Ulrich's 33rd Edition
INTERNATIONAL PERIODICALS DIRECTORY
1994-95

Ulrich's International Periodicals Directory
is compiled by
R.R. Bowker
A Reed Reference Publishing Company
Serials Bibliography Department

Albert Simmonds, Managing Director, Bibliographies

Editorial
Judith Salk, Executive Editor
Edvika Popilskis, Managing Editor
Ewa Kowalska, Dawn Lombardy, Senior Editors

Daniel Berek, Egill Halldorsson, Henry Wessells, Associate Editors
Laura Forbes, Christopher King, Zhaoxia Lian, Assistant Editors

Mary Crouthers, Editorial Assistant
O'Sheila Delgado, Mail Processing Clerk
Karen Pouliot, Administrative Coordinator

Terence Carlson, Michael Crouthers, Mary Jo Duffy, Karl Dusza, Joseph Gutkovich,
Michael Helme, Bronislaw Jan Kowalski, Margareta Leon, Zelda Salk, and
Eline van de Poel-Becker, Contributing Editors

Production
Doreen Gravesande, Production Director
Myriam Nunez, Managing Editor
Barbara Holton, Frank McDermott, Senior Editors

Computer Operations Group
Nick Wikowski, Director, Network/Computer Operations
Max Kobrinsky, Manager
Jack Murphy, Supervisor

International Computaprint Corporation
Karen Strong, Senior Account Manager
Donna Colahan, Account Manager

33rd Edition
Ulrich's
INTERNATIONAL PERIODICALS DIRECTORY
1994-95

including
Irregular Serials & Annuals

Volume 2

Subjects E-L

THE BOWKER INTERNATIONAL SERIALS DATABASE

R.R. BOWKER
A Reed Reference Publishing Company
New Providence, New Jersey

Published by R.R. Bowker
A Reed Reference Publishing Company
121 Chanlon Rd., New Providence, NJ 07974

Ira Siegel, President, CEO
Andrew W. Meyer, Executive Vice President
Peter E. Simon, Senior Vice President, Database Publishing
Stanley Walker, Senior Vice President, Marketing
Edward J. Roycroft, Senior Vice President, Sales

Copyright © 1994 by Reed Elsevier Inc.
All rights reserved

Ulrich's Hotline (U.S. only): 1-800-346-6049
Editorial (Canada only, call collect): 1-908-665-2875
Serials Fax (overseas users): 908-771-7725

Ulrich's is a trademark of Reed Properties Inc., used under license

No part of this publication may be reproduced or transmitted
in any form or by any means, stored in any information
storage and retrieval system, without prior written permission
of R.R. Bowker, 121 Chanlon Rd., New Providence
New Jersey 07974

International Standard Book Number 0-8352-3537-8
(5 Volume set)
International Standard Book Number 0-8352-3538-6
(Volume 1)
International Standard Book Number 0-8352-3539-4
(Volume 2)
International Standard Book Number 0-8352-3540-8
(Volume 3)
International Standard Book Number 0-8352-3541-6
(Volume 4)
International Standard Book Number 0-8352-3542-4
(Volume 5)
International Standard Serial Number 0000-0175

Library of Congress Catalog Card Number 32-16320

Printed and bound in the United States of America.

No payment is either solicited or accepted for the inclusion of entries in this publication. R.R. Bowker
has used its best efforts in collecting and preparing material for inclusion in this publication, but does not warrant
that the information herein is complete or accurate, and does not assume, and hereby disclaims any liability to any
person for the loss or damage caused by errors or omissions in this publication whether such errors or
omissions result from negligence, accident or any other cause.

ISBN 0-8352-3537-8

9 780835 235372

Contents

BOWKER/ULRICH'S SERIALS LIBRARIANSHIP AWARD WINNERS	vi
PREFACE	vii
USER'S GUIDE	ix
INTERNATIONAL STANDARD SERIAL NUMBER (ISSN)	xvii
ABBREVIATIONS	
General Abbreviations and Special Symbols	xix
Country of Publication Codes	xx
Document Suppliers	xxii
Micropublishers and Distributors	xxiii
Money Symbols	xxviii
Reprint Services	xxix
Wire Services	xxx
Abstracting and Indexing Services	xxxi
SUBJECT GUIDE TO ABSTRACTING AND INDEXING	xliv
SUBJECTS	xlv
CROSS-INDEX TO SUBJECTS	l

VOLUME 1

CLASSIFIED LIST OF SERIALS/SUBJECTS A to D	1

VOLUME 2

CLASSIFIED LIST OF SERIALS/SUBJECTS E to L	1909

VOLUME 3

CLASSIFIED LIST OF SERIALS/SUBJECTS M to Z	3733

VOLUME 4

REFEREED SERIALS	5985
CONTROLLED CIRCULATION SERIALS	6115
SERIALS AVAILABLE ON CD-ROM	6211
PRODUCER LISTING/SERIALS ON CD-ROM	6237
SERIALS AVAILABLE ONLINE	6241
VENDOR LISTING/SERIALS ONLINE	6335
CESSATIONS	6361
INDEX TO PUBLICATIONS OF INTERNATIONAL ORGANIZATIONS	6575
International Organizations	6575
International Congress Proceedings	6586
European Communities	6590
United Nations	6591
ISSN INDEX	6599
TITLE CHANGE INDEX	7299
TITLE INDEX	7321

VOLUME 5

PREFACE	vii
USER'S GUIDE	ix
ABBREVIATIONS	xii
DAILY NEWSPAPERS — US	1
WEEKLY NEWSPAPERS — US	97
TITLE INDEX	343
DAILY NEWSPAPER INDEX	411
WEEKLY NEWSPAPER INDEX	429
GEOGRAPHIC INDEX	481
CESSATIONS	547

Bowker/Ulrich's Serials Librarianship Award

Presented by the Serials Section
Association for Library Collections and Technical Services (ALCTS)
Division of the American Library Association (ALA)

Sponsored by R.R. Bowker

This annual award is given in recognition of distinguished and ongoing contributions to serials librarianship. Qualified individuals demonstrate leadership in serials-related activities through their participation in professional associations, groups, and/or library education programs; make significant contributions to serials literature; and, in general, strive to enhance our comprehension of the serials world.

AWARD RECIPIENTS

1985	Marcia Tuttle
1986	Ruth C. Carter
1987	James P. Danky
1988	Marjorie E. Bloss
1989	John E. Merriman
1990	Jean S. Cook
1991	Deana L. Astle/Charles A. Hamaker
1992	Linda K. Bartley
1993	Ann L. Okerson
1994	Tina Feick

Preface

For 62 years, **Ulrich's International Periodicals Directory** has been the premier serials reference source. **Ulrich's**, now in its 33rd edition, continues to uphold its reputation for excellence in the provision of serials bibliographic information. With the publication of this directory we, once again, provide numerous new features which will improve your access to and use of the serials information contained herein.

Over 10,000 newspapers published worldwide are included in the 33rd edition of **Ulrich's**. The fifth volume of **Ulrich's**, introduced last edition, reappears with nearly 7,000 daily and weekly U.S. newspapers listed. Topical or subject-oriented newspapers from the entire world, which have been included in **Ulrich's** for many years, are subject-classified and appear in the Classified List of Serials, Volumes 1-3. New to this edition and also contained in these volumes are listings for general-interest daily and weekly newspapers published outside the United States. This configuration represents the second phase of our plan to provide comprehensive worldwide newspaper coverage in **Ulrich's**.

Our coverage of document delivery services has been expanded to include Chemical Abstracts Service (CASDDS), SWETS, and UMI. Titles available for document delivery from nine different services (ADONIS™, British Library Document Supply Centre, Congressional Information Service, Engineering Information Inc., Faxon, UnCover, and the three new services mentioned above) are flagged in Volumes 1-3 of **Ulrich's**. For a full explanation of these useful data, please refer to the *User's Guide* beginning on page ix in the prefatory material of Volumes 1-4. Also new to this edition are the inclusion of toll-free telephone numbers for publishing companies, e-mail addresses, subscription fax numbers, distributor fax numbers, and a new personnel category — publisher's name.

Serials continue to be important as primary sources of current and topical news in all fields of endeavor, as evidenced by the vast number of serials published and their rapid development into electronic formats. The availability of serials in electronic formats, either online or on CD-ROM, continues to grow. This edition of **Ulrich's** includes 4,115 serials available exclusively online or in addition to hardcopy, and 1,119 serials available on CD-ROM. These serials are indicated by a notation and a bullet (●) in the main entry.

The 33rd edition of **Ulrich's** contains information on more than 147,000 serials published throughout the world, arranged under 967 subject headings. More than 112,000 entries have been updated to reflect the most current information available and more than 11,500 serials have been added. Also included in this edition is information on 9,532 titles that are known to have ceased or suspended publication in the last three years. The ceased or suspended titles are preceded by a dagger (†) in the *Title Index* for instant identification. Users can identify newer serials, over 3,600 of which are known to have begun publication since January 1, 1992, by looking for an upside-down solid triangle (▼) preceding entries in both the *Classified List of Serials* and the *Title Index*. In addition, over 7,000 refereed serials notations, over 50,000 brief descriptions; 34,595 LC Classification Numbers; 16,600 CODEN; and 3,096 vendor file names or numbers for 4,115 titles available in an online format appear in this edition.

Included in **Ulrich's** are serials which are currently available, issued more frequently than once a year and usually published at regular intervals, as well as publications issued annually or less frequently than once a year, or irregularly. Due to the vast number of serials, we have established certain criteria for inclusion, while maintaining our aim of maximum title coverage that will satisfy the widest range of use. We include all publications that meet the definition of a serial except administrative publications of major government agencies below state level that can be easily found elsewhere, membership directories, comic books, and puzzles and game books. This edition of **Ulrich's** is arranged within five volumes: the first three volumes comprise the *Classified List of Serials*; the fourth volume contains the *Refereed Serials, Controlled Circulation Serials, Serials Available on CD-ROM, Producer Listing/Serials on CD-ROM, Serials Available Online, Vendor Listing/Serials Online, Cessations, Index to International Organizations, ISSN, Title Change,* and *Title indexes*. The fifth volume comprises daily and weekly newspapers published in the United States.

International data inquiries are mailed annually to some 70,000 publishers to secure accurate and up-to-date information on current titles, as well as new titles, title changes, and cessations. In addition, updating of the database occurs daily from information received from publishers throughout the year. All post office returns are researched, and entries from publishers whose addresses cannot be verified are suspended from the file. Information about title changes, cessations, and new titles not received by the deadline for this edition will appear in **Ulrich's Update**; in the online database available through DIALOG Information Services, Inc., and BRS Information Technologies, Inc.; on **Ulrich's Plus**™ CD-ROM; and on **Ulrich's Microfiche**.

Your purchase and use of **Ulrich's** is complemented with some additional services. **Ulrich's Update**, provided free of charge, three times per year in November, February and May is a supplemental service to the annual directory. The **Ulrich's Hotline** is a toll-free number that subscribers can call to get help in solving particular serials research problems and questions. Canadian users are asked to call a special number collect, and our overseas users are asked to use a designated fax number. (Please see page iv for our address and telephone and fax numbers.) A former service, **Ulrich's News**, the quarterly publication sent free-of-charge to subscribers of **Ulrich's**, merged in September, 1992, with a quarterly newsletter from R.R. Bowker, **The Cornerstone**. **The Cornerstone** includes not only valuable information about serials and **Ulrich's**, as had **Ulrich's News**, but also contains news about other Bowker titles and pertinent topics.

As always, we continue to research, plan, and implement enhancements to the **Ulrich's** database and our database maintenance system. We consider feedback from our users to be essential, so please contact us and let us know your thoughts. We want **Ulrich's** and its family of products to provide all necessary reference information quickly and effectively. Comments and suggestions are encouraged in order to help keep our database and its bibliographic publications of the highest quality.

My sincere appreciation is extended to the senior staff of **Ulrich's** and to our fine staff of serial editors and contributing editors for their unflagging dedication and hard work in updating and maintaining the serials database in preparation of the 33rd edition of **Ulrich's**. Gratitude is also conveyed to Karen Strong, Senior Account Manager and Donna Colahan, Account Manager, at International Computaprint Corporation, for their competence, diligence, and patience in working closely with us again this year to produce this directory. Finally, I would like to thank the various information specialists and serialists throughout the world who have taken it upon themselves to provide us with hard-to-locate and/or esoteric serials data. We consider their participation and interest in the dissemination of accurate and comprehensive serials information to be of great value to **Ulrich's** and its users.

Judith Salk
Executive Editor

User's Guide

This directory offers two primary access methods for locating periodicals in Volumes 1-4: by subject in the CLASSIFIED LIST OF SERIALS, and alphabetically in the TITLE INDEX. Ceased serials are listed in a separate CESSATIONS section and are also accessible by means of the TITLE INDEX. Other indexes provide listings of selected periodicals in specific categories. These indexes are REFEREED SERIALS, CONTROLLED CIRCULATION SERIALS, SERIALS AVAILABLE ON CD-ROM, PRODUCER LISTING/SERIALS ON CD-ROM, SERIALS AVAILABLE ONLINE, VENDOR LISTING/SERIALS ONLINE, PUBLICATIONS OF INTERNATIONAL ORGANIZATIONS, ISSN INDEX, and TITLE CHANGE INDEX. See the User's Guide in Volume 5 for a content description and use instructions for the NEWSPAPER volume.

In addition, separate subheadings for "Abstracting, Bibliographies and Statistics" under major subject headings provide convenient access to these types of publications. Page references for these subheadings are given in the "Subject Guide to Abstracting and Indexing" on p. xliv. This Subject Guide provides an overview of subjects for which abstracting and indexing publications have been identified.

This "User's Guide" is separated into three divisions for ease of use: (I) Section Descriptions, (II) Full Entry Content Description, and (III) Cataloging Rules for Main Entry Title.

Section Descriptions

CLASSIFIED LIST OF SERIALS

This is the main section of the book, containing bibliographic information for currently published serials classified by subject. Entries are arranged alphabetically by title within each subject heading. Subject cross-references in the text direct the user to the location of subheadings.

Volume 1 contains subjects A-D, from "Abstracting and Indexing" through "Drug Abuse and Alcoholism." Volume 2 contains subjects E-L, "Earth Sciences" through "Lumber and Wood." Volume 3 contains subjects M-Z, from "Machine Theory" through "Zoology."

A complete listing of the "Subjects" used in the CLASSIFIED LIST OF SERIALS appears on p. xlv. To aid international users, this list is translated into four languages. For additional guidance on the subject classification scheme, the user should also consult the "Cross-Index to Subjects" on p. l, which contains additional key word references.

Each serial is listed with full bibliographic information only once. If a serial covers several subjects, title cross-references appear under the related headings, directing the user to the heading where the full entry is listed.

New serials (beginning publication within the last three years) are highlightened by a ▼ in front of the title.

The "Cataloging Rules for Main Entry Title" section of this "User's Guide" explains the title cataloging rules followed in compiling ULRICH'S.

REFEREED SERIALS

This section is an alphabetical listing by title of all serials known to be refereed, or peer reviewed. It includes the publisher name, address, and telephone number, if known. The italicized number at the end of each entry is the page number where the full entry appears in the CLASSIFIED LIST OF SERIALS.

CONTROLLED CIRCULATION SERIALS

This section is an alphabetical listing of all serials known to have controlled circulations. It includes the publisher name and address, telephone and fax numbers, and circulation figure, if known. The italicized number at the end of each entry is a reference to the page on which the full entry appears in the CLASSIFIED LIST OF SERIALS.

SERIALS AVAILABLE ON CD-ROM

This section is an alphabetical listing of all serials known to be available on CD-ROM, either in addition to hardcopy, or on CD-ROM only. It includes the publisher name, address, telephone and fax numbers, if known. It also includes the name of CD-ROM producers, when known. The italicized number at the end of each entry is the page number where the full entry appears in the CLASSIFIED LIST OF SERIALS.

PRODUCER LISTING/SERIALS ON CD-ROM

This section is an alphabetical listing of identified producers of serials on CD-ROM. Entries include the producer address, telephone and fax numbers, and an alphabetical listing of all serial titles known to be available. If known, the serial on CD-ROM product name is listed in parentheses after the serial title. All serials listed in this index also have full bibliographic entries in the CLASSIFIED LIST OF SERIALS. Consult the TITLE INDEX or the SERIALS AVAILABLE ON CD-ROM listing for page numbers.

SERIALS AVAILABLE ONLINE

This section is an alphabetical listing of all serials known to be available online, either in addition to hardcopy, or online only. Entries include publisher name, address, telephone and fax numbers, plus names of online vendors and file names or numbers if known. The number in parentheses at the end of each entry is the page number where the full entry appears in the CLASSIFIED LIST OF SERIALS.

VENDOR LISTING/SERIALS ONLINE

This section is an alphabetical listing of identified vendors of online periodicals. Entries include addresses, telephone and fax numbers for the vendor, and an alphabetical listing of all titles known to be available, with file names or numbers, if known. All serials listed in this index also have full bibliographic entries in the CLASSIFIED LIST OF SERIALS. Consult the TITLE INDEX or the SERIALS AVAILABLE ONLINE listing for page numbers.

CESSATIONS

In this section, entries for serials which have ceased in the past three years are listed alphabetically by title. The cessation entry includes: title, Dewey Decimal Classification number, former frequency of publication, publisher name and address, country-of-publication code, and, if available, other information such as ISSN, CODEN, LC number, subtitle, corporate author, year of first issue and year ceased. Titles which were originally planned as continuing series but which have closed are included in the CESSATIONS section although back issues may still be available.

If a title has "ceased" because a new title is being used, there will not be an entry in the CESSATIONS section. Instead, the entry is maintained in the CLASSIFIED LIST OF SERIALS under the new title, with a "Formerly" or "Former titles" indication.

INDEX TO PUBLICATIONS OF INTERNATIONAL ORGANIZATIONS

Complexity of corporate author structure, as well as title page variations in multilingual texts, compound the problems in cataloging international publications. This special index is provided so that the user may have one reference point for these titles. This index consists of four sections:

International Organizations
International Congress Proceedings
European Communities
United Nations

The index contains all current titles listed in the Bowker International Serials Database. The user must consult the CLASSIFIED LIST OF SERIALS for the full bibliographic information pertaining to these titles. Page references are provided.

ISSN INDEX

The ISSN INDEX lists serials in order by ISSN number. It includes all serials contained in the Bowker International Serials Database, whether current, ceased, or inactive, to which an ISSN has been assigned in our file. A dagger symbol (†) indicates that the title is ceased. If an ISSN appears twice, it usually indicates that the serial has split into two or more parts. Titles which have changed, and for which new ISSNs have been assigned, will show cross-references from one ISSN to the new ISSN. If no new ISSN has been assigned, the cross-reference is from ISSN to new title. Entries for inactive titles do not appear in the book.

Italicized type indicates the page number where a complete entry can be found for active titles. If a title has ceased in the last three years, the page reference will be to the listing in the CESSATION INDEX. If no page reference appears for ceased titles, it means the title ceased more than three years ago and is not listed in this edition. ISSNs of inactive titles likewise do not have page references and are not listed in this book.

A full description of the ISSN and its use is provided on p. xvii.

TITLE CHANGE INDEX

The TITLE CHANGE INDEX lists former titles alphabetically with references to new titles. Page numbers indicate where bibliographic entries are listed in the CLASSIFIED LIST OF SERIALS. This index cumulates all title changes recorded in the ULRICH'S database since the publication of the previous, or 32nd, edition.

TITLE INDEX

The TITLE INDEX, which is at the end of Volume 4, is the second major access point for serials. To locate a serial by its title, the user should be familiar with title cataloging rules as described in the "Cataloging Rules for Main Entry Titles" paragraphs of this "User's Guide."

The TITLE INDEX lists all current and ceased serials included in this directory. **Boldface** type indicates the page number where the complete entry will be found; page numbers in roman type refer to related subject categories.

For serials with identical titles published within a country, the city of publication is added in parentheses, and sometimes the year of first publication is given to further distinguish the titles.

If a serial title consists of or contains an acronym, a cross-reference is provided from the full name to the acronym form of the title.

Cross-references are provided from former titles and variant titles, and from the alternate language titles of multi-language publications. Recent title changes are noted, with a reference to the current title. The TITLE INDEX also lists the country code for all serials, along with the ISSN, if known.

The ▼ used in the "Classified List of Serials" to indicate new serials also appears in this index, preceding the title. A (†) appears preceding the title if the publication has ceased.

Full Entry Content Description

Basic Information
The following items are mandatory for listing and appear in all entries: main entry title, frequency of publication, publisher address, country code, and Dewey Decimal Classification number.

Dewey Decimal Classification Number
The Dewey Decimal number is printed at the top left of each entry. More than one Dewey number may have been assigned if a serial covers several subjects.

LC Classification Number
The Library of Congress classification number, if known, appears directly below the Dewey Decimal number. Shelf numbers are not included.

SAMPLE ENTRY

❶ 930.198 490.996   ❷ US   ❸ ISSN 1055-7644
❹ DZ991   ❺ CODEN: JAAPL9
❻ **JOURNAL OF ANTARCTIC ARCHAEOLOGY AND PROTOLINGUISTICS;** ❼ international communications and research.   ❽ (Supplement avail.)   ❾ (Text in English, French, Polynesian languages)   ❿ 1927.   ⓫ 2/yr.   ⓬ $39 to individuals; institutions $99 (includes supplement) (effective 1993); newsstand price: $1.50.   ⓭ (Societe d'Archaeologie et de Linguistique Pacifiques—Society of Pacific Archaeology and Linguistics)   ⓮ W.A. Translations (Subsidiary of: Temporary Culture),   ⓯ Box 43072, Upper Montclair, NJ 07043-7072.   ⓰ TEL 908-665-2869.
⓱ FAX 508-555-0010.   ⓲ TELEX 123458.   ⓳ E-mail: intl.@tien.bon.
⓴ (Subscr. to: Department of Archaeology and Proto-Linguistics, 7 Old College Walk, Arkham, MA 01901-1011. TEL 508-555-0110. FAX 508-555-4112;   ㉑ Dist. in Europe by: Editions d'Erlette, Ch. de Kerangat, 56120 Plumelec, France. TEL 33-76-63-94. FAX 33-76-205).   ㉒ (Co-sponsor: Miskatonic University, Department of Archaeology and Proto-Linguistics)   ㉓ Eds. A.H. Whateley, J.M. Snyrnat;
㉔ Pub. M.J. Smith.   ㉕ adv.: B&W page $400; trim 8 1/8 x 10;   ㉖ adv. contact: Arthur Dunwich.
㉗ bk.rev.; abstr.; bibl.; illus.; index;   ㉘ circ. 500 (paid); 500 (controlled).   ㉙ (also avail. in microform from SWZ, UMI; also avail. on diskette; back issues avail.; reprint service avail. from SWZ, UMI).
㉚ **Indexed:** Abstr. Anthropol., Br.Archaeol.Abstr.   ㉛ (1991–), Onoma (1986–), Ref.Zh.
㉜ **Document type:** academic/scholarly publication.
㉝ ● Also available online.   ㉞ Vendor(s): UTOPIA (Miskatonic).
㉟ Also available on CD-ROM.   ㊱ Producer(s): TEMPCULT (Miskatonic).
㊲ —BLDSC (9999.000000); CIS   ㊳ **CCC.**
㊴ **Supersedes (in 1986):** Miskatonic Annals of Antarctic Archaeology and Extraterrestrial Linguistics
㊵ (ISSN 0055-1298).
㊶ **Description:** Publishes archaeological field research on prehistoric civilizations in the Pacific Islands and Antarctica, with relevant contributions discussing worldwide linguistic evidence of contacts among civilizations.
㊷ *Refereed Serial*

KEY

❶ Dewey Decimal Classification
❷ Country Code
❸ ISSN
❹ LC Classification
❺ CODEN
❻ Main Entry Title
❼ Subtitle
❽ Bibliographic Note
❾ Language
❿ First Published
⓫ Frequency
⓬ Price
⓭ Corporate Author
⓮ Publishing Company
⓯ Address
⓰ Telephone
⓱ Fax
⓲ Telex
⓳ E-mail
⓴ Subscription Address, Tel & Fax
㉑ Distributor Address, Tel & Fax
㉒ Co-Sponsor
㉓ Editor
㉔ Publisher
㉕ Advertising Rate
㉖ Advertising Contact
㉗ Special Features
㉘ Circulation
㉙ Format
㉚ Indexed
㉛ Years of Coverage
㉜ Document Type
㉝ Online Availability
㉞ Online Vendor/File Name
㉟ CD-ROM Availability
㊱ CD-ROM Producer(s)
㊲ Document Suppliers
㊳ Copyright Clearance Center Registration Notation
㊴ Title Changes
㊵ Former ISSN
㊶ Brief Description
㊷ Refereed

USER'S GUIDE

Country Code
The Country Code is printed at the top right of each entry following the Dewey Decimal number. A complete list of country codes used will be found on p. xx.

ISSN
The ISSN for the main entry title is printed immediately following the country code. Not all publications have been assigned an ISSN, and lack of a number does not render a publication ineligible for listing.

CODEN
The CODEN designation, if known, is printed directly below the country code and ISSN. The CODEN is an alphanumeric code, applied uniquely to a specific publication. Devised by the American Society for Testing and Materials, it is used primarily for scientific and technical titles. New CODEN are assigned by Chemical Abstracts Service.

Title Information
The main title is printed in **boldface** and upper case as the first item in the entry. Titles are catalogued according to rules described below in the "Cataloging Rules for Main Entry Title" section. For multi-language publications, the parallel language title is also printed in upper case, immediately following the main entry title, and is separated from it by a slash.

A ▼ printed before the title indicates that the title began publishing within the last three years.

An asterisk (*) printed after the title indicates that the information in the entry was not verified by the publisher for this edition.

The subtitle is printed in lower case after the title.

Variant titles or translated edition titles are given within the entry and are labeled as such.

Former titles are given at the end of the entry, along with publication dates if known. If a former title also had an ISSN, the ISSN is listed in parentheses after the former title. Many entries contain extensive former title information, providing a history of changes which may be useful for bibliographic record-keeping.

The Key Title, which is assigned at the time of ISSN assignment by the responsible center of the International Serials Data System, is given only if it is different from the main entry title.

Year First Published
The year first published is given if provided by the publisher. If information is lacking, a volume number and specific year may be provided to indicate the approximate age of the publication.

Frequency
The frequency of publication is given in abbreviated form, such as "a." for annual, "irreg." for irregular, "m." for monthly, "3/yr." for three times per year. All abbreviations used are listed in the "General Abbreviations" on p. xix.

Price
Unless otherwise indicated, the price given is the annual price for an individual subscription in the currency of the country of origin. The price in U.S. dollars may also be given in parentheses if it is provided by the publisher. No attempt is made to convert foreign currency to U.S. dollars. Separate postage information is not given, since postal rates vary widely.

Publishing Company Information
Many serials are editorially controlled by a sponsoring organization or corporate author and published by a commercial publisher. In these instances, the commercial publishing company's name and address are given, and the name of the corporate author is given in parentheses immediately preceding. In other instances, either a sponsoring organization or a commercial publishing company has sole responsibility, and only one name is given. We avoid listing printers as publishing companies, preferring the name and address of someone with editorial responsibility. For the same reason, we avoid listing distributors as publishing companies.

If no publishing company name is given, it is assumed that the publishing company name is the same as the title.

Telephone, Fax, Telex Numbers and E-mail Addresses
Telephone, fax, telex numbers and e-mail addresses are given when provided by the publisher. U.S. and Canadian numbers are given in standard North American format. Toll-free numbers within U.S. and Canada are also included, when available. Numbers in other countries are provided in the same format as supplied by the publisher, resulting in some inconsistencies. Users are advised to consult an international operator before placing the calls.

Subscription or Distribution Address
A second address is given only if the address for ordering subscriptions is different from the publishing company's address. Distributors are listed only if we have been informed that a particular organization is the exclusive distributor. Additional subscription and/or distribution offices of international publishers are listed, if known. Telephone and fax numbers for subscription and/or distribution offices appear if provided by the publisher.

Editor
Usually only one name is given, preceded by the notation "Ed." Advanced degrees and titles are omitted, except for medical, military and religious titles; absence of a title does not mean that the editor has none. The abbreviation "Ed.Bd." indicates editorship by three or more persons.

Publisher
Only one or two names are given when known, preceded by the notation "Pub." or "Pubs." Advanced degrees and titles are omitted, except for medical, military and religious titles; absence of a title does not mean that the publisher has none.

If the publisher is also the editor, and no publishing company name is available, the person's name is given with the notation "Ed. & Pub."

Advertising Rates and Contact Name
When provided by the publisher, the name of the advertising contact, as well as full-page advertising rates and trim size are indicated. Most dimensions are listed in millimeters, except for US publications whose dimensions are usually in inches.

Special Features
A listing of special features may include such items as book or other types of reviews, advertising (usually meaning commercial, not classified advertising), charts, illustrations, bibliography section, article abstracts, and an annual index to the periodical's contents.

Reprint Services
If a serial is known to be available from a reprint service, a code referring to the service appears in the entry. More than one code may be listed. For a list of reprint services and a translation of the codes, please refer to p. xxix.

Circulation
All circulation figures used are approximate. Circulation is given only if provided by the publisher. The notation "controlled" indicates that the publication is available only to the qualified persons, usually members of a particular trade or profession.

Format
Formats other than standard magazine format are noted in parentheses. Other formats may be looseleaf, duplicated (mimeographed), tabloid, newspaper. If a publication is available in microform, a notation is made which includes a three-letter code for the vendor, if known. A list of names, addresses, telephone and fax numbers of micropublishers begins on p. xxiii.

Abstracting and Indexing
The notation "Indexed:" precedes a list of abbreviations for all abstracting and indexing services known to cover the serial on a regular basis. Years of coverage immediately follow each abstracting and indexing service code, if known. The complete names of the abstracting and indexing services are listed with their abbreviations on p. xxxi. All currently published abstracting and indexing services are also listed as entries in the CLASSIFIED LIST OF SERIALS.

Document Type
Notations are included to indicate type of publication, e.g. trade publication, newsletter, or abstracting/indexing. The words "**Document type:**" appear in boldface, followed by the document type description, in entries where this information is known. More than one document type may be listed for a single publication, if applicable.

Online Availability and CD-ROM Availability
If a serial is known to be available in a full-text online format and/or on CD-ROM, a bullet symbol (●) precedes the information. Online and CD-ROM availability are noted whether they exist in addition to hardcopy or in one or both formats exclusively. Online vendors and CD-ROM producers are also listed, if known.

For a listing of serials available online, consult the SERIALS AVAILABLE ONLINE index on p. 6241. Complete names and addresses of vendors, with a listing of serials known to be available through them, are in a separate index, VENDOR LISTING/SERIALS ONLINE on p. 6335.

For a listing of serials available on CD-ROM, consult the SERIALS AVAILABLE ON CD-ROM index on p. 6211. Complete names and addresses of producers, with a list of CD-ROMs known to be available through them, are in a separate index, PRODUCER LISTING/SERIALS ON CD-ROM on p. 6237.

Document Suppliers
The **Ulrich's** database and the individual databases of the following document suppliers were matched on the presence of ISSNs. When a match was successful, the appropriate document supplier code was noted. Not all serials titles in general, or in these individual databases, have ISSNs. Therefore, the absence of one or any document supplier code in an **Ulrich's** listing does not necessarily mean the title is unavailable from one or any of these suppliers.

ADONIS™
The notation, ADONIS, appearing in a serial entry indicates the availability of that serial for document delivery through ADONIS's service, by permission from the copyright owner. Such permission is subject to change without notice.

For further information, contact: ADONIS B.V., Spuistraat 112D, 1012VA Amsterdam, The Netherlands; tel: 31-20-6262629, fax: 31-20-6261437; ADONIS USA, 238 Main St., Cambridge, MA 02142; tel: 800-944-6415, fax: 617-876-7022.

British Library Document Supply Centre
The notation, BLDSC, appearing in a serial entry indicates the availability of that serial for document delivery from the British Library Document Supply Centre, by permission from the copyright owner. The BLDSC shelfmark number, a unique identifier of each serial, is preceded by an

em-dash (—) which is followed by the notation "BLDSC (0000.000000)." The format of the shelfmark is four digits, a decimal point, then six digits.

For further information about BLDSC's services, contact: Customer Services, BLDSC, Boston Spa, Wetherby, LS23 7BQ, UK; tel: 44-937-546060, fax: 44-937-546333.

Chemical Abstracts Service

The notation, CASDDS, appearing in a serial entry indicates the availability of that serial for document delivery through Chemical Abstracts Service Document Delivery Service.

For further information, contact Chemical Abstracts Service, Document Delivery Service, P.O. Box 3012, Columbus, OH 43210, USA; tel: 800-678-4337; fax: 614-447-3648; e-mail: dds65@cas.org.

Congressional Information Service, Inc.

The notation, CIS, appearing in a serial entry indicates the availability of that serial for document delivery through CIS Documents on Demand Service, by permission from the copyright owner. Such permission is subject to change without notice.

For further information, contact Congressional Information Service, Inc., 4520 East-West Hwy., Ste. 800, Bethesda, MD 20814-3389, USA; tel: 301-654-1550, 800-227-2477; fax: 301-657-3203.

Engineering Information Inc./ Article Express International, Inc.

The notation, EI, appearing in a serial entry indicates the availability of that serial for document delivery through Engineering Information, Inc./Article Express International, Inc.'s service, by permission from the copyright owner. Such permission is subject to change without notice.

For further information, contact Article Express International, Inc., 469 Union Ave., Westbury, NY 11590, USA; tel: 516-997-0699, 800-238-3458; fax: 516-997-0890; e-mail: DDS@WORK4U.ARTX.COM.

Faxon Research Services, Inc.

The notation, Faxon, appearing in a serial entry indicates the availability of that serial's table of contents in Faxon Finder™, and article delivery through Faxon Xpress™, by permission from the copyright owner. Such permission is subject to change without notice.

For further information, contact Faxon Research Services, Inc., 15 Southwest Park, Westwood, MA 02090, USA; tel: 800-999-3594; fax: 800-933-6831; e-mail: macintosh@faxon.com.

SWETS

The notation, SWETS, appearing in a serial entry indicates the availability of that serial for document delivery through the SwetScan-SwetDoc service, by permission from the copyright owner. Such permission is subject to change without notice.

For further information, contact Swets & Zeitlinger bv, Heereweg 347, P.O. Box 830, 2160 SZ Lisse, The Netherlands; tel: 31-2521-35111; fax: 31-2521-15888; telex: 41325.

UMI

The notation, UMI, appearing in a serial entry indicates the availability of that serial for document delivery through UMI's Article Clearinghouse service, by permission from the copyright owner. Such permission is subject to change without notice.

For further information, contact UMI Article Clearinghouse, 300 N. Zeeb Rd., P.O. Box 1346, Ann Arbor, MI 48106-1346, USA; tel: 800-521-0600, ext. 2786; fax: 313-761-1032, 313-665-7075; e-mail: ACHMAIL@UMI.COM.

The UnCover Company

The notation, UnCover, appearing in a serial entry indicates the availability of that serial for document delivery through UnCover's service, by permission from the copyright owner. Such permission is subject to change without notice.

For further information, contact The UnCover Co., 3801 E. Florida Ave., Ste. 200, Denver, CO 80210, USA; tel: 303-758-3030; fax: 303-758-5946; e-mail: uncover@carl.org.

Copyright Clearance Center, Inc.
The Copyright Clearance Center, Inc. (CCC) is a not-for-profit collective licensing organization. The CCC grants permissions to institutions and individuals to photocopy works of its registered publishers upon payment of publisher set royalties. The CCC does not supply copies of registered works directly to anyone.

The boldfaced **CCC** notation appears in the entries of titles for which CCC has been authorized by the publisher to grant photocopy permissions through its Transactional Reporting Service (TRS). Additional titles may be available for certain publishers who have authorized the CCC to grant photocopy permissions on any of their works. The same inclusive country-wide coverage is available for publishers in the following countries: Canada, the Commonwealth of Independent States, Germany, New Zealand, Norway, and Spain. To register with the CCC, please contact TRS Customer Service, 222 Rosewood Dr., Danvers, MA 01923, USA; tel: 508-750-8400; fax: 508-750-4470.

Brief Description
A brief description of the contents and editorial focus of the publication may be provided, preceded by the word

"Description:" at the end of the entry. These descriptions were submitted by the publisher or were written by editorial staff after examination of sample copies or publisher catalogs.

Refereed Serial

The manuscript peer review and evaluation system is utilized to protect, maintain and raise the quality of scholarly material published in serials. If a serial is known to be refereed or juried, the notation *"Refereed Serial"* appears in italics at the end of the entry. This information is generally provided by the serial publisher.

Newspaper-Specific Data Elements

Ownership

The name of the owner(s) of a newspaper is listed, usually accompanied by the owner(s) address, and telephone and fax numbers. The owner address may differ from the newspaper location address. Owner information is preceded by the notion "Owner(s):."

Wire Services

If a newspaper is known to use one or more news or photo wire services, abbreviations or names of the services used are listed in the entry. Such information is preceded by the words "Wire Service(s):." Abbreviations for wire services used are listed on page xxx of this volume.

Pages Per Issue; Columns Per Page

When known, the number of pages per issue (pp./issue:) and/or columns per page (cols./p.:) is/are noted.

Cataloging Rules for Main Entry Title

The majority of titles in the Bowker International Serials Database were cataloged according to *Anglo-American Cataloging Rules* prior to 1978, the date of the new edition of *Anglo-American Cataloging Rules*. The new *AACR II* reflects a trend toward the Key Title concept of cataloging as used by the International Serials Data System (ISDS) and published in its *International Standard Bibliographic Description for Serials* (1974).

Because recataloging a database the size of Bowker's was not feasible, our cataloging rules were modified but not radically changed. Cross-references are provided in the TITLE INDEX from variant forms of title, such as Key Title, to aid users searching by other methods.

Whenever possible, main entry title cataloging is done from a sample of the title page of the most recent issue, according to the following rules:

Articles at the beginning of titles are omitted, or are bypassed in filing.

Serials with distinctive titles are usually entered under title. For example:

Annual Bulletin of Historical Literature
Business Week
Milton Studies

If a title consists only of a generic term followed by the name of the issuing body, or if the name of the issuing body clarifies the content of the publication, entry is under the name of the issuing body. For example:

Newsletter of the American Theological Library Association

is entered as

American Theological Library Association. Newsletter

Economic Performance and Prospects, issued by the Private Development Corporation of the Philippines

is entered as

Private Development Corporation of the Philippines. Economic Performance and Prospects

A title which consists of a subject modified generic term followed by the name of the issuing body is considered nondistinctive and is entered under the name of the issuing body. For example:

Annual Meeting Scientific Proceedings of the American Animal Hospital Association

is entered as

American Animal Hospital Association. Annual Meeting Scientific Proceedings

Government publications with nondistinctive titles are entered under the name of the government jurisdiction of the issuing body, although distinctive titles of government organizations may be entered directly under title. For example:

Great Britain. Economic and Social Research Council. Annual Report

but

Statistical Abstract of Iceland

Titles which begin with the initials of the issuing body are entered under the initials. Cross-references from the full name are provided in the TITLE INDEX.

If a geographic name is part of the name of the issuing body, entry will be under the common form of the name of the body. For example:

University of the West Indies. Vice-Chancellor's Report

not

West Indies. University. Vice-Chancellor's Report

Note, however, that government publications retain similar cataloging as government jurisdiction.

Canada. Statistics Canada. Field Crop Reporting Series

Multilingual titles are entered under the first title given on the title page, or the first title reported by the publisher if the title page is not available. Titles in other languages are entered directly after the main entry title. Cross-references are provided in the TITLE INDEX for each language title.

FILING RULES

Due to the restrictions imposed by computer filing of titles, the following special filing rules should be noted.

Articles and prepositions within titles are alphabetized as words:

Journal of the West

precedes

Journal of Theological Studies

Hyphenated words are treated as separate words:

Pre-Text

precedes

Preaching

However, words indicating compass points (northeast, southwest, etc.) are filed as one word regardless of how printed:

Southeast Asia Builder
South-East Asia Stamp Catalogue
Southeast Dragster
South East Magazine

Titles entered under corporate author or government jurisdiction are sequenced before distinctive titles that begin with the same words:

British Columbia. Ministry of Energy, Mines and Petroleum Resources. Mineral Market Update

precedes

British Columbia Catholic

Acronyms and initials are treated as such and are listed at the beginning of each letter of the alphabet. Exceptions are the abbreviations of U.N. (United Nations), U.S. (United States), Gt. Britain (Great Britain), and St. (Saint), which are filed as words:

U R A M Newsletter
United Mutual Fund Sector
U.S. Environmental Protection Agency. Clean Water: Report to Congress

Titles in excess of 36 characters which are identical may not sort sequentially. The editors suggest that users scan the entire sequence of identical titles to locate specific entries.

Diacritical marks have been omitted. The German and Scandinavian umlaut has been replaced by the letter "e" following the vowels a, e, o, and u. In Danish, Norwegian and Swedish, the letter å is sequenced as "aa" and the letter ø as "oe."

International Standard Serial Number (ISSN)

1. What is the ISSN?

An internationally accepted, concise, unique, and unambiguous code for the identification of serial publications. One ISSN represents one serial title.

The ISSN consists of seven numbers with an eighth check digit calculated according to Modulus 11 and used to verify the number in computer processing. A hyphen is printed after the fourth digit, as a visual aid, and the acronym, ISSN, precedes the number.

2. How did the ISSN evolve as an international system?

The International Organization for Standardization Technical Committee 46 (ISO/TC 46) is the agency responsible for the development of the ISSN as an international standard. The organization responsible for the administration and coordination of ISSN assignments worldwide is the ISSN International Centre in Paris, which is supported by the French government and UNESCO.

ISSNs are assigned by over 50 national centers worldwide. The National Serials Data Program (NSDP) is the U.S. national center. The centers form a network which is coordinated by the ISSN International Centre located in Paris.

The implementation of the ISSN system started with the numbering of the 70,000 titles in the serials database of the R.R. Bowker Company (*Ulrich's International Periodicals Directory* and *Irregular Serials and Annuals*). The next serials database numbering was the *New Serials Titles 1950-70* cumulation listing 220,000 titles, cumulated, converted to magnetic tape, and published by the R.R. Bowker Company in collaboration with the Serials Record Division of the Library of Congress. These two databases were used as the starting base for the implementation of the ISSN.

3. What types of publications are assigned ISSNs?

For assignment of an ISSN, a serial is defined as a publication in print or non-print form, issued in successive parts, usually having numerical or chronological designations, and intended to be continued indefinitely.

4. How is the ISSN used?

The ISSN is employed as a component of bar codes and as a tool for the communication of basic information about a serial title and for such processes as ordering, billing, inventory control, abstracting, and indexing. In library processes, the ISSN is used in operations such acquisitions, claiming, binding, accessioning, shelving, cooperative cataloguing, circulation, interlibrary loans, and retrieval of requests.

5. May a publication have an International Standard Book Number (ISBN) and an ISSN?

Yes! Monographic series (separate works issued indefinitely under a common title, generally in a uniform format with numeric designations) and annuals or titles planned to be issued indefinitely under the same title may be defined as serials. The ISSN is assigned to the serial title, while an ISBN is assigned to each individual title or monograph in the series.

A new ISBN is assigned to each volume or edition by the publisher, while the ISSN, which is assigned by the ISSN International Centre or national ISSN centers, remains the same for each issue. Both numbers should be printed on the copyright page or other appropriate page of each volume, with their acronyms or words preceding each number for immediate identification. With the availability of both an ISSN and ISBN, the problem of defining the overlap of serials and monographs has been resolved.

SAMPLE TITLE

Advances in the Biosciences
ISSN 0065-3446

Vol. 1 Proceedings: Berlin. Schering Symposium of Endocrinology, Berlin. Ed. by Gerhard Raspe. 1969. 40.00 (ISBN 0-08-013395-9). Pergamon.

Vol. 2 Proceedings. Schering Symposium on Biodynamics & Mechanisms of Action of Steroid Hormones, Berlin. Ed. by Gerhard Raspe. 1969. 41.25 (ISBN 0-08-006942-8). Pergamon.

Vol. 3 Proceedings. Schering Workshop on Steroid Metabolism "in Vitro Versus in Vivo," Berlin. Ed. by Gerhard Raspe. 1969. 41.25 (ISBN 0-08-017544-9). Pergamon.

Vol. 4 Proceedings. Schering Symposium on Mechanisms Involved in Conception. Berlin. Ed. by Gerhard Raspe. 1970. text ed. 41.25 (ISBN 0-08-017546-5). Pergamon.

Vol. 25 Development of Responsiveness to Steroid Hormones. Alvin M. Kaye & Myra Kaye et al. LC 79-42938. 1980. 66.00 (ISBN 0-08-024949-X). Pergamon.

6. Where should the ISSN appear on the serial?

In a prominent position on or in each issue of the serial, such as the front cover, back cover, masthead, title, or copyright pages. The international standard recommendation is that the ISSN of a periodical be printed, whenever possible, in the upper right corner of the front cover.

Promotional and descriptive materials about the serial should include the ISSN.

7. When a title changes, is a new ISSN assigned?

In most instances, a new ISSN is assigned when a title changes. However, the determination is made by the ISSN International Centre or the appropriate national ISSN centers. Publishers should report all the title changes to their respective centers.

8. How does a publisher apply for an ISSN?

The publisher should contact the appropriate national ISSN center or the ISSN International Centre. Centers require bibliographic evidence of a serial, including a copy of the title page and cover. There is no charge to publishers for the assignment of ISSNs.

For full information, publishers should contact the national library or bibliographic center in the country where they are publishing. The address of the ISSN International Centre is:

> ISSN International Centre
> 20, rue Bachaumont
> 75002 Paris
> France
> **Tel:** 33-1-42 36 73 81
> **Fax:** 33-1-40 26 32 43
> **Telex:** 219847F

The address for the U.S. national ISSN center is:

> National Serials Data Program (NSDP)
> Library of Congress
> Washington, DC 20540-4160
> **Tel:** 202-707-6452
> **Fax:** 202-707-6333

9. What is SISAC?

SISAC stands for the Serials Industry Systems Advisory Committee. SISAC is an industry group formed to develop voluntary standardized formats for electronically transmitting serials business transaction information. SISAC provides a forum where serial (particularly journal) publishers, library system vendors, and librarians can discuss mutual concerns regarding the electronic transmission of serial information and develop cooperative solutions, in the form of standardized formats, to efficiently address these concerns.

10. What is the SISAC Symbol (SICI) and its relationship to the ISSN?

The Serial Item and Contribution Identifier (SICI) is a serial identification code which follows the ISSN and is a string of letters and/or numbers which uniquely identify a particular issue of a serial. Encoded in the SICI are chronological and enumeration data which identify serials by date and volume/issue numbers. According to SISAC, "the ANSI* standard extends the code down to the article level by adding location number and necessary title information, plus a record validation character. Code 128 is the bar code symbology selected by SISAC for displaying this number string in scannable form. When displayed in the Code 128 symbology, the SICI is called the SISAC symbol." The SICI is the ANSI standard; the SISAC symbol is the bar code.

*ANSI American National Standards Institute. Organization that coordinates the voluntary standards system in the United States. U.S. member of the International Standards Organization (ISO).

Abbreviations

General Abbreviations and Special Symbols

a.	annual	music rev.	music reviews
A&I	Abstracting and Indexing	N.S.	New Series
abstr.	abstracts	pat.	patents
approx.	approximately	play rev.	play reviews (theater reviews)
bi-m.	bimonthly (every two months)	pp./issue	pages per issue
bi-w.	biweekly (every two weeks)	Prof.	Professor
bibl.	bibliographies	Pub.	Publisher
bk.rev.	book reviews	q.	quarterly
CCC	Copyright Clearance Center	rec. rev.	record reviews
c/o	care of	s-a.	semiannually (twice annually)
circ.	circulation	s-m.	semimonthly (twice monthly)
cols./p.	columns per page	s-w.	semiweekly (twice weekly)
contr.	controlled	stat.	statistics
cum.index	cumulative index	subscr.	subscription
Cy.	county	tele.rev.	television reviews
d.	daily	3/m.	3 times a month
dance rev.	dance reviews	3/yr.	3 times a year
Dir.	Director	tr.lit.	trade literature (manufacturers' catalogues, reader response cards)
dist.	distributed		
Ed., Eds.	Editor, Editors	tr.mk.	trade marks
Ed.Bd.	Editorial Board	video rev.	video reviews
film rev.	film reviews	w.	weekly
fortn.	fortnightly (every two weeks)	‡	not available from a subscription agency
ISSN	International Standard Serial Number	*	not updated / unverified
illus.	illustrations	●	online and / or CD-ROM availability
irreg.	irregular	▼	new serial
m.	monthly	†	ceased
mkt.	market prices		

Country of Publication Codes

This list of countries and their codes has been taken from the list used by the Library of Congress in the MARC II format, 1992. The list used here is not the complete list of the MARC II format and is limited to countries and territories with publications listed in Ulrich's. The states of the United States, provinces and territories of Canada, and divisions of the United Kingdom are not listed separately.

The codes are mnemonic in most cases. Special codes not in the MARC format are used for publications of two international organizations: EI for European Communities and UN for United Nations and related organizations; and KR for Ukraine.

Country Code Sequence

Code	Country	Code	Country	Code	Country
AA	- ALBANIA	GH	- GHANA	PE	- PERU
AE	- ALGERIA	GI	- GIBRALTAR	PG	- GUINEA-BISSAU
AF	- AFGHANISTAN	GL	- GREENLAND	PH	- PHILIPPINES
AG	- ARGENTINA	GM	- GAMBIA	PK	- PAKISTAN
AI	- ARMENIA	GO	- GABON	PL	- POLAND
AJ	- AZERBAIJAN	GP	- GUADELOUPE	PN	- PANAMA
AN	- ANDORRA	GR	- GREECE	PO	- PORTUGAL
AO	- ANGOLA	GS	- GEORGIA	PP	- PAPUA NEW GUINEA
AQ	- ANTIGUA	GT	- GUATEMALA	PR	- PUERTO RICO
AS	- AMERICAN SAMOA	GU	- GUAM	PY	- PARAGUAY
AT	- AUSTRALIA	GV	- GUINEA	QA	- QATAR
AU	- AUSTRIA	GW	- GERMANY	RE	- REUNION
AY	- ANTARCTICA	GY	- GUYANA	RH	- ZIMBABWE
BA	- BAHRAIN	HK	- HONG KONG	RM	- RUMANIA
BB	- BARBADOS	HO	- HONDURAS	RU	- RUSSIA
BD	- BURUNDI	HT	- HAITI	RW	- RWANDA
BE	- BELGIUM	HU	- HUNGARY	SA	- SOUTH AFRICA
BF	- BAHAMAS	IC	- ICELAND	SE	- SEYCHELLES
BG	- BANGLADESH	IE	- IRELAND	SF	- SAO TOME E PRINCIPE
BH	- BELIZE	II	- INDIA	SG	- SENEGAL
BL	- BRAZIL	IO	- INDONESIA	SI	- SINGAPORE
BM	- BERMUDA	IQ	- IRAQ	SJ	- SUDAN
BN	- BOSNIA HERCEGOVINA	IR	- IRAN	SL	- SIERRA LEONE
BO	- BOLIVIA	IS	- ISRAEL	SM	- SAN MARINO
BP	- SOLOMON ISLANDS	IT	- ITALY	SO	- SOMALIA
BR	- UNION OF MYANMAR (FORMERLY BURMA)	IV	- IVORY COAST	SP	- SPAIN
BS	- BOTSWANA	JA	- JAPAN	SQ	- SWAZILAND
BT	- BHUTAN	JM	- JAMAICA	SR	- SURINAM
BU	- BULGARIA	JO	- JORDAN	SU	- SAUDI ARABIA
BW	- BELARUS	KE	- KENYA	SW	- SWEDEN
BX	- BRUNEI DARUSSALAM	KG	- KYRGYZSTAN	SX	- NAMIBIA (FORMERLY SOUTH-WEST AFRICA)
CB	- CAMBODIA	KN	- KOREA, NORTH	SY	- SYRIA
CC	- CHINA, PEOPLE'S REPUBLIC OF	KO	- KOREA, SOUTH	SZ	- SWITZERLAND
CD	- CHAD	KR	- UKRAINE	TA	- TAJIKISTAN
CE	- SRI LANKA	KU	- KUWAIT	TC	- TURKS AND CAICOS ISLANDS
CF	- CONGO (BRAZZAVILLE)	KZ	- KAZAKHSTAN	TG	- TOGO
CH	- CHINA, REPUBLIC OF	LB	- LIBERIA	TH	- THAILAND
CI	- CROATIA	LE	- LEBANON	TI	- TUNISIA
CJ	- CAYMAN ISLANDS	LH	- LIECHTENSTEIN	TK	- TURKMENISTAN
CK	- COLOMBIA	LI	- LITHUANIA	TO	- TONGA
CL	- CHILE	LO	- LESOTHO	TR	- TRINIDAD & TOBAGO
CM	- CAMEROON	LS	- LAOS	TS	- UNITED ARAB EMIRATES
CN	- CANADA	LU	- LUXEMBOURG	TU	- TURKEY
CQ	- COMOROS	LV	- LATVIA	TV	- TUVALU
CR	- COSTA RICA	LY	- LIBYA	TZ	- TANZANIA
CS	- CZECHOSLOVAKIA	MC	- MONACO	UA	- EGYPT (ARAB REPUBLIC OF EGYPT)
CU	- CUBA	MF	- MAURITIUS	UG	- UGANDA
CV	- CAPE VERDE	MG	- MALAGASY REPUBLIC (MADAGASCAR)	UI	- UNITED KINGDOM MISC. ISLANDS
CX	- CENTRAL AFRICAN REPUBLIC	MH	- MACAO	UK	- UNITED KINGDOM
CY	- CYPRUS	MJ	- MONTSERRAT	UN	- UNITED NATIONS
DK	- DENMARK	MK	- SULTANATE OF OMAN	US	- UNITED STATES
DM	- BENIN	ML	- MALI	UV	- BURKINA FASO
DQ	- DOMINICA	MM	- MALTA	UY	- URUGUAY
DR	- DOMINICAN REPUBLIC	MP	- MONGOLIA	UZ	- UZBEKISTAN
EA	- ERITREA	MQ	- MARTINIQUE	VB	- BRITISH VIRGIN ISLANDS
EC	- ECUADOR	MR	- MOROCCO	VC	- VATICAN CITY
EG	- EQUATORIAL GUINEA	MU	- MAURITANIA	VE	- VENEZUELA
EI	- EUROPEAN COMMUNITIES	MV	- MOLDOVA	VI	- U.S. VIRGIN ISLANDS
ER	- ESTONIA	MW	- MALAWI	VN	- VIETNAM
ES	- EL SALVADOR	MX	- MEXICO	WS	- WESTERN SAMOA
ET	- ETHIOPIA	MY	- MALAYSIA	XC	- MALDIVE ISLANDS
FA	- FAEROE ISLANDS	MZ	- MOZAMBIQUE	XE	- MARSHALL ISLANDS
FG	- FRENCH GUIANA	NA	- NETHERLANDS ANTILLES	XI	- SAINT KITTS-NEVIS
FI	- FINLAND	NE	- NETHERLANDS	XK	- SAINT LUCIA
FJ	- FIJI	NG	- NIGER	XM	- SAINT VINCENT
FK	- FALKLAND ISLANDS	NL	- NEW CALEDONIA	XN	- MACEDONIA
FM	- FEDERATED STATES OF MICRONESIA	NN	- VANUATU (NEW HEBRIDES)	XO	- SLOVAKIA
FP	- FRENCH POLYNESIA	NO	- NORWAY	XR	- CZECH REPUBLIC
FR	- FRANCE	NP	- NEPAL	XV	- SLOVENIA
FT	- DJIBOUTI	NQ	- NICARAGUA	YE	- YEMEN, REPUBLIC OF
GB	- KIRIBATI	NR	- NIGERIA	YU	- YUGOSLAVIA
GD	- GRENADA	NU	- NAURU	ZA	- ZAMBIA
GE	- GERMANY, EAST	NX	- NORFOLK ISLAND	ZR	- ZAIRE
		NZ	- NEW ZEALAND		

COUNTRY OF PUBLICATION CODES

Country Sequence

AFGHANISTAN - AF
ALBANIA - AA
ALGERIA - AE
AMERICAN SAMOA - AS
ANDORRA - AN
ANGOLA - AO
ANTARCTICA - AY
ANTIGUA - AQ
ARGENTINA - AG
ARMENIA - AI
AUSTRALIA - AT
AUSTRIA - AU
AZERBAIJAN - AJ
BAHAMAS - BF
BAHRAIN - BA
BANGLADESH - BG
BARBADOS - BB
BELARUS - BW
BELGIUM - BE
BELIZE - BH
BENIN - DM
BERMUDA - BM
BHUTAN - BT
BOLIVIA - BO
BOSNIA HERCEGOVINA - BN
BOTSWANA - BS
BRAZIL - BL
BRITISH VIRGIN ISLANDS - VB
BRUNEI DARUSSALAM - BX
BULGARIA - BU
BURKINA FASO - UV
BURUNDI - BD
CAMBODIA - CB
CAMEROON - CM
CANADA - CN
CAPE VERDE - CV
CAYMAN ISLANDS - CJ
CENTRAL AFRICAN REPUBLIC - CX
CHAD - CD
CHILE - CL
CHINA, REPUBLIC OF - CC
CHINA, PEOPLE'S REPUBLIC OF - CH
COLOMBIA - CK
COMOROS - CQ
CONGO (BRAZZAVILLE) - CF
COSTA RICA - CR
CROATIA - CI
CUBA - CU
CYPRUS - CY
CZECH REPUBLIC - XR
CZECHOSLOVAKIA - CS
DENMARK - DK
DJIBOUTI - FT
DOMINICA - DQ
DOMINICAN REPUBLIC - DR
ECUADOR - EC
EGYPT (ARAB REPUBLIC OF EGYPT) - UA
EL SALVADOR - ES
EQUATORIAL GUINEA - EG
ERITREA - EA
ESTONIA - ER
ETHIOPIA - ET
EUROPEAN COMMUNITIES - EI
FAEROE ISLANDS - FA
FALKLAND ISLANDS - FK
FEDERATED STATES OF MICRONESIA - FM
FIJI - FJ
FINLAND - FI
FRANCE - FR
FRENCH GUIANA - FG
FRENCH POLYNESIA - FP
GABON - GO
GAMBIA - GM
GEORGIA - GS

GERMANY - GW
GERMANY, EAST - GE
GHANA - GH
GIBRALTAR - GI
GREECE - GR
GREENLAND - GL
GRENADA - GD
GUADELOUPE - GP
GUAM - GU
GUATEMALA - GT
GUINEA - GV
GUINEA-BISSAU - PG
GUYANA - GY
HAITI - HT
HONDURAS - HO
HONG KONG - HK
HUNGARY - HU
ICELAND - IC
INDIA - II
INDONESIA - IO
IRAN - IR
IRAQ - IQ
IRELAND - IE
ISRAEL - IS
ITALY - IT
IVORY COAST - IV
JAMAICA - JM
JAPAN - JA
JORDAN - JO
KAZAKHSTAN - KZ
KENYA - KE
KIRIBATI - GB
KOREA, NORTH - KN
KOREA, SOUTH - KO
KUWAIT - KU
KYRGYZSTAN - KG
LAOS - LS
LATVIA - LV
LEBANON - LE
LESOTHO - LO
LIBERIA - LB
LIBYA - LY
LIECHTENSTEIN - LH
LITHUANIA - LI
LUXEMBOURG - LU
MACAO - MH
MACEDONIA - XN
MALAGASY REPUBLIC (MADAGASCAR) - MG
MALAWI - MW
MALAYSIA - MY
MALDIVE ISLANDS - XC
MALI - ML
MALTA - MM
MARSHALL ISLANDS - XE
MARTINIQUE - MQ
MAURITANIA - MU
MAURITIUS - MF
MEXICO - MX
MOLDOVA - MV
MONACO - MC
MONGOLIA - MP
MONTSERRAT - MJ
MOROCCO - MR
MOZAMBIQUE - MZ
NAMIBIA (FORMERLY SOUTH-WEST AFRICA) - SX
NAURU - NU
NEPAL - NP
NETHERLANDS - NE
NETHERLANDS ANTILLES - NA
NEW CALEDONIA - NC
NEW ZEALAND - NZ
NICARAGUA - NQ
NIGER - NG
NIGERIA - NR

NORFOLK ISLAND - NX
NORWAY - NO
PAKISTAN - PK
PANAMA - PN
PAPUA NEW GUINEA - PP
PARAGUAY - PY
PERU - PE
PHILIPPINES - PH
POLAND - PL
PORTUGAL - PO
PUERTO RICO - PR
QATAR - QA
REUNION - RE
RUMANIA - RM
RUSSIA - RU
RWANDA - RW
SAINT KITTS-NEVIS - XI
SAINT LUCIA - XK
SAINT VINCENT - XM
SAN MARINO - SM
SAO TOME E PRINCIPE - SF
SAUDI ARABIA - SU
SENEGAL - SG
SEYCHELLES - SE
SIERRA LEONE - SL
SINGAPORE - SI
SLOVAKIA - XO
SLOVENIA - XV
SOLOMON ISLANDS - BP
SOMALIA - SO
SOUTH AFRICA - SA
SPAIN - SP
SRI LANKA - CE
SUDAN - SJ
SULTANATE OF OMAN - MK
SURINAM - SR
SWAZILAND - SQ
SWEDEN - SW
SWITZERLAND - SZ
SYRIA - SY
TAJIKISTAN - TA
TANZANIA - TZ
THAILAND - TH
TOGO - TO
TONGA - TR
TRINIDAD & TOBAGO - TT
TUNISIA - TI
TURKEY - TU
TURKMENISTAN - TK
TURKS AND CAICOS ISLANDS - TC
TUVALU - TV
U.S. VIRGIN ISLANDS - VI
U.S.S.R. - UR
UGANDA - UG
UKRAINE - KR
UNION OF MYANMAR (FORMERLY BURMA) - BR
UNITED ARAB EMIRATES - TS
UNITED STATES - US
UNITED NATIONS - UN
UNITED KINGDOM - UK
UNITED KINGDOM MISC. ISLANDS - UI
URUGUAY - UY
UZBEKISTAN - UZ
VANUATU (NEW HEBRIDES) - NN
VATICAN CITY - VC
VENEZUELA - VE
VIETNAM - VN
WESTERN SAMOA - WS
YEMEN, REPUBLIC OF - YE
YUGOSLAVIA - YU
ZAIRE - ZR
ZAMBIA - ZA
ZIMBABWE - RH

Document Suppliers

ADONIS
ADONIS B.V. (main office)
Spuistraat 112D
1012 VA Amsterdam
The Netherlands
Tel: 31-20-6262629
Fax: 31-20-6261437

ADONIS USA
238 Main St.
Cambridge, MA 02142
USA
Tel: 800-944-6415
Fax: 617-876-7022

BLDSC
British Library Document Supply Center
Customer Services
Boston Spa, Wetherby
W. Yorkshire LS23 7BQ
England
Tel: 44-937-546060
Fax: 44-937-546333

CASDDS
Chemical Abstracts Service
Document Delivery Service
P.O. Box 3012
Columbus, OH 43210
USA
Tel: 800-678-4337
Fax: 614-447-3648
E-mail: dds65@cas.org

CIS
Congressional Information Service, Inc.
CIS Documents on Demand
4520 East-West Hwy., Ste. 800
Bethesda, MD 20814-3389
USA
Tel: 301-654-1550, 800-227-2477
Fax: 301-657-3203

EI
Engineering Information Inc.
Article Express International, Inc.
469 Union Ave.
Westbury, NY 11590
USA
Tel: 516-997-0699, 800-238-3458
Fax: 516-997-0890
E-mail: DDS@WORK4U.ARTX.COM

Faxon
Faxon Research Services, Inc.
15 Southwest Park
Westwood, MA 02090
USA
Tel: 800-999-3594
Fax: 800-933-6831
E-mail: macintosh@faxon.com

SWETS
Swets & Zeitlinger bv
Heereweg 347
P.O. Box 830
2160 SZ Lisse
The Netherlands
Tel: 31-2521-35111
Fax: 31-2521-15888
Telex: 41325

UMI
UMI Article Clearinghouse
300 N. Zeeb Rd.
P.O. Box 1346
Ann Arbor, MI 48106-1346
USA
Tel: 800-521-0600, ext. 2786
Fax: 313-761-1032, 313-665-7075
E-mail: ACHMAIL@UMI.COM

UnCover
The UnCover Co.
3801 E. Florida Ave., Ste. 200
Denver, CO 80210
USA
Tel: 303-758-3030
Fax: 303-758-5946
E-mail: UNCOVER@CARL.ORG

Micropublishers and Distributors

ACR **A.C.R.P.P.**
(Association pour la Conservation et la Reproduction Photographique de la Presse)
B.P. 21
77313 Marne-La-Vallee Cedex 21
France
Tel: 1-60-17-68-10; **Fax:** 1-60-17-68-05

ADL **Advanced Library Systems, Inc.**
100 Brickstone Sq.
P.O. Box 246
Andover, MA 01810-0005
USA
Tel: 508-470-0610; **Fax:** 508-475-1072

AFS **Fertility and Sterility**
(no longer producer)
2140 11 Ave. S., Ste. 200
Birmingham, AL 35205-2800
USA
Tel: 205-933-8494; **Fax:** 205-930-9904

AGU **American Geophysical Union**
2000 Florida Ave., N.W.
Washington, DC 20009
USA
Tel: 202-462-6900; **Fax:** 202-328-0566

AIP **American Institute of Physics**
500 Sunnyside Blvd.
Woodbury, NY 11797-2999
USA
Tel: 516-576-2270; Fax: 516-349-9704

AIR **Aircraft Technical Publishers**
101 S. Hill Dr.
Brisbane, CA 94005
USA
Tel: 415-468-1705; **Fax:** 415-468-1596

AJP **American Jewish Periodical Center**
Hebrew Union College - Jewish Institute of Religion
3101 Clifton Ave.
Cincinnati, OH 45220
USA
Tel: 513-221-1875; **Fax:** 513-221-0321

ALP **Alpha Com**
Sportallee 6
22335 Hamburg
Germany
Tel: 49-40-51302-123; **Fax:** 49-40-51302111

AMP **Adam Matthew Publications**
8 Oxford St.
Marlborough, Wiltshire SN8 1AP
England
Tel: 44-672-511921; **Fax:** 44-672-511663

AMS **AMS Press, Inc.**
(no longer producer)
56 E. 13th St.
New York, NY 10003
USA
Tel: 212-777-4700; **Fax:** 212-995-5413

ATL **American Theological Library Association, Preservation Board**
820 Church St., Ste. 300
Evanston, IL 60201
USA
Tel: 708-869-7788; **Fax:** 708-869-8513

BAR **Barbour Index plc**
New Lodge, Drift Rd.
Windsor, Berkshire SL4 4RQ
England
Tel: 44-344-884121; Fax: 44-344-884845

BHP **Brookhaven Press**
P.O. Box 2287
La Crosse, WI 54602-2287
USA
Tel: 608-781-0850; **Fax:** 608-781-3883

BIO **BIOSIS**
2100 Arch St.
Philadelphia, PA 19103-1399
USA
Tel: 215-587-4800, 800-523-4806
Fax: 215-587-2016

BKR **Bowker A&I Publishing**
(See: CIS)

BLC **Bloch & Company**
P.O. Box 18058
Cleveland, OH 44118
USA
Tel: 216-371-0979; **Fax:** 216-371-9493

BLH **Bell & Howell**
(Micropublishing now operated by UMI)

BLI **Balch Institute**
Research Library
18 S. 7th St.
Philadelphia, PA 19106
USA
Tel: 215-925-8090; **Fax:** 215-925-8195

BNB **British Library National Bibliographic Service**
Boston Spa, Wetherby
W. Yorkshire LS23 7BQ
England
Tel: 44-937-546585; **Fax:** 44-937-546586

MICROPUBLISHERS AND DISTRIBUTORS

BNQ **Bibliotheque national du Quebec**
Section de la Reproduction
125 rue Sherbrooke Ouest
Montreal, PQ H2X 1X4
Canada
Tel: 514-873-1100; **Fax:** 514-873-9932

BWC **Butterworth & Co., Ltd.**
88 Kingsway
London WC2B 6AB
England
Tel: 44-71-4056900; **Fax:** 44-71-4051332

CCM **Core Collection Micropublishers**
Div. of Roth Publishing, Inc.
185 Great Neck Rd.
Great Neck, NY 11021
USA
Tel: 516-466-3676, 800-327-0295
Fax: 516-829-7746

CDS **Current Digest of the Soviet Press**
3857 N. High St.
Columbus, OH 43214
USA
Tel: 614-292-4234; **Fax:** 614-267-6310

CHL **Chadwyck-Healey Ltd.**
Cambridge Place
Cambridge CB2 1NR
England
Tel: 44-223-311479; **Fax:** 44-223-66440
Chadwyck-Healey Inc.
1101 King St.
Alexandria, VA 22314-2944
USA
Tel: 703-683-4890; **Fax:** 703-683-7589

CIH **Canadian Institute for Historical Microreproductions**
P.O. Box 2428, Sta. D
Ottawa, ON K1P 5W5
Canada
Tel: 613-235-2628; **Fax:** 613-235-9752

CIS **Congressional Information Service, Inc.**
4520 East-West Hwy., Ste. 800
Bethesda, MD 20814-3389
USA
Tel: 301-654-1550, 800-638-8380
Fax: 301-654-4033

CLA **Canadian Library Association**
(no longer producer)
Microfilm Department
200 Elgin St., Ste. 602
Ottawa, ON K2P 1L5
Canada
Tel: 613-232-9625; **Fax:** 613-563-9895

CLS **CLASS**
(Cooperative Library Agency for
Systems & Services)
1415 Koll Circle, Ste. 101
San Jose, CA 95112-4698
USA
Tel: 408-453-0444; **Fax:** 408-453-5379

CMC **Computer Microfilm Corp.**
3900 Wheeler Ave.
Alexandria, VA 22304
USA
Tel: 703-823-0500; **Fax:** 703-823-0505

CML **Commonwealth Microfilm Products**
202 Amber St.
Markham, ON L3R 3J8
Canada
Tel: 905-415-9498; **Fax:** 905-415-9616

EDR **Eric Document Reproduction Service**
(See: CMC)

EEE **Institute of Electrical and Electronics Engineers Inc.**
345 E. 47th St.
New York, NY 10017
USA
Tel: 212-705-7900; **Fax:** 212-705-7682

EMP **Emmett Publishing, Ltd.**
W. House 21, West St.
Haslemere, Surrey GU27 2AB
England
Tel: 44-428-654443; **Fax:** 44-428-661582

FCM **Fairchild Books & Visuals**
7 W. 34th St.
New York, NY 10001
USA
Tel: 212-630-3880; **Fax:** 212-630-3868

GCS **Preston Publications**
7800 Merrimac Ave.
P.O. Box 48312
Niles, IL 60714
USA
Tel: 708-965-0566; **Fax:** 708-965-7639

GMC **General Microfilm Co.**
(acquired by OMNISYS Corp.)

HAW **The Haworth Press**
10 Alice St.
Binghamton, NY 13904
USA
Tel: 607-722-7259; **Fax:** 607-722-1424

HPL **Harvester Press Microfilm Publications Ltd.**
(Now wholly owned and operated
by Research Publications, Inc.)

IAM **SIAM Publications**
3600 University City Science Center
Philadelphia, PA 19104-2688
USA
Tel: 215-382-9800; **Fax:** 215-386-7999

ICS **Editions I.C.S.**
23 Ave. Villemain
75014 Paris
France
Tel: 33-1-45392244; **Fax:** 33-1-45434680

IDC **IDC Microform Publishers bv**
P.O. Box 11205
2301 EE Leiden
The Netherlands
Tel: 31-71142700; **Fax:** 31-71131721

MICROPUBLISHERS AND DISTRIBUTORS

IFA   **International Federation of Film Archives (FIAF)**
6 Nottingham St.
London W1M 3RB
England
Tel: 44-71-2240991; **Fax:** 44-71-2241203

ILO   **ILO Publications**
1828 L St., N.W., Ste. 801
Washington, DC 20036
USA
Tel: 202-653-7652; **Fax:** 202-653-7687

IMI   **Irish Microforms, Ltd.**
Unit 56
Sandyford Industrial Estate
Dublin 18
Ireland
Tel: 353-1-2893626; **Fax:** 353-1-2954270

IPC   **Institute of Paper Science & Technology, Inc.**
500 19th St. N.W.
Atlanta, GA 30318
USA
Tel: 404-853-9500; **Fax:** 404-853-9510

IRE   **International Research and Evaluation**
21098 IRE-Control Center
Eagan, MN 55121-0098
USA
Tel: 612-888-9635; **Fax:** 612-888-9124

ISI   **Institute for Scientific Information**
3501 Market St.
Philadelphia, PA 19104
USA
Tel: 215-386-0100
Fax: 215-386-6362, 215-386-2911

JAI   **JAI Press Inc.**
55 Old Post Rd., No. 2
P.O. Box 1678
Greenwich, CT 06836-1678
USA
Tel: 203-661-7602; **Fax:** 203-661-0792

JOH   **Johnson Reprint Microeditions**
(Out of business)

JSC   **J.S. Canner & Co.**
10 Charles St.
Needham Heights, MA 02194
USA
Tel: 617-449-9103; **Fax:** 617-449-1767

KGS   **K.G. Saur**
A Reed Reference Publishing Company
121 Chanlon Rd.
New Providence, NJ 07974
USA
Tel: 908-464-6800; **Fax:** 908-771-7725

KHS   **Kansas State Historical Society Microfilm Publications**
120 W. Tenth Ave.
Topeka, KS 66612-1291
USA
Tel: 913-296-3086; **Fax:** 913-296-1005

KTO   **Kraus Microform**
350 Saw Mill River Rd.
Millwood, NY 10546-1035
USA
Tel: 914-762-2200; **Fax:** 914-762-1195

LCP   **The Library of Congress Photoduplication Service**
101 Second St.
Washington, DC 20540
USA
Tel: 202-707-5640; **Fax:** 202-707-1771

LIB   **Library Microfilms**
1115 E. Arques Ave.
Sunnyvale, CA 94086
USA
Tel: 408-736-7444; **Fax:** 408-736-4397

LOP   **Lomond Publications**
P.O. Box 88
Mt. Airy, MD 21771
USA
Tel: 301-829-1496, 800-443-6299

MCA   **Microfilming Corporation of America**
(Acquired by UMI; operation phased out)

MCE   **Microcard Editions**
(See: CIS)

MDX   **Micromedex Inc.**
600 Grant St.
Denver, CO 80203
USA
Tel: 303-831-1400; **Fax:** 303-837-1717

MEL   **Metropolitan Library Service Agency (MELSA)**
570 Asbury St., Ste. 201
St. Paul, MN 55104-1849
USA
Tel: 612-645-5731; **Fax:** 612-649-3169

MIM   **Elsevier Science Ltd.**
Headington Hill Hall
Oxford OX3 0BW
England
Tel: 44-865-79414; **Fax:** 44-865-60285

MIS   **Moody's Investors Service**
Sales Department
99 Church St.
New York, NY 10007
USA
Tel: 212-553-0300; **Fax:** 212-553-4700

MML   **Micromedia Limited**
20 Victoria St.
Toronto, ON M5C 2N8
Canada
Tel: 416-362-5211, 800-387-2689
Fax: 416-362-6161

MMP   **McLaren Micropublishing Ltd.**
P.O. Box 972, Sta. F
Toronto, ON M4Y 2N9
Canada
Tel: 416-960-4801; **Fax:** 416-964-3745

MICROPUBLISHERS AND DISTRIBUTORS

MUE University Music Editions, Inc.
P.O. Box 192, Ft. George Sta.
New York, NY 10040
USA
Tel: 718-569-5340, 5393; **Fax:** 718-601-7226

NBI Newsbank, Inc.
58 Pine St.
New Canaan, CT 06840
USA
Tel: 203-966-1100, 800-243-7694
Fax: 203-966-6254

NRP Norman Ross Publishing, Inc.
330 W. 58th St., Ste. 214
New York, NY 10019
USA
Tel: 212-765-8200, 800-648-8850
Fax: 212-765-2393

NTI National Technical Information Service
5285 Port Royal Rd.
Springfield, VA 22161
USA
Tel: 703-487-4600; **Fax:** 703-321-8547

NYL New York Law Publishing Co.
345 Park Ave., S.
New York, NY 10010
USA
Tel: 212-779-9200; **Fax:** 212-696-4287

NYT New York Times Information Bank
(Operation phased out)
229 W. 43rd St.
New York, NY 10036
USA
Tel: 212-556-1234

OEC Organization for Economic Cooperation & Development, Publications & Information Center
2001 L St., N.W., Ste. 700
Washington, DC 20036-4910
USA
Tel: 202-785-6323; **Fax:** 202-785-0350

OMN OMNISYS Corp.
211 Second Ave.
Waltham, MA 02154
USA
Tel: 617-684-1234; **Fax:** 617-684-1245

OMP Oxford Microform Publication Ltd.
(Acquired by UMI)

PMC Princeton Microfilm Corp.
P.O. Box 2073
Princeton, NJ 08543
USA
Tel: 609-452-2066, 800-257-9502
Fax: 609-275-6201

PSL The Pretoria State Library
P.O. Box 397
Pretoria 0001
Republic of South Africa
Tel: 27-12-218931; **Fax:** 27-12-3255984

RPI Research Publications
12 Lunar Dr.
Drawer AB
Woodbridge, CT 06525
USA
Tel: 203-397-2600; **Fax:** 203-397-3893

RRI Fred B. Rothman & Co.
10368 W. Centennial Rd.
Littleton, CO 80127
USA
Tel: 303-979-5657, 800-457-1986
Fax: 303-978-1457

SAS Society for Applied Spectroscopy
198 Thomas Johnson Dr., Ste S2
Frederick, MD 21702
USA
Tel: 301-694-8122; **Fax:** 301-694-6860

SOC Societe Canadienne du Microfilm Inc. - Canadian Microfilming Co. Ltd.
464 rue Saint-Jean
Montreal, PQ H2Y 2S1
Canada
Tel: 514-288-5404; **Fax:** 514-843-4690

SWZ Swets & Zeitlinger B.V.
Backsets Department
P.O. Box 810
2160 SZ Lisse
The Netherlands
Tel: 31-2521-35334; **Fax:** 31-2521-15888

TMI Tennessee Microfilms
P.O. Box 23075
Nashville, TN 37202
USA
Tel: 615-242-3632

UMI University Microfilms International
(A Bell & Howell Company)
300 N. Zeeb Rd.
Ann Arbor, MI 48103
USA
Tel: 313-761-4700, 800-521-0600
Fax: 313-761-1203

UNW University of Wisconsin Library
Interlibrary Loan Department
728 State St., Rm. 231
Madison, WI 53706
USA
Tel: 608-262-3193; **Fax:** 608-262-4649

UPD Updata Publications, Inc.
1736 Westwood Blvd.
Los Angeles, CA 90024
USA
Tel: 310-474-5900; **Fax:** 310-474-4095

VCI VCH Publishers, Inc.
303 N.W. 12th Ave.
Deerfield Beach, FL 33442-1788
USA
Tel: 305-428-5566
Fax: 305-428-8201, 800-367-8247

VFN	**The Voltaire Foundation at the Taylor Institution** St. Giles' Oxford OX1 3NA England **Tel:** 44-865-270250; **Fax:** 44-865-270740	**WPI**	**Cadmus Journal Services** 428 E. Preston St. Baltimore, MD 21202 USA **Tel:** 410-528-8555; **Fax:** 410-528-8596
WDS	**Dawson Microfiche** (Distributor only) Cannon House Parkfarm Rd. Folkestone, Kent CT19 5EE England **Tel:** 44-303-850101; **Fax:** 44-303-850440	**WSH**	**William S. Hein & Co., Inc.** Hein Bldg., 1285 Main St. Buffalo, NY 14209-1987 USA **Tel:** 716-882-2600, 800-828-7571 **Fax:** 716-883-8100
WMP	**World Microfilm Publications Ltd** Microworld House, 2-6 Foscote Mews London W9 2HH England **Tel:** 44-71-2662202; **Fax:** 44-71-2662314	**WWS**	**Williams & Wilkins** 428 E. Preston St. Baltimore, MD 21202 USA **Tel:** 410-528-4309; **Fax:** 410-528-4312

Money Symbols

SYMBOL	UNIT	COUNTRY
A.	austral	Argentina
Arg.$	peso	Argentina
Aus.$	dollar	Australia
B.	baht	Thailand
B.$	dollar	Brunei Darussalam, Belize
BEF	franc	Belgium
Bl.	balboa	Panama
Bol.$	peso	Bolivia
Br.	birr	Ethiopia
Bs.	bolivar	Venezuela
BTN	bonus do tesouro nacional	Brazil
BTNF	bonus do tesouro nacional fiscal	Brazil
C.$	cordoba; dollar	Nicaragua, Cayman Islands
Can.$	dollar	Canada
CFPF	franc	New Caledonia
Col.	colon	Costa Rica, El Salvador
Col.$	peso	Colombia
Cr.$	cruzerio	Brazil
Cz.$	cruzado	Brazil
D.	dalasi	Gambia
DH., Dh.	dirham	Morocco, United Arab Emirates
DKK	krone	Denmark
DM.	mark	Germany
din.	dinar	Algeria, Jordan, Kuwait, Libya, Tunisia, Yugoslavia
$	dollar; peso	various
Dr.	drachma	Greece
E.	emalageni	Swaziland
EAs.	shilling	East Africa, Somalia, Tanzania, Uganda
EC$.	dollar	Dominica, St. Lucia
ECU	European currency unit	European Communities
EEK	kroon	Estonia
Esc.	escudo	Angola, Portugal, Mozambique
F.	franc	Djibouti, France, Guadeloupe, Mali, Martinique, Monaco, Rwanda
F$	dollar	Fiji
FIM	markka	Finland
fl.	guilder; florin	Netherlands, Netherlands Antilles, Surinam
FMG.	franc	Malagasy Republic
Fmk.	mark; markka	Finland
Fr.	franc	Belgium, Liechtenstein, Luxembourg, Switzerland
Fr.CFA	franc	African Financial Community, Benin, Burkina Faso, Burundi, Cameroon, Central African Republic, Chad, Congo, Gabon, Ivory Coast, Niger, Reunion, Senegal, Togo
Ft.	forint	Hungary
g.	guarani	Paraguay
Gde.	gourde	Haiti
G.$	dollar	Guyana
HK$	dollar	Hong Kong
HRD	dinar	Croatia
I£	pound	Ireland
I.D.	dinar	Iran, Iraq
IRI.	riyal	Iran
IS	shekel	Israel
ISK	krona	Iceland
J.$	dollar	Jamaica
Jam.$	dollar	Jamaica
K.	kina; kwacha	Malawi, Papua New Guinea, Zambia
Kc.	koruna	Czech Republic
Kcs.	koruny	Czechoslovakia
kip	kip	Laos
Kr.	krona; krone	Scandinavian countries
KShs.	shilling	Kenya
L.	lempira; lira	Honduras, Italy
Le.	leone	Sierra Leone
lei	lei	Rumania
Lit.	lira italiana	Italy
Ls.	lats	Latvia
Lt.	litas	Lithuania
lv.	lev	Bulgaria
M.$	dollar; ringgit	Malaysia
Mex.$	peso	Mexico
$m.n.	moneda nacional	various
mt.	metical	Mozambique
N$	new Uruguay peso	Uruguay
NC.	cedi	Ghana
NOK	krone	Norway
NT.$	dollar	Republic of China (Taiwan)
N.Z.$	dollar	New Zealand
ORI.	riyal	Oman
P.	pula; peso	Botswana, Philippines, various
QRI.	riyal	Qatar
£	pound	Ireland, Gt. Britain, Malta
£C	pound	Cyprus
£E	pound	Egypt
£L	pound; dinar	Lebanon
£N	pound; naira	Nigeria
£S	pound	Syria
ptas.	peseta	Spain
Q.	quetzal	Guatemala
R.	rand	South Africa, Lesotho, Namibia
RD.$	peso	Dominican Republic
Rps.	rupiah	Indonesia
Rs.	riel; rial; rupee	Cambodia, India, Iran, Mauritius, Nepal, Pakistan, Seychelles, Sri Lanka
Rub.	ruble	Commonwealth of Independent States
S/	sucre; sole	Ecuador, Peru
S.	schilling	Austria
S.$	dollar	Singapore
SEK	krona	Sweden
SFr.	franc	Liechtenstein, Switzerland
SI$	dollar	Solomon Islands
SK.	koruna	Slovakia
SL.	pound	Sudan
SLT	talar	Slovenia
SRI.	riyal	Saudia Arabia
$T.	dollar	Tonga
TK.	taka	Bangladesh
TL.	pound; lira	Turkey
T.T.$	dollar	Trinidad and Tobago
tugrik	tugrik	Mongolia
UM	ouguiya	Mauritania
Urg.$	peso	Uruguay
vatu	vatu	Vanuatu
VN.$	dollar	Vietnam
Won	won (hwan)	Korea
Y	yuan	People's Republic of China
Yen	yen	Japan
YRI.	rial	Yemen
Z	zaire	Zaire
Z.$	dollar	Zimbabwe
Zl.	zloty	Poland

Reprint Services

CIS   **Congressional Information Service, Inc.**
4520 East-West Hwy., Ste. 800
Bethesda, MD 20814-3389
USA
Tel: 301-654-1550, 800-227-2477
Fax: 301-657-3203

IRC   **International Reprint Corp.**
968 Admiral Callaghan Ln., #268
P.O. Box 12004
Vallejo, CA 94590
USA
Tel: 707-746-0722
Fax: 707-746-1643

ISI   **Institute for Scientific Information**
3501 Market St.
Philadelphia, PA 19104
USA
Tel: 215-386-0100
Fax: 215-386-6362, 215-386-2911

JOH   **Johnson Reprint Microeditions**
(out of business)

KTO   **Kraus Microform**
358 Saw Mill River Rd.
Millwood, NY 10546-1035
USA
Tel: 914-762-2200
Fax: 914-762-1195

RRI   **Fred B. Rothman & Co.**
10368 W. Centennial Rd.
Littleton, CO 80127
USA
Tel: 303-979-5657, 800-457-1986
Fax: 303-978-1457

SCH   **Schmidt Periodicals GmbH**
Dettendorf
D-8201 Bad Feilnbach 2
Germany
Tel: 49-8064221
Fax: 49-8064557

SWZ   **Swets & Zeitlinger bv**
Backsets Department
P.O. Box 810
2160 SZ Lisse
The Netherlands
Tel: 31-2521-35334
Fax: 31-2521-15888
Telex: 41325

UMI   **University Microfilms International**
(A Bell & Howell Company)
300 N. Zeeb Rd.
Ann Arbor, MI 48103
USA
Tel: 313-761-4700, 800-521-0600
Fax: 313-761-1203

WDS   **Dawson Microfiche**
Cannon House
Parkfarm Rd.
Folkestone, Kent CT19 5EE
England
Tel: 44-303-850101
Fax: 44-303-850440

WSH   **William S. Hein & Co., Inc.**
Hein Bldg., 1285 Main St.
Buffalo, NY 14209-1987
USA
Tel: 716-882-2600, 800-828-7571
Fax: 716-883-8100

Wire Services

AAP	Australian Associated Press Information Services
AFP	Agence France-Press
ANP	Algemeen Nederlands Persbureau (Netherlands Press Agency)
AP	Associated Press (USA)
APP	Associated Press of Pakistan
BNS	Baltic News Service
CanP	Canadian Press
EFE	Agencia EFE (Spain)
KR	Knight-Ridder Financial News
LAT-WP	Los Angeles Times-Washington Post News Service
NPA	New Zealand Associated Press
NYT	New York Times News Service
PAP	Polska Agencja Prasowa (Polish Press Agency)
PPI	Pakistan Press International
RN	Reuters News Agency
SAPA	South African Press Association
SHNA	Scripps-Howard Newspaper Alliance - Scripps-Howard News Service
TASS	Telegrafnoe Agentstvo Suverennykh Stran (Telegraphic Agency of the Sovereign Countries)
UK News	United Kingdom News
UPI	United Press International

Abstracting and Indexing Services

This list contains the full names of all abstracting and indexing services whose abbreviations are used in entries in the Classified List of Serials. For all currently published abstracting and indexing services, entries containing full bibliographic information will be found in the Classified List of Serials. Consult the Title Index for page numbers. (Bibliographic information for ceased titles can be found in the Bowker International Serials Database online.)

A

A.A.P.P.Abstr.	Amino Acids, Peptides & Proteins Abstracts (Now: Cambridge Scientific Biochemistry Abstracts, Part 3: Amino Acids, Peptides & Proteins)
AAR	Accounting Articles
ABC	Abstracts in BioCommerce
A.B.C.Pol.Sci.	ABC Pol Sci; A Bibliography of Contents: Political Science and Government
ABI Inform.	A B I-INFORM
ABTICS	Abstracts and Book Title Index Card Services (Ceased)
A.D.& D.	Alcohol, Drugs and Driving: Abstracts and Reviews (Now: Alcohol, Drugs and Driving)
AESIS	A E S I S Quarterly (Australian Earth Sciences Information System)
A.I.Abstr.	Artificial Intelligence Abstracts (United States) (Ceased)
A.I.C.P.	Anthropological Index to Current Periodicals in the Library of the Museum of Mankind Library
A.I.D.Res.Dev. Abstr.	A.I.D. Research & Development Abstracts (Agency for International Development)
A.I.P.P.	Annual Index to Poetry in Periodicals (Now: Roth's American Poetry Annual) (Ceased)
AIT Reports	AIT Reports and Publications on Renewable Energy Resources. Abstracts (Asian Institute of Technology) (Now: A I T Reports and Publications on Energy. Abstracts)
ALISA	A L I S A (Australian Library and Information Science Abstracts)
API Abstr.	A P I Abstracts: Literature (American Petroleum Institute) (Now: Literature Abstracts)
API Catal.	A P I Abstracts: Catalysts & Catalysis (Now: Literature Abstracts: Catalysts - Zeolites)
API Hlth.& Environ.	A P I Abstracts: Health & Environment (Now: Literature Abstracts: Health & Environment)
API Oil.	A P I Abstracts: Oilfield Chemicals (Now: Literature and Patent Abstracts: Oilfield Chemicals)
API Pet.Ref.	A P I Abstracts: Petroleum Refining and Petrochemicals (Now: Literature Abstracts: Petroleum Refining and Petrochemicals)
API Pet.Subst.	A P I Abstracts: Petroleum Substitutes (Now: Literature Abstracts: Petroleum Substitutes)
API Transport.	A P I Abstracts: Transportation and Storage (Now: Literature Abstracts: Transportation and Storage)
A.S.& T.Ind.	Applied Science & Technology Index
ASCA	Automatic Subject Citation Alert (Now: Research Alert (Philadelphia))
ASEAN Manage. Abstr.	A S E A N Management Abstracts (Association of South East Asian Nations)
ASSIA	A S S I A: Applied Social Sciences Index & Abstracts
ASTIS	A S T I S Bibliography (Arctic Science & Technology Information System)
Abr.R.G.	Abridged Readers' Guide to Periodical Literature
Abstr.Anthropol.	Abstracts in Anthropology
Abstr.Bk.Rev. Curr.Leg.Per.	Abstracts of Book Reviews in Current Legal Periodicals (Ceased)
Abstr.Bulg.Sci. Med.Lit.	Abstracts of Bulgarian Scientific Medical Literature
Abstr.Bull.Inst. Pap.Chem.	Institute of Paper Chemistry. Abstract Bulletin (Now: Institute of Paper Science and Technology. Abstract Bulletin)
Abstr.Crim.& Pen.	Abstracts on Criminology and Penology (Now: Criminology, Penology & Police Science Abstracts)
Abstr.Engl.Stud.	Abstracts of English Studies
Abstr.Folk.Stud.	Abstracts of Folklore Studies (Ceased)
Abstr.Health Care Manage. Stud.	Abstracts of Health Care Management Studies (Ceased)
Abstr.Health Eff. Environ.Pollut.	Abstracts on Health Effects of Environmental Pollutants (Ceased)
Abstr.Hosp. Manage.Stud.	Abstracts of Hospital Management Studies (Now: Abstracts of Health Care Management Studies) (Ceased)
Abstr.Hum.Comp. Inter.	Abstracts in Human-Computer Interaction
Abstr.Hyg.	Abstracts on Hygiene and Communicable Diseases
Abstr.Inter.Med.	Abstracts in Internal Medicine (Now: Abstracts in Medicine and Key Word Index)
Abstr.J.Earthq. Eng.	Abstract Journal in Earthquake Engineering
Abstr.Mil.Bibl.	Abstracts of Military Bibliography

Abstr.Musl.Rel.	European Muslims and Christian-Muslim Relations. Abstracts. (Ceased)
Abstr.N.Amer.Geol.	Abstracts of North American Geology (Ceased)
Abstr.Pop.Cult.	Abstracts of Popular Culture (Ceased)
Abstr.Rural Dev.Trop.	Abstracts on Rural Development in the Tropics
Abstr.Soc.Geront.	Abstracts in Social Gerontology: Current Literature on Aging
Abstr.Soc.Work.	Abstracts for Social Workers (Now: Social Work Abstracts)
Abstr.Trop.Agri.	Abstracts on Tropical Agriculture
Acad.Ind.	Academic Index
Access	Access: the Supplementary Index to Periodicals
Account.& Data Proc.Abstr.	Accounting & Data Processing Abstracts (Now: Accounting & Finance Abstracts) (Also see: Anbar)
Account.Ind.	Accountant's Index (Now: Accounting and Tax Index)
Acid Pre.Dig.	Acid Precipitation Digest (Ceased)
Acid Rain Abstr.	Acid Rain Abstracts (Now: Environment Abstracts)
Acid Rain Ind.	Acid Rain Annual Index (Now: Environment Abstracts Annual)
Acoust.Abstr.	Acoustics Abstracts
Adol.Ment.Hlth.Abstr.	Adolescent Mental Health Abstracts (Ceased)
Agri.Eng.Abstr.	Agricultural Engineering Abstracts
Agri.Ind.	Agricultural Index (Now: Biological & Agricultural Index)
Agrindex	Agrindex
Agroforest.Abstr.	Agroforestry Abstracts
Air Un.Lib.Ind.	Air University Library Index to Military Periodicals
Alloys Ind.	Alloys Index
Alt.Press Ind.	Alternative Press Index
Amer.Bibl.Slavic & E.Ear.Stud.	American Bibliography of Slavic and East European Studies
Amer.Hist.& Life	America: History & Life
Amer.Hum.Ind.	American Humanities Index
Amer.Stat.Ind.	American Statistics Index
Anal.Abstr.	Analytical Abstracts
Anbar	Anbar Management Services Abstracts (Now: Management Services & Production Abstracts; Marketing & Distribution Abstracts; Personal & Training Abstracts) (Also see: Account.& Data Proc.Abstr.; also see: Computer Abstr.; also see: Top Manage.Abstr.)
Anim.Behav.Abstr.	Animal Behavior Abstracts
Anim.Breed.Abstr.	Animal Breeding Abstracts
Anthropol.Lit.	Anthropological Literature
Ap.Ind.	Apple Index
Apic.Abstr.	Apicultural Abstracts
Appl.Ecol.Abstr.	Applied Ecology Abstracts (Now: Ecology Abstracts)
Appl.Mech.Rev.	Applied Mechanics Reviews
Aqua.Sci.& Fish.Abstr.	Aquatic Sciences & Fisheries Abstracts (Parts 1, 2)
Aquacult.Abstr.	A S F A Aquaculture Abstracts
Archit.Per.Ind.	Architectural Periodicals Index
Arct.Bibl.	Arctic Bibliography (Ceased)
Art & Archaeol.Tech.Abstr.	Art and Archaeology Technical Abstracts
Art Ind.	Art Index
Art.Hosp.& Tour.	Articles in Hospitality and Tourism
Art.Int.Abstr.	Artificial Intelligence Abstracts (England) (Ceased)
Artbibl.	Artbibliographies Current Titles
Artbibl.Mod.	Artbibliographies Modern
Arts & Hum.Cit.Ind.	Arts & Humanities Citation Index
Ash.G.Bot.Per.	Asher's Guide to Botanical Periodicals (Now: Guide to Botanical Periodicals) (Ceased)
Asian-Pac.Econ.Lit.	Asian-Pacific Economic Literature
Astron.& Astrophys.Abstr.	Astronomy and Astrophysics Abstracts
Astron.Jahresber.	Astronomischer Jahresbericht (Now: Astronomy and Astrophysics Abstracts)
Aus.Educ.Ind.	Australian Education Index
Aus.Leg.Mon.Dig.	Australian Legal Monthly Digest
Aus.P.A.I.S.	Australian Public Affairs Information Service (Now: APAIS: Australian Public Affairs Information Service)
Aus.Rd.Ind.	Australian Road Index (Ceased)
Aus.Sci.Ind.	Australian Science Index (Ceased)
Aus.Speleo Abstr.	Australian Speleo Abstracts
Avery Ind.Archit.Per.	Avery Index to Architectural Periodicals

B

B.C.I.R.A.	B.C.I.R.A. Abstracts of International Foundry Literature (British Cast Iron Research Association) (Now: B C I R A Abstracts on International Literature on Metal Casting Production)
BIM	Bibliography and Index of Micropaleontology
BMT	B M T Abstracts (British Maritime Technology)
B.P.I.	Business Periodicals Index
BPIA	Business Publications Index and Abstracts (Ceased)

ABSTRACTING AND INDEXING

B.R.I.	BioResearch Index (Now: Biological Abstracts - R R M (Reports, Reviews, Meetings))
BSL Biol.	Abstracts of Bulgarian Scientific Literature. Biology (Ceased)
BSL Econ.	Abstracts of Bulgarian Scientific Literature. Economics and Law (Ceased)
BSL Geo.	Abstracts of Bulgarian Scientific Literature. Geosciences (Ceased)
BSL Indus.	Abstracts of Bulgarian Scientific Literature. Industry, Building and Transport
BSL Math.	Abstracts of Bulgarian Scientific Literature. Mathematical and Physical Sciences (Ceased)
Bangladesh Agr. Sci.Abstr.	Bangladesh Agricultural Sciences Abstracts
Bank.Lit.Ind.	Banking Literature Index
Behav.Abstr.	Behavioural Abstracts (Ceased)
Behav.Med. Abstr.	Behavioral Medicine Abstracts (Now: Annals of Behavioral Medicine)
Ber.Biochem. Biol.	Berichte Biochemie und Biologie (Ceased)
Bibl Agri.	Bibliography of Agriculture
Bibl.& Ind.Geol.	Bibliography & Index of Geology (see: GeoRef)
Bibl.Cart.	Bibliographia Cartographica
Bibl.Dev.Med.& Child Neur.	Bibliography of Developmental Medicine & Child Neurology. Books and Articles Received
Bibl.Engl.Lang. & Lit.	Bibliography of English Language and Literature (Now: Annual Bibliography of English Language and Literature)
Bibl.Ind.	Bibliographic Index
Bibl.IULA	Bilbiographia I U L A (International Union of Local Authorities) (Ceased)
Bibl.Ling.	Linguistic Bibliography/Bibliographie Linguistique
Bibl.Repro.	Bibliography of Reproduction
Bibliogr.Bras. Odontol.	Bibliografia Brasileira de Odontologia
Bio-Contr.News & Info.	Bio-Control News and Information
Biodet.Abstr.	Biodeterioration Abstracts
Bioeng.Abstr.	Bioengineering Abstracts
Biog.& Gen. Master Ind.	Biography and Genealogy Master Index
Biog.Ind.	Biography Index
Biol.Abstr.	Biological Abstracts
Biol.& Agr.Ind.	Biological & Agricultural Index
Biol.Dig.	Biology Digest
Biostat.	Biostatistica
Biotech.Abstr.	Biotechnology Research Abstracts
Biul.Inst.Hod. Aklim.Rosl.	Instytut Hodowli i Aklimatyzacji Roslin. Biuletyn
Biwk.Pap.Rad. Chem.& Photochem.	Biweekly List of Papers on Radiation Chemistry and Photochemistry
Bk.Rev.Dig.	Book Review Digest
Bk.Rev.Ind.	Book Review Index
Bk.Rev.Mo.	Book Reviews of the Month (Ceased)
Br.Archaeol. Abstr.	British Archaeological Abstracts (Now: British Archaeological Bibliography)
Br.Ceram.Abstr.	British Ceramic Abstracts (Now: World Ceramics Abstracts)
Br.Educ.Ind.	British Education Index
Br.Geol.Lit.	British Geological Literature
Br.Hum.Ind.	British Humanities Index
Br.Rail.Bd.	British Railways Board. Monthly Review of Technical Literature (Ceased)
Br.Tech.Ind.	British Technology Index (Now: Current Technology Index)
Build.Manage. Abstr.	Building Management Abstracts (Now: Technical Information Service - TIS)
Bull.Anal.Ent. Med.Vet.	Bulletin Analytique d'Entomologie Medicale et Veterinaire (Ceased)
Bull.Signal.	Bulletin Signaletique (Now: P A S C A L Explore, P A S C A L Folio, P A S C A L Thema) (Programme Applique a la Selection et la Compilation Automatique de la Literature)
Bull.Thermodyn. & Thermochem.	Bulletin of Thermodynamics & Thermochemistry (Now: Bulletin of Chemical Thermodynamics) (Ceased)
Bus.Comput.Ind.	Business Computer Index
Bus.Educ.Ind.	Business Education Index
Bus.Ind.	Business Index

C

CAD CAM Abstr.	C A D - C A M Abstracts (Ceased)
CALL	C A L L (Current Awareness—Library Literature)
C.C.I.Ob.Gyn.	Combined Cumulative Index to Obstetrics and Gynecology
C.C.I.P.	Combined Cumulative Index to Pediatrics
C.C.L.P.	Contents of Current Legal Periodicals (Now: Legal Contents) (Ceased)
C.C.M.J.	Contents of Contemporary Mathematical Journals (Now: Current Mathematical Publications)
CCR	Current Christian Abstracts (Now: Current Thoughts & Trends)
CERDIC	Universite de Strasbourg. Centre de Recherche et de Documentation des Institutions Chretiennes. Bulletin du CERDIC (Ceased)
CHNI	Consumer Health & Nutrition Index
C.I.J.E.	Current Index to Journals in Education
CINAHL (also C.I.N.L.)	Cumulative Index to Nursing and Allied Health Literature
CIRF Abstr.	C I R F Abstracts (Now: T&D Abstracts) (Ceased)
CIRR	C I R R (Corporate and Industry Research Reports) (Ceased)

C.I.S. Abstr.	C I S Abstracts (Centre International d'Information de Securite et Hygiene du Travail) (Now: Safety and Health at Work)	**Child.Auth.& Illus.**	Children's Authors and Illustrators
		Child.Bk.Rev.Ind.	Children's Book Review Index
C.I.S. Ind.	C I S Index (Congressional Information Service)	**Child Devel.Abstr.**	Child Development Abstracts and Bibliography
CJPI	Criminal Justice Periodical Index	**Child.Lit.Abstr.**	Children's Literature Abstracts
C.L.I.	Current Law Index	**Chr.Per.Ind.**	Christian Periodical Index
CLOA	Current Literature on Aging (Now: Abstracts in Social Gerontology: Current Literature on Aging)	**Clin-Alert**	Clin-Alert
		Coll.Stud.Pers. Abstr.	College Student Personnel Abstracts (Now: Higher Education Abstracts)
CLOSS	Current Literature on Science of Science	**Commun.Abstr.**	Communication Abstracts
CMI	Canadian Magazine Index (Now: Canadian Index)	**Community Ment.Health Rev.**	Community Mental Health Review (Now: Prevention in Human Services)
C.P.I.	Current Physics Index	**Compumath**	Compumath Citation Index
C.R.E.J.	Contents of Recent Economics Journals	**Comput.Abstr.**	Computer Abstracts (Also see: Anbar)
C.R.I.Abstr.	C R I Abstracts (Cement Research Institute of India)	**Comput.& Contr. Abstr.**	Computer & Control Abstracts (Also see: INSPEC; also see: Sci.Abstr.)
CS Ind.	Canadian Statistics Index (Now: Directory of Statistics in Canada	**Comput.& Info. Sys.**	Computer and Information Systems Abstracts Journal
CSI Fed.Ind.	C S I Federal Index (Capitol Services, Inc.)	**Comput.Bus.**	Computer Business
CWHM	Current Work in the History of Medicine	**Comput.Cont.**	Computer Contents (Ceased)
Cab.Vid.Ind.	Cable-Video Index	**Comput.Dtbs.**	Computer Database
Cadscan	Cadscan	**Comput.Ind.**	Computer Index
Cal.Per.Ind.	California Periodicals Index	**Comput.Indus.Up.**	Computer Industry Update
Cal.Tiss.Abstr.	Calcified Tissue Abstracts (Now: Calcium and Calcified Tissue Abstracts)	**Comput.Lit.Ind.**	Computer Literature Index
Can.B.P.I.	Canadian Business Periodicals Index (Now: Canadian Index)	**Comput.Rev.**	Computing Reviews
		Concr.Abstr.	Concrete Abstracts
Can.Educ.Ind.	Canadian Education Index	**Consum.Ind.**	Consumers Index
Can.Lit.Ind.	Canadian Literature Index (Ceased)	**Cont.Pg.Educ.**	Contents Pages in Education
Can.Per.Ind.	Canadian Periodical Index	**Cont.Pg.Manage.**	Contents Pages in Management
Can.Rev.Comp. Lit.	Canadian Review of Comparative Literature	**Copper Abstr.**	Copper Abstracts (Now: International Copper Information Bulletin)
Can.Wom.Per. Ind.	Canadian Women's Periodicals Index	**Corros.Abstr.**	Corrosion Abstracts
Canadiana	Canadiana	**Cott.& Trop.Fibr. Abstr.**	Cotton and Tropical Fibres Abstracts (Now: Cotton and Tropical Fibres)
Canon Law Abstr.	Canon Law Abstracts	**Crim.Just.Abstr.**	Criminal Justice Abstracts
Carcinog.Abstr.	Carcinogenesis Abstracts (Now: Cancergram)	**Crime Delinq. Abstr.**	Crime and Delinquency Abstracts (Ceased)
Cath.Ind.	Catholic Periodical & Literature Index	**Crime Delinq.Lit.**	Crime & Delinquency Literature (Now: Criminal Justice Abstracts)
Ceram.Abstr.	Ceramic Abstracts		
Chem.Abstr.	Chemical Abstracts	**Crop Physiol. Abstr.**	Crop Physiology Abstracts
Chem.Eng.Abstr.	Chemical Engineering Abstracts	**Curr.Adv. Biochem.**	Current Advances in Biochemistry (Now: Current Advances in Protein Biochemistry)
Chem.Indus. Notes.	Chemical Industry Notes		
Chem.Infd.	Chemischer Informationsdienst (Now: ChemInform)	**Curr.Adv.Cancer Res.**	Current Advances in Cancer Research
Chem.Titles	Chemical Titles	**Curr.Adv.Cell & Devel.Biol.**	Current Advances in Cell and Developmental Biology
Chemorec.Abstr.	Chemoreception Abstracts		
Chicago Psychoanal. Lit.Ind.	Chicago Psychoanalytic Literature Index (Ceased)	**Curr.Adv.Clin. Chem.**	Current Advances in Clinical Chemistry
		Curr.Adv.Ecol. Sci.	Current Advances in Ecological Sciences (Now: Current Advances in Ecological and Environmental Sciences)
Chic.Per.Ind.	Chicano Periodical Index (Now: Chicano Index)		

Curr.Adv. Genetics & Molec.Biol.	Current Advances in Genetics and Molecular Biology
Curr.Adv. Immunol.	Current Advances in Immunology (Now: Current Advances in Immunology & Infectious Diseases)
Curr.Adv. Microbiol.	Current Advances in Microbiology (Now: Current Advances in Applied Microbiology & Biotechnology)
Curr.Adv. Neurosci.	Current Advances in Neuroscience
Curr.Adv. Pharmacol. & Toxicol.	Current Advances in Pharmacology & Toxicology (Now: Current Advances in Toxicology)
Curr.Adv.Physiol.	Current Advances in Physiology (Now: Current Advances in Endocrinology & Metabolism)
Curr.Adv.Plant Sci.	Current Advances in Plant Science
Curr.Aus.N.Z.Leg. Lit.Ind.	Current Australian and New Zealand Legal Literature Index (Ceased)
Curr.Bibl.Aquatic Sci.& Fish.	Current Bibliography for Aquatic Sciences & Fisheries (Now: Aquatic Sciences and Fisheries Abstracts. Parts 1,2,3)
Curr.Biotech. Abstr.	Current Biotechnology Abstracts (Now: Current Biotechnology)
Curr.Bk.Rev.Cit.	Current Book Review Citations (Ceased)
Curr.Chem.React.	Current Chemical Reactions
Curr.Cont.	Current Contents
Curr.Cont.Africa	Current Contents Africa
Curr.Cont.M.E.	Current Contents of Periodicals on the Middle East
Curr.Dig.Sov. Press	Current Digest of the Soviet Press (Now: Current Digest of the Post-Soviet Press)
Curr.Ind. Commonw. Leg.Per.	Current Index to Commonwealth Legal Periodicals (Now: Index to Commonwealth Legal Periodicals) (Ceased)
Curr.Ind.Stat.	Current Index to Statistics
Curr.Leather Lit.	Current Leather Literature (Now: Leather Science Abstracts)
Curr.Lit.Blood	Current Literature of Blood (Ceased)
Curr.Lit.Fam. Plan.	Current Literature in Family Planning
Curr.Pack.Abstr.	Current Packaging Abstracts (Ceased)
Curr.Pap.Phys.	Current Papers in Physics (Also see: INSPEC)
Curr.Ref. Fish Res.	Current References in Fish Research
Curr.Tit.Dent.	Current Titles in Dentistry
Curr.Tit. Electrochem.	Current Titles in Electrochemistry
Curr.Tit.Ocean	Current Titles in Ocean, Coastal, Lake & Waterway Sciences (Ceased)
Cyb.Abstr.	Cybernetics Abstracts

D

DAAI	Design and Applied Arts Index
DM&T	Defense Markets and Technology (Now: Aerospace Defense Markets and Technology) (Ceased)
DNP	Digest of Neurology & Psychiatry
DSH Abstr.	DSH Abstracts (Deafness, Speech and Hearing) (Ceased)
Dairy Sci.Abstr.	Dairy Science Abstracts
Data Process.Dig.	Data Processing Digest
Deep Sea Res.& Oceanogr.Abstr.	Deep Sea Research & Oceanographic Abstracts (Now: Oceanographic Literature Review)
Dent.Abstr.	Dental Abstracts
Dent.Ind.	Index to Dental Literature
Devindex	Devindex (Ceased)
Diab.Lit.Ind.	Diabetes Literature Index (Ceased)
Diar.Dis.Res.	Journal of Diarrhoeal Diseases Research
Doc.Geogr.	Documentatio Geographica (Now: Dokumentation zur Raumentwicklung) (Ceased)
Documentatie-blad	Documentatieblad: The Abstracts Journal of the African Studies Centre Leiden (Now: African Studies Abstracts)
Dok.Arbeitsmed.	Dokumentation Arbeitsmedizin (Now: Arbeitsmedizin)
Dok.Raum.	Dokumentation zur Raumentwicklung (Ceased)
Dok.Str.	Dokumentation Strasse

E

E & P Hlth.	Exploration and Production Health, Safety and Environment
EC Ind.	EC Index (European Communities)
E.I.	E I (Excerpta Indonesica)
ELLIS	E L L I S (European Legal Literature Information Service)
ERIC	Eric Clearinghouse (See: C.I.J.E.)
Ecol.Abstr.	Ecological Abstracts
Econ.Abstr.	Economic Abstracts (Now: Key to Economic Science)
Educ.Admin. Abstr.	Educational Administration Abstracts
Educ.Ind.	Education Index
Educ.Tech.Abstr.	Educational Technology Abstracts
Ekist.Ind.	Ekistic Index
Elec.& Electron. Abstr.	Electrical & Electronics Abstracts (Also see: INSPEC; also see: Sci.Abstr.)
Electroanal.Abstr.	Electroanalytical Abstracts (Ceased)
Electron.& Communic. Abstr.J.	Electronics and Communications Abstracts Journal
Endocrin.Abstr.	Endocrinology Abstracts (Now: C S A Neurosciences Abstracts)
Endocrin.Ind.	Endocrinology Index (Ceased)

Energy Abstr.	Energy Abstracts
Energy Ind.	Energy Index (Now: Energy Information Abstracts Annual)
Energy Info.Abstr.	Energy Information Abstracts
Energy Res.Abstr.	Energy Research Abstracts
Energy Rev.	Energy Review (Santa Barbara)
Eng.Ind.	Engineering Index (Now: Engineering Index Monthly)
Eng.Mat.Abstr.	Engineered Materials Abstracts
Entomol.Abstr.	Entomology Abstracts
Environ.Abstr.	Environment Abstracts
Environ.Ind.	Environment Index (Now: Environment Abstracts Annual)
Environ.Per.Bibl.	Environmental Periodicals Bibliography
Ergon.Abstr.	Ergonomics Abstracts
Except.Child Educ.Abstr.	Exceptional Child Education Abstracts (Now: Exceptional Child Education Resources)
Excerp.Bot.	Excerpta Botanica (Sections A, B)
Excerp.Criminol.	Excerpta Criminologica (Now: Criminology, Penology & Police Science Abstracts)
Excerp.Med.	Excerpta Medica

F

F.A.C.T.	Fuel Abstracts and Current Titles (Now: Fuel and Energy Abstracts)
FAMLI	F A M L I (Family Medicine Literature Index) (Ceased)
F.R.	Fanatic Reader
Fababean Abstr.	Fababean Abstracts (Ceased)
Farm & Garden Ind.	Farm & Garden Index (Ceased)
Fed Print	Fed in Print
Fert.Abstr.	Fertilizer Abstracts (Ceased)
Field Crop Abstr.	Field Crop Abstracts
Film Lit.Ind.	Film Literature Index
Fluidex	Fluidex consists of: Civil Engineering Hydraulics Abstracts (Now: Fluid Abstracts: Civil Engineering) Current Fluid Engineering Titles (Ceased) Fluid Flow Measurement Abstracts (Now: Fluid Abstracts: Process Engineering) Fluid Power Abstracts (Now: Fluid Abstracts: Process Engineering) Fluid Sealing Abstracts (Now: Fluid Abstracts: Process Engineering) Industrial Aerodynamics Abstracts (Now: Fluid Abstracts: Civil Engineering) Industrial Jetting Report (Ceased) Offshore Engineering Abstracts (Now: Fluid Abstracts: Civil Engineering) Pipelines Abstracts (Now: Fluid Abstracts: Process Engineering) Pumps & Other Fluids Machinery Abstracts (Now: Fluid Abstracts: Process Engineering) Pumps and Turbines (Ceased) River and Flood Control Abstracts (Ceased) Solid-Liquid Flow Abstracts (Now: Fluid Abstracts: Process Engineering) Tribos-Tribology Abstracts (Now: Tribology & Corrosion Abstracts) (Ceased) World Ports and Harbours Abstracts (Now: Fluid Abstracts: Civil Engineering) World Ports and Harbours News (Ceased)
Food Sci.& Tech. Abstr.	Food Science and Technology Abstracts
Foreign Leg.Per.	Index to Foreign Legal Periodicals
Forest.Abstr.	Forestry Abstracts
Forest Prod. Abstr.	Forest Products Abstracts
Foul.Prev.Res. Dig.	Fouling Prevention Research Digest (Now: Heat Transfer & Fluid Flow Service Digest)
Fuel & Energy Abstr.	Fuel & Energy Abstracts
Fut.Abstr.	Future - Abstracts
Fut.Surv.	Future Survey

G

G.Indian Per.Lit.	Guide to Indian Periodical Literature
G.Perf.Arts.	Guide to the Performing Arts (Ceased)
G.Soc.Sci.& Rel. Per.Lit.	Guide to Social Sciences and Religion in Periodical Literature
Gard.Lit.	Garden Literature
Gas Abstr.	Gas Abstracts
Gas Process.& Ppl.	Gas Processing and Pipelining
Gastroenterol. Abstr.& Cit.	Gastroenterology Abstracts & Citations (Ceased)
Gdlns.	Guidelines
Gen.Phys.Adv. Abstr.	General Physics Advance Abstracts
Gen.Sci.Ind.	General Science Index
Geneal.Per.Ind.	Genealogical Periodical Annual Index
Genet.Abstr.	Genetics Abstracts
Geo.Abstr.	Geographical Abstracts: Human Geography Geographical Abstracts: Physical Geography
Geol.Abstr.	Geological Abstracts
Geophys.Abstr.	Geophysical Abstracts (Ceased)
GeoRef	Bibliography and Index of Geology (Also known as GeoRef)
Geosci.Doc.	Geoscience Documentation
Geotech.Abstr.	Geotechnical Abstracts

Ger.J.Psych.	German Journal of Psychology	I.C.U.I.S.Abstr.	I C U I S Abstracts Service (Institute on the Church in Urban Industrial Society) (Now: I C U I S Justice Ministries) (Ceased)
Gleanings	Gleanings		
Graph.Arts Abstr.	Graphic Arts Abstracts (Now: G A T F World)		
Graph.Arts Lit. Abstr.	Graphic Arts Literature Abstracts (Now: Institute of Paper Science and Technology. Graphic Arts Bulletin)	I D A	International Development Abstracts
		IIS	Index to International Statistics
		I.M.M.Abstr.	I M M Abstracts (Institute of Mining & Metallurgy) (Now: I M M Abstracts and Index)

H

		I.N.E.P.	Index to New England Periodicals
HMA	Healthcare Marketing Abstracts	INIS Atomind.	I N I S Atomindex (International Nuclear Information System)
HR Rep.	Human Rights Internet Reporter		
HRIS	H R I S Abstracts (Now: Highway Research Abstracts)	INSPEC	INSPEC (The Institution of Electrical Engineers):
Helminthol.Abstr.	Helminthological Abstracts. Series A (Now: Helminthological Abstracts) Helminthological Abstracts. Series B (Now: Nematological Abstracts)		Computers & Control Abstracts (Alternative title: INSPEC, Section C. Represents: Science Abstracts. Section C) (Also see: Comput.& Contr.Abstr.; also see: Sci.Abstr.)
Herb.Abstr.	Herbage Abstracts (Now: Grasslands and Forage Abstracts)		Current Papers in Computers & Control Current Papers in Electrical & Electronics Engineering
High.Educ.Abstr.	Higher Education Abstracts		
High.Educ.Curr. Aware.Bull.	Higher Education Current Awareness Bulletin (Ceased)		Current Papers in Physics (Also see: Curr.Pap.Phys.)
Hisp.Amer.Per. Ind.	Hispanic American Periodicals Index		Electrical & Electronics Abstracts (Alternative title: INSPEC, Section B. Represents: Science Abstracts. Section B.) (Also see: Elec.& Electron.Abstr.; also see: Sci.Abstr.)
Hist.Abstr.	Historical Abstracts (Parts A, B)		
Hlth.Dev.Alerts	Health Devices Alerts		
Hlth.Ind.	Health Index		Key Abstracts - Advanced Materials Key Abstracts - Antennas & Propagation
Hlth.Phys.Educ. & Rec.	Health, Physical Education and Recreation Microform Publications Bulletin		Key Abstracts - Artificial Intelligence Key Abstracts - Business Automation
Hongkongiana	Hongkongiana		Key Abstracts - Computer Communication and Storage
Hort.Abstr.	Horticultural Abstracts		
Hosp.Abstr.	Hospital Abstracts (Now: Health Service Abstracts)		Key Abstracts - Computing in Electronics & Power
			Key Abstracts - Electronic Circuits
Hosp.Abstr.Serv.	Hospital Abstracts Service (Ceased)		Key Abstracts - Electronic Instrumentation
Hosp.Lit.Ind.	Hospital Literature Index		
Hospit.Ind.	Hospitality Index		Key Abstracts - Factory Automation
Hum.Ind.	Humanities Index		Key Abstracts - High-Temperature Superconductors
Human Resour. Abstr.	Human Resources Abstracts		Key Abstracts - Human-Computer Interaction
Hung.Build.Bull.	Hungarian Building Bulletin (Ceased)		Key Abstracts - Machine Vision
Hung.Lib.& Info. Sci.Abstr.	Hungarian Library and Information Science Abstracts		Key Abstracts - Measurements in Physics
Hwy.Res.Abstr.	Highway Research Abstracts (Now: Transportation Research Abstracts) (Ceased)		Key Abstracts - Microelectronics & Printed Circuits
			Key Abstracts - Microwave Technology
			Key Abstracts - Neural Networks

I

			Key Abstracts - Optoelectronics
			Key Abstracts - Power Systems & Applications
IBM PC Ind.	IBM PC Index (Personal Computer)		Key Abstracts - Robotics & Control
IBR	I B R (International Bibliography of Book Reviews of Scholarly Literature)		Key Abstracts - Semiconductor Devices
			Key Abstracts - Software Engineering
IBZ	Internationale Bibliographie der Zeitschriftenliteratur aus allen Gebieten des Wissens/International Bibliography of Periodicals from all Fields of Knowledge		Key Abstracts - Telecommunications
			Physics Abstracts (Alternative title: INSPEC, Section A. Represents: Science Abstracts. Section A) (Also see: Phys.Abstr.; also see: Sci.Abstr.)
		I.P.A.	International Pharmaceutical Abstracts

ABSTRACTING AND INDEXING

I.R.A.	Information Resources Annual (Ceased)
ISMEC	I S M E C Bulletin (Information Service in Mechanical Engineering) (Now: Mechanical Engineering Abstracts)
Immun.Abstr.	Immunology Abstracts
Ind.Agri.Am.Lat. Caribe	Indice Agricole de America Latina y el Caribe (Ceased)
Ind.Amer.Per. Verse	Index of American Periodical Verse
Ind.Aric.Jew. Stud.	Index of Articles on Jewish Studies
Ind.Bk.Rev.Hum.	Index to Book Reviews in the Humanities (Ceased)
Ind.Bus.Rep.	Index to Business Reports
Ind.Can.L.P.L.	Index to Canadian Legal Periodical Literature
Ind.Chem.	Index Chemicus
Ind.Child.Mag.	Subject Index to Children's Magazines (Now: Children's Magazine Guide)
Ind.Curr.Urb. Doc.	Index to Current Urban Documents
Ind.Develop. Abstr.	Industrial Development Abstracts
Ind.Free.Per.	Index to Free Periodicals
Ind.Heb.Per.	Index to Hebrew Periodicals
Ind.How To Do It	Index to How to Do It Information
Ind.Hyg.Dig.	Industrial Hygiene Digest
Ind.India	Index India
Ind.Islam.	Index Islamicus (Now: Quarterly Index Islamicus)
Ind.Jew.Per.	Index to Jewish Periodicals
Ind.Lit.Amer. Indian	Index to Literature on the American Indian (Ceased)
Ind.Lit.Dent.	Indice de la Literatura Dental Periodica en Castellano
Ind.Little Mag.	Index to Little Magazines (Ceased)
Ind.Med.	Index Medicus
Ind.Med.Esp.	Indice Medico Espanol
Ind.N.Z.Per.	Index to New Zealand Periodicals (Now: Index New Zealand)
Ind.Per.Art.Relat. Law	Index to Periodical Articles Related to Law
Ind.Per.Blacks	Index to Periodical Articles by and about Blacks (Now: Index to Black Periodicals)
Ind.Per.Lit.	Index to Indian Periodical Literature (Ceased)
Ind.Per.Negroes	Index to Periodical Articles by & about Negroes (Now: Index to Black Periodicals)
Ind.Phil.Per.	Index to Philippine Periodicals
Ind.Rheum.	Annual Index of Rheumatology (Ceased)
Ind.S.A.Per.	Index to South African Periodicals
Ind.Sci.Rev.	Index to Scientific Reviews
Ind.Sel.Per.	Index to Selected Periodicals (Now: Index to Black Periodicals)
Ind.SST.	Indice Espanol de Ciencia y Tecnologia
Ind.U.S.Gov.Per.	Index to U.S. Government Periodicals (Now: U S Government Periodicals Index)
Ind.Vet.	Index Veterinarius
Indian Educ. Abstr.	Indian Education Abstracts
Indian Lib.Sci. Abstr.	Indian Library Science Abstracts
Indian Psychol. Abstr.	Indian Psychological Abstracts
Indian Sci.Abstr.	Indian Science Abstracts
Indian Sci.Ind.	Indian Science Index (Ceased)
Info.Media & Tech.	Information Media and Technology (Now: Information Management & Technology)
Inform.Sci.Abstr.	Information Science Abstracts
Inpharma	InPharma
Instrum.Abstr.	Instrument Abstracts (Now: Metron) (Ceased)
Int.Abstr.Biol.Sci.	International Abstracts of Biological Sciences (Now: Current Awareness in Biological Sciences)
Int.Abstr.Oper. Res.	International Abstracts in Operations Research
Int.Aerosp.Abstr.	International Aerospace Abstracts
Int.Bibl.Soc.Sci.	International Bibliography of the Social Sciences: Anthropology, Political Science, Economics, Sociology (Ceased)
Int.Build.Serv. Abstr.	International Building Services Abstracts
Int.G.Class.Stud.	International Guide to Classical Studies (Ceased)
Int.Ind.Film Per.	International Index to Film Periodicals
Int.Lab.Doc.	International Labor Documentation
Int.Nurs.Ind.	International Nursing Index
Int.Packag.Abstr.	International Packaging Abstracts
Int.Polit.Sci.Abstr.	International Political Science Abstracts
Int.Sci.Rev.	International Science Review Series (Ceased)
Int.Z.Bibelwiss.	Internationale Zietschriften fuer Bibelwissenschaft und Grenzgebiete
Intl.Bibl.Burns.	International Bibliography on Burns
Intl.Bibl.S.S.Econ.	International Bibliography of the Social Sciences: Economics
Intl.Bibl.S.S.Pol. Sci.	International Bibliography of the Social Sciences: Political Science
Intl.Bibl.S.S. Soc.Cult.Anthro.	International Bibliography of the Social Sciences: Anthropology
Intl.Civil Eng. Abstr.	International Civil Engineering Abstracts
Intl.Ind.TV.	International Index to Television Periodicals
Intl.Mgmt.Info.	International Management Information Business Digest (Ceased)
Intl.Polym.Sci.& Tech.	International Polymer Science and Technology

ABSTRACTING AND INDEXING

Iron & Steel Indus.Pr.	Iron and Steel Industry Profiles (Ceased)
Irr.& Drain.Abstr.	Irrigation & Drainage Abstracts

J

JAMA	JAMA: The Journal of the American Medical Association
JCT	Japan Computer Technology and Applications Abstracts (Ceased)
JTA	Japanese Technical Abstracts (Now: Japan Technology Series) (Ceased)
J.Cont.Quant.Meth.	Journal Contents in Quantitative Methods
J.Curr.Laser Abstr.	Journal of Current Laser Abstracts
J.of Abstr.Int.Educ.	Journal of Abstracts in International Education
J.of Econ.Abstr. (also: J.of Econ.Lit.)	Journal of Economic Abstracts (Now: Journal of Economic Literature)
J.of Ferroc.	Journal of Ferrocement
Jap.Per.Ind.	Japanese Periodicals Index (Humanities and Social Sciences Section; Medical Sciences and Pharmacology (Ceased); Science and Technology)
Jazz Ind.	Jazz Index (Ceased)
Jun.High Mag.Abstr.	Junior High Magazine Abstracts

K

Key to Econ.Sci.	Key to Economic Science (Ceased)
Key Word Ind.Ser.Titl.	Keyword Index to Serial Titles
Key Word Ind.Wildl.Res.	Key Word Index of Wildlife Research

L

LAMP	L A M P (Literature Analysis of Microcomputer Publications)
LCR	Literary Criticism Register
LHTN	Library Hi Tech News
L.I.I.	Life Insurance Index (Ceased)
LISA	L I S A: Library & Information Science Abstracts
L.R.I.	Legal Resource Index (Now: LegalTrac)
Lab.Haz.Bull.	Laboratory Hazards Bulletin
Landwirt.Zentralbl.	Landwirtschaftliches Zentralblatt (Now: Agroselekt) (Ceased)
Lang.& Lang.Behav.Abstr.	Language and Language Behaviour Abstracts (Now: Linguistics and Language Behavior Abstracts)
Lang.Teach.& Ling.Abstr.	Language Teaching and Linguistics Abstracts (Now: Language Teaching)
Lat.Lit.Fam.Plan	Latest Literature in Family Planning (Ceased)
Law Ofc.Info.Svc.	Law Office Information Service
Lead Abstr.	Lead Abstracts (Now: Leadscan)
Left Ind.	Left Index
Leg.Cont.	Legal Contents (Ceased)
Leg.Info.Manage.Ind.	Legal Information Management Index
Leg.Per.	Index to Legal Periodicals
Lib.Lit.	Library Literature
Lib.Sci.Abstr.	Library Science Abstracts (Now: Library & Information Science Abstracts)
Lit.Automat.	Literature on Automation (Now: New Literature on Automation)

M

MEDOC	Medoc: Index to U.S. Government Publications in the Medical and Health Sciences
MEDSOC	Medical Socioeconomic Research Sources (Ceased)
MELSA	MELSA Messenger (Metropolitan Library Service)(Ceased)
M.L.A.	M L A Abstracts of Articles in Scholarly Journals (Ceased)
M.M.R.I.	Multi-Media Reviews Index (Now: Media Review Digest)
Mag.Ind.	Magazine Index
Maize Abstr.	Maize Abstracts
Manage.Abstr.	Management Abstracts (India) (Now: Indian Management)
Manage.Cont.	Management Contents
Mar.Aff.Bibl.	Marine Affairs Bibliography
Mar.Sci.Cont.Tab.	Marine Science Contents Tables
Mark.Res.Abstr.	Market Research Abstracts
Mass Spectr.Bull.	Mass Spectrometry Bulletin
Math.R.	Mathematical Reviews
Med.Abstr.	Medical Abstract Service (Ceased)
Med.Care Rev.	Medical Care Review
Media Rev.Dig.	Media Review Digest
Ment.Retard.Abstr.	Mental Retardation Abstracts (Now: Developmental Disabilities Abstracts) (Ceased)
Met.Abstr.	Metallurgical Abstracts (Now: Metals Abstracts)
Met.Finish.Abstr.	Metal Finishing Abstracts (Now: Surface Treatment Technology Abstracts)
Meteor.& Geoastrophys.Abstr.	Meteorological & Geoastrophysical Abstracts
Meth.Per.Ind.	Methodist Periodical Index (Now: United Methodist Periodical Index) (Ceased)
Mgmt.Abstr.	Management Abstracts (Trinidad) (Ceased)
Mgmt.& Market.Abstr.	Management & Marketing Abstracts
Mich.Mag.Ind.	Michigan Magazine Index (Ceased)
Microbiol.Abstr.	Microbiological Abstracts (Sections A, B, C)

Microcomp.Ind.	Microcomputer Index	Oper.Res.Manage.Sci.	Operations Research - Management Science
Microcomp.Indus.Up.	Microcomputer Industry Update	Ophthal.Lit.	Ophthalmic Literature
Mid.East: Abstr. & Ind.	Middle East: Abstracts and Index	Oral Res.Abstr.	Oral Research Abstracts (Ceased)
Mineral Abstr.	Mineralogical Abstracts	Ornam.Hort.	Ornamental Horticulture

P

Mkt.Inform.Guide	Marketing Information Guide (Ceased)
Mult.Ed.Abstr.	Multicultural Education Abstracts
Multi.Scler.Abstr.	Multiple Sclerosis Indicative Abstracts (Ceased)
Music Artic.Guide	Music Article Guide
Music Ind.	Music Index
Mycol.Abstr.	Abstracts of Mycology

N

NAA	N A A (Nordic Archaeological Abstracts)
NASA	N A S A Patent Abstracts Bibliography: A Continuing Bibliography. Section 2. Indexes (National Aeronautics and Space Administration)
NBA	Notiziario Bibliografico di Audiologia ORL e Foniatria
NRN	Nutrition Research Newsletter
Nav.Abstr.	Naval Abstracts (Ceased)
Neurosci.Abstr.	Neurosciences Abstracts (Now: CSA Neurosciences Abstracts)
New Per.Ind.	New Periodicals Index (Ceased)
New Sil.Tech.	New Silver Technology (Ceased)
New Test.Abstr.	New Testament Abstracts
Noise Pollut.Publ.Abstr.	Noise Pollution Publications Abstracts (Ceased)
Nucl.Sci.Abstr.	Nuclear Science Abstracts (Now INIS Atomindex)
Numis.Lit.	Numismatic Literature
Nurs.Abstr.	Nursing Abstracts
Nurs.Res.Abstr.	Nursing Research Abstracts
Nutr.Abstr.	Nutrition Abstracts & Reviews (Now: Nutrition Abstracts and Reviews Series A: Human and Experimental; Nutrition Abstracts and Reviews Series B: Livestock Feeds and Feeding)
Nutr.Plan.	Nutrition Planning (Ceased)

O

Occup.Saf.& Health Abstr.	Occupational Safety & Health Abstracts (Now: Safety and Health at Work)
Ocean.Abstr.	Oceanic Abstracts
Ocean.Abstr.Bibl.	Oceanographic Abstracts and Bibliography (Now: Oceanographic Literature Review)
Ocean.Ind.	Oceanic Index (Now: Oceanic Abstracts)
Off.Tech.	Offshore Technology
Old Test.Abstr.	Old Testament Abstracts
Oncol.Abstr.	Oncology Abstracts (Ceased)

P.A.I.S.	P A I S Bulletin (Public Affairs Information Service) (Now: P A I S International in Print)
P.A.I.S.For.Lang.Ind.	Public Affairs Information Service Foreign Language Index (Now: P A I S International in Print)
PC Abstr.	P C Abstracts (Personal Computing) (Ceased)
PCR2	P C R2 (Personal Computer Review - Squared)
PHRA	Poverty & Human Resources Abstracts (Now: Human Resources Abstracts)
P.I.R.A.	P.I.R.A. Marketing Abstracts (Packaging Industry Research Association) (Now: Management and Marketing Abstracts)
P.L.E.S.A.	Quarterly Index to Periodical Literature, Eastern and Southern Africa
P.L.I.I.	Property & Liability Insurance Index (Ceased)
P.M.I.	Photography Magazine Index (Ceased)
PMR	Popular Magazine Review (Now: Magazine Article Summaries)
P.N.I.	Pharmaceutical News Index
PROMT	Predicasts Overview of Markets and Technologies
PSI	Philanthropic Studies Index
Packag.Abstr.	Packaging Abstracts (Now: International Packaging Abstracts)
Packag.Sci.Tech.	Packaging Science and Technology Abstracts
Paper.& Bd.Abstr.	Paper and Board Abstracts
Past.Care & Couns.Abstr.	Pastoral Care & Counseling Abstracts (Now: Abstracts of Research in Pastoral Care and Counseling)
Peace Res.Abstr.	Peace Research Abstracts Journal
Peat Abstr.	Peat Abstracts
Per.Islam.	Periodica Islamica
Perf.Arts Biog.Master Ind.	Performing Arts Biography Master Index
Periodex	Periodex (Now: Point de Repere)
Pers.Lit.	Personnel Literature
Pers.Manage.Abstr.	Personnel Management Abstracts
Petrol.Abstr.	Petroleum Abstracts
Petrol.Energy B.N.I.	Petroleum - Energy Business News Index
Pharmacog.Tit.	Pharmacognosy Titles (Ceased)
Phil.Ind.	Philosopher's Index

Philip.Abstr.	Philippine Abstracts (Now: Philippine Science & Technology Abstracts)
Photo.Abstr.	Photographic Abstracts (Now: Imaging Abstracts)
Photo.Ind.	Photography Index
Phys.Abstr.	Physics Abstracts (Also see: INSPEC; also see: Sci.Abstr.)
Phys.Ber.	Physikalische Berichte (Now: Physics Briefs - Physikalische Berichte)
Phys.Ed.Ind.	Physical Education Index
Pig News & Info.	Pig News and Information
Pinpointer	Pinpointer (Ceased)
Plant Breed. Abstr.	Plant Breeding Abstracts
Plant Grow.Reg. Abstr.	Plant Growth Regulator Abstracts
Plast.Abstr.	Plastics Abstracts (Ceased)
Pol.Tech.Abstr.	Polish Technical Abstracts (Now: Polish Technical and Economic Abstracts)
Polit.Sci.Abstr.	Political Science Abstracts
Pollut.Abstr.	Pollution Abstracts
Pop.Mus.Per.Ind.	Popular Music Periodicals Index (Ceased)
Pop.Per.Ind.	Popular Periodical Index
Popul.Ind.	Population Index
Potato Abstr.	Potato Abstracts
Poult.Abstr.	Poultry Abstracts
Pr.Briefs	Predi-Briefs
Predi.F&S Ind. Eur.	Predicasts F & S Index Europe
Predi.F&S Ind.Intl.	Predicasts F & S Index International
Predi.F&S Ind.U.S.	Predicasts F & S Index United States
Print.Abstr.	Printing Abstracts
Protozool.Abstr.	Protozoological Abstracts
Psychoanal. Abstr.	Psychoanalysis Abstracts (Now: Psychoanalytic Abstracts)
Psychol.Abstr.	Psychological Abstracts
Psychol.R.G.	Psychological Reader's Guide (Ceased)
Psychopharmacol. Abstr.	Psychopharmacology Abstracts (Ceased)
Psycscan	Psycscan: Applied Psychology
Psycscan C.P.	Psycscan: Clinical Psychology
Psycscan D.P.	Psycscan: Developmental Psychology
Pt.de Rep.	Point de Repere (Formed by the merger of Periodex and RADAR)
Pub.Admin.Abstr.	Public Administration Abstracts and Index of Articles (Now: Documentation in Public Administration)

Q

Q.Abstr.	Quality Abstracts
Qual.Contr. Appl.Stat.	Quality Control and Applied Statistics

R

RADAR	Repertoire Analytique d'Articles des Revues du Quebec (Now: Point de Repere)
RAPRA	R A P R A Abstracts (Rubber and Plastics Research Association of Great Britain)
R.G.	Readers' Guide to Periodical Literature
R.G.Abstr.	Reader' Guide Abstracts
RICS	R I C S Abstracts and Reviews (Now: R I C S Library Information Service Abstracts and Reviews) (Royal Institute of Chartered Surveyors)
RILA	R I L A (International Repertory of the Literature of Art) (Now: BHA (Bibliography of the History of Art))
RILM	R I L M Abstracts of Music Literature (International Repertory of Music Literature)
Reac.	Reactions
Ref.Pt.Food Indus.Abstr.	Reference Point: Food Industry Abstracts
Ref.Sour.	Reference Sources (Ceased)
Ref.Zh.	Referativnyi Zhurnal
Refug.Abstr.	Refugee Abstracts
Rehabil.Lit.	Rehabilitation Literature (Ceased)
Rel.& Theol. Abstr.	Religious & Theological Abstracts
Rel.Ind.One	Religion Index One: Periodicals
Rel.Ind.Two	Religion Index Two: Multi-Author Works
Rel.Per.	Index to Religious Periodical Literature (Now: Religion Index One: Periodicals)
Res.Educ.	Research in Education (Now: Resources in Education)
Res.High.Educ. Abstr.	Research into Higher Education Abstracts
Resour.Ctr.Ind.	Resource Center Index
Rev.Appl. Entomol.	Review of Applied Entomology. Series A (Now: Review of Agricultural Entomology) Review of Applied Entomology. Series B (Now: Review of Medical and Veterinary Entomology)
Rev.Appl.Mycol.	Review of Applied Mycology (Now: Review of Plant Pathology)
Rev.Med.& Vet.Mycol.	Review of Medical and Veterinary Mycology
Rev.Plant Path.	Review of Plant Pathology
Rheol.Abstr.	Rheology Abstracts
Rice Abstr.	Rice Abstracts
Risk Abstr.	Risk Abstracts
Robomat.	Robomatix Reporter (Now: Robotics Abstracts) (Ceased)
Rom.Sci.Abstr.	Rumanian Scientific Abstracts
Rural Devel. Abstr.	Rural Development Abstracts

Rural Ext.Educ.& Tr.Abstr.	Rural Extension, Education and Training Abstracts (Ceased)	Soils & Fert.	Soils & Fertilizers
Rural Recreat. Tour.Abstr.	Rural Recreation and Tourism Abstracts (Now: Leisure, Recreation and Tourism Abstracts)	Solid St.Abstr.	Solid State Abstracts (Now: Solid State and Superconductivity Abstracts)
		Sorghum & Millets Abstr.	Sorghum and Millets Abstracts

S

		South.Bap.Per.Ind.	Southern Baptist Periodical Index (Ceased)
S.A.Waterabstr.	S.A. Waterabstracts (South Africa) (Ceased)	Soyabean Abstr.	Soyabean Abstracts
SCIMP	S C I M P (Selective Cooperative Index of Management Periodicals)	Sp.Ed.Needs Abstr.	Special Education Needs Abstracts
		Speleol.Abstr.	Speleological Abstracts
SOMA	School Organization & Management Abstracts	Sport Fish.Abstr.	Sport Fishery Abstracts (Now: Fisheries Review)
SOPODA	Social Planning, Policy and Development Abstracts	Sports Per.Ind.	Sports Periodicals Index (Ceased)
		Sportsearch	Sportsearch
SRI	Statistical Reference Index	Sri Lanka Sci. Ind.	Sri Lanka Science Index
SSCI	Social Science Citation Index		
Saf.Sci.Abstr.	Safety Science Abstracts Journal (Now: Health and Safety Science Abstracts)	St.Educ.J.Ind.	State Education Journal Index
		Stat.Theor.Meth. Abstr.	Statistical Theory and Method Abstracts
Sage Fam.Stud. Abstr.	Sage Family Studies Abstracts	Steel Cas.Abstr.	Steel Castings Abstracts (Ceased)
Sage Pub.Admin. Abstr.	Sage Public Administration Abstracts	Stud.Wom.Abstr.	Studies on Women Abstracts
		Sugar Ind.Abstr.	Sugar Industry Abstracts
Sage Urb.Stud. Abstr.	Sage Urban Studies Abstracts		

T

Sci.Abstr.	Science Abstracts A. Physics Abstracts (Also see: INSPEC; also see: Phys.Abstr.) B. Electrical & Electronics Abstracts (Also see: Elec.& Electron.Abstr.; also see: INSPEC) C. Computer & Control Abstracts (Also see: Comput.& Cont.Abstr.; also see: INSPEC)	TBRI	Technical Book Review Index (Ceased)
		T.C.E.A.	Theoretical Chemical Engineering Abstracts (Now: Theoretical Chemical Engineering)
		TOM	T O M (Text on Microfilm)
		Tech.Educ.Abstr.	Technical Education Abstracts (Now: Technical Education & Training Abstracts)
Sci.Cit.Ind.	Science Citation Index		
Sci.Res.Abstr.	Science Research Abstracts (Now: Solid State and Superconductivity Abstracts)	Tel.Abstr.	Telecommunications Abstracts (Ceased)
		Tel.Alert	Telecommunications Alert
Search	Search	Telegen	Telegen Reporter (Now: Telegen Abstracts) (Ceased)
Seed Abstr.	Seed Abstracts		
Sel.Bibl. Homosex.	Selected Bibliography of Homosexuality	Text.Dig.	Textile Digest (Ceased)
		Text.Tech.Dig.	Textile Technology Digest
Sel.J.Water.	Selected Journals on Water (Ceased)	Therm.Abstr.	Thermal Abstracts (Now: International Building Services Abstracts)
Sel. Water Res. Abstr.	Selected Water Resources Abstracts		
		Tob.Abstr.	Tobacco Abstracts
Sh.& Vib.Dig.	Shock and Vibration Digest	Tob.Bibl.	Tobacco Bibliography (Ceased)
Ship Abstr.	Ship Abstracts	Top Manage. Abstr.	Top Management Abstracts (Also see: Anbar)
Sinop.Odontol.	Sinopse de Odontologia (Ceased)		
Small Anim. Abstr.	Small Animal Abstracts (Now: Small Animals)	Tox.Abstr.	Toxicology Abstracts
		Tr.& Dev.Alert	Training and Development Alert
So.Pac.Per.Ind.	South Pacific Periodicals Index	Tr.& Indus.Ind.	Trade & Industry Index
Soc.Sci.Ind.	Social Sciences Index	Trans.Res.Abstr.	Transportation Research Abstracts (Ceased)
Soc.Work Res.& Abstr.	Social Work Research & Abstracts (Now: Social Work Abstracts)		
		Triticale Abstr.	Triticale Abstracts (Now: Wheat, Barley and Triticale Abstracts)
Sociol.Abstr.	Sociological Abstracts		
Sociol.Educ. Abstr.	Sociology of Education Abstracts	Trop.Abstr.	Tropical Abstracts (Now: Abstracts on Tropical Agriculture)
Soft.Abstr.Eng.	Software Abstracts for Engineers	Trop.Dis.Bull.	Tropical Diseases Bulletin

Trop.Oil Seeds Abstr.	Tropical Oil Seeds Abstracts (Now: Tropical Oil Seeds)	**Work Rel.Abstr.**	Work Related Abstracts
		World Agri.Econ. & Rural Sociol. Abstr.	World Agricultural Economics & Rural Sociology Abstracts

U

Urb.Aff.Abstr. — Urban Affairs Abstracts

World Alum. Abstr. — World Aluminum Abstracts

World Bank. Abstr. — World Banking Abstracts

V

Va.Hist.Abstr. — Virginia Historical Abstracts (Ceased)
Vert.File Ind. — Vertical File Index
Vet.Bull. — Veterinary Bulletin
Virol.Abstr. — Virology Abstracts (Now: Virology and AIDS Abstracts)
Vis.Ind. — Vision Index (Ceased)
VITIS — Vitis - Viticulture and Enology Abstracts

World Bibl.Soc.Sec. — World Bibliography of Social Security
World Fish.Abstr. — World Fisheries Abstracts (Ceased)
World Surf.Coat. — World Surface Coatings Abstracts
World Text.Abstr. — World Textile Abstracts

Y

Yrbk.Assoc.Educ. & Rehab.Blind — Association for Education and Rehabilitation of the Blind and Visually Impaired. Yearbook (Ceased)

W

W.R.C.Inf. — W.R.C. Information (Water Research Centre) (Now: Aqualine Abstracts)
Water Pollut. Abstr. — Water Pollution Abstracts (Now: Aqualine Abstracts)
Water Resour. Abstr. — Water Resources Abstracts (Now: Hydro-Abstracts)
Weed Abstr. — Weed Abstracts
Wild Life Rev. — Wildlife Review (Ceased)
Wom.Stud.Abstr. — Women Studies Abstracts

Z

Zent.Math. — Zentralblatt fuer Mathematik und ihre Grenzgebiete
Zincscan — Zincscan
Zion.Lit. — Zionist Literature
Zoo.Rec. — Zoological Record

Subject Guide to Abstracting and Indexing

The 132 subject headings listed below are major subjects which contain a sub-category headed "Abstracting, Bibliographies, Statistics." This sub-category, which follows the major subject headings in the Classified List of Serials, identifies publications which abstract and/or index publications in the relevant subject. Bibliographies and statistical publications pertaining to the subject are also included in this sub-category. This guide will enable users to quickly locate subject areas of interest for which abstracting and indexing publications have been identified and to build profiles by combination of relevant subject areas. Page numbers refer to the first page on which the sub-category appears.

SUBJECT CATEGORY	PAGE
Advertising and Public Relations	44
Aeronautics and Space Flight	75
Agriculture	152
Alternative Medicine	268
Animal Welfare	272
Anthropology	296
Archaeology	341
Architecture	264
Art	412
Arts and Handicrafts	419
Astronomy	435
Beauty Culture	440
Beverages	456
Biography	498
Biology	543
Birth Control	716
Building and Construction	763
Business and Economics	845
Ceramics, Glass and Pottery	1447
Chemistry	1477
Children and Youth	1547
Civil Defense	1578
Classical Studies	1586
Cleaning and Dyeing	1588
Clothing Trade	1595
Clubs	1612
Communications	1669
Computers	1738
Conservation	1860
Consumer Education and Protection	1868
Criminology and Law Enforcement	1888
Dance	1898
Drug Abuse and Alcoholism	1907
Earth Sciences	1920
Education	2067
Electronics	2193
Energy	2215
Engineering	2270
Environmental Studies	2441
Ethnic Interests	2516
Fire Prevention	2523
Fish and Fisheries	2542
Folklore	2553
Food and Food Industries	2584
Forests and Forestry	2616
Funerals	2626
Gardening and Horticulture	2651

SUBJECT CATEGORY	PAGE
Genealogy and Heraldry	2684
Geography	2824
Gerontology and Geriatrics	2840
Handicapped	2848
Heating, Plumbing and Refrigeration	2872
History	2898
Hobbies	3031
Home Economics	3038
Homosexuality	3047
Hospitals	3063
Hotels and Restaurants	3077
Housing and Urban Planning	3099
How-to and Do-it-Yourself	3103
Humanities: Comprehensive Works	3126
Instruments	3132
Insurance	3159
Interior Design and Decoration	3172
Jewelry, Clocks and Watches	3184
Journalism	3197
Labor Unions	3214
Law	3340
Leather and Fur Industries	3413
Library and Information Sciences	3476
Linguistics	3552
Literary and Political Reviews	3592
Literature	3693
Machinery	3745
Mathematics	3791
Martimony	3798
Medical Sciences	3911
Meetings and Congresses	4215
Metallurgy	4251
Meteorology	4276
Metrology and Standardization	4283
Military	4314
Mines and Mining Industry	4339
Motion Pictures	4363
Museums and Art Galleries	4382
Music	4443
Numismatics	4461
Nutrition and Dietetics	4474
Occupational Health and Safety	4486
Occupations and Careers	4497

SUBJECT CATEGORY	PAGE
Oriental Studies	4515
Packaging	4523
Paints and Protective Coatings	4527
Paleontology	4534
Paper and Pulp	4541
Parapsychology and Occultism	4547
Patents, Trademarks and Copyrights	4557
Petroleum and Gas	4587
Pharmacy and Pharmacology	4641
Philately	4656
Philosophy	4690
Photography	4704
Physical Fitness and Hygiene	4718
Physics	4749
Plastics	4792
Political Science	4873
Population Studies	4936
Printing	4961
Psychology	5016
Public Administration	5049
Public Health and Safety	5093
Publishing and Book Trade	5119
Real Estate	5144
Religions and Theology	5204
Rubber	5308
Sciences: Comprehensive Works	5371
Shoes and Boots	5380
Social Sciences: Comprehensive Works	5419
Social Services and Welfare	5456
Sociology	5491
Sound Recording and Reproduction	5498
Sports and Games	5539
Technology: Comprehensive Works	5687
Textile Industries and Fabrics	5703
Theater	5719
Tobacco	5723
Transportation	5742
Travel and Tourism	5904
Veterinary Science	5932
Water Resources	5951
Women's Interests	5977
Women's Studies	5983

Subjects

ENGLISH	FRENCH	GERMAN	SPANISH
Abstracting and Indexing Services	Services d'Analyse et Indexage	Referate- und Indexdienste	Servicios de Extractos e Indices
Advertising and Public Relations	Publicité et Relations Publiques	Reklamewesen und Public Relations	Publicidad y Relaciones Públicas
Aeronautics and Space Flight	Aéronautique et Astronautique	Luft- und Raumfahrt	Aeronáutica y Vuelo Espacial
Computer Applications	Applications des Ordinateurs	Computer Anwendung	Aplicaciones de los Ordenadores
Agriculture	Agriculture	Landwirtschaft	Agricultura
Agricultural Economics	Agriculture Économique	Agrarökonomie	Economía Agrícola
Agricultural Equipment	Outillage Agricole	Landwirtschaftsgeräte	Aparatos Agrícolas
Computer Applications	Applications des Ordinateurs	Computer Anwendung	Aplicaciones de los Ordenadores
Crop Production and Soil	Récolte et Terre	Ernte und Acker	Producción de Cosecha, Tierra
Dairying and Dairy Products	Production Laitière	Milchwirtschaft	Lechería y Productos Lácteos
Feed, Flour and Grain	Pature, Farine et Grain	Futter, Mehl und Getreide	Forraje, Granos y Harina
Poultry and Livestock	Élevage	Geflügel- und Viehwirtschaft	Ganadería
Alternative Medicine	Médecine Alternative	Alternative Heilkunde	Medicina Alternativa
Animal Welfare	Protection des Animaux	Tierschutz	Bienestar Animal
Anthropology	Anthropologie	Anthropologie	Antropología
Antiques	Antiquités	Antiquitäten	Antigüedades
Archaeology	Archeologie	Archaeologie	Arqueología
Computer Applications	Applications des Ordinateurs	Computer Anwendung	Aplicaciones de los Ordenadores
Architecture	Architecture	Architektur	Arquitectura
Computer Applications	Applications des Ordinateurs	Computer Anwendung	Aplicaciones de los Ordenadores
Art	Art	Kunst	Arte
Computer Applications	Applications des Ordinateurs	Computer Anwendung	Aplicaciones de los Ordenadores
Arts and Handicrafts	Arts et Métiers	Kunst und Handwerk	Artes y Obras de Mano
Astrology	Astrologie	Astrologie	Astrología
Astronomy	Astronomie	Astronomie	Astronomía
Computer Applications	Applications des Ordinateurs	Computer Anwendung	Aplicaciones de los Ordenadores
Beauty Culture	Soins de Beauté	Schönheitspflege	Belleza Personal
Perfumes and Cosmetics	Parfums et Cosmétiques	Kosmetik und Parfüme	Perfumes y Cosméticos
Beverages	Boissons	Getränke	Bebidas
Bibliographies	Bibliographies	Bibliographien	Bibliografías
Biography	Biographie	Biographie	Biografía
Biology	Biologie	Biologie	Biología
Bioengineering	Biogénie	Bioingenieurwesen	Bio-ingeniería
Biological Chemistry	Chimie Biologique	Biochemie	Química Biológica
Biophysics	Biophysique	Biophysik	Biofísica
Biotechnology	Biotechnologie	Biotechnologie	Biotecnología
Botany	Botanique	Botanik	Botánica
Computer Applications	Applications des Ordinatures	Computer Anwendung	Aplicaciones de los Ordenadores
Cytology and Histology	Cytologie et Histologie	Zytologie und Histologie	Citología e Histología
Entomology	Entomologie	Entomologie	Entomología
Genetics	Génétique	Genetik	Genética
Microbiology	Microbiologie	Mikrobiologie	Microbiología
Microscopy	Microscopie	Mikroskopie	Microscopia
Ornithology	Ornithologie	Ornithologie	Ornitología
Physiology	Physiologie	Physiologie	Fisiología
Zoology	Zoologie	Zoologie	Zoología
Birth Control	Limitation des Naissances	Geburtenregelung	Reglamentación del Nacimiento
Building and Construction	Bâtiment et Construction	Bauwesen	Edificios y Construcción
Carpentry and Woodwork	Charpenterie et Menuiserie	Zimmerhandwerk und Holzbau	Carpintería y Ebanistería
Hardware	Quincaillerie	Metallbaustoffe	Ferretería
Business and Economics	Affaires et Économie	Wirtschaft und Handel	Negocios y Economía
Accounting	Comptabilité	Rechnungswesen	Contabilidad
Banking and Finance	Banque et Finance	Bank- und Finanzwesen	Bancos y Finanzas

Banking and Finance-
    Computer Applications
	Banque et Finance-
	    Applications des Ordinateurs
		Bank- und Finanzwesen-
		    Computer Anwendung
			Bancos y Finanzas-
			    Aplicaciones de los Ordenadores

Chamber of Commerce
    Publications
	Publications des Chambres
	    de Commerce
		Veröffentlichungen von Handels-
		    kammern
			Publicaciones de las Cámaras de
			    Comercio

Computer Applications	Applications des Ordinateurs	Computer Anwendung	Aplicaciones de los Ordenadores
Cooperatives	Coopératives	Genossenschaften	Cooperativos
Domestic Commerce	Commerce Interieur	Binnenhandel	Comercio Interior

Economic Situation and
    Conditions
	Situations et Conditions
	    Économiques
		Wirtschaftliche Situation und
		    Verhältnisse
			Situaciones y Condiciones
			    Económicas

Economic Systems and Theories,
    Economic History
	Systèmes et Théories Économiques,
	    Histoire Économique
		Ökonomische Systeme und
		    Theorien, Wirtschafts-
		    geschichte
			Sistemas y Teorías Económicos,
			    Historia Económica

International Commerce	Commerce International	Aussenhandel	Comercio Internacional

International Development and
    Assistance
	Développement et Assistance
	    Internationaux
		Internationale Entwicklungshilfe	Desarrollo y Asistencia Inter-
			    nacionales

Investments	Investissements	Investitionen	Inversiones
Labor and Industrial Relations	Travail et Relations Industrielles	Arbeits und Industrielle Beziehungen	Trabajo y Relaciones Industriales
Macroeconomics	Macroéconomique	Makroökonomie	Macroeconomía
Management	Gestion	Betriebsführung	Gerencia
Marketing and Purchasing	Cours et Achats	Marketing und Kauf	Compra y Venta
Office Equipment and Services	Matériel et Entretien de Bureaux	Büroeinrichtung und Service	Equipo y Servicios de Oficinas
Personnel Management	Direction de Personnel	Personal Führung	Dirección de Empleados
Production of Goods and Services	Production	Produktion	Producción
Public Finance, Taxation	Finance Publique, Impots	Staatsfinanzen, Steuerwesen	Finanza Publica, Impuestos
Small Business	Petites et Moyennes Affaires	Kleinbetrieb	Negocios Pequeños

Trade and Industrial Directories	Directoires de Commerce et
	    Industrie
		Firmenverzeichnisse	Directorios de Comercio e
			    Industria

SUBJECTS

Ceramics, Glass and Pottery	Céramique, Verrerie et Poterie	Keramik, Glas und Töpferei	Cerámica, Vidrio y Porcelana
Chemistry	Chimie	Chemie	Química
Analytical Chemistry	Chimie Analytique	Analytische Chemie	Química Analítica
Computer Applications	Applications des Ordinateurs	Computer Anwendung	Aplicaciones de los Ordenadores
Crystallography	Cristallographie	Kristallographie	Cristalografía
Electrochemistry	Électrochimie	Elektrochemie	Electroquímica
Inorganic Chemistry	Chimie Inorganique	Anorganische Chemie	Química Inorgánica
Organic Chemistry	Chimie Organique	Organische Chemie	Química Orgánica
Physical Chemistry	Chimie Physique	Physikalische Chemie	Fisicoquímica
Children and Youth	Enfance et Adolescence	Kinder und Jugend	Niños y Jóvenes
About	Au Sujet de	Über	Acerca
For	Pour	Für	Para
Civil Defense	Defense Civile	Ziviler Bevölkerungsschutz	Defensa Civil
Classical Studies	Études Classiques	Klassische Studien	Estudios Clásicos
Cleaning and Dyeing	Nettoyage et Teinturerie	Reinigen und Färben	Limpieza y Tintura
Clothing Trade	Vêtement	Bekleidungsgewerbe	Industria de Vestidos
Fashions	Mode	Moden	Modas
Clubs	Clubs	Klubs	Clubes
College and Alumni	Université et Diplomés	Universitäten und Hochschulabsolventen	Universidades y Exalumnos
Communications	Communications	Nachrichtentechnik	Comunicaciones
Computer Applications	Applications des Ordinateurs	Computer Anwendung	Aplicaciones de los Ordenadores
Postal Affairs	Postes	Postwesen	Correo
Radio	Radio	Rundfunk	Radio
Telephone and Telegraph	Téléphone et Télégraphe	Telephon und Telegraph	Teléfono y Telégrafo
Television and Cable	Télévision	Fernsehen und Bildfrequenzkanal	Televisión y Cable
Video	Vidéo	Video	Video
Computers	Ordinateurs	Computer	Ordenadores
Artificial Intelligence	Intelligence Artificielle	Künstliche Intelligenz	Inteligencia Artificial
Automation	Automation	Automatisierung	Automación
Calculating Machines	Calculateurs	Rechenmaschine	Calculadores
Circuits	Circuits	Schaltungen	Circuitos
Computer Architecture	Architecture de la Machine	Computer Architektur	Arquitectura de los Ordenadores
Computer-Assisted Instruction	Enseignement Assisté par Ordinateur	Computerunterstuetzter Unterricht	Instrucción con la Ayuda de Ordenador
Computer Engineering	Technique d'Ordinateur	Computerentwicklung	Ingeniería de Ordenador
Computer Games	Jeux des Ordinateurs	Computer Spiele	Juegos de Ordenadores
Computer Graphics	Conception Assistée par Ordinateur	Computergraphik	Diseño con la Ayuda de Ordenador
Computer Industry	Industrie d'Ordinateur	Computerbetrieb	Industrias de los Ordenadores
Computer Industry Directories	Annuaire de la Industrie d'Ordinateur	Computerbetriebverzeichnisse	Directorios de los Ordenadores
Computer Industry, Vocational Guidance	Industrie d'Ordinateur, Orientation Professionnelle	Computerbetrieb Berufsberatung	Industria de los Ordenadores, Gobierno Práctico
Computer Music	Musique d'Ordinateur	Computer Musik	Música de Ordenadores
Computer Networks	Reseaux des Ordinateurs	Rechnernetz	Red para Transmisión de Datos
Computer Programming	Programme Machine	Rechnerprogrammierung	Programa de Ordenador
Computer Sales	Ventes des Ordinateurs	Computervertrieb	Ventas de Ordenadores
Computer Security	Protection des Ordinateurs	Computersicherheit	Protección de los Ordenadores
Computer Simulation	Simulation des Ordinateurs	Computersimulation	Simulación de los Ordenadores
Computer Systems	Systèmes des Ordinateurs	Computersystemen	Sistemas de los Ordenadores
Cybernetics	Cybernetiques	Kybernetik	Cibernéticas
Data Communications, Data Transmission Systems	Données de Communication	Datenübertragung, Datenübertragungssystem	Datos de Comunicación
Data Base Management	Gestion de Base de Données	Datenbankverwaltung	Gestión de Banco de Datos
Electronic Data Processing	Traitement de l'Information Électronique	Elektronische Datenverarbeitung	Proceso de Datos Electronico
Hardware	Materiel	Hardware	Equipo Físico
Information Science, Information Theory	Théorie de l'Information	Informationstheorie	Ciencia, Teoría de la Información
Machine Theory	Théorie de Machine	Maschinetheorie	Teoría de la Maquina
Microcomputers	Micro-Ordinateurs	Mikrocomputer	Microordenadores
Minicomputers	Mini-Ordinateurs	Minicomputer	Miniordenadores
Personal Computers	Ordinateurs Privés	Persoenlichecomputer	Ordenadores Personales
Robotics	Robotique	Robotersysteme	Robótica
Software	Logiciel	Software	Soporte Lógico
Theory of Computing	Théorie de Traitement	Computertheorie	Theoria de Cálculo
Word Processing	Traitement de Textes	Textverarbeitung	Proceso de la Palabras
Conservation	Conservation	Landschaftsschutz	Conservación
Consumer Education and Protection	Protection de Consommateur	Verbraucherwirtschaftsschutz	Protección del Consumidor
Criminology and Law Enforcement	Criminologie et Police	Kriminologie und Strafvollzug	Criminología y Acción Policial
Computer Applications	Applications des Ordinateurs	Computer Anwendung	Aplicaciones de los Ordenadores
Security	Sécurité	Sicherheit	Seguridad
Dance	Danse	Tanz	Baile
Drug Abuse and Alcoholism	Toxicomanie et Alcoolisme	Rauschgiftsucht und Alkoholismus	Drogadismo y Alcoholismo
Earth Sciences	Sciences Géologiques	Wissenschaften der Erde	Ciencias Geológicas
Computer Applications	Applications des Ordinateurs	Computer Anwendung	Aplicaciones de los Ordenadores
Geology	Géologie	Geologie	Geología
Geophysics	Géophysique	Geophysik	Geofísica
Hydrology	Hydrologie	Hydrologie	Hidrología
Oceanography	Océanographie	Ozeanographie	Oceanografía
Education	Éducation	Bildungswesen	Educación
Adult Education	Enseignement des Adultes	Erwachsenenbildung	Enseñanza de Adultos
Computer Applications	Applications des Ordinateurs	Computer Anwendung	Aplicaciones de los Ordenadores
Guides to Schools and Colleges	Guides d'Écoles et Colleges	Führer zur Schulen und Universitäten	Guías de Escuelas y Colegios
Higher Education	Enseignement Supérieur	Hochschulwesen	Enseñanza Superior
International Education Programs	Programmes d'Éducation Internationale	Internazionale Erziehungsprogramme	Programas de Enseñanza Internacional
School Organization and Administration	Organisation et Administration de l'École	Organisation und Verwaltung von dem Schule	Administración y Dirección de la Escuela
Special Education and Rehabilitation	Enseignement Special et Réhabilitation	Fachunterricht und Rehabilitierung	Enseñanza Especial y Rehabilitación
Teaching Methods and Curriculum	Méthodes Pédagogiques et Programmes Scolaires	Lehrmethoden und Lehrplan	Métodos de Enseñanza y Planes de Estudios

Electronics	Électronique	Elektronik	Electrónicos
Computer Applications	Applications des Ordinateurs	Computer Anwendung	Aplicaciones de los Ordenadores
Encyclopedias and General Almanacs	Encyclopédies et Almanachs Générales	Enzyklopädien und Allgemeine Nachschlagewerke	Enciclopedias y Almanaques Generales
Energy	Énergie	Energie	Energía
Computer Applications	Applications des Ordinateurs	Computer Anwendung	Aplicaciones de los Ordenadores
Electrical Energy	Énergie Électrique	Elektrizitätsenergie	Energía Eléctrica
Geothermal Energy	Énergie Géothermique	Thermalenergie	Energía Geotérmica
Hydroelectrical Energy	Énergie Hydraulique	Hydroelektroenergie	Energía Hidroeléctrica
Nuclear Energy	Énergie Nucléaire	Kernenergie	Energía Nuclear
Solar Energy	Énergie Solaire	Sonnenenergie	Energía Solar
Wind Energy	Énergie à Vent	Windenergie	Energía de Viento
Engineering	Génie	Ingenieurwesen	Ingeniería
Chemical Engineering	Génie Chimique	Chemieingenieurwesen	Ingeniería Química
Civil Engineering	Génie Civil	Bauingenieurwesen	Ingeniería Civil
Computer Applications	Applications des Ordinateurs	Computer Anwendung	Aplicaciones de los Ordenadores
Electrical Engineering	Génie Électrique	Elektrotechnik	Ingeniería Eléctrica
Engineering Mechanics and Materials	Méchanique de Génie et Materiels	Ingenieurwesen Mechanik und Materialien	Mecánica de Ingeniería y Materiales
Hydraulic Engineering	Génie Hydraulique	Wasserbau	Ingeniería Hidráulica
Industrial Engineering	Génie Industriel	Industrieingenieurwesen	Ingeniería Industrial
Mechanical Engineering	Génie Mécanique	Maschinenbau	Ingeniería Mecánica
Environmental Studies	Science de l'Environnement	Umweltschutz	Ciencias Ecológicas
Computer Applications	Applications des Ordinateurs	Computer Anwendung	Aplicaciones de los Ordenadores
Pollution	Pollution	Umweltverschmutzung	Contaminación
Toxicology and Environmental Safety	Toxicologie et Sécurité de l'Environnement	Toxokologie und Umweltsicherheit	Toxicología y Seguridad Ambiental
Waste Management	Gestion de Déchets	Abfallwirtschaft	Manejo de la Basura
Ethnic Interests	Publications de l'Orientation Ethnique	Allgemeine Völkerkunde	Publicaciones de Temas Etnicos
Fire Prevention	Précaution contre l'Incendie	Brandbekämpfung	Prevención del Fuego
Fish and Fisheries	Poisson et Pêche	Fische und Fischerei	Pesca y Pesquerías
Folklore	Folklore	Volkskunde	Folklore
Food and Food Industries	Alimentation et Industries Alimentaires	Nahrungsmittel und Lebensmittelindustrie	Alimentos e Industrias Alimenticias
Bakers and Confectioners	Boulangerie et Confiserie	Bäcker- und Konditorgewerbe	Panaderías y Dulcerías
Grocery Trade	Épicerie	Kolonialwarenhandel	Abacerías
Forest and Forestry	Forêts et Exploitation Forestière	Forstwesen und Waldwirtschaft	Bosques y Selvicultura
Lumber and Wood	Bois	Holz	Maderas
Funerals	Funérailles	Beerdigungen	Funerales
Gardening and Horticulture	Jardinage et Horticulture	Gartenpflege und Gartenbau	Jardinería y Horticultura
Florist Trade	Commerce des Fleurs	Blumenhandel	Floristas
Genealogy and Heraldry	Généalogie et Science Héraldique	Genealogie und Wappenkunde	Genealogía y Heráldica
Computer Applications	Applications des Ordinateurs	Computer Anwendung	Aplicaciones de los Ordenadores
General Interest Periodicals (Subdivided by country)	Publications d'Intérêt Général (Selon pays)	Allgemeine Zeitschriften (nach Land)	Periódicos de Interés General (por país)
Geography	Géographie	Geographie	Geografía
Computer Applications	Applications de Ordinateurs	Computer Anwendung	Aplicaciones de los Ordenadores
Gerontology and Geriatrics	Gérontologie	Gerontologie	Gerontología y Geriátrica
Giftware and Toys	Cadeaux et Jouets	Geschenkartikel und Spielwaren	Regalos y Juguetes
Handicapped	Handicapés	Behinderung	Desventajados
Computer Applications	Applications des Ordinateurs	Computer Anwendung	Aplicaciones de los Ordenadores
Hearing Impaired	Sourds	Schwerhörigkeit	Debilitado del Oído
Physically Impaired	Handicapés Physique	Körperbehinderung	Debilitado Físicamente
Visually Impaired	Aveugles	Blindheit	Debilitado Visualmente
Heating, Plumbing, and Refrigeration	Chauffage, Plomberie et Réfrigeration	Heizung, Kühlung und Installation	Calefacción, Plomería y Refrigeración
History	Histoire	Geschichte	Historia
Computer Applications	Applications des Ordinateurs	Computer Anwendung	Aplicaciones de los Ordenadores
History of Africa	Histoire de l'Afrique	Geschichte-Afrika	Historia de Africa
History of Asia	Histoire de l'Asie	Geschichte-Asien	Historia de Asia
History of Australasia	Histoire de l'Australasie	Geschichte-Australasien	Historia de Australasia
History of Europe	Histoire de l'Europe	Geschichte-Europa	Historia de la Europa
History of North and South America	Histoire de l'Amérique du Nord et du Sud	Geschichte-Nord- und Südamerika	Historia de la América del Norte y de la del Sur
History of Near East	Histoire du Proche-Orient	Geschichte-Nahe Osten	Historia del Cercano Oriente
Hobbies	Passe-Temps	Hobbies	Pasatiempos
Home Economics	Enseignement Ménager	Hauswirtschaft	Economía Doméstica
Homosexuality	Homosexualisme	Homosexualität	Homosexualismo
Hospitals	Hôpitaux	Krankenhäuser	Hospitales
Computer Applications	Applications des Ordinateurs	Computer Anwendung	Aplicaciones de los Ordenadores
Hotels and Restaurants	Hôtels et Restaurants	Hotels und Restaurants	Hoteles y Restaurantes
Computer Applications	Applications des Ordinateurs	Computer Anwendung	Aplicaciones de los Ordenadores
Housing and Urban Planning	Logement et Urbanisme	Wohnungswesen und Stadtplanung	Viviendas y Urbanismo
Computer Applications	Applications des Ordinateurs	Computer Anwendung	Aplicaciones de los Ordenadores
How-To and Do-It-Yourself	Bricolage	Selbstanfertigung	Cómo Hacerlo y Hágalo Si Mismo
Humanities: Comprehensive Works	Humanités: Oeuvres Compréhensives	Klassische Philologie	Humanidades: Obras Comprensivas
Computer Applications	Applications des Ordinateurs	Computer Anwendung	Aplicaciones de los Ordenadores
Instruments	Instruments	Instrumente	Instrumentos
Insurance	Assurances	Versicherungswesen	Seguros
Computer Applications	Applications des Ordinateurs	Computer Anwendung	Aplicaciones de los Ordenadores
Interior Design and Decoration	Agencements Intérieurs et Décoration	Innenarchitektur und Innenausstattung	Diseño del Interior y Ornamentación
Furniture and House Furnishing	Meubles et Articles pour la Maison	Möbel und Wohnungseinrichtung	Muebles y Articulos para el Hogar
Jewelry Clocks and Watches	Bijouterie et Horlogerie	Schmuck und Uhren	Joyería y Relojería
Journalism	Journalisme	Journalismus	Periodismo
Labor Unions	Syndicalisme	Gewerkschaften	Sindicatos

SUBJECTS

Law	Droit	Rechtswissenschaft	Derecho
Civil Law	Droit Civil	Zivilrecht	Derecho Civil
Computer Applications	Applications des Ordinateurs	Computer Anwendung	Aplicaciones de los Ordenadores
Constitutional Law	Droit Constitutionel	Verfassungsrecht	Derecho Constitucional
Corporate Law	Droit Commercial	Handelsrecht	Derecho Corporativo
Criminal Law	Droit Pénal	Strafrecht	Derecho Criminal
Estate Planning	Succession	Mobiliarvermögensrecht	Planificación de los Bienes
Family and Matrimonial Law	Droit Familial et Matrimonial	Ehegesetz und Familienrecht	Derecho Familial y Matrimonial
International Law	Droit International	Völkerrecht	Derecho Internacional
Judicial Systems	Système Judiciaire	Gerichtswesen	Sistemas Judiciales
Legal Aid	Assistance Judiciaire	Rechtshilfe	Ayuda Legal
Maritime Law	Droit Maritime	Seerecht	Derecho Marítimo
Military Law	Droit Militaire	Kriegsrecht	Derecho Militar
Leather and Fur Industries	Maroquinerie et Pelleterie	Leder und Pelz	Pieles y Cuero
Leisure and Recreation	Loisirs et Récréation	Freizeit und Unterhaltung	Ocio y Recreo
Library and Information Science	Bibliothéconomie et Informatique	Bibliothek- und Informationswissenschaft	Bibliotecología y Ciencia de la Información
Computer Applications	Applications des Ordinateurs	Computer Anwendung	Aplicaciones de los Ordenadores
Linguistics	Linguistique	Sprachwissenschaft	Lingüística
Computer Applications	Applications des Ordinateurs	Computer Anwendung	Aplicaciones de los Ordenadores
Literary and Political Reviews	Revues Littéraires et Politiques	Literarische und Politische Zeitschriften	Revistas Literarias y Políticas
Literature	Littérature	Literatur	Literatura
Adventure and Romance	Aventure et Romance	Abenteuer und Romantik	Aventura y Romance
Mystery and Detective	Mystère et Policier	Geheimnis und Detektivroman	Misterio y Detective
Poetry	Poésie	Poesie	Poesía
Science Fiction, Fantasy, Horror	Science-Fiction, Oeuvres Fantastiques, Oeuvre d'Epouvante	Zukunftsroman, Phantasiegebilde, Grausen	Ciencia Ficción, Fantasía, Horror
Machinery	Machines	Maschinenwesen	Maquinaria
Computer Applications	Applications des Ordinateurs	Computer Anwendung	Aplicaciones de los Ordenadores
Mathematics	Mathématiques	Mathematik	Matemática
Computer Applications	Applications des Ordinateurs	Computer Anwendung	Aplicaciones de los Ordenadores
Matrimony	Mariage	Ehestand	Matrimonio
Computer Applications	Applications des Ordinateurs	Computer Anwendung	Aplicaciones de los Ordenadores
Medical Sciences	Sciences Médicales	Medizinische Wissenschaften	Ciencias Médicas
Allergology and Immunology	Allergologie et Immunologie	Allergie und Immunologie	Alergología e Imunología
Anaesthesiology	Anesthésiologie	Anaesthesiology	Anestesiología
Cardiovascular Diseases	Maladies Cardiovasculaires	Kreislauferkrankungen	Enfermedades Cardiovasculares
Chiropractic, Homeopathy, Osteopathy	Chiropraxie, Homéopathie, Ostéopathie	Chiropraktik, Homöopathie, Osteopathie	Quiropráctica, Homeopatía, Osteopatía
Communicable Diseases	Maladies Contagieuses	Infektiöse Krankheiten	Enfermedades Contagiosas
Computer Applications	Applications des Ordinateurs	Computer Anwendung	Aplicaciones de los Ordenadores
Dentistry	Dentisterie	Zahnmedizin	Dentistería
Dermatology and Venereology	Dermatologie et Maladies Vénériennes	Dermatologie und Geschlechtskrankheiten	Dermatología y Venereología
Endocrinology	Endocrinologie	Endokrinologie	Endocrinología
Experimental Medicine Laboratory Technique	Médecine Expérimentale, Techniques de Laboratoire	Versuchsmedizin, Laboratoriumstechnik	Medicina Experimental, Tecnicas del Laboratorio
Forensic Sciences	Médecine Légale	Gerichtliche Medizin	Ciencias Forenses
Gastroenterology	Gastroentérologie	Gastroenterologie	Gastroenterología
Hematology	Hématologie	Hämatologie	Hematología
Hypnosis	Hypnose	Hypnose	Hipnotismo
Internal Medicine	Médecine Interne	Innere Medizin	Medicina Interna
Nurses and Nursing	Personnel et Soins Infirmiers	Krankenpflege	Enfermeros y Enfermería
Obstetrics and Gynecology	Obstétrique et Gynécologie	Gynäkologie und Geburtshilfe	Obstetricia y Ginecología
Oncology	Cancer	Onkologie	Oncología
Ophthalmology and Optometry	Ophtalmologie et Optométrie	Opthalmologie und Optometrie	Oftalmología y Optometría
Orthopedics and Traumatology	Orthopédie et Traumatologie	Orthopädie und Traumatologie	Ortopedia y Traumatología
Otorhinolaryngology	Otorhinolaryngologie	Otorhinolaryngologie	Otorinolaringología
Pediatrics	Pédiatrie	Pädiatrie	Pediatría
Physical Medicine and Rehabilitation	Médecine Physique et Réhabilitation	Physikalische Heilkunde und Rehabilitation	Medicina Física y Rehabilitación
Psychiatry and Neurology	Psychiatrie et Neurologie	Psychiatrie und Neurologie	Psiquiatría y Neurología
Radiology and Nuclear Medicine	Radiologie et Médecine Nucléaire	Radiologie und Nuklearmedizin	Radiología y Medicina Nuclear
Respiratory Diseases	Maladies Respiratoires	Atmungskrankheiten	Enfermedades Respiratorias
Rheumatology	Rhumatologie	Rheumatologie	Reumatología
Sports Medicine	Médecine du Sport	Sportmedizin	Medicina de Deportes
Sugery	Chirurgie	Chirurgie	Cirugía
Urology and Nephrology	Urologie et Néphrologie	Urologie und Nephrologie	Urología y Nefrología
Men's Health	Santé de l'Homme	Gesundheit von Männern	Salud Masculina
Men's Interests	Publications d'Intérêt Masculin	Männer Interessen	Intereses Masculinos
Men's Studies	Études de l'Homme	Männerstudien	Estudios de los Hombres
Meetings and Congresses	Réunions et Congrès	Tagungen und Kongresse	Conferencias y Congresos
Metallurgy	Métallurgie	Metallurgie	Metalurgia
Computer Applications	Applications des Ordinateurs	Computer Anwendung	Aplicaciones de los Ordenadores
Welding	Soudure	Schweissen	Soldadura
Meteorology	Météorologie	Meteorologie	Meteorología
Computer Applications	Applications des Ordinateurs	Computer Anwendung	Aplicaciones de los Ordenadores
Metrology and Standardization	Métrologie et Standardisation	Mass- und Gewichtskunde, Normung	Metrología y Normalización
Computer Applications	Applications des Ordinateurs	Computer Anwendung	Aplicaciones de los Ordenadores
Military	Militaires	Militärwesen	Militares
Mines and Mining Industry	Mines et Resources Minières	Bergwesen und Bergbauindustrie	Mines y Minerales
Computer Applications	Applicationes des Ordinateurs	Computer Anwendung	Aplicaciones de los Ordenadores
Motion Pictures	Cinéma	Film und Kino	Películas
Museums and Art Galleries	Musées et Galleries	Museen und Kunstgalerien	Museos y Galerías del Arte
Music	Musique	Musik	Música
Computer Applications	Applications des Ordinateurs	Computer Anwendung	Aplicaciones de los Ordenadores
Needlework	Travaux à l'Aiguille	Näherei	Bordado
New Age	Nouvelle Ere	New Age	Nueva Epoca
Numismatics	Numismatique	Numismatik	Numismática
Nutrition and Dietetics	Nutrition et Diététique	Ernährung und Diätetik	Nutrición y Dietética
Occupational Health and Safety	Médecine du Travail et Prévention	Berufsgesundheitspflege und Sicherheit	Sanidad y Seguridad de Oficio
Occupations and Careers	Occupations et Carrières	Berufe	Empleos y Ocupaciones
Oriental Studies	Études Orientales	Orientalistik	Estudios Orientales
Packaging	Emballage	Verpackung	Empaque
Computer Applications	Applications des Ordinateurs	Computer Anwendung	Aplicaciones de los Ordenadores

SUBJECTS xlix

Paints and Protective Coatings	Couleurs et Peintures	Farben und Beläge	Pinturas y Revestimientos Protectores
Paleontology	Paléontologie	Paleontologie	Paleontología
Computer Applications	Applications des Ordinateurs	Computer Anwendung	Aplicaciones de los Ordenadores
Paper and Pulp	Papier et Pulpe	Papier und Papierstoff	Papel y Pasta
Parapsychology and Occultism	Parapsychologie et Occultisme	Parapsychologie und Okkultismus	Parapsicología y Ocultismo
Patents, Trademarks and Copyrights	Brevets, Marques de Fabrique et Droits d'Auteur	Patente, Schutzmarken und Urheberrechte	Patentes, Marcas de Fabrica y Derechos de Autor
Petroleum and Gas	Pétrole et Gas Naturel	Petroleum und Gas	Petróleo y Gas Natural
Computer Applications	Applications des Ordinateurs	Computer Anwendung	Aplicaciones de los Ordenadores
Pets	Animaux Familiers	Haustiere	Animales Domésticos
Pharmacy and Pharmacology	Pharmacie et Pharmacologie	Pharmazie und Pharmakologie	Farmacia y Farmacología
Computer Applications	Applications des Ordinateurs	Computer Anwendung	Aplicaciones de los Ordenadores
Philately	Philatélie	Briefmarkenkunde	Filatelia
Philosophy	Philosophie	Philosophie	Filosofía
Photography	Photographie	Photographie	Fotografía
Computer Applications	Applications des Ordinateurs	Computer Anwendung	Aplicaciones de los Ordenadores
Physical Fitness and Hygiene	Santé Physique et Hygiène	Gesundheitszustand und Hygiene	Salud Física e Higiene
Physics	Physique	Physik	Física
Computer Applications	Applications des Ordinateurs	Computer Anwendung	Aplicaciones de los Ordenadores
Electricity	Électricité	Elektrizität	Electricidad
Heat	Chaleur	Wärme	Calor
Mechanics	Mécanique	Mechanik	Mecánica
Nuclear Physics	Physique Nucléaire	Kernphysik	Física Nuclear
Optics	Optique	Optik	Optica
Sound	Son	Schall	Sonido
Plastics	Plastiques	Kunststoffe	Plásticos
Computer Applications	Applications des Ordinateurs	Computer Anwendung	Aplicaciones de los Ordenadores
Political Science	Sciences Politiques	Politische Wissenschafte	Ciencias Políticas
Civil Rights	Droits Civiques	Bürgerrechte	Derechos Civiles
International Relations	Relations Internationales	Internationale Beziehungen	Relaciones Internacionales
Population Studies	Démographie	Bevölkerungswissenschaft	Demografía
Printing	Imprimerie	Druck	Imprenta
Computer Applications	Applications des Ordinateurs	Computer Anwendung	Aplicaciones de los Ordenadores
Psychology	Psychologie	Psychologie	Psicología
Public Administration	Administration Publique	Öffentliche Verwaltung	Administración Pública
Computer Applications	Applications des Ordinateurs	Computer Anwendung	Aplicaciones de los Ordenadores
Municipal Government	Gouvernement Municipal	Kommunalverwaltung	Gobierno Municipal
Public Health and Safety	Santé Publique et Prévention	Öffentliche Gesundheitspflege	Salud Pública y Seguridad
Publishing and Book Trade	Édition et Commence du Livre	Verlagswesen und Buchhandel	Editoriales y Libreria
Computer Applications	Applications des Ordinateurs	Computer Anwendung	Aplicaciones de los Ordenadores
Real Estate	Immobilières	Grundbesitz und Immobilien	Bienes Raíces
Computer Applications	Applications des Ordinateurs	Computer Anwendung	Aplicaciones de los Ordenadores
Religions and Theology	Religions et Théologie	Religion und Theologie	Religión y Teología
Buddhist	Bouddhisme	Buddhist	Budista
Eastern Orthodox	Églises Orthodoxes	Orthodox	Ortodoxo Oriental
Hindu	Hindou	Hindu	Hindú
Islamic	Islamique	Islamische	Islámico
Judaic	Judaïque	Jüdäistische	Judaico
Protestant	Protestant	Evangelische	Protestante
Roman Catholic	Catholique Romain	Römisch-katholische	Católico Romano
Other Sects	Autres Sectes	Andere Sekte	Otras Sectas
Rubber	Caoutchouc	Gummi	Caucho
Computer Applications	Applications des Ordinateurs	Computer Anwendung	Aplicaciones de los Ordenadores
Sciences: Comprehensive Works	Sciences: Oeuvres Compréhensives	Wissenschaften: Umfassende Werke	Ciencias: Obras Comprensivas
Computer Applications	Applications des Ordinateurs	Computer Anwendung	Aplicaciones de los Ordenadores
Shoes and Boots	Chaussures et Bottes	Schuhe und Stiefel	Zapatos y Botas
Singles' Interests and Lifestyles	Intérêts et Style de Vie Célibataire	Ledigenstandinteressen	Intereses y Estilos de Vivir de los Solteros
Social Sciences: Comprehensive Works	Sciences Sociales: Oeuvres Compréhensives	Sozialwissenschaften: Umfassende Werke	Ciencias Sociales: Obras Comprensivas
Social Service and Welfare	Service Social et Protection Sociale	Sozialpflege und Fürsorge	Asistencia Social y Bienestar
Sociology	Sociologie	Soziologie	Sociología
Computer Applications	Applications des Ordinateurs	Computer Anwendung	Aplicaciones de los Ordenadores
Sound Recording and Reproduction	Enregistrement et Reproduction du Son	Tonaufnahme und Tonwiedergabe	Grabaciones y Reproducciones Sonoras
Computer Applications	Applications des Ordinateurs	Computer Anwendung	Aplicaciones de los Ordenadores
Sports and Games	Sports et Jeux	Sport und Spiele	Deportes y Juegos
Ball Games	Jeux de Balle	Ballspiele	Juegos de Pelota
Bicycles and Motorcycles	Bicyclettes et Motocyclettes	Fahrräder und Motorräder	Bicicletas y Motocicletas
Boats and Boating	Bateaux et Canotage	Boote und Bootfahren	Botes y Bartelaje
Horses and Horsemanship	Equitation	Pferde und Reitsport	Caballos y Equitación
Outdoor Life	Vie en Plein Air	Im Freien	Vida de Campo
Statistics	Statistique	Statistik	Estadísticas
Technology: Comprehensive Works	Technologie: Oeuvres Compréhensives	Technologie: Umfassende Werke	Tecnología: Obras Comprensivas
Textile Industries and Fabrics	Textiles	Textil	Textiles y Telas
Computer Applications	Applications des Ordinateurs	Computer Anwendung	Aplicaciones de los Ordenadores
Theater	Théâtre	Theater	Teatro
Tobacco	Tabac	Tabak	Tabaco
Transportation	Transports	Transport	Transportación
Air Transport	Transport Aérien	Luftverkehr	Transporte Aéreo
Automobiles	Automobiles	Kraftfahrzeugen	Automóviles
Computer Applications	Applications des Ordinateurs	Computer Anwendung	Aplicaciones de los Ordenadores
Railroads	Chemins de Fer	Eisenbahnen	Ferrocarriles
Roads and Traffic	Routes et Circulation	Strassen und Strassenverkehr	Caminos y Tráfico
Ships and Shipping	Navires et Transport Maritimes	Schiffe und Schiffahrt	Barcos y Embarques
Trucks and Trucking	Transports Routiers	Lastkraftwagen	Camiones
Travel and Tourism	Voyages et Tourisme	Reisen und Tourismus	Viaje y Turismo
Airline Inflight and Hotel Inroom	Revues en Vol des Lignes Aériennes et en Chambre des Hôtels	Fluggesellschaft und Hotel Veröffentlichungen	Aerolínea En-Vuelo y Hotel En-Cuarto
Veterinary Sciences	Science Vétérinaire	Tierheilkunde	Veterinaria
Computer Applications	Applications des Ordinateurs	Computer Anwendung	Aplicaciones de los Ordenadores
Water Resources	Ressources de l'Eau	Wasserwirtschaft	Recursos de Aqua
Computer Applications	Applications des Ordinateurs	Computer Anwendung	Aplicaciones de los Ordenadores
Women's Health	Santé de la Femme	Gesundheit von Frauen	Salud Feminina
Women's Interests	Publications d'Intérêt Féminin	Fraueninteresse	Intereses Femininas
Women's Studies	Études de la Femme	Frauenstudien	Estudios de las Mujeres

Cross-Index to Subjects

A I D S see MEDICAL SCIENCES - Communicable Diseases 3962
A T M (Automated Teller Machine) see BUSINESS AND ECONOMICS - Banking And Finance - Computer Applications 981
Abortions see BIRTH CONTROL 713, see also MEDICAL SCIENCES - Obstetrics And Gynecology 4056
Abrasives see MACHINERY 3733, see also METALLURGY 4223
ABSTRACTING AND INDEXING SERVICES 1
Acarology see BIOLOGY - Entomology 628
Accessories see CLOTHING TRADE - Fashions 1596
Accident Prevention see OCCUPATIONAL HEALTH AND SAFETY 4474, see also TRANSPORTATION - Roads and Traffic 5811
Accounting see BUSINESS AND ECONOMICS - Accounting 903
Acid Rain see ENVIRONMENTAL STUDIES - Pollution 2446
Acoustics see PHYSICS - Sound 4780, see also SOUND RECORDING AND REPRODUCTION 5494
Acquired Immunodeficiency Syndrome see MEDICAL SCIENCES - Communicable Diseases 3962
Acting see COMMUNICATIONS - Television And Cable 1696, see also MOTION PICTURES 4344, THEATER 5704
Activation Analysis see PHYSICS - Nuclear Physics 4763
Actuarial Science see INSURANCE 3133, see also MATHEMATICS 3745
Acupressure see ALTERNATIVE MEDICINE 265
Acupuncture see ALTERNATIVE MEDICINE 265
Addictions see DRUG ABUSE AND ALCOHOLISM 1898
Adhesives see ENGINEERING - Chemical Engineering 2277
Administrative Law see LAW - Constitutional Law 3354
Adolescence see CHILDREN AND YOUTH - About 1529, see also CHILDREN AND YOUTH - For 1548
Adolescent Medicine see MEDICAL SCIENCES - Pediatrics 4110
Adoption And Fostering see CHILDREN AND YOUTH - About 1529, see also LAW - Family And Matrimonial Law 3375, SOCIAL SERVICES AND WELFARE 5421
Adult Education see EDUCATION - Adult Education 2075
Adventism see RELIGIONS AND THEOLOGY - Protestant 5225
Adventure And Romance see LITERATURE - Adventure And Romance 3696
ADVERTISING AND PUBLIC RELATIONS 28
ADVERTISING AND PUBLIC RELATIONS — Abstracting, Bibliographies, Statistics 44
Advertising Art see ADVERTISING AND PUBLIC RELATIONS 28
Aerobics see PHYSICAL FITNESS AND HYGIENE 4704, see also SPORTS AND GAMES 5498
Aerodynamics see PHYSICS - Mechanics 4758
AERONAUTICS AND SPACE FLIGHT 47, see also ENGINEERING - Mechanical Engineering 2379, TRANSPORTATION - Air Transport 5753
AERONAUTICS AND SPACE FLIGHT — Abstracting, Bibliographies, Statistics 75
AERONAUTICS AND SPACE FLIGHT — Computer Applications 76
Aerophysics see PHYSICS - Mechanics 4758
Aerosol Containers see ENVIRONMENTAL STUDIES - Pollution 2446, see also PACKAGING 4516
Aerospace Engineering see AERONAUTICS AND SPACE FLIGHT 47
Aerospace Medicine see MEDICAL SCIENCES 3799
Aesthetics see ART 364, see also PHILOSOPHY 4656
African American History see HISTORY - History Of North And South America 2977
African History see HISTORY - History of Africa 2902
African Studies see HISTORY - History of Africa 2902
Aging see GERONTOLOGY AND GERIATRICS 2826
Agnosticism see PHILOSOPHY 4656, see also RELIGIONS AND THEOLOGY 5145
Agribusiness see AGRICULTURE - Agricultural Economics 169
Agricultural Aviation see AERONAUTICS AND SPACE FLIGHT 47
Agricultural Chemistry see AGRICULTURE 76, see also CHEMISTRY 1448
Agricultural Economics see AGRICULTURE - Agricultural Economics 169
Agricultural Engineering see AGRICULTURE 76, see also ENGINEERING 2237
Agricultural Equipment see AGRICULTURE - Agricultural Equipment 186
Agricultural Marketing see AGRICULTURE - Agricultural Economics 169, see also FOOD AND FOOD INDUSTRIES - Grocery Trade 2591
AGRICULTURE 76, see also FOOD AND FOOD INDUSTRIES 2553, FORESTS AND FORESTRY 2597, GARDENING AND HORTICULTURE 2627
AGRICULTURE — Abstracting, Bibliographies, Statistics 152
AGRICULTURE — Agricultural Economics 169
AGRICULTURE — Agricultural Equipment 186
AGRICULTURE — Computer Applications 191
AGRICULTURE — Crop Production And Soil 192
AGRICULTURE — Dairying And Dairy Products 228
AGRICULTURE — Feed, Flour And Grain 236
AGRICULTURE — Poultry And Livestock 241
Agronomy see AGRICULTURE 76
Air Conditioning see HEATING, PLUMBING AND REFRIGERATION 2862
Air Defense see MILITARY 4283

Air Force see MILITARY 4283
Air Law see AERONAUTICS AND SPACE FLIGHT 47, see also LAW 3215, TRANSPORTATION - Air Transport 5753
Air Navigation see AERONAUTICS AND SPACE FLIGHT 47
Air Pollution see ENVIRONMENTAL STUDIES - Pollution 2446
Air Traffic Control see AERONAUTICS AND SPACE FLIGHT - Computer Applications 76
Air Transport see TRANSPORTATION - Air Transport 5753
Aircraft see AERONAUTICS AND SPACE FLIGHT 47, see also TRANSPORTATION - Air Transport 5753
Airline Inflight And Hotel Inroom see TRAVEL AND TOURISM - Airline Inflight And Hotel Inroom 5908
Airplanes see AERONAUTICS AND SPACE FLIGHT 47, see also TRANSPORTATION - Air Transport 5753
Airports see AERONAUTICS AND SPACE FLIGHT 47, see also TRANSPORTATION - Air Transport 5753
Alarms see CRIMINOLOGY AND LAW ENFORCEMENT - Security 1890, see also ELECTRONICS 2170, ENGINEERING - Electrical Engineering 2320
Alcoholic Beverages see BEVERAGES 443
Alcoholism see DRUG ABUSE AND ALCOHOLISM 1898
Algae see BIOLOGY - Botany 583
Algebra see MATHEMATICS 3745
Alimentary System see MEDICAL SCIENCES - Gastroenterology 4024
Allergology And Immunology see MEDICAL SCIENCES - Allergology And Immunology 3933
Alloys see METALLURGY 4223
Almanacs, General see ENCYCLOPEDIAS AND GENERAL ALMANACS 457
ALTERNATIVE MEDICINE 265
ALTERNATIVE MEDICINE — Abstracting, Bibliographies, Statistics 268
Aluminum see METALLURGY 4223, see also MINES AND MINING INDUSTRY 4315
Alumni see COLLEGE AND ALUMNI 1612
Alzheimer's Disease see GERONTOLOGY AND GERIATRICS 2826, see also MEDICAL SCIENCES - Psychiatry And Neurology 4125
Amateur Radio see COMMUNICATIONS - Radio 1678
American History see HISTORY - History Of North And South America 2977
Amusement Guides see COMMUNICATIONS - Television And Cable 1696, see also MUSIC 4382, THEATER 5704, TRAVEL AND TOURISM 5848
Anabaptist see RELIGIONS AND THEOLOGY - Protestant 5225
Anaesthesiology see MEDICAL SCIENCES - Anaesthesiology 3942
Analogue Computation see COMPUTERS - Hardware 1799, see also COMPUTERS - Theory of Computing 1836
Analysis see MATHEMATICS 3745
Analytical Chemistry see CHEMISTRY - Analytical Chemistry 1491
Anarchy see POLITICAL SCIENCE 4793
Anatomy see BIOLOGY 499, see also MEDICAL SCIENCES 3799
Ancient History see ARCHAEOLOGY 304, see also HISTORY 2872
Anemia see MEDICAL SCIENCES - Hematology 4030
Angiology see MEDICAL SCIENCES - Cardiovascular Diseases 3946
Anglicanism see RELIGIONS AND THEOLOGY - Protestant 5225
ANIMAL WELFARE 268
ANIMAL WELFARE — Abstracting, Bibliographies, Statistics 272
Animals see AGRICULTURE - Poultry and Livestock 241, see also ANIMAL WELFARE 268, BIOLOGY - Zoology 689, LEATHER AND FUR INDUSTRIES 3410, PETS 4591, SPORTS AND GAMES - Horses and Horsemanship 5579, VETERINARY SCIENCE 5913
Animation see ART - Computer Applications 413, see also COMMUNICATIONS - Television And Cable 1696, COMMUNICATIONS - Video 1715, MOTION PICTURES 4344, PHOTOGRAPHY 4691
Anorexia Nervosa see MEDICAL SCIENCES - Psychiatry And Neurology 4125, see also NUTRITION AND DIETETICS 4461
ANTHROPOLOGY 272, see also ARCHAEOLOGY 304
ANTHROPOLOGY — Abstracting, Bibliographies, Statistics 296
Anthropometry see ANTHROPOLOGY 272
Anthroposophy see RELIGIONS AND THEOLOGY - Other Denominations And Sects 5287
Anti-Semitism see POLITICAL SCIENCE 4793, see also POLITICAL SCIENCE - Civil Rights 4877
Antibiotics see PHARMACY AND PHARMACOLOGY 4600
Antiquarian Book Trade see PUBLISHING AND BOOK TRADE 5096
ANTIQUES 297
Antiquities see CLASSICAL STUDIES 1578
Antiwar Movement see POLITICAL SCIENCE 4793, see also POLITICAL SCIENCE - International Relations 4889
Anxiety see MEDICAL SCIENCES - Psychiatry And Neurology 4125, see also PSYCHOLOGY 4962

CROSS-INDEX TO SUBJECTS

Apartheid see POLITICAL SCIENCE 4793, see also POLITICAL SCIENCE - Civil Rights 4877
Apartments see HOUSING AND URBAN PLANNING 3078, see also REAL ESTATE 5124
Apiculture see AGRICULTURE 76
Apothecary see PHARMACY AND PHARMACOLOGY 4600
Apparatus see INSTRUMENTS 3128, see also MACHINERY 3733
Apparel see CLOTHING TRADE 1589
Appliances see ELECTRONICS 2170, see also HEATING, PLUMBING AND REFRIGERATION 2862, INTERIOR DESIGN AND DECORATION - Furniture and House Furnishings 3172, PHYSICS - Electricity 4754
Applied Mechanics see ENGINEERING - Engineering Mechanics and Materials 2359
Apprenticeship see OCCUPATIONS AND CAREERS 4487
Aquaculture see BIOLOGY - Zoology 689, see also FISH AND FISHERIES 2523
Aquariums see BIOLOGY - Zoology 689, see also FISH AND FISHERIES 2523, PETS 4591
Aqueducts see WATER RESOURCES 5933
Arachnology see BIOLOGY - Entomology 628
Arbitration see BUSINESS AND ECONOMICS - Labor And Industrial Relations 1189, see also LAW 3215
ARCHAEOLOGY 304, see also ANTHROPOLOGY 272, ART 364, HISTORY 2872
ARCHAEOLOGY — Abstracting, Bibliographies, Statistics 341
ARCHAEOLOGY — Computer Applications 342
Archery see SPORTS AND GAMES 5498
ARCHITECTURE 342, see also BUILDING AND CONSTRUCTION 716, ENGINEERING - Civil Engineering 2293, HOUSING AND URBAN PLANNING 3078
ARCHITECTURE — Abstracting, Bibliographies, Statistics 364
ARCHITECTURE — Computer Applications 364
Archives see HISTORY 2872, see also LIBRARY AND INFORMATION SCIENCES 3416, MUSEUMS AND ART GALLERIES 4364
Area Planning see HOUSING AND URBAN PLANNING 3078
Arithmetic see MATHEMATICS 3745
Armed Forces see MILITARY 4283
Arms And Ammunition see MILITARY 4283, see also SPORTS AND GAMES - Outdoor Life 5588
Arms Control see MILITARY 4283, see also POLITICAL SCIENCE - International Relations 4889
Army see MILITARY 4283
Aromatherapy see ALTERNATIVE MEDICINE 265
ART 364
ART — Abstracting, Bibliographies, Statistics 412
ART — Computer Applications 413
Art Exhibitions see MUSEUMS AND ART GALLERIES 4364
Art History see ART 364
Arteriosclerosis see MEDICAL SCIENCES - Cardiovascular Diseases 3946
Arthritis see MEDICAL SCIENCES - Rheumatology 4179
Arthropods see BIOLOGY - Entomology 628
Artificial Insemination see MEDICAL SCIENCES - Obstetrics And Gynecology 4056
Artificial Intelligence see COMPUTERS - Artificial Intelligence 1741
Artillery see MILITARY 4283
Arts see ART 364, see also DANCE 1893, LITERATURE 3592, MOTION PICTURES 4344, MUSIC 4382, THEATER 5704
ARTS AND HANDICRAFTS 413
ARTS AND HANDICRAFTS — Abstracting, Bibliographies, Statistics 419
Asbestos see BUILDING AND CONSTRUCTION 716, see also ENVIRONMENTAL STUDIES 2399, LAW 3215, PUBLIC HEALTH AND SAFETY 5070
Ashkenazim see ETHNIC INTERESTS 2466, see also RELIGIONS AND THEOLOGY - Judaic 5218
Ashram see RELIGIONS AND THEOLOGY - Hindu 5211
Asian History see HISTORY - History of Asia 2908
Asian Studies see HISTORY - History Of Asia 2908, see also ORIENTAL STUDIES 4498
Asphalt see BUILDING AND CONSTRUCTION 716, see also ENGINEERING - Civil Engineering 2293, TRANSPORTATION - Roads and Traffic 5811
Asthma see MEDICAL SCIENCES - Respiratory Diseases 4174
ASTROLOGY 419
Astronautics see AERONAUTICS AND SPACE FLIGHT 47
ASTRONOMY 421
ASTRONOMY — Abstracting, Bibliographies, Statistics 435
Astrophysics see ASTRONOMY 421
Atavism see BIOLOGY - Genetics 643
Atheism see PHILOSOPHY 4656
Athletics see MEDICAL SCIENCES - Sports Medicine 4183, see also SPORTS AND GAMES 5498
Atlases see GEOGRAPHY 2794
Atmospheric Sciences see METEOROLOGY 4259
Atomic Energy see ENERGY - Nuclear Energy 2223
Audio Equipment see ELECTRONICS 2170, see also SOUND RECORDING AND REPRODUCTION 5494
Audio-Visual Education see EDUCATION - Teaching Methods and Curriculum 2146, see also MOTION PICTURES 4344
Audiocassettes see MUSIC 4382, see also SOUND RECORDING AND REPRODUCTION 5494
Audiology see MEDICAL SCIENCES - Otorhinolaryngology 4104
Auditing see BUSINESS AND ECONOMICS - Accounting 903
Autism see EDUCATION - Special Education And Rehabilitation 2136, see also MEDICAL SCIENCES - Psychiatry And Neurology 4125
Autobiographies see BIOGRAPHY 490
Automated Teller Machines see BUSINESS AND ECONOMICS - Banking And Finance - Computer Applications 981
Automation see COMPUTERS - Automation 1746
Automobile Racing see SPORTS AND GAMES 5498
Automobiles see TRANSPORTATION - Automobiles 5765
Autopsy see MEDICAL SCIENCES - Forensic Sciences 4021
Avalanches see METEOROLOGY 4259
Aviation see AERONAUTICS AND SPACE FLIGHT 47, see also TRANSPORTATION - Air Transport 5753
Aviculture see BIOLOGY - Ornithology 671
Avionics see AERONAUTICS AND SPACE FLIGHT - Computer Applications 76
Ayurveda see ALTERNATIVE MEDICINE 265
Babism see RELIGIONS AND THEOLOGY - Other Denominations And Sects 5287
Baby see CHILDREN AND YOUTH - About 1529, see also MEDICAL SCIENCES - Obstetrics And Gynecology 4056, MEDICAL SCIENCES - Pediatrics 4110
Bachelors, Bachelorettes see SINGLES' INTERESTS AND LIFESTYLES 5380
Bacteriology see BIOLOGY - Microbiology 654, see also MEDICAL SCIENCES - Communicable Diseases 3962
Badminton see SPORTS AND GAMES 5498
Baha'ism see RELIGIONS AND THEOLOGY - Other Denominations And Sects 5287
Bakers And Confectioners see FOOD AND FOOD INDUSTRIES - Bakers And Confectioners 2586
Ball Games see SPORTS AND GAMES - Ball Games 5540
Ballet see DANCE 1893
Bank Notes see NUMISMATICS 4456, see also PRINTING 4949
Banking And Finance see BUSINESS AND ECONOMICS - Banking And Finance 920
Banking Law see BUSINESS AND ECONOMICS - Banking and Finance 920, see also LAW 3215
Bankruptcy see BUSINESS AND ECONOMICS - Banking And Finance 920
Bankruptcy Law see LAW 3215, see also LAW - Corporate Law 3355
Baptist see RELIGIONS AND THEOLOGY - Protestant 5225
Barbering see BEAUTY CULTURE 435
Barbiturates see DRUG ABUSE AND ALCOHOLISM 1898, see also PHARMACY AND PHARMACOLOGY 4600
Barrels see PACKAGING 4516
Bars see HOTELS AND RESTAURANTS 3064
Baseball see SPORTS AND GAMES - Ball Games 5540
Basketball see SPORTS AND GAMES - Ball Games 5540
Battered Women see LAW - Family And Matrimonial Law 3375, see also SOCIAL SERVICES AND WELFARE 5421, WOMEN'S INTERESTS 5953
Batteries see PHYSICS - Electricity 4754, see also TRANSPORTATION - Automobiles 5765
BEAUTY CULTURE 435
BEAUTY CULTURE — Abstracting, Bibliographies, Statistics 440
BEAUTY CULTURE — Perfumes And Cosmetics 440
Beekeeping see AGRICULTURE 76
Beer see BEVERAGES 443
Behavioral Sciences see PSYCHOLOGY 4962, see also SOCIOLOGY 5459
Bereavement see PSYCHOLOGY 4962
BEVERAGES 443, see also FOOD AND FOOD INDUSTRIES 2553
BEVERAGES — Abstracting, Bibliographies, Statistics 456
Bias Attacks see CRIMINOLOGY AND LAW ENFORCEMENT 1869, see also POLITICAL SCIENCE - Civil Rights 4877
Biblical Studies see RELIGIONS AND THEOLOGY 5145
BIBLIOGRAPHIES 457, see also ABSTRACTING AND INDEXING SERVICES 1, LIBRARY AND INFORMATION SCIENCES 3416, PUBLISHING AND BOOK TRADE 5096
Bicycles And Motorcycles see SPORTS AND GAMES - Bicycles And Motorcycles 5560
Billiards see SPORTS AND GAMES - Ball Games 5540
Biochemistry see BIOLOGY - Biological Chemistry 555
Biocybernetics see MEDICAL SCIENCES 3799
Bioenergetics see BIOLOGY 499, see also PHYSICAL FITNESS AND HYGIENE 4704
Bioengineering see BIOLOGY - Bioengineering 552
Biofeedback see MEDICAL SCIENCES 3799, see also PHYSICAL FITNESS AND HYGIENE 4704
BIOGRAPHY 490
BIOGRAPHY — Abstracting, Bibliographies, Statistics 498
Biological Chemistry see BIOLOGY - Biological Chemistry 555
Biological Warfare see MILITARY 4283
BIOLOGY 499, see also MEDICAL SCIENCES 3799
BIOLOGY — Abstracting, Bibliographies, Statistics 543
BIOLOGY — Bioengineering 552
BIOLOGY — Biological Chemistry 555
BIOLOGY — Biophysics 572
BIOLOGY — Biotechnology 575
BIOLOGY — Botany 583
BIOLOGY — Computer Applications 621
BIOLOGY — Cytology And Histology 621
BIOLOGY — Entomology 628
BIOLOGY — Genetics 643
BIOLOGY — Microbiology 654
BIOLOGY — Microscopy 669
BIOLOGY — Ornithology 671
BIOLOGY — Physiology 681
BIOLOGY — Zoology 689
Biometeorology see METEOROLOGY 4259
Biometry see BIOLOGY 499, see also STATISTICS 5613
Bionics see COMPUTERS - Cybernetics 1784
Biophysics see BIOLOGY - Biophysics 572
Biotechnology see BIOLOGY - Biotechnology 575, see also ENGINEERING - Chemical Engineering 2277
Birds see BIOLOGY - Ornithology 671, see also CONSERVATION 1837, PETS 4591
BIRTH CONTROL 713
BIRTH CONTROL — Abstracting, Bibliographies, Statistics 716
Birth Defects see BIOLOGY - Genetics 643, see also MEDICAL SCIENCES 3799, MEDICAL SCIENCES - Obstetrics And Gynecology 4056
Birth Rate see POPULATION STUDIES - Abstracting, Bibliographies, Statistics 4936
Black Magic see PARAPSYCHOLOGY AND OCCULTISM 4542
Black Studies see ETHNIC INTERESTS 2466
Blacksmiths see METALLURGY 4223, see also SPORTS AND GAMES - Horses And Horsemanship 5579
Bladder see MEDICAL SCIENCES - Urology And Nephrology 4203
Blind see EDUCATION - Special Education and Rehabilitation 2136, see also HANDICAPPED - Visually Impaired 2855, MEDICAL SCIENCES - Ophthalmology And Optometry 4083, SOCIAL SERVICES AND WELFARE 5421
Blood see MEDICAL SCIENCES - Hematology 4030
Blood Transfusion see MEDICAL SCIENCES - Cardiovascular Diseases 3946, see also MEDICAL SCIENCES - Hematology 4030

CROSS-INDEX TO SUBJECTS

Board Games see SPORTS AND GAMES 5498
Boats And Boating see SPORTS AND GAMES - Boats And Boating 5568
Bobsleighing see SPORTS AND GAMES - Outdoor Life 5588
Bodybuilding see PHYSICAL FITNESS AND HYGIENE 4704, see also SPORTS AND GAMES 5498
Bond Market see BUSINESS AND ECONOMICS - Investments 1150
Book Collecting see PUBLISHING AND BOOK TRADE 5096
Book Design see ART 364, see also PUBLISHING AND BOOK TRADE 5096
Book Illustrating see PUBLISHING AND BOOK TRADE 5096
Book Reviews see LITERARY AND POLITICAL REVIEWS 3555, see also LITERATURE 3592, PUBLISHING AND BOOK TRADE 5096
Book Trade see BIBLIOGRAPHIES 457, see also PRINTING 4949, PUBLISHING AND BOOK TRADE 5096
Bookbinding see PUBLISHING AND BOOK TRADE 5096
Bookkeeping see BUSINESS AND ECONOMICS - Accounting 903
Booksellers see PUBLISHING AND BOOK TRADE 5096
Boots see SHOES AND BOOTS 5378
Botanical Gardens see BIOLOGY - Botany 583, see also GARDENING AND HORTICULTURE 2627
Botany see BIOLOGY - Botany 583
Bottling see BEVERAGES 443, see also PACKAGING 4516
Bowling see SPORTS AND GAMES - Ball Games 5540
Boxes see PACKAGING 4516
Boxing see SPORTS AND GAMES 5498
Brahmanism see RELIGIONS AND THEOLOGY - Hindu 5211
Braille see HANDICAPPED - Visually Impaired 2855
Brain see MEDICAL SCIENCES - Psychiatry And Neurology 4125
Brand Names see PATENTS, TRADEMARKS, AND COPYRIGHTS 4547
Brass see METALLURGY 4223
Brass Instruments see MUSIC 4382
Brazing see METALLURGY - Welding 4256
Breastfeeding see MEDICAL SCIENCES - Obstetrics And Gynecology 4056, see also NUTRITION AND DIETETICS 4461
Breathing Disorders see MEDICAL SCIENCES - Respiratory Diseases 4174
Brethren see RELIGIONS AND THEOLOGY - Protestant 5225
Brewing see BEVERAGES 443
Bricks see BUILDING AND CONSTRUCTION 716, see also CERAMICS, GLASS AND POTTERY 1439
Brides And Bridal Apparel see CLOTHING TRADE - Fashions 1596, see also MATRIMONY 3796
Bridge see SPORTS AND GAMES 5498
Bridge Construction see ENGINEERING - Civil Engineering 2293
Broadcasting see COMMUNICATIONS - Radio 1678, see also COMMUNICATIONS - Television And Cable 1696
Bronchitis see MEDICAL SCIENCES - Respiratory Diseases 4174
Broncho-Esophagology see MEDICAL SCIENCES - Respiratory Diseases 4174
Bryology see BIOLOGY - Botany 583
Buddhism see RELIGIONS AND THEOLOGY - Buddhist 5206
Budget see BUSINESS AND ECONOMICS - Banking And Finance 920, see also BUSINESS AND ECONOMICS - Public Finance, Taxation 1335, HOME ECONOMICS 3031
BUILDING AND CONSTRUCTION 716, see also ARCHITECTURE 342, ENGINEERING - Civil Engineering 2293, HOUSING AND URBAN PLANNING 3078
BUILDING AND CONSTRUCTION — Abstracting, Bibliographies, Statistics 763
BUILDING AND CONSTRUCTION — Carpentry And Woodwork 767
BUILDING AND CONSTRUCTION — Hardware 770
Bulimia see MEDICAL SCIENCES - Psychiatry And Neurology 4125, see also NUTRITION AND DIETETICS 4461
Bullfighting see SPORTS AND GAMES 5498
Burial see FUNERALS 2625
Burns see MEDICAL SCIENCES - Orthopedics and Traumatology 4094
Buses see TRANSPORTATION - Automobiles 5765
Business Administration see BUSINESS AND ECONOMICS - Management 1227
BUSINESS AND ECONOMICS 772
BUSINESS AND ECONOMICS — Abstracting, Bibliographies, Statistics 845
BUSINESS AND ECONOMICS — Accounting 903
BUSINESS AND ECONOMICS — Banking And Finance 920
BUSINESS AND ECONOMICS — Banking And Finance - Computer Applications 981
BUSINESS AND ECONOMICS — Chamber Of Commerce Publications 983
BUSINESS AND ECONOMICS — Computer Applications 1004
BUSINESS AND ECONOMICS — Cooperatives 1008
BUSINESS AND ECONOMICS — Domestic Commerce 1013
BUSINESS AND ECONOMICS — Economic Situation And Conditions 1023
BUSINESS AND ECONOMICS — Economic Systems And Theories, Economic History 1090
BUSINESS AND ECONOMICS — International Commerce 1102
BUSINESS AND ECONOMICS — International Development And Assistance 1136
BUSINESS AND ECONOMICS — Investments 1150
BUSINESS AND ECONOMICS — Labor And Industrial Relations 1189
BUSINESS AND ECONOMICS — Macroeconomics 1224
BUSINESS AND ECONOMICS — Management 1227
BUSINESS AND ECONOMICS — Marketing And Purchasing 1264
BUSINESS AND ECONOMICS — Office Equipment And Services 1298
BUSINESS AND ECONOMICS — Personnel Management 1304
BUSINESS AND ECONOMICS — Production Of Goods And Services 1317
BUSINESS AND ECONOMICS — Public Finance, Taxation 1335
BUSINESS AND ECONOMICS — Small Business 1369
BUSINESS AND ECONOMICS — Trade And Industrial Directories 1377
Business Education see BUSINESS AND ECONOMICS 772, see also EDUCATION 1999
Business Law see LAW - Corporate Law 3355
Butane see PETROLEUM AND GAS 4558
C A D - C A M see COMPUTERS - Computer Graphics 1758
C A E (Computer Aided Engineering) see COMPUTERS - Computer Graphics 1758, see also ENGINEERING - Computer Applications 2316
C A T Scan see MEDICAL SCIENCES - Radiology And Nuclear Medicine 4164
C D - R O M see COMMUNICATIONS - Computer Applications 1673, see also COMPUTERS - Software 1827
C I M (Computer Integrated Manufacturing) see ENGINEERING - Computer Applications 2316
Cabinetry see BUILDING AND CONSTRUCTION - Carpentry And Woodwork 767
Cable Television see COMMUNICATIONS - Television And Cable 1696
Cables see COMMUNICATIONS - Telephone and Telegraph 1686, see also ENGINEERING - Electrical Engineering 2320
Cafeterias see HOTELS AND RESTAURANTS 3064
Calculating Machines see COMPUTERS - Calculating Machines 1753
Calculus see MATHEMATICS 3745
Calendars of Events see MEETINGS AND CONGRESSES 4210, see also TRAVEL AND TOURISM 5848
Calligraphy see ART 364
Calvinism see RELIGIONS AND THEOLOGY - Protestant 5225
Cameras see COMMUNICATIONS - Television And Cable 1696, see also COMMUNICATIONS - Video 1715, MOTION PICTURES 4344, PHOTOGRAPHY 4691
Camping see LEISURE AND RECREATION 3413, see also SPORTS AND GAMES - Outdoor Life 5588, TRAVEL AND TOURISM 5848
Canals see TRANSPORTATION - Ships and Shipping 5818
Cancer see ONCOLOGY 4069
Candy see FOOD AND FOOD INDUSTRIES - Bakers and Confectioners 2586
Canning and Preserving see FOOD AND FOOD INDUSTRIES 2553, see also HOME ECONOMICS 3031
Canoeing see SPORTS AND GAMES - Boats and Boating 5568
Canon Law see RELIGIONS AND THEOLOGY 5145
Cans see ENVIRONMENTAL STUDIES - Waste Management 2458, see also PACKAGING 4516
Canvas see TEXTILE INDUSTRIES AND FABRICS 5689
Capital Punishment see LAW 3215
Capitalism see BUSINESS AND ECONOMICS 772, see also POLITICAL SCIENCE 4793
Carbohydrates see CHEMISTRY - Organic Chemistry 1508, see also NUTRITION AND DIETETICS 4461
Carboniferous Geology see EARTH SCIENCES - Geophysics 1964
Card Games see SPORTS AND GAMES 5498
Cardboard see PACKAGING 4516, see also PAPER AND PULP 4535
Cardiology see MEDICAL SCIENCES - Cardiovascular Diseases 3946
Cardiovascular Diseases see MEDICAL SCIENCES - Cardiovascular Diseases 3946
Cardiovascular Surgery see MEDICAL SCIENCES - Surgery 4186
Careers see OCCUPATIONS AND CAREERS 4487
Cargo Handling see TRANSPORTATION - Ships and Shipping 5818
Caribbean History see HISTORY - History of North and South America 2977
Carpal Tunnel Syndrome see OCCUPATIONAL HEALTH AND SAFETY 4474
Carpentry And Woodwork see BUILDING AND CONSTRUCTION - Carpentry And Woodwork 767
Carpets and Rugs see INTERIOR DESIGN AND DECORATION - Furniture and House Furnishings 3172
Cartography see GEOGRAPHY 2794
Cartons see PACKAGING 4516
Cartoons see ART 364
Castings see METALLURGY 4223
Catamarans see SPORTS AND GAMES - Boats And Boating 5568
Cataracts see MEDICAL SCIENCES - Ophthalmology And Optometry 4083
Catechesis see RELIGIONS AND THEOLOGY 5145
Catering see HOTELS AND RESTAURANTS 3064
Catholicism see RELIGIONS AND THEOLOGY - Roman Catholic 5255
Cats see PETS 4591
Cattle see AGRICULTURE - Poultry and Livestock 241
Cavalry see MILITARY 4283
Caves see EARTH SCIENCES - Geology 1925
Cell Biology see BIOLOGY - Cytology And Histology 621
Cement see BUILDING AND CONSTRUCTION 716
Cemeteries see FUNERALS 2625
Censorship see JOURNALISM 3184, see also MOTION PICTURES 4344, POLITICAL SCIENCE - Civil Rights 4877, PUBLISHING AND BOOK TRADE 5096
Census see POPULATION STUDIES - Abstracting, Bibliographies, Statistics 4936
Central American History see HISTORY - History Of North And South America 2977
Central Heating see HEATING, PLUMBING AND REFRIGERATION 2862
CERAMICS, GLASS AND POTTERY 1439, see also ART 364, ARTS AND HANDICRAFTS 413
CERAMICS, GLASS AND POTTERY — Abstracting, Bibliographies, Statistics 1447
Cereals see AGRICULTURE - Feed, Flour and Grain 236, see also FOOD AND FOOD INDUSTRIES 2553
Cerebral Palsy see MEDICAL SCIENCES - Psychiatry and Neurology 4125
Cerebrum, Cerebellum see MEDICAL SCIENCES - Psychiatry And Neurology 4125
Chamber of Commerce Publications see BUSINESS AND ECONOMICS - Chamber of Commerce Publications 983
Chaplains see MILITARY 4283, see also RELIGIONS AND THEOLOGY 5145
Charities see SOCIAL SERVICES AND WELFARE 5421
Cheese see AGRICULTURE - Dairying And Dairy Products 228
Chemical Engineering see ENGINEERING - Chemical Engineering 2277
Chemical Warfare see MILITARY 4283
Chemical Wastes see ENVIRONMENTAL STUDIES - Pollution 2446, see also ENVIRONMENTAL STUDIES - Waste Management 2458
CHEMISTRY 1448
CHEMISTRY — Abstracting, Bibliographies, Statistics 1477
CHEMISTRY — Analytical Chemistry 1491
CHEMISTRY — Computer Applications 1500
CHEMISTRY — Crystallography 1501
CHEMISTRY — Electrochemistry 1503
CHEMISTRY — Inorganic Chemistry 1505
CHEMISTRY — Organic Chemistry 1508
CHEMISTRY — Physical Chemistry 1520
Chemotherapy see BIOLOGY - Biological Chemistry 555, see also MEDICAL SCIENCES - Oncology 4069, PHARMACY AND PHARMACOLOGY 4600
Chess see SPORTS AND GAMES 5498
Chest Diseases see MEDICAL SCIENCES - Respiratory Diseases 4174
Child Abuse see CHILDREN AND YOUTH - About 1529, see also LAW - Family And Matrimonial Law 3375, SOCIAL SERVICES AND WELFARE 5421

Child Care see CHILDREN AND YOUTH - About 1529, see also LAW - Family And Matrimonial Law 3375, SOCIAL SERVICES AND WELFARE 5421
Child Psychology see PSYCHOLOGY 4962
Child Welfare see CHILDREN AND YOUTH - About 1529, see also SOCIAL SERVICES AND WELFARE 5421
Childbirth see MEDICAL SCIENCES - Obstetrics And Gynecology 4056
Childhood Diseases see MEDICAL SCIENCES - Pediatrics 4110
CHILDREN AND YOUTH — About 1529
CHILDREN AND YOUTH — Abstracting, Bibliographies, Statistics 1547
CHILDREN AND YOUTH — For 1548
Chinese Traditional Medicine see ALTERNATIVE MEDICINE 265
Chiropractic, Homeopathy, Osteopathy see MEDICAL SCIENCES - Chiropractic, Homeopathy, Osteopathy 3959
Chlorofluorocarbons see ENGINEERING - Chemical Engineering 2277, see also ENVIRONMENTAL STUDIES - Pollution 2446
Chocolate see FOOD AND FOOD INDUSTRIES - Bakers And Confectioners 2586
Cholesterol see CHEMISTRY - Organic Chemistry 1508, see also MEDICAL SCIENCES 3799, NUTRITION AND DIETETICS 4461
Christianity see RELIGIONS AND THEOLOGY 5145, see also RELIGIONS AND THEOLOGY - Eastern Orthodox 5209, RELIGIONS AND THEOLOGY - Protestant 5225, RELIGIONS AND THEOLOGY - Roman Catholic 5255, RELIGIONS AND THEOLOGY - Other Denominations And Sects 5287
Chromatography see CHEMISTRY - Analytical Chemistry 1491
Church History see RELIGIONS AND THEOLOGY 5145
Cigarettes and Cigars see TOBACCO 5719
Cinematography see MOTION PICTURES 4344, see also PHOTOGRAPHY 4691
Circuits see COMPUTERS - Circuits 1753
Circulatory System see MEDICAL SCIENCES - Cardiovascular Diseases 3946
Circus see THEATER 5704
Cities and Towns see HOUSING AND URBAN PLANNING 3078, see also PUBLIC ADMINISTRATION - Municipal Government 5055
Citizenship see POLITICAL SCIENCE 4793
Citrus Fruits see AGRICULTURE - Crop Production and Soil 192, see also FOOD AND FOOD INDUSTRIES 2553, GARDENING AND HORTICULTURE 2627
City Planning see HOUSING AND URBAN PLANNING 3078
Civil Aeronautics see TRANSPORTATION - Air Transport 5753
CIVIL DEFENSE 1576, see also MILITARY 4283
CIVIL DEFENSE — Abstracting, Bibliographies, Statistics 1578
Civil Engineering see ENGINEERING - Civil Engineering 2293
Civil Law see LAW - Civil Law 3345
Civil Liberties see LAW - Constitutional Law 3354, see also POLITICAL SCIENCE - Civil Rights 4877
Civil Rights see POLITICAL SCIENCE - Civil Rights 4877
Civil Service see OCCUPATIONS AND CAREERS 4487, see also PUBLIC ADMINISTRATION 5017
Clairvoyance see NEW AGE PUBLICATIONS 4450, see also PARAPSYCHOLOGY AND OCCULTISM 4542
Classical Music see MUSIC 4382
CLASSICAL STUDIES 1578, see also ARCHAEOLOGY 304, HISTORY 2872, LINGUISTICS 3485, LITERATURE 3592
CLASSICAL STUDIES — Abstracting, Bibliographies, Statistics 1586
Classified Advertising see ADVERTISING AND PUBLIC RELATIONS 28
Clay see BUILDING AND CONSTRUCTION 716, see also CERAMICS, GLASS AND POTTERY 1439, EARTH SCIENCES - Geology 1925, MINES AND MINING INDUSTRY 4315
CLEANING AND DYEING 1586
CLEANING AND DYEING — Abstracting, Bibliographies, Statistics 1588
Climate Control see HEATING, PLUMBING AND REFRIGERATION 2862
Climatology see METEOROLOGY 4259
Clinical Medicine see MEDICAL SCIENCES 3799
Clinics see HOSPITALS 3047
Clocks see JEWELRY, CLOCKS AND WATCHES 3179
Cloning see BIOLOGY - Genetics 643
CLOTHING TRADE 1589
CLOTHING TRADE — Abstracting, Bibliographies, Statistics 1595
CLOTHING TRADE — Fashions 1596
CLUBS 1603
CLUBS — Abstracting, Bibliographies, Statistics 1612
Coaching see SPORTS AND GAMES 5498
Coal see ENERGY 2197, see also MINES AND MINING INDUSTRY 4315
Coast Guard see MILITARY 4283
Coastal Engineering see ENGINEERING - Hydraulic Engineering 2373
Coastal Waters see EARTH SCIENCES - Oceanography 1982
Coats Of Arms see GENEALOGY AND HERALDRY 2654
Cobbling see SHOES AND BOOTS 5378
Cocaine see DRUG ABUSE AND ALCOHOLISM 1898
Codependency see DRUG ABUSE AND ALCOHOLISM 1898, see also PSYCHOLOGY 4962
Coffee see BEVERAGES 443
Cogeneration see ENERGY 2197, see also ENVIRONMENTAL STUDIES - Waste Management 2458
Cognitive Studies see PSYCHOLOGY 4962
Coins see NUMISMATICS 4456
Colitis see MEDICAL SCIENCES - Gastroenterology 4024
Collectibles see ANTIQUES 297
Collections see MUSEUMS AND ART GALLERIES 4364
Collectors and Collecting see ANTIQUES 297, see also HOBBIES 3016
COLLEGE AND ALUMNI 1612, see also CLUBS 1603, EDUCATION - Higher Education 2095
College Management see EDUCATION - Higher Education 2095, see also EDUCATION - School Organization and Administration 2126
Colloids see CHEMISTRY - Physical Chemistry 1520, see also PHYSICS 4718
Colonialism see HISTORY - History Of Africa 2902, see also HISTORY - History Of Asia 2908, HISTORY - History Of North And South America 2977
Combat see MILITARY 4283
Combustion see CHEMISTRY - Physical Chemistry 1520, see also PHYSICS - Heat 4755

Comedy see LITERARY AND POLITICAL REVIEWS 3555, see also MOTION PICTURES 4344, THEATER 5704
Commerce see BUSINESS AND ECONOMICS - Domestic Commerce 1013, see also BUSINESS AND ECONOMICS - International Commerce 1102
Commercial Art see ADVERTISING AND PUBLIC RELATIONS 28, see also ART 364
Commercial Education see EDUCATION - Teaching Methods and Curriculum 2146
Commercial Law see BUSINESS AND ECONOMICS 772, see also LAW 3215, LAW - Corporate Law 3355
Commercials see ADVERTISING AND PUBLIC RELATIONS 28, see also COMMUNICATIONS - Radio 1678, COMMUNICATIONS - Television And Cable 1696
Common Cold see MEDICAL SCIENCES - Respiratory Diseases 4174
Communicable Diseases see MEDICAL SCIENCES - Communicable Diseases 3962
COMMUNICATIONS 1647, see also JOURNALISM 3184
COMMUNICATIONS — Abstracting, Bibliographies, Statistics 1669
COMMUNICATIONS — Computer Applications 1673
COMMUNICATIONS — Postal Affairs 1676
COMMUNICATIONS — Radio 1678
COMMUNICATIONS — Telephone And Telegraph 1686
COMMUNICATIONS — Television And Cable 1696
COMMUNICATIONS — Video 1715
Communism see BUSINESS AND ECONOMICS - Economic Systems and Theories, Economic History 1090, see also POLITICAL SCIENCE 4793
Community Affairs see PUBLIC ADMINISTRATION - Municipal Government 5055
Compact Disc see COMMUNICATIONS - Computer Applications 1673, see also MUSIC 4382, 5494
Company Law see LAW - Corporate Law 3355
Comparative Psychology see PSYCHOLOGY 4962
Compressed Air see ENGINEERING - Mechanical Engineering 2379
Computational Mathematics see MATHEMATICS - Computer Applications 3792
Computerized Axial Tomography see MEDICAL SCIENCES - Radiology And Nuclear Medicine 4164
COMPUTERS 1720, see also COMPUTERS - Information Science and Information Theory 1802
COMPUTERS — Abstracting, Bibliographies, Statistics 1738
COMPUTERS — Artificial Intelligence 1741, see also COMPUTERS - Cybernetics 1784
COMPUTERS — Automation 1746
COMPUTERS — Calculating Machines 1753
COMPUTERS — Circuits 1753, see also COMPUTERS - Computer Engineering 1754
COMPUTERS — Computer Architecture 1753, see also COMPUTERS - Computer Engineering 1754
COMPUTERS — Computer Assisted Instruction 1753, see also EDUCATION - Computer Applications 2083
COMPUTERS — Computer Engineering 1754, see also COMPUTERS - Computer Architecture 1753
COMPUTERS — Computer Games 1756
COMPUTERS — Computer Graphics 1758, see also PRINTING - Computer Applications 4961
COMPUTERS — Computer Industry 1763
COMPUTERS — Computer Industry Directories 1765
COMPUTERS — Computer Industry, Vocational Guidance 1766, see also EDUCATION 1999, OCCUPATIONS AND CAREERS 4487
COMPUTERS — Computer Music 1766, see also MUSIC - Computer Applications 4445
COMPUTERS — Computer Networks 1767
COMPUTERS — Computer Programming 1771, see also COMPUTERS - Software 1827
COMPUTERS — Computer Sales 1774, see also BUSINESS AND ECONOMICS - Marketing and Purchasing 1264
COMPUTERS — Computer Security 1776
COMPUTERS — Computer Simulation 1777
COMPUTERS — Computer Systems 1779, see also COMPUTERS - Computer Architecture 1753
COMPUTERS — Cybernetics 1784, see also COMPUTERS - Artificial Intelligence 1741
COMPUTERS — Data Base Management 1788
COMPUTERS — Data Communications And Data Transmission Systems 1790
COMPUTERS — Electronic Data Processing 1795, see also BUSINESS AND ECONOMICS - Banking and Finance - Computer Applications 981
COMPUTERS — Hardware 1799
COMPUTERS — Information Science And Information Theory 1802, see also COMPUTERS 1720
COMPUTERS — Machine Theory 1805
COMPUTERS — Microcomputers 1805, see also COMPUTERS - Personal Computers 1814
COMPUTERS — Minicomputers 1813
COMPUTERS — Personal Computers 1814, see also COMPUTERS - Microcomputers 1805
COMPUTERS — Robotics 1825
COMPUTERS — Software 1827, see also COMPUTERS - Computer Programming 1771
COMPUTERS — Theory Of Computing 1836
COMPUTERS — Word Processing 1836
Conchology see BIOLOGY - Zoology 689
Concrete see BUILDING AND CONSTRUCTION 716
Condominiums see REAL ESTATE 5124
Confectioners see FOOD AND FOOD INDUSTRIES - Bakers and Confectioners 2586
Conferences see MEETINGS AND CONGRESSES 4210
Confucianism see PHILOSOPHY 4656
Congenital Abnormalities see BIOLOGY - Genetics 643, see also MEDICAL SCIENCES 3799
Congresses see MEETINGS AND CONGRESSES 4210
CONSERVATION 1837, see also ENERGY 2197, ENVIRONMENTAL STUDIES 2399, FISH AND FISHERIES 2523, FORESTS AND FORESTRY 2597, WATER RESOURCES 5933
CONSERVATION — Abstracting, Bibliographies, Statistics 1860

CROSS-INDEX TO SUBJECTS

Constitutional Law see LAW - Constitutional Law 3354
Construction see BUILDING AND CONSTRUCTION 716, see also ENGINEERING - Civil Engineering 2293
Consumer Credit see BUSINESS AND ECONOMICS - Banking and Finance 920
CONSUMER EDUCATION AND PROTECTION 1860
CONSUMER EDUCATION AND PROTECTION — Abstracting, Bibliographies, Statistics 1868
Consumer Electronics see ELECTRONICS 2170
Contact Lenses see MEDICAL SCIENCES - Ophthalmology and Optometry 4083
Containers see PACKAGING 4516
Contamination see ENVIRONMENTAL STUDIES 2399, see also FOOD AND FOOD INDUSTRIES 2553, PUBLIC HEALTH AND SAFETY 5070
Contemporary Music see MUSIC 4382
Contraception see BIRTH CONTROL 713
Contractors see BUILDING AND CONSTRUCTION 716
Convention Dates see MEETINGS AND CONGRESSES 4210
Cookery see HOME ECONOMICS 3031, see also HOTELS AND RESTAURANTS 3064
Cooling see HEATING, PLUMBING AND REFRIGERATION 2862
Co-op Apartments see REAL ESTATE 5124
Cooperative Farming see AGRICULTURE 76
Cooperatives see BUSINESS AND ECONOMICS - Cooperatives 1008
Copper see METALLURGY 4223, see also MINES AND MINING INDUSTRY 4315
Coptic see RELIGIONS AND THEOLOGY - Other Denominations and Sects 5287
Copying and Duplicating see PHOTOGRAPHY 4691, see also PRINTING 4949
Copyrights see PATENTS, TRADEMARKS AND COPYRIGHTS 4547
Cordage see TEXTILE INDUSTRIES AND FABRICS 5689
Corn see AGRICULTURE - Feed, Flour And Grain 236
Coroners see MEDICAL SCIENCES - Forensic Sciences 4021
Corporate Law see LAW - Corporate Law 3355
Correctional Facilities see CRIMINOLOGY AND LAW ENFORCEMENT 1869
Correspondence Education see EDUCATION - Adult Education 2075
Corrosion see METALLURGY 4223, see also PAINTS AND PROTECTIVE COATINGS 4523
Cosmetic Surgery see MEDICAL SCIENCES - Surgery 4186
Cosmetics see BEAUTY CULTURE - Perfumes and Cosmetics 440
Cotton see AGRICULTURE - Crop Production And Soil 192, see also CLOTHING TRADE 1589, TEXTILE INDUSTRIES AND FABRICS 5689
Counseling see EDUCATION 1999, see also PSYCHOLOGY 4962, SOCIAL SERVICES AND WELFARE 5421
Courts see LAW - Judicial Systems 3398
Courtship see SINGLES' INTERESTS AND LIFESTYLES 5380
Crack Cocaine see DRUG ABUSE AND ALCOHOLISM 1898
Crafts see ARTS AND HANDICRAFTS 413
Creationism see RELIGIONS AND THEOLOGY 5145, see also SCIENCE: COMPREHENSIVE WORKS 5304
Credit and Collections see BUSINESS AND ECONOMICS - Banking and Finance 920
Credit Cards see BUSINESS AND ECONOMICS - Banking And Finance 920
Credit Unions see BUSINESS AND ECONOMICS - Banking and Finance 920
Cremation see FUNERALS 2625
Crewing see SPORTS AND GAMES - Boats And Boating 5568
Cricket see SPORTS AND GAMES 5498
Criminal Law see LAW - Criminal Law 3367
CRIMINOLOGY AND LAW ENFORCEMENT 1869
CRIMINOLOGY AND LAW ENFORCEMENT — Abstracting, Bibliographies, Statistics 1888
CRIMINOLOGY AND LAW ENFORCEMENT — Security 1890
Critical Care see MEDICAL SCIENCES - Orthopedics And Traumatology 4094
Crochet see NEEDLEWORK 4445
Crop Production And Soil see AGRICULTURE - Crop Production And Soil 192
Croquet see SPORTS AND GAMES - Ball Games 5540
Cross Stitch see NEEDLEWORK 4445
Cruises see TRAVEL AND TOURISM 5848
Cryogenic Engineering see ENGINEERING - Mechanical Engineering 2379
Cryogenics see PHYSICS - Heat 4755
Crystal Healing see ALTERNATIVE MEDICINE 265
Crystallography see CHEMISTRY - Crystallography 1501
Cultivators see AGRICULTURE - Agricultural Equipment 186
Cultural Theory see HUMANITIES: COMPREHENSIVE WORKS 3103, see also SOCIAL SCIENCES: COMPREHENSIVE WORKS 5382
Curating see MUSEUMS AND ART GALLERIES 4364
Currency see BUSINESS AND ECONOMICS - Banking and Finance 920
Curriculum and Teaching Methods see EDUCATION - Teaching Methods and Curriculum 2146
Customs and Excise see BUSINESS AND ECONOMICS - Public Finance, Taxation 1335
Cybernetic Medicine see MEDICAL SCIENCES 3799
Cybernetics see COMPUTERS - Cybernetics 1784
Cystic Fibrosis see MEDICAL SCIENCES 3799
Cytology And Histology see BIOLOGY - Cytology And Histology 621
Dairying And Dairy Products see AGRICULTURE - Dairying And Dairy Products 228
Dams see ENGINEERING - Civil Engineering 2293, see also WATER RESOURCES 5933
DANCE 1893, see also MUSIC 4382, THEATER 5704
DANCE — Abstracting, Bibliographies, Statistics 1898
Darkroom see PHOTOGRAPHY 4691
Data Base Management see COMPUTERS - Data Base Management 1788
Data Communications And Data Transmission Systems see COMPUTERS - Data Communications And Data Transmission Systems 1790
Data Processing see COMPUTERS - Electronic Data Processing 1793
Dating see SINGLES' INTERESTS AND LIFESTYLES 5380
Day Care see CHILDREN AND YOUTH - About 1529
Deaf see EDUCATION - Special Education and Rehabilitation 2136, see also HANDICAPPED - Hearing Impaired 2849, MEDICAL SCIENCES - Otorhinolaryngology 4104, SOCIAL SERVICES AND WELFARE 5421
Death see PHILOSOPHY 4656, see also RELIGIONS AND THEOLOGY 5145
Death Customs see FUNERALS 2625, see also RELIGIONS AND THEOLOGY 5145
Death Penalty see CRIMINOLOGY AND LAW ENFORCEMENT 1869, see also LAW 3215, POLITICAL SCIENCE - Civil Rights 4877

Decoration see INTERIOR DESIGN AND DECORATION 3162
Deep-Sea Diving see LEISURE AND RECREATION 3413, see also SPORTS AND GAMES - Outdoor Life 5588
Defense see CIVIL DEFENSE 1576, see also MILITARY 4283
Deforestation see ENVIRONMENTAL SCIENCES 2399, see also FORESTS AND FORESTRY 2597
Delinquency see CHILDREN AND YOUTH - About 1529, see also CRIMINOLOGY AND LAW ENFORCEMENT 1869, SOCIAL SERVICES AND WELFARE 5421
Democracy see POLITICAL SCIENCE 4793
Demography see POPULATION STUDIES 4924
Demolition see BUILDING AND CONSTRUCTION 716
Demonology see PARAPSYCHOLOGY AND OCCULTISM 4542
Dentistry see MEDICAL SCIENCES - Dentistry 3977
Department Stores see BUSINESS AND ECONOMICS - Marketing and Purchasing 1264
Depression see MEDICAL SCIENCES - Psychiatry And Neurology 4125
Dermatology And Venereology see MEDICAL SCIENCES - Dermatology And Venereology 3998
Desalination see ENVIRONMENTAL STUDIES 2399, see also WATER RESOURCES 5933
Design see ART 364, see also CLOTHING TRADE - Fashions 1596, INTERIOR DESIGN AND DECORATION 3162
Desktop Publishing see PUBLISHING AND BOOK TRADE - Computer Applications 5123
Detective Magazines see LITERATURE - Mystery And Detective 3698
Detectives see CRIMINOLOGY AND LAW ENFORCEMENT 1869
Developmental Disabilities see EDUCATION - Special Education And Rehabilitation 2136, see also HANDICAPPED 2844, MEDICAL SCIENCES - Psychiatry And Neurology 4125
Dharma see RELIGIONS AND THEOLOGY - Buddhist 5206, see also RELIGIONS AND THEOLOGY - Hindu 5211
Diabetes see MEDICAL SCIENCES - Endocrinology 4004
Dialectics see PHILOSOPHY 4656
Dialysis see MEDICAL SCIENCES - Urology and Nephrology 4203
Diarrhea see MEDICAL SCIENCES - Gastroenterology 4024
Diaspora see RELIGIONS AND THEOLOGY - Judaic 5218
Diecasting see ENGINEERING 2237
Diesel Engines see ENGINEERING - Mechanical Engineering 2379
Dietetics see NUTRITION AND DIETETICS 4461
Digestive System see MEDICAL SCIENCES - Gastroenterology 4024
Digital Computers see COMPUTERS - Hardware 1799
Dining see HOTELS AND RESTAURANTS 3064
Dinosaurs see PALEONTOLOGY 4528
Diplomatic Service see POLITICAL SCIENCE - International Relations 4889
Direct Marketing see ADVERTISING AND PUBLIC RELATIONS 28, see also BUSINESS AND ECONOMICS - Marketing and Purchasing 1264
Disability, Disabled see HANDICAPPED 2844, see also INSURANCE 3133, MEDICAL SCIENCES - Physical Medicine And Rehabilitation 4122, OCCUPATIONAL HEALTH AND SAFETY 4474, SOCIAL SERVICES AND WELFARE 5421
Disarmament see MILITARY 4283, see also POLITICAL SCIENCE 4793
Disaster Planning see CIVIL DEFENSE 1576, see also SOCIAL SERVICES AND WELFARE 5421
Disciples Of Christ see RELIGIONS AND THEOLOGY - Protestant 5225
Discrimination see POLITICAL SCIENCE - Civil Rights 4877
Disease Control see PUBLIC HEALTH AND SAFETY 5070
Disk Drives see COMPUTERS - Hardware 1799
Distilling see BEVERAGES 443
Divinity Schools see EDUCATION - Higher Education 2095, see also RELIGIONS AND THEOLOGY 5145
Divorce see LAW - Family And Matrimonial Law 3375, see also MATRIMONY 3796, SINGLES' INTERESTS AND LIFESTYLES 5380
Documentation see COMPUTERS - Computer Programming 1771, see also COMPUTERS - Software 1827
Dogs see PETS 4591
Domestic Animals and Birds see ANIMAL WELFARE 268, see also PETS 4591, VETERINARY SCIENCE 5913
Domestic Commerce see BUSINESS AND ECONOMICS - Domestic Commerce 1013
Domestic Relations see LAW - Family And Matrimonial Law 3375, see also MATRIMONY 3796
Down Syndrome see EDUCATION - Special Education And Rehabilitation 2136, see also HANDICAPPED 2844, MEDICAL SCIENCES - Psychiatry And Neurology 4125
Drafting see ENGINEERING 2237, see also TECHNOLOGY: COMPREHENSIVE WORKS 5663
Drama see LITERATURE 3592, see also THEATER 5704
Drawing and Sketching see ART 364
Dreams see MEDICAL SCIENCES - Psychiatry And Neurology 4125, see also PARAPSYCHOLOGY AND OCCULTISM 4542
Dressmaking see CLOTHING TRADE 1589, see also NEEDLEWORK 4445
Drilling see PETROLEUM AND GAS 4558
Drought see METEOROLOGY 4259
DRUG ABUSE AND ALCOHOLISM 1898
DRUG ABUSE AND ALCOHOLISM — Abstracting, Bibliographies, Statistics 1907
Drug Contamination see PUBLIC HEALTH AND SAFETY 5070
Drugs see PHARMACY AND PHARMACOLOGY 4600
Dry Goods see CLOTHING TRADE 1589, see also TEXTILE INDUSTRIES AND FABRICS 5689
Dyes and Dyeing see CLEANING AND DYEING 1586, see also TEXTILE INDUSTRIES AND FABRICS 5689
Dyslexia see EDUCATION - Special Education And Rehabilitation 2136
E C G see MEDICAL SCIENCES - Cardiovascular Diseases 3946
E E G see MEDICAL SCIENCES - Psychiatry and Neurology 4125
E F T (Electronic Funds Transfer) see BUSINESS AND ECONOMICS - Banking And Finance - Computer Applications 981
E K G see MEDICAL SCIENCES - Radiology And Nuclear Medicine 4164
E-mail see COMMUNICATIONS - Computer Applications 1673, see also COMPUTERS - Computer Networks 1767
E S P see PARAPSYCHOLOGY AND OCCULTISM 4542
Ear, Nose, Throat see MEDICAL SCIENCES - Otorhinolaryngology 4104

EARTH SCIENCES 1909
EARTH SCIENCES — Abstracting, Bibliographies, Statistics 1920
EARTH SCIENCES — Computer Applications 1924
EARTH SCIENCES — Geology 1925
EARTH SCIENCES — Geophysics 1964
EARTH SCIENCES — Hydrology 1977
EARTH SCIENCES — Oceanography 1982
Earthquakes see EARTH SCIENCES - Geophysics 1964
Eastern Orthodox see RELIGIONS AND THEOLOGY - Eastern Orthodox 5209
Eating Disorders see MEDICAL SCIENCES - Psychiatry And Neurology 4125, see also NUTRITION AND DIETETICS 4461
Ecclesiastical Art see ART 364, see also RELIGIONS AND THEOLOGY 5145
Ecclesiastical Law see RELIGIONS AND THEOLOGY 5145
Ecology see BIOLOGY 499, see also CONSERVATION 1837, ENVIRONMENTAL STUDIES 2399
Economic Geology see EARTH SCIENCES - Geology 1925
Economic Situation And Conditions see BUSINESS AND ECONOMICS - Economic Situation And Conditions 1023
Economic Systems And Theories, Economic History see BUSINESS AND ECONOMICS - Economic Systems And Theories, Economic History 1090
Economics see BUSINESS AND ECONOMICS 772
Ecosystems see BIOLOGY 499, see also ENVIRONMENTAL STUDIES 2399
Ecumenism see RELIGIONS AND THEOLOGY 5145
Editing see JOURNALISM 3184, see also PUBLISHING AND BOOK TRADE 5096
EDUCATION 1999, see also CHILDREN AND YOUTH - About 1529
EDUCATION — Abstracting, Bibliographies, Statistics 2067
EDUCATION — Adult Education 2075
EDUCATION — Computer Applications 2083, see also COMPUTERS - Computer Assisted Instruction 1753
EDUCATION — Guides To Schools And Colleges 2087
EDUCATION — Higher Education 2095
EDUCATION — International Education Programs 2122
EDUCATION — School Organization And Administration 2126
EDUCATION — Special Education And Rehabilitation 2136
EDUCATION — Teaching Methods And Curriculum 2146
Educational Films see EDUCATION - Teaching Methods and Curriculum 2146, see also MOTION PICTURES 4344
Educational Psychology see PSYCHOLOGY 4962
Egg Production see AGRICULTURE - Poultry And Livestock 241
Egyptology see ARCHAEOLOGY 304, see also ART 364, HISTORY - History of Africa 2902
Elections see POLITICAL SCIENCE 4793, see also PUBLIC ADMINISTRATION 5017
Electrical Energy see ENERGY - Electrical Energy 2219
Electrical Engineering see ENGINEERING - Electrical Engineering 2320
Electricity see PHYSICS - Electricity 4754
Electrochemistry see CHEMISTRY - Electrochemistry 1503
Electronic Data Processing see COMPUTERS - Electronic Data Processing 1793
Electronic Funds Transfer see BUSINESS AND ECONOMICS - Banking And Finance - Computer Applications 981
ELECTRONICS 2170
ELECTRONICS — Abstracting, Bibliographies, Statistics 2193
ELECTRONICS — Computer Applications 2194
Electrophysics see PHYSICS - Electricity 4754
Electroplating see ENGINEERING - Electrical Engineering 2320, see also METALLURGY 4223
Electrotherapy see MEDICAL SCIENCES - Psychiatry and Neurology 4125, see also MEDICAL SCIENCES - Radiology and Nuclear Medicine 4164
Embroidery see NEEDLEWORK 4445
Embryology see BIOLOGY 499, see also MEDICAL SCIENCES 3799
Emergency Medicine see MEDICAL SCIENCES - Orthopedics And Traumatology 4094
Emigration see POPULATION STUDIES 4924
Emission Control see ENVIRONMENTAL STUDIES - Pollution 2446
Emotional Disorders see MEDICAL SCIENCES - Psychiatry And Neurology 4125
Emotionally Disturbed Children see CHILDREN AND YOUTH - About 1529, see also EDUCATION - Special Education and Rehabilitation 2136
Emphysema see MEDICAL SCIENCES - Respiratory Diseases 4174
Empiricism see PHILOSOPHY 4656
Employee Benefits see BUSINESS AND ECONOMICS - Personnel Management 1304
Employment see BUSINESS AND ECONOMICS - Labor and Industrial Relations 1189, see also OCCUPATIONS AND CAREERS 4487
Encephalitis see MEDICAL SCIENCES - Psychiatry and Neurology 4125
ENCYCLOPEDIAS AND GENERAL ALMANACS 2194
Endocrinology see MEDICAL SCIENCES - Endocrinology 4004
Enduro Racing see SPORTS AND GAMES - Bicycles And Motorcycles 5560
ENERGY 2197
ENERGY — Abstracting, Bibliographies, Statistics 2215
ENERGY — Computer Applications 2219
ENERGY — Electrical Energy 2219
ENERGY — Geothermal Energy 2223
ENERGY — Hydroelectrical Energy 2223
ENERGY — Nuclear Energy 2223
ENERGY — Solar Energy 2234
ENERGY — Wind Energy 2237
ENGINEERING 2237
ENGINEERING — Abstracting, Bibliographies, Statistics 2270
ENGINEERING — Chemical Engineering 2277
ENGINEERING — Civil Engineering 2293
ENGINEERING — Computer Applications 2316
ENGINEERING — Electrical Engineering 2320
ENGINEERING — Engineering Mechanics And Materials 2359
ENGINEERING — Hydraulic Engineering 2373
ENGINEERING — Industrial Engineering 2377
ENGINEERING — Mechanical Engineering 2379
Engines see ENGINEERING - Mechanical Engineering 2379, see also TRANSPORTATION 5723
English Language - Study and Teaching see LINGUISTICS 3485
Engraving see ART 364, see also PRINTING 4949
Enterology see MEDICAL SCIENCES - Gastroenterology 4024

Entertainment see COMMUNICATIONS - Radio 1678, see also COMMUNICATIONS - Television And Cable 1696, COMMUNICATIONS - Video 1715, DANCE 1893, MOTION PICTURES 4344, MUSIC 4382, SPORTS AND GAMES 5498, THEATER 5704, TRAVEL AND TOURISM 5848
Entomology see BIOLOGY - Entomology 628
Entrepreneurship see BUSINESS AND ECONOMICS - Small Business 1369
Environmental Health see ENVIRONMENTAL STUDIES 2399, see also PUBLIC HEALTH AND SAFETY 5070
ENVIRONMENTAL STUDIES 2399, see also CONSERVATION 1837
ENVIRONMENTAL STUDIES — Abstracting, Bibliographies, Statistics 2441
ENVIRONMENTAL STUDIES — Computer Applications 2445
ENVIRONMENTAL STUDIES — Pollution 2446
ENVIRONMENTAL STUDIES — Toxicology And Environmental Safety 2452
ENVIRONMENTAL STUDIES — Waste Management 2458
Enzymes see BIOLOGY - Biological Chemistry 555, see also MEDICAL SCIENCES 3799
Ephemerides see ASTRONOMY 421
Epidemiology see PUBLIC HEALTH AND SAFETY 5070
Epilepsy see MEDICAL SCIENCES - Psychiatry and Neurology 4125
Episcopalianism see RELIGIONS AND THEOLOGY - Protestant 5225
Epistemology see PHILOSOPHY 4656
Equal Opportunity see BUSINESS AND ECONOMICS - Labor And Industrial Relations 1189, see also LAW 3215, POLITICAL SCIENCE - Civil Rights 4877
Equal Rights Amendment see POLITICAL SCIENCE - Civil Rights 4877, see also WOMEN'S STUDIES 5977
Equestrianism see SPORTS AND GAMES - Horses And Horsemanship 5579
Equipment see AGRICULTURE - Agricultural Equipment 186, see also MACHINERY 3733
Ergonomics see BUSINESS AND ECONOMICS - Labor and Industrial Relations 1189, see also PSYCHOLOGY 4962
Erosion see AGRICULTURE - Crop Production and Soil 192, see also CONSERVATION 1837
Esperanto see LINGUISTICS 3485
Espionage see MILITARY 4283, see also POLITICAL SCIENCE - International Relations 4889
Estate Planning Law see LAW - Estate Planning 3373
Esthetics see ART 364, see also PHILOSOPHY 4656
Ethics see PHILOSOPHY 4656, see also RELIGIONS AND THEOLOGY 5145
ETHNIC INTERESTS 2466
ETHNIC INTERESTS — Abstracting, Bibliographies, Statistics 2516
Ethnography see ANTHROPOLOGY 272, see also SOCIOLOGY 5459
Ethnology see ANTHROPOLOGY 272
Ethnopharmacology see ANTHROPOLOGY 272, see also PHARMACY AND PHARMACOLOGY 4600
Eugenics see BIOLOGY - Genetics 643
European History see HISTORY - History of Europe 2920
Euthanasia see MEDICAL SCIENCES 3799, see also PHILOSOPHY 4656, RELIGIONS AND THEOLOGY 5145
Evangelism see RELIGIONS AND THEOLOGY - Protestant 5225
Evangelization see RELIGIONS AND THEOLOGY 5145
Evolution see BIOLOGY 499, see also SCIENCES: COMPREHENSIVE WORKS 5304
Exceptional Children, Education see EDUCATION - Special Education and Rehabilitation 2136
Exchange Students see EDUCATION 1999, see also EDUCATION - International Education Programs 2122
Exercise see PHYSICAL FITNESS AND HYGIENE 4704
Exhibitions see MEETINGS AND CONGRESSES 4210, see also MUSEUMS AND ART GALLERIES 4364
Existentialism see LITERATURE 3592, see also PHILOSOPHY 4656
Exorcism see PARAPSYCHOLOGY AND OCCULTISM 4542, see also RELIGIONS AND THEOLOGY 5145
Experimental Medicine, Laboratory Technique see MEDICAL SCIENCES - Experimental Medicine, Laboratory Technique 4012
Exports and Imports see BUSINESS AND ECONOMICS - International Commerce 1102
Expositions see MEETINGS AND CONGRESSES 4210, see also MUSEUMS AND ART GALLERIES 4364
Extinction see BIOLOGY 499, see also CONSERVATION 1837, PALEONTOLOGY 4528
Extrasensory Perception see PARAPSYCHOLOGY AND OCCULTISM 4542
Extraterrestrials see AERONAUTICS AND SPACE FLIGHT 47, see also PARAPSYCHOLOGY AND OCCULTISM 4542
Eye Care see MEDICAL SCIENCES - Ophthalmology and Optometry 4083
Fables see FOLKLORE 2544, see also LITERATURE 3592
Fabrics see TEXTILE INDUSTRIES AND FABRICS 5689
Facilities Maintenance see BUSINESS AND ECONOMICS - Management 1227, see also BUSINESS AND ECONOMICS - Office Equipment And Services 1298
Facsimile Transmission see COMMUNICATIONS - Computer Applications 1673
Fairy Tales see FOLKLORE 2544, see also LITERATURE 3592
Family And Matrimonial Law see LAW - Family And Matrimonial Law 3375
Family History see GENEALOGY AND HERALDRY 2654
Family Planning see BIRTH CONTROL 713
Family Therapy see MATRIMONY 3796
Famine see SOCIAL SERVICES AND WELFARE 5421
Fantasy see LITERATURE - Science Fiction, Fantasy, Horror 3723
Farm Equipment see AGRICULTURE - Agricultural Equipment 186, see also MACHINERY 3733
Farm Management see AGRICULTURE 76
Farm Marketing see AGRICULTURE - Agricultural Economics 169
Farming see AGRICULTURE 76
Fashions see CLOTHING TRADE - Fashions 1596
Fate see PARAPSYCHOLOGY AND OCCULTISM 4542, see also PHILOSOPHY 4656, RELIGIONS AND THEOLOGY 5145
Fatherhood see LAW - Family And Matrimonial Law 3375, see also MEN'S INTERESTS 4216, MEN'S STUDIES 4222
Fauna see BIOLOGY - Zoology 689, see also CONSERVATION 1837
Fax see COMMUNICATIONS - Computer Applications 1673
Federalism see POLITICAL SCIENCE 4793
Feed, Flour And Grain see AGRICULTURE - Feed, Flour And Grain 236

Fellowships see EDUCATION - Higher Education 2095
Feminist Movement see POLITICAL SCIENCE - Civil Rights 4877, see also WOMEN'S INTERESTS 5953, WOMEN'S STUDIES 5977
Fencing see SPORTS AND GAMES 5498
Fertility see MEDICAL SCIENCES - Obstetrics And Gynecology 4056, see also MEN'S HEALTH 4215, WOMEN'S HEALTH 5952
Fertilizers see AGRICULTURE - Crop Production and Soil 192
Fiber Optics see COMMUNICATIONS - Computer Applications 1673, see also PHYSICS - Optics 4770
Fiction see LITERATURE 3592
Field Crops see AGRICULTURE - Crop Production And Soil 192
Film Processing see PHOTOGRAPHY 4691
Filmmaking see MOTION PICTURES 4344
Finance see BUSINESS AND ECONOMICS - Banking and Finance 920, see also BUSINESS AND ECONOMICS - Investments 1150
Finishing see PAINTS AND PROTECTIVE COATINGS 4523
FIRE PREVENTION 2517
FIRE PREVENTION — Abstracting, Bibliographies, Statistics 2523
Firearms see HOBBIES 3016, see also SPORTS AND GAMES 5498
Fireworks see ENGINEERING - Chemical Engineering 2277, see also FIRE PREVENTION 2517
First Aid see MEDICAL SCIENCES 3799, see also MEDICAL SCIENCES - Orthopedics And Traumatology 4094, PUBLIC HEALTH AND SAFETY 5070
FISH AND FISHERIES 2523, see also BIOLOGY - Zoology 689
FISH AND FISHERIES — Abstracting, Bibliographies, Statistics 2542
Fishing, Sport see SPORTS AND GAMES - Outdoor Life 5588
Flags see GENEALOGY AND HERALDRY 2654
Flax see AGRICULTURE - Crop Production and Soil 192, see also TEXTILE INDUSTRIES AND FABRICS 5689
Floor Coverings see INTERIOR DESIGN AND DECORATION - Furniture and House Furnishings 3172
Flora see BIOLOGY - Botany 583
Floral Decorations see ART 364, see also GARDENING AND HORTICULTURE 2627
Florist Trade see GARDENING AND HORTICULTURE - Florist Trade 2652
Flour see AGRICULTURE - Feed, Flour And Grain 236, see also FOOD AND FOOD INDUSTRIES - Bakers And Confectioners 2586
Flowers see BIOLOGY - Botany 583, see also GARDENING AND HORTICULTURE 2627
Flu see MEDICAL SCIENCES - Respiratory Diseases 4174
Fluid Power see ENGINEERING - Mechanical Engineering 2379
Flying see AERONAUTICS AND SPACE FLIGHT 47, see also TRANSPORTATION - Air Transport 5753
Flying Saucers see AERONAUTICS AND SPACE FLIGHT 47, see also LITERATURE - Science Fiction, Fantasy, Horror 3723
FOLKLORE 2544
FOLKLORE — Abstracting, Bibliographies, Statistics 2553
FOOD AND FOOD INDUSTRIES 2553
FOOD AND FOOD INDUSTRIES — Abstracting, Bibliographies, Statistics 2584
FOOD AND FOOD INDUSTRIES — Bakers And Confectioners 2586
FOOD AND FOOD INDUSTRIES — Grocery Trade 2591
Food Contamination see FOOD AND FOOD INDUSTRIES 2553, see also PUBLIC HEALTH AND SAFETY 5070
Food Inspection see FOOD AND FOOD INDUSTRIES 2553, see also HOTELS AND RESTAURANTS 3064, PUBLIC HEALTH AND SAFETY 5070
Football see SPORTS AND GAMES - Ball Games 5540
Footwear see LEATHER AND FUR INDUSTRIES 3410, see also SHOES AND BOOTS 5378
Foreign Affairs see POLITICAL SCIENCE - International Relations 4889
Foreign Aid see BUSINESS AND ECONOMICS - International Development and Assistance 1136
Foreign Commerce see BUSINESS AND ECONOMICS - International Commerce 1102
Foreign Legion see MILITARY 4283
Forensic Sciences see MEDICAL SCIENCES - Forensic Sciences 4021
Forest Fires see FIRE PREVENTION 2517, see also FORESTS AND FORESTRY 2597
FORESTS AND FORESTRY 2597
FORESTS AND FORESTRY — Abstracting, Bibliographies, Statistics 2616
FORESTS AND FORESTRY — Lumber And Wood 2618
Forges see METALLURGY 4223
Fortune Telling see PARAPSYCHOLOGY AND OCCULTISM 4542
Fossil Fuel Energy see ENERGY 2197, see also PETROLEUM AND GAS 4558
Fossils see ARCHAEOLOGY 304, see also PALEONTOLOGY 4528
Foundry Practices see METALLURGY 4223
Franchises see BUSINESS AND ECONOMICS - Small Business 1369
Fraternal Organizations see CLUBS 1603, see also COLLEGE AND ALUMNI 1612
Freezing see HEATING, PLUMBING AND REFRIGERATION 2862, see also PHYSICS - Heat 4755
Freight see TRANSPORTATION 5723
French Language - Study and Teaching see LINGUISTICS 3485
Frequency Modulation see COMMUNICATIONS - Radio 1678, see also COMMUNICATIONS - Television And Cable 1696, SOUND RECORDING AND REPRODUCTION 5494
Fresh Water Research see BIOLOGY - Zoology 689, see also EARTH SCIENCES - Hydrology 1977
Fretted Instruments see MUSIC 4382
Friction see PHYSICS - Mechanics 4758
Frozen Food see FOOD AND FOOD INDUSTRIES 2553
Fruit see AGRICULTURE - Crop Production and Soil 192, see also FOOD AND FOOD INDUSTRIES 2553, GARDENING AND HORTICULTURE 2627
Fuel see ENERGY 2197, see also HEATING, PLUMBING AND REFRIGERATION 2862, MINES AND MINING INDUSTRY 4315, PETROLEUM AND GAS 4558
Fundraising see SOCIAL SERVICES AND WELFARE 5421
FUNERALS 2625
FUNERALS — Abstracting, Bibliographies, Statistics 2626
Fur see LEATHER AND FUR INDUSTRIES 3410
Furnaces see HEATING, PLUMBING AND REFRIGERATION 2862, see also METALLURGY 4223
Furniture And House Furnishings see INTERIOR DESIGN AND DECORATION - Furniture And House Furnishings 3172

Gallbladder see MEDICAL SCIENCES - Gastroenterology 4024
Galleries see MUSEUMS AND ART GALLERIES 4364
Gambling see SPORTS AND GAMES 5498
Game Breeding see AGRICULTURE - Poultry and Livestock 241
Games see SPORTS AND GAMES 5498
Gangs see CHILDREN AND YOUTH - About 1529, see also CRIMINOLOGY AND LAW ENFORCEMENT 1869
Garages see TRANSPORTATION - Automobiles 5765
GARDENING AND HORTICULTURE 2627, see also AGRICULTURE 76, BIOLOGY - Botany 583
GARDENING AND HORTICULTURE — Abstracting, Bibliographies, Statistics 2651
GARDENING AND HORTICULTURE — Florist Trade 2652
Gas Chromatography see CHEMISTRY - Analytical Chemistry 1491
Gas Dynamics see PHYSICS - Mechanics 4758
Gas Turbines see ENGINEERING - Mechanical Engineering 2379
Gastroenterology see MEDICAL SCIENCES - Gastroenterology 4024
Gastronomy see HOME ECONOMICS 3031
Gauges see INSTRUMENTS 3128, see also METROLOGY AND STANDARDIZATION 4277
Gay see HOMOSEXUALITY 3039, see also MEN'S HEALTH 4215, MEN'S INTERESTS 4216
Gay Rights see HOMOSEXUALITY 3039, see also POLITICAL SCIENCE - Civil Rights 4877
Gemstones see JEWELRY, CLOCKS AND WATCHES 3179
Gender Bias see LAW 3215, see also POLITICAL SCIENCE - Civil Rights 4877
Gender Studies see MEN'S STUDIES 4222, see also WOMEN'S STUDIES 5977
GENEALOGY AND HERALDRY 2654
GENEALOGY AND HERALDRY — Abstracting, Bibliographies, Statistics 2684
GENEALOGY AND HERALDRY — Computer Applications 2684
GENERAL INTEREST PERIODICALS — Africa 2684
GENERAL INTEREST PERIODICALS — Albania 2686
GENERAL INTEREST PERIODICALS — Andorra 2686
GENERAL INTEREST PERIODICALS — Argentina 2686
GENERAL INTEREST PERIODICALS — Australasia 2687
GENERAL INTEREST PERIODICALS — Australia 2687
GENERAL INTEREST PERIODICALS — Austria 2689
GENERAL INTEREST PERIODICALS — Azerbaijan 2690
GENERAL INTEREST PERIODICALS — Bahrain 2690
GENERAL INTEREST PERIODICALS — Bangladesh 2690
GENERAL INTEREST PERIODICALS — Belarus 2691
GENERAL INTEREST PERIODICALS — Belgium 2691
GENERAL INTEREST PERIODICALS — Belize 2692
GENERAL INTEREST PERIODICALS — Benin 2692
GENERAL INTEREST PERIODICALS — Bermuda 2692
GENERAL INTEREST PERIODICALS — Bhutan 2692
GENERAL INTEREST PERIODICALS — Bolivia 2692
GENERAL INTEREST PERIODICALS — Botswana 2692
GENERAL INTEREST PERIODICALS — Brazil 2693
GENERAL INTEREST PERIODICALS — Bulgaria 2693
GENERAL INTEREST PERIODICALS — Burundi 2694
GENERAL INTEREST PERIODICALS — Cameroon 2694
GENERAL INTEREST PERIODICALS — Canada 2694
GENERAL INTEREST PERIODICALS — Central African Republic 2702
GENERAL INTEREST PERIODICALS — Central America 2702
GENERAL INTEREST PERIODICALS — Chile 2702
GENERAL INTEREST PERIODICALS — China 2702
GENERAL INTEREST PERIODICALS — Colombia 2705
GENERAL INTEREST PERIODICALS — Congo 2706
GENERAL INTEREST PERIODICALS — Cuba 2706
GENERAL INTEREST PERIODICALS — Cyprus 2706
GENERAL INTEREST PERIODICALS — Czech Republic 2707
GENERAL INTEREST PERIODICALS — Denmark 2707
GENERAL INTEREST PERIODICALS — Dominican Republic 2708
GENERAL INTEREST PERIODICALS — Ecuador 2709
GENERAL INTEREST PERIODICALS — Egypt 2709
GENERAL INTEREST PERIODICALS — Estonia 2709
GENERAL INTEREST PERIODICALS — Ethiopia 2709
GENERAL INTEREST PERIODICALS — European Communities 2709
GENERAL INTEREST PERIODICALS — Falkland Islands 2710
GENERAL INTEREST PERIODICALS — Finland 2710
GENERAL INTEREST PERIODICALS — France 2711
GENERAL INTEREST PERIODICALS — French Polynesia 2714
GENERAL INTEREST PERIODICALS — Gambia 2714
GENERAL INTEREST PERIODICALS — Germany 2714
GENERAL INTEREST PERIODICALS — Ghana 2724
GENERAL INTEREST PERIODICALS — Gibraltar 2724
GENERAL INTEREST PERIODICALS — Great Britain 2725
GENERAL INTEREST PERIODICALS — Greece 2732
GENERAL INTEREST PERIODICALS — Greenland 2732
GENERAL INTEREST PERIODICALS — Guatemala 2732
GENERAL INTEREST PERIODICALS — Guyana 2733
GENERAL INTEREST PERIODICALS — Haiti 2733
GENERAL INTEREST PERIODICALS — Hong Kong 2733
GENERAL INTEREST PERIODICALS — Hungary 2733
GENERAL INTEREST PERIODICALS — Iceland 2734
GENERAL INTEREST PERIODICALS — India 2735
GENERAL INTEREST PERIODICALS — Indonesia 2739
GENERAL INTEREST PERIODICALS — Iran 2740
GENERAL INTEREST PERIODICALS — Iraq 2740
GENERAL INTEREST PERIODICALS — Ireland 2740
GENERAL INTEREST PERIODICALS — Israel 2741
GENERAL INTEREST PERIODICALS — Italy 2742
GENERAL INTEREST PERIODICALS — Ivory Coast 2745
GENERAL INTEREST PERIODICALS — Japan 2745
GENERAL INTEREST PERIODICALS — Jordan 2747
GENERAL INTEREST PERIODICALS — Kazakhstan 2747
GENERAL INTEREST PERIODICALS — Kenya 2747
GENERAL INTEREST PERIODICALS — Korea 2748

CROSS-INDEX TO SUBJECTS

GENERAL INTEREST PERIODICALS — Kuwait 2748
GENERAL INTEREST PERIODICALS — Latvia 2748
GENERAL INTEREST PERIODICALS — Lebanon 2748
GENERAL INTEREST PERIODICALS — Lesotho 2748
GENERAL INTEREST PERIODICALS — Liberia 2748
GENERAL INTEREST PERIODICALS — Libya 2748
GENERAL INTEREST PERIODICALS — Lithuania 2748
GENERAL INTEREST PERIODICALS — Luxembourg 2749
GENERAL INTEREST PERIODICALS — Malagasy Republic 2749
GENERAL INTEREST PERIODICALS — Malawi 2749
GENERAL INTEREST PERIODICALS — Malaysia 2749
GENERAL INTEREST PERIODICALS — Malta 2749
GENERAL INTEREST PERIODICALS — Mexico 2750
GENERAL INTEREST PERIODICALS — Middle East 2751
GENERAL INTEREST PERIODICALS — Moldova 2752
GENERAL INTEREST PERIODICALS — Monaco 2752
GENERAL INTEREST PERIODICALS — Morocco 2752
GENERAL INTEREST PERIODICALS — Mozambique 2752
GENERAL INTEREST PERIODICALS — Namibia 2752
GENERAL INTEREST PERIODICALS — Nepal 2752
GENERAL INTEREST PERIODICALS — Netherlands 2752
GENERAL INTEREST PERIODICALS — New Zealand 2753
GENERAL INTEREST PERIODICALS — Nicaragua 2754
GENERAL INTEREST PERIODICALS — Niger 2754
GENERAL INTEREST PERIODICALS — Nigeria 2754
GENERAL INTEREST PERIODICALS — Norway 2755
GENERAL INTEREST PERIODICALS — Oceania 2756
GENERAL INTEREST PERIODICALS — Pakistan 2757
GENERAL INTEREST PERIODICALS — Panama 2757
GENERAL INTEREST PERIODICALS — Paraguay 2757
GENERAL INTEREST PERIODICALS — Peru 2757
GENERAL INTEREST PERIODICALS — Philippines 2758
GENERAL INTEREST PERIODICALS — Poland 2758
GENERAL INTEREST PERIODICALS — Portugal 2760
GENERAL INTEREST PERIODICALS — Puerto Rico 2760
GENERAL INTEREST PERIODICALS — Rumania 2760
GENERAL INTEREST PERIODICALS — Russia 2761
GENERAL INTEREST PERIODICALS — Saint Vincent 2762
GENERAL INTEREST PERIODICALS — Saudi Arabia 2762
GENERAL INTEREST PERIODICALS — Scandinavia 2762
GENERAL INTEREST PERIODICALS — Senegal 2762
GENERAL INTEREST PERIODICALS — Seychelles 2762
GENERAL INTEREST PERIODICALS — Sierra Leone 2762
GENERAL INTEREST PERIODICALS — Singapore 2762
GENERAL INTEREST PERIODICALS — Slovakia 2763
GENERAL INTEREST PERIODICALS — South Africa 2763
GENERAL INTEREST PERIODICALS — South America 2765
GENERAL INTEREST PERIODICALS — Spain 2765
GENERAL INTEREST PERIODICALS — Sri Lanka 2766
GENERAL INTEREST PERIODICALS — Sudan 2766
GENERAL INTEREST PERIODICALS — Sultanate Of Oman 2766
GENERAL INTEREST PERIODICALS — Surinam 2766
GENERAL INTEREST PERIODICALS — Swaziland 2766
GENERAL INTEREST PERIODICALS — Sweden 2767
GENERAL INTEREST PERIODICALS — Switzerland 2768
GENERAL INTEREST PERIODICALS — Syria 2769
GENERAL INTEREST PERIODICALS — Taiwan 2769
GENERAL INTEREST PERIODICALS — Tanzania 2770
GENERAL INTEREST PERIODICALS — Thailand 2770
GENERAL INTEREST PERIODICALS — Tonga 2770
GENERAL INTEREST PERIODICALS — Turkey 2771
GENERAL INTEREST PERIODICALS — Tuvalu 2771
GENERAL INTEREST PERIODICALS — Uganda 2772
GENERAL INTEREST PERIODICALS — Ukraine 2772
GENERAL INTEREST PERIODICALS — Union Of Myanmar 2772
GENERAL INTEREST PERIODICALS — United Arab Emirates 2772
GENERAL INTEREST PERIODICALS — United Kingdom Miscellaneous Islands 2773
GENERAL INTEREST PERIODICALS — United States 2773
GENERAL INTEREST PERIODICALS — Uruguay 2791
GENERAL INTEREST PERIODICALS — Venezuela 2791
GENERAL INTEREST PERIODICALS — Vietnam 2792
GENERAL INTEREST PERIODICALS — West Indies 2792
GENERAL INTEREST PERIODICALS — Yugoslavia 2793
GENERAL INTEREST PERIODICALS — Zambia 2793
GENERAL INTEREST PERIODICALS — Zimbabwe 2794
General Medical Practice see MEDICAL SCIENCES 3799
Generators see ENGINEERING - Electrical Engineering 2320, see also PHYSICS - Electricity 4754
Genetic Engineering see BIOLOGY - Bioengineering 552, see also BIOLOGY - Biotechnology 575, BIOLOGY - Genetics 643, ENGINEERING - Chemical Engineering 2277
Genetics see BIOLOGY - Genetics 643
Genitals see MEDICAL SCIENCES - Obstetrics And Gynecology 4056, see also MEDICAL SCIENCES - Urology And Nephrology 4203
Genocide see LAW - International Law 3379, see also POLITICAL SCIENCE - International Relations 4889
Geochemistry see EARTH SCIENCES - Geology 1925
Geodesy see EARTH SCIENCES - Geophysics 1964, see also GEOGRAPHY 2794
GEOGRAPHY 2794, see also TRAVEL AND TOURISM 5848
GEOGRAPHY — Abstracting, Bibliographies, Statistics 2824
GEOGRAPHY — Computer Applications 2825
Geology see EARTH SCIENCES - Geology 1925
Geomagnetism see EARTH SCIENCES - Geophysics 1964
Geometry see MATHEMATICS 3745
Geophysics see EARTH SCIENCES - Geophysics 1964
Geothermal Energy see ENERGY - Geothermal Energy 2223
German Baptist see RELIGIONS AND THEOLOGY - Protestant 5225
German Language - Study and Teaching see LINGUISTICS 3485

GERONTOLOGY AND GERIATRICS 2826
GERONTOLOGY AND GERIATRICS — Abstracting, Eibliographies, Statistics 2840
Ghosts see LITERATURE - Science Fiction, Fantasy, Horror 3723, see also PARAPSYCHOLOGY AND OCCULTISM 4542
GIFTWARE AND TOYS 2841
Gingivitis see MEDICAL SCIENCES - Dentistry 3977
Glaciology see EARTH SCIENCES - Geology 1925
Glandular System see MEDICAL SCIENCES - Endocrinology 4004
Glass see CERAMICS, GLASS AND POTTERY 1439
Glasses, Eye see MEDICAL SCIENCES - Ophthalmology and Optometry 4083
Glaucoma see MEDICAL SCIENCES - Ophthalmology and Optometry 4083
Glazing see CERAMICS, GLASS AND POTTERY 1439
Gliders see AERONAUTICS AND SPACE FLIGHT 47
Global Warming see ENVIRONMENTAL STUDIES 2399, see also METEOROLOGY 4259
Gnosticism see RELIGIONS AND THEOLOGY 5145
Gold see JEWELRY, CLOCKS AND WATCHES 3179, see also METALLURGY 4223, MINES AND MINING INDUSTRY 4315
Goldfish see PETS 4591
Golf see SPORTS AND GAMES - Ball Games 5498
Gourmet see FOOD AND FOOD INDUSTRIES 2553, see also HOME ECONOMICS 3031, HOTELS AND RESTAURANTS 3064
Government see POLITICAL SCIENCE 4793, see also PUBLIC ADMINISTRATION 5017, PUBLIC ADMINISTRATION - Municipal Government 5055
Grain see AGRICULTURE - Feed, Flour And Grain 236
Graphic Arts see ART 364, see also PRINTING 4949
Graphology see PSYCHOLOGY 4962
Gravity see PHYSICS - Mechanics 4758
Greek Catholic see RELIGIONS AND THEOLOGY - Roman Catholic 5255
Greek Orthodox see RELIGIONS AND THEOLOGY - Eastern Orthodox 5209
Greenhouse Effect see ENVIRONMENTAL STUDIES 2399, see also METEOROLOGY 4259
Greenhouses see GARDENING AND HORTICULTURE 2627
Greeting Cards see GIFTWARE AND TOYS 2841
Grieving see PSYCHOLOGY 4962, see also SOCIAL SERVICES AND WELFARE 5421
Grocery Trade see FOOD AND FOOD INDUSTRIES - Grocery Trade 2591
Guerrilla Warfare see MILITARY 4283
Guides To Schools And Colleges see EDUCATION - Guides To Schools And Colleges 2087
Gum Disease see MEDICAL SCIENCES - Dentistry 3977
Gun Control see CRIMINOLOGY AND LAW ENFORCEMENT 1869
Guns see MILITARY 4283, see also SPORTS AND GAMES 5498
Gymnastics see SPORTS AND GAMES 5498
Gyms see PHYSICAL FITNESS AND HYGIENE 4704
Gynecology see MEDICAL SCIENCES - Obstetrics and Gynecology 4056
H M O see HOSPITALS 3047, see also INSURANCE 3133
Habitat Protection see CONSERVATION 1837, see also ENVIRONMENTAL STUDIES 2399
Hair Removal see BEAUTY CULTURE 435
Hairdressing see BEAUTY CULTURE 435
Handbags see CLOTHING TRADE 1589, see also LEATHER AND FUR INDUSTRIES 3410
HANDICAPPED 2844
HANDICAPPED — Abstracting, Bibliographies, Statistics 2848
HANDICAPPED — Computer Applications 2849
HANDICAPPED — Hearing Impaired 2849
HANDICAPPED — Physically Impaired 2854
HANDICAPPED — Visually Impaired 2855
Handicrafts see ARTS AND HANDICRAFTS 413
Harbors see TRANSPORTATION - Ships and Shipping 5818
Hardware see BUILDING AND CONSTRUCTION - Hardware 770
Hardware (Computer) see COMPUTERS - Hardware 1799
Hare Krishna see RELIGIONS AND THEOLOGY - Hindu 5211
Harijan see RELIGIONS AND THEOLOGY - Hindu 5211
Harnesses see LEATHER AND FUR INDUSTRIES 3410
Hashish see DRUG ABUSE AND ALCOHOLISM 1898
Hasidim, Hasidism see RELIGIONS AND THEOLOGY - Judaic 5218
Hay Fever see MEDICAL SCIENCES - Allergology And Immunology 3933
Hazardous Substances see ENVIRONMENTAL STUDIES - Waste Management 2458
Headhunters see OCCUPATIONS AND CAREERS 4487
Health Clubs see PHYSICAL FITNESS AND HYGIENE 4704
Health Foods see FOOD AND FOOD INDUSTRIES 2553, see also NUTRITION AND DIETETICS 4461, PHYSICAL FITNESS AND HYGIENE 4704
Health Insurance see INSURANCE 3133
Health Maintenance Organization see HOSPITALS 3047, see also INSURANCE 3133
Healthcare Administration see HOSPITALS 3047
Hearing see MEDICAL SCIENCES - Otorhinolaryngology 4104
Hearing Impaired see HANDICAPPED - Hearing Impaired 2849
Heart Diseases see MEDICAL SCIENCES - Cardiovascular Diseases 3946
Heat see PHYSICS - Heat 4755
HEATING, PLUMBING AND REFRIGERATION 2862, see also BUILDING AND CONSTRUCTION 716, ENGINEERING - Mechanical Engineering 2379
HEATING, PLUMBING AND REFRIGERATION — Abstracting, Bibliographies, Statistics 2872
Helicopters see AERONAUTICS AND SPACE FLIGHT 47
Hematology see MEDICAL SCIENCES - Hematology 4030
Hemophilia see MEDICAL SCIENCES - Hematology 4030
Hepatology see MEDICAL SCIENCES - Gastroenterology 4024
Heraldry see GENEALOGY AND HERALDRY 2654
Herbal Medicine see ALTERNATIVE MEDICINE 265, see also BIOLOGY - Botany 583
Herbariums see BIOLOGY - Botany 583, see also GARDENING AND HORTICULTURE 2627
Herbs see AGRICULTURE 76, see also BIOLOGY - Botany 583, GARDENING AND HORTICULTURE 2627
Heredity see BIOLOGY - Genetics 643
Heroin see DRUG ABUSE AND ALCOHOLISM 1898
Herpetology see BIOLOGY - Zoology 689
Hi-Fi see SOUND RECORDING AND REPRODUCTION 5494

CROSS-INDEX TO SUBJECTS

Hides see LEATHER AND FUR INDUSTRIES 3410
Higher Education see EDUCATION - Higher Education 2095
Highways see ENGINEERING - Civil Engineering 2293, see also TRANSPORTATION - Roads and Traffic 5811
Hinayana see RELIGIONS AND THEOLOGY - Buddhist 5206
Hinduism see RELIGIONS AND THEOLOGY - Hindu 5211
Histochemistry see BIOLOGY - Cytology and Histology 621
Histology see BIOLOGY - Cytology and Histology 621
Historic Sites see HISTORY 2872, see also TRAVEL AND TOURISM 5848
HISTORY 2872, see also ARCHAEOLOGY 304, BIOGRAPHY 490, CLASSICAL STUDIES 1578
HISTORY — Abstracting, Bibliographies, Statistics 2898
HISTORY — Computer Applications 2902
HISTORY — History Of Africa 2902
HISTORY — History Of Asia 2908
HISTORY — History Of Australasia And Other Areas 2917
HISTORY — History Of Europe 2920
HISTORY — History Of North And South America 2977
HISTORY — History Of The Near East 3011
HIV see MEDICAL SCIENCES - Allergology And Immunology 3933
HOBBIES 3016, see also SPORTS AND GAMES 5498
HOBBIES — Abstracting, Bibliographies, Statistics 3031
Hockey see SPORTS AND GAMES 5498
Holidays see FOLKLORE 2544, see also TRAVEL AND TOURISM 5848
Holistic Medicine see ALTERNATIVE MEDICINE 265
Holocaust see ETHNIC INTERESTS 2466, see also HISTORY - History Of Europe 2920
Home Appliances see ELECTRONICS 2170, see also INTERIOR DESIGN AND DECORATION - Furniture And House Furnishings 3172
HOME ECONOMICS 3031
HOME ECONOMICS — Abstracting, Bibliographies, Statistics 3038
Home Improvement see BUILDING AND CONSTRUCTION 716, see also HOW-TO AND DO-IT-YOURSELF 3102
Home Remodeling And Repairs see BUILDING AND CONSTRUCTION 716, see also HOW-TO AND DO-IT-YOURSELF 3102
Homelessness see SOCIAL SERVICES AND WELFARE 5421
Homeopathy see MEDICAL SCIENCES - Chiropractic, Homeopathy, Osteopathy 3959
HOMOSEXUALITY 3039
HOMOSEXUALITY — Abstracting, Bibliographies, Statistics 3047
Hormones see MEDICAL SCIENCES - Endocrinology 4004
Horology see JEWELRY, CLOCKS AND WATCHES 3179
Horror see LITERATURE - Science Fiction, Fantasy, Horror 3723
Horses And Horsemanship see SPORTS AND GAMES - Horses And Horsemanship 5579
Horticulture see GARDENING AND HORTICULTURE 2627
Hosiery see CLOTHING TRADE 1589
Hospices see HOSPITALS 3047
Hospital Supplies see HOSPITALS 3047, see also PHARMACY AND PHARMACOLOGY 4600
HOSPITALS 3047, see also MEDICAL SCIENCES 3799
HOSPITALS — Abstracting, Bibliographies, Statistics 3063
HOSPITALS — Computer Applications 3064
HOTELS AND RESTAURANTS 3064
HOTELS AND RESTAURANTS — Abstracting, Bibliographies, Statistics 3077
House Furnishings see INTERIOR DESIGN AND DECORATION - Furniture and House Furnishings 3172
Household Management see HOME ECONOMICS 3031
Houses see BUILDING AND CONSTRUCTION 716, see also REAL ESTATE 5124
Housewares see CERAMICS, GLASS AND POTTERY 1439, see also INTERIOR DESIGN AND DECORATION - Furniture And House Furnishings 3172
HOUSING AND URBAN PLANNING 3078, see also BUILDING AND CONSTRUCTION 716, PUBLIC ADMINISTRATION 5017, REAL ESTATE 5124
HOUSING AND URBAN PLANNING — Abstracting, Bibliographies, Statistics 3099
HOW-TO AND DO-IT-YOURSELF 3102
HOW-TO AND DO-IT-YOURSELF — Abstracting, Bibliographies, Statistics 3103
Human Ecology see SOCIOLOGY 5459
Human Geography see GEOGRAPHY 2794, see also POPULATION STUDIES 4924
Human Immunodeficiency Virus see MEDICAL SCIENCES - Allergology And Immunology 3933, see also MEDICAL SCIENCES - Communicable Diseases 3962
Human Resources see BUSINESS AND ECONOMICS - Personnel Management 1304
Human Rights see POLITICAL SCIENCE - Civil Rights 4877
Humanism see PHILOSOPHY 4656
HUMANITIES: COMPREHENSIVE WORKS 3103
HUMANITIES: COMPREHENSIVE WORKS — Abstracting, Bibliographies, Statistics 3126
HUMANITIES: COMPREHENSIVE WORKS — Computer Applications 3127
Humor see LITERARY AND POLITICAL REVIEWS 3555
Hunger see SOCIAL SERVICES AND WELFARE 5421
Hunting see SPORTS AND GAMES - Outdoor Life 5588
Hurricanes see METEOROLOGY 4259
Hydraulic Engineering see ENGINEERING - Hydraulic Engineering 2373
Hydrodynamics see PHYSICS 4718
Hydroelectric Engineering see ENGINEERING - Electrical Engineering 2320
Hydroelectrical Energy see ENERGY - Hydroelectrical Energy 2223
Hydrography see WATER RESOURCES 5933
Hydrology see EARTH SCIENCES - Hydrology 1977
Hydroponics see AGRICULTURE - Crop Production And Soil 192
Hydrotherapy see ALTERNATIVE MEDICINE 265
Hygiene see OCCUPATIONAL HEALTH AND SAFETY 4474, see also PHYSICAL FITNESS AND HYGIENE 4704, PUBLIC HEALTH AND SAFETY 5070
Hyperglycemia see MEDICAL SCIENCES - Endocrinology 4004, see also NUTRITION AND DIETETICS 4461
Hypertension see MEDICAL SCIENCES - Cardiovascular Diseases 3946
Hypnosis see MEDICAL SCIENCES - Hypnosis 4035
Hypochondria see MEDICAL SCIENCES - Psychiatry And Neurology 4125
Hypoglycemia see MEDICAL SCIENCES - Endocrinology 4004, see also NUTRITION AND DIETETICS 4461
Ichthyology see BIOLOGY - Zoology 689

Idealism see PHILOSOPHY 4656
Illumination see ENGINEERING - Electrical Engineering 2320, see also PHYSICS - Electricity 4754
Immigration see POPULATION STUDIES 4924
Immunization see MEDICAL SCIENCES - Allergology And Immunology 3933, see also MEDICAL SCIENCES - Pediatrics 4110, PUBLIC HEALTH AND SAFETY 5070
Immunology see MEDICAL SCIENCES - Allergology And Immunology 3933
Imperialism see POLITICAL SCIENCE 4793
Imports see BUSINESS AND ECONOMICS - International Commerce 1102
Impotence see MEDICAL SCIENCES - Urology And Nephrology 4203, see also MEN'S HEALTH 4215
Incineration see ENVIRONMENTAL STUDIES - Waste Management 2458
Income Tax see BUSINESS AND ECONOMICS - Public Finance, Taxation 1335, see also HOME ECONOMICS 3031
Indexing Services see ABSTRACTING AND INDEXING SERVICES 1
Indoor Air Pollution see OCCUPATIONAL HEALTH AND SAFETY 4474
Indoor Games and Amusements see HOBBIES 3016, see also SPORTS AND GAMES 5498
Industrial Arts see TECHNOLOGY 5663
Industrial Chemistry see ENGINEERING - Chemical Engineering 2277
Industrial Design see ENGINEERING 2237, see also TECHNOLOGY: COMPREHENSIVE WORKS 5663
Industrial Engineering see ENGINEERING - Industrial Engineering 2377
Industrial Health And Safety see OCCUPATIONAL HEALTH AND SAFETY 4474
Industrial Hygiene see OCCUPATIONAL HEALTH AND SAFETY 4474
Industrial Relations see BUSINESS AND ECONOMICS - Labor and Industrial Relations 1189, see also BUSINESS AND ECONOMICS - Personnel Management 1304
Industrial Sanitation Engineering see ENGINEERING - Industrial Engineering 2377, see also ENVIRONMENTAL STUDIES - Toxicology And Environmental Safety 2452
Industry see BUSINESS AND ECONOMICS - Production of Goods and Services 1317
Infantry see MILITARY 4283
Infants see CHILDREN AND YOUTH - About 1529, see also MEDICAL SCIENCES - Obstetrics And Gynecology 4056, MEDICAL SCIENCES - Pediatrics 4110
Infectious Diseases see MEDICAL SCIENCES - Communicable Diseases 3962, see also PUBLIC HEALTH AND SAFETY 5070
Infertility see MEDICAL SCIENCES - Obstetrics And Gynecology 4056, see also MEN'S HEALTH 4215, WOMEN'S HEALTH 5952
Influenza see MEDICAL SCIENCES - Respiratory Diseases 4174
Information Science And Information Theory see COMPUTERS - Information Science And Information Theory 1802
Infrared see PHYSICS - Optics 4770
Injuries see MEDICAL SCIENCES - Orthopedics And Traumatology 4094
Inorganic Chemistry see CHEMISTRY - Inorganic Chemistry 1505
Input-Output Systems see COMPUTERS - Hardware 1799
Insecticides see AGRICULTURE - Crop Production And Soil 192, see also BIOLOGY - Entomology 628, ENGINEERING - Chemical Engineering 2277, PUBLIC HEALTH AND SAFETY 5070
Insects see BIOLOGY - Entomology 628
INSTRUMENTS 3128
INSTRUMENTS — Abstracting, Bibliographies, Statistics 3132
Insulation see BUILDING AND CONSTRUCTION 716, see also ENERGY 2197, HEATING, PLUMBING AND REFRIGERATION 2862
INSURANCE 3133
INSURANCE — Abstracting, Bibliographies, Statistics 3159
INSURANCE — Computer Applications 3162
Integrated Circuits see ELECTRONICS 2170
Intellectual Property see PATENTS, TRADEMARKS AND COPYRIGHTS 4547
Intensive Care Medicine see MEDICAL SCIENCES 3799
INTERIOR DESIGN AND DECORATION 3162, see also HOME ECONOMICS 3031
INTERIOR DESIGN AND DECORATION — Abstracting, Bibliographies, Statistics 3172
INTERIOR DESIGN AND DECORATION — Furniture And House Furnishings 3172
Internal Medicine see MEDICAL SCIENCES - Internal Medicine 4035
International Affairs see BUSINESS AND ECONOMICS - International Development and Assistance 1136, see also LITERARY AND POLITICAL REVIEWS 3555, POLITICAL SCIENCE - International Relations 4889
International Commerce see BUSINESS AND ECONOMICS - International Commerce 1102
International Development And Assistance see BUSINESS AND ECONOMICS - International Development And Assistance 1136
International Education Programs see EDUCATION - International Education Programs 2122
International Law see LAW - International Law 3379
International Relations see POLITICAL SCIENCE - International Relations 4889
Interplanetary Flight see AERONAUTICS AND SPACE FLIGHT 47
Inventions see PATENTS, TRADEMARKS AND COPYRIGHTS 4547, see also SCIENCES: COMPREHENSIVE WORKS 5304, TECHNOLOGY: COMPREHENSIVE WORKS 5663
Investments see BUSINESS AND ECONOMICS - Investments 1150
Ionization see CHEMISTRY - Electrochemistry 1503
Iron see METALLURGY 4223, see also MINES AND MINING INDUSTRY 4315
Irrigation see AGRICULTURE 76, see also CONSERVATION 1837, ENGINEERING - Hydraulic Engineering 2373, WATER RESOURCES 5933
Islam see RELIGIONS AND THEOLOGY - Islamic 5212
Isma'ilism see RELIGIONS AND THEOLOGY - Islamic 5212
Italian Language - Study and Teaching see LINGUISTICS 3485
Jails see CRIMINOLOGY AND LAW ENFORCEMENT 1869
Jainism see RELIGIONS AND THEOLOGY - Other Denominations And Sects 5287
Jaundice see MEDICAL SCIENCES - Gastroenterology 4024
Jaw see MEDICAL SCIENCES - Dentistry 3977
Jazz see MUSIC 4382
Jehovah's Witness see RELIGIONS AND THEOLOGY - Other Denominations And Sects 5287
Jet Engines see AERONAUTICS AND SPACE FLIGHT 47
JEWELRY, CLOCKS AND WATCHES 3179
JEWELRY, CLOCKS AND WATCHES — Abstracting, Bibliographies, Statistics 3184
Job Opportunities see BUSINESS AND ECONOMICS - Labor and Industrial Relations 1189, see also OCCUPATIONS AND CAREERS 4487
Jogging see PHYSICAL FITNESS AND HYGIENE 4704

CROSS-INDEX TO SUBJECTS

JOURNALISM 3184
JOURNALISM — Abstracting, Bibliographies, Statistics 3197
Judaism see RELIGIONS AND THEOLOGY - Judaic 5218
Judges see LAW - Judicial Systems 3398
Judicial Systems see LAW - Judicial Systems 3398
Judo see SPORTS AND GAMES 5498
Jurisprudence see LAW 3215
Jury see LAW - Criminal Law 3367
Jute see TEXTILE INDUSTRIES AND FABRICS 5689
Juvenile Delinquency see CHILDREN AND YOUTH - About 1529, see also CRIMINOLOGY AND LAW ENFORCEMENT 1869
Juvenile Literature see CHILDREN AND YOUTH - For 1548, see also PUBLISHING AND BOOK TRADE 5096
Ka'abah see RELIGIONS AND THEOLOGY - Islamic 5212
Kabala see RELIGIONS AND THEOLOGY - Judaic 5218
Karate see SPORTS AND GAMES 5498
Karma see RELIGIONS AND THEOLOGY - Buddhist 5206, see also RELIGIONS AND THEOLOGY - Hindu 5211
Keyboard Instruments see MUSIC 4382
Kibbutz see BUSINESS AND ECONOMICS - Cooperatives 1008, see also GENERAL INTEREST PERIODICALS - Israel 2741
Kidney see MEDICAL SCIENCES - Urology And Nephrology 4203
Kinetics see CHEMISTRY - Organic Chemistry 1508, see also CHEMISTRY - Physical Chemistry 1520, PHYSICS 4718
Knit Goods see CLOTHING TRADE 1589, see also TEXTILE INDUSTRIES AND FABRICS 5689
Knitting see NEEDLEWORK 4445
Koran see RELIGIONS AND THEOLOGY - Islamic 5212
L S D see DRUG ABUSE AND ALCOHOLISM 1898
Labels, Labeling see PACKAGING 4516
Labor And Industrial Relations see BUSINESS AND ECONOMICS - Labor And Industrial Relations 1189
Labor Law see BUSINESS AND ECONOMICS - Labor and Industrial Relations 1189, see also LAW 3215
LABOR UNIONS 3199
LABOR UNIONS — Abstracting, Bibliographies, Statistics 3214
Laboratory Animals see MEDICAL SCIENCES - Experimental Medicine, Laboratory Technique 4012
Laboratory Technique see MEDICAL SCIENCES - Experimental Medicine, Laboratory Technique 4012, see also SCIENCES - Comprehensive Works 5304
Lace see NEEDLEWORK 4445
Lamaism see RELIGIONS AND THEOLOGY - Buddhist 5206
Lamination see PAINTS AND PROTECTIVE COATINGS 4523, see also PLASTICS 4783
Land Management see CONSERVATION 1837, see also ENVIRONMENTAL STUDIES 2399
Land Reclamation see AGRICULTURE - Crop Production and Soil 192, see also ENVIRONMENTAL STUDIES 2399
Landfills see ENVIRONMENTAL STUDIES - Waste Management 2458
Landscaping see ARCHITECTURE 342, see also GARDENING AND HORTICULTURE 2627
Language, Study and Teaching see LINGUISTICS 3485
Laryngology see MEDICAL SCIENCES - Otorhinolaryngology 4104
Laser Printers see COMPUTERS - Hardware 1799, see also PUBLISHING AND BOOK TRADE - Computer Applications 5123
Lasers see PHYSICS - Optics 4770
Lathes see MACHINERY 3733
Latin American History see HISTORY - History of North and South America 2977
Latin Language and Literature see CLASSICAL STUDIES 1578, see also LINGUISTICS 3485
Latter-Day Saints see RELIGIONS AND THEOLOGY - Other Denominations And Sects 5287
Laundries see CLEANING AND DYEING 1586
LAW 3215
LAW — Abstracting, Bibliographies, Statistics 3340
LAW — Civil Law 3345
LAW — Computer Applications 3352
LAW — Constitutional Law 3354
LAW — Corporate Law 3355
LAW — Criminal Law 3367
Law Enforcement see CRIMINOLOGY AND LAW ENFORCEMENT 1869
LAW — Estate Planning 3373
LAW — Family And Matrimonial Law 3375
LAW — International Law 3379
LAW — Judicial Systems 3398
LAW — Legal Aid 3407
LAW — Maritime Law 3408
LAW — Military Law 3409
Lawns see GARDENING AND HORTICULTURE 2627
Lead see METALLURGY 4223, see also MINES AND MINING INDUSTRY 4315
Lead Poisoning see ENVIRONMENTAL STUDIES - Toxicology And Environmental Safety 2452, see also PUBLIC HEALTH AND SAFETY 5070
Leasing And Renting see BUSINESS AND ECONOMICS - Small Business 1369, see also LAW - Civil Law 3345, REAL ESTATE 5124
LEATHER AND FUR INDUSTRIES 3410, see also SHOES AND BOOTS 5378
LEATHER AND FUR INDUSTRIES — Abstracting, Bibliographies, Statistics 3413
Legal Aid see LAW - Legal Aid 3407
Legends see FOLKLORE 2544, see also LITERATURE 3592
Legionnaires see MILITARY 4283
Legislation see LAW 3215, see also POLITICAL SCIENCE 4793, PUBLIC ADMINISTRATION 5017
LEISURE AND RECREATION 3413
Lenses see MEDICAL SCIENCES - Ophthalmology And Optometry 4083, see also PHOTOGRAPHY 4691, PHYSICS - Optics 4770
Lepidoptera see BIOLOGY - Entomology 628
Leprosy see MEDICAL SCIENCES - Communicable Diseases 3962
Lesbian see HOMOSEXUALITY 3039, see also WOMEN'S HEALTH 5952, WOMEN'S INTERESTS 5953
Lesbian Rights see HOMOSEXUALITY 3039, see also POLITICAL SCIENCE - Civil Rights 4877
Leukemia see MEDICAL SCIENCES - Hematology 4030, see also MEDICAL SCIENCES - Oncology 4069
Lexicography see LINGUISTICS 3485
LIBRARY AND INFORMATION SCIENCES 3416, see also BIBLIOGRAPHIES 457, COMPUTERS - Information Science and Information Theory 1802, PUBLISHING AND BOOK TRADE 5096
LIBRARY AND INFORMATION SCIENCES — Abstracting, Bibliographies, Statistics 3476
LIBRARY AND INFORMATION SCIENCES — Computer Applications 3482
Library Bookbinding see LIBRARY AND INFORMATION SCIENCES 3416, see also PUBLISHING AND BOOK TRADE 5096
Licensing see PATENTS, TRADEMARKS AND COPYRIGHTS 4547
Lichenology see BIOLOGY - Botany 583
Lighting see INTERIOR DESIGN AND DECORATION - Furniture and House Furnishings 3172, see also PHYSICS - Electricity 4754
Limnology see EARTH SCIENCES - Hydrology 1977
LINGUISTICS 3485
LINGUISTICS — Abstracting, Bibliographies, Statistics 3552
LINGUISTICS — Computer Applications 3554
Liquor see BEVERAGES 443
LITERARY AND POLITICAL REVIEWS 3555, see also LITERATURE 3592
LITERARY AND POLITICAL REVIEWS — Abstracting, Bibliographies, Statistics 3592
Literary Criticism see LITERARY AND POLITICAL REVIEWS 3555, see also LITERATURE 3592
LITERATURE 3592, see also LINGUISTICS 3485, LITERARY AND POLITICAL REVIEWS 3555
LITERATURE — Abstracting, Bibliographies, Statistics 3693
LITERATURE — Adventure And Romance 3696
LITERATURE — Mystery And Detective 3698
LITERATURE — Poetry 3700, see also LITERARY AND POLITICAL REVIEWS 3555
LITERATURE — Science Fiction, Fantasy, Horror 3723
Lithography see PRINTING 4949
Lithotripsy see MEDICAL SCIENCES - Urology And Nephrology 4203
Little Magazines see LITERARY AND POLITICAL REVIEWS 3555
Liturgy see RELIGIONS AND THEOLOGY 5145
Liver Disorders see MEDICAL SCIENCES - Gastroenterology 4024
Livestock see AGRICULTURE - Poultry and Livestock 241, see also VETERINARY SCIENCE 5913
Locks see BUILDING AND CONSTRUCTION - Hardware 770
Logic see MATHEMATICS 3745, see also PHILOSOPHY 4656
Long-wave Electronics see ELECTRONICS 2170
Lotteries see BUSINESS AND ECONOMICS - Public Finance, Taxation 1335, see also SPORTS AND GAMES 5498
Lubrication and Lubricants see ENGINEERING - Mechanical Engineering 2379, see also PETROLEUM AND GAS 4558
Luggage see LEATHER AND FUR INDUSTRIES 3410
Lumber And Wood see FORESTS AND FORESTRY - Lumber And Wood 2618
Lungs see MEDICAL SCIENCES - Respiratory Diseases 4174
Lupus see MEDICAL SCIENCES - Allergology And Immunology 3933
Lutheranism see RELIGIONS AND THEOLOGY - Protestant 5225
Lymphoma see MEDICAL SCIENCES - Hematology 4030, see also MEDICAL SCIENCES - Oncology 4069
M R I (Magnetic Resonance Imaging) see MEDICAL SCIENCES - Radiology And Nuclear Medicine 4164
Machine Theory see COMPUTERS - Machine Theory 1805
Machine Translating see COMPUTERS - Computer Programming 1771, see also LINGUISTICS 3485
MACHINERY 3733, see also AGRICULTURE - Agricultural Equipment 186, ENGINEERING - Mechanical Engineering 2379, TECHNOLOGY: COMPREHENSIVE WORKS 5663
MACHINERY — Abstracting, Bibliographies, Statistics 3745
MACHINERY — Computer Applications 3745
Macroeconomics see BUSINESS AND ECONOMICS - Macroeconomics 1224
Macromolecules see CHEMISTRY - Organic Chemistry 1508
Magazine Business see PUBLISHING AND BOOK TRADE 5096
Magic see HOBBIES 3016
Magnetic Resonance Imaging see MEDICAL SCIENCES - Radiology And Nuclear Medicine 4164
Magnetism see PHYSICS 4718
Mahayana see RELIGIONS AND THEOLOGY - Buddhist 5206
Mail Order Business see BUSINESS AND ECONOMICS - Marketing and Purchasing 1264
Malacology see BIOLOGY - Zoology 689
Malpractice see LAW - Civil Law 3345, see also MEDICAL SCIENCES 3799
Mammalogy see BIOLOGY - Zoology 689
Mammography see MEDICAL SCIENCES - Obstetrics And Gynecology 4056, see also MEDICAL SCIENCES - Radiology And Nuclear Medicine 4164
Management see BUSINESS AND ECONOMICS - Management 1227
Mandala see RELIGIONS AND THEOLOGY - Buddhist 5206
Manic Depression see MEDICAL SCIENCES - Psychiatry And Neurology 4125
Manufacturing see BUSINESS AND ECONOMICS - Production of Goods and Services 1317
Maps see GEOGRAPHY 2794
Marijuana see DRUG ABUSE AND ALCOHOLISM 1898
Marine Biology see BIOLOGY 499, see also EARTH SCIENCES - Oceanography 1982
Marine Engineering see ENGINEERING 2237, see also TRANSPORTATION - Ships and Shipping 5818
Marine Policy see LAW - Maritime Law 3408
Marines see MILITARY 4283
Maritime Law see LAW - Maritime Law 3408
Marketing And Purchasing see BUSINESS AND ECONOMICS - Marketing And Purchasing 1264
Marriage see LAW - Family And Matrimonial Law 3375, see also MATRIMONY 3796
Martial Arts see PHYSICAL FITNESS AND HYGIENE 4704, see also SPORTS AND GAMES 5498

CROSS-INDEX TO SUBJECTS

Marxism see BUSINESS AND ECONOMICS - Economic Systems and Theories, Economic History 1090, see also POLITICAL SCIENCE 4793
Masonry see BUILDING AND CONSTRUCTION 716
Mass Transit see TRANSPORTATION 5723
Massage see MEDICAL SCIENCES - Physical Medicine And Rehabilitation 4122, see also PHYSICAL FITNESS AND HYGIENE 4704
Materialism see PHILOSOPHY 4656
Materials Handling see BUSINESS AND ECONOMICS - Management 1227
Materials Science see ENGINEERING - Engineering Mechanics And Materials 2359, see also METALLURGY 4223, PLASTICS 4783
Maternal-Fetal Medicine see MEDICAL SCIENCES - Obstetrics And Gynecology 4056
Mathematical Geography see GEOGRAPHY 2794
Mathematical Physics see PHYSICS 4718
MATHEMATICS 3745
MATHEMATICS — Abstracting, Bibliographies, Statistics 3791
MATHEMATICS — Computer Applications 3792
MATRIMONY 3796
MATRIMONY — Abstracting, Bibliographies, Statistics 3798
Mausoleums see FUNERALS 2625
Maxillofacial Surgery see MEDICAL SCIENCES - Dentistry 3977
Measurement see METROLOGY AND STANDARDIZATION 4277
Meat see FOOD AND FOOD INDUSTRIES 2553
Mechanical Drawing see ENGINEERING 2237, see also TECHNOLOGY: COMPREHENSIVE WORKS 5663
Mechanical Engineering see ENGINEERING - Mechanical Engineering 2379
Mechanical Handling see MACHINERY 3733, see also TECHNOLOGY: COMPREHENSIVE WORKS 5663, TRANSPORTATION 5723
Mechanical Translating see COMPUTERS - Computer Programming 1771, see also LINGUISTICS 3485
Mechanics see PHYSICS - Mechanics 4758
Medals And Medallions see NUMISMATICS 4456
Media see COMMUNICATIONS - Radio 1678, see also COMMUNICATIONS - Television And Cable 1696, JOURNALISM 3184
Medical Bacteriology see MEDICAL SCIENCES - Communicable Diseases 3962
Medical Centers see HOSPITALS 3047
Medical Economics see HOSPITALS 3047, see also MEDICAL SCIENCES 3799
Medical Engineering see MEDICAL SCIENCES 3799
Medical Examiners see MEDICAL SCIENCES - Forensic Sciences 4021
Medical Imaging Technology see MEDICAL SCIENCES - Radiology And Nuclear Medicine 4164
Medical Jurisprudence see MEDICAL SCIENCES - Forensic Sciences 4021
Medical Parasitology see MEDICAL SCIENCES - Communicable Diseases 3962
MEDICAL SCIENCES 3799, see also BIOLOGY 499, DRUG ABUSE AND ALCOHOLISM 1898, GERONTOLOGY AND GERIATRICS 2826, HOSPITALS 3047, NUTRITION AND DIETETICS 4461, OCCUPATIONAL HEALTH AND SAFETY 4474, PHARMACY AND PHARMACOLOGY 4600, PHYSICAL FITNESS AND HYGIENE 4704, PUBLIC HEALTH AND SAFETY 5070
MEDICAL SCIENCES — Abstracting, Bibliographies, Statistics 3911
MEDICAL SCIENCES — Allergology And Immunology 3933
MEDICAL SCIENCES — Anaesthesiology 3942
MEDICAL SCIENCES — Cardiovascular Diseases 3946
MEDICAL SCIENCES — Chiropractic, Homeopathy, Osteopathy 3959
MEDICAL SCIENCES — Communicable Diseases 3962
MEDICAL SCIENCES — Computer Applications 3974
MEDICAL SCIENCES — Dentistry 3977
MEDICAL SCIENCES — Dermatology And Venereology 3998
MEDICAL SCIENCES — Endocrinology 4004
MEDICAL SCIENCES — Experimental Medicine, Laboratory Technique 4012
MEDICAL SCIENCES — Forensic Sciences 4021
MEDICAL SCIENCES — Gastroenterology 4024
MEDICAL SCIENCES — Hematology 4030
MEDICAL SCIENCES — Hypnosis 4035
MEDICAL SCIENCES — Internal Medicine 4035
MEDICAL SCIENCES — Nurses And Nursing 4038
MEDICAL SCIENCES — Obstetrics And Gynecology 4056
MEDICAL SCIENCES — Oncology 4069
MEDICAL SCIENCES — Ophthalmology And Optometry 4083
MEDICAL SCIENCES — Orthopedics And Traumatology 4094
MEDICAL SCIENCES — Otorhinolaryngology 4104
MEDICAL SCIENCES — Pediatrics 4110
MEDICAL SCIENCES — Physical Medicine And Rehabilitation 4122
MEDICAL SCIENCES — Psychiatry And Neurology 4125
MEDICAL SCIENCES — Radiology And Nuclear Medicine 4164
MEDICAL SCIENCES — Respiratory Diseases 4174
MEDICAL SCIENCES — Rheumatology 4179
MEDICAL SCIENCES — Sports Medicine 4183
MEDICAL SCIENCES — Surgery 4186
MEDICAL SCIENCES — Urology And Nephrology 4203
Medical Technicians see MEDICAL SCIENCES 3799
Medieval Studies see HISTORY - History of Europe 2920, see also LITERATURE 3592, PHILOSOPHY 4656
Meditation see PHILOSOPHY 4656, see also RELIGIONS AND THEOLOGY 5145
MEETINGS AND CONGRESSES 4210
MEETINGS AND CONGRESSES — Abstracting, Bibliographies, Statistics 4215
Melkite Rite see RELIGIONS AND THEOLOGY - Roman Catholic 5255
Memory Structures see COMPUTERS - Hardware 1799
Mennonite see RELIGIONS AND THEOLOGY - Other Denominations And Sects 5287
Menopause see MEDICAL SCIENCES - Obstetrics And Gynecology 4056, see also WOMEN'S HEALTH 5952
MEN'S HEALTH 4215
MEN'S INTERESTS 4216
MEN'S STUDIES 4222
Menswear see CLOTHING TRADE 1589
Mental Health see PSYCHOLOGY 4962
Mental Hygiene see PUBLIC HEALTH AND SAFETY 5070
Mental Illness see MEDICAL SCIENCES - Psychiatry And Neurology 4125, see also PSYCHOLOGY 4962

Mental Retardation see EDUCATION - Special Education and Rehabilitation 2136, see also MEDICAL SCIENCES - Psychiatry and Neurology 4125, PSYCHOLOGY 4962
Merchandising see BUSINESS AND ECONOMICS - Marketing and Purchasing 1264
Mergers And Acquisitions see BUSINESS AND ECONOMICS 772, see also LAW - Corporate Law 3355
Messianism see RELIGIONS AND THEOLOGY - Judaic 5218
Metabolism see BIOLOGY - Physiology 681, see also MEDICAL SCIENCES - Endocrinology 4004
Metal Industries see METALLURGY 4223
METALLURGY 4223, see also MINES AND MINING INDUSTRY 4315
METALLURGY — Abstracting, Bibliographies, Statistics 4251
METALLURGY — Welding 4256
Metaphysics see NEW AGE PUBLICATIONS 4450, see also PHILOSOPHY 4656
METEOROLOGY 4259
METEOROLOGY — Abstracting, Bibliographies, Statistics 4276
Methodism see RELIGIONS AND THEOLOGY - Protestant 5225
Metric System see METROLOGY AND STANDARDIZATION 4277
METROLOGY AND STANDARDIZATION 4277
METROLOGY AND STANDARDIZATION — Abstracting, Bibliographies, Statistics 4283
Microbes see BIOLOGY - Microbiology 654, see also MEDICAL SCIENCES - Communicable Diseases 3962
Microbiology see BIOLOGY - Microbiology 654
Microcomputers see COMPUTERS - Microcomputers 1805
Microelectronics see ELECTRONICS 2170
Microfilming see PHOTOGRAPHY 4691
Micropaleontology see PALEONTOLOGY 4528
Microphotography see PHOTOGRAPHY 4691
Microscopy see BIOLOGY - Microscopy 669
Microwaves see ELECTRONICS 2170
Midwifery see MEDICAL SCIENCES - Obstetrics and Gynecology 4056
Migration see POPULATION STUDIES 4924
MILITARY 4283
MILITARY — Abstracting, Bibliographies, Statistics 4314
Military Engineering see ENGINEERING 2237
Military Law see LAW - Military Law 3409
Military Medicine see MEDICAL SCIENCES 3799
Milk see AGRICULTURE - Dairying And Dairy Products 228
Millinery see CLOTHING TRADE 1589
Milling see AGRICULTURE - Feed, Flour and Grain 236
Mineral Resources see EARTH SCIENCES - Geology 1925, see also MINES AND MINING INDUSTRY 4315
Mineralogy see MINES AND MINING INDUSTRY 1925
MINES AND MINING INDUSTRY 4315
MINES AND MINING INDUSTRY — Abstracting, Bibliographies, Statistics 4339
MINES AND MINING INDUSTRY — Computer Applications 4344
Minicomputers see COMPUTERS - Minicomputers 1813
Minorities see ETHNIC INTERESTS 2466, see also POLITICAL SCIENCE - Civil Rights 4877
Minting see NUMISMATICS 4456
Miscarriage see MEDICAL SCIENCES - Obstetrics And Gynecology 4056
Missiles see AERONAUTICS AND SPACE FLIGHT 47
Missionaries And Missions see RELIGIONS AND THEOLOGY 5145
Mobile Homes see HOUSING AND URBAN PLANNING 3078, see also TRANSPORTATION 5723
Modeling see CLOTHING TRADE - Fashions 1596, see also OCCUPATIONS AND CAREERS 4487
Models and Model Building see HOBBIES 3016
Modems see COMPUTERS - Hardware 1799
Molecular Physics see PHYSICS - Nuclear Physics 4763
Mollusca see BIOLOGY - Zoology 689
Monarchy see POLITICAL SCIENCE 4793
Mongoloidism see EDUCATION - Special Education And Rehabilitation 2136, see also MEDICAL SCIENCES - Psychiatry And Neurology 4125
Monitors see COMPUTERS - Hardware 1799
Monotheism see RELIGIONS AND THEOLOGY 5145
Moravian Church see RELIGIONS AND THEOLOGY - Protestant 5225
Mormonism see RELIGIONS AND THEOLOGY - Other Denominations And Sects 5287
Morphology see BIOLOGY 499, see also MEDICAL SCIENCES 3799
Mortality Rate see POPULATION STUDIES - Abstracting, Bibliographies, Statistics 4936
Mortuaries see FUNERALS 2625
Mosses see BIOLOGY - Botany 583
Motels see HOTELS AND RESTAURANTS 3064
Motherhood see LAW - Family And Matrimonial Law 3375, see also WOMEN'S INTERESTS 5953, WOMEN'S STUDIES 5977
MOTION PICTURES 4344
MOTION PICTURES — Abstracting, Bibliographies, Statistics 4363
Motocross see SPORTS AND GAMES - Bicycles And Motorcycles 5560
Motor Scooters see SPORTS AND GAMES - Bicycles and Motorcycles 5560
Motorcycles see SPORTS AND GAMES - Bicycles and Motorcycles 5560
Mountaineering see SPORTS AND GAMES - Outdoor Life 5588
Movies see MOTION PICTURES 4344
Multiple Sclerosis see MEDICAL SCIENCES - Psychiatry and Neurology 4125
Municipal Government see PUBLIC ADMINISTRATION - Municipal Government 5055
Municipal Law see LAW 3215, see also PUBLIC ADMINISTRATION - Municipal Government 5055
Municipal Transportation see TRANSPORTATION 5723
Murder see CRIMINOLOGY AND LAW ENFORCEMENT 1869
Muscular Dystrophy see MEDICAL SCIENCES - Rheumatology 4179
Musculoskeletal System see MEDICAL SCIENCES - Orthopedics And Traumatology 4094
MUSEUMS AND ART GALLERIES 4364
MUSEUMS AND ART GALLERIES — Abstracting, Bibliographies, Statistics 4382
Mushrooms see AGRICULTURE - Crop Production And Soil 192, see also BIOLOGY - Botany 583, GARDENING AND HORTICULTURE 2627
MUSIC 4382
MUSIC — Abstracting, Bibliographies, Statistics 4443

MUSIC — Computer Applications 4445, see also COMPUTERS - Computer Music 1766
Music Therapy see EDUCATION - Special Education and Rehabilitation 2136, see also MUSIC 4382
Musical Instruments see MUSIC 4382
Muslim see RELIGIONS AND THEOLOGY - Islamic 5212
Mutation see BIOLOGY - Biological Chemistry 555, see also BIOLOGY - Genetics 643
Mutual Funds see BUSINESS AND ECONOMICS - Investments 1150
Mycology see BIOLOGY - Botany 583
Mystery And Detective see LITERATURE - Mystery And Detective 3698
Mysticism see NEW AGE PUBLICATIONS 4450, see also PARAPSYCHOLOGY AND OCCULTISM 4542, RELIGIONS AND THEOLOGY 5145
Mythology see FOLKLORE 2544, see also LITERATURE 3592
N M R I see MEDICAL SCIENCES - Radiology And Nuclear Medicine 4164
Narcotics see DRUG ABUSE AND ALCOHOLISM 1898, see also PHARMACY AND PHARMACOLOGY 4600
National Government see PUBLIC ADMINISTRATION 5017
National Guard see MILITARY 4283
National Security see MILITARY 4283, see also POLITICAL SCIENCE 4793
Nationalism see POLITICAL SCIENCE 4793
Native American History see HISTORY - History Of North And South America 2977
Native Medical Sciences see ALTERNATIVE MEDICINE 265
Natural Foods see AGRICULTURE - Crop Production And Soil 192, see also FOOD AND FOOD INDUSTRIES 2553, NUTRITION AND DIETETICS 4461
Natural Gas see PETROLEUM AND GAS 4558
Natural Resources see CONSERVATION 1837, see also ENVIRONMENTAL STUDIES 2399
Naturalization see POLITICAL SCIENCE 4793
Naturopathy see ALTERNATIVE MEDICINE 265
Nautical Arts and Sciences see TRANSPORTATION - Ships and Shipping 5818
Naval Architecture see TRANSPORTATION - Ships and Shipping 5818
Naval Engineering see TRANSPORTATION - Ships and Shipping 5818
Naval Law see LAW - Maritime Law 3408, see also LAW - Military Law 3409
Naval Medicine see MEDICAL SCIENCES 3799
Navigation see AERONAUTICS AND SPACE FLIGHT 47, see also TRANSPORTATION - Air Transport 5753, TRANSPORTATION - Ships And Shipping 5818
Navy see MILITARY 4283
Nazarene see RELIGIONS AND THEOLOGY - Other Denominations And Sects 5287
Needlepoint see NEEDLEWORK 4445
NEEDLEWORK 4445
Nematology see BIOLOGY - Zoology 689
Neonatal Care And Medicine see MEDICAL SCIENCES - Obstetrics And Gynecology 4056
Neoplasms see MEDICAL SCIENCES - Oncology 4069
Nephrology see MEDICAL SCIENCES - Urology and Nephrology 4203
Nerves, Nervous System see MEDICAL SCIENCES - Psychiatry And Neurology 4125
Neurology see MEDICAL SCIENCES - Psychiatry and Neurology 4125
Neurophysiology see MEDICAL SCIENCES - Psychiatry and Neurology 4125
Neuroradiology see MEDICAL SCIENCES - Radiology and Nuclear Medicine 4164
Neurosurgery see MEDICAL SCIENCES - Psychiatry and Neurology 4125, see also MEDICAL SCIENCES - Surgery 4186
NEW AGE PUBLICATIONS 4450, see also PARAPSYCHOLOGY AND OCCULTISM 4542
New Testament see RELIGIONS AND THEOLOGY 5145
Newspaper Business see JOURNALISM 3184, see also PUBLISHING AND BOOK TRADE 5096
Nickel see METALLURGY 4223, see also MINES AND MINING INDUSTRY 4315
Nightclubs see HOTELS AND RESTAURANTS 3064
Noise Control see ENGINEERING - Mechanical Engineering 2379
Noise Pollution see ENVIRONMENTAL STUDIES - Pollution 2446
North American History see HISTORY - History of North and South America 2977
Nuclear Energy see ENERGY - Nuclear Energy 2223
Nuclear Magnetic Resonance Imaging see MEDICAL SCIENCES - Radiology And Nuclear Medicine 4164
Nuclear Medicine see MEDICAL SCIENCES - Radiology and Nuclear Medicine 4164
Nuclear Physics see PHYSICS - Nuclear Physics 4763
Nuclear Warfare see MILITARY 4283
Nudism see PHYSICAL FITNESS AND HYGIENE 4704
NUMISMATICS 4456
NUMISMATICS — Abstracting, Bibliographies, Statistics 4461
Nurseries see GARDENING AND HORTICULTURE - Florist Trade 2652
Nurses And Nursing see MEDICAL SCIENCES - Nurses And Nursing 4038
Nursing Homes see GERONTOLOGY AND GERIATRICS 2826, see also HOSPITALS 3047, SOCIAL SERVICES AND WELFARE 5421
NUTRITION AND DIETETICS 4461, see also FOOD AND FOOD INDUSTRIES 2553, HOSPITALS 3047, PHARMACY AND PHARMACOLOGY 4600, PHYSICAL FITNESS AND HYGIENE 4704
NUTRITION AND DIETETICS — Abstracting, Bibliographies, Statistics 4474
Nuts see AGRICULTURE - Crop Production And Soil 192, see also GARDENING AND HORTICULTURE 2627
Obesity see NUTRITION AND DIETETICS 4461, see also PHYSICAL FITNESS AND HEALTH 4704
Obstetrics And Gynecology see MEDICAL SCIENCES - Obstetrics And Gynecology 4056
Occultism see PARAPSYCHOLOGY AND OCCULTISM 4542
OCCUPATIONAL HEALTH AND SAFETY 4474
OCCUPATIONAL HEALTH AND SAFETY — Abstracting, Bibliographies, Statistics 4486
Occupational Therapy see EDUCATION - Special Education and Rehabilitation 2136, see also MEDICAL SCIENCES 3799
OCCUPATIONS AND CAREERS 4487, see also BUSINESS AND ECONOMICS - Labor and Industrial Relations 1189
OCCUPATIONS AND CAREERS — Abstracting, Bibliographies, Statistics 4497
Ocean Dumping see ENVIRONMENTAL SCIENCES - Pollution 2446
Oceanography see EARTH SCIENCES - Oceanography 1982
Ocular Disorders see MEDICAL SCIENCES - Ophthalmology And Optometry 4083
Odontology see MEDICAL SCIENCES - Dentistry 3977
Office Equipment And Services see BUSINESS AND ECONOMICS - Office Equipment And Services 1298

Oil Spills see ENVIRONMENTAL SCIENCES - Pollution 2446
Oil Wells see PETROLEUM AND GAS 4558
Oils and Fats see CHEMISTRY - Organic Chemistry 1508
Old Age see GERONTOLOGY AND GERIATRICS 2826
Old Testament see RELIGIONS AND THEOLOGY 5145, see also RELIGIONS AND THEOLOGY - Judaic 5218
Olfactory System see MEDICAL SCIENCES - Otorhinolaryngology 4104
Oncology see MEDICAL SCIENCES - Oncology 4069
Online Systems see COMPUTERS - Computer Networks 1767
Onomastics see LINGUISTICS 3485
Ontology see PHILOSOPHY 4656
Opera see MUSIC 4382
Operations Research see BUSINESS AND ECONOMICS - Management 1227, see also COMPUTERS 1720
Ophthalmology and Optometry see MEDICAL SCIENCES - Ophthalmology And Optometry 4083
Opium see DRUG ABUSE AND ALCOHOLISM 1898
Optics see PHYSICS - Optics 4770
Optimization see MATHEMATICS - Computer Applications 3792
Optometry see MEDICAL SCIENCES - Ophthalmology and Optometry 4083
Oral Surgery see MEDICAL SCIENCES - Dentistry 3977
Orchards see AGRICULTURE - Crop Production And Soil 192, see also GARDENING AND HORTICULTURE 2627
Ore see EARTH SCIENCES - Geology 1925, see also MINES AND MINING INDUSTRY 4315
Organic Chemistry see CHEMISTRY - Organic Chemistry 1508
Organic Farming see AGRICULTURE - Crop Production And Soil 192
Organic Foods see NUTRITION AND DIETETICS 4461
Organized Crime see CRIMINOLOGY AND LAW ENFORCEMENT 1869
ORIENTAL STUDIES 4498, see also HISTORY - History of Asia 2908, LINGUISTICS 3485, LITERATURE 3592, PHILOSOPHY 4656
ORIENTAL STUDIES — Abstracting, Bibliographies, Statistics 4515
Ornithology see BIOLOGY - Ornithology 671
Orphanages see SOCIAL SERVICES AND WELFARE 5421
Orthodontics see MEDICAL SCIENCES - Dentistry 3977
Orthopedics And Traumatology see MEDICAL SCIENCES - Orthopedics And Traumatology 4094
Orthotics see MEDICAL SCIENCES - Orthopedics And Traumatology 4094
Osteopathy see MEDICAL SCIENCES - Chiropractic Homeopathy, Osteopathy 3959
Osteoporosis see MEDICAL SCIENCES 3799
Otology see MEDICAL SCIENCES - Otorhinolaryngology 4104
Otorhinolaryngology see MEDICAL SCIENCES - Otorhinolaryngology 4104
Outdoor Life see SPORTS AND GAMES - Outdoor Life 5588
Ozone Depletion see ENVIRONMENTAL STUDIES 2399, see also METEOROLOGY 4259
PACKAGING 4516
PACKAGING — Abstracting, Bibliographies, Statistics 4523
Paganism see RELIGIONS AND THEOLOGY - Other Denominations And Sects 5287
PAINTS AND PROTECTIVE COATINGS 4523
PAINTS AND PROTECTIVE COATINGS — Abstracting, Bibliographies, Statistics 4527
Paleobotany see BIOLOGY - Botany 583
PALEONTOLOGY 4528
PALEONTOLOGY — Abstracting, Bibliographies, Statistics 4534
Paleozoology see PALEONTOLOGY 4528
Palmistry see PARAPSYCHOLOGY AND OCCULTISM 4542
PAPER AND PULP 4535, see also FORESTS AND FORESTRY - Lumber and Wood 2618
PAPER AND PULP — Abstracting, Bibliographies, Statistics 4541
Paper Money see NUMISMATICS 4456, see also PRINTING 4949
Papyrus see PAPER AND PULP 4535
Parachuting see SPORTS AND GAMES 5498
Parakeets see PETS 4591
Paramedics see MEDICAL SCIENCES - Orthopedics And Traumatology 4094
Paramilitary see MILITARY 4283
Paraplegia see MEDICAL SCIENCES - Psychiatry and Neurology 4125
PARAPSYCHOLOGY AND OCCULTISM 4542, see also NEW AGE PUBLICATIONS 4450
PARAPSYCHOLOGY AND OCCULTISM — Abstracting, Bibliographies, Statistics 4547
Parasitology see BIOLOGY 499, see also MEDICAL SCIENCES - Communicable Diseases 3962, PUBLIC HEALTH AND SAFETY 5070
Parent Teacher Associations see EDUCATION - School Organization and Administration 2126
Parenting see CHILDREN AND YOUTH - About 1529
Parkinson's Disease see MEDICAL SCIENCES - Psychiatry And Neurology 4125
Parks and Recreation Areas see CONSERVATION 1837, see also SPORTS AND GAMES - Outdoor Life 5588, TRAVEL AND TOURISM 5848
PATENTS, TRADEMARKS AND COPYRIGHTS 4547
PATENTS, TRADEMARKS AND COPYRIGHTS — Abstracting, Bibliographies, Statistics 4557
Pathology see MEDICAL SCIENCES 3799
Paving see BUILDING AND CONSTRUCTION 716, see also TRANSPORTATION - Roads and Traffic 5811
Payroll see BUSINESS AND ECONOMICS - Accounting 903, see also BUSINESS AND ECONOMICS - Public Finance and Taxation 1335
Peacekeeping see MILITARY 4283, see also POLITICAL SCIENCE - International Relations 4889
Pediatrics see MEDICAL SCIENCES - Pediatrics 4110
Penal Law see LAW - Criminal Law 3367
Penology see CRIMINOLOGY AND LAW ENFORCEMENT 1869
Pensions see BUSINESS AND ECONOMICS - Labor and Industrial Relations 1189, see also INSURANCE 3133, SOCIAL SERVICES AND WELFARE 5421
Pentecostalism see RELIGIONS AND THEOLOGY - Other Denominations And Sects 5287
Percussion Instruments see MUSIC 4382
Performing Arts see DANCE 1893, see also MOTION PICTURES 4344, MUSIC 4382, THEATER 5704
Perfumes And Cosmetics see BEAUTY CULTURE - Perfumes And Cosmetics 440

CROSS-INDEX TO SUBJECTS

Perinatal Care And Medicine see MEDICAL SCIENCES - Obstetrics And Gynecology 4056
Periodontics see MEDICAL SCIENCES - Dentistry 3977
Peripherals see COMPUTERS - Hardware 1799
Personal Computers see COMPUTERS - Personal Computers 1814
Personal Growth see NEW AGE PUBLICATIONS 4450, see also PSYCHOLOGY 4962
Personnel Management see BUSINESS AND ECONOMICS - Personnel Management 1304
Pest Control see AGRICULTURE 76, see also BIOLOGY - Entomology 628, PUBLIC HEALTH AND SAFETY 5070
Pesticides see AGRICULTURE - Crop Production And Soil 192, see also ENGINEERING - Chemical Engineering 2277, ENVIRONMENTAL STUDIES - Toxicology And Environmental Safety 2452
PETROLEUM AND GAS 4558
PETROLEUM AND GAS — Abstracting, Bibliographies, Statistics 4587
Petrology see EARTH SCIENCES - Geology 1925
PETS 4591
Pewter see METALLURGY 4223
PHARMACY AND PHARMACOLOGY 4600, see also MEDICAL SCIENCES 3799
PHARMACY AND PHARMACOLOGY — Abstracting, Bibliographies, Statistics 4641
PHARMACY AND PHARMACOLOGY — Computer Applications 4643
Phenomenology see PHILOSOPHY 4656
Philanthropy see SOCIAL SERVICES AND WELFARE 5421
PHILATELY 4643
PHILATELY — Abstracting, Bibliographies, Statistics 4656
Philology see CLASSICAL STUDIES 1578, see also LINGUISTICS 3485
PHILOSOPHY 4656
PHILOSOPHY — Abstracting, Bibliographies, Statistics 4690
Phobias see MEDICAL SCIENCES - Psychiatry And Neurology 4125
Phonetics see LINGUISTICS 3485
Phonographs see MUSIC 4382, see also SOUND RECORDING AND REPRODUCTION 5494
Photogrammetry see GEOGRAPHY 2794, see also PHOTOGRAPHY 4691
Photographic Surveying see ENGINEERING - Civil Engineering 2293
PHOTOGRAPHY 4691, see also MOTION PICTURES 4344
PHOTOGRAPHY — Abstracting, Bibliographies, Statistics 4704
PHOTOGRAPHY — Computer Applications 4704
Photomechanical Processing see PRINTING 4949
Phrenology see PARAPSYCHOLOGY AND OCCULTISM 4542
Physiatry see MEDICAL SCIENCES - Physical Medicine And Rehabilitation 4122
Physical Anthropology see ANTHROPOLOGY 272
Physical Chemistry see CHEMISTRY - Physical Chemistry 1520
Physical Education see EDUCATION - Teaching Methods and Curriculum 2146, see also PHYSICAL FITNESS AND HYGIENE 4704, SPORTS AND GAMES 5498
PHYSICAL FITNESS AND HYGIENE 4704
PHYSICAL FITNESS AND HYGIENE — Abstracting, Bibliographies, Statistics 4718
Physical Medicine And Rehabilitation see MEDICAL SCIENCES - Physical Medicine And Rehabilitation 4122
Physical Rehabilitation see MEDICAL SCIENCES - Physical Medicine And Rehabilitation 4122
Physical Therapy see MEDICAL SCIENCES - Physical Medicine And Rehabilitation 4122
Physically Impaired see HANDICAPPED - Physically Impaired 2854
Physician Assistants see MEDICAL SCIENCES 3799
Physicians see MEDICAL SCIENCES 3799
PHYSICS 4718
PHYSICS — Abstracting, Bibliographies, Statistics 4749
PHYSICS — Computer Applications 4754
PHYSICS — Electricity 4754
PHYSICS — Heat 4755
PHYSICS — Mechanics 4758
PHYSICS — Nuclear Physics 4763
PHYSICS — Optics 4770
PHYSICS — Sound 4780
Physiology see BIOLOGY - Physiology 681
Phytology see BIOLOGY - Botany 583
Phytopathology see BIOLOGY - Botany 583
Piano see MUSIC 4382
Pigeons see PETS 4591
Piloting see AERONAUTICS AND SPACE FLIGHT 47, see also TRANSPORTATION - Air Transport 5753
Pituitary Disorders see MEDICAL SCIENCES - Endocrinology 4004
Planned Parenthood see BIRTH CONTROL 713
Plant Breeding see AGRICULTURE - Crop Production and Soil 192, see also BIOLOGY - Botany 583, GARDENING AND HORTICULTURE 2627
Plasma see MEDICAL SCIENCES - Hematology 4030
Plasma Physics see PHYSICS 4718
Plastic Surgery see MEDICAL SCIENCES - Surgery 4186
PLASTICS 4783, see also CHEMISTRY - Physical Chemistry 1520, ENGINEERING - Chemical Engineering 2277
PLASTICS — Abstracting, Bibliographies, Statistics 4792
PLASTICS — Computer Applications 4793
Platinum see JEWELRY, CLOCKS AND WATCHES 3179, see also METALLURGY 4223
Platonism see PHILOSOPHY 4656
Plays see LITERATURE 3592, see also THEATER 5704
Pleurisy see MEDICAL SCIENCES - Respiratory Diseases 4174
Plumbing see HEATING, PLUMBING AND REFRIGERATION 2862
Pneumonia see MEDICAL SCIENCES - Respiratory Diseases 4174
Podiatry see MEDICAL SCIENCES 3799
Poetry see LITERATURE - Poetry 3700
Police see CRIMINOLOGY AND LAW ENFORCEMENT 1869
Poliomyelitis see MEDICAL SCIENCES - Psychiatry and Neurology 4125
Political Asylum see POLITICAL SCIENCE - Civil Rights 4877, see also POLITICAL SCIENCE - International Relations 4889
Political Reviews see LITERARY AND POLITICAL REVIEWS 3555
POLITICAL SCIENCE 4793, see also LITERARY AND POLITICAL REVIEWS 3555, PUBLIC ADMINISTRATION 5017
POLITICAL SCIENCE — Abstracting, Bibliographies, Statistics 4873
POLITICAL SCIENCE — Civil Rights 4877
POLITICAL SCIENCE — International Relations 4889
Pollution see ENVIRONMENTAL STUDIES - Pollution 2446
Polo see SPORTS AND GAMES - Horses And Horsemanship 5579
Polyandry see ANTHROPOLOGY 272, see also MATRIMONY 3796
Polygamy see ANTHROPOLOGY 272, see also MATRIMONY 3796
Polymers see CHEMISTRY 1448, see also ENGINEERING - Chemical Engineering 2277
Polynesian History see HISTORY - History Of Australasia And Other Areas 2917
Polyurethane see PAINTS AND PROTECTIVE COATINGS 4523, see also PLASTICS 4783
Ponies see SPORTS AND GAMES - Horses And Horsemanship 5579
Popular Music see MUSIC 4382
POPULATION STUDIES 4924
POPULATION STUDIES — Abstracting, Bibliographies, Statistics 4936
Ports see TRANSPORTATION - Ships and Shipping 5818
Portuguese LANGUAGE - Study and Teaching see LINGUISTICS 3485
Positivism see PHILOSOPHY 4656
Post-colonial History see HISTORY - History Of Africa 2902, see also HISTORY - History Of Asia 2908, HISTORY - History Of Australasia And Other Areas 2917, HISTORY - History Of North And South America 2977
Postage Stamps see COMMUNICATIONS - Postal Affairs 1676, see also PHILATELY 4643
Postal Affairs see COMMUNICATIONS - Postal Affairs 1676
Postcards see PHILATELY 4643
Postmarks see COMMUNICATIONS - Postal Affairs 1676, see also PHILATELY 4643
Pottery see CERAMICS, GLASS AND POTTERY 5145
Poultry And Livestock see AGRICULTURE - Poultry And Livestock 241
Poverty see BUSINESS AND ECONOMICS - International Development And Assistance 1136, see also SOCIAL SERVICES AND WELFARE 5421, SOCIOLOGY 5459
Power Plants see ENERGY 2197
Pragmatism see PHILOSOPHY 4656
Prayer see RELIGIONS AND THEOLOGY 5145
Preaching see RELIGIONS AND THEOLOGY 5145
Precipitation see METEOROLOGY 4259
Precision Mechanics see INSTRUMENTS 3128
Prefabricated Houses see BUILDING AND CONSTRUCTION 716
Pregnancy see MEDICAL SCIENCES - Obstetrics And Gynecology 4056
Prenatal Care And Medicine see MEDICAL SCIENCES - Obstetrics And Gynecology 4056
Presbyterianism see RELIGIONS AND THEOLOGY - Protestant 5225
Preschool Education see EDUCATION 1999
Presents see GIFTWARE AND TOYS 2841
Preservation And Conservation see ARCHITECTURE 342, see also ART 364
Preventive Medicine see PUBLIC HEALTH AND SAFETY 5070
Primary Education see EDUCATION 1999
Primatology see BIOLOGY - Zoology 689
PRINTING 4949
PRINTING — Abstracting, Bibliographies, Statistics 4961
PRINTING — Computer Applications 4961, see also COMPUTERS - Computer Graphics 1758
Prisons see CRIMINOLOGY AND LAW ENFORCEMENT 1869
Private Law see LAW - Civil Law 3345
Private Schools see EDUCATION - Guides to Schools and Colleges 2087, see also EDUCATION - School Organization and Administration 2126
Pro-Choice see BIRTH CONTROL 713, see also POLITICAL SCIENCE - Civil Rights 4877
Pro-Life see BIRTH CONTROL 713, see also POLITICAL SCIENCE - Civil Rights 4877
Probability see MATHEMATICS 3745
Probate see LAW - Estate Planning 3373
Probation And Parole see CRIMINOLOGY AND LAW ENFORCEMENT 1869
Proctology see MEDICAL SCIENCES - Gastroenterology 4024
Produce see FOOD AND FOOD INDUSTRIES 2553
Produce Marketing see AGRICULTURE - Agricultural Economics 169
Product Finishing see PAINTS AND PROTECTIVE COATINGS 4523
Production of Goods And Services see BUSINESS AND ECONOMICS - Production of Goods And Services 1317
Professional Recruiting see OCCUPATIONS AND CAREERS 4487
Programmed Instruction see EDUCATION - Teaching Methods and Curriculum 2146
Programming, Automatic see COMPUTERS - Computer Programming 1771
Proofreading see JOURNALISM 3184, see also PRINTING 4949
Prospecting see EARTH SCIENCES - Geology 1925, see also MINES AND MINING INDUSTRY 4315
Prostate see MEDICAL SCIENCES - Urology And Nephrology 4203
Prosthetics see MEDICAL SCIENCES - Orthopedics and Traumatology 4094
Protective Coatings see PAINTS AND PROTECTIVE COATINGS 4523
Protestantism see RELIGIONS AND THEOLOGY - Protestant 5225
Protozoology see BIOLOGY - Zoology 689
Psoriasis see MEDICAL SCIENCES - Dermatology And Venereology 3998
Psychiatry And Neurology see MEDICAL SCIENCES - Psychiatry And Neurology 4125
Psychic Phenomena see PARAPSYCHOLOGY AND OCCULTISM 4542
Psychical Research see PARAPSYCHOLOGY AND OCCULTISM 4542
Psychoanalysis see PSYCHOLOGY 4962
Psychological Testing see PSYCHOLOGY 4962
PSYCHOLOGY 4962
PSYCHOLOGY — Abstracting, Bibliographies, Statistics 5016
Psychopathology see PSYCHOLOGY 4962
Psychopathology see MEDICAL SCIENCES - Psychiatry And Neurology 4125
Psychosomatic Medicine see MEDICAL SCIENCES 3799
Psychotherapy see MEDICAL SCIENCES - Psychiatry and Neurology 4125
PUBLIC ADMINISTRATION 5017, see also POLITICAL SCIENCE 4793
PUBLIC ADMINISTRATION — Abstracting, Bibliographies, Statistics 5049
PUBLIC ADMINISTRATION — Computer Applications 5055
PUBLIC ADMINISTRATION — Municipal Government 5055
Public Affairs see POLITICAL SCIENCE 4793, see also PUBLIC ADMINISTRATION 5017, SOCIAL SCIENCES 5382

CROSS-INDEX TO SUBJECTS

Public Finance, Taxation see BUSINESS AND ECONOMICS - Public Finance, Taxation 1335
PUBLIC HEALTH AND SAFETY 5070, see also DRUG ABUSE AND ALCOHOLISM 1898, ENVIRONMENTAL STUDIES 2399, FIRE PREVENTION 2517, HOSPITALS 3047, MEDICAL SCIENCES 3799, OCCUPATIONAL HEALTH AND SAFETY 4474
PUBLIC HEALTH AND SAFETY — Abstracting, Bibliographies, Statistics 5093
Public Law see LAW - Constitutional Law 3354
Public Relations see ADVERTISING AND PUBLIC RELATIONS 28, see also ADVERTISING AND PUBLIC RELATIONS 28
Public Transportation see TRANSPORTATION 5723
Public Utilities see PETROLEUM AND GAS 4558, see also PUBLIC ADMINISTRATION 5017
Public Welfare see SOCIAL SERVICES AND WELFARE 5421
Public Works see BUILDING AND CONSTRUCTION 716, see also ENGINEERING - Civil Engineering 2293, HOUSING AND URBAN PLANNING 3078, PUBLIC ADMINISTRATION 5017
Publicity see ADVERTISING AND PUBLIC RELATIONS 28
PUBLISHING AND BOOK TRADE 5096, see also BIBLIOGRAPHIES 457, LIBRARY AND INFORMATION SCIENCES 3416, PATENTS, TRADEMARKS AND COPYRIGHTS 4547, PRINTING 4949
PUBLISHING AND BOOK TRADE — Abstracting, Bibliographies, Statistics 5119
PUBLISHING AND BOOK TRADE — Computer Applications 5123
Pulmonary Diseases see MEDICAL SCIENCES - Respiratory Diseases 4174
Pulp see PAPER AND PULP 4535
Puppets see HOBBIES 3016, see also THEATER 5704
Puzzles see SPORTS AND GAMES 5498
Pyrotechnics see ENGINEERING - Chemical Engineering 2277, see also FIRE PREVENTION 2517
Quakers see RELIGIONS AND THEOLOGY - Other Denominations And Sects 5287
Quality Control see BUSINESS AND ECONOMICS - Management 1227, see also METROLOGY AND STANDARDIZATION 4277
Quantum Chemistry see CHEMISTRY - Physical Chemistry 1520
Quantum Mechanics see PHYSICS 4718
Quarries see MINES AND MINING INDUSTRY 4315
Quilting see NEEDLEWORK 4445
Qur'an see RELIGIONS AND THEOLOGY - Islamic 5212
Race Relations see POLITICAL SCIENCE - Civil Rights 4877, see also SOCIOLOGY 5459
Racing see SPORTS AND GAMES - Horses and Horsemanship 5579, see also TRANSPORTATION - Automobiles 5765
Racquetball see SPORTS AND GAMES - Ball Games 5540
Radar see COMMUNICATIONS 1647
Radiation see ASTRONOMY 421, see also BIOLOGY - Biophysics 572, CHEMISTRY - Physical Chemistry 1520, MEDICAL SCIENCES - Radiology and Nuclear Medicine 4164, PHYSICS - Nuclear Physics 4763
Radiation Chemistry see CHEMISTRY 1448
Radio see COMMUNICATIONS - Radio 1678
Radio Advertising see ADVERTISING AND PUBLIC RELATIONS 28, see also COMMUNICATIONS - Radio 1678
Radioactive Waste see ENERGY - Nuclear Energy 2223, see also ENVIRONMENTAL STUDIES - Waste Management 2458
Radiobiology see BIOLOGY 499
Radiocarbon see PHYSICS - Nuclear Physics 4763
Radiological Contamination see ENERGY - Nuclear Energy 2223, see also ENVIRONMENTAL STUDIES - Waste Management 2458
Radiology And Nuclear Medicine see MEDICAL SCIENCES - Radiology And Nuclear Medicine 4164
Railroad Engineering see TRANSPORTATION - Railroads 5799
Railroads see TRANSPORTATION - Railroads 5799
Railway Ties see FORESTS AND FORESTRY - Lumber and Wood 2618, see also TRANSPORTATION - Railroads 5799
Rainfall see METEOROLOGY 4259
Rainforest see CONSERVATION 1837, see also ENVIRONMENTAL STUDIES 2399, FOREST AND FORESTRY 2597
Ramakrishna see RELIGIONS AND THEOLOGY - Hindu 5211
Rape see CRIMINOLOGY AND LAW ENFORCEMENT 1869, see also MEDICAL SCIENCES - Psychiatry And Neurology 4125
Rare Earths see CHEMISTRY - Inorganic Chemistry 1505
Rationalism see PHILOSOPHY 4656
Reading Guides and Aids see ABSTRACTING AND INDEXING SERVICES 1, see also BIBLIOGRAPHIES 457, EDUCATION - Teaching Methods and Curriculum 2146, LIBRARY AND INFORMATION SCIENCES 3416
REAL ESTATE 5124, see also BUILDING AND CONSTRUCTION 716, BUSINESS AND ECONOMICS 772, HOUSING AND URBAN PLANNING 3078, LAW 3373
REAL ESTATE — Abstracting, Bibliographies, Statistics 5144
Realism see ART 364, see also LITERATURE 3592, PHILOSOPHY 4656
Recorded Music see MUSIC 4382, see also SOUND RECORDING AND REPRODUCTION 5494
Recreation see DANCE 1893, see also HOBBIES 3016, LEISURE AND RECREATION 3413, SPORTS AND GAMES 5498
Recreation Areas see CONSERVATION 1837, see also TRAVEL AND TOURISM 5848
Recreational Vehicles see TRANSPORTATION - Automobiles 5765
Recycling see ENVIRONMENTAL STUDIES - Waste Management 2458
Red Cross see SOCIAL SERVICES AND WELFARE 5421
Reed Instruments see MUSIC 4382
Reference Books see ENCYCLOPEDIAS AND GENERAL ALMANACS 2194
Refineries see PETROLEUM AND GAS 4558
Refinishing see HOW-TO AND DO-IT-YOURSELF 3102, see also PAINTS AND PROTECTIVE COATINGS 4523
Reformed Church see RELIGIONS AND THEOLOGY - Protestant 5225
Refractories see CERAMICS, GLASS AND POTTERY 1439
Refrigeration see HEATING, PLUMBING AND REFRIGERATION 2862, see also PHYSICS - Heat 4755
Refugees see POLITICAL SCIENCE 4793, see also POLITICAL SCIENCE - International Relations 4889
Refuse see ENVIRONMENTAL STUDIES - Waste Management 2458
Regional Planning see HOUSING AND URBAN PLANNING 3078

Rehabilitation see EDUCATION - Special Education and Rehabilitation 2136, see also MEDICAL SCIENCES - Physical Medicine And Rehabilitation 4122, SOCIAL SERVICES AND WELFARE 5421
Reincarnation see NEW AGE PUBLICATIONS 445C, see also PARAPSYCHOLOGY AND OCCULTISM 4542, RELIGIONS AND THEOLOGY 5145
RELIGIONS AND THEOLOGY 5145
RELIGIONS AND THEOLOGY — Abstracting, Bibliographies, Statistics 5204
RELIGIONS AND THEOLOGY — Buddhist 5206
RELIGIONS AND THEOLOGY — Eastern Orthodox 5209
RELIGIONS AND THEOLOGY — Hindu 5211
RELIGIONS AND THEOLOGY — Islamic 5212
RELIGIONS AND THEOLOGY — Judaic 5218
RELIGIONS AND THEOLOGY — Other Denominations And Sects 5287
RELIGIONS AND THEOLOGY — Protestant 5225
RELIGIONS AND THEOLOGY — Roman Catholic 5255
Religious Freedom see POLITICAL SCIENCE 4793, see also POLITICAL SCIENCE - Civil Rights 4877
Religious History see RELIGIONS AND THEOLOGY 5145
Renal Disease see MEDICAL SCIENCES - Urology And Nephrology 4203
Repairs see HOW-TO AND DO-IT YOURSELF 3102
Reproduction and Fertility see BIOLOGY 499
Reproductive System see MEDICAL SCIENCES - Obstetrics And Gynecology 4056, see also MEDICAL SCIENCES - Urology And Nephrology 4203
Reprography see PHOTOGRAPHY 4691
Reptiles see BIOLOGY - Zoology 689
Research and Development see TECHNOLOGY: COMPREHENSIVE WORKS 5663
Reservoirs see WATER RESOURCES 5933
Resins see PLASTICS 4783
Resorts see HOTELS AND RESTAURANTS 3064, see also TRAVEL AND TOURISM 5848
Respiratory Diseases see MEDICAL SCIENCES - Respiratory Diseases 4174
Restaurants see HOTELS AND RESTAURANTS 3064
Retailing see BUSINESS AND ECONOMICS - Marketing and Purchasing 1264
Retardation (Retarded) see EDUCATION - Special Education And Rehabilitation 2136, see also MEDICAL SCIENCES - Psychiatry And Neurology 4125
Retirement see BUSINESS AND ECONOMICS - Banking And Finance 920, see also GERONTOLOGY AND GERIATRICS 2826
Rheology see PHYSICS - Mechanics 4758
Rheumatology see MEDICAL SCIENCES - Rheumatology 4179
Rhinology see MEDICAL SCIENCES - Otorhinolaryngology 4104
Right-to-Life Movement see BIRTH CONTROL 713, see also POLITICAL SCIENCE - Civil Rights 4877
Roads And Traffic see TRANSPORTATION - Roads And Traffic 5811
Robbery see CRIMINOLOGY AND LAW ENFORCEMENT 1869
Robotics see COMPUTERS - Robotics 1825, see also COMPUTERS - Artificial Intelligence 1741
Rock see EARTH SCIENCES - Geology 1925, see also MINES AND MINING INDUSTRY 4315
Rock and Roll see MUSIC 4382
Rock Climbing see SPORTS AND GAMES - Outdoor Life 5588
Rockets see AERONAUTICS AND SPACE FLIGHT 47
Rodeo see SPORTS AND GAMES - Horses and Horsemanship 5579
Roentgenology see MEDICAL SCIENCES - Radiology And Nuclear Medicine 4164
Roller Skating see SPORTS AND GAMES 5498
Roman Catholicism see RELIGIONS AND THEOLOGY - Roman Catholic 5255
Roofing see BUILDING AND CONSTRUCTION 716
RUBBER 5299, see also ENGINEERING - Chemical Engineering 2277, PLASTICS 4783
RUBBER — Abstracting, Bibliographies, Statistics 5303
Rugby see SPORTS AND GAMES - Ball Games 5540
Running see PHYSICAL FITNESS AND HYGIENE 4704, see also SPORTS AND GAMES 5498
S T D (Sexually Transmitted Diseases) see MEDICAL SCIENCES - Communicable Diseases 3962, see also MEDICAL SCIENCES - Dermatology And Venereology 3998
Safety Education see BUSINESS AND ECONOMICS - Labor and Industrial Relations 1189, see also FIRE PREVENTION 2517, OCCUPATIONAL HEALTH AND SAFETY 4474, PUBLIC HEALTH AND SAFETY 5070, TRANSPORTATION - Roads and Traffic 5811
Sailboarding see SPORTS AND GAMES - Outdoor Life 5588
Sailing see SPORTS AND GAMES - Boats and Boating 5568
Salaries see BUSINESS AND ECONOMICS - Labor And Industrial Relations 1189, see also BUSINESS AND ECONOMICS - Personnel Management 1304
Sales Promotion see ADVERTISING AND PUBLIC RELATIONS 28
Salesmanship see BUSINESS AND ECONOMICS - Marketing and Purchasing 1264
Salvation Army see RELIGIONS AND THEOLOGY - Other Denominations And Sects 5287, see also SOCIAL SERVICES AND WELFARE 5421
Samsara see RELIGIONS AND THEOLOGY - Buddhist 5206, see also RELIGIONS AND THEOLOGY - Hindu 5211
Sanitary Engineering see PUBLIC HEALTH AND SAFETY 5070
Sanitation see ENGINEERING - Civil Engineering 2293, see also ENVIRONMENTAL STUDIES - Waste Management 2458, PHYSICAL FITNESS AND HYGIENE 4704, PUBLIC HEALTH AND SAFETY 5070
Satanism see PARAPSYCHOLOGY AND OCCULTISM 4542, see also RELIGIONS AND THEOLOGY - Other Denominations And Sects 5287
Savings and Loan see BUSINESS AND ECONOMICS - Banking and Finance 920
Scales see INSTRUMENTS 3128, see also METROLOGY AND STANDARDIZATION 4277
Schizophrenia see MEDICAL SCIENCES - Psychiatry And Neurology 4125
Scholarships see EDUCATION - Higher Education 2095
Scholasticism see PHILOSOPHY 4656
School Organization And Administration see EDUCATION - School Organization And Administration 2126
Science Fiction, Fantasy, Horror see LITERATURE - Science Fiction, Fantasy, Horror 3723
SCIENCES: COMPREHENSIVE WORKS 5304
SCIENCES: COMPREHENSIVE WORKS — Abstracting, Bibliographies, Statistics 5371
SCIENCES: COMPREHENSIVE WORKS — Computer Applications 5376

CROSS-INDEX TO SUBJECTS

Scientific Jurisprudence see MEDICAL SCIENCES - Forensic Sciences 4021
Scientology see RELIGIONS AND THEOLOGY - Other Denominations And Sects 5287
Scooters see SPORTS AND GAMES - Bicycles and Motorcycles 5560
Scouting see CHILDREN AND YOUTH - About 1529, see also CHIDREN AND YOUTH - For 1548
Screen Printing see PRINTING 4949
Scuba Diving see LEISURE AND RECREATION 3413, see also SPORTS AND GAMES - Outdoor Life 5588
Sculpture see ART 364
Sealants see PAINTS AND PROTECTIVE COATINGS 4523
Seaweed see BIOLOGY - Botany 583, see also EARTH SCIENCES - Oceanography 1982
Secondary Education see EDUCATION 1999
Securities see BUSINESS AND ECONOMICS - Investments 1150
Security see CRIMINOLOGY AND LAW ENFORCEMENT - Security 1890
Sediment Data see ENGINEERING - Hydraulic Engineering 2373
Sedimentology see EARTH SCIENCES - Geophysics 1964
Seeds see AGRICULTURE - Crop Production and Soil 192
Segregation see POLITICAL SCIENCE - Civil Rights 4877
Seismology see EARTH SCIENCES - Geophysics 1964
Self-help see NEW AGE PUBLICATIONS 4450, see also PSYCHOLOGY 4962
Self-instruction see EDUCATION - Adult Education 2075
Selling see ADVERTISING AND PUBLIC RELATIONS 28, see also BUSINESS AND ECONOMICS - Marketing and Purchasing 1264
Semantics see LINGUISTICS 3485
Semiconductors see PHYSICS - Electricity 4754
Seminaries see EDUCATION - Higher Education 2095, see also RELIGIONS AND THEOLOGY 5145
Senior Citizens see GERONTOLOGY AND GERIATRICS 2826
Separatist Movement see POLITICAL SCIENCE - International Relations 4889
Sephardim see ETHNIC INTERESTS 2466, see also RELIGION AND THEOLOGY - Judaic 5218
Serology see MEDICAL SCIENCES - Allergology And Immunology 3933
Service Stations see TRANSPORTATION - Automobiles 5765
Sewage And Waste Treatment see ENVIRONMENTAL STUDIES - Waste Management 2458, see also PUBLIC ADMINISTRATION 5017, PUBLIC HEALTH AND SAFETY 5070, WATER RESOURCES 5933
Sewing see CLOTHING TRADE - Fashions 1596, see also NEEDLEWORK 4445
Sex Education see PHYSICAL FITNESS AND HYGIENE 4704
Sexology see MEDICAL SCIENCES 3799, see also PSYCHOLOGY 4962, SOCIAL SCIENCES 5382
Sexual Dysfunctions see MEDICAL SCIENCES - Psychiatry And Neurology 4125
Sexual Harassment see BUSINESS AND ECONOMICS - Labor And Industrial Relations 1189, see also LAW 3215, POLITICAL SCIENCE - Civil Rights 4877
Sexually Transmitted Diseases see MEDICAL SCIENCES - Communicable Diseases 3962, see also MEDICAL SCIENCES - Dermatology And Venereology 3998
Shamanism see ANTHROPOLOGY 272, see also RELIGIONS AND THEOLOGY - Other Denominations And Sects 5287
Shari'ah see LAW 3215, see also RELIGIONS AND THEOLOGY - Islamic 5212
Sheet Metal see METALLURGY 4223
Shellac see PAINTS AND PROTECTIVE COATINGS 4523
Shi'ism see RELIGIONS AND THEOLOGY - Islamic 5212
Shintoism see RELIGIONS AND THEOLOGY - Other Denominations And Sects 5287
Shipbuilding see TRANSPORTATION - Ships and Shipping 5818
Shipping see COMMUNICATIONS - Postal Affairs 1676, see also TRANSPORTATION 5723
Ships And Shipping see TRANSPORTATION - Ships And Shipping 5818
Shivism see RELIGIONS AND THEOLOGY - Hindu 5211
SHOES AND BOOTS 5378, see also LEATHER AND FUR INDUSTRIES 3410
SHOES AND BOOTS — Abstracting, Bibliographies, Statistics 5380
Shooting see SPORTS AND GAMES - Outdoor Life 5588
Shorthand see BUSINESS AND ECONOMICS - Office Equipment and Services 1298
Shortwave see COMMUNICATIONS - Radio 1678
Shortwave Electronics see ELECTRONICS 2170
Sick Building Syndrome see OCCUPATIONAL HEALTH AND SAFETY 4474
Sickle-cell Anemia see MEDICAL SCIENCES - Hematology 4030
Siding see BUILDING AND CONSTRUCTION 716
Sign Manufacturing see ADVERTISING AND PUBLIC RELATIONS 28
Sikhism see RELIGIONS AND THEOLOGY - Other Denominations And Sects 5287
Silicates see CERAMICS, GLASS AND POTTERY 1439
Silicosis see MEDICAL SCIENCES 3799
Silk see CLOTHING TRADE 1589, see also TEXTILE INDUSTRIES AND FABRICS 5689
Silver see JEWELRY, CLOCKS AND WATCHES 3179, see also METALLURGY 4223, MINES AND MINING INDUSTRY 4315
Silviculture see FORESTS AND FORESTRY 2597
SINGLES' INTERESTS AND LIFESTYLES 5380
Site Selection see HOUSING AND URBAN PLANNING 3078, see also REAL ESTATE 5124
Skating see SPORTS AND GAMES 5498
Skeet Shooting see SPORTS AND GAMES - Outdoor Life 5588
Skepticism see PHILOSOPHY 4656
Skiing see SPORTS AND GAMES - Outdoor Life 5588
Skin Care see BEAUTY CULTURE 435
Skin Disorders see MEDICAL SCIENCES - Dermatology And Venereology 3998
Slavery see HISTORY 2872, see also POLITICAL SCIENCE - Civil Rights 4877, SOCIOLOGY 5459
Slavonic Languages - Study and Teaching see LINGUISTICS 3485
Small Business see BUSINESS AND ECONOMICS - Small Business 1369
Smoking see DRUG ABUSE AND ALCOHOLISM 1898, see also PHYSICAL FITNESS AND HYGIENE 4704, PUBLIC HEALTH AND SAFETY 5070, TOBACCO 5719
Snack Foods see FOOD AND FOOD INDUSTRIES - Bakers and Confectioners 2586
Snowmobiles see SPORTS AND GAMES - Outdoor Life 5588
Soap see BEAUTY CULTURE - Perfumes and Cosmetics 440
Soccer see SPORTS AND GAMES - Ball Games 5540
Social Insurance see INSURANCE 3133, see also SOCIAL SERVICES AND WELFARE 5421
Social Medicine see PUBLIC HEALTH AND SAFETY 5070

Social Psychology see PSYCHOLOGY 4962, see also SOCIOLOGY 5459
SOCIAL SCIENCES: COMPREHENSIVE WORKS 5382
SOCIAL SCIENCES: COMPREHENSIVE WORKS — Abstracting, Bibliographies, Statistics 5419
Social Security see INSURANCE 3133, see also SOCIAL SERVICES AND WELFARE 5421
SOCIAL SERVICES AND WELFARE 5421
SOCIAL SERVICES AND WELFARE — Abstracting, Bibliographies, Statistics 5456
Socialism see BUSINESS AND ECONOMICS - Economic Systems and Theories, Economic History 1090, see also POLITICAL SCIENCE 4793
Society Of Friends see RELIGIONS AND THEOLOGY - Other Denominations And Sects 5287
SOCIOLOGY 5459, see also POPULATION STUDIES 4924
SOCIOLOGY — Abstracting, Bibliographies, Statistics 5491
SOCIOLOGY — Computer Applications 5493
Soft Drinks see BEVERAGES 443
Softball see SPORTS AND GAMES - Ball Games 5540
Software see COMPUTERS - Software 1827
Soil see AGRICULTURE - Crop Production and Soil 192, see also CONSERVATION 1837, ENGINEERING - Civil Engineering 2293
Soil Pollution see ENVIRONMENTAL STUDIES - Pollution 2446
Solar Energy see ENERGY. - Solar Energy 2234
Soldering see METALLURGY - Welding 4256
Soldiers see MILITARY 4283
Solid Waste see ENVIRONMENTAL STUDIES - Waste Management 2458
Somatology see ANTHROPOLOGY 272
Sonography see MEDICAL SCIENCES - Radiology And Nuclear Medicine 4164, see also PHYSICS - Sound 4780
Sophism see PHILOSOPHY 4656
Sororities see COLLEGE AND ALUMNI 1612
Sound see PHYSICS - Sound 4780
SOUND RECORDING AND REPRODUCTION 5494
SOUND RECORDING AND REPRODUCTION — Abstracting, Bibliographies, Statistics 5498
South American History see HISTORY - History of North and South America 2977
Souvenirs see GIFTWARE AND TOYS 2841
Space Flight see AERONAUTICS AND SPACE FLIGHT 47
Spacecraft see AERONAUTICS AND SPACE FLIGHT 47
Spanish Language - Study and Teaching see LINGUISTICS 3485
Spearfishing see SPORTS AND GAMES - Outdoor Life 5588
Special Education and Rehabilitation see EDUCATION - Special Education And Rehabilitation 2136
Spectrometry see CHEMISTRY - Analytical Chemistry 1491, see also PHYSICS - Optics 4770
Spectroscopy see CHEMISTRY - Analytical Chemistry 1491, see also PHYSICS - Optics 4770
Spectrum see PHYSICS - Optics 4770
Speech and Hearing Disorders see EDUCATION - Special Education and Rehabilitation 2136, see also HANDICAPPED - Hearing Impaired 2849, MEDICAL SCIENCES - Psychiatry and Neurology 4125
Speech - Study and Teaching see EDUCATION - Special Education and Rehabilitation 2136, see also LINGUISTICS 3485
Speleology see EARTH SCIENCES - Geophysics 1964
Spices see FOOD AND FOOD INDUSTRIES 2553
Spina Bifida see MEDICAL SCIENCES 3799
Spinal Cord see MEDICAL SCIENCES - Psychiatry And Neurology 4125
Spinning see NEEDLEWORK 4445
Spiritualism see NEW AGE PUBLICATIONS 4450, see also PARAPSYCHOLOGY AND OCCULTISM 4542
Spleen see MEDICAL SCIENCES - Hematology 4030
Spontaneous Abortion see MEDICAL SCIENCES - Obstetrics And Gynecology 4056
Sporting Goods see SPORTS AND GAMES 5498
SPORTS AND GAMES 5498
SPORTS AND GAMES — Abstracting, Bibliographies, Statistics 5539
SPORTS AND GAMES — Ball Games 5540
SPORTS AND GAMES — Bicycles And Motorcycles 5560
SPORTS AND GAMES — Boats And Boating 5568
SPORTS AND GAMES — Horses And Horsemanship 5579
SPORTS AND GAMES — Outdoor Life 5588
Sports Cards see HOBBIES 3016
Sports Cars see TRANSPORTATION - Automobiles 5765
Sports Medicine see MEDICAL SCIENCES - Sports Medicine 4183
Sportswear see CLOTHING TRADE 1589
Spreadsheets see COMPUTERS - Data Base Management 1788, see also COMPUTERS - Software 1827
Stained Glass see ART 364, see also ARTS AND HANDICRAFTS 413, CERAMICS, GLASS AND POTTERY 1439
Stainless Steel see METALLURGY 4223
Stamps see COMMUNICATIONS - Postal Affairs 1676, see also PHILATELY 4643
Standards see METROLOGY AND STANDARDIZATION 4277
Stationery and Office Equipment see BUSINESS AND ECONOMICS - Office Equipment and Services 1298
STATISTICS 5613, see also MATHEMATICS 3745, POPULATION STUDIES 4924
Steel see METALLURGY 4223
Stenography see BUSINESS AND ECONOMICS - Office Equipment and Services 1298
Stereo Equipment see ELECTRONICS 2170, see also SOUND RECORDING AND REPRODUCTION 5494
Sterility see MEDICAL SCIENCES - Obstetrics And Gynecology 4056, see also MEDICAL SCIENCES - Urology And Nephrology 4203, WOMEN'S HEALTH 5952
Sterilization see BIRTH CONTROL 713
Steroids see BIOLOGY - Biological Chemistry 555, see also MEDICAL SCIENCES - Endocrinology 4004, PHARMACY AND PHARMACOLOGY 4600
Stock and Stock-Breeding see AGRICULTURE - Poultry and Livestock 241
Stocks and Bonds see BUSINESS AND ECONOMICS - Investments 1150
Stoicism see PHILOSOPHY 4656
Stomach Disorders see MEDICAL SCIENCES - Gastroenterology 4024
Stomatology see MEDICAL SCIENCES - Dentistry 3977

CROSS-INDEX TO SUBJECTS

Stone see EARTH SCIENCES - Geology 1925, see also MINES AND MINING INDUSTRY 4315
Store Display and Promotion see ADVERTISING AND PUBLIC RELATIONS 28
Storms see METEOROLOGY 4259
Stress see PSYCHOLOGY 4962
Stringed Instruments see MUSIC 4382
Student Aid see EDUCATION 1999
Student Exchange Programs see EDUCATION 1999, see also EDUCATION - International Education Programs 2122
Substance Abuse see DRUG ABUSE AND ALCOHOLISM 1898
Suffrage see POLITICAL SCIENCE - Civil Rights 4877
Sufism see RELIGIONS AND THEOLOGY - Islamic 5212
Sugar see AGRICULTURE - Crop Production And Soil 192, see also FOOD AND FOOD INDUSTRIES 2553, FOOD AND FOOD INDUSTRIES - Bakers And Confectioners 2586
Suicide Prevention see MEDICAL SCIENCES - Psychiatry And Neurology 4125, see also SOCIAL SERVICES AND WELFARE 5421
Sunnis see RELIGIONS AND THEOLOGY - Islamic 5212
Superconductors see ENGINEERING - Electrical Engineering 2320, see also PHYSICS 4718
Supermarkets see FOOD AND FOOD INDUSTRIES - Grocery Trade 2591
Supersonic Transport see AERONAUTICS AND SPACE FLIGHT 47, see also TRANSPORTATION - Air Transport 5753
Surfing see SPORTS AND GAMES - Outdoor Life 5588
Surgery see MEDICAL SCIENCES - Surgery 4186
Surgical Instruments see MEDICAL SCIENCES - Surgery 4186
Surrogate Motherhood see LAW - Family And Matrimonial Law 3375, see also MEDICAL SCIENCES - Obstetrics And Gynecology 4056
Surveying see ENGINEERING - Civil Engineering 2293, see also GEOGRAPHY 2794
Swimming see SPORTS AND GAMES 5498
Synagogue see RELIGIONS AND THEOLOGY - Judaic 5218
Synthetic Fabrics see TEXTILE INDUSTRIES AND FABRICS 5689
Table Tennis see SPORTS AND GAMES - Ball Games 5540
Tailoring see CLOTHING TRADE 1589
Talking Books see HANDICAPPED - Visually Impaired 2855
Talmud see RELIGIONS AND THEOLOGY - Judaic 5218
Taoism see PHILOSOPHY 4656, see also RELIGIONS AND THEOLOGY - Other Denominations And Sects 5287
Tape Drives see COMPUTERS - Hardware 1799
Tape Recording see SOUND RECORDING AND REPRODUCTION 5494
Tapestry see NEEDLEWORK 4445
Tariffs see BUSINESS AND ECONOMICS - International Commerce 1102, see also BUSINESS AND ECONOMICS - Public Finance, Taxation 1335
Tatting see NEEDLEWORK 4445
Taverns see HOTELS AND RESTAURANTS 3064
Taxation see BUSINESS AND ECONOMICS - Public Finance, Taxation 1335
Taxicabs see TRANSPORTATION - Automobiles 5765
Tea see BEVERAGES 443
Teaching Methods And Curriculum see EDUCATION - Teaching Methods And Curriculum 2146
TECHNOLOGY: COMPREHENSIVE WORKS 5663
TECHNOLOGY: COMPREHENSIVE WORKS — Abstracting, Bibliographies, Statistics 5687
Teenagers see CHILDREN AND YOUTH - About 1529, see also CHILDREN AND YOUTH - For 1548, MEDICAL SCIENCES - Psychiatry And Neurology 4125
Teeth see MEDICAL SCIENCES - Dentistry 3977
Telecommunications see COMMUNICATIONS 1647, see also ENGINEERING - Electrical Engineering 2320
Telefacsimile see COMMUNICATIONS - Computer Applications 1673
Telepathy see NEW AGE PUBLICATIONS 4450, see also PARAPSYCHOLOGY AND OCCULTISM 4542
Telephone And Telegraph see COMMUNICATIONS - Telephone And Telegraph 1686
Television And Cable see COMMUNICATIONS - Television And Cable 1696
Tennis see SPORTS AND GAMES - Ball Games 5540
Terminals see COMPUTERS - Hardware 1799
Terrorism see CRIMINOLOGY AND LAW ENFORCEMENT 1869, see also POLITICAL SCIENCE - International Relations 4889
Textbooks see EDUCATION - Teaching Methods and Curriculum 2146, see also PUBLISHING AND BOOK TRADE 5096
TEXTILE INDUSTRIES AND FABRICS 5689
TEXTILE INDUSTRIES AND FABRICS — Abstracting, Bibliographies, Statistics 5703
Thanatology see MEDICAL SCIENCES - Psychiatry And Neurology 4125, see also PSYCHOLOGY 4962
THEATER 5704
THEATER — Abstracting, Bibliographies, Statistics 5719
Theology see RELIGIONS AND THEOLOGY 5145
Theory of Computing see COMPUTERS - Theory of Computing 1836
Theosophy see PHILOSOPHY 4656, see also RELIGIONS AND THEOLOGY 5145
Therapy see MEDICAL SCIENCES - Physical Medicine And Rehabilitation 4122
Theravada see RELIGIONS AND THEOLOGY - Buddhist 5206
Thermodynamics see CHEMISTRY - Physical Chemistry 1520, see also PHYSICS - Heat 4755
Thermometers see INSTRUMENTS 3128, see also METROLOGY AND STANDARDIZATION 4277
Thermophysics see PHYSICS - Heat 4755
Thoracic Surgery see MEDICAL SCIENCES - Surgery 4186
Thrombosis see MEDICAL SCIENCES - Cardiovascular Diseases 3946
Tiles see BUILDING AND CONSTRUCTION 716, see also CERAMICS, GLASS AND POTTERY 1439, INTERIOR DESIGN AND DECORATION 3162
Timber see FORESTS AND FORESTRY - Lumber and Wood 2618
Timetables see TRANSPORTATION 5723
Tin see METALLURGY 4223, see also MINES AND MINING INDUSTRY 4315
Tires see RUBBER 5299, see also TRANSPORTATION - Automobiles 5765
TOBACCO 5719
TOBACCO — Abstracting, Bibliographies, Statistics 5723
Toiletries see BEAUTY CULTURE 435
Tools see MACHINERY 3733

Topology see MATHEMATICS 3745
Toponyms see GEOGRAPHY 2794, see also LINGUISTICS 3485
Torah see RELIGIONS AND THEOLOGY - Judaic 5218
Totalitarianism see POLITICAL SCIENCE 4793
Touring see TRAVEL AND TOURISM 5848
Tourist Camps see HOTELS AND RESTAURANTS 3064, see also TRAVEL AND TOURISM 5848
Town Planning see HOUSING AND URBAN PLANNING 3078
Toxicology see ENVIRONMENTAL STUDIES - Toxicology And Environmental Safety 2452, see also MEDICAL SCIENCES 3799, PHARMACY AND PHARMACOLOGY 4600
Toxicology And Environmental Safety see ENVIRONMENTAL STUDIES - Toxicology And Environmental Safety 2452
Toys see GIFTWARE AND TOYS 2841
Track and Field see SPORTS AND GAMES - Outdoor Life 5588
Tractors see AGRICULTURE - Agricultural Equipment 186
Trade see BUSINESS AND ECONOMICS - Domestic Commerce 1013, see also BUSINESS AND ECONOMICS - International Commerce 1102
Trade And Industrial Directories see BUSINESS AND ECONOMICS - Trade And Industrial Directories 1377
Trade Shows see MEETINGS AND CONGRESSES 4210
Trade Unions see LABOR UNIONS 3199
Trademarks see PATENTS, TRADEMARKS AND COPYRIGHTS 4547
Traffic see TRANSPORTATION - Roads and Traffic 5811
Trailers see TRANSPORTATION 5723
Transistors see COMMUNICATIONS - Radio 1678, see also ELECTRONICS 2170
Translation Services see LINGUISTICS 3485
Transmittable Diseases see MEDICAL SCIENCES - Communicable Diseases 3962
TRANSPORTATION 5723
TRANSPORTATION — Abstracting, Bibliographies, Statistics 5742
TRANSPORTATION — Air Transport 5753
TRANSPORTATION — Automobiles 5765
TRANSPORTATION — Computer Applications 5799
Transportation Law see LAW 3215
TRANSPORTATION — Railroads 5799
TRANSPORTATION — Roads And Traffic 5811
TRANSPORTATION — Ships And Shipping 5818
TRANSPORTATION — Trucks And Trucking 5840
Trapping see LEATHER AND FUR INDUSTRIES 3410
Trapshooting see SPORTS AND GAMES - Outdoor Life 5588
Traumatology see MEDICAL SCIENCES - Orthopedics and Traumatology 4094
TRAVEL AND TOURISM 5848, see also GEOGRAPHY 2794, HOTELS AND RESTAURANTS 3064
TRAVEL AND TOURISM — Abstracting, Bibliographies, Statistics 5904
TRAVEL AND TOURISM — Airline Inflight And Hotel Inroom 5908
Treaties see LAW - International Law 3379
Trees see FORESTS AND FORESTRY 2597, see also GARDENING AND HORTICULTURE 2627
Triage see MEDICAL SCIENCES - Orthopedics And Traumatology 4094
Trial Law see LAW - Criminal Law 3367
Trigonometry see MATHEMATICS 3745
Trimurti see RELIGIONS AND THEOLOGY - Hindu 5211
Troops see MILITARY 4283
Tropical Diseases see MEDICAL SCIENCES - Communicable Diseases 3962
Tropical Fish see BIOLOGY - Zoology 689, see also PETS 4591
Trucks And Trucking see TRANSPORTATION - Trucks And Trucking 5840
Tsunami see EARTH SCIENCES - Geophysics 1964, see also METEOROLOGY 4259
Tuberculosis see MEDICAL SCIENCES - Respiratory Diseases 4174
Tumors see MEDICAL SCIENCES - Oncology 4069
Typewriters see BUSINESS AND ECONOMICS - Office Equipment and Services 1298
Typography see PRINTING 4949
U F O see AERONAUTICS AND SPACE FLIGHT 47
Ulcers see MEDICAL SCIENCES - Gastroenterology 4024
Ultrasonics see PHYSICS - Sound 4780
Ultrasonography see MEDICAL SCIENCES - Radiology And Nuclear Medicine 4164
Ultrasound see MEDICAL SCIENCES - Radiology And Nuclear Medicine 4164
Ultraviolet see PHYSICS - Optics 4770
Underground Organizations see POLITICAL SCIENCE 4793
Underground Periodicals see LITERARY AND POLITICAL REVIEWS 3555, see also POLITICAL SCIENCE 4793
Underwear see CLOTHING TRADE 1589
Unemployment see BUSINESS AND ECONOMICS - Labor and Industrial Relations 1189
Uniate Churches see RELIGIONS AND THEOLOGY - Roman Catholic 5255
Unidentified Flying Objects see AERONAUTICS AND SPACE FLIGHT 47
Unions see LABOR UNIONS 3199
Unitarianism see RELIGIONS AND THEOLOGY - Other Denominations And Sects 5287
U. S. Armed Forces see MILITARY 4283
Universalism see PHILOSOPHY 4656, see also RELIGIONS AND THEOLOGY - Other Denominations And Sects 5287
Universities And Colleges see COLLEGE AND ALUMNI 1612, see also EDUCATION - Higher Education 2095
Upholstery see INTERIOR DESIGN AND DECORATION - Furniture and House Furnishings 3172
Urban Renewal see HOUSING AND URBAN PLANNING 3078
Urinary Tract see MEDICAL SCIENCES - Urology And Nephrology 4203
Urology And Nephrology see MEDICAL SCIENCES - Urology And Nephrology 4203
Utilities see ENERGY 2197, see also ENGINEERING - Electrical Engineering 2320, PUBLIC ADMINISTRATION 5017, WATER RESOURCES 5933
Utopianism see PHILOSOPHY 4656
Vacations see TRAVEL AND TOURISM 5848
Vaccines see PHARMACY AND PHARMACOLOGY 4600
Vacuum Sciences see ENGINEERING - Mechanical Engineering 2379, see also PHYSICS - Mechanics 4758
Vaishnavism see RELIGIONS AND THEOLOGY - Hindu 5211
Vajrayana see RELIGIONS AND THEOLOGY - Buddhist 5206
Varnishes see PAINTS AND PROTECTIVE COATINGS 4523
Vedanta see RELIGIONS AND THEOLOGY - Hindu 5211

CROSS-INDEX TO SUBJECTS

Vegetables see AGRICULTURE - Crop Production And Soil 192, see also GARDENING AND HORTICULTURE 2627
Vegetarianism see NUTRITION AND DIETETICS 4461
Vending Machines see BUSINESS AND ECONOMICS - Marketing and Purchasing 1264, see also BUSINESS AND ECONOMICS - Small Business 1369
Venereology see MEDICAL SCIENCES - Dermatology and Venereology 3998
Ventilation see HEATING, PLUMBING AND REFRIGERATION 2862
Veterans see MILITARY 4283
VETERINARY SCIENCE 5913
VETERINARY SCIENCE — Abstracting, Bibliographies, Statistics 5932
Vibration see ENGINEERING - Engineering Mechanics And Materials 2359, see also PHYSICS - Mechanics 4758, PHYSICS - Sound 4780
Video see COMMUNICATIONS - Video 1715
Video Games see COMPUTERS - Computer Games 1756
Vineyards see AGRICULTURE - Crop Production And Soil 192
Virology see BIOLOGY - Microbiology 654
Virtual Reality see COMPUTERS - Computer Simulation 1777
Vision see MEDICAL SCIENCES - Ophthalmology And Optometry 4083
Visual Arts see ART 364, see also PHOTOGRAPHY 4691
Visually Impaired see HANDICAPPED - Visually Impaired 2855
Vital Statistics see POPULATION STUDIES 4924
Vitamins see PHARMACY AND PHARMACOLOGY 4600
Viticulture see AGRICULTURE - Crop Production and Soil 192
Vocational Education see EDUCATION - Teaching Methods and Curriculum 1999, see also OCCUPATIONS AND CAREERS 4487
Voice see MUSIC 4382
Volcanoes see EARTH SCIENCES - Geophysics 1964
Volleyball see SPORTS AND GAMES - Ball Games 5540
Volume Feeding see HOTELS AND RESTAURANTS 3064
Voodoo see PARAPSYCHOLOGY AND OCCULTISM 4542, see also RELIGIONS AND THEOLOGY - Other Denominations And Sects 5287
Voting see POLITICAL SCIENCE - Civil Rights 4877
Wages see BUSINESS AND ECONOMICS - Labor and Industrial Relations 1189
Wahhabism see RELIGIONS AND THEOLOGY - Islamic 5212
Waldensian Church see RELIGIONS AND THEOLOGY - Protestant 5225
Walking see PHYSICAL FITNESS AND HYGIENE 4704
War see HISTORY 2872, see also MILITARY 4283
Waste Management see ENVIRONMENTAL STUDIES - Waste Management 2458
Waste Reclamation see ENVIRONMENTAL STUDIES - Waste Management 2458
Wastewater Treatment see ENVIRONMENTAL STUDIES - Waste Management 2458, see also WATER RESOURCES 5933
Watchmaking see JEWELRY, CLOCKS AND WATCHES 3179
Water Pollution see ENVIRONMENTAL STUDIES - Pollution 2446
WATER RESOURCES 5933, see also AGRICULTURE 76, CONSERVATION 1837, ENVIRONMENTAL STUDIES 2399, PUBLIC HEALTH AND SAFETY 5070
WATER RESOURCES — Abstracting, Bibliographies, Statistics 5951
Water Sports see SPORTS AND GAMES 5498
Weapons see MILITARY 4283, see also SPORTS AND GAMES - Outdoor Life 5588
Weather see METEOROLOGY 4259
Weaving see NEEDLEWORK 4445, see also TEXTILE INDUSTRIES AND FABRICS 5689
Weddings see MATRIMONY 3796
Weight Control see NUTRITION AND DIETETICS 4461, see also PHYSICAL FITNESS AND HYGIENE 4704
Weightlifting see PHYSICAL FITNESS AND HYGIENE 4704, see also SPORTS AND GAMES 5498
Weights and Measures see METROLOGY AND STANDARDIZATION 4277
Welding see METALLURGY - Welding 4256
Welfare see SOCIAL SERVICES AND WELFARE 5421
Wells see WATER RESOURCES 5933
Wetlands see CONSERVATION 1837, see also ENVIRONMENTAL STUDIES 2399, WATER RESOURCES 5933

Who's Who see BIOGRAPHY 490
Wildlife see BIOLOGY 499, see also CONSERVATION 1837
Wills And Trusts see LAW - Estate Planning 3373
Wind Energy see ENERGY - Wind Energy 2237
Wind Instruments see MUSIC 4382
Window Coverings see INTERIOR DESIGN AND DECORATION - Furniture and House Furnishings 3172
Windows see BUILDING AND CONSTRUCTION 716, see also CERAMICS, GLASS AND POTTERY 1439
Windsurfing see LEISURE AND RECREATION 3413, see also SPORTS AND GAMES - Outdoor Life 5588
Wine see BEVERAGES 443
Wire see MACHINERY 3733, see also METALLURGY 3733
Wit and Humor see LITERARY AND POLITICAL REVIEWS 3555
Witchcraft see PARAPSYCHOLOGY AND OCCULTISM 4542
WOMEN'S HEALTH 5952, see also MEDICAL SCIENCES - Obstetrics and Gynecology 5952
WOMEN'S INTERESTS 5953
WOMEN'S INTERESTS — Abstracting, Bibliographies, Statistics 5977
Women's Liberation Movement see POLITICAL SCIENCE - Civil Rights 4877, see also WOMEN'S INTERESTS 5953
Women's Rights see POLITICAL SCIENCE - Civil Rights 4877, see also WOMEN'S INTERESTS 5953, WOMEN'S STUDIES 5977
WOMEN'S STUDIES 5977
WOMEN'S STUDIES — Abstracting, Bibliographies, Statistics 5983
Women's Wear see CLOTHING TRADE 1589
Wood see BUILDING AND CONSTRUCTION - Carpentry and Woodwork 767, see also FORESTS AND FORESTRY - Lumber and Wood 2618
Wood Pulp see PAPER AND PULP 4535
Woodwork see BUILDING AND CONSTRUCTION - Carpentry and Woodwork 767, see also HOW-TO AND DO-IT-YOURSELF 3102
Wool see CLOTHING TRADE 1589, see also TEXTILE INDUSTRIES AND FABRICS 5689
Word Processing see COMPUTERS - Word Processing 1836
Workers' Compensation see BUSINESS AND ECONOMICS - Labor And Industrial Relations 1189, see also INSURANCE 3133
Workstations see BUSINESS AND ECONOMICS - Computer Applications 1004, see also COMPUTERS - Hardware 1799
Worship see RELIGIONS AND THEOLOGY 5145
Wounds see MEDICAL SCIENCES - Orthopedics And Traumatology 4094
Wrestling see SPORTS AND GAMES 5498
Writers and Writing see JOURNALISM 3184, see also LITERATURE 3592, PUBLISHING AND BOOK TRADE 5096
X-Rays see MEDICAL SCIENCES - Radiology And Nuclear Medicine 4164, see also PHYSICS - Nuclear Physics 4763
Yachting see SPORTS AND GAMES - Boats and Boating 5568
Yoga see NEW AGE PUBLICATIONS 4450, see also PHILOSOPHY 4656, PHYSICAL FITNESS AND HYGIENE 4704
Youth see CHILDREN AND YOUTH - About 1529
Zen see RELIGIONS AND THEOLOGY - Buddhist 5206
Zinc see METALLURGY 4223, see also MINES AND MINING INDUSTRY 4315
Zionism see POLITICAL SCIENCE 4793
Zoning see HOUSING AND URBAN PLANNING 3078, see also LAW 3215, PUBLIC ADMINISTRATION - Municipal Government 5055
Zoology see BIOLOGY - Zoology 689
Zoos see BIOLOGY - Zoology 689
Zootechniques see AGRICULTURE - Poultry and Livestock 241, see also VETERINARY SCIENCE 5913
Zoroastrianism see RELIGIONS AND THEOLOGY - Other Denominations And Sects 5287

Classified List of Serials Subjects E-L

EARTH SCIENCES

see also Earth Sciences–Computer Applications; Earth Sciences–Geology; Earth Sciences–Geophysics; Earth Sciences–Hydrology; Earth Sciences–Oceanography

550   TH   ISSN 0301-4150
A G E CURRENT AWARENESS SERVICE. 1973. 6/yr. membership. Asian Geotechnical Engineering Information Center, c/o Asian Institute of Technology, Box 2754, Bangkok 10501, Thailand. TEL 66-2-524-5862. FAX 66-2-516-2126. TELEX 84276 TH. adv.; bk.rev.; abstr.; charts.

A N A R E REPORT. (Australian National Antarctic Research Expeditions) see *SCIENCES: COMPREHENSIVE WORKS*

550 574   GW   ISSN 0515-2712
                         CODEN: AARAAJ
ACTA ALBERTINA RATISBONENSIA. 1951. irreg. DM.30. Naturwissenschaftlicher Verein Regensburg e.V., Herzogspalais, Am Prebrunntor 4, 93047 Regensburg, Germany. TEL 0941-5073446. Ed. Helmuth Ackermann. circ. 1,200. (back issues avail.) **Document type:** academic/scholarly publication.

550 600   NO   ISSN 0800-3831
Q111   CODEN: ABOAAB
ACTA BOREALIA; A Nordic journal of circumpolar societies. (Text in English and Norwegian) 1878. s-a. $55 (foreign $55). (Tromsoe Museum) Novus Press, P.O. Box 748, Sentrum, N-0106 Oslo, Norway. TEL 47-22-71-74-50. FAX 47-22-71-81-07. adv. **Indexed:** Biol.Abstr., GeoRef.
   Incorporates (1952-1979): Acta Borealia B. Humaniora (ISSN 0065-1117); (1951-1975): Acta Borealia A. Scientia (ISSN 0065-1109); Which was formerly (until 1947): Tromsoe Museums Aarshefter (ISSN 0800-3998)
   Description: Focuses on the societies of the arctic and subarctic.

550 577   XV   ISSN 0583-6050
                         CODEN: ACLOBC
ACTA CARSOLOGICA/KRASOSLOVNI ZBORNIK. 1955. a. (Slovenska Akademija Znanosti in Umetnosti, Razred za Prirodoslovne Vede) Institut za Raziskovanje Krasa ZRC SAZU, Titov trg 2, 66230 Postojna, Slovenia. TEL 067-22781. FAX 061-331-033. Ed. Peter Habic. circ. 1,200. (also avail. in diskette format) **Indexed:** GeoRef.
—BLDSC (0608.550000).

ACTA HISTORIAE RERUM NATURALIUM NEC NON TECHNICARUM. see *HISTORY — History Of Europe*

550   CC   ISSN 1001-8166
ADVANCE IN EARTH SCIENCES. (Text in Chinese; abstracts in English) 1986. bi-m. Y30. Zhongguo Kexueyuan, Lanzhou Wenxian Qingbo Zhongxin - Chinese Academy of Sciences, Lanzhou Documentation and Information Centre, 236 Tianshui Rd., Lanzhou, Gansu Province 730000, People's Republic of China. TEL 86-931-25317. FAX 86-931-418667. (Co-sponsors: National Science Foundation of China, Earth Science Department; Developmental Bureau of Nature) Ed. Liu Quangen. **Document type:** academic/scholarly publication.
   Description: Reviews the developments of earth sciences, especially global change researches.

550   NE
ADVANCES IN POROUS MEDIA. (Text in English) 1991. irreg. price varies. Elsevier Science B.V., Books Division, P.O. Box 211, 1000 AE Amsterdam, Netherlands. TEL 31-20-5803911. FAX 31-20-5803705. TELEX 18582 ESPA NL. (Subscr. in U.S. and Canada to: Elsevier Science Inc., Box 882, Madison Sq. Sta., New York, NY 10159. TEL 212-989-5800) Ed. M.Y. Corapcioglu. **Document type:** monographic series.
   Refereed Serial

550 631.4   US   ISSN 0176-9340
S590   CODEN: ASSCEO
ADVANCES IN SOIL SCIENCES. 1985. irreg., vol.12, 1990. price varies. Springer-Verlag, 175 Fifth Ave., New York, NY 10010. TEL 212-460-1500. FAX 212-473-6272. (Also: Berlin, Heidelberg, Tokyo and Vienna) (reprint service avail. from ISI) **Document type:** monographic series.
—BLDSC (0711.410000); Faxon; UnCover; CASDDS.

550   PL   ISSN 0860-6307
AKADEMIA GORNICZO-HUTNICZA IM. STANISLAWA STASZICA. ZESZYTY NAUKOWE. FOLIA MALACOLOGICA. 1987. a., no.5, 1993. price varies. Wydawnictwo A G H, Al. Mickiewicz 30, 30-059 Krakow, Poland. TEL 48-12-338100. FAX 48-12-331014. TELEX 322203 AGH PL. (Dist. by: Ars Polona, Krakowskie Przedmiescie 7, 00-068, Warsaw, Poland) Ec. Z. Kleczek. illus. circ. 200. **Document type:** academic/scholarly publication.
—UnCover.

551   RU
AKADEMIYA NAUK C.S.S.R. VOSTOCHNO-SIBIRSKII FILIAL, IRKUTSK. INSTITUT GEOKHIMII. GEOKHIMYA ENDOGENNYCH PROTSESSOV. 1977. irreg. 1.19 Rub. per issue. Institut Geokhimii, Ul. Favorskogo, 1, 664033 Irkutsk, Russia. Ed. L. Tauson. circ. 700.

551   RU
AKADEMIYA NAUK C.S.S.R. VOSTOCHNO-SIBIRSKII FILIAL, IRKUTSK. INSTITUT GEOKHIMII. GEOKHIMICHESKIE METODY POISKOV, METODY ANALIZA. 1977. irreg. 1.40 Rub. per issue. Institut Geokhimii, Ul. Favorskogo, 1, 664033 Irkutsk, Russia. Ed. L. Tauson. circ. 700.

550   CN   ISSN 0034-5172
ALBERTA RESEARCH COUNCIL. BULLETINS. 1958. irreg. price varies. Alberta Research Council, Publications Dept., P.O. Box 8330, Sta. F, Edmonton, Alta. T6H 5X2, Canada. TEL 403-450-5390. FAX 403-461-2651. TELEX 037-2147. bibl.; charts; illus.; stat. **Indexed:** Geo.Abstr., GeoRef.
—UnCover.
   Description: Reports by the Alberta Research Council on the earth sciences.

550   CN
ALBERTA RESEARCH COUNCIL. EARTH SCIENCE REPORTS. 1955. irreg. price varies. Alberta Research Council, Publications Dept., P.O. Box 8330, Sta. F, Edmonton, Alta. T6H 5X2, Canada. TEL 403-450-5390. FAX 403-461-2651. TELEX 037-2147. **Indexed:** Geo.Abstr.
   Description: Reports by the Alberta Research Council on the earth sciences.

1910 EARTH SCIENCES

550 US ISSN 0002-9599
Q1 CODEN: AJSCAP
AMERICAN JOURNAL OF SCIENCE; devoted to the geological sciences and to related fields. 1818. m. (except July & Aug.). $40 to individuals; institutions $90 (effective 1992). (Yale University, Kline Geology Laboratory) American Journal of Science, Box 6666, Yale Sta., New Haven, CT 06511-8130. TEL 203-432-3131. FAX 203-432-5668. Ed.Bd. bk.rev.; bibl.; illus.; index. circ. 3,000. (also avail. in microform from UMI,PMC) **Indexed:** A.S.& T.Ind., AESIS, Biol.Abstr., Br.Ceram.Abstr., Br.Geol.Lit. (1972-), Bull.Thermodyn.& Thermochem., Cadscan, Chem.Abstr., Curr.Cont., Deep Sea Res.& Oceanogr.Abstr., E&P Hlth. (1993-), Eng.Ind., Environ.Abstr., Excerp.Med., Gas Process.& Ppl. (1993-), Gen.Sci.Ind., Geo.Abstr., GeoRef., Geotech.Abstr., Ind.Sci.Rev., INIS Atomind., Lead Abstr., Met.Abstr., Off.Tech. (1993-), Petrol.Abstr. (1961-), Sci.Abstr., Sci.Cit.Ind., Sel.Water Res.Abstr., Soils & Fert., W.R.C.Inf., Zincscan.
—BLDSC (0838.000000); Faxon; UnCover; SWETS; CASDDS.
Refereed Serial

ANNALS OF ARID ZONE. see *AGRICULTURE — Crop Production And Soil*

550 US ISSN 0084-6597
QE1 CODEN: AREPCI
ANNUAL REVIEW OF EARTH AND PLANETARY SCIENCES. 1973. a. $62 (foreign $67) (effective Jan. 1994). Annual Reviews Inc., 4139 El Camino Way, Box 10139, Palo Alto, CA 94303-0139. TEL 415-493-4400; 800-523-8635. FAX 415-855-9815. Ed. George W. Wetherill. adv. contact: Elizabeth Kao. bibl.; cum.index. (also avail. in microform from UMI; back issues avail.; reprint service avail.) **Indexed:** AESIS, Chem.Abstr., Curr.Cont., Deep Sea Res.& Oceanogr.Abstr., GeoRef., Ind.Sci.Rev., Int.Aerosp.Abstr., M.M.R.I., Sci.Cit.Ind. **Document type:** academic/scholarly publication.
—BLDSC (1522.350000); Faxon; UnCover; SWETS; UMI; CASDDS. **CCC.**
Description: Original reviews of critical literature and current developments in earth and planetary sciences.

ANTARCTIC JOURNAL OF THE UNITED STATES. see *SCIENCES: COMPREHENSIVE WORKS*

550 CC ISSN 1004-4078
ANTARCTIC RESEARCH. s-a. $49.50 to individuals (foreign $59.95); institutions $91.30 (foreign $101.30). Science Press, Marketing and Sales Department, 16 Donghuangchenggen Beijie, Beijing 100707, People's Republic of China. TEL 4010642. FAX 4012180. TELEX 210247 SPBJ CN. (Overseas dist. by: Science Press New York, Ltd., 63-117 Alderton St., Rego Park, NY 11374. TEL 718-459-4638)

550 SA ISSN 0003-5351
ANTARKTIESE BULLETIN/ANTARCTIC BULLETIN.* (Text in Afrikaans and English; summaries in English) 1964. q. R.2. South African Antarctic Association, 32 Park Ave., Bordeaux, Randburg, South Africa. Ed. Dr. D.G. Torr. charts; illus.; circ. 7,000 (controlled). (tabloid format)

ARCTIC AND ALPINE RESEARCH. see *SCIENCES: COMPREHENSIVE WORKS*

ARID LANDS NEWSLETTER. see *AGRICULTURE*

ARNOLDIA ZIMBABWE. see *BIOLOGY*

550 UK ISSN 0066-8044
ARTHUR HOLMES SOCIETY. JOURNAL. 1959-1981; resumed 1985. a. £2. Arthur Holmes Society, University of Durham, Department of Geological Sciences, South Rd., Durham DH1 3LE, England. TEL (0385)64971. FAX 091-374-3741. TELEX 537183 DURLIBG. Ed. A. C. Kerr. circ. 100. **Indexed:** GeoRef. **Document type:** academic/scholarly publication.
Formerly (until 1966): Durham University Geological Society. Journal.

550 AG ISSN 0325-0253
CODEN: RAASE9
ASOCIACION ARGENTINA DE MINERALOGIA, PETROLOGIA Y SEDIMENTOLOGIA. REVISTA. (Text in English, Spanish; abstracts in English) 1970. s-a. Arg.$10($30) (foreign $35). Asociacion Argentina de Mineralogia, Petrologia y Sedimentologia, Ciudad Universitaria, Pabellon, 2 piso 1 Nunez, 1428 Buenos Aires, Argentina. Ed. Hugo Corbella. bk.rev.; charts; illus. circ. 300. (back issues avail.) **Indexed:** GeoRef., Mineral.Abstr.
—CASDDS.

551.9 CN
ASSOCIATION OF EXPLORATION GEOCHEMISTS. SPECIAL PUBLICATIONS. irreg. price varies. Association of Exploration Geochemists, Box 523, Rexdale, Ont. M9W 5L4, Canada. **Indexed:** GeoRef.

550 NE ISSN 0926-4701
ATMOSPHERIC SCIENCES LIBRARY. 1982. irreg. price varies. Kluwer Academic Publishers, Postbus 17, 3300 AA Dordrecht, Netherlands. TEL 31-78-334911. FAX 31-78-334254. TELEX 29245 KAPG NL. (Dist. by: Kluwer Academic Publishers Group, P.O. Box 322, 3300 AH Dordrecht, Netherlands. TEL 31-78-524400; N. America dist. addr.: Box 358, Accord Sta., Hingham, MA 02018-0358. TEL 617-871-6600) Ed.Bd. **Indexed:** Meteor.& Geoastrophys.Abstr. **Document type:** monographic series.
Refereed Serial

550 AT ISSN 1035-9338
AUS-GEO NEWS. 1990. bi-m. free. Australian Geological Survey Organisation, G.P.O. Box 378, Canberra, A.C.T. 2601, Australia. TEL 06-249-9111. FAX 06-249-9999. **Document type:** government publication, newsletter.
Description: Designed to keep AGSO clients informed of research results, program changes, staff movements, new publications and data releases.

AUSTRALIA. BUREAU OF MINERAL RESOURCES, GEOLOGY AND GEOPHYSICS. AUSTRALIAN PETROLEUM ACCUMULATIONS REPORT. see *PETROLEUM AND GAS*

AUSTRALIA. BUREAU OF RESOURCE SCIENCES. MINERAL RESOURCE REPORT. see *MINES AND MINING INDUSTRY*

550 AT
QE340 CODEN: AGGBA9
AUSTRALIAN GEOLOGICAL SURVEY ORGANISATION. BULLETIN. 1932. irreg. price varies. Australian Geological Survey Organisation, G.P.O. Box 378, Canberra, A.C.T. 2601, Australia. TEL 06-249-9111. FAX 06-249-9999. **Indexed:** AESIS, Aus.Sci.Ind., Biol.Abstr., Geo.Abstr., GeoRef. **Document type:** government publication.
—CCC.
Formerly: Australia. Bureau of Mineral Resources, Geology and Geophysics. Bulletin (ISSN 0084-7089)

550 AT ISSN 0158-7285
QE48.A8
AUSTRALIAN GEOLOGICAL SURVEY ORGANISATION. YEARBOOK. 1977. a. free. Australian Geological Survey Organisation, G.P.O. Box 378, Canberra, A.C.T. 2601, Australia. TEL 06-249-9111. FAX 06-249-9999. **Document type:** government publication.
—BLDSC (2116.205000).
Formerly: Australia. Bureau of Mineral Resources, Geology and Geophysics. Yearbook.

AUSTRALIAN GEOLOGICAL SURVEY ORGANISATION. 1: 250000 GEOLOGICAL MAPS AND EXPLANATORY NOTES SERIES. see *EARTH SCIENCES — Geology*

550 551.6 US
AVALANCHE REVIEW. 1982. m. $30 to individuals; students $20. American Association of Avalanche Professionals, Inc., Box 34004, Truckee, CA 96160. TEL 916-587-3653. FAX 916-587-4313. Ed. Steve Conger. adv.; bk.rev.; bibl.; charts; illus.; stat.; cum.index. circ. 1,000. (tabloid format; back issues avail.) **Document type:** academic/scholarly publication.
Description: Current snow and avalanche information.

550 UK ISSN 0950-091X
QE571
BASIN RESEARCH. 1988. q. £116 in Europe; elsewhere £127.50 ($190) (effective 1994). (European Association of Exploration Geophysicists) Blackwell Scientific Publications Ltd., Osney Mead, Oxford OX2 0EL, England. TEL 0865-240201. FAX 0865-721205. TELEX 83355-MEDBOK-G. (Co-sponsor: International Association of Sedimentologists) Ed.Bd. bk.rev.; abstr.; bibl.; illus. circ. 850. (also avail. in microform from UMI; back issues avail.) **Indexed:** Br.Geol.Lit. (1972-), E&P Hlth. (1993-), Gas Process.& Ppl. (1993-), Off.Tech. (1993-), Petrol.Abstr. (1991-). **Document type:** academic/scholarly publication.
—BLDSC (1864.520000); Faxon; UnCover; SWETS; UMI. **CCC.**
Description: Presents original research papers on sedimentary basins, of interest to earth scientists in all specializations.
Refereed Serial

910 910 BL ISSN 0100-9761
BOLETIM DE GEOGRAFIA TEORETICA. (Text in English, Portuguese, Spanish; summaries in English, French) 1971. s-a. $50 or exchange basis. Associacao de Geografia Teoretica, Caixa Postal 178, 13500-230 Rio Claro, SP, Brazil. FAX 55-195-249622. Ed. Lucia H. de Oliveira Gerardi. bk.rev.; abstr.; bibl.; illus.; index. circ. 1,500. **Indexed:** Geo.Abstr., I D A, Ref.Zh. **Document type:** academic/scholarly publication.
—BLDSC (2151.950000).

550 520 BL ISSN 0102-6275
BOLETIM I G - U S P. PUBLICACAO ESPECIAL. 1984. irreg. $20 per no. Universidade de Sao Paulo, Instituto de Geociencias, Attn: Editorial Committee President, Cidade Universitaria, Caixa Postal 20899, 01498 Sao Paolo, Brazil. TEL 011-818-3973. circ. 450. **Document type:** academic/scholarly publication.
Supersedes in part (1970-1985): Boletim I G.
Description: Covers all aspects of earth science.

550 520 BL ISSN 0102-6283
CODEN: BICIE5
BOLETIM I G - U S P. SERIE CIENTIFICA. 1984. a. $20 per no. Universidade de Sao Paulo, Instituto de Geociencias, Attn: Editorial Committee President, Cidade Universitaria, Caixa Postal 20899, 01498 Sao Paolo, SP, Brazil. TEL 011-818-3973. circ. 450. **Document type:** bulletin.
—BLDSC (2131.449950); UnCover; CASDDS.
Supersedes in part (1970-1985): Boletim I G.
Description: Presents scientific papers on earth science.

550 520 BL ISSN 0102-6291
BOLETIM I G - U S P. SERIE DIDATICA. 1985. irreg. $20 per no. Universidade de Sao Paulo, Instituto de Geociencias, Attn: Editorial Committee President, Cidade Universitaria, Caixa Postal 20899, 01498 Sao Paolo, Brazil. TEL 011-818-3973. circ. 450. **Document type:** monographic series.
Supersedes in part (1970-1985): Boletim I G.
Description: Monographs on the earth sciences.

550 BO ISSN 0067-9828
CODEN: GBBLAB
BOLIVIA. SERVICIO GEOLOGICO. BOLETIN. 1961. irreg. price varies. Servicio Geologico, Casilla 2729, La Paz, Bolivia.

550 BO ISSN 0067-9836
BOLIVIA. SERVICIO GEOLOGICO. CIRCULARE. 1964. irreg. P.2($0.20) Servicio Geologico, Casilla 2729, La Paz, Bolivia.

550 BO ISSN 0067-9844
BOLIVIA. SERVICIO GEOLOGICO. INFORME. a. P.240($0.35) Servicio Geologico, Casilla 2729, La Paz, Bolivia.

BOLIVIA. SERVICIO GEOLOGICO. SERIE MINERALOGICA. CONTRIBUCIONE. see *MINES AND MINING INDUSTRY*

EARTH SCIENCES

550   IT   ISSN 0006-6710
QB275   CODEN: BGSAA9
BOLLETTINO DI GEODESIA E SCIENZE AFFINI. (Text in Italian; summaries in English, French, German, Italian, Spanish) 1941. q. L.44000. Istituto Geografico Militare, Via C. Battisti 10, 50100 Florence, Italy. TEL 055-27751. FAX 055-4378120. TELEX 575597 IGM FI l. Ed. Luciano Surace. adv.; bk.rev.; charts; illus.; index. circ. 800. **Indexed:** Bibl.Cart., Geo.Abstr., GeoRef.
    Description: Covers geodesy, cartography, remote sensing, and photogrammetry.

550   UK   ISSN 0144-9761
BRITISH NATURALIST. 1980. 2/yr. membership. British Naturalists Association, c/o Mrs. J. Pearton, 48 Russell Way, Higham Ferrers, Northants. NN10 8EJ, England. FAX 0933-314672. (Subscr. to: Mrs. Y. Griffiths, 1 Bracken Mews, Chingford, London E1X 7HE England) **Document type:** academic/scholarly publication.

BUFFALO SOCIETY OF NATURAL SCIENCES. BULLETIN.
see *SCIENCES: COMPREHENSIVE WORKS*

550   AA
BULETINI I SHKENCAVE NATYRES/BULLETIN DES SCIENCES NATURELLES. (Text in Albanian; summaries in French) 1957. q. $7.20. Enver Hoxha Universitet, Tirana, Albania. Ed. Muharrem Frasheri.

550   SZ
BULLETIN DE LA MURITHIENNE. (Text in French) 1862. a. 20 SFr. Societe Valaisanne des Sciences Naturelles, Case Postale 2175, CH-1950 Sion 2, Switzerland. TEL 027-216920. bk.rev. circ. 750. **Indexed:** Biol.Abstr. **Document type:** academic/scholarly publication.

550.5   II
BULLETIN OF EARTH SCIENCES. (Text in English) 1972. a. Rs.15($3) Indian Society of Earth Scientists, c/o Dept. of Geology, Poona University, Poona 411007, India. Ed. V.G. Phansalkar. adv.; illus. circ. 300.

550   UK
CAMBRIDGE EARTH SCIENCE SERIES. irreg., latest 1986. price varies. Cambridge University Press, Edinburgh Bldg., Shaftesbury Rd., Cambridge CB2 2RU, England. TEL 0223-312393. FAX 0223-315052. TELEX 851817256. (N. American addr.: Cambridge University Press, Journals Dept., 40 W. 20th St., New York, NY 10011. TEL 212-924-3900. FAX 212-691-3239) Ed.Bd. **Document type:** monographic series.

550   CN   ISSN 0008-3674
CODEN: CGJOAH
CANADIAN GEOTECHNICAL JOURNAL/REVUE CANADIENNE DE GEOTECHNIQUE. (Text mainly in English, occasionally in French) 1963. bi-m. Can.$72($76) to individuals; institutions Can.$190. National Research Council of Canada, Research Journals, Ottawa, Ont. K1A 0R6, Canada. TEL 613-993-9084. FAX 613-952-7656. (Co-sponsor: Canadian Geotechnical Society) Ed. R.J. Mitchell. adv.: B&W page Can.$550; trim 8 1/2 x 11; adv. contact: Hoda Jabbour. bk.rev.; bibl.; illus.; index. circ. 2,800. (also avail. in microform from UMI; back issues avail.; reprint service avail. from UMI) **Indexed:** Abstr.J.Earthq.Eng., Br.Geol.Lit., Chem.Abstr., Curr.Cont., Deep Sea Res.& Oceanogr.Abstr., E&P Hlth. (1993-), Eng.Ind., Excerp.Med., Fuel & Energy Abstr., Gas Process.& Ppl. (1993-), Geo.Abstr., GeoRef., Geotech.Abstr., Ind.Sci.Rev., INIS Atomind., Intl.Civil Abstr., Off.Tech. (1993-), Petrol.Abstr. (1966-), Risk Abstr., Sci.Cit.Ind., Sel.Water Res.Abstr., Soft.Abstr.Eng. **Document type:** academic/scholarly publication.
—BLDSC (3027.005000); EI; Faxon; UnCover; SWETS; UMI; CASDDS. **CCC.**
Refereed Serial

550   CN   ISSN 0008-4077
QE1   CODEN: CJESAP
CANADIAN JOURNAL OF EARTH SCIENCES/JOURNAL CANADIEN DES SCIENCES DE LA TERRE. (Text mainly in English, occasionally in French) 1964. m. Can.$108($113) to individuals; institutions Can.$335 (effective 1993). National Research Council of Canada, Research Journals, Ottawa, Ont. K1A 0R6, Canada. TEL 613-993-9084. FAX 613-952-7656. (Co-sponsor: Geological Association of Canada) Ed. D.J.W. Piper. adv.: B&W page Can.$550; trim 8 1/2 x 11; adv. contact: Hoda Jabbour. bibl.; charts; illus.; index. circ. 4,600. (also avail. in microform from UMI,PMC; back issues avail.; reprint service avail. from UMI) **Indexed:** Abstr.J.Earthq.Eng., AESIS, Bibl.& Ind.Geol., Biol.Abstr., Br.Geol.Lit., Chem.Abstr., Curr.Adv.Ecol.Sci., Curr.Cont., Curr.Tit.Ocean., Deep Sea Res.& Oceanogr.Abstr., E&P Hlth. (1993-), Energy Info.Abstr., Eng.Ind., Environ.Abstr., Gas Process.& Ppl. (1993-), Geo.Abstr., Geophys.Abstr., GeoRef., Geotech.Abstr., HRIS, Ind.Sci.Rev., INIS Atomind., Mass Spectr.Bull., Meteor.& Geoastrophys.Abstr., Nucl.Sci.Abstr., Ocean.Abstr., Off.Tech. (1993-), Petrol.Abstr. (1965-), Pollut.Abstr., Sci.Abstr., Sci.Cit.Ind., Sel.Water Res.Abstr., Soils & Fert., W.R.C.Inf. **Document type:** academic/scholarly publication.
—BLDSC (3031.150000); CIS; Faxon; UnCover; SWETS; UMI; CASDDS. **CCC.**
Refereed Serial

CARNEGIE INSTITUTION OF WASHINGTON. YEAR BOOK.
see *ASTRONOMY*

550 581 591   GW   ISSN 0176-3997
CODEN: CAROEJ
CAROLINEA; Beitraege zur Naturkundlichen Forschung in Suedwestdeutschland. (Text in English, German; summaries in English, French) 1864. a. DM.60. Staatliches Museum fuer Naturkunde Karlsruhe, Bibliothek, Erbprinzenstr. 13, 76133 Karlsruhe, Germany. TEL 0721-175-111. FAX 0721-175110. Ed. S. Rietschel. bk.rev.; charts; illus. circ. 700. (back issues avail.) **Indexed:** Biol.Abstr., GeoRef. **Document type:** academic/scholarly publication.
—BLDSC (3055.317000).
    Formerly (until 1982): Beitraege zur Naturkundlichen Forschung in Suedwestdeutschland (ISSN 0005-8122)

CEYLON GEOGRAPHER. see *GEOGRAPHY*

551.9   NE   ISSN 0009-2541
QE515   CODEN: CHGEAD
CHEMICAL GEOLOGY; an international journal. (Text in English, French, German) 1966. 32/yr. (in 8 vols.; 4 nos./vol.) fl.3008($1626) (effective 1994). (European Association for Geochemistry) Elsevier Science B.V., P.O. Box 211, 1000 AE Amsterdam, Netherlands. TEL 31-20-5803911. FAX 31-20-5803598. TELEX 18582 ESPA NL. (Subscr. in U.S. and Canada to: Elsevier Science Inc., Box 882, Madison Sq. Sta., New York, NY 10159-0882. TEL 212-989-5800. FAX 212-633-3990) Ed.Bd. adv.; bk.rev.; bibl.; charts; illus.; index. (also avail. in microform from UMI; reprint service avail. from SWZ) **Indexed:** AESIS, Br.Geol.Lit., Bull.Signal., Chem.Abstr., Curr.Cont., Deep Sea Res.& Oceanogr.Abstr., E&P Hlth. (1993-), Fuel & Energy Abstr., Gas Process.& Ppl. (1993-), Geo.Abstr., GeoRef., Ind.Sci.Rev., INIS Atomind., Mass Spectr.Bull., Mineral.Abstr., Ocean.Abstr., Off.Tech. (1993-), Petrol.Abstr. (1970-), Sci.Abstr., Sci.Cit.Ind., Sel.Water Res.Abstr., So.Pac.Per.Ind., Soils & Fert., W.R.C.Inf. **Document type:** academic/scholarly publication.
—BLDSC (3146.550000); Faxon; UnCover; SWETS; CASDDS. **CCC.**
    Incorporates (in 1993): Chemical Geology. Isotope Geoscience Section (ISSN 0168-9622); Which was formerly (1983-1985): Isotope Geoscience (ISSN 0167-6695)
    Description: Publishes original articles in the field of organic and inorganic geochemistry.
Refereed Serial

550 910   JA   ISSN 0022-135X
G1   CODEN: CGZAAL
CHIGAKU ZASSHI/JOURNAL OF GEOGRAPHY. (Text in Japanese; title, summaries and table of contents in English) 1889. bi-m. 14700 Yen (includes special issue). Tokyo Geographical Society - Tokyo Chigaku Kyokai, 12-2 Niban-cho, Chiyoda-ku, Tokyo 102, Japan. TEL 03-3251-0809. FAX 03-3263-0257. Ed. Tokihiko Matsuda. adv.; bk.rev.; index. circ. 1,100. (reprint service avail.) **Indexed:** Chem.Abstr., Geo.Abstr., GeoRef., INIS Atomind. **Document type:** academic/scholarly publication.
—BLDSC (4992.001000); UnCover; CASDDS.
    Description: Covers the broad field of earth science, including geography, geology and geophysics.

550 574   US
CHIHUAHUAN DESERT DISCOVERY. 1975. s-a. membership. Chihuahuan Desert Research Institute, Box 1334, Alpine, TX 79831. TEL 915-837-8370. circ. 1,000. **Document type:** newsletter.
    Description: Natural sciences in the Chihuahuan Desert Region of the United States and Mexico.

550 574   US
CHIHUAHUAN DESERT NEWSBRIEFS. 1983. s-a. free. Chihuahuan Desert Research Institute, Box 1334, Alpine, TX 79831. TEL 915-837-8370. circ. 5,000.

550   JA
CHIJIKI SEKAI SHIRYO KAISEKI SENTA NYUSU/DATA ANALYSIS CENTER FOR GEOMAGNETISM AND SPACE MAGNETISM. OPERATING WORLD DATA CENTER C2 FOR GEOMAGNETISM. (Text in Japanese) bi-m. Kyoto Dagaku, Rigakubu, Fuzoku Chijiki Sekai Shiryo Kaiseki Senta - Kyoto University, Faculty of Science, Data Analysis Center for Geomagnetism and Space Magnetism, Kitashirakawa Oiwakecho, Sakyo-ku, Kyoto 606, Japan.

550   JA   ISSN 0366-6611
CODEN: CKKAA8
CHIKYU KAGAKU/EARTH SCIENCE. (Text in English, Japanese) 1949. b-m. membership. Chigaku Dantai Kenkyukai - Association for the Geological Collaboration in Japan, 8-7, Minamiikebkuro 1-chome, Toshima-ku, Tokyo 171, Japan. **Indexed:** Biol.Abstr., Chem.Abstr., INIS Atomind., Jap.Per.Ind.
—CASDDS.

551   JA   ISSN 0386-4073
CODEN: CKNKDM
CHIKYU KAGAKU (TOKYO, 1967)/GEOCHEMISTRY. (Text in Japanese; summaries in English) 1967. s-a. Nihon Chikyu Kagakkai - Geochemical Society of Japan, Nihon Gakkai Jimu Senta, 16-9, Honkomagome 5-chome, Bunkyo-ku, Tokyo 113, Japan. **Indexed:** Chem.Abstr., INIS Atomind., Jap.Per.Ind.
—CASDDS.

550   JA   ISSN 0915-4523
CHIKYUKEN NYUSU RETA/GLOBAL INDUSTRIAL AND SOCIAL PROGRESS RESEARCH INSTITUTE. NEWSLETTER. (Text in Japanese) 1989. m. Chikyu Sangyo Bunka Kenkyujo - Global Industrial and Social Progress Research Institute, 8-21, Toranomon 3-chome, Minato-ku, Tokyo 105, Japan. **Document type:** newsletter.

550   US   ISSN 0898-5146
GB618.7   CODEN: CALREW
CHINESE JOURNAL OF ARID LAND RESEARCH. 1988. q. $300. Allerton Press, Inc., 150 Fifth Ave., New York, NY 10011. TEL 212-924-3950. FAX 212-463-9684. Ed. Zhao Songqiao. (back issues avail.) **Document type:** academic/scholarly publication.
—BLDSC (3180.295200); UnCover. **CCC.**
    Description: Covers arid land research in China, including desert management, reclamation and development.

550 330   GW   ISSN 0578-0160
CHRISTIANA ALBERTINA. 1965. s-a. DM.20. Christian Albrechts Universitaet zu Kiel, Presse- und Informationsstelle, Olshausenstr. 40, 24118 Kiel, Germany. FAX 0431-880-1355. TELEX 292656-CAUKID. Ec. Gerhard Bagan. circ. 1,200. (back issues avail.)

550   CU
CIENCIAS DE LA TIERRA Y EL ESPACIO. s-a. $15 in N. and S. America; Europe $16. (Academia de Ciencias de Cuba) Ediciones Cubanas, Obispo No. 527, Apdo. 605, Havana, Cuba.

EARTH SCIENCES

549 553   UK   ISSN 0009-8558
QE389.625   CODEN: CLMIAF
CLAY MINERALS. 1947. q. £89($150) Mineralogical Society, 41 Queen's Gate, London SW7 5HR, England. TEL 071-584-7516. FAX 071-823-8021. Ed. D.C. Bain. adv.; bk.rev.; abstr.; bibl.; charts; illus.; index. circ. 1,500. (back issues avail.) **Indexed:** Abstr.Bull.Inst.Pap.Chem., Br.Ceram.Abstr., Br.Geol.Lit., C.I.S. Abstr., C.R.I. Abstr., Chem.Abstr., Curr.Cont., Deep Sea Res.& Oceanogr.Abstr., Fuel & Energy Abstr., Geo.Abstr., GeoRef., Geotech.Abstr., Ind.Sci.Rev., Sci.Cit.Ind., Soils & Fert. **Document type:** academic/scholarly publication.
—BLDSC (3276.900000); EI; Faxon; UnCover; SWETS; CASDDS. **CCC.**
    Formerly: Clay Minerals Bulletin.

549   II   ISSN 0255-7193
     CODEN: CLRSD5
CLAY RESEARCH. s-a. Clay Minerals Society of India, Division of Agricultural Physics, New Delhi 110 012, India. Ed.Bd. **Indexed:** Chem.Abstr., Soils & Fert.
—CASDDS.

550   GT
COLECCION EDITORIAL UNIVERSITARIA. irreg., no.63, 1983. Universidad de San Carlos de Guatemala, Guatemala City, C.A., Guatemala.

628 550   JA   ISSN 0547-1435
COLLECTED PAPERS ON SCIENCES OF ATMOSPHERE AND HYDROSPHERE. (Text in English, Japanese) 1964. a. exchange basis. Nagoya Daigaku, Suiken Kagaku Kenkyujo - Nagoya University, Water Research Institute, Furo-cho, Chikusa-ku, Nagoya-shi, Aichi-ken 464, Japan. **Indexed:** GeoRef.

COLORADO SCHOOL OF MINES. PROFESSIONAL CONTRIBUTIONS. see MINES AND MINING INDUSTRY

COLORADO SCHOOL OF MINES QUARTERLY. see MINES AND MINING INDUSTRY

COMMONWEALTH SCIENTIFIC AND INDUSTRIAL RESEARCH ORGANIZATION. DIVISION OF GEOMECHANICS. TECHNICAL REPORT. see MINES AND MINING INDUSTRY

550   US   ISSN 0894-802X
     CODEN: CSGEAM
COMPASS (NORMAN); an honorary scientific society magazine devoted to the earth sciences. 1920. 4/yr. $24. Society of Sigma Gamma Epsilon, c/o Charles J. Mankin, University of Oklahoma, 100 E. Boyd St., Rm. N-131, Norman, OK 73019. TEL 405-325-3031. FAX 405-325-7069. Ed. Don C. Steinker. adv.; charts; illus. circ. 1,800. (back issues avail.) **Indexed:** GeoRef. **Document type:** academic/scholarly publication.
—BLDSC (3363.920000); UnCover. **CCC.**

COMPUTERS & GEOSCIENCES; an international journal. see EARTH SCIENCES — Computer Applications

CORSONAT. see CONSERVATION

550   UK   ISSN 0195-6671
QE685   CODEN: CRRSDD
CRETACEOUS RESEARCH; an international journal. 1980. bi-m. £250 (effective 1994). Academic Press Ltd. (Subsidiary of Harcourt Brace & Company Ltd.), 24-28 Oval Rd., London NW1 7DX, England. TEL 44-71-267-4466. FAX 44-71-482-2293. TELEX 25775-ACPRES-G. (Subscr. to: Harcourt Brace & Company Ltd., Foots Cray High St., Sidcup, Kent DA14 5HP, England. TEL 44-81-300-3322. FAX 44-81-309-0807) Eds. D. Batten, N. Mateer. **Indexed:** AESIS, Chem.Abstr., Deep Sea Res.& Oceanogr.Abstr., E&P Hlth. (1993-), Gas Process.& Ppl. (1993-), GeoRef, Off.Tech. (1993-), Petrol.Abstr. (1984-). **Document type:** academic/scholarly publication.
—BLDSC (3487.324000); Faxon; UnCover; SWETS; CASDDS. **CCC.**
    Description: Provides a forum for the rapid publication of research on all aspects of the Cretaceous Period, including its boundaries with the Jurassic and Tertiary.

550   UK   ISSN 0732-443X
QE1
CURRENT TOPICS IN CHINESE SCIENCE. SECTION F: EARTH SCIENCE. 1982. irreg., vol.3, 1985. Gordon & Breach Science Publishers, P.O. Box 90, Reading, Berks. RG1 8JL, England. TEL 0734-560080. FAX 0734-568211. TELEX 849870 SCIPUBG. (U.S. addr.: 820 Town Center Dr., Langhorne, PA 19047. TEL 215-750-2642. FAX 215-750-6343) (also avail. in microfilm; microfiche) **Document type:** monographic series.
    Refereed Serial

553   CY   ISSN 0574-8267
QE316
CYPRUS. GEOLOGICAL SURVEY DEPARTMENT. ANNUAL REPORT. 1956. a. free to institutions. Geological Survey Department, Nicosia, Cyprus. charts; illus.; stat.; index. (processed) **Indexed:** GeoRef.

550   CY
CYPRUS. GEOLOGICAL SURVEY DEPARTMENT. BULLETIN. 1963. irreg., no.7, 1977. price varies. Geological Survey Department, Nicosia, Cyprus. **Indexed:** GeoRef.
    Description: Papers on hydrogeology, economic and engineering geology and seismology of Cyprus.

550   CY   ISSN 0574-8259
QE316
CYPRUS. GEOLOGICAL SURVEY DEPARTMENT. MEMOIRS. (Text and summaries in English) 1959. irreg., latest no.8. £0.35. Geological Survey Department, Nicosia, Cyprus. charts; illus.
    Description: Detailed description of the geology and mineral resources of a specific area of Cyprus.

DECHENIANA-BEIHEFTE (BONN). see BIOLOGY

550 598.1   US   ISSN 0191-3875
QL666.C584
DESERT TORTOISE COUNCIL. PROCEEDINGS OF SYMPOSIUM. 1976. a. $20 to non-members; members $15. Desert Tortoise Council, Box 1738, Palm Desert, CA 92261-1738. circ. 600.

550 378.0025   US
QE47.A1
DIRECTORY OF GEOSCIENCE DEPARTMENTS. 1952. a. $26 (effective Jan. 1992). American Geological Institute, 4220 King St., Alexandria, VA 22302-1507. TEL 703-379-2480. FAX 703-379-7563. (Dist. by: AGI Publications Center, Box 205, Annapolis Junction, MD 20701. TEL 301-953-1744) Ed. Nicholas H. Claudy. adv.; index. circ. 1,500. (back issues avail.) **Document type:** directory.
    Former titles: Directory of Geoscience Departments, North America; Directory of Geoscience Departments, United States and Canada (ISSN 0364-7811)
    Description: Identifies more than 10,000 geoscientists in US, Canada, and Mexico by institution, rank, and specialty. Includes colleges, universities, selected national laboratories, natural history museums, and field courses and campus.

DORTMUNDER BEITRAEGE ZUR LANDESKUNDE. see BIOLOGY

550   FR   ISSN 1017-4613
E A R SE L ADVANCES IN REMOTE SENSING. (Text in English) 1991. 3/yr. 800 F. includes EARSeL newsletter. European Association of Remote Sensing Laboratories - Association Europeenne de Laboratoires de Teledetection, 2 av. Rapp, 75340 Paris Cedex 07, France. TEL 45-56-73-60. FAX 45-56-73-61. **Document type:** academic/scholarly publication.
—BLDSC (3643.009300).

E A R SE L DIRECTORY. (European Association of Remote Sensing Laboratories) see BUSINESS AND ECONOMICS — Trade And Industrial Directories

550   FR   ISSN 0257-0521
E A R SE L NEWSLETTER. 1977. q. 450 F. (effective 1992). European Association of Remote Sensing Laboratories - Association Europeenne de Laboratoires de Teledetection, 2 av. Rapp, 75340 Paris Cedex 07, France. TEL 45-56-73-60. FAX 45-56-73-61. Ed. John van Genderen. adv.; bk.rev. circ. 750. (back issues avail.) **Document type:** newsletter.
    Formerly (until 1990): E A R S L News.
    Description: Gives an overview on the latest news concerning remote sensing research in Europe and throughout the world.

550 620   US   ISSN 0270-8337
TH1095
E E R I NEWSLETTER. 1966. m. $109 individual membership; institutions $218; students $30 (effective 1994). Earthquake Engineering Research Institute, 499 14th Street, Suite 320, Oakland, CA 94612-1902. TEL 510-451-0905. FAX 510-451-5411. Ed. Diana Todd. bk.rev. circ. 2,175. (tabloid format; back issues avail.) **Document type:** newsletter.
—BLDSC (3663.444500).
    Description: Provides news of the institute and other related professions in earthquake hazard reduction.

550   US   ISSN 1056-148X
QE1
EARTH (WAUKESHA); the science of our planet. 1991. bi-m. $19.95 (foreign $26). Kalmbach Publishing Co., Box 1612, Waukesha, WI 53187. TEL 414-796-8776. FAX 414-896-0126. Ed. Tom Yulsman. illus. circ. 71,800. **Indexed:** Environ.Per.Bibl.
    Formerly (until Nov. 1991): Editors of Astronomy Look at Earth.
    Description: Covers different earth sciences topics for a general audience, including geology, planetology, oceanography, meteorology and mineralogy, as well as travel and exploration.

550   US   ISSN 0026-4539
TN210   CODEN: EMISAK
EARTH AND MINERAL SCIENCES. 1931. q. free. Pennsylvania State University, College of Earth & Mineral Sciences, 116 Deike Bldg., University Park, PA 16802. TEL 814-863-4667. Ed. Judy Kiusalaas. bibl.; charts; illus.; stat.; index, cum.index; circ. 18,000. (controlled). **Indexed:** Br.Ceram.Abstr., Ceram.Abstr., Chem.Abstr., GeoRef., INIS Atomind. **Document type:** bulletin.
—BLDSC (3643.050000); UnCover.
    Formerly: Mineral Industries.

550   NE   ISSN 0012-821X
QE1   CODEN: EPSLA2
EARTH AND PLANETARY SCIENCE LETTERS. (Summaries in English, French, German) 1966. 28/yr. (in 7 vols.; 4 nos./vol.) fl.2527($1366) (effective 1994). Elsevier Science B.V., P.O. Box 211, 1000 AE Amsterdam, Netherlands. TEL 31-20-5803911. FAX 31-20-5803598. TELEX 18582 ESPA NL. (Subscr. in U.S. and Canada to: Elsevier Science Inc., Box 882, Madison Sq. Sta., New York, NY 10159-0882. TEL 212-989-5800. FAX 212-633-3990) Ed.Bd. illus.; stat. (also avail. in microform from UMI; reprint service avail. from SWZ) **Indexed:** AESIS, Br.Archaeol.Abstr., Br.Geol.Lit., Bull.Signal., Cadscan, Chem.Abstr., Curr.Cont., Deep Sea Res.& Oceanogr.Abstr., E&P Hlth. (1993-), Excerp.Med., Gas Process.& Ppl. (1993-), Geo.Abstr., GeoRef., Ind.Sci.Rev., INIS Atomind., Int.Aerosp.Abstr., Lead Abstr., Mass Spectr.Bull., Meteor.& Geoastrophys.Abstr., Ocean.Abstr., Off.Tech. (1993-), Petrol.Abstr. (1969-), Phys.Ber., Pollut.Abstr., Sci.Abstr., Sci.Cit.Ind., W.R.C.Inf., Zincscan. **Document type:** academic/scholarly publication.
—BLDSC (3643.100000); Faxon; UnCover; SWETS; CASDDS. **CCC.**
    Description: Covers research into all aspects of lunar studies, plate tectonics, ocean floor spreading, and continental drift, as well as basic studies of the physical, chemical and mechanical properties of the Earth's crust and mantle, the atmosphere and the hydrosphere.
    Refereed Serial

EARTH SCIENCES

551 001.9   US   ISSN 1058-8981
THE EARTH CHANGES REPORT; the survival guide for the nineties. 1991. m. $50 (foreign $60) (effective 1994). Matrix Institute, Inc., Box 87, Westmoreland, NH 03467-0087. TEL 603-399-4916; 800-628-7493. FAX 603-399-4340. Eds. Gordon-Michael Scallion, Cynthia Keyes. adv.; stat. (back issues avail.) **Document type:** newsletter.
Description: Forecasts future trends, using intuitive methodologies, as they relate to Earth changes, Earth consciousness, personal and environmental health and healing, phenomena and the origins of Man.

550 333.7   UK
EARTH HERITAGE. 1968. s-a. £5.50 per no. to individuals; institutions £16.50. English Nature, Northminster House, Peterborough PE1 1UA, England. TEL 0733-340345. FAX 0733-68834. TELEX 931-2130132-NC-G. **Document type:** academic/scholarly publication.
—BLDSC (3643.460000).
Formerly (until Jan. 1994): Earth Science Conservation (ISSN 0142-2324)

550   US   ISSN 0885-1565
EARTH SCIENCE. (Subseries of: S I R S Science (ISSN 0885-1530)) 1985. a. $80. Social Issues Resources Series, Box 2348, Boca Raton, FL 33427-2348. TEL 407-994-0079; 800-232-7477. FAX 407-994-4704. (looseleaf format; also avail. in microfiche)
Description: Reprints 70 articles from the fields of climatology, ecology, meterology, oceanography, and paleontology that reflect important social issues.

550   NE   ISSN 0012-8252
QE1   CODEN: ESREAV
EARTH SCIENCE REVIEWS; the international geological journal bridging the gap between research articles and text books. 1966. 8/yr. (in 2 vols.; 4 nos./vol.). fl.812($439) (effective 1994). Elsevier Science B.V., P.O. Box 211, 1000 AE Amsterdam, Netherlands. TEL 31-20-5803911. FAX 31-20-5803598. TELEX 18582 ESPA NL. (Subscr. in U.S. and Canada to: Elsevier Science Inc., Box 882, Madison Sq. Sta., New York, NY 10159-0882. TEL 212-989-5800. FAX 212-633-3990) Ed.Bd. adv.; abstr.; charts; illus.; index. (also avail. in microform from UMI; reprint service avail. from SWZ) **Indexed:** AESIS, Biol.Abstr., Bull.Signal., Cadscan, Chem.Abstr., Curr.Cont., Deep Sea Res.& Oceanogr.Abstr., Gen.Sci.Ind., Geo.Abstr., GeoRef., Ind.Sci.Rev., INIS Atomind., Lead Abstr., Meteor.& Geoastrophys.Abstr., Phys.Ber., Sci.Abstr., Sci.Cit.Ind., Sel.Water Res.Abstr., Zincscan. **Document type:** academic/scholarly publication.
—BLDSC (3643.540000); Faxon; UnCover; SWETS; CASDDS. **CCC.**
Description: Provides information for instructors, students, research scientists, government agencies involved in program support management and in environmental assessment and control, private industries concerned with planetary resources, and the independent consultant.
Refereed Serial

550   UN   ISSN 0070-7910
AS4.U8
EARTH SCIENCES SERIES. (Text in English, French) 1969. irreg., latest no.18. Unesco, 7-9 Place de Fontenoy, 75700 Paris, France. TEL 45-77-16-10. (Dist. in U.S. by: Unipub, 4611-F Assembly Dr., Lanham, MD 20706-4391)

550 520   US   ISSN 1060-1848
TL787
EARTH SPACE REVIEW. a. 517 ECU (effective 1993). Gordon & Breach Science Publishers, 820 Town Center Dr., Langhorne, PA 19047. TEL 215-750-2642. FAX 215-750-6343. (UK subscr. to: P.O. Box 90, Reading, Berkshire RG1 8JL, England. TEL 0734-560-080) (also avail. in microform)
—**CCC.**

ECOLOGIA EN BOLIVIA. see *BIOLOGY*

550   JA   ISSN 0009-3831
QE48.J3
EDUCATION OF EARTH SCIENCE/CHIGAKU KYOIKU. (Text in Japanese; summaries in English) 1948. bi-m. $10. Japan Society of Earth Science Education - Nihon Chigaku Kyoiku Gakkai, c/o Tokyo Gakugei Daigaku Chigaku Kyoshitsu, 4-1, Nukui Kita-machi, Koganei-shi, Tokyo 184, Japan. Ed. Dr. H. Hirayama. bk.rev.; film rev.; abstr. circ. 1,500.

ELECTRICITE DE FRANCE. DIRECTION DES ETUDES ET RECHERCHES. COLLECTION DE NOTES INTERNES. BIOLOGIE, SCIENCES DE LA TERRE ET ENVIRONNEMENT. see *BIOLOGY*

550   NE   ISSN 0924-5405
ENVIRONMENTAL FLUID MECHANICS. 1982. irreg. price varies. Kluwer Academic Publishers, Postbus 17, 3300 AA Dordrecht, Netherlands. TEL 31-78-334911. FAX 31-78-334254. TELEX 29245 KAPG NL. (Dist. by: Kluwer Academic Publishers Group, P.O. Box 322, 3300 AH Dordrecht, Netherlands. TEL 31-78-524400. FAX 31-78-524474; N. America dist. addr.: Box 358, Accord Sta., Hingham, MA 02018-0358. TEL 617-871-6600. FAX 617-871-6528) Ed. G.T. Csanady. **Document type:** monographic series.
Refereed Serial

ENVIRONMENTAL NEWS DIGEST. see *ENVIRONMENTAL STUDIES*

550   GW   ISSN 0170-3188
CODEN: ERFODV
ERDWISSENSCHAFTLICHE FORSCHUNG. (Text in English, German) irreg., vol.29, 1993. price varies. (Akademie der Wissenschaften und der Literatur, Mainz, Kommission fuer Erdwissenschaftliche Forschung) Franz Steiner Verlag Wiesbaden GmbH, Birkenwaldstr. 44, 70191 Stuttgart, Germany. TEL 0711-2582-0. FAX 0711-2582290. TELEX 723636-DAZ-D. (Subscr. to: Postfach 101061, 70009 Stuttgart, Germany) Ed. Wilhelm Lauer. **Document type:** monographic series.

550   SP   ISSN 0367-0449
QE283   CODEN: EGLMA9
ESTUDIOS GEOLOGICOS. (Text and summaries in English, French, Spanish) 1945. bi-m. 5000 ptas.($45) (foreign 7500 ptas.). Museo Nacional de Ciencias Naturales, J. Gutierrez Abascal 2, 28006 Madrid, Spain. FAX 341-5645078. (Dist. by: Consejo Superior de Investigaciones Cientificas (Servicio de Publicaciones), Vitrubio 8, 28006 Madrid, Spain) Ed. Jose Lopez Ruiz. bk.rev. circ. 625. (back issues avail.) **Indexed:** Biol.Abstr., Bull.Signal., Chem.Abstr., GeoRef, I D A, Ind.SST, Mineral.Abstr.
—BLDSC (3812.750000); CASDDS. **CCC.**
Description: Publishes research papers concerned with mineralogy, petrology, geochemistry, geomorphology, stratigraphy and related topics.

550   GW   ISSN 0932-2205
EXCELLENCE IN ECOLOGY. (Text in English) irreg. Ecology Institute, Nordbuente 23, 21385 Oldendorf, Germany. TEL 04132-7127. FAX 04132-8883. Ed. O. Kinne. **Document type:** academic/scholarly publication.
—BLDSC (3835.146000).

550 551 560   GW   ISSN 0172-9179
QE640   CODEN: FACSEN
FACIES. (Text in English, German; summaries in English) 1979. s-a. DM.120. Universitaet Erlangen-Nuernberg, Institut fuer Palaeontologie, Loewenichstr. 28, 91054 Erlangen, Germany. TEL 09131-852622. FAX 09131-852690. Eds. E. Fluegel, E. Fluegel-Kahler. circ. 300. **Indexed:** E&P Hlth. (1993-), Gas Process.& Ppl. (1993-), Geo.Abstr., Off.Tech. (1993-), Petrol.Abstr. (1989-). **Document type:** bulletin.
—BLDSC (3863.425000).

550 520   HU   ISSN 1215-8690
FOLDGOMB. 1966. m. $26.50. Tudomanyos Ismeretterjeszto Tarsulat, Bocskai ut 37, 1113 Budapest XI, Hungary. TEL 186-8239. (Subscr. to: Kultura, Box 149, 1389 Budapest, Hungary) Ed. Artur Vasvary. bk.rev.; illus.; maps. circ. 3,300.
—BLDSC (3964.563000).
Formerly (until 199?): Fold es Eg (ISSN 0015-539X)

550 610   DK   ISSN 0105-7502
QH84.1
FORSKNING I GROENLAND-TUSAAT. (Text in Danish, Greenlandic) 1977. q. DKK 140. Danish Polar Center, Strandgade 100 H, DK-1401 Copenhagen K, Denmark. TEL 45-32-88-01-00. FAX 45-32-88-01-01. bk.rev.; illus.; cum.index. circ. 2,000. (back issues avail.)
Description: Features articles, understandable to the lay readers, on scientific research carried out in Greenland.

550   GW   ISSN 0071-9404
CODEN: FFRCAD
FREIBERGER FORSCHUNGSHEFTE. MONTANWISSENSCHAFTEN: REIHE C. GEOWISSENSCHAFTEN. Subseries title varies: Geologie, Geophysik, Mineralogie, Geochemie, Lagerstaettenlehre, Palaeontologie. irreg. price varies. (Bergakademie Freiberg) Deutscher Verlag fuer Grundstoffindustrie GmbH, Karl-Heine-Str. 27b, 04229 Leipzig, Germany. TEL 0341-49057-0. FAX 0341-4905720. **Indexed:** Chem.Abstr., INIS Atomind. **Document type:** academic/scholarly publication.
—BLDSC (4033.402000); SWETS; CASDDS.

550   US
G I S NEWSLETTER. 1966. bi-m. $40 (foreign $45). Geoscience Information Society, c/o American Geological Institute, 4220 King St., Alexandria, VA 22302. bibl.; circ. 300 (controlled). (processed; back issues avail.) **Indexed:** AESIS.
Formerly (until no.27, 1973): Geoscience Information Society. Newsletter (ISSN 0046-5801)

GACETA INFORMATIVA I N E G I. (Instituto Nacional de Estadistica, Geografia e Informatica) see *BUSINESS AND ECONOMICS — Economic Situation And Conditions*

550   US
GAEA. 1977. bi-m. $40. Association for Women Geoscientists, Geology Department, Macalester College, 1600 Grand Ave., St. Paul, MN 55105-1899. TEL 612-696-6448. FAX 612-696-6122. Ed. Sarah Stoll. adv. contact: Virginia Sand. bk.rev. circ. 1,100. (also avail. in diskette format; back issues avail.) **Document type:** newsletter.
●Also available online.
Description: Provides technical adn career information to geoscientists.

GAZETA OBSERWATORA I M G W/JOURNAL OF I M W M OBSERVER. (Instytut Meteorologii i Gospodarki Wodnej) see *METEOROLOGY*

550   JA   ISSN 0387-3498
GEKKAN CHIKYU/CHIKYU MONTHLY. (Text in Japanese) 1979. m. 2000 Yen per no. Kaiyo Shuppan Co., Ltd., 675-5, Misawa, Hino-shi, Tokyo 191, Japan.

550   GW   ISSN 0935-1523
GEO - INFORMATIONS - SYSTEME/GEO - INFORMATION - SYSTEMS; Zeitschrift fuer interdisziplinaeren Austausch innerhalb der Geowissenschaften - journal for cross-disciplinary exchange of knowledge in the geo-sciences. (Text in English, German; summaries in English, French, German) 1988. q. DM.134 (foreign DM.148). Herbert Wichmann Verlag GmbH, Amalienstr. 29, 76133 Karlsruhe, Germany. TEL 0721-91220-0 FAX 0721-9122020. Ed. Wolfgang Steinborn. index. circ. 5,000. **Document type:** academic/scholarly publication.
—BLDSC (4179.260000).

GEOBIOS; an international journal of life sciences on earth. see *BIOLOGY*

GEOBIOS NEW REPORTS. see *BIOLOGY*

551.9   JA   ISSN 0016-7002
QE514   CODEN: GEJOBE
GEOCHEMICAL JOURNAL. (Text in English) 1966. bi-m. $160. (Geochemical Society of Japan) Business Center for Academic Societies Japan, 5-16-9 Honkomagome, Bunkyo-ku, Tokyo 113, Japan. TEL 03-5814-5811. FAX 035814-5822. TELEX 2722268 BCJSP J. adv.; charts; stat. circ. 1,300. **Indexed:** AESIS, Biol.Abstr., Chem.Abstr, Curr.Cont., Deep Sea Res.& Oceanogr.Abstr., E&P Hlth. (1993-), Excerp.Med., Gas Process.& Ppl. (1993-), GeoRef., Ind.Sci.Rev., INIS Atomind., JTA, Off.Tech. (1993-), Petrol.Abstr. (1969-), Sci.Cit.Ind.
—BLDSC (4116.920000); Faxon; UnCover; UMI; CASDDS.

EARTH SCIENCES

551.9   US   ISSN 0016-7029
QE515   CODEN: GCINAP
GEOCHEMISTRY INTERNATIONAL. English translation of: Geokhimiya (RU ISSN 0016-7525) 1964. m. $1150 (Canada & Mexico $1270; elsewhere $1315). (Rossiiskaya Akademiya Nauk, RU - Russian Academy of Sciences) Scripta Technica, Inc. (Subsidiary of John Wiley & Sons, Inc.), 7961 Eastern Ave., Silver Spring, MD 20910. TEL 301-588-0484. FAX 301-588-5278. (Dist. by: John Wiley & Sons, Inc., Periodicals Division, 650 Third Ave., New York, NY 10158. TEL 212-692-6000) (Co-sponsors: American Geophysical Union; American Geological Institute) Ed. Charles P. Thornton. adv.; bk.rev.; bibl.; index. circ. 675. (also avail. in microform from UMI; reprint service avail. from KTO) **Indexed:** AESIS, Deep Sea Res.& Oceanogr.Abstr., E&P Hlth. (1993-), Excerp.Med., Gas Process.& Ppl. (1993-), Geo.Abstr., Off.Tech. (1993-), Petrol.Abstr. (1989-). **Document type:** academic/scholarly publication.
—BLDSC (0411.775000); Faxon; UnCover; SWETS; UMI. **CCC.**
     Formerly: Geochemistry.
     Description: Covers terrestrial and planetary rocks and atmospheres, rock evolution, parageneses and alteration, geochemical ore-prospecting techniques, ore-zone compositions and distribution, hydrocarbon generation and migration.

550   BL   ISSN 0101-9082
QE235   CODEN: GESPDU
GEOCIENCIAS. (Text in Portuguese; summaries in English, Portuguese) 1982. a. $30 or exchange basis. Universidade Estadual Paulista, Av. Vicente Ferreira, 1278, Caixa Postal 603, 17515-901 Marilia SP, Brazil. TEL 0144-33-1844. FAX 0144-22-2504. TELEX 111 9016 UJME BR. bibl.; charts; illus. circ. 1,000. **Indexed:** Bull.Signal., Curr.Adv.Ecol.Sci., Geo.Abstr. **Document type:** academic/scholarly publication.
—BLDSC (4117.300000).
     Incorporates: Noticia Geomorfologica.
     Description: Covers all areas of geology, mineralogy, paleontology and applied geophysics.

526.8   CI   ISSN 0016-710X
GEODETSKI LIST. (Contents page in English, French, German, Russian) 1947. q. 1500 din. (effective 1991)(typically set in Jan.). (Savez Geodetskih Inzenjera i Geometara S F R J) Savez Drustava Geodeta Hrvatske, Kaciceva 26, 41000 Zagreb, Croatia. Ed. Nedjeljko Francula. adv.; bk.rev.; abstr.; bibl.; charts; illus.; maps; index. **Indexed:** Bibl.Cart., GeoRef., Ref.Zh.

550   GW   ISSN 0170-3250
GEOECOLOGICAL RESEARCH. (Text in English) irreg., vol.7, 1993. price varies. Franz Steiner Verlag Wiesbaden GmbH, Birkenwaldstr. 44, 70191 Stuttgart, Germany. TEL 0711-2582-0. FAX 0711-2582290. TELEX 723636-DAZ-D. (Subscr. to: Postfach 101061, 70009 Stuttgart, Germany) Ed. Ulrich Schweinfurth. **Document type:** monographic series.
—BLDSC (4119.770000).

GEOFORUM; the international multi-disciplinary journal for the rapid publication of research results and critical review articles in the physical, human and regional geosciences. see *GEOGRAPHY*

GEOGRAPHIE - ECOLOGIE - ENVIRONNEMENT; organisation de l'espace. see *GEOGRAPHY*

GEOJOURNAL; international journal of physical, biological, social and economic geography and applications in environmental planning and ecology. see *GEOGRAPHY*

551.9 552 549   BU   ISSN 0324-1718
QE381.B8   CODEN: GMPED4
GEOKHIMIIA, MINERALOGIIA I PETROLOGIIA. (Text in various languages; summaries in English) 1975. 3/yr. price varies. (Bulgarska Akademiia na Naukite) Publishing House of the Bulgarian Academy of Sciences, Acad. G. Bonchev St., Bldg. 6, 1113 Sofia, Bulgaria. Ed. I. Kostov. illus. circ. 420. (reprint service avail. from IRC) **Indexed:** BSL Geo., Chem.Abstr., Int.Aerosp.Abstr.
—BLDSC (0047.984000); UnCover; CASDDS.

GEOLOGICAL SOCIETY OF CHINA. JOURNAL. see *EARTH SCIENCES — Geology*

550   GW   ISSN 0408-1552
GEOLOGISCHES LANDESAMT BADEN-WUERTTEMBERG. ABHANDLUNGEN. (Text in German; summaries in English, French and German) 1953. irreg. Geologisches Landesamt Baden-Wuerttemberg, Albertstr. 5, 79104 Freiburg, Germany. TEL 0761-204-4375. FAX 0761-204-4438. (back issues avail.) **Document type:** monographic series.

550   GW   ISSN 0408-1560
QE269.A19   CODEN: JGLBAV
GEOLOGISCHES LANDESAMT BADEN-WUERTTEMBERG. JAHRESHEFTE. (Text and summaries in English, French or German) 1955. a. Geologisches Landesamt Baden-Wuerttemberg, Albertstr. 5, 79104 Freiburg, Germany. TEL 0761-204-4375. FAX 0761-204-4438. cum.index. (back issues avail.) **Document type:** bulletin.
—CASDDS.

550   SZ   ISSN 0171-1687
GEOMETHODICA. Represents: Basler Geomethodisches Colloquium. Veroeffentlichungen - Basel Geomethodological Meeting. Proceedings. (Proceedings of 1st and 2nd meetings published in Basler Afrika Bibliographien. Mitteilungen, vol.15, 1976 and vol.19, 1977) (Text in German; summaries in English, French, German) 1976. a. 30 SFr. Basler Afrika Bibliographien, Postfach 2037, CH-4001 Basel, Switzerland. TEL 061-2713345. FAX 061-2713155. Ed. Hartmut Leser. illus. circ. 300. **Indexed:** Geo.Abstr. **Document type:** proceedings.
—BLDSC (4147.350000).

550   VE   ISSN 0016-7975
           CODEN: GMNSAX
GEOMINAS. 1964. irreg. exchange basis. Universidad de Oriente, Escuela de Geologia y Minas, c/o Comision de Publicaciones, La Sabanita, Ciudad Bolivar, 8001, Venezuela. Ed.Bd. bk.rev.; bibl.; charts; circ. controlled.
—CASDDS.

550   CN   ISSN 0315-0941
QE185   CODEN: GSCNA5
GEOSCIENCE CANADA. 1974. q. Can.$45. Geological Association of Canada, Dept. of Earth Sciences, Memorial Univ. of Newfoundland, St. John's, NF A1B 3X5, Canada. Ed. P. Thurston. adv.; bk.rev. circ. 3,300. (also avail. in microform from UMI; reprint service avail. from UMI) **Indexed:** Abstr.J.Earthq.Eng., AESIS, Curr.Cont., Deep Sea Res.& Oceanogr.Abstr., E&P Hlth. (1993-), Gas Process.& Ppl. (1993-), Geo.Abstr., Ind.Sci.Rev., INIS Atomind., Off.Tech. (1993-), Petrol.Abstr. (1980-), Sci.Cit.Ind.
—BLDSC (4158.838000); Faxon; UnCover; SWETS; UMI. **CCC.**
     Description: Contains state-of-the-art reviews, summaries of recent developments, and conference reports.

550   US   ISSN 0072-1409
QE48.85   CODEN: GISPAL
GEOSCIENCE INFORMATION SOCIETY. PROCEEDINGS. 1969. a. $45 to non-members. Geoscience Information Society, c/o American Geological Institute, 4220 King St., Alexandria, VA 22302. circ. 250. **Indexed:** AESIS, GeoRef.
—BLDSC (6704.350000).
     Description: Contains papers presented at symposium, technical and poster sessions held at annual meeting.

550   UK
GEOSOURCES. 1969. irreg. £25($50) Geosystems, P.O. Box 40, Didcot, Oxon. OX11 9BS, England. TEL 44-2385-813913. adv. **Document type:** bibliography.
● Also available on CD-ROM. Producer(s): NISC (GeoArchive).
     Formerly: Geoserials (ISSN 0072-1417)

GEOTECHNICAL ENGINEERING. see *ENGINEERING — Civil Engineering*

550   TH
GEOTECHNICAL ENGINEERING BULLETIN. 4/yr. membership. Asian Geotechnical Engineering Information Center, c/o Asian Institute of Technology, Box 2754, Bangkok 10501, Thailand. TEL 66-2-524-5862. FAX 66-2-516-2126. TELEX 84276 TH. bk.rev.
     Formerly (until 1992): A G E News (ISSN 0125-1767)

550   NE   ISSN 0926-5074
GEOTECHNIKA; selected translations of Russian geotechnical literature. (Text in English) 1991. irreg., latest vol.10, 1993. price varies. A.A. Balkema, P.O. Box 1675, 3000 BR Rotterdam, Netherlands. TEL 31-10-4145822. FAX 31-10-4135947. (Dist. in U.S. by: Ashgate Publishing Co., Old Post Rd., Brookfield, VT 05036. TEL 800-535-9544. FAX 802-276-3837)
Document type: monographic series.
     Description: Monographs on specific geotechnical topics, including soil mechanics and electromagnetic phenomena, and their applications in the design and construction of buildings.

550   UK   ISSN 0375-6505
GB1001   CODEN: GTMCAT
GEOTHERMICS; international journal of geothermal research and its applications. (Text and summaries in English, French) 1972. 6/yr. £275($425) (effective 1994). (International Institute for Geothermal Research, Pisa, IT) Elsevier Science Ltd., Pergamon, P.O. Box800, Kidlington, Oxford OX5 1DX, England. TEL 44-865-843000. FAX 44-865-843010. (Subscr. in U.S. and Canada to: Elsevier Science, 660 White Plains Rd., Tarrytown, NY 10591-5153. TEL 914-524-9200. FAX 914-333-2444) Eds. Enrico Barbier, M. Lippmann. adv.; charts; index. circ. 1,075. (also avail. in microfilm from UMI; reprint service avail. from UMI) **Indexed:** Abstr.J.Earthq.Eng., Agri.Eng.Abstr., Chem.Abstr., Deep Sea Res.& Oceanogr.Abstr., E&P Hlth. (1993-), Energy Info.Abstr., Environ.Per.Bibl. (1990-), Gas Process.& Ppl. (1993-), Off.Tech. (1993-), Petrol.Abstr. (1976-), Sci.Abstr. **Document type:** academic/scholarly publication.
—BLDSC (4161.040000); EI; Faxon; UnCover; SWETS; UMI; CASDDS. **CCC.**
     Description: Publishes papers addressing all aspects of the utilization of geothermal resources, including theory and new exploration techniques.
     Refereed Serial

550   US   ISSN 0016-8556
QE1   CODEN: GEOTAJ
GEOTIMES; news of the earth sciences. 1956. m. $24.95 (effective Jan. 1991). American Geological Institute, 4220 King St., Alexandria, VA 22302-1507. TEL 703-379-2480. FAX 703-379-7563. Ed. Julie A. Jackson. adv.; bk.rev.; illus.; index. circ. 13,000. (also avail. in microform from UMI; reprint service avail. from UMI) **Indexed:** AESIS, Biol.Abstr., C.I.J.E., Curr.Cont., Curr.Tit.Ocean, Deep Sea Res.& Oceanogr.Abstr., Geo.Abstr., GeoRef., Petrol.Abstr., Risk Abstr., Sel.Water Res.Abstr., So.Pac.Per.Ind.
—BLDSC (4161.050000); Faxon; UnCover; SWETS; UMI; CASDDS. **CCC.**

551   GW   ISSN 0933-0704
QE1   CODEN: GEOWEW
DIE GEOWISSENSCHAFTEN. 1983. m. DM.325($245) (Alfred-Wegener-Stiftung) Wilhelm Ernst und Sohn, Hohenzollerndamm 170, 10713 Berlin, Germany. TEL 030-860003-0. FAX 030-86000370. Ed. R. Thien. adv.; bk.rev. circ. 1,104. **Indexed:** Art & Archaeol.Tech.Abstr. **Document type:** academic/scholarly publication.
—BLDSC (4161.142000). **CCC.**
     Formerly: Geowissenschaften in Unserer Zeit (ISSN 0723-0834)

GOLDTHWAIT POLAR LIBRARY ACCESSIONS LIST. see *LIBRARY AND INFORMATION SCIENCES — Abstracting, Bibliographies, Statistics*

550 574 560   IT   ISSN 0391-5859
           CODEN: GMFNDF
GORTANIA; atti del Museo Friulano di Storia Naturale. (Text in English, French, German, Italian; summaries in English, French, German, Italian, Slovenian) 1979. a. exchange basis. Comune di Udine, Museo Friulano di Storia Naturale, Via Grazzano 1, 33100 Udine, Italy. TEL 0432-510221. Ed. Carlo Morandini. circ. 600. **Indexed:** Biol.Abstr., Zoo.Rec. **Document type:** bulletin.

EARTH SCIENCES

550   GT
GUATEMALA. INSTITUTO NACIONAL DE SISMOLOGIA, VULCANOLOGIA, METEOROLOGIA E HIDROLOGIA. BOLETIN. vol.7, 1974. m. $20. Instituto Nacional de Sismologia, Vulcanologia, Meteorologia e Hidrologia (INSIVUMEH), Ministerio de Comunicaciones y Obras Publicas, 7 Avenida 14-57, Zona 13, Guatemala, C.A., Guatemala. FAX 502-2-315005. Ed.Bd. bk.rev.; charts; stat. circ. 100.
  Former titles: I N S I V U M E H Boletin; Observatorio Nacional de Guatemala. Boletin.

550 665.5 531.64   US   ISSN 0891-4915
Z6026.G3
GUIDE TO U S G S GEOLOGIC AND HYDROLOGIC MAPS. (U.S. Geological Survey) 1986. biennial. $160. Documents Index, Inc., Box 195, McLean, VA 22101. TEL 703-356-2434. Ed. Laurie Andriot. **Document type:** abstracting/indexing.

550 540   NE
HANDBOOK OF ENVIRONMENTAL ISOTOPE GEOCHEMISTRY. 1980. irreg., vol.3, 1989. price varies. Elsevier Science B.V., Books Division, P.O. Box 211, 1000 AE Amsterdam, Netherlands. TEL 31-20-5803911. FAX 31-20-5803705. TELEX 18582 ESPA NL. (Subscr. in U.S. and Canada to: Elsevier Science Inc., Box 882, Madison Sq. Sta., New York, NY 10159. TEL 212-989-5800) (back issues avail.) **Document type:** monographic series.
  Refereed Serial

550 620   NE
HANDBOOK OF SOIL MECHANICS. (Text in English) 1974. irreg., vol.4, 1990. price varies. Elsevier Science B.V., Books Division, P.O. Box 211, 1000 AE Amsterdam, Netherlands. TEL 31-20-5803911. FAX 31-20-5803705. TELEX 18582 ESPA NL. (Subscr. in U.S. and Canada to: Elsevier Science Inc., Box 882, Madison Sta., New York, NY 10159. TEL 212-989-5800) **Document type:** monographic series.
  Refereed Serial

550   CC   ISSN 1003-5427
HUBO KEXUE/LAKE SCIENCE. (Text in Chinese) q. $67 for 60 vols. Science Press, 16 Donghuangchengge Beijie, Beijing 100707, People's Republic of China. TEL 4010642. FAX 4012180. TELEX 210247 SPBJ CN. **Document type:** academic/scholarly publication.

HUMBOLDT SOCIETY NEWSLETTER. see *HOMOSEXUALITY*

I E E E TRANSACTIONS ON GEOSCIENCE AND REMOTE SENSING. see *ENGINEERING — Electrical Engineering*

550   JA   ISSN 0910-9900
I S E I TECHNICAL REPORT. SERIES A. (Text in English) 1985. irreg. Okayama University, Institute for Study of the Earth's Interior - Okayama Daigaku Chikyu Naibu Kenkyu Senta, 827, Yamada, Misasacho, Tohaku-gun, Tottori-ken 682-02, Japan.
  —BLDSC (8715.910000); UnCover.

550   JA   ISSN 0911-4114
                     CODEN: TRIBE3
I S E I TECHNICAL REPORT. SERIES B. (Text in English) 1985. s-a. Okayama University, Institute for Study of the Earth's Interior - Okayama Daigaku Chikyu Naibu Kenkyu, 827, Yamada, Misasacho, Tohaku-gun, Tottori-ken 682-02, Japan. **Indexed:** Chem.Abstr.
  —UnCover; CASDDS.

550   JA   ISSN 0911-4122
                     CODEN: TRICE6
I S E I TECHNICAL REPORT. SERIES C. (Text in Japanese) 1985. irreg. Okayama University, Institute for Study of the Earth's Interior - Okayama Daigaku Chikyu Naibu Kenkyu Senta, 827, Yamada, Masasacho, Tohaku-gun, Tottori-ken 682-02, Japan.
  —CASDDS.

I T C JOURNAL. see *GEOGRAPHY*

555.4   II
INDIAN ACADEMY OF GEOSCIENCE. JOURNAL. (Text in English) vol.14, 1972. a. $24. Indian Academy of Geoscience, Osmania University, Department of Geology, Hyderabad 500007, Andhra Pradesh, India. (Subscr. to: Prints India, 11 Darya Ganj, New Delhi 110002, India) illus.
  Continues: Indian Geoscience Association. Journal.

550   II   ISSN 0253-4126
QE1   CODEN: PIESDS
INDIAN ACADEMY OF SCIENCES. PROCEEDINGS. EARTH AND PLANETARY SCIENCES. (Text in English) 1934. 4/yr. Rs.75($75) Indian Academy of Sciences, C.V. Raman Ave., P.O. Box 8005, Bangalore 560 080, India. TEL 342546. TELEX 0845-2178-ACAD-IN. Ed. V.K. Gaur. bibl.; illus.; index. circ. 1,000. (also avail. in microfilm from UMI; reprint service avail. from ISI,UMI) **Indexed:** Curr.Cont., Environ.Abstr., Met.Abstr., Meteor.& Geoastrophys.Abstr., Sci.Abstr., Sci.Cit.Ind., Soils & Fert. **Document type:** academic/scholarly publication.
  —BLDSC (6709.940000); UnCover; UMI; CASDDS.

550   II   ISSN 0046-8983
TA710   CODEN: IGTJAG
INDIAN GEOTECHNICAL JOURNAL. (Text in English) 1962. q. Rs.100($30) Indian Geotechnical Society, Central Soil and Materials Station, Olof Palme Marg, Haus Khas, New Delhi 110 016, India. Ed. R. Kuberan. adv.; bk.rev.; bibl.; charts; illus. circ. 1,200. **Indexed:** Abstr.J.Earthq.Eng., Appl.Mech.Rev., C.R.I. Abstr., Geotech.Abstr.
  Formerly (until 1971): Indian National Society for Soil Mechanics and Foundation Engineering. Journal.

560.5   II   ISSN 0379-5128
QE295   CODEN: IJEAB4
INDIAN JOURNAL OF EARTH SCIENCES. (Text in English) 1974. 4/yr. Rs.90($50) Indian Society of Earth Sciences, Department of Geology, Presidency College, Calcutta 700 073, India. Ed. A.K. Saha. adv.; bk.rev.; charts; stat. circ. 500. **Indexed:** Biol.Abstr., C.R.I. Abstr., Geo.Abstr., Herb.Abstr., INIS Atomind., Mineral.Abstr., Petrol.Abstr.
  —Faxon; UnCover; CASDDS.

INSTITUT FRANCAIS D'ETUDES ANDINES. BULLETIN/INSTITUTO FRANCES DE ESTUDIOS ANDINOS. BOLETIN. see *SOCIAL SCIENCES: COMPREHENSIVE WORKS*

INSTITUT FRANCAIS D'ETUDES ANDINES. TRAVAUX. see *SOCIAL SCIENCES: COMPREHENSIVE WORKS*

INSTITUTION OF MINING AND METALLURGY. TRANSACTIONS. SECTION B: APPLIED EARTH SCIENCE. see *MINES AND MINING INDUSTRY*

550   CL   ISSN 0073-9871
G845   CODEN: IACSCK
INSTITUTO ANTARTICO CHILENO. CONTRIBUTION. SERIE CIENTIFICA. (Text in Spanish; summaries in English) 1964; N.S. 1969. a. exchange basis. Instituto Antartico Chileno, Luis Thayer Ojeda 814, Casilla 16521, Correo 9, Santiago, Chile. FAX 2320440. TELEX 346261 INACH CK. Ed. Daniel Torres. circ. 600. **Indexed:** Deep Sea Res.& Oceanogr.Abstr., Sel.Water Res.Abstr.
  Supersedes: Instituto Antartico Chileno. Publicacion.

550   PO   ISSN 0871-1798
INSTITUTO DE INVESTIGACAO CIENTIFICA TROPICAL. COMUNICACOES. SERIE DE CIENCIAS DA TERRA. 1989. irreg. price varies. Instituto de Investigacao Cientifica Tropical, Rua Jau, 54, 1300 Lisbon, Portugal. TEL 364-5321. FAX 363-1460. (Subscr. to: Centro de Documentacao e Informacao, Rua Jau 47, 1300 Lisbon, Portugal) circ. 1,000. **Document type:** monographic series.

550   RM   ISSN 0254-7112
QE287   CODEN: MIGRAX
INSTITUTUL GEOLOGIE SI GEOFIZICA. MEMOIRE. (Text in English, French, German or Rumanian; contents page in French; summaries in English) 1924. a. price varies. Institutul de Geologie si Geofizica, Str. Caransebes Nr. 1, 78344 Bucharest, Rumania. bk.rev.; abstr.; charts; illus. **Indexed:** Bull.Signal., Ref.Zh.

INTERNATIONAL CONFERENCE ON PORT AND OCEAN ENGINEERING UNDER ARCTIC CONDITIONS. PROCEEDINGS. see *ENGINEERING*

INTERNATIONAL GEOSCIENCE AND REMOTE SENSING SYMPOSIUM DIGEST. see *GEOGRAPHY*

INTERNATIONAL HYDROGRAPHIC REVIEW. see *EARTH SCIENCES — Oceanography*

INTERNATIONAL JOURNAL FOR NUMERICAL AND ANALYTICAL METHODS IN GEOMECHANICS. see *ENGINEERING — Civil Engineering*

550 681   UK   ISSN 0143-1161
G70.4   CODEN: IJSEDK
INTERNATIONAL JOURNAL OF REMOTE SENSING. 1980. 18/yr. £756($1270) Taylor & Francis Ltd., Rankine Rd., Basingstoke, Hants RG24 8PR, England. TEL 0256-840366. FAX 0256-479438. TELEX 858540. Ed. A.P. Cracknell. adv.; bk.rev.; bibl. circ. 800. **Indexed:** AESIS, Curr.Tit.Ocean, Excerp.Med., Forest.Abstr., Geo.Abstr., I D A, Int.Aerosp.Abstr., Meteor.& Geoastrophys.Abstr., Rice Abstr., Sci.Abstr., Triticale Abstr. **Document type:** academic/scholarly publication.
  —BLDSC (4542.528000); EI; Faxon; UnCover; SWETS. **CCC.**
  Description: Covers sensors, image processing, use of remotely-sensed data, economic surveys and cost-benefit analyses.
  Refereed Serial

550   CC   ISSN 1001-6279
INTERNATIONAL SILT RESEARCH/GUOJI NISHA YANJIU. (Text in English) c. Guoji Nisha Yanjiu Zhongxin - International Silt Research Center, 1 Fuxingmenwai Dajie, Beijing 100860, People's Republic of China. TEL 868941. Ed. Ding Lianzhen.

551   BU   ISSN 0204-7934
TA705   CODEN: IGKHD2
INZENERNA GEOLOGIIA I KHIDROGEOLOGIIA. (Text in various languages) 1975. 3/yr. 0.75 lv. per no. (Bulgarska Akademiia na Naukite, Geologicheski Institut) Publishing House of the Bulgarian Academy of Sciences, Acad. G. Bonchev St., Bldg. 6, 1113 Sofia, Bulgaria. Ed. M. Minkov. illus. circ. 450. (reprint service avail. from IRC) **Indexed:** BSL Geo.
  —BLDSC (0086.175000).
  Supersedes in part: Bulgarska Akademiia na Naukite. Geologicheski Institut. Izvestiia.

550   KR
IONOSFERA. 1990. irreg. Kharkivskyi Politekhnichnyi Instytut, Ul. Frunze, 21, Kharkov 310002, Ukraine.

550 551   IE   ISSN 0790-1763
QE1   CODEN: IJESER
IRISH JOURNAL OF EARTH SCIENCES. 1978. s-a. I£15 to individuals; institutions I£30. Royal Irish Academy, 19 Dawson St., Dublin 2, Ireland. TEL 01-762570. FAX 01-762346. Ed.Bd. (back issues avail.) **Indexed:** Biol.Abstr., Br.Geol.Lit., Geo.Abstr., Soils & Fert. **Document type:** academic/scholarly publication.
  —BLDSC (4571.930000); CASDDS.
  Formerly: Journal of Earth Sciences (ISSN 0332-1851)

550   IS   ISSN 0021-2164
QE318   CODEN: IJERAK
ISRAEL JOURNAL OF EARTH SCIENCES. (Text in English) 1951. 4/yr. $160. Laser Pages Publishing (1992) Ltd., P.O. Box 50257, Jerusalem 91502, Israel. TEL 972-2-829770. FAX 972-2-818782. Ed. Y. Bartov. bk.rev.; charts; illus.; index. circ. 625. **Indexed:** AESIS, Biol.Abstr., Chem.Abstr., Curr.Cont., Deep Sea Res.& Oceanogr.Abstr., E&P Hlth. (1993-), Excerp.Med., Gas Process.& Ppl. (1993-), Geo.Abstr., Ind.Sci.Rev., INIS Atomind., Irr.& Drain.Abstr., Of.Tech. (1993-), Petrol.Abstr. (1965-), Sci.Abstr., Sci.Cit.Ind., Sel.Water Res.Abstr., Soils & Fert. **Document type:** academic/scholarly publication.
  —Faxon; UnCover; CASDDS.
  Refereed Serial

550 540   RU
ISSLEDOVANIYA V OBLASTI KHIMII REDKOZEMEL'NYKH ELEMENTOV. 1969. irreg. 0.55 Rub. Saratovskii Universitet, Saratov, Russia.

ISTITUTO UNIVERSITARIO NAVALE, NAPOLI. ANNALI. see *TRANSPORTATION — Ships And Shipping*

550   JA   ISSN 0373-3602
JAPAN. MARITIME SAFETY AGENCY. HYDROGRAPHIC DEPARTMENT. REPORT OF HYDROGRAPHIC RESEARCH. (Text in English, Japanese) 1966. a. exchange basis. Kaijo Hoancho, Suirobu - Maritime Safety Agency Hydrographic Department, 3-1, Tsukiji 5-chome, Chuo-ku, Tokyo 104, Japan.

EARTH SCIENCES

550   JA   ISSN 0075-3343
CODEN: JADRDY
JAPANESE ANTARCTIC RESEARCH EXPEDITION DATA REPORTS. (Text in English) 1966. irreg., no.191, 1993. exchange basis. National Institute of Polar Research - Kokuritsu Kyokuchi Kenkyujo, Library, 9-10, Kaga 1-chome, Itabashi-ku, Tokyo 173, Japan. TEL 03-3962-4711. FAX 03-3962-2529. TELEX 272-3515 POLRSCJ. Ed. Takao Hoshiai. circ. 600. **Indexed:** Biol.Abstr., GeoRef., Meteor.& Geoastrophys.Abstr. **Document type:** academic/scholarly publication.
   Description: Discusses upper atmosphere physics, ionosphere, meteorology, earth science, glaciology, seismology, geochemistry, oceanography, marine biology and terrestrial biology.

551   JA
JAPANESE ANTARCTIC RESEARCH REPORT TO S C A R. (Scientific Committee on Antarctic Research) (Text in English) 1985. a. National Institute of Polar Research - Kokuritsu Kyokuchi Kenkyujo, 9-10, Kaga 1-chome, Itabashi-ku, Tokyo 173, Japan.

550   JA   ISSN 0022-0442
QE304   CODEN: JEASAD
JOURNAL OF EARTH SCIENCES. 1953. a. exchange basis. Nagoya Daigaku, Rigakubu, Chikyu Kagaku Kyoshitsu - Nagoya University, Faculty of Science, Department of Earth Sciences, Furocho, Chikusa-ku, Nagoya-shi, Aichi-ken 464, Japan. FAX 052-782-7091. Ed.Bd. circ. 376. **Indexed:** Biol.Abstr., Br.Geol.Lit., Chem.Abstr., Deep Sea Res.& Oceanogr.Abstr., GeoRef., INIS Atomind., Nutr.Abstr. —BLDSC (4971.000000); UnCover; CASDDS.

JOURNAL OF ELECTROTOPOGRAPHY. see *PHYSICS*

551.9   NE   ISSN 0375-6742
TN270.A1   CODEN: JGCEAT
JOURNAL OF GEOCHEMICAL EXPLORATION. 1972. 9/yr. (in 3 vols.; 3 nos./vol.) fl.1188($642) (effective 1994). (Association of Exploration Geochemists) Elsevier Science B.V., P.O. Box 211, 1000 AE Amsterdam, Netherlands. TEL 31-20-5803911. FAX 31-20-5803598. TELEX 18582 ESPA NL. (Subscr. in U.S. and Canada to: Elsevier Science Inc., Box 882, Madison Sq. Sta., New York, NY 10159-0882. TEL 212-989-5800. FAX 212-633-3990) Ed. E.M. Cameron. illus.; index. (also avail. in microform from UMI; reprint service avail. from ISI,SWZ) **Indexed:** AESIS, Br.Geol.Lit., Bull.Signal., Chem.Abstr., Curr.Cont., Deep Sea Res.& Oceanogr.Abstr., E&P Hlth. (1993-), Eng.Ind., Environ.Abstr., Excerp.Med., Fluidex, Gas Process.& Ppl. (1993-), Geo.Abstr., GeoRef., Ind.Sci.Rev., INIS Atomind., Mineral.Abstr., Off.Tech. (1993-), Petrol.Abstr. (1975-), Sci.Cit.Ind., Soils & Fert., W.R.C.Inf. **Document type:** academic/scholarly publication.
—BLDSC (4991.900000); EI; Faxon; UnCover; SWETS; CASDDS. **CCC.**
   Description: Covers all aspects of the application of geochemistry to the search for mineral deposits, including petroleum.
Refereed Serial

550   JA   ISSN 0449-2560
QE1   CODEN: JOGSAB
JOURNAL OF GEOSCIENCES/OSAKA-SHIRITSU DAIGAKU RIGAKUBU CHIGAKU KIYO. (Text in English) 1957. a. exchange basis. Osaka City University, Department of Geosciences - Osaka-shiritsu Daigaku Rigakubu Chigaku Kyoshitsu, Faculty of Science, 3-3-138 Sugimoto, Sumiyoshi-ku, Osaka 558, Japan. **Indexed:** Biol.Abstr., Deep Sea Res.& Oceanogr.Abstr.
—BLDSC (4995.060000); UnCover.

JOURNAL OF NATURAL & PHYSICAL SCIENCES. see *SCIENCES: COMPREHENSIVE WORKS*

JOURNAL OF QUATERNARY SCIENCE. see *SCIENCES: COMPREHENSIVE WORKS*

550   US   ISSN 0022-4472
QE420   CODEN: JSEPAK
JOURNAL OF SEDIMENTARY PETROLOGY. 1931. bi-m. $154 to non-members. S E P M, Box 4756, Tulsa, OK 74159-0756. TEL 918-743-9765. FAX 918-743-2498. Ed. J. Southard. bk.rev.; index. circ. 5,000. (also avail. in microform from UMI,PMC; back issues avail.) **Indexed:** AESIS, Biol.Abstr., Br.Geol.Lit., C.R.I. Abstr., Chem.Abstr., Curr.Cont., Deep Sea Res.& Oceanogr.Abstr., E&P Hlth. (1993-), Excerp.Med., Gas Process.& Ppl. (1993-), Geo.Abstr., GeoRef., Ind.Sci.Rev., INIS Atomind., Ocean.Abstr., Off.Tech. (1993-), Petrol.Abstr. (1963-), Sel.Water Res.Abstr., Soils & Fert. **Document type:** academic/scholarly publication.
—Faxon; UnCover; UMI. **CCC.**
   Description: Covers the basic research and most recent advances in the study of sediments, through papers, discussions, and replies to previously published papers.
Refereed Serial

550   UK   ISSN 0895-9811
QE200   CODEN: JAESE9
JOURNAL OF SOUTH AMERICAN EARTH SCIENCES; including Central America, the Caribbean and the Antarctic Peninsula. 1988. 4/yr. £165($255) (effective 1994). Elsevier Science Ltd., Pergamon, P.O. Box 800, Kidlington, Oxford OX5 1DX, England. TEL 44-865-843000. FAX 44-865-843010. (Subscr. in U.S. and Canada to: Elsevier Science, 660 White Plains Rd., Tarrytown, NY 10591-5153. TEL 914-524-9200. FAX 914-333-2444) Eds. Richardson B. Allen, Alan E.M. Nairn. circ. 350. (also avail. in microfilm from UMI; back issues avail.) **Indexed:** E&P Hlth. (1993-), Gas Process.& Ppl. (1993-), Off.Tech. (1993-), Petrol.Abstr. (1989-). **Document type:** academic/scholarly publication.
—BLDSC (5066.002400); Faxon; UnCover; SWETS; UMI. **CCC.**
   Description: Covers all aspects of earth sciences in the South American continent and surrounding oceans.
Refereed Serial

550 574   JA   ISSN 0385-4019
CODEN: KDCSAR
KAGOSHIMA DAIGAKU RIGAKUBU KIYO. CHIGAKU, SEIBUTSUGAKU/KAGOSHIMA UNIVERSITY. FACULTY OF SCIENCE. REPORTS. EARTH SCIENCES AND BIOLOGY. (Text in English and Japanese; summaries in English) 1967. a. Kagoshima Daigaku, Rigakubu - Kagoshima University, Faculty of Science, 21-35 Koorimoto 1-chome, Kagoshima-shi, Kagoshima-ken 890, Japan. **Indexed:** Chem.Abstr., Jap.Per.Ind.
—BLDSC (7467.160000).

550 551.46   JA   ISSN 0385-2687
KAIYO JIHO/CURRENT OCEANOGRAPHY. 1976. q. 3000 Yen. Ocean Association of Japan, New Diamond Bldg., 1-4-4, Kasumigaseki, Chiyoda-ku, Tokyo, Japan. circ. 2,000. (back issues avail.)

KAZE NI KANSURU SHINPOJUMU KOEN YOSHISHU/PROCEEDINGS OF THE WIND SYMPOSIUM. see *METEOROLOGY*

KENSETSU KOGAKU KENKYUJO HOKOKU/CONSTRUCTION ENGINEERING RESEARCH INSTITUTE FOUNDATION REPORT. see *ENGINEERING — Engineering Mechanics And Materials*

KEVO SUBARCTIC RESEARCH INSTITUTE. REPORTS. see *BIOLOGY*

550   SU
KING ABDUL AZIZ UNIVERSITY. FACULTY OF EARTH SCIENCES. BULLETIN. no.4, 1981. a. King Abdul Aziz University, Faculty of Earth Sciences, P.O. Box 1540, Jeddah 21441, Saudi Arabia. TEL 6952386. FAX 6952381. TELEX 601141 KAUNI SJ.

KOBLENZER GEOGRAPHISCHES KOLLOQUIUM. see *GEOGRAPHY*

550   JA
KOKURITSU KYOKUCHI KENKYUJO KYODO KENKYU HOKOKUSHO/NATIONAL INSTITUTE OF POLAR RESEARCH. JOINT RESEARCH REPORT. (Text in Japanese) 1977. irreg. National Institute of Polar Research - Kokuritsu Kyokuchi Kenkyujo, 9-10, Kiga 1-chome, Itabashi-ku, Tokyo 173, Japan.

550   JA
KOKURITSU KYOKUCHI KENKYUJO NENPO/NATIONAL INSTITUTE OF POLAR RESEARCH. ANNUAL REPORT. (Text in Japanese) 1974. a. National Institute of Polar Research - Kokuritsu Kyokuchi, 9-10, Kaga 1-chome, Itabashi-ku, Tokyo 173, Japan.

551.22   ISSN 0910-6324
KOKUSAI JISHIN OYOBI JISHIN KOGAKU KENSHU NENPO/INTERNATIONAL STUDY REPORT ON THE EARTHQUAKE AND EARTHQUAKE ENGINEERING. (Text in Japanese) 1972. a. Kensetsusho, Kenchiku Kenkyujo - Ministry of Construction, Building Research Institute, 1, Tachihara, Tsukuba-shi, Ibaraki-ken 305, Japan.

KONGELIGE DANSKE VIDENSKABERNES SELSKAB. BIOLOGISKE SKRIFTER. see *BIOLOGY*

550   JA   ISSN 0911-0410
KYOKUCHIKEN NYUSU/NATIONAL INSTITUTE OF POLAR RESEARCH. NEWS. (Text in Japanese) 1974. bi-m. National Institute of Polar Research - Kokuritsu Kyokuchi Kenkyujo, 9-10, Kaga 1-chome, Itabashi-ku, Tokyo 173, Japan.

550   JA   ISSN 0289-5250
KYOTO DAIGAKU KYOYOBU CHIGAKU HOKOKU/KYOTO UNIVERSITY. COLLEGE OF LIBERAL ARTS AND SCIENCES. EARTH SCIENCE REPORT. (Text in Japanese) 1966. a. Kyoto Daigaku, Kyoyobu, Chigaku Kyoshitsu - Kyoto University, Faculty of General Education, Institute of Earth Science, Yoshida Nihonmatsucho, Sakyo-ku, Kyoto 606, Japan.

550   JA   ISSN 0453-0276
KYUSHU DAIGAKU KYOYOBU CHIGAKU KENKYU HOKOKU/KYUSHU UNIVERSITY. COLLEGE OF GENERAL EDUCATION. REPORTS ON EARTH SCIENCE. (Text in English, Japanese) 1955. irreg. Kyushu Daigaku, Kyoyobu, Chigaku Kyoshitsu - Kyushu University, College of General Education, Department of Earth Science, 2-1, Ropponmatsu 4-chome, Chuo-ku, Fukuoka-shi, Fukuoka-ken 810, Japan. **Indexed:** Chem.Abstr., INIS Atomind., Jap.Per.Ind.

550   JA   ISSN 0916-7390
QE1   CODEN: MFKDAO
KYUSHU UNIVERSITY. FACULTY OF SCIENCE. MEMOIRS. SERIES D: EARTH AND PLANETARY SCIENCES/KYUSHU DAIGAKU RIGAKUBU KIYO D. CHIKYUWAKUSEI KAGAKU. (Text in English) 1940. a. exchange basis. Kyushu University, Faculty of Science, Department of Earth and Planetary Sciences - Kyushu Daigaku Rigakubu Chikyuwakusei Kagaku Kyoshitsu, 6-10-1 Hakozaki, Higashi-ku, Fukuoka-shi, Fukuoka-ken 812, Japan. circ. 1,050. **Indexed:** Biol.Abstr., Chem.Abstr, Deep Sea Res.& Oceanogr.Abstr., Geo.Abstr., GeoRef.
—BLDSC (5600.500000); UnCover.
   Formerly (until 1991): Kyushu University. Faculty of Science. Memoirs. Series D: Geology (ISSN 0023-6179)

L P I TECHNICAL REPORT. (Lunar and Planetary Institute) see *ASTRONOMY*

550   UK   ISSN 0898-5812
S622   CODEN: LDREE7
LAND DEGRADATION AND REHABILITATION; an international journal devoted to land degradation, land degradation avoidance, land degradation mitigation, and rehabilitation of degraded land. 1989. q. $165 (effective 1993). John Wiley & Sons Ltd., Journals, Baffins Ln., Chichester, Sussex PO19 1UK, England. TEL 0243-779777. FAX 0243-775878. TELEX 86290 WIBOOK G. Ed. C.J. Barrow. **Indexed:** Environ.Per.Bibl. (1990-).
—BLDSC (5146.796800); SWETS; UMI. **CCC.**
   Description: Seeks to promote rational study of the recognition, monitoring, control, and rehabilitation of degradation in terrestrial environments.

550   RU   ISSN 0131-1719
QE420   CODEN: LIPADJ
LITOLOGIYA I PALEOGEOGRAFIYA. 1972. triennial. 1 Rub. Sankt-Peterburgskii Universitet, Kafedra Litologii i Morskoi Geologii, Universitetskaya Nab. 7-9, St. Petersburg V-164, Russia. TEL 218-9656. (Dist. by: Mezhdunarodnaya Kniga, ul. Dimitrova 39, Moscow G-200, Russia) Ed. N.V. Logvinenko. bibl.; illus. circ. 600. **Indexed:** GeoRef., Ref.Zh.
   Description: Deals with the sedimentary deposition and paleogeography within various regions in Russia and other countries.

EARTH SCIENCES 1917

LUNAR AND PLANETARY INFORMATION BULLETIN. see *ASTRONOMY*

551.46 NE ISSN 0304-4203
GC109 CODEN: MRCHBD
MARINE CHEMISTRY; an international journal for studies of all chemical aspects of the marine environment. 1972. 16/yr. (in 4 vols.; 4 nos./vol.). fl.1604($867) (effective 1994). Elsevier Science B.V., P.O. Box 211, 1000 AE Amsterdam, Netherlands. TEL 31-20-5803911. FAX 31-20-5803598. TELEX 18582 ESPA NL. (Subscr. in U.S. and Canada to: Elsevier Science Inc., Box 882, Madison Sq. Sta., New York, NY 10159-0882. TEL 212-989-5800. FAX 212-633-3990) Ed. P.J. Wangersky. adv.; bk.rev.; bibl.; charts; illus.; index, cum.index. (also avail. in microform from UMI) Indexed: Biol.Abstr., Bull.Signal., Cadscan, Chem.Abstr., Curr.Adv.Ecol.Sci., Curr.Cont., Deep Sea Res.& Oceanogr.Abstr., E&P Hlth. (1993-), Energy Ind., Energy Info.Abstr., Environ.Per.Bibl., Excerp.Med., Gas Process.& Ppl. (1993-), Geo.Abstr., GeoRef., Ind.Sci.Rev., INIS Atomind., Lead Abstr., Mar.Sci.Cont.Tab., Nutr.Abstr., Ocean.Abstr., Off.Tech. (1993-), Petrol.Abstr. (1978-), Pollut.Abstr., Sel.Water Res.Abstr., W.R.C.Inf., Zincscan. Document type: academic/scholarly publication.
—BLDSC (5373.760000); Faxon; UnCover; SWETS; CASDDS. **CCC.**
Refereed Serial

MEDITERRANEE; revue geographique des pays mediterraneens. see *GEOGRAPHY*

LA MER. see *BIOLOGY*

550 JA
METEORITES NEWS. (Text in English) 1982. irreg. National Institute of Polar Research - Kokuritsu Kyokuchi Kenkyujo, 9-10, Kaga 1-chome, Itabashi-ku, Tokyo 173, Japan.

METEORITICS. see *ASTRONOMY*

551.9 551 NE ISSN 0076-6895
CODEN: MGEGAA
METHODS IN GEOCHEMISTRY AND GEOPHYSICS. (Text in English) 1964. irreg., vol.31, 1994. price varies. Elsevier Science B.V., Books Division, P.O. Box 211, 1000 AE Amsterdam, Netherlands. TEL 31-20-5803911. FAX 31-20-5803705. TELEX 18582 ESPA NL. (Subscr. in U.S. and Canada to: Elsevier Science Inc., Box 882, Madison Sq. Sta., New York, NY 10159. TEL 212-989-5800) Indexed: Deep Sea Res.& Oceanogr.Abstr., GeoRef. Document type: monographic series.
—CASDDS. **CCC.**
Refereed Serial

MINERALOGIA POLONICA. see *MINES AND MINING INDUSTRY*

MINERALOGICAL RECORD. see *HOBBIES*

MINERALOGICHESKII ZHURNAL; vsesoyuznyi nauchno-teoreticheskii zhurnal. see *MINES AND MINING INDUSTRY*

550 GW ISSN 0938-9563
MODELING OF GEO-BIOSPHERE PROCESS. 1991. q. DM.198. Catena Verlag, Brockenblich 8, 38162 Cremlingen-Destedt, Germany. TEL 05306-1530. FAX 05306-1560. (N. America subscr. to: 810 E. 10th St., Box 1897, Lawrence, KS 66044-8897, USA. TEL 913-843-1221) Ed. Y. Mualem. Document type: academic/scholarly publication.
—BLDSC (5883.525460). **CCC.**
Description: Concerned with the micro- and macroscale process in the systems of the geo-biosphere.

550 XR ISSN 0521-2359
AS142 CODEN: CAMMAI
MORAVSKE ZEMSKE MUZEUM. CASOPIS. VEDY PRIRODNI/ACTA MUSEI MORAVIAE - SCIENTIAE NATURALES. (Supplement avail.: Acta Musei Moraviae. Supplementum: Folia Mendeliana (ISSN 0085-0748)) (Text in Czech, English, German; summaries in English, German) 1901. a. $69. Moravske Zemske Muzeum, Zelny trh 6, 659 37 Brno, Czech Republic. TEL 42-5-22241. FAX 42-5-25279. Eds. M. Novak, I. Vavrinova. Document type: academic/scholarly publication.
—BLDSC (0582.300000).

550 US ISSN 0276-4741
GB500
MOUNTAIN RESEARCH AND DEVELOPMENT. (Text in English; summaries in French, German; occasionally in Spanish) 1981. q. $36 to individuals (foreign $43); institutions $76 (foreign $83); students $22 (foreign $29) (effective 1994). (International Mountain Society) University of California Press, Journals Division, 2120 Berkeley Way, Berkeley, CA 94720. TEL 510-643-7154. FAX 510-642-9917. Ed. Jack D. Ives. adv.; bk.rev.; index. circ. 960. (also avail. in microfilm from UMI; back issues avail.) Indexed: Anthropol.Lit., Curr.Adv.Ecol.Sci., Curr.Cont., Forest.Abstr., I D A, Irr.& Drain.Abstr., Risk Abstr., Rural Devel.Abstr., Sci.Cit.Ind., Soils & Fert., World Agri.Econ.& Rural Sociol.Abstr. Document type: academic/scholarly publication.
—BLDSC (5978.990000); Faxon; UnCover; UMI. **CCC.**
Description: Takes an interdisciplinary approach to mountain regions and the exploitation of their resources, as well as the well-being of mountain peoples.
Refereed Serial

550 574 FR ISSN 0246-1196
QE1 CODEN: MMNCAH
MUSEE NATIONAL D'HISTOIRE NATURELLE, PARIS. MEMOIRES. NOUVELLE SERIE. SERIE C. SCIENCES DE LA TERRE. 1950. irreg. price varies. Musee National d'Histoire Naturelle, 57 rue Cuvier, 75005 Paris, France. TEL 40-79-30-00. FAX 40-79-34-84. TELEX 202 641 F. Ed. Jean-Lou Justine. adv. circ. 600. Indexed: Biol.Abstr., Deep Sea Res.& Oceanogr.Abstr., GeoRef., Ocean.Abstr., Pollut.Abstr.
Description: Covers earth sciences, geology and paleontology.

MUSEO CIVICO DI STORIA NATURALE DI TRIESTE. ATTI. see *BIOLOGY*

550 IT
MUSEO CIVICO DI STORIA NATURALE DI VERONA. MEMORIE. SERIE 2, SEZIONE B: SCIENZE DELLA TERRA. 1977. irreg., vol.3, 1986. price varies. Museo Civico di Storia Naturale di Verona, Lungadige Porta Vittoria, 9, 37129 Verona, Italy.
Formerly: Museo Civico di Storia Naturale di Verona. Memorie. Serie 2, Part 2: Abiologica.

550 BL ISSN 0103-4278
QE235 CODEN: BMPTET
MUSEU PARAENSE EMILIO GOELDI. BOLETIM. SERIE CIENCIAS DA TERRA. (Text in Portuguese; abstracts in English) 1957. s-a. Cr.$34000($10) per no. Conselho Nacional de Desenvolvimento Cientifico e Tecnologico, Museu Paraense Emilio Goeldi, Caixa Postal 399, 66017-970 Belem, Para, Brazil. TEL 091-228-2341. FAX 091-229-1412. TELEX 091-1419. bibl.; charts; illus.; stat. circ. 1,000. Indexed: Biol.Abstr., Curr.Adv.Ecol.Sci., GeoRef.
—BLDSC (2143.430000).
Formerly (until 1988): Museu Paraense Emilio Goeldi. Boletim. Nova Serie: Geologia (ISSN 0077-2224)
Description: Publishes original papers in earth sciences.

333.1 US
N R R I NOW. 1987. q. free. University of Minnesota, Duluth, Natural Resources Research Institute, 5013 Miller Trunk Hwy., Duluth, MN 55811. TEL 218-720-4300. FAX 218-720-4219. Ed. Lisa Hawkinson Wydra. circ. 4,000 (controlled). (back issues avail.)
Description: Reports the institute's activities in promoting the economic development of Minnesota's natural resources in an environmentally sound manner.

550 JA ISSN 0386-8559
NAGASAKIKEN CHIGAKKAISHI/NAGASAKI EARTH SCIENCE ASSOCIATION. JOURNAL. (Text in Japanese) 1962. s-a. Nagasakiken Chigakkai, Nagasaki Daigaku Kyoikugakubu Chigaku Kyoshitsu, 1-14, Bunkyo-machi, Nagasaki-shi, Nagasaki-ken 852, Japan.

550 559 JA ISSN 0386-5533
CODEN: MNISDG
NATIONAL INSTITUTE OF POLAR RESEARCH. MEMOIRS. SERIES C: EARTH SCIENCES. (Text and summaries in English) 1964. irreg., no.16, 1984. exchange basis. National Institute of Polar Research - Kokuritsu Kyokuchi Kenkyujo, Library, 9-10, Kaga 1-chome, Itabashi-ku, Tokyo 173, Japan. TEL 03-3962-4711. FAX 03-3962-2529. TELEX 272-3515 POLRSCJ. Ed. Takao Hoshiai. circ. 1,000. Indexed: GeoRef. Document type: monographic series.
Supersedes: Japanese Antarctic Research Expedition, 1956-1962. Scientific Reports. Series C: Earth Sciences (ISSN 0075-3378)

550 JA ISSN 0386-0744
CODEN: MNIRDD
NATIONAL INSTITUTE OF POLAR RESEARCH. MEMOIRS. SPECIAL ISSUE. (Text and summaries in English) 1967. irreg., no.48, 1987. exchange basis. National Institute of Polar Research - Kokuritsu Kyokuchi Kenkyujo, Library, 9-10, Kaga 1-chome, Itabashi-ku, Tokyo 173, Japan. TEL 03-3962-4711. FAX 03-3962-2529. TELEX 272-3515 POLRSCJ. Ed. Takao Hoshiai. circ. 1,000. Indexed: Geo.Abstr., GeoRef. Document type: proceedings.
Formerly (1967-1972): Japanese Antarctic Research Expedition Scientific Reports. Special Issue (ISSN 0386-5452)

NATIONAL RESEARCH COUNCIL, CANADA. ASSOCIATE COMMITTEE ON GEOTECHNICAL RESEARCH. TECHNICAL MEMORANDUM. see *ENGINEERING*

NATUR UND MENSCH: JAHRESMITTEILUNGEN DER NATURHISTORISCHEN GESELLSCHAFT NUERNBERG. see *BIOLOGY*

550 IT ISSN 0392-4149
NATURA ALPINA. 1950. q. L.15000 membership. (Societa di Scienze Naturali del Trentino) Museo Tridentino di Scienze Naturali, Via Calepina 14, C.P. 393, 38100 Trent, Italy. Ed. Gino Tomasi.

550 NE ISSN 0921-030X
GB5000 CODEN: NAHZEL
NATURAL HAZARDS. 1988. 6/yr. fl.552($289) (effective 1994). (International Society for the Prevention and Mitigation of Natural Hazards) Kluwer Academic Publishers, Postbus 17, 3300 AA Dordrecht, Netherlands. TEL 31-78-334911. FAX 31-78-334254. TELEX 29245 KAPG NL. (Dist. by: Kluwer Academic Publishers Group, P.O. Box 322, 3300 AH Dordrecht, Netherlands. TEL 31-78-524400. FAX 31-78-524474; N. America dist. addr.: Box 358, Accord Sta., Hingham, MA 02018-0358. TEL 617-871-6600. FAX 617-871-6528) Ed.Bd. (also avail. in microform from UMI; back issues avail.; reprint service avail. from SWZ) Indexed: Abstr.J.Earthq.Eng., Curr.Cont., Environ.Per.Bibl., Geo.Abstr., Geol.Abstr., INSPEC, Meteor.& Geoastrophys.Abstr. Document type: academic/scholarly publication.
—BLDSC (6037.780000); UnCover; SWETS; UMI. **CCC.**
Description: Publishes original research work on the physical aspects of natural hazards, the statistics of forecasting catastrophic events, risk assessment, and the nature of precursors of natural and/or technological hazards.
Refereed Serial

550 333.7 UN ISSN 0077-6092
CODEN: NRSRAV
NATURAL RESOURCES RESEARCH. French edition: Recherches sur les Ressources Naturelles (ISSN 0503-423X) 1963. irreg., vol.21, 1985. price varies. Unesco, 7-9 Place de Fontenoy, 75700 Paris, France. TEL 45-77-16-10. (Dist. in U.S. by: Unipub, 4611-F Assembly Dr., Lanham, MD 20706-4391) Indexed: Biol.Abstr., Forest.Abstr., Forest Prod.Abstr., GeoRef.

550 001.3 FR ISSN 1240-1307
▼**NATURES - SCIENCES - SOCIETES.** (Text in French, occasionally in English) 1993. 4/yr. 620 F. Dunod, 15 rue Gossin, 92543 Montrouge Cedex, France. TEL 40-92-65-00. FAX 40-92-65-97. TELEX 634 916 F. (Subscr. to: Centrale des Revues, 11 rue Gossin, 92543 Montrouge Cedex, France. TEL 46-54-52-66) Ed.Bd. adv.
—BLDSC (6048.C18000).
Description: Examines the relationship of man to the physical and living world which is responsible for environmental problems.

EARTH SCIENCES

NATURHISTORISCHE GESELLSCHAFT HANNOVER. BEIHEFTE ZU DEN BERICHTEN. see *BIOLOGY*

550   GW   ISSN 0365-9844
QH5   CODEN: BENHAP
NATURHISTORISCHE GESELLSCHAFT HANNOVER. BERICHTE. (Summaries in English, German) 1800. a. DM.40. Naturhistorische Gesellschaft Hannover, Postfach 510153, 30631 Hannover, Germany. TEL 0511-6432471. FAX 0511-6432304. circ. 900. **Indexed**: Biol.Abstr., GeoRef. **Document type**: proceedings.

NATURHISTORISCHE GESELLSCHAFT NUERNBERG. ABHANDLUNGEN. see *ARCHAEOLOGY*

NATURWISSENSCHAFTLICHE ZEITSCHRIFT FUER NIEDERBAYERN. see *BIOLOGY*

NATURWISSENSCHAFTLICHER VEREIN FUER SCHWABEN. BERICHTE. see *BIOLOGY*

NATUURWETENSCHAPPELIJKE STUDIEKRING VOOR SURINAME EN DE NEDERLANDSE ANTILLEN. UITGAVEN. see *BIOLOGY*

550   AU
NEUE DENKSCHRIFTEN DES NATURHISTORISCHEN MUSEUMS IN WIEN. 1977. irreg. price varies. Verlag Ferdinand Berger und Soehne GmbH, Wienerstr. 21-23, A-3580 Horn, Austria. TEL 02982-2317-0. Eds. Ortwin Schultz, Friedrich Bachmayer. circ. 500. **Indexed**: Biol.Abstr., GeoRef. **Document type**: monographic series.

550   JA
NIHON CHIKYU KAGAKKAI NYUSU/GEOCHEMICAL SOCIETY OF JAPAN. NEWS. (Text in Japanese) 1954. 4/yr. Nihon Chikyu Kagakkai, Nihon Gakkai Jimu Senta, 16-9, Honkomagome 5-chome, Bunkyo-ku, Tokyo 113, Japan.

551   JA   ISSN 0911-4971
NIHON DAIGAKU BUNRIGAKUBU SHIZEN KAGAKU KENKYUJO KENKYU KIYO. OYO CHIGAKU/NIHON UNIVERSITY. INSTITUTE OF NATURAL SCIENCES. PROCEEDINGS. APPLIED EARTH SCIENCES. (Text in English, Japanese) a. Nihon Daigaku, Bunrigakubu, Shizen Kagaku Kenkyujo - Nihon University, College of Humanities and Sciences, Institute of Natural Sciences, 25-40, Sakurajosui 3-chome, Setagaya-ku, Tokyo 156, Japan.

550   JA
O T C CHOSA HOKOKUSHO/OFFSHORE TECHNOLOGY CONFERENCE. REPORT. (Text in English, Japanese) a. Kaiyo Kagaku Gijutsu Senta - Japan Marine Science and Technology Center, 2-15, Natsushimacho, Yokosuka-shi, Kanagawa-ken 237, Japan.

OESTERREICHISCHE GEOGRAPHISCHE GESELLSCHAFT. MITTEILUNGEN. see *GEOGRAPHY*

550 574   JA   ISSN 0289-7857
OKINAWA TOSHO KENKYU/ISLAND STUDIES IN OKINAWA. (Text in English, Japanese) 1983. a. Ryukyu Daigaku, Rigakubu Seibutsugakka, Iriomote Yamaneko Seitai Jikken Kenkyushitsu - University of Ryukyus, College of Science, Department of Biology, Iriomote Cat Research Laboratory, 1, Senbaru, Nishiharacho, Nakagami-gun, Okinawa-ken 903-01, Japan.

550 331   CN   ISSN 0706-0092
L222.O6
ONTARIO EDUCATION RELATIONS COMMISSION. ANNUAL REPORT. (Editions in English, French) 1975. a. Education Relations Commission, 111 Ave. Rd., Ste. 400, Toronto, Ont. M5R 3J8, Canada. TEL 416-922-7679. circ. 2,000. (back issues avail.)

ORNITHOLOGISCHER VEREIN ZU HILDESHEIM. MITTEILUNGEN. see *BIOLOGY — Ornithology*

550   US
OUTREACH. 1991. bi-m. free. Pennsylvania State University, College of Earth and Mineral Sciences, Earth System Science Center, 248 Deike Bldg., University Park, PA 16802. Ed. Thomas Ackerman. **Document type**: newsletter.

P & A: PAYSAGE ET AMENAGMENT. see *CONSERVATION*

PALAEOGEOGRAPHY, PALAEOCLIMATOLOGY, PALAEOECOLOGY; an international journal for the geo-sciences. see *PALEONTOLOGY*

551.3   CC   ISSN 1002-0160
PEDOSPHERE/TURANG QUAN; a quarterly journal of soil science. (Text in English) 1991. q. $160. (Zhongguo Kexueyuan, Turangsuo - Chinese Academy of Sciences, Institute of Soil Science) Science Press, Marketing and Sales Department, 16 Donghuangchenggen Beijie, Beijing 100707, People's Republic of China. TEL 4010642. FAX 4012180. TELEX 210247-SPBJ-CN. (Subscr. to: P.O. Box 821, 71 East Beijing Rd., Nanjing 210008, P.R. China. TEL 025-3353934. FAX 025-3353590; Overseas dist by: Science Press New York, Ltd., 63-117 Alderton St., Rego Park, NY 11374. TEL 718-459-4638) Ed. Du Rongmin. **Document type**: academic/scholarly publication.
—BLDSC (6417.798000).
Description: Covers the fields of protection of soil resources, promotion of soil fertility and improvement of ecological environment.
Refereed Serial

PERIODICO DI MINERALOGIA. see *MINES AND MINING INDUSTRY*

614.7   US   ISSN 0272-3646
G1
PHYSICAL GEOGRAPHY. 1980. 6/yr. $229 (foreign $251). V.H. Winston & Son, Inc., c/o Bellwether Publishing, Ltd., 8640 Guilford Rd., Ste. 200, Columbia, MD 21046. TEL 410-290-3870. FAX 410-290-8726. Ed. Antony R. Orme. abstr.; bibl.; charts; illus.; stat.; index. circ. 400. (back issues avail.) **Indexed**: ASCA, Curr.Tit.Ocean, Geo.Abstr., GeoRef, Meteor.& Geoastrophys.Abstr. **Document type**: academic/scholarly publication.
—BLDSC (6475.615000); Faxon; UnCover. **CCC**.
Refereed Serial

550   UK   ISSN 0079-1946
QE501   CODEN: PCEAAV
PHYSICS AND CHEMISTRY OF THE EARTH; an international review journal. 1956. 6/yr. £357($550) (effective 1994). Elsevier Science Ltd., Pergamon, P.O. Box 800, Kidlington, Oxford OX5 1DX, England. TEL 44-865-843000. FAX 44-865-843010. (Subscr. in U.S. and Canada to: Elsevier Science, 660 White Plains Rd., Tarrytown, NY 10591-5153. TEL 914-524-9200. FAX 914-333-2444) index. (also avail. in microfilm from UMI) **Indexed**: Chem.Abstr., Curr.Cont., Deep Sea Res.& Oceanogr.Abstr., GeoRef., Sci.Abstr. **Document type**: academic/scholarly publication.
—Faxon; UnCover; UMI; CASDDS. **CCC**.
Description: Covers significant developments in the physics and chemistry of the earth and planets, including geophysics and geochemistry, physical and chemical oceanography and atmospheric physics and chemistry.
Refereed Serial

PLANETARY AND SPACE SCIENCE. see *ASTRONOMY*

919   GW   ISSN 0032-2490
G600   CODEN: POLFAT
POLARFORSCHUNG. (Text in English, German) 1931. 3/yr. DM.120. Deutsche Gesellschaft fuer Polarforschung e.V. - German Society of Polar Research, c/o Alfred-Wegener-Institut fuer Polar- und Meeresforschung, Postfach 120161, 27515 Bremerhaven, Germany. FAX 0471-4831149. TELEX 0238695-POLAR-D. Eds. D.K. Fuetterer, E. Treude. adv.; bk.rev.; bibl.; charts; illus.; stat. circ. 1,000. **Indexed**: Chem.Abstr., GeoRef., Meteor.& Geoastrophys.Abstr. **Document type**: academic/scholarly publication.

550   PL   ISSN 0239-7277
CODEN: BAESEN
POLISH ACADEMY OF SCIENCES. BULLETIN. EARTH SCIENCES. (Text in English, French, German) 1953. q. $100. Polska Akademia Nauk, Centrum Upowszechniania Nauki, Palac Kultury i Nauki, Pietro XXIII, pok. 23-10, 00-901 Warsaw, Poland. (Dist. by: Ars Polona, Krakowskie Przedmiescie 7, 00-068 Warsaw, Poland) Ed. R. Ney. adv. contact: Ewa Bartkowiak. bibl.; charts; illus. circ. 250. **Indexed**: Biol.Abstr., Chem.Abstr., GeoRef. **Document type**: monographic series, bulletin.
—CASDDS.
Formerly (until 1983): Academie Polonaise des Sciences. Bulletin. Serie des Sciences de la Terre (ISSN 0001-4109)

550   PL   ISSN 0138-0338
POLISH POLAR RESEARCH. (Text in English; summaries in Polish) 1980. q. $15. (Polska Akademia Nauk, Komitet Badan Polarnych) Wydawnictwo Naukowe P W N - Polish Scientific Publishers P W N Ltd., Ul. Miodowa 10, 00-251 Warsaw, Poland. TEL 48-22-260207. FAX 48-22-267163. Ed. Krzysztof Jazdzewski. charts; illus.; maps.
—BLDSC (6543.721000).
Description: Presents original scientific papers containing the results of investigations carried out in polar regions, expedition reports, reminiscences.

550   PL
POLITECHNIKA WROCLAWSKA. INSTYTUT GEOTECHNIKI I HYDROTECHNIKI. PRACE NAUKOWE. KONFERENCJE. (Text in Polish; summaries in English, Russian) 1972. irreg., no.32, 1992. price varies. Wydawnictwo Politechniki Wroclawskiej, Wybrzeze Wyspianskiego 27, 50-370 Wroclaw, Poland. FAX 22-36-64. TELEX 712559 PWRPL. (Dist. by: Ars Polona-Ruch, Krakowskie Przedmiescie 7, Warsaw, Poland)
Formerly: Politechnika Wroclawska. Instytut Geotechniki. Prace Naukowe. Konferencje (ISSN 0370-0836)

550   PL
POLITECHNIKA WROCLAWSKA. INSTYTUT GEOTECHNIKI I HYDROTECHNIKI. PRACE NAUKOWE. MONOGRAFIE. (Text in Polish; summaries in English, French, Russian) 1971. irreg., no.20, 1990. price varies. Wydawnictwo Politechniki Wroclawskiej, Wybrzeze Wyspianskiego 27, 50-370 Wroclaw, Poland. (Dist. by: Ars Polona-Ruch, Krakowskie Przedmiescie 7, Warsaw, Poland) **Document type**: monographic series.
—EI.
Formerly: Politechnika Wroclawska. Instytut Geotechniki. Prace Naukowe. Monografie (ISSN 0084-2834)

550   PL   ISSN 0084-2842
POLITECHNIKA WROCLAWSKA. INSTYTUT GEOTECHNIKI. PRACE NAUKOWE. STUDIA I MATERIALY. (Text in Polish; summaries in English, French, Russian) 1969. irreg., no.11, 1985. price varies. Wydawnictwo Politechniki Wroclawskiej, Wybrzeze Wyspianskiego 27, 50-370 Wroclaw, Poland. FAX 22-36-64. TELEX 712559 PWRPL. (Dist. by: Ars Polona-Ruch, Krakowskie Przedmiescie 7, Warsaw)

550   GW   ISSN 0341-9665
CODEN: MIPOD4
POLLICHIA. MITTEILUNGEN. (Summaries in English, French, German) 1888. a. DM.50. Pollichia Verein fuer Naturforschung und Landespflege, Hermann-Schaefer-Str. 17, 67098 Bad Duerkheim, Germany. Ed. K. Stapf. circ. 3,000. (back issues avail.) **Indexed**: Biol.Abstr., GeoRef. **Document type**: academic/scholarly publication.

550 560   GW   ISSN 0941-0414
▼**PROFIL.** (Text in English or German; summaries in English, French, German, Spanish) 1992. 4/yr. Universitaet Stuttgart, Institut fuer Geologie und Palaeontologie, Herdweg 51, 70174 Stuttgart, Germany. TEL 0711-1211344. FAX 0711-1211341. Ed. Dr. Manfred Krautter. **Document type**: academic/scholarly publication.

REMOTE SENSING TECHNOLOGY AND APPLICATION. see *GEOGRAPHY*

RENEWABLE RESOURCES JOURNAL. see *ENVIRONMENTAL STUDIES*

550   GW   ISSN 0935-7238
RESEARCH & DEVELOPMENT. 1989. s-m. DM.480. T N V GmbH, An den Eichen, 53773 Hennef, Germany. TEL 02248-1881. Ed. Stephen Wright.

RESEARCH INSTITUTE NEDRI-AS. BULLETIN. see *BIOLOGY — Botany*

550   FR
REUNION DES SCIENCES DE LA TERRE; resumes des communications. 1973. biennial. price varies. Societe Geologique de France, 77 rue Claude Bernard, 75005 Paris, France. TEL 43-31-77-35. FAX 45-35-79-10. illus. **Indexed**: GeoRef. **Document type**: proceedings.
—BLDSC (7785.785400).
Formerly: Reunion Annuelle des Sciences de la Terre (ISSN 0249-7557)

EARTH SCIENCES

550   BL
REVISTA BRASILEIRA DE GEOCIENCIAS. (Text in English, French, Portuguese, Spanish) 1971. q. $34. (Sociedade Brasileira de Geologia) Editora Edgard Bluecher Ltda., Rua Pedroso Alvarenga 1245, 04531 Sao Paulo, Brazil. Ed. Paulo Milton Barbosa Landim. index. circ. 4,000. **Indexed:** AESIS, GeoRef.

REVISTA DE GEOGRAFIA CANARIA. see *GEOGRAPHY*

REVUE D'AUVERGNE. see *HISTORY — History Of Europe*

RIKAGAKKAISHI/JOURNAL OF PHYSICS, CHEMISTRY AND EARTH SCIENCE. see *SCIENCES: COMPREHENSIVE WORKS*

ROTUNDA. see *ART*

550   UK   ISSN 0263-5933
                              CODEN: TRSSDZ
ROYAL SOCIETY OF EDINBURGH. TRANSACTIONS. (EARTH SCIENCES). 1783. 4/yr. £82. Royal Society of Edinburgh, 22 George St., Edinburgh EH2 2PQ, Scotland. TEL 031-225-6057. FAX 031-220-6889. Ed. J.B. Dawson. circ. 900. (also avail. in microform from PMC) **Indexed:** AESIS, Biol.Abstr., Br.Geol.Lit., Chem.Abstr., Curr.Adv.Ecol.Sci., Deep Sea Res.& Oceanogr.Abstr., Eng.Ind., Geo.Abstr., GeoRef., Ind.Med., Math.R., Met.Abstr., Sci.Abstr. **Document type:** academic/scholarly publication.
—UnCover; SWETS; CASDDS.
Description: Covers all aspects of earth and related planetary sciences and contains contributions that emphasize principles and represent a worldwide authorship rather than locally orientated topics.

550   US
QE1
RUSSIAN ACADEMY OF SCIENCES. TRANSACTIONS (DOKLADY). EARTH SCIENCE SECTIONS. English translation in part of: Rossiiskaya Akademiya Nauk. Doklady. 1959. 9/yr. $1400 (Canada & Mexico $1490; elsewhere $1523.75). (Rossiiskaya Akademiya Nauk, RU - Russian Academy of Sciences) Scripta Technica, Inc. (Subsidiary of: John Wiley & Sons, Inc.), 7961 Eastern Ave., Silver Spring, MD 20910. TEL 301-588-0484. FAX 301-588-5278. (Dist by: John Wiley & Sons, Inc. Periodicals Division, 650 Third Ave., New York, NY 10158. TEL 212-692-6000) (Co-sponsor: American Geological Institute) Ed. V.A. Kabanov. acv.; bibl.; charts; illus.; index. circ. 500. (also avail. in microform from UMI; reprint service avail. from UMI) **Indexed:** AESIS, Deep Sea Res.& Oceanogr.Abstr., Excerp.Med., GeoRef., Potato Abstr. **Document type:** academic/scholarly publication.
—BLDSC (0427.860000); EI; Faxon; UnCover; SWETS; UMI. **CCC.**
Former titles: U S S R Academy of Sciences. Transactions (Doklady). Earth Science Sections (ISSN 0891-5571); (until 1985): Academy of Sciences of the U S S R. Doklady. Earth Science Sections (ISSN 0012-494X)

SAINT MARY'S UNIVERSITY. OCCASIONAL PAPERS IN GEOGRAPHY. see *GEOGRAPHY*

550   JA
SAITAMA DAIGAKU KYOIKUGAKUBU CHIKYU KAGAKU KANSOKU JIKKENSHITSU KENKYU HOKOKU/SAITAMA UNIVERSITY. FACULTY OF EDUCATION. EARTH SCIENCE LABORATORY. BULLETIN. (Text in English, Japanese) 1979. triennial. Saitama Daigaku, Kyoikugakubu, Chikyu Kagaku Kansoku Jikkenshitsu, 255, Shimookubo, Urawa-shi, Saitama-ken 338, Japan.

SCIENCES DE LA TERRE: SERIE INFORMATIQUE GEOLOGIQUE. see *EARTH SCIENCES — Geology*

553.2   NE
SEDIMENTARY BASINS OF THE WORLD. (Text in English) 1989. irreg., vol.2, 1993. price varies. Elsevier Science B.V., Books Division, P.O. Box 211, 1000 AE Amsterdam, Netherlands. TEL 31-20-5803911. FAX 31-20-5803705. TELEX 18582 ESPA NL. (Subscr. in U.S. and Canada to: Elsevier Science Inc., Box 882, Madison Sq. Sta., New York, NY 10159. TEL 212-989-5800) **Document type:** monographic series.
Refereed Serial

550 551   JA   ISSN 0373-1006
SEPPYO/JAPANESE SOCIETY OF SNOW AND ICE. JOURNAL. (Text in Japanese; summaries in English) 1939. q. Nihon Seppyo Gakkai - Japanese Society of Snow and Ice, 3-12, Kojimachi, Chiyoda-ku, Tokyo 102, Japan. Ed. Gorow Wakahama. circ. 1,200. **Indexed:** Jap.Per.Ind.

620 550   SZ   ISSN 0080-9004
                             CODEN: SRSMC
SERIES ON ROCK AND SOIL MECHANICS. 1971. irreg. (4-6/yr.). price varies. Trans Tech Publications, Hardstr. 13, P.O. Box 100, CH-4714 Aedermannsdorf, Switzerland. FAX 062-741058. Ed. Dr. R.H. Wohlbier. **Indexed:** GeoRef., Geotech.Abstr.

SEVERO-KAVKAZSKII NAUCHNYI TSENTR VYSSHEI SHKOLY. ESTESTVENNYE NAUKI. IZVESTIYA/NORTH-CAUCASUS SCIENTIFIC CENTER OF HIGH SCHOOL. NATURAL SCIENCES. NEWS. see *MATHEMATICS*

550   JA   ISSN 0389-9128
SHIGA SHIZEN KYOIKU KENKYU SHISETSU KENKYU GYOSEKI/INSTITUTE OF NATURE EDUCATION IN SHIGA HEIGHTS. BULLETIN. (Text in Japanese; summaries in English and Japanese) 1962. a. Shinshu Daigaku, Kyoikugakubu Fuzoku Shiga Shizen Kyoiku Kenkyu Shisetsu - Shinshu University, Faculty of Education, Institute of Nature Education in Shiga Heights, 1-Ha 7148 Shiga Kogen, Hirao, Yamanouchi-machi, Shimotakai-gun, Nagano-ken 381-04, Japan. Ed. Kenzo Haneda. (back issues avail.) **Indexed:** Biol.Abstr., Jap.Per.Ind.
—BLDSC (2581.802000).

550   JA   ISSN 0388-6298
SHIZUOKA DAIGAKU CHIKYU KAGAKU KENKYU HOKOKU/SHIZUOKA UNIVERSITY. GEOSCIENCE REPORTS. (Text in English, Japanese) 1975. a. Shizuoka Daigaku, Rigakubu, Chikyu Kagaku Kyoshitsu - Shizuoka University, Faculty of Science, Institute of Geosciences, 836, Oya, Shizuoka-shi, Shizuoka-ken 422, Japan.

SHUILI FADIAN/HYDROELECTRIC POWER. see *WATER RESOURCES*

550   US   ISSN 0081-0274
QE1   CODEN: SCESBH
SMITHSONIAN CONTRIBUTIONS TO THE EARTH SCIENCES. 1969. irreg., no.31, 1993. free. Smithsonian Institution Press, 470 L'Enfant Plaza, Ste. 7100, Washington, DC 20560. TEL 202-287-3738. FAX 202-287-3637. Ed. Don Fisher. circ. 1,900. (reprint service avail. from UMI) **Indexed:** Biol.Abstr., Deep Sea Res.& Oceanogr.Abstr., GeoRef., Meteor.& Geoastrophys.Abstr. **Document type:** monographic series.
—CASDDS.

550   MX
SOCIEDAD MEXICANA DE HISTORIA NATURAL. REVISTA. (Text in Spanish; summaries in English) 1940. a. Mex.$250($25) Sociedad Mexicana de Historia Natural, Ave. Dr. Vertiz 724, Mexico City 12 D.F., Mexico. Ed. Ambrosio Gonzalez Cortes. bk.rev. circ. 1,000. (back issues avail.) **Indexed:** Biol.Abstr., Deep Sea Res.& Oceanogr.Abstr., GeoRef.

SOCIETA SARDA DI SCIENZE NATURALI. BOLLETTINO. see *BIOLOGY*

SOCIETE DES NATURALISTES LUXEMBOURGEOIS. BULLETIN. see *BIOLOGY*

550   US   ISSN 0037-9913
SOCIETY OF INDEPENDENT PROFESSIONAL EARTH SCIENTISTS. NEWSLETTER. 1964. q. $15. Society of Independent Professional Earth Scientists, 4925 Greenville, Ste. 170, Dallas, TX 75206-4008. adv. circ. 1,500.

736   SA   ISSN 0038-237X
SOUTH AFRICAN LAPIDARY MAGAZINE. 1967. 3/yr. $22. Federation of South African Gem & Mineralogical Societies, P.O. Box 28744, Sunnyside 0132, South Africa. TEL 27-12-44-4620. Ed. L. Dreyer. adv. bk.rev.; circ. 600 (controlled). **Indexed:** GeoRef., Ind.S.A.Per. **Document type:** consumer publication.
Description: Amateur publication for those interested in collecting minerals, lapidary, geology and related fields.

550 622   AT   ISSN 0726-1527
                              CODEN: SPSEE3
SOUTH AUSTRALIA. DEPARTMENT OF MINES AND ENERGY. SPECIAL PUBLICATIONS. 1982. irreg. price varies. Department of Mines and Energy, P.O. Box 151, Eastwood, S.A. 5063, Australia. TEL 08-274-7500. FAX 08-272-7597. circ. 300. (back issues avail.) **Indexed:** AESIS, GeoRef. **Document type:** government publication.
Description: Historical, scientific or general interest publications dealing with special subjects, particularly those not accomodated by other departmental titles.

551 622   SP
SPAIN. INSTITUTO TECNOLOGICO GEOMINERO DE ESPANA. COLECCION TEMAS GEOLOGICOS - MINEROS. 1977. irreg., no.11, 1989. price varies. Instituto Tecnologico Geominero de Espana, Cristobal Bordiu, 34, 28003 Madrid, Spain. TEL 3495730. FAX 3495762. **Document type:** monographic series.
Formerly: Spain. Instituto Geologico y Minero. Coleccion Temas Geologicos - Mineros.
Description: Covers diverse themes of geology and mining. Many volumes cover congresses, symposiums or courses.

550 398 910   IT   ISSN 0394-5057
SPELEO. 1978. q. L.10000 8. Speleo Club Firenze, Via Torre del Gallo, 30, 50125 Florence, Italy. TEL 055-8448155. FAX 055-8448301. Ed. Franco Utili. adv.; bk.rev.; bibl. circ. 10,000. (back issues avail.)

550 910   JA   ISSN 0386-233X
GB601.A1
SPELEOLOGICAL SOCIETY OF JAPAN. JOURNAL. (Text in English, Japanese) 1976. a. 3000 Yen($25) Speleological Society of Japan - Nihon Kokutsu Gakkai, Akiyoshidai Kagaku Hakubutsukan, Akiyoshi, Shuhocho, Mine-gun, Yamaguchi-ken 754-05, Japan. Eds. T. Kuramoto, K. Yoshimura. circ. 250. (back issues avail.)
—BLDSC (4902.790000).

550   CH   ISSN 1017-0839
QC801   CODEN: TAOSEX
T A O: TERRESTRIAL, ATMOSPHERIC AND OCEANIC SCIENCES/DIQIU KEXUE JIKAN. (Text in Chinese, English) 1990. c. Academia Sinica, Institute of Earth Sciences, P.O. Box 23-59, Taipei, Taiwan, Republic of China. Ed.Bd. **Document type:** academic/scholarly publication.
—BLDSC (8796.065000).
Incorporates (in 1990): Papers in Meteorological Research & Bulletin of Geophysics.
Description: Serves as a medium for the publication of research papers on the atmosphere, the ocean and the solid earth.

550   UK   ISSN 0954-4879
QE1   CODEN: TENOEA
TERRA NOVA. 1989. bi-m. £192 in Europe; elsewhere £211 ($314) (includes Terra Abstracts (ISSN 0954-4887). (European Union of Geosciences) Blackwell Scientific Publications Ltd., Osnew Mead, Oxford OX2 0EL, England. TEL 0865-240201. FAX 0865-721205. TELEX 83355-MEDBOK-G. Ed. R. Muir Wood. adv.; bk.rev.; bibl.; illus.; index. circ. 2,600. (also avail. in microform from UMI; back issues avail.) **Indexed:** Environ.Per.Bibl. (1991-). **Document type:** academic/scholarly publication.
—BLDSC (8794.761100); Faxon; UnCover; SWETS; UMI. **CCC.**
Description: Contains papers on all aspects of significant earth and planetary sciences research.
Refereed Serial

TEXAS. NATURAL RESOURCES INFORMATION SYSTEM. NEWSLETTER. see *ENVIRONMENTAL STUDIES*

551.9   JA   ISSN 0910-688X
TOKYO DAIGAKU RIGAKUBU CHIKAKU KAGAKU JIKKEN SHISETSU IHO/LABORATORY FOR EARTHQUAKE CHEMISTRY. BULLETIN. (Text in Japanese; summaries in English) 1979. irreg. Tokyo Daigaku, Rigakubu, Chikaku Kagaku Jikken Shisetsu - University of Tokyo, Faculty of Science, Laboratory for Earthquake Chemistry, 3-1, Hongo 7-chome, Bunkyo-ku, Tokyo 113, Japan.

EARTH SCIENCES — ABSTRACTING, BIBLIOGRAPHIES, STATISTICS

550   JA   ISSN 0913-6800
TSUKUBA DAIGAKU SUGADAIRA KOGEN JIKKEN SENTA KENKYU HOKOKU/UNIVERSITY OF TSUKUBA. SUGADAIRA MONTANE RESEARCH CENTER. BULLETIN. (Text in English, Japanese) 1967. a. Tsukubu Daigaku, Sugadaira Kogen Jikken Senta - University of Tsukuba, Sugadaira Montane Research Center, Sugadaira, Sanadamachi, Chiisagata-gun, Nagano-ken 386-22, Japan.

549 631.4   CC   ISSN 0564-3910
TURANG/PEDOLOGY. (Text in Chinese) bi-m. Zhongguo Kexueyuan, Nanjing Turang Yanjiusuo - Chinese Academy of Sciences, Nanjing Institute of Pedology, 71 Beijing Donglu, Nanjing, Jiangsu 210008, People's Republic of China. TEL 713781. Ed. Zhao Qiguo.

549 631.4   CC   ISSN 0254-010X
                  CODEN: TUJID
TURANG XUE JINZHAN/ADVANCES IN PEDOLOGY. (Text in Chinese) bi-m. Zhongguo Kexueyuan, Nanjing Turang Yanjiusuo - Chinese Acacemy of Sciences, Nanjing Institute of Pedology, 71 Beijing Donglu, Nanjing, Jiangsu 210008, People's Republic of China. TEL 713781. Ed. Shi Hua.
—CASDDS.

549   CC   ISSN 0564-3929
S590   CODEN: TJHPAE
TURANG XUEBAO/ACTA PEDOLOGICA SINICA. (Text in Chinese; summaries in English) 1948. q. $56.80. Science Press, Marketing and Sales Department, 16 Donghuangchenggen Beijie, Beijing 100707, People's Republic of China. TEL 4010642. FAX 4012180. TELEX 210247-SPBJ-CN. adv. circ. 11,000. **Indexed:** Biol.Abstr., Chem.Abstr, Cott.&Trop.Fibr.Abstr., Curr.Adv.Ecol.Sci., Excerp.Med., GeoRef, Rice Abstr., Soils & Fert. **Document type:** academic/scholarly publication.
—BLDSC (0644.400000); CASDDS.
     Description: Reports on improvement and utilization of soil, provides original theses on this subject. Contains news and information on technology and devices, as well as reviews and discussions of the subject.
     Refereed Serial

550   TU
▼**TURK YERBILIMLERI DERGISI.** (Text in Turkish) 1992. 2/yr. $50. Scientific and Technical Research Council of Turkey - TUBITAK - Turkiye Bilimsel ve Teknik Arastirma Kurumu, Ataturk Bulvari, No. 221, Kavaklidere, Ankara 06100, Turkey. TEL 90-312-468-5300. FAX 90-312-4271336. TELEX 43186 BTAK TR. **Document type:** academic/scholarly publication.
     Supersedes in part (in 1994): Doga Turkish Journal of Earth Sciences - Doga Turk Yerbilimleri Dergisi.
     Refereed Serial

550   TU
▼**TURKISH JOURNAL OF EARTH SCIENCES.** (Text in English) 1992. a. $50. Scientific and Technical Research Council of Turkey - TUBITAK - Turkiye Bilimsel ve Teknik Arastirma Kurumu, Ataturk Bulvari, No. 221, Kavaklidere, 06100 Ankara, Turkey. TEL 90-312-4685300. FAX 90-312-4271336. TELEX 43186 BTAK TR. Ed. Okan Tekeli. **Document type:** academic/scholarly publication.
     Supersedes in part (in 1994): Doga Turkish Journal of Earth Sciences - Doga Turk Yerbilimleri Dergisi.
     Refereed Serial

550   CL   ISSN 0069-357X
UNIVERSIDAD DE CHILE. DEPARTAMENTO DE GEOLOGIA. SERIE COMUNICACIONES. (Text in Spanish; summaries in English) 1960. a. $10. Universidad de Chile, Departamento de Geologia, Casilla 13518, Correo 21, Santiago, Chile. FAX 69630509. TELEX 240523 CENET GL. Ed. Estanislao Godoy. bk.rev. circ. 400.
     Description: Original papers on Andean geology, including economic and structural geology and geochronology, petrology, and volcanology.

550   UY   ISSN 0250-6521
UNIVERSIDAD DE LA REPUBLICA. FACULTAD DE HUMANIDADES Y CIENCIAS. REVISTA. SERIE CIENCIAS DE LA TIERRA. N.S. 1979. irreg. exchange basis. Universidad de la Republica, Facultad de Humanidades y Ciencias, Seccion Revista, Tristan Narvaja 1674, Montevideo, Uruguay. Dir. Beatriz Martinez Osorio.
     Supersedes in part: Universidad de la Republica. Facultad de Humanidades y Ciencias. Revista.

550   BL
UNIVERSIDADE FEDERAL DE PERNAMBUCO. DEPARTAMENTO DE GEOLOGIA. SERIE B. ESTUDOS E PESQUISAS. (Text in Portuguese; summaries in English, French or German) 1971. irreg. exchange basis. Universidade Federal de Pernambuco, Centro de Tecnologia, Recife, PE, Brazil. Ed. J.M. Mabesoone. circ. 1,000.
     Formerly: Universidade Federal de Pernambuco. Instituto de Geosciencias. Serie B: Estudos e Pesquisas (ISSN 0080-0244)

550   BL   ISSN 0100-5375
UNIVERSIDADE FEDERAL DO RIO GRANDE DO SUL. INSTITUTO DE GEOCIENCIAS. PESQUISAS. (Text in English, French, Portuguese, Spanish; summaries in English) 1972. s-a. exchange basis. Universidade Federal do Rio Grande do Sul, Instituto de Geociencias, Av. Bento Goncalves, 9500, Predio 43113, 91540-000 Porto Alegre, RS, Brazil. TEL 051-336-93-22. FAX 051-336-50-11. Ed. Yvonne T. Sanginetti. adv.; bibl. **Indexed:** Geosci.Doc. **Document type:** academic/scholarly publication.

550   BL   ISSN 0104-4338
▼**UNIVERSIDADE FEDERAL DO RIO GRANDE DO SUL. INSTITUTO DE GEOCIENCIAS. PESQUISAS. SERIE MAPAS.** (Text in English, French, Portuguese, Spanish; abstracts in English) 1992. irreg. exchange basis. Universidade Federale do Rio Grande do Sol, Instituto de Geociencias, Av. Bento Goncalves, 9500, Predio 43113, 91540-000 Porto Alegre RS, Brazil. TEL 051-336-98-22. FAX 051-336-50-11. Ed. Ricardo Norberto Ayup-Zouain. **Document type:** academic/scholarly publication.

UNIVERSITE DE SHERBROOKE. DEPARTMENT DE GEOGRAPHIE. BULLETIN DE RECHERCHE. see *GEOGRAPHY*

550   US   ISSN 0068-645X
QE1   CODEN: UCGSAE
UNIVERSITY OF CALIFORNIA PUBLICATIONS IN GEOLOGICAL SCIENCES. 1893. irreg., vol.137, 1993. price varies. University of California Press, 2120 Berkeley Way, Berkeley, CA 94720. TEL 510-642-4247. FAX 510-643-7127. (Orders to: California-Princeton Fulfillment Services, 1445 Lower Ferry Rd., 2120 Berkeley, CA 94720. TEL 800-777-4726. FAX 800-999-1958) Ed.Bd. (back issues avail.; reprint service avail. from JOH) **Indexed:** Biol.Abstr., Deep Sea Res.& Oceanogr.Abstr. **Document type:** monographic series.
—BLDSC (9105.150000); UnCover.
     Refereed Serial

UNIVERSITY OF COLORADO. INSTITUTE OF ARCTIC AND ALPINE RESEARCH. OCCASIONAL PAPERS. see *SCIENCES: COMPREHENSIVE WORKS*

550   JA
QE1
UNIVERSITY OF TOKYO. FACULTY OF SCIENCE. JOURNAL. SECTION 2: GEOLOGY, MINERALOGY, GEOGRAPHY, GEOPHYSICS/TOKYO DAIGAKU RIGAKUBU KIYO, DAI-2-RUI, CHISHITSUGAKU, KOBUTSUGAKU, CHIRIGAKU, CHIKYU BUTSURIGAKU. (Text in English) 1925. a. price varies. c/o Faculty of Science - Library, 3-1, Hongo 7-chome, Bunkyo-ku, Tokyo 113, Japan. TEL 03-3812-2111. (Subscr. to: Maruzen Co., Ltd., 2-3-10 Nihonbashi, Chuo-ku, Tokyo 103, Japan; Overseas subscr. to: Import and Export Dept., P.O. Box 5050, Tokyo International, Tokyo 100-31, Japan) Ed. Hidehiko Shimazaki. bibl.; charts; illus. circ. 800. **Indexed:** Biol.Abstr., Chem.Abstr., Deep Sea Res.& Oceanogr.Abstr., GeoRef., JTA, Met.Abstr. **Document type:** academic/scholarly publication.
—BLDSC (4751.000000); UnCover.
     Former titles: University of Tokyo. Faculty of Science. Journal. Section 2: Geology, Mineralogy, Geography, Earth and Planetary Physics; University of Tokyo. Faculty of Science. Journal. Section 2: Geology, Mineralogy, Geography, Geophysics (ISSN 0368-2250)

UNIVERSITY OF TORONTO. FACULTY OF FORESTRY. RESEARCH REPORT. see *FORESTS AND FORESTRY*

UNIVERSITY OF WISCONSIN-MILWAUKEE. FIELD STATION BULLETIN. see *BIOLOGY*

550   JA   ISSN 0288-3155
URBAN KUBOTA. (Text in Japanese) 1969. a. Kubota Corp., 2-47, Shikitsu Hagashi 1-chome, Naniwa-ku, Osaka 556-91, Japan.

VEGETATION HISTORY AND ARCHAEOBOTANY. see *BIOLOGY — Botany*

WASEDA DAIGAKU KYOIKUGAKUBU GAKUJUTSU KENKYU. SEIBUTSUGAKU, CHIGAKU HEN/WASEDA UNIVERSITY. SCHOOL OF EDUCATION. SCIENTIFIC RESEARCHES: BIOLOGY, GEOLOGY. see *BIOLOGY*

WESTERN CONTRACTOR. see *MINES AND MINING INDUSTRY*

WHO'S DRILLING. see *PETROLEUM AND GAS*

550   CC
WUTAN HUATAN YICONG. (Text in Chinese) bi-m. Dizhi Kuangchan Bu, Diqiu Wuli Diqiu Huaxue Kanca Yanjiusuo - Ministry of Geology and Mineral Products, Institute of Geophysics and Geochemistry Prospecting, Baiwanzhuang, Fuchengmenwai, Beijing 100037, People's Republic of China. TEL 8311133. Ed. Li Xingyi.

WYOMING GEOLOGICAL ASSOCIATION. GUIDEBOOK. see *PETROLEUM AND GAS*

550   JA   ISSN 0289-9787
YAMAGUCHI CHIGAKKAISHI/YAMAGUCHI EARTH SCIENCE ASSOCIATION. JOURNAL. (Text in Japanese) s-a. Yamaguchi Chigakkai - Yamaguchi Earth Science Association, Kenritsu Yamaguchi Hakubutsukan, 8-2, Kasugacho, Yamaguchi-shi, Yamaguchi-ken 753, Japan.

550   XR   ISSN 0232-0916
Z DEJIN GEODEZIE A KARTOGRAFIE. 1981. irreg. exchange basis. Narodni Technicke Muzeum, Kostelni 42, Prague 7, Czech Republic. bibl.; illus.

550   CC   ISSN 1000-694X
ZHONGGUO SHAMO/CHINESE DESERT. (Text in Chinese) q. Zhongguo Kexueyuan, Lanzhou Shamo Yanjiusuo - Chinese Academy of Sciences, Lanzhou Institute of Desert Research, 174 Donggang Xilu, Lanzhou, Gansu 730000, People's Republic of China. TEL 26725. Ed. Zhu Zhenda.

550   CC   ISSN 1000-3037
ZIRAN ZIYUAN XUEBAO/JOURNAL OF NATURAL RESOURCES. (Text in Chinese) 1986. q. $63.60. (Zhongguo Kexueyuan, Ziran Ziyuan Zonghe Kaocha Weiyuanhui - Academia Sinica, Comprehensive Exploration Committee of Natural Resource) Science Press, Marketing and Sales Department, 16 Donghuangchenggen Beijie, Beijing 100707, People's Republic of China. TEL 4010642. FAX 4012180. TELEX 210247-SPBJ-CN.
     Refereed Serial

EARTH SCIENCES — Abstracting, Bibliographies, Statistics

016 550   AT   ISSN 0313-704X
A E S I S QUARTERLY. (Australian Earth Sciences Information System) 1976. q. Aus.$325 to individuals; educational organizations Aus.$275. Australian Mineral Foundation, 63 Conyngham St., Glenside, S.A. 5065, Australia. TEL 08-3790444. FAX 08-3794634. index. circ. 500. **Indexed:** AESIS. ●Also available online. Vendor(s): Info-One International Pty Ltd.

550 620 016   TH
A G E REFDEX. (Text in English) 1973. a. membership. Asian Geotechnical Engineering Information Center, c/o Asian Institute of Technology, Box 2754, Bangkok, Thailand. TEL 66-2-524-5862. FAX 66-2-516-2126. TELEX 84276 TH. abstr.; circ. 300 (controlled). (microfiche)
     Formerly: Asian Geotechnical Engineering Abstracts (ISSN 0301-4169)

551   US
A M Q U A PROGRAM AND ABSTRACTS. 1970. biennial. $8 membership. American Quaternary Association, c/o Julie Brigham-Grette, Department of Geology - Geography, University of Massachusetts, Box 35820, Amherst, MA 01003-5820. TEL 413-545-4840. FAX 413-545-1200. circ. 1,000. **Document type:** academic/scholarly publication.
     Description: Abstracts of a topical nature with different themes each issue related to the interdisciplinary fields in the Quarternary.

EARTH SCIENCES — ABSTRACTING, BIBLIOGRAPHIES, STATISTICS

A S F A MARINE BIOTECHNOLOGY ABSTRACTS. (Aquatic Sciences & Fisheries Abstracts) see *BIOLOGY — Abstracting, Bibliographies, Statistics*

011 CN ISSN 0226-1685
A S T I S BIBLIOGRAPHY. (Not avail. in printed format) 1979. a. Can.$110. Arctic Science & Technology Information System, Arctic Institute of North America, University of Calgary, 2500 University Dr. N.W. Calgary, AB T2N 1N4, Canada. TEL 403-220-4036. Ed. C. Ross Goodwin. circ. 100. (also avail. in microfiche) **Document type:** bibliography.
●Also available online. Vendor(s): QL Systems Ltd. Also available on CD-ROM.
—BLDSC (1747.067000).
Description: Contains the complete contents of the ASTIS database, including detailed subject, geographic, author and title indexes.

ABSTRACT JOURNAL IN EARTHQUAKE ENGINEERING. see *ENGINEERING — Abstracting, Bibliographies, Statistics*

551 CC ISSN 0258-6746
ABSTRACTS OF CHINESE GEOLOGICAL LITERATURE. (Text in English) 1985. q. $80. National Geological Library, Kan Kia Ko, Fu Wai, Beijing, People's Republic of China. TEL 0086-01-8327337. FAX 0086-01-8323270. (Dist. by: China National Publications Import & Export Corporation, P.O. Box 88, Beijing, People's Republic of China. TEL 0086-01-5063069) Ed. Chen Minghui. circ. 100. (reprint service avail.) **Document type:** abstracting/indexing.
Description: Provides bibliographic information on Chinese geological literature.

551.7 560 560 US ISSN 0192-7272
CODEN: APSPC6
AMERICAN ASSOCIATION OF STRATIGRAPHIC PALYNOLOGISTS. ABSTRACTS OF PAPERS PRESENTED AT THE ANNUAL MEETINGS. a. $2. American Association of Stratigraphic Palynologists Foundation., c/o Robert T. Clarke, Mobil R & D Corp.-D R L, Box 819047, Dallas, TX 75381. TEL 214-851-8481. FAX 214-851-8185. **Indexed:** GeoRef.

551 US
ARCTIC & ANTARCTIC REGIONS (COLD REGIONS 1800-PRESENT). s-a. $795. National Information Services Corporation (NISC), Ste. 6, Wyman Towers, 3100 St. Paul St., Baltimore, MD 21218. TEL 301-243-0797. FAX 301-243-0982.
●Available only on CD-ROM. Producer(s): NISC.
Description: Information resource for polar literature citations and abstracts.

796.525 AT ISSN 0313-2846
AUSTRALIAN SPELEO ABSTRACTS. 1970. irreg. price varies. Sydney Speleological Society, P.O. Box 198, Broadway, N.S.W. 2007, Australia. FAX 02-660-1217. Ed. Ross Ellis. adv. contact: Ross Ellis. index, cum.index. circ. 125. **Document type:** abstracting/indexing.

551 PL ISSN 0373-1987
BIBLIOGRAFIA GEOLOGICZNA POLSKI. 1920. a. price varies. Panstwowy Instytut Geologiczny, Ul. Rakowiecka 4, 00-975 Warsaw, Poland. TEL 48-22-495351. TELEX 815541. index. circ. 400. (back issues avail.) **Document type:** bibliography.
Description: Focuses on the fields of geophysics, geomorphology, stratigraphy, paleontology, mineralogy, petrography, hydrogeology and drilling.

551.4 PL ISSN 0239-6246
BIBLIOGRAFIA HYDROLOGII I OCEANOLOGII/BIBLIOGRAPHY OF HYDROLOGY AND OCEANOLOGY. (Text in English, French, German, Polish, Russian) 1936. irreg. $75. Instytut Meteorologii i Gospodarki Wodnej - Institute of Meteorology and Water Management, 61 Podlesna St., 01-673 Warsaw, Poland. FAX 48-22-345466. TELEX 814331. circ. 150. **Document type:** bibliography.
Description: Articles on hydrology, groundwaters, surface waters, oceanology, hydrometeorology, instruments.

551 016 US ISSN 0098-2784
Z6031 CODEN: BBIGB
BIBLIOGRAPHY AND INDEX OF GEOLOGY. 1969. m. $1295 (effective Jan. 1991). American Geological Institute, 4220 King St., Alexandria, VA 22302-1507. TEL 703-379-2480. FAX 703-379-7563. Ed. Sharon Tahirkheli. index. circ. 620. (also avail. in microform from PMC)
●Also available online. Vendor(s): CISTI, DIALOG Information Services, Inc., Orbit Search Service (GEOR), STN International (GeoRef).
Also available on CD-ROM. Producer(s): SilverPlatter Information, Inc. (GeoRef).
—BLDSC (2001.800000); UnCover.
Formed by the merger of: Bibliography of North American Geology; Bibliography and Index of Geology Exclusive of North America (ISSN 0006-1522).

551 016 SA ISSN 0584-2360
Z6034.S57 CODEN: BSIGDW
BIBLIOGRAPHY AND SUBJECT INDEX OF SOUTH AFRICAN GEOLOGY. (Text in English) 1957. irreg., latest 1991. price varies. Geological Survey, Private Bag X112, Pretoria 0001, South Africa. TEL 27-12-841-1911. FAX 27-12-841-1203. TELEX 350286-SAGEO. circ. 2,000. **Document type:** bibliography.
Description: Lists geological articles appearing in South African publications for a particular year with an abstract of each.

551.22 016 UK ISSN 0523-2988
CODEN: BISEB2
BIBLIOGRAPHY OF SEISMOLOGY. 1965. s-a. £90. International Seismological Centre, Pipers Lane, Thatcham, Newbury, Berks. RG13 4NS, England. TEL 0635-61022. FAX 0635-72351. (back issues avail.) **Indexed:** GeoRef.
—BLDSC (2011.000000).

012 559 FJ ISSN 0252-8398
BIBLIOGRAPHY OF THE GEOLOGY OF FIJI. 1969. irreg. price varies. Mineral Resources Department, P.M. Bag, Suva, Fiji. Ed. Peter Rodda. circ. 500. **Document type:** bibliography.
Description: Works on geology, geophysics, and mining on the islands and ocean areas of Fiji.

557 016 US ISSN 0067-7272
BIBLIOGRAPHY OF THE GEOLOGY OF MISSOURI. 1956. a. price varies. Department of Natural Resources, Division of Geology and Land Survey, Box 250, Rolla, MO 65401. TEL 314-368-2125.

BIBLIOGRAPHY ON COLD REGIONS SCIENCE & TECHNOLOGY. see *ENGINEERING — Abstracting, Bibliographies, Statistics*

BIULETIN ZA NOVONABAVENI KNIGI NA CHUZHDI EZITZI. SERIIA B: ESTESTVENI I PRILOZHNI NAUKI. see *BIOLOGY — Abstracting, Bibliographies, Statistics*

354 BS
BOTSWANA. GEOLOGICAL SURVEY DEPARTMENT. ANNOTATED BIBLIOGRAPHY AND INDEX OF THE GEOLOGY OF BOTSWANA. 1968. irreg. $3. Geological Survey Department, Lobatse, Botswana. FAX 332013. Ed. C. Siyumbwa. circ. 400. **Document type:** government publication, bibliography.

551 016 UK ISSN 0140-7813
BRITISH GEOLOGICAL LITERATURE; a bibliography and index of geology (and related topics) of the British Isles and adjacent sea areas. 1972. q. £60($115) Bibliographic Press, 52 Little Paddocks, Ferring, Worthing, W. Sussex BN12 5NH, England. TEL 44-903-504019. Ed. N. Edwards. abstr.; bibl.; index. circ. 300. **Document type:** abstracting/indexing.
—BLDSC (2301.050000).
Description: Contains a continuing regional bibliography and index of papers and articles in journals, as well as conference proceedings.

557 016 CN ISSN 0707-2996
QE185
CANADA. GEOLOGICAL SURVEY. INDEX OF PUBLICATIONS OF THE GEOLOGICAL SURVEY OF CANADA. 1900. irreg. price varies. Geological Survey of Canada, 601 Booth St., Ottawa, ON K1A 0E8, Canada. TEL 613-995-4342. index, cum.index: 1959-1974, 1975-1979.
—CCC.

557 016 CN
CANADA. GEOLOGICAL SURVEY. INFORMATION CIRCULAR/CANADA. COMMISSION GEOLOGIQUE. BULLETIN D'INFORMATION. (Text in English, French) 1973. m. free. Geological Survey of Canada - Commission Geologique du Canada, 601 Booth St., Ottawa, ON K1A 0E8, Canada. TEL 613-995-4342. bibl. circ. 5,100. **Document type:** government publication.
Formerly: Canada. Geological Survey. Monthly Information Circular.
Description: Announces the publication of new reports and maps (and reprints), and the release of open files.

551.49 JA
CHIKA SUII JIBAN CHINKA KANSOKU KIROKU/OBSERVATIONS OF UNDERGROUND WATER LEVEL AND SUBSIDENCE OF GROUND IN HOKKAIDO. (Text in Japanese) 1976. a. Hokkaidoritsu Chika Shigen Chosajo - Geological Survey of Hokkaido, Nishi 12-chome, K ta 19-jo, Kita-ku, Sapporo-shi, Hokkaido 060, Japan. TEL 011-747-2211. FAX 011-737-9071.

622 669 550 015 JA ISSN 0011-3301
CURRENT BIBLIOGRAPHY ON SCIENCE AND TECHNOLOGY: EARTH SCIENCE, MINING AND METALLURGY/KAGAKU GIJUTSU BUNKEN SOKUHO. KINZOKU KOGAKU KOZAN KOGAKU, CHIKYU NO KAGAKU-HEN. (Text in Japanese) 1958. s-m. $2080. Japan Information Center of Science and Technology - Nihon Kagaku Gijutsu Joho Senta, 5-2 Nagata-cho, 2-chome, Chiyoda-ku, Tokyo 100, Japan. TEL 03-381-6411. FAX 03-3581-6446. index. circ. 600.
●Also available on ine. Vendor(s): JICST.

CURRENT CONTENTS: PHYSICAL, CHEMICAL & EARTH SCIENCES. see *CHEMISTRY — Abstracting, Bibliographies, Statistics*

551.44 011 UK
CURRENT TITLES IN SPELEOLOGY. 1969. a. £13.50. British Cave Research Association, c/o Bryan Ellis, 20 Woodland Avenue, Westonzoyland, Bridgewater, Somerset TA7 0LQ, England. Ed. R.W. Mansfield. circ. 500. (back issues avail.) **Document type:** abstracting/indexing.
Description: Bibliographical details of papers published worldwide that deal with caves and caving.

551.22 CC
DIZHEN WENZHAI/SEISMOLOGY ABSTRACTS. (Text in Chinese) bi-m. Guojia Dizhen-ju, Keji Qingbao Zhongxin - State Seismological Bureau, Science and Technology Information Center, 63 Fuxing Lu, Beijing 100036, People's Republic of China. TEL 8115331. Ed. Cheng Ronglian.

550 016 AT ISSN 0311-3531
EARTH SCIENCE AND RELATED INFORMATION; selected annotated titles. 1973. m. Aus.$150. Australian Mineral Foundation, 63 Conyngham St., Glenside, S.A. 5065, Australia. TEL 08-3790444. FAX 08-3794634. bk.rev.; bibl. circ. 400. **Indexed:** AESIS.

EARTHQUAKE ENGINEERING ABSTRACTS DATABASE. see *ENGINEERING — Abstracting, Bibliographies, Statistics*

GEOGRAPHICAL ABSTRACTS: PHYSICAL GEOGRAPHY. see *GEOGRAPHY — Abstracting, Bibliographies, Statistics*

551 HU ISSN 0230-7065
GEOLOGIAI ES GEOFIZIKAI SZAKIRODALMI TAJEKOZTATO/GEOLOGY AND GEOPHYSICS ABSTRACTS. 1983. m. 6000 Ft. Orszagos Muszaki Informacios Kozpont es Konyvtar (O.M.I.K.K.) - National Technical Information Centre and Library, Muzeum u. 17, Box 12, 1428 Budapest, Hungary. (Subscr. to: Kultura, Box 149, 1389 Budapest, Hungary) Ed. Otto Tomschey. abstr.; index. circ. 270.

EARTH SCIENCES — ABSTRACTING, BIBLIOGRAPHIES, STATISTICS

551 UK ISSN 0954-0512
QE1
GEOLOGICAL ABSTRACTS. 1977. 12/yr. (plus a. cumulation). £600($925) (effective 1994). Elsevier - Geo Abstracts (Subsidiary of: Elsevier Science Ltd.), Regency House, 34 Duke St., Norwich NR3 3AP, England. TEL 44-603-626327. FAX 44-603-667934. TELEX 975247 CHACOM G. (Subscr. to: Elsevier Science Ltd., Oxford Fulfilment Centre, P.O. Box 800, Kidlington, Oxford OX5 1DX, England. TEL 44-865-843000. FAX 44-865-843010; Subscr. in U.S. and Canada to: Elsevier Science, 660 White Plains Rd., Tarrytown, NY 10591-5153. TEL 914-524-9200. FAX 914-333-2444) Eds. A. Hall, S. Stone. index. circ. 600. (back issues avail.; reprint service avail. from KTO) **Indexed:** AESIS. **Document type:** abstracting/indexing.
●Also available online. Vendor(s): DIALOG Information Services, Inc. (File no.292), Orbit Search Service (GEOB).
—BLDSC (4131.230000). **CCC.**
Formed by the 1989 merger of: Geological Abstracts: Geophysics and Tectonics (ISSN 0268-7941); Geological Abstracts: Economic Geology (ISSN 0268-800X); Geological Abstracts: Palaeontology and Stratigraphy (ISSN 0268-8018); Geological Abstracts: Sedimentary Geology; Geological Abstracts: Geophysics and Tectonics was formerly: Geophysics and Tectonics Abstracts (ISSN 0262-0847) which was formerly: Geophysical Abstracts (ISSN 0309-4332); Geological Abstracts: Sedimentary Geology was formerly: Sedimentology (ISSN 0268-8026).
Description: International abstracting service for geologists.

551 016 US ISSN 0016-7592
QE1 CODEN: GAAPBC
GEOLOGICAL SOCIETY OF AMERICA. ABSTRACTS WITH PROGRAMS. 1969. a. $73 (effective 1995). Geological Society of America, 3300 Penrose Pl., Box 9140, Boulder, CO 80301. TEL 303-447-2020. FAX 303-447-1133. Ed. J. Clark. circ. 7,000. **Indexed:** GeoRef., INIS Atomind.
—BLDSC (0567.950000). **CCC.**
Description: Abstracts of scientific papers to be presented at the Society's annual meetings, and program of events.

550 AT
GEOLOGICAL SOCIETY OF AUSTRALIA. ABSTRACTS SERIES. 1980. irreg., no.34, 1993. price varies. Geological Society of Australia, Inc., 606 Wynardt Jouse, 301 George St., Sydney, N.S.W. 2000, Australia. TEL 02-290-2194. FAX 02-290-2198. **Indexed:** AESIS. **Document type:** abstracting/indexing.

557 016 US
GEORGIA GEOLOGIC SURVEY. CIRCULAR 1. LIST OF PUBLICATIONS. (Subseries of its Circular series) 14th ed., 1973. irreg., 21st ed., 1990. free. Department of Natural Resources, Georgia Geologic Survey, 19 Martin Luther King Jr. Dr., S.W., Rm. 400, Atlanta, GA 30334. TEL 404-656-3214.
Formerly: Georgia Geological Survey. Circular 1. List of Publications.
Description: Listing and charges for all geologic survey publications.

550 016 UK ISSN 0016-8483
QE1
GEOSCIENCE DOCUMENTATION; a bi-monthly journal for the study of geoscience literature. 1969. bi-m. £60($120) Geosystems, P.O. Box 40, Didcot, Oxon. OX11 9BX, England. TEL 44-235-813913. bk.rev.; pat.; stat.; index. **Indexed:** AESIS, Bibl.Cart. **Document type:** abstracting/indexing.
●Also available online. Vendor(s): DIALOG Information Services, Inc.
Also available on CD-ROM. Producer(s): NISC (GeoArchive).
—UnCover.

011 614.7 CN ISSN 0831-5000
GEOTECHNICAL SCIENCE LABORATORIES. PUBLICATIONS, REPORTS, AND THESES. 1972. a. free. Geotechnical Science Laboratories, Geography Department, Carleton University, 1125 Colonel By Dr., Ottawa, ON K1S 5B6, Canada. TEL 613-788-2600. FAX 613-788-4301. index, cum.index: 1976-1984. circ. 550. **Document type:** academic/scholarly publication, bibliography.
Description: Lists scientific reports, papers in journals, theses and other items available.

550 016 UK ISSN 0952-2700
GEOTITLES; geoscience bibliography. 1969. m. £400($800) Geosystems, P.O. Box 40, Didcot, Oxon. OX11 9BX, England. TEL 44-235-813913. adv. (also avail. in magnetic tape) **Document type:** bibliography.
●Also available online. Vendor(s): DIALOG Information Services, Inc. (File no. 58).
Also available on CD-ROM. Producer(s): NISC (GeoArchive).
—BLDSC (4161.090000).
Formerly (until 1985): Geotitles Weekly (ISSN 0016-8564)

550 US ISSN 1050-4818
QE1
GLOBAL VOLCANISM NETWORK. BULLETIN. 1978. m. $75 in US, Canada, Mexico; elsewhere $150. (Smithsonian Institution) U.S. National Technical Information Service, 5825 Port Royal Rd., Springfield, VA 22161. TEL 703-487-4630. **Document type:** bulletin.
Formerly (until 1989): Scientific Event Alert Network. Bulletin (ISSN 0731-7573)
Description: Reports timely information on worldwide natural science events such as volcanic eruptions, earthquakes, fireballs, meteorite falls and finds, mammal strandings and sitings, discoveries of unusual natural history specimens, and population biology events including migrations, diseases and afflictions, and mortalities.

551 CC
GUOWAI KEJI ZILIAO MULU - DIZHIXUE/FOREIGN SCIENCE AND TECHNOLOGY CATALOGUE - GEOLOGY. (Text in Chinese) q. Zhongguo Dizhi Kuangchan Xinxi Yanjiuyuan - Chinese Institute of Geology and Mineral Products Information, 277, Fuchengmenwai Beijie, Beijing 100037, People's Republic of China. TEL 892243. Ed. Bao Yongquan.

011 551.46 FR ISSN 1250-5811
HORIZON. BULLETIN BIBLIOGRAPHIQUE O R S T O M. 1989. s-a. 370 F. (Institut Francais de Recherche Scientifique pour le Developpement en Cooperation) O R S T O M Editions - Diffusion, 72 Route d'Aulnay, 93143 Bondy Cedex, France. TEL 48-02-55-00. FAX 48-47-30-88. circ. 250. **Document type:** abstracting/indexing.
Formed by the 1993 merger of: Horizon. Bulletin Bibliographique O R S T O M Oceanographie Hydrobiologie (ISSN 1142-2505) & Horizon. Bulletin Bibliographique O R S T O M Sante (ISSN 0998-478X) & Horizon. Bulletin Bibliographique O R S T O M Science de la Terre (ISSN 0998-4771) & Horizon. Bulletin Bibliographique O R S T O M Sciences du Monde Vegetal et Animal (ISSN 1142-2521) & Horizon. Bulletin Bibliographique O R S T O M Sciences Economiques et Sociales (ISSN 1142-2513); Horizon. Bulletin Bibliographique O R S T O M Sciences et Techniques Fondamentales Sciences de l'Ingenieur (ISSN 1142-253X).

016.551 UK ISSN 0953-7589
HYDROTITLES; hydroscience bibliography. 1989. bi-m. $160 (Europe £80) (effective Jan. 1994). Geosystems, P.O. Box 40, Didcot, Oxon. OX11 9BX, England. TEL 44-235-813913. Ed. Roger F. Templeman. bk.rev. **Document type:** abstracting/indexing.
●Also available online. Vendor(s): DIALOG Information Services, Inc.
Also available on CD-ROM. Producer(s): NISC (GeoArchive).
Description: Covers hydrology, hydroelectric power, climate change, glaciology, and fluvial geomorphology.

I M M ABSTRACTS AND INDEX; a survey of world literature on the economic geology and mining of all minerals (except coal), mineral processing and non-ferrous extraction metallurgy. (Institution of Mining and Metallurgy) see MINES AND MINING INDUSTRY — Abstracting, Bibliographies, Statistics

550 IS
ISRAEL. GEOLOGICAL SURVEY. BIBLIOGRAPHY SERIES. (Text in English, French, German, Hebrew) irreg. $15 per no. Geological Survey Library, 30 Malke Yisrael St., Jerusalem 95 501, Israel. TEL 972-2-314266. **Document type:** bibliography.

555 IS ISSN 0334-3510
ISRAEL. GEOLOGICAL SURVEY. CURRENT BIBLIOGRAPHY OF MIDDLE EAST GEOLOGY. (Text in English) 1972. m. $24. Geological Survey Library, 30 Malke Israel Street, Jerusalem 95 501, Israel. TEL 972-2-314266. bibl. circ. 320. (back issues avail.) **Indexed:** GeoRef. **Document type:** bibliography.
Formerly: Selected Bibliography of Middle East Geology.
Description: Compendium of all geology books printed in Israel and the Arab world, classified by country and by subject.

551.22 JA
JISHIN KOGAKU BUNKEN MOKUROKU/BIBLIOGRAPHY OF EARTHQUAKE ENGINEERING. (Text in English, Japanese) 1968. biennial. 700 Yen per no. Doboku Gakkai, Taishin Kogaku linkai - Japan Society of Civil Engineers, Earthquake Engineering Committee, Yotsuya 1-chome, Shinjuku-ku, Tokyo 160, Japan. **Document type:** bibliography.

KYOKUIKI SEIBUTSU SHINPOJUMU KOEN YOSHISHU/ABSTRACTS OF THE SYMPOSIUM ON POLAR BIOLOGY. see BIOLOGY — Abstracting, Bibliographies, Statistics

551 CN
MANITOBA ENERGY AND MINES. BIBLIOGRAPHY SERIES. irreg. Manitoba Energy and Mines, 555-330 Graham Ave., Winnipeg, MB R3C 4E3, Canada. TEL 204-945-6541. FAX 204-945-0586. **Document type:** bibliography, government publication.
Formerly: Manitoba. Mineral Resources Division. Bibliography Series.
Description: Bibliographic reference material on the geology of Manitoba.

MARINE POLLUTION RESEARCH TITLES. see ENVIRONMENTAL STUDIES — Abstracting, Bibliographies, Statistics

MARINE SCIENCE CONTENTS TABLES. see BIOLOGY — Abstracting, Bibliographies, Statistics

METEOROLOGICAL AND GEOASTROPHYSICAL ABSTRACTS. see METEOROLOGY — Abstracting, Bibliographies, Statistics

N T I S ALERTS: NATURAL RESOURCES & EARTH SCIENCES. see CONSERVATION — Abstracting, Bibliographies, Statistics

621.4 016 US
N T I S ALERTS: OCEAN TECHNOLOGY & ENGINEERING. w. $135 (foreign $195). U.S. National Technical Information Service, 5285 Port Royal Rd., Springfield, VA 22161. TEL 703-487-4630. FAX 703-321-8547. TELEX 64617. index. (back issues avail.)
Former titles: Abstract Newsletter: Ocean Technology & Engineering; Weekly Abstract Newsletter: Ocean Technology and Engineering; Weekly Government Abstracts. Ocean Technology and Engineering (ISSN 0364-6424)

550 JA
NIHON CHIKYU KAGAKKAI NENKAI KOEN YOSHISHU/GEOCHEMICAL SOCIETY OF JAPAN. ABSTRACTS OF REPORTS ON ANNUAL MEETING. (Text in English, Japanese) a. Nihon Chikyu Kagakkai, Nihon Gakkai Jimu Senta, 16-19, Honkomagome 5-chome, Bunkyo-ku, Tokyo 113, Japan. **Document type:** abstracting/indexing.

551 JA ISSN 0917-3404
NIHON CHISHITSU GAKKAI KANTO SHIBU SHINPOJUMU KOEN YOSHISHU/GEOLOGICAL SOCIETY OF JAPAN. ABSTRACTS OF KANTO BRANCH SYMPOSIUM. (Text in Japanese) s-a. Nihon Chishitsu Gakkai, Kanto Shibu - Geological Society of Japan, Kanto Branch, Gunma Daigaku Kyoikugakubu Chigaku Kyoshitsu, 4-2, Aramaki-cho, Maebashi-shi, Gunma-ken 371, Japan.

551.46 JA
NIHON KAISUI GAKKAI KENKYU GIJUTSU HAPPYOKAI KOEN YOSHISHU/SOCIETY OF SEA WATER SCIENCE, JAPAN. ABSTRACTS OF MEETING. (Text in Japanese) a. Nihon Kaisui Gakkai, 15-14, Roppongi 7-chome, Minato-ku, Tokyo 106, Japan. **Document type:** abstracting/indexing.

551.48 JA
NIHON RIKUSUI GAKKAI KOEN YOSHISHU/JAPANESE SOCIETY OF LIMNOLOGY. ABSTRACTS OF MEETING. (Text in Japanese) a. Nihon Rikusui Gakkai, Tokyo Toritsu Daigaku Rigakubu Kagaku Kyoshitsu, 1-1, Minamiosawa, Hachioji-shi, Tokyo 192-03, Japan. **Document type:** abstracting/indexing.

551.46 016 US ISSN 0748-1489
GC1 CODEN: OABTAE
OCEANIC ABSTRACTS. 1964. m. $1045 (foreign $1250). Cambridge Scientific Abstracts, 7200 Wisconsin Ave., 6th Fl., Bethesda, MD 20814. TEL 301-961-6750. FAX 301-961-6720. adv.; bibl.; index, cum.index. (also avail. in magnetic tape; back issues avail.) **Indexed:** Cal.Tiss.Abstr., Chemorec.Abstr., Comput.& Info.Sys., Nutr.Abstr., Oncol.Abstr., Pollut.Abstr. **Document type:** abstracting/indexing.
•Also available online. Vendor(s): DIALOG Information Services, Inc. (File no.28), European Space Agency (File no.17/OCEANIC), STN International.
Supersedes: Oceanic Index (ISSN 0029-8093); Oceanic Citation Index (ISSN 0029-8085)
Description: Covers marine biology, oceanography, ships and shipping, marine pollution, and offshore engineering.

551.46 011 UK ISSN 0967-0653
Z6004.P6
OCEANOGRAPHIC LITERATURE REVIEW. 1967. 12/yr. £568($875) (effective 1994). Elsevier Science Ltd., Pergamon, P.O. Box 800, Kidlington, Oxford OX5 1DX, England. TEL 44-865-843000. FAX 44-865-843010. (Subscr. in U.S. and Canada to: Elsevier Science, 660 White Plains Rd., Tarrytown, NY 10591-5153. TEL 914-524-9200. FAX 914-333-2444) Ed. Sally Stone. adv.; bk.rev.; bibl.; charts; illus.; pat.; index. (also avail. in microfilm from UMI) **Indexed:** Biol.Abstr., Chem.Abstr., Curr.Adv.Ecol.Sci., Curr.Tit.Ocean, Eng.Ind., Excerp.Med., Geo.Abstr., GeoRef., Ind.Sci.Rev., Meteor.& Geoastrophys.Abstr., Ocean.Abstr., Petrol.Abstr., Pollut.Abstr., Sci.Abstr., Sci.Cit.Ind., So.Pac.Per.Ind. **Document type:** academic/scholarly publication, bibliography.
•Also available on CD-ROM. Producer(s): NISC (Oceanographic & Marine Resources - Vol.1).
—BLDSC (6232.130000); SWETS; UMI. **CCC.**
Former titles (until 1993): Deep-Sea Research. Part B: Oceanographic Literature Review (ISSN 0198-0254); (until 1979): Oceanographic Abstracts and Bibliography (ISSN 0146-6305); (until 1977): Deep-Sea Research. Oceanographic Abstracts and Oceanographic Bibliography Section (ISSN 0418-4890)
Description: Annotated bibliography to international research literature in all disciplines pertaining to oceanography.
Refereed Serial

551.46 JA
OCEANOGRAPHICAL SOCIETY OF JAPAN. ABSTRACTS ON THE CONFERENCE/NIHON KAIYO GAKKAI TAIKAI KOEN YOSHISHU. (Text in English, Japanese) s-a. 2500 Yen per no. Oceanographical Society of Japan - Nippon Kaiyo Gakkai, 6-14, Minamidai 1-chome, Nakano-ku, Tokyo 164, Japan. **Document type:** abstracting/indexing.

520 016 551 FR ISSN 1146-545X
P A S C A L. E 48: ENVIRONNEMENT COSMIQUE TERRESTRE, ASTRONOMIE ET GEOLOGIE EXTRATERRESTRE. (Text in English, French) 1984. 10/yr. 1240 F. (outside EC 1320 F.). Centre National de la Recherche Scientifique, Institut de l'Information Scientifique et Technique, 2 allee du Parc de Brabois, 54514 Vandoeuvre-Les-Nancy, France. TEL 83-50-46-00. FAX 83-50-46-50. adv. contact: Veronique Guinvarc'h. index, cum.index. (also avail. in microfiche) **Document type:** bibliography.
•Also available online. Vendor(s): DIALOG Information Services, Inc. (File no.144), European Space Agency (File no.14), Telesystemes - Questel. Also available on CD-ROM.
Former titles: P A S C A L Explore. E 48: Environnement Cosmique Terrestre, Astronomie et Geologie Extraterrestre (ISSN 0761-2109); P A S C A L Explore. Part 48: Environnement Cosmique Terrestre, Astronomie et Geologie Extraterrestre; Which supersedes in part (in 1984): Bulletin Signaletique. Part 120: Geophysique Externe. Astronomie et Astrophysique; Which supersede in part: Bulletin Signaletique. Part 120: Astronomie - Physique Spatiale - Geophysique (ISSN 0240-849X)

551 016 FR ISSN 1146-5174
P A S C A L. F 40: MINERALOGIE. GEOCHIMIE. GEOLOGIE EXTRATERRESTRE. (Text in English, French) 1984. 10/yr. 1370 F. (outside EC 1450 F.). (Bureau de Recherches Geologiques et Minieres) Centre National de la Recherche Scientifique, Institut de l'Information Scientifique et Technique, 2 allee du Parc de Brabois, 54514 Vandoeuvre-Les-Nancy Cedex, France. TEL 83-50-46-00. FAX 83-50-46-50. adv. contact: Veronique Guinvarc'h. (also avail. in microfiche) **Document type:** bibliography.
•Also available online. Vendor(s): DIALOG Information Services, Inc. (File no.144), European Space Agency (File no.14), Telesystemes - Questel. Also available on CD-ROM.
Former titles: P A S C A L Folio. F 40: Mineralogie. Giochimie. Geologie Extraterrestre (ISSN 0761-1811); P A S C A L Folio. Part 40: Mineralogie. Geochimie. Geologie Extraterrestre; Which supersedes (in 1984): Bulletin Sigignaletique: Bibliographie des Sciences de la Terre. Section 220. Mineralogie. Geochimie. Geologie Extraterrestre (ISSN 0300-9262)

652 016 FR ISSN 1146-5190
P A S C A L. F 42: ROCHES CRISTALLINES. (Text in English, French) 1984. 10/yr. 695 F. (outside EC 735 F.). (Bureau de Recherches Geologiques et Minieres) Centre National de la Recherche Scientifique, Institut de l'Information Scientifique et Technique, 2 allee du Parc de Brabois, 54514 Vandoeuvre-Les-Nancy Cedex, France. TEL 83-50-46-00. FAX 83-50-46-50. adv. contact: Veronique Guinvarc'h. (also avail. in microfiche) **Document type:** bibliography.
•Also available online. Vendor(s): DIALOG Information Services, Inc. (File no.144), European Space Agency (File no.14), Telesystemes - Questel. Also available on CD-ROM.
Former titles: P A S C A L Folio. F 42: Roches Cristallines (ISSN 0761-1838); P A S C A L Folio. Part 42: Roches Cristallines; Which supersedes (in 1984): Bulletin Signaletique: Bibliographie des Sciences de la Terre. Section 222: Roches Cristallines (ISSN 0300-9289)

551.46 016 552.5 FR ISSN 1146-5204
P A S C A L. F 43: ROCHES SEDIMENTAIRES. GEOLOGIE MARINE. (Text in English, French) 1984. 10/yr. 790 F. (outside EC 840 F.). (Bureau de Recherches Geologiques et Minieres) Centre National de la Recherche Scientifique, Institut de l'Information Scientifique et Technique, 2 allee du Parc de Brabois, 54514 Vandoeuvre-Les-Nancy Cedex, France. TEL 83-50-46-00. FAX 83-50-46-50. adv. contact: Veronique Guinvarc'h. (also avail. in microfiche) **Document type:** bibliography.
•Also available online. Vendor(s): DIALOG Information Services, Inc. (File no.144), European Space Agency (File no.14), Telesystemes - Questel. Also available on CD-ROM.
Former titles: P A S C A L Folio. F 43: Roches Sedimentaires. Geologie Marine (ISSN 0761-1846); P A S C A L Folio. Part 43: Roches Sedimentaires. Geologie Marine; Which supersedes (in 1984): Bulletin Signaletique: Bibliographie des Sciences de la Terre. Section 223. Roches Sedimentaires. Geologie Marine (ISSN 0300-9297)

551 016 FR ISSN 1146-5212
P A S C A L. F 44: STRATIGRAPHIE, GEOLOGIE REGIONALE, GEOLOGIE GENERALE. (Text in English, French) 1985. 10/yr. 1010 F. (outside EC 1065 F.). (Bureau de Recherches Geologiques et Minieres) Centre National de la Recherche Scientifique, Institut de l'Information Scientifique et Technique, 2 allee du Parc de Brabois, 54514 Vandoeuvre-Les-Nancy Cedex, France. TEL 83-50-46-00. FAX 83-50-46-50. adv. contact: Veronique Guinvarc'h. (also avail. in microfiche) **Document type:** bibliography.
•Also available online. Vendor(s): DIALOG Information Services, Inc. (File no.144), European Space Agency (File no.14), Telesystemes - Questel. Also available on CD-ROM.
Former titles: P A S C A L Folio. F 44: Stratigraphie. Geologie Regionale. Geologie Generale (ISSN 0761-1854); P A S C A L Folio. Part 44: Stratigraphie. Geologie Regionale. Geologie Generale; Which supersedes (in 1984): Bulletin Signaletique: Bibliographie des Sciences de la Terre. Section 224: Stratigraphie, Geologie, Regionale et Generale; Bulletin Signaletique. Bibliographie des Sciences de la Terre. Section 224. Stratigraphie, Geologie, Regionale et Geologie Generale. (ISSN 0300-9300)

551.8 016 FR ISSN 1146-5220
P A S C A L. F 45: TECTONIQUE, GEOPHYSIQUE INTERNE. (Text in English, French) 1985. 10/yr. 1165 F. (outside EC 1230 F.). (Bureau de Recherches Geologiques et Minieres) Centre National de la Recherche Scientifique, Institut de l'Information Scientifique et Technique, 2 allee du Parc de Brabois, 54514 Vandoeuvre-Les-Nancy Cedex, France. TEL 83-50-46-00. FAX 83-50-46-50. adv. contact: Veronique Guinvarc'h. (also avail. in microfiche) **Document type:** bibliography.
•Also available online. Vendor(s): DIALOG Information Services, Inc. (File no.144), European Space Agency (File no.14), Telesystemes - Questel. Also available on CD-ROM.
Former titles: P A S C A L Folio. F 45: Tectonique. Geophysique Interne (ISSN 0761-1862); P A S C A L Folio. Part 45: Tectonique. Geophysique Interne; Which supersedes (in 1984): Bulletin Signaletique: Bibliographie des Sciences de la Terre. Section 225: Tectonique Geophysique Interne (ISSN 0240-8503); Bulletin Signaletique: Bibliographie des Sciences de la Terre. Section 225. Tectonique (ISSN 0300-9319)

551.4 016 FR ISSN 1146-5239
P A S C A L. F 46: HYDROLOGIE. GEOLOGIE DE L'INGENIEUR. FORMATIONS SUPERFICIELLES. (Text in English, French) 1984. 10/yr. 2005 F. (outside EC 2120 F.). (Bureau de Recherches Geologiques et Minieres) Centre National de la Recherche Scientifique, Institut de l'Information Scientifique et Technique, 2 allee du Parc de Brabois, 54514 Vandoeuvre-Les-Nancy Cedex, France. TEL 83-50-46-00. FAX 83-50-46-50. adv. contact: Veronique Guinvarc'h. index, cum.index. (also avail. in microfiche) **Document type:** bibliography.
•Also available online. Vendor(s): DIALOG Information Services, Inc. (File no.144), European Space Agency (File no.14), Telesystemes - Questel. Also available on CD-ROM.
Former titles: P A S C A L Folio. F 46: Hydrologie. Geologie de l'Ingenieur. Formations Superficielles (ISSN 0761-1870); P A S C A L Folio. Part 46: Hydrologie. Geologie de l'Ingenieur. Formations Superficielles; Which supersedes (in 1984): Bulletin Signaletique: Bibliographie des Sciences de la Terre. Section 226: Hydrologie. Geologie de l'Ingenieur. Formations Superficielles (ISSN 0300-9327)

550 FR ISSN 1164-5989
P A S C A L. V.4 SCIENCES DE LA TERRE. (Text in English, French) 1961. 10/yr. 7485 F. (outside EC 7935 F.). Centre National de la Recherche Scientifique, Institut de l'Information Scientifique et Technique, 2 allee du Parc de Brabois, 54514 Vandoeuvre-les-Nancy Cedex, France. TEL 83-50-46-00. FAX 83-50-46-50. adv. contact: Veronique Guinvarc'h. (also avail. in microfiche) **Document type:** bibliography.
•Also available online. Vendor(s): DIALOG Information Services, Inc. (File no.144), European Space Agency (File no.14), Telesystemes - Questel. Also available on CD-ROM.
Former titles (until 1992): P A S C A L. Vol. 4: Terre Ocean Espace (ISSN 1146-5018); (until 1990): P A S C A L Thema. T 022: Sciences de la Terre (ISSN 0761-1633); (until 1984): Bulletin Signaletique. Part 22. Sciences de la Terre (ISSN 0245-9531)

551 UK ISSN 0957-5073
Z6005.P7
POLAR AND GLACIOLOGICAL ABSTRACTS. 1931. q. £60($99) to individuals (overseas £76); institutions £69 (overseas £85 ($125)). (Scott Polar Research Institute) Cambridge University Press, Edinburgh Bldg., Shaftesbury Rd., Cambridge CB2 2RU, England. TEL 0223-312393. FAX 0223-315052. TELEX 851517256. (N. American addr.: Cambridge University Press, Journals Dept., 40 W. 20th St., New York, NY 10011. TEL 212-924-3900. FAX 212-691-3239) Ed. William Mills. adv. (back issues avail.) **Document type:** abstracting/indexing.
•Also available online. Vendor(s): QL Systems Ltd.. Also available on CD-ROM.
—UMI.
Supersedes (in 1990): Recent Polar and Glaciological Literature (ISSN 0263-547X); Formerly: Recent Polar Literature.
Description: Covers literature relating to both polar regions and adjacent areas.

EARTH SCIENCES — COMPUTER APPLICATIONS

526 016   RU   ISSN 0375-9717
REFERATIVNYI ZHURNAL. GEODEZIYA I AEROS'EMKA. 1963. m. 36 Rub. (including index 37.80 Rub.). Vsesoyuznyi Institut Nauchno-Tekhnicheskoi Informatsii (VINITI), Baltiiskaya ul., 14, Moscow A-219, Russia. (Subscr. to: Mezhdunarodnaya Kniga, Dimitrova ul. 39, 113095 Moscow, Russia) **Indexed:** Chem.Abstr. **Document type:** abstracting/indexing.
 Formerly: Referativnyi Zhurnal. Geodeziya (ISSN 0034-2351)

551 016   RU   ISSN 0034-236X
REFERATIVNYI ZHURNAL. GEOFIZIKA. 1957. m. 155 Rub. (including index 175 Rub.). Vsesoyuznyi Institut Nauchno-Tekhnicheskoi Informatsii (VINITI), Baltiiskaya ul., 14, Moscow A-219, Russia. (Subscr. to: Mezhdunarodnaya Kniga, Dimitrova ul. 39, 113095 Moscow, Russia) **Indexed:** Chem.Abstr., GeoRef. **Document type:** abstracting/indexing.

550 016   RU   ISSN 0486-2309
CODEN: RZGLAJ
REFERATIVNYI ZHURNAL. GEOLOGIYA. 1954. m. 308 Rub. (including index 336 Rub.). Vsesoyuznyi Institut Nauchno-Tekhnicheskoi Informatsii (VINITI), Baltiiskaya ul., 14, Moscow A-219, Russia. (Subscr. to: Mezhdunarodnaya Kniga, Dimitrova ul. 39, 113095 Moscow, Russia) **Indexed:** Chem.Abstr. **Document type:** abstracting/indexing.
 —CASDDS.

551   AT
REGIONAL BIBLIOGRAPHY SERIES. 1989. irreg. price varies. Sydney Speleological Society, P.O. Box 198, Broadway, N.S.W. 2007, Australia. FAX 02-660-1217. Ed. Ross Ellis. adv. contact: Ross Ellis. circ. 100. **Document type:** bibliography.

622.1 016   US   ISSN 1055-9922
G70.4   CODEN: QLRRDK
REMOTE SENSING OF EARTH RESOURCES: A QUARTERLY BIBLIOGRAPHY. 1974. q. $175 in U.S.; India $220; foreign $185. University of New Mexico, Earth Data Analysis Center, 2500 Yale Blvd. S.E., Ste.100, Albuquerque, NM 87131-6031. TEL 505-277-3622. FAX 505-277-3614. TELEX 660461-ASBKS-UNM-ABQ. (Co-sponsor: U.S. National Aeronautics and Space Administration) Ed. Jeanette Albany. abstr.; circ. 130 (controlled). (back issues avail.) **Document type:** bibliography.
 Former titles (until 1990): Remote Sensing of Natural Resources: A Quarterly Literature Review (ISSN 0160-8754); Quarterly Review of the Remote Sensing of Natural Resources; Quarterly Review of Remote Sensing.
 Description: Collection of abstracts and citations in earth observing technology and remote sensing theory and application literature.
 Refereed Serial

551   US
SCARECROW AREA BIBLIOGRAPHY SERIES. irreg. no.2, 1994. Scarecrow Press, Inc., 52 Liberty St., Box 4167, Metuchen, NJ 08840. TEL 908-548-8600; 800-537-7107. FAX 908-548-5767. **Document type:** bibliography.

597 551.46 016   US   ISSN 0887-4220
SEA GRANT ABSTRACTS; publications from the nation's Sea Grant programs. 1985. q. free to qualified personnel. (National Sea Grant Depository) Woods Hole Data Base, Inc., Box 712, Woods Hole, MA 02543. TEL 508-548-2743. (Subscr. to: Box 84, Woods Hole, MA 02543) Eds. Frank Shephard, Cynthia Murray. bk.rev. circ. 6,000. (back issues avail.) **Document type:** abstracting/indexing.
 ●Also available on CD-ROM. Producer(s): NISC (Oceanographic & Marine Resources - Vol.2).
 Description: Documents and facilitates the acquisition of publications originating from the Program.

551.22   JA
SEISMOLOGICAL SOCIETY OF JAPAN. PROGRAMME AND ABSTRACTS. (Text in English, Japanese) 1980. s-a. Jishin Gakkai - Seismological Society of Japan, Tokyo Daigaku Jishin Kenkyujo, 1-1, Yayoi 1-chome, Bunkyo-ku, Tokyo 113, Japan.

551.4 011   US   ISSN 0037-136X
TC1   CODEN: SWRABW
SELECTED WATER RESOURCES ABSTRACTS. (Not avail. in printed format as of 1992) 1968. m. $115 (with index $145). U.S. Geological Survey, Water Resources Scientific Information Center, 425 National Center, Reston, VA 22092. TEL 703-648-6820. (Dist. by: NTIS, Springfield, VA 22161) Ed. R.A. Jensen. index. circ. 2,000. **Indexed:** Petrol.Abstr. **Document type:** abstracting/indexing.
 ●Also available online. Vendor(s): DIALOG Information Services, Inc. (File no.117).
 Also available on CD-ROM. Producer(s): Cambridge Scientific Abstracts, NISC, SilverPlatter Information, Inc.

551.44   SZ   ISSN 0253-8296
Z6033.C3
SPELEOLOGICAL ABSTRACTS/BULLETIN BIBLIOGRAPHIQUE SPELEOLOGIQUE. (Text in English, French) 1969. a. 28.50 SFr. International Union of Speleology, Bibliotheque de la Societe Suisse de Speleologie, Ch. des Invuex, CH-1614 Granges, Switzerland. FAX 021-9475378. adv.; bk.rev. circ. 1,000. **Indexed:** GeoRef. **Document type:** abstracting/indexing.

526.9   JA
SUIJUN KIHYO SOKURYO SEIKAHYO/REPORTS ON THE SURVEY OF LEVEL REFERENCE POINTS. (Text in Japanese) a. Tokyo Doboku Gijutsu Kenkyujo - Tokyo Metropolitan Government, Institute of Civil Engineering, 9-15, Shinsuna 1-chome, Koto-ku, Tokyo 136, Japan. stat.
 Description: Contains statistical reports on the survey of level reference points.

551 011   UK   ISSN 0954-4887
TERRA ABSTRACTS. 1989. irreg. included with subscr. to Terra Nova (ISSN 0954-4879). (European Union of Geosciences) Blackwell Scientific Publications Ltd., Osney Mead, Oxford OX2 OEL, England. TEL 0865-240201. FAX 0865-721205. TELEX 83355-MEDBOK-G. Ed. R. Muir Wood. **Document type:** abstracting/indexing.
 —BLDSC (8794.400000).
 Supersedes in part: Terra Cognita.
 Description: Abstracts meetings and conferences on earth sciences.

551.46   US
UNDERWATER AND HYPERBARIC MEDICINE: ABSTRACTS FROM THE LITERATURE. bi-m. $100. Undersea and Hyperbaric Medical Society, Inc., 9650 Rockville Pike, Bethesda, MD 20814. TEL 301-571-1818. FAX 301-571-1815. Ed. Leon J. Greenbaum, Jr. circ. 250. **Document type:** academic/scholarly publication, abstracting/indexing.
 Former titles: Underwater Medicine: Abstracts from the Literature (ISSN 0886-3474); Underwater Physiology Abstracts.

551.46 016   VE   ISSN 0590-3343
CODEN: OUIBAX
UNIVERSIDAD DE ORIENTE. INSTITUTO OCEANOGRAFICO BIBLIOTECA. BOLETIN BIBLIOGRAFICO. 1964. a. $1. Universidad de Oriente, Instituto Oceanografico, Biblioteca, Apdo. Postal 94, Cumana, Sucre, Venezuela. Ed. Francisco V. Pinto C. bibl.; circ. 1,000 (controlled).
 Description: Journal of research in oceanography.

551.31   US
WORLD DATA CENTER A FOR GLACIOLOGY (SNOW AND ICE). NEW ACCESSIONS LIST. no.46, 1990. irreg., 3-4/yr. free. World Data Center A for Glaciology (Snow and Ice), National Snow and Ice Data Center, CIRES, Campus Box 449, University of Colorado, Boulder, CO 80309. TEL 303-492-5171. FAX 303-492-2468. TELEX 7401426 WDCA UC. Ed. Ann Brennan.

WYOMING GEOLOGICAL ASSOCIATION. OIL & GAS FIELDS SYMPOSIUM. see *PETROLEUM AND GAS*

551 016   GW   ISSN 0340-5109
CODEN: ZGPAAK
ZENTRALBLATT FUER GEOLOGIE UND PALAEONTOLOGIE. TEIL I: ALLGEMEINE, ANGEWANDTE, REGIONALE UND HISTORISCHE GEOLOGIE. (Text in English, German) 1807. 13/yr. price varies. E. Schweizerbart'sche Verlagsbuchhandlung, Johannesstr. 3A, 70176 Stuttgart, Germany. TEL 0711-625001. FAX 0711-625005. TELEX 723363-SCHB-D. Ed.Bd. adv.; bk.rev. **Indexed:** Bibl.Cart., Chem.Abstr., Deep Sea Res.& Oceanogr.Abstr., GeoRef. **Document type:** academic/scholarly publication.
 —UnCover; SWETS.

ZENTRALBLATT FUER MINERALOGIE. TEIL II: PETROGRAPHIE, TECHNISCHE MINERALOGIE, GEOCHEMIE UND LAGERSTAETTENKUNDE. see *MINES AND MINING INDUSTRY — Abstracting, Bibliographies, Statistics*

551 549   CC
ZHONGGUO DIZHI WENZHAI. English edition: Chinese Geology Abstracts. (Text in Chinese) m. Zhongguo Dizhi Kuangchan Xinxi Yanjiuyuan - Chinese Institute of Geology and Mineral Product Information, 277, Fuchengmenwai Beijie, Beijing 100037, People's Republic of China. TEL 892243. Eds. Bao Yongquan, Li Meiqiu.

EARTH SCIENCES — Computer Applications

550   US
C O G S LETTER. 1986. m. $34 includes membership. Computer Oriented Geological Society, Box 1317, Denver, CO 80201. TEL 303-751-8553. circ. 1,100.

620 550   UK   ISSN 0098-3004
QE48.8   CODEN: CGEODT
COMPUTERS & GEOSCIENCES; an international journal. 1975. 10/yr. £605($930) (effective 1994). (International Association for Mathematical Geology) Elsevier Science Ltd., Pergamon, P.O. Box 800, Kidlington, Oxford OX5 1DX, England. TEL 44-865-843000. FAX 44-865-843010. (Subscr. in U.S. and Canada to: Elsevier Science, 660 White Plains Rd., Tarrytown, NY 10591-5153. TEL 914-524-9200. FAX 914-333-2444) Ed. Dr. Daniel F. Merriam. adv.; bk.rev.; charts; illus.; index. circ. 1,100. (also avail. in microfilm from UMI) **Indexed:** AESIS, Chem.Abstr., Compumath, Comput.Abstr., Comput.Cont., Cyb.Abstr., Deep Sea Res.& Oceanogr.Abstr., E&P Hlth. (1993-), Gas Process.& Ppl. (1993-), Geo.Abstr., GeoRef., Ind.Sci.Rev., Intl.Civil Eng.Abstr., Ocean.Abstr., Off.Tech. (1993-), Petrol.Abstr. (1978-), Sci.Abstr., Sci.Cit.Ind., Soft.Abstr.Eng., Soils & Fert. **Document type:** academic/scholarly publication.
 —BLDSC (3394.695000); EI; Faxon; UnCover; SWETS; UMI; CASDDS. **CCC.**
 Incorporates: Geocom Programs (ISSN 0305-0017)
 Description: Covers all aspects of the application of computers to the geosciences, including algorithms, programming, computational problem-solving techniques, as well as data processing and file maintenance concerns.
 Refereed Serial

COMPUTERS & MINING. see *MINES AND MINING INDUSTRY — Computer Applications*

550 551   XO
CZECHOSLOVAK NATIONAL WORKSHOP ON SEISMIC DATA ACQUISITION AND COMPUTER PROCESSING. PROCEEDINGS. (Text in English) 1984. a. free. (Slovak Academy of Sciences, Geophysical Institute) Veda, Publishing House of the Slovak Academy of Sciences, Klemensova 19, 814 30 Bratislava, Slovakia. TELEX 93373 SEIS C. (Subscr. to: Dubravska cesta 9, 842 28 Bratislava, Slovakia) Eds. Klara Mrazova, Libuse Ruprechtova. circ. 250.
 Description: Contains papers presented at the annual Czechoslovak workshop on seismic data acquisition and computer processing.

550   US
PUBLIC DOMAIN SOFTWARE FOR EARTH SCIENTISTS. 1991. a. $40 (foreign $50). Gibbs Associates, Box 706, Boulder, CO 80306. TEL 303-444-6032. Eds. Betty Gibbs, Stephen Krajewski. **Document type:** directory.
 Description: Contains information on public domain software from government agencies, universities, and individuals. Includes shareware programs and inexpensive software.

EARTH SCIENCES — Geology

see also Mines and Mining Industry

A A P G BULLETIN. (American Association of Petroleum Geologists) see *PETROLEUM AND GAS*

A A P G EXPLORER. (American Association of Petroleum Geologists) see *PETROLEUM AND GAS*

A A P G STUDIES IN GEOLOGY SERIES. (American Association of Petroleum Geologists) see *PETROLEUM AND GAS*

551   US   ISSN 0888-305X
A E G NEWS. 1958. q. $20. Association of Engineering Geologists, 323 Boston Post Rd., Ste. 2D, Box 132, Sudbury, MA 01776. TEL 508-443-4639. Ed. William Smith. adv.; bibl.; tr.lit. circ. 3,600. **Indexed:** GeoRef. **Document type:** newsletter.
 Formerly: A E G Newsletter (ISSN 0514-9142)
 Description: Contains reports, news, technical news articles, and annual meeting announcements and information.

551   AT   ISSN 1320-1271
QE340
A G S O JOURNAL OF AUSTRALIAN GEOLOGY AND GEOPHYSICS. 1976. q. Aus.$80 to individuals; corporations Aus.$120. Australian Geological Survey Organisation, G.P.O. Box 378, Canberra, A.C.T. 2601, Australia. TEL 61-6-2499519. FAX 61-6-2499982. Ed. Karl H. Wolf. **Indexed:** AESIS, Aus.Rd.Ind., Biol.Abstr., Chem.Abstr., Deep Sea Res.& Oceanogr.Abstr., Geo.Abstr., INIS Atomind., Ocean.Abstr., Petrol.Abstr., Sci.Abstr., Sel.Water Res.Abstr. **Document type:** government publication.
 —BLDSC (0771.914500); UnCover; SWETS. **CCC.**
 Formerly: B M R Journal of Australian Geology and Geophysics (ISSN 0312-9608)
 Description: Contains the results of geoscientific research carried out by the A G S O, both on land and on the continental margin, and in the Australian Antarctic territory.

551   AT   ISSN 1039-0073
A G S O RECORD. 1942. irreg. price varies. Australian Geological Survey Organisation, G.P.O. Box 378, Canberra, A.C.T. 2601, Australia. TEL 06-249-9111. FAX 06-249-9999. **Document type:** government publication.
 Formerly: B M R Record.

551   AT   ISSN 0813-751X
A G S O RESEARCH NEWSLETTER. 1984. s-a. free. Australian Geological Survey Organisation, G.P.O. Box 378, Canberra, A.C.T. 2601, Australia. TEL 06-249-9111. FAX 06-249-9999. **Document type:** government publication, newsletter.
 Formerly: B M R Research Newsletter.

A M C JOURNAL. (American Mining Congress) see *MINES AND MINING INDUSTRY*

549   AT   ISSN 0045-0707
TN1   CODEN: AMBNBT
A M D E L BULLETIN. 1966. a. free. Australia Mineral Development Laboratories, Flemington St., Frewville, S.A. 5063, Australia. Ed. K.J. Henley. circ. 800. **Indexed:** Chem.Abstr., Eng.Ind., Mineral.Abstr.

551   DK   ISSN 0105-8258
AARHUS UNIVERSITET. GEOLOGISK INSTITUT. GEOKOMPENDIER. irreg., no.31, 1992. price varies. Aarhus Universitet, Geologisk Institut, Biblioteket, C.F. Mollers Alle bygn. 120, 8000 Aarhus C, Denmark. FAX 86-139248. illus.

551   DK   ISSN 0105-8266
AARHUS UNIVERSITET. GEOLOGISK INSTITUT. GEORAPPORTER. 1978. irreg., no. 13, 1992. price varies. Aarhus Universitet, Geologisk Institut, Biblioteket, C.F. Mollers Alle Bygn. 120, DK-8000 Aarhus C, Denmark. FAX 86-139248. illus.

551 910   DK   ISSN 0105-824X
AARHUS UNIVERSITET. GEOLOGISK INSTITUT. GEOSKRIFTER. irreg., no.42, 1992. price varies. Aarhus Universitet, Geologisk Institut, C.F. Mollers Alle, Bygn. 120, 8000 Aarhus C, Denmark. FAX 86-139248. illus. **Indexed:** Geo.Abstr.
 —BLDSC (4158.896000).
 Formerly: Skrifter i Fysisk Geografi.

ABSTRACTS OF CHINESE GEOLOGICAL LITERATURE. see *EARTH SCIENCES — Abstracting, Bibliographies, Statistics*

550   CU
ACADEMIA DE CIENCIAS DE CUBA. INSTITUTO DE GEOLOGIA. RESUMENES, COMUNICACIONES Y NOTAS DEL CONSEJO CIENTIFICO.* irreg. Academia de Ciencias de Cuba, Instituto de Geologia, Calfada no. 851, Esq. a Calle 4, Havana 4, Cuba. illus.
 Formerly: Academia de Ciencias de Cuba. Instituto de Geologia. Resumenes del Consejo Cientifico.

557   CU
ACADEMIA DE CIENCIAS DE CUBA. INSTITUTO DE GEOLOGIA. SERIE GEOLOGICA.* (Text in Spanish; summaries in English) 1968. irreg. (3-4/yr.). exchange basis. Academia de Ciencias de Cuba, Instituto de Geologia, Calzada no. 851, Esq. a Calle 4, Havana 4, Cuba. bibl.; charts; illus.; stat.; circ. controlled. **Indexed:** GeoRef.

551   US   ISSN 1050-8309
ACADEMIC PRESS GEOLOGY SERIES. 1981. irreg., vol.10, 1991. Academic Press, Inc., 525 B St., Ste. 1900, San Diego, CA 92101-4495. TEL 619-231-0926. FAX 619-699-6715. (Subscr. to: Order Dept., 6277 Sea Harbor Dr., 4th Fl., Orlando, FL 32887. TEL 800-321-5068) (reprint service avail. from ISI)
 Refereed Serial

ACTA ALBERTINA RATISBONENSIA. see *EARTH SCIENCES*

ACTA GEOGRAPHICA AC GEOLOGICA ET METEOROLOGICA DEBRECINA. see *GEOGRAPHY*

551   SP   ISSN 0567-7505
    CODEN: ACGHAX
ACTA GEOLOGICA HISPANICA. (Text in English or Spanish; summaries in English, French, Spanish) 1966. 4/yr. 4000 ptas.($40) or exchange basis. Universidad de Barcelona, Institut de Ciencies de la Terra Jaume Almera, c/o Marti i Franques s-n, 08028 Barcelona, Spain. TEL 3-402-1420. FAX 3-402-1340. Dir. Pere Busquets. bibl.; charts; illus.; index. circ. 600. **Indexed:** Biol.Abstr., Bull.Signal., Chem.Abstr., Geo.Abstr., GeoRef., Ind.SST. **Document type:** academic/scholarly publication.
 —BLDSC (0620.350000); CASDDS. **CCC.**
 Refereed Serial

550   HU   ISSN 0236-5278
QE1   CODEN: AGHUE7
ACTA GEOLOGICA HUNGARICA. (Text in English) 1952. q. $80 (effective 1992). (Magyar Tudomanyos Akademia) Akademiai Kiado, Publishing House of the Hungarian Academy of Sciences, P.O. Box 245, H-1519 Budapest, Hungary. TEL 181-2134. FAX 166-6466. TELEX 22-6228 AKNYO H. Ed. Janos Haas. bibl.; charts; illus.; index. **Indexed:** Biol.Abstr., Chem.Abstr., INIS Atomind., Mineral.Abstr.
 —UnCover; CASDDS.
 Formerly (until 1982): Academia Scientiarum Hungarica. Acta Geologica (ISSN 0001-5695)
 Description: Covers all fields of geology, including crystallography, mineralogy, petrography, geochemistry and paleontology.

550   AG   ISSN 0567-7513
QE231   CODEN: AGELAT
ACTA GEOLOGICA LILLOANA. (Text in Spanish; summaries in English, French, German, Italian) 1957. irreg., vol.17, no.1, 1989. Fundacion Miguel Lillo, Miguel Lillo 251, 4000 Tucuman, Argentina. Ed. Dr. Jose A. Haedo Rossi. bibl.; charts; illus.; stat.; index. circ. 500. (back issues avail.) **Indexed:** Biol.Abstr., Bull.Signal., GeoRef., Ref.Zh.
 —BLDSC (0620.500000).

550   PL   ISSN 0001-5709
QE1   CODEN: AGLPA8
ACTA GEOLOGICA POLONICA. (Text in English; summaries in Polish) 1950. q. $84. (Polska Akademia Nauk, Komitet Nauk Geologicznych) Wydawnictwo Naukowe P W N, Ul. Miodowa 10, 00-251 Warsaw, Poland. (Dist. by: Ars Polona, Krakowskie Przedmiescie 7, 00-068 Warsaw) Ed. A. Radwanski. charts; illus.; maps; index. circ. 680. **Indexed:** Biol.Abstr., Chem.Abstr., GeoRef., INIS Atomind., Petrol.Abstr.
 —BLDSC (0621.000000); UnCover; CASDDS.

550.1   CH   ISSN 0065-1265
QE1   CODEN: SRTUAW
ACTA GEOLOGICA TAIWANICA. Key Title: Yanjiu Baogao - Guoli Taiwan Daxue Lixueyuan Dizhixue Xi. (Text in English) 1947. a. exchange basis. National Taiwan University, Department of Geology, Taipei, Taiwan 10764, Republic of China. FAX 02-363-6095. Ed. Cheng-Hong Chen. bk.rev. circ. 600. **Indexed:** Biol.Abstr., Chem.Abstr., Deep Sea Res.& Oceanogr.Abstr., GeoRef., Mineral.Abstr. **Document type:** academic/scholarly publication.
 —BLDSC (8156.000000); UnCover; CASDDS.

ACTA NATURALIA ISLANDICA. see *BIOLOGY — Botany*

550   XR   ISSN 0001-7132
QE1   CODEN: AUCGAY
ACTA UNIVERSITATIS CAROLINAE: GEOLOGICA. (Text in Czech, English, German, Russian) 1954. q. 40 Kcs.($60) Universita Karlova, Prirodovedecka Fakulta, Vinicna 5, 128 44 Prague 2, Czech Republic. (Dist. by: Geological Library, Faculty of Science, Albertov 6, 128 43 Prague 2, Czech Republic) Ed.Bd. illus.; maps. circ. 700. **Indexed:** Biol.Abstr., Chem.Abstr., GeoRef.
 —BLDSC (0584.510000); UnCover; CASDDS.

550 551   PL   ISSN 0525-4132
QE1   CODEN: PGEMBS
ACTA UNIVERSITATIS WRATISLAVIENSIS. PRACE GEOLOGICZNO - MINERALOGICZNE. (Text in Polish; summaries in English) 1969. irreg. price varies. (Uniwersytet Wroclawski) Wydawnictwo Uniwersytetu Wroclawskiego, Pl. Uniwersytecki 9-13, 50-137 Wroclaw, Poland. TEL 44-10-06. (Dist. by: Ksiegarnia Uniwersytetu Wroclawskiego, Pl. Uniwersytecki 9-13, 50-137 Wroclaw, Poland) Ed. Irena Wojciechowska. charts; illus.; maps. circ. 250. **Document type:** academic/scholarly publication.

551   NE
ADVANCES IN EARTH AND PLANETARY SCIENCES; a series of conference proceedings volumes. 1977. irreg. price varies. Kluwer Academic Publishers, Postbus 17, 3300 AA Dordrecht, Netherlands. TEL 31-78-334911. FAX 31-78-334254. TELEX 29245 KAPG NL. (Dist. by: Kluwer Academic Publishers Group, P.O. Box 322, 3300 AH Dordrecht, Netherlands. TEL 31-78-524400; N. America dist. addr.: Box 358, Accord Sta., Hingham, MA 02018-0358. TEL 617-871-6600) Ed. T. Rikitake. **Indexed:** Chem.Abstr.
 Refereed Serial

ADVANCES IN GEOPHYSICAL DATA PROCESSING; a research annual. see *COMPUTERS*

ADVANCES IN PETROLEUM GEOCHEMISTRY. see *PETROLEUM AND GAS*

551.9   US   ISSN 0722-3269
    CODEN: APGEDG
ADVANCES IN PHYSICAL GEOCHEMISTRY. 1981. irreg., vol.7, 1988. price varies. Springer-Verlag, 175 Fifth Ave., New York, NY 10010. TEL 212-460-1500. FAX 212-473-6272. (Also: Berlin, Heidelberg, Tokyo and Vienna) Ed. S. Saxena. (reprint service avail. from ISI) **Indexed:** Chem.Abstr. **Document type:** monographic series.
 —Faxon; CASDDS.

551   PL   ISSN 0372-9427
QE1   CODEN: ZNAGDF
AKADEMIA GORNICZO-HUTNICZA IM. STANISLAWA STASZICA. ZESZYTY NAUKOWE. GEOLOGIA. (Text in English, Polish; summaries in English, Polish, Russian) 1956. irreg., no.54, 1992. price varies. Wydawnictwo A G H, Al. Mickiewicza 30, paw. A-1, 30-059 Krakow, Poland. (Dist. by: Ars Polona, Krakowskie Przedmiescie 7, 00-068 Warsaw, Poland) Ed Z. Kleczek. illus. circ. 200. **Document type:** academic/scholarly publication.
 —BLDSC (9512.150152); UnCover; CASDDS.

EARTH SCIENCES — GEOLOGY

551   PL   ISSN 0138-0974
QE1   CODEN: GEOLDW
AKADEMIA GORNICZO-HUTNICZA IM. STANISLAWA STASZICA. ZESZYTY NAUKOWE. GEOLOGIA. KWARTALNIK. (Text in English or Polish; summaries in English, Polish) 1975. q. 40000 Zl. per issue (effective 1993). Wydawnictwo A G H, Al. Mickiewicza 30, 30-059 Krakow, Poland. TEL 48-12-338100. FAX 48-12-331014. TELEX 322203 AGH PL. (Dist. by: Ars Polona, Krakowskie Przedmiescie 7, 00-068 Warsaw, Poland) Ed. Z. Kleczek. illus. circ. 460. **Document type:** academic/scholarly publication.
—BLDSC (9512.150150); CASDDS.

550   AJ
AKADEMIYA NAUK AZERBAIJANA. IZVESTIYA. SERIYA NAUKI O ZEMLE. (Text in Azerbaijani, Russian) 1958. bi-m. 22.50 Rub. Izdatel'stvo Elm, Ul. Narimanova, 37, 370073 Baku, Azerbaijan. charts; illus.; index. **Indexed:** Art & Archaeol.Tech.Abstr., Chem.Abstr., GeoRef., INIS Atomind.
—CCC.
Formerly: Akademiya Nauk Azerbaidzhanskoi S.S.R. Izvestiya. Seriya Nauki o Zemle (ISSN 0002-3124)

550   KZ
QE1
AKADEMIYA NAUK KAZAKHSTANA. IZVESTIYA. SERIYA GEOLOGICHESKAYA. 1940. bi-m. $16.20. Gylym, Ul. Pushkina 111-113, 480100 Alma-Ata, Kazakhstan. TEL 3272-611877. Ed. Sh.E. Esenov. charts; illus.; maps. **Indexed:** Chem.Abstr., GeoRef., INIS Atomind.
—CCC.
Formerly (until 1992): Akademiya Nauk Kazakhskoi S.S.R. Izvestiya. Seriya Geologicheskaya (ISSN 0002-3175)

AKADEMIYA NAUK TAJIKISTANA. IZVESTIYA. OTDELENIE FIZIKO-MATEMATICHESKIKH I GEOLOGO-KHIMICHESKIKH NAUK. see *PHYSICS*

AKADEMIYA NAUK TURKMENISTANA. IZVESTIYA. SERIYA FIZIKO-TEKHNICHESKIKH, KHIMICHESKIKH I GEOLOGICHESKIKH NAUK. see *PHYSICS*

557   US   ISSN 0065-5635
QE81   CODEN: AGAFAP
ALABAMA GEOLOGICAL SOCIETY. GUIDEBOOK FOR THE ANNUAL FIELD TRIP. 1964. a. price varies. Alabama Geological Society, Box 6184, Tuscaloosa, AL 35486. TEL 205-349-2852. circ. 150. **Indexed:** GeoRef.
Refereed Serial

551   US
ALASKA. DIVISION OF GEOLOGICAL AND GEOPHYSICAL SURVEYS. GEOLOGIC - PROFESSIONAL REPORT. 1969. irreg. price varies. Department of Natural Resources, Division of Geological and Geophysical Surveys, 794 University Ave., Ste.200, Fairbanks, AK 99709-3645. TEL 907-474-7147. FAX 907-479-4779.
Formerly: Alaska. Division of Geological and Geophysical Surveys. Laboratory Report (ISSN 0065-5775)
Refereed Serial

557   US   ISSN 0065-5759
                   CODEN: AGICCO
ALASKA. DIVISION OF GEOLOGICAL AND GEOPHYSICAL SURVEYS. INFORMATION CIRCULAR. irreg. free. Department of Natural Resources, Division of Geological and Geophysical Surveys, 794 University Ave. Ste. 200, Fairbanks, AK 99709-3645. TEL 907-474-7147. FAX 907-479-4779.
Refereed Serial

551   US
ALASKA. DIVISION OF GEOLOGICAL AND GEOPHYSICAL SURVEYS. REPORT OF INVESTIGATIONS. irreg. price varies. Department of Natural Resources, Division of Geological and Geophysical Surveys, 794 University Ave., Ste. 200, Fairbanks, AK 99709-3645. TEL 907-474-7147. FAX 907-479-4779.
Former titles: Alaska. Division of Geological and Geophysical Surveys. Open-File Report; Alaska. Division of Geological and Geophysical Surveys. Laboratory Note (ISSN 0065-5767)
Refereed Serial

551   US   ISSN 0360-3881
               CODEN: SRASD2
ALASKA. DIVISION OF GEOLOGICAL AND GEOPHYSICAL SURVEYS. SPECIAL REPORT. 1967. irreg. price varies. Department of Natural Resources, Division of Geological and Geophysical Surveys, 794 University Ave. Ste. 200, Fairbanks, AK 99709-3645. TEL 907-474-7147. FAX 907-479-4779. **Indexed:** Chem.Abstr., GeoRef.
—CASDDS.
Refereed Serial

556   AE
QE329   CODEN: ASMBBM
ALGERIA. OFFICE NATIONALE DE LA GEOLOGIE. BULLETIN. irreg. (approx. 2/yr.). price varies. Office Nationale de la Geologie, 18A Ave. Mustapha el-Ouali, Algiers, Algeria. TEL 74-08-64. **Indexed:** Bull.Signal., GeoRef.
Formerly: Algeria. Service Geologique. Bulletin (ISSN 0401-345X)

ALTENBURGER NATURWISSENSCHAFTLICHE FORSCHUNGEN. see *BIOLOGY*

551 665.5   US   ISSN 0065-731X
                  CODEN: MAPGAN
AMERICAN ASSOCIATION OF PETROLEUM GEOLOGISTS. MEMOIR. 1962. irreg., no.45, 1988. price varies. American Association of Petroleum Geologists, Box 979, Tulsa, OK 74101. TEL 918-584-2555. cum.index: 1956-65, 1966-70, 1971-75, 1976-80, 1981-85. **Indexed:** AESIS, Biol.Abstr., GeoRef.
—CCC.
Description: Book series of reference titles of current and future value.

AMERICAN ASSOCIATION OF STRATIGRAPHIC PALYNOLOGISTS. CONTRIBUTIONS SERIES. see *PALEONTOLOGY*

551.7 560   CN   ISSN 0192-7299
                  CODEN: NASPDB
AMERICAN ASSOCIATION OF STRATIGRAPHIC PALYNOLOGISTS. NEWSLETTER. 1968. q. membership. American Association of Stratigraphic Palynologists Foundation, Inc., c/o Judith Lentin, 665 8th St., S.W., Ste. 700, Calgary, AB T2P 3K7, Canada. TEL 403-264-0173. FAX 403-262-1629. bk.rev. circ. 1,100. **Indexed:** GeoRef. **Document type:** newsletter.
Description: News of the organization's activities and information of interest to palynologists.

ANDRIAS. see *BIOLOGY — Botany*

550   AO   ISSN 0003-3456
                CODEN: AGMBA5
ANGOLA. DIRECCAO PROVINCIAL DOS SERVICOS DE GEOLOGIA E MINAS. BOLETIM. (Text in English, French, Portuguese) 1960. irreg. Esc.50. Direccao Provincial dos Servicos de Geologia e Minas, C.P. 1260-C, Luanda, Angola. (Co-sponsor: Instituto Nacional de Geologia) charts; illus.; maps; stat. **Indexed:** GeoRef.

550.1   FI   ISSN 0066-197X
Q60   CODEN: AAFGAB
ANNALES ACADEMIAE SCIENTIARUM FENNICAE. SERIES A, III: GEOLOGICA-GEOGRAPHICA. (Text in English, French, German) 1941. irreg. price varies. Suomalainen Tiedeakatemia - Academia Scientiarum Fennica, Mariankatu 5, FIN-00170 Helsinki, Finland. (Orders to: The Bookstore Tiedekirja, Kirkkokatu 14, SF-00170 Helsinki, Finland) Ed. Toive Aartolahti. circ. 540. (also avail. in microform; back issues avail.) **Indexed:** Biol.Abstr., Bull.Signal., Doc.Geogr., Geo.Abstr., GeoRef., INIS Atomind., Psychol.Abstr., Ref.Zh.
—UnCover.

ANNALES UNIVERSITATIS MARIAE CURIE-SKLODOWSKA. SECTIO B. GEOGRAPHIA, GEOLOGIA, MINERALOGIA ET PETROGRAPHIA. see *GEOGRAPHY*

551.31   UK   ISSN 0260-3055
                  CODEN: ANGLDN
ANNALS OF GLACIOLOGY. 1980. a. price varies. International Glaciological Society, Lensfield Rd., Cambridge CB2 1ER, England. TEL 0223-355974. FAX 0223-336543. illus. circ. 800. **Indexed:** Chem.Abstr., Deep Sea Res.& Ocean.Abstr., Geo.Abstr., Meteor.& Geoastrophys.Abstr. **Document type:** academic/scholarly publication.
—BLDSC (1040.830000); Faxon; UnCover; CASDDS.

556 016   ZA   ISSN 0066-2410
ANNOTATED BIBLIOGRAPHY AND INDEX OF THE GEOLOGY OF ZAMBIA. 1959. irreg., latest issue 1980. price varies. Geological Survey, P.O. Box R.W. 50135, Lusaka, Zambia.

ANTARCTIC METEORITE NEWSLETTER. see *ASTRONOMY*

ANUARIO DE LA MINERIA DE CHILE. see *MINES AND MINING INDUSTRY*

551 666 614.7 624   NE   ISSN 0169-1317
                           CODEN: ACLSER
APPLIED CLAY SCIENCE; an international journal on the application and technology of clays and clay minerals. 1985. 6/yr. fl.541($292) (effective 1994). Elsevier Science B.V., P.O. Box 211, 1000 AE Amsterdam, Netherlands. TEL 31-20-5803911. FAX 31-20-5803598. TELEX 18582 ESPA NL. (Subscr. in U.S. and Canada to: Elsevier Science Inc., Box 882, Madison Sq. Sta., New York, NY 10159-0882. TEL 212-989-5800. FAX 212-633-3990) Ed.Bd. adv.; bk.rev. (also avail. in microform from UMI; back issues avail.) **Indexed:** Eng.Ind., Excerp.Med., Sel.Water Res.Abstr., Soils & Fert., Weed Abstr. **Document type:** academic/scholarly publication.
—BLDSC (1571.936000); El; SWETS; CASDDS. CCC.
Description: Publishes research papers, reviews and short communications in the field of applied clay science and clay technology in a broad sense.
Refereed Serial

551.9   UK   ISSN 0883-2927
QE514   CODEN: APPGEY
APPLIED GEOCHEMISTRY. 1986. 6/yr. £195($300) (effective 1994). (International Association of Geochemistry and Cosmochemistry) Elsevier Science Ltd., Pergamon, P.O. Box 800, Kidlington, Oxford OX5 1DX, England. TEL 44-865-843000. FAX 44-865-843010. (Subscr. in U.S. and Canada to: Elsevier Science, 660 White Plains Rd., Tarrytown, NY 10591-5153. TEL 914-524-9200. FAX 914-333-2444) Ed. Brian Hitchon. index. (also avail. in microfilm from UMI; back issues avail.) **Indexed:** E&P Hlth. (1993-), Gas Process.& Ppl. (1993-), Off.Tech. (1993-), Petrol.Abstr. (1989-), Sel.Water Res.Abstr., Soils & Fert. **Document type:** academic/scholarly publication.
—BLDSC (1572.585000); El; Faxon; UnCover; SWETS; UMI; CASDDS. CCC.
Description: International journal devoted to original research papers in geochemistry and cosmochemistry.
Refereed Serial

AQUA; mensile di acqua, natura, vita. see *EARTH SCIENCES — Hydrology*

550   PL   ISSN 0066-6912
QE351   CODEN: ARWMAT
ARCHIWUM MINERALOGICZNE. (Text in Polish, English or French; summaries in English, French or Polish) 1925. s-a. 240 Zl. price varies. Polska Akademia Nauk, Instytut Nauk Geologicznych, Ul. Zwirki Wigury 93, 02-089 Warsaw, Poland. (Dist. by: Ars Polona-Ruch, Krakowskie Przedmiescie 7, Warsaw) **Indexed:** Chem.Abstr., GeoRef.
—BLDSC (1661.400000); UnCover; CASDDS.

ARHIV ZA RUDARSTVO I GEOLOGIJU. see *MINES AND MINING INDUSTRY*

557   US   ISSN 0066-7412
QE85   CODEN: AGSDA7
ARIZONA GEOLOGICAL SOCIETY DIGEST. 1958. irreg., no.18, 1987. price varies. Arizona Geological Society, Box 40952, Tucson, AZ 85717. (Subscr. to: Arizona Geological Survey, 845 N. Park Ave., Tucson, AZ 85719) Ed. Judith P. Jenney. adv. circ. 1,000. **Indexed:** GeoRef.

ARIZONA GEOLOGICAL SURVEY. SPECIAL PUBLICATION. see *PETROLEUM AND GAS*

EARTH SCIENCES — GEOLOGY

531.64 551 US ISSN 1045-4802
TN24.A6
ARIZONA GEOLOGY; investigation, service, information. 1971. q. free in US. Arizona Geological Survey, 845 N. Park Ave., Ste. 100, Tucson, AZ 85719. TEL 602-882-4795. FAX 602-628-5106. Ed. Evelyn M. VandenDolder. bk.rev.; bibl.; charts; illus.; cum.index: 1971-1989. circ. 3,000. (back issues avail.) **Document type**: academic/scholarly publication.
 Formerly (until vol.18, no.3, 1988): Fieldnotes.
 Description: Semitechnical articles on Arizona's geology, summaries of survey research and activities, and announcements of new publications.

557 US
ARKANSAS. GEOLOGICAL COMMISSION. INFORMATION CIRCULARS. no.8, 1936. irreg., no.30, 1986. price varies. Geological Commission, Vardelle Parham Geology Center, 3815 W. Roosevelt Rd., Little Rock, AR 72204. TEL 501-663-9714. illus. (back issues avail.)

557 US
ARKANSAS. GEOLOGICAL COMMISSION. MISCELLANEOUS PUBLICATIONS. 1940. irreg., no.21, 1988. price varies. Geological Commission, Vardelle Parham Geology Center, 3815 W. Roosevelt Rd., Little Rock, AR 72204. FAX 501-663-7360. illus. circ. 1,000. (back issues avail.) **Document type**: monographic series.

557 US
ARKANSAS. GEOLOGICAL COMMISSSION. BULLETIN. no.5, 1930. irreg., no.23, 1987. price varies. Geological Commission, Vardelle Parham Geology Center, 3815 W. Roosevelt Rd., Little Rock, AR 72204. TEL 501-663-9714. (back issues avail.) **Document type**: bulletin.

550 AG ISSN 0004-4822
 CODEN: AAREDY
ASOCIACION GEOLOGICA ARGENTINA. REVISTA. 1946. q. price varies. Librart s.r.l., Casilla Correo 5047, Buenos Aires, Argentina. charts; illus.; maps. **Indexed**: Biol.Abstr., Chem.Abstr., GeoRef.
 —CASDDS.
 Supersedes: Sociedad Geologica Argentina. Revista (ISSN 0370-7288)

551 US ISSN 0004-5691
TA705 CODEN: AEGBBU
ASSOCIATION OF ENGINEERING GEOLOGISTS. BULLETIN. 1963. q. $80. Association of Engineering Geologists, 323 Boston Post Rd., Ste. 2D, Box 132, Sudbury, MA 01776. TEL 508-443-4639. Ed. Normetan R. Tilford. adv.; abstr.; charts; illus. circ. 3,500. (back issues avail.) **Indexed**: AESIS, Chem.Abstr., Excerp.Med., Fuel & Energy Abstr., Geotech.Abstr., HRIS, INIS Atomind., Sel.Water Res.Abstr., W.R.C.Inf. **Document type**: bulletin.
 —BLDSC (2396.965000); Faxon; UnCover.
 Description: Publishes selected technical papers in the field of engineering geology.

551 US
ASSOCIATION OF ENGINEERING GEOLOGISTS. SPECIAL PUBLICATIONS. irreg. price varies. Association of Engineering Geologists, 323 Boston Post Rd., Ste. 2D, Box 132, Sudbury, MA 01776. TEL 508-443-4639. **Document type**: monographic series.

ASSOCIATION OF MARINE LABORATORIES OF THE CARIBBEAN. NEWSLETTER. see EARTH SCIENCES — Oceanography

ASSOCIATION OF MARINE LABORATORIES OF THE CARIBBEAN. PROCEEDINGS. see EARTH SCIENCES — Oceanography

551.3 CN ISSN 0843-5561
GC380 CODEN: ATGEEB
ATLANTIC GEOLOGY. (Text in English; abstract in English, French) 1965. 3/yr. Can.$26($26) to individuals; institutions Can.$38($38). Atlantic Geoscience Society, c/o Acadia Centre for Estuarine Research, Box 115, Acadia University, Wolfville, NS BOP 1X0, Canada. TEL 902-542-2201. FAX 902-542-1454. Ed.Bd. bk.rev.; abstr.; index, cum.index. circ. 400. **Indexed**: Biol.Abstr., Deep Sea Res.& Oceanogr.Abstr., E&P Hlth. (1993-), Fluidex, Gas Process.& Ppl. (1993-), Geo.Abstr., GeoRef., Off.Tech. (1993-), Petrol.Abstr. (1971-). **Document type**: academic/scholarly publication.
 —BLDSC (1765.903000); Faxon; SWETS. **CCC**.
 Former titles (until 1990): Maritime Sediments and Atlantic Geology (ISSN 0711-1150); (until 1982): Maritime Sediments (ISSN 0025-3456)
 Description: Publishes papers, notes and discussions on original research and review papers on all aspects of the geology of Atlantic Canada and related areas.
 Refereed Serial

ATLANTIC SUMMARY REPORT - INDEX. see PETROLEUM AND GAS

551 GW ISSN 0004-7856
 CODEN: AFSLAO
DER AUFSCHLUSS. 1950. bi-m. DM.84 (foreign DM.96). Vereinigung der Freunde der Mineralogie und Geologie e.V., Blumenthalstr. 40, 69120 Heidelberg, Germany. TEL 06221-413411. circ. 6,500. **Document type**: academic/scholarly publication.
 —CASDDS.

526 AT
AUSTRALIAN GEOLOGICAL SURVEY ORGANISATION. 1: 250000 GEOLOGICAL MAPS AND EXPLANATORY NOTES SERIES. irreg. Aus.$9 per sheet. Australian Geological Survey Organisation, G.P.O. Box 378, Canberra, A.C.T. 2601, Australia. TEL 06-249-9111. FAX 06-249-9999. **Document type**: government publication.
 Formerly: Australia. Bureau of Mineral Resources, Geology and Geophysics. 1: 250000 Geological Maps and Explanatory Notes Series.

AUSTRALIAN INSTITUTE OF PETROLEUM. ANNUAL REPORT. see PETROLEUM AND GAS

551 AT ISSN 0812-0099
QE340 CODEN: AJESE7
AUSTRALIAN JOURNAL OF EARTH SCIENCES. 1953. bi-m. Aus.$275($325) (Geological Society of Australia) Blackwell Scientific Publications (Australia) Pty. Ltd., P.O. Box 378, Carlton, Vic. 3055, Australia. TEL 03-347-0300. FAX 03-347-5001. Ed. A.E. Cockbain. adv.: B&W page $680, color page $1450. bibl.; illus.; index, circ. 3,200. (also avail. in microform from UMI; back issues avail.; reprint service avail. from UMI) **Indexed**: AESIS, Chem.Abstr., Curr.Cont., E&P Hlth. (1993-), Gas Process.& Ppl. (1993-), Geo.Abstr., Geotech.Abstr.,Ind.Sci.Rev., INIS Atomind., Off.Tech. (1993-), Petrol.Abstr. (1986-), Phys.Abstr., Sci.Cit.Ind., Sel.Water Res.Abstr.
 —BLDSC (1807.555000); Faxon; UnCover; SWETS; UMI; CASDDS. **CCC**.
 Supersedes: Geological Society of Australia. Journal (ISSN 0016-7614)
 Description: Covers original contributions ranging from those of a purely theoretical nature to those of more general interest to geoscientists working in and around the southern continents.

551 549 AT ISSN 0819-6508
AUSTRALIAN MINERALOGIST. vol.4, 1989. q. Aus.$28($26) Gemcraft Pty. Ltd., 293 Wattletree Rd., E. Malvern, Vic. 3145, Australia. TEL 03-509-1666. Eds. W.D. Birch, C. Kovac. circ. 1,200. (back issues avail.)

551 AT
 CODEN: ANUGA7
AUSTRALIAN NATIONAL UNIVERSITY, CANBERRA. GEOLOGY DEPARTMENT. ANNUAL REPORT. 1962. a. free. Australian National University, Department of Geology, Faculty of Science, Canberra, A.C.T. 0200, Australia. TEL 249-2056. FAX 249-5544. circ. 500.
 Formerly (until 1989): Australian National University, Canberra. Geology Department. Publication (ISSN 0084-750X)

BADISCHER LANDESVEREIN FUER NATURKUNDE UND NATURSCHUTZ, FREIBURG. MITTEILUNGEN. NEUE FOLGE. see BIOLOGY

BASE LINE. see GEOGRAPHY

BAYERISCHE STAATSSAMMLUNG FUER PALAEONTOLOGIE UND HISTORISCHE GEOLOGIE. MITTEILUNGEN. see PALEONTOLOGY

551 US ISSN 0005-7266
 CODEN: BGOBAQ
BAYLOR GEOLOGICAL STUDIES BULLETIN. 1961. s-a. $5. Baylor University, Geology Department, Box 97354, Waco, TX 76798-7354. TEL 817-755-2361. FAX 817-755-2673. Ed. Janet L. Burton. bibl.; charts; illus.; index. circ. 700. (also avail. in microfilm) **Indexed**: Abstr.N.Amer.Geol., Chem.Abstr., Geo.Abstr., GeoRef. **Document type**: academic/scholarly publication, bulletin.
 —BLDSC (1871.241000); UnCover; UMI.

550 GW ISSN 0939-7086
BEITRAEGE ZUR MATHEMATISCHEN GEOLOGIE UND GEOINFORMATIK. 1991. irreg., vol.5, 1993. DM.48. Verlag Sven von Loga, Gerhard-vom-Rath-Str. 55, 50968 Cologne, Germany. TEL 0221-383680. FAX 0221-386737. Ed. Gerald Peschel. **Document type**: monographic series.

BEITRAEGE ZUR NATURKUNDE IN OSTHESSEN. see BIOLOGY

BERICHTE DER DEUTSCHEN MINERALOGISCHEN GESELLSCHAFT. see MINES AND MINING INDUSTRY

BIBLIOGRAFIA GEOLOGICZNA POLSKI. see EARTH SCIENCES — Abstracting, Bibliographies, Statistics

BIBLIOGRAPHY OF THE GEOLOGY OF FIJI. see EARTH SCIENCES — Abstracting, Bibliographies, Statistics

BIOLOGY AND ENVIRONMENT; proceedings of the Royal Irish Academy. see CHEMISTRY

551 UK ISSN 0260-714X
BLACK COUNTRY GEOLOGIST. 1981. a. Black Country Geological Society, c/o Hon. Sec., 16 St. Nicholas Gardens, Kings Norton, Birmingham B38 8TW, England. illus.

551 558 VE ISSN 0257-8611
BOLETIN DE GEOCIENCIAS. 1985. s-a. $15. Sociedad Venezolana de Historia de las Geociencias, Apdo. 47334, Caracas 1041A, Venezuela. FAX 58-2-662-7845. Ed. F. Urbani. bk.rev. circ. 250. (back issues avail.)

558 CK ISSN 0120-1425
QE239 CODEN: BGINBX
BOLETIN GEOLOGICO. (Text in Spanish; summaries in English) 1953. 3/yr. price varies. Instituto Nacional de Investigaciones en Geociencias, Mineria y Quimica, Diagonal 53 No. 34-53, Apdo. Aereo 4865, Bogota D.E., Colombia. FAX 2220797. **Indexed**: Chem.Abstr., GeoRef. **Document type**: bulletin.
 —CASDDS.

551 622 SP ISSN 0366-0176
 CODEN: BGMIA3
BOLETIN GEOLOGICO Y MINERO. 1874. bi-m. 5400 ptas. Instituto Tecnologico Geominero de Espana, Cristobal Bordiu, 34, 28003 Madrid, Spain. TEL 3495730. FAX 3495762. bibl.; charts; index. **Indexed**: GeoRef.
 —CASDDS. **CCC**.
 Former titles (until 1968): Instituto Geologico y Minero de Espana. Boletin (ISSN 0366-0168); Instituto Geologico y Minero de Espana. Notas y Comunicaciones (ISSN 0369-5050)

551 622 SP
BOLETIN GEOLOGICO Y MINERO. PUBLICACIONES ESPECIALES. 1980. irreg., no.14, 1992. price varies. Instituto Tecnologico Geominero de Espana, Cristobal Bordiu, 34, 28003 Madrid, Spain. TEL 3495730. FAX 3495762.
 Description: Selected articles from the Boletin Geologico y Minero on specific topics.

BOOKS IN THE EARTH SCIENCES; and related topics. see BIBLIOGRAPHIES

EARTH SCIENCES — GEOLOGY

551 560   NO   ISSN 0300-9483
CODEN: BRESB3
BOREAS; an international journal of quaternary research. (Text in English) 1972. q. NOK 835 in the Nordic countries; elsewhere NOK 900. Scandinavian University Press, P.O. Box 2959, N-0608 Oslo, Norway. TEL 472-67-7600. FAX 472-67-7575. (U.S. addr.: Scandinavian University Press, 200 Meacham Ave., Elmont, NY 11003. TEL 516-352-7300) Ed. Christian Hjort. bk.rev.; illus. circ. 700. (also avail. in microform from UMI; back issues avail.; reprint service avail. from ISI) **Indexed:** AESIS, ASTIS, Bibl.& Ind.Geol., Biol.Abstr., Br.Geol.Lit., Chem.Abstr., Curr.Adv.Ecol.Sci., Curr.Cont., Curr.Tit.Ocean, Deep Sea Res.& Oceanogr.Abstr., Ecol.Abstr., Excerp.Bot., Geo.Abstr., GeoRef., Ind.Sci.Rev., INIS Atomind., Plant Breed.Abstr., Sci.Cit.Ind., Soils & Fert.
—BLDSC (2251.385000); Faxon; UnCover; SWETS; UMI. **CCC.**

BOTSWANA. GEOLOGICAL SURVEY DEPARTMENT. ANNOTATED BIBLIOGRAPHY AND INDEX OF THE GEOLOGY OF BOTSWANA. see *EARTH SCIENCES — Abstracting, Bibliographies, Statistics*

354   BS
BOTSWANA. GEOLOGICAL SURVEY DEPARTMENT. ANNUAL REPORTS. 1953. a. $3. Geological Survey Department, Lobatse, Botswana. FAX 332013. Ed. C. Siyumbwa. illus. circ. 300. **Document type:** government publication, academic/scholarly publication.
Formerly: Botswana. Geological Survey and Mines Department. Annual Reports.

354   BS
BOTSWANA. GEOLOGICAL SURVEY DEPARTMENT. BULLETINS. 1966. irreg. $3. Geological Survey Department, Lobatse, Botswana. FAX 332013. Ed. C. Siyumbwa. circ. 300. **Document type:** government publication, bulletin.

354   BS
BOTSWANA. GEOLOGICAL SURVEY DEPARTMENT. DISTRICT MEMOIRS. 1973. irreg. $4. Geological Survey Department, Lobatse, Botswana. FAX 332013. Ed. C. Siyumbwa. circ. 450. **Document type:** government publication.

354   BS
BOTSWANA. GEOLOGICAL SURVEY DEPARTMENT. MINERAL RESOURCES REPORTS. 1959. irreg. $3. Geological Survey Department, Lobatse, Botswana. FAX 332013. Ed. C. Siyumbwa. circ. 300. **Document type:** government publication.

354   BS
BOTSWANA. GEOLOGICAL SURVEY DEPARTMENT. RECORDS OF THE GEOLOGICAL SURVEY. 1958. irreg. $2. Geological Survey Department, Lobatse, Botswana. FAX 332013. Ed. C. Siyumbwa. circ. 300. **Document type:** government publication.

BRAGANTIA. see *AGRICULTURE*

558   BL
BRAZIL. DEPARTAMENTO NACIONAL DA PRODUCAO MINERAL. SERIE GEOLOGIA. 1976. irreg., no.27, 1985. price varies. Departamento Nacional da Producao Mineral, Setor de Autarquias Norte, Quadra 1, Bloco B, 70040 Brasilia D.F., Brazil. TEL 061-224-2670.

554   SP   ISSN 0520-9455
QE283   CODEN: BGAOAT
BREVIORA GEOLOGICA ASTURICA. (Text in English, Spanish) 1957. q. Universidad de Oviedo, Instituto de Geologia Aplicada, Oviedo, Spain. Ed.Bd. bibl.; illus. **Indexed:** Biol.Abstr., GeoRef., Ind.SST.

557   US
BRIGHAM YOUNG UNIVERSITY GEOLOGY STUDIES. 1954. a. $25. Brigham Young University, Department of Geology, Box 24646, Provo, UT 84602-4646. TEL 801-378-3918. FAX 801-378-2265. Ed. Bart J. Kowallis. cum.index (1954-1992). circ. 600. (also avail. in microfilm; back issues avail.) **Indexed:** E&P Hlth. (1993-), Gas Process.& Ppl. (1993-), GeoRef., Off.Tech. (1993-), Petrol.Abstr. (1965-). **Document type:** academic/scholarly publication.
—BLDSC (2283.970000); Faxon; UnCover.
Former titles: Brigham Young University. Department of Geology. Geology Studies (ISSN 0068-1016); (until 1960): Brigham Young University Research Studies. Geology Series.

557   CN   ISSN 0226-9430
CODEN: PMERDJ
BRITISH COLUMBIA. MINISTRY OF ENERGY, MINES AND PETROLEUM RESOURCES. PAPER SERIES. 1978. irreg. price varies. Ministry of Energy, Mines and Petroleum Resources, Mineral Resources Division, 5th Fl., 1810 Blanshard St., Victoria, BC V8V 1X4, Canada. (Subscr. to: Crown Publications, 546 Yates St., Victoria, BC V8W 1K8, Canada. TEL 604-386-4636) (back issues avail.) **Document type:** government publication.
—CASDDS.
Description: Consists primarily of geological research reports representing the culmination of major project activity or annual reviews of the Geological Survey as a whole.

622 557   CN   ISSN 0068-144X
TN27
BRITISH COLUMBIA. MINISTRY OF ENERGY, MINES AND PETROLEUM RESOURCES. BULLETIN. 1940; N.S. 19?? irreg. price varies. (Ministry of Energy, Mines and Petroleum Resources, Publications Distribution Section) Queen's Printer, Victoria, 563 Superior St., Victoria, B.C. V8V 1X4, Canada. (Dist. by: Crown Publications, 546 Yates St., Victoria, B.C. V8W 1K8, Canada. TEL 604-386-4636) **Indexed:** Eng.Ind., GeoRef.

554   UK   ISSN 0367-3928
BRITISH REGIONAL GEOLOGY. 1935. irreg. price varies. Natural Environment Research Council, British Geological Survey, Kingsley Dunham Centre, Keyworth, Nottingham NG12 5GG, England. TEL 0602-361000. FAX 0602-362000. TELEX 378173-BGSKEY-G. (Subscr. to: H.M.S.O., c/o Liaison Officer, Nine Elms, London SW8 5DR, England) illus. circ. 15,000. **Document type:** government publication.
Description: Describes the various geological regions in the United Kingdom.

551 560   PL
BUDOWA GEOLOGICZNA POLSKI. (Text in English, Polish; summaries in English, Russian) 1968. irreg. price varies. Panstwowy Instytut Geologiczny, Ul. Rakowiecka 4, 00-975 Warsaw, Poland. TEL 48-22-495351. TELEX 815541. bibl. circ. 1,500. **Indexed:** Bull.Signal., Ref.Zh.
Description: Explores the areas of paleontolgy, stratigraphy, tectonics and economic geology.

551 622   AA   ISSN 0254-5276
QE1   CODEN: BSGJDT
BULETINI I SHKENCAVE GJEOLOGJIKE. (Text in Albanian; summaries in French) 1965. q. Instituti i Studimeve dhe i Projektimeve te Gjeologjise, Tirana, Albania. TEL 355-22411. FAX 42-34031. TELEX 6044204 MIMEN AB. (Co-sponsor: Universiteti Politeknik, Fakulteti i Gjeologjise dhe i Minierave) Ed. Afat Serjani. circ. 650. **Indexed:** GeoRef.
—CASDDS.
Formerly (until 1982): Instituti i Studimeve dhe Kerkimeve Industriale e Minerale. Permbledhje Studimesh (ISSN 0370-1638)

550   BU   ISSN 0007-3938
CODEN: SBGDA8
BULGARSKO GEOLOGICHESKO DRUZHESTVO. SPISANIE. (Summaries in English, French, German, Russian) 1927. 3/yr. 1.65 lv. per no. (Bulgarska Akademiia na Naukite) Publishing House of the Bulgarian Academy of Sciences, Acad. G. Bonchev St., Bldg. 6, 1113 Sofia, Bulgaria. (Dist. by: Hemus, 6, Rouski Blvd., 1000 Sofia) Ed. Khr. Spasov. bk.rev.; abstr.; illus.; index. circ. 1,090. (reprint service avail. from IRC) **Indexed:** Biol.Abstr., BSL Geo., Chem.Abstr.
—BLDSC (0166.370000); CASDDS.

551   II   ISSN 0970-4639
QE1
BULLETIN OF PURE & APPLIED SCIENCES. SECTION F: GEOLOGY. 1982. 2/yr. Rs.40($8) to individuals; institutions Rs.80($12). Dr. A.K. Sharma, Ed. & Pub., P.O. Box 38, Modinagar 201 204, India. adv.; bk.rev. **Document type:** academic/scholarly publication.
—BLDSC (2884.510000). **CCC.**

C O G S LETTER. (Computer Oriented Geological Society) see *EARTH SCIENCES — Computer Applications*

551.3   FR
CODEN: COPEB6
CAHIERS DE PEDOLOGIE. (Text in French; summaries in English) 1962. s-a. 270 F. (Institut Francais de Recherche Scientifique pour le Developpement en Cooperation) O R S T O M Editions - Diffusion, 72 Route d'Aulnay, 93143 Bondy Cedex, France. TEL 48-02-55-00. FAX 48-47-30-88. circ. 800. (back issues avail.) **Indexed:** Agri.Eng.Abstr., Biol.Abstr., Chem.Abstr., Forest.Abstr., Geo.Abstr., INIS Atomind., Sel.Water Res.Abstr., Soils & Fert. **Document type:** academic/scholarly publication.
—BLDSC (2948.440000); Faxon; SWETS; CASDDS.
Formerly: Cahiers O R S T O M Serie Pedologie (ISSN 0029-7259)

551   FR   ISSN 0008-0241
CAHIERS GEOLOGIQUES. (Text and summaries in English, French) 1950. 2/yr. 200 F. Association des Amis et Ancien Eleves du Laboratoire de Geologie, l, Universite Paris VI, Tour 14-15-16, 4 place Jussieu, 4 Etage, 75005 Paris, France. Ed. J.P. Michel. adv.; bk.rev.; abstr.; bibl.; illus.; stat.; index. circ. 1,000. **Indexed:** Biol.Abstr., Chem.Abstr., GeoRef. **Document type:** academic/scholarly publication, bibliography, bulletin.
—Faxon.

551   US   ISSN 0008-1000
TN24.C2   CODEN: CDMBA6
CALIFORNIA. DIVISION OF MINES AND GEOLOGY. BULLETIN. 1888. irreg. (2-3/yr.). Division of Mines and Geology, 801 K St., MSC 14-33, Sacramento, CA 95814-3532. TEL 916-445-5716. (Subscr. to: Box 2980, Sacramento, CA 95812) index. **Indexed:** GeoRef. **Document type:** government publication.

551 622   US   ISSN 0527-0014
TN24.C2   CODEN: CCGRA
CALIFORNIA. DIVISION OF MINES AND GEOLOGY. SPECIAL REPORT.* irreg. Division of Mines and Geology, 801 K St. - MSC12 30, Sacramento, CA 95814-3531. TEL 916-445-1825.

557 549   US   ISSN 0026-4555
QE89   CODEN: CGEOAQ
CALIFORNIA GEOLOGY. 1948. bi-m. $10. Division of Mines and Geology, 801 K St., MSC 14-33, Sacramento, CA 95814-3532. TEL 916-445-5716. (Subscr. to: Box 2980, Sacramento, CA 95812) bk.rev.; abstr.; bibl.; charts; illus.; mkt.; stat.; index, cum.index every 10 yrs. circ. 10,000. (also avail. in microform from UMI; reprint service avail. from UMI) **Indexed:** Abstr.J.Earthq.Eng., Cal.Per.Ind. (1978-), E&P Hlth. (1993-), Gas Process.& Ppl. (1993-), Geo.Abstr., GeoRef., INIS Atomind., Off.Tech. (1993-), Petrol.Abstr. (1972-). **Document type:** government publication.
—BLDSC (3013.700000); Faxon; UnCover; UMI. **CCC.**
Formerly: Mineral Information Service.

551   UK
CAMBRIDGE PLANETARY SCIENCE SERIES. 1981. irreg., no.5, 1986. price varies. Cambridge University Press, Edinburgh Bldg., Shaftesbury Rd., Cambridge CB2 2RU, England. TEL 0223-312393. FAX 0223-315052. TELEX 851817256. (N. American addr.: Cambridge University Press, Journals Dept., 40 W. 20th St., New York, NY 10011. TEL 212-924-3900. FAX 212-691-3239) **Document type:** monographic series.

557   CN   ISSN 0068-7626
QE185   CODEN: CMGEAE
CANADA. GEOLOGICAL SURVEY. BULLETIN. (Text in English, French) 1945. irreg. price varies. Geological Survey of Canada, 601 Booth St., Ottawa, ON K1A 0E8, Canada. TEL 613-995-4342. index, cum.index: 1945-1969. circ. 800. **Indexed:** AESIS, Biol.Abstr., GeoRef., Petrol.Abstr.
—BLDSC (5607.000000); UnCover; CASDDS. **CCC.**
Incorporates: Canada. Geological Survey. Memoir (ISSN 0068-7634) & Canada. Geological Survey. Economic Geology Reports.

EARTH SCIENCES — GEOLOGY

557   CN
QE185   CODEN: CGCPAJ
CANADA. GEOLOGICAL SURVEY. CURRENT RESEARCH. (In series A-G) (Text in English, French) 1935. irreg. price varies. Geological Survey of Canada, 601 Booth St., Ottawa, Ont. K1A 0E8, Canada. TEL 513-995-4343. bibl.; index, cum.index. circ. 800. **Indexed:** AESIS, Biol.Abstr., E&P Hlth. (1993-), Gas Process.& Ppl. (1993-), Off.Tech. (1993-), Petrol.Abstr. (1963-).
—UnCover; CASDDS. **CCC.**
    Supersedes: Canada. Geological Survey. Paper (ISSN 0068-7650); Canada. Earth Physics Branch. Seismological Series (ISSN 0084-8387); Canada. Earth Physics Branch. Gravity Map Series; Canada. Earth Physics Branch. Geothermal Series (ISSN 0704-3066); Canada. Earth Physics Branch. Geomagnetic Series (ISSN 0704-3015); Canadian Earthquakes - Tremblements de Terre Canadiens (ISSN 0225-6002); Canada. Earth Physics Branch. Geodynamic Series.

557   CN   ISSN 0068-7642
QE185   CODEN: CGSRA3
CANADA. GEOLOGICAL SURVEY. MISCELLANEOUS REPORT. 1960. irreg. price varies. Geological Survey of Canada, 601 Booth St., Ottawa, ON K1A 0E8, Canada. TEL 613-995-4342. circ. 800. **Indexed:** GeoRef.
—BLDSC (5825.150000); UnCover.

549   CN   ISSN 0008-4476
CODEN: CAMIA6
CANADIAN MINERALOGIST; crystallography, geochemistry, mineralogy, petrology, mineral deposits. (Text in English or French, summaries in English, French) 1957. q. Can.$70($70) to individuals; institutions Can.$250. Mineralogical Association of Canada, Business Office, Cityview 78087, Nepean, ON K2G 5W2, Canada. TEL 613-226-4651. FAX 613-226-4651. Ed. R.F. Martin. bk.rev.; charts; illus.; index. circ. 2,000. **Indexed:** Acid Pre.Dig., AESIS, Chem.Abstr., Curr.Cont., GeoRef., Ind.Sci.Rev., INIS Atomind., Mineral.Abstr., Petrol.Abstr., Sci.Cit.Ind.
—BLDSC (3040.300000); El; Faxon; UnCover; SWETS; CASDDS. **CCC.**
    Description: Results of original research in crystallography, geochemistry, mineralogy, petrology and mineral deposits.

CANADIAN MINING JOURNAL. see *MINES AND MINING INDUSTRY*

551   US   ISSN 0891-2556
CODEN: CAEVE9
CARBONATES AND EVAPORITES. 1986. 2/yr. $30 to individuals (foreign $40); institutions $52 (foreign $62) (effective 1994). Northeastern Science Foundation, Inc., 15 Third St., Box 746, Troy, NY 12181-0746. TEL 518-273-3247. Ed. Gerald M. Friedman. index. (back issues avail.) **Indexed:** Gas Process.& Ppl. (1993-), Off.Tech. (1993-), Petrol.Abstr. (1987-). **Document type:** academic/scholarly publication.
—BLDSC (3050.996800); UnCover; SWETS; CASDDS. **CCC.**
    Description: Professional reports on all aspects of carbonates and evaporites.
Refereed Serial

558   CL   ISSN 0716-0194
CARTA GEOLOGICA DE CHILE. (Text in Spanish; summaries in English) 1959. irreg. $30 (effective 1994) or exchange basis. Servicio Nacional de Geologia y Mineria, Casilla 10465, Santiago, Chile. TEL 56-2-7375050. FAX 56-2-7372026. Ed.Bd. circ. 1,000. **Document type:** government publication.

558   BL
CARTA GEOLOGICA DO BRASIL AO MILIONESIMO. 1974. irreg., no.19, 1979. 1 BTN($1) Departamento Nacional da Producao Mineral, Setor Autarquias Norte, Quadra 1, Bloco B, 70040 Brasilia, D.F., Brazil. TEL 061-224-2670. charts.

558   CL   ISSN 0716-7555
CARTA HIDROGEOLOGICA DE CHILE. (Text in Spanish; summaries in English) 1990. irreg. $25 (effective 1994). Servicio Nacional de Geologia y Mineria, Casilla 10465, Santiago, Chile. TEL 56-2-7375050. FAX 56-2-372026. Ed.Bd. circ. 1,000. **Document type:** government publication.

551.44   US   ISSN 0008-7211
CASCADE CAVER;* international journal of vulcanospeleology. 1961. 10/yr. $7.50. National Speleological Society, Cascade Grotto, c/o National Society, Cave Ave., Huntsville, AL 35810. Ed. Mark Sherman. bk.rev.; abstr.; charts; illus. circ. 150. (processed) **Indexed:** Geo.Abstr., GeoRef.

551   US
CASEBOOKS IN EARTH SCIENCES. 1984. irreg. price varies. Springer-Verlag, 175 Fifth Ave., New York, NY 10010. TEL 212-460-1500. FAX 212-473-6272. (Also: Berlin, Heidelberg, Tokyo and Vienna) (reprint service avail. from ISI) **Document type:** monographic series.

550 549   XR   ISSN 0008-7378
QE351   CODEN: CAPMAX
CASOPIS PRO MINERALOGII A GEOLOGII/JOURNAL OF MINERALOGY AND GEOLOGY. (Text in Czech, English, French, German, Russian; summaries in Czech, English, German) 1956. q. DM.168. (Ceskoslovenska Spolecnost pro Mineralogii a Geologii Bohemoslovaca) Academia, Publishing House of the Czechoslovak Academy of Sciences, Vodickova 40, 112 29 Prague 1, Czech Republic. TEL 221-413. (Dist. in Western countries by: Kubon & Sagner, P.O. Box 34 01 08, 8000 Munich 34, Germany) Ed. Jan Petranek. adv.; bk.rev.; charts; illus.; index. circ. 900. **Indexed:** Chem.Abstr., E&P Hlth. (1993-), Gas Process.& Ppl. (1993-), GeoRef., Off.Tech. (1993-), Petrol.Abstr. (1963-).
    Description: All fields of geology, mineralogy, paleontology and applied geophysics.

551   NE   ISSN 0341-8162
CODEN: CIJPD3
CATENA; an interdisciplinary journal of soil science, hydrology, geomorphology. (Supplement avail. (0722-0723)) (Text and summaries in English) 1973. 8/yr. (in 2 vols., 4 nos./vol.) fl.672($363) (effective 1994). Elsevier Science B.V., P.O. Box 211, 1000 AE Amsterdam, Netherlands. TEL 31-20-5803911. FAX 31-20-5803598. (Subscr. in U.S. and Canada to: Elsevier Science Inc., Box 882, Madison Sq. Sta., New York, NY 10159-0882. TEL 212-989-5800. FAX 212-633-3990) Ed.Bd. index. circ. 1,000. (back issues avail.) **Indexed:** Chem.Abstr., Curr.Cont., Geo.Abstr., Sci.Cit.Ind., Sel.Water Res.Abstr. **Document type:** academic/scholarly publication.
—BLDSC (3092.590000); UnCover; SWETS; CASDDS. **CCC.**
    Description: Publishes original research contributions in geoecology and landscape evolution.
Refereed Serial

551   NE   ISSN 0722-0723
CATENA SUPPLEMENT. (Text and summaries in English) 1982. 2/yr. price varies. Elsevier Science B.V., P.O. Box 211, 1000 AE Amsterdam, Netherlands. TEL 31-20-5803911. FAX 31-20-5803598. (Subscr. in U.S. and Canada to: Elsevier Science Inc., Box 882, Madison Sq. Sta., New York, NY 10159-0882. TEL 212-989-5800. FAX 212-633-3990) index. circ. 1,000. (back issues avail.) **Indexed:** Chem.Abstr., Curr.Cont., Geo.Abstr., Sci.Cit.Ind. **Document type:** proceedings.
—BLDSC (3092.700000); UnCover. **CCC.**

551.44   US
CAVE GEOLOGY. 1976. irreg., vol.2, no.3, 1992. price varies. National Speleological Society, Section of Cave Geology and Geography, 542 Glenn Rd., State College, PA 16803. TEL 814-237-3187. Eds. W.B. & E.L. White. bk.rev. circ. 200. (back issues avail.) **Document type:** academic/scholarly publication.
    Description: Covers geology with emphasis on caves and karst systems.

551.44   UK   ISSN 0263-760X
CAVE SCIENCE: TRANSACTIONS OF THE BRITISH CAVE RESEARCH ASSOCIATION. 1974. irreg. (3/yr.). £16 to non-members. British Cave Research Association, c/o Bryan Ellis, 20 Woodland Ave., Westonzoyland, Bridgwater, Somerset TA7 0LQ, England. Ed. T.D. Ford. adv.; index. circ. 1,400. **Indexed:** Br.Archaeol.Abstr., Geo.Abstr., GeoRef. **Document type:** academic/scholarly publication.
—BLDSC (3094.000000). **CCC.**
    Former titles: British Cave Research Association. Transactions (ISSN 0305-859X); Cave Research Group of Great Britain. Transactions (ISSN 0069-1305); Cave Science; British Hypogean Fauna and Biological Records.
    Description: Covers all aspects of science, technology and exploration associated with caves and limestones.

CAVES AND CAVERNS; national caves association directory. see *TRAVEL AND TOURISM*

551.44   UK   ISSN 0142-1832
CAVES & CAVING. 1973. q. £8.50 (foreign £10). British Cave Research Association, c/o Bryan Ellis, 20 Woodland Ave., Westonzoyland, Bridgwater, Somerset TA7 0LQ, England. Ed. M. Dougherty. adv.; bk.rev. circ. 2,000. **Indexed:** GeoRef. **Document type:** bulletin.
—BLDSC (3094.019000). **CCC.**
    Supersedes: British Speleological Association. Bulletin (ISSN 0045-3153); Supersedes: Cave Research Group of Great Britain Newsletter.

551.4   FR   ISSN 0068-4791
CENTRE DE GEOMORPHOLOGIE, CAEN. BULLETIN. 1967. 3/yr. exchange basis. Centre National de la Recherche Scientifique, Centre de Geomorphologie, Rue des Tilleuls, 14000 Caen, France. FAX 31-45-56-00. **Indexed:** Geo.Abstr., GeoRef.

556   FR   ISSN 0769-0541
CENTRE INTERNATIONAL POUR LA FORMATION ET LES ECHANGES GEOLOGIQUES. PUBLICATION OCCASIONNELLE/INTERNATIONAL CENTER FOR TRAINING AND EXCHANGES IN THE GEOSCIENCES. OCCASIONAL PUBLICATION. (Text and summaries in English, French) 1983. irreg., latest no.24, 1993. price varies. Centre International pour la Formation et les Echanges Geologiques - International Center for Training and Exchanges in the Geosciences, B.P. 6517, Av. de Concyr, 45065 Orleans Cedex 2, France. TEL 38-54-36-57. FAX 38-64-34-72. TELEX 780 258. Ed. Jean-Claude Bidet. circ. 600.
    Description: Scientific papers on geosciences, mainly extended abstracts of conferences on African geology.

CENTRES DE RECHERCHES EXPLORATION - PRODUCTION ELF AQUITAINE. BULLETIN. see *PETROLEUM AND GAS*

CEPHALOPOD NEWSLETTER. see *BIOLOGY — Zoology*

796.525   UK   ISSN 0045-6381
CHELSEA SPELAEOLOGICAL SOCIETY. NEWSLETTER. 1959. m. £5. Chelsea Speleological Society, Chelsea Community Centre, Worlds End Estate, Kings Rd., Chelsea, London SW3, England. Ed. L. Ramsay. charts; index. circ. 150. (processed)

796.525   UK   ISSN 0309-409X
CHELSEA SPELAEOLOGICAL SOCIETY. RECORDS. irreg. Chelsea Speleological Society, Chelsea Community Centre, Worlds End Estate, Kings Rd., Chelsea, London SW3, England. Ed. Harry Pearman. circ. 250. (processed) **Indexed:** GeoRef.

550   GW   ISSN 0009-2819
QE1   CODEN: CERDAA
CHEMIE DER ERDE/GEOCHEMISTRY; Zeitschrift fuer chemische Mineralogie, Petrographie, Bodenkunde, Geochemie und Meteoritenkunde - journal for chemical problems of the geo-sciences and extraterrestrial mineralogy. (Text and summaries in English, German) 1914. 4/yr. DM.244 (foreign DM.248). Gustav Fischer Verlag Jena, Villengang 2, 07745 Jena, Germany. TEL 03641-27332. FAX 03641-22638. (Subscr. to: Postfach 100537, 07705 Jena, Germany) Ed. K. Heide. adv.; bk.rev.; bibl.; charts; illus.; index, cum.index: vols.1-45. (reprint service avail. from ISI,KTO) **Indexed:** Chem.Abstr., Deep Sea Res.& Oceanogr.Abstr., Excerp.Med., GeoRef., INIS Atomind., Mineral.Abstr., Ref.Zh. **Document type:** academic/scholarly publication.
—BLDSC (3156.000000); UnCover; CASDDS. **CCC.**

EARTH SCIENCES — GEOLOGY

551.3   **CC**   **ISSN 1000-0550**
CODEN: CHXUEE
CHENJI XUEBAO/ACTA SEDIMENTOLOGICA SINICA. (Text in Chinese; summaries in English) 1983. q. $89.20. Science Press, Marketing and Sales Department, 16 Donghuangchenggen Beijie, Beijing 100707, People's Republic of China. TEL 4010642. FAX 4012180. TELEX 210247-SPBJ-CN. adv. circ. 4,000.
—BLDSC (0663.259000); CASDDS.
Refereed Serial

550   **JA**
CHIBAKEN KOGAI KENKYUJO CHIKA SHIGEN JIBAN SAIGAI KENKYU SHIRYO/RESEARCH REPORT OF GEOLOGICAL SURVEY AND LANDSUBSIDENCE IN CHIBA PREFECTURE. (Text in Japanese) a. Chibaken Kogai Kenkyujo - Chiba Prefectural Research Institute for Environmental Pollution, 8-8, Iwasaki Nishi 1-chome, Ichihara-shi, Chiba-ken 290, Japan. stat. **Document type:** academic/scholarly publication.

551   **JA**
CHIDANKEN SENPO/ASSOCIATION FOR GEOLOGICAL COLLABORATION IN JAPAN. BULLETIN. (Text in Japanese; summaries in English) 1972. irreg. Chigaku Dantai Kenkyukai - Association for Geological Collaboration in Japan, 8-7, Minamiikebukuro 1-chome, Toshima-ku, Tokyo 171, Japan. **Document type:** bulletin.

551   **JA**   **ISSN 0388-5208**
CHIGAKU DANTAI KENKYUKAI SOKUHO/ASSOCIATION FOR THE GEOLOGICAL COLLABORATION IN JAPAN. NEWS. (Text in Japanese) m. Chigaku Dantai Kenkyukai, 8-7, Minamiikebukuro 1-chome, Toshima-ku, Tokyo 171, Japan.

551   **JA**   **ISSN 0366-5933**
CODEN: CGKUA6
CHIGAKU KENKYU/GEOSCIENCE MAGAZINE. (Text in Japanese) 1046. q. 1500 Yen per no. Nippon Chigaku Kenkyukai, Karasuma Demizu Nishi Iru, Kamigyo-ku, Kyoto 602, Japan. **Indexed:** Chem.Abstr., INIS Atomind., Jap.Per.Ind.
—CASDDS.

550 624   **JA**
CHIKA KUKAN RIYO SHINPOJUMU/SYMPOSIUM ON UTILITY OF UNDERGROUND SPACE. (Text in Japanese; summaries in English) 1988. a. 5000 Yen. Doboku Gakkai - Japan Society of Civil Engineers, Yotsuya 1-chome, Shinjuku-ku, Tokyo 160, Japan.

555.2   **JA**   **ISSN 0441-0785**
CODEN: CHCHB3
CHIKA SHIGEN CHOSAJO HOKOKU/GEOLOGICAL SURVEY OF HOKKAIDO. REPORT. (Text in Japanese; summaries in English) 1950. a. exchange basis. Hokkaidoritsu Chika Shigen Chosajo - Geological Survey of Hokkaido, Nishi 12-chome, Kita 19-jo, Kita-ku, Sapporo-shi, Hokkaido 060, Japan. FAX 011-737-9071. Ed. Fukutoshi Hayakawa. circ. 900. **Indexed:** Chem.Abstr., Jap.Per.Ind. **Document type:** bulletin.
Formerly (until 1958): Hokkaido Chika Shigen Chosa Hokoku (ISSN 0286-7583)

551   **JA**   **ISSN 0389-1755**
CHIKEI/JAPANESE GEOMORPHOLOGICAL UNION. TRANSACTIONS. (Text in English, Japanese) 1980. q. 4000 Yen. Nihon Chikeigaku Rengo - Japanese Geomorphological Union, Kyoto Daigaku Bosai Kenkyujo, Chikei Dojo Saigai Kenkyu Bumon, Gokanosho, Uji-shi, Kyoto 611, Japan.
—BLDSC (8975.117000).

550   **CL**   **ISSN 0020-3939**
QE237   CODEN: BIGCA3
CHILE. SERVICIO NACIONAL DE GEOLOGIA Y MINERIA. BOLETIN. (Text in Spanish; summaries in English) 1958. irreg. price varies or on exchange. Servicio Nacional de Geologia y Mineria, Casilla de Correo 10465, Santiago, Chile. TEL 56-2-7375050. FAX 56-2-372026. Ed.Bd. charts; illus. circ. 1,000. **Indexed:** GeoRef. **Document type:** government publication.
—BLDSC (2188.475000).

551   **CH**   **ISSN 1012-6821**
CHINA, REPUBLIC. CENTRAL GEOLOGICAL SURVEY. BULLETIN. (Text in Chinese, English) 1981. irreg. $30 (effective 1991)(typically set in July). Ministry of Economic Affairs, Central Geological Survey, 2 Lane 109, Huahsin St., Chungho, Taipei, Taiwan, Republic of China. FAX 886-2-9429291. (Subscr. to: Central Geological Survey, Ministry of Economic Affairs, P.O. Box 968, Taipei, Taiwan) Ed. Tunyow Huang. circ. 750.
—BLDSC (2435.950000).
Supersedes: China, Republic. Geological Survey of Taiwan. Bulletin.

555   **CC**   **ISSN 1002-0063**
CHINESE GEOGRAPHICAL SCIENCE/ZHONGGUO DILI KEXUE. Chinese edition: Dili Kexue (ISSN 1000-0690) (Text in English) 1991. q. $110 to individuals (foreign $130); institutions $225 (foreign $245). (Zhongguo Kexueyuan, Changchun Dilisuo - Chinese Academy of Sciences, Changchun Geology Institute) Science Press, Marketing and Sales Department, 16 Donghuangchenggen Beijie, Beijing 100707, People's Republic of China. TEL 4010642. FAX 4012180. TELEX 210247-SPBJ-CN. (Overseas dist by: Science Press New York, Ltd., 63-117 Alderton St., Rego Park, NY 11374. TEL 718-459-4638) Ed. Huang Xichou.
—BLDSC (3180.278900).
Refereed Serial

551.9 552   **CC**   **ISSN 1000-9426**
CODEN: CJGEEV
CHINESE JOURNAL OF GEOCHEMISTRY. Chinese edition: Diqiu Huaxue (ISSN 0379-1726) (Text in English) 1982. q. DM.410 (effective 1994). Science Press, Marketing and Sales Department, 16 Donghuangchenggen Beijie, Beijing 100707, People's Republic of China. TEL 4010642. FAX 4012180. TELEX 210247-SPBJ-CN. (Dist. outside China by: V S P, P.O. Box 346, 3700 AH Zeist, Netherlands. TEL 31-3404-25790. FAX 31-3404-32081) Ed. Tu Guangzhi. adv. circ. 6,000. (back issues avail.) **Indexed:** E&P Hlth. (1993-), Gas Process.& Ppl. (1993-), Off.Tech. (1993-), Petrol.Abstr. (1988-). **Document type:** academic/scholarly publication.
—BLDSC (3180.335000); CASDDS.
Formerly: Geochemistry (ISSN 0253-486X)
Description: Includes research on petrology, mineralogy and economic geology, as well as isotopic geology, cosmochemistry, and quaternary geology.
Refereed Serial

555   **JA**   **ISSN 0016-7665**
QE1   CODEN: CHCGAX
CHISHITSU CHOSAJO GEPPO/GEOLOGICAL SURVEY OF JAPAN. BULLETIN. (Text in English, Japanese) 1950. m. Kogyo Gijutsuin, Chishitsu Chosajo - Agency of Industrial Science and Technology, Geological Survey of Japan, 1-3, Higashi 1-chome, Tsukuba-shi, Ibaraki-ken 305, Japan. Dir. Isamu Kobayashi. charts; illus.; index, cum.index every 5 yrs. circ. 1,950. **Indexed:** Biol.Abstr., Chem.Abstr., Eng.Ind., INIS Atomind., Jap.Per.Ind., Petrol.Abstr.
—BLDSC (2533.000000); UnCover; CASDDS.

551   **JA**   **ISSN 0366-5542**
CHISHITSU CHOSAJO HOKOKU/GEOLOGICAL SURVEY OF JAPAN. REPORT. (Text in Japanese; summaries in English, Japanese) 1907. irreg. Kogyo Gijutsuin, Chishitsu Chosajo - Agency of Industrial Science, Geological Survey of Japan, 1-3, Higashi 1-chome, Tsukuba-shi, Ibaraki-ken 305, Japan. **Indexed:** Biol.Abstr., INIS Atomind., Jap.Per.Ind.
—BLDSC (7484.910000).

551   **JA**
CHISHITSU CHOSAJO KENKYU KOENKAI SHIRYO/GEOLOGICAL SURVEY OF JAPAN. PROCEEDINGS OF THE ANNUAL MEETING. (Text in Japanese) a. 2500 Yen. (Kogyo Gijutsuin, Chishitsu Chosajo - Agency of Industrial Science and Technology, Geological Survey of Japan) Nihon Sangyo Gijutsu Shinko Kyokai - Japan Industrial Technology Association, 19-5, Toranomon 1-chome, Minato-ku, Tokyo 105, Japan. **Document type:** proceedings.

551   **JA**
CHISHITSU CHOSAJO NENPO/GEOLOGICAL SURVEY OF JAPAN. ANNUAL REPORT. (Text in Japanese) 1882. a. Kogyo Gijutsuin, Chishitsu Chosajo - Agency of Industrial Science and Technology, Geological Survey of Japan, 1-3, Higashi 1-chome, Tsukuba-shi, Ibaraki-ken 305, Japan.

555   **JA**   **ISSN 0009-4854**
QE1   CODEN: CHNYB7
CHISHITSU NYUSU/MONTHLY REVIEW OF GEOLOGY. (Text in Japanese) 1953. m. 700 Yen per no. (Kogyo Gijutsuin, Chishitsu Chosajo - Agency of Industrial Science and Technology, Geological Survey of Japan) Jitsugyo Kohosha Co., Ltd., 1-12, Kudan Minami 4-chome, Chiyoda-ku, Tokyo 102, Japan. Ed. Hiroshi Takahashi. bk.rev. circ. 6,000. **Indexed:** Art & Archaeol.Tech.Abstr., Chem.Abstr.
—CASDDS.

552 551.3   **JA**   **ISSN 0385-8545**
QE304   CODEN: CSGRBS
CHISHITSUGAKU RONSHU/GEOLOGICAL SOCIETY OF JAPAN. MEMOIRS. 1968. irregg. 5000 Yen. Nihon Chishitsu Gakkai - Geological Society of Japan, 10-4, Kajicho 1-chome, Chiyoda-ku, Tokyo 101, Japan. circ. 1,500. (back issues avail.) **Indexed:** Jap.Per.Ind.
—CASDDS. **CCC.**
Description: Original papers on geoscientific topics.

555   **JA**   **ISSN 0016-7630**
CODEN: CHTZA5
CHISHITSUGAKU ZASSHI/GEOLOGICAL SOCIETY OF JAPAN. JOURNAL. (Text in English, Japanese) 1893. m. 12000 Yen. Nihon Chishitsu Gakkai - Geological Society of Japan, 10-4, Kajicho 1-chome, Chiyoda-ku, Tokyo 101, Japan. Ed. Yasumoto Suzuki. adv.; bk.rev.; index. circ. 5,500. **Indexed:** Biol.Abstr., Chem.Abstr., INIS Atomind., Jap.Per.Ind.
—BLDSC (4757.000000).
Description: Original papers on earth sciences.

913 520 551   **UK**
CHRONOLOGY & CATASTROPHISM REVIEW. 1976. a. £15.50. Society for Interdisciplinary Studies, c/o Veronica Shelley-Pearce, 29 Cudham Ln., N., Orpington, Kent BR6 6BX, England. Ed. B. Newgrosh. adv.; bk.rev.; charts, illus. circ. 500. (back issues avail.) **Document type:** academic/scholarly publication.
Formerly: S I S Review (ISSN 0308-3276)

796.525   **IT**   **ISSN 0009-7268**
CODEN: CSPNAQ
CIRCOLO SPELEOLOGICO ROMANO. NOTIZIARIO. (Text in Italian; summaries in English, Italian) 1947. a. $9. Circolo Speleologico Romano, Via Ulisse Aldrovandi 18, 00197 Rome, Italy. TEL 06-3216223. Ed. Giorgio Marzolla. adv.; bk.rev.; bibl.; charts; illus. circ. 1,000. **Indexed:** Appl.Mech.Rev., GeoRef., Math.R.
Description: Covers speleology, subterranean hydrology, geology, and speleogenesis.

554   **GW**   **ISSN 0009-8523**
QE269   CODEN: CGEAAI
CLAUSTHALER GEOLOGISCHE ABHANDLUNGEN. 1965. q. price varies. Verlag Sven von Loga, Gerhard-vom-Rath-Str. 55, 50968 Cologne, Germany. TEL 0221-383680. FAX 0221-386737. circ. 500. **Indexed:** Chem.Abstr., GeoRef. **Document type:** academic/scholarly publication.

550   **GW**   **ISSN 0069-4584**
CLAUSTHALER TEKTONISCHE HEFTE. 1959. irreg., no.28, 1993. DM.29.80. Verlag Sven von Loga, Gerhard-vom-Rath-Str. 55, 50968 Cologne, Germany. TEL 0221-383680. FAX 0221-386737. Eds. S. Schultheiss, W. Goos. **Document type:** monographic series.

558   **CK**
COLOMBIA. MINISTERIO DE MINAS Y ENERGIA. MEMORIA AL CONGRESO DE LA REPUBLICA. 1940. a. Ministerio de Minas y Energia, Oficina de Planeacion-Investigaciones Economicas, Bogota, Colombia. circ. 1,500.
Continues: Colombia. Ministerio de Minas y Petroleos. Informe.

551   **FR**   **ISSN 0074-9427**
COMMISSION FOR THE GEOLOGICAL MAP OF THE WORLD. BULLETIN. (Text in English, French) 1962. a. 150 F.($25) Commission for the Geological Map of the World (CGMW), Maison de la Geologie, 77 rue Claude-Bernard, 75005 Paris, France. TEL 47-07-22-84. FAX 33-1-43-36-76-55. TELEX 206 411 F. Ed. P. Bouysse. adv.; bk.rev.; illus. circ. 300. **Indexed:** GeoRef. **Document type:** bulletin.
Description: Details CGMW's activities in the preceeding year.

COMPUTERS & MINING. see *MINES AND MINING INDUSTRY — Computer Applications*

EARTH SCIENCES — GEOLOGY

550 500 US
CONNECTICUT GEOLOGIC AND NATURAL HISTORY BULLETINS. irreg. Department of Environmental Protection, 165 Capitol Ave., Hartford, CT 06160. TEL 203-566-7719. illus.

551 US
CONTRIBUTION TO PRECAMBRIAN GEOLOGY. 1969. irreg., no.18, 1987. Department of Natural Resources, Division of Geology and Land Survey, Box 250, Rolla, MO 65401. TEL 314-368-2125. bibl.; charts; illus. circ. 1,500.

CONTRIBUTIONS IN BIOLOGY AND GEOLOGY. see *BIOLOGY*

551 II
CONTRIBUTIONS TO HIMALAYAN GEOLOGY. (Text in English) 1979. irreg., vol.4, 1989. price varies. Hindustan Publishing Corp., 6-U.B. Jawahar Nagar, New Delhi 110007, India. TEL 2915059. FAX 6863511. Ed. V.J. Gupta.

552 549 GW ISSN 0010-7999
CODEN: CMPEAP
CONTRIBUTIONS TO MINERALOGY AND PETROLOGY. 1947. 16/yr. (in 4 vols., 4 nos./vol.). DM.3396($2123) Springer-Verlag, Heidelberger Platz 3, 14197 Berlin, Germany. TEL 030-8207-1. FAX 030-8214091. (Subscr. in N. America to: Springer-Verlag New York, Inc., 44 Hartz Way, Secaucus, NJ 07096-2491. TEL 201-348-4033. FAX 201-348-4505) Eds. T. Grove, J. Hoefs. adv.; bibl.; charts; illus.; index. (also avail. in microform from UMI; reprint service avail. from ISI) **Indexed:** AESIS, Br.Geol.Lit., Chem.Abstr., Curr.Cont., Deep Sea Res.& Oceanogr.Abstr., Geo.Abstr., GeoRef., Ind.Sci.Rev., INIS Atomind., Mineral.Abstr., Petrol.Abstr., Sci.Cit.Ind., So.Pac.Per.Ind. **Document type:** academic/scholarly publication.
—BLDSC (3461.020000); Faxon; UnCover; SWETS; UMI; CASDDS. **CCC.**
Description: Original articles presenting essentially new scientific findings on geochemistry. Includes isotope geology; the petrology and genesis of igneous, metamorphic, and sedimentary rocks; experimental petrology and mineralogy; and distribution and significance of elements and their isotopes in the rocks.
Refereed Serial

551.3 GW ISSN 0343-4125
CODEN: CBSDAS
CONTRIBUTIONS TO SEDIMENTOLOGY. (Text in English, German) 1973. irreg. price varies. E. Schweizerbart'sche Verlagsbuchhandlung, Johannesstr. 3A, 70176 Stuttgart, Germany. TEL 0711-625001. FAX 0711-625005. TELEX 723363-SCHB-D. Ed. H. Fuechtbauer. **Indexed:** Deep Sea Res.& Oceanogr.Abstr., GeoRef., Petrol.Abstr. **Document type:** monographic series.
—CCC.

CUBA. MINING AND GEOLOGY. see *MINES AND MINING INDUSTRY*

557 551 US ISSN 0092-9565
QE47.M9
CURRENT GEOLOGICAL AND GEOPHYSICAL STUDIES IN MONTANA. (Subseries of: Montana. State Bureau of Mines and Geology. Open-File Reports) 1969. a. Bureau of Mines and Geology, Montana College of Mineral Science and Technology, Room 200, Main Hall, Butte, MT 59701-8997. TEL 406-496-4167. FAX 406-496-4451. Comp. Richard B. Berg. stat. circ. 700.
Description: Listing of all on-going research studies in the geosciences being conducted by students, faculty and individuals from both federal and state agencies.

551 II ISSN 0971-1481
CURRENT TRENDS IN GEOLOGY. 1978. a. $75. Today and Tomorrow's Printers and Publishers, 24B-5 Desh Bandhu Gupta Rd., Karol Bagh, New Delhi 110 005, India. TEL 5721928. (Dist. in U.S. by: Scholarly Publications, 7310 Elcreata Dr., Houston, Texas 77083. TEL 713-781-0070. FAX 713-781-2112) Ed. P.S. Saklani.

551 DK ISSN 0109-2367
D G U INFORMATION. 1984. q. free. Danmark Geologiske Undersoegelse, 8 Thoravej, DK-2400 Copenhagen V, Denmark. (Subscr. to: Geografforlaget, 5464 Brenderup, Denmark. TEL 45-64-44-16-83) Ed. Knud Binzer. illus. circ. 3,000. **Indexed:** NAA. **Document type:** government publication.

551 CC ISSN 1001-1552
QE601 CODEN: DGYXEW
DADI GOUZAO YU CHENGKUANGXUE/GEOTECTONICA ET METALLOGENIA. (Text in Chinese) 1977. q. $74. Science Press, Marketing and Sales Department, 16 Donghuangchenggen Beijie, Beijing 100707, People's Republic of China. TEL 4010642. FAX 4012180. TELEX 210247-SPBJ-CN. adv. circ. 5,500.
—BLDSC (4160.530000); CASDDS.
Description: Covers the structure of the earth and the formation of mineral deposits.
Refereed Serial

551 DK ISSN 0901-0270
DANMARKS GEOLOGISKE UNDERSOEGELSE. SERIE A/GEOLOGICAL SURVEY OF DENMARK. SERIES A. Key Title: D G U, Danmarks Geologiske Undersoegelse. Serie A. 1976. irreg. price varies. Danmarks Geologiske Undersoegelse - Geological Survey of Denmark, 8 Thoravej, DK-2400 Copenhagen, Denmark. TEL 31 10 66 00. FAX 31-19-68-68. TELEX 19999 DANGEO DK. **Indexed:** Biol.Abstr., Curr.Adv.Ecol.Sci., NAA. **Document type:** monographic series.
Formerly (until 1979): Danmarks Geologiske Undersoegelse. Serie A (ISSN 0105-6980)

551 DK ISSN 0901-0289
DANMARKS GEOLOGISKE UNDERSOEGELSE. SERIE B/GEOLOGICAL SURVEY OF DENMARK. SERIES B. Key Title: D G U, Danmarks Geologiske Undersoegelse. Serie B. 1977-1983; resumed 1986. irreg. Danmarks Geologiske Undersoegelse - Geological Survey of Denmark, 8 Thoravej, DK-2400 Copenhagen, Denmark. TEL 31-10-66-00. FAX 31-19-68-68. TELEX 19999 DANGEO DK. **Document type:** monographic series.
Formerly (until 1983): Danmarks Geologiske Undersoegelse. Serie B (ISSN 0105-7197)

551 DK ISSN 0900-6362
CODEN: DSECEL
DANMARKS GEOLOGISKE UNDERSOEGELSE. SERIE C. Key Title: D G U Serie. C. irreg. price varies. Danmarks Geologiske Undersoegelse - Geological Survey of Denmark, Thoravej 8, DK-2400 Copenhagen, Denmark. TEL 31 10 66 00. FAX 31-19-68-68. TELEX 19999 DANGEO DK.

551 DK ISSN 0900-6257
DANMARKS GEOLOGISKE UNDERSOEGELSE. SERIE D. Key Title: D G U Serie. D. irreg. Danmarks Geologiske Undersoegelse - Geological Survey of Denmark, Thoravej 8, DK 2400 Copenhagen NV, Denmark. TEL 31 10 66 00. FAX 31-19-68-68. TELEX 19999 DANGEO DK. **Document type:** monographic series.

551 US ISSN 0895-0717
DELAWARE GEOLOGICAL SURVEY. INFORMATION SERIES. 1986. irreg., no.7, 1992. Delaware Geological Survey, University of Delaware, Newark, DE 19716. TEL 302-831-2833.

557 US ISSN 0070-3273
QE95 CODEN: DGSBAY
DELAWARE GEOLOGICAL SURVEY BULLETINS. 1953. irreg., no.18, 1988. Geological Survey, University of Delaware, Newark, DE 19716. TEL 302-831-2833. FAX 302-831-3579. **Indexed:** Abstr.N.Amer.Geol., GeoRef. **Document type:** bulletin.

557 US ISSN 0011-7749
QE95 CODEN: DGRIAG
DELAWARE GEOLOGICAL SURVEY REPORTS OF INVESTIGATIONS. 1957. irreg., no. 50, 1992. Geological Survey, University of Delaware, Newark, DE 19716. TEL 302-831-2833. FAX 302-831-3579. **Indexed:** Abstr.N.Amer.Geol., Chem.Abstr., GeoRef.
—UnCover.

796.525 UK ISSN 0046-0036
DESCENT; the magazine for cavers. 1969. bi-m. £11.70($20) Ambit Publications, Fuller Ct., Ste. 1, Lower Quay St., Gloucester GL2 2LW, England. FAX 44-452-423430. Ed. Chris Howes. adv.; bk.rev.; charts; illus. circ. 3,000. **Indexed:** Sportsearch.
—BLDSC (3555.750000).
Description: Covers aspects of speleology.

551 GW
DEUTSCHE GEOLOGISCHE GESELLSCHAFT. 1969. a. DM.90. (Deutsche Geologische Gesellschaft) Ferdinand Enke Verlag, Postfach 101254, 70011 Stuttgart, Germany. TEL 0711-135798-0. FAX 0711-135798-30. circ. 3,300. (back issues avail.; reprint service avail. from IRC) **Document type:** academic/scholarly publication.

551 GW ISSN 0012-0189
CODEN: ZDGGA6
DEUTSCHE GEOLOGISCHE GESELLSCHAFT. ZEITSCHRIFT. (Text and summaries in English, French, German) 2/yr. DM.90. Ferdinand Enke Verlag, Postfach 101254, 70011 Stuttgart, Germany. TEL 0711-135798-0. FAX 0711-135798-30. TELEX 07252275-GTV-D. Ed. H. Vossmerbaeumer. index. (reprint service avail. from IRC) **Indexed:** Deep Sea Res.& Oceanogr.Abstr., Geotech.Abstr. **Document type:** academic/scholarly publication.
—BLDSC (9442.000000); UnCover; SWETS; CASDDS. **CCC.**
Description: Scientific publication covering historical and regional geology, stratigraphy, petrography, deposits, and hydrogeology, mainly in central Europe.

551 NE
DEVELOPMENTS IN EARTH AND PLANETARY SCIENCES; a series of monographs. 1980. irreg. price varies. Kluwer Academic Publishers, Postbus 17, 3300 AA Dordrecht, Netherlands. TEL 31-78-334911. FAX 31-78-334254. TELEX 29245 KAPG NL. (Dist. by: Kluwer Academic Publishers Group, P.O. Box 322, 3300 AH Dordrecht, Netherlands. TEL 31-78-524400; N. America dist. addr.: Box 358, Accord Sta., Hingham, MA 02018-0358. TEL 617-871-6600) Ed. T. Rikitake. **Document type:** monographic series.
Refereed Serial

550 NE
DEVELOPMENTS IN EARTH SURFACE PROCESSES. (Text in English) 1990. irreg., vol.3, 1992. price varies. Elsevier Science B.V., Books Division, P.O. Box 211, 1000 AE Amsterdam, Netherlands. TEL 31-20-5803911. FAX 31-20-5803705. TELEX 18582 ESPA NL. (Subscr. in U.S. and Canada to: Elsevier Science Inc., Box 882, Madison Sq. Sta., New York, NY 10159. TEL 212-989-5800) (back issues avail.) **Document type:** monographic series.
Refereed Serial

551 NE ISSN 0168-6178
CODEN: DGEOD6
DEVELOPMENTS IN ECONOMIC GEOLOGY. (Text in English) 1975. irreg., vol.28, 1994. price varies. Elsevier Science B.V., Books Division, P.O. Box 211, 1000 AE Amsterdam, Netherlands. TEL 31-20-5803911. FAX 31-20-5803705. TELEX 18582 ESPA NL. (Subscr. in U.S. and Canada to: Elsevier Science Inc., Box 882, Madison Sq. Sta., New York, NY 10159. TEL 212-989-5800) (back issues avail.) Indexed: GeoRef. **Document type:** monographic series.
—BLDSC (3579.071000); Faxon; CASDDS.
Refereed Serial

551 NE ISSN 0921-3198
CODEN: DEVEEE
DEVELOPMENTS IN GEOCHEMISTRY. 1978. irreg., vol.6, 1991. price varies. Elsevier Science B.V., Books Division, P.O. Box 211, 1000 AE Amsterdam, Netherlands. TEL 31-20-5803911. FAX 31-20-5803705. TELEX 18582 ESPA NL. (Subscr. in U.S. and Canada to: Elsevier Science Inc., Box 882, Madison Sq. Sta., New York, NY 10159. TEL 212-989-5800) (back issues avail.) **Document type:** monographic series.
—BLDSC (3579.071900); CASDDS.
Refereed Serial

EARTH SCIENCES — GEOLOGY

551.8 NE ISSN 0419-0254
CODEN: DEVGAG
DEVELOPMENTS IN GEOTECTONICS. 1965. irreg., vol.23, 1992. price varies. Elsevier Science B.V., Books Division, P.O. Box 211, 1000 AE Amsterdam, Netherlands. TEL 31-20-5803911. FAX 31-20-5803705. TELEX 18582 ESPA NL. (Subscr. in U.S. and Canada to: Elsevier Science Inc., Box 882, Madison Sq. Sta., New York, NY 10159. TEL 212-989-5800) **Indexed:** GeoRef. **Document type:** monographic series.
—BLDSC (3579.074000).
Refereed Serial

549 NE ISSN 0167-4528
CODEN: DMPRDA
DEVELOPMENTS IN MINERAL PROCESSING. 1977. irreg., vol.12, 1992. price varies. Elsevier Science B.V., Books Division, P.O. Box 211, 1000 AE Amsterdam, Netherlands. TEL 31-20-5803911. FAX 31-20-5803705. TELEX 18582 ESPA NL. (Subscr. in U.S. and Canada to: Elsevier Science Inc., Box 882, Madison Sq. Sta., New York, NY 10159. TEL 212-989-5800) (back issues avail.) **Document type:** monographic series.
—BLDSC (3579.085300); CASDDS. **CCC.**
Refereed Serial

552 NE ISSN 0167-2894
CODEN: DEPEDH
DEVELOPMENTS IN PETROLOGY. (Text in English) 1971. irreg., vol.13, 1991. price varies. Elsevier Science B.V., Books Division, P.O. Box 211, 1000 AE Amsterdam, Netherlands. TEL 31-20-5803911. FAX 31-20-5803705. TELEX 18582 ESPA NL. (Subscr. in U.S. and Canada to: Elsevier Science Inc., Box 882, Madison Sq. Sta., New York, NY 10159. TEL 212-989-5800) (back issues avail.) **Document type:** monographic series.
—CASDDS.
Refereed Serial

551 NE ISSN 0166-2635
CODEN: DPGEDF
DEVELOPMENTS IN PRECAMBRIAN GEOLOGY. (Text in English) 1978. irreg., vol.10, 1993. price varies. Elsevier Science B.V., Books Division, P.O. Box 211, 1000 AE Amsterdam, Netherlands. TEL 31-20-5803911. FAX 31-20-5803705. TELEX 18582 ESPA NL. (Subscr. in U.S. and Canada to: Elsevier Science Inc., Box 882, Madison Sq. Sta., New York, NY 10159. TEL 212-989-5800) **Indexed:** Chem.Abstr. **Document type:** monographic series.
—CASDDS.
Refereed Serial

551.3 NE ISSN 0070-4571
CODEN: DVSDA9
DEVELOPMENTS IN SEDIMENTOLOGY. (Text in English) 1964. irreg., vol.52, 1993. price varies. Elsevier Science B.V., Books Division, P.O. Box 211, 1000 AE Amsterdam, Netherlands. TEL 31-20-5803911. FAX 31-20-5803705. TELEX 18582 ESPA NL. (Subscr. in U.S. and Canada to: Elsevier Science Inc., Box 882, Madison Sq. Sta., New York, NY 10159. TEL 212-989-5800) (back issues avail.) **Indexed:** Chem.Abstr., GeoRef. **Document type:** monographic series.
—BLDSC (3579.087900); Faxon; CASDDS. **CCC.**
Refereed Serial

550 NE
DEVELOPMENTS IN STRUCTURAL GEOLOGY. 1988. irreg. price varies. Elsevier Science B.V., Books Division, P.O. Box 211, 1000 AE Amsterdam, Netherlands. TEL 31-20-5803911. FAX 31-20-5803705. TELEX 18582 ESPA NL. (Subscr. in U.S. and Canada to: Elsevier Science Inc., Box 882, Madison Sq. Sta., New York, NY 10159. TEL 212-989-5800) **Document type:** monographic series.
Refereed Serial

551 CC ISSN 0253-4959
QE640 CODEN: DICZEA
DICENGXUE ZAZHI/JOURNAL OF STRATIGRAPHY. (Text in Chinese) 1966. q. $61.60. (Zhongguo Kexueyuan, Nanjing Dizhi Gushengwu Yanjiusuo) Science Press, Marketing and Sales Department, 16 Donghuangchenggen Beijie, Beijing 100707, People's Republic of China. TEL 4010642. FAX 4012180. TELEX 210247-SPBJ-CN. adv. circ. 7,000. **Indexed:** GeoRef.
—BLDSC (5066.873500).
Formerly: Acta Stratigraphica Sinica.
Description: Contains treatises and articles on biostratigraphy, petrostratigraphy, chronostratigraphy, tectonic stratigraphy, paleogeography, paleoclimatology, and paleomagnetism. Introduces and discusses new techniques, methods, and achievements in stratigraphic research.
Refereed Serial

551 CC ISSN 1001-8107
DILIXUE YU GUOTU YANJIU. (Text in Chinese) q. Hebei Sheng Kexueyuan, Dili Yanjiusuo - Hebei Provincial Academy of Sciences, Institute of Geology, 24 Fanxi Lu, Shijiazhuang, Hebei 050011, People's Republic of China. TEL 49375. Ed. Si Youyuan.

555 540 CC ISSN 0379-1726
QE514 CODEN: TCHHCB
DIQIU HUAXUE. English edition: Chinese Journal of Geochemistry (ISSN 1000-9426) (Text in Chinese; summaries in English) 1972. q. $63.60. Science Press, Marketing and Sales Department, 16 Donghuangchenggen Beijie, Beijing 100707, People's Republic of China. TEL 4010642. FAX 4012180. TELEX 210247-SPBJ-CN. adv.; bk.rev. circ. 11,000. **Indexed:** Chem.Abstr., Geo.Abstr., Ind.Sci.Rev., INIS Atomind.
—BLDSC (4116.990000); CASDDS.
Description: Covers research on isotopic geology, cosmochemistry, organic, structural, environmental and experimental geochemistry, quaternary geology, petrology, and applied geochemistry.
Refereed Serial

DIRECTORY OF BRITISH CAVING CLUBS (YEAR). see *SPORTS AND GAMES — Outdoor Life*

551 CC ISSN 1001-7410
DISIJI YANJIU/QUATERNARIA SINICA. (Text in Chinese; summaries in English) 1980. q. $51.20. (China Quaternaria Research Committee) Science Press, Marketing and Sales Department, 16 Donghuangchenggen Beijie, Beijing 100707, People's Republic of China. TEL 4010642. FAX 4012180. TELEX 210247-SPBJ-CN. adv. circ. 4,000.
Refereed Serial

551 540 560 MY ISSN 0126-9046
DISTRICT MEMOIR. (Text in English) 1937. irreg. M.30. Geological Survey Malaysia, P.O. Box 1015, Ipoh, Perak, Malaysia. FAX 05-557685. (back issues avail.) **Indexed:** Biol.Abstr.

DIVREI HA-AKADEMIA HA-LEUMIT HA-YISRAELIT LEMADAIM-HA-HATIVA LE-MADAEI HA-TEVA. see *SCIENCES: COMPREHENSIVE WORKS*

DIZHEN DIZHI/SEISMOLOGY AND GEOLOGY. see *EARTH SCIENCES — Geophysics*

DIZHEN WENZHAI/SEISMOLOGY ABSTRACTS. see *EARTH SCIENCES — Abstracting, Bibliographies, Statistics*

551 CC
DIZHI KEJI DONGTAI/GEOLOGY SCIENCE AND TECHNOLOGY DEVELOPMENT. (Text in Chinese) s-m. Zhongguo Dizhi Kuangchan Xinxi Yanjiuyuan - Chinese Institute of Geology and Mineral Products Information, 277, Fuchengmenwai Beijie, Beijing 100037, People's Republic of China. TEL 892243. Ed. Qin Guoxing.

DIZHI KEJI GUANLI/SCIENTIFIC AND TECHNOLOGICAL MANAGEMENT IN GEOLOGICAL EXPLORATION. see *BUSINESS AND ECONOMICS — Management*

551 CC ISSN 0563-5020
QE1 CODEN: TCKHAO
DIZHI KEXUE. English edition: Scientia Geologica Sinica (ISSN 1004-3543) (Text in Chinese; summaries in English) 1958. q. $6 per no. Science Press, Marketing and Sales Department, 16 Donghuangchenggen Beijie, Beijing 100707, People's Republic of China. TEL 4010642. FAX 4012180. TELEX 210247-SPBJ-CN. adv. circ. 12,000. **Indexed:** Biol.Abstr., Chem.Abstr, GeoRef.
—BLDSC (8172.300000); CASDDS.
Description: Contains representative theses on geology, reports of achievements, and comments.
Refereed Serial

551 CC
DIZHI LUN-PING/GEOLOGICAL REVIEW. (Text in Chinese) bi-m. $1.60 per no. Guoji Shudian, Qikan Bu - China International Book Trading Corp., Chegongzhuang Xilu 21, P.O. Box 399, Beijing 100044, People's Republic of China.

550 CC ISSN 0001-5717
QE1 CODEN: TCHPAX
DIZHI XUEBAO. English edition: Acta Geologica Sinica (ISSN 1000-9515) (Text in Chinese; summaries in English) 1952. q. $55.20. (Institute of Scientific and Technological Information of China) Science Press, Marketing and Sales Department, 16 Donghuangchenggen Beijie, Beijing 100707, People's Republic of China. TEL 4010642. FAX 4012180. TELEX 210247-SPBJ-CN. adv.; charts; illus.; maps. circ. 12,000. **Indexed:** Biol.Abstr., Chem.Abstr., Curr.Cont., Geo.Abstr., GeoRef., Ind.Sci.Rev., Petrol.Abstr., Sci.Cit.Ind.
—BLDSC (0621.500000); CASDDS.
Description: Contains theses relating to stratigraphy, geological history, paleontology, rocks and minerals, geochemistry, structural geology, ore-deposit geology, hydrogeology, engineering geology, regional geology, and other multi-disciplinary topics.
Refereed Serial

551 CC ISSN 1001-1412
DIZHI ZHAOKUANG LUNCONG. (Text in Chinese; summaries in English) 1980. q. $60. Tianjin Dizhi Yanjiusuo - Tianjin Geological Academy, 42 Youyi Lu, Hexi Qu, Tianjin 300061, People's Republic of China. TEL 86-22-835-3819. FAX 86-22-835-7460. Ed. Li Qingpo. **Document type:** academic/scholarly publication.
Description: Covers geology and mineral resource researches.

DOJIN/ASSOCIATION OF JAPANESE CAVERS. JOURNAL. see *PALEONTOLOGY*

E A N H S BULLETIN. (East Africa Natural History Society) see *BIOLOGY*

551 UK
EARTH SCIENCES PROGRAMME NEWSLETTER. 1952. bi-m. £6. Commonwealth Science Council, Geological Surveys Consultative Group, Marlborough House, Pall Mall, London SW1Y 5HX, England. bk.rev. circ. 700. **Indexed:** GeoRef.
Formerly: Commonwealth Geological Liaison Office. Newsletter (ISSN 0588-7739)

551.3 UK ISSN 0197-9337
GB400 CODEN: ESPLDB
EARTH SURFACE PROCESSES AND LANDFORMS. 1976. 9/yr. $635 (effective 1994). (British Geomorphological Research Group) John Wiley & Sons Ltd., Journals, Baffins Ln., Chichester, Sussex PO19 1UD, England. TEL 0243-779777. FAX 0243-775878. Ed. Michael J. Kirkby. (reprint service avail. from ISI,SWZ,UMI,) **Indexed:** AESIS, Agri.Eng.Abstr., Br.Geol.Lit., Chem.Abstr., Curr.Cont., Curr.Tit.Ocean, Eng.Ind., Environ.Per.Bibl. (1990-), Fluidex, Forest.Abstr., Geo.Abstr., Geotech.Abstr., Ind.Sci.Rev., INSPEC, Irr.& Drain.Abstr., Sci.Abstr., Sci.Cit.Ind., Sel.Water Res.Abstr., Soils & Fert. **Document type:** academic/scholarly publication.
—BLDSC (3643.564030); El; Faxon; UnCover; SWETS; UMI; CASDDS. **CCC.**
Formerly (until Jan. 1981): Earth Surface Processes (ISSN 0360-1269)
Description: Contains important research papers on all aspects of geomorphology interpreted in its widest sense, including both pure and applied.

EARTH SCIENCES — GEOLOGY

551 US ISSN 0891-4176
QE531
EARTHQUAKE RESEARCH IN CHINA. 1987. q. $395. (Chinese State Seismological Bureau, CC) Allerton Press, Inc., 150 Fifth Ave., New York, NY 10011. TEL 212-924-3950. FAX 212-463-9684. Ed. Chen Yong. **Document type:** academic/scholarly publication.
—BLDSC (3643.595220). **CCC.**

550 HK
EAST ASIAN TERTIARY - QUATERNARY NEWSLETTER. 1987. a. HK.$200($25) University of Hong Kong, Centre of Asian Studies, Pokfulam Rd., Hong Kong. Ed. Nina G. Jablonski. bk.rev.; abstr. (back issues avail.) **Document type:** newsletter.
Description: Contains original contributions, news items regarding research projects (in progress or planned) and travel information.

554 SZ ISSN 0012-9402
CODEN: EGHVAG
ECOLOGAE GEOLOGICAE HELVETIAE. (Text in English, French, German and Italian) 1888. 3/yr. 498 SFr.($348) (Schweizerische Geologische Gesellschaft - Swiss Geological Society) Birkhaeuser Verlag, P.O. Box 133, CH-4010 Basel, Switzerland. TEL 061-2717400. FAX 061-2717666. TELEX 963475-BIRKH-CH. (Dist. in N. America by: Springer-Verlag, Mercedes Distribution Center, 160 Imlay St., Brooklyn, NY 11231, USA) Ed. H. Funk. charts; illus.; index, cum.index. **Indexed:** Biol.Abstr., Chem.Abstr., Curr.Cont., Deep Sea Res.& Oceanogr.Abstr., E&P Hlth. (1993-), Gas Process.& Ppl. (1993-), GeoRef., Off.Tech. (1993-), Petrol.Abstr. (1961-). **Document type:** academic/scholarly publication.
—BLDSC (3648.000000); UnCover; SWETS; UMI. **CCC.**

553 US ISSN 0361-0128
QE1 CODEN: ECGLAL
ECONOMIC GEOLOGY AND THE BULLETIN OF THE SOCIETY OF ECONOMIC GEOLOGISTS. 1906. 8/yr. $65. (Society of Economic Geologists) Economic Geology Publishing Co., 101 Vowell Hall, University of Texas, El Paso, TX 79968. FAX 915-544-7416. TELEX 915-533-1965. Ed. Brian J. Skinner. adv.; bk.rev.; charts; illus.; index. circ. 7,000. (also avail. in microfilm from UMI,PMC; reprint service avail. from UMI) **Indexed:** A.S.& T.Ind., AESIS, Br.Geol.Lit., Chem.Abstr., Curr.Cont., Deep Sea Res.& Oceanogr.Abstr., Energy Ind., Energy Info.Abstr., Eng.Ind., Fuel & Energy Abstr., Geo.Abstr., GeoRef., Ind.Sci.Rev., INIS Atomind., Mass Spectr.Bull., Petrol.Abstr., Sci.Cit.Ind., So.Pac.Per.Ind. **Document type:** bulletin.
—BLDSC (3653.120000); EI; Faxon; UnCover; SWETS; CASDDS. **CCC.**
Formerly: Economic Geology (ISSN 0013-0109)

551 ER ISSN 1018-7669
QE1
EESTI TEADUSTE AKADEEMIA. TOIMETISED. GEOLOOGIA/ESTONIAN ACADEMY OF SCIENCES. PROCEEDINGS. GEOLOGY. (Text and summaries in English, Estonian, Russian) 1956. q. $40 (effective 1994). Teaduste Akadeemia Kirjastus, Estonia pst.7, EE-0100 Tallinn, Estonia. TEL 7-3722-454156. **Indexed:** INIS Atomind. **Document type:** academic/scholarly publication.
—UnCover.
Formerly (until 1990): Akademiya Nauk Estonskoi S.S.R. Izvestiya. Geologiya (ISSN 0201-8136); Supersedes in part (in 1978): Akademiya Nauk Estonskoi S.S.R. Izvestiya. Khimiya. Geologiya.

551 560 JA ISSN 0422-7727
CODEN: EDKCDO
EHIME DAIGAKU KIYO. SHIZEN KAGAKU: D SHIRIZU, CHIGAKU/EHIME UNIVERSITY. MEMOIRS. NATURAL SCIENCE: SERIES D, EARTH SCIENCES. (Text in Japanese; summaries in English) 1950. a. Ehime Daigaku, 10-13, Dogo Himachi, Matsuyama-shi, Ehimeken 790, Japan. Ed. Shuichiro Maeda. circ. 400. **Indexed:** Deep Sea Res.& Oceanogr.Abstr.

551.34 GW ISSN 0013-2705
EISBERICHT. 1903. d. (during Winter & Spring). DM.358.50. Bundesamt fuer Seeschiffahrt und Hydrographie, Bernhard-Nocht Str. 78, 20359 Hamburg, Germany. TEL 040-3190-0. FAX 040-3190-5000. TELEX 211138-BSHHH-D. Ed. Gerhard Koslowski. charts. **Document type:** academic/scholarly publication.

557 US ISSN 0013-676X
QE145 CODEN: ESGGAG
EMPIRE STATE GEOGRAM. 1962. a. free. (Geological Survey) New York State Museum, 3140 Cultural Education Center, Albany, NY 12230. Eds. William B. Rogers, John B. Skiba. bibl.; charts; illus.; stat. circ. 1,300. **Indexed:** GeoRef. **Document type:** government publication.
Description: Reports on current research in geology in New York State and lists geologic publications available from the New York State Museum.

ENERGY EXPLORATION AND EXPLOITATION. see ENERGY

ENTWICKLUNGSLAENDER-STUDIEN; Bibliographie entwicklungslaenderbezogener Forschungsarbeiten. see BUSINESS AND ECONOMICS — Abstracting, Bibliographies, Statistics

551 GW ISSN 0943-0105
ENVIRONMENTAL GEOLOGY. 1975. 8/yr. (in 2 vols., 4 nos./vol.). DM.496($310) Springer-Verlag, Heidelberger Platz 3, 14197 Berlin, Germany. TEL 030-8207-1. FAX 030-8214091. (Subscr. in N. America to: Springer-Verlag New York, Inc., 44 Hartz Way, Secaucus, NJ 07096-2491. TEL 201-348-4033. FAX 201-348-4505) Ed. P.E. LaMoreaux. adv.; charts; illus. (also avail. in microform from UMI; back issues avail.; reprint service avail. from ISI) **Indexed:** Acid Pre.Dig., Chem.Abstr., Curr.Adv.Ecol.Sci., Curr.Cont., Curr.Tit.Ocean., Deep Sea Res.& Oceanogr.Abstr., Energy Info.Abstr., Energy Rev., Environ.Abstr., Environ.Ind., Environ.Per.Bibl. (1975-), Excerp.Med., GeoRef., HRIS, Ind.Sci.Rev., Ocean.Abstr., Petrol.Abstr., Pollut.Abstr., Risk Abstr., Sci.Cit.Ind., Sel.Water Res.Abstr., Soils & Fert., W.R.C.Inf. **Document type:** academic/scholarly publication.
—BLDSC (3791.466930); Faxon; UnCover; SWETS; UMI. **CCC.**
Former titles (until 1993): Environmental Geology and Water Sciences (ISSN 0177-5146); (until 1984): Environmental Geology (ISSN 0099-0094)

551 UK ISSN 0705-3797
QE1 .I762 CODEN: EPSDDF
EPISODES (NOTTINGHAM); international geoscience newsmagazine. 1978. q. International Union of Geological Sciences, c/o British Geological Society, Keyworth, Nottingham NG12 5GG, England. TEL 44-602-363100. FAX 44-602-363474. TELEX 378173 BGSKEY G. E-mail: k-rdw@va.nkw.ac.uk. (Subscr. to: Computer Posting Group Ltd., 120-126 Lavender Ave., Mitcham, Surrey CR4 3HP, England. TEL 44-81-646-1031. FAX 44-81-6484873) Ed. Rodney D. Walshaw. adv.; bk.rev. circ. 3,000. **Indexed:** AESIS, Chem.Abstr., Curr.Cont., Excerp.Med., Geo.Abstr., GeoRef., INIS Atomind., Petrol.Abstr. **Document type:** academic/scholarly publication.
—BLDSC (3793.838000); Faxon; UnCover; SWETS; CASDDS. **CCC.**
Supersedes: International Union of Geological Sciences. Geological Newsletter (ISSN 0047-1267)
Description: Covers developments of regional and global importance in the earth sciences.

554 GW ISSN 0071-1160
QE1 CODEN: EGABAN
ERLANGER GEOLOGISCHE ABHANDLUNGEN. 1952. 2/yr. DM.40. Universitaet Erlangen - Nuernberg, Institut fuer Geologie und Mineralogie, Schlossgarten 5, 91054 Erlangen, Germany. FAX 09131-859295. Ed. W. Buggisch. **Indexed:** GeoRef. **Document type:** academic/scholarly publication.
—BLDSC (3810.510000).

ESTUDÓS TECNOLOGICOS. see SCIENCES: COMPREHENSIVE WORKS

EUROPEAN JOURNAL OF MINERALOGY. see MINES AND MINING INDUSTRY

551 CC ISSN 1001-6112
EXPERIMENTAL PETROLEUM GEOLOGY/SHUYOU SHIYAN DIZHI. (Text in Chinese, English) 1979. q. P.O. Box 916, Wuxi, Jiangsu, People's Republic of China. TEL 0510-302724. (Dist. by: China Publishing Industry Trading Corporation, P.O. Box 782, Beijing, P.R.C.) Ed. Lu Peide. **Document type:** academic/scholarly publication.
—BLDSC (3840.035000).
Description: Studies the formation and evolution of petroliferous sedimentary basins, as well as the formation and distribution patterns of oil, gas fields.

551 622 UK ISSN 0964-1823
CODEN: EMGEE6
▼**EXPLORATION & MINING GEOLOGY.** 1992. 4/yr. £110($170) (effective 1994). (Canadian Institute of Metallurgy, Geological Society, CN) Elsevier Science Ltd., Pergamon, P.O. Box 800, Kidlington, Oxford OX5 1DX, England. TEL 44-865-843000. FAX 44-865-843010. (Subscr. in U.S. and Canada to: Elsevier Science, 660 White Plains Rd., Tarrytown, NY 10591-5153. TEL 914-524-9200. FAX 914-333-2444) Ed.Bd. index. (also avail. in microfilm from UMI) **Document type:** academic/scholarly publication.
—BLDSC (3842.155280); UnCover; UMI; CASDDS. **CCC.**
Description: Deals with mineral deposits, mining geology, geomathematics, and directly related environmental and earth science studies.
Refereed Serial

557 622 CN ISSN 0823-2059
TN270
EXPLORATION IN BRITISH COLUMBIA. 1969. a. price varies. Ministry of Energy, Mines and Petroleum Resources, Mineral Resources Division, 5th Fl., 1810 Blanshard St., Victoria, BC V8V 1X4, Canada. (Subscr. to: Crown Publications, 546 Yates St., Victoria, BC V8W 1K8, Canada. TEL 604-386-4636) **Document type:** government publication.
Supersedes in part: Geology, Exploration, and Mining in British Columbia (ISSN 0085-1027); Which was formerly: Lode Metals in British Columbia.
Description: Records the results of mineral exploration and development in British Columbia.

551 US
EXPLORATION OF THE DEEP CONTINENTAL CRUST. 1986. irreg. price varies. Springer-Verlag, 175 Fifth Ave., New York, NY 10010. TEL 212-460-1500. FAX 212-473-6272. (Also: Berlin, Heidelberg, Tokyo, Vienna) (reprint service avail. from ISI) **Document type:** academic/scholarly publication.

FACIES. see EARTH SCIENCES

551 US ISSN 0096-2651
QE1 CODEN: FLDGAV
FIELDIANA: GEOLOGY. 1895. irreg. (Field Museum of Natural History, Library - Publications Division) Field Museum Press, Roosevelt Rd. at Lake Shore Dr., Chicago, IL 60605-2498. TEL 312-922-9410. FAX 312-427-7269. bibl.; charts; illus. circ. 475. (back issues avail.; reprint service avail. from UMI) **Indexed:** Biol.Abstr., Chem.Abstr., Deep Sea Res.& Oceanogr.Abstr., GeoRef.
Description: Contains primarily paleontological studies involving Field Museum collections and field research.
Refereed Serial

559 FJ
FIJI. MINERAL RESOURCES DEPARTMENT. BULLETIN. (Text in English) 1976. irreg. price varies. Mineral Resources Department, P.M. Bag, Suva, Fiji. Ed. Peter Rodda. **Indexed:** GeoRef. **Document type:** bulletin.
Former titles: Fiji. Mineral Resources Division. Bulletin (ISSN 0379-1580); (until 1972): Fiji. Geological Survey. Bulletin (ISSN 0250-7242)
Description: Description and map of geology of parts of Fiji.

559 FJ ISSN 0250-7277
FIJI. MINERAL RESOURCES DEPARTMENT. GEOTHERMAL REPORT. (Text in English) 1980. irreg. price varies. Mineral Resources Department, P.M. Bag, Suva, Fiji. Ed. Peter Rodda. circ. 300.
Description: Results of investigations of geothermal areas.

551 FJ ISSN 1011-7512
FIJI. MINERAL RESOURCES DEPARTMENT. HYDROGEOLOGICAL REPORT. (Text in English) 1988. irreg. price varies. Mineral Resources Department, P.M. Bag, Suva, Fiji. TEL 381-611. FAX 679-386-864. TELEX 2330 SOPAC PRO FJ. Ed. Peter Rodda. circ. 300.
—UnCover.
Description: Results of hydrogeological investigations in Fiji.

551 FJ ISSN 1016-2135
FIJI. MINERAL RESOURCES DEPARTMENT. INFORMATION NOTES. (Text in English, Fijian or Hindi) 1986. irreg. free. Mineral Resources Department, P.M. Bag, Suva, Fiji. circ. 10,000.

EARTH SCIENCES — GEOLOGY

551   FJ
FIJI. MINERAL RESOURCES DEPARTMENT. MEMOIR. (Text in English) irreg. price varies. Mineral Resources Department, P.M. Bag, Suva, Fiji. Ed. Peter Rodda. circ. 300. **Indexed:** GeoRef.
Former titles: Fiji Mineral Resources Division. Memoir (ISSN 0252-2497); (until 1972): Fiji. Geological Survey. Memoir (ISSN 0250-7269)
Description: Results of investigations into earth sciences in Fiji.

551   FJ
FIJI. MINERAL RESOURCES DEPARTMENT. REPORT. (Text in English) irreg. price varies. Mineral Resources Department, P.M. Bag, Suva, Fiji. Ed. Peter Rodda. circ. 300.
—UnCover.
Former titles (until 1986): Fiji. Mineral Resources Division. Report (ISSN 0250-7234); (until 1980): Fiji. Geological Survey. Report; (until 1961): Fiji. Geological Survey. Long Report (ISSN 0250-720X)

551   US   ISSN 1052-6536
QE99
FLORIDA GEOLOGICAL SURVEY. BIENNIAL REPORT. 1985. biennial. free. Florida Geological Survey, 903 W. Tennessee St., Tallahassee, FL 32304. TEL 904-488-9380. circ. 1,000. **Document type:** government publication.
Description: Presents a summary of the extended services and activities of the FGS.

557   US   ISSN 0271-7832
QE99
FLORIDA GEOLOGICAL SURVEY. BULLETIN. 1908. irreg., latest no.63, 1991. price varies. Florida Geological Survey, 903 W. Tennessee St., Tallahassee, FL 32304. TEL 904-488-9380. circ. 1,000. **Indexed:** GeoRef.
Formerly: Florida. Bureau of Geology. Geological Bulletins (ISSN 0085-0608)

557   US
QE99
FLORIDA GEOLOGICAL SURVEY. INFORMATION CIRCULARS. 1948. irreg., latest no.108. price varies. Florida Geological Survey, 903 W. Tennessee St., Tallahassee, FL 32304. TEL 904-488-9380. circ. 1,000.
Formerly: Florida. Bureau of Geology. Information Circulars (ISSN 0085-0616)

557   US
FLORIDA GEOLOGICAL SURVEY. MAP SERIES. 1952. irreg., latest no.139. price varies. Florida Geological Survey, 903 W. Tennessee St., Tallahassee, FL 32304. TEL 906-488-9380. circ. 1,000. **Indexed:** GeoRef.
Formerly: Florida. Bureau of Geology. Map Series (ISSN 0085-0624)

557   US   ISSN 1053-0533
QE99
FLORIDA GEOLOGICAL SURVEY. REPORT OF INVESTIGATIONS. 1934. irreg., latest no.98. price varies. Florida Geological Survey, 903 W. Tennessee St., Tallahassee, FL 32304. TEL 904-488-9380. circ. 1,000. **Indexed:** GeoRef.
Former titles (until 1986): Florida. Bureau of Geology. Report of Investigations (ISSN 0096-0489); Florida. Division of Geology. Report of Investigations (ISSN 0160-1016)

557   US
FLORIDA GEOLOGICAL SURVEY. SPECIAL PUBLICATIONS. 1956. irreg., latest no.36. price varies. Florida Geological Survey, 903 W. Tennessee St., Tallahassee, FL 32304. TEL 904-488-9380. circ. 1,000. **Indexed:** GeoRef.
Formerly: Florida. Bureau of Geology. Special Publications (ISSN 0085-0640)

551.44   US   ISSN 0071-6006
FLORIDA SPELEOLOGICAL SOCIETY. SPECIAL PAPERS. 1961. irreg. membership. Florida Speleological Society, Box 12581, University Sta., Gainesville, FL 32604. TEL 904-372-0521. FAX 904-392-2831. Ed. Mardi Krause. circ. 150.

551.44   US
FLORIDA SPELEOLOGIST. 1961. q. membership or exchange basis. Florida Speleological Society, Box 12581, University Sta., Gainesville, FL 32604. TEL 904-372-0521. FAX 904-332-2276. Ed. Mardi Krause. bk.rev. circ. 100.

550   HU   ISSN 0015-542X
CODEN: FOKOA9
FOLDTANI KOZLONY. (Text in Hungarian; summaries in English, French, German or Russian) 1871. q. $26. Magyarhoni Foldtani Tarsulat, Fo u. 68, 1027 Budapest, Hungary. Ed. G. Hamor. adv.; bk.rev.; charts; illus.; cum.index: 1901-1960. **Indexed:** Biol.Abstr., Chem.Abstr., Deep Sea Res.& Oceanogr.Abstr., Petrol.Abstr.
—CASDDS.

550   XR
FOLIA FACULTATIS SCIENTIARUM NATURALIUM UNIVERSITATIS MASARYKIANAE BRUNENSIS: GEOLOGIA. a. price varies. Masarykova Universita, Prirodovedecka Fakulta - Masaryk University, Faculty of Sciences, Kotlarska 2, 611 37 Brno, Czech Republic. **Indexed:** GeoRef. **Document type:** monographic series.
Formerly: Folia Facultatis Scientiarum Naturalium Universitatis Purkynianae Brunensis: Geologia (ISSN 0323-0139)

FOLIA GEOGRAPHICA. GEOGRAPHICA-PHYSICA. see *GEOGRAPHY*

554   GW   ISSN 0071-8009
CODEN: FGRWAC
FORTSCHRITTE IN DER GEOLOGIE VON RHEINLAND UND WESTFALEN. (Text in German; summaries in English, French) 1958. irreg., no.36, 1991. price varies. Geologisches Landesamt Nordrhein-Westfalen, Postfach 1080, 47710 Krefeld, Germany. TEL 02151-8971. FAX 02151-897505. Ed. Rainer Wolf. circ. 900. **Indexed:** Biol.Abstr., Fuel & Energy Abstr., Petrol.Abstr. **Document type:** monographic series.
—BLDSC (4021.400000).
Description: Studies earth sciences, mainly in the area of North Rhine-Westphalia.

FOSSILIEN; Zeitschrift fuer Sammler und Hobbypalaeontologen. see *PALEONTOLOGY*

551   IQ
AL-FRAHEEDI NEWSLETTER. (Text in Arabic, English) q. $10. Al- Fraheedi Geoscience Bureau, P.O. Box 3038 Alwiya, Baghdad 12902, Iraq. TEL 8872518. Ed. Ismail I.M. Kassab. bibl. **Document type:** newsletter.
Description: News, publications, conferences and resource materials in the earth sciences.

551   FR   ISSN 0221-2536
CODEN: DOBRDM
FRANCE. BUREAU DE RECHERCHES GEOLOGIQUES ET MINIERES. DOCUMENTS. (Text in French) 1973; N.S. 1979. irreg. (15-20/yr.). price varies. Editions B R G M, B.P. 6009, 45060 Orleans Cedex, France. **Indexed:** Bull.Signal., Chem.Abstr., Geo.Abstr., Ocean.Abstr., Ref.Zh.
—CASDDS.

554   FR   ISSN 0246-0874
CODEN: GEFRE6
FRANCE. BUREAU DE RECHERCHES GEOLOGIQUES ET MINIERES. GEOLOGIE DE LA FRANCE. 1889. q. 650 F. Bureau de Recherches Geologiques et Minieres, Division Edition et Vente, B.P. 6009, 45060 Orleans Cedex, France. (Dist. by: Gauthier-Villars, Centrale des Revues, 11 rue Gossin, 92543 Montrouge Cedex, France. TEL 1-46-56-52-66) Eds. C. Cavelier, J.P. Burg. abstr.; charts; illus.; index. circ. 1,500. **Indexed:** Bull.Signal., Chem.Abstr., Geo.Abstr., Ref.Zh. **Document type:** bulletin.
—EI; CASDDS.
Former titles: France. Bureau de Recherches Geologiques et Minieres. Bulletin. Section 1: Geologie de la France (ISSN 0007-6104); Service de la Carte Geologique de la France. Bulletin.
Description: Covers essentially the notes and works of collaborators and organizations responsible for the geological mapping of France.

551 622   FR   ISSN 0245-9345
FRANCE. BUREAU DE RECHERCHES GEOLOGIQUES ET MINIERES. MANUELS ET METHODES. 1980. irreg. (2-3/yr.). price varies. Editions B R G M, B.P. 6009, 45060 Orleans Cedex, France. Ed. Jacqueline E. Goyallon. **Indexed:** Bull.Signal., Chem.Abstr., Geo.Abstr., Ref.Zh.
—BLDSC (5365.766600).

554   FR   ISSN 0766-7167
FRANCE. BUREAU DE RECHERCHES GEOLOGIQUES ET MINIERES. RESUME DES PRINCIPAUX RESULTATS SCIENTIFIQUES ET TECHNIQUES. a. 150 F. Bureau de Recherches Geologiques et Minieres, Division Edition et Vente, B.P. 6009, 45060 Orleans Cedex, France. illus.

551   CC   ISSN 1001-3970
FUJIAN DIZHI/FUJIAN GEOLOGY. (Text in Chinese) q. Y12. Fujiansheng Dizhi Kuangchan Ju, Fujian Dizhi Bianjibu - Fujian Provincial Bureau of Geology and Mineralogy, Editorial Department of Fujian Geology, 285 Wusi St., Fuzhou, Fujian 350003, People's Republic of China. TEL 0591-845388. FAX 0591-845666. (Dist. overseas by: China National Publishing Trading Corp., P.O. Box 782, Beijing, P.R.C.) Ed. Gao Tianjun. **Document type:** academic/scholarly publication.
Description: Covers stratigraphy, palaeontology, petrology, mineralogy, geophysics and other fields associated with geology.

FUNDACION MIGUEL LILLO. MISCELANEA. see *BIOLOGY — Botany*

551   SW   ISSN 1103-5897
QE1   CODEN: GFSFA4
G F F. (Text in English) 1872. q. SEK 480 to non-members (effective 1994). Swedish Science Press, P.O. Box 118, S-751 04 Uppsala, Sweden. TEL 018-36-55-66. FAX 018-36-52-77. (Co-sponsor: Geologiska Foereningen) Ed. Bjoern Sundquist. adv.; bk.rev.; abstr.; bibl.; charts; illus.; index, cum.index (every 10 vols.). circ. 1,000. **Indexed:** AESIS, Art & Archaeol.Tech.Abstr., Biol.Abstr., Chem.Abstr., E&P Hlth. (1993-), Gas Process.& Ppl. (1993-), Geo.Abstr., Geotech.Abstr., INIS Atomind., Off.Tech. (1993-), Petrol.Abstr. (1978-).
—BLDSC (4146.300000); UnCover; CASDDS.
Formerly (until 1994): Geologiska Foereningens i Stockholm Foerhandlingar (ISSN 0016-786X)

551   US   ISSN 1052-5173
QE1
G S A TODAY. 1978. m. $45 to non-members (foreign $55) (effective 1995). Geological Society of America, 3300 Penrose Pl., Box 9140, Boulder, CO 80301. TEL 303-447-2020. FAX 303-447-1133. Ed. Faith Rogers. adv. circ. 17,500. (tabloid format)
—BLDSC (4223.692500); UnCover. **CCC.**
Former titles (until 1991): Geological Society of America. News and Information (ISSN 8755-4976); (until 1983): G S A News and Information (ISSN 0164-5854)
Description: For professional geologists in academia, government, industry, and business. News items about the Society's activities and the geologic community at large.

551   NE
G U A PAPERS OF GEOLOGY. (Text in English) 1972. irreg. Stichting G U A Papers of Geology, c/o Geologisch Instituut, Nieuwe Prinsengracht 130, Amsterdam, Netherlands. Ed.Bd.

551   JA
GAKEKUZURE SAIGAI NO JITTAI/RESEARCH DATA OF LANDSLIDE DISASTERS. (Text in Japanese) irreg. Kensetsusho, Doboku Kenkyujo - Ministry of Construction, Public Works Research Institute, 1, Asahi, Tsukuba-shi, Ibaraki-ken 305, Japan.

GANBAN RIKIGAKU NI KANSURU SHINPOJUMU RONBUNSHU/SYMPOSIUM ON ROCK MECHANICS. PROCEEDINGS. see *ENGINEERING — Civil Engineering*

581   PO   ISSN 0378-1240
QE337   CODEN: GOGLAP
GARCIA DE ORTA: SERIE DE GEOLOGIA. 1973. 2/yr. price varies. Instituto de Investigacao Cientifica Tropical, Rua Jau 54, 1300 Lisbon, Portugal. TEL 364-5321. FAX 363-1460. (Subscr. to: Centro de Documentacao e Informacao, Rua Jau 47, 1300 Lisbon, Portugal) circ. 1,000. **Document type:** academic/scholarly publication.

551 551.46 GW ISSN 0276-0460
QE39 CODEN: GMLEDI
GEO-MARINE LETTERS; an international journal of marine geology. 1980. 4/yr. DM.298($186) Springer-Verlag, Heidelberger Platz 3, 14197 Berlin. TEL 030-8207-1. FAX 030-8214091. (Subscr. in N. America to: Springer-Verlag New York, Inc., 44 Hartz Way, Secaucus, NJ 07096-2491. TEL 201-348-4033. FAX 201-348-4505) Ed. A.H. Buoma. adv. (also avail. in microform from UMI; reprint service avail. from ISI) **Indexed:** Curr.Cont., Curr.Tit.Ocean., Deep Sea Res.& Oceanogr.Abstr., E&P Hlth. (1993-), Gas Process.& Ppl. (1993-), Off.Tech. (1993-), Petrol.Abstr. (1985-), Sel.Water Res.Abstr. **Document type:** academic/scholarly publication.
—BLDSC (4147.230000); Faxon; UnCover; SWETS; CASDDS. **CCC.**
Description: Publishes short articles in such fields as marine geology, marine chemistry, marine geophysics, and marine environment.

GEOCARTO INTERNATIONAL; multi-disciplinary journal of remote sensing. see *GEOGRAPHY*

551.9 540 US
GEOCHEMICAL SOCIETY. SPECIAL PUBLICATION. 1987. irreg., no.4, 1992. $40 to non-members; members $30. Geochemical Society, Dept. of Chemistry, Univ. of Houston, Houston, TX 77204-5641. TEL 713-743-8282. FAX 713-743-8281. **Document type:** monographic series.

551 II ISSN 0368-2323
QE514 CODEN: JGSIBK
GEOCHEMICAL SOCIETY OF INDIA. JOURNAL. (Text in English) 1965. a. Rs.35($8) Geochemical Society of India, Patna 5, India. Ed. R.C. Sinha. bk.rev.; bibl.; charts; illus. **Indexed:** Chem.Abstr.

551 UK ISSN 0016-7037
QE351 CODEN: GCACAK
GEOCHIMICA ET COSMOCHIMICA ACTA. (Supplement avail.) (Text in English, French, German) 1950. 24/yr. £580($895) (effective 1994). (Geochemical Society) Elsevier Science Ltd., Pergamon, P..O. Box 800, Kidlington, Oxford OX5 1DX, England. TEL 44-865-843000. FAX 44-865-843010. (Subscr. in U.S. and Canada to: Elsevier Science, 660 White Plains Rd., Tarrytown, NY 10591-5153. TEL 914-524-9200. FAX 914-333-2444) (Co-sponsor: Meteoritical Society) Ed. Gunter Faure. adv.; bk.rev.; abstr.; bibl.; charts; index. circ. 3,800. (also avail. in microfilm from UMI; back issues avail.; reprint service avail. from UMI) **Indexed:** AESIS, Biol.Abstr., Br.Geol.Lit., Chem.Abstr., Curr.Cont., Deep Sea Res.& Oceanogr.Abstr., E&P Hlth. (1993-), Excerp.Med., Fuel & Energy Abstr., Gas Process.& Ppl. (1993-), Geo.Abstr., GeoRef., Ind.Sci.Rev., INIS Atomind., Int.Aerosp.Abstr., Mass Spectr.Bull., Meteor.& Geoastrophys.Abstr., Ocean.Abstr., Off.Tech. (1993-), Petrol.Abstr. (1961-), Pollut.Abstr., Sci.Abstr., Sci.Cit.Ind., Sel.Water Res.Abstr., So.Pac.Per.Ind., Soils & Fert., W.R.C.Inf. **Document type:** academic/scholarly publication.
—BLDSC (4117.000000); Faxon; UnCover; SWETS; UMI; CASDDS. **CCC.**
Description: Original research covering the entire spectrum of geochemistry and cosmochemistry, incorporating chemistry, geology, physics and astronomy.
Refereed Serial

551 FR ISSN 0153-8446
QE1 CODEN: FBGGAA
GEOCHRONIQUE. (Text in French; summaries in English) 1968. q. 210 F. (foreign 230 F.). Bureau de Recherches Geologiques et Minieres, Societe Geologiques de France, 77 rue Claude Bernard, 75005 Paris, France. FAX 38-64-39-50. TELEX BRGM 780258F. Eds. Jacques-Marie Bardintzeff, Claude Megnien. adv.: page 3950 F.; adv. contact: G. Faury. bk.rev.; abstr.; charts; illus.; index. circ. 4,300. **Indexed:** Bull.Signal., Chem.Abstr., Deep Sea Res.& Oceanogr.Abstr., Geo.Abstr., GeoRef., INIS Atomind., Petrol.Abstr. (1985), Ref.Zh.
Formerly (until 1982): France. Bureau de Recherches Geologiques et Minieres. Bulletin Section 4: Geologie Generale (ISSN 0007-6112)
Description: Earth science magazine featuring geological news, synoptic articles, news of organizations, society activities and calendar.

551 NE
GEODE. 1974. 10/yr. fl.30 membership only. Association of Collectors of Minerals - Fossils, c/o A.J. Zantvoort-van Bossum, Prinsessenpark 28, 3331 GZ Zwijndrecht, Netherlands. Ed. D.M.A. Houtman. adv. circ. 500.
Description: Covers news and information of interest to mineral collectors, including meetings and excursions.

551 910.02 FR ISSN 0985-3111
G1 CODEN: GACTE3
GEODINAMICA ACTA. 1928. q. $227 (typically set in Jan.). Masson - Periodiques, Villa Laromiguiere, 75005 Paris, France. TEL 1-40-46-62-00. FAX 1-40-46-62-01. Ed. J.P. Burg. bibl.; charts; illus. circ. 800. (also avail. in microform from UMI; reprint service avail. from ISI) **Indexed:** Chem.Abstr., Curr.Cont., Deep Sea Res.& Oceanogr.Abstr., Geo.Abstr., GeoRef.
—BLDSC (4119.751000); UnCover; SWETS; UMI. **CCC.**
Former titles: Revue de Geologie Dynamique et de Geographie Physique (ISSN 0241-1407); Revue de Geographie Physique et de Geologie Dynamique (ISSN 0035-1164)

554 SP ISSN 0213-683X
GEOGACETA. m.? 2500 ptas. (foreign 3500 ptas.). Sociedad Geologica de Espana, c/o Museo Nacional de Ciencias Naturales, Jose Gutierrez Abascal 2, 28006 Madrid, Spain. TEL 91-411-13-28-156. Ed. Juan Antonio Vera Torres.
—BLDSC (4122.070000).

551.31 IT ISSN 0391-9838
QE696 CODEN: GFDQDX
GEOGRAFIA FISICA E DINAMICA QUATERNARIA. (Text mainly in Italian; occasionally in English, French and German) 1914. s-a. price varies. Comitato Glaciologico Italiano, Via Academia delle Scienze N. 5, 10123 Turin, Italy. bk.rev.; charts; illus. circ. 375. **Indexed:** GeoRef.
—CASDDS.
Former titles (until 1977): Comitato Glaciologico Italiano. Bollettino (ISSN 0084-8948); (until 1947): Comitato Glaciologico Italiano e Commissione Glaciologica. Bollettino (ISSN 1120-3692)

GEOKATALOG. see *GEOGRAPHY*

551 RU ISSN 0016-7525
QE515 CODEN: GEOKAQ
GEOKHIMIYA. English translation: Geochemistry International (US ISSN 0016-7029) (Text in Russian; contents page and summaries in English) 1956. m. 57 Rub. (Rossiiskaya Akademiya Nauk, Institut Geokhimii i Analiticheskoi Khimii im. V.I. Vernadskogo) Izdatel'stvo Nauka, 90 Profsoyuznaya ul., 117864 Moscow, Russia. (Dist. by: Mezhdunarodnaya Kniga, ul. Dimitrova D.39, 113095 Moscow, Russia) Ed. A.P. Vinogradov. charts; illus.; index. **Indexed:** Biol.Abstr., Chem.Abstr., Curr.Cont., Deep Sea Res.& Oceanogr.Abstr., Eng.Ind., GeoRef., Ind.Sci.Rev., INIS Atomind., Petrol.Abstr., Sci.Cit.Ind. **Document type:** academic/scholarly publication.
—BLDSC (0047.980000); CASDDS. **CCC.**

551.9 KR ISSN 0130-1128
CODEN: GKROAR
GEOKHIMIYA I RUDOOBRAZOVANIE; respublikanskii mezhvedomstvennyi sbornik nauchnykh trudov. (Text in Russian) 1972. a. (Akademiya Nauk Ukrainy, Institut Geokhimii i Fiziki Mineralov) Vidavnitstvo Naukova Dumka, Vul. Tereshchenivska 3, 252601 Kiev, Ukraine. TEL 044-224-4068. FAX 044-224-7060. (Dist. by: Mezhdunarodnaya Kniga, B. Yakimanka 39, 117049 Moscow, Russia) Ed. N.P. Semenenko. **Indexed:** Chem.Abstr.
—BLDSC (0047.983000); CASDDS.

551 CN
GEOLOG. 1970. 4/yr. Can.$15. (Geological Association of Canada) G A C Publications, Department of Earth Sciences, Memorial University of Newfoundland, St. John's, NF A1B 3X5, Canada. TEL 709-737-7660. FAX 709-737-2532. Ed. Michael Easton. adv.; bk.rev.
Description: Reports on current happenings in the Canadian geological community.

551 FI ISSN 0046-5720
CODEN: GEOHAH
GEOLOGI. (Text in Finnish, Swedish, English; summaries in English) 1949. 8/yr. FIM 100. Suomen Geologinen Seura - Geological Society of Finland, Betonimiehenkuja 4, SF-02150 Espoo 15, Finland. FAX 358-0-462-205. TELEX 123185 GEOLO SF. Ed. Paivi Toikkanen. adv.; bk.rev.; cum.index. circ. 1,200. (tabloid format) **Indexed:** Biol.Abstr., Chem.Abstr., NAA, Soils & Fert. **Document type:** newsletter.
—CASDDS.

550 PL
GEOLOGIA. 1961. irreg., vol.14, 1993. price varies. Adam Mickiewicz University Press, Nowowiejskiego 55, 61-287 Poznan, Poland. TEL 527-380. FAX 61-526425. TELEX 413260 UAMPL. circ. 350. **Document type:** academic/scholarly publication.
—BLDSC (9120.468000).
Formerly: Uniwersytet im. Adama Mickiewicza w Poznaniu. Wydzia Biologii i Nauk o Ziemi. Prace. Seria Geologia (ISSN 0083-4238)
Description: Every volume contains current research results of one author in the field of earth sciences, including Ph.D. works and monographs.

551 624 IT ISSN 0435-3870
QE272 CODEN: GAIDBG
GEOLOGIA APPLICATA E IDROGEOLOGIA. (Text and summaries in English, Italian) 1986. a. Istituto di Geologia Applicata e Geotecnica, Universita di Bari, Facolta di Ingegneria, Via re David 200, 70125 Bari, Italy. TEL 080 242362. (Co-sponsor: Italian National Research Council (C.N.R.)) charts; illus. circ. 1,000. (back issues avail.)
—CASDDS.

558 CK ISSN 0072-0992
CODEN: GECBA7
GEOLOGIA COLOMBIANA. (Text in Spanish; summaries in English, French, German, Italian) 1962. irreg. $10 per no. Universidad Nacional de Colombia, Departamento de Geociencias, Apdo. Aereo 14490, Bogota, D.E., Colombia. TEL 2682289. FAX 2682289. Ed.Bd. bk.rev.; circ. 1,000 (controlled). **Indexed:** GeoRef.

550 PL ISSN 0072-100X
QE276.5 CODEN: GLSDA6
GEOLOGIA SUDETICA. (Text in English, Polish; summaries in English) 1964. s-a. price varies. Polska Akademia Nauk, Instytut Nauk Geologicznych, Ul. Zwirki i Wigury 93, 02-089 Warsaw, Poland. (Dist. by: Ars Polona-Ruch, Krakowskie Przedmiescie 7, Warsaw, Poland) Ed. Maria Borkowska. **Indexed:** Chem.Abstr.
—BLDSC (4130.420000); UnCover; CASDDS.

550 BU ISSN 0324-0894
QE287 CODEN: GEBAD2
GEOLOGICA BALCANICA. 1975. 6/yr. 11 lv.($12) (Bulgarska Akademiia na Naukite) Publishing House of the Bulgarian Academy of Sciences, 7 Noemvri St. 1, 1040 Sofia, Bulgaria. (Dist. by: Hemus, 6, Rouski Blvd., 1000 Sofia, Bulgaria) (reprint service avail. from IRC) **Indexed:** Biol.Abstr., BSL Geo., Chem.Abstr, Deep Sea Res.& Oceanogr.Abstr., Geo.Abstr., GeoRef.
—BLDSC (4130.900000); UnCover; CASDDS.

554 GW ISSN 0016-755X
QE269 CODEN: GEBAAX
GEOLOGICA BAVARICA. 1949. irreg., vol.97, 1993. DM.50. Bayerisches Geologisches Landesamt, Hessstr. 123, 80797 Munich, Germany. TEL 089-12000600. FAX 089-12000647. Ed. H. Risch. charts; illus.; maps. circ. 800. **Indexed:** Biol.Abstr., Chem.Abstr., GeoRef. **Document type:** academic/scholarly publication.
—BLDSC (4131.000000).
Description: Covers the regional geology of Bavaria, including mineral deposits.

1936 EARTH SCIENCES — GEOLOGY

550 XO ISSN 1210-2695
GEOLOGICA CARPATHICA - CLAYS; international clay journal. (Text in English) s-a. $15 to individuals; institutions $40. (Slovenska Akademia Vied, Geologicki Ustav - Slovak Academy of Sciences, Geological Institute) Slovak Academic Press Ltd., P.O. Box 57, Nam. Slobody 6, 810 05 Bratislava, Slovakia. Ed. Maria Ovciarkova. adv. contact: Eva Chorvatova. bk.rev.
 Description: Publishes original contributions to: chemical, mineralogical, geochemical and physical properties and behaviour of clay minerals; geological aspects of clay research; experimental clay mineralogy; clay occurrences and deposits; geotechnical and environmental application of clays.

551 560 GW ISSN 0072-1018
        CODEN: GPALA2
GEOLOGICA ET PALAEONTOLOGICA. (Text in English, German) 1967. a. N.G. Elwert Verlag, Reitgasse 7-9, 35037 Marburg, Germany. Eds. M. Lindstroem, W. Schmidt. circ. 500. **Indexed:** AESIS, GeoRef. **Document type:** academic/scholarly publication.
—BLDSC (4131.070000); UnCover. **CCC.**

554 NE ISSN 0072-1026
QE1   CODEN: GEULAP
GEOLOGICA ULTRAIECTINA; mededelingen van de Faculteit Aardwetenschappen, Universiteit Utrecht. (Text in English) 1957. irreg., no.110, 1993. fl.65 per no. or exchange basis (effective 1993). Universiteit Utrecht, Faculteit Aardwetenschappen, Budapestlaan 4, 3584 CD Utrecht, Netherlands. TEL 31-30-534994. FAX 31-30-535030. circ. 200. **Indexed:** GeoRef. **Document type:** academic/scholarly publication.
—CASDDS.
 Description: Devoted to scientific research in the earth sciences.

551 UN ISSN 0302-069X
GEOLOGICAL CORRELATION; report of the international geological correlation programme. French edition: Correlation Geologique (ISSN 0302-0703) 1973. a. free to qualified personnel. Unesco, International Geological Correlation Programme, 7 place de Fontenoy, 75007 Paris, France. TEL 45-68-41-23. FAX 43-06-11-22. TELEX 204461 PARIS. Ed. V. Babuska. circ. 5,500. (back issues avail.) **Indexed:** AESIS.

557 CN ISSN 0381-243X
QE187
GEOLOGICAL FIELDWORK. a. price varies. Ministry of Energy, Mines and Petroleum Resources, Mineral Resources Division, 5th Fl., 1810 Blanshard St., Victoria, BC V8V 1X4, Canada. (Subscr. to: Crown Publications, 546 Yates St., Victoria, BC V8W 1K8, Canada. TEL 604-386-4636) Ed. Brian Grant. (back issues avail.) **Document type:** government publication.
 Description: Summarizes field activity and current research of the geological survey branch of the division.

554 UK ISSN 0072-1050
QE1   CODEN: GELJA8
GEOLOGICAL JOURNAL. 1966. q. $295 (effective 1994). (Liverpool Geological Society) John Wiley & Sons Ltd., Journals, Baffins Ln., Chichester, Sussex PO19 1UD, England. TEL 0243-779777. FAX 0243-775878. TELEX 86290 WIBOOK G. (Co-sponsor: Manchester Geological Society) Ed. A.E. Adams. adv.; bk.rev. circ. 463. (reprint service avail. from ISI,UMI) **Indexed:** Br.Geol.Lit., Chem.Abstr., Curr.Cont., Deep Sea Res.& Oceanogr.Abstr., E&P Hlth. (1993-), Gas Process.& Ppl. (1993-), Geo.Abstr., GeoRef., Ind.Sci.Rev., INSPEC, Off.Tech. (1993-), Petrol.Abstr. (1966-), Sci.Abstr., Sci.Cit.Ind. **Document type:** academic/scholarly publication.
—BLDSC (4133.600000); Faxon; UnCover; SWETS; UMI; CASDDS. **CCC.**
 Formerly (until 1964): Liverpool and Manchester Geological Journal.

551 UK ISSN 0016-7568
QE1   CODEN: GEMGA4
GEOLOGICAL MAGAZINE. 1864. bi-m. £142($263) (overseas £170). (Fellows of the Geological Society of Longon) Cambridge University Press, Edinburgh Bldg., Shaftesbury Rd., Cambridge CB2 2RU, England. TEL 0223-312393. FAX 0223-315052. TELEX 851817256. (N. American addr.: Cambridge University Press, Journals Dept., 40 W. 20th St., New York, NY 10011. TEL 212-924-3900. FAX 212-691-3239) (Co-sponsors: Geological Society of Australia; Geological Society of New Zealand; European Union of Geosciences; Geologists' Association) Ed.Bd. adv.; bk.rev.; abstr.; bibl.; charts; illus.; maps; index, cum.index 1904-1963. (also avail. in microform from BHP,UMI; back issues avail.; reprint service avail. from UMI) **Indexed:** AESIS, Biol.Abstr., Br.Ceram.Abstr., Br.Geol.Lit., Br.Tech.Ind., Chem.Abstr., Curr.Cont, Deep Sea Res.& Oceanogr.Abstr., E&P Hlth. (1993-), Eng.Ind., Gas Process.& Ppl. (1993-), Geo.Abstr., GeoRef., Ind.Sci.Rev., Off.Tech. (1993-), Petrol.Abstr. (1961-), Sci.Cit.Ind., So.Pac.Per.Ind. **Document type:** academic/scholarly publication.
—BLDSC (4134.000000); Faxon; UnCover; SWETS; UMI; CASDDS. **CCC.**

550 553 II ISSN 0016-7576
QE1   CODEN: BGMSAX
GEOLOGICAL, MINING AND METALLURGICAL SOCIETY OF INDIA. BULLETIN. (Text in English) 1936. irreg. price varies. Geological, Mining and Metallurgical Society of India, Geology Department, University of Calcutta, 35 Ballygunge Circular Rd., Calcutta 700019, India. TEL 9133-4753681. Eds. Sanjib C. Sarkar, Dhruba Mukhopadhyay. charts; illus.; maps. circ. 300. **Document type:** academic/scholarly publication, bulletin.
—BLDSC (2524.500000).

551 CN
GEOLOGICAL REFERENCE BOOK. a. Can.$112. Ministry of Energy, Mines and Petroleum Resources, Energy Resources Division, 7th Fl., 1810 Blanshard St., Victoria, B.C. V8V 1X4, Canada. (Subscr. to: Crown Publications, 546 Yates St., Victoria, B.C. V8W 1K8, Canada. TEL 604-386-4636) (looseleaf format; back issues avail.)
 Description: Indicates the Division's interpretation of the various pools in the province with interpretative net pay maps.

551 UK ISSN 0016-7649
QE1   CODEN: JGSLAS
GEOLOGICAL SOCIETY. JOURNAL. 1845. 6/yr. £260($524) (foreign £312). (Geological Society of London) Geological Society Publishing House, Unit 7, Brassmill Enterprise Centre, Brassmill Ln., Bath BA1 3JN, England. TEL 0225-445046. FAX 0225-442836. Ed. M.J. Le Bas. adv.; bibl.; illus.; maps; index, cum.index approx. every 50 vols. circ. 5,000. **Indexed:** AESIS, ASCA, Biol.Abstr., Br.Archaeol.Abstr., Br.Geol.Lit., Chem.Abstr., Curr.Cont., E&P Hlth. (1993-), Eng.Ind., Gas Process.& Ppl. (1993-), Geo.Abstr., GeoRef., Off.Tech. (1993-), Petrol.Abstr. (1963-1964, 1972-), Sci.Cit.Ind. **Document type:** academic/scholarly publication.
—BLDSC (4755.900000); Faxon; UnCover; SWETS; UMI; CASDDS. **CCC.**
 Formerly: Geological Society of London. Quarterly Journal.

551 US ISSN 0016-7606
QE1   CODEN: BUGMAF
GEOLOGICAL SOCIETY OF AMERICA. BULLETIN. 1888. m. $205 (foreign $215) (effective 1995). Geological Society of America, 3300 Penrose Pl., Box 9140, Boulder, CO 80301. TEL 303-447-2020. FAX 303-447-1133. adv.; bibl.; illus.; maps; index, cum.index every 10 yrs. circ. 7,500. (also avail. in microform from PMC,UMI; back issues avail.; reprint service avail. from UMI) **Indexed:** A.S.& T.Ind., Abstr.J.Earthq.Eng., AESIS, Bibl.Agri., Biol.Abstr., Br.Geol.Lit., Chem.Abstr., Curr.Cont., Curr.Tit.Ocean, Deep Sea Res.& Oceanogr.Abstr., E&P Hlth. (1993-), Energy Info.Abstr., Eng.Ind., Environ.Abstr., Gas Process.& Ppl. (1993-), Gen.Sci.Ind., Geo.Abstr., GeoRef, Geotech.Abstr., HRIS, Ind.Sci.Rev., Int.Aerosp.Abstr., Ocean.Abstr., Off.Tech. (1993-), Petrol.Abstr. (1961, 1963-), Pollut.Abstr., Risk Abstr., Sci.Cit.Ind., Sel.Water Res.Abstr., So.Pac.Per.Ind.
●Also available on CD-ROM.
—BLDSC (4136.800000); EI; Faxon; UnCover; SWETS; UMI; CASDDS. **CCC.**
 Description: Presents papers on the results of international research on all earth science disciplines.
Refereed Serial

551 560 US ISSN 0072-1069
        CODEN: GSAMAQ
GEOLOGICAL SOCIETY OF AMERICA. MEMOIRS. (Each vol. has distinctive title) 1888. irreg., no.183, 1993. price varies. Geological Society of America, 3300 Penrose Pl., Box 9140, Boulder, CO 80301. TEL 303-447-2020. FAX 303-447-1133. index. (reprint service avail. from UMI) **Indexed:** AESIS, Biol.Abstr., Chem.Abstr., Deep Sea Res.& Oceanogr.Abstr., E&P Hlth. (1993-), Gas Process.& Ppl. (1993-), GeoRef., Off.Tech. (1993-), Petrol.Abstr. (1965-).
—UnCover; CASDDS. **CCC.**
 Description: Presents results of long-term geological studies and projects.

551 US ISSN 0091-5041
QE21   CODEN: GSCMB3
GEOLOGICAL SOCIETY OF AMERICA. MEMORIALS. Key Title: Memorials - Geological Society of America. 1973. a. price varies. Geological Society of America, 3300 Penrose Pl., Box 9140, Boulder, CO 80301. TEL 303-447-2020. FAX 303-447-1133. bibl.; illus. **Indexed:** GeoRef.
—**CCC.**
 Description: Contains memorials to deceased fellows and society members. Most include bibliographies of their work.

551 560 US ISSN 0072-1077
        CODEN: GSAPAZ
GEOLOGICAL SOCIETY OF AMERICA. SPECIAL PAPERS. (Each vol. has distinctive title) 1934. irreg., no.289, 1994. price varies. Geological Society of America, 3300 Penrose Pl., Box 9140, Boulder, CO 80301. TEL 303-447-2020. FAX 303-447-1133. index. (reprint service avail. from UMI) **Indexed:** AESIS, Biol.Abstr., Chem.Abstr., Deep Sea Res.& Oceanogr.Abstr., E&P Hlth. (1993-), Gas Process.& Ppl. (1993-), Geo.Abstr., Off.Tech. (1993-), Petrol.Abstr. (1965-).
—BLDSC (8368.000000); CASDDS. **CCC.**
 Description: State of the art research in the earth sciences.
Refereed Serial

GEOLOGICAL SOCIETY OF AUSTRALIA. ABSTRACTS SERIES. see *EARTH SCIENCES — Abstracting, Bibliographies, Statistics*

559.4 AT ISSN 0072-1085
        CODEN: GSASBB
GEOLOGICAL SOCIETY OF AUSTRALIA. SPECIAL PUBLICATION. 1967. irreg., no.14, 1989. price varies. Blackwell Scientific Publications (Australia) Pty. Ltd., P.O. Box 378, Carlton, Vic. 3053, Australia. TEL 03-347-0300. FAX 03-347-5001. **Indexed:** AESIS, GeoRef.
—**CCC.**

EARTH SCIENCES — GEOLOGY

551 550   CH   ISSN 1018-7057
QE1   CODEN: JGSCE5
GEOLOGICAL SOCIETY OF CHINA. JOURNAL. (Text in English) 1958. q. $80. Geological Society of China, 2, Lane 109, Hua Hsin St., Chung Ho 23557, Taipei, Taiwan, Republic of China. (Editorial addr.: P.O. Box 23-59, Taipei, Taiwan 10764, Republic of China) (Co-sponsor: Academia Sinica, Institute of Earth Sciences) Ed. H.J. Lo. (back issues avail.) **Indexed:** AESIS, Biol.Abstr., Deep Sea Res.& Oceanogr.Abstr.
—BLDSC (4756.250000); UnCover; CASDDS.
Formerly (until 1992): Zhongguo Dizhi Xuehui Huikan - Geological Society of China. Proceedings (ISSN 0431-2155)

554   DK   ISSN 0011-6297
                              CODEN: MDGFAU
GEOLOGICAL SOCIETY OF DENMARK. BULLETIN. (Text in English; summaries in Danish) 1894. 4/yr. DKK 400 to individuals; institutions DKK 530; students DKK 200. (Dansk Geologisk Forening) C.A. Reitzels Forlag, Norregade 20, DK-1165 Copenhagen K, Denmark. Ed. Walter Kegel Christensen. adv.; bk.rev.; bibl.; charts; illus.; cum.index. circ. 1,100. **Indexed:** Biol.Abstr., Br.Geol.Lit., Chem.Abstr., GeoRef., INIS Atomind., Petrol.Abstr.
—UnCover; CASDDS.
Formerly (until 1970): Meddelelser fra Dansk Geologisk Forening (ISSN 0105-1040)

550   II   ISSN 0016-7622
QE1   CODEN: JGSIAJ
GEOLOGICAL SOCIETY OF INDIA. JOURNAL. (Text in English) 1959. m. Rs.1000($100) Geological Society of India, Post Box 1922, Gavipuran, Bangalore 560 019, India. Ed. R. Vaidyanadhan. bk.rev.; charts; illus.; index. circ. 2,000. (also avail. in microform from UMI; back issues avail.) **Indexed:** Biol.Abstr., C.R.I.Abstr., Chem.Abstr., Curr.Cont., E&P Hlth. (1993-), Gas Process.& Ppl. (1993-), Geo.Abstr., INIS Atomind., Mineral.Abstr., Off.Tech. (1993-), Petrol.Abstr. (1978-1980, 1992-). **Document type:** academic/scholarly publication.
●Also available online. Vendor(s): DIALOG Information Services, Inc. (File no.89).
—BLDSC (4756.800000); UnCover; UMI; CASDDS. **CCC.**

551   JM   ISSN 0435-401X
                              CODEN: JGSJBN
GEOLOGICAL SOCIETY OF JAMAICA. JOURNAL. 1958. a. (plus special issues). membership. Geological Society of Jamaica, c/o Dept. of Geology, University of the West Indies, Mona Campus, Kingston 7, Jamaica, W.I. TEL 809-927-2728. FAX 809-927-1640. Ed. Yolanda Drakapoulos. adv.; bk.rev.; charts; illus. circ. 500. **Indexed:** Biol.Abstr., GeoRef., Met.Abstr., World Alum.Abstr.
Formerly (until 1965): Geonotes.

555   MY   ISSN 0126-6187
QE299.5   CODEN: BPMAEC
GEOLOGICAL SOCIETY OF MALAYSIA. BULLETIN. (Text in English) 1968. irreg., no.32, 1992. price varies. Geological Society of Malaysia, c/o Department of Geology, University of Malaya, 59100 Kuala Lumpur, Malaysia. TEL 603-7577036. FAX 603-7563900. Ed. Teh Guan Hoe. circ. 700. (back issues avail.) **Indexed:** Biol.Abstr. **Document type:** bulletin.
—BLDSC (2525.800000).
Description: Studies the geology of the South-East Asian region and surrounding marine areas.

556   SA   ISSN 0256-3029
GEOLOGICAL SOCIETY OF SOUTH AFRICA. GEOBULLETIN/GEOLOGIESE VERENIGING VAN SUID-AFRICA. GEOBULLETIN. Key Title: Geobulletin. (Text in English; occasional articles in Afrikaans) 1958. q. R.48. Geological Society of South Africa - Geologiese Vereniging van Suid-Afrika, P.O. Box 44283, Linden 2104, South Africa. TEL 27-11-888-2288. FAX 27-11-888-2181. Ed. Neil Gardyne. bk.rev.; charts; illus. circ. 800. **Indexed:** AESIS, Geo.Abstr., INIS Atomind. **Document type:** bulletin.
Formerly (until 1984): Geological Society of South Africa. Quarterly News Bulletin - Geologiese Vereniging van Suid-Afrika. Kwartaalikse Nuusbulletin (ISSN 0016-7657)
Description: Provides news and information in the field of geology, including technical articles, reports, society and branch news, and announcements of events of interest to geologists.

556   SA
GEOLOGICAL SOCIETY OF SOUTH AFRICA. SPECIAL PUBLICATION. 1970. irreg., SP13, 1986. price varies. Geological Society of South Africa, P.O. Box 44283, Linden 2104, South Africa. TEL 27-11-888-2288. FAX 27-11-888-2181. circ. 2,000. **Indexed:** Geo.Abstr., GeoRef.

557   US   ISSN 0270-5451
GEOLOGICAL SOCIETY OF THE OREGON COUNTRY. GEOLOGICAL NEWSLETTER. 1935. m. $13 (typically set in Jan.). Geological Society of the Oregon Country, Box 907, Portland, OR 97207. Ed. Donald Barr. bk.rev.; index. circ. 300. (back issues avail.) **Document type:** newsletter.
Description: News items and announcements pertaining to the members and activities of the society.

551   II   ISSN 0378-4029
QE295   CODEN: GSINB2
GEOLOGICAL SURVEY OF INDIA. NEWS. (Text in English) 1970. m. free. Geological Survey of India, 29 Jawaharlal Nehru Rd., Calcutta 700016, India. Ed. T.K. Kurien. adv.; charts; illus. circ. 2,500.

554   IE   ISSN 0085-0985
QE265   CODEN: GSVIBI
GEOLOGICAL SURVEY OF IRELAND. BULLETIN. 1970. irreg., vol.4, pt.2, 1989. £5.50. Geological Survey of Ireland, Department of Energy, Beggars Bush, Haddington Rd., Dublin 4, Ireland. TEL 01-609511. FAX 01-681-782. cum.index. circ. 650. **Indexed:** Br.Geol.Lit., Geo.Abstr. **Document type:** bulletin.

554   IE   ISSN 0790-0260
GEOLOGICAL SURVEY OF IRELAND. GUIDE SERIES. 1976. irreg., latest 1983. price varies. Geological Survey of Ireland, Department of Energy, Beggars Bush, Haddington Rd., Dublin 4, Ireland. TEL 01-609511. FAX 01-681-782.
—BLDSC (4229.906000).

554   IE   ISSN 0085-0993
GEOLOGICAL SURVEY OF IRELAND. INFORMATION CIRCULARS. 1970. irreg., latest 1989. price varies. Geological Survey of Ireland, Department of Energy, Beggars Bush, Haddington Rd., Dublin 4, Ireland. TEL 01-609511. FAX 01-681-782. circ. 500.

554   IE   ISSN 0790-0279
GEOLOGICAL SURVEY OF IRELAND. REPORT SERIES. irreg., latest 1989. price varies. Geological Survey of Ireland, Department of Energy, Beggars Bush, Haddington Rd., Dublin 4, Ireland. TEL 01-609511. FAX 01-681-782. **Indexed:** Deep Sea Res.& Oceanogr.Abstr., Geo.Abstr.

554   IE   ISSN 0085-1019
GEOLOGICAL SURVEY OF IRELAND. SPECIAL PAPERS. 1971. irreg. latest 1988. price varies. Geological Survey of Ireland, Department of Energy, Beggars Bush, Haddington Rd., Dublin 4, Ireland. TEL 01-609511. circ. 600. **Indexed:** Geo.Abstr.

551   JA
GEOLOGICAL SURVEY OF JAPAN. CRUISE REPORT. (Text in English) 1974. irreg. Kogyo Gijutsuin, Chishitsu Chosajo - Agency of Industrial Science and Technology, Geological Survey of Japan, 1-3, Higashi 1-chome, Tsukuba-shi, Ibaraki-ken 305, Japan. Ed. Hideo Takeda. charts; illus. **Indexed:** Biol.Abstr., Deep Sea Res.& Oceanogr.Abstr.

556   SX
GEOLOGICAL SURVEY OF NAMIBIA. COMMUNICATIONS. (Text in English) 1985. a. price varies. Ministry of Mines and Energy, Geological Survey of Namibia, 45 Mugabe Ave., P.O. Box 2168, Windhoek 9000, Namibia. TEL 061-37240. FAX 061-228324. TELEX 50-908-487 WK. circ. 800.
—UnCover.
Formerly (until vol.5, 1989): Geological Survey of South West Africa - Namibia. Communications (ISSN 0256-1697)

556   SX
GEOLOGICAL SURVEY OF NAMIBIA. MEMOIRS. (Text in English) 1965. irreg., no.16, 1993. price varies. Ministry of Mines and Energy, Geological Survey of Namibia, 45 Mugabe Ave., P.O. Box 2168, Windhoek 9000, Namibia. TEL 061-37240. FAX 061-228324. TELEX 50-908-487 WK. circ. 800. **Document type:** monographic series.
Former titles (until 1990): Geological Survey of South West Africa - Namibia. Memoirs; (until 1981): South West Africa Series. Memoirs.

556   SX
GEOLOGICAL SURVEY OF NAMIBIA. REPORTS ON OPEN FILE. C D M MINERAL SURVEYS. (Text in English) irreg. price varies. Ministry of Mines and Energy, Geological Survey of Namibia, 45 Mugabe Ave., P.O. Box 2168, Windhoek 9000, Namibia. TEL 061-37240. FAX 061-228324. TELEX 50-908-487 WK. **Document type:** government publication.

553   SX
GEOLOGICAL SURVEY OF NAMIBIA. REPORTS ON OPEN FILE. ECONOMIC GEOLOGY. (Text in English, occasionally in Afrikaans) 1921. irreg., no.86, 1990. price varies. Ministry of Mines and Energy, Geological Survey of Namibia, 45 Mugabe Ave., P.O. Box 2168, Windhoek 9000, Namibia. TEL 061-37240. FAX 061-228324. TELEX 50-908-487 WK. **Document type:** government publication.
Description: Series of preliminary reports on topics in economic geology.

556 620   SX
GEOLOGICAL SURVEY OF NAMIBIA. REPORTS ON OPEN FILE. ENGINEERING GEOLOGY. (Text in English) 1983. irreg. price varies. Ministry of Mines and Energy, Geological Survey of Namibia, 45 Mugabe Ave., P.O. Box 2168, Windhoek 9000, Namibia. TEL 061-37240. FAX 061-228324. TELEX 50-908-487 WK. **Document type:** government publication.
Description: Series of preliminary reports on topics in engineering geology.

556   SX
GEOLOGICAL SURVEY OF NAMIBIA. REPORTS ON OPEN FILE. MINERAL RESOURCE SERIES. irreg., no.47, 1992. price varies. Ministry of Mines and Energy, Geological Survey of Namibia, 45 Mugabe Ave., P.O. Box 2168, Windhoek 9000, Namibia. TEL 061-37240. FAX 061-228324. TELEX 50-908-487 WK. **Document type:** government publication.
Description: Series of preliminary reports from mineral resource studies.

556   SX
GEOLOGICAL SURVEY OF NAMIBIA. REPORTS ON OPEN FILE. REGIONAL GEOLOGY. (Text in English, occasionally in Afrikaans) 1970. irreg., no.7, 1984. price varies. Ministry of Mines and Energy, Geological Survey of Namibia, 45 Mugabe Ave., P.O. Box 2168, Windhoek 9000, Namibia. TEL 061-37240. FAX 061-228324. TELEX 50-908-487 WK. **Document type:** government publication.
Description: Series of preliminary reports on topics in regional geology.

559.4   AT   ISSN 0016-7673
GEOLOGICAL SURVEY OF SOUTH AUSTRALIA. BULLETIN. 1912. irreg., no.53, 1987. price varies. Department of Mines and Energy, P.O. Box 151, Eastwood, S.A. 5063, Australia. TEL 08-274-7500. FAX 08-272-7597. Ed. John F. Drexel. circ. 1,000. (also avail. in microfiche; back issues avail.) **Indexed:** AESIS. **Document type:** government publication.
Description: Regional geological research studies. Includes information on groundwater and mineral resources.

551   AT   ISSN 0572-0125
GEOLOGICAL SURVEY OF SOUTH AUSTRALIA. EXPLANATORY NOTES. 1972. irreg. Aus.$21 including map. Department of Mines and Energy, P.O. Box 151, Eastwood, S.A. 5063, Australia. TEL 08-274-7500. FAX 08-274-7597. (back issues avail.) **Indexed:** AESIS, Eng.Ind., GeoRef. **Document type:** government publication.
Description: Explanatory notes to the standard 1:250000 geological map sheets, containing summaries of geology, stratigraphy and tectonics.

551   AT   ISSN 0016-7681
QE345   CODEN: AMGNAJ
GEOLOGICAL SURVEY OF SOUTH AUSTRALIA. REPORT OF INVESTIGATIONS. 1954. irreg. price varies. Department of Mines and Energy, P.O. Box 151, Eastwood, S.A. 5063, Australia. TEL 08-274-7500. FAX 08-272-7597. (back issues avail.) **Indexed:** Eng.Ind., GeoRef. **Document type:** government publication.
—UnCover.
Description: Technical accounts of investigations in applied geology.

EARTH SCIENCES — GEOLOGY

557 US
GEOLOGICAL SURVEY OF WYOMING. BULLETIN. 1911. irreg., no.69, 1990. price varies. Geological Survey of Wyoming, Box 3008, University Sta., Laramie, WY 82071. TEL 307-766-2286. **Indexed:** GeoRef. **Document type:** bulletin.
Description: Covers extensive treatment of variable topics for public and technical readers.

551 US
GEOLOGICAL SURVEY OF WYOMING. EDUCATIONAL SERIES. 1989. irreg. price varies. Geological Survey of Wyoming, Box 3008, University Sta., Laramie, WY 82071. TEL 307-766-2286.
Description: Covers a broad range of geological topics for the general public and public school audiences. Classroom activity suggestions and other teaching materials upon request.

557 US
GEOLOGICAL SURVEY OF WYOMING. PUBLIC INFORMATION CIRCULARS. 1976. irreg., no.31, 1991. price varies. Geological Survey of Wyoming, Box 3008, University Sta., Laramie, WY 82071. **Document type:** consumer publication.
Description: Covers geologic hazards, and earth resources for a nontechnical audience.

557 US
GEOLOGICAL SURVEY OF WYOMING. REPORT OF INVESTIGATIONS. 1934. irreg., no.47, 1991. price varies. Geological Survey of Wyoming, Box 3008, University Sta., Laramie, WY 82071. TEL 307-766-2286. **Document type:** consumer publication.
Description: For technical and mineral industry personnel.

550 KR ISSN 0367-4290
QP1 CODEN: GEZHA4
GEOLOGICHESKII ZHURNAL; nauchnyi zhurnal. (Text in Russian; summaries in English, Russian) 1934. bi-m. 10.20 Rub.($19.80) (Akademiya Nauk Ukrainy, Otdelenie Nauk o Zemle) Vydavnitstvo Naukova Dumka, Vul. Tereshchenkivska 3, 252601 Kiev, Ukraine. TEL 044-216-38-76. FAX 044-224-70-60. (Subscr. to: Mezhdunarodnaya Kniga, Moscow, G-200, Russia) Ed. Ya.N. Belevtsev. charts; illus. **Indexed:** Chem.Abstr., INIS Atomind.
—BLDSC (0047.370000); CASDDS. **CCC**.
Formerly (until 1968): Geologichnii Zhurnal (Ukrainian) (ISSN 0016-7703)

550 AI ISSN 0016-769X
GEOLOGICHESKII ZHURNAL ARMENII. (Text and summaries in Armenian, Russian) 1966. bi-m. $13.20. Akademiya Nauk Armenii, Pr. Marshala Bagamayana, 24, 375019 Erevan, Armenia. charts; illus.; index.

550 XR ISSN 0016-772X
QE33 CODEN: GEYPAN
GEOLOGICKY PRUZKUM/GEOLGICKY PRIESKUM/GEOLOGICAL SURVEYING; a special journal for techniques, methodics and economy of exploration and problems related to raw materials. (Text in Czech and Slovak; contents page and summaries in English, German, Russian) 1959. m. $60.10. (Cesky Geologicky Urad) Nakladatelstvi Technicke Literatury, Spalena 51, Prague 1, Czech Republic. TELEX 122 540 UUG. (Dist. by: Artia, Ve Smeckach 30, 111 27 Prague 1, Czech Republic) (Co-sponsor: Slovensky Geologicky Urad) Ed. Jindrich Hauft. adv.; bk.rev.; charts; illus.; index. circ. 2,500. **Indexed:** Chem.Abstr., Geotech.Abstr.
—CASDDS.

550 XO ISSN 0016-7738
QE1 CODEN: GECAE8
GEOLOGICKY ZBORNIK/GEOLOGICA CARPATHICA; international geological journal. (Subseries avail: Geologica Carpathica - Clays (ISSN 1210-2695)) (Text and summaries in English, French, German, Russian) 1950. bi-m. $120. (Slovenska Akademia Vied, Geologicky Ustav - Slovak Academy of Sciences, Geological Institute) Slovak Academic Press Ltd., P.O. Box 57, 810 05 Bratislava, Slovakia. Ed. Maria Ovciarkova. adv. contact: Eva Chorvatova. bk.rev.; charts; illus.; maps; cum.index: 1950-1959 in 1 vol. circ. 1,100. **Indexed:** Biol.Abstr., Chem.Abstr., Geo.Abstr., INIS Atomind.
Description: Publishes original scientific works from all geological disciplines, including stratigraphic geology, depositary geology, geochemistry, paleontology, petrography, tectonics, and engineering geology. Focuses chiefly on the Carpathian and Balkan mountain ranges with occasional contributions concerning adjacent European mountain ranges.

551 GW
GEOLOGIE. 1973. q. DM.35($20) Steinknoeck 3, 91054 Erlangen-Sieglitzhof, Germany. TEL 09131-51815. Ed. Johan C. van Soeren. (back issues avail.) **Document type:** academic/scholarly publication.
Description: Covers geology: caves, minerals, fossils.

556 FR
Z6034.A25
GEOLOGIE AFRICAINE/AFRICAN GEOLOGY. (Text in English, French) 1976. a. 550 F.($110) Centre International pour la Formation et les Echanges Geologiques (CIFEG) - International Center for Training and Exchanges in the Geosciences, B.P. 6517 av. de Concyr, 45065 Orleans Cedex 2, France. TEL 33-38-64-36-57. FAX 33-38-64-34-72. TELEX 780 258 CIFEG. bk.rev.; bibl. **Document type:** bibliography.
Formerly: Association des Services Geologiques Africains. Bulletin d'Information et de Liaison. Information and Liaison Bulletin (ISSN 0396-8863)

551 622 NE ISSN 0016-7746
CODEN: GEMIAA
GEOLOGIE EN MIJNBOUW/GEOLOGY AND MINING; an international journal. (Text in English; occasionally in German, French, Spanish, and Dutch; summaries in English) 1921. 4/yr. fl.293($153) (effective 1994). (Koninklijk Nederlands Geologisch Mijnbouwkundig Genootschap - Royal Geological and Mining Society of the Netherlands) Kluwer Academic Publishers, Postbus 17, 3300 AA Dordrecht, Netherlands. TEL 31-78-334911. FAX 31-78-334254. TELEX 29245 KAPG NL. (Dist. by: Kluwer Academic Publishers Group, Distribution Center, Postbus 322, 3300 AM Dordrecht, Netherlands. TEL 31-78-524400. FAX 31-78-524474; N. America dist. addr.: Box 358, Accord Sta., Hingham, MA 02018-0358. TEL 617-871-6600. FAX 617-871-6528) Ed. W.J.M. van der Linden. adv.; bk.rev.; abstr.; charts; illus.; index, cum.index. circ. 2,250. (also avail. in microform from UMI; reprint service avail. from SWZ) **Indexed:** AESIS, Biol.Abstr., Br.Geol.Lit., Chem.Abstr., Deep Sea Res.& Oceanogr.Abstr., E&P Hlth. (1993-), Eng.Ind., Gas Process.& Ppl. (1993-), Geo.Abstr., INIS Atomind., Off.Tech. (1993-), Petrol.Abstr. (1961-). **Document type:** academic/scholarly publication.
—BLDSC (4143.000000); UnCover; SWETS; UMI; CASDDS. **CCC**.
Refereed Serial

554 FR ISSN 0397-2844
QE350.2 CODEN: AUPGDY
GEOLOGIE MEDITERRANEENNE. 1974. q. 274.30 F. (EC 260 F., elsewhere 280 F.). Universite d'Aix-Marseille I (Universite de Provence), Centre St. Charles, U.E.R. de Sciences Naturelles, Place Victor Hugo, 13331 Marseille Cedex 3, France. **Indexed:** Chem.Abstr., Geo.Abstr.
—BLDSC (4143.300000); CASDDS.
Description: Articles on the geology of the Mediterranean countries.

551 GW ISSN 0176-148X
GEOLOGIE UND PALAEONTOLOGIE IN WESTFALEN. 1983. irreg. (2-4/yr.). price varies. Westfaelisches Museum fuer Naturkunde, Sentruperstr. 285, 48161 Muenster, Germany. charts; illus.; maps. **Document type:** academic/scholarly publication.

550 XV ISSN 0016-7789
QE 287 CODEN: GERPAM
GEOLOGIJA; razprave in porocila. (Text in English, French, German, Serbocroatian, Slovenian) 1953. biennial. 400 din.($14) Geoloski Zavod - Geological Survey, Parmova Ul. 33, 1000 Ljubljana, Slovenia. (Co-sponsor: Slovensko Geolosko Drustvo) Ed. Stefan Kolenko. bk.rev.; charts; illus.; index. circ. 1,000. **Indexed:** Chem.Abstr.
—BLDSC (4144.100000); CASDDS.

551 560 GW ISSN 0341-4043
GEOLOGISCHE ABHANDLUNGEN HESSEN. 1976. a. price varies. Hessisches Landesamt fuer Bodenforschung, Leberberg 9, 65193 Wiesbaden, Germany. TEL 0611-701034. (Subscr. to: Hessisches Landesamt fuer Bodenforschung, Vertriebsstelle, Hasengartenstr. 26, 6200 Wiesbaden, Germany) (back issues avail.)

554 GW ISSN 0016-7797
CODEN: GBNBA7
GEOLOGISCHE BLAETTER FUER NORDOST-BAYERN UND ANGRENZENDE GEBIETE. 1951. irreg. (1-4/yr.). DM.45. Universitaet Erlangen - Nuernberg, Institut fuer Geologie und Mineralogie, Schlossgarten 5, 91054 Erlangen, Germany. FAX 09131-859295. Ed. R. Rossner. adv.; bk.rev.; charts; illus. **Indexed:** Biol.Abstr., Chem.Abstr. **Document type:** academic/scholarly publication.
—UMI.
Description: Studies geological and paleontological topics relating to Northern Bavaria.

551 AU ISSN 0378-0864
CODEN: AGBDAO
GEOLOGISCHE BUNDESANSTALT, VIENNA. ABHANDLUNGEN. (Text mainly in German; occasionally in other languages) 1852. irreg. price varies. Geologische Bundesanstalt, Rasumofskygasse 23, Postfach 127, A-1031 Vienna, Austria. FAX 01-712567456. Ed. Albert Daurer. circ. 1,250. (also avail. in microfilm) **Indexed:** Ref.Zh. **Document type:** monographic series.
—BLDSC (0540.749800).

551 560 AU ISSN 0016-7800
CODEN: JAGBAW
GEOLOGISCHE BUNDESANSTALT, VIENNA. JAHRBUCH. (Text and summaries in English, German) 1850. q. price varies. Geologische Bundesanstalt, Rasumofskygasse 23, Postfach 127, A-1031 Vienna, Austria. FAX 01-712567456. Ed. Albert Daurer. (also avail. in microfilm) **Indexed:** Biol.Abstr., GeoRef. **Document type:** bulletin.
—CASDDS.

551 GW ISSN 0016-7835
QE1 CODEN: GERUA3
GEOLOGISCHE RUNDSCHAU; international journal of earth sciences. (Text in English, French, German) 4/yr. DM.480. (Geologische Vereinigung) Springer-Verlag, Heidelberger Platz 3, 14197 Berlin, Germany. TEL 030-8207-1. FAX 030-8214091. (Subscr. in N. America to: Springer-Verlag New York, Inc., 44 Hartz Way, Secaucus, NJ 07096-2491. TEL 201-348-4033. FAX 201-348-4505) Ed.Bd. (also avail. in microfiche from BHP; reprint service avail. from IRC) **Indexed:** AESIS, Bibl.Cart., Br.Geol.Lit., Chem.Abstr., Deep Sea Res.& Oceanogr.Abstr., E&P Hlth. (1993-), Gas Process.& Ppl. (1993-), Geo.Abstr., Ind.Sci.Rev., INIS Atomind., Off.Tech. (1993-), Petrol.Abstr. (1961-), Sci.Cit.Ind. **Document type:** academic/scholarly publication.
—BLDSC (4145.000000); Faxon; UnCover; SWETS; CASDDS. **CCC**.
Description: Contains original contributions and reviews of the entire field of geology and related sciences. Covers regional geology, stratigraphy, structural geology, tectonics, geodynamics and more.

EARTH SCIENCES — GEOLOGY

554 560   GW   ISSN 0341-6399
QE269   CODEN: GJRABD
GEOLOGISCHES JAHRBUCH. REIHE A: ALLGEMEINE UND REGIONALE GEOLOGIE B.R. DEUTSCHLAND UND NACHBARGEBIETE, TEKTONIK, STRATIGRAPHIE, PALAEONTOLOGIE. (Text in German; summaries in English, French, Italian, Russian and Spanish) 1972. irreg. price varies. (Bundesanstalt fuer Geowissenschaften und Rohstoffe) E. Schweizerbart'sche Verlagsbuchhandlung, Johannesstr. 3A, 70176 Stuttgart, Germany. TEL 0711-625001. FAX 0711-625005. TELEX 723363-SCHB-D. illus. **Indexed:** Chem.Abstr., Deep Sea Res.& Oceanogr.Abstr., E&P Hlth. (1993-), Gas Process.& Ppl. (1993-), Off.Tech. (1993-), Petrol.Abstr. (1983-). **Document type:** monographic series.
—BLDSC (4145.320000). **CCC.**
Supersedes in part: Geologisches Jahrbuch (ISSN 0016-7851); Which was formerly: Beihefte zum Geologischen Jahrbuch (ISSN 0005-8017)

554   GW   ISSN 0341-6402
QE1   CODEN: GJRBAF
GEOLOGISCHES JAHRBUCH. REIHE B: REGIONALE GEOLOGIE AUSLAND. (Text in German; summaries in English, French, German, Russian) 1972. irreg. price varies. (Bundesanstalt fuer Geowissenschaften und Rohstoffe) E. Schweizerbart'sche Verlagsbuchhandlung, Johannesstr. 3A, 70176 Stuttgart, Germany. TEL 0711-625001. FAX 0711-625005. TELEX 723363-SCHB-D. illus. **Indexed:** Chem.Abstr., Deep Sea Res.& Oceanogr.Abstr., Petrol.Abstr. **Document type:** academic/scholarly publication, monographic series.
—UnCover; CASDDS. **CCC.**
Supersedes in part: Geologisches Jahrbuch (ISSN 0016-7851); Which was formerly: Beihefte zum Geologischen Jahrbuch (ISSN 0005-8017)

551   GW   ISSN 0341-6410
GB651   CODEN: GJRCAI
GEOLOGISCHES JAHRBUCH. REIHE C: HYDROGEOLOGIE. INGENIEURGEOLOGIE. (Text in German; summaries in English, French, German, Russian) 1972. irreg. price varies. (Bundesanstalt fuer Geowissenschaften und Rohstoffe) E. Schweizerbart'sche Verlagsbuchhandlung, Johannesstr. 3A, 70176 Stuttgart, Germany. TEL 0711-625001. FAX 0711-625005. TELEX 723363-SCHB-D. illus. **Indexed:** Chem.Abstr., Deep Sea Res.& Oceanogr.Abstr., INIS Atomind., Petrol.Abstr. **Document type:** academic/scholarly publication, monographic series.
—UnCover. **CCC.**
Supersedes in part: Geologisches Jahrbuch (ISSN 0016-7851); Which was formerly: Beihefte zum Geologischen Jahrbuch (ISSN 0005-8017)

551 549   GW   ISSN 0341-6429
QE351   CODEN: GJRDAL
GEOLOGISCHES JAHRBUCH. REIHE D: MINERALOGIE. PETROGRAPHIE, GEOCHEMIE, LAGERSTAETTENKUNDE. (Text in German, summaries in English, French, German, Russian) 1972. irreg. price varies. (Bundesanstalt fuer Geowissenschaften und Rohstoffe) E. Schweizerbart'sche Verlagsbuchhandlung, Johannesstr. 3A, 70176 Stuttgart, Germany. TEL 0711-625001. FAX 0711-625005. TELEX 723363-SCHB-D. illus. **Indexed:** Chem.Abstr., Deep Sea Res.& Oceanogr.Abstr., E&P Hlth. (1993-), Gas Process.& Ppl. (1993-), INIS Atomind., Off.Tech. (1993-), Petrol.Abstr. (1983-). **Document type:** academic/scholarly publication, monographic series.
—BLDSC (4145.350000); CASDDS. **CCC.**
Supersedes in part: Geologisches Jahrbuch (ISSN 0016-7851); Which was formerly: Beihefte zum Geologischen Jahrbuch (ISSN 0005-8017)

551   GW   ISSN 0341-6437
QE500   CODEN: GJREAO
GEOLOGISCHES JAHRBUCH. REIHE E: GEOPHYSIK. (Text in English, German; summaries in English, French, German, Russian) 1972. irreg. price varies. (Bundesanstalt fuer Geowissenschaften und Rohstoffe) E. Schweizerbart'sche Verlagsbuchhandlung, Johannesstr. 3A, 70176 Stuttgart, Germany. TEL 0711-625001. FAX 0711-625005. TELEX 723363-SCHB-D. illus. **Indexed:** Biol.Abstr., Deep Sea Res.& Oceanogr.Abstr., INIS Atomind., Petrol.Abstr. **Document type:** academic/scholarly publication, monographic series.
—UnCover. **CCC.**

551   GW   ISSN 0341-6445
S599.4.G3   CODEN: GJRFAR
GEOLOGISCHES JAHRBUCH. REIHE F: BODENKUNDE. (Text in English, German; summaries in English, French, German, Russian) 1973. irreg. price varies. (Bundesanstalt fuer Geowissenschaften und Rohstoffe) E. Schweizerbart'sche Verlagsbuchhandlung, Johannesstr. 3A, 70176 Stuttgart, Germany. TEL 0711-625001. FAX 0711-625005. TELEX 723363-SCHB-D. **Indexed:** Chem.Abstr., Deep Sea Res.& Oceanogr.Abstr., Soils & Fert. **Document type:** academic/scholarly publication, monographic series.
—**CCC.**

551 560   GW   ISSN 0341-4027
QE269.A19   CODEN: GJHEDB
GEOLOGISCHES JAHRBUCH HESSEN. 1976. a. price varies. Hessisches Landesamt fuer Bodenforschung, Leberberg 9, 65193 Wiesbaden, Germany. TEL 0611-701034. (Subscr. to: Hessisches Landesamt fuer Bodenforschung, Vertriebsstelle, Hasengartenstr. 26, 6200 Wiesbaden, Germany) Ed.Bd. (back issues avail.) **Indexed:** E&P Hlth. (1993-), Gas Process.& Ppl. (1993-), Off.Tech. (1993-), Petrol.Abstr. (1983-).
—BLDSC (4145.310000); CASDDS.

554   GW   ISSN 0940-0834
GEOLOGISCHES LANDESAMT BADEN - WUERTTEMBERG. INFORMATIONEN. 1990. irreg. Geologisches Landesamt Baden-Wuerttemberg, Albertstr. 5, 79104 Freiburg, Germany. TEL 0761-2044375. FAX 0761-2044438. Ed. Diethard H. Storch. (back issues avail.) **Document type:** monographic series.

551   UK   ISSN 0016-7878
     CODEN: PGAEAH
PROCEEDINGS OF THE GEOLOGISTS' ASSOCIATION. 1859. q. £80($134) (Geologists' Association) Geological Society Publishing House, Brassmill Enterprise Centre, Unit 7, Brassmill Ln., Bath BA1 3JN, England. TEL 225-445046. FAX 225-442836. Ed. D.H. Keen. adv.; bk.rev.; charts; illus.; index covering 10 yrs. circ. 2,600. **Indexed:** AESIS, Biol.Abstr., Br.Geol.Lit., Chem.Abstr., Geo.Abstr., Ocean.Abstr., Pollut.Abstr. **Document type:** academic/scholarly publication.
—BLDSC (6704.000000); Faxon; UnCover. **CCC.**
Description: Contains articles on the pectrum of the geological sciences, including results of current research and reviews of progress in rapidly advancing areas of the science.

551   UK   ISSN 0260-0463
GEOLOGIST'S DIRECTORY. 1980. a. £20 (effective 1993). Geological Society, Unit 7, Brassmill Enterprise Centre, Brassmill Ln., Bath BA1 3JN, England. TEL 0225-445046. FAX 0225-442836. Ed. G.M. Reeves. adv. circ. 2,000. **Document type:** directory.
—BLDSC (4146.412000).
Description: Directory of U.K. geological activities in government, academia and industry.

551   RU   ISSN 0016-7886
     CODEN: GGASAS
GEOLOGIYA I GEOFIZIKA. English translation: Russian Geology and Geophysics (US ISSN 1068-7971) (Text in Russian; summaries in English) 1960. m. 12000 Rub.($200) Rossiskaya Akademiya Nauk, Sibirskoe Otdelenie, Institut Geologii i Geofiziki, Universitetskii pr. 3, 630090 Novosibirsk, Russia. TEL 38332-354650. FAX 3832-351351. TELEX 133123 KORA SU. (Subscr. addr.: Ul. Sovetskaya 18, 630099 Novosibirsk, Russia. TEL 3832-226988) Ed. Nikoai L. Dobretsov. illus.; index. circ. 930. **Indexed:** Chem.Abstr., Deep Sea Res.& Oceanogr.Abstr., E&P Hlth. (1993-), Gas Process.& Ppl. (1993-), INIS Atomind., Off.Tech. (1993-), Petrol.Abstr. (1963-), Sci.Abstr.
—BLDSC (0047.480000); CASDDS. **CCC.**
Formerly: Geofizicheskii Byulleten' (ISSN 0072-1182)
Description: Presents theoretical and methodological papers on all problems of geology and geophysics.

551   KR   ISSN 0135-2164
TN260
GEOLOGIYA I GEOKHIMIYA GORYUCHIKH ISKOPAEMYKH; respublikanskii mezhvedomstvennyi sbornik nauchnykh trudov 1965. s-a. (Akademiya Nauk Ukrainy, Institut Geologii i Geokhimii Goryuchikh Iskopaemykh) Vidavnitstvo Naukova Dumka, Vul. Tereshchenkivska 3, 252601 Kiev, Ukraine. TEL 044-224-4068. FAX 044-224-7060. Ed. V.E. Zabigailo. **Indexed:** Deep Sea Res.& Oceanogr.Abstr.
—BLDSC (0047.490000). **CCC.**
Formerly (until 1974): Geologiya i Geokhimiya Goryuchikh Kopalin (ISSN 0435-4117)

551   US   ISSN 0091-7613
QE1   CODEN: GLGYBA
GEOLOGY (BOULDER). 1973. m. $170 to non-members (foreign $180) (effective 1995). Geological Society of America, 3300 Penrose Pl., Box 9140, Boulder, CO 80301. TEL 303-447-2020. FAX 303-447-1133. Ed. F. Rogers. adv.; bk.rev. circ. 9,500. (also avail. in microform from UMI; back issues avail.; reprint service avail. from UMI) **Indexed:** A.S.& T.Ind., AESIS, Art & Archaeol.Tech.Abstr., Biol.Abstr., Br.Geol.Lit., Chem.Abstr., Curr.Cont., Curr.Tit.Ocean., Deep Sea Res.& Oceanogr.Abstr., E&P Hlth. (1993-), Excerp.Med., Fuel & Energy Abstr., Gas Process.& Ppl. (1993-), Gen.Sci.Ind., Geo.Abstr., GeoRef., Ind.Sci.Rev., INIS Atomind., Int.Aerosp.Abstr., Off.Tech. (1993-), Petrol.Abstr. (1976-), Risk Abstr., Sci.Cit.Ind., Sel.Water Res.Abstr.
—BLDSC (4146.432000); EI; Faxon; UnCover; SWETS; UMI; CASDDS. **CCC.**
Description: Topical scientific papers on all earth science disciplines worldwide.
Refereed Serial

555   JA
GEOLOGY AND MINERAL RESOURCES OF JAPAN/NIHON CHISHITSU KOSANSHI.* (Text in English) 1956. irreg. exchange basis. Kogyo Gijutsuin, Chishitsu Chosajo - Agency of Industrial Science and Technology, Geological Survey of Japan, 1-3, Higashi 1-chome, Tsukuba-shi, Ibaraki-ken 305, Japan.

551   US
TN799.5
GEOLOGY AND WORLD DEPOSITS. 1984. irreg. $82. Metal Bulletin Inc., 220 Fifth Ave., 19th Fl., New York, NY 10001. TEL 800-638-2525. FAX 212-213-6273. Eds. P.W. Harben, R.L. Bates. **Document type:** trade publication.
Formerly: Geology of Nonmetallics (ISSN 0266-1411)
Description: Covers geology and uses of 50 industrial rocks and minerals.

551   GW   ISSN 0720-8863
GEOLOGY OF PETROLEUM. (Text in English) 1981. irreg., no.7, 1983. price varies. Ferdinand Enke Verlag, Postfach 101254, 70011 Stuttgart, Germany. TEL 0711-135798-0. FAX 0711-135798-30. TELEX 07252275-GTV-D. Ed. H. Beckmann. (reprint service avail. from IRC) **Document type:** monographic series.

551   PL   ISSN 0138-0389
QE276.5
GEOLOGY OF POLAND. (Text in English) 1979. irreg. (approx. a.). price varies. Panstwowy Instytut Geologiczny - Polish Geological Institute, Ul. Rakowiecka 4, 00-975 Warsaw, Poland. TEL 48-22-495351. FAX 48-22-495342. circ. 400. **Indexed:** Chem.Abstr., Geo.Abstr.

551   US   ISSN 8755-075X
GEOLOGY OF THE PACIFIC OCEAN. 12/yr. (in 2 vols., 6 nos./vol.). 513 ECU per vol. (effective 1993). Harwood Academic Publishers, 820 Town Center Dr., Langhorne, PA 19047. TEL 215-750-2642. FAX 215-750-6343. (UK subscr. to: P.O. Box 90, Reading, Berkshire RG1 8JL, England. TEL 0734-560-080) Ed. N.A. Shilo. (also avail. in microform) **Indexed:** E&P Hlth. (1993-), Gas Process.& Ppl. (1993-), Off.Tech. (1993-), Petrol.Abstr. (1993-).
Refereed Serial

EARTH SCIENCES — GEOLOGY

551 UK ISSN 0266-6979
QE1
GEOLOGY TODAY. 1985. bi-m. £27.50 to individuals in Europe (elsewhere £30.50 ($46)); institutions in Europe £105 (elsewhere £115.50 ($172)) (effective 1994). (Geological Society) Blackwell Scientific Publications Ltd., Osney Mead, Oxford OX2 OEL, England. TEL 0865-240201. FAX 0865-721205. TELEX 83355-MEDBOK-G. (Co-sponsor: Geologists' Association) Ed. P. Smith. adv.; bk.rev.; illus.; charts; maps. circ. 3,100. (also avail. in microform from UMI; back issues avail.) **Indexed:** AESIS. **Document type:** academic/scholarly publication.
—BLDSC (4146.640000); Faxon; UnCover; SWETS; UMI. **CCC.**
Refereed Serial

550 CI ISSN 0016-7924
QE1 CODEN: GEVJAO
GEOLOSKI VJESNIK. (Text in Serbo-Croatian) 1947. irreg. exchange basis. (Hrvatsko Geolosko Drustvo) Institut za Geoloska Istrazivanja u Zagrebu, Sachsova 2, 41000 Zagreb, Croatia. FAX 38-41-519-149. Ed. Branko Crnkovic. **Indexed:** Biol.Abstr., Chem.Abstr.

GEOMAGNETISM AND AERONOMY. see *EARTH SCIENCES — Geophysics*

GEOMIMET. see *MINES AND MINING INDUSTRY*

551 NE ISSN 0169-555X
CODEN: GEMPEZ
GEOMORPHOLOGY. 1987. 12/yr. (in 3 vols.) 4 nos./vol.). fl.1098($594) (effective 1994). Elsevier Science B.V., P.O. Box 211, 1000 AE Amsterdam, Netherlands. TEL 31-20-5803911. FAX 31-20-5803598. TELEX 18582 ESPA NL. (Subscr. in U.S. and Canada to: Elsevier Science Inc., Box 882, Madison Sq. Sta., New York, NY 10159. TEL 212-989-5800. FAX 212-633-3990) Ed. M. Morisawa. adv.; bk.rev.; illus. (also avail. in microform from UMI; back issues avail.) **Document type:** academic/scholarly publication.
—BLDSC (4147.680000); Faxon; UnCover; SWETS. **CCC.**
Description: Publishes review articles, research papers and letters related to pure and applied geomorphology, including modelling of landforms, extraterrestrial landforms, tectonic and climatological geomorphology.
Refereed Serial

555 PK ISSN 0435-4311
QE295 CODEN: GGSPB8
GEONEWS. (Text in English) 1968. irreg., vol. 2, 1972. Geological Survey of Pakistan, c/o Chief Librarian, Box 15, Quetta, Pakistan. TEL 73055.

GEOOEKODYNAMIK. see *GEOGRAPHY*

557 US
GEORGIA GEOLOGIC SURVEY. BULLETIN. 1894. irreg, no.124, 1990. price varies. Department of Natural Resources, Georgia Geologic Survey, 19 Martin Luther King Jr. Dr., S.W., Rm. 400, Atlanta, GA 30334. TEL 404-656-3214. **Document type:** bulletin.
Description: Discusses geologic and mineral resources on a multi-region and statewide basis.

550 US
GEORGIA GEOLOGIC SURVEY. CIRCULAR. (Has subseries for Circulars 1, 2 and 3) 1981. irreg., no.14, 1991. price varies. Department of Natural Resources, Georgia Geologic Survey, 19 Martin Luther King Jr. Dr., S.W., Rm. 400, Atlanta, GA 30334. TEL 404-656-3214.
Description: Provides information on the Survey and its facilities and data.

557 US
GEORGIA GEOLOGIC SURVEY. GEOLOGIC GUIDE. 1977. irreg., no.9, 1985. price varies. Department of Natural Resources, Georgia Geologic Survey, 19 Martin Luther King Jr. Dr., S.W., Rm. 400, Atlanta, GA 30334. TEL 404-656-3214.
Description: Brief reports detailing the geology of some of Georgia's parks.

551 US
GEORGIA GEOLOGIC SURVEY. GEOLOGIC REPORT. 1971. irreg., no.7, 1992. price varies. Department of Natural Resources, Georgia Geologic Survey, 19 Martin Luther King Jr. Dr., S.W., Rm. 400, Atlanta, GA 30334. TEL 404-656-3214.
Description: Brief reports discussing specific commodities and geologic topics in specific areas of the State.

557 US
GEORGIA GEOLOGIC SURVEY. GUIDEBOOK. 1962. irreg., no.22, 1980. price varies. Department of Natural Resources, Georgia Geologic Survey, 19 Martin Luther King Jr. Dr., S.W., Rm. 400, Atlanta, GA 30334. TEL 404-656-3214.
Description: Detailed field trips conducted by the Georgia Geological Society.

557 US
GEORGIA GEOLOGIC SURVEY. MISCELLANEOUS PUBLICATION. 1963. irreg., no.7, 1984. price varies. Department of Natural Resources, Georgia Geologic Survey, 19 Martin Luther King Jr. Dr., S.W., Rm. 400, Atlanta, GA 30334. TEL 404-656-3214.
Formerly: Georgia Geologic Survey. Special Publication.
Description: Hydrologic topics of special time-limited interest.

557 US
GEORGIA GEOLOGIC SURVEY. OPEN FILE REPORT. 1979. irreg., no.92-4, 1992. price varies. Department of Natural Resources, Georgia Geologic Survey, 19 Martin Luther King Jr. Dr., S.W., Rm. 400, Atlanta, GA 30334. TEL 404-656-3214.

557 US
GEORGIA GEOLOGIC SURVEY. PROJECT REPORT. 1966. irreg., no.17, 1992. price varies. Department of Natural Resources, Georgia Geologic Survey, 19 Martin Luther King Jr. Dr., S.W., Rm. 400, Atlanta, GA 30334. TEL 404-656-3214.
Description: Concerned with the potential for mineral resources in the coastal zone of the Georgia Coastal Plain.

551 VE ISSN 0435-5601
CODEN: GEOSAG
GEOS. (Text in Spanish; summaries in English) 1959. a. $15. Fundacion Geos, Apdo. 54008, Caracas 1053A, Venezuela. Ed. Franco Urbani. circ. 1,000. (back issues avail.) **Indexed:** Bull.Signal, GeoRef.
—CASDDS

557 US ISSN 0164-2049
QE179 CODEN: GEWIDT
GEOSCIENCE WISCONSIN. 1977. irreg., no.14, 1991. price varies. Geological and Natural History Survey, University of Wisconsin - Extension, 3817 Mineral Point Rd., Madison, WI 53705. TEL 608-262-1705. FAX 608-262-8086. **Document type:** government publication.
—BLDSC (4158.879000); CASDDS.

551 UK ISSN 0961-5628
QE1
GEOSCIENTIST. 1991. bi-m. £37($70) (foreign £42). Geological Society Publishing House, Unit 7, Brassmill Enterprise Centre, Brassmill Ln., Bath BA1 3JN, England. TEL 0225-445046. FAX 0225-442836. Ed. Roger Beck. adv.; bk.rev circ. 7,500. **Document type:** academic/scholarly publication.
—BLDSC (4158.892500).
Incorporates: British Geologist (ISSN 0144-0063)

091 FR ISSN 0150-5505
CODEN: GENEE7
GEOSTANDARDS NEWSLETTER. 1977. 2/yr. $105. Association Nationale de la Recherche Technique, International Working Group "Analytical Standards of Minerals, Ores, and Rocks", C R P G, B.P. 20, 54501 Vandoeuvre Cedex, France. TEL 33-83-51-22-13. FAX 33-83-51-17-98. TELEX 960431 ADNANCY. Ed. K. Govindaraju; Pub. K. Govindaraju. circ. 650. **Indexed:** Br.Ceram.Abstr., Chem.Abstr., Deep Sea Res.& Oceanogr.Abstr., Ind.Sci.Rev., Sci.Cit.Ind. **Document type:** newsletter.
—BLDSC (4158.896800); Faxon; SWETS; CASDDS. **CCC.**

551 CN ISSN 0823-650X
GEOTECHNICAL NEWS. 1982. q. Can.$45($45) (outside N. America Can.$60). BiTech Publishers Ltd., 173 - 11860 Hammersmith Way, Richmond, BC V7A 5G1, Canada. TEL 604-277-4250. FAX 604-277-8125. Ed. John W. Gadsby. adv. contact: Lynn Pugh. bk.rev. circ. 6,000. **Document type:** newsletter, trade publication.
—EI.
Formerly: C G S News (ISSN 0710-0477)
Description: Contains news on geotechnical activities in Canada, the US, Mexico and Europe including special sections on waste geotechnics and geosynthetics and a calendar of geotechnical events.

551 624.176 US
GEOTECHNICAL SPECIAL PUBLICATIONS. irreg. American Society of Civil Engineers, 345 E. 47th St., New York, NY 10017-2398. TEL 212-705-7520. FAX 212-980-4681. **Document type:** academic/scholarly publication, monographic series.

GEOTECHNIK. see *ENGINEERING*

551 CI
GEOTEHNIKA; informativno glasilo radne zajednice Geotehnika. 1965. irreg. Geotehnika, Kupska 2, Zagreb, Croatia. Ed. Zvonko Jelic. **Indexed:** Chem.Abstr.

551 RU ISSN 0016-853X
CODEN: GTKTA2
GEOTEKTONIKA. English translation: Geotectonics (US ISSN 0016-8521) 1965. bi-m. 32.10 Rub. (Rossiiskaya Akademiya Nauk, Otdelenie Nauk o Zemle) Iadatel'stvo Nauka, Profsoyuznaya 90, 117864 GSP-7 Moscow, V-485, Russia. bk.rev.; charts; illus.; index. **Indexed:** Chem.Abstr., Deep Sea Res.& Oceanogr.Abstr., E&P Hlth. (1993-), Gas. Process.& Ppl. (1993-), INIS Atomind., Off.Tech. (1993-), Petrol.Abstr. (1988-).
—CASDDS. **CCC.**

551.8 BU ISSN 0324-1661
QE601 CODEN: GTGED8
GEOTEKTONIKA, TEKTONOFIZIKA I GEODINAMIKA. (Text in Bulgarian; summaries in English and French) 1975. 3/yr. (Bulgarska Akademiia na Naukite) Publishing House of the Bulgarian Academy of Sciences, Acad. G. Bonchev St., Bldg. 6, 1113 Sofia, Bulgaria. Ed. J. Karagiuleva. circ. 450. (reprint service avail. from IRC) **Indexed:** Deep Sea Res.& Oceanogr.Abstr., Geo.Abstr.
—BLDSC (0047.785000).

551 VE ISSN 0253-1062
GEOTERMIA. (Text in Spanish; summaries in English) 1981. 2/yr. Bs.150($8) (Universidad Central de Venezuela) Sociedad Venezolana de Historia de las Geociencias, Apdo. 47334, Caracas 1041A, Venezuela. Ed. Franco Urbani. circ. 500. (back issues avail.) **Indexed:** GeoRef.

GEOTHERMAL HOTLINE. see *ENERGY — Geothermal Energy*

551 US ISSN 0890-5363
GB1199.5
GEOTHERMAL SCIENCE AND TECHNOLOGY. 4/yr. (in 1 vol., 4 nos./vol.). 361 ECU (effective 1993). Gordon & Breach Science Publishers, 820 Town Center Dr., Langhorne, PA 19047. TEL 215-750-2642. FAX 215-750-6343. (UK subscr. to: P.O. Box 90, Reading, Berkshire RG1 8JL, England. TEL 0734-560-080) Ed. James C. Bresee. (also avail. in microform) **Indexed:** Environ.Per.Bibl. (1991-).
—BLDSC (4161.032500). **CCC.**
Refereed Serial

551 GW ISSN 0341-7522
GEOWISSEN KOMPAKT. 1976. irreg., vol.9, 1985. price varies. Ferdinand Enke Verlag, Postfach 101254, 70011 Stuttgart, Germany. TEL 0711-135798-0. FAX 0711-135798-30. TELEX 07252275-GTV-D. (reprint service avail. from IRC) **Document type:** monographic series.

550 GW ISSN 0340-4056
DER GESCHIEBESAMMLER. 1966. q. DM.50. Frank Rudolph, Ed. & Pub., Achtern Hoeven 6, 24601 Wankendorf, Germany. TEL 04326-2205. adv.; bk.rev. **Document type:** newsletter.

EARTH SCIENCES — GEOLOGY

551 551.4 560   AU
QE1
GESELLSCHAFT DER GEOLOGIE- UND BERGBAUSTUDENTEN. MITTEILUNGEN. 1949. a. S.450. Gesellschaft der Geologie- und Bergbaustudenten, Universitaetsstr. 7-III, A-1010 Vienna, Austria. FAX 4300-2520. Eds. Richard Lein, Marion Jarnik. adv.; bk.rev. circ. 450. (back issues avail.)

551   IT   ISSN 0017-0291
QE1   CODEN: GGMGAI
GIORNALE DI GEOLOGIA; rivista di geologia sedimentaria e geologia marina. (Text in English, French, German and Italian; summaries in English and Italian) 1926. s-a. L.60000. Via Zamboni, 63, 40127 Bologna, Italy. FAX 051-354522. Ed. Franco Ricci-Lucchi. adv.; bk.rev. circ. 600. (back issues avail.) **Indexed:** Biol.Abstr., Chem.Abstr. **Document type:** bulletin.
—BLDSC (4178.025000).
    Description: Covers geology of the Alps and seas around Italy, with an emphasis on high resolution seismic stratigraphy of plio-quaternary sediments, as well as other regional geography.

551.31   US   ISSN 0149-1776
GB2401
GLACIOLOGICAL DATA. 1977. irreg. exchange basis. World Data Center A for Glaciology (Snow and Ice), National Snow and Ice Data Center, CIRES, Campus Box 449, University of Colorado, Boulder, CO 80309. TEL 303-492-5171. FAX 303-492-2468. TELEX 7401426 WDCA UC. Eds. R.G. Barry, Ann M. Brennan. bk.rev.; index. circ. 1,100. (back issues avail.) **Indexed:** Meteor.& Geoastrophys.Abstr. **Document type:** monographic series.
—BLDSC (4180.060000); UnCover.
    Supersedes the quarterly issued from 1960-1976: Glaciological Notes (ISSN 0017-0712)

551 910   NE   ISSN 0924-5006
GLACIOLOGY AND QUATERNARY GEOLOGY. 1985. irreg., latest 1991. price varies. Kluwer Academic Publishers, Postbus 17, 3300 AA Dordrecht, Netherlands. TEL 31-78-334911. FAX 31-78-334254. TELEX 29245 KAPG NL. (Dist. by: Kluwer Academic Publishers Group, P.O. Box 322, 3300 AH Dordrecht, Netherlands. TEL 31-78-524400; N. America dist. addr.: Box 358, Accord Sta., Hingham, MA 02018-0358. TEL 617-871-6600) **Indexed:** Meteor.& Geoastrophys.Abstr. **Document type:** monographic series.
    Refereed Serial

551   NE   ISSN 0921-8181
QE1   CODEN: GPCHE4
GLOBAL AND PLANETARY CHANGE. (Supplement to: Palaeogeography, Palaeoclimatology, Palaeoecology (ISSN 0031-0182)) (Text in English) 1988. 8/yr. (in 2 vols.; 4 nos./vol.) fl.752($406) (effective 1994). Elsevier Science B.V., P.O. Box 211, 1000 AE Amsterdam, Netherlands. TEL 31-20-5803911. FAX 31-20-5803598. TELEX 18582 ESPA NL. (Subscr. in U.S. and Canada to: Elsevier Science Inc., Box 882, Madison Sq. Sta., New York, NY 10159. TEL 212-989-5800. FAX 212-633-3990) Ed.Bd. adv.; bk.rev. (also avail. in microform from UMI; back issues avail.) **Indexed:** Environ.Per.Bibl (1992-), Meteor.& Geoastrophys.Abstr., Sel.Water Res.Abstr. **Document type:** academic/scholarly publication.
—BLDSC (4195.345000); Faxon; UnCover; SWETS. **CCC.**
    Description: Focuses on the causes, processes and limits of variability in planetary change, the record of change in earth history, the analysis and prediction of recent and future changes. Includes discussions of ocean, climate and atmosphere, geophysics, human geography and global ecology.
    Refereed Serial

551   GW   ISSN 0163-3171
GLOBAL TECTONICS AND METALLOGENY. (Text in English) 1978. irreg. DM.128. E. Schweizerbart'sche Verlagsbuchhandlung, Johannesstr. 3A, 70176 Stuttgart, Germany. TEL 0711-625001. FAX 0711-625005. TELEX 723363-SCHB-D. Ed. Jan Kutina. **Indexed:** AESIS. **Document type:** academic/scholarly publication.
—BLDSC (4195.476000); UnCover. **CCC.**

GREAT BRITAIN. COMMONWEALTH ASSOCIATION OF SURVEYING AND LAND ECONOMY. SURVEY REVIEW.
see *ENGINEERING — Civil Engineering*

551   UK
GREAT BRITAIN. NATURAL ENVIRONMENT RESEARCH COUNCIL. BRITISH GEOLOGICAL SURVEY. TECHNICAL REPORT. FLUID PROCESSES SERIES. m. Natural Environment Research Council, British Geological Survey, Fluid Process Research Group, Kingsley Dunham Centre, Keyworth, Nottingham NG1 5GG, England. TEL 06077-6111. FAX 06077-6602. TELEX 378173-BGSKEY-G. (Subscr. to: H.M.S.O., Liaison Officer, Nine Elms, London, SW8 5DR, England) Ed.Bd. **Document type:** government publication.

551 557   UK
GREAT BRITAIN. NATURAL ENVIRONMENT RESEARCH COUNCIL. BRITISH GEOLOGICAL SURVEY. CLASSICAL AREAS OF BRITISH GEOLOGY. 1968. irreg. Natural Environment Research Council, British Geological Survey, Kingsley Dunham Centre, Keyworth, Nottingham NG12 5GG, England. TEL 0602-361000. FAX 0602-362000. TELEX 378173-BGSKEY-G. (Subscr. to: H.M.S.O., c/o Liaison Officer, Nine Elms, London SW8 5DR, England) circ. 2,500. **Document type:** government publication.
    Formerly (until Jan. 1984): Great Britain. Institute of Geological Sciences. Classical Areas of British Geology.
    Description: Guide to the geology of various areas.

554 560   UK
GREAT BRITAIN. NATURAL ENVIRONMENT RESEARCH COUNCIL. BRITISH GEOLOGICAL SURVEY. MEMOIRS. 1846. irreg. price varies. Natural Environment Research Council, British Geological Survey, Kingsley Dunham Centre, Keyworth, Nottingham NG12 5GG, England. TEL 0602-361000. FAX 0602-362000. TELEX 378173-BGSKEY-G. (Subscr. to: H.M.S.O., c/o Liaison Officer, Nine Elms, London SW8 5DR, England) illus. circ. 2,000. **Document type:** government publication.
    Formerly (until Jan. 1984): Great Britain. Institute of Geological Sciences. Memoirs of the Geological Survey of Great Britain (ISSN 0072-6494)
    Description: Presents geological studies of Great Britain and Northern Ireland.

551   UK   ISSN 0030-7467
TN57   CODEN: OGMRA3
GREAT BRITAIN. NATURAL ENVIRONMENT RESEARCH COUNCIL. BRITISH GEOLOGICAL SURVEY. OVERSEAS GEOLOGY AND MINERAL RESOURCES. 1950. irreg. price varies. Natural Environment Research Council, British Geological Survey, Kingsley Dunham Centre, Keyworth, Nottingham NG12 5GG, England. TEL 0602-361000. FAX 0602-362000. TELEX 378173-BGSKEY-G. (Subscr. to: H.M.S.O., c/o Liaison Officer, Nine Elms, London SW8 5DR, England) illus. circ. 1,500. **Indexed:** GeoRef. **Document type:** government publication.
—UnCover; CASDDS. **CCC.**
    Formerly (until Jan. 1984): Great Britain. Institute of Geological Sciences. Overseas Geology and Mineral Resources (ISSN 0073-9332)
    Description: Examines papers on geological aspects of the developing areas of the world.

551   UK   ISSN 0951-6646
GREAT BRITAIN. NATURAL ENVIRONMENT RESEARCH COUNCIL. BRITISH GEOLOGICAL SURVEY. OVERSEAS MEMOIRS. 1976. irreg. price varies. Natural Environment Research Council, British Geological Survey, Kingsley Dunham Centre, Keyworth, Nottingham NG12 5GG, England. TEL 0602-361000. FAX 0602-362000. TELEX 378173-BGSKEY-G. (Subscr. to: H.M.S.O., c/o Liaison Officer, Nine Elms, London SW8 5DR, England) illus.; maps. circ. 1,250. **Document type:** government publication.
—BLDSC (6316.690000). **CCC.**
    Formerly (until Jan. 1984): Great Britain. Institute of Geological Sciences. Overseas Memoirs (ISSN 0308-5325)
    Description: Studies the geology of various countries.

551.44   GR   ISSN 0011-8117
GREEK SPELEOLOGICAL SOCIETY. DELTION/SOCIETE SPELEOLOGIQUE DE GRECE. BULLETIN TRIMESTRIEL. (Text in Greek; summaries in French) 1952. q. membership or on exchange basis. Greek Speleological Society, 11 Mantzarou St., Athens 135, Greece. bibl.; index. circ. 600. **Document type:** bulletin.

559.82   DK   ISSN 0105-3507
          CODEN: BGGUA9
GROENLANDS GEOLOGISKE UNDERSOEGELSE. BULLETIN/GEOLOGICAL SURVEY OF GREENLAND. BULLETIN. (Nos.1-114 also published in Meddelelser Om Groenland) (Text mainly in English) 1948. irreg. (1-3/yr.). price varies. Groenlands Geologiske Undersoegelse, Oester Voldgade 10, DK-1350 Copenhagen K, Denmark. TEL 45-33-11-88-66. FAX 45-33-93-53-52. **Document type:** bulletin.
—BLDSC (2551.360000).

559.82   DK   ISSN 0418-6559
          CODEN: GRGUA5
GROENLANDS GEOLOGISKE UNDERSOEGELSE. RAPPORT. (Text mainly in English) 1964. irreg. (approx. 5/yr.). price varies. Groenlands Geologiske Undersoegelse, Oester Voldgade 10, DK-1350 Copenhagen K, Denmark. TEL 45-33-11-88-66. FAX 45-33-93-53-52. Ed. Stuart Watt. bibl.; charts; illus. **Indexed:** Geo.Abstr., INIS Atomind., Petrol.Abstr.

551   NE   ISSN 0017-4505
GRONDBOOR EN HAMER. (Text in Dutch; summaries in English) 1955. bi-m. fl.40 (foreign fl.55). Nederlandse Geologische Vereniging, Hortensialaan 64, 7101 XH Winterswyk, Netherlands. adv.; bk.rev.; bibl.; charts; illus.; index. cum.index. circ. 1,800. **Document type:** bulletin.
—BLDSC (4217.910000).

551 910   IT
GROTTE D'ITALIA. 1927. a. Societa Speleologica Italiana, Via Zamboni, 67, I-40127 Bologna, Italy. FAX 3951-354522. Ed. Paolo Forti. circ. 1,000.

796.525   VE   ISSN 0583-774X
          CODEN: BSVGAO
GUACHARO; boletin de divulgacion espeleologica. (Text in Spanish; summaries in English) 1968. a. Bs.50($5) Sociedad Venezolana de Espeleologia, Apdo. 47334, Caracas 1041A, Venezuela. Ed. F. Urbani. circ. 500. (back issues avail.) **Indexed:** Speleol.Abstr.

555   CC
GUANGDONG DIZHI/GUANGDONG GEOLOGY. (Text in Chinese; abstracts in English) 1986. q. Y12 (foreign $25). Guangdong Sheng Dizhi Kuangchan Ju - Bureau of Geology and Mineral Resources of Guangdong Province, No. 739, Dongfeng Road East, Guangzhou, Guangdong 510080, People's Republic of China. TEL 778992. Ed. Ouyang Chi. adv. contact: Yue Gongshang. circ. 1,000. **Document type:** academic/scholarly publication.
    Description: Carries academic articles on geological sciences, and latest developments in science and technology.

551   CC
GUOWAI DIZHI/GEOLOGY ABROAD. (Text in Chinese) bi-m. Zhongguo Kexueyuan, Dizhi Yanjiusuo - Chinese Academy of Sciences, Institute of Geology, Qijia Huozi, Deshengmenwai, Beijing 100029, People's Republic of China. TEL 4016611. Ed. Yi Shanfeng.

551   CC
GUOWAI DIZHI KEJI/FOREIGN GEOLOGY SCIENCE AND TECHNOLOGY. (Text in Chinese) 8/yr. Zhongguo Dizhi Kuangchan Xinxi Yanjiuyuan - Chinese Institute of Geology and Mineral Products Information, 277, Fuchengmenwai Beijie, Beijing 100037, People's Republic of China. TEL 892243. Ed. Wang Liwen.

GUOWAI KEJI ZILIAO MULU - DIZHIXUE/FOREIGN SCIENCE AND TECHNOLOGY CATALOGUE - GEOLOGY.
see *EARTH SCIENCES — Abstracting, Bibliographies, Statistics*

551   CC   ISSN 1001-5825
GUOWAI YOUQI KANTAN. (Text in Chinese) bi-m. Nengyuan Bu, Dili Wuli Kantan Ju, P.O. Box 11-1, Zuozhou, Hebei 072751, People's Republic of China. TEL 2901.

557   GY
GUYANA. GEOLOGY & MINES COMMISSION. ANNUAL REPORT. a. $5. Geology and Mines Commission, P.O. Box 1028, Georgetown, Guyana. FAX 53047.
    Formerly: Guyana. Geological Survey Department. Annual Reports (ISSN 0072-9108)

EARTH SCIENCES — GEOLOGY

557   GY
GUYANA. GEOLOGY & MINES COMMISSION. MINERAL RESOURCES PAMPHLET. 1953. irreg., no.15, 1980. Geology & Mines Commission, P.O. Box 1028, Georgetown, Guyana. FAX 53047.
Formerly: Guyana. Geological Survey Department. Mineral Resources Pamphlet (ISSN 0072-9124)

551   GW   ISSN 0936-8515
HAECKEL BUECHEREI. 1990. irreg., no.2, 1991. price varies. Ferdinand Enke Verlag, Postfach 101254, 70011 Stuttgart, Germany. TEL 0711-135798-0. FAX 0711-135798-30. TELEX 07252275-GTV-D. Ed.Bd. (reprint service avail. from IRC) **Document type:** monographic series.

550   GW   ISSN 0943-4658
▼**HAMBURGER MINERALISCHEN MUSEUM. SCHRIFTEN.** 1992. irreg. DM.36.80. Verlag Sven von Loga, Gerhard-vom-Rath-Str. 55, 50968 Cologne, Germany. TEL 0221-383680. FAX 0221-386737. Ed. W. Liessmann. **Document type:** monographic series.

551   NE   ISSN 0168-6275
HANDBOOK OF EXPLORATION GEOCHEMISTRY. (Text in English) 1981. irreg., vol.5, 1992. price varies. Elsevier Science B.V., Books Division, P.O. Box 211, 1000 AE Amsterdam, Netherlands. TEL 31-20-5803911. FAX 31-20-5803705. TELEX 18582 ESPA NL. (Subscr. in U.S. and Canada to: Elsevier Science Inc., Box 882, Madison Sq. Sta., New York, NY 10159. TEL 212-989-5800) Ed. G.J.S. Govett. **Document type:** monographic series.
Refereed Serial

551   NE
HANDBOOK OF STRATA-BOUND AND STRATIFORM ORE DEPOSITS. 1976. irreg., vol.14, 1986. price varies. Elsevier Science B.V., Books Division, P.O. Box 211, 1000 AE Amsterdam, Netherlands. TEL 31-20-5803911. FAX 31-20-5803705. TELEX 18582 ESPA NL. (Subscr. in U.S. and Canada to: Elsevier Science Inc., Box 882, Madison Sq. Sta., New York, NY 10159. TEL 212-989-5800) Ed. K.H. Wolf. **Document type:** monographic series.
Refereed Serial

551.44 574 628.44   AT   ISSN 0017-9973
CODEN: HELIBH
HELICTITE; journal of Australasian cave research. 1962. s-a. Aus.$20. Speleological Research Council Ltd., P.O. Box 183, Broadway, N.S.W. 2007, Australia. Ed.Bd. adv.; bk.rev.; abstr.; charts; illus.; cum.index. circ. 180. **Indexed:** AESIS. **Document type:** academic/scholarly publication.
—BLDSC (4285.250000).

551 549   FR   ISSN 0982-3816
CODEN: HERCEW
HERCYNICA. 1969. s-a. 250 F. (Societe Geologique et Mineralogique) Universite de Rennes I, Institut de Geologie, Av. du General Leclerc, 35042 Rennes Cedex, France. FAX 99-28-67-00. Eds. P. Jegouzo, M. Robardet. adv.; bk.rev.; bibl.; charts; illus. circ. 500. **Indexed:** Biol.Abstr., Br.Geol.Lit., Bull.Signal., GeoRef., Soils & Fert.
Formerly (until 1985): Societe Geologique et Mineralogique de Bretagne. Bulletin, Serie C (ISSN 0560-5466)

555   II   ISSN 0379-5101
QE319.H5   CODEN: HMLGBX
HIMALAYAN GEOLOGY. (Text in English) 1971. a. $100. (Wadia Institute of Himalayan Geology) Hindustan Publishing Corp., 6-U.B. Jawahar Nagar, Delhi 110007, India. TEL 2915059. FAX 6863511. (back issues avail.) **Indexed:** Chem.Abstr.
—CASDDS.

555   JA   ISSN 0073-2303
CODEN: HIRDAP
HIROSHIMA DAIGAKU CHIGAKU KENKYU HOKOKU/HIROSHIMA UNIVERSITY. GEOLOGICAL REPORT. (Text in Japanese; summaries in English) 1951. a. not for sale. Hiroshima Daigaku, Rigakubu, Chishitsugaku Kobutsugaku Koyoshitsu - Hiroshima University, Faculty of Science, Institute of Geology and Mineralogy, 1-3, Kagamiyama, Higashi Hiroshima-shi, Hiroshima-ken 724, Japan. **Indexed:** Biol.Abstr., Jap.Per.Ind.
—BLDSC (4136.000000).

551 549   JA   ISSN 0075-4374
CODEN: JSHCAU
HIROSHIMA UNIVERSITY. JOURNAL OF SCIENCE. SERIES C. GEOLOGY AND MINERALOGY/HIROSHIMA DAIGAKU RIGAKUBU KIYO, CHIKYU WAKUSEI. (Text in English, French and German) 1951. irreg., vol.9, no.4, 1993. Hiroshima University, Faculty of Science - Hiroshima Daigaku Rigakubu Chikyu Wakuseiguku, Kagamiyama, Higashihiroshima 724, Japan. TEL 0824-24-7459. FAX 0824-24-0735. index. **Indexed:** Biol.Abstr., JTA, Met.Abstr. **Document type:** bulletin.
—UnCover.

551 558   VE   ISSN 0258-3135
HISTORIA DE LAS GEOCIENCIAS EN VENEZUELA. BOLETIN. 1984. 3/yr. $15. Sociedad Venezolana de Historia de las Geociencias, Apdo. 47334, Caracas 1041A, Venezuela. FAX 58-2-6627845. Ed. F. Urbani. bk.rev.; index. circ. 300. (back issues avail.)

HOBETSU-CHORITSU HAKUBUTSUKAN KENKYU HOKOKU/HOBETSU MUSEUM. BULLETIN. see *PALEONTOLOGY*

551.44   AU   ISSN 0018-3091
GB601.A1   CODEN: HOHLA7
DIE HOEHLE; Zeitschrift fuer Karst- und Hoehlenkunde. 1950. q. S.140($12) Verband Oesterreichischer Hoehlenforscher, Obere Donaustr. 97-1-61, A-1020 Vienna, Austria. Ed. Hubert Trimmel. bk.rev.; index. circ. 2,000. **Indexed:** Biol.Abstr. **Document type:** academic/scholarly publication.
—BLDSC (4322.200000).

551.44   SZ   ISSN 0018-3105
HOEHLENPOST. 1963. 3/yr. 17 SFr. (foreign 20 SFr.). Ostschweizerische Gesellschaft fuer Hoehlenforschung, c/o Rene Scherrer, Bruggwiesenstr. 6, CH-8442 Hettlingen, Switzerland. TEL 052-391737. adv. circ. 180. **Document type:** bulletin.

HOKKAIDO KYOIKU DAIGAKU KIYO. DAI-2-BU, B. SEIBUTSUGAKU, CHIGAKU, NOGAKU- HEN/HOKKAIDO UNIVERSITY OF EDUCATION. JOURNAL. SECTION 2 B. BIOLOGY, GEOLOGY, AND AGRICULTURE. see *BIOLOGY*

555 553 549   JA   ISSN 0018-3474
CODEN: JFHGAJ
HOKKAIDO UNIVERSITY. FACULTY OF SCIENCE. JOURNAL. SERIES 4: GEOLOGY AND MINERALOGY. (Text in English) 1930. s-a. Hokkaido University, Faculty of Science - Hokkaido Daigaku Rigakubu, Nishi-8-chome, Kita-10-jo, Kita-ku, Sapporo 060, Japan. FAX 011-716-0394. Ed. M. Kato. circ. 850. (back issues avail.) **Indexed:** Biol.Abstr., Chem.Abstr., INIS Atomind., Sci.Abstr.
—BLDSC (4748.500000); UnCover; CASDDS.

551.22   JA
HOKKAIDO UNIVERSITY. URAKAWA SEISMOLOGICAL OBSERVATORY. BULLETIN. (Text in English) s-a. exchange basis. Hokkaido University, Urakawa Seismological Observatory, 956-2, Kamikineusu, Urakawa-machi, Urakawa-gin, Hokkaido 057-01, Japan. **Document type:** bulletin.

557   US   ISSN 0018-6686
CODEN: BHGLA
HOUSTON GEOLOGICAL SOCIETY. BULLETIN. 1958. m. (Sep.-Jun.). $25 (effective July 1991). Houston Geological Society, 7171 Harwin, Ste. 314, Houston, TX 77036. TEL 713-785-6402. FAX 713-785-0553. Ed. Lynne Feldkamp. adv. contact: John King. bk.rev.; abstr.; charts; illus. circ. 5,400. **Indexed:** GeoRef. **Document type:** bulletin.

HYDROCARBON AND BYPRODUCT RESERVES. see *PETROLEUM AND GAS*

HYDROCARBONS RESERVE TAPE. see *PETROLEUM AND GAS*

551.31   UK   ISSN 0019-1043
GB2401   CODEN: ICEXAN
ICE. 1958. 3/yr. $36 (effective 1994). International Glaciological Society, Lensfield Rd., Cambridge CB2 1ER, England. TEL 0223-355974. FAX 0223-336543. Ed. H. Richardson. adv.; bk.rev. circ. 1,200. **Document type:** bulletin.

557 622   US   ISSN 0734-3825
IDAHO. GEOLOGICAL SURVEY. BULLETIN. 1920. irreg., no.26, 1982. price varies. Idaho Geological Survey, Morrill Hall, Rm. 332, University of Idaho, Moscow, ID 83843. TEL 208-885-7991. **Document type:** bulletin.
Formerly (until 1984): Idaho. Bureau of Mines and Geology. Bulletin (ISSN 0073-442X)

517 622   US
IDAHO. GEOLOGICAL SURVEY. INFORMATION CIRCULAR. 1957. irreg., no.40, 1986. price varies. Idaho Geological Survey, Morrill Hall, Rm.332, University of Idaho, Moscow, ID 83843. TEL 208-885-7991.
Formerly (until 1984): Idaho. Bureau of Mines and Geology. Information Circular (ISSN 0073-4446)

551   US
IDAHO. GEOLOGICAL SURVEY. TECHNICAL REPORT. 1978. irreg. (6-10/yr.). Idaho Geological Survey, Morrill Hall, Rm. 332, University of Idaho, Moscow, ID 83843. TEL 208-885-7991.
Formerly (until 1984): Idaho. Geological Survey. Open-File Report.

557   US   ISSN 0073-5051
CODEN: ILGBAU
ILLINOIS. STATE GEOLOGICAL SURVEY. BULLETIN. 1906. irreg., no.99, 1993. price varies. State Geological Survey, Natural Resources Bldg., 615 E. Peabody Dr., Champaign, IL 61820. TEL 217-333-4747. abstr.; bibl.; charts; illus.; maps. circ. 1,200. **Indexed:** Biol.Abstr., GeoRef. **Document type:** bulletin.

557   US   ISSN 0073-506X
CODEN: ILGCAX
ILLINOIS. STATE GEOLOGICAL SURVEY. CIRCULAR. 1932. irreg., no.553, 1993. price varies. State Geological Survey, Natural Resources Bldg., 615 E. Peabody Dr., Champaign, IL 61820. TEL 217-333-4747. abstr.; bibl.; charts; illus.; maps; stat. **Indexed:** Biol.Abstr., Geo.Abstr., GeoRef.
—CASDDS.

557   US   ISSN 0073-5078
CODEN: IGSEAU
ILLINOIS. STATE GEOLOGICAL SURVEY. EDUCATIONAL SERIES. 1931. irreg., no.13, 1990. price varies. State Geological Survey, Natural Resources Bldg., 615 E. Peabody Dr., Champaign, IL 61820. TEL 217-333-4747. charts; illus.; stat. circ. 5,000. **Indexed:** GeoRef.

557   US   ISSN 1060-1988
QE105   CODEN: IEGNAH
ILLINOIS. STATE GEOLOGICAL SURVEY. ENVIRONMENTAL GEOLOGY. 1965. irreg., no.144, 1993. price varies. State Geological Survey, Natural Resources Bldg., 615 E. Peabody Dr., Champaign, IL 61820. TEL 217-333-4747. abstr.; bibl.; charts; illus.; stat. **Indexed:** Bibl.& Ind.Geol., Biol.Abstr.
Formerly: Illinois. State Geological Survey. Environmental Geology Notes (ISSN 0073-5086)

557   US   ISSN 0073-5094
QE105.   CODEN: IGSSA4
ILLINOIS. STATE GEOLOGICAL SURVEY. GUIDEBOOK SERIES. 1950. irreg., no.24, 1992. price varies. State Geological Survey, Natural Resources Bldg., 615 E. Peabody Dr., Champaign, IL 61820. TEL 217-333-4747. FAX 217-244-7004. abstr.; bibl.; charts; illus.; stat. circ. 1,000. **Indexed:** Biol.Abstr., GeoRef.

ILLINOIS MINERALS. see *MINES AND MINING INDUSTRY*

ILLINOIS PETROLEUM. see *PETROLEUM AND GAS*

551.3   II
INDIAN ASSOCIATION OF SEDIMENTOLOGISTS. JOURNAL. (Text in English) 1981. s-a. $30. Hindustan Publishing Corp., 6-U.B. Jawahar Nagar, Delhi 110007, India. TEL 2915059. FAX 6863511. Ed. S.M. Mathur.

551   II   ISSN 0379-5098
INDIAN GEOLOGISTS' ASSOCIATION. BI-ANNUAL BULLETIN. 1968. s-a. Rs.75($45) to members; institutions Rs.400($80). Indian Geologists' Association, c/o N. Kochhar, Secretary, Department of Geology, Panjab University, Chandigarh 160 014, India. TEL 0172-541-740. FAX 0172-541-409. TELEX 3957464 RSIC IN. Ed. N. Chawdhri. adv.; bk.rev.; charts; illus. circ. 350. (back issues avail.) **Document type:** bulletin.

EARTH SCIENCES — GEOLOGY

550 553   II   ISSN 0970-1354
QE1   CODEN: IJOGE7
INDIAN JOURNAL OF GEOLOGY. (Text in English) 1926. q. $55. Geological Mining and Metallurgical Society of India, Geology Department, University of Calcutta, 35 Ballygunge Circular Rd., Calcutta 700019, India. TEL 9133-4753681. Eds. Sarijib C. Sarkar, Dhruba Mukhopadhyay. adv.; bk.rev.; charts; illus.; index. circ. 500. **Indexed:** Chem.Abstr., GeoRef. **Document type:** academic/scholarly publication, bulletin.
—BLDSC (4413.300000); Faxon; UnCover.
Formerly: Geological, Mining and Metallurgical Society of India. Quarterly Journal (ISSN 0016-7584)

INDIAN MINERALOGIST. see *MINES AND MINING INDUSTRY*

551.3   II   ISSN 0970-3918
CODEN: TISTEA
INDIAN SOCIETY OF DESERT TECHNOLOGY. TRANSACTIONS. 1976. a. $20. Indian Society of Desert Technology, A-42 Shastri Nagar, Jodphur 342 003, India. Ed. Alam Singh. adv.; bk.rev. circ. 1,000. **Indexed:** Agroforest.Abstr., Chem.Abstr., Curr.Adv.Ecol.Sci., Excerp.Med., Field Crop Abstr., Irr.& Drain.Abstr., Maize Abstr., Plant Grow.Reg.Abstr., Ref.Zh., Soils & Fert., Sorghum & Millets Abstr.
—CASDDS. **CCC.**
Formerly (until 1987): Indian Society of Desert Technology and University Centre of Desert Studies. Transactions (ISSN 0379-0568)

INDIAN SOCIETY OF EARTHQUAKE TECHNOLOGY. BULLETIN; journal of international earthquake engineering. see *ENGINEERING — Civil Engineering*

551.3   II
INDIAN STRATIGRAPHY. (Text in English) 1973. irreg. price varies. Hindustan Publishing Corp., 6-U.B. Jawahar Nagar, Delhi 110007, India.
FAX 6863511.

551.3   BE   ISSN 0374-6291
INSTITUT ROYAL DES SCIENCES NATURELLES DE BELGIQUE. BULLETIN. SERIE SCIENCES DE LA TERRE. (Text in English, French, German) 1930. a. 1650 BEF (foreign 1900 BEF). Koninklijk Belgisch Instituut voor Natuurwetenschappen - Institut Royal des Sciences Naturelles de Belgique, Vautierstraat 29, 1040 Brussels, Belgium. abstr.; bibl.; charts; illus.; cum.index. (back issues avail.) **Indexed:** Biol.Abstr., Bull.Signal., Ref.Zh., Zoo.Rec. **Document type:** academic/scholarly publication.

538.7   BE   ISSN 0770-4569
INSTITUT ROYAL METEOROLOGIQUE DE BELGIQUE. ANNUAIRE: MAGNETISME TERRESTRE/KONINKLIJK METEOROLOGISCH INSTITUUT VAN BELGIE. JAARBOEK: AARDMAGNETISME. Key Title: Annuaire Magnetisme Terrestre - Jaarboek Aardmagnetisme. (Text in Dutch, French) 1964. a. 750 BEF (effective 1994). Institut Royal Meteorologique de Belgique - Koninklijk Meteorologisch Instituut van Belgie, Ave. Circulaire 3, 1180 Brussels, Belgium.
TEL 32-2-3730502. FAX 32-2-3751259. TELEX 21315 METEOBRU. circ. 150.

INSTITUTE FOR THE STUDY OF EARTH AND MAN NEWSLETTER. see *ARCHAEOLOGY*

559   NZ   ISSN 1171-9168
INSTITUTE OF GEOLOGICAL AND NUCLEAR SCIENCES. GEOLOGICAL MAP. irreg. price varies. Institute of Geological and Nuclear Sciences Ltd., P.O. Box 30-368, Lower Hutt, New Zealand.
TEL 64-4-569-9059. FAX 64-4-569-5016. Ed. D. Heron. circ. 450.
Supersedes: New Zealand Geological Survey Map Series.
Description: Includes geological maps mostly about New Zealand regional geology, usually at scale 1-50 thousand.

559   NZ   ISSN 1172-028X
INSTITUTE OF GEOLOGICAL AND NUCLEAR SCIENCES. MONOGRAPH. 1993. irreg. price varies. Institute of Geological and Nuclear Sciences Ltd., P.O. Box 30-368, Lower Hutt, New Zealand.
TEL 64-4-569-9059. FAX 64-4-569-5016. Ed. J.G. Gregory. bibl.; charts; illus. circ. 450. (back issues avail.) **Document type:** monographic series.
—BLDSC (6345.322000).
Formed by the merger of: New Zealand Geological Survey Basin Studies & New Zealand Geological Survey Bulletin; Which was formerly: New Zealand. Department of Scientific and Industrial Research. Geological Survey. Bulletin (ISSN 0077-9628) & New Zealand Geological Survey Paleontological Bulletin (ISSN 0114-2283); Which was formerly: New Zealand. Department of Scientific and Industrial Research. Paleontological Bulletin (ISSN 0078-8589).
Description: Monographs about New Zealand regional geology, paleontology, basin studies, petrology, minerals, and volcanoes.

559   NZ   ISSN 1171-9184
▼**INSTITUTE OF GEOLOGICAL AND NUCLEAR SCIENCES. SCIENCE REPORTS.** 1992. irreg. price varies. Institute of Geological and Nuclear Sciences Ltd., P.O. Box 30-368, Lower Hutt, New Zealand.
TEL 64-4-569-9059. FAX 64-4-569-5016.
Description: Specific topics in earth and isotope sciences.

558   CK
INSTITUTO NACIONAL DE INVESTIGACIONES EN GEOCIENCIAS, MINERIA Y QUIMICA. INFORME ANUAL DE ACTIVIDADES. a., latest 1991. Instituto Nacional de Investigaciones en Geociencias, Mineria y Quimica, Diagonal 53 No.34-53, Apdo. Aereo 4865, Bogota D.E., Colombia.
Formerly: Instituto Nacional de Investigaciones Geologico Mineras. Informe Anual de Actividades.

558   CK
INSTITUTO NACIONAL DE INVESTIGACIONES EN GEOCIENCIAS, MINERIA Y QUIMICA. PUBLICACIONES GEOLOGICAS ESPECIALES DEL INGEOMINAS. (Text in English or Spanish) 1978. irreg., no.19, 1993. Instituto Nacional de Investigaciones en Geociencias, Mineria y Quimica, Diagonal 53 No. 34-53, Apdo. Aereo 4865, Bogota D.E., Colombia. **Document type:** monographic series.
Formerly: Instituto Nacional de Investigaciones Geologico Mineras. Publicaciones Geologicas Especiales del Ingeominas.

550   RM   ISSN 0250-2933
INSTITUTUL DE GEOLOGIE SI GEOFIZICA. ANUARUL. (Text in English, French and Rumanian; summaries in English) 1908. a. price varies. Institutul de Geologie si Geofizica, Str. Caransebes, Nr. 1, 78344 Bucharest, Rumania. **Indexed:** Bull.Signal., Ref.Zh.

550   RM
INSTITUTUL DE GEOLOGIE SI GEOFIZICA. STUDII TEHNICE SI ECONOMICE. (Text in English, French and Rumanian; summaries in English, French and German) 1933. irreg. price varies. Institutul de Geologie si Geofizica, Str. Caransebes, Nr. 1, 78344 Bucharest, Rumania. **Indexed:** Chem.Abstr., Ref.Zh.

624.151   FR   ISSN 0074-1612
TA705   CODEN: BIEGB6
INTERNATIONAL ASSOCIATION OF ENGINEERING GEOLOGY. BULLETIN. (Text in French, English) 1970. s-a. 450 F. A I G I, Laboratoire Central des Ponts et Chaussees, 58 bd. Lefebvre, 75732 Paris Cedex 15, France. FAX 40-43-54-98. TELEX LCPARI 200361 F. Ed. L. Primel. adv.; bk.rev. circ. 4,500. **Indexed:** AESIS, Chem.Abstr., Geotech.Abstr. **Document type:** bulletin.
—BLDSC (2586.725000); SWETS; CASDDS.

551   US   ISSN 0740-5162
TP325   CODEN: PITCEM
INTERNATIONAL COAL TESTING CONFERENCE; proceedings of the conference. 1981. a. $100. Standard Laboratories, Inc., Box 1970, Ashland, KY 41105. TEL 606-325-1970. FAX 606-325-2689. Ed. Tamra H. Broam. circ. 1,000. (back issues avail.) **Document type:** proceedings.
—BLDSC (4538.698000); CASDDS.

551   US   ISSN 0020-6814
QE1   CODEN: IGREAP
INTERNATIONAL GEOLOGY REVIEW. (Translation of selected papers from Russian journals) 1958. m. $849 (foreign $905). (International Union of Geological Science) V.H. Winston & Son, Inc., c/o Bellwether Publishing, Ltd., 8640 Guilford Rd., Ste. 200, Columbia, MD 21046. TEL 410-290-3870. FAX 410-290-8726. Eds. Kevin Burke, Brian Skinner. bibl.; charts; illus.; stat.; index. circ. 500. (back issues avail.; reprint service avail. from CCC) **Indexed:** AESIS, Chem.Abstr., Deep Sea Res.& Oceanogr.Abstr., E&P Hlth. (1993-), Gas Process.& Ppl. (1993-), Geo.Abstr., GeoRef., INIS Atomind., Off.Tech. (1993-), Petrol.Abstr. (1961-). **Document type:** academic/scholarly publication.
—BLDSC (4540.500000); Faxon; UnCover; SWETS. **CCC.**
Description: Presents original papers in English from Enlish- and foreign-language journals.

551 622.33   NE   ISSN 0166-5162
TN799.9   CODEN: IJCGDE
INTERNATIONAL JOURNAL OF COAL GEOLOGY. (Text in English) 1980. 8/yr. (in 2 vols.; 4 nos./vol.). fl.862($466) (effective 1994). Elsevier Science B.V., P.O. Box 211, 1000 AE Amsterdam, Netherlands. TEL 31-20-5803911.
FAX 31-20-5803598. TELEX 18582 ESPA NL. (Subscr. in U.S. and Canada to: Elsevier Science Inc., Box 882, Madison Sq. Sta., New York, NY 10159. TEL 212-989-5800. FAX 212-633-3990) Ed. R.R. Dutcher. adv.; bk.rev.; charts; illus. (also avail. in microform from UMI; back issues avail.) **Indexed:** AESIS, Chem.Abstr., Curr.Cont., E&P Hlth. (1993-), Energy Info.Abstr., Gas Process.& Ppl. (1993-), Geo.Abstr., Ind.Sci.Rev., Off.Tech. (1993-), Petrol.Abstr. (1982-), Sci.Cit.Ind. **Document type:** academic/scholarly publication.
—BLDSC (4542.172200); EI; Faxon; UnCover; SWETS; CASDDS. **CCC.**
Description: Covers basic and applied aspects of the geology and petrology of coal.
Refereed Serial

551.44   IT   ISSN 0020-7691
GB601.A1   CODEN: ISPEAV
INTERNATIONAL JOURNAL OF SPELEOLOGY. (Text in English, French and German) 1964. q. (International Union of Speleology) International Journal of Speleology, c/o Dept. Biologia Animale Dell Uomo, Viale dell'Universita 32, 00185 Rome, Italy. Ed.Bd. adv.; bk.rev.; charts; illus. circ. 600. **Indexed:** Biol.Abstr., Chem.Abstr. **Document type:** academic/scholarly publication.

INTERNATIONAL OIL AND GAS DEVELOPMENT YEARBOOK. see *PETROLEUM AND GAS*

INTERNATIONAL OIL SCOUTS ASSOCIATION. OFFICIAL PUBLICATION. see *PETROLEUM AND GAS*

INTERNATIONAL OIL SCOUTS ASSOCIATION DIRECTORY. see *BUSINESS AND ECONOMICS — Trade And Industrial Directories*

INTERNATIONAL PEAT JOURNAL. see *MINES AND MINING INDUSTRY*

INTERNATIONAL PEAT SOCIETY. BULLETIN/INTERNATIONALE MOOR- UND TORF-GESELLSCHAFT. MITTEILUNGEN. see *MINES AND MINING INDUSTRY*

551.3   GW   ISSN 0074-7904
INTERNATIONAL SEDIMENTOLOGICAL CONGRESS. GUIDEBOOK. Represents International Sedimentological Congress. Proceedings) 1946. quadrennial. DM.48. Institut fuer Sediment Forschung Postfach 103020, 69020 Heidleberg, Germany.

INTERNATIONAL SOCIETY FOR ROCK MECHANICS. CONGRESS. PROCEEDINGS. see *ENGINEERING — Civil Engineering*

555   IR   ISSN 0075-0484
CODEN: IGSRB2
IRAN. GEOLOGICAL SURVEY. REPORT. 1964. irreg. price varies. Geological Survey, Box 1555, Teheran, Iran. circ. 2,000. **Document type:** academic/scholarly publication.

EARTH SCIENCES — GEOLOGY

551　　　　　　IQ
　　　　　　　　CODEN: GSIJAN
IRAQI GEOLOGICAL JOURNAL. (Text in Arabic, English) 1968. a. $32. (Union of Iraqi Geologists) Al-Fraheedi Geoscience Bureau, P.O. Box 3038 Alwiya, Baghdad 12902, Iraq. TEL 8872518. Ed. Muzahim A. Basi. bk.rev.; charts; illus. circ. 500. **Document type:** academic/scholarly publication.
　Formerly (until vol.23, 1992): Geological Society of Iraq. Journal (ISSN 0533-8301)

IRISH JOURNAL OF EARTH SCIENCES. see *EARTH SCIENCES*

550　　　　　　AT　　ISSN 1038-4871
QE511.4
▼**THE ISLAND ARC.** (Text in English) 1992. q. Aus.$150 (foreign $105). (Geological Society of Japan, JA) Blackwell Scientific Publications (Australia) Pty. Ltd., P.O. Box 378, Carlton, Vic 3053, Australia. TEL 03-347-0300. FAX 03-347-5001. Eds. M. Komatsu, K. Kodama, A. Taira. adv.: page $680; trim 275 x 210. circ. 1,000.
　—UMI. **CCC.**
　Description: Focuses on the geological, geochemical and geophysical problems related to modern and ancient plate convergent processes, of the western Pacific Rim in particular.

555　　　　　　IS　　ISSN 0075-1200
QE319.I8　　　　　　CODEN: ISGBBC
ISRAEL. GEOLOGICAL SURVEY. BULLETIN. Key Title: Bulletin - Geological Survey of Israel. (Text in English; summaries in Hebrew) 1956. irreg., no.83, 1992. price varies. Geological Survey Library, 30 Malkhe Israel St., Jerusalem 95501, Israel. TEL 972-2-314266. Ed.Bd. circ. 1,200. **Indexed:** Biol.Abstr., Deep Sea Res.& Oceanogr.Abstr. **Document type:** bulletin.

ISRAEL. GEOLOGICAL SURVEY. CURRENT BIBLIOGRAPHY OF MIDDLE EAST GEOLOGY. see *EARTH SCIENCES — Abstracting, Bibliographies, Statistics*

555　　　　　　IS　　ISSN 0333-6425
QE48.I75
ISRAEL. GEOLOGICAL SURVEY. CURRENT RESEARCH. (Text in English) 1975. a. $10. Geological Survey, 30 Malkhe Israel Street, Jerusalem 95 501, Israel.
　—BLDSC (4137.350000).

ISRAEL JOURNAL OF EARTH SCIENCES. see *EARTH SCIENCES*

551 549　　　　RU　　ISSN 0202-7348
ITOGI NAUKI I TEKHNIKI: GEOKHIMIYA - MINERALOGIYA - PETROGRAFIYA. irreg., vols.15-16, 1989. price varies. Vsesoyuznyi Institut Nauchno-Tekhnicheskoi Informatsii (VINITI), Baltiiskaya ul. 14, Moscow A-219, Russia. (Subscr. to: Mezhdunarodnaya Kniga, Dimitrova ul. 39, 113095 Moscow, Russia)
　—BLDSC (0047.985000).

552　　　　　　RU　　ISSN 0302-542X
TN4　　　　　　　　CODEN: IMGIAO
ITOGI NAUKI I TEKHNIKI: MESTOROZHDENIYA GORYUCHIKH POLEZNYKH ISKOPAEMYKH. irreg., vol.16, 1988. 5.40 Rub. Vsesoyuznyi Institut Nauchno-Tekhnicheskoi Informatsii (VINITI), Baltiiskaya ul. 14, Moscow A-219, Russia. (Subscr. to: Mezhdunarodnaya Kniga, Dimitrova ul. 39, 113095 Moscow, Russia) **Indexed:** Chem.Abstr.
　—BLDSC (0108.065000).

551　　　　　　RU　　ISSN 0202-7372
QE1　　　　　　　　CODEN: INOGBW
ITOGI NAUKI I TEKHNIKI: OBSHCHAYA GEOLOGIYA. irreg., vols.24-26, 1989. price varies. Vsesoyuznyi Institut Nauchno-Tekhnicheskoi Informatsii (VINITI), Baltiiskaya ul. 14, Moscow A-219, Russia. **Indexed:** Chem.Abstr.
　—BLDSC (0126.705300).

IVORY COAST. DIRECTION DES MINES ET DE LA GEOLOGIE. RAPPORT PROVISOIRE SUR LES ACTIVITES DU SECTEUR. see *MINES AND MINING INDUSTRY*

550　　　　　　RU　　ISSN 0016-7762
QE1　　　　　　　　CODEN: IVUGAF
IZVESTIYA VYSSHIKH UCHEBNYKH ZAVEDENII. SERIYA GEOLOGIYA I RAZVEDKA. 1958. m. 34.80 Rub. (Moskovskii Institut Geologii i Razvedki) Izdatel'stvo Vysshaya Shkola, Prospekt Marksa 18, 103009 Moscow K-9, Russia. (Subscr. to: Mezhdunarodnaya Kniga, Moscow, G-200, Russia) (Co-sponsor: Ministerstvo Mysshego i Srednego Spetsial'nogo Obrazovaniya) Ed.Bd. bk.rev.; charts; illus.; maps. circ. 2,500. **Indexed:** AESIS, Chem.Abstr., INIS Atomind., Petrol.Abstr., Ref.Zh.
　—BLDSC (0077.430000); CASDDS. **CCC.**

550　　　　　　JA　　ISSN 0911-0143
JIBAN KOGAKU KENKYUJO HOKOKU/GEOTECHNICAL RESEARCH INSTITUTE. TECHNICAL REPORTS. (Text in Japanese; summaries in English, Japanese) 1985. a. Nishinippon Kogyo Daigaku, Jiban Kogaku Kenkyujo - Nishinippon Institute of Technology, Geotechnical Research Institute, 1633, Aratsu, Kanda-machi, Miyako-gun, Fukuoka-ken 800-03, Japan.

550　　　　　　JA　　ISSN 0913-7882
JIOTEKISUTAIRU SHINPOJUMU HAPPYO RONBUNSHU/SYMPOSIUM ON INTERNATIONAL GEOTEXTILE SOCIETY. PROCEEDINGS. (Text and summaries in English, Japanese) 1986. a. Kokusai Jiotekisutairu Gakkai, Nihon Shibu - International Geotextile Society, Japan Chapter, Doshitsu Kogakkai, 2-23, Kanda Awaji-cho, Chiyoda-ku, Tokyo 101, Japan.

551 551.31 551.4　IC　ISSN 0449-0576
GB2496.I3　　　　　　CODEN: JOKUA3
JOEKULL. (Text in English and Icelandic) 1951. a. $35 membership. Joeklarannsoknafelag Islands - Iceland Glaciological Society, Science Institute, University of Iceland, Dunhaga 3, 107 Reykjavik, Iceland. FAX 354-1-28911. TELEX 2307 ISINFO IS. (Subscr. to: Box 5128, Reykjavik, Iceland) (Co-sponsor: Jardfraedafelag Islands - Geoscience Society of Iceland) Eds. Helgi Bjoernsson, Leo Kristjansson. bk.rev. circ. 1,100. (back issues avail.) **Indexed:** Deep Sea Res.& Oceanogr.Abstr., Geo.Abstr. **Document type:** academic/scholarly publication.

551　　　　　　US　　ISSN 0075-3890
　　　　　　　　　　CODEN: JHUGAU
JOHNS HOPKINS UNIVERSITY STUDIES IN GEOLOGY. 1922. irreg., no.21, 1973. price varies. (Johns Hopkins University, Department of Earth and Planetary Sciences) Johns Hopkins University Press, 701 W. 40th St., Ste. 275, Baltimore, MD 21211. TEL 410-516-6900. FAX 410-516-6998. (reprint service avail. from UMI) **Indexed:** GeoRef.
　Refereed Serial

556　　　　　　UK　　ISSN 0899-5362
QE320　　　　　　　CODEN: JOASEJ
JOURNAL OF AFRICAN EARTH SCIENCES (AND THE MIDDLE EAST). 1983. 8/yr. £437($675) (effective 1994). Elsevier Science Ltd., Pergamon, P.O. Box 800, Kidlington, Oxford OX5 1DX, England. TEL 44-865-843000. FAX 44-865-843010. (Subscr. in U.S. and Canada to: Elsevier Science, 660 White Plains Rd., Tarrytown, NY 10591-5153. TEL 914-524-9200. FAX 914-333-2444) Ed. C.A. Kogbe. (also avail. in microfilm from UMI; back issues avail.) **Indexed:** ASCA, Bibl.& Ind.Geol., Chem.Abstr., Curr.Cont., Deep Sea Res.& Oceanogr.Abstr., E&P Hlth. (1993-), Gas Process.& Ppl. (1993-), Geo.Abstr., Off.Tech. (1993-), Petrol.Abstr. (1989-). **Document type:** academic/scholarly publication.
　—BLDSC (4919.989000); UnCover; SWETS; UMI; CASDDS. **CCC.**
　Formerly (until 1987): Journal of African Earth Sciences (ISSN 0731-7247)
　Refereed Serial

JOURNAL OF COASTAL RESEARCH; an international forum for the littoral sciences. see *EARTH SCIENCES — Oceanography*

JOURNAL OF GEODYNAMICS. see *EARTH SCIENCES — Geophysics*

550.07　　　　　US　　ISSN 0022-1368
QE40　　　　　　　CODEN: JGEEA5
JOURNAL OF GEOLOGICAL EDUCATION. 1951. 5/yr. $33 (foreign $37). National Association of Geology Teachers, Inc., Box 5443, Bellingham, WA 98227-5443. TEL 206-650-3587. FAX 206-650-7295. Ed. J.H. Shea. adv.; bk.rev.; abstr.; illus.; index, cum.index: 1951-1979. circ. 2,800. (also avail. in microform from UMI; back issues avail.; reprint service avail. from UMI) **Indexed:** C.I.J.E., Chem.Abstr., Cont.Pg.Educ., Educ.Ind., Excerp.Med., Geo.Abstr., GeoRef., Ind.Sci.Rev. **Document type:** academic/scholarly publication.
　—BLDSC (4992.400000); Faxon; UnCover; SWETS; UMI.
　Description: Fosters improvement in teaching of earth sciences at all levels of instruction, emphasizes the cultural and environmental significance of the field, and disseminates information on related topics of interest.

551　　　　　　US　　ISSN 0022-1376
QE1　　　　　　　　CODEN: JGEOAZ
JOURNAL OF GEOLOGY. 1893. bi-m. $45 to individuals; institutions $78; students $20. University of Chicago Press, Journals Division, 5720 S. Woodlawn Ave., Chicago, IL 60637. TEL 312-753-3347. FAX 312-753-0811. (Subscr. to: Box 37005, Chicago, IL 60637) Eds. Alfred T. Anderson, Jr., Robert C. Newton. adv.; bk.rev.; illus.; index, cum.index. circ. 2,400. (also avail. in microform from UMI,PMC; reprint service avail. from ISI,UMI) **Indexed:** A.S.& T.Ind., AESIS, Biol.Abstr., Br.Geol.Lit., Chem.Abstr., Curr.Cont., Curr.Tit.Ocean., Deep Sea Res.& Oceanogr.Abstr., E&P Hlth. (1993-), Gas Process.& Ppl. (1993-), Geo.Abstr., GeoRef., Geotech.Abstr., Ind.Sci.Rev., INIS Atomind., Int.Aerosp.Abstr., Ocean.Abstr., Off.Tech. (1993-), Petrol.Abstr. (1961-), Phys.Ber., Sci.Abstr., Sci.Cit.Ind., Sel.Water Res.Abstr., So.Pac.Per.Ind., Soils & Fert. **Document type:** academic/scholarly publication.
　—BLDSC (4993.000000); Faxon; UnCover; SWETS; UMI; CASDDS. **CCC.**
　Refereed Serial

538.7　　　　　JA　　ISSN 0022-1392
QC801　　　　　　　CODEN: JGEGAB
JOURNAL OF GEOMAGNETISM AND GEOELECTRICITY. (Text in English) 1949. m. 47000 Yen. (Nihon Chikyu Denki Jiki Gakkai - Society of Geomagnetism and Earth, Planetary and Space Sciences) Terra Scientific Publishing Company, 302 Jiyugaoka Komatsu Bldg., 24-17 Midorigaoka 2-chome, Meguro-ku, Tokyo 152, Japan. FAX 03-3718-4403. Eds. T. Oguchi, T. Yukatake. adv.; bk.rev. circ. 1,500. **Indexed:** Chem.Abstr., Curr.Cont., Deep Sea Res.& Oceanogr.Abstr., Geo.Abstr., GeoRef., Ind.Sci.Rev., INIS Atomind., JTA, Meteor.& Geoastrophys.Abstr., Petrol.Abstr., Sci.Abstr., Sci.Cit.Ind.
　—BLDSC (4994.000000); Faxon; UnCover; SWETS; UMI; CASDDS.

JOURNAL OF GEOTECHNICAL ENGINEERING. see *ENGINEERING — Civil Engineering*

551.31　　　　　UK　　ISSN 0022-1430
GB2401　　　　　　　CODEN: JOGLAO
JOURNAL OF GLACIOLOGY. 1947. 3/yr. $270 (effective 1994). International Glaciological Society, Lensfield Rd., Cambridge CB2 1ER, England. TEL 0223-355974. FAX 0223-336543. abstr.; illus. circ. 1,500. **Indexed:** Chem.Abstr., Curr.Cont., Deep Sea Res.& Oceanogr.Abstr., Geo.Abstr., GeoRef., Ind.Sci.Rev., Meteor. & Geoastrophys.Abstr., Sci.Abstr., Sci.Cit.Ind., Sel.Water Res.Abstr. **Document type:** academic/scholarly publication.
　—BLDSC (4996.000000); Faxon; UnCover; SWETS; CASDDS.

551　　　　　　II　　ISSN 0970-0951
QE319.H5
JOURNAL OF HIMALAYAN GEOLOGY. (Text in English) 1990. s-a. $100. (Wadia Institute of Himalayan Geology) Indian Petroleum Publishers, 100-9 Naishville Rd., Dehra Dun 248001, India. (Dist. by: Hindustan Publishing Corp., 6-U.B. Jawahar Nagar, Delhi 110007, India. TEL 9-11-2915059. FAX 9-11-6863511) Ed. V.C. Thakur.

EARTH SCIENCES — GEOLOGY

551   US   ISSN 0263-4929
QE475.A2   CODEN: JMGEER
JOURNAL OF METAMORPHIC GEOLOGY. 1982. bi-m. $500 to individuals; institutions $435. Blackwell Scientific Publications, Inc., 238 Main St., Ste. 501, Cambridge, MA 02142-1413. TEL 617-876-7000. FAX 617-876-7022. Ed.Bd. adv.; bk.rev.; bibl.; charts; illus. circ. 364. **Indexed:** AESIS, Chem.Abstr., Curr.Cont., Deep Sea Res.& Oceanogr.Abstr., Mineral.Abstr. **Document type:** academic/scholarly publication.
—BLDSC (5018.500000); Faxon; UnCover; SWETS; UMI; CASDDS. **CCC.**
Description: Covers entire range of metamorphic studies from the scale of the individual crystal to that of the lithospheric plate; includes geochemistry.
Refereed Serial

551 549 553   JA   ISSN 0914-9783
CODEN: GANKEV
JOURNAL OF MINERALOGY, PETROLOGY AND ECONOMIC GEOLOGY. (Text in English, Japanese; summaries in English) 1929. m. 11000 Yen($40) Japanese Association of Mineralogists, Petrologists and Economic Geologists, Tohoku Daigaku Rigakubu, Aoba, Aramaki, Aoba-ku, Sendai-shi, Miyagi-ken 980, Japan. FAX 22-224-3852. Ed. Mizuhiko Akizuki. adv.; bk.rev. circ. 1,300. (back issues avail.) **Indexed:** Chem.Abstr., GeoRef., INIS Atomind., Jap.Per.Ind., JTA, Mineral.Abstr.
—BLDSC (5020.144000). **CCC.**
Formerly: Japanese Association of Mineralogists, Petrologists and Economic Geologists. Journal (ISSN 0021-4825)
Description: Publishes original scientific papers for researchers and professionals in mineralogy, petrology, and economic geology.

JOURNAL OF MINING RESEARCH. see *MINES AND MINING INDUSTRY*

JOURNAL OF MINING SCIENCE. see *MINES AND MINING INDUSTRY*

JOURNAL OF PETROLEUM SCIENCE AND ENGINEERING. see *PETROLEUM AND GAS*

552   UK   ISSN 0022-3530
QE420   CODEN: JPTGAD
JOURNAL OF PETROLOGY. 1960. 6/yr. £170($295) (effective 1994). Oxford University Press, Oxford Journals, Walton St., Oxford OX2 6DP, England. TEL 0865-56767. FAX 0865-56646. TELEX 837330-OXPRES-G. (U.S. subscr. to: Oxford University Press Inc., 2001 Evans Rd., Cary, NC 27513. TEL 919-677-0977) Eds. B.G.J. Upton, B.M. Wilson. adv.; bk.rev.; bibl.; charts; illus.; index, cum.index every 4 yrs. circ. 1,200. (also avail. in microform from UMI) **Indexed:** AESIS, Br.Ceram.Abstr., Br.Geol.Lit., Cadscan, Chem.Abstr., Curr.Cont., Deep Sea Res.& Oceanogr.Abstr., Geo.Abstr., GeoRef., Ind.Sci.Rev., Lead Abstr., Mineral.Abstr., Sci.Abstr., Sci.Cit.Ind., Zincscan. **Document type:** academic/scholarly publication.
—BLDSC (5031.200000); Faxon; UnCover; SWETS; UMI; CASDDS. **CCC.**
Description: Presents papers on the physics and chemistry of rocks, experimental petrology and mineralogy, rock-forming minerals and their paragenesis, microstructure of rocks, and isotope geochemistry and geochronology as applied to problems of petrogenesis.

551   UK   ISSN 0743-9547
JOURNAL OF SOUTH-EAST ASIAN EARTH SCIENCES. 1987. 8/yr. £319($490) (effective 1994). Elsevier Science Ltd., Pergamon, P.O. Box 800, Kidlington, Oxford OX5 1DX, England. TEL 44-865-843000. FAX 44-865-843010. (Subscr. in U.S. and Canada to: Elsevier Science, 660 White Plains Rd., Tarrytown, NY 10591-5153. TEL 914-524-9200. FAX 914-333-2444) Eds. B.K. Tan, T.T. Khoo. (also avail. in microfilm from UMI; back issues avail.) **Indexed:** AESIS, E&P Hlth. (1993-), Gas Process.& Ppl. (1993-), Geo.Abstr., Off.Tech. (1993-), Petrol.Abstr. (1989-). **Document type:** academic/scholarly publication.
—BLDSC (5066.006000); Faxon; UnCover; SWETS; UMI. **CCC.**
Description: Publishes research results on regional geology, economic geology, geochemistry, petroleum geology and petrology, palaeontology, geophysics, tectonics, geomorphology, Quaternary geology and analysis of sedimentary basins.
Refereed Serial

551.44   US   ISSN 0022-4693
JOURNAL OF SPELEAN HISTORY. 1968. q. $7 to individuals; libraries $6. American Spelean History Association, c/o Jack H. Speece, 711 E. Atlantic Ave., Altoona, PA 16602. TEL 814-946-3155. Ed. James Hedges. adv.; bk.rev.; bibl.; charts; illus. circ. 150. (also avail. in microfiche; reprint service avail.) **Indexed:** GeoRef. **Document type:** academic/scholarly publication.
Description: Exploration of caves.

551   UK   ISSN 0191-8141
QE601   CODEN: JSGEDY
JOURNAL OF STRUCTURAL GEOLOGY. 1979. 12/yr. £414($640) (effective 1994). Elsevier Science Ltd., Pergamon, P.O. Box 800, Kidlington, Oxford OX5 1DX, England. TEL 44-865-843000. FAX 44-865-843010. (Subscr. in U.S. and Canada to: Elsevier Science, 660 White Plains Rd., Tarrytown, NY 10591-5153. TEL 914-524-9200. FAX 914-333-2444) Ed. Susan H. Treagus. adv. circ. 2,000. (also avail. in microfilm from UMI) **Indexed:** AESIS, Appl.Mech.Rev., Chem.Abstr., Curr.Cont., Deep Sea Res.& Oceanogr.Abstr., E&P Hlth. (1993-), Gas Process.& Ppl. (1993-), Geo.Abstr., GeoRef., Ind.Sci.Rev., Off.Tech. (1993-), Petrol.Abstr. (1980-), Sci.Abstr. **Document type:** academic/scholarly publication.
—BLDSC (5066.878000); EI; Faxon; UnCover; SWETS; UMI; CASDDS. **CCC.**
Description: Covers all aspects and processes of deformation in rocks, including folds, fracture and fabrics, structural associations in orogenic rocks, strike slip zones, and related phenomena.
Refereed Serial

JOURNAL OF VOLCANOLOGY AND GEOTHERMAL RESEARCH; an international journal on the geophysical, geochemical, petrological and economic aspects of geothermal and volcanological research. see *EARTH SCIENCES — Geophysics*

551 574   CI   ISSN 0351-3297
CODEN: RJAZBM
JUGOSLAVENSKA AKADEMIJA ZNANOSTI I UMJETNOSTI. RAZRED ZA PRIRODNE ZNANOSTI. RAD. (Text and summaries in Croatian, English, French and German) 1866. a. $30. Jugoslavenska Akademija Znanosti i Umjetnosti, Razred za Prirodne Znanosti - Yugoslav Academy of Sciences and Arts, Brace Kavurica 1, 41000 Zagreb, Croatia. **Indexed:** Biol.Abstr.

551   NE   ISSN 0165-7720
K.N.G.M.G. NIEUWSBRIEF. 1975. 10/yr. membership. Koninklijk Nederlands Geologisch Mijnbouwkundig Genootschap - Royal Geological and Mining Society of the Netherlands, P.O. Box 157, 2000 AD Haarlem, Netherlands. TEL 21-23-300300. FAX 31-23-367064. Eds. C.W. Dubelaar, J.C. Blom. adv.; bk.rev.; bibl. circ. 2,000. **Document type:** newsletter.

551 551.4   CI   ISSN 0454-5478
GB608.67   CODEN: KJCIA5
K R S JUGOSLAVIJE/CARSUS JUGOSLAVIAE. (Text and summaries in Croatian, English, French and German) 1957. q. $28. Jugoslavenska Akademija Znanosti i Umjetnosti - Yugoslav Academy of Sciences and Arts, Brace Kavurica 1, 41000 Zagreb, Croatia. **Indexed:** Biol.Abstr., GeoRef.

557   US   ISSN 0097-4471
CODEN: KSGBAX
KANSAS GEOLOGICAL SURVEY. BULLETIN. 1913. irreg., no.228, 1989. price varies. Geological Survey, 1930 Constant Ave., Campus West, University of Kansas, Lawrence, KS 66047. TEL 913-864-3965. illus.; maps. **Document type:** bulletin.
—CASDDS.

557   US   ISSN 0731-616X
KANSAS GEOLOGICAL SURVEY. EDUCATIONAL SERIES. 1973. irreg., no.10, 1990. price varies. Geological Survey, 1930 Constant Ave., Campus West, University of Kansas, Lawrence, KS 66047. TEL 913-864-3965. **Indexed:** GeoRef.

551   US   ISSN 0731-2784
KENTUCKY GEOLOGICAL SURVEY. ANNUAL REPORT. 1979. a. Kentucky Geological Survey, 228 Mining and Mineral Resources Bldg., University of Kentucky, Lexington, KY 40506-0107. TEL 606-257-5500. Ed. Donald W. Hutcheson.
Description: Describes major research and service activities of the Kentucky Geological Survey during the preceding year.

557   US   ISSN 0075-5575
KENTUCKY GEOLOGICAL SURVEY. GUIDEBOOK TO GEOLOGICAL FIELD TRIPS. 1952. irreg. price varies. Kentucky Geological Survey, 228 Mining and Mineral Resources Bldg., University of Kentucky, Lexington, KY 40506-0107. TEL 606-257-5500. Ed. Donald W. Hutcheson. **Document type:** monographic series.
Description: Guidebooks for the annual Field Conference of the Geological Society of Kentucky.

557   US   ISSN 0075-5559
KENTUCKY GEOLOGICAL SURVEY. SERIES 11. BULLETIN. 1879. irreg., no.3, 1992. price varies. Kentucky Geological Survey, 228 Mining and Mineral Resources Bldg., University of Kentucky, Lexington, KY 40506-0107. TEL 606-257-5500. Ed. Donald W. Hutcheson. **Document type:** bulletin.
Description: Detailed treatment of a subject and extensive interpretation of geologic data.

557   US   ISSN 0075-5567
CODEN: KGUCBN
KENTUCKY GEOLOGICAL SURVEY. SERIES 11. COUNTY REPORT. 1912. irreg., no.2, 1982. price varies. Kentucky Geological Survey, 228 Mining and Mineral Resources Bldg., University of Kentucky, Lexington, KY 40506-0107. TEL 606-257-5500. Ed. Donald W. Hutcheson. **Document type:** monographic series.
Description: Summary of the geology and mineral resources of individual counties.

557   US   ISSN 0075-5583
KENTUCKY GEOLOGICAL SURVEY. SERIES 11. INFORMATION CIRCULAR. 1951. irreg., no.43, 1993. price varies. Kentucky Geological Survey, 228 Mining and Mineral Resources Bldg., University of Kentucky, Lexington, KY 40506-0107. TEL 606-257-5500. Ed. Donald W. Hutcheson.
Description: Mainly data compilations, with some interpretation provided.

551   US
KENTUCKY GEOLOGICAL SURVEY. SERIES 11. MAP AND CHART SERIES. 1989. irreg., no.5, 1993. price varies. Kentucky Geological Survey, 228 Mining and Mineral Resources Bldg., University of Kentucky, Lexington, KY 40506-0107. TEL 606-257-5500. Ed. Donald W. Hutcheson.
Description: Includes maps, cross sections, and charts that are larger than 8.5 by 11 inches.

557   US   ISSN 0075-5591
CODEN: KUSRAJ
KENTUCKY GEOLOGICAL SURVEY. SERIES 11. REPORT OF INVESTIGATIONS. 1949. irreg., no.6, 1992. price varies. Kentucky Geological Survey, 228 Mining and Mineral Resources Bldg., University of Kentucky, Lexington, KY 40506-0107. TEL 606-257-5500. Ed. Donald W. Hutcheson.
—BLDSC (7557.720000); UnCover.
Description: Reports current research findings.

557   US   ISSN 0075-5605
CODEN: KGRSAL
KENTUCKY GEOLOGICAL SURVEY. SERIES 11. REPRINTS. 1925. irreg., no.38, 1993. price varies. Kentucky Geological Survey, 228 Mining and Mineral Resources Bldg., University of Kentucky, Lexington, KY 40506-0107. TEL 606-257-5500. Ed. Donald W. Hutcheson.
Description: Reprints of articles dealing with the geology or mineral resources of Kentucky.

557   US   ISSN 0075-5613
QE115   CODEN: KUSSBN
KENTUCKY GEOLOGICAL SURVEY. SERIES 11. SPECIAL PUBLICATION. 1953. irreg., no.19, 1993. price varies. Kentucky Geological Survey, 228 Mining and Mineral Resources Bldg., University of Kentucky, Lexington, KY 40506-0107. TEL 606-257-5500. Ed. Donald W. Hutcheson.
—UnCover.
Description: Covers the geology of Kentucky parks and scenic areas and other reports.

557   US   ISSN 0075-5621
QE115   CODEN: KGTSAV
KENTUCKY GEOLOGICAL SURVEY. SERIES 11. THESIS SERIES. 1966. irreg., no.5, 1993. price varies. Kentucky Geological Survey, 228 Mining and Mineral Resources Bldg., University of Kentucky, Lexington, KY 40506-0107. TEL 606-257-5500. Ed. Donald W. Hutcheson.
Description: Masters and doctoral theses about Kentucky geology.

EARTH SCIENCES — GEOLOGY

KISHO KINZOKU KOBUTSU SHIGEN NO FUZON JOKYO CHOSA HOKOKUSHO/INVESTIGATION OF UNDERGROUND RARE METALS. see *METALLURGY*

KOBIE, REVISTA DE BELLAS ARTES Y CIENCIAS: SERIE CIENCIAS NATURALES. see *SCIENCES: COMPREHENSIVE WORKS*

551   JA   ISSN 0389-0295
KOCHI UNIVERSITY. FACULTY OF SCIENCE. MEMOIRS. SERIES E, GEOLOGY. (Text in English) 1980. a. Kochi University, Faculty of Science - Kochi Daigaku Rigakubu, 5-1, Akebonocho 2-chome, Kochi-shi, Kochi-ken 780, Japan.
—BLDSC (5597.838000).

551   DK   ISSN 0906-0294
KOEBENHAVNS UNIVERSITET. GEOLOGISK CENTRALINSTITUT. AARSBERETNING. 1970. a. free. Koebenhavns Universitet, Geologisk Institut, Oester Voldgade 10, DK-1350 Copenhagen K, Denmark. TEL 33-11-22-32. circ. 525 (controlled).

551   JA
KOIKI CHISHITSU KOZO CHOSA HOKOKUSHO/GEOLOGICAL STRUCTURE SURVEY OF JAPAN. (Text in Japanese) 1971. a. Shigen Enerugicho - Agency of Natural Resources and Energy, 3-1, Kasumigaseki 1-chome, Chiyoda-ku, Tokyo 100, Japan. **Document type:** government publication.

549   KZ
KOMPLEKSNOE ISPOL'ZOVANIE MINERAL'NOGO SYR'YA. 1978. m. 43.20 Rub. (Akademiya Nauk Kazakhstana) Gylym, Ul. Pushkina 111-113, 480100 Alma-Ata, Kazakhstan. TEL 3272-611877. **Indexed:** Chem.Abstr., INIS Atomind.

551 622   NE   ISSN 0075-6741
QE1   CODEN: VGMGAD
KONINKLIJK NEDERLANDS GEOLOGISCH MIJNBOUWKUNDIG GENOOTSCHAP. VERHANDELINGEN. (Before 1969 published in 2 series: Geologische Serie, and Mijnbouwkundige Serie) (Text in English) 1912. irreg., no. 32, 1980. price varies. (Koninklijk Nederlands Geologisch Mijnbouwkundig Genootschap - Royal Geological and Mining Society of the Netherlands) Kluwer Academic Publishers, Postbus 17, 3300 AA Dordrecht, Netherlands. TEL 31-78-334911. FAX 31-78-334254. TELEX 29245 KAPG NL. (Dist. by: Kluwer Academic Publishers Group, P.O. Box 322, 3300 AH Dordrecht, Netherlands. TEL 31-78-524400; N. America dist. addr.: Box 358, Accord Sta., Hingham, MA 02018-0358. TEL 617-871-6600) **Document type:** monographic series.
—CCC.
Refereed Serial

552   XR   ISSN 0454-5524
CODEN: KRYSAV
KRYSTALINIKUM; contributions to the geology and petrology of crystalline complexes. (Text in English) vol. 11, 1975. irreg., vol. 20, 1989. price varies. Academia, Publishing House of the Czechoslovak Academy of Sciences, Vodickova 40, 112 29 Prague 1, Czech Republic. TEL 23-63-065. (Dist. in Western countries by: E. Schweizerbart'sche Verlagsbuchhandlung, Johannesstr. 3A, 7000 Stuttgart 1, Germany) bibl.; charts; illus. **Indexed:** Br.Geol.Lit., Chem.Abstr.
—CASDDS.

KUANGCHAN YU DIZHI/MINERALS AND GEOLOGY. see *METALLURGY*

KUANGSHAN DIZHI. see *MINES AND MINING INDUSTRY*

555   JA
KUMAMOTO UNIVERSITY. DEPARTMENT OF GEOLOGY. JOURNAL. (Text in English) 1952. irreg. on exchange basis. Kumamoto Daigaku, Rigakubu Chigaku Kyoshitsu - Kumamoto University, Faculty of Science, Department of Geology, 39-1, Kurokami 2-chome, Kumamoto-shi, Kumamoto-ken 860, Japan.

550   PL   ISSN 0023-5873
QE1   CODEN: KWGEA2
KWARTALNIK GEOLOGICZNY/GEOLOGICAL QUARTERLY. (Text and summaries in English and Polish) 1957. q. Panstwowy Instytut Geologiczny, Rakowiecka 4, 00-975 Warsaw, Poland. TEL 48-22-495351. charts. circ. 1,000. **Indexed:** Appl.Mech.Rev., Bull.Signal., Chem.Abstr., Geo.Abstr., GeoRef., INIS Atomind., Petrol.Abstr., Ref.Zh. **Document type:** academic/scholarly publication.
—BLDSC (5134.750000); CASDDS.

555 549   JA   ISSN 0454-7810
QE304   CODEN: KFMGAL
KYOTO UNIVERSITY. FACULTY OF SCIENCE. MEMOIRS. SERIES OF GEOLOGY AND MINERALOGY. (Text in English) 1924. a. exchange basis. Kyoto University, Faculty of Science - Kyoto Daigaku Rigakubu, Oiwake-cho, Kitashirakawa, Sakyo-ku, Kyoto 606, Japan. **Indexed:** Biol.Abstr., Deep Sea Res.& Oceanogr.Abstr., GeoRef., INIS Atomind.
—BLDSC (5597.870000); CASDDS.

551 560 665.5   JA   ISSN 0385-8278
CODEN: KRKHAU
KYUSHU UNIVERSITY. DEPARTMENT OF EARTH AND PLANETARY SCIENCES. SCIENCE REPORTS/KYUSHU DAIGAKU RIGAKUBU KENKYU HOKOKU CHIKYU-WAKUSEI-KAGAKU. (Text in Japanese; summaries in English) 1941. irreg. exchange basis only. Kyushu University 33, Department of Earth and Planetary Sciences, 6-10-1 Hakozaki, Higashi-ku, Fukuoka 812, Japan. TEL 81-92-641-1101. FAX 81-92-632-2736. Ed. Hakuyu Okada. circ. 650. **Indexed:** Chem.Abstr., Geo.Abstr., GeoRef., INIS Atomind. **Document type:** academic/scholarly publication.
—UnCover.
Formerly (until 1990): Kyushu University. Department of Geology. Science Reports.

LANDESMUSEUM JOANNEUM. ABTEILUNG FUER GEOLOGIE UND PALAEONTOLOGIE. MITTEILUNGEN. see *PALEONTOLOGY*

551.44   AU
LANDESVEREIN FUER HOEHLENKUNDE IN DER STEIERMARK. MITTEILUNGEN. 1972. a. S.100. Landesverein fuer Hoehlenkunde in der Steiermark, Brandhofgasse 18, A-8010 Graz, Austria. Ed. Mag. Volker Weissensteiner. adv.; bk.rev.; bibl.; illus. circ. 300. **Document type:** bulletin.

551   CC   ISSN 1000-6273
LIAONING DIZHI/LIAONING GEOLOGY. (Text in Chinese) 1984. q. Y2. (Liaoning Dizhi Kuangchan-ju - Liaoning Bureau of Geology and Mineral Resources) Liaoning Dizhi Bianjibu, No. 29, Beiling Dajie, Shenyang, Liaoning 110032, People's Republic of China. TEL 646573. FAX 024-662688. Ed. Chen Shichi. circ. 2,000. **Document type:** academic/scholarly publication.
Description: Publishes geology research results and progress in and around Liaoning Province.

LIETUVOS AUKSTUJU MOKYKLU MOKSLO DARBAI. GEOGRAFIJA. see *GEOGRAPHY*

550   LI
LIETUVOS AUKSTUJU MOKYKLU MOKSLO DARBAI. GEOLOGIJA. 1961. a. (Vilniaus Universitetas) Leidykla Academia, A. Gostauto 12, 2600 Vilnius, Lithuania. TEL 626851. **Document type:** monographic series.
—BLDSC (0122.616300).
Formerly (until 1990): Lietuvos T S R Aukstuju Mokyklu Mokslo Darbai. Geologija (ISSN 0202-327X); Supersedes in part (in 1980): Lietuvos T S R Aukstuju Mokslo Darbai. Geografija ir Geologija (ISSN 0459-3448)

LINNEAN SOCIETY OF NEW SOUTH WALES. PROCEEDINGS. see *BIOLOGY — Zoology*

552 553   US   ISSN 0024-4902
TN1   CODEN: LTMRAR
LITHOLOGY AND MINERAL RESOURCES. English Translation of: Litologiya i Poleznye Iskopaemye (RU ISSN 0024-497X) 1966. bi-m. $1195 (foreign $1395) (effective 1994). (Russian Academy of Sciences, RU) Plenum Publishing Corp., Consultants Bureau, 233 Spring St., New York, NY 10013-1578. TEL 212-620-8468. FAX 212-463-0742. TELEX 23-421139. Ed. V.N. Kholodov. (also avail. in microfilm from JSC; back issues avail.) **Indexed:** AESIS, Eng.Ind., INIS Atomind., Met.Abstr. **Document type:** academic/scholarly publication.
—BLDSC (0415.580000); Faxon; UnCover; UMI. **CCC.**
Refereed Serial

549 552 551.9   NE   ISSN 0024-4937
QE1   CODEN: LITHAN
LITHOS; an international journal of mineralogy, petrology, and geochemistry. (Text in English) 1968. 12/yr. (in 3 vols.; 4 nos./vol.) fl.978($529) (effective 1994). Elsevier Science B.V., P.O. Box 211, 1000 AH Amsterdam, Netherlands. TEL 31-20-5803911. FAX 31-20-5803598. TELEX 18582 ESPA NL. (Subscr. in U.S. and Canada to: Elsevier Science Inc., Box 882, Madison Sq. Sta., New York, NY 10159-0882. TEL 212-989-5800. FAX 212-633-3990) Ed. R. Gorbatschev. adv.; bk.rev.; bibl.; charts; illus.; index. circ. 1,000. (also avail. in microform from UMI; back issues avail.) **Indexed:** AESIS, Bull.Signal., Chem.Abstr., Curr.Cont., Deep Sea Res.& Oceanogr.Abstr., GeoRef., Ind.Sci.Rev. **Document type:** academic/scholarly publication.
—BLDSC (5277.300000); Faxon; UnCover; SWETS; CASDDS. **CCC.**
Description: Publishes original research papers on mineralogy, petrology and geochemistry, emphasizing the application of mineralogy and geochemistry to petrogenetic problems.
Refereed Serial

557   US   ISSN 0459-8474
GB705.L8   CODEN: LGWBA6
LOUISIANA. GEOLOGICAL SURVEY. WATER RESOURCES BULLETIN. 1960. irreg., no.20, 1975. $5 per no. Geological Survey, Box G, University Sta., Baton Rouge, LA 70893. TEL 504-388-5320. illus. (back issues avail.) **Indexed:** GeoRef. **Document type:** bulletin.

538.7   SW   ISSN 0076-1354
LOVOE GEOMAGNETIC OBSERVATORY YEARBOOK. (Text in English) 1930. a. SEK 25. Sveriges Geologiska Undersoekning - Geological Survey of Sweden, Box 670, S-751 28 Uppsala, Sweden. TEL 46-18-17-93-96. FAX 46-18-17-93-06.

551.44   US
M S S LIAISON. 1959. m. $5. Missouri Speleological Survey, Inc., c/o Ronald H. Jones, 2851 A Victor St., St. Louis, MO 63104-2334. TEL 314-782-3560. Ed. Gary Zumwalt. bk.rev.
Description: Exploration of caves.

796.525   AT   ISSN 1035-4697
M U C G - RAKER. 1977. a. Aus.$2.50. Macquarie University Caving Group, c/o Macquarie University Sports Association, Macquarie University, N.S.W. 2109, Australia. TEL 02-805-7635. FAX 02-888-5179. Ed. Lucinda Coates. circ. 100.
Formerly (until no.10, 1989): Quaver (ISSN 0155-2880)
Description: Presents caving as a sport and science, as well as discussing canyoning, bushwalking, conservation and related club activities.

553   ZR   ISSN 0250-538X
TN119.Z3   CODEN: MAADDA
MAADINI; bulletin d'information de la GECAMINES. 1974. q. Generale des Carrieres et des Mines, Division des Relations Publiques, B.P. 450, Lubumbashi, Zaire. Ed. Kamuanga Tshiayembela. illus. circ. 5,000. **Indexed:** Chem.Abstr.

556   MG
MADAGASCAR. SERVICE GEOLOGIQUE. RAPPORT D'ACTIVITE: GEOLOGIE. (Text in French) 1975. a. FMG.7000. Service Geologique de Madagascar, B.P. 322, Antananarivo, Malagasy Republic. TELEX 22450 MIEM.
Description: Features articles on geological research findings.

EARTH SCIENCES — GEOLOGY

551   **US**
MAINE GEOLOGIST. 1973. irreg. (approx. 4/yr.). $7. Geological Society of Maine, Inc., c/o Marc Loiselle, Maine Geological Survey, State House, Sta. 22, Augusta, ME 04333. TEL 207-287-2801. Ed. Susan Weddle. circ. 250. (tabloid format)

554   **GW**   **ISSN 0340-4404**
QE269   **CODEN: MZGMAZ**
MAINZER GEOWISSENSCHAFTLICHE MITTEILUNGEN. (Text in English, German; summaries in English, French, German) 1972. a. price varies. Geologisches Landesamt, Emmeransstr. 36, 55116 Mainz, Germany. TEL 06131-232261. FAX 06131-236007. charts; illus. circ. 800. (back issues avail.) **Document type:** academic/scholarly publication.
—BLDSC (5352.645000).
Description: Studies earth sciences and paleontology of the Rhineland-Palatinate area.

556   **MW**   **ISSN 0076-311X**
MALAWI. GEOLOGICAL SURVEY DEPARTMENT. ANNUAL REPORT. 1923. a. price varies. Geological Survey Department, Box 27, Zomba, Malawi. TEL 265-50-522-166. TELEX 44382.
Description: Activities of the Survey: mineral exploration, staff matters.

559   **MY**   **ISSN 0127-0559**
QE299.5   **CODEN: AGSMD3**
MALAYSIA. GEOLOGICAL SURVEY. ANNUAL REPORT. (Text in English) 1949. a. M.$20. Geological Survey, c/o Library, Kuching, Sarawak, Malaysia. FAX 082-415290. Ed. Yin Ee Heng. circ. 500. **Indexed:** Biol.Abstr.

557   **CN**
MANITOBA ENERGY AND MINES. ECONOMIC GEOLOGY PAPER SERIES. 1979. irreg. price varies. Manitoba Energy and Mines, 555-330 Graham Ave., Winnipeg, MB R3C 4E3, Canada. TEL 204-945-6541. FAX 204-945-0586. **Document type:** government publication.
Formerly: Manitoba. Mineral Resources Division. Economic Geology Paper Series.
Description: Contains overviews on specific economic geology topics relating to Manitoba.

557   **CN**
MANITOBA ENERGY AND MINES. EDUCATIONAL SERIES. 1976. irreg. price varies. Manitoba Energy and Mines, 555-330 Graham Ave., Winnipeg, MB R3C 4E3, Canada. TEL 204-945-6541. FAX 204-945-0586. **Document type:** government publication.
Formerly: Manitoba. Mineral Resources Division. Educational Series.
Description: General information about geology and mineral resources of Manitoba.

551   **CN**
MANITOBA ENERGY AND MINES. GEOLOGICAL PAPER. 1968. irreg. price varies. Manitoba Energy and Mines, 555-330 Graham Ave., Winnipeg, MB R3C 4E3, Canada. TEL 204-945-6541. **Indexed:** GeoRef. **Document type:** government publication.
Formerly: Manitoba. Mineral Resources Division. Geological Paper (ISSN 0076-387X)
Description: Deals with specific geological topic or introduces new data or concepts.

557   **CN**
MANITOBA ENERGY AND MINES. GEOLOGICAL REPORT. 1937. irreg. price varies. Manitoba Energy and Mines, 555-330 Graham Ave., Winnipeg, MB R3C 4E3, Canada. TEL 204-945-6541. FAX 204-945-0586. **Document type:** government publication.
Former titles: Manitoba. Mineral Resources Division. Geological Report; Manitoba. Mines Branch. Publication (ISSN 0085-3070)
Description: Results of comprehensive geological studies of specific projects.

557   **CN**
MANITOBA ENERGY AND MINES. OPEN FILE REPORT SERIES. 1976. irreg. price varies. Manitoba Energy and Mines, 555-330 Graham Ave., Winnipeg, MB R3C 4E3, Canada. TEL 204-945-6541. FAX 204-945-0586. **Document type:** government publication.
Formerly: Manitoba. Mineral Resources Division. Open File Report Series.
Description: Information on specific geological topics or results of other activities which may be of immediate interest to the public.

557   **CN**
MANITOBA ENERGY AND MINES. REPORT OF FIELD ACTIVITIES. 1968. a. price varies. Manitoba Energy and Mines, 555-330 Graham Ave., Winnipeg, MB R3C 4E3, Canada. TEL 204-945-6541. FAX 204-945-0586. **Document type:** government publication.
Former titles: Manitoba. Mineral Resources Division. Report of Field Activities; Manitoba. Mines Branch. Summary of Geological Field Work.
Description: Summarizes field activities carried out by the Minerals Division of the Department.

551   **UK**   **ISSN 0264-8172**
QE39   **CODEN: MPEGD8**
MARINE AND PETROLEUM GEOLOGY. q. £300 in UK and Europe; elsewhere £330. (Geological Society) Butterworth - Heinemann (Subsidiary of: Reed International PLC), Linacre House, Jordan Hill, Oxford OX2 8DP, England. TEL 0865-310366. FAX 0865-310898. TELEX 83111 BHPOXF G. (Subscr. to: Turpin Transactions Ltd., Distribution Centre, Blackhorse Rd., Letchworth, Herts SG6 1HN, England. TEL 0462-672555) Ed. D.G. Roberts. adv.; bk.rev.; illus.; index. (also avail. in microform from UMI; back issues avail.) **Indexed:** E&P Hlth. (1993-), Energy Info.Abstr., Environ.Abstr., Gas Process.& Ppl. (1993-), Off.Tech. (1993-), Petrol.Abstr. (1985-). **Document type:** academic/scholarly publication.
—BLDSC (5373.632100); EI; Faxon; UnCover; SWETS; UMI; CASDDS. CCC.
Description: For explorationists in industry, government and academia. Multidisciplinary concepts and technologies of direct relevance to all concerned with marine and petroleum geology.
Refereed Serial

MARSCHENRAT ZUR FOERDERUNG DER FORSCHUNG IM KUESTENGEBIET DER NORDSEE. NACHRICHTEN. see *SCIENCES: COMPREHENSIVE WORKS*

557   **US**   **ISSN 0076-4779**
QE121   **CODEN: MGSBBW**
MARYLAND. GEOLOGICAL SURVEY. BULLETIN. 1944. irreg., latest no.37, 1990. price varies. Maryland Geological Survey, 2300 St. Paul St., Baltimore, MD 21218. TEL 301-554-5500. FAX 301-554-5502. index. **Indexed:** Chem.Abstr., GeoRef. **Document type:** bulletin.

557   **US**   **ISSN 0076-4787**
QE121   **CODEN: MGSVBO**
MARYLAND. GEOLOGICAL SURVEY. EDUCATIONAL SERIES. 1964. irreg., no.6, 1989. price varies. Maryland Geological Survey, 2300 St. Paul St., Baltimore, MD 21218. TEL 301-554-5500. FAX 301-554-5502. **Indexed:** GeoRef.

557   **US**   **ISSN 0076-4795**
   CODEN: MGICAI
MARYLAND. GEOLOGICAL SURVEY. INFORMATION CIRCULAR. 1963. irreg., latest no.50. price varies. Maryland Geological Survey, 2300 St. Paul St., Baltimore, MD 21218. TEL 301-554-5500. FAX 301-554-5502.

557   **US**   **ISSN 0076-4809**
QE121   **CODEN: MGRIAD**
MARYLAND. GEOLOGICAL SURVEY. REPORT OF INVESTIGATIONS. 1965. irreg., latest no.53. price varies. Maryland Geological Survey, 2300 St. Paul St., Baltimore, MD 21218. TEL 301-554-5500. FAX 301-554-5502. **Indexed:** Deep Sea Res.& Oceanogr.Abstr., GeoRef.
—BLDSC (7657.730000); EI.

550   **XR**
MASARYK UNIVERSITY. FACULTY OF SCIENCES. SCRIPTA GEOLOGIA. (Text in English, French, German and Russian) 1971. a. price varies. Masarykova Universita, Prirodovedecka Fakulta - Masaryk University, Faculty of Sciences, Kotlarska 2, 611 37 Brno, Czech Republic. Ed. Antonin Prichystal. illus. **Document type:** academic/scholarly publication.
Former titles: Scripta Facultatis Scientiarum Naturalium Univeritatis Masaykianae Brunensis. Geologia; Scripta Facultatis Scientiarum Naturalium Universitatis Purkynianae Brunensis. Geologia (ISSN 0322-824X)

551   **NE**   **ISSN 0924-4972**
MATERIALS SCIENCE OF MINERALS AND ROCKS. 1983. irreg. price varies. Kluwer Academic Publishers, Postbus 17, 3300 AA Dordrecht, Netherlands. TEL 31-78-334911. FAX 31-78-334254. TELEX 29245 KAPG NL. (Dist. by: Kluwer Academic Publishers Group, P.O. Box 322, 3300 AH Dordrecht, Netherlands. TEL 31-78-524400. FAX 31-78-524474; N. America dist. addr.: Box 358, Accord Sta., Hingham, MA 02018-0358. TEL 617-871-6600. FAX 617-871-6528) Ed. I. Sunagawa. **Document type:** monographic series.
Refereed Serial

551 526   **US**   **ISSN 0882-8121**
QE1   **CODEN: MATGED**
MATHEMATICAL GEOLOGY. 1969. 8/yr. $455 (foreign $530) (effective 1994). Plenum Publishing Corp., 233 Spring St., New York, NY 10013-1578. TEL 212-620-3000. FAX 212-463-0742. TELEX 23-421139. Ed. Robert Ehrlich. adv.; bk.rev. (also avail. in microfilm from JSC; back issues avail.) **Indexed:** AESIS, Appl.Mech.Rev., Chem.Abstr., Compumath, Curr.Cont., Curr.Ind.Stat., Deep Sea Res.& Oceanogr.Abstr., Eng.Ind., GeoRef., INIS Atomindx., Irr.& Drain.Abstr., Math.R., Petrol.Abstr., Ref.Zh., Sci.Cit.Ind., Soils & Fert., Zent.Math. **Document type:** academic/scholarly publication.
—BLDSC (5402.200000); Faxon; UnCover; SWETS; UMI; CASDDS. CCC.
Formerly: International Association for Mathematical Geology. Journal (ISSN 0020-5958)
Refereed Serial

551 581   **DK**   **ISSN 0106-1046**
QE70   **CODEN: GRGEDS**
MEDDELELSER OM GROENLAND, GEOSCIENCE. (Text mainly in English, occasionally in Danish, French or German) 1979. irreg. price varies. (Kommissionen for Videnskabelige Undersoegelser i Groenland, GL - Commission for Scientific Research in Greenland) Geografforlaget ApS, Fruerhoejvej 43, DK-5464 Brenderup, Denmark. Ed. S. Funder. charts; illus.; maps. **Indexed:** Biol.Abstr., Chem.Abstr., GeoRef. **Document type:** academic/scholarly publication.
—BLDSC (5487.250000).
Formerly: Greenland Biosciences; Supersedes in part (1878-1979): Meddelelser om Groenland (ISSN 0025-6676)

554   **BE**   **ISSN 0408-9510**
MEMOIRES POUR SERVIR A L'EXPLICATION DES CARTES GEOLOGIQUES ET MINIERES DE LA BELGIQUE. (Text in Dutch, English, French, German) 1955. irreg. price varies. Ministry of Economical Affairs, Service Geologique de Belgique, 13, rue Jenner, 1040 Brussels, Belgium. TEL 32-2-647-64-00. FAX 32-2-647-73-59. Ed.Bd. charts. circ. 1,500. **Document type:** government publication.

551   **IT**   **ISSN 0391-8602**
MEMORIE DI SCIENZE GEOLOGICHE. (Text in English, French, German, Italian; summaries in English and Italian) 1912. a. L.120000. Universita di Padova, Dipartimento di Geologia, Paleontologia e Geofisica, Via Giotto 1, 35137 Padua, Italy. FAX 87-50-367. Ed.Bd. **Indexed:** Biol.Abstr.

554   **UK**   **ISSN 0025-990X**
QE262.M6   **CODEN: MGEOAY**
MERCIAN GEOLOGIST. 1964. s-a. £6 per part. East Midlands Geological Society, Dept. of Geology, The University, Leicester LE1 7RH, England. TEL 0533-523610. FAX 0533-523918. Ed. R.J. Aldridge. bk.rev.; bibl.; charts; illus.; maps; cum.index. circ. 600. (back issues avail.) **Indexed:** AESIS, Br.Geol.Lit., Chem.Abstr., Deep Sea Res.& Oceanogr.Abstr., Fuel & Energy Abstr., Geo.Abstr., GeoRef. **Document type:** academic/scholarly publicat on.
—BLDSC (5679.100000).

EARTH SCIENCES — GEOLOGY

551 GW ISSN 0076-7689
QE269 CODEN: MEYNAF
MEYNIANA; Veroeffentlichungen aus dem Geologischen Institut der Universitaet Kiel. 1952. a. price varies. Universitaet Kiel, Geologisch-Palaeontologisches Institut, Olshausenstr. 40, 24118 Kiel, Germany. TEL 0431-8803254. FAX 0431-8804376. (Co-sponsor: Museum der Universitaet Kiel) Ed. Kyaw Winn. circ. 300. (back issues avail.) **Indexed:** Biol.Abstr., Deep Sea Res.& Oceanogr.Abstr., Geo.Abstr., GeoRef. **Document type:** bulletin.
—BLDSC (5752.000000).

557 US ISSN 0543-8497
QE125 CODEN: MGDRA4
MICHIGAN. GEOLOGICAL SURVEY DIVISION. BULLETIN. 1964. irreg., no.6, 1976. price varies. Department of Natural Resources, Geological Survey Division, Box 30028, Lansing, MI 48909. TEL 517-334-6907. Ed. S.E. Wilson. illus.; maps. **Indexed:** GeoRef. **Document type:** bulletin.

557 US
MICHIGAN. GEOLOGICAL SURVEY DIVISION. REPORT OF INVESTIGATION. 1963. irreg., latest no.28. price varies. Department of Natural Resources, Geological Survey Division, Box 30028, Lansing, MI 48909. TEL 517-373-1256. Ed. S.E. Wilson. illus.; maps. **Indexed:** GeoRef. **Document type:** monographic series.
Formerly: Michigan. Department of Conservation. Geological Survey Division. Progress Report (ISSN 0096-5022)

551 CN ISSN 1189-6000
▼**MINERAL MATTERS/PARLONS MINERAUX.** 1992. irreg. free. Department of Natural Resources and Energy - Ministere des Ressources Naturelles et de l'Energie, Box 6000, Fredericton, NB E3B 5H1, Canada. TEL 506-453-2614. FAX 506-457-4881. **Document type:** newsletter.

555 549 PK
MINERAL REVIEW. (Text in English and Urdu) q. free. Pakistan Mineral Development Corporation, P I D C House, Dr. Ziauddin Ahmed Rd., Karachi-4, Pakistan. Ed. Sajid Hussain. circ. 1,000.

MINERALES. see *MINES AND MINING INDUSTRY*

551 549 551.9 GW ISSN 0026-4598
QE351 CODEN: MIDEBE
MINERALIUM DEPOSITA; international journal of geology, mineralogy, and geochemistry of mineral deposits. (Text and summaries in English, French or German) 1966. 6/yr. DM.648($405) (Society for Geology Applied to Mineral Deposits) Springer-Verlag, Heidelberger Platz 3, 14197 Berlin, Germany. TEL 030-8207-1. FAX 030-8214091. (Subscr. in N. America to: Springer-Verlag New York, Inc., 44 Hartz Way, Secaucus, NJ 07096-2491. TEL 201-348-4033. FAX 201-348-4505) Ed.Bd. adv.; bk.rev.; charts; illus.; index. (also avail. in microform from UMI; back issues avail.; reprint service avail. from ISI) **Indexed:** AESIS, Br.Geol.Lit., Cadscan, Chem.Abstr., Curr.Cont., Eng.Ind., GeoRef., Lead Abstr., Zincscan. **Document type:** academic/scholarly publication.
—BLDSC (5786.200000); Faxon; UnCover; SWETS; UMI; CASDDS. **CCC.**
Description: Introduces new observations, principles, and interpretations from the fields of economic geology and applied geochemistry, with emphasis on mineral deposits.

551 549 US ISSN 0343-2181
MINERALS AND ROCKS; monograph series of theoretical and experimental studies. 1968. irreg. price varies. Springer-Verlag, 175 Fifth Ave., New York, NY 10010. TEL 212-460-1500. FAX 212-473-6272. (Also: Berlin, Heidelberg, Tokyo and Vienna) Ed. P.J. Wyllie. (reprint service avail. from ISI) **Indexed:** GeoRef. **Document type:** monographic series.
Former titles: Mineralogie und Petrographie in Einzel Darstellungen; Minerals, Rocks and Inorganic Materials (ISSN 0076-8944)

MINFO; New South Wales mining and exploration quarterly. see *MINES AND MINING INDUSTRY*

MINING, GEOLOGICAL AND METALLURGICAL INSTITUTE OF INDIA. TRANSACTIONS. see *MINES AND MINING INDUSTRY*

557 US ISSN 0076-9169
QE127 CODEN: MGSBAV
MINNESOTA. GEOLOGICAL SURVEY. BULLETIN. 1889. irreg., latest no.47, 1986. price varies. Geological Survey, 2642 University Ave., St. Paul, MN 55114-1057. TEL 612-627-4780. **Indexed:** GeoRef. **Document type:** bulletin.
—BLDSC (2617.000000).

551 US ISSN 0544-3083
CODEN: MGSEB7
MINNESOTA. GEOLOGICAL SURVEY. EDUCATIONAL SERIES. no.2, 1979. irreg., latest no.7, 1990. price varies. Geological Survey, 2642 University Ave., St. Paul, MN 55114-1057. TEL 612-627-4780. **Document type:** monographic series.
—BLDSC (3662.504000).

551 US ISSN 0192-6268
CODEN: MGLGAB
MINNESOTA. GEOLOGICAL SURVEY. GUIDEBOOK SERIES. no.14, 1982. irreg., latest no.19, 1992. Geological Survey, 2642 University Ave., St. Paul, MN 55114-1057. TEL 612-627-4780.

557 US ISSN 0544-3105
QE127 CODEN: MGSIBJ
MINNESOTA. GEOLOGICAL SURVEY. INFORMATION CIRCULARS. 1962. irreg., latest no.39, 1993. price varies. Geological Survey, 2642 University Ave., St. Paul, MN 55114-1057. TEL 612-627-4780. (back issues avail.) **Document type:** monographic series.
Description: Results of scientific test drilling for minerals in southwestern Minnesota.

557 US ISSN 0076-9177
QE127
MINNESOTA. GEOLOGICAL SURVEY. REPORT OF INVESTIGATIONS. 1963. irreg., latest no.42, 1993. price varies. Geological Survey, 2642 University Ave., St. Paul, MN 55114-1057. TEL 612-627-4780. Ed. N.H. Balaban. circ. 400. (back issues avail.) **Indexed:** GeoRef. **Document type:** monographic series.
—BLDSC (7657.750000); UnCover.

557 US ISSN 0275-8555
QE129
MISSISSIPPI GEOLOGY. 1980. q. free. Department of Environmental Quality, Office of Geology, Box 20307, Jackson, MS 39289. TEL 601-961-5500. FAX 601-961-5521. Eds. Michael B.E. Bograd, David Dockery. bk.rev.; bibl.; charts; illus.; stat. circ. 800. (back issues avail.) **Indexed:** GeoRef., Petrol.Abstr. **Document type:** government publication.
Description: Articles and abstracts on geological research in the state, with news items, reviews, and lists of relevant publications.

551.44 US ISSN 0026-671X
CODEN: MSSPA
MISSOURI SPELEOLOGY. 1959. a. $12 per vol. Missouri Speleological Survey, Inc., c/o Ronald H. Jones, 2851 A Victor St., St. Louis, MO 63104-2334. TEL 314-771-8285. Ed. Jo Schaper. bk.rev.; charts; illus. circ. 275. (back issues avail.) **Indexed:** GeoRef.
—UnCover.

551 US ISSN 0026-7775
QE1 CODEN: MOGEB3
MODERN GEOLOGY. 1969. 4/yr. (in 1 vol., 4 nos./vol.). 223 ECU (effective 1993). Gordon and Breach Science Publishers, 820 Town Center Dr., Langhorne, PA 19047. TEL 215-750-2642. FAX 215-750-6343. (UK subscr. to: P.O. Box 90, Reading, Berkshire RG1 8JL, England. TEL 0734-560-080) Eds. Douglas Palmer, Hughes Tomeas. adv.; bk.rev.; charts; illus.; index. (also avail. in microform from MIM) **Indexed:** Biol.Abstr., Chem.Abstr., Curr.Cont., Geo.Abstr., GeoRef., Intl.Civil Eng.Abstr., Petrol.Abstr., Sci.Abstr., Soft.Abstr.Eng.
—BLDSC (5886.650000); Faxon; UnCover; SWETS; CASDDS. **CCC.**
Refereed Serial

557 US ISSN 0077-1090
CODEN: MBGBA4
MONTANA. BUREAU OF MINES AND GEOLOGY. BULLETIN. 1919. irreg., no.131, 1993. price varies. Bureau of Mines and Geology, Montana College of Mineral Science and Technology, Butte, MT 59701-8997. TEL 406-496-4167. FAX 406-496-4451. **Indexed:** GeoRef. **Document type:** bulletin.
—CASDDS.
Incorporates (in 1960): Montana. Bureau of Mines and Geology. Ground Water Reports (ISSN 0077-1112)
Description: Series includes data sources, catalogs, bibliographies, indexes, categorized studies and information.

557 622 US ISSN 0077-1120
CODEN: MBGMA3
MONTANA. BUREAU OF MINES AND GEOLOGY. MEMOIR. 1928. irreg., no.64, 1993. Bureau of Mines and Geology, Montana College of Mineral Science and Technology, Butte, MT 59701-8997. TEL 406-496-4167. FAX 406-496-4451. **Indexed:** GeoRef.
Description: Detailed, scientific study of a specific subject on earth science.

557 US ISSN 0077-1139
CODEN: MBGSAL
MONTANA. BUREAU OF MINES AND GEOLOGY. SPECIAL PUBLICATIONS. (Continues numbering of Miscellaneous Contributions, 1932-1957) 1957. irreg., no.105, 1993. price varies. Bureau of Mines and Geology, Montana College of Mineral Science and Technology, Butte, MT 59701-8997. TEL 406-496-4167. FAX 406-496-4451. **Document type:** government publication.
—CASDDS.
Description: Compilation of various works, guidebooks, proceedings, multiple authorships; may include treatments suitable for laymen.

551 US ISSN 0145-8752
QE1 CODEN: MUGBD4
MOSCOW UNIVERSITY GEOLOGY BULLETIN. English translation of: Moskovskii Universitet. Vestnik. Seriya 4: Geologiya (RU ISSN 0579-9406) 1974. bi-m. $815. (Moskovskii Universitet, RU) Allerton Press, Inc., 150 Fifth Ave., New York, NY 10011. TEL 212-924-3950. FAX 212-463-9684. Ed. V.F. Trofimov. charts; illus.; index. **Indexed:** Excerp.Med., GeoRef. **Document type:** academic/scholarly publication.
—BLDSC (0416.238500). **CCC.**

550 RU ISSN 0366-1318
Q60 CODEN: BMPGAK
MOSKOVSKII GOSUDARSTVIENNYI UNIVERSITET. MOSKOVSKOE OBSHCHESTVO ISPYTATELEI PRIRODY. OTDEL GEOLOGICHESKII. BYULLETEN. (Text in Russian; summaries in English) 1922. bi-m. 30.60 Rub. (Moskovskii Gosudarstviennyi Universitet, Moskovskoe Obshchestvo Ispytatelei Prirody) Izdatel'stvo Moskovskogo Gosudarstvennogo Universiteta, Ul. Gerzena, 6, Moscow 103009, Russia. Ed. D.P. Naidin. bk.rev.; abstr.; bibl.; charts; illus. circ. 900. **Indexed:** Biol.Abstr., Chem.Abstr., GeoRef., INIS Atomind.
—BLDSC (0022.050000); CASDDS. **CCC.**
Formerly: Moskovskii Universitet. Moskovskoe Obshchestvo Ispytatelei Prirody. Geologicheskii Otdel. Byulleten (ISSN 0007-7682)

550 RU ISSN 0579-9406
QE1 CODEN: VMUGAR
MOSKOVSKII UNIVERSITET. VESTNIK. SERIYA 4: GEOLOGIYA. English translation: Moscow University Geology Bulletin (US ISSN 0145-8752) (Contents page in English) bi-m. 22.80 Rub. Moskovskii Universitet, Ul. Gertsena 5-7, 103009 Moscow, Russia. bk.rev.; bibl.; index. **Indexed:** Bibl.Cart., Chem.Abstr.
—BLDSC (0032.510000); CASDDS.

MOSKOVSKOE OBSHCHESTVO ISPYTATELEI PRIRODY. BIOLOGICHESKII OTDEL. BYULLETEN/MOSCOW SOCIETY OF NATURALISTS. BIOLOGICAL SERIES. BULLETIN. see *BIOLOGY*

EARTH SCIENCES — GEOLOGY

551 US ISSN 0027-254X
QE79 CODEN: MOGEA2
MOUNTAIN GEOLOGIST. 1964. q. $15. Rocky Mountain Association of Geologists, 5139 Raleigh St., Denver, CO 80212-2609. Ed. Penny Frush. adv.; charts; illus.; index, cum.index. circ. 2,600. (also avail. in microfiche; back issues avail.) **Indexed:** Chem.Abstr., Geo.Abstr., GeoRef., Petrol.Abstr.
—BLDSC (5978.900000); Faxon; UnCover. **CCC.**

MUENCHNER GEOWISSENSCHAFTLICHE ABHANDLUNGEN. REIHE A: GEOLOGIE UND PALAEONTOLOGIE. see *PALEONTOLOGY*

551 GW ISSN 0931-8739
MUENCHNER GEOWISSENSCHAFTLICHE ABHANDLUNGEN. REIHE B: ALLGEMEINE UND ANGEWANDTE GEOLOGIE. (Text in English, French, German) 1988. irreg. price varies. Verlag Dr. Friedrich Pfeil, Postfach 650086, 81214 Munich, Germany. TEL 089-188058. FAX 089-8341873. Ed. Friedrich H. Pfeil. circ. 500. (back issues avail.) **Document type:** monographic series.
Description: Covers all areas of geology and applied geology.

551 BE ISSN 0368-489X
MUSEE ROYAL DE L'AFRIQUE CENTRALE. ANNALES - SCIENCES GEOLOGIQUES. SERIE IN 8/KONINKLIJK MUSEUM VOOR MIDDEN-AFRIKA. ANNALEN - GEOLOGISCHE WETENSCHAPPEN. REEKS IN 8. 1948. irreg., no.98, 1990. price varies. Musee Royal de l'Afrique Centrale - Koninklijk Museum voor Midden-Afrika, 13 Steenweg op Leuven, B-3080 Tervuren, Belgium. TEL 32-2-7675401. FAX 32-7670242. charts; illus. **Indexed:** Biol.Abstr. **Document type:** monographic series.
—BLDSC (0933.975000).

551 BE ISSN 0378-0953
MUSEE ROYAL DE L'AFRIQUE CENTRALE. DEPARTEMENT DE GEOLOGIE ET DE MINERALOGIE. RAPPORT ANNUEL. 1957. biennial, latest 1991 (for the years 1989-1990). 650 BEF. Musee Royal de l'Afrique Centrale, Departement de Geologie et de Mineralogie, 13 Steenweg op Leuven, B-3080 Tervuren, Belgium. TEL 32-2-7675401. FAX 32-2-7670242. Ed. J. Klerkx. charts. circ. 1,000. **Indexed:** Biol.Abstr., Chem.Abstr., GeoRef.

550 AG ISSN 0027-3880
QE231 CODEN: MCNRAQ
MUSEO ARGENTINO DE CIENCIAS NATURALES "BERNARDINO RIVADAVIA." INSTITUTO NACIONAL DE INVESTIGACION DE LAS CIENCIAS NATURALES. REVISTA. GEOLOGIA. 1949. irreg., vol.9, no.1, 1989. free. Museo Argentino de Ciencias Naturales "Bernardino Rivadavia", Instituto Nacional de Investigacion de las Ciencias Naturales, Avda. Angel Gallardo 470, Casilla de Correo 220-Sucursal 5, Buenos Aires, Argentina. illus.
Supersedes: Museo Argentino de Ciencias Naturales "Bernardino Rivadavia." Instituto Nacional de Investigacion de las Ciencias Naturales. Revista y Comunicaciones; Formerly: Buenos Aires. Museo Argentino de Ciencias Naturales Bernardino Rivadavia. Instituto Nacional de Investigacion de las Ciencias Naturales. Revista. Ciencias Geologicas.

500.907 AG ISSN 0539-3027
MUSEO MUNICIPAL DE HISTORIA NATURAL DE SAN RAFAEL. INSTITUTO DE CIENCIAS NATURALES. NOTAS. 1957. irreg. on exchange basis. Museo Municipal de Historia Natural de San Rafael, Parque Mariano Moreno, 5600 San Rafael, Mendoza, Argentina. FAX 54-0627-21244. Ed. Humberto A. Lagiglia. circ. 1,200. **Document type:** monographic series.
Formerly: Museo de Historia Natural de San Rafael. Instituto de Ciencias Naturales. Notas.

551 FR ISSN 0181-0642
QE1 CODEN: BMNMDV
MUSEUM NATIONAL D'HISTOIRE NATURELLE. BULLETIN - SECTION C (SCIENCES DE LA TERRE: PALEONTOLOGIE, GEOLOGIE, MINERALOGIE). q. 430 F. Museum National d'Histoire Naturelle, 57 rue Cuvier, 75005 Paris, France. TEL 40-79-30-00. FAX 40-79-34-84. TELEX MUSNAHN 202641F. Eds. Philippe Taquet, Leonard Ginsburg.

550 PL ISSN 0032-6275
CODEN: PMUZAI
MUZEUM ZIEMI. PRACE. (Text in English or Polish) 1958. irreg., approx. 1-2/yr. Polska Akademia Nauk, Muzeum Ziemi, Ul. Na Skarpie 20-26, 00-488 Warsaw, Poland. TEL 48-22-298061. Ed. Antoni Laszkiewicz. **Indexed:** Chem.Abstr.
—BLDSC (6588.440000).

N C A CAVE TALK. (National Caves Association) see *TRAVEL AND TOURISM*

551 US
N C G S OPEN-FILE REPORT. 1966. irreg., no.89, 1989. price varies. (Department of Environment, Health, and Natural Resources, Division of Land Resources) North Carolina Geological Survey, Box 27687, Raleigh, NC 27611-7687. TEL 919-733-2423.

554 NO ISSN 0332-5768
QE281 CODEN: NGUBBJ
N G U BULLETIN. Key Title: Bulletin - Norges Geologiske Undersoekelse. (Text in English) 1890. irreg. price varies. Norges Geologiske Undersoekelse - Geological Survey of Norway, Leiv Erikssons vei 39, P.O. Box 3006 Lade, N-7002 Trondheim, Norway. TEL 47-73-90-40-11. FAX 7-92-16-20. Ed. David Roberts. bibl.; charts; illus. **Indexed:** Biol.Abstr., Br.Geol.Lit., Chem.Abstr., Geo.Abstr., GeoRef. **Document type:** bulletin.
—BLDSC (6129.000000); UnCover; CASDDS. **CCC.**
Description: Comprises scientific contributions to the earth sciences of regional Norwegian, general or specialist interest.

351 NO ISSN 0377-8894
QE281 CODEN: NGUSB2
N G U SKRIFTER. (Text in Norwegian; summaries in English) 1972. irreg. price varies. Norges Geologiske Undersoekelse - Geological Survey of Norway, Leiv Erikssons vei 39, P.O. Box 3006 Lade, N-7002 Trondheim, Norway. TEL 47-73-90-40-11. FAX 7-92-16-20. Ed. David Roberts. **Indexed:** Br.Geol.Lit., Geo.Abstr.
—CASDDS.
Description: Consists of descriptions og geological map sheets, either bedrock or Quaternary geology.

551 NO ISSN 0801-5961
N G U SPECIAL PUBLICATION. (Text in English) 1987. irreg. price varies. Norges Geologiske Undersoekelse - Geological Survey of Norway, P.O. Box 3006 Lade, 7002 Trondheim, Norway. TEL 47-73-90-40-11. FAX 47-7-92-16-20. TELEX 55 4 17 NGU N. Ed. David Roberts. circ. 1,000. **Document type:** academic/scholarly publication, government publication, proceedings.
—BLDSC (8379.629800).
Description: Presents papers and proceedings from national and international symposia or meetings dealing with Norwegian and international geology, geophysics and geochemistry; features some thematic articles.

551 JA ISSN 0914-2029
QE350
N I P R SYMPOSIUM ON ANTARCTIC GEOSCIENCES. PROCEEDINGS. (Text in English) 1987. irreg., no.6, 1993. exchange basis. National Institute of Polar Research - Kokuritsu Kyokuchi Kenkyujo, Library, 9-10, Kaga 1-chome, Itabashi-ku, Tokyo 173, Japan. TEL 03-3962-4711. FAX 03-3962-2529. TELEX 272-3515 POLRSCJ. Ed. Takao Hoshiai. circ. 1,000. **Indexed:** Geo.Abstr., GeoRef. **Document type:** proceedings.
—BLDSC (6848.270500); UnCover.
Supersedes in part (in 1987): National Institute of Polar Research. Memoirs. Special Issue (ISSN 0386-0744); Which was formerly (1967-1972): Japanese Antarctic Research Expedition Scientific Reports. Special Issue (ISSN 0386-5452)

551 JA ISSN 0914-5621
QB755.5.A6 CODEN: PNMEES
N I P R SYMPOSIUM ON ANTARCTIC METEORITES. PROCEEDINGS. (Text and summaries in English) 1988. irreg., no.6, 1993. exchange basis. National Institute of Polar Research - Kokuritsu Kyokuchi Kenkyujo, Library, 9-10, Kaga 1-chome, Itabashi-ku, Tokyo 173, Japan. Ed. Takao Hoshiai. circ. 1,000. **Indexed:** Geo.Abstr., GeoRef., Meteor.& Geoastrophys.Abstr. **Document type:** proceedings.
—BLDSC (6848.270520); CASDDS.
Supersedes in part (in 1987): National Institute of Polar Research. Memoirs. Special Issue (ISSN 0386-0744); Which was formerly (1967-1972): Japanese Antarctic Research Expedition Scientific Reports. Special Issue (ISSN 0386-5452)

551 JA ISSN 0914-2037
QC994.75
N I P R SYMPOSIUM ON POLAR METEOROLOGY AND GLACIOLOGY. PROCEEDINGS. (Text in English) 1987. irreg., no.6, 1993. exchange basis. National Institute of Polar Research - Kokuritsu Kyokuchi Kenkyujo, Library, 9-10, Kaga 1-chome, Itabashi-ku, Tokyo 173, Japan. TEL 03-3962-4711. FAX 03-3962-2529. TELEX 272-3515 POLRSCJ. Ed. Takao Hoshiai. circ. 1,000. **Indexed:** Geo.Abstr., GeoRef., Meteor.& Geoastrophys.Abstr. **Document type:** proceedings.
—BLDSC (6848.270600).
Supersedes in part (in 1987): National Institute of Polar Research. Memoirs. Special Issue (ISSN 0386-0744); Which was formerly (1967-1972): Japanese Antarctic Research Expedition Scientific Reports. Special Issue (ISSN 0386-5452)

553.53 US ISSN 0077-5673
CODEN: NSGCAZ
N S G A CIRCULAR. 1928. irreg., no. 120, 1973. price varies. National Sand and Gravel Association, 900 Spring St., Silver Spring, MD 20910.
TEL 301-587-1400. Ed. R.D. Gaynor. circ. 1,000.

551.31 US
N S I D C NOTES. 1991. q. free. World Data Center A for Glaciology (Snow and Ice), National Snow and Ice Data Center, CIRES, Campus Box 449, University of Colorado, Boulder, CO 80309. TEL 303-492-5171. FAX 303-492-2468. TELEX 7401426 WDCA UC. Ed. Ann Brennan. **Document type:** newsletter.
Formerly (until 1992): C D M S Notes.
Description: Provides news of relevant topics for users of National Snow and Ice Data Center data.

551.44 US ISSN 0146-9517
GB601 CODEN: NSSBDR
N S S BULLETIN. 1940. s-a. $18 to non-members. National Speleological Society, Inc., Cave Ave., Huntsville, AL 35810. TEL 205-852-1300. FAX 205-851-9241. Ed. Andrew Flurkey. bibl.; charts; illus.; index, cum.index every 5 yrs. circ. 9,000. (back issues avail.) **Indexed:** Biol.Abstr., Chem.Abstr., Geo.Abstr., GeoRef. **Document type:** bulletin.
—BLDSC (6130.581000); Faxon; UnCover; CASDDS.
Formerly (until 1974): National Speleological Society. Bulletin (ISSN 0028-0216)
Description: Discusses cave science.

551.44 US ISSN 0027-7010
GV200.6
N S S NEWS. 1943. m. $18. National Speleological Society, Inc., Cave Ave., Huntsville, AL 35810. TEL 205-852-1300. FAX 205-851-9241. Ed. Glenda Rhodes. adv.; bk.rev.; bibl.; charts; illus.; stat.; index. circ. 9,500. (back issues avail.) **Indexed:** Biol.Abstr., GeoRef. **Document type:** newsletter.
—BLDSC (6180.583000); UnCover.
Description: Discusses cave exploration.

551.44 AT ISSN 1037-4361
NARGUN. 1967. 10/yr. Aus.$20. Victorian Speleological Association Inc., G.P.O. Box 5425cc, Melbourne, Vic.3001, Australia. Ed. S. White. adv.; bk.rev. circ. 170. **Indexed:** Aus.Speleo.Abstr.

1950 EARTH SCIENCES — GEOLOGY

551   JA   ISSN 0385-244X
QE304   CODEN: BNSPD4
NATIONAL SCIENCE MUSEUM. BULLETIN. SERIES C: GEOLOGY & PALEONTOLOGY. (Text in English) 1939. q. Monbusho, Kokuritsu Kagaku Hakubutsukan - Ministry of Education, Science and Culture, National Science Museum, 7-20 Ueno Koen, Taito-ku, Tokyo 110, Japan. illus. **Indexed:** Biol.Abstr., Deep Sea Res.& Oceanogr.Abstr., GeoRef., INIS Atomind. **Document type:** academic/scholarly publication, bulletin.
—BLDSC (2644.040000); UnCover.
Formerly: National Science Museum. Bulletin. Series C: Geology; Which superseded in part (in 1975): National Science Museum. Bulletin (ISSN 0028-0119)

NATTURUFRAEDISTOFNUN ISLANDS. FJOELRIT. see *BIOLOGY*

NATUR UND MENSCH: JAHRESMITTEILUNGEN DER NATURHISTORISCHEN GESELLSCHAFT NUERNBERG. see *BIOLOGY*

551   UK   ISSN 0968-0462
QE1
NATURAL HISTORY MUSEUM. BULLETIN. GEOLOGY. 1949. a. £78.75. Intercept Ltd., P.O. Box 716, Andover, Hants. SP10 1YG, England. TEL 0264-334748. FAX 0264-334058. bibl.; illus.; stat.; index. circ. 750. **Indexed:** Biol.Abstr., Br.Geol.Lit. (1972-), Chem.Abstr., Curr.Adv.Ecol.Sci., E&P Hlth. (1993-), Gas Process.& Ppl. (1993-), GeoRef., Off.Tech. (1993-), Petrol.Abstr. (1969-). **Document type:** academic/scholarly publication, bulletin.
—BLDSC (2644.269000); UnCover.
Formerly (until 1992): British Museum (Natural History) Bulletin. Geology (ISSN 0007-1471); Which incorporates: British Museum (Natural History) Bulletin. Mineralogy (ISSN 0007-148X)

NATURE AND RESOURCES; international news about research on environment, resources, and conservation of nature. see *CONSERVATION*

NATURHISTORISCHES MUSEUM BASEL. VEROEFFENTLICHUNGEN. see *SCIENCES: COMPREHENSIVE WORKS*

NATURWISSENSCHAFTLICHER VEREIN FUER SCHWABEN. BERICHTE. see *BIOLOGY*

NATURWISSENSCHAFTLICHER VEREIN WUPPERTAL. JAHRESBERICHTE. see *BIOLOGY — Botany*

526   RU
NAUCHNO-ISSLEDOVATEL'SKII INSTITUT PRIKLADNOI GEODEZII. TRUDY. 1976. irreg. 0.80 Rub. per issue. Izdatel'stvo Tsniigaik, Ul. Onezhskaya, 26, Moscow A-Y13, Russia. Ed. V. Chernikov. abstr.; charts. circ. 500.

554   BU   ISSN 0204-5109
TN860   CODEN: NVGEDV
NEFTENA I VUGLISTNA GEOLOGIIA/PETROLEUM AND COAL GEOLOGY. (Text in Bulgarian or Russian; summaries in English, French and German) 1975. irreg. 1.15 lv. per no. (Bulgarska Akademiia na Naukite) Publishing House of the Bulgarian Academy of Sciences, Acad. G. Bonchev St., Bldg. 6, 1113 Sofia, Bulgaria. (Dist. by: Hemus, 6, Rouski Blvd., 1000 Sofia, Bulgaria) illus. circ. 420. (reprint service avail. from IRC) **Indexed:** BSL Geo., Chem.Abstr., Geo.Abstr., GeoRef.
—CASDDS.
Formerly: Bulgarska Akademiia na Naukite. Geologicheski Institut. Izvestiia. Seriie Neftena i Vuglishtna Geologiia.

554   NE   ISSN 0077-7617
NETHERLANDS. RIJKS GEOLOGISCHE DIENST. JAARVERSLAG/NETHERLANDS GEOLOGICAL SURVEY. ANNUAL REPORT. (Text in Dutch and English) 1968. a. free. Rijks Geologische Dienst, Postbus 157, 2000 AD Haarlem, Netherlands. TEL 31-23-300300. FAX 31-23-351614. TELEX 71105 GEOLD NL. **Indexed:** GeoRef. **Document type:** government publication.

551 560   GW   ISSN 0077-7749
                      CODEN: NEJPAP
NEUES JAHRBUCH FUER GEOLOGIE UND PALAEONTOLOGIE. ABHANDLUNGEN. 1807. irreg. (2-3 vols./yr., 3 nos./vol.). price varies. E. Schweizerbart'sche Verlagsbuchhandlung, Johannesstr. 3A, 70176 Stuttgart, Germany. TEL 0711-625001. FAX 0711-625005. TELEX 723363-SCHB-D. Ed.Bd. adv.; index. **Indexed:** Biol.Abstr., Chem.Abstr., Deep Sea Res.& Oceanogr.Abstr., Petrol.Abstr.
—BLDSC (6078.000000); UnCover; SWETS. **CCC.**
Supersedes in part and continues volume numbering of: Neues Jahrbuch fuer Mineralogie, Geologie und Palaeontologie. Abhandlungen.

551 560   GW   ISSN 0028-3630
QE1   CODEN: NJGMA2
NEUES JAHRBUCH FUER GEOLOGIE UND PALAEONTOLOGIE, MONATSHEFTE. (Text in English and German) 1900. m. E. Schweizerbart'sche Verlagsbuchhandlung, Johannesstr. 3A, 70176 Stuttgart, Germany. TEL 0711-625001. FAX 0711-625005. TELEX 723363-SCHB-D. Ed.Bd. adv.; bk.rev.; bibl.; charts; illus. **Indexed:** Biol.Abstr., Chem.Abstr., Deep Sea Res.& Oceanogr.Abstr., Petrol.Abstr. **Document type:** academic/scholarly publication.
—BLDSC (6078.100000); UnCover; SWETS; CASDDS. **CCC.**

NEUES JAHRBUCH FUER MINERALOGIE. ABHANDLUNGEN. see *MINES AND MINING INDUSTRY*

NEUES JAHRBUCH FUER MINERALOGIE. MONATSHEFTE. see *MINES AND MINING INDUSTRY*

557 622   US
NEVADA. BUREAU OF MINES AND GEOLOGY. BULLETIN. 1904. irreg. no.107, 1993. price varies. Bureau of Mines and Geology, University of Nevada at Reno, Reno, NV 89557-0088. TEL 702-784-6691. **Indexed:** GeoRef. **Document type:** government publication, bulletin.

557   US
NEVADA. BUREAU OF MINES AND GEOLOGY. OPEN-FILE REPORTS. irreg., latest 1993. price varies. Bureau of Mines and Geology, University of Nevada at Reno, Reno, NV 89557-0088. TEL 702-784-6691. **Document type:** government publication.

557 622   US   ISSN 0095-5264
TN24.N3   CODEN: RNMGDL
NEVADA. BUREAU OF MINES AND GEOLOGY. REPORT. Key Title: Report - Nevada Bureau of Mines and Geology. 1962. irreg., no.47, 1992. Bureau of Mines and Geology, University of Nevada at Reno, Reno, NV 89557-0088. TEL 702-784-6691. illus. **Indexed:** GeoRef. **Document type:** government publication.
—CASDDS.
Supersedes: Nevada. Bureau of Mines. Report.

557   US
NEVADA. BUREAU OF MINES AND GEOLOGY. SPECIAL PUBLICATIONS. 1975. irreg., no.15, 1993. price varies. Bureau of Mines and Geology, University of Nevada at Reno, Reno, NV 89557-0088. TEL 702-784-6691. FAX 702-784-6691. **Document type:** government publication.

557   US
NEVADA GEOLOGY. 1988. q. free. Bureau of Mines and Geology, Mackay School of Mines, University of Nevada at Reno, Reno, NV 89557-0088. TEL 702-784-6691. FAX 702-784-1709. Ed. Dick Meeuwig. bk.rev.; charts; maps; stat. **Document type:** government publication, newsletter.
Description: News of projects and publications sponsored by the Nevada Bureau of Mines and Geology.

557   US
NEVADA MINERAL INDUSTRY (YEAR). 1979. a. price varies. Bureau of Mines and Geology, University of Nevada at Reno, Reno, NV 89557-0088. TEL 702-784-6691. FAX 702-784-1709. **Document type:** government publication.
Description: Includes listing of active mines.

NEW CALEDONIA. SERVICE DES MINES ET DE L'ENERGY. RAPPORT ANNUEL. see *MINES AND MINING INDUSTRY*

557   US
NEW JERSEY. GEOLOGICAL SURVEY. BULLETIN. 1910. irreg. price varies. Geological Survey, CN-029, Trenton, NJ 08625. Ed. David P. Harper. circ. 500. **Indexed:** GeoRef. **Document type:** government publication, bulletin.
Formerly: New Jersey. Bureau of Geology and Topography. Bulletin.

557   US   ISSN 0741-7357
Z6034.U5
NEW JERSEY. GEOLOGICAL SURVEY. REPORT SERIES. 1959. irreg., no.20, 1989. price varies. Geological Survey, CN-029, Trenton, NJ 08625. Ed. David P. Harper. circ. 500. **Indexed:** GeoRef. **Document type:** government publication.
Formerly: New Jersey. Bureau of Geology and Topography. Geologic Report Series.

557   US   ISSN 0077-8567
QE1   CODEN: NMGGA5
NEW MEXICO GEOLOGICAL SOCIETY. GUIDEBOOK, FIELD CONFERENCE. 1950. irreg., no.44, 1993. price varies. New Mexico Geological Society, Inc., Campus Station, Socorro, NM 87801. TEL 505-835-5410. Ed. Spencer Lucas. adv. circ. 1,500. **Indexed:** GeoRef.

551   US
NEW MEXICO GEOLOGY. 1979. q. $6. Bureau of Mines and Mineral Resources, Campus Station, Socorro, NM 87801. TEL 505-835-5410. Ed. Carol A. Hjellming. bk.rev.; index. circ. 1,200. (back issues avail.)

559.4   AT   ISSN 0155-5561
                      CODEN: NSWGAP
NEW SOUTH WALES. GEOLOGICAL SURVEY. BULLETIN. 1922. irreg., no.32, 1988. price varies. Department of Mineral Resources, P.O. Box 536, St. Leonards, N.S.W. 2065, Australia. TEL 02-901-8262. Ed. H. Basden. index. circ. 400. **Indexed:** AESIS, GeoRef. **Document type:** bulletin.

559.4   AT   ISSN 0077-8710
QE341   CODEN: NGMGAR
NEW SOUTH WALES. GEOLOGICAL SURVEY. MEMOIRS: GEOLOGY. 1887. irreg., no. 12, 1993. price varies. Department of Mineral Resources, P.O. Box 536, St. Leonards, N.S.W. 2065, Australia. TEL 02-901-8262. Ed. H. Basden. index. circ. 400. **Indexed:** AESIS, GeoRef.

551 549   AT
NEW SOUTH WALES. GEOLOGICAL SURVEY. METALLOGENIC STUDY AND MINERAL DEPOSIT DATA SHEETS. 1972. irreg. price varies. Department of Mineral Resources, P.O. Box 536, St. Leonards, N.S.W. 2065, Australia. TEL 02 901-8262. Ed. H. Basden. circ. 400. **Document type:** government publication.
Former titles: New South Wales. Geological Survey. Mineral Deposit Data Sheets and Metallogenic Study; New South Wales. Geological Survey. Mine Data Sheets and Metallogenic Study (ISSN 0727-9418)
Description: Contains mineral deposit inventory with geological and metallogenic discussion.

NEW SOUTH WALES. GEOLOGICAL SURVEY. MINERAL INDUSTRY SERIES. see *MINES AND MINING INDUSTRY*

NEW SOUTH WALES. GEOLOGICAL SURVEY. MINERAL RESOURCES SERIES. see *MINES AND MINING INDUSTRY*

551   AT   ISSN 0155-3410
QE341   CODEN: QNGSDG
NEW SOUTH WALES. GEOLOGICAL SURVEY. QUARTERLY NOTES. 1970. q. Aus.$10. Department of Mineral Resources, P.O. Box 536, St. Leonards, N.S.W. 2065, Australia. TEL 02 901-8262. Ed. H. Basden. circ. 700. **Indexed:** AESIS. **Document type:** government publication.
—BLDSC (7196.750000).
Description: Directed to academic and minerals-industry geologists.

EARTH SCIENCES — GEOLOGY

559.4 AT ISSN 0155-3372
NEW SOUTH WALES. GEOLOGICAL SURVEY. RECORDS.
1889. irreg., no.23, 1986. price varies. Department of Mineral Resources, P.O. Box 536, St. Leonards, N.S.W. 2065, Australia. TEL 02 901-8262. Ed. H. Basden. circ. 400. **Indexed:** AESIS, GeoRef. **Document type:** government publication.
—BLDSC (7319.450000).
Description: Papers on geology and mineral deposits.

551 US ISSN 0097-3793
NEW YORK STATE MUSEUM. MAP AND CHART SERIES.
1960. irreg., no.43, 1993. price varies. New York State Museum, 3140 Cultural Education Center, Albany, NY 12230. **Document type:** government publication.
Description: Geologic maps and charts of New York State, with annotation and commentary.

551 559.3 NZ ISSN 0028-8306
QE1 CODEN: NEZOAY
NEW ZEALAND JOURNAL OF GEOLOGY AND GEOPHYSICS. 1958. q. NZ.$220($190) (effective 1993). (Royal Society of New Zealand) S I R Publishing, P.O. Box 399, Wellington, New Zealand. TEL 04-472-7421. FAX 04-473-1841. (Subscr. addr. in U.S.: SIR Publishing, 810 East 10th St., P.O. Box 1897, Lawrence, KS 66044-8897. TEL 913-843-1221) Ed. R. Lynch. abstr.; bibl.; charts; illus.; index. circ. 650. (back issues avail.) **Indexed:** Abstr.J.Earthq.Eng., AESIS, Biol.Abstr., Chem.Abstr., Curr.Cont., Deep Sea Res.& Oceanogr.Abstr., Geo.Abstr., GeoRef., Ind.Sci.Rev., Ocean.Abstr., Petrol.Abstr., Pollut.Abstr., Sel.Water Res.Abstr., So.Pac.Per.Ind., Soils & Fert.
—BLDSC (6094.500000); Faxon; UnCover; CASDDS. **CCC.**
Description: Publishes papers on all aspects of earth sciences with particular interest in papers of the circum-Pacific region.

557 CN
NEWFOUNDLAND. GEOLOGICAL SURVEY BRANCH. BULLETIN. 1934. irreg., no.38, 1969. price varies. Department of Mines and Energy, Geological Survey Branch, P.O. Box 8700, St. John's, Nfld. A1B 4J6, Canada. TEL 709-576-6487. FAX 709-576-3493. **Document type:** bulletin.
Formerly: Newfoundland. Mineral Development Division. Geological Survey. Bulletin. (ISSN 0078-0308)

557 CN ISSN 0078-0383
NEWFOUNDLAND. MINES BRANCH. GEOLOGICAL SURVEY OF NEWFOUNDLAND. REPORT SERIES. 1953. irreg. price varies. Department of Mines and Energy, Geological Survey Branch, P.O. Box 8700, St. John's, Nfld. A1B 4J6, Canada. TEL 709-576-6487. FAX 709-576-3493.

551.7 GW ISSN 0078-0421
QE640 CODEN: NLSGAO
NEWSLETTERS ON STRATIGRAPHY. (Text in English or German) 1970. 3/yr. price varies. Gebrueder Borntraeger Verlagsbuchhandlung, Johannesstr. 3A, 70176 Stuttgart, Germany. TEL 0711-625001. FAX 0711-625005. TELEX 723363-SCHB-D. Ed. Gerd Luettig. adv.; abstr.; charts; illus. **Indexed:** Biol.Abstr., Br.Geol.Lit., GeoRef, Petrol.Abstr. **Document type:** academic/scholarly publication, newsletter.
—BLDSC (6108.740000); UnCover. **CCC.**

NIGERIAN MINING AND GEOSCIENCES SOCIETY. JOURNAL. see MINES AND MINING INDUSTRY

551 JA ISSN 0912-6627
NIHON CHISHITSU GAKKAI KANSAI SHIBU KAIHO/GEOLOGICAL SOCIETY OF JAPAN. KANSAI BRANCH. PROCEEDINGS. (Text in Japanese) irreg. Nihon Chishitsu Gakkai, Jansai Shibu - Geological Society of Japan, Kansai Branch, Osaka Shiritsu Daigaku Rigakubu Chigaku Kyoshitsu, 3-138, Sugimoto 3-chome, Sumiyoshi-ku, Osaka 558, Japan. **Document type:** proceedings.

NIHON DOKETSUGAKU KENKYUJO HOKOKU/SPELEOLOGICAL RESEARCH INSTITUTE OF JAPAN. ANNUAL. see PALEONTOLOGY

551 JA
NIHON OYO CHISHITSU GAKKAI KENKYU HAPPYOKAI KOEN RONBUNSHU/JAPAN SOCIETY OF ENGINEERING GEOLOGY. PROCEEDINGS OF MEETING. (Text in Japanese) a. Nihon Oyo Chishitsu Gakkai - Japan Society of Engineering Geology, 1-9, Takadanobaba 2-chome, Shinjuku-ku, Tokyo 169, Japan. **Document type:** proceedings.

551 JA ISSN 0917-2289
NIHON OYO CHISHITSU GAKKAI KYUSHU SHIBU KAIHO/JAPAN SOCIETY OF ENGINEERING GEOLOGY. KYUSHU BRANCH REPORT. (Text in Japanese) a. Nihon Oyo Chishitsu Gakkai, Kyushu Shibu - Japan Society of Engineering Geology, Kyushu Branch, Nihon Chiken K.K., 25-25, Morooka 5-chome, Hakata-ku, Fukuoka-shi, Fukuoka-ken 816, Japan.

555 549 JA ISSN 0369-5638
NIIGATA UNIVERSITY. FACULTY OF SCIENCE. SCIENCE REPORTS. SERIES E: GEOLOGY AND MINERALOGY/NIIGATA DAIGAKU RIGAKUBU KENKYU HOKOKU. E-RUI, CHISHITSU KOBUTSUGAKU. (Text in English) 1952. a. exchange basis. Niigata Daigaku, Rigakubu - Niigata University, Faculty of Science, 8050 Igarashi Nino-cho, Niigata-shi, Nigata-ken 950-21, Japan. **Indexed:** Biol.Abstr.
Supersedes in part (in 1964): Niigata University. Faculty of Science. Journal. Series 2: Biology, Geology, and Mineralogy (ISSN 0549-4842)

NISHINIHON GANBAN KOGAKU SHINPOJUMU RONBUNSHU/PROCEEDINGS OF WEST JAPAN SYMPOSIUM ON ROCK ENGINEERING. see ENGINEERING — Civil Engineering

NONRENEWABLE RESOURCES. see MINES AND MINING INDUSTRY

551 NO ISSN 0333-4112
NORGES GEOLOGISKE UNDERSOEKELSE. AARSMELDING.
1922. a. free. Norges Geologiske Undersoekelse - Geological Survey of Norway, Leiv Erikssons vei 39, P.O. Box 3006 Lade, Trondheim 7002, Norway. FAX 7-92-16-20. TELEX 55417-NGU-N. Ed. Anne Katharine Dahl. illus. circ. 5,000.

551 NO ISSN 0029-196X
QE1 CODEN: NOGTAO
NORSK GEOLOGISK TIDSSKRIFT/NORWEGIAN JOURNAL OF GEOLOGY. (Text in English) 1905. q. NOK 740 in the Nordic countries; elsewhere NOK 810. (Norwegian Geological Society) Scandinavian University Press, P.O. Box 2959-Toeyen, N-0608 Oslo, Norway. TEL 472-67-7600. FAX 472-67-7575. (U.S. addr.: Scandinavian University Press, 200 Meacham Ave., Elmont, NY 11003. TEL 516-352-7300) Ed. Allan Krill. bk.rev.; charts; illus.; index. circ. 1,400. (also avail. in microform from UMI; back issues avail.; reprint service avail. from ISI) **Indexed:** Bibl.& Ind.Geol., Biol.Abstr., Br.Geol.Lit., Chem.Abstr., Curr.Cont., Energy Res.Abstr., Geo.Abstr., Ind.Sci.Rev., Met.Abstr., NAA, Petrol.Abstr., Sci.Cit.Ind., World Alum.Abstr.
—BLDSC (6140.000000); Faxon; UnCover; UMI; CASDDS. **CCC.**
Description: Main journal for Norwegian geological research, distributed to all members of the Norwegian Geological Society and internationally.

508.982 NO ISSN 0085-4271
G575 CODEN: NPOAAE
NORSK POLARINSTITUTT. AARBOK. 1960. a. free. Norsk Polarinstitutt, Postboks 158, 1330 Oslo Lufthavn, Norway. FAX 02-123854. TELEX 74745 POLAR. **Indexed:** Deep Sea Res.& Oceanogr.Abstr., Meteor.& Geoastrophys.Abstr. **Document type:** academic/scholarly publication.
Description: Annual report of the Norwegian Polar Research Institute.

551 NO ISSN 0373-5605
CODEN: NPMEAG
NORSK POLARINSTITUTT. MEDDELELSER. (Editions in English, Norwegian) 1926. irreg., no.121, 1992. Norsk Polarinstitutt, Postboks 158, 1330 Oslo Lufthavn, Norway. FAX 02-123854. TELEX 74745 POLAR. **Indexed:** Deep Sea Res.& Oceanogr.Abstr., Meteor.& Geoastrophys.Abstr.
Formerly: Norges Svalbard- og Ishavs-Undersoekelser.
Description: Non-refereed science publication treating subjects concerning the polar regions.

551 NO ISSN 0474-8042
NORSK POLARINSTITUTT. POLARHAANDBOK. Short title: Polarhaandbok. (Editions in English, Norwegian) 1964. irreg., latest vol.5, 1990. Norsk Polarinstitutt, Postboks 158, 1330 Oslo Lufthavn, Norway. FAX 02-123854. TELEX 74745 POLAR. **Document type:** academic/scholarly publication.
Description: Each handbook on a separate subject concerning the polar regions.

551 NO ISSN 0369-5417
Q115 CODEN: NPOSAY
NORSK POLARINSTITUTT. SKRIFTER. (Editions in English, French or German) 1929. irreg., no.191, 1989. Norsk Polarinstitutt, Postboks 158, 1330 Oslo Lufthavn, Norway. FAX 02-123854. TELEX 74745 POLAR. **Indexed:** Biol.Abstr., Br.Geol.Lit., Deep Sea Res.& Oceanogr.Abstr., Geo.Abstr., GeoRef. **Document type:** academic/scholarly publication.
—UnCover.
Former titles: Norges Svalbard- og Ishavs-Undersoekelser. Skrifter; Skrifter om Svalbard og Ishavet; Skrifter om Svalbard og Nordishavet; Norske Statsunderstoettede Spitsbergenekspedisjoner. Resultater.
Description: Monographic papers on subjects within the field of polar research.
Refereed Serial

551 US
NORTH CAROLINA. DEPARTMENT OF ENVIRONMENT, HEALTH, AND NATURAL RESOURCES. DIVISION OF LAND RESOURCES. BULLETIN. 1893. irreg., no.91, 1989. price varies. North Carolina Geological Survey, Box 27687, Raleigh, NC 27611. TEL 919-733-2423. **Indexed:** GeoRef. **Document type:** bulletin.
Former titles: North Carolina. Department of Natural Resources and Community Development. Division of Land Resources. Bulletin; North Carolina. Division of Mineral Resources. Bulletin.

551 US
NORTH CAROLINA. DEPARTMENT OF ENVIRONMENT, HEALTH, AND NATURAL RESOURCES. DIVISION OF LAND RESOURCES. INFORMATION CIRCULAR. 1940. irreg., no.25, 1989. price varies. North Carolina Geological Survey, Box 27687, Raleigh, NC 27611. TEL 919-733-2423. **Indexed:** GeoRef.
Former titles: North Carolina. Department of Natural Resources and Community Development. Division of Land Resources. Information Circular; North Carolina. Division of Mineral Resources. Information Circular.

557 US ISSN 0546-5001
GB705.N9
NORTH DAKOTA. GEOLOGICAL SURVEY. BULLETIN.
1920. irreg., latest 1989. free. Geological Survey, 600 E. Boulevard Ave., Bismarck, ND 58505-0840. TEL 701-224-4109. (back issues avail.) **Indexed:** GeoRef. **Document type:** bulletin.

557 US ISSN 0091-9004
QE149 CODEN: NDGSBD
NORTH DAKOTA. GEOLOGICAL SURVEY. EDUCATIONAL SERIES. Key Title: Educational Series - North Dakota Geological Survey. 1972. irreg., no.22, 1993. price varies. Geological Survey, 600 E. Boulevard Ave., Bismarck, ND 58505-0840. TEL 701-224-4109. illus. (back issues avail.) **Indexed:** GeoRef.

557 US ISSN 0078-1576
QE149 CODEN: NDGXAR
NORTH DAKOTA. GEOLOGICAL SURVEY. MISCELLANEOUS SERIES. 1957. irreg., no.79, 1993. price varies. Geological Survey, 600 E. Boulevard Ave., Bismarck, ND 58505-0840. TEL 701-224-4109. (back issues avail.) **Indexed:** GeoRef.
—BLDSC (5827.200000); UnCover.

552 US ISSN 0889-3594
NORTH DAKOTA. GEOLOGICAL SURVEY. NEWSLETTER.
Key Title: N D G S Newsletter. 1973. q. free. Geological Survey, 600 E. Boulevard Ave., Bismarck, ND 58505-0840. TEL 701-224-4109. Ed. Robert Biek. circ. 3,000. (back issues avail.) **Document type:** newsletter.
—UnCover.

EARTH SCIENCES — GEOLOGY

551 US
NORTH DAKOTA. GEOLOGICAL SURVEY. REPORT OF INVESTIGATIONS. 1955. irreg., no.96, 1993. price varies. Geological Survey, 600 E. Boulevard Ave., Bismarck, ND 58505-0840. TEL 701-224-4106. illus. circ. 1,500. (back issues avail.)

557 US ISSN 0194-1453
QE78.3
NORTHEASTERN GEOLOGY. 1979. q. $35 to individuals (foreign $45); institutions $52 (foreign $62) (effective 1994). Northeastern Science Foundation, Inc., 15 Third St., Box 746, Troy, NY 12181-0746. TEL 518-273-3247. Ed. Gerald M. Friedman. adv.; bk.rev.; charts; illus.; index. (back issues avail.) **Indexed:** GeoRef., Sel.Water Res.Abstr. **Document type:** academic/scholarly publication.
—BLDSC (6150.297000); Faxon. **CCC.**
Incorporates (1982-1990): Northeastern Environmental Science (ISSN 0730-630X)
Description: Research papers on the geology of northeastern North America.

O.R.S.T.O.M. RESUMES DES TRAVAUX. OCEANOGRAPHIE. (Office de la Recherche Scientifique et Technique Outre-Mer) see EARTH SCIENCES — Oceanography

551 GW ISSN 0078-2947
CODEN: JMOGAZ
OBERRHEINISCHER GEOLOGISCHER VEREIN. JAHRESBERICHTE UND MITTEILUNGEN. 1911. a. price varies. E. Schweizerbart'sche Verlagsbuchhandlung, Johannesstr. 3a, 70176 Stuttgart, Germany. TEL 0711-625001. FAX 0711-625005. TELEX 723363-SCHB-D. Ed. P. Rothe. **Indexed:** GeoRef. **Document type:** academic/scholarly publication.
—**CCC.**

OCEANOLOGICAL SOCIETY OF KOREA. JOURNAL. see EARTH SCIENCES — Oceanography

551 560 AU ISSN 0251-7493
OESTERREICHISCHE GEOLOGISCHE GESELLSCHAFT. MITTEILUNGEN. (Text in German; summaries in English) 1908. a. S.380. Oesterreichische Geologische Gesellschaft, Universitaet Str. 7, A-1010 Vienna, Austria. Eds. Alexander and Edith Tollmann. adv.; bk.rev. circ. 1,300. **Indexed:** Biol.Abstr., Deep Sea Res.& Oceanogr.Abstr.
Supersedes: Geologische Gesellschaft, Vienna. Mitteilungen (ISSN 0016-7843)

557 US ISSN 0097-5478
CODEN: ODGBA6
OHIO. DIVISION OF GEOLOGICAL SURVEY. BULLETIN. 1903. irreg., no.69, 1991. price varies. Ohio Department of Natural Resources, Division of Geological Survey, 4383 Fountain Square Dr., Columbus, OH 43224-1362. TEL 614-265-6605. FAX 614-447-1918. illus. (back issues avail.) **Indexed:** GeoRef. **Document type:** government publication, bulletin.
—UnCover.

557 US ISSN 0472-6685
OHIO. DIVISION OF GEOLOGICAL SURVEY. EDUCATIONAL LEAFLET. 1956. irreg. no.15, 1989. free. Ohio Department of Natural Resources, Division of Geological Survey, 4383 Fountain Square Dr., Columbus, OH 43224-1362. TEL 614-265-6605. FAX 614-447-1918. (back issues avail.) **Document type:** government publication.

557 US
OHIO. DIVISION OF GEOLOGICAL SURVEY. GEOLOGICAL NOTE. 1975. irreg., no.6, 1979. price varies. Ohio Department of Natural Resources, Division of Geological Survey, 4383 Fountain Square Dr., Columbus, OH 43224-1362. TEL 614-265-6605. FAX 614-447-1918. illus. (back issues avail.) **Document type:** government publication.

557 US ISSN 0097-9473
QE151 CODEN: OGSGA
OHIO. DIVISION OF GEOLOGICAL SURVEY. GUIDEBOOK. Key Title: Guidebook - State of Ohio, Department of Natural Resources, Division of Geological Survey. 1973. irreg., no.13, 1994. price varies. Ohio Department of Natural Resources, Division of Geological Survey, 4383 Fountain Square Dr., Columbus, OH 43224-1362. TEL 614-265-6605. FAX 614-447-1918. illus. (back issues avail.) **Document type:** government publication, monographic series.

557 US
OHIO. DIVISION OF GEOLOGICAL SURVEY. INFORMATION CIRCULAR. 1946. irreg., no.57, 1992. price varies. Ohio Department of Natural Resources, Division of Geological Survey, 4383 Fountain Square Dr., Columbus, OH 43224-1362. TEL 614-265-6605. FAX 614-447-1918. illus. (back issues avail.) **Document type:** government publication.

557 US ISSN 0361-0519
CODEN: MOGSDD
OHIO. DIVISION OF GEOLOGICAL SURVEY. MISCELLANEOUS REPORT. Key Title: Miscellaneous Report - State of Ohio, Department of Natural Resources, Division of Geological Survey. 1974. irreg., no.6, 1992. Ohio Department of Natural Resources, Division of Geological Survey, 4383 Fountain Square Dr., Columbus, OH 43224-1362. TEL 614-265-6605. FAX 614-447-1918. (back issues avail.) **Indexed:** Chem.Abstr. **Document type:** government publication.

557 US
OHIO. DIVISION OF GEOLOGICAL SURVEY. REPORT OF INVESTIGATIONS. 1947. irreg., no.144, 1993. price varies. Ohio Department of Natural Resources, Division of Geological Survey, 4383 Fountain Square Dr., Columbus, OH 43224. TEL 614-265-6605. FAX 614-447-1918. illus. (back issues avail.) **Indexed:** GeoRef. **Document type:** government publication.

OIL AND GAS; monthly report on drilling in Illinois. see PETROLEUM AND GAS

552 CN
OIL AND GAS FIELD DESIGNATIONS. q. Can.$24. Ministry of Energy, Mines and Petroleum Resources, Energy Resources Division, 7th Fl., 1810 Blanshard St., Victoria, BC V8V 1X4, Canada. (Subscr. to: Crown Publications, 546 Yates St., Victoria, BC V8W 1K8, Canada. TEL 604-386-4636) (processed; back issues avail.)
Description: Field descriptions consisting of the lands contained within each field.

552 665.5 CN
OIL AND GAS POOL DESCRIPTIONS. q. Can.$60. Ministry of Energy, Mines and Petroleum Resources, Energy Resources Division, 7th Fl., 1810 Blanshard St., Victoria, BC V8V 1X4, Canada. (Subscr. to: Crown Publications, 546 Yates St., Victoria, BC V8W 1K8, Canada. TEL 604-386-4636)
Description: Descriptions of oil and gas pools as designated or amended.

OILFIELD REVIEW. see PETROLEUM AND GAS

551.23 JA ISSN 0289-3134
OITAKEN ONSEN CHOSA HOKOKU/OITA PREFECTURE. ANNUAL DATA OF HOT SPRING RESEARCH. (Text in Japanese) 1959. a. Oitaken Hoken Kankyobu - Oita Prefectural Government, Health and Environment Division, 1-1, Otemachi 3-chome, Oita-shi, Oita-ken 870, Japan. **Document type:** government publication.

551.23 JA ISSN 0289-2413
OITAKEN ONSEN CHOSA KENKYUKAI HOKOKU/HOT SPRING RESEARCH ASSOCIATION OF OITA PREFECTURE. ANNUAL BULLETIN. (Text in Japanese) 1949. a. Oitaken Onsen Chosa Kenkyukai, Oitaken Kankyo Hokenbu, 1-1, Otemachi 3-chome, Oita-shi, Oita-ken 870, Japan.

550 624 JA ISSN 0917-5687
OKINAWA DOSHITSU KOGAKU KENKYU HAPPYOKAI KOEN GAIYOSHU/OKINAWA GEOTECHNICAL SOCIETY. PAPERS OF ANNUAL MEETING. (Text in Japanese) 1988. a. Okinawa Doshitsu Kogaku Kenkyukai, Ryukyu Daigaku Kogakubu Doboku Kogakka, 1, Senbaru, Nakagami-gun, Okinawa-ken 903-01, Japan.

557 US ISSN 0078-4389
QE153 CODEN: OKGBAL
OKLAHOMA GEOLOGICAL SURVEY. BULLETIN. 1908. irreg., no.145, 1992. price varies. Oklahoma Geological Survey, University of Oklahoma, 100 E. Boyd, Rm. N-131, Norman, OK 73019. TEL 405-325-3031. bibl.; charts; illus.; index. circ. 500. (also avail. in microfilm; back issues avail.) **Indexed:** Chem.Abstr., GeoRef., Petrol.Abstr. **Document type:** bulletin.
—BLDSC (2670.000000); UnCover.

557 US ISSN 0078-4397
QE153 CODEN: OKGCAO
OKLAHOMA GEOLOGICAL SURVEY. CIRCULAR. 1908. irreg. no.94, 1992. price varies. Oklahoma Geological Survey, University of Oklahoma, 100 E. Boyd, Rm. N-131, Norman, OK 73019. TEL 405-325-3031. bibl.; charts; illus.; stat.; index. circ. 500. (microfilm; back issues avail.) **Indexed:** Biol.Abstr., Chem.Abstr., Geo.Abstr., GeoRef., Petro.Abstr.
—BLDSC (3249.650000); UnCover; CASDDS.
Refereed Serial

557 US ISSN 0160-8746
CODEN: OGSEBT
OKLAHOMA GEOLOGICAL SURVEY. EDUCATIONAL PUBLICATION. 1971. irreg., no.4, 1981. price varies. Oklahoma Geological Survey, University of Oklahoma, 100 E. Boyd, R. N-131, Norman, OK 73019. TEL 405-321-3031. circ. 1,200. (reprint service avail. from UMI)

557 US ISSN 0078-4400
QE153 CODEN: OGGBAR
OKLAHOMA GEOLOGICAL SURVEY. GUIDEBOOK. 1953. irreg., no.28, 1993. price varies. Oklahoma Geological Survey, University of Oklahoma, 100 E. Boyd, Rm. N-131, Norman, OK 73019. TEL 405-325-3031. circ. 500. (reprint service avail. from UMI)

557 US ISSN 0275-0929
OKLAHOMA GEOLOGICAL SURVEY. SPECIAL PUBLICATION SERIES. irreg., latest no.93-2. Oklahoma Geological Survey, University of Oklahoma, 100 E. Boyd, Rm. N-131, Norman, OK 73019. TEL 405-325-3031. (reprint service avail. from UMI)
—BLDSC (8379.655000).
Refereed Serial

557 US ISSN 0030-1736
TN1 CODEN: OKGNAN
OKLAHOMA GEOLOGY NOTES. 1941. bi-m. $6. Oklahoma Geological Survey, University of Oklahoma, 100 E. Boyd, Rm. N-131, Norman, OK 73019. TEL 405-325-3031. Ed. Christie Cooper. bk.rev.; bibl.; charts; illus.; index. circ. 1,500. (also avail. in microfilm from UMI; reprint service avail. from UMI) **Indexed:** Biol.Abstr., Chem.Abstr., Geo.Abstr., GeoRef., Petrol.Abstr.
—UnCover; UMI.
Formerly (until vol.15, 1956): Hopper.
Refereed Serial

551.23 JA ISSN 0369-7665
CODEN: ONKOBY
ONSEN KOGAKKAISHI/SOCIETY OF ENGINEERS FOR MINERAL SPRINGS. JOURNAL. (Text in Japanese; summaries in English, Japanese) 1963. 2/yr. 1500 Yen per no. Onsen Kogakkai - Society of Engineers for Mineral Springs, Chuo Onsen Kenkyujo, 42-10, Takada 3-chome, Toshima-ku, Tokyo 171, Japan. **Indexed:** INIS Atomind., Jap.Per.Ind.
—CASDDS.

557 622 CN
ONTARIO GEOLOGICAL SURVEY. GUIDE BOOKS. 1968. irreg. (1-2/yr.). price varies. Ontario Geological Survey, 933 Ramsey Lake Rd., Sudbury, ON P3E 6B5, Canada. TEL 416-314-3800. FAX 416-314-3797. (Subscr. to: Mines & Minerals Information Centre, Rm. M2-17, MacDonald Block, 900 Bay St., Toronto, ON M7A 1C3, Canada) (also avail. in microfiche; back issues avail.) **Document type:** government publication.
Formerly: Ontario. Division of Mines. Guide Books.

ONTARIO GEOLOGICAL SURVEY. REPORT. see MINES AND MINING INDUSTRY

ONTARIO GEOLOGICAL SURVEY. REPORT OF ACTIVITIES, RESIDENT GEOLOGISTS. see MINES AND MINING INDUSTRY

OPERA LILLOANA. see BIOLOGY — Botany

EARTH SCIENCES — GEOLOGY

551 NE ISSN 0169-1368
CODEN: OGREER
ORE GEOLOGY REVIEWS; journal for comprehensive studies of ore genesis and ore exploration. (Text in English) 1986. 6/yr. fl.566($306) (effective 1994). Elsevier Science B.V., P.O. Box 211, 1000 AE Amsterdam, Netherlands. TEL 31-20-5803911. FAX 31-20-5803598. TELEX 18582 ESPA NL. (Subscr. in U.S. and Canada to: Elsevier Science Inc., Box 882, Madison Sq. Sta., New York, NY 10159. TEL 212-989-5800. FAX 212-633-3990) Ed.Bd. (also avail. in microform from UMI; back issues avail.) Indexed: Curr.Cont., Eng.Ind., Geo.Abstr., Mineral.Abstr. Document type: academic/scholarly publication.
—BLDSC (6280.830000); EI; Faxon; UnCover; SWETS; CASDDS. CCC.
 Description: Aims to familiarize all earth scientists with recent advances in a number of interconnected disciplines related to the study of, and search for, ore deposits.
 Refereed Serial

557 622 US ISSN 0078-5709
QE155 CODEN: OGMBAN
OREGON. DEPARTMENT OF GEOLOGY AND MINERAL INDUSTRIES. BULLETIN. 1938. irreg., no.103, 1987. price varies. Department of Geology and Mineral Industries, 800 N.E. Oregon St., No. 28, Ste. 965, Portland, OR 97232-2109. TEL 503-731-4100. FAX 503-731-4066. Document type: bulletin.

OREGON. DEPARTMENT OF GEOLOGY AND MINERAL INDUSTRIES. OIL AND GAS INVESTIGATIONS. see *PETROLEUM AND GAS*

550 US
OREGON. DEPARTMENT OF GEOLOGY AND MINERAL INDUSTRIES. OPEN FILE REPORTS. 1966. irreg., latest 1993. price varies. Department of Geology and Mineral Industries, 800 N.E. Oregon St., No. 28, Ste. 965, Portland, OR 97232-2109.
TEL 503-731-4100. FAX 503-731-4066. stat.

551 US
OREGON. DEPARTMENT OF GEOLOGY AND MINERAL INDUSTRIES. SPECIAL PAPERS. 1978. irreg., no.26, 1992. price varies. Department of Geology and Mineral Industries, 800 N.E. Oregon St., No. 28, Ste. 965, Portland, OR 97232-2109.
TEL 503-731-4100. FAX 503-731-4066.

553 553 US ISSN 0164-3304
TN1 CODEN: ORGEEF
OREGON GEOLOGY. 1939. bi-m. $8. Department of Geology and Mineral Industries, 800 N.E. Oregon St., No. 28, Ste. 965, Portland, OR 97232-2109. TEL 503-731-4100. FAX 503-731-4066. Ed. B. Vogt. bk.rev.; bibl.; charts; illus. circ. 2,000. (back issues avail.) Indexed: Geo.Abstr., GeoRef., Petrol.Abstr.
 Formerly (until vol.40, no.12, 1978): Ore Bin (ISSN 0148-1827)
 Refereed Serial

ORGANIC GEOCHEMISTRY. see *CHEMISTRY — Organic Chemistry*

OSNOVANIYA, FUNDAMENTY I MEKHANIKA GRUNTOV. see *ENGINEERING — Civil Engineering*

OUTER CONTINENTAL SHELF RESOURCE DEVELOPMENT NEWS. see *EARTH SCIENCES — Oceanography*

551 JA ISSN 0286-7737
OYO CHISHITSU/JAPAN SOCIETY OF ENGINEERING GEOLOGY. JOURNAL. (Text in Japanese; summaries in English) 1960. 4/yr. Nihon Oyo Chishitsu Gakkai - Japan Society of Engineering Geology, 1-9, Takadanobaba 2-chome, Shinjuku-ku, Tokyo 169, Japan. Indexed: Jap.Per.Ind.

551 JA ISSN 0912-6325
OYO CHISHITSU NENPO/OYO TECHNICAL REPORT. (Text in English, Japanese; summaries in English) 1979. a. Oyo Chishitsu - Oyo Corp., 2-6, Kudan Kita 4-chome, Chiyoda-ku, Tokyo 102, Japan.

P A S C A L. F 44: STRATIGRAPHIE, GEOLOGIE REGIONALE, GEOLOGIE GENERALE. see *EARTH SCIENCES — Abstracting, Bibliographies, Statistics*

P E G G. (Professional Engineer, Geologist, Geophysicist) see *ENGINEERING*

555 PK ISSN 0078-8163
QE295 CODEN: RGPAAY
PAKISTAN. GEOLOGICAL SURVEY. RECORDS. (Text in English) 1949. irreg. price varies. Geological Survey of Pakistan, c/o Chief Librarian, P.O. Box 15, Quetta, Pakistan. TEL 73055. circ. 1,500.

PALAEOCLIMATES: DATA AND MODELLING. see *METEOROLOGY*

554 560 UK
PALAEONTOGRAPHICAL SOCIETY. MONOGRAPHS (LONDON). (Text in English; summaries in French, German, Russian) 1848. a. £22 to individuals; institutions £44. Palaeontographical Society, c/o Secretary, British Geological Survey, Keyworth, Nottingham NG12 5GG, England. Ed. J.E. Hutt. circ. 750. (also avail. in microfiche; back issues avail.) Indexed: Biol.Abstr. Document type: monographic series.

PALEOBIOS. see *PALEONTOLOGY*

PALYNOLOGY. see *PALEONTOLOGY*

556 FR ISSN 0760-1751
PANGEA. (Text and summaries in English, French) 1983. 2/yr. 400 F. Centre International pour la Formation et les Echanges Geologiques - International Center for Training and Exchanges in the Geosciences, B.P. 6517, Av. de Concyr, 45065 Orleans Cedex 2, France. TEL 38-64-33-67. FAX 38-64-34-72. TELEX 780 258. Ed. Jean-Claude Bidet. bk.rev. circ. 600.
—BLDSC (6357.371500).
 Description: Scientific and technical information on various aspects of international research in the geosciences: training, congresses and colloquia, cooperative research programs, syntheses.

551 560 PL ISSN 0208-645X
QE1 CODEN: IGEPAR
PANSTWOWY INSTYTUT GEOLOGICZNY. PRACE. (Text in Polish; occasionally in English, French; summaries in English, Russian) 1921. irreg., (2-4/yr.). price varies. Panstwowy Instytut Geologiczny, Ul. Rakowiecka 4, 00-975 Warsaw, Poland.
TEL 48-22-495351. TELEX 815541. abstr.; bibl.; charts; illus. circ. 400. (back issues avail.) Indexed: Bull.Signal., Ref.Zh. Document type: monographic series.
 Description: Contains research on the regional geology of Poland.

558 BL ISSN 0102-6887
PAULO-COUTIANA. (Text in Portuguese or Spanish; summaries in English) 1967. irreg., no.4, 1990. price varies. Fundacao Zoobotanica do Rio Grande do Sul, Museu de Ciencias Naturais, Caixa Postal 1188, 90960-000 Porto Alegre, RS, Brazil. Eds. A. Lise, Hilda Gastal. bibl.; illus. circ. 600. Indexed: Biol.Abstr., GeoRef.
—CCC.
 Formerly (until 1986, no.11): Iheringia. Serie Geologia (ISSN 0073-4713)

557 US ISSN 0048-3214
QE157 CODEN: PAGYBW
PENNSYLVANIA GEOLOGY. 1969. bi-m. free. Department of Environmental Resources, Bureau of Topographic and Geologic Survey, Box 8453, Harrisburg, PA 17105-8453. TEL 717-787-2169. FAX 717-783-7267. Eds. Christine Dodge, Donald M. Hoskins. bk.rev.; bibl.; charts; illus. circ. 3,000. Indexed: GeoRef. Document type: government publication, academic/scholarly publication.
—Faxon; UnCover.

551 UK ISSN 1045-6740
GB641 CODEN: PEPPED
PERMAFROST AND PERIGLACIAL PROCESSES. 1990. q. $245 (effective 1994). John Wiley & Sons Ltd., Journals, Baffins Ln., Chichester, Sussex PO19 1UD, England. TEL 0243-779777. FAX 0243-775878. TELEX 86290 WIBOOK G. Ed. H.M. French. circ. 159. Document type: academic/scholarly publication.
—BLDSC (6426.685000); Faxon; UnCover; UMI.
 Description: Presents papers on earth surface cryogenic processes, landforms, and sediments present in arctic, antarctic, and high-mountain environments.

PETROLEUM GEOLOGY: A DIGEST OF RUSSIAN LITERATURE ON PETROLEUM GEOLOGY. see *PETROLEUM AND GAS*

PETROLEUM GEOLOGY OF TAIWAN/T'AIWAN SHIH-YU TI-CHIH. see *PETROLEUM AND GAS*

PETROLEUM GEOLOGY SPECIAL PAPER SERIES. see *PETROLEUM AND GAS*

550 NE ISSN 0924-1957
PETROLOGY AND STRUCTURAL GEOLOGY. (Text in English) 1986. irreg., vol.5, 1991. Kluwer Academic Publishers, Postbus 17, 3300 AA Dordrecht, Netherlands. TEL 31-78-334911.
FAX 31-78-334254. (Dist. by: Kluwer Academic Publishers Group, P.O. Box 322, 3300 AH Dordrecht, Netherlands. TEL 31-78-524400; N. America dist. addr.: Box 358, Accord Sta., Hingham, MA 02018-0358. TEL 617-871-6600) Ed. Adolphe Nicolas. Document type: monographic series, proceedings.

551 BE
PIERRE ET MARBRE/STEEN EN MARMER. s-a. 900 Fr. Federation Belge des Associations de Maitres Tailleurs de Pierres, Galerie du Centre 220, Rue des Fripiers, B-1000 Brussels, Belgium. FAX 2230538.

PLINIUS. see *MINES AND MINING INDUSTRY*

POLAR GEOGRAPHY AND GEOLOGY. see *GEOGRAPHY*

550 PL ISSN 0079-3361
QE276.5 CODEN: PRGLA9
POLSKA AKADEMIA NAUK. ODDZIAL W KRAKOWIE. KOMISJA NAUK GEOLOGICZNYCH. PRACE GEOLOGICZNE. (Text in Polish; summaries in English and Russian) 1960. irreg., no.136, 1992. price varies. Ossolineum, Publishing House of the Polish Academy of Sciences, Rynek 9, 50-106 Wroclaw, Poland. TEL 48-71-386-25. FAX 48-71-448-103. TELEX 0712771 OSS PL. Ed. Roman Ney. index. Indexed: GeoRef. Document type: monographic series.
 Description: Monographs in regional and applied geology, geochemistry and petrography of mineral products, works in geophysics and hydrogeology.

550 PL ISSN 0079-3396
QE351 CODEN: PAPMB7
POLSKA AKADEMIA NAUK. ODDZIAL W KRAKOWIE. KOMISJA NAUK MINERALOGICZNYCH. PRACE MINERALOGICZNE. (Text in English or Polish; summaries in English or Russian) 1965. irreg., no.82, 1992. price varies. Ossolineum, Publishing House of the Polish Academy of Sciences, Rynek 9, 50-106 Wroclaw Poland. TEL 48-71-386-25. FAX 48-71-448-103. TELEX 0712771 OSS PL. Ed. Andrzej Bolewski. Indexed: Chem.Abstr. Document type: monographic series.
—BLDSC (6588.990000); CASDDS.

551 PO ISSN 0037-2730
QE284 CODEN: CGEPAT
PORTUGAL. SERVICOS GEOLOGICOS. COMUNICACOES. (Text and summaries in English, French, Portuguese) 1887. irreg., no. 476, 1989. price varies. Direccao-Geral de Geologia e Minas, Servicos Geologicos, Rua Academia das Ciencias 19-2, 1200 Lisbon, Portugal. FAX 3511-3424609. circ. 1,500. Indexed: Biol.Abstr., GeoRef.
—BLDSC (3397 000000); UnCover; CASDDS.

550 910 PL ISSN 0137-9771
POZNANSKIE TOWARZYSTWO PRZYJACIOL NAUK. KOMISJA GEOGRAFICZNO-GEOLOGICZNA. PRACE. (Text in Polish; summaries in English) 1936. irreg., vol.20, 1980. price varies. Poznanskie Towarzystwo Przyjaciol Nauk, Komisja Geograficzno-Geologiczna, Ul. Mielzynskiego 27-29, 61-725 Poznan, Poland. (Dist. by: Ars Polona, Krakowskie Przedmiescie 7, 00-068 Warsaw, Poland) Ed. Andrzej Karczewski. bibl. circ. 400.
—BLDSC (6586.500000).

1954 EARTH SCIENCES — GEOLOGY

551   NE   ISSN 0301-9268
QE653   CODEN: PCBRBY
PRECAMBRIAN RESEARCH. 1974. 24/yr. (in 6 vols.; 4 nos./vol.). fl.2256($1219) (effective 1994). (International Union of Geological Sciences, Subcommission on Precambrian Stratigraphy) Elsevier Science B.V., P.O. Box 211, 1000 AE Amsterdam, Netherlands. TEL 31-20-5803911. FAX 31-20-5803598. TELEX 18582 ESPA NL. (Subscr. in U.S. and Canada to: Elsevier Science Inc., Box 882, Madison Sq. Sta., New York, NY 10159-0882. TEL 212-989-5800. FAX 212-633-3990) Eds. B. Nagy, A. Kroener. adv.; bk.rev.; index. **Indexed:** AESIS, Biol.Abstr., Br.Geol.Lit., Bull.Signal., Chem.Abstr., Curr.Cont., Geo.Abstr., GeoRef., Mineral.Abstr., Sci.Abstr. **Document type:** academic/scholarly publication.
—BLDSC (6603.860000); Faxon; UnCover; SWETS; CASDDS. **CCC.**
Description: Publishes studies on all aspects of the early stages of the history and evolution of the Earth and its planetary neighbors.
Refereed Serial

550   US
PRINCIPLES OF GEOLOGY. a. University of Chicago Press, 5720 S. Woodlawn Ave., Chicago, IL 60637. TEL 312-753-3347. FAX 312-702-0694. Ed. Charles Lyell. bibl.; index.

549 550 560   YU   ISSN 0367-4983
                             CODEN: GPBAA8
PRIRODNJACKI MUZEJ U BEOGRADU. GLASNIK. SERIJA A: MINERALOGIJA, GEOLOGIJA, PALEONTOLOGIJA. 1948. irreg. Prirodnjacki Muzej u Beogradu, Njegoseva 51, Belgrade, Yugoslavia. Ed. Vojislav Vasic. **Indexed:** GeoRef.
—BLDSC (0050.220000).

551 551.4   CI   ISSN 0448-0155
QH178.Y8   CODEN: AGJAAL
PRIRODOSLOVNA ISTRAZIVANJA: ACTA GEOLOGICA. (Text and summaries in Croatian, English, French and German) 1913. s-a. $10. Jugoslavenska Akademija Znanosti i Umjetnosti - Yugoslav Academy of Sciences and Arts, Brace Kavurica 1, 41000 Zagreb, Croatia. TEL 041 449-867. Ed. Milan Herak. circ. 800. (back issues avail.) **Indexed:** Biol.Abstr., GeoRef.

550 551.4   US   ISSN 0279-0521
PROFESSIONAL GEOLOGIST. 1964. m. $25. American Institute of Professional Geologists, 7828 Vance Dr., Ste. 103, Arvada, CO 80003-2125. TEL 303-431-0831. FAX 303-431-1332. Ed. Charles Dimmick. adv. circ. 6,000. (back issues avail.)
—UnCover.
Description: Covers proposed legislation and regulations of concern to geologists, business news, public attitudes and trends, on-the-job techniques, current research and recent publications of interest.

551.3 551 624   II
TA710.A1
PROGRESS IN GEOTECHNICAL ENGINEERING. 1984. a. $50. Divyajyoti Prakashan, 5 Bhagat-ki-kothi, Jodhpur 342 003, India. (Co-sponsor: Geo-Environ Academia) Ed. Alan Singh. **Document type:** academic/scholarly publication.
—BLDSC (3501.318000).
Formerly (until 1988): Current Practices in Geotechnical Engineering (ISSN 0253-5122)

557   CN
PROVINCIAL GEOLOGISTS JOURNAL (VICTORIA). 1983. a. price varies. Ministry of Energy, Mines and Petroleum Resources, Mineral Resources Division, 5th Fl., 1810 Blanshard St., Victoria, BC V8V 1X4, Canada. (Subscr. to: Crown Publications, 546 Yates St., Victoria, BC V8W 1K8, Canada. TEL 604-386-4636) maps. **Document type:** government publication.

550   PL   ISSN 0033-2151
QE1   CODEN: PRZGAL
PRZEGLAD GEOLOGICZNY/GEOLOGICAL REVIEW. (Text in English or Polish; summaries in English and Russian; table of contents in English, Polish, Russian) 1953. m. $63. Panstwowy Instytut Geologiczny - Polish Geological Institute, Rakowiecka 4, 00-975 Warsaw, Poland. TEL 44-22-495351. FAX 48-22-495342. Ed. Tadeusz Peryt. adv.; bk.rev.; bibl.; charts; illus.; index. circ. 1,600. **Indexed:** Bibl.Cart., Chem.Abstr., GeoRef., Geotech.Abstr.
—BLDSC (6942.000000); CASDDS.
Description: Focuses on geology, hydrogeology, engineering geology, geophysics and environmental protection.

551   NE   ISSN 0924-1973
QUANTITATIVE GEOLOGY AND GEOSTATISTICS. 1985. irreg. price varies. Kluwer Academic Publishers, Postbus 17, 3300 AA Dordrecht, Netherlands. TEL 31-78-334911. FAX 31-78-334254. TELEX 29245 KAPG NL. (Dist. by: Kluwer Academic Publishers Group, P.O. Box 322, 3300 AH Dordrecht, Netherlands. TEL 31-78-524400. FAX 31-78-524474; N. America dist. addr.: Box 358, Accord Sta., Hingham, MA 02018-0358. TEL 617-871-6600. FAX 617-871-6528) **Document type:** monographic series.
Refereed Serial

551   AT   ISSN 0584-3219
QE345   CODEN: SGQGAY
QUARTERLY GEOLOGICAL NOTES. 1962. q. free. Department of Mines and Energy, P.O. Box 151, Eastwood, S.A. 5063, Australia. TEL 08-274-7500. FAX 08-272-7597. cum.index: vols.1-75. (back issues avail.) **Indexed:** AESIS, Eng.Ind., Geo.Ref. **Document type:** government publication.
—BLDSC (7181.340000); CASDDS.
Description: Includes definitions of geological units.

QUARTERLY JOURNAL OF ENGINEERING GEOLOGY. see *ENGINEERING — Civil Engineering*

551   FR   ISSN 1142-2904
                           CODEN: QUATE5
QUATERNAIRE. (Summaries in English, French, German) 1964. q. 300 F. (foreign 400 F.)(effective 1994). Association Francaise pour l'Etude du Quaternaire, Centre de Geomorphologie, Rue des Tilleuls, 14000 Caen, France. TEL 31-45-57-24. FAX 31-45-57-57. Dir. J.C. Miskovsky. adv.; bk.rev.; charts; illus.; index. circ. 450. **Indexed:** Geo.Abstr., GeoRef.
—BLDSC (7209.960000).
Formerly: Association Francaise pour l'Etude du Quaternaire. Bulletin (ISSN 0004-5500)
Description: International journal dealing with all aspects related to the Quaternary.

QUATERNARIA NOVA. see *PALEONTOLOGY*

551   UK   ISSN 1040-6182
QE696   CODEN: QUINER
QUATERNARY INTERNATIONAL. 1989. 4/yr. £163($250) (effective 1994). (International Union for Quaternary Research) Elsevier Science Ltd., Pergamon, P.O. Box 800, Kidlington, Oxford OX5 1DX, England. TEL 44-865-8430001. FAX 44-865-843010. (Subscr. in U.S. and Canada to: Elsevier Science, 660 White Plains Rd., Tarrytown, NY 10591-5153. TEL 914-524-9200. FAX 914-333-2444) Eds. Nat Rutter, N.R. Catto. (also avail. in microfilm from UMI; back issues avail.) **Document type:** academic/scholarly publication.
—BLDSC (7210.043000); Faxon; UnCover; SWETS; UMI. **CCC.**
Description: Publishes original research from the full spectrum of physical and natural sciences addressing problems in Quaternary science.
Refereed Serial

557   CN
QUEBEC (PROVINCE). DEPARTMENT OF ENERGY AND RESOURCES. GEOLOGICAL REPORTS. (Text mainly in French) 1886. irreg. price varies. Department of Energy and Resources, Centre de Diffusion des Donnees Geoscientifiques - Ministere de l'Energie et des Ressources, 5700, 4e Av. Ouest, 2e etage, Charlesbourg, Que. G1H 6R1, Canada. TEL 418-643-4601. FAX 418-644-3814. Ed. Raymond Boivin. circ. 1,200. (also avail. in microfiche)
Formerly: Quebec (Province). Department of Natural Resources. Geological Reports (ISSN 0079-8738)

557   CN
QUEBEC (PROVINCE). MINISTERE DE L'ENERGIE ET DES RESOURCES. RAPPORT DES GEOLOGUES RESIDENTS SUR L'ACTIVITE MINIERE REGIONALE. 1927. a. Can.$4. Ministere de l'Energie et des Ressources, Centre de Diffusion, 5700 4e Av. Ouest, Local A-201, Charlesbourg, PQ G1H 6R1, Canada. TEL 418-643-4601. FAX 418-644-3814. **Document type:** government publication.
Former titles: Quebec (Province). Department d'Energie et Resources. Rapport des Representants Regionaux; (until 1985): Quebec (Province). Ministere des Richesses Naturelles. Travaux sur le Terrain (ISSN 0079-8746)

551   SW   ISSN 0348-7377
QUFO. (Text in Swedish) 1979. irreg., no.3, 1986. price varies. (Societas Upsaliensis pro Geologia Quaternaria) Uppsala Universitet, Geovetenskap Kvartaergeologi, Norbyvaegen 18 B, S-752 36 Uppsala, Sweden. TEL 46-18-18-25-00. FAX 46-18-18-25-91. Ed. L.K Koenigsson. **Document type:** academic/scholarly publication, monographic series.

551   DK
RAASTOFPRODUKTION I DANMARK, HAVOMRAADE; produktionsmaengden fra samtlige optagningslokaliteter samt udlosningssteder og maengder. 1982. a. DKK 25. Miljoeministeriet, Skov- og Natursstyrelsen, Copenhagen, Denmark. Ed. Willy Nicolaisen.
Former titles: Raastofproduktionen, Havomraadet (ISSN 0109-7466); Raastofproduktionsopgoerelse fra Havbunden.

551   DK   ISSN 0908-0945
RAASTOFPRODUKTION I DANMARK, LANDOMRAADE. 1982. a. DKK 50. Miljoeministeriet, Skov- og Natursstyrelsen, Copenhagen, Denmark. Eds. Steen Andersen, Kirsten Skipper.
Formed by the 1990 merger of: Raastofproduktionen, Landomraadet. Produktionen af Geologiske Raastoffer Fordelt paa Amtskommuner og Kommuner (ISSN 0109-7458); Raastofproduktionen, Landomraadet. Handelsvarer og Anvendelse, Graveforhold, Arealforhold (ISSN 0109-7474); **Formerly:** Raastofproduktionsopgoerelse (ISSN 0109-503X)

REAL SOCIEDAD ESPANOLA DE HISTORIA NATURAL. BOLETIN. ACTAS. see *BIOLOGY*

554   SP   ISSN 0583-7510
QE1   CODEN: BRSGA2
REAL SOCIEDAD ESPANOLA DE HISTORIA NATURAL. BOLETIN. SECCION GEOLOGICA. (Text in Spanish; summaries in English, French) 1871. a. 10000 ptas. Real Sociedad Espanola de Historia Natural, Facultades de Biologia y Geologia, Ciudad Universitaria, 28040 Madrid, Spain. TEL 394-50-00. Ed. Antonio Perejon Rincon. (reprint service avail.) **Document type:** bulletin.
—CASDDS. **CCC.**
Supersedes in part (in 1950): Real Sociedad Espanola de Historia Natural. Boletin (ISSN 0365-9755)

551   II
RECENT RESEARCHES IN GEOLOGY. (Text in English) 1973. irreg., vol.14, 1993. price varies. Hindustan Publishing Corp., 6-U.B. Jawahar Nagar, Delhi 110007, India. TEL 2915059. FAX 6863511. **Indexed:** GeoRef. **Document type:** monographic series.

550   II
▼**RECENT RESEARCHES IN SEDIMENTOLOGY.** (Text in English) 1993. a. price varies. Hindustan Publishing Corp., 6-U.B. Jawahar Nagar, Delhi 110007, India. TEL 2915059. FAX 6863511. Ed. Vinay Jhingran.

556   UG
RECORDS OF GEOLOGICAL SURVEY AND MINES. 1950. a. price varies. Geological Survey and Mines Department, P.O. Box 9, Entebbe, Uganda.
Formerly: Uganda. Geological Survey and Mines Department. Annual Report (ISSN 0082-7215)

REGIONAL BIBLIOGRAPHY SERIES. see *EARTH SCIENCES — Abstracting, Bibliographies, Statistics*

EARTH SCIENCES — GEOLOGY

551 GW
RELIEF, BODEN, PALAEOKLIMA. 1981. irreg. price varies. (Kommission fuer Geomorphologie der Bayerischen Akademie der Wissenschaften) Gebrueder Borntraeger Verlagsbuchhandlung, Johannesstr. 3A, 70176 Stuttgart, Germany. TEL 0711-625001. FAX 0711-625005. TELEX 723363-SCHB-D. Ed. H. Hagedorn. **Document type:** academic/scholarly publication.

557 CR ISSN 0256-7024
REVISTA GEOLOGICA DE AMERICA CENTRAL. 1984. a. $20. Editorial de la Universidad de Costa Rica, Apdo 75-2060, Ciudad Universitaria Rodrigo Facio, 2050 San Pedro de Montes de Oca, San Jose, Costa Rica. TEL 506-25-3133. FAX 506-24-9367. TELEX UNICORI 2544. Dir. Siegfried Kussmaul. **Document type:** academic/scholarly publication.

558 CL ISSN 0716-0208
REVISTA GEOLOGICA DE CHILE. (Text in Spanish or English; summaries in English, Spanish) 1974. s-a. $40 (effective 1994) or exchange basis. Servicio Nacional de Geologia y Mineria, Casilla 10465, Santiago, Chile. TEL 56-2-7375050. FAX 56-2-372026. Ed. Francisco Herve A. circ. 1,000. **Indexed:** Chem.Abstr., GeoRef. **Document type:** government publication.
—BLDSC (7858.230000).

551 CU
REVISTA TECNOLOGIA: GEOLOGIA. s-a. $12. (Ministerio de la Industria Basica) Ediciones Cubanas, Obispo No. 461, Apdo. 605, Havana, Cuba. TEL 32-5556.

551 560 SZ ISSN 0253-6730
REVUE DE PALEOBIOLOGIE. (Text in English and French) 1982. s-a. exchange basis. 1 Route de Malagnou, Case Postale 434, CH-1211 Geneva 6, Switzerland. Ed.Bd. adv.; index. (back issues avail.)
—BLDSC (7940.800000).

REVUE DES SCIENCES NATURELLES D'AUVERGNE. see *BIOLOGY*

551 RM ISSN 1220-529X
QE287 CODEN: RRGGBH
REVUE ROUMAINE DE GEOLOGIE. (Text in English, French, German and Russian) 1957. a. $32. (Academia Romana) Editura Academiei Romane, Calea Victoriei 125, 79717 Bucharest, Rumania. (Dist. by: Rompresfilatelia, Calea Grivitei 64-66, P.O. Box 12-201, 78104 Bucharest, Rumania) bk.rev.; charts; illus.; index. **Indexed:** Chem.Abstr., GeoRef, Soils & Fert.
—CASDDS.
Formerly (until 1991): Revue Roumaine de Geologie, Geophysique et Geographie (ISSN 0556-8102); Which supersedes in part (in 1963): Revue de Geologie et de Geographie (ISSN 1220-1855)

554 NE ISSN 0165-1951
QE273
RIJKS GEOLOGISCHE DIENST. MEDEDELINGEN. NIEUWE SERIE. (Text in Dutch, English, French) 1946. irreg. (1-3/yr.). price varies. Rijks Geologische Dienst - Geological Survey of the Netherlands, Postbus 157, 2000 AD Haarlem, Netherlands. TEL 31-23-300300. FAX 31-23-401754. TELEX 71105 GEOLD NL. Ed. Th.E. Wong. circ. 1,000.
Formerly (until 1968): Geologische Stichting. Mededelingen. Nieuwe Serie.

551 IT
RIVISTA ITALIANA DI GEOTECNICA. (Text in English, Italian) 1967. q. L.110000 to individuals; institutions L.155000; foreign L.200000 (effective 1993). Edizioni Scientifiche Italiane S.p.A., Via Chiatamone, 7, 80121 Naples, Italy. TEL 081-7645768. FAX 081-7646477. Ed. Arrigo Croce. adv. circ. 2,400. **Indexed:** Intl.Civil Eng.Abstr., Soft.Abstr.Eng.

552 624.151 AU ISSN 0723-2632
TA710.A1 CODEN: RMREDX
ROCK MECHANICS AND ROCK ENGINEERING. (Text in English, French and German) 1929. 4/yr. DM.272($187) (effective 1994). Springer-Verlag, Sachsenplatz 4-6, Postfach 89, A-1201 Vienna, Austria. TEL 0222-330-2416. FAX 0222-330-2426. (N. American subscr. to: Journal Fulfillment Services, Box 2485, Secaucus, NJ 07096-2491. TEL 800-777-4643. FAX 201-348-4505; Elsewhere: Heidelberger Platz 3, 1000 Berlin 33, Germany. TEL 030-8207-1. FAX 030-821-4091) Ed. K. Kovari. adv.; bk.rev.; charts; illus.; index. (also avail. in microform from UMI) **Indexed:** Appl.Mech.Rev., ASCA, Chem.Abstr., Curr.Cont., Eng.Ind., Fuel & Energy Abstr., GeoRef., Intl.Civil Eng.Abstr., Nucl.Sci.Abstr., Petrol.Abstr., Sel.Water Res.Abstr., Soft.Abstr.Eng., W.R.C.Inf. **Document type:** academic/scholarly publication.
—BLDSC (8001.806000); Faxon; UnCover; SWETS; UMI. **CCC.**
Former titles: Rock Mechanics (ISSN 0035-7448); Felsmechanik und Ingenieur Geologie.
Description: Covers the experimental and theoretical aspects of rock mechanics.

ROCKS AND MINERALS; mineralogy, geology, lapidary. see *MINES AND MINING INDUSTRY*

550 RU
ROSSIISKAYA AKADEMIYA NAUK IZVESTIYA. SERIYA GEOLOGICHESKAYA. (Text in Russian; contents page in English) 1936. m. 66 Rub. Izdatel'stvo Nauka, 90 Profsoyuznaya ul., 117864 Moscow, Russia. (Dist. by: Mezhdunarodnaya Kniga, B. Yakimanka 39, 117049 Moscow, Russia) Ed. V.V. Menner. bk.rev.; bibl.; charts; illus.; maps; index. circ. 2,550. (reprint service avail. from KTO) **Indexed:** Biol.Abstr., Chem.Abstr., Deep Sea Res.& Oceanogr.Abstr., Eng.Ind., Geo.Abstr., INIS Atomind.
—**CCC.**
Formerly: Akademiya Nauk S.S.S.R. Izvestiya. Seriya Geologicheskaya (ISSN 0002-3345)

551 BU ISSN 0204-5311
TN95.B8 CODEN: RPMNDM
RUDOOBRAZUVATELNI PROTSESI I MINERALNI NAKHODISHTA. (Text in various languages) 1975. 3/yr. price varies. (Bulgarska Akademiia na Naukite) Publishing House of the Bulgarian Academy of Sciences, Acad. G. Bonchev St., Bldg. 6, 1113 Sofia, Bulgaria. circ. 420. (reprint service avail. from IRC) **Indexed:** Chem.Abstr., Geo.Abstr.
—CASDDS.

551 554 US ISSN 1068-7971
QE1
RUSSIAN GEOLOGY AND GEOPHYSICS. English translation of: Geologiya i Geofizika (UR ISSN 0016-7886) 1974. m. $920. (Russian Academy of Sciences, Siberian Division, Institute of Geology and Geophysics, RU) Allerton Press, Inc., 150 Fifth Ave., New York, NY 10011. TEL 212-924-3950. FAX 212-463-9684. Ed. M.L. Dobretsov. **Indexed:** Deep Sea Res.& Oceanogr.Abstr., GeoRef., Sci.Abstr. **Document type:** academic/scholarly publication.
—Faxon; UnCover. **CCC.**
Formerly: Soviet Geology and Geophysics (ISSN 0361-7149); Which was formed by the merger of: Soviet Geology; Soviet Geophysics.

913 520 551 UK ISSN 0951-5984
S.I.S. CHRONOLOGY & CATASTROPHISM WORKSHOP. 1978. q. £5($10.50) to non-members. Society for Interdisciplinary Studies, 29 Cudham Ln. N., Orpington, Kent BR6 6BX, England. Ed. B. Newsgrosh. bk.rev. circ. 500. (back issues avail.) **Document type:** academic/scholarly publication.
—BLDSC (3188.440000).
Formerly: S.I.S. Workshop (ISSN 0260-2806)

551.44 AT
S U S S BULLETIN. 1950. 4/yr. Aus.$20 membership (typically set in Dec.). Sydney University Speleological Society, P.O. Box 35, Holme Bldg., University of Sydney, Sydney, N.S.W. 2006, Australia. TEL 660-3399. Ed. Lorraine O'Keeffe. bk.rev.; circ. 180 (paid). **Indexed:** Aus.Speleo Abstr. **Document type:** bulletin.
Description: Exploration and study of caves and karst.

SAND PAPER. see *HOBBIES*

551 JA
SANGYO CHISHITSU KAGAKU KENKYUJO KENKYU NENPO/INSTITUTE OF INDUSTRIAL GEOLOGICAL SCIENCES. ANNUAL REPORT. (Text in Japanese) 1990. a. Sangyo Chishitsu Kagaku Kenkyujo, 13-6, Heijima 1-chome, Niigata-shi, Niigata-ken 950-21, Japan.

550 RU
AS262
SANKT-PETERBURGSKII UNIVERSITET. SERIYA GEOLOGIYA I GEOGRAFIYA. (Text in Russian; contents page and summaries in English) 1946. q. 18.60 Rub. Sankt-Peterburgskii Universitet, Universitetskaya Nab., 7-9, St. Petersburg V-164, Russia. (Subscr. to: Mezhdunarodnaya Kniga, Moscow, G-200, Russia) Ed. L.E. Smirnov. bk.rev.; abstr.; charts; illus.; index. circ. 1,225. **Indexed:** Bibl.Cart., Chem.Abstr., Geo.Abstr.
—UMI. **CCC.**
Formerly (until 1992): Leningradskii Universitet. Vestnik. Seriya Geologiya i Geografiya (ISSN 0024-0834)

554 RU
AS262
SANKT-PETERBURGSKII UNIVERSITET. UCHENYE ZAPISKI. SERIYA GEOLOGICHESKIKH NAUK. 1950. irreg. 1.40 Rub. Sankt-Peterburgskii Universitet, Geologicheskii Fakultet, Universitetskaya Nab. 7-9, St. Petersburg V-164, Russia. illus. **Indexed:** GeoRef.
Formerly: Leningradskii Universitet. Uchenye Zapiski. Seriya Geologichekikh Nauk (ISSN 0459-0805)
Description: Provides articles on research in geology, geochemistry and geophysics.

SANTA BARBARA MUSEUM OF NATURAL HISTORY. OCCASIONAL PAPERS. see *ANTHROPOLOGY*

550 XR ISSN 0036-5270
QE697 CODEN: SGANA9
SBORNIK GEOLOGICKYCH VED: ANTROPOZOIKUM/JOURNAL OF GEOLOGICAL SCIENCES: ANTHROPOZOIC. (Text and summaries in Czech, English, French and German) 1951. irreg. Cesky Geologicky Ustav, Malostranske nam. 19, 118 21 Prague 1, Czech Republic. (Dist. by: Artia, Ve Smeckach 30, 111 27 Prague 1, Czech Republic) Ed. Jaroslav Tyracek. charts; illus. circ. 600. (back issues avail.) **Indexed:** Bull.Signal., Chem.Abstr., GeoRef., Ref.Zh.
—CASDDS.

551 XR ISSN 0581-9172
QE267.C8 CODEN: SGVGAP
SBORNIK GEOLOGICKYCH VED: GEOLOGIE/JOURNAL OF GEOLOGICAL SCIENCES: GEOLOGY. (Text in Czech, English or German; summaries also in French, Russian) 1921. irreg. (1-3/yr.). Cesky Geologicky Ustav, Malostranske nam. 19, 118 21 Prague 1, Czech Republic. (Dist. by: Artia, Ve Smeckach 30, 111 27 Prague 1, Czech Republic) Ed. Zdenek Kukal. charts; illus.; maps. circ. 850. **Indexed:** Bull.Signal, Chem.Abstr., GeoRef., Ref.Zh.
—UnCover; CASDDS.

551 XR ISSN 0581-9180
QE267.C8 CODEN: SVLMDX
SBORNIK GEOLOGICKYCH VED: LOZISKOVA GEOLOGIE, MINERALOGIE/JOURNAL OF GEOLOGICAL SCIENCES: ECONOMIC GEOLOGY, MINERALOGY. (Text in Czech, English or German; summaries also in French and Russian) 1963. irreg. Cesky Geologicky Ustav, Malostranske nam. 19, 118 21 Prague 1, Czech Republic. (Dist. by: Artia, Ve Smeckach 30, 111 27 Prague 1, Czech Republic) Ed. Milan Drabek. charts; illus. circ. 600. (back issues avail.) **Indexed:** Bull.Signal., Chem.Abstr., GeoRef., Ref.Zh.
—CASDDS.

550 XR ISSN 0036-5300
CODEN: SGVTAU
SBORNIK GEOLOGICKYCH VED: TECHNOLOGIE, GEOCHEMIE/JOURNAL OF GEOLOGICAL SCIENCES: TECHNOLOGY, GEOCHEMISTRY. (Text in Czech, English or German; summaries in Czech and Russian) 1962. irreg. Cesky Geologicky Ustav, Malostranske nam. 19, 118 21 Prague 1, Czech Republic. (Dist. by: Artia, Ve Smeckach 30, 111 27 Prague 1, Czech Republic) (Co-sponsor: Ustav Nerostnyc Surovin, Kutna Hora) Ed. Jiri Vtelensky. charts; illus. circ. 600. (back issues avail.) **Indexed:** Bull.Signal., Chem.Abstr., GeoRef., Ref.Zh.
—BLDSC (4992.620000); CASDDS.

EARTH SCIENCES — GEOLOGY

SCARECROW AREA BIBLIOGRAPHY SERIES. see *EARTH SCIENCES — Abstracting, Bibliographies, Statistics*

551   GW   ISSN 0323-8946
CODEN: SGWID5
SCHRIFTENREIHE FUER GEOLOGISCHE WISSENSCHAFTEN/SERIALS IN GEOLOGICAL SCIENCES. (Text in English and German; summaries in English, German and Russian) 1974. irreg., vol.28, 1990. price varies. (Vorstand der Gesellschaft fuer Geologische Wissenschaften) Akademie Verlag GmbH, Muehlenstr. 33-34, 13187 Berlin, Germany. TEL 030-47889348. FAX 030-47889357. Ed.Bd. **Indexed:** GeoRef. **Document type:** monographic series.
—CASDDS.
Description: Original papers on the history of geological sciences, and problems facing geologists today.

SCHWEIZERISCHE MINERALOGISCHE UND PETROGRAPHISCHE MITTEILUNGEN/BULLETIN SUISSE DE MINERALOGIE ET PETROGRAPHIE/BOLLETTINO SVIZZERO DI MINERALOGIA E PETROGRAFIA/SWISS BULLETIN OF MINERALOGY AND PETROLOGY; eine europaeische Zeitschrift fuer Mineralogie, Geochemie und Petrographie. see *MINES AND MINING INDUSTRY*

551.23   JA   ISSN 0030-2821
SCIENCE OF HOT SPRINGS/ONSEN KAGAKU.* (Text in Japanese; summaries in English) 1933. 4/yr. 6000 Yen. Balneological Society of Japan - Nippon Onsen Kagakukai, c/o Tokyo Toritsu Daigaku Rigakubu, 1-1, Minamiosawa, Hachiozi-shi, Tokyo 192-03, Japan. Ed. Kimio Noguchi. circ. 500.

551 550   FR   ISSN 0335-9255
CODEN: STIGDK
SCIENCES DE LA TERRE: SERIE INFORMATIQUE GEOLOGIQUE. Cover title: Sciences de la Terre: Informatique Geologique. (Text in English and French) 1973. irreg., no.31, 1992. price varies. Association Scientifique pour la Geologie et ses Applications, 94 av. de Lattre de Tassigny, 54000 Nancy, France. TEL 83-50-30-30. FAX 83-51-23-12. (Subscr. to: Sciences de la Terre, rue du Doyen Roubault, B.P. 40, 54501 Vandoeuvre-les-Nancy, France.) Ed. J.J. Royer. play rev. circ. 400. (back issues avail.) **Indexed:** Chem.Abstr., GeoRef. **Document type:** proceedings.
—UnCover; CASDDS.

551   FR
SCIENCES DE LA TERRE: SERIE MEMOIRES. 1955. irreg., no.51, 1990. price varies. Association Scientifique pour la Geologie et ses Applications, 94 av. de Lattre de Tassigny, 54000 Nancy, France. TEL 83-50-30-30. FAX 83-51-23-12. (Subscr. to: Rue du Doyen Marcel Roubault, B.P. 40, 54501 Vandoeuvre-les-Nancy, France. TEL 83-55-35-23) (back issues avail.)

551   FR   ISSN 0302-2692
QE269   CODEN: BIGPA8
SCIENCES GEOLOGIQUES. BULLETIN. (Text in English, French; summaries in English) 1920. q. price varies. Universite Louis Pasteur de Strasbourg, Institut de Geologie, 1 rue Blessig, 67084 Strasbourg Cedex, France. TEL 88-35-85-31. FAX 88-36-72-35. Ed. Bertrand Fritz. charts; illus.; index, cum.index circ. 775. **Indexed:** Bull.Signal., Chem.Abstr., Geo.Abstr., GeoRef.
—UnCover; CASDDS.
Formerly: Service de la Carte Geologique d'Alsace et de Lorraine. Bulletin (ISSN 0037-2560)

554   FR   ISSN 0302-2684
QE269   CODEN: SGQMAI
SCIENCES GEOLOGIQUES - MEMOIRES. 1929. irreg. (1-2/yr.). price varies. Universite Louis Pasteur de Strasbourg, Institut de Geologie, 1 rue Blessig, 67084 Strasbourg Cedex, France. TEL 88-35-85-31. FAX 88-36-72-35. Ed. Bertrand Fritz. adv.; bk.rev. circ. 1,000. **Indexed:** Chem.Abstr., Geo.Abstr., GeoRef.
Formerly: Service de la Carte Geologique d'Alsace et de Lorraine. Memoires (ISSN 0080-9020)

551   CC   ISSN 1004-3543
▼**SCIENTIA GEOLOGICA SINICA.** Chinese edition: Dizhi Kexue (ISSN 0563-5020) (Text in English) 1992. q. $88 to individuals (foreign $108); institutions $164 (foreign $184). (Chinese Academy of Sciences, Institute of Geology) Science Press, Marketing and Sales Department, 16 Donghuangchenggen Beijie, Beijing 100707, People's Republic of China. (Overseas dist. by: Science Press New York, Ltd., 63-117 Alderton St., Rego Park, NY 11374. TEL 718-459-4638) Ed. Wang Sijing. **Document type:** academic/scholarly publication.
—BLDSC (8172.310000).
Description: Covers geology and its broader branches, including mineralogy, petrology and palaeontology, structural geology and regional tectonics, sedimentology and stratigraphy, geochemistry and geophysics, and more.
Refereed Serial

554   UK   ISSN 0036-9276
QE1   CODEN: SJGEAX
SCOTTISH JOURNAL OF GEOLOGY. 1965. 2/yr. £68($114) Geological Society Publishing House, Unit 7, Brassmill Enterprise Centre, Brassmill Ln., Bath BA1 3JN, England. TEL 225-445046. FAX 225-442836. (Co-sponsors: Geological Societies of Edinburgh & Glasgow) adv. circ. 1,500. **Indexed:** AESIS, ASCA, Biol.Abstr., Br.Geol.Lit., Chem.Abstr., Curr.Adv.Ecol.Sci., Curr.Cont., Fuel & Energy Abstr., Geo.Abstr., GeoRef, Petrol.Abstr. **Document type:** academic/scholarly publication.
—BLDSC (8210.500000); Faxon; UnCover. **CCC.**
Description: Contains original papers on all aspects of the geology of Scotland and neighboring areas including Europe, the North Sea and the margins of the North Atlantic.

551   NE   ISSN 0375-7587
QE1   CODEN: SCGLA5
SCRIPTA GEOLOGICA. (Text in English; occasionally in French, German or Spanish) 1971. irreg. price varies. Nationaal Natuurhistorisch Museum - National Museum of Natural History, Postbus 9517, 2300 RA Leiden, Netherlands. TEL 31-71-143844. FAX 31-71-133344. bibl.; charts; illus.; circ. 575 (controlled). **Indexed:** AESIS, Deep Sea Res.& Oceanogr.Abstr., GeoRef., Mineral.Abstr. **Document type:** academic/scholarly publication.
—BLDSC (8212.600000).

551.3   CN   ISSN 0080-8482
QE471
SEDIMENT DATA FOR SELECTED CANADIAN RIVERS. (Issued in separate regional volumes) 1965. a. free. Environment Canada, Inland Waters Directorate, Ottawa, Ont. K1A OH3, Canada.
TEL 613-953-3680. FAX 613-997-8701. Ed. Dorothy Whyte. charts. circ. 500. (also avail. in microfiche) **Indexed:** Eng.Ind., GeoRef.
●Also available online.
Also available on CD-ROM.
Description: Provides information on sediment data for certain Canadian rivers.

551.3   NE   ISSN 0037-0738
QE471   CODEN: SEGEBX
SEDIMENTARY GEOLOGY; international journal of pure and applied sedimentology. (Text in English, French, German) 1967. 24/yr. (in 6 vols.; 4 nos./vol.). fl.2196($1187) (effective 1994). Elsevier Science B.V., P.O. Box 211, 1000 AE Amsterdam, Netherlands. TEL 31-20-5803911.
FAX 31-20-5803598. TELEX 18582 ESPA NL. (Subscr. in N. America to: Elsevier Science Inc., Box 882, Madison Sq. Sta., New York, NY 10159. TEL 212-989-5800. FAX 212-633-3990) Ed.Bd. adv.; bk.rev.; abstr.; charts; illus.; index. (also avail. in microform from UMI; reprint service avail. from SWZ) **Indexed:** AESIS, ASCA, Biol.Abstr., Br.Geol.Lit., Bull.Signal., Chem.Abstr., Curr.Cont., Deep Sea Res.& Oceanogr.Abstr., Fuel & Energy Abstr., Geo.Abstr., GeoRef., Petrol.Abstr., Sel.Water Res.Abstr. **Document type:** academic/scholarly publication.
—BLDSC (8217.320000); Faxon; UnCover; SWETS; CASDDS. **CCC.**
Description: Provides a forum for the publication of research papers across the entire subject, from analytical techniques to regional or geodynamical aspects of sedimentary systems and basin analysis.
Refereed Serial

551.3   UK   ISSN 0037-0746
QE471   CODEN: SEDIAT
SEDIMENTOLOGY. (Text in English, French and German) 1952. 6/yr. £264 in Europe; elsewhere £291 ($434) (effective 1994). (International Association of Sedimentologists) Blackwell Scientific Publications, Ltd., Osney Mead, Oxford OX2 OEL, England. TEL 0865-240201. FAX 0865-721205. TELEX 83355-MEDBOK-G. Ed.Bd. adv.; bk.rev.; abstr.; charts; illus.; index, cum.index: vols. 1-10. circ. 3,200. (also avail. in microform from UMI; back issues avail; reprint service avail. from ISI) **Indexed:** AESIS, ASCA, Biol.Abstr., Br.Geol.Lit., Chem.Abstr., Curr.Cont., Curr.Tit.Ocean, Deep Sea Res.& Oceanogr.Abstr., Fuel & Energy Abstr., Geo.Abstr., GeoRef., Petrol.Abstr., Sci.Cit.Ind., Sel.Water Res.Abstr., W.R.C.Inf. **Document type:** academic/scholarly publication.
—BLDSC (8217.400000); Faxon; UnCover; SWETS; UMI; CASDDS. **CCC.**
Refereed Serial

SEMINAR ON PETROLIFEROUS BASINS OF INDIA. PROCEEDINGS. see *PETROLEUM AND GAS*

SENCKENBERGIANA LETHAEA. see *PALEONTOLOGY*

557   US   ISSN 0037-3257
QE153   CODEN: SHSKAT
SHALE SHAKER. 1950. bi-m. $15. Oklahoma City Geological Society, Inc., 227-W Park Ave., Oklahoma City, OK 73102. TEL 405-236-8086.
FAX 405-236-8085. Ed. Kathy Fowler. adv.; bibl.; charts; circ. 1,250 (controlled). **Indexed:** GeoRef., Petrol.Abstr.
—BLDSC (8254.588000).

555   CC   ISSN 1000-002X
SHANDI YANJIU/MOUNTAIN RESEARCH. (Text in Chinese) 1983. q. $33.20. (Chinese Academy of Sciences, Chengdu Institute of Geography) Science Press, Marketing and Sales Department, 16 Donghuangchenggen Beijie, Beijing 100707, People's Republic of China. TEL 4010642.
FAX 4012180. TELEX 210247-SPBJ-CN. adv. circ. 5,500.
Refereed Serial

551 333.7   JA   ISSN 0918-2454
CODEN: SHCHEC
SHIGEN CHISHITSU/MINING GEOLOGY. (Text in English, Japanese) 1951. 6/yr. 2500 Yen per no. Shigen Chishitsu Gakkai - Society of Resource Geology, 6-41, Akasaka 9-chome, Minato-ku, Tokyo 107, Japan.
—BLDSC (7777.602560); CASDDS.

551   JA   ISSN 0287-816X
SHIMANE DAIGAKU CHISHITSUGAKU KENKYU HOKOKU/SHIMANE UNIVERSITY. GEOLOGICAL REPORTS. (Text in English, Japanese; summaries in English) 1982. a. Shimane Daigaku, Rigakubu, Chishitsugaku Kyoshitsu - Shimane University, Faculty of Science, Department of Geology, 1060, Nishikawatsucho, Matsue-shi, Shimane-ken 690, Japan.

551   CC   ISSN 1000-7210
TN270.A1
SHIYOU DILI WULI KANTAN/OIL GEOPHYSICAL PROSPECTING. (Text in Chinese, English) 1966. bi-m. $60. Nengyuan Bu, Dili Wuli Kantan Ju, P.O. Box 11-1, Zuozhou, Hebei 072751, People's Republic of China. TEL 3234-332901. TELEX 222998 BGPPC CN. (Dist. outside China by: China International Book Trading Corp., P.O. Box 399, Beijing 100044, P.R. China) Ed. Yu Shoupeng. adv.: B&W page $1000, color page $2000; trim 188 x 260; adv. contact: Huang Xiangxiu. circ. 10,000. **Document type:** academic/scholarly publication.
Description: Provides information on the new technical developments in geophysical exploration.

552   CC
SHIYOU YU TIANRANQI DIZHI/OIL AND GAS GEOLOGY. (Text in Chinese) q. $1 per no. Guoji Shudian, Qikan Bu - China International Book Trading Corp., P.O. Box 399, Beijing 100044, People's Republic of China. **Indexed:** Chem.Abstr.

EARTH SCIENCES — GEOLOGY 1957

551 JA ISSN 0285-0753
SHIZUOKA CHIGAKU/SHIZUOKA GEOSCIENCE LETTERS.
(Text in Japanese) 1964. s-a. Shizuokaken Chigakkai - Shizuoka Geoscience Association, Shizuoka Daigaku Kyoikugakubu Chigaku Kyoshitsu, 836, Oya, Shizuoka-shi, Shizuoka-ken 422, Japan.
—BLDSC (8267.371700).

558 PE ISSN 0079-1091
QE1 CODEN: BOGPAG
SOCIEDAD GEOLOGICA DEL PERU. BOLETIN. (Text in Spanish; summaries in English, French, Spanish) 1925. irreg. S/1500($20) Sociedad Geologica del Peru, Apdo. 2559, Lima, Peru. TEL 633947. Ed. O. Orrego. adv.; bk.rev.; cum.index: vols.1-18 (1925-45), vols.19-27 (1946-55), vols.20-50 (1947-75), vols.51-81 (1976-1990). circ. 800. **Indexed:** Biol.Abstr., Deep Sea Res.& Oceanogr.Abstr., GeoRef. **Document type:** academic/scholarly publication, bulletin.

796.525 VE ISSN 0583-7731
CODEN: SVEBAU
SOCIEDAD VENEZOLANA DE ESPELEOLOGIA. BOLETIN. (Text in Spanish; summaries in English) 1967. a. Bs.100($10) Sociedad Venezolana de Espeleologia, Apdo. 47334, Caracas 1041A, Venezuela. Ed. F. Herrera. circ. 1,000. (back issues avail.) **Indexed:** Biol.Abstr., GeoRef., Speleol.Abstr. **Document type:** bulletin.

551 VE
SOCIEDAD VENEZOLANA DE GEOLOGOS. BOLETIN.
1965. 3/yr. $90. Sociedad Venezolana de Geologos, Apdo. 2006, Caracas 1010A, Venezuela. FAX 582-573-3968. TELEX 21470 CIVFC VE. Ed. Anibal R. Martinez. adv. circ. 1,000. **Document type:** academic/scholarly publication, bulletin.

554 IT ISSN 0037-8763
G17 CODEN: BOGIAT
SOCIETA GEOLOGICA ITALIANA. BOLLETTINO. (Text in Italian; summaries in English, French, German) 1882. 3/yr. price varies. Societa Geologica Italiana, Citta Universitaria, 00100 Rome, Italy. Ed. Dr. Achille Zuccari. bibl.; charts; illus.; mkt.; index, cum.index. circ. 2,200. **Indexed:** Biol.Abstr., Chem.Abstr., Geo.Abstr., GeoRef., INIS Atomind. **Document type:** bulletin.
—BLDSC (2230.500000); UnCover; CASDDS.

551 IT ISSN 0375-9857
CODEN: MSGLAH
SOCIETA GEOLOGICA ITALIANA. MEMORIE. irreg. Societa Geologica Italiana, Citta Universitaria, 00100 Rome, Italy. **Document type:** monographic series.
—BLDSC (5675.155000).

SOCIETAT D'HISTORIA NATURAL DE LES BALEARS. BOLLETI. see *BIOLOGY*

551 PL ISSN 0208-9068
QE1 CODEN: ASGPD2
SOCIETATIS GEOLOGORUM POLONIAE. ANNALES/POLSKIE TOWARZYSTWO GEOLOGICZNE. ROCZNIK. Key Title: Annales Societatis Geologorum Poloniae. (Text in English) 1921. q. £25($42.50) to individuals; institutions £30($50). Polskie Towarzystwo Geologiczne - Geological Society of Poland, Ul. Oleandry 2A, 30-063 Krakow, Poland. FAX 48-12-372243. (Dist. in UK by: UCL Press, University College of London, Gower St., London WC1E 6BT, England) (Co-sponsor: Polska Akademia Nauk, Komitet Badan Naukowych) Ed. Grzegorz Haczewski. adv.: Page $250. bk.rev.; bibl.; charts; illus.; index. circ. 900. **Document type:** academic/scholarly publication.
—BLDSC (0946.420000); UnCover; CASDDS.
Formerly (until 1981): Polskie Towarzystwo Geologiczne. Rocznik (ISSN 0079-3663)
Description: Publishes scientific contributions from all fields of geological science.

551 BE ISSN 0772-9464
SOCIETE BELGE DE GEOLOGIE. BULLETIN/BELGISCHE VERENIGING VOOR GEOLOGIE. BULLETIN. Cover title: Geologie. (Text mainly in English, French; occasionally in other European languages) 1887. 2/yr. 1200 BEF. Societe Belge de Geologie - Belgische Vereniging voor Geologie, 13 rue Jenner, B-1040 Brussels, Belgium. TEL 32-2-6476400. FAX 32-2-6477359. Ed. Michiel Dusar. adv.; bk.rev.; bibl.; charts; illus.; index. circ. 1,300. **Indexed:** Biol.Abstr., Chem.Abstr., Eng.Ind., GeoRef. **Document type:** academic/scholarly publication.
—UnCover.
Formerly (until 1974): Societe Belge de Geologie, de Paleontologie et d'Hydrologie. Bulletin (ISSN 0037-8909)
Description: Papers on the regional geology of Belgium and neighboring areas, with reports of current research in earth science institutes in Belgium, and discussions of applied geology, including hydrogeology, building materials, remote sensing, and conservation issues.

554 BE ISSN 0037-9395
QE1 CODEN: ASGBAP
SOCIETE GEOLOGIQUE DE BELGIQUE. ANNALES. (Text in English, French) 1874. s-a. 1800 Fr. Societe Geologique de Belgique, Universite de Liege, 7 Place du Vingt-Aout, 4000 Liege, Belgium. Ed. M. Streel. adv.; bk.rev.; abstr.; charts; illus.; index. circ. 900. **Indexed:** Biol.Abstr., Br.Geol.Lit. (1972-), Chem.Abstr., Curr.Tit.Ocean, Geo.Abstr., GeoRef., INIS Atomind. **Document type:** academic/scholarly publication.
—BLDSC (0948.000000); UnCover; CASDDS.

554 FR ISSN 0037-9409
QE1 CODEN: BSGFAE
SOCIETE GEOLOGIQUE DE FRANCE. BULLETIN. (Text in English, French) 1830. 6/yr. 660 F. (foreign 720 F.). Societe Geologique de France, 77 rue Claude Bernard, 75005 Paris, France. TEL 43-31-77-35. FAX 45-35-79-10. index; cum.index: 1830-1958 (in 6 vols.). circ. 2,800. (also avail. in microfilm from BHP) **Indexed:** Biol.Abstr., Br.Geol.Lit., Chem.Abstr., Curr.Cont., Deep Sea Res.& Oceanogr.Abstr., E&P Hlth. (1993-), Eng.Ind., Gas Process.& Ppl. (1993-), Geo.Abstr., GeoRef., INIS Atomind., Int.Aerosp.Abstr., Off.Tech. (1993-), Petrol.Abstr. (1961, 1965-), Risk Abstr., Sci.Cit.Ind., Sel.Water Res.Abstr. **Document type:** academic/scholarly publication.
—BLDSC (2742.000000); Faxon; UnCover; SWETS; CASDDS. CCC.
Incorporates: Societe Geologique de France. Compte Rendu Sommaire des Seances (ISSN 0037-9417)
Description: Papers in geological sciences.

554 FR ISSN 0249-7549
SOCIETE GEOLOGIQUE DE FRANCE. MEMOIRES. (Text in English, French) 1962. irreg. (1-4/yr.). price varies. Societe Geologique de France, 77, rue Claude-Bernard, 75005 Paris, France. TEL 43-31-77-35. FAX 45-35-79-10. **Indexed:** Biol.Abstr., Br.Geol.Lit., Geo.Abstr., GeoRef. **Document type:** academic/scholarly publication.
—BLDSC (5569.000000).
Description: Scientific papers on geological subjects; each volume studies a particular theme.

554 FR ISSN 0336-9994
SOCIETE GEOLOGIQUE DE NORMANDIE ET DES AMIS DU MUSEUM DU HAVRE. BULLETIN TRIMESTRIEL. 1871. q. 300 F. (Societe Geologique de Normandie et des Amis du Museum du Havre) Editions du Museum du Havre, Place du Vieux Marche, 76600 le Havre, France. (Co-sponsor: Museum d'Histoire Naturelle du Havre) Ed. G. Breton. bk.rev.; illus. circ. 1,000. **Indexed:** Biol.Abstr., GeoRef. **Document type:** academic/scholarly publication, bulletin.
—BLDSC (2922.000000).
Supersedes: Societe Geologique de Normandie, Le Havre. Bulletin.

551 FR ISSN 0767-7367
SOCIETE GEOLOGIQUE DU NORD. ANNALES. (Text in English and French; summaries in English, French, Spanish) 1870. q. 365 F. (outside Europe 400 F.). Societe Geologique du Nord, Universite des Sciences et Techniques de Lille, Sciences de le Terre, B.P. 36, F-59655 Villeneuve d'Ascq, France.
TEL 20-43-41-45. Ed. Paule Corsin. bk.rev. **Indexed:** Biol.Abstr., Br.Geol.Lit. (1972-), GeoRef., Petrol.Abstr. **Document type:** bulletin.
—BLDSC (0949.100000).

SOCIETE LINNEENNE DE BORDEAUX. BULLETIN. see *BIOLOGY — Entomology*

SOCIETE LINNEENNE DE PROVENCE. BULLETIN. see *BIOLOGY*

551 BU ISSN 0324-0479
QE287 CODEN: GSUFE7
SOFIISKI UNIVERSITET. GEOLOGO-GEOGRAFSKI FAKULTET. GEOLOGIIA. GODISHNIK. (Text in Bulgarian; summaries in English, French and German) 1905. irreg. 50 lv. per issue. Izdatelstvo Sv. Kliment Ohridski, 125 Tsarigradsko Shosse Blvd., Bl.4, 1113 Sofia, Bulgaria. Ed. Drmiter Tashev. circ. 550. **Indexed:** Geo.Abstr. **Document type:** academic/scholarly publication.
—BLDSC (0051.070000); CASDDS.

SOLOS E ROCHAS/SOILS AND ROCKS; revista brasileira de geotecnia - Brazilian geotechnical journal. see *ENGINEERING*

796.525 551.44 CN ISSN 0827-9772
SOUS TERRE. 1983. q. $15 to individuals; institutions $25. Societe Quebecoise de Speleologie, 4545 Av. Pierre-de-Coubertin, C.P. 1000, Succ. M, Montreal, Que. H1V 3R2, Canada. TEL 514-252-3006. FAX 514-251-8038. Ed. Daniel Caron. circ. 12,000. **Formerly:** Societe Quebecoise de Speleologie. Bulletin.
Description: Covers the activities of cavers and cave research.

SOUTH AFRICA. DEPARTMENT OF MINERAL AND ENERGY AFFAIRS. ANNUAL REPORT. see *MINES AND MINING INDUSTRY*

551 SA
QE325
SOUTH AFRICA. GEOLOGICAL SURVEY. ANNUAL TECHNICAL REPORT. (Text in Afrikaans, English) 1962. irreg., latest 1992. price varies. Geological Survey, Private Bag X112, Pretoria 0001, South Africa. TEL 27-12-841-1911.
FAX 27-12-841-1203. TELEX 350286-SAGEO. **Indexed:** GeoRef., Ind.S.A.Per., INIS Atomind. **Document type:** academic/scholarly publication.
—BLDSC (1025.290000).
Formerly (until 1988): South Africa. Geological Survey. Annals (SSN 0584-2352)
Description: Summary of research papers by staff members on various aspects of southern African geology, geophysics, geochemistry, and engineering geology. Includes annual report of the Chief Director, and progress reports on Geological Survey projects.

551 SA
SOUTH AFRICA. GEOLOGICAL SURVEY. BULLETIN. (Text in Afrikaans, English) 1934. irreg., latest no.115. price varies. Geological Survey, Private Bag X112, Pretoria 0001, South Africa. TEL 27-12-841-1911. FAX 27-12-841-1203. TELEX 350286-SAGEO. **Indexed:** GeoRef **Document type:** academic/scholarly publication, bulletin.
Description: Presents the results of geological investigations of localized scope.

556 SA
SOUTH AFRICA. GEOLOGICAL SURVEY. CONTRIBUTIONS TO ENGINEERING GEOLOGY. 1989. irreg. price varies. Geological Survey, Private Bag X112, Pretoria 0001, South Africa. TEL 27-12-841-1911. FAX 27-12-841-1203. TELEX 350286 SAGEO. (Co-sponsor: South African Institute of Engineering Geologists) stat. **Document type:** academic/scholarly publication.
Description: Publishes short research papers on different aspects of Southern African engineering geology.

551 SA
SOUTH AFRICA. GEOLOGICAL SURVEY. GEOLOGICAL MAPS. (Text in Afrikaans, English) 1911. irreg. price varies. Geological Survey, Private Bag X112, Pretoria 0001, South Africa. TEL 27-12-841-1911. FAX 27-12-841-1203. TELEX 350286-SAGEO. **Indexed:** GeoRef. **Document type:** academic/scholarly publication.
Formerly: South Africa. Geological Survey. Special Publications.
Description: The 1:250,000-scale series provides the basis for geological mapping of the whole country; the more detailed 1:50,000-scale series concentrates on growth points and areas with a strong mining potential.

EARTH SCIENCES — GEOLOGY

556   SA
SOUTH AFRICA. GEOLOGICAL SURVEY. GEOLOGICAL MAPS. EXPLANATIONS. (Text in Afrikaans, English) 1957. irreg., latest 1993. price varies. Geological Survey, Private Bag X112, Pretoria 0001, South Africa. TEL 27-12-841-1911. FAX 27-12-841-1203. TELEX 350286-SAGEO. **Document type:** academic/scholarly publication.
Description: Geological explanatory notes to accompany published geological maps.

550   SA   ISSN 0560-9208
CODEN: RMGHAI
SOUTH AFRICA. GEOLOGICAL SURVEY. HANDBOOK. (Text in Afrikaans, English) 1959. irreg., latest no.14. price varies. Geological Survey, Private Bag X112, Pretoria 0001, South Africa. TEL 27-12-841-1911. FAX 27-12-841-1203. TELEX 350286-SAGEO. **Indexed:** GeoRef. **Document type:** academic/scholarly publication.
Description: Deals with investigations having a countrywide scope.

551   SA
SOUTH AFRICA. GEOLOGICAL SURVEY. MEMOIRS. (Text in English) 1905. irreg., latest no.82. price varies. Geological Survey, Private Bag X112, Pretoria 0001, South Africa. TEL 27-12-841-1911. FAX 27-12-841-1203. TELEX 350286-SAGEO. **Indexed:** GeoRef. **Document type:** academic/scholarly publication, monographic series.
Description: Presents the results of comprehensive research in a specified field, or on a geological subject or entity.

556   SA
SOUTH AFRICA. GEOLOGICAL SURVEY. OPEN FILE REPORTS. (Text in English) irreg., latest 0-372, 1991. price varies. Geological Survey, Private Bag X112, Pretoria 0001, South Africa. TEL 27-12-841-1911. FAX 27-12-841-1203. TELEX 350286 SAGEO. stat. **Document type:** academic/scholarly publication.

556   SA
SOUTH AFRICA. GEOLOGICAL SURVEY. SOUTH AFRICAN COMMITTEE FOR STRATIGRAPHY. CIRCULAR. 1987. irreg. price varies. Geological Survey, South African Committee for Stratigraphy, Private Bag X112, Pretoria 0001, South Africa. TEL 27-12-841-1911. FAX 27-12-841-1203. TELEX 350286 SAGEO. **Document type:** academic/scholarly publication.
Description: Guidelines for standardized lithostratigraphic descriptions.

556   SA
SOUTH AFRICA. GEOLOGICAL SURVEY. SOUTH AFRICAN COMMITTEE FOR STRATIGRAPHY. CATALOGUE OF SOUTH AFRICAN LITHOSTRATIGRAPHIC UNITS. 1989. irreg., latest vol.4. price varies. Geological Survey, South African Committee for Stratigraphy, Private Bag X112, Pretoria 0001, South Africa. TEL 27-12-841-1911. FAX 27-12-841-1203. TELEX 350286 SAGEO. **Document type:** catalog.
Description: Comprehensive descriptions in brief of igneous, metamorphic and sedimentary units.

556   SA
SOUTH AFRICA. GEOLOGICAL SURVEY. SOUTH AFRICAN COMMITTEE FOR STRATIGRAPHY. CHRONOSTRATIGRAPHIC SERIES. 1989. irreg. price varies. Geological Survey, South African Committee for Stratigraphy, Private Bag X112, Pretoria 0001, South Africa. TEL 27-12-841-1911. FAX 27-12-841-1203. TELEX 350286 SAGEO. **Document type:** academic/scholarly publication.
Description: Provides detailed descriptions of formal chronostratigraphic units according to international principles.

551   SA
SOUTH AFRICA. GEOLOGICAL SURVEY. SOUTH AFRICAN COMMITTEE FOR STRATIGRAPHY. LITHOSTRATIGRAPHIC SERIES. 1987. irreg., no.25, 1993. Geological Survey, South African Committee for Stratigraphy, Private Bag X112, Pretoria 0001, South Africa. TEL 27-12-841-1911. FAX 27-12-841-1023. TELEX 350286-SAGEO. circ. 2,000. **Document type:** academic/scholarly publication.
Description: Provides detailed descriptions of formal lithostratigraphic formations according to international principles.

556   SA   ISSN 1012-0750
QE1   CODEN: SAJGET
SOUTH AFRICAN JOURNAL OF GEOLOGY. (Text in English; occasional articles in Afrikaans) 1896. q. R.210. (Geological Society of South Africa) Foundation for Education, Science & Technology, P.O. Box 1758, Pretoria 0001, South Africa. TEL 27-12-322-6422. Ed. S. McCourt. bibl.; illus.; cum.index every 10 yrs. circ. 2,400. (also avail. in microfiche from BHP) **Indexed:** AESIS, Biol.Abstr., Chem.Abstr., Geo.Abstr., Ind.S.A.Per., Petrol.Abstr., Sel.Water Res.Abstr. **Document type:** academic/scholarly publication.
—BLDSC (8338.868000); EI; Faxon; UnCover; UMI; CASDDS. **CCC.**
Former titles (until 1987): Geological Society of South Africa. Transactions (ISSN 0371-7208); Geological Society of South Africa. Transactions and Proceedings.

551   AT   ISSN 0159-7043
TN122
SOUTH AUSTRALIA. DEPARTMENT OF MINES AND ENERGY. ANNUAL REPORT. 1912. a. avail. on exchange basis, free in Australia. Department of Mines and Energy, P.O. Box 151, Eastwood, S.A. 5063, Australia. TEL 08-274-7500. FAX 08-272-7597. Ed J. Selby. circ. 1,750. **Indexed:** AESIS, Eng.Ind., GeoRef. **Document type:** government publication, academic/scholarly publication.

551   US   ISSN 0272-9873
QE161   CODEN: SCGYDD
SOUTH CAROLINA GEOLOGY. 1957. a. $10. Geological Survey, 5 Geology Rd., Columbia, SC 29210. TEL 803-896-7700. FAX 803-896-7695. Ed. Arthur H. Maybin, III. abstr.; illus. circ. 200. (processed; back issues avail.; reprint service avail.) **Indexed:** Deep Sea Res.& Oceanogr.Abstr., GeoRef. **Document type:** academic/scholarly publication.
—BLDSC (8350.087000).
Formerly: Geologic Notes (ISSN 0016-7541)

557   US   ISSN 0085-6479
QE163   CODEN: SDGBB
SOUTH DAKOTA GEOLOGICAL SURVEY. BULLETIN. 1894. irreg., no.33, 1989. price varies. Geological Survey, Science Center University, Vermillion, SD 57069. TEL 605-677-5227. FAX 605-677-5895. circ. controlled. **Indexed:** GeoRef. **Document type:** government publication, academic/scholarly publication.

557   US   ISSN 0085-6487
SOUTH DAKOTA GEOLOGICAL SURVEY. CIRCULAR. 1917. irreg., no.44, 1989. price varies. Geological Survey, Science Center University, Vermillion, SD 57069. TEL 605-677-5227. FAX 605-677-5895. circ. controlled. **Indexed:** GeoRef. **Document type:** government publication, academic/scholarly publication.

557   US   ISSN 0085-6495
CODEN: SDGRAU
SOUTH DAKOTA GEOLOGICAL SURVEY. REPORTS OF INVESTIGATION. 1929. irreg., no.113, 1990. price varies. Geological Survey, Science Center University, Vermillion, SD 57069. TEL 605-677-5227. FAX 605-677-5895. circ. controlled. **Indexed:** Biol.Abstr., GeoRef. **Document type:** government publication, academic/scholarly publication.
—UnCover.

557   US   ISSN 0038-3678
CODEN: SOGEAY
SOUTHEASTERN GEOLOGY. 1959. irreg., vol.34, 1992. $15 per vol. to individuals; institutions $20; foreign $24. Duke University, Geology Department, Box 90233, Durham, NC 27708-0233. TEL 919-684-5321. FAX 919-684-5833. Ed. S. Duncan Heron, Jr. charts; illus. circ. 600 (paid). (also avail. in microform from UMI; reprint service avail. from UMI) **Indexed:** Abstr.N.Amer.Geol., Biol.Abstr., Chem.Abstr., Deep Sea Res.& Oceanogr.Abstr., GeoRef., Mineral.Abstr., Petrol.Abstr., Sel.Water Res.Abstr. **Document type:** academic/scholarly publication.
—Faxon; UnCover; UMI. **CCC.**
Refereed Serial

551.44   AT   ISSN 0157-8464
SOUTHERN CAVER. 1967. irreg., no.56, 1993. Aus.$5 (overseas Aus.$8) (effective 1994). Southern Caving Society, P.O. Box 121, Moonah, Tas. 7009, Australia. TEL 61-02-325302. FAX 61-02-238620. Ed. Jeff Butt. adv.; bk.rev. circ. 60. **Indexed:** Geo.Abstr. **Document type:** newsletter.
Description: Reports activities and views of society members; especially new discoveries, surveys, technical and human articles related to caving in Tasmania.

550   RU   ISSN 0038-5069
QE1   CODEN: SVGLA2
SOVETSKAYA GEOLOGIYA. (Text in Russian; summaries in English) 1958. m. 53.40 Rub. (Ministerstvo Geologii) Izdatel'stvo Nedra, Pl. Belorusskogo Vokzala, 3, 125047 Moscow, Russia. TEL 250-52-55. bk.rev.; charts; illus.; index. (tabloid format) **Indexed:** Chem.Abstr., Eng.Ind., GeoRef., Petrol.Abstr. **Document type:** government publication, academic/scholarly publication.
—**CCC.**

551   US   ISSN 0896-7571
QE1   CODEN: SRGREU
SOVIET SCIENTIFIC REVIEWS. SECTION G: GEOLOGY REVIEWS. a. 108 ECU (effective 1993). Harwood Academic Publishers, 820 Town Center Dr., Langhorne, PA 19047. TEL 215-750-2642. FAX 215-750-6343. (UK subscr. to: P.O. Box 90, Reading, Berkshire RG1 8JL, England. TEL 0734-560-080) Ed. B.S. Sokolov. (also avail. in microform) **Document type:** academic/scholarly publication.
—BLDSC (8359.915405). **CCC.**
Description: Includes contributions on Precambrian and Cambrian geology and paleontology, evolution of the biosphere, and the geological history of the earth's climate.
Refereed Serial

551 622   SP
SPAIN. INSTITUTO TECNOLOGICO GEOMINERO DE ESPANA. COLECCION MEMORIAS. 1854. irreg., no.103, 1992. price varies. Instituto Tecnologico Geominero de Espana, Cristobal Bordiu, 34, 28003 Madrid, Spain. TEL 3495730. FAX 3495762. **Indexed:** GeoRef. **Document type:** monographic series.
Formerly: Spain. Instituto Geologico y Minero. Coleccion Memorias.

551 622   SP
SPAIN. INSTITUTO TECNOLOGICO GEOMINERO DE ESPANA. INFORMES. (In 4 subseries: 1. Geologia; 2. Mineria; 3. Monografias; 4. Aguas Subterraneas) 1972. irreg. 1500 ptas. Instituto Tecnologico Geominero de Espana, Cristobal Bordiu, 34, 28003 Madrid, Spain. TEL 3495730. FAX 3495762. **Document type:** monographic series.
Formerly: Spain. Instituto Geologico y Minero. Informes.

SPELEO NEDERLAND. see *EARTH SCIENCES — Geophysics*

551.44   IT   ISSN 0038-7290
SPELEOLOGIA EMILIANA.* 1968. bi-m. L.2000($5) (Unione Speleologica Bolognese) Speleologia Emiliana, Cassero di Porta Lame, Piazza VII Novembre 1944, 40122 Bologna, Italy.

551.44   SZ   ISSN 0038-9226
STALACTITE. (Text in French, German) 1950. 2/yr. 30 SFr. Societe Suisse de Speleologie, Bibliotheque, Ch. des Invuex, CH-1614 Granges, Sitzerland. FAX 021-9475378. Ed.Bd. bk.rev.; charts. circ. 1,400. **Indexed:** GeoRef, Sportsearch. **Document type:** bulletin.
—BLDSC (8430.200000).

551   US   ISSN 0039-0089
QE1   CODEN: SGJOAN
STATE GEOLOGISTS JOURNAL. 1949. a. $10. Association of American State Geologists, c/o Ohio Geological Survey, 4383 Fountain Sq. Dr., Columbus, OH 43224-1362. TEL 614-265-6576. FAX 614-447-1918. Ed. Thomas M. Berg. circ. 200 (controlled). (back issues avail.) **Indexed:** GeoRef. **Document type:** trade publication.
—UnCover.
Description: Summary of activities for State Geological Surveys.

EARTH SCIENCES — GEOLOGY

551   RU
STRATIGRAFIYA. GEOLOGICHESKAYA KORRELYATSIYA. English translation: Stratigraphy and Geological Correlation (US ISSN 0869-5938) (Text in Russian) 6/yr. (Rossiiskaya Akademiya Nauk, Geologicheskii Institut) Interperiodica, Staromonetnyi Per., 22, 109180 Moscow, Russia. TEL 7-095-231-2164. FAX 7-095-233-5590. Ed.Bd.

551   US   ISSN 0869-5938
▼**STRATIGRAPHY AND GEOLOGICAL CORRELATION**; journal of the fundamental and applied aspects of stratigraphy and the correlation of geologic events and processes in time and space. English translation of: Stratigrafiya, Geologicheskaya Korrelyatsiya. 1993. 6/yr. $540 (outside N. America $576). (Russian Academy of Sciences, RU) Interperiodica, Box 1831, Birmingham, AL 35201-1831. TEL 205-995-1567; 800-633-4931. FAX 205-995-1588. Ed. Boris S. Sokolov.
—BLDSC (0425.890200).

551   SW   ISSN 0345-0074
CODEN: STREDP
STRIAE; a monograph series for quaternary studies. (Text in English, French and German) 1975. irreg., no.35, 1992. price varies. (Societas Upsaliensis pro Geologia Quaternaria) Uppsala Universitet, Geovetenskap Kvartaergeologi, Norbyvaegen 18 B, S-752 36 Uppsala, Sweden. TEL 46-18-18-25-00. FAX 46-18-18-25-91. Eds. B.G. Andersen, Lars-Koenig Koenigsson. circ. 400. **Indexed:** Geo.Abstr., GeoRef. **Document type:** academic/scholarly publication, monographic series.
Description: Monographs for dissertations or other major research reports, for geologists.

551   SW   ISSN 0348-4386
STRIOLAE. (Text in English, French, German) 1979. irreg. price varies. (Societas Upsaliensis pro Geologia Quaternaria) Uppsala Universitet, Geovetenskap Kvartaergeologi, Norbyvaegen 18 B, S-752 36 Uppsala, Sweden. TEL 46-18-18-25-00. FAX 46-18-18-25-91. circ. 400. **Indexed:** Geo.Abstr., NAA. **Document type:** academic/scholarly publication, monographic series.

550   IT   ISSN 0392-0534
CODEN: STSGD2
STUDI TRENTINI DI SCIENZE NATURALI. ACTA GEOLOGICA. 1968. q. L.50000 (foreign L.90000) (effective 1990). Museo Tridentino di Scienze Naturali, Via Calepina 14, Casella Postale 393, 38100 Trent, Italy. Ed. G. Tomasi.
—CASDDS.
Formerly (until 1976): Studi Trentini di Scienze Naturali. Sezione A. Abiologica (ISSN 0585-5608)

550   PL   ISSN 0081-6426
QE1   CODEN: SGPOAJ
STUDIA GEOLOGICA POLONICA. (Text in English and Polish) 1958. irreg. price varies. Polska Akademia Nauk, Instytut Nauk Geologicznych, Ul. Zwirki Wigury 93, 02-089 Warsaw, Poland. (Dist. by: Ars Polona-Ruch, Krakowskie Przedmiescie 7, Warsaw, Poland) **Indexed:** Biol.Abstr., Geo.Abstr., Petrol.Abstr. **Document type:** academic/scholarly publication.
—BLDSC (8482.500000); UnCover.

551   SP   ISSN 0211-8327
STUDIA GEOLOGICA SALMANTICENSIA. 1970. a. 1500 ptas. Ediciones Universidad de Salamanca, Apdo. 325, 37080 Salamanca, Spain. TEL 923-26-14-54. Dir. Emiliano Jimenez Fuentes. **Document type:** academic/scholarly publication.

STUDIA I MATERIALY DO DZIEJOW ZUP SOLNYCH W POLSCE. see ARCHAEOLOGY

STUDIA SOCIETATIS SCIENTIARUM TORUNENSIS. SECTIO C. GEOGRAFIA ET GEOLOGIA. see GEOGRAPHY

550   RM
QE1   CODEN: SBBGAQ
STUDIA UNIVERSITATIS "BABES-BOLYAI". GEOLOGIA. (Text in English, French, German, Rumanian) 1958. s-a. exchange basis. Universitatea "Babes-Bolyai", Biblioteca Centrala Universitara, Str. Clinicilor. Nr. 2, Cluj-Napoca 3400, Rumania. TEL 95-117092. FAX 95-117633. charts; illus.; maps; index. **Indexed:** Biol.Abstr., Chem.Abstr., GeoRef. **Document type:** academic/scholarly publication.
Supersedes in part (in 1990): Studia Universitatis "Babes-Bolyai". Geologia - Geographia (ISSN 0039-341X)

551.44   UK   ISSN 0585-718X
CODEN: STSPAQ
STUDIES IN SPELEOLOGY. 1964. a. £12 to non-members. William Pengelly Cave Studies Trust Ltd., 107 Andover Rd., Newbury, Berks. RG14 6JH, England. Ed. R.G. Cooper. adv.; bk.rev.; index. circ. 600. **Indexed:** A.I.C.P., Biol.Abstr., Br.Archaeol.Abstr., GeoRef. **Document type:** academic/scholarly publication.

557   US   ISSN 0081-8747
QE171   CODEN: SVTGB
STUDIES IN VERMONT GEOLOGY. 1970. irreg., no.4, 1988. $4 per no. Vermont Geological Survey, Agency of Natural Resources, 103 S. Main St. (Center Bldg.), Waterbury, VT 05671-0401. TEL 802-244-5164. Ed. Charles A. Ratte. illus. **Indexed:** Biol.Abstr., GeoRef. **Document type:** academic/scholarly publication.
Description: Presents topical geologic studies of a specific site or area in Vermont.

551   RM   ISSN 1220-4994
STUDII SI CERCETARI DE GEOLOGIE/STUDIES AND RESEARCH IN GEOLOGY. 1958. a. 55 lei($32) (Academia Romana) Editura Academiei Romane, Calea Victoriei 125, 79717 Bucharest, Rumania. (Dist. by: Rompresfilatelia, Calea Grivitei 64-66, P.O. Box 12-201, 78104 Bucharest, Rumania) Ed. Dan Radulescu. **Document type:** academic/scholarly publication.
Former titles (until 1990): Studii si Cercetari de Geologie, Geofizica si Geographie. Geologie (ISSN 0567-6096); (until 1964): Studii si Cercetari de Geologie (ISSN 1010-688X)

526.9   MY   ISSN 0127-4937
SURVEYOR. (Text in English) 1963. q. M.$24 (Asia & Australia $20; Europe $50; America $80). Institution of Surveyors, Malaysia, P.O. Box 171, 46720 Petaling Jaya, Selangor, Malaysia. TEL 03-756-9728. FAX 03-755-0253. Ed. Gurjit Singh. adv.; bk.rev.; charts; illus. circ. 2,600. **Indexed:** RICS, W.R.C.Inf.
—BLDSC (8552.650000).

551   US   ISSN 0733-8813
SURVIEW. 1980. s-a. free. Geological and Natural History Survey, University of Wisconsin - Extension, 3817 Mineral Point Rd., Madison, WI 53705. TEL 608-262-1705. FAX 608-262-8086. Ed. Mindy James. bk.rev.; bibl. circ. 3,500. (back issues avail.) **Document type:** government publication.

554   SW   ISSN 0082-0024
QE282
SVERIGES GEOLOGISKA UNDERSOEKNING. SERIE C. AVHANDLINGAR OCH UPPSATSER/GEOLOGICAL SURVEY OF SWEDEN. SERIES C. MEMOIRS AND NOTICES. (Text in English, German and Swedish; summaries in English) 1868. irreg., no.819, 1988. price varies. Sveriges Geologiska Undersoekning - Geological Survey of Sweden, P.O. Box 670, S-751 28 Uppsala, Sweden. cum.index: 1858-1958. **Document type:** government publication.
—BLDSC (8568.960000); UnCover.

554   SW   ISSN 1103-3363
QE282   CODEN: SGUAA2
SVERIGES GEOLOGISKA UNDERSOEKNING. SERIE CA. AVHANDLINGAR OCH UPPSATSER I KVARTO/GEOLOGICAL SURVEY OF SWEDEN. SERIES CA. NOTICES IN FOLIO AND QUARTO. 1900. irreg., no.71, 1988. price varies. Sveriges Geologiska Undersoekning - Geological Survey of Sweden, P.O. Box 670, S-751 28 Uppsala, Sweden. **Document type:** government publication.

538.7   SW   ISSN 0281-1049
SVERIGES GEOLOGISKA UNDERSOEKNING. SERIE CB. JORDMAGNETISKA PUBLIKATIONER/GEOLOGICAL SURVEY OF SWEDEN. GEOMAGNETIC PUBLICATIONS. (Text in English) 1922. irreg. SEK 50. Sveriges Geologiska Undersoekning - Geological Survey of Sweden, P.O. Box 670, S-751 28 Uppsala, Sweden. **Document type:** government publication, academic/scholarly publication.
Formerly (until 1976): Jordmagnetiska Publikationer (ISSN 0075-403X)

556 622   SQ   ISSN 0081-9999
CODEN: SGMDA5
SWAZILAND. GEOLOGICAL SURVEY AND MINES DEPARTMENT. ANNUAL REPORT. 1947. a. price varies. Geological Survey and Mines Department, P.O. Box 9, Mbabane, Swaziland. FAX 09268-452:5. Ed. Ettie Ngubonde. circ. 500. **Indexed:** GeoRef. **Document type:** government publication.
Description: Provides a brief description of current work and progress on mining geology, research, chemical analysis and statistics.

556 622   SQ   ISSN 0082-0008
CODEN: SGMBAX
SWAZILAND. GEOLOGICAL SURVEY AND MINES DEPARTMENT. BULLETIN. 1961. a. price varies. Geological Survey and Mines Department, P.O. Box 9, Mbabane, Swaziland. FAX 09268-45215. Ed. Ettie Ngubonde. circ. 500. **Indexed:** GeoRef. **Document type:** government publication.
Description: Covers special topics related to mineral-bearing regions in mining geology, geochemistry and geophysics in Swaziland.

796.525   AT
SYDNEY SPELEOLOGICAL SOCIETY. JOURNAL. 1957. m. Aus.$38. Sydney Speleological Society, P.O. Box 198, Broadway, N.S.W. 2007, Australia. FAX 02-692-09C8. Ed. Ross Ellis. adv. contact: Ross Ellis. bk.rev.; illus.; index. circ. 200. **Indexed:** Aus.Speleo Abstr. **Document type:** newsletter.
Former titles (until 1970): Stop Press; Communications: S S S Newsletter.

551.44   AT
SYDNEY SPELEOLOGICAL SOCIETY. OCCASIONAL PAPER. 1965. irreg. price varies. Sydney Speleological Society, P.O. Box 198, Broadway, Sydney, N.S.W. 2007, Australia. FAX 02-660-1217. Ed. Ross A. Ellis. circ. 2,600. **Indexed:** Aus.Speleo Abstr., GeoRef.
Formerly: Sydney Speleological Society. Communications (ISSN 0085-7017)

796.525   AT
▼**SYDNEY SPELEOLOGICAL SOCIETY. REPRINT SERIES.** 1993. irreg. price varies. Sydney Speleological Society, P.O. Box 198, Broadway, N.S.W. 2007, Australia. FAX 02-660-1217. Ed. Ross A. Ellis. adv. contact: Ross Ellis. circ. 2,300. **Document type:** monographic series.

551   JA   ISSN 0285-1555
TAISEKIGAKU KENKYUKAIHO/SEDIMENTOLOGICAL SOCIETY OF JAPAN. JOURNAL. (Text in English, Japanese) 1969. s-a. Taisekigaku Kenkyukai - Sedimentologica Society of Japan, Kyushu Daigaku Rigakubu, Chikyu Wakusei Kagaku Kyoshitsu, 10-1, Hakozaki 6-chome, Higashi-ku, Fukuoka-shi, Fukuoka-ken 812, Japan.

559.4   AT
TASMANIA. DEPARTMENT OF RESOURCES AND ENERGY. DIVISION OF MINES AND MINERAL RESOURCES. GEOLOGICAL SURVEY BULLETINS. 1907. irreg., no.66, 1989. price varies. Geological Survey of Tasmania, P.O. Box 56, Rosny Park, Tas. 7018, Australia. FAX 61-02-44-2217. Ed. E.L. Martin. circ. 300. **Indexed:** GeoRef. **Document type:** government publication, academic/scholarly publication.
—UnCover.
Formerly: Tasmania. Department of Mines. Geological Survey Bulletins (ISSN 0082-2043)
Description: Publishes articles in the field of geology, mining mineral resources, water resources, and palaeontology.

559.4   AT
TASMANIA. DEPARTMENT OF RESOURCES AND ENERGY. DIVISION OF MINES AND MINERAL RESOURCES. REPORT (YEARS). irreg? Geological Survey of Tasmania, P.O. Box 56, Rosny Park, Tas. 7018, Australia. TEL 002-30-8333. FAX 002-44-2117. **Document type:** government publication.

1960 EARTH SCIENCES — GEOLOGY

551 371.3   UK   ISSN 0957-8005
TEACHING EARTH SCIENCES. 1976. q. £15. Institute of Earth Studies, University of Wales, Aberstwyth, Dyfed SY23 3DB, Wales. TEL 0970-622639. FAX 0970-622659. (Subscr. to: S. Rogers, 4 Middledyke Lane, Cottingham, N. Humberside HU16 4NH, England) Ed. Denis E.B. Bates. adv.; bk.rev.; film rev.; bibl.; charts; illus.; stat. circ. 1,100. **Indexed:** Cont.Pg.Educ. **Document type:** academic/scholarly publication.
—BLDSC (8614.090000).
    Formerly (until 1989): Geology Teaching (ISSN 0308-1567)

550   PL
TECHNIKA POSZUKIWAN GEOLOGICZNYCH, GEOSYNOPTYKA I GEOTERMIA/EXPLORATION TECHNOLOGY, GEOSYNOPTICS AND GEOTHERMAL ENERGY. (Text in Polish; summaries in English and Russian) 1962. bi-m. $60. Polska Akademia Nauk, Centrum Podstawowych Problemow Gospodarki Surowcami Mineralnymi i Energia - Polish Academy of Sciences, Minerals and Energy Economy Research Centre, Ul. Jozefa Wybickiego 7, 31-261 Krakow, Poland. TEL 48-12-36-24-35. FAX 48-12-36-35-24. (Co-sponsor: Osrodek Badawczo-Rozwojowy Techniki Geologicznej) Ed. Julian Sokolowski. adv.; bk.rev.; charts; illus.; pat.; tr.lit.; tr.mk.; index. circ. 500. **Indexed:** Chem.Abstr. **Document type:** academic/scholarly publication.
    Former titles (until 1988): Technika Poszukiwan Geologicznych (ISSN 0304-520X); (until 1974): Technika Poszukiwan (ISSN 0040-1161)
    Description: Addresses drilling, hydrogeological engineering and geophysical techniques.

549   KR   ISSN 0375-7773
TEKTONIKA I STRATIGRAFIYA; respublikanskii mezhvedomstvennyi sbornik nauchnykh trudov. 1972. s-a. (Akademiya Nauk Ukrainy, Institut Geologicheskikh Nauk) Vidavnitstvo Naukova Dumka, Vul. Tereshchenkivska 3, 252601 Kiev, Ukraine. (Dist. by: Mezhdunarodnaya Kniga, B. Yakimanka 39, 117049 Moscow, Russia) Ed. V.G. Bondarchuk. **Indexed:** GeoRef. **Document type:** academic/scholarly publication.
—CCC.

551 560   NE   ISSN 0308-9649
QE691
TERTIARY RESEARCH. 1970. 4/yr. fl.104($58) (Tertiary Research Group, UK) Universal Book Services, c/o Dr. W. Backhuys, Warmonderweg 80, 2341 KZ Oegstgeest, Netherlands. TEL 31-71-170208. FAX 31-71-171856. Ed. Dr. J.J. Hooker. circ. 350. (back issues avail.) **Indexed:** Geo.Abstr., GeoRef. **Document type:** academic/scholarly publication.
—BLDSC (8796.152000).
    Supersedes in part (in 1976): Tertiary Times (ISSN 0144-2236)

TEXAS ENERGY. see *ENERGY*

551.44 060   US
TEXAS MEMORIAL MUSEUM. SPELEOLOGICAL MONOGRAPHS. 1966. irreg., no.3, 1992. price varies. Texas Memorial Museum, University of Texas at Austin, 2400 Trinity, Austin, TX 78705. TEL 512-471-1604. **Document type:** academic/scholarly publication.

551   US   ISSN 0730-3300
QD901   CODEN: TEMIDK
TEXTURES AND MICROSTRUCTURES. 1972. 8/yr. (in 2 vols., 4 nos./vol.). 215 ECU per vol. (effective 1993). Gordon & Breach Science Publishers, 820 Town Center Dr., Langhorne, PA 19047. TEL 215-750-2642. FAX 215-750-6343. (UK subscr. to: P.O. Box 90, Reading, Berkshire RG1 8JL, England. TEL 0734-560-080) Ed. H.J. Bunge. adv.; bibl.; charts; illus.; index. (also avail. in microform) **Indexed:** ASCA, Chem.Abstr., Met.Abstr., Sci.Abstr., World Alum.Abstr. **Document type:** academic/scholarly publication.
—BLDSC (8813.784000); Faxon; CASDDS. CCC.
    Formerly: Texture of Crystalline Solids (ISSN 0309-7951)
    Refereed Serial

THALASSAS; revista de ciencias del mar. see *BIOLOGY*

TIANRANQI GONGYE/NATURAL GAS INDUSTRY. see *PETROLEUM AND GAS*

551 560   JA   ISSN 0082-4658
    CODEN: TDRCAH
TOHOKU DAIGAKU RIGAKUBU CHISHITSUGAKU KOSEIBUTSUGAKU KYOSHITSU KENKYU HOBUN HOKOKU/TOHOKU UNIVERSITY. FACULTY OF SCIENCE. INSTITUTE OF GEOLOGY AND PALEONTOLOGY. CONTRIBUTIONS. (Text in Japanese; summaries in English) 1921. irreg., no.91, 1988. exchange basis. Tohoku Daigaku, Rigakubu Chishitsugaku Koseibutsugaku Kyoshitsu, Chishitsugaku Koseibutsugaku Kyoshitsu - Tohoku University, Faculty of Science, Institute of Geology and Paleontology, Aoba, Aramaki, Aoba-ku, Sendai-shi, Miyagi-ken 980, Japan. Ed.Bd. circ. 750. **Indexed:** Biol.Abstr., GeoRef., Jap.Per.Ind. **Document type:** academic/scholarly publication.
—BLDSC (3445.000000); UnCover.

551 560   JA   ISSN 0082-464X
Q77.T55   CODEN: STUGA9
TOHOKU UNIVERSITY. SCIENCE REPORTS. SECOND SERIES: GEOLOGY/TOHOKU DAIGAKU RIKA HOKOKU. DAI 2-SHU, CHISHITSUGAKU. (Text and summaries in English) 1912. s-a. exchange basis. Tohoku Daigaku, Rigakubu, Chishitsugaku Koseibutsugaku Kyoshitsu - Tohoku University, Faculty of Science, Institute of Geology and Paleontology, Aoba, Aramaki, Aoba-ku, Sendai-shi, Miyagi-ken 980, Japan. Ed.Bd. circ. 750. **Indexed:** Biol.Abstr. **Document type:** academic/scholarly publication.
—BLDSC (8157.000000); UnCover.

TOHOKU UNIVERSITY. SCIENCE REPORTS. THIRD SERIES: MINERALOGY, PETROLOGY AND ECONOMIC GEOLOGY/TOHOKU DAIGAKU RIKA HOKOKU. DAI 3-SHU, GANSEKIGAKU KOBUTSUGAKU KOSHOGAKU. see *MINES AND MINING INDUSTRY*

551 574   US   ISSN 0275-0120
    CODEN: TBGBDG
TOPICS IN GEOBIOLOGY. 1980. irreg., vol.11, 1993. price varies. Plenum Publishing Corp., 233 Spring St., New York, NY 10013-1578. TEL 212-620-8000. FAX 212-463-0742. TELEX 23-421139. Eds. Francis G. Stehli, D.S. Jones. **Document type:** monographic series.
—BLDSC (8867.441000); CASDDS.
    Refereed Serial

551   SP   ISSN 0474-9588
    CODEN: TBGLA9
TRABAJOS DE GEOLOGIA. 1967. a. price varies. Universidad de Oviedo, Facultad de Geologia, 33005 Oviedo, Spain. (Subscr. to: Servicio de Publicaciones, Un. de Oviedo, Calle Arias de Velasco s-n, 33005 Oviedo, Spain) Ed. Maria Martinez Chacon. abstr.; illus. circ. 1,000. **Indexed:** Biol.Abstr., Bull.Signal., GeoRef., Ind.SST, Zoo.Rec. **Document type:** academic/scholarly publication.
—CASDDS. CCC.

TRAPANANDA. see *HISTORY — History Of North And South America*

551 560   US   ISSN 0041-4018
QE1   CODEN: TSGEB6
TULANE STUDIES IN GEOLOGY AND PALEONTOLOGY. 1962. q. $20 (foreign $22). Tulane University, Department of Geology, New Orleans, LA 70118. TEL 504-865-5198. Eds. Hubert C. Skinner, Emily H. Vokes. bk.rev.; abstr.; charts; illus. circ. 1,000. **Indexed:** Chem.Abstr., GeoRef., Petrol.Abstr. **Document type:** academic/scholarly publication.
—BLDSC (9070.395000); UnCover.
    Formerly: Tulane Studies in Geology (ISSN 0096-4077)
    Description: Devoted to the geology and paleontology of the coasts and adjacent land areas of the Gulf of Mexico and the Caribbean Sea.
    Refereed Serial

TURUN YLIOPISTO. JULKAISUJA. SARJA A. II. BIOLOGICA - GEOGRAPHICA - GEOLOGICA. see *BIOLOGY*

551.44   AU
U I S BULLETIN. (Union Internationale de Speleologie) 1970. s-a. $2. International Union of Speleology, c/o Hubert Trimmel, Pres., Draschestr. 77, A-1232 Vienna, Austria. bk.rev. circ. 2,200.

550   UA
UNITED ARAB REPUBLIC JOURNAL OF GEOLOGY. (Text in English; summaries in Arabic and English) 1957. s-a. $30. Egyptian Geological Society, Tager Bldg., 1 Osoris St., Garden City, Cairo, Egypt. Ed. S. Al-Ansary. charts; illus. **Indexed:** Biol.Abstr., Chem.Abstr., GeoRef.
    Former titles: Egyptian Journal of Geology; (until 1971): Journal of Geology of the United Arab Republic (ISSN 0022-1384); (until 1960): United Arab Republic Journal of Geology.

551 669   MX   ISSN 0581-5207
QE1   CODEN: UAIFA5
UNIVERSIDAD AUTONOMA DE SAN LUIS POTOSI. INSTITUTO DE GEOLOGIA. FOLLETO TECNICO. 1962. irreg., no.117, 1993. exchange basis. Universidad Autonoma de San Luis Potosi, Instituto de Geologia, Av. Dr. Manuel Nava 5, San Luis Potosi S.L.P., Mexico. TEL 48-17-10-39. Ed. Guillerno Labarthe. **Indexed:** Chem.Abstr. **Document type:** academic/scholarly publication.
—CASDDS.
    Formerly: Universidad Autonoma de San Luis Potosi. Instituto de Geologia y Metalurgia. Folleto Tecnico.

550   CK   ISSN 0120-0283
UNIVERSIDAD INDUSTRIAL DE SANTANDER. BOLETIN DE GEOLOGIA. (Text in Spanish, occasionally in English and French) 1958. irreg. $8 for 2 yrs. or exchange basis. Universidad Industrial de Santander, Biblioteca, Apdo. Aereo 678, Bucaramanga, Santander, Colombia. FAX 5776-351946. abstr.; charts; illus. circ. 1,200. **Indexed:** Biol.Abstr., Chem.Abstr. **Document type:** academic/scholarly publication.

557   MX   ISSN 0185-0962
QE201   CODEN: RUNGD7
UNIVERSIDAD NACIONAL AUTONOMA DE MEXICO. INSTITUTO DE GEOLOGIA. REVISTA. (Supersedes an experimental publication of the same title issued 1975-1976) (Text mainly in English; occasionally in French, Spanish) 1977. s-a. $36 for vol.10 (effective 1992-93). Universidad Nacional Autonoma de Mexico, Instituto de Geologia, Apdo. 70-296, Deleg. Coyoacan, 04510 Mexico, D.F., Mexico. FAX 5-550-66-44. Ed. Arturo Gomez C. charts. circ. 1,200. (reprint service avail.) **Indexed:** Biol.Abstr., Chem.Abstr., GeoRef., Sel.Water Res.Abstr. **Document type:** academic/scholarly publication.
    Description: Publishes the results of work carried out at the institution.

551   BL   ISSN 0101-5400
    CODEN: BCDGDT
UNIVERSIDADE FEDERAL DO RIO GRANDE DO NORTE. DEPARTAMENTO DE GEOLOGIA. BOLETIM. (Text in Portuguese; abstracts in English.) 1981. q. Universidade Federal do Rio Grande do Norte, Departamento de Geologia, Campus Universitario, Cx. Postal 1639, 59000 Natal RN, Brazil. Ed. Peter Christian Hackspacher. adv.; abstr.; bibl.; illus.; charts. circ. 1,000. **Indexed:** Chem.Abstr. **Document type:** academic/scholarly publication, bulletin.
—CASDDS.

551 560   IT
UNIVERSITA DEGLI STUDI DI FERRARA. DIPARTIMENTO DI SCIENZE GEOLOGICHE E PALEONTOLOGICHE. ANNALI. SEZIONE: SCIENZE DELLA TERRA. (Text in English, French or Italian) 1951. irreg., vol.3, no.2, 1981. exchange basis. Universita degli Studi di Ferrara, Dipartimento de Scienze Geologiche e Paleontologiche, C.So Ercole 1 d'Este 32, 44100 Ferrara, Italy. index. circ. 450. **Document type:** academic/scholarly publication.
    Former titles: Universita degli Studi di Ferrara. Istituto di Geologia. Annali. Sezione 9. Scienze Geologiche; Universite degli Studi di Ferrara. Istituto di Geologia, Paleontologia e Paleontologia Umana. Annali. Sezione 9. Scienze Geologiche (ISSN 0071-4550)

554 560   IT
UNIVERSITA DEGLI STUDI DI FERRARA. ISTITUTO DI GEOLOGIA. PUBBLICAZIONI. (Text in English, French or Italian) 1950. a. available on exchange. Universita degli Studi di Ferrara, Istituto di Geologia, C.So Ercole 1 d' Este, 32, Ferrara, Italy. index. circ. 450. **Document type:** academic/scholarly publication.
    Formerly: Universita degli Studi di Ferrara. Istituto di Geologia, Paleontologia e Paleontologia Umana. Pubblicazioni (ISSN 0071-4577)

EARTH SCIENCES — GEOLOGY

551   IT   ISSN 0041-8978
QE272   CODEN: AGUGAQ
UNIVERSITA DEGLI STUDI DI GENOVA. ISTITUTO DI GEOLOGIA. ATTI.* 1963. 2/yr. Universita degli Studi di Genova, Istituto di Geologia, Via Balbi 5, Genoa, Italy. Ed.Bd. **Document type:** academic/scholarly publication.

554 560   GW   ISSN 0072-1115
QE1   CODEN: MGPHBZ
UNIVERSITAET HAMBURG. GEOLOGISCH-PALAEONTOLOGISCHES INSTITUT. MITTEILUNGEN. (Text in English and German) 1948. a. DM.35($5) Universitaet Hamburg, Geologisch-Palaeontologisches Institut, Bundesstr. 55, 20146 Hamburg, Germany. TEL 040-41234989. FAX 040-41235270. Ed. Wolfgang Weitschat. **Indexed:** Biol.Abstr., Deep Sea Res.& Oceanogr.Abstr. **Document type:** academic/scholarly publication.
—BLDSC (5846.250000).

554   AU
UNIVERSITAET INNSBRUCK. ALPENKUNDLICHE STUDIEN. (Subseries of: Universitaet Innsbruck. Veroeffentlichungen) 1968. irreg., vol.10, 1972. price varies. Oesterreichische Kommissionsbuchhandlung, Maximilianstrasse 17, A-6020 Innsbruck, Austria. Ed. Franz Fliri. **Document type:** academic/scholarly publication.

551   GW   ISSN 0175-9302
UNIVERSITAET KIEL. GEOLOGISCH-PALAEONTOLOGISCHES INSTITUT. BERICHTE - REPORTS. 1983. irreg., vol.64, 1993. price varies. Universitaet Kiel, Geologisch-Palaeontologisches Institut, Olshausenstr. 40, 24118 Kiel, Germany. TEL 0431-8803254. FAX 0431-8804376. **Document type:** monographic series.

554   GW   ISSN 0069-5874
UNIVERSITAET ZU KOELN. GEOLOGISCHES INSTITUT. SONDERVEROEFFENTLICHUNGEN. (Text in German; summaries in English) 1956. irreg., no.87, 1992. price varies. Universitaet zu Koeln, Geologisches Institut, Zuelpicher Str. 49, 50674 Cologne, Germany. FAX 0221-4705149. Ed. E. Kempf. **Document type:** monographic series.

550   RM   ISSN 0379-7902
QE287.6   CODEN: ASJSAN
UNIVERSITATEA "AL. I. CUZA" DIN IASI. ANALELE STIINTIFICE. GEOLOGIE - GEOGRAFIE. (Text in English, French, Rumanian, Russian) 1955. a. 35 lei. Universitatea "Al. I. Cuza" din Iasi, Calea M. Eminescu 11, Jassy, Rumania. (Subscr. to: ILEXIM, Str. 13 Decembrie Nr.3, P.O. Box 136-137, Bucharest, Rumania) Eds. V. Erhan, I. Donisa. circ. 350. **Document type:** academic/scholarly publication.
Formed by the merger of: Universitatea "Al. I. Cuza" din Iasi. Analele Stiintifice. Sectiunea 2b: Geologie (ISSN 0365-6594); Universitatea "Al. I. Cuza" din Iasi. Analele Stiintifice. Sectiunea 2c: Geografie (ISSN 0365-7256)
Description: Articles on geomorphology, climatology, hydrology, economic geography, petrology, geochemistry and paleontology.

553   RM   ISSN 1220-5079
UNIVERSITATEA TEHNICA PETROSANI. LUCRARI STIINTIFICE. (Text in English, French, German and Russian) 1958. s-a. 1000 lei. Universitatea Tehnica Petrosani - Technical University of Petrosani, Str. Universitatii Nr. 20, 2675 Petrosani, Rumania. TEL 935-42580. FAX 935-43491. TELEX 72524 INMIN. Ed. Nicolae/Ilias. adv. contact: Mioara Costinas. bk.rev.; illus. circ. 400. **Document type:** academic/scholarly publication.
Formerly: Institutul de Mine Petrosani. Lucrari Stiintifice.
Description: The papers comprise new mining, ore-dressing, electrification and automation technologies used in the mining industry resulting from the scientific research carried out by the university's teaching staff.

551   TU   ISSN 0253-1216
             CODEN: CFSGDY
UNIVERSITE D'ANKARA. FACULTE DES SCIENCES. COMMUNICATIONS. SERIE C1. GEOLOGIE. (Text in English, French, German) 1947. a. exchange basis. University of Ankara, Faculty of Sciences, Besevler, Ankara, Turkey. circ. 250. (back issues avail.) **Indexed:** Biol.Abstr. **Document type:** academic/scholarly publication.

557   CN   ISSN 0705-3207
UNIVERSITY OF BRITISH COLUMBIA. DEPARTMENT OF GEOLOGICAL SCIENCES. REPORT. 1962. irreg., no.19, 1990. Can.$3 per no. or on exchange basis. University of British Columbia, Department of Geological Sciences, Vancouver, BC V6T 2B4, Canada. TEL 604-228-2211. FAX 604-822-6088. Ed. W.R. Danner. circ. 400. **Document type:** academic/scholarly publication.
Formerly: University of British Columbia. Department of Geology. Report (ISSN 0068-1733)

556   SA
UNIVERSITY OF CAPE TOWN. DEPARTMENT OF GEOLOGICAL SCIENCES. PRECAMBRIAN RESEARCH UNIT. BULLETIN. 1965. irreg., no.38, 1993. R.200($60) or exchange basis. University of Cape Town, Department of Geological Sciences, Precambrian Research Unit, Rondebosch 7700, South Africa. TEL 27-21-6502917. Ed. C.W. Stowe. bibl.; charts. circ. 375. **Indexed:** AESIS. **Document type:** academic/scholarly publication, bulletin.
Formerly: University of Cape Town. Department of Geology. Precambrian Research Unit. Bulletin (ISSN 0041-9478)

553 557   US   ISSN 0082-3287
             CODEN: TGARBX
UNIVERSITY OF TEXAS AT AUSTIN. BUREAU OF ECONOMIC GEOLOGY. ANNUAL REPORT. 1960. a. free. University of Texas at Austin, Bureau of Economic Geology, University Station, Box X, University Sta., Austin, TX 78713. TEL 512-471-7721. FAX 512-471-0140. (reprint service avail. from UMI) **Indexed:** AESIS, GeoRef. **Document type:** academic/scholarly publication.
—BLDSC (1132.600000).
Description: Provides advisory, technical, and informational services relating to the resources and geology of Texas.

557   US   ISSN 0082-3309
             CODEN: GCUGDX
UNIVERSITY OF TEXAS AT AUSTIN. BUREAU OF ECONOMIC GEOLOGY. GEOLOGICAL CIRCULAR. 1965. irreg., latest no.91-2. price varies. University of Texas at Austin, Bureau of Economic Geology, Box X, University Sta., Austin, TX 78713. TEL 512-471-7721. FAX 512-471-0140. (reprint service avail. from UMI) **Indexed:** AESIS. **Document type:** academic/scholarly publication.

557   US   ISSN 0363-4132
             CODEN: TEGGAF
UNIVERSITY OF TEXAS AT AUSTIN. BUREAU OF ECONOMIC GEOLOGY. GUIDEBOOK. 1958. irreg, no.25, 1990. price varies. University of Texas at Austin, Bureau of Economic Geology, Box X, University Sta., Austin, TX 78713. TEL 512-471-7721. FAX 512-471-0140. (reprint service avail. from UMI) **Indexed:** AESIS.
Formerly: University of Texas. Bureau of Economic Geology. Guidebook (ISSN 0082-3295)

553   US   ISSN 0082-3333
UNIVERSITY OF TEXAS AT AUSTIN. BUREAU OF ECONOMIC GEOLOGY. MINERAL RESOURCE CIRCULARS. 1930. irreg., no.81, 1989. price varies. University of Texas at Austin, Bureau of Economic Geology, Box X, University Sta., Austin, TX 78713. TEL 512-471-7721. FAX 512-471-0140. (back issues avail.; reprint service avail. from UMI) **Indexed:** Geo.Abstr. **Document type:** academic/scholarly publication.

557   US   ISSN 0082-335X
QE167   CODEN: TUGRAO
UNIVERSITY OF TEXAS AT AUSTIN. BUREAU OF ECONOMIC GEOLOGY. REPORT OF INVESTIGATIONS. 1946. irreg., no.200, 1991. price varies. University of Texas at Austin, Bureau of Economic Geology, Box X, University Sta., Austin, TX 78713. TEL 512-471-7721. FAX 512-471-0140. (reprint service avail. from UMI) **Indexed:** AESIS, Geo.Abstr. **Document type:** academic/scholarly publication.
—BLDSC (7659.200000).

551   US   ISSN 0193-0990
UNIVERSITY OF TEXAS AT AUSTIN. BUREAU OF ECONOMIC GEOLOGY. SPECIAL PUBLICATIONS. irreg. price varies. University of Texas at Austin, Bureau of Economic Geology, Box X, University Sta., Austin, TX 78713. TEL 512-471-7721. FAX 512-471-0140. **Document type:** academic/scholarly publication.
Refereed Serial

550   PK
UNIVERSITY OF THE PUNJAB. INSTITUTE OF GEOLOGY. GEOLOGICAL BULLETIN. (Text in English) 1961. a. Rs.50. University of the Punjab, Institute of Geology, Qaid-E-Azam Campus, Lahore, Pakistan. Ed. F.A. Shams. bk.rev.; circ. controlled. (back issues avail.) **Indexed:** Biol.Abstr., Mineral.Abstr. **Document type:** academic/scholarly publication, bulletin.

551   JA   ISSN 0388-6182
UNIVERSITY OF TSUKUBA. INSTITUTE OF GEOSCIENCE. SCIENCE REPORTS. SECTION B: GEOLOGICAL SCIENCES. (Text in English) 1980. a. University of Tsukuba, Institute of Geoscience - Tsukuba Daigaku Chikyu Kagakukei, 1-1, Tennodai 1-chome, Tsukuba-shi, Ibarak-ken 305, Japan.
—BLDSC (8153.820000); UnCover.

559.8 597 551.9   NZ   ISSN 0110-2192
QE350   CODEN: RUWADY
UNIVERSITY OF WAIKATO. ANTARCTIC RESEARCH UNIT. REPORT. 1972. a. free. University of Waikato, Private Bag, Hamilton, New Zealand. circ. 350. **Indexed:** Chem.Abstr., GeoRef. **Document type:** academic/scholarly publication.

551   US   ISSN 0010-7980
QE1   CODEN: WUGGAO
UNIVERSITY OF WYOMING. CONTRIBUTIONS TO GEOLOGY. 1962. s-a. $20. University of Wyoming, Department of Geology and Geophysics, Box 3006, University Sta., Laramie, WY 82071. TEL 307-766-3386. FAX 307-766-6679. TELEX 9109494949. Ed Ms. Buff Moore. bk.rev.; bibl.; charts; illus.; cum.index: 1962-1986. circ. 680. (back issues avail.) **Indexed:** Biol.Abstr., Chem.Abstr., Eng.Ind., Geo.Abstr., GeoRef., Mineral.Abstr. **Document type:** academic/scholarly publication.
—BLDSC (3458.600000); UnCover; CASDDS.
Description: Items dealing with geological problems especially pertinent to the Rocky Mountain region.
Refereed Serial

796.525   PL   ISSN 0208-5534
UNIWERSYTET SLASKI W KATOWICACH. PRACE NAUKOWE. GEOLOGIA. (Text in Polish; summaries in English, Russian) 1977. irreg. price varies. Wydawnictwo Uniwersytetu Slaskiego, Ul. Bankowa 12B, 40-007 Katowice, Poland. TEL 48-32-596-915. FAX 48-32-599-699. TELEX 0315584 USKPL (Dist. by: CHZ Ars Polona, P.O. Box 1001, 00-950 Warsaw, Poland) Ed. Barbara Woznica. **Document type:** academic/scholarly publication.
Description: Covers basic geology, palaeontology, stratigraphy, geochemistry, mineralogy, petrography, hydrogeology, engineering geology, geology of deposits.

796.525   PL   ISSN 0137-5482
GB601.A1
UNIWERSYTET SLASKI W KATOWICACH. PRACE NAUKOWE. KRAS I SPELEOLOGIA. (Text in English, Polish; summaries in English, French, Polish) 1977. irreg. Wydawnictwo Uniwersytetu Slaskiego, Ul. Bankowa 12B, 40-007 Katowice, Poland. TEL 48-32-596-915. FAX 48-32-599-605. TELEX 315584 USKTL. (Dist. by: CHZ Ars Polona, P.O. Box 1001, 00-950 Warsaw, Poland) Ed. Barbara Woznica. **Document type:** academic/scholarly publication.
Description: Covers karst in Poland and Europe, with thermokarst and pseudokarst, and cave explorations.

550   PL   ISSN 0067-9003
             CODEN: BGLGAQ
UNIWERSYTET WARSZAWSKI. WYDZIAL GEOLOGII. BIULETYN GEOLOGICZNY. (Text in Polish; summaries in English) 1961. irreg., no.31, 1988. price varies. (Uniwersytet Warszawski, Wydzial Geologii) Wydawnictwa Uniwersytetu Warszawskiego, Ul. Obozna 8, 00-032 Warsaw, Poland. (Dist. by: Ars Polona-Ruch, Krakowskie Przedmiescie 7, 00-068 Warsaw, Poland) Ed. Barbara Grabowska-Olszewska. circ. 400. **Indexed:** GeoRef. **Document type:** academic/scholarly publication.
—BLDSC (2105.310000).

EARTH SCIENCES — GEOLOGY

551   SW
UPPSALA UNIVERSITET. GEOLOGICAL INSTITUTION. BULLETIN. (Subseries of: Acta Universitatis Upsaliensis) (Text in English) N.S. 1970. irreg. price varies. A W I International AB, P.O. Box 4627, S-116 91 Stockholm, Sweden. TEL 468-40-8800. FAX 468-641-1180. Eds. Bengt Collini, Richard A. Reyment. bibl.; charts; illus. **Indexed:** Biol.Abstr. **Document type:** academic/scholarly publication, bulletin.

550   XR   ISSN 0042-4730
QE267.C8
USTREDNI USTAV GEOLOGICKY. VESTNIK/GEOLOGICAL SURVEY. BULLETIN. (Text in Czech, English, French, German; summaries in English, German) 1925. bi-m. DM.146. Academia, Publishing House of the Czechoslovak Academy of Sciences, Vodickova 40, 112 29 Prague 1, Czech Republic. TEL 53-36-41. (Dist. in Western countries by: Kubon & Sagner, P.O. Box 34 01 08, 8000 Munich 34, Germany) Ed. Jan H. Bernard. bk.rev.; bibl.; charts; illus. circ. 950. (back issues avail.) **Indexed:** Biol.Abstr., Chem.Abstr. **Document type:** academic/scholarly publication, bulletin.
—UnCover.
    Formerly (until 1951): Statni Ustav Geologicky. Vestnik (ISSN 0042-1359)
    Description: Reports of geological studies and investigations made by Czechoslovak specialists at home and abroad; information about recent foreign research relevant to Czechoslovak geology.

557   US   ISSN 0083-484X
UTAH GEOLOGICAL ASSOCIATION. ANNUAL GUIDEBOOK. (Not published 1978) 1971. a. price varies. Utah Geological Association, Box 11334, Salt Lake City, UT 84147. TEL 801-467-7970. (Subscr. to: Utah Geological Survey, 2363 Foothill Dr., Salt Lake City, UT 84109-1491) adv. circ. 850.
    Description: Presents papers on a specific area's geology and related topics, with emphasis on field trips.

557 553   US
QE169
UTAH GEOLOGICAL SURVEY. BULLETIN. no.35, 1948. irreg., no.127, 1993. price varies. Utah Geological Survey, 2363 Foothill Dr., Salt Lake City, UT 84109-1491. TEL 801-467-7970. FAX 801-467-4070. illus. **Indexed:** AESIS, Chem.Abstr., GeoRef. **Document type:** government publication, academic/scholarly publication.
    Formerly: Utah. Geological and Mineral Survey. Bulletin (ISSN 0098-4825)

557 553   US
         CODEN: UGMSA4
UTAH GEOLOGICAL SURVEY. SPECIAL STUDIES. 1962. irreg., no.83, 1993. price varies. Utah Geological Survey, 2363 Foothill Dr., Salt Lake City, UT 84109-1491. TEL 801-467-7970. FAX 801-467-4070. **Indexed:** GeoRef. **Document type:** government publication, academic/scholarly publication.
—UnCover; CASDDS.
    Formerly: Utah. Geological and Mineral Survey. Special Studies (ISSN 0098-115X)

557 553   US   ISSN 1061-7930
QE169
UTAH GEOLOGICAL SURVEY. SURVEY NOTES. 1964. 3/yr. free in U.S. Utah Geological Survey, 2363 Foothill Dr., Salt Lake City, UT 84109-1491. TEL 801-467-7970. FAX 801-467-4070. Ed. J. Stringfellow. bk.rev.; charts; illus.; stat. circ. 3,600. **Indexed:** AESIS, GeoRef. **Document type:** government publication, academic/scholarly publication.
—UnCover.
    Former titles: Utah. Geological and Mineral Survey. Survey Notes (ISSN 0362-6288); Utah. Geological and Mineral Survey. Quarterly Review (ISSN 0042-1421)

550   UZ   ISSN 0042-1693
         CODEN: UZGZAQ
UZBEKSKII GEOLOGICHESKII ZHURNAL. (Text in Russian) 1957. bi-m. 13.50 Rub. (Akademiya Nauk Uzbekistana) Izdatel'stvo Fan, Ul. Gogolya 70, k. 105, 700000 Tashkent, Uzbekistan. charts; illus.; index. **Indexed:** Chem.Abstr., GeoRef., Protozool.Abstr.
—BLDSC (0384.040000). **CCC.**

559   NN   ISSN 0077-8443
QE349.N43   CODEN: NHGRA3
VANUATU. GEOLOGICAL SURVEY. REPORTS. (Numbering of reports has been discontinued) 1966. irreg. price varies. Geological Survey, G.P.O., Port Vila, Vanuatu. FAX 22213. TELEX 1040 NH VANGOV. **Document type:** academic/scholarly publication.
—BLDSC (4110.810000).
    Formerly: New Hebrides. Condominium Geological Survey. Report.
    Description: Descriptive reports of geology of island groups within Vanuatu. Reports published separately from geological maps.

550   VE   ISSN 0006-6281
QE251   CODEN: VMMGAL
VENEZUELA. MINISTERIO DE ENERGIA Y MINAS. BOLETIN DE GEOLOGIA. (Summaries in English and Spanish) 1951. irreg. price varies. Ministerio de Energia y Minas, Direccion de Geologia, Torre Norte, Torre oeste, Piso 4, Caracas, Venezuela. Ed.Bd. **Indexed:** Biol.Abstr. **Document type:** government publication, academic/scholarly publication.

VEREINIGUNG SCHWEIZERISCHER PETROLEUM-GEOLOGEN UND -INGENIEURE. BULLETIN/ASSOCIATION SUISSE DES GEOLOGUES ET INGENIEURS DU PETROLE. BULLETIN. (Vereinigung Schweizerischer Petroleum-Geologen und -Ingenieure) see *PETROLEUM AND GAS*

557   US
QE171   CODEN: VGSBAS
VERMONT DIVISION OF GEOLOGY AND MINERAL RESOURCES. BULLETIN. 1950. irreg., no.32, 1984. price varies. Vermont Geological Survey, Agency of Natural Resources, 103 S. Main St., Center Bldg., Waterbury, VT 05671-0301. TEL 802-241-3601. **Indexed:** Biol.Abstr., GeoRef. **Document type:** government publication, academic/scholarly publication.
    Formerly: Vermont Geological Survey. Bulletin (ISSN 0083-5757)
    Description: Covers the geology of 15-minute quadrangles in Vermont.

557 551   US
QE171
VERMONT DIVISION OF GEOLOGY AND MINERAL RESOURCES. ECONOMIC GEOLOGY. 1966. irreg., no.8, 1972. $1 per no. Vermont Division of Geology and Mineral Resources, 103 S. Main St.-Center Bldg., Waterbury, VT 05676. TEL 802-241-3601. illus. **Document type:** academic/scholarly publication.
    Formerly: Vermont Geological Survey. Economic Geology (ISSN 0531-8262)
    Description: Contains information on magnetic, geochemical, resistivity surveys and geology of economic mineral desposits in Vermont.

557 551.4   US
VERMONT DIVISION OF GEOLOGY AND MINERAL RESOURCES. ENVIRONMENTAL GEOLOGY. 1971. irreg., no.7, 1975. $2 per no. Vermont Geological Survey, Agency of Natural Resources, 103 S. Main St., Center Bldg., Waterbury, VT 05676. TEL 802-244-5164. Ed. Charles A. Ratte. illus. **Indexed:** AESIS, Cadscan, Deep Sea Res.& Oceanogr.Abstr., GeoRef., Lead Abstr., W.R.C.Inf., Zincscan. **Document type:** academic/scholarly publication.
    Formerly: Vermont Geological Survey. Evironmental Geology (ISSN 0071-0857)
    Description: Regional information on simplified surficial and bedrock geology, ground-water potential, sand and gravel resources and waste disposal for land use planning.

557   US
VERMONT DIVISION OF GEOLOGY AND MINERAL RESOURCES. SPECIAL BULLETIN. 1968. irreg., no.11, 1989. price varies. Vermont Geological Survey, Agency of Natural Resources, 103 S. Main St., Center Bldg., Waterbury, VT 05671-0301. TEL 802-241-3601. illus. **Document type:** government publication, bulletin.
    Formerly: Vermont Geological Survey. Special Bulletin (ISSN 0506-7553)
    Description: Covers the geology of Vermont.

557 551.4   US
QE747.V4   CODEN: VGSPA2
VERMONT GEOLOGICAL SURVEY. SPECIAL PUBLICATION. 1962. irreg., no.3, 1982. price varies. Vermont Geological Survey, Agency of Natural Resources, 103 S. Main St., Center Bldg., Waterbury, VT 05671-0301. TEL 802-241-3601. illus. **Indexed:** GeoRef. **Document type:** government publication.
    Formerly: Vermont Geological Survey. Special Publications (ISSN 0083-5765)
    Description: General-interest publications on Vermont geology.

559.4   AT   ISSN 0085-7750
VICTORIA, AUSTRALIA. GEOLOGICAL SURVEY. BULLETIN. 1903. irreg. price varies. Geological Survey of Victoria, Department of Energy of Minerals, P.O. Box 98, E. Melbourne, Vic. 3002, Australia. TEL 03-665-0600. FAX 03-663-6325. circ. 750. **Indexed:** AESIS, GeoRef. **Document type:** government publication, monographic series.

559.4   AT   ISSN 0085-7769
VICTORIA, AUSTRALIA. GEOLOGICAL SURVEY. MEMOIRS. 1903. irreg. price varies. Geological Survey of Victoria, Department of Energy of Minerals, P.O. Box 98, E. Melbourne, Vic. 3002, Australia. TEL 03-665-0600. FAX 03-663-6325. circ. 750. **Indexed:** AESIS, Biol.Abstr., GeoRef. **Document type:** government publication, monographic series.

559.4   AT   ISSN 0810-6959
VICTORIA, AUSTRALIA. GEOLOGICAL SURVEY. REPORTS. 1968. irreg. price varies. Geological Survey of Victoria, Department of Energy of Minerals, P.O. Box 98, E. Melbourne, Vic. 3002, Australia. TEL 03-665-0600. FAX 03-663-6325. **Document type:** government publication, monographic series.

VIRGINIA. DIVISION OF MINERAL RESOURCES. PUBLICATIONS. see *MINES AND MINING INDUSTRY*

557   US   ISSN 0507-1259
VIRGINIA POLYTECHNIC INSTITUTE AND STATE UNIVERSITY. DEPARTMENT OF GEOLOGICAL SCIENCES. GEOLOGICAL GUIDEBOOKS. 1961. irreg., no.9, 1973. price varies. Virginia Polytechnic Institute and State University, Department of Geological Sciences, 4044 Derring Hall, Blacksburg, VA 24061. TEL 703-961-6521. circ. controlled. (back issues avail.) **Indexed:** GeoRef.
    Formerly: Virginia Polytechnic Institute, Blacksburg. Engineering Extension Division. Geological Guidebook.

526   BU   ISSN 0324-1114
QB275   CODEN: VGEOEZ
VISSHA GEODEZIIA. (Text in various languages) 1975. irreg. 1.10 lv. per no. (Bulgarska Akademiia na Naukite) Publishing House of the Bulgarian Academy of Sciences, Acad. G. Boncev St., Bldg. 6, 1113 Sofia, Bulgaria. circ. 480. (reprint service avail. from IRC) **Indexed:** BSL Geo. **Document type:** academic/scholarly publication.
—BLDSC (0040.631000).

549   RU
QE351   CODEN: ZVMOAG
VSEROSSIISKOE MINERALOGICHESKOE OBSHCHESTVO. ZAPISKI. (Text in Russian; abstracts and contents page in English) 1866. bi-m. $132.80 (typically set in Jan.). 21 Line, 2, St. Petersburg, 199026, Russia. TEL 812-218-86-40. FAX 812-213-26-13. TELEX 121494 LGIP SU. (Co-sponsor: Russian Academy of Sciences, Department of Geology, Geophysics, Geochemistry and Mining) Ed. Yury B. Marin. bk.rev.; abstr.; charts; illus.; index. circ. 1,000. (tabloid format; also avail. in microform; reprint service avail.) **Indexed:** AESIS, Eng.Ind., GeoRef. **Document type:** academic/scholarly publication.
—CCC.
    Formerly (until 1992): Vsesoyuznoe Mineralogicheskoe Obshchestvo. Zapiski (ISSN 0044-1805)
    Description: Informs readers about the main achievements of Russian scientists in the fields of mineralogy, petrology, crystallography, geochemistry and the science of mineral deposits. Covers the scientific-public activities of the society.

EARTH SCIENCES — GEOLOGY

551 **MY**
WARTA GEOLOGI. (Text in English) 1967. bi-m. M.$51.40($20) Geological Society of Malaysia, c/o Department of Geology, University of Malaya, 59100 Kuala Lumpur, Malaysia. TEL 603-7577036. FAX 603-7563900. Ed. Teh Guan Hoe. circ. 700. (back issues avail.) **Indexed:** Biol.Abstr., GeoRef.
Formerly: Geological Society of Malaysia Newsletter (ISSN 0126-5539)
Description: Articles, progress reports, and general information for members.

557 622 **US**
WASHINGTON (STATE). DEPARTMENT OF NATURAL RESOURCES. DIVISION OF GEOLOGY AND EARTH RESOURCES. BULLETIN. 1910. irreg., no.79, 1990. price varies. Department of Natural Resources, Division of Geology and Earth Resources, Olympia, WA 98504. TEL 902-902-1450. FAX 206-902-1785. (back issues avail.) **Document type:** government publication, monographic series.
Description: Provides technical information on various aspects of the geology of the state of Washington.

WASHINGTON (STATE). DEPARTMENT OF NATURAL RESOURCES. DIVISION OF GEOLOGY AND EARTH RESOURCES. INFORMATION CIRCULAR. see *MINES AND MINING INDUSTRY*

551 **US**
WASHINGTON (STATE). DEPARTMENT OF NATURAL RESOURCES. DIVISION OF GEOLOGY AND EARTH RESOURCES. REPORT OF INVESTIGATIONS. 1926. irreg., no. 31, 1992. price varies. Department of Natural Resources, Division of Geology and Earth Resources, MS PY-12, Olympia, WA 98504. TEL 206-902-1450. FAX 206-902-1785. Ed. Katherine Reed. circ. 1,000. **Document type:** government publication, monographic series.
Description: Information on a single topic of the geology of the state of Washington.

557 **US** **ISSN 1058-2134**
QE175 **CODEN: WGNLAA**
WASHINGTON GEOLOGY. 1973. q. free. Department of Natural Resources, Division of Geology and Earth Resources, Olympia, WA 98504. TEL 206-902-1450. FAX 206-902-1785. circ. 4,100. **Indexed:** GeoRef. **Document type:** government publication.
—UnCover.
Formerly: Washington Geologic Newsletter (ISSN 0094-2820)
Description: Provides information about the geology of the state of Washington for an informed readership.

551.44 **UK**
WESSEX CAVE CLUB JOURNAL. 1934. irreg. (approx. 6/yr.). £10. Wessex Cave Club, Upper Pitts, Priddy, Somerset BA5 3AX, England. TEL 0749-672310. Ed. N.J. Williams. bk.rev.; index. circ. 300. **Indexed:** GeoRef. **Document type:** newsletter.
Formerly: Wessex Cave Club Occasional Publication (ISSN 0083-811X)
Description: Features articles by members of the club on earth science, speleology, sport caving and exploration.

557 **US**
WEST TEXAS GEOLOGICAL SOCIETY. FIELDTRIP GUIDEBOOK. a. West Texas Geological Society, Box 1595, Midland, TX 79702. TEL 915-683-1573. FAX 951-686-7827.

557 **US**
WEST TEXAS GEOLOGICAL SOCIETY. SPECIAL PUBLICATIONS. 1939. a. West Texas Geological Society, Box 1595, Midland, TX 79702. TEL 915-683-1573. FAX 915-686-7827. adv. **Indexed:** GeoRef.

551 **US**
WEST VIRGINIA. GEOLOGICAL AND ECONOMIC SURVEY. ANNUAL REPORT. 1897. a. free. Geological and Economic Survey, Box 879, Morgantown, WV 26507-0879. TEL 304-594-2331. circ. 3,000. **Document type:** government publication.
Description: Covers activities, research, personnel and finances of the survey.

559.4 **AT** **ISSN 0085-8137**
QE348 **CODEN: AWGBAJ**
WESTERN AUSTRALIA. GEOLOGICAL SURVEY. BULLETIN. 1896. irreg., latest 1992. price varies. Geological Survey of Western Australia, Mineral House, 100 Plain St., E. Perth, W.A. 6004, Australia. TEL 09-222-3333. FAX 09-222-3633. (also avail. in microfiche; back issues avail.) **Indexed:** GeoRef. **Document type:** government publication, monographic series.
—BLDSC (2541.000000); UnCover.
Description: Provides technical reports on geology of Western Australia.

559.4 **AT** **ISSN 0085-8145**
WESTERN AUSTRALIA. GEOLOGICAL SURVEY. REPORT. 1969. irreg. latest 1993. price varies. Geological Survey of Western Australia, 100 Plain St., E. Perth, W.A. 6004, Australia. TEL 09-222-3333. FAX 09-222-3633. **Indexed:** AESIS, GeoRef. **Document type:** government publication, monographic series.
Description: Specific reports on aspects of Western Australian geology.

551 910 **AT**
WESTERN AUSTRALIA. GEOLOGICAL SURVEY. 1: 250,000 GEOLOGICAL SERIES. EXPLANATORY NOTES. 1966. irreg. Geological Survey of Western Australia, Mineral House, 100 Plain St., E. Perth, W.A. 6004, Australia. TEL 09-222-3333. FAX 09-222-3633. (back issues avail.) **Document type:** government publication.
Description: Provides geological maps of the state of Western Australia.

551.44 **AT**
WESTERN CAVER. 1960. a. Aus.$7.50. Western Australian Speleological Group, P.O. Box 67, Nedlands, W.A. 6009, Australia. TEL 09-495-1661. Ed. Steven Brooks. adv.; bk.rev.; circ. 200 (controlled).

557 **US**
WISCONSIN. GEOLOGICAL AND NATURAL HISTORY SURVEY. BULLETIN. 1898. irreg., no.89, 1982. price varies. Geological and Natural History Survey, University of Wisconsin - Extension, 3817 Mineral Point Rd., Madison, WI 53705. TEL 608-262-1705. FAX 608-262-8086. **Indexed:** Biol.Abstr. **Document type:** government publication.

551 **US**
WISCONSIN. GEOLOGICAL AND NATURAL HISTORY SURVEY. FIELD TRIP GUIDE BOOKS. 1978. irreg., no.13, 1986. price varies. Geological and Natural History Survey, University of Wisconsin, 3817 Mineral Point Rd., Madison, WI 53705. TEL 608-262-1705. FAX 608-262-8086. **Document type:** government publication.

551 **US**
WISCONSIN. GEOLOGICAL AND NATURAL HISTORY SURVEY. GEOSCIENCE EDUCATIONAL SERIES. Variant title: Educational Series. no.2, 1977. irreg., no.37, 1991. price varies. Geological and Natural History Survey, University of Wisconsin - Extension, 3817 Mineral Point Rd., Madison, WI 53705. TEL 608-262-1705. FAX 608-262-8086. **Document type:** government publication.
Supersedes (1953-1976?): Wisconsin. Geological and Natural History Survey. Geoscience Information Series.

557 **US** **ISSN 0512-0640**
QE179 **CODEN: WGICA**
WISCONSIN. GEOLOGICAL AND NATURAL HISTORY SURVEY. INFORMATION CIRCULARS. 1955. irreg., no.73, 1991. price varies. Geological and Natural History Survey, University of Wisconsin - Extension, 3817 Mineral Point Rd., Madison, WI 53705-4096. TEL 608-262-1705. FAX 608-262-8086. **Document type:** government publication.

557 **US**
WISCONSIN. GEOLOGICAL AND NATURAL HISTORY SURVEY. PROGRAMS AND ACTIVITIES. 1854. biennial. free. Geological and Natural History Survey, University of Wisconsin - Extension, 3817 Mineral Point Rd., Madison, WI 53705. TEL 608-262-1705. FAX 608-262-8086. **Document type:** government publication.
Former titles (until 1984): Wisconsin. Geological and Natural History Survey. Biennial Report; (until 1880): Wisconsin Geological Survey. Annual Report.

557 **US** **ISSN 0512-0659**
CODEN: SUWSDV
WISCONSIN. GEOLOGICAL AND NATURAL HISTORY SURVEY. SPECIAL REPORT. 1967. irreg., no.13, 1991. price varies. Geological and Natural History Survey, University of Wisconsin - Extension, 3817 Mineral Point Rd., Madison, WI 53705. TEL 608-262-1705. FAX 608-262-8086. **Document type:** government publication.

551 **US**
WYOMING GEO-NOTES. 1977. q. $10. Geological Survey of Wyoming, Box 3008, University Sta., Laramie, WY 82071. TEL 307-766-2286. bk.rev.; stat. circ. 300. **Document type:** government publication.
Description: Describes the state's geology and mineral resources, and activities. Includes minerals exploration and production information.

551 **US** **ISSN 0096-9842**
HD9506.U63
WYOMING MINERAL YEARBOOK. 1971. a. free. Department of Commerce, Division of Economic and Community Development, Energy Section, Barrett Bldg., Cheyenne, WY 82002. TEL 307-777-7284. FAX 307-777-5840. Ed. Dale Hoffman. circ. 1,000 (controlled). **Indexed:** SRI. **Document type:** government publication.

551 **CC** **ISSN 1000-8527**
CODEN: XIDZEV
XIANDAI DIZHI/GEOSCIENCE. (Text in Chinese) 1987. q. Y12. (Zhongguo Dizhi Daxue, China University of Geosciences - China University of Geosciences) Publishing House of China University of Geosciences, 29 Xueyuan Road, Beijing 100083, People's Republic of China. TEL 2022244. FAX 2014874. Ed. Shi Zhunli. circ. 800. **Document type:** academic/scholarly publication.
—BLDSC (4158.770000).

551 **JA** **ISSN 0911-8179**
YAMAGATA OYO CHISHITSU/APPLIED GEOLOGY OF YAMAGATA. (Text in Japanese) 1981. a. membership. Yamagata Oyo Chishitsu Kenkyukai - Association of Applied Geology of Yamagata, Yamagata Daigaku Kyoyobu Chigaku Kyoshitsu, 4-12, Koshirakawamachi 1-chome, Yamagata-shi, Yamagata-ken 990, Japan.

YAMAGUCHI GANBAN KENKYU/YAMAGUCHI ROCK ENGINEERING SOCIETY. SELECTED RESEARCH. see *ENGINEERING*

YAMAGUCHI KEIBINGU KURABU KAIHO/YAMAGUCHI CAVING CLUB. REPORT. see *PALEONTOLOGY*

526.9 **CC** **ISSN 0254-5357**
CODEN: YACEEK
YANKUANG CESHI/ROCK AND MINERAL ANALYSIS. (Text in Chinese) q. (Dizhi Kuangchan Bu, Yankuang Ceshi Yanjiusuo) Dizhi Chubanshe, 29 Xueyuan Lu, Haidian-qu, Beijing, People's Republic of China. TEL 8311133. (Dist. outside China by: China International Book Trading Corporation, P.O. Box 399, Beijing, P.R.C.) Ed. Ma Guangzu.
—CASDDS.

552 **CC** **ISSN 1000-0569**
YANSHI XUEBAO/ACTA PETROLOGICA SINICA. (Text in Chinese; summaries in English) 1985. q. $56.80. Science Press, Marketing and Sales Department, 16 Donghuangchenggen Beijie, Beijing 100707, People's Republic of China. TEL 4010642. FAX 4012180. TELEX 210247-SPBJ-CN. adv. circ. 6,000. **Document type:** academic/scholarly publication.
Description: Publishes research papers on petrological, petrogeochemical, petrogenetic, and petrotectonic studies of igneous, metamorphic, and sedimentary rocks. Also includes some papers on related topics, such as mineralogy and metallogeny.
Refereed Serial

551 **UK** **ISSN 0044-0604**
YORKSHIRE GEOLOGICAL SOCIETY. PROCEEDINGS. 1871. s-a. £55($92) (Yorkshire Geological Society) Geological Society Publishing House, Unit 7, Brassmill Enterprise Centre, Brassmill Ln., Bath BA1 3JN, England. TEL 0225-445046. FAX 0225-442836. Eds. D. Millward, I.C. Burgess. adv.; bibl.; illus.; maps; index. circ. 1,200. **Document type:** academic/scholarly publication.
—BLDSC (6834.750000); Faxon; UnCover.
Description: Contains original research papers on the geology of northern England.

EARTH SCIENCES — GEOPHYSICS

556   ZA   ISSN 0084-473X
QE327.R55   CODEN: ARGZDP
ZAMBIA. GEOLOGICAL SURVEY. ANNUAL REPORTS.
1951. a. price varies. Geological Survey, P.O. Box R.W. 50135, Lusaka, Zambia. **Indexed:** GeoRef. **Document type:** government publication.

556   ZA   ISSN 0084-4748
TN119.R38   CODEN: ZGSEAD
ZAMBIA. GEOLOGICAL SURVEY. ECONOMIC REPORTS.
1964. irreg. price varies. Geological Survey, P.O. Box R.W. 50135, Lusaka, Zambia. **Indexed:** GeoRef. **Document type:** government publication.

556   ZA   ISSN 0084-4756
ZAMBIA. GEOLOGICAL SURVEY. OCCASIONAL PAPERS.
irreg., latest no.121. price varies. Geological Survey, P.O. Box R.W. 50135, Lusaka, Zambia. **Indexed:** GeoRef. **Document type:** government publication.

556   ZA   ISSN 0084-4764
ZAMBIA. GEOLOGICAL SURVEY. REPORTS. 1954. irreg., latest no.69. price varies. Geological Survey, P.O. Box R.W. 50135, Lusaka, Zambia. **Indexed:** GeoRef. **Document type:** government publication.

556   ZA
ZAMBIA. GEOLOGICAL SURVEY. TECHNICAL REPORTS.
irreg., latest no.101. price varies. Geological Survey, P.O. Box R.W. 50135, Lusaka, Zambia. **Indexed:** GeoRef. **Document type:** government publication.

550   GW   ISSN 0044-2259
QE1   CODEN: ZANGAK
ZEITSCHRIFT FUER ANGEWANDTE GEOLOGIE. (Text in German; summaries in English, German) 1955. 2/yr. DM.38. (Bundesanstalt fuer Geowissenschaften und Rohstoffe) E. Schweizerbart'sche Verlagsbuchhandlung, Johannesstr. 3A3-4, 70176 Stuttgart, Germany. TEL 0711-625001. FAX 0711-625005. TELEX 723363-SCHB-D. Ed. Andrea Sobe. adv.; bk.rev.; abstr.; bibl.; charts; illus.; stat.; index, cum.index. **Indexed:** Bibl.Cart., Br.Geol.Lit., Chem.Abstr., Curr.Cont., Geotech.Abstr., Petrol.Abstr. **Document type:** academic/scholarly publication.
—BLDSC (9448.700000); CASDDS.

551.4   GW   ISSN 0372-8854
G1   CODEN: ZGMPAG
ZEITSCHRIFT FUER GEOMORPHOLOGIE/ANNALS OF GEOMORPHOLOGY/ANNALES DE GEOMORPHOLOGIE.
(Supplements avail.) (Text and title in English, French and German) N.S. 1957. 4/yr. price varies. Gebrueder Borntraeger Verlagsbuchhandlung, Johannesstr. 3A, 70176 Stuttgart, Germany. TEL 0711-625001. FAX 0711-625005. TELEX 723363-SCHB-D. Ed. H. Bremer. adv.; bk.rev.; abstr.; bibl.; charts; illus.; pat.; index. (back issues avail.) **Indexed:** AESIS, Bibl.Cart., Br.Geol.Lit., Bull.Signal., Chem.Abstr., Curr.Cont.Africa, Geo.Abstr., GeoRef., So.Pac.Per.Ind., Soils & Fert. **Document type:** academic/scholarly publication.
—BLDSC (9462.600000); Faxon; UnCover; SWETS. **CCC.**

ZEITSCHRIFT FUER GEOMORPHOLOGIE, SUPPLEMENTBAENDE/ANNALS OF GEOMORPHOLOGY, SUPPLEMENT VOLUMES/ANNALES DE GEOMORPHOLOGIE, SUPPLEMENTS. see *GEOGRAPHY*

551.31   AU   ISSN 0044-2836
QE575   CODEN: ZGGGAR
ZEITSCHRIFT FUER GLETSCHERKUNDE UND GLAZIALGEOLOGIE. (Text in English, French, German, Italian and Spanish; summaries in English, German and original language of text) 1949. s-a. S.980. Universitaetsverlag Wagner, Andreas-Hofer-Str. 13, Postfach 165, A-6010 Innsbruck, Austria. FAX 0512-582209. Eds. G. Patzelt, M. Kuhn. bk.rev.; bibl.; charts; illus.; maps; index. (back issues avail.) **Indexed:** Bibl.Cart., Chem.Abstr., GeoRef., Meteor.& Geoastrophys.Abstr. **Document type:** academic/scholarly publication.
—BLDSC (9464.000000).

551   CC   ISSN 1000-3657
ZHONGGUO DIZHI/CHINESE GEOLOGY. (Text in Chinese) m. Dizhi Kuangchan Bu - Ministry of Geology and Mineral Products, P.O. Box 259, Beijing 101149, People's Republic of China. TEL 658561. Ed. Cheng Yuqi.

551   CC   ISSN 1001-4810
ZHONGGUO YANRONG/CARSOLOGICA SINICA. (Text in Chinese) 1982. q. Y2.50 per no. (Chinese Academy of Geological Sciences, Institute of Karst Geology) Guilin Karst Research Institute, 40 Qixing Lu, Guilin, Guangxi 541004, People's Republic of China. TEL 445151. (Co-sponsor: Geological Society of China) Ed. Han Xingrui.
—BLDSC (3055.810000).

ZIMBABWE. MINISTRY OF ENERGY AND WATER RESOURCES AND DEVELOPMENT. HYDROLOGICAL SUMMARIES. see *ENGINEERING — Hydraulic Engineering*

ZITTELIANA; Abhandlungen der Bayerischen Staatssammlung fuer Palaeontologie und historische Geologie. see *PALEONTOLOGY*

EARTH SCIENCES — Geophysics

A G S O JOURNAL OF AUSTRALIAN GEOLOGY AND GEOPHYSICS. (Australian Geological Survey Organisation) see *EARTH SCIENCES — Geology*

A G S O RECORD. (Australian Geological Survey Organisation) see *EARTH SCIENCES — Geology*

A G S O RESEARCH NEWSLETTER. (Australian Geological Survey Organisation) see *EARTH SCIENCES — Geology*

551   HU   ISSN 0236-5758
          CODEN: AGGHEV
ACTA GEODAETICA, GEOPHYSICA ET MONTANISTICA HUNGARICA. (Text in English) 1959. q. $76 (effective 1992). (Magyar Tudomanyos Akademia) Akademiai Kiado, Publishing House of the Hungarian Academy of Sciences, P.O. Box 245, H-1519 Budapest, Hungary. TEL 181-2134. FAX 166-6466. TELEX 22-6228 AKNYO H. Eds. Jozsef Somogyi, Jozsef Vero. adv.; bk.rev.; bibl.; charts; illus. **Indexed:** Geo.Abstr., GeoRef., INIS Atomind., Sci.Abstr. **Document type:** academic/scholarly publication.
—EI. **CCC.**
Formerly (until 1982): Academiae Scientiarum Hungarica. Acta Geodaetica, Geophysica et Montanistica (ISSN 0374-1842); Supersedes (in 1965): Acta Technica. Series Geodaetica et Geophysica (ISSN 0567-8145).
Description: Publishes original research papers in the field of geodesy, geophysics and mining engineering.

551   PL   ISSN 0001-5725
QC801   CODEN: AGPOAP
ACTA GEOPHYSICA POLONICA. (Text in English) 1953. q. $50 (effective 1993). Polska Akademia Nauk, Instytut Geofizyki - Polish Academy of Sciences, Institute of Geophysics, Ul. Ksiecia Janusza 64, 01-452-Warsaw, Poland. Ed. S.J. Gibowicz. charts; index. circ. 700. **Indexed:** Chem.Abstr., Deep Sea Res.& Oceanogr.Abstr., E&P Hlth. (1993-), Gas Process.& Ppl. (1993-), Geo.Abstr., GeoRef., INIS Atomind., Meteor.& Geoastrophys.Abstr., Off.Tech. (1993-), Petrol.Abstr. (1972-), Sci.Abstr. **Document type:** academic/scholarly publication.
—BLDSC (0622.000000); UnCover; CASDDS.

551   SW   ISSN 0072-4815
QC801
ACTA REGIAE SOCIETATIS SCIENTIARUM ET LITTERARUM GOTHOBURGENSIS. GEOPHYSICA. (Text in various languages) 1968. irreg., no.3, 1990. price varies; also exchange basis. Kungliga Vetenskaps- och Vitterhets-Samhaellet i Goeteborg, c/o Goeteborgs Universitetsbibliotek, P.O. Box 5096, S-402 22 Goeteborg, Sweden. **Document type:** monographic series.
Supersedes in part: Goeteborgs Kungliga Vetenskaps- och Vitterhets-Samhaelle. Handlingar.

551.22   CC   ISSN 1000-9116
QE531
ACTA SEISMOLOGICA SINICA. Chinese edition: Dizhen Xuebao (ISSN 0253-3782) (Text in English) 1988. 4/yr. $160 (effective 1994). Seismological Society of China, c/o Institute of Geophysics, State Seismological Bureau, No.5 Minzuxueyuan Nanlu, Haidian District, Beijing 100081, People's Republic of China. TEL 86-1-8417744. FAX 86-1-8415372. Ed. Chen Yuntai. adv.; bk.rev. (also avail. in microform; back issues avail.) **Document type:** academic/scholarly publication.
—BLDSC (0663.271000); UMI.
Description: A comprehensive academic journal on seismological science.
Refereed Serial

ACTA UNIVERSITATIS WRATISLAVIENSIS. PRACE GEOLOGICZNO - MINERALOGICZNE. see *EARTH SCIENCES — Geology*

551   IT
ACTA VULCANOLOGICA. 1991. a. L.20000 to individuals; institutions L.60000. (National Volcanic Group of Italy) Giardini Editori e Stampatori, Via delle Sorgenti 23, 56010 Agnano Pisano (PI), Italy. TEL 050-855390. FAX 050-856106. Ed.Bd. **Document type:** monographic series.

551   NE   ISSN 0921-9366
ADVANCES IN EXPLORATION GEOPHYSICS. (Text in English) 1987. irreg., vol.3, 1990. price varies. Elsevier Science B.V., Books Division, P.O. Box 211, 1000 AE Amsterdam, Netherlands. TEL 31-20-5803911. FAX 31-20-5803911. TELEX 18582 ESPA NL. (Subscr. in U.S. and Canada to: Elsevier Science Inc., Box 882, Madison Sq. Sta., New York, NY 10159. TEL 212-989-5800) Ed. A.J. Berkhout. (back issues avail.) **Document type:** monographic series.
—BLDSC (0706.200000).
Refereed Serial

551   US   ISSN 0065-2687
QC801   CODEN: ADGOAR
ADVANCES IN GEOPHYSICS. 1952. irreg., vol.34, 1993. Academic Press, Inc., 525 B St., Ste. 1900, San Diego, CA 92101-4495. TEL 619-231-0926. FAX 619-699-6715. (Subscr. to: Order Dept., 6277 Sea Harbor Dr., Orlando, FL 32887. TEL 800-321-5068) Ed. Barry Saltzman. index. (reprint service avail. from ISI) **Indexed:** Deep Sea Res.& Oceanogr.Abstr., Fuel & Energy Abstr., INIS Atomind., Petrol.Abstr. **Document type:** academic/scholarly publication.
—BLDSC (0709.000000); Faxon; UnCover. **CCC.**
Refereed Serial

551   PL   ISSN 0860-7109
AKADEMIA GORNICZO-HUTNICZA IM. STANISLAWA STASZICA. ZESZYTY NAUKOWE. GEOFIZYKA STOSOWANA. 1988. irreg., no.13, 1993. price varies. Wydawnictwo A G H, Al. Mickiewicza 30, paw. A-1, 03-059 Krakow, Poland. TEL 48-12-338100. FAX 48-12-331014. TELEX 322203 AGH PL. (Dist. by: Ars Polona, Krakowskie Przedmiscie 7, 00-068 Warsaw, Poland) Ed. Z. Kleczek. illus. circ. 200. **Document type:** academic/scholarly publication.
—UnCover.

551 526.9   PL   ISSN 0239-9288
AKADEMIA ROLNICZA IM. HUGONA KOLLATAJA W KRAKOWIE. ZESZYTY NAUKOWE. SERIA: GEODEZJA.
(Text in Polish; summaries in English) 1969. a. price varies. Akademia Rolnicza im. Hugona Kollataja w Krakowie, Al. 29 Listopada 46, 31-425 Krakow, Poland. TEL 48-12-119144. FAX 48-12-336245. TELEX 322469 PL. Ed. Zdzislaw Piskornik. circ. 120 (paid). **Document type:** academic/scholarly publication.
Former titles (until 1979): Akademia Rolnicza w Krakowie. Zeszyty Naukowe. Geodezja (ISSN 0137-1835); (until 1973): Wyzsza Szkola Rolnicza w Krakowie. Zeszyty Naukowe. Geodezja (ISSN 0137-205X)

EARTH SCIENCES — GEOPHYSICS

551   GW   ISSN 0514-8790
CODEN: DZPVA8
AKADEMIE DER WISSENSCHAFTEN DER D.D.R. ZENTRALINSTITUT FUER PHYSIK DER ERDE. VEROEFFENTLICHUNGEN. Key Title: Veroeffentlichungen der Zentralinstitut fuer Physik der Erde. 1949. irreg. exchange basis. Akademie der Wissenschaften der D.D.R., Zentralinstitut fuer Physik der Erde, Telegrafenberg A17, 14473 Potsdam, Germany. Ed. H. Kautzleben. circ. 500. **Indexed:** GeoRef., Math.R.
—UnCover; CASDDS.
Formerly (1949-1969): Akademie der Wissenschaften der D.D.R. Geodaetisches Institut. Veroeffentlichungen (ISSN 0065-5015)

ALASKA. DIVISION OF GEOLOGICAL AND GEOPHYSICAL SURVEYS. GEOLOGIC - PROFESSIONAL REPORT. see *EARTH SCIENCES — Geology*

ALASKA. DIVISION OF GEOLOGICAL AND GEOPHYSICAL SURVEYS. INFORMATION CIRCULAR. see *EARTH SCIENCES — Geology*

ALASKA. DIVISION OF GEOLOGICAL AND GEOPHYSICAL SURVEYS. REPORT OF INVESTIGATIONS. see *EARTH SCIENCES — Geology*

ALASKA. DIVISION OF GEOLOGICAL AND GEOPHYSICAL SURVEYS. SPECIAL REPORT. see *EARTH SCIENCES — Geology*

551   US
AMERICAN GEOPHYSICAL UNION. GEOPHYSICAL MONOGRAPHS BOOK SERIES. 1956. irreg. price varies. American Geophysical Union, 2000 Florida Ave., N.W., Washington, DC 20009. TEL 202-462-6900. Ed.Bd. (reprint service avail. from ISI) **Indexed:** Deep Sea Res.& Oceanogr.Abstr., GeoRef. **Document type:** monographic series.
—BLDSC (4154.500000). **CCC.**
Formerly: American Geophysical Union. Geophysical Monograph (ISSN 0065-8448)
Refereed Serial

551   GW   ISSN 0992-7689
QC801   CODEN: ANNGEA
ANNALES GEOPHYSICAE. (Text in English, French and German; summaries in English) 1983. 12/yr. DM.998($624) (European Geophysical Society) Springer-Verlag, Heidelberger Platz 3, 14197 Berlin, Germany. TEL 030-8207-1. FAX 030-8214091. (U.S. subscr. to: Springer-Verlag New York, Inc., 44 Hartz Way, Secaucus, NJ 07096-2491. TEL 201-348-4033) Ed. M. Fulchignoni. adv.; abstr.; bibl.; illus.; index. circ. 600. **Indexed:** Chem.Abstr., Curr.Cont., Deep Sea Res.& Oceanogr.Abstr., GeoRef., Ind.Sci.Rev., Meteor. & Geoastrophys.Abstr., Phys.Ber., Sci.Abstr. **Document type:** academic/scholarly publication.
—BLDSC (0977.900000); SWETS; UMI; CASDDS. **CCC.**
Formerly (until 1988): Atmospheres, Hydrospheres, Space Sciences; Formed by the 1985 merger of: Annales de Geophysicae. Serie A: Upper Atmosphere and Space Sciences (ISSN 0980-8752); Annales Geophysicae. Serie B: Terrestrial and Planetary Physics (ISSN 0980-8760)
Description: Information on interplanetary medium, magnetosphere and upper atmosphere of the earth and planets, terrestrial and planetary boundary layers.
Refereed Serial

551.22   IT   ISSN 0394-5596
ANNALES TECTONICAE. s-a. L.60000 (foreign L.85000). Editrice Sedicesimo, Via Mannelli 29r, 50136 Florence, Italy. TEL 055-2476781. FAX 055-2478568.
—BLDSC (1001.900000); UnCover.

551   US
ANTARCTIC RESEARCH BOOK SERIES. 1964. irreg. price varies. American Geophysical Union, 2000 Florida Ave., N.W., Washington, DC 20009. TEL 202-462-6900. Ed.Bd. (reprint service avail. from ISI) **Indexed:** Biol.Abstr., Deep Sea Res.& Oceanogr.Abstr., Meteor.& Geoastrophys.Abstr.
—BLDSC (1542.130000). **CCC.**
Formerly: Antarctic Research Series (ISSN 0066-4634)

AQUA; mensile di acqua, natura, vita. see *EARTH SCIENCES — Hydrology*

ARCHIVES OF HYDRO-ENGINEERING AND ENVIRONMENTAL MECHANICS. see *WATER RESOURCES*

ARCTIC. see *SCIENCES: COMPREHENSIVE WORKS*

ASTRONOMICHESKII VESTNIK. see *ASTRONOMY*

AUSTRALIA - NEW ZEALAND CONFERENCE ON GEOMECHANICS PROCEEDINGS. see *ENGINEERING — Civil Engineering*

551 559.4   AT   ISSN 1035-1515
AUSTRALIAN GEOMAGNETISM REPORT. 1953. m. Australian Geological Survey Organisation, G.P.O. Box 378, Canberra, A.C.T. 2601, Australia. TEL 06-249-9111. FAX 06-249-9999. charts; stat. **Indexed:** AESIS, Chem.Abstr., Geo.Abstr. **Document type:** government publication.
Formerly: Australia. Bureau of Mineral Resources, Geology and Geophysics. Geophysical Observatory Group. Report (ISSN 0433-5015)

AUSTRIA. ZENTRALANSTALT FUER METEOROLOGIE UND GEODYNAMIK. JAHRBUCH. see *METEOROLOGY*

551.22   CC   ISSN 1000-0240
QE575   CODEN: BDONEB
BINGCHUAN DONGTU/JOURNAL OF GLACIOLOGY AND GEOCRYOLOGY. (Text in Chinese; summaries in English) 1978. q. $58.40 per no. (Chinese Academy of Sciences, Lanzhou Institute of Galciology and Geocryology) Science Press, Marketing and Sales Department, 16 Donghuangchenggen Beijie, Beijing 100707, People's Republic of China. TEL 4010642. FAX 4012180. TELEX 210247-SPBJ-CN. adv. circ. 6,000.
—BLDSC (4996.060000).
Former English title: Journal of Glaciology and Cryopedology.
Description: Covers the physical and chemical properties of ice and frozen ground, glaciers, glaciation, and environment in quaternary, permafrost, seasonally frozen ground, glacial deposits and geomorphology, periglacial landforms, glacial debris flow, avalanches, snow-drifts, sea ice, river ice, and lake ice. Also includes reviews, short communications, and news of scientific activities.

551   PL   ISSN 0067-9038
QE1   CODEN: BIPEAK
BIULETYN PERYGLACJALNY. (Text in English) 1954. irreg., no.31, 1986. price varies. Lodzkie Towarzystwo Naukowe, Ul. Piotrkowska 179, 90-447 Lodz, Poland. TEL 48-42-3610026. FAX 48-22-362415. TELEX 884519 PAN PL. (Co-sponsor: Komitet Badan Naukowych) Ed. A. Dylikowa. **Indexed:** Br.Geol.Lit., GeoRef., Soils & Fert. **Document type:** government publication.
—BLDSC (2105.450000).
Description: Contains articles by Polish and foreign authors on periglacial structures, continental glaciation, laboratory experiments documented with line-drawings, photographs and tables.

551.22   IT   ISSN 0006-6729
QC801   CODEN: BGTAAE
BOLLETTINO DI GEOFISICA, TEORICA ED APPLICATA. (Text in English) 1959. q. L.85000($80) (effective 1993). Osservatorio Geofisico Sperimentale di Trieste, Casella Postale 2011, 34016 Trieste, Italy. TEL 040-21401. FAX 040-327307. TELEX 460329 OGS I. Ed. I. Finetti. bk.rev.; abstr.; charts; illus.; index. circ. 500. **Indexed:** Abstr.J.Earthq.Eng., Deep Sea Res.& Oceanogr.Abstr., E&P Hlth. (1993-), Gas Process.& Ppl. (1993-), Geo.Abstr., GeoRef., INIS Atomind., Meteor.& Geoastrophys.Abstr., Off.Tech. (1993-), Petrol.Abstr. (1963-), Sci.Abstr. **Document type:** academic/scholarly publication.
—BLDSC (2236.800000); UnCover.
Description: Covers theoretical and applied geophysics.

551   DK   ISSN 0901-9413
BRORFELDE GEOMAGNETIC OBSERVATORY MAGNETIC RESULTS (YEAR). 1983. a. free. Danish Meteorological Institute, Division of Research and Development, Lyngbyvej 100, DK-2100 Copenhagen OE, Denmark. FAX 45-39-157460. TELEX 15835 GEOMI DK. illus. circ. 300. **Document type:** academic/scholarly publication.
Formerly (until 1985): Brorfelde Magnetic Results (ISSN 0109-2170)

551   GW   ISSN 0007-4632
QB294   CODEN: BGDQAG
BULLETIN GEODESIQUE. (Text in English or French) 1924. 4/yr. DM.198($124) (International Union of Geodesy and Geophysics) Springer-Verlag, Heidelberger Platz 3, 14197 Berlin, Germany. TEL 030-8207-1. FAX 030-8214091. (Subscr. in U.S. and Canada to: Springer-Verlag New York, Inc., 44 Hartz Way, Secaucus, NJ 07096-2491. TEL 201-348-4033. FAX 201-348-4505) Ed. C.C. Tscherning. adv.; bk.rev.; charts. circ. 1,200. (also avail. in microfiche) **Indexed:** Amer.Hist.& Life, Deep Sea Res.& Oceanogr.Abstr., Geophys.Abstr., GeoRef., Hist.Abstr., Int.Aerosp.Abstr., Math.R., Ocean.Abstr., Pollut.Abstr., Sci.Abstr. **Document type:** academic/scholarly publication, bulletin.
—BLDSC (2855.000000); UnCover; SWETS; UMI. **CCC.**

551.21   JA   ISSN 0525-1524
CODEN: BVOEA4
BULLETIN OF VOLCANIC ERUPTIONS. (Issued with "Bulletin Volcanologique," published by the co-sponsor) (Text in English) 1961. a. membership. Volcanological Society of Japan - Nihon Kazan Gakkai, c/o Earthquake Research Institute, University of Tokyo, 1-1-1 Yayoi, Bunkyo-ku, Tokyo 113, Japan. TEL 03-3684-2549. (Co-sponsor: International Association of Volcanology and Chemistry of the Earth's Interior) Ed.Bd. adv.; bk.rev. circ. 2,500. **Indexed:** Deep Sea Res.& Oceanogr.Abstr., GeoRef.
—UnCover.

551.21   GW   ISSN 0258-8900
CODEN: BUVOEW
BULLETIN OF VOLCANOLOGY. 1924. 8/yr. DM.708($443) (International Association of Volcanology and Chemistry of the Earth's Interior) Springer-Verlag, Heidelberger Platz 3, 14197 Berlin, Germany. TEL 030-8207-1. FAX 030-8214091. (Subscr. in N. America to: Springer-Verlag New York, Inc., 44 Hartz Way, Secaucus, NJ 07096-2491. TEL 201-348-4033. FAX 201-348-4505) Eds. H.U. Schmincke, G.A. Mahood. **Indexed:** AESIS, Chem.Abstr., Deep Sea Res.& Oceanogr.Abstr., Geo.Abstr., GeoRef., So.Pac.Per.Ind. **Document type:** academic/scholarly publication.
—BLDSC (2925.020000); Faxon; UnCover; SWETS; UMI; CASDDS. **CCC.**
Formerly (until 1984): Bulletin Volcanologique.
Description: Covers articles relating to the understanding of volcanic phenomena.

551   JA   ISSN 0912-7984
BUTSURI TANSA/GEOPHYSICAL EXPLORATION. (Text in English, Japanese) 1948. bi-m. Butsuri Tansa Gakkai - Society of Exploration Geophysicists of Japan, 2-18, Nakamagome 2-chome, Ota-ku, Tokyo 143, Japan. **Indexed:** INIS Atomind., Jap.Per.Ind., Sci.Abstr.
—BLDSC (4150.200000).

551   JA
BUTSURI TANSA CHOSA KENKYU ICHIRAN/GEOPHYSICAL ACTIVITY. (Text in Japanese) 1956. a. Kogyo Gijutsuin, Chishitsu Chosajo - Agency of Industrial Science and Technology, Geological Survey of Japan, 1-3, Higashi 1-chome, Tsukuba-shi, Ibaraki-ken 305, Japan.

551   JA
BUTSURI TANSA GAKKAI GAKUJUTSU KOENKAI KOEN RONBUNSHU/SOCIETY OF EXPLORATION GEOPHYSICISTS OF JAPAN. CONFERENCE. PROCEEDINGS. (Text in English, Japanese; summaries in English) 1984. s-a. Butsuri Tansa Gakkai, 2-18, Nakamagome 2-chome, Ota-ku, Tokyo 143, Japan.

551.22   US
C U S E C JOURNAL. irreg. free. Central United States Earthquake Consortium, 2630 Holmes Rd. E., Memphis, TN 38118-8001. TEL 901-345-0932. FAX 901-345-0998. circ. 3,000. **Document type:** newsletter.
Formerly (until vol.4, 1992): Fault Line.

EARTH SCIENCES — GEOPHYSICS

622.15   CN
CANADIAN JOURNAL OF EXPLORATION GEOPHYSICS. 1965. s-a. Can.$45 per no. Canadian Society of Exploration Geophysicists, 206 7th Ave., S.W., Ste. 406, Calgary, Alta. T2P 0W7, Canada. adv.; charts; illus. circ. 2,200. **Indexed:** GeoRef. **Document type:** academic/scholarly publication.
—CCC.
Formerly (until 1988): Canadian Society of Exploration Geophysicists. Journal (ISSN 0008-5022)

551   PO   ISSN 0870-4716
CENTRO DE FISICA DA ATMOSFERA DE LISBOA. BOLETIM. 1955. m. Esc.1900. Instituto de Meteorologia, Centro de Fisica da Atmosfera de Lisboa, Rua C do Aeroporto, 1700 Lisbon, Portugal. TEL 8472880. FAX 802370. TELEX 12742 DIRMET P. charts; stat. (processed) **Document type:** bulletin.
Formerly (until 1977): Boletim Geoelectrico (ISSN 0006-5994)
Description: Observations of the electric field of the atmosphere.

551   JA   ISSN 0913-9214
CHIBA DAIGAKU EIZO KAKUSOKU KENKYU SENTA. SENTA NENPO/CHIBA UNIVERSITY. REMOTE SENSING AND IMAGE RESEARCH CENTER. ANNUAL REPORT. 1987. a. Chiba Daigaku, Eizo Kakusoku Kenkyu Senta - Chiba University, Remote Sensing and Image Research Center, 1-33, Yayoicho, Inage-ku, Chiba-shi, Chiba-ken 263, Japan.

551   JA
CHIJIKI KANSOKUJO GIJUTSU HOKOKU/KAKIOKA MAGNETIC OBSERVATORY. TECHNICAL REPORT. (Text in Japanese) s-a. Kishocho, Chijiki Kansokujo - Japan Meteorological Agency, Kakioka Magnetic Observatory, 595, Kakioka, Yasato-cho, Niihari-gun, Ibaraki-ken 315-01, Japan.

551   JA
CHIJIKI KANSOKUJO YOHO/KAKIOKA MAGNETIC OBSERVATORY. MEMOIRS. (Text in English, Japanese) 1938. s-a. Kishocho, Chijiki Kansokujo - Japan Meteorological Agency, Kakioka Magnetic Observatory, 594, Kakioka, Yasato-cho, Niihari-gun, Ibaraki-ken 315-01, Japan.

551   JA
CHIKYU DENJIKI CHIKYU WAKUSEIKEN GAKKAI KAIHO/SOCIETY OF GEOMAGNETISM AND EARTH, PLANETARY AND SPACE SCIENCES. NEWS. (Text in Japanese) 4/yr. Chikyu Denjiki Chikyu Wakuseiken Gakkai - Society of Geomagnetism and Earth, Planetary and Space Sciences, Nihon Gakkai Jimu Senta, 16-9, Honkomagome 5-chome, Bunkyo-ku, Tokyo 113, Japan.

551   JA
CHIKYU DENJIKI CHIKYU WAKUSEIKEN GAKKAI KOENKAI KOEN YOKOSHU/SOCIETY OF GEOMAGNETISM AND EARTH, PLANETARY AND SPACE SCIENCES. PREPRINTS OF THE MEETING. (Text in Japanese; summaries in English) s-a. 2000 Yen per no. Chikyu Denjiki Chikyu Wakuseiken Gakkai, Nihon Gakkai Jimu Senta, 16-9, Honkomagome 5-chome, Bunkyo-ku, Tokyo 113, Japan.

551   JA
CHIKYU JIKI KANSOKU HOKOKU/GEOMAGNETIC OBSERVATIONS AT MIZUSAWA AND KANOZAN. (Text in English) 1982. a. Kokudo Chiriin - Geographical Survey Institute, 1, Kitasato, Tsukuba-shi, Ibaraki-ken 305, Japan.

551   US   ISSN 0898-9591
QC801
CHINESE JOURNAL OF GEOPHYSICS. English translation of: Diqiu Wuli Xuebao (CC ISSN 0001-5733) 1988. q. $375. (Chinese Geophysical Society, CC) Allerton Press, Inc., 150 Fifth Ave., New York, NY 10011. TEL 212-924-3950. FAX 212-463-9684. Ed. Liu Guang-ding. (back issues avail.) **Document type:** academic/scholarly publication.
—UnCover. CCC.
Description: Covers geophysical research in China, including seismology, physics of the earth's interior, and geodesy.
Refereed Serial

CHINETSU/JAPAN GEOTHERMAL ENERGY ASSOCIATION. JOURNAL. see *ENERGY — Geothermal Energy*

CHINETSU GIJUTSU/GEOTHERMAL ENERGY RESEARCH AND DEVELOPMENT CO., LTD. JOURNAL. see *ENERGY — Geothermal Energy*

CIEL ET TERRE. see *ASTRONOMY*

551   US
CRUSTAL AND UPPER MANTLE STRUCTURE IN EUROPE. MONOGRAPHS. 1976. irreg. price varies. (European Seismological Commission) Springer-Verlag, 175 Fifth Ave., New York, NY 10010. TEL 212-460-1500. FAX 212-473-6272. (Also: Berlin, Heidelberg, Tokyo and Vienna) (reprint service avail. from ISI) **Document type:** monographic series.

CURRENT GEOLOGICAL AND GEOPHYSICAL STUDIES IN MONTANA. see *EARTH SCIENCES — Geology*

624.151   XR   ISSN 0139-9292
CZECH SEISMOLOGICAL STATIONS: PRYHONICE, PRAHA, KASPERSK HORY. BULLETIN. (Text in English) 1965. a. free. (Czechoslovak Academy of Sciences) Academia, Publishing House of the Czechoslovak Academy of Sciences, Vodickova 40, 112 29 Prague 1, Czech Republic. circ. 250.
Supersedes in part (in 1966): Czechoslovak Seismological Stations: Pryhonice, Praha, Kaspersk Hory, Cheb, Bratislava, Srobarova, Hurbanovo and Skalnate Pleso (ISSN 0139-9209)

CZECHOSLOVAK NATIONAL WORKSHOP ON SEISMIC DATA ACQUISITION AND COMPUTER PROCESSING. PROCEEDINGS. see *EARTH SCIENCES — Computer Applications*

551   DK   ISSN 0109-1972
CODEN: CGIBA7
D G I - BULLETIN. Variant title: Danish Geotechnical Institute. Bulletin. (Text in various languages) 1956. irreg., no.36, 1985. price varies. Akademiet for de Danske Videnskaber, Geoteknisk Institut, 1 Maglebjergvej, DK-2800 Lyngby, Denmark. **Indexed:** Geotech.Abstr. **Document type:** academic/scholarly publication, bulletin.
Formerly (until 1979): Geoteknisk Institut. Bulletin (ISSN 0069-987X)

DADI GOUZAO YU CHENGKUANGXUE/GEOTECTONICA ET METALLOGENIA. see *EARTH SCIENCES — Geology*

538 384   JA   ISSN 0389-8229
DATA IN WORLD DATA CENTER C2 FOR IONOSPHERE. CATALOGUE. (Text in English) 1958. a. Yuseisho, Tsushin Sogo Kenkyujo - Ministry of Posts and Telecommunications, Communications Research Laboratory, 2-1, Nukui Kitamachi 4-chome, Koganei-shi, Tokyo 184, Japan. **Document type:** catalog.

551.22   TU
DEPREM ARASTIRMA BULTENI. (Text in Turkish, summaries in English, Turkish) 1973. q. free. Ministry of Public Works and Settlement, Earthquake Research Department - Afet Isleri Genel Mudurlugu - Deprem Arastirma Enstitusu, Posta Kutusu 763, Kizilay, Ankara, Turkey. Ed. Erol Aytac; Pub. Oktay Ergunay. adv.; abstr.; bibl.; stat. circ. 1,250. **Indexed:** Abstr.J.Earthq.Eng. **Document type:** government publication, academic/scholarly publication.
Formerly: Deprem Arastirma Enstitusu Bulteni.

551 510   NE
DEVELOPMENTS IN GEOMATHEMATICS. 1974. irreg., vol. 6, 1988. price varies. Elsevier Science B.V., Books Division, P.O. Box 211, 1000 AE Amsterdam, Netherlands. TEL 31-20-5803911. FAX 31-20-5803705. TELEX 18582 ESPA NL. (Subscr. in N. America to: Elsevier Science Inc., Box 882, Madison Sq. Sta., New York, NY 10159. TEL 212-989-5800) **Indexed:** GeoRef. **Document type:** monographic series.
Refereed Serial

551   NE   ISSN 0419-0297
CODEN: DSEGA
DEVELOPMENTS IN SOLID EARTH GEOPHYSICS. (Text in English) 1964. irreg., vol.19, 1990. price varies. Elsevier Science B.V., Books Division, P.O. Box 211, 1000 AE Amsterdam, Netherlands. TEL 31-20-5803911. FAX 31-20-5803705. TELEX 18582 ESPA NL. (Subscr. in U.S. and Canada to: Elsevier Science Inc., Box 882, Madison Sq. Sta., New York, NY 10159. TEL 212-989-5800) (back issues avail.) **Indexed:** Deep Sea Res.& Oceanogr.Abstr., GeoRef. **Document type:** monographic series.
—CCC.
Refereed Serial

551.21   NE
DEVELOPMENTS IN VOLCANOLOGY. 1983. irreg., vol.3, 1983. price varies. Elsevier Science B.V., Books Division, P.O. Box 211, 1000 AE Amsterdam, Netherlands. TEL 31-20-5803911. FAX 31-20-5803705. TELEX 18582 ESPA NL. (Subscr. in U.S. and Canada to: Elsevier Science Inc., Box 882, Madison Sq. Sta., New York, NY 10159. TEL 212-989-5800) **Document type:** monographic series.
Refereed Serial

DICENGXUE ZAZHI/JOURNAL OF STRATIGRAPHY. see *EARTH SCIENCES — Geology*

551   CC   ISSN 0001-5733
QC801   CODEN: TCWHAG
DIQIU WULI XUEBAO/ACTA GEOPHYSICA SINICA. English translation: Chinese Journal of Geophysics (CC ISSN 0898-9591) (Text in Chinese; summaries in English) 1948. bi-m. Y13($7) per no. (Chinese Academy of Sciences, Institute of Geophysics and Meteorology) Science Press, Marketing and Sales Department, 16 Donghuangchenggen Beijie, Beijing 100707, People's Republic of China. TEL 4010642. FAX 4012180. TELEX 210247-SPBJ-CN. adv. circ. 12,000. **Indexed:** Chem.Abstr., Curr.Cont., Deep Sea Res.& Oceanogr.Abstr., GeoRef., Ind.Sci.Rev., Sci.Abstr., Sci.Cit.Ind. **Document type:** academic/scholarly publication.
—BLDSC (0622.500000). CCC.
Description: Covers geophysical research in China, including seismology, physics of the earth's interior, and geodesy.
Refereed Serial

551 530   UK   ISSN 0361-3666
HV553
DISASTERS; the journal of disaster relief and management. 1977. q. £48($89.50) to individuals; institutions £75($122). (Relief and Development Institute) Basil Blackwell Ltd., 108 Cowley Rd., Oxford OX4 1JF, England. TEL 0865-791100. FAX 0865-791347. TELEX 837022-OXBOOK-G. Ed. David Turton. adv.; bk.rev.; charts; illus.; stat.; index. circ. 2,000. (also avail. in microform from MIM,UMI; reprint service avail. from SWZ,UMI). **Indexed:** Abstr.Hyg., Abstr.J.Earthq.Eng., Abstr.Rural Dev.Trop., Curr.Cont., Environ.Abstr., Excerp.Med, Geo.Abstr., GeoRef., Int.Lab.Doc., Nutr.Abstr., Refug.Abstr., Risk Abstr., Rural Devel.Abstr., Rural Recreat.Tour.Abstr., SSCI, Trop.Dis.Bull., World Agri.Econ.& Rural Sociol.Abstr.
—BLDSC (3595.510000); Faxon; UnCover; SWETS; UMI. CCC.

551.22   CC   ISSN 1000-3274
DIZHEN/JOURNAL OF SEISMOLOGY. (Text in Chinese) bi-m. $77.40. (Zhongguo Dizhen Xuehui, Dizhen Qianzhao Zhuanye Weiyuanhui - Chinese Seismological Society, Special Committee on Seismic Precursors) Science Press, Marketing and Sales Department, 16 Donghuangchenggen Beijie, Beijing 100707, People's Republic of China. TEL 4010642. FAX 4012180. TELEX 210247-SPBJ-CN. adv. circ. 31,000.
—BLDSC (3643.571000).
Description: Aims to publicize the study of seismic precursors and earthquake prediction. Covers theories and methods of earthquake prediction, application of observation techniques, and analysis of available data.

551.22   CC
DIZHEN DICI GUANCE YU YANJIU/OBSERVATION AND STUDY OF EARTHQUAKES AND GEOMAGNETISM. (Text in Chinese) bi-m. Guojia Dizhenju, Diqiu Wuli Yanjiusuo - National Bureau of Seismology, Institute of Geophysics, Qinghua Donglu, Beijing 100083, People's Republic of China. TEL 2011116. Ed. Chen Peishan.

EARTH SCIENCES — GEOPHYSICS

551.22 551 CC ISSN 0253-4967
QE531 CODEN: DDIZD4
DIZHEN DIZHI/SEISMOLOGY AND GEOLOGY. (Text in Chinese) 1979. q. $4080. Guojia Dizhenju, Dizhi Yanjiusuo - State Seismology Administration, Institute of Geology, Qijia Huozi, Deshengmenwai, Beijing 100029, People's Republic of China. TEL 86-1-2023377. FAX 86-1-2028617. Ed. Ma Xingyuan. bk.rev.; abstr.; index. circ. 1,200. **Indexed:** Abstr.J.Earthq.Eng., Sci.Abstr. **Document type:** academic/scholarly publication.
—BLDSC (8227.750000).
Description: Academic publication covers the latest development in earth sciences, especially in the fields of seismology and geology.
Refereed Serial

551.22 CC
DIZHEN DIZHI YICONG/TRANSLATED LITERATURE ON SEISMOLOGY AND GEOLOGY. (Text in Chinese) bi-m. Guojia Dizhenju, Dizhi Yanjiusuo - National Bureau of Seismology, Institute of Geology, Qijia Huozi, Deshengmenwai, Beijing 100029, People's Republic of China. TEL 4016611. Ed. Ma Xingheng.

551.22 CC ISSN 1000-1301
DIZHEN GONGCHENG YU GONGCHENG ZHENDONG/EARTHQUAKE ENGINEERING AND ENGINEERING VIBRATION. (Text in Chinese) 1981. q. $66.40. Science Press, Marketing and Sales Department, 16 Donghuangchenggen Beijie, Beijing 100707, People's Republic of China. TEL 4010642. FAX 4012180. TELEX 210247-SPBJ-CN. adv. circ. 6,000.
Description: Contains research papers on both theory and applications.
Refereed Serial

551.22 CC ISSN 0253-3782
QE531 CODEN: ASSID7
DIZHEN XUEBAO. English edition: Acta Seismologica Sinica (ISSN 1000-9116) (Text in Chinese; summaries in English) 1979. q. Y139.20($330) Science Press, Marketing and Sales Department, 16 Donghuangchenggen Beijie, Beijing 100707, People's Republic of China. TEL 4010642. FAX 4012180. TELEX 210247-SPBJ-CN. adv. circ. 12,000. **Indexed:** GeoRef., Sci.Abstr.
—BLDSC (0663.270000).
Description: Publishes articles on research work in seismology, and papers on basic geophysical studies of seismology, seismotectonics, seismic precursor, earthquake engineering, and related technology. Contains reviews and information on activities.
Refereed Serial

551 IE ISSN 0070-7422
CODEN: CDDBDW
DUBLIN INSTITUTE FOR ADVANCED STUDIES. SCHOOL OF COSMIC PHYSICS. GEOPHYSICAL BULLETIN. Titles varies: Dublin Institute for Advanced Studies. Communications. Series D. 1950. irreg., no. 42, 1989. price varies. Dublin Institute for Advanced Studies, 10 Burlington Rd., Dublin 4, Ireland. TEL 680748. FAX 680561. **Indexed:** GeoRef. **Document type:** academic/scholarly publication.

551.22 US
EARTHQUAKE HISTORY OF THE UNITED STATES. 1928. irreg. (approx. every 5 yrs.). price varies. National Oceanic and Atmospheric Administration, National Geophysical Data Center, 325 Broadway, Boulder, CO 80303-3328. TEL 303-497-6419. Ed.Bd. stat. (also avail. in microfiche from NTI) **Document type:** government publication.
●Also available on CD-ROM.
Description: Tells the location and effects of U.S. earthquakes from earliest recorded history to present.

EARTHQUAKE RESEARCH IN CHINA. see *EARTH SCIENCES — Geology*

551 US ISSN 8755-2930
TA654.6
EARTHQUAKE SPECTRA. 1984. q. $75 to individuals; institutions $120 (effective 1994). Earthquake Engineering Research Institute, 499 14th Street, Ste.320, Oakland, CA 94612-1902. TEL 510-451-0905. FAX 510-451-5411. Ed. Jack P. Moehle. bk.rev. circ. 2,400. (back issues avail.) **Indexed:** Abstr.J.Earthq.Eng. **Document type:** academic/scholarly publication.
—BLDSC (3643.595800); EI; Faxon; UnCover; SWETS.
Description: For those professions involved in earthquake hazards reduction.

ELECTROMAGNETICS. see *ENGINEERING — Electrical Engineering*

ENGINEERING GEOLOGY & GEOTECHNICAL ENGINEERING SYMPOSIUM. PROCEEDINGS. see *ENGINEERING — Civil Engineering*

551 US ISSN 0096-3941
QE500 CODEN: EOSTA
EOS. 1919. w. $230 to non-members. American Geophysical Union, 2000 Florida Ave., N.W., Washington, DC 20009. TEL 202-462-6900. FAX 202-328-0566. TELEX 710-822-9300. Ed. A.F. Spilhaus. adv. contact: Karol Snyder. bk.rev.; abstr.; bibl.; charts; illus.; index. circ. 30,000. (tabloid format; also avail. in microform from AGU; reprint service avail. from ISI) **Indexed:** Abstr.J.Earthq.Eng., Art & Archaeol.Tech.Abstr., Biol.Abstr., Curr.Adv.Ecol.Sci., Deep Sea Res.& Oceanogr.Abstr., Eng.Ind., Geo.Abstr., GeoRef., HRIS, INIS Atomind., Meteor.& Geoastrophys.Abstr., Petrol.Abstr., Rev.Appl.Entomol., Sci.Abstr., Sel.Water Res.Abstr.
—BLDSC (3793.065000); SWETS. **CCC.**
Formerly (until 1969): American Geophysical Union. Transactions (ISSN 0002-8606)
Description: For geophysicists; carries articles on recent research; news; employment opportunities; meeting programs and reports; announcements of grants and fellowships; and AGU activities.
Refereed Serial

551 HU ISSN 0524-8655
CODEN: MAGJBM
EOTVOS LORAND GEOPHYSICAL INSTITUTE OF HUNGARY. ANNUAL REPORT/MAGYAR ALLAMI EOTVOS LORAND GEOFIZIKAI INTEZET EVI JELENTESE. (Text in English, Hungarian and Russian) 1966. s-a. Eotvos Lorand Geophysical Institute of Hungary, Columbus u. 17-23, 1145 Budapest, Hungary. TEL 36-11632835. FAX 36-1-1637-256. TELEX 22-6194-ELGI-H. Ed. Zsuzsanna Hegybiro. charts; illus.; maps. circ. 1,400. **Indexed:** INIS Atomind. **Document type:** government publication.
Description: Contains results of raw materials prospecting, methodological and instrumental research, earth physics and lithospheric studies of ELGI.

EUROPEAN EARTHQUAKE ENGINEERING; international journal of earthquake engineering and engineering seismology. see *ENGINEERING*

551 AT ISSN 0812-3985
TN269 CODEN: EXGEEF
EXPLORATION GEOPHYSICS. (Supplement avail.) 1970. q. Aus.$100 in Australasia; elsewhere Aus.$160. Australian Society of Exploration Geophysicists, P.O. Box 354, Hawthorn, Vic. 3122, Australia. TEL 61-3-818-1272. FAX 61-3-818-1286. Ed. John Denham. adv.; cum.index: 1970-1987. circ. 1,200. (also avail. in microfiche) **Indexed:** AESIS, E&P Hlth. (1993-), Gas Process.& Ppl. (1993-), Geo.Abstr., Off.Tech. (1993-), Petrol.Abstr. (1976-).
—BLDSC (3842.155750); UnCover; CASDDS. **CCC.**
Formerly: Australian Society of Exploration Geophysicists. Bulletin (ISSN 0314-2876)

551.22 UK ISSN 0144-2376
FELT AND DAMAGING EARTHQUAKES. 1976. a. £5. International Seismological Centre, Pipers Lane, Thatcham, Newbury, Berks. RG13 4NS, England. TEL 0635-61022. FAX 0635-72351. **Indexed:** Abstr.J.Earthq.Eng.

551 FI ISSN 0782-6087
FINNISH METEOROLOGICAL INSTITUTE. GEOPHYSICAL PUBLICATIONS/ILMATIETEEN LAITOS. GEOFYSIKAALISIA JULKAISUJA. irreg. Ilmatieteen Laitos - Finnish Meteorological Institute, P.O. Box 503, SF-00101 Helsinki, Finland. FAX 1929218. TELEX 124435 EFKL SF. (Dist. by) Oy Painatuskeskus AB, P.O. Box 516, FIN-00101 Helsinki, Finland) **Indexed:** Meteor.& Geoastrophys.Abstr. **Document type:** government publication.
—BLDSC (4156.400000).

551 FI ISSN 1235-4732
FINNISH METEOROLOGICAL INSTITUTE. MAGNETIC RESULTS. (Text in English) a. price varies. Ilmatieteen Laitos, P.O. Box 503, SF-0101 Helsinki, Finland. FAX 1929218. (Dist. by) Oy Painatuskeskus AB, Publ. Division, P.O. Box 516, SF-00101, Helsinki, Finland) **Document type:** government publication.

551 UK ISSN 0263-5046
FIRST BREAK. 1983. m. £91 to individuals in Europe (elsewhere £106.50 ($159)); institutions in Europe £228 (elsewhere £268 ($399) (effective 1994). (European Association of Exploration Geophysicists, NE) Blackwell Scientific Publications Ltd., Osney Mead, Oxford OX2 0EL, England. TEL 0865-240201. FAX 0865-721205. TELEX 83355-MEDBOK-G. Ed. A. Lucas. adv.; bk.rev.; bibl.; charts; illus.; index. circ. 4,900. **Indexed:** AESIS, E&P Hlth. (1993-), Gas Process.& Ppl. (1993-), Off.Tech. (1993-), Petrol.Abstr. (1984-). **Document type:** academic/scholarly publication.
—BLDSC (3934.438000); Faxon; UnCover; SWETS; UMI. **CCC.**
Refereed Serial

526 RU ISSN 0016-7126
QB275 CODEN: GZKGA5
GEODEZIYA I KARTOGRAFIYA. 1956. m. $19.80. (Glavnoe Upravlenie Geodezii i Kartografii pri Sovete Ministrov) Izdatel'stvo Nedra, Pl. Belorusskogo Vakzala, 3, 125047 Moscow, Russia. TEL 250-52-55. bibl.; index. **Indexed:** Bibl.Cart., Geo.Abstr.
—BLDSC (0047.320000).

526 PL ISSN 0016-7134
QB275 CODEN: GEJKAZ
GEODEZJA I KARTOGRAFIA. (Text in Polish; summaries in English) 1952. q. $32. (Polska Akademia Nauk, Komitet Geodezji) Wydawnictwo Naukowe P W N, Ul. Miodowa 10, 00-251 Warsaw, Poland. Ed. A. Makowski. bibl.; illus.; index. circ. 1,040. **Indexed:** Bibl.Cart., Geo.Abstr., GeoRef.

551 FR ISSN 0766-5105
QC801
GEODYNAMIQUE. 1957. s-a. 260 F. (Institut Francais de Recherche Scientifique pour le Developpement en Cooperation) O R S T O M Editions - Diffusion, 72 Route d'Aulnay, 93143 Bondy Cedex, France. TEL 48-02-55-00. FAX 48-47-30-88. circ. 500. (back issues avail.) **Indexed:** Br.Geol.Lit. **Document type:** academic/scholarly publication.
—BLDSC (4119.757000); Faxon; UnCover.
Formed by the 1985 merger of: Geophysique (ISSN 0398-3218); Cahiers O R S T O M Serie Geologie (ISSN 0029-7232); *Supersedes:* Cahiers O R S T O M Serie Geophysique.

551 IT
▼**GEOFISICA DELL'AMBIENTE E DEL TERRITORIO.** 1992. irreg., no.2, 1993. price varies. Liguori Editore s.r.l., Via Mezzocanone, 19, 80134 Naples, Italy. TEL 081-5527139. Ed. Antonio Rapolla. **Document type:** monographic series.

551 MX ISSN 0016-7169
QC801 CODEN: GFINAC
GEOFISICA INTERNACIONAL. (Text in English, French and Spanish) 1961. q. $50. Universidad Nacional Autonoma de Mexico, Instituto de Geofisica, Circuito Exterior, Mexico 20, D.F., Mexico. Ed. Jaime Urrutia. bibl.; charts; index. circ. 1,200. **Indexed:** Chem.Abstr., Deep Sea Res.& Oceanogr.Abstr., GeoRef., INIS Atomind., Meteor.& Geoastrophys.Abstr.
—BLDSC (4120.300000); UnCover; CASDDS.

551 KR ISSN 0203-3100
QC801 CODEN: GEZHD7
GEOFIZICHESKII ZHURNAL/JOURNAL OF GEOPHYSICS; nauchno-teoretichskii zhurnal. English translation: Geophysical Journal (UK ISSN 0275-9128) (Text in Russian; summaries in English) 1979. bi-m. 7.20 Rub. (Akademiya Nauk Ukrainy, Otdelenie Nauk o Zemle) Vicavnitstvo Naukova Dumka, Vul. Tereshchenkivska 3, 252601 Kiev, Ukraine. TEL 444-11-65. (Dist. by: Mezhdunarodnaya Kniga, B. Yakimanka 39, 117049 Moscow, Russia; Dist. in U.S. by: Victor Kamkin Inc., 4956 Boiling Brook Pkwy., Rockville, MD 20852. TEL 301-881-5973. FAX 301-881-1637) Ed. A.V. Chekunov. **Indexed:** Chem.Abstr., Deep Sea Res.& Oceanogr.Abstr., GeoRef., INIS Atomind., Phys.Ber., Sci.Abstr. **Document type:** academic/scholarly publication.
—BLDSC (0047.850000); CASDDS.
Formerly: Geofizicheskii Sbornik (ISSN 0568-6989)

EARTH SCIENCES — GEOPHYSICS

551   CI   ISSN 0352-3659
GEOFIZIKA. 1923. a. exchange basis only. (Sveuciliste u Zagrebu, Prirodoslovno-Matematicki Fakultet) Geofizicki Zavod, Horvatovac bb, p.p. 224, 41000 Zagreb, Croatia. TEL 041-420-222. FAX 041-432-462. TELEX 22575 GEOZAG YU. Ed. Mirko Orlic. bk.rev. circ. 350. **Indexed:** Amer.Hist.& Life, Hist.Abstr., Meteor.& Geostrophys.Abstr. **Document type:** academic/scholarly publication.
—BLDSC (4121.260000).
    Formerly: Sveuciliste u Zagrebu. Prirodoslovno-Matematicki Fakultet. Radovi.

GEOLOGICAL SOCIETY OF CHINA. JOURNAL. see *EARTH SCIENCES — Geology*

GEOLOGICAL SURVEY OF NAMIBIA. REPORTS ON OPEN FILE. C D M MINERAL SURVEYS. see *EARTH SCIENCES — Geology*

556   SX
GEOLOGICAL SURVEY OF NAMIBIA. REPORTS ON OPEN FILE. GEOPHYSICS. (Text in English, occasionally in Afrikaans) 1971. irreg., no.42, 1985. price varies. Ministry of Mines and Energy, Geological Survey of Namibia, 45 Mugabe Ave., P.O. Box 2168, Windhoek 9000, Namibia. TEL 061-37240. FAX 061-228324. TELEX 50-908-487. **Document type:** government publication.
    Description: Series of preliminary reports on topics in geophysics.

GEOLOGICKY PRUZKUM/GEOLGICKY PRIESKUM/GEOLOGICAL SURVEYING; a special journal for techniques, methodics and economy of exploration and problems related to raw materials. see *EARTH SCIENCES — Geology*

GEOLOGISCHE ABHANDLUNGEN HESSEN. see *EARTH SCIENCES — Geology*

GEOLOGISCHES JAHRBUCH HESSEN. see *EARTH SCIENCES — Geology*

GEOLOGIYA I GEOFIZIKA. see *EARTH SCIENCES — Geology*

551   US
GEOMAGNETIC INDICES BULLETIN. m. $21 (effective 1993). National Oceanic and Atmospheric Administration, National Geophysical Data Center, 325 Broadway, E-GC4, Boulder, CO 80303-3328. TEL 303-497-6223. (looseleaf format; back issues avail.) **Document type:** government publication, bulletin.

538.7 551   US   ISSN 0016-7932
QC811   CODEN: GMARAX
GEOMAGNETISM AND AERONOMY. English translation of: Geomagnetizm i Aeronomiya (UR ISSN 0016-7940) 1961. 6/yr. $545 for vol.32 to non-members (foreign $555); members $436 (foreign $446). (Russian Academy of Sciences, RU) American Geophysical Union, 2000 Florida Ave., N.W., Washington, DC 20009. TEL 202-462-6900. FAX 202-328-0566. TELEX 710-822-9300. (Germany addr.: Postfach 49, 37189 Katlenburt-Lindau, Germany. TEL 49-5556-1440) charts; illus.; index. (reprint service avail. from ISI) **Indexed:** Deep Sea Res.& Oceanogr.Abstr., Meteor.& Geostrophys.Abstr., Sci.Abstr.
—BLDSC (0411.800000); Faxon; UnCover. **CCC.**

538   RU   ISSN 0016-7940
    CODEN: GEAEA6
GEOMAGNETIZM I AERONOMIYA. English translation: Geomagnetism and Aeronomy (US ISSN 0016-7932) 1961. bi-m. 39.90 Rub. (Rossiiskaya Akademiya Nauk) Izdatel'stvo Nauka, 90 Profsoyuznaya ul., 117864 Moscow, Russia. Ed. Yu.D. Kalinin. bk.rev.; charts; illus.; index. (tabloid format) **Indexed:** Chem.Abstr., Curr.Cont., Ind.Sci.Rev., INIS Atomind., Int.Aerosp.Abstr., Meteor.& Geostrophys.Abstr., Phys.Ber., Sci.Abstr., Sci.Cit.Ind.
—BLDSC (0047.740000); CASDDS. **CCC.**

551   US   ISSN 0309-1929
QC809.F5   CODEN: GAFDD3
GEOPHYSICAL AND ASTROPHYSICAL FLUID DYNAMICS. 1970. 28/yr. (in 7 vols., 4 nos./vol.). 234 ECU per vol. to individuals (effective 1993). Gordon and Breach Science Publishers, 820 Town Center Dr., Langhorne, PA 19047. TEL 215-750-2642. FAX 215-750-6343. (UK subscr. to: P.O. Box 90, Reading, Berkshire RG1 8JL, England. TEL 0734-560-080) Eds. Paul H. Roberts, Andrew Soward. adv.; bk.rev.; charts; illus.; cum.index. (also avail. in microform) **Indexed:** Appl.Mech.Rev., Astron.& Astrophys.Abstr., Curr.Cont., Deep Sea Res.& Oceanogr.Abstr., Geo.Abstr., Ind.Sci.Rev., Int.Aerosp.Abstr., Math.R., Phys.Ber., Sci.Abstr., Sci.Cit.Ind. **Document type:** academic/scholarly publication.
—BLDSC (4148.600000); UnCover; SWETS. **CCC.**
Refereed Serial

551   US
GEOPHYSICAL DIRECTORY. 1946. a. $50 (foreign $65). Geophysical Directory, Inc., 2200 Welch Ave., Box 130508, Houston, TX 77219. TEL 713-529-8789. FAX 713-529-3646. Ed. Claudia La Calli. adv. contact: Claudia LaCalli. circ. 5,000. (also avail. in diskette format) **Document type:** directory.
    Description: Lists oil companies and key personnel that use geophysical techniques as well as supply and service companies in the petroleum and mineral exploration industry worldwide.

551   US   ISSN 0275-9128
QC801   CODEN: GJOUDQ
GEOPHYSICAL JOURNAL. English translation of: Geofizicheskii Zhurnal (UR ISSN 0203-3100) vol.3, 1982. 12/yr. (in 2 vols., 6 nos./vol.). 361 ECU per vol. (effective 1993). (Akademiya Nauk Ukrainy, Otdelenie Nauk o Zemle, KR) Gordon and Breach Science Publishers, 820 Town Center Dr., Langhorne, PA 90471. TEL 215-750-2642. FAX 215-750-6343. (UK subscr. to: P.O. Box 90, Reading, Berkshire RG1 8JL, England. TEL 0734-560-080) Ed. Anatoly Chekunov. (also avail. in microform) **Indexed:** E&P Hlth. (1993-), Gas Process.& Ppl. (1993-), Geo.Abstr., Ind.Sci.Rev., Int.Aerosp.Abstr., Off.Tech. (1993-), Petrol.Abstr. (1993-), Sci.Abstr., Sci.Cit.Ind.
—BLDSC (0411.930000). **CCC.**
Refereed Serial

551   UK   ISSN 0956-540X
QC806   CODEN: GEJOEH
GEOPHYSICAL JOURNAL INTERNATIONAL. 1958. m. £530 in Europe (elsewhere £585 ($872) (effective 1994). (Royal Astronomical Society) Blackwell Scientific Publications Ltd., Osney Mead, Oxford OX2 0EL, England. TEL 0865-240201. FAX 0865-721205. TELEX 83355-MEDBOK-G. (Co-sponsors: Deutsche Geophysikalische Gesellschaft, European Geophysical Society) Ed. M.A. Khan. abstr.; bibl.; charts; illus.; index. circ. 1,800. (also avail. in microform from UMI; back issues avail.) **Indexed:** ASCA, Br.Geol.Lit., Chem.Abstr., Curr.Cont., E&P Hlth. (1993-), Gas Process.& Ppl. (1993-), Geo.Abstr., INIS Atomind., Meteor.& Geostrophys.Abstr., Off.Tech. (1993-), Petrol.Abstr. (1961-), Sci.Abstr., Sci.Cit.Ind. **Document type:** academic/scholarly publication.
—BLDSC (4150.800000); Faxon; UnCover; SWETS; UMI; CASDDS. **CCC.**
    Formerly (until 1989): Geophysical Journal (ISSN 0952-4592); Which incorporates in part (in 1987): Annales Geophysicae. Series B: Terrestrial and Planetary Physics (ISSN 0980-8760) & Royal Astronomical Society Geophysical Journal (ISSN 0016-8009); Which was formerly: Royal Astronomical Society. Monthly Notices. Geophysical Supplement.
Refereed Serial

551   JA   ISSN 0016-8017
QC801   CODEN: GEOMAW
GEOPHYSICAL MAGAZINE/KISHOCHO OBUN IHO. (Text in English) 1926. a. 3296 Yen. (Japan Meteorological Agency - Kishocho) Japan Weather Association, 2-9-2, Kanda-nishikicho, Chiyoda-ku, Tokyo 101, Japan. circ. 849. **Indexed:** Appl.Mech.Rev., Chem.Abstr., INIS Atomind., JTA, Meteor.& Geostrophys.Abstr., Sci.Abstr.

622.15   UK   ISSN 0016-8025
TN269   CODEN: GPPRAR
GEOPHYSICAL PROSPECTING. (Text in English, French or German; summaries in English) 1953. 8/yr. £205 in Europe; elsewhere $249 ($369) (effective 1994). (European Association of Exploration Geophysicists, NE) Blackwell Scientific Publications Ltd., Osney Mead, Oxford OX2 0EL, England. TEL 0865-240201. FAX 0865-721205. TELEX 83355-MEDBOK-G. Ed. D.W. March. bk.rev.; abstr.; bibl.; charts; illus.; index, cum.index. circ. 4,750. (also avail. in microform from UMI; back issues avail.) **Indexed:** AESIS, ASCA, Br.Geol.Lit., Chem.Abstr., Curr.Cont., Deep Sea Res.& Oceanogr.Abstr., E&P Hlth. (1993-), Eng.Ind., Fuel & Energy Abstr., Gas Process.& Ppl. (1993-), Geo.Abstr., Geotech.Abstr., Ind.Sci.Rev., INIS Atomind., Off.Tech. (1993-), Petrol.Abstr. (1961-), Sci.Abstr., Sci.Cit.Ind., W.R.C.Inf.
—BLDSC (4156.000000); EI; Faxon; UnCover; SWETS; UMI. **CCC.**
Refereed Serial

551   US   ISSN 0094-8276
QE500   CODEN: GPRLAJ
GEOPHYSICAL RESEARCH LETTERS. 1974. s-m. $590 to non-members (foreign $614); members $65 (foreign $89); students $33 (foreign $57). American Geophysical Union, 2000 Florida Ave., N.W., Washington, DC 20009. TEL 202-462-6900. FAX 202-328-0566. TELEX 710-822-9300. Ed. Philip Russell. bibl.; illus.; index. (also avail. in microform from AGU; reprint service avail. from ISI) **Indexed:** Chem.Abstr., Curr.Cont., Deep Sea Res.& Oceanogr.Abstr., E&P Hlth. (1993-), Excerp.Med., Gas Process.& Ppl. (1993-), Geo.Abstr., Ind.Sci.Rev., INIS Atomind., Int.Aerosp.Abstr., Mass Spectr.Bull., Meteor.& Geostrophys.Abstr., Ocean.Abstr., Off.Tech. (1993-), Petrol.Abstr. (1978-), Phys.Ber., Sci.Abstr., Sci.Cit.Ind., Sel.Water Res.Abstr.
—BLDSC (4156.900000); Faxon; UnCover; SWETS; CASDDS. **CCC.**
    Description: Provides a forum for the rapid dissemination of current research of broad geophysical interest.
Refereed Serial

551   HU   ISSN 0016-7177
QC801.M3   CODEN: GEKOAI
GEOPHYSICAL TRANSACTIONS/GEOFIZIKAI KOZLEMENYEK/GEOFIZICHESKII BYULLETEN'. (Text in English; abstracts in Hungarian and Russian) 1952. q. $90. Eotvos Lorand Geophysical Institute of Hungary, Columbus u. 17-23, 1145 Budapest, Hungary. TEL 36-11632-835. FAX 36-1-1637-256. TELEX 22-6194-ELGI-H. Ed. Zsuzsanna Hegybiro. charts; illus.; maps. circ. 1,400. **Indexed:** Appl.Mech.Rev., Chem.Abstr., Deep Sea Res.& Oceanogr.Abstr., INIS Atomind., Petrol.Abstr., Phys.Abstr., Ref.Zh., Sci.Abstr. **Document type:** government publication.
—BLDSC (4157.700500); UnCover.
    Description: Contains methodological and instrumental research and occasional studies on regional problems of central Europe.

551   US   ISSN 0016-8033
QE500   CODEN: GPYSA7
GEOPHYSICS. 1936. m. $250 (foreign $265). Society of Exploration Geophysicists, Box 702740, Tulsa, OK 74170-2740. TEL 918-493-3516. Ed. Bob A. Hardage. adv. contact: David Yowell. bk.rev.; abstr.; illus.; pat.; index. circ. 19,000. (also avail. in microform from UMI; reprint service avail. from UMI) **Indexed:** A.S.& T.Ind., AESIS, Appl.Mech.Rev., Biol.Abstr., Chem.Abstr., Curr.Cont., Deep Sea Res.& Oceanogr.Abstr., E&P Hlth. (1993-), Energy Ind., Energy Info.Abstr., Eng.Ind., Gas Process.& Ppl. (1993-), Geo.Abstr., Geotech.Abstr., Ind.Sci.Rev., INIS Atomind., Ocean.Abstr., Off.Tech. (1993-), Petrol.Abstr. (1961-), Phys.Ber., Pollut.Abstr., Sci.Abstr., Sci.Cit.Ind. **Document type:** academic/scholarly publication.
—BLDSC (4158.000000); EI; Faxon; UnCover; SWETS; UMI; CASDDS. **CCC.**

GEOPHYSICS AND ASTROPHYSICS MONOGRAPHS; a series of graduate-level textbooks and monographs on plasma astrophysics and geophysics, including magnetospheric, solar, and stellar physics. see *ASTRONOMY*

EARTH SCIENCES — GEOPHYSICS

551   GW   ISSN 0138-2357
CODEN: GEGED5
GEOPHYSIK UND GEOLOGIE; geophysikalische Veroeffentlichungen der Karl-Marx-Universitaet Leipzig. Dritte Serie. 1974. irreg., vol.4, no.4, 1992. price varies. (Universitaet Leipzig) Akademie Verlag GmbH, Muehlenstr. 33-34, 13187 Berlin, Germany. TEL 030-47889348. FAX 030-47889357. Ed. R. Lauterbach. **Indexed:** Chem.Abstr. **Document type:** monographic series.
—CASDDS.
Formerly: Leipzig. Universitaet. Geophysikalisches Institut. Veroeffentlichungen. Zweite Serie (ISSN 0016-8041)

551.8   US   ISSN 0016-8521
QE500   CODEN: GEOTBK
GEOTECTONICS. English translation of: Geotektonika (UR ISSN 0016-853X) 1967. 6/yr. $395 for vol.26 to non-members (foreign $405); members $316 (foreign $326). (Russian Academy of Sciences, Division of Earth Sciences, RU) American Geophysical Union, 2000 Florida Ave. N.W., Washington, DC 20009. TEL 202-462-6900. FAX 202-328-0566. TELEX 710-822-9300. (Germany addr.: Postfach 49, 37189 Katlenburg-Lindau, Germany. TEL 49-5556-1440) bibl.; charts; maps; illus.; index. circ. 245. (reprint service avail. from ISI) **Indexed:** Abstr.J.Earthq.Eng., AESIS, Curr.Cont., Deep Sea Res.& Oceanogr.Abstr., Ind.Sci.Rev., Phys.Ber., Sci.Cit.Ind.
—BLDSC (0411.950000); UnCover; SWETS. **CCC.**

551.8   GW   ISSN 0016-8548
QE601   CODEN: GKTFAA
GEOTEKTONISCHE FORSCHUNGEN. (Text in English and German; summaries in English, French, German, Italian and Spanish) 1937. 3/yr. price varies. E. Schweizerbart'sche Verlagsbuchhandlung, Johannesstr. 3A, 70176 Stuttgart, Germany. TEL 0711-625001. FAX 0711-625005. TELEX 723363-SCHB-D. Ed. K. Weber. charts; illus. **Indexed:** Chem.Abstr., GeoRef. **Document type:** academic/scholarly publication.
—UnCover. **CCC.**

551   US   ISSN 0149-8991
CODEN: RGRCDJ
GEOTHERMAL RESOURCES COUNCIL. SPECIAL REPORT. no.3, 1973. irreg., no.17, 1992. price varies. Geothermal Resources Council, Box 1350, Davis, CA 95617. TEL 916-758-2360. FAX 916-758-2839. (Street addr.: 2001 Second St., Ste. 5, Davis, CA 95616) **Document type:** monographic series.
—BLDSC (8394.410000).

551   US   ISSN 0193-5933
GB1199.5   CODEN: TGRCD7
GEOTHERMAL RESOURCES COUNCIL. TRANSACTIONS. 1977. a. price varies. Geothermal Resources Council, Box 1350, Davis, CA 95617. TEL 916-758-2360. FAX 916-758-2839. **Document type:** proceedings.
—BLDSC (8933.220000); CASDDS.

551   DK   ISSN 0109-4300
GODHAVN MAGNETIC RESULTS. 1983. a. free. Danish Meteorological Institute, Division of Research and Development, Lyngbyvej 100, DK-2100 Copenhagen OE, Denmark. FAX 31-293400. TELEX 15835 GEOMI DK. illus. circ. 250. **Document type:** government publication.
Formerly: Godhavn Geophysical Observatory. Magnetic Results.

538.7   UK
GREAT BRITAIN. NATURAL ENVIRONMENT RESEARCH COUNCIL. BRITISH GEOLOGICAL SURVEY. GEOMAGNETIC BULLETIN. 1969. irreg. price varies. Natural Environment Research Council, British Geological Survey, Kingsley Dunham Centre, Keyworth, Nottingham NG12 5GG, England. TEL 0602-361000. FAX 0602-362000. TELEX 378173-BGSEKY-G. (Subscr. to: H.M.S.O., c/o Liaison Officer, Nine Elms, London SW8 5DR, England) circ. 600. **Document type:** bulletin, government publication.
—BLDSC (4147.070000).
Formerly (until Jan. 1984): Great Britain. Institute of Geological Sciences. Geomagnetic Bulletin (ISSN 0073-9316)

551.2   CC
GUOJI DIZHEN DONGTAI/RECENT DEVELOPMENTS OF WORLD SEISMOLOGY. (Text in Chinese) m. $0.50 per no. Guoji Shudian, Qikan Bu - China International Book Trading Corp., Chegongzhuang Xilu 21, P.O. Box 399, Beijing 100044, People's Republic of China.

551.22   CC   ISSN 0253-4975
GUOJI DIZHEN DONGTAI/INTERNATIONAL SEISMOLOGY DEVELOPMENT. (Text in Chinese) m. Guojia Dizhenju, Diqiu Wuli Yanjiusuo - National Bureau of Seismology, Institute of Geophysics, Qinghua Donglu, Beijing 100083, People's Republic of China. TEL 2011116. Ed. Zou Qijia.

551   UK
HANDBOOK OF GEOPHYSICAL EXPLORATION. (Series not published in numerical sequence.) 1983. irreg., vol.21, 1988. price varies. Elsevier Science Ltd., Books Division, P.O. Box 800, Kidlington, Oxford OX5 1DK, England. TEL 44-865-843000. FAX 44-865-8743010. (And: Elsevier Science, 660 White Plains Rd., Tarrytown, NY 10591-5153. TEL 914-524-9200. FAX 914-333-2444) Eds. S. Treitel, K. Helbig. index. circ. 2,000. (back issues avail.) **Document type:** academic/scholarly publication.
Description: Encyclopedia of current information for geophysicists, geologists, seismologists and engineers.

551   JA   ISSN 0439-3503
HOKKAIDO DAIGAKU CHIKYU BUTSURIGAKU KENKYU HOKOKU/HOKKAIDO UNIVERSITY. GEOPHYSICAL BULLETIN. (Text in Japanese; summaries in English) 1951. s-a. Hokkaido Daigaku, Rigakubu, Chikyu Butsurigaku Kyoshitsu - Hokkaido University, Faculty of Science, Department of Geophysics, Nishi 8-chome, Kita 10-jo, Kita-ku, Sapporo-shi, Hokkaido 060, Japan. **Indexed:** Jap.Per.Ind.

551.22   JA
HOKKAIDO JISHIN KAZAN GEPPO/SEISMOLOGICAL AND VOLCANOLOGICAL MONTHLY REPORT IN HOKKAIDO. (Text in Japanese) 1984. m. Kishocho, Sapporo Kanku Kishodai - Japan Meteorological Agency, Sapporo District Meteorological Observatory, 1, Nishi 18-chome, Kita 2-jo, Chuo-ku, Sapporo-shi, Hokkaido 060, Japan.

551.2   JA
HOKKAIDO JISHIN KAZAN NENPO/SEISMOLOGICAL AND VOLCANOLOGICAL ANNUAL REPORT IN HOKKAIDO. (Text in Japanese) a. Kishocho, Sapporo Kanku Kishodai - Japan Meteorological Agency, Sapporo District Meteorological Observatory, 2, Nishi 18-chome, Kita 2-jo, Chuo-ku, Sapporo-shi, Hokkaido 060, Japan.

551   JA   ISSN 0441-067X
HOKKAIDO UNIVERSITY. FACULTY OF SCIENCE. JOURNAL. SERIES 7: GEOPHYSICS. (Text in English) 1957. a. exchange basis. Hokkaido University, Faculty of Science - Hokkaido Daigaku Rigakubu, Nishi-8-chome, Kita-10-jo, Kita-ku, Sapporo 060, Japan. FAX 011-716-0394. Ed. K. Kikuchi. circ. 400. (back issues avail.) **Indexed:** Geo.Abstr., Meteor.& Geoastrophys.Abstr. **Document type:** academic/scholarly publication.
—BLDSC (4749.010000).

551   CC
HUABEI DIZHEN KEXUE. (Text in Chinese) q. Hebei Dizhen-ju - Hebei Seismology Bureau, Shijiazhuang, Hebei 050021, People's Republic of China. TEL 615956. Ed. Yang Lihua.

551.22   CC
HUANAN DIZHEN/SOUTH-CHINA SEISMOLOGY. (Text in Chinese) q. Guangdong Sheng Dizhen Ju, No. 81, Xianlie Lu, Guangzhou, Guangdong 510070, People's Republic of China. TEL 778583. Ed. Ding Yuanzhang.

HVAR OBSERVATORY BULLETIN. see *ASTRONOMY*

538.7   UK   ISSN 0536-1095
I A G A NEWS. 1963. a. free. International Association of Geomagnetism and Aeronomy - Association Internationale de Geomagnetisme et d'Aeronomie, c/o Prof. M. Gadsden, Ed., Physics Department, Aberdeen University, Aberdeen AB9 2UE, Scotland. circ. 2,400.

551 526   BE   ISSN 0047-1259
QC801
I U G G CHRONICLE. (Text in English, French) 1957. irreg., 5-6/yr. $66. International Union of Geodesy and Geophysics, c/o Observatoire Royal de Belgique, Ave. Circulaire 3, 1180 Brussels, Belgium. TEL 32-2-3730267. FAX 32-2-3749822. Ed. Paul Melchior. bk.rev. circ. 1,400. **Indexed:** Deep Sea Res.& Oceanogr.Abstr., GeoRef.

INGEGNERIA SISMICA. see *ENGINEERING*

551.44   RM   ISSN 0065-0498
QH89   CODEN: TISPBT
INSTITUT DE SPEOLOGIE EMIL RACOVITZA. TRAVAUX. (Text in English, French, German) 1962. a. 60 lei($40) Editura Academiei Romane, Calea Victoriei 125, 79717 Bucharest, Rumania. (Subscr. to: Rompresfilatelia, Calea Grivitei 64-66, P.O. Box 12-201, 78104 Bucharest, Rumania) bk.rev. circ. 450. **Indexed:** Biol.Abstr., Ref.Zh., Zoo.Rec.

551   BE   ISSN 0020-2525
INSTITUT ROYAL METEOROLOGIQUE DE BELGIQUE. BULLETIN MENSUEL: OBSERVATIONS GEOPHYSIQUES/KONINKLIJK METEOROLOGISCH INSTITUUT VAN BELGIE. MAANDBULLETIN. GEOFYSISCHE WAARNEMINGEN. Key Title: Bulletin Mensuel: Observations Geophysiques - Maandbulletin: Geofysische Waarnemingen. (Text in Dutch, French) 1961. m. 2500 BEF. Institut Royal Meteorologique - Koninklijk Meteorologische Instituut van Belgie, Ave. Circulaire 3, 1180 Brussels, Belgium. TEL 32-2-3730502. FAX 32-2-3751259. TELEX 21315 METEOBRU. charts; stat. circ. 220. **Document type:** bulletin.

INSTITUTE FOR PETROLEUM RESEARCH AND GEOPHYSICS, HOLON, ISRAEL. REPORT. see *PETROLEUM AND GAS*

551   RM   ISSN 0068-306X
INSTITUTUL DE GEOLOGIE SI GEOFIZICA. DARI DE SEAMA ALE SEDINTELOR. (Text in English, French and Rumanian; summaries in English and French; contents page in French) 1907. 5/yr. price varies. Institutul de Geologie si Geofizica, Str. Caransebes Nr. 1, 78344 Bucharest, Rumania. bk.rev. **Indexed:** Bull.Signal., Ref.Zh. **Document type:** academic/scholarly publication.

526 551   BE   ISSN 0542-6766
QC809.E2   CODEN: MTBIBP
INTERNATIONAL ASSOCIATION OF GEODESY. COMMISSION PERMANENTE DES MAREES TERRESTRES. MAREES TERRESTRES BULLETIN D'INFORMATION. 1957. 4/yr. 1000 BEF($33) International Association of Geodesy, Commission Permanente des Marees Terrestres, c/o Observatoire Royal de Belgique, 3 Av. Circulaire, B-1180 Brussels, Belgium. TEL 32-2-3730267. FAX 32-2-3749822. TELEX 21565. Ed. P. Melchior. **Document type:** academic/scholarly publication, bulletin.
—UnCover.
Description: Covers earth tides, geophysics, and geodynamics.

551   US   ISSN 0074-6142
CODEN: IGPSAN
INTERNATIONAL GEOPHYSICS SERIES. 1959. irreg., vol.47, 1991. Academic Press, Inc., 525 B St., Ste. 1900, San Diego, CA 92101-4495. TEL 619-231-0926. FAX 619-699-6715. (Subscr. to: Order Dept., 6277 Sea Harbor Dr., 4th Fl., Orlando, FL 32887. TEL 800-321-5068) Ed. William L. Donn. (reprint service avail. from ISI) **Document type:** academic/scholarly publication.
—BLDSC (4540.610000).

531.14   FR
INTERNATIONAL GRAVIMETRIQUE BUREAU. BULLETIN D'INFORMATION. (Text in English or French) 1960. s-a. 70 F. Bureau Gravimetric International, 18 av. Edouard Belin, 31055 Toulouse Cedex, France. TEL 61-33-29-80. FAX 33-61-25-30-98. adv.; circ. 350 (controlled). **Document type:** bulletin.
Description: Presents technical results achieved by individuals, as well as internal matters and the status of the Bureau's database.

1970 EARTH SCIENCES — GEOPHYSICS

551.22 624.151 JA ISSN 0074-655X
INTERNATIONAL INSTITUTE OF SEISMOLOGY AND EARTHQUAKE ENGINEERING. BULLETIN. (Text in English) 1964. a. International Institute of Seismology and Earthquake Engineering, Building Research Institute-Ministry of Construction, 1 Tatehara, Tsukuba-city, Ibaraki Prefecture 305, Japan. Ed. Yoshikazu Kitagawa. circ. 820. **Indexed:** Abstr.J.Earthq.Eng., Geo.Abstr.
Description: Interdisciplinary study of seismology and earthquake engineering.

551.22 JA
INTERNATIONAL INSTITUTE OF SEISMOLOGY AND EARTHQUAKE ENGINEERING. INDIVIDUAL STUDIES BY PARTICIPANTS AT I I S E E. 1965. a. International Institute of Seismology and Earthquake Engineering, Building Research Institute-Ministry of Construction, 1 Tatehara, Tsukuba-city, Ibaraki Prefecture 305, Japan. Ed. Yoshikazu Kitagawa. circ. 560. **Indexed:** Abstr.J.Earthq.Eng.
—BLDSC (4437.530000).
Formerly: International Institute of Seismology and Earthquake Engineering. Report of Individual Study by Participants to I S E E E (ISSN 0074-6606)

551.22 JA ISSN 0074-6614
INTERNATIONAL INSTITUTE OF SEISMOLOGY AND EARTHQUAKE ENGINEERING. YEAR BOOK. 1964. biennial. International Institute of Seismology and Earthquake Engineering, Building Research Institute-Ministry of Construction, 1 Tatehara, Tsukuba-city, Ibaraki Prefecture 305, Japan. Ed. Yoshikazu Kitagawa. circ. controlled. **Indexed:** Geo.Abstr.
Description: For the exchange of information between the Institute and developing countries.

551.22 UK ISSN 0020-8671
QE532.I56 CODEN: ISCBBQ
INTERNATIONAL SEISMOLOGICAL CENTRE. BULLETIN. 1964. m. £125. International Seismological Centre, Pipers Lane, Thatcham, Newbury, Berks. RG13 4NS, England. TEL 0635-61022. FAX 0635-72351.
Description: Covers seismology.

551.22 UK ISSN 0034-334X
QE532 CODEN: RCEABK
INTERNATIONAL SEISMOLOGICAL CENTRE. REGIONAL CATALOGUE OF EARTHQUAKES. 1964. s-a. £50. International Seismological Centre, Pipers Lane, Thatcham, Newbury, Berks. RG13 4NS, England. TEL 0635-61022. FAX 0635-72351.

INTERNATIONAL UNION OF GEODESY AND GEOPHYSICS. MONOGRAPH. see GEOGRAPHY

551 910 BE ISSN 0074-9419
INTERNATIONAL UNION OF GEODESY AND GEOPHYSICS. PROCEEDINGS OF THE GENERAL ASSEMBLY. (Text in English, French) 1921. quadrennial. $20. International Union of Geodesy and Geophysics, c/o Observatoire Royal de Belgique, Ave. Circulaire 3, 1180 Brussels, Belgium. TEL 32-2-3730267. FAX 32-2-3749822. circ. 3,500. **Document type:** proceedings.

538 RU ISSN 0202-7275
QC811 CODEN: ITGAEJ
ITOGI NAUKI I TEKHNIKI: GEOMAGNETIZM I VYSOKIE SLOI ATMOSFERY. irreg., vol.8, 1986. price varies. Vsesoyuznyi Institut Nauchno-Tekhnicheskoi Informatsii (VINITI), Ul. Baltiiskaya, 14, Moscow A-219, Russia. illus.
—BLDSC (0047.750000).

IZVESTIYA VYSSHIKH UCHEBNYKH ZAVEDENII. SERIYA GEOLOGIYA I RAZVEDKA. see EARTH SCIENCES — Geology

551 US
J G R: JOURNAL OF GEOPHYSICAL RESEARCH: OCEANS. 1896. m. $1950 to non-members (includes J G R: Atmospheres) (foreign $2026); members $77 (foreign $107); students $39 (foreign $69. American Geophysical Union, 2000 Florida Ave., N.W., Washington, DC 20009. TEL 202-462-6900. FAX 202-328-0566. TELEX 710-822-9300. abstr.; bibl.; charts; illus.; index, cum.index: 1959-1965, 1966-1972. (also avail. in microform from AGU; reprint service avail. from ISI) **Indexed:** Appl.Mech.Rev., Biol.Abstr., Chem.Abstr., Eng.Ind., Environ.Abstr., Excerp.Med., GeoRef., INIS Atomind., Mass Spectr.Bull., Meteor.& Geoastrophys.Abstr., Ocean.Abstr., Pollut.Abstr., Sci.Abstr., Sel.Water Res.Abstr. **Document type:** academic/scholarly publication.
—CCC.
Formerly: J G R: Journal of Geophysical Research: Oceans and Atmospheres. C - D (ISSN 0196-2256)
Description: Covers the physics, chemistry, and biology of the air-sea interface, the ocean, and the marine boundary layer.
Refereed Serial

551 US
J G R: JOURNAL OF GEOPHYSICAL RESEARCH: SOLID EARTH. m. $1570 to non-members (foreign $1624); members $143 (foreign $197); students $72 (foreign $126). American Geophysical Union, 2000 Florida Ave., N.W., Washington, DC 20009. TEL 202-462-6900. FAX 202-328-0566. TELEX 710-822-9300. (also avail. in microform from AGU) **Indexed:** Art & Archaeol.Tech.Abstr., GeoRef., INIS Atomind., Mass Spectr.Bull., Meteor.& Geoastrophys.Abstr., Sci.Abstr., Sel.Water Res.Abstr. **Document type:** academic/scholarly publication.
—CCC.
Supersedes in part (in 1991): J G R: Journal of Geophysical Research: Solid Earth and Planets; **Formerly:** J G R: Journal of Geophysical Research: Solid Planets. B (ISSN 0196-6936)
Refereed Serial

551 US ISSN 0196-6928
J G R: JOURNAL OF GEOPHYSICAL RESEARCH: SPACE PHYSICS. m. $1435 to non-members (foreign $1481); members $126 (foreign $172); students $63 (foreign $109). American Geophysical Union, 2000 Florida Ave., N.W., Washington, DC 20009. TEL 202-462-6900. FAX 202-328-0566. TELEX 710-822-9300. (also avail. in microform from AGU) **Indexed:** Chem.Abstr., INIS Atomind., Mass Spectr.Bull., Meteor.& Geoastrophys.Abstr., Sci.Abstr. **Document type:** academic/scholarly publication.
—CCC.
Description: Covers aeronomy, terrestrial and planetary magnetospheric physics, external solar and interplanetary physics, cosmic rays, comets, and active space plasma experimentation.

551 JA
JAPAN METEOROLOGICAL AGENCY. REPORT OF MAGNETIC PULSATIONS. (Text in English) 1976. a. Japan Meteorological Agency, Kakioka Magnetic Observatory - Kishocho Chijiki Kansokujo, Kakioka 595, Yasato-cho, Niibari-gun, Ibaraki-ken 315-01, Japan. FAX 02994-3-1154.

551.22 JA ISSN 0446-5059
QE531
JAPAN METEOROLOGICAL AGENCY. SEISMOLOGICAL BULLETIN/JISHIN GEPPO. (Text in English) 1951. m. $347. Japan Meteorological Agency - Kishocho, 3-4, Otemachi 1-chome, Chiyoda-ku, Tokyo 100, Japan. stat. **Document type:** bulletin.

511.22
JAPAN UNIVERSITY NETWORK EARTHQUAKE CATALOG/KOKURITSU DAIGAKU KANSOKUMO JISHIN KATAROGU. (Text in English, Japanese) s-a. Tokyo Daigaku, Jishin Kenkyujo - University of Tokyo, Earthquake Research Institute, 1-1, Yayoi 1-chome, Bunkyo-ku, Tokyo 113, Japan. **Document type:** catalog.

551.22 JA ISSN 0037-1114
CODEN: ZIZIA6
JISHIN/SEISMOLOGICAL SOCIETY OF JAPAN. JOURNAL. (Text in English, Japanese; summaries in English) 1948. q. $20. Jishin Gakkai - Seismological Society of Japan, Tokyo Daigaku Jishin Kenkyjo, 1-1, Yayoi 1-chome, Bunkyo-ku, Tokyo 113, Japan. abstr.; index. **Indexed:** Abstr.J.Earthq.Eng., GeoRef., JTA, Sci.Abstr.
—UnCover.

551.22 JA ISSN 0916-2720
JISHIN GAKKAI NYUSU RETA/SEISMOLOGICAL SOCIETY OF JAPAN. NEWSLETTER. (Text in Japanese) 1989. b-m. Jishin Gakkai, Tokyo Daigaku Jishin Kenkyujo, 1-1, Yayoi 1-chome, Bunkyo-ku, Tokyo 113, Japan. **Document type:** newsletter.

551.22 JA ISSN 0912-5779
JISHIN JANARU/ASSOCIATION FOR THE DEVELOPMENT OF EARTHQUAKE PREDICTION. JOURNAL. (Text in Japanese) 1986. s-a. Jishin Yochi Sogo Kenkyu Shinkokai, 3, Kanda Mitoshirocho, Chiyoda-ku, Tokyo 101, Japan.

551.22 JA ISSN 0289-2723
JISHIN KANSOKU HOKOKU/MATSUSHIRO SEISMOLOGICAL OBSERVATORY. SEISMOLOGICAL BULLETIN. (Text in English) 1973. s-a. Kishocho, Jishin Kansokujo - Japan Meteorological Agency, Matsushiro Seismological Observatory, 3511, Nishijo, Matsushiro-cho, Nagano-shi, Nagano-ken 381-12, Japan.

551.22 JA
JISHIN KOGAKU KENKYU HAPPOYOKAI KOEN GAIYO/JAPAN SOCIETY OF CIVIL ENGINEERS. EARTHQUAKE ENGINEERING SYMPOSIUM. PROCEEDIGS. (Text in Japanese) 1968. biennial. Doboku Gakkai, Taishin Kogaku Iinkai - Japan Society of Civil Engineers, Earthquake Engineering Committee, Yotsuya 1-chome, Shinjuku-ku, Tokyo 160, Japan. **Document type:** proceedings.

551.22 JA
JISHIN KOGAKU SHINKOKAI NYUSU/JAPAN SOCIETY FOR EARTHQUAKE ENGINEERING PROMOTION NEWS. (Text in Japanese) 1962. bi-m. 2000 Yen per no. Shinsai Yobo Kyokai - Association for Earthquake Disaster Prevention, Kenchiku Kaikan, 26-20, Shiba 5-chome, Minato-ku, Tokyo 108, Japan.

551.22 368 JA
JISHIN SAIGAI YOSOKU NO KENKYU/SEISMICITY AND SEISMIC HAZARD. (Text in Japanese; summaries in English) 1984. a. Songai Hoken Ryoritsu Santeikai - Fire and Marine Insurance Rating Association of Japan, 7, Kanda Mitoshiro-cho, Chiyoda-ku, Tokyo 101, Japan.

551.22 JA ISSN 0386-0086
JISHIN TO YOCHI/EARTHQUAKE AND PREDICTION. (Text in Japanese) 1974. m. 200 Yen per no. Nihon Jishin Yochi Kurabu - Japan Earthquake Prediction Club, 2573, Tsuhahara, Minamiashigara-shi, Kanagawa-ken 250-01, Japan.

551.22 JA
JISHIN YOCHI RENRAKUKAI KAIHO/COORDINATING COMMITTEE FOR EARTHQUAKE PREDICTION. REPORT. (Text in Japanese) 1969. s-a. Kokudo Chiriin - Geographical Survey Institute, 1, Kitasato, Tsukuba-shi, Ibaraki-ken 305, Japan.

551 JA ISSN 0285-2926
QE599.A1 CODEN: JISUD4
JISUBERI/LANDSLIDES. (Text in Japanese, English) 1963. q. Jisuberi Gakkai - Japan Landslide Society, 30-7, Shinbashi 5-chome, Minato-ku, Tokyo 105, Japan. Ed. Shinichi Yamaguchi. circ. 2,300. (back issues avail.)
—CASDDS.

551.2 JA
JISUBERI KYUKEISHACHI NO CHOSA TO TAISAKU KOZA/INVESTIGATION OF LANDSLIDE AND THEIR CONTROL. (Text in Japanese) a. Zenkoku Jisuberi Gake Kuzure Taisaku Kyogikai - National Conference of Landslide and Slope Fall Control, Niigataken Dobokubu Saboka, 4-1, Shinkocho, Niigata-shi, Niigata-ken 950, Japan.

JOEKULL. see EARTH SCIENCES — Geology

622.15 NE ISSN 0926-9851
TN1.A1 CODEN: JAGPEA
JOURNAL OF APPLIED GEOPHYSICS. (Text in English, French and German) 1963. 8/yr. (in 2 vols.; 4 nos./vol.) fl.772($417) (effective 1994). Elsevier Science B.V., P.O. Box 211, 1000 AE Amsterdam, Netherlands. TEL 31-20-5803911. FAX 31-20-5803598. TELEX 18582 ESPA NL. (Subscr. in U.S. and Canada to: Elsevier Science Inc., Box 882, Madison Sq. Sta., New York, NY 10159-0882. TEL 212-989-5800. FAX 212-633-3990) Eds. T.E. Owen, D.S. Parasnis. adv.; bk.rev.; bibl.; charts; illus.; index. (also avail. in microform from UMI; reprint service avail. from SWZ) **Indexed:** AESIS, Br.Geol.Lit., Bull.Signal., Chem.Abstr., Curr.Cont., E&P Hlth. (1993-), Eng.Ind., Excerp.Med., Gas Process.& Ppl. (1993-), GeoRef., Geotech.Abstr., Ind.Sci.Rev., INIS Atomind., Off.Tech. (1993-), Petrol.Abstr. (1965-), Sci.Abstr., Sci.Cit.Ind. **Document type:** academic/scholarly publication.
—BLDSC (4942.614000); EI; Faxon; UnCover; SWETS. **CCC.**
Formerly (until vol.29, 1992): Geoexploration (ISSN 0016-7142)
Description: Publishes papers on a wide variety of applied geophysical topics such as environmental, geotechnical engineering and hydrological geophysics, mining and petroleum geophysics and petrophysics.
Refereed Serial

551 UK ISSN 0021-9169
QC801 CODEN: JATPA3
JOURNAL OF ATMOSPHERIC AND TERRESTRIAL PHYSICS. 1950. 14/yr. £810($1245) (effective 1994). Elsevier Science Ltd., Pergamon, P.O. Box 800, Kidlington, Oxford OX5 1DX, England. TEL 44-865-843000. FAX 44-865-843010. (Subscr. in U.S. and Canada to: Elsevier Science, 660 White Plains Rd., Tarrytown, NY 10591-5153. TEL 914-524-9200. FAX 914-333-2444) Ed. Michael J. Rycroft. adv.: B&W page $550, color page $1350. bk.rev. circ. 1,350. (also avail. in microfilm from UMI; reprint service avail. from UMI) **Indexed:** Chem.Abstr., Curr.Cont., Deep Sea Res.& Oceanogr.Abstr., GeoRef., Ind.Sci.Rev., INIS Atomind., Int.Aerosp.Abstr., Meteor.& Geoastrophys.Abstr., Phys.Ber., Sci.Abstr., Sci.Cit.Ind. **Document type:** academic/scholarly publication.
—BLDSC (4948.000000); Faxon; UnCover; SWETS; UMI; CASDDS. **CCC.**
Refereed Serial

551.2 CC ISSN 1002-1604
▼**JOURNAL OF EARTHQUAKE PREDICTION RESEARCH.** (Text in English) 1992. q. $200 (effective 1994). State Seismological Bureau, National Center for Seismic Data and Information, 56 Sanlihe Rd., Beijing 100045, People's Republic of China. TEL 861-8530337. (Co-sponsor: Russian Academy of Sciences) Eds. Guoming Zhang, V.N. Strakhov. circ. 190. **Document type:** academic/scholarly publication.
Description: Covers the advances in earthquake prediction research in China, Russia and other countries. Also covers geophysics, earthquake engineering and countermeasurements for disaster reduction.

551 551.9 UK ISSN 0264-3707
QE500 CODEN: JOGEE7
JOURNAL OF GEODYNAMICS. (Text and summaries in English) 1984. 8/yr. £295($455) (effective 1994). Elsevier Science Ltd., Pergamon, P.O. Box 800, Kidlington, Oxford OX5 1DX, England. TEL 44-865-843000. FAX 44-865-843010. (Subscr. in U.S. and Canada to: Elsevier Science, 660 White Plains Rd., Tarrytown, NY 10591-5153. TEL 914-524-9200. FAX 914-333-2444) Eds. Nicholas Rast, Wolf Jacoby. adv.; index. circ. 900. (also avail. in microform from UMI; back issues avail.) **Indexed:** AESIS, Deep Sea Res.& Oceanogr.Abstr., Geosci.Doc., Int.Aerosp.Abstr., Sci.Abstr., SSCI. **Document type:** academic/scholarly publication.
—BLDSC (4991.950000); Faxon; UnCover; SWETS; UMI. **CCC.**
Description: Publishes research on the dynamics and the dynamic history of the earth, with emphasis on deep-seated foundations of geological phenomena, including investigations of movements and deformations, past and present, of the lithosphere and all relevant properties of the earth's interior.
Refereed Serial

JOURNAL OF GEOMAGNETISM AND GEOELECTRICITY.
see *EARTH SCIENCES — Geology*

551 526 JA ISSN 0022-3743
QE500 CODEN: JPHEAF
JOURNAL OF PHYSICS OF THE EARTH. (Text in English) 1953. bi-m. $115. (Jishin Gakkai - Seismological Society of Japan) Center for Academic Publications Japan, 2-4-16 Yayoi, Bunkyo-ku, Tokyo 113, Japan. TEL 3817-5825. FAX 3817-5830. (Dist. by: Business Center for Academic Societies Japan, 5-16-9 Honkomagome, Bunkyo-ku, Tokyo 113, Japan) (Co-sponsors: Volcanological Society of Japan, Geodetic Society of Japan) adv.; illus.; mkt.; cum.index every 13 yrs. circ. 800. **Indexed:** Abstr.J.Earthq.Eng., Appl.Mech.Rev., Chem.Abstr., Curr.Cont., Deep Sea Res.& Oceanogr.Abstr., Geo.Abstr., GeoRef., INIS Atomind., Phys.Ber., Sci.Abstr. **Document type:** academic/scholarly publication.
—BLDSC (5037.000000); Faxon; UnCover; SWETS; CASDDS.

551.2 NE ISSN 0377-0273
QE521.5 CODEN: JVGRDQ
JOURNAL OF VOLCANOLOGY AND GEOTHERMAL RESEARCH; an international journal on the geophysical, geochemical, petrological and economic aspects of geothermal and volcanological research. (Text in English) 1976. 24/yr. (in 6 vols.; 4 nos./vol.). fl.2136($1155) (effective 1994). Elsevier Science B.V., P.O. Box 211, 1000 AE Amsterdam, Netherlands. TEL 31-20-5803911. FAX 31-20-5803598. TELEX 18582 ESPA NL. (Subscr. in N. America to: Elsevier Science Inc., Box 882, Madison Sq. Sta., New York, NY 10159. TEL 212-989-5800. FAX 212-633-3990) Ed.Bd. adv.; bk.rev. (also avail. in microform from UMI; reprint service avail. from ISI,SWZ) **Indexed:** Chem.Abstr., Curr.Cont., Deep Sea Res.& Oceanogr.Abstr., E&P Hlth. (1993-), Gas Process.& Ppl. (1993-), Geo.Abstr., GeoRef., Ind.Sci.Rev., INIS Atomind., Int.Aerosp.Abstr., Mineral.Abstr., Off.Tech. (1993-), Petrol.Abstr. (1981-), Phys.Ber., Risk Abstr. **Document type:** academic/scholarly publication.
—BLDSC (5072.513000); EI; Faxon; UnCover; SWETS; CASDDS. **CCC.**
Description: Provides volcanologists, petrologists and geochemists with a source of information and an outlet for rapid publication of papers in the field.
Refereed Serial

551 JA ISSN 0914-5753
QB275
KAIJO HOANCHO. SUIROBU KANSOKU HOKOKU. EISEI SOKUCHI HEN/DATA REPORT OF HYDROGRAPHIC OBSERVATIONS. SERIES OF SATELLITE GEODESY. (Text in English, Japanese; summaries in English) 1988. a. Kaijo Hoancho, Suirobu - Maritime Safety Agency, Hydrographic Department, 3-1, Tsukiji 5-chome, Chuo-ku, Tokyo 104, Japan. **Document type:** government publication.

551.4 JA ISSN 0287-2633
KAIJO HOANCHO. SUIROBU KANSOKU HOKOKU. TENMON SOKUCHI HEN/DATA REPORT OF HYDROGRAPHIC OBSERVATIONS. SERIES OF ASTRONOMY AND GEODESY. (Text in English, Japanese; summaries in English) 1966. a. Kaijo Hoancho, Suirobu - Maritime Safety Agency, Hydrographic Department, 3-1, Tsukiji 5-chome, Chuo-ku, Tokyo 104, Japan. stat. **Document type:** government publication.

551 JA
KAKIOKA MAGNETIC OBSERVATORY. REPORT. GEOELECTRICITY/KISHOCHO CHIJIKI KANSOKUJO HOKOKU. CHIKYU DENKI. (Text in English) a. Kishocho, Chijiki Kansoku - Japan Meteorological Agency, Kakioka Magnetic Observatory, 595, Kakioka, Yasato-cho, Niihari-gun, Ibaraki-ken 315-01, Japan.

551 JA
KAKIOKA MAGNETIC OBSERVATORY. REPORT. GEOMAGNETISM/KISHOCHO CHIJIKI KANSOKUJO HOKOKU. CHIKYU JIKI. (Text in English) a. Kishocho, Chijiki Kansokuro - Japan Meteorological Agency, Kakioka Magnetic Observatory, 595, Kakioka, Yasatocho, Niihari-gun, Ibaraki-ken 351-01, Japan.

KANKYO CHISHITSUGAKU SHINPOJUMU KOEN RONBUNSHU/SYMPOSIUM ON GEO-ENVIRONMENTS. PROCEEDINGS. see *ENVIRONMENTAL STUDIES*

551.2 JA ISSN 0389-9713
KAZAN FUNKA YOCHI RENRAKUKAI KAIHO/COORDINATING COMMITTEE FOR PREDICTION OF VOLCANIC ERUPTION. REPORT. (Text in Japanese) 1974. 3/yr. Kishocho - Japan Meteorological Agency, 3-4, Otemachi 1-chome, Chiyoda-ku, Tokyo 100, Japan.

551.21 JA ISSN 0447-3892
KAZAN HOKOKU/JAPAN METEOROLOGICAL AGENCY. (Text in English, Japanese) 1962. q. $284. Kishocho - Japan Meteorological Agency, 1-3-4 Otemachi, Chiyoda-ku, Tokyo 100, Japan.

551.22 JA
KENSHIN JIHO/QUARTERLY JOURNAL OF SEISMOLOGY. (Text in Japanese; summaries in English) 1925. q. 5768 Yen. (Japan Meteorological Agency - Kishocho) Japan Weather Association, 2-9-2, Kanda-nishikicho, Chiyoda-ku, Tokyo 101, Japan. circ. 535. **Indexed:** Jap.Per.Ind., Sci.Abstr.

551 SW ISSN 0453-9478
KIRUNA GEOPHYSICAL DATA; data summary. (Supplements avail.) (Text in English) 1959. q. SEK 50 per no. (free to qualified institutions and libraries). Swedish Institute of Space Physics, P.O. Box 812, S-981 28 Kiruna, Sweden. TEL 0980-79000. FAX 0980-79050. TELEX 8754-IRF-S. Ed. Sheila Kirkwood. charts. circ. 300.
—BLDSC (5097.640000).

551 JA
KISHO YORAN/GEOPHYSICAL REVIEW. (Text in Japanese) 1890. m. Kishocho - Japan Meteorological Agency, 3-4, Otemachi 1-chome, Chiyoda-ku, Tokyo 100, Japan.

551 JA ISSN 0447-3868
KISHOCHO GIJUTSU HOKOKU/JAPAN METEOROLOGICAL AGENCY. TECHNICAL REPORT. (Text in Japanese) 1960. irreg. price varies. Kishocho - Japan Meteorological Agency, 3-4, Otemachi 1-chome, Chiyoda-ku, Tokyo 100, Japan. circ. 575.

551.22 JA ISSN 0388-7359
KISHOCHO JISHIN KANSOKUJO GIJUTSU HOKOKU/MATSUSHIRO SEISMOLOGICAL OBSERVATORY. TECHNICAL REPORTS. (Text in Japanese; summaries in English) 1980. a. Kishocho, Jishin Kansokujo - Japan Meteorological Agency, Matsushiro Seismological Observatory, 3511, Nishijo, Matsushiro-cho, Nagano-shi, Nagano-ken 381-12, Japan.

551.22 JA
KOCHI UNIVERSITY. EARTHQUAKE OBSERVATORY. SEISMOLOGICAL BULLETIN. (Text in English) 1973. q. Kochi Daigaku, Earthquake Observatory - Kochi University, Asakura, Kochi 780, Japan. stat.

551 JA
KODO RIMOTO SENSHINGU GIJUTSU SHIRYO/TECHNICAL NOTE OF HIGH ALTITUDE REMOTE SENSING. (Text in English, Japanese) 1977. irreg. Shigen Kansoku Kaiseki Senta - Earth Resources Satellite Data Analysis Center, 4-5, Azabudai 2-chome, Minato-ku, Tokyo 106, Japan.

551.2 JA
KOKUSAI JISUBERI NYUSU RETA/LANDSLIDE NEWS. (Editions in English, Japanese) 1987. a. 1000 Yen. Jisuberi Gakkai - Japan Landslide Society, 30-7, Shinbashi 5-chome, Minato-ku, Tokyo 105, Japan.

551 JA ISSN 0910-5395
KYOTO DAIGAKU RIGAKUBU CHIKYU BUTSURIGAKU KENKYU SHISETSU HOKOKU/KYOTO UNIVERSITY. GEOPHYSICAL RESEARCH STATION. REPORTS. (Text in English, Japanese) 1960. biennial. Kyoto Daigaku, Rigakubu, Fuzoku Chikyu Butsurigaku Kenkyu Shisetsu - Kyoto University, Faculty of Science, Geophysical Research Station, 3088-7, Noguchihara, Beppu-shi, Oita-ken 874, Japan.

551.22 JA ISSN 0454-7659
KYOTO UNIVERSITY. ABUYAMA SEISMOLOGICAL OBSERVATORY. SEISMOLOGICAL BULLETIN/KYOTO DAIGAKU ABUYAMA JISHIN KANSOKU HOKOKU. (Text in English) 1952. s-a. free. Kyoto University, Abuyama Seismological Observatory - Kyoto Daigaku Abuyama Jishin Kansokujo, Nasahara, Takatsuki 569, Japan. circ. 300.

EARTH SCIENCES — GEOPHYSICS

551.2   JA   ISSN 0285-0958
KYUSHU CHIIKI KAZAN KIDO KANSOKU JISSHI HOKOKU/REPORT OF VOLCANO OBSERVATION IN KYUSHU DISTRICT. (Text in Japanese) 1981. a. Kishocho, Fukuoka Kanku Kishodai - Japan Meteorological Agency, Fukuoka District Meteorological Observatory, 2-36, Ohori 1-chome, Chuo-ku, Fukuoka-shi, Fukuoka-ken 810, Japan.

551   JA   ISSN 0916-2259
KYUSHU DAIGAKU RIGAKUBU SHIMABARA JISHIN KAZAN KANSOKUJO KENKYU HOKOKU/KYUSHU UNIVERSITY. FACULTY OF SCIENCE. SHIMABARA EARTHQUAKE AND VOLCANO OBSERVATORY. SCIENCES REPORTS. (Text in Japanese; summaries in English) 1965. a. exchange basis. Kyushu Daigaku, Rigakubu, Shimabara Jishin Kazan Kansokujo - Kyushu University, Faculty of Science, Shimabara Earthquake and Volcano Observatory, 5643-29, Shin'yama 2-chome, Shimabara-shi, Nagasaki-ken 855, Japan. TEL 0957-62-6621. FAX 0957-63-0225. Ed. Kazuya Ohta. circ. 500. **Document type:** academic/scholarly publication.
Former titles (until 1985): Kyushu Daigaku Rigakubu Shimabara Kazan Kansokujo Kenkyu Hokoku (ISSN 0385-8286); (until 1971): Kyushu Daigaku Rigakubu Shimabara Kazan Onsen Kenkyujo Kenkyu Hokoku (ISSN 0454-8205)
Description: Contains seismological and volcanological reports, especially concerning Unzen volcano, Kyushu, Japan.

551   US   ISSN 0075-790X
LANDOLT-BOERNSTEIN, ZAHLENWERTE UND FUNKTIONEN AUS NATURWISSENSCHAFTEN UND TECHNIK. NEUE SERIE. GROUP 5: GEOPHYSICS. 1981. irreg. price varies. Springer-Verlag, 175 Fifth Ave., New York, NY 10010. TEL 212-460-1500. FAX 212-473-6272. (Also: Berlin, Heidelberg, Tokyo and Vienna) (reprint service avail. from ISI) **Document type:** academic/scholarly publication.

551   US   ISSN 1070-485X
TN269
THE LEADING EDGE. 1982. m. $70 (foreign $85). Society of Exploration Geophysicists, Box 702740, Tulsa, OK 74170-2740. TEL 918-493-3516. Ed. Dean Clark. adv. contact: David Yowell. charts; illus.; stat.; index. circ. 20,205. **Indexed:** AESIS, E&P Hlth. (1993-), Gas Process.& Ppl. (1993-), Off.Tech. (1993-), Petrol.Abstr. (1984-). **Document type:** academic/scholarly publication.
—BLDSC (5162.872500); Faxon; UnCover; SWETS. **CCC.**
Formerly: Geophysics: The Leading Edge of Exploration (ISSN 0732-989X)

551   HU   ISSN 0025-0120
QC801.M3   CODEN: MAGFA9
MAGYAR GEOFIZIKA. (Text in Hungarian; summaries in English and Russian) 1960. bi-m. $30. (Magyar Geofizikusok Egyesulete - Association of Hungarian Geophysicists) Lapkiado Vallalat, Lenin korut 9-11, 1073 Budapest 7, Hungary. TEL 222-408. (Subscr. to: Kultura, Box 149, H-1389 Budapest, Hungary) Ed. Karoly Sebestyen. adv.; bk.rev. circ. 850. **Indexed:** GeoRef., INIS Atomind., Sci.Abstr.

551   GW   ISSN 0340-8825
                                      CODEN: MANGEH
MANUSCRIPTA GEODAETICA. 1978. 6/yr. DM.298($186) Springer-Verlag, Heidelberger Platz 3, 14197 Berlin, Germany. TEL 030-8207-1. FAX 030-8214091. (Subscr. in N. America to: Springer-Verlag New York, Inc., 44 Hartz Way, Secaucus, NJ 07096-2491. TEL 201-348-4033. FAX 201-348-4505) Ed. P. Vanicek, C. Tscherning. (also avail. in microform from UMI; back issues avail.; reprint service avail. from ISI) **Document type:** academic/scholarly publication.
—BLDSC (5368.275000); SWETS; UMI. **CCC.**
Description: Publishes articles of a fundamental nature in geodesy and geodynamics, focusing on physical and mathematical theories and numerical methods.

MARINE GEOPHYSICAL RESEARCHES; an international journal for the study of the earth beneath the sea. see *EARTH SCIENCES — Oceanography*

551.4   RU   ISSN 0130-3686
GB2401
MATERIALY GLYATSIOLOGICHESKIKH ISSLEDOVANII/DATA OF GLACIOLOGICAL STUDIES. (Text in Russian; abstracts in English) 1961. 3/yr. exchange basis. Rossiiskaya Akademiya Nauk, Geofizicheskii Komitet - Russian Academy of Sciences, Geophysical Committee, Molodezhnaya ul., 3, Moscow GSP-1, Russia. (Co-sponsor: Russian Academy of Sciences, Institute of Geography) Ed. V.M. Kotlyakov. circ. 950. **Document type:** academic/scholarly publication.
—BLDSC (0102.260000).

551 510   NE   ISSN 0169-295X
MATHEMATICAL APPROACHES TO GEOPHYSICS. 1983. irreg. price varies. Kluwer Academic Publishers, Postbus 17, 3300 AA Dordrecht, Netherlands. TEL 31-78-334911. FAX 31-78-334254. TELEX 29245 KAPG NL. (Dist. by: Kluwer Academic Publishers Group, P.O. Box 322, 3300 AH Dordrecht, Netherlands. TEL 31-78-524400. FAX 31-78-524474; N. America dist. addr.: Box 358, Accord Sta., Hingham, MA 02018-0358. TEL 617-871-6600. FAX 617-871-6528) **Indexed:** Math.R. **Document type:** monographic series.
Refereed Serial

551   JA   ISSN 0385-2016
MATSUSHIRO GUNPATSU JISHIN SHIRYO HOKOKU/BULLETIN OF DATA AND INFORMATION ON THE MATSUSHIRO EARTHQUAKE SWARM. (Text in Japanese) 1972. a. Matsushiro Jishin Senta - Research Center of Matsushiro Earthquake Swarm, Kishocho Jishin Kansokujo, 3511, Nishijo, Matsushiro-machi, Nagano-shi, Nagano-ken 381-12, Japan.

MAUSAM. see *METEOROLOGY*

MEMORIE DI SCIENZE GEOLOGICHE. see *EARTH SCIENCES — Geology*

METEOROLOGISCHE ZEITSCHRIFT. see *METEOROLOGY*

METHODS IN GEOCHEMISTRY AND GEOPHYSICS. see *EARTH SCIENCES*

MIZUSAWA ASTROGEODYNAMICS OBSERVATORY. ANNUAL REPORT. see *ASTRONOMY*

551   NE   ISSN 0924-6096
MODERN APPROACHES IN GEOPHYSICS. 1985. irreg. price varies. Kluwer Academic Publishers, Postbus 17, 3300 AA Dordrecht, Netherlands. TEL 31-78-334911. FAX 31-78-334254. TELEX 29245 KAPG NL. (Dist. by: Kluwer Academic Publishers Group, P.O. Box 322, 3300 AH Dordrecht, Netherlands. TEL 31-78-524400. FAX 31-76-524474; N. America dist. addr.: Box 358, Accord Sta., Hingham, MA 02018-0358. TEL 617-871-6600. FAX 617-871-6528) **Document type:** monographic series.
Formerly (until 1988): Seismology and Exploration Geophysics (ISSN 0924-6088)
Refereed Serial

551   MZ
MOZAMBIQUE. INSTITUTO NACIONAL DE GEOLOGIA. BOLETIM GEOMAGNETICO PRELIMINAR. 1957. m. free. Instituto Nacional de Geologia, C.P. 217, Maputo, Mozambique. TEL 424031-4. TELEX 6-584 GEOMI MO. stat. (processed) **Document type:** government publication.
Former titles: Mozambique. Instituto Nacional de Geologia. Departamento Geofisica Global. Boletim Geomagnetico Preliminar; Mozambique. Servico Meteorologico. Boletim Geomagnetico Preliminar (ISSN 0006-6001)

551.22   MZ
MOZAMBIQUE. INSTITUTO NACIONAL DE GEOLOGIA. BOLETIM SEISMIQUE. 1957. m. free. Instituto Nacional de Geologia, C.P. 217, Maputo, Mozambique. TEL 424031-4. TELEX 6-584 GEOMI MO. stat. (processed) **Document type:** bulletin, government publication.
Formerly: Mozambique. Servico Meteorologico. Boletim Seismique (ISSN 0006-6095)
Description: Concentrates on seismology.

MOZAMBIQUE. INSTITUTO NACIONAL DE METEOROLOGIA. BOLETIM METEOROLOGICO PARA AGRICULTURA. see *METEOROLOGY*

551.5 520   MZ
MOZAMBIQUE. INSTITUTO NACIONAL DE METEOROLOGIA. INFORMACOES DE CARACTER ASTRONOMICO. 1955. a. 20000 mt($7) (effective 1992). Instituto Nacional de Meteorologia, C.P. 256, Maputo, Mozambique. TEL 491061-3. TELEX SMMMP 6-259. stat. **Document type:** government publication.
Formerly: Mozambique. Servico Meteorologico. Informacoes de Caracter Astronomico.

NATIONAL ASTRONOMICAL OBSERVATORY. MIZUSAWA ASTROGEODYNAMICS OBSERVATORY. MIZUSAWA KANSOKU CENTER. TECHNICAL REPORT. see *ASTRONOMY*

551.22   JA
NATIONAL RESEARCH CENTER FOR DISASTER PREVENTION. SEISMOLOGICAL BULLETIN. (Text in English) 1970. irreg. exchange basis. National Research Center for Disaster Prevention - Kokuritsu Bosai Kagaku Gijutsu Senta, 3-chome, Tennodai, Sakura-mura, Ibaraki-ken 305, Japan. circ. 200.

NEW MEXICO GEOLOGY. see *EARTH SCIENCES — Geology*

NEW ZEALAND JOURNAL OF GEOLOGY AND GEOPHYSICS. see *EARTH SCIENCES — Geology*

551.2   JA   ISSN 0388-6735
NIHON CHINETSU GAKKAISHI/GEOTHERMAL RESEARCH SOCIETY OF JAPAN. JOURNAL. (Text in English, Japanese) 1979. q. Nihon Chinetsu Gakkai, 25-18-602, Hongo 5-chome, Bunkyo-ku, Tokyo 113, Japan.
—BLDSC (4757.501000).

551.22   JA
NIHON JISHIN KOGAKU SHINPOJUMU KOENSHU/JAPAN EARTHQUAKE ENGINEERING SYMPOSIUM. PROCEEDINGS. (Text in English, Japanese; summaries in English) 4/yr. membership. Jishin Gakkai - Seismological Society of Japan, Tokyo Daigaku Jishin Kenkyujo, 1-1, Yayoi 1-chome, Bunkyo-ku, Tokyo 113, Japan. **Document type:** proceedings.

551   NO   ISSN 0078-1193
TA710.A1   CODEN: NGIPBZ
NORGES GEOTEKNISKE INSTITUTT. PUBLIKASJON/NORWEGIAN GEOTECHNICAL INSTITUTE. PUBLICATIONS. (Text mainly in English; occasionally French, German and Norwegian) 1953. irreg. (2-5/yr.) price varies. Norges Geotekniske Institutt - Norwegian Geotechnical Institute, P.O. Box 3930 Ullevaal Hageby, N-0806 Oslo, Norway. TEL 47-22-02-30-00. FAX 47-2-230448. TELEX 19787 NGI N. Ed. Kjell Hauge. cum.index: no.1-30. circ. 9,000. **Indexed:** Dok.Str., Geo.Abstr., GeoRef., Geotech.Abstr., HRIS.
—BLDSC (7152.800000); EI.
Description: Results of research and practical work in the field of soil mechanics, engineering geology, rock engineering, snow mechanics, and field instrumentation and performance monitoring.

551 539.7   UK   ISSN 0969-8086
QE501.4.N9   CODEN: NUGEEP
NUCLEAR GEOPHYSICS; a journal of nuclear techniques in the earth and environmental sciences, mineral exploration, mining and process control. 1987. 6/yr. £339($520) (effective 1994). Elsevier Science Ltd., Pergamon, P.O. Box 800, Kidlington, Oxford OX5 1DX, England. TEL 44-865-843000. FAX 44-865-843010. (Subscr. in U.S. and Canada to: Elsevier Science, 660 White Plains Rd., Tarrytown, NY 10591-5153. TEL 914-524-9200. FAX 914-333-2444) Ed. Colin G. Clayton. (also avail. in microfilm from UMI; back issues avail.) **Indexed:** Energy Info.Abstr. **Document type:** academic/scholarly publication.
—BLDSC (6180.783000); ADONIS; EI; Faxon; SWETS; CASDDS. **CCC.**
Formerly (until 1993): International Journal of Radiation Applications and Instrumentation. Part E: Nuclear Geophysics (ISSN 0886-0130)
Description: Original scientific and technological papers on the development and application of nuclear techniques in the geosciences and in those areas of economic activity involved in the use of earth materials.
Refereed Serial

OBSERVATORIO NACIONAL RIO DE JANEIRO. PUBLICACOES. see *ASTRONOMY*

EARTH SCIENCES — GEOPHYSICS

551.2 CR
OBSERVATORIO VULCANOLOGICO DE ARENAL. BOLETIN. 1988. irreg. Instituto Costarricense de Electricidad (ICE), Direccion de Planificacion Electrica, Departamento de Geologia, Apdo. 10032, San Jose, Costa Rica.

OESTERREICHISCHE BEITRAEGE ZU METEOROLOGIE UND GEOPHYSIK. see *METEOROLOGY*

551 SG
OFFICE DE LA RECHERCHE SCIENTIFIQUE ET TECHNIQUE OUTRE-MER DE M'BOUR. CENTRE DE GEOPHYSIQUE. BULLETIN SEISMIQUE.* (Text in French) 1974. m. Office de la Recherche Scientifique et Technique Outre-Mer de M'Bour, Centre de Geophysique, B.P. 50, M'Bour, Senegal. charts; stat.

OHIO STATE UNIVERSITY. BYRD POLAR RESEARCH CENTER. CONTRIBUTION SERIES. see *SCIENCES: COMPREHENSIVE WORKS*

OHIO STATE UNIVERSITY. BYRD POLAR RESEARCH CENTER. MISCELLANEOUS SERIES. see *SCIENCES: COMPREHENSIVE WORKS*

OHIO STATE UNIVERSITY. BYRD POLAR RESEARCH CENTER. REPORT SERIES. see *SCIENCES: COMPREHENSIVE WORKS*

OILFIELD REVIEW. see *PETROLEUM AND GAS*

P A S C A L F 45: TECTONIQUE, GEOPHYSIQUE INTERNE. see *EARTH SCIENCES — Abstracting, Bibliographies, Statistics*

551.05 BO
PAN AMERICAN INSTITUTE OF GEOGRAPHY AND HISTORY. COMMISSION ON GEOPHYSICS. BOLETIN. irreg. Instituto Panamericano de Geografia e Historia, Casilla 6003, La Paz, Bolivia.

PAPERS IN METEOROLOGY AND GEOPHYSICS. see *METEOROLOGY*

551 NE ISSN 0031-9201
QE500 CODEN: PEPIAM
PHYSICS OF THE EARTH AND PLANETARY INTERIORS. 1967. 24/yr. (in 6 vols.; 4 nos./vol.). fl.2436($1317) (effective 1994). Elsevier Science B.V., P.O. Box 211, 1000 AE Amsterdam, Netherlands. TEL 31-20-5803911. FAX 31-20-5803598. TELEX 18582 ESPA NL. (Subscr. in N. America to: Elsevier Science Inc., Box 882, Madison Sq. Sta., New York, NY 10159-0882. TEL 212-989-5800. FAX 212-633-3990) Ed.Bd. (also avail. in microform from UMI; reprint service avail. from SWZ) **Indexed:** Bull.Signal., Chem.Abstr., Curr.Cont., Deep Sea Res.& Oceanogr.Abstr., Geo.Abstr., GeoRef., Int.Aerosp.Abstr., Petrol.Abstr., Phys.Ber., Risk Abstr., Sci.Abstr., So.Pac.Per.Ind. **Document type:** academic/scholarly publication.
—BLDSC (6478.525000); Faxon; UnCover; SWETS; CASDDS. **CCC.**
Description: Devoted to observational and experimental studies of the earth and planetary interiors and their theoretical interpretation by the physical sciences.
Refereed Serial

551 PL ISSN 0137-2440
POLISH ACADEMY OF SCIENCES. INSTITUTE OF GEOPHYSICS. PUBLICATIONS. SERIES A: PHYSICS OF THE EARTH'S INTERIOR. Key Title: Publications of the Institute of Geophysics. A: Physics of the Earth's Interior. (Text in English; summaries in English and Polish) 1963. irreg. price varies. Polska Akademia Nauk, Instytut Geofizyki - Polish Academy of Sciences, Institute of Geophysics, Ul. Ksiecia Janusza 64, 01-452 Warsaw, Poland. Ed. Roman Teisseyre. **Indexed:** GeoRef. **Document type:** academic/scholarly publication.
Supersedes in part: Polska Akademia Nauk. Instytut Geofizyki. Materialy i Prace (ISSN 0079-3574)

551 PL ISSN 0138-0109
POLISH ACADEMY OF SCIENCES. INSTITUTE OF GEOPHYSICS. PUBLICATIONS. SERIES B: SEISMOLOGY. Key Title: Publications of the Institute of Geophysics. B: Seismology. (Text in English; summaries in English and Polish) irreg. price varies. Polska Akademia Nauk, Instytut Geofizyki - Polish Academy of Sciences, Institute of Geophysics, Ul. Ksiecia Janusza 64, 01-452 Warsaw, Poland. **Document type:** academic/scholarly publication.
—UnCover.
Supersedes in part: Polska Akademia Nauk. Instytut Geofizyki. Materialy i Prace (ISSN 0079-3574)

551 PL ISSN 0138-0117
QC830.H39
POLISH ACADEMY OF SCIENCES. INSTITUTE OF GEOPHYSICS. PUBLICATIONS. SERIES C: GEOMAGNETISM. Key Title: Publications of the Institute of Geophysics. C: Geomagnetism. (Text and summaries in English and Polish) irreg. price varies. Polska Akademia Nauk, Instytut Geofizyki - Polish Academy of Sciences, Institute of Geophysics, Ul. Ksiecia Janusza 64, 01-452 Warsaw, Poland. **Document type:** academic/scholarly publication.
Supersedes in part: Polska Akademia Nauk. Instytut Geofizyki. Materialy i Prace (ISSN 0079-3574)

551 PL ISSN 0138-0125
CODEN: PIGPDT
POLISH ACADEMY OF SCIENCES. INSTITUTE OF GEOPHYSICS. PUBLICATIONS. SERIES D: PHYSICS OF THE ATMOSPHERE. Key Title: Publications of the Institute of Geophysics. D: Physics of the Atmosphere. (Text in English and French; summaries in English and Polish) irreg. price varies. Polska Akademia Nauk, Instytut Geofizyki - Polish Academy of Sciences, Institute of Geophysics, Ul. Ksiecia Janusza 64, 01-452 Warsaw, Poland. **Document type:** academic/scholarly publication.
—CASDDS.
Supersedes in part: Polska Akademia Nauk. Instytut Geofizyki. Materialy i Prace (ISSN 0079-3574)

551 PL ISSN 0138-0141
POLISH ACADEMY OF SCIENCES. INSTITUTE OF GEOPHYSICS. PUBLICATIONS. SERIES F: PLANETARY GEODESY. Key Title: Publications of the Institute of Geophysics. F: Planetary Geodesy. (Text in English; summaries in English and Polish) irreg. price varies. Polska Akademia Nauk, Instytut Geofizyki - Polish Academy of Sciences, Institute of Geophysics, Ul. Ksiecia Janusza 64, 01-452 Warsaw, Poland. **Document type:** academic/scholarly publication.
Supersedes in part: Polska Akademia Nauk. Instytut Geofizyki. Materialy i Prace (ISSN 0079-3574)

551 PL ISSN 0138-015X
CODEN: PGPMEI
POLISH ACADEMY OF SCIENCES. INSTITUTE OF GEOPHYSICS. PUBLICATIONS. SERIES M: MISCELLANEA. Key Title: Publications of the Institute of Geophysics. M: Miscellanea. (Text and summaries in English and Polish) irreg. price varies. Polska Akademia Nauk, Instytut Geofizyki - Polish Academy of Sciences, Institute of Geophysics, Ul. Ksiecia Janusza 64, 01-452 Warsaw, Poland. **Document type:** academic/scholarly publication.
—BLDSC (7081.835000).
Supersedes in part: Polska Akademia Nauk. Instytut Geofizyki. Materialy i Prace (ISSN 0079-3574)

551 993 US
POWER PLACES OF CALIFORNIA. 1988. irreg. $10. Louise Lacey, Ed. & Pub., Box 489, Berkeley, CA 94701. TEL 510-232-9865. bk.rev.; abstr.; bibl.; illus. circ. 250. (back issues avail.) **Document type:** newsletter.
Description: Locates specific geomagnetic anomalies producing physical and perceptual responses, and speculates on their implications.

551 RU
PRIKLADNAYA GEOFIZIKA. vol.85, 1977. irreg. 1.00 Rub. per no. (Vsesoyuznyi Nauchno-Issledovatel'skii Institut Geofizicheskikh Metodov Razvedki) Izdatel'stvo Nedra, Pl. Belorusskogo Vokzala, 3, 125047 Moscow, Russia. TEL 250-52-55. Ed. M. Polshkov. abstr. circ. 25,000. **Indexed:** Chem.Abstr., GeoRef., Sci.Abstr.

PROGRESS IN GEOTECHNICAL ENGINEERING. see *EARTH SCIENCES — Geology*

526 PL ISSN 0033-2127
PRZEGLAD GEODEZYJNY. 1924. m. $71.50. (Stowarzyszenie Geodetow Polskich) Wydawnictwo Czasopism i Ksiazek Technicznych SIGMA - NOT, Ul. Ratuszowa 11, P.O. 1004, 00-950 Warsaw, Poland. TEL 48-22-180918. FAX 48-22-192187. TELEX 814550 SIGMA PL. (Dist. by: SIGMA NOT Ltd., Ul. Bartycka 20, 00-716 Warsaw, Poland) bk.rev.; index. circ. 1,400 **Indexed:** Appl.Mech.Rev., Bibl.Cart., Geo.Abstr., Meteor.& Geoastrophys.Abstr.

551 PL ISSN 0033-2135
QC851 CODEN: PRGEAM
PRZEGLAD GEOFIZYCZNY/REVIEW OF GEOPHYSICS. (Text in Polish; summaries in English) 1948. q. $36. (Polskie Towarzystwo Geofizyczne - Polish Society of Geophysics) Wydawnictwo Naukowe P W N, Miodowa 10, CO-251 Warsaw, Poland. Ed. Z. Mikulski. bk.rev.; charts; illus.; maps; index. circ. 860. **Indexed:** Bibl.Cart., Deep Sea Res.& Oceanogr.Abstr., GeoRef., Meteor.& Geoastrophys.Abstr.
Formerly (until 1956): Przeglad Meteorologiczny i Hydrologiczny.

PRZEGLAD GEOLOGICZNY/GEOLOGICAL REVIEW. see *EARTH SCIENCES — Geology*

551.22 FI ISSN 0079-774X
PUBLICATIONS IN SEISMOLOGY.* (Text in English; occasionally in Finnish) 1960. irreg. exchange basis. Helsingin Yliopisto, Seismologian Laitos - University of Helsinki, Institute of Seismology, Et. Hesperiankatu 4, Helsinki 10, Finland. Ed. Ekjo Vesanen.

551 SZ ISSN 0033-4553
QC801 CODEN: PAGYAV
PURE AND APPLIED GEOPHYSICS. (Text in English, French, and German) 1939. 8/yr. 1380 SFr.($940) Birkhaeuser Verlag, P.O. Box 133, CH-4010 Basel, Switzerland. TEL 061-2717400. FAX 061-2717656. TELEX 963475-BIRKH-CH. (Dist. in N. America by: Springer-Verlag, Mercedes Distribution Center, 160 Imlay St., Brooklyn, NY 11231, USA) Ed. H. Kanamori. bk.rev.; illus.; index. **Indexed:** AESIS, Chem.Abstr., Curr.Cont., Deep Sea Res.& Oceanogr.Abstr., Excerp.Med., Geo.Abstr., GeoRef., Int.Aerosp.Abstr., Meteor.& Geoastrophys.Abstr., Petrol.Abstr., Phys.Ber., Sci.Abstr. **Document type:** academic/scholarly publication.
—BLDSC (7161.400000); Faxon; UnCover; SWETS; UMI; CASDDS. **CCC.**
Formerly: Geofisica.

QUEENSLAND MUSEUM, BRISBANE. MEMOIRS. see *MUSEUMS AND ART GALLERIES*

551 537.534 US ISSN 0048-6604
QC851 CODEN: RASCAD
RADIO SCIENCE. 1928. bi-m. $265 to non-members (foreign $275); members $46 (foreign $56); students $23 (foreign $33). American Geophysical Union, 2000 Florida Ave., N.W., Washington, DC 20009. TEL 202-462-6900. FAX 202-328-0566. TELEX 710-822-9300. Ed. David Chang. charts; illus.; index. (also avail. in microform from AGU,MIM,UMI; reprint service avail. from ISI,UMI) **Indexed:** A.S.& T Ind., Chem.Abstr., Curr.Cont., Eng.Ind., Excerp.Med., GeoRef., INSPEC, Int.Aerosp.Abstr., Meteor.& Geoastrophys.Abstr., Petrol.Abstr., Phys.Ber., Sci.Abstr., Tel.Abstr.
—BLDSC (7232.999500); EI; Faxon; UnCover; SWETS; CASDDS. **CCC.**
Former titles (until 1965): National Bureau of Standards. Journal of Research. D, Radio Science (ISSN 0502-2558); (until 1963): National Bureau of Standards. Journal of Research. D, Radio Propagation (ISSN 1060-1783); **Superseded in part** (in 1959): National Bureau of Standards. Journal of Research (ISSN 0091-0635); Which was formerly (until 1934): Bureau of Standards. Journal of Research (ISSN 0091-1801).
Description: Contains original articles on all aspects of electromagnetic phenomena related to physical problems.
Refereed Serial

EARTH SCIENCES — GEOPHYSICS

551   SP
REAL INSTITUTO Y OBSERVATORIO DE LA ARMADA. OBSERVACIONES METEOROLOGICAS, MAGNETICAS Y SISMICAS. ANALES. (Former issuing body: Instituto y Observatorio de Marina) 1870. a. 500 ptas. Real Instituto y Observatorio de la Armada, Seccion de Geofisica, San Fernando (Cadiz), Spain. circ. 400.
   Formerly: Instituto y Observatorio de Marina. Observaciones Meteorologicas, Magneticas y Sismicas. Anales (ISSN 0080-5955)

551   523.01   US   ISSN 8755-1209
QC801   CODEN: REGEEP
REVIEWS OF GEOPHYSICS. 1963. 4/yr. $220 to non-members (foreign $225); members $25 (foreign $30); students $13 (foreign $18). American Geophysical Union, 2000 Florida Ave., N.W., Washington, DC 20009. TEL 202-462-6900. FAX 202-328-0566. TELEX 710-822-9300. Ed. Alan Chave. abstr.; bibl.; charts; illus.; index. circ. 3,000. (also avail. in microform from AGU; reprint service avail. from ISI) **Indexed:** Cadscan, Chem.Abstr., Curr.Cont., Deep Sea Res.& Oceanogr.Abstr., Environ.Abstr., Excerp.Med., Geo.Abstr., Int.Aerosp.Abstr., Lead Abstr., Math.R., Meteor.& Geoastrophys.Abstr., Phys.Ber., Sci.Abstr., Sel.Water Res.Abstr., Zincscan.
   —BLDSC (7790.760000); Faxon; UnCover; SWETS; CASDDS. **CCC.**
   Former titles: Reviews of Geophysics and Space Physics (ISSN 0034-6853); (until 1969): Reviews of Modern Physics (ISSN 0096-1043); Reviews of Geophysics.
   Description: Covers all areas of earth and space science. Examines recent research and explains the current level of of understanding within a field.
   Refereed Serial

551   SP   ISSN 0034-8279
QC801   CODEN: RGNGA8
REVISTA DE GEOFISICA. (Text in Spanish; summaries in English) 1942. s-a. 3300 ptas. (foreign 4950 ptas.). Consejo Superior de Investigaciones Cientificas (C.S.I.C.), Catedra de Geofisico, Vitruvio, 8, 28006 Madrid, Spain. Ed. Prof. A. Udias. adv.; bk.rev.; abstr.; charts; illus.; index. circ. 2,140. **Indexed:** Appl.Mech.Rev., Chem.Abstr., GeoRef., Ind.SST, Phys.Abstr., Sci.Abstr., Soils & Fert.
   Description: Contains original works on the phenomena and forces that affect the Earth, including geodesy, seismology, geomagnetism, oceanography, and the studies of volcanoes, the atmosphere, and tectonic plates.

551   MX   ISSN 0252-9769
QC801
REVISTA GEOFISICA. 1971. s-a. $34 (C. & N. America $38; S. America & Europe $43; Asia $48). Instituto Panamericano de Geografia e Historia, Ex-Arzobispado 29, Col. Observatorio, Deleg. Miguel Hidalgo, 11860 Mexico, D.F., Mexico. TEL 525-277-5888. FAX 525-271-6271. Ed. Alberto Gieselke. illus. (reprint service avail. from UMI) **Indexed:** Deep Sea Res.& Oceanogr.Abstr., GeoRef. **Document type:** academic/scholarly publication.
   Supersedes (in 1975): Geofisica Panamericana.

551   RM   ISSN 1220-5303
                               CODEN: RRGPA9
REVUE ROUMAINE DE GEOPHYSIQUE. (Text in English, French, German and Russian) 1957. a. 60 lei($32) (Academia Romana) Editura Academiei Romane, Calea Victoriei 125, 79717 Bucharest, Rumania. (Dist. by: Rompresfilatelia, Export-Import Press, Calea Grivitei 64-66, P.O. Box 12-201, 78104 Bucharest) Ed. Sabba Stefanescu. bk.rev.; charts; illus.; index. **Indexed:** GeoRef.
   Formerly (until 1990): Revue Roumaine de Geologie, Geophysique et Geographie. Geophysique (ISSN 0556-8110); Which supersedes in part (in 1963): Revue de Geologie et de Geographie (ISSN 1220-1855)

551.4   RU   ISSN 0568-6245
REZULTATY ISSLEDOVANII PO MEZHDUNARODNYM GEOFIZICHESKIM PROEKTAM. GLYATSIOLOGICHESKIE ISSLEDOVANIYA/RESULTS OF RESEARCHES ON THE INTERNATIONAL GEOPHYSICAL PROJECTS. GLACIOLOGICLA RESEARCHES. 1959. irreg.; latest no.76. exchange basis. Rossiiskaya Akademiya Nauk, Geofizicheskii Komitet - Russian Academy of Sciences, Geophysical Committee, Molodezhnaya ul., 3, Moscow GSP-1, Russia. Eds. V.M. Kotlyakov. adv. circ. 1,000. (also avail. in microfilm) **Indexed:** Ref.Zh.

552.06 551   JA   ISSN 0385-2520
ROCK MAGNETISM AND PALEOGEOPHYSICS. (Text in English) 1973. a. free. Rock Magnetism and Paleogeophysics Research Group in Japan, c/o Department of Geology and Mineralogy, Kyoto University, Kyoto 606-01, Japan. TEL 81-75-7534163. FAX 81-75-7534189. TELEX 5422302 SCIKYUJ. Eds. Masayuki Torii, Yozo Hamano. circ. 500 (controlled). **Indexed:** GeoRef. **Document type:** abstracting/indexing, academic/scholarly publication.
   —BLDSC (8001.775000).

551   RU
QC801
ROSSIISKAYA AKADEMIYA NAUK. IZVESTIYA. SERIYA FIZIKA ZEMLI. English translation: Russian Academy of Sciences. Izvestiya. Physics of the Solid Earth. 1965. m. 53.40 Rub. Izdatel'stvo Nauka, 90 Profsoyuznaya ul., 117864 Moscow, Russia. (Dist. by: Mezdunarodnaya Kniga, ul. Dimitrova D.39, 113095 Moscow, Russia) Ed. V.A. Magnitzkij. bk.rev.; charts; illus.; index. (tabloid format) **Indexed:** Chem.Abstr., INIS Atomind., Math.R., Sci.Abstr. **Document type:** academic/scholarly publication.
   —**CCC.**
   Formerly: Akademiya Nauk S.S.S.R. Izvestiya. Seriya Fizika Zemli (ISSN 0002-3337); Supersedes: Akademiya Nauk S.S.S.R. Izvestiya. Seriya Geofizicheskaya.

551   US
QC801
RUSSIAN ACADEMY OF SCIENCES. IZVESTIYA. PHYSICS OF THE SOLID EARTH. English translation of: Rossiiskaya Akademiya Nauk. Izvestiya. Seriya Fizika Zemli. 1965. 12/yr. $565 for vol.28 to non-members (foreign $575); members $425 (foreign $435). (Russian Academy of Sciences, RU) American Geophysical Union, 2000 Florida Ave., N.W., Washington, DC 20009. TEL 202-462-6900. FAX 202-328-0566. TELEX 710-822-9300. (Germany addr.: Postfach 49, 37189 Katlenburg-Lindau, Germany. TEL 49-5556-1440) bibl.; charts; illus.; index. (reprint service avail. from ISI) **Indexed:** Appl.Mech.Rev., Geo.Abstr., Math.R., Phys.Ber., Sci.Abstr. **Document type:** academic/scholarly publication.
   —Faxon; UnCover; SWETS. **CCC.**
   Formerly: Academy of Sciences of the U S S R. Izvestiya. Physics of the Solid Earth (ISSN 0001-4354)

RUSSIAN GEOLOGY AND GEOPHYSICS. see *EARTH SCIENCES — Geology*

551   XR   ISSN 0036-5319
                               CODEN: SGVUAX
SBORNIK GEOLOGICKYCH VED: UZITA GEOFYZIKA/JOURNAL OF GEOLOGICAL SCIENCES: APPLIED GEOPHYSICS. (Text in Czech, English, German and Russian) 1963. irreg. Cesky Geologicky Ustav, Malostranske nam. 19, 118 21 Prague 1, Czech Republic. (Dist. by: Artia, Ve Smeckach 30, 111 27 Prague 1, Czech Repulbic) (Co-sponsor: Geofyzika, n.p. Brno) Ed. Karel Cidlinsky. charts; illus. circ. 600. (back issues avail.) **Indexed:** Bull.Signal., GeoRef., Ref.Zh.

551   US
SCHOOL OF OCEAN AND EARTH SCIENCE AND TECHNOLOGY. BIENNIAL REPORT. biennial. School of Ocean and Earth Science and Technology, 2525 Correa Rd., Honolulu, HI 96822. TEL 808-956-7059.
   Former titles: Hawaii Institute of Geophysics. Technical Reports and Special Publications; S O E S T Special Publications.

551   GW   ISSN 0934-4365
QE511   CODEN: SCDREC
SCIENTIFIC DRILLING; geophysics, geochemistry, technology. 1989. 6/yr. DM.218($136) Springer-Verlag, Heidelberger Platz 3, 14197 Berlin, Germany. TEL 030-8207-1. FAX 030-8214091. (Subscr. in N. America to: Springer-Verlag New York, Inc., 44 Hartz Way, Secaucus, NJ 07096-2491. TEL 201-348-4033. FAX 201-348-4505) Ed. R.N. Anderson. **Document type:** academic/scholarly publication.
   —BLDSC (8178.495000); UMI; CASDDS. **CCC.**
   Description: Covers geophysics and geochemistry of rocks penetrated by the drillbit, technological developments, as well as disseminating information on new discoveries made in hydrocarbon and mineral exploration wells.

551.22   US   ISSN 0747-9239
QE541   CODEN: SIEEEK
SEISMIC INSTRUMENTS. 1979. irreg., latest vol. 23. $165 per vol. Allerton Press, Inc., 150 Fifth Ave., New York, NY 10011. TEL 212-924-3950. FAX 212-463-9684. **Document type:** academic/scholarly publication.
   —BLDSC (0420.805500). **CCC.**

551.22   CC   ISSN 1003-3246
SEISMOLOGICAL AND GEOMAGNETIC OBSERVATION AND RESEARCH. bi-m. Y39. Seismological Society of China, Observation Technology Committee, c/o Institute of Geophysics, State Seismological Bureau, No. 5, Minzuxueyuan Nanlu, Haidian District, Beijing 100081, China. TEL 86-1-8417744. FAX 86-1-8415372. Ed. Peishan Chen.

551.22   US   ISSN 0895-0695
QE531   CODEN: SRLEEG
SEISMOLOGICAL RESEARCH LETTERS. 1929. q. $15 to individuals (foreign $18); institutions $20 (foreign $25); (effective 1993). Seismological Society of America, 201 Plaza Professional Bldg., El Cerrito, CA 94530-4003. TEL 510-525-5474. FAX 510-525-7204. Ed. Arch Johnston. adv.; charts; illus.; stat. circ. 700. (also avail. in microform from UMI; reprint service avail. from UMI) **Indexed:** Abstr.J.Earthq.Eng., Deep Sea Res.& Oceanogr.Abstr., Eng.Ind., GeoRef., Sci.Abstr. **Document type:** academic/scholarly publication.
   —BLDSC (8227.200000); SWETS.
   Formerly (until vol.57, 1986): Earthquake Notes (ISSN 0012-8287)
   Description: Publishes articles pertaining to eastern North American earthquakes, with emphasis on intarplate seismotectonics and earthquake engineering.
   Refereed Serial

551.22   US   ISSN 0037-1106
QE531   CODEN: BSSAAP
SEISMOLOGICAL SOCIETY OF AMERICA. BULLETIN. 1911. bi-m. $135 (foreign $145) (effective 1994). Seismological Society of America, 201 Plaza Professional Bldg., El Cerrito, CA 94530. TEL 510-525-5474. FAX 510-525-7204. Ed. Charles M. Langston. bk.rev.; bibl.; charts; illus.; index, cum.index. circ. 2,500. (also avail. in microfiche; microfilm; back issues avail.) **Indexed:** A.S.& T.Ind, Abstr.J.Earthq.Eng., Appl.Mech.Rev., Curr.Cont., Deep Sea Res.& Oceanogr.Abstr., GeoRef., Geotech.Abstr., INIS Atomind., Int.Aerosp.Abstr., Math.R., Petrol.Abstr., Risk Abstr., Sci.Abstr., Sci.Cit.Ind., So.Pac.Per.Ind., Soils & Fert. **Document type:** academic/scholarly publication, bulletin.
   —BLDSC (2711.000000); EI; Faxon; UnCover; SWETS.
   Description: Publishes scientific papers on the various aspects of seismology, including investigation of specific earthquakes, theoretical and observational studies of seismic waves and earthquake hazard and risk estimation.

SEPPYO/JAPANESE SOCIETY OF SNOW AND ICE. JOURNAL. see *EARTH SCIENCES*

551.22   CC   ISSN 1000-6265
SHANXI DIZHEN/EARTHQUAKE RESEARCH IN SHANXI. (Text in Chinese) 1973. q. Y1.50 per no. Shanxi Dizhen-ju - Shanxi Seismology Bureau, 10 Xinjian Lu, Taiyuan, Shanxi 030002, People's Republic of China. TEL 222090. Ed. Sun Guoxue. circ. 2,000.

551 333.7   JA
SHIGEN KANSOKU KAISEKI KOKUSAI SHINPOJUMU KOENSHU/EARTH RESOURCES SATELLITE DATA ANALYSIS CENTER. PROCEEDINGS OF INTERNATIONAL SYMPOSIUM. (Text in English, Japanese) 1982. irreg. Shigen Kansoku Kaiseki Senta, 4-5, Azabudai 2-chome, Minato-ku, Tokyo 106, Japan. **Document type:** proceedings.

551.22   CC
SHIJIE DIZHEN YICONG. (Text in Chinese) bi-m. Guojia Dizhenju, Diqiu Wuli Yanjiusuo - National Bureau of Seismology, Institute of Geophysics, Qinghua Donghua, Beijing 100083, People's Republic of China. TEL 2011116. Ed. Chen Yuntai.

EARTH SCIENCES — GEOPHYSICS

551   XO   ISSN 0586-4607
QC801   CODEN: CGISAO
SLOVAK ACADEMY OF SCIENCES. GEOPHYSICAL INSTITUTE. CONTRIBUTIONS. (Text and summaries in English and Russian) 1971. irreg. price varies. Veda, Publishing House of the Slovak Academy of Sciences, Klemensova 19, 814 30 Bratislava, Slovakia. TEL 503 55. (Dist. by: Slovart, Nam. Slobody 6, 817 64 Bratislava, Slovakia) Ed. Melania Bielekova. circ. 600. **Indexed:** GeoRef., Sci.Abstr. **Document type:** academic/scholarly publication.
   Description: Contains geophysical scientific papers concerning the theory of geophysical potential fields, mathematical statistics applied to geodetic and geophysical measurements, analysis of gravity anomalies.

551   XO   ISSN 0139-9349
SLOVAK SEISMOGRAPHIC STATIONS: BRATISLAVA, SROBAROVA, HURBANOVO AND SKALNATE PLESO. BULLETIN. (Text and summaries in English) 1965. a. 17($2.85) (Slovenska Akademia Vied, Geofyzikalny Ustav) Veda, Publishing House of the Slovak Academy of Sciences, Klemensova 19, 814 30 Bratislava, Slovakia. (Dist. by: Slovart, Nam. Slobody 6, 817 64 Bratislava, Slovakia) Ed. Klara Mrazova. abstr. circ. 500. (tabloid format)
   Supersedes in part (in 1966): Czechoslovak Seismological Stations: Pryhonice, Praha, Kaspersk Hory, Cheb, Bratislava, Srobarova, Hurbanovo and Skalnate Pleso. Bulletin (ISSN 0139-9209)

SOCIETA ITALIANA DI FISICA. NUOVO CIMENTO C; geophysics and space physics. see *PHYSICS*

622.15   US
SOCIETY OF EXPLORATION GEOPHYSICISTS. SPECIAL PUBLICATIONS (SYMPOSIA) SERIES. 1947. irreg. price varies. Society of Exploration Geophysicists, Box 702740, Tulsa, OK 74170-2740. TEL 918-493-3516. adv. contact: David Yowell. bk.rev. circ. 19,000. (also avail. in microform) **Document type:** monographic series.
   Refereed Serial

551 624.176   UK   ISSN 0267-7261
TA710.A1
SOIL DYNAMICS AND EARTHQUAKE ENGINEERING. 1981. 6/yr. £334($515) (effective 1994). Elsevier Science Ltd., Oxford Fulfilment Centre, P.O. Box 800, Kidlington, Oxford OX5 1DX, England. TEL 44-865-843000. FAX 44-865-843010. (Subscr. in U.S. and Canada to: Elsevier Science, 660 White Plains Rd., Tarrytown, NY 10591-5153. TEL 914-524-9200. FAX 914-333-2444) Eds. A.S. Cakmak. adv. circ. 500. (back issues avail.) **Indexed:** Comput.& Info.Sys., Curr.Cont., Eng.Ind., Environ.Per.Bibl., Sci.Abstr. **Document type:** academic/scholarly publication.
—BLDSC (8322.225000); EI; Faxon; UnCover; SWETS. **CCC.**
   Formerly (until 1984): International Journal of Soil Dynamics and Earthquake Engineering (ISSN 0261-7277)
   Description: Covers applications of mechanics, mathematics, engineering and other applied sciences to problems in the field of earthquake and geotechnical engineering.
   Refereed Serial

SOLAR-GEOPHYSICAL DATA. PART 1 - PROMPT REPORTS. see *ASTRONOMY*

SOLAR-GEOPHYSICAL DATA: PART 2 - COMPREHENSIVE REPORTS. see *ASTRONOMY*

551   US
SOLAR INDICES BULLETIN. m. $21 (effective 1993). National Oceanic and Atmospheric Administration, National Geophysical Data Center, Mail Code E-GC2, 325 Broadway, Boulder, CO 80303. TEL 303-497-6133. Ed. John McKinnon. **Document type:** government publication, bulletin.
   Description: Contains monthly compilations of sunspot numbers and solar radio flux from radio observatories around the world.

551.527   JA   ISSN 0386-5444
QC801   CODEN: SERJD3
SOLAR TERRESTRIAL ENVIRONMENTAL RESEARCH IN JAPAN. (Text in English) 1949. irreg. (3-4/yr.). Ministry of Education, Science and Culture, Institute of Space and Aeronautical Science - Uchu Kagaku Kenkyujo, 4-6-1 Komaba, Meguro-ku, Tokyo 153, Japan. Ed.Bd. abstr. circ. 1,200. (also avail. in microfilm) **Indexed:** Appl.Mech.Rev., Chem.Abstr., INIS Atomind., Meteor.& Geostrophys.Abstr., Sci.Abstr.
—BLDSC (8327.212000).
   Former titles (until 1976): Report of Ionosphere and Space Research in Japan (ISSN 0034-4672); (until 1959): Report of Ionosphere Research in Japan.

551.22   SA
SOUTH AFRICA. GEOLOGICAL SURVEY. SEISMOLOGIC SERIES. (Text in Afrikaans, English) 1972. irreg., latest no.23. price varies. Geological Survey, Private Bag X112, Pretoria 0001, South Africa. TEL 27-12-841-1911. FAX 27-12-841-1203. TELEX 350286-SAGEO. **Indexed:** GeoRef. **Document type:** government publication.
   Description: Documents natural and man-induced earthquakes occurring in Southern Africa and provides a forum for publishing research work in this field.

551   NE   ISSN 0167-224X
SPELEO NEDERLAND. (Text in Dutch; summaries in English and French) 1971; N.S. 1976. q. fl.20. Nederlandse Vereniging voor Grot- en Karstonderzoek, Binnensingel 4, 3134 NE Vlaardingen, Netherlands. Ed. H.W. de Swart. adv.; bk.rev. circ. 250.

551   SW   ISSN 0348-0755
    CODEN: RGINE8
STATENS GEOTEKNISKA INSTITUT. RAPPORT/SWEDISH GEOTECHNICAL INSTITUTE. REPORT. (Text in English or Swedish; summaries in English) 1977. irreg. (2-3/yr.). price varies. Statens Gotekniska Institut - Swedish Geotechnical Institute, 581 93 Linkoeping, Sweden. TEL 46-13-11-51-00. FAX 46-13-13-16-96. TELEX 501 25 (VTISGI S). circ. 1,000. **Indexed:** Dok.Str., GeoRef., Geotech.Abstr. **Document type:** government publication, monographic series.
   Former titles: Statens Geotekniska Institut. Meddelanden; Statens Geotekniska Institut. Saertryck och Preliminaera Rapporter (ISSN 0562-0953); Statens Geotekniska Institut. Proceedings (ISSN 0081-5705)
   Description: Presents the research and development work of the Institute.

551.22   PO   ISSN 0039-0356
STATION SEISMOGRAPHIQUE DE LISBOA. BULLETIN SEISMIQUE. 1946. 6/yr. free to scientific institutions. Instituto Geofisico do Infante D. Luis, R. Escola Politecnica, Lisbon 2, Portugal. TELEX 404-65869 FCULIS-P. Ed. Prof. Jose Pinto Peixoto. charts. circ. 230.

551.22   JA   ISSN 0563-7902
STRONG-MOTION EARTHQUAKE RECORDS IN JAPAN/KYOSHIN KIROKU. (Text in English) 1960. s-a. exchange basis. Science and Technology Agency, National Research Institute for Earth Science and Disaster Prevention - Kagaku Gijutsucho Bosai Kagaku Gijutsu Kenkyujo, 3-1, Tennodai, Tsukuba-shi, Ibaraki-ken 305, Japan. Ed. Makoto Miyamoto. stat.

551.4   PL   ISSN 0081-6434
QE260   CODEN: SGCAAE
STUDIA GEOMORPHOLOGICA CARPATHO-BALCANICA. (Text in English) 1967. a. price varies. (Polska Akademia Nauk, Oddzial w Krakowie, Komisja Nauk Geograficznych) Ossolineum, Publishing House of the Polish Academy of Sciences, Rynek 9, 50-106 Wroclaw, Poland. TEL 48-17-386-25. FAX 48-71-448-103. TELEX 0712771 OSS PL. Ed. Leszek Starkel. **Indexed:** Geo.Abstr., GeoRef. **Document type:** academic/scholarly publication.
—BLDSC (8482.700000).

551 526   US   ISSN 0039-3169
QC801   CODEN: SGEGA8
STUDIA GEOPHYSICA ET GEODAETICA; a journal of geophysics, geodesy, meteorology and climatology. (Text and summaries in English, French, German, Russian) 1957. c. $445 (foreign $530) (effective 1994). (Czechoslovak Academy of Sciences, Geophysical Institute, CS) Plenum Publishing Corp., 233 Spring St., New York, NY 10013-1578. TEL 212-620-8000. FAX 212-463-0742. TELEX 23-421139. (Co-publisher: Academia, CS) Ed. Milan Bursa. bk.rev.; abstr.; charts; illus.; maps; index. circ. 800. **Indexed:** ASCA, Chem.Abstr., Curr.Cont., Geo.Abstr., GeoRef., Int.Aerosp.Abstr., Meteor.& Geoastrophys.Abstr., Petrol.Abstr., Sci.Abstr. **Document type:** academic/scholarly publication.
—BLDSC (8482.800000); UnCover; UMI; CASDDS. **CCC.**
   Description: Papers on original research into geophysics, geodesy, meteorology and climatology.
   Refereed Serial

STUDIA GEOTECHNICA ET MECHANICA. see *ENGINEERING*

551   RM
STUDII SI CERCETARI DE GEOFIZICA. vol.18, 1980. a. $32. (Academia Romana) Editura Academiei Romane, Calea Victoriei 125, 79717 Bucharest, Rumania. TEL 50-76-80. (Dist. by: Rompresfilatelia, Export-Import Press, Calea Grivitei 64-66, P.O. Box 12-201, 78104 Bucharest, Rumania) Ed. Sabba Stefanescu. **Indexed:** GeoRef.
   Formerly (until 1989): Studii si Cercetari de Geologie, Geofizica si Geographie. Geofizica.

526   FI   ISSN 0085-6932
QB296.F5   CODEN: VFGIAG
SUOMEN GEODEETTISEN LAITOKSEN. JULKAISUJA/FINNISH GEODETIC INSTITUTE. PUBLICATIONS/FINNISCHE GEODAETISCHE INSTITUT. VEROEFFENTLICHUNGEN. (Text and summaries in English, French or German) 1923. irreg., no.116, 1993. price varies. Suomen Geodeettinen Laitos - Finnish Geodetic Institute, Ilmalankatu 1 A, SF-00240 Helsinki 24, Finland. circ. 800. **Indexed:** Deep Sea Res.& Oceanogr.Abstr. **Document type:** government publication.
—BLDSC (7062.600000).

551   FI   ISSN 0355-1962
SUOMEN GEODEETTISEN LAITOKSEN. TIEDONANTOJA./FINNISH GEODETIC INSTITUTE. REPORTS. (Text in English) 1973. irreg. price varies. Suomen Geodeettinen Laitos - Finnish Geodetic Institute, Ilmalankatu 1 A, 00240 Helsinki 24, Finland. **Indexec:** Deep Sea Res.& Oceanogr.Abstr. **Document type:** government publication.
—BLDSC (7470.950000).

551   NE   ISSN 0169-3298
QE1   CODEN: SUGEEC
SURVEYS IN GEOPHYSICS; an international review journal of geophysics and planetary sciences. (Text in English) 1973. 6/yr. fl.566($295) (effective 1994). (European Geophysical Society) Kluwer Academic Publishers, Postbus 17, 3300 AA Dordrecht, Netherlands. TEL 31-78-334911. FAX 31-78-334254. TELEX 29245 KAPG NL. (Dist. by: Kluwer Academic Publishers Group, P.O. Box 322, 3300 AH Dordrecht, Netherlands. TEL 31-78-524400. FAX 31-78-524474; N. America dist. addr.: Box 358, Accord Sta., Hingham, MA 02018-0358. TEL 617-871-6600. FAX 617-871-6523) Ed. K.M. Creer. adv.; bk.rev.; illus. (also avail. in microform from UMI; reprint service avail. from SWZ) **Indexed:** AESIS, Appl.Mech.Rev., ASCA, Astron.& Astrophys.Abstr., Curr.Cont., Deep Sea Res.& Oceanogr.Abstr., Geo.Abstr., GeoRef., Ind.Sci.Rev., Int.Aerosp.Abstr., Petrol.Abstr., Phys.Ber., Ref.Zh., Sci.Abstr., Sci.Cit.Ind. **Document type:** academic/scholarly publication.
—BLDSC (8549.377000); Faxon; UnCover; SWETS; UMI. **CCC.**
   Formerly: Geophysical Surveys (ISSN 0046-5763)
   Description: Publishes articles covering the study of the physical processes of the atmosphere, oceans and interior of the Earth, Moon and other planets of the solar system.
   Refereed Serial

EARTH SCIENCES — GEOPHYSICS

551 SW ISSN 0284-169X
SWEDISH INSTITUTE OF SPACE PHYSICS. ANNUAL REPORT. 1985. a. free. Swedish Institute of Space Physics, P.O. Box 812, Library, S-98128 Kiruna, Sweden. TEL 46 980 790 50. FAX 46-980-790-50. TELEX 8754-IRFS-S. Eds. Lars Eliasson, Bengt Holback. circ. 1,000. **Document type:** government publication, academic/scholarly publication.
Formerly: Kiruna Geophysical Institute. Annual Report (ISSN 0283-1686)

551 SW ISSN 0284-1703
SWEDISH INSTITUTE OF SPACE PHYSICS. SCIENTIFIC REPORT. (Text in English) 1973. irreg. free. Institutet foer Rymdfysik - Swedish Institute of Space Physics, P.O. Box 812, Library, S-981 28 Kiruna, Sweden. TEL 46-0980-79000. FAX 46-0980-79050. TELEX 8754-IRF-S. Ed. Aake Steen. charts. circ. 500. (back issues avail.) **Document type:** government publication. —BLDSC (4567.808900).
Former titles: Kiruna Geophysical Institute. Scientific Report (ISSN 0283-1694); Kiruna Geophysical Institute. Report (ISSN 0347-6405)
Description: Features investigations of various phenomena of concern to physicists.

551 SW ISSN 0284-172X
SWEDISH INSTITUTE OF SPACE PHYSICS. SOFTWARE REPORT. (Text in English) 1977. irreg. price varies (free to qualified institutions, libraries and personnel). Swedish Institute of Space Physics, Box 812, S-98128 Kiruna, Sweden. TEL 0980-79000. FAX 0980-79050. TELEX 8754-IRF-S. (back issues avail.) **Document type:** government publication.
Formerly: Kiruna Gephysical Institute. Software Report (ISSN 0349-2664)
Description: Monographs on computer software.

551 SW ISSN 0284-1738
SWEDISH INSTITUTE OF SPACE PHYSICS. TECHNICAL REPORT. (Text and summaries in English and Swedish) 1969. irreg. free. Swedish Institute of Space Physics, P.O. Box 812, Library, S-981 28 Kiruna, Sweden. TEL 0980-79000. FAX 0980-79050. TELEX 8754-IRF-S. (back issues avail.) **Document type:** government publication.
Formerly: Kiruna Geophysical Institute. Technical Report (ISSN 0349-2672)

TECHNIKA POSZUKIWAN GEOLOGICZNYCH, GEOSYNOPTYKA I GEOTERMIA/EXPLORATION TECHNOLOGY, GEOSYNOPTICS AND GEOTHERMAL ENERGY. see *EARTH SCIENCES — Geology*

551 US ISSN 0278-7407
QE601 CODEN: TCTNDM
TECTONICS. 1982. bi-m. $330 to non-members (foreign $345); members $75 (foreign $90); students $38 (foreign $53). American Geophysical Union, 2000 Florida Ave., N.W., Washington, DC 20009. TEL 202-462-6900. FAX 202-328-0566. TELEX 710-822-9300. (German addr.: Postfach 49, 37189 Katlenburg-Lindau, Germany. TEL 49-5556-1440) (Co-sponsor: European Geophysical Society) Ed. Kevin Burke. charts; illus. (also avail. in microform from AGU) **Indexed:** AESIS, ASCA, Deep Sea Res.& Oceanogr.Abstr., Int.Aerosp.Abstr., Petrol.Abstr., Sci.Abstr.
—BLDSC (8763.003500); Faxon; UnCover; SWETS. **CCC**.
Description: Contains leading papers on the structure and evolution of the lithosphere; analytical, synthetic, and integrative tectonics; and tectonic process.

551.8 NE ISSN 0040-1951
CODEN: TCTOAM
TECTONOPHYSICS; international journal of geotectonics and the geology and physics of the interior of the earth. (Text in English, French and German) 1964. 56/yr. (in 14 vols.; 4 nos./vol.). fl.4494($2429) (effective 1994). Elsevier Science B.V., P.O. Box 211, 1000 AE Amsterdam, Netherlands. TEL 31-20-5803911. FAX 31-20-5803598. TELEX 18582 ESPA NL. (Subscr. in U.S. and Canada to: Elsevier Science Inc., Box 882, Madison Sq. Sta., New York, NY 10159-0882. TEL 212-989-5800. FAX 212-633-3990) Eds. M. Friedman, S. Uyeda. adv.; bk.rev.; abstr.; charts. (also avail. in microform from UMI; reprint service avail. from SWZ) **Indexed:** Abstr.J.Earthq.Eng., AESIS, ASCA, Bull.Signal., Chem.Abstr., Curr.Cont., Deep Sea Res.& Oceanogr.Abstr., Eng.Ind., Geo.Abstr., Geosci.Doc., Geotech.Abstr., Int.Aerosp.Abstr., Petrol.Abstr., Phys.Ber., Risk Abstr., Sci.Abstr., So.Pac.Per.Ind. **Document type:** academic/scholarly publication.
—BLDSC (8763.020000); Faxon; UnCover; SWETS; CASDDS. **CCC**.
Description: Publishes original research studies and comprehensive reviews in the field of geotectonics and structural geology.
Refereed Serial

551 DK ISSN 0280-6495
QC880 CODEN: TSAOD8
TELLUS. SERIES A: DYNAMIC METEOROLOGY AND OCEANOGRAPHY. (Text in English, French or German; summaries in English) 1949. 5/yr. DKK 850 (with Series B DKK 1300). (Svenska Geofysiska Foerening, SW - Swedish Geophysical Society) Munksgaard International Publishers Ltd., P.O. Box 2148, DK-1016 Copenhagen K, Denmark. TEL 33-127030. FAX 33-129387. Ed. H. Sundquist. abstr.; charts; illus.; stat.; index. circ. 1,000. (reprint service avail. from ISI,KTO) **Indexed:** Acid Pre.Dig., Acid Rain Abstr., Acid Rain Ind., Appl.Mech.Rev., ASCA, Biol.Abstr., Chem.Abstr., Curr.Adv.Ecol.Sci., Curr.Cont., Deep Sea Res.& Oceanogr.Abstr., Environ.Abstr., Excerp.Med., Geo.Abstr., Int.Aerosp.Abstr., Math.R., Meteor.& Geoastrophys.Abstr., Pollut.Abstr., Sci.Abstr., Sel.Water Res.Abstr., Soils & Fert. **Document type:** academic/scholarly publication.
—BLDSC (8789.000100); Faxon; UnCover; SWETS. **CCC**.
Supersedes in part: Tellus (ISSN 0040-2826)
Refereed Serial

551 DK ISSN 0280-6509
QC879.6 CODEN: TSBMD7
TELLUS. SERIES B: CHEMICAL AND PHYSICAL METEOROLOGY. (Text in English, French or German; summaries in English) 1949. 5/yr. DKK 800 (with Series A DKK 1300). (Swedish Geophysical Society, SW) Munksgaard International Publishers Ltd., 35 Noerre Soegade, P.O. Box 2148, DK-1016 Copenhagen K, Denmark. TEL 33-127030. FAX 33-129387. Ed. H. Rodhe. abstr.; charts; illus.; stat.; index. circ. 1,000. (reprint service avail. from ISI,KTO) **Indexed:** Acid Pre.Dig., Acid Rain Abstr., Acid Rain Ind., Appl.Mech.Rev., Biol.Abstr., Chem.Abstr., Curr.Adv.Ecol.Sci., Curr.Cont., Deep Sea Res.& Oceanogr.Abstr., Environ.Abstr., Excerp.Med., Int.Aerosp.Abstr., Meteor.& Geoastrophys.Abstr., Ocean.Abstr., Pollut.Abstr., Sci.Abstr., Soils & Fert. **Document type:** academic/scholarly publication.
—BLDSC (8789.000150); Faxon; UnCover; SWETS; CASDDS. **CCC**.
Supersedes in part: Tellus (ISSN 0040-2826)
Refereed Serial

551 NE ISSN 0257-4284
TIDAL GRAVITY CORRECTIONS. 1970. a. fl.40 (effective 1994). European Association of Exploration Geophysicists, Postbus 298, 3700 AG Zeist, Netherlands. TEL 31-3404-56997. FAX 31-3404-62640. circ. 150.

551 JA ISSN 0040-8794
QC801 CODEN: STUEA3
TOHOKU GEOPHYSICAL JOURNAL; science reports of Tohoku University, fifth series. (Text in English) 1949. irreg. (3-4/yr.). exchange basis. Tohoku Daigaku, Rigakubu Chikyu-butsurigaku Ka - Tohoku University, Faculty of Science, Geophysical Institute, Aoba, Aramaki, Sendai-shi, Miyagi-ken 980, Japan. FAX 81-22-227-3671. Ed. Yoshiaki Toba. bibl.; charts; illus.; index. circ. 700. (also avail. in microform from PMC) **Indexed:** Chem.Abstr., GeoRef., Meteor.& Geoastrophys.Abstr., Sci.Abstr. **Document type:** academic/scholarly publication.
—BLDSC (8859.994400).
Formerly: Tohoku University. Science Reports. Series 5: Geophysics.

551 JA ISSN 0917-6217
TOHOKU NO YUKI TO SEIKATSU/SNOW AND LIFE IN TOHOKU. (Text in Japanese) 1986. a. 1000 Yen. Nihon Seppyo Gakkai, Tohoku Shibu - Japanese Society of Snow and Ice, Tohoku Branch, 1-2, Nakagawara, Motouchi, Fukushima-shi, Fukushima-ken 960-01, Japan.

U.S. AIR FORCE GEOPHYSICS LABORATORY. A F G L (SERIES). see *MILITARY*

551.22 US ISSN 0364-7072
U.S. NATIONAL EARTHQUAKE INFORMATION SERVICE. PRELIMINARY DETERMINATION OF EPICENTERS, MONTHLY LISTING. Key Title: Preliminary Determination of Epicenters. m. $14. U.S. Geological Survey, National Earthquake Information Service, Stop 967, Box 25046, Denver Federal Center, Denver, CO 80225. TEL 303-273-8500. FAX 303-273-8450. TELEX 510-601-4123 ESL UD. (Dist. by: Supt. of Documents, Washington, DC 20402) **Document type:** government publication.

551.22 US ISSN 0091-1429
QE535.2.U6 CODEN: XGEQAP
UNITED STATES EARTHQUAKES. 1928. a. price varies. U.S. Geological Survey, Open-File Services Section, Box 25425, Federal Center, Denver, CO 80225. TEL 303-273-8419. Ed. James W. Dewey. illus. (also avail. in microfilm) **Indexed:** GeoRef. **Document type:** government publication.
Description: Lists earthquakes that occurred in the U.S. during the year and describes their effects.

551 MX
UNIVERSIDAD NACIONAL AUTONOMA DE MEXICO. INSTITUTO DE GEOFISICA. BOLETIN SISMOLOGICO. 1949. m. $30. Universidad Nacional Autonoma de Mexico, Instituto de Geofisica, Circuto Exterior, Ciudad Universitaria, Mexico 20, D.F., Mexico. Ed. Francisco Graffe.

551 MX ISSN 0076-7204
UNIVERSIDAD NACIONAL AUTONOMA DE MEXICO. INSTITUTO DE GEOFISICA. MONOGRAFIAS. 1959-1963; resumed 1981. irreg. Universidad Nacional Autonoma de Mexico, Instituto de Geofisica, Circuito Exterior, Ciudad Universitaria, Mexico 20, D.F., Mexico. Ed. Francisco Graffe.

551 GW ISSN 0343-7493
QC830.F8
UNIVERSITAET MUENCHEN. GEOPHYSIKALISCHES OBSERVATORIUM, FUERSTENFELDBRUCK. VEROEFFENTLICHUNGEN. SERIE A. 1959. a. exchange basis. Universitaet Muenchen, Geophysikalisches Observatorium, Ludwigshoehe 8, 82256 Fuerstenfeldbruck, Germany. **Document type:** academic/scholarly publication.

551 GW ISSN 0077-2100
UNIVERSITAET MUENCHEN. GEOPHYSIKALISCHES OBSERVATORIUM, FUERSTENFELDBRUCK. VEROEFFENTLICHUNGEN. SERIE B. 1960. irreg., no.8, 1985. exchange basis. Universitaet Muenchen, Geophysikalisches Observatorium, Ludwigshoehe 8, 82256 Fuerstenfeldbruck, Germany. **Document type:** academic/scholarly publication.

551 551.5 GW ISSN 0069-5882
QC801
UNIVERSITAET ZU KOELN. INSTITUT FUER GEOPHYSIK UND METEOROLOGIE. MITTEILUNGEN. (Text in English and German) 1965. irreg., no.82, 1991. DM.15. Universitaet zu Koeln, Institut fuer Geophysik und Meteorologie, Albertus-Magnus-Platz, 50923 Cologne, Germany. TEL 0221-4702552. FAX 0221-4705198. Ed.Bd. Meteor.& Geoastrophys.Abstr. **Document type:** academic/scholarly publication.

UNIVERSITEIT TE GENT. STERRENKUNDIG OBSERVATORIUM. MEDEDELINGEN: METEOROLOGIE EN GEOFYSICA. see *METEOROLOGY*

551   US   ISSN 0041-9362
QC801
UNIVERSITY OF ALASKA. GEOPHYSICAL INSTITUTE. REPORT SERIES. 1948. irreg. free. University of Alaska at Fairbanks, Geophysical Institute, Box 757320, Fairbanks, AK 99775-7320. TEL 907-474-7503.

551.22   US   ISSN 0041-946X
UNIVERSITY OF CALIFORNIA. SEISMOGRAPHIC STATIONS. BULLETIN. 1910. s-a. $10. University of California, Berkeley, Seismographic Station, 475 Earth Sciences Bldg., Berkeley, CA 94720. TEL 415-642-3977. FAX 643-5811. Ed. Robert A. Uhrhammer. charts; circ. 450. (processed; also avail. in microfiche)
Description: Lists local, regional and worldwide earthquakes recorded by the seismographic network.

551.22   US   ISSN 0092-4288
QE531
UNIVERSITY OF NEVADA. SEISMOLOGICAL LABORATORY. BULLETIN. Key Title: Bulletin of the Seismological Laboratory (Reno). 1970. irreg. latest 1987. free. University of Nevada, Seismological Laboratory, Makay School of Mines, Reno, NV 89557. TEL 702-784-4975. Ed. A.A. Aburto. illus. circ. 100. **Indexed:** GeoRef.

551.22   JA   ISSN 0040-8972
QE531   CODEN: TDJKAZ
UNIVERSITY OF TOKYO. EARTHQUAKE RESEARCH INSTITUTE. BULLETIN/TOKYO DAIGAKU JISHIN KENKYUJO IHO. 1926. q. price varies. University of Tokyo, Earthquake Research Institute - Tokyo Daigaku Jishin Kenkyujo, 1-1-1 Yayoi, Bunkyo-ku, Tokyo 113, Japan. Ed.Bd. circ. 1,150. **Indexed:** Abstr.J.Earthq.Eng., Deep Sea Res.& Oceanogr.Abstr., Eng.Ind., GeoRef., Jap.Per.Ind., JTA, Phys.Abstr., Sci.Abstr. **Document type:** bulletin.
—EI; UnCover.

551.22   JA   ISSN 0915-0862
UNIVERSITY OF TOKYO. EARTHQUAKE RESEARCH INSTITUTE. SPECIAL BULLETIN. (Text in English, Japanese) 1943. irreg. price varies. University of Tokyo, Earthquake Research Institute - Tokyo Daigaku Jishin Kenkyujo, 1-1-1 Yayoi, Bunkyo-ku, Tokyo 113, Japan. Ed.Bd. circ. 1,150. **Document type:** bulletin.

551   JA
UNIVERSITY OF TOKYO. FACULTY OF SCIENCE. GEOPHYSICAL INSTITUTE. ANNUAL REPORT. (Text in English) a. University of Tokyo, Faculty of Science, Geophysical Institute - Tokyo Daigaku Rigakubu Chikyu Butsurigakka, 3-1, Hongo 7-chome, Bunkyo-ku, Tokyo 113, Japan.

551   JA
UNIVERSITY OF TOKYO. GEOPHYSICS RESEARCH LABORATORY. ACTIVITY REPORT. (Text in English) 1979. triennial. University of Tokyo, Faculty of Science, Geophysics Research Laboratory - Tokyo Daigaku Rigakubu Fuzoku Chikyu Butsuri Kenkyu Shitesu, 3-1, Hongo 7-chome, Bunkyo-ku, Tokyo 113, Japan.

551   JA   ISSN 0285-3175
UNIVERSITY OF TSUKUBA. INSTITUTE OF GEOSCIENCE. ANNUAL REPORT. (Text in English) 1975. a. University of Tsukuba, Institute of Geoscience - Tsukuba Daigaku Chikyu Kagakukei, 1-1, Tennodai 1-chome, Tsukuba-shi, Ibaraki-ken 305, Japan. Ed.Bd. **Indexed:** Geo.Abstr., GeoRef., Meteor.& Geoastrophys.Abstr.
—BLDSC (1302.983000); UnCover.

VERMONT DIVISION OF GEOLOGY AND MINERAL RESOURCES. ECONOMIC GEOLOGY. see *EARTH SCIENCES — Geology*

551   RU   ISSN 0065-0099
VOEIKOV MAIN GEOPHYSICAL OBSERVATORY. LENINGRAD. RESULTS OF GROUND OBSERVATIONS OF ATMOSPHERIC ELECTRICITY. THE WORLD NETWORK. ADDITIONAL ISSUE. (Text and tables in English and Russian) irreg. Glavnaya Geofizicheskaya Observatoriya im. A.I. Voeikova, Karbysheva, 7, St. Petersburg 194018, Russia.

551   RU   ISSN 0136-4863
VOEIKOV MAIN GEOPHYSICAL OBSERVATORY. LENINGRAD. RESULTS OF GROUND OBSERVATIONS OF ATMOSPHERIC ELECTRICITY. THE WORLD NETWORK. (Text and tables in English, Russian) m. Glavnaya Geofizicheskaya Observatoriya im. A.I. Voeikova, Karbysheva 7, St. Petersburg 194018, Russia.

551.2   JA   ISSN 0453-4360
                      CODEN: KAZAAX
VOLCANOLOGICAL SOCIETY OF JAPAN. BULLETIN/KAZAN. (Text in English, Japanese; summaries in English) 1957. q. 2500 Yen per no. Volcanological Society of Japan - Nihon Kazan Gakkai, Tokyo Daigaku Jishin Kenkyujo, 1-1, Yayoi 1-chome, Bunkyo-ku, Tokyo 113, Japan. **Indexed:** Chem.Abstr., INIS Atomind., Jap.Per.Ind. **Document type:** academic/scholarly publication.
—CASDDS.

551   US   ISSN 0742-0463
QE521   CODEN: VULSD9
VOLCANOLOGY & SEISMOLOGY. English translation of: Vulkanologiya i Seiomologiya. 12/yr. (in 2 vols., 6 nos./vol.). 361 ECU per vol. (effective 1993). Gordon & Breach Science Publishers, 820 Town Center Dr., Langhorne, PA 19047. TEL 215-750-2642. FAX 215-750-6343. (UK subscr. to: P.O. Box 90, Reading, Berkshire RG1 8JL, England. TEL 0734-560-080) Ed. L.N. Rykunov. index. (also avail. in microform; back issues avail.) **Document type:** academic/scholarly publication.
—Faxon; UnCover. **CCC.**
Refereed Serial

551   XO   ISSN 0231-7737
                      CODEN: RGOOE7
VYSLEDKY GEOMAGNETICKYCH POZOROVANI V GEOMAGNETICKOM OBSERVATORIU V HURBANOVE V ROKU (YEAR)/RESULTS OF GEOMAGNETIC OBSERVATIONS AT THE HURBANOVO GEOMAGNETIC OBSERVATORY IN (YEAR). (Text in English, Russian and Slovak) 1953. a. free. Slovenska Akademia Vied, Geofizikaly Ustav - Slovak Academy of Science, Geophysical Institute, Dubravska Cesta 9, 842 28 Bratislava, Slovakia. TEL 373 368. TELEX 98527 GFYZ C. Ed. Jozef Podsklan. circ. 500. (back issues avail.)
Description: Contains tables with results of geomagnetic observations performed on the Geomagnetic Observatory in Hurbanovo.

551.22   CC   ISSN 1001-4683
ZHONGGUO DIZHEN/CHINESE SEISMOLOGY. (Editions in Chinese, English) q. Guojia Dizhen-ju, Zhongguo Dizhen Bianjibu - State Seismological Bureau, Editorial Office of Chinese Seismology, 63 Fuxing Lu, Beijing 100036, People's Republic of China. TEL 811398. Ed. Ding Guoyu.

EARTH SCIENCES — Hydrology

A M S NEWSLETTER (BOSTON). (American Meteorological Society) see *METEOROLOGY*

551.48 370   PL   ISSN 0208-6158
ACTA UNIVERSITATIS LODZIENSIS: FOLIA LIMNOLOGICA. (Text in Polish; summaries in various languages) 1955-1974; N.S. 1983. irreg. Wydawnictwo Uniwersytetu Lodzkiego, Ul. Jaracza 34, Lodz, Poland. TEL 331671. (Dist. by: Ars Polona-Ruch, Krakowskie Przedmiescie 7, Warsaw, Poland) **Document type:** academic/scholarly publication.
Supersedes in part: Uniwersytet Lodzki. Zeszyty Naukowe. Seria 2: Nauki Matematyczno-Przyrodnicze (ISSN 0076-0366)
Description: Publishes the original works in the field of limnology: taxonomy, morphology, biology, ecology and biogeography of organisms living in inland waters.

551.48   PL   ISSN 0208-5348
QH96.A1   CODEN: AUNLD5
ACTA UNIVERSITATIS NICOLAI COPERNICI. PRACE LIMNOLOGICZNE. 1965. irreg. price varies. Uniwersytet Mikolaja Kopernika, Biblioteka Uniwersytecka, Ul. Gagarina 13, 87-100 Torun, Poland. TEL 233-52. TELEX 552382. (Dist. by: Osrodek Rozpowszechniania Wydawnictw Naukowych PAN, Palac Kultury i Nauki, 00-901 Warsaw, Poland) **Indexed:** Biol.Abstr., Curr.Adv.Ecol.Sci.
—BLDSC (0585.280000).

ADVANCES IN POROUS MEDIA. see *EARTH SCIENCES*

AKITA PREFECTURAL COLLEGE OF AGRICULTURE. BULLETIN. see *AGRICULTURE*

ALBERTA RESEARCH COUNCIL. RIVER ENGINEERING AND SURFACE HYDROLOGY REPORTS. see *ENGINEERING — Civil Engineering*

ALGOLOGICAL STUDIES; Archiv fuer Hydrobiologie, Supplementbaende. see *BIOLOGY*

AMERICAN INSTITUTE OF HYDROLOGY. BULLETIN. see *WATER RESOURCES*

AMERICAN METEOROLOGICAL SOCIETY. BULLETIN. see *METEOROLOGY*

AMERICAN SHORE AND BEACH PRESERVATION ASSOCIATION. NEWSLETTER. see *ENVIRONMENTAL STUDIES*

551.48   FR   ISSN 0003-4088
                      CODEN: ANLIB3
ANNALES DE LIMNOLOGIE. (Text in English, French) 1965. 3/yr. 620 F. (Universite Paul Sabatier (Toulouse)) Gauthier-Villars, 15 rue Gossin, 92543 Montrouge Cedex, France. TEL 33-1-40-92-65-00. FAX 33-1-40-92-65-97. TELEX 634 916 F. (Subscr. to: Centrale des Revues, 11 rue Gossin, 92543 Montrouge Cedex, France. TEL 33-1-46-56-52-66) Ed. H. Laville. bk.rev. (reprint service avail. from ISI) **Indexed:** Biol.Abstr., Curr.Adv.Ecol.Sci., Excerp.Med., GeoRef., Sel.Water Res.Abstr., W.R.C.Inf.
—BLDSC (0981.050000); Faxon; UnCover; SWETS; CASDDS. **CCC.**
Description: Covers continental waters ecology with respect to micro-organisms, sea weeds, vertebrate and invertebrate macrophytes, ecosystems as well as to the physical and chemical aspects of aquatic environment.

070 551.4   FR   ISSN 0373-3629
VK798   CODEN: AHDGAG
ANNALES HYDROGRAPHIQUES. 1848. irreg., vol.10, 1992. price varies. Service Hydrographique et Oceanographique de la Marine, 3 av. Octave Greard, 00300 Armees, France. TEL 98-22-10-80. FAX 98-43-18-11. TELEX HYDRO 940568. (Subscr. to: EPSHOM, B.P. 426, 29275 Brest Cedex, France) charts; illus.; index, cum.index. circ. 400. **Indexed:** Chem.Abstr., Deep Sea Res.& Oceanogr.Abstr., Meteor.& Geoastrophys.Abstr. **Document type:** government publication.
—BLDSC (0980.000000); CASDDS.

551.4   UN
ANUARIO HIDROLOGICO DEL ISTMO CENTROAMERICANO. 1966. a. free. United Nations Central American Hydrometeorological Project, Regional Committee for Water Resources, Apdo. 4328, Managua, Nicaragua. Ed. Eduardo Basso. circ. 300. (back issues avail.)

551.4   GW   ISSN 0941-2816
▼**APPLIED HYDROLOGY.** 1992. q. DM.120. (International Association of Hydrologists) Verlag Heinz Heise GmbH und Co. KG, Helstorfer. 7, 30625 Hannover, Germany. TEL 0511-5352-0. FAX 0511-5352-129. TELEX 923173-HEISE-D. (Subscr. to: P.O. Box 610407, 30604 Hannover, Germany) Ed. E S. Simpson. **Document type:** academic/scholarly publication.
—BLDSC (1573.070000).
Description: Covers a wide range of hydrogeological specialities. Provides new information and theoretical papers of merit for practicing hydrogeologists.
Refereed Serial

551 551.46   IT   ISSN 0394-6568
AQUA; mensile di acqua, natura, vita. 1986. m. (11/yr.). L.57200 (foreign L.80000). Editrice Portoria S.r.l., Via Chiossetto, 1, 20122 Milan, Italy. TEL 02-783541. FAX 02-782601. Ed. Luca Oriani. adv.; bk.rev. circ. 100,000.

551.4　　　　SZ　ISSN 1015-1621
GB651　　　　　CODEN: AQSCEA
AQUATIC SCIENCES; multidisciplinary journal for theoretical and applied limnology, fisheries science and water technology. (Text in English, French and German) 1920. 4/yr. 238 SFr.($162) (Swiss Academy of Sciences) Birkhaeuser Verlag, P.O. Box 133, CH-4010 Basel, Switzerland. TEL 061-2717400. FAX 061-2717666. TELEX 963475-BIRKH-CH. (Dist. in N. America by: Springer-Verlag, Mercedes Distribution Center, 160 Imlay St., Brooklyn, NY 11231, USA) Ed. P. Bossard. circ. 600. **Indexed:** Biol.Abstr., Chem.Abstr., Curr.Adv.Ecol.Sci., Curr.Cont., Deep Sea Res.& Oceanogr.Abstr., Environ.Abstr., Excerp.Med., Fluidex, Geo.Abstr., GeoRef., Sel.Water Res.Abstr., W.R.C.Inf., Water Pollut.Abstr. **Document type:** academic/scholarly publication.
—BLDSC (1582.430000); UnCover; SWETS; UMI. **CCC.**
Formerly: Swiss Journal of Hydrology (ISSN 0036-7842)

ARCHIV FUER HYDROBIOLOGIE. see *BIOLOGY*

ARCHIVIO DI OCEANOGRAFIA E LIMONOLOGIA. see *EARTH SCIENCES — Oceanography*

551.46　　　　AT　ISSN 0812-5090
AUSTRALIAN HYDROGRAPHIC NEWSLETTER. 1979. q. Aus.$20. Australian Hydrographers Association, 94 Rogers St., P.O. Box E205, Queen Victoria Terrace, A.C.T. 2600, Australia. TEL 062-725833. FAX 062-724526. adv.; charts; illus. circ. 250.
Description: Covers water measurement instrumentation and techniques. Provides a forum for the interchange of information and ideas on technology.

BAYERISCHES LANDESAMTES FUER WASSERWIRTSCHAFT. SCHRIFTENREIHE. see *WATER RESOURCES*

551.4 333.91 910
627　　　　　GW　ISSN 0343-0987
BEITRAEGE ZUR HYDROLOGIE. (Text and summaries in English, German) 1971. s-a. DM.48.90. Ibenstalstr. 20, 79199 Kirchzarten, Germany. Ed. Karl-Rainer Nippes. adv.; bk.rev.; cum.index: 1971-1984. circ. 700. (back issues avail.) **Indexed:** Geo.Abstr.
—BLDSC (1884.275000).

BIBLIOGRAFIA HYDROLOGII I OCEANOLOGII/BIBLIOGRAPHY OF HYDROLOGY AND OCEANOLOGY. see *EARTH SCIENCES — Abstracting, Bibliographies, Statistics*

551.48　　　　GW　ISSN 0067-8643
　　　　　　　　　CODEN: BNGWAU
DIE BINNENGEWAESSER; Einzeldarstellungen aus der Limnologie und ihren Grenzgebieten. (Text in English and German) 1926. irreg. price varies. E. Schweizerbart'sche Verlagsbuchhandlung, Johannesstr. 3A, 70176 Stuttgart, Germany. TEL 0711-625001. FAX 0711-625005. TELEX 723363-SCHB-D. Ed. H. Kausch, W. Lampert. **Indexed:** Ber.Biochem.Biol., Biol.Abstr., Deep Sea Res.& Oceanogr.Abstr. **Document type:** academic/scholarly publication.

551.48　　　　CR　ISSN 0067-9747
BOLETIN HIDROLOGICO. 1962. a. Instituto Costarricense de Electricidad (ICE), Apto. 10032, San Jose, Costa Rica. charts; illus.; stat.; index; circ. controlled.

551.4　　　　US　ISSN 0575-4968
TD224.C3　　　　CODEN: RUCCD8
CALIFORNIA. WATER RESOURCES CENTER. ANNUAL REPORT. no.79, 1992. a. Water Resources Center, University of California, Rubidoux Hall-094, Riverside, CA 92521-0436. TEL 909-787-4327. FAX 909-787-5295. Ed. Rex J. Woods. illus. circ. 265. **Document type:** government publication.
—BLDSC (7393.984000).
Description: Examines the center's objectives, research program activities and conferences.

551.49　　　　CN
CANADA. MARINE ENVIRONMENTAL DATA SERVICE. MONTHLY AND TEN YEARLY MEANS WATER LEVELS - MOYENNES MENSUELLES ET ANNUELLES DES NIVEAUX D'EAU. (Text in English and French) 1972. quinquennial. free. Marine Environmental Data Service, 1202-200 Kent St., Ottawa, Ont. K1A 0E6, Canada. TEL 613-990-0268. FAX 613-990-5510. TELEX 053-4228. circ. 100. **Document type:** government publication.

CHINESE JOURNAL OF OCEANOLOGY AND LIMNOLOGY. see *EARTH SCIENCES — Oceanography*

553.79　　　　US　ISSN 0094-9671
GB1001
CONFERENCE ON GROUND WATER. PROCEEDINGS. Key Title: Proceedings - Conference on Ground Water. biennial. $5. University of California, Davis, Water Resources Center, Davis, CA 95616. TEL 916-752-1544. (Co-sponsor: California Department of Water Resources)
—UnCover.

DEUTSCHE GEWAESSERKUNDLICHE MITTEILUNGEN; Mitteilungsblatt der gewaesserkundlichen Dienststellen des Bundes und der Laender. see *WATER RESOURCES*

DEUTSCHES GEWAESSERKUNDLICHES JAHRBUCH. DONAUGEBIET. see *WATER RESOURCES*

DEUTSCHES GEWAESSERKUNDLICHES JAHRBUCH. KUESTENGEBIET DER NORD- UND OSTSEE. see *WATER RESOURCES*

DEUTSCHES GEWAESSERKUNDLICHES JAHRBUCH. RHEINGEBIET TEIL 2: MAIN. see *WATER RESOURCES*

DEVELOPMENTS IN HYDROBIOLOGY. see *BIOLOGY*

DEVELOPMENTS IN WATER SCIENCE. see *WATER RESOURCES*

551.48　　　　EC
ECUADOR. INSTITUTO NACIONAL DE METEOROLOGIA E HIDROLOGIA. ANUARIO HIDROLOGICO. 1963. a. exchange basis. Instituto Nacional de Meteorologia e Hidrologia, Paris 270 y Gaspar de Villarroel, Quito, Ecuador. index. **Document type:** government publication.
Supersedes: Ecuador. Servicio Nacional de Meteorologia e Hidrologia. Anuario Hidrologico (ISSN 0070-8933)

551.4　　　　SZ
EIDGENOESSISCHE TECHNISCHE HOCHSCHULE ZUERICH. VERSUCHSANSTALT FUER WASSERBAU, HYDROLOGIE UND GLAZIOLOGIE. JAHRESBERICHT. 1971. a. free. Eidgenoessische Technische Hochschule Zuerich, Versuchsanstalt fuer Wasserbau, Hydrologie und Glaziologie, ETH-Zentrum, CH-8092 Zurich, Switzerland. Ed. D. Vischer. illus. **Document type:** academic/scholarly publication.
Description: Includes information on hydraulics, water engineering, and glaciology.

551.4 627　　　　SZ
EIDGENOESSISCHE TECHNISCHE HOCHSCHULE ZUERICH. VERSUCHSANSTALT FUER WASSERBAU, HYDROLOGIE UND GLAZIOLOGIE. MITTEILUNGEN. (Text in English and German) 1971. a. free. Eidgenoessische Technische Hochschule Zuerich, Versuchsanstalt fuer Wasserbau, Hydrologie und Glaziologie, ETH-Zentrum, CH-8092 Zurich, Switzerland. Ed. D. Vischer. illus. **Document type:** academic/scholarly publication.
Description: Includes information on glaciology, water engineering, and hydraulics.

551.48　　　　GW　ISSN 0071-1128
QH98　　　　　CODEN: ERLIA6
ERGEBNISSE DER LIMNOLOGIE/ADVANCES IN LIMNOLOGY. (Supplement to: Archiv fuer Hydrobiologie) (Text in English and German) 1964. irreg. price varies. (Internationale Vereinigung fuer Theoretische und Angewandte Limnologie) E. Schweizerbart'sche Verlagsbuchhandlung, Johannesstr. 3A, 70176 Stuttgart, Germany. TEL 0711-625001. FAX 0711-625005. TELEX 723363-SCHB-D. Eds. H. Kausch, W. Lampert. adv. **Indexed:** Biol.Abstr., Chem.Abstr., Sel.Water Res.Abstr., W.R.C.Inf. **Document type:** monographic series.
—BLDSC (3807.130000); UnCover; SWETS; CASDDS. **CCC.**

368 627　　　　US
FLOOD REPORT.* 1983. m. $89. (Emergency Management Marketing Analysis, Inc.) E M M A, Inc., c/o ELSEY, Box 222273, Chantilly, VA 22022-2273. circ. 1,000. (looseleaf format; back issues avail.)

551.48　　　　DK
FOLIO LIMNOLOGICA SCANDINAVICA. (Text in English) 1943. irreg. no.18, 1982. price varies. Koebenhavns Universitet, Freshwater Biological Laboratory, 51 Helsingoersgade, DK-3400 Hilleroed, Denmark. Ed.Bd. (back issues avail.) **Document type:** academic/scholarly publication.

551.4　　　　FR　ISSN 0246-1641
GB651
FRANCE. BUREAU DE RECHERCHES GEOLOGIQUES ET MINIERES. HYDROGEOLOGIE. (Text in French; summaries in English) 1963. q. 700 F. Bureau de Recherches Geologiques et Minieres, Division Edition et Vente, B.P. 6009, 45060 Orleans cedex, France. (Dist. by: Gauthier-Villars, Centrale des Revues, 11 rue Gossin, 92543 Montrouge Cedex, France. TEL 1-46-56-52-66) Ed. J. Margat. abstr.; charts; illus.; index. circ. 1,500. **Indexed:** Bull.Signal., Chem.Abstr., Excerp.Med., Geo.Abstr., GeoRef., Ref.Zh. **Document type:** bulletin.
—EI; Faxon; SWETS.
Former titles: France. Bureau de Recherches Geologiques et Minieres. Bulletin. Section 3: Hydrologie-Geologie de l'Ingenieur (ISSN 0300-936X); France. Bureau de Recherches Geologiques et Minieres. Bulletin. Section 3: Hydrogeologie (ISSN 0007-6120)
Description: Features original articles and reviews which are sometimes devoted to hydrogeology, notably underground hydrodynamics geothermal resources, appraisal of water sources and management, general hydrology, protection of water quality.

551.48　　　　JA
FRONT. (Text in Japanese) 1988. m. 1600 Yen per no. Riba Furonto Seibi Senta - Technology Research Center for River Front Development, Ichibancho Eito Wan Biru, 6F, 6-4, Ichibacho, Chiyoda-ku, Tokyo 102, Japan.

GEOLOGIA APPLICATA E IDROGEOLOGIA. see *EARTH SCIENCES — Geology*

GEOLOGISCHES JAHRBUCH. REIHE C: HYDROGEOLOGIE. INGENIEURGEOLOGIE. see *EARTH SCIENCES — Geology*

GEOOEKODYNAMIK. see *GEOGRAPHY*

GESELLSCHAFT DER GEOLOGIE- UND BERGBAUSTUDENTEN. MITTEILUNGEN. see *EARTH SCIENCES — Geology*

GIDROBIOLOGICHESKII ZHURNAL; nauchnyi zhurnal. see *BIOLOGY*

559.82　　　　DK　ISSN 0903-7322
GROENLANDS GEOLOGISKE UNDERSOEGELSE. OPEN FILE SERIES. 1981. irreg. (approx. 8/yr.). price varies. Groenlands Geologiske Undersoegelse - Geological Survey of Greenland, Oester Voldgade 10, DK-1350 Copenhagen K, Denmark. TEL 45-33-11-88-66. FAX 45-33-93-53-52. illus. **Document type:** government publication.
Formerly (until 1987): Groenlands Geologiske Undersoegelse. Gletscher-Hydrologiske Meddelelser (ISSN 0109-2073)
Description: Unedited reports on the geology of Greenland, primarily topics of interest to the mining and petroleum industries.

GROTTE D'ITALIA. see *EARTH SCIENCES — Geology*

EARTH SCIENCES — HYDROLOGY

551.49 628.11 US ISSN 0017-467X
GB1001 CODEN: GRWAAP
GROUND WATER. Variant title: Journal of Ground Water. 1963. bi-m. $90 (foreign $110). (National Water Well Association) Ground Water Publishing Co., 6375 Riverside Dr., Dublin, OH 43017. TEL 614-761-3222. Ed. J. Bredehoeft. abstr.; bibl.; charts; illus.; index. circ. 15,500. (also avail. in microform from UMI; reprint service avail. from UMI) **Indexed:** A.S.& T.Ind., Acid Pre.Dig., Acid Rain Abstr., Acid Rain Ind., AESIS, Biol.Abstr., Br.Geol.Lit., Chem.Abstr., Curr.Adv.Ecol.Sci., Curr.Cont., Energy Ind., Energy Info.Abstr., Energy Rev., Eng.Ind., Environ.Abstr., Environ.Per.Bibl. (1981-), Excerp.Med., Fluidex, Geo.Abstr., Geotech.Abstr., I D A, Ind.Sci.Rev., INIS Atomind., Irr.& Drain.Abstr., Petrol.Abstr. (1966-1987), Sci.Cit.Ind., Sel.J.Water, Sel.Water Res.Abstr., Soils & Fert., W.R.C.Inf.
—BLDSC (4219.450000); CIS; El; Faxon; UnCover; SWETS; UMI; CASDDS. **CCC.**
Refereed Serial

551.49 US
GB1001 CODEN: GWMRDU
GROUND WATER MONITORING & REMEDIATION. 1981. q. $30 (foreign $49). Ground Water Publishing Co., 6375 Riverside Dr., Dublin, OH 43017. TEL 614-761-3222. Ed. Michael Barcelona. adv. circ. 16,000. (back issues avail.) **Indexed:** Chem.Abstr., Curr.Adv.Ecol.Sci., Energy Info.Abstr., Energy Rev., Environ.Abstr., Environ.Per.Bibl., Excerp.Med., Fluidex, Geo.Abstr., Sel.Water Res.Abstr., W.R.C.Inf.
—Faxon; UnCover; SWETS. **CCC.**
Formerly: Ground Water Monitoring Review (ISSN 0277-1926)
Refereed Serial

551.48 US ISSN 0090-5070
CODEN: GWNEDU
THE GROUNDWATER NEWSLETTER. 1972. s-m. $327 (foreign $357) (effective Jan. 1994). Water Information Center, Inc., 1099 18th St., Ste. 2150, Denver, CO 80202. TEL 303-391-8799. Ed. Judith M. Schoek. bk.rev. (looseleaf format; back issues avail.) **Document type:** newsletter.
—**CCC.**
Description: Provides news on groundwater exploration, development, management, recharge, pollution, and waste disposal.

HABITAT - CALABRIA. see *METEOROLOGY*

551.4 JA ISSN 0914-3009
HAIDOROROJI/HYDROLOGY. (Text in English, Japanese; summaries in English) 1967. 3/yr. Nihon Suimon Kagakkai - Japanese Association of Hydrological Science, Tsukuba Daigaku Chikyu Kagakukei, 1-1, Tennodai 1-chome, Tsukuba-shi, Ibaraki-ken 305, Japan.

HAIYANG YU HUZHAO. see *EARTH SCIENCES — Oceanography*

551.4 CC ISSN 1000-1980
CODEN: HEDXEP
HEHAI DAXUE XUEBAO/HOHAI UNIVERSITY. JOURNAL. (Text in Chinese) 1957. bi-m. $6. Hehai Daxue, 1 Xikang Lu, Nanjing, Jiangsu 210024, People's Republic of China. TEL 6632106. Ed. Xiang Darun. **Document type:** academic/scholarly publication.
Description: Publishes original papers in the field of development, management and protection of water resources.

HELICTITE; journal of Australasian cave research. see *EARTH SCIENCES — Geology*

HYDROBIOLOGIA. see *BIOLOGY*

HYDROBIOLOGICAL JOURNAL. see *BIOLOGY*

551.46 UK ISSN 0309-7846
VK588
HYDROGRAPHIC JOURNAL. 1972. q. £40 to non-members (effective 1994). Hydrographic Society, International Headquarters, University of East London, Longbridge Rd., Dagenham, Essex RM8 2AS, England. TEL 081-597-1946. FAX 081-590-9730. Ed. J. Kitching. adv.; bk.rev. circ. 2,500. (back issues avail.) **Document type:** academic/scholarly publication.
—BLDSC (4346.100000); Faxon.
Incorporates: Information Bulletin.
Description: Contains authoritative articles and papers dealing with all aspects of hydrographic surveying and related sciences authored by acknowledged experts.

551 UK ISSN 0885-6087
GB651 CODEN: HYPRE3
HYDROLOGICAL PROCESSES: AN INTERNATIONAL JOURNAL. 1987. bi-m. $345 (effective 1994). John Wiley & Sons Ltd., Journals, Baffins Ln., Chichester, W. Sussex PO19 1UD, England. TEL 0243-779777. FAX 0243-775878. TELEX 86290 WIBOOK G. Ed. M.G. Anderson. adv.; bk.rev.; illus.; maps. circ. 318. (reprint service avail. from SWZ) **Indexed:** Curr.Cont., Eng.Ind., Environ.Abstr., Environ.Per.Bibl. (1990-), Geotech.Abstr., Sel.J.Water, Sel.Water Res.Abstr. **Document type:** academic/scholarly publication.
—BLDSC (4347.625600); El; Faxon; SWETS; UMI. **CCC.**
Description: Reflects the findings on environmental hydrology with an emphasis on field processes, their modelling and forecasting.

HYDROLOGICAL SCIENCE AND TECHNOLOGY. see *WATER RESOURCES*

551.4 UK ISSN 0262-6667
GB651 CODEN: HSJODN
HYDROLOGICAL SCIENCES JOURNAL/JOURNAL DES SCIENCES HYDROLOGIQUES. (Text in English and French) 1956. bi-m. £105($160) (Institute of Hydrology) I A H S Press, Wallingford, Oxford OX10 8BB, England. TEL 0491-838800. FAX 0491-832256. E-mail: 849365-HYDROL-G. Ed. Terrence O'Donnell. adv.; bk.rev.; index. circ. 1,000. (back issues avail.; reprint service avail. from ISI) **Indexed:** Acid Pre.Dig., ASCA, Chem.Abstr., Curr.Adv.Ecol.Sci., Curr.Cont., Curr.Ref.Fish Res., Eng.Ind., Excerp.Med., Fluidex, Geo.Abstr., Geotech.Abstr., Int.Abstr.Oper.Res., Irr.& Drain.Abstr., Meteor.& Geoastrophys.Abstr., Sel.Water Res.Abstr., Soils & Fert., W.R.C.Inf. **Document type:** academic/scholarly publication.
—BLDSC (4347.628100); El; Faxon; UnCover; SWETS; UMI; CASDDS. **CCC.**
Former titles (until 1981): Hydrological Sciences Bulletin (ISSN 0303-6936); (until 1971): International Association of Scientific Hydrology. Bulletin (ISSN 0020-6024)
Description: Disseminates news and opinion on important developments in hydrology.
Refereed Serial

551.48 IS ISSN 0073-4217
HYDROLOGICAL YEARBOOK OF ISRAEL/SHENATON HIDROLOGI LE-YISRAEL. (Text in English and Hebrew) 1946. a. $36. Ministry of Agriculture Water Commission, Hydrological Service, P.O. Box 6381, Jerusalem 91063, Israel. TEL 972-2-381101. FAX 972-2-388704. Ed. A. Ben-Zvi. circ. 250. **Document type:** government publication.
—BLDSC (4347.750000).
Description: Data on streamflow and springflow in Israel.

HYDROLOGIE CONTINENTALE. see *WATER RESOURCES*

HYDROTITLES; hydroscience bibliography. see *EARTH SCIENCES — Abstracting, Bibliographies, Statistics*

551.4 333.91 US ISSN 0741-8507
I G W M C GROUND WATER MODELING NEWSLETTER. 1981. q. free. International Ground Water Modeling Center, Colorado School of Mines, Institute for Ground Water Research and Education, Golden, CO 80401. TEL 303-273-3103. Ed. Paul K.M. van der Heijde. bk.rev.; software rev. circ. 4,000. (back issues avail.) **Document type:** newsletter.
Description: Technical level of interest for engineers and water resources experts in groundwater modeling. Contains announcements of new publications, events and short courses.

551.48 JA ISSN 0289-9531
IBARAKI UNIVERSITY. ITAKO HYDROBIOLOGICAL STATION. PUBLICATIONS. (Text in English) 1984. a. Ibaraki University, Faculty of Science, Itako Hydrobiological Station - Ibaraki Daigaku Rigakubu Fuzoku Itako Rinko Jikkenjo, 1375, Ou Itako-cho, Namekata-gun, Ibaraki-ken 311-24, Japan.

INSTITUT FUER WASSERWIRTSCHAFT, HYDROLOGIE UND LANDWIRTSCHAFTLICHEN WASSERBAU. MITTEILUNGEN. see *WATER RESOURCES*

551.4 627 RM
INSTITUTUL POLITEHNIC DIN IASI. BULETINUL. SECTIA VII: HIDROTEHNICA. (Text in English, French, German, Italian, Russian, Spanish) 1946. s-a. exchange basis. Institutul Politehnic din Iasi, Bd. Copou 11, 6600 Jassy, Rumania. TEL 46577. FAX 40-81-47923. Eds. Alfred Braier, Hugo Rosman. bk.rev.

551.4 PL ISSN 0239-6297
GB651
INSTYTUT METEOROLOGII I GOSPODARKI WODNEJ. MATERIALY BADAWCZE. SERIA: HYDROLOGIA I OCEANOLOGIA/INSTITUTE OF METEOROLOGY AND WATER MANAGEMENT. RESEARCH PAPERS SERIES: HYDROLOGY AND OCEANOLOGY. (Text in Polish; summaries in English and Russian) 1977. irreg. $15. Instytut Meteorologii i Gospodarki Wodnej - Institute of Meteorology and Water Management, 61 Podlesna St., 01-673 Warsaw, Poland. FAX 48-22-345456. TELEX 814331. circ. 200.
Description: Articles on hydrology, oceanology, methodics, forecastings, measurements, instruments and research works.

INTERAFRICAN COMMITTEE FOR HYDRAULIC STUDIES. LIAISON BULLETIN. see *WATER RESOURCES*

551.4 UK ISSN 0579-6733
CODEN: IAHMAP
INTERNATIONAL ASSOCIATION OF HYDROGEOLOGISTS. MEMOIRES. irreg. International Association of Hydrogeologists, c/o Dr. Andrew Skinner, Sec.-Gen., National Rivers Authority, Sapphire East, 550 Streetsbrook Rd., Solihull B91 1QT, England. TEL 44-21-7225802. FAX 44-21-7225824. **Document type:** monographic series.

551.48 GW ISSN 0538-4680
CODEN: IVTMAS
INTERNATIONAL ASSOCIATION OF THEORETICAL AND APPLIED LIMNOLOGY. COMMUNICATIONS/INTERNATIONALE VEREINIGUNG FUER THEORETISCHE UND ANGEWANDTE LIMNOLOGIE. MITTEILUNGEN. (Text in English and German) 1953. irreg. price varies. (International Association of Theoretical and Applied Limnology) E. Schweizerbart'sche Verlagsbuchhandlung, Johannesstr. 3A, 70176 Stuttgart, Germany. TEL 0711-625001. FAX 0711-625005. TELEX 723363-SCHB-D. Ed. R.G. Wetzel. circ. 4,000. **Indexed:** Biol.Abstr. **Document type:** monographic series.
—BLDSC (3352.000000); CASDDS. **CCC.**

551.48 GW ISSN 0368-0770
QH98 CODEN: IVTLAP
INTERNATIONAL ASSOCIATION OF THEORETICAL AND APPLIED LIMNOLOGY. PROCEEDINGS/INTERNATIONALE VEREINIGUNG FUER THEORETISCHE UND ANGEWANDTE LIMNOLOGIE. VERHANDLUNGEN. (Text in English, French and German) 1922. triennial. price varies. E. Schweizerbart'sche Verlagsbuchhandlung, Johannesstr. 3A, 70176 Stuttgart, Germany. TEL 0711-625001. FAX 0711-625005. TELEX 723363-SCHB-D. Ed. A. Sladeckova. index. circ. 3,000. **Indexed:** Biol.Abstr., Chem.Abstr., Deep Sea Res.& Oceanogr.Abstr., Excerp.Med., Sel.Water Res.Abstr., W.R.C.Inf. **Document type:** proceedings.
—BLDSC (6728.000000); SWETS; CASDDS. **CCC.**

INTERNATIONAL HYDROGRAPHIC BULLETIN. see *EARTH SCIENCES — Oceanography*

INTERNATIONAL HYDROGRAPHIC CONFERENCE. REPORTS OF PROCEEDINGS. see *EARTH SCIENCES — Oceanography*

INTERNATIONAL HYDROGRAPHIC ORGANIZATION. YEARBOOK. see *EARTH SCIENCES — Oceanography*

INTERNATIONAL HYDROGRAPHIC REVIEW. see *EARTH SCIENCES — Oceanography*

EARTH SCIENCES — HYDROLOGY

551.4   JA   ISSN 0912-7410
INTERNATIONAL LAKE ENVIRONMENT COMMITTEE FOUNDATION. NEWSLETTER. ENGLISH EDITION.
Japanese edition (ISSN 0912-7402) 1986. a. Kokusai Kosho Kankyo Iinkai - International Lake Environment Committee Foundation, Shiga Kaikan, 4-22, Kyomachi 3-chome, Otsu-shi, Shiga-ken 520, Japan. **Document type:** newsletter.

551.4   JA   ISSN 0912-7402
INTERNATIONAL LAKE ENVIRONMENT COMMITTEE FOUNDATION. NEWSLETTER. JAPANESE EDITION.
English edition (ISSN 0912-7410) 1986. irreg. Kokusai Kosho Kankyo Iinkai - International Lake Environment Committee Foundation, Shiga Kaikan, 4-22, Kyomachi 3-chome, Otsu-shi, Shiga-ken 520, Japan. **Document type:** newsletter.

551.4   GW   ISSN 0344-5259
GB731
INTERNATIONALES HYDROLOGISCHES PROGRAMM: OPERATIONELLES HYDROLOGISCHES PROGRAMM: JAHRBUCH BUNDESREPUBLIK DEUTSCHLAND UND BERLIN (WEST)/INTERNATIONAL HYDROLOGICAL PROGRAMME: OPERATIONAL HYDROLOGICAL PROGRAMME: YEARBOOK FEDERAL REPUBLIC OF GERMANY AND BERLIN (WEST). (Text in English and German) 1965; N.S. 1968. a. exchange basis. Bundesanstalt fuer Gewaesserkunde, Postfach 309, 56003 Koblenz, Germany. TEL 0261-1306-0. FAX 0261-1306302. TELEX 8-62499. circ. 700. **Document type:** government publication.
Formerly: Internationale Hydrologische Dekade: Yearbook of the Federal Republic of Germany (ISSN 0538-7779)
Description: Surveys hydrological processes in Germany by means of selected stations.

551.4   RU   ISSN 0202-7356
GB1001   CODEN: INGGDS
ITOGI NAUKI I TEKHNIKI: GIDROGEOLOGIYA. INZHENERNAYA GEOLOGIYA. irreg., vol.11, 1989. price varies. Vsesoyuznyi Institut Nauchno-Tekhnicheskoi Informatsii (VINITI), Baltiiskaya ul. 14, Moscow A-219, Russia. (Subscr. to: Mezhdunarodnaya Kniga, Dimitrova ul. 39, 113095 Moscow, Russia) **Indexed:** GeoRef.
—BLDSC (0048.493000).

551.48   JA   ISSN 0021-5104
CODEN: RIZAAU
JAPANESE JOURNAL OF LIMNOLOGY/RIKUSUI GAKU ZASSHI. (Text in English and Japanese) 1931. q. 10000 Yen. Japanese Society of Limnology - Nihon Rikusui Gakkai, Shiga University, Faculty of Education, 2-5-1 Hiratsu Ohotsu-shi, Shiga 520, Japan. TEL 0426-77-2531. FAX 0426-77-2525. Ed. Yasuhiko Tezuka. adv.; bk.rev.; charts; illus. circ. 1,200. **Indexed:** Chem.Abstr., Curr.Tit.Ocean, Excerp.Med., Geo.Abstr., GeoRef., Sel.Water Res.Abstr. **Document type:** academic/scholarly publication.
—BLDSC (4656.000000); UnCover; CASDDS.

JOEKULL. see EARTH SCIENCES — Geology

JOURNAL OF CONTAMINANT HYDROLOGY. see ENVIRONMENTAL STUDIES — Pollution

551.48 614.7   US   ISSN 0270-5060
QH541.5.F7   CODEN: JFREDW
JOURNAL OF FRESHWATER ECOLOGY. 1981. q. $48 (foreign $60). Oikos Publishers, Inc., Box 2558, La Crosse, WI 54602-2558. TEL 608-526-9577. Ed. Joseph A. Kawatski. circ. 500. **Indexed:** Acid Rain Abstr., Acid Rain Ind., Biol.Abstr., Chem.Abstr., Curr.Adv.Ecol.Sci., Curr.Cont., Curr.Ref.Fish Res., Environ.Abstr., Environ.Per.Bibl. (1990-), Sel.Water Res.Abstr. **Document type:** academic/scholarly publication.
—BLDSC (4986.540000); Faxon; UnCover; SWETS; CASDDS.

JOURNAL OF GREAT LAKES RESEARCH; devoted to research on large lakes of the world. see ENVIRONMENTAL STUDIES

551.4 333.9   JA   ISSN 0913-4182
GB1001
JOURNAL OF GROUNDWATER HYDROLOGY/CHIKASUI GAKKAISHI. (Text in English, Japanese) 1959. q. 6000 Yen. Japanese Association of Groundwater Hydrology - Nippon Chikasui Gakkai, c/o Dept. of Earth Sciences, Faculty of Science, Chiba University, 1-33 Yayoi-cho, Inage-ku, Chiba 263, Japan. TEL 81-43-290-2846. Ed. Makoto Nishigakiwa. adv.; bk.rev.; index. **Indexed:** Excerp.Med., GeoRef., Sel.Water Res.Abstr. **Document type:** academic/scholarly publication.
Formerly: Japanese Association of Groundwater Hydrology. Journal (ISSN 0029-0602)

551.4   NE   ISSN 0022-1694
GB651   CODEN: JHYDA7
JOURNAL OF HYDROLOGY. (Text in English, French, German) 1963. 48/yr. (in 12 vols.; 4 nos./vol.). fl.4272($2309) (effective 1994). Elsevier Science B.V., P.O. Box 211, 1000 AE Amsterdam, Netherlands. TEL 31-20-5803911. FAX 31-20-5803598. TELEX 18582 ESPA NL. (Subscr. in U.S. and Canada to: Elsevier Science Inc., Box 882, Madison Sq. Sta., New York, NY 10159-0882. TEL 212-989-5800. FAX 212-633-3990) Ed.Bd. adv.; bk.rev.; charts; illus.; index. (also avail. in microform from UMI; reprint service avail. from ISI,SWZ) **Indexed:** Acid Pre.Dig., Acid Rain Abstr., Acid Rain Ind., AESIS, Agri.Eng.Abstr., Appl.Mech.Rev., Biol.Abstr., Bull.Signal., Chem.Abstr., Curr.Adv.Ecol.Sci., Curr.Cont., Curr.Ref.Fish Res., Deep Sea Res.& Oceanogr.Abstr., Energy Info.Abstr., Environ.Abstr., Excerp.Med., Field Crop Abstr., Fluidex, Forest.Abstr., Forest Prod.Abstr., Geo.Abstr., GeoRef., Geotech.Abstr., Herb.Abstr., I D A, Ind.Sci.Rev., Irr.& Drain.Abstr., Maize Abstr., Meteor.& Geoastrophys.Abstr., Sci.Cit.Ind., Sel.J.Water, Sel.Water Res.Abstr., So.Pac.Per.Ind., Soils & Fert., Triticale Abstr., W.R.C.Inf. **Document type:** academic/scholarly publication.
—BLDSC (5003.700000); EI; Faxon; UnCover; SWETS; CASDDS. **CCC.**
Description: Presents original studies, research results and reviews on the chemical and physical aspects of surface and groundwater hydrology, hydrometeorology, hydrogeology, parametric and stochastic hydrology, agrohydrology, hydrology of arid zones, and applied hydrology.
Refereed Serial

551.4   NZ   ISSN 0022-1708
GB651   CODEN: JLHYAD
JOURNAL OF HYDROLOGY. NEW ZEALAND. 1962. s-a. NZ.$40 to members and institutions (effective 1993). New Zealand Hydrological Society, P.O. Box 12-300, Wellington, New Zealand. TEL 64-3-351-7099. FAX 64-3-351-7091. Ed. M.K. Stewart. adv.; bk.rev.; abstr.; charts; illus.; cum.index every 5 yrs.; circ. 500 (paid). (also avail. in microfilm) **Indexed:** Agri.Eng.Abstr., Appl.Mech.Rev., Biol.Abstr., Eng.Ind., Excerp.Med., Geo.Abstr., GeoRef., Intl.Civil Eng.Abstr., Meteor.& Geoastrophys.Abstr., Sel.Water Res.Abstr., Soft.Abstr.Eng., Soils & Fert., W.R.C.Inf. **Document type:** academic/scholarly publication.
—BLDSC (5003.750000); UMI. **CCC.**
Refereed Serial

551.4 627   IQ   ISSN 0255-0148
JOURNAL OF WATER RESOURCES. (Text in Arabic, English) 1982. s-a. $30. I H P - Iraqi National Committee, Box 26054 Waziriya, Baghdad, Iraq. TELEX 212290 IK. Ed. Nadhir A. Al-Ansari. adv.; bk.rev.; charts.
—BLDSC (5072.539000).
Description: Presents papers on original or applied research related to the fields of hydrology and water resources.

K R S JUGOSLAVIJE/CARSUS JUGOSLAVIAE. see EARTH SCIENCES — Geology

551.48   JA   ISSN 0914-8272
KAIJO HOANCHO. SUIROBU KANSOKU HOKOKU. CHORYU HEN/DATA REPORT OF HYDROGRAPHIC OBSERVATIONS. SERIES OF TIDAL STREAM. (Text in English, Japanese) 1987. a. Kaijo Hoancho, Suirobu - Maritime Safety Agency, Hydrographic Department, 3-1, Tsukiji 5-chome, Chuo-ku, Tokyo 104, Japan.

551.48   JA   ISSN 0448-3308
KAIJO HOANCHO. SUIROBU KANSOKU HOKOKU. CHOSEKI HEN/DATA REPORT OF HYDROGRAPHIC OBERVATIONS. SERIES OF TIDE. (Text in English) 1965. a. Kaijo Hoancho, Suirobu - Maritime Safety Agency, Hydrographic Department, 3-1, Tsukiji 5-chome, Chuo-ku, Tokyo 104, Japan.

551.48   JA   ISSN 0910-9102
KAIJO HOANCHO. SUIROBU KANSOKU HOKOKU. HACHIJO SUIRO KANSOKUJO CHIJIKI KANSOKU NENPO/DATA REPORT OF HYDROGRAPHIC OBSERVATIONS. HATIZYO HYDROGRAPHIC OBSERVATORY. GEOMAGNETIC OBSERVATIONS. (Text in English) a. Kaijo Hoancho, Suirobu - Maritime Safety Agency, Hydrographic Department, 3-1, Tsukiji 5-chome, Chuo-ku, Tokyo 104, Japan.

551.48   JA
KAIJO HOANCHO. SUIROBU KANSOKU HOKOKU. HARO HEN/DATA REPORT OF HYDROGRAPHIC OBSERVATIONS. WAVE OBSERVATIONS. (Text in English, Japanese) a. Kaijo Hoancho, Suirobu - Maritime Safety Agency, Hydrographic Department, 3-1, Tsukiji 5-chome, Chuo-ku, Tokyo 104, Japan.

551.48   JA
KAIJO HOANCHO. SUIROBU KANSOKU HOKOKU. KAIYO HEN/DATA REPORT OF HYDROGRAPHIC OBSERVATIONS. SERIES OF OCEANOGRAPHY. (Text in English) 1965. a. Kaijo Hoancho, Suirobu - Maritime Safety Agency, Hydrographic Department, 3-1, Tsukiji 5-chome, Chuo-ku, Tokyo 104, Japan.

551.48   JA   ISSN 0021-4485
KAIJO HOANCHO SUIROBU SUIRO YOHO/MARITIME SAFETY AGENCY. HYDROGRAPHIC DEPARTMENT. HYDROGRAPHIC BULLETIN. 1922. a. price varies. Kaijo Hoancho, Suirobu - Maritime Safety Agency, Hydrographic Department, 1-3, Kasumigaseki 2-chome, Chiyoda-ku, Tokyo 100, Japan. FAX 03-545-2885. TELEX 2522452 HDJODC J. Ed. Takahiro Sato.

KASEN JOHO KENKYUJO HOKOKU/INSTITUTE OF RIVER AND BASIN INTEGRATED COMMUNICATIONS. REPORT. see WATER RESOURCES

551.4   JA   ISSN 0287-4660
KIKAN SUIRO. (Text in Japanese) 1972. q. 400 Yen per no. Nihon Suiro Kyokai - Japan Hydrographic Association, 15-16, Toranomon 1-chome, Minato-ku, Tokyo 105, Japan.

KYOTO UNIVERSITY. OTSU HYDROBIOLOGICAL STATION. COLLECTED PAPERS. see BIOLOGY

551.48   JA   ISSN 0289-3363
LAKE BIWA STUDY MONOGRAPHS/BIWAKO KENKYU MONOGURAFU. (Text in English; summaries in English, Japanese) 1984. irreg. free. Lake Biwa Research Institute - Shigaken Biwako Kenkyujo, 1-10, Uchide-hama, Otsu-shi, Shiga-ken 520, Japan. TEL 0775-26-4800. FAX 0775-26-4803. Ed. Tatuo Kira. circ. 400. **Document type:** monographic series.

551.4   LO
LESOTHO. MINISTRY OF NATURAL RESOURCES. HYDROLOGICAL YEARBOOK. (Former name of issuing body: Lesotho. Ministry of Water, Energy and Mining) (Text in English) 1970. quinquennial. $5. Ministry of Natural Resources, Water Affairs Department, P.O. Box MS 772, Maseru 100, Lesotho. FAX 310437. TELEX 4431. circ. (controlled). (back issues avail.) **Document type:** government publication.

551.48   SP   ISSN 0213-8409
LIMNETICA. (Text and summaries in English, Spanish) 1985. a. 7000 ptas.($84) (effective 1992). Asociacion Espanola de Limnologia, Museo Nacional de Ciencias Naturales, C. Jose Gutierrez Abascal, 2, 28006 Madrid, Spain. TEL 91-4649881. FAX 91-3974168. Ed. Luis Cruz-Pizarro. index. circ. 600. (back issues avail.) **Indexed:** Zoo.Rec.
—BLDSC (5219.400000).
Description: Covers research and studies in limnology from the Iberian peninsula.
Refereed Serial

EARTH SCIENCES — HYDROLOGY

551.48 GW ISSN 0075-9511
QH96.A1 CODEN: LMNOA8
LIMNOLOGICA; ecology and management of inland waters. 1962. 4/yr. DM.344 (foreign DM.350). Gustav Fischer Verlag Jena, Villengang 2, 07745 Jena, Germany. TEL 03641-27332. FAX 03641-22638. (Subscr. to: Postfach 100537, 07705 Jena, Germany) Ed. J. Casper. **Indexed:** Biol.Abstr., Chem.Abstr., Deep Sea Res.& Oceanogr.Abstr., Excerp.Med., GeoRef., INIS Atomind., Sel.J.Water, Sel.Water Res.Abstr., W.R.C.Inf. **Document type:** academic/scholarly publication.
—BLDSC (5219.450000); UnCover; SWETS; CASDDS.

551.48 551.46 US ISSN 0024-3590
GC1 CODEN: LIOCAH
LIMNOLOGY AND OCEANOGRAPHY. 1956. 8/yr. $160. American Society of Limnology and Oceanography, Inc., School of Oceanography, WB-10, University of Washington, Seattle, WA 98195. FAX 206-543-8655. (Subscr. to: c/o Karen Hickey, Bus. Mgr., 810 E. 10th St., Lawrence, KS 66044. TEL 800-627-0629) Ed. Raelyn Cole. bk.rev.; charts; illus.; index. circ. 5,300. **Indexed:** Abstr.Bull.Inst.Pap.Chem., Acid Pre.Dig., Acid Rain Abstr., Acid Rain Ind., Aqua.Sci.& Fish.Abstr., Biol.Abstr., Biol.& Agr.Ind., Cadscan, Chem.Abstr., Curr.Adv.Ecol.Sci., Curr.Cont., Curr.Ref.Fish Res., Deep Sea Res.& Oceanogr.Abstr., Energy Ind., Energy Info.Abstr., Excerp.Med., Geo.Abstr., GeoRef., Helminthol.Abstr., Ind.Sci.Rev., INIS Atomind., Lead Abstr., Mar.Sci.Cont.Tab., Meteor.& Geoastrophys.Abstr., Ocean.Abstr., Pollut.Abstr., Rice Abstr., Risk Abstr., Sel.J.Water, Sel.Water Res.Abstr., So.Pac.Per.Ind., Soils & Fert., W.R.C.Inf., Zincscan. **Document type:** academic/scholarly publication.
—BLDSC (5219.500000); Faxon; UnCover; SWETS; UMI; CASDDS.
Description: Covers all areas of aquatic research (except fisheries and pollution) at research level or advanced graduate studies.
Refereed Serial

LIST OF HYDROBIOLOGICAL PAPERS OF BRITISH FRESH WATERS. see *ENVIRONMENTAL STUDIES — Abstracting, Bibliographies, Statistics*

LOUISIANA WATER RESOURCES RESEARCH INSTITUTE. ANNUAL REPORT. see *WATER RESOURCES*

MARINE MICROBIAL FOOD WEBS. see *BIOLOGY — Microbiology*

MEMORIE DI SCIENZE GEOLOGICHE. see *EARTH SCIENCES — Geology*

MISSOURI. DIVISION OF GEOLOGICAL SURVEY AND WATER RESOURCES. WATER RESOURCES REPORT. see *WATER RESOURCES*

MONDO SOMMERSO; international magazine on nature, ecology, environment, sea diving activities, and travels. see *EARTH SCIENCES — Oceanography*

MONO LAKE COMMITTEE NEWSLETTER. see *WATER RESOURCES*

551.4 DK ISSN 0900-0267
N H P RAPPORT. 1981. irrege. price varies. Nordisk Hydrologisk Forening, c/o Miljoestyrelsen, Vandressource Kontoret, Strandgade 29, 1401 Copenhagen K, Denmark. illus.

NATIONAL DRILLERS BUYERS GUIDE. see *WATER RESOURCES*

NATIONAL SYMPOSIUM ON MINING. PROCEEDINGS. see *MINES AND MINING INDUSTRY*

551.48 US
NEW MEXICO. BUREAU OF MINES AND MINERAL RESOURCES. HYDROLOGIC REPORT. 1948. irreg., no.7, 1984. price varies. Bureau of Mines and Mineral Resources, Socorro, NM 87801. TEL 505-835-5410. illus. also avail. in microfiche) **Indexed:** GeoRef. **Document type:** government publication.
Supersedes (in 1971): Ground-Water Reports.

NEW MEXICO GEOLOGY. see *EARTH SCIENCES — Geology*

NEW WAVES (COLLEGE STATION). see *WATER RESOURCES*

NEW ZEALAND JOURNAL OF MARINE AND FRESHWATER RESEARCH. see *EARTH SCIENCES — Oceanography*

NIHON RIKUSUI GAKKAI KOEN YOSHISHU/JAPANESE SOCIETY OF LIMNOLOGY. ABSTRACTS OF MEETING. see *EARTH SCIENCES — Abstracting, Bibliographies, Statistics*

441.48 JA ISSN 0913-4859
NIHON RIKUSUI GAKKAI KOSHIN'ETSU SHIBUKAI KAIHO/LIMNOLOGICAL SOCIETY OF KOSHIN'ETSU DISTRICT. BULLETIN. (Text in Japanese; summaries in English, Japanese) 1977. a. Nihon Rikusui Gakkai - Japanese Society of Limnology, Tokyo Toritsu Daigaku Rigakubu Kagaku Kyoshitsu, 1-1, Minamiosawa, Hachioji-shi, Tokyo 192-03, Japan.

551.46 JA
NIHON SUIRO KYOKAI CHOSA KENKYU SHIRYO/JAPAN HYDROGRAPHIC ASSOCIATION. RESEARCH REPORTS. (Text in Japanese) 4/yr. Nihon Suiro Kyokai, 15-16, Toranomon 1-chome, Minato-ku, Tokyo 100, Japan.

551.4 DK ISSN 0029-1277
GB651 CODEN: NOHYBB
NORDIC HYDROLOGY; an international journal. (Text and summaries in English) 1970. 5/yr. DKK 423 (effective 1994). Nordic Association of Hydrology, c/o ISVA, Technical University of Denmark, Bldg. 115, DK-2800 Lyngby, Denmark. TEL 45-42-88-48-29. FAX 45-45-93-28-60. TELEX 37529 DTHDIA DK. Ed. Dan Rosberg. bk.rev.; bibl.; charts; illus. circ. 400. **Indexed:** Acid Rain Abstr., Acid Rain Ind., Agri.Eng.Abstr., Biol.Abstr., Chem.Abstr., Curr.Adv.Ecol.Sci., Curr.Cont., Energy Info.Abstr., Environ.Abstr., Excerp.Med., Fluidex, Forest.Abstr., Geo.Abstr., GeoRef., Ind.Sci.Rev., Intl.Civil Eng.Abstr., Irr.& Drain.Abstr., Meteor.& Geoastrophys.Abstr., Ocean.Abstr., Sci.Cit.Ind., Sel.Water Res.Abstr., Soft.Abstr.Eng., Soils & Fert., W.R.C.Inf.
—BLDSC (6117.920000); EI; UnCover; SWETS; CASDDS.
Description: Publishes articles on hydrology, hydrometeorology, hydrodynamics with the emphasis on hydrological cycle; also covers physics and chemistry of water.

551 NO
NORSK INSTITUTT FOR VANNFORSKNING. AARSBERETNING. 1958. a. free. Norsk Institutt for Vannforskning - Norwegian Institute for Water Research, Postboks 69 Korsvoll, 0808 Oslo 8, Norway. TEL 02-235280. FAX 02-394189. illus. **Indexed:** Deep Sea Res.& Oceanogr.Abstr.
Formerly: Norsk Institutt for Vannforskning. Aarbok.

551 NO
NORSK INSTITUTT FOR VANNFORSKNING. RESEARCH REPORTS. irreg. NOK 150. Norsk Institutt for Vannforskning - Norwegian Institute for Water Research, Postboks 69 Korsvoll, 0808 Oslo 8, Norway. TEL 02-235280. charts; illus.
Formerly: Norsk Institutt for Vannforskning. Temarapport.

551.48 JA
OMIA/LAKE BIWA RESEARCH INSTITUTE. NEWS. (Text in Japanese) 1982. irreg. Shigaken Biwako Kenkyujo - Lake Biwa Research Institute, 1-10, Uchidehama, Otsu-shi, Shiga-ken 520, Japan.

551.48 UN ISSN 0379-1335
QC851 CODEN: WMOHBC
OPERATIONAL HYDROLOGY REPORT. 1973. irreg., latest no.38. price varies. World Meteorological Organization, 41 Av. Giuseppe Motta, CH-1211 Geneva 2, Switzerland. TEL 730-8111. (Dist. in U.S. by: American Meteorological Society, 45 Beacon St., Boston, MA 02108. TEL 617-227-2425) **Indexed:** Meteor.& Geoastrophys.Abstr.
Description: Technical reports about operational hydrology.

P A S C A L. F 46: HYDROLOGIE. GEOLOGIE DE L'INGENIEUR. FORMATIONS SUPERFICIELLES. see *EARTH SCIENCES — Abstracting, Bibliographies, Statistics*

PRIRODOSLOVNA ISTRAZIVANJA: ACTA GEOLOGICA. see *EARTH SCIENCES — Geology*

551.4 US
PROCEEDINGS OF THE ARIZONA SECTION, AMERICAN WATER RESOURCES ASSOCIATION AND THE HYDROLOGY SECTION, ARIZONA-NEVADA ACADEMY OF SCIENCE. 1971. a. $14. American Water Resources Association, Arizona Section, Office of Arid Lands Studies, 845 N. Park Ave., Tucson, AZ 85719. Ed.Bd. charts; illus.; stat. (back issues avail.)

PROFESSIONAL GEOLOGIST. see *EARTH SCIENCES — Geology*

REPORTS OF INVESTIGATIONS ABOUT LAKE BIWA. see *PUBLIC HEALTH AND SAFETY*

551.4 628.167 FR ISSN 0992-7158
CODEN: RSEAEX
REVUE DES SCIENCES DE L'EAU; journal of water science. (Text in English or French; summaries in English, French) 1982. q. 660 F. Lavoisier Abonnements, 11 rue Lavoisier, 75384 Paris Cedex 08, France. Ed. M. Dore. circ. 1,000. **Indexed:** Chem.Abstr., Curr.Adv.Ecol.Sci., Environ.Abstr., Environ.Per.Bibl., W.R.C.Inf.
—BLDSC (7947 650000); EI; Faxon; CASDDS. CCC.
Formed by the 1988 merger of: Revue Internationale des Sciences de l'Eau (ISSN 0830-9590) & Sciences de l'Eau (ISSN 0298-6663); Which was formerly (until 1986): Revue Francaise des Sciences de l'Eau (ISSN 0750-7186); Incorporates: Journal Francais d'Hydrologie (ISSN 0335-9581)
Description: Devoted to water sciences.

RUSSIAN METEOROLOGY AND HYDROLOGY. see *METEOROLOGY*

SAVE THE HARBOR - SAVE THE BAY NEWSLETTER. see *ENVIRONMENTAL STUDIES*

551.4 XR ISSN 0036-5289
GB1001 CODEN: SGVHAS
SBORNIK GEOLOGICKYCH VED: HYDROGEOLOGIE, INZENYRSKA GEOLOGIE/JOURNAL OF GEOLOGICAL SCIENCES: HYDROGEOLOGY, ENGINEERING GEOLOGY. (Text and summaries in Czech, English, French, German, Russian) 1964. irreg. Cesky Geologicky Ustav, Malostranske nam. 19, 118 21 Prague 1, Czech Republic. (Dist. by: Artia, Ve Smeckach 30, 111 27 Prague 1, Czech Republic) Ed. Jan Jetel. charts; illus. circ. 600. (back issues avail.) **Indexed:** Bull.Signal., GeoRef., Ref.Zh.

551.48 CN ISSN 0382-2915
SELECTED STREAMFLOW DATA FOR ONTARIO. 1969. a. Ministry of the Environment, Water Resources Branch, 1 St. Clair Avenue W., 4th Fl., Toronto, Ont. M4V 1K6, Canada. TEL 416-965-6141. (Subscr. to: Environment Canada, 75 Farkuahar St., Guelph, Ont. N1H 3N7, Canada) (diskette format)

SELECTED WATER RESOURCES ABSTRACTS. see *EARTH SCIENCES — Abstracting, Bibliographies, Statistics*

551.48 JA ISSN 0914-3068
SHIGA DAIGAKU KYOIKUGAKUBU KOSHO JISSHU SHISETSU RONBUNSHU/SHIGA UNIVERSITY. FACULTY OF EDUCATION. INSTITUTE OF LAKE SCIENCES. ANNUAL REPORT. (Text in Japanese; summaries in English, Japanese) 1961. a. Shiga Daigaku, Kyoikugakubu, Kosho Jisshu Shisetsu, 5-1, Hiratsu 2-chome, Otsu-shi, Shiga-ken 520, Japan.

551.48 JA ISSN 0289-7636
SHIGA KENRITSU BIWAKO BUNKAKAN KENKYU KIYO/BIWAKO BUNKAKAN. ANNUAL REPORT. (Text in Japanese) 1983. a. Shiga Kenritsu Biwako Bunkakan, 1-1 Uchidehama, Otu-shi, Shiga-ken 520, Japan.

551.48 JA ISSN 0288-1330
SHIGAKEN BIWAKO KENKYUJO SHOHO/LAKE BIWA RESEARCH INSTITUTE. BULLETIN. (Text in English) 1982. a. Shigaken Biwako Kenkyojo, 1-10, Uchidehama, Otsu-shi, Shiga-ken 520, Japan. **Document type:** bulletin.

551.48 574 JA ISSN 0916-3255
SHINSHU DAIGAKU RIGAKUBU FUZOKU SUWA RINKO JIKKENJO HOKOKU/SHINSHU UNIVERSITY. SUWA HYDROBIOLOGICAL STATION. REPORT. (Text in English, Japanese; summaries in English) 1976. irreg. Shinshu Daigaku, Rigakubu, Fuzoku Suwa Rinko Jikkenjo - Shinshu University, Faculty of Science, Suwa Hydrobiological Station, 2-4, Kogan Dori 5-chome, Suwa-shi, Nagano-ken 392, Japan.

1982 EARTH SCIENCES — OCEANOGRAPHY

SHUISHENG SHENGWU XUEBAO/ACTA HYDROBIOLOGICA SINICA. see *BIOLOGY*

551.4 CC
SHUIWEN DIZHI GONGCHENG DIZHI/HYDROGEOLOGY AND ENGINEERING GEOLOGY. (Text in Chinese; abstracts in English) 1957. bi-m. Y16.80 (effective 1994). Dizhi Kuangchan Bu - Ministry of Geology and Mineral Resources, 20 Dahui Si, Haidian District, Beijing 100081, People's Republic of China. TEL 8950262. FAX 8350261. (Subscr. to: 504 Anhuali, Andingmenwai, Beijing, P.R. China. TEL 861-4215031) Ed. Yu Huanxin. adv.: page $500; adv. contact: Gao Yansong. **Document type:** academic/scholarly publication.

SOUTHERN AFRICAN JOURNAL OF AQUATIC SCIENCES. see *BIOLOGY*

551.4 CE
SRI LANKA. IRRIGATION DEPARTMENT. HYDROLOGY DIVISION. HYDROLOGICAL ANNUAL. a. Irrigation Department, Hydrology Division, Bauddhaloka Mawatha, Colombo 7, Sri Lanka. illus. **Document type:** government publication.

551.48 US ISSN 0376-4826
CODEN: SBHYA8
STEIRISCHE BEITRAEGE ZUR HYDROGEOLOGIE. a. price varies. Springer-Verlag, 175 Fifth Ave., New York, NY 10010. TEL 212-460-1500. (Also Berlin, Heidelberg, Tokyo and Vienna) Ed. Josef Zoetl. (reprint service avail. from ISI) **Indexed:** GeoRef. —CCC.

551.48 UN ISSN 0081-7449
CODEN: IHSRB9
STUDIES AND REPORTS IN HYDROLOGY SERIES. (Text in English) 1969. irreg., latest no.49. Unesco, 7-9 Place de Fontenoy, 75700 Paris, France. TEL 45-77-16-10. (Dist. in U.S. by: Unipub, 4611-F Assembly Dr., Lanham, MD 20706-4391) (also avail. in microform) **Indexed:** GeoRef.
—BLDSC (8489.370000).

STUDIES IN VERMONT GEOLOGY. see *EARTH SCIENCES — Geology*

627 RM
STUDII DE HIDRAULICA. (Text in Rumanian; summaries in English and French) a. Academia de Stiinte Agricole si Silvice, Institutul de Cercetari Pentru Imbunatatiri Funciare, B-dul Marasti Nr. 61, Bucharest, Rumania. (Subscr. to: ILEXIM, Str. 13 Decembrie Nr. 3, P.O. Box 136-137, Bucharest)

551.4 628.1 JA
SUIMON MIZU SHIGEN GAKKAI NYUSU/JAPAN SOCIETY OF HYDROLOGY AND WATER RESOURCES NEWS. (Text in Japanese) 1988. s-a. Suimon Mizu Shigen Gakkai, Nihon Gakkai Jimu Senta, 16-9, Honkomagome 5-chome, Bunkyo-ku, Tokyo 113, Japan.

551.4 628.1 JA ISSN 0915-1389
SUIMON MIZU SHIGEN GAKKAISHI/JAPAN SOCIETY OF HYDROLOGY AND WATER RESOURCES. JOURNAL. (Text in Japanese; summaries in English, Japanese) 1988. s-a. Suimon Mizu Shigen Gakkai, Nihon Gakkai Jimu Senta, 16-9, Honkomagome 5-chome, Bunkyo-ku, Tokyo 113, Japan.

551.48 JA
SUIRO SOKURYO NO KIROKU/RECORD OF HYDROGRAPHIC SURVEY. (Text in Japanese) a. Kaijo Hoancho, Suirobu - Maritime Safety Agency, Hydrographic Department, 3-1, Tsukiji 5-chome, Chuo-ku, Tokyo 104, Japan.

551.4 JA ISSN 0288-5301
SUIROBBU GIHO/TECHNICAL BULLETIN ON HYDROGRAPHY. (Text in English, Japanese) 1984. a. Kaijo Hoancho, Suirobu - Maritime Safety Agency, Hydrographic Department, 3-1, Tsukiji 5-chome, Chuo-ku, Tokyo 104, Japan.

551.48 UN ISSN 0082-2310
GB651 CODEN: TPHYAF
TECHNICAL PAPERS IN HYDROLOGY SERIES. 1970. irreg., vol.27, 1992-94. Unesco, 7-9 Place de Fontenoy, 75700 Paris, France. TEL 45-77-16-10. (Dist. in U.S. by: Unipub, 4611-F Assembly Dr., Lanham, MD 20706-4391) (also avail. in microform)
—BLDSC (8704.422200).

551.4 MX
UNIVERSIDAD NACIONAL AUTONOMA DE MEXICO. INSTITUTO DE GEOFISICA. DATOS GEOFISICOS A TABLAS DE PREDICCION DE MAREAS, PUERTOS DEL GOLFO DE MEXICO Y MAR CARIBE. 1963. a. $20. Universidad Nacional Autonoma de Mexico, Instituto de Geofisica, Circuito Exterior, Ciudad Universitaria, Mexico 20, D.F., Mexico. Ed. Francisco Graffe.

551.4 MX
UNIVERSIDAD NACIONAL AUTONOMA DE MEXICO. INSTITUTO DE GEOFISICA. DATOS GEOFISICOS A TABLAS DE PREDICCION DE MAREAS, PUERTOS DEL OCEANO PACIFICO. 1963. a. $20. Universidad Nacional Autonoma de Mexico, Instituto de Geofisica, Circuito Exterior, Ciudad Universitaria, Mexico 20, D.F., Mexico. Ed. Francisco Graffe.

574 BL ISSN 0100-7068
UNIVERSIDADE FEDERAL DO RIO GRANDE DO NORTE. CENTRO DE BIOCIENCIAS. DEPARTAMENTO DE OCEANOGRAFIA E LIMNOLOGIA. BOLETIM. 1964. irreg., vol.8, 1991. exchange basis. (Universidade Federal do Rio Grande do Norte, Departamento de Oceanografia e Limnologia) Conselho Editorial, Praia de Mae Luiza, s-n, 59020 Natal RN, Brazil. FAX 842296. Ed. Francisca de Assis de Sousa. circ. 1,000. **Indexed:** Biol.Abstr. **Document type:** bulletin.
Formerly (until vol.5, 1971): Universidade Federal do Rio Grande do Norte. Instituto de Biologia Marinha. Boletim (ISSN 0041-8927)
Description: Covers hydrology, marine biology, and aquaculture.

551.4 SZ ISSN 0724-7087
GB658.8.S9
UNIVERSITE DE NEUCHATEL. CENTRE D'HYDROGEOLOGIE. BULLETIN. (Text in French and German) 1976. a. 25 SFr. (Universite de Neuchatel, Centre d'Hydrogeologie) Verlag Peter Lang AG, Jupiterstr. 15, CH-3000 Bern 15, Switzerland. TEL 031-9411122. FAX 031-9411131. TELEX 912651-PELA-CH. circ. 250. **Document type:** bulletin.
Description: Studies the hydrogeology of fissured and karstified rocks, the hydrochemistry and isotopes of groundwater, pollution and protection of groundwater, groundwater resources exploration, the modelling of underground flow and mass transport, geophysical methods applied to hydrogeology, regional studies and technical notes.

VERMONT DIVISION OF GEOLOGY AND MINERAL RESOURCES. ENVIRONMENTAL GEOLOGY. see *EARTH SCIENCES — Geology*

VERMONT GEOLOGICAL SURVEY. SPECIAL PUBLICATION. see *EARTH SCIENCES — Geology*

VODNI HOSPODARSTVI/WATER MANAGEMENT. see *ENGINEERING — Hydraulic Engineering*

VODNYE RESURSY. see *WATER RESOURCES*

WATER RESOURCES. see *WATER RESOURCES*

WATER RESOURCES RESEARCH. see *WATER RESOURCES*

WATER RESOURCES SUMMARY. see *WATER RESOURCES*

WEATHER AND FORECASTING. see *METEOROLOGY*

WELL LOG. see *WATER RESOURCES*

551.4 US
WESTERN SNOW CONFERENCE. PROCEEDINGS. 1948. a. $25. Western Snow Conference, Box 2646, Portland, OR 97208-2646. TEL 503-641-7142. Ed. Charles Troendle. circ. 800. **Document type:** academic/scholarly publication.

EARTH SCIENCES — Oceanography

551.46 AT
A I M S MONOGRAPH SERIES. 1976. irreg. price varies. Australian Institute of Marine Science, Private Mail Bag 3, Townsville M.C., Qld. 4810, Australia. **Indexed:** Biol.Abstr., Deep Sea Res.& Oceanogr.Abstr. **Document type:** monographic series.

A M S NEWSLETTER (BOSTON). (American Meteorological Society) see *METEOROLOGY*

A S F A MARINE BIOTECHNOLOGY ABSTRACTS. (Aquatic Sciences & Fisheries Abstracts) see *BIOLOGY — Abstracting, Bibliographies, Statistics*

551.46 628 US
A S L O BULLETIN. 1990. 3/yr. $40. American Society of Limnology and Oceanography, Department of Biology, Whitman College, Walla Walla, WA 99362. TEL 509-527-5948. FAX 509-527-5961. (Subscr. to: Karen Hickey, Allen Press, Box 1897, Lawrence, KS 66044-8897. TEL 913-843-1221. FAX 913-843-1274) Ed. C. Susan Weiler. adv.; circ. 3,700 (paid). (back issues avail.) **Document type:** newsletter.
Description: Informs members of society events and provides a forum to discuss issues.

551.46 CU ISSN 0138-6328
ACADEMIA DE CIENCIAS DE CUBA. INSTITUTO DE OCEANOLOGIA. REPORTE DE INVESTIGACION. (Text in Spanish; summaries in English) 1982. irreg. free. Academia de Ciencias de Cuba, Instituto de Oceanologia, Avda. 1ra. no. 18406, Playa, Havana, Cuba. TEL 21-9988. TELEX 511290. Dir. Guillermo Garcia Montero. illus. **Indexed:** Meteor.& Geoastrophys.Abstr.
Supersedes (after no.187): Academia de Ciencias de Cuba. Instituto de Oceanologia. Informes Cientificos Tecnicos.

551.46 MM
ACROSS THE OCEANS. 1982. irreg. free. International Ocean Institute, P.O. Box 3, Gzire GZR 01, Malta. TEL 356-346529. FAX 356-346502.

551.46 CI ISSN 0001-5113
QH93 CODEN: AADRAY
ACTA ADRIATICA. 1932. a. exchange basis. Institut za Oceanografiju i Ribarstvo - Institute of Oceanography and Fisheries, Mose Pijade 63, Box 114, 58001 Split, Croatia. TELEX 46593. Ed. Mira Zore Armanda. circ. 400. **Indexed:** Biol.Abstr., Chem.Abstr., Curr.Adv.Ecol.Sci., Deep Sea Res.& Oceanogr.Abstr., GeoRef., Ocean.Abstr., Pollut.Abstr., Sel.Water Res.Abstr.
—BLDSC (0588.000000); CASDDS.

551.46 EC ISSN 1010-4402
ACTA OCEANOGRAFICA DEL PACIFICO. (Text in Spanish; summaries in English and Spanish) 1980. s-a. free. Instituto Oceanografico de la Armada, Avenida 25 de Julio Box 5940, Guayaquil, Ecuador. TEL 593-4-431300. FAX 593-4-442151. TELEX 4-3572 ED. Dir. Hernan Moreano Andrade. circ. 3,000 (controlled). (tabloid format) **Indexed:** Curr.Tit.Ocean.
Description: Covers physical, biological, chemical, geological oceanography, and their incidence in living resources, wheather and climate.

551.4 CH ISSN 0379-7481
GC1 CODEN: AOTADS
ACTA OCEANOGRAPHICA TAIWANICA. (Text in English; summaries in Chinese and English) 1971. s-a. $20. National Taiwan University, College of Science, Institute of Oceanography, Box 23-13, Taipei, Taiwan, Republic of China. TEL 886-2-3625983. FAX 886-2-3636092. Ed. Ju-chin Chen. bk.rev. circ. 800. **Indexed:** Chem.Abstr., Curr.Adv.Ecol.Sci., Deep Sea Res.& Oceanogr.Abstr., GeoRef., Meteor.& Geoastrophys.Abstr., Ocean.Abstr., Pollut.Abstr. **Document type:** academic/scholarly publication.
—BLDSC (0641.620000); CASDDS.
Description: Contains original articles, notes, and letters on oceanographic research.

551.46 CC ISSN 0253-505X
GC1 CODEN: AOSIEE
ACTA OCEANOLOGICA SINICA. Chinese edition: Haiyang Xuebao (ISSN 0253-4193) (Text in English) 1979. 4/yr. $360 (effective 1994). (Chinese Society of Oceanography) China Ocean Press, International Department, Haimao Dalou, 1 Fuxingmenwai St., Beijing 100860, People's Republic of China. TEL 8032211. FAX 8033515. TELEX 22536 NBO CN. Ed. Su Jilan. circ. 1,500. **Indexed:** Chem.Abstr., Curr.Adv.Ecol.Sci., Curr.Tit.Ocean., Deep Sea Res.& Oceanogr.Abstr., Environ.Per.Bibl. (1990-), Sel.Water Res.Abstr. **Document type:** academic/scholarly publication.
—BLDSC (0641.623050); UnCover; UMI. **CCC**.
Description: Publishes scholarly papers on marine science and technology, including physics, chemistry, biology, hydrology, meteorology, aquaculture, engineering, remote sensing, instrumentation and meters.
Refereed Serial

EARTH SCIENCES — OCEANOGRAPHY

ADVANCED SERIES ON OCEAN ENGINEERING. see *ENGINEERING*

ADVANCES IN MARINE BIOLOGY. see *BIOLOGY*

551.46   UK   ISSN 0952-1798
ADVANCES IN UNDERWATER TECHNOLOGY, OCEAN SCIENCE AND OFFSHORE ENGINEERING. irreg., latest no.27. £67.45. (Society for Underwater Technology) Graham & Trotman Ltd. (Subsidiary of: Kluwer Academic Publishers Group), Sterling House, 66 Wilton Rd., London SW1V 1DE, England. TEL 44-71-821-1123. FAX 44-71-630-5229. (Dist. by: Kluwer Academic Publishers Group, P.O. Box 322, 3300 AH Dordrecht, Netherlands. TEL 31-78-524400. FAX 31-78-524474; In N. America: Box 358, Accord St., Hingham, MA 02018-0358. TEL 617-871-6600. FAX 617-871-6528) **Document type:** monographic series.
—BLDSC (0711.678200).

551.46   US   ISSN 1060-202X
    CODEN: AWAQE4
ADVANCES IN WORLD AQUACULTURE. 1990. irreg., vol.5, 1991. price varies. World Aquaculture Society, 143 J M Parker Coliseum, Louisiana State University, Baton Rouge, LA 70803. TEL 504-388-3137. FAX 504-388-3493. Ed. D. Aiken. **Document type:** monographic series.
Refereed Serial

551.46   UY
ALMANAQUE. a. Servicio de Oceanografia e Hidrografia, Capurro 980, Casilla de Correo 1381, Montevideo, Uruguay.

AMERICAN METEOROLOGICAL SOCIETY. BULLETIN. see *METEOROLOGY*

AMERICAN SHORE AND BEACH PRESERVATION ASSOCIATION. NEWSLETTER. see *ENVIRONMENTAL STUDIES*

551.46   II   ISSN 0066-1686
ANDHRA UNIVERSITY MEMOIRS IN OCEANOGRAPHY. (Text in English) 1954. irreg. price varies. Andhra University Press and Publications, Waltair, Visakhapatnam 530003, Andhra Pradesh, India. Ed. E.C. la Fond.

551.46   FR   ISSN 0180-989X
ANNUAIRE DES MAREES POUR L'AN. TOME 1. PORTS DE FRANCE. 1839. a. 44 F. Service Hydrographique et Oceanographique de la Marine, 3 av. Octave Greard, 00300 Armees, France. TEL 98-22-10-80. FAX 98-43-18-11. TELEX HYDRO 940568. (Subscr. to: EPSHOM, B.P. 426, 29275 Brest Cedex, France) index. circ. 10,000. (tabloid format) **Document type:** government publication.

551.46   FR   ISSN 0180-9962
ANNUAIRE DES MAREES POUR L'AN. TOME 2. PORTS D'OUTRE MER. 1885. a. 70 F. Service Hydrographique et Oceanographique de la Marine, 3 av. Octave Greard, 00300 Armees, France. TEL 98-22-10-80. FAX 98-43-18-11. TELEX HYDRO 940568. (Subscr. to: EPSHOM, B.P. 426, 29275 Brest Cedex, France) **Document type:** government publication.

551.46 620   UK   ISSN 0141-1187
TC1501   CODEN: AOCRDS
APPLIED OCEAN RESEARCH. 1979. 6/yr. £229($355) (effective 1994). Elsevier Science Ltd., Oxford Fulfilment Centre, P.O. Box 800, Kidlington, Oxford OX5 1DX, England. TEL 44-865-843000. FAX 44-865-843010. (Subscr. in U.S. and Canada to: Elsevier Science, 660 White Plains Rd., Tarrytown, NY 10591-5153. TEL 914-524-9200. FAX 914-333-2444) Ed. C.L. Kirk. adv. (back issues avail.) **Indexed:** Abstr.J.Earthq.Eng., Appl.Mech.Rev., BMT, Curr.Tit.Ocean, Deep Sea Res.& Oceanogr.Abstr., E&P Hlth. (1993-), Eng.Ind., Environ.Per.Bibl. (1985-), Fluidex, Gas Process.& Ppl. (1993-), GeoRef., Met.Abstr., Meteor.& Geoastrophys.Abstr., Ocean.Abstr., Off.Tech. (1993-), Petrol.Abstr. (1984-), World Alum.Abstr.
Document type: academic/scholarly publication.
—BLDSC (1576.240000); El; Faxon; UnCover; SWETS. **CCC.**
    Description: Provides current information about various aspects of ocean research and development, especially those related to offshore engineering.
Refereed Serial

AQUA; mensile di acqua, natura, vita. see *EARTH SCIENCES — Hydrology*

551.46   FR   ISSN 0295-0448
AQUA REVIEW. (Text in French; summaries in English, Spanish) 1985. bi-m. 250 F. (foreign 310 F.). Societe d'Editions Aquapresse, 55 Cours Georges Clemenceau, 33000 Bordeaux, France. TEL 56-44-62-08. FAX 56-44-28-76. Ed. Bernard-Marie Thomas. adv.: B&W page 3700 F., color page 5800 F. bk.rev. circ. 2,300. **Document type:** newspaper.
—BLDSC (1581.864250).
    Description: Treats marine and continental aquaculture.

551.46   BE   ISSN 1018-9661
AQUACULTURE EUROPE MAGAZINE. 1976. q. 2300 BEF to non-members. European Aquaculture Society (EAS), Coupure Rechts 168, B-9000 Gent, Belgium. TEL 32-9-2237722. FAX 32-9-2237604. Ed. P. Lavens. adv.; bk.rev. circ. 1,000. (back issues avail.) **Document type:** bulletin.
    Formerly (until 1992): European Aquaculture Society Quarterly Newsletter (ISSN 0773-6940)

AQUAPHYTE. see *BIOLOGY — Botany*

AQUATIC CONSERVATION: MARINE AND FRESHWATER ECOSYSTEMS. see *CONSERVATION*

ARCHAEONAUTICA. see *ARCHAEOLOGY*

ARCHIVES OF HYDRO-ENGINEERING AND ENVIRONMENTAL MECHANICS. see *WATER RESOURCES*

551.46 551.48   IT   ISSN 0066-667X
    CODEN: AOLVAE
ARCHIVIO DI OCEANOGRAFIA E LIMONOLOGIA. (Text in Italian or congress languages; summaries in English and Italian) 1941. irreg., vol.21, no.3, 1989. L.5000 per no. Istituto di Biologia del Mare, Riva 7 Martiri 1364-A, 30122 Venice, Italy. FAX 041-5204126. Ed. B. Battaglia. bk.rev. circ. 500. **Indexed:** Biol.Abstr., Deep Sea Res.& Oceanogr.Abstr., Ocean.Abstr., Pollut.Abstr.
—CASDDS.

551.4   BL   ISSN 0374-5686
QH91.A1   CODEN: AQCMBP
ARQUIVOS DE CIENCIAS DO MAR. (Text and summaries in English, Portuguese) 1961. s-a. Cr.$400($40) or exchange basis. Universidade Federal do Ceara, Laboratorio de Ciencias do Mar, Av. da Universidade 2853, 60000 Fortaleza, Brazil. Ed. Regine Helena S.F Vieira. circ. 1,500. (back issues avail.) **Indexed:** Biol.Abstr., Chem.Abstr., Curr.Tit.Ocean, Deep Sea Res.& Oceanogr.Abstr., Zoo.Rec.
    Formerly: Universidade Federal do Ceara. Estacao de Biologia Marinha. Arquivos.

551.46   HK   ISSN 1018-8673
ASIA - PACIFIC UPLANDS; a newsletter for scientists. (Text in English) 1991. s-a. Pacific Science Association (Hong Kong), University of Hong Kong, Department of Geography & Geology, Hong Kong. Ed. R.D. Hill. **Document type:** newsletter.
—BLDSC (1742.262300).

574 551.46   PR
ASSOCIATION OF MARINE LABORATORIES OF THE CARIBBEAN. NEWSLETTER. (English and Spanish issues) 1986. q. $5. Association of Marine Laboratories of the Caribbean, University of Puerto Rico, Dept. of Marine Science, Mayaguez, PR 00708. FAX 809-834-3031. TELEX UPR MAY 3452024. adv.; bk.rev.; index. **Document type:** newsletter.

574 551   PR
ASSOCIATION OF MARINE LABORATORIES OF THE CARIBBEAN. PROCEEDINGS. (Former name of issuing body: Association of Island Marine Laboratories of the Caribbean) 1957. irreg., vol.22, 1989. $5. Association of Marine Laboratories of the Caribbean, University of Puerto Rico, Dept. of Marine Sciences, Mayaguez, PR 00708. FAX 809-265-2880. TELEX UPR MAY 3452024. Ed. Lucy Bunkley-Williams. circ. 500.
    Formerly: Association of Island Marine Laboratories of the Caribbean. Proceedings (ISSN 0066-9571)

ATMOSPHERE - OCEAN. see *METEOROLOGY*

551.46   US   ISSN 1063-7184
GC190
ATMOSPHERE - OCEAN SYSTEM. 1986. 4/yr. 78 ECU (effective 1993). Gordon and Breach Science Publishers, 820 Town Center Dr., Langhorne, PA 19047. TEL 215-750-2642. FAX 215-750-6343. (UK subscr. to: P.C. Box 90, Reading, Berkshire RG1 8JL, England. TEL 0734-560-080) Ed. Kristina Katsaros. (also avail. in microfilm; back issues avail.)
—BLDSC (6231.271900). **CCC.**
    Formerly: Ocean-Air Interactions (ISSN 0743-0876)
Refereed Serial

551.46   AT
AUSTRALIAN INSTITUTE OF MARINE SCIENCE. ANNUAL REPORT. 1972. a. Australian Institute of Marine Science, Private Mail Bag 3, Townsville M.C., Qld. 4810, Australia. charts; illus. circ. 2,000. **Document type:** corporate report.
    Formerly: Australian Institute of Marine Science. Yearly Report.

551.46 551.48   AT   ISSN 0067-1940
GC1   CODEN: AJMFA4
AUSTRALIAN JOURNAL OF MARINE AND FRESHWATER RESEARCH. 1950. 8/yr. Aus.$220($220) (effective 1994). C.S.I.R.O., 314 Albert St., E. Melbourne, Vic. 3002, Australia. TEL 61-3-418-7333. FAX 61-3-419-4096. Ed. A. Grant. adv.; index. circ. 1,100. (also avail. in microform from UMI; back issues avail.) **Indexed:** AESIS, Biol.Abstr., Cadscan, Chem.Abstr., Curr.Adv.Ecol.Sci., Curr.Cont., Curr.Ref.Fish Res., Curr.Tit.Ocean, Deep Sea Res.& Oceanogr.Abstr., Environ.Abstr., Environ.Per.Bibl. (1974-), Excerp.Med., Food Sci.& Tech.Abstr., Forest.Abstr., Geo.Abstr., GeoRef., Helminthol.Abstr., Ind.Sci.Rev., Ind.Vet., INIS Atomind., Irr.& Drain.Abstr., Lead Abstr., Nutr.Abstr., Ocean.Abstr., Pollut.Abstr., Sci.Cit.Ind., Sel.Water Res.Abstr., Soils & Fert., W.R.C.Inf., Weed Abstr., Zincscan. **Document type:** academic/scholarly publication.
—BLDSC (1810.000000); CIS; Faxon; UnCover; SWETS; UMI; CASDDS. **CCC.**
    Description: Presents research in physical oceanography, marine chemistry, marine and estuarine biology and limnology.

551.46   AT
AUSTRALIAN MARINE SCIENCE BULLETIN. 1962. q. membership. Australian Marine Sciences Association Inc., School of Marine Sciences, University of Queensland, Qld. 4072, Australia. FAX 002-24-0530. Ed. I. Tibbetts. adv.; bk.rev. circ. 1,200. **Indexed:** Curr.Tit.Ocean. **Document type:** bulletin.
    Former titles: Australian Marine Sciences Association. Bulletin (ISSN 0157-6429); (until 1970): Australian Marine Science Newsletter.

AUSTRALIAN METEOROLOGICAL AND OCEANOGRAPHIC SOCIETY. BULLETIN. see *METEOROLOGY*

AUTOMAZIONE NAVALE; tecnologie per il mare. see *TRANSPORTATION — Ships And Shipping*

551.46   CN   ISSN 0846-9121
GC59.15   CODEN: SRHAEI
BEDFORD INSTITUTE OF OCEANOGRAPHY. SCIENCE REVIEW. (Editions in English, French) 1968. a. free. Department of Fisheries and Oceans, Bedford Institute of Oceanography, Dartmouth, N.S. B2Y 4A2, Canada. TEL 902-426-4093. FAX 902-426-2256. circ. 5,000 (controlled). **Indexed:** Aqua.Sci.& Fish.Abstr., GeoRef.
    Former titles: Bedford Institute of Oceanography. Review (ISSN 0229-8910); Bedford Institute of Oceanography. Biennial Review (ISSN 0067-480X)
    Description: Describes the federal marine science and fisheries research programs performed by the Institute, the Halifax Fisheries Research Laboratory, and the St. Andrews Biological Station.

551.46   GW   ISSN 0067-5148
GC1   CODEN: BMEKAB
BEITRAEGE ZUR MEERESKUNDE/CONTRIBUTIONS TO MARINE SCIENTIFIC RESEARCH. 1961. irreg., no.63, 1993. price varies. Akademie Verlag GmbH, Muehlenstr. 33-34, 13187 Berlin, Germany. TEL 030-47889348. FAX 030-47889357. **Indexed:** Curr.Adv.Ecol.Sci., Deep Sea Res.& Oceanogr.Abstr., GeoRef., Ocean.Abstr., Pollut.Abstr. **Document type:** monographic series.
—BLDSC (1885.350000); UnCover; CASDDS.
    Description: Original articles on marine scientific research: physical and chemical oceanology, marine geology and biology, marine research technology.

EARTH SCIENCES — OCEANOGRAPHY

551.46 614.7   BM
BERMUDA. BIOLOGICAL STATION FOR RESEARCH. SPECIAL PUBLICATIONS. 1969. irreg. price varies. Biological Station for Research, Inc., Ferry Reach GE01, Bermuda. FAX 809-297-8143. circ. 250. (back issues avail.) **Indexed:** Biol.Abstr, Deep Sea Res.& Oceanogr.Abstr., GeoRef.

BIBLIOGRAFIA HYDROLOGII I OCEANOLOGII/BIBLIOGRAPHY OF HYDROLOGY AND OCEANOGRAPHY. see EARTH SCIENCES — Abstracting, Bibliographies, Statistics

551.46   GW   ISSN 0930-8148
BIOLOGISCHE ANSTALT HELGOLAND. BERICHTE.. 1986. irreg. free to students and scientists. Biologische Anstalt Helgoland, Notkestr. 31, 22607 Hamburg, Germany. TEL 040-896930. FAX 040-89693115. Ed. Dr. W. Hickel. abstr.; bibl.; charts; illus. **Document type:** academic/scholarly publication.

BIOLOGIYA MORYA/MARINE BIOLOGY. see BIOLOGY

551.46   IT   ISSN 0393-196X
GC1
BOLLETTINO DI OCEANOLOGIA; teorica ed applicata. 1983. q. $75. Osservatorio Geofisico Sperimentale, P.O. Box 2011, 34016 Opicina, Trieste, Italy. TEL 4021401. FAX 40-327307. TELEX 460329 OGS I. Ed. A. Brambati. bk.rev. circ. 300. (back issues avail.) **Indexed:** Deep Sea Res.& Oceanogr.Abstr.
Description: Deals with general and physical oceanology, marine geosciences, ocean engineering and marine technology.

551.46 574.92   US   ISSN 0007-4977
GC1   CODEN: BMRSAW
BULLETIN OF MARINE SCIENCE. 1950. bi-m. $70 to individuals (foreign $90); institutions $175 (foreign $200); students $35 (foreign $55) (effective 1994). Rosenstiel School of Marine and Atmospheric Science, 4600 Rickenbacker Causeway, Miami, FL 33149. TEL 305-361-4190. Ed. William J. Richards. bk.rev.; circ. 1,000 (paid). (reprint service avail. from SWZ) **Indexed:** Aqua.Sci.& Fish.Abstr., Biol.Abstr., Chem.Abstr., Curr.Adv.Ecol.Sci., Curr.Cont., Curr.Ref.Fish Res., Deep Sea Res.& Oceanogr.Abstr., E&P Hlth. (1993-), Environ.Abstr., Excerp.Med., Gas Process.& Ppl. (1993-), Geo.Abstr., GeoRef, Helminthol.Abstr., Ind.Sci.Rev., Meteor.& Geoastrophys.Abstr., Ocean.Abstr., Off.Tech. (1993-), Petrol.Abstr. (1963-), Pollut.Abstr., Sci.Cit.Ind., Sel.Water Res.Abstr., So.Pac.Per.Ind., Zoo.Rec. **Document type:** academic/scholarly publication, bulletin.
—BLDSC (2866.990000); Faxon; UnCover; SWETS; CASDDS.
Formerly: Bulletin of Marine Science of the Gulf and Caribbean.
Refereed Serial

551.46   GW
VK597.G4   CODEN: JDHIDE
BUNDESAMT FUER SEESCHIFFAHRT UND HYDROGRAPHIE. JAHRESBERICHT. 1947. a. DM.10.70. Bundesamt fuer Seeschiffahrt und Hydrographie, Bernhard-Nocht-Str. 78, 20359 Hamburg, Germany. TEL 040-3190-0. FAX 040-3190-5000. TELEX 211138-BSHHH-D. circ. 2,000. **Indexed:** GeoRef. **Document type:** academic/scholarly publication.
Formerly: Deutsches Hydrographisches Institut. Jahresbericht (ISSN 0070-4458)

C - C O R E NEWS. (Centre for Cold Ocean Resources Engineering) see ENGINEERING

551.46 620   US
THE C E R CULAR; information exchange bulletin. 1976. q. free. U.S. Coastal Engineering Research Center, c/o Fred E. Camfield, 3909 Halls Ferry Rd., Waterways Experiment Sta., Vicksburg, MS 39180-6199. TEL 601-634-2012. circ. 2,700.
Description: Presents reports on activities of the laboratory.

551.46   US
C G O U TECHNICAL REPORT.* 1964. irreg. U.S. Coast Guard, Oceanographic Unit, 400 Seventh St., S.W., Washington, DC 20590. TEL 703-426-2158. (Dist. by: N T I S, Springfield, VA 22151) circ. 300.

551.46 574.92   FR   ISSN 0007-8603
C M A S BULLETIN D'INFORMATION/C M A S NEWSLETTER. (Confederation Mondiale des Activites) 1959. 4/yr. 80 F. World Underwater Federation, Viale Tiziano 74, 00196 Rome, Italy. bk.rev.; illus. circ. 2,000. **Document type:** newsletter.

574 351.46   IS   ISSN 0792-6073
C M S NEWS. (Text in English) 1978. s-a. Haifa University, Center for Maritime Studies, Ha-Carmel, Haifa 31905, Israel. FAX 972-4-240493. TELEX 46060-UNIHA-IL. Ed. Nira Karmon. circ. 1,000. **Document type:** newsletter.

C S I R O DIVISION OF FISHERIES. RESEARCH REPORT. (Commonwealth Scientific and Industrial Research Organization) see FISH AND FISHERIES

551.46   AT   ISSN 1031-9964
GC59.89
C S I R O DIVISION OF OCEANOGRAPHY. RESEARCH REPORT. 1961. biennial. free. Commonwealth Scientific and Industrial Research Organization, Division of Oceanography, G.P.O. Box 1538, Hobart, Tas. 7001, Australia. TEL 002-32-5222. FAX 002-32-5000. TELEX AA57182. circ. 1,000. **Indexed:** Biol.Abstr., Meteor.& Geoastrophys.Abstr.
—BLDSC (7761.171500).
Supersedes in part (in 1984): Commonwealth Scientific and Industrial Research Organization. Marine Laboratories. Research Report (ISSN 0726-4291); Which superseded: Commonwealth Scientific Industrial Research Organization. Division of Fisheries and Oceanography. Report (ISSN 0069-7397)

551.46 540   II
C S M C R I NEWSLETTER. 1982. q. free. Central Salt and Marine Chemicals Research Institute, Gijubhai Badheka Marg, Bhavnagar 364 002, Gujarat, India. TEL 24496. FAX 0278-26970. TELEX 0182-230 ABC SALT IN. Ed. Shri K.D. Padia. adv.; bk.rev. circ. 700. **Document type:** newsletter.

CALANUS. see BIOLOGY

CALYPSO LOG. see ENVIRONMENTAL STUDIES

CANADIAN INDUSTRY REPORT OF FISHERIES AND AQUATIC SCIENCES. see FISH AND FISHERIES

CANADIAN MANUSCRIPT REPORT OF FISHERIES AND AQUATIC SCIENCES. see ENVIRONMENTAL STUDIES

CANADIAN METEOROLOGICAL AND OCEANOGRAPHIC SOCIETY. ANNUAL CONGRESS. see METEOROLOGY

623.894   CN   ISSN 0068-9882
CANADIAN TIDE AND CURRENT TABLES. Continues a publication with the same title issued by the Hydrographic Service. 1967. a. Can.$0.50. Department of Fisheries and Oceans, Canadian Hydrographic Service, P.O. Box 8080, 1675 Russell Rd., Ottawa, Ont. K1G 3H6, Canada. TEL 613-995-3065.
—CCC.

CENTRAL MARINE FISHERIES RESEARCH INSTITUTE. BULLETIN. see FISH AND FISHERIES

581   FR   ISSN 0528-4465
QH3   CODEN: BBERAN
CENTRE D'ETUDES ET DE RECHERCHES SCIENTIFIQUES DE BIARRITZ. BULLETIN. (Text in French) 1956-1984; resumed 1985. irreg. 70 F. Centre d'Etudes et de Recherches Scientifiques de Biarritz, BP 89, Plateau de l'Atalaye, 64200 Biarritz, France. TEL 59-24-41-98. FAX 59-22-33-34. Ed. J. Harambillet. illus.; index. circ. 500. (back issues avail.) **Indexed:** Biol.Abstr. **Document type:** bulletin.
—CASDDS.

551.46   MG
CENTRE D'INFORMATION ET DE DOCUMENTATION SCIENTIFIQUE ET TECHNIQUE. ARCHIVES DU CENTRE NATIONAL DE RECHERCHES OCEANOGRAPHIQUES. a. Centre d'Information et de Documentation Scientifique et Technique, 27 rue Fernand Kasanga, Tsimbazaza, B.P. 6224, 101 Antananarivo, Malagasy Republic. TEL 33288. TELEX 225 39 MRS-MG.

551.4   IV
CENTRE DE RECHERCHES OCEANOGRAPHIQUES D'ABIDJAN. DOCUMENTS SCIENTIFIQUES. (Text in French; summaries in English) 1970. q. free. Centre de Recherches Oceanographiques d'Abidjan, B.P. V 18, Abidjan, Ivory Coast. FAX 35-11-55. TELEX 214235 MIX CROA. Ed. Amon Kothias. illus. circ. 300. **Indexed:** Deep Sea Res.& Oceanogr.Abstr., Ocean.Abstr.

551.46 574   JA   ISSN 0916-6025
CHIBA DAIGAKU RIGAKUBU KAIYO SEITAIKEI KENKYU SENTA NENPO/CHIBA UNIVERSITY. MARINE ECOSYSTEM RESEARCH CENTER. ANNUAL REPORT. (Text in Japanese) 1990. a. Chiba Daigaku, Rigakubu, Kaiyo Seitaikei Kenkyu Senta - Chiba University, Faculty of Science, Marine Ecosystem Research Center, 1-33, Yayoicho, Inage-ku, Chiba-shi, Chhiba-ken 263, Japan.
—BLDSC (1144.360000).

CHINA OCEAN ENGINEERING. see ENGINEERING

551.46 551.48   CC   ISSN 0254-4059
CODEN: CJOLEO
CHINESE JOURNAL OF OCEANOLOGY AND LIMNOLOGY. Chinese edition: Haiyang yu Huzhao. (Text in English) 1982. q. DM.410 (effective 1994). Science Press, Marketing and Sales Department, 16 Donghuangchenggen Beijie, Beijing 100707, People's Republic of China. TEL 4010642. FAX 4012180. TELEX 210247-SPBJ-CN. (Dist. outside China by: V S P, P.O. Box 346, 3700 AH Zeist, Netherlands. TEL 31-3404-25790. FAX 31-3404-32081) Ed. C.K. Tseng. adv. circ. 6,000. **Indexed:** Anim.Breed.Abstr., Deep Sea Res.& Oceanogr.Abstr. **Document type:** academic/scholarly publication.
—BLDSC (3180.450000); CASDDS. **CCC.**
Description: Covers hydrophysics, hydrochemistry, hydrobiology, geomorphology, apparatus research and manufacture, comprehensive reviews, and academic activities.
Refereed Serial

551.46   JA
CHOI NENPO/YEARBOOK OF TIDAL RECORDS. (Text in Japanese) 1966. a. Kokudo Chiriin - Geographical Survey Institute, Ministry of Construction, Kitasato-1, Tsukuba-shi, Ibaraki-ken 305, Japan. circ. 400. **Document type:** government publication.

551.46   JA
CHOSEKI KANSOKU/TIDAL OBSERVATIONS. (Text in English, Japanese) 1925. a. Kishocho - Japan Meteorological Agency, 3-4, Otemachi 1-chome, Chiyoda-ku, Tokyo 100, Japan.

551.46   JA   ISSN 0910-0458
CHOSEKIHYO 1. NIHON OYOBI FUKIN/TIDE TABLES 1. JAPAN AND ITS VICINITIES. (Text in English, Japanese) 1920. s-a. Kaijo Hoancho, Suirobu - Maritime Safety Agency, Hydrographic Department, 3-1, Tsukiji 5-chome, Chuo-ku, Tokyo 104, Japan.

551.46   JA   ISSN 0910-0466
CHOSEKIHYO 2. TAIHEIYO OYOBI INDOYO/TIDE TABLES 2. PACIFIC AND INDIAN OCEANS. (Text in English, Japanese) 1920. a. Kaijo Hoancho, Suirobu - Maritime Safety Agency, Hydrograhic Department, 3-1, Tsukiji 5-chome, Chuo-ku, Tokyo 104, Japan.

551.46   CL   ISSN 0716-2006
CIENCIA Y TECNOLOGIA DEL MAR. (Text in Spanish; summaries in English) 1975. a. free. Comite Oceanografico Nacional, Errauriz 232, Casilla 324, Valparaiso, Chile. TEL 056-032-282697. FAX 056-032-283537. TELEX 23-0362 HIDRO CL. circ. 500. **Indexed:** GeoRef.

351.46   JA
CLASS N K MAGAZINE. (Text in English) 1973. a. free. Nippon Kaiji Kyokai, 4-7, Kioicho, Chiyoda-ku, Tokyo 102, Japan. TEL 03-3200-1201. FAX 03-0230-3524. Ed. Yokio Sakamoto.
Former titles (until 1994): Overseas (ISSN 0913-204X); (until 1980): N K Overseas (ISSN 0913-2422)

EARTH SCIENCES — OCEANOGRAPHY

551.46   US
COAST AND SEA; marine and coastal research in Louisiana's universities. 1972. q. free. Louisiana State University, Louisiana Sea Grant College Program, Baton Rouge, LA 70803-7507. TEL 504-388-6449. FAX 504-388-6331. Ed. Elizabeth Coleman. bk.rev.; illus. circ. 2,500. (back issues avail.) **Indexed:** Environ.Abstr., Fluidex.
Document type: academic/scholarly publication.
  Supersedes (in 1992): Aquanotes.

COASTAL ENGINEERING RESEARCH COUNCIL. PROCEEDINGS. see *ENGINEERING — Civil Engineering*

551.46 341.7   US   ISSN 0892-0753
                                   CODEN: CMANEF
COASTAL MANAGEMENT; an international journal of marine environment, resources, law and society. 1973. q. $140. Taylor & Francis, 1900 Frost Rd., Ste. 101, Bristol, PA 19007. TEL 215-785-5800. FAX 215-785-5515. Ed. Marc J. Hershman. adv.; bk.rev.; abstr.; bibl.; charts; illus.; stat.; index, cum.index. **Indexed:** Abstr.Bk.Rev.Curr.Leg.Per., C.L.I., Curr.Adv.Ecol.Sci., Curr.Cont., Curr.Tit.Ocean, Ecol.Abstr., Energy Info.Abstr., Energy Rev., Eng.Ind, Environ.Abstr., Environ.Ind., Environ.Per.Bibl. (1988-), Geo.Abstr., I D A, Ind.Per.Art.Relat.Law, Ind.Sci.Rev., Leg.Per., Mar.Aff.Bibl., Meteor.& Geostrophys.Abstr., Ocean.Abstr., P.A.I.S., Petrol.Abstr., Pollut.Abstr., Sci.Cit.Ind., Sel.Water Res.Abstr.
—BLDSC (3292.413150); CIS; EI; Faxon; UnCover; SWETS. **CCC.**
  Formerly: Coastal Zone Management Journal (ISSN 0090-8339)
  Description: Explores the technical, legal, political, social, and policy issues surrounding the utilization of valuable and unique coastal environments and resources.
Refereed Serial

551.46   US   ISSN 0271-5376
COASTAL RESEARCH. 1962. 3/yr. $6 (effective 1993-94). Florida State University, Geology Department, Tallahassee, FL 32306. TEL 904-644-5860. FAX 904-644-4214. Ed. W.F. Tanner. bk.rev. circ. 400. (back issues avail.) **Indexed:** Geo.Abstr., GeoRef. **Document type:** newsletter.
  Formerly: Coastal Research Notes (ISSN 0578-5677)
  Description: Covers science, engineering and other matters of coastal interest.
Refereed Serial

COASTAL ZONE MANAGEMENT; newsletter of coastal resource development, conservation & enhancement. see *CONSERVATION*

333.9   US
COASTWATCH. 1970. bi-m. $12. North Carolina Sea Grant College Program, Box 8605, North Carolina State University, Raleigh, NC 27695-8605. TEL 919-515-2454. FAX 919-515-7095. Ed. Kathy Hart. bk.rev.; abstr. circ. 4,000. (processed) **Indexed:** Ocean.Abstr.
  Formerly: University of North Carolina. Sea Grant College Newsletter (ISSN 0161-8369)

COLLECTANEA MARITIMA. see *HISTORY — History Of Europe*

COMMONWEALTH SCIENTIFIC AND INDUSTRIAL RESEARCH ORGANIZATION. MARINE LABORATORIES. REPORT. see *FISH AND FISHERIES*

551.46   UK   ISSN 0278-4343
GC85   CODEN: CSHRDZ
CONTINENTAL SHELF RESEARCH. 1982. 15/yr. £495($760) (effective 1994). Elsevier Science Ltd., Pergamon, P.O. Box 800, Kidlington, Oxford OX5 1DX, England. TEL 44-865-843000. FAX 44-865-843010. (Subscr. in U.S. and Canada to: Elsevier Science, 660 White Plains Rd., Tarrytown, NY 10591-5153. TEL 914-524-9200. FAX 914-333-2444) Eds. M.B. Collins, R.W. Sternberg. (also avail. in microfilm from UMI). **Indexed:** Curr.Adv.Ecol.Sci., Curr.Tit.Ocean, Deep Sea Res.& Oceanogr.Abstr., Environ.Per.Bibl. (1992-), Fluidex, Ind.Sci.Rev., Meteor.& Geoastrophys.Abstr., Sci.Abstr., Sci.Cit.Ind., Sel.Water Res.Abstr. **Document type:** academic/scholarly publication.
—BLDSC (3425.640000); Faxon; UnCover; SWETS; UMI; CASDDS. **CCC.**
  Description: Presents research results in physical oceanography, chemistry, ecology, sedimentology, and applied aspects of continental shelf research.
Refereed Serial

551.46   GW
                                 CODEN: CORFDL
CORAL REEFS. 1982. 4/yr. DM.274($171) (International Society for Reef Studies) Springer-Verlag, Heidelberger Platz 3, 14197 Berlin, Germany. TEL 030-8207-1. FAX 030-8214091. (Subscr. in N. America to: Springer-Verlag New York, Inc., 44 Hartz Way, Secaucus, NJ 07096-2491. TEL 201-348-4033. FAX 201-348-4505) Ed. R.W. Grigg. adv. (also avail. in microform from UMI; reprint service avail. from ISI) **Indexed:** Curr.Adv.Ecol.Sci., Curr.Tit.Ocean, Deep Sea Res.& Oceanogr.Abstr., Environ.Per.Bibl. (1990-), Sel.Water Res.Abstr. **Document type:** academic/scholarly publication.
—BLDSC (3470.325000); Faxon; UnCover; SWETS; UMI; CASDDS. **CCC.**
  Formerly: International Society for Reef Studies. Journal (ISSN 0722-4028)
  Description: Covers reef structure and morphology, biogeochemical cycles, behavioral ecology, sedimentology, and evolutionary ecology of the reef biota.

551.46   DK   ISSN 0070-2668
Q115   CODEN: DNRPAI
DANA-REPORT. (Text in English; occasionally French or German) 1934. irreg. price varies. (Carlsberg Foundation) Scandinavian Science Press Ltd. (Subsidiary of: E.J. Brill), Universitetsparken 15, 1260 Copenhagen, Denmark. Ed. E. Bertelsen. cum.index: 1934-1969. **Indexed:** Biol.Abstr. **Document type:** monographic series.
  Description: Covers the Carlsberg Foundation's oceanographical expedition round the world 1928-30 and previous Dana expeditions.
Refereed Serial

551.46   UK   ISSN 0967-0637
GC1   CODEN: DRORE7
DEEP-SEA RESEARCH. PART 1: OCEANOGRAPHIC RESEARCH PAPERS. 1953. 12/yr. £1015($1565) includes Part 2 (effective 1994). Elsevier Science Ltd., Pergamon, P.O. Box 800, Kidlington, Oxford OX5 1DX, England. TEL 44-865-843000. FAX 44-865-843010. (Subscr. in U.S. and Canada to: Elsevier Science, 660 White Plains Rd., Tarrytown, NY 10591-5153. TEL 914-524-9200. FAX 914-333-2444) Ed. John Milliman. adv.; bk.rev.; abstr.; bibl.; charts; illus.; index. (also avail. in microfilm from UMI) **Indexed:** Biol.Abstr., Chem.Abstr., Curr.Adv.Ecol.Sci., Curr.Tit.Ocean, Deep Sea Res.& Oceanogr.Abstr., Eng.Ind., Environ.Per.Bibl. (1989-), Excerp.Med., Geo.Abstr., GeoRef., Ind.Sci.Rev., Meteor.& Geostrophys.Abstr., Ocean.Abstr., Petrol.Abstr., Pollut.Abstr., Sci.Abstr., Sci.Cit.Ind., So.Pac.Per.Ind. **Document type:** academic/scholarly publication.
—BLDSC (3540.955500); EI; Faxon; UnCover; CASDDS. **CCC.**
  Former titles (until 1993): Deep-Sea Research. Part A: Oceanographic Research Papers (ISSN 0198-0149); uUntil 1979): Deep-Sea Research (ISSN 0146-6291); (until 1977): Deep-Sea Research and Oceanographic Abstracts (ISSN 0011-7471); Supersedes (in 1962): Deep-Sea Research (ISSN 0146-6313)
  Description: Publishes original research results, and instrumentation and methodological developments.
Refereed Serial

551.46   UK   ISSN 0967-0645
GC1   CODEN: DSROEK
▼**DEEP-SEA RESEARCH. PART 2: TOPICAL STUDIES IN OCEANOGRAPHY.** 1993. 6/yr. £441($680) (effective 1994) Elsevier Science Ltd., Pergamon, P.O. Box 800, Kidlington, Oxford OX5 1DX, England. TEL 44-865-843000. FAX 44-865-843010. (Subscr. in U.S. and Canada to: Elsevier Science, 660 White Plains Rd., Tarrytown, NY 10591-5153. TEL 914-524-9200. FAX 914-333-2444) (also avail. in microfilm from UMI) **Document type:** academic/scholarly publication.
—BLDSC (8867.412700); UnCover; SWETS; CASDDS. **CCC.**
  Description: Forum for collected papers on specific topics reflecting important international and interdisciplinary research projects undertaken.
Refereed Serial

DELAWARE SEA GRANT REPORTER. see *FISH AND FISHERIES*

551.48   GW   ISSN 0012-0308
VK588   CODEN: DHYZA7
DEUTSCHE HYDROGRAPHISCHE ZEITSCHRIFT. (Text in English or German; summaries in English, French, German) 1948. 6/yr. DM.128.40. Bundesamt fuer Seeschiffahrt und Hydrographie, Bernhard-Nocht-Str. 78, 20359 Hamburg, Germany. TEL 040-3190-0. FAX 040-3190-5000. TELEX 211138-BSHHH-D. Eds. G. Heise, D. Voppel. bk.rev.; bibl.; charts; illus.; index. circ. 650. **Indexed:** Bibl.Cart., Biol.Abstr., Chem.Abstr., Deep Sea Res.& Oceanogr.Abstr., Excerp.Med., Fluidex, INIS Atomind., Meteor.& Geoastrophys.Abstr., Ocean.Abstr., Pollut.Abstr., Sel.Water Res.Abstr.
—BLDSC (3569 000000).

551.46   GW   ISSN 0070-4164
DEUTSCHE HYDROGRAPHISCHE ZEITSCHRIFT. ERGAENZUNGSHEFT. REIHE A. 1952. irreg., no.17, 1991. Bundesamt fuer Seeschiffahrt und Hydrographie, Bernhard-Nocht-Str. 78, 2000 Hamburg 36, Germany. TEL 040-3190-0. FAX 040-3190-5000. TELEX 211138-BSHHH-D. Eds. G. Heise, D. Voppel. **Indexed:** Meteor.& Geoastrophys.Abstr.
—BLDSC (3569 500000).

551.46   GW   ISSN 0070-4172
DEUTSCHE HYDROGRAPHISCHE ZEITSCHRIFT. ERGAENZUNGSHEFT. REIHE B. 1956. irreg., no.24, 1991. Bundesamt fuer Seeschiffahrt und Hydrographie, Bernhard-Nocht-Str. 78, 2000 Hamburg 36, Germany. TEL 040-3190-0. FAX 040-3190-5000. TELEX 211138-BSHHH-D. Eds. G. Heise, D. Voppel. **Document type:** academic/scholarly publication.

551.46   NE   ISSN 0163-6995
                                     CODEN: DMBIDF
DEVELOPMENTS IN MARINE BIOLOGY. 1979. irreg., vol.2, 1980. price varies. Elsevier Science B.V., Books Division, P.O. Box 211, 1000 AE Amsterdam, Netherlands. TEL 31-20-5803911. FAX 31-20-5803705. TELEX 18582 ESPA NL. (Subscr. in U.S. and Canada to: Elsevier Science Inc., Box 882, Madison Sq. Sta., New York, NY 10159. TEL 212-989-5800) **Document type:** monographic series.
—CASDDS.
Refereed Serial

DEVELOPMENTS IN MARINE TECHNOLOGY. see *ENGINEERING — Mechanical Engineering*

DYNAMICS OF ATMOSPHERES AND OCEANS; planetary fluids, climatic and biogeochemical systems. see *METEOROLOGY*

551.46   US   ISSN 1068-2678
EARTH SYSTEM MONITOR. 1990. q. free. National Oceanic and Atmospheric Administration, Office of Environmental Information Services, NOAA - NESDIS Ex2, Universal Bldg., Rm. 506, 1825 Connecticut Ave., N.W., Washington, DC 20235. TEL 202-606-4561. Ed. Richard J. Abram. **Document type:** government publication.
  Description: Reports on NOAA environmental data and information management programs and activities, describes new NOAA data and information products and services.

EARTH SCIENCES — OCEANOGRAPHY

551.46 574.92   CK   ISSN 0120-8993
QH121   CODEN: BOECE5
ECOTROPICA. ECOSISTEMAS TROPICALES. BOLETIN. (Text in Spanish; summaries in English) 1970. irreg. price varies. Universidad de Bogota Jorge Tadeo Lozano, Museo del Mar, Calle 23 No. 4-47, Bogota, Colombia. TEL 57-1-3422961. FAX 57-1-2826197. Ed. Elvira Maria Alvarado-Chacon. bibl.; illus.; circ. 1,200 (controlled). (cards) **Document type:** bulletin.
    Formerly (until 1985): Universidad de Bogota Jorge Tadeo Lozano. Museo del Mar. Boletin.

551.46   NE   ISSN 0422-9894
CODEN: ELOSA9
ELSEVIER OCEANOGRAPHY SERIES. (Text in English) 1964. irreg., vol.59, 1993. price varies. Elsevier Science B.V., Books Division, P.O. Box 211, 1000 AE Amsterdam, Netherlands. TEL 31-20-5803911. FAX 31-20-5803705. TELEX 18582 ESPA NL. (Subscr. in U.S. and Canada to: Elsevier Science Inc., Box 882, Madison Sq. Sta., New York, NY 10159. TEL 212-989-5800) (back issues avail.) **Indexed:** Biol.Abstr., Chem.Abstr., GeoRef., Math.R. **Document type:** monographic series.
  —BLDSC (3732.380000); CASDDS.
    Supersedes: Oceanography Series (ISSN 0078-3226)
    Refereed Serial

551.46   JA   ISSN 0914-3882
ENGAN KAIYO KENKYU NOTO/BULLETIN ON COASTAL OCEANOGRAPHY. (Text in Japanese; summaries in English, Japanese) 1962. s-a. Nihon Kaiyo Gakkai, Engan Kaiyo Kenkyu Bukai - Oceanographical Society of Japan, Coastal Oceanography Research Committee, Tokai Daigaku Kaiyogakubu, 20-1, Orido 3-chome, Shimizu-shi, Shizuoka-ken 424, Japan.

EPIMENIDES/EPIMENIS. see ASTRONOMY

551.46   UK   ISSN 0272-7714
GC96   CODEN: ECSSD3
ESTUARINE, COASTAL AND SHELF SCIENCE. 1973. m. (2 vols./yr.). £315. Academic Press Ltd. (Subsidiary of: Harcourt Brace & Company Ltd.), 24-28 Oval Rd., London NW1 7DX, England. TEL 44-71-267-4466. FAX 44-71-482-2293. TELEX 25775-ACPRES-G. (Subscr. to: Harcourt Brace & Company Ltd., Foots Cray High St., Sidcup, Kent DA14 5HP, England. TEL 44-81-300-3322. FAX 44-81-309-0807) Eds. N.C. Flemming, E. Naylor. **Indexed:** Abstr.Bull.Inst.Pap.Chem., Biol.Abstr., Cadscan, Chem.Abstr., Curr.Adv.Ecol.Sci., Curr.Tit.Ocean, Deep Sea Res.& Oceanogr.Abstr., E&P Hlth. (1993-), Environ.Abstr., Environ.Per.Bibl. (1977-), Excerp.Med., Fluidex, Gas Process.& Ppl. (1993-), Geo.Abstr., GeoRef., Helminthol.Abstr., Ind.Sci.Rev., INIS Atomind., Lead Abstr., Meteor.& Geoastrophys.Abstr., Ocean.Abstr., Off.Tech. (1993-), Petrol.Abstr. (1980-), Pollut.Abstr., Sci.Cit.Ind, Sel.Water Res.Abstr., Soils & Fert., W.R.C.Inf., Zincscan. **Document type:** academic/scholarly publication.
  —BLDSC (3812.599200); CIS; Faxon; UnCover; SWETS; CASDDS. **CCC.**
    Formerly (until 1982): Estuarine and Coastal Marine Science (ISSN 0302-3524)
    Description: Devoted to the analysis of saline water phenomena ranging from the outer edge of the continental shelf to the upper limits of the tidal zone.

551.4   CL   ISSN 0071-173X
ESTUDIOS OCEANOLOGICOS. (Text in Spanish; abstracts in English, Spanish) 1965-1966; resumed 1983. a., vol.12, 1992. $30 or exchange basis. Universidad de Antofagasta, Facultad de Recursos del Mar, Casilla 170, Antofagasta, Chile. FAX 083-247542. TELEX 325054 UANTOF CK. Ed. Oscar Zuniga Romero. charts; illus.; stat.; circ. 600 (controlled). **Indexed:** Aqua.Sci.& Fish.Abstr., Deep Sea Res.& Oceanogr.Abstr.
    Description: Provides research in aquatic sciences, with emphasis on the Pacific Ocean.

551.46 597   BE   ISSN 0774-0689
EUROPEAN AQUACULTURE SOCIETY. SPECIAL PUBLICATIONS. 1976. irreg. price varies. European Aquaculture Society (EAS), Coupure Rechts 168, B-9000 Gent, Belgium. TEL 32-9-2237722. FAX 32-9-2237604. Ed.Bd. **Document type:** proceedings.

551.4   FI   ISSN 0357-1076
GC3.F4   CODEN: FMRED3
FINNISH MARINE RESEARCH. (Text mainly in English) 1920. irreg., no.261, 1992. price varies. Finnish Institute of Marine Research, P.O. Box 33, SF-00931 Helsinki 93, Finland. FAX 0-331-376. TELEX 125731 IMR. Ed. Pentti Malkki. circ. 800. (back issues avail.) **Indexed:** Aqua.Sci.& Fish.Abstr., Biol.Abstr., Chem.Abstr., Curr.Adv.Ecol.Sci., Deep Sea Res.& Oceanogr.Abstr., Meteor.& Geoastrophys.Abstr., Ocean.Abstr., Pollut.Abstr., Ref.Zh.
  —BLDSC (3929.185000); CASDDS.
    Formerly (until 1978): Finland. Merentutkimuslaitoksen. Julkaisu (ISSN 0025-9985)

FLINDERS INSTITUTE FOR ATMOSPHERIC AND MARINE SCIENCES. COMPUTING REPORTS. see *METEOROLOGY*

551.5   AT   ISSN 0311-6883
FLINDERS INSTITUTE FOR ATMOSPHERIC AND MARINE SCIENCES. CRUISE REPORTS. 1972. irreg., no.7, 1978. Aus.$30 per no. Flinders Institute for Atmospheric and Marine Sciences, Flinders University of South Australia, P.O. Box 2100, Australia. Ed. M. Tomezak. circ. 150.

FLINDERS INSTITUTE FOR ATMOSPHERIC AND MARINE SCIENCES. RESEARCH REPORTS. see *METEOROLOGY*

FLINDERS INSTITUTE FOR ATMOSPHERIC AND MARINE SCIENCES. TECHNICAL REPORTS. see *METEOROLOGY*

551.46   FR   ISSN 0761-3962
CODEN: ACIFE7
FRANCE. IFREMER. CENTRE DE BREST. COLLOQUES. ACTES. 1971. irreg., no.12, 1991. 300 F. per no. (Institut Francais de Recherche pour l'Exploitation de la Mer (IFREMER), Centre de Brest, Service Documentation et Publications) Editions de l' IFREMER, B.P. 70, 29280 Plouzane, France. TEL 98-22-40-13. FAX 98-22-45-86. TELEX 940 627 F. Ed. Raoul Piboubes. (back issues avail.) **Indexed:** Biol.Abstr., Bull.Signal., Chem.Abstr., GeoRef., Ocean.Abstr., Ocean.Abstr.Bibl., Pollut.Abstr. **Document type:** proceedings.
  —BLDSC (0675.113340); CASDDS.
    Formerly: France. Centre National pour l'Exploitation des Oceans. Colloques. Actes (ISSN 0335-8259)

551.46 576   JA   ISSN 0388-3531
FUCHAKU SEIBUTSU KENKYU/MARINE FOULING. (Text in English, Japanese) 1979. irreg. Fuchaku Seibutsu Kenkyukai - Japan Research Group of Marine Fouling Organisms, Kankyo Seibutsu Kenkyujo, 3-8 Nakameguro 1-chome, Meguro-ku, Tokyo 153, Japan.

551.46 574   JA   ISSN 0917-8147
FUKUYAMA DAIGAKU FUZOKU NAIKAI SEIBUTSU SHIGEN KENKYUJO HOKOKU/FUKUYAMA UNIVERSITY. RESEARCH INSTITUTE OF MARINE BIORESOURCES. REPORT. (Text in English, Japanese) 1991. irreg. Fukuyama Daigaku, Fuzoku Naikai Seibutsu Shigen Kenkyujo, Ohamacho, Innoshima-shi, Hiroshima-ken 722-21, Japan.

551.4 574.92   JA   ISSN 0287-6779
CODEN: GLXADP
GALAXEA. 1982. s-a. exchange basis. University of the Ryukyus, Sesoko Marine Science Center - Ryukyu Daigaku Nettai Kaiyo Kagaku Senta, 3422, Sesoko, Motobu-cho, Kunigami-gun, Okinawa-ken 903-01, Japan. FAX 0980-47-4919. Ed. Makoto Tsuchiya. illus. **Indexed:** Biol.Abstr., Curr.Adv.Ecol.Sci., W.R.C.Inf.
  —BLDSC (4066.590000); CASDDS.

551.46   JA
GEKKAN AKUA RAIFU/AQUAL LIFE. (Text in Japanese) 1979. m. 760 Yen per no. Marin Kikaku - Marine Planning Co., Ltd., 2-3, Sarugakucho 2-chome, Chiyoda-ku, Tokyo 101, Japan.

551.46   JA   ISSN 0916-2011
GEKKAN KAIYO/OCEANOGRAPHY MONTHLY. (Text in Japanese) 1969. m. 2000 Yen per no. Kaiyo Shuppan Co., Ltd., 675-5, Misawa, Hino-shi, Tokyo 191, Japan.

GEO-MARINE LETTERS; an international journal of marine geology. see *EARTH SCIENCES — Geology*

551.4   GW   ISSN 0084-9774
GEZEITENTAFELN. (Issued in 2 parts) 1879. a. DM.36.10. Bundesamt fuer Seeschiffahrt und Hydrographie, Bernhard-Nocht-Str. 78, 20359 Hamburg, Germany. TEL 040-3190-0. FAX 040-3190-5000. TELEX 211138-BSHHH-D. circ. 6,300. (tabloid format) **Document type:** academic/scholarly publication.

551.46   SW
GOETEBORGS UNIVERSITET. OCEANOGRAFISKA INSTITUTIONEN. REPORTS. (Text in English) 1969. irreg., no.42, 1982. free. Goeteborgs Universitet, Oceanografiska Institutionen, Box 4038, 400 40 Goeteborg, Sweden. circ. 100. **Indexed:** Deep Sea Res.& Oceanogr.Abstr.
    Supersedes (1930-1964, no.31): Oceanografiska Institutet, Goeteborg. Meddelanden (ISSN 0072-5072)

551.46   AT   ISSN 0156-5842
GREAT BARRIER REEF MARINE PARK AUTHORITY WORKSHOP SERIES. 1978. irreg. price varies. Great Barrier Reef Marine Park Authority, P.O. Box 1379, Townsville, Qld. 4810, Australia. TEL 077-818811. FAX 077-726093. circ. 250. **Document type:** academic/scholarly publication.
    Description: Covers workshops on marine sciences held by the Marine Park Authority.

551.46   US   ISSN 0072-9027
GC1   CODEN: GURRA4
GULF RESEARCH REPORTS. 1961. a., latest 1992. price varies; free to qualified personnel. Gulf Coast Research Laboratory, P.O. Box 7000, Ocean Springs, MS 39564. TEL 601-872-4200. FAX 601-872-4204. Ed. Thomas D. McIlwain. circ. 900. (reprint service avail. from UMI) **Indexed:** Aqua.Sci.& Fish.Abstr., Biol.Abstr., Curr.Adv.Ecol.Sci., Curr.Cont., Deep Sea Res.& Oceanogr.Abstr., Helminthol.Abstr., Mar.Sci.Cont.Tab., Ocean.Abstr. **Document type:** academic/scholarly publication.
  —BLDSC (4230.400000); UnCover.

HAFRANNSOKNIR. see *FISH AND FISHERIES*

551.46   CC
HAIYANG/OCEANS. (Text in Chinese) m. $0.40 per no. (China Oceanic Society) Guoji Shudian, Qikan Bu - China International Book Trading Corp., Chegongzhuang Xilu 21, P.O. Box 399, Beijing 100044, People's Republic of China.

551.46   CC   ISSN 1003-2029
HAIYANG JISHU/OCEAN TECHNOLOGY. (Text in Chinese; abstracts in English) 1982. q. Y8. Guojia Haiyang-ju, Haiyang Jishu Yanjiusuo - State Oceanic Administration, Institute of Ocean Technology, 60 Xianyang Road, Tianjin 300111, People's Republic of China. TEL 022-736-7821. TELEX 23174 TJPTB CN. Ed. Li Yunwu. circ. 1,500. **Document type:** academic/scholarly publication.

551.46   CC   ISSN 1000-3096
HAIYANG KEXUE/MARINE SCIENCES. (Text in Chinese; summaries in English) 1977. bi-m. $43.20. (Chinese Academy of Sciences, Institute of Oceanology) Science Press, Marketing and Sales Press, 16 Donghuangchenggen Beijie, Beijing 100707, People's Republic of China. TEL 4010642. FAX 4012180. TELEX 210247-SPBJ-CN. adv. circ. 10,000. **Document type:** academic/scholarly publication.
  —BLDSC (5378.144000).
    Description: Covers marine physics, geology, chemistry, biology, engineering, instruments, and environmental protection. Devoted to the construction and modernization of China.

551.46   CC   ISSN 1001-5043
HAIYANG SHIJIE/OCEAN WORLD. (Text in Chinese) 1975. m. Y1.20 per no. (Zhongguo Haiyang Xuehui - Chinese Society of Oceanography) Haiyang Chubanshe - China Ocean Press, Haimao Dalou, 1 Fuxingmenwai St., Beijing 100860, People's Republic of China. TEL 86-1-868941. Ed. Tan Zheng. adv.: B&W page $1000, color page $3500; adv. contact: Guo Wei. circ. 20,000.
    Description: Publishes articles on all aspects of ocean science, such as geography, geology, biology and physics.

EARTH SCIENCES — OCEANOGRAPHY

551.46   CC   ISSN 1001-6392
HAIYANG TONGBAO. (Text in Chinese) 1982. bi-m. $150. Guojia Haiyang-ju, Haiyang Keji Qingbao Yanjiusuo, No. 93, Liu (6) Wei Lu, Hedong Qu, Tianjin 300171, People's Republic of China. TEL 086-22-244161. FAX 086-22-314408. Ed. Yu Zhouwen. **Document type:** bulletin.
—BLDSC (5378.134100).

551.46   CC   ISSN 1001-0157
HAIYANG WENZHAI. (Text in Chinese) 1962. bi-m. Y120. Guojia Haiyang-ju, Haiyang Qingbao Yanjiusuo, P.O. Box 75, Tianjin 300171, People's Republic of China. TEL 086-22-244161. FAX 086-022-314408. TELEX 23138 NODC CN. Ed. Chen Boyong. **Document type:** abstracting/indexing.

551.65   CC
HAIYANG XINXI. (Text in Chinese) 1986. m. Y120. Guojia Haiyang-ju, Haiyang Xinxi Zhongxin, No. 93, Liu (6) Wei Lu, Tianjin 300171, People's Republic of China. TEL 086-22-244161. FAX 086-022-314408. TELEX 23138 NODC CN. Ed. Chen Boyong. adv. **Document type:** newsletter.

551.46   CC   ISSN 0253-4193
GC1   CODEN: HYPADJ
HAIYANG XUEBAO. English edition: Acta Oceanologica Sinica (ISSN 0253-505X) (Text in Chinese) bi-m. (Chinese Society of Oceanography) China Ocean Press, International Department, Haimao Dalou, 1 Fuxingmenwai St., Beijing 100860, People's Republic of China. TEL 8032211. FAX 8033515. TELEX 22536 NBO CN. Ed. Su Jilan. **Document type:** academic/scholarly publication.
—BLDSC (0641.623000); CASDDS.
Description: Publishes scholarly papers on marine science and technology, including physics, chemistry, biology, hydrology, meteorology, aquaculture, engineering, remote sensing, instrumentation and meters.
Refereed Serial

551.46 551.48   CC
GC1   CODEN: HYHCAG
HAIYANG YU HUZHAO. English edition: Chinese Journal of Oceanology and Limnology (ISSN 0254-4059) (Text in Chinese; summaries in English) 1957. bi-m. $95.30. (Chinese Academy of Sciences) Science Press, Marketing and Sales Department, 16 Donghuangchenggen Beijie, Beijing 100707, People's Republic of China. TEL 4010642. FAX 4012180. TELEX 210247-SPBJ-CN. adv. circ. 7,000. **Indexed:** Biol.Abstr., Curr.Adv.Ecol.Sci., Deep Sea Res.& Oceanogr.Abstr., GeoRef., Sel.Water Res.Abstr.
—BLDSC (6234.150000); UnCover; CASDDS.
Formerly: Oceanologia et Limnologia Sinica (ISSN 0029-814X)
Description: Covers hydrophysics, hydrochemistry, hydrobiology, geomorphology, equipment and apparatus research and manufacture, comprehensive reviews, and academic activities.
Refereed Serial

551.46   CC
HAIYANG YUBAO. (Text in Chinese) q. Guojia Haiyang Ju, Haiyang Huanjing Yubao Zhongxin, 8, Dahui Si, Beijing 100081, People's Republic of China. TEL 8313947. Ed. Du Bilan.

551.46   JA
HAKODATE KAIYO KISHODA. KAIYO SOKUHO/HAKODATE MARINE OBSERVATORY. OCEANOGRAPHIC OBSERVATION REPORT. (Text in Japanese) 1963. q. Kishocho, Hakodate Kaiyo Kishodai - Japan Meteorological Agency, Hakodate Marine Observatory, 4-4, Mihara 3-chome, Hakodate-shi, Hokkaido 041, Japan.

551.46 620   US
HARBOR BRANCH NEWS. 1986. fortn. Harbor Branch Oceanographic Institution, Inc., 5600 Old Dixie Hwy., Fort Pierce, FL 34946. TEL 407-465-2400. FAX 407-465-2446. TELEX 52-2886. circ. 700. (back issues avail.)

551.46   JA
HARO CHOSA HOKOKUSHO/RESEARCH REPORT OF WAVES. (Text in Japanese) 1966. biennial. Suisancho, Gyokubo - Fisheries Agency, Oceanic Fisheries Department, 2-1, Kasumigaseki 1-chome, Chiyoda-ku, Tokyo 100, Japan.

551.2   GW   ISSN 0174-3597
QH301   CODEN: HEMEDC
HELGOLAENDER MEERESUNTERSUCHUNGEN; marine investigations - recherches marines. (Text in English and German) 1937. 4/yr. DM.175. Biologische Anstalt Helgoland, Notkestr. 31, 22607 Hamburg, Germany. TEL 040-896930. FAX 040-89693115. Eds. H.-D. Franke, K. Luening. adv.; bk.rev.; abstr.; bibl.; charts; illus. circ. 750. **Indexed:** Aqua.Sci.& Fish.Abstr., Biol.Abstr., Chem.Abstr., Curr.Cont., Curr.Ref.Fish Res., Curr.Tit.Ocean, Deep Sea Res.& Oceanogr.Abstr., Excerpt.Med., Helminthol.Abstr., Ind.Sci.Rev., INIS Atomind., Mar.Sci.Cont.Tab., Ocean.Abstr., Pollut.Abstr., Sci.Cit.Ind., Sel.Water Res.Abstr., W.R.C.Inf. **Document type:** academic/scholarly publication.
—BLDSC (4284.970000); UnCover; SWETS; CASDDS.
Formerly (until 1980): Helgolaender Wissenschaftliche Meeresuntersuchungen (ISSN 0017-9957)

551.46 574   JA   ISSN 0285-9416
HIROSAKI DAIGAKU RIGAKUBU FUZOKU FUKAURA RINKAI JISSHUJO HOKOKU/HIROSAKI UNIVERSITY. FUKAURA MARINE BIOLOGICAL LABORATORY. REPORT. (Text in English, Japanese; summaries in English) 1969. biennial. Hirosaki Daigaku, Rigakubu - Hirosaki University, Faculty of Science, 3 Bunkyocho, Hirosaki-shi, Aomori-ken 036, Japan. **Indexed:** Jap.Per.Ind.
—BLDSC (7482.310000).

551.46 574   JA   ISSN 0289-2197
HIROSHIMA UNIVERSITY. MUKAISHIMA MARINE BIOLOGICAL STATION. CONTRIBUTIONS. (Text in English; summaries in English, Japanese) 1933. a. Hiroshima University, Mukaishima Marine Biological Station - Hiroshima Daigaku Rigakubu Fuzoku Mukaishima Rinkai Jikkenjo, Mukaishimacho, Mitsugi-gun, Hiroshima-ken 722, Japan.

551.46   GW   ISSN 0172-8253
HOCH- UND NIEDRIGWASSERZEITEN FUER DIE DEUTSCHE BUCHT UND DEREN FLUSSGEBIETE. 1947. a. DM.3.60. Bundesamt fuer Seeschiffahrt und Hydrographie, Bernhard-Nocht-Str. 78, 20359 Hamburg, Germany. TEL 040-3190-0. FAX 040-3190-5000. TELEX 211138-BSHHH-D. **Document type:** academic/scholarly publication.

551.46 639.2   JA   ISSN 0439-3511
GC791
HOKKAIDO UNIVERSITY. FACULTY OF FISHERIES. DATA RECORD OF OCEANOGRAPHIC OBSERVATIONS AND EXPLORATORY FISHING/KAIYO CHOSA GYOGYO SHIKEN YOHO. (Text in Japanese and European languages) 1957. a. exchange basis. Hokkaido University, Faculty of Fisheries, 3-1-1 Minato-machi, Hakodate, Hokkaido 041, Japan. circ. 600.

551.46   JA
HOKKAIDO UNIVERSITY. INSTITUTE OF ALGOLOGICAL RESEARCH. SCIENTIFIC PAPERS/HOKKAIDO DAIGAKU RIGAKUBU KAISO KENKYUJO OBUN HOKOKU. (Text in English) 1935. irreg. exchange basis. Hokkaido University, Faculty of Science, Institute of Algological Research - Hokkaido Daigaku Rigakubu Kaiso Kenkyujo, 1-13, Bokoi Minamimachi, Muroran-shi, Hokkaido 051, Japan. **Indexed:** Biol.Abstr.

HORIZON. BULLETIN BIBLIOGRAPHIQUE O R S T O M.
see EARTH SCIENCES — Abstracting, Bibliographies, Statistics

551.46   CC   ISSN 1000-7199
HUANG BOHAI HAIYANG. (Text in Chinese) q. Guojia Haiyang-ju, Di 1 Haiyang Yanjiusuo, No. 13, Hongdao Zhilu, Qingdao, Shandong 286810, People's Republic of China. TEL 286810. Ed. Chen Zeshi.

551.46 639.3   UK   ISSN 1054-3139
GC1   CODEN: ICESEC
I C E S JOURNAL OF MARINE SCIENCE. (Text and summaries in English or French) 1926. q. £103 (effective 1994). (International Council for the Exploration of the Sea) Academic Press Ltd. (Subsidiary of: Harcourt Brace & Company Ltd.), 24-28 Oval Rd., London NW1 7DX, England. TEL 44-71-267-4466. FAX 44-71-482-2293. TELEX 25775-ACPRESS-G. (Subscr. to: Harcourt Brace & Company Ltd., Foots Cray High St., Sidcup, Kent DA14 5HP, England. TEL 44-81-300-3322. FAX 44-80-309-0307) Ed. R.J.H. Beverton. bk.rev.; cum.index: vols.1-25. circ. 1,000. (back issues avail.) **Indexed:** Biol.Abstr., Chem.Abstr., Deep Sea Res.& Oceanogr.Abstr., Environ.Abstr., Environ.Per.Bibl. (1991-), Ocean.Abstr., Pollut.Abstr. **Document type:** academic/scholarly publication.
—BLDSC (4361.491000); Faxon; UnCover; SWETS.
Former titles (until 1991): Conseil International pour l'Exploration de la Mer. Journal (ISSN 0020-6466); (until 1968): Conseil Permanent International pour 'Exploration de la Mer. Journal (ISSN 0902-3232)
Description: Contains original papers within the broad field of marine and fisheries science. References subjects including ecology, population studies, plankton research, and physical and chemical oceanography.

I C E S MARINE SCIENCE SYMPOSIA/ACTES DU SYMPOSIUM. (International Council for the Exploration of the Sea) see FISH AND FISHERIES

551.46   DK   ISSN 0106-6935
I C E S OCEANOGRAPHIC DATA LISTS AND INVENTORIES. (Text in English) 1963. irreg., no.68, 1986. price varies. International Council for the Exploration of the Sea, Palaegade 2-4, DK-1261 Copenhagen K, Denmark. FAX 33-934215. TELEX 22498 ICES DK. (Subscr. to: C.A. Reitzels Boghandel, Noerregade 20, DK-1165 Copenhagen K, Denmark) circ. 300. (back issues avail.) **Document type:** bulletin.
Supersedes (in 1971): I C E S Oceanographic Data Lists (ISSN 0074-4328); Conseil International pour l'Exploration de la Mer. Bulletin Hydrographique.

I E E E JOURNAL OF OCEANIC ENGINEERING. see ENGINEERING — Electrical Engineering

551.46 621.3   US
I E E E WORKING CONFERENCE ON CURRENT MEASUREMENT. PROCEEDINGS. 1978. irreg., 3rd, 1986. (I E E E, Oceanic Engineering Society) Institute of Electrical and Electronics Engineers, Inc., 345 E. 47th St., New York, NY 10017-2394. TEL 212-705-7900. FAX 212-705-7682. (Subscr. to: Box 1331, 445 Hoes Ln., Piscataway, NJ 08855-1331)
Description: Focuses on addressing problems associated with measuring currents in the oceans.

551.46 574.92   UN   ISSN 0020-7918
I M S NEWSLETTER. (International Marine Science) Spanish edition: Boletin Internacional de Ciencias del Mar (ISSN 0379-5276); French edition: Bulletin International des Sciences de la Mer (ISSN 0251-4451) (Text in English, French and Spanish) 1963. q. free to qualified personnel. Unesco, Marine Information Centre, 7 Place de Fontenoy, 75700 Paris, France. Ed. Gary Wright. circ. 8,000 (controlled). **Indexed:** Curr.Adv.Ecol.Sci. **Document type:** newsletter.
—BLDSC (4371.665000).
Formerly (until 1970): International Marine Science (ISSN 1013-2813)

551.46   MM
I O I NEWS. 1988. irreg. free. International Ocean Institute, P.O. Box 3, Gzira GZR 01, Malta. TEL 356-346529. FAX 356-346502.

551.46   JA   ISSN 0917-3382
I.O.P. DIVING NEWS/IZU KAIYO KAIYO TSUSHIN. (Text in Japanese; summaries in English) 1990. m. 250 Yen per no. Izu Ocean Academy Corp. - Izu Kaiyo Akademi, Ikedayama Haitsu 1502, 22-33, Higashigotanda 5-chome, Shinagawa-ku, Tokyo 141, Japan.

EARTH SCIENCES — OCEANOGRAPHY

551.4   II   ISSN 0379-5136
GC721   CODEN: IJMNBF
INDIAN JOURNAL OF MARINE SCIENCES. (Text in English) 1972. q. Rs.160($65) Council of Scientific and Industrial Research, Publications and Information Directorate, Hillside Rd., New Delhi 110012, India. TEL 5784846. (Co-sponsor: Indian National Science Academy) Ed. K. Satyanarayana. illus. **Indexed:** Biol.Abstr., Chem.Abstr., Curr.Adv.Ecol.Sci., Curr.Cont., Curr.Ref.Fish Res., Curr.Tit.Ocean, Deep Sea Res.& Oceanogr.Abstr., Helminthol.Abstr., INIS Atomind., Nutr.Abstr., Pollut.Abstr., Sci.Abstr., Sel.Water Res.Abstr., Soils & Fert.
—BLDSC (4416.050000); Faxon; SWETS; CASDDS.

639.2 551.46   SP   ISSN 1130-782X
INFORMES TECNICOS DE SCIENTIA MARINA. (Text in English, Spanish; summaries in English) 1972. 10/yr. 3000 ptas. (foreign 4600 ptas.). Consejo Superior de Investigaciones Cientificas (C.S.I.C.), Instituto de Ciencias del Mar, Paseo Nacional s-n, 08039 Barcelona, Spain. TEL 310-64-50. FAX 319-98-42. Ed. Josep-Maria Gili. bibl. circ. 600. **Indexed:** Biol.Abstr., Chem.Abstr., Deep Sea Res.& Oceanogr.Abstr., Ind.SST.
Former titles (until 1990, no.155): Informes Tecnicos de Investigacion Pesquera; (until 1987): Instituto de Investigaciones Pesqueras. Informes Tecnicos (ISSN 0304-5161)

551.46   FR   ISSN 0078-9682
GC1   CODEN: AIOPA3
INSTITUT OCEANOGRAPHIQUE. ANNALES. (Text in English, French) 2/yr. 810 F. Gauthier-Villars, 15 rue Gossin, 92543 Montrouge Cedex, France. TEL 33-1-40-92-65-00. FAX 33-1-40-92-65-97. TELEX 634 916 F. (Subscr. to: Centrale des Revues, 11 rue Gossin, 92543 Montrouge Cedex, France. TEL 33-1-46-56-52-66) Ed. G. Grau. bk.rev.; abstr.; bibl.; illus. circ. 525. **Indexed:** Appl.Mech.Rev., Biol.Abstr., Chem.Abstr., Curr.Adv.Ecol.Sci., Deep Sea Res.& Oceanogr.Abstr., Helminthol.Abstr., Mar.Sci.Cont.Tab., Ocean.Abstr., Pollut.Abstr., Sci.Cit.Ind., So.Pac.Per.Ind.
—BLDSC (0926.000000); SWETS; CASDDS. **CCC**.

551.46   MC   ISSN 0304-5722
CODEN: BULCAA
INSTITUT OCEANOGRAPHIQUE. BULLETIN. (Text in English or French) 1904. irreg., no.1440, 1993. price varies. Musee Oceanographique, Service des Publications, Avenue Saint-Martin, MC 98000, Monaco. TEL 93-15-36-00. FAX 93-50-52-97. TELEX 469 037 MC. illus. (back issues avail.) **Indexed:** Biol.Abstr., Ref.Zh. **Document type:** bulletin.
—BLDSC (2574.000000).
Description: Monographic studies on taxonomy of marine animals. Catalogues of the oceanographic museum collection.

551.46   MC   ISSN 0304-5714
CODEN: MIOGA6
INSTITUT OCEANOGRAPHIQUE. MEMOIRES. (Text in English, French) 1970. irreg., no.17, 1993. price varies. Musee Oceanographique, Service des Publications, Av. Saint-Martin, MC 98000, Monaco. TEL 93-15-36-00. FAX 93-50-52-97. TELEX 469 037 MC. Ed. Jacqueline Carpine-Lancre. illus. circ. 850. (back issues avail.) **Indexed:** Biol.Abstr., Curr.Adv.Ecol.Sci., Deep Sea Res.& Oceanogr.Abstr., Ref.Zh.
Description: Monographic studies on taxonomy of marine animals.

551.46   UK
INSTITUTE OF OCEANOGRAPHIC SCIENCES. DEACON LABORATORY. ANNUAL REPORT. 1973. a. £8. Institute of Oceanographic Sciences, Deacon Laboratory, Wormley, Godalming, Surrey GU8 5UB, England. FAX 0428-683066. TELEX 858833-OCEANS-G. **Indexed:** Biol.Abstr., Deep Sea Res.& Oceanogr.Abstr., GeoRef., Ocean.Abstr. **Document type:** corporate report.
Formerly: Institute of Oceanographic Sciences. Annual Report (ISSN 0309-4472)

551.46   SP   ISSN 0074-0195
GC1   CODEN: BOEA3
INSTITUTO ESPANOL DE OCEANOGRAFIA. BOLETIN. (Text in Spanish; summaries in English) 1948. s-a. 1800 ptas. per no. Instituto Espanol de Oceanografia, Avda. del Brasil, 31, 28020 Madrid, Spain. TEL 5974443. FAX 5974770. TELEX 44460. (Dist. by: Centro de Publicaciones, Ministerio de Agricultura, Pesca y Alimentacion, Paseo Infanta Isabel, 1, 28014 Madrid, Spain. TEL 3475551) **Indexed:** Biol.Abstr., Curr.Adv.Ecol.Sci., Deep Sea Res.& Oceanogr.Abstr., Helminthol.Abstr., Ind.SST, Sel.Water Res.Abstr. **Document type:** bulletin.
—BLDSC (2171.000000).

551.46   SP   ISSN 0214-1949
INSTITUTO ESPANOL DE OCEANOGRAFIA. MONOGRAFIAS. (Text in Spanish; summaries in English) irreg. price varies. Instituto Espanol de Oceanografia, Avda. del Brasil, 31, 28020 Madrid, Spain. TEL 5974443. FAX 5974770. TELEX 44460. (Dist. by: Centro de Publicaciones, Ministerio de Agricultura, Pesca y Alimentacion, Paseo Infanta Isabel, 1, 28014 Madrid. TEL 3475551) **Indexed:** Deep Sea Res.& Oceanogr.Abstr., Ind.SST. **Document type:** monographic series.
Formerly (until 1983): Instituto Espanol de Oceanografia. Trabajos (ISSN 0074-0209)

551.46   SP   ISSN 0214-7378
INSTITUTO ESPANOL DE OCEANOGRAFIA. PUBLICACIONES ESPECIALES. (Text in Spanish; summaries in English) 1988. irreg. price varies. Instituto Espanol de Oceanografia, Avda. del Brasil, 31, 28020 Madrid, Spain. TEL 5974443. FAX 5974770. TELEX 44460. (Dist. by: Centro de Publicaciones, Ministerio de Agricultura Pesca y Alimentacion, Paseo Infanta Isabel 1, 28014 Madrid, Spain. TEL 3475551) **Document type:** monographic series.

INSTYTUT METEOROLOGII I GOSPODARKI WODNEJ. MATERIALY BADAWCZE. SERIA: HYDROLOGIA I OCEANOLOGIA/INSTITUTE OF METEOROLOGY AND WATER MANAGEMENT. RESEARCH PAPERS SERIES: HYDROLOGY AND OCEANOLOGY. see EARTH SCIENCES — Hydrology

551.46   PL
INSTYTUT METEOROLOGII I GOSPODARKI WODNEJ. ODDZIAL MORSKI W GDYNI. MATERIALY. WARUNKI SRODOWISKOWE POLSKIEJ STREFY POLUDNIOWEGO BALTYKU. (Text in English, Polish) 1987. a. $20. Instytut Meteorologii i Gospodarki Wodnej, Oddzial Morski w Gdyni, 42 Waszyngtona St., 81-342 Gdynia, Poland. TEL 4858-205221. FAX 4858-201641. TELEX 54216 PL. Ed.Bd. charts; illus. circ. 120.
Description: Covers physics, chemistry and pollution of sea water in the Polish zone of Southern Baltic Sea.

551.46   PL
INSTYTUT METEOROLOGII I GOSPODARKI WODNEJ. ODDZIAL MORSKI W GDYNI. MATERIALY. ZLODZENIE POLSKIEJ STREFY PRZYBRZEZNEJ. (Text in English, Polish) 1987. a. $20. Instytut Meteorologii i Gospodarki Wodnej, Oddzial Morski w Gdyni, 42 Waszyngtona St., 81-342 Gdynia, Poland. TEL 4858-20701. FAX 4858-201641. TELEX 54216 PL. Ed. Alicja Wisniewska-Michalska. illus.; maps. circ. 120.
Description: Covers ice-conditions in the Polish coastal zone of the Baltic Sea.

551.46   UN   ISSN 0074-1175
INTERGOVERNMENTAL OCEANOGRAPHIC COMMISSION. TECHNICAL SERIES. French edition: Commission Oceanographique Intergouvernementale. Serie Technique (ISSN 0251-9607); Russian edition: Mezpravitel'stvennaja Okeanograficeskaja Komissia. Mehaniceskaja Serija (ISSN 0251-9593); Spanish edition: Comision Oceanografica Intergubernamental. Coleccion Tecnica (ISSN 0538-3900) (Text in English) 1965. irreg., no.30, 1984. price varies. Unesco, 7-9 Place de Fontenoy, 75700 Paris, France. TEL 45-77-16-10. (Dist. in U.S. by: Unipub, 4611-F Assembly Dr., Lanham, MD 20706-4391) **Indexed:** Biol.Abstr., Meteor.& Geoastrophys.Abstr., Ocean.Abstr.

551.46   US
INTERNATIONAL ASSOCIATION FOR THE PHYSICAL SCIENCE OF THE OCEAN. PROCES-VERBAUX. (Text in English or French) 1934. quadrennial. free. International Association for the Physical Sciences of the Ocean, c/o Dr. Robert E. Stevenson, Ed., Box 1161, Del Mar, CA 92014. circ. 1,000. (back issues avail.) **Document type:** proceedings.
Formerly: International Association for the Physical Science of Oceanography. Proces-Verbaux.

551.46   US
INTERNATIONAL ASSOCIATION FOR THE PHYSICAL SCIENCES OF THE OCEAN. PUBLICATIONS SCIENTIFIQUE. irreg., latest no.35, 1992. free. International Association for the Physical Sciences of the Ocean, c/o Dr. Robert E. Stevenson, Box 1161, Del Mar, CA 92014. **Document type:** academic/scholarly publication.

INTERNATIONAL ASSOCIATION OF THEORETICAL AND APPLIED LIMNOLOGY. PROCEEDINGS/INTERNATIONALE VEREINIGUNG FUER THEORETISCHE UND ANGEWANDTE LIMNOLOGIE. VERHANDLUNGEN. see EARTH SCIENCES — Hydrology

551.4   MC   ISSN 0020-6938
INTERNATIONAL HYDROGRAPHIC BULLETIN. (Text in English, French) 1928. m. 250 F. International Hydrographic Bureau, 7 av. President J.F. Kennedy, B.P. 445 MC 98011, Monaco. TEL 93-50-65-87. bk.rev.; bibl.; charts; illus.; index. circ. 600. (reprint service avail. from ISI,UMI) **Indexed:** Curr.Tit.Ocean, Fluidex, Ocean.Abstr., Pollut.Abstr.
—Faxon.

551.48   MC   ISSN 0074-6274
INTERNATIONAL HYDROGRAPHIC CONFERENCE. REPORTS OF PROCEEDINGS. (Editions in English, French) 1919. quinquennial, 14th, 1992, Monte Carlo. 150 F. per vol. International Hydrographic Bureau, 7 av. President J. F. Kennedy, B.P. 445, MC 98011 Cedex, Monaco. TEL 93-50-65-87. (reprint service avail. from ISI,UMI)

551.46   MC
INTERNATIONAL HYDROGRAPHIC ORGANIZATION. YEARBOOK. (Text in English, French) 1928. a. 125 F. International Hydrographic Bureau, 7 av. President J.F. Kennedy, B.P. 445, MC 98011 Cedex, Monaco. TEL 93-50-65-87. circ. 550. (reprint service avail. from ISI, UMI)
Formerly: International Hydrographic Bureau. Yearbook (ISSN 0074-6282)

551.4   MC   ISSN 0020-6946
CODEN: IHYRA4
INTERNATIONAL HYDROGRAPHIC REVIEW. (Editions in English, French) 1923. s-a. 350 F. International Hydrographic Bureau, 7 av. President J.F. Kennedy, B.P. 445, MC 98011 cedex, Monaco. TEL 93-50-65-87. adv.; bk.rev.; bibl.; charts; illus.; maps; cum.index every 5 yrs. circ. 1,050. (also avail. in microform from UMI; reprint service avail. from ISI, UMI; back issues avail.) **Indexed:** Bibl.Cart., Curr.Cont., Curr.Tit.Ocean, Deep Sea Res.& Oceanogr.Abstr., Fluidex, Geo.Abstr., I D A, Ocean.Abstr.
—BLDSC (4541.000000); Faxon; UnCover; UMI.

INTERNATIONAL JOURNAL OF OFFSHORE AND POLAR ENGINEERING. see ENGINEERING — Mechanical Engineering

551.46   MM
INTERNATIONAL OCEAN INSTITUTE. OCCASIONAL PAPERS. Short title: I O I Occasional Papers. 1973. irreg., no.8, 1981. price varies. International Ocean Institute, P.O. Box 3, Gzira GZR 01, Malta. TEL 356-346529. FAX 356-346502. circ. 200. **Indexed:** Chem.Abstr., Ocean.Abstr.
Formerly: University of Malta. International Ocean Institute. Occasional Papers.
Description: Research papers and commissioned studies on various aspects of international law of the sea and NIED.

EARTH SCIENCES — OCEANOGRAPHY

551.46   MM
INTERNATIONAL OCEAN INSTITUTE. PACEM IN MARIBUS. PROCEEDINGS. 1971. irreg. (every 12-18 mos.). price varies. International Ocean Institute, P.O. Box 3, Gzira GZR 01, Malta. TEL 356-346529. FAX 356-346502. circ. 200. **Document type:** proceedings.
Description: Collected papers and discussion of issues under consideration at PIM. Always related to international law and NIED.

551.46   UN   ISSN 0538-8880
INTERNATIONAL OCEANOGRAPHIC TABLES. (Prepared under the supervision of the Joint Panel on Oceanographic Tables and Standards.) (Text in English, French, Russian and Spanish) 1966. a. (National Institute of Oceanography, UK) Unesco Press, 7 Place de Fontenoy, F-75700 Paris, France. TEL 33 1 568-10-00. (Dist. in U.S. by: Unipub, 4611-F Assembly Dr., Lanham, MD 20706-4391)

INTERNATIONAL SEAWEED SYMPOSIUM. PROCEEDINGS. see *BIOLOGY — Botany*

551.4 623.82   UK   ISSN 0267-1085
TC1501
INTERNATIONAL UNDERWATER SYSTEM DESIGN. 1979. 6/yr. £51 (US $145; elsewhere £71). A.P. Publications Ltd., 377 St. John St., London EC1V 4LD, England. TEL 071-837-5921. FAX 071-837-1197. Ed. Ed Patterson. adv.: B&W page £935; trim 254 x 178; adv. contact: Tony Barrett. bk.rev. circ. 10,100. **Document type:** trade publication.
—BLDSC (4551.460000); Faxon; SWETS.
Formerly (until 1991): Underwater System Design.
Description: Discusses underwater engineering, instrumentation, and military technology.

551.4   IS   ISSN 0792-0911
GC59.81.I75   CODEN: BRIREN
ISRAEL OCEANOGRAPHIC AND LIMNOLOGICAL RESEARCH. BIENNIAL REPORT. (Text and summaries in English) 1971. biennial. free. Israel Oceanographic and Limnological Research Ltd., P.O. Box 8030, Haifa 31080, Israel. TEL 972-4-515202. FAX 972-4-511911. Ed.Bd. bibl.; charts; illus.; stat. circ. 500. **Indexed:** Aqua.Sci.& Fish.Abstr., Meteor.& Geoastrophys.Abstr.
Former titles (until 1982): Israel Oceanographic and Limnological Research. Triennial Report (ISSN 0334-6145); (until 1976): Israel Oceanographic and Limnological Research. Annual Report (ISSN 0304-7423)

ISTITUTO RICERCHE PESCA MARITTIMA. QUADERNI. see *FISH AND FISHERIES*

551.46   IT   ISSN 0082-6456
ISTITUTO SPERIMENTALE TALASSOGRAFICO DI TRIESTE. PUBBLICAZIONE. 1919. irreg., no.690, 1993. price varies or exchange basis. Consiglio Nazionale delle Ricerche, Istituto Sperimentale Talassografico di Trieste, Viale Romolo Gessi, 2, 34123 Trieste, Italy. TEL 040-305312. FAX 040-308941. **Indexed:** Ocean.Abstr., Pollut.Abstr. **Document type:** academic/scholarly publication.
Description: Reprints of articles prepared by reseachers of the institute and published in the journals of different publishers.

551.42   JA   ISSN 0915-2636
J A M S T E C. (Text in Japanese) 1989. q. free. Japan Marine Science and Technology Center - Kaiyo Kagaku Gijutsu Senta, 2-15 Natsushima-cho, Yokosuka-shi, Kanagawa-ken 237, Japan.

551.46   JA
J O D C CATALOGUE. (Text in Japanese) 1981. irreg. Maritime Safety Agency, Hydrographic Department, Japan Oceanographic Data Center - Kaijo Hoancho Suirobu Nihon Kaiyo Deta Senta, 3-1, Tsukiji 5-chome, Chuo-ku, Tokyo 104, Japan. **Document type:** catalog.

551.46   JA   ISSN 0287-2609
J O D C NEWS. (Text in Japanese) 1971. s-a. Maritime Safety Agency, Hydrographic Department, Japan Oceanographic Data Center - Kaijo Hoancho Suirobu Nihon Kaiyo Deta Senta, 3-1, Tsukiji 5-chome, Chuo-ku, Tokyo 104, Japan.

JAPAN INSTITUTE OF NAVIGATION. JOURNAL/NIHON KOKAI GAKKAI RONBUNSHU. see *TRANSPORTATION — Ships And Shipping*

JAPAN SEA REGIONAL FISHERIES RESEARCH INSTITUTE. BULLETIN/NIHONKAIKU SUISAN KENKYUJO KENKYU HOKOKU. see *FISH AND FISHERIES*

551.46   US   ISSN 0075-3858
                   CODEN: JHOSA2
JOHNS HOPKINS OCEANOGRAPHIC STUDIES. 1962. irreg., no.6, 1977. price varies. Johns Hopkins University Press, 701 W. 40th St., Ste. 275, Baltimore, MD 21211. TEL 410-516-6900. FAX 410-516-6998. (reprint service avail. from UMI) **Indexed:** Biol.Abstr., Deep Sea Res.& Oceanogr.Abstr., GeoRef.
Refereed Serial

JOURNAL OF ATMOSPHERIC AND OCEANIC TECHNOLOGY. see *METEOROLOGY*

613.7 551.46   US   ISSN 0749-0208
GB450   CODEN: JCRSEK
JOURNAL OF COASTAL RESEARCH; an international forum for the littoral sciences. 1985. q. $58 to individuals (foreign $68); institutions $125 (foreign $135); students $43 (foreign $53). Coastal Education & Research Foundation, 4310 N.E. 25th Ave., Fort Lauderdale, FL 33308. TEL 305-565-1051. FAX 305-565-1051. Ed. Charles W. Finkl. adv.; bk.rev.; bibl.; charts; illus.; stat.; index. circ. 800. (back issues avail.) **Indexed:** Aqua.Sci.& Fish.Abstr., Curr.Cont., Curr.Ref.Fish Res., Deep Sea Res.& Oceanogr.Abstr., Ecol.Abstr., Excerp.Med., Geo.Abstr., Mar.Sci.Cont.Tab., Meteor.& Geoastrophys.Abstr., Ocean.Abstr., Phys.Abstr., Pollut.Abstr., Sel.Water Res.Abstr. **Document type:** academic/scholarly publication.
—BLDSC (4958.793700); Faxon; UnCover; SWETS. CCC.
Description: Dedicated to all aspects of coastal (marine) research. Encourages the dissemination of knowledge and understanding of the coastal zone by promoting cooperation and communication between specialists in different disciplines.

JOURNAL OF MARINE ENVIRONMENTAL ENGINEERING. see *ENVIRONMENTAL STUDIES*

551.46   NE   ISSN 0924-7963
GC1   CODEN: JMASE5
JOURNAL OF MARINE SYSTEMS. (Text in English) 1990. 6/yr. fl.566($306) (effective 1994). (European Association of Marine Sciences and Techniques) Elsevier Science B.V., P.O. Box 211, 1000 AE Amsterdam, Netherlands. TEL 31-20-5803911. FAX 31-20-5803598. TELEX 18582 ESPA NL. (Subscr. in U.S. and Canada to: Elsevier Science Inc., Box 882, Madison Sq. Sta., New York, NY 10159-0882. TEL 212-989-5800. FAX 212-633-3990) Ed.Bd. adv.; bk.rev.; charts; illus. (also avail. in microform from UMI; back issues avail.) **Indexed:** Aqua.Sci.& Fish.Abstr., Environ.Abstr., Environ.Per.Bibl. (1990-), Mar.Sci.Cont.Tab., Meteor.& Geoastrophys.Abstr. **Document type:** academic/scholarly publication.
—BLDSC (5012.033000); EI; UnCover; SWETS. CCC.
Description: Aims to provide a medium of exchange for those engaged in marine research where there exists an interplay between geology, chemistry, biology, and physics.
Refereed Serial

551.46   JA   ISSN 0916-8370
GC1   CODEN: JOOCE7
JOURNAL OF OCEANOGRAPHY. (Text in English) 1941. q. 3900 Yen (effective 1992). (Oceanographical Society of Japan - Nippon Kaiyo Gakkai) Terra Scientific Publishing Company, 302 Jiyugaoka Komatsu Bldg., Midoriqaoka 2-24-17, Meguro, Tokyo 152, Japan. TEL 03-3718-4403. FAX 81-3-3843-5015. Ed. Shizuo Tsunogai. adv.; bk.rev.; abstr.; charts; illus.; maps; index. circ. 2,100. **Indexed:** Biol.Abstr., Chem.Abstr., Geo.Abstr., GeoRef., Helminthol.Abstr., Meteor.& Geoastrophys.Abstr., Ocean.Abstr., Pollut.Abstr., Sel.Water Res.Abstr.
—BLDSC (5026.151000); CASDDS.
Formerly (until 1992): Oceanographical Society of Japan. Journal (ISSN 0029-8131)
Description: Contains original papers in oceanography and related fields.

551.46   US   ISSN 0022-3670
GC1   CODEN: JPYOBT
JOURNAL OF PHYSICAL OCEANOGRAPHY. 1971. m. $235 (foreign $255). American Meteorological Society, 45 Beacon St., Boston, MA 02108-3693. TEL 617-227-2425. FAX 617-742-8718. Ed. Eli Joel Katz. abstr.; bibl.; charts; illus.; stat.; index. circ. 1,397. (back issues avail.; reprint service avail.) **Indexed:** Appl.Mech.Rev., Biol.Abstr., Chem.Abstr., Curr.Cont., Deep Sea Res.& Oceanogr.Abstr., Fluidex, GeoRef., Ind.Sci.Rev., INIS Atomind., Int.Aerosp.Abstr., Meteor.& Geoastrophys.Abstr., Ocean.Abstr., Petrol.Abstr., Pollut.Abstr., Sci.Abstr., Sel.Water Res.Abstr., W.R.C.Inf. **Document type:** academic/scholarly publication.
—BLDSC (5036.210000); Faxon; UnCover; SWETS. CCC.
Description: Publishes research related to the physics of the ocean and of the processes operating at its boundaries.
Refereed Serial

JOURNAL OF PLANKTON RESEARCH. see *BIOLOGY*

JOURNAL OF WATERWAY, PORT, COASTAL, AND OCEAN ENGINEERING. see *ENGINEERING — Civil Engineering*

K W M NEWSLETTER. (Kendall Whaling Museum) see *MUSEUMS AND ART GALLERIES*

551.46   JA
KAGOSHIMA DAIGAKU. NANSEICHIIKI KENKYU SHIRYO SENTA. HOKOKU/KAGOSHIMA UNIVERSITY. REFERENCE CENTER OF THE SCIENTIFIC RESEARCHES FOR THE SOUTHWEST PACIFIC AREA. REPORTS. (Text in Japanese) 1967. s-a. free. Kagoshima Daigaku, Nanseichiiki Kenkyu Shiryo Senta - Kagoshima University, Reference Center of the Scientific Researches for the Southwest Pacific Area, 21-35 Korimoto 1-chome, Kagoshima-shi 890, Japan. FAX 81-992-85-7460. Ed. Eiji Nitta. circ. 550. (back issues avail.) **Document type:** bulletin.
—BLDSC (7589.230000).
Formerly: Kagoshima Daigaku. Nankanen Shiryo Senta. Hokoku (ISSN 0287-7791)

551.46   JA
KAIGAN SHOKO KENCHI SENTA CHOI NENPO/COAST RISE AND FALL SURVEY CENTER. ANNUAL TIDAL OBSERVATIONS. (Text in Japanese) 1967. a. Kokudo Chiriin - Geographical Survey Institute, 1, Kitasato, Tsukuba-shi, Ibaraki-ken 305, Japan.

KAISHO NENPO/ANNUAL REPORT OF MARITIME METEOROLOGY. see *METEOROLOGY*

551   JA   ISSN 0472-4666
KAISHO TO KISHO/OCEANOGRAPHY AND METEOROLOGY. (Text in English, Japanese) 1947. irreg. Kishocho, Nagasaki Kaiyo Kishodai - Japan Meteorological Agency, Nagasaki Marine Observatory, 11-51, Minamiyamatecho, Nagasaki-shi, Nagasaki-ken 850, Japan.
—BLDSC (6234.000000).

551.46   JA   ISSN 0915-2997
KAIYO CHOSA GIJUTSU/JAPAN SOCIETY FOR MARINE SURVEYS AND TECHNOLOGY. JOURNAL. (Text in Japanese; summaries in English) 1989. s-a. membership. Kaiyo Chosa Gijutsu Gakkai - Japan Society for Marine Surveys and Technology, Nihon Suiro Kyokai, 3-1, Tsukiji 5-chome, Chuo-ku, Tokyo 104, Japan.

551.46   JA
KAIYO CHOSA HOKOKU ICHIRAN/NATIONAL OCEANOGRAPHIC PROGRAM OF JAPAN. (Text in Japanese) a. Kaijo Hoancho, Suirobu, Nihon Kaiyo Deta Senta - Maritime Safety Agency, Hydrographic Department, Japan Oceanographic Data Center, 3-1, Tsukiji 5-chome, Chuo-ku, Tokyo 104, Japan.

551.46   JA
KAIYO CHOSA YOHO/DATA RECORD OF OCEANOGRAPHIC OBSERVATIONS. (Text in English) biennial. Hokkaidoriku Chuo Suisan Shikenjo - Hokkaido Central Fisheries Experimental Station, 238, Hamanakacho, Yoichi-machi, Yoichi-gun, Hokkaido 046, Japan.

551.46   JA
KAIYO ENKAKU TANSA. KAIYO RIMOTO SENSHINGU GIJUTSU NO KENKYU. KENKYU SEIKASHU/REPORT OF MARINE REMOTE SENSING TECHNIQUE. (Text in Japanese) a. Kagaku Gijutsu-cho, Kenkyu Kaihatsukyoku - Science and Technology Agency, Research and Development Bureau, 2-1, Kasumigaseki 2-chome, Chiyoda-ku, Tokyo 100, Japan.

KAIYO JIHO/CURRENT OCEANOGRAPHY. see EARTH SCIENCES

551.46   JA
KAIYO KAGAKU GIJUTSU SENTA NENPO/JAPAN MARINE SCIENCE AND TECHNOLOGY CENTER. ANNUAL REPORT. (Text in Japanese) 1972. a. free. Kaiyo Kagaku Gijutsu Senta - Japan Marine Science and Technology Center, 2-15 Natsushima-cho, Yokosuka-shi, Kanagawa-ken 237, Japan. Ed.Bd. circ. 1,000.

551.46   JA   ISSN 0387-382X
GC1   CODEN: KKKHEJ
KAIYO KAGAKU GIJUTSU SENTA SHIKEN KENKYU HOKOKU/JAPAN MARINE SCIENCE AND TECHNOLOGY CENTER. TECHNICAL REPORT. (Text in English, Japanese) 1977. s-a. free. Kaiyo Kagaku Gijutsu Senta, 2-15 Natsushima-cho, Yokosuka-shi, Kanagawa-ken 237, Japan. Ed.Bd. circ. 700.
—BLDSC (7526.754000).

551.46   JA   ISSN 0912-4829
KAIYO KAGAKU KENKYU/RESEARCH INSTITUTE OF OCEANOCHEMISTRY. TRANSACTIONS. (Text in English, Japanese) 1986. s-a. Kaiyo Kagaku Kenkyujo - Research Institute of Oceanochemistry, Kyoto Daigaku Rigakubu, Kita-Shirakawa Oiwakecho, Kyoto-shi, Kyoto 606, Japan.

551.46   JA   ISSN 0912-8549
KAIYO KAIHATSU NYUSU/JAPAN OCEAN INDUSTRIES ASSOCIATION. NEWS. (Text in Japanese) 1973. bi-m. Nihon Kaiyo Kaihatsu Sangyo Kyokai - Japan Ocean Industries Association, 8-10, Toranomon 2-chome, Minato-ku, Tokyo 105, Japan.

551.46   JA
KAIYO KAIHATSU SUISHIN KEIKAKU/MARINE SCIENCE AND TECHNOLOGY DEVELOPMENT IN JAPAN. (Text in Japanese) 1970. a. 5000 Yen. (Kaiyo Kagaku Gijutsu Kaihatsu Suishin Renraku Kaigi - Coordinating Committee for the Promotion and Development of Marine Science and Technology) Okurasho Insatsukyoku - Ministry of Finance, Printing Bureau, 2-4, Toranomon 2-chome, Minato-ku, Tokyo 105, Japan. Document type: government publication.

551.4   JA   ISSN 0287-2293
KAIYO KANSOKU DETA/DATA OF OCEANIC OBSERVATIONS. (Text in Japanese) 1980. a. Tokai Daigaku, Kaiyogakubu - Tokai University, Faculty of Marine Science and Technology, 20-1, Orido 3-chome, Shimizu-shi, Shizuoka-ken 424, Japan.

551.46 623.82   JA
KAIYO KOGAKU SHINPOJUMU/OCEAN ENGINEERING SYMPOSIUM. (Text in English, Japanese; summaries in English) 1975. biennial. Nihon Zosen Gakkai - Society of Naval Architects of Japan, 15-16, Toranomon 1-chome, Minato-ku, Tokyo 105, Japan.

551.46   JA   ISSN 0910-5425
KAIYO KYOKAIHO/JAPAN OCEAN DEVELOPMENT CONSTRUCTION ASSOCIATION. NEWS. (Text in Japanese) 1976. q. Nihon Kaiyo Kaihatsu Kensetsu Kyokai - Ocean Development Construction Association, Tokyo Kensetsu Kaikan, 5-1, Hatchobori 2-chome, Chuo-ku, Tokyo 104, Japan.

KAIYO ONKYO GAKKAISHI. see PHYSICS — Sound

551.46   JA   ISSN 0912-8123
KAIYO SANGYO KENKYU SHIRYO/RESEARCH MATERIALS ON OCEAN ECONOMICS. (Text in Japanese) 1970. irreg. Kaiyo Sangyo Kenkyukai - Research Institute for Ocean Economics, 1-10, Shinbashi 3-chome, Minato-ku, Tokyo 105, Japan.

KAIYO SEIBUTSU KANKYO KENKYUJO KENKYU HOKOKU/MARINE ECOLOGY RESEARCH INSTITUTE. REPORT. see BIOLOGY

551.46 574.5   JA   ISSN 0285-4376
KAIYO TO SEIBUTSU/AQUABIOLOGY. (Text in Japanese; summaries in English) 1979. bi-m. 1400 Yen per no. Seibutsu Kenkyusha Co., Ltd., 19-5 Higashigotanda 2-chome, Shinagawa-ku, Tokyo 141, Japan.
—BLDSC (1581.865700).

551.46 574   JA
KANAZAWA DAIGAKU RIGAKUBU FUZOKU NOTO RINKAI JIKKENJO KENKYU GAIYO NENJI HOKOKU/KANAZAWA UNIVERSITY. NOTO MARINE LABORATORY. ANNUAL PROGRESS REPORTS. (Text in Japanese) 1987. a. Kanazawa Daigaku, Rigakubu, Fuzoku Noto Rinkai Jikkenjo - Kanazawa University, Faculty of Science, Noto Marine Laboratory, Ogi, Uchiuramachi, Suzu-gun, Ishikawa-ken 927-05, Japan.

551.46   JA
KENCHO KIROKU/TIDAL RECORD. (Text in Japanese) 1930. a. Kokudo Chiriin - Geographical Survey Institute, 1, Kitasato, Tsukuba-shi, Ibaraki-ken 305, Japan.

551.46   JA
KISHOCHO KAIHYO KANSOKU SHIRYO/RESULTS OF SEA ICE OBSERVATIONS. (Text in Japanese) 1983. a. Kishocho - Japan Meteorological Agency, 3-4, Ote-machi 1-chome, Chiyoda-ku, Tokyo 100, Japan.

551.46   JA
KOBE KAIYO KISHODAI. KAIYO SOKUHO/KOBE MARINE OBSERVATORY. OCEANOGRAPHIC PROMPT REPORT. (Text in Japanese) 1956. irreg. Kishocho, Kobe Kaiyo Kishodai - Japan Meteorological Agency, Kobe Marine Observatory, 14-1, Nakayamate Dori 7-chome, Chuo-ku, Kobe-shi, Hyogo-ken 650, Japan.

551   JA   ISSN 0368-5969
                            CODEN: KKKIAI
KOBE KAIYO KISHODAI IHO/KOBE MARINE OBSERVATORY. BULLETIN. (Text in Japanese; summaries in English) 1925. irreg. free to qualified personnel. Kishocho, Kobe Kaiyo Kishodai - Japan Meteorological Agency, Kobe Marine Observatory, 7-14-1, Nakayamate-dori, Chuo-ku, Kobe-shi 650, Japan. Ed.Bd. circ. 400. Indexed: Deep Sea Res.& Oceanogr.Abstr., Meteor.& Geoastrophys.Abstr.
—BLDSC (2600.100000).

551.46   JA
KOCHI UNIVERSITY. MARINE SCIENCES AND FISHERIES. BULLETIN. (Text in Japanese, English) 1979. a. exchange basis. Kochi University, Usa Marine Biological Institute, Usa-cho, Tosa, Kochi 781-11, Japan. TEL 0888-56-0422. FAX 0888-56-0425. Ed.Bd. Document type: bulletin.
Formerly (until Dec. 1989): Kochi University. Usa Marine Biological Institute. Report (ISSN 0387-9763); Which was formed by the merger of: Usa Marine Biological Station. Reports (ISSN 0452-2478); Kochi Daigaku Suisan Jikkenjo Kenkyu Hokoku (ISSN 0387-9755)

551.46   JA
KOGYO JIJI TSUSHIN. KAIYO KAIHATSUBAN/INDUSTRIAL NEWS. MARINE DEVELOPMENT SERIES. (Text in Japanese) s-w. 90000 Yen. Kogyo Jiji Tsushinsha - Industrial News Agency, 13-9, Iidabashi 2-chome, Chiyoda-ku, Tokyo 102, Japan.

551.4 623 333.7 GW   ISSN 0452-7739
TC203   CODEN: KUSTAP
DIE KUESTE; Archiv fuer Forschung und Technik an der Nord- und Ostsee. 1952. irreg. (1-2/yr.). price varies. (Kuratorium fuer Forschung im Kuesteningenieurwesen) Westholsteinische Verlagsanstalt Boyens und Co., Am Wulf-Isebrand-Platz, 25746 Heide, Germany. TEL 0481-691-0. Ed. Harald Goehren. illus. Indexed: GeoRef.
—BLDSC (5131.500000).

551.46   JA   ISSN 0913-1302
KUROSHIO/KOCHI UNIVERSITY. INSTITUTE OF THE KUROSHIO SPHERE. REPORT. (Text in Japanese) 1986. a. Kochi Daigaku, Kuroshioken Kenkyujo - Kochi University, Institute of the Kuroshio Sphere, Kochi Daigaku Jimukyoku, 5-1, Akebonocho 2-chome, Kochi-shi, Kochi-ken 780, Japan.

551.46   JA   ISSN 0914-7225
KUROSHIO. TOKUBETSUGO/KOCHI UNIVERSITY. INSTITUTE OF THE KUROSHIO SPHERE. REPORT. SPECIAL SERIES. (Text in Japanese) 1987. a. Kochi Daigaku, Kuroshioken Kenkyujo - Kochi University, Institute of the Kuroshio Sphere, Kochi Daigaku Jimukyoku, 5-1, Akebonochi 2-chome, Kochi-shi, Kochi-ken 780, Japan.

551.46   JA
KUROSHIO NO KAIHATSU RIYO CHOSA KENKYU SEIKA HOKOKUSHO/KUROSHIO EXPLOITATION RESEARCH AND UTILIZATION REPORT. (Text in Japanese; summaries in English, Japanese) 1978. a. Kagaku Gijutsucho, Kenkyu Kaihatsukyoku - Science and Technology Agency, Research and Development Bureau, 2-1, Kasumigaseki 2-chome, Chiyoda-ku, Tokyo 100, Japan.

551.46 639.3   JA
KYOTO FURITSU KAIYO SENTA JIGYO GAIYO/KYOTO INSTITUTE OF OCEANIC AND FISHERY SCIENCE. REPORT. (Text in Japanese) a. Kyoto Furitsu Kaiyo Senta, Odashukuno, Miyazu-shi, Kyoto 626, Japan.

551.46 639.2   JA   ISSN 0289-9515
KYOTO FURITSU KAIYO SENTA KENKYU GYOSEKISHU/KYOTO INSTITUTE OF OCEANIC AND FISHERY SCIENCE. CONTRIBUTIONS. (Text in English, Japanese) 1983. irreg. Kyoto Furitsu Kaiyo Senta, Odashukno, Miyazu-shi, Kyoto 626, Japan.

639.2   JA   ISSN 0386-5290
KYOTO FURITSU KAIYO SENTA KENKYU HOKOKU/KYOTO INSTITUTE OF OCEANIC AND FISHERY SCIENCE. BULLETIN. (Text in English, Japanese) 1977. a. Kyoto Furitsu Kaiyo Senta, Odashukuno, Miyazu-shi, Kyoto 626, Japan. Indexed: Agrindex. Document type: bulletin.

551.46 639.2   JA   ISSN 0286-617X
KYOTO FURITSU KAIYO SENTA KENKYU RONBUN/KYOTO INSTITUTE OF OCEANIC AND FISHERY SCIENCE. SPECIAL REPORT. (Text in English, Japanese) 1982. irreg. Kyoto Furitsu Kaiyo Senta, Odashukuno, Miyazu-shi, Kyoto 626, Japan.

551.46   US   ISSN 0724-5890
                            CODEN: LNCSEA
LECTURE NOTES ON COASTAL AND ESTUARINE STUDIES. 1980. irreg. price varies. Springer-Verlag, 175 Fifth Ave., New York, NY 10010. TEL 212-460-1500. FAX 212-473-6272. (Also: Berlin, Heidelberg, Tokyo and Vienna) Ed.Bd. (reprint service avail. from ISI) Document type: monographic series.

LIMNOLOGY AND OCEANOGRAPHY. see EARTH SCIENCES — Hydrology

LIVING WITH THE SHORE. see ENVIRONMENTAL STUDIES

599   US
LONG ISLAND SOUND STUDY UPDATE. 1988. bi-m. membership. Long Island Sound Taskforce, Stamford Marine Center, Magee Ave., Stamford, CT 06902. TEL 203-327-9786. FAX 203-967-2677. (Co-sponsor: Long Island Sound Study (EPA)) Ed. Richard Schreiner. adv. circ. 6,200.
Former titles: Long Island Sound Report; Taffrail.

551.46 669   US
THE LOOKDOWN. 1980. q. membership. Virginia Marine Science Museum, 717 General Booth Blvd., Virginia Beach, VA 23451. TEL 804-437-4949. FAX 804-437-4976. Ed. Mary Reid Barrow. (back issues avail.)
Description: Presents information to members about museum programs and trips, Virginia's marine environment and museum research and promotes ecological awareness.

551.46   US
M I T SEA GRANT QUARTERLY REPORT. 1979. q. Massachusetts Institute of Technology, Sea Grant College Program, E38-302 Kendall Sq., 292 Main St., Cambridge, MA 02139-9910. TEL 617-253-5944. circ. 2,000. Indexed: Environ.Abstr. Document type: academic/scholarly publication.

EARTH SCIENCES — OCEANOGRAPHY

551.46   II   ISSN 0542-0938
GC1   CODEN: MHSGAJ
MAHASAGAR. (Text in English) 1968. q. Rs.70($35) National Institute of Oceanography, Dona Paula, Goa 403004, India. (Affiliate: Council of Scientific and Industrial Research) Ed. H.N. Siddiquie. adv.; bk.rev.; bibl.; charts; illus. circ. 400. (also avail. in microfilm) **Indexed:** Aqua.Sci.& Fish.Abstr., Chem.Abstr., Curr.Adv.Ecol.Sci., Curr.Tit.Ocean, Deep Sea Res.& Oceanogr.Abstr., GeoRef., INIS Atomind., Meteor.& Geoastrophys.Abstr., Ocean.Abstr.
—BLDSC (5351.465000); CASDDS. **CCC.**
Incorporates: International Indian Ocean Expedition.

551.46   JA   ISSN 0022-7811
MAIZURU KAIYO KISHODAI. KAIYO SOKUHO/MAIZURU MARINE OBSERVATORY. OCEANOGRAPHIC PROMPT REPORTS. (Text in Japanese) 1950. irreg. Kishocho, Maizuru Kaiyo Kishodai - Japan Meteorological Agency, Maizuru Marine Observatory, 901, Shimofukui, Maizuru-shi, Kyoto 624, Japan. bk.rev.; abstr.; charts.

551.46   US   ISSN 0745-2896
MAKAI. 1979. m. free. University of Hawaii, Sea Grant College Program, 1000 Pope Rd., Rm. 200, Honolulu, HI 96822. TEL 808-956-7410. FAX 808-956-2880. Ed. Jill Ladwig Katter. bk.rev. circ. 2,000. **Indexed:** Environ.Abstr. **Document type:** newsletter.
Formerly: University of Hawaii. Sea Grant College Program. Sea Grant Newsletter.

551.46   SP   ISSN 1131-9240
MAR (MADRID, 1964). 1964. m. free. Ministerio de Trabajo y Seguridad Social, Instituto Social de la Marina, Genova, 24-6 planta, 28004 Madrid, Spain. TEL 1-410-4626. FAX 1-319-9134. TELEX 23743. Ed. Vidal Mate Herreros. adv. circ. 350,000.
Formerly (until 1987): Hoja del Mar.

551.46 333.7   JA
MARIN PABIRION/MARINE PAVILION. (Text in Japanese) 1971. m. 50 Yen per no. Kushimoto Kaichu Koen Senta - Kushimoto Marine Park Center, 1157 Arita, Kushimotocho, Nishimuro-gun, Wakayama-ken 649-35, Japan.

551.46   JA   ISSN 0289-6095
MARINE. (Text in Japanese) 1969. m. 1130 Yen per no. Nikkan Kaiji Tsushinsha - Daily the Kaiji, 23-6, Nishishinbashi 3-chome, Minato-ku, Tokyo 105, Japan.

MARINE ACOUSTICS SOCIETY OF JAPAN. JOURNAL. see *PHYSICS — Sound*

MARINE ACOUSTICS SOCIETY OF JAPAN. PROCEEDINGS OF THE MEETING/KAIYO ONKYO GAKKAI KENKYU HAPPYOKAI KOEN RONBUNSHU. see *PHYSICS — Sound*

551.46   II   ISSN 0970-9967
MARINE AND ATMOSPHERIC RESEARCH. (Text in English) 1963. irreg. Rs.20 per no. University of Cochin, Department of Marine Sciences, Foreshore Rd., Ernakulam, Cochin 16, Kerala, India. Ed. C.V. Kurian. (back issues avail.) **Indexed:** GeoRef.
Former titles (until 1988): University of Cochin. School of Marine Sciences. Bulletin (ISSN 0970-9886); (until 1986): University of Cochin. Department of Marine Sciences. Bulletin (ISSN 0970-9878); (until 1973): University of Cochin. Department of Marine Biology and Oceanography. Bulletin (ISSN 0970-986X); (until 1971): University of Kerala. Central Research Institute. Bulletin, Series C.

MARINE BIOLOGICAL ASSOCIATION OF INDIA. JOURNAL. see *BIOLOGY*

MARINE CONSERVATION NEWS; "for all at last returns to the sea - the beginning and the end." Rachel Carson. see *CONSERVATION*

MARINE ENGINEERING SOCIETY IN JAPAN. JOURNAL. see *ENGINEERING*

MARINE ENVIRONMENTAL RESEARCH. see *ENVIRONMENTAL STUDIES — Pollution*

551.46   NE   ISSN 0025-3227
QE39   CODEN: MAGEA6
MARINE GEOLOGY; international journal of marine geology, geochemistry and geophysics. (Text in English, French and German) 1964. 28/yr. (in 7 vols.; 4 nos./vol.) fl.2562($1385) (effective 1994). Elsevier Science B.V., P.O. Box 211, 1000 AE Amsterdam, Netherlands. TEL 31-20-5803911. FAX 31-20-5803598. TELEX 18582 ESPA NL. (Subscr. in U.S. and Canada to: Elsevier Science Inc., Box 882, Madison Sq. Sta., New York, NY 10159-0882. TEL 212-989-5800. FAX 212-633-3990) Ed. D.A. McManus. adv.; bk.rev.; abstr.; bibl.; charts; illus.; index per vol. (also avail. in microform from UMI; reprint service avail. from SWZ) **Indexed:** AESIS, Br.Geol.Lit., Chem.Abstr., Curr.Cont., Deep Sea Res.& Oceanogr.Abstr., E&P Hlth. (1993-), Gas Process.& Ppl. (1993-), Geo.Abstr., GeoRef., Ind.Sci.Rev., INIS Atomind., Ocean.Abstr., Off.Tech. (1993-), Petrol.Abstr. (1964-), Pollut.Abstr., Sel.Water Res.Abstr., So.Pac.Per.Ind. **Document type:** academic/scholarly publication.
—BLDSC (5375.400000); EI; Faxon; UnCover; SWETS; CASDDS. **CCC.**
Description: Original research and comprehensive reviews in the fiedl of marine geology, geochemistry, and geophysics.
Refereed Serial

551.46 551   NE   ISSN 0025-3235
QE501   CODEN: MGYRA7
MARINE GEOPHYSICAL RESEARCHES; an international journal for the study of the earth beneath the sea. 1970. 6/yr. fl.740($385.50) (effective 1994). Kluwer Academic Publishers, Postbus 17, 3300 AA Dordrecht, Netherlands. TEL 31-78-334911. FAX 31-78-334254. TELEX 29245 KAPG NL. (Dist. by: Kluwer Academic Publishers Group, P.O. Box 322, 3300 AH Dordrecht, Netherlands. TEL 31-78-524400. FAX 31-78-524474; N. America dist. addr.: Box 358, Accord Sta., Hingham, MA 02018-0358. TEL 617-871-6600. FAX 617-871-6528) Eds. F.K. Duennebier, J.-C. Sibuet. adv.; bk.rev.; illus. (also avail. in microform from UMI; reprint service avail. from SWZ) **Indexed:** Chem.Abstr., Curr.Adv.Ecol.Sci., Curr.Cont., Curr.Tit.Ocean, Deep Sea Res.& Oceanogr.Abstr., E&P Hlth. (1993-), Eng.Ind., Gas Process.& Ppl. (1993-), Geo.Abstr., Geophys.Abstr, GeoRef., Ind.Sci.Rev., Mar.Sci.Cont.Tab., Ocean.Abstr., Off.Tech. (1993-), Petrol.Abstr. (1978-), Phys.Ber., Pollut.Abstr., Sci.Abstr., Sci.Cit.Ind. **Document type:** academic/scholarly publication.
—BLDSC (5375.500000); EI; Faxon; UnCover; SWETS; UMI. **CCC.**
Refereed Serial

551.46 623   US   ISSN 1064-119X
TN264   CODEN: MGGEEI
MARINE GEORESOURCES AND GEOTECHNOLOGY. 1993. q. $131. Taylor & Francis, 1900 Frost Rd., Ste. 101, Bristol, PA 19007. TEL 215-785-5800. FAX 215-785-5515. Ed. Ronald Chaney. adv.; bk.rev.; abstr.; charts; illus.; stat.; index. circ. 260. (also avail. in microform from UMI; reprint service avail. from UMI) **Indexed:** A.S.& T.Ind., Aqua.Sci.& Fish.Abstr., BIM, Biol.Abstr., Br.Geol.Lit., Curr.Cont., Deep Sea Res.& Oceanogr.Abstr., E&P Hlth. (1993-), Eng.Ind., Fluidex, Gas Process.& Ppl. (1993-), Geo.Abstr., GeoRef., Geotech.Abstr., I.M.M.Abstr., Ind.Sci.Rev., Mar.Sci.Cont.Tab., Ocean.Abstr., Off.Tech. (1993-), Petrol.Abstr. (1978-). **Document type:** academic/scholarly publication.
—BLDSC (5375.520000); CIS; EI; Faxon; UnCover; SWETS; CASDDS. **CCC.**
Formed by the merger of (1975-1993): Marine Geotechnology (ISSN 0360-8867); (1977-1993): Marine Mining (ISSN 0149-0397)
Description: Devoted to all scientific and engineering aspects of seafloor sediment and rocks.
Refereed Serial

MARINE LAWS; navigation and safety. see *LAW — Maritime Law*

551.46   US   ISSN 0824-0469
QL713.2   CODEN: MMSCEC
MARINE MAMMAL SCIENCE. vol.1, 1985. q. $100. (Society for Marine Mammalogy) Allen Press, Inc., 1041 New Hampshire St., Box 1897, Lawrence, KS 66044-8897. TEL 913-843-1221. FAX 913-843-1274. bk.rev. (back issues avail.) **Indexed:** Curr.Adv.Ecol.Sci., Curr.Cont., Deep Sea Res.& Oceanogr. Abstr., Environ.Per.Bibl. (1985-), Geo.Abstr., Ref.Zh., Sci.Cit.Ind., Wild Life Rev. **Document type:** academic/scholarly publication.
—BLDSC (5376.170000); Faxon; UnCover; SWETS. **CCC.**
Description: Presents original research and observations on marine mammals, their evolution, form, function, husbandry, health, populations, and ecological relationships.

MARINE MICROBIAL FOOD WEBS. see *BIOLOGY — Microbiology*

MARINE OBSERVER; a quarterly journal of maritime meteorology. see *METEOROLOGY*

343.09   UK   ISSN 0308-597X
GC1000
MARINE POLICY. 1977. bi-m. £205 in UK and Europe; elsewhere £220. Butterworth - Heinemann (Subsidiary of: Reed International PLC), Linacre House, Jordan Hi l, Oxon. OX2 8DP, England. TEL 0865-310366. FAX 0865-310898. TELEX 83111 BHPOXF G. (Subscr. to: Turpin Transactions Ltd., Distribution Centre, Blackhorse Rd., Letchworth, Herts. SG6 1HN, England. TEL 0462-672555) Ed. Jennifer Nicholson. bk.rev.; abstr.; illus. (also avail. in microform from UMI; back issues avail.) **Indexed:** Curr.Adv.Ecol.Sci. Curr.Cont., Curr.Tit.Ocean, Deep Sea Res.& Oceanogr.Abstr., ELLIS, Energy Ind., Energy Info.Abstr., Energy Rev., Environ.Abstr., Environ.Per.Bibl. (1979-), Excerpt.Med., Fluidex, Fut.Surv., Geo.Abstr., GeoRef., I D A, Ind.Sci.Rev., Key to Econ.Sci., Mar.Aff.Bibl., Ocean.Abstr., P.A.I.S., Pollut.Abstr., Risk Abstr., Sel.Water Res.Abstr., SSCI, World Agri.Econ.& Rural Sociol.Abstr. **Document type:** academic/scholarly publication.
—BLDSC (5377.250000); CIS; Faxon; UnCover; SWETS; UMI. **CCC.**
Description: Offers researchers, analysts and policy makers a combination of legal, political, social and economic analysis. Major articles are written by international lawyers, political scientists, fishery specialists and marine economists.
Refereed Serial

551.4   IO   ISSN 0079-0435
GC1   CODEN: MRINAQ
MARINE RESEARCH IN INDONESIA. (Text in English and German) 1956. irreg. $10 per no. Centre for Oceanological Research and Development, Documentation and Information Division - Pusat Penelitian den Pergembangan Oseanologi, Jalan Pasir Putih No.1, Ancol Timur Box 580, Jakarta 11001, Indonesia TEL 683850. TELEX 45879-PDIN-IA. Ed. Kasijan Romimohtarto. circ. 500. **Indexed:** Biol.Abstr., Deep Sea Res.& Oceanogr.Abstr.

MARINE RESOURCE BULLETIN; a sea grant advisory service. see *FISH AND FISHERIES*

EARTH SCIENCES — OCEANOGRAPHY

623 US ISSN 0025-3324
GC1 CODEN: MTSJBB
MARINE TECHNOLOGY SOCIETY JOURNAL. 1963. q. $60 (foreign $74) (typically set in Sep.). Marine Technology Society, Inc., c/o Allen Beard Young, 1828 L St., N.W., 9th Fl., Washington, DC 20036. TEL 202-775-5966. FAX 202-429-9417. Ed. William S. Busch. adv.; bk.rev.; abstr.; bibl.; charts; illus.; stat. circ. 3,200. (also avail. in microfilm; back issues avail.) Indexed: A.S.& T.Ind., Aqua.Sci.& Fish.Abstr., Biol.Abstr., Biol.& Agr.Ind., BMT, C.I.S. Abstr., Chem.Abstr., Corros.Abstr., Curr.Adv.Ecol.Sci., Curr.Cont., Curr.Tit.Ocean, Deep Sea Res.& Oceanogr.Abstr., Energy Info.Abstr., Eng.Ind., Environ.Abstr., Environ.Per.Bibl., Excerpt.Med., Fluidex, Geo.Abstr., GeoRef., Ind.Sci.Rev., INIS Atomind., Mar.Sci.Cont.Tab., Ocean.Abstr., Petrol.Abstr., Pollut.Abstr., Sci.Abstr., Sel.Water Res.Abstr.
●Also available online.
Also available on CD-ROM.
—BLDSC (5378.700000); CIS; Faxon; UnCover; SWETS; UMI. **CCC.**
  Incorporates: Ocean Soundings (ISSN 0048-1386)
  Description: International interdisciplinary journal devoted to ocean and marine engineering, science, and policy.
  Refereed Serial

MARINER'S MIRROR. see *HISTORY*

MARINERS WEATHER LOG; a climatic review of North Atlantic and North Pacific Ocean and Great Lake areas. see *METEOROLOGY*

551.46 US ISSN 0025-3472
GC1 CODEN: MRTMBB
MARITIMES. 1957. q. free. University of Rhode Island, Graduate School of Oceanography, S. Ferry Rd., Narragansett, RI 02882-1197. TEL 401-792-6211. FAX 401-792-6486. Ed. Jackleen de La Harpe. charts; illus.; index. circ. 4,500. Indexed: Biol.Abstr., Deep Sea Res.& Oceanogr.Abstr., GeoRef., Ocean.Abstr., Pollut.Abstr. **Document type:** academic/scholarly publication.
—UnCover.
  Description: Reports the activities of the school and the work of its faculty and staff, including independent studies and cooperative participation in international programs.

MEMOIRS OF THE HOURGLASS CRUISES. see *BIOLOGY*

574.92 551.46 IT ISSN 0390-492X
QH152 CODEN: MBMOA5
MEMORIE DI BIOLOGIA MARINA E DI OCEANOGRAFIA. (Text and summaries in English, French, German, Italian) 1930-1940; N.S. 1971. bi-m. L.10000. Universita degli Studi di Messina, Istituto di Zoologia, Stazione di Biologia Marina, Messina, Italy. Ed. Carmelo Cavallaro. adv.; bk.rev. circ. 350. (back issues avail.) Indexed: Biol.Abstr., Chem.Abstr., Deep Sea Res.& Oceanogr.Abstr.
—BLDSC (5675.450000).

551.46 FI ISSN 0356-0023
MERI. (Text in English, Finnish, Swedish; summaries in English) 1975. irreg. (1-2/yr.), no.20, 1993. price varies. Finnish Institute of Marine Research, P.O. Box 33, SF-00931 Helsinki 93, Finland. TEL 358-0-331044. FAX 358-0-331376. TELEX 125731 IMRSF. Ed. Pentti Malkki. circ. 300. (back issues avail.)

551.46 MX
MEXICO. DIRECCION GENERAL DE OCEANOGRAFIA. CALENDARIO GRAFICO DE MAREAS. 1971. a. $8. Universidad Nacional Autonoma de Mexico, Instituto de Geofisica, Circuito Exterior, Ciudad Universitaria, Mexico 20, D.F., Mexico.

551.46 JA ISSN 0916-0752
MINAMI TAIHEIYO KENKYU/SOUTH PACIFIC STUDY. (Text in English, Japanese) 1980. s-a. Kagoshima University, Research Center for the South Pacific, 1-21-24, Korimoto, Kagoshima 890, Japan.
—BLDSC (8352.127000).
  Formerly (until 1988): Nankaiken Kiyo (ISSN 0389-5351)

333.9 US ISSN 0095-6783
GC1021.M7
MISSISSIPPI MARINE RESOURCES COUNCIL. ANNUAL REPORT.* Key Title: Annual Report - Mississippi Marine Resources Council. a. free. Mississippi Marine Resources Council, 2620 W. Beach Blvd, Biloxi, MS 39531. TEL 601-864-4602. illus.

551.4 797.2 IT ISSN 0026-9573
MONDO SOMMERSO; international magazine on nature, ecology, environment, sea diving activities, and travels. (Text in English, Italian) 1959. m. L.90000($57.50) Media Sea Communication s.r.l., Via G.A. Amadeo 41, 20133 Milan, Italy. TEL 02-70100020. FAX 02-70101709. Ed. Fabrizio de Checchi. adv. circ. 52,000. (reprint service avail.) **Document type:** consumer publication.
  Description: Spreads scientific and biological news related to seas, lakes, rivers and their inhabitants. Covers diving resorts worldwide and diving techniques.

551.46 UN ISSN 0077-104X
CODEN: MNOMAP
MONOGRAPHS ON OCEANOGRAPHIC METHODOLOGY. 1966. irreg., latest no.9. $41. Unesco, 7-9 Place de Fontenoy, 75700 Paris, France. TEL 577-16-10. (Dist. in U.S. by: Unipub, 4611-F Assembly Dr., Lanham, MD 20706-4391) (also avail. in microform) Indexed: Biol.Abstr. **Document type:** monographic series.

551.46 JA
NAGASAKI KAIYO KISHODAI. KAIYO SOKUHO/NAGASAKI MARINE OBSERVATORY. OCEANOGRAPHIC PROMPT REPORT. (Text in Japanese) 1950. irreg. Kishocho, Nagasaki Kaiyo Kishodai - Japan Meteorological Agency, Nagasaki Marine Observatory, 11-51, Minamiyamatecho, Nagasaki-shi, Nagasaki-ken 850, Japan.

551.46 JA
NAGOYA UNIVERSITY. WATER RESEARCH INSTITUTE. PUBLICATION LIST. (Text in English, Japanese) 1983. a. Nagoya Daigaku, Suiken Kagaku Kenkyujo - Nagoya University, Water Research Institute, Furocho, Chikusa-ku, Nagoya-shi, Aichi-ken 464, Japan.

551.46 639.2 JA ISSN 0910-3694
NANSEIKAI BUROKKU KAIYO KENKYUKAI HOKOKU/SOCIETY OF NANSEI NATIONAL FISHERIES RESEARCH INSTITUTE. JOURNAL. (Text in Japanese) 1984. a. Suisancho, Nansei Kaiku Suisan Kenkyujo - Fisheries Agency, Nansei National Fisheries Research Institute, 17-5, Maruishi 2-chome, Onomachi, Saeki-gun, Hiroshima-ken 739-04, Japan.

551.468 JA
NATIONAL INSTITUTE OF POLAR RESEARCH. MEMOIRS. SERIES D: OCEANOGRAPHY. (Text and summaries in English) 1964. irreg. exchange basis. National Institute of Polar Research - Kokuritsu Kyokuchi Kenkyujo, Library, 9-10, Kaga 1-chome, Itabashi-ku, Tokyo 173, Japan. TEL 03-3962-4711. FAX 03-3962-2529. TELEX 272-3515 POLRSCJ. Ed. Takao Hoshiai. circ. 1,000. **Document type:** monographic series.
  Supersedes: Japanese Antarctic Research Expedition, 1956-1962. Scientific Reports. Series D: Oceanography (ISSN 0075-3386)

551.46 US ISSN 1054-240X
CODEN: NURREH
NATIONAL UNDERSEA RESEARCH PROGRAM. RESEARCH REPORT. 1988. a.? National Oceanic & Atmospheric Administration, National Undersea Research Program, 6010 Executive Blvd., Rockville, MD 20852.
—BLDSC (6033.199000).

551.46 JA
NATSUSHIMA/JAPAN MARINE SCIENCE AND TECHNOLOGY CENTER NEWS. (Text in Japanese) 1973. bi-m. Kaiyo Kagaku Gijutsu Senta - Japan Marine Science and Technology Center, 2-15, Natsushima-cho, Yokosuka-shi, Kanagawa-ken 237, Japan.

623.82 PL ISSN 0548-0523
VK4
NAUTOLOGIA. 1966. q. $40. Polskie Towarzystwo Nautologiczne, Ul. Sienkiewicza 3, 81-374 Gdynia, Poland. TEL 20-49-75. (Dist. by: Ars Polona-Ruch, Krakowskie Przedmiescie 7, Warsaw, Poland) Ed. S. Machalinski. (reprint service avail.) Indexed: Curr.Tit.Ocean. **Document type:** academic/scholarly publication.
  Description: Devoted to maritime problems.

551.46 JA ISSN 0387-5504
NAVAL ARCHITECTURE AND OCEAN ENGINEERING. (Text in English) 1968. a. 4000 Yen. Nihon Zosen Gakkai - Society of Naval Architects of Japan, 15-16 Toranomon 1-chome, Minato-ku, Tokyo 105, Japan. Indexed: Eng.Ind.
—**CCC.**

NAVY NEWS & UNDERSEA TECHNOLOGY. see *MILITARY*

551.46 NE ISSN 0165-9162
NETHERLANDS INSTITUTE FOR SEA RESEARCH. ANNUAL REPORT. (Subseries of: Netherlands Institute for Sea Research. Publications Series (ISSN 0923-330X)) (Text in English) 1971. a. exchange basis. Netherlands Institute for Sea Research, P.O. Box 59, 1790 AB Den Burg, Texel, Netherlands. TEL 31-2220-69362. FAX 31-2220-19674. Ed. J.J. Beukema. **Document type:** corporate report.

551.46 NE ISSN 0923-330X
NETHERLANDS INSTITUTE FOR SEA RESEARCH. PUBLICATIONS SERIES. (Supplement to: Netherlands Journal of Sea Research (ISSN 0077-7579)) (Text in English) 1978. irreg., no.19, 1992. exchange basis (free with Netherlands Journal of Sea Research). Netherlands Institute for Sea Research, P.O. Box 59, 1790 AB Den Burg, Texel, Netherlands. TEL 31-2220-69362. FAX 31-2220-19674. Ed. J.J. Beukema. **Document type:** academic/scholarly publication.
  Description: Publishes contributions dealing with the various fields of marine science and the annual reports of the institute.

551.46 NE ISSN 0077-7579
GC1 CODEN: NJSRBA
NETHERLANDS JOURNAL OF SEA RESEARCH. (Text in English) 1961. 8/yr. fl.400 (or exchange basis). Netherlands Institute for Sea Research, P.O. Box 59, 1790 AB Den Burg, Texel, Netherlands. TEL 31-2220-69362. FAX 31-2220-19674. Ed. J.J. Beukema. circ. 1,100. Indexed: Biol.Abstr., Chem.Abstr., Curr.Adv.Ecol.Sci., Curr.Cont., Curr.Ref.Fish Res., Curr.Tit.Ocean, Deep Sea Res.& Oceanogr.Abstr., Energy Info.Abstr., Environ.Abstr., Environ.Ind., Excerpt.Med., Geo.Abstr., Helminthol.Abstr, Ocean.Abstr., Sel.Water Res.Abstr. **Document type:** academic/scholarly publication.
—BLDSC (6077.020000); CIS; Faxon; UnCover; SWETS; CASDDS.
  Description: Contains papers on marine research with emphasis on non-applied aspects and contributions to the understanding of the functioning of marine ecosystems, including abiotic aspects.

551.46 551.48
574.92 NZ ISSN 0028-8330
QH91.A1 CODEN: NZJMBS
NEW ZEALAND JOURNAL OF MARINE AND FRESHWATER RESEARCH. 1967. q. NZ.$200($170) (effective 1993). (Royal Society of New Zealand) S I R Publishing, P.O. Box 399, Wellington, New Zealand. TEL 04-472-7421. FAX 04-473-1841. (U.S. subscr. to: S I R Publishing, 810 E. Tenth St., Box 1897, Lawrence, KS 66044-8897. TEL 913-843-1221) Ed. J. Jasperse. abstr.; bibl.; charts; illus.; index. circ. 500. (back issues avail.) Indexed: Anim.Breed.Abstr., Biol.Abstr., Chem.Abstr., Curr.Adv.Ecol.Sci., Curr.Cont., Curr.Tit.Ocean, Deep Sea Res.& Oceanogr.Abstr., Energy Ind., Energy Info.Abstr., Environ.Abstr., Environ.Per.Bibl. (1990-), Excerpt.Med., Geo.Abstr., GeoRef., Helminthol.Abstr., Ind.Vet., Ocean.Abstr., Ocean Abstr., Pollut.Abstr., Protozool.Abstr., Sel.Water Res.Abstr., So.Pac.Per.Ind., Soils & Fert., W.R.C.Inf., Weed Abstr., Zoo.Rec.
—BLDSC (6094.550000); CIS; Faxon; UnCover; CASDDS. **CCC.**
  Description: Publishes papers on all fields of fisheries and acquatic science in the Pacific and Antarctic region.

NEW ZEALAND MARINE SCIENCES SOCIETY REVIEW. see *BIOLOGY*

551.46   NZ   ISSN 0083-7903
GC1   CODEN: NZOMAI
NEW ZEALAND OCEANOGRAPHIC INSTITUTE. MEMOIR. 1955. irreg. price varies. New Zealand Oceanographic Institute, P.O. Box 14-901, Kilbirnie, Wellington, New Zealand. TEL 04-386-1189. FAX 04-386-2153. Ed. Dennis P. Gordon. index. circ. 660. **Indexed:** Chem.Abstr., Curr.Adv.Ecol.Sci., Deep Sea Res.& Oceanogr.Abstr., GeoRef., Ocean.Abstr. Document type: academic/scholarly publication, monographic series.
—CASDDS.
Description: Memoirs feature monographic treatment of mainly systematic monographs, occasionally marine geology and physical oceanography.

NEWSLETTER GOLD, SILVER AND URANIUM FROM SEAS AND OCEANS PROGRESS UPDATE. see ENGINEERING — Chemical Engineering

NIHON KAISUI GAKKAI KENKYU GIJUTSU HAPPYOKAI KOEN YOSHISHU/SOCIETY OF SEA WATER SCIENCE, JAPAN. ABSTRACTS OF MEETING. see EARTH SCIENCES — Abstracting, Bibliographies, Statistics

551.46 621.3   JA   ISSN 0369-4550
                      CODEN: NKAGBU
NIHON KAISUI GAKKAISHI/SOCIETY OF SEA WATER SCIENCE, JAPAN. BULLETIN. (Text in English, Japanese) 1947. bi-m. 6000 Yen($60) Nihon Kaisui Gakkai - Society of Sea Water Science, Japan, 7-15-14 Roppongi, Minato-ku, Tokyo 106, Japan. TEL 03-3402-6414. Ed. Noboru Ogata. index, cum.index. circ. 1,000. (back issues avail.) **Indexed:** Chem.Abstr., INIS Atomind., Jap.Per.Ind.
—BLDSC (2758.680000); CASDDS.

551.46   US
NOR'EASTER (NARRAGANSETT). 1989. 2/yr. free. Northeast Sea Grant Programs, University of Rhode Island, Rhode Island Sea Grant, Narragansett, RI 02882-1197. Ed.Bd. adv. **Indexed:** Environ.Abstr.
Description: Presents marine-related issues to the general public.

551.46   US   ISSN 0148-9836
GC1   CODEN: NGSCDE
NORTHEAST GULF SCIENCE. 1977. s-a. $4. Marine Environmental Sciences Consortium of Alabama, c/o Dauphin Island Sea Lab, Box 369-370, Dauphin Island, AL 36528. TEL 205-861-2141. FAX 205-460-7357. Ed. Robert L. Shipp. bk.rev. circ. 350. **Indexed:** Biol.Abstr., Curr.Cont., Curr.Tit.Ocean., Deep Sea Res.& Oceanogr.Abstr., Ocean.Abstr., Sel.Water Res.Abstr.
—BLDSC (6150.273000); UnCover.
Formerly: Journal of Marine Science (ISSN 0364-1988)

551.46   FR
NOUVEAU GLOSSAIRE NAUTIQUE D'AUGUSTIN JAL. irreg. price varies. (Centre National de la Recherche Scientifique) C N R S Editions, 20-22 rue St. Amand, 75015 Paris, France. TEL 45-33-16-00. FAX 45-33-92-13. TELEX 200 356 F. adv.; bk.rev.; index; circ. 1,250 (controlled).

551.46   JA   ISSN 0289-9078
O D P NYUSU RETA/O D P NEWSLETTER. (Ocean Drilling Program) (Text in English, Japanese) 1984. irreg. O D P Kokunai Kenkyu Renrakukai - National Committee for Ocean Drilling Program, Tokyo Daigaku Kaiyo Kenkyujo, 15-1, Minamidai 1-chome, Nakano-ku, Tokyo 164, Japan. **Document type:** newsletter.

551.46   US
O P D I N UPDATE. q. Ocean Pollution Data and Information Network, c/o National Oceanographic Data Center, 1825 Connecticut Ave., N.W., Washington, DC 20235.
Description: Designed to facilitate exchange of information among the agencies that are members of National Ocean Pollution Policy Board.

551.46   NL
O.R.S.T.O.M. RESUMES DES TRAVAUX. OCEANOGRAPHIE. (Text in French; summaries in English, French) 1969. biennial. avail. on exchange. Office de la Recherche Scientifique et Technique Outre-Mer, Centre O.R.S.T.O.M., B.P. A5, Noumea, New Caledonia. TEL 687 261000. FAX 687-264326. TELEX 3193 NM ORSTOM. Ed. Rene Grandperrin. circ. 270.
Formerly: O.R.S.T.O.M. Recueils des Travaux. Oceanographie (ISSN 0078-2130)

551.46   UK   ISSN 0964-5691
GC1000   CODEN: OCMAEU
OCEAN & COASTAL MANAGEMENT; international journal dedicated to the study of all aspects of ocean and coastal management. 1973. 12/yr. (in 4 vols., 3 nos./vol.). £368($565) (effective 1994). Elsevier Science Ltd., Oxford Fulfilment Centre, P.O. Box 800, Kidlington, Oxford OX5 1DX, England. TEL 44-865-843000. FAX 44-865-843010. (Subscr. in U.S. and Canada to: Elsevier Science, 660 White Plains Rd., Tarrytown, NY 10591-5153. TEL 914-524-9200. FAX 914-333-2444) Eds. B. Cicin-Sain, R.W. Knecht. adv.; bk.rev.; charts. (also avail. in microform from UMI; reprint service avail. from SWZ) **Indexed:** Biol.Abstr., Curr.Adv.Ecol.Sci., Curr.Cont., Deep Sea Res.& Oceanogr.Abstr., Energy Ind., Energy Info.Abstr., Energy Rev., Environ.Abstr., Environ.Per.Bibl. (1974-), Excerp.Med., Geo.Abstr., GeoRef., Key to Econ.Sci., Mar.Aff.Bibl., Mar.Sci.Cont.Tab., Ocean.Abstr., Sel.Water Res.Abstr. **Document type:** academic/scholarly publication.
—BLDSC (6231.271920); EI; Faxon; UnCover; SWETS. **CCC.**
Former titles (until 1992): Ocean and Shoreline Management (ISSN 0951-8312); (until 1988): Ocean Management (ISSN 0302-184X)
Description: Covers all aspects of ocean and coastal management at local, regional, national and international levels.
Refereed Serial

551.46   UK   ISSN 0959-0161
OCEAN CHALLENGE. 1990. 4/yr. £70. Challenger Society for Marine Science, Deacon Laboratory, Institute of Oceanographic Sciences, Wormley, Godalming, Surrey GU8 5UB, England. FAX 051-653-6269. (Subscr. to: Parjon Information Services, P.O. Box 144, Haywards Heath, W. Sussex RH16 2YX, England) Ed. Angela Colling. adv.; bk.rev. circ. 500.
Supersedes (1975-1989): Challenger Society. Newsletter (ISSN 0306-7335); Which supersedes: Challenger Society. Proceedings.
Description: Contains articles of wide interest on marine science, accounts of the meetings of the Challenger Society and other oceanographic organizations together with notices of new marine science publications.

551.46   US   ISSN 0090-8320
JX1
OCEAN DEVELOPMENT AND INTERNATIONAL LAW; the journal of marine affairs. 1973. bi-m. $92 to individuals; institutions $183. Taylor & Francis, 1900 Frost Rd., Ste. 101, Bristol, PA 19007-1598. TEL 215-785-5800. FAX 215-785-5515. Ed. Jon L. Jacobson. adv.; bk.rev.; abstr.; charts; stat.; index, cum.index. **Indexed:** Amer.Bibl.Slavic & E.Eur.Stud, C.L.I., Curr.Cont., Deep Sea Res.& Oceanogr.Abstr., Econ.Abstr., Environ.Abstr., Environ.Per.Bibl. (1980-), Ind.Per.Art.Relat.Law., Int.Polit.Sci.Abstr., J.of Econ.Abstr., L.R.I., Leg.Cont., Leg.Per., Mar.Aff.Bibl., Ocean.Abstr., P.A.I.S., Pollut.Abstr., Ref.Zh., Sel.Water Res.Abstr., So.Pac.Per.Ind., SSCI.
—BLDSC (6231.275000); Faxon; UnCover; SWETS. **CCC.**
Formerly: Ocean Development and International Law Journal.
Description: Focuses on the international aspects of ocean regulation, affairs and all forms of ocean utilization.
Refereed Serial

551.46   US   ISSN 0884-5883
QE39   CODEN: PODRET
OCEAN DRILLING PROGRAM. PROCEEDINGS, PART A: INITIAL REPORTS. irreg. approx. 6/yr. $48 per no. (foreign $53). Texas A&M University, Ocean Drilling Program, 1000 Discovery Dr., College Station, TX 77845-9547. TEL 409-845-2016. FAX 409-845-4857. TELEX 62760290. circ. 50 (paid); 1,550 (controlled). **Indexed:** Chem.Abstr., GeoRef, INSPEC, Petrol.Abstr. **Document type:** proceedings.
—BLDSC (6780.600000); CASDDS.
Formerly (until 1987): Scripps Institution of Oceanography. Deep Sea Drilling Project. Initial Reports (ISSN 0080-8334)
Description: Report on the results of investigations of the Earth's crust beneath the world's ocean basins, as determined from core samples.

551.46   US   ISSN 0884-5891
QE39   CODEN: POSRE2
OCEAN DRILLING PROGRAM. SCIENTIFIC RESULTS. PROCEEDINGS. PART B: SCIENTIFIC RESULTS. 1988. irreg. approx. 6/yr. $48 per no. (foreign $53). Texas A&M University, Ocean Drilling Program, 1000 Discovery Dr., College Sta., TX 77845-9547. TEL 409-845-2016. FAX 409-845-4857. TELEX 62760290. circ. 50 (paid); 1,550 (controlled). **Indexed:** Chem.Abstr., GeoRef, INSPEC, Petrol.Abstr. **Document type:** proceedings.
—BLDSC (6780.620000); CASDDS.
Description: Report on the results of investigations of the Earth's crust beneath the world's ocean basins, as determined from core samples.
Refereed Serial

623   UK   ISSN 0029-8018
TC1501   CODEN: OCENBQ
OCEAN ENGINEERING; an international journal of research and development. 1968. 8/yr. £385($595) (effective 1994). Elsevier Science Ltd., Pergamon, P.O. Box 800, Kidlington, Oxford OX5 1DX, England. TEL 44-865-843000. FAX 44-865-843010. (Subscr. in U.S. and Canada to: Elsevier Science, 660 White Plains Rd., Tarrytown, NY 10591-5153. TEL 914-524-9200. FAX 914-333-2444) Eds. Michael E. McCormick, R. Bhattacharyya. adv.; bk.rev.; bibl.; charts; illus. circ. 1,200. (also avail. in microfilm from UMI; back issues avail.) **Indexed:** A.S.& T.Ind., Appl.Mech.Rev., BMT, Br.Tech.Ind., Chem.Abstr., Curr.Cont., Curr.Tit.Ocean, Deep Sea Res.& Oceanogr.Abstr., Energy Rev., Eng.Ind., Environ.Per.Bibl. (1972-), Excerp.Med., Fluidex, GeoRef., Met.Abstr., Ocean.Abstr., Petrol.Abstr., Pollut.Abstr., Sci.Abstr., World Alum.Abstr. **Document type:** academic/scholarly publication.
—BLDSC (6231.280000); EI; Faxon; UnCover; SWETS; UMI. **CCC.**
Description: Covers the design and building of ocean structures; submarine soil mechanics; coastal engineering; ocean energy; underwater instrumentation, marine resources and other related issues.
Refereed Serial

551.46   US   ISSN 1041-8091
GC2
OCEAN PERSPECTIVES JOURNAL. 1987. q.? Ocean Church, 481 8th Ave., Box G21, New York, NY 10001.

551.46   US   ISSN 0029-8069
OCEAN SCIENCE NEWS. 1959. 3/m. $365 (foreign $385). Nautilus Press, Inc., 1201 National Press Bldg., Washington, DC 20045. TEL 202-347-3043. Ed. John R. Botzum Jr. bk.rev.; film rev.; charts; tr.lit. **Document type:** newsletter.
Incorporates: Global Climate Change.
Description: Reports on U.S. and international developments in ocean and atmosphere science, technology, research, and engineering, and offers detailed coverage of Capitol Hill.

551.46 333.91   US
OCEAN SCIENCE, RESOURCES AND TECHNOLOGY. 1980. irreg., latest 1980. Academic Press, Inc., 525 B St., Ste. 1900, San Diego, CA 92101-4495. TEL 619-231-0926. FAX 619-699-6715. (Subscr. to: Order Dept. 6277 Sea Harbor Dr., 4th Fl, Orlando, FL 32887. TEL 800-321-5068) Ed. D.S. Cronan. (reprint service avail. from ISI)

551.46   CC   ISSN 1001-1862
                    CODEN: QHDXE9
OCEAN UNIVERSITY OF QINGDAO. JOURNAL/QINGDAO HAIYANG DAXUE XUEBAO. (Text in Chinese, English) 1959. q. $2.50 per no. Qingdao Haiyang Daxue Chubanshe No. 5, Yushan Lu, Qingdao, Shandong, People's Republic of China. TEL 264361. FAX 0532-279091. (Dist. overseas by: China International Book Trading Corp., P.O. Box 399, Beijing, P.R.C.) Ed. Wen Shengchang. **Indexed:** Chem.Abstr., Curr.Adv.Ecol.Sci., Deep Sea Res.& Oceanogr.Abstr. **Document type:** academic/scholarly publication.
—BLDSC (4834.480000); UnCover.
Formerly (until 1988): Shandong College of Oceanology. Journal.

EARTH SCIENCES — OCEANOGRAPHY

551.46 333.9   US   ISSN 0191-8575
GC1000
OCEAN YEARBOOK. 1978. irreg. (approx. every 18 mos.). price varies. (International Ocean Institute, MM) University of Chicago Press, Journals Division, 5720 S. Woodlawn Ave., Chicago, IL 60637. TEL 312-753-3347. FAX 312-753-0811. (Subscr. to: Box 37005, Chicago, IL 60637) Eds. Norton M. Ginsburg, Joseph Morgan. bibl.; index. (also avail. in microform from UMI,PMC; reprint service avail. from ISI,UMI) **Indexed:** Biol.Abstr., GeoRef., Mar.Aff.Bibl. **Document type:** academic/scholarly publication.
—UMI.
   Description: Devoted to assessing the resources, ecology, technology, and strategic importance of the world's oceans.
   Refereed Serial

551.46   FR   ISSN 0182-0745
GC1   CODEN: OCAND8
OCEANIS; serie de documents oceanographiques. Represents: Revue des Seminaires de l'Institut Oceanographique. 1976. 6/yr. $110. Fondation Albert 1er de Monaco, Institut Oceanographique, 195 rue Saint-Jacques, 75005 Paris, France. FAX 40-51-73-16. Ed. G. Grau. bk.rev. circ. 250. (back issues avail.) **Indexed:** Aqua.Sci.& Fish.Abstr., Chem.Abstr., Curr.Tit.Ocean, Deep Sea Res.& Oceanogr.Abstr., Mar.Sci.Cont.Tab. **Document type:** academic/scholarly publication.
—BLDSC (6231.600000); Faxon; CASDDS.

OCEANOGRAPHIC LITERATURE REVIEW. see *EARTH SCIENCES — Abstracting, Bibliographies, Statistics*

OCEANOGRAPHIC RESEARCH INSTITUTE. INVESTIGATIONAL REPORT. see *BIOLOGY — Zoology*

551.46 574.92   SA   ISSN 1017-298X
OCEANOGRAPHIC RESEARCH INSTITUTE. POSTER SERIES. 1987. irreg., no.23, 1990. exchange basis. Oceanographic Research Institute, P.O. Box 10712, Marine Parade, Durban 4056, South Africa. TEL 27-31-373536. FAX 27-31-372132. (poster format) **Document type:** proceedings.
   Description: Provides a permanent record for the scholarly community of data presented at conferences in poster format.

551.46   SA
OCEANOGRAPHIC RESEARCH INSTITUTE. SPECIAL PUBLICATION. irreg., no.2, 1993. Oceanographic Research Institute, P.O. Box 10712, Marine Parade 4056, South Africa. TEL 27-31-373536. FAX 27-31-372132. (back issues avail.) **Document type:** monographic series.
   Description: Reports on expeditions surveys and workshops or provides bibliographic and technical information.

551.46   JA   ISSN 0369-707X
CODEN: OCMAAQ
OCEANOGRAPHICAL MAGAZINE/KISHOCHO OBUN KAIYO HOKOKU. (Text in English) 1949. a. 1900 Yen. Kishocho - Japan Meteorological Agency, 3-4, Otemachi 1-chome, Chiyoda-ku, Tokyo 100, Japan. circ. 788. **Indexed:** Deep Sea Res.& Oceanogr.Abstr., INIS Atomind., Meteor.& Geoastrophys.Abstr.
—CASDDS.

OCEANOGRAPHICAL SOCIETY OF JAPAN. ABSTRACTS ON THE CONFERENCE/NIHON KAIYO GAKKAI TAIKAI KOEN YOSHISHU. see *EARTH SCIENCES — Abstracting, Bibliographies, Statistics*

551.46   JA   ISSN 0029-8131
OCEANOGRAPHICAL SOCIETY OF JAPAN. JOURNAL/NIHON KAIYO GAKKAISHI. (Text in English, Japanese) 1942. bi-m. 2200 Yen per no. Oceanographical Society of Japan - Nippon Kaiyo Gakkai, 6-14, Minamidai 1-chome, Nakano-ku, Tokyo 164, Japan. **Indexed:** Biol.Abstr., Chem.Abstr., INIS Atomind., Jap.Per.Ind.

551.46 574.92   UK   ISSN 0078-3218
GC1   CODEN: OCMBAT
OCEANOGRAPHY AND MARINE BIOLOGY: AN ANNUAL REVIEW. 1963. a. price varies. Aberdeen University Press, Farmers Hall, Aberdeen AB9 2XT, Scotland. TEL 0224-641672. FAX 0224-643286. Ed. Margaret Barnes. **Indexed:** Biol.Abstr., Chem.Abstr., Curr.Adv.Ecol.Sci., Deep Sea Res.& Oceanogr.Abstr., Geo.Abstr., Helminthol.Abstr.
—BLDSC (6233.996000); UnCover; SWETS; CASDDS.

551.46   PL   ISSN 0078-3234
GC1   CODEN: OCEGA4
OCEANOLOGIA. (Text in English) 1971. irreg., no.33, 1992. price varies. Polska Akademia Nauk, Instytut Oceanologii - Polish Academy of Sciences, Institute of Oceanology, Ul. Powstancow Warszawy 55, 81-712 Sopot, Poland. TEL 48-58-512130. TELEX 051 2785. E-mail: library@ocean.iopan.gda.pl. (Dist. by: ORWN PAN, Palac Kultury i Nauki, 00-901 Warsaw, Poland) (Co-sponsor: Polska Akademia Nauk, Instytut Badan Morza - Polish Academy of Sciences, National Scientific Committee on Oceanic Research) Ed. Jerzy Dera. (reprint service avail. from UMI) **Indexed:** Curr.Tit.Ocean, Deep Sea Res.& Oceanogr.Abstr., Environ.Abstr., GeoRef., Meteor.& Geoastrophys.Abstr., Pollut.Abstr. **Document type:** academic/scholarly publication.
—UMI.
   Description: Works concerning maritime biology, physics, chemistry and other problems connected with maritime phenomena.

551.46   FR   ISSN 0399-1784
GC1   CODEN: OCACD9
OCEANOLOGICA ACTA; revue europeenne d'oceanologie. (Text in English, French) 1978. 6/yr. 1500 F. Gauthier-Villars, 15 rue Gossin, 92543 Montrouge Cedex, France. TEL 33-1-40-92-65-00. FAX 33-1-40-92-65-97. TELEX 634 916 F. (Subscr. to: Centrale des Revues, 11 rue Gossin, 92543 Montrouge Cedex, France. TEL 33-1-46-56-52-66) Ed. J. Boutler. adv. (also avail. in microform) **Indexed:** Anim.Breed.Abstr., Biol.Abstr., Chem.Abstr., Curr.Adv.Ecol.Sci., Curr.Adv.Genetics & Molec.Biol., Curr.Cont., Curr.Tit.Ocean, Deep Sea Res.& Oceanogr.Abstr., Ecol.Abstr., Excerp.Med., Geo.Abstr., GeoRef., Helminthol.Abstr., Meteor.& Geoastrophys.Abstr., Ocean.Abstr., Pollut.Abstr., Sci.Abstr., So.Pac.Per.Ind. **Document type:** academic/scholarly publication.
—BLDSC (6234.155000); Faxon; UnCover; SWETS; CASDDS. **CCC.**
   Description: Presents results of works in all sections of oceanography and from all parts of the oceans and their adjacent estuaries and brackish water systems.

551.46   KO   ISSN 0374-8049
CODEN: HHHCAX
OCEANOLOGICAL SOCIETY OF KOREA. JOURNAL. (Text in English and Korean) 1966. q. $15. Korean Federation of Science and Technology Societies, Yugsam-dong 635-4, Kangnam-gu, Seoul 135, S. Korea. TEL 02-553-2181. (Subscr. to: Oceanological Society of Korea, Seoul University, Dept. of Oceanography, Seoul 151) Ed.Bd. (back issues avail.) **Indexed:** INIS Atomind.
—CASDDS.
   Description: Oceanographic studies of the Yellow Sea, the Sea of Japan, and Korean coastal regions.

551.46   JA
OCEANS CHOSA HOKOKU/JAPAN MARINE SCIENCE AND TECHNOLOGY CENTER. RESEARCH REPORT ON OCEANS. (Text in Japanese) a. Kaiyo Kagaku Gijutsu Senta - Japan Marine Science and Technology Center, 2-15, Natsushima-cho, Yokosuka-shi, Kanagawa-ken 237, Japan.

551.46   US   ISSN 0029-8182
GC1   CODEN: OCEAAK
OCEANUS; reports on research at the Woods Hole Oceanographic Institution. 1952. s-a. Woods Hole Oceanographic Institution, 86 Water St., Woods Hole, MA 02543-9903. TEL 508-457-2000. FAX 508-457-2182. Ed. Vicky Cullen. adv.; bk.rev.; charts; illus.; index, cum.index: vols.1-14. circ. 16,035. (magnetic tape; also avail. in microform from UMI; back issues avail.; reprint service avail. from UMI) **Indexed:** A.S.& T.Ind., Acad.Ind., Aqua.Sci.& Fish.Abstr., Biol.Abstr., Biol.Dig., Chem.Abstr., Curr.Adv.Ecol.Sci., Curr.Cont., Curr.Ref.Fish Res., Curr.Tit.Ocean, Deep Sea Res.& Oceanogr.Abstr., Environ.Abstr., Environ.Ind., Environ.Per.Bibl. (1977-), Excerp.Med., Fluidex, Fut.Surv., Gen.Sci.Ind., Geo.Abstr., GeoRef., Mar.Sci.Cont.Tab., Meteor.& Geoastrophys.Abstr., Ocean.Abstr., Phys.Abstr., Pollut.Abstr., Sci.Cit.Ind. **Document type:** academic/scholarly publication.
●Also available online.
Also available on CD-ROM.
—BLDSC (6234.400000); Faxon; UnCover; SWETS; UMI. **CCC.**
   Incorporates in 1994: Woods Hole Oceanographic Institution. Reports on Research (ISSN 1062-2160)
   Description: Covers marine science and policy for the educated lay reader and specialist alike.

551.46 574   JA
OCHANOMIZU UNIVERSITY. TATEYAMA MARINE LABORATORY. CONTRIBUTIONS. (Text in English) 1975. a. Ochanomizu University, Tateyama Marine Laboratory - Ochanomizu Joshi Digaku Rigakubu Fuoku Rinkai Jikkenjo, 11-12, Koyatsu, Tateyama-shi, Chiba-ken 294-03, Japan.

OFFSHORE MECHANICS AND ARCTIC ENGINEERING SYMPOSIUM. PROCEEDINGS. see *ENGINEERING — Mechanical Engineering*

551.4   BU   ISSN 0324-0878
GC1   CODEN: OKEADB
OKEANOLOGIIA. 1975. irreg. 1.36 lv. per no. (Bulgarska Akademiia na Naukite) Publishing House of the Bulgarian Academy of Sciences, Acad. G. Bonchev St., Bldg. 6, 1113 Sofia, Bulgaria. circ. 580. (reprint service avail. from IRC) **Indexed:** BSL Biol., Chem.Abstr., Deep Sea Res.& Oceanogr.Abstr., Ocean.Abstr.

551.46 639.3   IO   ISSN 0125-9830
OSEANOLOGI DI INDONESIA. (Text and summaries in English and Indonesian) 1974. q. Rps.3200($3) Indonesian Institute of Sciences, Centre for Oceanological Research and Development - Lembaga Ilmu Pengetahuan Indonesia, Pusat Penelitian dan Pengembangan Oseanologi, Jl. Pasir Putih No. 1, Ancol Timur, Box 580 - DAK, Jakarta Utara, Indonesia. Ed. Dr. Subagjo Soemodihardjo. circ. 450. (back issues avail.) **Indexed:** Deep Sea Res.& Oceanogr.Abstr.

551.46   JA   ISSN 0388-5747
OTSUCHI RINKAI KENKYU SENTA HOKOKU/OTSUCHI MARINE RESEARCH CENTER REPORT. (Text in English, Japanese; summaries in Japanese) 1974. a. Tokyo Daigaku, Kaiyo Kenkyujo, Otsuchi Rinkai Kenkyu Senta - University of Tokyo, Ocean Research Institute, Otsuchi Marine Research Center, 106-1, Akahama 2-chome, Otsuchi-cho, Kamihei-gun, Iwate-ken 028-11, Japan.

551.46   US
OUTER CONTINENTAL SHELF RESOURCE DEVELOPMENT NEWS. 1982. q. free. Geological Survey, Department of Natural Resources, Box G, University Sta., Baton Rouge, LA 70893. TEL 504-383-5320. Ed. Dianne Lindstedt. circ. 1,200.
   Description: Covers the outer continental resources such as oil, gas, sulphur and fisheries.

551.46   US
PACIFIC RIM RESEARCH SERIES. vol.2, 1977. irreg. price varies. D.C. Heath & Company, 125 Spring St., Lexington, MA 02173. TEL 617-862-6650. index. **Document type:** monographic series.

PACIFIC SOCIETY. JOURNAL/TAIHEIYO GAKKAI SHI. see *ANTHROPOLOGY*

551.46 574   AE   ISSN 0031-4137
PELAGOS. (Text in French; summaries in English) 1963. s-a. 60 din. Organisme National de la Recherche Scientifique, Centre de Recherches Oceanographiques et des Peches, Jetee Nord, Amiraute, Algiers, Algeria. (Dist. in U.S. by: African Imprint Library Services, 236 Main St., Falmouth, MA 02540. TEL 508-540-5378) illus. **Indexed:** Biol.Abstr., Ocean.Abstr., Pollut.Abstr.

551.46   NE   ISSN 0928-5105
GC1
PHYSICAL OCEANOGRAPHY. Translation of: Morskoi Gidrofizicheskii Zhurnal (KR ISSN 0233-7584) (Text in English) 1987. bi-m. DM.690 (effective 1994). V S P, P.O. Box 346, 3700 AH Zeist, Netherlands. TEL 31-3404-25790. FAX 31-3404-32081. TELEX 40217 VSP NL. Ed. V.N. Eremeev. **Document type:** academic/scholarly publication.
—BLDSC (0416.823000).
   Formerly (until vol.4, 1993): Soviet Journal of Physical Oceanography (ISSN 0920-5047)
   Description: Provides coverage of recent advances in physical oceanography research.

551.46   JA
PRELIMINARY REPORT OF THE HAKUHO MARU CRUISE. (Text in English) 1968. a. Tokyo Daigaku, Kaiyo Kenkyujo - University of Tokyo, Ocean Research Institute, 15-1, Minamidai 1-chome, Nakano-ku, Tokyo 164, Japan.

EARTH SCIENCES — OCEANOGRAPHY

551.46   UK   ISSN 0079-6611
GC1   CODEN: POCNA8
PROGRESS IN OCEANOGRAPHY. 1963. 8/yr. (in 2 vols.). £457($705) (effective 1994). Elsevier Science Ltd, Pergamon, P.O. Box 800, Kidlington, Oxford OX5 1DX, England. TEL 44-865-843000. FAX 44-865-843010. (Subscr. in U.S. and Canada to: Elsevier Science, 660 White Plains Rd., Tarrytown, NY 10591-5153. TEL 914-524-9200. FAX 914-333-2444) Eds. Martin V. Angel, Robert Lloyd Smith. index. (also avail. in microfilm from UMI) **Indexed:** Appl.Mech.Rev., Biol.Abstr., Chem.Abstr., Curr.Adv.Ecol.Sci., Curr.Tit.Ocean, Deep Sea Res.& Oceanogr.Abstr., Energy Rev., Environ.Per.Bibl. (1981-), GeoRef., Meteor.& Geoastrophys.Abstr., Ocean.Abstr., Sci.Abstr., Sel.Water Res.Abstr. **Document type:** academic/scholarly publication.
—BLDSC (6871.300000); EI; Faxon; UnCover; SWETS; UMI. **CCC.**
   Description: Publishes extended reviews of specific topics in oceanography and treatises on oceanographic subjects.
Refereed Serial

551.46 341   NE   ISSN 0924-1922
PUBLICATIONS ON OCEAN DEVELOPMENT; a series of studies on the international, legal, institutional and policy aspects of the ocean development. (Text in English) 1976. irreg., vol.20, 1993. price varies. Kluwer Academic Publishers, Postbus 17, 3300 AA Dordrecht, Netherlands. TEL 31-78-334911. FAX 31-78-334254. TELEX 29245 KAPG NL. (Dist. by: Kluwer Academic Publishers Group, P.O. Box 322, 3300 AH Dordrecht, Netherlands. TEL 31-78-524400. FAX 31-78-524474; N. America dist. addr.: Box 358, Accord Sta., Hingham, MA 02018-0358. TEL 617-871-6600. FAX 617-871-6528) Ed. Shigeru Oda. (back issues avail.) **Document type:** monographic series.
   Formerly (until 1983): Sijthoff Publications on Ocean Development (ISSN 0167-5362)
Refereed Serial

551   JA   ISSN 0915-9851
GC38
R N O D C ACTIVITY REPORT. 1990. a. (Responsible National Oceanographic Data Center) Japan Oceanographic Data Center, Hydrographic Department, Maritime Safety Agency, 5-3-1 Tukiji, Chuo-ku, Tokyo 104, Japan. TEL 81-3-3541-3811. Ed. Kunio Saiki. circ. 600. **Document type:** government publication, newsletter.
   Description: Covers JODC activities for data contributors, data users, oceanographic communities and other national oceanographic data centers.

551.46   JA   ISSN 0287-5098
R N O D C NEWSLETTER FOR WESTPAC. (Text in English) 1982. a. (Responsible National Oceanographic Data Center, Hydrographic Department) Japan Oceanographic Data Center, Maritime Safety Agency, 3-1, Tsukiji 5-chome, Chuo-ku, Tokyo 104, Japan.

551.46   JA
R O V CHOSA HOKOKUSHO/TECHNICAL REPORT OF REMOTELY OPERATED VEHICLE. (Text in Japanese) a. Kaiyo Kagaku Gijutsu Senta - Japan Marine Science and Technology Center, 2-15, Natsushima-cho, Yokosuka-shi, Kanagawa-ken 237, Japan.

551.46   US
R O V REVIEW (YEAR). (Remotely Operated Vehicles) bienneial. $90 in the U.S. and Canada; overseas $105. Technology Systems Corporation, 3337 S.W. Bessey Creek Trail, Box 2174, Palm City, FL 34990-1803. TEL 407-221-7720. FAX 407-221-7715. **Document type:** trade publication.
   Description: Presents a guide to the remotely operated vehicle industry with more than 100 vehicles photographed, categorized and listed with complete specifications and manufacturer contact. Includes subsea services firms, technology manufacturerers, manufacturers' representatives, consultants and engineering firms.

551.46   CC   ISSN 1000-3053
GC880   CODEN: REHAEI
REDAI HAIYANG/TROPIC OCEANOLOGY. (Text in Chinese; summaries in English) 1982. q. $80.40. (Chinese Academy of Sciences, Institute of South China Sea) Science Press, Marketing and Sales Department, 16 Donghuangchenggen Beijie, Beijing 100707, People's Republic of China. TEL 4010642. FAX 4012180. TELEX 210247-SPBJ-CN. adv. circ. 4,000.
—CASDDS.
   Description: Publishes papers and research results on the tropical and sub-tropical zones, mainly in the South China Sea and its adjacent oceans. Covers physical oceanography and meteorology, marine physics, geotectonics, sedimentation, coasts and estuaries, marine biology, chemistry, and pollution.
Refereed Serial

551.46   FR   ISSN 1240-1153
REPERES OCEAN. 1971. irreg., latest no.4. (Institut Francais de Recherche pour l'Exploitation de la Mer (IFREMER), Centre de Brest) Editions de l' IFREMER, B.P. 70, 29280 Plouzane, France.
TEL 98-22-40-13. FAX 98-22-45-86. TELEX 940 627 F. Ed. Raoul Piboubes. charts; stat. **Indexed:** Biol.Abstr., Bull.Signal., Chem.Abstr., GeoRef., Ocean Abstr.Bibl., Ocean.Abstr., Pollut.Abstr., Zoo.Rec.
   Supersedes (in 1992): Campagnes Oceanographiques Francaise; France. IFREMER. Centre de Brest. Publications. Serie: Rapports Economiques et Juridiques (ISSN 0761-3938); France. IFREMER. Centre de Brest. Publications. Serie: Rapports Scientifique et Techniques (ISSN 0761-3970); Campagnes Oceanographiques Francaises was formerly: France. I.F.Re.Mer. Centre de Brest. Publications. Serie: Resultat des Campagnes a la Mer (ISSN 0761-3989); France. Centre National pour l'Exploitation des Oceans. Publications. Serie: Resultats des Campagnes a la Mer (ISSN 0339-2902); France. IFREMER. Centre de Brest. Publications. Serie: Rapports Economiques et Juridiques was formerly: France. Centre National pour l'Exploitation des Oceans. Publications. Serie: Rapports Economiques et Juridiques (ISSN 0339-2910); France. IFREMER. Centre de Brest. Publications. Serie: Rapports Scientifiques et Techniques was formerly: France. Centre National pour l'Exploitation des Oceans. PublicatioRapports Scientifiques et Techniques (ISSN 0339-2899).

551.48   JA
RESULTS OF OCEANOGRAPHICAL OBSERVATIONS. (Text in English) 1947. a. Kishocho - Japan Meteorological Agency, 3-4, Otemachi 1-chome, Chiyoda-ku, Tokyo 100, Japan.

551.46 597   CL   ISSN 0716-1069
REVISTA INVESTIGACIONES MARINAS. 1970. a. $40. (Universidad Catolica de Valparaiso, Escuela de Ciencias del Mar) Ediciones Universitarias de Valparaiso, Casilla 1415, Valparaiso, Chile.
TEL 032-252900. FAX 032-212746. TELEX 230389 UCVAL CL. bk.rev. circ. 500. **Indexed:** Biol.Abstr., Meteor.& Geoastrophys.Abstr., Sel.Water Res.Abstr. **Document type:** academic/scholarly publication.

REVUE INTERNATIONALE D'OCEANOGRAPHIE MEDICALE. see *MEDICAL SCIENCES*

ROSSIISKAYA AKADEMIYA NAUK. INSTITUT OBSHCHEI FIZIKI. TRUDY. see *PHYSICS*

551.46   RU   ISSN 0375-8419
ROSSIISKAYA AKADEMIYA NAUK. INSTITUT OKEANOLOGII IM. P.P. SHIRSHOVA. TRUDY. (Text in Russian; summaries in English) 1946. irreg. price varies. Izdatel'stvo Nauka, 90 Profsoyuznaya ul., 117864 Moscow, Russia. **Indexed:** Biol.Abstr., Chem.Abstr. **Document type:** monographic series.
   Formerly: Akademiya Nauk S.S.S.R. Institut Okeanologii. Trudy (ISSN 0002-3450)

ROSSIISKAYA AKADEMIYA NAUK. IZVESTIYA. SERIYA FIZIKA ATMOSFERY I OKEANA. see *METEOROLOGY*

551.46   RU
GC1.A47   CODEN: OKNOAR
ROSSIISKAYA AKADEMIYA NAUK. OKEANOLOGIYA.
English translation: Russian Academy of Sciences. Oceanology. 1961. bi-m. 39.90 Rub. Rossiiskaya Akademiya Nauk. P.P. Shirshov Institute of Oceanography, 23, Krasikova St., 117218 Moscow, Russia. Ed. L.M. Brekhovskikh. bk.rev.; index. (tabloid format) **Indexed:** Biol.Abstr., Chem.Abstr., Curr.Adv.Ecol.Sci., Curr.Cont., Geo.Abstr., GeoRef., Meteor.& Geoastrophys.Abstr., Sci.Abstr., Sel.Water Res.Abstr.
—BLDSC (0127.400000); CASDDS. **CCC.**
   Formerly: Akademiya Nauk S.S.S.R. Okeanologiya (ISSN 0030-1574)

RUSSIAN ACADEMY OF SCIENCES. INSTITUTE OF GENERAL PHYSICS. PROCEEDINGS. see *PHYSICS*

RUSSIAN ACADEMY OF SCIENCES. IZVESTIYA. ATMOSPHERIC AND OCEANIC PHYSICS. see *METEOROLOGY*

551.46   US
GC1
RUSSIAN ACADEMY OF SCIENCES. OCEANOLOGY.
English translation of: Rossiiskaya Akademiya Nauk. Okeanologiya. 1961. 6/yr. $490 for vol.32 to non-members (foreign $500); members $392 (foreign $402). (Russian Academy of Sciences, RU) American Geophysical Union, 2000 Florida Ave., N.W., Washington, DC 20009. TEL 202-462-6900. FAX 202-328-0566. TELEX 710-822-9300. (Germany addr.: Postfach 49, 37189 Katlenburt-Lindau Germany. TEL 49-5556-1440) index. (reprint service avail. from ISI) **Document type:** academic/scholarly publication.
—BLDSC (0416.645000); Faxon; UnCover; SWETS. **CCC.**
   Formerly: Academy of Sciences of the U S S R. Oceanology (ISSN 0001-4370); **Supersedes:** Soviet Oceanography.

551.46   UK
S U T NEWS. q. Society for Underwater Technology, 76 Mark Lane, London EC3R 7JN, England.
TEL 071-481-0750. FAX 071-481-4001. **Document type:** academic/scholarly publication.
   Formerly (until 1993): Underwater and Marine Technology News (ISSN 0965-5468)

551.46   JA   ISSN 0914-6105
SCIENCE AND TECHNOLOGY. (Text in English, Japanese) 1988. q. Kokusai Kaiyo Kagaku Gijutsu Kyokai - Japan International Marine Science and Technology Federation, 3-5, N honbashi Kakigaracho 1-chome, Chuo-ku, Tokyo 103, Japan.

351.46 639   SP   ISSN 0214-8358
SH285   CODEN: SCIMEM
SCIENTIA MARINA. (Text in English or Spanish) 1955. 4/yr. 11000 ptas ($190) (foreign 19300 ptas.) (effective 1992). Consejo Superior de Investigaciones Cientificas (C.S.I.C.), Instituto de Ciencias del Mar, Paseo Nacional s-n, 080039 Barcelona, Spain. TEL 221-64-50. FAX 221-73-40. TELEX 59367 INPB E. Ed. Josep-Maria Gili. bibl.; charts; illus.; index circ. 800. (back issues avail.) **Indexed:** Aqua.Sci.& Fish.Abstr., Biol.Abstr., Chem.Abstr., Curr.Cont., Deep Sea Res.& Oceanogr.Abstr., Food Sci.& Tech.Abstr., Geo.Abstr., Helminthol.Abstr., nd.SST, Ocean.Abstr., Pollut.Abstr., Ref.Zh., Sel.Water Res.Abstr., Zoo.Abstr. **Document type:** academic/scholarly publication.
●Also available online.
Also available on CD-ROM.
—BLDSC (8172.550000); UMI.
   Formerly (until 1988): Investigacion Pesquera (ISSN 0020-9953)
   Description: Contains articles of multi-disciplinary nature related to marine biology and ecology, fisheries, physical and chemical oceanography, and marine geology.
Refereed Serial

551.46	US	ISSN 1046-9443
GC58		CODEN: ARSODI

SCRIPPS INSTITUTION OF OCEANOGRAPHY. ANNUAL REPORT. (Report year ends June 30) 1971. a. Scripps Institution of Oceanography, Technical Publications, University of California, San Diego, La Jolla, CA 92093-0233. TEL 619-534-2309. illus. **Document type:** academic/scholarly publication.
Former titles (until 1984): Scripps Institution of Oceanography (Year) (ISSN 0194-2816); (until 1978): S I O Scripps Institution of Oceanography (ISSN 0160-7596); (until 1976): Scripps Institution of Oceanography. Annual Report (ISSN 0147-6203); (until 1972): S I O: A Report on the Work and Programs of Scripps Institution of Oceanography (ISSN 0091-1518)

551.46	US	ISSN 0080-8318
QH95		CODEN: BUUNAK

SCRIPPS INSTITUTION OF OCEANOGRAPHY. BULLETIN. 1927. irreg., vol.28, 1993. price varies. University of California Press, 2120 Berkeley Way, Berkeley, CA 94720. TEL 415-642-4247. FAX 415-643-7127. (Orders to: California-Princeton Fulfillment Services, 1445 Lower Ferry Rd., Ewing, NJ 08618. TEL 800-777-4726. FAX 800-999-1958) Ed.Bd. (back issues avail.) **Indexed:** Biol.Abstr., Deep Sea Res.& Oceanogr.Abstr. **Document type:** monographic series.
—UnCover.
Description: Publishes research on deep-sea flora and fauna.
Refereed Serial

551.46	US	

SCRIPPS INSTITUTION OF OCEANOGRAPHY. CONTRIBUTIONS. NEW SERIES. 1930. a. exchange basis only. Scripps Institution of Oceanography, Technical Publications, University of California, San Diego, La Jolla, CA 92093-0233. TEL 619-534-2309.
Formerly: Scripps Institution of Oceanography. Contributions (ISSN 0080-8326)

551.46	US	ISSN 0897-2249

SEA FRONTIERS. 1954. bi-m. $24. 400 S.E. Second Ave., 4th Fl., Knight Centre, Miami, FL 33131. TEL 305-375-8498. Ed. Bonnie Bilyeu Gordon. adv.; bk.rev.; index. circ. 50,000. (also avail. in microform from UMI,ISI) **Indexed:** Acad.Ind., Biol.Dig., Bk.Rev.Ind. (1991-), C.I.J.E., Child.Bk.Rev.Ind. (1991-), Deep Sea Res.& Oceanogr.Abstr., Energy Info.Abstr., Energy Rev., Environ.Abstr., Environ.Per.Bibl. (1990-), Gen.Sci.Ind., Mag.Ind., Meteor.& Geoastrophys.Abstr., So.Pac.Per.Ind.
—Faxon; UnCover; UMI.
Former titles: Sea Frontiers - Sea Secrets; Sea Frontiers (ISSN 0886-9448); Which incorporates: Sea Secrets (ISSN 0037-0029)
Description: Covers the latest news in marine science.

SEA TECHNOLOGY; for design engineering and application of equipment and services for the marine environment. see *ENGINEERING*

SEA TECHNOLOGY BUYERS GUIDE - DIRECTORY. see *ENGINEERING*

SEA WIND. see *ENVIRONMENTAL STUDIES*

SEARS FOUNDATION FOR MARINE RESEARCH. MEMOIRS. see *BIOLOGY*

551.46 574.92	GW	ISSN 0080-889X
QE39		CODEN: SEMADJ

SENCKENBERGIANA MARITIMA. ZEITSCHRIFT FUER MEERESGEOLOGIE UND MEERESBIOLOGIE. irreg. DM.98. (Senckenbergische Naturforschende Gesellschaft) Verlag Dr. Waldemar Kramer, Bornheimer Landwehr 57a, 60385 Frankfurt a.M., Germany. FAX 069-449064. Eds. G. Hertweck, S. Little-Gadow. **Indexed:** Biol.Abstr., Curr.Adv.Ecol.Sci., Deep Sea Res.& Oceanogr.Abstr., Geo.Abstr., GeoRef., Ocean.Abstr., Pollut.Abstr. **Document type:** academic/scholarly publication.
—BLDSC (8241.040000); SWETS; UMI.

551.46 574	SG	ISSN 0850-1602

SENEGAL. CENTRE DE RECHERCHE OCEANOGRAPHIQUE. DOCUMENT SCIENTIFIQUE. (Text in French) 1966. irreg., no.137, 1993. 65000 Fr.CFA. Centre de Recherche Oceanographique de Dakar-Thiaroye, B.P. 2241, Dakar, Senegal. (also avail. in microfiche; back issues avail.) **Document type:** monographic series.

SHIMA MARINELAND. SCIENCE REPORT. see *BIOLOGY*

SHIPPING AND MARINE INDUSTRIES JOURNAL; devoted to shipping and shipbuilding industries, fisheries and oceanography. see *TRANSPORTATION — Ships And Shipping*

SHUISHENG SHENGWU XUEBAO/ACTA HYDROBIOLOGICA SINICA. see *BIOLOGY*

551.46	UN	ISSN 0379-2463

SIREN; news from UNEP's Oceans and Coastal Areas Programme. French Edition: Sirene (ISSN 0379-2498); Spanish Edition: Sirena (ISSN 1014-0212) (Text in English) 1978. 4/yr. free. United Nations Environment Programme (UNEP), Oceans and Costal Areas Programme Activity Centre, P.O. Box 30552, Nairobi, Kenya. TEL 254-2-621234. FAX 254-2-230127. TELEX 22068 UNEP KE. Joan Chamberlin. circ. 11,000. **Indexed:** Environ.Abstr. **Document type:** newsletter.
Description: Intended for an informal presentation of news from OCA-PAC, the oceans and coastal areas program of UNEP.

551.46	US	ISSN 0196-0768
		CODEN: SCSCD7

SMITHSONIAN CONTRIBUTIONS TO THE MARINE SCIENCES. 1977. irreg., no.36, 1993. free. Smithsonian Institution Press, 470 L'Enfant Plaza, Ste. 7100, Washington, DC 20560. TEL 202-287-3738. FAX 202-287-3637. Ed. Don Fisher. abstr.; bibl.; charts; illus. circ. 1,800. (back issues avail.; reprint service avail. from UMI) **Indexed:** Biol.Abstr., Curr.Adv.Ecol.Sci., Deep Sea Res.& Oceanogr.Abstr., GeoRef. **Document type:** monographic series.
—Faxon.

SNOWY MOUNTAINS ENGINEERING CORPORATION. ANNUAL REPORT. see *ENGINEERING*

SORA TO UMI/SKY AND MARINE. see *AERONAUTICS AND SPACE FLIGHT*

551.46		UK

SOUTH WALES PORTS TIDES TABLES. a. £0.50. Associated British Ports, South Wales Group Office, Pierhead Bldng., Bute Docks, Cardiff CF1 5TH, Wales. TEL 0229-822911. FAX 0229-835822. circ. 5,000.

551.46		UK

SOUTHAMPTON PORT TIDE TABLES. 1927. a. Association British Ports (Southampton), Dock House, Canute Rd., Southampton SO9 1PZ, England. circ. 6,000.

551.46	SP	ISSN 0212-1565
		CODEN: ITIOE3

SPAIN. INSTITUTO ESPANOL DE OCEANOGRAFIA. INFORMES TECNICOS. (Text in Spanish, summaries in English) 1982. irreg. price varies. Instituto Espanol de Oceanografia, Avda. del Brasil, 31, 28020 Madrid, Spain. TEL 5974443. FAX 5974770. TELEX 44460. (Dist. by: Centro de Publicaciones, Ministerio de Agricultura, Pesca y Alimentacion, Paseo Infanta Isabel, 1, 28014 Madrid, Spain. TEL 3475551) **Document type:** monographic series.

551.46	PL	ISSN 0208-421X
		CODEN: SMOCDN

STUDIA I MATERIALY OCEANOLOGICZNE. (Text in English) 1972. irreg., no.65, 1993. price varies. Polska Akademia Nauk, Komitet Badan Morza - Polish Academy of Sciences, National Scientific Commiittee on Oceanic Research, Ul. Powstancow Warszawy 55, 81-712 Sopot, Poland. TEL 48-58-512130. TELEX 051-2785. E-mail: library@ocean.iopan.gda.pl. (Dist. by: ORWN PAN, Palac Kultury i Nauki, 00-901 Warsaw, Poland) (Co-sponsor: Polska Akademia Nauk, Instytut Oceanologii - Polish Academy of Sciences, Institute of Oceanology) Ed. Krzysztof Korzeniewski. **Indexed:** GeoRef. **Document type:** academic/scholarly publication.
—CASDDS.
Description: A series of sheets on various problems of the sea, including sea dynamics, sea physics and more.

551.46	US	ISSN 0081-8720
QH91.A1		

STUDIES IN TROPICAL OCEANOGRAPHY. 1963. irreg., no.15, 1992. price varies. Office of the Bulletin of Marine Science, 4600 Rickenbacker Causeway, Miami, FL 33149-1098. TEL 305-361-4190. Ed. William Richards. **Indexed:** Biol.Abstr., Curr.Cont., Zoo.Rec.

551.46		IT

SUBACQUEO. m. (11/yr.). L.25000. Cuba S.p.A., Via Orti della Farnesina 137, 00194 Rome, Italy. Ed. Calogero Cascio. adv. circ. 70,000.

551.46	CC	ISSN 1000-8160

TAIWAN HAIXIA/JOURNAL OF OCEANOGRAPHY IN TAIWAN STRAIT. (Text in Chinese; abstracts in English) 1982. q. $10 per no. Guojia Haiyang-ju, Disan Haiyang Yanjiusuo - State Oceanic Administration, Third Institute of Oceanography, P.O. Box 0570, Xiamen, Fujian 361005, People's Republic of China. TEL 0592-2085880. FAX 0592-2086646. Ed. Zhang Jinbiao. bk.rev.; circ. 1,000 (controlled). **Document type:** academic/scholarly publication.
—BLDSC (5026.153000).
Description: Covers researches on oceanography in East China Sea, especially the Taiwan Strait and its adjacent sea area.

TERRA ET AQUA. see *TRANSPORTATION — Ships And Shipping*

551.46	US	ISSN 0069-9640
GC1		

TEXAS A & M UNIVERSITY. COLLEGE OF GEOSCIENCES. CONTRIBUTIONS IN OCEANOGRAPHY. 1950. irreg. price varies or exchange basis. Texas A & M University, Department of Oceanography, College Sta., TX 77843. TEL 409-845-7327. FAX 409-845-6331. Comp. Gloria Guffy. abstr. circ. controlled. **Indexed:** GeoRef.
Description: A collection of reprints.

THALASSAS; revista de ciencias del mar. see *BIOLOGY*

551.46	DK	ISSN 0106-8334
VK623		

TIDEVANDSTABELLER FOR DANMARK. (Text in Danish and English) 1977. a. DKK 100. Farvandsvaesenet, Oceanografisk Tjeneste, Overgaden O. Vandet 62B, DK-1023 Copenhagen K, Denmark. TEL 45-33-93-13-51. FAX 45-33-32-23-75. Ed. Palle Bo Nielsen. **Document type:** government publication.

551.461	DK	ISSN 0106-8342
VK614.F2		

TIDEVANDSTABELLER FOR FAEROERNE. 1977. a. DKK 50. Farvandsvaesenet, Oceanografisk Tjeneste, Overgaden O. Vandet 62B, DK-1023 Copenhagen K, Denmark. TEL 45-33-93-13-51. FAX 45-33-32-23-75. Ed. Palle Bo Nielsen. **Document type:** government publication.

551.461	DK	ISSN 0107-0398
VK614.G7		

TIDEVANDSTABELLER FOR GROENLAND. (Text in Danish and English) 1966. a. DKK 75. Farvandsvaesenet, Oceanografisk Tjeneste, Overgaden O. Vandet 62B, DK-1023 Copenhagen K, Denmark. TEL 45-33-93-13-51. FAX 45-33-32-23-75. Ed. Palle Bo Nielsen. **Document type:** government publication.

551.46	JA	ISSN 0287-2099

TOKAI DAIGAKU KAIYO KAGAKU HAKUBUTSUKAN NENPO/TOKAI UNIVERSITY. MARINE SCIENCE MUSEUM. ANNUAL REPORT. (Text in English, Japanese) 1972. a. Tokai Daigaku, Kaiyo Kagaku Hakubutsukan, 2389, Miho, Shimizu-shi, Shizuoka-ken 424, Japan.

551.46	JA	ISSN 0289-680X

TOKAI DAIGAKU KAIYO KENKYUJO KENKYU HOKOKU/TOKAI UNIVERSITY. INSTITUTE OF OCEAN RESEARCH AND DEVELOPMENT. BULLETIN. (Text in English, Japanese) 1979. a. Tokai Daigaku, Kaiyo Kenkyujo, 20-1, Orito 3-chome, Shimizu-shi, Shizuoka-ken 424, Japan. **Document type:** bulletin.

551.46	JA	ISSN 0287-1467

TOKAI DAIGAKU KAIYO KENKYUJO NENPO/TOKAI UNIVERSITY. INSTITUTE OF OCEANIC RESEARCH AND DEVELOPMENT. ANNUAL REPORT. (Text in Japanese) 1979. a. Tokai Daigaku, Kaiyo Kenkyujo, 20-1, Orito 3-chome, Shimizu-shi, Shizuoka-ken 424, Japan.

EARTH SCIENCES — OCEANOGRAPHY

551.46   JA   ISSN 0389-2050
TOKAI DAIGAKU KAIYOGAKUBU GYOSEKISHU/TOKAI UNIVERSITY. FACULTY OF MARINE SCIENCE AND TECHNOLOGY. COLLECTED REPRINTS. (Text in English, Japanese) a. Tokai Daigaku, Kaiyogakubu, 20-1, Orido 3-chome, Shimizu-shi, Shizuoka-ken 424, Japan.

551.46   JA   ISSN 0375-3271
CODEN: TDKYBF
TOKAI DAIGAKU KIYO. KAIYOGAKUBU/TOKAI UNIVERSITY. FACULTY OF MARINE SCIENCE AND TECHNOLOGY. JOURNAL. (Text in English, Japanese) 1966. s-a. Tokai Daigaku, Kaiyogakubu - Tokai University, Faculty of Marine Science and Technology, 20-1, Orido 3-chome, Shimizu-shi, Shizuoka-ken 424, Japan. **Indexed:** Agrindex, Biol.Abstr., Jap.Per.Ind. **Document type:** academic/scholarly publication.
—BLDSC (4745.900000); CASDDS.

551.46 574   JA
TOKYO DAIGAKU RIGAKUBU FUZOKU RINKAI JIKKENJO NENPO/UNIVERSITY OF TOKYO. MISAKI MARINE BIOLOGICAL STATION. ANNUAL REPORT. (Text in Japanese) 1951. a. Tokyo Daigaku, Rigakubu, Fuzoku Rinkai Jikkenjo - University of Tokyo, Faculty of Science, Misaki Marine Biological Station, 1024, Koajiro, Misakicho, Miur-shi, Kanagawa-ken 238-02, Japan.

551.46   JA   ISSN 0916-4820
TOKYOKO HARO KANSOKU NENPO/ANNUAL REPORT OF OBSERVATION WAVES IN TOKYO BAY. (Text in Japanese) a. Tokyoto Kowankyoku - Tokyo Metropolitan Government, Bureau of Port and Harbour, 8-1 Nishishinjuku 2-chome, Shinjuku-ku, Tokyo 163-01, Japan.

551   US
TOPICS IN ATMOSPHERIC AND OCEANOGRAPHIC SCIENCES. 1982. irreg. price varies. Springer-Verlag, 175 Fifth Ave., New York, NY 10010. TEL 212-460-1500. FAX 212-473-6272. (Also: Berlin, Heidelberg, Tokyo and Vienna) Eds. M. Ghil, J. Suenderman. **Document type:** monographic series.

551.46   JA
TSUKUBA DAIGAKU ENGAN KANSOKU HOKOKU/UNIVERSITY OF TSUKUBA. REPORT OF COASTAL OBSERVATION. (Text in Japanese) a. Tsukuba Daigaku, Shimoda Rinkai Jikken Senta - University of Tsukuba, Shimoda Marine Research Center, 10-1, Shimodashi 5-chome, Shizuoka-ken 415, Japan.

TSUKUBA INSTITUTE. TECHNICAL REPORT/TSUKUBA KENKYUJO GIHO. see *TRANSPORTATION — Ships And Shipping*

551.46 639.3   TI   ISSN 0579-7926
QH90.A1   CODEN: INOBAG
TUNISIA. INSTITUT NATIONAL SCIENTIFIQUE ET TECHNIQUE D'OCEANOGRAPHIE ET DE PECHE. BULLETIN. (Text in French; summaries in Arabic, English, and French) 1966 N.S. irreg. Institut National Scientifique et Technique d'Oceanographie et de Peche, Salammbo, Tunisia. circ. 1,150. **Indexed:** Bull.Signal. **Document type:** bulletin.

551.46   UN
U N E P REGIONAL SEAS REPORTS AND STUDIES. 1982. 10/yr. free. United Nations Environment Programme, Oceans and Coastal Areas, Programme Activity Centre, P.O. Box 30552, Nairobi, Kenya. FAX 254-2-621234. TELEX 25164 UNEPRS KE. circ. 500. (also avail. in microfiche from CIS) **Indexed:** IIS, Meteor.& Geoastrophys.Abstr. **Document type:** academic/scholarly publication.
Description: Contains reports and studies of the Kenyan waters concerning marine and riparian environments, pollution, conservation, and marine mammals.

551.46   JA   ISSN 0386-4197
UMI NO HAKUBUTSUKAN/TOKAI UNIVERSITY. MARINE SCIENCE MUSEUM. JOURNAL. (Text in Japanese) 1971. bi-m. 600 Yen. Tokai Daigaku, Kaiyo Kagaku Hakubutsukan - Tokai University, Marine Science Museum, 2389, Miho, Shimizu-shi, Shizuoka-ken 424, Japan. **Document type:** academic/scholarly publication.

UMI NO KISHO/MARINE METEOROLOGY. see *METEOROLOGY*

551.46 614.7   JA   ISSN 0912-7437
UMI TO ANZEN. 1958. m. 4000 Yen. Nihon Kainan Boshi Kyokai - Japan Association for Preventing Marine Accidents, 1-14-1 Toranomon, Minato-ku, Tokyo 105, Japan. FAX 03-3581-6136. Ed. Inoue Isao. circ. 6,500. **Document type:** bulletin.
Description: Propagates the prevention of marine accidents and pollution.

551.46   JA   ISSN 0385-5597
UMI TO NINGEN/TOBA MARITIME MUSEUM. ANNUAL. (Text in Japanese) 1973. a. Umi no Hakubutsukan - Toba Maritime Museum, 1731, Okitsu, Uramuracho, Toba-shi, Mie-ken 517, Japan.

UMI TO SORA/SEA AND SKY. see *METEOROLOGY*

551.46   US   ISSN 1061-5776
▼**UNDERCURRENTS.** 1992. q. $10 to non-members; members $6. Mystic Marinelife Aquarium, Membership Dept., 55 Coogan Blvd., Mystic, CT 06355-1997. TEL 203-536-4200. FAX 203-572-0761. Ed. William J. Kelly. circ. 15,700.
Description: Describes classes, trips and programs available to members. Contains articles on marine life and aquatic habitats.

591   US   ISSN 0041-6606
QH91.A1   CODEN: UWNAAX
UNDERWATER NATURALIST. 1962. q. membership. American Littoral Society, Sandy Hook, Highlands, NJ 07732. TEL 908-291-0055. Ed. D.W. Bennett. adv.; bk.rev.; charts; illus. circ. 9,000. (also avail. in microform from UMI; reprint service avail. from UMI) **Indexed:** Biol.Abstr., Biol.Dig., Environ.Per.Bibl. (1973-), Ocean.Abstr., Pollut.Abstr. **Document type:** newsletter.
—BLDSC (9090.013000); UnCover; UMI.

551.46   US   ISSN 1069-6547
CODEN: WAVEEP
UNDERWATER NEWS & TECHNOLOGY. 1981. bi-m. $45 in the U.S. and Canada; overseas $75. Technology Systems Corporation, 3337 S.W. Bessey Creek Trail, Box 2174, Palm City, FL 34990-1803. TEL 407-221-7720. FAX 407-221-7715. adv.: B&W page $1125, color page $1625; trim 8 1/2 x 11. bk.rev. circ. 5,000. (back issues avail.) **Document type:** trade publication.
—SWETS.
Former titles (until June 1993): Waves (ISSN 1055-0348); (until Jan. 1991): Subnotes (ISSN 0889-7166)
Description: Covers international underwater ocean technology. Applications include: search and salvage, defense, manned submersibles, diving, ocean instrumentation, and surface ocean technology.

551.46   UK
UNDERWATER TECHNOLOGY. 1975. q. £60 (foreign £68). Society for Underwater Technology, 76 Mark Lane, London EC3R 7JN, England. TEL 071-481-0750. FAX 071-481-4001. TELEX 886841-IMARE. Ed. Rowena Morton. adv.; bk.rev.; illus. circ. 1,500. **Indexed:** Fluidex, Ocean.Abstr. **Document type:** academic/scholarly publication.
—BLDSC (9090.017900); EI; SWETS.
Formerly (until 1984): Society for Underwater Technology. Journal (ISSN 0141-0814)

UNDERWATER U S A. see *SPORTS AND GAMES*

551.47   US
U.S. DEPARTMENT OF COMMERCE. NATIONAL OCEANIC AND ATMOSPHERIC ADMINISTRATION. OCEANOGRAPHIC MONTHLY SUMMARY. 1981. m. $27 (foreign $33 75). U.S. Department of Commerce, National Oceanic and Atmospheric Administration, NOAA/NOS/OPB, World Weather Bldg., 5200 Auth Rd., Camp Springs, MD 20746. TEL 301-763-8294. (Subscr. to: Superintendent of Documents, U.S. Government Printing Office, Box 371954, Pittsburgh, PA 15250-7954. TEL 202-783-3238. FAX 202-512-2233) Ed. Paul T. Reilly. charts; illus. circ. 700. (also avail. in microfiche from CIS; reprint service avail. from CIS) **Indexed:** Amer.Stat Ind. (1981-), Ind.U.S.Gov.Per. **Document type:** government publication.
—UnCover.
Formerly: U.S. National Weather Service. Oceanographic Monthly Summary (ISSN 0277-6197); Formed by the merger of (1966-1980): Gulfstream (ISSN 0565-8543); Fishing Information
Description: Compiles sea-surface temperature information for all major oceans, including some thermal ocean fronts and eddy analyses, and climatological anomalies. Includes brief articles about oceanography.

551.46   US   ISSN 0276-4849
VK589
U.S. HYDROGRAPHIC CONFERENCE. BIENNIAL MEETING. PROCEEDINGS. 1984. biennial. price varies. Hydrographic Society of America, Box 732, Rockville, MD 20848-0732. TEL 301-460-4768. FAX 301-460-4768. (back issues avail.) **Document type:** proceedings.

U.S. NATIONAL OCEANIC AND ATMOSPHERIC ADMINISTRATION. ENGINEERING SUPPORT OFFICE. TECHNICAL MEMORANDUM. 1969. irreg. free. U.S. National Oceanic and Atmospheric Administration, Engineering Support Office, Rockville, MD 20852. TEL 301-655-4000 circ. 3,000. **Indexed:** Geo.Abstr., Ocean.Abstr., Pollut.Abstr.
Former titles: U.S. National Oceanic and Atmospheric Administration. Test and Evaluation Office. Technical Memorandum; U.S. National Oceanographic Instrumentation Center. Technical Memorandum.

U.S. NATIONAL OCEANIC AND ATMOSPHERIC ADMINISTRATION. NATIONAL UNDERSEA RESEARCH PROGRAM SUMMARY. see *ENGINEERING*

551.46   US
U.S. NATIONAL OCEANIC AND ATMOSPHERIC ADMINISTRATION. TECHNICAL BULLETIN. 1964. irreg. free. U.S. National Oceanic and Atmospheric Administration, Engineering Support Office, Rockville, MD 20852. TEL 301-655-4000. circ. 3,000.
Former titles: U.S. National Oceanic and Atmospheric Administration. Test and Evaluation Laboratory. Technical Bulletin; U.S. National Oceanographic Instrumentation Center. Technical Bulletin.

551.46   US   ISSN 0091-9500
GC37.5   CODEN: KORADQ
U.S. NATIONAL OCEANOGRAPHIC DATA CENTER. KEY TO OCEANOGRAPHIC RECORDS DOCUMENTATION. 1973. irreg., no.19, 1994. U.S. National Oceanographic Data Center, NOAA-NESDIS, E-OC2, Universal Bldg., Rm. 415, 1825 Connecticut Ave., N.W., Washington, DC 20235. TEL 202-606-4549. (Subscr. to: Superintendent of Documents, U.S. Government Printing Office, Box 371954, Pittsburgh, PA 15250-7954. TEL 202-783-3238. FAX 202-512-2233) Ed. Richard Abram. **Document type:** government publication.
Description: Describes the data holdings, products and services of the center.

551.46   VE   ISSN 0020-417X
CODEN: BOUOAF
UNIVERSIDAD DE ORIENTE. INSTITUTO OCEANOGRAFICO. BOLETIN. (Text and summaries in English and Spanish) 1961. s-a. Bol.$25($7) Universidad de Oriente Instituto Oceanografico, Bilbioteca, Apdo. Posta 94, Cumana, Sucre, Venezuela. Ed. E.K. Ganesan. adv.; bk.rev.; abstr.; bibl.; charts; illus. circ. 2,000. **Indexed:** Biol.Abstr., GeoRef., Ocean.Abstr.
Description: Covers study on the Caribbean and Atlantic oceans.

EARTH SCIENCES — OCEANOGRAPHY

551.46   BL   ISSN 0373-5524
QH1   CODEN: BOCNAO
UNIVERSIDADE DE SAO PAULO. INSTITUTO OCEANOGRAFICO. BOLETIM. (Text in various languages; summaries in English) 1950. biennial. $17 or exchange basis. Universidade de Sao Paulo, Instituto Oceanografico, Cidade Universitaria, Butanta, 05508 Sao Paulo, SP, Brazil. circ. 650.
Indexed: Aqua.Sci.& Fish.Abstr., Biol.Abstr., Curr.Adv.Ecol.Sci., Deep Sea Res. & Oceanogr.Abstr., Deep Sea Res.& Oceanogr.Abstr., Ocean.Abstr., Sel.Water Res.Abstr., Zoo.Rec.

550   BL   ISSN 0100-5146
UNIVERSIDADE DE SAO PAULO. INSTITUTO OCEANOGRAFICO. PUBLICACAO ESPECIAL. (Multilingual text; summaries in English) 1972. irreg., no.4, 1977. price varies or exchange basis. Universidade de Sao Paulo, Instituto Oceanografico, Cidade Universitaria, Butanta, 05508 Sao Paulo, SP, Brazil. circ. 650.

551   BL   ISSN 0100-5197
GC1
UNIVERSIDADE DE SAO PAULO. INSTITUTO OCEANOGRAFICO. RELATORIO DE CRUZEIROS. (Text in various languages; summaries in English) 1976. irreg., no.6, 1985. price varies or exchange basis. Universidade de Sao Paulo, Instituto Oceanografico, Cidade Universitaria, Butanta, 05508 Sao Paulo, S.P., Brazil. Ed. W. Besuard. circ. 650.

551   BL   ISSN 0100-5243
UNIVERSIDADE DE SAO PAULO. INSTITUTO OCEANOGRAFICO. RELATORIO INTERNO. (Text in various languages; summaries in English) 1974. irreg., no.14, 1985. price varies; exchange basis. Universidade de Sao Paulo, Instituto Oceanografico, Cidade Universitaria, Butanta, 05508 Sao Paulo, S.P., Brazil. circ. 200.

551.46   US
UNIVERSITY OF CALIFORNIA, SANTA CRUZ. INSTITUTE FOR MARINE SCIENCES. SPECIAL PUBLICATION. 1974. irreg., no.9, 1978. price varies. University of California, Santa Cruz, Institute of Marine Sciences, Santa Cruz, CA 95064. TEL 408-429-2464. FAX 408-429-0146. circ. 500.
Former titles: University of California, Santa Cruz. Center for Marine Studies. Special Publication; University of California, Santa Cruz. Coastal Marine Laboratory. Special Publication.

551.46   DK
UNIVERSITY OF COPENHAGEN. DEPARTMENT OF PHYSICAL OCEANOGRAPHY. REPORT. 1968. 2/yr. free. University of Copenhagen, Department of Physical Oceanography, Haraldsgade 6, DK-2200 Copenhagen N, Denmark. TEL 45-31-83-47-64. FAX 45-35-82-25-65. TELEX 16469 UCPHGI DK. Ed.Bd. illus. circ. 250.
Formerly: University of Copenhagen. Institute of Physical Oceanography. Report.

551.46   US
UNIVERSITY OF SOUTH CAROLINA. BELLE W. BARUCH LIBRARY IN MARINE SCIENCE AND COASTAL RESEARCH. COLLECTED PAPERS. 1973. irreg. (approx. 2/yr.). $49.95. University of South Carolina Press, c/o Ribin Sumner, Rights & Permissions, Columbia, SC 29208. TEL 803-777-5243. charts; illus.
Refereed Serial

551.46   JA   ISSN 0564-6898
UNIVERSITY OF TOKYO. OCEAN RESEARCH INSTITUTE. BULLETIN/TOKYO DAIGAKU KAIYO KENKYUJO. (Text in English) 1967. a. exchange basis. University of Tokyo, Ocean Research Institute - Tokyo Daigaku Kaiyo Kenkyujo, 15-1 Minami-Dai 1-chome, Nakano-ku, Tokyo 164, Japan. FAX 81-3-3375-6716. TELEX J25607-ORIUT. stat. **Indexed:** Biol.Abstr., Curr.Adv.Ecol.Sci., Deep Sea Res.& Oceanogr.Abstr., GeoRef. **Document type:** academic/scholarly publication, bulletin.

551.48   JA
UNIVERSITY OF TOKYO. OCEAN RESEARCH INSTITUTE. PUBLICATION LIST. (Text in English) a. Tokyo Daigaku, Kaiyo Kenkyujo - University of Tokyo, Ocean Research Institute, 15-1, Minamidai 1-chome, Nakano-ku, Tokyo 164, Japan.

551.46 574   JA
UNIVERSITY OF TSUKUBA. SHIMODA MARINE RESEARCH CENTER. CONTRIBUTIONS. (Text in English, Japanese) 1954. irreg. Tsukuba Daigaku, Shimoda Rinkai Jikken Senta - University of Tsukuba, Shimoda Marine Research Center, 10-1, Shimodashi 5-chome, Shizuoka-ken 415, Japan.

551.46   PL   ISSN 0867-8413
UNIWERSYTET GDANSKI. WYDZIAL BIOLOGII, GEOGRAFII I OCEANOLOGII. ZESZYTY NAUKOWE. OCEANOGRAFIA. (Text in Polish; summaries in English and Russian) 1973. irreg., latest no.13. price varies. Uniwersytet Gdanski, Wydzial Biologii, Geografii i Oceanologii, c/o Biblioteka Glowna, Ul. Armii Krajowej 110, 81-824 Sopot, Poland. TEL 51-0061. TELEX 051 2247 BMOR PL. (Dist. by: Ars Polona-Ruch, Krakowskie Przedmiescie 7, 00-680 Warsaw, Poland) Ed. Krystyna Wiktor. **Document type:** academic/scholarly publication.
Formerly: Uniwersytet Gdanski. Wydzial Biologii i Nauk o Ziemi. Zeszyty Naukowe. Oceanografia (ISSN 0302-3125)
Description: Covers marine biology (plankton, benthos, ichtiology), biology and morphometrics, physical and chemical oceanography, water pollution, and marine geology.

550   UY
URUGUAY. SERVICIO DE OCEANOGRAFIA E HIDROGRAFIA. AVISOS A LOS NAVEGANTES. 1974. m. Urg.$5 per no. Servicio de Oceanografia e Hidrografia, Capurro 980, Casilla de Correo No. 1381, Montevideo, Uruguay.
Continues: Uruguay. Servicio de Hidrografia. Avisos a los Navegantes.

551.46   US
VIRGINIA INSTITUTE OF MARINE SCIENCE. CONTRIBUTIONS. 1940. irreg., latest 1979. exchange basis. Virginia Institute of Marine Science, Library, Gloucester Point, VA 23062. TEL 804-642-7116. FAX 804-642-7113.

551.46   US
VIRGINIA INSTITUTE OF MARINE SCIENCE, GLOUCESTER POINT. SPECIAL REPORT IN APPLIED MARINE SCIENCE AND OCEAN ENGINEERING. 1955. irreg., no.304, 1990. price varies. Virginia Institute of Marine Science, Gloucester Point, VA 23062. TEL 804-642-7116. FAX 804-642-7113. (also avail. in microfiche) **Indexed:** Ocean.Abstr.

551.46   RU
VSESOYUZNYI NAUCHNO-ISSLEDOVATEL'SKII INSTITUT MORSKOGO RYBNOGO KHOZYAISTVA I OKEANOGRAFII (V N I R O). TRUDY. vol.117, 1976. irreg. price varies. Ul.Verkhnyaya Krasnosel'skaya, 17, Moscow 107140, Russia. Ed. K. Yablonskaya. circ. 500.
Indexed: Biol.Abstr., Chem.Abstr, Food Sci.& Tech.Abstr., Geo.Abstr., GeoRef., Helminthol.Abstr.

551.46   US
WASHINGTON LETTER OF OCEANOGRAPHY. 1973. fortn. $56. Compass Publications, Inc. (Arlington), Ste. 1000, 1117 N. 19 St., Arlington, VA 22209. TEL 703-524-3136. FAX 703-841-0852. bk.rev.; bibl. (reprint service avail. from UMI) **Document type:** trade publication.
Description: Contains comprehensive, factual news on plans and programs in both government and industry, particularly marketing information, legislation, contracts, proposals and interpretations of significant news in the oceanology.

551.46   US
WHALING ACCOUNT. 1965-1991; resumed 1992. q. $20. Whaling Museum Society, Inc., Box 25, Cold Spring Harbor, NY 11724. TEL 516-367-3418. Ed. Ann M. Gill. bk.rev. circ. 700.

351.46   US   ISSN 1062-2152
GC1
WOODS HOLE OCEANOGRAPHIC INSTITUTION - ANNUAL REPORT. 1932. a. Woods Hole Oceanographic Institution, Woods Hole, MA 02543. TEL 508-457-2000. FAX 508-457-2182. Ed. Vicky Cullen. **Document type:** corporate report.
Former titles (until 1990): Woods Hole Oceanographic Institution (ISSN 1053-9352); (until 1989): Woods Hole Oceanographic Institution. Annual Report (ISSN 0099-3808)

551.46   US   ISSN 1041-5602
WORLD AQUACULTURE. q. $30 (foreign $40) (effective 1993). World Aquaculture Society, 143 J.M. Parker Coliseum, Louisiana State Univ., Baton Rouge, LA 70803. TEL 504-388-3137. FAX 504-388-3493. Ed. David E. Aiken.
—BLDSC (9352.912430).
Formerly: World Aquaculture Society. Newsletter.
Description: Contains aquaculture science and technology news and information.

551.46   US   ISSN 0893-8849
SH138   CODEN: JWASE7
WORLD AQUACULTURE SOCIETY. JOURNAL. q. $90 (Canada, Mexico & S. America $100; elsewhere $115). World Aquaculture Society, 143 J M Parker Coliseum, Louisiana State University, Baton Rouge, LA 70803. TEL 504-388-3137. FAX 504-388-3493. Ed. Ronald Thune. adv. (back issues avail.) **Document type:** academic/scholarly publication.
—BLDSC (4917.434000); UnCover; SWETS; CASDDS.
Former titles: World Mariculture Society. Journal (ISSN 0735-0147); World Mariculture Society. Proceedings.
Description: Covers all aspects of the culture of plants and animals: culture systems, nutrition, water quality, disease, economics and marketing, physiology, reproduction and breeding and genetics.
Refereed Serial

551.46   US
WORLD AQUACULTURE SOCIETY. WORKSHOP SERIES. 1991. a. price varies. World Aquaculture Society, 143 J.M. Parker Coliseum, Lousiana State Univ., Baton Rouge, LA 70803. TEL 504-388-3137. FAX 504-388-3493. **Document type:** proceedings.

WORLD AQUATIC NEWS & TRAVEL. see *TRAVEL AND TOURISM*

WORLD METEOROLOGICAL ORGANIZATION. COMMISSION FOR HYDROLOGY. ABRIDGED FINAL REPORT OF THE (NO.) SESSION. see *METEOROLOGY*

551.46   UN   ISSN 0084-2001
WORLD METEOROLOGICAL ORGANIZATION. REPORTS ON MARINE SCIENCE AFFAIRS. 1970. irreg., no.16, 1991. price varies. World Meteorological Organization, 41 Av. Giuseppe Motta, 1211 Geneva 2, Switzerland. TEL 730-8111. (Dist. in U.S. by: American Meteorological Society, 45 Beacon St., Boston, MA 02108. TEL 617-227-2425) **Indexed:** Biol.Abstr.

WORLD SURVEY OF CLIMATOLOGY. see *METEOROLOGY*

551.46   GW   ISSN 0936-949X
ZENTRUM FUER MEERES- UND KLIMAFORSCHUNG. BERICHTE. 1962. a. exchange basis. Universitaet Hamburg, Institut fuer Meereskunde, Bundestr. 55, 22765 Hamburg, Germany. FAX 4940-4123-4644. TELEX 212586-IFMHHHD. Ed. Walter Nellen. illus. circ. 200. **Indexed:** Deep Sea Res.& Oceanogr.Abstr., Meteor.& Geoastrophys.Abstr.
Former titles: Universitaet Hamburg. Zentrum fuer Meereskunde- und Klimaforschung. Berichte; Universitaet Hamburg. Institut fuer Meereskunde. Mitteilungen.

EDUCATION

EASTERN ORTHODOX

see Religions and Theology–Eastern Orthodox

ECONOMIC SITUATION AND CONDITIONS

see Business and Economics–Economic Situation and Conditions

ECONOMIC SYSTEMS AND THEORIES, ECONOMIC HISTORY

see Business and Economics–Economic Systems and Theories, Economic History

ECONOMICS

see Business and Economics

EDUCATION

see also Education–Adult Education; Education–Computer Applications; Education–Guides to Schools and Colleges; Education–Higher Education; Education–International Education Programs; Education–School Organization and Administration; Education–Special Education and Rehabilitation; Education–Teaching Methods and Curriculum

A A T S E E L NEWSLETTER. (American Association of Teachers of Slavic and East European Languages) see LINGUISTICS

A A U W NEW YORKER. (American Association of University Women) see COLLEGE AND ALUMNI

370 028.5   CC
A B C PINPIN DUDU HUABAO/A B C SPELLING AND READING PICTORIAL. (Text in Chinese) m. $24. Shanghai Jiaoyu Chubanshe - Shanghai Educational Publishing House, 123 Yongfu Road, Shanghai 200031, People's Republic of China. TEL 4377165. Ed. Zhang Wenjie. **Document type:** academic/scholarly publication.

A C A S BULLETIN. (Association of Concerned Africa Scholars) see ETHNIC INTERESTS

613.7 370   AT   ISSN 1321-0394
A C H P E R HEALTHY LIFESTYLES JOURNAL. 1954. q. Aus.$28 (foreign Aus.$35) (effective 1993). Australian Council for Health, Physical Education and Recreation Inc., P.O. Box 304, Hindmarsh, S.A. 5007, Australia. TEL 08-340-3388. FAX 08-340-3399. Ed. Michael Reynods. adv.; bk.rev.; charts; film rev.; illus.; stat. circ. 3,500. (also avail. in microform from UMI; reprint service avail. from UMI) **Indexed:** Rural Recreat.Tour.Abstr., Sportsearch (1983-), World Agri.Econ.& Rural Sociol.Abstr.
—BLDSC (0576.546000); UMI.
Former titles (until 1994): A C H P E R National Journal (ISSN 0813-2283); (until 1983): A J H P E R. Australian Journal for Health, Physical Education and Recreation (ISSN 0813-2275); (until 1977): Australian Journal for Health, Physical Education and Recreation (ISSN 0312-827X); (until 1975): Australian Journal of Physical Education (ISSN 0312-8261); Which was formerly (until 1960): Physical Education Journal (ISSN 0004-9492).

A C J S TODAY. (Academy of Criminal Justice Sciences) see CRIMINOLOGY AND LAW ENFORCEMENT

370   AT
A C S S O POLICY DOCUMENT (YEAR). a. Aus.$10. Australian Council of State School Organisations, Hughes Primary School, Kent St., Hughes, A.C.T. 2605, Australia. TEL 062-825-150. FAX 062-851-351. circ. 200.
Formerly (until 1994): A C S S O Policy (Year).

A D A TODAY; a newsletter for liberal activists. (Americans for Democratic Action) see POLITICAL SCIENCE

371   US   ISSN 0194-8849
A E A ADVOCATE. 1914. 6/yr. $3 to non-members. Arizona Education Association, 2102 W. Indian School Rd., Phoenix, AZ 85015. TEL 602-264-1774. Ed. Daphne Atkeson. adv.; bk.rev.; bibl.; illus. circ. 22,000. (tabloid format; also avail. in microform from UMI) **Indexed:** Educ.Ind. —UMI.
Former titles (until 1979): Arizona Educator Advocate; Arizona Teacher (ISSN 0004-1653)

370   US
A E A NEWSLETTER. 1940. m. $10 includes membership. American Education Association, Box 463, Center Moriches, NY 11934. Ed. Rudolph P. Blaum. bk.rev. circ. 250. **Document type:** newsletter.
Formerly (until 1987): Signpost (New York).

A F T ISSUES BULLETIN. (American Federation of Teachers) see LABOR UNIONS

370   US   ISSN 1041-956X
A H A F JOURNAL. 1967. bi-m. $50. American Handwriting Analysis Foundation, 1844 Law St., San Diego, CA 92109-2232. TEL 619-274-0522. Ed. Shari Lee Galve. adv.: B&W page $75; adv. contact: Shari Lee Galve. bk.rev.; charts; illus. circ. 500. (back issues avail.) **Document type:** newsletter.
Formerly (until 1985): A H A F News.
Description: Covers educational material pertaining to graphology and questioned documents. Includes international graphological "hand-holding" exchange with analysts around the world.
Refereed Serial

370   US
A I S NEWSLETTER. 1979. q. $30 individual membership; institutional $50; students $15. Association for Integrative Studies (Oxford), c/o Prof. William Newell, School of Interdisciplinary Studies, Miami University, Oxford, OH 45056. TEL 513-529-2213. FAX 513-529-5849. adv.; bk.rev.; circ. 550 (paid). **Document type:** newsletter.
Description: Provides a forum for the exchange of ideas among scholars and administrators in the arts and sciences on intellectual and organizational issues related to furthering integrative or interdisciplinary studies.

370   US   ISSN 0882-438X
A M S STUDIES IN EDUCATION. 1974. irreg., no.8, 1987. price varies. A M S Press, Inc., 56 E. 13th St., New York, NY 10003. TEL 212-777-4700. FAX 212-995-5413. (back issues avail.)
Description: Series of monographs, reference works and bibliographies on various aspects of education.

370   BL   ISSN 0101-5028
A N D E. 1981. 2/yr. $12. Associacao Nacional de Educacao, Rua Bartira 387, 05009-000 Sao Paulo, Brazil. TEL 011-872-3209. Ed. Lia Rosenberg. bk.rev.; index. circ. 8,000. (also avail. in microform; back issues avail.) **Document type:** academic/scholarly publication, bulletin.

370 296 320   US
A O J T NEWS; of the New York City public schools. 1965. bi-m. membership. Association of Orthodox Jewish Teachers, 1577 Coney Island Ave., Brooklyn, NY 11230. TEL 718-258-3585. FAX 718-258-3586. Ed. Yehoshua Leiman. adv.; bk.rev. circ. 9,300. (tabloid format)

370   US
A P SPECIAL; the newsletter for assistant principals. 1985. q. National Association of Secondary School Principals, 1904 Association Dr., Reston, VA 22091. TEL 703-860-0200. FAX 703-476-5432. Ed. Jackie Rough. circ. 10,000. (also avail. in microfilm from UMI; back issues avail.) **Document type:** newsletter.
Description: Addresses issues of interest to secondary school assistant principals.

A P U PRESS ALASKANA BOOK SERIES. (Alaska Pacific University Press) see HISTORY — History Of North And South America

370   UK
A R E L S BROCHURE; learn English in Britain. 1984. a. free. Association of Recognised English Language Services, 2 Pontypcol Pl., Valentine Pl., London SE1 8QF, England. TEL 071-242 3136. FAX 071-928-9378. TELEX 916655-AF. Ed. Oksana Higglesden. adv. contact: Christine Edington. circ. 130,000.
Former titles: A R E L S - F E L C O Brochure; A R E L S Brochure; A R E L S Handbook.
Description: Contains details of English language courses and services provided by 200 member schools and colleges in the U.K.

A S T C NEWSLETTER. (Association of Science-Technology Centers) see MUSEUMS AND ART GALLERIES

370   US   ISSN 0889-6488
A T E A JOURNAL. 1953. 4/yr. $30. American Technical Education Association, Inc., North Dakota State College of Science, Wahpeton, ND 58076. TEL 701-671-2240. FAX 701-671-2260. Ed. Betty Krump. adv.; bk.rev. circ. 3,000. **Indexed:** Cont.Pg.Educ. **Document type:** newsletter.
Formerly: Technical Education Newsletter (ISSN 0040-0939)

370.7   US   ISSN 0001-2718
A T E NEWSLETTER. vol.5, 1973. 6/yr. $75 to individuals; libraries $60. Association of Teacher Educators, 1900 Association Dr., Reston, VA 22091-1599. TEL 703-620-3110. Ed. Gloria Chernay. circ. 4,000. **Document type:** newsletter.
Formerly: A S T Newsletter.

371   AT
A T F ANNUAL REPORT.* 1943. a. Aus.$15. Australian Teachers Union, c/o Australian Educators Union, 220 Clavendon St., E Melbourne, Vic. 3002, Australia. TEL 03-254-1800. FAX 03-254-1805. adv.; circ. controlled. (processed) **Indexed:** Aus.Educ.Ind.
Formerly: A T F Monthly Report (ISSN 0001-2726)

A T G BULLETIN. (Accord on Teachers' Guild, Inc.) see MUSIC

373   UK
A T L REPORT. 1978. 8/yr. £8 (overseas £12). Association of Teachers and Lecturers, 7 Northumberland St., London WC2N 5DA, England. TEL 071-930-6441. FAX 071-930-1359. Ed. Julia Hagedorn. adv.; charts; circ. 130,000 (controlled). **Indexed:** High.Educ.Curr.Aware.Bull., Rehabil.Lit. **Document type:** trade publication.
Formerly (until 1993): Assistant Masters and Mistresses Association Report (ISSN 0142-3134); Which supersedes (in July 1978): A.M.A. (ISSN 0001-1819)
Description: Provides news and analysis of events in British (excluding Scottish) education.

371.33   HU
A - V KOMMUNIKACIO/A - V COMMUNICATIONS. 1964. bi-m. 420 Ft. Orszagos Muszaki Informacios Kozpont es Konyvtar (O.M.I.K.K.) - National Technical Information Centre and Library, Muzeum u. 17, PO Box 12, 1428 Budapest, Hungary. (Subscr. to: Kultura, PO Box 149, 1389 Budapest, Hungary) Ed. Ivan Arkos. adv.; bibl.; index. circ. 2,600.
Formerly: Audio-Vizualis Kozlemenyek - Audio-Visual Review (ISSN 0231-2379); Supersedes (in 1973): Audio-Vizual s Technikai es Modszertani Kozlemenyek (ISSN 0004-7600)

370   SW   ISSN 0065-0196
AARSBOK FOER SKOLAN. 1964. a. SEK 300 (effective 1994). Laerarfoerlaget, P.O. Box 12239, S-102 26 Stockholm, Sweden. TEL 46-8-737-65-00. FAX 46-8-619-00-88. Ed. Eva Olson. circ. 10,000. **Supersedes (1920-1953):** Folkskolans Aarsbok.

ABHANDLUNGEN ZUR PHILOSOPHIE, PSYCHOLOGIE UND PAEDAGOGIK. see PHILOSOPHY

EDUCATION

370 AT ISSN 0310-5822
ABORIGINAL CHILD AT SCHOOL. 1973. 5/yr. Aus.$24. University of Queensland, Department of Education, St. Lucia, Qld. 4067, Australia. FAX 07-365-7199. Ed. D.M. Muir. bk.rev. circ. 2,200. **Indexed:** Aus.Educ.Ind., Cont.Pg.Educ., Rural.Ext.Educ.& Tr.Abstr., Sp.Ed.Needs Abstr.
Description: National journal for the teachers of aboriginal learners, focuses on classroom teaching and curriculum development.

ACADEMIA; a monthly magazine of academic titles and information. see *PUBLISHING AND BOOK TRADE*

370 CL ISSN 0716-0526
F3099
ACADEMIA.* 1981. s-a. Esc.2000($25) Universidad Metropolitana de Ciencias de la Educacion, Av. Jose Pedro Alessandri 774, Nunoa, Santiago, Chile. Ed. Tomas P. MacHale. adv. circ. 1,500.

ACADEMIA. see *CHILDREN AND YOUTH — For*

370 US ISSN 0895-4852
AS30 CODEN: ACQUEO
ACADEMIC QUESTIONS. 1988. q. $40 to individuals (foreign $64); institutions $96 (foreign $120). Transaction Publishers, Transaction Periodicals Consortium, Department 3091, Rutgers University, New Brunswick, NJ 08903. TEL 908-932-2280. FAX 908-932-3138. Ed. Herbert I. London. adv.; bk.rev. circ. 4,500. (also avail. in microform from UMI) **Document type:** academic/scholarly publication. —UnCover; UMI. **CCC.**
Description: Explores interdisciplinary issues related to politics, ideology, and scholarship in academe.

ACCELERATOR. see *SCIENCES: COMPREHENSIVE WORKS*

370 US
ACCESS (NEW YORK, 1979); the information on global, international and foreign language education. 1979. 6/yr. $30 (Canada $36; foreign $51). American Forum for Global Education, 45 John St., Ste. 908, New York, NY 10038. TEL 212-732-8606. FAX 212-791-4132. Ed. Elizabeth Mahony. bk.rev.; bibl. circ. 2,000. (back issues avail.)
Description: Serves as an open forum for ideas and inquiries on global education; includes articles, resource reviews, job opportunities, program announcements, teaching aids and a calendar of events for all global educators.

ACCOUNTING EDUCATION NEWS. see *BUSINESS AND ECONOMICS — Accounting*

ACORN STORYTELLER. see *CHILDREN AND YOUTH — For*

ACTA COLLOQUII DIDACTICI CLASSICI; didactica classica gandensia. see *LINGUISTICS*

370 HU ISSN 0230-6476
ACTA PAEDAGOGICA DEBRECINA. (Text in Hungarian; summaries in German and Russian) 1962. irreg., vol.92, 1990. Kossuth Lajos Tudomanyegyetem, Nevelestudomanyi Tanszek, Egyetem Ter 1, 4010 Debrecen, Hungary. bibl.
—BLDSC (0642.330000).
Supersedes in part (in 1980): Neveles, Muvelodes. Acta Paedagogica Debrecina (ISSN 0324-6957); Which was formerly (until 1967): Acta Paedagogica Debrecina (ISSN 0567-7912); Which supersedes in part (in 1963): Acta Marxistica et Pedagogica Debrecina.

ACTA UNIVERSITATIS LODZIENSIS: FOLIA ARCHAEOLOGICA. see *ARCHAEOLOGY*

ACTA UNIVERSITATIS LODZIENSIS: FOLIA BIOCHIMICA ET BIOPHYSICA. see *BIOLOGY — Biological Chemistry*

ACTA UNIVERSITATIS LODZIENSIS: FOLIA BOTANICA. see *BIOLOGY — Botany*

ACTA UNIVERSITATIS LODZIENSIS: FOLIA CHIMICA. see *CHEMISTRY*

ACTA UNIVERSITATIS LODZIENSIS: FOLIA ETHNOLOGICA. see *ANTHROPOLOGY*

ACTA UNIVERSITATIS LODZIENSIS: FOLIA GEOGRAPHICA. see *GEOGRAPHY*

ACTA UNIVERSITATIS LODZIENSIS: FOLIA HISTORICA. see *HISTORY*

ACTA UNIVERSITATIS LODZIENSIS: FOLIA IURIDICA. see *LAW*

ACTA UNIVERSITATIS LODZIENSIS: FOLIA LIMNOLOGICA. see *EARTH SCIENCES — Hydrology*

ACTA UNIVERSITATIS LODZIENSIS: FOLIA LINGUISTICA. see *LINGUISTICS*

ACTA UNIVERSITATIS LODZIENSIS: FOLIA LITTERARIA. see *LITERATURE*

ACTA UNIVERSITATIS LODZIENSIS: FOLIA MATHEMATICA. see *MATHEMATICS*

ACTA UNIVERSITATIS LODZIENSIS: FOLIA OECONOMICA. see *BUSINESS AND ECONOMICS*

ACTA UNIVERSITATIS LODZIENSIS: FOLIA PAEDAGOGICA ET PSYCHOLOGICA. see *PSYCHOLOGY*

ACTA UNIVERSITATIS LODZIENSIS: FOLIA PHILOSOPHICA. see *PHILOSOPHY*

ACTA UNIVERSITATIS LODZIENSIS: FOLIA PHYSICA. see *PHYSICS*

ACTA UNIVERSITATIS LODZIENSIS: FOLIA SCIENTIAE ARTIUM ET LITTERARUM. see *HUMANITIES: COMPREHENSIVE WORKS*

ACTA UNIVERSITATIS LODZIENSIS: FOLIA SOCIOLOGICA. see *SOCIOLOGY*

ACTA UNIVERSITATIS LODZIENSIS: FOLIA ZOOLOGICA ET ANTHROPOLOGICA. see *BIOLOGY — Zoology*

301 PL ISSN 0208-5267
ACTA UNIVERSITATIS NICOLAI COPERNICI. SOCJOLOGIA WYCHOWANIA. (Text in Polish; summaries in English) 1976. irreg. price varies. Uniwersytet Mikolaja Kopernika, Biblioteka Uniwersytecka, Ul. Gagarina 13, 87-100 Torun, Poland. TEL 233-52. TELEX 552382. (Dist. by: Osrodek Rozpowszechniania Wydawnictw Naukowych PAN, Palac Kultury i Nauki, 00-901 Warsaw, Poland)
Formerly: Uniwersytet Mikolaja Kopernika, Torun. Nauki Humanistyczno-Spoleczne. Socjologia.

ACTA UNIVERSITATIS SZEGEDIENSIS DE ATTILA JOZSEF NOMINATAE. ACTA BIBLIOTHECARIA. see *LIBRARY AND INFORMATION SCIENCES*

ACTA UNIVERSITATIS SZEGEDIENSIS DE ATTILA JOZSEF NOMINATAE. SECTIO PAEDAGOGICA ET PSYCHOLOGICA. see *PSYCHOLOGY*

370 PL ISSN 0137-1096
LA843
ACTA UNIVERSITATIS WRATISLAVIENSIS. PRACE PEDAGOGICZNE. (Text in Polish; summaries in English or French or Russian) 1973. irreg. price varies. (Uniwersytet Wroclawski) Wydawnictwo Uniwersytetu Wroclawskiego, Pl. Uniwersytecki 9-13, 50-137 Wroclaw, Poland. (Dist. by: Ksiegarnia Uniwersytetu Wroclawskiego, Pl. Uniwersytecki 9-13, 50-137 Wroclaw, Poland) Ed.Bd. circ. 600. **Indexed:** Geo.Abstr., Rural Recreat.Tour.Abstr., World Agri.Econ.& Rural Sociol.Abstr. **Document type:** academic/scholarly publication.

370 US
ACTION (CLEARWATER). 1962. m. free. Pinellas Classroom Teachers Association, Inc., 650 Seminole Blvd., Largo, FL 34640-3625. TEL 813-585-6518. Ed. Jade T. Moore. adv.; bk.rev.; illus. circ. 5,600. (tabloid format)
Former titles: New Pinellas Teacher; Pinellas Teacher (ISSN 0031-9872)

378 US ISSN 0001-7442
ACTION LINE (BALTIMORE). 1968. w. $2. Maryland State Teachers Association, 344 N. Charles St., Baltimore, MD 21201-4374. TEL 301-727-7676. Ed. Dorothy D. Lloyd. adv.; charts; illus. circ. 34,000. (tabloid format)

370 UV
ACTION - REFLEXION - CULTURE. 1968. 8/yr. 6000 Fr.CFA($30) Ministere de l'Education Nationale, Institut Pedagogique de Burkina, B.P. 7043, Ouagadougou, Burkina Faso. bk.rev.; bibl. circ. 1,000.

370 FR ISSN 0065-177X
ACTION UNIVERSITAIRE. 1970; N.S. m. 40 F. Union Nationale Inter-Universitaire, 6, rue de Musset, 75016 Paris, France. TEL 45-25-34-65. Ed. Frederic Deloffre. bk.rev. circ. 45,000.
Description: Forum for students, teachers and personnel at the University.

371.26 US ISSN 0001-7620
ACTIVITY. 1960. q. free. American College Testing, 2201 N. Dodge St., Box 168, Iowa, IA 52243. TEL 319-337-1410. FAX 319-339-3020. circ. 105,000. (tabloid format; back issues avail.) **Indexed:** Curr.Cont.
Description: Covers education at all levels, career planning, and educational measurement research.

ACTU ECO; werkkrant voor het economie-onderwijs. see *BUSINESS AND ECONOMICS*

ACTUA PRESS (EDITION FRANCAISE). see *LINGUISTICS*

ACTUA PRESS (ENGLISH EDITION). see *LINGUISTICS*

ACTUA PRESS (NEDERLANDS EDITIE). see *LINGUISTICS*

ADOLESCENCE; an international quarterly devoted to the physiological, psychological, psychiatric, sociological, and educational aspects of the second decade of human life. see *CHILDREN AND YOUTH — About*

370 IE
ADULT EDUCATION COLLEGE: AN GRIANAN PROGRAMME. 1954. a. 70p. per issue. Irish Countrywomen's Association, An Grianan, Termonfechine, Co. Louth, Ireland. TEL 041-22119. circ. 5,000. **Document type:** newsletter.
Formerly: Irish Countrywomen's Association: An Grianan Programme.
Description: Outlines weekly courses for the year taught by the Irish Countrywomen's Association.

370 UK
ADULT EDUCATION PROGRAMME. 1965. a. Bradford and Ilkley Community College, Great Horton Rd., Bradford, W. Yorks. BD7 1AY, England. TEL 44-274-753089. FAX 44-274-753173. Ed. R.T. Sweeney. circ. 50,000.

372.21 US ISSN 0270-4021
HV854
ADVANCES IN EARLY EDUCATION AND DAY CARE; a research annual. 1980. a. $58.50 to institutions. J A I Press Inc., 55 Old Post Rd., No. 2, Box 1678, Greenwich, CT 06836-1678. TEL 203-661-7602. Ed. Sally J. Kilmer. **Indexed:** Psychol.Abstr. —BLDSC (0704.340000); Faxon. **CCC.**

370 II ISSN 0001-8694
ADVANCES IN EDUCATION. (Text in English) vol.5, 1970. a. Maharaja Sayajirao University of Baroda, Centre for Advanced Study in Education, Faculty of Education and Psychology, Baroda 390002, Gujarat, India. Ed. Dr. A.S. Patel. bk.rev.; bibl.

ADVANCES IN PHYSIOLOGY EDUCATION. see *BIOLOGY — Physiology*

370 US ISSN 0735-0171
ADVANCES IN READING - LANGUAGE RESEARCH. 1982. a. $58.50 to institutions. J A I Press Inc., 55 Old Post Rd., No. 2, Box 1678, Greenwich, CT 06836-1678. TEL 203-661-7602. FAX 203-661-0792. (Addr. in the U.K. and the rest of Europe: J A I Press Ltd., The Courtyard, Hampton Hill, Mddx. TW12 1PD, England. TEL 44-81-943-9296. FAX 44-81-943-9317) Ed. Barbara A. Hutson. **Indexed:** Psychol.Abstr. —Faxon. **CCC.**

ADVANCES IN TEST ANXIETY RESEARCH. see *PSYCHOLOGY*

370 331.8 US
THE ADVOCATE (PITTSBURGH). q. $5. Pennsylvania Federation of Teachers, 53 S. 10th St., Pittsburgh, PA 15203. TEL 412-431-5900. FAX 412-431-6882. Ed. John Tarka. adv.; bk.rev. circ. 43,000. **Document type:** newspaper.
Formerly (until 1992): Pennsylvania Teacher.

EDITION 2001

370 US ISSN 1053-3362
ADVOCATE (ST. PAUL). Key Title: Advocate - Minnesota Education Association. Variant title: M E A Advocate. 1979. 10/yr. $12 to non-members. Minnesota Education Association, 41 Sherburne Ave., St. Paul, MN 55103. TEL 612-227-9541. FAX 612-227-4868. Ed. Tom Nordby. adv.; bk.rev.; illus.; circ. 46,000 (controlled). (tabloid format) **Document type:** newspaper.
  Formerly (until 1990): M E A Advocate (ISSN 0889-2474)
  Description: Contains articles, opinion and photos covering K-12 and postsecondary education topics.

370 US
ADVOCATE'S VOICE. vol.9, 1979. 9/yr. $2. National Education Association of New Mexico, 130 S. Capitol, Santa Fe, NM 87504. TEL 505-982-1916. Ed. Steve Lemken. adv. circ. 8,500.
  Formerly: N E A - N M Advocate.

371.04 US ISSN 1067-9219
AERO-GRAMME. 1989. 3/yr. $15 (foreign $20). Jerry Mintz, Ed. & Pub., 417 Roslyn Rd., Roslyn Heights, NY 11577. TEL 516-621-2195. FAX 516-625-3257. bk.rev. circ. 5,000. (back issues avail.) **Document type:** newsletter.
  Description: Networking information for alternative educators, including homeschoolers.

AFFINITY. see HOMOSEXUALITY

370 374 KE ISSN 1016-8826
AFRICAN ASSOCIATION FOR LITERACY AND ADULT EDUCATION. JOURNAL. 1985. s-a. $10 per no. African Association for Literacy and Adult Education, P.O. Box 50768, Nairobi, Kenya. TEL 254-2-331512. FAX 254-2-340849. TELEX 23240 NAIROBI. **Indexed:** P.L.E.S.A (1988-).

AGAZEN. see CONSERVATION

370 US ISSN 1055-1247
LA217.2
AGENDA (NEW YORK, 1991); America's schools for the 21st century. 1991. 3/yr. $18. Scholastic Inc., 555 Broadway, New York, NY 10012-3999. TEL 212-343-6100. Ed. Eileen Garred. circ. 250,000 (controlled). **Document type:** trade publication.
  Description: Addresses educational reform issues at all levels of the American educational system.

370 US
AGENDA: JEWISH EDUCATION; a journal of public policy magazine. 1949. 2/yr. $12. Jewish Education Service of North America, Inc., 730 Broadway, 2nd Fl., New York, NY 10003-9540. TEL 212-529-2000. FAX 212-529-2009. Ed. Arthur Vernon. bk.rev.; bibl. circ. 2,000. **Indexed:** Ind.Jew.Per.
  Formerly (until 1992): Pedagogic Reporter (ISSN 0031-3793)

THE AGRICULTURAL EDUCATION MAGAZINE. see AGRICULTURE

AHAD. see POLITICAL SCIENCE

370 613.7 JA ISSN 0288-4712
AICHI KYOIKU DAIGAKU TAIIKU KYOSHITSU KENKYU KIYO/AICHI UNIVERSITY OF EDUCATION. BULLETIN OF THE PHYSICAL EDUCATION AND SPORT RESEARCH. (Text in English, Japanese; summaries in English) 1976. a. Aichi Kyoiku Daigaku, Taiiku Kyoshitsu - Aichi University of Education, Department of Physical Education, 1, Hirosawa, Igayacho, Kariya-shi, Aichi-ken 448, Japan.

AID FOR EDUCATION REPORT. see PUBLIC ADMINISTRATION

AIIKU TSUSHIN/LETTERS OF HUMAN GROWTH. see PSYCHOLOGY

AISTHESIS; revista chilena de investigaciones esteticas. see PHILOSOPHY

AKTUELNOSTI U VASPITANJU I OBRAZOVANJU. see EDUCATION — Teaching Methods And Curriculum

370 US ISSN 0002-435X
L11
ALABAMA SCHOOL JOURNAL.* 1921. bi-m. $7 to non-members. Alabama Education Association, Box 4177, Montgomery, AL 36103-4177. TEL 205-834-9790. Ed. Paul R. Hubbert. adv.; bk.rev.; charts; illus.; tr.lit.; index. circ. 47,000. (tabloid format)

ALBARREGAS. see HUMANITIES: COMPREHENSIVE WORKS

370 CN ISSN 0002-4805
LB1028 CODEN: AJEDAQ
ALBERTA JOURNAL OF EDUCATIONAL RESEARCH. 1955. q. Can.$32 to individuals; institutions Can.$40. University of Alberta, Publication Services, 4-116 Education North, Edmonton, AB T6G 2G5, Canada. TEL 403-492-4024. FAX 403-492-0390. Ed. Judy Cameron. adv.; bk.rev.; bibl.; charts; index. circ. 700. (back issues avail.) **Indexed:** C.I.J.E., Can.Educ.Ind., Can.Wom.Per.Ind., Cont.Pg.Educ., Curr.Cont., Educ.Admin.Abstr., Educ.Tech.Abstr., Lang.& Lang.Behav.Abstr., Mult.Ed.Abstr., Psychol.Abstr., Res.High.Educ.Abstr., Sociol.Educ.Abstr., SOMA, Sp.Ed.Needs Abstr., SSCI, Stud.Wom.Abstr.
  —BLDSC (0786.585000); Faxon; UnCover. **CCC.**

370 IS
ALEI CHINNUCH. 3/yr. IS.50 (effective 1994). United Kibbutz Federation, 10 Dubnov St., Tel Aviv, Israel. TEL 972-3-5452560. Ed. Shlomo Bahar. bk.rev. circ. 700. **Document type:** newsletter.
  Formerly (until 1993): Igeret Lechinuch (ISSN 0536-3535)

370 LY
AL-FATEH UNIVERSITY. FACULTY OF EDUCATION. BULLETIN. a. Al-Fateh University, Faculty of Education, P.O. Box 13040, Tripoli, Libya. TEL 36010. TELEX 20629. **Document type:** bulletin.

371 CN ISSN 0711-6829
L'ALLIANCE (MONTREAL). (Text in French) 1963. 6/yr. Alliance des Professeurs de Montreal, 8225 Blvd. Saint-Laurent, Montreal, Que. H2P 2M1, Canada. TEL 514-383-4880. FAX 514-384-5756. Ed. Pierre Dubuc. adv.; bk.rev.; illus. circ. 10,000. **Indexed:** CERDIC.

377.9 US ISSN 0002-6093
ALLIANCE REVIEW. vol.12, 1947. a. membership. American Friends of the Alliance Israelite Universelle Inc., 420 Lexington Ave., Ste. 1733, New York, NY 10170-0001. FAX 212-983-0094. Ed. Warren Green. bk.rev.; illus. circ. 5,000.
  Description: Highlights the activities and projects of the Alliance Israelite Universelle and its network of schools in Europe, the Middle East and Canada.

370 IS ISSN 0334-5076
ALON LAMORAH LESIFRUT. 1972. a. Atlas Ltd., 49 Chelnov St., Tel Aviv, Israel.

ALPHA - MATHEMATISCHE SCHUELERZEITSCHRIFT. see MATHEMATICS

370 PE
AMAUTA; revista de investigacion educacional. 1971. s-a. Universidad Nacional de Trujillo, Departamento Academico de Ciencias de la Educacion, Ciudad Universitaria, Apdo. 152, Trujillo, Peru. Ed. Yeconias Culquichicon Gomez.

AMERICAN ARTIST DIRECTORY OF ART SCHOOLS & WORKSHOPS. see ART

370 US ISSN 0002-8312
L11
AMERICAN EDUCATIONAL RESEARCH JOURNAL. 1964. q. $37 to individuals; institutions $46. American Educational Research Association, 1230 17th St., N.W., Washington, DC 20036-3078. TEL 202-223-9485. FAX 202-775-1824. Ed.Bd. adv.; bk.rev.; abstr.; bibl.; index. circ. 17,400. (also avail. in microform from UMI) **Indexed:** Adol.Ment.Hlth.Abstr., C.I.J.E., Commun.Abstr., Cont.Pg.Educ., Curr.Cont., Educ.Ind., Educ.Tech.Abstr., Except.Child.Educ.Abstr., Lang.& Lang.Behav.Abstr., Mid.East: Abstr.& ind., Mult.Ed.Abstr., Psychol.Abstr., Res.High.Educ.Abstr., SOMA, SSCI, Stud.Wom.Abstr. **Document type:** academic/scholarly publication.
  —BLDSC (0813.650000); Faxon; UnCover; SWETS; UMI.
  Description: Reports original research, both empirical and theoretical, and brief synopses of research.

371.1 331.8 US ISSN 0148-432X
L11
AMERICAN EDUCATOR. 1977. q. $8. American Federation of Teachers, 555 New Jersey Ave., N.W., Washington, DC 20001. TEL 202-879-4400. FAX 202-879-4534. Ed. Elizabeth McPike. adv.; bk.rev.; illus. circ. 600,000. (also avail. in microfilm; reprint service avail. from UMI) **Indexed:** Biog.Ind., C.I.J.E., Cont.Pg.Educ., Educ.Ind., Mag.Ind., PMR, R.G.
  —BLDSC (0813.670000); Faxon; UnCover; UMI.

AMERICAN FEDERATION OF TEACHERS. ACTION. see LABOR UNIONS

AMERICAN FORENSIC ASSOCIATION NEWSLETTER. see COMMUNICATIONS

370 914 US ISSN 0163-0040
AMERICAN HUNGARIAN EDUCATOR. 1978. 3/yr. $15 includes membership. American Hungarian Educators' Association, Box 4103, Silver Spring, MD 20904. TEL 301-384-4657. Ed. Ilena Lantos. bk.rev. circ. 250. (back issues avail.) **Document type:** newsletter.
  Description: News of publications, courses, programs and exchanges in Hungarian studies; includes articles on Hungarian studies.

AMERICAN INDIAN JOURNAL. see HISTORY — History Of North And South America

370 US ISSN 0195-6744
L11
AMERICAN JOURNAL OF EDUCATION. 1893. 4/yr. $25.50 to individuals; institutions $51; students $21. University of Chicago Press, Journals Division, 5720 S. Woodlawn Ave., Chicago, IL 60637. TEL 312-753-3347. FAX 312-753-0811. TELEX 25-4603. (Subsc. to: Box 37005, Chicago, IL 60637) Ed.Bd. adv.; bk.rev.; charts; illus.; stat.; index. circ. 2,500. (also avail. in microform from UMI,PMC; reprint service avail. from UMI,KTO) **Indexed:** Abstr.Pop.Cult., Bibl.Ind., C.I.J.E., Chic.Per.Ind., Cont.Pg.Educ., Curr.Cont., Educ.Admin.Abstr., Educ.Ind., Educ.Tech.Abstr., Lang.& Lang.Behav.Abstr., Mid.East: Abstr.& Ind., Mult.Ed.Abstr., Psychol.Abstr., Sociol.Abstr., Sp.Ed.Needs Abstr., SSCI. **Document type:** academic/scholarly publication.
  —BLDSC (0824.560000); Faxon; UnCover; SWETS; UMI. **CCC.**
  Formerly (until vol.88, Nov. 1979): School Review (ISSN 0036-6773)
  Refereed Serial

428.5 US ISSN 0895-3562
AMERICAN READING FORUM. YEARBOOK. 1981. a. $20. American Reading Forum, c/o Dept. of Elementary Education, Utah State University, Logan, UT 84322-2805. TEL 801-797-0399. Eds. Bernie Hayes, Kay Camperell. **Indexed:** C.I.J.E. **Document type:** academic/scholarly publication.

373 US ISSN 0003-1003
LA222
AMERICAN SECONDARY EDUCATION. 1970. q. $18. Ohio Association of Secondary School Administrators, c/o JoAnne Martin-Reynolds, Ed., Rm. 531 Education Bldg., Bowling Green State University, Bowling Green, OH 43403. TEL 419-372-7379. adv.; bk.rev. circ. 3,300. (also avail. in microform from UMI; reprint service avail. from UMI) **Indexed:** Cont.Pg.Educ., Educ.Ind. **Document type:** academic/scholarly publication.
  —BLDSC (0857.C27000); Faxon; UnCover; UMI.

EDUCATION

AMERICAN STRING TEACHER. see *MUSIC*

AMERICAN TEACHER. see *LABOR UNIONS*

371.8   IT   ISSN 0003-1720
AMICIZIA; rivista mensile per studenti esteri. 1964. m. L.10000($10) Ufficio Centrale Studenti Esteri in Italia, Via Monti Parioli 57-59, 00197 Rome, Italy. TEL 06-3104491. Dir. Nuccio Fava. bk.rev.; charts; illus.; index.
    Description: Includes articles on students studying in Italy, various exchange programs, and new numbers of students in Italy.

AMIGO. see *CHILDREN AND YOUTH — For*

AMISOL. see *CHILDREN AND YOUTH — For*

AMNESTY INTERNATIONAL AUSTRALIAN NEWSLETTER. see *POLITICAL SCIENCE — Civil Rights*

370   NE   ISSN 0926-5201
AMSTERDAM PAEDOLOGICAL CENTER. PUBLICATIONS. (Text in English) 1991. irreg. fl.34.50($26) Swets & Zeitlinger bv, Heereweg 347, 2161 CA Lisse, Netherlands. TEL 31-2521-35111. FAX 31-2521-15888. TELEX 41325. (Dist. in N. America by: Swets & Zeitlinger, 440 Creamery Way, Ste. A, Exton, PA 19341. TEL 800-447-9387. FAX 610-524-5366) **Document type:** monographic series.
    Refereed Serial

AMTLICHES MITTEILUNGSBLATT DER MARKTGEMEINDE LEOBERSDORF. see *PUBLIC ADMINISTRATION — Municipal Government*

370   GW   ISSN 0003-2190
AMTLICHES SCHULBLATT FUER DEN REGIERUNGSBEZIRK DUESSELDORF. 1909. m. DM.34.80. August Bagel Verlag, Grafenberger Allee 100, 40237 Duesseldorf, Germany. adv.

370   GW
ANALYSEN;* Zeitschrift zur Wissenschafts und Berufspraxis. 1971. m. DM.28. Aspekte Verlag GmbH, Xantener Str. 5, 1000 Berlin 15, Germany. adv.; bk.rev.; bibl.; charts; illus. circ. 100,000.

800 371.2 370   GW
ANDREANER; Schuelerzeitung am Gymnasium Andreanum. (Text in German, Latin; summaries in German) 1948. q. DM.5($4) Hagentorwall 17, 31134 Hildesheim, Germany. Ed.Bd. adv.; bk.rev.; bibl.; film rev.; illus.; stat.; index. circ. 1,500. (back issues avail.)

ANGEBOTE FUER SCHULEN, KINDER- UND JUGENDGRUPPEN FORTBILDUNGSANGEBOTE FUER PAEDAGOGEN. see *MUSEUMS AND ART GALLERIES*

ANGLISTIK UND ENGLISCHUNTERRICHT. see *HUMANITIES: COMPREHENSIVE WORKS*

375   CC   ISSN 1001-5116
ANHUI JIAOYU XUEYUAN XUEBAO (SHEHUI KEXUE BAN)/ANHUI INSTITUTE OF EDUCATION. JOURNAL (SOCIAL SCIENCE EDITION). (Text in Chinese) q. Y3.20. Anhui Jiaoyu Xueyuan - Anhui Institute of Education, 261 Jinzhai Lu, Hefei, Anhui 230061, People's Republic of China. TEL 254523.
    Description: Covers education and teaching theory for basic, higher, and adult education. Includes language and literature, history, and humanities teaching, and scientific research results.

ANIMAL KEEPERS' FORUM. see *BIOLOGY — Zoology*

370   FR   ISSN 0395-0840
ANIMATION ET EDUCATION. 1976. bi-m. 69 F. Office Central de la Cooperation a l'Ecole, 101 bis rue du Ranelagh, 75016 Paris, France. TEL 45-25-46-07. Ed. Gerard Gentil.

370   IT   ISSN 0392-2804
ANIMAZIONE ED ESPRESSIONE - TEMPO SERENO. 1976. bi-m. L.53000. Editrice La Scuola S.p.A., Via Cadorna 11, 25186 Brescia, Italy. TEL 030-29931. Ed. Remo Bernacchia.

370   PL   ISSN 0867-2040
ANNALES UNIVERSITATIS MARIAE CURIE-SKLODOWSKA. SECTIO J. PAEDAGOGIA - PSYCHOLOGIA. (Text and summaries in English or Polish) 1988. a. price varies. Uniwersytet Marii Curie-Sklodowskiej, Wydawnictwo, Pl. M. Curie-Sklodowskiej 5, 20-031 Lublin, Poland. TEL 48-81-375304. FAX 48-81-336699. TELEX 0643223. Ed. Stanislaw Popek. circ. 500. **Document type:** academic/scholarly publication.

ANNUAIRE DES COMMUNAUTES D'ENFANTS. see *CHILDREN AND YOUTH — About*

372   US
ANNUAL EDITIONS: EARLY CHILDHOOD EDUCATION. 1977. a. $11.95. Dushkin Publishing Group, Inc., Sluice Dock, Guilford, CT 06437-9989. TEL 203-453-4351. FAX 203-453-6000. Eds. Joyce Huth Munro, Karen Menke Paciorek; Pub. Lan Nielsen. illus. **Document type:** academic/scholarly publication.
    Refereed Serial

370   US   ISSN 0095-5787
LB41
ANNUAL EDITIONS: EDUCATION. 1973. a. $11.95. Dushkin Publishing Group, Inc., Sluice Dock, Guilford, CT 06437-9989. TEL 203-453-4351. FAX 203-453-6000. Ed. Fred Schultz; Pub. Lan Nielsen. illus. **Document type:** academic/scholarly publication.
    Formerly: Annual Editions: Readings in Education.
    Refereed Serial

ANNUAL EDITIONS: EDUCATIONAL PSYCHOLOGY. see *PSYCHOLOGY*

370   US   ISSN 0085-4077
LA337
ANNUAL EDUCATIONAL SUMMARY, NEW YORK STATE. 1904. a. free. Education Department, Instruction & Program Development, Education Bldg. Annex, Rm. 381, Albany, NY 12234. TEL 518-474-7082. FAX 518-474-4351. charts; stat.; circ. controlled. (processed; also avail. in microfiche from CIS; back issues avail.) **Indexed:** SRI. **Document type:** government publication.

370 600   CN
ANNUAL REVIEW OF GLOBAL EDUCATION. 1979. a. £8.50. International Institute for Global Education, Univ. of Toronto, Fac. of Education, 371 Bloor St. W., Ontario M5S 2R7, Canada. TEL 416-978-3223. Ed. David E. Selby. adv.; bk.rev. circ. 500. **Indexed:** Cont.Pg.Educ.
    Formerly: World Studies Journal (ISSN 0144-4298)

574.92   US   ISSN 0270-1480
GC1005.2
ANNUAL STUDENT SYMPOSIUM ON MARINE AFFAIRS. PROCEEDINGS. 1976. a. free to qualified personnel. Hawaiian Academy of Science, Box 11689, Honolulu, HI 96828. Ed. Jean A. Curtis. circ. 200. **Document type:** proceedings.

372   US   ISSN 0197-5129
LB1050
ANNUAL SUMMARY OF INVESTIGATIONS RELATING TO READING. a. International Reading Association, Inc., 800 Barksdale Rd., Box 8139, Newark, DE 19714-8139. TEL 302-731-1600. FAX 302-731-1057. TELEX 5106002813READING. (reprint service avail. from UMI) **Document type:** bibliography.
—BLDSC (8524.495000).

370 267   GW
ANTENNE AKTUELL. 1972. 4/yr. DM.14. Gemeinschaften Christlichen Lebens Jugendverbaende, Sterngasse 3, 86150 Augsburg, Germany. TEL 0821-5010127. FAX 0821-5010140. circ. 1,500. (back issues avail.) **Document type:** newsletter.
    Formerly: Antenne.

ANTHROPOLOGY & EDUCATION QUARTERLY. see *ANTHROPOLOGY*

370   US   ISSN 0895-7347
LB3051
APPLIED MEASUREMENT IN EDUCATION. 1988. q. $36 to individuals (foreign $61); institutions $170 (foreign $195). (Buros Institute of Mental Measurements) Lawrence Erlbaum Associates, Inc., 365 Broadway, Hillsdale, NJ 07642. TEL 201-666-4110. FAX 201-666-2394. Eds. Barbara S. Plake, James C. Impara. **Indexed:** Mult.Ed.Abstr., Sp.Ed.Needs Abstr.
—BLDSC (1574.300000); UnCover; SWETS.
    Description: Designed to improve measurement practice by enhancing the communication between academicians and educational measurement practitioners. Describes original research studies, innovative strategies and integrative reviews of current approaches.
    Refereed Serial

370 500 700   TI
ARAB LEAGUE EDUCATIONAL, SCIENTIFIC, AND CULTURAL ORGANIZATION. INFORMATION NEWSLETTER.* (Text in Arabic, English) 1972. 3/yr. exchange basis. Arab League Educational, Scientific, and Cultural Organization, Department of Documentation and Information, Boite Postale 1120, Tunis, Tunisia. Ed. Raouf Ali Hafez. bk.rev.; illus. (also avail. in microfiche)
    Formerly: A L E S C O Newsletter.

370   GW   ISSN 0066-569X
ARBEITEN ZUR PAEDAGOGIK. 1963. irreg., vol.27, 1991. price varies. Calwer Verlag, Scharnhauserstr.44, 70599 Stuttgart, Germany. TEL 0711-452019. FAX 0711-4560660. Eds. Otto Duerr, Helmut Frik. **Document type:** monographic series.

ARBITRATION IN THE SCHOOLS. see *BUSINESS AND ECONOMICS — Labor And Industrial Relations*

370 060   PL   ISSN 0066-6831
ARCHIWUM Z DZIEJOW OSWIATY. (Text in Polish) 1959. irreg., vol.10, 1981. price varies. Polska Akademia Nauk, Instytut Historii Nauki, Oswiaty i Techniki, Ul. Nowy Swiat 72, 00-330 Warsaw, Poland. (Dist. by: Ars Polona-Ruch, Krakowskie Przedmiescie 7, Warsaw, Poland) Ed. Kalina Bartnicka. circ. 1,000.

370   AG   ISSN 0066-7021
ARGENTINA. DEPARTAMENTO DE ESTADISTICA EDUCATIVA. BOLETIN INFORMATIVO.. 1965. a. free. Ministerio de Cultura y Educacion, Departamento de Estadistica Educativa, Avda. Eduardo Madero 235, 1 Piso, Buenos Aires, Argentina.

ARGOS; revue des B C D et C D I. see *LIBRARY AND INFORMATION SCIENCES*

ARGUMENTATION & ADVOCACY. see *COMMUNICATIONS*

379   US   ISSN 0095-5310
L120
ARIZONA. DEPARTMENT OF EDUCATION. SUPERINTENDENT OF PUBLIC INSTRUCTION. ANNUAL REPORT. Key Title: Annual Report of the Superintendent of Public Instruction. a. $5.69. Department of Education, Superintendent of Public Instruction, Central Distribution Center, 1535 W. Jefferson, Phoenix, AZ 85007. TEL 602-542-3088. FAX 602-542-3099. illus.; stat. (also avail. in microfiche from CIS) **Indexed:** SRI.

371.9   US
ARIZONA DEPARTMENT OF EDUCATION. MIGRANT CHILD EDUCATION. STATE PLAN. 1967. a. free. Department of Education, 1535 W. Jefferson, Phoenix, AZ 85007. TEL 602-542-5138. FAX 602-542-3013. Ed. Jane Hunt. illus.; stat. circ. 75. **Document type:** government publication.
    Formerly: Arizona State Plan for the Education of Migratory Children.

370   US   ISSN 0161-7753
ARKANSAS EDUCATOR. 1923. 10/yr. $4. Arkansas Education Association, 1500 W. Fourth St., Little Rock, AR 72201. TEL 501-375-4611. FAX 501-632-0624. Ed. Don Murphy, Jr. adv.; bk.rev.; charts; illus. circ. 18,293. (also avail. in microfilm from UMI; reprint service avail. from UMI) **Document type:** trade publication.
    Formerly (until 1975): Journal of Arkansas Education (ISSN 0021-9061)

ART & CRAFT; a magazine for all primary school teachers of art and craft. see *ARTS AND HANDICRAFTS*

707 370   US   ISSN 0004-3125
N81
ART EDUCATION. 1948. bi-m. $50 to non-members (includes N A E A News). National Art Education Association, 1916 Association Dr., Reston, VA 22091. TEL 703-860-8000. Ed. Ronald MacGregor. adv.; bk.rev.; illus. circ. 14,000. (also avail. in microform from UMI; reprint service avail. from UMI,KTO) **Indexed:** C.I.J.E., Cont.Pg.Educ., Educ.Ind., Yrbk.Assoc.Educ.& Rehab.Blind. **Document type:** academic/scholarly publication.
—BLDSC (1733.400000); Faxon; UnCover; SWETS; UMI.
    Incorporates (1970-1980): Art Teacher (ISSN 0163-3651)

370 700   CN   ISSN 0708-5354
ART EDUCATION. 1972. q. Can.$20 to non-members. (Saskatchewan Society for Education Through Art) Saskatchewan Teachers' Federation, Box 1108, Saskatoon, SK S7K 3N3, Canada. Ed. Grant McLaughlin. bk.rev. circ. 200.
    Formerly: Discovery Through Art (ISSN 0315-9027)

ARTLINK. see *ART*

ASIAN JOURNAL OF PSYCHOLOGY AND EDUCATION. see *PSYCHOLOGY*

370   DK   ISSN 0106-7478
ASKOV LAERLINGE. 1904. a. DKK 50. Askov Hoejskoles Elevforening, Maltvej 1, 6600 Vejen, Denmark. illus.

370   PR
ASOMA. vol.6, 1977. q.? membership. Asociacion de Maestros de Puerto Rico, Apdo. 1088, Hato Rey, PR 00919. Ed. Wanda Garcia. charts; illus. (tabloid format)
    Formerly: Vocero Informativo.

370   UK   ISSN 0066-8672
L16
ASPECTS OF EDUCATION. 1964. 2/yr. £6 per no. University of Hull, Institute of Education, Cottingham Rd., Hull HU6 7RX, England. TEL 0482-465406. FAX 0482-466205. TELEX 592592 KHMAIL G HULIB 375. Ed. V.A. McClelland. bk.rev. circ. 500. (back issues avail.) **Indexed:** Br.Educ.Ind., Cont.Pg.Educ., Curr.Cont., SSCI. **Document type:** academic/scholarly publication.
—BLDSC (1745.910000).
    Description: Covers social, political, economic, and cultural facets of education.

370   UK   ISSN 0969-594X
▼**ASSESSMENTS IN EDUCATION: PRINCIPLES, POLICY AND PRACTICE**. 1994. 3/yr. $54 to individuals; institutions $198 (effective 1994). Carfax Publishing Co., P.O. Box 25, Abingdon, Oxon. OX14 3UE, England. TEL 44-235-553355. FAX 44-235-553559. (N. American subscr. to: Carfax Publishing Co., Box 2025, Dunnellon, FL 34430-2025) Ed. Patricia Broadfoot. adv.; index. (also avail. in microfiche) **Document type:** academic/scholarly publication.

370 371.0025   BL   ISSN 0102-0471
ASSOCIACAO MINEIRA DE ACAO EDUCACIONAL. REVISTA. 1967. 8/yr. $14. Associacao Mineira de Acao Educacional, Av. Bernardo Monteiro 861, CEP 30.150, Belo Horizonte-MG, Brazil. circ. 12,000. (back issues avail.)
    Description: Covers all aspects of education in the state of Minas Gerais.

370   NE   ISSN 0165-0343
ASSOCIATIE MEMORIAAL. 1972. 4/yr. fl.24. (Stichting Nederlandse Associate voor Praktijkexamens) WoltersgroepGroningen b.v., Postbus 58, 9700 MB Groningen, Netherlands. TEL 31-50-226922. FAX 31-50-264866.

370   CN   ISSN 0004-5306
ASSOCIATION CANADIENNE D'EDUCATION. BULLETIN. (Text in French) 1965. 9/yr. Can.$15 (foreign $15). Association Canadienne d'Education - Canadian Education Association, 252 Bloor St. W., Ste. 8-200, Toronto, ON M5S 1V5, Canada. TEL 416-924-7721. FAX 416-924-3188. Ed. Daniel Fitzgerald. adv.; bk.rev.; illus. circ. 1,100. (back issues avail.) **Document type:** newsletter.
    Description: Covers education policies and initiatives, curriculum changes, developments, new publications, events and conventions.

370   US
ASSOCIATION CONTACT. fortn. Connecticut Education Association, Capitol Place, Ste. 500, 21 Oak St., Hartford, CT 06106-8001. TEL 203-525-5641. FAX 203-725-6323. Ed. Cheryl Yost.
    Formerly: Connecticut Education Association. News Bulletin.

370   CN   ISSN 0228-7730
ASSOCIATION DES COLLEGES PRIVES DU QUEBEC ANNUAIRE. 1968. a. free. Association des Colleges Prives du Quebec, 1940 Blvd. Henri-Bourassa est, Montreal, PQ H2B 1S2, Canada. TEL 514-381-8891. adv. circ. 3,000.
    Formerly: Association des Colleges du Quebec Annuaire.

370   CN
ASSOCIATION DES ENSEIGNANTES ET DES ENSEIGNANTS FRANCOPHONES DU NOUVEAU-BRUNSWICK. NOUVELLES. (Text in French) 1970. m. Presses de la Federation des Enseignants du Nouveau-Brunswick, C.P. 712, Fredericton, NB E3B 5B4, Canada. TEL 506-452-8921. FAX 506-453-9795. Ed. Nicole Dupere. circ. 4,800. **Document type:** newsletter.
    Formerly: Federation des Enseignants du Nouveau-Brunswick. Nouvelles (ISSN 0229-7558)

370   FR   ISSN 0765-9482
ASSOCIATION NATIONALE DES COMMUNAUTES EDUCATIVES. BULLETIN HEBDOMADAIRE D'INFORMATIONS. w. 190 F. Association Nationale des Communautes Educatives, 145 bd. de Magenta, 75010 Paris, France. TEL 48-78-13-30. FAX 42-85-56-14. circ. controlled.

370   FR   ISSN 0245-5668
ASSOCIATION NATIONALE DES COMMUNAUTES EDUCATIVES. BULLETIN MENSUEL D'INFORMATIONS. m. 270 F. Association Nationale des Communautes Educatives, 145 bd. de Magenta, 75010 Paris, France. TEL 44-63-51-15. FAX 42-85-56-14. circ. controlled.

ASSOCIATION OF AMERICAN LAW SCHOOLS. NEWSLETTER. see *LAW*

378   US   ISSN 0004-5659
L13.A6994
ASSOCIATION OF COLLEGE UNIONS - INTERNATIONAL. BULLETIN. 1933. 6/yr. $20 to non-members. Association of College Unions - International, 400 E. 7th St., Bloomington, IN 47405. TEL 812-332-8017. FAX 812-333-8050. Ed. Nancy Davis. bk.rev. charts; illus. circ. 4,500. (also avail. in microfiche) **Document type:** academic/scholarly publication.
    Description: Articles for college union and student activities personnel dealing with program, operations, and student development.

378   US   ISSN 0004-5667
ASSOCIATION OF COLLEGE UNIONS - INTERNATIONAL. UNION WIRE. 1969. m. membership. Association of College Unions - International, 400 E. 7th St., Bloomington, IN 47405. TEL 812-332-8017. FAX 812-333-8050. Ed. Richard D. Blackburn. bk.rev. circ. 1,800. **Document type:** newsletter.
    Description: Lists building projects, conferences and new members.

370 500   FR   ISSN 0297-9373
ASTER; recherches en Didactique des Sciences Experimentales. 2/yr. 165 F. (foreign 190 F.). Institut National de Recherche Pedagogique, 29 rue d'Ulm, 75230 Paris Cedex 05, France. TEL 46-34-90-00.

ASTRONOMIE IN DER SCHULE. see *ASTRONOMY*

373   BE   ISSN 0004-6590
L'ATHENEE. (Text mainly in French; occasionally in Dutch, English, German) 1912. 3/m. (Sept.-June). 950 BEF. Federation de l'Enseignement Moyen Officiel du Degre Superieur de Belgique (FEMO), Place des Deportes 9, B-4000 Liege, Belgium. TEL 041-52-02-38. Ed. Jeanne Muyters. adv.; bk.rev.; bibl. circ. 700. **Indexed:** M.L.A.

373   GR
ATHENS COLLEGE BULLETIN. 1959. 3/yr. free. Athens College, P.O. Box 65005, 154 10 Psyhico, Athens, Greece. Ed. Dimitris Karamanos. bk.rev.; illus. circ. 10,000. **Document type:** bulletin.

370   IO
ATMA JAYA RESEARCH CENTRE. EDUCATION DEVELOPMENT RESEARCH REPORT/PUSAT PENELITIAN ATMA JAYA. STUDI TENTANG PENGEMBANGAN PENDIDIKAN. 1980. irreg. Atma Jaya Research Centre - Pusat Penelitian Atma Jaya, Jalan Jenderal Sudirman 51, P.O. Box 2639-JKT, Jakarta 10001, Indonesia. **Document type:** monographic series.

370   CN
AU FIL DES EVENEMENTS. (Text in French) 1965. w. free. Universite Laval, Communication Department, Quebec, PQ G1K 7P4, Canada. TEL 418-656-2571. FAX 418-656-2809. TELEX 051-31621 UNILAVAL QBC. Ed. Jean-Euces Landry. adv.; B&W page Can.$1000; trim 10 1/2 x 14 1/4. bk.rev. circ. 20,000. (tabloid format; also avail. in microform)

370 001.3 500   SP   ISSN 0214-3402
AULA. 1985. a. 1000 ptas. Ediciones Universidad de Salamanca, Apdo. 325, 37080 Salamanca, Spain. TEL 923-26-14-54. Dir. Pilar de la Puente Samaniego. **Document type:** academic/scholarly publication.
    Description: Contains studies on pedagogy, humanities and science.

370   PE
AULA ABIERTA. 1976. irreg. Instituto Nacional de Investigacion y Desarrollo de la Educacion, Centro Nacional de Documentacion e Informacion Educacional, Van de Velde 160, San Borja, Lima 100, Peru. bibl.; charts; illus.

370   CL   ISSN 0716-9299
AULA XXI. irreg.? Universidad Metropolitana de Ciencias de la Educacion, Av. Jose Pedro Alessandri 774, Nunoa, Santiago, Chile.

370   AT   ISSN 1032-4623
AUSTRALIA. DEPARTMENT OF EMPLOYMENT, EDUCATION AND TRAINING. ANNUAL REPORT. 1988. a. price varies. Australian Government Publishing Service, G.P.O. Box 84, Canberra, A.C.T. 2601, Australia. TEL 61-6-295-4612. FAX 61-6-295-4500. **Document type:** government publication.
    Formed by the merger of (1968-1987): Australia. Commonwealth Department of Education. Annual Report (ISSN 1030-8229); **(1982-1987):** Australia. Department of Employment and Industry Relations. Annual Report (ISSN 0729-1213)

370   AT   ISSN 1039-4001
AUSTRALIAN AND NEW ZEALAND JOURNAL OF VOCATIONAL EDUCATION RESEARCH. 1985. s-a. Aus.$25 per no. National Centre for Vocational Education Research Ltd., 252 Kensington Rd., Leabrook, S.A. 5068, Australia. TEL 08-332-7822. FAX 08-332-3988. Ed. Dr. W.C. Hall. bk.rev.; abstr. circ. 300. **Document type:** academic/scholarly publication.
—BLDSC (1796.920000).
    Formerly (until May 1993): Australian Journal of T A F E Research and Development (ISSN 0816-2018)
    Description: Provides articles based on vocational education and training research and development activities in Australia and New Zealand.

AUSTRALIAN ART EDUCATION. see *ART*

EDUCATION

370   AT   ISSN 0813-3085
AUSTRALIAN COLLEGE OF EDUCATION. NEW SOUTH WALES CHAPTER NEWSLETTER. no.86-1, 1986. q. Aus.$10 to non-members. Australian College of Education, New South Wales Chapter, 54 Hawthorne Ave., Chatswood, N.S.W. 2067, Australia. TEL 02-419-4466. FAX 02-411-5483. Ed. P. Evans. adv.; bk.rev. circ. 1,800. (back issues avail.)
Description: Features Chapter activities, and broad coverage of educational issues in all sectors of education.

370   AT
AUSTRALIAN COUNCIL FOR EDUCATIONAL RESEARCH. ANNUAL REPORT. a. Australian Council for Educational Research, Private Bag 55, Camberwell, Vic. 3124, Australia. TEL 03-277-5555. FAX 03-277-5500. *Document type:* corporate report.
Description: Financial, divisional reports with administrative organization and staff list.

370   AT
AUSTRALIAN COUNCIL FOR EDUCATIONAL RESEARCH. RESEARCH MONOGRAPH. irreg. Australian Council for Educational Research, Private Bag 55, Camberwell, Vic. 3124, Australia. TEL 03-277-5555. FAX 03-277-5500. Ed. Graeme Withers. *Document type:* monographic series.
Formerly: Australian Council for Educational Research. Research Series.
Description: Monograph series consisting of individual titles covering the research activities of the Australian Council for Educational Research and some work of non-ACER authors.

372.21   AT
AUSTRALIAN EARLY CHILDHOOD ASSOCIATION. VICTORIAN BRANCH. JOURNAL. 1960. q. Aus.$20. Australian Early Childhood Association, Victorian Branch, Private Bag 10, Kew, Vic. 3101, Australia. FAX 03-854-3348. Ed. Lee Tregloan. adv.; bk.rev. circ. 250. *Indexed:* Aus.Educ.Ind.
Former titles: Australian Early Childhood Association. Victorian Branch. Newsletter; Australian Pre-School Association. Victoria Branch. Newsletter.

370   AT   ISSN 0311-6875
AUSTRALIAN EDUCATION REVIEW. irreg. Australian Council for Educational Research, Private Bag 55, Camberwell, Vic. 3124, Australia. TEL 03-277-5555. FAX 03-277-5500. Ed. L. Splitter. stat. circ. 400. *Indexed:* Aus.Educ.Ind.
—BLDSC (1798.720000). **CCC.**
Formerly: Quarterly Review of Australian Education. (ISSN 0033-5762)
Description: Devoted to topics on educational interest.

370   AT   ISSN 0311-6999
AUSTRALIAN EDUCATIONAL RESEARCHER. 1974. 3/yr. Aus.$65. Australian Association for Research in Education, Department of Administrative and Higher Education Studies, University of New England, Armidale, N.S.W. 2351, Australia. FAX 067-733363. TELEX 166050. (Subscr. to: Mr. P. Jeffrey, c/o Australian Council for Educational Research, Box 210, Hawthorn, Vic. 3122, Australia) Ed. V. Lynn Meek. adv.; bk.rev. circ. 600. *Indexed:* Aus.Educ.Ind., Cont.Pg.Educ. *Document type:* academic/scholarly publication.
—BLDSC (1798.740000).
Formerly: A.A.R.E. Newsletter.

331.8   AT
AUSTRALIAN EDUCATOR. 1982. q. Aus.$16. Australian Education Union, 220 Clavendon St., E. Melbourne, Vic. 3002, Australia. FAX 03-416-2651. Ed.Bd. adv.; bk.rev. circ. 120,000. *Indexed:* Aus.Educ.Ind., Cont.Pg.Educ.
Formerly: Australian Teacher (ISSN 0728-8387)
Description: Educational, industrial and other news, analysis and resource information for teachers.

372.21 372   AT   ISSN 0312-5033
AUSTRALIAN JOURNAL OF EARLY CHILDHOOD. 1976. q. Aus.$39 (effective 1993). Australian Early Childhood Association, P.O. Box 105, Knox St., Watson, A.C.T. 2602, Australia. TEL 06-2-416900. FAX 06-2-425547. Ed. Jim Clough. adv.; bk.rev.; abstr.; bibl.; charts; illus.; stat.; index. circ. 2,500. (also avail. in microfilm from UMI; back issues avail.) *Indexed:* Aus.Educ.Ind., C.I.J.E., Mult.Ed.Abstr., Sp.Ed.Needs Abstr. *Document type:* academic/scholarly publication.
—BLDSC (1807.550000); UnCover; UMI.
Description: Forum for the discussion of new and controversial ideas in the field of early childhood.

370   AT   ISSN 0004-9441
L91
AUSTRALIAN JOURNAL OF EDUCATION. 1957. 3/yr. Aus.$65 (foreign Aus.$79). Australian Council for Educational Research, Private Bag 55, Camberwell, Vic. 3124, Australia. TEL 03-277-5555. FAX 03-277-5500. Ed. Richard Smith. bk.rev.; abstr.; index. circ. 1,000. *Indexed:* Adol.Ment.Hlth.Abstr., Aus.Educ.Ind., Aus.P.A.I.S., C.I.J.E., Cont.Pg.Educ., Curr.Cont., Educ.Tech.Abstr., Lang.& Lang.Behav.Abstr., Mult.Ed.Abstr., Psychol.Abstr., Res.High.Educ.Abstr., SOMA, Sp.Ed.Needs Abstr., SSCI, Stud.Wom.Abstr.
—BLDSC (1807.600000); Faxon; UnCover; SWETS; UMI. **CCC.**
Description: Papers on theory and practice of education.

370   AT   ISSN 1034-7992
AUSTRALIAN RESEARCH COUNCIL AWARDS. 1979. a. price varies. Australian Government Publishing Service, G.P.O. Box 84, Canberra, A.C.T. 2601, Australia. TEL 61-6-295-4612. FAX 61-6-295-4500. stat. (back issues avail.) *Document type:* government publication.
Formerly (until 1989): Australian Research Grants Scheme. Marine Sciences and Technologies Grants Scheme. National Research Fellowships Scheme. Queen Elizabeth II Fellowship (ISSN 1034-9022); Which was formed by the 1987 merger of: Australian Research Grants Scheme. Report on Grants Approved for ... (ISSN 0812-9509); Report on Marine Sciences and Technologies Grants for ... Grants Approved and Fellowships Awarded (ISSN 0817-3818); Report on Fellowships Awarded for ... (ISSN 0815-3183)

370   AT   ISSN 0819-3053
AUSTRALIAN STUDY OPPORTUNITIES. (Text mainly in English, one section in Chinese, French, Indonesian, Japanese, Korean, Thai) 1985. a. Aus.$19.95. (International Development Program) New Hobsons Press Pty. Ltd., 553 Elizabeth St., Surry Hills, N.S.W. 2010, Australia. TEL 02-310-2257. FAX 02-310-2243. Ed. Catherine Etteridge. adv. contact: Colin Ritchie. circ. 25,000. *Document type:* directory.
Description: Lists accredited courses for international students studying in Australia, including secondary school, TAFE and university courses. Also contains articles on the further education system, admission and visa requirements.

AUSTRALIAN TEACHER OF THE DEAF. see *HANDICAPPED — Hearing Impaired*

370   AT   ISSN 1037-3292
AUSTRALIAN TRAINING REVIEW. 1991. s-a. Aus.$28 for 4 nos. National Centre for Vocational Education Research, 252 Kensington Rd., Leabrook, S.A. 5068, Australia. TEL 08-332-7822. FAX 08-332-3988. Ed. Carol Cheshire. *Document type:* bulletin.
Description: Contains articles and information on industry case studies, policy plans, training techniques and materials, conferences in Australia and overseas.

AVIMO INFO. see *RELIGIONS AND THEOLOGY*

370   NR
AWORERIN. m.? Ministry of Education, General Publishing Section, Ibada, Nigeria. circ. 125,000.

370   US
B C E A REPORTER. q. membership. Bergen County Education Association, 210 W. Englewood Ave., Teaneck, NJ 07666. TEL 201-833-9166. Eds. Cherylin J. Roeser, Carol S. Pierce.

371   CN   ISSN 0005-2957
B.C. TEACHER. 1921. 8/yr. B.C. Teachers' Federation, 2235 Burrard St., Vancouver, B.C. V6J 3H9, Canada. TEL 604-731-8121. Ed. Nancy Hinds. adv.; bk.rev.; charts; illus.; index. circ. 41,000. *Indexed:* Can.Educ.Ind., CMI.

B D GUIDE. (Band Director) see *MUSIC*

370   GW   ISSN 0171-8495
B L L V BAYERISCHE SCHULE. Key Title: Bayerische Schule. 1947. 11/yr. DM.15. (Bayerischer Lehrer und Lehrerinnen Verband) B L L V, Bavariaring 37, 80336 Munich, Germany. adv.; bk.rev. circ. 46,500. *Document type:* bulletin.

BABEL. see *EDUCATION — Teaching Methods And Curriculum*

370   BF
BAHAMAS. MINISTRY OF EDUCATION AND CULTURE. ANNUAL REPORT. a. Ministry of Education and Culture, N 7147, Nassau, Bahamas. illus.

370 895.1   CC   ISSN 1001-4039
BAIJIA ZUOWEN ZHIDAO. (Text in Chinese) bi-m. Daqing Shi Jiaoyu Xueyuan - Daqing Institute of Education, Zhongyang Dajie, Daqing, Heilongjiang 163712, People's Republic of China. TEL 55462. Ed. Yang Puqing.
Description: Provides guidance on how to write a Chinese composition.

650.07 371.3   US   ISSN 0005-4232
HF1101
BALANCE SHEET. 1919. bi-m. free to qualified teachers. South-Western Publishing Co., 5101 Madison Rd., Cincinnati, OH 45227. TEL 513-271-8811. FAX 513-527-6973. Ed. Robert E. Lewis. adv.; bibl.; charts; stat.; index. circ. 151,000. (also avail. in microform from UMI) *Indexed:* AAR, Bus.Educ.Ind., C.I.J.E., Educ.Ind., Ind.Free Per.
—Faxon; UnCover.

370   US
BALDWIN LECTURES. 1957. a. $1.50. Northeast Missouri State University, Office of the President, Kirksville, MO 63501. TEL 816-785-4000. circ. 200.
Formerly: Baldwin Lectures in Teacher Education (ISSN 0067-303X)

370 340   US   ISSN 1055-0100
BALDWIN'S OHIO SCHOOL LAW JOURNAL. 1975. bi-m. $135. Banks - Baldwin Law Publishing Co., University Center, Box 1974, Cleveland, OH 44106. TEL 216-721-7373. FAX 216-721-8055. Ed. Mary A. Lentz.
Formerly: Baldwin's Ohio School Service.
Description: Original commentary on school district liability, education reform, handicapped education, property taxes, and labor disputes. Reports on State Board of Education administrative rule changes and key state and federal judicial and legislative developments.

371   US
BALTIMORE CITY PUBLIC SCHOOLS STAFF NEWSLETTER.* 1948. s-m. free. Baltimore City Public Schools, Division of Publications and Public Information, 200 E. North Ave, Baltimore, MD 21202. TEL 301-396-8700. Eds. John A. Robbins, Jr., Sandra P. Jubilee. circ. 16,500. *Indexed:* Educ.Ind. *Document type:* newsletter.
Formerly: Baltimore City Public Schools Staff Newsletter and Community Newsletter (ISSN 0005-4488)

370   SW   ISSN 0005-6006
BARN I HEM-SKOLA-SAMHAELLE. 1947. 8/yr. SEK 190. (Riksfoerbundet Hem och Skola (RHS)) Carlstedt Foerlag, Artillerigatan 2, S-114 51 Stockholm, Sweden. Ed. Jan Erik Carlstedt. adv. circ. 50,000. (also avail. in audio cassette)

BARN OCH KULTUR/CHILDREN AND CULTURE. see *LIBRARY AND INFORMATION SCIENCES*

370   US   ISSN 0196-4984
L13
BASIC EDUCATION. 1956. 10/yr. (Sep.-Jun.). $25. Council for Basic Education, 1319 F St., N.W., Ste. 900, Washington, DC 20004-1106. TEL 202-347-4171. Ed. Patle Barth. bk.rev.; charts; stat. circ. 6,000. *Indexed:* Cont.Pg.Educ.
Formerly: C B E Bulletin (ISSN 0007-7933)

379   GW   ISSN 0931-4059
BAYERISCHEN STAATSMINISTERIEN FUER UNTERRICHT UND KULTUS UND WISSENSCHAFT UND KUNST. AMTSBLATT. TEIL 1. 1865. irreg. DM.120. Verlagsgruppe Jehle - Rehm, Einsteinstr. 172, 81675 Munich, Germany. TEL 089-416006-0. FAX 089-4706998. Ed.Bd. index. circ. 7,600. (tabloid format) *Document type:* academic/scholarly publication.
Former titles (until 1986): Bayerisches Staatsministerium fuer Unterricht und Kultus. Amtsblatt. Teil 1 (ISSN 0722-5105); Supersedes in part (in 1974): Bayerisches Staatsministerium fuer Unterricht und Kultus. Amtsblatt (ISSN 0005-7207)

379 GW ISSN 0931-4075
BAYERISCHEN STAATSMINISTERIEN FUER UNTERRICHT UND KULTUS UND WISSENSCHAFT UND KUNST. AMTSBLATT. TEIL 2. 1974. irreg. DM.115. Verlagsgruppe Jehle - Rehm, Einsteinstr. 172, 81675 Munich, Germany. TEL 089-416006-0. FAX 089-4706998. **Document type:** academic/scholarly publication.
Formerly (until 1986): Bayerisches Staatsministerium fuer Unterricht und Kultus. Amtsblatt. Teil 2 (ISSN 0722-5113); Supersedes in part (in 1974): Bayerisches Staatsministerium fuer Unterricht und Kultus. Amtsblatt (ISSN 0005-7207)

407 370 US
BEACON (GEORGIA). 1966. 2/yr. $15 membership. Georgia Southern University, Department of Foreign Languages, Statesboro, GA 30460. TEL 912-681-5278. (Co-sponsor: Foreign Language Association of Georgia) Ed. Judy Schomber. adv.; bk.rev.; bibl.; circ. 1,000 (controlled).
Formerly: Foreign Language Beacon (ISSN 0015-7198)
Description: Presents language study and teaching methods.

370 CC ISSN 1000-7997
BEIJING JIAOYU/BEIJING EDUCATION. (Text in Chinese) m. Y18. (Beijing Jiaoyu-ju - Beijing Education Bureau) Beijing Jiaoyu Zazhishe - Beijing Education Magazine Office, 201 Qianmen Dajie, Beijing 100600, People's Republic of China. TEL 3015815. Ed. Niu Chensheng. adv.: B&W page Y1000, color page Y1200.

BEIKOKU TOKKYO SHOROKU. SOKUTEI, SEIMITSU KIKI, INSATSU, ONKYO, KYOIKU HEN/U.S. PATENT ABSTRACTS. MEASURING, PRECISION INSTRUMENT, PRINTING, SOUND RECORDING, EDUCATION. see *PATENTS, TRADEMARKS AND COPYRIGHTS — Abstracting, Bibliographies, Statistics*

370 BE
BELGIUM. MINISTERE DE L'EDUCATION NATIONALE. RAPPORT ANNUEL. a. Ministere de l'Education Nationale, Cite Administrative de l'Etat, Bd. Pacheco, 1010 Brussels, Belgium.
Formerly: Belgium. Ministere de l'Education Nationale et de la Culture Francaise. Rapport Annuel (ISSN 0067-5598)

370 BE
BELGIUM. MINISTERE DE L'EDUCATION NATIONALE. REVUE. 10/yr. 150 Fr. Ministere de l'Education Nationale, Administrative de l'Etat, Bd. Pacheco, 1010 Brussels, Belgium. (Subscr. to: 123 rue Royale, 1000 Brussels, Belgium)
Former titles: Belgium. Ministere de l'Education Nationale et de la Culture Francaise. Revue & Belgium. Ministere de l'Education Nationale et de la Culture Francaise. Bulletin d'Information (ISSN 0026-5284)

370 AU ISSN 0005-9471
BERUF UND GESINNUNG. 1946. m. (except July & Aug.). membership. Lehrerbund der O V P Steiermark, Keplerstr. 92, A-8020 Graz, Austria. Ed. Hermann Thueringer. adv.; bk.rev.; illus.; index. circ. 4,000.

BERUFSAUSBILDUNG JUGENDARBEITSLOSIGKEIT. see *SOCIAL SERVICES AND WELFARE*

370 SZ ISSN 0005-9501
BERUFSBERATUNG UND BERUFSBILDUNG/ORIENTATION ET FORMATION PROFESSIONNELLES. (Text in French, German; summaries in French) 1915. bi-m. 45 SFr. (foreign 60 SFr.). Schweizerischer Verband fuer Berufsberatung - Association Suisse pour l'Orientation Scolaire et Professionnelle, Zuerichstr. 98, CH-8600 Duebendorf, Switzerland. TEL 01-8220022. FAX 01-8221488. adv.: B&W page 600 SFr.; trim 126 x 200. bk.rev.; film rev.; bibl.; charts; illus.; stat.; index. **Document type:** academic/scholarly publication.

373.246 GW ISSN 0005-9536
BERUFSBILDUNG; Zeitschrift fuer Theorie und Praxis der beruflichen Bildung und Erziehung. 1946. m. DM.44. Erhard Friedrich Verlag GmbH, Im Brande 15, 30936 Seelze, Germany. TEL 0511-40004-0. FAX 0511-40004-19. (Subscr. to: Postfach 100150, 30917 Seelze, Germany) Ed. Wolfgang Heyn. adv.; bk.rev.; abstr.; bibl.; charts; illus.; stat. **Indexed:** Int.Lab.Doc.
—BLDSC (1941.470000); SWETS.

370 US
BEYOND Z. 1990. 6/yr. $35 includes membership. Citizens Education Center, 310 First Ave. S., Ste. 330, Seattle, WA 98104-2536. TEL 206-624-9955. circ. 10,000. (back issues avail.)
Description: Discusses issues surrounding restructuring public education.

BIBLIOGRAPHIE PAEDAGOGIK. REIHE A: ZEITSCHRIFTENAUFSAETZE. see *BIBLIOGRAPHIES*

BIBLIOGRAPHIE PAEDAGOGIK. REIHE B: BUECHER - SONDERSAMMELGEBIET BILDUNGSFORSCHUNG IN ERLANGEN. see *BIBLIOGRAPHIES*

370 BL
BIBLIOTECA DE EDUCACAO. 1982. irreg., vol.2, 1982. Edicoes Graal Ltda., Rua Hermenegildo de Barros, 31-A, Gloria 20240, Rio de Janeiro, Brazil.

BIBLIOTHEQUE DE TRAVAIL. see *CHILDREN AND YOUTH — For*

372 027.625 FR ISSN 0005-3120
BIBLIOTHEQUE DE TRAVAIL JUNIOR. Short title: B T J. 1965. 15/yr. 239 F. Ecole Moderne Francaise-Pedagogie Freinet, B.P. 109, 06322 Cannes - La Bocca Cedex, France.

373 027.626 FR ISSN 0005-3414
BIBLIOTHEQUE DE TRAVAIL 2D DEGRE. Short title: B T 2. 1968. 12/yr. 243 F. Ecole Moderne Francaise-Pedagogie Freinet, B.P. 109, 06322 Cannes - La Bocca Cedex, France.

372 UK ISSN 0954-9803
THE BIG PAPER; exploring design and technology across the primary school curriculum. 1987. 6/yr. £10($24) Design Council, 28 Haymarket, London SW1Y 4SU, England. TEL 071-839-8000. (Subscr. to: The Big Paper, Subscr., P.O. Box 167, Sittingbone, Kent ME10 1BR, England) Ed. Laurie Johnston. adv. contact: Steve Welch. bk.rev.
Description: Covers the use of the arts and design in primary education.

370 CC ISSN 1003-7667
BIJIAO JIAOYU. (Text in Chinese) bi-m. Y11. Beijing Shifan Daxue - Beijing Normal University, Xinjiekouwai, Beijing 100875, People's Republic of China. TEL 2011144. Ed. Gu Mingyuan. **Document type:** academic/scholarly publication.
Formerly: Waiguo Jiaoyu Dongtai.

370 GW ISSN 0172-0147
BILDUNG KONKRET. 1970. m. membership. Deutscher Lehrerverband, Nordstr. 53, 53111 Bonn, Germany. Ed. Ernst Kiel. adv.; bk.rev. circ. 100,000.

370 GW ISSN 0006-2456
BILDUNG UND ERZIEHUNG. 1948. q. DM.98. Boehlau Verlag GmbH, Theodor-Heuss-Str. 76, 51149 Cologne, Germany. TEL 02203-307021. FAX 02203-307349. Ed.Bd. adv.; bk.rev. circ. 1,000. **Document type:** academic/scholarly publication.
—SWETS. CCC.

370 GW ISSN 0172-0171
BILDUNG UND WISSENSCHAFT (BONN). English edition: Education and Science (ISSN 0177-4212) (Editions in Arabic, English, German, French, Russian and Spanish) 1965. m. (q. Arabic and Russian eds.). free. Inter Nationes e.V., Kennedyallee 91-103, 53175 Bonn, Germany. TEL 0228-880-0. FAX 0228-880457. TELEX 17228308. Ed. Ivan Tapia. bk.rev.; index. circ. 3,000. (reprint service avail. from UMI) **Indexed:** ERIC. **Document type:** academic/scholarly publication.
Formerly: Education in Germany.
Description: Articles on German educational developments and policies of the German government. Focus on higher education, grade schools, vocational education.

370 GW ISSN 0944-937X
BILDUNG UND WISSENSCHAFT (LUDWIGSBURG). Short title: B & W. m. DM.66. (G E W Baden-Wuerttemberg) Sueddeutscher Paedagogischer Verlag GmbH, Sudetenstr. 32, 71638 Ludwigsburg, Germany. TEL 07141-879080. FAX 07141-875105. circ. 33,500. (back issues avail.) **Document type:** academic/scholarly publication.
Formerly: Lehrerzeitung Baden-Wuerttemberg (ISSN 0170-4605)

370 SZ ISSN 0252-9955
BILDUNGSFORSCHUNG UND BILDUNGSPRAXIS/EDUCATION ET RECHERCHE. 3/yr. 53 SFr. (foreign 60 SFr.). Universitaetsverlag Freiburg, Perolles 42, CH-1700 Freiburg, Switzerland. Ed.Bd. **Document type:** academic/scholarly publication.
—BLDSC (2059.730000).

BILINGUAL REVIEW/REVISTA BILINGUE. see *LINGUISTICS*

BILL OF RIGHTS IN ACTION. see *LAW — Constitutional Law*

370 500 XR ISSN 1210-3349
BIOLOGIE, CHEMIE, ZEMEPIS. (Text in Czech, Slovak; summaries German, Russian) 1949. 5/yr. 60 Kcs.($22.90) (Ministerstvo Skolstvi, Mladezy a Telovychovy Ceske Republiky) Statni Pedagogicke Nakladatelstvi, Ostrovni 30, 113 01 Prague 1, Czech Republic. TEL 42-2-203850. FAX 42-2-293883 Ed. Hana Fricova. circ. 6,500. **Document type:** academic/scholarly publication.
Formerly (until 1991): Prirodni Vedy ve Skole (ISSN 0231-5130)

BIOPSYCHE; rivista di scienze antropologiche. see *PSYCHOLOGY*

BIOTECHNOLOGY EDUCATION. see *BIOLOGY — Biotechnology*

370 IS ISSN 0523-1469
BISDEH HEMED. (Text in Hebrew) 1957. m. $25. Organizations of Religious Teachers in Israel, 166 Ibn Gabirol St., Tel Aviv 62032, Israel. TEL 972-3-5442151. FAX 972-3-5468942. (Subscr. in U.S. to: Associated Talmud Toras, 2828 W. Pratt Blvd., Chicago, IL 60645) Ed. Y. Eisenberg. **Document type:** bulletin.
Description: Covers educational and instructional issues.

370 GW
BISMARCKSCHULE. 1932. s-a. Bismarckstr. 2, 25335 Elmshorn, Germany. TEL 04121-2310. adv.; bk.rev. circ. 1,400.
Description: News concerning school and education, forum for young writers.

BLACK EMPLOYMENT AND EDUCATION. see *ETHNIC INTERESTS*

372.21 DK ISSN 0006-5633
BOERN & UNGE. 1932. w. (50/yr.). DKK 550. (Boerne- og Ungdomspaedagogernes Landsforbund) Fagbladet Boern og Unge, Blegdamsvej 124, 4, DK-2100 Copenhagen Oe, Denmark. TEL 35-43-10-00. FAX 35-43-22-99. Ed.Bd. adv.: B&W page DKK 12960; trim 220 x 320; adv. contact: Laila Christiansen. bk.rev.; illus.; circ. 46,415 (controlled).
Formerly: Boernehaven.

370 BL
BOLETIM U E R J. 1965. 3/yr. free. Universidade do Estado do Rio de Janeiro, R. Sao Francisco Xavier, 524 sala T-01, CEP 20550 Maracana, Rio de Janeiro, Brazil. bk.rev.; bibl.; charts; stat.; circ. 2,000 (controlled). (cards)
Formerly: U E G Boletim (ISSN 0041-5057)

370 MP
BOLOVSROL/EDUCATION. (Text in Mongolian) 10/yr. Ministry of Education, Ulan Bator, Mongolia.

370 CN ISSN 0381-6028
BOOKMARK. q. Can.$60.67. British Columbia Teachers' Federation, British Columbia Teacher-Librarians' Association, 2235 Burrard, Vancouver, B.C. V6J 3H9, Canada. TEL 604-731-8121. adv.; bk.rev.; bibl.; index; circ. 1,300 (controlled). (back issues avail.)

BORE DA. see *CHILDREN AND YOUTH — For*

370 BL
BRAZIL. INSTITUTO NACIONAL DE ESTUDOS E PESQUISAS EDUCACIONAIS. INFORMATIVO. 1981. s-a. Instituto Nacional de Estudos e Pesquisas Educacionais, Campus da Universidade da Brazil, Acesso Sul, 70910-900, 70312 Brasilia, D.F., Brazil. TEL 061-3478970. FAX 061-2733233.
Description: Presents a review of current research.

EDUCATION

370 300   BL   ISSN 0102-549X
BRAZIL. SERVICO NACIONAL DE APRENDIZAGEM COMERCIAL. BOLETIM TECNICO. 1974. 3/yr. free. Servico Nacional de Aprendizagem Comercial, Rua Dona Mariana, 48, 7 andar, Botafogo, 22280 Rio de Janeiro RJ, Brazil. FAX 2860645. TELEX (021) 31129. Ed. Ana Lucia Bosisio. circ. 1,700. (back issues avail.) **Document type:** bulletin.

BRIEF AUS WAHLWIES; Mitteilungen aus dem Pestalozzi Kinder- und Jugenddorf. see *CHILDREN AND YOUTH — About*

379.70   CN   ISSN 0709-8383
L222.B8
BRITISH COLUMBIA. MINISTRY OF EDUCATION. ANNUAL REPORT. 1871. a. free. Ministry of Education, Parliament Bldgs., Victoria, BC V8V 2M4, Canada. TEL 604-356-2500. FAX 604-356-5945. circ. 6,000 (controlled). **Document type:** government publication.
Description: Summarizes a wide array of data and survey results, provides descriptionso f programs and student activities, describes the effectiveness of the school system.

371.4   CN   ISSN 0705-8802
BRITISH COLUMBIA SCHOOL COUNSELLORS' ASSOCIATION. NEWSLETTER. 1956. irreg. Can.$45 to non-members; members Can.$35; students Can.$25. B.C. Teachers' Federation, 2235 Burrard St., Vancouver, B.C. V6J 3H9, Canada. TEL 604-731-8121. circ. 525.
Formerly: British Columbia Counsellors' Association. Newsletter (ISSN 0045-2947)

370   UK   ISSN 0141-1926
LB1028   CODEN: BERJEL
BRITISH EDUCATIONAL RESEARCH JOURNAL. 1975. 5/yr. $123 to individuals; institutions $449 (effective 1994). (British Educational Research Association) Carfax Publishing Co., P.O. Box 25, Abingdon, Oxon. OX14 3UE, England. TEL 44-235-555335. FAX 44-235-553559. (U.S. subscr. to: Carfax Publishing Co., Box 2025, Dunnellon, FL 34430-2025) Ed. Barry Troyna. adv.; bk.rev.; illus.; stat.; index. (also avail. in microfiche; back issues avail.) **Indexed:** Cont.Pg.Educ., Educ.Tech.Abstr., High.Educ.Curr.Aware.Bull., Lang.Teach.& Ling.Abstr., Mult.Ed.Abstr., Psychol.Abstr., Res.High.Educ.Abstr., SOMA, SSCI, Stud.Wom.Abstr. **Document type:** academic/scholarly publication.
—BLDSC (2299.250000); Faxon; UnCover; SWETS. **CCC.**
Formerly (until vol.4, 1978): Research Intelligence (ISSN 0307-9023)
Refereed Serial

BRITISH JOURNAL OF EDUCATIONAL PSYCHOLOGY. see *PSYCHOLOGY*

370   UK   ISSN 0007-1005
L16
BRITISH JOURNAL OF EDUCATIONAL STUDIES. 1952. q. £32.50($72.50) to individuals; institutions £78 ($183). Basil Blackwell Ltd., 108 Cowley Rd., Oxford OX4 1JF, England. TEL 0865-791100. FAX 0865-791347. TELEX 837022-OXBOOK-G. Ed. Richard Pring. adv.; bk.rev.; index. circ. 1,300. (also avail. in microform from UMI; reprint service avail. from SWZ) **Indexed:** Amer.Hist.& Life, Br.Educ.Ind., Cont.Pg.Educ., Curr.Cont., Educ.Admin.Abstr., Educ.Ind., Educ.Tech.Abstr., High.Educ.Curr.Aware.Bull., Hist.Abstr., Lang.& Lang.Behav.Abstr., Mult.Ed.Abstr., Res.High.Educ.Abstr., SSCI. **Document type:** academic/scholarly publication.
—BLDSC (2307.720000); Faxon; UnCover; SWETS; UMI. **CCC.**

BRITISH JOURNAL OF HOLOCAUST EDUCATION. see *HISTORY — History Of Europe*

370 301   UK   ISSN 0142-5692
LC191.8.G7
BRITISH JOURNAL OF SOCIOLOGY OF EDUCATION. 1980. q. $134 to individuals; institutions $366 (effective 1994). Carfax Publishing Co., P.O. Box 25, Abingdon, Oxon. OX14 3UE, England. TEL 44-235-555335. FAX 44-235-553559. (U.S. subscr. to: Carfax Publishing Co., Box 2025, Dunnellon, FL 34430-2025) Ed. Len Barton. adv.; bk.rev.; index. (also avail. in microfiche; back issues avail.) **Indexed:** ASSIA, C.I.J.E., Cont.Pg.Educ., Curr.Cont., Educ.Tech.Abstr., High.Educ.Curr.Aware.Bull., Lang.& Lang.Behav.Abstr., Mult.Ed.Abstr., Res.High.Educ.Abstr., Rural Ext.Educ.& Tr.Abstr., Sociol.Abstr. (1980-), SOMA, Sp.Ed.Needs Abstr., SSCI, Stud.Wom.Abstr. **Document type:** academic/scholarly publication.
—BLDSC (2324.803000); Faxon; UnCover; SWETS. **CCC.**
Refereed Serial

BRITISH JOURNAL OF VISUAL IMPAIRMENT. see *HANDICAPPED — Visually Impaired*

370.15   UK   ISSN 0262-4087
BRITISH PSYCHOLOGICAL SOCIETY. EDUCATION SECTION. REVIEW. 1979. 2/yr. £8 to non-members; members £2. British Psychological Society, St. Andrews House, 48 Princess Rd., E., Leicester LE1 7DR, England. Ed. Kevin Wheldall. adv.; bk.rev. circ. 550. (reprint service avail. from ISI)
—BLDSC (3661.334600).
Description: Publishes material in educational psychology which is likely to be of general interest to the membership.

370   UK   ISSN 0141-5972
L915
BRITISH QUALIFICATIONS. 1969. a. £34.50 hardback; paperback £26.50. Kogan Page Ltd., 120 Pentonville Rd., London N1 9JN, England. TEL 071-278-0433. FAX 071-837-6348. TELEX 263088 KOGAN G. adv. **Document type:** academic/scholarly publication, directory.
—BLDSC (2340.380000).
Description: Comprehensive listing of all academic, educational, technical and professional qualifications available in Britain today.

370   BE
BRUG. 1957. 8/yr. (N.C.O.V. (Nacionale Confederatie voor Oudervereningingen)) Publicarto N.V., Langestraat 170, B-1150 Brussels, Belgium. TEL 32-2-7790000. FAX 32-2-7791616. circ. 41,236 (controlled).
Description: For parents and members of school's parents-board in Dutch-speaking part of Belgium.

653.07 370   GW   ISSN 0863-4912
DER BUEROPRAKTIKER; Zeitschrift fuer Stenografie, Maschinenschreiben, Buerowirtschaft, Textverarbeitung. 1952. m. DM.57.60. Verlag Die Wirtschaft GmbH, Am Friedrichshain 22, 10407 Berlin, Germany. TEL 030-4287237. FAX 030-4287234. illus. **Document type:** trade publication.
Formerly: Stenopraktiker (ISSN 0039-1174)
Description: Includes exercises for the practice of shorthand, shorthand news, association news.

BULLDOG WEEKLY. see *COLLEGE AND ALUMNI*

370   KE
BUREAU OF EDUCATIONAL RESEARCH. DISCUSSION PAPERS. (Text in English) w. Kenyatta University College, Bureau of Educational Research, P.O. Box 43844, Nairobi, Kenya. Ed. George O. Onyango. **Document type:** academic/scholarly publication.

370   KE
BUREAU OF EDUCATIONAL RESEARCH. SEMINAR PAPERS. (Text in English) bi-w. Kenyatta University College, Bureau of Educational Research, P.O. Box 43844, Nairobi, Kenya. **Document type:** academic/scholarly publication.

BUSINESS EDUCATION FILMS CATALOG. see *BUSINESS AND ECONOMICS*

BUTSURI KYOIKU/PHYSICS EDUCATION SOCIETY OF JAPAN. JOURNAL. see *PHYSICS*

370   US   ISSN 0271-1451
C A P E OUTLOOK. m. $10 (typically set in June). (Council for American Private Education) Serif Press, 1331 H St. N.W., No. 1102-LL, Washington, DC 20005. TEL 202-737-4650. FAX 202-783-1931. (Subscr. to: 1726 M St. N.W., Ste. 1102, Washington, DC 20036-4502) Ed. Greg D. Kubiak. circ. 3,400. (back issues avail.)

370   US
C B E REPORT. 1976. m. $30. Association for Community Based Education, 1805 Florida Ave., N.W., Washington, DC 20009. TEL 202-462-6333. Ed. V. Fay Mays. bk.rev.; index. circ. 200. (back issues avail.)
Description: Keeps community-based educators informed about literacy, community-organizing, economic development issues, federal policies, funding opportunities, fellowships, awards, program ideas, resource materials, workshops and conferences.

370   US   ISSN 0007-8050
C E A ADVISOR. 1958. m. (Sep.-Jun.). $15. Connecticut Education Association, Capitol Place, Ste. 500, 21 Oak St., Hartford, CT 06106-8001. TEL 203-525-5641. FAX 203-725-6323. Ed. Michael G. Lydick. adv.; bk.rev. circ. 30,150.

371.2   CN   ISSN 0068-8657
C E A HANDBOOK/KI-ES-KI. (Text in English or French) 1949. a. Can.$40 (foreign Can.$45). Canadian Education Association, 252 Bloor St. W., Ste. 8-200, Toronto, ON M5S 1V5, Canada. TEL 416-924-7721. FAX 416-924-3188. Ed. H. Goldsborough. circ. 2,500. **Document type:** directory.
Formerly: Directory of Administrative Officials in Public Education - Canada.
Description: Names, titles and addresses of the Canadian Ministries of Education, school boards, teacher training institutions, community colleges and universities, educational organizations and associations, federal departments involved in education and education publications.

370   US   ISSN 0882-5017
C E A VOICE. vol.51, 1970. q. membership. Columbus Education Association, 929 E. Broad St., Columbus, OH 43205. TEL 614-253-4731. FAX 614-253-0465. Ed. Bob Buelow. bk.rev.; illus. circ. 10,000. (tabloid format)
Formerly (until 1985): C E A Spotlight (ISSN 0007-8107)

370   DK   ISSN 0905-7765
C E U - BLADET.* 1977. irreg. free. Center for Europaeisk Uddannelse, Krusaa, Denmark. bk.rev.
Formerly (until 1989): Euro - Laerer Nyt (ISSN 0107-5624)

370   CU
C I C. BOLETIN INFORMATIVO. s-m. Ministerio de Comunicaciones, Centro de Informacion de Comunicaciones, Obispo No. 527, Apdo. 605, Havana, Cuba.

370   II   ISSN 0007-8425
C.I.E. NEWSLETTER.* no.48, 1967. irreg. (3-4/yr.). Central Institute of Education, Patel Mar, University Campus, Delhi 1100016, India. Ed. Dr. R.S. Vashishj. bk.rev.

371.42   UY   ISSN 0577-2931
C I N T E R F O R ESTUDIOS Y MONOGRAFIAS. 1967. irreg. price varies. Centro Interamericano de Investigacion y Documentacion sobre Formacion Profesional, Avda. Uruguay 1238, Casilla de Correo 1761, Montevideo, Uruguay. FAX 921305. **Indexed:** CIRF Abstr.

C M L E A JOURNAL. (California Media and Library Educators Association) see *LIBRARY AND INFORMATION SCIENCES*

C N L. (Colonial Newsletter Foundation, Inc.) see *NUMISMATICS*

370　　　　　　UK　　ISSN 0308-6909
C O R E. (Collected Original Resources in Education); an international journal of educational research published in microfiche. 1977. 3/yr. $560 (effective 1994). Carfax Publishing Co., P.O. Box 25, Abingdon, Oxon. OX14 3UE, England. TEL 44-235-555335. FAX 44-235-553559. (U.S. subscr. to: Carfax Publishing Co., Box 2025, Dunnellon, FL 34430-2025) Ed. Derek Cherrington. bk.rev.; abstr.; bibl.; charts; illus.; stat.; index. (microfiche; back issues avail.) **Indexed:** Cont.Pg.Educ., Educ.Tech.Abstr., Res.High.Educ.Abstr., SOMA, Stud.Wom.Abstr. **Document type:** abstracting/indexing.
—BLDSC (3300.791000). **CCC.**
Refereed Serial

370　　　　　　ZR
C R I D E CAHIERS. 1974. 5/yr. $4. Universite de Kisangani, Centre de Recherches Interdisciplinaires pour le Developpement de l'Education (CRIDE), B.P. 1386, Kisangani, Zaire. Ed. Mbaya Mudimba. circ. 150.

370　　　　　　BL　　ISSN 0100-1574
CADERNOS DE PESQUISA; revista de estudos e pesquisas em educacao. (Text in Portuguese; summaries in English and Portuguese) 1971. q. $30. (Fundacao Carlos Chagas, Departamento de Pesquisas Educacionais) Cortez Editora, Rua Bartira 387, 05009 Sao Paulo, SP, Brazil. TELEX 011-83823. Ed. Fulvia Rosemberg. bk.rev.; bibl.; charts. circ. 3,000. **Indexed:** Bibliogr.Bras.Odontol.
Description: Original research or analytical summaries in the areas of education and women's studies.

370　　　　　　BL
CADERNOS PEDAGOGICOS. 3/yr. Cr.$100. Centro Educacional, Av. Ernai do Amaral Peixoto, 836, Niteroi, R.J., Brazil. Dir. Roberto Ballalai. illus.

370　　　　　　FR　　ISSN 0008-042X
CAHIERS PEDAGOGIQUES. 1946. 10/yr. 280 F. (foreign 400 F.). Cercle de Recherche et d'Action Pedagogiques (CRAP), 5 Impasse Bon Secours, 75543 Paris Cedex 11, France. TEL 43-48-22-30. Ed. J.M. Zakhartchouk. adv.; bk.rev. circ. 10,000. **Indexed:** Amer.Hist.& Life, Hist.Abstr., Lang.& Lang.Behav.Abstr. **Document type:** academic/scholarly publication.
—BLDSC (2951.550000); SWETS.

370　　　　　　AG
CALENDARIO ESCOLAR. a. Ministerio de Educacion y Justicia, Secretaria de Educacion, Directorio 1801, Buenos Aires, Argentina. circ. 20,000.

CALIFORNIA CABLETTER; current community perspectives and directions. see *COMMUNICATIONS*

371　　　　　　US
CALIFORNIA SCHOOL BOARDS JOURNAL. 1942. q. $15 (foreign $30). California School Board Association, 3100 Beacon Blvd., Box 1660, W. Sacramento, CA 95819. TEL 916-371-4691. FAX 916-371-3407. Ed. Kevin Swartzendruber. adv.; bk.rev.; illus.; cum.index. circ. 7,000. **Indexed:** ERIC.
Formerly: California School Boards (ISSN 0008-1507)
Description: Covers policy and legislative issues affecting public education administration in the state.
Refereed Serial

370 331　　　　US　　ISSN 0410-3556
CALIFORNIA TEACHER. 6/yr. $3. California Federation of Teachers, One Kaiser Plaxa, Ste. 1440, Oakland, CA 94612. TEL 510-832-8812. FAX 510-832-5044. Ed. Fred Glass. adv.; charts; illus.; stat.; tr.lit. circ. 50,000. (tabloid format; back issues avail.)

371　　　　　　US
CALL TO ACTION. 1980. m. Board of Education, 5057 Woodward, Detroit, MI 48202. TEL 313-494-1000. Ed. Charles Alexander. circ. 22,000 (controlled).
Supersedes: Detroit Public Schools Reporter; Detroit Schools (ISSN 0011-9679)

370　　　　　　GW
CALYPSO; Schuelerzeitung Gymnasium Bondenwald. 1987. q. DM.6($15) Calypso Verlag, Am Langdiek 16a, 22453 Hamburg, Germany. TEL 040-586696. Ed.Bd. adv.; bk.rev. circ. 825. (back issues avail.)

371.8 378　　　PH　　ISSN 0008-252X
CAMPUS LEADER. (Text in English, Filipino and Spanish) 1927. m. $1. University of Manila, 546 Dr. M.V. de los Santos St., Manila D-403, Philippines. Ed. Honorato A. Victoria. adv.; bk.rev.; play rev.; charts; illus.; circ. 8,000 (controlled).

CANADA & THE WORLD; the magazine for students of current events. see *SOCIAL SCIENCES: COMPREHENSIVE WORKS*

370　　　　　　CN　　ISSN 0315-1409
CANADIAN AND INTERNATIONAL EDUCATION/EDUCATION CANADIENNE ET INTERNATIONALE. (Text and summaries in English, French) 1972. s-a. Can.$20 to individuals; institutions Can.$25 (typically set in Jan.). Comparative and International Education Society of Canada, c/o Faculty of Education, Univ. of Western Ontario, London, ON N6G 1G7, Canada. TEL 519-661-3182. FAX 519-661-3833. Eds. Douglas Ray, David Radcliffe. bk.rev.; bibl. circ. 400. (also avail. in microform from MML,UMI) **Indexed:** Cont.Pg.Educ., Educ.Admin.Abstr., Mid.East: Abstr.& Ind., Mult.Ed.Abstr., SOMA, Sp.Ed.Needs Abstr., Stud.Wom.Abstr. **Document type:** academic/scholarly publication.
—BLDSC (3017.140000); UnCover.

CANADIAN ATHLETIC DIRECTOR AND COACH. see *SPORTS AND GAMES*

370　　　　　　CN　　ISSN 0008-4557
AS4.U825
CANADIAN COMMISSION FOR UNESCO. BULLETIN/COMMISSION CANADIENNE POUR L'UNESCO. BULLETIN. (Text and summaries in English, French) 1965. 4/yr. free. Canadian Commission for UNESCO, PO Box 1047, Ottawa, ON K1P 5V8, Canada. TEL 613-566-4325. bibl.; illus. circ. 5,200.

370　　　　　　CN　　ISSN 0008-3445
CANADIAN EDUCATION ASSOCIATION. NEWSLETTER. 1947. 9/yr. Can.$15. Canadian Education Association, 252 Bloor St. W., Ste. 8-200, Toronto, ON M5S 1V5, Canada. TEL 416-924-7721. FAX 416-924-3188. Ed. Harriett Goldsborough. bk.rev.; illus.; stat. circ. 9,000. (reprint service avail. from MMI) **Indexed:** Can.Educ.Ind. **Document type:** newsletter.
Description: Events, people and policies in Canadian elementary and secondary education.

370　　　　　　CN　　ISSN 0380-2361
LA410
CANADIAN JOURNAL OF EDUCATION/REVUE CANADIENNE DE L'EDUCATION. (Text in English, French) 1976. q. Can.$100 (foreign $100). Canadian Society for the Study of Education, Ottawa Secretariat, c/o Tim Howard, One Stewart St., Ste. 205, Ottawa, ON K1N 6H7, Canada. TEL 613-230-3532. FAX 613-230-2746. Ed. Michael Manley-Casimir. bk.rev.; bibl. circ. 1,460. (also avail. in microfilm from UMI,MML) **Indexed:** C.I.J.E., Can.Per.Ind., Can.Wom.Per.Ind., CMI, Cont.Pg.Educ., Educ.Ind., Educ.Tech.Abstr., Mult.Ed.Abstr., P.A.I.S., Psychol.Abstr., Res.High.Educ.Abstr., Sociol.Educ.Abstr., SOMA, Sp.Ed.Needs Abstr., Stud.Wom.Abstr.
—BLDSC (3031.250000); Faxon; UnCover; UMI. **CCC.**
Description: Provides a national forum for the discussion of the problems and issues confronting education in Canada.

CANADIAN JOURNAL OF HISTORY OF SPORT/REVUE CANADIENNE DE L'HISTOIRE DES SPORTS. see *SPORTS AND GAMES*

370 970.1　　　CN　　ISSN 0710-1481
CANADIAN JOURNAL OF NATIVE EDUCATION. 1973. 2/yr. Can.$22.50 (foreign Can.$30). University of Alberta, Publications Services, 4-116 Education North, Edmonton, AB T6G 2G5, Canada. TEL 403-492-4204. FAX 403-492-0390. TELEX 0372979. Eds. C. Urion, Jo-ann Archibald. adv.; bk.rev.; bibl. circ. 350. (back issues avail.) **Indexed:** C.I.J.E., Cont.Pg.Educ., Mult.Ed.Abstr. **Document type:** academic/scholarly publication.
—BLDSC (3033.200000); UnCover.
Formerly: Indian-Ed (ISSN 0318-8647)

CANADIAN JOURNAL OF SCHOOL PSYCHOLOGY. see *PSYCHOLOGY*

CANADIAN MODERN LANGUAGE REVIEW/REVUE CANADIENNE DES LANGUES VIVANTES. see *LINGUISTICS*

CANADIAN MUSIC EDUCATOR. see *MUSIC*

704　　　　　　CN　　ISSN 0706-8107
CANADIAN REVIEW OF ART EDUCATION RESEARCH AND ISSUES. (Text mainly in English; occasionally in French) 1977. irreg. Can.$65 includes Newsletter and Journal. Canadian Society for Education Through Art, 1487 Parish La., Oakville, ON L6M 2Z6, Canada. circ. 400. **Indexed:** Cont.Pg.Educ.
—BLDSC (3044.631000).
Formerly (until 1988): Canadian Review of Art Education Research (ISSN 0384-1839)

704　　　　　　CN
CANADIAN SOCIETY FOR EDUCATION THROUGH ART. JOURNAL. a. Can.$65. Canadian Society for Education Through Art, 1487 Parish La., Oakville, ON L6M 2Z6, Canada. bk.rev. circ. 700.
—BLDSC (4723.C95000).
Formerly (until 1988): Canadian Society for Education Through Art. Annual Journal (ISSN 0068-9645)

704　　　　　　CN　　ISSN 0045-5369
CANADIAN SOCIETY FOR EDUCATION THROUGH ART. NEWSLETTER. 1955. 4/yr. Can.$65. Canadian Society for Education Through Art, 1497 Parish La., Oakville, ON L6M 2Z6, Canada. adv.; bk.rev. circ. 400. (also avail. in microform from UMI) **Document type:** newsletter.

371.4　　　　　UK
CAREERS COP: I S C O CAREERS BULLETIN. 1947. 3/yr. £10. Independent Schools Careers Organisation, 12a-18a Princess Way, Camberley, Surrey GU15 3SP, England. Ed. Anna Alston. bk.rev.; index. circ. 33,000. (back issues avail.) **Indexed:** Build.Manage.Abstr.
Formerly: I S C O Careers Bulletin (ISSN 0267-9981)

370　　　　　　JM　　ISSN 0376-7701
LA475
CARIBBEAN JOURNAL OF EDUCATION. 1974. triennial. $18. University of the West Indies, Faculty of Education, Mona, Kingston 7, Jamaica, W.I. TEL 809-927-2431. FAX 809-927-7581. Ed.Bd. adv.; bk.rev.; bibl. circ. 1,000. (also avail. in microform from UMI) **Indexed:** Cont.Pg.Educ., ERIC, Mult.Ed.Abstr., Rural Ext.Educ.& Tr.Abstr., Sp.Ed.Needs Abstr. **Document type:** academic/scholarly publication.
—BLDSC (3053.030000); UMI.

CARMELUS; commentarii ab Instituto Carmelitano editi. see *RELIGIONS AND THEOLOGY — Roman Catholic*

371　　　　　　US　　ISSN 0069-0651
CARNEGIE FOUNDATION FOR THE ADVANCEMENT OF TEACHING. ANNUAL REPORT. 1906. a. free. Carnegie Foundation for the Advancement of Teaching, 5 Ivy Ln., Princeton, NJ 08540. TEL 609-452-1780. FAX 609-520-1712. Ed. Jeanine Natriello. circ. 1,700. (also avail. in microfiche from BHP)
Description: Features a message from the President of the foundation, and financial information about the foundation.

370　　　　　　US
CASE STUDIES IN EDUCATION AND CULTURE.* irreg. price varies. Holt, Rinehart and Winston, Inc., c/o Harcourt Brace Jovenovich, Orlando, FL 32887. TEL 407-345-2500.

370　　　　　　US
▼**CATALOG OF FEDERAL EDUCATION GRANTS.** 1993. 12/yr. $200. Capitol Publications Inc., 1101 King St., Ste. 444, Alexandria, VA 22314. TEL 703-683-4100. FAX 703-739-6517. **Document type:** newsletter.

371.42 016　　　UY　　ISSN 0069-1046
CATALOGO DE PUBLICACIONES LATINOAMERICANAS SOBRE FORMACION PROFESIONAL. 1964. a. price varies. Centro Interamericano de Investigacion y Documentacion Sobre Formacion Profesional, Avda. Uruguay 1238, Casilla de Correo 1761, Montevideo, Uruguay. FAX 921305. **Indexed:** CIRF Abstr.

CATHOLIC EDUCATION. see *RELIGIONS AND THEOLOGY — Roman Catholic*

EDUCATION

CATHOLIC MUSIC EDUCATOR. see *MUSIC*

370   CJ
CAYMAN ISLANDS. EDUCATION DEPARTMENT. REPORT OF THE CHIEF EDUCATION OFFICER. a. Education Department, Grand Cayman, Cayman Islands, British W.I. illus.

370 658.048   AT
CE MOIS-CI A L'ALLIANCE. (Text in French; summaries in English) 1976. m. Aus.$40. Alliance Francaise de Canberra Inc., P.O. Box 125, O'Connor, A.C.T. 2601, Australia. TEL 06-257-1984. FAX 06-257-6696. Ed. Jean Poncet. adv. circ. 1,000. (reprint service avail.)
    Formerly (until 1988): Chantecler.

340 370   US   ISSN 0276-203X
KF4102
CENTER FOR LAW AND EDUCATION. NEWSNOTES. 1979. q. free. Center for Law and Education, Inc., 955 Massachusetts Ave., Cambridge, MA 02139. TEL 617-876-6611. FAX 617-876-0203. Ed. Sharon Schumack. bk.rev. circ. 5,500. (looseleaf format; reprint service avail. form UMI) **Indexed:** Rehabil.Lit. **Document type:** newsletter.
    Description: Covers education advocacy, key legal developments, noteworthy advocacy efforts, and useful resources for persons who represent low-income parents and students.

372   US
CENTER FOR PARENT EDUCATION NEWSLETTER. 1978. bi-m. $28 (Canada $33; elsewhere $38). Center for Parent Education, 81 Wyman St., No. 6, Waban, MA 02168-1519. TEL 617-964-2442. FAX 617-965-8827. Ed. Burton L. White. bk.rev.; index. circ. 200. (back issues avail.) **Document type:** newsletter.
    Description: Serving professional needs in parent education during the first three years of life; evaluating new research, assessment techniques, books, films; monitoring developments in the field.

CENTER FOR PEACE AND CONFLICT STUDIES - DETROIT COUNCIL FOR WORLD AFFAIRS. NEWSLETTER. see *POLITICAL SCIENCE — International Relations*

370   FR
CENTRE REGIONAL DE DOCUMENTATION PEDAGOGIQUE. STUDI. (Text in Breton and French) 1974. 4/yr. 40 F. (Faculte des Lettres de Brest, Section Celtique) Centre Regional de Documentation Pedagogique, 92 rue d'Antrain, 35000 Rennes, Brittany, France. bibl. circ. 600.
    Formerly: Centre Regional de Recherche et de Documentation Pedagogiques de Rennes. Studi.

370   FR   ISSN 0069-2069
CENTRE REGIONAL DE DOCUMENTATION PEDAGOGIQUE DE TOULOUSE. ANNALES; dossier d'information et de perfectionnement (Francais-Mathematiques). (Supplement to: Bulletin Regional d'Informations Universitaires) 1970. irreg. price varies. Centre Regional de Documentation Pedagogique de Toulouse, 3 rue Roquelaine, 31000 Toulouse, France. **Document type:** academic/scholarly publication, bulletin.

371.42   UY   ISSN 0577-2907
CENTRO INTERAMERICANO DE INVESTIGACION Y DOCUMENTACION SOBRE FORMACION PROFESIONAL. BOLETIN. 1969. 4/yr. $30. Centro Interamericano de Investigacion y Documentacion sobre Formacion Profesional, Avda. Uruguay 1238, Casilla de Correo 1761, Montevideo, Uruguay. FAX 921305. cum.index.
    Supersedes: C I N T E R F O R Noticias.

374.013   UY
CENTRO INTERAMERICANO DE INVESTIGACION Y DOCUMENTACION SOBRE FORMACION PROFESIONAL. INFORMES. 1964. irreg. price varies. Centro Interamericano de Investigacion y Documentacion sobre Formacion Profesional, Avda. Uruguay 1238, Casilla de Correo 1761, Montevideo, Uruguay. FAX 921305.

371.42 016   UY
CENTRO INTERAMERICANO DE INVESTIGACION Y DOCUMENTACION SOBRE FORMACION PROFESIONAL. SERIE BIBLIOGRAFICA. 1968. irreg. Centro Interamericano de Investigacion y Documentacion sobre Formacion Profesional, Avda. Uruguay 1238, Casilla de Correo 1761, Montevideo, Uruguay. FAX 921305. bk.rev.; abstr.; bibl.

370 491.86 891.86   XR   ISSN 0009-0786
CESKY JAZYK A LITERATURA; casopis pro metodiku. (Text in Czech; contents page also in German) 1950. 5/yr. 57.50 Kcs. (Ministerstvi Skolstvi, Mladezy a Telovychovy Ceske Republiky) Statni Pedagogicke Nakladatelstvi, Ostrovni 30, 113 01 Prague 1, Czech Republic. TEL 2-203787. FAX 2-293883. (Subscr. to: Pelit, Opatoricka 22, Prague 1, Czech Republic) Ed. Marie Cechova. bk.rev. **Indexed:** Bibl.Ling. **Document type:** academic/scholarly publication.

372   AT   ISSN 0311-0486
CHALLENGE. 1971. 4/yr. Aus.$9.50. (Ministry of Education and Training) Marayanga Publications, P.O. Box 258, Prahran, Vic. 3181, Australia. TEL 03-525-2088. FAX 03-525-2184. Ed. Sue Galley. circ. 35,500.
    Description: Reading material for children in upper primary school.

370 360   US
CHALLENGING TIMES; educating children and youth at risk. 5/yr. $49.90 (effective 1994). National Professional Resources, Inc., 25 S. Regent St., Port Chester, NY 10573. TEL 914-937-8879; 800-453-7461. **Document type:** newsletter.
    Incorporates (in 1994): Educating At-Risk Youth & Substance Abuse in Schools.
    Description: Addresses issues and news of interest to service providers for children and youth at risk, including such topics as drop-out prevention, substance abuse, HIV, teen suicide, youth violence.

379.15   US
CHAMPIONS FOR CHILDREN; New Hampshire school administrators newsletter. 1955. m. membership. New Hampshire School Administrators Association, Morrill Hall, Durham, NH 03824. TEL 603-862-1384. FAX 603-862-1084. Ed. Elinor A. Fox. adv.; bk.rev.; abstr.; charts; illus.; stat. circ. 1,500. (tabloid format) **Document type:** newsletter.
    Former titles (until 1993): Granite State School Leader; New Hampshire School Boards Association Newsletter; Granite State School Leader (ISSN 0027-660X)

370   IS
HACHEINUCH VE SIVEVO. 1977. a. free. College of Education, Kibbutz Seminar, 149 Namir Rd., Tel Aviv, Israel. FAX 410269. Ed. Yoel Snir. bk.rev.

CHEMIE IN DER SCHULE. see *CHEMISTRY*

370   US
CHICAGO UNION TEACHER. 1937. 10/yr. 222 Merchandise Mart, Ste. 400, Chicago, IL 60654. TEL 312-329-9100. FAX 312-329-6200. Ed. Ellen Schur Brown. adv.; bk.rev. circ. 35,000.
    Description: For teachers and Chicago school employees; articles on topics of education, labor, politics and child development.

CHILD AND FAMILY. see *CHILDREN AND YOUTH — About*

370   US
CHILD AND FAMILY POLICY. 1981. irreg., vol.6, 1988. price varies. Ablex Publishing Corporation, 355 Chestnut St., Norwood, NJ 07648. TEL 201-767-8450. FAX 201-767-6717. TELEX 135-393. Eds. James J. Gallagher, Ron Haskins.

370   UK   ISSN 0009-3890
CHILD AND MAN; a journal for contemporary education. 1948. s-a. £4.80. Steiner Schools Fellowship, The Sprig, Ashdown Rd., Forest Row, E. Sussex RH18 5BN, England. TEL 0342-822115. Ed. Brien Masters. adv.; bk.rev.; illus. circ. 5,000. **Document type:** academic/scholarly publication.
    —BLDSC (3172.915500).

372   UK   ISSN 0009-3947
CHILD EDUCATION; for teachers of young children to 8 years of age. 1924. m. £27.50 (foreign £33.20). Scholastic Publications Ltd., Villiers House, Clarendon Ave., Leamington Spa, Warks CV32 5PR, England. TEL 0926-887799. FAX 0926-883331. TELEX 312138 SPLSG. Ed. Gill Moore. adv.; bk.rev.; illus.; index. circ. 67,744. (also avail. in microfilm from UMI) **Indexed:** Cont.Pg.Educ. **Document type:** academic/scholarly publication.
    —UnCover; SWETS; UMI. CCC.

155.4   US   ISSN 0009-4005
LB1101   CODEN: CSJOD2
CHILD STUDY JOURNAL. 1970. q. $16 to individuals; institutions $32; students $6. State University of New York at Buffalo, Behavioral and Humanistic Studies, Bacon Hall 306, 1300 Elmwood Ave., Buffalo, NY 14222-1095. TEL 716-878-5302. Ed. Donald E. Carter. bk.rev.; illus.; index. circ. 500. (also avail. in microfilm from UMI; reprint service avail. from UMI; back issues avail.) **Indexed:** C.I.J.E., Child Devel.Abstr., Cont.Pg.Educ., Curr.Cont., Educ.Ind., Except.Child Educ.Abstr., Lang.& Lang.Behav.Abstr., Mult.Ed.Abstr., Psychol.Abstr., Psycscan D.P., Sociol.Abstr., Sp.Ed.Needs Abstr., SSCI.
    —BLDSC (3172.949000); Faxon; UnCover; UMI.
    Formerly: Child Study Center Bulletin.
    Description: Theory and research on child and adolescent development.
    Refereed Serial

372   US   ISSN 0009-4056
LB1141
CHILDHOOD EDUCATION; a journal for teachers, teachers-in-training, teacher educators, parents, day care workers, librarians, pediatricians and other child caregivers. 1924. 5/yr. $45 to individuals; institutions $78 (includes Journal of Reasearch in Childhood Education); students $26; retirees $23. Association for Childhood Education International, 11501 Georgia Ave., Ste. 312, Wheaton, MD 20902. TEL 301-942-2443. Ed. Anne Watson Bauer. adv.; bk.rev.; abstr.; bibl.; charts; illus.; tr.lit.; index. circ. 11,700. (also avail. in microfilm from UMI,PMC; back issues avail.; reprint service avail. from UMI) **Indexed:** Acad.Ind., Adol.Ment.Hlth.Abstr., Bk.Rev.Ind. (1965-), C.I.J.E., Child.Bk.Rev.Ind. (1965-), Child Devel.Abstr., Cont.Pg.Educ., Educ.Ind., Except.Child.Educ.Abstr., Nutr.Abstr., Psychol.Abstr., Rehabil.Lit. **Document type:** trade publication.
    —BLDSC (3172.955000); Faxon; UnCover; SWETS; UMI.
    Incorporates (in 1991): A C E I Exchange (ISSN 0732-5371)
    Description: Articles cover current research and each issue focuses on a single theme.

CHILDREN TODAY; an interdisciplinary journal for the professions serving children. see *CHILDREN AND YOUTH — About*

CHILDREN'S BOOKS OF THE YEAR. see *CHILDREN AND YOUTH — For*

CHILDREN'S HOUSE - CHILDREN'S WORLD; a magazine for parents, teachers and professionals about today's children. see *CHILDREN AND YOUTH — About*

CHILDREN'S LITERATURE IN EDUCATION; an international quarterly. see *CHILDREN AND YOUTH — About*

CHINA INSTITUTE IN AMERICA. BULLETIN.. see *ORIENTAL STUDIES*

370 951   US   ISSN 1061-1932
LA1130
CHINESE EDUCATION AND SOCIETY; a journal of translations. 1968. bi-m. $429 (foreign $472). M.E. Sharpe, Inc., 80 Business Park Dr., Armonk, NY 10504. TEL 914-273-1800. FAX 914-273-2106. Ed. Stanley Rosen. adv.; index. (also avail. in microform from UMI; back issues avail.) **Indexed:** C.I.J.E., Cont.Pg.Educ., Curr.Cont., Educ.Ind., Educ.Tech.Abstr., Mult.Ed.Abstr., Rural Ext.Educ.& Tr.Abstr., SSCI. **Document type:** academic/scholarly publication.
    —BLDSC (3180.278000); Faxon; UnCover; UMI.
    Formerly: Chinese Education (ISSN 0009-4560)
    Refereed Serial

CHINESE LANGUAGE TEACHERS ASSOCIATION. JOURNAL. see *LINGUISTICS*

CHINESE LANGUAGE TEACHERS ASSOCIATION. MONOGRAPH SERIES. see *LINGUISTICS*

CHRISTENE SCHOOL. see *RELIGIONS AND THEOLOGY*

CHRISTOPHORUS. see *RELIGIONS AND THEOLOGY — Roman Catholic*

370 CU
CIENCIAS PEDAGOGICAS. 1980. s-a. $12. (Ministerio de Educacion, Instituto Central de Ciencias Pedagogicas) Ediciones Cubanas, Obispo No. 527, Apdo. 605, Havana, Cuba. Ed.Bd. bk.rev.; bibl.; charts; illus. circ. 3,000.

CITIZENSHIP EDUCATOR. see *LAW*

370 407 XR
CIZI JAZYKY; casopis pro vyucovani cizim jazykum - zejmena anglictine, nemcine, francouzstine, spanelstine, rustine a latine. (Texts in Czech or Slovak; contents page also in English, French, German and Russian) 1957. 10/yr. 30 Kcs.($15) Ministerstvo Skolstvi, Mladezy a Telovychovy Ceske Republiky, c/o Editorial Office, Branicak 114, 147 00 Prague 4, Czech Republic. (Subscr. to: PNS, Ustredni Expedice a Dovoz Tisku Praha, Zavod 01, Administrace Vyvozu Tisku, Kovpakova 26, 160 00 Prague 6, Czech Republic) Ed. Vaclav Simecek. bk.rev.; abstr.; charts; illus.; index. **Indexed:** Lang.Teach.& Ling.Abstr., M.L.A.
    Formerly: Cizi Jazyky ve Skole (ISSN 0009-8205)

CLASSICAL JOURNAL. see *CLASSICAL STUDIES*

CLASSICAL OUTLOOK. see *CLASSICAL STUDIES*

370 FR ISSN 1243-4450
▼**CLE...S A VENIR;** l'innovation on sait faire. 1992. 3/yr. Centre National de Documentation Pedagogique, 29 rue d'Ulm, 75320 Paris Cedex 05, France. (Co-sponsor: Centre Regional de Documentation Pedagogique (Nancy))

373 US ISSN 0009-8655
L11
THE CLEARING HOUSE; a journal for middle schools, junior and senior high schools. 1925. bi-m. $29 to individuals; institutions $51. (Helen Dwight Reid Educational Foundation) Heldref Publications, 1319 Eighteenth St., N.W., Washington, DC 20036-1802. TEL 202-296-6267. FAX 202-296-5149. Ed. Judy Cusick. adv. contact: Raymond Rallo. charts. circ. 4,100. (also avail. in microform; back issues avail.; reprint service avail.) **Indexed:** Acad.Ind., Access, Bus.Educ.Ind., C.I.J.E., CERDIC, Cont.Pg.Educ., Educ.Admin.Abstr., Educ.Ind., Mag.Ind., Sp.Ed.Needs Abstr. **Document type:** academic/scholarly publication.
    —BLDSC (3278.530000); Faxon; UnCover; UMI. CCC.
    Refereed Serial

COGNITION AND INSTRUCTION. see *PSYCHOLOGY*

370 US
COGNITION AND LITERACY. 1987. irreg. price varies. Ablex Publishing Corporation, 355 Chestnut St., Norwood, NJ 07648. TEL 201-767-8450. FAX 201-767-6717. TELEX 135-393. Ed. Judith Orasanu.

374.013 UY
COLECCIONES BASICAS C I N T E R F O R. (Text in Portuguese and Spanish) 1970. irreg. price varies. Centro Interamericano de Investigacion y Documentacion sobre Formacion Profesional, Avda. Uruguay 1238, Casilla de Correo 1761, Montevideo, Uruguay. FAX 921305. **Indexed:** CIRF Abstr.

370 VE ISSN 0010-0633
COLEGIO DE PROFESORES DE VENEZUELA. SECCIONAL NO.1. BOLETIN INFORMATIVO.* 1969. 8/yr. free. Colegio de Profesores de Venezuela, Apdo. de Correo 6642, Caracas 101, Venezuela. Ed. Teodoro Perez Peralta. adv.; bk.rev.; illus.; cum.index.

370 BL ISSN 0080-3103
COLEGIO MILITAR DO RIO DE JANEIRO. REVISTA DIDACTICA.* 1902. a. free. Colegio Militar do Rio de Janeiro, Rua Sao Francisco Xavier 267, ZC-11 Rio de Janeiro, Brazil.

COLLECTION ORIENTATIONS. see *PSYCHOLOGY*

370 FR
COLLECTION SCIENCES DE L'EDUCATION. irreg. price varies. Editions Scientifiques et Psychologiques, 6 bis, rue Andre Chenier, 29130 Issy-les-Moulineaux, France. TEL 46-45-38-12. FAX 40-95-73-32. TELEX 270 105 F. Ed. L. Marmoz.

370 FR
COLLECTIONS EDUCATION - PEDAGOGIE. irreg. price varies. Editions Scientifiques et Psychologiques, 6 bis, rue Andre Chenier, 92130 Issy-les-Moulineaux, France. TEL 46-45-38-12. FAX 40-95-73-32. TELEX 270 105 F. Ed. J.L. Bernaud.

370 020 US
COLLEGE CATALOG COLLECTION ON MICROFICHE. 1973. s-a. price varies. Career Guidance Foundation, 8090 Engineer Rd., San Diego, CA 92111. TEL 619-560-8051. FAX 619-278-8960. Ed.Bd. abstr.; charts; illus.; stat. circ. 100,000. (microfiche; back issues avail.) **Document type:** catalog.

COLLEGE MEDIA REVIEW. see *JOURNALISM*

370 UK ISSN 0010-1842
COLSTONIAN. 1894. a. £5. Colston's Collegiate School, Stapleton, Bristol, England. TEL 0272-655207. Ed. M.E. Davies. adv.: Page £100; adv. contact: M.E. Davies. illus. circ. 650. **Document type:** consumer publication.
    Description: Records activities of the school year, together with literary and artistic contributions by pupils.

370 360 NE ISSN 0167-9163
COMENIUS; wetenschappelijk forum voor opvoeding, onderwijs en cultuur. (Text mainly in Dutch; occasionally in English, French, German) 1981. q. fl.93.50. Uitgeverij S U N, Postbus 1609, 6501 BP Nijmegen, Netherlands. TEL 31-80-221700. FAX 31-80-235493. adv.: B&W page fl.350. bk.rev. circ. 650. **Indexed:** Bull.Signal., Cont.Pg.Educ., E.I., Sociol.Abstr., Sociol.Educ.Abstr., Stud.Wom.Abstr. **Document type:** academic/scholarly publication.
    Description: Contains articles and opinions on education, schooling, culture and women's studies.

372 AT ISSN 0158-4243
COMET. 1970. 4/yr. Aus.$9.50. (Ministry of Education and Training) Marayanga Publications, P.O. Box 258, Prahran, Vic. 3181, Australia. TEL 03-525-2088. FAX 03-525-2184. circ. 25,000.
    Description: Educational activities and fun reading for infants to age 7.

370 US
COMMITTEE FOR THE EDUCATIONAL RIGHTS OF STUDENTS NEWSLETTER. irreg. membership. Committee for the Educational Rights of Students, Box 47432, Seattle, WA 98146.
    Description: Dedicated to protecting the rights of all students.

331.2 AT ISSN 0311-8991
COMMONWEALTH TEACHING SERVICE. ANNUAL REPORT. (Subseries of: Australia. Parliament. Parliamentary Papers) 1972. a. price varies. Australian Government Publishing Service, G.P.O. Box 84, Canberra, A.C.T. 2601, Australia. TEL 61-6-295-4612. FAX 61-6-295-4500. illus. **Document type:** government publication.

370 CN
COMMUNICATE (IQALUIT). vol.10, 1986. 8/yr. Can.$10. Northwest Territories Teachers Association, Box 761, Iqaluit, NT X0A 0H0, Canada. TEL 403-873-8501. FAX 403-873-2236. Ed. John Maurice. adv.; bk.rev. circ. 900.

420 370 US ISSN 0363-4523
PN4071
COMMUNICATION EDUCATION. 1952. 4/yr. $75 membership. Speech Communication Association, 5105 Backlick Rd., Bldg. E., Annandale, VA 22003. TEL 703-750-0533. FAX 703-914-9471. Ed. Lawrence B. Rosenfeld. adv.; bk.rev.; abstr.; charts; index, cum.index. circ. 4,200. (also avail. in microform from UMI; reprint service avail. from UMI) **Indexed:** Acad.Ind., C.I.J.E., Cont.Pg.Educ., Curr.Cont., Educ.Ind., Lang.& Lang.Behav.Abstr., M.L.A., Media Rev.Dig., Psychol.Abstr., SSCI.
    —BLDSC (3359.830000); Faxon; UnCover; SWETS; UMI.
    Formerly (until 1976): Speech Teacher (ISSN 0038-7177)
    Description: Presents studies and research on communication in instructional settings.

371.897 US ISSN 0010-3535
PN4788
COMMUNICATION: JOURNALISM EDUCATION TODAY. Short title: C: J E T. 1967. q. $35 to teachers, advisers, associates; institutions $40; retired teachers $20; students $25. Journalism Education Association, Inc., Kedzie Hall 103, Kansas State University, Manhattan, KS 66506. TEL 913-532-5532. FAX 913-532-7309. Ed. Molly J. Clemons. adv.; bk.rev.; bibl.; charts; illus.; stat.; index. circ. 1,800. (also avail. in microform from UMI; reprint service avail. from ERIC) **Indexed:** C.I.J.E. —UMI.
    Description: Journal for high school journalism educators and anyone interested in high school journalism.

370 US ISSN 0363-7751
PN4077
COMMUNICATION MONOGRAPHS. 1934. 4/yr. $75 membership. Speech Communication Association, 5105 Backlick Rd., Bldg. E., Annandale, VA 22003. TEL 703-750-0533. Ed. Judy Burgoon. bibl.; illus.; index, cum.index: vols.1-36, 1934-1969. circ. 3,400. (also avail. in microform from UMI; reprint service avail. from UMI) **Indexed:** Acad.Ind., Amer.Hist.& Life, Biol.Abstr., C.I.J.E., Commun.Abstr., Educ.Ind., Except.Child.Educ.Abstr., Hist.Abstr., Lang.& Lang.Behav.Abstr., Lang.Teach.& Ling.Abstr., M.L.A., Mid.East: Abstr.& Ind., Psychol.Abstr., Sage Fam.Stud.Abstr., Sage Pub.Admin.Abstr., SSCI. —BLDSC (3361.150000); Faxon; UnCover; SWETS; UMI.
    Formerly (until vol.42): Speech Monographs (ISSN 0038-7169)

808.5 370 US ISSN 0146-3373
PN4071
COMMUNICATION QUARTERLY. 1953. q. $25 (foreign $28). Eastern Communication Association, c/o Jerry L. Allen, Exec. Sec., Department of Communication & Marketing, University of New Haven, 300 Orange Ave., West Haven, CT 06516. TEL 203-932-7208. FAX 203-937-0756 Ed. Raymie E. McKerrow. adv.; bk.rev.; bibl.; index. circ. 3,000. (also avail. in microform from UMI,MIM) **Indexed:** C.I.J.E., Commun.Abstr., Cont.Pg.Educ., Educ.Ind., Hum.Ind., Lang.& Lang.Behav.Abstr., Mid.East: Abstr.& Ind., Mult.Ed.Abstr., Sociol.Abstr., Sp.Ed.Needs Abstr., Stud.Wom.Abstr. **Document type:** academic/scholarly publication.
    —BLDSC (3363.020000); Faxon; UnCover; SWETS; UMI.
    Formerly: Today's Speech (ISSN 0040-8573)

370 BE
COMMUNICATIONES. 1959. s-a. 600 BEF. World Association for Educational Research, Henri Dunantlaan 1, B-9000 Ghent, Belgium. Ed. M.L. van Herreweghe.
    Description: Journal on educational sciences about and for World Association for Educational Research members.

370 US ISSN 1040-4848
COMMUNICATIONS INSTITUTE. TRANSCRIPT. 1983. q. $20. Communications Institute, Communications Library, Lockbox 472139, Marina Station, San Francisco, CA 94147-2139. TEL 415-626-5050. Ed. T.S. Connelly. bk.rev. **Document type:** newsletter.
    Description: Timely topics related to the field of communications education which can be of assistance to the teacher and professor of communications in the classroom.

370 US ISSN 0045-7736
COMMUNITY EDUCATION JOURNAL. 1971-1975; resumed. q. $25. National Community Education Association, 3929 Old Lee Hwy., Ste. 91-A, Fairfax, VA 22030-2401. TEL 703-359-8973. FAX 703-359-0972. Ed. Ursula Ellis. adv.; index. circ. 3,300. (tabloid format; also avail. in microform from UMI) **Indexed:** Acad.Ind., C.I.J.E., Educ.Admin.Abstr., Mult.Ed.Abstr. **Document type:** academic/scholarly publication.
    —BLDSC (3363.624150); UnCover; UMI.
    Description: Provides a forum for the exchange of ideas and practices in community education, including reports of successful programs and research projects of interest to community educators.

EDUCATION

370   UK   ISSN 0262-706X
COMMUNITY EDUCATION NETWORK. 1981. 10/yr. £12.50 (foreign £15). Community Education Development Centre (CEDC), Lyng Hall, Blackberry Lane, Coventry CV2 3JS, England. TEL 0203-638660. FAX 0203-681161. Ed. Brian Sayer. adv.; bk.rev.; charts; illus. circ. 3,000.

COMPANY; a magazine of the American Jesuits. see *RELIGIONS AND THEOLOGY — Roman Catholic*

370   US   ISSN 0010-4043
COMPARATIVE AND INTERNATIONAL EDUCATION SOCIETY. NEWSLETTER. (Includes: Comparative Education Review) 1960. q. $10. Comparative and International Education Society, Secretariat Office, School of Education, University of Akron, Akron, OH 44325. TEL 216-972-6953. (Subscr. to: University of Chicago Press, Journals Division, Box 37005, Chicago, IL 60637) Ed. Dr. A. Al-Rubaiy. bk.rev.; bibl. circ. 2,600. (processed; reprint service avail.) **Document type:** academic/scholarly publication. —SWETS.
  Description: Information on new research and teaching activities, and information about the annual meetings.

370   UK   ISSN 0305-0068
L16
COMPARATIVE EDUCATION; an international journal of comparative studies. 1965. 3/yr. $132 to individuals; institutions $362 (effective 1994). Carfax Publishing Co., P.O. Box 25, Abingdon, Oxon. OX14 3UE, England. TEL 44-235-555335. FAX 44-235-553559. (U.S. subscr. to: Carfax Publishing Co., Box 2025, Dunnellon, FL 34430-2025) Ed. Patricia Bradfoot. adv.; bk.rev.; illus.; index. circ. 1,200. (also avail. in microfiche; back issues avail.) **Indexed:** C.I.J.E., Cont.Pg.Educ., Curr.Cont., Educ.Ind., Educ.Tech.Abstr., High.Educ.Curr.Aware.Bull., Lang.& Lang.Behav.Abstr., Mid.East: Abstr.& Ind., Mult.Ed.Abstr., Res.High.Educ.Abstr., Rural Ext.Educ.& Tr.Abstr., Rural Recreat.Tour.Abstr., So.Pac.Per.Ind., SOMA, Sp.Ed.Needs Abstr., SSCI, Stud.Wom.Abstr., World Agri.Econ.& Rural Sociol.Abstr. **Document type:** academic/scholarly publication.
—BLDSC (3363.760000); Faxon; UnCover; SWETS. **CCC.**
Refereed Serial

370   US   ISSN 0010-4086
L11
COMPARATIVE EDUCATION REVIEW. 1956. q. $31 to individuals; institutions $67. (Comparative and International Education Society) University of Chicago Press, Journals Division, 5720 S. Woodlawn Ave., Chicago, IL 60637. TEL 312-702-3347. FAX 312-753-0811. TELEX 25-4603. (Subscr. to: Box 37005, Chicago, IL 60637) Ed. Erwin H. Epstein. adv.; bk.rev.; bibl.; charts; index. circ. 2,300. (also avail. in microform from MIM,UMI; reprint service avail. from ISI,SCH,UMI) **Indexed:** Amer.Bibl.Slavic & E.Eur.Stud., C.I.J.E., Cont.Pg.Educ., Curr.Cont., Educ.Ind., Educ.Tech.Abstr., High.Educ.Curr.Aware.Bull., Lang.& Lang.Behav.Abstr., Mid.East: Abstr.& Ind., Mult.Ed.Abstr., P.A.I.S., Res.High.Educ.Abstr., Rural Ext.Educ.& Tr.Abstr., Rural Recreat.Tour.Abstr., SOMA, Sp.Ed.Needs Abstr., SSCI, World Agri.Econ.& Rural Sociol.Abstr. **Document type:** academic/scholarly publication.
—BLDSC (3363.780000); Faxon; UnCover; SWETS; UMI. **CCC.**
  Description: Publishes interdisciplinary research on educational policies and problems throughout the world, covering practical, theoretical, and methodological issues.
Refereed Serial

370   BE   ISSN 0588-9049
COMPARATIVE EDUCATION SOCIETY IN EUROPE. PROCEEDINGS OF THE GENERAL MEETING. Represents: C E S E Conference. Proceedings. (Text in English and French) 1963. biennial, 15th, 1992, Dijon. Comparative Education Society in Europe (CESE), c/o Dr. Miguel Pereira, Secy., Universidad de Granada, Facultad de Filosofia y Letras, Campus Univ. "La Cartuja, Granada 18071, Spain. FAX 34-58-236761. **Document type:** proceedings.

370   UK   ISSN 0305-7925
COMPARE; a journal of comparative education. 1971. 3/yr. £110 to individuals; institutions $346 (effective 1994). (British and International Comparative Education Society) Carfax Publishing Co., P.O. Box 25, Abingdon, Oxon. OX14 3UE, England. TEL 44-235-555335. FAX 44-235-553559. (U.S. subscr. to: Carfax Publishing Co., Box 2025, Dunnellon, FL 34430-2025) Ed. Nicholas Beattie. adv.; bk.rev.; illus.; index. (also avail. in microfiche; back issues avail.) **Indexed:** C.I.J.E., Cont.Pg.Educ., Curr.Cont., Educ.Tech.Abstr., High.Educ.Curr.Aware.Bull., Lang.& Lang.Behav.Abstr., Mult.Ed.Abstr., Res.High.Educ.Abstr., Rural Ext.Educ.& Tr.Abstr., SOMA, Sp.Ed.Needs Abstr., SSCI, Stud.Wom.Abstr. **Document type:** academic/scholarly publication.
—BLDSC (3363.890000); Faxon; SWETS. **CCC.**
Refereed Serial

COMUNICACION, LENGUAJE Y EDUCACION; metodos y tecnicas para el educador en las areas del curriculum. see *LINGUISTICS*

370   SP
COMUNIDAD ESCOLAR. 44/yr. 4700 ptas. (Europe 12550 ptas.; elsewhere 13950 ptas.) (effective 1992). Ministerio de Educacion y Ciencia, Centro de Publicaciones, Ciudad Universitaria, 28040 Madrid, Spain. TEL 549 77 00. Dir. Concha Gomez. **Document type:** newspaper.

370   US
CONCERNS (WASHINGTON). q. free. Council of Chief State School Officers, One Massachusetts Ave., N.W., Ste. 700, Washington, DC 20001. TEL 202-408-5505. Ed. Cynthia G. Brown. (back issues avail.)
  Description: Covers news of educational equity, including legislative news.

370   US   ISSN 1053-0053
LB1775.2
CONDITION OF TEACHING. 1983. irreg. (Carnegie Foundation) Princeton University Press, 41 William St., Princeton, NJ 08540. TEL 609-258-4900. FAX 609-258-6305. **Document type:** monographic series.

370   UK   ISSN 0265-4458
CONFERENCE & COMMON ROOM. 1963. 3/yr. £7. (Headmasters' Conference) Belgrave Educational Publishing, P.O. Box 140, Ipswich IP6 9PL, England. TEL 0449-79550. Ed. C.J. Driver Esq. adv.; bk.rev. circ. 3,000. **Document type:** trade publication.
—BLDSC (3408.779400).
  Formerly (until Feb. 1982): Conference (ISSN 0305-7658)
  Description: Contains news and developments in independent education regarding teaching methods, equipment, new buildings and experiments in particular schools.

379   US
LC1046.C8
CONNECTICUT. STATE COUNCIL ON VOCATIONAL-TECHNICAL EDUCATION. VOCATIONAL EDUCATION EVALUATION REPORT. Key Title: Vocational Education Evaluation Report. 1969. a. $10. Advisory Council on Vocational-Technical Education, 61 Woodland St., Hartford, CT 06105. TEL 203-566-4035. Ed. Richard G. Rausch. circ. 1,000. (also avail. in microfiche)
  Formerly: Connecticut. Advisory Council on Vocational and Career Education. Vocational Education Evaluation Report (ISSN 0363-650X)
  Description: Includes an evaluation of the vocational - technical education program delivery systems assisted under the Carl D. Perkins Vocational Education Act (PL 98-524), and the Job Training Partnership Act (PL 97-300) in terms of their adequacy and effectiveness in achieving their respective purposes.

370 340   US
CONNECTICUT EDUCATION ASSOCIATION. LEGISLATIVE BULLETIN. irreg. Connecticut Education Association, Capitol Place, Ste. 500, 21 Oak St., Hartford, CT 06106-8001. TEL 203-525-5641. FAX 203-725-6323. Ed. Michael Cooper.

370 800 420   US
CONNECTICUT ENGLISH JOURNAL. 1968. s-a. $15. Connecticut Council of Teachers of English, Central Connecticut State University, New Britain, CT 06050. TEL 203-827-7000. Ed. Diane P. Shugert. adv.; bk.rev.; index. circ. 600. (also avail. in microfiche from EDR) **Indexed:** ERIC.

CONNECTIONS (DAYTON). see *POLITICAL SCIENCE*

372.21   UK   ISSN 0308-0633
CONTACT (LONDON, 1961). 1969. m. (except Aug. & Jan.). £12. Pre-School Playgroups Association, 61-63 Kings Cross Rd., London WC1X 9LL, England. TEL 01-833 0991. Ed. Ann Henderson. adv.; bk.rev.; index, cum.index. circ. 20,000. (back issues avail.) **Indexed:** CERDIC.

370   ML
CONTACT: BULLETIN PEDAGOGIQUE.* (Text in French) 1973. q. 700 F. Ministere de l'Enseignement Superieur Secondaire et de la Recherche Scientifique, Institut Pedagogique National, B.P. 1583, Bamako, Mali. Ed. S. Tounkara. charts; illus.; stat.
  Description: Covers information regarding educational programs.

370   UK
CONTEMPORARY ANALYSES IN EDUCATION. 1979. 3/yr. £21($52) Taylor & Francis Ltd., Rankine Rd., Basingstoke, Hants. RF24 0PR, England. Eds. P. Taylor, C. Richards. adv.; bk.rev. circ. 750. (back issues avail.) **Indexed:** Educ.Tech.Abstr., Rural Ext.Educ.& Tr.Abstr., Stud.Wom.Abstr.
—CCC.
  Formerly: Educational Analysis (ISSN 0260-0994)
Refereed Serial

370   US   ISSN 0010-7476
L11
CONTEMPORARY EDUCATION. 1929. q. $12 to individuals (foreign $16); institutions $16 (foreign $19). Indiana State University, School of Education, Statesman Towers, Rm. 1005, Terre Haute, IN 47809. TEL 812-237-2970. FAX 812-237-4348. Ed. David A. Gilman. bk.rev.; illus.; index. circ. 1,500. (also avail. in microform from MIM,UMI; back issues avail.; reprint service avail. from UMI) **Indexed:** Amer.Hist.& Life, Bk.Rev.Ind. (1976-), C.I.J.E., Child.Bk.Rev.Ind. (1976-), Cont.Pg.Educ., Curr.Cont., Educ.Ind., Educ.Tech.Abstr., Hist.Abstr., Lang.& Lang.Behav.Abstr., Mid.East: Abstr.& Ind., Mult.Ed.Abstr., Sp.Ed.Needs Abstr., SSCI, Stud.Wom.Abstr. **Document type:** academic/scholarly publication.
—BLDSC (3425.180000); Faxon; UnCover; SWETS; UMI.
  Formerly: Teachers College Journal.

370.15   US   ISSN 0361-476X
LB1051
CONTEMPORARY EDUCATIONAL PSYCHOLOGY. 1976. q. $165 (foreign $208). Academic Press, Inc., Journal Division, 525 B St., Ste. 1900, San Diego, CA 92101-4495. TEL 619-230-1840. FAX 619-699-6800. (Subscr. to: Box 620000, Orlando, FL 32891-8340. TEL 800-543-9534) Ed. Raymond W. Kulhavy. illus.; index. (back issues avail.) **Indexed:** C.I.J.E., Child Devel.Abstr., Cont.Pg.Educ., Curr.Cont., Educ.Ind., Educ.Tech.Abstr., Mult.Ed.Abstr., Psychol.Abstr., Res.High.Educ.Abstr., SOMA, SSCI. **Document type:** academic/scholarly publication.
—BLDSC (3425.181000); Faxon; UnCover; SWETS. **CCC.**
  Description: Journal of empirical research and theory that demonstrates the application of psychological methods and research to problems in education. Covers the process of education through the life span, and presents a clear relationship of topic to data and theory.

CONTEMPORARY WALES; an annual review of economic and social research. see *SOCIAL SCIENCES: COMPREHENSIVE WORKS*

370   US   ISSN 0196-707X
CONTRIBUTIONS TO THE STUDY OF EDUCATION. 1981. irreg., no.57, 1992. price varies. Greenwood Press, Inc. (Subsidiary of: Greenwood Publishing Group Inc.), Box 5007, 88 Post Rd. W., Westport, CT 06881-5007. TEL 203-226-3571. FAX 203-222-1502.
—BLDSC (3461.454000).

371.42   US   ISSN 0069-9810
COOPERATIVE EDUCATION ASSOCIATION MEMBERSHIP DIRECTORY. 1965. a. $80. Cooperative Education Association, Inc., 11710 Beltsville Dr., Ste. 520, Beltsville, MD 20705-3102. TEL 301-572-2329. FAX 301-572-3916. circ. 3,000. **Document type:** directory.

370   US   ISSN 0010-843X
COOPERATIVE EDUCATION ASSOCIATION NEWSLETTER. 1969. 4/yr. $25. Cooperative Education Association, Inc., 11710 Beltsville Dr., Ste. 520, Beltsville, MD 20705-3102. TEL 301-572-2329. FAX 301-572-3916. Ed. Dawn E. Pettit. circ. 3,000. (tabloid format) **Document type:** newsletter.

371.3   US
CO-OPERATIVELY SPEAKING. 1970. 4/yr. $15. Parent Cooperative Preschools International, Box 90410, Indianapolis, IN 46290-0410. TEL 317-849-0992. (In Canada: 86 Saint George St., London, ON N6A 2Z7, Canada) illus.; index. circ. 10,000. **Document type:** newsletter.
  Formerly (until 1984): Parent Cooperative Preschools International Journal (ISSN 0048-2978)

370   IT   ISSN 0010-8502
COOPERAZIONE EDUCATIVA. 1952. q. L.40000 (foreign L.50000) (effective 1993). Nuova Italia Editrice S.p.a., Via Ernesto Codignola, 50018 Scandicci (FI), Italy. Ed. Giorgio Testa.

370   ZA
COPPERBELT EDUCATION. (Text in English) irreg. (1-2/yr.). PO Box 1552, Ndola, Zambia. illus.

CORPORATE SUPPORT OF EDUCATION. see *BUSINESS AND ECONOMICS*

370   BL
CORREIO DA UNESCO. 1972. m. $65 (effective 1994). (Instituto de Documentacao) Fundacao Getulio Vargas, C.P. 9052, 22272-970 Rio de Janeiro, R.J., Brazil. FAX 021-551-7801. TELEX 21-36811. illus. circ. 5,500.
  Description: Covers articles about the arts, education, sciences, communication and cultures.

370   US
CORRESPONDENCE EDUCATIONAL DIRECTORY. (4th ed. announced, never published) 1976-1993; suspended. quadrennial, 4th ed., 1993. $75. Racz Publishing Company, 6000 S. Eastern Ave., Bldg. 7, Ste. D, Las Vegas, NV 89119. TEL 702-795-8832. FAX 702-798-7471. Ed. John Harding Jones. adv.; bk.rev. circ. 10,000. **Document type:** directory.
  Description: Complete listings of institutions in the English-speaking countries offering correspondence education.

370   US   ISSN 0070-069X
COUNCIL FOR BASIC EDUCATION. OCCASIONAL PAPERS. 1961. irreg., latest no.33. $2 per no. Council for Basic Education, 1319 F St., N.W., Ste. 900, Washington, DC 20004-1106. TEL 202-347-4171. circ. 10,000.

COUNCIL FOR RESEARCH IN MUSIC EDUCATION. BULLETIN. see *MUSIC*

370   EI   ISSN 0252-0591
LA620
COUNCIL OF EUROPE. DOCUMENTATION CENTRE FOR EDUCATION IN EUROPE. NEWSLETTER. (Text in English or French) 1968. 5/yr. 160 F. Council of Europe, Publishing and Documentation Service, 67075 Strasbourg Cedex, France. TEL 33-88-41-25-93. FAX 33-88-41-27-80. TELEX 870943. (Dist. in U.S. by: Manhattan Publishing Co., One Croton Point Ave., P.O. Box 650, Croton, NY 10520) Ed. Wilson Barrett. adv. circ. 4,500. **Indexed:** High.Educ.Curr.Aware.Bull. **Document type:** newsletter.
  Description: Provides information on educational developments in European countries.

370   US
T61
COUNCIL ON TECHNOLOGY TEACHER EDUCATION. YEARBOOK. 1952. a. $18.96 to non-members. (American Council on Technology Teacher Education) Macmillan - McGraw-Hill, Glencoe Division, c/o Dr. Peggy Wild, 15319 Chatsworth St., Mission Hills, CA 91345. TEL 309-691-4454. (Addr. of Council: c/o Illinois State University, Department of Industrial Technology, 210 Turner Hall, Normal, IL 61761) Ed. Trudy Muller. circ. 1,500. (also avail. in microform from UMI; reprint service avail. from UMI) **Indexed:** Educ.Ind.
  Former titles: American Council on Industrial Arts Teacher Education. Yearbook (ISSN 0084-6333); American Industrial Arts Association. Yearbook (ISSN 0065-8634)
  Description: Devoted to current concerns and issues in technology education.

371.4   US   ISSN 0193-7375
COUNSELING AND HUMAN DEVELOPMENT. 1968. 9/yr. $30 (effective 1994). Love Publishing Co., 1777 S. Bellaire St., Denver, CO 80222. TEL 303-757-2579. FAX 303-782-5683. Ed. S.F. Love. bk.rev.; index, cum.index. circ. 1,500. (also avail. in microform from UMI; reprint service avail. from UMI)
  —UnCover; UMI.
  Formerly (until Sep. 1977): Focus on Guidance (ISSN 0015-5136)

COUNSELOR EDUCATION AND SUPERVISION. see *PSYCHOLOGY*

371.4   US   ISSN 0271-5368
L901
COUNSELOR PREPARATION (YEAR); programs, personnel, trends. (In 2 vols.: Vol. 1 Personnel and Programs, Vol. 2 Status, Trends, and Implications) 1971. triennial, 8th ed., 1993. $49.95 (vol.1 $34.95; vol.2 $25.95). Accelerated Development Inc., 3808 W. Kilgore Ave., Muncie, IN 47304-4896. TEL 317-284-7511. FAX 317-284-2535. Ed. Cindy Long. adv. contact: Janet Merchant. circ. 800. **Document type:** directory.
  Formerly: Counselor Education Directory: Personnel and Programs (ISSN 0190-2199)
  Description: Lists all counselor-education programs in the United States. Program areas include: counseling psychology, counseling, marriage and family therapy, and counselor education.

370   US   ISSN 0899-9376
COUNTRY TEACHER. 1985. 3/yr. $35 library membership includes Rural Educator and National Rural Education News (foreign $50) (not avail. separately) (effective 1994). National Rural Education Association, 230 Education Bldg., Colorado State University, Fort Collins, CO 80523-0001. TEL 303-491-7022. FAX 303-491-1317. Ed. Joseph T. Newlin. circ. 3,000 (paid). **Document type:** newspaper.
  Description: Covers issues in rural education.

370   CN
COVEN. w. Humber College of Applied Arts and Technology, Journalism Department, Box 1900, Rexdale, Ont. M9W 5L7, Canada. TEL 416-675-3111. Ed. Bruce Gates. adv.

CREATIVE CHILD AND ADULT QUARTERLY. see *CHILDREN AND YOUTH — About*

371.42   US
CREATIVE TRAINING TECHNIQUES; a newsletter of tips, tactics and how-tos for delivering effective training. 1988. 12/yr. $99 in U.S.; Canada $109; elsewhere $119. Lakewood Publications (Subsidiary of: Maclean Hunter Publishing Company), 50 S. Ninth St., Minneapolis, MN 55402. TEL 612-333-0471. FAX 612-333-6526. Ed. Bob Pike. **Document type:** newsletter.
  Description: Provides tips on tactics and how to provide effective training.

CREATIVITY IN ACTION. see *BUSINESS AND ECONOMICS — Management*

370   US   ISSN 0011-1171
CRESCENDO (INTERLOCHEN). 1964. 3/yr. free. Interlochen Arts Academy, Interlochen Arts Camp, Interlochen, MI 49643. TEL 616-276-7200. FAX 616-276-6321. illus.; circ. 51,000 (controlled). **Document type:** newsletter.
  Description: Guide to schools.

CRIT. see *ARCHITECTURE*

370   AT   ISSN 1033-808X
CRITICAL PEDAGOGY NETWORKER. 1988. q. Aus.$15 (effective Jan. 1991). Flinaers University of South Australia, School of Education, P.O. Box 2100, Adelaide, S.A. 5001, Australia. TEL 08-201-2277. circ. 500.

377.8   UK   ISSN 0260-6313
CROSSCURRENT. 1980. 3/yr. £7. National Society, Church House, Great Smith St., Westminster, London SW1P 3NZ, England. TEL 071-222-1672. FAX 071-233-2592. Ed. Joanna Yates. adv.; bk.rev. circ. 3,000. **Document type:** consumer publication.
  Description: For teachers and clergy interested in the Church's work in education.

370   CL   ISSN 0716-0496
CUADERNOS DE EDUCACION. 1973. m. Esc.250($17.50) Centro de Investigacion y Desarrollo de Educacion, Casilla 13608, Santiago 1, Chile. Ed. Francisco Alvarez Martin. adv.; bk.rev.; bibl.; charts; illus. index. circ. 1,000.

370   SP   ISSN 0210-0630
CUADERNOS DE PEDAGOGIA; revista mensual de educacion. 1975. m. (11/yr.). $60. Editorial Fontalba, S.A., Valencia 359, 6o, 1a, 08009 Barcelona, Spain. TEL 93-458-5508. FAX 93-458-6602. TELEX 97835 FON E. bibl.; illus.; stat. circ. 20,000.
  —SWETS.

370   IT   ISSN 0011-2771
AS221
CULTURA E SCUOLA. q. L.24000. Istituto della Enciclopedia Italiana, Piazza Paganica 4, 00186 Rome, Italy. adv.; bk.rev.; charts; play rev. **Indexed:** M.L.A.
  —BLDSC (3491.655000).
  Description: Focuses on the problems of educational curricula, up-dating teachers, and proposals for the suggested sequence of subjects to be studied.

370 301.16   US   ISSN 0097-952X
BR115.C8
CULTURAL INFORMATION SERVICE; the magazine for lifelong learners. 1972. 10/yr. $37 (foreign $49). C I S-tems, Inc., Box 786, New York, NY 10159. TEL 212-691-5240. Ed. Frederic A. Brussat. bk.rev.; index.
  Description: Discusses education and media.

CURRENT (NEWARK) the journal of marine education. see *BIOLOGY*

300   US   ISSN 0011-3131
AP2
CURRENT (WASHINGTON, 1960); significant new material from all sources on the frontier problems of today. 1960. m. (except Mar.-Apr., Jul.-Aug. combined). $32 to individuals; institutions $56. (Helen Dwight Reid Educational Foundation) Heldref Publications, 1319 18th St., N.W., Washington, DC 20036-1802. TEL 202-296-6267. FAX 202-296-5149. Ed. Joyce Horn. adv.: B&W page $330; adv. contact: Raymond Rallo. abstr.; bibl.; charts; index. circ. 4,600. (also avail. in microform; back issues avail.; reprint service avail.) **Indexed:** Arts & Hum.Cit.Ind., Cont.Pg.Educ., Curr.Cont., G.Soc.Sci.& Rel.Per.Lit., Human Resour.Abstr., Mid.East: Abstr.& Ind., R.G., Sp.Ed.Needs Abstr., SSCI. **Document type:** academic/scholarly publication.
  —Faxon; UnCover UMI.
  Refereed Serial

CURRENT (WASHINGTON, 1982). see *COMMUNICATIONS — Television And Cable*

CURRENT EVENTS. see *CHILDREN AND YOUTH — For*

377.9   US
CURRENT ISSUES IN CATHOLIC HIGHER EDUCATION. 1975. s-a. price varies. Association of Catholic Colleges and Universities, One Dupont Circle, Ste. 650, Washington, DC 20036. TEL 202-457-0650. FAX 202-728-0977. Ed. Paul Gallagher. circ. 2,000. (also avail. in microform from EDR; reprint service avail. from UMI) **Indexed:** ERIC.
  Supersedes (1975-1980): National Catholic Educational Association. Occasional Papers.

EDUCATION

371 US ISSN 1059-7107
▼**CURRENT ISSUES IN MIDDLE LEVEL EDUCATION.**
1992. 2/yr. $15. West Georgia College, School of Education, Carrollton, GA 30118.
TEL 404-836-6560. FAX 404-836-6729. Ed. John W. Myers. bk.rev. **Document type:** academic/scholarly publication.
Description: Focuses on discussion of issues in middle level education, philosophy, curriculum and instruction, and research.
Refereed Serial

CURRENT SCIENCE. see *CHILDREN AND YOUTH — For*

372.21 US ISSN 0363-8332
LB1140.A1
CURRENT TOPICS IN EARLY CHILDHOOD EDUCATION.
1977. irreg., vol.7, 1987. price varies. Ablex Publishing Corporation, 355 Chestnut St., Norwood, NJ 07648. TEL 201-767-8450.
FAX 201-767-6717. TELEX 135-393. Ed. Lilian G. Katz.

370 CN
CYCLOPEDIA. 1981. a. free. Student Enterprises & Assistance League, Box 250, Station P., Toronto, Ont. M5S 2T9, Canada. illus.; circ. 25,000 (controlled).

370 CY ISSN 0045-9429
CYPRUS TO-DAY. 1963. q. free. Press and Information Office, Nicosia, Cyprus. TEL 357-2-446981.
FAX 357-2-453730. TELEX 2526-PIONIC. Ed. Yiannis Katsouris. adv.; bk.rev.; illus. circ. 15,000.
Document type: government publication.
—BLDSC (3506.735000); UnCover.

CZLOWIEK I SPOLECZENSTWO. see *PSYCHOLOGY*

370 DK ISSN 0107-301X
D S - KONTAKT. 1981. q. membership. Danmarks Skolelederforening, Ved Stranden 16, 1061 Copenhagen K, Denmark. adv. circ. 3,000.

DANCE AUSTRALIA. see *DANCE*

DANCE TEACHER NOW; the practical magazine of dance. see *DANCE*

370 DK ISSN 0900-5781
DANMARKS LAERERHOEJSKOLE. INSTITUT FOR INFORMATIK. ARBEJDSPAPIR. 1984. irreg. free. Danmarks Laererhoejskole, Institut for Informatik - Royal Danish School of Educational Studies, Institute of Informatics, Emdrupvej 115B, 2400 Copenhagen NV, Denmark. circ. 500.

370 150 DK ISSN 0107-1637
DANMARKS LAERERHOEJSKOLE. INSTITUT FOR PAEDAGOGIK OG PSYKOLOGI. TESTSAMLING. 1978. irreg. DKK 40 (effective 1991). Danmarks Laererhoejskole, Institut for Paedagogik og Psykologi, Copenhagen, Denmark. Ed. Ole Varming.

370 DK ISSN 0011-6408
DANSK PAEDAGOGISK TIDSSKRIFT/DANISH JOURNAL OF EDUCATION. 1953. 8/yr. DKK 150. Kongelundsvej 353, DK-2770 Kastrup, Denmark. Ed.Bd. adv.; bk.rev.; illus.; index. circ. 4,600.

DANYAG; journal of studies in the humanities, education and the sciences, basic and applied. see *HUMANITIES: COMPREHENSIVE WORKS*

370 SP ISSN 0070-2897
DATOS Y CIFRAS DE LA ENSENANZA EN ESPANA. 1978. irreg., latest 1982. Ministerio de Educacion y Ciencia, Centro de Publicaciones, Ciudad Universitaria, s-n, 28040 Madrid, Spain. TEL 549 77 00.

370 US ISSN 0091-6188
LB2803.D3
DELAWARE. DEPARTMENT OF PUBLIC INSTRUCTION. EDUCATIONAL PERSONNEL DIRECTORY. 1921. a. $7.50. Department of Public Instruction, Division of Planning, Research & Evaluation, Townsend Bldg., Dover, DE 19903. Ed. Wilmer E. Wise. circ. 3,500.
Document type: directory, government publication.

370 US ISSN 0362-8787
LA252
DELAWARE. STATE BOARD OF EDUCATION. REPORT OF EDUCATIONAL STATISTICS. Key Title: Report of Educational Statistics. 1921. a. State Board of Education, Townsend Bldg., Box 1402, Dover, DE 19901. TEL 302-736-4629. circ. 300. (also avail. in microfiche from CIS) **Indexed:** SRI.

DELFIN; eine deutsche Zeitschrift fuer Konstruktion, Analyse und Kritik. see *ART*

370 028.5 NZ ISSN 0110-4748
DELTA RESEARCH MONOGRAPH. 1967. s-a. NZ.$25. Massey University, Education Department, Palmerston N., New Zealand.
FAX 064-6-35505635. Ed. Dr. John A. Codd. bk.rev. circ. 500. (back issues avail.) **Indexed:** Mult.Ed.Abstr., Sociol.Educ.Abstr.
—BLDSC (3548.298000). **CCC.**
Formerly (until 1977): Delta (Palmerston North) (ISSN 0419-9855)

370 US
DEMOCRACY AND EDUCATION. 1986. q. $25 to individuals; institutions $30. Institute for Democracy in Education, Ohio University, College of Education, 313 McCracken Hall, Athens, OH 45701-2979.
TEL 614-593-4531. FAX 614-593-0177. Ed.Bd. adv.; bk.rev. circ. 650.
Refereed Serial

370 DK ISSN 0107-4652
DENMARK. STATENS PAEDAGOGISKE FORSOEGSCENTER. ARBEJDSBESKRIVELSE. 1980. a. free. Statens Paedagogiske Forsoegscenter, Ungdomsbyens Skole, Islevgaard Alle 5, 2610 Roedovre, Denmark. illus.
Formerly: Denmark. Statens Paedagogiske Forsoegscenter. Projektbeskrivelser.

370 DK
DENMARK. STATENS UDDANNELSESSTOETTE. HAANDBOG. 1970. a. DKK 55 (typically set in Jan.). Statens Uddannelsesstoette, Danasvej 30, DK-1780 Copenhagen V607, Denmark. TEL 31-21-46-66.
FAX 45-31-23-75-70. (Subscr. to: Statens Information, Nr. Farimagsgade 65, P.O. Box 1103, 1009 Copenhagen K, Denmark. TEL 45 33 37 92 00) Ed. Lone Hedegaard Hansen. circ. 10,000.
Document type: government publication.
Formerly: Denmark. Statens Uddannelsesstoette. Regelsamling for Stoetteaaret (ISSN 0107-5152)

370 340 US ISSN 1058-4919
KF4114
DESKBOOK ENCYCLOPEDIA OF AMERICAN SCHOOL LAW.
1981. a. Data Research Inc., 4635 Nicols Rd., Ste. 100, Eagan, MN 55122. (Subscr. to : Box 409, Rosemount, MN 55068)

371 US ISSN 0011-9695
DETROIT TEACHER. vol.34, 1975. s-m. $4 to non-members. Detroit Federation of Teachers, A F L - C I O, Local 231, 7451 Third Ave., Detroit, MI 48202. TEL 313-875-3500. FAX 313-875-3512. Ed. Lois Vagnozzi. adv.; bk.rev.; charts; illus. circ. 16,500. **Document type:** newspaper.

DEUTSCHE OSTKUNDE; Vierteljahresschrift fuer Wissenschaft, Erziehung und Unterricht. see *HISTORY — History Of Europe*

370 GW ISSN 0012-0731
DIE DEUTSCHE SCHULE; Zeitschrift fuer Erziehungswissenschaft, Bildungspolitik und paedagogische Praxis. 1908. q. DM.75 (students DM.64). (Gewerkschaft Erziehung und Wissenschaft) Juventa Verlag GmbH, Ehretstr. 3, 69469 Weinheim, Germany. TEL 06201-61035.
FAX 06201-13135. Ed.Bd. adv.; bk.rev.; index. circ. 1,500. **Document type:** academic/scholarly publication.
—SWETS. **CCC.**

370 GW ISSN 0012-1460
DEUTSCHUNTERRICHT (BERLIN). 1948. 11/yr. DM.60.50. Paedagogischer Zeitschriftenverlag, Postfach 269, 10107 Berlin, Germany.
TEL 030-20343431. FAX 030-20343432. Ed. Christel Ende. adv.; bk.rev.; abstr.; index. **Indexed:** Bibl.Ling. **Document type:** academic/scholarly publication.

370 GW ISSN 0340-2258
DER DEUTSCHUNTERRICHT; Beitraege zu seiner Praxis und wissenschaftlichen Grundlegung. 1948. 6/yr. DM.99.60. Erhard Friedrich Verlag GmbH, Im Brande 17, 30926 Seelze, Germany.
TEL 0511-40004-0. (Subscr. to: Postfach 100150, 30917 Seelze, Germany) Ed.Bd. cum.index: vols.1-30, 1948-1978. circ. 15,000. **Indexed:** Bibl.Ling., Lang.& Lang.Behav.Abstr., M.L.A.
Document type: academic/scholarly publication.
—BLDSC (3578.530000); Faxon; SWETS. **CCC.**

DEUTSCHUNTERRICHT IM SUEDLICHEN AFRIKA. see *LINGUISTICS*

DEVELOPMENT COMMUNICATION REPORT. see *TECHNOLOGY: COMPREHENSIVE WORKS*

370 PK ISSN 0080-1321
DEVELOPMENT OF EDUCATION IN PAKISTAN. Variant title: Report on the Progress of Education in Pakistan. (Text in English) 1965. a. Ministry of Education, Documentation Section, Curriculum Wing, Sector H-9, P.O. Shaigan, Industrial Area, Islamabad, Pakistan.

DIALOG. see *POLITICAL SCIENCE*

507 370 IT ISSN 0012-2106
DIALOGOS; problemi dell'istruzione e della ricerca scientifica. 1960. 5/yr. L.20000($30) Libreria Editrice Romana, Casella Postale 30098, Rome 47, Italy. Ed. Dr. Saverio Avveduto. adv.; bk.rev.; index. circ. 6,000. **Indexed:** Phil.Ind.

DIDAKOMETRY AND SOCIOMETRY. see *PSYCHOLOGY*

370 500 FR
▼**DIDASKALIA**; recherches sur la communication et l'apprentissage des sciences et des techniques. 1993. 3/yr. 400 F. (foreign 500 F.). Institut National de Recherche Pedagogique, 29 rue d'Ulm, 75230 Paris Cedex 05, France. TEL 46-34-90-00.

370 BL ISSN 0101-059X
L45 CODEN: DIDAD7
DIDATICA; serie educacao. (Text in Portuguese; summaries in English and Portuguese) 1964-1977; resumed 1979. a. $30 or exchange basis. Universidade Estadual Paulista, Av. Vicente Ferreira 1278, Caixa Postal 603, 17515-901 Marilia, SP, Brazil. TEL 0144-33-1844. FAX 0144-22-2504.
TELEX 111 9016 UJME BR. bibl.; charts. circ. 1,000. **Indexed:** Cont.Pg.Educ., Psychol.Abstr.
Document type: academic/scholarly publication.
Description: Presents articles and reviews which examine the process of education at all levels.

DIMENSIO. see *MATHEMATICS*

300 CN ISSN 0709-2334
DIMENSIONS (MONTREAL). (Text in French) 1979. q. Commission des Ecoles Catholiques de Montreal, 3737 Sherbrooke St. E., Montreal, PQ H1X 3B3, Canada. TEL 514-596-6116. FAX 514-596-7525. Ed. Jean-Pierre Issenhuth. adv.: Page Can.$900; 19 x 24. circ. 11,000. **Indexed:** Pt.de Rep. (1979-). **Document type:** academic/scholarly publication.

370 TS
DIRASAT TARBAWIYYAH/EDUCATIONAL STUDIES.* (Text in Arabic) 1977. q. exchange basis. Mintaqat Al-Ain al-Ta'limiyyah, Qism al-Buhuth wal-Tawthiq - Al-Ain Educational Region, Department of Research and Documentation, P.O. Box 1008, Al-Ain, United Arab Emirates. TEL 655877. circ. 500.
Description: Covers all aspects of education studies, including administration, teacher training, Arabic language instruction, leadership, theoretical and practical observations on teaching methods.

DIRECTORY OF COMPUTER AND HIGH TECHNOLOGY GRANTS. see *SOCIAL SERVICES AND WELFARE*

DIRECTORY OF DEVELOPMENT AND TRAINING INSTITUTES IN AFRICA. see *BUSINESS AND ECONOMICS — International Development And Assistance*

374 US ISSN 0084-991X
DIRECTORY OF EDUCATIONAL INSTITUTIONS IN NEW MEXICO; approved for the education of veterans, war orphans and other eligible persons. (Subseries of its Bulletin) 1966. a. free. Department of Education, Veterans Approval Division, Box 4277, Santa Fe, NM 87501. Dir. Rudy Silva.

DIRECTORY OF INTERNATIONAL MUSIC EDUCATION DISSERTATIONS IN PROGRESS. see *MUSIC*

DIRECTORY OF MUSIC FACULTIES IN COLLEGES & UNIVERSITIES U S AND CANADA. see *MUSIC*

370 US ISSN 1041-6331
L901
DIRECTORY OF PUBLIC ELEMENTARY AND SECONDARY EDUCATION AGENCIES. irreg., latest 1989-90. price varies. U.S. Department of Education, National Center for Education Statistics, 555 New Jersey Ave., N.W., Washington, DC 20208. TEL 800-424-1616. (Dist. by: Superintendant of Documents, Washington, DC 20402)
Former titles: Education Directory. Local Education Agencies (ISSN 0273-4346); Education Directory. Public Schools Systems (ISSN 0083-2677)

370 US
DIRECTORY OF STATE EDUCATION AGENCIES. a. $25. Council of Chief State School Officers, One Massachusetts Ave., N.W., Ste. 700, Washington, DC 20001. TEL 202-408-5505. Ed. Wendy Campbell. circ. 3,000.
Description: Lists key personnel at the 50 state education departments, the District of Columbia, five US territories, and the Department of Defense dependents schools. Also provides addresses for U.S. governors, national edecation associations, and key personnel of the U.S. Department of Education.

DIRECTORY OF UNDERGRADUATE POLITICAL SCIENCE FACULTY (YEAR). see *POLITICAL SCIENCE*

371.2 US
DISPATCH (DES MOINES). 1930. 7/yr. free to Iowa teachers and administrators. Department of Education, Grimes State Office Bldg., Des Moines, IA 50319-0146. TEL 515-281-3797. Ed. Lisa Bartusek. circ. 56,000.
Former titles: D P I Dispatch; Educational Bulletin (ISSN 0013-1679)
Description: Focuses on educational administration.

370 AT ISSN 0158-7919
DISTANCE EDUCATION. 1980. s-a. Aus.$48. (Open and Distance Learning Association of Australia) U S Q Publications, Distance Education Centre, Darling Heights, Toowoomba, Qld. 4350, Australia. TEL 61-76-312290. FAX 61-76-312868. TELEX 40010. Ed. Ian Mitchell. adv.; bk.rev. circ. 1,000. (back issues avail.; reprint service avail. from EDR) Indexed: C.I.J.E., Cont.Pg.Educ., Educ.Tech.Abstr., Mult.Ed.Abstr., Res.High.Educ.Abstr. Document type: academic/scholarly publication.
—BLDSC (3602.520000); Faxon; UnCover; SWETS; UMI. **CCC**.
Description: Publishes papers on the history, politics, theory, practice and administration of distance and open education.

370 FR
DITS ET VECUS POPULAIRES. 1983. 6/yr. 54 F. to individuals; professionals 46 F. Ecole Moderne Francaise - Pedagogie Freinet, B.P. 109, 06332 Cannes - La Bocca Cedex, France.

370 IT
DOCETE. 1946. m. L.30000 (effective Sep. 1993). Federazione Istituti di Attivita Educative, Via della Pigna 13-A, Rome, Italy. TEL 06-6791341. FAX 06-6791097. Ed. Giuseppe Gioia. adv.; bk.rev.; index. circ. 4,000.
Description: Covers educational issues, aimed especially at headmasters and teachers of free Italian schools.

370 BL
DOCUMENTA. (Text in Portuguese; summaries in English, French, Spanish) 1962. m. Cr.$8800($219) (for 2 years). (Conselho Federal de Educacao) Fundacao Mariana Rezende Costa, Av. Dom Jose Gaspar, 500, Bairro Coracao Eucaristico, 30000 Belo Horizonte M.G., Brazil.

DOCUMENTATION PAR L'IMAGE; revue des activites d'eveil. see *SCIENCES: COMPREHENSIVE WORKS*

DOCUMENTI DELLA SCUOLA. see *CHILDREN AND YOUTH — About*

372.21 RU ISSN 0012-561X
DOSHKOL'NOE VOSPITANIE. 1928. m. $17. (Ministerstvo Prosveshcheniya) Izdatel'stvo Prosveshchenie, 3-i Proezd Mar'inoi Roshchi, 41, Moscow, Russia. TEL 095-289-1405. (Co-sponsor: Ministerstvo Narodnogo Obrazovaniya) Ed. M.A. Vasil'eva. bk.rev.; bibl.; illus. circ. 983,474.
Description: Aimed at pre-school and kindergarten pedagogues.

DRAGON'S TEETH. see *CHILDREN AND YOUTH — About*

DRAMATICS; devoted to the advancement of theatre arts in the secondary schools. see *THEATER*

370 150 US
DREAM SWITCHBOARD. 1988. q. $10. (Community Dreamsharing Network) Dream Switchboard, Box 8032, Hicksville, NY 11802-8032. TEL 516-796-9455. FAX 516-731-2395. Ed. Harold R. Ellis. adv.; bk.rev.; film rev.; play rev. circ. 500. Document type: newsletter.
Description: Provides elementary and secondary school classroom assistance to help students understand dreams.
Refereed Serial

DUKE UNIVERSITY LIBRARIES. see *LIBRARY AND INFORMATION SCIENCES*

370 GW ISSN 0070-7767
DURCH STIPENDIEN STUDIEREN. 1964. a. DM.18. Verein Freunde und Foerderer der Deutschen Studentenschaft e.V., Untere Hausbreite 11, 80939 Munich, Germany. Ed. Gundolf Seidenspinner. adv.

372 GW
DURCHBRUCH; Zeitung der kreisschueler innenvertretung des Main - Taunus - Kreises. 1986. q. DM.8. Kreisschueler Innenvertretung des Main - Taunus - Kreises, Gartenstr. 28, 65719 Hofheim, Germany. TEL 06192-24322. Ed. Stefan Diefenbach. adv.; bk.rev.

371.33 UK ISSN 0952-3987
LB1043
E D I. EDUCATIONAL MEDIA INTERNATIONAL. 1961. q. £37($70) (International Council for Educational Media) Kogan Page Ltd., 120 Pentonville Rd., London N1 9JN, England. TEL 071-278-0433. FAX 071-837-6348. TELEX 263088 KOGAN G. Ed. John Bell. adv.; bk.rev. circ. 500. (also avail. in microfilm from UMI; reprint service avail. from UMI) Indexed: Abstr.Hum.Comp.Inter., C.I.J.E., Commun.Abstr., Cont.Pg.Educ., Educ.Ind., Excerp.Med., High.Educ.Curr.Aware.Bull., Lang.& Lang.Behav.Abstr., Mid.East: Abstr.& Ind., Res.High.Educ.Abstr., SOMA. Document type: academic/scholarly publication.
—BLDSC (3733.490000); Faxon; UnCover; SWETS; UMI.
Former titles (until 1986): Educational Media International (ISSN 0004-7597); (until 1971): Audio-Visual Media (ISSN 0571-8716)
Description: Discusses audiovisual aids.

370 UK ISSN 0962-4244
E D I T. (European Dimension in Teaching) 1991. irreg. price varies. U.K. Centre for European Education, Central Bureau, Seymour Mews House, Seymour Mews, London W1H 9PE, England. TEL 071-486-5101. FAX 071-935-5741. TELEX 21368-CBEVEX-G. circ. 12,000. Document type: academic/scholarly publication.

370 US
E R I C - C R E S S BULLETIN. 1966. 3/yr. free. Educational Resources Information Center, Clearinghouse on Rural Education and Small Schools, 1031 Quarrier St., Box 1348, Charleston, WV 25325. TEL 304-347-0437. FAX 304-347-0487. Ed. Pat Cahape. bk.rev.; film rev.; abstr.; bibl. circ. 4,000. (looseleaf format; back issues avail.) Document type: newsletter.
Formerly (until 1988): C R E S S Notes.

370 362.7 917.306 US ISSN 0889-8022
E R I C - C U E TRENDS AND ISSUES. 1985. irreg. price varies. Educational Resource Information Center, Clearinghouse on Urban Education, Box 40, Teachers College, Columbia University, New York, NY 10027. TEL 212-678-3433. (Co-sponsor: Institute for Urban and Minority Education) Ed. Wendy Schwartz. bibl.; stat. (also avail. in microfiche; back issues avail.) Indexed: Res.Educ. Document type: monographic series.

370 US ISSN 0889-8030
E R I C - C U E URBAN DIVERSITY SERIES. 1972. irreg. price varies. Educational Resource Information Center, Clearinghouse on Urban Education, Box 40, Teachers College, Columbia University, New York, NY 10027. TEL 212-678-3433. Ed. Wendy Schwartz. bibl.; stat. circ. 1,000. (also avail. in microfiche; back issues avail.) Indexed: ERIC, Res.Educ. Document type: monographic series.

370 US
E R I C CLEARINGHOUSE ON TEACHING AND TEACHER EDUCATION. CURRENT ISSUES PUBLICATIONS. irreg. (4-5/yr.). E R I C Clearinghouse on Teaching and Teacher Education. One Dupont Circle, Ste. 610, Washington, DC 20036. TEL 202-293-2450. (also avail. in microfiche; reprint service avail. from UMI,EDR) Document type: monographic series.
Formerly: E R I C Clearinghouse on Teacher Education. Current Issues Publications.

370 362.7 917.306 US ISSN 0889-8049
E R I C CLEARINGHOUSE ON URBAN EDUCATION. DIGEST. (Educational Resources Information Center) 1980. irreg. (Institute for Urban and Minority Education) E R I C Clearinghouse on Urban Education, Box 40 Teachers College, Columbia University, New York, NY 10027. TEL 212-678-3433. Ed. Wendy Schwartz. bibl. (also avail. in microfiche; back issues avail.) Indexed: Res.Educ. Document type: academic/scholarly publication.
●Also available online. Vendor(s): The Source.

E R I C - I R UPDATE. (Educational Resources Information Center - Information Resources) see *LIBRARY AND INFORMATION SCIENCES — Computer Applications*

371.3 US ISSN 1053-1912
LB1743604
E T IDEAS. 1966. 10/yr. $35. Princeton Educational Publishers, Box 280, Plainsboro, NJ 08536. TEL 908-297-6920. charts; illus. circ. 23,000. Document type: newsletter.
Formerly (until 1991): Elementary Teacher's Ideas and Materials Workshop (ISSN 0013-5992)

370 US
E T S POLICY INFORMATION REPORT. irreg. price varies. Educational Testing Service, Princeton, NJ 08541-0001. TEL 609-921-9000. (Subscr. to: Little Brown, 200 West St., Waltham, MA 02254. TEL 800-759-0190; Institutional subscr. to: Special Sales, Warner Book, Inc., Time & Life Bldg., 1271 Ave. of the Americas, New York, NY 10020. TEL 212-522-7381)

370 US
E T S POLICY NOTES. irreg. (2-3/yr.). Educational Testing Service, Princeton, NJ 08541-0001. TEL 609-921-9000. (Subscr. to: Little Brown, 200 West St., Waltham, MA 02254. TEL 800-759-0190; Institutional subscr. to: Special Sales, Warner Book, Inc., Time & Life Bldg., 1271 Ave. of the Americas, New York, NY 10020. TEL 212-522-7381) Document type: newsletter.
Description: Discloses research results relating to education policy.

370 US
E T S RESEARCH REPORTER. 3/yr. free. Educational Testing Service, Princeton, NJ 08541-0001. TEL 609-921-9000. (Dist. by: Office of Research Administration, E.T.S., 19-D, Rosedale Rd., Princeton, NJ 08541) Document type: newsletter.
Description: Keeps E.T.S. staff and colleagues up-to-date on E.T.S research projects and activities.

370 US
E T S TODAY. a.? free. Educational Testing Service, Princeton, NJ 08541-0001. TEL 609-921-9000. (Subscr. to: Little Brown, 200 West St., Waltham, MA 02254. TEL 800-759-0190; Institutional subscr. to: Special Sales, Warner Book, Inc., Time & Life Bldg., 1271 Ave. of the Americas, New York, NY 10020. TEL 212-522-7381)

370 IT
E T V. (Educazione e Televisione); rivista di attualita-cultura-economia. 1982. s-a. L.10000. Queriniana Unione Editoriale Rivista Cinematografia Istruzione Audiovisia (QUERCIA), Via Paisiello 12, 00198 Rome, Italy

EDUCATION

370   **GW**
E U INFORMATIONEN FUER DIE SCHULE. (Europaeische Union) 1990. q. Europaeische Kommission, Vertretung in der Bundesrepublik Deutschland, Zitelmannstr. 22, 53113 Bonn, Germany. TEL 0228-53009-0. FAX 0228-5300950. adv. circ. 40,000. (back issues avail.) **Document type:** bulletin.
    Former titles (until 1993): E G Informationen fuer die Schule; Schule in der Europaeischen Gemeinschaft.

370   **US**
EAGLE (PRICE). 1937. bi-m. $12. College of Eastern Utah, 451 E. 4th North, Price, UT 84501. TEL 801-637-2120. FAX 801-637-4102. Ed. Elisha Ray. adv.; bk.rev.; film rev.; play rev.; charts; illus.; tr.lit. circ. 1,500. (tabloid format; back issues avail.; reprint service avail.)

372   **US**   **ISSN 0885-2006**
EARLY CHILDHOOD RESEARCH QUARTERLY. 1986. q. $45 to individuals; institutions $120. Ablex Publishing Corporation, 355 Chestnut St., Norwood, NJ 07648. TEL 201-767-8450. FAX 201-767-6717. TELEX 135-393. Ed. Lilian G. Katz. index. circ. 1,700. **Indexed:** Psychol.Abstr. —BLDSC (3642.960300); Faxon; UnCover; SWETS. CCC.

372 001.642
621.381   **US**
EARLY CHILDHOOD TEACHER; instructor's magazine for preschool and primary professionals. 1986. s-a. free. Scholastic Inc., 555 Broadway, New York, NY 10012-3999. TEL 212-343-6100. Ed. Anne Marie DiTeodoro. adv.; bk.rev.; circ. 60,000 (controlled). **Document type:** trade publication.
    Formerly: E C E Teacher.
    Description: Aimed at classroom teachers of children ages 3 to 6. Contains a variety of articles of interest to preschool and primary instructors.

370.15 150   **US**   **ISSN 1040-9289**
LB1101
EARLY EDUCATION AND DEVELOPMENT. 1989. q. $55 to individuals; institutions $105 (effective 1994). Wide Range Inc., Box 3410, Wilmington, DE 19804-0250. TEL 800-221-9728. FAX 302-652-1644. Ed. Richard R. Abidin. bk.rev. circ. 350. **Document type:** academic/scholarly publication.
—BLDSC (3642.964800); UnCover.
    Description: Presents empirical research in early childhood education and child development, with emphasis on practical implications for practitioners.

EAST AND CENTRAL AFRICAN JOURNAL OF SURGERY. see *MEDICAL SCIENCES — Surgery*

370   **US**   **ISSN 0899-0247**
EAST-WEST EDUCATION. 1977-1989; resumed 1992. s-a. $20 to individuals; institutions $40. Office of East-West Education, Dept. of History, Andrews University, Berrien Springs, MI 49104. TEL 616-471-3291. (Co-sponsors: Arbeitsstelle fuer Vergleichende Bildungsforschung, Ruhr-Universitaet, Bochum, GW) Ed. John J. Markovic. adv.; bk.rev.; bibl. circ. 400. (back issues avail.) **Indexed:** Amer.Bibl.Slavic & E.Eur.Stud., Cont.Pg.Educ. **Document type:** academic/scholarly publication. —UnCover.
    Formerly (until 1986): Slavic and European Education Review (ISSN 0149-9858)

371   **SZ**   **ISSN 0012-9143**
ECHO. (Text in English, French, Japanese, Spanish) 1959. 5/yr. 25 Fr.($15) World Confederation of Organizations of the Teaching Profession, 5 Avenue du Moulin, CH-1110 Morges, Switzerland. TEL 021-8017467. FAX 021-8017469. TELEX 458219-WCTP-CH. Ed. Nick Grisewood. illus. circ. 90,000.

ECHO. see *HOME ECONOMICS*

ECHO DE LA LIBERTE DE L'OUEST; organe mensuel independant de Defense des Libertes Scolaires et Familiales. see *POLITICAL SCIENCE — Civil Rights*

373   **GW**
ECKENBRUELLER; Schuelerzeitung am Gymnasium Balingen. 1983. 3/yr. DM.0.50($1.20) Der Eckenbrueller, Gymnasiumstr. 31, 72336 Balingen, Germany. circ. 500. (back issues avail.)

370   **IT**   **ISSN 0012-9496**
ECO DELLA SCUOLA NUOVA. 1945. m. L.20000. Federazione Nazionale Insegnanti, Via del Tritone 46, 000187 Rome, Italy. TEL 06-6788918. Ed. Luisa La Malfa. adv.; bk.rev.; bibl.; tr.lit. circ. 3,000. (tabloid format)

370   **FR**
ECOLE ET LA FAMILLE. (Three Series: Pink (Primary), Yellow (Levels 1&2), Blue (Levels 3&4)) 1873. m. 229 F.(Pink), 228 F.(Yellow), 227 F.(Blue). Editions E. Robert, 28 rue du Bon Pasteur, B.P. 4384, 69242 Lyon Cedex 04, France. FAX 78-29-31-03. Ed. Armand Rouveyrol. adv.; bk.rev.; illus. circ. 5,000.

370 329.9   **FR**
ECOLE ET LA NATION-ACTUALITES. 1975. q. Parti Communiste Francais, 2 place Colonel Fabien, 75167 Paris Cedex 19, France. TEL 40-40-12-13. FAX 40-40-13-56. Ed. Jean-Paul Legrand. adv. contact: Nicole Borvo. **Document type:** academic/scholarly publication.

200   **LU**
ECOLE ET VIE; bulletin syndical, pedagogique, culturel. (Text in French, German) 1947. 8/yr. 1000 Fr. Syndicat National des Enseignants, 5 rue des Ardennes, 1133 Luxembourg, Luxembourg. Ed. Roby Schmitz. adv.; bk.rev. circ. 2,500.
    Former titles: Syndicat National des Enseignants. Ecole et Vie; Association des Instituteurs Reunis du Grand-Duche de Luxembourg. Bulletin d'Information.

370   **GV**
ECOLE NOUVELLE. m. Conakry, Guinea.

370   **UK**   **ISSN 0013-0893**
EDINBURGH ACADEMY CHRONICLE. 1893. 3/yr. £2.50. Edinburgh Academy, Henderson Row, Edinburgh EH3 5BL, Scotland. Ed. M.R. Richards. adv.; illus.; index; circ. 4,100 (controlled).

EDITOR'S REVENGE. see *JOURNALISM*

370   **US**
EDNEWS. 1972. 5/yr. free. Department of Education, Office of Communication Services, 1933 Capital Plaza Tower, Frankfort, KY 40601. TEL 502-564-3421. FAX 502-564-6771. bk.rev.; illus.; circ. 50,000 (controlled). (tabloid format)
    Formerly: School News (ISSN 0036-6692)

370   **US**
EDPRESS NEWS. 1939. m. $50 to individuals; institutions $120; corporations $200. Educational Press Association of America, Rowan College of New Jersey, Glassboro, NJ 08028. TEL 609-863-7349. FAX 609-863-5012. Ed. Lloyd W. Kline. bk.rev.; charts; illus.; stat.; tr.lit. circ. 900. **Document type:** newsletter.
    Formerly: EdPress Newsletter (ISSN 0013-1024)
    Description: Covers news about EdPress and its members, educational issues, print communication and technology, and professional development.

370   **PO**
EDUCACAO. 1990. 2/yr. Esc.1100. Rua da Restauracao 365, 4099 Porto, Portugal. TEL 2-2005813. FAX 2-313072. TELEX 27205. circ. 15,000.

370   **BL**   **ISSN 0100-3143**
EDUCACAO E REALIDADE. 1976. q. Cr.$3500 or exchange basis. Universidade Federal do Rio Grande do Sul, Faculdade de Educacao, Av. Pualo Gama, 8 andar, sala 801, 90000 Porto Alegre, Brazil. Ed. Juracy C. Marques. illus. circ. 1,000.

370   **BL**   **ISSN 0101-7330**
EDUCACAO E SOCIEDADE; revista quadrimestral de ciencia da educacao. 1978. 3/yr. Centro de Estudos de Educacao e Sociedade, Caixa postal 6022, 13081 Campinas SP, Brazil. TEL 0192-39-1598. Ed.Bd. **Document type:** academic/scholarly publication.

370   **PR**   **ISSN 0013-1067**
EDUCACION. (Text occasionally in English) 1960. 3/yr. free. Department of Education, Box 190759, Hato Rey, PR 00919. TEL 809-754-8610. FAX 809-753-7926. Ed. Jose Galarza Rodriguez. bk.rev.; bibl.; illus. circ. 40,000. **Document type:** academic/scholarly publication.
    Description: Contains articles on education and other related fields. Focuses on research articles and educational innovations and projects.

379   **VE**   **ISSN 0013-1075**
.L45
EDUCACION;* revista para el magisterio. vol. 37, 1975. q. free. Ministerio de Educacion, Ministerio de Relacciones Exteriores, Direccion de Relaciones Culturales, Caracas, Venezuela. Ed. Ligia de Lima de Bianchi. bibl.; charts; illus.; stat.; cum.index. circ. 30,000. **Indexed:** Amer.Hist.& Life, Hist.Abstr.

370   **MX**   **ISSN 0185-0547**
EDUCACION. 1957. 4/yr. Consejo Nacional Tecnico de la Educacion, Calle Luis Gonzalez Obregon No. 21, CP 06020, Mexico. Ed.Bd. bibl.; charts. circ. 5,000.

370   **PE**
EDUCACION; revista del maestro peruano. 1970. irreg. Instituto Nacional de Investigacion y Desarrollo de la Educacion, Centro Nacional de Documentacion e Informacion Educacional, Van de Velde 160, San Borja, Lima 100, Peru. Ed. Raul Vargas Vega. bibl.; charts; illus.

370   **US**   **ISSN 0250-6130**
EDUCACION; revista interamericana de desarrollo educativo. (Text in Spanish; occasionally in English and Portuguese; summaries in Spanish) 1956. q. $15. Organization of American States, 1889 F. St. N.W., Washington, DC 20006-4499. TEL 202-458-3323. Ed. Osvaldo Kriemer. circ. 8,500. (also avail. in microfiche from CIS) **Indexed:** Amer.Hist.& Life, Hist.Abstr., IIS, Int.Lab.Doc., Rural Ext.Educ.& Tr.Abstr.

370   **CU**
EDUCACION (HAVANA). 1971. s-a. $12 in S. America; N. America $14; elsewhere $16. (Ministerio de Educacion, Direccion de Divulgacion y Publicaciones) Ediciones Cubanas, Obispo No. 527, Apdo. 605, Havana, Cuba. Ed.Bd. bk.rev.; bibl.; charts; illus.; index, cum.index. circ. 80,000.

370   **AG**
EDUCACION CUYO. s-a. Universidad Nacional de Cuyo, Departamento de Ciencias de la Educacion y Formacion, Centro Universitario, 5500 Mendoza, Argentina.

370   **UY**
EDUCACION PARA EL DESARROLLO. suspended 1978; resumed 19?? q. free. Confederacion Latinoamericana de Asociaciones Cristianas de Jovenes, Casilla 172, Montevideo, Uruguay. Ed. Edgardo G. Crovetto. illus.

370   **CU**
EDUCACION SUPERIOR CONTEMPORANEA. q. $28. (Ministerio de Educacion Superior) Ediciones Cubanas, Obispo No. 527, Apdo. 605, Havana, Cuba.

371   **BO**
EDUCACION Y PUEBLO. 1986. 2/yr. Equipo Interinstitucional del Educacion Popular, Comite de Redaccion, Casilla 6522, La Paz, Bolivia.

370   **SP**   **ISSN 0013-1113**
EDUCADORES. 1959. q. $48 (effective Jan. 1994). Federacion Espanola de Religiosos de Ensenanza, Conde de Penalver, 45-4, 28006 Madrid, Spain. TEL 402-13-00. FAX 309-17-40. Ed. Millan Arroyo. adv.; bk.rev.; bibl.; index, cum.index. circ. 1,750. **Indexed:** Amer.Hist.& Life, Hist.Abstr. **Document type:** academic/scholarly publication.
    Description: Contains articles and studies in all areas of education. Covers teacher training, curriculum and methods, foundations of education, moral and religious education, and social education.

370   **GW**
EDUCADORES DEL MUNDO. English edition: Teachers of the World (ISSN 0863-0070); French edition: Revue Internationale des Enseignants. German edition: Lehrer der Welt. 1978. q. $5 to individuals and teachers; $10 to institutions. World Federation of Teachers' Unions (FISE), Wilhelm-Wolff-Strasse 21, 13156 Berlin, Germany. TEL 4800591. Ed. Gabriele Vavra. adv.; bk.rev. circ. 19,000.

370 SA ISSN 0250-152X
LC2808.S7
EDUCAMUS. (Text in English) 1954. 6/yr. free to qualified personnel. Department of Education and Training, Rm. 561, Magister Bldg., Private Bag X212, Pretoria 0001, S. Africa.
TEL 27-12-312-5285. TELEX 321378-SA. charts; illus.; stat.; index. circ. 60,000. **Indexed:** Ind.S.A.Per., Rural Ext.Educ.& Tr.Abstr., Rural Recreat.Tour.Abstr., World Agri.Econ. & Rural Sociol.Abstr. **Document type:** academic/scholarly publication, government publication.
Formerly: Bantu Education Journal - Bantoe Onderwysblad (ISSN 0005-5662)
  Description: Contains mainly articles on the practice and theory of teaching.

370 CK ISSN 0120-162X
EDUCAR.* 1977. m. Ministerio de Educacion Nacional, Division de Documentacion e Informacion Educativa, Avda Eldorado, Of. 501, Bogota, Colombia. illus.

370 SA
EDUCARE. (Text in Afrikaans and English) 1972. s-a. R.13.80 (overseas $7.50) (effective 1994). University of South Africa, Faculty of Education, P.O. Box 392, Pretoria 0001, South Africa.
FAX 27-12-429-3221. TELEX 350068. Ed. T.L. Verster. adv.; bk.rev. circ. 5,500. (back issues avail.) **Indexed:** Ind.S.A.Per. **Document type:** academic/scholarly publication.

370 FR ISSN 0013-113X
EDUCATEUR. (Supplement avail.) 1928. 15 nos. per school yr. 240 F. Ecole Moderne Francaise-Pedagogie Freinet, B.P. 109, 06322 Cannes - La Bocca Cedex, France.

370 SZ
EDUCATEUR: JOURNAL CORPORATIF ET SYNDICAL. 1981. 20/yr. 90 SFr. includes both Educateur editions. (Societe Pedagogique Romande) Editions de la Tour S.A., Case Postale 880, CH-1001 Lausanne, Switzerland. **Document type:** academic/scholarly publication.
  Supersedes in part (in 1981): Educateur et Bulletin Corporatif.

370 SZ
EDUCATEUR: REVUE DE PEDAGOGIE ET D'EDUCATION. 1864. 9/yr. 67 SFr. (97 SFr. for both Educateur editions). (Societe Pedagogique Romande) Editions de la Tour S.A., Case Postale 880, CH-1001 Lausanne, Switzerland. TEL 021-652-9941. Ed. Rene Blind. adv.; bk.rev.; abstr.; bibl.; charts; illus.; play rev.; stat. circ. 9,500. (tabloid format) **Document type:** academic/scholarly publication.
  Supersedes in part (in 1981): Educateur et Bulletin Corporatif (ISSN 0013-1148)

370 II ISSN 0013-1180
LAW
EDUCATION. (Text and summaries in English and Hindi) 1921. m. Rs.40. S. Kumar and Associates, Mass Communications Division, 32 Sarojini Debi Lane, Maqboolganj, Lucknow 226078, Uttar Pradesh, India. TEL 91-52-224-1010. Ed. Parimal Mandke. adv.; bk.rev.; bibl.; cum.index 1948-1978; circ. 2,000 (controlled). **Document type:** academic/scholarly publication.

370 UK ISSN 0013-1164
L16
EDUCATION. 1903. w. £72 (Europe £79; elsewhere £83). (Society of Education Officers) Longman Group UK Ltd., Westgate House, The High, Harlow, Essex CM20 1YR, England. TEL 0279-442601. FAX 0279-444501. Ed. George Low. adv.; bk.rev.; illus.; s-a. index. (also avail. in microform from UMI; reprint service avail. from UMI) **Indexed:** Br.Educ.Ind., Cont.Pg.Educ., Res.High.Educ.Abstr. **Document type:** academic/scholarly publication.
—BLDSC (3661.164000); Faxon; SWETS; UMI. **CCC.**

370 US ISSN 0013-1172
L11 CODEN: EDUCD6
EDUCATION. 1880. q. $20 to individuals; institutions $26. Project Innovation of Mobile, Box 8508, Spring Hill Sta., Mobile, AL 36608. TEL 205-343-1878. Ed. George E. Uhlig. adv.; bk.rev.; index. circ. 3,500. (also avail. in microform from UMI,PMC; reprint service avail. from UMI,KTO) **Indexed:** Acad.Ind., C.I.J.E., Cont.Pg.Educ., Educ.Admin.Abstr., Educ.Ind., High.Educ.Curr.Aware.Bull., Lang.& Lang.Behav.Abstr., Psychol.Abstr., Sociol.Abstr. **Document type:** academic/scholarly publication.
—BLDSC (3661.162000); UnCover; SWETS; UMI.

370 IE
EDUCATION. 12/yr. 1 Pembroke Pl., Ballsbridge, Dublin 4, Ireland. TEL 682750. FAX 685184.

370 MM
EDUCATION. 2/yr. $5 (effective 1994). University of Malta, Faculty of Education, Msida, Malta. TEL 356-333903. FAX 356-336450. TELEX 407 HIEDUC. Ed. C.J. Farruga. circ. 1,000. **Document type:** academic/scholarly publication.
  Description: Publishes scholarly articles about education generally, looking at issues affecting teachers in Malta and elsewhere in the World.

370 CN
EDUCATION. 1985. irreg. price varies. University of Ottawa Press, 542 King Edward, Ottawa, ON K1N 6N5, Canada. TEL 613-564-2270. Ed. Evelyn Gagne.
  Description: Studies all aspects of education (philosophy, history, psychology).

370 AT ISSN 0013-1156
EDUCATION (SYDNEY). 1919. fortn. (during school term). Aus.$45. New South Wales Teachers Federation, 300 Sussex St., Sydney, N.S.W. 2000, Australia. FAX 2675221. TELEX 71402 TEFED. Ed. Diane Hague. adv.; bk.rev.; index. circ. 70,000. **Indexed:** Aus.Educ.Ind., Br.Educ.Ind., Educ.Ind.
  Incorporates: Teacher Feedback (ISSN 0311-2772)

370.193 CN
EDUCATION ADVISORY. 1975. irreg. (approx. 2/yr.). Can.$3. 2267 Kings Ave., West Vancouver, B.C. V7V 2C1, Canada. Ed. Tunya Audain. bk.rev. circ. 3,000.

370 371.42 SA
EDUCATION & CAREERS IN SOUTH AFRICA. (Text in Afrikaans and English) a. R.45. Erudita Publications (Pty) Ltd., Cnr. 11th Ave. & Main Rd., P.O. Box 29159, Melville, Johannesburg 2109, South Africa. adv.

370.968 SA ISSN 0259-2029
EDUCATION & CULTURE/ONDERWYS EN KULTUUR. (Text in Afrikaans, English) 1976. 3/yr. free. Department of Education and Culture, Private Bag X55, Pretoria 0001, South Africa.
TEL 012-200189. FAX 3234880. TELEX 322024. Ed. M. Garbers. bk.rev. circ. 8,000. **Indexed:** Ind.S.A.Per. **Document type:** government publication, academic/scholarly publication.

370 EI
EDUCATION AND CULTURE. SECTION 1: CULTURAL DEVELOPMENT. 1979. irreg. Council of Europe, Council for Cultural Co-Operation, Publications Section, Strasbourg, France. FAX 33-88-41-27-81. (Dist. in US by: Manhattan Publishing Co., Box 650, Croton-on-Hudson, NY 10520)

370 EI
EDUCATION AND CULTURE. SECTION 2: HIGHER EDUCATION AND RESEARCH. 1979. irreg. Council of Europe, Council for Cultural Co-Operation, Publications Section, Strasbourg, France.
FAX 33-88-41-27-81. (Dist. in US by: Manhattan Publishing Co, Box 650, Croton-on-Hudson, NY 10520)

370 US ISSN 0279-0688
LB1028
EDUCATION AND PSYCHOLOGICAL RESEARCH. 1967. q. $3. University of Southern Mississippi, School of Education and Psychology, Box 5028, Southern Sta., Hattiesburg, MS 39401. TEL 601-266-4568. Ed. Dr. Richard Kazelskis. charts; stat. circ. 300. (also avail. in microform from UMI; reprint service avail. from UMI) **Indexed:** Except.Child.Educ.Abstr., Psychol.Abstr.
Formerly: Southern Journal of Education Research (ISSN 0038-4267)

370 150 II ISSN 0046-1385
EDUCATION AND PSYCHOLOGY REVIEW. (Text in English) 1961. q. Rs.10($3) Maharaja Sayajirao University of Baroda, Faculty of Education and Psychology, Baroca 390002, Gujarat, India. Ed. Prof. D.M. Desai. bk.rev.; stat. circ. 400. **Indexed:** Cont.Pg.Educ., Psychol.Abstr.

370 AT ISSN 0726-2655
LC189.8
EDUCATION AND SOCIETY. 1983. 2/yr. $60 to individuals; institutions $95. James Nicholas Publishers, P.O. Box 244, Albert Park, Vic. 3206, Australia. TEL 03-596-5545. FAX 613-699-2040. Ed. Joseph Zajda. **Indexed:** Cont.Pg.Educ., Educ.Tech.Abstr., Mult.Ed.Abstr., SOMA, Sp.Ed.Needs Abstr. **Document type:** academic/scholarly publication.
—BLDSC (3661.196500). **CCC.**
  Description: Examines the relationship between schooling and society, and its impact on culture, ideology and power. Explores social, cultural and economic factors affecting schooling and society.

EDUCATION AND SOCIETY IN THE MIDDLE AGES AND THE RENAISSANCE. see HISTORY — History Of Europe

EDUCATION AND THE LAW. see LAW

374.013 UK ISSN 0040-0912
T61 CODEN: EDTRDC
EDUCATION AND TRAINING. 1959. 8/yr. $1189.95. M C B University Press Ltd., 60-62 Toller Ln., Bradford, W. Yorks BD8 9BY. England. TEL 0274-499821. FAX 0274-547143. TELEX 51317-MCBUNI-G. Ed. Richard Holden. bk.rev.; illus.; index. (also avail. in microform from UMI; reprint service avail. from UMI) **Indexed:** Account.& Data Proc.Abstr., Anbar, Br.Tech.Ind., Cont.Pg.Educ., Educ.Tech.Abstr., High.Educ.Curr.Aware.Bull., Mult.Ed.Abstr., Res.High.Educ.Abstr., Sci.Abstr., SOMA, Tr.& Dev.Alert. **Document type:** academic/scholarly publication.
—BLDSC (3661.198000); SWETS; UMI.
Formerly: Technical Education.
  Description: Covers subjects ranging from qualifications and career choices for students to current policies and approaches in universities, colleges and industry. Covers unemployment and training, the psychology of winning, marketing, law and finance, choosing a career.

301.34 370 US ISSN 0013-1245
LC5101
EDUCATION AND URBAN SOCIETY. 1968. q. $45 to individuals (foreign $51); institutions $135 (foreign $141). Corwin Press, Inc. (Subsidiary of: Sage Publications, Inc.), 2455 Teller Rd., Thousand Oaks, CA 91320. TEL 805-499-0721.
FAX 805-499-0871. (And: Sage Publications, Ltd., 6 Bonhill St., London EC2A 4PU, England) Ed.Bd. adv.: B&W page $225. bk.rev.; index. (also avail. in microfilm from UMI; reprint service avail. from UMI; back issues avail.) **Indexed:** A.B.C.Pol.Sci., Adol.Ment.Hlth.Abstr., Amer.Hist.& Life, ASSIA, C.I.J.E., Chic.Per.Ind., Cont.Pg.Educ., Curr.Cont., Educ.Admin.Abstr., Educ.Ind., Educ.Tech.Abstr., ERIC, Hist.Abstr., Human Resour.Abstr., Lang.& Lang.Behav.Abstr., Mid.East: Abstr.& Ind., Mult.Ed.Abstr., P.A.I.S., Sage Fam.Stud.Abstr., Sage Pub.Admin.Abstr., Sage Urb.Stud.Abstr., Soc.Sci.Ind., Sociol.Abstr., SOMA, SSCI, Urb.Aff.Abstr.
—BLDSC (3661.204000); Faxon; UnCover; SWETS; UMI. **CCC.**
  Description: Contains theme-organized articles prepared by guest editors on education as a social institution within urban contexts.

370.58 UK ISSN 0070-9131
L915
EDUCATION AUTHORITIES' DIRECTORY AND ANNUAL. 1902. a. £60. School Government Publishing Co. Ltd., Darby House, Bletchingley Rd., Merstham, Redhill, Surrey RH1 3DN, England.
TEL 0737-642223 FAX 0737-644283. Ed. Marjorie McCormack. adv. circ. 8,000. (also avail. in microform) **Document type:** directory.
●Also available online.
  Description: Lists the names, addresses and telephone numbers of more than 13,500 local education authorities, secondary and independent schools, colleges and other educational institutions in the United Kingdom.

EDUCATION

370 US ISSN 1058-4226
EDUCATION BEAT. 1990. fortn. $110. 926 J. St., Rm. 121B, Sacramento, CA 95814.
TEL 916-446-3956. FAX 916-446-5302. Ed. Larry Lynch. circ. 400. **Document type:** newsletter.
Description: News of issues in California education from kindergarten through graduate school.

370 CN ISSN 0013-1253
L11
EDUCATION CANADA. (Text mainly in English; some French) 1949. q. Can.$25($25) Canadian Education Association, 252 Bloor St. W., Ste. 8-200, Toronto, ON M5S 1V5, Canada.
TEL 416-924-7721. FAX 416-924-3188. Ed. Harriett Goldsborough. bk.rev.; illus.; index. circ. 4,800. (also avail. in microform from MML,UMI; reprint service avail. from UMI) **Indexed:** C.I.J.E., Can.Educ.Ind., Can.Per.Ind., Can.Wom.Per.Ind., CMI, Cont.Pg.Educ., Curr.Cont., Educ.Admin.Abstr., Educ.Ind., Mult.Ed.Abstr., Sp.Ed.Needs Abstr.
Document type: consumer publication.
—BLDSC (3661.220000); UnCover; SWETS; UMI.
CCC.
Supersedes: Canadian Education and Research Digest.
Description: Covers current issues and trends in elementary and secondary education in Canada.

370 362.4 US ISSN 0013-1261
L11.E38
EDUCATION DAILY; the American educator's independent, daily news service. 1968. d. (5/w.). $581 (foreign $831). Capitol Publications Inc., 1101 King St., Ste. 444, Box 1455, Alexandria, VA 22314. TEL 703-683-4100. FAX 703-739-6517. Ed. Joe McGavin. q. index. (looseleaf format; also avail. in microform from UMI; reprint service avail. from UMI) **Document type:** newsletter.
●Also available online. Vendor(s): NewsNet (ED08).
—CCC.
Incorporates: Higher Education Daily (ISSN 0194-2239)
Description: Current reports on national, state and local events pertinent to top-level education officials everywhere. Includes news from the Education Department, Congress, the White House and the courts. Reports on the latest education research, education of handicapped children, and higher education.

375 US ISSN 0424-5407
EDUCATION DEVELOPMENT CENTER. ANNUAL REPORT. 1967. a. Education Development Center, Inc., 55 Chapel St., Newton, MA 02160.
TEL 617-969-7100. FAX 617-069-5979. illus. circ. 2,500. **Document type:** corporate report.

370 US ISSN 0013-127X
L11
THE EDUCATION DIGEST. 1935. m. (Sep.-May). $36. Prakken Publications, Inc., Box 8623, Ann Arbor, MI 48107. TEL 313-769-1211. FAX 313-769-8383. Ed. Kenneth Schroeder. adv.; bk.rev.; index. circ. 26,000. (also avail. in microform from UMI; reprint service avail. from UMI,BLH) **Indexed:** Abr.R.G., Acad.Ind., Adol.Ment.Hlth.Abstr., Educ.Ind., Except.Child.Educ.Abstr., Hlth.Ind., Jun.High.Mag.Abstr., Mag.Ind., PMR, R.G., TOM.
●Also available online.
—BLDSC (3661.240000); Faxon; UnCover; SWETS; UMI.

372 FR ISSN 0013-1288
EDUCATION ENFANTINE; revue des ecoles maternelles, classes enfantines, cours preparatoires. 1904. 9/yr. 264 F. Librairie Fernand Nathan, 9 rue Mechain, 75680 Paris Cedex 14, France. TEL 45-87-50-00. TELEX 204 525. Ed. Monica Cubertafon. illus. circ. 100,000.
—CCC.

370 CN ISSN 0849-1089
EDUCATION ET FRANCOPHONIE; revue d'education des communautes francophones canadiennes. 1971. q. Can.$24. Association Canadienne d'Education de Langue Francaise, 268 rue Marie-de-l'Incarnation, Quebec, PQ G1N 3G4, Canada.
TEL 418-681-4661. FAX 418-681-3389. Ed. Helene Landry. adv.; bk.rev. circ. 1,000. **Indexed:** Pt.de Rep. (1989-). **Document type:** academic/scholarly publication.
Formerly: Association Canadienne d'Education de Langue Francaise. Revue.
Description: Promotes and protects French language education

370 UK ISSN 0266-9145
EDUCATION FOR TOMORROW. 1948. 5/yr. £5.40. Education for Tomorrow Collective, Haddon, The Street, Wickham Skeith, Eye, Suffolk IP23 8LP, England. Ed. Ian Gunn.
Formerly: Education Today and Tomorrow.

373 CN ISSN 0840-9269
EDUCATION FORUM; the magazine for secondary school professionals. 1922. 3/yr. (during school year). Can.$20 (foreign Can.$24). Ontario Secondary School Teachers' Federation, 60 Mobile Dr., Toronto, ON M4A 2P3, Canada. TEL 416-751-8300. FAX 416-751-3394. Ed. Neil Walker. adv.; bk.rev.; illus.; circ. 46,000 (controlled). (also avail. in microform from MML; reprint service avail. from MML) **Indexed:** Can.Educ.Ind., Can.Per.Ind., CMI.
Former titles: Forum (Toronto) (ISSN 0319-2121); (until 1984): O S S T F Forum; (until 1975): O S S T F Bulletin (ISSN 0029-7275)

370 AT ISSN 0013-1334
EDUCATION GAZETTE. 1905. fortn. (during school year). Department of School Education, G.P.O. Box 33, Sydney, N.S.W. 2001, Australia. Ed. B. Williams. circ. 23,000.
Description: Information to teachers employed by the New South Wales Department of Education.

370 US ISSN 1056-2656
EDUCATION GRANTS ALERT. 1991. w. $299 (foreign $349). Capitol Publications Inc., 1101 King St., Ste. 444, Alexandria, VA 22314. TEL 703-683-4100. FAX 703-739-6517. Ed. Leslie Ratzlaff. (back issues avail.) **Document type:** newsletter.
—CCC.
Description: Covers federal and private funding opportunities and funding trends in education, especially designed for those seeking grants for elementary and secondary education programs.

370 UN ISSN 0257-845X
EDUCATION IN ASIA AND THE PACIFIC: REVIEWS, REPORTS AND NOTES. French edition: Education en Asie (ISSN 1014-3513) (Nos. 1-3 issued as: Unesco Regional Office for Education in Asia. Bulletin. Supplement) (Text in English) 1972. a. price varies. (Library and Documentation Service) Unesco, Principal Regional Office for Asia and the Pacific, P.O. Box 1425, Bangkok 10500, Thailand. FAX 301-459-0056. TELEX 20591 TH. (Dist. in U.S. by: Unipub, 4611-F Assembly Dr., Lanham, MD 20706-4391) bk.rev.; abstr.; bibl. circ. 2,650. **Indexed:** ERIC, Mid.East: Abstr.& Ind., Rural Ext.Educ.& Tr.Abstr.
Former titles: Education in Asia and Oceania: Reviews, Reports and Notes (ISSN 0251-4648); Education in Asia: Reviews, Reports and Notes.

370 KE ISSN 0046-1423
EDUCATION IN EASTERN AFRICA.* 1970. s-a. EAs.28($8) (Regional Council for Education) Kenya Literature Bureau, Box 30022, Nairobi, Kenya. Ed. John C.B. Bigala. adv.; bk.rev.; stat. circ. 2,000. **Indexed:** Cont.Pg.Educ.

370 EI
EDUCATION IN EUROPE. CULTURAL DEVELOPMENT. 1974. irreg. price varies. Council of Europe, Council for Cultural Co-Operation, Publishing and Documentation Service, 67000 Strasbourg, France. FAX 33-88-41-27-81. (Dist. in U.S. by: Manhattan Publishing Co., Box 650, Croton-on-Hudson, NY 10520)

370 US ISSN 1049-7250
EDUCATION IN FOCUS. 1990. s-a. $18 in US and Canada; elsewhere $28 for 6 issues. Books for All Times, Inc., Box 2, Alexandria, VA 22313. TEL 703-548-0457. Ed. Joe David. adv.; bk.rev. circ. 1,000. (back issues avail.) **Document type:** newsletter.
Description: Focuses on education: its failures, its successes.

370 II
EDUCATION IN INDIA. (Issued in 2 Vols.) (Text in English) 1950. irreg. price varies. Ministry of Education and Social Welfare, Department of Education, Shastri Bhavan, New Delhi 110001, India. (Subscr. to: Controller of Publications, Government of India, Civil Lines, Delhi 110054, India)

370 JA ISSN 0070-9220
L611
EDUCATION IN JAPAN; A GRAPHIC PRESENTATION. (Text in English) 1954. irreg., 8th ed., 1971. 1400 Yen. Ministry of Education, 3-2-2 Kasumigaseki, Chiyoda-ku, Tokyo 100, Japan. (Subscr. to: Government Publications Service Center, 1-2-1 Kasumigaseki, Chiyoda-ku, Tokyo 100, Japan)

370 FR
EDUCATION IN O E C D COUNTRIES: COMPENDIUM OF STATISTICAL INFORMATION. (Text in English, French) 1974. irreg. price varies. Organization for Economic Cooperation and Development, 2 rue Andre-Pascal, 75775 Paris Cedex 16, France. (U.S. orders to: O.E.C.D. Publications and Information Center, 2001 L St., N.W., Ste. 700, Washington, D.C. 20036-4910. TEL 202-785-6323) (also avail. in microfiche from OEC)
Former titles: Educational Statistics in O E C D Countries; Educational Statistics Yearbook.

370 UK ISSN 1351-0371
EDUCATION IN RUSSIA, THE INDEPENDENT STATES AND EASTERN EUROPE. 1982. s-a. £6($18) to individuals; institutions £8($25). Study Group on Education in Russia, the Independent States and Eastern Europe, 24 Cholmeley Park, London N6 5EU, England. TEL 081-340-4277. Ed. Bryan Woodriff. bk.rev.; abstr. (back issues avail.) **Document type:** academic/scholarly publication.
—BLDSC (2770.532500).
Formerly: Soviet Education Study Bulletin.
Description: All matters relating to education in the former Soviet Union, Tsarist Russia, the CIS and Eastern Europe.

507 370 UK ISSN 0013-1377
EDUCATION IN SCIENCE. 1962. 5/yr. £24 (overseas £34) (effective Jan. 1994). Association for Science Education, College Ln., Hatfield, Herts. AL10 9AA, England. TEL 0707-267411. FAX 0707-266532. Ed. D.S. Moore. adv. circ. 24,000. (also avail. in microform from UMI; reprint service avail. from UMI) **Indexed:** C.I.J.E., CAD CAM Abstr., Cont.Pg.Educ., Educ.Tech.Abstr., High.Educ.Curr.Aware.Bull.
—BLDSC (3661.334000); SWETS; UMI.

370 UK ISSN 0424-5512
EDUCATION IN THE NORTH; the journal of Scottish education. 1965. bi-a. £3.60. Northern College of Education, Hilton Place, Aberdeen AB9 1FA, Scotland. TEL 0224-283500. FAX 0224-487046. Eds. R. Jackson, W. W. McPhillimy. adv. contact: Page 1000. bk.rev. circ. 1,000. **Indexed:** Br.Educ.Ind., High.Educ.Curr.Aware.Bull. **Document type:** academic/scholarly publication.
—BLDSC (3661.306000).
Description: Covers all aspects of education in Scotland.

370 UK ISSN 0261-8966
EDUCATION IN THE ROYAL COUNTY OF BERKSHIRE. 1981. irreg. (Berkshire Education Department) Coles & Sons, 223 Southampton St., Reading RG1 2RB, England. illus.

370 SA ISSN 0259-207X
EDUCATION JOURNAL. (Includes: Education News) a. R.24 (foreign R.35). South African Teachers' Association, 6 Park Rd., Rondebosch, Cape Province 7700, South Africa. TEL 27-21-686-8521. FAX 27-21-689-2998. adv.; bk.rev. circ. 5,000. **Indexed:** Ind.S.A.Per.
Supersedes in part: Education (ISSN 0013-1202)

EDUCATION LAW JOURNAL. see LAW

EDUCATION LAW REPORTS. see LAW

EDUCATION LIBRARIES. see LIBRARY AND INFORMATION SCIENCES

EDUCATION LIBRARIES JOURNAL. see LIBRARY AND INFORMATION SCIENCES

370 320 AT ISSN 0814-6802
EDUCATION LINKS. 1976. 3/yr. Aus.$18 to individuals & schools (foreign Aus.$20); other institutions Aus.$30 (foreign Aus.$35). Education Links, 37 Cavendish St., Stanmore, N.S.W. 2048, Australia. Ed.Bd. adv.; bk.rev. circ. 1,500. (back issues avail.)
Description: Advocates socialist change in Australian schooling.

EDUCATION 2017

370 CN ISSN 0704-2671
EDUCATION MANITOBA. 1974. 5/yr. Can.$12. Manitoba Education and Training, Communications Services Branch, 210 Osborne St., N., 3rd Fl., Winnipeg, MB R3C 1V4, Canada. TEL 204-945-6183. FAX 204-948-2147. Ed. Joan Dougherty. adv.; bk.rev.; circ. 16,000 (controlled). (also avail. in microform from MIM,UMI; reprint service avail. from UMI) **Indexed:** Can.Educ.Ind. **Document type:** government publication.
 Description: Includes policies, events and resources of the department as well as events and issues from the education community.

370 SA
EDUCATION NEWS. (Includes: Education Journal) 1890. 5/yr. R.20 (foreign R.35). South African Teachers' Association, 6 Park Rd., Rondebosch, Cape Province 7700, South Africa. TEL 27-21-6868521. FAX 27-21-6892998. adv.; bk.rev. circ. 5,000.
 Supersedes in part: Education (ISSN 0013-1202)

370 US
EDUCATION NEWS. 1961. m. free. Superintendent of Public Instruction, Old Capitol Bldg., Box 47200, Olympia, WA 98504-7200. TEL 206-753-6725. FAX 206-664-0756. Ed. Charlotte Manning. charts; illus.; stat. circ. 73,500. (tabloid format)
 Formerly (until vol.6, 1989): Your Public Schools (ISSN 0044-1104)

370 280 US
EDUCATION NEWSLINE. 1983. bi-m. $20. National Association of Christian Educators, Citizens for Excellence in Education, Box 3200, Costa Mesa, CA 92628. TEL 714-546-5931. FAX 714-546-6323. Ed. Kathi Hudson. bk.rev.; bibl.; illus. circ. 18,000. **Document type:** newsletter.
 Formerly: Christians in Education.
 Description: Information on issues of interest to Christian parents, teachers, and public school administrators.

372 FR ISSN 0246-4438
EDUCATION PAR LE JEU ET L'ENVIRONNEMENT. q. 120 F. (foreign 170 F.). (Association Francaise pour l'Education par le Jeu) Groupe des Revues Associees, 25, rue Dagorno, 75012 Paris, France.

370 361 FR ISSN 0339-7513
EDUCATION PERMANENTE. 1969. 4/yr. 380 F. (foreign 500 F.). Education Permanente, 16 rue Berthollet, 94113 Arcueil, France. TEL 16-1-46-63-94-70. FAX 16-1-46-63-94-69. Ed. Guy Jobert. adv.; bk.rev. circ. 3,500. **Indexed:** Cont.Pg.Educ., Int.Lab.Doc.
 —BLDSC (3661.312000); SWETS.

370 II ISSN 0013-1482
EDUCATION QUARTERLY. (Text in English) 1949. q. Rs.32($11.52) Government of India, Department of Publication, Civil Lines, Delhi 110 054, India. TEL 11-2517409. bk.rev.; cum.index: vols.1-25, 1949-1974. **Indexed:** Cont.Pg.Educ.
 Incorporates: Youth (ISSN 0513-3297); Secondary Education (ISSN 0582-3692)

370 PH
EDUCATION QUARTERLY. (Text in English) 1953. q. P.36($15) University of the Philippines, College of Education, Diliman, Quezon City, Philippines. Ed. Celeste O. Botor. bk.rev.; abstr.; bibl.; circ. controlled. **Indexed:** Ind.Phil.Per.

370 US ISSN 0013-1512
EDUCATION REPORTER. 1966. 6/yr. membership. Education Writers Association, 1001 Connecticut Ave., N.W., Ste. 310, Washington, DC 20036-5541. TEL 202-429-9680. FAX 202-872-4016. Ed. Bert Menninga. bk.rev.; circ. 700 (controlled). **Document type:** newsletter.

370 US
EDUCATION REPORTS. 1979. 50/yr. $327. (National Center for Education Information) Feistritzer Publications, 4401-A Connecticut Ave., N.W., Ste. 212, Washington, DC 20088. TEL 202-362-3444. FAX 202-362-3493. Ed. David T. Chester. **Document type:** newsletter.
 Description: Reports events and decisions affecting education with analysis.

370 FR ISSN 0395-7691
EDUCATION RURALE. 1946. 5/yr. 100 F. (effective 1991). Association Nationale des Maitres Agricoles, Lycee Professionnel Horticole, 59463 Lomme Cedex, France. TEL 20-92-47-61. Ed. Michel Enchery. adv.; bk.rev. circ. 1,500.

370 US
EDUCATION SAN DIEGO COUNTY. 1943. 4/yr. free to qualified personnel. Department of Education, Superintendent of Schools, 6401 Linda Vista Rd., San Diego, CA 92111. TEL 619-292-3500. Ed. Doug Langdon. circ. 13,000 (controlled).
 Formerly: Education Newsletter (ISSN 0013-144X)

001.3 RW
EDUCATION, SCIENCE ET CULTURE/UBUREZI, UBUHANGA N'UMUCO. 1978. q. $3. Ministere de l'Enseignement Superieur et de la Recherche Scientifique, B.P. 624, Kigali, Rwanda. FAX 250-82162. adv.
 Former titles (until 1982): Education et Culture - Uburezi n'Uburere; Vie Familiale; Vie Feminine et Enseignement Familial.

370 613.62 US ISSN 1059-0595
EDUCATION SPECIAL INTEREST SECTION NEWSLETTER. (Consists of 9 sections: Administration and Management; Developmental Disabilities; Education; Gerontology; Mental Health; Physical Disabilities; Sensory Integration; Technology; Work Programs) 1991. q. American Occupational Therapy Association, Inc., 1383 Piccard Dr., Box 1725, Rockville, MD 20850-0822. TEL 301-948-9626. FAX 301-948-5512. **Document type:** newsletter.

370 UK
EDUCATION STATISTICS FOR THE UNITED KINGDOM. a. price varies. (Department of Education and Science) H.M.S.O., P.O. Box 276, London SW8 5DT, England. **Document type:** government publication.

370 UK ISSN 0013-1547
EDUCATION TODAY. 1950. 4/yr. £82.50 (Europe £84; elsewhere £90). (College of Preceptors) Longman Group UK Ltd., Westgate House, 6th Fl., The High, Harlow, Essex CM20 1YR, England. TEL 0279-442601. FAX 0279-444501. (Subscr. to: Journals Dept., Fourth Ave., Harlow, Essex CM19 5AA, England. TEL 0279-623924) Ed. Brian Holmes. adv.; bk.rev. circ. 3,900. (also avail. in microfilm; microfiche; back issues avail.; reprint service avail. from UMI) **Indexed:** Cont.Pg.Educ., Stud.Wom.Abstr. **Document type:** academic/scholarly publication.
 —BLDSC (3661.346000); UMI.
 Refereed Serial

370 US ISSN 0013-1571
EDUCATION U S A. 1958. fortn. $128 (foreign $154). Capitol Publications Inc., 1101 King St., Ste. 444, Alexandria, VA 22314. TEL 703-683-4100. FAX 703-739-6517. Ed. Joe McGavin. bk.rev.; s-a. index. (also avail. in microform from UMI; reprint service avail. from UMI) **Indexed:** SSCI. **Document type:** newsletter.
 —UMI.

370 US
EDUCATION UPDATE (ST. PAUL). 1966. 5/yr. Department of Education, 550 Cedar St., Capitol Square Bldg., St. Paul, MN 55101. TEL 612-297-1928. FAX 612-297-7201. Ed. Cynthia Hanson. circ. 59,500. **Document type:** government publication, newspaper.
 Formerly: Minnesota Education Report (ISSN 0026-5454)
 Description: Communicates policies and programs of Minnesota Department of Education and State Board of Education and information about programs in Minnesota public schools.

370 US ISSN 0277-4232
EDUCATION WEEK; American education's newspaper of record. 1981. 40/yr. $59.94 (foreign $117.20). Editorial Projects in Education, Inc., 4301 Connecticut Ave., N.W., Ste. 432, Washington, DC 20008. TEL 202-364-4114. (Subscr. to: Box 2083, Marion, OH 43306) Ed. Virginia Edwards. adv.; bk.rev.; index. circ. 50,000. (also avail. in microform from UMI; microfiche from CIS) **Indexed:** SRI. **Document type:** newspaper.
 ●Also available online.
 —UMI. **CCC.**

370 UK ISSN 0143-5469
EDUCATION YEAR BOOK. 1939. a. £69. (Society of Education Officers) Longman Group UK Ltd., Westgate, 6th Fl., The High, Harlow, Essex CM20 1YR, England. TEL 0279-442601. FAX 0279-444501. Ed. Deborah Lyltelton. adv.: B&W page £345; 203 x 128. **Document type:** academic/scholarly publication.
 —BLDSC (3661.352500).
 Formerly: Education Committees Year Book (ISSN 0070-9158)

370 UK ISSN 0300-4279
EDUCATION 3-13. 1973. 3/yr. £16.50 to individuals (foreign £19.75); institutions £35 (foreign £39.50). (Primary Schools Research and Development Group) Longman Group UK Ltd., Westgate House, 6th Fl., The High, Harlow, Essex CM20 1YR, England. TEL 0279-442601. FAX 0279-444501. (Subscr. to: Journals, Fourth Ave., Harlow, Essex CM19 5AA, England. TEL 0279-623924) Ed. J. Campbell. adv.; bk.rev.; charts; illus.; index. circ. 3,000. (also avail. in microfiche from UMI; microfilm; back issues avail.; reprint service avail. from UMI) **Indexed:** C.I.J.E., Cont.Pg.Educ., Educ.Tech.Abstr., Mult.Ed.Abstr., SOMA. **Document type:** academic/scholarly publication.
 —BLDSC (3661.356000); UMI. **CCC.**
 Description: Focuses on a stimulating ways of teaching rather than relying on a series of tips.

EDUCATIONAL AND PSYCHOLOGICAL INTERACTIONS. see *PSYCHOLOGY*

EDUCATIONAL AND PSYCHOLOGICAL MEASUREMENT; devoted to the development and application of measures of individual differences. see *PSYCHOLOGY*

370 US ISSN 1062-7197
LB3051
▼**EDUCATIONAL ASSESSMENT.** 1993. q. $30 to individuals (foreign $55); institutions $95 (foreign $120). Lawrence Erlbaum Associates, Inc., 365 Broadway, Hillsdale, NJ 07642. TEL 201-666-4110. FAX 201-666-2394. Ed. Robert C. Calfee. adv. **Document type:** academic/scholarly publication.
 —BLDSC (3661.366800); UnCover.
 Description: Publishes original research and scholarship on the assessment of individuals, groups and programs in educational settings. Covers a broad range of issues related to theory, empirical research, and practice in the appraisal of educational achievements by students and teachers, young children and adults, and novices and experts.

370 US ISSN 0146-9282
LC1047.822.K2
EDUCATIONAL CONSIDERATIONS. 1973. 2/yr. $6 (effective 1993). Kansas State University, College of Education, Bluemont Hall 313, Manhattan, KS 66506. TEL 913-532-5543. Ed.Bd. bk.rev.; charts; illus.; stat. circ. 1,200. **Indexed:** Educ.Admin.Abstr.
 —BLDSC (3661.382500); UnCover.

370 UK
EDUCATIONAL COURSES IN GREAT BRITAIN AND AMERICA.* 1980. bi-m. Dominion Press Ltd., Signal House, Lyon Rd., Harrow, Middx HA1 2QE, England.

370 CN ISSN 0046-1482
EDUCATIONAL DIGEST. 1969. 5/yr. Can.$40 (foreign Can.$60). Zanny Publications Ltd., 11966 Woodbine Ave., Gormley, ON L0H 1G0, Canada. TEL 905-887-4813. FAX 905-479-4839. Ed. Amy Margaret.; Pub. Janey Gardiner. adv.: B&W page Can.$3270, color page Can.$4395; trim 8 1/4 x 10 3/4. bk.rev.; film rev.; tr.lit. circ. 18,506. (also avail. in microform from UMI; reprint service avail. from UMI) **Indexed:** Bk.Rev.Ind. (1977-), Child.Bk.Rev.Ind. (1977-), Cont.Pg.Educ.
 —UMI.
 Formerly: T A D (ISSN 0040-0556)

EDUCATION

370 US ISSN 0162-3737
LB1028
EDUCATIONAL EVALUATION & POLICY ANALYSIS. 1979. q. $37 to individuals; institutions $46. American Educational Research Association, 1230 17th St., N.W., Washington, DC 20036-3078. TEL 202-223-9485. FAX 202-775-1824. Ed. Lorraine McDonnell. circ. 5,000. (also avail. in microform from UMI; reprint service avail. from UMI) **Indexed:** C.I.J.E., Cont.Pg.Educ., Educ.Ind., Psychol.Abstr.
—BLDSC (3661.402000); Faxon; UnCover; SWETS; UMI.
Description: Focuses on practical, theoretical, and methodological issues in educational evaluation and educational policy analysis.

371.6 US
EDUCATIONAL FACILITY PLANNER.* 1969. bi-m. $25 to non-members. Council of Educational Facility Planners, 8687 E. Via de Ventura, Ste. 311, Scottsdale, AZ 85258-3347. TEL 614-442-1811. adv.; bk.rev.; illus.; circ. controlled. (processed; also avail. in microform from UMI; reprint service avail. from UMI) **Indexed:** C.I.J.E., Educ.Admin.Abstr.
Formerly: C E F P Journal (ISSN 0007-8220)

370 US ISSN 0013-1741
KF4124.A15
EDUCATIONAL FREEDOM. 1962-1973; resumed 1977. s-a. $7 (effective Feb. 1991). Educational Freedom Foundation, 110 E. Rose Ave., Saint Louis, MO 63119-4720. Ed. Daniel D. McGarry. bk.rev. circ. 2,000.
Description: Contains articles concerning and supporting unpenalized freedom of choice and content in education.

370 US ISSN 0013-175X
L11
EDUCATIONAL HORIZONS. 1921. q. $18 (foreign $25). Pi Lambda Theta, Inc., Box 6626, Bloomington, IN 47407-6626. TEL 812-339-3411. FAX 812-339-3462. Ed. Juli Knutson. adv.; bk.rev.; software rev.; index. circ. 14,000. (also avail. in microform from UMI; reprint service avail. from UMI) **Indexed:** C.I.J.E., Cont.Pg.Educ., Curr.Cont., Educ.Ind., Except.Child.Educ.Abstr., Lang.& Lang.Behav.Abstr., Mid.East: Abstr.& Ind., Mult.Ed.Abstr., Sociol.Abstr., Sp.Ed.Needs Abstr. **Document type:** academic/scholarly publication.
—BLDSC (3661.417000); Faxon; UnCover; UMI.

370 II ISSN 0013-1768
EDUCATIONAL INDIA. (Text in English) vol.32, 1965. m. Rs.5.50. Vidya Bhavan, Jagannath Puram, Masulipatnam, Andhra Pradesh, India. Ed. M. Venkatarangaiya. adv.; bk.rev.; illus.; index.

370 SA
EDUCATIONAL JOURNAL. 8/yr. R.2. Teachers' League of South Africa, Upper Bloem St., Cape Town 8001, South Africa. Ed. H.N. Kies. adv.

EDUCATIONAL MARKETER. see *PUBLISHING AND BOOK TRADE*

371.2 US ISSN 0731-1745
LB3051
EDUCATIONAL MEASUREMENT: ISSUES AND PRACTICE. 1982. q. $20 to individuals; institutions $25. National Council on Measurement in Education, 1230 17th St. N.W., Washington, DC 20036-3078. TEL 202-223-9318. FAX 202-775-1824. Ed. Anthony J. Nitko. adv.; bk.rev. circ. 2,500. (reprint service avail. from UMI) **Indexed:** C.I.J.E., Cont.Pg.Educ., Educ.Ind., Psychol.Abstr.
—BLDSC (3661.446000); Faxon; UnCover; SWETS; UMI.
Supersedes: National Council on Measurement in Education. Measurement News (ISSN 0025-6315); **Formerly:** N C M E Newsletter.

370 II
EDUCATIONAL MISCELLANY. s-a. Directorate of Higher Education, Publications Unit, Old Flowers Corner Bldg., Melarmath, Agartala, Tripura 799001, India.

371.7 US ISSN 0013-1849
EDUCATIONAL PERSPECTIVES. 1962. s-a. $5. University of Hawaii at Manoa, College of Education, 1776 University Ave., Honolulu, HI 96822. TEL 808-948-7988. FAX 808-956-2512. Ed. Dr. Alex L. Pickens. bk.rev.; illus. circ. 1,000. (also avail. in microform from UMI; back issues avail.; reprint service avail. from UMI) **Indexed:** C.I.J.E., Cont.Pg.Educ., Educ.Tech.Abstr., Mult.Ed.Abstr., So.Pac.Per.Ind., Sp.Ed.Needs Abstr.
—Faxon; UnCover; UMI.

370 AT ISSN 0013-1857
EDUCATIONAL PHILOSOPHY AND THEORY. 1969. s-a. Aus.$20 (foreign Aus.$25) to individuals; institutions Aus.$40 (foreign Aus.$50). Philosophy of Education Society of Australasia, Monash University, Faculty of Education, Clayton, Vic. 3168, Australia. TEL (03) 565 2800. FAX 61-3-565-2901. TELEX MONASH AA32691. (Subscr. to: Educational Philosophy and Theory, P.O. Box 517, Belmont, Vic. 3216, Australia) Ed. D. Aspin. bk.rev. circ. 700. (also avail. in microfiche from UMI,KTO; back issues avail.; reprint service avail. from UMI) **Indexed:** Aus.Educ.Ind., Aus.P.A.I.S., Cont.Pg.Educ., Educ.Admin.Abstr., High.Educ.Curr.Aware.Bull., Phil.Ind. **Document type:** academic/scholarly publication.
—BLDSC (3661.480000); Faxon; UnCover; SWETS; UMI.
Description: Publishes articles concerned with all aspects of educational philosophy.

370 US ISSN 0895-9048
LC89
EDUCATIONAL POLICY; an interdisciplinary journal of policy and practice. 1987. q. $42 to individuals (foreign $48); institutions $125 (foreign $131). Corwin Press, Inc. (Subsidiary of: Sage Publications, Inc.), 2455 Teller Rd., Thousand Oaks, CA 91320. TEL 805-499-0721. FAX 805-499-0871. (And: Sage Publications, Ltd., 6 Bonhill St., London EC2A 4PU, England) Ed. Philip Altbach. adv.; B&W page $225. bk.rev.; charts; illus.; index. (also avail. in microform from UMI; back issues avail.) **Indexed:** ASSIA, Mult.Ed.Abstr., SOMA, SSCI.
—BLDSC (3661.483400); UnCover; SWETS; UMI.
Description: Provides analysis and research on educational policy at the local, national and international level.
Refereed Serial

EDUCATIONAL PSYCHOLOGIST. see *PSYCHOLOGY*

EDUCATIONAL PSYCHOLOGY; an international journal of experimental educational psychology. see *PSYCHOLOGY*

EDUCATIONAL PSYCHOLOGY IN PRACTICE. see *PSYCHOLOGY*

370.15 150 US ISSN 1040-726X
LB1051 CODEN: EPSREO
EDUCATIONAL PSYCHOLOGY REVIEW. 1989. q. $135 (foreign $160) (effective 1994). Plenum Publishing Corp., 233 Spring St., New York, NY 10013-1578. TEL 212-620-8000. FAX 212-463-0742. TELEX 23-421139. Ed. Stephen L. Benton. adv. (also avail. in microfilm from JSC; back issues avail.) **Indexed:** Mult.Ed.Abstr., Pyschol.Abstr., Sp.Ed.Needs Abstr. **Document type:** academic/scholarly publication.
—BLDSC (3661.545000); UnCover; SWETS; UMI. **CCC.**
Description: Publishes review articles in general education psychology: learning, cognition, measurement, school-related counseling, and development.
Refereed Serial

379 US ISSN 0013-1873
L11 CODEN: EDREAS
EDUCATIONAL RECORD; the magazine of higher education. 1920. q. $25. American Council on Education, One Dupont Circle, Washington, DC 20036. TEL 202-939-9300. Ed. Wendy Bresler. bk.rev.; charts; index. circ. 12,000. (also avail. in microform from MIM,UMI,PMC; reprint service avail. from UMI) **Indexed:** Chic.Per.Ind., Cont.Pg.Educ., Curr.Cont., Educ.Admin.Abstr., Educ.Ind., Lang.& Lang.Behav.Abstr., Mid.East: Abstr.& Ind., P.A.I.S., Psychol.Abstr., Res.High.Educ.Abstr., Sage Pub.Admin.Abstr., SSCI.
—BLDSC (3661.820000); Faxon; UnCover; SWETS; UMI.

370 II ISSN 0046-1539
EDUCATIONAL REPORTER. (Text in English) 1970. m. Rs.20($9) Educational Journalists Forum, 159 Golf Links, New Delhi 110003, India. Ed. Madhu Bala. adv.; bk.rev.; bibl.; index. circ. 4,000.

370 UK ISSN 0013-1881
CODEN: EDURAE
EDUCATIONAL RESEARCH. 1958. 3/yr. £28 (foreign £33) to individuals; institutions £62 (foreign £72). (National Foundation for Educational Research) Routledge, 11 New Fetter Ln., London EC4P 4EE, England. TEL 071-583-9855. FAX 071-583-0701. TELEX 263398-ROUT-G. (Subscr. to: ITPS Ltd., Cheriton House, Andover, Hants SP10 5BE, England. TEL 0264-342919. FAX 0264-342807) Eds. Clare Burstall, Seamus Hegarty. adv.; bk.rev. circ. 2,500. (also avail. in microfiche from SWZ; back issues avail.; reprint service avail. from SWZ) **Indexed:** Adol.Ment.Hlth.Abstr., Br.Educ.Ind., C.I.J.E., Child Devel.Abstr., Cont.Pg.Educ., Curr.Cont., Educ.Ind., Educ.Tech.Abstr., High.Educ.Curr.Aware.Bull., Lang.Teach.& Ling.Abstr., Mid.East: Abstr.& Ind., Mult.Ed.Abstr., Psychol.Abstr., Res.High.Educ.Abstr., Rural Ext.Educ.& Tr.Abstr., SOMA, Sp.Ed.Needs Abstr., SSCI, Stud.Wom.Abstr. **Document type:** academic/scholarly publication.
—BLDSC (3661.840000); Faxon; UnCover; SWETS. **CCC.**
Description: Presents research findings in all levels of education from policy-making to classroom teaching.

370 US ISSN 0196-5042
L11
EDUCATIONAL RESEARCH QUARTERLY. 1950. q. $36.50 to individuals; institutions $46.50 (foreign $56.50). Gambling State University, Adams 105, Grambling, LA 71245. Ed. Robert M. Hashway. adv.; bk.rev.; bibl.; charts; index. circ. 1,374. (also avail. in microfilm from UMI; reprint service avail. from UMI) **Indexed:** C.I.J.E., Cont.Pg.Educ., Curr.Cont., Educ.Ind., Educ.Tech.Abstr., Lang.& Lang.Behav.Abstr., Mid.East: Abstr.& Ind., Psychol.Abstr., Res.High.Educ.Abstr., SOMA, Sp.Ed.Needs Abstr., SSCI. **Document type:** academic/scholarly publication.
—BLDSC (3661.953200); Faxon; UnCover; SWETS; UMI.
Formerly (until 1976): California Journal of Educational Research (ISSN 0008-1213)

370 KE
EDUCATIONAL RESEARCH WORKING PAPERS. (Text in English) 1973. q. Kenyatta University College, Bureau of Educational Research, P.O. Box 43844, Nairobi, Kenya. **Document type:** academic/scholarly publication.

370 US ISSN 0013-189X
L11
EDUCATIONAL RESEARCHER. 1972. 9/yr. $37 to individuals; institutions $46. American Educational Research Association, 1230 17th St. N.W., Washington, DC 20036-3078. TEL 202-223-9485. FAX 202-775-1824. Ed.Bd. adv. circ. 19,000. (also avail. in microform from UMI; processed offset format; reprint service avail. from UMI) **Indexed:** Adol.Ment.Hlth.Abstr., C.I.J.E., Cont.Pg.Educ., Educ.Admin.Abstr., Educ.Ind., Educ.Tech.Abstr., Except.Child.Educ.Abstr., Mid.East: Abstr.& Ind., Mult.Ed.Abstr., Res.High.Educ.Abstr.
—BLDSC (3661.955000); Faxon; UnCover; SWETS; UMI.
Description: Contains news and features of general significance in educational research.

370 II ISSN 0013-192X
EDUCATIONAL REVIEW. 1895. m. Rs.35($1.35) 41 Sunkuwar St., Triplicane, Madras 600005, India. Ed. A.N. Parasuram. adv.; bk.rev. circ. 1,000. (also avail. in microform from UMI; reprint service avail. from UMI) **Indexed:** C.I.J.E., Curr.Cont., Educ.Tech.Abstr., High.Educ.Curr.Aware.Bull., Res.High.Educ.Abstr., Sage Fam.Stud.Abstr., SSCI.
Description: Discusses all issues of educational interest.

EDUCATION 2019

370   UK   ISSN 0013-1911
L16
EDUCATIONAL REVIEW. 1948. 3/yr. $134 to individuals; institutions $362 (effective 1994). Carfax Publishing Co., P.O. Box 25, Abingdon, Oxon. OX14 3UE, England. TEL 44-235-555335. FAX 44-235-553559. (U.S. subscr. to: Carfax Publishing Co., Box 2025, Dunnellon, FL 34430-2025) Ed. Barrie Wade. adv.; bk.rev.; bibl.; index. (also avail. in microfiche from SWZ; back issues avail.; reprint service avail. from SWZ) **Indexed:** Br.Educ.Ind., C.I.J.E., Cont.Pg.Educ., Curr.Cont., Educ.Ind., Mult.Ed.Abstr., Psychol.Abstr., SOMA, Sp.Ed.Needs Abstr., SSCI, Stud.Wom.Abstr. **Document type:** academic/scholarly publication.
—BLDSC (3661.960000); Faxon; UnCover; SWETS. **CCC.**
Refereed Serial

370   JA
EDUCATIONAL STANDARDS IN JAPAN. (Text in English) 1959. irreg. Ministry of Education, 3-2-2 Kasumigaseki, Chiyoda-ku, Tokyo 100, Japan. illus.; stat.

370   US   ISSN 0013-1946
L11
EDUCATIONAL STUDIES; a journal of book reviews of the foundational areas in education. 1970. q. $25 to individuals (foreign $30); institutions $35 (foreign $40) (effective 1993). American Educational Studies Association, c/o Harvey Neufeldt, Box 5193, Tennessee Tech University, Cookeville, TN 38505. TEL 615-372-3377. FAX 615-372-3898. adv.; bk.rev.; index. circ. 1,300. (also avail. in microfilm from UMI; back issues avail.) **Indexed:** Amer.Bibl.Slavic & E.Eur.Stud., Bk.Rev.Dig., Bk.Rev.Ind. (1977-), C.I.J.E., Child.Bk.Rev.Ind. (1977-), Cont.Pg.Educ., Educ.Ind., Educ.Tech.Abstr., Phil.Ind., Psychol.Abstr., SSCI.
—Faxon; UnCover; UMI.

370   UK   ISSN 0305-5698
L16
EDUCATIONAL STUDIES. 1975. 3/yr. $130 to individuals; institutions $372 (effective 1994). Carfax Publishing Co., P.O. Box 25, Abingdon, Oxon. OX14 3UE, England. TEL 44-235-555335. FAX 44-235-553559. (U.S. subscr. to: Carfax Publishing Co., Box 2025, Dunnellon, FL 32630) Ed. Derek Cherrington. adv.; bk.rev.; index. (also avail. in microfiche; back issues avail.) **Indexed:** Bk.Rev.Ind., C.I.J.E., Cont.Pg.Educ., Curr.Cont., Educ.Ind., High.Educ.Curr.Aware.Bull., Lang.& Lang.Behav.Abstr., Lang.Teach.& Ling.Abstr., Mid.East: Abstr.& Ind., Mult.Ed.Abstr., Psychol.Abstr., Res.High.Educ.Abstr., SOMA, Sp.Ed.Needs Abstr., SSCI, Stud.Wom.Abstr. **Document type:** academic/scholarly publication.
—BLDSC (3662.513000); SWETS. **CCC.**
Refereed Serial

370   UN   ISSN 0070-9344
EDUCATIONAL STUDIES AND DOCUMENTS. French edition: Etudes et Documents d'Education (ISSN 0501-3550) 1953. irreg., no.59, 1993. price varies. Unesco, 7-9 Place de Fontenoy, 75700 Paris, France. TEL 45-77-16-10. (Dist. in U.S. by: Unipub, 4611-F Assembly Dr., Lanham, MD 20706-4391) (also avail. in microfiche from CIS) **Indexed:** IIS, Rural Recreat.Tour.Abstr., World Agri.Econ.& Rural Sociol.Abstr.

EDUCATIONAL STUDIES IN MATHEMATICS; an international journal. see *MATHEMATICS*

371.3   US   ISSN 0013-1962
LB1043
EDUCATIONAL TECHNOLOGY; the magazine for managers of change in education. 1961. m. $119 (foreign $139). Educational Technology Publications, Inc., 700 Palisade Ave., Englewood Cliffs, NJ 07632. TEL 201-871-4007. FAX 201-871-4009. Ed. Lawrence Lipsitz. adv.; bk.rev.; charts; illus.; index. circ. 5,000. (also avail. in microfilm from UMI; reprint service avail. from UMI) **Indexed:** C.I.J.E., Comput.Cont., Comput.Dtbs., Cont.Pg.Educ., Educ.Admin.Abstr., Educ.Ind., Educ.Tech.Abstr., Except.Child Educ.Abstr., High.Educ.Curr.Aware.Bull., Lang.& Lang.Behav.Abstr., LHTN, Media Rev.Dig., Microcomp.Ind., Psychol.Abstr., Res.High.Educ.Abstr., Sci.Abstr., SOMA, SSCI, Tr.& Dev.Alert. **Document type:** trade publication.
—BLDSC (3662.530000); Faxon; UnCover; SWETS; UMI.
Description: For educators at all levels involved with technology. Articles cover telecommunications, computer-aided instruction, information retrieval, educational television and electronic media in the classroom.

EDUCATIONAL THEATRE NEWS. see *THEATER*

370   US   ISSN 0013-2004
L11
EDUCATIONAL THEORY; a medium of expression for the John Dewey Society and the Philosophy of Education Society. 1951. q. $20 to individuals (foreign $22); institutions $30 (foreign $32). University of Illinois at Urbana-Champaign, College of Education, 1310 S. Sixth St., Champaign, IL 61820. TEL 217-333-3003. FAX 217-244-3711. Ed. Nicholas C. Burbules. adv. contact: Diane E. Beckett. bk.rev.; index. circ. 2,200. (also avail. in microform from UMI,MIM; reprint service avail. from UMI) **Indexed:** C.I.J.E., Cont.Pg.Educ., Curr.Cont., Educ.Ind., Educ.Tech.Abstr., ERIC, Lang.& Lang.Behav.Abstr., Mult.Ed.Abstr., Phil.Ind., Res.High.Educ.Abstr., Sp.Ed.Needs Abstr., SSCI, Stud.Wom.Abstr. **Document type:** academic/scholarly publication.
—BLDSC (3662.550000); Faxon; UnCover; SWETS; UMI. **CCC.**

EDUCATIONAL TRAVEL; the original guide to adult learning vacations around the world. see *TRAVEL AND TOURISM*

370   II
EDUCATIONAL TRENDS.* (Text in English) vol.6, 1972. s-a. Rs.10($2) National Council of Educational Research and Training, Regional College of Education, Alumni Association, Sri Aurobindo Marg, New Delhi, India. Ed. G.N. Bhardwaj. bk.rev.; bibl.; charts. circ. 1,000.

370   IT   ISSN 0391-6375
EDUCATORE. 1953. fortn. L.58000 (foreign L.65000). R C S Libri & Grandi Opere, Divisione Scuola, Via Mecenate 91, 20138 Milan, Italy. TEL 02-50951. FAX 55400398. Ed. Sergio Neri. adv. circ. 50,000.
Formerly (until 1976): Educatore Italiano.

370   US   ISSN 0013-2047
EDUCATORS' ADVOCATE. 1884. m. (except Dec., June, July). $5 to non-members. S D E A - N E A, 411 E. Capital Ave., Pierre, SD 57501. TEL 605-224-9263. FAX 605-658-5456. Ed. Cynthia Menzel. adv. circ. 7,800. **Document type:** newsletter.

EDUCATORS' GUIDE TO CORPORATE AND VOLUNTARY SUPPORT. see *BUSINESS AND ECONOMICS*

370   PL   ISSN 0239-6858
EDUKACJA. 1975. q. $40. (Ministerstwo Edukacji Narodowej) Edukacja, Ul. Gorczeska 8, 01-180, Poland. TEL 48-22-3320221. FAX 48-22-321895. (Dist. by: Ars Polona-Ruch, Krakowskie Przedmiescie 7, Warsaw, Poland) Ed. Miroslaw Szymanski. circ. 1,500. **Document type:** academic/scholarly publication.
Formerly: Badania Oswiatowe.

370   DK   ISSN 0108-8262
EFTERSKOLER. FORTEGNELSE. 1971. a. free. Undervisningsministeriet, Folkeoplysningsafdelingen, Copenhagen, Denmark. circ. 7,500. **Document type:** government publication, consumer publication, catalog.

370   TU
EGITIM BULTENI/EDUCATION BULLETIN. (Text in Turkish) 1972. m. Ministry of National Education & Culture, Lefkosa - Nicosia, Mersin 10, Turkey. TEL 520-83136. FAX 520-82334. circ. 3,000. **Document type:** bulletin.

373   GW
EIBE. 1973. q. DM.12. Rudolf-Steiner-Schulverein Ottersberg e.V., Amtshof 5, 28807 Ottersberg, Germany. TEL 04205-2066. FAX 04205-8510. Ed. Bert Blumenthal. adv.: B&W page DM.200; adv. contact: Peter Stuehl. circ. 1,400. **Document type:** bulletin.
Description: Contains information on pedagogical matters.

370   IS
EIGERET LECHINUCH. s-a. 10 Dubnov St., Tel Aviv 64 732, Israel.

EINHARD INTERN; Schulzeitschrift des staedtischen Einhard-Gymnasiums Aachen. see *CHILDREN AND YOUTH — About*

101   IS   ISSN 0334-2565
EIUNIM BICHEINUCH. Added title: Studies in Education. (Text in Hebrew; summaries in English) 1973. s-a. Haifa University, School of Education, Mount Carmel, Haifa 31999, Israel. Ed. Adir Cohen. bk.rev. circ. 1,000. **Indexed:** Inc.Heb.Per. **Document type:** academic/scholarly publication.

ELEMENTA; matematik, fysik och kemi. see *SCIENCES: COMPREHENSIVE WORKS*

ELEMENTARY SCHOOL GUIDANCE & COUNSELING. see *PSYCHOLOGY*

372   US   ISSN 0013-5984
L11   CODEN: ELSJA2
ELEMENTARY SCHOOL JOURNAL. 1900. bi-m. (Sep.-May). $29.50 to individuals; institutions $56; students $19.50. University of Chicago Press, Journals Division, 5720 S. Woodlawn Ave., Chicago, IL 60637. TEL 312-753-3347. FAX 312-753-0811. (Subscr. to: Box 37005, Chicago, IL 60637) Ed. Thomas L. Good. adv.; abstr.; index. circ. 6,000. (also avail. in microform from MIM,UMI,PMC; reprint service avail. from UMI,ISI) **Indexed:** Acad.Ind., C.I.J.E., Chic.Per.Ind., Cont.Pg.Educ., Curr.Cont., DSH Abstr., Educ.Admin.Abstr., Educ.Ind., Educ.Tech.Abstr., Except.Child.Educ.Abstr., Lang. & Lang.Behav.Abstr., Mult.Ed.Abstr., Psychol.Abstr., SOMA, Sp.Ed.Needs Abstr., SSCI. **Document type:** academic/scholarly publication.
—BLDSC (3727.200000); Faxon; UnCover; SWETS; UMI. **CCC.**
Refereed Serial

ELEMENTARY SCHOOL LIBRARY COLLECTION. see *LIBRARY AND INFORMATION SCIENCES*

ELTERN. see *CHILDREN AND YOUTH — About*

370   SZ   ISSN 0013-645X
DER ELTERNBRIEF; Anregungen und Hilfen fuer die Erziehung. 1957. m. 52.80 SFr. Verlag die Kommenden AG, Steigstr. 59, CH-8201 Schaffhausen, Switzerland. TEL 053-250023. FAX 053-833404. circ. 3,000. **Document type:** bulletin.

370   GW   ISSN 0934-8662
ELTERNFORUM; Zeitschrift fuer Eltern und alle, die an Erziehung und Schule interressiert sind. 1967. q. DM.25. Katholische Elternschaft Deutschlands, Baumschulallee 9-13, 53115 Bonn, Germany. TEL 0228-650052. FAX 0228-696217. Ed. Annegret Jonas. bk.rev.; index. circ. 3,000. (back issues avail.) **Document type:** academic/scholarly publication.

370   BL   ISSN 0104-1037
EM ABERTO. 1981. 4/yr. Cr.$3600($800) (effective Nov. 1993). Instituto Nacional de Estudos e Pesquisas Educacionais, Campus da Universidade de Brasilia, Ala Sul, 70910-900 Brasilia, DF, Brazil. TEL 061-347-8970 FAX 061-273-3233. Ed. Arsenio C. Becker. adv.; bk.rev.; bibl.; cum.index: 1981-1987. circ. 12,500. (looseleaf format; back issues avail.)
●Also available online.
Description: Looks at relevant and current issues related to Brazilian education.
Refereed Serial

ENGLISCH; eine Zeitschrift fuer Englischlehrerinnen und Englischlehrer. see *LINGUISTICS*

ENGLISH ACADEMY REVIEW. see *LITERATURE*

420.07 370 US ISSN 0007-8204
LA632
ENGLISH EDUCATION. 1969. 4/yr. $55 membership. (Conference on English Education) National Council of Teachers of English, 1111 W. Kenyon Rd., Urbana, IL 61801-1096. TEL 217-328-3870. FAX 217-328-9645. Ed. Patricia Lambert Stock. adv.; bk.rev.; index. circ. 3,200. (also avail. in microfilm from UMI; reprint service avail. from UMI). **Indexed:** C.I.J.E., Cont.Pg.Educ., Curr.Cont., Educ.Ind., SSCI. **Document type:** academic/scholarly publication.
—BLDSC (3773.490000); Faxon; UnCover; UMI.
Formerly: C E E Newsletter.

370 US ISSN 0425-0508
ENGLISH IN TEXAS. 1969. q. $15. Texas Council of Teachers of English, Fort Worth, TX 76129-0001. TEL 817-921-7221. FAX 817-921-7333. (Co-sponsor: Texas Christian University) Ed. Christina Murphy. adv.; bk.rev.; circ. 3,000 (paid). **Indexed:** ERIC. **Document type:** academic/scholarly publication.
Description: Publishes articles on English and language arts instruction from elementary through university levels, as well as poetry and fiction.

420.07 370 US ISSN 0013-8274
PE1
ENGLISH JOURNAL. 1912. 8/yr. (Sep.-Apr.) $40 individual membership; institutions $50. National Council of Teachers of English, 1111 W. Kenyon Rd., Urbana, IL 61801-1096. TEL 217-328-3870. FAX 217-328-9645. Ed. Leila Christenbury. adv.; bk.rev.; rec.rev.; index. circ. 56,000. (also avail. in microform from UMI,PMC; reprint service avail. from UMI,KTO) **Indexed:** Abstr.Engl.Stud., Acad.Ind., Bk.Rev.Ind. (1965-), C.I.J.E., Child.Bk.Rev.Ind. (1965-), Cont.Pg.Educ., Curr.Cont., Educ.Ind., Except.Child.Educ.Abstr., Film Lit.Ind. (1973-), Jun.High.Mag.Abstr., Lang.& Lang.Behav.Abstr., Lang.Teach.& Ling.Abstr., M.L.A., Mag.Ind., PSI, R.G., SSCI, TOM. **Document type:** academic/scholarly publication.
—BLDSC (3775.020000); Faxon; UnCover; SWETS; UMI.

ENGLISH QUARTERLY. see *EDUCATION — Teaching Methods And Curriculum*

370 CN ISSN 0046-2101
ENSEIGNANTS; mensuel national d'information pedagogique. 1970. m. Can.$18. Journal "Les Enseignants" Limitee, 767 Demers, Saint-Jean, Que. J3B 4W1, Canada. TEL 514-348-8718. Ed. Fernand Houde. adv.; bk.rev.; circ. 4,500. (also avail. in microfilm from BNQ)

372 RM ISSN 0256-5129
L'ENSEIGNEMENT ET LA PEDAGOGIE EN ROUMANIE. (Text in French; table of contents in English and French) 1978. a. $30 (exchange basis to foreign subscribers). Biblioteca Centrala Pedagogica, Str. Zalomit Nr. 12, Sector 1, 70714 Bucharest, Rumania. TEL 157571. (Co-sponsor: Soros Foundation) Eds. George Anca, Luminita Burciu. bk.rev.; abstr.; bibl.; index. circ. 2,000.
Description: Covers secondary and higher education in Rumania.

100 FR ISSN 0986-1653
L'ENSEIGNEMENT PHILOSOPHIQUE. 1950. 6/yr. 220 F. (foreign 250 F.). Association des Professeurs de Philosophie de l'Enseignement Public, c/o Claude Brochard, Les Bertons, 17350 St. Savinien, France. TEL 46-90-17-73. bk.rev.; bibl.; charts; stat.; cum.index 1950-1988. **Indexed:** Amer.Hist.& Life, Hist.Abstr. **Document type:** academic/scholarly publication.
—BLDSC (3776.301100).
Formerly: Revue de l'Enseignement Philosophique (ISSN 0035-1393)

370 FR ISSN 0223-5986
ENSEIGNEMENT PUBLIC. 1945. m. 220 F. Federation de l'Education Nationale, 48 rue la Bruyere, 75440 Paris Cedex 9, France. TEL 42-85-71-01. FAX 40-16-05-92. TELEX FENTELX 648 356 F. Ed. Yannick Simbron. adv. circ. 418,100.

378.666 IV
ENSEIGNEMENT SUPERIEUR EN COTE-D'IVOIRE. 1980. a. 60 Fr. Universite Nationale de Cote d'Ivoire, B.P. 859, Abidjan-08, Ivory Coast. adv.

ENTRANCE REQUIREMENTS FOR NURSING EDUCATION PROGRAMS IN CANADA. see *MEDICAL SCIENCES — Nurses And Nursing*

ENVIRONMENTAL COMMUNICATOR. see *ENVIRONMENTAL STUDIES*

ENVIRONMENTAL EDUCATION. see *ENVIRONMENTAL STUDIES*

370.193 US
LB3062
EQUITY & EXCELLENCE IN EDUCATION. 1963. 3/yr. $60 (effective 1992). (University of Massachusetts, School of Education) Greenwood Press, Inc. (Subsidiary of: Greenwood Publishing Group Inc.), 88 Post Rd. W., Westport, CT 06881. TEL 203-226-3571. FAX 203-222-1502. Ed. Byrd Jones. adv.; bk.rev.; bibl. circ. 3,000. (also avail. in microform from UMI,MIM; reprint service avail. from UMI) **Indexed:** Acad.Ind., C.I.J.E., Curr.Cont., Educ.Admin.Abstr., Educ.Ind., Ind.Per.Negroes-, P.A.I.S., Sociol.Abstr., Stud.Wom.Abstr. **Document type:** academic/scholarly publication.
—Faxon; UnCover.
Former titles: Equity and Excellence (ISSN 0894-0681); Integrateducation (ISSN 0020-4862)

370 DK ISSN 0906-7892
HD5715.5.D4
ERHVERVSUDDANNELSER EFTER 9. OG 10. KLASSE.* 1979. a. free. Raadet for Uddannelses- og Erhvervsvejledning, Copenhagen, Denmark. illus.
Former titles (until 1991): Erhvervsuddannelser (ISSN 0906-0065); (until 1990): Om Laerlinge- og E F G - Uddannelserne (ISSN 0109-9914); (until 1984): Om E F G - Uddannelserne (ISSN 0901-5353)

370 028.5 CC ISSN 1002-4042
ERTONG CHUANGZHAO/CHILDREN'S CREATION. (Text in Chinese) 1987. m. Y0.50 per no. Nanning Shi Jiaoyu Ju - Nanning Municipal Bureau of Education, Minle Lu, Nanning, Guangxi 530012, People's Republic of China. TEL 207323. FAX 0771-205614. Ed. Ma Zuowen. circ. 250,000.

370 AU ISSN 0014-0325
ERZIEHUNG UND UNTERRICHT; Oesterreichische paedagogische Zeitschrift. (Supplement avail.: Heilpaeagogik) 1850. 10/yr. (supplement 5/yr.). S.545. Oesterreichischer Bundesverlag Gesellschaft mbH, Schwarzenbergstr. 5, Postfach 79, A-1010 Vienna, Austria. FAX 0222-51405210. TELEX 131159. Ed.Bd. adv.; bk.rev.; abstr.; bibl.; charts; illus. circ. 4,100.

370 GW ISSN 0342-0671
ERZIEHUNG UND WISSENSCHAFT; allgemeine Deutsche Lehrer-Zeitung. 1948. m. DM.22.80. (Gewerkschaft Erziehung und Wissenschaft) Stamm-Verlag GmbH, Goldammerweg 16, 45134 Essen, Germany. adv.; bk.rev.; illus.; stat. circ. 187,000.
Formerly: Allgemeine Deutsche Lehrerzeitung (ISSN 0002-5836)

370 GW ISSN 0170-0723
ERZIEHUNG UND WISSENSCHAFT NIEDERSACHSEN. m. DM.10.80. (Landesverband Niedersachsen, Gewerkschaft Erziehung und Wissenschaft) Stamm-Verlag GmbH, Goldammerweg 16, 45134 Essen, Germany. TEL 0201-41757. circ. 34,300.
Description: Deals with issues important to teachers in Niedersachsen.

370 GW ISSN 0014-0333
ERZIEHUNGSKUNST; Monatsschrift zur Paedagogik R. Steiners. 1927. m. DM.59. (Bund der Freien Waldorfschulen e.V.) Verlag Freies Geistesleben GmbH, Haussmannstr. 76, 70188 Stuttgart, Germany. TEL 0711-283255. FAX 0711-2624606. Ed. Klaus Schickert. adv.; bk.rev.; illus.; index. circ. 9,000.
—CCC.

370 BE
ESPACE DE LIBERTES. 10/yr. 600 Fr. (foreign 900 Fr.). Centre d'Action Laique, Campus de la Plaine ULB, CP 236 bd. du Triomphe, 1050 Brussels, Belgium. TEL 647-52-39. FAX 647-61-21. Ed. Jean Schouters.

370 IT
ESPERIENZE E PROGETTI. 1974. bi-m. L.15000. Centro Studi ed Esperienze Scout Baden-Powell, Via Achille Papa n.17, 00195 Rome, Italy. (Subscr. to: Via Bonci n.4, 40137 Bologna, Italy) circ. 3,000.

ESPRIT LIBRE. see *PSYCHOLOGY*

371.8 BL ISSN 0103-6831
LA555
ESTUDOS EM AVALIACAO EDUCACIONAL. s-a. Fundacao Carlos Chagas, Nucleo de Testes e Medidas, Av. Prof. Francisco Morato, 1565, 05513 Sao Paulo, SP, Brazil. TEL 011-813-4511. FAX 011-815-1059. TELEX 11-83823 CHAF BR. Ed. Heraldo Marelim Vianna. charts; stat.
Formerly (until 1990): Educacao e Selecao (ISSN 0101-3823)

ETHICS JOURNAL. see *BUSINESS AND ECONOMICS — Management*

370 ET ISSN 0425-4414
ETHIOPIAN JOURNAL OF EDUCATION. 1967. 2/yr. $16 per no. to individuals; institutions $20 per no. Addis Ababa University, Institute of Educational Research, P.O. Box 1176, Addis Ababa, Ethiopia. Ed. Lakew Tekle. adv. circ. 2,000. **Indexed:** P.L.E.S.A.

370 RW ISSN 1011-4874
ETUDES RWANDAISES. SCIENCES NATURELLES ET APPLIQUEES. (Text in French) 1975. q. Institut Pedagogique National du Rwanda, B.P. 77, Butare, Rwanda.
Supersedes in part: Etudes Rwandaises. Lettres et Sciences Humaines; **Formerly (until 1981):** Rencontres.

L'ETUDIANT. see *CHILDREN AND YOUTH — For*

370 UK ISSN 0260-8979
EUROEDNEWS. 1980. 2/yr. free. U.K. Centre for European Education, Central Bureau, Seymour Mews House, Seymour Mews, London W1H 9PE, England. TEL 071-486-5101. FAX 071-935-5741. TELEX 21368-CBEVEX-G. Ed. K.R. Tillin. bk.rev. circ. 12,000. **Document type:** newsletter.
—BLDSC (3829.267900).
Description: Reports on educational developments in Europe including research articles, conference reports, project reports, news from education centers and members.

370 US ISSN 1056-4934
LA622
EUROPEAN EDUCATION; a journal of translations. (Text in English) 1969. q. $315 (foreign $347). M.E. Sharpe, Inc., 80 Business Park Dr., Armonk, NY 10504. TEL 914-273-1800. FAX 914-273-2106. Ed. Susanne M. Shafer. adv. contact: Barbara Ladd. circ. 220 (paid). (back issues avail.) **Indexed:** C.I.J.E., Cont.Pg.Educ., Curr.Cont., Educ.Ind., Educ.Tech.Abstr., Mid.East: Abstr.& Ind., Psychol.Abstr., Sociol.Educ.Abstr. **Document type:** academic/scholarly publication.
—BLDSC (3829.697730); Faxon; UnCover; UMI.
Formerly: Western European Education (ISSN 0043-3675)
Description: Contains articles selected and translated from leading European journals. Also includes research reports and documents from research centers and school authorities.
Refereed Serial

370 US ISSN 1053-640X
L914.5
EUROPEAN FACULTY DIRECTORY. 1991. a. Gale Research Inc., 835 Penobscot Bldg., Detroit, MI 48226-4094. TEL 313-961-2242. FAX 313-961-6083. **Document type:** directory.

370   UK   ISSN 0141-8211
L101.A2   CODEN: EJEDE6
EUROPEAN JOURNAL OF EDUCATION; research, development and policies. 1964. q. $144 to individuals; institutions $398 (effective 1994). (European Institute of Education and Social Policy, Paris, FR) Carfax Publishing Co., P.O. Box 25, Abingdon, Oxon. OX14 3UE, England. TEL 44-235-555335. FAX 44-235-553559. (U.S. subscr. to: Carfax Publishing Co., Box 2025, Dunnellon, FL 34430-2025) Ed. Jean-Pierre Jallade. bk.rev.; index. (also avail. in microfiche; back issues avail.) **Indexed:** C.I.J.E., Cont.Pg.Educ., Educ.Tech.Abstr., High.Educ.Curr.Aware.Bull., Mult.Ed.Abstr., Res.High.Educ.Abstr., SOMA, Sp.Ed.Needs Abstr., Stud.Wom.Abstr. **Document type:** academic/scholarly publication.
—BLDSC (3829.728400); Faxon; UnCover; SWETS. CCC.
   Formerly: Paedagogica Europaea (ISSN 0078-7787)
   Refereed Serial

EUROPEAN JOURNAL OF ENGINEERING EDUCATION. see *ENGINEERING*

370.15 150   PO   ISSN 0256-2928
   CODEN: EJPDER
EUROPEAN JOURNAL OF PSYCHOLOGY OF EDUCATION. (Text in English) 1986. q. $50 to individuals (outside Europe $55); institutions $77 (outside Europe $83) (effective 1994). Instituto Superior de Psicologia Aplicada, Rua Jardim do Tabaco, 44, 1100 Lisbon, Portugal. TEL 886-31-84. FAX 886-09-54. (Co-sponsors: Universite de Provence; University of Neuchatel) Ed. Michel Gilly. adv.; bk.rev.; bibl.; charts. **Indexed:** Mult.Ed.Abstr., Psychol.Abstr., Sp.Ed.Needs Abstr. **Document type:** academic/scholarly publication.
—BLDSC (3829.738000); SWETS.
   Description: Provides original articles on empirical research in the psychology of education.

370   UK   ISSN 0261-9768
EUROPEAN JOURNAL OF TEACHER EDUCATION. 1978. 3/yr. $124 to individuals; institutions $348 (effective 1994). (Association for Teacher Education in Europe) Carfax Publishing Co., P.O. Box 25, Abingdon, Oxon. OX14 3UE, England. TEL 44-235-555335. FAX 44-235-553559. (U.S. subscr. to: Carfax Publishing Co., Box 2025, Dunnellon, FL 34430-2025) Ed. Marco Todeschini. bk.rev.; index. (also avail. in microfiche; back issues avail.) **Indexed:** C.I.J.E., Cont.Pg.Educ., Educ.Tech.Abstr., Mult.Ed.Abstr., Res.High.Educ.Abstr., SOMA, Sp.Ed.Needs Abstr., Stud.Wom.Abstr. **Document type:** academic/scholarly publication.
—BLDSC (3829.746000); SWETS. CCC.
   Formerly (until vol.4, 1981): Revue A T E E Journal (ISSN 0379-606X)
   Refereed Serial

370   UK   ISSN 0950-0790
L16   CODEN: EREEEV
EVALUATION AND RESEARCH IN EDUCATION; Durham and Newcastle research review. 1950. 3/yr. £14($27) to individuals; group rate £37 ($74); students £9 ($18). Multilingual Matters Ltd., Frankfurt Lodge, Clevedon Hall, Victoria Rd., Clevedon, Avon BS21 7SJ, England. TEL 0275-876519. FAX 0275-343096. Ed. Roy Bevan. adv.; bk.rev.; bibl.; index. circ. 750. (also avail. in microform; back issues avail.) **Indexed:** Br.Educ.Ind., Br.Hum.Ind., Cont.Pg.Educ., High.Educ.Curr.Aware.Bull., Mult.Ed.Abstr., Res.High.Educ.Abstr., Sociol.Abstr., SOMA, Sp.Ed.Needs Abstr., SSCI, Stud.Wom.Abstr. **Document type:** trade publication.
—BLDSC (3830.568000); SWETS.
   Former titles: Durham and Newcastle Research Review (ISSN 0141-108X); Durham Research Review.
   Description: Makes methods of evaluation and research in education available to teachers, administrators and research workers.

370   US
EVALUATION COMMENT; the journal of educational evaluation. 1968. a. free. University of California, Los Angeles, Center for the Study of Evaluation, 145 Moore Hall, Graduate School of Education, 405 Hilgard Ave., Los Angeles, CA 90024-1522. TEL 213-206-1512. Ed.Bd. circ. 10,000.
●Also available online.

370 330.1   NE   ISSN 0924-5391
EVALUATION IN EDUCATION AND HUMAN SERVICES. (Text in English) 1982. irreg., vol.35, 1993. price varies. Kluwer Academic Publishers, Postbus 17, 3300 AA Dordrecht, Netherlands. TEL 31-78-334911. FAX 31-78-334254. TELEX 29245 KAPG NL. (Dist. by: Kluwer Academic Publishers Group, P.O. Box 322, 3300 AH Dordrecht, Netherlands. TEL 31-78-524400. FAX 31-78-524474; N. America dist. addr.: Box 358, Accord Sta., Hingham, MA 02018-0358. TEL 617-871-6600. FAX 617-871-6528) **Document type:** monographic series.
   Refereed Serial

377.8 268   GW   ISSN 0014-3413
DER EVANGELISCHE ERZIEHER; Zeitschrift fuer Paedagogik und Theologie. 1945. bi-m. DM.48. Verlag Moritz Diesterweg GmbH, Waechtersbacher Str. 89, 60386 Frankfurt a.M., Germany. TEL 069-42081-0. FAX 069-1301-100. TELEX 413234-MDD. Ed.Bd. adv.; bk.rev.; abstr.; index. circ. 3,500. **Document type:** academic/scholarly publication.
—BLDSC (3830.710000). CCC.

377.9   GW   ISSN 0344-1466
EVANGELISCHE FACHHOCHSCHULEN DARMSTADT, FREIBURG, LUDWIGSHAFEN, REUTLINGEN. HOCHSCHULBRIEF. 1972. a. Evangelische Fachhochschulen Darmstadt, Freiburg, Ludwigshafen, Reutlingen, Zweifalltorweg 12, 64293 Darmstadt, Germany. FAX 06151-879858. **Document type:** academic/scholarly publication.

EXCEPTIONAL CHILDREN. see *CHILDREN AND YOUTH — About*

EXCLAIMER. see *EDUCATION — Higher Education*

370   US   ISSN 1065-5115
▼**EXECUTIVE SUMMARY OF CALIFORNIA EDUCATION.** 1993. m. (10/yr.). $50 to individuals; institutions $75. Caddo Gap Press, 3145 Geary Blvd., Ste. 275, San Francisco, CA 94118. TEL 415-750-9978. FAX 415-668-5450. Ed. Alan H. Jones. circ. 1,000. **Document type:** academic/scholarly publication.
   Description: Features condensations of reports, research, and practice specifically relevant to education at all levels in California.

372   AT   ISSN 0313-8747
EXPLORE. 1971. 4/yr. Aus.$9.50. (Ministry of Education and Training) Marayanga Publications, P.O. Box 258, Prahran, Vic. 3181, Australia. TEL 03-525-2088. FAX 03-525-2184. circ. 25,000.
   Description: Reading and class activities for middle primary level children.

377.8   PO
EXPOSITOR DOMINICAL. q. Esc.220. Casa Publicadora das Assembleias de Deus, Av. Alm. Gago Coutinho 158, 1700 Lisbon, Portugal. Ed. Fernando Martinez da Silva. circ. 2,200.

F A E UPDATE. (Foundation for Accounting Education) see *BUSINESS AND ECONOMICS — Accounting*

370   PH
F A P E REVIEW. (Text in English) 1970. s-a. free. Fund for Assistance to Private Education, M.C.P.O. Box 947, Makati 1299, Philippines. FAX 818-0013. Ed. Bettina R. Olmedo. bk.rev.; illus. circ. 2,000. **Indexed:** Ind.Phil.Per.
   Description: Serves as a forum for the articulation of issues and problems affecting private education in the Philippines.

370   FR   ISSN 0751-8145
F E N - HEBDO. w. 160 F. Federation de l'Education Nationale (FEN), 48 rue la Bruyere, 75440 Paris Cedex 09, France. Ed. Yannick Simbron. adv.; illus. circ. 10,000.
   Formerly: F E N Informations.

F F A ADVISORS MAKING A DIFFERENCE. see *AGRICULTURE*

F F A NEW HORIZONS. (Future Farmers of America) see *AGRICULTURE*

370   GW
F H PRESSE. 1979. bi-m. free. Fachhochschule Dortmund, Sonnenstr. 96, 44139 Dortmund, Germany. TEL 0231-9112-0. FAX 0231-9112313. adv.; bk.rev. circ. 2,500. (back issues avail.) **Document type:** newsletter.

373   FR   ISSN 1016-6998
F I P E S O NEWSLETTER. French edition: Nouvelles de la F I P E S O (ISSN 1016-7048) 1921. 8/yr. 120 F. Federation Internationale des Professeurs de l'Enseignement Secondaire Officiel, 7 rue de Villersexel, 75007 Paris, France. TEL 40-63-29-35. FAX 40-63-29-36. Ed. Claude Aufort. bk.rev. circ. 600. **Document type:** newsletter.
   Formerly (until 1988): International Federation of Secondary Teachers. International Bulletin.
   Description: Aims to develop international cooperation among secondary teachers.

370 528 410   SZ
F I P L V WORLD NEWS. (Text in English, French, German) 1984. 3/yr. free. Federation Internationale des Professeurs de Langues Vivantes, Seestr. 247, CH-8038 Zurich, Switzerland. TEL 06421-282141. FAX 06421-285710. TELEX 482372-UMR-D. Ed. Reinhold Freudenstein. bk.rev. circ. 600. **Document type:** newsletter.
   Supersedes (in 1984): Unesco. A L S E D Newsletter (Anthropology and Language Science in Educational Development).

371.8   US
F.S.S.C. NEWSLETTER. 1966. irreg. (2-4/yr.). free. Foreign Student Service Council, 2337 18th St., N.W., Washington, DC 20009. TEL 202-232-4979. FAX 202-667-9305. Ed. Susanna Ball. circ. 2,000. (tabloid format) **Document type:** newsletter.
   Formerly: International Student Newsletter (ISSN 0020-8809)

370   CN   ISSN 0381-9183
F W T A O NEWSLETTER. 1982. 6/yr. Can.$23 (US Can.$27, elsewhere Can.$42). Federation of Women Teachers' Associations of Ontario, 1260 Bay St., Toronto, ON M5R 2B8, Canada. TEL 416-964-1232. FAX 416-774-6093. Ed. Mary Labatt. bk.rev. circ. 53,000. **Document type:** newspaper.

370   GW
FACHHOCHSCHULE AALEN. INFO. 1971. q. free. Fachhochschule Aalen, Beethovenstr. 1, 73430 Aalen, Germany. TEL 07361-5760. Ed. Joerg Linser. adv.; bk.rev circ. 1,400. **Document type:** bulletin.
   Formerly: Fachhochschule Aalen. Bulletin.

371   US
FACT BOOK; a statistical handbook. 1967. a. free. Department of Education, 200 W. Baltimore St., Baltimore, MD 21201. TEL 301-333-2664. FAX 301-333-2017. Ed. Kathie Hiatt. charts. circ. 8,500. **Indexed:** SR. **Document type:** government publication.
   Former titles: Facts about Maryland Public Education (ISSN 0092-461X); Facts about Maryland Schools.
   Description: Provides statistical information about Maryland's 24 school systems, including enrollment, staff, state aid, per pupil cost, and average teacher salary.

FAMILIENMAGAZIN. see *CHILDREN AND YOUTH — About*

FAMILLE ET DEVELOPPEMENT. see *PUBLIC HEALTH AND SAFETY*

FAMILY LIFE EDUCATOR. see *PSYCHOLOGY*

FAMILY MEDICINE. see *MEDICAL SCIENCES*

FAMILY RELATIONS; journal of applied family & child studies. see *SOCIOLOGY*

FANLIGHT NEWS. see *MEDICAL SCIENCES*

EDUCATION

370 960 SX ISSN 0256-5994
FASETTE/FACETS/FACETTEN. (Text in English, occasionally in Afrikaans, German) 1983. s-a. free. Council of the Windhoek College of Education, Private Bag 16003, Windhoek, Namibia. TEL 061-42421. Ed. Emma Kirchner. bk.rev.; abstr.; bibl.; illus. circ. 500. (back issues avail.) **Indexed:** Documentatieblad. **Document type:** academic/scholarly publication.
  Description: Publishes in all fields of education

350 338.9 US ISSN 0148-4109
FEDERAL RESEARCH REPORT; weekly report on federal grants and contracts available to research institutions. 1965. w. $245. Business Publishers, Inc., 951 Pershing Dr., Silver Spring, MD 20910-4464. TEL 301-587-6300. FAX 301-585-9075. Ed. Leonard Eiserer. bk.rev.; stat. (looseleaf format; back issues avail.) **Document type:** newsletter.
●Also available online. Vendor(s): NewsNet (RD10).
  Description: Covers funding and fellowship opportunities for researchers and administrators in all fields.

370 AT ISSN 1036-3904
FEDERATION NEWS (ABBOTSFORD). 1990. w. (during school term). Aus.$40 to non-members. Federated Teachers' Union of Victoria, 112 Trenerry Cress, Abbotsford, Vic. 3067, Australia. TEL 03-417-2822. FAX 03-417-6198. Ed. Charles Smith. adv.; bk.rev.; illus.; index. circ. 36,000. (tabloid format; also avail. in microfiche; back issues avail.) **Document type:** newspaper.
  Formed by the merger of (1982-1990): Tech Teacher; (1985-1990): V T U Journal; Which was formerly (1917-1984): Teachers'Journal (ISSN 0040-0483)

370 CN ISSN 0700-9070
FEDERATION OF C.P.T.A. ASSOCIATIONS OF ONTARIO. NEWSLETTER. 1974. q. Can.$15 membership. Federation of Catholic Parent-Teacher Associations of Ontario, 80 Sheppard Ave E., Toronto, Ont. M2N 6E8, Canada. TEL 416-229-5333. FAX 416-512-3428. Ed. Patrick Smith. bk.rev. circ. 70,000. **Document type:** newsletter.

370 CN
FEDERATION QUEBECOISE DES DIRECTEURS ET DIRECTRICES D'ECOLE. REVUE INFORMATION. 1963. 5/yr. Can.$15. Federation Quebecoise des Directeurs et Directrices d'Ecole, 7855 Bd. L.H. Lafontaine, Ste. 100, Anjou, Que. H1K 4E4, Canada. TEL 514-353-7511. FAX 514-353-2064. adv.; illus. circ. 5,000. (back issues avail.)
  Formerly: Federation Quebecoise des Directeurs d'Ecole. Revue Information.

370 HU ISSN 0209-9608
FELNOTTNEVELES, MUVELODES. ACTA ANDRAGOGIAE ET CULTURAE. irreg., vol.12, 1991. Kossuth Lajos Todomanyegyetem, Egyetem ter 1, 4010 Debrecen, Hungary. TEL 0036-52-416666. FAX 0036-52-412336. Ed. Kalman Rubovszky. bibl. circ. 500. **Document type:** academic/scholarly publication.
—BLDSC (0642.330000).
  Supersedes in part (in 1980): Neveles, Muvelodes. Acta Paedagogica Debrecina (ISSN 0324-6957); Which was formerly (until 1963): Acta Paedagogica Debrecina (ISSN 0567-7912).

370 US ISSN 0015-0037
FERGUSON-FLORISSANT SCHOOLS. 1945. q. Ferguson-Florissant School District, Board of Education, 1005 Waterford Dr., Florissant, MO 63033-3649. FAX 314-831-1535. Ed. Donna Corno. illus. circ. 32,000. (tabloid format) **Document type:** newsletter.

FEUILLETS D'INFORMATIONS PEDAGOGIQUES. see GEOGRAPHY

370 FJ
FIJI. MINISTRY OF EDUCATION, SCIENCE AND TECHNOLOGY. ANNUAL REPORT. (Subseries of: Fiji. Parliament. Parliamentary Paper) 1918. a. $2.50. Ministry of Education, Science and Technology, Suva, Fiji. TEL 679-314477. FAX 679-303511. circ. 500. **Document type:** government publication.
  Former titles: Fiji. Ministry of Education. Report; (until 1977): Fiji. Ministry of Education, Youth and Sport. Report (ISSN 0377-3728)
  Description: Activities of all functional units of the ministry in the year reported on.

371 PH ISSN 0015-1009
FILIPINO TEACHER. (Text in English and Filipino) 1945. m. (except Apr.-May). P.300($12) (effective 1991). 373 Quezon Ave., Quezon City, Philippines. Ed. Minda C. Sutaria. adv.; illus.; circ. 42,000(controlled).
  Description: Contains instructural materials, news, views, literary articles and other features.

FILM AUSTRALIA EDUCATION CATALOGUE. see MOTION PICTURES

FILM UND FERNSEHEN IN FORSCHUNG UND LEHRE. see MOTION PICTURES

FILOZOFSKI FAKULTET - ZADAR. RAZDIO FILOZOFIJE, PSIHOLOGIJE, SOCIOLOGIJE I PEDAGOGIJE. RADOVI. see PHILOSOPHY

370 US ISSN 0744-7434
FIRST TEACHER; for people who care for young children. 1979. 6/yr. $24. First Teacher, Inc., 28 Tamarack Rd., Weston, MA 02193. TEL 617-893-7274; 800-825-0061. FAX 617-891-1260. (Subscr. to: Box 6781, Syracuse, NY 13217) Ed. Lisa L. Durkin. adv.; bk.rev. circ. 15,000. (back issues avail.)
  Description: Includes practical articles, ideas, and recipes for preschool and kindergarten teachers.

370.193 GW
DER FISCH; Mitteilungen fuer Eltern und Freunde. 1981. 2/yr. free. Freies Katholisches Schulwerk Friedrichshafen e.V., Bodensee-Schule St. Martin, Zeisigweg 1, 88045 Friedrichshafen, Germany. TEL 07541-2109193. adv.; illus. circ. 1,500. **Document type:** newsletter.

371 US
FLORIDA. DEPARTMENT OF EDUCATION. PROFESSIONAL PRACTICES COUNCIL. REPORT. 1969. a. free. Department of Education, Professional Practices Council, Tallahassee, FL 32304. TEL 904-488-2481. Ed. Hugh Ingram. circ. 300.

370 US
FLORIDA EDUCATIONAL RESEARCH COUNCIL. RESEARCH BULLETIN. 1965. 4/yr. $4 per no. Florida Educational Research Council, Inc., Box 506, Sanibel, FL 33957. TEL 813-472-4397. Ed. Charlie T. Council. abstr.; bibl. circ. 5,100. (tabloid format; also avail. in microfiche) **Indexed:** ERIC.
—BLDSC (7722.620000).
  Formerly: Florida Educational Research and Development Council. Research Bulletin (ISSN 0015-4024)

FLORIDA LEADER. see COLLEGE AND ALUMNI

FLORIDA MUSIC DIRECTOR. see MUSIC

372 US ISSN 0015-4261
FLORIDA READING QUARTERLY. 1964. 4/yr. $20 (foreign $22). Florida Reading Association, 11775 Raintree Dr., Tampa, FL 33617-2706. TEL 813-988-0442. FAX 803-453-2509. Ed. Evelyn Searls. adv. contact: Barbara Clark. bk.rev.; bibl.; charts; illus.; stat.; index. circ. 3,300. (also avail. in microform from UMI; reprint service avail. from UMI) **Indexed:** Educ.Ind. **Document type:** academic/scholarly publication.
—UnCover; UMI.
  Description: For members and others interested in reading.

FLORIDA SCHOOL HERALD. see HANDICAPPED — Hearing Impaired

370 SW ISSN 0015-6167
FOENSTRET. 1922. 12/yr. SEK 125. Arbetarnas Bildningsfoerbund, P.O. Box 522, 101 30 Stockholm, Sweden. TEL 08-6135000. FAX 08-246956. Ed. Eva Swedenmark. adv. contact: Ann-Kristine Roeyseng. bk.rev.; illus. circ. 36,000. (also avail. in audio cassette)
  Formerly (until 1954): A.B.F.

372.21 SW ISSN 0015-5292
FOERSKOLAN.* 1918. 10/yr. SEK 190. Sveriges Foerskollaerares Riksfoerening, Klara norra kyrkog. 21, 111 22 Stockholm, Sweden. FAX 086190088. Ed. Leif Mathiasson. adv.; bk.rev.; charts; illus.; index. circ. 52,000.
  Former titles (until 1969): Barntraedgaarden; (until 1940): Tidskrift - Svenska Froebelfoerbundet.

370 DK ISSN 0015-5810
FOLK OG FRITID. 1966. bi-m. membership. Folkeligt Oplysnings Forbund, Moellevej 9, DK-5683 Haarby, Denmark. Ed. Poul A. Joergensen. adv.; bk.rev.; circ. 7,500 (controlled).

370 DK ISSN 0015-5837
FOLKESKOLEN. 1884. w. DKK 600. Danmarks Laererforening, Vandkunsten 12, 1467 Copenhagen, Denmark. TEL 45-33-118255. FAX 45-33-938990. TELEX 112617 DLF. Ed. Thorkild Thejsen. adv.; bk.rev.; index. circ. 80,000. (reprint service avail.)

FOLKSONG IN THE CLASSROOM; a network of teachers of history, literature, music and the humanities - a newsletter. see MUSIC

370 US
FOR SENIORS ONLY; a magazine for H.S. seniors. 1970. s-a. $5. Campus Communications, Inc. (New City), 339 N. Main St., Ste. 4, New City, NY 10956. TEL 914-638-0333. circ. 350,000. **Document type:** academic/scholarly publication.
  Description: Directed to high school seniors and juniors. Special single-sponsor editions for seniors only are developed and tailored for individual corporations, institutions.

FORD FOUNDATION ANNUAL REPORT. see SOCIAL SCIENCES: COMPREHENSIVE WORKS

FORENSIC. see COMMUNICATIONS

FORENSIC QUARTERLY. see COMMUNICATIONS

370 JA
FOREST OF EDUCATION/KYOIKU-NO-MORI. (Text in Japanese) 1977. m. 5400 Yen. Mainichi Newspapers, 1-1-1, Hitotsubashi, Chiyoda-ku, Tokyo 100-51, Japan. TEL 03-3212-0321. FAX 03-3211-0895. TELEX 22324. Ed. Kyohei Fujita.

370 SP
FORJA. 1964. q. free. Colegio Nacional General Primo de Rivera, Calle Leon 7. Albacete, Spain.

371.4 FR ISSN 0395-9740
FORMATION FRANCE.* 1972-1982; resumed 19?? 10/yr. 300 F. Editions Generation, 27 rue du Chemin Vert, 75011 Paris, France. TEL 48-07-41-41. FAX 47-00-79-80. Ed. Sylvie Karsenty. adv. circ. 20,000.

FORMAZIONE E LAVORO. see OCCUPATIONS AND CAREERS

FORUM LOCCUM. see POLITICAL SCIENCE

370 US ISSN 1062-4686
▼**FOUNDATION & CORPORATION GRANTS ALERT.** 1993. 12/yr. $245. Capitol Publications Inc., 1101 King St., Ste. 444, Alexandria, VA 22314. TEL 703-739-6517. FAX 703-739-6517. **Document type:** newsletter.
—CCC.

370 JA
FOUR CORNERS.* 1983. 3/yr. Doshisha International High School - Doshi-sha Kokusai Koko, Tatara, Tanabe-cho, Tsuzuki-gun, Kyoto 610-03, Japan. Eds. Hillel Weintraub, Masahiko Amenomiya. bk.rev. (back issues avail.)

370 GW
FRAENKISCHE SCHULE. 1965. bi-m. DM.12. B L L V Oberfranken, Eichenwaldstr. 22, 91361 Pinzberg, Germany. TEL 09191-5754. (Subscr. to: Postfach 85, 95170 Schoenwald, Germany) Ed. Gerald Lippert. adv.; bk.rev.; illus. circ. 5,000. (back issues avail.) **Document type:** academic/scholarly publication.

EDUCATION

370 FR ISSN 0015-9395
PC2065
LE FRANCAIS DANS LE MONDE. (Includes 2 special issues and 3 cassettes) 1961. 8/yr. 375 F.($70) to individuals; institutions 455 F. ($83). Hachette Edicef, 58 rue Jean Bleuzen, 92178 Vanves Cedex, France. TEL 1-46-62-10-50. FAX 1-40-95-11-33. TELEX 631 124 F. (Subscr. to: 99, rue d'Amsterdam, 75008 Paris, France) Ed. Jacques Pecheur. adv.; bk.rev. circ. 15,000. (also avail. in microfilm; back issues avail.) **Indexed:** C.I.J.E., Lang.Teach.& Ling.Abstr., Lang.Teach.& Ling.Abstr., M.L.A., Sociol.Abstr.
—BLDSC (4032.160000); Faxon; SWETS; UMI.
Description: Covers culture and society of France, and surveys pedagogical developments for French teacher's use.

371.3 FR ISSN 0395-6601
AP20
FRANCE. CENTRE NATIONAL DE DOCUMENTATION PEDAGOGIQUE. TEXTES ET DOCUMENTS POUR LA CLASSE.. 1956. 20/yr. 350 F. (foreign 610 F.). Centre National de Documentation Pedagogique, 29 rue d'Ulm, 75230 Paris Cedex 05, France. TEL 46-57-11-17. FAX 46-57-57-31. (Subscr. to: B.P. 21, Square St. Charles, 75012 Paris, France) Ed. Evelyne Lattanzio. adv.; bk.rev.; charts; illus. circ. 40,000.
Formerly: France. Institut National de Recherche et de Documentation Pedagogiques. Textes et Documents pour la Classe (ISSN 0040-4799)
Description: Committed to offering its readers well-rounded knowledge by covering a wide variety of topics. Intended primarily for students.

370 FR ISSN 0291-5871
L391
FRANCE. MINISTERE DE L'EDUCATION NATIONALE. BULLETIN OFFICIEL. w. 375 F. (foreign 615 F.). (Ministere de l'Education Nationale) Centre National de Documentation Pedagogique, 29 rue de l'Ulm, 75230 Paris Cedex 05, France. (Subscr. to: CNDP-Service Abonnement, B.P. 7, 21 Square St. Charles, 75012 Paris, France) circ. 100,000.

370 FR ISSN 0220-0562
FRANCE. OFFICE NATIONAL D'INFORMATION SUR LES ENSEIGNEMENTS ET LES PROFESSIONS. BULLETIN D'INFORMATION.. m. 280 F. (foreign 313 F.). Office National d'Information sur les Enseignements et les Professions (ONISEP), 75635 Paris Cedex 13, France. TEL 40-77-60-00. FAX 45-86-60-85. TELEX 202 962 F ONISEP N. **Document type:** bulletin.
Formerly: France. Office National d'Information sur les Enseignements. Bulletin d'Information.

370 US ISSN 0836-0073
FREE MATERIALS FOR SCHOOLS AND LIBRARIES. 1979. 5/yr. $20. Connaught Education Service, Dept. 349, Box 34069, Seattle, WA 98124. TEL 604-876-3377. Ed. Jim Clark. (looseleaf format) **Document type:** newsletter.
Formerly: Free! The Newsletter of Free Materials and Services (ISSN 0708-4625)
Description: Provides schools and libraries with a list of recommended free materials and services.

370 SA ISSN 0042-9228
FREE STATE EDUCATIONAL NEWS/VRYSTAATSE ONDERWYSNUUS. (Text in Afrikaans and English) 1968. s-a. free. (Education Department) Ficksburg Press (Pty) Ltd., P.O. Box 380, Ficksburg, Orange Free State, South Africa. Ed.Bd. charts; illus.; stat.; circ. 1,000 (controlled).

370 AU ISSN 0016-075X
FREIE LEHRERSTIMME. 1895. q. S.60 for non-members. Sozialistischer Lehrerverein Oesterreichs, Landstr. Hauptstr. 96, A-1030 Vienna, Austria. Ed. Dr. Oskar Achs. adv.; bk.rev.; abstr. circ. 25,000.

370 335 GW ISSN 0067-589X
FREIE UNIVERSITAET BERLIN. OSTEUROPA-INSTITUT. ERZIEHUNGSWISSENSCHAFTLICHE VEROEFFENTLICHUNGEN. 1964. irreg., vol.21, 1991. price varies. (Freie Universitaet Berlin, Osteuropa-Institut) Harrassowitz Verlag, Taunusstr. 14, 65183 Wiesbaden, Germany. TEL 0611-530-0. FAX 0611-530570. TELEX 4186135. (Subscr. to: Postfach 2929, 65019 Wiesbaden, Germany) Ed. Oskar Anweiler, Siegfried Baske. **Document type:** monographic series.

370 AU
FREIHEITLICHER OBEROESTERREICHISCHER LEHRERVEREIN. ZEITSCHRIFT. 1956. q. S.96. Freiheitlicher Oberoesterreichischer Lehrerverein, Bluetenstr. 21-1, 4044 Linz, Austria. adv.; bk.rev. circ. 10,000.
Formerly: Freiheitlicher Oberoesterreichischer Landeslehrer Verein. Zeitschrift (ISSN 0016-0903)

370 DK ISSN 0109-9108
FREINET NYT. 1980. q. membership. Arbejdsgruppen af Freinetpaedagoger, c/o Kamma Ditlevsen, Gillesager 6, 7th, 2650 Hvidovre, Denmark. TEL 45-75-13-22-51. FAX 45-75-13-49-49. illus. circ. 200.

FREMDSPRACHEN; Zeitschrift fuer Theorie und Praxis der Sprachmittlung. see LINGUISTICS

FREMDSPRACHENUNTERRICHT. see LINGUISTICS

DER FREMDSPRACHLICHE UNTERRICHT; textarbeit, landeskunde, sprachpraxis und methodenfragen. see LINGUISTICS

FRESH PERSPECTIVE. see CHILDREN AND YOUTH — For

FRIEDENSFORSCHUNG AKTUELL. see POLITICAL SCIENCE

371.2 US
FROM THE BOARD ROOM. 1961. m. $10. Vermont School Boards Association, 2 Prospect St., Montpelier, VT 05602. TEL 802-223-3580. Ed. Donald E. Jamieson. adv.; bk.rev. circ. 2,200. (processed)
Former titles: V S B A Newsletter; V S S D A Newsletter (ISSN 0042-191X)

370 CC ISSN 0427-7058
FUJIAN JIAOYU/FUJIAN EDUCATION. (Text in Chinese) m. Y11.56. Fujian Jiaoyu Weiyuanhui - Fujian Education Commission, No. 7, Dameng Shan, Fuzhou, Fujian 350001, People's Republic of China. TEL 557027. (Dist. overseas by: Jiangsu Publications Import & Export Corp., 56 Gao Yun Ling, Nanjing, Jiangsu, P.R.C.) Ed. Yang Qingchu.

373 CC
FUJIAN ZHONGXUE JIAOXUE/FUJIAN MIDDLE SCHOOL TEACHING. (Text in Chinese) m. Fujian Jiaoyu Xueyuan - Fujian Institute of Education, 5 Ximen Dameng Shan, Fuzhou, Fujian 350001, People's Republic of China. TEL 557838. (Dist. overseas by: Jiangsu Publications Import & Export Corp., 56 Gao Yun Ling, Nanjing, Jiangsu, P.R.C.) Ed. Meng Jing.
Description: Aims to raise the quality of middle-school teaching.

370 US
G E A EDUCATOR. 1966. bi-m. free. Grossmont Education Association, 5464 Grossmont Center Dr., Ste. 330, La Mesa, CA 91942-3035. TEL 619-460-3465. FAX 619-460-9325. Ed. Joan Vandenberg. circ. 900. (processed) **Document type:** newsletter.
Former titles: Grossmont Educator (ISSN 0016-3635); G U H S D T A News.
Description: Contains information for teachers regarding education within the district and at the state and national levels.

370 700 DK ISSN 0109-9442
G L B. q. DKK 100. Gymnasiet Laerere i Billedkunst, Soroe, Denmark. illus.

G L V MITTEILUNGEN. (Graphische Lehr- und Versuchsanstalt) see PRINTING

G P N NEWSLETTER. (Great Plains National Instructional Television Library) see COMMUNICATIONS — Television And Cable

370 CC ISSN 1002-5111
GAODENG SHIFAN JIAOYU YANJIU. (Text in Chinese) bi-m. Y12. Beijing Shifan Daxue - Beijing Normal University, Xinjiekouwai, Beijing 100875, People's Republic of China. TEL 20110867. Ed. Gu Mingyuan. **Document type:** academic/scholarly publication.

370 IT ISSN 0016-5719
GAZZETTINO DELLA SCUOLA; quindicinale di problemi didattico-pedagogici e d'informazione scolastica. 1962. s-m. L.1000. Facolta di Magistero, Palazzo dei Capitani, 35100 Padova, Italy. Ed. Francesco Agnello. adv.; bk.rev.; film rev.; play rev.; bibl.; illus. circ. 20,000. (tabloid format)

370 GW ISSN 0016-5875
JA86
GEGENWARTSKUNDE; Gesellschaft, Staat, Erziehung. 1951. q. DM.36 (students DM.28). Verlag Leske und Budrich GmbH, Postfach 300551, 51334 Leverkusen, Germany. TEL 02171-2079. FAX 02171-41209. Ed.Bd. adv.; bk.rev.; charts; illus.; index, cum index covering 5 yrs. circ. 7,000. **Indexed:** Amer.Hist.& Life, ELLIS, Hist.Abstr., SSCI. **Document type:** academic/scholarly publication.
—BLDSC (4096.120000). **CCC.**
Description: Scientific information for teachers on economical, political and sociological matters.

370 UK ISSN 0954-0253
CODEN: GEEDER
GENDER AND EDUCATION. 1989. 3/yr. $68 to individuals; institutions $270 (effective 1994). Carfax Publishing Co., P.O. Box 25, Abingdon, Oxon. OX14 3UE, England. TEL 44-235-555335. FAX 44-235-553559. (U.S. subscr. to: Carfax Publishing Co., Box 2025, Dunnellon, FL 34430-2025) Ed. Lynda Measir. adv.; bk.rev. (also avail. in microfiche) **Indexed:** Mult.Ed.Abstr., SOMA, Sp.Ed.Needs Abstr. **Document type:** academic/scholarly publication.
—BLDSC (4096.401200); Faxon; UnCover. **CCC.**
Description: Covers all aspects of education in relation to gender.
Refereed Serial

374 II ISSN 0072-0720
GENERAL EDUCATION READING MATERIAL SERIES.* (Text in English and Hindi) 1959. irreg. price varies. Aligarh Muslim University, Aligarh, Uttar Pradesh, India.

370 UK ISSN 0142-2154
GENERAL TEACHING COUNCIL FOR SCOTLAND. BULLETIN. 1976. irreg. General Teaching Council for Scotland, 5 Royal Terrace, Edinburgh EH2 4DF, Scotland. circ. 85,000. **Document type:** bulletin.

GEOGRAFIE EDUCATIEF. see GEOGRAPHY

GEOGRAFIYA V SHKOLE. see GEOGRAPHY

GEOGRAPHY TEACHER. see GEOGRAPHY

370 US ISSN 0435-5261
GEORGIA ALERT; a look at education's role today. 1966. q. free. Department of Education, Public Information and Publications Division, 2052 Twin Towers E., Atlanta, GA 30334-5010. TEL 404-656-2476. Ed. Kristin L. Summerlin. illus. circ. 13,000.

GERMAN LIFE AND LETTERS. see LITERATURE

GERMAN QUARTERLY. see LINGUISTICS

370 900 GW ISSN 0176-943X
GESCHICHTE BETRIFFT UNS. 1983. 6/yr. DM.63. Bergmoser und Hoeller Verlag GmbH, Karl-Friedrich-Str. 76, 52072 Aachen, Germany. TEL 0241-1730925. FAX 0241-1730934. Ed. Dieter Tiemann. adv.; bk.rev. circ. 2,600. (looseleaf format; back issues avail.) **Document type:** academic/scholarly publication.
Description: Includes educational planning material for teachers of grades 9-13. Covers topics in the history of politics, sociology, economy or technology and aims to involve students actively in the subjects.

370 GW ISSN 0933-3096
GESCHICHTE LERNEN. 1988. bi-m. DM.95.70. Erhard Friedrich Verlag GmbH, Im Brande 17, 30926 Seelze, Germany. TEL 0511-40004-0. (Subscr. to: Postfach 100150, 30917 Seelze, Germany) Ed. Michael Sauer. bk.rev.; index. circ. 5,500. (back issues avail.) **Document type:** academic/scholarly publication.

GESCHICHTE, POLITIK UND IHRE DIDAKTIK. see HISTORY — History Of Europe

EDUCATION

373.246   **GW**
GEWERKSCHAFTLICHE BILDUNGSPOLITIK; Stellungnahmen - Analysen - Informationen. 1973. m. free. Deutscher Gewerkschaftsbund, Hans-Boeckler-Str. 39, 40476 Duesseldorf, Germany. Ed. Ulf Fink. bk.rev.; stat. circ. 35,000.
Indexed: Int.Lab.Doc.
Formerly: Berufliche Bildung (ISSN 0005-948X)

370   **GH**
GHANA JOURNAL OF EDUCATION.* vol.4, 1973. q. 30 per no. Ministry of Education, P.O. Box M 45, Accra, Ghana. adv.; bk.rev.; bibl.; illus.
Formerly: Ghana Teacher's Journal (ISSN 0016-9595)

GISTER EN VANDAG/YESTERDAY AND TODAY. see *HISTORY*

370   **UK**
GLASGOW UNIVERSITY STUDENTS' HANDBOOK. 1972. a. £1. Students Representative Council, John McIntyre Bldg., The University, Glasgow G12 8QQ, Scotland. TEL 041-339-8541. FAX 041-337-3557. adv.; circ. 8,000 (controlled). **Document type:** bulletin.
Formerly: Students Representative Council. Handbook.

370 057.85   **US**   **ISSN 1042-3745**
GLOS NAUCZYCIELA; kwartalnik. (Text in Polish) 1986. q. $15 to individuals; institutions $25. Polish American Congress, Commission on Education, 5631 W. Waveland Ave., Chicago, IL 60634. TEL 312-545-6522. Ed. Helena Ziolkowska. adv. contact: Helena Ziolkowska. bk.rev.; bibl.; illus. (back issues avail.) **Document type:** trade publication.
Description: Covers educational and instructional materials about Poland, its culture, literature, language, customs, geography, Polish and Polish-American history.

370 331.8   **PL**   **ISSN 0017-1263**
GLOS NAUCZYCIELSKI. 1917. w. $23. (Zwiazek Nauczycielstwa Polskiego - Polish Teachers' Union) Glos Nauczycielski, Ul. Spasowskiego 6-8, 00-389 Warsaw, Poland. TEL 48-22-263420. (Dist. by: Ars Polona-Ruch, Krakowskie Przedmiescie 7, Warsaw, Poland) Ed. Wojciech Sierakowski. adv.; illus.; index. circ. 59,900. **Document type:** newsletter.

370   **SW**   **ISSN 0436-1121**
GOETEBORG STUDIES IN EDUCATIONAL SCIENCES. (Subseries of Acta Universitatis Gothoburgensis) (Text in English and Swedish) 1966. irreg., no.82, 1991. price varies; also exchange basis. Acta Universitatis Gothoburgensis, P.O. Box 5096, S-402 22 Goeteborg, Sweden. Ed.Bd. **Document type:** monographic series.

370 371.2 350 792   **GW**
GOETIKUSS. 1978. bi-m. DM.1.80($5) Goetikuss Goethe-Gymnasium, Seestr. 37, 71638 Ludwigsburg, Germany. Ed. Eva Mueller. adv.; bk.rev.; charts. circ. 1,000. (back issues avail.)

GOLD-BAERCHI. see *CHILDREN AND YOUTH — For*

GOPHER MUSIC NOTES. see *MUSIC*

THE GOSPEL HERALD AND SUNDAY SCHOOL TIMES. see *RELIGIONS AND THEOLOGY*

GOVERNMENT PROGRAMS. see *SOCIAL SERVICES AND WELFARE*

372 613.7   **US**   **ISSN 0743-5606**
GREAT ACTIVITIES NEWSPAPER; an elementary physical education publication. 1984. bi-m. $18. Great Activities Publishing Co., Box 51158, Durham, NC 27717-1158. TEL 919-493-6977. Ed. Artie Kamiya. circ. 5,000.
Description: Kindergarten through grade six elementary newspaper.

370   **UK**
GREAT BRITAIN. DEPARTMENT OF EDUCATION AND SCIENCE. ANNUAL REPORT. a. price varies. (Department of Education and Science) H.M.S.O., P.O. Box 276, London SW8 5DT, England. (Dist. by: Elizabeth House, York Rd., London SE1 7PH, England) **Document type:** government publication.
Formerly: Education and Science (ISSN 0070-9115)

370   **UK**   **ISSN 0072-5897**
GREAT BRITAIN. DEPARTMENT OF EDUCATION AND SCIENCE. EDUCATION SURVEYS. 1967. irreg. price varies. (Department of Education and Science) H.M.S.O., P.O. Box 276, London SW8 5DT, England. **Document type:** government publication.
—CCC.

GREAT BRITAIN. DEPARTMENT OF EDUCATION AND SCIENCE. SAFETY IN EDUCATION. see *PUBLIC HEALTH AND SAFETY*

373   **UK**   **ISSN 0072-7121**
GREAT BRITAIN. SCHOOLS COUNCIL PUBLICATIONS. EXAMINATIONS BULLETINS. 1963. irreg. price varies. Routledge, 11 New Fetter Ln., London EC4P 4EE, England. TEL 071-583-9855. FAX 071-583-0701. **Document type:** bulletin.

370   **UK**   **ISSN 0072-713X**
GREAT BRITAIN. SCHOOLS COUNCIL PUBLICATIONS. WORKING PAPERS. 1965. irreg. price varies. Routledge, 11 New Fetter Ln., London EC4P 4EE, England. TEL 071-583-9855. FAX 071-583-0701. **Document type:** bulletin.

GREEN PAGES; California's school business directory. see *BUSINESS AND ECONOMICS — Trade And Industrial Directories*

370   **US**   **ISSN 1056-2192**
▼**GREENWOOD EDUCATORS' REFERENCE COLLECTION.** 1992. irreg. price varies. Greenwood Press, Inc. (Subsidiary of: Greenwood Publishing Group Inc.), 88 Post Rd. W., Box 5007, Westport, CT 06881-5007. TEL 203-226-3571. FAX 203-222-1502. **Document type:** monographic series.

370   **US**   **ISSN 0271-9509**
GREENWOOD ENCYCLOPEDIA OF AMERICAN INSTITUTIONS. 1977. irreg. price varies. Greenwood Press, Inc. (Subsidiary of: Greenwood Publishing Group Inc.), 88 Post Rd. W., Box 5007, Westport, CT 06881-5007. TEL 203-226-3571. FAX 203-222-1502.

GRLICA/TURTLEDOVE; revija za glasbeno vzgojo. see *MUSIC*

370 362.7   **US**   **ISSN 0745-5305** LC40
GROWING WITHOUT SCHOOLING. 1977. bi-m. $25. Holt Associates, 2269 Massachusetts Ave., Cambridge, MA 02140. TEL 617-864-3100. FAX 617-864-9235. Ed. Susannah Sheffer. adv. contact: Patricia Farenga. bk.rev. circ. 5,000. (back issues avail.)
Description: Forum for discussion on learning, teaching, home education, and schooling in contemporary society.

370 500   **GW**
GRUNDLAGEN UND PERSPEKTIVEN FUER BILDUNG UND WISSENSCHAFT. BERUFSBILDUNGSBERICHT. a. DM.14.80. (Bundesminister fuer Bildung und Wissenschaft) Verlag K.H. Bock, Reichenbergerstr. 11e, Postfach 1145, 53604 Bad Honnef, Germany. TEL 02224-5443. FAX 02224-78310.

370   **GW**
GRUNDSCHULUNTERRICHT. 1954. 11/yr. DM.58.30. Paedagogischer Zeitschriftenverlag, Postfach 269, 10107 Berlin, Germany. TEL 030-20343431. FAX 030-20343432. bk.rev.; charts; illus.; index. circ. 35,000. **Document type:** academic/scholarly publication.
Formerly: Unterstufe (ISSN 0042-0638)

370   **CC**
GUANGDONG JIAOYU/GUANGDONG EDUCATION. (Text in Chinese) m. Guangdong Sheng Jiaoyu Weiyuanhui - Guangdong Provincial Education Commission, No. 14, Guangwei Lu, 7th Fl., Guangzhou, Guangdong 510030, People's Republic of China. TEL 330351. Ed. Liu Dazhong.

370   **CC**
GUANGZHOU JIAOYU/GUANGZHOU EDUCATION. (Text in Chinese) bi-m. Guangzhou Shi Jiaoyu-ju - Guangzhou Municipal Bureau of Education, 83-503 Xihu Lu, Guangzhou, Guangdong 510030, People's Republic of China. TEL 345161. Ed. Shao Haiqiang.

371.4   **CN**   **ISSN 0831-5493**
GUIDANCE & COUNSELLING. 1944. 5/yr. Can.$40. Ontario Institute for Studies in Education, Guidance Centre, 712 Gordon Baker Rd., Toronto, ON M2H 3R7, Canada. TEL 416-502-1262; 800-668-6247. FAX 416-502-1101. Ed. David Studd. adv.; bk.rev.; film rev. circ. 3,000. (also avail. in microform from UMI; reprint service avail. from UMI) **Indexed:** C.I.J.E., Can.Educ.Ind., Educ.Ind. **Document type:** academic/scholarly publication.
—UnCover; UMI.
Formerly: School Guidance Worker (ISSN 0048-9409)
Description: Devoted to serving all practitioners and educators in guidance and counselling.

372.21   **JA**
GUIDANCE OF INFANTS/YOJI-NO-SHIDO. (Text in Japanese) 1955. m. 8160 Yen. Gakken Co. Ltd., 40-5, 4-chome, Kamiikedai, Ohta-ku, Tokyo 145, Japan. Ed. Toshiyuki Fuse.

373   **US**
GUIDE TO DELEGATE PREPARATION. MODEL U.N. SURVIVAL KIT. a. $10. United Nations Association of the USA, 485 Fifth Ave., New York, NY 10017. Ed. James P. Muldoon, Jr.

GUNMA SEIBUTSU/GUNMA BIOLOGICAL EDUCATION SOCIETY. BULLETIN. see *BIOLOGY*

371 331.8   **MY**
GURU MALAYSIA. (Text in English, Malay) 1964. m. M.$2.40. National Union of Teachers of Malaysia, Box 169, Taiping, Perak, Malaysia. Ed. Francis Mathews. adv.; bk.rev.; illus.; stat. circ. 20,000.
Formerly: Educator (ISSN 0013-2012)

373   **DK**   **ISSN 0017-5927**
GYMNASIESKOLEN. 1916. bi-w. DKK 459.02 (typically set in Jan.). Gymnasieskolernes Laereforening - Union of Secondary School Teachers, Magistrenes Hus, Lyngbyvej 32, 2100 Copenhagen OE, Denmark. FAX 31-20-95-91. Ed. Torben Lynge Hansen. adv.; bk.rev.; index. circ. 11,350.

373   **SZ**   **ISSN 0017-5951**
GYMNASIUM HELVETICUM; Zeitschrift fuer die schweizerische Mittelschule. (Text in French and German) 1947. 6/yr. 95 SFr. (foreign 103 SFr.). (Verein Schweizerischer Gymnasiallehrer) Sauerlaender AG, Laurenzenvorstadt 89, CH-5001 Aarau, Switzerland. TEL 064-268626. FAX 064-245780. TELEX 981195-SAG-CH. Ed. Verena Mueller. adv.: B&W page 773 SFr.; trim 135 x 203. bk.rev.; charts; index. circ. 6,000. **Document type:** academic/scholarly publication.
—CCC.
Description: Information and evaluation of secondary education in Switzerland, and comparisons to that in other countries. Includes reports of events, and positions available.

373   **GW**
DAS GYMNASIUM IN BAYERN. m. Bayerische Philologenverband, Implerstr. 25A, 81371 Munich, Germany. TEL 089-774004-05.

H C J COMMUNICATIONS REPORT. see *POLITICAL SCIENCE — International Relations*

370   **US**
H E A ADVOCATE. (Former name of issuing body: Houston Teachers Association) 1971. m. membership. Houston Education Association, 1415 Southmore, Houston, TX 77004. TEL 713-528-1968. FAX 713-528-1960. Ed. John Small. adv. circ. 17,000.
Former titles: H T A Advocate; H T A Today; Which supersedes: H T A Contact (ISSN 0017-6265)

370 378   **AT**   **ISSN 0157-1826**
H E R D S A NEWS. 1978. 3/yr. membership. Higher Education Research and Development Society of Australasia, c/o T.E.R.C., University of New South Wales, Kensington, N.S.W. 2033, Australia. TEL 02 697 4937. Ed. P. Nightingale. bk.rev. circ. 800. (back issues avail.)
—BLDSC (4298.815100).
Description: Informal and practical articles on teaching and learning in higher education.

EDUCATION

370   GW
H L Z; Zeitschrift der G E W Hamburg. 1922. 10/yr. DM.40. (Gewerkschaft Erziehung und Wissenschaft, Landesverband Hamburg) Curio Verlag Erziehung und Wissenschaft GmbH, Rothenbaumchaussee 19a, 20148 Hamburg, Germany. TEL 040-4101055. Ed. Frieder Bachteler. adv.; bk.rev.; index. circ. 12,000. **Document type:** academic/scholarly publication.
Formerly: Hamburger Lehrerzeitung (ISSN 0017-6966)

370   US
H S A HAPPENINGS. 1986. m. $20. Homeschoolers' Support Association, Box 413, Maple Valley, WA 98038. TEL 206-432-9805. Ed. Sherry Wiltsey. adv.; bk.rev. circ. 484. **Document type:** newsletter.
Formerly: Homeschoolers' Voice.
Description: Provides current news and information on homeschooling to the local community.

370   IS
HADRACHA DIGEST. (Editions in English, French, Spanish) 1982. s-a. World Zionist Organization, Youth and Hechalutz Department, Educational Resource Centre, P.O. Box 92, Jerusalem 91920, Israel. TEL 02-732312. FAX 02-732159. TELEX SUMINIL 25375. Ed. Henrique Cymerman. circ. 1,500.
Description: Intended for youth leaders and community workers around the world.

373 001.6   US   ISSN 0743-0221
                                                            CODEN: HSONDB
HANDS ON! (CAMBRIDGE). 1977. 2/yr. $10 contribution. T E R C, 2067 Massachusetts Ave., Cambridge, MA 02140. TEL 617-547-0430. Ed. Peggy Kapisovsky. circ. 20,000. **Indexed:** Comput.Lit.Ind., Sci.Abstr. **Document type:** newsletter.
Description: For elementary through college level educators and administrators. Each issue contains feature articles on science, math, and technology in education.

370   US
HARBINGER (DETROIT).* 1953. q. $1.50. (Warren Education Association) Harpress Publications, c/o Richard Wirth, Ed., Box 283, Algonac, MI 48001-0283. adv.; bk.rev.; bibl.; stat. circ. 2,000. (tabloid format; also avail. in microform from UMI)
Formerly: Profile (ISSN 0033-0256)

372   US   ISSN 8755-3716
HARVARD EDUCATION LETTER. 1985. bi-m. $26 (Canada & Mexico $34, elsewhere $36). Harvard University, Graduate School of Education, 6 Appian Way, Gutman Library, No. 301, Cambridge, MA 02138-3752. TEL 617-496-9984. (Subscr. to: Box 8900, Braintree, MA 02184. TEL 800-422-2681) Ed. Edward Miller. index. circ. 14,000. (looseleaf format; back issues avail.) **Document type:** newsletter.
Description: Applies the latest educational research to practical concerns in education today; for parents and educators.

370.7   US   ISSN 0017-8055
L11   CODEN: HVERAP
HARVARD EDUCATIONAL REVIEW. 1931. q. $39 to individuals; institutions $76. Harvard University, Graduate School of Education, Gutman Library, Ste. 349, 6 Appian Way, Cambridge, MA 02138. TEL 617-495-3432. adv.; bk.rev.; bibl.; charts; index. circ. 10,500. (also avail. in microform from UMI,KTO; reprint service avail. from KTO) **Indexed:** Amer.Hist.& Life, Bk.Rev.Ind. (1965-), C.I.J.E., Child.Bk.Rev.Ind. (1965-), Cont.Pg.Educ., Curr.Cont., Educ.Admin.Abstr., Educ.Ind., Educ.Tech.Abstr., Except.Child.Educ.Abstr., High.Educ.Curr.Aware.Bull., Hist.Abstr., Mid.East: Abstr.& Ind., Mult.Ed.Abstr., P.A.I.S., Psychol.Abstr., Res.High.Educ.Abstr., Soc.Work Res.& Abstr., Sociol.Abstr., Sociol.Educ.Abstr., SOMA, Sp.Ed.Needs Abstr., SSCI, Stud.Wom.Abstr. **Document type:** academic/scholarly publication.
—BLDSC (4265.900000); Faxon; UnCover; SWETS; UMI. **CCC.**
Formerly: Harvard Teachers Record (ISSN 0361-8021)

370.7   US   ISSN 0046-6905
HARVARD UNIVERSITY. GRADUATE SCHOOL OF EDUCATION. BULLETIN. 1956. 3/yr. free. Harvard University, Graduate School of Education, Appian Way, Cambridge, MA 02138. TEL 617-495-3615. Ed. Gillian Charters. adv.; bk.rev.; circ. 19,500 (controlled). **Document type:** bulletin.
Description: Articles and news about alumni and the Graduate School of Education at Harvard.

370 379   II   ISSN 0017-825X
HARYANA JOURNAL OF EDUCATION. (Text in English) vol.3, 1970. q. Rs.6. Department of Education, 650 Sector 16-2, Chandigarh 17, India. Ed. D.l. Lall. adv.; bk.rev.; bibl.

370.25   US   ISSN 0092-1777
L903.H3
HAWAII. DEPARTMENT OF EDUCATION. EDUCATIONAL DIRECTORY: STATE & DISTRICT OFFICE. 1924. a. $1.50. Department of Education, Office of Business Services, Box 2360, Honolulu, HI 96804. illus.

371.2   US
HAWAII. DEPARTMENT OF EDUCATION. OFFICE OF BUSINESS SERVICES. PUBLIC AND PRIVATE SCHOOL ENROLLMENT. 1970? a. Department of Education, Office of Business Services, Box 2360, Honolulu, HI 96804. circ. 650.
Formerly: Hawaii. Department of Education. Office of Research and Planning. Information Systems Branch. Public and Private School Enrollment.

HAWAII'S NATIONAL GAY COMMUNITY NEWS; Hawaii and Western States. see *HOMOSEXUALITY*

370   TS
HAWLIYAH KULLIYAH AL-TARBIYYAH/EDUCATIONAL JOURNAL.* (Text in Arabic) 1986. a. exchange basis. United Arab Emirates University, College of Education, P.O. Box 15551, Al-Ain, United Arab Emirates. TEL 677700. TELEX 33521 JAMEAH EM. circ. 1,000.
Description: Publishes research in education and conference reports.

370   UK   ISSN 0017-873X
HEAD TEACHERS REVIEW. 1910. 9/yr. £6. National Association of Head Teachers, 1 Heath Sq., Boltro Rd., Haywards Heath, W. Sussex RH16 1BL, England. TEL 0444-458133. FAX 0444-416326. Ed. David M. Hart. adv.; bk.rev. circ. 42,000. **Indexed:** Cont.Pg.Educ., SOMA. **Document type:** academic/scholarly publication.
—BLDSC (4274.620000).

613.7 370   JA   ISSN 0018-3350
HEALTH AND PHYSICAL EDUCATION/HOKEN TAIIKU KYOSHITSU. (Text in Japanese) 1967. q. 620 Yen. Taishukan Publishing Co. Ltd., 3-24 Kanda Nishikicho, Chiyoda-ku, Tokyo 101, Japan. FAX 03-3295-4107. Ed. Toshio Saeki. adv.; bk.rev.; charts; circ. 5,000 (controlled).

370 613 331   US   ISSN 0888-9465
HEALTH PROFESSIONS REPORT; the independent bi-weekly newsletter on the education & training of medical, nursing and health professionals. 1971. bi-w. $260. Whitaker Newsletters Inc., 313 South Ave., Fanwood, NJ 07023. TEL 908-889-6336. FAX 908-889-6339. (Subscr. to: Box 192, Fanwood, NJ 07023) Ed. Anne Bittner. charts; stat. (looseleaf format; back issues avail.) **Document type:** newsletter.
—UnCover. **CCC.**
Former titles: Health Planning and Manpower Report (ISSN 0362-3165); Health Manpower Report (ISSN 0161-6781)
Description: Reports on the education and training of doctors, nurses and allied health professionals. Includes pending legislation, information on public and private funding sources, cost-cutting measures, new medical breakthroughs, curriculum ideas, and admissions policies.

370   CC   ISSN 1004-6208
HEBEI JIAOYU/HEBEI EDUCATION. (Text in Chinese) 1949. m. Y18 (effective 1994). Hebei Sheng Jiaoyu Weiyuanhui - Hebei Provincial Education Commission, 4, Shigang Dajie, Shijiazhuang, Hebei 050061, People's Republic of China. TEL 86-311-743498. Ed. Liu Xinzong. adv. contact: Yan Zhanji. bk.rev. circ. 130,000.

370   IS   ISSN 0017-9493
HED HACHINUCH. 1926. m. Israel Teachers Union - Histadrut Hamorim, 8 Ben Saruk St., Tel Aviv 62 969, Israel. TEL 03-5432911. FAX 03-5432928. Ed. Dalia Lachman. adv.; bk.rev.; charts; illus.; stat.; index. circ. 40,000. **Indexed:** Ind.Heb.Per.

370   IS   ISSN 0334-2263
HED HAGAN; bulletin for early childhood. (Text in Hebrew) 1935. s-a. IS.32. Israel Teachers Union - Histadrut Hamorim, 8 Ben Saruk St., Tel Aviv 62 969, Israel. TEL 03-543911. FAX 03-5432928. Ed. Ziva Pedahzur. bk.rev. circ. 6,300.

370   CC   ISSN 0438-9050
HEILONGJIANG JIAOYU/HEILONGJIANG EDUCATION. (Text in Chinese) m. Heilongjiang Sheng Jiaoyu Weiyuanhui - Heilongjiang Education Commission, Fu 4, Xuefu Lu, Harbin, Heilongjiang 150080, People's Republic of China. TEL 53562. Ed. Zhu Mantang.

373   US   ISSN 0018-1498
L11
HIGH SCHOOL JOURNAL. 1917. 4/yr. $19 (foreign $25). (University of North Carolina at Chapel Hill, Department of English) University of North Carolina Press, Box 2288, Chapel Hill, NC 27515-2288. TEL 919-966-3561. FAX 919-966-3829. Ed. Gerald Unks. bk.rev.; index. circ. 1,900. (also avail. in microform from UMI; reprint service avail. from UMI) **Indexed:** Adol.Ment.Hlth.Abstr., C.I.J.E., Cont.Pg.Educ., Curr.Cont., Curr.Lit.Fam.Plan., Educ.Admin.Abstr. Educ.Ind., Educ.Tech.Abstr., Mult.Ed.Abstr., Psychol.Abstr., Stud.Wom.Abstr.
—BLDSC (4307.358000); Faxon; UnCover; SWETS; UMI. **CCC.**
Refereed Serial

370 378   AT   ISSN 0729-4360
HIGHER EDUCATION RESEARCH AND DEVELOPMENT. RESEARCH PAPERS. 1982. s-a. Aus.$45. Higher Education Research & Development Society of Australasia Inc. (HERDSA Inc.), Centre for Learning and Teaching, University of Technology, Sydney, P.O. Box 123, Broadway, N.S.W. 2007, Australia. FAX 02-692-4331. Ed. K. Trigwell. adv.; bk.rev. circ. 1,000. (back issues avail.) **Indexed:** Cont.Pg.Educ., Mult.Ed.Abstr., Sp.Ed.Needs Abstr. **Document type:** academic/scholarly publication.
—BLDSC (4307.389000); SWETS.

370   IS   ISSN 0334-4568
HA-HINUKH HA-MESHUTAF. 1958. q. IS.7.50($4) Ha-Kibbutz ha-Artzi, Department of Education, Rehov Leonardo de Vinci 13, Tel Aviv 61 400, Israel. Ed. Yehiel Kadmi. circ. 2,000.

HISPANIA; a journal devoted to the interests of the teaching of Spanish and Portuguese. see *LINGUISTICS*

HISPANORAMA. see *LITERATURE*

370   FR   ISSN 0221-6280
HISTOIRE DE L'EDUCATION. 1978. 3/yr. 128 F. (foreign 180 F.). Institut National de Recherche Pedagogique, 29 rue d'Ulm, 75230 Paris Cedex 05, France. TEL 46-34-90-00.
—SWETS.

370   SP   ISSN 0212-0267
HISTORIA DE LA EDUCACION. 1982. a. 3000 ptas. Ediciones Universidad de Salamanca, Apdo. 325, 37080 Salamanca, Spain. TEL 923-26-14-54. Dir. Agustin Escolano. **Document type:** academic/scholarly publication.

HISTORIENS ET GEOGRAPHES. see *HISTORY*

HISTORISCHE UND PAEDAGOGISCHE STUDIEN. see *HISTORY*

EDUCATION

370.9   UK   ISSN 0046-760X
LA5
HISTORY OF EDUCATION. 1972. q. £145($244) (History of Education Society) Taylor & Francis Ltd., Rankine Rd., Basingstoke, Hants RG24 8PR, England. TEL 0256-840366. FAX 0256-479438. TELEX 858540. Ed. R.A. Lowe. adv.; bk.rev. (back issues avail.) **Indexed:** Amer.Hist.& Life, Cont.Pg.Educ., Educ.Ind., Hist.Abstr., Res.High.Educ.Abstr. **Document type:** academic/scholarly publication.
—BLDSC (4318.110000); Faxon; SWETS. CCC.
   Description: Intended for social historians and others interested in the development of education worldwide. Articles range from schooling in Britain and abroad to teaching in schools and universities, to government policy and to philosophy of education.
Refereed Serial

370   US   ISSN 0018-2680
L11
HISTORY OF EDUCATION QUARTERLY. 1961. q. $30 to individuals; institutions $57; students $15. (History of Education Society) Indiana University, School of Education, Bloomington, IN 47405. FAX 812-856-8440. Ed. William J. Reese. adv.; bk.rev.; cum.index: 1961-1990. circ. 1,800. (also avail. in microfilm from UMI; back issues avail.; reprint service avail. from UMI) **Indexed:** Amer.Hist.& Life, C.I.J.E., CERDIC, Cont.Pg.Educ., Curr.Cont., Educ.Ind., Educ.Tech.Abstr., ERIC, Hist.Abstr., Mid.East: Abstr.& Ind., Res.High.Educ.Abstr., SSCI. **Document type:** academic/scholarly publication.
—BLDSC (4318.125000); Faxon; UnCover; SWETS; UMI.

370   AT   ISSN 0819-8691
HISTORY OF EDUCATION REVIEW. 1972. s-a. Aus.$30 (effective 1993). Australian and New Zealand Education Society, c/o Dr. G. Rodwell, Business Manager, Faculty of Education, Northern Territory University, P.O. Box 40146, Casuarina, N.T. 0811, Australia. Ed. M. Theobald. bk.rev.; cum.index 1972-1988. circ. 350. (back issues avail.) **Indexed:** Amer.Hist.& Life, Cont.Pg.Educ., Hist.Abstr. **Document type:** academic/scholarly publication.
—BLDSC (4318.130000).
   Formerly (until 1983): A N Z H E S Journal (ISSN 0311-3248)

370   UK   ISSN 0018-2699
LA630
HISTORY OF EDUCATION SOCIETY BULLETIN. 1968. s-a. £24 to individuals; institutions £16. History of Education Society, 4 Marydene Dr., Evington, Leicester LE5 6HD, England. Ed. R. Betts. adv.; bibl. circ. 500. (also avail. in microfilm from UMI) **Document type:** bulletin.
—BLDSC (2555.080000); UMI.
   Description: Discusses the history of education.

HISTORY TEACHER. see *HISTORY*

373   GW
HOCHSCHULE BREMEN. FACHBEREICH WIRTSCHAFT. VERANSTALTUNGSVERZEICHNIS. 1982. 2/yr. Hochschule Bremen, Fachbereich Wirtschaft, Werderstr. 73, 28195 Bremen, Germany. TEL 0421-5905102. Ed. Prof. Leuthold.

373   GW   ISSN 0018-2974
DAS HOCHSCHULWESEN. 1953. bi-m. DM.112. Luchterhand Verlag, Heddesdorferstr. 31, 56564 Neuwied, Germany. TEL 02631-801-0. FAX 02631-801210. adv.; bk.rev.; abstr.; bibl.; stat.; index. **Document type:** academic/scholarly publication.

378   GW   ISSN 0018-3083
DIE HOEHERE SCHULE. 1947. m. DM.9. (Deutscher Philologenverband) Pädagogik und Hochschul Verlag, Raderfeld 30, 47807 Krefeld, Germany. adv.; index. circ. 24,000.
—BLDSC (4322.170000).

370   JA   ISSN 0386-4499
HOKKAIDO KYOIKU DAIGAKU KIYO. DAI-1-BU, C. KYOIKUGAKU HEN/HOKKAIDO UNIVERSITY OF EDUCATION. JOURNAL. SECTION 1 C. EDUCATION. vol.32, 1982. s-a. exchange basis. Hokkaido University of Education - Hokkaido Kyoiku Daigaku, Ainosoto 5-jo, 3-chome, Kita-ku, Sapporo 002, Hokkaido, Japan.

370   US   ISSN 0898-0926
LC1011
HOLISTIC EDUCATION REVIEW. 1987. q. $35 to individuals; institutions $55 (effective 1994). Psychology Press, Inc., Box 328, Brandon, VT 05733-0328. TEL 802-247-8312. FAX 802-247-8312. Ed. Jeffrey Kane. adv. contact: C.S. Jakeila. bk.rev.; illus.; circ. 1,600 (paid). **Indexed:** Alt.Press Ind. **Document type:** academic/scholarly publication.
—BLDSC (4322.302190).
   Description: Considers all aspects of innovative education theory and practice, emphasizing the 'wholeness' of the human/educational experience. For parents, teachers, administrators and trainers.
Refereed Serial

370.193   UK   ISSN 0305-1536
HOME AND SCHOOL. 1974. q. £1.50. Hobsons Publishing plc., Bateman St., Cambridge CB2 1LZ, England. TEL 0223-354551. FAX 0223-323154. TELEX 81546-HOBCAM-G. adv. contact: Debbie Mendelson. bk.rev. circ. 10,000.
   Former titles: Parent - Teacher; N C P T A News.
   Description: Contains educational information for parents of school-age children in the U.K.

640   US
HOME ECONOMICS EDUCATOR. 1927. s-a. membership. Home Economics Education Association, Box 603, Gainesville, VA 22065. TEL 703-349-4676. Ed. Stephanie H. Price. bk.rev. circ. 2,000. **Document type:** monographic series.
   Former titles: Home Economics Education Association. Newsletter; Home Economics Education Association. Bulletin (ISSN 0073-3091)
   Description: Timely articles covering the changing times and offering guidelines for the teaching of classroom units.

HOME SCHOOL GAZETTE. see *JOURNALISM*

370   US   ISSN 1054-8033
HOME SCHOOL RESEARCHER. 1985. q. $25 to individuals; institutions $40 (effective 1993). National Home Education Research Institute, Western Baptist College, 5000 Deer Park Dr., Salem, OR 97301-9330. TEL 503-581-8600. FAX 503-585-4316. Ed. Brian D. Ray. adv.; bk.rev. (back issues avail.) **Document type:** academic/scholarly publication.
   Description: Covers research topics relating to home education or home schooling in the US and in other countries.
Refereed Serial

370 340   US   ISSN 1051-5771
KF4222
HOME SCHOOLING LAWS IN ALL FIFTY STATES. 1986. biennial, 6th ed. $22. Companion Press, 167 Walnut Bottom Rd., Box 310, Shippensburg, PA 17257-0310. TEL 717-532-3040. FAX 717-532-9291. (Subscr. to: 228 Central Dr., Briarcliff Manor, NY 10510-1213. TEL 914-923-0838) Ed. Steve Deckard. (back issues avail.; reprint service avail.)
   Description: Describes state laws on educating a child at home. Name, address, and telephone number for each state contact is listed, as well as the application process, curriculum, record-keeping, testing and teacher requirements.

370   HO
HONDURAS. UNIVERSIDAD NACIONAL AUTONOMA. REVISTA DE LA UNIVERSIDAD; publicacion cientifico y cultural. 1909. irreg., no.26, 1990. $6. (Universidad Nacional Autonoma) Editorial Universitaria U N A H, Ciudad Universitaria, Tegucigalpa, Honduras. TEL 504-32-4772. FAX 504-31-0675. bk.rev. circ. 1,000. (reprint service avail.)

HOOSHARAR - MIOUTUNE. see *SOCIAL SERVICES AND WELFARE*

371.2   US
LA283
HOOSIER PRINCIPAL. 1956. 2/yr. membership. Indiana Association of School Principals, Box 503250, 8091 Center Run Dr., Indianapolis, IN 46250-3250. TEL 317-576-5400. FAX 317-576-5408. Dir. F. Edward Wall. adv.; bk.rev. circ. 2,000. (tabloid format)
   Formerly: Hoosier Schoolmaster (ISSN 0018-4810)
   Description: Articles on research and curriculum of interest to school building-level administrators.

370   PH   ISSN 0018-5019
HORIZONS UNLIMITED. vol.10, 1970. q. P.3. Foundation University, Dumaguete City 6200, Philippines. TEL 37-44. Ed. Edgar Libre-Grino. bk.rev.; charts. **Indexed:** Ind.Phil.Per.

HOW TO DO IT MANUALS FOR SCHOOL AND PUBLIC LIBRARIANS. see *LIBRARY AND INFORMATION SCIENCES*

370   CC   ISSN 1000-5560
HUADONG SHIFAN DAXUE XUEBAO (JIAOYU BAN)/EAST CHINA NORMAL UNIVERSITY. JOURNAL (EDUCATION EDITION). (Text in Chinese) q. Huadong Shifan Daxue, Xuebao Bianjibu, 3663 Zhongshan Beilu, Shanghai 200062, People's Republic of China. TEL 2577577.
—UnCover.

HUAXUE JIAOXUE/CHEMISTRY TEACHING. see *CHEMISTRY*

HUMAN POTENTIAL MAGAZINE. see *PSYCHOLOGY*

001.3   US   ISSN 0018-7577
HUMANITIES IN THE SOUTH. 1951. s-a. free to qualified personnel. Southern Humanities Council, c/o Division of Humanities, Lander College, Greenwood, SC 29646. Ed. Carol Wilson. bk.rev. circ. 11,500. **Indexed:** Amer.Hum.Ind., M.L.A.
   Description: Focuses on ideas, directions and methods in the humanities, with emphasis on higher education.

370   MP
HUN BOLOH BAGAASAA/GROWING UP. (Text in Mongolian) bi-m. Ministry of Education, Ulan Bator, Mongolia. Ed. N. Tsevgee. circ. 23,400.

370 150   US
HYMAN BLUMBERG SYMPOSIUM SERIES. 1973. irreg., no.6, 1977. price varies. Johns Hopkins University Press, 701 W. 40th St., Ste. 275, Baltimore, MD 21211. TEL 410-516-6900. FAX 410-516-6998. (reprint service avail. from UMI)

HYPERNEXUS; journal of hypermedia and multimedia studies. see *COMPUTERS — Computer Assisted Instruction*

I A S L CONFERENCE PROCEEDINGS. (International Association of School Librarianship) see *LIBRARY AND INFORMATION SCIENCES*

I C B. (International Communication Bulletin) see *JOURNALISM*

370   FR
I C E M REVIEW.* 1964. q. 18 Fr. International Council for Educational Media, c/o Centre National de Documentation Pedagogique, 29 rue d'Ulm, 75230 Paris Cedex 05, France. Ed. Kevin Hogan. adv.; bk.rev.

I C L A R M EDUCATION SERIES. (International Center for Living Aquatic Resources Management) see *FISH AND FISHERIES*

370 331.88   US
I E A - N E A ADVOCATE. 1971. m. (8/yr.) $10 to non-members. Illinois Education Association, National Education Association, 100 E. Edwards St., Springfield, IL 62704. TEL 217-544-0706. Ed. Gordon R. Jackson. adv.; bk.rev.; illus. circ. 78,000. **Document type:** trade publication.
   Formerly: Advocate (Springfield) (ISSN 0097-6164)

371.14   US
I E A REPORTER (YEAR). vol.27, 1972. m. (Sep.-May). $10. Idaho Education Association, 620 N. Sixth St., Box 2638, Boise, ID 83701. TEL 208-344-1341. Ed. Gayle L. Moore. circ. 8,653.
   Former titles: I E A - N E A Reporter; I E A Reporter (ISSN 0046-8495); Idaho Education News (ISSN 0019-1183)

I E E E TRANSACTIONS ON EDUCATION. see *ENGINEERING — Electrical Engineering*

EDUCATION 2027

I E R FLAMBEAU. a. to individuals; institutions $10. Addis Ababa University, Institute of Educational Research, P.O. Box 1176, Addis Ababa, Ethiopia. Ed. Tassew Zewdie.
  Supersedes: Addis Ababa University. Institute of Educational Research. News Bulletin; Which was formerly: Addis Ababa University. Educational Research Centre. News Bulletin.

370   AU   ISSN 0018-9715
I F M - S E I BULLETIN.* (Editions in English, Finnish, French, German, Spanish and Swedish) 1970. 10/yr. $2. International Falcon Movement - Socialist Educational International, Ruahensteingasse 5, A-1011 Vienna, Austria. Ed. Miguel Angel Martinez.

370   US   ISSN 0019-0624
I S E A COMMUNIQUE. 1962. 8/yr. $4 to non-members. Iowa State Education Association, 4025 Tonawanda Dr., Des Moines, IA 50312. TEL 515-279-9711. Ed. Lana O. Schlapkohl. adv.; illus. circ. 37,000. (tabloid format; back issues avail.) **Document type:** newspaper.

370   II
I S P T INTERNATIONAL JOURNAL OF EDUCATIONAL SCIENCES. s-a. Rs.50($50) Institute for Studies in Psychological Testing, 17 Karanpur, Dehradun 248 001 (UP), India. Ed. S.P. Kulshrestha.

152.8   II   ISSN 0251-0146
I S P T JOURNAL OF RESEARCH IN EDUCATIONAL & PSYCHOLOGICAL MEASUREMENT. 1977. s-a. Rs.100($25) Institute for Studies in Psychological Testing, 101 Doon Vihar, Jakhan, Dehradun 248009, India. Ed. S.P. Kulshrestha. adv.; bk.rev. circ. 500. (back issues avail.) **Indexed:** Indian Psychol.Abstr.
  Description: Devoted to the fields of educational, psychological measurement, evaluation, testing and other allied subjects.

370   US
I S T A ADVOCATE. 1972. 5/yr. $6. Indiana State Teachers Association, 150 W. Market St., Indianapolis, IN 46204. TEL 317-634-1515. Ed. Kathleen A. Berry. adv. circ. 50,000. **Document type:** newsletter.
  Formerly: Teacher Advocate (ISSN 0300-6298); **Supersedes:** Indiana Teacher (ISSN 0019-6797); I S T A News.
  Description: Provides timely information on state and national civil liberties developments.

371.394 600   US   ISSN 1040-4694
I S T E UPDATE; people, events and news in education technology. 1988. 7/yr. $12 to non-members. International Society for Technology in Education, 1787 Agate St., Eugene, OR 97403-1923. TEL 503-346-4414. FAX 503-346-5890. Ed. Anita Best. (back issues avail.) **Document type:** newsletter. ●Also available online.
  —CCC.
  Description: Articles on current issues by leaders in the field of technology in education.

I T L REVIEW OF APPLIED LINGUISTICS. see *LINGUISTICS*

370   FR   ISSN 0249-6372
IANUS BIFRONS. 1991-1993 (Spr.). 4/yr. 220 F. (foreign 330 F.). Presses Universitaires de Nancy, 25 rue Baron Louis, 54001 Nancy Cedex, France. TEL 83-37-37-65. Dir. Jean-Marie Bonnet. circ. 600.

370   CN
IBIDEM: GLENDON COLLEGE STUDENT HANDBOOK. a. Glendon College, Student Union, 2275 Bayview Ave., Toronto, Ont. M4N 3M6, Canada. TEL 416-487-6720. adv. circ. 1,000.

370   US   ISSN 1049-2437
IDAHO. DEPARTMENT OF EDUCATION. NEWS AND REPORTS. 1972. 5/yr. free. Department of Education, Len B. Jordan Bldg., Boise, ID 83720. TEL 208-334-3300. FAX 208-334-2228. Ed. Lindy High. bk.rev. circ. 20,000. (tabloid format) **Document type:** newspaper.

371.9   US   ISSN 0093-7223
E97.65.I2
IDAHO. STATE SUPERINTENDENT OF PUBLIC INSTRUCTION. ANNUAL REPORT. STATE OF IDAHO JOHNSON-O'MALLEY PROGRAM. Key Title: Annual Report: State of Idaho Johnson-O'Malley Program. Cover title: Indian Education Annual Report. 1966. irreg. State Department of Education, Adult Education, Boise, ID 83720. TEL 208-334-3300. FAX 208-334-2228. circ. 20.

370   US   ISSN 0073-4497
IDAHO EDUCATION ASSOCIATION. PROCEEDINGS. a. membership. Idaho Education Association, 620 N. Sixth St., Box 2638, Boise, ID 83702. TEL 208-344-1341. **Document type:** proceedings.

370   II   ISSN 0019-1353
IDEAL EDUCATION.* (Text in English) 1964. m. Rs.10.($2) V.M. Sinkar, Ed. & Pub., "Prabhat", 47-A Gophale Rd. (North), Dadar, Bombay 28, India. adv.; bk.rev.; charts; tr.lit. circ. 2,000.

IGAKU KYOIKU/MEDICAL EDUCATION. see *MEDICAL SCIENCES*

379   US   ISSN 0147-2860
L142
ILLINOIS. STATE BOARD OF EDUCATION. ANNUAL REPORT. a. State Board of Education, 100 N. First St., Springfield, IL 62777. TEL 217-782-4648. Ed. Lee Milner. illus.; stat. **Document type:** government publication.
  Supersedes: Illinois. Department of Public Instruction. Annual State of Education Message (ISSN 0098-0269)

370   US   ISSN 0019-2236
L11
ILLINOIS SCHOOLS JOURNAL. 1967. 3/yr. $4. Chicago State University, 95th St. at King Dr., Chicago, IL 60628. TEL 312-995-2000. Ed. G. Lopardo. bibl.; charts; illus.; stat.; index. cum.index. circ. 7,000. (also avail. in microform from UMI; reprint service avail. from UMI) **Indexed:** C.I.J.E., Curr.Cont., Educ.Ind., Except.Child.Educ.Abstr., Sociol.Abstr.
  —BLDSC (4365.530000); Faxon; UnCover; UMI.
  Supersedes: Chicago Schools Journal.

ILLUSTRATOR. see *ART*

370   US
IMPACT ON INSTRUCTIONAL IMPROVEMENT. 1966. q. $10. New York State Association for Supervision and Curriculum Development, c/o Peter Incalcaterra, 44 Ridgewood Ave. RD5, Kingston, NY 12401. Ed. Mildred Ness. circ. 1,000. (back issues avail.) **Indexed:** PROMT.
  Formerly: Impact.

372   CN   ISSN 0823-695X
IN THE MIDDLE. 1982. 3/yr. Can.$15. (Saskatchewan Middle Years Association) Saskatchewan Teachers' Federation, Box 1108, Saskatoon, Sask. S7K 3N3, Canada. Ed. Elaine Bergh. adv.

370   US   ISSN 0145-9635
LC47
INDEPENDENT SCHOOL. 1941. 3/yr. $17.50. National Association of Independent Schools, 1620 L St., N.W., Washington, DC 20036-5605. Ed. Catherine O'Neill. adv.; bk.rev.; index. circ. 7,500. (also avail. in microfilm from UMI; reprint service avail. from UMI) **Indexed:** C.I.J.E., Educ.Ind., Media Rev.Dig.
  —UnCover; UMI.
  Formerly: Independent School Bulletin (ISSN 0019-3755)

370   II
INDIA. MINISTRY OF HUMAN RESOURCE DEVELOPMENT. DEPARTMENT OF EDUCATION. REPORT. 1948. a. free. Ministry of Human Resource Development, Department of Education, Shastri Bhavan, New Delhi 110001, India. (Subscr. to: Assistant Educational Adviser (Publications), Ministry of Human Resource Development, Department of Education, EX AFO Hutments, Dr. Rajendra Prasad Rd., New Delhi 110001, India) circ. 3,500. **Document type:** government publication.
  Formerly: India. Ministry of Education and Social Welfare. Department of Education. Report (ISSN 0073-6201)

370   II   ISSN 0019-4689
INDIAN EDUCATION (KANPUR).* 1960. m. Rs.25($8) All India Federation of Educational Associations, Iha Seshadri Khattry Bhanan, P.O. Box 52, Kanpur 208 001, India. Ed. V.F. Rghavachari. adv.; bk.rev. circ. 2,000. **Indexed:** Cont.Pg.Educ.

370   II   ISSN 0019-4700
LB1028.A1   CODEN: IEREDE
INDIAN EDUCATIONAL REVIEW. (Text in English) 1966. q. Rs.26($18) National Council of Educational Research and Training, Publication Department, Sri Aurbindo Marg, New Delhi 110016, India. Ed. R.P. Singh. bk.rev. circ. 1,000. **Indexed:** Cont.Pg..Educ., Educ.Admin.Abstr., Psychol.Abstr., Res.High.Educ.Abstr., Rural Ext.Educ.& Tr.Abstr., Sociol.Educ.Abstr.
  —SWETS.

INDIAN JOURNAL OF PSYCHOMETRY AND EDUCATION. see *PSYCHOLOGY*

INDIAN MUSIC JOURNAL; devoted to general reader and student. see *MUSIC*

370 622.07   II   ISSN 0304-1158
TN213.D52
INDIAN SCHOOL OF MINES. ANNUAL REPORT. Key Title: Annual Report - Incian School of Mines. (Text in English) 1968. a. free. Indian School of Mines, Dhanbad 826004, Bihar, India. FAX 0326-2840. adv.; illus.
  Description: Reports the school's annual education & research activities.

INDIANA DIRECTORY OF MUSIC TEACHERS. see *MUSIC*

372.21   UK   ISSN 0269-9524
INFANT PROJECTS. 1974. 6/yr. £14.50 (foreign £16). Scholastic Publications Ltd., Villiers House, Clarendon Ave., Leamington Spa, Warks. CV32 5PR, England. TEL 0926-887799. FAX 0926-883331. TELEX 312138 SFLSG. Ed. Margot O'Keeffe. bk.rev. circ. 39,949. (also avail. in microform from UMI) **Indexed:** Cont.Pg.Educ. **Document type:** academic/scholarly publication.
  Former titles: Child Education Special (ISSN 0262-7507); Child Education Quarterly (ISSN 0045-6640)

INFANZIA Y APRENDIZAJE. see *PSYCHOLOGY*

370   US   ISSN 0020-0115
INFORMATION LEGISLATIVE SERVICE. 1961. w. $150 to non-members. Pennsylvania School Boards Association, 774 Limekiln Rd., New Cumberland, PA 17070-2398. TEL 717-774-2331. FAX 717-774-0713. Ed. Lynn H. Mannion. index. circ. 11,300. (back issues avail.)

INFORMATION TECHNOLOGY, EDUCATION AND SOCIETY. see *COMPUTERS — Information Science And Information Theory*

370   GW   ISSN 0343-7868
INFORMATIONEN - BILDUNG, WISSENSCHAFT. 1970. m. free. Bundesministerium fuer Bildung und Wissenschaft, Referat Oeffentlichkeitsarbeit, 53170 Bonn, Germany. TEL 0228-572045. FAX 0228-572094. circ. 20,000. **Document type:** government publication.

370 430   AU   ISSN 0721-9954
INFORMATIONEN ZUR DEUTSCHDIDAKTIK; Zeitschrift fuer den Deutschunterricht in Wissenschaft und Schule. 1976. 4/yr. $40. Verband der Wissenschaftlichen Gesellschaften Oesterreichs, Lindengasse 37, A-1070 Vienna, Austria. TEL 932166. Ed. Werner Wintersteiner. bk.rev.; index.

INFORMATIONEN ZUR POLITISCHEN BILDUNG/INFORMATION FOR CIVIC EDUCATION. see *POLITICAL SCIENCE*

370   SP
INFORMATIVO ENSENANZA ANDALUZA. 1981. 12/yr. Union de Sindicatos de Trabajadores de la Ensenanza de Andalucia, Aparejo 2, 1o A-B, Apdo. de Correos 3127, 29080 Malaga, Spain. TEL 52-392-412. FAX 52-28-64-43. Dir. Dalmiro Garcia. circ. 8,000. **Document type:** trade publication.

EDUCATION

370 US ISSN 0046-9572
INNOVATOR (ANN ARBOR). 1969. irreg. free. University of Michigan, School of Education, E. & S. University Aves., Ann Arbor, MI 48109. TEL 313-763-4880. FAX 313-763-1229. Ed. Eric Warden. bk.rev. circ. 53,000. (tabloid format)

371.2 340 US ISSN 1069-0190
INQUIRY & ANALYSIS. 1979. bi-m. $75. National School Boards Association, 1680 Duke St., Alexandria, VA 22314. TEL 703-838-6722. FAX 703-683-7590. Ed. Naomi Gittins. circ. 3,000. (looseleaf format; back issues avail.) **Document type:** newsletter.
   Description: For attorneys representing public schools. Focuses on Supreme Court and national legal issues.

INSIDE STORY. see *LITERATURE*

INSIDER'S REPORT; a special bulletin for leaders. see *LABOR UNIONS*

373 US
INSIGHT (HUBBARD). 1965. 4/yr. free. Hubbard Exempted Village School District, Office of Superintendent, 150 Hall Ave., Hubbard, OH 44425. TEL 216-534-1921. Ed. Kevin S. Turner. bk.rev.; charts; illus. circ. 6,000. **Document type:** newsletter.
   Formerly (until 1976): Hubbard School System Office of Curriculum and Instruction. Digest Newsletter (ISSN 0018-6961)

370 CN ISSN 0073-8123
INSIGHTS. 1964. irreg. (2-4/yr.) membership. John Dewey Society, Graduate Student Education, Brock University, St. Catharines, ON L2S 3A1, Canada. (Subscr. to: Robert C. Morris, Secondary Education, West Georgia College, 1600 Maple St., Carrollton, GA 30118) Ed. John M. Novak. bk.rev. circ. 400. **Document type:** academic/scholarly publication.
   Description: Focuses on themes of cultural and educational interest.

370 CN ISSN 0020-2029
INSITE (SASKATOON). 1968. irreg., vol.23, no.3, 1993. Can.$10. (Saskatchewan Industrial Education Association) Saskatchewan Teachers' Federation, Box 1108, Saskatoon, SK S7K 3N3, Canada. Ed. Kevin Kaiser. adv.; bk.rev.; film rev.; illus. circ. 500. (processed)

370 FR
INSTITUT COLLEGIAL EUROPEEN. ACTES DES COLLOQUES DE LOCHES. 1963. a. 75 F. (Institut Collegial Europeen) Editions Universitaires, 77 av. de Vaugirard, 75006 Paris, France. Ed. Gilbert Gadoffre. circ. 300. (back issues avail.)
   Formerly: Institute Collegial Europeen. Bulletin (ISSN 0073-8174)

370 613 UK ISSN 0307-3289
INSTITUTE OF HEALTH EDUCATION. JOURNAL. 1962. 3/yr. £15 to non-members (effective 1994). Institute of Health Education, 9 Elm Ridge Dr., Hale Barns, Altrincham, Ches. WA15 0JE, England. TEL 061-980-8276. FAX 061-980-7446. Ed. A.S. Blinkhorn. adv.; bk.rev.; film rev.; index; circ. 1,000 (paid). **Indexed:** Abstr.Hyg., Curr.Adv.Ecol.Sci., Trop.Dis.Bull. **Document type:** academic/scholarly publication.
   —BLDSC (4776.200000).

370 BL ISSN 0020-367X
INSTITUTO BRASIL - ESTADOS UNIDOS. BOLETIM. (Text in English and Portuguese) 1943. bi-m. free. Instituto Brasil - Estados Unidos, Av. N.S. de Copacabana, 690 - 5 andar, Rio de Janeiro, R.A., Brazil. TEL 255-8939. adv.; bk.rev.; bibl.; illus. circ. 2,000.

370 PE
INSTITUTO CULTURAL PERUANO NORTEAMERICANO. NEWSLETTER. (Text in English, Spanish) 1939. m. free. Instituto Cultural Peruano Norteamericano, Jiron Cuzco 446, Avda. Arequipa 4798, Apdo 304, Lima, Peru. TEL 46-0381. Ed. Maria de Ortiz de Vallate. illus. circ. 3,000. **Document type:** newsletter.
   Formerly: Instituto Cultural Peruano Norteamericano. Boletin (ISSN 0020-3718)
   Description: Calendar of events, plus description of highlights.

INSTITUTO DE CIENCIAS PARA LA FAMILIA. see *LAW*

INSTITUTUL DE SUBINGINERI ORADEA. LUCRARI STIINTIFICE: SERIA PEDAGOGIE, PSIHOLOGIE, METODICA. see *PSYCHOLOGY*

370 NE ISSN 0020-4277
L11 CODEN: INLSBJ
INSTRUCTIONAL SCIENCE; an international journal of learning and cognition. (Text in English) 1971. 6/yr. fl.493($257) (effective 1994). Kluwer Academic Publishers, Postbus 17, 3300 AA Dordrecht, Netherlands. TEL 31-78-334911. FAX 31-78-334254. TELEX 29245 KAPG NL. (Dist. by: Kluwer Academic Publishers Group, P.O. Box 322, 3300 AH Dordrecht, Netherlands. TEL 31-78-524400. FAX 31-78-524474; N. America dist. addr.: Box 358, Accord Sta., Hingham, MA 02018-0358. TEL 617-871-6600. FAX 617-871-6528) Ed. Peter Goodyear. adv.; bk.rev.; illus.; index, cum.index. (also avail. in microform from UMI; reprint service avail. from SWZ) **Indexed:** Br.Educ.Ind., C.I.J.E., Commun.Abstr., Comput.Abstr., Comput.Rev., Cont.Pg.Educ., Curr.Cont., Educ.Ind., Educ.Tech.Abstr., Mult.Ed.Abstr., Psychol.Abstr., Psychol.R.G., Sociol.Abstr., Sociol.Educ.Abstr., SSCI. **Document type:** academic/scholarly publication.
   —BLDSC (4524.950000); Faxon; UnCover; SWETS; UMI. **CCC.**
   Refereed Serial

372 US ISSN 1049-5851
INSTRUCTOR. 1891. 9/yr. $14.95 (foreign $27.95). Scholastic Inc., 555 Broadway, New York, NY 10012-3999. TEL 212-313-6100. (Subscr. to: 1 E. First St., Duluth, MN 55802) Ed. Deborah Martorell. adv.; bk.rev.; film rev.; illus.; index. circ. 254,361. (also avail. in microform from UMI) **Indexed:** Acad.Ind., Bk.Rev.Ind. (1965-), Bus.Ind., C.I.J.E., Child.Bk.Rev.Ind. (1965-), Educ.Ind., Except.Child.Educ.Abstr., Ind.Child.Mag., Jun.High.Mag.Abstr., Mag.Ind., Media Rev.Dig., Tr.& Indus.Ind. **Document type:** trade publication.
   —Faxon; UMI.
   Former titles: Instructor and Teacher (ISSN 0279-3369); Instructor (ISSN 0020-4285); Incorporates (in May 1981): Teacher (ISSN 0148-6578); Which was formerly: Grade Teacher (ISSN 0017-2782)
   Description: Features articles on a variety of topics of interest to elementary school teachers. Includes articles on computer applications for teaching techniques, educational software reviews and children's fiction book reviews.

INSTRUMENTALIST; a magazine for school and college band and orchestra directors, professional instrumentalists, teacher-training specialists in instrumental music education and instrumental teachers. see *MUSIC*

INSURANCE INSTITUTE OF AMERICA. INSTITUTE INSIGHTS. see *INSURANCE*

INSURANCE INSTITUTE OF AMERICA. KEY INFORMATION. see *INSURANCE*

370 FR ISSN 0020-5001
INTER AUTO ECOLES DE FRANCE - INTER AUTO ROUTE. 1961. m. 75 F. Publi-Inter, 89 rue Carnot, 92305 Levallois-Perret Cedex, France. TEL 47-48-09-00. FAX 47-48-13-16. TELEX 612 942. Ed. Bertrand Tarisien. adv.; bk.rev.; abstr.; illus. circ. 8,000.
   Description: For driving school instructors.

370 500 US ISSN 0074-0829
F1405.5 1959
INTER-AMERICAN COUNCIL FOR EDUCATION, SCIENCE, AND CULTURE. FINAL REPORT. (Text in English, French, Portuguese and Spanish) a. $4. Organization of American States, Department of Publications, 1889 F St., N.W., Washington, DC 20006. TEL 703-941-1617. circ. 2,000. (also avail. in microfiche from CIS) **Indexed:** IIS.

370 NE ISSN 0826-4805
L11 CODEN: INDOE4
INTERCHANGE; quarterly review of education. 1970. 4/yr. fl.285($149) (effective 1994). (Ontario Institute for Studies in Education) Kluwer Academic Publishers, Postbus 17, 3300 AA Dordrecht, Netherlands. TEL 31-78-334911. FAX 31-78-334254. TELEX 29245 KAPG NL. (Dist. by: Kluwer Academic Publishers Group, P.O. Box 322, 3300 AH Dordrecht, Netherlands. TEL 31-78-524400. FAX 31-78-524474; N. America dist. addr.: Box 358, Accord Sta., Hingham, MA 02018-0358. TEL 617-871-6600. FAX 617-871-6528) Ed. Ian Winchester. bk.rev.; charts. circ. 1,000. (also avail. in microform from UMI; reprint service avail. from UMI) **Indexed:** C.I.J.E., Can.Educ.Ind., Commun.Abstr., Cont.Pg.Educ., Curr.Cont., Educ.Admin.Abstr., Educ.Tech.Abstr., Mult.Ed.Abstr., Psychol.Abstr., Res.High.Educ.Abstr., Sociol.Educ.Abstr., SOMA, Sp.Ed.Needs Abstr., Stud.Wom.Abstr. **Document type:** academic/scholarly publication.
   —BLDSC (4532.500000); Faxon; UnCover; SWETS; UMI. **CCC.**
   Formerly (until 1984): Interchange on Education (ISSN 0833-9856); (until 1983): Interchange on Educational Policy (ISSN 0822-9848); (until 1979): Interchange (ISSN 0020-5230)
   Refereed Serial

371.3 US ISSN 0047-0457
INTERCHANGE (PORTLAND). 1964. 3/yr. membership. Oregon Educational Media Association, 16695 S.W. Rosa Rd., Beaverton, OR 97007. TEL 503-649-5764. Ed. Jennifer Vaught. adv.; bk.rev.; illus.; circ. controlled. (tabloid format; reprint service avail. from EDR) **Indexed:** Curr.Lit.Fam.Plan.

370 GW ISSN 0935-0993
INTERKULTURELL; Forum fuer interkulturelle Kommunikation, Erziehung und Beratung. 1980. q. DM.63. Forschungsstelle Migration und Integration, Paedagogische Hochschule, Kunzenweg 21, 79117 Freiburg, Germany. TEL 0761-682-311. FAX 0761-682402. Ed. Guido Schmitt. adv.; bk.rev.; bibl.; index. circ. 750. **Document type:** academic/scholarly publication.
   Description: For teachers and social workers: focus on bilingual and intercultural education.

370 FR
INTERNATIONAL ASSOCIATION FOR EDUCATIONAL AND VOCATIONAL INFORMATION. STUDIES AND REPORTS. irreg. International Association for Educational and Vocational Information, 20 rue de l'Estrapade, 75005 Paris, France.

658.3 370 US ISSN 0020-6016
LB1027.5
INTERNATIONAL ASSOCIATION OF PUPIL PERSONNEL WORKERS. JOURNAL. vol.14, 1970. q. membership (libraries $30). International Association of Pupil Personnel Workers, c/o Janice Chmela, Ed., 2025 Juneway Dr., Michigan City, IN 46360-1474. (Subscr. to: William D. Chmela, Exec. Dir., 2025 Juneway Dr., Long Beach, IN 46360) adv.; bk.rev.; index. circ. 1,000. (also avail. in microform from UMI; reprint service avail. from UMI) **Indexed:** C.I.J.E.

370 SZ
INTERNATIONAL BACCALAUREATE ORGANISATION. ANNUAL BULLETIN. (Editions in English, French, Spanish) 1968. a. 15 SFr. International Baccalaureate Organisation - Organisation du Baccalaureat International, Route des Morillons 15, CH-1218 Grand-Saconnex, Switzerland. TEL 022-7910274. FAX 022-7910277. (U.S. subscr. to: International Baccalaureate North America, 200 Madison Ave., New York, NY 10016) Ed. Roger M. Peel. circ. 5,000 (approx.). **Document type:** bulletin.
   Former titles: International Baccalaureate Office. Annual Bulletin (ISSN 0074-1973); (until 1972): International Baccalaureate Office. Semi-Annual Bulletin.

INTERNATIONAL BRAIN DOMINANCE REVIEW. see *MEDICAL SCIENCES — Psychiatry And Neurology*

EDUCATION

370   UN
INTERNATIONAL CONFERENCE ON EDUCATION. FINAL REPORT/CONFERENCE INTERNATIONAL DE L'EDUCATION. RAPPORT FINAL. (Editions in Arabic, Chinese, English, French, Russian, and Spanish) 1934, 3rd (none 1940-45, 1969). a. until 33rd, 1971; thereafter biennial. free. Unesco, International Bureau of Education, Case Postale 199, CH-1211 Geneva 20, Switzerland. TEL 41-22-7981455. FAX 41-22-7981486. TELEX 22644. (also avail. in microfiche)
Former titles: International Conference on Education. Proceedings (ISSN 0074-3275); (until no.32, 1970): International Conference on Public Education. Proceedings.
Description: Deliberations, speeches at opening and closing ceremonies, and lists of documents and reports distributed.

371.9   US
INTERNATIONAL CONFERENCE ON PIAGETIAN THEORY AND THE HELPING PROFESSIONS. PROCEEDINGS. 8th, 1978. a. price varies. (Childrens Hospital of Los Angeles, University Affiliated Program) University of Southern California, Department of Sociology and Social Research, University Park, Los Angeles, CA 90089-2539. TEL 213-743-7610.

371.4   NE   ISSN 0165-0653
BF637.C6   CODEN: IJACER
INTERNATIONAL JOURNAL FOR THE ADVANCEMENT OF COUNSELLING. (Text in English) 1978. 4/yr. fl.281($148) (effective 1994). Kluwer Academic Publishers, Postbus 17, 3300 AA Dordrecht, Netherlands. TEL 31-78-334911. FAX 31-78-334254. TELEX 29245 KAPG NL. (Dist. by: Kluwer Academic Publishers Group, P.O. Box 322, 3300 AH Dordrecht, Netherlands. TEL 31-78-524400. FAX 31-78-524474; N. America dist. addr.: Box 358, Accord Sta., Hingham, MA 02018-0358. TEL 617-871-6600. FAX 617-871-6528) (Co-sponsors: International Association for Educational and Vocational Guidance; International Round Table for the Advancement of Counselling) Ed. Len Stewin. (also avail. in microform from UMI; back issues avail.; reprint service avail. from SWZ) **Indexed:** Psychol.Abstr., SSCI. **Document type:** academic/scholarly publication.
—BLDSC (4541.573000); UnCover; SWETS; UMI. **CCC**.
Description: Promotes the exchange of information about counselling activities throughout the world.
Refereed Serial

370   UK   ISSN 0957-4964
INTERNATIONAL JOURNAL OF COGNITIVE EDUCATION & MEDIATED LEARNING. 1990. 3/yr. £21 to individuals; institutions £45. Sharron Publishing Co., 27 Frederick St., Hockley, Birmingham B1 3HH, England. TEL 021-212-0919. FAX 021-212-0919. Ed. Martha Coulter. circ. 350. **Document type:** academic/scholarly publication.
—BLDSC (4542.172250).

379   UK   ISSN 0966-9760
▼**INTERNATIONAL JOURNAL OF EARLY YEARS EDUCATION.** 1993. 3/yr. Trentham Books Ltd., Westview House, 734 London Rd., Oakhill, Stoke-on-Tent, Staffs. ST4 5NP, England. TEL 0782-745567. FAX 0782-745553. Ed. Elizabeth Coates. **Document type:** academic/scholarly publication.
—BLDSC (4542.193000).

370   UK   ISSN 0738-0593
L16
INTERNATIONAL JOURNAL OF EDUCATIONAL DEVELOPMENT. 1981. 4/yr. £188($290) (effective 1994). Elsevier Science Ltd, Pergamon, P.O. Box 800, Kidlington, Oxford OX5 1DX, England. TEL 44-865-843000. FAX 44-865-843010. (Subscr. in U.S. and Canada to: Elsevier Science, 660 White Plains Rd., Tarrytown, NY 10591-5153. TEL 914-524-9200. FAX 914-333-2444) Ed. Keith Watson. adv.; bk.rev.; index. (also avail. in microform from UMI) **Indexed:** Cont.Pg.Educ., Curr.Cont., Educ.Tech.Abstr., I D A, Mult.Ed.Abstr., Res.High.Educ.Abstr., Rural Ext.Educ.& Tr.Abstr., SOMA, Sp.Ed.Needs Abstr., Stud.Wom.Abstr. **Document type:** academic/scholarly publication.
—BLDSC (4542.199500); SWETS; UMI. **CCC**.
Description: Reports key developments in national systems of education as they emerge, including new structures of schooling, curriculum innovation and change, new approaches to educational management, and studies of achievement and student participation rates, as well as research and analysis of theoretical, practical and planning issues.
Refereed Serial

370   US   ISSN 1056-7879
L11
▼**INTERNATIONAL JOURNAL OF EDUCATIONAL REFORM.** 1992. q. $65. Technomic Publishing Co., Inc., 851 New Holland Ave., Box 3535, Lancaster, PA 17604. TEL 717-291-5609. FAX 717-295-4538. TELEX 230-753565 (TECHNOMIC UD). Eds. Fenwick W. English, Betty E. Steffy. circ. 210. **Document type:** academic/scholarly publication.
—BLDSC (4542.199780); UMI. **CCC**.
Description: Provides a forum for information and analysis of the many reforms now in progress around the world. Discusses reform theory, strategy, policy, and movements.
Refereed Serial

370   II   ISSN 0252-8576
INTERNATIONAL JOURNAL OF EDUCATIONAL SCIENCES. (Text in English) 1984. a. Rs.100($25) Institute for Studies in Psychological Testing, 101 Doon Vihar, Jakhan, Dehradun 248009, India. Ed. Sr. S.P. Kulshaestha. adv.; bk.rev. circ. 1,000. (back issues avail.)
Description: Forum for research in the educational sciences.

INTERNATIONAL JOURNAL OF EDUCOLOGY. see *EDUCATION — Adult Education*

INTERNATIONAL JOURNAL OF ENGINEERING EDUCATION. see *ENGINEERING*

INTERNATIONAL JOURNAL OF MUSIC EDUCATION. see *MUSIC*

370   UK   ISSN 0951-8398
LB1028   CODEN: QSEEEY
INTERNATIONAL JOURNAL OF QUALITATIVE STUDIES IN EDUCATION. q. £44($75) to individuals; institutions £88($148). Taylor & Francis Ltd., Rankine Rd., Basingstoke, Hants RG24 8PR, England. TEL 0256-840366. FAX 0256-479438. TELEX 858540. Eds. J. Amos Hatch, Richard Wisniewski. **Indexed:** Mult.Ed.Abstr., SOMA. **Document type:** academic/scholarly publication.
—BLDSC (4542.509700); UnCover; SWETS. **CCC**.
Description: Aims to enhance the theory and practice of qualitative research in education by reporting experience of a variety of techniques, including ethnographic observation and interviewing, grounded theory, life history, qualitative evaluation, curriculum criticism and phenomenology.
Refereed Serial

370 500   UK   ISSN 0950-0693
Q181.A1   CODEN: ISEDEB
INTERNATIONAL JOURNAL OF SCIENCE EDUCATION. (Text in English; summaries in French and German) 1979. bi-m. £151($254) Taylor & Francis Ltd., Rankine Rd., Basingstoke, Hants RG24 8PR, England. TEL 0256-840366. FAX 0256-479438. TELEX 858540. Ed. John Gilbert. adv.; bk.rev.; bibl.; charts; illus.; index. circ. 700. (also avail. in microfiche; back issues avail.) **Indexed:** Biol.Abstr., Br.Educ.Ind., C.I.J.E., Child Devel.Abstr., Cont.Pg.Educ., Educ.Tech.Abstr., Excerp.Med., INSPEC, Res.High.Educ.Abstr., Sci.Abstr., SSCI, Stud.Wom.Abstr., Tech.Educ.Abstr. **Document type:** academic/scholarly publication.
—BLDSC (4542.544000); Faxon; UnCover; SWETS. **CCC**.
Formerly: European Journal of Science Education (ISSN 0140-5284)
Description: Aims to bridge the gap between research and practice; provides information, ideas and opinions that serve as a medium for placing these research findings in the context of the classroom.
Refereed Serial

INTERNATIONAL JOURNAL OF SOCIAL EDUCATION. see *SOCIAL SCIENCES: COMPREHENSIVE WORKS*

INTERNATIONAL NEWSLETTER ON CHEMICAL EDUCATION. see *CHEMISTRY*

370   US   ISSN 0278-2731
Q179.98   CODEN: IRCDES
INTERNATIONAL RESEARCH CENTERS DIRECTORY. 1982. biennial. $410 (effective Aug. 1993). Gale Research Inc., 835 Penobscot Bldg., Detroit, MI 48226. TEL 313-961-2242; 800-877-4253. FAX 313-961-6083. TELEX 810-221-7086. Ed. Annettee Piccirelli.
●Also available online. Vendor(s): DIALOG Information Services, Inc.
—BLDSC (4545.830800); CASDDS.
Description: Guide to research centers worldwide.

370   NE   ISSN 0020-8566
L18   CODEN: IRVEAK
INTERNATIONAL REVIEW OF EDUCATION/INTERNATIONALE ZEITSCHRIFT FUER ERZIEHUNGSWISSENSCHAFT/REVUE INTERNATIONALE DE PEDAGOGIE. (Text, title and summaries in English, French, German) 1955. 6/yr. fl.280($146) (effective 1994). (Unesco Institute for Education, UN) Kluwer Academic Publishers, Postbus 17, 3300 AA Dordrecht, Netherlands. TEL 31-78-334911. FAX 31-78-334254. TELEX 29245 KAPG NL. (Dist. by: Kluwer Academic Publishing Group, P.O. Box 322, 3300 AH Dordrecht, Netherlands. TEL 31-78-524400. FAX 31-78-524474; N. America dist. addr.: Box 358, Accord Sta., Hingham, MA 02018-0358. TEL 617-871-6600. FAX 617-871-6528) Ed. P. Sutton. adv.; bk.rev.; index. (also avail. in microform from UMI; reprint service avail. from SWZ) **Indexed:** Br.Educ.Ind., C.I.J.E., Cont.Pg.Educ., Curr.Cont., Educ.Ind., Educ.Tech.Abstr., High.Educ.Curr.Aware.Bull., I D A, Int.Lab.Doc., Lang.& Lang.Behav.Abstr., Lang.Teach.& Ling.Abstr., Mid.East: Abstr.& Ind., Mult.Ed.Abstr., Res.High.Educ.Abstr., Rural Ext.Educ.& Tr.Abstr., SOMA, Sp.Ed.Needs Abstr., SSCI.
—BLDSC (4547.100000); Faxon; UnCover; SWETS; UMI. **CCC**.
Description: Provides departments and institutes of education, teacher training institutions and professional readers worldwide with scholarly information on major educational innovations, research projects and trends.
Refereed Serial

INTERNATIONAL SOCIETY FOR MUSIC EDUCATION. PROCEEDINGS. see *MUSIC*

371.7 614.8   BE   ISSN 0074-9524
INTERNATIONAL UNION OF SCHOOL AND UNIVERSITY HEALTH AND MEDICINE. CONGRESS REPORTS.* quadrennial, 1975, 7th, Mexico City. International Union of School and University Health and Medicine, c/o Dr. Guy Roggen, Pres., Serv. Medical de l'ULB, Ave. Paul Heger 28, B-1050 Brussels, Belgium.

EDUCATION

920 370   UK
INTERNATIONAL WHO'S WHO IN EDUCATION. 1974. irreg. price varies. Melrose Press Ltd., 3 Regal Ln., Soham, Ely, Cambridgeshire CB7 5BA, England. TEL 0353-721091. FAX 0353-721839. (Dist. in U.S. by: Taylor and Francis Inc., 1900 Frost Rd., Ste. 101, Bristol, PA 19007-1598) **Document type:** directory.

L'INTERPRETE. see *LINGUISTICS*

370 301   US
INTERPRETIVE PERSPECTIVES ON EDUCATION AND POLICY. 1990. irreg. price varies. Ablex Publishing Corporation, 355 Chestnut St., Norwood, NJ 07648. TEL 201-767-8405. FAX 201-767-6717. TELEX 135-393. Eds. George Noblit, William Pink.

373   RM
INVATAMINTUL LICEAL SI TEHNIC PROFESIONAL. m. (10/yr.). 40 lei($10) Ministerul Educatiei si Invatamintului, Str. Spiru Haret Nr. 12, Bucharest, Rumania. (Dist. by: ILEXIM, Str. 13 Decembr i Nr. 3, P.O. Box 136-137, Bucharest, Rumania) illus. **Formerly:** Invatamintul Profesional si Tehnic.

370   SP
INVESTIGACION EN LA ESCUELA. 1987. s-a. (E.U. de Magisterio, Departamento de Didactica de las Ciencias) Universidad de Sevilla, Servicio de Publicaciones, Valparaiso 5, 41013 Seville, Spain. TEL 954-231958. FAX 954-232245. (Subscr. to: Avda. Ciudad Jardin, 22, 41005 Seville, Spain)

370   NE   ISSN 0021-0307
INZICHT. 1878. 5/yr. fl.35. Vereniging voor Openbaar Onderwijs, Blekerstraat 20, 1315 AH Almere, Netherlands. TEL 31-36-5331500. FAX 31-36-5340464. Ed. L. van Zyl. adv.; bk.rev.; illus. circ. 35,000. **Formerly:** Volksonderwijs.

IOWA MEDIA MESSAGE. see *LIBRARY AND INFORMATION SCIENCES*

IOWA MUSIC EDUCATOR. see *MUSIC*

370.193   US   ISSN 0021-0617
IOWA P T A BULLETIN. 1920. m. (Sep.-May). $4. Iowa Congress of Parents and Teachers, 610 Merle Hay Towers, Des Moines, IA 50310. bk.rev. (processed) **Document type:** bulletin.

370 800   IQ
IRAQ. MINISTRY OF EDUCATION. AL-MU'ALLEM AL-JADID. 1935. 4/yr. ID.600 to individuals; students and teachers ID.1000. Ministry of Education, Adhamiya P.B. 14051, Baghdad, Iraq. Ed. Ahmed Shahhath. bk.rev. circ. 180,000. **Document type:** government publication.

370   IE   ISSN 0021-1257
IRISH JOURNAL OF EDUCATION/IRIS EIREANNACH AN OIDEACHAIS. 1967. s-a. I£3($8) St. Patrick's College, Educational Research Centre, Dublin 9, Ireland. TEL 01-373789. FAX 01-378997. Ed. Thomas Kellaghan. adv.; bk.rev.; charts; stat.; cum.index every 2 yrs. circ. 1,000. (also avail. in microform from UMI; reprint service avail. from UMI) **Indexed:** Br.Educ.Ind., Cont.Pg.Educ., Educ.Tech.Abstr., Mult.Ed.Abstr., Psychol.Abstr., Res.High.Educ.Abstr., Sociol.Educ.Abstr., SOMA, SSCI. **Document type:** academic/scholarly publication.
—BLDSC (4571.950000); UMI.

370 297   PK   ISSN 0578-8056
ISLAMIC EDUCATION. (Text in English) 1968. bi-m. Rs.12($2.50) All-Pakistan Islamic Education Congress, 7 Friends Colony, Multan Rd., Lahore, Pakistan. Ed. Muzaffar Hussain. adv.; bk.rev.; bibl. circ. 500. **Indexed:** Cont.Pg.Educ.

370   US   ISSN 1058-1634
ISSUES AND CONCEPTS IN THE POSTMODERN THEORY OF EDUCATION. irreg. price varies. Peter Lang Publishing, Inc., 62 W. 45th St., 4th Fl., New York, NY 10036. TEL 212-302-7640. Eds. Joe Kincheloe, Shirley Steinberg. **Document type:** academic/scholarly publication.
Description: Focuses on issues and concepts in the postmodern theory of education.

ISSUES IN ACCOUNTING EDUCATION. see *BUSINESS AND ECONOMICS — Accounting*

370   US
ISSUES IN INTEGRATIVE STUDIES. 1982. a. $20 to individuals; institutions $30; students $10. Association for Integrative Studies (San Francisco), c/o Prof. Stanley Bailis, Ed., Social Science Program (Interdisciplinary), San Francisco State University, San Francisco, CA 94132. TEL 415-338-2982. adv.; bk.rev. circ. 400. (also avail. in microform) **Description:** Provides articles on interdisciplinary theory and method, integrative research, empirical evaluations of interdisciplinary curricular models and programs, cross-campus surveys on the status of interdisciplinary programs, and pedagogical approaches.

ISSUES IN LANGUAGE EDUCATION. see *LINGUISTICS*

370   IT   ISSN 0021-258X
ISTITUTO TECNICO; rassegna trimestrale di cultura. q. Casella Postale 4, 66034 Lanciano, Italy. circ. 1,000.

607 650.07 370   IT   ISSN 0393-2680
ISTRUZIONE TECNICA E PROFESSIONALE. 1937. q. L.55000. (Ministero della Pubblica Istruzione) Casa Editrice Fratelli Palombi, Via dei Gracchi 181-185, 00192 Rome, Italy. TEL 06-354456. FAX 06-319806. Dir. Donato P. Moro. adv.; bk.rev.; index. **Indexed:** C.I.S. Abstr.
Former titles (until 1973): Istruzione Tecnica (ISSN 0021-2679); (until 1967): Istruzione Tecnica e Professionale (ISSN 0535-899X)
Description: Covers life in a technical vocational school.

370 659.2   US   ISSN 0021-2717
IT STARTS IN THE CLASSROOM; the public relations newsletter for classroom teachers, principals and district administrators. 1941. m. (Sep.-May). $70. National School Public Relations Association, 1501 Lee Hwy., Ste. 201, Arlington, VA 22209. TEL 703-528-5840. Ed. Judi Cowan. circ. 3,000. **Document type:** newsletter.

ITALICA (MADISON). see *LITERATURE*

370   US   ISSN 0098-7549
IT'S HAPPENING. 1974. irreg. membership. National Association for Creative Children and Adults, 8080 Springvalley Dr., Cincinnati, OH 45236-1395. TEL 513-631-1777. Ed. Ann F. Isaacs. adv. circ. 2,000. (reprint service avail. from UMI)

370   CN   ISSN 0022-0701
L11
J E T: JOURNAL OF EDUCATIONAL THOUGHT/REVUE DE LA PENSEE EDUCATIVE. 1967. 3/yr. Can.$30 to individuals; institutions Can.$40. University of Calgary, Faculty of Education, Rm. 1304 Education Tower, Calgary, AB T2N 1N4, Canada. TEL 403-220-5629. FAX 403-282-5849. Ed. Emma Plattor. bk.rev.; bibl. circ. 575. (also avail. in microfilm from UMI; reprint service avail. from UMI) **Indexed:** C.I.J.E., Can.Educ.Ind., Can.Wom.Per.Ind., Cont.Pg.Educ., Educ.Admin.Abstr., Educ.Ind., Educ.Tech.Abstr., Lang.& Lang.Behav.Abstr., Mid.East: Abstr.& Ind., Mult.Ed.Abstr., Sociol.Educ.Abstr., SOMA, SSCI, Stud.Wom.Abstr.
—BLDSC (4973.260000); Faxon; UnCover; SWETS; UMI. CCC.
Formerly: Journal of Educational Thought.
Description: Promotes speculative, critical and historical research concerning the theory and practice of education in a variety of areas. *Refereed Serial*

370   GW   ISSN 0940-4961
J U M A. 1974. q. Tiefdruck Schwann Bagel GmbH, Frankfurterstr. 128, 51065 Cologne, Germany. TEL 0221-693061. FAX 0221-699344. Ed. Ch. Vogeler. circ. 700,000. **Document type:** academic/scholarly publication.
Former titles: Jugendmagazin (ISSN 0935-8927); Jugendscala (ISSN 0341-3071); Scala Jugendmagazin.
Description: Written for foreign youths learning German; edited in a readily understandable language.

370   GW
JAHRBUCH FUER LEHRER. 1981. a. DM.29.80. (G E W Baden-Wuerttemberg) Sueddeutscher Paedagogischer Verlag GmbH, Sudetenstr. 32, 71638 Ludwigsburg, Germany. TEL 07141-879080. FAX 07141-875105. circ. 20,000. **Document type:** academic/scholarly publication.

370   GW
▼**JAHRBUCH FUER PAEDAGOGIK.** 1992. a. DM.39. Peter Lang GmbH Europaeischer Verlag der Wissenschaften, Eschborner Landstr. 42-50, 60489 Frankfurt a.M., Germany. TEL 069-7807050. FAX 069-785893. Eds. Karl-Christoph Lingelbach, Hasko Zimmer. **Document type:** academic/scholarly publication.

370   UA
JAMI'AT AL-MANUFIYYAH. KULLIYYAT AL-TARBIYYAH. MAJALLAH/MENOUFIA UNIVERSITY. FACULTY OF EDUCATION. JOURNAL. (Text in Arabic) 1986. irreg. Jami'at al-Manufiyyah, Kulliyyat al-Tarbiyyah - Manoufia University, Faculty of Education, Shebeen El-Kom, Menoufia, Egypt.

370   JA   ISSN 0385-1990
JAPAN. NATIONAL INSTITUTE FOR EDUCATIONAL RESEARCH. NEWSLETTER; UNESCO-NIER programme for educational research in Asia. (Text in English) 1969. 3/yr. free. National Institute for Educational Research, 5-22, Shimo-Meguro 6-chome, Meguro-ku, Tokyo 153, Japan. TEL 03-714-0111. FAX 03-714-5294. Ed. T. Kanaya. circ. 1,000. (back issues avail.) **Document type:** newsletter.

370   JA   ISSN 0289-405X
JAPAN COMPARATIVE EDUCATION SOCIETY. BULLETIN. 1975. a. 3000 Yen($15) Japan Comparative Education Society, c/o National Institute for Education Research, 6-5-22, Shimomeguro, Meguro-Ku, Tokyo 153, Japan. Ed. Masaharu Amano. adv.; bk.rev. circ. 700. (back issues avail.)

JAPANESE JOURNAL OF EDUCATIONAL PSYCHOLOGY. see *PSYCHOLOGY*

370 150   XO   ISSN 0021-5805
JEDNOTNA SKOLA; journal for pedagogical theory and praxis and psychology. (Text in Slovak; summaries in English and Russian) 1945. 5/yr. $40. (Ministerstvo Skolstva Slovenskej Republiky) Slovenske Pedagogicke Nakladatelstvo, Sasinkova 5, 815 60 Bratislava, Slovakia. (Dist. by: PNS, s.p., Pribinova 25, 813 81 Bratislava, Slovakia) Ed. Jarmila Antosikova. circ. 1,500. **Indexed:** Psychol.Abstr.

JERSEY JOURNEYS. see *HISTORY — History Of North And South America*

JEWISH CURRENT EVENTS. see *ETHNIC INTERESTS*

377.9   US   ISSN 0021-6429
JEWISH EDUCATION. 1929. q. $15. Council for Jewish Education, 730 Broadway, 2nd Fl., New York, NY 10003-9540. TEL 212-529-2000. Ed. Alvin Schiff. adv.; bk.rev.; index, cum.index: 5 yrs. and 25 yrs. (vols.1-43). circ. 1,500. (also avail. in microform from UMI; reprint service avail. from UMI) **Indexed:** Cont.Pg.Educ., Educ.Ind., Ind.Jew.Per., Mid.East: Abstr.& Ind., Psychol.Abstr., Rel.& Theol.Abstr. (1981-).
—BLDSC (4668.352000); UnCover; UMI.

375   PL   ISSN 0446-7965
JEZYKI OBCE W SZKOLE. 1957. bi-m. $10. (Ministerstwo Edukacji Narodowej) Wydawnictwa Szkolne i Pedagogiczne, Pl. Dabrowskiego 8, 00-950 Warsaw, Poland. TEL 48-22-265451. FAX 48-22-266313. (Dist. by: Ars Polona-Ruch, Krakowskie Przedmiescie 7, Warsaw, Poland) Ed. Maria Gorzelak. circ. 6,200. **Indexed:** Bibl.Ling., Lang.Teach.& Ling.Abstr.
Incorporates: Jezyk Rosyjski (ISSN 0137-7647)
Description: Covers issues in teaching English, French, German, Russian and Latin in primary, secondary, and post-secondary schools. Discusses the latest achievements in general pedagogy and in the methodology of teaching individual languages, as well as linguistics, psychology, psycholinguistics, sociolinguistics, and literary and cultural studies.

370   CC
JIANGXI JIAOYU XUEYUAN XUEBAO/JIANGXI INSTITUTE OF EDUCATION. JOURNAL. (Text in Chinese) q. .Y4. Jiangxi Jiaoyu Xueyuan - Jiangxi Institute of Education, 87 Beijing Donglu, Nanchang, Jiangxi 330029, People's Republic of China.
Description: Presents basic theoretical research in secondary and adult education. Includes teaching materials and methods, education science and management, psychology, school history, philosophy, history, politics, economics, Marxist-Leninist theory, and political education.

EDUCATION

370   CC
JIAOYU KEXUE/SCIENCE OF EDUCATION. (Text in Chinese) q. Liaoning Shifan Daxue - Liaoning Normal University, Dalian, Liaoning 116022, People's Republic of China. TEL 401181. Ed. Zhao Hanzhang.

370   CC
JIAOYU PINGLUN/EDUCATION REVIEW. (Text in Chinese) bi-m. Y7.20. Fujian Jiaoyu Kexue Yanjiusuo - Fujian Institute of Education Science, No. 104, Wusi Lu, Fuzhou, Fujian 350003, People's Republic of China. TEL 556730. (Dist. overseas by: Jiangsu Publications Import & Export Corp., 56 Gao Yun Ling, Nanjing, Jiangsu, P.R.C.) (Co-sponsor: Fujian Jiaoyu Xuehui) Ed. Lin Tianqing.
Description: Publishes results of scientific research on education, introduces up-to-date educational information at home and abroad and presents institutional and personal experience.

370   CC
JIAOYU YANJIU/EDUCATIONAL RESEARCH. (Text in Chinese; table of contents in English) m. Y20.40($65.70) (Zhongyang Jiaoyu Kexue Yanjiusuo - Central Institute of Educational Science) Jiaoyu Yanjiu Bianjibu, 46, Beisanhuan Zhonglu, Beijing 100088, People's Republic of China. TEL 2011873. (Dist. outside China by: China International Book Trading Corp., P.O. Box 2820, Beijing, P.R.C.; Dist. in US by: China Books & Periodicals, Inc., 2929 24th St., San Francisco, CA 94110. TEL 415-282-2994) Ed. Zhao Deqiang. abstr.; bibl.; charts.

370   CC
JIAOYU ZHANWANG/EDUCATIONAL PROSPECTS. (Text in Chinese) q. Zhongguo Duiwai Fanyi Chuban Gongsi - China International Translation Publishing Company, 4 Taipingqiao Dajie, Beijing 100810, People's Republic of China. TEL 662134. Ed. Mei Zupei.

370   JA   ISSN 0912-9111
JISSEN KYOIKU/PRACTICAL TECHNOLOGY EDUCATION. (Text in Japanese) 1986. 3/yr. Jissen Kyoiku Kikaikei Kenkyukai - Society for the Practical Technology Education, Tokyo Shokugyo Kunren Tanki Daigakko, 32-1, Ogawa Nishi-cho 2-chome, Kodaira-shi, Tokyo 187, Japan.

JOHANN WILHELM KLEIN; literarische Zeitschrift fuer Blinde. see *HANDICAPPED — Visually Impaired*

370   FR   ISSN 0021-8073
JOURNAL DES INSTITUTEURS ET DES INSTITUTRICES; nouvelle presentation. vol. 112, 1991. 9/yr. 92 F. Librairie Fernand Nathan, 9 rue Mechain, 75680 Paris Cedex 14, France. adv.; bk.rev.; bibl.; illus.
—CCC.

JOURNAL FUER MATHEMATIK-DIDAKTIK; Zeitschrift der Gesellschaft fuer Didaktik der Mathematik. see *MATHEMATICS*

JOURNAL OF ADOLESCENT RESEARCH. see *CHILDREN AND YOUTH — About*

JOURNAL OF ADVENTIST EDUCATION. see *RELIGIONS AND THEOLOGY — Other Denominations And Sects*

370 100   US   ISSN 0021-8510
N1   CODEN: JAEDBT
JOURNAL OF AESTHETIC EDUCATION. 1966. q. $22 to individuals (foreign $29); institutions $35 (foreign $42). (University of Illinois at Urbana-Champaign) University of Illinois Press, 1325 S. Oak St., Champaign, IL 61820. TEL 217-333-0950. FAX 217-244-8082. Ed. Ralph A. Smith. adv.: B&W page $160; adv. contact: Cat Warren. bk.rev.; charts; illus.; index. circ. 1,250. (also avail. in microform from JAI,MIM,UMI; reprint service avail. from UMI) **Indexed:** Abstr.Engl.Stud., Artbibl.Mod., Arts & Hum.Cit.Ind., Bk.Rev.Ind. (1980-), C.I.J.E., Child.Bk.Rev.Ind. (1980-), Cont.Pg.Educ., Curr.Cont., Educ.Ind., Educ.Tech.Abstr., Film Lit.Ind. (1974-), Hum.Ind., Ind.Bk.Rev.Hum., Music Artic.Guide, Phil.Ind., Psychol.Abstr., SSCI. **Document type:** academic/scholarly publication.
—BLDSC (4919.984000); Faxon; UnCover; SWETS; UMI. **CCC.**
Refereed Serial

JOURNAL OF AMERICAN INDIAN EDUCATION. see *ETHNIC INTERESTS*

JOURNAL OF BEHAVIORAL EDUCATION. see *PSYCHOLOGY*

JOURNAL OF BELIEFS AND VALUES. see *RELIGIONS AND THEOLOGY*

JOURNAL OF BIOLOGICAL EDUCATION. see *BIOLOGY*

JOURNAL OF BLACK STUDIES. see *SOCIAL SCIENCES: COMPREHENSIVE WORKS*

JOURNAL OF BROADCASTING AND ELECTRONIC MEDIA. see *COMMUNICATIONS — Television And Cable*

JOURNAL OF CHRISTIAN EDUCATION. see *RELIGIONS AND THEOLOGY*

JOURNAL OF CHRISTIAN EDUCATION OF THE AFRICAN METHODIST EPISCOPAL CHURCH. see *RELIGIONS AND THEOLOGY — Protestant*

370   US   ISSN 0749-4025
LB1034
JOURNAL OF CLASSROOM INTERACTION. (Supplements avail.) 1965. s-a. $36 to institutions in N. America; elsewhere $33; individuals in N. America $31; elsewhere $40, for 2 yrs. c/o H. Jerome Freiberg, Ed., Farish Hall, Rm. 350, College of Education, University of Houston, Houston, TX 77204-5872. TEL 713-743-4953. FAX 713-743-9870. adv.; bk.rev.; abstr.; bibl.; charts; stat. circ. 1,000. (processed; also avail. in microform from UMI; reprint service avail. from UMI) **Indexed:** C.I.J.E., Cont.Pg.Educ., Educ.Tech.Abstr., ERIC, Mult.Ed.Abstr., Psychol.Abstr. **Document type:** academic/scholarly publication.
—BLDSC (4958.369700); Faxon; UnCover; SWETS; UMI.
Formerly: Classroom Interaction Newsletter (ISSN 0009-8485)

370   US   ISSN 0022-0132
LB1029.C6
JOURNAL OF COOPERATIVE EDUCATION. 1964. 3/yr. $30 (foreign $45). Cooperative Education Association, Inc., 11710 Beltsville Dr., Ste. 520, Beltsville, MD 20705-3102. TEL 301-572-2329. FAX 301-572-3916. Ed. Jim Wilson. stat.; circ. 3,000 (controlled). (tabloid format; also avail. in microform from UMI; reprint service avail. from UMI) **Indexed:** C.I.J.E., Cont.Pg.Educ., Educ.Ind., Pers.Lit.
—BLDSC (4965.280000); Faxon; UnCover; UMI.

364 370   US   ISSN 0022-0159
HV8875
JOURNAL OF CORRECTIONAL EDUCATION.* 1949. q. $35 to individuals; libraries $50; institutions $75. (Correctional Educational Association) Karcz, McGing & Associates, Inc., 45 Syndicate St. S, St. Paul, MN 55105-2612. TEL 612-699-5403. (Subscr. to: 8025 Laurel Lakes Court, Laurel, MD 20707) Ed. Stan A. Karcz. adv.; bk.rev.; bibl.; charts; illus.; tr.lit.; index, cum.index: 1959-1966. circ. 3,300. (also avail. in microform from UMI; reprint service avail. from UMI) **Indexed:** C.I.J.E., Cont.Pg.Educ., Crim.Just.Abstr., ERIC.
Description: Covers topics in the field of correctional education.

150 370   US   ISSN 0022-0175
BF408
JOURNAL OF CREATIVE BEHAVIOR. 1967. q. $36 (Canada and Mexico $39; elsewhere $46). Creative Education Foundation, Inc., 1050 Union Rd., Buffalo, NY 14224. TEL 716-675-3181. FAX 716-675-3209. Ed. Dean Keith Simonton. adv.; bk.rev.; bibl.; charts; illus.; stat.; index. circ. 2,000. (also avail. in microform from UMI; reprint service avail. from UMI) **Indexed:** Adol.Ment.Hlth.Abstr., ASSIA, C.I.J.E., Commun.Abstr., Cont.Pg.Educ., Curr.Cont., Educ.Ind., Except.Child.Educ.Abstr., Lang.& Lang.Behav.Abstr., Pers.Lit., Psychol.Abstr., Soc.Sci.Ind., Soc.Work Res.& Abstr., SSCI.
—BLDSC (4965.500000); Faxon; UnCover; SWETS; UMI.

JOURNAL OF CRIMINAL JUSTICE EDUCATION. see *CRIMINOLOGY AND LAW ENFORCEMENT*

JOURNAL OF DRUG EDUCATION. see *DRUG ABUSE AND ALCOHOLISM*

370   US   ISSN 0022-0574
L11   CODEN: JEBUA
JOURNAL OF EDUCATION. 1875. 3/yr. $26 to individuals (Canada and foreign $28); institutions $28 (Canada and foreign $31); students $10. Trustees of Boston University, School of Education, 605 Commonwealth Ave., Boston, MA 02215. TEL 617-353-3230. FAX 617-353-3924. Ed.Bd. adv.; bk.rev.; charts; illus. circ. 2,000. (also avail. in microform from UMI,MIM; reprint service avail. from UMI) **Indexed:** Acad.Ind., Bk.Rev.Ind. (1977-), C.I.J.E., Child.Bk.Rev.Ind. (1977-), Commun.Abstr., Cont.Pg.Educ., Educ.Admin.Abstr., Educ.Ind., Educ.Tech.Abstr., Lang.& Lang.Behav.Abstr., Mid.East: Abstr.& Ind., Mult.Ed.Abstr., Psychol.Abstr., Sp.Ed.Needs Abstr., Stud.Wom.Abstr. **Document type:** academic/scholarly publication.
—BLDSC (4973.100000); Faxon; UnCover; SWETS; UMI.

370 150   II   ISSN 0022-0590
L61
JOURNAL OF EDUCATION AND PSYCHOLOGY. (Text in English) 1943. q. Rs.25($10) individuals; Rs. 30 institutions. Sardar Patel University, Department of Education, Vallabh Vidyanagar, Gujarat, India. Ed. Jayendradave. adv.; bk.rev.; index. circ. 300. **Indexed:** Curr.Cont.

370.15   US   ISSN 1047-4412
LB2799
JOURNAL OF EDUCATIONAL AND PSYCHOLOGICAL CONSULTATION. 1990. q. $36 to individuals (foreign $61); institutions $165 (foreign $190). (Association for Educational and Psychological Consultants) Lawrence Erlbaum Associates, Inc., 365 Broadway, Hillsdale, NJ 07642. TEL 201-666-4110. FAX 201-666-2394. Ed. Howard Margolis. **Document type:** academic/scholarly publication.
—BLDSC (4973.154050).
Description: Serves as a forum for the exchange of ideas, theories, and research among the fields of school psychology, special education, and reading.
Refereed Serial

371.26   US   ISSN 0022-0655
LB1131.A1   CODEN: JEDMAA
JOURNAL OF EDUCATIONAL MEASUREMENT. 1964. q. $45 to individuals; institutions $50. National Council on Measurement in Education, 1230 17th St., N.W., Washington, DC 20036-3078. TEL 202-223-9318. FAX 202-775-1824. Ed. James Algina. adv.; bk.rev.; cum.index. circ. 3,200. (also avail. in microform from UMI; reprint service avail. from UMI) **Indexed:** C.I.J.E., Chic.Per.Ind., Cont.Pg.Educ., Curr.Cont., Educ.Ind., Lang.& Lang.Behav.Abstr., Pers.Lit., Psychol.Abstr., Res.High.Educ.Abstr., SSCI. **Document type:** academic/scholarly publication.
—BLDSC (4973.157000); Faxon; UnCover; SWETS; UMI.
Supersedes: National Council on Measurement in Education. Yearbook.

JOURNAL OF EDUCATIONAL MEDIA AND LIBRARY SCIENCES. see *LIBRARY AND INFORMATION SCIENCES*

JOURNAL OF EDUCATIONAL PUBLIC RELATIONS; the school PR magazine. see *COMMUNICATIONS*

370   US   ISSN 0022-0671
L11   CODEN: JEDRAP
THE JOURNAL OF EDUCATIONAL RESEARCH. 1920. bi-m. $35 to individuals; institutions $70. (Helen Dwight Reid Educational Foundation) Heldref Publications, 1319 18th St., N.W., Washington, DC 20036-1802. TEL 202-296-6267. FAX 202-296-5149. Ed. Jeanne Bebo. adv. contact: Raymond Rallo. bib.; charts; index. circ. 3,500. (also avail. in microform from PMC; reprint service avail.) **Indexed:** C.I.J.E., Child Devel.Abstr., Cont.Pg.Educ., Curr.Cont., Educ.Admin.Abstr., Educ.Ind., Educ.Tech.Abstr., Except.Child Educ.Abstr., G.Soc.Sci.& Rel.Per.Lit., High.Educ.Curr.Aware.Bull., Lang.& Lang.Behav Abstr., Mult.Ed.Abstr., Psychol.Abstr., Res.High.Educ.Abstr., Sociol.Abstr., Sociol.Educ.Abstr., SOMA, SSCI, Stud.Wom.Abstr. **Document type:** academic/scholarly publication.
—Faxon; UnCover; SWETS; UMI. **CCC.**
Refereed Serial

EDUCATION

370   MY   ISSN 0126-6020
LA1235
JOURNAL OF EDUCATIONAL RESEARCH/JURNAL PENDIDIKAN. (Text in English, Malay) 1970. a. $15. Penerbit Universiti Kebangsaan Malaysia, 43600 UKM Bangi Selangor, Malaysia. TEL 8250001. TELEX UNIKEB-MA-31496. **Document type:** academic/scholarly publication.
    Description: Contains research, reports, commentaries and articles in the field of teaching and learning: primary, secondary and higher education.

373   II   ISSN 0022-068X
JOURNAL OF EDUCATIONAL RESEARCH AND EXTENSION. (Text in English) 1963. q. Rs.35($15) Sri Ramakrishna Mission Vidyalaya College of Education, Sri Ramakrishna Vidyalaya P.O., Coimbatore 641020, Tamil Nadu, India. Ed. Swami Bhaktirupananda. adv.; bk.rev.; abstr.; index. circ. 600. **Indexed:** Cont.Pg.Educ.
—BLDSC (4973.250000).

370 630   US   ISSN 0022-0140
JOURNAL OF EXTENSION. (Not avail in print) 1963. q. free. (National Association of Land-Grant Colleges and State Universities) Virginia Tech, 233 Smyth Hall, Blacksburg, VA 24061-0452.
TEL 703-231-7880. E-mail: almanac@joe.uwex.edu. (Co-sponsor: Extension Committee on Organization) Ed. Michael Lambur. bk.rev.; bibl.; index, cum.index. circ. 12,500. (also avail. in microform from UMI; reprint service avail. from UMI) **Indexed:** Abstr.Soc.Work., C.I.J.E., Cont.Pg.Educ., Curr.Cont., Farm & Garden Ind., Lang.& Lang.Behav.Abstr., Rural Recreat.Tour.Abstr., Soc.Work Res.& Abstr., Sociol.Abstr., World Agri.Econ.& Rural Sociol.Abstr.
●Available only online.
—BLDSC (4983.200000); Faxon; UnCover; UMI.
    Formerly: Journal of Cooperative Extension.
    Description: Covers successful educational applications, original and applied research findings, scholarly opinions, educational resources, and challenges on issues of critical importance to adult educators.

378   US   ISSN 0021-3667
L11
JOURNAL OF GENERAL EDUCATION. Short title: J G E. 1946. q. $20 to individuals (foreign $27); institutions $30 (foreign $35). Pennsylvania State University Press, Barbara Bldg., Ste. C, 820 N. University Dr., University Park, PA 16802-1003. TEL 814-865-1327. FAX 814-863-1408. Ed. James Ratcliff. adv.; bk.rev.; charts; index. circ. 1,000. (also avail. in microform from UMI; reprint service avail. from UMI,KTO) **Indexed:** Abstr.Engl.Stud., Adol.Ment.Hlth.Abstr., Amer.Hist.& Life, Bk.Rev.Ind. (1965-1988), C.I.J.E., Child.Bk.Rev.Ind. (1965-1988), Cont.Pg.Educ., Educ.Ind., Except.Child.Educ.Abstr., Hist.Abstr., Lang.& Lang.Behav.Abstr., M.L.A. **Document type:** academic/scholarly publication.
—Faxon; UnCover; SWETS. **CCC**
    Refereed Serial

JOURNAL OF GEOGRAPHY. see *GEOGRAPHY*

JOURNAL OF HUMANISTIC EDUCATION AND DEVELOPMENT. see *PSYCHOLOGY*

370   II   ISSN 0377-0435
JOURNAL OF INDIAN EDUCATION. (Text in English) 1975. bi-m. Rs.16($17) National Council of Educational Research and Training, Publication Department, Sri Aurbindo Marg, New Delhi 110016, India. TEL 662708. (Dist. by: International Publications Service, 303 Park Ave. S., New York, NY 10010) Ed. R.P. Singh. circ. 1,200. **Indexed:** Cont.Pg.Educ.
—UnCover.
    Supersedes: N I E Journal (ISSN 0027-6634)

150 370   US   ISSN 0094-1956
LB1051
JOURNAL OF INSTRUCTIONAL PSYCHOLOGY. 1974. q. $25. V.U. Publishing Co., Box 8826, Mobile, AL 36608. TEL 205-343-1878. Ed. George E. Uhlig. bk.rev. circ. 400. (also avail. in microform from UMI; back issues avail.; reprint service avail. from UMI) **Indexed:** Educ.Ind., ERIC, Psychol.Abstr., Sociol.Abstr., Sp.Ed.Needs Abstr. **Document type:** academic/scholarly publication.
—BLDSC (5007.513000); Faxon; UnCover; UMI.

370   US   ISSN 1060-6041
▼**JOURNAL OF INVITATIONAL THEORY AND PRACTICE.** 1992. s-a. $10 to non-members. International Alliance for Invitational Education, School of Education, University of North Carolina, Greensboro, Greensboro, NC 27412-5001. TEL 919-334-5100. FAX 919-334-5060. Ed. John J. Schmidt. bk.rev. circ. 2,000. **Document type:** academic/scholarly publication.
    Description: Invitational theory and practice in schools and other organizations. Theory founded on self-concept and perceptional psychology.

JOURNAL OF LAW AND EDUCATION. see *LAW*

JOURNAL OF LEGAL EDUCATION. see *LAW*

150 370   US   ISSN 0749-596X
BF455.A1
JOURNAL OF MEMORY AND LANGUAGE. 1962. bi-m. $205 (foreign $249). Academic Press, Inc., Journal Division, 525 B St., Ste. 1900, San Diego, CA 92101-4495. TEL 619-230-1840. FAX 619-699-6800. (Subscr. to: Box 620000, Orlando, FL 32891-8340. TEL 800-543-9534) Ed. George Murphy. adv.; charts; illus.; index. (back issues avail.) **Indexed:** Abstr.Anthropol., ASSIA, Bibl.Ling., C.I.J.E., Child Devel.Abstr., Commun.Abstr., Cont.Pg.Educ., Curr.Cont., Ergon.Abstr., High.Educ.Curr.Aware.Bull., Lang.& Lang.Behav.Abstr. (1972-), Lang.Teach.& Ling.Abstr., M.L.A., Mid.East: Abstr.& Ind., Psychol.Abstr., Soc.Sci.Ind., SSCI. **Document type:** academic/scholarly publication.
—BLDSC (5017.630000); Faxon; UnCover; SWETS. **CCC**
    Formerly: Journal of Verbal Learning and Verbal Behavior (ISSN 0022-5371)
    Description: Contributes to the formulation of scientific issues and theories in the areas of memory, language comprehension and production, and cognitive processes.

JOURNAL OF MOTOR BEHAVIOR. see *PSYCHOLOGY*

JOURNAL OF MUSIC TEACHER EDUCATION. see *MUSIC*

370 301.451   US   ISSN 0022-2984
LC2701   CODEN: JNEEAK
JOURNAL OF NEGRO EDUCATION. 1932. q. $16 to individuals; institutions $20. Howard University, School of Education, 2600 Sixth St., N.W., Washington, DC 20059. TEL 202-806-8120. FAX 202-806-8130. Ed. Dr. Sylvia T. Johnson. adv.; bk.rev.; index, cum.index: 1963-1979; 1980-1989. circ. 2,000. (also avail. in microform from MIM,UMI,PMC; reprint service avail. from UMI,KTO) **Indexed:** Amer.Hist.& Life, Bk.Rev.Ind. (1965-), C.I.J.E., Child.Bk.Rev.Ind. (1965-), Cont.Pg.Educ., Curr.Cont., Educ.Admin.Abstr., Educ.Ind., Except.Child.Educ.Abstr., Hist.Abstr., Ind.Sel.Per., Lang.& Lang.Behav.Abstr., Mag.Ind., P.A.I.S., Psychol.Abstr., Sage Fam.Stud.Abstr., Soc.Work Res.& Abstr., Sociol.Abstr., Sociol.Educ.Abstr., SSCI. **Document type:** academic/scholarly publication, abstracting/indexing.
—BLDSC (5021.395000); Faxon; UnCover; UMI.
    Description: Collects and disseminates information about the education of blacks and minorities in the USA.

JOURNAL OF NORTHERN LUZON; a semi-annual research forum. see *SOCIOLOGY*

370   US   ISSN 0022-3336
LB3481
JOURNAL OF OUTDOOR EDUCATION. 1966. a. free. Northern Illinois University, Department of Outdoor Teacher Education, Taft Field Campus, Box 299, Oregon, IL 61061. TEL 815-732-2111. Ed. Robert L. Vogl. bk.rev.; circ. 2,500 (controlled). (also avail. in microform from UMI; reprint service avail. from UMI) **Indexed:** C.I.J.E., Educ.Ind.
—Faxon; UnCover.

370 658.3   US   ISSN 0920-525X
LB2838
JOURNAL OF PERSONNEL EVALUATION IN EDUCATION. 1987. q. fl.324($169.50) (effective 1994). Kluwer Academic Publishers Boston, Box 358, Accord Sta., Hingham, MA 02018-0358. TEL 617-871-6600. FAX 617-871-6528. TELEX 200190. (Dist. outside N. America by: Kluwer Academic Publishers Group, P.O. Box 322, 3300 AH Dordrecht, Netherlands. TEL 31-78-524400. FAX 31-78-524474) Ed. Edward F. Iwanicki. adv. (also avail. in microform from UMI; back issues avail.; reprint service avail. from SWZ,UMI) **Indexed:** High.Educ.Abstr., Sociol.Educ.Abstr. **Document type:** academic/scholarly publication.
—BLDSC (5030.970000); SWETS; UMI. **CCC**
    Description: Publishes research and applied scholarship on current issues in the evaluation of teacher and administrator performance.
    Refereed Serial

370   US   ISSN 0890-913X
HB95
JOURNAL OF PRIVATE ENTERPRISE. 1985. a. $12. Association of Private Enterprise Education, 112 Business Administration Bldg., University of Tennessee, Martin, Martin, TN 38238.
TEL 901-587-7208. FAX 901-587-7228. Ed. J.R. Clark. bk.rev. circ. 750. (back issues avail.) **Document type:** academic/scholarly publication.
    Description: Brings together scholars in the fields of economics, management, entrepreneurship, marketing, finance, ethics, religion and education who have done research on topics pertaining to the American system of private enterprise.

372   US   ISSN 0022-4103
L11   CODEN: JRDNB3
JOURNAL OF READING. 1957. 8/yr. (Sep.-May; Dec. & Jan. combined). $38 in developed countries; developing countries $19. International Reading Association, Inc., 800 Barksdale Rd., Box 8139, Newark, DE 19714-8139. TEL 302-731-1600. FAX 302-731-1057. TELEX 5106002813READING. Ed. Janet R. Binkley. adv. contact: Linda Hunter. bk.rev.; illus.; index. circ. 20,000. (also avail. in microform from UMI; reprint service avail. from UMI) **Indexed:** Acad.Ind., Bk.Rev.Ind. (1976-), C.I.J.E., Chic.Per.Ind., Child.Bk.Rev.Ind. (1976-), Cont.Pg.Educ., Curr.Cont., Educ.Ind., Except.Child.Educ.Abstr., Lang.& Lang.Behav.Abstr., Mid.East: Abstr.& Ind., Sociol.Abstr., Sp.Ed.Needs Abstr., SSCI. **Document type:** academic/scholarly publication.
—BLDSC (5047.500000); Faxon; UnCover; SWETS; UMI. **CCC**
    Formerly: Journal of Developmental Reading (ISSN 0731-3667)
    Description: Covers adolescent and adult readers.
    Refereed Serial

JOURNAL OF READING BEHAVIOR. see *LINGUISTICS*

370   US   ISSN 0022-426X
LB1028.A1   CODEN: JRDMBY
JOURNAL OF RESEARCH AND DEVELOPMENT IN EDUCATION. 1967. q. $15 to individuals; institutions $25. University of Georgia, College of Education, 427 Tucker Hall, Athens, GA 30602.
TEL 404-542-1154. Ed. A. Guy Larkins. index. circ. 1,300. (also avail. in microform from UMI; reprint service avail. from UMI) **Indexed:** Adol.Ment.Hlth.Abstr., Behav.Abstr., Bull.Signal., C.I.J.E., Comput.Lit.Ind., Cont.Pg.Educ., Educ.Admin.Abstr., Educ.Ind., Educ.Tech.Abstr., Lang.& Lang.Behav.Abstr., Mid.East: Abstr.& Ind., Mult.Ed.Abstr., Psychol.Abstr., SOMA, SSCI, Stud.Wom.Abstr. **Document type:** academic/scholarly publication.
—BLDSC (5052.002000); Faxon; UnCover; SWETS; UMI.
    Description: Presents articles on a wide variety of topics in education.
    Refereed Serial

370 362.7   US   ISSN 0256-8543
LB1028
JOURNAL OF RESEARCH IN CHILDHOOD EDUCATION; an international journal of research on the education of children. 1986. 2/yr. $38 to non-members; members $28; institutions $78 (includes Childhood Education). Association for Childhood Education International, 11501 Georgia Ave., Ste. 312, Wheaton, MD 20902. TEL 301-942-2443. Ed. Steven B. Silvern. adv. **Indexed:** Psychol.Abstr. **Document type:** trade publication.
—BLDSC (5052.003500); Faxon; UnCover; SWETS; UMI.
  Description: Development from infancy through early adolesence.

372   UK   ISSN 0141-0423
LB1050.6
JOURNAL OF RESEARCH IN READING. (Text and summaries in English and French) 1978. s-a. £18.50($43.50) to individuals; institutions £30($69.50). (United Kingdom Reading Association) Basil Blackwell Ltd., 108 Cowley Rd., Oxford OX4 1JF, England. TEL 0865-791100. FAX 0865-791347. TELEX 837022-OXBOOK-G. Ed. D. Vincent. adv.; bk.rev.; abstr.; bibl.; charts. circ. 1,250. (also avail. in microform from UMI; reprint service avail. from UMI) **Indexed:** Br.Educ.Ind., C.I.J.E., Child Devel.Abstr., Cont.Pg.Educ., Educ.Tech.Abstr., High.Educ.Curr.Aware.Bull., Lang. & Lang. Behav.Abstr., Lang.Teach.& Ling.Abstr., Psychol.Abstr.
—BLDSC (5052.027000); UnCover; SWETS; UMI. CCC.

JOURNAL OF RESEARCH IN SCIENCE TEACHING. see *SCIENCES: COMPREHENSIVE WORKS*

JOURNAL OF SCHOOL HEALTH. see *PUBLIC HEALTH AND SAFETY*

370 500   US   ISSN 1059-0145
Q183.3.A1   CODEN: JSEEEP
▼**JOURNAL OF SCIENCE EDUCATION AND TECHNOLOGY.** 1992. q. $125 (foreign $145) (effective 1994). Plenum Publishing Corp., 233 Spring St., New York, NY 10013-1578. TEL 212-620-8000. FAX 212-463-0742. TELEX 23-421139. Ed. Karen C. Cohen. adv. **Document type:** academic/scholarly publication.
—BLDSC (5054.980000); Faxon; UnCover; UMI. CCC.
  Description: Forum for the discussion of issues and policies relating to improvement of U.S. science education at all levels, including legislative, administrative, and implementation issues.
  Refereed Serial

371.8 155.3   US   ISSN 0161-4576
HQ1   CODEN: JSETE2
JOURNAL OF SEX EDUCATION AND THERAPY. 1976. q. $30 to individuals (foreign $45); institutions $70 (foreign $85) (effective 1994). (American Association of Sex Educators, Counselors and Therapists) Guilford Publications, Inc., 72 Spring St., 4th Fl., New York, NY 10012. TEL 212-431-9800. FAX 212-966-6708. Ed. R. Taylor Segraves. adv.; bk.rev. circ. 3,000. (reprint service avail. from UMI) **Indexed:** Abstr.Anthropol., Cont.Pg.Educ., Curr.Lit.Fam.Plan., Mid.East: Abstr.& Ind., Psychol.Abstr., Soc.Work Res.& Abstr.
—BLDSC (5064.019000); Faxon; UnCover; UMI. CCC.
  Description: Presents research and clinical articles, field reports, and reviews of new materials.
  Refereed Serial

JOURNAL OF SOCIAL WORK EDUCATION. see *SOCIAL SERVICES AND WELFARE*

370   UK   ISSN 0140-671X
JOURNAL OF SOURCES IN EDUCATIONAL HISTORY. 1978. 3/yr. $338 (effective 1994). Carfax Publishing Co., P.O. Box 25, Abingdon, Oxon. OX14 3UE, England. TEL 44-235-555335. FAX 44-235-553559. (U.S. subscr. to: Carfax Publishing Co., Box 2025, Dunnellon, FL 34430-2025) Ed. Keith Dent. (also avail. in microfiche; back issues avail.) **Indexed:** Res.High.Educ.Abstr. **Document type:** abstracting/indexing.
—BLDSC (5065.950000). CCC.

370   UK   ISSN 0964-0606
▼**JOURNAL OF TEACHER DEVELOPMENT.** 1992. 3/yr. £19 (Europe £20; elsewhere £21.50) to individuals; institutions £37(Europe £38; elsewhere £43). Longman Group UK Ltd., Westgate House, 6th Fl., The High, Harlow, Essex CM20 1YR, England. TEL 0279-442601. FAX 0279-444501. (Subscr. to: Journals Dept., Fourth Ave., Harlow, Essex CM19 4AA, England. TEL 0279-623924) Ed. R. Deem. circ. 1,000. **Document type:** academic/scholarly publication.
—BLDSC (5068.284500).

370 382   US   ISSN 0897-5930
HD62.4   CODEN: JTIBE9
JOURNAL OF TEACHING IN INTERNATIONAL BUSINESS. 1989. q. $36 to individuals; institutions $48; libraries $60. Haworth Press, Inc., 10 Alice St., Binghamton, NY 13904. TEL 607-722-5857; 800-342-9678. FAX 607-722-1424. TELEX 4932599. Ed. Erdener Kaynak. adv.; bk.rev. (also avail. in microfiche from UMI; reprint service avail. from HAW) **Indexed:** Cont.Pg.Manage., Ind.Per.Art.Relat.Law, Tech.Educ.Abstr.
—BLDSC (5068.285600).
  Description: Aimed at practicing international business educators and curriculum developers - focuses on successful methods and techniques for better business teaching.
  Refereed Serial

JOURNAL OF TEACHING PRACTICE. see *EDUCATION — Teaching Methods And Curriculum*

808.025   US   ISSN 0047-2816
T11   CODEN: JTWCAA
JOURNAL OF TECHNICAL WRITING AND COMMUNICATION. 1971. q. $36 to individuals; institutions $107. Baywood Publishing Co., Inc., 26 Austin Ave., Box 337, Amityville, NY 11701. TEL 516-691-1270. FAX 516-691-1770. Ed. David Carson. bk.rev.; abstr.; charts; illus. (back issues avail.) **Indexed:** Commun.Abstr., Cont.Pg.Educ., Curr.Cont., Eng.Ind., Int.Aerosp.Abstr., Lang.& Lang.Behav.Abstr., Sp.Ed.Needs Abstr., SSCI. **Document type:** academic/scholarly publication.
—BLDSC (5068.295000); Faxon; UnCover; SWETS.
  Description: Contains essays on oral, as well as written communication, for purposes from pure research to needs of business and industry.
  Refereed Serial

370.15 150   US   ISSN 1050-8406
L11   CODEN: JLSBE3
JOURNAL OF THE LEARNING SCIENCES, a journal of ideas and their applications. 1991. q. $37.50 to individuals (foreign $62.50); institutions $120 (foreign $145). Lawrence Erlbaum Associates, Inc., 365 Broadway, Hillsdale, NJ 07642. TEL 201-666-4110. FAX 201-666-2394. Ed. Janet L. Kolodner. **Document type:** academic/scholarly publication.
—BLDSC (5010.231000); UnCover.
  Description: Provides a multidisciplinary forum for the presentation and discussion of research on teaching and learning.
  Refereed Serial

JOURNAL OF VISUAL IMPAIRMENT & BLINDNESS. see *HANDICAPPED — Visually Impaired*

370   DK
JOURNAL OF WORLD EDUCATION. (Text in English) 1970. q. DKK 100. Association for World Education, Nordenfjord World University, 7752 Snedsted, Thy, Denmark. Ed. Aage R. Nielsen. adv.; bk.rev. circ. 3,000. (back issues avail.)

JUCO REVIEW. see *SPORTS AND GAMES*

370   DK   ISSN 0107-8887
JULEHILSEN. 1962. a. Elevforeningen for Hoven Ungdomsskole, 6880 Tarm, Denmark. illus.

370   LB
JULIUS C. STEVENS ANNUAL LECTURES IN EDUCATION.* irreg. University of Liberia, William V.S. Tubman Teachers College, Monrovia, Liberia.

371.3   UK   ISSN 0309-3484
JUNIOR EDUCATION. 1977. m. £19.50 (foreign £33.20). Scholastic Publications Ltd., Villiers House, Clarendon Ave., Leamington Spa, Warks CV32 5PR, England. TEL 0925-887799. FAX 0926-883331. TELEX 312138 SPLSG. Ed. Terry Saunders. adv.; bk.rev.; illus. circ. 36,650. **Indexed:** Cont.Pg.Educ., Ind.Child.Mag. **Document type:** academic/scholarly publication.
—BLDSC (5075.137000); UMI.
  Incorporates (in Mar. 1982): Pictorial Education (ISSN 0048-4121); **Supersedes:** Teachers World (ISSN 0049-3139)

371.3   UK   ISSN 0966-7113
JUNIOR FOCUS. 1927. 6/yr. £14.50 (foreign £16). Scholastic Publications Ltd., Villiers House, Clarendon Ave., Leamington Spa, Warks. CV32 5PR, England. FAX 043-28-2205. TELEX 312138 SPLSG. Ed. Margot O'Keeffe. illus. circ. 23,395. (also avail. in microform from UMI) **Document type:** academic/scholarly publication.
—UMI.
  Former titles: Junior Projects (ISSN 0269-9532); Junior Education Special (ISSN 0262-7515); (until Mar. 1982): Pictorial Education Special (ISSN 0142-4963); Pictorial Education Quarterly (ISSN 0048-413X)

JUNIOR SCHOLASTIC. see *CHILDREN AND YOUTH — For*

370   AT
JUNIOR TOPICS. 1982. bi-m. Aus.$24 (foreign Aus.$35). Ashton Scholastic Pty. Ltd., Railway Crescent, Lisarow, N.S.W. 2250, Australia. TEL 043 28-3555. FAX 043-28-2205. (Subscr. to: P.O. Box 579, Gosford, N.S.W. 2250, Australia. TEL 02-4164000) Ed. Ann Bingaman. circ. 8,000.

JURIMETRICS JOURNAL; journal of law, science and technology. see *LAW*

JURISTISCHE SCHULUNG; Zeitschrift fuer Studium und praktische Ausbildung mit JUS-Kartei und JUS-Lernbogen. see *LAW*

JUSTICE AND THE J.P. see *CRIMINOLOGY AND LAW ENFORCEMENT*

150 300 370   FI   ISSN 0075-4625
        CODEN: JYSEAV
JYVASKYLA STUDIES IN EDUCATION, PSYCHOLOGY AND SOCIAL RESEARCH. (Text in English or Finnish; summaries in English) 1962. irreg. price varies. Jyvaskylan Yliopisto - University of Jyvaskyla, Library, PL 35, 4C100 Jyvaskyla 10, Finland. TEL 941-601-211. FAX 603-371. TELEX 28219JYK SF. Ed.Bd. circ. 450. **Indexed:** Cont.Pg.Educ., Psychol.Abstr. **Document type:** monographic series.

370 613.7   US   ISSN 1071-2577
K A H P E R D JOURNAL. 1964. 2/yr. $5 per no. Kentucky Association for Health, Physical Education, Recreation and Dance, c/o Burch E. Oglesby, Western Kentucky University, Bowling Green, KY 42101. TEL 502-742-3347. TELEX 745-6474. Ed. Dr. William Meadors. adv.; bk.rev.; bibl. circ. 1,000. **Indexed:** Sportsearch (1985-).
  Formerly: K A H P E R Journal (ISSN 0022-7269)

372   II
K A P T UNION PATHRIKA. (Text in Malayalam & English) 1975. m. Rs.20. Kerala Aided Primary Teachers' Union, Carrier Station Rd., Cochin 682016, Kerala, India. Ed. M.K. Kurian. adv. circ. 3,500.
  Supersedes: Vijnanevedi.

370   US   ISSN 0164-3959
K E A NEWS. 1964. 10/yr. $5. Kentucky Education Association, 401 Capitol Ave., Frankfort, KY 40601-2836. TEL 800-231-4532. FAX 502-227-8062. Ed. Mary Ann Blankenship. illus. circ. 36,000. **Document type:** newsletter.
  Formerly: Kentucky Education News (ISSN 0023-0170)

377.8   AU
K L O E IMPULSE. 1906. q. S.50. Katholische Lehrerschaft Oesterreichs, Stephansplatz 5-2-4, A-1010 Vienna, Austria. adv.; bk.rev.; bibl.; charts; film rev.; illus.; stat.; index. circ. 15,000.
  Formerly: Oesterreichische Paedagogische Warte (ISSN 0029-9383)

EDUCATION

KAGAKU KYOIKU KENKYU/JOURNAL OF SCIENCE EDUCATION IN JAPAN. see *SCIENCES: COMPREHENSIVE WORKS*

KAGAKU TO KYOIKU/CHEMICAL EDUCATION. see *CHEMISTRY*

KAGAWA DAIGAKU KYOIKUGAKUBU KENKYU HOKOKU. DAI-2-BU/KAGAWA UNIVERSITY. FACULTY OF EDUCATION. MEMOIRS. PART 2. see *SCIENCES: COMPREHENSIVE WORKS*

KAGOSHIMA DAIGAKU KYOIKUGAKUBU KENKYU KIYO. SHIZEN KAGAKU HEN/KAGOSHIMA UNIVERSITY. FACULTY OF EDUCATION. BULLETIN. NATURAL SCIENCE. see *SCIENCES: COMPREHENSIVE WORKS*

372   US   ISSN 0893-6226
KALEIDOSCOPE (MADISON). 1986. 9/yr. $15 (foreign $18). Wisconsin Academy of Sciences, Arts and Letters, 1922 University Ave., Madison, WI 53705. TEL 608-263-1692. FAX 608-265-3039. Ed. Linda Pils. circ. 650. (back issues avail.) **Document type:** academic/scholarly publication.
  Description: Instructs K-3 grade teachers on how to incorporate simple science concepts and activities into a daily curriculum.

370   JA
KANAZAWA UNIVERSITY. FACULTY OF EDUCATION. BULLETIN: HUMANITIES, SOCIAL AND EDUCATIONAL SCIENCES/KANAZAWA DAIGAKU KYOIKUGAKUBU KIYO. JINBUN, SHAKAI KYOIKU KAGAKU. (Text in Japanese; summaries and some articles in English) irreg. Kanazawa Daigaku, Kyoikugakubu - Kanazawa University, Faculty of Education, 1-1 Marunouchi, Kanazawa-shi, Ishikawa-ken 920, Japan.

377.8   NE   ISSN 0022-8354
KANDELAAR. 1947. m. fl.47.50. Nederlandse Vereniging van Vrijzinnige Zondagsscholen, c/o Mevr M. Spyker v.d. Laan, Maskweg 28, 6871 kx Renkuu, Netherlands. Ed. C. van Santen-Teeling. bk.rev. circ. 1,200.

KANSAS BIOLOGY TEACHER. see *BIOLOGY*

370   US   ISSN 0022-8834
KANSAS TEACHER. 1914. m. (8/yr.). $5 to non-members; members $3. Kansas-National Education Association, 715 W. 10th St., Topeka, KS 66612. TEL 913-232-8271. Ed. Anna Mary Lyle. adv.; charts; illus.; stat.; index. circ. 26,000. (tabloid format)

370   US
THE KAPPA PROFILE. 1949. s-a. membership. National Kappa Kappa Iota, 1875 E. 15, Tulsa, OK 74104-4610. TEL 918-744-0389. Ed. Emily Sleeth. circ. 9,600. **Document type:** newsletter.
  Former titles: Kappa Kappa Iota Newsletter; Kappa Kappa Iota Bulletin.

370.7   II   ISSN 0022-4979
KARNATAK UNIVERSITY. COLLEGE OF EDUCATION. JOURNAL. (Text in English, Kannada) vol. 19, 1972. s-a. Rs.10. Karnatak University, College of Education, Dharwad 580003, Karnataka, India. Ed. T.K. Hiregange. bk.rev.; charts.

KATALOG FOR SKOLEBIBLIOTEKER. SKOLEBIBLIOTEKARENS. see *BIBLIOGRAPHIES*

KATALOG FOR SKOLEBIBLIOTEKER. TITELKATALOG. see *BIBLIOGRAPHIES*

KATOLICKI UNIWERSYTET LUBELSKI. ZESZYTY NAUKOWE. see *RELIGIONS AND THEOLOGY — Roman Catholic*

370   GW   ISSN 0724-7613
KAUFMAENNISCHE SCHULE. 1955. 11/yr. membership. (Verband der Lehrer an Wirtschaftsschulen und Kollegschulen in NW e.V.) Verlag & Offestdruckerei Rainer Meyer, Binterimstr. 12, 40223 Duesseldorf, Germany. TEL 0211-348093-7. FAX 0211-317615. TELEX 8588886-VEME-D. adv.; bk.rev. circ. 6,000.
  Description: Publication for teachers and professors in tradeschools. Discusses education, curriculum, use of computers in schools, and new books.

370   JA
KENKYU SHUROKU. s-a. free or on exchange basis. National Institute for Educational Research, Planning Section of External Service, 6-5-22 Shimo-Meguro, Meguro-ku, Tokyo 153, Japan.

KENTUCKY ENGLISH BULLETIN. see *LINGUISTICS*

370   KE   ISSN 0075-5869
KENYA. MINISTRY OF EDUCATION. ANNUAL REPORT. a. latest 1984. EAs.24. Government Printing and Stationery Department, Box 30128, Nairobi, Kenya.

370   KE
KENYA. MINISTRY OF EDUCATION. NEWSLETTER. (Text in English) 1974. bi-m. Ministry of Education, Science and Technology, Public Relations Officer, Commercial House, Moi Ave., P.O. Box 30040, Nairobi, Kenya. Ed.Bd. **Document type:** government publication, newsletter.
  Formerly: Kenya. Ministry of Education, Science and Technology Newsletter.

370   KE   ISSN 0023-0413
KENYA EDUCATION JOURNAL.* 1958. 3/yr. EAs.1 per no. Ministry of Education, POB 2768, Nairobi, Kenya. Ed. W.G. Bowman. adv.; bk.rev.; bibl.; charts. circ. 5,000. **Indexed:** Cont.Pg.Educ.

377.8   US   ISSN 0023-0839
BV1500
KEY TO CHRISTIAN EDUCATION. 1962. q. $6.95. Standard Publishing, 8121 Hamilton Ave., Cincinnati, OH 45231. TEL 513-931-4050. FAX 513-931-0904. Ed. Barbara Bolton. index. circ. 68,000. **Indexed:** CERDIC, Chr.Per.Ind.
  Description: Ideas for Sunday school teachers and leaders.

KING SAUD UNIVERSITY. JOURNAL. EDUCATIONAL SCIENCES AND ISLAMIC STUDIES/JAMI'AT AL-MALIK SA'UD. MAJALLAH. AL-'ULUM AL-TARBAWIYYAH WAL-DIRASAT AL-ISLAMIYYAH. see *RELIGIONS AND THEOLOGY — Islamic*

370   GW
DER KLECKS; Schuelerzeitung des Thomas-Morus-Gymnasiums Daun. 1966. 2/yr. DM.4. Der Klecks, Michael-Reineke-Str. 6, 54550 Daun, Germany. TEL 06592-4117.

KLEIO. see *HISTORY*

KNOW YOUR WORLD EXTRA. see *CHILDREN AND YOUTH — For*

KOBLENZER GEOGRAPHISCHES KOLLOQUIUM. see *GEOGRAPHY*

370 500   JA   ISSN 0389-0449
Q77   CODEN: KDKDDP
KOCHI DAIGAKU KYOIKUGAKUBU KENKYU HOKOKU. DAI-3-BU/KOCHI UNIVERSITY. FACULTY OF EDUCATION. BULLETIN. SERIES 3. (Text in Japanese; summaries in English) 1951. a. Kochi Daigaku, Kyoikugakubu - Kochi University, Faculty of Education, 5-1 Akebono-cho 2-chome, Kochi-shi, Kochi-ken 780, Japan. **Indexed:** Jap.Per.Ind. —CASDDS.

KOCHNIANO ANEES/ANEES FOR CHILDREN. see *CHILDREN AND YOUTH — For*

370   DK
KOEBENHAVNS KOMMUNESKOLE.* 40/yr. Koebenhavns Laererforening, Frydendalsvej 24, DK-1809 Frederiksberg C, Denmark. Ed. Per Agner. adv. circ. 4,500.

370 200   GW
KORRESPONDENZBLATT EVANGELISCHER SCHULEN UND HEIME. 1960. bi-m. DM.22. Evangelischer Schulbund in Nordwestdeutschland und Berlin, Koenigsweg 1, 33617 Bielefeld, Germany. TEL 0521-1443610. circ. 1,850.

KOULULAINEN/PUPIL. see *CHILDREN AND YOUTH — For*

370   RM
KOZOKTATAS. (Text in Hungarian) 1957. m. Ministry of Education and Science, Piata Presei Libere 1, 71341 Bucharest, Rumania. (Co-sponsor: Trade Union of Workers in Education, Science and Cultural Institutions) Ed. Stefan Banto. circ. 4,000.
  Formerly (until 1989): Tanugyi Ujsag.

370   GW
KRANICH. 1955. q. Kranich Gymnasium, An der Windmuehle 23-25, 38226 Salzgitter, Germany. TEL 05341-40970. circ. 800. (back issues avail.)

613.7   NO   ISSN 0333-0141
KROPPSOEVING. 1951. 8/yr. NOK 300. Landslaget Fysisk Fostring i Skolen, Moellegt. 10, N-3111 Toensberg, N-3111 Toensberg, Norway. TEL 47-33-31-53-00. FAX 47-33-31-52-66. Ed. Finn Ellingsen. adv.; bk.rev.; circ. 2,500 (controlled).

KUMAR. see *ART*

370   PL   ISSN 0023-5938
L51
KWARTALNIK PEDAGOGICZNY. 1956. q. $27. (Uniwersytet Warszawski, Instytut Pedagogiki) Wydawnictwa Uniwersytetu Warszawskiego, Ul. Obozna 8, 00-032 Warsaw, Poland. Ed. Wincenty Okon. bk.rev. circ. 8,100. **Indexed:** Cont.Pg.Educ.

370   JA   ISSN 0023-5997
KYOIKU HYORON/EDUCATIONAL REVIEW. (Includes 3 special nos.) (Text in Japanese) 1951. m. 6000 Yen. Japan Teachers' Union - Nikkyoso, Nihon Kyoiku-Kaikan, 2-6-2 Hitotsubashi, Kanda, Chiyoda-ku, Tokyo, Japan. Ed. Hiroshi Morioka. adv.; bk.rev.; film rev.; play rev.; charts; illus.; stat.; circ. 20,000 (controlled).

370   JA   ISSN 0452-3318
KYOIKU KENKYU/EDUCATIONAL STUDIES. (Text in English and Japanese) 1958. a. $5. International Christian University, Institute for Educational Research and Service - Kokusai Kirisutokyo Daigaku, 3-10 Osawa, Mitaka, Tokyo 181, Japan. FAX 0422-33-9887. Ed. Terumi Nakano. circ. 500. (back issues avail.)

KYOIKU SHINRIGAKU NENPO/ANNUAL REPORT OF EDUCATIONAL PSYCHOLOGY IN JAPAN. see *PSYCHOLOGY*

370   US   ISSN 0162-3052
L A E NEWS. 1977. m. (8/yr.). $25 to non-members; members $3. Louisiana Association of Educators, Box 479, Baton Rouge, LA 70821. TEL 504-343-9243. FAX 504-343-9272. Ed. Jeff Simon. adv.: B&W page $550; trim 11 x 15. circ. 23,000. (tabloid format)
  Formerly: Louisiana Teachers' Tabloid.
  Description: Publication directed to the education community in Louisiana, seeking to update educators on important happenings within the LAE-NEA, as well as cover education news of a more general nature.

L I N K LINE. (Library and Information Network) see *BIRTH CONTROL*

L M S - LINGUA. (Riksfoereningen foer Laerarna i Moderna Spraak) see *LINGUISTICS*

370   US   ISSN 0023-7140
LADUE PUBLIC SCHOOLS BULLETIN. 1960. bi-m. free. Ladue Board of Education, c/o Elizabeth Schwartz, Ed., School District of the City of Ladue, 9703 Conway Rd., St. Louis, MO 63124. TEL 314-994-7080. FAX 314-994-0441. Ed. E. Schwartz. circ. 12,000 (controlled). **Document type:** bulletin.

370   FI   ISSN 0356-7842
LAERAREN/TEACHER. (Text in Swedish) 1894. 30/yr. FIM 280. Finlands Svenska Laerarfoerbund R.F. - Trade Union of Teachers in Swedish Finland, Jaernvaegsmannagatan 6, 00520 Helsinki 52, Finland. FAX 90-142-748. Ed. Carl-Erik Rusk. adv. contact: Bo Gerkman. bk.rev.; film rev.; illus. circ. 4,300. **Document type:** trade publication.
  Formerly: Skolnytt (ISSN 0049-0660)

600   SW   ISSN 1101-2633
LAERARNAS TIDNING. Variant title: L. 1967. 33/yr. SEK 470. Laerarfoerbundet - Swedish Union of Teachers, P.O. Box 12239, 102 26 Stockholm 12, Sweden. Ed. Anders Ternstroem. adv.; bk.rev.; illus.; stat.; index. circ. 180,000.
  Formed by the 1990 merger of: Laerartidningen, Svensk Skoltidning (ISSN 0023-849X) & Facklaereraren (ISSN 0014-6463)

EDUCATION

370   NG   ISSN 0331-9237
LAGOS EDUCATION REVIEW. 1978. biennial. $10. Joja Educational Research and Publishers Limited, 13 B Ikorodu Rd., Maryland, P.M.B. 21526, Ikeja, Lagos, Nigeria. TEL 01-933866. (Subscr. to: Office of the Dean, Faculty of Education, University of Lagos, Akoka, Yaba, Lagos, Nigeria) Ed. M.N. Okenimkpe. adv.; bk.rev.; circ. 3,000 (controlled).
Description: Presents discussions of topics on all areas of education and reports of research.

LANGENSCHEIDTS SPRACH-ILLUSTRIERTE; a German language journal. see *LINGUISTICS*

420.07 370   US   ISSN 0360-9170
LB1576.A1
LANGUAGE ARTS. 1924. 8/yr. (Sep.-Apr.). $40 individual membership; institutions $50. National Council of Teachers of English, 1111 W. Kenyon Rd., Urbana, IL 61801-1096. TEL 217-328-3870. FAX 217-328-9645. Ed. William Teale. adv.; bk.rev.; film rev.; bibl. circ. 21,000. (also avail. in microform from UMI; reprint service avail. from UMI,KTO) **Indexed:** Acad.Ind., Bk.Rev.Ind. (1975-), C.I.J.E., Child.Bk.Rev.Ind. (1975-), Cont.Pg.Educ., Curr.Cont., Educ.Ind., Lang.& Lang.Behav.Abstr., Lang.Teach.& Ling.Abstr. **Document type:** academic/scholarly publication.
—BLDSC (5155.708300); Faxon; UnCover; SWETS; UMI.
Formerly (until 1975?): Elementary English (ISSN 0013-5968)
Description: Provides a forum for elementary study and teaching methods.

LANGUAGE LEARNING; a journal of research in language studies. see *LINGUISTICS*

LANGUAGE LEARNING JOURNAL. see *LINGUISTICS*

LANGUAGE MATTERS. see *BUSINESS AND ECONOMICS*

LANGUAGE QUARTERLY. see *LINGUISTICS*

370   SA   ISSN 0023-8422
AP18
LANTERN; cultural journal. (Text in Afrikaans and English) 1949. q. R.30 (effective 1994). Foundation for Education, Science and Technology, P.O. Box 1758, Pretoria 0001, South Africa. TEL 27-12-322-6404. FAX 27-12-320-7803. Ed. Riena van Graan. illus. circ. 5,000. **Indexed:** Artbibl.Mod., Ind.S.A.Per.
Incorporates: Young Academic.

LASER QUEST. see *INSTRUMENTS*

371.3   US
LAST RESORT. 1973. q. $10. End Violence Against the Next Generation, Inc., 977 Keeler Ave., Berkeley, CA 94708-1498. TEL 510-527-0454. Ed. Adah Maurer. bk.rev. circ. 1,000. **Document type:** newsletter.
Description: Publishes researches regarding the relationship between physical punishment and behavior problems. Promotes alternative methods of raising and educating children.

LAW-RELATED EDUCATION NEWSLETTER. see *LAW*

370 011   US   ISSN 8755-2620
LC1756
LEADER IN ACTION. 1981. q. $25 (members $20). American Association of University Women, 1111 16th St., N.W., Washington, DC 20036. TEL 202-785-7738. FAX 202-872-1425. Ed. Jodi Lipson. adv.; illus. circ. 18,000. (back issues avail.)
Description: Presents information to assist AAUW's leaders in their effort for equity for women and positive societal change.

LEADER IN THE CHURCH SCHOOL TODAY. see *RELIGIONS AND THEOLOGY — Protestant*

373   US
LA229
LEADERSHIP (RESTON). 1974. m. (Sep.-May). $10. National Association of Secondary School Principals, 1904 Association Dr., Reston, VA 22091. TEL 703-860-0200. FAX 703-476-5432. Ed. Jackie Rough. circ. 25,000. (also avail. in microform from UMI; reprint service avail. from UMI)
Former titles: Student Activities (ISSN 0746-3545); (until 1983): Student Advocate (ISSN 0094-0836); Supersedes (1962-1974): Student Life Highlights (ISSN 0039-2766); Student Life.
Description: Articles of interest to student councils, honor societies and other student activity participants.

370   US   ISSN 1062-1474
LEADERSHIP EDUCATION (YEAR); a source book. 1987. biennial. $59.95. Center for Creative Leadership, One Leadership Pl., Box 26300, Greensboro, NC 27438-6300. TEL 919-288-7210. FAX 919-288-3999. Eds. Frank H. Freeman, Sara N. King. bk.rev.; film rev, video rev.; index.
Description: Provides readers with current information on the latest resources in leadership development. Includes sections on courses and programs, leadership technologies, and resource persons in leadership education.

372   US   ISSN 0090-3167
LB5
LEARNING (YEAR); creative ideas and insights for teachers. 1972. 8/yr. (Aug.-May). $20. Springhouse Corporation (Subsidiary of: Reed Elsevier Medical Group), 1111 Bethlehem Pike, Box 908, Springhouse, PA 19477-0908. TEL 215-646-8700; 800-346-7844. FAX 215-646-4399. (Subscr. to: Box 2580, Boulder, CO 80322) Ed. Charlene Gaynor. adv. contact: Mary Wardlaw. bk.rev.; film rev.; charts; illus.; stat. circ. 285,000. (also avail. in microform from UMI) **Indexed:** Bk.Rev.Ind. (1984-), C.I.J.E., Child.Bk.Rev.Ind. (1984-), Educ.Ind., ERIC, Ind.Child.Mag., R.G. **Document type:** trade publication.
—BLDSC (5179.325700); Faxon; UnCover; UMI. CCC.
Description: Contains teaching tips and curriculum ideas for kindergarten through middle school.

LEARNING AND INDIVIDUAL DIFFERENCES; a multidisciplinary journal in education. see *PSYCHOLOGY*

370   UK   ISSN 0959-4752
LA620   CODEN: LEAIE9
LEARNING AND INSTRUCTION. (Section of: International Journal of Educational Research (ISSN 0883-0355)) 1991. 4/yr. £109($170) (effective 1994). (European Association for Research on Learning and Instruction) Elsevier Science Ltd., Pergamon, P.O. Box 800, Kidlington, Oxford OX5 1DX, England. TEL 44-865-843000. FAX 44-865-843010. (Subscr. in U.S. and Canada to: Elsevier Science, 660 White Plains Rd., Tarrytown, NY 10591-5153. TEL 914-524-9200. FAX 914-333-2444) Ed. Erik DeCorte. index. (also avail. in microfilm from UMI; back issues avail.) **Document type:** academic/scholarly publication.
—BLDSC (5179.325890); UnCover. CCC.
Description: Presents papers and review articles on the processes of learning, development, instruction, and teaching representing a variety of theoretical perspectives, and different methodological approaches.
Refereed Serial

150 370   US   ISSN 0023-9690
BF1   CODEN: LNMVAV
LEARNING AND MOTIVATION. 1970. q. $176 (foreign $226). Academic Press, Inc., Journal Division, 525 B St., Ste. 1900, San Diego, CA 92101-4495. TEL 619-230-1840. FAX 619-699-6800. (Subscr. to: Box 620000, Orlando, FL 32891-8340. TEL 800-543-9534) Ed. Steven F. Maier. adv.; charts; illus. (back issues avail.) **Indexed:** Adol.Ment.Hlth.Abstr., Biol.Abstr., Commun.Abstr., Cont.Pg.Educ., Curr.Cont., Mid.East: Abstr.& Ind., Psychol.Abstr., Soc.Sci.Ind., SSCI. **Document type:** academic/scholarly publication.
—Faxon; UnCover; SWETS. CCC.
Description: Features original experimental research studies devoted to the analysis of basic phenomena and mechanisms of learning, memory, and motivation.

LEBENDE SPRACHEN; Zeitschrift fuer fremde Sprachen in Wissenschaft und Praxis. see *LINGUISTICS*

LEBLANC BELL. see *MUSIC*

LEGAL VIDEO REVIEW. see *LAW*

LEHRBUECHER UND MONOGRAPHIEN ZUR DIDAKTIK DER MATHEMATIK see *MATHEMATICS*

370   GW
LEHREN UND LERNEN. 1975. m. DM.66. (Landesinstitut fuer Erziehung und Unterricht Stuttgart) Neckar Verlag GmbH, Postfach 1820, 78008 Villingen-Schwenningen, Germany. TEL 07221-8987-0. FAX 07221-898750. adv. circ. 3,000. **Document type:** academic/scholarly publication.

370   GW
LEHRERINNEN- UND LEHRERKALENDER. 1977. a. DM.14.80. Anabas-Verlag Guenter Kaempf KG, Unterer Hardthof 25, 35398 Giessen, Germany. FAX 0641-67356 adv.; bk.rev. circ. 20,000. **Document type:** bulletin.

370   GW   ISSN 0173-0614
LERNEN IN DEUTSCHLAND. 1980. 2/yr. DM.42. Schneider Verlag Hohengehren GmbH, Wilhelmstr. 13, 73666 Baltmannsweiler, Germany. TEL 07153-41206. FAX 07153-48761. Ed. Alfred J. Tumat. **Document type:** academic/scholarly publication.
—CCC.

370   GW   ISSN 0722-1843
LERNEN KONKRET. 1981. 4/yr. DM.11.80. Verlag Duerr und Kessler GmbH, Maarweg 30, 53619 Rheinbreitbach, Germany. TEL 02224-77050. FAX 02224-79243. adv.; bk.rev.; illus. circ. 4,000.

LESBIAN & GAY TEACHER'S ASSOCIATION NEWSLETTER. see *HOMOSEXUALITY*

370   LO
LESOTHO. MINISTRY OF EDUCATION, SPORTS AND CULTURE. ANNUAL REPORT OF THE PERMANENT SECRETARY. 1966. a. Ministry of Education, Sports and Culture, P.O. Box 47, Maseru, Lesotho. **Document type:** government publication.
Formerly: Lesotho. Ministry of Education and Culture. Annual Report of the Permanent Secretary.

LET'S FIND OUT. see *CHILDREN AND YOUTH — For*

LEVENDE TALEN. see *LINGUISTICS*

370   CC   ISSN 1002-8196
LIAONING JIAOYU/LIAONING EDUCATION. (Text in Chinese) 1972. m. Y18. (Liaoning Sheng Jiaoyu Ting - Liaoning Provincial Bureau of Education) Liaoning Jiaoyu Zazhishe, 29 Ningshan Zhonglu, Huangu Qu, Shenyang, Liaoning 110031, People's Republic of China. TEL 6853324. Ed. Wei Guanghua.

370   UK   ISSN 0267-8500
LIB ED; a magazine for the liberation of learning. 1967. 3/yr. $29 to indivuduals; institutions $46. Phoenix House, 170 Wells Rd., Bristol BS4 2AG, England. FAX 0272-778453. adv.; bk.rev. circ. 1,500. **Document type:** academic/scholarly publication.
Formerly: Libertarian Education.
Description: News items and feature articles on the practical and philosophic issues associated with freedom in education and learning in schools and colleges through alternatives to authoritarianism and elitism; contains lists of sources and associations.

370   IT
LIBERTA DI EDUCAZIONE; Rivista di Cultura e Politica Scolastica. 1976. bi-m. L.35000. Centro Servizi Didattici, Piazza Maria alla Fontana, 3, 20159 Milan, Italy. TEL 02-606377. FAX 02-6880981. Ed. Fiorenzo Tagiabue. adv.; bk.rev. circ. 5,500.

LIBRARY ADMINISTRATOR'S DIGEST. see *LIBRARY AND INFORMATION SCIENCES*

370   SP   ISSN 0075-9201
LIBROS Y MATERIAL DE ENSENANZA. 1958. a. free. Instituto Nacional del Libro Espanol, Comision Asesora de Editores de Libros de Ensenanza, Santiago Rusinol, 8, Madrid-3, Spain. Ed. Ramon Grimaldo Huete. adv.; bk.rev. circ. 10,000.

EDUCATION

370   UN
LIFELONG EDUCATION NETWORK. 1980. irreg. DM.6. Unesco Institute for Education, Feldbrunnenstr. 58, D-2000 Hamburg 13, Germany. TEL 040-447843. FAX 040-4107723. TELEX 2-164-146 UIE D. (Dist. in U.S. by: Unipub, 4611-F Assembly Dr., Lanham, MD 20706-4391) Eds. Ursula Giere, Yasushi Maehira.
   Description: Directory of writers on lifelong education.

LINGUISTICS AND EDUCATION; an international research journal. see *LINGUISTICS*

370   CN
LINK (BURNABY). 1966. bi-w. Can.$20. British Columbia Institute of Technology, Student Association, 3700 Willingdon Ave., Burnaby, B.C. V5G 3H2, Canada. TEL 604-434-5734. Ed. Paul Dayson. adv.; bk.rev. circ. 5,000. (tabloid format)

LITERARY CAVALCADE. see *CHILDREN AND YOUTH — For*

LITERATURNAYA UCHEBA. see *CHILDREN AND YOUTH — For*

330   II   ISSN 0024-5917
LOK RAJYA. (Editions in English & Marathi) 1945. s-m. Rs.10. Directorate of Information and Public Relations, Sachivalaya, Bombay 400032, India. Ed. Shri S.K. Sagane. bk.rev.; illus. circ. 3,650 (English ed.); 13,250 (Marathi ed.). (back issues avail.)

370   US
LOOK AT US! 1956. 4/yr. free. Vestal Board of Education, Vestal Central School District, Vestal, NY 13850. TEL 607-757-2205. FAX 607-757-2227. Ed. Katie Ellis. bk.rev. circ. 13,500. **Document type:** newsletter.
   Former titles: V C S Newsletter; Report from Your Vestal Schools; Status of Your Vestal Schools (ISSN 0039-0755)

LOOK - LISTEN PROJECT REPORT. see *COMMUNICATIONS — Television And Cable*

370   US
LOUISIANA PHILOSOPHY OF EDUCATION JOURNAL. 1975. a. $14. Louisiana Philosophy of Education Society, Department of Education, Louisiana State University in Shreveport, One University Pl., Shreveport, LA 71115. TEL 318-797-5032. Ed. Joe L. Green. circ. 30. **Document type:** proceedings.

LUCKY; the magazine for young readers. see *CHILDREN AND YOUTH — For*

LUMEN VITAE (ENGLISH EDITION); revue internationale de la formation religieuse. see *RELIGIONS AND THEOLOGY — Roman Catholic*

370 377.8   US   ISSN 0024-7448
LC573
LUTHERAN EDUCATION. 1865. 5/yr. $9 (foreign $12). Concordia University, 7400 Augusta St., River Forest, IL 60305-1499. TEL 708-209-3073. FAX 708-209-3176. Ed. Wayne Lucht. adv.; bk.rev.; illus.; index. circ. 4,200. (also avail. in microfilm from UMI) **Indexed:** CERDIC, Educ.Ind.
   —BLDSC (5307.810000); UMI.

M A A FOCUS. (Mathematical Association of America) see *MATHEMATICS*

370   US
M E A TODAY. 1924. m. membership. Montana Education Association, 1232 E. Sixth Ave., Helena, MT 59601. TEL 406-442-4250. FAX 406-443-5081. Ed. Nancy L. Robbins. adv.; bk.rev.; illus. circ. 9,800. (also avail. in microfilm from UMI) **Indexed:** Educ.Ind.
   Formerly: Montana Education (ISSN 0026-993X)

370 614.7 300   YU   ISSN 0353-1074
M I. (Text in Serbo-Croatian; summaries in English) 1981. bi-m. free. Mladi Istrazivaci Srbije - Young Researchers' Movement of Serbia, Ho Si Minova 27, 11070 Belgrade, Yugoslavia. TEL 011 138-942. Ed. Zvezdan Djruic. adv.; bk.rev.; index. circ. 4,000.

370   US
M T A TODAY. m. Massachusetts Teachers Association, 20 Ashburton Pl., Boston, MA 02108-2727. TEL 617-742-7950. FAX 617-742-7046. Ed. Andrew D. Linebaugh. circ. 70,000.

370   US
M T I REPORTER. 1968. w. (during school yr.). $15. Madison Teachers, Inc., 821 Williamson St., Madison, WI 53703. TEL 608-257-0491. Ed. John A. Matthews. adv.; illus.; circ. controlled. **Document type:** bulletin, newsletter.
   Formerly: Merrimac (ISSN 0026-0169)

M.3. see *CHILDREN AND YOUTH — For*

370   CN   ISSN 0024-9033
MCGILL JOURNAL OF EDUCATION. (Text in English, French) 1966. 3/yr. Can.$25. McGill University, Faculty of Education, 3700 McTavish St., Montreal, PQ H3A 1Y2, Canada. TEL 514-398-4246. FAX 514-398-4679. Ed. William M. Talley. bk.rev.; bibl.; charts; illus.; stat.; cum.index. circ. 1,000. (also avail. in microfilm from UMI; microform from MML) **Indexed:** Can.Educ.Ind., Cont.Pg.Educ., Educ.Tech.Abstr., ERIC, Mult.Ed.Abstr., Res.High.Educ.Abstr., Sociol.Abstr., Sociol.Educ.Abstr., SOMA, Sp.Ed.Needs Abstr. —BLDSC (5413.427500); Faxon; UnCover; UMI.

MACQUARIE UNIVERSITY FRENCH MONOGRAPHS. see *LINGUISTICS*

377.8   IT
MAESTRI FRIULANI. 1967. m. free. (Associazione Italiana Maestri Cattolici di Udine) A I M C, Vicolo Sillio, 3, 33100 Udine, Italy. TEL 0432-295442. circ. 2,000.

MAESTRO. see *RELIGIONS AND THEOLOGY — Roman Catholic*

370   SP
MAGISTERIO ESPANOL. 1866. w. 2128($14) Siena, S.A., Lopez de Hoyos, 5 2o Izda., 28006 Madrid, Spain. TEL 91-5624105. FAX 91-5611200. Dir. Mercedes Eguibar Galarza. circ. 23,691.

370   HU   ISSN 0025-0260
L56
MAGYAR PEDAGOGIA/HUNGARIAN JOURNAL OF EDUCATIONAL RESEARCH. (Text in Hungarian; summaries in English) 1892. q. 400 Ft.($8) Jozsef Attila Tudomanyegyetem, Department of Education, Petofi sgt. 30-34, 6722 Szeged, Hungary. TEL 36-62-321034. (Subscr. in Hungary to: Hirlapelofizetesi es Lapellatasi Iroda, Lehel u. 10-A, 1900 Budapest, Hungary) (Co-sponsor: Hungarian Academy of Sciences, Educational Committee) Ed. Beno Csapo. adv.; bk.rev. **Indexed:** Cont.Pg.Educ., Curr.Cont., Lang.& Lang.Behav.Abstr. **Document type:** academic/scholarly publication.
   Description: Publishes empirical, theoretical, methodological, and state of the art studies and papers.
   Refereed Serial

370   II
MAHARASHTRA STATE INSTITUTE OF EDUCATION. RESEARCH BULLETIN. (Text in English) vol.5, 1975. q. free. Maharashtra State Institute of Education, Poona 411030, India. Ed. M.S. Sadashiv Peth. bk.rev.; bibl.; charts; illus. circ. 500. **Indexed:** Res.Educ.

370   US   ISSN 0199-6045
MAILBOX. (In 3 editions: Preschool/Kindergarten; Primary (Grades 1-3); Intermediate (Grades 4-6)) bi-m. $19.95 (foreign $28.95). Education Center Inc., 1606 Battleground Ave., Box 9753, Greensboro, NC 27429. TEL 800-334-0298.

370   US   ISSN 0025-0775
MAINE TEACHER. 1940. 9/yr. (Sep.-May). $6 to non-members. Maine Teachers' Association, 35 Community Dr., Augusta, ME 04330. TEL 207-622-5866. Ed. Keith C. Harvie. adv.; charts; illus. circ. 21,000.

MAISON - DIEU; revue specialisee de liturgique. see *RELIGIONS AND THEOLOGY*

370   TS
MAJALLAT AL-ANSHITTAH AL-TARBAWIYYAH/EDUCATIONAL ACTIVITIES MAGAZINE. (Text in Arabic) 1988. irreg. free. Ministry of Education, Private Education Administration, P.O. Box 295, Abu Dhabi, United Arab Emirates. TEL 330216. circ. 1,000.
   Description: Discusses the state of private education in the U.A.E., focussing on present activities of private educational institutions and future projects.

372   GW
MAL UND BASTELSTUNDE; Arbeitsblaetter fuer bildhaftes und konstruktives Gestalten. 1978. 3/yr. DM.20. A L S Verlag GmbH, Voltastr. 3, 63128 Dietzenbach, Germany. TEL 06074-25051. FAX 06074-27322. Ed. Ingrid Kreide. illus.; cum.index: 1978-1993. circ. 48,000. (looseleaf format; back issues avail.) **Document type:** academic/scholarly publication.

372   KR   ISSN 0025-1453
MALYATKO. 1960. m. $85. (Soyuz Molodezhnikh Organizatsii Ukrainy) Vidavnitstvo Molod, Vul. Parkhomenko 38-44, 252119 Kiev, Ukraine. TEL 044-213-1160. (Dist in U.S. by: Victor Kamkin Inc., Boiling Brook Pkwy., Rockville, MD 20852. TEL 044-213-1160) Ed. Svitlana Yefimenko. illus.; index. circ. 240,000.

370   II
MAMANE. (Text in English and Kannada) 1970. m. Rs.10($2) Mamane International Academy, 265-I-N Block, Rajajinagar, Bangalore 560010, India. Ed. V.K. Javali. adv.; bk.rev. circ. 500.

MANAGEMENT IN EDUCATION. see *BUSINESS AND ECONOMICS — Management*

370   UK
MANCHESTER TEACHER. 1980. bi-m. Manchester Teachers' Association, c/o Whalley Range High School, Doncaster Ave., Manchester M20 8DN, England. Ed. R. Flint. circ. 3,750.

370   CN
MANITOBA ASSOCIATION FOR SCHOOLING AT HOME NEWSLETTER. 1984. bi-m. Can.$20. Manitoba Association for Schooling at Home, 89 Edkar Cres., Winnipeg, MB R2G 3H8, Canada. TEL 204-334-4763. Ed. Michelle Davidow. adv. circ. 100. **Document type:** newsletter.
   Description: Provides information on events, resources and legislation on education at home. Includes a contact directory.

507 370   CN   ISSN 0315-9159
MANITOBA SCIENCE TEACHER. 3/yr. membership. Science Teachers' Association of Manitoba, 155 Kingsway Ave., Winnipeg, Man. R3R 0G3, Canada. Ed. Raj Goyal. adv.; bk.rev. circ. 800.

370   CN   ISSN 0025-228X
MANITOBA TEACHER. 1919. 10/yr. Can.$12. Manitoba Teachers' Society, 191 Harcourt St., Winnipeg, MB R3J 3H2, Canada. TEL 204-888-7961. FAX 204-831-0877. Ed. Ramon Job. adv. contact: Joy Montgomery. circ. 17,000.

370   NZ   ISSN 0076-4280
MAORI EDUCATION FOUNDATION. ANNUAL REPORT. 1962. a. NZ.$6.45 per no. Maori Education Foundation, P.O. Box 3745, Wellington, New Zealand. TEL 64-4-801-8041. FAX 64-4-801-8046. (Subscr. to: G P Legislation, P.O. Box 12418, Thorndon, Wellington, New Zealand)

MARYLAND MUSIC EDUCATOR. see *MUSIC*

370.193   US   ISSN 0025-4339
MARYLAND P T A BULLETIN.* 1950. m. (9/yr.). Maryland Congress of Parents and Teachers, 3121 Saint Paul St., Ste. 25, Baltimore, MD 21218-3857. TEL 301-685-0865. Ed. Gary Jones. bk.rev.; illus.; circ. controlled.

370   MY   ISSN 0126-5024
MASALAH PENDIDIKAN; bulletin on current issues in education. (Text in English and Malay) 1965. a. M.$10. University of Malaya, Faculty of Education - Universiti Malaya. Fakulti Pendidikan, Lembah Pantai, 59100 Kuala Lumpur, Malaysia. Ed. Raja Maznah Raja Hussain. circ. 800.
   —UnCover.

MASARYKOVA UNIVERSITA. FILOZOFICKA FAKULTA. SBORNIK PRACI. I: RADA PEDAGOGICKO - PSYCHOLOGICKA. see *PSYCHOLOGY*

MASSACHUSETTS MUSIC NEWS. see *MUSIC*

EDUCATION

370 US ISSN 0889-6259
MASTER TEACHER. 1970. w. $21.60 (typically set in Sep.). Master Teacher, Inc., Leadership Lane, Box 1207, Manhattan, KS 66502-0013. TEL 913-539-0555. FAX 913-539-7739. Ed. Robert L. DeBruyn. charts. circ. 214,000. **Document type:** monographic series.
  Description: In-service program provided to teachers by principals and superintendents.

370 016 US ISSN 0076-5112
Z5816.I6
MASTER'S THESES IN EDUCATION. 1952. a. $40. Master's Theses Directories, Box 92, Cedar Falls, IA 50613. TEL 319-273-6412. FAX 319-273-2742. Ed. H.M. Silvey.

370 510 530 XR ISSN 1210-1761
MATEMATIKA, FYZIKA, INFORMATIKA. (Text in Czech, Slovak; summaries in English, German, Russian) 1970. 5/yr. 60 Kcs.($17.60) (Ministerstvo Skolstvi, Mladezy a Telovychovy Ceske Republiky) Statni Pedagogicke Nakladatelstvi, Ostrovni 30, 113 01 Prague 1, Czech Republic. TEL 42-2-203851. FAX 42-2-393883. Ed. Josef Fuka. bk.rev. **Indexed:** Ref.Zh. **Document type:** academic/scholarly publication.
  Formerly (until 1991): Matematika a Fyzika ve Skole (ISSN 0323-1690); Formed by the merger of: Fyzika ve Skole (ISSN 0016-3376); Matematika ve Skole.

370 GW ISSN 0173-3842
MATERIALIEN AUS DER BILDUNGSFORSCHUNG. (Text in German; summaries in English) 1972. irreg., vol.45, 1993. price varies. Max-Planck-Institut fuer Bildungsforschung - Max-Planck-Institute for Human Development and Education, Lentzeallee 94, 14195 Berlin, Germany. TEL 030-82995-1. **Document type:** monographic series.
  Description: Monographic series of reports on works-in-progress at the Institute.

MATHEMATICAL PIE. see MATHEMATICS

THE MATHEMATICS EDUCATION. see MATHEMATICS

370 510 301 NE ISSN 0924-4921
MATHEMATICS EDUCATION LIBRARY. 1983. irreg., vol.4, 1986. price varies. Kluwer Academic Publishers, Postbus 17, 3300 AA Dordrecht, Netherlands. TEL 31-78-334911. FAX 31-78-334254. TELEX 29245 KAPG NL. (Dist. by: Kluwer Academic Publishers Group, P.O. Box 322, 3300 AH Dordrecht, Netherlands. TEL 31-78-524400; N. America dist. addr.: Box 358, Accord Sta., Hingham, MA 02018-0358. TEL 617-871-6600) Ed. A. Bishop. bibl.; illus. (back issues avail.) **Document type:** monographic series.
  Refereed Serial

MATHEMATICS TEACHING IN THE MIDDLE SCHOOL. see MATHEMATICS

370 MF
MAURITIUS INSTITUTE OF EDUCATION. ANNUAL REPORT. a. Mauritius Institute of Education, Reduit, Mauritius.

370 MF
MAURITIUS INSTITUTE OF EDUCATION. JOURNAL. (Text in English) 1977. a. Mauritius Institute of Education, Reduit, Mauritius. **Indexed:** P.L.E.S.A.

371.4 US ISSN 0748-1756
LB1027.5
MEASUREMENT AND EVALUATION IN COUNSELING AND DEVELOPMENT. 1968. 4/yr. $23. (Association for Measurement and Evaluation in Counseling and Development) American Counseling Association, 5999 Stevenson Ave., Alexandria, VA 22304-3300. TEL 703-823-9800. FAX 703-823-0252. Ed. Jo-Ida C. Hansen. adv.; bk.rev.; abstr.; charts; stat.; index. circ. 3,175. (also avail. in microform from UMI; back issues avail.; reprint service avail. from UMI) **Indexed:** ASCA, C.I.J.E., Curr.Cont., Educ.Ind., Psychol.Abstr., Soc.Work Res.& Abstr., Sp.Ed.Needs Abstr., SSCI. —BLDSC (5413.560800); Faxon; UnCover; SWETS; UMI. **CCC.**
  Formerly (until 1984): Measurement and Evaluation in Guidance (ISSN 0025-6307)
  Description: Focuses on the latest research and applications for counselors, administrators, educators, researchers and students.

MEDIA FOCUS/MEDIAFOKUS. see LIBRARY AND INFORMATION SCIENCES

371.33 UK ISSN 0262-0251
LB1044.7.A2 CODEN: MDETDV
MEDIA IN EDUCATION & DEVELOPMENT. 1967-1990. q. £45($85) to institutions. British Council, 65 Davies St., London W1Y 2AA, England. Ed. G. Grimmet. adv.; bk.rev.; film rev.; charts; illus.; index. circ. 1,500. (back issues avail.) **Indexed:** C.I.J.E., Cont.Pg.Educ., Educ.Ind., Educ.Tech.Abstr., High.Educ.Curr.Aware.Bull., Ind.Vet., Intl.Ind.TV, Lang.Teach.& Ling.Abstr., Rural Ext.Educ.& Tr.Abstr., Rural Recreat.Tour.Abstr., Sci.Abstr., Sp.Ed.Needs Abstr., World Agri.Econ.& Rural Sociol.Abstr. —UnCover. **CCC.**
  Former titles: Educational Broadcasting International (ISSN 0013-1970); Educational Television International.
  Description: Concerned with the application of communications technology and techniques to educational and societal development.

MEDIELAERERFORENINGEN FOR GYMNASIET OG H F. MEDDELELSER. see MOTION PICTURES

MEDIEN AKTIV. see PHOTOGRAPHY

MEDIEN & ERZIEHUNG; Zweimonatsschrift fuer audiovisuelle Kommunikation. see COMMUNICATIONS — Television And Cable

MEDIENCONCRET; Magazin fuer die paedagogische Praxis. see COMMUNICATIONS

370 AT ISSN 0076-6275
L101.A8
MELBOURNE STUDIES IN EDUCATION. 1957. a. Aus.$25 to institutions (foreign Aus.$26.50). (University of Melbourne, School of Education) La Trobe University Press, Bundoora, Vic. 3085, Australia. (Dist. by: International Specialized Book Services, Inc., P.O. Box 1632, Beaverton, OR 97075-3640) Ed. Imelda Palmer. circ. 2,000. **Indexed:** Aus.P.A.I.S.
  —BLDSC (5536.820000); UnCover. **CCC.**

370 370.15 US
MENSA RESEARCH JOURNAL. 3/yr. $21. Mensa Education and Research Foundation, 2626 E. 14th St., Brooklyn, NY 11235-3992. TEL 201-655-4225. FAX 201-655-7382. Ed. Phyllis Miller. adv.; bk.rev. circ. 1,000. (back issues avail.) **Document type:** academic/scholarly publication.
  Description: Covers research on intelligence; aimed particularly at the gifted.

370 US ISSN 1045-4985
MENTOR; recreating community through the art and practice of mentoring. 1989. q. $24. Watermarks, Box 4382, Overland Park, KS 66204. TEL 913-362-7889. Ed. Maureen Waters. adv.; bk.rev.; illus.; circ. 300 (paid). (back issues avail.) **Indexed:** A.I.P.P. **Document type:** newsletter.

370 SA ISSN 0025-9713
MENTOR. (Text in English) 1918. 3/yr. R.20 (effective 1993). Natal Teachers' Society, 178 Florida Rd., Durban 4001, South Africa. FAX 239637. Ed. P. Londal. adv.; bk.rev. circ. 4,700.

MERRILL - PALMER QUARTERLY. see PSYCHOLOGY

370 GO
MESSAGE;* bulletin de liaison des enseignants gabonais. irreg. 600 Fr.CFA. Direction de l'Enseignement du Premier Degre, B.P. 221, Libreville, Gabon.
  Formerly: Tam-Tam.

370 AA
MESUESI/INSTITUTEUR. (Text in Albanian) w. $10.80. Ministria e Arsimit dhe e Kultures - Ministry of Education and Culture, Tirana, Albania. TELEX 4203. Ed. Thoma Qendro.

METHODIST THEOLOGICAL SCHOOL IN OHIO. STORY. see RELIGIONS AND THEOLOGY — Protestant

METODICKI OGLEDI. see PHILOSOPHY

379.15 US ISSN 0026-153X
METROPOLITAN NASHVILLE BOARD OF EDUCATION. NEWS AND VIEWS; official publication of the public schools of metropolitan Nashville Davidson County. 1954. q. free. Metropolitan Nashville Board of Education, 2601 Bransford Ave., Nashville, TN 37204. TEL 615-259-8400. circ. 7,500 (controlled).
  Description: Information on events and activities in the public schools of Nashville including recognition of outstanding incividuals, awards and new school construction.

370 MX
MEXICO. SECRETARIA DE EDUCACION PUBLICA. INFORME DE LABORES. 1970. a. Secretaria de Educacion Publica, Direccion General de Planeacion, Programacion y Presupuesto, Mexico D.F., Mexico. **Document type:** government publication.
  Description: Report of activities regarding organization and administration of education in Mexico.

373 US ISSN 0026-2013
MICHIGAN ASSOCIATION OF SECONDARY SCHOOL PRINCIPALS' BULLETIN. vol.16, 1974. m. (Sep.-May). membership. Michigan Association of Secondary School Principals, 418 Erickson Hall, Michigan State University, E. Lansing, MI 48823. Ed. Jock Bittle. adv.; bk.rev.; circ. controlled. (looseleaf format; also avail. in microfilm; reprint service avail. from UMI) **Document type:** bulletin.
  Formerly: Journal of Secondary Education.

371.42 US ISSN 0093-9137
LC1046.M5
MICHIGAN COUNCIL ON VOCATIONAL EDUCATION. BIENNIAL EVALUATION REPORT (YEAR). Key Title: Biennial Report of the Michigan State Advisory Council for Vocational Education. 1970. biennial. free. Michigan Council on Vocational Education, Box 30008, Lansing, MI 48909. TEL 517-373-6407. FAX 517-335-1324. circ. 1,525.
  Formerly: Michigan. Advisory Council for Vocational Education. Annual Report.

370 US ISSN 0047-7125
LB1049.9
MICHIGAN READING JOURNAL. 1967. 3/yr. $2 to non-members. Michigan Reading Association, Charles Peters, Oakland Schools, 2100 Pontiac Lake Rd., Pontiac, MI 48054. TEL 313-698-2098. bk.rev. circ. 2,400.

370 US
MICHIGAN STATE UNIVERSITY. INTERNATIONAL NETWORKS IN EDUCATION AND DEVELOPMENT. PUBLICATIONS. 1962. irreg. Michigan State University, International Networks in Education and Development (INET), College of Education, 237 Erickson Hall, E. Lansing, MI 48824-1034. TEL 517-335-5522.
  Formerly: Michigan State University. Institute for International Studies in Education. Publications.

370 UK
MIDDLE EAST EDUCATION & TRAINING BUYERS GUIDE. (Editions in Arabic, English) 1982. a. $60. International Business Publications Ltd., Queensway House, 2 Queensway, Redhill, Surrey RH1 1QS, England. Ed. Geoff Napier. adv.

370 US ISSN 0092-2986
LA205
MIDWEST HISTORY OF EDUCATION SOCIETY. JOURNAL. Key Title: Journal of the Midwest History of Education Society. 1972. a. $4. Midwest History of Education Society, Univ. of Dayton, Dayton, OH 45469-0525. TEL 513-229-3328. Ed. Joseph Watras. circ. 100. **Indexed:** Amer.Hist.& Life (1993-), Hist.Abstr. (1993-).
  Description: Current research in all aspects of the history of education.

MINNESOTA. GEOLOGICAL SURVEY. EDUCATIONAL SERIES. see EARTH SCIENCES — Geology

EDUCATION

370 CC ISSN 1001-7178
MINZU JIAOYU YANJIU/ETHNIC EDUCATION STUDIES. (Text in Chinese) 1989. q. (Zhongyang Minzu Xueyuan - Central Institute of National Minorities) Minzu Jiaoyu Yanjiu Bianjibu, Zhongyang Minzu Xueyuan, 27 Baishiqiao, Beijing, 100081, People's Republic of China. TEL 8420077. FAX 01-8422954. (Dist. overseas by: China International Book Trading Corp., P.O. Box 399, Beijing, P.R. China) Ed. Geng Jinsheng. circ. 2,000. **Document type:** academic/scholarly publication.
  Description: Probes the principles of ethnic education.

MIRA; a monthly journal of Indian culture. see *LITERARY AND POLITICAL REVIEWS*

MISCELANEA COMILLAS; revista de teologia y ciencias humanas. see *RELIGIONS AND THEOLOGY*

MISSISSIPPI MUSIC EDUCATOR. see *MUSIC*

MISSOURI SCHOOL MUSIC. see *MUSIC*

370 US ISSN 0745-1237
L168
MISSOURI SCHOOLS. 1935. q. Department of Elementary and Secondary Education, Box 480, Jefferson City, MO 65102. TEL 314-751-3469. FAX 314-751-1179. Ed. James L. Morris. charts; illus.; stat. circ. 7,500. **Document type:** government publication.

MIXED MEDIA. see *ART*

377.8 US
MOMENTUM (WASHINGTON). 1970. 4/yr. $20. National Catholic Educational Association, 1077 30 St., N.W., Ste. 100, Washington, DC 20007. TEL 202-337-6232. Ed. Patricia Feistritzer. bk.rev.; bibl.; charts; illus.; cum.index. circ. 25,000. (also avail. in microfilm from UMI; reprint service avail. from UMI) **Indexed:** C.I.J.E., Cath.Ind., Chic.Per.Ind., Curr.Cont., Educ.Ind.
  —BLDSC (5901.590000); UnCover; UMI.
  Formerly: Catholic School Bulletin (ISSN 0026-914X)

370 FR ISSN 0337-9213
LE MONDE DE L'EDUCATION. 1975. m. 235 F. (foreign 329 F.). Le Monde, 15 rue Falguiere, 75501 Paris Cedex 15, France. TEL 40-65-25-25. TELEX 650 572. (Subscr. to: Immeuble Sirius, 1 place Hubert-Beuve-mery, 94852 Ivry-sur-Seine Cedex, France. TEL 49-60-32-90) Ed. F. Gaussen. circ. 115,000. (also avail. in microfilm from RPI) **Indexed:** CERDIC, ELLIS, High.Educ.Curr.Aware.Bull. **Document type:** newspaper.
  —BLDSC (5906.915000).

373 157.61 US ISSN 0190-9185
HQ796
MONITORING THE FUTURE; questionnaire responses from the nation's high school seniors. 1975. a. $40. Institute for Social Research, University of Michigan, Box 1248, Ann Arbor, MI 48106. TEL 313-764-8271.

370 US ISSN 0026-9808
MONMOUTH EDUCATOR;* M C E A monitor. 1948. 10/yr. membership. Monmouth County Education Association, 1049 Broadway, West Long Branch, NJ 07764-1307. TEL 908-542-8254. illus. circ. 7,500.

370 US
MONTANA SCHOOLS. 1956. q. free. Office of Public Instruction, State Capitol, Box 202501, Helena, MT 59620-2501. TEL 406-444-4397. Ed. Sanna Kiesling. illus. circ. 12,000. (tabloid format) **Document type:** government publication.

MONTEREY PENINSULA MUSEUM OF ART NEWS. see *ART*

370 US ISSN 0889-6720
MONTESSORI NEWS. 1979. 2/yr. membership (free to qualified personnel). International Montessori Society, 912 Thayer Ave., Silver Spring, MD 20910. TEL 301-589-1127. Ed. Lee Havis. circ. 4,000. (tabloid format) **Document type:** newsletter, newspaper, academic/scholarly publication.
  Description: Expands awareness and practical application of Montessori principles with children.

372 US ISSN 0889-5643
MONTESSORI OBSERVER. 1980. 4/yr. $20 to individuals; institutions $25. International Montessori Society, 912 Thayer Ave., Silver Spring, MD 20910. TEL 301-589-1127. Ed. Lee Havis. adv.; bk.rev. circ. 2,000. **Document type:** newsletter, academic/scholarly publication.
  Description: Provides news and information about the development of Montessori education and attempts to promote an awareness of its principals.

372 JA
MONTHLY EDUCATION JOURNAL/GEKKAN KYOIKU JOURNAL. (Text in Japanese) 1963. m. 1800 Yen. Gakken Co. Ltd., 40-5, 4-chome, Kamiikedai, Ohta-ku, Tokyo 145, Japan. Ed. Mitsunobu Hayakawa.

370 US ISSN 0027-1055
MORELAND NEWS AND VIEWS. vol.8, 1970. bi-w. free to qualified personnel. Moreland School District, 4710 Campbell Ave., San Jose, CA 95130. TEL 408-379-1370. Ed. Keith Clawson. bk.rev. circ. 500. (processed)

370 US ISSN 0047-8121
MORNING STAR PEOPLE. 1965. 4/yr. free. St. Labre Indian School, Ashland, MT 59004. Ed. Mary Jo Burkholder. **Document type:** newsletter.
  Description: Informative newsletter from the St. Labre Indian School about the activities of its Native American pupils, both attending and alumni.

370 FR ISSN 1167-993X
MOUV'ANCE. 1992. m. 300 F. Association Nationale des Communautes Educatives, 145 bd. Magenta, 75010 Paris, France. TEL 44-63-51-15. FAX 42-85-56-14.

370 TS
AL-MU'ALLIM. 1982. m. Sharjah Teachers Society, P.O. Box 839, Sharjah, United Arab Emirates. TEL 248877. Ed. Salih al-Marzogi. circ. 3,500.
  Formerly: Sawt al-Mu'allim.
  Description: Covers international and local educational issues, and society activities.

370 US
▼**MULTICULTURAL EDUCATION.** 1993. q. $40 (effective 1993). (National Association for Multicultural Education) Caddo Gap Press, 3145 Geary Blvd., Ste. 275, San Francisco, CA 94118. TEL 415-750-9978. FAX 415-668-5450. Ed. Priscilla H. Walton. bk.rev.; film rev. circ. 10,000. **Document type:** academic/scholarly publication.
  Description: Features articles, interviews, promising practices, and listing of resources in multicultural education.

MURZILKA. see *CHILDREN AND YOUTH — For*

MUSIC TEACHERS LIBRARY. see *MUSIC*

MUSIK IN DER SCHULE; Zeitschrift fuer Theorie und Praxis des Musikunterrichts. see *MUSIC*

372 GW
MUSISCHE STUNDE; Unterrichtshilfen fuer Bewegungserziehung, Spielgestaltung, Musikalische Frueherziehung, Darstellung und Tanz. 1985. 2/yr. DM.19. A L S Verlag GmbH, Voltastr. 3, 63128 Dietzenbach, Germany. TEL 06074-25051. FAX 06074-27322. Ed. Ingrid Kreide. cum.index: 1985-1993. circ. 10,000. (looseleaf format; back issues avail.) **Document type:** academic/scholarly publication.

MUZIEK EN ONDERWIJS. see *MUSIC*

MUZIKA. see *MUSIC*

MY PRESCHOOLER. see *CHILDREN AND YOUTH — For*

MYND. see *CHILDREN AND YOUTH — For*

N A B E JOURNAL. (National Association for Bilingual Education) see *LINGUISTICS*

N A B E NEWS. (National Association for Bilingual Education) see *LINGUISTICS*

N A E A NEWS. (National Art Education Association) see *ART*

372 US ISSN 0094-0208
N A E P NEWSLETTER. 1967. 4/yr. free. (Educational Testing Service) National Assessment of Educational Progress, CN 6710, Princeton, NJ 08541-6710. Ed. Eleanor Driscoll. charts. circ. 40,000. **Document type:** newsletter.

371.8 US ISSN 0027-5824
LB2375
N A F S A NEWSLETTER. 1948. 8/yr. $35 (foreign $50). National Association for Foreign Student Affairs, Association of International Educators, 1875 Connecticut Ave., N.W., Ste. 1000, Washington, DC 20009-5728. TEL 202-462-4811. FAX 202-667-3419. Ed. Steven Kennedy. adv. circ. 7,000. **Document type:** newsletter.

N A T S JOURNAL. (National Association of Teachers of Singing, Inc.) see *MUSIC*

370 CN ISSN 0317-5227
N B T A NEWS. 1969. m. free. New Brunswick Teachers' Association, Box 752, Fredericton, NB E3B 5R6, Canada. TEL 506-452-8921. FAX 506-453-9795. Ed. Jim Dysart. circ. 8,200 (controlled). **Document type:** newsletter.

370 US ISSN 0027-6189
N C A E NEWS BULLETIN. 1970. 5/yr. $2.50. North Carolina Association of Educators, 700 S. Salisbury St., Box 27347, Raleigh, NC 27611. TEL 919-832-3000. Ed. Jacqueline Vaughn. circ. 56,000. (tabloid format) **Document type:** bulletin.
  Formerly: N C E A News Bulletin.

370 US ISSN 1043-3511
L11
N C A QUARTERLY. 1926. q. $15. North Central Association of Colleges and Schools, Arizona State University, Tempe, AZ 85287-3011. TEL 602-965-8700. bk.rev.; index. circ. 10,500. (also avail. in microform from UMI) **Indexed:** C.I.J.E., Educ.Ind.
  —BLDSC (6149.200000); Faxon; UnCover.
  Formerly (until 1989): North Central Association Quarterly (ISSN 0029-2648)

377.9 US ISSN 0550-5682
N C E A NOTES. 5/yr. membership. National Catholic Educational Association, 1077 30 St., N.W., Ste. 100, Washington, DC 20007. TEL 202-337-2632.
  Description: For members in elementary and secondary schools and superintendents-diocesan administrators.

370 II ISSN 0302-508X
N C E R T NEWSLETTER; a monthly house journal. (Text in English) 1974. m. National Council of Educational Research and Training, Publication Department, Sri Aurobindo Marg, New Delhi 110016, India. TEL 662708. Ed. T.S. Sarma. bk.rev. circ. 5,500. **Document type:** newsletter.

N C F E MOTIVATOR. (National Center for Financial Education) see *BUSINESS AND ECONOMICS — Banking And Finance*

N C S E REPORTS. (National Center for Science Education) see *SCIENCES: COMPREHENSIVE WORKS*

370 US
N E A NEW YORK. 1976. 9/yr. $10. National Education Association of New York, 217 Lark St., Albany, NY 12210. TEL 518-462-6451. FAX 518-462-1731. Ed. Mollie T. Marchione. adv.; illus. circ. 35,000. (tabloid format) **Document type:** newspaper.
  Formerly: N Y E A Advocate (ISSN 0161-7982)

370 US ISSN 0744-0154
N E A NOW. 1972. 37/yr. National Education Association of the United States, 1201 16th St., N.W., Washington, DC 20036. TEL 202-822-7207. Ed. Marian Clayton. circ. 115,000.

370 011　　　US　　ISSN 0734-7219
N E A TODAY. 1982. 8/yr. $15 to libraries (foreign $22). National Education Association of the United States, 1201 16th St., N.W., Washington, DC 20036. TEL 202-822-7207. FAX 202-822-7206. Ed. William Fischer. charts; illus. circ. 2,100,000. (also avail. in microform from UMI; reprint service avail. from UMI) **Indexed:** Mag.Ind., PSI, TOM. **Document type:** newspaper.
—BLDSC (6067.941500); UnCover; UMI.
Supersedes: N E A Reporter (ISSN 0027-6405); Supersedes in part (1913-1987): Today's Education (Annual Edition) (ISSN 0737-1888); Which was formerly: Today's Education (General Edition) (ISSN 0272-3573); Which superseded in part: Today's Education (ISSN 0040-8484); Which was formerly: N E A Journal.
Description: Features insights on the education challenges facing our nation today.

372　　　SA
N E O N. (Natal Education - Onderwys in Natal) (Text in Afrikaans or English) 1969. irreg. (approx. 2-3/yr.). free. Natal Education Department, Private Bag 9044, Pietermaritzburg 3200, South Africa. FAX 0331-943808. Ed. M.J. Marwick. bk.rev.; illus. circ. 3,500. **Indexed:** Ind.S.A.Per.
Description: Provides information on educational activities in the province as well as on topics of general educational interest and value.

370 300 301.412　PH　ISSN 0115-852X
N F E - W I D EXCHANGE - ASIA. NEWSLETTER. (Text and summaries in English) 1981. 3/yr. University of the Philippines at Los Banos, College of Agriculture, Department of Agricultural Education, Laguna 3720, Philippines. Ed. Dr. Priscilla A. Juliano. circ. 800. (back issues avail.) **Document type:** newsletter.

370　　　JA
N I E R. OCCASIONAL PAPER. (Text in English) 1981. irreg. (3-5/yr). free. National Institute for Educational Research, Section for International Cooperation in Education, Attn: Mr. N. Higuchi, 6-5-22 Shimo-Meguro, Meguro-ku, Tokyo 153, Japan. FAX 03-714-5294. Ed. T. Kanaya. circ. 300.

N O L P E SCHOOL LAW REPORTER. see *LAW*

371　　　US　　ISSN 0027-6987
N R T A BULLETIN. vol.11, 1970. m. membership. (National Retired Teachers Association) American Association of Retired Persons (Washington), 601 E St., N.W., Washington, DC 20049. TEL 202-434-2277. Ed. Elliot Carlson. adv.; illus. circ. 23,000,000.
Description: Focuses on subjects of interest to retired teachers such as educational trends, pension plans, development from Congress and state legislatures.

370　　　US
N S C T E MONOGRAPHS. (National Society of College Teachers of Education) a. price varies. Society of Professors of Education, c/o Richard Wisniewski, College of Education, Univ. of Tennessee, Knoxville, TN 37996-3400. TEL 615-974-2201. FAX 615-974-8718.

370　　　UK
N S E. (National Student Extra) 6/yr. £30. N U S Services Ltd., Bleaklow House, Howard Town Mills, Mill St., Glossop SK13 8PT, England. Ed. David Healy. circ. 100,000. **Document type:** consumer publication.
Former titles: N S M; National Student.

370 500　　　US
N S T A REPORTS. 6/yr. membership. National Science Teachers Association, 1840 Wilson Blvd., Arlington, VA 22201. Ed. Ann L. Wild. adv. circ. 47,000. **Document type:** newspaper.
Description: Presents information of interest to K-12 science teachers.

N T U BULLETIN. (Newark Teachers Union) see *LABOR UNIONS*

370　　　UK
N U S ACTION. 1922. fortn. £40. National Union of Students, 461 Holloway Rd., London N7 6LJ, England. circ. 3,500.
Former titles: N U S News; (1981): N U S Yearbook (ISSN 0077-5932)

378　　　UK　　ISSN 0951-7855
L16
N U T EDUCATION REVIEW. 1987. 2/yr. £14 to non-members; members £6; foreign £24. National Union of Teachers, Hamilton House, Mabledon Pl., London WC1H 9BD, England. TEL 071-388-6191. FAX 071-387-8458. Ed. Michael Barber. adv.; bk.rev. circ. 4,000. **Indexed:** Br.Educ.Ind., Br.Hum.Ind., Cont.Pg.Educ., Educ.Tech.Abstr., Mult.Ed.Abstr., SOMA, Stud.Wom.Abstr. **Document type:** academic/scholarly publication.
Formed by the merger of (1975-1987): Primary Education Review (ISSN 0141-6022); (1970-1987): Secondary Education Journal (ISSN 0143-1749); Which was formerly: Secondary Education (ISSN 0018-1595); Higher Education Journal.

371.4　　　US
N Y S C A NEWS. 1973. 5/yr. New York School Counselor Association, c/o Wes Berkowitz, Ed., Sachem High School, Sachem, NY 11779. adv.; bibl.; illus. circ. 2,000.
Formerly: New York School Counselor Association Newsletter.

370　　　NZ　　ISSN 0111-2821
N Z C E R NEWSLETTER. 1965. s-a. free. New Zealand Council for Educational Research, P.O. Box 3237, Wellington, New Zealand. TEL 64-4-3847-939. FAX 64-4-3847-933. Ed.Bd. bibl.; illus. circ. 5,000. (also avail. in microfilm from UMI) **Document type:** newsletter.
Description: Accounts of educational research in progress and completed, staff movements, and general news.

370　　　NZ　　ISSN 0114-8206
N Z E I ROUROU. 1990. 21/yr. NZ.$20. New Zealand Educational Institute, P.O. Box 466, Wellington 1, New Zealand. TEL 04-384-9689. FAX 04-385-1772. Ed. Cathy Jackson. adv. contact: Alastair Duncan. bk.rev.; charts; illus.; stat. circ. 16,000. **Indexed:** Cont.Pg.Educ. **Document type:** trade publication.
—CCC.
Formed by the 1990 merger of: National Education (ISSN 0027-9188) & Nat Ed Newsletter (ISSN 0111-395X)
Description: Provides industrial news and professional information to NZEI members in the primary education sector.

372　　　RU　　ISSN 0027-7371
NACHAL'NAYA SHKOLA. 1933. m. 2.40 Rub. (Ministerstvo Prosveshcheniya) Izdatel'stvo Prosveshchenie, 3-i Proezd Mar'inoi Roshchi, 41, Moscow, Russia. TEL 289-42-35. TELEX 111999 PARK. (Co-sponsor: Ministerstvo Narodnogo Obrazovaniya R.S.F.S.R.) Ed. V.G. Goretskii. bk.rev.; bibl.; illus. **Document type:** trade publication.
Description: Aimed at elementary school pedagogues.

370　　　RU　　ISSN 0027-8033
NARODNOE OBRAZOVANIE. 1918. m. $87 (foreign $114). Izdatels'stvo Pedagogika, Smolensky per. 4, 100034 Moscow, Russia. TEL 095-246-5969. (Dist. in U.S. by: Victor Kamkin Inc., 4956 Boiling Brook Pkwy, Rockville, MD 20852. TEL 301-881-5973) Ed. B. Ermidaev. abstr.; bibl.; illus.; index. circ. 131,435.

370　　　BN　　ISSN 0027-8262
NASI DANI. 1954. w. 80 din. Savez Socijalisticke Omladine Bosne i Hercegovine, Marsala Tita 44, Sarajevo, Bosnia Hercegovina. Ed. Djuro Kozar.

370　　　YU　　ISSN 0547-3330
NASTAVA I VASPITANJE. 1952. 6/yr. Pedagosko Drustvo SR Srbije, Terazije 26, Belgrade, Yugoslavia. bk.rev.; bibl.

373.1　　　US
NATIONAL ASSOCIATION FOR THE EDUCATION OF YOUNG CHILDREN. RESEARCH MONOGRAPHS. irreg., vol.5, 1992. price varies. National Association for the Education of Young Children, 1509 16th St., N.W., Washington, DC 20036-1426. TEL 202-232-8777. FAX 202-328-1846. **Document type:** monographic series.

371　　　US　　ISSN 0550-7421
L13
NATIONAL ASSOCIATION OF INDEPENDENT SCHOOLS. ANNUAL REPORT. Key Title: Annual Report - National Association of Incependent Schools. 1963. a. National Association of Independent Schools, 1620 L St., N.W., Washington, DC 20036-5605. stat. (reprint service avail. from UMI)

370　　　UK　　ISSN 0263-9696
NATIONAL ASSOCIATION OF INSPECTORS AND EDUCATIONAL ADVISORS. JOURNAL. 1974. s-a. £3. National Association of Inspectors and Educational Advisors, Nebo House, New Inn, Devanden, Chepstow, Gwent NP6 6NW, Wales. Ed. Eric Williams. circ. 1,600.

619　　　US
NATIONAL ASSOCIATION OF LABORATORY SCHOOLS. JOURNAL. 1976. q. $25 membership. National Association of Laboratory Schools, c/o John R. Johnson, 104 Davis Hall, University School, Indiana University of Pennsylvania, Indiana, PA 15705. TEL 412-357-2480. FAX 412-357-2434. Ed. Robert Hymer. bk.rev.; circ. 500 (paid). **Document type:** academic/scholarly publication.

370　　　US
NATIONAL COALITION NEWS. Variant title: N C A C S News. 4/yr. $20 membership. National Coalition of Alternative Community Schools, Box 15036, Santa Fe, NM 87506. TEL 505-474-4312. charts; illus. **Document type:** newsletter.
Description: Contains events, happenings, thoughts, and opinions from around the coalition and the world of alternative education. Emphasis is on international news

NATIONAL COUNCIL OF TEACHERS OF MATHEMATICS. PROFESSIONAL REFERENCE SERIES. see *MATHEMATICS*

NATIONAL COUNCIL OF TEACHERS OF MATHEMATICS. YEARBOOK. see *MATHEMATICS*

373 790.1　　　US
NATIONAL DIRECTORY OF HIGH SCHOOL COACHES. 1963. a. $42.95. Athletic Publishing Co., 2540 E. Fifth St., Montgomery, AL 36107. TEL 205-263-4436. Ed. Christine Bearley; Pub. Allen Dees. adv.: B&W page $785, color page $1225; trim 6 x 9; adv. contact: John Allen Dees. circ. 12,000. **Document type:** directory.

NATIONAL DIRECTORY OF STORYTELLING. see *LITERATURE*

370　　　US
NATIONAL EDUCATION ASSOCIATION OF THE UNITED STATES. PROCEEDINGS OF THE REPRESENTATIVE ASSEMBLY. 1860. a. $15.95 to non-members; members $5. National Education Association of the United States, 1201 16th St., N.W., Washington, DC 20036. TEL 800-229-4200. (Subscr. to: NEA Professional Library, Box 509, West Haven, CT 06516) index. **Document type:** proceedings.
Former titles: National Education Association of the United States. Proceedings of the Annual Meeting (ISSN 0190-7662); National Education Association of the United States. Addresses and Proceedings (ISSN 0077-4243)

370　　　US　　ISSN 0886-9979
NATIONAL EDUCATION ASSOCIATION RHODE ISLAND. NEWSLINE. m. (8/yr.). membership. National Education Association Rhode Island, 99 Bald Hill Rd., Cranston, RI 02920-2631. TEL 401-463-9630. Ed. Karen Comiskey Jenkins. adv. circ. 7,000.
Former titles: National Education Association Rhode Island. Journal; National Education Association. Journal (ISSN 0080-2751)

371.202　　　US　　ISSN 0027-9196
NATIONAL EDUCATIONAL SECRETARY. 1934. 4/yr. $20 to non-members. National Association of Educational Office Personnel, Box 12619, Wichita, KS 67277-2619. FAX 316-942-7100. Ed. Kay Barclay. adv.; bk.rev.; illus.; stat. circ. 7,000. (also avail. in microform from UMI; reprint service avail. from UMI)
—UnCover; UMI.

NATIONAL EDUCATOR. see *GENERAL INTEREST PERIODICALS — United States*

NATIONAL ENDOWMENT FOR THE ARTS. APPLICATION GUIDELINES: ARTS IN EDUCATION. see *ART*

EDUCATION

NATIONAL FORENSIC JOURNAL. see *COMMUNICATIONS*

370 US ISSN 0895-3880
NATIONAL FORUM OF APPLIED EDUCATIONAL RESEARCH JOURNAL. Short title: National Forum A E R J. 1987. 2/yr. $30 to individuals; libraries $50. (Wright State University) National Forum Journals, 1930 Nicholas St., Lake Charles, LA 70605. TEL 318-474-6976. Ed. William Allan Kritsonis. circ. 10,000. (back issues avail.) **Document type:** academic/scholarly publication.
—BLDSC (6023.644000). **CCC.**
 Description: Scholarly articles bridging the gap between educational theoreticians and practitioners in schools.
 Refereed Serial

NATIONAL FORUM OF INSTRUCTIONAL TECHNOLOGY JOURNAL. see *EDUCATION — Computer Applications*

370 US ISSN 1049-2658
LB1715
NATIONAL FORUM TEACHER EDUCATION JOURNAL. Short title: N F T E J. 1990. a. $80. (McNeese State University) National Forum Journals, 1930 Nicholas St., Lake Charles, LA 70605. TEL 318-474-6976. Ed. William Allan Kritsonis. **Document type:** academic/scholarly publication.
—BLDSC (6023.646200).
 Description: Addresses the roles, problems and progress of teacher education.
 Refereed Serial

370 US
NATIONAL HOMESCHOOL ASSOCIATION NEWSLETTER. 1988. q. $15. National Homeschool Association, Box 157290, Cincinnati, OH 45215-7290. Ed. Meg McClorey. bk.rev. **Document type:** newsletter.
 Description: Provides current news and information on home schooling.

370 JA ISSN 0085-378X
L67 CODEN: RBNRD9
NATIONAL INSTITUTE FOR EDUCATIONAL RESEARCH. RESEARCH BULLETIN. (Text in English) 1959. irreg. free. National Institute for Educational Research, Planning Section, 6-5-22 Shimo-Meguro, Meguro-ku, Tokyo 153, Japan. Ed. Bd. charts; illus.; stat.; circ. controlled. (tabloid format) **Indexed:** Psychol.Abstr. **Document type:** bulletin.

370 PP
NATIONAL RESEARCH INSTITUTE. DIVISION OF EDUCATIONAL RESEARCH. OCCASIONAL PAPERS. 1977. irreg. price varies. National Research Institute, Division of Educational Research, P.O. Box 5854, Boroko, NCD, Papua New Guinea. TEL 675-26-0300. FAX 675-26-0312.

370 PP
NATIONAL RESEARCH INSTITUTE. DIVISION OF EDUCATIONAL RESEARCH. RESEARCH PAPERS. 1972. irreg. price varies. National Research Institute, Division of Educational Research, P.O. Box 5854, Boroko, NCD, Papua New Guinea. TEL 675-26-0300. FAX 675-26-0312.

370 PP
NATIONAL RESEARCH INSTITUTE. DIVISION OF EDUCATIONAL RESEARCH. SPECIAL REPORT. 1985. irreg. price varies. National Research Institute, Division of Educational Research, P.O. Box 5854, Boroko, NCD, Papua New Guinea. TEL 675-26-0300. FAX 675-26-0312.

370 PP
NATIONAL RESEARCH INSTITUTE. DIVISION OF EDUCATIONAL RESEARCH. WORKING PAPERS. irreg. price varies. National Research Institute, Division of Educational Research, P.O. Box 5854, Boroko, NCD, Papua New Guinea. TEL 675-26-0300. FAX 675-26-0312.

370 US ISSN 0036-0023
LC5146
NATIONAL RURAL EDUCATION NEWS. 1948. q. $35 library membership includes Rural Educator and Country Teacher (foreign $50) (not avail. separately) (effective 1994). National Rural Education Association, 230 Education Bldg., Colorado State University, Fort Collins, CO 80523-0001. TEL 303-491-7022. FAX 303-491-1317. Ed. Joseph T. Newlin. adv.; bk.rev.; circ. 1,000 (paid). **Indexed:** ERIC. **Document type:** newsletter.
 Incorporates (1976-1980): Rural - Regional Education News (ISSN 0276-072X); **Formerly:** Rural Education News.

370 US ISSN 0077-5762
LB5
NATIONAL SOCIETY FOR THE STUDY OF EDUCATION. YEARBOOK. 1902. a. (in 2 parts). price varies. National Society for the Study of Education, University of Chicago, Judd Hall, Chicago, IL 60637. TEL 312-702-1582. (Subscr. to: Univ. of Chicago Press, 5835 Kimbark Ave., Chicago, IL 60637) Ed. Kenneth J. Rehage. circ. 2,700. **Indexed:** Educ.Ind.
—BLDSC (9394.100000).

370 CH
NATIONAL TAIWAN NORMAL UNIVERSITY. GRADUATE INSTITUTE OF EDUCATION. BULLETIN. (Text in Chinese and English) 1959. a. $9. National Taiwan Normal University, Graduate Institute of Education, Ho-Ping East Road, Taipei, Taiwan, Republic of China. TEL 02-3225146. FAX 02-3939468. Ed. Wu Chen-Tsou. bk.rev. circ. 1,500.

370 II
NAYI TALIM/BASIC EDUCATION. (Text in Hindi) 1952. bi-m. Rs.12 per no. All India Basic Education Council - All India Nai Talim Samiti, Sevagram, Wardha, Maharashtra, India. Ed. Shriman Narayan. adv.; bk.rev. circ. 3,000.

370 613.7 US
NEBRASKA JOURNAL. s-a. $10. Nebraska Association for Health, Physical Education, Recreation & Dance, School of HPER, Univ. of Nebraska-Lincoln, 204 MABL, Lincoln, NE 68588-0229. TEL 402-554-2670. Ed. Tom Sharpe. adv. circ. 350. (back issues avail.) **Indexed:** Phys.Ed.Ind.

NEBRASKA MUSIC EDUCATOR. see *MUSIC*

370 NE ISSN 0169-1872
NEDERLANDS TIJDSCHRIFT VOOR OPVOEDING, VORMING, EN ONDERWIJS. (Text in Dutch; summaries in English) 1984. bi-m. fl.77.50. (Nederlandse Vereniging van Onderwijskundigen) Van Gorcum en Co. B.V., P.O. Box 43, 9400 AA Assen, Netherlands. TEL 31-5920-46864. FAX 31-5920-72064. Ed. R. van der Kooij. adv.; bk.rev. circ. 2,500. **Document type:** academic/scholarly publication.
—SWETS.

370 US ISSN 0548-1384
NEED A LIFT? 1951. a. $2. American Legion, Need a Lift, Box 1055, Indianapolis, IN 46206. Ed. Robert K. Caudell. adv. circ. 100,000.
 Description: Covers sources of career, scholarship and loan information for not only children of veterans but for all children. Includes information that leads students to millions of dollars in scholarships, fellowships, loans and part-time jobs to help finance their education.

373 NE ISSN 0922-2472
NEEM MIJNOU. 1970. 10/yr. fl.19.50. Landelijk Centrum voor Gereformeerd Jeugdwerk, Postbus 99, 3970 AB Driebergen, Netherlands. TEL 03438-23251.
 Former titles: Voetnoot; Weerwoord; Risiko (ISSN 0035-5569).
 Description: Provides information for Dutch Reformed youth groups in the age range of 16 through 25.

370 910.03 US ISSN 0548-1457
NEGRO EDUCATIONAL REVIEW. 1950. q. $15. Negro Educational Review, Inc., Box 2895, West Bay Annex, Jacksonville, FL 32203. Ed. R. Grann Lloyd. adv.; bk.rev.; index, cum.index every 25 yrs. circ. 5,000. (tabloid format) **Indexed:** C.I.J.E., Cont.Pg.Educ., Educ.Ind., Ind.Per.Blacks, Sociol.Educ.Abstr.
—BLDSC (6075.160000); UnCover.

370 NE
NETHERLANDS. MINISTERIE VAN ONDERWIJS EN WETENSCHAPPEN. ONDERWIJSVERSLAG. 1973. a. price varies. Staatsuitgeverij, Chr. Plantijnstraat, The Hague, Netherlands. circ. 1,000.

NETWORK (ARLINGTON). see *ADVERTISING AND PUBLIC RELATIONS*

370 US ISSN 1041-8520
NETWORK FOR PUBLIC SCHOOLS. 1975. bi-m. $15. National Committee for Citizens in Education, 900 Second St., N.E., Ste. 8, Washington, DC 20002-3557. TEL 202-408-0447. FAX 202-408-0452. Ed. Susan Hlesciak Hall. adv.; bk.rev.; charts; illus. circ. 10,000. (back issues avail.)
 Formerly: Network.
 Description: Features articles on school issues and a direct mail catalogue of publications focused on public involvement and school improvement.

370 GW
NEUE DEUTSCHE SCHULE. 1949. s-m. DM.43. (Gewerkschaft Erziehung und Wissenschaft, Landesverband Nordrhein-Westfalen) Neue Deutsche Schule Verlagsgesellschaft mbH, Nuenningstr. 11, 45141 Essen, Germany. adv.; bk.rev. circ. 42,500. (back issues avail.)

370 GW ISSN 0028-3355
AP30
NEUE SAMMLUNG; Vierteljahres-Zeitschrift fuer Erziehung und Gesellschaft. 1961. q. DM.145. Erhard Friedrich Verlag, Im Brande 15, 30926 Seelze, Germany. FAX 0511-40004-19. (Subscr. to: Postfach 100150, 30917 Seelze, Germany) Ed. Gerold Becker. adv.; bk.rev.; bibl.; index. circ. 1,600. (reprint service avail. from KTO) **Indexed:** Amer.Hist.& Life, Hist.Abstr.
—Faxon; SWETS. **CCC.**
 Formerly: Sammlung.

NEUE WEGE; Kulturzeitschrift junger Menschen. see *CHILDREN AND YOUTH — For*

DIE NEUEREN SPRACHEN; Zeitschrift fuer Forschung, Unterricht und Kontaktstudium auf dem Fachgebiet der modernen Fremdsprachen. see *LINGUISTICS*

NEUSPRACHLICHE MITTEILUNGEN AUS WISSENSCHAFT UND PRAXIS. see *LINGUISTICS*

NEW CATALYST. see *ENVIRONMENTAL STUDIES*

370 US ISSN 0164-7989
H62.A1
NEW DIRECTIONS FOR PROGRAM EVALUATION. 1979. q. $54 to individuals; institutions $75. (American Evaluation Association) Jossey-Bass Inc., Publishers, 350 Sansome St., 5th Fl., San Francisco, CA 94104. TEL 415-433-1767. FAX 415-433-0499. Ed. William Shadish. circ. 2,850. (also avail. in microform from UMI; back issues avail.; reprint service avail. from UMI) **Indexed:** C.I.J.E., Cont.Pg.Educ., Educ.Ind. **Document type:** monographic series.
—BLDSC (6083.406000); Faxon; UnCover; UMI.
 Description: Outlines techniques and procedures for conducting useful evaluation studies of all types of programs, from educational curricula to health programs.

370 US ISSN 0271-0633
LB1025.2
NEW DIRECTIONS FOR TEACHING AND LEARNING. 1980. q. $47 to individuals; institutions $62. Jossey-Bass Inc., Publishers, 350 Sansome St., 5th Fl., San Francisco, CA 94104. TEL 415-433-1767. FAX 415-433-0499. Ed. Robert J. Menges. circ. 900. (back issues avail.; reprint service avail. from UMI) **Indexed:** C.I.J.E., Chic.Per.Ind., Educ.Ind., Psychol.Abstr. **Document type:** monographic series.
—BLDSC (6083.469500); UnCover; SWETS; UMI.
 Description: Presents ideas and techniques for improving college teaching based on both the practical expertise of seasoned instructors and on the latest research findings of educational and psychological researchers.

370　　　　　　　AT　ISSN 0156-0905
L91
NEW EDUCATION. 1978. 2/yr. $60 to individuals; institutions $95. James Nicholas Publishers, P.O. Box 244, Albert Park, Vic. 3206, Australia. TEL 03-696-5545. FAX 613-699-2040. Ed. Rea Zajda. adv.; bk.rev.; index. (back issues avail.) **Indexed:** Aus.Educ.Ind., Cont.Pg.Educ., Educ.Tech.Abstr., Lang.& Lang.Behav.Abstr., Rural Ext.Educ.& Tr.Abstr., Sociol.Abstr., Sociol.Educ.Abstr., Sp.Ed.Needs Abstr. **Document type:** academic/scholarly publication.
—CCC.
Description: Investigates current trends in educational practice and theory, by focusing on educational reforms, teaching methods, curriculum evaluation and comparative studies in education and social change.

370　　　　　　　AT　ISSN 0811-5982
NEW ENGLAND MONOGRAPHS IN CONTINUING EDUCATION (NO.). 1983. irreg. University of New England, Department of Continuing Education, Armidale, N.S.W. 2351, Australia. TEL 067-732287.

420.07 370　　US　ISSN 0028-4882
NEW ENGLAND READING ASSOCIATION. JOURNAL. 1966. 3/yr. $10. New England Reading Association, Box 997, Portland, ME 04104-0997. TEL 207-772-6540. Ed. Donald L. Landry. adv.; bk.rev. circ. 3,000. (also avail. in microform from UMI; reprint service avail. from UMI) **Indexed:** Educ.Ind.
—Faxon; UnCover; UMI.

966.7　　　　　GH　ISSN 0028-4998
NEW ERA.* 1968. m. $5. Nananom Publishers, Box 5446, Accra, Ghana.

407 370　　　　UK
L16
NEW ERA IN EDUCATION. 1920. 3/yr. £17 to individuals; institutions £23. World Education Fellowship, c/o Helen Pearson, 20 Queen Sq., Leeds LS2 8AF, England. Ed.Bd. adv.; bk.rev.; index. circ. 2,000. (also avail. in microform from UMI; reprint service avail. from UMI) **Indexed:** Br.Educ.Ind., Sp.Ed.Needs Abstr. **Document type:** bulletin.
—UnCover.
Formerly (until 1988): New Era (ISSN 0028-5048); Which incorporated: World Studies Bulletin and Ideas.

NEW HAMPSHIRE BUSINESS EDUCATION ASSOCIATION. NEWSLETTER. see *BUSINESS AND ECONOMICS*

370　　　　　　US　ISSN 0028-5234
NEW HAMPSHIRE EDUCATOR. 1920. 8/yr. $3.60 to non-members. New Hampshire Education Association, 103 N. State St., Concord, NH 03301. TEL 603-224-7751. Ed. Carol Carstarphen. adv.; bk.rev.; film rev.; illus. circ. 7,800. (tabloid format) **Document type:** newsletter.

NEW HAMPSHIRE QUARTER NOTES. see *MUSIC*

370　　　　　　AT　ISSN 0028-5382
NEW HORIZONS IN EDUCATION. 1937. s-a. Aus.$12. World Education Fellowship (Australia), P.O. Box 367, Launceston, Tas. 7250, Australia. TEL 003-243281. Ed. Edward Bromhall. adv.; bk.rev. circ. 1,000.
Description: Covers current issues, policies, and developments concerning education in Australia. Includes reports of events.

370 331.8 340　US　ISSN 0279-8557
NEW JERSEY EDUCATION LAW REPORT; the authority on labor relations in New Jersey schools. 1980. m. $189. Whitaker Newsletters Inc., 313 South Ave., Fanwood, NJ 07023-0192. TEL 908-889-6336. FAX 908-889-6339. (Subscr. to: Box 192, Fanwood, NJ 07034) Ed. Irving Evers. bk.rev. (back issues avail.) **Document type:** newsletter.
—CCC.
Description: Covers news and administrative and court decisions pertaining to the law, the courts and New Jersey schools. Emphasizes decisions by the Commissioner of Education and the Public Employees Relations Commission.

NEW JERSEY JOURNAL OF SCHOOL PSYCHOLOGY. see *PSYCHOLOGY*

370.193　　　　US　ISSN 0028-5897
NEW JERSEY PARENT TEACHER. 1915. 8/yr. (Sep.-Jun.). $4. New Jersey Congress of Parents and Teachers, 900 Berkeley Ave., Trenton, NJ 08618. TEL 609-393-6709. Ed. Pat Frey. illus.; stat. circ. 4,000. **Document type:** bulletin.
Description: Provides news of local and national issues affecting youth and public education, parental involvement in schools and communities, and legislation for public education, news regarding PTA events.

370　　　　　　　US
NEW SCHOOLS EXCHANGE. DIRECTORY AND RESOURCE GUIDE. 1969. a. $5. New Schools Exchange, Pettigrew, AR 72752. Ed. Grace Dailey-Harwood. adv.; bk.rev.; bibl.; film rev.; cum.index. circ. 3,000. (back issues avail.)

370　　　　　　　PK　ISSN 0077-8826
NEW TEACHER. (Text in English, Urdu and Pashto) 1952. a. Rs.8. University of Peshawar, College of Education, Peshawar, Pakistan. Ed.Bd.

NEW TREND; independent forum for the oppressed Muslim masses. see *RELIGIONS AND THEOLOGY — Islamic*

NEW TRENDS IN PHYSICS TEACHING. see *PHYSICS*

370 340　　　　US　ISSN 0896-4122
NEW YORK EDUCATION LAW REPORT. m. $125. Whitaker Newsletters Inc., 313 South Ave., Fanwood, NJ 07023. TEL 908-889-6336. FAX 908-889-6339. (Subscr. to: Box 192, Fanwood, NJ 07023) Ed. Fred Rossi. bk.rev. **Document type:** newsletter.
—CCC.
Description: Covers new and administrative and court decisions pertaining to the law, the courts and New York schools. Emphasizes decisions by the Commissioner of Education and the Public Employment Relations Board.

NEW YORK STATE SCHOOL BOARDS ASSOCIATION. EMPLOYEE RELATIONS NEWS. see *EDUCATION — School Organization And Administration*

NEW YORK TEACHER. see *LABOR UNIONS*

370 379　　　　NZ　ISSN 0077-958X
NEW ZEALAND. CENTRAL ADVISORY COMMITTEE ON THE APPOINTMENTS AND PROMOTION OF PRIMARY TEACHERS. REPORT TO THE MINISTER OF EDUCATION. 1961. quinquennial. free. (Central Advisory Committee) Government Printing Office, c/o Department of Education, Private Bag, Government Buildings, Wellington, New Zealand. circ. controlled. **Document type:** government publication.

370　　　　　　　NZ　ISSN 0028-8276
LA2120　　　　　CODEN: NZESDN
NEW ZEALAND JOURNAL OF EDUCATIONAL STUDIES. 1966. s-a. $60 to individuals; institutions $95. New Zealand Council for Educational Research, Attn.: Zona Steer, P.O. Box 3237, Wellington, New Zealand. Eds. John Codd, Joy Cullen. adv.; bk.rev.; charts; illus.; stat.; index, cum.index. **Indexed:** Cont.Pg.Educ., Curr.Cont., Educ.Tech.Abstr., Lang.& Lang.Behav.Abstr., Psychol.Abstr., Res.High.Educ.Abstr., So.Pac.Per.Ind., Sociol.Educ.Abstr., Sp.Ed.Needs Abstr., SSCI, Stud.Wom.Abstr. **Document type:** academic/scholarly publication.
—BLDSC (6093.540000); UnCover. CCC.

370　　　　　　　CN　ISSN 0380-1047
NEWFOUNDLAND TEACHERS' ASSOCIATION. BULLETIN. 1954. 8/yr. (during school yr.). Can.$7($8) Newfoundland Teachers' Association, 3 Kenmount Rd., St. John's, Nfld. A1B 1W1, Canada. TEL 709-726-3223. FAX 709-726-4302. adv. **Document type:** bulletin, trade publication.

370　　　　　　　US　ISSN 0271-8472
LB3051
NEWS ON TESTS. 1979-1993 (Dec.). q. $45. Educational Testing Service, Test Collection, Princeton, NJ 08541. TEL 609-734-5682. FAX 609-734-5410. Ed. Marilyn Halpern. index. circ. 650. (also avail. in microfiche; back issues avail.) **Document type:** newsletter.
Supersedes: Test Collection Bulletin (ISSN 0563-1874)

370　　　　　　　US
NEWSLINER (LITTLE ROCK).* q. National Association of State Education, Department Information Officers, RR1 Box 55B, Bigelow, AR 72016-9705. TEL 501-378-2344. Ed. Mary Laurie.
Description: Exchange of information among members.

491.8 370　　　US
DK1
NEWSNET. 1960. 5/yr. $20 to non-members. American Association for the Advancement of Slavic Studies, Jordan Quad - Acacia Bldg., Stanford University, Stanford, CA 94305-4130. TEL 415-723-9668. adv. circ. 4,000. **Document type:** newsletter.
Formerly: American Association for the Advancement of Slavic Studies. Newsletter (ISSN 0883-9549)

370　　　　　　　NR　ISSN 0189-2916
LA1630
NIGERIA EDUCATIONAL FORUM. JOURNAL. (Special issues avail.) 1974. s-a. £N240. Ahmadu Bello University, Institute of Education, Zaria, Nigeria. TEL 51216. Ed. R.A. Omojuwa. adv.; bk.rev. circ. 500. **Indexed:** Rural Ext.Educ.& Tr.Abstr.
Formerly: Ahmadu Bello University. Institute of Education. Paper (ISSN 0065-4752)
Description: Deals with a variety of educational topics covering school subjects.

370　　　　　　　NR　ISSN 0029-0157
NIGERIAN SCHOOLMASTER. 1969. 3/yr. L.3. Nigeria Union of Teachers, P.M.B. 1044 Yaba, Lagos, Nigeria. Ed. Gabriel O. Falade. adv.; bk.rev.; play rev.; illus. circ. 20,000.
Description: Contains organization news.

NIHON KYOIKUHO GAKKAI NENPO. see *LAW*

NIIGATAKEN SEIBUTSU KYOIKU KENKYUKAISHI/NIIGATA PREFECTURAL BIOLOGICAL SOCIETY FOR EDUCATION. BULLETIN. see *BIOLOGY*

370 331.8　　　JA　ISSN 0029-0505
NIKKYOSO KYOIKU SHINBUN. 1949. w. 1500 Yen. Japan Teachers' Union - Nikkyoso, Nihon Kyoiku-Kaikan, 2-6-2 Hitotsubashi, Kanda, Chiyoda-ku, Tokyo, Japan. Ed.Bd. adv.; charts; illus.; stat. circ. 450,000. **Document type:** newspaper.

370　　　　　　　US　ISSN 0077-9253
NONPUBLIC SCHOOL ENROLLMENT AND STAFF, NEW YORK STATE. 1966. a. free. Education Department, Instruction & Program Development, Education Bldg. Annex, Rm. 381, Albany, NY 12234. TEL 518-474-7082. FAX 518-474-4351. charts; stat.; circ. controlled. (back issues avail.) **Document type:** government publication.
Formerly: Survey of Nonpublic Schools in New York State.

370　　　　　　　NO　ISSN 0901-8050
NORDISK PEDAGOGIK/POHJOIISMAINEN PEDAGOGIKA. (Text in English, Scandinavian languages; summaries in English, Finnish) 1980. q. NOK 470 in the Nordic countries; elsewhere NOK 505. (Nordisk Forening for Pedagogisk Forskning (NFPF) - Nordic Society for Educational Research) Scandinavian University Press, P.O. Box 2959 Toeyen, N-0608 Oslo, Norway. TEL 47-22-57-54-00. FAX 47-22-57-53-53. Ed. Bjoern Hasselgren.
Formerly (until 1986): Tidskrift foer Nordisk Foerening foer Pedagogisk Forskning (ISSN 0349-6732)
Description: Publishes scholarly articles, lively debate and information on issues in education in the Nordic countries.

370　　　　　　　NO　ISSN 0029-2052
NORSK PEDAGOGISK TIDSSKRIFT/NORWEGIAN JOURNAL OF EDUCATION. 1917. bi-m. NOK 410 in the Nordic countries, elsewhere NOK 485. Scandinavian University Press, P.O. Box 2959-Toeyen, N-0608 Oslo, Norway. TEL 472-67-7600. FAX 472-67-7575. (U.S. addr.: Scandinavian University Press, 200 Meacham Ave., Elmont, NY 11003. TEL 516-352-7300) Ed.Bd. adv.; bk.rev.; abstr.; ndex. circ. 3,000. (back issues avail.) **Document type:** trade publication.
Description: Deals with theoretical and practical issues in education.

EDUCATION

370   NO   ISSN 0029-2117
NORSK SKOLEBLAD. 1934. w. (40/yr.). NOK 350. Norsk Laererlag - Norwegian Union of Teachers, Rosenkrantzgt. 15, Oslo 1, Norway. TEL 02-41-58-75. FAX 02-425137. Ed. Knut Hovland. adv.; bk.rev.; index; circ. 58,600 (controlled). (reprint service avail.) **Document type:** trade publication.
—CCC.

370   US   ISSN 0029-2451
NORTH CAROLINA EDUCATION. 1906. q. $2.50. North Carolina Association of Educators, 700 S. Salisbury St., Box 27347, Raleigh, NC 27611. TEL 919-832-3000. Ed. Jacqueline Vaughn. adv.; bk.rev.; index. circ. 56,000.

371.14   US   ISSN 0048-0681
NORTH DAKOTA EDUCATION NEWS. 1968. 9/yr. $85 membership only. North Dakota Education Association, Box 5005, Bismarck, ND 58502. TEL 701-223-0450. FAX 701-224-8535. Ed. Richard J. Palmer. adv. circ. 8,500. (tabloid format) **Document type:** newspaper.

370   CN   ISSN 0029-3253
NORTHIAN. 1964. q. Can.$6. Society for Indian and Northern Education, Univ. of Saskatchewan, Saskatoon, Sask. S7N 0W0, Canada. TEL 306-343-2100. Ed. D. Koenig. bk.rev.; illus.; index. circ. 500. (also avail. in microform from UMI) Indexed: C.I.J.E., Can.Educ.Ind.

NORTHWEST ASSOCIATION OF SCHOOLS AND COLLEGES. CONVENTION PROCEEDINGS. see EDUCATION — Higher Education

370   US
NORTHWEST ASSOCIATION OF SCHOOLS AND COLLEGES. NEWSLETTER. 1968. s-a. membership. Northwest Association of Schools and Colleges, Boise State University, Boise, ID 83725. TEL 208-334-3226. FAX 208-334-3228. Ed. David G. Steadman. bibl.; circ. controlled. (processed) **Document type:** newsletter.
Former titles: Northwest Association of Schools and Colleges. Committee on Research and Service. Newsletter; Northwest Association of Secondary and Higher Schools. Committee on Research and Service. Newsletter. (ISSN 0029-3326)

370   IT
NOSTRI BAMBINI; incontri tra scuola materna e famiglia. 1972. 7/yr. L.5000. Associazione Genitori, P.O. Box 602, 40100 Bologna, Italy. circ. 15,000.

370   IT   ISSN 0029-3792
NOSTRI RAGAZZI; incontri tra scuola elementare e famiglia. 1958. 7/yr. L.5000. Associazione Genitori, P.O. Box 217, 40100 Bologna, Italy. circ. 15,000.

378   PH   ISSN 0048-0932
NOTRE DAME JOURNAL. 1965. s-a. P.500. Notre Dame University, Cotabato City, Philippines. TEL 063-64-214313. Ed. Eliseo R. Mercado. bk.rev. circ. 500. Indexed: Curr.Cont., Ind.Phil.Per. **Document type:** academic/scholarly publication.
Description: Publishes papers, research reports and thesis abstracts on education.

370   FR   ISSN 0029-4748
NOUVELLE FAMILLE EDUCATRICE. 1947. 8/yr. 25 F. (Union Nationale des Associations de Parents d'Eleves de l'Enseignement Libre (UNAPEL)) Societe d'Edition de la Famille Educatrice, 277 rue Saint Jacques, 75005 Paris, France. TEL 46-33-62-89. FAX 46-34-70-33. adv.; bk.rev.; bibl.; film rev.; illus.; stat.; tr.lit.; tr.mk. circ. 819,092. (tabloid format)

373   FR
NOUVELLE REVUE PEDAGOGIQUE. 1969. 9/yr. 280 F. Librairie Fernand Nathan, 9 rue Mechain, 75680 Paris Cedex 14, France. adv. circ. 76,000.

370   CN   ISSN 0710-5568
NOUVELLES C E Q. (Text in French) 1970. 5/yr. free. Centrale de l'Enseignement du Quebec, 9405 Sherbrooke St., E., Montreal, PQ H1L 6P3, Canada. TEL 514-356-8888. FAX 514-356-9999. Ed. Luc Allaire. adv.; bk.rev. circ. 100,000. (back issues avail.) Indexed: RADAR.
Former titles: Mouvements (ISSN 0823-5651); Magazine C E Q (ISSN 0710-300X); Ligne Directe (ISSN 0315-4998); Enseignement (ISSN 0046-211X)

378   EI   ISSN 0378-8172
NOUVELLES UNIVERSITAIRES EUROPEENES/EUROPEAN UNIVERSITY NEWS. (Text in Dutch, English, French, German, Italian) vol. 5, 1970. bi-m. Commission of the European Communities, University Information, 200 rue de la Loi, B-1049 Brussels, Belgium. FAX 236-07-52. (Subscr. to: Office for Official Publications, 2 rue Mercier, L-2985 Luxembourg, Luxembourg; Dist. in U.S. by: European Community Information Service, 2100 M St., N.W., Ste. 707, Washington, DC 20037) Ed. Gilbert Germain. bk.rev. circ. 6,000. Indexed: Cont.Pg.Educ., EC Ind. **Document type:** newsletter.
Description: Carries news for and from universities in Europe, especially on courses and lectures in European studies and research, calendar of forthcoming events and useful addresses.

370   BL   ISSN 0103-0116
NOVA ESCOLA. 1986. m. $55. Fundacao Victor Civita, Rua Haddock Lobo 403-D, 01414-903 Sao Paulo SP, Brazil. TEL 011-284-1040. (Subscr. to: Rua do Curtume 769, 05065-900 Sao Paulo, Brazil. TEL 011-823-9100) Ed. Ana Maria Sanchez. adv.; bk.rev.; charts, illus. circ. 80,000. **Document type:** trade publication.
Description: For elementary school teachers.

NOVA SCOTIA CRAFT NEWS. see ARTS AND HANDICRAFTS

370   PL   ISSN 0029-537X
NOWA SZKOLA; miesiecznik spoleczno-pedagogiczny. 1945. 10/yr. $42. (Ministerstwo Edukacji Narodowej) Wydawnictwa Szkolne i Pedagogiczne, Pl. Dabrowskiego 8, 00-950 Warsaw, Poland. TEL 48-22-261327. FAX 48-22-266313. (Dist. by: Ars Polona-Ruch, Krakowskie Przedmiescie 7, Warsaw, Poland) bk.rev.; illus.; index. circ. 6,000.
Description: Focuses on contemporary problems of instruction and education, presents teachers' experiences, publishes reports on educational research and experiments undertaken at schools, and reports on the life of schools and other educational institutions.

370   PN
NUEVA ESCUELA. N.S. 1990. q. Instituto de Estudios Nacionales, La Colina, Estafeta Universitaria, Universidad de Panama, Panama, Panama. TEL 69-1412. Ed. Alfredo Figueroa Navarro. circ. 500.

370   GW
NUMERUS CLAUSUS - FINESSEN. 1973. a. DM.18. Verein Freunde und Foerderer der Deutschen Studentenschaft e.V., Untere Hausbreite 11, 80939 Munich, Germany. Ed. Gundolf Seidenspinner. adv.
Former titles: Numerus Clausus - Alternativen; Numerus Clausus - Ersatzstudiengaenge.

370   IT   ISSN 0469-2454
NUOVA RIVISTA PEDAGOGICA.* 1951. bi-m. L.4000. Via deila Camilluccia 177, 00135 Rome, Italy. Ed. Nino Sammartano.

370   IT
NUOVA SECONDARIA. 1983. m. L.70000. Editrice la Scuola S.p.A., Via Cadorna 11, 25186 Brescia, Italy. TEL 030-29931. Ed. Evandro Agazzi.

372 373   IC   ISSN 0258-3747
NY MENNTAMAL. 1983. q. ISK 1350. Bandalag Kennarafelaga, Lagmula 7, 108 Reykjavik, Iceland. TEL 354-1-31117. FAX 354-1-679239. Ed. Hannes I. Olafsson. adv.; bk.rev. circ. 5,700. (back issues avail.) **Document type:** academic/scholarly publication, trade publication.
Description: Devoted to education on the elementary and secondary level.

371.3   US   ISSN 0743-7986
O E A FOCUS. 1919. 10/yr. $5 to non-members. Oklahoma Education Association, Box 18485, 323 E. Madison, Oklahoma City, OK 73154. TEL 405-528-7785. FAX 405-524-0350. Ed. Bill Guy. adv. contact: Bill Guy. bk.rev.; illus.; index. circ. 49,500. (tabloid format; also avail. in microform from UMI; reprint service avail. from UMI) **Document type:** newspaper.
—UMI.
Formerly (until 1982): Oklahoma Teacher (ISSN 0030-1884)

377.8   CN
O E C T A REPORTER. 1968. 5/yr. Can.$18 membership. Ontario English Catholic Teachers Association, 65 St. Clair Ave. E., Toronto, ON M4T 2Y8, Canada. TEL 416-925-2493. FAX 416-925-7764. Ed. Aleda O'Connor. adv.; bk.rev.; abstr.; illus. circ. 32,000.
Formerly (until 1975): O E C T A Reporter (ISSN 0384-5621); Which was formed by the merger of: O E C T A News and Views (ISSN 0384-563X); O E C T A Review (ISSN 0384-5613)
Description: Publishes articles on educational innovations, curriculum development, education philosophies for practising teachers in Catholic school systems in Ontario.

377 282   BE   ISSN 0770-1683
LC461
O I E C BULLETIN. (Text in English, French, Spanish) 1969. N.S. 1993. 4/yr. 600 BEF($20) in Europe; elsewhere 750 BEF($25). Office International de l'Enseignement Catholique - Catholic International Education Office, 60 rue des Eburons, B-1040 Brussels, Belgium. TEL 32-2-2307252. FAX 32-2-2309745. Ed. Father Andres Delgado Hernandez; Pub. Claire Fijolek. adv. contact: Josu de Aguirre. bk.rev. circ. 700. (processed) Indexed: HR Rep. **Document type:** bulletin.
Former titles: Catholic International Education Office. Bulletin Nouvelle Serie; Catholic International Education Office. Bulletin Trimestriel (ISSN 0084-8638)
Description: Aim is to make widely known the major trends affecting education in schools today and shaping tomorrow's educational policies.

O I O NEWS. (Oklahomans for Indian Opportunity) see ETHNIC INTERESTS

370   UK   ISSN 0953-5543
O R INSIGHT. 1988. 4/yr. £40 to non-members; institutions £50. Operational Research Society, Publications Unit, Neville House, Waterloo St., Birmingham B2 5TX, England. TEL 021-643-0236. FAX 021-631-3485. Ed. S.C. Ward. adv.; bk.rev. Indexed: Comput.Abstr., Cont.Pg.Manage. **Document type:** academic/scholarly publication.
—BLDSC (6277.373000).

371.4   CN   ISSN 1193-9524
O S C A REPORTS. 1976. 4/yr. Can.$60. Ontario School Counsellors' Association, 19 Treadgold Cres., Don Mills, ON M3A 1X1, Canada. TEL 416-449-9321. FAX 416-449-9321. Ed. Al Oakley. adv.; bk.rev.; illus. circ. 1,200.
Former titles (until 1990): O S C A R. Ontario School Counsellors' Association Reports (ISSN 0843-154X); (until 1980): O S C A Reports (ISSN 0383-9931); (until 1976): Ontario School Counsellors' Association. Newsletter (ISSN 0317-3992)

370   US   ISSN 0095-6694
L13
O S S C BULLETIN. 1957. 9/yr. $55. University of Oregon College of Education, Oregon School Study Council, 1787 Agate St., Eugene, OR 97403-5207. TEL 503-346-5043. FAX 503-346-2334. Ed. Stuart C. Smith. circ. 800 (paid). (also avail. in microfiche) Indexed: ERIC. **Document type:** monographic series.
●Also available online.
Formerly: Oregon School Study Council. Bulletin.
Description: Reports on a single, important educational topic or issue, combining evidence from research literature with descriptions of actual school programs in each number.

370 370.15 100   CI   ISSN 0351-4889
ODGOJ I SAMOUPRAVLJANJE. (Text in Croatian; summaries in English and Russian) 1981. a. $5. (Institute for Pedagogy of the Philosophic Faculty) SIZ Znanosti SR Hrvatske, Opaticka 10, 41000 Zagreb, Croatia. TEL 041-274 261. circ. 1,000.

OFFSPRING - BOING. see CHILDREN AND YOUTH — For

EDUCATION

370   TU
OGRETMEN. (Text in Turkish) 1972. 3/yr. Kibris Turk Orta Egitim Ogretmenler Sendikasi - Cyrpus Turkish Secondary School Teachers Union, Abdullah Parla Sokagi, Lefkosa Kibris, Mersin 10, Turkey. TEL 90-392-2287971. FAX 90-392-2288648. Ed. Ali Alnar. circ. 1,500. (tabloid format) **Document type:** newspaper.
    Description: Examines events, problems and devlopments in the field of teaching in Northern Cyprus at the secondary school level.

OHIO MEDIA SPECTRUM. see *LIBRARY AND INFORMATION SCIENCES*

370.193   US   ISSN 0199-0918
OHIO P T A NEWS. 1923. 8/yr. $6. Ohio Congress of Parents & Teachers, Inc., 427 E. Town St., Columbus, OH 43215. TEL 614-221-4844. Ed. Barbara Sprague. charts, illus. circ. 2,500. **Document type:** newsletter.
    Formerly (until vol.57, May 1979): Ohio Parent Teacher (ISSN 0030-1019)

372   US   ISSN 0030-1035
OHIO READING TEACHER; a journal of education whose objective is to improve reading instruction in Ohio schools. 1967. q. $12. International Reading Association, Inc., Ohio Council, 401 McGuffey Hall, Miami University, Oxford, OH 45056. TEL 513-529-6451. Ed. Carolyn Andrews-Beck. adv.; bk.rev.; bibl. circ. 2,000. (also avail. in microform from UMI; reprint service avail. from UMI) **Indexed:** Lang.& Lang.Behav.Abstr. **Document type:** academic/scholarly publication.
—UMI.

370   US   ISSN 0030-1086
OHIO SCHOOLS. 1923. 9/yr. $18 to libraries. Ohio Education Association, 225 E. Broad St., Box 2550, Columbus, OH 43216. TEL 614-228-4526. FAX 614-228-8771. Ed. Richard J. Baker. adv. contact: Maxine Pauli. bibl.; illus. circ. 108,000. (also avail. in microform from UMI; reprint service avail. from UMI) **Indexed:** Educ.Ind. **Document type:** academic/scholarly publication.
—Faxon; UnCover; UMI.

OIKOGENEIA KAI SKOLEIO/FAMILY AND SCHOOL; dimenaio pedagogiko periodiko. see *CHILDREN AND YOUTH — About*

370.193   US   ISSN 0030-1817
OKLAHOMA PARENT - TEACHER. 1923. q. $4. Oklahoma Congress of Parents and Teachers, 224 S.E., 4th Fl., Moore, OK 73160. circ. 1,500.

379.15   US   ISSN 0030-185X
OKLAHOMA SCHOOL BOARD JOURNAL. 1950. m. $5. Oklahoma State School Boards Association, 2801 N. Lincoln Blvd., Oklahoma City, OK 73105. TEL 405-528-3571. FAX 405-528-5695. Ed. Bob Mooneyham. adv.; illus.; circ. 4,600 (controlled). (tabloid format)

370   IR
OLUM-E TARBIATI/EDUCATION. (Text in Persian; abstracts in European languages) 1971. q. Rs.400. Daneshgah-e Tehran, Daneshkade-ye Olum-e Tarbiati - Teheran University, Faculty of Education, Al-Ahmad Ave., P.O. Box 14155-6346, Tehran, Iran. TEL 970062. Ed. Kamal Dorrani. circ. 2,000. **Document type:** academic/scholarly publication.
    Former titles (until 1991): University of Teheran. Faculty of Education. Journal of Education - Daneshgah-e Tehran. Daneshkade-ye 'Olum-e Tarbiyati. Nashriyeh; University of Teheran. Faculty of Education. Journal.
    Description: Disseminates theoretical and practical findings from research and studies in education.

370   NE   ISSN 0030-2481
L21
ONDERWIJS EN OPVOEDING; algemeen onderwijskundig tijdschrift. 1949. m. (10/yr.) fl.42.50 to individuals, fl.27.50 to students. Bosch en Keuning N.V., Box 1, Baarn, Netherlands. Ed.Bd. adv.; bk.rev.; charts; illus. circ. 10,000.

370   CN   ISSN 0317-6436
L222.06
ONTARIO. MINISTRY OF EDUCATION. REPORT. a. (Ministry of Education) Goot Publications, 880 Bay St., Toronto, Ont., Canada. TEL 416-965-2054.

370.25   CN   ISSN 0316-8549
L906.06
ONTARIO DIRECTORY OF EDUCATION. a. Can.$10 per no. (Ministry of Education) Goot Publications, 50 Grosvenor St., Toronto, Ont. M7A 1N8, Canada. TEL 416-326-5300. (Subscr. to: Publications Services, Ministry of Government Services, 880 Bay St., 5th Fl.,Toronto, Ont. M7A 1N8, Canada)

370   AT
OPEN BOOK. 1972. irreg. Aus.$5. 21 Smith St., Thornbury, Vic. 3071, Australia. Ed.Bd.

370   US
OPEN EXCHANGE. 1974. 6/yr. $12. Community Resource Institute, Box 7880, Berkeley, CA 94707. TEL 510-526-7190. FAX 510-540-1057. Ed. Bart Brodsky. adv.; bk.rev.; illus. circ. 105,000. (tabloid format)
    Formerly: Open Education Exchange.

370 374.4   UK
OPEN PRAXIS. 1983. 2/yr. $65 individual membership; libraries $50. International Council for Distance Education, National Extension College, 18 Brooklands, Ave., Cambridge CB2 2HN, England. TEL 44-223-316644. FAX 44-223-313586. Ed. Ros Morpeth. bk.rev. circ. 1,100. **Document type:** bulletin.
    Formerly: International Council for Distance Education. Bulletin (ISSN 0264-0201)

OPERA AMERICA NEWSLINE. see *MUSIC*

385   FI   ISSN 0355-3965
OPETTAJA/TEACHER. 1906. w. FIM 385. Opettajien Ammattijarjesto - Trade Union of Teachers in Finland, Rautatielaisenkatu 6, SF-00520 Helsinki 52, Finland. TEL 358-0-150271. FAX 358-0-1502281. Ed. Hannu Laaksola. adv. contact: Jyrki Ehnqvist. bk.rev. circ. 75,461. **Document type:** trade publication.
    Incorporates: Opettajain Lehti & Oppikoululehti.

370   DK   ISSN 0109-1255
OPGAVESAET TIL DANSK SKRIFTLIG FREMSTILLING, FOLKESKOLENS AFGANGSPROEVE; dagproeve aftenproeve, ekstraordinaere proevetermin. 1983. a. DKK 20. Dansklaererforeningen-Folkeskolefraktionen, Noerre Soegade 49C, 1370 Copenhagen K, Denmark. circ. 20,000.
    Formerly: Opgavesaet til Dansk Skr. Fremstilling, Folkeskolens Udvidede Afgangsproeve (ISSN 0109-1247)

370   CN   ISSN 0030-4433
L11
ORBIT; ideas about teaching and learning. 1970. q. Can.$32.10 (foreign $30). Ontario Institute for Studies in Education, 252 Bloor St. W., Toronto, ON M5S 1V6, Canada. TEL 416-696-2295. (Subscr. to: CNS Circulation, P.O. Box 10, Sta. F, Toronto, ON M4Y 2L4, Canada) Ed. Heather Berkeley. circ. 7,000. (also avail. in microform from UMI; reprint service avail. from UMI) **Indexed:** Can.Educ.Ind., ERIC.
—Faxon; UMI.

370   US   ISSN 0030-4689
OREGON EDUCATION. 1926. m. (9/yr., Sep.-June). $10. Oregon Education Association, 6900 S.W. Haines Rd., Tigard, OR 97223. TEL 503-684-3300. FAX 503-684-8063. Ed. Shari Forbes Thomas. adv.; charts; illus. circ. 38,000.

OREGON SCIENCE TEACHER. see *SCIENCES: COMPREHENSIVE WORKS*

370   IT   ISSN 0030-5391
L36
ORIENTAMENTI PEDAGOGICI; rivista internazionale di scienze dell'educazione. (Text in Italian; summaries in several languages) 1954. bi-m. L.53000 (foreign L.90000). (Universita Pontificia Salesiana, Facolta di Scienze dell'Educazione, VC) Societa Editrice Internazionale, Corso R. Margherita 176, 10152 Turin, Italy. TEL 011-52 27 1. FAX 011-5211320. Ed. Sergio Giordani. bk.rev.; charts. circ. 3,900. **Indexed:** CERDIC. **Document type:** academic/scholarly publication.

370   DK   ISSN 0106-7125
ORIENTING OM SKOLEAARET. (Subseries of: Denmark. Folkeskolens Forsoegsraad. Publikation) 1978. a. free. Folkeskolens Udviklingsraad, c/o The Secretariat of the Innovation Council, Frederiksholms Kanal 26, DK-1220 Copenhagen K, Denmark. TEL 45-33-92-51-39. **Document type:** government publication.

370   XV   ISSN 0030-6681
OTROK IN DRUZINA; revija za druzinsko in druzbeno vzgojo. (Text in Slovenian) 1952. m. 20 din. (foreign DM.3). Zveza Prijateljev Mladine Slovenije, Miklosiceva 16-II, 61000 Ljubljana, Slovenia. (Co-sponsor: Zveza Pedagoskih Drustev Slovenije) Ed. Biserka Marolt-Meden. circ. 18,000.

OUR REVIEW/MABAT SHELANV. see *HANDICAPPED — Hearing Impaired*

370   CN   ISSN 0384-6636
OUR SCHOOLS. 1972. m. free. Winnipeg School Division No. 1, 1577 Wall T. E., Winnipeg, MB R3E 2S5, Canada. TEL 204-775-0231. illus. circ. 25,000. **Document type:** newspaper.
    Formerly: Focus on Winnipeg Schools (ISSN 0384-6628)

370.971   CN   ISSN 0840-7339
OUR SCHOOLS, OUR SELVES; a magazine for Canadian education activists. 1988. bi-m. Can.$34 to individuals; institutions Can.$50. Our Schools, Our Selves Education Foundation, 1698 Gerrard St. E., Toronto, ON M6K 2A3, Canada. **Indexed:** Alt.Press Ind.

OXFORD. see *LITERARY AND POLITICAL REVIEWS*

370   UK   ISSN 0305-4985
L16
OXFORD REVIEW OF EDUCATION. 1975. q. $84 to individuals; institutions $198 (effective 1994). Carfax Publishing Co., P.O. Box 25, Abingdon, Oxon. OX14 3UE, England. TEL 44- 235-555335. FAX 44-235-553559. (U.S. subscr. to: Carfax Publishing Co., Box 2025, Dunnellon, FL 34430-2025) Eds. David Phillips, John Wilson. adv.; index. (also avail. in microfiche; back issues avail.) **Indexed:** C.I.J.E., Chic.Per.Ind., Cont.Pg.Educ., Curr.Cont, Educ.Inc., Educ.Tech.Abstr., High.Educ.Curr.Aware.Bull., Lang.& Lang.Behav.Abstr., Res.High.Educ.Abstr., SOMA, Sp.Ed.Needs Abstr., SSCI, Stud.Wom.Abstr. **Document type:** academic/scholarly publication.
—BLDSC (6321.0.7000); Faxon; UnCover; SWETS. CCC.
    Refereed Serial

370   UK   ISSN 0961-2149
OXFORD STUDIES IN COMPARATIVE EDUCATION. 1991. s-a. £24 to individuals; institutions £48. Triangle Journals Ltd., P.O. Box 65, Wallingford, Oxfordshire OX10 0YG, England. TEL 0491-838013. FAX 0491-834968. **Indexed:** SOMA. **Document type:** academic/scholarly publication.
—BLDSC (6321.021900).
    Description: Devotes each volume to a specific topic.

P A C E. (Professional Approaches for Christian Educators) see *RELIGIONS AND THEOLOGY*

372   AU
P A - KONTAKTE. 1972. irreg. free. International Institute for Children's Literature and Reading Research, Mayerhofgasse 6, A-1040 Vienna, Austria. Ed. Karin Sollat. bk.rev.; bibl. **Document type:** academic/scholarly publication.

P & A. (Preiswert & Attraktiv) see *POLITICAL SCIENCE*

370   NE   ISSN 0165-7933
P C O - MAGAZINE. 1975. w. fl.235.20. Protestants Christelijke Onderwijsvakorganisatie, Postbus 87868, 2508 DG The Hague, Netherlands. TEL 31-70-3522541. FAX 31-70-3522841. Ed.Bd. adv.; illus.
    Incorporates (1982-1986): Protestants Christelijke Onderwijsvakorganisatie. Special (ISSN 0920-7252); (1937-1986): Magazine Voortgezet Onderwijs (ISSN 0920-5276); Which was formerly: Bereopsonderwijs; Ons Beroepsonderwijs (ISSN 0030-2635).

EDUCATION

370   CN   ISSN 0383-199X
P E I T F NEWSLETTER. 1948. q. free. Prince Edward Island Teachers Federation, P.O. Box 6000, Charlottetown, PE C1A 8B4, Canada. TEL 902-569-4157. FAX 902-569-3682. Ed. Robert G. MacRae. circ. 2,400 (controlled). (back issues avail.) **Document type:** newsletter.
   Description: Describes and comments on activities of the federation and education in the province and nationally.

P M E A NEWS. (Pennsylvania Music Educators Association, Inc.) see *MUSIC*

P P F BULLETIN. (Public Policy Forum) see *PUBLIC ADMINISTRATION — Municipal Government*

P R R C: EMERGING TRENDS. (Princeton Religion Research Center, Inc.) see *RELIGIONS AND THEOLOGY*

370.193   US   ISSN 1072-3242
P T A IN PENNSYLVANIA. 1924. 8/yr. $5. Pennsylvania Congress of Parents and Teachers, 4804 Derry St., Box 4384, Harrisburg, PA 17111-0384. TEL 717-564-8985. FAX 717-564-9046. **Document type:** bulletin.
   Former titles: Pennsylvania Parent Teacher Bulletin; P T A in Pennsylvania; Pennsylvania Parent Teacher.

370.193   US   ISSN 0195-2781
LC231
P T A TODAY. 1906. 5/yr. $10 (typically set in Mar.). National Parent - Teacher Association, 330 N. Wabash Ave., Ste. 2100, Chicago, IL 60611-3690. TEL 312-670-6782. FAX 312-670-6783. Ed. Pamela Schrom Reynolds. bk.rev.; index. circ. 38,000. (also avail. in microform from UMI; reprint service avail. from UMI) **Indexed:** C.I.J.E., Human Resour.Abstr., Sage Fam.Stud.Abstr. **Document type:** consumer publication.
—BLDSC (6946.566500); UMI.
   Supersedes (in 1975): P T A Magazine.
   Description: Practical information on parenting.

907 370   BE   ISSN 0030-9230
PAEDAGOGICA HISTORICA; international journal of the history of education. (Text in English, French, German, Spanish) 1961. 3/yr. 3000 BEF. Universiteit Gent - University of Ghent, A. Baertsoenkaai 3, B-9000 Ghent, Belgium. TEL 32-9-2240224. FAX 32-9-2259311. Ed. Frank Simon. bk.rev. circ. 700. (also avail. in microform; reprint service avail. from SWZ) **Indexed:** Amer.Hist.& Life, Bull.Signal., C.I.J.E., Hist.Abstr., Res.High.Educ.Abstr. **Document type:** academic/scholarly publication.
—Faxon; UnCover; SWETS.
   Description: Publishes international methodological articles on intellectual history and social, cultural, economic and political aspects of the history of education, conference reports, announcements, review articles and an overview of contents of national journals in the history of education.
   Refereed Serial

370   GW
PAEDAGOGIK. 1968. m. DM.104. Verlag Julius Beltz GmbH, Am Hauptbahnhof 10, Postfach 100154, 69469 Weinheim, Germany. TEL 06201-60070. FAX 06201-17464. TELEX 465500-BELTZD. Ed. Peter Kalb. adv.; bk.rev.; index. circ. 8,000. **Indexed:** Lang.& Lang.Behav.Abstr.
—CCC.
   Former titles: Paedagogik Heute - Paedagogische Beitraege; Paedagogik Heute (ISSN 0179-9401); Betrifft: Erziehung (ISSN 0045-1789)

370   GW
L31
PAEDAGOGIK UND SCHULALLTAG. 1946. m. DM.55.20. Luchterhand Verlag, Lindenstr. 54A, 1086 Berlin, Germany. TEL 030-20343431. FAX 030-20343432. adv.; bk.rev.; charts; illus.; index. circ. 40,000(combined). **Indexed:** Ger.J.Psych. **Document type:** academic/scholarly publication.
—SWETS.
   Formerly: Paedagogik (ISSN 0030-9249)

370   AU
PAEDAGOGISCHE INSTITUTE. MITTEILUNGEN. 1962. 10/yr. S.120. Paedagogisches Institut der Stadt Wien, Burgasse 14-16, 1070 Vienna, Austria. (Dist. by: Verlag fuer Jugend und Volk, Anschutzgasse 1, 1150 Vienna, Austria) Ed. Johanna Juna. circ. 1,500.
   Formerly: Paedagogisches Institut der Stadt Wien. Mitteilungen (ISSN 0030-9281)

370   GW   ISSN 0933-6389
PAEDAGOGISCHE KORRESPONDENZ; Zeitschrift fuer kritische Zeitdiagnostik in Paedagogik und Gesellschaft. 1987. s.a. DM.32. (Institut fuer Paedagogik und Gesellschaft) Buechse der Pandora Verlag GmbH, Postfach 2820, 35538 Wetzlar, Germany. FAX 06441-43216. (back issues avail.)

370   GW   ISSN 0030-9273
PAEDAGOGISCHE RUNDSCHAU. 1946. bi-m. DM.118. Peter Lang GmbH Europaeischer Verlag der Wissenschaften, Eschborner Landstr. 42-50, 60489 Frankfurt a.M., Germany. TEL 069-7807050. FAX 069-785893. Eds. Rudolf Lassahn, Birgit Ofenbach. adv.: B&W page DM.800; trim 120 x 190. bk.rev.; abstr.; illus.; index. circ. 835. **Indexed:** SSCI. **Document type:** academic/scholarly publication.
—BLDSC (6333.168000); SWETS. **CCC**.

370   CY
PAEDIKI CHARA/CHILDREN'S JOY. (Text in Greek) m. Pan-Cyprian Greek Teachers Union, 18 Archbishop Makarios III Ave., Nicosia, Cyprus. TEL 02-442683. Ed. Costas Protopapas. circ. 15,000.
   Description: Developed for Greek-Cypriot children.

370 028.5   US
THE PAGE (SEATTLE). 1980. m. $35 includes membership. Citizens Education Center, 310 First Ave. S., Ste. 330, Seattle, WA 98104-2536. TEL 206-624-9955. Ed. Diana Tanner. circ. 400. (back issues avail.)
   Description: Updates members on center's activities and meetings, and items of interest around the state.

PAIDEIA. see *PHILOSOPHY*

370   PL   ISSN 0137-3943
PAIDEIA; international pedagogical review. (Text in English, French and German) a. price varies. (Polska Akademia Nauk, Komitet Nauk Pedagogicznych) Ossolineum, Publishing House of the Polish Academy of Sciences, Rynek 9, 50-106 Wroclaw, Poland. TEL 48-71-386-25. FAX 48-71-448-103. TELEX 0712771 OSS PL. Ed. B. Suchodolski. **Document type:** academic/scholarly publication.
   Description: Papers on adult education, secondary and academic schools in Europe, U.S.A. and in the Third World countries.

PAIDEUSIS. see *PHILOSOPHY*

370   PK   ISSN 0078-8287
PAKISTAN. MINISTRY OF EDUCATION. YEARBOOK. (Text in English) a. Ministry of Education, Documentation Section, Curriculum Wing, Sector H-9, P.O. Shaigan, Industrial Area, Islamabad, Pakistan.
   Formerly: Pakistan. Central Bureau of Education. Yearbook (ISSN 0078-7922)

370   IS
PANIM LEKAN VELEKAN. 1988. bi-m. IS.25. Institute for Education in Democracy, Levinsky College, Israel. FAX 972-3-6993546. Ed. Shlomo Tzidkiyahu. circ. 2,000.

370   PP   ISSN 0048-2919
PAPUA AND NEW GUINEA EDUCATION GAZETTE. 1967. m. (exc. Jan.& Dec.). free. Department of Education, P.S.A. Haus, Private Mail Bag, Boroko, Papua New Guinea. Ed. J. Oberlenter. bk.rev. circ. 8,000. **Indexed:** Aus.Educ.Ind.

370   PP   ISSN 0031-1472
LA2270.P3
PAPUA NEW GUINEA JOURNAL OF EDUCATION. 1961. 2/yr. K.10 (foreign K.38($40)). University of Papua New Guinea, Department of Education, P.O. Box 320, University P.O., Papua New Guinea. TEL 267-430. FAX 267-187. TELEX NE22193. (Subscr. to: Eudcation Research Officer, Policy, Research & Evaluation, NDOW, PSA HAUS, Private Mail Bag, NCD, Papua New Guinea) Ed. Richard Guy. adv.; bk.rev.; bibl.; charts; illus.; stat. circ. 400. **Indexed:** Cont.Pg.Educ., Rural Ext.Educ.& Tr.Abstr.

370.193   AT   ISSN 0726-7126
PARENT AND CITIZEN. 1939. q. Aus.$10. Federation of Parents & Citizens Associations of New South Wales, 210 Crown St., East Sydney, P.O. Box 789, Dalinghurst 2000, Australia. TEL 02-360-2481. FAX 02-361-6835. Ed. Gail Nicholls. adv.; bk.rev. circ. 24,000.
   Description: Aimed at informing parents on school and educational matters.

372.21   US
PARENT COOPERATIVE PRESCHOOLS INTERNATIONAL. DIRECTORY. 1969. a. membership. Parent Cooperative Preschools International, Box 90410, Indianapolis, IN 46290-0410. TEL 317-849-0992. (In Canada: 86 Saint George St., London, Ontario N6A 2Z7) adv.; bk.rev. circ. 6,500. **Document type:** directory.
   Description: Listing of cooperative preschool programs and cooperative preschool councils in the US and Canada.

370   US
PARENTS CHOICE (ARLINGTON). 1959. q. $20. Citizens for Educational Freedom, 927 S. Walter Reed Dr., Ste. 1, Arlington, VA 22204. TEL 703-486-8311. Eds. Martin and Mae Duggan. circ. 10,000. (tabloid format; back issues avail.) **Document type:** newsletter.
   Former titles: Choice in Education; Freedom in Education.

370.193   FR
PARENTS D'ELEVES. 1932. 4/yr. 15 F. Federation Nationale des Associations des Parents d'Eleves de l'Enseignement Public, 27 rue du Faubourg Poissonniere, 75009 Paris, France. adv.; bk.rev. circ. 80,000.

PARENTS MAKE THE DIFFERENCE; practical ideas for parents to help their children. see *CHILDREN AND YOUTH — About*

PARENTS STILL MAKE THE DIFFERENCE; practical ideas for parents to help their children. see *CHILDREN AND YOUTH — About*

377.9   US
PARISH COORDINATORS - DIRECTORS OF RELIGIOUS EDUCATION. q. membership. (National Forum of Religious Educators) National Catholic Educational Association, 1077 30 St. N.W., Ste. 100, Washington, DC 20007. TEL 202-337-6232.
   Formerly: Parish Coordinator of Religious Education.

PARK WATCH. see *CONSERVATION*

362   US   ISSN 1041-1542
PARTNERS IN EDUCATION. 1976. m. (except July-Aug.). $100 to non-members; members free. National Association of Partners in Education, Inc., 209 Madison St., Ste. 401, Alexandria, VA 22314. TEL 703-836-4880. FAX 703-836-6941. bk.rev.; index. circ. 6,000. (tabloid format)
   Former titles: Volunteer in Education; School Volunteer; V A S T; Volunteer Views (ISSN 0042-868X)
   Description: Clearinghouse for information regarding parent-community-business partnerships including education policy issues, legislation, research, funding sources, and innovative programs.

370 330   US   ISSN 1042-6590
PARTNERSHIPS IN EDUCATION JOURNAL. 1987. m. $48 (foreign $61) (effective 1994). InfoMedia Inc., Box 210, Ellenton, FL 34222-0210. TEL 813-776-2535. Ed. Don Adams. **Document type:** newsletter.

370   US
PASSING THE WORD. 4/yr. free. Illinois State Library, Literacy Office, 431 S. Fourth St., Springfield, IL 62701. TEL 217-785-6521. Eds. Jan Grimes, Julie Dutton. **Document type:** newsletter.
   Description: Discusses literacy campaign activities in Illinois schools, libraries, and prisons.

370   UK · ISSN 0264-3944
PASTORAL CARE IN EDUCATION. 1983. 3/yr.
£35($70.50) to individuals; institutions £53($111).
Basil Blackwell Ltd., 108 Cowley Rd., Oxford OX4
1JF, England. TEL 0865-791100.
FAX 0865-791347. TELEX 837022-OXBOOK-G.
Ed. R. Best. circ. 4,500. (reprint service avail. from
UMI) **Indexed:** Cont.Pg.Educ., Educ.Tech.Abstr.,
High.Educ.Curr.Aware.Bull.
—BLDSC (6409.230000); UMI. **CCC.**

370.7   US   ISSN 0031-3432
PEABODY JOURNAL OF EDUCATION. 1923. q. $40 to
individuals; institutions $60. Vanderbilt University,
George Peabody College for Teachers, Box 41,
Nashville, TN 37203. TEL 615-322-8963.
FAX 615-343-7094. Ed. Susan Atkisson. circ.
2,600. (also avail. in microform from MIM,UMI;
reprint service avail. from UMI,KTO) **Indexed:** C.I.J.E.,
Cont.Pg.Educ., Curr.Cont., Educ.Ind.,
Educ.Tech.Abstr., Except.Child.Educ.Abstr.,
Res.High.Educ.Abstr., SOMA, SSCI.
—BLDSC (6413.750000).

370   IT   ISSN 0031-3777
PEDAGOGIA E VITA. 1952. bi-m. L.54000. Editrice La
Scuola S.p.A., Via Cadorna N.11, 25186 Brescia,
Italy. TEL 030-29931. Ed. Remo Bernacchia. adv.;
bk.rev.; bibl.; index. **Indexed:** CERDIC.

370   HU   ISSN 0031-3785
L56
PEDAGOGIAI SZEMLE/PEDAGOGICAL REVIEW. (Text in
Hungarian; summaries in English and Russian)
1951. m. $23. Magyar Pedagogiai Tarsasag,
Konyves Kalman krt. 48-52, 1087 Budapest,
Hungary. (Subscr. to: Kultura, Box 149, 1389
Budapest, Hungary) (Co-sponsor: Orszagos
Pedagogiai Intezet) Ed. Tamas Sutler. adv.; bk.rev.;
abstr.; index.

370   SA   ISSN 0256-520X
L81
PEDAGOGIEKJOERNAAL/JOURNAL OF PEDAGOGICS.
(Text in Afrikaans, Dutch, English) 1967. s-a. R.30
(effective 1992). University of Pretoria, Faculty of
Education, Pretoria 0002, South Africa.
FAX 27-12-342-2914. Ed. W.J. Louw. bk.rev. circ.
500. **Indexed:** Ind.S.A.Per., Psychol.Abstr. **Document
type:** academic/scholarly publication.
Formerly (until 1980): Suid-Afrikaanse Tydskrif vir
die Pedagogiek.

370   YU   ISSN 0031-3807
L51
PEDAGOGIJA; casopis Saveza pedagoskih drustava.
(Text in Serbo-Croatian) 1963. q. 100 din.($10.)
Savez Pedagoskih Drustava Jugoslavije, Mose Pijade
12, Box 331, 11001 Belgrade, Yugoslovia. Ed.
Nikola Potkonjak.

370   XR   ISSN 0031-3815
L51
PEDAGOGIKA/PEDAGOGY; casopis pro pedagogicke
vedy. (Text in Czech or Slovak; summaries in
English, German, Russian) 1951. bi-m. DM.136.
(Czechoslovak Academy of Sciences, Comenius
Institute of Education) Academia, Publishing House
of the Czechoslovak Academy of Sciences, Vodickova
40, 112 29 Prague 1, Czech Republic.
TEL 214-8092. (Dist. in Western countries by:
Kubon & Sagner, Postfach 34-01-08, 8000 Munich
34, Germany) Ed. Jarmila Skalkova. bk.rev.; abstr.;
bibl.; charts; illus.; stat.; index. **Indexed:**
Cont.Pg.Educ., Educ.Tech.Abstr., Psychol.Abstr.
Description: Contains original articles from all
spheres of pedagogical sciences; general
pedagogical theory, theory of education, educational
psychology, history of education, etc.

370   RU
L51
PEDAGOGIKA. (Text in Russian; contents page in
English) 1937. m. $88. Rossiiskaya Akademiya
Pedagogicheskikh Nauk, Nauchno-Issledovatel'skii
Institut Pedagogicheskoi Metodologii Standartov,
Pogodinskaya ul. 8, 119905 Moscow, Russia.
TEL 095-245-1641. (Dist. in U.S. by: Victor Kamkin
Inc., 4956 Boiling Brook Pkwy., Rockville, MD
20852. TEL 301-881-5973. FAX 301-881-1637)
Ed. S.A. Chernik. bk.rev.; bibl.; index. circ. 75,000.
Indexed: Psychol.Abstr.
Formerly: Sovetskaya Pedagogika (ISSN
0038-5093)

370.15   BE   ISSN 0166-5855
PEDAGOGISCH TIJDSCHRIFT. 1967. 6/yr. fl.69 to
individuals; institutions fl.99; students fl.58 (effective
1994). (Faculteit der Psychologie en Pedagogische
Wetenschappen) Institute of Psychology,
Tiensestraat 102, B-3000 Leuven, Belgium.
TEL 32-16-286102. FAX 32-16-286000. Ed. Paul
Smeyers. bk.rev.; index. circ. 750. **Document type:**
academic/scholarly publication.
—SWETS.
Formerly: Pedagogisch Tijdschrift - Forum voor
Opvoedkunde; Which was formed by the merger of:
Pedagogisch Forum (ISSN 0031-3823); Tijdschrift
voor Opvoedkunde (ISSN 0040-7577)

370   NE   ISSN 0552-7775
PEDAGOGISCHE STUDIEN; tijdschrift voor
onderwijskunde en opvoedkunde. 1924. 6/yr. fl.135
(students fl.87.50). WoltersgroepGroningen b.v.
(Subsidiary of: Wolters Kluwer N.V.), Postbus 58,
9700 MB Groningen, Netherlands.
TEL 31-50-226922. Ed. Dr. J. Lowyck. abstr. circ.
2,700. **Indexed:** Psychol.Abstr. **Document type:**
academic/scholarly publication.
—SWETS.

370   SW   ISSN 0346-5047
PEDAGOGISKA HJAELPMEDEL. 1971. irreg. Malmoe
School of Education, Inst. foer Pedagogik och
Specialmetodik, Box 23501, S-20045 Malmoe,
Sweden. Ed. Aake Bjerstedt. (back issues avail.)
Indexed: Psychol.Abstr. **Document type:**
academic/scholarly publication.

370   SW   ISSN 0281-6776
PEDAGOGISKA RAPPORTER/EDUCATIONAL REPORTS.
(Text in English or Swedish) 1969 N.S. 1984. irreg.
free. Umeaa Universitet, Pedagogiska Institutionen,
S-901 87 Umeaa, Sweden. FAX 46-90166203.
TELEX 54005. Ed. Jarl Backman. circ. 200.
Document type: academic/scholarly publication.
Formerly: Pedagogiska Rapporter Umeaa (ISSN
0348-9388)

PEDAGOGUSOK LAPJA. see *LABOR UNIONS*

370   CI   ISSN 0031-384X
PEDAGOSKI RAD. 1946. bi-m. 70 din. per no.
Pedagosko Drustvo SR Hrvatske, Trg Marsala Tita 4,
Zagreb, Croatia. Ed. Valentin Puzevski. bk.rev. circ.
5,000.

370   YU   ISSN 0031-3858
PEDAGOSKI ZIVOT; bilten Prosvetno pedagoskog zavoda
zrenjanin. (Text in Serbo-Croatian) 1963. 3/yr.
3.50 din. per no. Prosvetno-Pedagoski Zavod
Zrenjanin, Ul. Dr. M. Tirsa 2, Zrenjanin, Yugoslavia.
Ed. Vojislav Arsenijevic. bk.rev. circ. 1,200.

372.6 652.1   CN   ISSN 0031-4315
PENMEN'S NEWS LETTER. 1950. 6/yr. $15.
(International Association of Master Penmen and
Teachers of Handwriting) Eileen Richardson, Ed. &
Pub., 34 Broadway Ave., Ottawa, Ont. K1S 2V6,
Canada. TEL 613-232-3014. (Address from Nov. to
May: 19125 S.W. 107 Lane, Dunnellon, FL 32630,
U.S.A.) bk.rev.; circ. 300 (controlled).

370   US   ISSN 0031-4455
LA355
PENNSYLVANIA EDUCATION. 1968. 8/yr. free.
Department of Education, Bureau of Press and
Communications, 333 Market St., Harrisburg, PA
17126-0333. TEL 717-783-9802.
FAX 717-783-4517. Ed. Beth Bayer. bk.rev. circ.
190,000. (looseleaf format)
Formerly: Pennsylvania Basic Education.
Description: Communicates educational
information to teachers in Pennsylvania schools,
administrators, and the public.

370 331.8 340   US
PENNSYLVANIA EDUCATION LAW REPORT. m. $114.
Capital Publications, 1101 King St., Alexandria, VA
22314. TEL 703-683-4100. Ed. Anne Bittner.
index. (back issues avail.)
Description: Covers administrative law, court
decisions regarding schools and teachers in
Pennsylvania. Emphasizes decisions by the Secretary
of Education and the Pennsylvania Labor Relations
Board.

EDUCATION   2045

370   US   ISSN 0079-0508
PENNSYLVANIA SCHOOL STUDY COUNCIL. REPORTS.
1947. irreg. (20-25/yr.). price varies (free to
members). Pennsylvania School Study Council, 308
Rackley Bldg., Pennsylvania State University,
University Park, PA 16802. TEL 814-865-0321.
Ed. Oscar Knade. bk.rev. circ. 250. **Document type:**
academic/scholarly publication.

371.2   US
PENNSYLVANIA SCHOOLMASTER. 1970. q.
membership. Pennsylvania Association of Secondary
School Principals, 801 N. Second St., Harrisburg, PA
17102-3297. TEL 717-233-3001. Ed. Joseph
Mamana. adv.; bk.rev.; circ. 3,200 (controlled).
Document type: academic/scholarly publication.
Description: Scholarly articles by principals,
superintendents and college professors on successful
administrative practices.

370 301   US   ISSN 1063-7877
LC191.4
▼**PEOPLE AND EDUCATION;** the human side of schools.
1993. q. $38 to individuals; institutions $80.
Corwin Press, Inc. (Subsidiary of: Sage Publications
Inc.), 2455 Teller Rd., Thousand Oaks, CA 91320.
TEL 805-499-0721. FAX 805-499-0871. (And:
Sage Publications, Ltd., 6 Bonhill St., London EC2A
4PU, England. TEL 071-374-0645) Ed. Jerry J.
Herman. adv.; B&W page $225.
—BLDSC (6422.872500).

370 150   FI   ISSN 0781-2477
Z5815.S25
**PEPSY. PEDAGOGISK OCH PSYKOLOGISK LITTERATUR I
NORDEN.** (Text in Danish, English, Finnish, Icelandic,
Norwegian, Swedish) 1983. Nordisk Arbetsgrupp
foer Pedagogik och Psykologi, Jyvaskylae University
Library, Seminaarink. 15, SF-40100 Jyvaeskylae,
Finland. **Document type:** bibliography.
●Available only online.

370   FR   ISSN 0989-6465
PERIOSCOPE. 1988. m. (10/yr.). 290 F. Centre
National de Documentation Pedagogique, 29 rue
d'Ulm, 75230 Paris Cedex 05, France.

370   FR
PERISCOPE. 1983. 5/yr. 168 F. Ecole Moderne
Francaise - Pedagogie Freinet, B.P. 109, 06332
Cannes - La Bocca Cedex, France.

370   SP   ISSN 0210-2331
PERSPECTIVA ESCOLAR. (Text in Catalan) 1974. m.
4900 ptas. Rosa Sensat, Corsega 271, 08008
Barcelona, Spain. FAX 4153680. Ed.Bd. adv.;
bk.rev.; bibl.; illus.; cum.index: 1974-1985. circ.
7,000.

PERSPECTIVE (MADISON); the campus legal monthly.
see *LAW*

370   UN
PERSPECTIVES; revue trimestrielle de l'education.
English edition: Prospects; Quarterly Review of
Education (ISSN 0033-1538); Spanish edition:
Perspectivas (ISSN 0304-3053); Arabic edition:
Mustaqbaliyyat (ISSN 0254-119X) 1971. q. $28.
Unesco, International Bureau of Education, Case
Postale 199, 1211 Geneva 20, Switzerland. (Dist.
in U.S. by: Unipub, 4611-F Assembly Dr., Lanham,
MD 20706-4391. TEL 800-274-4888) Ed. J.C.
Tedesco. bk.rev.; bibl; charts. circ. 2,125.
Formerly: Perspectives de l'Education (ISSN
1010-6952)

378   US   ISSN 0890-9792
LB2361.5
PERSPECTIVES (COLUMBUS). 1969. 2/yr. $30 for
libraries. Association for General and Liberal Studies,
c/o Tamar March, Ed., Vice Pres. of Academic
Affairs, New England College, 7 Mian St., Henniker,
NH 03242-3293. (Subscr. to: c/o Bruce Busby,
Ohio Dominican College, 1216 Sunbury Rd.,
Columbus, OH 43219-2099) bk.rev. circ. 500.
(also avail. in microform from UMI; reprint service
avail. from UMI) **Indexed:** ERIC. **Document type:**
academic/scholarly publication.
—Faxon; UMI.
Former titles (until 1981): Interdisciplinary
Perspectives (ISSN 0148-1959); (until 1976):
Perspectives: Journal of General and Liberal Studies
(ISSN 0031-5958)

ULRICH'S INTERNATIONAL PERIODICALS DIRECTORY 1994-95

2046 EDUCATION

370   FR   ISSN 1148-4519
PERSPECTIVES DOCUMENTAIRES EN EDUCATION. 3/yr. 145 F. (foreign 182 F.). Institut National de Recherche Pedagogique, 29 rue d'Ulm, 75230 Paris Cedex 05, France. TEL 46-34-90-00.
Former titles (until 1990): Perspectives Documentaires en Sciences de l'Education (ISSN 0760-7962); (until 1983): Informations Bibliographiques en Sciences de l'Education (ISSN 0760-7970)

PERSPECTIVES IN PSYCHOLOGICAL RESEARCHES. see *PSYCHOLOGY*

370   PE
PERU. MINISTERIO DE EDUCACION PUBLICA. OFICINA SECTORIAL DE PLANIFICACION. PLAN BIENAL. irreg. Ministerio de Educacion Publica, Oficina Sectorial de Planificacion, Lima, Peru. illus.

370   US
PHI DELTA KAPPA FASTBACKS. 1972. 16/yr. $1.25 per no. (Phi Delta Kappa Educational Foundation) Phi Delta Kappa, Inc., Box 789, Bloomington, IN 47402-0789. TEL 812-339-1156. FAX 812-339-0018. Ed. Donovan Walling. bibl. (back issues avail.) **Indexed:** Educ.Ind., ERIC. **Document type:** monographic series.

370   US   ISSN 0031-7217
LJ121
PHI DELTA KAPPAN. 1915. m. (Sep.-June). $35. Phi Delta Kappa, Inc., Box 789, Bloomington, IN 47402-0789. TEL 812-339-1156. FAX 812-339-0018. Ed. Pauline B. Gough. adv.; bk.rev.; stat.; index. circ. 150,000. (also avail. in microfilm from UMI; microfiche from CIS; reprint service avail. from UMI,KTO) **Indexed:** Acad.Ind., Biog.Ind., Bk.Rev.Ind. (1979-1991), C.I.J.E., Child.Bk.Rev.Ind. (1979-1991), Cont.Pg.Educ., Curr.Cont., Educ.Admin.Abstr., Educ.Ind., Except.Child.Educ.Abstr., Fut.Surv., Mag.Ind., Mult.Ed.Abstr., PMR, PSI, R.G., Res.High.Educ.Abstr., Sage Pub.Admin.Abstr., SOMA, SRI, SSCI. **Document type:** academic/scholarly publication.
—BLDSC (6449.400000); Faxon; UnCover; SWETS; UMI.

PHI KAPPA PHI NEWSLETTER. see *COLLEGE AND ALUMNI*

370   PH
PHILIPPINE EDUCATION QUARTERLY;* journal of fact and opinion. (Text in English & occasionally Filipino) 1969. q. P.20($12) (Arellano University) Bookman Printing House, P.O. Box 709, Manila, Philippines. Ed. Jose T. Enriquez. bk.rev.; abstr.; index. circ. 800. (back issues avail.) **Indexed:** Cont.Pg.Educ.

370   PH   ISSN 0031-7527
PHILIPPINE EDUCATIONAL FORUM. s-a. P.26($4.50) Philippine Women's University, Taft Ave., Manila 2801, Philippines. Ed. Ester Vallado-Daroy. circ. 1,000.

370   US   ISSN 0160-7561
L107
PHILOSOPHICAL STUDIES IN EDUCATION. 1968. a. $15 to individuals; institutions $13.50. Ohio Valley Philosophy of Education Society, c/o Susan Martin, Indiana State University, Terre Haute, IN 47809. TEL 812-237-2927. FAX 812-237-4348. circ. 220. (microfiche from EDR; reprint service avail. from UMI) **Indexed:** Phil.Ind. **Document type:** proceedings.
Formerly: Ohio Valley Philosophy of Education Society. Proceedings of the Annual Meetings (ISSN 0078-4044)

370   US   ISSN 8756-6575
L13
PHILOSOPHY OF EDUCATION; proceedings of the annual meeting. (Proceedings for 1st-13th meetings not published) 1958, 14th meeting proceedings. a. $35 (effective 1992). Philosophy of Education Society, c/o College of Education, University of Illinois, 1310 Sixth St., Champaign, IL 61821. TEL 217-333-3003. FAX 217-244-3711. circ. 1,200. (also avail. in microfiche) **Indexed:** Phil.Ind., Res.Educ., SSCI. **Document type:** proceedings.
—BLDSC (6464.900000).
Formerly: Philosophy of Education Society. Proceedings of the Annual Meetings (ISSN 0079-1733)

PHYLLIS SCHLAFLY REPORT. see *WOMEN'S INTERESTS*

370   IS   ISSN 0333-5259
PHYSICAL EDUCATION AND SPORT. 1944. bi-m. IS.69($33) (effective 1993). Wingate Institute, Wingate Post 42902, Israel. TEL 972-9-639480. FAX 972-9-639482. Ed. Adi Gross. adv.; bk.rev. circ. 3,500. **Indexed:** Ind.Heb.Per. **Document type:** academic/scholarly publication.
Description: Information, research and applied material for Israeli physical education instructors and coaches.

613.7 370   US   ISSN 0031-8981
GV201
PHYSICAL EDUCATOR; a magazine for the profession. 1940. 4/yr. $25. Phi Epsilon Kappa Fraternity, 901 W. New York St., Indianapolis, IN 46202. TEL 317-637-8431. Ed. Robert Pangrazi. bk.rev.; illus.; index. circ. 5,000. (also avail. in microfilm from UMI; reprint service avail. from UMI) **Indexed:** C.I.J.E., Cont.Pg.Educ., Educ.Ind., Phys.Ed.Ind., Sportsearch (1952-). **Document type:** academic/scholarly publication.
—BLDSC (6475.550000); Faxon; UnCover; SWETS; UMI.

370   US
PINE TORCH. vol.52, no.4, 1992. q. Piney Woods Country Life School, Piney Woods, MS 39148. Ed. Bevelyn D. Young. **Document type:** newsletter.
Description: News and activities of the school, its staff and alumni.

370   ZR
PISTES ET RECHERCHES. 1986. 2/yr. Institut Superieur Pedagogique, B.P. 258, Kikwit, Zaire. **Indexed:** P.L.E.S.A.

PLANETARIAN. see *ASTRONOMY*

370   PL   ISSN 0867-518X
PLASTYKA I WYCHOWANIE W SZKOLE. (Until 1984 supplement to: Wychowanie Techniczne w Szkole) 1961. 6/yr. $21. (Ministerstwo Edukacji Narodowej) Wydawnictwa Szkolne i Pedagogiczne, Pl. Dabrowskiego 8, 00-950 Warsaw, Poland. TEL 48-22-265451. FAX 48-22-266313. (Dist. by: Ars Polona-Ruch, Krakowskie Przedmiescie 7, Warsaw, Poland) Ed. Jacek Bukowski. circ. 7,000.
Formerly: Plastyka w Szkole (ISSN 0324-8844)
Description: For plastic arts teachers, with articles on the theory and history of art, comtemporary plastics art, the psychology of creativity and education. Presents both Polish and foreign ideas of education through art.

372.21   US   ISSN 0032-1443
PLAY SCHOOLS NEWSLETTER. 1969. a. free to qualified personnel. Play Schools Association, 9 E. 38th St., 8th Fl., New York, NY 10016. TEL 212-725-6540. Ed. Joseph Corrado. bk.rev.; illus.; circ. 2,500 (controlled). **Document type:** newsletter.

370   UK
POLESTAR. 1976. bi-m. £3.50($7.50) Ann Rignall, Ed. & Pub., 42 St. Peter's Court, Rock Ferry, Merseyside L42 1PF, England. TEL 051-645-7185. (Subscr. to: 7 Lynwood Ave., Aughton, Lancs L39 5BB, England; U.S. subscr. to: 1156 15th St. NW, Ste. 910, Washington, DC 20005) adv.; bk.rev. circ. 1,500. (tabloid format; back issues avail.) **Document type:** academic/scholarly publication.

370   IT
POLITICA DELLA SCUOLA. 1972. s-a. L.15000($20) Associazione Nazionale per Il Progresso della Scuola Italiana, Piazza SS, Apostoli N. 80, Rome, Italy.

370   PL
POLSKA AKADEMIA NAUK. KOMISJA NAUK PEDAGOGICZNYCH. ROCZNIK. (Text in Polish; summaries in English) a. price varies. Ossolineum, Publishing House of the Polish Academy of Sciences, Rynek 9, 50-106 Wroclaw, Poland. TEL 48-71-386-25. FAX 48-71-448-103. TELEX 0712771 OSS PL. **Document type:** academic/scholarly publication.
Description: Original papers and research reports on various aspects of children and adult education and history of pedagogical research.

370   PL   ISSN 0079-3418
L53
POLSKA AKADEMIA NAUK. ODDZIAL W KRAKOWIE. KOMISJA NAUK PEDAGOGICZNYCH. ROCZNIK. (Text in Polish; summaries in English, French, German, Russian) 1961. s-a. price varies. Ossolineum, Publishing House of the Polish Academy of Sciences, Rynek 9, 50-106 Wroclaw, Poland. TEL 48-71-386-25. FAX 48-71-448-103. TELEX 0712771 OSS PL. Ed. Czeslaw Majorek. **Document type:** academic/scholarly publication.
Description: Presents original works in all areas of basic educational research, particulary on topics spanning history, theory, methodology and application.

370   PL   ISSN 0079-340X
POLSKA AKADEMIA NAUK. ODDZIAL W KRAKOWIE. KOMISJA NAUK PEDAGOGICZNYCH. PRACE. (Text in Polish; summaries in English and Russian) 1958. irreg., no.19, 1980. price varies. Ossolineum, Publishing House of the Polish Academy of Sciences, Rynek 9, 50-106 Wroclaw, Poland. TEL 48-71-386-25. FAX 48-71-448-103. TELEX 0712771 OSS PL. **Document type:** monographic series.

370   BL   ISSN 0101-465X
PONTIFICIA UNIVERSIDADE CATOLICA DO RIO GRANDE DO SUL. EDUCACAO. 1978. 2/yr. Cr.$10($9) Editora da P U C R S, c/o Antoninho M. Naime, Caixa Postal, 12001, 90620 Porte Alegre RS, Brazil. bk.rev.; charts. circ. 1,000.

POPULATION EDUCATION IN ASIA AND THE PACIFIC NEWSLETTER AND FORUM. see *POPULATION STUDIES*

370   PO
PORTUGAL. INSTITUTO NACIONAL DE ESTATISTICA. ESTATISTICAS DA EDUCACAO. CONTINENTE, ACORES E MADEIRA. 1940. a. Esc.4200. Instituto Nacional de Estatistica, Av. Antonio Jose de Almeida, 1078 Lisbon Codex, Portugal. (Orders to: Imprensa Nacional, Casa da Moeda, Direccao Comercial, rua D. Francisco Manuel de Melo 5, 1000 Lisbon, Portugal)
Formerly: Portugal. Instituto Nacional de Estatistica. Estatisticas de Educacao (ISSN 0079-4155)

370   US   ISSN 1040-0494
POSITIVE INK. 1985. m. $25 (effective 1994). Power of Positive Students International Foundation, 4325 Dick Pond Rd., Myrtle Beach, SC 29575. TEL 803-650-7677; 800-521-2741. FAX 803-650-7681. Ed. Michael A. Mitchell. circ. 10,000 (paid). **Document type:** newsletter.
Formerly (until 1988): P O P S Ink (ISSN 0887-5839)
Description: Contains motivational articles and ideas for educators, classroom strategies, staff development ideas and more.

370   FR
POURQUOI, COMMENT; pedagogie Freinet. 1982. 5/yr. 125 F. to individuals; 88 F. to professionals. Ecole Moderne Francaise - Pedagogie Freinet, B.P. 109, 06332 Cannes - La Bocca Cedex, France.

PRAKTIKA; Forum fuer den Russischunterricht. see *LINGUISTICS*

370   GW   ISSN 0934-5256
PRAXIS SPIEL UND GRUPPE. q. DM.36 (students DM.32). Matthias Gruenewald Verlag GmbH, Max-Hufschmidt-Str. 4a, 55130 Mainz-Weisenau, Germany. TEL 06131-839055. circ. 2,000. (back issues avail.)
Formerly (until 1988): Schwalbacher Blaetter.

370   GW
PRAXIS VERKEHRSERZIEHUNG. (In two editions for different scholastic levels) 1965. 6/yr. DM.8 per no. Rot-Gelb-Gruen Lehrmittel GmbH, Theodor-Heuss-Str. 3, Postfach 3922, 38122 Braunschweig, Germany. FAX 0531-80907-21. TELEX 952357. adv.; bk.rev. circ. 10,000.
Formerly (until 1990): Lehrer-Briefe zur Verkehrserziehung (ISSN 0075-8612)

372 001.642
621.381   US   ISSN 0888-3009
PRE-K TODAY. 8/yr. $19.95. Scholastic Inc., 555 Broadway, New York, NY 10012-3999. TEL 212-343-6100. Ed. Helen Benham. **Document type:** trade publication.

EDUCATION 2047

372.21   XO   ISSN 0032-7220
PREDSKOLSKA VYCHOVA; casopis pre pracovnicky jasiel a materskych skol. 1946. m. 30 Kcs.($12) (Ministerstvo Skolstva Slovenskej Republiky) Slovenske Pedagogicke Nakladatelstvo, Sasinkova 5, 815 60 Bratislava, Slovakia. TEL 603-03. (Dist. by: Slovart, Gottwaldovo nam. 6, 817 64 Bratislava, Slovakia) Ed. Luboslava Klindova. bk.rev.; charts; illus. circ. 30,000.

370   BL
PREMIO GRANDES EDUCADORES BRASILEIROS. 1984. a. $150 (effective Dec. 1991). Instituto Nacional de Estudos e Pesquisas Educacionais, C.P. 04162-04-0366, 70312 Brasilia D.F., Brazil. TEL 061-347-8970. FAX 061-2733233.

370   UK   ISSN 0963-8601
PREP SCHOOL. q. £7. (Incorporated Association of Preparatory Schools) Belgrave Educational Publishing, P.O. Box 140, Ipswich, Suffolk IP6 9PL, England. TEL 0449-79550. (Co-sponsor: Society of Assistants Teaching in Preparatory Schools) Ed. Anne Kiggell. adv.; bk.rev. circ. 5,500. (back issues avail.) **Document type:** academic/scholarly publication.
—BLDSC (6607.820000).
Formerly: Preparatory Schools Review.
Description: News and developments in junior independent education regarding teching methods, equipment, new buildings and experiments in particular schools.

PRESENCE DE L'ENSEIGNEMENT AGRICOLE PRIVE. see *AGRICULTURE*

PRESERVATION EDUCATION DIRECTORY. see *LIBRARY AND INFORMATION SCIENCES*

PREVENTING SEXUAL ABUSE. see *PSYCHOLOGY*

372   UK
PRIMARY & MIDDLE SCHOOL EQUIPMENT. 1974. 11/yr. £17 (foreign £22). Bouverie Publishing Company Ltd., 131-135 Temple Chambers, Temple Ave., London EC4Y 0DT, England. TEL 071-583-3030. FAX 071-583-6481. Ed. Garry Parker. adv.; bk.rev.; illus. circ. 10,272. **Document type:** trade publication.
Former titles: 5 - 13 Education; Primary and Middle School Equipment (ISSN 0262-5717); Education Equipment, Primary and Middle School Edition (ISSN 0140-3230); Junior Education Equipment (ISSN 0022-6564)
Description: For professionals involved in the education of young children.

372   AT   ISSN 0048-5284
PRIMARY EDUCATION. 1970. bi-m. Aus.$35.95. Collins Dove, 22-24 Joseph St., North Blackburn, Vic. 3130, Australia. TEL 03-895-8195. FAX 03-895-8181. Ed. Christine Powers. adv. contact: Annie Walsh. bk.rev.; index. circ. 2,000. (also avail. in microfilm from UMI; reprint service avail. from UMI) **Indexed:** Aus.Educ.Ind.
Description: Committed to the open communication of ideas about primary education in Australia.

370   UK   ISSN 0962-8789
LA633
▼**PRIMARY LIFE**; the practical journal for primary and middle school teachers. 1992. 3/yr. Basil Blackwell Ltd., 108 Cowley Rd., Oxford OX4 1JF, England. TEL 0865-791100. FAX 0865-791347. TELEX 837022-OXBOOK-G.
—BLDSC (6612.909700); UMI. **CCC.**

PRIMARY SCIENCE REVIEW. see *SCIENCES: COMPREHENSIVE WORKS*

370   CN   ISSN 0032-8359
PRIME AREAS. 1958. 3/yr. Can.$51 to non-members; members Can.$35; students Can.$17.50. (B.C. Primary Teachers' Association) B.C. Teachers' Federation, 2235 Burrard St., Vancouver, B.C. V6J 3H9, Canada. TEL 604-731-8121. bk.rev. circ. 3,500. **Indexed:** Can.Educ.Ind.

370   SP
PRIMERAS NOTICIAS COMUNICACION Y PEDAGOGIA. 12/yr. Cerdena 259, 08013 Barcelona, Spain. TEL 3-207-50-52. Ed. J. Aliaga Serrnao.

370   CN   ISSN 1188-8644
PRISM. vol.69, 1980. 2/yr. Can.$8($11) (Includes NTA Bulletin). Newfoundland Teachers Association, 3 Kenmount Rd., St. John's, Nfld. A1B 1W1, Canada. TEL 709-726-3223. FAX 709-726-4302. Ed. Jacqui Tam. adv.; bk.rev.; charts; illus. circ. 10,000. **Indexed:** Can.Per.Ind.
Former titles (until 1992): Professional Development Journal (ISSN 0834-0633); (until 1984): N T A Journal (ISSN 0027-7037)

PRISMA (KASSEL). see *SCIENCES: COMPREHENSIVE WORKS*

377.8   NO   ISSN 0032-8847
PRISMET; pedagogisk tidsskrift. 1950. bi-m. NOK 310 in the Nordic countries; elsewhere NOK 370. (Institutt for Kristen Oppseding - Institute for Christian Education) Scandinavian University Press, P.O. Box 2959-Toeyen, N-0608 Oslo, Norway. TEL 472-67-7600. FAX 472-67-7575. (U.S. addr.: Scandinavian University Press, 200 Meacham Ave., Elmont, NY 11003. TEL 516-352-7300) Ed. Erling Birkedal. adv.; bk.rev.; index. circ. 2,500.
Description: Examines the pedagogy of religion, particularly the place and function of Christian beliefs in the bringing up of children at school and in the home and parish.

PRIVATE EDUCATION LAW REPORT. see *BUSINESS AND ECONOMICS — Labor And Industrial Relations*

370   CN   ISSN 1188-777X
PRIVE. 1973. 4/yr. free. Federation des Associations d'Etablissements Prives, 1940 Est, bd. Henri Bourassa, Montreal, PQ H2B 1S2, Canada. TEL 514-381-8891. FAX 514-381-4086. Ed. Rose-Aimee Michaud. bk.rev.; abstr.; bibl.; charts; stat.; index. circ. 1,000.
Formerly (until 1992): Bivoie (ISSN 0315-2138)

370   RM   ISSN 1220-8825
PROBLEME DE PEDAGOGIE CONTEMPORANA. 1970. a. $15. Biblioteca Centrala Pedagogica, Str. Zalomit Nr. 12, Sector 1, 70714 Bucharest, Rumania. TEL 15-75-71. Eds. George Anca, Ana Sincai. index. circ. 5,000.
Supersedes: Buletin de Informare Pedagogica (ISSN 0007-3792)
Description: Summaries of articles or books tackling problems of secondary education in the world.

370   IT   ISSN 0032-9347
PROBLEMI DELLA PEDAGOGIA. 1955. bi-m. L.69000 (foreign L.80000) (effective 1993). Marzorati Editore, Via Pordoi, 8, 20019 Settimo (Milan), Italy. TEL 02-33501314. FAX 02-33500046. Dir. Ignazio Volpicelli. adv.; bk.rev.; film rev.; charts; illus.; stat.; cum.index 1955-1965. circ. 2,500.

370.15   PL   ISSN 0552-2188
PROBLEMY OPIEKUNCZO-WYCHOWAWCZE. 1961. m. $35. (Ministerstwo Edukacji Narodowej) Wydawnictwa Szkolne i Pedagogiczne, Pl. Dabrowskiego 8, 00-950 Warsaw, Poland. TEL 48-22-265451. (Dist. by: Ars Polona-Ruch, Krakowskie Przedmiescie 7, Warsaw, Poland) Ed. Jadwiga Raczkowska. circ. 7,868.
Description: For teachers in boarding schools, foster parents and inter-school educational centres.

370   FR
PROFESSION EDUCATION. 10/yr. S G E N - C F D T, 5 rue Mayran, 75442 Paris Cedex 09, France. TEL 42-47-72-85. FAX 42-47-72-74. Ed. J. Michel Lebrun. circ. 40,000.

370   UK   ISSN 0269-0411
PROFESSIONAL TEACHER. 1970. 5/yr. £7.50. Professional Association of Teachers, 2 St. James Court, Friar Gate, Derby DE1 1BT, England. TEL 0332-372337. FAX 0332-292431. Ed. Jackie Miller. adv.; bk.rev. circ. 33,000. **Document type:** trade publication.

370   RU
PROFESSIONAL'NO-TEKHNICHESKOE OBRAZOVANIE. 1941. m. Ul. Chernyakhovskogo 9, 125319 Moscow, Russia. Ed. Vladimir G. Chernykh.

370   PO
PROFESSOR. 12/yr. Rua de S. Bernardo 14, 1200 Lisbon, Portugal. TEL 1-670193. FAX 1-668793. TELEX 65791.

378   AU
PROFESSOR AN A H S & B H S. (Text and summaries in German) 1953. m. or bi-m. S.50. Verband der Professoren Oesterreichs, c/o Dr. Walter Marinovic, Gentzgasse 132-3, A-1180 Vienna, Austria. adv.; bk.rev. circ. 7,500. (tabloid format)
Formerly: Professor (ISSN 0033-0221)

370   US
PROGRAM TRENDS IN MUSEUM EDUCATION. 1991-1993. m. $95. Learning Resources Network, 1554 Hayes Dr., Manhattan, KS 66502. TEL 913-539-5376. Ed. Mary Ellen Sills.

370   II   ISSN 0033-0663
PROGRESS OF EDUCATION; a journal devoted to the discussion of problems relating to the theory, practice & administration of education. (Text in English) 1924. m. Rs.50($10) Pune Vidyarthi Griha Prakashan, 1786 Sadashiv Peth, Poona 411 030, India. TEL 430573. Ed. N.S. Mujumdar. adv.; bk.rev.; stat. circ. 1,350. **Indexed:** Cont.Pg.Educ., Educ.Ind., G.Indian Per.Lit., SOMA. **Document type:** academic/scholarly publication.

370   US   ISSN 0033-0825
PROGRESSIVE TEACHER. 1894. q. $6.95. Progressive Publishing Co., 2678 Henry St., Augusta, GA 30904. Ed. M. S. Adcock. adv.; bk.rev.; film rev.; record rev.; illus.; index. circ. 10,450. **Indexed:** Curr.Cont. **Document type:** academic/scholarly publication.

370   US
PROJECTIONS OF EDUCATION STATISTICS. 1964. a. U.S. Department of Education, National Center for Education Statistics. 555 New Jersey Ave., N.W., Washington, DC 20208. TEL 800-424-1616. (Dist. by: Supt. of Documents, Washington DC 20402) Ed. Debra E. Gerald. charts; stat. **Document type:** academic/scholarly publication.

PROLOGUE (MEDFORD). see *THEATER*

370   UN   ISSN 0033-1538
PROSPECTS; quarterly review of education. French edition: Perspectives; Revue Trimestrielle de l'Education. (Editions in English, French, Spanish) 1969. q. 100 F.($35) Unesco, International Bureau of Education, Case Postale 199, 1211 Geneva 20, Switzerland. (Dist. in US by: Unipub, 4611-F Assembly Dr., Lanham, MD 20706-4391. TEL 800-274-4888) Ed. J.C. Tedesco. bk.rev.; bibl. circ. 9,000 (English & French eds.). **Indexed:** C.I.J.E., Educ.Ind., Educ.Tech.Abstr., High.Educ.Curr.Aware.Bull., Lang.& Lang.Behav.Abstr., Rural Ext.Educ.& Tr.Abstr., SSCI.
—Faxon; UnCover; SWETS.

370   XV   ISSN 0033-1643
PROSVETNI DELAVEC; list delavcev v vzgojnoizobravevalnih zavodih. (Text in Slovenian) 1949. 20/yr. 380 S.T. Prosvetni Delavec, p.o., Poljanski nasip 28, 61000 Ljubljana, Slovenia. adv.; bk.rev. circ. 7,000.

370   YU   ISSN 0033-1651
PROSVETNI PREGLED; list prosvetnih i kulturnih radnika SR Srbije. 1944. w. 140 din. Privredni Pregled, Marsala Birjuzova 3-5, 11000 Belgrade, Yugoslavia. Ed. Rade Vukovic.

370   XN   ISSN 0033-1635
PROSVETNI RABOTNIK. (Text in Macedonian) 1953. fortn. 40 din. Rabotnicki Dom II-VIII, Soba 185, 91000 Skopje, Macedonia. Ed. Miso Kitanoski.

370   BN   ISSN 0033-1678
PROSVJETNI LIST. 1952. fortn. 80 din.($6.25) Sindikat Radnika Drustvenih Djelatnosti SR Bosne i Hercegovina, Dure Dakovica 4, Sarajevo, Bosnia Hercegovina. Ed. Nikoa Nikic.

370   YU   ISSN 0033-1686
PROSVJETNI RAD; list prosvjetnih i naucnih radnika socijalisticke republike Crne Gore. 1953? bi-w. 20 din. Sindikat Radnika Drustvenih Djelatnosti Crne Gore, Novaka Miloseva 9a, Box 253, Titograd, Yugoslavia. Ed. Vukale Derkovic.

EDUCATION

370   PL   ISSN 0867-0420
PRZYSPOSOBIENIE OBRONNE W SZKOLE. 1955. bi-m. $18 per number. (Ministerstwo Edukacji Narodowej) Wydawnictwa Szkolne i Pedagogiczne, Pl. Dabrowskiego 8, 00-950 Warsaw, Poland. TEL 48-22-265451. (Dist. by: Ars Polona-Ruch, Krakowskie Przedmiescie 7, Warsaw, Poland) Ed. Tadeusz Siuda.
Description: Covers civil defence instruction in secondary schools.

PSYCH DISCOURSE. see *PSYCHOLOGY*

PSYCHOLOGIA A SKOLA. see *PSYCHOLOGY*

370.15   PL   ISSN 0033-2860
LB1051.A2
PSYCHOLOGIA WYCHOWAWCZA/EDUCATIONAL PSYCHOLOGY. bi-m. $25. (Ministerstwo Edukacji Narodowej) Wydawnictwa Szkolne i Pedagogiczne, Pl. Dabrowskiego 8, 00-950 Warsaw, Poland. TEL 48-22-265451. (Dist. by: Ars Polona Ruch, Krakowskie Przedmiescie 7, Warsaw, Poland) Ed. Ziemowit Wlodarski. circ. 2,340. **Indexed:** Child Devel.Abstr., Educ.Tech.Abstr., Lang.& Lang.Behav.Abstr., Psychol.Abstr. **Document type:** academic/scholarly publication.
—BLDSC (6946.282000).
Description: Discusses problems of human development, learning and teaching. Publishes reports on empirical research, presents original theoretical conceptions, reviews of psychological problems, and information on practical work of psychologist in education.

370.15 150   FR   ISSN 0151-2137
PSYCHOLOGIE ET EDUCATION. 1962. q. 300 F. Association Francaise des Psychologues Scolaires, c/o Georges Lelouey, 24 rue de Bougainville, 50130 Octeville, France. TEL 64-59-94-46. FAX 64-59-32-83. Dir. Jo Herve. bk.rev. circ. 2,000. (back issues avail.)
Formerly (until 1990): Psychologie Scolaire.

370   GW   ISSN 0342-183X
LB1051   CODEN: PEUNDV
PSYCHOLOGIE IN ERZIEHUNG UND UNTERRICHT; Organ der Deutschen Gesellschaft fuer Psychologie. 1954. 4/yr. DM.86. Ernst Reinhardt Verlag, Kemnatenstr. 46, 80639 Munich, Germany. TEL 089-1783005. FAX 089-1781827. Eds. K. Heller, H. Nickel. adv.; bk.rev. circ. 1,400. (reprint service avail. from ISI and UMI) **Indexed:** Cont.Pg.Educ., Curr.Cont., Ger.J.Psych., Psychol.Abstr., Sp.Ed.Needs Abstr., SSCI. **Document type:** academic/scholarly publication.
—BLDSC (6946.532000). **CCC**.
Formerly: Schule und Psychologie.

PSYKOLOGISK PAEDAGOGISK RAADGIVNING/JOURNAL OF SCHOOL PSYCHOLOGY; tidsskrift for paedagogisk psykologi og raadgivning. see *PSYCHOLOGY*

370   US
PUBLIC EDUCATION ALERT. 1970. 4/yr. $25. Public Education Association, 39 W. 32nd St., New York, NY 10001-3803. TEL 212-868-1640. FAX 212-268-7344. Ed. Judith Baum. bk.rev.; bibl.; circ. 5,000 (controlled). **Document type:** newsletter.
Former titles (until 1986): P E A Reports; Public Education Association Newsletter.
Description: Devoted to issues affecting the education of children in the New York City public school system, grades pre-K through 12. Presents summaries and extracts of the organization's research, analysis, coalition-building, model programs, legal action and extensive information program.

378.1   US
PUBLIC SCHOOL ENROLLMENT AND STAFF, NEW YORK STATE. 1961. a. free. Education Department, Instruction & Program Development, Education Bldg. Annex, Rm. 381, Albany, NY 12234. TEL 518-474-7082. FAX 518-474-4351. charts; stat.; circ. controlled. (back issues avail.) **Document type:** government publication.
Formerly: New York (State) Education Department. Survey of Enrollment, Staff and School Housing.

370   US   ISSN 0077-9229
PUBLIC SCHOOL PROFESSIONAL PERSONNEL REPORT, NEW YORK STATE. 1967. a. free. Education Department, Instruction & Program Development, Education Bldg. Annex, Rm. 381, Albany, NY 12234. TEL 518-474-7082. FAX 518-474-4351. charts; illus.; circ. controlled. (back issues avail.) **Document type:** government publication.
Formerly: New York (State) Education Department. Public School Professional Personnel Report (ISSN 0077-9245)

PUBLIKATIONEN ZU WISSENSCHAFTLICHEN FILMEN. SEKTION GESCHICHTE, PUBLIZISTIK. see *MOTION PICTURES*

370   UY
PUNTO 21. q. Centro de Investigacion y Experimentacion Pedagogica, Jaime Cibils 2810, Montevideo, Uruguay. (Subscr. to: Libreria Adolfo Linardi, Juan C. Gomez 1435, Montevideo, Uruguay) Ed.Bd. charts.

PURPLE AND GOLD. see *CLUBS*

370   CC
QI MENG. (Text in Chinese) m. Tianjin Jiaoyu Zazhishe, No. 47, 11 Jing Lu, Hedong Qu, Tianjin 300171, People's Republic of China. TEL 413876. Ed. Huang Lizhu.

370   UK   ISSN 0968-4883
▼**QUALITY ASSURANCE IN EDUCATION**. 1993. 3/yr. $219.95. M C B University Press Ltd., 60-62 Toller Ln., Bradford, W. Yorks BD8 9BY, England. TEL 0274-499821. FAX 0274-547143. TELEX 51317-MCBUNI-G. (N. American subscr. to: M C B University Press Limited, Box 1943, Birmingham, AL 35201) Eds. Gerard McElwee, George Holmes. **Document type:** academic/scholarly publication.

QUARTERLY JOURNAL OF MUSIC TEACHING AND LEARNING. see *MUSIC*

420.07 370   US   ISSN 0033-5630
PN4071
QUARTERLY JOURNAL OF SPEECH. 1915. 4/yr. $75 membership. Speech Communication Association, 5105 Backlick Rd., Bldg. E., Annandale, VA 22003. TEL 703-750-0533. Ed. Martha Solomon. adv.; bk.rev.; index, cum.index vol.1-55 (1915-1969). circ. 5,400. (also avail. in microform from UMI,PMC; reprint service avail. from UMI) **Indexed:** Abstr.Engl.Stud., Acad.Ind., Amer.Hist.& Life, Bk.Rev.Ind. (1965-), C.I.J.E., Child.Bk.Rev.Ind. (1965-), Commun.Abstr., Cont.Pg.Educ., Curr.Cont., Educ.Ind., Except.Child.Educ.Abstr., Hist.Abstr., Hum.Ind., Lang.& Lang.Behav.Abstr., Lang.Teach.& Ling.Abstr., M.L.A., Psychol.Abstr., SSCI.
—BLDSC (7195.930000); Faxon; UnCover; SWETS; UMI.

370.193   CN   ISSN 0033-5967
QUEBEC HOME & SCHOOL NEWS. 1948. 5/yr. during school yr. Can.$12. Quebec Federation of Home and School Associations, 3285 Cavendish Blvd., Ste. 562, Montreal, PQ H4B 2L9, Canada. TEL 514-481-5619. Ed. Charlene de Conde. adv.; bk.rev.; circ. 6,200 (paid); 1,800. (tabloid format) **Document type:** newspaper.
Description: Communication and information medium for parents and others interested in education in Quebec and in Canada.

370.193   CN
QUEBEC HOMESCHOOLING ADVISORY NEWSLETTER. (Text in English, French) 1983. 4/yr. Can.$10. Quebec Homeschooling Advisory, Box 1278, 1002 Rosemarie, Val David, PQ J0T 2N0, Canada. TEL 819-322-6495. Ed. Elizabeth Edwards. adv. circ. 80. (looseleaf format; back issues avail.) **Document type:** newsletter.
Description: Provides legal and pedagogical advice, as well as local contacts regarding home schooling in Quebec.

370   AT
QUEENSLAND. DEPARTMENT OF EDUCATION. RESEARCH AND EVALUATION UNIT. EDUCATIONAL RESEARCH REPORT. 1975. irreg. Department of Education, Research and Evaluation Unit, P.O. Box 33, 50 Albert St., Brisbane, Qld. 4002, Australia. TEL 07-237-0970. FAX 07-237-0203.
Former titles (until May 1987): Queensland. Department of Education. Research Services. Research Series (ISSN 0816-3782); (Until 1983): Queensland. Department of Education. Research Branch. Research Series.

370   AT   ISSN 0033-6238
QUEENSLAND TEACHERS' JOURNAL. 1895. m. Aus.$22. Queensland Teachers' Union, P.O. Box 310, Spring Hill, Qld. 4004, Australia. FAX 07-832-3644. Ed. John Battams. adv.; bk.rev.; index. circ. 32,000. (tabloid format) **Indexed:** Aus.Educ.Ind. **Document type:** trade publication.
Description: For teachers in Queensland's State Education system.

370   CN   ISSN 0380-240X
QUERY. 1970. 4/yr. Can.$15 membership. Saskatchewan Reading Council, Box 1108, Saskatoon, SK S7K 3N3, Canada. TEL 306-373-1660. Ed. Cheryl Craik. bk.rev. circ. 1,000. **Indexed:** Can.Educ.Ind., Can.Per.Ind.

QUILL AND SCROLL. see *JOURNALISM*

370   FR   ISSN 0395-6725
QUINZAINE UNIVERSITAIRE. 1905. s-m. 435 F. (typically set in Sep.). Syndicat National des Lycees et Colleges, 4 rue de Trevise, 75009 Paris, France. TEL 45-23-05-14. FAX 42-46-26-60. Ed. C. Ters. adv.; bk.rev.; abstr. circ. 20,000. **Document type:** academic/scholarly publication.

370 808.5   US   ISSN 0273-6705
PN6081
QUOTE; the speakers digest. 1940. m. $37.95 (Canada and Mexico $40; elsewhere $45). Cheallaigh Shamrock, Box 815, Las Cruces, NM 88004-0815. TEL 505-522-7744. FAX 505-521-7315. E-mail: TTKELLY@DELPHI.COM. Ed. Tom Kelly. adv.; bk.rev. circ. 5,000. (also avail. in microform from UMI; reprint service avail. from UMI)
—UMI.
Formerly: Quote Magazine (ISSN 0033-667X)
Description: Collection of quips, jokes, one liners, and topical selections from a variety of sources, edited for public speakers, ministers, sales motivators and idea presenters.

507   MY   ISSN 0377-3450
Q183.4.A7
R E C S A M ANNUAL REPORT. (Text in English) 1972. a. free. Southeast Asian Ministers of Education Organisation, Regional Centre for Education in Science and Mathematics, 11700 Glugor, Penang, Malaysia. TEL 883266. illus. circ. 150.

R E L C JOURNAL; a journal of language teaching and research in Southeast Asia. (Regional Language Centre) see *LINGUISTICS*

370 800   US   ISSN 0364-8389
R I F NEWSLETTER. 1971. 3/yr. free. Reading Is Fundamental, Inc., Smithsonian Institution, 600 Maryland Ave., S.W., Rm. 600, Washington, DC 20560. TEL 202-287-3220. FAX 202-287-3196. Ed. Gail Oerke. circ. 18,000. (back issues avail.) **Indexed:** ERIC. **Document type:** newsletter.
Description: Reports on projects, book distribution and other activities conducted throughout the U.S. to encourage reading at all levels of elementary and secondary education.

R S A JOURNAL. see *ART*

371   US   ISSN 0085-4093
RACIAL - ETHNIC DISTRIBUTION OF PUBLIC SCHOOL STUDENTS AND STAFF, NEW YORK STATE. 1968. a. free. Education Department, Instruction & Program Development, Education Bldg. Annex, Rm. 381, Albany, NY 12234. TEL 518-474-7082. FAX 518-474-4351. charts; stat.; circ. controlled. (back issues avail.) **Document type:** government publication.

370   UK   ISSN 0305-6147
RADICAL EDUCATION. no.4, 1975. q. £1 to individuals; institutions £2. 86 Eleanor Rd., London E.8., England. Ed.Bd. adv.; bk.rev. circ. 3,500.

EDUCATION

370 US ISSN 0191-4847
L11
RADICAL TEACHER; a news journal of socialist theory and practice. 1975. 3/yr. $10 to individuals; institutions $16. Boston Women's Teachers' Group, Box 102, Cambridge, MA 02142. Ed. Susan O'Malley. adv.; bk.rev. circ. 2,400. (back issues avail.) **Indexed:** Alt.Press Ind., Left Ind. (1982-), M.L.A. **Document type:** academic/scholarly publication.
—BLDSC (7228.099100); UnCover.

370 KR ISSN 0033-8605
RADYANS'KA OSVITA.* 1940. s-w. $7.20. Ministerstvo Osvity, Kiev, Ukraine.

373 II ISSN 0033-9083
RAJASTHAN BOARD JOURNAL OF EDUCATION. (Text in English, Hindi) 1964. q. Rs.25 (teachers Rs. 15). Board of Secondary Education, Rajasthan, Ajmer, India. TEL 20346. Ed. Panna Lal Verma. adv.; bk.rev.; stat.; index. circ. 20,000.
Description: Provides teachers and educational administrators with the latest developments in the field of secondary education.

RANDSE AFRIKAANSE UNIVERSITEIT. JAARBOEK. see EDUCATION — Higher Education

370 IT ISSN 0393-4586
RASSEGNA AMMINISTRATIVA DELLA SCUOLA.* m. L.55000. Edizioni Romane, Via degli Ubertini 32, 34, 00100 Rome, Italy. Dir. Luciano Molinari.

RASSEGNA DI CULTURA E VITA SCOLASTICA. see LITERARY AND POLITICAL REVIEWS

370 IT ISSN 0033-9571
RASSEGNA DI PEDAGOGIA/PAEDAGOGISCHE UMSCHAU. (Text in French, German, Italian; summaries in English, French, German, Italian) 1941. q. L.16000. (Universita degli Studi di Padova, Istituto di Pedagogia) Giardini Editori e Stampatori, Via Biesiano 28, 56100 Pisa, Italy. Ed. Giuseppe Flores D'Arcais. bk.rev.; bibl.; index. circ. 1,200.

370 200 US
REACH (NEW HAVEN). 1970. q. membership. Religious Education Association, 409 Prospect St., New Haven, CT 06511-2177. TEL 203-865-6142. FAX 203-865-6142. Ed. Barbara Ryan. circ. 2,000 (controlled). **Document type:** newsletter.

READ MAGAZINE. see CHILDREN AND YOUTH — For

READ, SEE AND HEAR. see LIBRARY AND INFORMATION SCIENCES

READAPTATION. see EDUCATION — Special Education And Rehabilitation

372 UK ISSN 0034-0472
LB1050
READING; a journal for the study and improvement of reading and related skills. 1967. 3/yr. £25.50($58.50) to individuals; institutions £44($103). Basil Blackwell Ltd., 108 Cowley Rd., Oxford OX4 1JF, England. TEL 0865-791100. FAX 0865-791347. TELEX 837022-OXBOOK-G. Ed. David Way. adv.; bk.rev. circ. 2,200. (also avail. in microform from MIM,UMI; reprint service avail. from UMI) **Indexed:** Child.Lit.Abstr., Cont.Pg.Educ., High.Educ.Curr.Aware.Bull., Lang.& Lang.Behav.Abstr., Lang.Teach.& Ling.Abstr., Sociol.Abstr., Sp.Ed.Needs Abstr.
—BLDSC (7300.800000); UnCover; UMI. **CCC.**

READING AND WRITING; an interdisciplinary journal. see LINGUISTICS

372 US ISSN 0034-0553
LB1050 CODEN: RRQUA6
READING RESEARCH QUARTERLY. (Summaries in French, Spanish, German) 1965. 4/yr. $38 in developed countries; developing countries $19. International Reading Association, Inc., 800 Barksdale Rd., Box 8139, Newark, DE 19714-8139. TEL 302-731-1600. FAX 302-731-1057. TELEX 5106002813READING. Ed. Michael Kamil. adv.; abstr.; charts; illus.; stat.; index. circ. 10,000. (also avail. in microform from UMI; reprint service avail. from UMI) **Indexed:** C.I.J.E., Cont.Pg.Educ., Curr.Cont., Educ.Ind., Except.Child.Educ.Abstr., High.Educ.Curr.Aware.Bull., Lang.& Lang.Behav.Abstr., Lang.Teach.& Ling.Abstr., Mid.East: Abstr.& Ind., Psychol.Abstr., Sp.Ed.Needs Abstr., SSCI. **Document type:** academic/scholarly publication.
—BLDSC (7301.310000); Faxon; UnCover; SWETS; UMI. **CCC.**
Description: Technically oriented for those interested in reading research.
Refereed Serial

370 US ISSN 0737-4208
READING TODAY. bi-m. $19 in developed countries; developing countries $9.50. International Reading Association, Inc., 800 Barksdale Rd., Box 8139, Newark, DE 19714-8139. TEL 302-731-1600. FAX 302-731-1057. TELEX 5106002813 READING. Ed. John Micklos. circ. 94,000. (reprint service avail. from UMI) **Indexed:** Jun.High.Mag.Abstr. **Document type:** newspaper.
—SWETS. **CCC.**
Formerly: Reading.
Description: News and features about the reading profession and practical information for educators and parents about Association activities, publications and meetings.

373 GW ISSN 0342-829X
DIE REALSCHULE; Zeitschrift fuer Schulpaedagogik und Bildungspolitik. 1887. 10/yr. DM.50. (Verband Deutscher Realschullehrer) Schroedel Schulbuchverlag GmbH, Hildesheimer Str. 202-206, 30519 Hannover, Germany. TEL 0511-8388-0. TELEX 9-23527-HSVHAD. (Subscr. to: Oeding Druck GmbH, Wilhelmstr. 1, 3300 Braunschweig, Germany) (Co-Publisher: Ernst Klett Schulbuchverlag GmbH) Ed. Horst Wollenweber. circ. 11,900.

370 BE ISSN 0777-0820
LA810
RECHERCHE EN EDUCATION; theorie et pratique. (Text in French) 1990. 4/yr. 400 Fr. (foreign 500 Fr.). Centre Bruxellois de Recherche et de Documentation Pedagogiques, Service Enseignement, Avenue Louise 166, 1050 Brussels, Belgium. TEL 02-643-0364. (Co-sponsor: Commission Communautaire Francaise) Ed. Jeannine Blomart.

RECHT DER JUGEND UND DES BILDUNGSWESENS. see CHILDREN AND YOUTH — About

370 US ISSN 0034-3315
REGION SIX SENTINEL. 1960. m. $1. Michigan Education Association. Region Six, 5460 Arden, Warren, MI 48092. TEL 313-987-8668. Eds. R.M. Wirth, Oscar Maxfield. adv.; bk.rev.; bibl.; cum.index. circ. 6,000. (tabloid format)

370 SJ
REGIONAL EDUCATIONAL BUILDING INSTITUTE FOR AFRICA. LETTER/INSTITUT REGIONAL POUR LES CONSTRUCTIONS SCOLAIRES EN AFRIQUE. LETTRE.* q. Regional Educational Building Institute of Africa, Section de Documentation, B.P. 1720, Khartoum, Sudan. illus.

REGISTER OF MUSICIANS IN EDUCATION. see MUSIC

REGISTER OF PROFESSIONAL PRIVATE MUSIC TEACHERS. see MUSIC

377.8 FR
RELIGIEUSES ENSEIGNANTES. 1968. 4/yr. 10 bis rue Jean Bart, 75006 Paris, France. Ed. S. Denizet. adv.

377.9 US ISSN 1056-7224
LC405
RELIGION & PUBLIC EDUCATION. 1984. 3/yr. $25. National Council on Religion and Public Education, Webster University, 470 E.. Lockwood, Webster Groves, MO 63119. TEL 314-968-7135. adv.; bk.rev. **Document type:** academic/scholarly publication.
Description: Aims to provide readers with an overview of issues and curriculum related to the academic study of religion.

377.8 GW
RELIGION HEUTE: SUPPLEMENT. (Supplement to: Religion Heute) 1982. q. DM.39 to individuals; students DM.26.75. Erhard Friedrich Verlag, Im Brande 15, 30926 Seelze, Germany. FAX 0511-40004-19. (Subscr. to: Postfach 100150, 30917 Seelze, Germany) Ed. Wolfgang Thorns. adv.; bk.rev.
—BLDSC (7356.463000).
Incorporates: Informationen zum Religionsunterricht; Formerly: Zeitschrift fuer Religionspaedagogik (ISSN 0722-9151)

RELIGION IN AMERICA. see RELIGIONS AND THEOLOGY

RELIGIONE E SCUOLA; mensile per l'animazione culturale e la ricerca religiosa. see RELIGIONS AND THEOLOGY — Roman Catholic

377.8 GW ISSN 0341-8960
RELIGIONSUNTERRICHT AN HOEHEREN SCHULEN. 1958. bi-m. DM.47 (foreign DM.58). (Bundesverband der Katholischen Religionslehrer an Gymnasien e.V.) Patmos Verlag GmbH, Am Wehrhahn 100, 40211 Duesseldorf, Germany. TEL 0211-167950. FAX 0211-1679575. Ed. Theo Ahrens. adv.; bk.rev.; index. circ. 2,000. **Indexed:** CERDIC. **Document type:** academic/scholarly publication.
—CCC.
Description: Discusses topics in Catholic education; includes reports of current events and issues, and new publications.

RELIGIOUS EDUCATION; a platform for the free discussion of issues in the field of religion and their bearing on education. see RELIGIONS AND THEOLOGY

370 CC ISSN 0448-9365
RENMIN JIAOYU/PEOPLE'S EDUCATION. (Text in Chinese) 1950. m. Y11.40($34.10) (effective 1993). (Guojia Jiaoyu Weiyuanhui - State Education Commission) China Education Periodicals Company, 35 Damucang Hutong, Xidan, Beijing 100816, People's Republic of China. TEL 6014986. (Dist. outside China by: China International Book Trading Corp., P.O. Box 399, Beijing, P.R.C.; Dist. in US by: China Books & Periodicals, Inc., 2929 24th St., San Francisco, CA 94110. TEL 415-282-2994) adv. circ. 300,000.
Description: Covers all aspects of education in China.

REPERTORIO DE SERVICIOS IBEROAMERICANOS DE DOCUMENTACION E INFORMACION EDUCATIVAS/REPERTORIO DE SERVICOS IBERO-AMERICANOS DE DOCUMENTACAO E INFORMACAO EDUCATIVAS. see LIBRARY AND INFORMATION SCIENCES

370 US ISSN 0034-4699
LB1028
REPORT ON EDUCATION RESEARCH; the independent bi-weekly newsletter on research in education and learning. 1969. bi-w. $247 (foreign $273). Capitol Publications Inc., 1101 King St., Ste. 444, Alexandria, VA 22314. TEL 703-683-4100. FAX 703-739-6517. Ed. Annette Licitra. bibl.; charts; illus.; stat.; s-a. index. (looseleaf format) **Document type:** newsletter.
—CCC.
Incorporates: How to Evaluate Education Programs (ISSN 0270-157X)
Description: Provides current research initiatives, results and funding from the Education Department, its labs and centers and education policy groups.

2050 EDUCATION

370 US ISSN 1046-6150
REPORT ON LITERACY PROGRAM. 1989. bi-w. $247. Business Publishers, Inc., 951 Pershing Dr., Silver Spring, MD 20910-4464. TEL 301-587-6300. FAX 301-585-9075. Ed. Dave Speights. (looseleaf format; back issues avail.) **Document type:** newsletter.
●Also available online. Vendor(s): NewsNet (ED10).
—CCC.
Description: Provides news and information on ways and efforts to improve literacy in the United States, both in the workplace and at home.

370 US
REPORT ON PRESCHOOL PROGRAMS; the bi-weekly newsletter on federal programs for early childhood development. 1968. bi-w. $273. Business Publishers, Inc., 951 Pershing Dr., Silver Spring, MD 20910-4464. TEL 301-587-6300. FAX 301-585-9075. Ed. Charles Devaries. bibl.; charts; illus.; stat. (looseleaf format; back issues avail.) **Document type:** newsletter.
●Also available online. Vendor(s): NewsNet.
—CCC.
Formerly: Report on Preschool Education (ISSN 0034-4702)
Description: Ideal for administrators of preschool programs, includes reports of new studies of the most effective teaching methods.

REPORT ON SCHOOL-AGE CHILD CARE. see *CHILDREN AND YOUTH — About*

370 UK ISSN 1351-086X
REPORTBACK. 1969. 2/yr. Workers' Educational Association, 17 Victoria Park Sq., London E2 9PB, England. TEL 081-983-1515. FAX 081-983-4840. Ed. Mel Doyle. adv.; bk.rev. circ. 15,000. **Document type:** bulletin.
Formerly (until 1991): W E A News.
Description: Reports on news and events concerning adult education both inside and outside the W E A.

370 070 US ISSN 0739-3121
REPORTER - YOUR EDITORIAL ASSISTANT. 1972. m. (exc. July & Aug.). $36. George Dubow Agency, 7015 Prospect Pl., N.E., Albuquerque, NM 87110. TEL 505-884-7636. FAX 505-888-0477. Ed. Pat Johnston. (back issues avail.) **Document type:** newsletter.

370 CN ISSN 0315-369X
REPORTING CLASSROOM RESEARCH/COMPTE-RENDU DE RECHERCHES PEDAGOGIQUES. (Text in English; occasional papers in French) 1972. q. Can.$11.50 to non-members (effective 1992). Ontario Educational Research Council - Conseil Ontarien de Recherches Pedagogiques, c/o Dr. Mary Hookey, Nipissing University, 100 College Dr., North Bay, Ont. P1B 8L7, Canada. TEL 705-474-3461. FAX 705-474-1947. Ed. Dormer Ellis. circ. 7,000. **Document type:** newsletter.
Description: Features articles on educational research.

370 US
REPORTS MAGAZINE. irreg., no.29, 1991. $7.50. World Education, Publications Department, 210 Lincoln St., Boston, MA 02111. **Document type:** academic/scholarly publication.

370 CN ISSN 0080-1437
LB1773.C28
REQUIREMENTS FOR TEACHING CERTIFICATES IN CANADA. (Text in English and French) 1971. every 5 years, latest 1993. Can.$6. Canadian Education Association, 252 Bloor St. W. Ste. 8-200, Toronto, ON M5S 1V5, Canada. TEL 416-924-7721. FAX 416-924-3188. Ed. Harriett Goldsborough. circ. 1,400. **Document type:** monographic series.
Description: Guide to types of certificates and licenses necessary for teaching in Canada.

370.15 US ISSN 1046-3364
RESEARCH AND TEACHING IN DEVELOPMENTAL EDUCATION. Short title: R T D E. 1984. s-a. $35 to members; institutions $30. New York College Learning Skills Association, Finger Lakes Community College, 4355 Lake Shore Dr., Canandaigua, NY 14424. TEL 716-394-3500. FAX 716-394-5005. Ed. Patricia A. Malinowski. adv.; bk.rev. circ. 800. **Indexed:** Sp.Ed.Needs Abstr. **Document type:** academic/scholarly publication.
—BLDSC (7716.075000); UnCover.
Description: Interdisciplinary journal which focuses on theoretically based articles on pedagogy, evaluation, program design and delivery in the areas of mathematics, writing and reading.
Refereed Serial

370 378 AT ISSN 0155-6223
RESEARCH DEVELOPMENT IN HIGHER EDUCATION. PUBLICATIONS. 1979. a. Aus.$20($22) Higher Education Research and Development Society of Australasia, c/o T.E.R.C., University of New South Wales, Kensington, N.S.W. 2033, Australia. circ. 400. (back issues avail.)
Description: Selected papers from the annual conference of Higher Education Research and Development Society of Australasia.

374.4 CN ISSN 0843-8854
RESEARCH IN DISTANCE EDUCATION; a forum for researchers in distance education. 1989. irreg. free. Centre for Distance Education, Athabasca University, Box 10000, Athabasca, AB T0G 2R0, Canada. TEL 403-675-6179. FAX 403-675-6477. Eds. Bob Spencer, Eugene Rubin. bk.rev. **Document type:** academic/scholarly publication.
—BLDSC (7738.874500).

370 UK ISSN 0034-5237
LB1028.A1
RESEARCH IN EDUCATION. 1969. s-a. £35($70) to individuals; institutions £60 ($120). Manchester University Press, Oxford Rd., Manchester M13 9PL, England. TEL 061-273-5539. FAX 061-274-3346. TELEX 666517-UNIMAN. Ed. Ivan Reid; Pub. Francis Brooke. adv. circ. 700. (back issues avail.) **Indexed:** Cont.Pg.Educ., Curr.Cont., E.I., Educ.Ind., High.Educ.Curr.Aware.Bull., Lang.Teach.& Ling.Abstr., Mult.Ed.Abstr., Psychol.Abstr., Res.High.Educ.Abstr., SOMA, SSCI. **Document type:** academic/scholarly publication.
—BLDSC (7738.930000); UnCover; SWETS; UMI.
Description: Sociology and psychology of education, with emphasis on current practical issues in teaching.

370 UK ISSN 0263-5143
RESEARCH IN SCIENCE & TECHNOLOGICAL EDUCATION. 1983. s-a. $109 to individuals; institutions $308 (effective 1994). Carfax Publishing Co., P.O. Box 25, Abingdon, Oxon. OX14 3UE, England. TEL 44-235-555335. FAX 44-235-553559. (U.S. subscr. to: Carfax Publishing Co., Box 2025, Dunnellon, FL 34430-2025) Ed. Chris Brown. adv.; illus.; stat.; index. (also avail. in microfiche; back issues avail.) **Indexed:** C.I.J.E., Cont.Pg.Educ., Educ.Tech.Abstr., Psychol.Abstr., Res.High.Educ.Abstr., SOMA, Stud.Wom.Abstr. **Document type:** academic/scholarly publication.
—BLDSC (7769.692500); Faxon; SWETS. **CCC.**
Refereed Serial

370.19 US ISSN 0197-5080
LC189.8
RESEARCH IN SOCIOLOGY OF EDUCATION AND SOCIALIZATION; a research annual. 1980. a. $63.50 to institutions. J A I Press Inc., 55 Old Post Rd., No. 2, Box 1678, Greenwich, CT 06836-1678. TEL 203-661-7602. Ed. Ron Corwin. **Indexed:** Lang.& Lang.Behav.Abstr., Sociol.Abstr. (1981-). **Document type:** academic/scholarly publication.
—BLDSC (7770.718000); Faxon. **CCC.**

370 UK ISSN 0267-1522
RESEARCH PAPERS IN EDUCATION. 1986. 3/yr. £35 (foreign £40) to individuals; institutions £78 (foreign £88). (National Foundation for Educational Research) Routledge, 11 New Fetter Ln., London EC4P 4EE, England. TEL 071-583-9855. FAX 071-583-0701. TELEX 263398-ROUT-G. (Subscr. to: ITPS Ltd., Cheriton House, Andover, Hants SP10 5BE, England. TEL 0264-342919. FAX 0264-342807) Ed. Ted Wragg. adv.; bk.rev.; illus.; stat.; index, cum.index. (also avail. in microfiche) **Indexed:** Cont.Pg.Educ., Mult.Ed.Abstr., SOMA, Sp.Ed.Needs Abstr., Stud.Wom.Abstr. **Document type:** academic/scholarly publication.
—BLDSC (7755.034960); Faxon; UnCover.
Description: Provides authoritative research reports on educational policy and practice.

RESOURCES IN EDUCATION ANNUAL CUMULATION. see *EDUCATION — Abstracting, Bibliographies, Statistics*

370 US ISSN 0895-6855
LA390
RETHINKING SCHOOLS; an urban educational journal. 1987. q. (during school yr.). $12.50 (effective 1994). Rethinking Schools Limited, 1001 E. Keefe Ave., Milwaukee, WI 53212. TEL 414-694-9646. FAX 414-964-7220. bk.rev. **Document type:** newspaper.
Description: Independent, nonprofit, educational journal published by classroom teachers and educators. Helps parents, teachers, and students solve the many problems in our schools.

REVIEW (WASHINGTON); rehabilitation and education for blindness and visual impairment. see *HANDICAPPED — Visually Impaired*

REVIEW OF CHILD DEVELOPMENT RESEARCH. see *CHILDREN AND YOUTH — About*

REVIEW OF EDUCATION; critical analysis of recent books. see *EDUCATION — Abstracting, Bibliographies, Statistics*

370 II
REVIEW OF EDUCATION IN INDIA. 1950. a. Ministry of Education and Social Welfare, Department of Education, Shastri Bhavan, New Delhi 110001, India. (Subscr. to: Assistant Educational Adviser (Publications), Ministry of Human Resource Development, Department of Education Ex. AFO Hutments, Dr.Rajendra Prasad Road, New Delhi 110001, India)

370 US ISSN 0034-6543
L11 CODEN: REDRAB
REVIEW OF EDUCATIONAL RESEARCH. 1931. q. $37 to individuals; institutions $46. American Educational Research Association, 1230 17th St., N.W., Washington, DC 20036-3078. TEL 202-223-9485. FAX 202-775-1824. Eds. Frank Murray, James Raths. adv.; bibl.; index. circ. 17,200. (also avail. in microform from UMI,MIM,PMC; reprint service avail. from UMI) **Indexed:** Adol.Ment.Hlth.Abstr., C.I.J.E., Child Devel.Abstr., Commun.Abstr., Cont.Pg.Educ., Educ.Admin.Abstr., Educ.Ind., Educ.Tech.Abstr., Except.Child.Educ.Abstr., High.Educ.Curr.Aware.Bull., Lang.& Lang.Behav.Abstr., Lang.Teach.& Ling.Abstr., Mid.East: Abstr.& Ind., Mult.Ed.Abstr., Psychol.Abstr., Res.High.Educ.Abstr., SOMA, Sp.Ed.Needs Abstr., SSCI.
—BLDSC (7790.300000); Faxon; UnCover; SWETS; UMI.
Description: Contains integrative reviews and interpretations of the research literature on substantive and methodological issues.

REVIEW OF ENGLISH LANGUAGE TEACHING. see *LINGUISTICS*

370 YU ISSN 0351-0697
REVIJA OBRAZOVANJA. (Text in Serbo-Croatian; summaries in English, French and Russian) 1957-1971; resumed 19?? 6/yr. 10000 din.($50) Republicki Zavod za Unapredjivanje Vaspitanja i Obrazovanja SR Srbije, Draze Pavlovica 15, 11124 Belgrade, Yugoslavia. TEL 765-366. Ed. Cedo Nedeljkovic. bk.rev.; abstr.; bibl.; charts; index. circ. 1,000.
Formerly (until 1977): Revija Skolstva i Prosvetna Dokumentacija (ISSN 0034-6896)

309.2 BL
REVISTA AMAZONENSE DE DESENVOLVIMENTO. 1973. q. Cr.$20000. Centro de Desenvolvimento, Pesquisa e Tecnologia do Estado do Amazonas, Rua Emilio Moreira, 1308, 69000-Manaus-AM, Brazil. stat.
Formerly: R A D.

370 BL ISSN 0034-7183
L45
REVISTA BRASILEIRA DE ESTUDOS PEDAGOGICOS. (Text in Portuguese; summaries in English, French, Portuguese, Spanish) 1944-1980; resumed 1983. 3/yr. $750 (effective Feb. 1992). Instituto Nacional de Estudos e Pesquisas Educacionais, Campus da Universidade da Brasil, Acesso Sul, 70910-900, 70132 Brasilia D.F., Brazil. TEL 061-347-8970. FAX 061-273-3233. Ed. Jair Santana Moraes. bk.rev.; abstr.; bibl.; stat.; cum.index: 1944-1984. circ. 3,000. Indexed: Hisp.Amer.Per.Ind. Document type: academic/scholarly publication.
Description: Covers research, study and debates of various topics in education.
Refereed Serial

613.7 370 AG ISSN 0034-7884
REVISTA DE DERECHO DEPORTIVO. vol.3, 1964. s-a. Agricol de Bianchetti, Paraguay 1307, Buenos Aires, Argentina. Ed.Bd. adv.

377.8 BL
REVISTA DE EDUCACAO A E C. 1945. 4/yr. $8. Associacao de Educacao Catolica do Brasil, SBN Quadra 1, Bloco H, loja 40, 70040 Brasilia D.F., Brazil. TEL 061-223-2947. Ed. Jose Paulo II. bk.rev. circ. 6,000.
Formerly: Associacao de Educacao Catolica do Brasil. Boletim.

370 BL ISSN 0482-5527
REVISTA DE EDUCACAO E CULTURA.* 1960. a. Secretaria de Estado de Educacao de Cultura, Rua Ulhoa Cintra s-n, Recife-Pernambuco, Brazil.

370 AG ISSN 0034-8074
L45
REVISTA DE EDUCACION. N.S. 1956. q. free to schools, institutions & libraries. Ministerio de Cultura y Educacion, Calle 57, No. 777, La Plata, Buenos Aires, Argentina. bk.rev.; illus.; index.

370 CR ISSN 0379-7082
L45
REVISTA DE EDUCACION. 1977. s-a. Col.750($20) Editorial de la Universidad de Costa Rica, Apdo. 75-2060, Ciudad Universitaria Rodrigo Facio, 2050 San Pedro de Montes de Oca, San Jose, Costa Rica. TEL 506-25-3133. FAX 506-24-9367. TELEX UNICORI 2544. Document type: academic/scholarly publication.

370 SP
REVISTA DE EDUCACION (GRANADA). 1987. a. price varies. Universidad de Granada, Servicio de Publicaciones, Antiguo Colegio Maximo, Campus de Cartuja, 18071 Granada, Spain. TEL 243930. Document type: academic/scholarly publication.

370 SP ISSN 0034-8082
REVISTA DE EDUCACION (MADRID). vol.66, 1967. 3/yr. 3000 ptas. (foreign 3500 ptas). Ministerio de Educacion y Ciencia, Secretaria General Tecnica, Centro de Publicaciones, Ciudad Universitaria, 28040 Madrid, Spain. TEL 549-77-00. bk.rev.; abstr.
—SWETS.

370 CL
REVISTA DE TECNOLOGIA EDUCATIVA. q. (Organization of American States) Centro de Perfeccionamiento, Experimentacion e Investigaciones Pedagogica de Chile, Casilla 16162, Providencia, Santiago, Chile. Ed. Clifton B. Chadwick. circ. 2,000. (back issues avail.)

370 SP ISSN 0034-9461
L41
REVISTA ESPANOLA DE PEDAGOGIA. (Text in Spanish) 1943. q. 3300 ptas.($24) (foreign 5000 ptas.). Consejo Superior de Investigaciones Cientificas (C.S.I.C.), Vitruvio, 8, 28006 Madrid, Spain. Ed. Jose A. Ibanez-Martin. adv.; bk.rev.; bibl.; charts; illus.; cum.index. circ. 1,000. Indexed: Amer.Hist.& Life, Hist.Abstr.
—SWETS.
Description: Contains articles on all aspects of teaching.

370 MX ISSN 0185-1284
L43
REVISTA LATINOAMERICANA DE ESTUDIOS EDUCATIVOS. (Text in Spanish; summaries in English, Spanish) 1971. q. Mex.$150($50) (outside Latin America $60) (effective 1993). Centro de Estudios Educativos, A.C., Revolucion 1291, Deleg. Alvaro Obregon, 01040 Mexico, D.F., Mexico. TEL 593-59-77. FAX 664-3039. Ed. Salvador Martinez Licon. adv.; bk.rev.; abstr.; charts; stat.; index, cum.index. circ. 1,500. (back issues avail.) Indexed: Curr.Cont., Hisp.Amer.Per.Ind., Int.Lab.Doc., Res.High.Educ.Abstr., SSCI.
—BLDSC (7863.420000); SWETS.
Formerly (until 1979): Centro de Estudios Educativos. Revista (ISSN 0045-6128)

370 AA ISSN 0304-3509
REVISTA PEDAGOGJIKE. vol.31, 1976. q. 49 lek($19) Institut des Etudes Pedagogiques, Tirana, Albania. Erit Temo. bk.rev.; bibl. circ. 4,850.

370 CU
REVISTA REFERATIVA DE EDUCACION. 1974-1975; resumed 1980. 3/yr. free. Ministerio de Educacion, Direccion de Divulgacion y Publicaciones, Obispo 160, Havana, Cuba. Ed.Bd. bk.rev.; bibl. circ. 2,000.

370 UY
REVISTA URUGUAYA DE ESTUDIOS INTERNACIONALES. irreg., latest 1990. $5 per no. Instituto de Estudios Internacionales, Plaza Independencia 830, Casilla de Correo 903, Montevideo, Uruguay. Ed. Alphonse Max. adv.; bk.rev. circ. 5,000.
Description: Covers various issues and history of the Uruguian territory, also contains essays topics in the field of economy, geopolitics and education.

370 CU
REVISTA VARONA. s-a. $9 in N. and S. America; Europe $11; elsewhere $12. (Ministerio de Educacion) Ediciones Cubanas, Obispo No. 527, Apdo. 605, Havana, Cuba.

370 ZR
REVUE AFRICAINE DES SCIENCES DE L'EDUCATION/AFRICAN REVIEW OF EDUCATIONAL SCIENCES. (Text and summaries in English and French) 1976. s-a. 80 Fr.CFA($35) African Bureau of Educational Sciences, Box 14, Ksangani, Zaire. Ed. A.S. Mungala. circ. 150.

REVUE BELGE DE PSYCHOLOGIE ET DE PEDAGOGIE. see *PSYCHOLOGY*

378 AE
REVUE DE L'ENSEIGNEMENT SUPERIEUR ET DE LA RECHERCHE SCIENTIFIQUE. 1956. q. 20 F. 11 Chemin Mokhtar Doudou, Ben-Aknoun, Algiers, Algeria. TEL 78-87-18. illus.; index. circ. 8,000.
Formerly: Revue de l'Enseignement Superieur (ISSN 0035-1407)

372 BE ISSN 0035-1997
REVUE DES ECOLES. 1880. bi-m. 750 Fr. Imprimerie Artistic, 179 Av. de Maire, 7500 Tournai, Belgium. Ed. A. Gille. adv.; bk.rev.; bibl.; charts; film rev.; play rev.; record rev.; index. circ. 2,200.
Formerly: Bulletin des Ecoles Primaires.

370 HT
REVUE L'EDUCATEUR. m. Grand Rue, B.P. 164, Port-au-Prince, Haiti. TEL 1-2-2297. TELEX 0533. circ. 8,000.

370.15 ZR
REVUE ZAIROISE DE PSYCHOLOGIE ET DE PEDAGOGIE. (Text in French; some summaries in English) 1972. 2/yr. $8 per no. Universite de Kisangani, Faculte de Psychologie et des Sciences de l'Education, B.P. 1386, Kisangani, Zaire. Ed. Bamwisho Mihia.

370 IT
RICERCHE DI SOCIOLOGIA DELL'EDUCAZIONE E PEDAGOGIA COMPARATA. 1974. irreg. (Universita degli Studi di Messina, Istituto di Pedagogia) Peloritana Editrice, Messina, Italy. Dir. Giuseppe Catalfamo.
Description: Covers educational sociology and comparitive teaching.

370 IT ISSN 0035-5046
RICERCHE DIDATTICHE. 1951. m. L.25000($7) Movimento Circoli della Didattica, Via Crescenzio 25, Rome 00193, Italy.
—SWETS.
Description: Explores diverse didatic tactics and arguments regarding the discipline of studying.

370 PE
RIDECAB; boletin informativo. 1980. s-a. Instituto Nacional de Investigacion y Desarrollo de la Educacion, Centro Nacional de Documentacion e Informacion Educacional, Van de Velde 160, San Borja, Lima 100, Peru.

370 IT ISSN 0035-5240
RIFORMA DELLA SCUOLA/SCHOOL REFORM. 1955. m. L.51000 (L.77000 foreign). Editori Riuniti, Via Serchio 9-11, 00198 Rome, Italy. TEL 06-866383. FAX 06-8416095. TELEX EDIRIU I 625292. Ed. Tullio De Mauro. adv.; bk.rev.; bibl.; illus.; index. circ. 15,000. (tabloid format)
—SWETS.

370 US
RIO GRANDE EDUCATIONAL ASSOCIATION NEWSLETTER. 1971. s-a. $10. Rio Grande Educational Association, Box 2241, Santa Fe, NM 87501. Ed. Ed Nagel. bk.rev.; bibl.; illus. circ. 300.

370 US
RITENOUR NEWS. 1971. 4/yr. free. Ritenour School District, 2420 Woodson Rd., Overland, MO 63114. TEL 314-429-3500. FAX 314-426-7144. Ed. Cindy L. Gibson. circ. 25,000.
Former titles (until 1979): Ritenour School District News (ISSN 0035-5631); Ritenour School Bulletin.
Description: Information, feature articles and sports schedules concerning the Ritenour School District.

370 US
RITENOUR REPORTER. 1970. m. (during school year). free. Ritenour School District, 2420 Woodson Rd., Overland, MO 63114. TEL 314-429-3500. FAX 314-426-7144. Ed. Cindy L. Gibson. illus. circ. 1,200.
Former titles (until 1979): Intercom (Overland) (ISSN 0035-564X); Ritenour Staff Newsletter.

370 IT ISSN 0394-8447
RIVISTA DELL'ISTRUZIONE; sistema formativo e produttivita scolastica. 1985. bi-m. L.125000 (effective 1994). Maggioli Editore, Viale Vespucci 12-n, Casella Postale 290, 47037 Rimini, Italy. TEL 0541-626777. FAX 0541-622020. Ed.Bd. adv.: B&W page L 1200000, color page L.1800000; trim 115 x 180.

370 PL ISSN 0137-9585
ROCZNIK PEDAGOGICZNY. irreg., vol.13, 1991. price varies. (Polska Akademia Nauk, Komitet Nauk Pedagogicznych) Ossolineum, Publishing House of the Polish Academy of Sciences, Rynek 9, Wroclaw, Poland. TEL 48-71-386-25. FAX 48-71-448-103. TELEX 0712771 OSS PL. Ed. H. Muszynski. Document type: academic/scholarly publication.
Description: Pedagogical dissertations.

370 XO ISSN 0231-6463
RODINA A SKOLA; casopis pro rodinu a skolu. 1953. 10/yr. 30 Kcs. (Ministry of Education, Slovak Socialist Republic) Slovenske Pedagogicke Nakladatelstvo, Sasinkova 5, 815-60 Bratislava, Slovakia. TEL 697-64. (Subscr. to: Slovart, Gottwaldovo nam. 6, 805-32 Bratislava, Slovakia) Ed. Viera Chrostekova. circ. 37,000.

371 PL ISSN 0485-3504
RODZINA I SZKOLA; miesiecznik dla rodzicow i wychowawcow. 1959. m. $11. Wydawnictwo Wspolczesne R S W "Prasa-Ksiazka-Ruch", Ul. Wiejska 12, 00-420 Warsaw, Poland. (Subscr. to: RSW "Prasa-Ksiazka-Ruch" Centrala Kolportazu Prasy i Wydawnictw, ul. Towarowa 28, 00-958 Warsaw, Poland) Ed. Zofia Dabrowska-Caban.

2052 EDUCATION

370   US   ISSN 0278-3193
ROEPER REVIEW; a journal on gifted education. 1978. q. $37 to individuals; institutions $50. Roeper School, Box 329, Bloomfield Hills, MI 48303. TEL 810-642-1500. FAX 810-642-1500. Ed. Ruthan Brodsky; Pub. Ruthan Brodsky. adv. contact: Vicki Rossbach. bk.rev.; index; circ. 3,000 (paid). (also avail. in microform from UMI; back issues avail.; reprint service avail. from UMI) **Indexed:** C.I.J.E., Educ.Ind., Psychol.Abstr. **Document type:** academic/scholarly publication.
—BLDSC (8019.158000); Faxon; UnCover; UMI.
    Description: Focuses on issues, teaching strategies, academic theory and research regarding gifted education.
Refereed Serial

ROSICRUCIAN DIGEST. see *PHILOSOPHY*

370 970.1   US
ROUGH ROCK NEWS. 1966. m. (during school year). $4. Rough Rock Demonstration School, Rough Rock, AZ 86503. TEL 602-728-3243. Ed. Daisy Kiyaani. adv.; bk.rev.; play rev.; illus. circ. 400. (tabloid format)

370   PL   ISSN 0080-4754
ROZPRAWY Z DZIEJOW OSWIATY. 1958. a. price varies. Polska Akademia Nauk, Instytut Historii Nauki, Oswiaty i Techniki, Zaklad Dziejow Oswiaty, Ul. Nowy Swiat 72, 00-330 Warsaw, Poland. (Dist. by: Ars Polona-Ruch, Krakowskie Przedmiescie 7, Warsaw, Poland) Ed. Jozef Miaso. bk.rev. circ. 600. **Document type:** academic/scholarly publication.
—BLDSC (8035.670000).
    Description: Papers on the history and problems of education in Poland and abroad.

370 330   DK   ISSN 0109-0984
RUE-REVUE. 1983. q. free. Raadet for Uddannelses- og Erhvervsvejledning, Aebeloegade 7, 2100 Copenhagen OE, Denmark. illus. circ. 8,800.

RUIMZICHT. see *RELIGIONS AND THEOLOGY*

370   US   ISSN 0273-446X
LB1567
RURAL EDUCATOR. 1980. 3/yr. $35 library membership includes Country Teacher and National Rural Education News (foreign $50) (not avail. separately) (effective 1994). National Rural Education Association, 230 Education Bldg., Colorado State University, Fort Collins, CO 80523-0001. TEL 303-491-7022. FAX 303-491-1317. Ed. Joseph T. Newlin. adv.; bk.rev.; circ. 1,000 (paid). (also avail. in microfiche; back issues avail.; reprint service avail. from UMI) **Indexed:** C.I.J.E., Cont.Pg.Educ. **Document type:** academic/scholarly publication.
—BLDSC (8052.434500); UnCover; UMI.

RUSISTIKA. see *LINGUISTICS*

400   US   ISSN 1060-9393
L11
RUSSIAN EDUCATION AND SOCIETY; a journal of translations. 1958. m. $506 (foreign $558). M.E. Sharpe, Inc., 80 Business Park Dr., Armonk, NY 10504. TEL 914-273-1800. FAX 914-273-2106. Ed. Anthony Jones. adv.; index. (back issues avail.) **Indexed:** ASCA, C.I.J.E., Cont.Pg.Educ., Curr.Cont., Educ.Ind., Educ.Tech.Abstr., P.A.I.S., SSCI.
—BLDSC (8052.698000); Faxon; UnCover; SWETS; UMI.
    Formerly: Soviet Education (ISSN 0038-5360)
Refereed Serial

RUSSIAN LANGUAGE JOURNAL. see *LINGUISTICS*

THE S A L T PROGRAMME FOR 8 TO 10. see *RELIGIONS AND THEOLOGY*

370   US
S C E A EMPHASIS. 9/yr. $5 to non-members. South Carolina Education Association, 421 Zimalcrest Dr., Columbia, SC 29210. TEL 803-772-6553. FAX 803-772-0922. Ed. Sandor I. Ketzis. adv.; bk.rev. circ. 20,000.
    Formerly: South Carolina Education News Emphasis (ISSN 0038-3066)
    Description: Informs members of education news and association news.

370   TH   ISSN 0858-673X
▼**S E A M E O CANADA CHRONICLER**. (Text in English) 1992. s-a. exchange basis. Southeast Asian Ministers of Education Organization, 920 Sukhumvit Rd., Bangkok 10110, Thailand. TEL 66-2-391-0144. FAX 66-2-381-2587. TELEX 086-22683 SEAMES TH. circ. 1,500. **Document type:** newsletter.
    Description: News about activities in connection with SEAMEO-Canada Programme of Cooperation.

370   TH   ISSN 0858-6721
▼**S E A M E O UPDATE**. (Text in English) 1993. m. exchange basis. Southeast Asian Ministers of Education Organization, 920 Sukhumvit Rd., Bangkok 10110, Thailand. TEL 62-2-391-0144. FAX 66-2-381-2587. TELEX 086-22683 SEAMES TH. circ. 1,500. **Document type:** newsletter.
    Description: Contains news about the organization's activities.

370 100   US
S E R IN ACTION NEWSLETTER. 3/yr. membership. Society for Educational Reconstruction, c/o Dean S. Yarhrough, Jr., Ed., 468 Concord Rd., Sudbury, MA 01776. bk.rev. circ. 200. **Document type:** newsletter.
    Description: Covers goals and activities of the society.

370   NZ   ISSN 0110-6376
S E T: RESEARCH INFORMATION FOR TEACHERS. 1974. s-a. NZ.$32. New Zealand Council for Educational Research, P.O. Box 3237, Wellington, New Zealand. TEL 64-4-3847-939. FAX 64-4-3847-933. (Co-sponsor: Australian Council for Educational Research) Ed. Llewelyn Richards. bibl. circ. 5,500. (looseleaf format; also avail. in microfilm from UMI) **Document type:** academic/scholarly publication.
—CCC.

370   SQ
S I E R BULLETIN. no.2, 1979. a. $10. University of Swaziland, Swaziland Institute for Educational Research, Private Bag, Kwaluseni, Swaziland. TEL 09268-85108. FAX 09268-85276. TELEX 2087 WD. Ed. B. Putsoa. **Indexed:** P.L.E.S.A. **Document type:** bulletin.

370   CI   ISSN 0039-288X
S L. (Studentski List) 1945. w. 1000 din. Savez Socijalisticke Omladine Hrvatske, Zagreb, Sveucilisna Konferencija, Trg Zrtava Fasizma 13, 41001 Zagreb, Croatia. Ed. Zoran Milovic. bk.rev. circ. 10,000.

370   DK   ISSN 0108-3856
S L F INFORMATION; for laerere ved boernehave, fritidspaedagog- og socialpaedagogiske seminarier. 1979. irreg. (6-8/yr.). DKK 100 to non-members. Seminarielaererforeningen, Schleppegrellsgade 10, 2200 Copenhagen N, Denmark.
    Formerly: B F L Information.

370   US   ISSN 0882-1100
S P E MONOGRAPH SERIES. irreg. Society of Professors of Education, c/o Richard Wisniewski, College of Education, Univ. of Tennessee, Knoxville, TN 37996-3400. TEL 615-974-2201. FAX 615-974-8718.
—EI.
    Formerly: National Society of College Teachers of Education. Monographs.

370 366   US   ISSN 1068-1752
S R A T E JOURNAL. 1991. a. $15. Southeastern Regional Association of Teacher Educators, c/o Scott Hopkins, Ed., Department of Curriculum and Instruction, College of Education, University of South Alabama, Mobile, AL 36688-0002. TEL 205-380-2895. circ. 250. **Document type:** academic/scholarly publication.

370   IS
SADA-A-TARBIYA; educational and social problems in Israel. (Text in Arabic) m. Israel Teacher's Union, 8 Ben Saruk St., Tel Aviv 62 969, Israel. TEL 03-543911. FAX 03-5432928.

370   LE   ISSN 0581-2984
SAHIFAT AL-TAKHTIT AL-TARBAWI FI AL-BILAD AL-ARABIYAH/REVUE DE PLANIFICATION DE L'EDUCATION DANS LES PAYS ARABES. (Text in Arabic; summaries in English and French) 1963. 3/yr. Markaz al-Iqlimi, Centre Regional, B.P. 5233, Bir-Hassan, Beirut, Lebanon. bibl.; illus.

378   UA   ISSN 0036-2654
SAHIFAT AL-TARBIYA.* (Text in Arabic; summaries in English) 1948. q. P.T.60. Association of the Graduates of the Institutes and Faculties of Education, 13 Tahrir Sq., Cairo, Egypt. Ed. Aziz Mohammed Habib. bk.rev. circ. 3,000.

SAITAMA SEIBUTSU/SAITAMA BIOLOGICAL SOCIETY OF HIGH SCHOOL TEACHERS. see *BIOLOGY*

SALESIAN. see *RELIGIONS AND THEOLOGY — Roman Catholic*

SALEZIJANSKI VESTNIK; glasilo salezijanske druzine. see *RELIGIONS AND THEOLOGY — Roman Catholic*

SANTUARIO DE APARECIDA. see *RELIGIONS AND THEOLOGY*

379   BL
SAO PAULO, BRAZIL (STATE). SECRETARIA DA EDUCACAO. ATIVIDADES DESENVOLVIDAS. 1973. irreg. Secretaria da Educacao, Sao Paulo, Brazil.

370   CN   ISSN 0036-4886
SASKATCHEWAN BULLETIN. 1933. fortn. Can.$7. Saskatchewan Teachers' Federation, 2317 Arlington Ave., Box 1108, Saskatoon, Sask. S7K 3N3, Canada. TEL 306-373-1160. FAX 306-374-1122. Ed. Connie Burrows. adv.; bk.rev.; film rev.; illus.; stat.; circ. 22,300 (controlled). (tabloid format; also avail. in microfilm from CML) **Indexed:** Can.Educ.Ind.

371.4   CN   ISSN 0048-9190
SASKATCHEWAN GUIDANCE AND COUNSELLING ASSOCIATION. GUIDELINES. 1964. s-a. Can.$20. Saskatchewan Teachers' Federation, Box 1108, Saskatoon, SK S7K 3N3, Canada. TEL 306-373-1160. Ed. Janice Solem. adv.; bk.rev. circ. 250. **Indexed:** Can.Educ.Ind.

371.4   CN
SASKATCHEWAN GUIDANCE AND COUNSELLING ASSOCIATION. NEWSLETTER. s-a. Can.$50 to individuals; institutions Can.$100. Saskatchewan Teachers' Federation, Box 1108, Saskatoon, SK S7K 3N3, Canada. Ed. Janice Solem. **Document type:** newsletter.

370   FR
SAVOIR EDUCATION FORMATION. 1989. q. 475 F. (foreign 560 F.). Editions Sirey-Diffusion Dalloz, 22 rue Sufflot, 75005 Paris, France. (Subscr. to: 35 rue Tournefort, 75240 Paris Cedex 05, France. TEL 1-40-51-54-54) (back issues avail.)
    Description: Studies the political, economical, judicial and social aspects of education.

SCAN (NEW YORK). see *ETHNIC INTERESTS*

370   UK   ISSN 0031-3831
                       CODEN: SJERAS
SCANDINAVIAN JOURNAL OF EDUCATIONAL RESEARCH. (Text in English) 1957. q. $78 to individuals; institutions $202 (effective 1994). Carfax Publishing Co., P.O. Box 25, Abingdon, Oxon. OX14 3UE, England. TEL 44-235-555335. FAX 44-235-553559. (U.S. subscr. to: Carfax Publishing Co., Box 2025, Dunnellon, FL 34430-2025) Ed. Asmund L. Stroemnes. adv.; bk.rev.; bibl.; charts; index. (also avail. in microform from UMI) **Indexed:** C.I.J.E., Child Devel.Abstr., Cont.Pg.Educ., Educ.Tech.Abstr., Lang.& Lang.Behav.Abstr., Mult.Ed.Abstr., Psychol.Abstr., SOMA, Sp.Ed.Needs Abstr. **Document type:** academic/scholarly publication.
—BLDSC (8087.506000); Faxon; UnCover; SWETS. CCC.
    Formerly: Pedagogisk Forskning.
Refereed Serial

370   GW
SCHECKHEFT STUDIUM. 1980. a. DM.25. Verein Freunde und Foerderer der Deutschen Studentenschaft, Untere Hausbreite 11, 80939 Munich, Germany. Ed. Gundolf Seidenspinner. adv.; bk.rev. circ. 100. **Document type:** academic/scholarly publication.

028.5 370   IT   ISSN 0036-5955
SCHEDARIO; periodico di letteratura giovanile. vol.17, 1970. q. L.25000 (foreign L.55000). Biblioteca di Documentazione Pedagogica, Sezione di Letteratura Giovanile, Via M. Buonarroti 10, 50122 Florence, Italy. (Subscr. to: c/o Giunti Marzocco, Via Gioberti 34, 50100 Florence, Italy) (Co-sponsor: Ministero Pubblica Istruzione) Dir. Antonio Augenti. adv.; bk.rev.; bibl.; illus. circ. 8,000. (also avail. in microfiche)

370   GW
SCHLESWIG-HOLSTEIN. MINISTERIN FUER BILDUNG, WISSENSCHAFT, KULTUR UND SPORT. NACHRICHTENBLATT; als besondere Ausgabe des Amtsblatts fuer Schleswig-Holstein. 1949. m. DM.52. Ministerin fuer Bildung, Wissenschaft, Kultur und Sport, Duesternbrooker Weg 64, 24105 Kiel, Germany. TEL 0431-5961. FAX 596-4835. (Subscr. to: Schmidt und Klaunig, Ringstr. 19, 2300 Kiel 1, Germany) bk.rev.; index. circ. 2,900. (reprint service avail.; back issues avail.) **Document type:** government publication.
   Former titles (until 1992): Schleswig-Holstein. Ministerin fuer Bildung, Wissenschaft, Jugend und Kultur. Nachrichtenblatt (ISSN 0937-0005); (until 1989): Schleswig-Holstein. Kulturminister. Nachrichtenblatt (ISSN 0023-7868); (until 1960): Schleswig-Holsteinische Schulwesen. Nachrichtenblatt.
   Description: Government publication listing laws and regulations of schools, higher education, and trade schools concerning exams and organization. Includes positions available.

370   GW
SCHO WIDA. 1979. irreg. DM.1 per no. Scho Wida, Chiemgau Gymnasium, Brunnwiese 1, 83278 Traunstein, Germany. bk.rev.; film rev.; illus.; play rev. circ. 650. (back issues avail.)

SCHOENBERGER HEFTE. see *RELIGIONS AND THEOLOGY — Protestant*

SCHOLASTIC NEWS: NEWS EXPLORER. see *CHILDREN AND YOUTH — For*

SCHOLASTIC NEWS: NEWS PILOT. see *CHILDREN AND YOUTH — For*

SCHOLASTIC NEWS: NEWS RANGER. see *CHILDREN AND YOUTH — For*

SCHOLASTIC NEWS: NEWSTIME. see *CHILDREN AND YOUTH — For*

SCHOLASTIC NEWS TRAILS. see *CHILDREN AND YOUTH — For*

370   US   ISSN 0036-6412
SCHOLASTIC SCOPE. 1964. 20/yr. $6.95. Scholastic Inc., 555 Broadway, New York, NY 10012-3999. TEL 212-361-6100. Ed. Karen Glenn. adv.; film rev.; index. circ. 823,000. (also avail. in microform from UMI; reprint service avail. from UMI, BLH)
—UnCover; UMI.

SCHOLASTIC UPDATE. see *CHILDREN AND YOUTH — For*

371   NE   ISSN 0377-5054
SCHOOL; opinieblad voor de onderwijspraktijk. 1972. m. (10/yr.) fl.92.50. Koninklijke Boom Pers, P.O. Box 1064, 7940 KB Meppel, Netherlands. TEL 31-5220-54646. Ed. J. Ahlers. adv.; illus. circ. 5,000.
—SWETS.

370   US   ISSN 0272-9997
SCHOOL. (Supplement to: S I R S Social Issues (ISSN 0740-3127)) 1975. a. price varies; a. supplement $17. Social Issues Resources Series, Box 2348, Boca Raton, FL 33427-2348. TEL 407-994-0079; 800-232-7477. FAX 407-994-4704. (looseleaf format; also avail. in microfiche; back issues avail.)
   Description: Reprints articles that investigate all aspects of public education.

371   US   ISSN 1045-3970
SCHOOL AND COLLEGE; education facilities, business, systems, services, and administration. 1962. m. $30 (effective 1993-94). Peter Li Education Group, 2451 E. River Rd., Dayton, OH 45439. TEL 800-523-4625. FAX 513-294-7840. Ed. Roger Morton. adv.; bk.rev.; charts; film rev.; illus.; tr.lit.; circ. 50,000 (controlled). (also avail. in microform from UMI; reprint service avail. from UMI) **Indexed:** Bus.Ind., Tr.& Indus.Ind.
●Also available online. Vendor(s): DIALOG Information Services, Inc.
—UMI. **CCC**.
   Former titles (until 1986): School and College Product News (ISSN 0893-4126); School Product News (ISSN 0036-6749)
   Description: Covers current issues, equipment and technology.

370   US   ISSN 0036-6447
SCHOOL AND COMMUNITY. 1915. 4/yr. $10 (foreign $12.50). Missouri State Teachers Association, Box 458, Columbia, MO 65205. TEL 314-442-3127. FAX 314-443-5079. Ed. Bruce Moe. adv.; bk.rev.; illus.; index. circ. 30,000. (also avail. in microform from UMI; reprint service avail. from UMI) **Indexed:** Educ.Ind. **Document type:** trade publication.
—Faxon; UnCover; UMI.

370   CN   ISSN 0382-7879
LB3034
SCHOOL CALENDAR/CALENDRIER SCOLAIRE; opening and closing dates, number of working days and prescribed holidays in Canada. (Text in English and French) 1969. a. Can.$5. Canadian Education Association - Association Canadienne d'Education, 252 Bloor St. W., Ste. 8-200, Toronto, ON M5S 1V5, Canada. TEL 416-924-7721. FAX 416-924-3188. Ed. H. Goldsborough. circ. 600. **Indexed:** Can.Educ.Ind. **Document type:** monographic series.
   Description: Official school dates in Canada.

SCHOOL COUNSELOR. see *PSYCHOLOGY*

370   NE   ISSN 0924-3453
                          CODEN: SEFIE9
SCHOOL EFFECTIVENESS AND SCHOOL IMPROVEMENT; an international journal of research, policy and practice. 1990. q. $70 to individuals; institutions $140. Swets & Zeitlinger bv, Heereweg 347, 2161 CA Lisse, Netherlands. TEL 31-2521-35111. FAX 31-2521-15888. TELEX 41325. (Dist. in N. America by: Swets & Zeitlinger, 440 Creamery Way, Ste. A, Exton, PA 19341. TEL 800-447-9387. FAX 610-524-5366) Ed.Bd. (back issues avail.; reprint service avail. from SWZ) **Indexed:** SOMA. **Document type:** academic/scholarly publication.
—BLDSC (8092.734000); SWETS. **CCC**.
   Refereed Serial

370   UK
SCHOOL GOVERNOR. 1987. q. £14. Ream Ltd., c/o Felicity Taylor, Ed., 10 Brookfield Park, London NW5 1ER, England. TEL 01-485-4258. FAX 01-287-1989. (Subscr. to: 607 Hockley Hill, Hockley, Birmingham B18 5AA, England) Ed. Felicity Taylor. adv.; bk.rev.; film rev. circ. 5,000.
   Description: Independent magazine dealing with all aspects of a changing educational system in Britain.

SCHOOL LAW BULLETIN (CHAPEL HILL). see *LAW*

370 360   UG
SCHOOL LEAVER. 1973. 3/yr. EAs.100($45) Uganda School Leavers Association, Box 5145, Kampala, Uganda. Ed. John Ken-Lukyamuzi. adv.; bk.rev.; illus. circ. 8,500.

SCHOOL LIBRARIES IN CANADA. see *LIBRARY AND INFORMATION SCIENCES*

SCHOOL LIBRARY JOURNAL; the magazine of children, young adults & school librarians. see *LIBRARY AND INFORMATION SCIENCES*

SCHOOL LIBRARY MEDIA QUARTERLY. see *LIBRARY AND INFORMATION SCIENCES*

370 600   US
SCHOOL SCENE. 1968. q. $10. Technology Student Association, 1914 Association Dr., Reston, VA 22091. TEL 703-860-9000. FAX 703-620-4483. Ed. Ceil Holland. adv.; bk.rev. circ. 60,000. **Document type:** newspaper.
   Description: Provides networking and educational material to develop basic technological literacy and leadership skills among students.

SCHOOL SCIENCE; quarterly journal for secondary schools. see *SCIENCES: COMPREHENSIVE WORKS*

507 370   US   ISSN 0036-6803
Q1   CODEN: SSMAAC
SCHOOL SCIENCE AND MATHEMATICS; journal for all science and mathematical teachers. 1901. m. (Oct.-May). $32 (foreign $40) (effective 1993). School Science and Mathematics Association, Inc., Memorial Gym 300 B, Virgina Tech. C. & I., Blacksburg, VA 24061. TEL 703-231-5558. FAX 703-231-3717. (Subscr. to: Donald Pratt, Exec. Secy., Dept. of Education, McCormick Ctr., Bloomsburg Univ. Bloomsburg, PA 17815. TEL 717-389-4639) Ed. Robert Underhill. adv.; bk.rev.; bibl.; charts; illus.; tr.lit.; index, cum.index: 1900-1960. circ. 4,000. (also avail. in microform from UMI,PMC; back issues avail.; reprint service avail. from UMI.) **Indexed:** Acad.Ind., C.I.J.E., Chem.Abstr., Conf.Pg.Educ., Educ.Ind., Excerp.Med. **Document type:** academic/scholarly publication.
—BLDSC (8092.950000); Faxon; UnCover; SWETS; UMI.

SCHOOL SECURITY REPORT. see *CRIMINOLOGY AND LAW ENFORCEMENT — Security*

SCHOOL TRANSPORTATION NEWS. see *TRANSPORTATION*

370 910.09   UK
SCHOOL VISITS GUIDE. 1985. a. £5 free to U.K. schools. British Trades Alphabet, Thames View Business Centre, Thames View Industrial Park, Abingdon, Oxon. OX14 3LF, England. TEL 0235-553233. FAX 0235-553356. Ed. A. Rothery.
   Description: Reference guide for teachers planning school holidays or outings (field trips). Details transportation, accommodations, museums, farms and more.

362   US
SCHOOL VOLUNTEERING; linking school volunteers nationwide. (Special issue of: Partners in Education) q. $20 to non-members; members free. National Association of Partners in Education, Inc., 209 Madison St., Ste. 401, Alexandria, VA 22314. TEL 703-836-4880. FAX 703-836-6941. illus. (tabloid format)
   Description: Focuses on program management, tips for enhancing volunteer skills, and ideas for expanding the roles of individual school volunteers.

370   NE   ISSN 0036-6889
SCHOOLBLAD. 1850. w. fl.4.35 per no. Algemene Bond van Onderwijs Personeel, Herengracht 54, 1015 BN Amsterdam, Netherlands. Ed.Bd. adv.; bk.rev. circ. 45,000.

372   US   ISSN 0746-2018
SCHOOLDAYS; practical guides for primary teachers. 1982. 4/yr. $18. Frank Schaffer Publications, Inc., 23740 Hawthorne Blvd., Torrance, CA 90505. TEL 213-378-1133. FAX 213-375-5090. (Subscr. to: Box 10783, Des Moines, IA 50340-0783) Ed. Marsha Elyn Wright. adv.; bk.rev. circ. 161,000. (back issues avail.) **Document type:** trade publication.
   Description: Devoted to teachers of grades K-1-2-3, containing reproducible worksheets, activities and ideas for the classroom.

SCHOOLS AND THE COURTS; briefs of selected court cases involving secondary and elementary schools. see *LAW*

370   US   ISSN 0276-4482
LB1623.5
SCHOOLS IN THE MIDDLE; theory into practice. 1981. q. $10 membership. National Association of Secondary School Principals, 1904 Association Dr., Reston, VA 22091. TEL 703-860-0200. FAX 703-476-5432. Ed. Patricia George. circ. 23,000. (back issues avail.)
—UnCover; SWETS.
   Description: Addresses issues in middle level education.

SCHULE- UND SPORTSTAETTE. see *BUILDING AND CONSTRUCTION*

371.33   GW   ISSN 0036-7125
SCHULFERNSEHEN (MUNICH). 1964. m. DM.12. Bayerischer Rundfunk, Rundfunkplatz 1, 80335 Munich, Germany. Ed. Rosemarie v. Hornstein. play rev.; charts; illus. circ. 8,000. (cards)

370   GW   ISSN 0586-965X
SCHULREPORT; Tatsachen und Meinungen zur Bildungspolitik in Bayern. 1970. 6/yr. Bayerisches Staatsministerium fuer Unterricht, Kulturs, Wissenschaft und Kunst, Salvatorstr. 2, 80333 Munich, Germany. TEL 089-2186-1511. FAX 089-2186-1803. TELEX 898300-0. Ed. Hartmut Pramstaller. circ. 132,000. **Document type:** government publication.
Description: For educators and teachers in Bavaria.

SCHWAMM. see *CHILDREN AND YOUTH — For*

377.8   SZ   ISSN 0036-7443
SCHWEIZER SCHULE. 1914. s-m. 68 Fr. Brunner Druck AG, Arsenalstr. 24, CH-6010 Kriens, Switzerland. adv.; bk.rev.; rec.rev.; bibl.; charts; illus.; index. circ. 4,500.

370   SZ   ISSN 0036-7214
SCHWEIZERISCHE ARBEITSLEHRERINNEN-ZEITUNG. 1918. m. (10/yr.). 40 Fr. Schweizerischer Arbeitslehrerinnen-Verein, c/o Anita Keller, Huttenstr. 55, CH-8006 Zurich, Switzerland. adv.; bk.rev.; illus. circ. 55,000. **Document type:** trade publication.
Formerly: Schweiz Arbeitslehrerinnen-Zeitung.

370   SZ   ISSN 0036-7656
SCHWEIZERISCHE LEHRERZEITUNG. (Text in German) 1855. bi-w. 124 SFr. (Dachverband Schweizer Lehrerinnen und Lehrer) Zuerichsee Medien AG, Seestr. 86, CH-7612 Staefa, Switzerland. TEL 01-9285611. adv.; bk.rev.; bibl.; illus.; index; circ. 16,500 (controlled). **Document type:** trade publication.

507 370   US   ISSN 0036-8121
Q181.A1
SCIENCE ACTIVITIES; the teacher's classroom guide. 1969. 4/yr. $30 to individuals; institutions $54. (Helen Dwight Reid Educational Foundation) Heldref Publications, 1319 Eighteenth St., N.W., Washington, DC 20036-1802. TEL 202-296-6267. FAX 202-296-5149. Ed. Claire M. Wilson. adv. contact: Raymond Rallo. bk.rev.; film rev.; charts; illus.; stat.; index. circ. 1,500. (also avail. in microform; back issues avail.) reprint service avail.) **Indexed:** C.I.J.E., Educ.Ind. **Document type:** academic/scholarly publication.
—Faxon; UnCover; UMI. **CCC.**
Refereed Serial

SCIENCE AND CHILDREN. see *SCIENCES: COMPREHENSIVE WORKS*

SCIENCE & EDUCATION; contributions from history, philosophy & sociology of science and mathematics. see *SCIENCES: COMPREHENSIVE WORKS*

SCIENCE EDUCATION. see *SCIENCES: COMPREHENSIVE WORKS*

SCIENCE MATTERS. see *SCIENCES: COMPREHENSIVE WORKS*

THE SCIENCE TEACHER. see *SCIENCES: COMPREHENSIVE WORKS*

370.4   BE   ISSN 0582-2351
L10   CODEN: SPEXDN
SCIENTIA PAEDAGOGICA EXPERIMENTALIS; international journal. Short title: S P E. 1964. s-a. 1200 BEF. State University Ghent, Labo Pedagogiek, Blandijnberg 2, B-9000 Gent, Belgium. TEL 32-9-2643952. FAX 32-9-2646498. adv.; bk.rev.; abstr. circ. 600. (back issues avail.) **Indexed:** Curr.Cont., Lang.& Lang.Behav.Abstr., Psychol.Abstr., SSCI. **Document type:** academic/scholarly publication.
—BLDSC (8172.800000); UnCover; SWETS.
Refereed Serial

SCIENTIFIC WORLD. see *SCIENCES: COMPREHENSIVE WORKS*

378   IS   ISSN 0036-9020
SCOPUS. (Text in English) a. free. Hebrew University of Jerusalem, Mount Scopus, Jerusalem 91905, Israel. Ed. Lisa Clayton. adv.; illus. circ. 20,000.

370   UK
SCOTTISH EDUCATIONAL JOURNAL. 1876. 6/yr. £8.10 (rest of Europe £9.20; elsewhere £13). Educational Institute of Scotland, 46 Moray Pl., Edinburgh, EH3 6BH, Scotland. TEL 031-225-6244. FAX 031-220-3151. Ed. Simon G. Macauley. adv.; bk.rev. circ. 18,000. (tabloid format; back issues avail.) **Document type:** newspaper.

370   CN   ISSN 0838-4525
SCRUTINY. 1987. 8/yr. Can.$8 to individuals; institutions Can.$16. Don Cochrane, Ed. & Pub., Post Box 1, Sub Post Office 6, Saskatoon, SK S7N 0W0, Canada. TEL 306-966-7521. FAX 306-966-8719. circ. 300. (looseleaf format; back issues avail.)
Description: Bulletin of independent analysis, discussion, and controversy on issues vital to education in Saskatchewan.

370   IT
SCUOLA DOMENICALE. 1879. q. L.26,000 (effective July 1993). (Federazione dell Chiese Evangeliche in Italia) Servizio Istruzione ed Educazione, Via Porro Lambertenghi 28, 20159 Milano, Italy. TEL 02-69-000883.

370   IT   ISSN 0036-9853
L36
SCUOLA E CITTA; rivista de problemi educativi e di politica scolastica. 1950. m. L.50000 (foreign L.60000) (effective 1993). Nuova Italia Editrice S.p.a., Via Ernesto Codignola, 50018 Scandicci (FI), Italy. Ed.Bd. bibl.; illus.; index. circ. 4,500.
—BLDSC (8213.330000); SWETS.

372   IT   ISSN 0036-9861
SCUOLA E DIDATTICA. 1955. fortn. L.68000. Editrice La Scuola S.p.A., Via Cadorna 11, 25186 Brescia, Italy. TEL 030-29931. Ed. Giuseppe Vico. adv.; illus.; index.
—SWETS.

377.8   IT   ISSN 0036-987X
SCUOLA E L'UOMO. 1944. m. L.40000. Unione Cattolica Italiana Insegnanti Medi, Via Crescenzio 25, 00193 Rome, Italy. Dir. Cesarina Checcacci. adv.; bk.rev. circ. 22,000.
Description: Explains education in a global sense concerning family problems, religious education, etc.

372   IT   ISSN 0036-9888
SCUOLA ITALIANA MODERNA. 1893. fortn. L.60000. Editrice La Scuola S.p.A., Via Cadorna 11, 25186 Brescia, Italy. TEL 030-29931. Ed. Mario Cattaneo. adv.; charts; illus.; index.

372   IT
SCUOLA NOSTRA.* 1953. m. membership. Sindacato Nazionale Autonomo della Scuola Elementare, Via del Tritone 46, 00187 Rome, Italy.

372   IT
SCUOLA PRIMARIA. q. L.6000. Argalia Editore, Via N. Sauro 1, 61029 Urbino, Italy. Eds. Augusto Scocchera, Aldo Fabi.

370   IT   ISSN 0036-9926
SCUOLA VIVA; mensile per educatori. 1964. m. L.39000 (foreign L.68500). Societa Editrice Internazionale, Corso Regina Margherita 176, 10152 Torino, Italy. TEL 011-52271. FAX 011-5211320. Ed. Sergio Giordani. adv.; bk.rev.; play rev.; bibl.; illus. circ. 7,000. **Document type:** academic/scholarly publication.

373   US   ISSN 0160-6778
SECONDARY EDUCATION TODAY. 1958. a. $40. Michigan Association of Secondary School Principals, 418 Erickson Hall, Michigan State University, East Lansing, MI 48823. Ed. Dr. Philip Cusick. adv.; bk.rev. circ. 2,460. (also avail. in microform from UMI; reprint service avail. from UMI) **Indexed:** Amer.Hist.& Life, Hist.Abstr. **Document type:** academic/scholarly publication.
—UMI.
Formerly (until 1972): Michigan Journal of Secondary Education (ISSN 0026-2226)

373   US
SECONDARY SCHOOL ADMISSION TEST BOARD. ANNUAL REPORT.* 1984. a. Secondary School Admission Test Board, 12 Stockton St., Princeton, NJ 08540-6813. TEL 609-683-4440. Ed. Regan Kenyon. circ. 1,000. (back issues avail.)
Description: Reports on the organization's activities with a look at the future.

SEIBUTSU KENKYU/JAPAN ASSOCIATION OF BIOLOGY EDUCATION. RESEARCH REPORT. see *BIOLOGY*

SEIBUTSU KYOIKU/JAPANESE JOURNAL OF BIOLOGICAL EDUCATION. see *BIOLOGY*

370   II
SELECTIONS FROM EDUCATIONAL RECORDS OF THE GOVERNMENT OF INDIA. (Text in English) 1976. irreg. Jawaharlal Nehru University, Zakir Husain Centre for Educational Studies, New Delhi 110 067, India. Ed. Joseph Bara. bibl. circ. 100.

658.8   US   ISSN 1054-4593
HD9810.U6
SELLING TO THE OTHER EDUCATIONAL MARKETS; how to sell audiocassettes, books, educational toys and games, software programs, videos and other educational products to homeschoolers, afterschoolers, curriculum developers and correspondence schools. 1990. a. $39.95. Bluestocking Press, Dept. U, Box 1014, Placerville, CA 95667. TEL 916-621-1123. FAX 916-632-2501. Ed. Jane A. Williams. index. circ. 150.
Description: Explains how to reach the estimated 500,000 to one million homeschoolers and educators that comprises today's alternative education market. Over 200 listings including names, addresses, telephone numbers, fax numbers, contact people, circulation figures, editorial descriptions, and marketing tips.

370   PO   ISSN 0037-203X
SEMPRE PRONTO; mensario escotista. 1945. m. Esc.450($4) Associacao dos Escoteiros de Portugal, Trav: Das Galeotas, 1, 1300 Lisbon, Portugal. Ed. Rui F.T. Fonseca. adv. circ. 2,000.

370.193   RU   ISSN 0131-7377
SEM'YA I SHKOLA. 1946. m. $53 (foreign $60). (Rossiiskaya Akademiya Obrazovaniya) Sem'ya i Shkola, Ul. Pavla Korchagina 7, 129278 Moscow, Russia. (Dist. in U.S. by: Victor Kamkin Inc., 4956 Boiling Brook Pkwy, Rockville, MD 20852. TEL 301-881-5973) Ed. V.F. Smirnov. index. circ. 1,140,000. **Indexed:** Curr.Dig.Sov.Press.

370   AT
SENIOR TOPICS. 1985. bi-m. Aus.$24 (foreign Aus.$35). Ashton Scholastic Pty. Ltd., Railway Crescent, Lisarow, N.S.W 2250, Australia. TEL 043-28-3555. FAX 043-23-3827. (Subscr. to: P.O. Box 579, Gosford, N.S.W. 2250, Australia. TEL 02-4164000) Ed. Ann Bingaman. circ. 8,000.

SEQUENCES. see *MOTION PICTURES*

370   UY   ISSN 0797-650X
LA544.S68
▼**SERIE: EDUCACION Y MERCOSUR.** 1992. a. Ministerio de Educacion y Cultura, Direccion de Educacion, Reconquista 535, Piso 6, 11000 Montevideo, Uruguay. TEL 95-38-57. FAX 96-26-32. Ed. Carlos Romero. **Document type:** government publication, academic/scholarly publication.

370   BL
SERIE MEMORIA VIVA DA EDUCACAO BRASILEIRA. 1991. irreg. Cr.$1500($150) (effective Dec. 1991). Instituto Nacional de Estudos e Pesquisas Educacionais, Campus da UNB, Acesso Sul - Asa Norte, 70910-900 Brasilia, Brazil. TEL 061-347-8970. FAX 061-273-3232.
Refereed Serial

370   US
SERIE MONOGRAFIAS Y ESTUDIOS DE LA EDUCACION. (Published by host country) (Text in Spanish) 1974. irreg. Organization of American States, 1889 F St. N.W., Washington, DC 20006-4499. TEL 703-789-3319. circ. 2,000. (back issues avail.) **Document type:** academic/scholarly publication.

371.2   IT   ISSN 0037-279X
SERVIZIO INFORMAZIONI AVIO; periodico mensile di educazione, cultura e lavoro. 1954. bi-m. L.40000. Casa Editrice Armando s.r.l., Viale Trastevere u. 236, 00153 Rome, Italy. TEL 06-5817245. FAX 06-5818564. bibl.; charts; illus.; stat. circ. 15,000.

EDUCATION

327   IR
SHAHID CHAMRAN UNIVERSITY EDUCATIONAL JOURNAL. (Text in English, Farsi) 1972. s-a. Rs.100. Shahid Chamran University, Faculty of Education, Ahwaz, Iran. Ed. K. C. Chehrezad. circ. 2,000.
    Formerly (until 1983): Jundi Shapur University Educational Journal.

370   CC
SHANGHAI JIAOYU (XIAOXUE BAN)/SHANGHAI EDUCATION (ELEMENTARY SCHOOL EDITION). (Text in Chinese) m. Shanghai Shi Jiaoyu-ju - Shanghai Municipal Bureau of Education, 500 Shaanxi Beilu, Shanghai 200041, People's Republic of China. TEL 2534408. Ed. Song Xuhui.

370   CC
SHANGHAI JIAOYU (ZHONGXUE BAN)/SHANGHAI EDUCATION (MIDDLE SCHOOL EDITION). (Text in Chinese) m. Shanghai Shi Jiaoyu-ju - Shanghai Municipal Bureau of Education, 500 Shaanxi Beilu, Shanghai 200041, People's Republic of China. TEL 2534408. Ed. Shen Mianrong.

370   CC
SHANGHAI JIAOYU KEYAN/SHANGHAI EDUCATION RESEARCH. (Text in Chinese) 1982. bi-m. Y1.80 per no. Shanghai Shi Jiaoyu Kexue Yanjiusuo - Shanghai Educational Research Institute, 251 Baoshan Rd., Shanghai 200071, People's Republic of China. TEL 86-21-6630212. FAX 86-21-2551217. Ed. Li Hongceng. adv. contact: Fu Lu-jing. bk.rev. circ. 6,000. **Document type:** academic/scholarly publication.
    Description: Contains research information, methods, and research papers on education.

SHANGHAI ZHONGXUE SHUXUE/SHANGHAI SECONDARY SCHOOL MATHEMATICS. see *MATHEMATICS*

370   US
SHARING SPACE. 3/yr. $15. Children's Creative Response to Conflict, 521 N. Broadway, Box 271, Nyack, NY 10960. TEL 914-353-1796. FAX 914-358-1924. TELEX 152243432. Ed. Kay Reynolds. bk.rev. circ. 1,500. (back issues avail.) **Document type:** newsletter.

SHENGWUXUE JIAOXUE/BIOLOGY TEACHING. see *BIOLOGY*

SHENZHEN DAXUE XUEBAO (RENWEN SHEKE BAN)/SHENZHEN UNIVERSITY. JOURNAL (HUMANITIES, SOCIAL SCIENCES EDITION). see *HUMANITIES: COMPREHENSIVE WORKS*

371.33   JA   ISSN 0037-3664
SHICHOKAKU KYOIKU/AUDIO-VISUAL EDUCATION. (Text in Japanese) 1947. m. 10400 Yen. Japan Audio-Visual Education Association - Nihon Shichokaku Kyoiku Kyokai, 1-17-1 Toranomon, Minato-ku, Tokyo 105, Japan. FAX 81-3-3597-0564. Ed. M. Okabe. adv.; bk.rev.; play rev.; abstr.; bibl.; pat.; stat.; tr.lit.; index, cum.index; circ. 5,000 (controlled). (tabloid format) **Document type:** trade publication.
    Description: Features study and teaching manuals and materials on audio-visual education.

SHIJIE YANJIU DONGTAI. see *HISTORY*

370   JA
SHIZUOKA DAIGAKU KYOIKUGAKUBU KENKYU HOKOKU. KYOKA KYOIKUGAKU HEN/SHIZUOKA UNIVERSITY. FACULTY OF EDUCATION. BULLETIN. EDUCATIONAL RESEARCH SERIES. (Text in English, Japanese) a. Shizuoka Daigaku, Kyoikugakubu, 836 Oya, Shizuoka-shi, Shizuoka-ken 422, Japan. TEL 054-237-1170. FAX 054-237-9376.

370   RU   ISSN 0037-4024
SHKOLA I PROIZVODSTVO. 1957. m. 10.20 Rub. Izdatel'stvo Pedagogika, Smolensky per. 4, 100032 Moscow, Russia. TEL 095-246-5969. Ed. Yu.Ye. Rives-Korobkov. bk.rev.; illus. circ. 205,000.

370   AU
SHOMERNIK. (Text in English) 1985. q. S.30. Fleischmarkt 1B, A-1010 Vienna, Austria. Ed. Haschomer Hazair. circ. 4,500.

SI DE KA MAGAZINE. see *LAW*

370   CC
SICHUAN JIAOYU/SICHUAN EDUCATION. (Text in Chinese) m. Sichuan Sheng Jiaoyu Weiyuanhui - Sichuan Commission of Education, 44 Xuedao Jie, Chengdu, Sichuan 610016, People's Republic of China. TEL 28782. Ed. Li Ruolin.

370   SL
SIERRA LEONE. MINISTRY OF EDUCATION. MONTHLY NEWSLETTER. (Text in English) 1966. m. Ministry of Education, c/o Publications Branch, New England, Freetown, Sierra Leone. circ. 250.

370   SL   ISSN 0080-9551
SIERRA LEONE. MINISTRY OF EDUCATION. REPORT. 1961. a. Ministry of Education, Freetown, Sierra Leone. circ. 1,200.

370   SL   ISSN 0022-0582
SIERRA LEONE JOURNAL OF EDUCATION. 1966. s-a. $0.42 per no. Ministry of Education, New England, Freetown, Sierra Leone. Ed.Bd. adv.; bk.rev.; bibl.; charts. **Indexed:** C.I.J.E., Except.Child.Educ.Abstr., Psychol.Abstr.

SIGNAL; approaches to children's books. see *CHILDREN AND YOUTH — About*

370.15   II
SIKSHA. (Text in Bengali) m. Aijtkumar Basu, 1A College Rd., Calcutta 700009, India.

370   II   ISSN 0037-5160
SIKSHA - O - SAHITYA; teachers' journal. (Text in Bengali & English) 1921. m. Rs.24 to non-members; members Rs.15. All Bengal Teachers' Association, 15 Bankim Chatterjee St., Calcutta 700009, India. Eds. Sashimohon Bhattachuya, Amitava Sen. adv.; bk.rev.; abstr.; charts; stat.; index. circ. 10,000.

372.21   CU
SIMIENTES; circulos infantiles. 1962. 3/yr. $16 in S. America; N. America $18; elsewhere $20. (Ministerio de Educacion, Direccion de Divulgacion y Publicaciones) Ediciones Cubanas, Obispo No. 527, Aptdo. 605, Havana, Cuba. Ed.Bd. bk.rev.; bibl.; charts; illus. circ. 8,000.

SIMPLIFIED SPELLING SOCIETY. JOURNAL. see *LINGUISTICS*

370   PK   ISSN 0560-0871
SIND UNIVERSITY JOURNAL OF EDUCATION. (Text in English) 1955. a. $5. (University of Sind, Faculty of Education & Research) Sind University Press, Hyderabad 6, Pakistan. TEL 0221-25228. bk.rev.; bibl. circ. 1,000.

370   SI   ISSN 0129-4776
LA1239.5
SINGAPORE JOURNAL OF EDUCATION. (Text in English) 1978. s-a. S.$15($22) (National Institute of Education) Longman Singapore Publishers (Pte) Ltd., 25 First Lok Yang Rd., Singapore 2262, Singapore. Ed. Dorothy Lim. adv.; bk.rev.; illus. circ. 1,500. **Document type:** academic/scholarly publication.
—BLDSC (8285.463700); UnCover.
    Description: Contains articles, research papers, and reviews on educational developments and pedagogy.

370   NE   ISSN 0005-9390
SINT BERNARDUS; blad voor school en beroep. 1921. 3/mo. fl.2 per no. Katholieke Vereniging van Directies, Docenten en Consulten bij het Beroepsonderwijs en het Leerlingwezen, Stationsweg 56, The Hague, Netherlands. adv.; bk.rev. circ. 8,500.
    Formerly: Nijverheidsschool.

370   UY
▼**SIRFO FLASH C I N T E R F O R.** 1993. q. $30. Centro Interamericano de Investigacion y Documentacion sobre Formacion Profesional, Avda. Uruguay 1238, Casilla de Correo 1761, Montevideo, Uruguay. FAX 921305.

SISTEMA DE INDICADORES SOCIO-ECONOMICOS Y EDUCATIVOS DE LA O E I. see *SOCIAL SCIENCES: COMPREHENSIVE WORKS*

370   CC   ISSN 1002-588X
SIXIANG ZHENGZHIKE JIAOXUE. (Text in Chinese) m. Y18. Beijing Shifan Daxue - Beijing Normal University, Beitaipingzhuang, Beijing 100875, People's Republic of China. TEL 2012288. Ed. He Yunqing. **Document type:** academic/scholarly publication.

944   FR   ISSN 0755-8848
SKOL VREIZH- L'ECOLE BRETONNE. NOUVELLE SERIE. (Text in Breton, French) 1933. q. 190 F.($17) (foreign 250 F.). (Skolaerien ha Kelennerien Ar Falz - Instituteurs et Professeurs Laiques Bretons) Editions Skol Vreizh, 20 rue de Kerscoff, 29600 Morlaix, Brittany, France. TEL 98-62-17-20. FAX 98-62-02-38. bk.rev.; charts; illus. circ. 2,500. (back issues avail.) **Document type:** monographic series.
    Formerly: Skol Vreizh- l'Ecole Bretonne (ISSN 0037-6442)

370   BN   ISSN 0037-6450
SKOLA DANAS. (Text in Serbo-Croatian) 1964. q. $5. Prosvjetno Pedagoski Zavod Mostar, Ante Zuanica 14, Mostar, Bosnia Hercogovina. Ed. Alija Bijavica. circ. 1,500.

370   US
SKOLE; the journal of alternative education. 1985. s-a. $15 to non-members (effective 1993). Down to Earth Books, 72 Philip St., Albany, NY 12202. TEL 518-432-1578. FAX 518-432-8984. Ed. Mary Leue. adv.; bk.rev. circ. 300. **Document type:** academic/scholarly publication.
    Description: Articles related to the subject of alternatives or innovations in education, critiques of other forms of education, theoretical considerations associated with schools, schooling, learning and teaching, as well as accounts of individual schools.

370   DK   ISSN 0108-4593
SKOLE-BLADET;* magasinet for undervisning og forskning. 1982. bi-m. DKK 280 (incl. advertising, DKK 1760). Tidsskriftsforlaget ApS, Postbox 2610, 2100 Copenhagen Oe, Denmark. TEL 45-35-43-36-37. FAX 45-35-43-28-23. Ed. Finn Heitmann. adv.; bk.rev.; illus. circ. 8,500.

SKOLE OG LANDBRUG. see *AGRICULTURE*

SKOLEBIBLIOTEKET. see *LIBRARY AND INFORMATION SCIENCES*

370   DK   ISSN 0109-8985
SKOLEN I NORDEN. Variant title: Skolan i Norden. Finnish edition: Pohjoismaiden Kouluoloista (ISSN 0109-8993) (Text in Danish, Norwegian and Swedish; summaries in Icelandic) 1984. 3/yr. free. Nordisk Ministerraad, Sekretariatet, Store Strandstraede 18, DK-1255 Copenhagen K, Denmark. TEL 45-33-96-02-00. FAX 45-33-93-63-44. Erla Sigurdardottir. bk.rev.; illus. circ. 18,000.
    Formerly: Information om Skolen i Norden (ISSN 0106-2107)
    Description: Focuses on Nordic co-operation in education and the school system.

370   DK   ISSN 0107-3028
SKOLESTART. 1978. a DKK 24.40. Ole Camaae, Lerbjergstien 18, 3460 Birkeroed, Denmark. TEL 45-42-276282. illus.

370   SW   ISSN 0037-6515
SKOLLEDAREN. 1930. 10/yr. SEK 160($7) Sveriges Skolledarfoerbund - Swedish Association of School Leaders, P.O. Box 3266, S-103 65 Stockholm, Sweden. FAX 08-249811. Ed. Kerstin Loeoev. adv.; bk.rev. circ. 6,800.
    Formerly (until 1966): Svensk Skolledartidning.

SKOLSKA TELEVIZIJA. see *COMMUNICATIONS — Television And Cable*

370   CI   ISSN 0037-6531
SKOLSKE NOVINE. 1950. w. 160000 din. Brace Kavurica 40, P.O. Box 785, 41000 Zagreb, Croatia. TEL 041 433-415. Ed. Ivo Klaric. circ. 15,000. (also avail. in microfiche)
    Description: Contains educational news from Croatia and abroad, cultural information.

370   CI   ISSN 0037-654X
SKOLSKI VJESNIK; casopis za pedagoska i prosvjetna pitanja. (Text in Serbo-Croatian) 1950. q. $5. Pedagoska Akademija, Split, Zrtava Fasizma 6, Box 118, Split, Croatia. Ed. Jerko Matosic.

EDUCATION

370   SW   ISSN 0037-6566
SKOLVAERLDEN. 1901. 22/yr. SEK 400 (effective 1994). Laerarnas Riksfoerbund, P.O. Box 3529, 103 69 Stockholm, Sweden. Ed. Elisabeth Wiechel. adv.; bk.rev.; charts; illus. circ. 51,059. (tabloid format) **Document type:** academic/scholarly publication.
    Formerly (until 1963): Tidningen foer Sveriges Laeroverk.

371.3   UK   ISSN 0037-6817
SLEEP-LEARNING ASSOCIATION. JOURNAL. vol.7, 1970. q. £3. Sleep-Learning Association, 64 Grange Rd., Ealing, London W5 5BX, England. Ed. Geoffrey Stocker. bk.rev.; bibl.; charts; illus.; stat.

370 301   US
SOCIAL AND POLICY ISSUES IN EDUCATION. 1990. irreg. price varies. Ablex Publishing Corporation, 355 Chestnut St., Norwood, NJ 07648. TEL 201-767-8450. FAX 201-767-6717. TELEX 135-393. Ed. Kathryn Borman.

SOCIAL EDUCATION. see *SOCIAL SCIENCES: COMPREHENSIVE WORKS*

370   CH
SOCIAL EDUCATION YEARLY.* (Text in Chinese) a. Social Education Society of China, Ministry of Education, Social Education Dept., Chungshan S. Rd., Taipei, Taiwan, Republic of China. Ed. Shing Chou Wang. abstr.; charts; stat.; index, cum.index. (processed)

SOCIAL EUROPE. see *SOCIAL SERVICES AND WELFARE*

300 370   US   ISSN 0037-7996
D16.3
THE SOCIAL STUDIES. 1909. bi-m. $31 to individuals; institutions $51. (Helen Dwight Reid Educational Foundation) Heldref Publications, 1319 Eighteenth St., N.W., Washington, DC 20036-1802. TEL 202-296-6267. FAX 202-296-5149. Ed. Helen Kress. adv. contact: Raymond Rallo. bk.rev.; bibl.; index. circ. 2,600. (also avail. in microform; reprint service avail.) **Indexed:** Acad.Ind., Amer.Hist.& Life, Arts & Hum.Cit.Ind., Bk.Rev.Dig., Bk.Rev.Ind. (1965-), C.I.J.E., Child.Bk.Rev.Ind. (1965-), Cont.Pg.Educ., Curr.Cont., Educ.Ind., Hist.Abstr., P.A.I.S., PSI, Sp.Ed.Needs Abstr., SSCI. **Document type:** academic/scholarly publication.
    —BLDSC (8318.209000); Faxon; UnCover; SWETS; UMI. **CCC.**
    Refereed Serial

360.07   US   ISSN 0037-8062
SOCIAL WORK EDUCATION REPORTER. 1953. 3/yr. membership. Council on Social Work Education, 1600 Duke St., Alexandria, VA 22314-3421. TEL 202-683-8080. FAX 703-683-8099. adv.; cum.index through 1973. circ. 3,800. (also avail. in microform from UMI; reprint service avail. from UMI) **Indexed:** ASSIA, Soc.Work Res.& Abstr. **Document type:** newsletter.
    —UMI.
    Supersedes: Social Work Education.
    Description: News, information, and announcements pertaining to the activities and members of the Council, which promotes the dissemination of information on developments, innovations, and problems pertaining to social education at the undergraduate, master's, and postgraduate levels.

370   SP   ISSN 0213-3636
LA919.P34
SOCIEDAD DE ESTUDIOS VASCOS. CUADERNOS DE SECCION. EDUCACION. 1985. irreg. Eusko Ikaskuntza, Legazpi, 10-1, 20004 Donostia-San Sebastian, Spain. TEL 425 111.

SOCIETY FOR ITALIC HANDWRITING. JOURNAL. see *ART*

SOCIETY FOR ITALIC HANDWRITING. NEWSLETTER. see *ART*

370   US   ISSN 0882-7141
SOCIETY OF PROFESSORS OF EDUCATION. OCCASIONAL PAPERS. 1974. irreg. price varies. Society of Professors of Education, c/o Richard Wisniewski, College of Education, Univ. of Tennessee, Knoxville, TN 37996-3400. TEL 615-974-2201. FAX 615-974-8718. circ. controlled. **Document type:** monographic series.
    Formerly: National Society of College Teachers of Education. Occasional Papers.

SOCIOLOGY OF EDUCATION; a journal of research in socialization and social structure. see *SOCIOLOGY*

370   XV   ISSN 0038-0474
SODOBNA PEDAGOGIKA. (Text in Slovenian) 1950. 5/yr. 50 din. Zveza Pedagoskih Drustev Slovenije, Gosposka 3-1, Ljubljana, Slovenia. Ed. France Strmcnik. circ. 2,800.

370   PR   ISSN 0034-933X
EL SOL. 4/yr. Asociacion de Maestros de Puerto Rico, Ave. Ponce de Leon, Num. 452, Hato Rey, PR 00919. Ed. Evelyn Cruz de Soto. adv.; bk.rev.; charts; illus. circ. 35,000.

370   GW   ISSN 0038-1357
SONDERSCHULE. (Issued in two parts: Ausgabe A, Ausgabe B) 1956. bi-m. Luchterhand Verlag, Lindenstr. 54A, 1086 Berlin, Germany. TEL 030-20343431. FAX 030-20343432. adv.; bk.rev.; abstr.; charts; illus.; index. circ. 9,500. **Indexed:** Lang.& Lang.Behav.Abstr. **Document type:** academic/scholarly publication.

268 370   GW   ISSN 0012-2580
SONNTAGSCHULMITARBEITER; religionspaedagogisches Monatsblatt. 1971. q. DM.25.60. Oncken Verlag GmbH, Muendener Str. 13, 34123 Kassel, Germany. TEL 0561-52005-0. Ed. Siegfried Holtz. bk.rev.; stat.; index. circ. 7,000. **Document type:** newsletter.
    —CCC.
    Formed by the merger of: Dienst am Kinde; Sonntags Schulhelfer.

370.193   US
SOUND-OFF. 197? 10/yr. $6 (typically set in June). Utah Congress of Parents & Teachers, 1037 East South Temple, Salt Lake City, UT 84102. TEL 801-359-3875. Ed. Sherma Yeates. adv. circ. 3,200.
    Supersedes: Utah P T A Bulletin (ISSN 0042-1472)

370   US
SOUNDS OF READING. 1973. m. $25. Reading Reform Foundation, Box 98785, Tacoma, WA 98498-0785. bk.rev.; bibl. circ. 17,000.
    Formerly (until Jan. 1989): Reading Informer.

370   SA
SOUTH AFRICA. DEPARTMENT OF EDUCATION AND TRAINING. ANNUAL REPORT. 1961. a. price varies. Department of Education and Training, Private Bag X212, Pretoria 0001, South Africa. (Subscr. to: Government Printer, Bosman St., Private Bag X85, Pretoria 0001, South Africa) **Document type:** government publication.
    Formerly: South Africa. Department of Bantu Education. Annual Report (ISSN 0081-2188)

SOUTH AFRICAN MUSIC TEACHER/SUID-AFRIKAANSE MUSIEKONDERWYSER. see *MUSIC*

370   AT   ISSN 0049-1438
SOUTH AUSTRALIA. DEPARTMENT OF EDUCATION. EDUCATION GAZETTE. 1883. m. (during school year). Aus.$40($17) Education Department, Box 1152, G.P.O., Adelaide, S.A. 5001, Australia. FAX 08-226-1605. Ed. Carole Bowser-Nott. s-a. index. circ. 8,500. **Indexed:** Aus.Educ.Ind.
    Description: An internal communications document providing teachers in schools and administration centres throughout the state with information on education policy matters.

370   US   ISSN 0038-3171
SOUTH CAROLINA SCHOOLS. 1949. 5/yr. free. Department of Education, 1001 Rutledge Bldg., 1429 Senate St., Columbia, SC 29201. TEL 803-734-8500. FAX 803-734-8624. Ed. Janice Larrymore. circ. 45,000. (tabloid format; back issues avail.)
    Description: Publication devoted to developments in education affecting state classrooms.

780.07 370   US   ISSN 0038-3341
SOUTH DAKOTA MUSICIAN. 1970. 3/yr. $8 during school year (effective Fall 1990). South Dakota Music Educators Association, Northern State University, Music Department, Aberdeen, SD 57401. TEL 605-622-7759. Ed. Janis Pearson. adv.: B&W & color, B&W page $130; trim 8 1/2 x 11. circ. 1,300.

370 331.8   II   ISSN 0038-3481
SOUTH INDIAN TEACHER. (Text in English) 1966. m. Rs.5. South India Teachers' Union, Rajah Annamalaipuram, Madras 28, India. adv.; bk.rev.; charts; illus.

370   PH   ISSN 0038-3600
SOUTHEAST ASIA JOURNAL. s-a. P.30($5) Central Philippine University, Box 231, Iloilo City 5000, Philippines. Ed. Elma S. Herradura. adv.; bibl.

370   US   ISSN 0038-3813
LB2301
SOUTHERN ASSOCIATION OF COLLEGES AND SCHOOLS. PROCEEDINGS. 1945. bi-m. $10 to non-members. Southern Association of Colleges and Schools, 1866 Southern Ln., Decatur, GA 30033-4097. TEL 404-679-4500. FAX 679-4556. Ed. Teresa Greer. bk.rev. circ. 18,000. **Document type:** proceedings.

370   US   ISSN 0081-3060
SOUTHERN REGIONAL EDUCATION BOARD. ANNUAL REPORT. a. price varies. Southern Regional Education Board, 592 Tenth St., N.W., Atlanta, GA 30318-5790. TEL 404-875-9211. Ed. Margaret Sullivan. circ. 2,200. **Document type:** corporate report.

370   AI   ISSN 0038-5026
SOVETAKAN MANKAVARZH. vol.38, 1966. m. 9.60 Rub. Ministerstvo Kul'tury, Ul. Isahakian, 28, Erevan, Armenia. Ed. R.H. Dallakian. bk.rev.; bibl.; charts; illus.; stat.

SOVETSKII SHKOL'NIK. see *CHILDREN AND YOUTH — For*

370   AU   ISSN 0038-6146
SOZIALISTISCHE ERZIEHUNG; Zeitschrift fuer die Bildungsarbeit der sozialistischen Bewegung Oesterreichs. 1921. 4/yr. S.50. Sozialistische Partei Oesterreichs, Frei Schule Kinderfreunde, Rauhensteingasse 5, A-1010 Vienna, Austria. TEL 0222-5121298. Ed. Sepp Steiner. adv.; bk.rev.; abstr.; bibl.; charts; stat.; index, cum.index. circ. 6,000.

370   GW   ISSN 0038-6189
SOZIALPAEDAGOGIK. 1959. bi-m. DM.48.60. Guetersloher Verlagshaus Chr. Kaiser, Carl-Bertelsmann-Str. 256, 33335 Guetersloh, Germany. TEL 05241-7405-0. FAX 05241-740548. Ed. Albrecht Mueller-Schoell. adv.; bk.rev. **Document type:** academic/scholarly publication.

370 300   GW   ISSN 0340-2304
SOZIALWISSENSCHAFTLICHE INFORMATIONEN FUER UNTERRICHT UND STUDIUM. 1972. q. DM.54. (Arbeitskreis Sozialwissenschaftliche Informationen) Erhard Friedrich Verlag GmbH, Im Brande 17, 30926 Seelze, Germany. TEL 0511-40004-0. (Subscr. to: Postfach 100150, 30917 Seelze, Germany) Ed.Bd. circ. 3,000. **Document type:** academic/scholarly publication.

SPAIN. MINISTERIO DE EDUCACION Y CIENCIA. BOLETIN OFICIAL: COLECCION LEGISLATIVA. see *LAW*

370 500   SP
SPAIN. MINISTERO DE EDUCACION Y CIENCIA. GUIA. irreg. Ministerio de Educacion y Ciencia, Centro de Publicaciones, Ciudad Universitaria, 28040 Madrid, Spain. TEL 549-77-00.

370   US   ISSN 0731-8413
SPECIAL ASPECTS OF EDUCATION. 1984. irreg., vol.14, 1990. Gordon & Breach Science Publishers, 820 Town Center Dr., Langhorne, PA 19047. TEL 215-750-2642. FAX 215-750-6343. (UK addr.: P.O. Box 90, Reading, Berkshire RG1 8JL, England. TEL 0734-560-080) Ed. R. Evans. (also avail. in microform) **Document type:** monographic series.
    —BLDSC (8361.897000).
    Refereed Serial

370   DK   ISSN 0905-975X
SPECIALISTEN. 1982. irreg. (4-6/yr.). free. Danmarks Specialpaedagogiske Forening, Noerregade 48, 7400 Herning, Denmark. TEL 97-22-08-45. Ed. Preben Eriksen. bk.rev.; illus. circ. 700.
    Formerly (until 1990): Aksel (ISSN 0109-3762)

371.9   YU ISSN 0038-6936
SPECIJALNA SKOLA. (Text in Serbo-Croatian) 1952. bi-m. 40 din. Savez Drustava Defektologa Jugoslavije, Kosovska 8, Belgrade, Yugoslavia. Ed. Borivoje Novcic.

370   US
SPECTRA. 1964. m. (exc. Jul.). $18. Speech Communication Association, 5105 Backlick Rd., Bldg. E., Annandale, VA 22003. TEL 703-750-0533. Ed. James Gaudino. circ. 6,000.

370   AT ISSN 1037-2040
SPECTRUM. 1967. 6/yr. free to qualified personnel. Department of Education and the Arts, 116 Bathurst St., Hobart, Tas. 7000, Australia. TEL 002-337721. FAX 002-347991. Ed. Rod MacDonald. index. circ. 3,300.
Former titles (until May 1991): Tasmania. Department of Education and the Arts. Gazette (ISSN 1035-5014); Tasmanian Eudcation Gazette (ISSN 0039-9760)

SPEECH AND DRAMA. see *THEATER*

SPEKTATOR; tijdschrift voor neerlandistiek. see *LITERATURE*

SPEKTRUM (GELNHAUSEN). see *CHILDREN AND YOUTH — For*

373   RU ISSN 0869-5210
LC1047.R9   CODEN: SSOBET
SPETSIALIST. 1954. m. 70 Rub. per issue (effective 1993). Ul. Moskvina, d.5, 103031 Moscow K-31, Russia. Ed. E.N. Kolosov. bk.rev.; index. **Document type:** academic/scholarly publication.
—BLDSC (0166.309000).
Formerly (until 1992): Srednee Spetsial'noe Obrazovanie (ISSN 0131-9590)

SPHINX. see *CHILDREN AND YOUTH — For*

SPIEL-EBENE; Spieleberatung und Information. see *COMPUTERS — Computer Games*

370 362.7   GW
SPIELEN UND LERNEN. m. DM.75.60 (foreign DM.85.20). Velber Verlag GmbH, Im Brande 15c, 30926 Seelze, Germany. TEL 0511-40003-0. FAX 0511-4000370. adv. contact: Bernd Sandvoss. circ. 121,768. **Document type:** academic/scholarly publication.

SPOKESMAN. see *TECHNOLOGY: COMPREHENSIVE WORKS*

SPORT SCENE; focus on youth programs. see *SPORTS AND GAMES*

SPORT SUPPLEMENT. see *SPORTS AND GAMES*

SPOT. see *PHOTOGRAPHY*

370   BF
SPOTLIGHT. 1976. irreg. $1 per no. Ministry of Education and Culture, Box N 7147, Nassau, Bahamas.

370   US ISSN 0038-8602
SPRINGFIELD PUBLIC SCHOOLS. NEWS AND VIEWS. 1953. q. (during school yr.). free. Springfield Public Schools, Board of Education, 940 N. Jefferson, Springfield, MO 65802. Ed. Dick Grosenbaugh. bk.rev.; circ. 50,000 (controlled). (tabloid format)

372.21   JA ISSN 0388-4953
SPROUT/ME. (Text in Japanese) 1980. m. 8380 Yen. Seibundo Shinkosha Publishing Co., Ltd., 1-5-5 Kanda Nishikicho, Chiyoda-ku, Tokyo 101, Japan. Ed. Hiroshi Kubota. circ. 15,000. (back issues avail.)

370   II ISSN 0970-7417
SRI AUROBINDO INTERNATIONAL CENTRE OF EDUCATION. BULLETIN. (Supplement avail. with Hindi translation) (Text in English and French) 1949. q. Rs.30 (foreign $8); English-French-Hindi ed. Rs.35 (foreign $10). Sri Aurobindo Ashram Trust, Pondicherry 605002, India. circ. 800. **Document type:** bulletin.

STAR TRACK. see *LIBRARY AND INFORMATION SCIENCES*

370   US ISSN 0736-7511
L11
STATE EDUCATION LEADER. 1966. 3/yr. $15. Education Commission of the States, 707 17th St., Ste. 2700, Denver, CO 80202-3427. TEL 303-299-3600. FAX 303-296-8332. Ed. Sherry Walker. bk.rev.; charts; illus.; stat. circ. 4,500. (tabloid format; also avail. in microform from UMI; back issues avail.) **Indexed:** C.I.J.E., Educ.Ind., Except.Child.Educ.Abstr.
—Faxon.
Former titles (until 1981): Interstate Compact for Education (ISSN 0275-4592); (until 1979): Compact (ISSN 0010-3934)
Description: In-depth examination of major topics in education policy making.

379.544   II
STATE INSTITUTE OF EDUCATION, RAJASTHAN. ANNUAL REPORT. (Text in English) a. State Institute of Education, Udaipur, Rajasthan, India.

370   US ISSN 1041-9764
STATE UNIVERSITY OF NEW YORK. RESEARCH. 1981. 3/yr. free to qualified personnel. State University of New York at Albany, Research Foundation, State University Plaza, Albany, NY 12246. TEL 518-434-7180. FAX 518-434-7290. Ed. Frances Ghee Ross. bk.rev.; circ. 15,000 (controlled). **Document type:** academic/scholarly publication.
Former titles (until vol.8, no.3, 1988): S U N Y Research (Year) (ISSN 0897-330X); Chronica (ISSN 0009-594X)
Description: Features articles on research conducted by the State University of New York faculty for a research audience.

371   SO
STATISTICS OF EDUCATION IN SOMALIA.* irreg. Ministry of Education, Department of Planning, Mogadishu, Somalia. illus.; stat.

371.8   IT ISSN 0039-1433
STIL NOVO.* 1963. 3/yr. free. Manzi Pietro, Via Castellino Ola Castello 10, Milan, Italy. charts; illus. circ. 600. (looseleaf format)

STORYWORKS. see *CHILDREN AND YOUTH — For*

370   YU ISSN 0039-2693
STUDENT; list beogradskih studenata. (Text in Serbo-Croatian) 1936. w. Savez Studenata Beograda, Balkanska 4, Belgrade, Yugoslavia. Ed. Nebojsa Dragosavac. bk.rev. circ. 8,000.

373   US
▼**STUDENT CONTACT BOOK.** 1992. triennial. $29.95. Gale Research Inc., 835 Penobscot Bldg., Detroit, MI 48226. TEL 313-961-2242. FAX 313-961-6083. **Document type:** directory.

371.83 280   US ISSN 1073-8487
STUDENT LEADERSHIP JOURNAL. 1988. q. $4 per no. to non-members. Inter-Varsity Christian Fellowship of the United States of America, 6400 Schroeder Rd., Box 7895, Madison, WI 53707-7895. TEL 608-274-9001. FAX 608-274-7882. Ed. Jeff Yourison. bk.rev.; cum.index every 2 yrs. circ. 8,000. (back issues avail.)
Description: A practical and theoretical journal for Christian students on secular college campuses.

373   JO
STUDENT'S MESSAGE/RISALAT AL-TALIB.* (Text in Arabic) 1963. m. Box 2087, Amman, Jordan. Ed. Abdullah Abu Mughly.

371.8   GH
STUDENTS WORLD. (Text in English) 1974. m. POB M18, Accra, Ghana. TEL 774248. TELEX 2171. Ed. Eric Ofei. circ. 10,000.

STUDI DI PSICOLOGIA DELL'EDUCAZIONE. see *PSYCHOLOGY*

370   IT ISSN 0392-1948
STUDI DI STORIA DELL'EDUCAZIONE. 1980. 3/yr. L.45000 (foreign L.80000) (effective 1993). Casa Editrice Armando s.r.l., Viale Trastevere 236, 00153 Rome, Italy. TEL 06-5806420. FAX 06-5817245. Ed. Fabrizio Ravaglioli. bibl.; charts; illus.; stat.

370   IT ISSN 0392-2146
STUDI SULL'EDUCAZIONE. 1981. irreg., no.32, 1993. price varies. Liguori Editore s.r.l., Via Mezzocannone 19, 80134 Naples, Italy. TEL 081-5527139. Eds. Raffaele Laporta, Paolo Orefice. **Document type:** monographic series.

370   SP ISSN 0210-7546
LA910
STUDIA PAEDAGOGICA. 1978. a. 1200 ptas. Ediciones Universidad de Salamanca, Apdo. 325, 37080 Salamanca, Spain. TEL 923-26-14-54. Dir. Carlos Schramm Martin. **Document type:** academic/scholarly publication.
Description: Contains theoretical and experimental studies in education science.

370.15   SW
STUDIA PSYCHOLOGICA ET PAEDAGOGICA; series altera. (Text in English or Swedish; summaries in English) 1946. irreg. price varies. (University of Lund) A W I International AB, P.O. Box 4627, S-116 19 Stockholm, Sweden. TEL 468-640-8800. FAX 468-641-1180. (Co-sponsor: Malmoe Institute of Education) Ed. Aake Bjerstedt.

STUDIA UNIVERSITATIS "BABES-BOLYAI". PSICHOLOGIA - PEDAGOGIA. see *PSYCHOLOGY*

370   GW ISSN 0076-5627
STUDIEN UND BERICHTE. (Text usually in German; summaries in English) 1965. irreg., vol.56, 1993. price varies. Max-Planck-Institut fuer Bildungsforschung - Max-Planck-Institute for Human Development and Education, Lentzeallee 94, 14195 Berlin, Germany. (Dist. by: Edition Sigma Rainer Bohn Verlag, 10965 Berlin, Germany) **Document type:** monographic series.

370   GW
STUDIEN ZU BILDUNG UND WISSENSCHAFT. 1984. irreg., no.104, 1992. price varies. (Bundesminister fuer Bildung und Wissenschaft) Verlag K.H. Bock, Reichenbergerstr. 11e, Postfach 1145, 53604 Bad Honnef, Germany. TEL 02224-5443. FAX 02224-78310.

370   GW
DER STUDIENBEGINN. 1968. a. DM.10. Verein Freunde und Foerderer der Deutschen Studentenschaft e.V., Untere Hausbreite 11, 80939 Munich, Germany. Ed. Gundolf Seidenspinner. adv.

707   US ISSN 0039-3541
N81
STUDIES IN ART EDUCATION; a journal of issues and research in art education. 1959. 4/yr. $25. National Art Education Association, 1916 Association Dr., Reston, VA 22091. TEL 703-860-8000. Ed. Karen A. Hamblen. adv.; bk.rev.; bibl.; charts; illus. circ. 3,500. (also avail. in microform from UMI; reprint service avail. from KTO,UMI) **Indexed:** Artbibl., Artbibl.Mod., C.I.J.E., Cont.Pg.Educ., Educ.Ind. **Document type:** academic/scholarly publication.
—BLDSC (8489.530000); Faxon; UnCover; SWETS; UMI.
Description: Research and issues pertaining to visual art education.

370   US
STUDIES IN COMPARATIVE EDUCATION. 1978. irreg. price varies. Praeger Publishers (Subsidiary of: Greenwood Publishing Group Inc.), 88 Post Rd. W., Box 5007, Westport CT 06881-5007. TEL 203-226-3571. FAX 203-222-1502. **Document type:** monographic series.

370.15   SW
STUDIES IN EDUCATION AND PSYCHOLOGY. (Text in English) 1977. irreg. price varies. (Stockholm University, Institute of Education) A W I International AB, P.O. Box 4627, S-116 91 Stockholm, Sweden. TEL 468-640-8800. FAX 468-641-1180. Ed.Bd.

370 375   II ISSN 0254-0185
STUDIES IN EDUCATION AND TEACHING TECHNIQUES. 1979. irreg. Bahri Publications, 997-A, Street No. 9, Gobindpuri, Kalkaji, New Delhi 110 019, India. TEL 644-5710. Ed. Ujjal Singh Bahri. **Document type:** academic/scholarly publication, monographic series.
Description: Studies of education and information about educational software innovations.

EDUCATION

370　　　　　　UK　　ISSN 0191-491X
LB1570
STUDIES IN EDUCATIONAL EVALUATION. 1974. 4/yr. £171($265) (effective 1994). (University of California, Los Angeles, Center for the Study of Evaluation, US) Elsevier Science Ltd., Pergamon, P.O. Box 800, Kidlington, Oxford OX5 1DX, England. TEL 44-865-843000. FAX 44-865-843010. (Subscr. in U.S. and Canada to: Elsevier Science, 660 White Plains Rd., Tarrytown, NY 10591-5153. TEL 914-524-9200. FAX 914-333-2444) (Co-sponsors: Tel Aviv University School of Education, IS; University of Kiel, GW) Ed. Arieh Lewy. (also avail. in microfilm from UMI) **Indexed:** C.I.J.E., Cont.Pg.Educ. **Document type:** academic/scholarly publication.
—BLDSC (8490.468000); Faxon; UnCover; SWETS; UMI. **CCC.**
Description: Reports on aspects of education evaluation including curriculum evaluation, educational systems and organizations, teaching and learning strategies, and assessment of student performance.
Refereed Serial

370　　　　　　IS　　ISSN 0333-9661
BM100
STUDIES IN JEWISH EDUCATION. 1983. irreg., vol.6, 1992. price varies. (Hebrew University, Samuel Mendel Melton Centre for Jewish Education in Jerusalem) Magnes Press, Hebrew University, Jerusalem, P.O. Box 7695, Jerusalem 91076, Israel. TEL 972-2-660341. FAX 972-2-633370. circ. 1,000. (back issues avail.) **Document type:** monographic series.

370 100　　　　NE　　ISSN 0039-3746
L11　　　　　　　　CODEN: SPYEAT
STUDIES IN PHILOSOPHY AND EDUCATION. (Text in English) 1960. 4/yr. fl.274($148) (effective 1994). Kluwer Academic Publishers, Postbus 17, 3300 AA Dordrecht, Netherlands. TEL 31-78-334911. FAX 31-78-334254. TELEX 29245 KAPG NL. (Dist. by: Kluwer Academic Publishers Group, P.O. Box 322, 3300 AH Dordrecht, Netherlands. TEL 31-78-524400. FAX 31-78-524474; N. America dist. addr.: Box 358, Accord Sta., Hingham, MA 02018-0358. TEL 617-871-6600. FAX 617-871-6528) Ed. David P. Ericson. (also avail. in microfilm from UMI; reprint service avail. from SWZ) **Indexed:** Aus.Educ.Ind., High.Educ.Abstr., Phil.Ind., Sociol.Abstr., Sociol.Educ.Abstr. **Document type:** academic/scholarly publication.
—BLDSC (8491.220000); UMI. **CCC.**
Description: Focuses on philosophical, normative and conceptual problems and issues in educational research, policy and practice.
Refereed Serial

373　　　　　　GW
DAS STUDIUM AN MUENCHNER HOCHSCHULEN. LEHRBUECHER. 1985. a. Verlag K.H. Bock, Reichenbergerstr. 11e, 53604 Bad Honnef, Germany. TEL 02224-5443. FAX 02224-78310. **Document type:** academic/scholarly publication.

370　　　　　　LS
SUKSA MAY. (Text in Lao) m. Ministry of Education, Sports and Fine Arts, Vientiane, Laos.

379　　　　　　US　　ISSN 0094-8268
L162
SUMMARY OF EXPENDITURE DATA FOR MICHIGAN PUBLIC SCHOOLS. a. free. Department of Education, Box 30009, Lansing, MI 48909. TEL 517-373-0424. charts; stat.

331.1　　　　　US　　ISSN 0094-2308
LB2833.3.D4
SUPPLY AND DEMAND: EDUCATIONAL PERSONNEL IN DELAWARE. Variant title: Educational Personnel in Delaware. a. Department of Public Instruction, Division of Planning, Research & Evaluation, Townsend Building, Dover, DE 19903. TEL 302-736-4583. illus.
Formerly: Delaware. Department of Public Instruction. Teacher Supply and Demand.

370　　　　　　SP
SURGAM. 6/yr. Apdo. 40115, 28080 Madrid, Spain. Ed. Tomas Roca.

SVIVOT/ENVIRONMENTS; semi-annual on questions in environmental education. see *ENVIRONMENTAL STUDIES*

370　　　　　　SW　　ISSN 0348-6397
SWEDEN. STATISTISKA CENTRALBYRAAN. UTBILDNINGSSTATISTISK AARSBOK/SWEDISH EDUCATIONAL STATISTICS YEARBOOK. a. price varies. Statistiska Centralbyraan, Publishing Unit, S-701 89 Oerebro, Sweden.

373　　　　　　CM
SYLLABUS. (Text in English, French) 1964. q. Universite de Yaounde, Ecole Normale Superieure, B.P. 47, Yaounde, Cameroun. TEL 23-12-15. charts.
Supersedes: Revue Camerounaise de Pedagogie (ISSN 0556-7262)

SYNERGIST. see *PUBLIC ADMINISTRATION*

370 620　　　　US　　ISSN 0082-1217
SYSTEMS ENGINEERING OF EDUCATION SERIES. 1965. irreg. (1-2/yr.). price varies. Education and Training Consultants Co. (ETC), Box 2085, Sedona, AZ 86339-2085. TEL 602-282-3009. Ed. Leonard C. Silvern. circ. 2,000. **Indexed:** ERIC. **Document type:** monographic series.

370　　　　　　PL　　ISSN 0137-8171
SZKOLA ZAWODOWA. 10/yr. $42. (Ministerstwo Edukacji Narodowej) Szkola Zawodowa, Ul. Smulikowskiego 6-8, 00-389 Warsaw, Poland. TEL 48-22-261011. Ed. Janusz Moos. circ. 3,500.
Description: For teachers of vocational subjects, school inspectors and educational administrators, and organizers of vocational courses in factories.

370　　　　　　US　　ISSN 0039-8292
T E A NEWS. 1969. m. membership. Tennessee Education Association, 801 Second Ave. N., Nashville, TN 37201-1099. TEL 615-242-8392. Ed. Gene Bryant. circ. 43,000. (tabloid format; also avail. in microform from UMI; back issues avail.; reprint service avail. from UMI) **Indexed:** C.I.J.E. —UMI.

370　　　　　　US　　ISSN 0039-8306
T E A NEWSLETTER; a professional journal for a united teaching profession. 1957. bi-w. $10. Tucson Education Association, 4625 E. Second St., Tucson, AZ 85711. TEL 602-795-8870. Ed. Brian Koppy. bk.rev.; bibl.; charts; illus.; stat.; index, cum.index: 1957-1967. circ. 3,800. (tabloid format) **Document type:** newsletter.

T.I.C. NEWSLETTER. (Teacher Information Center) see *BUSINESS AND ECONOMICS — Labor And Industrial Relations*

370　　　　　　US　　ISSN 0364-3409
BF637.C6
T P G A JOURNAL. 1972. s-a. $8. Texas Personnel and Guidance Association, Austin Elementary-Opportunity School, 621 West Euclid, San Antonio, TX 78212. TEL 512-472-3403. (Or: 316 W. 12th St., Ste. 402, Austin, TX 78701) Ed. Margie Norman. adv.; bk.rev.; charts; illus.; index. circ. 3,000. (tabloid format; also avail. in microform from UMI; reprint service avail. from UMI) **Indexed:** C.I.J.E., Coll.Stud.Pers.Abstr., Psychol.Abstr.
Formerly: T A C D Journal.

370　　　　　　US
T S T A ADVOCATE. 1981. 8/yr. Texas State Teachers Association, 316 W. 12th St., Austin, TX 78701-1840. TEL 512-476-5355. FAX 512-469-0766. Ed. Deborah Turner. illus.

370　　　　　　CH
T'AI-WAN CHIAO YU/TAIWAN EDUCATION REVIEW. (Text in Chinese) 1952. m. NT.$500 (effective 1992). Taiwan Provincial Education Association - Taiwan Sheng Chiao Yu Hui, 2F, No. 51, Tsingtao E. Rd., Taipei, Taiwan, Republic of China. TEL 02-3519671. FAX 02-3519242. Ed. Kao Wen-Yi.

370　　　　　　US
TAKING SIDES: CLASHING VIEWS ON CONTROVERSIAL EDUCATIONAL ISSUES. irreg., 6th ed., 1991. $12.95. Dushkin Publishing Group, Inc., Sluice Dock, Guilford, CT 06437-9989. TEL 203-453-4351. FAX 203-453-6000. Ed. James William Noll; Pub. Lan Nielsen. illus. **Document type:** academic/scholarly publication.

370　　　　　　US
TALBOT'S STUDENT PLANNING BOOK. 1971. a. free. Dexter Publishing Co., Inc., 1 Hollis St., Ste. 110, Wellesley, MA 02181. TEL 617-237-0920. Ed. Jill E. Talbot. adv. circ. 530,000.
Description: Contains articles on questions students should ask about college and career planning.

370　　　　　　MU
TALIM. (Text in Arabic and French) q. Institut Pedagogique National - Al-Mahad al-Tarbawi al-Watani, Box 616, Nouakchott, Mauritania.

370　　　　　　HU　　ISSN 0082-1632
TANULMANYOK A NEVELESTUDOMANY KOREBOL. (Text in Hungarian; summaries in English and Russian) 1958. irreg. price varies. (Magyar Tudomanyos Akademia) Akademiai Kiado, Publishing House of the Hungarian Academy of Sciences, P.O. Box 245, H-1519 Budapest, Hungary. TEL 181-2134. FAX 166-6466. TELEX 22-6228 AKNYO H.

370　　　　　　TZ　　ISSN 0039-9477
TANZANIA EDUCATION JOURNAL. (Text in English; occasionally in Swahili) 1964. 3/yr. EAs.9. Ministry of National Education, Institute of Education, Box 9121, Dar es Salaam, Tanzania. Ed. A. Rugumyemheto. adv.; bk.rev.; illus.; mkt. circ. 8,000. **Indexed:** Cont.Pg.Educ.

370　　　　　　QA
AL-TARBIYYAH/EDUCATION. (Text in Arabic, English) 1970. q. free. National Commission for Education, Culture and Science, P.O. Box 9865, Doha, Qatar. TEL 861412. FAX 820911. TELEX 4672 NATCOM DH. Ed. Fahd Bin Jassem Al-Thani. bk.rev. circ. 2,500. (also avail. in microfilm)

370　　　　　　TS
AL-TARBIYYAH/EDUCATION. (Text in Arabic) 1979. m. Wizarat al-Tarbiyyah wal-Ta'lim, Idarat al-Ilaqat al-Aama - Ministry of Education, Public Relations Department, P.O. Box 295, Abu Dhabi, United Arab Emirates. TEL 321950. Ed. Da'in Jum'ah Ahmad al-Qubaisi. circ. 2,000.
Description: Covers education issues and developments in the U.A.E. and the Arab world.

370　　　　　　PE
TAREA; revista de educacion y cultura. 1980. 3/yr. $16 (outside Latin America $20). (Tarea Asociacion de Publicaciones Educativas) Ediciones Tarea, Horacio Urteaga 976, Apdo. Postal 2234, Lima 100, Peru. TEL 230935. Dir. Maria Amelia Palacios. bk.rev. **Document type:** academic/scholarly publication.
Former titles: Chaski; Tarea.

TASMANIAN EDUCATION REVIEW. see *LABOR UNIONS*

TAYLOR TALK; the yearbook magazine. see *JOURNALISM*

370　　　　　　MM　　ISSN 0040-0416
TEACHER.* 1920. q. free. Malta Union of Teachers, Movement of United Teachers, Teachers' Institute, Republic St., Valletta, Malta. Ed. A.M. Farrugia. adv.; bk.rev.; stat. circ. 4,000.

371　　　　　　CN　　ISSN 0841-9574
TEACHER (VANCOUVER). 1960. irreg. (approx. 13/yr.). B.C. Teachers' Federation, 2235 Burrard St., Vancouver, B.C. V6J 3H9, Canada. TEL 604-731-8121. Ed. Clive Cocking. circ. 41,000.
Former titles (until 1988): B C T F Newsletter (ISSN 0709-9800); (until 1979): British Columbia Teachers' Federation. Newsletter (ISSN 0005-2965)

TEACHER AND LIBRARIAN. see *LIBRARY AND INFORMATION SCIENCES*

370　　　　　　II　　ISSN 0379-3400
TEACHER EDUCATION. (Text in English) 1960. q. Rs.40($35) non-members; members Rs.24($30). Indian Association of Teacher Educators, 8B Bundh Rd., Allenganj, Allahabad, India. Ed. D.D. Tewari. adv.; bk.rev.; bibl. circ. 1,000.
Description: Deals with problems of teacher education, education and education research.

EDUCATION 2059

370 US
TEACHER EDUCATION REPORTS. 1979. 24/yr. $237. (National Center for Education Information) Feistritzer Publications, 4401-A Connecticut Ave., N.W., Ste. 212, Washington, DC 20008. TEL 202-362-3444. FAX 202-362-3493. Ed. David T. Chester. **Document type:** newsletter.
 Description: Provides information on teaching and teacher education at the federal, state and local levels.

378 RH ISSN 1018-4910
TEACHER IN ZIMBABWE. 1974. m. $22. (Ministry of Education and Culture) Zimbabwe Publishing House, P.O. Box 350, Harare, Zimbabwe. TEL 47548. FAX 47554. TELEX 26035 ZPH ZW. Ed. Jonathan Kadye. adv.: B&W page Z.$3200, color page Z.$8000; bleed 280 x 215; adv. contact: Monica Mutero. bk.rev.; circ. 55,000. **Document type:** government publication.
 Formerly (until 1991): Teachers' Forum.
 Description: Provides a forum for exchange of views and discussion of teaching methods, current issues and news of interest.

370 US
TEACHER SUPPLY AND DEMAND IN FLORIDA. a. Department of Education, Central Plaza, Level 8, Tallahassee, FL 32301. TEL 904-487-1630.
 Formerly: Areas of Critical Teacher Needs in Florida.

370 US ISSN 0161-4681
L11
TEACHERS COLLEGE RECORD; a professional journal of ideas, research and informed opinion. 1900. q. (Sep.-May). $30 to individuals; institutions $55. Columbia University, Teachers College Record Office, 525 W. 120th St., New York, NY 10027. TEL 212-678-3719. FAX 212-678-4048. Ed. Ellen Condliffe Lagemann. adv.; bk.rev.; film rev.; bibl.; charts; illus.; index. circ. 5,000. (also avail. in microform from UMI,MIM; reprint service avail. from UMI,KTO) **Indexed:** Amer.Hist.& Life, ASCA, Bk.Rev.Ind. (1965-), C.I.J.E., Child.Bk.Rev.Ind. (1965-), Coll.Stud.Pers.Abstr., Cont.Pg.Educ., Curr.Cont., Educ.Admin.Abstr., Educ.Ind., Educ.Tech.Abstr., Except.Child.Educ.Abstr., Fut.Surv., Hist.Abstr., Lang.& Lang.Behav.Abstr., Mult.Ed.Abstr., Psychol.Abstr., Sociol.Abstr., Sociol.Educ.Abstr., SOMA, SSCI, Stud.Wom.Abstr.
 —BLDSC (8613.710000); Faxon; UnCover; SWETS; UMI. **CCC.**

370 NR
TEACHERS' FORUM.* (Text in English) 1955. bi-m. Ministry of Education, 3 Moloney St., Lagos, Nigeria. charts.
 Formerly: Teachers' Monthly.

370 US
TEACHER'S HELPER MAGAZINE. (In 4 editions: Kindergarten; Grade 1; Grades 2-3; Grades 4-5) 4/yr. $14.95 (foreign $20.95). Education Center, Inc., 1607 Battleground Ave., Box 9753, Greensboro, NC 27429. TEL 800-334-0298.
 Formerly: Worksheet Magazine.

370 US
TEACHER'S INTERACTION; a magazine for Sunday school teachers. 1960. m. $10.25. (Lutheran Church - Missouri Synod, Board for Parish Services) Concordia Publishing House, 3558 Jefferson Ave., St. Louis, MO 63118. TEL 314-664-7000. Ed. Jane Haas. bk.rev.; illus.; index. circ. 17,000. (also avail. in microform from UMI) **Indexed:** Curr.Cont. **Document type:** consumer publication.
 Formerly: Interaction (ISSN 0020-5117)
 Description: Articles on teaching resources and personal enrichment for volunteer teachers in the church.

370 NR
TEACHERS JOURNAL. 6/yr. POB 139, Lagos, Nigeria.

370 UK
TEACHERS OF HISTORY IN THE UNIVERSITIES OF THE UNITED KINGDOM. a. £6. University of London, Institute of Historical Research, Senate House, London WC1E 7HU, England. TEL 071-636-0272. FAX 071-436-2183. Ed. Joyce M. Horn. index. circ. 350. (processed) **Document type:** directory.
 Former titles: Teachers of History in the Universities and Polytechnics of the United Kingdom (ISSN 0268-6732); Teachers of History in the Universities of the United Kingdom (ISSN 0085-7114)
 Description: Comprehensive listing of teachers of history in all universities with details of position held, degrees and honors.

370 331.88 GW ISSN 0863-0070
TEACHERS OF THE WORLD; international pedagogical and trade union review. (Editions in English, French, German and Spanish) 1951. q. $5 to individuals; institutions $10. World Federation of Teachers' Unions (FISE), Wilhelm-Wolff-Str. 21, 13156 Berlin, Germany. TEL 4800591. Ed.Bd. adv.; bk.rev.; charts; illus. circ. 19,000. **Indexed:** Mid.East: Abstr.& Ind.
 Description: Worldwide educational issues and problems are discussed from FISE's point of view. Covers all levels of education.

370 US
TEACHER'S PROFESSIONAL UPDATE; personal, financial, and career development. s-m. $24 includes Special Education Briefing. Prentice Hall, 24 Rope Ferry Rd., Waterford, CT 06386. TEL 203-434-6764.
 Supersedes (in Mar. 1993): Teaching Gifted Children.
 Description: Addresses the personal and professional needs and questions of teachers grades K through 12.

TEACHER'S TAX GUIDE. see *BUSINESS AND ECONOMICS — Public Finance, Taxation*

TEACHERS TRAVEL GAZETTE. see *TRAVEL AND TOURISM*

370 BG ISSN 0040-0521
TEACHER'S WORLD; quarterly journal of education and research. 1961. q. $1.50. University of Dhaka, Institute of Education and Research, Ramna, Dhaka 2, Bangladesh. Ed. Noorul Huq. bk.rev.; bibl.; index. circ. 1,000.

TEACHING AND LEARNING IN MEDICINE; an international journal. see *MEDICAL SCIENCES*

370 US ISSN 1047-6210
LB1715
TEACHING EDUCATION. 1987. s-a. $25 to individuals; institutions $35 (effective 1993). University of South Carolina, College of Education, Columbia, SC 29208. TEL 803-777-6301. FAX 803-777-3090. Ed. James Sears. adv.; bk.rev.; circ. 1,200 (controlled). **Indexed:** Educ.Ind., SOMA. **Document type:** academic/scholarly publication.
 —BLDSC (8614.095000); Faxon; UnCover.

972.8 US
TEACHING FOR CHANGE. 1987. q. $15 to individuals; institutions $25. Network of Educators on the Americas, 1118 22nd St., N.W., Washington, DC 20037. TEL 202-429-0137. FAX 202-429-9766. Ed. Deborah Menkart. adv.; bk.rev.; bibl.; illus. circ. 1,000. (back issues avail.) **Document type:** newsletter.
 Formerly: Central America in the Classroom (ISSN 1048-3543)
 Description: Serves as a forum for educators to share strategies, ideas and concerns. Includes news, classroom handouts and activities.

370 US
TEACHING FOR LEARNING. 2/yr. $15 for 4 issues. Anderson-Shea, Inc., 515 Hahaione St., No. 18C, Honolulu, HI 96825-1455. TEL 808-395-5677. Ed. Charlene Anderson-Shea.

TEACHING GEOGRAPHY. see *GEOGRAPHY*

370 331.1 US ISSN 0889-8839
TEACHING OPPORTUNITIES OVERSEAS - BULLETIN. 1975. m. $34. Overseas Academic Opportunities, 72 Franklin Ave., Ocean Grove, NJ 07756. TEL 718-706-4900. Ed. Susan Towey. circ. 2,800. **Document type:** newsletter.
 Description: Provides information on teaching positions at elementary and secondary schools all over the world.

TEACHING SCIENCE. see *SCIENCES: COMPREHENSIVE WORKS*

TEACHING THINKING & PROBLEM SOLVING NEWSLETTER. see *PSYCHOLOGY*

370 UK
TEACHING TODAY. 1921. 3/yr. £6. N A S U W T, Hillscourt Education Centre, Rose Hill, Rednal, Birmingham B45 8RS, England. TEL 021-453-6150. FAX 021-453-7224. Ed. Graham Terrell. adv.; bk.rev. circ. 120,000. **Document type:** trade publication.
 Former titles: N A S U W T Career Teacher Journal; Schoolmaster and Career Teacher.

370 US ISSN 1066-2847
LC1099.3
TEACHING TOLERANCE. 1991. 2/yr. free to educators. Southern Poverty Law Center, 400 Washington Ave., Montgomery, AL 36104. TEL 205-264-0286. FAX 205-264-3121. Ed. Sara Bullard. circ. 200,000. **Document type:** academic/scholarly publication.
 —UnCover.
 Description: Provides teachers with resources and ideas to help promote harmony in the classroom.

TECHNOLOGY ACCIDENT PREVENTION EDUCATION. see *OCCUPATIONAL HEALTH AND SAFETY*

TECHNOLOGY CONNECTION; the newsletter for school library media specialists. see *LIBRARY AND INFORMATION SCIENCES*

TECHNOLOGY IN EDUCATION. see *TECHNOLOGY: COMPREHENSIVE WORKS*

TECHNOLOGY TEACHER. see *TECHNOLOGY: COMPREHENSIVE WORKS*

TEKSTIILIOPETTAJA/TEXTILLAREN. see *HOME ECONOMICS*

TELEMEDIUM. see *COMMUNICATIONS — Television And Cable*

370 US ISSN 0739-0408
TENNESSEE EDUCATION. 1971. 3/yr. $4.50 (foreign $6). University of Tennessee at Knoxville, College of Education, 212 Claxton, Knoxville, TN 37996-3400. TEL 615-974-2272. FAX 615-974-8718. Ed. Sue Carey. bk.rev. circ. 2,500. (also avail. in microform from UMI) **Indexed:** C.I.J.E.
 —UMI.
 Description: Publishes general education articles, some specific to Tennessee schools or systems.

TENNESSEE MUSICIAN. see *MUSIC*

370.193 US
TENNESSEE PARENT - TEACHER BULLETIN. 1924. 10/yr. (Aug.-May). $3. Tennessee Congress of Parents and Teachers, 1905 Acklen Ave., Nashville, TN 37212. TEL 615-383-9740. Ed. Billy F. Davis. film rev.; circ. 1,400 (controlled). (processed)
 Supersedes (in 197?): Tennessee Parent - Teacher (ISSN 0049-3392)

370 371.2 US ISSN 0747-6159
TENNESSEE SCHOOL BOARDS JOURNAL. 1983. q. $20. Pollock Printing Co., 928 6th Ave., South, Nashville, TN 37203. TEL 615-255-0526. (Subscr. to: 500 13th Ave. N., Nashville, TN 37203) Ed. Holly Hewitt. circ. 1,700. (back issues avail.)
 Description: Informs school board members, school superintendents and other school administrators about education issues.

EDUCATION

370 US ISSN 0040-3407
TENNESSEE TEACHER. 1934. m. (Aug.-Apr.). $5 (effective Aug. 1992; typically set in Apr.). Tennessee Education Association, 801 Second Ave. N., Nashville, TN 37201-1099.
TEL 615-242-8392. Ed. Dawn Charles. adv.; bk.rev.; illus. circ. 42,000. (also avail. in microform from UMI; reprint service avail. from UMI) **Indexed:** Lang.& Lang.Behav.Abstr.
—UnCover; UMI.

370 SP ISSN 1130-3743
LB14.7
TEORIA DE LA EDUCACION. 1986. a. 1800 ptas. Ediciones Universidad de Salamanca, Apdo. 325, 37080 Salamanca, Spain. TEL 923-26-14-54. Dir. Joaquin Garcia Carrasco. **Document type:** academic/scholarly publication.

TERAPIA FAMILIARE. see *PSYCHOLOGY*

TEST - INFO. see *COLLEGE AND ALUMNI*

370 LI
TEVYNES SVIESA. 1953. w. Antakalnio 31, Vilnius 232055, Lithuania. TEL (0122) 741-571. Ed. Juozas Subacius.

373 US ISSN 0040-4705
TEXAS STUDY OF SECONDARY EDUCATION RESEARCH BULLETIN. 1948. s-a. $15. Texas Association of Secondary School Principals, 1833 South 1 H 35, Austin, TX 78741. TEL 512-442-2100.
FAX 512-443-3343. Ed. Julian Shaddix. adv.; charts; illus.; stat. circ. 4,000. (tabloid format) **Document type:** trade publication.
Formerly: Texas Journal of Secondary Education.

TEXTBOOK LETTER. see *EDUCATION — Teaching Methods And Curriculum*

TEXTILARBEIT UND UNTERRICHT. see *CLOTHING TRADE — Fashions*

THEATRE JOURNAL (BALTIMORE). see *THEATER*

370 100 SP
THEMATA. 1984. a. price varies. Universidad de Sevilla, Facultad de Filosofia y Ciencias de la Educacion, Servicio de Publicaciones, Valparaiso 5, 41013 Seville, Spain. TEL 954-231958. FAX 954-232245.

THEOLOGICAL EDUCATION. see *RELIGIONS AND THEOLOGY*

370 US ISSN 0040-5841
LB1028 CODEN: THPRAC
THEORY INTO PRACTICE. 1962. 4/yr. $30 to individuals (foreign $35); institutions $55 (foreign $60). Ohio State University, College of Education, 146 Arps Hall, 1945 N. High St., Columbus, OH 43210-1172. TEL 614-292-3407. Eds. Robert Donmoyer, Merryfield. index. circ. 5,000. (also avail. in microform from UMI; back issues avail.) **Indexed:** Adol.Ment.Hlth.Abstr., C.I.J.E., Cont.Pg.Educ., Curr.Cont, Educ.Admin.Abstr., Educ.Ind., ERIC, Mult.Ed.Abstr., Psychol.Abstr., Sage Fam.Stud.Abstr., SOMA. **Document type:** academic/scholarly publication.
—BLDSC (8814.632000); Faxon; UnCover; SWETS; UMI.
Supersedes: Educational Research Bulletin.
Refereed Serial

370 US ISSN 1055-9272
LB1590.3
THINK. 1991. 4/yr. $20 (foreign $26). ECS Learning Systems, Inc., Box 791437, San Antonio, TX 78279-1437. TEL 210-438-4262.
FAX 210-438-4263. Ed. Sam Mammen. adv.; bk.rev. **Document type:** trade publication.
Description: Directed to teachers teaching creative and critical thinking skills.

370 US ISSN 0196-9641
LA267
THRESHOLDS IN EDUCATION. 1975. q. $20. Thresholds in Education Foundation, Box 771, Dekalb, IL 60115. TEL 815-753-9357.
FAX 815-753-9388. Ed. Byron F. Radebaugh. adv.; bk.rev.; index. circ. 500. (back issues avail.) **Document type:** academic/scholarly publication.
Formerly: Thresholds in Secondary Education.
Description: Informs educators about future trends and contemporary issues related to research and practice in education.

373 US ISSN 1055-2243
LB2805
THRUST FOR EDUCATIONAL LEADERSHIP. 1971. 7/yr. $30. Association of California School Administrators, 1517 L St., Sacramento, CA 95814.
TEL 916-444-3216. Ed. Thomas K. DeLapp. adv.; bk.rev.; bibl.; charts; illus.; index. circ. 17,000. (also avail. in microform from UMI; reprint service avail. from UMI) **Indexed:** Cal.Per.Ind. (1980-), Educ.Ind.
—BLDSC (8820.371000); Faxon; UnCover; UMI.
Formerly (until 1990): Thrust (Sacramento) (ISSN 0145-2061); Which superseded: Journal of Secondary Education (ISSN 0022-4464)

370 CC ISSN 0493-2099
TIANJIN JIAOYU/TIANJIN EDUCATION. (Text in Chinese) m. Tianjin Jiaoyu Zazhishe, No. 47, 11 Jing Lu, Hedong Qu, Tianjin 300171, People's Republic of China. TEL 413876. Ed. Huang Lizhu.

370 US
TIDBITS. 1976. s-a. $10. National Association for the Legal Support of Alternative Schools, Box 2823, Santa Fe, NM 87501. TEL 505-471-6928. Ed. Ed Nagel. bk.rev. circ. 3,000. **Document type:** newsletter.

371 DK ISSN 0108-6278
TIDENS SKOLE.* 1898. 20/yr. DKK 260. Danmarks Realskoleforening, Vester Alle 7, 8000 Aarhus C, Denmark. (Co-sponsor: Frie Grundskolers Laererforening) Ed. Jais Jensen. adv.; bk.rev. circ. 4,600.
Formerly (until 1973): Danske Realskole (ISSN 0045-964X)

370 SW ISSN 0040-6856
TIDSKRIFT FOER YRKESUTBILDNING.* 1920. 9/yr. SEK 25. Svenska Yrkesutbildningsfoereningen, Box 137, 771 01 Ludvika 1, Sweden. Ed. Bert Holmqvist. adv.; bk.rev.; illus. circ. 6,000.
Formerly: Tidskrift for Praktiska Ungdomsskolor.

TIDSSKRIFTINDEKS FOR SKOLEBIBLIOTEKER. see *BIBLIOGRAPHIES*

370 NE ISSN 0929-2039
TIJDSCHRIFT VOLWASSENEN EDUCATIE. 1988. 6/yr. Nederlands Bibliotheek en Lektuur Centrum, Landelijke Studie en Ontwikkelingscentrum Volwasseneneducatie, Postbus 93054, 2509 AB The Hague, Netherlands.
—SWETS.
Formerly (until 1993): Basiseducatie (ISSN 0922-0933); Which was formed by the merger of (1986-1988): Nieuwsbrief Basiseducatie (ISSN 0920-6930); (1951-1988): Vorming (ISSN 0165-0998); Which was formerly (until 1973): Volksopvoeding.

370 NE ISSN 0166-591X
TIJDSCHRIFT VOOR ONDERWIJSRESEARCH. 1975. 6/yr. fl.132.50 to individuals; institutions fl.204.05 (effective 1994). (Vereniging voor Onderwijsresearch) Swets & Zeitlinger bv, Heereweg 347, 2161 CA Lisse, Netherlands.
TEL 31-2521-35111. FAX 31-2521-15888. TELEX 41325 SZLIS NL. (Dist. in N. America by: Swets & Zeitlinger, 440 Creamery Way, Ste. A, Exton, PA 19341. TEL 800-447-9387. FAX 610-524-5366) Ed.Bd. (back issues avail.) **Indexed:** Psychol.Abstr. **Document type:** academic/scholarly publication.
—BLDSC (8843.500000); SWETS.

370 UK ISSN 0040-7887
L16
TIMES EDUCATIONAL SUPPLEMENT. 1910. w. $120. Times Supplements Ltd., Admiral House, 66-68 E. Smithfield, London E1 9YY, England.
TEL 071-782-3000. FAX 071-782-3200. Ed. Patricia Rowan. adv.; bk.rev.; illus. circ. 124,618. (tabloid format; also avail. in microform from RPI) **Indexed:** Acad.Ind., Bk.Rev.Ind. (1977-), Child.Bk.Rev.Ind. (1977-), Child.Lit.Abstr., Educ.Ind., High.Educ.Curr.Aware.Bull., Lang.Teach.& Ling.Abstr., Res.High.Educ.Abstr. **Document type:** academic/scholarly publication.
—BLDSC (8853.500000).
Description: Provides news and opinions on issues at all levels of education from nursery schools to universities.

377.8 US ISSN 0040-8441
LC461
TODAY'S CATHOLIC TEACHER. 1967. 8/yr. $14.95 (effective 1993-94). Peter Li Education Group, 330 Progress Rd., Dayton, OH 45449.
TEL 513-847-5900. FAX 513-847-5910. Ed. Ruth A. Matheny. adv.; bk.rev.; film rev.; charts; illus.; stat. circ. 50,000. **Indexed:** Biol.Dig., Cath.Ind., CERDIC.
—UMI.
Description: Articles, columns, and announcements on Catholic education in the school and at home, for parents, teachers, and administrators.

TOERUSTING; tijdschrift voor kerk en educatie met werkmateriaal. see *RELIGIONS AND THEOLOGY*

370 UK ISSN 0953-895X
TOPIC; practical applications of research in education. 1989. s-a. £23.50($43) National Foundation for Educational Research, The Mere, Upton Park, Slough, Berkshire SL1 2DQ, England.
TEL 0753-574123. FAX 0753-691632. Ed. David Upton. circ. 400. (looseleaf format; also avail. in microfiche) **Document type:** academic/scholarly publication.
Description: Highlights the practical implications of research findings for teachers.

370 AT ISSN 1038-9563
▼**TOURISM EDUCATION DIRECTORY.** 1992. a. Aus.$19.95. (Australian Tourist Commission) New Hobsons Press Pty. Ltd., 553 Elizabeth St., Surry Hills, N.S.W. 2010, Australia. TEL 02-310-2257.
FAX 02-310-2243. (Co-sponsor: Australian Tourism Industry Association) Eds. June Beck, Elisabeth Richardson. adv.; page Aus.$980; adv. contact: Colin Ritchie. circ. 4,500. **Document type:** directory.
Description: Lists tourism courses from Australia, New Zealand, and the South Pacific region offered by TAFEs, Polytechnics, and universities. Identifies course levels, prerequisites and duration, and provides job descriptions in the tourism industry.

TOYAMAKEN KOTO GAKKO KYOIKU KENKYUKAI SEIBUTSU BUNKAIHO/TOYAMA BIOLOGICAL EDUCATION SOCIETY. REPORT. see *BIOLOGY*

370 658 US
TRAINING DIRECTORS' FORUM NEWSLETTER. vol.4, 1988. 12/yr. $118 (Canada $128; elsewhere $138). Lakewood Publications (Subsidiary of: Maclean Hunter Publishing Company), 50 S. Ninth St., Minneapolis, MN 55402. TEL 612-333-0471.
FAX 612-333-6526. Ed. Brian McDermott. **Indexed:** Tr.& Dev.Alert. **Document type:** newsletter.

370 UK ISSN 0958-9856
TRAINING DIRECTORY (YEAR). 1985. a. £25. (British Association for Commercial and Industrial Education) Kogan Page Ltd., 120 Pentonville Rd., London N1 9JN, England. TEL 071-278-0433.
FAX 071-837-6348. TELEX 263088 KOGAN G. (Co-sponsor: Institute of Training and Development) **Document type:** directory.
—BLDSC (8883.503050).
Former titles (until 1989): Trainer's Yearbook; Directory of Trainer Support Services.

370 371.42 US
TRAINING TODAY.* 1982. bi-m. membership only. American Society for Training and Development, Chicagoland Chapter, 203 N. Wabash Ave., Ste. 806, Chicago, IL 60601-2411.
TEL 312-236-3327. Ed. Shel Newman. adv.; bk.rev. circ. 1,000.

378 US ISSN 0194-0988
LB2360
TRANSFER CREDIT PRACTICES OF DESIGNATED EDUCATIONAL INSTITUTIONS. biennial. $20 to non-members; members $15. American Association of Collegiate Registrars and Admissions Officers, One Dupont Circle, N.W., Ste. 330, Washington, DC 20036-1171. TEL 202-293-9161.
FAX 202-872-8857. Ed. James Christensen. (reprint service avail. from UMI) **Document type:** directory.
Formerly: Report of Credit Given by Educational Institutions (ISSN 0569-2482)
Description: Describes selected institutional credit acceptance practices within each state.

EDUCATION 2061

370 SA ISSN 0041-171X
TRANSVAAL. EDUCATION DEPARTMENT. EDUCATION BULLETIN/TRANSVAAL. ONDERWYSDEPARTMENT. ONDERWYSBULLETIN. Key Title: Onderwysbulletin (Pretoria). (Text and summaries in Afrikaans, English) 1956. 2/yr. free. Transvaal Education Department - Transvaalse Onderwysdepartment, Private Bag X76, Pretoria 0001, South Africa. Ed.Bd. bk.rev.; abstr.; bibl.; charts; stat. circ. 6,000. **Indexed:** Ind.S.A.Per.
 Description: Contains articles for teachers and administrators, including results of recent educational research and relevant developments in education in South Africa and overseas.

370 SA ISSN 0013-1830
TRANSVAAL. EDUCATION DEPARTMENT. EDUCATIONAL NEWS FLASHES/TRANSVAAL. ONDERWYSDEPARTMENT. ONDERWYSNUUSFLITSE. (Text in Afrikaans, English) 1964. 3/yr. free to qualified personnel. Transvaal Education Department - Transvaalse Onderwysdepartment, Private Bag X76, Pretoria 0001, South Africa. charts; illus.; stat. circ. 20,000.
 Description: Articles and photographs of general interest on educational issues, and news of the TED head office.

370 SA ISSN 0041-1728
TRANSVAAL EDUCATIONAL NEWS. 1904. 4/yr. R.20. Transvaal Teachers' Association, 38 Honey St., Berea, Johannesburg 2198, Transvaal, South Africa. TEL 27-11-642-5139. FAX 27-11-484-2628. Ed. H.D. Ackermann. adv.; bk.rev. circ. 6,500. (also avail. in microfiche) **Indexed:** Ind.S.A.Per. **Document type:** academic/scholarly publication.

TRAVAUX DE L'INSTITUTE DE LINGUISTIQUE DE LUND. see *LINGUISTICS*

TREELINES. see *FORESTS AND FORESTRY*

TRENDS IN COLLEGE MEDIA. see *JOURNALISM*

TRENDS IN HIGH SCHOOL MEDIA. see *JOURNALISM*

TRIAD (COLUMBUS). see *MUSIC*

370 US
TRIANGLE COALITION NETWORK NEWS. 1986. bi-m. free. Triangle Coalition for Science & Technology Education, 5112 Berwyn Rd., 3rd Fl., College Park, MD 20740. TEL 301-220-3164. FAX 301-474-4381. Ed. H.K. Larson. circ. 3,000.
 Description: Highlights the Coalition's membership and affiliate programs and activities in science and technology education.

370 RM
TRIBUNA SCOLII. 1970. m. Ministry of Education and Science, Piata Presei Libere 1, 71341 Bucharest, Rumania. (Co-sponsor: Trade Union of Workers in Education, Science and Cultural Institutions) Ed. Tirea Doina. circ. 67,000.

TRICOLOR; revista Venezolana para los ninos. see *CHILDREN AND YOUTH — For*

372 IE ISSN 0790-9136
TUARASCAIL. 1979. m. £15. Irish National Teachers' Organization, 35 Parnell Square, Dublin 1, Ireland. FAX 01-722462. Ed. Billy Sheehan. adv.; index. circ. 21,000. (back issues avail.) **Document type:** trade publication.

TUTTITALIA. see *LINGUISTICS*

370 IT
TUTTOSCUOLA. 1975. m. L.49000 (effective Sep. 1993). Editoriale Tuttoscuola s.r.l., Via della Scrofa 39, 00186 Rome, Italy. TEL 6-6880-23-26. Dir. Giovanni Vinciguerra. adv.; bk.rev. circ. 150,000. **Document type:** newspaper.

TYDSKRIF VIR TAALONDERRIG. see *LINGUISTICS*

370 US ISSN 0042-1413
U E A ACTION. 1969. m. $4. Utah Education Association, 875 E. 5180 South St., Murray, UT 84107. TEL 801-266-4461. FAX 800-265-2249. Ed. Steve Hale. adv.; bk.rev.; charts; illus.; index; circ. 16,550 (paid). **Document type:** trade publication.
 Formerly: Utah Educational Review.

370 UN ISSN 0251-5989
U I E CASE STUDIES. (Text in English, French and Spanish) irreg., no.9b, 1990. price varies. Unesco Institute for Education, Feldbrunnenstr. 58, D 2000 Hamburg 13, Germany. TEL 040-447843. TELEX 2164-146-UIE-D. (Dist. in U.S. by: Associates-Unipub, 4611-F Assembly Dr., Lanham, MD 20706-4391)
 Description: Experimentation and reform in Germany, Norway, the Dominican Republic, Spain, Tanzania, Venezuela, Sri Lanka, Poland, Netherlands, Hungary and the USA.

370 UN ISSN 0251-9674
U I E MONOGRAPHS. French edition: Monographie de l'I U E (ISSN 0251-9682) 1973. irreg., no.14b, 1990. DM.14. Unesco Institute for Education, Felbrunnenstr. 58, D-2000 Hamburg 13, Germany. (Dist. in U.S. by: Unipub, 4611-F Assembly Dr., Lanham, MD 20706-4391) **Document type:** monographic series.
 Description: Comparative studies on lifelong education.

320 US ISSN 0161-7389
L11
U S A TODAY. 1915. m. $24. Society for the Advancement of Education, 99 W. Hawthorne Ave., Ste. 518, Valley Stream, NY 11580-6101. TEL 516-568-9191. Ed. Stanley Lehrer. adv.; bk.rev.; bibl.; index. circ. 251,000. (also avail. in microform from UMI,MIM,PMC; reprint service avail. from UMI) **Indexed:** Acad.Ind., Amer.Bibl.Slavic & E.Eur.Stud., Bk.Rev.Ind. (1984-1987), C.I.J.E., Child.Bk.Rev.Ind. (1984-1987), Coll.Stud.Pers.Abstr., Curr.Cont., Educ.Admin.Abstr., Educ.Ind., Film Lit.Ind. (1978-), Hlth.Ind., Ind.Per.Art.Relat.Law, Mag.Ind., PMR, R.G., SSCI, TOM, Wom.Stud.Abstr. **Document type:** consumer publication.
 ●Also available online. Vendor(s): DIALOG Information Services, Inc., Mead Data Central, Inc., VU/TEXT Information Services, Inc.
 —BLDSC (9124.840000); UnCover; SWETS; UMI.
 Former titles (until 1978): Intellect; School and Society (ISSN 0036-6455)

371 US
U T D TODAY. 1947. m. $5 to non-members. United Teachers of Dade, 2929 S.W. 3rd Ave., Miami, FL 33129. TEL 305-854-0220. Ed. Pat L. Tornillo. adv.; bk.rev.; charts; illus.; stat. circ. 20,000. (tabloid format)
 Formerly: Dade County Teacher (ISSN 0011-524X)

370 RU
UCHITEL'SKAYA GAZETA. 1924. w. Proezd Sapunova 13-15, 103635 Moscow, Russia. Ed. P. Polozhevetz. **Document type:** newspaper.

370 XO ISSN 0139-5769
UCITEL'SKE NOVINY. 1951. w. 36 Kcs. (Ministry of Education of Slovak Republic) Slovenske Pedagogicke Nakladatelstvo, Sasinkova 5, 815 60 Bratislava, Slovakia. (Subscr. to: Slovart, Gottwaldovo nam. 6, 805-32 Bratislava, Slovakia) Ed. Herlinda Novakova. circ. 30,000.

370 330 DK
UDDANNELSES OG ERHVERVSVALGET; orientering for gymnasiet og HF. 1966. a. DKK 30. Raadet for Uddannelses- og Erhvervsvejledning, Aebeloegade 7, DK-2100 Copenhagen Oe, Denmark. (Dist. by: Danske Boghendleres Kommissionsanstalt, Siljangade 6, 2300 Copenhagen S, Denmark)
 Formerly (until 1992): Studie- og Erhvervsvalget (ISSN 0108-6944)

370 DK ISSN 0900-226X
UDDANNELSESHISTORIE. 1967. a. DKK 200. (Selskabet for Dansk Skolehistorie) Odense Universitetsforlag, Campusvej 55, DK-5230 Odense M, Denmark. Ed. Harry Haue. bk.rev. circ. 1,000. **Document type:** academic/scholarly publication.
 Formerly (until 1984): Dansk Skolehistorie. Aarbog (ISSN 0107-1661)
 Description: Features articles and reviews on Danish educational history.

370 DK ISSN 0108-7886
UDVIKLINGSTENDENSERNE PAA DE LANGVARIGT UDDANNEDES ARBEJDSMARKED. 1980. a. free. Undervisningsministeriet, Datakontoret, DK-1220 Copenhagen, Denmark. (Subscr to: Undervisningsministeriets Tekstbehandlingsenhed, Frederiksholms Kanal 25, DK-1220 Copenhagen K, Denmark)

370 UG ISSN 0049-5026
UGANDA SCHOOLS NEWSLETTER. (Text in English) vol.4, 1972. m. free. Ministry of Information, Broadcasting and Tourism, P.O. Box 7142, Kampala, Uganda. illus. circ. 10,000.

UNDERSTANDING JAPAN. see *GENERAL INTEREST PERIODICALS — Japan*

370 309 KE
UNDUGU BULLETIN. (Text in Dutch, English, French and German) 1979. q. free. Undugu Society of Kenya, Box 40417, Nairobi, Kenya. FAX 505888. Ed. Herbert Kassamani. circ. 740.
 Description: Covers the progress of the Undugu Society.

370 UN
UNESCO. PRINCIPAL REGIONAL OFFICE FOR ASIA AND THE PACIFIC. BULLETIN. (Text in English) 1966. a. price varies. Unesco, Principal Regional Office for Asia and the Pacific, P.O. Box 1425, Bangkok 10500, Thailand. FAX 391-0866. TELEX 20591 TH. (Dist. in U.S. by: Unipub, 4611-F, Assembly Dr., Lanham, MD 20706-4391) circ. 3,200. (also avail. in microfiche from CIS) **Indexed:** ERIC, IIS, Mid.East: Abstr.& Ind., Rural Ext.Educ.& Tr.Abstr.
 Former titles: Unesco. Regional Office for Education in Asia and the Pacific. Bulletin (ISSN 1010-9854); Unesco. Regional Office for Education in Asia and Oceania Bulletin (ISSN 0251-4745); Unesco. Regional Office for Education in Asia. Bulletin. (ISSN 0503-4450)

UNESCO. STUDIES ON BOOKS AND READING. see *PUBLISHING AND BOOK TRADE*

060 370 UN ISSN 0041-5294
UNESCO PHILIPPINES. 1962-1967; resumed 1984. biennial. free. Unesco National Commission of the Philippines, PICC Bldg., Rm.512, Roxas Blvd., Manila, Philippines. TEL 832-03-09. TELEX 40257 UNESCO PM. Ed. Apolinario Y. Tating. illus.; cum.index 1962-1954. circ. 3,000.
 Description: Features significant programs, projects and activities undertaken by Unesco, especially the Unesco National Commision of the Philippines.

370 DK ISSN 0900-1395
UNGDOMSUDDANNELSER. 1985. a. DKK 225. Ole Camaae, Lerbjergstien 18, 3460 Birkeroed, Denmark. TEL 45-42-276282. FAX 45-42-277880. illus.

370 DK
UNGE PAEDAGOGER; periodical for Socialist teachers of Denmark. 1939. m. (8/yr.). DKK 100. Foreningen Unge Paedagoger, Edvard Griegsgade 2, DK-2100 Copenhagen OE, Denmark. TEL 01-291548. adv.; bk.rev.; index, cum.index.

370 AU
UNI-PRESS. (Text in German) 1977. 6/yr. free. Oesterreichische Hochschuelerzeitung an der Universitaet Salzburg, Residenzplatz 1, A-5020 Salzburg, Austria. Ed. Viktor Mayer-Schoenberger. adv.; bk.rev.; illus.; tr.lit. circ. 4,500.
 Supersedes: De Facto (ISSN 0014-6536)

370 AT ISSN 0311-4775
LA2100
UNICORN. 1975. 4/yr. Aus.$36 to non-members. Australian College of Education, P.O. Box 323, Curtin, A.C.T. 2605, Australia. TEL 06-281-1677. FAX 06-285-1262. Ed. N. Dempster. adv.; bk.rev. circ. 6,500. **Indexed:** Aus.Educ.Ind., Aus.P.A.I.S., Cont.Pg.Educ., Educ.Tech.Abstr., ERIC, Sociol.Educ.Abstr., Sp.Ed.Needs Abstr., Stud.Wom.Abstr. **Document type:** academic/scholarly publication.
 —BLDSC (9090.551500).
 Description: Provides information on new ideas and significant developments in education; informs members of the activities of the college.

EDUCATION

370   SA   ISSN 0259-5591
DIE UNIE. (Text in Afrikaans) 1905. bi-m. R.20.90. Suid-Afrikaanse Onderwysersunie, P.O. Box 196, Cape Town 8000, South Africa. TEL 27-21-461-6340. FAX 27-21-461-9238. Ed. M.J.L. Olivier. adv.; bk.rev.; circ. 8,500 (controlled).

370   US
UNION CONNECTION. 1923. q. $10. Florida Education Association - United, 118 N. Monroe St., Tallahassee, FL 32399-1700. TEL 904-224-1161. FAX 904-681-2905. Ed. Elisia Norton. adv.; bk.rev.; film rev.; charts; illus.; tr.lit.; index. circ. 60,000. (also avail. in microform from UMI; reprint service avail. from UMI) Document type: newsletter.
    Former titles: Forum (Tallahassee) (ISSN 1063-8393); (until 1987): F E A - United's Forum Magazine (ISSN 1071-619X); (until 1984): Forum (ISSN 1071-6181); (until 1984): F E A - U's Forum (ISSN 0744-6063); And (until 1982): F E A United's Forum (ISSN 0279-862X); (until 1980): Forum (ISSN 0274-8738); (until 1980): United Teacher; Florida Education (ISSN 0015-4016).

330.9   MG
UNION ECONOMIQUE. Union des Syndicats d'Interet Economique de Madagascar, Place Roland Garros, Antananarivo, Malagasy Republic. illus.

370   US
UNION LEADER (TALLAHASSEE). q. Florida Education Association - United, 118 N. Monroe St., Tallahassee, FL 32399-1700. TEL 904-224-1161. FAX 904-681-2905. Ed. Elisia Norton. circ. 60,000. (back issues avail.) Document type: newsletter.
    Former titles: Focus (Tallahassee); Solidarity's Focus.
    Description: Covers education issues and union trends in the K-12 area of education.

UNION NATIONALE DE L'ENSEIGNEMENT AGRICOLE PRIVE. ANNUAIRE. see *AGRICULTURE*

370   US
UNITED PARENTS ASSOCIATION OF NEW YORK CITY. NEWSLETTER.* vol.6, 1975. m. during school year. $15. United Parents Associations of New York City, 45 John St., Ste. 607, New York, NY 10038-3706. TEL 212-619-0095.

370.6   II
UNITED SCHOOLS ORGANISATION OF INDIA. ANNUAL REPORT. (Text in English) 19th ed., 1969. a. United Schools Organisation of India, U S O House, 6 Special Institutional Area, New Delhi 110 067, India. FAX 09111-6862042. illus.

370 500 380.5   US
U.S. OFFICE OF TECHNOLOGY ASSESSMENT. REPORTS. SCIENCE, EDUCATION, AND TRANSPORTATION PROGRAM. irreg. price varies. U.S. Office of Technology Assessment, Publication Distribution, U.S. Congress, 600 Pennsylvania Ave., S.E., Washington, DC 20510-8025. TEL 202-224-8996. FAX 202-228-6098. E-mail: PUBREQUEST@OTA.GOV. (Dist. by: Superintendent of Documents, U.S. Government Printing Office, Box 371954, Pittsburgh, PA 15250-7954. TEL 202-783-3238. FAX 202-512-2250; And: National Technical Information Service, 5285 Port Royal Rd., Springfield, VA 22161. TEL 703-487-4650. FAX 703-321-8547) (also avail. in microfiche from CIS; back issues avail.; reprint service avail. from CIS) Document type: monographic series, government publication.
    Formed by the merger of: U.S. Office of Technology Assessment. Reports. Science, Transportation, and Innovation Program & U.S. Office of Technology Assessment. Reports. Transportation Program & U.S. Office of Technology Assessment. Reports. Research and Development Program.
    Description: Reports provide technical information on various transportation issues, particularly those dealing with mass transit, and on ways to improve public education and reduce adult illiteracy.

UNIVERSE IN A CLASSROOM; a newsletter on astronomy for teachers. see *ASTRONOMY*

370   CK
UNIVERSIDAD DE ANTIOQUIA. ASOCIACION DE PROFESIONALES DE LA EDUCACION. ESTUDIOS EDUCATIVOS. 1973. 2/yr. Col.$800($15) Universidad de Antioquia, Asociacion de Profesionales de la Educacion, Facultad de la Educacion, Apdo. Aereo 1226, Medellin, Colombia. Ed. Luis Oscar Londono Zapata. bk.rev. circ. 2,000.

370   SP   ISSN 0212-8322
UNIVERSIDAD DE MURCIA. ANALES DE PEDAGOGIA. 1955. a. 1000 ptas. Universidad de Murcia, Secretariado de Publicaciones e Intercambio Cientifico, Santo Cristo, 1, 30001 Murcia, Spain. TEL 968-239450.
    Supersedes in part (in 1983): Universidad de Murcia. Filosofia y Letras. Anales (ISSN 0463-9863)

370   SP
UNIVERSIDAD DE NAVARRA. FACULTAD DE CIENCIAS DE LA EDUCACION. COLECCION. 1969. irreg., no.31, 1989. price varies. Ediciones Universidad de Navarra, S.A., Apdo. 396, 31080 Pamplona, Spain. TEL 94 825 6850.
    Formerly: Universidad de Navarra. Instituto de Ciencias de la Educacion. Coleccion I C E (ISSN 0078-8686)

370   SP
UNIVERSIDAD DE SEVILLA. SERIE: INSTITUTO DE CIENCIAS DE LA EDUCACION. irreg., latest no.5. Universidad de Sevilla, Instituto de Ciencias de la Educacion, Servicio de Publicaciones, Valparaiso 5, 41013 Seville, Spain. TEL 954-231958. FAX 954-232245. (Subscr. to: Avda. Ramon y Cajal, 1, 51005 Seville, Spain)

UNIVERSIDAD DE SEVILLA. SERIE: TESTIMONIO UNIVERSITARIO. see *BIBLIOGRAPHIES*

378   MX   ISSN 0026-1750
UNIVERSIDAD NACIONAL AUTONOMA DE MEXICO. REVISTA. 1945. m. Mex.$65.($8) Universidad Nacional Autonoma de Mexico, Direccion General de Difusion Cultural, Villa Obregon, Ciudad Universitaria, Mexico 20, D.F., Mexico. Ed. Gaston Garcia Cantu. **Indexed:** Hisp.Amer.Per.Ind.

370   BL   ISSN 0102-2555
UNIVERSIDADE DE SAO PAULO. FACULDADE DE EDUCACAO. REVISTA. (Text in Portuguese; summaries in English) 1975. s-a. $10. Universidade de Sao Paulo, Faculdade de Educacao, Av. da Universidade, 308, 05508-900 Sao Paulo SP, Brazil. TEL 011-211-0011 ext. 3433. FAX 011-815-4272. Ed. Nilson Jose Machado. bk.rev. circ. 1,500. **Document type:** academic/scholarly publication.
    Supersedes (1955-1967): Revista de Pedagogia.
    Description: Covers psychology, methodology, philosophy, history, and administration of education, and comparative education.

370   IT   ISSN 0082-6480
UNIVERSITA DEGLI STUDI DI TRIESTE. ISTITUTO DI PEDAGOGIA. QUADERNI. 1966. irreg. price varies. Casa Editrice Felice Le Monnier, Via A. Meucci 2, Casella Postale 202, 50100 Florence, Italy.

370   GW   ISSN 0722-8481
UNIVERSITAET-GESAMTHOCHSCHULE DUISBURG. UNIVERSITAETS-REPORT. 1982. q. Universitaet-Gesamthochschule Duisburg, Lotharstr. 65, 47048 Duisburg, Germany. TEL 0203-379-0. FAX 0203-379-3333. TELEX 855793-UNIDUD. adv. circ. 6,000. **Document type:** bulletin.
    Description: Covers all general issues, news and information of the University of Duisburg.

378   DR   ISSN 0041-9044
UNIVERSITARIO.* 1970. s-m. Universidad Autonoma de Santo Domingo, Escuela de Ciencias de la Informacion Publica, Santo Domingo, Dominican Republic. Ed. Dr. Gonzalez Tirado. charts; illus.

370   FR
UNIVERSITE DE BRETAGNE OCCIDENTALE. GUIDE DE L'ETUDIANT. 1971. a. free. Universite de Bretagne Occidentale, Rue de Archives, 29269 Brest, France. TEL 98-31-60-20. FAX 98-31-60-01. circ. controlled. (processed)

370   NO   ISSN 0800-6113
UNIVERSITET I OSLO. PEDAGOGISK FORSKNINGSINSTITUTT. RAPPORT. 1977. irreg. price varies. Universitet i Oslo, Pedagogisk Forskningsinstitutt, P.O. Box 1092, Blindern, N-0317 Oslo, Norway. TEL 47-22-85-70-75. FAX 47-22-85-42-50. circ. 175. **Document type:** academic/scholarly publication.

370 331.8   SW   ISSN 0282-4973
UNIVERSITETSLAERAREN. 1950. 18/yr. SEK 250. Sveriges Universitetslaerarfoerbund, P.O. Box 1227, S-111 82 Stockholm, Sweden. TEL 46-8-21-61-82. FAX 46-8-21-61-82. Ed. Lars-Goeran Heldt. adv.: B&W page SEK 11400, color page SEK 27400; adv. contact: Lena Loevenmark-Andre. bk.rev. circ. 14,000.
    Formed by the 1985 merger of: S U H A F - Tidningen (ISSN 0036-2018); U L F.

370   MY
UNIVERSITI KEBANGSAAN MALAYSIA. LAPURAN TAHUNAN - ANNUAL REPORT. (Text mainly in Malay) 1971. a. free. Penerbit Universiti Kebangsaan Malaysia, 436000 UKM Bangi Selangor, Malaysia. TEL 8250001. stat.

370   II   ISSN 0084-621X
UNIVERSITY OF ALLAHABAD. EDUCATION DEPARTMENT. RESEARCHES AND STUDIES. 1950. a. exchange basis. University of Allahabad, Education Department, Allahabad 211002, Uttar Pradesh, India. Ed. R.S. Pandey. bk.rev.; circ. controlled.

371.42   PH   ISSN 0070-8259
UNIVERSITY OF EASTERN PHILIPPINES. RESEARCH CENTER. REPORT. 1965. irreg. $2. University of Eastern Philippines, Research Center, University Town, Northern Samar, Philippines. Ed. Andres F. Celestino. circ. 3,000. (processed)

370   FI   ISSN 0073-179X
UNIVERSITY OF HELSINKI. DEPARTMENT OF EDUCATION. RESEARCH BULLETIN. (Text in English, French or German) 1957. irreg., no.85, 1993. exchange basis. University of Helsinki, Department of Education, P.O. Box 39, SF-00014 University of Helsinki, Finland. FAX 358-0-1918073. circ. 325. (also avail. in microfiche) **Indexed:** ERIC, Psychol.Abstr.

370   NR
UNIVERSITY OF IBADAN. INSTITUTE OF EDUCATION. ANNUAL REPORT. a. University of Ibadan, Institute of Education, Ibadan, Nigeria. TEL 62550-1495. Ed. J.D. Obemeata.

370   NR   ISSN 0073-4314
UNIVERSITY OF IBADAN. INSTITUTE OF EDUCATION. OCCASIONAL PUBLICATIONS. irreg. price varies. University of Ibadan, Institute of Education, Ibadan, Nigeria. TEL 62550-1495. Ed. J.D. Obemeata.

370   MM
UNIVERSITY OF MALTA. FACULTY OF EDUCATION. NEWSLETTER. irreg. (2-3/yr.). free. University of Malta, Faculty of Education, Msida, Malta. TEL 356-333903. FAX 356-336450. Ed. Paul Pace. bk.rev.; bibl. circ. 650. **Document type:** newsletter.
    Description: Reports on conferences, meeting and seminars attended by faculty members and staff, and lists publications by faculty and staff.

370   US
UNIVERSITY OF MINNESOTA. CENTER FOR RESEARCH IN LEARNING, PERCEPTION & COGNITION. REPORT AND FELLOWSHIP OFFERINGS. 1965. a. $3. University of Minnesota, Center for Research in Learning, Perception & Cognition, 205 Elliott Hall, Minneapolis, MN 55455. TEL 612-615-9367. circ. 1,000.
    Former titles: University of Minnesota. Center for Research in Human Learning. Report and Fellowship Offerings; University of Minnesota. Center for Research in Human Learning. Report (ISSN 0076-9282)

370 410   SA   ISSN 0378-5335
UNIVERSITY OF THE NORTH. COMMUNIQUE. (Text in Afrikaans, English) 1975. a. R.4.50. University of the North, Private Bag X1106, Sovenga 0727, South Africa. TEL 015-224-310. FAX 01522-4351. Ed. J.E. Nel. bk.rev. circ. 1,400.

370   PH
UNIVERSITY OF THE PHILIPPINES GAZETTE. 1970. q. University of the Philippines, Diliman, Quezon City, Philippines. Ed. Leonardo de Castro. circ. 1,000.

EDUCATION

378   CN   ISSN 0042-031X
UNIVERSITY OF WATERLOO. GAZETTE. vol.10, 1970. w. free. University of Waterloo, Internal Communications Department, Waterloo, ON N2L 3G1, Canada. TEL 519-885-1211. FAX 519-746-8652. Ed. Chris Redmond. illus.; circ. 10,000 (controlled). (tabloid format)

370   XO   ISSN 0083-4165
UNIVERZITA KOMENSKEHO. FILOZOFICKA FAKULTA. ZBORNIK: PAEDAGOGICA. (Text in Slovak; summaries in English, German, Russian) 1968. irreg. exchange basis. Univerzita Komenskeho, Filozoficka Fakulta, c/o Ustredna Kniznica Filozofickej Fakulty, Gondova 2, 818 01 Bratislava, Slovakia. Ed. Stefan Svec. circ. 700. **Document type:** academic/scholarly publication.

378   BN   ISSN 0042-0425
UNIVERZITET DANAS. vol.7, 1966. m. 60 din.($6) Zajednica Jugoslovenskih Univerziteta, Obaca 7, Sarajevo, Bosnia Hercegovina. Ed. Franko Kozul.

370 150   PL   ISSN 1230-607X
LA840
UNIWERSYTET GDANSKI. ZESZYTY NAUKOWE. PEDAGOGIKA, HISTORIA WYCHOWANIA. (Text in Polish; summaries in English and Russian) 1966. irreg., latest no.24. price varies. Uniwersytet Gdanski, Wydzial Humanistyczny, c/o Biblioteka Glowna, Ul. Armii Krajowej 110, 81-824 Sopot, Poland. TEL 51-0061. TELEX 051-2247 BMOR PL. (Dist. by: Ars Polona-Ruch, Krakowskie Przedmiescie 7, 00-680 Warsaw, Poland) circ. 250. **Document type:** academic/scholarly publication.
Former titles (until 1990): Uniwersytet Gdanski. Wydzial Humanistyczny. Zeszyty Naukowe. Pedagogika, Historia Wychowania (ISSN 0208-4767); (until 1979): Uniwersytet Gdanski. Wydzial Humanistyczny. Zeszyty Naukowe. Pedagogika, Psychologia, Historia Wychowania (ISSN 0302-2269); (until 1972): Wyzsza Szkola Pedagogiczna. Gdanskie Zeszyty Humanistyczne. Pedagogika, Psychologia, Historia Wychowania (ISSN 0072-047X)
Description: Covers theory of education, didactics, and pedagogics, teaching of first-graders, andragogics, and history of education in the region of Pomerania.

UNIWERSYTET JAGIELLONSKI. ZESZYTY NAUKOWE. PRACE PSYCHOLOGICZNO-PEDAGOGICZNE. see *PSYCHOLOGY*

370   PL   ISSN 0208-5526
UNIWERSYTET SLASKI W KATOWICACH. PRACE NAUKOWE. PEDAGOGIKA PRACY KULTURALNO-OSWIATOWEJ. (Text in Polish; summaries in English and Russian) 1976. irreg. price varies. Wydawnictwo Uniwersytetu Slaskiego, Ul. Bankowa 12B, 40-007 Katowice, Poland. TEL 48-32-596-915. FAX 48-32-599-605. TELEX 0315584 USKPL. (Dist. by: CHZ Ars Polona, P.O. Box 1001, 00-950 Warsaw, Poland) Ed. Barbara Woznica. **Document type:** academic/scholarly publication.
Description: Covers collateral education, creative activities in the free time, cultural education of children, youth and adults, changes in the cultural life of Southern Silesia.

370   PL   ISSN 0208-5429
UNIWERSYTET SLASKI W KATOWICACH. PRACE NAUKOWE. PRACE PEDAGOGICZNE. (Text in Polish; summaries in English and Russian) 1972. irreg. price varies. Wydawnictwo Uniwersytetu Slaskiego, Ul. Bankowa 12B, 40-007 Katowice, Poland. TEL 48-32-596-915. FAX 48-32-599-605. TELEX 0315584 USKPL. (Dist. by: CHZ Ars Polona, P.O. Box 1001, 00-950 Warsaw, Poland) Ed. Barbara Woznica. **Document type:** academic/scholarly publication.
Description: Covers: social pedagogy, protective pedagogy, resocialization, theory and methodological practice and history of education.

UNIWERSYTET SLASKI W KATOWICACH. PRACE NAUKOWE. Z TEORII I PRAKTYKI DYDAKTYCZNEJ JEZYKA POLSKIEGO. see *LINGUISTICS*

370   GW
DER UNTERMIETER. 1966. irreg. DM.5. Verein Freunde und Foerderer der Deutschen Studentenschaft e.V., Untere Hausbreite 11, 80939 Munich, Germany. Ed. Peter Gantzer. adv.

370   GW   ISSN 0340-4099
L31
UNTERRICHTSWISSENSCHAFT. 1973. q. DM.98 (students DM.84). Juventa Verlag GmbH, Ehretstr. 3, 69469 Weinheim, Germany. TEL 06201-61035. FAX 06201-13135. Ed. P. Strittmatter. adv.; bk.rev.; index. circ. 900. **Document type:** academic/scholarly publication.
—BLDSC (9121.325000). **CCC.**

UNTERSCHIEDE. see *WOMEN'S INTERESTS*

370   SW   ISSN 0347-1314
UPPSALA STUDIES IN EDUCATION. (Subseries of Acta Universitatis Upsaliensis) (Text in English and Swedish; summaries in English) 1976. irreg. price varies. (Uppsala Universitet, Pedagogiska Institutionen - University of Uppsala, Department of Education) A W I International AB, P.O. Box 4627, S-116 91 Stockholm, Sweden. TEL 468-640-8800. FAX 468-641-1180. Ed.Bd. index. circ. 750. **Indexed:** Psychol.Abstr.
Supersedes: Studia Scientiae Paedagogicae Upsaliensia (ISSN 0081-6892)

370   US   ISSN 0042-0859
LC5101
URBAN EDUCATION. 1966. q. $45 to individuals (foreign $51); institutions $145 (foreign $151). Corwin Press, Inc. (Subsidiary of: Sage Publications, Inc.), 2455 Teller Rd., Thousand Oaks, CA 91320. TEL 805-499-0721. FAX 805-499-0871. (And: Sage Publications, Ltd., 6 Bonhill St., London EC2A 4PU, England) Ed. Kofi Limotey. adv.: B&W page $225. bk.rev.; charts; stat.; index. (also avail. in microfilm from UMI; back issues avail.) **Indexed:** Adol.Ment.Hlth.Abstr., Biol.Abstr., C.I.J.E., Cont.Pg.Educ., Curr.Cont., Educ.Admin.Abstr., Educ.Ind., Educ.Tech.Abstr., Human Resour.Abstr., Lang.& Lang.Behav.Abstr., Sage Pub.Admin.Abstr., Sage Urb.Stud.Abstr., Sociol.Abstr., Sociol.Educ.Abstr., SSCI, Stud.Wom.Abstr., Urb.Aff.Abstr.
—BLDSC (9123.370000); Faxon; UnCover; SWETS; UMI. **CCC.**
Description: Informs practitioners and academics about difficult issues, and possible solutions, confronting urban education today.
Refereed Serial

370   US   ISSN 0042-0972
LC5101
THE URBAN REVIEW; issues and ideas in public education. 1966. q. $125 (foreign $145) (effective 1993). Human Sciences Press, Inc. (Subsidiary of: Plenum Publishing Corp.), 233 Spring St., New York, NY 10013. TEL 212-620-8000. FAX 212-463-0742. TELEX 23-421139. Eds. David E. Kapel, William T. Pink. adv.; bibl.; index. (also avail. in microform from UMI; reprint service avail. from UMI) **Indexed:** Adol.Ment.Hlth.Abstr., C.I.J.E., Chic.Per.Ind., Educ.Admin.Abstr., Educ.Ind., Psychol.Abstr., Sage Urb.Stud.Abstr., Sociol.Abstr., Sp.Ed.Needs Abstr. **Document type:** academic/scholarly publication.
—BLDSC (9123.689700); Faxon; UnCover; UMI. **CCC.**
Description: Intended for urban educators, scholars, administrators and all others concerned with improving public education in urban communities.
Refereed Serial

370   GW   ISSN 0936-8299
URSPRING NACHRICHTEN. (Text in English, French, German) 1964. a. DM.15. Altursspringbund e.V, Urspringschule, Postfach 66, 89601 Schelkingen, Germany. TEL 07394-2460. Ed. Liesel Mueller-Hermelink. circ. 2,250.
Description: Information on student life for alumni.

370   UY   ISSN 0797-6275
LA600
▼**URUGUAY. DIRECCION DE EDUCACION. REVISTA.** 1992. s-a. Ministerio de Educacion y Cultura, Direccion de Educacion, Reconquista 535, Montevideo, Uruguay. **Document type:** government publication.

370   AT
V A T F NEWSLETTER. 1976. m. Aus.$30. Victorian Affiliated Teachers Federation, 11 Glenwood Ave., Glen Waverly, Vic. 3150, Australia. TEL 03-561-5933. FAX 03-561-5834. Ed. P. Hicks. circ. 2,000. (back issues avail.) **Document type:** newsletter.
Description: Covers teaching, conditions of work, curriculum, school organization.

370   US   ISSN 0042-1790
V E A NEWS. vol.8, 1966. m. (Sep.-May). membership. Virginia Education Association, 116 South Third St., Richmond, VA 23219. TEL 804-648-5801. Ed. Trudy Willis. illus. circ. 50,000. (tabloid format)

371.42   US   ISSN 1040-4538
V I C A PROFESSIONAL: VP. 1965. 8/yr. $10 membership. Vocational Industrial Clubs of America, 14001 James Monroe Hwy., Box 3000, Leesburg, VA 22075. TEL 703-777-8810. FAX 703-777-8999. James Dawson. adv.; bk.rev.; stat.; tr.lit. cite. 18 000. (back issues avail.) **Document type:** newsletter.
Formerly: V I C A Professional Ed. (ISSN 0162-5012)
Description: Directed to vocational-technical education instructors, particularly those who advise local chapters of VJ.C.A. Includes national and state association news, as well as ideas for industry representatives in various chapters and success stories.

370   AT   ISSN 0049-6154
V I E R BULLETIN. 1957. 2/yr. Aus.$10 (effective 1994). Victorian Institute of Educational Research, c/o Kevin Hall, Ed., Institute of Education, University of Melbourne, Parkville, Vic. 3052, Australia. TEL 03-344-8418. FAX 03-347-2468. adv.; bk.rev. circ. 500. **Indexed:** Aus.Educ.Ind., Aus.P.A.I.S. **Document type:** academic/scholarly publication, bulletin.
Description: Presents reviews of research issues in the field of education and teacher development with particular emphasis to the Australian context.

370   NE   ISSN 0042-2053
VACATURE; nieuws- en advertentieblad voor het onderwijs. 1889. 3/m. fl.11.50. Uitgeverij Edu'Actief, Postbus 1056, 7940 KB Meppel, Netherlands. TEL 05220-62222. adv.; illus. (tabloid format)

VAN TAAL TOT TAAL. see *LINGUISTICS*

370   YU   ISSN 0350-1094
VASPITANJE I OBRAZOVANJE. 1975. 6/yr. Republicki Zavod za Unapredjivanje Skolstva, Novaka Miloseva 12, Titograd, Montenegro, Yugoslavia. bk.rev.

370   VE
VENEZUELA. DEPARTAMENTO DE INVESTIGACIONES EDUCACIONALES. SECCION DE ESTADISTICA. ESTADISTICAS EDUCACIONALES.* 1971. a. Ministerio de Educacon, Departamento de Investigaciones Educacionales, Ministerio de Relaciones Exteriores, Direccion de Relaciones Culturales, Caracas, Venezuela. illus.; stat.

372   CN   ISSN 0315-2235
VENTURE FORTH. 1969. 3/yr. Can.$16 (foreign Can.$20). (Early Childhood Education Council) Saskatchewan Teachers' Federation, Box 1108, Saskatoon, SK S7K 3N3, Canada. TEL 306-525-0368 Ed. Margaret E. Smith-Windsor. bk.rev. circ. 1,063. (back issues avail.)
Formerly: It's Our Bag.

370   US
VERMONT - N E A TODAY. 1933. m. (Aug.-Jun.). $6. Vermont National Education Association, Box 567, Montpelier, VT 05602. Ed. Laurie B. Huse. adv. circ. 8,000.
Former titles: V E A Today; Vermont Blackboard (ISSN 0042-4137)

370   SP   ISSN 1130-7471
VETE A SABER!. 1986. m. free. (Departamento de Educacion y Cultura) Gobierno de Navarra, Fondo de Publicaciones, Navas de Tolosa, 21, 31002 Pamplona, Spain. TEL 10-71-21. FAX 22-76-73.

2064 EDUCATION

370   NZ   ISSN 0083-6036
VICTORIA UNIVERSITY OF WELLINGTON. AWARDS HANDBOOK. 1969. a. free. (Victoria University of Wellington, Administration Office) Victoria University Press, P.O. Box 600, Wellington, New Zealand. circ. 1,450.

370.193   AT
VICTORIAN PARENTS COUNCIL NEWSLETTER. 1962. 5/yr. Aus.$20. Victorian Parents Council Inc., G.P.O. Box 2463 V, Melbourne, Vic. 3001, Australia. TEL 03-419-3693. Ed. R. Vallance. adv.; bk.rev. circ. 1,000. **Document type:** newsletter.
   Description: Informs parents about educational changes, problems and funding.

VIDA HISPANICA. see *LINGUISTICS*

370   US   ISSN 0083-6354
L903.V8
VIRGINIA EDUCATIONAL DIRECTORY. a. $3.50. Department of Education, Box 2120, Richmond, VA 23216-2120. TEL 804-225-2020.

370   US   ISSN 0270-837X
VIRGINIA JOURNAL OF EDUCATION.* 1907. m. (Sep.-May). membership. Virginia Education Association, 116 S. Third St., Richmond, VA 23219. Ed. Joseph W. Bland, Jr. adv.; bk.rev.; charts; illus.; stat.; tr.lit.; index. circ. 50,000. (also avail. in microform from UMI) **Indexed:** Educ.Ind.
—UMI.
   Former titles (until 1980): Journal of Virginia Education (ISSN 0198-3504); Virginia Journal of Education (ISSN 0042-6563)

370.193   US   ISSN 0042-6709
VIRGINIA P T A BULLETIN. (Parents and Teachers Association) vol.56, 1973. 8/yr. $8. Virginia Congress of Parents and Teachers, 3810 Augusta Ave., Richmond, VA 23230. TEL 804-355-2816. Ed. Mary S. Cottrell. circ. 6,500. **Document type:** newsletter.
   Description: Serves as the main communication link among national, state, and local levels of the P.T.A. in Virginia.

VISIBLE LANGUAGE; the quarterly concerned with all that is involved in our being literate. see *COMMUNICATIONS*

VISION (PASADENA). see *RELIGIONS AND THEOLOGY*

370   IT   ISSN 0042-7241
VITA DELL'INFANZIA. 1952. m. L.39000 (foreign L.52000). Giunti Gruppo Editoriale S.p.A., Via Vincenzo Gioberti, 34, 50121 Florence, Italy. TEL 055-66791. FAX 055-268312. Ed. Marziola Pignatari. adv.; bk.rev.; bibl.; illus.; index, cum.index. circ. 8,000.

VITA GIUSEPPINA. see *RELIGIONS AND THEOLOGY — Roman Catholic*

370   IT   ISSN 0042-7349
VITA SCOLASTICA; rassegna quindicinale della istruzione primaria. 1947. s-m. L.43000 (foreign L.66000). Giunti Gruppo Editoriale S.p.A., Via Vincenzo Gioberti, 34, 50121 Florence, Italy. TEL 055-66791. FAX 055-268312. Ed. Giuseppe Lisciani. adv.; bk.rev.; bibl.; charts; illus. circ. 100,000.

VITAE SCHOLASTICAE. see *BIOGRAPHY*

370   GR   ISSN 0042-7594
VIVLIOTHIKI GHONEON.* 1948. 8/yr. Dr.50.($2) Panagiotis Pavlouros, Ed. & Pub., Theras 113, Athens 220, Greece. stat.; index. circ. 2,000.

VOCE SERAFICA DELLA SARDEGNA. see *RELIGIONS AND THEOLOGY — Roman Catholic*

370   US   ISSN 0883-573X
VOICE (EAST LANSING). 1923. m. $15 to non-members. Michigan Education Association, Box 2573, E. Lansing, MI 48826-2573. TEL 517-332-6551. FAX 517-337-5414. Ed. Dennis Keenon. adv.; illus.; index. circ. 118,000. (tabloid format) **Document type:** newspaper, trade publication.
   Former titles: Teacher's Voice (ISSN 0026-2129); Michigan Education Journal.

370   US   ISSN 0896-6605
VOICE FOR EDUCATION. 1969. 9/yr. (Sep.-June). $8. Pennsylvania State Education Association, 400 N. Third St., Box 1724, Harrisburg, PA 17105. TEL 717-255-7000. FAX 717-255-7124. Ed. William H. Johnson, Jr. charts; illus.; stat.; tr.lit. circ. 125,000. **Document type:** newsletter.
   Formerly: Voice of P S E A (ISSN 0507-2298)

370   US
VOICES IN EDUCATION. bi-m. Pen & Ink, Inc., 61 North Rd., Cromwell, CT 06416-1007. TEL 203-635-0522. Ed. John Vecchitto.

370.193   FR   ISSN 0049-6693
VOIX DES PARENTS. 1932. q. 3.50 F. Federation des Parents d'Eleves de l'Enseignement Publique, 91 bd. Berthier, 75017 Paris, France. Ed. Jacques Hui. adv.; bk.rev.; film rev.; bibl.; illus. circ. 520,000.

370   GW
VOLKSHOCHSCHULE. 1949. bi-m. DM.76. (Landesverband der Volkshochschulen von Nordrhein-Westfalen) W. Kohlhammer GmbH, Hessbruehlstr. 69, 70565 Stuttgart, Germany. TEL 0711-7863-1. Eds. Bert Donnepp, Horst Wiedefeld. adv.; bk.rev.; film rev.; play rev.; record rev.; abstr.; charts; illus.; stat.; tr.lit.; index. circ. 3,000.
   Formerly: Volkshochschule im Westen (ISSN 0042-8515)

370   US   ISSN 0896-8934
VOX POP NEWSLETTER. 1983. m. $12. Vox Pop, Box 3511, West Sedona, AZ 86340-3511. circ. 1,500. **Document type:** newsletter.
   Description: Covers news of Vox Pop, a non-profit tax-exempt education corporation, and the community of Greater Sedona.

370 150   XO   ISSN 0139-6919
VYCHOVAVATEL. 1955. 10/yr. 30 Kcs. (Ministry of Education of the Slovak Socialist Republic) Slovenske Pedagogicke Nakladatelstvo, Sasinkova 5, 815-60 Bratislava, Slovakia. TEL 21-42-49. (Subscr. to: Slovart, Gottwaldovo nam. 6, Bratislava, Slovakia) Ed. Jan Farkas. circ. 12,500.

370   US   ISSN 8750-8133
W & J MAGAZINE. 1972. q. Washington & Jefferson College, 60 S. Lincoln St., Washington, PA 15301-9982. TEL 412-223-6507. Ed. Edward A. Marotta. circ. 11,500. (back issues avail.)
   Formerly: W and J News.

W C O T P BIENNIAL REPORT. (World Confederation of Organizations of the Teaching Profession) see *EDUCATION — School Organization And Administration*

370 001.3   US
W E S AUTHORS' AND PUBLISHERS' SERVICE NEWSLETTER.* 1977. 6/yr. $5. Watman Educational Services, Box 457, Henniker, NH 03242. bk.rev.; bibl. circ. 1,500.
   Supersedes: W E S Bulletin.

370   CC
WAIGUO JIAOYU ZILIAO/FOREIGN EDUCATION MATERIAL.* (Text in Chinese) bi-m. Huadong Shifan Daxue, Jiaoyu Kexue Xueyuan - East China Normal University, College of Education, c/o Du Diankun, Ed., 3663 Zhongshan Beilu, Shanghai 200062, People's Republic of China. TEL 2549677.

370   US
WASHINGTON EDUCATION DIRECTORY. 1973. a. $12. (Superintendent of Public Instruction) Barbara Krohn and Associates, 835 Securities Bldg., Seattle, WA 98101-1162. TEL 206-622-3538. Ed. Barbara Krohn. circ. 8,500. **Document type:** directory.
   Description: Includes all public school districts (K-12), state-approved private schools (K-12), public and private universities and colleges, community colleges, education agencies and associations.

370   AT   ISSN 1036-3912
THE WEB. q. Aus.$20. Federated Teachers' Union of Victoria, 112 Trenerry Cress, Abbotsford, Vic. 3067, Australia. TEL 03-417-2822. FAX 03-417-6198. Ed. Lyn Baird. circ. 2,600.
   Description: Focuses on women's education and equal opportunities.

WEEKLY READER. SUMMER EDITION A. PRE K - GRADE 1. see *CHILDREN AND YOUTH — For*

WEEKLY READER. SUMMER EDITION B. GRADES 2-6. see *CHILDREN AND YOUTH — For*

WELLA AKTIENGESELLSCHAFT. REPORT; Mitarbeitermagazin fuer Mitarbeiter und Pensionaere der weltweiten Wella-Unternehmen. see *BUSINESS AND ECONOMICS*

WELSH HISTORIAN/HANESYDD CYMREIG. see *HISTORY — History Of Europe*

370   UK   ISSN 0957-297X
WELSH JOURNAL OF EDUCATION. (Text in English, Welsh) 1989. s-a. £10. (University of Wales, Faculty of Education) University of Wales Press, 6 Gwennyth St., Cathays, Cardiff CF2 4YD, Wales. TEL 0222-231919. FAX 0222-230908. Eds. Gareth Jones, Anthony Packer. adv.; bk.rev. circ. 750. (back issues avail.) **Indexed:** SOMA. **Document type:** academic/scholarly publication.
—BLDSC (9294.652000).

370   NE   ISSN 0165-4772
DE WERELD VAN HET JONGE KIND. 1955. m. fl.67.50 (foreign fl.80) (effective 1994). Uitgeverij Dijkstra Zeist B.V., Hermesweg 2, 3741 GP Baarn, Netherlands. TEL 31-2154-25011. FAX 31-2154-24958. Eds. J.C. Snip, W.E. Westerman; Pub. J. Carla Snip. adv.; bk.rev.; abstr.; bibl.; index. circ. 10,000. (reprint service avail.) **Document type:** academic/scholarly publication.
   Formerly (until 1974): Kleuterwereld (ISSN 0023-2106)

370   NR   ISSN 0043-2997
L81
WEST AFRICAN JOURNAL OF EDUCATION. (Text in English) 1957. 3/yr. $35. University of Ibadan, Institute of Education, Ibadan, Nigeria. TEL 62550-1495. Ed. J.D. Obemeata. adv.; bk.rev.; illus. circ. 2,550. **Indexed:** Documentatieblad. **Document type:** academic/scholarly publication.
—UMI.

370.5   II
WEST BENGAL. BUREAU OF EDUCATIONAL AND PSYCHOLOGICAL RESEARCH. (Text in English) 1971. s-a. free. Bureau of Educational and Psychological Research, 25-3 Ballygunge Circular Rd., Calcutta 19, India. Ed. Maya Mukherjee.

370 307   US
WEST SIDE STORY. 1968. m. $10. Iowa City Community Schools, West High School, 2901 Melrose Ave., Iowa City, IA 52246. TEL 319-339-6817. Ed.Bd. adv.; bk.rev.; film rev.; play rev.; charts; illus. circ. 2,000. (also avail. in microfilm)
   Description: Serves to supplement the educational environment of West High School by providing news and information to the school and all its components.

370   US   ISSN 0085-8099
WEST VIRGINIA EDUCATION DIRECTORY. 1934. a. free. Department of Education, Capitol Complex, Bldg. B-204, Charleston, WV 25305. TEL 304-348-3667. Ed. Kim Nuzum. charts. circ. 5,000. **Document type:** directory, government publication.
   Description: Lists schools and personnel in West Virginia by district and county.

370   US   ISSN 0274-8606
L11
WEST VIRGINIA SCHOOL JOURNAL. Abbreviated title: W V School Journal. 1881. 12/yr. $5 to non-members. West Virginia Education Association, 1558 Quarrier St., Charleston, WV 25311. TEL 304-346-5315. FAX 304-346-4325. Ed. Jackie Goodwin. adv.; bk.rev.; charts; illus. circ. 18,000. (tabloid format; also avail. in microform from UMI) **Document type:** academic/scholarly publication.
—UMI.
   Former titles: W V E A School Journal (ISSN 0094-176X); West Virginia School Journal (ISSN 0043-3322)

WEST VIRGINIA UNIVERSITY ALUMNI MAGAZINE. see *COLLEGE AND ALUMNI*

WESTERN NEW YORK CATHOLIC. see *RELIGIONS AND THEOLOGY — Roman Catholic*

370		AT	

WESTERN TEACHER. 1971. every 4 wks. (except Jan.). Aus.$15. State School Teachers Union of W.A. (Inc.), 150-152 Adelaide Terrace, Perth, Australia. TEL 09-325-5311. FAX 09-221-2394. Ed. John Bartley. adv.; bk.rev.; abstr.; bibl.; charts; illus.; stat. circ. 12,000. (tabloid format) **Document type:** newspaper.
  Formerly: W.A. Teachers' Journal (ISSN 0042-949X)

370   UK   ISSN 0140-6728
WESTMINSTER STUDIES IN EDUCATION. 1978. a. $70 to individuals; institutions $206 (effective 1994). Carfax Publishing Co., P.O. Box 25, Abingdon, Oxon. OX14 3UE, England. TEL 44-235-555335. FAX 44-235-553559. (U.S. subscr. to.: Carfax Publishing Co., Box 2025, Dunnellon, FL 34430-2025) Ed. Ian Lewis. bk.rev.; illus.; stat. (also avail. in microfiche; back issues avail.) **Indexed:** Cont.Pg.Educ., Educ.Tech.Abstr., High.Educ.Curr.Aware.Bull., Mult.Ed.Abstr., Psychol.Abstr., Res.High.Educ.Abstr., SOMA, Sp.Ed.Needs Abstr., Stud.Wom.Abstr. **Document type:** academic/scholarly publication.
  —BLDSC (9304.770000). **CCC.**

370 360   US   ISSN 0732-8362
WHAT'S HAPPENING IN WASHINGTON. vol.21, 1992. bi-m. $6. National Parent - Teacher Association, Office of Governmental Relations, 2000 L St., N.W., Ste. 600, Washington, DC 20036. TEL 202-331-1380. (Subscr. to: National PTA, 330 N. Wabash Ave., Ste. 2100, Chicago, IL 60611-3604. TEL 312-951-6782) Ed. Susan Kushner. circ. 34,000. **Document type:** newsletter.
  Description: Informs PTA members and concerned citizens about federal legislation that has an impact on the education, health and welfare of children.

WHAT'S NEW IN HOME ECONOMICS. see *HOME ECONOMICS*

370 362.7   US   ISSN 1053-2609
WHAT'S WORKING IN PARENT INVOLVEMENT. (Includes supplement: Successful Ideas for Staff) 1990. 10/yr. (m. Sep.-June). $89. Parent Institute, Box 7474, Fairfax Station, VA 22039-7474. TEL 703-323-9170; 800-756-5525. FAX 703-323-9173. Ed. John H. Wherry; Pub. John H. Wherry. bk.rev. (back issues avail.) **Document type:** newsletter.
  Description: Practical ideas for schools to promote parent involvement in the education of their children.

105   US
WHOLISTIC EDUCATION; journal of humanistic and transpersonal education. 1978. s-a. $12 to individuals; institutions $15. Institute for Wholistic Education, Box 575, Amherst, MA 01002. Eds. Jack Canfield, Paula Klimek. adv.; bk.rev.; tr.lit. circ. 1,000.
  Formerly: Journal for Humanistic and Transpersonal Education.

WHO'S WHO IN AMERICAN EDUCATION. see *BIOGRAPHY*

WIR (MINDEN). see *CHILDREN AND YOUTH — For*

WIRKENDES WORT; deutsche Sprache und Literatur in Forschung und Lehre. see *LINGUISTICS*

WIRTSCHAFT UND ERZIEHUNG. see *BUSINESS AND ECONOMICS — Economic Systems And Theories, Economic History*

WIRTSCHAFT UND UNTERRICHT; Informationen fuer Paedagogen in Schule und Betrieb. see *BUSINESS AND ECONOMICS*

370   GW   ISSN 0340-3084
DAS WIRTSCHAFTSSTUDIUM - W I S U; Zeitschrift fuer Studium und Examen. 1972. m. DM.157.20 (students DM.119.60). Lange Verlag GmbH, Poststr. 12, 40213 Duesseldorf, Germany. TEL 0211-864190. FAX 0211-320000. adv.; bk.rev. circ. 10,000. **Document type:** academic/scholarly publication.

371.33   US   ISSN 0361-2120
LB1044.8
WISCONSIN. EDUCATIONAL COMMUNICATIONS BOARD. BIENNIAL REPORT. Key Title: Biennial Report-Educational Communications Board. biennial. free. Educational Communications Board, 3319 W. Beltline Hwy., Madison, WI 53713. FAX 608-264-9622.
  Description: Provides a description of agency functions in public broadcasting and a summary of activities over the previous two years.

WOMEN AND MATHEMATICS EDUCATION NEWSLETTER. see *MATHEMATICS*

370   BE
WORLD ASSOCIATION FOR EDUCATIONAL RESEARCH. CONGRESS REPORTS. 1953. quadrennial, 11th 1993, Jerusalem. 2000 BEF. World Association for Educational Research, Henri Dunantlaan 1, B-9000 Ghent, Belgium. Ed. M.L. van Herreweghe. **Document type:** proceedings.
  Formerly: International Association for the Advancement of Educational Research. Congress Reports (ISSN 0074-154X)
  Description: Papers and discussions on Congress presented and discussed when Congress meets.

370   UK
WORLD COUNCIL OF COMPARATIVE EDUCATION SOCIETIES. NEWSLETTER/CONSEIL MONDIAL DES SOCIETES D'EDUCATION COMPAREE. BULLETIN D'INFORMATION. (Text in English and French) 1972. q. free. World Council of Comparative Education Societies, c/o Raymond Ryba, University of Manchester, Department of Education, Manchester M13 9PL, England. FAX 061-275-3519. Ed. Douglas Ray. bk.rev. circ. 3,000.

WORLD DIRECTORY OF HUMAN RIGHTS RESEARCH AND TRAINING INSTITUTIONS. see *BUSINESS AND ECONOMICS — Trade And Industrial Directories*

WORLD ENGLISHES; journal of English as an international and intranational language. see *LINGUISTICS*

WORLD MEETINGS: SOCIAL & BEHAVIORAL SCIENCES, HUMAN SERVICES AND MANAGEMENT. see *MEETINGS AND CONGRESSES*

371.8   NE   ISSN 0139-746X
LB3602
WORLD STUDENT NEWS. French edition: Etudiants du Monde (ISSN 0014-2255); German edition: Studenten Nachrichten (ISSN 0139-7311); Spanish edition: Mundo Estudiantil (ISSN 0323-2093) 1947. m. $5. International Union of Students, 211 Lann Van Meerdervoort, The Hague, Netherlands. Ed. Zakaria Abdourahman. circ. (controlled). **Indexed:** HR Rep.
  Description: Devoted to the problem of students in a wide range of educational, social and political perspectives.

370   UK   ISSN 0084-2508
L101.G8
WORLD YEARBOOK OF EDUCATION. (Each vol. has distinctive subtitle) 1968. a. £34. Kogan Page Ltd., 120 Pentonville Rd., London N1 9JN, England. TEL 071-278-0433. FAX 071-837-6348. TELEX 263088 KOGAN G. Ed. Duncan Harris. **Indexed:** High.Educ.Curr.Aware.Bull. **Document type:** abstracting/indexing.
  —BLDSC (9360.450000).
  Description: Collects articles by international authorities to report on a variety of themes.

374   CN   ISSN 0820-6686
WORLDLIT. 1967. s-a. Can.$25. World Literacy of Canada, 59 Front St. E., Toronto, ON M5E 1B3, Canada. TEL 416-863-6262. FAX 416-601-6984. Ed.Bd. bk.rev.; illus. circ. 3,000. **Document type:** newsletter.
  Former titles (until 1982): World Literacy of Canada. Newsletter (ISSN 0700-5350); World Literacy of Canada, News and Views (ISSN 0705-8829)

WORT UND ANTWORT; Zeitschrift fuer Fragen des Glaubens. see *RELIGIONS AND THEOLOGY — Roman Catholic*

WRITING (MIDDLETOWN); the continuing guide to written communication. see *LITERATURE*

370   US   ISSN 0889-6143
CODEN: WCEJE3
WRITING CENTER JOURNAL. 1979. 2/yr. $10. National Writing Centers Association, c/o Nancy Grimm, Michigan Technological University, Humanities Department, 1400 Townsend Dr., Houghton, MI 49931. TEL 906-487-3265. Ed.Bd. adv.; bk.rev. —BLDSC (9364.757400).

808 372   US   ISSN 0894-5837
LB1576
WRITING TEACHER (SAN ANTONIO). 1987. 5/yr. (during school yr.). $25 (foreign $31). ECS Learning Systems, Inc., Box 791437, San Antonio, TX 78279-1437. TEL 210-438-4262. FAX 210-438-4263. Ed. Sam Mammen. adv.; bk.rev. **Document type:** trade publication.
  Description: For teachers K-8. Provides practical ideas for classroom activities and to teach writing.

WYCHOWANIE MUZYCZNE W SZKOLE. see *MUSIC*

WYCHOWANIE TECHNICZNE W SZKOLE. see *ENGINEERING*

370   PL   ISSN 0137-8082
WYCHOWANIE W PRZEDSZKOLU. 1948. m. $28.80. (Ministerstwo Edukacji Narodowej) Wydawnictwa Szkolne i Pedagogiczne, Pl. Dabrowskiego 8, 00-950 Warsaw, Poland. TEL 48-22-265451. (Dist.by: Ars Polona-Ruch, Krakowskie Przedmiescie 7, Warsaw, Poland) Ed. Ryszard Wieckowski. circ. 7,900.
  Description: Publishes articles on psychology, pedagogy, the history of education, the theory and practice of nursery education, and educational policy in the field, with discussions of experiences in nursery schools, and problems encountered in the dialogue between parents and schools.

370   US
WYOMING. DEPARTMENT OF EDUCATION. EDUCATION DIRECTORY. a. $5 (effective 1994). Department of Education, Hathaway Bldg., 2nd Fl., 2300 Capitol Ave., Cheyenne, WY 82002-0050. TEL 307-777-7673.

370   US   ISSN 0043-9681
WYOMING EDUCATION NEWS. 1935. 5/yr. $10 to non-members. Wyoming Education Association, 115 E. 22nd St., Cheyenne, WY 82001. TEL 307-634-7991. FAX 307-778-8161. Ed. Ronald P. Sniffin. adv.; illus. circ. 6,500. **Document type:** newsletter.

370   PL   ISSN 0239-6769
WYZSZA SZKOLA PEDAGOGICZNA IM. KOMISJI EDUKACJI NARODOWEJ W KRAKOWIE. PROBLEMY STUDIOW NAUCZYCIELSKICH. 1964. irreg., vol.4, 1990. price varies. Wydawnictwo Naukowe W S P, Ul. Karmelicka 41, 31-128 Krakow, Poland. TEL 33-78-20. (Co-sponsor: Ministerstwo Edukacji Narodowej)

370   PL   ISSN 0239-2356
WYZSZA SZKOLA PEDAGOGICZNA IM. KOMISJI EDUKACJI NARODOWEJ W KRAKOWIE. ROCZNIK NAUKOWO-DYDAKTYCZNY. PRACE PEDAGOGICZNE. 1972. irreg., no.12, 1991. price varies. Wydawnictwo Naukowe W S P, Ul. Karmelicka 41, 31-128 Krakow, Poland. TEL 33-78-20. (Co-sponsor: Ministerstwo Edukacji Narodowej)

370   PL   ISSN 0860-1046
WYZSZA SZKOLA PEDAGOGICZNA IM. KOMISJI EDUKACJI NARODOWEJ W KRAKOWIE. ROCZNIK NAUKOWO-DYDAKTYCZNY. PRACE Z HISTORII OSWIATY I WYCHOWANIA. 1984. irreg., no.2, 1989. price varies. Wydawnictwo Naukowe W S P, Ul. Karmelicka 41, 31-128 Krakow, Poland. FAX 33-78-20. (Co-sponsor: Ministerstwo Edukacji Narodowej)

370   CC
XIAOXUESHENG XUEXI ZHIDAO/STUDY GUIDE FOR ELEMENTARY STUDENTS. (Text in Chinese) m. Liaoning Shaonian Ertong Chubanshe, 2, Nanjing Jie 6 Duan 1 Li, Shenyang, Liaoning 110001, People's Republic of China. TEL 365076. Ed. Zhang Fenghe.

370   CC
XIZANG JIAOYU/TIBETAN EDUCATION. (Editions in Chinese, Tibetan) bi-m. Xizang Minzu Jiaoyu Yanjiusuo - Tibetan Institute of Minority Education, Kang'ang Donglu, Lhasa, Xizang (Tibet) 850000, People's Republic of China. TEL 22562. Ed. Liu Qinghui.

EDUCATION

370 CC ISSN 1002-5308
XUEKE JIAOYU. (Text in Chinese) q. Y18. Beijing Shifan Daxue - Beijing Normal University, Beitaipingzhuang, Beijing 100875, People's Republic of China. TEL 2012288. Ed. Yan Jinduo. **Document type:** academic/scholarly publication.

370 CC ISSN 0439-7843
XUEQIAN JIAOYU/PRESCHOOL EDUCATION. (Text in Chinese) 1980. m. Y0.95 per no. (Beijing Jiaoyu-ju - Beijing Bureau of Education) Beijing Jiaoyu Zazhishe - Beijing Educatin Magazine Office, 201 Qianmen Dajie, Beijing 100050, People's Republic of China. TEL 3015815. Ed. Niu Chensheng; Pub. Chen Yankang. adv.: B&W page Y1600, color page Y2100. **Document type:** academic/scholarly publication.
Formerly (until 1984): Youjiao Tongxun.

YEARBOOK OF EDUCATIONAL LAW. see LAW

370 ET ISSN 0044-0310
YEMEMHIRAN DIMTS. (Text in Amharic) 1962. 2/yr. Eth.$2 per no. Ethiopian Teacher's Association, Box 1639, Addis Ababa, Ethiopia. Ed. Bisrat Dilnessahu. adv.; bk.rev. circ. 30,000.

370 EA ISSN 0044-0329
YEMEMHIRAN MELKT/TEACHERS' MESSAGE.* (Editions in Amharic and English) irreg. Eth.$1 per no. Teachers Association of Ethiopia, Eritrea Branch, Box 954, Asmara, Eritrea.

370 KO ISSN 0044-0345
YEON-GU WEOLBO.* 1964. m. Jeon la Bug-do Gyo Yug Yeon Gu Won, Jeon Ju, S. Korea. (Subscr. to: Assembly Library, Seoul, S. Korea) Ed. Bag Byeong-Gweon. bk.rev.; bibl.; charts; illus.; stat.; index, cum.index; circ. 2,500 (controlled).

370 JA ISSN 0513-5656
YOKOHAMA NATIONAL UNIVERSITY. EDUCATIONAL SCIENCES/YOKOHAMA KOKURITSU DAIGAKU KYOIKU KIYO. (Text in English, Japanese) 1962. a. exchange basis. Yokohama Kokuritsu Daigaku, Kyoikugakubu - Yokohama National University, Faculty of Education, 156 Tokiwadai, Hodogaya-ku, Yokohama-shi, Kanagawa-ken 240, Japan. cum.index nos. 11-15, 1971-1975.

YOUNG FARMER UPDATE. see AGRICULTURE

YOUNG HORIZONS INDIGO. see CHILDREN AND YOUTH — About

377.9 296.68 US ISSN 0044-1007
YOUR CHILD. 1967. 3/yr. $3. United Synagogue of Conservative Judaism, Commission on Jewish Education, 155 5th Ave., New York, NY 10010. TEL 212-260-8450. Ed. Kay E. Pomerantz. bk.rev. circ. 3,000. **Document type:** newsletter.
Description: Discusses parenting from a Conservative Jewish perspective.

370 ZA ISSN 0084-487X
ZAMBIA. MINISTRY OF EDUCATION. ANNUAL REPORT. 1964. a. Ministry of Education, Box 50093, Lusaka, Zambia. (Dist. by: Government Printer, Box 30136, Lusaka, Zambia)

370 ZA ISSN 0556-9001
ZAMBIA. TEACHING SERVICE COMMISSION. ANNUAL REPORT. 1963. a. K.150. Zambia Government Printing Department, P.O. Box 60136, Lusaka, Zambia. **Document type:** government publication.
Description: Contains information on functions of the commision, appointments, promotions, results of examinations, and other events.

370 ZA
ZAMBIA EDUCATIONAL JOURNAL. 1971. a. $13. University of Zambia, School of Education, Department of Education, Box 32379, Lusaka, Zambia. Ed. P.M. Haamujompa. bk.rev.; charts; illus.
Formerly: Educational Front.

370 ZA ISSN 0255-0695
ZAMBIA EDUCATIONAL REVIEW. 1979. s-a. $13. University of Zambia, Department of Education, Box 32379, Lusaka, Zambia. Ed.Bd. adv.; bk.rev.; abstr. circ. 400. **Indexed:** Cont.Pg.Educ.

370 YU ISSN 0514-6151
LB5
ZBORNIK ZA ISTORIJU SKOLSTVA I PROSVETE. (Text in Serbo-Croatian, Slovenian; summaries in English, French, German) 1968. a. 3000 din.($10) Pedgoski Muzej, Uzun Mirkova 14, 11000 Belgrade, Yugoslavia. Ed. Valdeta Tesic. bk.rev. circ. 800. (back issues avail.)

ZEITSCHRIFT FUER ENTWICKLUNGSPAEDAGOGIK. see SOCIAL SCIENCES: COMPREHENSIVE WORKS

ZEITSCHRIFT FUER ENTWICKLUNGSPSYCHOLOGIE UND PAEDAGOGISCHE PSYCHOLOGIE. see PSYCHOLOGY

370 GW ISSN 0044-3247
L31
ZEITSCHRIFT FUER PAEDAGOGIK. 1949. m. DM.128. Verlag Julius Beltz GmbH, Am Hauptbahnhof 10, 69469 Weinheim, Germany. TEL 06201-60070. FAX 06201-17464. TELEX 465500-BELTZD. Ed. H.-Elmar Tenorth. adv.; bk.rev.; index. circ. 4,200. **Indexed:** Cont.Pg.Educ., Curr.Cont., Educ.Tech.Abstr., Lang.& Lang.Behav.Abstr., Sp.Ed.Needs Abstr., Stud.Wom.Abstr.
—BLDSC (9475.800000); SWETS. **CCC.**
Description: Comprehensive coverage of education and schools.

ZEITSCHRIFT FUER VERKEHRSERZIEHUNG. see TRANSPORTATION — Roads And Traffic

ZEITUNGS - DOKUMENTATION BILDUNGSWESEN. see CHILDREN AND YOUTH — About

ZEMEDELSKA SKOLA. see AGRICULTURE

370 320 CC
ZHENGZHI JIAOYU/POLITICAL EDUCATION. (Text in Chinese) no.103, 1990. m. $30. (Guojia Jiaoyu Weiyuanhui - State Education Commission) Shanghai Jiaoyu Chubanshe - Shanghai Educational Publishing House, 123 Yongfu Road, Shanghai 200031, People's Republic of China. TEL 4377165. Ed. Chen He. **Document type:** academic/scholarly publication.
Description: Contains articles and papers on political education in China, as well as other economic and political issues.

370 CC
ZHONGGUO CHAOXIANZU JIAOYU/KOREAN CHINESE EDUCATION. (Text in Korean) m. Yanbian Jiaoyu Weiyuanhui, Yanji, Jilin 133000, People's Republic of China. TEL 512771.

370 US
ZHONGGUO JIAOYU BAO/CHINESE EDUCATION NEWS. (Text in Chinese) 2/w. $202.10. China Books & Periodicals, Inc., 2929 24th St., San Francisco, CA 94110. TEL 415-282-2994. FAX 415-282-0994. **Document type:** newspaper.

370 CC
ZHONGGUO JIAOYU NIANJIAN/CHINA EDUCATION YEARBOOK. a. Y35. Renmin Jiaoyu Chubanshe, 55, Shatan Houjie, Beijing 100009, People's Republic of China.
Description: Summarizes educational policies, activities, and situations nationwide.

370 CC ISSN 1002-4808
ZHONGGUO JIAOYU XUEKAN/CHINA EDUCATION ASSOCIATION. JOURNAL. (Text in Chinese) bi-m. Y10. Zhongguo Jiaoyu Xuehui, 35 Damucang Hutong, Xidan, Beijing 100816, People's Republic of China. TEL 6097082. Ed. Zhang Jian.

370 CC ISSN 1002-5952
ZHONGGUO MINZU JIAOYU/NATIONALITIES EDUCATION OF CHINA. (Text in Chinese) bi-m. $18. Zhongguo Minzu Jiaoyu Chubanshe - China Nationalities Education Press, Xinan Minzu Xueyuan, Chengdu, Sichuan 610041, People's Republic of China. TEL 028-583730. FAX 028-589294. (Co-sponsor: State Education Commission, Department of Education for Minorities) Ed. Chen Hongtao.
Formerly (until 1991): Minzu Jiaoyu.

ZHONGWEN ZIXIU/CHINESE SELF-STUDY. see LINGUISTICS

ZHONGWEN ZIXUE ZHIDAO/GUIDE TO TEACHING YOURSELF CHINESE. see LINGUISTICS

370 CC ISSN 0412-3921
ZHONGXUE JIAOYU/SECONDARY SCHOOL EDUCATION. (Text in Chinese) 1979. m. Y14.40 (effective 1993). Shanghai Jiaoyu Xueyuan - Shanghai Institute of Education, 1045 Huaihai Zhonglu, Shanghai 200031, People's Republic of China. TEL 4314823. Ed. Zhang Jiaxiang. bk.rev. circ. 50,000. **Document type:** academic/scholarly publication.
Description: Covers the theories and practices of secondary school education, including education psychology, and school administration.

373 500 CC
ZHONGXUE KEJI/MIDDLE SCHOOL SCIENCE & TECHNOLOGY. (Text in Chinese) m. $36.80. Shanghai Keji Jiaoyu Chubanshe, 393, Guanshengyuan Lu, Shanghai 200233, People's Republic of China. TEL 437808. (Dist. in US by: China Books & Periodicals, Inc., 2929 24th St., San Francisco, CA 94110. TEL 415-282-2994) Ed. Yi Fangben.

373 CC
ZHONGXUESHENG/MIDDLE SCHOOL STUDENT. (Text in Chinese) m. $21.20. Zhongguo Shaonian Ertong Chubanshe - China Juvenile Press, 21 Dongsi Shi'ertiao, Beijing 100708, People's Republic of China. TEL 444761-225. (Dist. in US by: China Books & Periodicals, Inc., 2929 24th St., San Francisco, CA 94110. TEL 415-282-2994) Ed. Liu Xiliang.

370 CC
ZHONGXUESHENG KEXUE JIAOYU/MIDDLE-SCHOOL STUDENT SCIENCE EDUCATION. (Text in Chinese) m. Beijing Keji Ribao - Beijing Science and Technology Daily, A-5, Beiwa Lu, Beijing 100036, People's Republic of China. TEL 8417774. Ed. Wei Yi.

370 RH ISSN 1013-3445
LB1028.25.Z55 CODEN: ZJERE7
ZIMBABWE JOURNAL OF EDUCATIONAL RESEARCH. 1989. 3/yr. Z.$80 to individuals (foreign $60); institutions Z.$130 (foreign $90) (effective 1994). University of Zimbabwe, Faculty of Education, Human Resources Research Centre, P.O. Box MP 167, Mount Pleasant, Harare, Zimbabwe. TEL 263-4-302182. FAX 263-4-333407. Ed. Levi M. Nyagura. abstr. **Indexed:** Documentatieblad, P.L.E.S.A. **Document type:** academic/scholarly publication.
—BLDSC (9513.250300).
Description: Publishes scholarly articles reporting on research findings and policy issues relating to education in sub-Saharan Africa, as well as news reports of research initiatives in progress, relevant literature and organizations of interest.
Refereed Serial

370 CI ISSN 0044-4855
ZIVOT I SKOLA; casopis za pedagoska i kulturnoprosvjetna pitanja. (Text in Serbo-Croatian) 1952. bi-m. 70 din. per issue. Zavod za Pedagoska i Kulturno Prosvjetna Pitanja, Strossmayerova 6, Osijek, Croatia. Ed. Branko Ratkovcic.

370 GW
ZULASSUNGSARBEIT. 1972. irreg. DM.10. Verein Freunde und Foerderer der Deutschen Studentenschaft e.V., Untere Hausbreite 11, 80939 Munich, Germany. Ed. Gundolf Seidenspinner. adv.

370 895.1 CC ISSN 1001-571X
ZUOWEN CHENGGONG ZHI LU/WAYS TO A SUCCESSFUL COMPOSITION. (Text in Chinese) 1987. m. Y1 per no. (Daqing Jiaoyu Xueyuan - Daqing Institute of Education) Zuowen Chenggong zhi Lu Chubanshe, 4-34 Donggeng Xincun, Daqing, Heilongjiang 163311, People's Republic of China. TEL 0459-36650. Ed. Wang Yuhai. adv. contact: Wang Xinyun. bk.rev. circ. 500,000. **Document type:** academic/scholarly publication.
Description: Guides high school students to successful composition.

370 GW
ZUSAMMENSTELLUNG STUDIENEINFUEHRENDER SCHRIFTEN. 1974. irreg. DM.2. Verein Freunde und Foerderer der Deutschen Studentenschaft e.V., Untere Hausbreite 11, 80939 Munich, Germany. adv.; bk.rev.

ZWISCHENSCHRITTE; Beitraege zu einer morphologischen Psychologie. see PSYCHOLOGY

370　　　　　　　　PL　　ISSN 0137-7310
ZYCIE SZKOLY. 1946. 10/yr. $24. (Ministerstwo Edukacji Narodowej) Wydawnictwa Szkolne i Pedagogiczne, Pl. Dabrowskiego 8, 00-950 Warsaw, Poland. TEL 48 22 26-89-711. (Dist. by: Ars Polona-Ruch, Krakowskie Przedmiescie 7, Warsaw, Poland) circ. 15,764.
  Description: Covers issues in elementary education, for teachers, theoreticians of elementary pedagogy and students in pedagogical schools.

370　　　　　　　　GW
ZZAP; Schuelerzeitung Schillerschule. (Text in English and German) 1956. 4/yr. free. c/o Joerg Thiel, Albert-Schweitzer-Hof 21, D-3000 Hannover 71, Germany. TEL 0511-526462. adv.; bk.rev.; abstr.; bibl.; charts; illus.; stat. circ. 600.
  Supersedes (in 1987): Glocke (ISSN 0017-1247)

EDUCATION — Abstracting, Bibliographies, Statistics

378.025　　　　　　　US
A A C C STATISTICAL YEARBOOK (YEAR). 1950. a. $44 to non-members; members $33.50. American Association of Community Colleges, One Dupont Circle, N.W., Ste. 410, Washington, DC 20036. TEL 202-728-0200. FAX 202-223-9390. (Subscr. to: AACC Publications, Box 1737, Salisbury, MD 21802. TEL 410-546-0391) Eds. Edgar Jimenez, Jim Mahoney. (also avail. in microfiche from CIS) **Indexed:** ERIC, SRI. **Document type:** directory.
  Former titles: A A C J C Statistical Yearbook; Community, Technical, and Junior Colleges Directory: A Statistical Analysis; Community, Technical, and Junior College Directory; Community and Junior College Directory; Junior College Directory (ISSN 0075-4552)
  Description: Lists enrollment figures for fall of 1990 and 1991; number of full- and part-time faculty, administrators, part- and full-time students; and tuitition charged at every accredited community, technical, or junior college in the US and most of Canada.

378 615.53　　　　　　US
A A C O M ANNUAL STATISTICAL REPORT. 1981. a. $13. American Association of Colleges of Osteopathic Medicine, 6110 Executive Blvd., Ste. 405, Rockville, MD 20852. TEL 301-468-0990. Ed. Dr. Allen M. Singer. circ. 400. (back issues avail.) **Document type:** trade publication.
  Description: Statistical data relating to the characteristics of applicants and matriculants in osteopathic medical colleges, faculty, curriculum, sources of grants and loans, and distribution of revenues and expenditures.

100 370 016　　　　　　BU
ABSTRACTS OF BULGARIAN SCIENTIFIC LITERATURE. PHILOSOPHY, SOCIOLOGY, SCIENCE OF SCIENCES, PSYCHOLOGY AND PEDAGOGICS. (Editions in English and Russian) 1958. q. 3.44 lv.($8) (Bulgarska Akademiia na Naukite) Publishing House of the Bulgarian Academy of Sciences, 7 Noemvri St. 1, 1040 Sofia, Bulgaria. (Dist. by: Hemus, 6, Rouski Blvd., 1000 Sofia, Bulgaria) Ed.Bd. abstr.; author index. circ. 390 (English edt.). (reprint service avail. from IRC)
  Formerly: Abstracts of Bulgarian Scientific Literature. Philosophy, Psychology and Pedagogics (ISSN 0001-3528)

370 016　　　　　　　NR
ABSTRACTS OF EDUCATIONAL STUDIES AND RESEARCH.* 1971. w. £N1.50($2.25) University of Ife, Department of Education, Ile-Ife, Nigeria. Ed. Adeniji Adaralegbe. abstr.; stat. (back issues avail.)

ACADEMIC INDEX. see *HUMANITIES: COMPREHENSIVE WORKS — Abstracting, Bibliographies, Statistics*

370　　　　　　　US
AMERICAN STATISTICAL ASSOCIATION. SECTION ON STATISTICAL EDUCATION. PROCEEDINGS. 4th ed., 1982. a., 14th ed. $45 to non-members; members $28. American Statistical Association, 1429 Duke St., Alexandria, VA 22314-3402. TEL 703-684-1221. FAX 703-684-2037. **Document type:** proceedings.

ANNUAL REPORT ON ALLIED DENTAL HEALTH EDUCATION. see *MEDICAL SCIENCES — Abstracting, Bibliographies, Statistics*

ANNUAL REPORT ON DENTAL EDUCATION. see *MEDICAL SCIENCES — Abstracting, Bibliographies, Statistics*

370 016　　　　　　　AG
ARGENTINA. MINISTERIO DE CULTURA Y EDUCACION. BOLETIN BIBLIOGRAFICO. no.5, 1976. q. free. Centro de Documentacion e Informacion Educativa, Paraguay 1657-ler. piso, 1062-Capital Federal, Argentina. bibl.

370.982 318　　　　　　AG
ARGENTINA. MINISTERIO DE CULTURA Y EDUCACION. ESTADISTICAS DE LA EDUCACION. 1974. a. Ministerio de Cultura y Educacion, Departamento de Estadistica Educativa, Avenida E. Madero 235, Buenos Aires, Argentina. illus.; stat.
  Formerly: Estadistica Educativa.

370 016　　　　　　　US
AUDIOCASSETTE & C D FINDER. 1986. irreg., 3rd ed., 1992. $125. (National Information Center for Educational Media) Plexus Publishing, Inc., 143 Old Marlton Pike, Medford, NJ 08055-8750. TEL 609-654-4888. FAX 609-654-4309. abstr.; cum.index: 1971-1989. (back issues avail.)
  ●Also available online. Vendor(s): DIALOG Information Services, Inc. (File no.46).
  Former titles (until 1992): Audiocassette Finder; (until 1986): N I C E M Index to Educational Audio Tapes.
  Description: Subject guide of 29,000 titles of literary materials on audiocassette.

379.121　　　　　AT　　ISSN 1031-0282
AUSTRALIA. BUREAU OF STATISTICS. EXPENDITURE ON EDUCATION, AUSTRALIA. 1963. a. Aus.$10.50. Australian Bureau of Statistics, P.O. Box 10, Belconnen, A.C.T. 2616, Australia. TEL 062-527911. FAX 062-516009. stat. circ. 322. **Document type:** government publication.
  Description: Indicates the extent and direction of both government and private expenditure in the field of education.

AUSTRALIA. BUREAU OF STATISTICS. LABOUR FORCE STATUS AND EDUCATIONAL ATTAINMENT, AUSTRALIA. see *BUSINESS AND ECONOMICS — Abstracting, Bibliographies, Statistics*

370　　　　　AT　　ISSN 1037-9096
AUSTRALIA. BUREAU OF STATISTICS. PARTICIPATION IN EDUCATION, AUSTRALIA. 1988. a. Aus.$12.50. Australian Bureau of Statistics, P.O. Box 10, Belconnen, A.C.T.2616, Australia. **Document type:** government publication.
  Formerly: Australia. Bureau of Statistics. Labour Force Status and Educational Attendance, Australia (ISSN 1033-3185)

378　　　　　AT　　ISSN 0729-171X
AUSTRALIA. BUREAU OF STATISTICS. RESEARCH AND EXPERIMENTAL DEVELOPMENT, HIGHER EDUCATION ORGANISATIONS, AUSTRALIA. 1978. biennial. Australian Bureau of Statistics, P.O. Box 10, Belconnen, A.C.T. 2616, Australia. **Document type:** government publication.
  Description: Covers expenditure and human resources devoted to research and experimental development carried out by higher education organizations in Australia.

AUSTRALIA. BUREAU OF STATISTICS. SCHOOLS, AUSTRALIA. see *PUBLIC ADMINISTRATION — Abstracting, Bibliographies, Statistics*

AUSTRALIA. BUREAU OF STATISTICS. SCHOOLS, AUSTRALIA, PRELIMINARY. see *PUBLIC ADMINISTRATION — Abstracting, Bibliographies, Statistics*

370　　　　　AT　　ISSN 1031-7627
AUSTRALIA. BUREAU OF STATISTICS. TASMANIAN OFFICE. EDUCATION, TASMANIA. 1988. a. Aus.$12. Australian Bureau of Statistics, Tasmanian Office, G.P.O. Box 66A, Hobart, Tas. 7001, Australia. **Document type:** government publication.
  Description: Includes information for government and non-government schools and tertiary education institutions.

AUSTRALIA. BUREAU OF STATISTICS. TRANSITION FROM EDUCATION TO WORK, AUSTRALIA. see *OCCUPATIONS AND CAREERS — Abstracting, Bibliographies, Statistics*

370 016 020　　　AT　　ISSN 0004-9026
Z5813
AUSTRALIAN EDUCATION INDEX. 1957. 3/yr. plus a. cumulation. Aus.$185 (foreign Aus.$255). Australian Council for Educational Research, Private Bag 55, Camberwell, Vic. 3124, Australia. TEL 03-277-5555. FAX 03-277-5500. Ed.Bd. circ. 400.
  ●Also available online. Vendor(s): AUSINET.
  —CCC.
  Description: Comprehensive index with abstracts provided for many documents.

372.21　　　　　　　AU
AUSTRIA. STATISTISCHES ZENTRALAMT. DIE KINDERGAERTEN (KINDERTAGESHEIME). (Subseries of its Beitraege zur Oesterreichschen Statistik) a. S.470. Oesterreichisches Statistisches Zentralamt, Hintere Zollamtsstr. 2b, A-1033 Vienna, Austria. TEL 0222-71128 FAX 0222-7156828. **Document type:** government publication.
  Description: Data on all aspects of the development of the kindergarten.

370 012　　　　UN　　ISSN 0211-8335
Z5813
B I B E QUARTERLY BULLETIN. (International Bulletin of Bibliography on Education) (Text in English, French, German, Italian, Portuguese and Spanish) 1981. q. $352. B I B E Project, Apdo. 52, 28200 San Lorenzo del Escorial, Madrid, Spain. **Document type:** bibliography, abstracting/indexing.

370　　　　　　　　BA
BAHRAIN. EDUCATIONAL DOCUMENTATION LIBRARY. ACQUISITIONS LIST. m. Ministry of Education, Educational Documentation Library, P.O. Box 43, Manama, Bahrain. TEL 25840. TELEX 9094.

370　　　　　　　　BA
BAHRAIN. EDUCATIONAL DOCUMENTATION LIBRARY. BIBLIOGRAPHIC LISTS. a. Ministry of Education, Educational Documentation Library, P.O. Box 43, Manama, Bahrain. TEL 25840. TELEX 9094.

370 016　　　　TH　　ISSN 0067-3498
BANGKOK, THAILAND. COLLEGE OF EDUCATION. THESIS ABSTRACT SERIES.* (Editions in English and Thai) 1967. a. $1. Suan Sunautha Teacher College, Samsen, Bangkok 4, Thailand.

370　　　　　　　　BG
BANGLADESH EDUCATION IN STATISTICS (YEAR). (Text in English) a. Tk.1CO($15) Ministry of Planning, Statistics Division, Bureau of Statistics, Secretariat, Dhaka 2, Bangladesh. **Document type:** government publication.

370　　　　　BE　　ISSN 0773-5820
BELGIUM. MINISTERE DE L'EDUCATION NATIONALE. ETUDES ET DOCUMENTS. (Text in French) 1957. a. free. Ministere de l'Education Nationale, Cite Administrative de l'Etat, Bd. Pacheco, 1010 Brussels, Belgium.
  Former titles: Belgium. Ministere de l'Education Nationale et de la Culture Francaise. Annuaire Statistique de l'Enseignement & Belgium. Institut National de Statistique. Annuaire Statistique de l'Enseignement (ISSN 0067-5423)

370　　　　　BL　　ISSN 0067-6632
Z5815.B7
BIBLIOGRAFIA BRASILEIRA DE EDUCACAO. 1954-1979; resumed 1982. s-a Cr.$5000($500) (effective Dec. 1993). Instituto Nacional de Estudos e Pesquisas Educacionais, Campus da Universidade da Brasil, Acesso Sul, CP 10910-900, 70312 Brasilia, D.F., Brazil. TEL 061-347-8970. FAX 061-273-3233. (Or: C.P. 04662, 70132 Brasilia, D.F., Brazil) circ. 2,000. (back issues avail.) **Document type:** bibliography.
  Description: Covers all subject areas of education, especially postgraduate school.

371.9　　　　　FI　　ISSN 0357-2498
BIBLIOGRAFIA ERITYISIRYHMIEN LIIKUNNAN TUTKIMUKSESTA/BIBLIOGRAPHY ON RESEARCH IN PHYSICAL EDUCATION AND SPORT FOR THE HANDICAPPED. (Text in English and Finnish) 1975. irreg. Liikunnan ja Kansanterveyden Edistaemisaeaetion Tutkmuslaitos - Research Institute of Physical Culture and Health, Uimahalli, Yliopiston Alue, 40100-Jyvaeskylae 10, Finland. bibl. circ. 500.

EDUCATION — ABSTRACTING, BIBLIOGRAPHIES, STATISTICS

370 011 US ISSN 0147-6505
BIBLIOGRAPHIC GUIDE TO EDUCATION.* 1975. a. $300 (foreign $330). G.K. Hall & Co., c/o MacMillan Publishing Co., 866 Third Ave., 18th Fl., New York, NY 10022. TEL 212-702-6789. (Orders to: MacMillan Distribution Center, 100 Front St., Box 500, Riverside, NJ 08075-7500. TEL 800-257-5755) bibl. **Document type:** bibliography, abstracting/indexing.
Description: Covers all aspects of education. Lists materials recorded on the OCLC tapes of Columbia University Teachers College during the past year, including additional entries from New York Public Library.

370 US ISSN 0742-6917
BIBLIOGRAPHIES AND INDEXES IN EDUCATION. 1984. irreg. price varies. Greenwood Press, Inc. (Subsidiary of: Greenwood Publishing Group Inc.), 88 Post Rd. W., Box 5007, Westport, CT 06881-5007. TEL 203-226-3571. FAX 203-222-1502.
—BLDSC (1993.097350).

370 370.15 300
020 AT ISSN 0811-0174
Z5815.A8
BIBLIOGRAPHY OF EDUCATION THESES IN AUSTRALIA. 1982. a. Aus.$49.95. Australian Council for Educational Research, Radford House, P.O. Box 210, Hawthorn, Vic. 3122, Australia. TEL 61-3-819-1400. FAX 61-3-819-5502. Ed. Judith Fawcett. bibl. circ. 350. (back issues avail.) **Document type:** bibliography.
●Also available online. Vendor(s): AUSINET. Also available on CD-ROM.
—CCC.

370 314 GW ISSN 0938-1104
BILDUNG IM ZAHLENSPIEGEL. 1974. a. DM.20.60. Statistisches Bundesamt, 65180 Wiesbaden, Germany. TEL 0611-75-1. FAX 0611-724000. TELEX 61186-STBA-D. stat. **Document type:** government publication.

370 US ISSN 1044-7962
BIO-BIBLIOGRAPHIES IN EDUCATION. 1989. irreg. price varies. Greenwood Press, Inc. (Subsidiary of: Greenwood Publishing Group Inc.), 88 Post Rd. W., Box 5007, Westport, CT 06881-5007. TEL 203-226-3571. FAX 203-222-1502. **Document type:** monographic series.

BIOLOGY EDUCATION. see *BIOLOGY*

BRAILLE BOOKS (LARGE PRINT EDITION). see *HANDICAPPED — Abstracting, Bibliographies, Statistics*

372 BL
BRAZIL. MINISTERIO DA EDUCACAO. SERVICO DE ESTATISTICA DA EDUCACAO E CULTURA. SINOPSE ESTATISTICA DA EDUCACAO PRE-ESCOLAR. 1984. a. Ministerio da Educacao, Servico de Estatistica da Educacao e Cultura, Esplanada dos Ministerios, Bloco L - Anexo II - Terreo, 70.047 Brasilia-DF, Brazil.
Supersedes (1968-1973): Brazil. Servico de Estatistica da Educacao e Cultura. Sinopse Estatistica do Ensino Primario.

378 BL
BRAZIL. SERVICO DE ESTATISTICA DA EDUCACAO E CULTURA. SINOPSE ESTATISTICA DO ENSINO SUPERIOR. 1954. a. Ministerio da Educacao e Cultura, Servico de Estatistica da Educacao e Cultura, Esplanada dos Ministerios, Bloco L - Anexo II - Terreo, 70.047-Brasilia, DF, Brazil.

372 BL
BRAZIL. SERVICO DE ESTATISTICA DA EDUCACAO. SINOPSE ESTATISTICA DO ENSINO REGULAR DE 1O GRAU. irreg. Ministerio da Educacao, Servico de Estatistica da Educacao, Esplanada dos Ministerios, Bloco L - Anexo II - Terreo, 70047 Brasilia DF, Brazil. charts; stat.

370 016 UK ISSN 0007-0637
Z5813
BRITISH EDUCATION INDEX. 1961. a. (plus 4 quarterly issues). £92 (foreign £103) (effective 1993). British Education Index, Brotherton Library, University of Leeds, Leeds LS2 9JT, England. TEL 0532-335524. FAX 0532-336017. Ed. Philip W. Sheffield. circ. 1,000. **Document type:** abstracting/indexing.
●Also available online. Vendor(s): DIALOG Information Services, Inc. (File no.121).
—BLDSC (2299.200000).
Description: Subject and author index to articles of permanent educational interest in a wide range of British and some European periodicals.

371 362.4 UK
BRITISH INSTITUTE OF LEARNING DISABILITIES. CURRENT AWARENESS SERVICE. 1979. m. £25 to individuals; institutions £31.50 (Ireland £36.50; rest of Europe £41; elsewhere £42.50) (effective 1994). British Institute of Learning Disabilities (BILD), Wolverhampton Rd., Kidderminster, Worcs. DY10 3PP, England. TEL 0562-850251. FAX 0562-851197. Ed. Mrs. Lindaaverill. adv. circ. 1,000. **Document type:** bibliography.
Formerly: British Institute of Mental Handicap. Current Awareness Service (ISSN 0143-0289)
Description: Bibliography of current books, articles, educational events, and audiovisual materials covering all aspects of learning disabilities.

370 GW
BUECHER FUER DAS STUDIUM - GEISTESWISSENSCHAFTEN; Paedagogik, Didaktik, Psychologie, Philologie, Germanistik. a. Dr. Lothar Rossipaul Verlagsgesellschaft mbH, Menzingerstr. 37, 80638 Munich, Germany. TEL 089-179106-0. FAX 089-179106-22. Ed. Rainer Rossipaul. circ. 25,000. **Document type:** bibliography.
Description: Bibliography of available books for students.

BUECHER FUER DAS STUDIUM - MEDIZIN. see *MEDICAL SCIENCES — Abstracting, Bibliographies, Statistics*

BUECHER FUER DAS STUDIUM - NATURWISSENSCHAFTEN; Mathematik, Physik, Chemie, Biologie, Botanik, Zoologie, Geowissenschaften. see *SCIENCES: COMPREHENSIVE WORKS — Abstracting, Bibliographies, Statistics*

375 650 016 US ISSN 0068-4414
BUSINESS EDUCATION INDEX. 1940. a. $25. Delta Pi Epsilon Graduate Business Education Society, National Office, Box 4340, Little Rock, AR 72214. TEL 501-562-1233. FAX 501-562-1293. Ed. Pat Graves. circ. 11,000. (also avail. in microform from UMI; diskette format; reprint service avail. from UMI) **Document type:** abstracting/indexing.
—UMI.
Description: Contains an index of business education articles compiled from a selected list of periodicals and yearbooks published during each calendar year.

370 410 US ISSN 1046-0675
Z5818.E5
C C C C BIBLIOGRAPHY OF COMPOSITION AND RHETORIC. 1987. a. (Conference on College Composition and Communication) Southern Illinois University Press, Box 3697, Carbondale, IL 62902-3697. TEL 618-453-6610. FAX 618-453-1221. Eds. G.E. Hawisher, C.L. Selfe. bibl.; index. (back issues avail.) **Document type:** bibliography.
Description: Offers teachers and researchers an annotated list of scholarship on teaching written English.

378 CN ISSN 0832-6657
LB2328
CANADA. STATISTICS CANADA. COMMUNITY COLLEGES AND RELATED INSTITUTIONS, POSTSECONDARY ENROLMENT AND GRADUATES. (Catalogue 81-222) (Text in English and French) 1969. a. Can.$27($32) (foreign $38). Statistics Canada, Publications Sales and Services, Ottawa, Ont. K1A 0T6, Canada. TEL 613-951-7277. FAX 613-951-1584. (also avail. in microform from MML)
Formerly: Canada. Statistics Canada. Enrolment in Community Colleges (ISSN 0382-0920)
Description: Presents enrollment, graduation and distribution data on full-time students of the community college system in Canada.

371.2 CN ISSN 0704-6596
LC145.C2
CANADA. STATISTICS CANADA. ELEMENTARY - SECONDARY SCHOOL ENROLMENT. (Catalogue 81-210) (Text in English and French) 1958. a. Can.$26($31) (foreign $36). Statistics Canada, Publications Sales and Services, Ottawa, Ont. K1A 0T6, Canada. TEL 613-951-7277. FAX 613-951-1584. (also avail. in microform from MML)
Description: Presents national and provincial enrollment statistics, including data for public school systems, private schools and schools operated under the auspices of the federal government.

310 370 CN ISSN 0703-9328
LB2890
CANADA. STATISTICS CANADA. FINANCIAL STATISTICS OF EDUCATION. (Catalogue 81-208) (Text in English and French) 1954. a. Can.$39($47) (foreign $55). Statistics Canada, Publications Sales and Services, Ottawa, Ont. K1A 0T6, Canada. TEL 613-951-7277. FAX 613-951-1584. (also avail. in microform from MML)
Description: Presents five years of consolidated financial statistics on all levels of education and highlights revenues by direct source of funds and expenditures by object of various public and private educational institutions.

016 370 CN ISSN 0008-3453
Z5815.C3
CANADIAN EDUCATION INDEX/REPERTOIRE CANADIEN SUR L'EDUCATION. (Text in English or French) 1965. 4/yr. (4th issue - a. cumulation). Can.$425. (Canadian Education Association) Micromedia Ltd., 20 Victoria St., Toronto, ON M5C 2N8, Canada. TEL 416-362-5211. FAX 416-362-6161. Ed. Beth Kirkwood. (back issues avail.) **Document type:** abstracting/indexing.
●Also available online.
Also available on CD-ROM.
Description: Indexes Canadian education report and journal literature.

CANADIAN INDEX. see *BUSINESS AND ECONOMICS — Abstracting, Bibliographies, Statistics*

613.7 016 UK
CENTRE FOR SPORTS SCIENCE AND HISTORY. SERIAL HOLDINGS. (Text in English and other languages) 1974. a. free. Centre for Sports Science and History, Main Library, University of Birmingham, Edgbaston, Birmingham B15 2TT, England. TEL 021-414-5843. Ed.Bd. circ. 333. **Document type:** abstracting/indexing, bibliography.
Former titles (until 1993): Sports Documentation Centre. Serial Holdings; Sports Documentation Centre. List of Periodical and Abstracting and Indexing Journal Holdings.
Description: Lists of national and international periodicals, abstracts, and indexing journals on sports, physical education, and recreation held in the library of the Centre.

310 370 UK ISSN 0309-5614
LA630
CHARTERED INSTITUTE OF PUBLIC FINANCE AND ACCOUNTANCY. EDUCATION STATISTICS. ACTUALS. 1948. a. £42. Chartered Institute of Public Finance and Accountancy, 3 Robert St., London WC2N 6BH, England. TEL 071-895-8823. FAX 071-895-8825. stat. (back issues avail.)

310 370 UK ISSN 0307-0514
LA630
CHARTERED INSTITUTE OF PUBLIC FINANCE AND ACCOUNTANCY. EDUCATION STATISTICS. ESTIMATES. 1974. a. £60. Chartered Institute of Public Finance and Accountancy, 3 Robert St., London WC2N 6BH, England. TEL 071-895-8823. FAX 071-895-8825. (back issues avail.)
—BLDSC (3661.336300).

CHEMISTRY EDUCATION. see *CHEMISTRY*

370 US ISSN 0098-4752
L112
CONDITION OF EDUCATION; a statistical report on the condition of American education. 1975. a. price varies. U.S. Department of Education, National Center for Education Statistics, 555 New Jersey Ave., N.W., Washington, DC 20208. TEL 800-424-1616. (Dist. by: Supt. of Documents, Washington, DC 20402) stat. **Indexed:** SRI.
—Faxon.

EDUCATION — ABSTRACTING, BIBLIOGRAPHIES, STATISTICS

370   UK   ISSN 0265-9220
Z5813
CONTENTS PAGES IN EDUCATION. 1986. m. $579 (effective 1994). Carfax Publishing Co., P.O. Box 25, Abingdon, Oxon. OX14 3UE, England. TEL 44-235-555335. FAX 44-235-553559. (U.S. subscr. to: Carfax Publishing Co., Box 2025, Dunnellon, FL 34430-2025) Ed. Graham Hobbs. index. (also avail. in microfiche; back issues avail.) **Document type:** abstracting/indexing.
—CCC.

378.1   CN   ISSN 0382-912X
LA418.O6
COUNCIL OF ONTARIO UNIVERSITIES. RESEARCH DIVISION. APPLICATION STATISTICS. 1973. a. Council of Ontario Universities, Research Division, 444 Yonge St., Ste 203, Toronto, Ont. M5B 2H4, Canada. TEL 416-979-2165. FAX 416-979-8635. (reprint service avail from MML)

370 016   PE
CUADERNOS DE INFORMACION EDUCACIONAL. 3/yr. Instituto Nacional de Investigacion y Desarrollo de la Educacion, Centro Nacional de Documentacion e Informacion Educacional, Van de Velde 160, San Borja, Lima 100, Peru.
Formerly: Cuadernos de Bibliografia Educacional.

CURRENT CONTENTS: SOCIAL & BEHAVIORAL SCIENCES. see *SOCIOLOGY — Abstracting, Bibliographies, Statistics*

370 016   US   ISSN 0011-3565
Z5813   CODEN: CIJEA
CURRENT INDEX TO JOURNALS IN EDUCATION. 1969. m. $235 (foreign $270) s-a. cum. $235 (foreign $270) (effective 1992). (Educational Resources Information Center) Oryx Press, 4041 N. Central Ave., No. 700, Phoenix, AZ 85012-3397. TEL 602-265-2651. FAX 602-265-6250. **Document type:** abstracting/indexing.
●Also available online. Vendor(s): BRS Online Products, CISTI, DIALOG Information Services, Inc. (File no.1/ERIC), Orbit Search Service (ERIC). Also available on CD-ROM. Producer(s): NISC (ERIC), O C L C, SilverPlatter Information, Inc. (ERIC).
—BLDSC (3498.180000).
Description: Annotated index to education literature, including elementary, secondary and higher education, as well as administrative issues and concerns.

370 312   CY
LA1480
CYPRUS. DEPARTMENT OF STATISTICS AND RESEARCH. EDUCATION STATISTICS. (Text in English) 1969. a. £C4. Ministry of Finance, Department of Statistics and Research, Nicosia, Cyprus.
Formerly: Statistics of Education in Cyprus (ISSN 0253-8733)
Description: Statistical data on education at all levels.

378 330   US
DELTA PI EPSILON. INDEX TO DOCTORAL DISSERTATIONS IN BUSINESS EDUCATION. (Supplements avail.) 1975. every 5 yrs. price varies. Delta Pi Epsilon Graduate Business Education Society, National Office, Box 4340, Little Rock, AR 72214. TEL 501-562-1233. FAX 501-562-1293. **Document type:** abstracting/indexing.

378   DK   ISSN 0108-4267
LA878
DENMARK. UNDERVISNINGSMINISTERIET. DATAKONTORET. STATISTIK FOR DE VIDEREGAAENDE UDDANNELSER. a. DKK 60. Undervisningsministeriet, Datakontoret, Frederiksholms Kanal 25 G, DK-1220 Copenhagen K, Denmark.
Formerly: Denmark. Undervisningsministeriet. Oekonomisk-Statistiske Konsulent. Statistik for de Videregaaende Uddannelser.

DEUTSCHE NATIONALBIBLIOGRAPHIE. HOCHSCHULSCHRIFTEN-VERZEICHNIS. see *PUBLISHING AND BOOK TRADE — Abstracting, Bibliographies, Statistics*

378   US   ISSN 0883-5330
R850.A1
DIRECTORY OF BIOMEDICAL AND HEALTH CARE GRANTS. 1985. a. $84.50 (effective 1993). Oryx Press, 4041 N. Central Ave., No. 700, Phoenix, AZ 85012-3397. TEL 602-265-2651. FAX 602-265-6250. Eds. Millie Hannum, Janet Woolum. **Document type:** directory.
●Also available online. Vendor(s): DIALOG Information Services, Inc.
Description: Lists more than 3,000 federal, state and private grants and funding programs in health and related fields, including sponsoring organizations, application procedures, addresses, and restrictions.

378   US   ISSN 0887-0551
AZ188.U5
DIRECTORY OF GRANTS IN THE HUMANITIES. 1986. a. $84.50. Oryx Press, 4041 N. Central Ave., No. 700, Phoenix, AZ 85012-3397. TEL 602-265-2651. FAX 602-265-6250. Eds. Millie Hannum, Janet Woolum.
●Also available online. Vendor(s): DIALOG Information Services, Inc.
Description: Lists nearly 4,000 grants and funding programs in the humanities, with sponsoring organizations, application procedures, addresses, and restrictions.

370 016   CH   ISSN 0419-3733
AS448
DIRECTORY OF THE CULTURAL ORGANIZATIONS OF THE REPUBLIC OF CHINA. (In four parts; Learned Societies, Universities and Colleges, Libraries, and Social Educational Centers) (Text in English) 5th ed., 1978. irreg. (every 2-3/yrs.), 7th ed., 1992. $40. National Central Library, Bureau of International Exchange of Publications, 20 Chungshan S. Rd., Taipei, Taiwan 10040, Republic of China. FAX 02-311-0155. Ed. Teresa Wang Chang. circ. 1,000. **Document type:** directory.
Description: Lists cultural organizations on Taiwan, indexed by subject and name. Includes official name, address, phone and fax number, president or director, aims, activities, plans, facilities, collection, services, and publications.

370   US   ISSN 0077-9210
DISTRIBUTION OF HIGH SCHOOL GRADUATES AND COLLEGE GOING RATE, NEW YORK STATE. 1967. a. free. Education Department, Instruction & Program Development, Education Bldg. Annex, Rm. 381, Albany, NY 12234. TEL 518-474-7082. FAX 518-474-4351. circ. controlled. **Document type:** government publication.

370   GW   ISSN 0724-4401
DOKUMENTATIONSDIENST BILDUNG UND KULTUR. 1977. fortn. DM.120. Luchterhand Verlag, Heddesdorferstr. 31, 56564 Neuwied, Germany. TEL 02631-8010. FAX 02631-801210. bibl.; stat. circ. 600. (back issues avail.) **Document type:** abstracting/indexing.

016   CN   ISSN 0712-4635
E D U Q; bibliographie analytique sur l'education au Quebec. 1981. a. Can.$52($57) Services Documentaires Multimedia Inc., 75 Port-Royal E., No. 300, Montreal, Que. H3L 3T1, Canada. TEL 514-382-0895. FAX 514-384-9139. (back issues avail.)
●Also available online.

370   US   ISSN 1062-0508
Z695.1.E3
E R I C IDENTIFIER AUTHORITY LIST. 1987. irreg., latest 1992. $55. (Educational Resources Information Center) Oryx Press, 4041 N. Central Ave., No. 700, Phoenix, AZ 85012-3397. TEL 602-265-2651. FAX 602-265-6250. Eds. Carolyn Weller, James E. Houston. **Document type:** abstracting/indexing.
Description: Lists over 45000 retrieval identifiers for the ERIC database.

370 016   GW   ISSN 0378-7192
E U D I S E D - R & D BULLETIN. (European Documentation and Information System for Education) (Text in English, French and German) 1976. 4/yr. DM.228. (Council of Europe, EI) K.G. Saur Verlag KG, A Reed Reference Publishing Company, Part of the Reed Elsevier group, Ortlerstr. 8, 81373 Munich, Germany. TEL 089-76902-0. FAX 089-76902150. TELEX 5212067-SAUR-D. (Subscr. to: Postfach 701620, 81316 Munich, Germany) Ed. Wilson Barret. circ. 500. (also avail. in microfiche; back issues avail.) **Document type:** academic/scholarly publication.
●Also available online. Vendor(s): European Space Agency (File no.24/EUDISED R&D).
Also available on CD-ROM.
—BLDSC (3824 400000); SWETS. CCC.

370   BL   ISSN 0103-5770
EDUCACAO; indicadores sociais. 1981. a. Fundacao Instituto Brasileiro de Geografia e Estatistica, Av. Franklin Roosevelt, 166 Centro, 20021 Rio de Janeiro RJ, Brazil. TEL 011-284-7690. FAX 011-228-9575. Ed. Olga Lopes da Cruz. **Document type:** government publication.

370   CL
EDUCACION. 1911. a. Instituto Nacional de Estadisticas, Av. Bulnes 418, Casilla 498, Correo 3 Santiago, Chile.

370   AT   ISSN 0729-8528
EDUCATION GUIDELINES. 1979. 3/yr. (plus a. cumulation). Aus.$28. Bibliographic Services, P.O. Box 2, Mount Waverley, Vic. 3149, Australia. Ed. K.S. Darling. circ. 500. (also avail. in microfiche) **Document type:** abstracting/indexing.
Description: Subject index to Australian education journals and journals of teaching associations.

370   CN   ISSN 0706-3679
LA412
EDUCATION IN CANADA; a statistical review. (Catalogue 81-229) (Text in English and French) 1973. a. Can.$50($60) (foreign $70). Statistics Canada, Publications Sales and Services, Ottawa, ON K1A 0T6, Canada. TEL 613-951-1500; 800-267-6677. FAX 613-951-9040. circ. 800 (paid). (also avail. in microform from MML) **Document type:** government publication.
Description: Summarizes information on institutions, enrollment, graduates, teachers and finance for all levels of education and provides an analysis of the data.

378 011   KE
EDUCATION IN KENYA; index of articles on education. 1977. a. $70. Kenyatta University Library, Box 43844, Nairobi, Kenya. Ed. E.W. Kaberia. circ. 200.
Description: Indexes different subjects and indicates public response to contemporary issues in education.

370 016   US   ISSN 0013-1385
Z5813
EDUCATION INDEX. 1929. m. (Sep.-Jun.) plus q. and a. cumulations. service basis. H.W. Wilson Co., 950 University Ave., Bronx, NY 10452. TEL 800-367-6770. FAX 718-590-1617. TELEX 4990003HWILSON. Ed. Barbara Berry. (also avail. in magnetic tape) **Document type:** abstracting/indexing.
●Also available online. Vendor(s): BRS Online Products (WEDI), Wilsonline (File EDI).
Also available on CD-ROM. Producer(s): H.W. Wilson (WILSONDISC).
—BLDSC (3661.234000).
Description: Author-subject index to educational publications in the English language.

370   CN   ISSN 1195-2261
▼**EDUCATION QUARTERLY REVIEW.** (Catalog no. 81-003) (Text and summaries in English, French) 1993. q. Can.$60($72) Statistics Canada, Ottawa, ON K1A 0T6, Canada. TEL 613-951-1500; 800-267-6677. FAX 613-951-9040. Ed. Jim Seidle. circ. 800 (paid). (also avail. in microfiche) **Document type:** government publication.

EDUCATION — ABSTRACTING, BIBLIOGRAPHIES, STATISTICS

370　　　　　US
EDUCATION STATISTICS, NEW YORK STATE; prepared especially for members of the Legislature. 1968. a. free. Education Department, Instruction & Program Development, Education Bldg. Annex, Rm. 381, Albany, NY 12234. TEL 518-474-7082. FAX 518-474-4351. charts; stat.; circ. controlled. (back issues avail.) **Document type:** government publication.

370　　　　　TZ　　ISSN 0856-0005
EDUCATIONAL ABSTRACTS FOR TANZANIA. 1983. s-a. $28. Library Services Board, National Documentation Centre, P.O. Box 9283, Dar es Salaam, Tanzania. Ed. D.A. Sekimang'a. circ. 1,000.

371 016　　　US　　ISSN 0013-1601
LB2805
EDUCATIONAL ADMINISTRATION ABSTRACTS. 1966. q. $79 to individuals (foreign $84); institutions $250 (foreign $256). Corwin Press, Inc. (Subsidiary of: Sage Publications, Inc.), 2455 Teller Rd., Thousand Oaks, CA 91320. TEL 805-499-0721. FAX 805-499-0871. (And: Sage Publications, Ltd., 6 Bonhill St., London EC2A 4PU, England) Ed. Gracia A. Alkema. adv.: B&W page $225. index. (also avail. in microform from UMI; back issues avail.; reprint service avail. from UMI,ISI) **Document type:** abstracting/indexing.
—UMI.
Formerly: Educational Abstracts.
Description: Provides abstracts from more than 100 professional journals relating to education and educational administration.

EDUCATIONAL FILM & VIDEO LOCATOR. see MOTION PICTURES — Abstracting, Bibliographies, Statistics

370　　　　　BA
EDUCATIONAL INDEX OF ARABIC PERIODICALS. m. Ministry of Education, Educational Documentation Library, P.O. Box 43, Manama, Bahrain. TEL 25840. TELEX 9094.

370　　　　　BA
EDUCATIONAL INDEX OF FOREIGN PERIODICALS. m. Ministry of Education, Educational Documentation Library, P.O. Box 43, Manama, Bahrain. TEL 25840. TELEX 9094.

370　　　　　BA
EDUCATIONAL INDICATIVE ABSTRACTS. 3/yr. Ministry of Education, Educational Documentation Library, P.O. Box 43, Manama, Bahrain. TEL 25840. TELEX 9094.

370　　　　　BA
EDUCATIONAL INFORMATION ABSTRACTS. 3/yr. Ministry of Education, Educational Documentation Library, P.O. Box 43, Manama, Bahrain. TEL 25840. TELEX 9094.

370 350　　　BA
EDUCATIONAL LEGISLATION INDEX. m. Ministry of Education, Educational Documentation Library, P.O. Box 43, Manama, Bahrain. TEL 25840. TELEX 9094.

370　　　　　US　　ISSN 1053-1378
LB2331.63
EDUCATIONAL RANKINGS ANNUAL. a. $135. Gale Research Inc., 835 Penobscot Bldg., Detroit, MI 48266. TEL 313-961-2242. FAX 313-961-6083. Ed. Lynn C. Hattendorf.

370　　　　　BA
EDUCATIONAL SELECTIVE ABSTRACTS. bi-m. Ministry of Education, Educational Documentation Library, P.O. Box 43, Manama, Bahrain. TEL 25840. TELEX 9094.

371.3 011　　UK　　ISSN 0266-3368
EDUCATIONAL TECHNOLOGY ABSTRACTS. 1985. 6/yr. $175 to individuals; institutions $407 (effective 1994). Carfax Publishing Co., P.O. Box 25, Abingdon, Oxon. OX14 3UE, England. TEL 44-235-555335. FAX 44-35-553559. (U.S. subscr. to: Carfax Publishing Co., Box 2025, Dunnellon, FL 34430-2025) Ed. V.M. Johnston. adv.; bk.rev.; index. (also avail. in microfiche; back issues avail.) **Document type:** abstracting/indexing.
—BLDSC (3662.530500). **CCC**.

016 370　　　US　　ISSN 0000-0825
Z5813
EL-HI TEXTBOOKS AND SERIALS IN PRINT; including related teaching materials K-12. 1969. a. $139.95. R.R. Bowker, A Reed Reference Publishing Company, Part of the Reed Elsevier group, 121 Chanlon Rd., New Providence, NJ 07974. TEL 908-464-6800. FAX 908-665-3502. TELEX 138 755. (Subscr. to: Order Dept., Box 31, New Providence, NJ 07974-9903. TEL 800-521-8110) (also avail. in magnetic tape) **Document type:** bibliography, directory.
●Also available on CD-ROM. Producer(s): Bowker - Reed Reference Electronic Publishing.
Former titles: Textbooks in Print; El-Hi Textbooks in Print (ISSN 0070-9565)
Description: Provides complete bibliographic and ordering information for elementary, junior and senior high school textbooks, text series, periodicals, references, tests, teaching aids, and pedagogical and professional books and serials, arranged by subject and indexed by author, title and series, with a key to book publishers' and distributors' addresses.

378　　　　　EI
ERASMUS DIRECTORY. a. $45. Office for Official Publications of the European Communities, L-2985 Luxembourg, Luxembourg. (Dist. by: UNIPUB, 4611-F Assembly Dr., Lantham, MD 20706-4391. TEL 800-274-4888. FAX 301-459-0056)
Description: Covers inter-university cooperation programs, including guidelines for applicants, lists of national grant awarding authorities, academic recognition and measures to promote student mobility in the community.

370 318　　　MX
ESTADISTICA BASICA DEL SISTEMA EDUCATIVO NACIONAL. 1970. irreg. Secretaria de Educacion Publica, Direccion General de Planeacion, Programacion y Presupuesto, Mexico, D. F., Mexico.
Description: National statistics on education in Mexico from kindergarten to college.

370 310　　　PN　　ISSN 0378-4967
ESTADISTICA PANAMENA. SITUACION CULTURAL. SECCION 511. EDUCACION. 1957. a. Bl.0.75. Direccion de Estadistica y Censo, Contraloria General, Apartado 5213, Panama 5, Panama. FAX 69-7294. circ. 900. **Document type:** government publication, bulletin.

370　　　　　CL
ESTADISTICAS DE EDUCACION EXTRAESCOLAR. 1976. a. Instituto Nacional de Estadisticas, Av. Bulnes 418, Casilla 498, Correo 3 Santiago, Chile.

371.9 016　　US　　ISSN 0160-4309
Z5814.C52
EXCEPTIONAL CHILD EDUCATION RESOURCES. 1969. 4/yr. $75 to non-members (foreign $80); members $60. Council for Exceptional Children, 1920 Association Dr., Reston, VA 22091-1589. TEL 703-620-3660. FAX 703-264-9494. circ. 700. **Document type:** abstracting/indexing.
●Also available online. Vendor(s): DIALOG Information Services, Inc. (File no.54).
—SWETS.
Formerly (until May 1977): Exceptional Child Education Abstracts (ISSN 0014-4010)
Description: Computerized database containing more than 80,000 abstracts in the field of special education. Every citation gives author, title, source, publication date, availability date, subject terms, and a descriptive summary of the document or journal article.

370 016　　　FR　　ISSN 1157-3708
Z5813
F R A N C I S. 520: SCIENCES DE L'EDUCATION. (Text in English, French) 1947. q. 540 F. (outside EEC 570 F.). Centre National de la Recherche Scientifique, Institut de l'Information Scientifique et Technique, 2 allee du Parc de Brabois, 54514 Vandoeuvre-les-Nancy Cedex, France. TEL 83-50-46-00. FAX 83-50-46-50. Ed. C. Patou. adv. contact: Veronique Guinvarc'h. index, cum.index. **Document type:** bibliography.
●Also available online. Vendor(s): Telesystemes - Questel.
Also available on CD-ROM.
Formerly: Bulletin Signaletique. Part 520: Sciences de l'Education (ISSN 0223-341X)

370 016　　　US　　ISSN 0898-1582
FILM & VIDEO FINDER. 1987. irreg., 3rd ed., 1991. $295. (National Information Center for Educational Media) Plexus Publishing, Inc., 143 Old Marlton Pike, Medford, NJ 08055-8750. TEL 609-654-4888. FAX 609-654-4309.
●Also available online. Vendor(s): DIALOG Information Services, Inc. (File no.46).
Also available on CD-ROM. Producer(s): SilverPlatter Information, Inc..
Formed by the merger of (1967-1987): N I C E M Index to 16mm Educational Films (ISSN 0734-5488); (1971-1987): N I C E M Index to Educational Video Tapes (ISSN 0734-6921)
Description: Lists 92,000 films and videos by subject heading outline and index. Includes subject section by title and distributor code, producers and distributors.

370 016　　　US
FILMSTRIP AND SLIDE SET FINDER. vol.6, 1976. irreg., latest 1990. $225. (National Information Center for Educational Media) Plexus Publishing, Inc., 143 Old Marlton Pike, Medford, NJ 08055-8750. TEL 609-654-6500. FAX 609-654-4309.
●Also available online.
Also available on CD-ROM.
Formerly: N I C E M Index to 35mm Educational Filmstrips.

310 370　　　CN　　ISSN 0708-5168
FINANCIAL STATISTICS OF UNIVERSITIES AND COLLEGES/STATISTIQUES FINANCIERES DES UNIVERSITES ET COLLEGES. (Text in English, French) a. Can.$35 (US Can.$40, elsewhere Can.$45). (Canadian Association of University Business Officers - Association Canadienne du Personnel Administratif Universitaire) Association of Universities and Colleges of Canada - Association des Universites et Colleges du Canada, 600-350 Albert, Ottawa, ON K1R 1B1, Canada. TEL 613-563-1236. FAX 613-563-9745.
Description: Reports on the individual income and expenditures of institutions and provides aggregate results.

379　　　　　US
FLORIDA. DEPARTMENT OF EDUCATION. FLORIDA STATEWIDE ASSESSMENT PROGRAM: STATE, DISTRICT AND REGIONAL REPORT OF STATEWIDE ASSESSMENT RESULTS. 1976. s-a. free. Department of Education, Division of Public Schools, Student Assessment Section, Tallahassee, FL 32301. TEL 904-448-8198. FAX 904-487-1889. stat. **Document type:** government publication.
Formerly: Florida. Department of Education. Florida Statewide Assessment Program: Capsule Report (ISSN 0094-1468)
Description: Reports the results of the high school competing test.

370 016　　　DK　　ISSN 0901-9332
FOLKESKOLEN. OVERSIGTKATALOG.* 1979. a. DKK 27.60. Landscentralen for Undervisningsmidler, Gammel Kongevej 164, 1850 Copenhagen V, Denmark.
Formerly (until 1986): Undervisningsmidler for Folkeskolen. Katalog (ISSN 0106-5823)

370　　　　　DK　　ISSN 0905-7293
FOLKESKOLENS NYHEDSKATALOG.* 1980. a. DKK 31.60. Landscentralen for Undervisningsmidler, Gammel Kongevej 164, 1850 Copenhagen V, Denmark.
Formerly (until 1990): Undervisningsmidler for Folkeskolen. Nyhedskatalog (ISSN 0107-4296)

FOR YOUNGER READERS, BRAILLE AND TALKING BOOKS (LARGE PRINT EDITION). see HANDICAPPED — Abstracting, Bibliographies, Statistics

016 370　　　DK　　ISSN 0107-1491
FORLAGSSERIEKATALOG FOR BOERNE- OG SKOLEBIBLIOTEKER. 1980. a. DKK 188.15. Dansk BiblioteksCenter as, Tempovej 7-11, DK-2750 Ballerup, Denmark. TEL 45-44-97-40-00. FAX 45-44-68-24-42.
●Also available online.
Also available on CD-ROM.
Formerly: Forlagsseriekatalog.

EDUCATION — ABSTRACTING, BIBLIOGRAPHIES, STATISTICS

370.967   GO
GABON. MINISTERE DE L'EDUCATION NATIONALE. ANNUAIRE STATISTIQUE DE L'ENSEIGNEMENT. a. Ministere de l'Education Nationale, Service des Statistiques Scolaires et de l'Emploi, B.P. 334, Libreville, Gabon. illus.
Formerly: Statistiques de l'Enseignement au Gabon.

370   GM
GAMBIA. CENTRAL STATISTICS DEPARTMENT. EDUCATION STATISTICS. a. D.10. Central Statistics Department, Wellington St., Banjul, Gambia. stat.
Former titles: Gambia. Education Department. Education Statistics; Gambia. Education Department. Annual Report and Statistics.

370 314   GW   ISSN 0072-1778
GERMANY. STATISTISCHES BUNDESAMT. FACHSERIE 11: BILDUNG UND KULTUR. (Consists of several subseries) 1960. a. price varies. 65180 Wiesbaden, Germany. TEL 0611-75-1. FAX 0611-724000. TELEX 61186-STBA-D. **Document type:** government publication.

370 310   GH
GHANA. MINISTRY OF EDUCATION. EDUCATIONAL STATISTICS. a. NC.2. Ministry of Education, P.O. Box M 45, Accra, Ghana. charts.

370 310   UK   ISSN 0072-5900
GREAT BRITAIN. DEPARTMENT OF EDUCATION AND SCIENCE. STATISTICS OF EDUCATION. (In 6 parts) 1961. a. £12.95 price varies. (Department of Education and Science) H.M.S.O., P.O. Box 276, London SW8 5DT, England. **Document type:** government publication.
—CCC.

GRENADA SCHOOL DIRECTORY AND BASIC EDUCATIONAL STATISTICS. see EDUCATION — *Guides To Schools And Colleges*

370   US
GUIDE TO AMERICAN EDUCATIONAL DIRECTORIES. 1972. biennial. $65. Todd Publications, 18 N. Greenbush Rd., W. Nyack, NY 10994. TEL 914-358-6213. Ed. Barry Klein. **Document type:** directory.

370 016   DK   ISSN 0901-9308
GYMNASIET OG HF.* 1973. a. DKK 27.45. Landscentralen for Undervisningsmidler, Gammel Kongevej 164, DK-1850 Copenhagen V, Denmark.
Formerly (until 1986): Undervisningsmidler for Gymnasiet og Hf (ISSN 0106-5955); Which supersedes in part (in 1978): Danske Skole- og Laereboeger (ISSN 0107-6426)

370 016   KO
HAN'GUK BAKSA MIT SOKSA HAGWI NONMUN CH'ONGMONGNOK/LIST OF THESES FOR THE DOCTOR'S AND MASTER'S DEGREE IN KOREA. Variant spelling: Hankuk Baksa mit Seuksa Hakwee Nonmun Chong Mokrok. (Text in Korean) 1969. a. free. National Assembly Library - Kukhoe Tosogwan, 1 Yoido-dong, Seoul, S. Korea. FAX 02-788-4194. circ. 1,600.

370   II   ISSN 0579-6105
LA1150
INDIA. MINISTRY OF EDUCATION AND SOCIAL WELFARE. PROVISIONAL STATISTICS OF EDUCATION IN THE STATES. (Text in English) 1954. a. free. Ministry of Education and Social Welfare, Department of Education, Shastri Bhavan, New Delhi 110001, India. circ. controlled.

370 016   II   ISSN 0019-4697
INDIAN EDUCATION ABSTRACTS. 1955. q. Rs.15.60($5.62) Ministry of Education and Social Welfare, Department of Education, Shastri Bhavan, New Delhi 110001, India. abstr.; bibl.; index; circ. controlled. **Document type:** abstracting/indexing.

INDICE ESPANOL DE CIENCIAS SOCIALES. SERIES A: PSYCHOLOGY AND EDUCATIONAL SCIENCES. see PSYCHOLOGY — *Abstracting, Bibliographies, Statistics*

378 310   IS
ISRAEL. CENTRAL BUREAU OF STATISTICS. INPUTS IN RESEARCH AND DEVELOPMENT IN ACADEMIC INSTITUTIONS. (Text in English and Hebrew) 1970. irreg. price varies. Central Bureau of Statistics, P.O.B. 13015, Jerusalem 91 130, Israel. TEL 02-21 12 11. (Co-sponsor: National Council for Research and Development) charts; stat.

372   IS   ISSN 0075-1065
ISRAEL. CENTRAL BUREAU OF STATISTICS. SCHOOLS AND KINDERGARTENS. (Subseries of its Special Series) (Text in English and Hebrew) 1954. irreg., latest issue, no.701, 1982. $5.50. Central Bureau of Statistics, Box 13015, Jerusalem 91 130, Israel. TEL 02-21 12 11.

310   IS   ISSN 0333-600X
ISRAEL. CENTRAL BUREAU OF STATISTICS. STAFF IN UNIVERSITIES. (Text in English, Hebrew) 1981. biennial. Central Bureau of Statistics, Hakirya, Romema, Jerusalem 91 130, Israel. TEL 02-21 12 11. Ed. Ms. Lifshitz. (back issues avail.)

370   IS
ISRAEL. CENTRAL BUREAU OF STATISTICS. STUDENTS IN UNIVERSITIES. (Subseries of its Special Series) 1964. irreg. price varies. Central Bureau of Statistics, P.O. Box 13015, Jerusalem 91 130, Israel. TEL 02-21 12 11.
Formerly: Israel. Central Bureau of Statistics. Students in Academic Institutions (ISSN 0075-1081)

372   IT
▼**ITALY. ISTITUTO NAZIONALE DI STATISTICA. STATISTICHE DELLA SCUOLA MATERNA ED ELEMENTARE.** 1993. a. Istituto Nazionale di Statistica, Via Cesare Balbo 16, 00100 Rome, Italy.

372   IT
▼**ITALY. ISTITUTO NAZIONALE DI STATISTICA. STATISTICHE DELLA SCUOLA MEDIA INFERIORE.** 1992. a. L.13000. Istituto Nazionale di Statistica, Via Cesare Balbo 16, 00100 Rome, Italy.

373   IT
▼**ITALY. ISTITUTO NAZIONALE DI STATISTICA. STATISTICHE DELLE SCUOLE SECONDARIE SUPERIORI.** 1992. a. L.31000 (effective 1992). Istituto Nazionale di Statistica, Via Cesare Balbo 16, 00100 Rome, Italy.

372   QA
JAMI'AT QATAR. AL-TAQRIR AL-IHSA'I AL-SANAWI LIL-AAM AL-JAMI'I/UNIVERSITY OF QATAR. ANNUAL STATISTICAL REPORT FOR THE SCHOOL YEAR. a. University of Qatar, Cultural Affairs Administration, Statistical Section, P.O. Box 2173, Doha, Qatar. TEL 83-2222. TELEX 4630.

370 296   IS
JEWISH EDUCATIONAL STATISTICS. irreg., latest vol.5. Magnes Press, Hebrew University, Jerusalem, P.O. Box 7695, Jerusalem 91076, Israel. TEL 972-2-660341. FAX 972-2-633370.

370.196 016   US   ISSN 0094-2383
JOURNAL OF ABSTRACTS IN INTERNATIONAL EDUCATION. Abbreviated title: J A I E. 1970. s-a. $10 to individuals; institutions $30. University of Akron, College of Education, c/o Zook Hall, Akron, OH 44325. (Subscr. to: c/o A. Al-Rubaiy, Educational Foundation, College of Education, University of Akron, Akron OH 44325-4208. TEL 216-972-6953) adv.; bk.rev.; abstr. circ. 450. (back issues avail.) **Document type:** abstracting/indexing.

JOURNAL OF CHEMICAL EDUCATION: SOFTWARE. SERIES B; for MS-DOS - IBM PC compatible computers. see EDUCATION — *Computer Applications*

JOURNAL OF CHEMICAL EDUCATION: SOFTWARE. SERIES C; for Apple Macintosh computers. see EDUCATION — *Computer Applications*

JOURNAL OF CHEMICAL EDUCATION: SOFTWARE. SERIES D; for Windows. see EDUCATION — *Computer Applications*

JOURNAL OF CHEMICAL EDUCATION: SOFTWARE. SPECIAL ISSUE SERIES. see EDUCATION — *Computer Applications*

370 310   II   ISSN 0970-3500
JOURNAL OF EDUCATION AND SOCIAL CHANGE. (Text in English) 1987. q. (Indian Institute of Education) Wiley Eastern Ltd., Journals Division, 4835-24 Ansari Rd., Daryaganj, New Delhi 110 002, India. TEL 3267996. FAX 91-11-3267437. TELEX 031-66507-WE_IN. circ. 1,000.

370 310   US   ISSN 0362-9791
LB2846
JOURNAL OF EDUCATIONAL STATISTICS. 1976. q. $48 to individuals; institutions $55. American Educational Research Association, 1230 17th St., N.W., Washington, DC 20036-3078. TEL 202-223-9485. FAX 202-775-1824. (Co-sponsor: American Statistical Association) Ed. Jan de Leeuw. circ. 3,400. (also avail. in microform from UMI; reprint service avail. from UMI) **Indexed:** Biostat., C.I.J.E., Cont.Pg.Educ., J.Cont.Quant.Meth., Oper.Res.Manage.Sci., Psychol.Abstr., Psyscan, Qual.Contr.Appl.Stat., Res.High.Educ.Abstr.
—BLDSC (4973.257000); Faxon; UnCover; SWETS; UMI.
Description: Demonstrates how educational statistics can contribute to sound, creative educational decision making and practice.

370   US   ISSN 1045-5493
JUNIOR HIGH MAGAZINE ABSTRACTS. 1989. bi-m. $139. EBSCO Publishing (Subsidiary of: EBSCO Industries, Inc.), 83 Pine St., Peabody, MA 01960. TEL 508-887-6667. FAX 508-887-3923. Ed. Melissa Kummerer. index. **Document type:** abstracting/indexing.

370   US
K E A RESEARCH PUBLICATIONS. (Includes Research Report, Bulletin, Brief and Memo) 1964. s-a. price varies. Kentucky Education Association, 401 Capitol Ave., Frankfort, KY 40601-2836. TEL 800-755-2889. FAX 502-227-8062. Ed. Gretchen Lampe. abstr.; charts; stat. circ. 2,500. **Document type:** academic/scholarly publication.
Formerly: K E A Publications (ISSN 0022-7307)

378.1   US
KENTUCKY COLLEGE AND UNIVERSITY DEGREES AND OTHER FORMAL AWARDS (YEAR). a. Council on Higher Education, W. Frankfort Office Complex, 1050 US 127 S., Ste. 101, Frankfort, KY 40601. TEL 502-564-3553.
Description: Contains data for degrees conferred by Kentucky's state-supported and independent colleges and universities, business colleges, and theological seminaries.

378.1   US
KENTUCKY COLLEGE AND UNIVERSITY ENROLLMENTS (YEAR). a. Council on Higher Education, W. Frankfort Office Complex, 1050 US 127 S., Frankfort, KY 40601-4395. TEL 502-564-3553.

378.1   US
KENTUCKY COLLEGE AND UNIVERSITY ORIGIN OF ENROLLMENTS. 1968. a. free. Council on Higher Education, 1050 US 127 S., Ste. 101, Frankfort, KY 40601-4395. TEL 502-564-3553. FAX 502-564-2063. Asso. Dir. Sue D. McDade. stat. circ. 500.
Former titles: Kentucky. Council on Higher Education. Origin of Kentucky College and University Enrollments; Kentucky. Council on Public Higher Education. Origin of Enrollments, Accredited Colleges and Universities (ISSN 0098-9770)
Description: Lists and tables of enrollments of state-supported and independent senior, junior, and community colleges in the state, by the Kentucky county, state, and foreign country of origin of the students and number of first-time freshmen.

LANGUAGE TEACHING. see LINGUISTICS — *Abstracting, Bibliographies, Statistics*

LIBRARY AND INFORMATION SCIENCE EDUCATION STATISTICAL REPORT. see LIBRARY AND INFORMATION SCIENCES — *Abstracting, Bibliographies, Statistics*

370   GW
LITERATURINFORMATIONEN AUS DER BILDUNGSFORSCHUNG. 1968. m. DM.60. Max-Planck-Institut fuer Bildungsforschung, Lentzeallee 94, 14195 Berlin, Germany. Ed.Bd. **Document type:** abstracting/indexing.
Formerly: Literatur aus der Bildungsforschung (ISSN 0174-0601)

EDUCATION — ABSTRACTING, BIBLIOGRAPHIES, STATISTICS

370   MH
MACAO. DIRECCAO DOS SERVICOS DE ESTATISTICA E CENSOS. INQUERITO AO ENSINO/MACAO. CENSUS AND STATISTICS DEPARTMENT. EDUCATION SURVEY. (Text in Chinese, Portuguese) 1984. a. free. Direccao dos Servicos de Estatistica e Censos, Rua Inacio Baptista, No.4-6, P.O. Box 3022, Macao. TEL 3995311. FAX 307825. **Document type:** government publication.
    Description: Presents statistics on all levels of education in Macau, including data for public and private schools.

371   MM   ISSN 0076-3489
MALTA. CENTRAL OFFICE OF STATISTICS. EDUCATION STATISTICS. a. L.1. Central Office of Statistics, Auberge d'Italie, Valletta, Malta. (Subscr. to: Publications Bookshop, Auberge de Castille, Valletta, Malta) **Document type:** government publication.

378 013   US   ISSN 0898-9095
Z5055.U49
MASTERS ABSTRACTS INTERNATIONAL; catalog of selected masters theses on microfilm. 1962. bi-m. $150. University Microfilms International, 300 N. Zeeb Rd., Ann Arbor, MI 48106. TEL 313-761-4700; 800-521-0600. FAX 313-761-1203. index. **Indexed:** Biol.Abstr., E&P Hlth. (1993-), Gas Process.& Ppl. (1993-), Off.Tech. (1993-), Petrol.Abstr. (1980-). **Document type:** abstracting/indexing.
    ●Also available online. Vendor(s): BRS Online Products, DIALOG Information Services, Inc. (File no.35), STN International.
    Also available on CD-ROM. Producer(s): University Microfilms International.
    —UMI.
    Formerly: Masters Abstracts (ISSN 0025-5106)

MATHEMATICAL EDUCATION. see *MATHEMATICS*

370 310   MF
MAURITIUS. CENTRAL STATISTICAL OFFICE. DIGEST OF EDUCATIONAL STATISTICS. 1984. a. Rs.100. Central Statistical Office, Port-Louis, Mauritius. (Subscr. to: G.P.O., La Tour Koenig, Port-Louis, Mauritius. TEL 2345294. FAX 2084011).

370 658.3   II   ISSN 0971-1848
MEDIA AND TECHNOLOGY FOR HUMAN RESOURCE DEVELOPMENT. (Text in English) 1988. q. Rs.150($50) (All India Association for Educational Technology) Wiley Eastern Ltd., Journals Division, 4835-24 Ansari Rd., Daryaganj, New Delhi 110 002, India. TEL 3267996. FAX 91-11-3267437. TELEX 031-66507-WELIN. circ. 1,200.

370 016   MX
MEXICO. CENTRO DE INFORMACION TECNICA Y DOCUMENTACION. INDICE DE ARTICULOS SOBRE EDUCACION Y ADIESTRAMIENTO. 1972. q. Mex.$80($5) Mexico. Servicio Nacional de Adiestramiento Rapido de la Mano de Obra en la Industria, Calzada Atzcapotzalco-la Villa 209, Mexico 16, D.F., Mexico. Ed. Gilberto Diaz Santana. cum.index 1972-1977. circ. 2,500. (also avail. in microfilm)

370 016 301.16   MX
MEXICO. CENTRO DE INFORMACION TECNICA Y DOCUMENTACION. INDICE DE REVISTAS. SECCION DE EDUCACION Y COMUNICACION. 1973. w. Mex.$327($17) Mexico. Servicio Nacional de Adiestramiento Rapido de la Mano de Obra en la Industria, Calzada Atzcapotzalco-la Villa 209, Mexico 16, D.F., Mexico. Ed. Gilberto Diaz Santana. circ. 164.

370 315   KO
MINISTRY OF EDUCATION. BASIC STATISTICS OF EDUCATION. a. Ministry of Education, Korean Educational Development Institute, 92-6 Umyeon-dong, Seocho-gu, Seoul 137-791, S. Korea. charts; stat.

370 016   UK   ISSN 0260-9770
MULTICULTURAL EDUCATION ABSTRACTS. 1982. q. $140 to individuals; institutions $328 (effective 1994). Carfax Publishing Co., P.O. Box 25, Abingdon, Oxon. OX14 3UE, England. TEL 44-235-555335. FAX 44-235-553559. (U.S. subscr. to: Carfax Publishing Co., Box 2025, Dunnellon, FL 34430-2025) Ed. Derek Cherrington. adv.; bk.rev.; cum.index. (also avail. in microfiche; back issues avail.) **Document type:** abstracting/indexing.
    —CCC.

N I C E M INDEX TO A V PRODUCERS AND DISTRIBUTORS. (National Information Center for Educational Media) see *MOTION PICTURES — Abstracting, Bibliographies, Statistics*

372   NE   ISSN 0168-4809
NEDERLANDSE JEUGD EN HAAR ONDERWIJS/NETHERLANDS YOUTH AND ITS EDUCATION. (Text in Dutch and English) 1947. a. Centraal Bureau voor de Statistiek, Prinses Beatrixlaan 428, Voorburg, Netherlands. (Orders to: SDU - Publishers, Christoffel Plantijnstraat, The Hague, Netherlands) **Document type:** government publication.

371 379   NE   ISSN 0168-7905
NETHERLANDS. CENTRAAL BUREAU VOOR DE STATISTIEK. STATISTIEK VAN DE UITGAVEN DER OVERHEID VOOR ONDERWIJS/NETEHRLANDS. CENTRAL BUREAU OF STATISTICS. STATISTICS OF THE EXPENDITURE OF THE STATE, THE PROVINCES AND THE MUNICIPALITIES ON EDUCATION. (Text in Dutch and English) 1964. a. Centraal Bureau voor de Statistiek, Prinses Beatrixlaan 428, Voorburg, Netherlands. (Dist. by: SDU - Publishers, Christoffel Plantijnstraat 2, Postbus 20014, 2500 EA The Hague, Netherlands) **Document type:** government publication.

370   NE   ISSN 0168-5708
NETHERLANDS. CENTRAAL BUREAU VOOR DE STATISTIEK. STATISTIEK VAN HET BEROEPSONDERWIJS: BEROEPSBEGELEIDEND ONDERWIJS LEERLINGWEZEN. a. Centraal Bureau voor de Statistiek, Prinses Beatrixlaan 428, Voorburg, Netherlands. (Dist. by: SDU - Publishers, Christoffel Plantijnstraat, The Hague, Netherlands) stat. **Document type:** government publication.

378   NE   ISSN 0168-5503
NX354.A1
NETHERLANDS. CENTRAAL BUREAU VOOR DE STATISTIEK. STATISTIEK VAN HET BEROEPSONDERWIJS: KUNSTONDERWIJS/NETHERLANDS. CENTRAL BUREAU OF STATISTICS. STATISTICS OF PROFESSIONAL EDUCATION: ART EDUCATION. (Text in Dutch and English) 1966. a. Centraal Bureau voor de Statistiek, Prinses Beatrixlaan 428, Voorburg, Netherlands. (Dist. by: SDU - Publishers, Christoffel Plantijnstraat 2, Postbus 20014, 2500 EA The Hague, Netherlands) **Document type:** government publication.
    Formerly: Netherlands. Centraal Bureau voor de Statistiek. Statistiek van het Kunstonderwijs. Statistics on Art Colleges (ISSN 0077-7307)

378   NE   ISSN 0168-5651
NETHERLANDS. CENTRAAL BUREAU VOOR DE STATISTIEK. STATISTIEK VAN HET BEROEPSONDERWIJS: OPLEIDINGSSCHOLEN KLEUTERLEIDSTERS EN PEDAGOGISCHE ACADEMIES. (Text in Dutch and English) 1943. a. Centraal Bureau voor de Statistiek, Prinses Beatrixlaan 428, Voorburg, Netherlands. (Dist. by: SDU - Publishers, Christoffel Plantijnstraat, The Hague, Netherlands) **Document type:** government publication.
    Formerly: Netherlands. Centraal Bureau voor de Statistiek. Statistiek van het Kweekschoolonderwijs. Statistics on Teacher Training Colleges (ISSN 0077-7323)

370   NE   ISSN 0168-5600
NETHERLANDS. CENTRAAL BUREAU VOOR DE STATISTIEK. STATISTIEK VAN HET BEROEPSONDERWIJS: SOCIAAL-PEDAGOGISCH ONDERWIJS/NETHERLANDS. CENTRAL BUREAU OF STATISTICS. STATISTICS OF PROFESSIONAL EDUCATION: SOCIO-PEDAGOGIC EDUCATION. (Text in Dutch and English) 1968. a. Centraal Bureau voor de Statistiek, Prinses Beatrixlaan 428, Voorburg, Netherlands. (Dist. by: SDU - Publishers, Christoffel Plantijnstraat 2, Postbus 20014, 2500 EA The Hague, Netherlands) **Document type:** government publication.
    Formerly: Netherlands. Centraal Bureau voor de Statistiek. Statistiek van het Sociaal-Pedagogisch Onderwijs (ISSN 0077-7374)

375 314   NE   ISSN 0168-5457
NETHERLANDS. CENTRAAL BUREAU VOOR DE STATISTIEK. STATISTIEK VAN HET BEROEPSONDERWIJS: TECHNISCH EN NAUTISCH ONDERWIJS. (Text in Dutch and English) 1968. a. price varies. Centraal Bureau voor de Statistiek, Prinses Beatrixlaan 428, Voorburg, Netherlands. (Dist. by: SDU - Publishers, Christoffel Plantijnstraat, The Hague, Netherlands) **Document type:** government publication.
    Formerly: Netherlands. Centraal Bureau voor de Statistiek. Statistiek van het Beroepsonderwijs (ISSN 0077-7285)

375 314   NE
NETHERLANDS. CENTRAAL BUREAU VOOR DE STATISTIEK. STATISTIEK VAN HET HOGER BEROEPSONDERWIJS: AGRARISCH ONDERWIJS. (Text in Dutch and English) 1940. a. Centraal Bureau voor de Statistiek, Prinses Beatrixlaan 428, Voorburg, Netherlands. (Dist. by: SDU - Publishers, Christoffel Plantijnstraat, The Hague, Netherlands) **Document type:** government publication.
    Former titles: Netherlands. Centraal Bureau voor de Statistiek. Statistiek van het Beroepsonderwijs: Landbouwonderwijs; Netherlands. Centraal Bureau voor de Statistiek. Statistiek van het Land- en Tuinbouwonderwijs. Statistics Concerning Agricultural and Horticultural Education (ISSN 0077-7331); Netherlands. Centraal Bureau voor de Statistiek. Statistiek van het Beroepsonderwijs: Agrarisch Onderwijs (ISSN 0169-1007)

378   NE   ISSN 0168-5058
LA828.N48a
NETHERLANDS. CENTRAAL BUREAU VOOR DE STATISTIEK. STATISTIEK VAN HET WETENSCHAPPELIJK ONDERWIJS/NETHERLANDS. CENTRAL BUREAU OF STATISTICS. STATISTICS OF UNIVERSITY EDUCATION. (Text in Dutch and English) 1937. a. Centraal Bureau voor de Statistiek, Prinses Beatrixlaan 428, Voorburg, Netherlands. (Dist. by: SDU - Publishers, Christoffel Plantijnstraat 2, Postbus 20014, 2500 EA The Hague, Netherlands) **Document type:** government publication.

371 373   NE   ISSN 0168-5856
NETHERLANDS. CENTRAAL BUREAU VOOR DE STATISTIEK. STATISTIEK VAN HET W V O, H A V O EN M A V O: SCHOLEN EN LEERLINGEN. (Text in Dutch and English) 1950. a. Centraal Bureau voor de Statistiek, Prinses Beatrixlaan 428, Voorburg, Netherlands. (Dist. by: SDU - Publishers, Christoffel Plantijnstraat, The Hague, Netherlands) **Document type:** government publication.
    Former titles: Netherlands. Centraal Bureau voor de Statistiek. Statistiek van het W V O, H A V O en M A V O: Instroom, Doorstroom en Uitstroom van Leerlingen; Netherlands. Centraal Bureau voor de Statistiek. Statistiek van het Voorbereidend Hoger en Middelbaar Onderwijs: Leraren - Statistics of Secondary Education: Teachers (ISSN 0077-7404)

373   NE   ISSN 0168-485X
LA826
NETHERLANDS. CENTRAAL BUREAU VOOR DE STATISTIEK. VOORTGEZET ONDERWIJS REGIONAAL BEZIEN. 1949. a. Centraal Bureau voor de Statistiek, Prinses Beatrixlaan 428, Voorburg, Netherlands. (Dist. by: SDU - Publishers, Christoffel Plantijnstraat, The Hague, Netherlands) circ. 500. **Document type:** government publication.

370 500 016   NE   ISSN 0167-6644
Z5815.N45
NETHERLANDS. MINISTERIE VAN ONDERWIJS EN WETENSCHAPPEN. ONDERWIJSLITERATUUR. 1946. m. fl.56.50. Staatsuitgeverij, Chr. Plantijnstraat 1, The Hague, Netherlands. bk.rev.; abstr.; bibl.; charts; index. circ. 1,700.
    Former titles: Netherlands. Ministerie van Onderwijs en Wetenschappen. Documentatieblad (ISSN 0012-4540); Netherlands. Ministerie van Onderwijs, Kunsten en Wetenschappen. Documentatieblad.

370 015   NE   ISSN 0028-2987
NETHERLANDS. MINISTERIE VAN ONDERWIJS EN WETENSCHAPPEN. PEDAGOGISCHE BIBLIOGRAFIE. 1960. m. fl.54.50. Staatsuitgeverij, Christoffel Plantijnstraat 1, The Hague, Netherlands. bk.rev.; bibl. circ. 1,200.

EDUCATION — ABSTRACTING, BIBLIOGRAPHIES, STATISTICS

379   US
NORTH DAKOTA. DEPARTMENT OF PUBLIC INSTRUCTION. BIENNIAL REPORT OF THE SUPERINTENDENT OF PUBLIC INSTRUCTION. 1888. biennial. Department of Public Instruction, Bismarck, ND 58505. TEL 701-224-2260. FAX 201-224-2261. Ed. Joe Linnertz. circ. 5,000.

310.9   UK   ISSN 0048-0770
NORTHERN IRELAND. MINISTRY OF EDUCATION. EDUCATION STATISTICS. 1965. s-a. price varies. H.M.S.O. (N. Ireland), 64 Chichester St., Belfast BT1 4PS, N. Ireland. index. (reprint service avail. from UMI)

371   NO   ISSN 0800-2169
NORWAY. STATISTISK SENTRALBYRAA. UTDANNINGSSTATISTIKK. (Subseries of its Norges Offisielle Statistikk, issued in three vols.: Grunnskoler; Videre Gaende Skoler; Universiteter Og Hogskoler) (Text in Norwegian and English) 1952. a. NOK 60 per vol. Statistisk Sentralbyraa, P.O. Box 8131-Dep., N-0033 Oslo 1, Norway. TEL 47-22-864500. FAX 47-22-864973. circ. 1,400. **Document type:** government publication.

370 016   US   ISSN 0029-3962
NOTES AND ABSTRACTS IN AMERICAN AND INTERNATIONAL EDUCATION. 1963. 2/yr. $10 to individuals; institutions $15. (University of Michigan, Associates in the Social Foundations of Education) Caddo Gap Press, 3145 Geary Blvd., Ste. 275, San Francisco, CA 94118. TEL 415-750-9978. FAX 415-668-5450. Eds. Claude A. Eggertsen, Alan H. Jones. bk.rev.; abstr.; bibl. circ. 400. (back issues avail.) **Document type:** academic/scholarly publication.
Description: Features news, essays, dissertation abstracts, and other materials relevant to the social foundation of education and international education.

378 314   AU   ISSN 0067-2343
OESTERREICHISCHE HOCHSCHULSTATISTIK. (Subseries of: Beitraege zur Oesterreichischen Statistik) 1953. a. S.430. Oesterreichisches Statistisches Zentralamt, Hintere Zollamtsstr. 2b, A-1033 Vienna, Austria. TEL 0222-71128-0. FAX 0222-7156828. circ. 440. **Document type:** government publication.
Description: Data on students at universities and at arts colleges.

378.771   US   ISSN 0094-6109
L188
OHIO HIGHER EDUCATION. BASIC DATA SERIES. 1970. biennial. latest 1991. free. Board of Regents, 30 E. Broad St., Columbus, OH 43266-0417. TEL 614-466-6000. FAX 614-466-5866. Ed. Patty Hill. illus. circ. 500. **Indexed:** ERIC. **Document type:** government publication.

370 310   PK   ISSN 0078-7914
L578.5
PAKISTAN. CENTRAL BUREAU OF EDUCATION. EDUCATIONAL STATISTICS BULLETIN SERIES. (Text in English) 1966. irreg. Central Bureau of Education, Sector H-9, Cultural Area, Islamabad, Pakistan. **Document type:** bulletin.

370 314   PL   ISSN 0079-2799
POLAND. GLOWNY URZAD STATYSTYCZNY. ROCZNIK STATYSTYCZNY SZKOLNICTWA/POLAND. CENTRAL STATISTICS OFFICE. YEARBOOK OF EDUCATION STATISTICS. (Subseries of its: Statystyka Polski) 1967. a., latest 1988. Zaklad Wydawnictw Statystycznych, Al. Niepodleglosci 208, 00-925 Warsaw, Poland. TEL 48 22 25-03-45.

370   UN
POPULATION EDUCATION ACCESSIONS LIST. (Text in English) s-a. Unesco, Principal Regional Office for Asia and the Pacific, Population Education Programme Service, P.O. Box 1425, Bangkok 10500, Thailand. TEL 391-0577. FAX 391-0866. TELEX 20591 TH.
Description: Output from Unesco computerized bibliographic data base.

370 015   XR   ISSN 0139-9489
PREHLED PEDAGOGICKE LITERATURY. (In two parts: Rada A: Vyberova Bibliografie Ceskych Clanku a Knih; Rada B: vyberova Bibliografie Zahranicnich Clanku a Knih) (Text in Czech, Slovak) 1949. bi-m. $24. Ustav pro Informace ve Vzdelavani, Statni Pedagogicka Knihovna Komenskeho, Mikulandska 5, Prague 1, Czech Republic. TEL 42-2-294062. (Subscr. to.: Senovazne nam.26, 111 121 Prague 1, Czech Republic) Eds. Stanislava Brozova, Alice Koskova. bk.rev. circ. 350. **Document type:** bibliography.
Former titles: Novinky Literatury: Prehled Pedagogicke Literatury (ISSN 0032-7344); Czechoslovakia. Statni Knihovna. Novinky Literatury: Spolecenske Vedy.
Description: Annotated bibliography of articels form Czech and foreign periodicals and books in the field of education that are available in the Czech Republic.

370.196   SU
PROGRESS OF EDUCATION IN SAUDI ARABIA; a statistical review. (Text in English) irreg. Ministry of Education, Center for Statistical Data, Box 2871, Riyadh, Saudi Arabia. TEL 47-68695. TELEX TATWIR 20554050.

PSYCSCAN: LEARNING DISORDERS AND MENTAL RETARDATION. see *PSYCHOLOGY — Abstracting, Bibliographies, Statistics*

310   US
PUBLIC EDUCATION FINANCES. 1977. a. $3.50 per no. U.S. Department of Commerce, U.S. Bureau of the Census, Government Division, Washington, DC 20233. TEL 301-763-5086. FAX 301-763-6153. (back issues avail.) **Document type:** government publication.
Formerly (until 1988): Finances of Public School Systems (ISSN 0270-8868)

658.5 016 311   US   ISSN 0033-5207
TS156.A1
QUALITY CONTROL AND APPLIED STATISTICS; international literature digest service. 1956. bi-m. $149 (foreign $176) (effective 1994). Executive Sciences Institute, 1005 Mississippi Ave., Davenport, IA 52803. TEL 319-324-4463. Ed. Bruce Brocka. abstr.; bibl.; charts; illus.; stat.; index. **Document type:** abstracting/indexing.
—BLDSC (7168.140000); SWETS.

REHABILITATION INDEX. see *MEDICAL SCIENCES — Abstracting, Bibliographies, Statistics*

016 370   YU
REPUBLICKI ZAVOD ZA UNAPREDJIVANJE VASPITANJA I OBRAZOVANJA. BIBLIOGRAFIJA; lista bibliografskih podataka novonabavljenih knjiga i clanaka iz domace i inostrane pedagoske literature. 1972. m. 80 din. Republicki Zavod za Unapredjivanje Vaspitanja i Obrazovanja, Draze Pavlovica 15, Belgrade, Yugoslavia. Ed. Marija Sladojevic.
Formerly: Institut za Istrazivanje i Razvoj Obrazovanja. Bibliograija.

370   CN
RESEARCH AND STUDIES. (In 4 vols.: Science, Engineering, Social Sciences, Arts) 1970. biennial. free. Carleton University, Faculty of Graduate Studies and Research, Office of Research Administration, Dunton Tower, Rm. 1501, Ottowa, Ont. K1S 5B6, Canada. TEL 613-788-2516. FAX 613-788-2521. Ed. Anne Burgess.
Description: Lists all publications, research projects, grants and research funding awards, and patents of University faculty members, with activities of the organized research units, and comparative statistics for the faculties and departments.

370 016   UK   ISSN 0080-1674
RESEARCH IN THE HISTORY OF EDUCATION: A LIST OF THESES FOR HIGHER DEGREES IN THE UNIVERSITIES OF ENGLAND AND WALES. (1969 edt. includes Ireland) 1969. a. £2.40. History of Education Society, 4 Marydene Dr., Evington, Leicester LE5 6HD, England. Ed. V.F. Gilbert. circ. 250.
—BLDSC (5272.051000).
Description: Lists completed research in the history of education accepted by British and Irish universities.

378 016   UK   ISSN 0034-5326
LB2331
RESEARCH INTO HIGHER EDUCATION ABSTRACTS. 1966. 3/yr. $140 to individuals; institutions $328 (effective 1994). (Society for Research into Higher Education) Carfax Publishing Co., P.O. Box 25, Abingdon, Oxon. OX14 3UE, England. TEL 44-235-555335. FAX 44-235-553559. (U.S. subscr. to: Carfax Publishing Co., Box 2025, Dunnellon, FL 34430-2025) Ed. Ian McNay. adv.; bk.rev.; cum.index. (also avail. in microfiche; back issues avail.) **Document type:** abstracting/indexing.
—BLDSC (7741.250000). **CCC.**

370 016   US   ISSN 0098-0897
Z5813
RESOURCES IN EDUCATION. Short title: R I E. (Cumulated as: Resources in Education. Annual Cumulation (ISSN 0197-9973)) 1966. m. (with s-a. & a. cumulations). $73 (foreign $91.25). (U.S. Department of Education, Bureau of Research, Office of Education) E R I C Facility, 1301 Piccard Dr., Ste. 300, Rockville, MD 20850. TEL 301-258-5500. E-mail: ericfac@inet.ed.gov. (Subscr. to: Superintendent of Documents, U.S. Government Printing Office, Box 371954, Pittsburgh, PA 15250-7954. TEL 202-783-3238. FAX 202-512-2233) Ed. Carolyn Weller. bibl.; s-a. index. circ. 4,000. (also avail. in microform from UMI; back issues avail.; reprint service avail. from UMI) **Indexed:** Educ.Tech.Abstr. MEDOC, Mid.East: Abstr.& Ind., Rural Ext.Educ.& Tr.Abstr., World Agri.Econ.& Rural Sociol.Abstr. **Document type:** abstracting/indexing, government publication.
●Also available online. Vendor(s): BRS Online Products, CISTI, DIALOG Information Services, Inc. (File no.1/ERIC).
Also available on CD-ROM. Producer(s): DIALOG Information Services, Inc., NISC (ERIC), O C L C, SilverPlatter Information, Inc. (ERIC).
—BLDSC (7777.608100); UMI.
Formerly (until 1975): Research in Education (ISSN 0034-5229)
Description: Provides up-to-date information about educational research sponsored by the Bureau. Designed to keep teachers, administrators, research specialists, and others in the eductional community, as well as the public, informed about the latest major findings in educational research.

370   US   ISSN 0197-9973
L11
RESOURCES IN EDUCATION ANNUAL CUMULATION. 1979. a. $345 (foreign $395) for 3-vol. set. (Education Resources Information Center) Oryx Press, 4041 N. Central Ave., No. 700, Phoenix, AZ 85012-3397. TEL 602-265-2651. FAX 602-265-6250. Ed.Bd. index. circ. 1,000. (also avail. in microfiche; back issues avail.) **Document type:** abstracting/indexing.
●Also available on CD-ROM. Producer(s): NISC (ERIC).
Description: Index to annotated abstracts of current educational research literature, including technical reports, speeches, books, and unpublished manuscripts.

370 016   CL   ISSN 0716-0151
LA540
RESUMENES ANALITICOS EN EDUCACION. 1972. 2/yr. $30. Centro de Investigacion y Desarrollo de Educacion, Casilla 13608, Santiago 1, Chile. TEL 6986495. Ed. Gonzalo Gutierrez. abstr.; bibl.; index. circ. 1,500.

370   US   ISSN 0098-5597
L11   CODEN: TREDEN
REVIEW OF EDUCATION; critical analysis of recent books. 1975. 4/yr. (in 1 vol., 4 nos./vol.) 48 ECU (effective 1993). Gordon and Breach Science Publishers, 820 Town Center Dr., Langhorne, PA 19047. TEL 215-750-2642. FAX 215-750-6343. (UK subscr. to: P.O. Box 90, Reading, Berkshire RG1 8JL, England. TEL 0734-560-080) Ed. Steven Gelb. adv.; bk.rev.; index. (also avail. in microform from MIM,UMI; reprint service avail. from UMI) **Indexed:** Arts & Hum.Cit.Ind., Bk.Rev.Ind., Cont.Pg.Educ., Educ.Ind., MLA.
—BLDSC (7790.265000); Faxon; UnCover. **CCC.**
Description: Publishes critical and integrative essays on recent titles.
Refereed Serial

EDUCATION — ABSTRACTING, BIBLIOGRAPHIES, STATISTICS

370   RW   ISSN 1019-4940
RWANDA. MINISTERE DE L'ENSEIGNEMENT PRIMAIRE ET SECONDAIRE. DIRECTION DE LA PLANIFICATION. BULLETIN DES STATISTIQUES DE L'ENSEIGNEMENT. 1966. a. 10 F.($32) Ministere de l'Enseignement Primaire et Secondaire, Direction de la Planification, B.P. 622, Kigali, Rwanda. circ. 150. **Document type:** government publication.
   Formerly: Rwanda. Ministere de l'Education Nationale. Direction de la Planification, Statistique et Information. Statistique de l'Enseignement.

370.196   SU
SAUDI ARABIA. MINISTRY OF EDUCATION. ANNUAL STATISTICAL REPORT. (Text in Arabic) a. Ministry of Education, Center for Statistical Data, Box 2871, Riyadh, Saudi Arabia. TEL 4768695. TELEX TATWIR 205540 SG.

370.196   SU
SAUDI ARABIA. MINISTRY OF EDUCATION. EDUCATIONAL ABSTRACTS. (Text in Arabic) s-a. Ministry of Education, Center for Statistical Data, P.O. Box 2871, Riyadh, Saudi Arabia. TEL 4768695. TELEX TATWIR 205540 SG. **Document type:** abstracting/indexing.

370.953   SU
SAUDI ARABIA. MINISTRY OF EDUCATION. EDUCATIONAL STATISTICS. (Text in Arabic, English) irreg. Ministry of Education, Statistics, Research and Education Documents Unit, Statistics Section, P.O. Box 2871, Riyadh, Saudi Arabia. TEL 4768695. TELEX TATWIR 205540 SG. illus.

370 016   UK   ISSN 0261-2755
SCHOOL ORGANISATION & MANAGEMENT ABSTRACTS. 1982. q. $140 to individuals; institutions $328 (effective 1994). Carfax Publishing Co., P.O. Box 25, Abingdon, Oxon. OX14 3UE, England. TEL 44-235-555335. FAX 44-235-553559. (U.S. subscr. to: Carfax Publishing Co., Box 2025, Dunnellon, FL 34430-2025) Ed. David Smetherham. cum.index. (also avail. in microfiche; back issues avail.) **Document type:** abstracting/indexing.
—CCC.

370 016   UK   ISSN 0038-0415
SOCIOLOGY OF EDUCATION ABSTRACTS. 1965. q. $205 to individuals; institutions $430 (effective 1994). Carfax Publishing Co., P.O. Box 25, Abingdon, Oxon. OX14 3UE, England. TEL 44-235-555335. FAX 44-235-553559. (U.S. subscr. to: Carfax Publishing Co., Box 2025, Dunnellon, FL 34430-2025) Ed. Chris Shilling. cum.index. (also avail. in microfiche; back issues avail.) **Indexed:** E.I. **Document type:** abstracting/indexing.
—UnCover. **CCC.**

378 316.8   SA
SOUTH AFRICA. CENTRAL STATISTICAL SERVICE. STATISTICAL RELEASE. FINANCIAL STATISTICS OF UNIVERSITIES AND TECHNIKONS. (No. P9103) a., latest 1989. free. Central Statistical Service - Sentral Statistiekdiens, Private Bag X44, Pretoria 0001, South Africa. TEL 27-12-310-8911. FAX 27-12-310-8500. **Document type:** government publication.

371.4   UK   ISSN 0954-0822
SPECIAL EDUCATIONAL NEEDS ABSTRACTS. 1989. q. $140 to individuals; institutions $328 (effective 1994). Carfax Publishing Co., P.O. Box 25, Abingdon, Oxon. OX14 3UE, England. TEL 44-235-555335. FAX 44-235-553559. (U.S. subscr. to: Carfax Publishing Co., Box 2025, Dunnellon, FL 34430-2025) Ed. Derek Cherrington. adv.; bk.rev. (also avail. in microfiche) **Document type:** abstracting/indexing.
—CCC.

420 808.5   US   ISSN 0190-2075
PN4073
SPEECH COMMUNICATION DIRECTORY. 1935. a. $16. Speech Communication Association, 5105 Backlick Rd., Bldg. E., Annandale, VA 22003. TEL 703-750-0533. Ed. Penny Demo. circ. 2,000. **Document type:** directory.
   Former titles: Speech Communication Directory of S C A and the Regional Speech Communication Organizations; Speech Communication Association. Directory (ISSN 0081-3648); Speech Association of America. Directory.

613.7 016 790.1   UK   ISSN 0142-1794
SPORTS DOCUMENTATION MONTHLY BULLETIN. (Text in English and other languages; summaries in English) 1971. m. £38 to individuals; institutions £49. Centre for Sports Science and History, Main Library, University of Birmingham, Edgbaston, Birmingham B15 2TT, England. TEL 021-414-5843. Ed.Bd. cum.index. circ. 330. **Indexed:** Ergon.Abstr. **Document type:** bulletin.
—BLDSC (8419.834000).
   Formerly: Sports Information Monthly Bulletin.
   Description: Lists of recent periodical articles and conference papers on the scientific and medical aspects of sport, physical education, and recreation, with indexes of authors and subject matter.

SPORTSEARCH. see *SPORTS AND GAMES — Abstracting, Bibliographies, Statistics*

370 016   US   ISSN 0039-0046
Z5811
STATE EDUCATION JOURNAL INDEX; an annotated index to materials in the field of education. 1962. s-a. $78. State Education Journal Index Publications, Box 244, Westminster, CO 80030. TEL 303-494-8073. Ed. L. Stanley Ratliff. bk.rev.; bibl. circ. 500. **Document type:** abstracting/indexing.

378   US   ISSN 0081-4644
LA340.5
STATISTICAL ABSTRACT OF HIGHER EDUCATION IN NORTH CAROLINA. 1968. a. free. University of North Carolina, Box 2688, Chapel Hill, NC 27515-2688. TEL 919-962-1000. FAX 919-962-0488. Ed. Linda F. Balfour. circ. 2,500. (also avail. in microfiche from CIS) **Indexed:** ERIC, SRI.

370   UK   ISSN 0951-1245
LA662
STATISTICS OF EDUCATION IN WALES: HIGHER & FURTHER EDUCATION. 1975. a. £5 per issue. Welsh Office, Statistical Directorate, New Crown Bldg., Cathays Park, Cardiff CF1 3NQ, Wales. TEL 0222-825044. FAX 0222-825350. TELEX 498228. Ed. E. Swires-Hennessy. stat. circ. 600. **Document type:** government publication.
—BLDSC (8453.536220). **CCC.**
   Supersedes in part (in 1987): Statistics of Education in Wales (ISSN 0262-8317)

370   UK   ISSN 0951-1237
LA660
STATISTICS OF EDUCATION IN WALES: SCHOOLS. 1975. a. £6. Welsh Office, Statistical Directorate, New Crown Bldg., Cathays Park, Cardiff CF1 3NQ, Wales. TEL 022-825044. FAX 0222-825350. TELEX 498228. Ed. E. Swires-Hennessy. stat. circ. 625. **Document type:** government publication.
—CCC.
   Supersedes in part (in 1987): Statistics of Education in Wales (ISSN 0262-8317)
   Description: Specifics on school services, teachers, teacher training and finance.

361   US   ISSN 0091-7192
HV11
STATISTICS ON SOCIAL WORK EDUCATION IN THE UNITED STATES. 1952. a. $12. Council on Social Work Education, 1600 Duke St., Alexandria, VA 22314-3421. TEL 703-683-8080. FAX 703-683-8099. circ. 1,400.
   Formerly: Statistics on Social Work Education (ISSN 0081-5217)

370 150 016   XR
STATNI VEDECKA KNIHOVNA. VYBER NOVINEK. SERIE F: PEDAGOGIKA, PSYCHOLOGIE. 1974. 6/yr. 18 Kcs. (35 Kcs. for 7 vols. series: A-G). Statni Vedecka Knihovna, Kounicova 5-7, 601 87 Brno, Czech Republic. Ed. Eva Tauwinklova. circ. 300.

370.196 310   CY
SURVEY ON GRADUATING STUDENTS ABROAD. irreg. £C3 per no. Ministry of Finance, Department of Statistics and Research, 13, Lord Byron Ave., Nicosia, Cyprus. TEL 30-3208. FAX 456712.
   Description: Estimates the number of graduates who remain abroad and examines the employment situation of those returning to Cyprus one year after their graduation.

370 316   SQ
SWAZILAND. CENTRAL STATISTICAL OFFICE. EDUCATION STATISTICS. 1968. a., latest 1991. free. Central Statistical Office, Box 456, Mbabane, Swaziland. TEL 43765. circ. 700. **Document type:** government publication.

370   SW   ISSN 0282-3470
SWEDEN. STATISTISKA CENTRALBYRAAN. STATISTISKA MEDDELANDEN. SERIE U, UTBILDNING OCH FORSKNING. (Text in Swedish; table heads and summaries in English) 1963 N.S. irreg. SEK 910. Statistiska Centralbyraan, Publishing Unit, S-701 89 Oerebro, Sweden. circ. 2,000.
   Supersedes in part (in 1985): Sweden. Statistiska Centralbyraan. Statistiska Meddelanden. Serie U, Utbildning, Forskning och Kultur.

370   SZ
SWITZERLAND. BUNDESAMT FUER STATISTIK. SCHUELERINNEN, SCHUELER UND STUDIERENDE - ELEVES ET ETUDIANTS. (Text in French and German) 1976. a. 13 SFr. Bundesamt fuer Statistik, Schwarztorstr. 96, CH-3003 Bern, Switzerland. TEL 031-3236011. FAX 031-3236061. **Document type:** government publication.
   Formerly: Switzerland. Bundesamt fuer Statistik. Schuelerstatistik - Statistique des Eleves.

T O M. (Text on Microfilm) see *ABSTRACTING AND INDEXING SERVICES*

373 372 016   UK   ISSN 0141-982X
TEACHING STATISTICS; an international journal for teachers of pupils aged 9 to 19. 1979. 3/yr. £16.95 (foreign £21.50($45)). Teaching Statistics Trust, Dept. of Probability and Statistics, University of Sheffield, Sheffield S37 7RH, England. TEL 0742-824117. FAX 0742-824292. Ed. N. Hunt. adv.; bk.rev. circ. 1,300. **Indexed:** Cont.Pg.Educ., Curr.Ind.Stat., Oper.Res.Manage.Sci., Qual.Contr.Appl.Stat., Zent.Math. **Document type:** academic/scholarly publication.
—BLDSC (8614.343000); SWETS.

600 378 016   UK   ISSN 0966-162X
T61
TECHNICAL EDUCATION & TRAINING ABSTRACTS. 1961. q. $140 to individuals; institutions $328 (effective 1994). Carfax Publishing Co., P.O. Box 25, Abingdon, Oxon. OX14 3UE, England. TEL 44-235-555335. FAX 44-235-553559. (U.S. subscr. to: Carfax Publishing Co., Box 2025, Dunnellon, FL 34430-2025) Ed. Roy Kirk. cum.index. (also avail. in microfiche; back issues avail.) **Indexed:** Build.Manage.Abstr. **Document type:** abstracting/indexing.
—CCC.
   Formerly: Technical Education Abstracts (ISSN 0040-0920)

378   IS   ISSN 0792-7355
TECHNION - ISRAEL INSTITUTE OF TECHNOLOGY. ABSTRACTS OF RESEARCH THESES. (Text in English) 1983. a. $16. Technion - Israel Institute of Technology, Graduate School, Technion City, Haifa 32000, Israel. FAX 972-4-221600. circ. 500. **Document type:** abstracting/indexing.

370 020   US   ISSN 1051-2993
Z695.1.E3
THESAURUS OF E R I C DESCRIPTORS. (Educational Resources Information Center) 1967. irreg., 12th ed., 1990. $69.50 (foreign $83.40) (effective 1992). Oryx Press, 4041 N. Central Ave., No. 700, Phoenix, AZ 85012-3397. TEL 602-265-2651. FAX 602-265-6250. Ed.Bd. index. circ. 6,000. **Document type:** abstracting/indexing.
●Also available on CD-ROM. Producer(s): NISC (ERIC).
   Description: Lists the vocabulary of descriptors and terms used by the ERIC system in indexing and abstracting education literature. Has an extensive introduction describing the ERIC system providing keys for using the thesaurus.

315.61   TU
TURKEY. DEVLET ISTATISTIK ENSTITUSU. KAMU KURUMU VE KURULUSLARI HIZMET ONCESI VE HIZMET ICI EGITIM ISTATISTIKLERI/TURKEY. STATE INSTITUTE OF STATISTICS. STATISTICS ON TRAINING IN STATE INSTITUTIONS. (Text in English, Turkish) 1987. a. $15. Devlet Istatistik Enstitusu - State Institute of Statistics, Necatibey Caddesi No. 114, 06100 Ankara, Turkey. TEL 90-4-4176440. FAX 90-4-4253387. circ. 5,000. **Document type:** government publication.

315.61 TU
TURKEY. DEVLET ISTATISTIK ENSTITUSU. MILLI EGITIM ISTATISTIKLERI ORGUN EGITIM/TURKEY. STATE INSTITUTE OF STATISTICS. NATIONAL EDUCATIONAL STATISTICS FORMAL EDUCATION. (Text in English, Turkish) 1988. a. $60. Devlet Istatistik Enstitusu - State Institute of Statistics, Necatibey Caddesi No. 114, 06100 Ankara, Turkey. TEL 90-312-4185027. FAX 90-312-4170432. circ. 925. (also avail. in diskette format) **Document type:** government publication.
 Description: Contains statistical information on state and private education from kindergarten through high school, including vocational and technical high schools.

315.61 TU
TURKEY. DEVLET ISTATISTIK ENSTITUSU. MILLI EGITIM ISTATISTIKLERI: OGRETIM YILI BASI. 1933. a., latest 1986. free or on exchange basis. Devlet Istatistik Enstitusu - State Institute of Statistics, Necatibey Caddesi No. 114, 06100 Ankara, Turkey. TEL 90-4-4176440. FAX 90-4-4253387. **Document type:** government publication.

315.61 TU
TURKEY. DEVLET ISTATISTIK ENSTITUSU. MILLI EGITIM ISTATISTIKLERI YAYGIN EGITIM/TURKEY. STATE INSTITUTE OF STATISTICS. NATIONAL EDUCATION STATISTICS ADULT EDUCATION. (Text in English, Turkish) 1978. a. $40. Devlet Istatistik Enstitusu - State Institute of Statistics, Necatibey Caddesi No. 114, 06100 Ankara, Turkey. TEL 90-312-4185027. FAX 90-312-4170432. circ. 925. **Document type:** government publication.
 Description: Provides statistical information on private teaching centers, private courses, apprenticeship training programs, Koran courses, illiteracy campaign activities and practical trade schools for girls.

378 PH
U P THESIS AND DISSERTATION ABSTRACTS. (Text in English and Filipino) 1983. a. P.50($10) University of the Philippines, Office of Research Coordination, Rm. 309 Malcolm Hall, Diliman, Quezon City, Philippines. **Document type:** abstracting/indexing.

370 UN
UNESCO. PRINCIPAL REGIONAL OFFICE FOR ASIA AND PACIFIC. ABSTRACT BIBLIOGRAPHY SERIES ON POPULATION EDUCATION. (Text in English) a. Unesco, Principal Regional Office for Asia and the Pacific, Population Education Programme Service, P.O. Box 1425, Bangkok 10500, Thailand. FAX 391-0866. TELEX 20591 TH. abstr.; bibl.; index. **Document type:** abstracting/indexing.
 Formerly: Unesco. Regional Office for Education in Asia and the Pacific. Abstract Bibliography Series on Population Education.
 Description: Covers women's role and status in the socio-economic development of the Asian and Pacific areas.

370 016 UN
UNESCO LIST OF DOCUMENTS AND PUBLICATIONS. (Text in English, French, Spanish; summaries in English) 1973. 4/yr. (plus a. cum.). free. Unesco, Computerized Documentation Service, 7-9 Place de Fontenoy, 75700 Paris, France. TEL 45-77-16-10. (Dist. in U.S. by: Unipub, 4611-F Assembly Dr., Lanham, MD 20706-4391)

370 016 DK ISSN 0901-9294
UNGDOMS- OG VOKSENUNDERVISNING.* 1979. a. DKK 27.75. Landscentralen for Undervisningsmidler, Gammel Kongevej 164, 1850 Copenhagen V, Denmark.
 Former titles (until 1986): Undervisningsmidler for Ungdoms- og Voksenundervisning (ISSN 0106-5971); Supersedes in part: Danske Skole- og Laereboeger.

378 US
U.S. DEPARTMENT OF EDUCATION. NATIONAL CENTER FOR EDUCATION STATISTICS. ACADEMIC LIBRARIES. irreg., latest 1988. U.S. Department of Education, National Center for Education Statistics, 555 New Jersey Ave., N.W., Washington, DC 20208. TEL 800-424-1616. (Dist. by: Supt. of Documents, Washington, DC 20402)
 Formerly: U.S. Department of Education. National Center for Education Statistics. Library Statistics of Colleges and Universities.

378 US
U.S. DEPARTMENT OF EDUCATION. NATIONAL CENTER FOR EDUCATION STATISTICS. COMPLETIONS IN INSTITUTIONS OF HIGHER EDUCATION. 1948. irreg., latest 1987. U.S. Department of Education, 555 New Jersey Ave., N.W., Washington, DC 20208. TEL 800-424-1616. (Dist. by: Office of Educational Research and Improvement, Washington, DC 20208) **Indexed:** Educ.Ind., R.G.
 Formerly: U.S. Department of Education. National Center for Education Statistics. Earned Degrees Conferred (ISSN 0565-744X)

370 US
U.S. DEPARTMENT OF EDUCATION. NATIONAL CENTER FOR EDUCATION STATISTICS. DIGEST OF EDUCATION STATISTICS. 1962. a. U.S. Department of Education, National Center for Education Statistics, 555 New Jersey Ave., N.W., Washington, DC 20208. TEL 800-424-1616. (Dist. by: Supt. of Documents, Washington, DC 20402)
 Formerly: U.S. National Center for Education Statistics. Digest of Educational Statistics (ISSN 0083-2634)

378 US ISSN 0362-5036
LA227.3
U.S. DEPARTMENT OF EDUCATION. NATIONAL CENTER FOR EDUCATION STATISTICS. FALL ENROLLMENT IN HIGHER EDUCATION. 1947. a. price varies. U.S. Department of Education, National Center for Education Statistics, 555 New Jersey Ave., N.W., Washington, DC 20208. TEL 800-424-1616. (Dist. by: Office of Educational Research and Improvement, Washington, DC 20402)
 Formerly: Opening Fall Enrollment in Higher Education (ISSN 0083-2758)

372 373 310 US
U.S. DEPARTMENT OF EDUCATION. NATIONAL CENTER FOR EDUCATION STATISTICS. PUBLIC ELEMENTARY AND SECONDARY STATE AGGREGATE DATA, BY STATE. 1954. a. U.S. Department of Education, National Center for Education Statistics, 555 New Jersey Ave., N.W., Washington, DC 20208. TEL 800-424-1616. (Dist. by: Office of Education Research and Improvement, Washington, DC 20208)
 Supersedes: U.S. National Center for Education Statistics. Revenues and Expenditures for Public Elementary and Secondary Education (ISSN 0149-2497); U.S. National Center for Education Statistics. Expenditures and Revenues for Public Elementary and Secondary Education (ISSN 0090-7618); Incorporates: U.S. National Center for Education Statistics. Statistics of Public Elementary and Secondary School Systems; Which was formerly: U.S. National Center for Education Statistics. Statistics of Public Elementary and Secondary Day Schools.

378 US
U.S. DEPARTMENT OF EDUCATION. NATIONAL CENTER FOR EDUCATION STATISTICS. STATE HIGHER EDUCATION PROFILES. irreg., latest 1987. price varies. U.S. Department of Education, National Center for Education Statistics, 555 New Jersey Ave., N.W., Washington, DC 20208. TEL 800-424-1616. (Dist. by: Supt. of Documents, Washington DC 20402)
 Formerly: U.S. National Center for Education Statistics. Financial Statistics of Institutions of Higher Education (ISSN 0095-6716)

370 BL
UNIVERSIDADE FEDERAL DE PERNAMBUCO. ANUARIO ESTATISTICO. (Includes University Master Plan) 1972. a. (with supplement). free. Universidade Federal de Pernambuco, Assessoria da Area de Informacao, Cidade Universitaria, Av. Prof. Morais Rego, Recife, Pernambuco, Brazil. stat.

378 CN ISSN 0829-7177
UNIVERSITY FINANCE TREND ANALYSIS/FINANCE DES UNIVERSITES ANALYSE DES TENDANCES. (Text in English, French) 1983. a. Can.$29($47) Statistics Canada, Publications Sales and Services, Ottawa, Ont. K1A 0T6, Canada. FAX 613-951-1584. stat.; circ. 200 (controlled). (back issues avail.)
 Description: Presents a review of financing of Canadian universities.

EDUCATION — ADULT EDUCATION 2075

378 US ISSN 0070-3044
UNIVERSITY OF DAYTON. SCHOOL OF EDUCATION. ABSTRACTS OF RESEARCH PROJECTS. 1968. irreg., vol.8, 1989. free. University of Dayton, School of Education, Dayton, OH 45469. TEL 513-229-3146. Ed. L. Gordon Fuchs. index. **Document type:** abstracting/indexing.
 Description: Projects completed by candidates for the M.S.

378 016 BN
UNIVERZITET U SARAJEVU. DOKTORSKE DISERTACIJE. REZIMEI. (Supplement to: Univerzitet u Sarajevu. Bilten) 1969. a. Univerzitet u Sarajevu, Vojvode Stepe obala 7-111, 71000 Sarajevo, Bosnia Hercegovina. TEL 213-296. illus.
 Description: Summary of doctoral dissertations on education.

370 AT ISSN 1034-0815
VOCATIONAL EDUCATION AND TRAINING DATABASE. q. Aus.$100. National Centre for Vocational Education Research, 252 Kensington Rd., Leabrook, S.A. 5068, Australia. TEL 08-332-7822. FAX 08-332-3988. Ed. Carol Cheshire. circ. 1,400. **Document type:** abstracting/indexing.
 Description: Contains bibliographic entries describing publications by and about technical, vocational and further education in Australia and the Asian Pacific Region, entries covering research in progress in vocational training.

370 AT ISSN 0812-1311
WESTERN AUSTRALIA. MINISTRY OF EDUCATION. EDUCATION STATISTICS BULLETIN. 1983. s-a. Aus.$7. Ministry of Education, Information Services, 151 Royal St., East Perth, W.A. 6004, Australia. stat. circ. 1,600. (back issues avail.) **Document type:** bulletin.
 Description: Compilation of education statistics.

370 US
WHO'S WHO AMONG AMERICAN HIGH SCHOOL STUDENTS. (In 16 vols., by region) 1967. a. $34.95. Educational Communications, Inc. (Lake Forest), 721 N. McKinley, Lake Forest, IL 60045. TEL 708-295-6650. Ed. Paul C. Krouse. illus.; stat.

370 011 US
WHO'S WHO AMONG AMERICA'S TEACHERS. 1990. biennial (in 2vols.). $69.95. Educational Communications, Inc. (Lake Forest), 721 N. McKinley, Lake Forest, IL 60045. TEL 708-295-6650.

YEARBOOK OF ADULT CONTINUING EDUCATION. see *EDUCATION — Adult Education*

370 314 YU
YUGOSLAVIA. SAVEZNI ZAVOD ZA STATISTIKU. OSNOVNA I SREDNJE. (Subseries of its Statisticki Bilten) irreg. 30 din.($1.11) Savezni Zavod za Statistiku, Kneza Milosa 20, Belgrade, Yugoslavia. TEL 681-999. circ. 1,000.

370 314 YU ISSN 0513-0832
YUGOSLAVIA. SAVEZNI ZAVOD ZA STATISTIKU. UCENICI U PRIVREDI. (Subseries of its Statisticki Bilten) irreg. 20 din.($1.11) Savezni Zavod za Statistiku, Kneza Milosa 20, Belgrade, Yugoslavia. TEL 681-999. circ. 1,000.

011 GW ISSN 0172-9357
Z E U S; Zentralblatt fuer Erziehungswesen und Schule. (Text in Dutch, English, French, German) 1985. 6/yr. DM.495. Verlag fuer Paedagogische Dokumentation GmbH, Postfach 130840, 47108 Duisburg, Germany TEL 0203-89159. Ed. Heiner Schmidt. s-a. index. circ. 390. **Document type:** bibliography.

EDUCATION — Adult Education

374 AT ISSN 1320-2162
A A A C E NEWS. 7/yr. Aus.$30 (foreign Aus.$40). Australian Association of Adult and Community Education, P.O. Box 308, Jamison Centre, A.C.T. 2614, Australia. TEL 06-251-7933. Ed. Alastair Crombie. **Document type:** newsletter.
 Formerly: Australian Association of Adult Education. Newsletter (ISSN 0727-4386)

A A C E BONUS BRIEFS: careers, education, and work pulling together. (American Association for Career Education) see *OCCUPATIONS AND CAREERS*

EDUCATION — ADULT EDUCATION

A A C E CAREERS UPDATE. (American Association for Career Education) see *OCCUPATIONS AND CAREERS*

A A C E DISTINGUISHED MEMBER SERIES; careers, education, and work pulling together. (American Association for Career Education) see *OCCUPATIONS AND CAREERS*

374   KE
A A E A NEWSLETTER. 1978. s-a. free. African Adult Education Association, Box 50768, Nairobi, Kenya. Ed. Paul Wangoola. circ. 1,200. (back issues avail.) **Document type:** newsletter.

374   US
A C S D E RESEARCH MONOGRAPH. 1990. irreg., no.9, 1993. price varies. (American Center for the Study of Distance Education) Pennsylvania State University, College of Education, 403 S. Allen St., Ste. 206, University Park, PA 16801-5202. TEL 814-863-3764. FAX 814-865-5878. Ed. Michael G. Moore. **Document type:** monographic series.
   Description: Publishes symposium papers and studies on a variety of topics relating to distance education, including computer applications, studies of international interest, and research issues.

374.013   GW   ISSN 0937-8375
A K S B - INFORM. (Former name of issuing body: Verein zur Foerderung Katholisch-Sozialer Bildungswerke) 1974. bi-m. Arbeitsgemeinschaft Katholisch-Sozialer Bildungswerke, Heilsbachstr. 6, 53123 Bonn, Germany. TEL 0228-645058. FAX 0228-6420910. Ed. Johannes Tessmer. bk.rev. **Document type:** bulletin.

374   IE   ISSN 0790-7214
A O N T A S DIRECTORY OF ADULT AND COMMUNITY EDUCATION AGENCIES IN IRELAND. 1980. a? A O N T A S National Association of Adult Education, 22 Earlsfort Terrace, Dublin 2, Ireland. TEL 01-754121.
   Formerly (until 1985): National Directory of Adult and Community Education Agencies (ISSN 0332-1770)

374   IE
A O N T A S NEWSLETTER; newsletter of Irish adult education. 1987. bi-m. membership. A O N T A S National Association of Adult Education, 22 Earlsfort Terrace, Dublin 2, Ireland. TEL 01-754121. FAX 01-780084. Ed. Isobel Crowe. bk.rev. circ. 1,000. **Document type:** newsletter.

A R T I NEWS LETTER. (Agrarian Research and Training Institute) see *AGRICULTURE*

374 371.9   US
A V K O NEWSLETTER. 1974. q. membership. A V K O Educational Research Foundation, Inc., 3084 W. Willard Rd., Clio, MI 48420. TEL 810-686-9283. Ed. R.J. Rayl. bk.rev. (back issues avail.) **Document type:** newsletter.
   Description: Contains news and information to assist members of the foundation.

ACCESS (GLENSIDE); information and education for the mining and petroleum industry. see *MINES AND MINING INDUSTRY*

374   US
ADULT & COMMUNITY EDUCATION ORGANIZATIONS & LEADERS DIRECTORY.* 1977. a. $40. M & O Communications, 120 E. 34th St., 7th Fl., New York, NY 10016. TEL 202-638-0348. Ed. Lester A. Barrer.

374   US   ISSN 0001-8473
ADULT & CONTINUING EDUCATION TODAY. 1970. bi-w. $95. Learning Resources Network, 1554 Hayes Dr., Manhattan, KS 66502. TEL 913-539-5376. Ed. William A. Draves. adv.; bk.rev.; bibl.; stat.; index, cum.index. circ. 2,600. (looseleaf format; back issues avail.) **Indexed:** Res.High.Educ.Abstr. **Document type:** newsletter.
   Incorporates (in 1984): Learning Connection.
   Description: Newsletter of articles, editorials, and letters on contemporary continuing education.

371   US   ISSN 1052-231X
LC5201
ADULT BASIC EDUCATION. 1977. 3/yr. $25 in US and Canada; elsewhere $35. Commission on Adult Basic Education, Box 592053, Orlando, FL 32859-2053. TEL 407-836-3590. FAX 407-836-3523. Ed. Ken Melichar. adv.; bk.rev.; abstr.; bibl.; stat.; index. circ. 1,000. (also avail. in microfilm from UMI) **Indexed:** C.I.J.E., Educ.Ind.
   —BLDSC (0696.637000); Faxon; UnCover; SWETS; UMI.
   Formerly (until vol.14, no.3, 1990): Adult Literacy and Basic Education (ISSN 0147-8354)

374   UN   ISSN 0379-8348
ADULT EDUCATION INFORMATION NOTES. Arabic edition: Ta'lim al-Kibar (ISSN 1014-8736); French edition: Unesco Education des Adultes (ISSN 0376-4907); Russian edition: Unesko Obrazovanie Vzroslyh (ISSN 0379-8356); Spanish edition: Unesco Educacion de Adultos (ISSN 0379-833X) 1973. q. free. Unesco, Adult Education Section, 7-9 Place de Fontenoy, 75700 Paris, France. TEL 577-16-10. bibl.
   Incorporates: Literacy: a Newsletter (ISSN 0047-4770)

374   US   ISSN 0741-7136
LC5201
ADULT EDUCATION QUARTERLY.* 1950. q. $36 (foreign $43). American Association for Adult and Continuing Education, 1101 Connecticut Ave., N.W., Ste. 700, Washington, DC 20036. TEL 703-522-2234. Ed. Roger Hiemstra. adv.; bk.rev.; index. circ. 5,500. (also avail. in microform (ISSN 0364-9911) from UMI) **Indexed:** Bibl.Ind., Bk.Rev.Ind. (1965-), Br.Educ.Ind., C.I.J.E., Child.Bk.Rev.Ind. (1965-), Cont.Pg.Educ., Educ.Ind., High.Educ.Curr.Aware.Bull., Mid.East: Abstr.& Ind., Mult.Ed.Abstr., Psychol.Abstr., Rural Ext.Educ.& Tr.Abstr., SOMA, SSCI, Stud.Wom.Abstr.
   —BLDSC (0696.667000); Faxon; UnCover; SWETS; UMI.
   Formerly (until 1983): Adult Education (ISSN 0001-8481)
   Description: Research and theory journal on the field of adult education.
   Refereed Serial

374   US   ISSN 1045-1595
LC5251
ADULT LEARNING.* 1960. 8/yr. $37 (foreign $45). American Association for Adult and Continuing Education, 1101 Connecticut Ave., N.W., Ste. 700, Arlington, VA 20036. TEL 703-522-2234. Ed. Jeanette Smith. circ. 6,000. (also avail. in microform from UMI; reprint service avail. from UMI) **Indexed:** Acad.Ind., Bk.Rev.Ind. (1977-), C.I.J.E., Child.Bk.Rev.Ind. (1977-), CLOA, Cont.Pg.Educ., Educ.Ind., Tr.& Dev.Alert.
   —BLDSC (0696.680100); Faxon; UnCover; SWETS; UMI.
   Supersedes (in 1989): Lifelong Learning (ISSN 0740-0578); Which was formerly (1977-1983): Lifelong Learning: The Adult Years (ISSN 0148-2165); Adult Leadership; A A C E Dateline; Techniques for Teachers of Adults (ISSN 0040-1358)
   Description: Practical applications of research, innovative instructional strategies.

374   AT   ISSN 0157-4833
ADULT LITERACY CONTACTS VICTORIA. 1983. a. free. Victorian Adult Literacy and Basic Education Council (VALBEC), Ross House, 247 Flinders Ln., Melbourne, Vic. 3000, Australia. TEL 03-650 6906. FAX 03-654-1321. Ed. Barbara Money. circ. 1,000.
   Description: Names, addresses and descriptions of Victorian adult literacy programs.

374   UK   ISSN 0955-2308
LC5201
ADULTS LEARNING. 1989. m. £17.50 (foreign £22.50). National Institute of Adult Continuing Education, 21 De Montfort St., Leicester LE1 7GE, England. TEL 0533-551451. FAX 0533-854514. Ed. Christopher Feeney. adv.; bk.rev.; index. circ. 3,000. (back issues avail.) **Indexed:** Mult.Ed.Abstr. **Document type:** academic/scholarly publication.
   —BLDSC (0696.684887); SWETS; UMI.
   Description: Covers full range of adult learning, particularly women's education.

374   KE
AFRICAN ADULT EDUCATION ASSOCIATION. JOURNAL. (Text in English; summaries in French) 1979. irreg. $6.50 to non-members; members $4. African Adult Education Association, Box 50768, Nairobi, Kenya. Ed. Paul Wangoola. circ. 500. (back issues avail.)

AFRICAN ASSOCIATION FOR LITERACY AND ADULT EDUCATION. JOURNAL. see *EDUCATION*

374 384.55   GW   ISSN 0941-5491
LB1043.2.G4
AGENDA; magazine for media, education and culture. (Includes: AgendaService) 1978. bi-m. DM.65. Deutscher Volkshochschul-Verband e.V., Adolf Grimme Institut, Eduard-Weitsch-Weg 25, 45768 Marl, Germany. TEL 02365-9189-0. FAX 02365-918989. Ed. Ulrich Timmermann. adv.; bk.rev. circ. 3,000. **Document type:** consumer publication.
   Formerly (until 1992): W and M (ISSN 0170-866X)
   Description: Covers adult education and the media. Features education through television, radio, video, movies, and computers. Includes television program listing.

374   US
ALASKA ADULT EDUCATION. a. Department of Education, 801 W. 10th St., Ste. 200, Juneau, AK 99801-1894. **Document type:** government publication.

374.4   US   ISSN 0892-3647
AMERICAN JOURNAL OF DISTANCE EDUCATION. 1987. 3/yr. $30 to individuals (Canada & Mexico $36; elsewhere $45); institutions $55 (Canada & Mexico $61; elsewhere $70) (effective 1993). Pennsylvania State University, College of Education, 403 S. Allen St., Ste. 206, University Park, PA 16801-5202. TEL 814-863-3764. FAX 815-865-5878. Ed. Michael G. Moore. bk.rev. (back issues avail.) **Indexed:** Tr.& Dev.Alert. **Document type:** academic/scholarly publication.
   —BLDSC (0824.305000); Faxon; UnCover; SWETS.
   Description: Serves as a forum for criticism and debate about research and practice of distance education in the Americas, examining program ideas, developments in methods and systems for the delivery of education at a distance, management and administration, evaluation and assessment.

374   GW   ISSN 0720-9118
ARBEITSHILFEN FUER DIE ERWACHSENENBILDUNG. 1976. s-a. DM.10. Paedagogische Arbeitsstelle fuer Erwachsenenbildung in Baden-Wuerttemberg, Panoramastr. 19, 70174 Stuttgart, Germany. TEL 0711-293685. bk.rev. circ. 2,200. (back issues avail.) **Document type:** bulletin.

ASSOCIATION EDUCATION DIRECTOR. see *BUSINESS AND ECONOMICS — Management*

ASSOCIATION OF COLLEGES FOR FURTHER AND HIGHER EDUCATION. HANDBOOK. see *EDUCATION — Higher Education*

387   CN   ISSN 0703-5357
ATLANTIC CO-OPERATOR. 1933. m. Can.$15($16) Box 1386, Antigonish, NS B2G 2L7, Canada. TEL 902-863-2776. FAX 902-863-8077. Ed. Brenda MacKinnon. adv.; bk.rev. circ. 63,000. (tabloid format) **Document type:** consumer publication.
   Formerly: Maritime Co-Operator (ISSN 0025-3405)

374.013   GW   ISSN 0004-8100
DER AUSBILDER. 1952. m. DM.34.80. W. Bertelsmann Verlag, Postfach 100633, 33506 Bielefeld, Germany. TEL 0521-9110126. FAX 0521-9110179. Ed. Dr. Kieslinger. bk.rev. charts; index. circ. 4,700. **Document type:** trade publication.
   —CCC.

AUSTIN GENEALOGICAL SOCIETY QUARTERLY. see *GENEALOGY AND HERALDRY*

AUSTRALIAN BUSINESS EDUCATION DIRECTORY. see *BUSINESS AND ECONOMICS*

EDUCATION — ADULT EDUCATION

374   AT   ISSN 1035-0462
LC5201   CODEN: AJAEED
AUSTRALIAN JOURNAL OF ADULT & COMMUNITY EDUCATION. 1961. 3/yr. Aus.$33 (foreign Aus.$36). Australian Association of Adult and Community Education, P.O. Box 308, Jamison Centre, A.C.T. 2614, Australia. TEL 06-251-7933. adv.; bk.rev.; index every 3 yrs. circ. 800. (also avail. in microfiche from UMI; back issues avail.) **Indexed:** Aus.Educ.Ind., Aus.P.A.I.S., C.I.J.E., Cont.Pg.Educ., Educ.Admin.Abstr., Res.High.Educ.Abstr., Sociol.Educ.Abstr. **Document type:** academic/scholarly publication.
—BLDSC (1801.699800); UMI.
Formerly: Australian Journal of Adult Education (ISSN 0004-9387)

AVIATION EDUCATION NEWS BULLETIN. see *AERONAUTICS AND SPACE FLIGHT*

374   BG   ISSN 0070-8135
BANGLADESH. EDUCATION DIRECTORATE. REPORT ON PILOT PROJECT ON ADULT EDUCATION. Bengali edition: Barshika Bibarani Bayaska Siksha Parikshya Prakalpa Bangladesh. (Text in English) 1964. a. Tk.2 per no. Education Directorate, Adult Education Branch, B E E R I, Dhanmond, Dhaka 5, Bangladesh. circ. 500.
Supersedes: East Pakistan. Education Directorate. Adult Education Branch. Report on Pilot Project on Adult Education.

BANKING & FINANCIAL TRAINING. see *BUSINESS AND ECONOMICS — Banking And Finance*

374   GW   ISSN 0934-3814
BAUSTEINE GRUNDSCHULE. 1988. q. DM.58.27. Bergmoser und Hoeller Verlag GmbH, Karl-Friedrich-Str. 76, 52072 Aachen, Germany. TEL 0241-1730926. FAX 0241-1730934. circ. 5,000. (looseleaf format; back issues avail.) **Document type:** academic/scholarly publication.

374   CC   ISSN 1002-414X
BEIJING CHENGREN JIAOYU/BEIJING ADULT EDUCATION. (Text in Chinese) m. Y12. Beijing Chengren Jiaoyu Zazhishe, Beijing 100088, People's Republic of China. TEL 2012890. Ed. Ma Guifeng.

374   SZ
BERUFSAUSBILDUNG (YEAR)/FORMATION PROFESSIONNELLE (YEAR). (Text in French and German) 1978. a. 14 SFr. Bundesamt fuer Statistik, Schwarztorstr. 96, CH-3003 Bern, Switzerland. TEL 031-3236011. FAX 031-3236061. **Document type:** government publication.

374.013   GW   ISSN 0005-951X
DIE BERUFSBILDENDE SCHULE. 1949. m. DM.59. (Bundesverband der Lehrer an Beruflichen Schulen) Heckner Druck und Verlag, Postfach 1559, 38285 Wolfenbuettel, Germany. FAX 05331-800858. Eds. R. Bader, P. Grothe. adv.; bk.rev.; bibl.; illus.; stat.; index. **Indexed:** Int.Lab.Doc. **Document type:** academic/scholarly publication.
—BLDSC (1941.460000). CCC.

BETRIEBLICHE AUSBILDUNGSPRAXIS; Merkblaetter fuer Ausbilder in der Eisen- und Metallindustrie. see *METALLURGY*

374   AU
BILDUNGSIMPULS; Zeitschrift fuer Erwachsenenbildung. 1951. q. free to qualified personnel. Servicestelle fuer Erwachsenenbildung, Ursulinenhof, Landstr. 31, A-4020 Linz, Austria. TEL 0732-2720-5500. Ed. Herbert Saminger. bk.rev. circ. 10,000. (processed) **Document type:** government publication.
Formerly: Oberoesterreichisches Volksbildungswerk. Mitteilungen (ISSN 0026-6922)

374   SZ
BILDUNGSSTATISTIK SCHLUESSEL FUER BERUFSAUSBILDUNG/STATISTIQUE SCOLAIRE CODE DE LA FORMATION PROFESSIONELLE. (Text in French and German) 1986. a. 7 SFr. Bundesamt fuer Statistik, Schwarztorstr. 96, CH-3003 Bern, Switzerland. TEL 031-3236011. FAX 031-3236061. **Document type:** government publication.
Formerly: Schluessel fuer Berufsausbildung.

BOLETIN DE RESUMENES ANALITICOS. see *EDUCATION — Higher Education*

374   MX
BOLETIN INFORMATIVO CREFAL - REDUC. 1990. s-a. exchange basis. Centro de Cooperacion Regional para la Educacion de Adultos en America Latina y el Caribe - CREFAL, Quinta Erendira s-n, 61600 Patzcuaro, Mich., Mexico.

BUSINESS EXECUTIVE. see *BUSINESS AND ECONOMICS — Management*

374   US
C A E L FORUM AND NEWS. 1977. 3/yr. $15 (foreign $20) to non-members. Council for Adult and Experiential Learning, 223 W. Jackson Blvd., Ste. 510, Chicago, IL 60606-6904. TEL 312-922-5909. FAX 312-922-1769. adv.; bk.rev. circ. 3,500.
Formerly: C A E L News.
Description: Fosters experiential learning and improvement of services to the adult learner.

C C E T S W NEWS. (Central Council for Education and Training in Social Work) see *SOCIAL SERVICES AND WELFARE*

374 375.4   II
C I I L ADULT LITERACY SERIES. (Text in Assamese, English) 1976. irreg., latest 1983. Ministry of Human Resource Development, Central Institute of Indian Languages, Manasagangotri, Mysore 570 006, India. bibl.

374 375.4   II
C I I L BORDER AND TRIBAL LANGUAGES. ADULT LITERACY SERIES. 1978. irreg., latest 1981. price varies. Ministry of Human Resource Development, Central Institute of Indian Languages, Manasagangotri, Mysore 570 006, India. Ed.Bd.

374 378 375   US
C R L A NEWSLETTER. (Former name of issuing body: Western College Reading and Learning Association) 1977. 3/yr. $40. College Reading and Learning Association, c/o Tom Gier, English Dept., University of Alaska Anchorage, 3211 Providence Dr., Anchorage, AK 99508. TEL 907-786-1926. Ed. Thomas L. Pasternack. bk.rev. circ. 900. **Document type:** newsletter.
Former titles: W C R L A Newsletter; W C R A Newsletter.
Description: Addresses learning needs in colleges and universities: reading, learning assistance, developmental education and tutorial assistance.

CAMPUS - FREE COLLEGE DEGREES. see *EDUCATION — Higher Education*

374.971   CN   ISSN 0835-4944
CANADIAN JOURNAL FOR THE STUDY OF ADULT EDUCATION/REVUE CANADIENNE POUR L'ETUDE DE L'EDUCATION DES ADULTES. 1987. Can.$30 to non-members. Canadian Association for the Study of Adult Education - Association Canadienne pour l'Etude de l'Education des Adultes, Department of Adult Education, Ontario Institute for Studies in Education, 252 Bloor St. W., 7-107, Toronto, ON M5S 1V6, Canada. Ed.Bd. bk.rev. circ. 500. (also avail. in microfiche) **Document type:** academic/scholarly publication.
—BLDSC (3035.780000).
Description: Committed to the dissemination of knowledge derived from disciplined inquiry in the field of adult and continuing education.
Refereed Serial

CANADIAN JOURNAL OF UNIVERSITY CONTINUING EDUCATION. see *EDUCATION — Higher Education*

374.4   CN   ISSN 0827-1224
CANADIAN UNIVERSITY DISTANCE EDUCATION DIRECTORY/REPERTOIRE DE L'ENSEIGNEMENT A DISTANCE DANS LES UNIVERSITES CANADIENNES. (Text in English, French) 1957. a. Can.$20 (US Can.$21, elsewhere Can.$22). (Canadian Association for University Continuing Education) Association of Universities and Colleges of Canada, 600-350 Albert, Ottawa, ON K1R 1B1, Canada. TEL 613-563-1236. FAX 613-563-7739. E-mail: jrondeau@aucc.ca. circ. 1,000.
Former titles (until 1984): Directory of University Correspondence Courses (ISSN 0708-2193); Canadian Correspondence Courses for University Credit (ISSN 0068-855X)
Description: Lists universities offering distance education courses in Canada.

374   AT   ISSN 0310-1649
CANBERRA PAPERS IN CONTINUING EDUCATION. 1972; N.S. 1981. irreg., latest no.5, 1985. price varies. Australian National University, Centre for Continuing Education, c/o The Director, Canberra, A.C.T. 0200, Australia. TEL 06-2492892. FAX 06-257421.

CARAVAN; a resource for those engaged in animating adult faith formation. see *RELIGIONS AND THEOLOGY — Roman Catholic*

374 370   US
CAREER EDUCATION. 1936. bi-m. $35. Career College Association, 750 First St., N.E., Ste. 900, Washington, DC 20002-4242. TEL 202-336-6700. FAX 202-336-6828. Ed. Christopher Davis. adv.; bk.rev. **Indexed:** Bus.Educ.Ind.
Incorporates (in 1991): A I C S Compass (Association of Independent Colleges and Schools) (ISSN 0010-4205); (1983-1991): Career Training.

CAREER EDUCATION THAT WORKS FOR AMERICA; handbook of accredited trade & technical schools - handbook of private accredited independent colleges and schools. see *EDUCATION — Guides To Schools And Colleges*

371.42   US   ISSN 0736-1920
HF5381.A1
CAREER PLANNING & ADULT DEVELOPMENT JOURNAL. 1982. q. $30 to non-members (foreign $50). Career Planning and Adult Development Network, 4965 Sierra Rd., San Jose, CA 95132. TEL 408-559-4946. FAX 408-559-8211. Ed. Richard L. Knowdell. adv.; bk.rev.; film rev. circ. 1,000. (back issues avail.) **Indexed:** ERIC, Tr.& Dev.Alert.
—BLDSC (3051.762000).
Description: Articles on group and individual career counseling techniques, assessment, and job search skills for career counselors.

374 370.15 150   US   ISSN 0898-1353
CAREER PLANNING AND ADULT DEVELOPMENT NETWORK NEWSLETTER; a newsletter for career counselors, educators, and human resource specialists. 1979. m. $50 to non-members (foreign $70). Career Planning and Adult Development Network, 4965 Sierra Rd., San Jose, CA 95132. TEL 408-559-4946. FAX 498-559-8211. Ed. Richard L. Knowdell. bk.rev.; film rev. circ. 1,000. (back issues avail.) **Indexed:** ERIC. **Document type:** newsletter.
Description: Listing of workshops, conferences, films, books and counseling techniques for career counselors.

CAREER WORLD. see *OCCUPATIONS AND CAREERS*

374.013   UY
CATALOGO DE PUBLICACIONES DIDACTICAS LATINOAMERICANAS DE FORMACION PROFESIONAL. 1976. irreg. price varies. Centro Interamericano de Investigacion y Documentacion Sobre Formacion Profesional, Avda. Uruguay 1238, Casilla de Correo 1761, Montevideo, Uruguay. FAX 921305.
Supersedes (1969-1976): Catalogo de Manuales Latinoamericanos.

259 150.19   US
CATALOGUE OF CONFERENCES, SEMINARS, WORKSHOP. 1958. 3/yr. $5. Wainwright House, Inc., Wainwright House, 260 Stuyvesant Ave., Rye, NY 10580. TEL 914-967-6080. FAX 914-967-6114. Ed. Stacy C. Orphanos. bk.rev. circ. 35,000.
Former titles: Trends (Rye); Laymen's Movement Review (ISSN 0023-9518)

CENTENNIAL STATE LIBRARIES. see *LIBRARY AND INFORMATION SCIENCES*

374 301.412 640   US   ISSN 0736-3044
CENTER FOR SELF-SUFFICIENCY UPDATE. 1984. a. $1. Center for Self-Sufficiency, Publishing Division, c/o Prosperity & Profits Unlimited, Distribution Services, Box 416, Denver, CO 80201-0416. Ed. A. Doyle. circ. 2,000. (looseleaf format; back issues avail.) **Document type:** newsletter.

CENTRAL COUNCIL FOR EDUCATION AND TRAINING IN SOCIAL WORK. REPORT OF COUNCIL MEETING. see *SOCIAL SERVICES AND WELFARE*

EDUCATION — ADULT EDUCATION

377   FR   ISSN 0242-259X
CENTRE I N F F O. GUIDES TECHNIQUES. 1979. irreg. Centre I N F F O, Tour Europe, 92049 Paris Cedex 7 (La Defense), France. TEL 47-78-13-50. FAX 47-73-74-20. TELEX 615 383.

374   UK
CITY AND GUILDS HANDBOOK; guidance on the accreditation of prior learning. 1988. a. City and Guilds of London Institute, 76 Portland Place, London W1N 4AA, England. TEL 071-278-2468. circ. 17,500.

377   FR   ISSN 0769-0142
CLE POUR. 1986. irreg. Centre I N F F O, Tour Europe, 92049 Paris Cedex 7 (La Defense), France. TEL 47-78-13-50. FAX 47-73-74-20. TELEX 615 383.

374   UK   ISSN 0256-0925
COMMUNITY EDUCATION INTERNATIONAL. 1984. q. £20($100) to member institutions; developing countries £10. International Community Education Association, Lyng Hall, Blackberry Ln., Coventry, CV2 3JS, England. TEL 0203-638-670. FAX 0203-681161. Ed. Alan Blackhurst. bk.rev. circ. 2,000. (back issues avail.)
Formerly: I C E A Newsletter.

378 374   US
LB2328   CODEN: CJCOD6
COMMUNITY JUNIOR COLLEGE JOURNAL OF RESEARCH AND PRACTICE. 1976. bi-m. $80. (University of North Texas, Department of Higher Education) Taylor & Francis, 1900 Frost Rd., Ste. 101, Bristol, PA 19007-1598. TEL 800-821-8312. FAX 215-785-5515. Ed. D. Barry Lumsden. adv.; bk.rev.; abstr.; bibl.; charts; illus.; index. circ. 500. (also avail. in microform from UMI; back issues avail.; reprint service avail. from UMI) **Indexed:** C.I.J.E., Chic.Per.Ind., Curr.Cont.
—UnCover. **CCC.**
Former titles: Community Junior College Research Quarterly of Research and Practice (ISSN 0277-6774); (until vol.6, 1981): Community Junior College Research Quarterly (ISSN 0361-6975)
Description: Devoted to all aspects, domestic and international, research and practical, of two-year college education.
Refereed Serial

374   US   ISSN 0739-9227
LC215
COMMUNITY SERVICES CATALYST. 1971. 3/yr. $40. National Council on Community Services & Continuing Education, c/o Darrel A. Clowes, Ed., Virginia Polytechnic Institute & State University, Blacksburg, VA 24061-0313. TEL 703-231-5269. FAX 703-231-9075. bk.rev. circ. 1,200. (also avail. in microform; back issues avail.) **Indexed:** C.I.J.E., ERIC.
●Also available online.
—BLDSC (3363.669000); UMI.

374.8   US   ISSN 0361-6908
LC5252.C2
CONTINUATION EDUCATION. 1975. 3/yr. $5 to individuals; institutions $10. California Continuation Education Association, 6501 Balboa Blvd., Van Nuys, CA 91406. Ed. A.C. Laudon. charts; stat. circ. 600.
Formerly: Alternatives (ISSN 0273-0839)

374.013   US   ISSN 0736-1696
CONTINUING EDUCATION ALTERNATIVES UPDATE. 1983. a. $4. Update Publicare Co., c/o Prosperity & Profits Unlimited, Box 416, Denver, CO 80201-0416. TEL 303-575-5676. Ed. A. Doyle. adv.; bibl. circ. 1,000. (also avail. in microfiche; back issues avail.) **Document type:** newsletter.
—**CCC.**

267.5   NE   ISSN 0166-7831
CONTOUR. 1922. 8/yr. fl.50. Y W C A of the Netherlands, F.C. Dondersstraat 23, 3572 JB Utrecht, Netherlands. FAX 31-30-715525. Ed.Bd. bk.rev.; illus. circ. 1,600. **Indexed:** CERDIC. **Document type:** newsletter.
Formerly: Federatie Contact (ISSN 0014-9284)

374   CN   ISSN 0010-8146
LC5201   CODEN: COVEE5
CONVERGENCE; international journal of adult education. (Text and summaries in English, French, Spanish) 1968. q. $39 (students $26; Third World subscribers $30). International Council for Adult Education - Conseil International d'Education des Adultes, 720 Bathurst St., Ste. 500, Toronto, ON M5S 2R4, Canada. TEL 416-588-1211. FAX 416-588-5725. E-mail: icae@web.apc.org. Ed. Karen Yarmol-Franko. bk.rev.; abstr. circ. 2,000. (also avail. in microform from UMI,MML; back issues avail.) **Indexed:** C.I.J.E., Can.Educ.Ind., Can.Per.Ind., Cont.Pg.Educ., Educ.Ind., ERIC, Mid.East: Abstr.& Ind., Mult.Ed.Abstr., Rural Devel.Abstr., Rural Ext.Educ.& Tr.Abstr., Rural Recreat.Tour.Abstr., World Agri.Econ.& Rural Sociol.Abstr. **Document type:** academic/scholarly publication.
—BLDSC (3463.550000); Faxon; UnCover; SWETS; UMI. **CCC.**
Description: Provides a forum for international exchange on developments in adult education.
Refereed Serial

374   US
COURSE TRENDS. m. $95. Learning Resources Network, 1554 Hayes Dr., Manhattan, KS 66502. TEL 913-539-5376. Ed. Julie Coates. circ. 2,000. (back issues avail.) **Document type:** newsletter.
Incorporates: Marketing Classes for Adults; Formerly: Course Trends in Adult Learning.
Description: Newsletter of information and trends in continuing education courses, programs, workshops, and seminars in all fields throughout the United States.

374   MX
CREFAL CIRCULAR INFORMATIVA. q. exchange basis. Centro de Cooperacion Regional para la Educacion de Adultos en America Latina y el Caribe - CREFAL, Quinta Erendira s-n, 61600 Patzcuaro, Mich., Mexico.

374 301   BO
CUADERNOS C I P C A (SERIE POPULAR). 1974. irreg. price varies. Centro de Investigacion y Promocion del Campesinado, Casilla 5854, La Paz, Bolivia.
Description: Presents study and teaching methods.

374   MX
CUATRO TITULOS. 1988. irreg. Mex.$18.75($6) Centro de Cooperacion Regional para la Educacion de Adultos en America Latina y el Caribe - CREFAL, Quinta Erendira, 61600 Patzcuaro, Mich., Mexico.

374.013   GW   ISSN 0174-2809
D S K ZEITSCHRIFT; Zeitschrift fuer berufsbegleitendes Studium. 1961. q. DM.72. Deutscher Studienkreis e.V., Weimarische Str. 12, 10715 Berlin, Germany. TEL 030-8542356. FAX 030-8536357. Ed. Christian Mann. adv.; bk.rev. circ. 3,800. (back issues avail.) **Document type:** newsletter.
Formerly: Deutscher Studienkreis (ISSN 0174-2809)

374   DK
DANISH FOLKEHOEJSKOLE TODAY. 1981. a. free. Hoejskolernes Sekretariat - Folkehoejskolernes Information Office, Nytorv 7, DK-1450 Copenhagen K, Denmark. TEL 45-33-13-98-22. FAX 45-33-13-98-70. Eds. Arne Andresen, Sigurd Kvaerndrup. illus. circ. 5,000.
Formerly: Danish Folk High School Today.

430 375   GW   ISSN 0341-3675
DEUTSCH LERNEN; Zeitschrift fuer den Sprachunterricht mit auslaendischen Arbeitnehmern. 1976. q. DM.32. (Sprachverband Deutsch fuer Auslaendische Arbeitnehmer e.V.) Schneider Verlag Hohengehren GmbH, Wilhelmstr. 13, 73666 Baltmannsweiler, Germany. TEL 07153-41206. FAX 07153-48761. adv.; bk.rev. (reprint service avail. from UMI; back issues avail.) **Indexed:** Lang.Teach.& Ling.Abstr. **Document type:** academic/scholarly publication.

374.013   GW   ISSN 0721-5932
DIDAKTIK DER BERUFS- UND ARBEITSWELT; Giessener Blaetter zur Arbeitslehre. 1982. q. DM.30. Karl-Gloecker-Str. 21, 35394 Giessen, Germany. TEL 0641-7025270. Ed. Lothar Beinke. abstr.; bibl.; illus.; index. circ. 250. (back issues avail.)

DIRECTORY OF PRIVATE VOCATIONAL SCHOOLS. see
EDUCATION — Guides To Schools And Colleges

DRIVING INSTRUCTOR'S MANUAL. see
TRANSPORTATION — Automobiles

DUNGEONMASTER. see *HOMOSEXUALITY*

374   NE
E B A E NEWSLETTER. (Text in English; summaries in French and Spanish) 1978. q. fl.30. European Bureau of Adult Education - Bureau Europeen de l'Education Populaire, Nieuweweg 4, P.O. Box 367, 3800 AJ Amersfoort, Netherlands. TEL 033-631114. FAX 033-616627. Ed. Agaath Earl. adv.; bk.rev. circ. 800. **Indexed:** ERIC. **Document type:** newsletter.
Formerly (until 1989): E B A E - I C A E Newsletter.
Description: Covers the activities of the bureau and relevant news and initiatives in European adult education.

374 362.7   FR   ISSN 0424-2238
ECOLE DES PARENTS. 1949. m. (10/yr.). 280 F. (foreign 360 F.). Federation Nationale des Ecole des Parents et des Educateurs, 5 impasse Bon-Secours, 75543 Paris Cedex 11, France. TEL 43-48-00-16. FAX 43-48-81-53. Ed. Odile Naudin. adv.; bk.rev. circ. 15,000. **Indexed:** Bull.Signal.
—SWETS.
Description: For parents and educators. Contains information, research and regular chronicles such as books, toys and music.

EDUCACION SUPERIOR Y SOCIEDAD. see
EDUCATION — Higher Education

EDUCATIONAL AND VOCATIONAL GUIDANCE - BULLETIN A I O S P, I A E V G, I V S B B. (Association Internationale d'Orientation Scolaire et Professionnelle) see *OCCUPATIONS AND CAREERS*

374   US   ISSN 0360-1277
LC5201   CODEN: EDGEDA
EDUCATIONAL GERONTOLOGY; an international journal. 1976. 8/yr. $173. Taylor & Francis, 1900 Frost Rd., Ste. 101, Bristol, PA 19007-1598. TEL 800-821-8312. FAX 215-785-5515. Ed. D. Barry Lumsden. adv.; bk.rev.; abstr.; bibl.; charts; index. circ. 600. (also avail. in microform from UMI; back issues avail.; reprint service avail. from UMI) **Indexed:** A.D.& D., Biol.Abstr., C.I.J.E., CINAHL, CLOA, Cont.Pg.Educ., Curr.Cont., Educ.Admin.Abstr., Educ.Ind., Excerp.Med., Mult.Ed.Abstr., Psychol.Abstr., Res.High.Educ.Abstr., Sage Fam.Stud.Abstr., Sage Pub.Admin.Abstr., Soc.Sci.Ind., SSCI. **Document type:** academic/scholarly publication.
—BLDSC (3661.415000); Faxon; UnCover; SWETS. **CCC.**
Description: Covers original advances in gerontology, adult education and the social and behavioral sciences.
Refereed Serial

374 370.196   US
ELDERHOSTEL CATALOG. 1978. 8/yr. free in U.S. (foreign $35). Elderhostel, Inc., 75 Federal St, Ste. 300, Boston, MA 02110-1941.
TEL 617-426-7788. circ. 600,000. (tabloid format) **Document type:** catalog.
Description: Information on domestic and overseas educational programs for adults age 60 and older.

374   JA
ENERGETIC LIFE/KASSEI. (Text in Japanese) 1977. m. 7680 Yen. Gakken Co. Ltd., 40-5, 4-chome, Kamiikedai, Ohta-ku, Tokyo 145, Japan. Ed. Hiroyoshi Tayama.

374   JA
ENLIGHTENMENT/KEIHATSU. (Text in Japanese) 1974. m. 5980 Yen. Gakken Co. Ltd., 40-5, 4-chome, Kamiikedai, Ohta-ku, Tokyo 145, Japan. Ed. Ken'ichi Yamana.

EPILETTER. see *SOCIAL SERVICES AND WELFARE*

374.013   DK   ISSN 0105-6662
ERHVERVSNOEGLEN. 1978. a. DKK 225. Noegleforlaget ApS, Haslevej 12-14, 6000 Kolding, Denmark. TEL 75-538620. Ed. R. Poulsen. circ. 4,000.

374   GW
ERWACHSENENBILDUNG. q. DM.42 (foreign DM.52). Patmos Verlag GmbH, Am Wehrhahn 100, 40211 Duesseldorf, Germany. TEL 0211-16795-0. FAX 0211-1679575. **Document type:** academic/scholarly publication.

EDUCATION — ADULT EDUCATION

379   AU
ERWACHSENENBILDUNG IN OESTERREICH. 1959. 10/yr. S.200. (Bundesministerium fuer Unterricht und Kunst) Oesterreichischer Bundesverlag, Schwarzenbergstr. 5, A-1015 Vienna, Austria. TEL 0222-5262091. FAX 0222-526209111. Eds. Gerda Clauss, Regina Weissenboeck. adv.; bk.rev. circ. 2,000. **Document type:** academic/scholarly publication.
    Formerly: Neue Volksbildung.
    Description: Six issues focus on adult education; four issues focus on public libraries in Austria.

374   US
F E A A NEWSLETTER. 1982. q. $10 to non-members and students; institutions $50; membership $20. Folk Education Association of America, 39 Wagon Trail Rd., Black Mountain, NC 28711. TEL 704-669-5914. (Subscr. to: 2606 14th St., Two Rivers, WI 54241; Alt. addr.: 107 Vernon St., Northampton, MA 01060. TEL 413-585-8755) Ed. Janet Trader. circ. 350. (looseleaf format; back issues avail.) **Document type:** newsletter.
    Formerly: Folk School Association of America Newsletter.
    Description: Covers non-formal, non-competitive education and emphasizes individual and community development; inspired by folk-schools of Scandinavia, but not limited to them.

374   FR   ISSN 1166-0600
FICHES PRATIQUES DE LA FORMATION CONTINUE. MISE A JOUR. m. 730 (foreign 1007 F.). Centre I N F F O, Tour Europe, 92049 Paris Cedex 7 (La Defense), France. TEL 47-78-13-50. FAX 47-73-74-20. TELEX 615 383.

374   US
FIVE MINUTES WITH A C H E. 1977. 9/yr. membership. Association for Continuing Higher Education, Inc., c/o Dr. Wayne Whelan, Exec. VP, Trident Technical College, Box 118067, CE-P, Charleston, SC 29423-8067. TEL 803-722-5570. FAX 803-722-5520. bk.rev. circ. 1,600. (processed) **Document type:** newsletter.
    Former titles: Association for Continuing Higher Education. Newsletter & Association of University Evening Colleges. Newsletter (ISSN 0004-5845)

374   SW   ISSN 0348-4769
FOLKHOEGSKOLAN. 1920. 8/yr. SEK 350 (effective 1991). Svenska Folkhoegskolans Laerarfoerbund, P.O. Box 6087, 17206 Sundbyberg, Sweden. FAX 08-282034. Ed. Annika Jansson. adv.; bk.rev. circ. 3,100.
    Formerly (until Jan. 1979): Tidskrift foer Svenska Folkhoegskolan (ISSN 0040-6899)
    Description: Covers different issues in adult education, focusing on activities in the Swedish higher education system.

374   FR   ISSN 1148-8204
FORMATION PROFESSIONNELLE CONTINUE. 1989. irreg. Centre I N F F O, Tour Europe, 92049 Paris Cedex 7 (La Defense), France. TEL 47-73-74-20. FAX 47-73-74-20. TELEX 615 383.

FORSCHUNGSDOKUMENTATION ZUR ARBEITSMARKT- UND BERUFSFORSCHUNG. see *BUSINESS AND ECONOMICS — Labor And Industrial Relations*

374   GW   ISSN 0176-3687
DAS FORUM (MUNICH, 1961). 1961. q. DM.20. Bayerischer Volkshochschulverband, Faeustlestr. 5, 80339 Munich, Germany. TEL 089-51080-0. FAX 089-5023812. Ed. Hermann Kumpfmueller. adv.; bk.rev.; illus.; index. circ. 4,000. (back issues avail.) **Document type:** academic/scholarly publication.

FORUM (WASHINGTON, 1970). see *LIBRARY AND INFORMATION SCIENCES*

374   CC
FUJIAN ZIXUE KAOSHI/FUJIAN EXAMINATION GUIDE TO THE SELF-TAUGHT. (Text in Chinese) bi-m. Y6. Zixue Kaoshi Zhidao Weiyuanhui, Fujian, No.24, Xihukou Houcao, Fuzhou, Fujian 350001, People's Republic of China. TEL 557205. (Dist. overseas by: Jiangsu Publications Import & Export Corp., 56 Gao Yun Ling, Nanjing, Jiangsu, P.R.C.)
    Description: Adult education journal focusing on remedial learning and passing exams.

640 301.42   JA
FUJIN NO TOMO/WOMEN'S FRIEND. (Text in Japanese) 1903. m. 7040 Yen. 20-16, Nishi-Ikebukuro 2-chome, Toshima-ku, Tokyo, Japan. FAX 03-3987-8958. Ed. Yoko Utsnomiya. circ. 150,000. **Document type:** consumer publication.

374   US   ISSN 0896-0518
G E D ITEMS. (Graduate Equivalency Diploma) 1983. 5/yr. free. American Council on Education, One Dupont Circle, Washington, DC 20036. TEL 202-939-9490. FAX 202-775-8578. Ed. Colleen A. Allen. adv. contact: Lisa Richardo. circ. 22,000. (back issues avail.) **Document type:** newsletter.
    Description: For GED teachers, administrators, program staff; state departments of education and directors; adult educators. Includes teaching tips, success stories, research articles.

374 376   TG
GAME SU. (Text in Ewe) 1972. m. Ministry of Social and Women's Affairs, 19 ave de la Nouvelle Marche, B.P.1247, Lome, Togo. TEL 21-28-44. circ. 6,000.
    Description: For the newly literate.

GEWERKSCHAFTLICHE BILDUNGSPOLITIK; Stellungnahmen - Analysen - Informationen. see *EDUCATION*

374   US   ISSN 1055-3371
HF5549.5.T7
▼**GLOBAL CONNECTOR**; the complete resource directory for international training. 1992. a. $245. PASport Publications International, 20 Libertyship Way, Ste. 190, Sausalito, CA 94965. TEL 415-331-2606. FAX 415-331-3903. Ed. Ellen Mischka. **Document type:** directory.

374.013   US
GOVERNMENT TRAINING NEWS. 1976. m. $175. Business Publishers, Inc., 951 Pershing Dr., Silver Spring, MD 20910-4464. TEL 301-587-6300. FAX 301-587-1081. Ed. Henry Kleiner. bk.rev. (looseleaf format) **Document type:** newsletter.
    Description: Provides current reports on the latest training trends and opportunities, cost and effectiveness studies, and overall personnel training policy.

374   FR
GUIDE DE LA FAMILLE. 1964. bi-m. 48 F. EDICEF, 23 rue du Sommerard, 75005 Paris, France.

374 371.3   SP   ISSN 0213-0610
GUINIGUADA. 1984. a. $15 to individuals; institutions $20. Universidad de La Laguna, Escuela del Profesorado de E.G.B. (Las Palmas and Tenerife), Secretariado de Publicaciones, San Agustin, 30, 38201 La Laguna-Tenerife, Islas Canarias, Spain. TEL 922-25-81-27. adv.
    Description: Devoted to the educational and pedagogical research.

374   GW   ISSN 0932-8297
H V V RUNDSCHREIBEN. 1980. s-m. Hessischer Volkshochschulverband, Winterbachstr. 38, 60320 Frankfurt a.M., Germany. TEL 069-5600080. circ. 265.
    Description: Contains various reports and articles on adult education

374   JA
HEALTH LIFE. (Text in Japanese) 1981. m. 5400 Yen. Gakken Co. Ltd., 40-5, 4-chome, Kamiikedai, Ohta-ku, Tokyo 145, Japan. Ed. Kenji Watanabe.
    Formerly: Gold Life.

374   IS
HED HA-ULPAN. (Text in Hebrew) 1974. 3/yr. Ministry of Education and Culture, Division of Adult Education, P.O. Box 292, Jerusalem 91 002, Israel. Ed. Ido Bassok.

374   GW   ISSN 0018-103X
HESSISCHE BLAETTER FUER VOLKSBILDUNG. 1951. q. DM.39. (Hessischer Volkshochschulverband) Dipa Verlag, Nassauerstr. 1-3, 60439 Frankfurt a.M., Germany. TEL 069-586910. FAX 069-576128. Ed. Rudi Rohlmann. adv.; bk.rev.; charts; stat.; index. circ. 2,500. **Document type:** bulletin.
    —CCC.

HINTS FOR JOB HUNTERS. see *OCCUPATIONS AND CAREERS*

HOKEN KANRI SENTA DAYORI. see *PUBLIC HEALTH AND SAFETY*

642.5 910.09   US
HOSPITALITY & TOURISM EDUCATOR. 1988. 4/yr. $50 to non-members; foreign $60. Council on Hotel, Restaurant and Institutional Education, 1200 17th St., Washington, DC 20036-3047. TEL 202-331-5990. FAX 202-785-2511. Ed. Michael Lefever. adv.; index.; illus.; stat.; tr.lit.; circ. 2,000. (back issues avail.) **Indexed:** Art.Hosp.& Tour.
    Formerly: Hospitality Educator.
    Description: Features articles written by educators and industry professionals. Offers insights on the latest hospitality and tourism trends in education and the industry.

374   CN   ISSN 0834-9789
I C A E NEWS. (Editions in English, French, Spanish) 1981. q. International Council for Adult Education, 720 Bathurst St., Ste. 500, Toronto, ON M5S 2R4, Canada. TEL 416-588-1211. FAX 416-588-5725. E-mail: icae@web.apc.org. Ed. Thuraya Khalil-Khouri. circ. 1,500. (looseleaf format) **Document type:** newsletter.

374   US   ISSN 1058-6962
PS536.2
I L R JOURNAL. 1991. a. $10. Institute for Learning in Retirement, Education & Policy Research Bldg., 2115 N. Campus Dr., Evanston, IL 60208-2650.
    Description: Provides original stories, memoires, poetry and art by older learners.

379   US
IDAHO. STATE DIVISION OF VOCATIONAL EDUCATION. ANNUAL PERFORMANCE REPORT. 1963. a. State Division of Vocational Education, 650 W. State St., Boise, ID 83720. TEL 208-334-3216. circ. 40. **Document type:** government publication.
    Formerly: Idaho. State Board for Vocational Education. Annual Descriptive Report of Program Activities for Vocational Education (ISSN 0091-5882)

374   II   ISSN 0019-5006
LC5201
INDIAN JOURNAL OF ADULT EDUCATION. (Text in English) 1939. q. Rs.40($15) (Indian Adult Education Association) J.L. Sachdeva, Pub., 17-B Indraprastha Marg, New Delhi 110 002, India. TEL 3319282. FAX 011-3315460. Ed. B.B. Mohanty. adv.; bk.rev.; abstr.; bibl.; illus.; index. circ. 2,000. (also avail. in microform from UMI; reprint service avail. from UMI) **Indexed:** C.I.J.E., Cont.Pg.Educ., Int.Lab.Doc., Mult.Ed.Abstr., Rural Ext.Educ.& Tr.Abstr., Rural Recreat.Tour.Abstr., Sp.Ed.Needs Abstr., Stud.Wom.Abstr., World Agri.Econ.& Rural Sociol.Abstr.
    —UnCover; UMI.

374   II   ISSN 0537-1996
S544.5.I5
INDIAN JOURNAL OF EXTENSION EDUCATION. (Text in English) 1965. s-a. Rs.70($30) Indian Society of Extension Education, Division of Agricultural Extension, Indian Agricultural Research Institute, Delhi 110 012, India. Ed. Y.P. Singh. **Indexed:** Cont.Pg.Educ.

374 658.3   US   ISSN 8755-9269
INFO-LINE. 1984. m. $119 to non-members; members $79. American Society for Training and Development, 1640 King St., Box 1443, Alexandria, VA 22313. TEL 703-683-8136. FAX 703-683-8103. Ed. Barbara Darraugh. bibl.; charts; illus.; tr.lit. (back issues avail.) **Indexed:** Tr.& Dev.Alert.
    —SWETS.

INFORMATORE DI URIO. see *RELIGIONS AND THEOLOGY — Roman Catholic*

374   UK   ISSN 0968-1876
INKLING; magazine of the Oxfordshire adult literacy and basic education scheme. 1978. irreg. (3-4/yr.). free. Oxfordshire County Education Department, Community Education, Macclesfield House, Oxford, England.

INTERNATIONAL JOURNAL OF CONTINUING ENGINEERING EDUCATION. see *ENGINEERING*

EDUCATION — ADULT EDUCATION

374   AT   ISSN 0818-0563
INTERNATIONAL JOURNAL OF EDUCOLOGY. 1987. 2/yr. Aus.$35. Educology Research Associates, P.O. Box 216, Terrigal, N.S.W. 2260, Australia. Eds. James Christensen, James E. Fisher. bk.rev.; index; circ. 1,500 (controlled). (back issues avail.) **Document type:** academic/scholarly publication.
Description: Examines various aspects of the educational process from an educological perspective.

374   UK   ISSN 0260-1370
LC5201
INTERNATIONAL JOURNAL OF LIFELONG EDUCATION. 1982. bi-m. £115($194) Taylor & Francis Ltd., Rankine Rd., Basingstoke, Hants RG24 8PR, England. TEL 0256-840366. FAX 0256-479438. TELEX 858540. Eds. P. Jarvis, J.E. Thomas. abstr.; index. **Indexed:** C.I.J.E., Cont.Pg.Educ., Educ.Tech.Abstr., High.Educ.Curr.Aware.Bull., Mult.Ed.Abstr., Res.High.Educ.Abstr., Rural Ext.Educ.& Tr.Abstr., Stud.Wom.Abstr. **Document type:** academic/scholarly publication.
—BLDSC (4542.321300); Faxon; UnCover; SWETS. CCC.
Description: Provides an international forum for the debate of the principles and practice of lifelong, continuing, recurrent, adult and initial education.
Refereed Serial

374   CN
INTERNATIONAL JOURNAL OF UNIVERSITY ADULT EDUCATION. 1962. 3/yr. $40. International Congress of University Adult Education, c/o Dr. John F. Morris, Sec. Treas., Department of Extension and Summer Session, University of New Brunswick, Box 4400, Fredericton, NB E3B 5A3, Canada. TEL 506-453-4646. FAX 506-453-3572. Ed. C. Duke. adv.; bk.rev. circ. 500. **Indexed:** Mult.Ed.Abstr.
—BLDSC (4542.696800); SWETS.
Formerly: International Congress of University Adult Education. Journal (ISSN 0074-3992)

374   GW   ISSN 0074-9818
INTERNATIONALES JAHRBUCH DER ERWACHSENENBILDUNG/INTERNATIONAL YEARBOOK OF ADULT EDUCATION. 1969. a. DM.68. Boehlau Verlag GmbH, Theodor-Heuss-Str. 76, 51149 Cologne, Germany. TEL 02203-307021. FAX 02203-307349. Ed. Joachim Knoll. **Document type:** academic/scholarly publication.

374.013 658   US   ISSN 1065-464X
ISSUES & OBSERVATIONS. 1980. q. free. Center for Creative Leadership, One Leadership Pl., Box 26300, Greensboro, NC 27438-6300. TEL 919-288-7210. FAX 919-288-3999. Ed. Martin J. Wilcox. circ. 45,000. **Indexed:** Tr.& Dev.Alert. **Document type:** academic/scholarly publication, newsletter.
Description: Covers management education, executive development, and leadership development.

374.013   CC
JIAOYU YU ZHIYE/EDUCATION AND OCCUPATION. (Text in Chinese) m. Zhonghua Zhiye Jiaoyu She, 4 Taipingqiao Dajie, Xicheng-qu, Beijing 100810, People's Republic of China. TEL 6011155.

374   FR
JOURNAL DE LA FORMATION CONTINUE. 1972. 26/yr. $42. 2 rue d'Amsterdam, 75009 Paris, France. TEL 42-81-54-27. Ed. S. Errera. adv.; bk.rev. circ. 21,000.

JOURNAL FOR VOCATIONAL SPECIAL NEEDS EDUCATION. see EDUCATION — Special Education And Rehabilitation

374   TZ   ISSN 0856-1109
JOURNAL OF ADULT EDUCATION. (Text in English) 1977. a. $15. Institute of Adult Education, Box 20679, Dar es Salaam, Tanzania. Ed. Lawrence Kagaruki. adv.; bk.rev. circ. 1,500.
Formerly (until 1977): Fikara.
Description: Contains articles with one main theme, especially in the field of adult education.

028   US
JOURNAL OF COLLEGE AND ADULT READING. 1962. s-a. $20. North Central Reading Association, Simpson College, 701 North "C" St., Indianola, IA 50125. Eds. Joseph Fisher, Kay E. Fisher. bk.rev. circ. 1,000. (also avail. in microform from EDR)
Former titles: N C R A Yearbook; College and Adult Reading (ISSN 0069-553X)
Description: Topics include research, programs, professional issues and evaluation in reading and study skills programs.
Refereed Serial

374   UK   ISSN 0263-5909
JOURNAL OF COMMUNITY EDUCATION. 2/yr. £19.50. Community Education Development Centre (CEDC), Lyng Hall, Blackberry Lane, Coventry CV2 3JS, England. TEL 0203-638660. FAX 0203-681161.

374.8   US   ISSN 0737-7363
JOURNAL OF CONTINUING HIGHER EDUCATION. 1952. 3/yr. $25 to non-members (foreign $35). Association for Continuing Higher Education (University Park), 210 J. Orvis Keller Bldg., Pennsylvania State University, University Park, PA 16802. TEL 814-863-7752. FAX 814-865-3003. Ed. Donna S. Queeney. bk.rev. circ. 2,800. **Document type:** academic/scholarly publication.
—BLDSC (4965.247940); Faxon.
Former titles: Continuing Higher Education; Association for Continuing Higher Education. Newsletter.
Description: Serves as a forum for the reporting and exchange of information based on research, observations, and experiences relevant to continuing higher education.
Refereed Serial

370   CN   ISSN 0830-0445
JOURNAL OF DISTANCE EDUCATION. (Text in English, French) 1986. s-a. $40. Canadian Association for Distance Education, 151 Slater St., Ottawa, Ont. K1P 5N1, Canada. FAX 604-291-4964. Eds. Joan Collinge, Monique Layton. adv.; bk.rev. circ. 800.
—BLDSC (4969.840000); Faxon; SWETS.
Description: Aims to promote and encourage scholarly work of empirical and theoretical nature relating to distance education in Canada and throughout the world.
Refereed Serial

374.8   UK
KOGAN PAGE MATURE STUDENTS HANDBOOK; a nationwide guide to full-time, part-time and distance learning courses for mature students. 1988. a. £12.95. Kogan Page Ltd., 120 Pentonville Rd., London N1 9JN, England. TEL 071-278-0433. FAX 071-837-6348. TELEX 263088 KOGAN G. Ed. Margaret Korving. **Document type:** catalog.
Formerly: Make a Fresh Start (Year).
Description: Includes regional listings of all institutions for different kinds of courses, entry requirements and available grants.

374.2   NO   ISSN 0803-2149
KUNNSKAP & KULTUR. 1991. q. NOK 180. Folkeuniversitetet, Tollbugt 11, N-0152 Oslo 1, Norway.
Description: Devoted to people interested in adult education.

374   FI   ISSN 0788-2211
LA1010
L E I F - LIFE AND EDUCATION IN FINLAND. (Text in English) 1964. s-a. FIM 110($25) in Scandinavia; elsewhere FIM 150 ($35). Kansanvalistusseura - Society for Culture and Education, Museokatu 18 A 2, 00100 Helsinki 10, Finland. TEL 358-0-441-602. FAX 358-0-441-345. Eds. Christoffer Groenholm, Jussi T. Koski. adv. circ. 2,000. **Indexed:** C.I.J.E., Cont.Pg.Educ., Rural Recreat.Tour.Abstr., World Agri.Econ.& Rural Sociol.Abstr. **Document type:** academic/scholarly publication.
—BLDSC (5208.912800); UnCover.
Formerly (until 1990): Adult Education in Finland (ISSN 0001-8503)

374   DK   ISSN 0905-5487
L V U FAGBLADET.* 11/yr. Landsforbundet af Voksen- og Ungdomsundervisere, Vesterbrogade 31-3, 1620 Copenhagen V, Denmark. adv. circ. 6,000.
Former titles (until 1990): A og U Fagbladet (ISSN 0108-2752); (until 1982): Aften- og Ungdomsskolen (ISSN 0902-4255)

LABOUR EDUCATION. see BUSINESS AND ECONOMICS — Labor And Industrial Relations

374   CC
LAONIAN JIAOYU/EDUCATION FOR THE ELDERLY. (Text in Chinese) bi-m. Shandong Laonian Daxue - Shandong University of the Elderly, No. 3, Qianfoshan Xilu, Jinan, Shandong 250014, People's Republic of China. TEL 614704. Ed. Yuan Shishuo.

374   US   ISSN 1066-7377
LAUBACH LITERACY INTERNATIONAL ANNUAL REPORT. 1957. a. free to qualified personnel. Laubach Literacy International, 1320 Jamesville Ave., Box 131, Syracuse, NY 13210. TEL 315-422-9121. FAX 315-422-6369. Ed. Glenn H. Ivers. **Document type:** corporate report.
Description: Documents organization's annual report and financial statement.

374   CN   ISSN 0381-1387
LEARNING. 1976. irreg. Can.$24. Canadian Association for Adult Education, 29 Prince Arthur Ave., Toronto, ON M5R 1B2, Canada. TEL 416-964-0559. Ed. Lionel Orlikow. bk.rev.; tr.lit. circ. 1,500. **Indexed:** C.I.J.E., CMI.
—UMI.

374   US
LEARNING INDEPENDENTLY; a directory of self-instruction resources. 1979. irreg., 3rd ed., 1987. $220. Gale Research Inc., 835 Penobscot Bldg., Detroit, MI 48226. TEL 313-961-2242. FAX 313-961-6083. TELEX 810-221-7086. Ed. Steven R. Wasserman. **Document type:** directory.
Description: Guide to mail and other autodidactic learning help.

374.013   DK   ISSN 0109-9299
LEDER. KURSUSKATALOG. a. DKK 32. Kobenhavns Universitet, Krystalgade 25, DK-1172 Copenhagen K, Denmark.

374   US   ISSN 0047-4142
LITERACY ADVANCE. 1971. q. $10. (Laubach Literacy Action) Laubach Literacy International, 1320 Jamesville Ave., Box 131, Syracuse, NY 13210. TEL 315-422-9121. FAX 315-422-6369. Ed. Joan Warrender. bk.rev.; bibl.; illus. circ. 60,000. (tabloid format) **Document type:** newspaper.
Formerly: Laubach Literacy News.

374   US
LITERACY ADVOCATE. 1990. s-a. free to qualified personnel. Laubach Literacy International, 1320 Jamesville Ave., Box 131, Syracuse, NY 13210. TEL 315-422-9121. Ed. Glenn H. Ivers. circ. 20,000. **Document type:** newspaper.

374   AT   ISSN 0158-3026
LITERACY LINK. 1980. q. Aus.$30 to individuals; institutions Aus.$60. Australian Council For Adult Literacy, G.P.O. Box 2283, Canberra, A.C.T. 2601, Australia. TEL 60-258-7873. Ed. Simon Wallace. bk.rev. circ. 400. (back issues avail.) **Indexed:** Aus.Educ.Ind.

374   JA
LIVE. (Text in Japanese) 1971. m. 5980 Yen. Gakken Co. Ltd., 40-5, 4-chome, Kamiikedai, Ohta-ku, Tokyo 145, Japan. Ed. Ken'ichi Yamana.

374   US
M P A E A NEWSLETTER. no.2, 1975-76. q. $20 (with membership). Mountain Plains Adult Education Association, Newsletter, c/o Bill Shupe, Box 80 Pinecrest, Clancy, MT 59634. TEL 406-933-8327. bk.rev. circ. 550. **Document type:** newsletter.

374.013 658.3   CN   ISSN 0846-5274
MAGAZINE AVENIR; pour mieux gerer et former vos ressources humaines. (Text in French) 1984. 10/yr. Can.$25($40) Editions de Montr Royal Inc., 3715 Av. Lacombe, Ste. 200, Montreal, PQ H3T 1M3, Canada. TEL 514-341-7916. FAX 514-341-2644. Ed. Michel Guenard. adv.; bk.rev. circ. 30,000. (back issues avail.) **Indexed:** Pt.de Rep. (1991-).
Former titles: Avenir (ISSN 0838-6900); (until Oct. 1987): Magazine Ressources Humaines (ISSN 0826-3515)

EDUCATION — ADULT EDUCATION

379 US ISSN 0094-1506
LC1046.M5
MICHIGAN STATE PLAN FOR VOCATIONAL EDUCATION. Variant title- Annual and Long Range State Plan for Vocational Education. 1917. a. free. Department of Education, Division of Vocational Education, Box 30009, Lansing, MI 48909. TEL 517-373-3373. FAX 517-373-8776. illus. circ. 1,700.

374 US ISSN 0090-4244
LC5201
MOUNTAIN PLAINS JOURNAL OF ADULT EDUCATION. 1972. s-a. $20 membership. Mountain Plains Adult Education Association, Journal, College of Education, University of Wyoming, Box 3374, Laramie, WY 82071. TEL 307-766-3042. FAX 307-766-6668. Eds. Burton Sisco, Donna Whitson. bk.rev.; bibl. circ. 650. Indexed: ERIC.
—BLDSC (4918.944500); UnCover.
  Description: Provides a regional forum for discussion of current issues and research in adult education, its evolution and future.
  Refereed Serial

374 US
MYRIN INSTITUTE FOR ADULT EDUCATION PROCEEDINGS. 1954. irreg., latest no.38. $2 per no. Myrin Institute, Inc., 136 E. 64th St., New York, NY 10021. TEL 212-758-6475. FAX 212-758-6784. Ed.Bd. bk.rev.; bibl. circ. 2,000. **Document type:** proceedings.

374 AU ISSN 0027-7363
NACH DER ARBEIT. 1947. 10/yr. S.20. Volkshochschule Linz, Coulinstrasse 18, A-4020 Linz, Austria. Ed. Erich Leichtenmueller. bk.rev. circ. 1,300.

NARA JOSHI DAIGAKU HOKEN KANRI SENTA NENPO/NARA WOMEN'S UNIVERSITY. HEALTH ADMINISTRATION CENTER. ARCHIVES OF HEALTH CARE. see *PUBLIC HEALTH AND SAFETY*

NATIONAL ASSOCIATION OF CAREER & GUIDANCE TEACHERS. JOURNAL. see *EDUCATION — School Organization And Administration*

NATIONAL DIRECTORY OF ART INTERNSHIPS. see *ART*

NEIL MUSCOTT'S SUCCESS NEWSLETTER; strategies and stories for successful people. see *PSYCHOLOGY*

NETWORK NEWS. see *CHILDREN AND YOUTH — About*

NETWORK NEWS (CLEVELAND). see *PSYCHOLOGY*

374 US ISSN 1052-2891
LC5251
NEW DIRECTIONS FOR ADULT AND CONTINUING EDUCATION. 1979. q. $47 to individuals; institutions $62. Jossey-Bass Inc., Publishers, 350 Sansome St., 5th Fl., San Francisco, CA 94104. TEL 415-433-1767. FAX 415-433-0499. Ed. Ralph G. Brockett. bibl. circ. 850. (also avail. in microform from UMI; back issues avail.; reprint service avail. from UMI) Indexed: C.I.J.E., Chic.Per.Ind., Educ.Ind. **Document type:** monographic series.
—BLDSC (6083.312500); UnCover; SWETS; UMI.
  Formerly: New Directions for Continuing Education (ISSN 0195-2242)
  Description: Combines research findings on adult students and programs with the practical experience of continuing education directors and staff.

NEWFOUNDLAND AND LABRADOR WOMEN'S INSTITUTES. NEWSLETTER. see *WOMEN'S INTERESTS*

374 US ISSN 0884-3910
NEWS FOR YOU. 1959. w. $14.40. New Readers Press (Subsidiary of: Laubach Literacy International), 1320 Jamesville Ave., Box 131, Syracuse, NY 13210. TEL 800-448-8878. FAX 315-422-5561. Ed. Nancy Izuno; Pub. Dennis Cook. charts; illus.; stat.; tr.lit.; circ. 110,000 (paid). (tabloid format) Indexed: Jun.High.Mag.Abstr. **Document type:** newspaper.
  Formed by the 1985 merger of: News for You (Edition A) (ISSN 0162-8518); News for You (Edition B) (ISSN 0162-850X)
  Description: News and information for adults and older youth at reading levels 4-6, including supplementary worksheet.

374 US ISSN 0886-0165
NON-CREDIT LEARNING NEWS; the newsletter for directors of non-credit programs. 1986. 10/yr. $74. Learning for All Seasons, Inc., Box 579X, Lexington, MA 02173. TEL 617-861-0379. FAX 617-860-0237. Ed. Susan B. Capon. adv.; bk.rev.; tr.lit. circ. 1,300. (back issues avail.) **Document type:** newsletter.
  Description: Information and announcements on continuing education courses, programs, workshops, and seminars in all fields.

NONGCUN QINGNIAN/COUNTRY YOUTH. see *CHILDREN AND YOUTH — For*

NORDBAYERN. LANDESARBEITSAMT. BUNDESANSTALT FUER ARBEIT. BERATUNGS- UND VERMITTLUNGSDIENSTE. INFORMATIONEN. see *BUSINESS AND ECONOMICS*

374 US
ONLINE WITH ADULT AND CONTINUING EDUCATORS.* 1960. 8/yr. $25 (foreign $32). American Association for Adult and Continuing Education, 1101 Connecticut Ave., N.W., Ste. 700, Washington, DC 20036. TEL 703-522-2234. Ed. Jeanette Smith. circ. 4,000. (also avail. in microform from UMI; reprint service avail. from UMI)
  Former titles (until 1987): A A A C E Newsletter; (until 1982): Pulse of Public Continuing and Adult Education; Pulse of Public School Adult Education (ISSN 0033-4219)
  Description: Information on trends, statistics, issues, innovative programs, grants, job vacancies in the field of adult and continuing education.

OPEN PRAXIS. see *EDUCATION*

374 US
OPTION. 1977. s-a. $10 to non-members and students; institutions $50; membership $20. Folk Education Association of America, 39 Wagon Trail Rd., Black Mountain, NC 28711. TEL 704-669-5914. (Subscr. to: c/o Janet Trader, 2606 14th St., Two Rivers, WI 54241) Ed. Kathryn Parke. bk.rev. circ. 350. (back issues avail.)
  Description: Contains articles on current practice and history of popular education and culture nationally and internationally.

374 XO ISSN 0231-7613
OSVETA. 10/yr. (Vyskumny Ustav Kultury) Obzor, Ceskoslovenskej Armady 35, 815 85 Bratislava, Slovakia.

374 XO ISSN 0231-8911
OSVETOVA PRACA. 26/yr. $55. (Ministerstvo Kultury Slovenskej Republiky) Obzor, Ceskoslovenskej Armady 35, 815 85 Bratislava, Slovakia.

374 GW ISSN 0720-910X
P A E - MITTEILUNGEN. a. free. Paedagogische Arbeitsstelle fuer Erwachsenenbildung in Baden-Wuerttemberg, Panaoramastr. 19, 70174 Stuttgart, Germany. TEL 0711-293685. **Document type:** bulletin.

P H - F R. (Paedagogische Hochschule Freiburg) see *EDUCATION — Teaching Methods And Curriculum*

374 GW ISSN 0723-7197
PAEDAGOGISCHE ARBEITSSTELLE FUER ERWACHSENENBILDUNG. SCHRIFTEN. irreg., latest no.18. price varies. Paedagogische Arbeitsstelle fuer Erwachsenenbildung in Baden-Wuerttemberg, Panoramastr. 19, 70174 Stuttgart, Germany. TEL 0711-293685. **Document type:** monographic series.

374 200 US
PARENTING FOR PEACE & JUSTICE NETWORK NEWSLETTER. 1981. bi-m. $25. Parenting for Peace & Justice Network, Institute for Peace & Justice, 4144 Lindell Blvd., Ste. 124, St. Louis, MO 63108. TEL 314-533-4445. Eds. Jim & Nanette Ford. bk.rev.; film rev.; video rev.; bibl. circ. 2,500. (tabloid format; back issues avail.) **Document type:** newsletter.
  Description: Peace, justice and environmental resources and action suggestions for families and educators working with children and families.

PEACE GAZETTE. see *POLITICAL SCIENCE*

374 MX
PEDAGOGIA PARA EL ADIESTRAMIENTO. 1971. q. Mex.$80($5) (Centro de Informacion Tecnica y Documentacion) Mexico. Servicio Nacional de Adiestramiento Rapido de la Mano de Obra en la Industria, Av. Atzcapotzalco la Villa 209, Mexico 16 D.F., Mexico. Ed. Marsella Cruz. abstr.; bibl.; index; cum.index. circ. 4,000. (also avail. in microfilm)

374 658.3 SW
PERSONAL & LEDARSKAP. 1970. 8/yr. SEK 525. Epok Media AB, P.O. Box 22022, 702 02 Oerebro, Sweden. TEL 46-19-30-63-00. FAX 46-19-30-63-03. (Subscr. to: P.O. Box 21083, 100 31 Stockholm, Sweden) Ed. Kent Seifors. adv.; bk.rev.; abstr.; cum.index. circ. 11,200.
  Formerly: Utbildningstidningen (ISSN 0049-5735)

PERSPECTIVE (WHEATON). see *RELIGIONS AND THEOLOGY*

266 SA ISSN 0079-4341
CODEN: WBPNBQ
POTCHEFSTROOM UNIVERSITY FOR CHRISTIAN HIGHER EDUCATION. WETENSKAPLIKE BYDRAES. REEKS B: NATUURWETENSKAPPE. SERIES. irreg. free. Potchefstroom University for Christian Higher Education - Potchefstroomse Universiteit vir Christelike Hoer Onderwys, Potchefstroom, South Africa. Indexed: Biol.Abstr.

374 II
PRASAR; journal devoted to theory, research and field practices in adult continuing education. (Text in English or Hindi) 1973. q. Rs.18($10) University of Rajasthan, Department of Adult & Continuing Education, Gandhi Nagar, Jaipur 302004, India. Ed. C.K. Dandiya. adv.; bk.rev.; bibl.; charts; stat. circ. 250.

374 GW
PRAXIS DER VERKUENDIGUNG. q. DM.25.60. J.G. Oncken Nachf. GmbH, Postfach 102829, 34028 Kassel, Germany. TEL 0561-52005-0. FAX 0561-5200550. Ed. Rev. Hinrich Schmidt. circ. 3,000. **Document type:** bulletin.

374 US
PROFILE (WHEATON). 1967. 2/yr. free. Evangelical Training Association, 110 Bridge St., Box 327, Wheaton, IL 60139-0327. TEL 708-668-6400. FAX 708-668-8437. circ. 10,000. **Document type:** newsletter.
  Formerly: Teacher Training Profile.

374 420 AT ISSN 0814-7094
PROSPECT; a journal of Australian TESOL. 3/yr. Aus.$30 to individuals (foreign Aus.$45); institutions Aus.$50 (foreign Aus.$65). National Centre for English Language Teaching and Research, Macquarie University, New South Wales 2109, Australia. TEL 61-2-805-7673. FAX 61-2-805-7849. TELEX MACUNI AA122377. Ed. Anne Burns. adv.; bk.rev.; circ. 1,500 (paid). Indexed: Lang.Teach.& Ling.Abstr. **Document type:** academic/scholarly publication.
—BLDSC (6927.447800); UnCover.
  Description: Publishes research articles, notes, reports and reviews on applied linguistic and teaching concerns related to adult education.

R A S D UPDATE. (Reference and Adult Services Division) see *LIBRARY AND INFORMATION SCIENCES*

374.4 GW ISSN 0938-0345
RATGEBER FUER FERNUNTERRICHT; mit amtlichem Verzeichnis aller zugelassenen Fernlehrgaenge. 1980. a. Staatliche Zentralstelle fuer Fernunterricht, Peter-Welter-Platz 2, 50676 Cologne, Germany. TEL 0221-921207-0. FAX 0221-921207-20. circ. 20,000. **Document type:** directory.

374 US
READER (SYRACUSE). 1979. 4/yr. $25 lifetime subscription. Literacy Volunteers of America, Inc., 5795 Widewaters Pkwy., Syracuse, NY 13214. TEL 315-445-8000. FAX 315-445-8006. Ed. Jeff Charboneau. bk.rev. circ. 50,000. (back issues avail.) **Document type:** newsletter.
  Description: Addresses the problem of adult illiteracy and describes US efforts to promote literacy.

2082 EDUCATION — ADULT EDUCATION

374 FR ISSN 1247-6242
REGARDS SUR LA FORMATION. irreg. Centre I N F F O, Tour Europe, 92049 Paris Cedex 7 (La Defense), France. TEL 47-78-13-50. FAX 47-73-74-20. TELEX 615 383.

RESEARCH IN DISTANCE EDUCATION; a forum for researchers in distance education. see *EDUCATION*

RESOURCES IN AGING; an international newsletter featuring new developments in aging. see *GERONTOLOGY AND GERIATRICS*

374 MX
RETABLOS DE PAPEL. 1980-1988 (no.17). s-a. Centro Regional de Educacion de Adultos y Alfabetizacion Funcional para America Latina, Quinta Erendira, 61600 Patzcuaro, Mich., Mexico. circ. 2,500.

374 MX ISSN 1016-8087
REVISTA INTERAMERICANA DE EDUCACION DE ADULTOS. 1978. q. Mex.$14.40($15) (Organization of American States) Centro de Cooperacion Regional para la Educacion de Adultos en America Latina y el Caribe - CREFAL, Quinta Erendira s-n, 61600 Patzcuaro, Michoacan, Mexico. circ. 3,000. (back issues avail.)

S I L - A A I B OCCASIONAL PAPERS. (Summer Institute of Linguistics, Australian Aborigines and Islanders Branch) see *LINGUISTICS*

374 GW
SCHULDRUCKER.* 1964. 3/yr. DM.15. Graulheck 24A, 6685 Schiffweiler, Germany. Ed. P. Treitz. adv.; bibl.; illus. circ. 250.

374 GW
SCHULE HEUTE; Information und Meinung. 1960. m. DM.33. (Verband Bildung und Erziehung Nordrhein - Westfalen) Verlag Ferdinand Kamp GmbH & Co. KG, Postfach 101309, 44713 Bochum, Germany. TEL 0234-91420. FAX 0234-9142142. adv.; bk.rev. circ. 19,000. (back issues avail.) **Document type:** academic/scholarly publication.

374 338 US ISSN 0740-2791
SEMINARS, WORKSHOPS & CLASSES. 1985. biennial. $4. Training Manuals, Etc., c/o Prosperity & Profits Unlimited, Box 416, Denver, CO 80201-0416. TEL 303-575-5676. circ. 1,500. (also avail. in microfiche; back issues avail.) **Document type:** newsletter.
Description: Provides information on educational opportunities.

SHALOM; magazine for alumni of Israel training courses. see *BUSINESS AND ECONOMICS — International Development And Assistance*

374 CC ISSN 0488-5406
SHANGHAI JIAOYU (CHENGREN JIAOYU BAN)/SHANGHAI EDUCATION (ADULT EDUCATION EDITION). (Text in Chinese) m. Shanghai Shi Jiaoyu-ju - Shanghai Municipal Bureau of Education, 500 Shaanxi Beilu, Shanghai 200041, People's Republic of China. TEL 2530739. Ed. Liu Yuanzhang.

371.26 FR ISSN 0049-1063
SOCIETE D'ETUDES. REVUE D'ETUDES; revue mensuelle pour l'enseignement par correspondance. 1920. m. 270 F. Societe d'Etudes, 5 bd. Beaumarchais, 75180 Paris Cedex 04, France. TEL 42-72-23-39. Ed. J. Jore. bibl.; charts.

SOUTH AFRICAN JOURNAL OF AGRICULTURAL EXTENSION/SUID-AFRIKAANSE TYDSKRIF VIR LANDBOUVOORLIGTING. see *AGRICULTURE*

374.013 DK ISSN 0107-4733
SPECIALARBEJDERKURSER. 1973. a. free. Arbejdsmarkedsstyrelsen, P.O. Box 2722, Blegdamsvej 56, DK-2100 Copenhagen Oe, Denmark. TEL 45-35-28-81-00. FAX 45-35-36-24-11. illus. **Document type:** government publication, catalog.
Formerly: Specialarbejderkurser paa Specialarbejderskolerne.

374.013 DK ISSN 0108-3430
SPECIALARBEJDERSKOLEN. 1980. 10/yr. DKK 6 per no. Laerersammenslutningen ved Specialarbejderskolerne, c/o Ole Dam Pedersen, Hovedvejen 16, Hjarnoe, 8700 Horsens, Denmark. illus.
Formerly: L V S Bladet (ISSN 0108-3457)

374 CE
SRI LANKA FOUNDATION INSTITUTE. NEWS. (Text in English, Sinhalese, or Tamil) irreg. Rs.3. Sri Lanka Foundation Institute, 100 Independence Square, Colombo 8, Sri Lanka. **Indexed:** Sri Lanka Sci.Ind.

374 GW
STAATLICHE ZENTRALSTELLE FUER FERNUNTERRICHT. AMTLICHES MITTEILUNGSBLATT. 1973. s-a. DM.10. Staatliche Zentralstelle fuer Fernunterricht, Peter-Welter-Platz 2, 50676 Cologne, Germany. TEL 0221-921207-0. FAX 0221-921207-20. Ed. Michael Vennemann. adv.; bk.rev. **Document type:** bulletin.

377 FR ISSN 0996-9713
STAGES AGREES PAR L'ETAT. 1980. a. Centre I N F F O, Tour Europe, 92049 Paris Cedex 7 (La Defense), France. TEL 47-78-13-50. FAX 47-73-74-20. TELEX 615 383.

374 AT
STEPPING STONES. 1978. q. Department of Employment, Vocational Education and Training, Adult Literacy Services Bureau, 445 Murray St., Perth, W.A. 6000, Australia. TEL 09-320-3888. FAX 09-481-2448. Ed. Brenda Conochie. (back issues avail.)
Incorporates (1978-1992): T A F E - Adult Literacy Tutors' Newsletter.
Description: Anthology of adult literacy students' writing.

374 IT ISSN 0039-2057
STRADE APERTE. 1959. m. membership. Movimento Adulti Scouts Cattolici Italiani, Via Gualtiero Castellini 24, Rome 00197, Italy. FAX 06-877647. adv.; bk.rev.; film rev.; charts; illus.; stat.; index. circ. 7,000.

374 TZ ISSN 0856-0560
STUDIES IN ADULT EDUCATION. 1971. q. $12 per no. Institute of Adult Education, Box 20679, Dar es Salaam, Tanzania. Ed. W.I. Mjema. circ. 500.
Indexed: C.I.J.E., Educ.Ind., Int.Lab.Doc., Res.High.Educ.Abstr.
Description: Deals with specific issues on adult education.

374 UK ISSN 0266-0830
CODEN: SEDAE9
STUDIES IN THE EDUCATION OF ADULTS. 1969. s-a. £17.50 (foreign £20). National Institute of Adult Continuing Education, 21 De Montfort St., Leicester LE1 7GE, England. TEL 0533-551451. FAX 0533-854514. Ed. John Wallis. adv.; bk.rev.; bibl.; illus.; index. circ. 750. (reprint service avail.)
Indexed: C.I.J.E., Cont.Pg.Educ., Educ.Ind., Educ.Tech.Abstr., High.Educ.Curr.Aware.Bull., Mult.Ed.Abstr., Rural Ext.Educ.& Tr.Abstr., SOMA. **Document type:** academic/scholarly publication.
—BLDSC (8490.466300); Faxon; UnCover; SWETS; UMI.
Formerly: Studies in Adult Education (ISSN 0039-3525)

374 US
SYRACUSE UNIVERSITY PUBLICATIONS IN CONTINUING EDUCATION. LANDMARK AND NEW HORIZONS SERIES.* 1971. irreg. Syracuse University, Publications in Continuing Education, 356 Huntington Hall, 150 Marshall St., Syracuse, NY 13244. TEL 315-443-3421.

374 US
SYRACUSE UNIVERSITY PUBLICATIONS IN CONTINUING EDUCATION. NOTES AND ESSAYS. no.72, 1972. irreg. price varies. Syracuse University, Publications in Continuing Education, 356 Huntington Hall, 150 Marshall St., Syracuse, NY 13244. TEL 315-443-3421. bibl.; illus.

374 US ISSN 0082-1179
SYRACUSE UNIVERSITY PUBLICATIONS IN CONTINUING EDUCATION. OCCASIONAL PAPERS.* irreg., no.46, 1976. Syracuse University, Publications in Continuing Education, 356 Huntington Hall, 150 Marshall St., Syracuse, NY 13244. TEL 315-443-3421.

T E S O L MATTERS. (Teachers of English to Speakers of Other Languages) see *LINGUISTICS*

TANZEN. see *DANCE*

374.013 GW
DIE TECHNIKSTUNDE; paedagogische Arbeitsblaetter fuer zeitgemaessen Technikunterricht. 1969. 2/yr. DM.18. A L S Verlag GmbH, Voltastr. 3, 63128 Dietzenbach, Germany. TEL 06074-25051. FAX 06074-27322. Ed. Ingrid Kreide. cum.index: 1992-1993. circ. 7,000. (back issues avail.)
Document type: academic/scholarly publication.
Formerly (until 1992): Werkstunde.

374 CI
THELEME; casopis za istrazivanje edukacije i kulture. (Text in Croatian; summaries in English) 1955. q. $36. Andragoski Centar, Vojnoviceva 42-II, 41001 Zagreb, Croatia. TEL 041-412-523. Ed. Vjerocka Ban. adv. circ. 1,000.
Former titles (until no.12, 1990): Andragogija (ISSN 0029-764X); (until 1969): Obrazovanje Odraslih; (until 1959): Narodno Sveuciliste.

367 370 US
TOGETHER WE CAN. 1989. m. (Waynesboro Education Association) Valley Uniserv Unit, 620 Hawkins St., No.A, Harrisonburg, VA 22801-4412. TEL 800-725-5564. Ed. H. Aylor. circ. 170. (looseleaf format; back issues avail.)
Description: Contains information about meetings, workshops, and other general information.

374 NE
TOORTS. 1925. 6/yr. fl.25. Centraal Bestuur NIVON, Nieuwe Herengracht 119, 1011 SB Amsterdam, Netherlands. bk.rev.; film rev.; illus.; index. circ. 23,000.
Incorporates: Stuwing (ISSN 0039-4211)

378 630 UN ISSN 0251-1495
S530
TRAINING FOR AGRICULTURE AND RURAL DEVELOPMENT. French edition: Formation pour l'Agriculture et le Developpement Rural (ISSN 0251-1487); Spanish edition: Adiestramiento para el Desarrollo Agropecuario y Rural (ISSN 0251-1479) 1967. irreg. $25. Food and Agriculture Organization of the United Nations, Agricultural Education and Training Service, c/o UNIPUB, 4611-F Assembly Dr., Lanham, MD 20706-4391. FAX 301-459-0056.
Former titles: Training for Agriculture; (until 1972): Extension; (until 1971): Agricultural Education and Training (ISSN 1014-0964)

374 US
TRAINING TRENDS. 1985. q. T P C Training Systems (Subsidiary of: Telemedia Inc.), 750 Lake Crook Rd., Buffalo Grove, IL 60089-5080. TEL 708-537-6610. Ed. Patricia Horn. bk.rev.; charts; illus.; stat. circ. 25,000. (looseleaf format; back issues avail.)

374.8 UN
U I E STUDIES ON POST-LITERACY AND CONTINUING EDUCATION. (Text in English, French) 1984. irreg., no.7, 1989. DM.24. Unesco Institute for Education, Feldbrunnenstr. 58, 2000 Hamburg 13, Germany. TEL 040-447843. TELEX 2164-146-UIE-D. **Document type:** monographic series.
Description: Series reporting learning strategies in numerous countries.

374.013 DK ISSN 0107-3435
UDDANNELSESNOEGLEN. 1974. a. DKK 225. Noegleforlaget ApS, Haslevej 12-14, 6000 Kolding, Denmark. TEL 75-538620. illus.
Formerly: Uddannelsesvejviser.

374 CN
UNIVERSITY OF BRITISH COLUMBIA. CENTER FOR CONTINUING EDUCATION. MONOGRAPHS ON COMPARATIVE AND AREA STUDIES IN ADULT EDUCATION. 1977. irreg. price varies. University of British Columbia, Center for Continuing Education, Vancouver, BC V6T 1Z1, Canada. TEL 604-222-5282. FAX 604-222-5249. (Co-sponsor: International Council for Adult Education) circ. 500. **Document type:** monographic series.

UNIVERSITY OF SUSSEX. CENTRE FOR CONTINUING EDUCATION. OCCASIONAL PAPER. see *HISTORY*

EDUCATION — COMPUTER APPLICATIONS

374.9 ZA
UNIVERSITY OF ZAMBIA. CENTRE FOR CONTINUING EDUCATION. REPORT OF THE ANNUAL RESIDENT TUTORS' CONFERENCE. 1975. a, 8th, 1976. free. University of Zambia, Centre for Continuing Education, Box 516, Lusaka, Zambia. circ. 1,000.
Formerly: University of Zambia. Centre for Continuing Education. Report of the Annual Staff Conference.

373.246 US ISSN 1044-0151
LC1045
V I C A JOURNAL. (Special edition for teachers and administrators also avail: VICA Professional - VP (ISSN 1040-4538)) 1966. 4/yr. $8 to non-members. Vocational Industrial Clubs of America, Inc., Box 3000, Leesburg, VA 22075. TEL 703-777-8810. FAX 703-777-8999. Ed. E. Thomas Hall. adv. contact: Donald Canham. bk.rev.; stat.; tr.lit.; circ. 240,000 (paid). (back issues avail.) **Document type:** consumer publication.
Formerly: V I C A (ISSN 0042-1839)
Description: Directed to VICA student members in high schools, vocational-technical centers, and junior and community colleges. Covers career information, job-seeking tips, and professional development articles.

VIVE LA DIFFERENCE. see SOCIOLOGY

374 UK ISSN 0305-7879
CODEN: VAEDES
VOCATIONAL ASPECT OF EDUCATION. 1949. 3/yr. £24 to individuals; institutions £54. Triangle Journals Ltd., P.O. Box 65, Wallingford, Oxfordshire OX10 0YG, England. TEL 0491-838013. FAX 0491-834968. adv.; bk.rev.; illus.; index. circ. 1,000. Indexed: Br.Educ.Ind., C.I.J.E., Cont.Pg.Educ., High.Educ.Curr.Aware.Bull., Int.Lab.Doc., Res.High.Educ.Abstr., Rural Ext.Educ.& Tr.Abstr., Sp.Ed.Needs Abstr. **Document type:** academic/scholarly publication.
—BLDSC (9250.450000); UnCover; SWETS.

374.013 US ISSN 0884-8009
LC1041
VOCATIONAL EDUCATION JOURNAL. 1926. m. (8/yr.). $32 to non-members. American Vocational Association, 1410 King St., Alexandria, VA 22314. TEL 703-683-3111. FAX 703-683-7424. Ed. Paul Plawin. adv. contact: Fred Kurst. circ. 42,000. (also avail. in microform from UMI) Indexed: Acad.Ind., Bus.Educ.Ind., C.I.J.E., Educ.Ind. **Document type:** trade publication.
—BLDSC (9250.463000); Faxon; UnCover; SWETS; UMI.
Former titles: VocEd (ISSN 0164-9175); American Vocational Journal (ISSN 0003-1496)
Description: Focuses on trends and professional issues affecting vocational technical education.

374.013 HK
VOCATIONAL TRAINING COUNCIL. ANNUAL REPORT. a. Vocational Training Council, Information and Public Relations Section, Vocational Training Council Tower, 14th Fl., 27 Wood Rd., Wanchai, Hong Kong. TEL 5-836-1046. FAX 5-838-0667.

374.013 HK
VOCATIONAL TRAINING NEWS. 1986. bi-m. free. Vocational Training Council, Information and Public Relations Section, Vocational Training Council Tower, 14th Fl., 27 Wood Rd., Wanchai, Hong Kong. TEL 5-836-1046. FAX 5-838-0667. Ed.Bd. circ. 4,000. **Document type:** newsletter.
Description: Follows activities and developments of the council and is targeted to readers in government, employment, educational and social services circles.

374 DK ISSN 0107-8135
VOKSENUDDANNELSE; tidsskrift for amtskommunale enkeltfagkurser. 1980. 6/yr. DKK 80. Benne Vagn Jensen Ed. & Pub., Gyldenrisvej 12, 4470 Svebolle, Denmark. adv.; bk.rev.; illus. circ. 2,000.

374 GW
VOLKSHOCHSCHULE FLENSBURG. ARBEITSPLAN. 1949. s-a. Volkshochschule Flensburg, Suederhofenden 40-42, 24937 Flensburg, Germany. TEL 0461-852023. FAX 0461-852971.

VOX LATINA. see LITERATURE

374 US
W V A VIEWS & VISIONS. vol.6, 1970. 5/yr. membership. Wisconsin Vocational Association, 518 Potomac Ln., Madison, WI 53719. TEL 608-833-5858. FAX 608-833-3011. Ed. Bette Lou Esser. adv.; bk.rev.; illus. circ. 2,500. **Document type:** newsletter.
Former titles: W V A Lifeline; W A V A E News (ISSN 0042-9503)

W W T - WEITERBILDUNG IN WIRTSCHAFT UND TECHNIK; Zeitschrift fuer die berufliche Weiterbildung. see BUSINESS AND ECONOMICS

374 GW ISSN 0935-3097
WEITERBILDUNG; Magazin fuer die Fuehrungskraefte. 1988. bi-m. DM.48. Juenger Verlag, Schumannstr. 161, 63069 Offenbach a.M., Germany. TEL 069-840003-0. FAX 069-84000333. Ed. Helmut Juenger.

374 AU ISSN 0026-6906
WIENER URANIA. MITTEILUNGEN. 1910. m. S.30. Wiener Urania, Volksbildungshaus, Uraniastr. 1, A-1010 Vienna, Austria. Ed. Wilhelm Petrasch. adv.; bk.rev. circ. 8,000.

WOMEN'S EDUCATION/EDUCATION DES FEMMES. see WOMEN'S INTERESTS

370 331 II
WORKERS EDUCATION JOURNAL. 1966. q. free. Central Board for Workers Education, 1400 West High Court, Gokulpeth, Nagpur 440010, India. Ed. K.R. Khamborkar. adv.; bk.rev.; illus.; circ. 2,000 (controlled).
Description: Textual and pictorial booklets on trade unionism, industrial relations, labor economics and tools and techniques.

WORLDLIT. see EDUCATION

374 US ISSN 0084-2486
L900
WORLDWIDE REGISTER OF ADULT EDUCATION; directory of home study schools. 1960. irreg., latest 1973 (with 1980 supp.). $8.95. Aurea Publications, 207 Allen Ave., Allenhurst, NJ 07711. TEL 908-531-4535. Ed. Alex Sandri-White. **Document type:** directory.
Description: Lists hundreds of correspondence schools, including those accredited by the National Home Study Council, as well as many other vocational and university extension programs.

374 US
THE WRITTEN WORD; promoting communications in the field of functional illiteracy. 1979. m. $18. Contact Publications, 3900 Industrial Ave., N., 2nd Fl., Box 81826, Lincoln, NE 68501-1826. TEL 402-464-0602. FAX 402-464-5931. Ed. Su Perk Davis. bk.rev. circ. 1,000. (back issues avail.) **Document type:** newsletter.
Description: For local community programs combating functional illiteracy.

374 UK ISSN 0265-1726
LC5201
YEARBOOK OF ADULT CONTINUING EDUCATION. 1961. a. £9.95 (foreign £10.95). National Institute of Adult Continuing Education, 21 De Montfort St., Leicester LE1 7GE, England. TEL 0533-551451. FAX 0533-854514. bk.rev.; index. circ. 2,000. (also avail. in microfiche; reprint service avail.) **Document type:** directory.
Formerly: Yearbook of Adult Education (ISSN 0084-3601)
Description: Directory of organizations in the UK and guide to sources of information.

374 CC
ZHONGGUO DIANDA JIAOYU/CHINESE TELEVISION UNIVERSITY EDUCATION. (Text in Chinese) m. Zhongyang Guangbo Dianshi Daxue, 83, Fuxing Lu, Beijing 100856, People's Republic of China. TEL 8212629. Ed. Li Fuzhi.

374 US
ZI XUE/SELF-TEACHING. (Text in Chinese) m. $35. China Books & Periodicals, Inc., 2929 24th St., San Francisco, CA 94110. TEL 415-282-2994. FAX 415-282-0994.

ZIELSPRACHE ENGLISCH; Zeitschrift fuer den Englischunterricht in der Erwachsenbildung. see LINGUISTICS

374 GW
ZWEIWOCHEN DIENST; Bildung - Wissenschaft - Kulturpolitik. 1935. fortn. DM.156 to individuals; institutions DM.300. Zweiwochendienst Verlag GmbH, Pressehaus I, Rm. 234, Heussallee 2-10, 53113 Bonn, Germany. TEL 0228-217375. FAX 0228-215226. Ed. Brigitte Lausch. bibl.; stat. circ. 1,000. (back issues avail.) **Document type:** newsletter.

EDUCATION — Computer Applications

see also Computers–Computer Assisted Instruction

370 UK
▼ **A L T - J. ASSOCIATION FOR LEARNING TECHNOLOGY JOURNAL.** 1993. biennial. £60 per double vol. (Association for Learning Technology) University of Wales Press, 6 Gwennyth St., Catjays, Cardiff CF2 4YD, Wales. TEL 44-222-231919. FAX 44-222-230908. Ed. Gabriel Jacobs. **Document type:** academic/scholarly publication.
Description: Devoted to research and good practice in the use of learning technologies in higher education.

A V VIDEO; production and presentation technology. see COMMUNICATIONS — Video

A X I S. see COMPUTERS

APPLE EDUCATION NEWS; an information service for educators and trainers. see COMPUTERS — Personal Computers

BIBLIOGRAPHIE INFORMATIK FUER SCHULE, HOCHSCHULE UND WEITERBILDUNG. see COMPUTERS — Information Science And Information Theory

370 621.381 US ISSN 0742-7778
P53.28
C A L I C O JOURNAL. 1983. q. $35 to individuals; institutions $65; corporations $125. Computer Assisted Language & Instruction Consortium, 014 Language Bldg., Box 90267, Duke University, Durham, NC 27708-0267. TEL 919-660-3180. FAX 919-660-3133. Ed. Frank Borchardt. adv.; bk.rev. circ. 1,200. (also avail. in microfiche; back issues avail.) Indexed: ERIC, Lang.Teach.& Ling.Abstr. **Document type:** academic/scholarly publication.
—BLDSC (3010.760000); Faxon; UnCover; SWETS.
Description: Provides information on the applications of technology in teaching and learning languages.
Refereed Serial

C M E A NEWS. (California Music Educators Association) see MUSIC

371.394 US
C U E NEWSLETTER; serving computer-using educators internationally. 1978. bi-m. $25 (Foreign $50). Computer Using Educators, Inc., 1210 Marina Village Pkwy., Ste. 100, Alameda, CA 94501-1945. TEL 408-496-2935. Ed. Sue Talley. adv.; bk.rev. circ. 9,500. **Document type:** newsletter.
Formerly: Computer-Using Educators Newsletter (ISSN 0739-9553)
Description: Feature articles, columns, announcements, letters, and advertiser's index pertaining to the application of computer systems to learning and education throughout the United States and abroad.

370 US ISSN 1043-7290
CAUSE. PROCEEDINGS OF NATIONAL CONFERENCE. a. $75 to non-members. Cause, 4840 Pearl E. Circle, Ste. 302E, Boulder, CO 80301. TEL 303-449-4430. FAX 303-440-0461. Ed. Julia A. Rudy. circ. 1,300. **Document type:** proceedings.
Description: Activities and professional papers from national conference of professionals in the field of higher education information technology management.

EDUCATION — COMPUTER APPLICATIONS

370   US   ISSN 0164-534X
CAUSE - EFFECT MAGAZINE. 1978. q. $96 to non-members; campus libraries $24. Cause, 4830 Pearl E. Cir., Ste. 302E, Boulder, CO 80301. TEL 303-449-4430. FAX 303-440-0461. Ed. Julia A. Rudy. bk.rev.; bibl.; index. circ. 3,400. (also avail. in microfilm from UMI; back issues avail.) Indexed: C.I.J.E., Comput.Lit.Ind., ERIC, High.Educ.Abstr. **Document type:** academic/scholarly publication.
—BLDSC (3093.470000); Faxon; UnCover; UMI.
Description: For managers and users of information technology in higher education. Each issue features an article on the management and use of information technology at a CAUSE college or university. Other articles cover practical applications and problem solving, management and organizational issues, and general issues related to the use and evaluation of information technology in higher education.

371.9   US   ISSN 0886-1935
CLOSING THE GAP. 1982. 6/yr. $26 (Canada $41; elsewhere $50). Closing the Gap, Inc., Box 68, Henderson, MN 56044. TEL 612-248-3294. FAX 612-248-3810. Ed. Budd Hagen. adv.; bk.rev. circ. 10,000.
Description: For people working with disabled and those interested in the use of microcomputers in special education and rehabilitation. Each issue contains information emphasizing the practical applications of microcomputers as personal tools and educational aids for the handicapped.

370   CN   ISSN 0822-0638
COMMUNICATING TOGETHER. 1982. q. Can.$25 to non-members; members Can.$20. Sharing to Learn Inc., P.O. Box 986, Thornhill, ON L3T 4A5, Canada. TEL 416-771-1491. adv.; bk.rev. circ. 1,200.
—BLDSC (3341.385000).
Description: Studies augmentative and alternative communication systems for nonspeaking people, especially graphic systems.

COMMUNICATION OUTLOOK; focusing on communication aids and techniques. see COMMUNICATIONS — Computer Applications

COMPUTER ACCESS FOR THE BLIND IN EDUCATION AND EMPLOYMENT; project cable resource manual. see HANDICAPPED — Visually Impaired

COMPUTER-ASSISTED COMPOSITION JOURNAL. see COMPUTERS — Computer Assisted Instruction

370   US
COMPUTER ASSISTED LANGUAGE & INSTRUCTION CONSORTIUM. ANNUAL WILLIAMSBURG CONFERENCE. PROCEEDINGS. a. $12.95. Computer Assisted Language & Instruction Consortium, 014 Language Bldg., Box 90267, Duke University, Durham, NC 27708-0267. TEL 919-660-3180. FAX 919-660-3183. **Document type:** proceedings.

COMPUTER ASSISTED LANGUAGE LEARNING; an international journal. see LINGUISTICS — Computer Applications

370 371.394   UK   ISSN 0010-4590
QA76.27   CODEN: CPECBK
COMPUTER EDUCATION; a journal for teachers (especially of 11-18 age range) interested in computers & computing. 1969. 3/yr. £20. Staffordshire University, Computer Education Group, c/o Dr. H.L.W. Jackson, Beaconside, Stafford ST18 0AD, England. Ed. I. Selwood. adv.; bk.rev.; index every 2 yrs. circ. 1,500. **Indexed:** Comput.Cont., Curr.Cont., High.Educ.Curr.Aware.Bull., Res.High.Educ.Abstr., Sci.Abstr. **Document type:** academic/scholarly publication.
—BLDSC (3393.920000); SWETS.

COMPUTER SCIENCE EDUCATION. see COMPUTERS

370   US
COMPUTER STUDIES: COMPUTERS IN EDUCATION. 1985. a. $11.95. Dushkin Publishing Group, Inc., Sluice Dock, Guilford, CT 06437-9989. TEL 203-453-4351. FAX 203-453-6000. Eds. John Hirschbuhl, Loretta Wilkenson; Pub. Lan Nielsen. illus. circ. 10,000. **Document type:** academic/scholarly publication.
Description: Features articles on computer applications in education, including computer literacy, software, hardware, programming languages and their effectiveness. Contains discussions on the logistics and administrative problems surrounding the introduction of computers into a school system.
Refereed Serial

370   GW   ISSN 0930-3227
COMPUTERBILDUNG; didaktische Materialen fuer Unterricht, Ausbildung und Weiterbildung. 1987. q. DM.28. B und B Verlagsgesellschaft mbH, Rathenaustr. 16, 33102 Paderborn, Germany. TEL 05251-34024. FAX 05251-31414. Ed. Gerhard Ortner. adv.; bk.rev.; bibl.; illus. circ. 5,000. (back issues avail.)

COMPUTERS AND COMPOSITION; a journal for teachers of writing. see COMPUTERS — Computer Assisted Instruction

004 371.3   UK   ISSN 0360-1315
LB2846   CODEN: COMEDR
COMPUTERS & EDUCATION; an international journal. 1977. 8/yr. £392($605) (effective 1994). Elsevier Science Ltd., Pergamon, P.O. Box 800, Kidlington, Oxford OX5 1DX, England. TEL 44-865-843000. FAX 44-865-843010. (Subscr. in U.S. and Canada to: Elsevier Science, 660 White Plains Rd., Tarrytown, NY 10591-5153. TEL 914-524-9200. FAX 914-333-2444) Eds. Rachelle Heller, Michael R. Kibby. adv.; bk.rev.; charts; illus.; index. circ. 1,100. (also avail. in microfilm from UMI) **Indexed:** Abstr.Hum.Comp.Inter., C.I.J.E., CAD CAM Abstr., Compumath., Comput.Cont., Comput.Lit.Ind., Cont.Pg.Educ., Curr.Cont., Cyb.Abstr., Educ.Tech.Abstr., High.Educ.Curr.Aware.Bull., LAMP, Res.High.Educ.Abstr., Sci.Abstr., SSCI. **Document type:** academic/scholarly publication.
—BLDSC (3394.677000); Faxon; UnCover; SWETS; UMI. **CCC.**
Description: For users of analog, digital and hybrid computers in all aspects of higher education. Presents technical research papers covering a broad range of subjects.
Refereed Serial

371.394 001.6   US
  CODEN: CWLJDP
COMPUTERS IN EDUCATION JOURNAL. 1965. q. $45 (foreign $65). American Society for Engineering Education, Computers in Education Division, Box 68, Port Royal Sq., Port Royal, VA 22535. TEL 804-742-5611. Ed. W.W. Everett. adv.; bk.rev.; illus. circ. 1,250. (processed; back issues avail.) **Indexed:** A.I.Abstr., CAD CAM Abstr., Comput.Cont., Cont.Pg.Educ., Eng.Ind., Sci.Abstr. **Document type:** academic/scholarly publication.
—BLDSC (3292.795000); Faxon.
Formerly: CoED Journal (ISSN 0736-8607); Formed by the merger of: A S E E Computers in Education Division. Newsletter; A S E E Computers in Education Division. Application Notes (ISSN 0736-895X); A S E E Computers in Education Division. CoED Transactions (ISSN 0271-5902); Which was formerly: Analog-Hybrid Computer Educational Society. A C E S Transactions (ISSN 0276-8542)
Description: Covers transactions, scholarly research papers, applications notes, and teaching methods.
Refereed Serial

370 621.381   US   ISSN 0738-0569
LB1028.43
COMPUTERS IN THE SCHOOLS; the interdisciplinary journal of practice, theory, and applied research. 1984. q. $34 to individuals; institutions $75; libraries $115. Haworth Press, Inc., 10 Alice St., Binghamton, NY 13904. TEL 607-722-5857; 800-342-9678. FAX 607-722-1424. Ed. D. LaMont Johnson. adv.; bk.rev.; bibl.; charts; illus. circ. 536. (also avail. in microfiche from HAW; reprint service avail. from HAW) **Indexed:** C.I.J.E., Comput.Cont., Comput.Rev., Cont.Pg.Educ., Educ.Tech.Abstr., Except.Child Educ.Abstr., LAMP, Ref.Zh., Sci.Abstr., Sociol.Educ.Abstr.
—BLDSC (3394.937500); Faxon; UnCover; SWETS.
Description: For educators and school administrators. Features articles that combine theory and practical applications of small computers in schools.
Refereed Serial

COMPUTING NEWS. see COMPUTERS

COMPUTING TEACHER. see COMPUTERS

370 621.381   US
DATA BASE (CINCINNATI); new directions in computer education. 1983. s-a. free to qualified personnel. South-Western Publishing Co., 5101 Madison Rd., Cincinnati, OH 45227. TEL 513-271-8811. FAX 513-527-6973. Ed. Robert First. adv.; software rev. circ. 62,000. **Indexed:** Bus.Educ.Ind., Compumath. **Document type:** newsletter.
Description: Aimed at teachers in computer education. Covers computer teaching and computer-assisted instruction.

DATA CHANNELS. see COMPUTERS — Electronic Data Processing

370 621.381   DK   ISSN 0108-3708
DATALOGI OE. 1973. irreg. free. Koebenhavns Universitet, Datalogisk Institut, Universitetsparken 1, DK-2100 Copenhagen OE, Denmark. TEL 45-33-32-18-18. FAX 45-35-32-14-01. illus.

E P I E GRAM; the newsletter of software and networks for learning. (Educational Products Information Exchange Institute) see COMPUTERS — Computer Assisted Instruction

EARLY CHILDHOOD TEACHER; instructor's magazine for preschool and primary professionals. see EDUCATION

370   US   ISSN 1065-6901
▼**ED - TECH REVIEW.** 1993. q. Association for the Advancement of Computing in Education, Box 2966, Charlottesville, VA 22902. TEL 804-973-3987. FAX 804-978-7449. adv.; B&W page $1025; trim 8 1/2 x 11. circ. 10,000. **Document type:** academic/scholarly publication.
Description: Publishes articles on the issues and applications of educational technology to enhance learning and teaching in all disciplines and levels.

EDUCATIONAL I R M QUARTERLY. see EDUCATION — Teaching Methods And Curriculum

370 001.642   US
EDUCATIONAL SOFTWARE REVIEW. 1991. m. $33.75. Growth Systems, Inc., 855 Normandy Rd., Encinitas, CA 92024. Ed. Stewart Walton. illus.

EDUCATIONAL TECHNOLOGY; the magazine for managers of change in education. see EDUCATION

EDUCATION — COMPUTER APPLICATIONS

378 US ISSN 1045-9146
LB2300 CODEN: EDREEW
EDUCOM REVIEW. 1966. bi-m. $60 (foreign $75). (Educom) Sheridan Press, 450 Fame Ave., Hanover, PA 17331. TEL 717-632-3535. (Subscr. to: Educom, 1112 16th St., N.W., Ste. 600, Washington, DC 20036. TEL 202-872-4200. FAX 202-872-4318) Ed. John Gehl. adv.; bk.rev.; charts; illus.; stat.; index. circ. 20,000. (also avail. in microfiche; microfilm; back issues avail.) **Indexed:** C.I.J.E., Comput.Lit.Ind., Curr.Cont., ERIC, Sci.Abstr. **Document type:** academic/scholarly publication.
●Also available online.
—BLDSC (3663.253300); Faxon; UnCover; UMI; CASDDS.
Former titles (until vol.23, no.4, 1989): Educom Bulletin (ISSN 1045-9154); (until 1984): Educom (ISSN 0424-6268)
Description: Articles cover current issues and applications in the planning, management, and use of information technology in higher education.

378 US ISSN 1069-8183
CODEN: EDUPEC
EDUCOM UPDATE. 1992. bi-m. membership. Educom, 1112 16th St., N.W., Ste. 600, Washington, DC 20036. TEL 202-872-4200.
Description: Contains news and information pertaining to information technology in higher education.

371.3 US ISSN 0278-3258
LB1028.5 CODEN: ELEADA
ELECTRONIC LEARNING. 1981. 8/yr. $19.95. Scholastic Inc., 555 Broadway, New York, NY 10012-3999. TEL 212-343-6100. (Subscr. to: Box 3024, Southeast, PA 19398. TEL 800-544-2917) Ed. Jon Goodspeed. adv.; bk.rev.; illus.; index. circ. 85,000. (reprint service avail. from BLH, UMI) **Indexed:** C.I.J.E., Comput.Cont., Comput.Dtbs., Cont.Pg.Educ., Educ.Ind., Jun.High.Mag.Abstr., LAMP, Mag.Ind., Microcomp.Ind., PCR2, Sci.Abstr., TOM. **Document type:** trade publication.
●Also available online. Vendor(s): DIALOG Information Services, Inc.
—BLDSC (3702.578000); Faxon; UnCover; SWETS; UMI.
Description: Aimed at K-12 and college-level educators and educational administrators. Features articles on the applications and advances of technology in education.

370 UK
ELECTRONICS EDUCATION. 1982. 3/yr. £9. I.E.E, Michael Faraday House, Six Hills Way, Stevenage, Herts. SG1 2AY, England. TEL 0438-313311. FAX 0438-742840. TELEX 825578-IEESTV-G. (Subscr. to: Publication Sales Dept., P.O. Box 96, Stevenage, Herts. SG1 2SD, England; U.S. addr. INSPEC/IEEE, Box 1331, 445 Hoes Ln., Piscataway, NJ 08855-1331. TEL 908-562-5549) Ed. A. M. Finney. adv.; bk.rev. circ. 12,000. (back issues avail.) **Document type:** academic/scholarly publication.
—CCC.
Formerly: Electronic Systems News (ISSN 0265-0096)
Description: Geared toward teachers of electronics and computing in schools.

FOUR CORNERS. see *EDUCATION*

HANDS ON! (CAMBRIDGE). see *EDUCATION*

HIGH - SCOPE BUYER'S GUIDE TO CHILDREN'S SOFTWARE; annual survey of computer programs for children ages 3 to 7. see *COMPUTERS — Software*

378 US ISSN 1065-2086
HIGHER EDUCATION PRODUCT COMPANION. Abbreviated title: H E P C. 1991. 7/yr (Sep.-Jun.). $24 to individuals; institutions $60. Syllabus Press, Box 2716, Sunnyvale, CA 94087. TEL 408-773-0670. FAX 408-746-2711. Ed. Jeff Baskin. adv.: B&W page $3000, color page $3900; trim 8 1/2 x 10 7/8; adv. contact: Lynn Richardson. bk.rev. circ. 60,000. **Document type:** trade publication.
Description: Includes information about mainstream hardware and software as well as lesser-known educational products. Focuses on desktop computing applications, hardware, audiovisual products, and curriculum products.

I I C S REPORTER. (International Interactive Communications Society) see *COMMUNICATIONS — Computer Applications*

370 025 US ISSN 1055-3916
INFORMATION SEARCHER. 1988. q. $34. Datasearch, Inc., 14 Hadden Rd., Scarsdale, NY 10583. TEL 914-723-3156. Ed. Pam Berger. adv.; bk.rev. **Document type:** newsletter.
Formerly: Online Searcher.
Description: Dedicated to online and CD-ROM searching in schools.

370 US
INSIDER'S LETTER. 1986. 9/yr. $75. National School Boards Association, Institute for the Transfer of Technology to Education., 1680 Duke St., Alexandria, VA 22314-3493. TEL 703-838-6722. FAX 703-683-7590. bk.rev. circ. 4,000. **Document type:** newsletter.
Description: Covers new applications of computer and other technologies, and their impact on education at primary and secondary school levels. Considers policy, curriculum development, school environment, administrative concerns, and more, as they relate to technology.

370 US ISSN 1049-4820
LB1028.3
INTERACTIVE LEARNING ENVIRONMENTS. 1990. q. $45 to individuals; institutions $105. Ablex Publishing Corporation, 355 Chestnut St., Norwood, NJ 07648. TEL 201-767-8450.
FAX 201-767-6717. TELEX 135-393. Ed. Elliot Soloway. circ. 300. **Indexed:** Environ.Abstr.
—BLDSC (4531.872180).
Formerly (until 1990): Artificial Intelligence and Education.

370 001.6 US ISSN 0163-6626
QA76.27 CODEN: INFCDB
INTERFACE: THE COMPUTER EDUCATION QUARTERLY.*
Key Title: Interface (Santa Cruz). 1979. q. $14 to individuals; institutions $26. Mitchell Publishing, Inc., 55 Francisco St. Ste. 200, San Francisco, CA 94133-2109. TEL 408-724-0195.
FAX 408-728-2582. Eds. Erika Berg, John Ambrose. adv.; bk.rev.; charts; illus.; tr.lit. circ. 2,000. (back issues avail.) **Indexed:** Abstr.Hum.Comp.Inter., CAD CAM Abstr., Comput.Cont., Comput.Lit.Ind., Cont.Pg.Educ., LAMP, Sci.Abstr.
—BLDSC (4533.452000); Faxon; SWETS.
Description: For university and community college teachers emphasizing computer curriculum and classroom issues.

INTERNATIONAL VISUAL LITERACY ASSOCIATION. ANNUAL CONFERENCE READINGS. see
EDUCATION — Teaching Methods And Curriculum

370 CC
JISUANJI JIAO YU XUE/COMPUTER TEACHING AND LEARNING. (Text in Chinese) 1985. bi-m. Y5.28. Shanghai Shifan Daxue - Shanghai Normal University, 715 Kangding Lu, Shanghai 200040, People's Republic of China. TEL 2531905. (Co-sponsor: Shanghai Jiaoyuju - Shanghai Municipal Bureau of Education) Ed. Sun Yuanqing. adv.; bk.rev. circ. 50,000. **Document type:** academic/scholarly publication.

370 001.536 US ISSN 1043-1020
LB1028.43 CODEN: JAIEEL
JOURNAL OF ARTIFICIAL INTELLIGENCE IN EDUCATION; an international journal of research and applications on using intelligent computer technologies in education. Short title: J A I E. 1989. q. $65 to individuals (foreign $80); institutions and libraries $93 (foreign $113). Association for the Advancement of Computing in Education, Box 2966, Charlottesville, VA 22902-2966.
TEL 804-973-3987. Ed. John Self. (also avail. in microfiche; back issues avail.) **Document type:** academic/scholarly publication.
—BLDSC (4947.211800); UnCover; SWETS; UMI. CCC.
Description: Publishes articles on how intelligent computer technologies can be used in education to enhance learning and teaching. Reports on research, developments, integration, and applications of AI in education.
Refereed Serial

370 001.642 US ISSN 1050-429X
QD1
JOURNAL OF CHEMICAL EDUCATION: SOFTWARE. SERIES B; for MS-DOS - IBM PC compatible computers. 1988. 2/yr. $100 (foreign $140) (effective 1994). American Chemical Society, Division of Chemical Education, Inc.. c/o Dept. of Chemistry, Montana State University, Bozeman, MT 59717-0340. TEL 406-994-5393. FAX 406-994-5407. (Subscr. to: Journal of Chemical Education: Software, University of Wisconsin at Madison, Dept. of Chemistry, 1101 University Ave., Madison, WI 53706. TEL 608-262-5153. FAX 608-262-0381) Ed. John W. Moore. circ. 1,000. (diskette format; back issues avail.) **Indexed:** Chem.Abstr. **Document type:** academic/scholarly publication.
Description: Publishes instructional soft on disk with ancillary printed materials for students and teachers.
Refereed Serial

370 001.642 US ISSN 1050-4303
JOURNAL OF CHEMICAL EDUCATION: SOFTWARE. SERIES C; for Apple Macintosh computers. 1989. 2/yr. $100 (foreign $140) (effective 1994). American Chemical Society, Division of Chemical Education, Inc., c/o Dept. of Chemistry, Montana State University, MT 59717-0340. TEL 406-994-5393. FAX 406-994-5407. (Subscr. to: Journal of Chemical Education: Software, University of Wisconsin at Madison, Dept. of Chemistry, 1101 University Ave., Madison, WI 53706. TEL 608-262-5153. FAX 608-262-0381) Ed. John W. Moore. circ. 1,000. (diskette format; back issues avail.) **Indexed:** Chem.Abstr. **Document type:** academic/scholarly publication.
Description: Publishes instructional software on disk with ancillary printed materials for students and teachers.
Refereed Serial

370 001.642 US
▼**JOURNAL OF CHEMICAL EDUCATION: SOFTWARE. SERIES D**; for Windows. 1993. 2/yr. $100 (foreign $140). American Chemical Society, Division of Chemical Education, Inc., 238 Kent Rd., Springfield, Bozeman, PA 19C64. TEL 215-542-7862. FAX 202-872-4615. TELEX 440159 ACSP UI. (Subscr. to: Journal of Chemical Education: Software, University of Wisconsin at Madison, Dept. of Chemistry, 1101 University Ave., Madison, WI 53706) Ed. John W. Moore. circ. 500. (also avail. in diskette format; back issues avail.; reprint service avail. from UMI) **Indexed:** Chem.Abstr. **Document type:** academic/scholarly publication.
Description: Abstracts journals of instructional software published on disk with ancillary printed materials for students and teachers.
Refereed Serial

370 001.642 US ISSN 1050-6942
JOURNAL OF CHEMICAL EDUCATION: SOFTWARE. SPECIAL ISSUE SERIES. 1989. irreg. $100 (foreign $140). American Chemical Society, Division of Chemical Education, Inc., c/o Dept. of Chemistry, Montana State University, Bozeman, MT 59717-0340. TEL 406-994-5393. FAX 406-994-5407. (Subscr. to: Journal of Chemical Education Software, University of Wisconsin at Madison, Dept. of Chemistry, 1101 University Ave., Madison, WI 53706. TEL 608-262-5153. FAX 608-262-0381) Ed. John W. Moore. circ. 1,500. (diskette format; back issues avail.) **Indexed:** Chem.Abstr. **Document type:** academic/scholarly publication.
Refereed Serial

JOURNAL OF COMPUTER ASSISTED LEARNING. see
COMPUTERS — Computer Assisted Instruction

JOURNAL OF COMPUTER SCIENCE EDUCATION. see
COMPUTERS

JOURNAL OF COMPUTERS IN MATHEMATICS AND SCIENCE TEACHING. see *MATHEMATICS — Computer Applications*

EDUCATION — COMPUTER APPLICATIONS

370   US   ISSN 1043-1055
LB1028.5   CODEN: JCOEEV
JOURNAL OF COMPUTING IN CHILDHOOD EDUCATION; an international journal of research and applications on using computer technologies in the education of children. Short title: J C C E. 1989. q. $65 to individuals (foreign $80); institutions $73 (foreign $93). Association for the Advancement of Computing in Education, Box 2966, Charlottesville, VA 22902-2966. TEL 804-973-3987. Ed. Daniel Shade. (also avail. in microfiche; back issues avail.) **Document type:** academic/scholarly publication.
—BLDSC (4963.850000); UMI. **CCC.**
    Description: Serves as a forum and information source to report the research and applications on using computer technology in the education of children.
    Refereed Serial

370   US   ISSN 1042-1726
LB2395.7   CODEN: JHIEE2
JOURNAL OF COMPUTING IN HIGHER EDUCATION. 1989. 2/yr. $35 to individuals; institutions $55 (foreign $70) (effective 1994). (Lederle Graduate Research Center) Norris Publishers, Box 2593, Amherst, MA 01004. TEL 413-545-4232. FAX 413-545-3203. Ed. Carol B. MacKnight. adv.: Full page $500. bk.rev.; software rev.; illus.; cum.index. circ. 400. (back issues avail.) **Indexed:** Comput.Abstr., Comput.& Contr.Abstr. **Document type:** academic/scholarly publication.
—BLDSC (4963.950000); Faxon; UnCover.
    Description: Publishes scholarly essays, reviews, reports and research articles that contribute to the understanding of the issues, problems and research associated with instructional technology. Articles cover all aspects of academic and administrative computing.
    Refereed Serial

370   US   ISSN 0735-6331
    CODEN: JERSEY
JOURNAL OF EDUCATIONAL COMPUTING RESEARCH. 1984. 8/yr. (in 2 vols., 4 nos./vol.) $95 to individuals; institutions $173. Baywood Publishing Co., Inc., 26 Austin Ave., Box 337, Amityville, NY 11701. TEL 516-691-1270. FAX 516-691-1770. Ed. Robert H. Seidman. bk.rev.; abstr.; charts. (back issues avail.) **Indexed:** Comput.Abstr., Comput.Lit.Ind., Cont.Pg.Educ., Psychol.Abstr., Stud.Wom.Abstr. **Document type:** academic/scholarly publication.
—BLDSC (4973.154700); Faxon; UnCover; SWETS.
    Description: Includes original research papers, critical analyses, reports on research in progress, design and development studies, article reviews, grant award listings, and readers' opinions.
    Refereed Serial

370   US   ISSN 1055-8896
LB1028.5   CODEN: JEMHEA
▼**JOURNAL OF EDUCATIONAL MULTIMEDIA AND HYPERMEDIA.** Variant title: J E M H. 1992. q. $65 to individuals (foreign $80); institutions $83 (foreign $103). Association for the Advancement of Computing in Education, Box 2966, Charlottesville, VA 22902-2966. TEL 804-973-3987. Ed. David Jonassen. (also avail. in microfiche; back issues avail.) **Document type:** academic/scholarly publication.
—BLDSC (4973.170000); SWETS. **CCC.**
    Description: Provides a multi-disciplinary information source to present research and applications on multimedia and hypermedia tools that allow the integration of images, sounds, text, and data in learning and teaching.
    Refereed Serial

371.3   US   ISSN 0047-2395
LB1028.3   CODEN: JETSB7
JOURNAL OF EDUCATIONAL TECHNOLOGY SYSTEMS. 1972. q. $112. (Society for Applied Learning Technology) Baywood Publishing Co., Inc., 26 Austin Ave., Box 337, Amityville, NY 11701. TEL 516-691-1270. FAX 516-691-1770. Eds. Thomas T. Liao, David C. Miller. abstr.; charts; illus.; stat. (back issues avail.) **Indexed:** Abstr.Hum.Comp.Inter., C.I.J.E., Comput.Lit.Ind., Cont.Pg.Educ., Educ.Ind., Educ.Tech.Abstr., Eng.Ind., Sci.Abstr. **Document type:** academic/scholarly publication.
—BLDSC (4973.259000); Faxon; UnCover; SWETS.
    Formerly: Journal of Educational Instrumentation.
    Description: Deals with the nature of technological devices (hardware) that are useful for teaching and learning; focuses on the techniques and approaches (software) for using technology in all types of educational systems.

370   US
LB1028.3
JOURNAL OF INSTRUCTION DELIVERY SYSTEMS. 1987. q. $60 (foreign $75). (Society for Applied Learning Technology) Learning Technology Institute, 50 Culpeper St., Warrenton, VA 22186. TEL 703-347-0055. FAX 703-349-3169. Ed. Barbara Clinton. **Indexed:** A.I.Abstr., Tr.& Dev.Alert. **Document type:** trade publication.
—**CCC.**
    Formerly (until 1992): Instruction Delivery System (ISSN 0892-4872)
    Description: Articles and commentary on uses of interactive multimedia to enhance productivity through appropriate applications of technology in education, training and job performance.

370 375   US   ISSN 1040-0370
JOURNAL OF INTERACTIVE INSTRUCTION DEVELOPMENT. 1988. q. $60 (foreign $75). (Society for Applied Learning Technology) Learning Technology Institute, 50 Culpeper St., Warrenton, VA 22186. TEL 703-347-0055. FAX 703-349-3169. Ed. Ann Barron. **Indexed:** Tr.& Dev.Alert. **Document type:** trade publication.
—BLDSC (5007.539500). **CCC.**
    Description: Articles and commentary on the development of interactive multimedia instruction materials for use in education, training and job performance improvement.

370 610   US   ISSN 1056-2478
JOURNAL OF MEDICAL EDUCATION TECHNOLOGIES. 1990. q. $60 (foreign $75). (Society for Applied Learning Technologies) Learning Technology Institute, 50 Culpeper St., Warrenton, VA 22186. TEL 703-347-0055. FAX 703-349-3169. Ed. Robert Macura. **Document type:** trade publication.
—**CCC.**
    Description: Articles and commentary on developments utilizing technology-based learning systems to train health care professionals and educate students involved in the various health care disciplines.

370 310   US
LB2846   CODEN: JRCEE8
JOURNAL OF RESEARCH ON COMPUTING IN TEACHER EDUCATION. 1967. q. $65 to non-members (foreign $75); members $30 (foreign $40). International Society for Technology in Education, Special Interest Group for Teacher Educators (SIGTE), 1787 Agate St., Eugene, OR 97403-1923. TEL 503-346-4414. FAX 503-346-5890. Eds. William C. Bozeman, Dennis Spuck. bk.rev.; charts; stat.; index; circ. 2,500 (controlled). (also avail. in microform from UMI; reprint service avail. from UMI) **Indexed:** C.I.J.E., Comput.Cont., Comput.Lit.Ind., Comput.Rev., Cont.Pg.Educ., Educ.Admin.Abstr., Educ.Ind., Educ.Tech.Abstr., Sci.Abstr. **Document type:** academic/scholarly publication.
—BLDSC (5052.004000); Faxon; UnCover; SWETS; UMI. **CCC.**
    Former titles: Journal of Research on Computing in Education (ISSN 0888-6504); A E D S Journal (ISSN 0001-1037)
    Description: Original research and detailed system and project evaluations.

JOURNAL OF SPECIAL EDUCATION TECHNOLOGY. see *EDUCATION — Special Education And Rehabilitation*

370   US   ISSN 1059-7069
LB1705
▼**JOURNAL OF TECHNOLOGY AND TEACHER EDUCATION.** Variant title: J T A T E. 1992. q. $65 to individuals (foreign $80); institutions $83 (foreign $103). Association for the Advancement of Computing in Education, Box 2966, Charlottesville, VA 22901-2966. TEL 804-973-3987. Eds. Jerry Willis, Dee Anna Willis. (also avail. in microfiche; back issues avail.) **Document type:** academic/scholarly publication.
    Description: Serves as an international forum to report research and applications of technology in teacher education - pre-service, in-service, and graduate teacher education.
    Refereed Serial

370   US   ISSN 1045-1064
T61
JOURNAL OF TECHNOLOGY EDUCATION. 1989. s-a. $8 to individuals (foreign $12); institutions $15 (foreign $18). Virginia Polytechnic Institute, Technology Education Program, c/o Mark Sanders, Ed., 144 Smyth Hall, Blacksburg, VA 24061-0432. FAX 703-231-4188. bk.rev. circ. 500. **Document type:** academic/scholarly publication.
●Also available online.
—BLDSC (5068.560000).
    Description: Provides a forum for scholarly discussion of the philosophy, theory, practice, and research related to technology education.

JOURNAL OF VISUAL LITERACY. see *EDUCATION — Teaching Methods And Curriculum*

370   DK   ISSN 0107-8283
KOEBENHAVNS UNIVERSITET. DATALOGISK INSTITUT. RAPPORT. irreg. free. Koebenhavns Universitet, Datalogisk Institut, Universitetsparken 1, DK-2100 Copenhagen OE, Denmark. TEL 45-35-32-18-18. FAX 45-35-32-14-01.
—BLDSC (7264.280000).

THE LATEST AND BEST OF T E S S; the educational software selector. see *COMPUTERS — Software*

LIBRARY SOFTWARE REVIEW. see *COMPUTERS — Software*

001.6 370   GW   ISSN 0720-8642
LOG IN; Informatik und Computer in der Schule. 1981. 6/yr. DM.74.60. F U Berlin, Habelschwerdter Allee 45, 14195 Berlin, Germany. **Document type:** academic/scholarly publication.
—BLDSC (5292.304800). **CCC.**
    Description: Devoted to the use of computers and information technology in education. Features practice and methods, application, readers' letters, calendar of events.

371.3 001.642   US   ISSN 0888-6970
QA76.73.L63
LOGO EXCHANGE. 1986. q. $30 to non-members (foreign $40); members $20 (foreign $30). International Society for Technology in Education, Special Interest Group for Logo-Using Educators, 1787 Agate St., Eugene, OR 97403-1923. TEL 503-346-4414. FAX 503-346-5890. Ed. Sharon Yoder. bk.rev. circ. 2,000. (also avail. in microform; back issues avail.) **Indexed:** ERIC, PCR2. **Document type:** academic/scholarly publication.
—**CCC.**
    Incorporates: International Logo Exchange (ISSN 0883-1505); Supersedes (1982-1985): National Logo Exchange Newsletter; National Logo Exchange (ISSN 0734-1717)
    Description: Current information on Logo research, resources and methods.

370   US   ISSN 1047-7926
MANAGE I T. (Information Technology) 1990. q. free to qualified personnel. Cause, 4840 Pearl E. Circle, Ste. 302E, Boulder, CO 80301. TEL 303-449-4430. FAX 303-440-0461. Ed. Karen McBride. circ. 4,000. **Document type:** newsletter.
    Description: For information technology administrators in colleges, universities and higher education administration.

MATHEMATICA IN EDUCATION. see *MATHEMATICS*

MEDIA & METHODS; educational products, technologies & programs for schools & universities. see *EDUCATION — Teaching Methods And Curriculum*

EDUCATION — GUIDES TO SCHOOLS AND COLLEGES

371.33   US
MICROCOMPUTERS IN EDUCATION.* 1980. m. $38. John Mongillo, Ed. & Pub., 470 Big Water Rd., Wakefield, RI 02879-1823. TEL 203-655-3798. adv.; bk.rev. circ. 1,000. **Indexed:** Comput.Cont., LAMP. **Document type:** newsletter.
●Also available online. Vendor(s): NewsNet (EC59).
Description: A newsletter for educators at all levels. Offers educational software reviews, hardware reviews, and industry developments.

370
NATIONAL FORUM OF INSTRUCTIONAL TECHNOLOGY JOURNAL. 1991. 2/yr. $80 to institutions. National Forum Journals, 1930 Nicholas St., Lake Charles, LA 70605. TEL 318-474-6976. Ed. William Allan Kritsonis. bk.rev.; abstr. **Document type:** academic/scholarly publication.
Description: Publishes articles on research and development in the field of instructional technology.
Refereed Serial

O L S NEWS. (Open Learning Systems) see *EDUCATION — Teaching Methods And Curriculum*

PRE-K TODAY. see *EDUCATION*

378   US   ISSN 1065-206X
LB2341
QUERY (SUNNYVALE). 1991. q. $55 (typically set in July). Syllabus Press, Box 2716, Sunnyvale, CA 94087-0716. TEL 408-773-0670. FAX 408-746-2711. Ed. Mary Grush. adv.: B&W page $3000, color page $3900; trim 8 1/2 x 10 7/8; adv. contact: Lynne Richardson. bk.rev. (also avail. in diskette format; back issues avail.) **Document type:** newsletter.
●Also available online.
Description: Covers the integration of computer technology in the administrative area of higher education. Features news, resources, and advice about how campuses can improve the computer environment.

S A C E BULLETIN. (Saskatchewan Association for Computers in Education) see *COMPUTERS — Computer Assisted Instruction*

370   US   ISSN 0097-8418
QA76.27   CODEN: SIGSD3
S I G C S E BULLETIN. q. $30. Association for Computing Machinery, Special Interest Group on Computer Science Education, 1515 Broadway, 17th Fl., New York, NY 10036. TEL 212-869-7440. **Indexed:** Sci.Abstr. **Document type:** bulletin.
—BLDSC (8275.265000); UnCover.

370 651.8   US
S I G C U E BULLETIN. 1967. q. $20 to non-members; members $10. Association for Computing Machinery, Special Interest Group on Computer Uses in Education, 1515 Broadway, 17th Fl., New York, NY 10036. TEL 212-869-7440. adv.; bk.rev.; abstr.; bibl.; index. circ. 1,000. (also avail. in microform from UMI; reprint service avail. from UMI) **Indexed:** Abstr.Hum.Comp.Inter., Sci.Abstr. **Document type:** bulletin.
Formerly: Interface (ISSN 0020-5427)

370   US
S I G T C CONNECTIONS; the journal for technology coordinators. q. $25 to non-members; members $16; student members $8. International Society for Technology in Education, Special Interest Group for Technology Coordinators, 1787 Agate St., Eugene, OR 97403-1923. TEL 503-346-4414. FAX 503-346-5890. **Document type:** academic/scholarly publication.
Description: Provides a forum to identify problems and solutions and to share information on issues facing technology coordinators today.

370   UK   ISSN 1351-4644
SIMULATION AND GAMING YEARBOOK (YEAR). INTERACTIVE LEARNING. a. £32. (Society for Advancement of Games and Simulations in Education and Training) Kogan Page Ltd., 120 Pentonville Rd., London N1 9JN, England. TEL 071-278-0433. FAX 071-837-6348. TELEX 263088-KOGAN-G. Ed. Danny Saunders. **Document type:** directory.

350   US   ISSN 0894-4393
H61.3   CODEN: CSOSE6
SOCIAL SCIENCE COMPUTER REVIEW. 1982. q. $48 to individuals (foreign $56); institutions $88 (foreign $86); students $24 (foreign $32). (North Carolina State University, Social Science Research and Instructional Computing Lab) Duke University Press, Box 90660, Durham, NC 27708-0660. TEL 919-687-3600. FAX 919-688-4574. Ed. G. David Garson. adv.; bk.rev. circ. 1,000. (back issues avail.) **Indexed:** Comput.Lit.Ind., Curr.Cont., Psychol.Abstr. **Document type:** academic/scholarly publication.
—BLDSC (8318.159500); Faxon; UnCover; SWETS; UMI. **CCC.**
Formed by the merger of: Social Science Microcomputer Review (ISSN 8755-3031); Computers and the Social Sciences (ISSN 0748-9269); Formerly (until 1984): Political Science Micro Review.
Description: Disseminates research and teaching applications of microcomputers for social scientists. Features include pertinent software reviews, new product announcements and tutorials for beginners.
Refereed Serial

371.3   US
SOCIETY FOR APPLIED LEARNING TECHNOLOGY. NEWSLETTER. 1972. q. Society for Applied Learning Technology, 50 Culpeper St., Warrenton, VA 22186. TEL 703-347-0055. FAX 703-349-3169. circ. 27,000. **Document type:** newsletter.
Description: Primarily for professionals in instructional technology. Includes organizational news, conference information and publications.

SOFTWARE DEVELOPER'S MONTHLY. see *COMPUTERS — Computer Programming*

378   US   ISSN 1065-2051
SYLLABUS (SUNNYVALE). 1988. bi-m. $75 (typically set in July). Syllabus Press, Box 2716, Sunnyvale, CA 94087-0716. TEL 408-773-0670. FAX 408-746-2711. Ed. Jeff Baskin. adv.: B&W page $3000, color page $3900; trim 8 1/2 x 10 7/8; adv. contact: David Kastrinen. bk.rev. circ. 55,000. (also avail. in diskette format; back issues avail.)
●Also available online.
Incorporates: Computer Science Syllabus.
Description: Covers how technology can improve teaching and learing at the postsecondary level. Features technology overviews, case studies, interviews, product information, news, and resources for instructors and software developers.

370   US   ISSN 0192-592X
LB1028.3   CODEN: THEJD4
T H E JOURNAL. (Technological Horizons in Education) 1973. 11/yr. $29. Ed Warnshius Ltd., 150 El Camino Real, Ste. 112, Tustin, CA 92680-3670. TEL 714-730-4011. FAX 714-730-3739. Ed. Sylvia Charp. adv.; bk.rev.; charts; illus.; stat.; circ. 146,000 (controlled). (also avail. in microform from UMI; back issues avail.) **Indexed:** C.I.J.E., Comput.Cont., Comput.Dtbs., Comput.Lit.Ind., Educ.Admin.Abstr., Educ.Ind., Microcomp.Ind., Sci.Abstr. **Document type:** academic/scholarly publication.
—Faxon; UnCover; UMI.
Description: Contains material of interest to educators of all levels; focuses on a specific topic for each issue as well as technological innovations as they apply to education.

371.394 001.6   US   ISSN 1053-6728
LB1028.43
TECHNOLOGY AND LEARNING; the leading magazine of electronic education. 1980. m. (8/yr.). $24 (effective 1993-94). Peter Li Education Group, 330 Progress Rd., Dayton, OH 45449. TEL 513-847-5900. FAX 513-847-5910. Ed. Holly Brady. adv.; bk.rev.; charts; illus. circ. 80,000. (back issues avail.) **Indexed:** C.I.J.E., Comput.Cont., Comput.Dtbs., Cont.Pg.Educ., Educ.Ind., Ind.Child.Mag., Microcomp.Ind., PCR2, PSI, Sci.Abstr.
●Also available online. Vendor(s): DIALOG Information Services, Inc.
—UnCover; SWETS; UMI.
Former titles (until 1990): Classroom Computer Learning (ISSN 0746-4223); (until 1983): Classroom Computer News (ISSN 0731-9398)
Description: Features, reviews, news, and announcements of educational activities and opportunities in programming, software development, and hardware configurations.

370 791.4   US   ISSN 1060-5649
LB1028.3
TECHNOS; quarterly for education and technology. 1966. q. $20 to individuals; libraries $16; foreign $24. Agency for Instructional Technology, Box A, Bloomington, IN 47402-0120. TEL 812-339-2203. FAX 812-333-4218. Ed. Carole Novak. circ. 4,000. **Document type:** academic/scholarly publication.
—UnCover.
Former titles (until vol.22, no.2, 1991): A I T Newsletter (ISSN 0193-578X); (until 1970): N I T Newsletter (ISSN 0027-6731)
Description: Provides a forum for the discussion of ideas about the use of technology in education, with focus on reform

TECHTRENDS; for leaders in education and training. see *EDUCATION — Teaching Methods And Curriculum*

370 384   US
TELECOMMUNICATIONS IN EDUCATION NEWS. Abbreviated title T.I.E. News. q. $25 to non-members; members $16. International Society for Technology in Education, S I G Tel, 1787 Agate St., Eugene, OR 97403-1923. TEL 503-346-4414. FAX 503-346-5890. **Document type:** academic/scholarly publication.
Description: Covers communications, projects, research, publications, international connections and training.

370   US
U C C C TECHNICAL UPDATE. 1973. q. free. University of Cincinnati Computing Center, Instruction and Research Information Technology, B-3 Beecher Hall, ML 88, Cincinnati, OH 45221-0088. TEL 513-556-9022. Ed. Mary J. Clark. bk.rev.; stat.; index. circ. 3,250.

UCITELJ/TEACHER. see *CHILDREN AND YOUTH — For*

370.285 410.285   NE   ISSN 0924-1868
QA76.9.H85   CODEN: UMUIEQ
USER MODELLING AND USER-ADAPTED INTERACTION; an international journal. (Text in English) 1991. 4/yr. fl.371($194) (effective 1994). Kluwer Academic Publishers, Postbus 17, 3300 AA Dordrecht, Netherlands. TEL 31-78-334911. FAX 31-78-334254. TELEX 29245 KAPG NL. (Dist. by: Kluwer Academic Publishers Group, P.O. Box 322, 3300 AH Dordrecht, Netherlands. TEL 31-78-524400. FAX 31-78-524474; N. America dist. addr.: Box 358, Accord Sta., Hingham, MA 02018-0358. TEL 617-871-6600. FAX 617-871-6528) Ed. Alfred Kobsa. (also avail. in microform from UMI; back issues avail.) **Indexed:** INSPEC. **Document type:** academic/scholarly publication.
—BLDSC (9133.045900); UMI. **CCC.**
Description: Interdisciplinary forum for research results in user modelling and user-adapted interaction, including intelligent information retrieval, recognition, conceptual models, response tailoring, and explanation strategies.
Refereed Serial

VIDEOGRAPHY. see *COMMUNICATIONS — Video*

EDUCATION — Guides To Schools And Colleges

371.0025 850   UK
A A B'S GUIDE TO ITALIAN PRIVATE ENGLISH LANGUAGE SCHOOLS & ITALIAN LANGUAGE SCHOOLS FOR OVERSEAS & ITALY. 1986. a. £29.95. A A B British Book Services (Oxford), Editorial Research Centre, P.O. Box 342, Oxford OX1 1NN, England. TEL 0865-79261C. FAX 0865-792611. Ed. Luigi Gigliotti. circ. 55,000. **Document type:** directory.

371.0025 420
375.4   UK
A A B'S GUIDE TO PRIVATE ENGLISH LANGUAGE SCHOOLS IN THE U.K. FOR OVERSEAS STUDENTS. 1985. a. £29.95. A A B British Book Services (Oxford), Editorial Research Centre, P.O. Box 342, Oxford OX1 1NN, England. TEL 0865-792610. FAX 0865-792611. Ed. Luigi Gigliotti. circ. 60,000. **Document type:** directory.

A A C C STATISTICAL YEARBOOK (YEAR). (American Association of Community Colleges) see *EDUCATION — Abstracting, Bibliographies, Statistics*

EDUCATION — GUIDES TO SCHOOLS AND COLLEGES

371.0025 285   US
A A C S NEWSLETTER.* 1985. m. American Association of Christian Schools, 4500 Selsa Rd., Blue Springs, MO 64015-2221. TEL 703-818-7150. Ed. Carl Herbster. circ. 1,500. (back issues avail.) **Document type:** newsletter.

378.0025   US
A S C U S STAFFER.* q. $10 to non-members. Association for School, College and University Staffing, Inc., c/o High School, 1600 Dodge Ave., Ste. 5-330, Evanston, IL 60204.

378
ACCREDITATION FACT SHEET. 1980. irreg. $6 per issue. National Association of Private Non-Traditional Schools and Colleges, 182 Thompson Rd., Grand Junction, CO 81503. TEL 303-243-5441. Ed. H. Earl Heusser.
   Description: Information concerning accreditation criteria for private, nontraditional schools and colleges with history and general facts about accreditation.

378.025   US   ISSN 0270-1715
L901
ACCREDITED INSTITUTIONS OF POSTSECONDARY EDUCATION. 1964. a. $35. Oryx Press, 4041 N. Central Ave., Ste. 700, Phoenix, AZ 85012-3397. TEL 602-265-2651. circ. 8,000. **Document type:** directory.
   Former titles: Accredited Institutions of Postsecondary Education and Programs (ISSN 0361-9362); Accredited Institutions of Post Secondary Education; Accredited Institutions of Higher Education (ISSN 0065-0862)

371.0025   US   ISSN 0091-729X
RK91
ADMISSION REQUIREMENTS OF U S AND CANADIAN DENTAL SCHOOLS. 1963. a. $22. American Association of Dental Schools, 1625 Massachusetts Ave., N.W., Washington, DC 20036-2212. TEL 202-667-9433. circ. 3,000. (reprint service avail.) **Document type:** directory.
   Formerly: Admission Requirements of American Dental Schools (ISSN 0065-1990)
   Description: Contains comprehensive details of requirements for application and admission to all US and Canadian dental schools.

AFTERMARKET TRAINING GUIDE. see *TRANSPORTATION — Automobiles*

610 378.0025   US   ISSN 0194-3766
R847
ALLIED HEALTH EDUCATION DIRECTORY. 1968. a. $45 to non-members; members $30. American Medical Association, 515 N. State St., Chicago, IL 60610. TEL 312-464-0183. FAX 312-464-5834. Ed. Gloria C. Gupta. **Document type:** directory.
   Formerly: Allied Medical Education Directory (ISSN 0163-2590)

ALMANAC OF HIGHER EDUCATION. see *EDUCATION — Higher Education*

371.0025 285   US
AMERICAN ASSOCIATION OF CHRISTIAN SCHOOLS. DIRECTORY.* 1972. a. $25. American Association of Christian Schools, 4500 Selsa Rd., Blue Springs, MO 64015-2221. TEL 703-818-7150. Ed. Carl Herbster. circ. 1,500. **Document type:** directory.
   Description: Listing of all AACS member schools.

370   US   ISSN 0516-9313
LB1715
AMERICAN ASSOCIATION OF COLLEGES FOR TEACHER EDUCATION. DIRECTORY. a. $50. American Association of Colleges for Teacher Education, One Dupont Circle, N.W., Ste. 610, Washington, DC 20036-1186. TEL 202-293-2450. FAX 202-457-8095. **Document type:** directory.

660 540 016   US   ISSN 0193-5011
CODEN: ACDGAF
AMERICAN CHEMICAL SOCIETY. DIRECTORY OF GRADUATE RESEARCH. 1955. biennial. $60. American Chemical Society, Committee on Professional Training, 1155 16th St., N.W., Washington, DC 20036. TEL 800-227-5558. FAX 202-872-4615. (back issues avail.) **Document type:** academic/scholarly publication, directory.
   ●Also available online.
   —CASDDS.

371.0025   US   ISSN 0517-564X
T73
AMERICAN TRADE SCHOOLS DIRECTORY. base vol. (plus m. supplements). $99.95. Croner Publications, Inc., 34 Jericho Turnpike, Jericho, NY 11753. TEL 516-333-9085. FAX 516-338-4986. Ed. Carol Sixt. adv. (looseleaf format) **Document type:** directory.
   Description: Directory of trade, technical and vocational schools arranged by state.

370.025 378   US   ISSN 0066-0922
LA226
AMERICAN UNIVERSITIES AND COLLEGES. 1928. quadrennial. price varies. (American Council on Education) Walter de Gruyter, Inc., 200 Saw Mill River Rd., Hawthorne, NY 10532. TEL 914-747-0110. FAX 914-747-1326. TELEX 646677. Ed.Bd.
—CCC.

ASSOCIACAO MINEIRA DE ACAO EDUCACIONAL. REVISTA. see *EDUCATION*

ASSOCIATION OF THEOLOGICAL SCHOOLS IN THE UNITED STATES AND CANADA. DIRECTORY. see *RELIGIONS AND THEOLOGY*

378   AT
AUSTRALIAN DIRECTORY OF VOCATIONAL EDUCATION AND TRAINING. irreg. (2-3/yr.). Aus.$45 per no. Auslib Press, P.O. Box 622, Blackwood, S.A. 5051, Australia. TEL 08-278-4363. FAX 08-270-4000. circ. 1,500. **Document type:** directory.
   Formerly: Australian T A F E Directory.
   Description: Brings up-to-date details of all TAFE colleges and associated organizations in Australia.

378 330
BARRON'S GUIDE TO GRADUATE BUSINESS SCHOOLS. biennial, latest 8th ed. $14.95. Barron's Educational Series, Inc., 250 Wireless Blvd., Hauppage, NY 11788. TEL 516-434-3311.

378.0025   US
BARRON'S PROFILES OF AMERICAN COLLEGES. 1964. biennial, 19th ed., 1992. $18.95. Barron's Educational Series, Inc., 250 Wireless Blvd., Hauppauge, NY 11788. TEL 516-434-3311.
   ●Also available on CD-ROM.
   Formed by the merger of: Barron's Profiles of American Colleges. Vol. 1: Descriptions of the Colleges; Barron's Profiles of American Colleges. Vol. 2: Index of College Major Areas of Study.

371.0025 378   UK   ISSN 0951-872X
BOARDING SCHOOLS & COLLEGES. 1987. a. £9.95. (Gabbitas, Truman & Thring Educational Trust) John Catt Educational Ltd., Great Glemham, Saxmundham, Suffolk IP17 2DH, England. TEL 0728-78666. FAX 0728-663415. Ed. Derek Bingham. adv.; charts; illus. circ. 3,000. (back issues avail.) **Document type:** directory.
   Description: Provides information on more than 390 independent and state boarding schools in the U.K. and the rest of Europe.

BRICKER'S INTERNATIONAL DIRECTORY, VOLUME 1: LONG-TERM UNIVERSITY-BASED EXECUTIVE PROGRAMS (YEAR). see *BUSINESS AND ECONOMICS — Management*

BRICKER'S INTERNATIONAL DIRECTORY, VOLUME 2: SHORT-TERM UNIVERSITY-BASED EXECUTIVE PROGRAMS (YEAR). see *BUSINESS AND ECONOMICS — Management*

371.002   UK
BRITAIN'S INDEPENDENT SCHOOLS DIRECTORY; the definitive and essential guide for parents. a. £6.95. Peerage Publications, 9 Mortlake Terr., Kew Green, Richmond-upon-Thames, Surrey TW9 3DT, England. TEL 081-747-0385. Ed. Sara Marden-King. adv.: B&W page £375, color page £475; trim 297 x 210. **Document type:** directory.

378.0025   UK
BRITISH UNIVERSITIES' GUIDE TO GRADUATE STUDY.* 1973. a. £30. Association of Commonwealth Universities, John Foster House, 36 Gordon Sq., London WC1H OPF, England. TEL 071-387-8572. FAX 071-387-2655. (Co-sponsor: United Kingdom Committee of Vice-Chancellors and Principals)
   Former titles: Postgraduate Courses in United Kingdom Universities (ISSN 0263-6182); Schedule of Postgraduate Courses in United Kingdom Universities (ISSN 0306-1728)

371.0025   US   ISSN 0162-9646
L903.W27
C I C'S STATE SCHOOL DIRECTORIES. (Published by state in 51 vols.) 1976. a. $1075 per set; price varies per vol. (typically set in Oct.) (Curriculum Information Center) Market Data Retrieval, Inc., 16 Progress Dr., P.O. Box 2117, Shelton, CT 06484-1117. TEL 203-926-4800. FAX 203-926-0721.
   ●Also available online. Vendor(s): DIALOG Information Services, Inc.
   Supersedes: School Universe Data Book (ISSN 0146-4329)

371.0025 384.5   US   ISSN 0742-3632
P91.5.U5
C I N C O M: COURSES IN COMMUNICATIONS. 1983. a. $35. Communications Institute, Communications Library, Lockbox 472139, Marina Station, San Francisco, CA 94147-2139. TEL 415-626-5050. bk.rev. circ. 5,000. (looseleaf format) **Document type:** directory.
   Description: Contains over 1,200 accredited American, Asian, Canadian, European, and Middle Eastern IHEs offering courses and degrees in communications, data telecom, telephony, telecommunications and CATV.

371.0025   US   ISSN 0098-5147
L903.C2
CALIFORNIA PRIVATE SCHOOL DIRECTORY. 1969. a. $16. Department of Education, Bureau of Publications, 515 L St., Box 271, Sacramento, CA 95812-0271. TEL 916-445-1260. FAX 916-323-0823. Ed. Bob Klingensmith. index. circ. 4,000. **Document type:** directory.
   Formerly: Directory of Private Elementary Schools and High Schools in California.

370.025   US   ISSN 0068-5771
L903.C2
CALIFORNIA PUBLIC SCHOOL DIRECTORY. 1928. a. $16. Department of Education, Bureau of Publications, 515 L St., Box 271, Sacramento, CA 95812-0271. TEL 916-445-1260. FAX 916-323-0823. Ed. Bob Klingensmith. index. circ. 15,000. **Document type:** directory.
   Formerly (until 1970): Directory of Administrative and Supervisory Personnel of California Public Schools.

371.0025   US
T64
CAREER EDUCATION THAT WORKS FOR AMERICA; handbook of accredited trade & technical schools - handbook of private accredited independent colleges and schools. 1966. a. free. Career College Association, 750 First St., N.E., Ste. 900, Washington, DC 20002-4242. TEL 202-336-6700. Ed.Bd. circ. 440,000.
   Formerly (until 1992): Trade and Technical Careers and Training (ISSN 0278-4920)

CAREERS & MAJORS. see *OCCUPATIONS AND CAREERS*

378.002 540   US   ISSN 1058-1227
QD47
▼**CHEMICAL SCIENCES GRADUATE SCHOOL FINDER.** 1992. a. American Chemical Society, 1155 16th St. N.W., Washington, DC 20036.
—CCC.

371.002 371.42   US
CHICAGO SCHOOLS AND CAREERS.* m. free. K B Communications, 2240 W. 23rd PL., Chicago, IL 60608-3904. TEL 312-944-0100. FAX 312-915-5906. Ed. Joe Brar.

378.0025   US   ISSN 0191-3670
L901
CHRONICLE FOUR-YEAR COLLEGE DATABOOK. 1979. a. $28.11. Chronicle Guidance Publications, Inc., Box 1190, Moravia, NY 13118. TEL 315-497-0330. FAX 315-497-3359. circ. 6,800.
   Formerly: Guide to Four-Year College Databook (ISSN 0361-8927); Supersedes in part: Chronicle College Charts (ISSN 0163-9242)

EDUCATION — GUIDES TO SCHOOLS AND COLLEGES

378.0025 US ISSN 0191-3662
L901
CHRONICLE TWO-YEAR COLLEGE DATABOOK. 1979. a. $28.08. Chronicle Guidance Publications, Inc., Box 1190, Moravia, NY 13118. TEL 315-497-0330. FAX 315-497-3359. circ. 6,800.
Former titles (until 1978): Chronicle Guide to Two-Year College Majors and Careers; Guide to Two-Year College Majors and Careers (ISSN 0362-420X); Supersedes in part: Chronicle College Charts (ISSN 0163-9242)

378.0025 US ISSN 0276-0371
L901
CHRONICLE VOCATIONAL SCHOOL MANUAL. 1979. a. $28.10. Chronicle Guidance Publications, Inc., Box 1190, Moravia, NY 13118. TEL 315-497-0330. FAX 315-497-3359. charts. circ. 6,200.
Formerly: Chronicle Annual Vocational School Manual (ISSN 0163-4100)

378.1 US
COLLEGE ADMISSIONS DATA HANDBOOK.* Spine title: College Admissions Data. 1960. a. (in 4 vols.). $160 (effective 1992). Orchard House, Inc., 629 Cherokee St., New Orleans, LA 70118-5049. Ed. Maura Kelly. circ. 10,000.
Formerly: College Admissions Data Service.

378.0025 US
COLLEGE ADMISSIONS INDEX OF MAJORS & SPORTS.* 1987. a. $28 (effective 1992). Orchard House, Inc., 629 Cherokee St., New Orleans, LA 70118-5049. TEL 508-369-0467. FAX 508-369-9472. Ed.Bd. circ. 2,000. **Document type:** abstracting/indexing.

370.025 US ISSN 0069-5572
LA226
COLLEGE BLUE BOOK. (5-vol. set) 1923. biennial. $225 (CD-ROM ed. $475). Macmillan Publishing Company, 866 Third Ave., New York, NY 10022. TEL 212-702-4296.
●Also available on CD-ROM.

COLLEGE BOUND. see EDUCATION — Higher Education

COLLEGE BOUND ADMISSIONS SURVEY. see EDUCATION — Higher Education

378.0025 US
COLLEGE COST BOOK (YEAR). a. College Board, 45 Columbus Ave., New York, NY 10023. TEL 212-713-8000. FAX 212-713-8143. Ed.Bd. (reprint service avail.)
Description: For high school students, parents, and counselors. Provides current facts on costs plus financial aid and scholarship availability at 3,200 two- and four-year institutions.

378 US ISSN 0069-5688
L901
COLLEGE FACTS CHART. 1956. a. $5. National Beta Club, Box 730, Spartanburg, SC 29304. TEL 803-583-4553. Ed. Marggi Roldan. circ. 15,000. **Document type:** directory.

371.0025 US
COLLEGE OUTLOOK AND CAREER OPPORTUNITIES. 1977. a. free. Townsend Outlook Publishing Co., Inc., 20 E. Gregory St., Kansas City, MO 64114. TEL 800-274-8867. FAX 816-361-6164. circ. 1,340,000.
Description: Provides High School counselors and college-bound students information about higher education opportunities.

378.0025 US
COLLEGE TRANSFER GUIDE. a. $10. School Guide Publications, 210 N. Ave., New Rochelle, NY 10801. TEL 914-632-7771. Ed. Marie Castrovilla. adv. circ. 60,000. **Document type:** directory.

371.0025 FR ISSN 0245-2030
COMMUNAUTES EDUCATIVES. 1972. q. 330 F. Association Nationale des Communautes Educatives, 145 bd. Magenta, 75010 Paris, France. TEL 44-63-51-15. FAX 42-85-56-14. adv.

COMMUNICATION DISCIPLINES IN HIGHER EDUCATION: A DIRECTORY. see COMMUNICATIONS — Television And Cable

378.0025 US
COMMUNITY COLLEGE TIMES. 1989. bi-w. $46. American Association of Community Colleges, One Dupont Circle, N.W., Ste. 410, Washington, DC 20036. TEL 202-728-0200. FAX 202-223-9390. Ed. Bill Reinhard. adv. (tabloid format) **Document type:** newspaper.
Formerly: Community, Technical, and Junior College Times.
Description: Covers the happenings and people at community, technical, and junior colleges.

378.0025 US ISSN 0893-1216
COMPARATIVE GUIDE TO AMERICAN COLLEGES; for students, parents and counselors. a. $11.95. Harper & Row, Publishers, Inc., 10 E. 53 St., New York, NY 10022. TEL 212-207-7000.
—BLDSC (3363.782100).
Description: Takes a consumer view of how to choose a college.

COMPENDIUM OF HIGHER EDUCATION. see EDUCATION — Higher Education

371 378 US ISSN 1049-6238
LB2353.57
CRACKING THE SYSTEM: THE S A T & P S A T. a. (Princeton Review) Random House, Vintage Books, 201 E. 50th St., New York, NY 10022. TEL 212-572-2128. FAX 212-572-2593. TELEX 960550. Eds. Adam Robinson, John Katzman.

DANCE MAGAZINE COLLEGE GUIDE; a directory to dance in North American colleges and universities. see DANCE

371.0025 DK ISSN 0108-3082
DANMARKS FOLKEHOEJSKOLER. 1950. a. free. Hoejskolernes Sekretariat, Nytorv 7, 1450 Copenhagen K, Denmark. TEL 45-33-13-98-22. FAX 45-33-13-98-70. Ed. Arne Andresen. illus. circ. 250,000.
Formerly: Danmarks Hoejskoler.

370.025 GW
DEUTSCHER HOCHSCHULFUEHRER. 1925. irreg., vol.54, 1992. DM.128. Dr. Josef Raabe Verlag GmbH, Weberstr. 118, 53113 Bonn, Germany. TEL 0228-223071. FAX 0228-221783. adv. circ. 3,000. **Document type:** monographic series.

370 CK ISSN 0120-5056
LB2341.8.C7
DIRECTORIO DE LA EDUCACION SUPERIOR EN COLOMBIA. 1977. a. Col.500($10) Instituto Colombiano para el Fomento de la Educacion Superior, Calle 17 N. 3-40, Apdo. Aereo 6319, Bogota, D.E., Colombia. (Co-sponsor: Division de Recursos Bibliograficos) circ. 5,000. (also avail. in microfiche)

370.025 US
DIRECTORY OF ACCREDITED HOME STUDY SCHOOLS. 1953. a. free. National Home Study Council, 1601 18th St., N.W., Washington, DC 20009. TEL 202-234-5100. Ed. Sally R. Welch. circ. 40,000. **Document type:** directory.
Formerly: Directory of Accredited Private Home Study Schools (ISSN 0070-5055)
Description: Lists accredited home study schools.

378 CN ISSN 0706-2338
L905
DIRECTORY OF CANADIAN UNIVERSITIES (YEAR)/REPERTOIRE DES UNIVERSITES CANADIENNES (YEAR). (Text in English and French) 1956. biennial. Can.$27.95 (US Can.$28.95, elsewhere Can.$30.95). Association of Universities and Colleges of Canada, 600-350 Albert, Ottawa, ON K1R 1B1, Canada. TEL 613-563-1236. FAX 613-563-9745. circ. 2,000. **Document type:** directory.
Former titles: Directory of Canadian Universities and Colleges; Universities and Colleges of Canada (ISSN 0083-3932)

378.025 US
DIRECTORY OF COLLEGE FACILITIES AND SERVICES FOR PEOPLE WITH DISABILITIES. 1983. irreg., 3rd ed. 1991. $115. Oryx Press, 4041 N. Central Ave., No. 700, Phoenix, AZ 85012-3397. TEL 602-265-2651. FAX 602-265-6250. Eds. Carol H. Thomas, James L. Thomas. **Document type:** directory.
Formerly (until 1991): Directory of College Facilities and Services for the Disabled.
Description: Provides information on programs and services available for the disabled in approximately 3600 postsecondary institutions within the U.S., Canada and outlying areas.

360 US ISSN 1049-5657
HV11
DIRECTORY OF COLLEGES AND UNIVERSITIES WITH ACCREDITED SOCIAL WORK DEGREE PROGRAMS. a. $10. Council on Social Work Education, 1600 Duke St., Alexandria, VA 22314-3421. TEL 703-683-8080. FAX 703-683-8099. **Document type:** directory.
Former titles: Colleges and Universities with Accredited Social Work Degree Programs; Colleges and Universities with Accredited Undergraduate Social Work Programs.

371.0025 296 US
DIRECTORY OF DAY SCHOOLS IN THE UNITED STATES AND CANADA. biennial. $10. Torah Umesorah, National Society for Hebrew Day Schools, 5723 18th Ave., Brooklyn, NY 11204-1932. TEL 718-259-1223. FAX 718-259-1795. Ed. Rabbi Yaakov Fruchter. circ. 2,500. **Document type:** directory.
Formerly: Directory of Day Schools in the United States, Canada and Latin America.
Description: Lists addresses, phone and fax numbers of elementary and secondary Hebrew Day Schools (Yeshivas) in the United States and Canada. Also includes administrative personnel, grades, and language of instruction.

DIRECTORY OF GEOSCIENCE DEPARTMENTS. see EARTH SCIENCES

378.0025 616.8 US
DIRECTORY OF GRADUATE TRAINING IN BEHAVIOR THERAPY. 1980. irreg., latest 1992. $20. Association for Advancement of Behavior Therapy, 305 Seventh Ave., Ste. 16A, New York, NY 10001. circ. 1,000. **Document type:** directory.
Formerly: Directory of Behavioral Graduate Study.
Description: Listing of 308 psychology programs including courses, faculty, specialties offered, supervision and funding.

378.025 UK
DIRECTORY OF HIGHER EDUCATION (D O H E); a complete guide to first degree, HNCs, HNDs and DIPHE courses. a. £46.95 (hardcover £51.95). (Careers Research and Advisory Centre) Hobsons Publishing plc., Bateman St., Cambridge CB2 1LZ, England. TEL 0223-354551. FAX 0223-323154. TELEX 81546-HOBCAM-G. Ed. Emma Al Hudairi. adv. contact: Bella Mitchell. circ. 3,200. **Document type:** directory.
Formerly: Directory of United Kingdom Higher Education (D U K H E).

378.0025 975 US
DIRECTORY OF HISTORY DEPARTMENTS AND ORGANIZATIONS (YEAR); colleges, universities, and research institutions in the United States and Canada. 1975. a. $50 to non-members; members $45. American Historical Association, 400 A St., S.E., Washington, DC 20003-3889. TEL 202-544-2422. FAX 202-544-8307. Ed. Roxanne Myers Spencer. stat.; index. circ. 2,500. (back issues avail.) **Document type:** directory.
Formerly: Guide to Departments of History (Year).
Description: Lists programs, faculty, and staff of more than 780 departments and research institutions.

DIRECTORY OF MEDICAL SCHOOLS WORLDWIDE. see MEDICAL SCIENCES

378.774 US
DIRECTORY OF MICHIGAN INSTITUTIONS OF HIGHER EDUCATION. a. Department of Education, Box 30008, Lansing, MI 48909. TEL 517-373-3360. **Document type:** directory.

EDUCATION — GUIDES TO SCHOOLS AND COLLEGES

DIRECTORY OF MODEL - TALENT AGENCIES AND SCHOOLS USA AND INTERNATIONAL. see *BUSINESS AND ECONOMICS — Trade And Industrial Directories*

370.025   US   ISSN 0898-2317
L901
DIRECTORY OF POSTSECONDARY INSTITUTIONS. 1967. biennial. price varies. U.S. Department of Education, National Center for Education Statistics, 555 New Jersey Ave., N.W., Washington, DC 20208. TEL 800-424-1616. (Dist. by: Supt. of Documents, Washington, DC 20402) **Document type:** directory.
     Former titles: Education Directory (School Year) - Colleges and Universities; Directory of U.S. Institutions of Higher Education (ISSN 0070-654X)

371.002 374.013   US
DIRECTORY OF PRIVATE VOCATIONAL SCHOOLS. 1968. a. free. Department of Education, Division of Vocational Education, Office of Private Schools, CN 500, Trenton, NJ 08625-0500. TEL 609-292-9696. FAX 609-633-0658. Ed. Detri Oliver. circ. 500. **Document type:** directory.
     Formerly: Directory of Private Schools; Which was formed by the merger of: Directory of Private Trade, Technical and Art Schools; Directory of Private Business Correspondence Schools (ISSN 0092-4202)

378.0025 370.15   US
DIRECTORY OF PSYCHOLOGY INTERNSHIPS: PROGRAMS OFFERING BEHAVIORAL TRAINING. 1989. a. $25. Association for Advancement of Behavior Therapy, 305 Seventh Ave., Ste. 16A, New York, NY 10001. circ. 1,000. **Document type:** directory.
     Description: Lists hundreds of behavioral therapy training programs for mental health practitioners and professionals.

371   US
DIRECTORY OF PUBLIC SCHOOLS IN THE U S.* a. $60 to non-members. Association for School, College and University Staffing, Inc., c/o High School, 1600 Dodge Ave., Ste. 5-330, Evanston, IL 60204. circ. 1,000. **Document type:** directory.

371.002   US
DIRECTORY OF PUBLIC VOCATIONAL TECHNICAL SCHOOLS AND INSTITUTES. Variant title: Directory of Public Vocational Technical Schools. 1982. biennial. $65. Media Marketing Group, Box 611, DeKalb, IL 60115. TEL 815-895-6842. (Co-publisher: Minnesota Scholarly Press) Ed. Marliss Johnston. **Document type:** directory.

DIRECTORY OF SERVICES AND FACILITIES FOR THE LEARNING DISABLED. see *EDUCATION — Special Education And Rehabilitation*

DIRECTORY OF SPECIAL PROGRAMS FOR MINORITY GROUP MEMBERS; CAREER INFORMATION SERVICES, EMPLOYMENT SKILLS, BANKS, FINANCIAL AID SOURCES. see *BUSINESS AND ECONOMICS — Trade And Industrial Directories*

371.002   UK   ISSN 0309-5290
T61
DIRECTORY OF TECHNICAL AND FURTHER EDUCATION. 1956. a. £65. Longman Group UK Ltd., Westgate House, 6th Fl., The High, Harlow, Essex CM20 1YR, England. TEL 0279-442601. FAX 0279-444501. index. **Document type:** directory.
     Former titles: Yearbook of Technical and Further Education; Yearbook of Technical Education and Training for Industry (ISSN 0084-4020)

378.0025 300.7   UK   ISSN 0269-2554
E S R C STUDENTSHIP HANDBOOK; postgraduate studentships in the social sciences. 1970. a. free. Economic and Social Research Council, Polaris House, N. Star Ave., Swindon, Wilts. SN2 1UJ, England. TEL 0793-413000. FAX 0793-413001. **Document type:** corporate report.
     Former titles (until 1984): S S R C Studentship Handbook; Social Science Research Council (Gt. Brit.) Postgraduate Studentships in the Social Sciences.

371   FR   ISSN 0012-9585
ECOLE MATERNELLE FRANCAISE. 1922. m. (9/yr.). 34 ECU($39) Armand Colin (Subsidiary of: Masson), 103 bd. Saint Michel, 75005 Paris, France. TEL 1-46-34-19-12. FAX 1-43-26-06-38. TELEX 201 269 F. Ed. J. Talamon. adv. circ. 18,000.

610 378   UN   ISSN 0013-1091
EDUCACION MEDICA Y SALUD. (Text in Spanish) 1966. q. $20. Pan American Health Organization, Pan American Sanitary Bureau, Regional Office of the World Health Organization, 525 23rd St., N.W., Washington, DC 20037. TEL 202-293-8130. FAX 202-338-0869. bk.rev.; abstr.; charts; index. circ. 6,000. (also avail. in microfiche from CIS; back issues avail.) **Indexed:** Abstr.Hyg., Biol.Abstr., Curr.Adv.Ecol.Sci., Dent.Ind., IIS, Ind.Med., INIS Atomind., Protozool.Abstr., Trop.Dis.Bull.
—BLDSC (3661.136000); SWETS.

371.0025 378   UK   ISSN 0965-2396
EDUCATION AFTER SIXTEEN. 1986. a. £7.95. (Gabbitas, Truman & Thring Educational Trust) John Catt Educational Ltd., Great Glemham, Saxmundham, Suffolk IP17 2DH, England. TEL 0728-78666. FAX 0728-663415. Ed. Derek Bingham. adv.; charts; illus. circ. 2,000. (back issues avail.) **Document type:** directory.
     Former titles (until 1992): Gabbitas, Truman and Thring Education after 16 (ISSN 0269-588X); Gabbitas, Truman and Thring Guide to Independent Further Education.
     Description: Lists institutions providing vocational courses, in addition to FE colleges, professional schools and colleges, and colleges of the arts.

371.002   UK
EDUCATION & TRAINING NEWS. 1988. a. Bradford and Ilkley Community College, Great Horton Rd., Bradford, W. Yorks. BD7 1AY, England. TEL 44-274-753089. FAX 44-274-753173. Ed. R.T. Sweeney. adv. circ. 12,000. (back issues avail.) **Document type:** newspaper.
     Formerly (until 1993): What Next.
     Description: Contains news for trainers in commerce and higher education.

374   US
EDUCATIONAL OPPORTUNITIES OF GREATER BOSTON. 1923. a. $15.95. Education Resources Institute, Attn.: Educational Opportunities, 330 Stuart St., Ste. 500, Boston, MA 02116-5237. TEL 617-426-0681. FAX 617-426-7114. Ed. Kathy Weinkle. circ. 3,500.

374   UK   ISSN 0956-3709
FLOODLIGHT; London's guide to part-time day and evening classes. 1936. a. £2. A L A - L B A, 36 Old Queen Street, London SW1H 9JF, England. TEL 071-222-0193. FAX 071-799-2339. Ed. Philippa Miller. adv. circ. 150,000. **Document type:** directory.
     Description: Lists over 16,600 classes under 5,420 subject headings, plus enrolment and fee information, for inner London's 43 universities, colleges and educational institutes.

FLORIDA. STATE BOARD OF INDEPENDENT COLLEGES AND UNIVERSITIES. REPORT. see *EDUCATION — Higher Education*

370.025   US
FLORIDA EDUCATION DIRECTORY. a. Department of Education, Knott Building, Tallahassee, FL 32304. TEL 904-488-3284.

371.0025   DK   ISSN 0107-4504
FOLKEHOEJSKOLER. 1971. a. free. Kulturministeriet, Vestergade 29-31, 1456 Copenhagen K, Denmark.

374   UK   ISSN 0967-0165
▼**FULL-TIME FLOODLIGHT;** Greater London's guide to full-time courses. 1992. a. £4.95. A L A - L B A, 36 Old Queen St., London SW1H 9JF. Ed. Philippa Miller. circ. 10,000. **Document type:** directory.
     Description: Includes 97 public-sector colleges and universities, with over 7,000 courses in more than 3,500 subjects, leading to A-Levels, BTEC awards, first degrees, GCSEs, and postgraduate degrees.

378.002   GW
G H K PUBLIK. 1978. m. DM.10. Universitaet Gesamthochschule Kassel, Moenchebergstr. 19, 34109 Kassel, Germany. TEL 0561-8042216. FAX 0561-8042330. circ. 6,500. (tabloid format; back issues avail.) **Document type:** directory.

378   US
GEORGIA'S POSTSECONDARY SCHOOLS. 1966. a. free. Georgia Student Finance Commission, 2082 E. Exchange Pl., Ste. 200, Tucker, GA 30084. TEL 404-493-5402. FAX 404-414-3133. adv.; illus. circ. 80,000. **Document type:** government publication.
     Former titles: Georgia Postsecondary School Directory: A Guide to Colleges, Vocational-Technical Schools and Special Purpose Institutions; Directory: A Guide to Colleges, Vocational-Technical Schools and Special Purpose Institutions; Directory: A Guide to Colleges, Vocational-Technical and Diploma Schools of Nursing; Directory of Educational Opportunities in Georgia (ISSN 0419-2559)
     Description: Outlines programs of study at Georgia postsecondary schools. Includes information on location, enrollment, admissions, and financial aid.

GLOBAL DIRECTORY OF SCHOOLS OF LAW OUTSIDE OF THE UNITED STATES OF AMERICA. see *LAW*

378.025   US   ISSN 1065-6049
JA88.U6
GRADUATE FACULTY AND PROGRAMS IN POLITICAL SCIENCE. 1972. triennial. $45 to non-members; members $25. American Political Science Association, 1527 New Hampshire Ave., N.W., Washington, DC 20036. TEL 202-483-2512. FAX 202-483-2657. Ed. Patricia Spellman. circ. 2,500. **Document type:** directory.
     Formerly (until 1994): Guide to Graduate Study in Political Science (ISSN 0091-9632)

350   US
GRADUATE PROGRAMS IN PUBLIC AFFAIRS AND PUBLIC ADMINISTRATION. Variant titles: Directory: Graduate Programs in Public Affairs and Administration. Programs in Public Affairs and Administration. 1972. biennial. $12.50. National Association of Schools of Public Affairs and Administration, 1120 G St., N.W., Ste. 730, Washington, DC 20005. TEL 202-628-8965. FAX 202-626-4978. Ed. Alfred M. Zuck. circ. 1,500. **Indexed:** C.I.J.E.
     Formerly: Graduate School Programs in Public Affairs and Public Administration (ISSN 0094-6648)

378.002   US
GRADUATE SCHOOL GUIDE. a. $10. School Guide Publications, 210 N. Ave., New Rochelle, NY 10801. TEL 914-632-7771. Ed. Marie Castrovilla. adv.; stat. circ. 80,000. **Document type:** directory.

GRADUATE STUDY IN PSYCHOLOGY. see *PSYCHOLOGY*

371.002 310   GD
GRENADA SCHOOL DIRECTORY AND BASIC EDUCATIONAL STATISTICS. a. Ministry of Education, Statistical Unit, St. George's, Grenada, W.I. **Document type:** government publication, directory.

377   SP   ISSN 0211-4410
GUIA DE CENTROS EDUCATIVOS CATOLICOS. 1970. triennial. 7000 ptas. Federacion Espanola de Religiosos de la Ensenanza (F.E.R.E.), Servicio Estadistico, Conde de Penalver, 45, 28006 Madrid, Spain. TEL 91-4021300. FAX 91-3091740. Ed.Bd. adv.; stat. circ. 1,000.
     Formerly: Guia de Centros Docentes de la Iglesia.
     Description: Provides information on all Catholic centers of education at all levels, from preschool to university.

378.002   ES
GUIA UNIVERSITARIA SALVADORENA. a. Instituto Salvadoreno de Estudios Politicos, Apdo. Postal 2687, Col. Escalon, San Salvador, El Salvador. circ. 500. **Document type:** directory.

371.002   IT
▼**GUIDA RAGIONATA ALLE SCUOLE D'INGLESE IN ITALIA.** (Supplement to: Rivista delle Lingue) 1992. biennial. Edizioni Linguistic Club, Via Principe Amedeo 15, 00044 Frascati (Rome), Italy. TEL 06-941-68-57. FAX 06-941-68-58. Ed. Carlo Nofri. **Document type:** directory.

378.0025 371.42   AT
GUIDE TO CAMPUS RECRUITING. 1981. a. $10. Graduate Careers Council of Australia Ltd., P.O. Box 28, Parkville, Vic. 3052, Australia. TEL 03-344-4666. FAX 03-347-7298. Ed. Catherine Buchanan. adv. circ. 2,500.
     Formerly: Employers Guide to Recruiting in Australian Universities and Colleges of Advanced Education.

EDUCATION — GUIDES TO SCHOOLS AND COLLEGES

371.0025 378.0025 US
TX911.5
GUIDE TO COLLEGE PROGRAMS IN HOSPITALITY & TOURISM; a directory of CHRIE member colleges and universities. 1989. irreg. $15.95. John Wiley & Sons, Inc., 605 Third Ave., New York, NY 10158. TEL 212-850-6572. FAX 212-850-6088. TELEX 12-7063. Ed. Karen Stiegler. **Document type:** directory.
  Former titles: Guide to Hospitality and Tourism Education (ISSN 1050-933X); Directory of C H R I E Member Schools.
  Description: Guide to colleges and universities offering degrees or certificates in hospitality and tourism related fields.

371.0025 US
GUIDE TO DOCTORAL PROGRAMS IN BUSINESS AND MANAGEMENT. 1985. irreg., revised 1992. $10 (foreign $15). American Assembly of Collegiate Schools of Business, 600 Emerson Rd., Ste. 300, St. Louis, MO 63141-6762. TEL 314-872-8481. FAX 314-872-8495. Ed. Charlotte Kurst. **Document type:** directory.

371 US
GUIDE TO GRADUATE EDUCATION IN SPEECH - LANGUAGE PATHOLOGY AND AUDIOLOGY. 1982. biennial. price varies. American Speech - Language - Hearing Association, 10801 Rockville Pike, Rockville, MD 20852. TEL 301-897-5700. FAX 301-571-0457. circ. 5,000. **Document type:** directory.
  Description: Contains profiles of education and training programs, degree and admission requirements, costs and financial assistance programs.

378.025 US ISSN 0072-8500
GUIDE TO GRADUATE STUDY IN BOTANY FOR THE UNITED STATES AND CANADA. 1966. irreg., latest 1988. $10. Botanical Society of America, Inc. (Columbus), Business Office, 1735 Neil Ave., Columbus, OH 43210. TEL 614-292-3519.
  Description: Provides data on degree programs and faculty of plant science departments in the United States and Canada.

378.002 US ISSN 1052-9586
LC1090
GUIDE TO INTERNATIONAL EDUCATION IN THE UNITED STATES. 1991. biennial. Gale Research Inc., 835 Penobscot Bldg., Detroit, MI 48226. TEL 313-961-2242. FAX 313-961-6083.

GUIDE TO PROGRAMS IN GEOGRAPHY IN THE UNITED STATES AND CANADA - A A G MEMBERSHIP DIRECTORY (YEAR). see GEOGRAPHY

370.025 US ISSN 0072-8705
GV193
GUIDE TO SUMMER CAMPS AND SUMMER SCHOOLS. 1936. irreg., 26th ed, 1990-1991. $26 cloth; paper $21. Porter Sargent Publishers, Inc., 11 Beacon St., Ste. 1400, Boston, MA 02108. TEL 617-523-1670. FAX 617-523-1021. adv.; illus.; stat.; index. circ. 4,000. **Document type:** directory.
  Description: Guides parents to all types of summer camps and educational summer opportunities for children, as well as specialized programs for children with physical or emotional handicaps or learning disabilities.

378 UK
HANDBOOK OF DEGREE AND ADVANCED COURSES IN INSTITUTES-COLLEGES OF HIGHER EDUCATION, COLLEGES OF EDUCATION, POLYTECHNICS, UNIVERSITY DEPARTMENTS OF EDUCATION. 1954. a. £8.50. National Association of Teachers in Further and Higher Education in England and Wales, 27 Britannia St., London WC2X 9JP, England. Ed. Jonathan R. Garnett.

378.0025 620 II
HANDBOOK OF ENGINEERING EDUCATION. (Text in English) irreg., latest 1993. price varies. Association of Indian Universities, A.I.U. House, 16 Kotla Marg, New Delhi 110 002, India. TEL 11-3310059. FAX 11-3315105. TELEX 31-66180-AIU-IN. circ. 2,200.

378 610 II
HANDBOOK OF MEDICAL EDUCATION. (Text in English) irreg., latest 1994. price varies. Association of Indian Universities, A.I.U. House, 16 Kotla Marg, New Delhi 110 002, India. TEL 11-3310059. FAX 11-3315105. TELEX 31-66180-AIU-IN. circ. 2,200.

371.0025 US ISSN 0072-9884
L901
HANDBOOK OF PRIVATE SCHOOLS; an annual descriptive survey of independent education. 1914. a. $80 (effective 1994). Porter Sargent Publishers, Inc., 11 Beacon St., Ste. 1400, Boston, MA 02108. TEL 617-523-1670. FAX 617-523-1021. Ed.Bd. adv.; illus.; stat.; index. circ. 5,000. **Document type:** directory.
  Description: Guides parents in choosing a private school; includes statistics on enrollments, tuition, graduates, administrators, and faculty, as well as summer educational programs.

378.002 US ISSN 0160-4961
HEALTH SERVICES ADMINISTRATION EDUCATION. 1979. biennial. $20.45. Association of University Programs in Health Administration, 1911 N. Fort Myer Dr., Ste. 503, Arlington, VA 22209. TEL 703-524-5500. Ed. Donna Royston. **Document type:** directory.
  Description: Contains higher education and continuing education health administration program information, featuring admission requirement, application, curriculum, cost, and student aid information.

378.0025 028.5
296 US
HILLEL GUIDE TO JEWISH LIFE ON CAMPUS (YEAR). 1981. biennial. $14.95. B'nai B'rith Hillel Foundations (Washington), 1640 Rhode Island Ave., N.W., Washington, DC 20036. TEL 202-857-6560. FAX 202-857-6693. Ed. Ruth Fredman Cernea. adv.; index. circ. 10,000. **Document type:** directory.
  Description: Discription of Jewish life on approximately 500 college campuses designed to assist students in choosing colleges.

371.0025 UK
THE I S I S MAGAZINE. 1972. 3/yr. £3.50 (institutions £5) (overseas £6). Independent Schools Information Service, 56 Buckingham Gate, London SW1E 6AG, England. TEL 071-630-8793. Ed. D.J. Woodhead. adv.; bk.rev. circ. 50,000. (back issues avail.)
  Former titles: I S I S News; (until 1986): I S I S Newsletter.
  Description: Targeted to parents and staff of English independent schools: senior and junior, day and boarding, girls', boys' and coeducational. News and features about independent education.

371.0025 US
I S S DIRECTORY OF OVERSEAS SCHOOLS. 1981. a. $34.95. International Schools Services, Inc., Box 5910, Princeton, NJ 08543. TEL 609-452-0990. FAX 609-452-2690. TELEX 843-308 SCHOLSERV PRIN. Ed. Mea Kaemmerlen. adv. circ. 4,000. **Document type:** directory.

371.002 US
IDAHO EDUCATIONAL DIRECTORY. 1919. a. $5. Department of Education, Division of Finance and Administration, Len B. Jordan Bldg., Boise, ID 83720. TEL 208-334-3330. FAX 208-334-2228. Ed. Dorian D. Weineke. circ. 5,000. **Document type:** directory.

373 370.025 US ISSN 0073-5779
INDEPENDENT SCHOOLS ASSOCIATION OF THE SOUTHWEST. MEMBERSHIP LIST. 1966. a. free. Independent Schools Association of the Southwest, Box 52297, Tulsa, OK 74152-0297. TEL 918-749-5927. FAX 918-749-5937. Ed. Richard W. Ekdahl. circ. 700.
  Description: Lists schools accredited by the Association.

370.025 UK
INDEPENDENT SCHOOLS OF THE UNITED KINGDOM. (Includes: Continental Tutors and Special Training Sections) 1910. a. £14.99. J. Burrow & Co. Ltd., Publicity House, Streatham Hill, London SW2 4TR, England. TEL 081-674-4122. FAX 081-674-8489. Ed. K. Knowler. adv. contact: K. Neale. circ. 9,000. **Document type:** directory.
  Former titles: Schools of the United Kingdom; (until 1989): Schools of England, Wales, Scotland and Ireland (ISSN 0080-6919)

370.025 374.4 US ISSN 0733-6020
LC5951
THE INDEPENDENT STUDY CATALOG: N U C E A'S GUIDE TO INDEPENDENT STUDY THROUGH CORRESPONDENCE INSTRUCTION. 1964. triennial. $16.95. (National University Continuing Education Association) Peterson's Guides, Inc., 202 Carnegie Center, Box 2123, Princeton, NJ 08543-2123. TEL 609-243-9111. FAX 609-243-9150. **Document type:** directory.
—CCC.
  Former titles (until 1977): Guide to Independent Study Through Correspondence Instruction (ISSN 0149-1083); Guide to Correspondence Studies in Colleges and Universities (ISSN 0072-8322)
  Description: Covers over 12,000 high school, undergraduate, graduate and non-credit correspondence courses offered by over 70 colleges and universities

371.002 US ISSN 1067-6554
INDIANA SCHOOL DIRECTORY. a. $5. Department of Education, 227 State House, Indianapolis, IN 46204. TEL 317-232-6610. **Document type:** directory.

378.002 150 US ISSN 1061-7132
INSIDER'S GUIDE TO GRADUATE PROGRAMS IN CLINICAL PSYCHOLOGY. 1990. biennial. $17.95. Guilford Publications, Inc., 72 Spring St., 4th Fl., New York, NY 10012. TEL 212-431-9800. FAX 212-966-6708. charts; stat.
  Description: Outlines strategies for getting in to graduate school n psychology and gives an inside look at all to the programs available in the US and Canada.

378 AT
INSTITUTE OF EDUCATION. HANDBOOK. a. Aus.$3. University of Melbourne, Institute of Education, Parkville, Vic. 3052, Australia. TEL 03-344-4000. TELEX AA35185. circ. 3,000. (also avail. in microfiche; back issues avail.)
  Formerly: Melbourne College of Advanced Education. Handbook (ISSN 0812-230X)

INTERNATIONAL ASSOCIATION OF EDUCATORS FOR WORLD PEACE. CIRCULATION NEWSLETTER. see EDUCATION — International Education Programs

370.025 IE ISSN 0075-0662
IRELAND DEPARTMENT OF EDUCATION. LIOSTA DE IAR-BHUNSCOILEANNA AITHEANTA - LIST OF RECOGNISED POST-PRIMARY SCHOOLS. 1968. a. Government Publications Sales Office, Sun Alliance House, Molesworth St., Dublin 2, Ireland. **Document type:** government publication.

JOURNALISM AND MASS COMMUNICATION DIRECTORY. see JOURNALISM

JOURNALIST'S ROAD TO SUCCESS. see JOURNALISM

371.002 GW
KATHOLISCHE UNIVERSITAET EICHSTAETT. VORLESUNGSVERZEICHNIS. 1960. s-a. DM.8. Katholische Universitaet Eichstaett, Ostenstr. 26, 85072 Eichstaett, Germany. TEL 08421-20248. adv.; bibl.; stat. circ. 4,500. **Document type:** directory.

370 US ISSN 0091-0775
L152
KENTUCKY SCHOOL DIRECTORY. 1975. a. $20. Department of Education, Office of Communication Services, 1912 Capital Plaza Tower, 1500 Mero St., 19th Fl., Frankfort, KY 40601. TEL 502-564-3421. Ed. Sheila Shouse. stat. circ. 6,500. (processed) **Document type:** directory.

378.0025 371.42 US
KEY - A GUIDE TO COLLEGE AND CAREERS. (In 3 editions: High School Junior, High School Senior, Junior-Community College Transfer) a. free. Target Marketing, Inc., 5 Victory Lane, Ste. 101, Liberty, MO 64068. TEL 816-781-7557. FAX 816-792-3892. Ed.Bd. adv. circ. 1,400,000.
  Description: Focuses on educational options, campus life, financial aid sources and military and career opportunities.

378.002 JA ISSN 0389-4088
KOCHI GAKUEN COLLEGE. BULLETIN. (Text in English or Japanese; summaries in English) 1970. a. $10. Kochi Gakuen College, 292 Asahitenjin-Cho, Kochi-Shi 780, Japan. Ed. Hajime Iwakura. circ. 500. (back issues avail.) **Document type:** bulletin.

EDUCATION — GUIDES TO SCHOOLS AND COLLEGES

LAW SCHOOL SUMMER SCHOOL PROGRAMS AT HOME AND ABROAD. see *LAW*

371.0025 378   UK   ISSN 0969-9015
▼**LEARN FOR YOURSELF.** 1993. a. £9.95. John Catt Educational Ltd., Great Glemham, Saxmundham, Suffolk IP17 2DH, England. TEL 0728-663666. FAX 0728-663415. Ed. Derek Bingham. circ. 2,000. **Document type:** directory.
Description: Provides details on more than 5,000 courses in 200 subjects, from GCSE to degrees and professional qualifications, their duration and cost.

371.0025 378.0025   UK   ISSN 0965-240X
LEARNING LANGUAGES IN EUROPE. 1988. a. £7.95. (Gabbitas, Truman & Thring Educational Trust) John Catt Educational Ltd., Great Glemham, Saxmundham, Suffolk IP17 2DH, England. TEL 0728-78666. FAX 0728-663415. Ed. Derek Bingham. adv.; charts; illus. circ. 2,000. (back issues avail.) **Document type:** directory.
Formerly (until 1992): Learning English in Britain (ISSN 0953-2617)
Description: Provides information on language schools in Europe where students can learn the language of the country.

LONDON AND SOUTH EAST REGION ADVISORY COUNCIL FOR EDUCATION AND TRAINING. INDEX OF COURSES. see *EDUCATION — Higher Education*

370.025   US   ISSN 0076-132X
LA226
LOVEJOY'S COLLEGE GUIDE. 1940. s-a. $40 cloth; paper $21. Prentice Hall, 15 Columbus Cir., New York, NY 10023. TEL 212-373-8500. Ed. Barbarasue Lovejoy Straughn.

378 371   US   ISSN 0024-7022
LOVEJOY'S GUIDANCE DIGEST. 1946. 10/yr. $60. Lovejoy's College Guide Inc., Box Q, Red Bank, NJ 07701. TEL 908-741-5640. Ed. Charles T. Straughn. adv.; index. circ. 5,000.

371   US
MAJOR DECISIONS;* a guide to college majors. 1990. biennial. $15 (effective 1992). Orchard House, Inc., 629 Cherokee St., New Orleans, LA 70118-5049. Eds. Joseph Despres, Richard Blumenthal. circ. 2,000.

378   US
MARKETING RECREATION CLASSES. 1987. m. $95. Learning Resources Network, 1554 Hayes Dr., Manhattan, KS 66502. TEL 913-539-5376.
Description: Newsletter and articles on art, music, personal skills, health, business, and other nonacademic-oriented courses, seminars, workshops, and programs throughout the United States.

378.774   US
MICHIGAN POSTSECONDARY ADMISSIONS & FINANCIAL ASSISTANCE HANDBOOK. a. Department of Education, Box 30008, Lansing, MI 48909. TEL 517-373-0457. illus.
Formerly: Michigan. Department of Education. College Admissions and Financial Assistance Handbook (ISSN 0094-3754)

370   US   ISSN 0092-7899
L903.M6
MISSISSIPPI EDUCATIONAL DIRECTORY. 1977. a. $8. Department of Education, c/o Management Information System, Box 771, Jackson, MS 39205. TEL 601-359-3487. FAX 601-359-2326. Ed. Patricia Dalton. circ. 2,000. **Document type:** directory.
Formerly: Educational Directory of Mississippi Schools (ISSN 0363-874X)

377.82   US   ISSN 0147-8044
LC501
N C E A GANLEY'S CATHOLIC SCHOOLS IN AMERICA. 1974. a. $37.50. (National Catholic Educational Association) Fisher Publishing Company, Box 1073, Montrose, CO 81402. TEL 303-249-1303. FAX 303-290-9308. Ed. Mary Mahar. circ. 500.
Former titles: Ganley's Catholic Schools in America - Elementary, Secondary; Catholic Schools in the United States (ISSN 0091-9527)

371.0025 700   US
NATIONAL ASSOCIATION OF SCHOOLS OF ART AND DESIGN. DIRECTORY. 1977. a. $11. National Association of Schools of Art and Design, 11250 Roger Bacon Dr., Ste. 21, Reston, VA 22090. TEL 703-437-0700. Ed. David Bading. circ. 1,000. **Document type:** directory.
Formerly: National Association of Schools of Art. Directory.

378.002   CN
NATIONAL CO-OPERATIVE EDUCATION DIRECTORY. (Text in English, French) 1989. a. Can.$95. Canadian Association for Co-operative Education, 1209 King St., W., Ste. 203, Toronto, ON M6K 1G2, Canada. TEL 416-535-6993. FAX 416-535-3994. Eds. Michael Baldwin, Julie Rohmer. charts; stat. circ. 500.
Description: Lists co-operative education programs at Canadian universities and colleges according to province. Includes program schedules, co-op fees, addresses, phone-fax numbers, staff and enrollment date.

371.0025   US   ISSN 1062-0869
L901
NATIONAL DIRECTORY OF ALTERNATIVE SCHOOLS. biennial. $15. National Coalition of Alternative Community Schools, Box 15036, Santa Fe, NM 87506. TEL 505-474-4312. Ed. Michael Traugot. bibl. **Document type:** directory.
Description: Contains a list of alternative schools in the United States and foreign countries, and descriptions of programs.

378.0025   US
HQ1060
NATIONAL DIRECTORY OF EDUCATIONAL PROGRAMS IN GERONTOLOGY AND GERIATRICS. 1976. triennial, 6th ed., 1993. $54.50. Association for Gerontology in Higher Education, 1001 Connecticut Ave., N.W., Ste. 410, Washington, DC 20036-5504. TEL 202-429-9277. Ed. Joy C. Lobenstine. circ. 1,000. (back issues avail.) **Document type:** directory.
Formerly: National Directory of Educational Programs in Gerontology (ISSN 0148-4508)
Description: Listings and descriptions of 1,000 gerontology programs and contact persons in accredited institutions of higher education in the US and Canada.

NATIONAL DIRECTORY OF NONPROFIT ORGANIZATIONS. see *SOCIAL SERVICES AND WELFARE*

NATIONAL UNIVERSITY CONTINUING EDUCATION ASSOCIATION. DIRECTORY. see *EDUCATION — Higher Education*

NETHERLANDS. CENTRAAL BUREAU VOOR DE STATISTIEK. STATISTIEK VAN HET BEROEPSONDERWIJS: KUNSTONDERWIJS/NETHERLANDS. CENTRAL BUREAU OF STATISTICS. STATISTICS OF PROFESSIONAL EDUCATION: ART EDUCATION. see *EDUCATION — Abstracting, Bibliographies, Statistics*

NEW YORK CITY MODEL AGENCY DIRECTORY. see *BUSINESS AND ECONOMICS — Trade And Industrial Directories*

371.42   JA
NIKKEI VOCATIONAL SCHOOL GUIDE. a. Nikkei Custom Publishing Services, Inc. (Subsidiary of: Nihon Keizai Shimbun, Inc.), 2-8-4 Kanda Tsukasa-cho, Chiyoda-ku, Tokyo 101, Japan. TEL 03-5256-6924.
Description: A guide for students continuing their education at vocational schools. Also contains valuable employment information.

371.002   UK
NORVICENSIAN. 1873. a. Norwich School, 71A The Close, Norwich NR1 4DD, England. Ed. P.J. Carpmael. adv. contact: T. Hilton. circ. 2,200. **Document type:** corporate report.

371.002   US   ISSN 0731-8650
OCCUPATIONAL PROGRAMS IN CALIFORNIA PUBLIC COMMUNITY COLLEGES. 1980. biennial. $25.50. Leo A. Meyer Associates, Inc., 23850 Clawiter Rd., Ste. 1, Hayward, CA 94545. TEL 510-785-1091. FAX 510-785-1099. index. circ. 2,000.
Description: Reference lists for vocational counselors, administrators, libraries, students, and career centers, providing general information, charts of program locations, and information about specific colleges.

370.025   US   ISSN 0078-5679
OREGON SCHOOL DIRECTORY. 1972. a. $8. Department of Education, 700 Pringle Pkwy., S.E., Salem, OR 97310. TEL 503-378-3589. FAX 503-373-7968. Ed. Sharon Lesh. circ. 10,000. (also avail. in microfiche) **Document type:** directory.
Formerly (until 1973): Oregon School-Community College Directory.

OVERBACHER BRUECKE. see *CHILDREN AND YOUTH — For*

PARALEGAL SCHOOL DIRECTORY. see *LAW*

378.0025   US
PAREGIAN DIRECTORY OF COLLEGES. bi-w. $2 per no. M.G. Paregian, Publisher, 733 Childs Ave., Drexel Hill, PA 19026. TEL 215-259-3864. **Document type:** directory.

371.0025   US
PAREGIAN DIRECTORY OF INDEPENDENT - PRIVATE SCHOOLS. bi-w. $2 per no. M.G. Paregian, Publisher, 733 Childs Ave., Drexel Hill, PA 19026. TEL 215-259-3864. **Document type:** directory.

370.025   US   ISSN 0079-0230
L901
PATTERSON'S AMERICAN EDUCATION. 1904. a. $79 to individuals; schools & libraries $69. Educational Directories Inc., Box 199, Mount Prospect, IL 60056-0199. TEL 708-459-0605. FAX 708-459-0608. Ed. Douglas Moody. index. **Document type:** directory.
Description: Directory to more than 11,400 public school districts; 34,000 public, private and Catholic high, junior high and middle schools; 300 parochial superintendents; 400 territorial schools; 400 State Dept. of Education personnel; and 400 educational associations.

371.0025   US   ISSN 1044-1417
L901
PATTERSON'S ELEMENTARY EDUCATION. 1989. a. $79 to individuals; schools & libraries $69. Educational Directories Inc., Box 199, Mount Prospect, IL 60056-0199. TEL 708-459-0605. Ed. Douglas Moody. **Document type:** directory.
Description: Directory to more than 13,000 public school districts; 71,000 public, private and Catholic elementary and middle schools; 1,600 territorial schools; and 400 State Dept. of Education personnel.

371.0025   US   ISSN 0553-4054
L901
PATTERSON'S SCHOOLS CLASSIFIED. (Also incl. in Patterson's American Education) 1951. a. $15. Educational Directories Inc., Box 199, Mount Prospect, IL 60056-0199. TEL 708-459-0605. Ed. Wayne Moody. (processed) **Document type:** directory.
Description: Directory to more than 7,000 accredited postsecondary schools. Schools are commingled under 50 academic diciplines but retain their school type identification.

378.0025   US   ISSN 1062-3205
LB2337.2
PAYING LESS FOR COLLEGE (YEAR). 1983. a. $22.95. Peterson's Guides, Inc., 202 Carnegie Center, Box 2123, Princeton, NJ 08543-2123. TEL 609-243-9111. FAX 609-243-9150.
Formerly: College Money Handbook (ISSN 0894-9395)
Description: Details costs and financial aid at more than 1,700 accredited four-year colleges in the United States.

PEACE PROGRESS; I A E W P journal of education. see *EDUCATION — International Education Programs*

378.002   GW
PERSONAL- UND VORLESUNGSVERZEICHNIS DER UNIVERSITAET WUERZBURG. s-a. DM.10.80. (Julius Maximilian Universitaet Wuerzburg) Echter Wuerzburg, Fraenkische Gesellschaftsdruckerei und Verlag GmbH, Juliuspromenade 64, 97070 Wuerzburg, Germany. TEL 0931-3091-0. circ. 9,800. (back issues avail.) **Document type:** academic/scholarly publication.

EDUCATION — GUIDES TO SCHOOLS AND COLLEGES

378.0025   US   ISSN 0887-0152
LB2351.2
PETERSON'S COMPETITIVE COLLEGES (YEAR). 1981. a. $13.95. Peterson's Guides, Inc., 202 Carnegie Center, Box 2123, Princeton, NJ 08543-2123. TEL 609-243-9111. FAX 609-243-9150.
Description: Covers over 300 selective accredited colleges in the United States.

378.0025   US   ISSN 0742-4973
L903.N38
PETERSON'S GUIDE TO COLLEGES IN NEW ENGLAND (YEAR). 1984. a. $12.95. Peterson's Guides, Inc., 202 Carnegie Center, Box 2123, Princeton, NJ 08543-2123. TEL 609-243-9111. FAX 609-243-9150.
Description: Covers all accredited four-year and private two-year colleges in New England.

378.0025   US   ISSN 0742-4965
L903.N7
PETERSON'S GUIDE TO COLLEGES IN NEW YORK (YEAR). 1984. a. $12.95. Peterson's Guides, Inc., 202 Carnegie Center, Box 2123, Princeton, NJ 08543-2123. TEL 609-243-9111. FAX 609-243-9150.
Description: Covers all accredited four-year and private two-year colleges in New York State.

378.0025   US   ISSN 0742-4957
L903.M54
PETERSON'S GUIDE TO COLLEGES IN THE MIDDLE ATLANTIC STATES (YEAR). 1984. a. $12.95. Peterson's Guides, Inc., 202 Carnegie Center, Box 2123, Princeton, NJ 08543-2123. TEL 609-243-9111. FAX 609-243-9150.
Description: Covers all accredited four-year and private two-year colleges in the Middle Atlantic States.

378.0025   US   ISSN 0742-4949
L903.M57
PETERSON'S GUIDE TO COLLEGES IN THE MIDWEST (YEAR). 1984. a. $12.95. Peterson's Guides, Inc., 202 Carnegie Center, Box 2123, Princeton, NJ 08543-2123. TEL 609-243-9111. FAX 609-243-9150.
Description: Covers all accredited four-year and private two-year colleges in the Midwest.

378.0025   US   ISSN 0882-309X
L903.S84
PETERSON'S GUIDE TO COLLEGES IN THE SOUTHEAST (YEAR). 1985. a. $12.95. Peterson's Guides, Inc., 202 Carnegie Center, Box 2123, Princeton, NJ 08543-2123. TEL 609-243-9111. FAX 609-243-9150.
Description: Covers all accredited four-year and private two-year colleges in the Southeast.

378.0025   US   ISSN 0882-3103
L903.S85
PETERSON'S GUIDE TO COLLEGES IN THE SOUTHWEST (YEAR). 1985. a. $12.95. Peterson's Guides, Inc., 202 Carnegie Center, Box 2123, Princeton, NJ 08543-2123. TEL 609-243-9111. FAX 609-243-9150.
Description: Covers all accredited four-year and private two-year colleges in the Southwest.

378.0025   US   ISSN 0888-8159
L903.W39
PETERSON'S GUIDE TO COLLEGES IN THE WEST (YEAR). 1986. a. $12.95. Peterson's Guides, Inc., 202 Carnegie Center, Box 2123, Princeton, NJ 08543-2123. TEL 609-243-9111. FAX 609-243-9150.
Description: Covers all accredited four-year and private two-year colleges in the western United States.

370.025 378   US   ISSN 0894-9336
L901
PETERSON'S GUIDE TO FOUR-YEAR COLLEGES (YEAR). 1970. a. $18.95. Peterson's Guides, Inc., 202 Carnegie Center, Box 2123, Princeton, NJ 08543-2123. TEL 609-243-9111. FAX 609-243-9150.
●Also available online. Vendor(s): BRS Online Products (PETE), CompuServe, Inc. (PCG), DIALOG Information Services, Inc. (File no.214), Dow Jones News Retrieval (SCHOOL).
—CCC.
Former titles: Guide to Four-Year Colleges (ISSN 0737-3163); Which supersedes in part (as of 1970): Peterson's Annual Guide to Undergraduate Study (ISSN 0147-8451); Annual Guide to Undergraduate Study (ISSN 0091-0465)
Description: Covers the 1,950 accredited institutions in the United States and Canada that grant baccalaureate degrees.

370.025   US   ISSN 0894-9344
L901
PETERSON'S GUIDE TO GRADUATE AND PROFESSIONAL PROGRAMS: AN OVERVIEW (YEAR) (BOOK 1). Key Title: Peterson's Annual Guides to Graduate Study. Book 1. Peterson's Guides to Graduate and Professional Programs. 1966. a. $23.95. Peterson's Guides, Inc., 202 Carnegie Center, Box 2123, Princeton, NJ 08543-2123. TEL 609-243-9111. FAX 609-243-9150. **Document type:** directory.
●Also available online. Vendor(s): DIALOG Information Services, Inc. (File no.273).
Also available on CD-ROM. Producer(s): SilverPlatter Information, Inc. (PETERSON'S GRADLINE).
Former titles (until 1989): Peterson's Annual Guides to Graduate Study. Book 1. Accredited Institutions Offering Graduate Work (ISSN 0887-8358); (until 1982): Peterson's Annual Guides to Graduate Study. Book 1. Graduate Institutions of the U.S. and Canada; (1976-1980): Peterson's Annual Guides to Graduate Study. Book 1: Graduate and Professional Programs (ISSN 0887-834X)
Description: Covers all accredited institutions offering postbaccalaureate programs in the United States and Canada.

378.0025   US   ISSN 0897-6023
L901
PETERSON'S GUIDE TO GRADUATE PROGRAMS IN BUSINESS, EDUCATION, HEALTH, AND LAW (YEAR) (BOOK 6). 1966. a. $23.95. Peterson's Guides, Inc., 202 Carnegie Center, Box 2123, Princeton, NJ 08543-2123. TEL 609-243-9111. FAX 609-243-9150.
●Also available online. Vendor(s): DIALOG Information Services, Inc. (File no.273).
Also available on CD-ROM. Producer(s): SilverPlatter Information, Inc. (PETERSON'S GRADLINE).
Description: Covers postbaccalaureate programs in the professional areas of business, education, health, and law in the United States and Canada.

370.025 620   US   ISSN 0894-9387
L901
PETERSON'S GUIDE TO GRADUATE PROGRAMS IN ENGINEERING AND APPLIED SCIENCES (YEAR) (BOOK 5). 1966. a. $35.95. Peterson's Guides, Inc., 202 Carnegie Center, Box 2123, Princeton, NJ 08543-2123. TEL 609-243-9111. FAX 609-243-9150. **Document type:** directory.
●Also available online. Vendor(s): DIALOG Information Services, Inc. (File no.273).
Also available on CD-ROM. Producer(s): SilverPlatter Information, Inc. (PETERSON'S GRADLINE).
Former titles (until 1989): Peterson's Annual Guides - Graduate Study. Book 5. Graduate Programs in Engineering and Applied Sciences (ISSN 0887-8617); (1976-1983): Peterson's Annual Guides to Graduate Study. Book 5: Engineering and Applied Sciences (ISSN 0887-8609)
Description: Covers postbaccalaureate programs in engineering and applied sciences in the United States and Canada.

370.025 570   US   ISSN 0894-9360
L901
PETERSON'S GUIDE TO GRADUATE PROGRAMS IN THE BIOLOGICAL AND AGRICULTURAL SCIENCES (YEAR) (BOOK 3). Key Title: Peterson's Annual Guides to Graduate Study. Book 3. Peterson's Guide to Graduate Programs in the Biological and Agricultural Sciences. 1966. a. $40.95. Peterson's Guides, Inc., 202 Carnegie Center, Box 2123, Princeton, NJ 08543-2123. TEL 609-243-9111. FAX 609-243-9150. **Document type:** directory.
●Also available online. Vendor(s): DIALOG Information Services, Inc. (File no.273).
Also available on CD-ROM. Producer(s): SilverPlatter Information, Inc. (PETERSON'S GRADLINE).
Former titles (until 1989): Peterson's Annual Guides - Graduate Study. Book 3. Graduate Programs in the Biological, Agricultural, and Health Sciences (ISSN 0887-8412); (until 1984): Peterson's Annual Guides to Graduate Study. Book 3. Biological, Agricultural, and Health Sciences. (ISSN 0278-5358); (1976-1977): Peterson's Annual Guides to Graduate Study. Book 3: Biological and Health Sciences (ISSN 0887-8404)
Description: Covers postbaccalaureate programs in biological and agricultural sciences in the United States and Canada.

370.025 650   US   ISSN 0894-9352
L901
PETERSON'S GUIDE TO GRADUATE PROGRAMS IN THE HUMANITIES AND SOCIAL SCIENCES (YEAR) (BOOK 2). 1966. a. $34.95. Peterson's Guides, Inc., 202 Carnegie Center, Box 2123, Princeton, NJ 08543-2123. TEL 609-243-9111. FAX 609-243-9150. **Document type:** directory.
●Also available online. Vendor(s): DIALOG Information Services, Inc. (File no.273).
Also available on CD-ROM. Producer(s): SilverPlatter Information, Inc. (PETERSON'S GRADLINE).
Former titles (until 1989): Peterson's Graduate Programs in the Humanities and Social Sciences (ISSN 0887-8382). (1976-1983): Peterson's Annual Guides to Graduate Study. Book 2: Humanities and Social Sciences. (ISSN 0887-8374)
Description: Covers postbaccalaureate programs in the humanities and social sciences in the United States and Canada.

370.025 500   US   ISSN 0894-9379
L901
PETERSON'S GUIDE TO GRADUATE PROGRAMS IN THE PHYSICAL SCIENCES AND MATHEMATICS (YEAR) (BOOK 4). Key Title: Peterson's Annual Guides to Graduate Study. Book 4. Peterson's Guide to Graduate Programs in the Physical Sciences and Mathematics. 1966. a. $30.95. Peterson's Guides, Inc., 202 Carnegie Center, Box 2123, NJ 08543-2123. TEL 609-243-9111. FAX 609-243-9150. **Document type:** directory.
●Also available online. Vendor(s): DIALOG Information Services, Inc. (File no.273).
Also available on CD-ROM. Producer(s): SilverPlatter Information, Inc. (PETERSON'S GRADLINE).
Former titles (until 1989): Peterson's Annual Guides to Graduate Study. Book 4. Graduate Programs in the Physical Sciences and Mathematics. (ISSN 0887-8595); (until 1984): Peterson's Annual Guides to Graduate Study. Book 4. Physical Sciences and Mathematics (ISSN 0887-8587); (1976-1982): Peterson's Guides. Annual Guides to Graduate Study. Book 4: Physical Sciences (ISSN 0887-8579)
Description: Covers postbaccalaureate programs in the physical sciences and mathematics in the United States and Canada.

378.0025   US   ISSN 0894-9409
L900
PETERSON'S GUIDE TO INDEPENDENT SECONDARY SCHOOLS (YEAR). 1980. a. $22.95. Peterson's Guides, Inc., 202 Carnegie Center, Box 2123, Princeton, NJ 08543-2123. TEL 609-243-9111. FAX 609-243-9150.
Description: Covers over 1,300 college-preparatory secondary schools in the United States and abroad.

EDUCATION — GUIDES TO SCHOOLS AND COLLEGES

378.002 US ISSN 0894-9328
L901
PETERSON'S GUIDE TO TWO-YEAR COLLEGES (YEAR). 1960. a. $15.95. Peterson's Guides, Inc., 202 Carnegie Center, Box 2123, Princeton, NJ 08543-2123. TEL 609-243-9111. FAX 609-243-9150.
●Also available online. Vendor(s): BRS Online Products (PETE), CompuServe, Inc. (PCG), DIALOG Information Services, Inc. (File no.214), Dow Jones News Retrieval (SCHOOL).
—CCC.
Supersedes in part (as of 1970): Peterson's Annual Guide to Undergraduate Study (ISSN 0147-8451)
Description: Covers the 1,450 accredited institutions in the United States that grant associate degrees.

378.0025 US ISSN 1046-2406
L901
PETERSON'S REGISTER OF HIGHER EDUCATION (YEAR). 1988. a. $44.95 hardbound. Peterson's Guides, Inc., 202 Carnegie Center, Box 2123, Princeton, NJ 08543-2123. TEL 609-243-9111. FAX 609-243-9150.
Formerly: Peterson's Higher Education Directory (Year) (ISSN 0896-2944)
Description: Profiles all U.S. postsecondary institutions (over 3,500).

POLITIK UND UNTERRICHT; Zeitschrift zur Gestaltung des politischen Unterrichts. see EDUCATION — Teaching Methods And Curriculum

371.0025 UK ISSN 0950-4508
PRIMARY EDUCATION DIRECTORY. 1986. a. £36. School Government Publishing Co. Ltd., Darby House, Bletchingley Rd., Merstham, Redhill, Surrey RH1 3DN, England. TEL 0737-642223. FAX 0737-644283. TELEX 9312102503 SG G. adv.: page £100; trim 178 x 106. circ. 1,600. **Document type:** directory.
●Also available online.
Description: Lists 26,000 state and independent schools in the UK.

378.002 UK ISSN 0951-6883
PRISM. 1986. every 3 wks. free. University of Strathclyde, Public Relations Service, McCance Bldg., 16 Richmond St., Glasgow G1 1XQ, Scotland. TEL 041-552-4400. FAX 041-552-0775. Ed. Sally Watson. adv. circ. 4,000. (back issues avail.) **Document type:** newsletter.

370.025 US ISSN 0079-5399
L901
PRIVATE INDEPENDENT SCHOOLS (YEAR); the Bunting and Lyon Blue Book. 1943. a. $95. Bunting and Lyon, Inc., 238 N. Main St., Wallingford, CT 06492. TEL 203-269-3333. FAX 203-269-5697. Ed.Bd. adv. **Document type:** directory.
Description: Comprehensive guide to more than 1,200 elementary and secondary private schools and summer programs in the United States and abroad.

371.025 DK ISSN 0905-1449
DE PRIVATE SKOLER I DE ENKELTE KOMMUNER. 1979. a. DKK 250. Undervisningsministeriet, Folkeskoleafdelingen, Frederiksholms Kanal 21-23, DK-1220 Copenhagen K, Denmark. TEL 45-33-92-53-79. FAX 45-33-92-53-02. circ. 1,000.
Formerly (until 1989): Folkeskolen i de Enkelte Kommuner (ISSN 0106-2530)

378.0025 US ISSN 0097-5206
L901
RANDAX EDUCATION GUIDE; to colleges seeking students. 1971. a. $15.95. Education Guide, Inc., Box 421, Randolph, MA 02368. TEL 617-961-2217. FAX 617-963-8268. Ed. Stephen E. Marshall. adv.; bk.rev. circ. 20,000.

REAL TALK. see CHILDREN AND YOUTH — For

378.0025 US
RECREATIONAL SPORTS DIRECTORY. 1975. a. $25.95. National Intramural Recreational Sports Association, 850 S.W. 15th St., Corvallis, OR 97333-4145. TEL 503-737-2088. FAX 503-737-2026. Ed. Will Holsberry. circ. 2,000. **Document type:** directory.
Description: Lists recreational sports programs in colleges and universities in the U.S., Canada and U.S. military installations.

378.0025 IE
SCHOOL AND COLLEGE; exam and career guide for students. 1980. 8/yr. £0.40. School and College Service, Taney Rd., Dundrum, Dublin 14, Ireland. illus.; charts.

370 US
SCHOOL GUIDE. (Avail. in 11 regional editions.) 1935. a. $10. School Guide Publications, 210 North Ave., New Rochelle, NY 10801. TEL 914-632-7771. Ed. Virginina Spiridigliozzi. adv.; stat. circ. 280,000. **Document type:** directory.

SCHOOLS IN THE UNITED STATES AND CANADA OFFERING GRADUATE EDUCATION IN PHARMACOLOGY. see PHARMACY AND PHARMACOLOGY

SCHWENDEMAN'S DIRECTORY OF COLLEGE GEOGRAPHY OF THE UNITED STATES. see GEOGRAPHY

378.0025 JA ISSN 0286-4932
SEI MARIANNA IKA DAIGAKU KIYO. IPPAN KYOIKU/ST. MARIANNA UNIVERSITY SCHOOL OF MEDICINE. BULLETIN (GENERAL EDUCATION). (Text in Japanese; summaries in English) 1972. a. St. Marianna University School of Medicine, 2-16-1 Sugao Miyamae-ku, Kawasaki-shi 216, Japan. TEL 044-977-8111. FAX 044-977-9835. Ed. Tetsuro Asao. circ. 1,000. (back issues avail.)
Indexed: Chem.Abstr. **Document type:** academic/scholarly publication.

378.0025 SP
SERIE GUIAS DE LOS ESTUDIOS UNIVERSITARIOS. 1977. irreg., no.13, 1984. (Universidad de Navarra, Instituto de Ciencias de la Educacion) Ediciones Universidad de Navarra, S.A., Apdo. 396, 31080 Pamplona, Spain. TEL 94 825 6850.

371 378 UK
STAFFROOM JOURNAL. 1980. 2/school term. free. M B & A Publishing, Box 10, Wetherby, W. Yorkshire LS23 7EL, England. TEL 0937-844515. FAX 0937-541445. Ed. Lynn Dorward. adv.; bk.rev. circ. 32,000. (back issues avail.)

STATE-APPROVED SCHOOLS OF NURSING - L.P.N. - L.V.N.. see MEDICAL SCIENCES — Nurses And Nursing

STATE-APPROVED SCHOOLS OF NURSING - R.N.. see MEDICAL SCIENCES — Nurses And Nursing

371 US
STUDENT GUIDE TO GRADUATE LAW STUDY PROGRAMS. biennial. $19. Joint Committee on Law Study Programs, 154 Stuart St., Boston, MA 02116. TEL 617-451-0010. Eds. Ellen Wayne, Betsy McCombs.

371.0025 378.0025 US ISSN 1043-8378
STUDENT GUIDE TO THE S A T. (Scholastic Aptitude Test) 1989. s-m. $49. Krell Software Corp., P.O. Box 1252, Lake Grove, NY 11755. TEL 516-584-7900. Ed. Ben Ephraim. adv.; bk.rev. circ. 8,231. (back issues avail.)
Description: For students and teachers who need help or information about the Scholastic Aptitude Test.

600 371 US ISSN 1045-6171
T73.1
TECHNICAL, TRADE & BUSINESS SCHOOL DATA HANDBOOK.* 1984. biennial (in 2 vols.). $95 (effective 1992). Orchard House, Inc., 629 Cherokee St., New Orleans, LA 70118-5049. Ed. Deborah Otaguro. circ. 4,500.

371 US ISSN 0363-4566
L903.T4
TEXAS SCHOOL DIRECTORY. 1915. a. $15. Texas Education Agency, Resource Center Library, 1701 N. Congress Ave., Austin, TX 78701-1494. TEL 512-463-9744. circ. 15,000. **Document type:** directory.
Former titles: Public School Directory of the State of Texas; Texas Public School Directory.

378 CN ISSN 0706-4713
U - CHOOSE: A GUIDE TO CANADIAN UNIVERSITIES. irreg. (every 3-4 yrs.). Can.$12.95 per no. Moving Publications Ltd., 44 Upjohn Rd., Don Mills, ON M3B 2W1, Canada. TEL 416-441-1168. FAX 416-441-1641. Ed. Frank Stephan. adv. contact: Anita Wood. **Document type:** consumer publication.

378.025 IT ISSN 0392-8411
L935
UNIVERSITA DEGLI STUDI IN ITALIA. ANNUARIO. 1981. biennial. L.150000($93) (Istituto Nazionale dell'Informazione) Editoriale Italiana, Via Viglieria 10, 00192 Rome, Italy. TEL 06-3212653. FAX 06-3211359. Ed. Giordano Treveri Gennari. adv. circ. 50,000. (also avail. in diskette format) **Document type:** directory.
Description: Provides information on Italian universities, including faculties, curricula, and degrees offered.

378 II ISSN 0377-6336
UNIVERSITIES HANDBOOK. (Text in English) 1927. biennial. $140. Association of Indian Universities, A.I.U. House, 16 Kotla Marg, New Delhi 110 002, India. TEL 11-3310059. FAX 11-3315105. TELEX 31-66180-AIU-IN. circ. 2,500.

UNIVERSITY OF LIVERPOOL POST GRADUATE PROSPECTUS. see EDUCATION — Higher Education

UNIVERSITY OF LIVERPOOL PROSPECTUS. see EDUCATION — Higher Education

378.0025 AT
UNIVERSITY OF TECHNOLOGY, SYDNEY. POSTGRADUATE STUDIES GUIDE. 1987. a. free. University of Technology, Sydney, P.O. Box 123, City Campus, Broadway, N.S.W. 2007, Australia. TEL 02-330-1524. FAX 02-330-1200. circ. 15,000.
Description: Includes courses, admission requirements and applications procedures.

371 US
UTAH PUBLIC SCHOOL DIRECTORY. a. $2. State Board of Education, 250 E. Fifth, S., Salt Lake City, UT 84111. TEL 801-533-5431. circ. 2,000. **Document type:** directory.

V S T A NEWS. (Victorian Secondary Teachers Association) see EDUCATION — Teaching Methods And Curriculum

378.002 GW
VERANSTALTUNGSKALENDER. 1972. 7/yr. Ludwig Maximilians Universitaet Muenchen, Geschwister-Scholl-Platz 1, 80539 Munich, Germany. TEL 089-2180-3423. FAX 089-338297. Eds. Dietmar Schmidt, Ursula Haubner. circ. 2,600.

VOICES OF YOUTH. see CHILDREN AND YOUTH — For

378.0025 659.1 US
WHERE SHALL I GO TO STUDY ADVERTISING & PUBLIC RELATIONS?. 1965. a. $5. Advertising Education Publications, 623 Meadow Bend Dr., Baton Rouge, LA 70820. TEL 504-767-0988. FAX 504-273-4007. Eds. Billy I. Ross, Keith F. Johnson. circ. 3,000. **Document type:** consumer publication.
Former titles: Where Shall I Go to College to Study Advertising and Public Relations; (until 1992): Where Shall I Go to College to Study Advertising?
Description: Aimed at students and counselors seeking information on U.S. universities that have advertising and public relations education programs.

378 US
WHERE THE COLLEGES RANK.* irreg., latest 1973. $2. College-Rater, Inc., 2121 South 12th St., Allentown, PA 18103.

370.025 UK ISSN 0952-083X
WHICH SCHOOL?. 1924. a. £12.95. John Catt Educational Ltd., Great Glemham, Saxmundham, Suffolk IP17 2DH, England. TEL 0728-663666. FAX 0728-78415. Ed. Derek Bingham. adv. circ. 3,500. **Document type:** directory.
—BLDSC (9310.897000).
Former titles (until 1986): Schools (ISSN 0080-6897); (until 1982): Directory of Catholic Schools and Colleges (ISSN 0070-5233)
Description: Lists independendent schools in Britain for children between five and 18 years of age.

EDUCATION — HIGHER EDUCATION

371.0025 278   UK
▼**WHICH SCHOOL? FOR A LEVELS.** 1994. a. £7.95. John Catt Educational Ltd., Great Glemham, Saxmundham, Suffolk IP17 2DH, England. TEL 0728-663666. FAX 0728-663415. Ed. Derek Bingham. circ. 2,000. **Document type:** directory.
   Description: Lists independent schools and colleges offering A-level courses, as well as schools and colleges offering the International Baccalaureate diploma.

371.0025 371.9   UK   ISSN 0965-1004
▼**WHICH SCHOOL? FOR SPECIAL NEEDS.** 1992. a. £7.95. John Catt Educational Ltd., Great Glemham, Saxmundham, Suffolk IP17 2DH, England. TEL 0728-663666. FAX 0728-663415. Ed. Derek Bingham. circ. 2,000. **Document type:** directory.
   Description: Lists independent and maintained schools in Britain for pupils with learning, educational and behavioral difficulties, physical or mental handicaps, or dyslexia.

378.025   US
L901
WHO'S WHO IN COMMUNITY COLLEGES (YEAR). 1986. a. $57.50 to non-members; members $43. American Association of Community Colleges, One Dupont Circle, N.W., Ste. 410, Washington, DC 20036. TEL 202-728-0200. FAX 202-223-9390. (Subscr. to: AACC Publications, Box 1737, Salisbury, MD 21802. TEL 410-546-0391) Ed. Bonnie Gardner. **Document type:** directory.
   Former titles: Who's Who in Community, Technical and Junior Colleges (ISSN 1061-8023); A A C J C Guide to Community, Technical and Junior Colleges; Directory of Community, Junior, and Technical Colleges; Who's Who in American Community, Technical, and Junior Colleges.
   Description: Lists all US and most foreign community, technical, and junior colleges whether or not they are members of AACC, as well as top 14 administrators by name on each campus.

371.0025   US
L216
WISCONSIN SCHOOL DIRECTORY. a. $10.02 in Wisconsin; outside Wisconsin $15.50. Department of Public Instruction, 125 S. Webster St., Madison, WI 53702. TEL 608-266-2188. Ed. Greg M. Doyle. **Document type:** directory, government publication.
   Former titles: Wisconsin Public - Private School Directory; Wisconsin Public School Directory (ISSN 0148-5059)

370.025 378   UK   ISSN 0084-1889
L900
WORLD LIST OF UNIVERSITIES, OTHER INSTITUTIONS OF HIGHER EDUCATION AND UNIVERSITY ORGANISATIONS/LISTE MONDIALE DES UNIVERSITES. Variant title: World List of Universities. 1952. triennial. £65. (International Association of Universities, IX) Macmillan Press, Brunel Rd., Houndmills, Basingstoke, Hants. RG21 2XS, England. TEL 0256-817245. FAX 0253-28339. (Dist. in the U.S. by: Stockton Press, 49 W. 24th St., New York, NY 10010. TEL 212-673-4400. FAX 212-673-9842) Ed. Julian Ashby. index. **Document type:** directory.
   —BLDSC (9356.558520).
   Description: Contains information on more than 9,000 universities, university organizations, and other centers of higher learning in 160 countries.

370.025   UK   ISSN 0084-2117
AS2   CODEN: WOLED4
WORLD OF LEARNING. 1947. a. $380. Europa Publications, Ltd., 18 Bedford Sq., London WC1B 3JN, England. TEL 071-580-8236. FAX 071-636-1664. TELEX 21540-EUROPA-G. (Dist. in North America by: Gale Research Inc., Department 77748, Detroit, MI 48277-0748) **Document type:** directory.
   —BLDSC (9356.400000); CASDDS. **CCC.**
   Description: Guide and directory of learned societies, research institutes, libraries, museums, and universities.

378.0025   FI   ISSN 0355-1784
YLIOPPILASAINEITA. 1948. a. FIM 48. Suomalaisen Kirjallisuuden Seura, Hallituskatu 1, P.O. Box 259, 00170 Helsinki 17, Finland. TEL 358-0-131231. FAX 358-0-13123220. circ. 15,000.

EDUCATION — Higher Education

see also College and Alumni

378 268   US   ISSN 0094-260X
BV4019
A A B C NEWSLETTER. 1958. 3/yr. $6. American Association of Bible Colleges, Box 1523, Fayetteville, AR 72702. TEL 501-521-8164. FAX 501-521-9202. Ed. Randall E. Bell. bk.rev. circ. 1,300. (also avail. in microfilm; microfiche) **Document type:** newsletter.

378   US
A A C R A O CONFERENCE PAPERS. a. $30 to non-members; members $25. American Association of Collegiate Registrars and Admissions Officers, One Dupont Circle, N.W., Ste. 330, Washington, DC 20036-1171. TEL 202-293-9161. FAX 202-872-8857. Ed. James Menzel. **Document type:** proceedings.
   Formerly: A A C R A O Proceedings.

378   US   ISSN 1040-8924
A A C R A O DATA DISPENSER. 1981. 10/yr. $30 to non-members (overseas $40). American Association of Collegiate Registrars and Admissions Officers, One Dupont Circle, N.W., Ste. 330, Washington, DC 20036-1171. TEL 202-293-9161. FAX 202-872-8495. Ed. Eileen M. Kennedy. bk.rev. circ. 8,900. (back issues avail.) **Document type:** newsletter.
   Description: For professional higher education administrators, covering Association news, issues in higher education, and international education.

330 378   US   ISSN 0360-697X
A A C S B NEWSLINE. 1971. 4/yr. $15 (foreign $20). American Assembly of Collegiate Schools of Business, 600 Emerson Rd., Ste. 300, St. Louis, MO 63141-6762. TEL 314-872-8481. FAX 314-872-8495. Ed. Sharon Barber. circ. 8,000. **Document type:** newsletter.
   Incorporates (in Apr. 1977): International Dimension.
   Description: Reports on activities of the Assembly as well as trends and issues in management education.

378   US   ISSN 0162-7910
LB2300
A A H E BULLETIN. 1948. m. (except Jul.-Aug.). $35. American Association for Higher Education, One Dupont Circle, Ste. 360, Washington, DC 20036-1110. TEL 202-293-6440. FAX 202-293-0073. illus. circ. 8,000. (also avail. in microform from UMI) **Indexed:** Res.High.Educ.Abstr. **Document type:** bulletin.
   —BLDSC (0537.260000); Faxon; UMI.
   Formerly (until Sep. 1978): A A H E College and University Bulletin (ISSN 0001-2971)

A A M C DIRECTORY OF AMERICAN MEDICAL EDUCATION. (Association of American Medical Colleges) see *EDUCATION — School Organization And Administration*

378   US
A A S C U ISSUES. 1970. irreg. price varies. American Association of State Colleges and Universities, One Dupont Circle, N.W., Ste. 700, Washington, DC 20036. TEL 202-293-7070. FAX 202-296-5819.
   Formerly: A A S C U Studies (ISSN 0065-7344)

378   GH   ISSN 0855-0174
LB2301.A493
A A U NEWSLETTER. 3/yr. free. Association of African Universities, Box 5744, Accra, Ghana. Ed. Daniel Mboungou-Mayenque. **Document type:** newsletter.
   Formerly: Association of African Universities. Information Bulletin.
   Description: Carries information on the activities of AAU member universities and the AAU secretariat and lists vacancy announcements as well as applications for employment in African universities and new publications.

378   US
LC1756.A2
A A U W OUTLOOK. 1882. 4/yr. $15 to non-members. American Association of University Women, 1111 16th St., N.W., Washington, DC 20036. TEL 202-785-7700. FAX 202-872-1425. Ed. Sheila Buckmaster. adv.; bk.rev.; illus.; biennial index. circ. 135,000. (also avail. in microfilm from UMI; reprint service avail. from UMI) **Indexed:** C.I.J.E., P.A.I.S., PMR.
   —UnCover.
   Former titles (until 1988): Graduate Woman (ISSN 0161-5661); (1962-1978): A A U W Journal (ISSN 0001-0278)

378 323.4   US
A A W C J C NEWSLETTER. q. American Association of Women in Community and Junior Colleges, c/o Barb Cannell (North Campus), Milwaukee Area Technical College, 5555 W. Highland Rd., Meguon, WI 53092. TEL 414-242-6500.

378   CN   ISSN 0839-0088
A C C C COMMUNITY.* (Text in English, French) 5/yr. Can.$35. Association of Canadian Community Colleges, 1223 Michael St. N., Ste. 200, Ottawa, ON K1J 7T2, Canada TEL 613-746-2222. FAX 613-746-6721. Ed. Peggy Robinson. circ. 11,000.
   Description: Addresses issues of interest to all five of the association's constituent groups: CEOs, faculty, administration, staff and students. Features columns that highlight literacy and human resource development.

A C E ACTION NEWSLETTER. (Association of Collegiate Entrepreneurs) see *BUSINESS AND ECONOMICS — Small Business*

378   AT
A C E R NEWSLETTER. 1969. 3/yr. free. Australian Council for Educational Research, Private Bag 55, Canberwell, Vic. 3124, Australia. TEL 03-277-5555. FAX 03-277-5500. Ed. Rhonda Idczak. circ. 22,000. (back issues avail.) **Document type:** newsletter.
   Description: Includes articles on ACER's research and features on new publications.

A C H A ACTION. (American College Health Association) see *PHYSICAL FITNESS AND HYGIENE*

378 345   US
A C J S PROGRAM BOOK. a. Academy of Criminal Justice Sciences, 402 Nunn Hall, Northern Kentucky University, Highland Heights, KY 41099-5998. TEL 606-572-5434. FAX 606-572-6665. circ. 1,400 (controlled).
   Description: Complete program and abstracts of annual meeting.

378   US   ISSN 0569-3993
                              CODEN: ACRRCI
A C T RESEARCH REPORT. 1965. irreg. free. American College Testing, Box 168, Iowa City, IA 52243. TEL 319-337-1077 circ. 3,354. (also avail. in microfiche) **Indexed:** Coll.Stud.Pers.Abstr., ERIC, Psychol.Abstr.
   Formerly: A C T Research Service Report (ISSN 0065-7840)

378   UK   ISSN 0044-9563
A C U BULLETIN OF CURRENT DOCUMENTATION (ABCD). 1971. 5/yr. membership only. Association of Commonwealth Universities, John Foster House, 36 Gordon Sq., London WC1H OPF, England. TEL 071-387-8572. FAX 071-387-2655. Ed. G.B. Woolven. adv.; bk.rev; bibl.; circ. controlled. **Indexed:** High.Educ.Curr.Aware.Bull. **Document type:** bulletin.
   —BLDSC (0677.900000).

A C U T A NEWS. (Association of College and University Telecommunications Administrators) see *COMMUNICATIONS — Computer Applications*

A D F L BULLETIN. (Association of Departments of Foreign Languages) see *LINGUISTICS*

371.2   US   ISSN 0738-3460
A G B NOTES. 1970. bi-m. $40 includes Reports. Association of Governing Boards of Universities and Colleges, One Dupont Circle, Ste. 400, Washington, DC 20036. TEL 202-296-8400. FAX 202-223-7053. Ed. Daniel J. Levin. bk.rev. circ. 32,000. (reprint service avail. from UMI)
   Formerly (until 1982): A G B News Notes (ISSN 0199-7939)

EDUCATION — HIGHER EDUCATION

371.2　　　　　　US　ISSN 0044-961X
LB2341
A G B REPORTS. vol.7, 1965. bi-m. $40 includes Notes. Association of Governing Boards of Universities and Colleges, One Dupont Circle, Ste. 400, Washington, DC 20036. TEL 202-296-8400. FAX 202-223-7053. Ed. Daniel J. Levin. illus. circ. 32,000. (reprint service avail. from UMI) **Indexed:** C.I.J.E., PSI.
—UnCover.

A G H E EXCHANGE. (Association for Gerontology in Higher Education) see *GERONTOLOGY AND GERIATRICS*

A I D VERBRAUCHERDIENST; Zeitschrift fuer Fach-, Lehr- und Beratungskraefte im Bereich Ernaehrung. (Auswertungs- und Informationsdienst fuer Ernaehrung, Landwirtschaft und Forsten e.V.) see *NUTRITION AND DIETETICS*

378　　　　　　　US　ISSN 1053-8933
A J C U HIGHER EDUCATION REPORT.* 1976. m. (except Jul. and Aug.). $17.50. Association of Jesuit Colleges and Universities, 1 Dupont Cir., N.E., Ste. 405, Washington, DC 20036-1110.
TEL 202-667-3889. FAX 202-328-8643. Ed. Lewis Hill Rowan. circ. 900. (back issues avail.)
Description: Discusses secondary education issues as well as relevant points of interest concerning the 28 Jesuit institutions in the United States.

370 510　　　　US　ISSN 0740-8404
A M A T Y C REVIEW. 1979. s-a. $50 membership. American Mathematical Association of Two-Year Colleges, c/o Joseph Browne, Ed., Onondaga Community College, Syracuse, NY 13215.
TEL 315-469-2649. adv. contact: Lawrence Lance. bk.rev.; software rev. circ. 3,000. (back issues avail.) **Document type:** academic/scholarly publication.
Description: Provides a forum for mathematics educators to exchange their views, ideas, and experiences pertinent to two-year college teachers and students.
Refereed Serial

378　　　　　　　US
A R A NEWSLETTER. 1986. bi-m. (American Romanian Academy of Arts and Sciences) A R A Publications (Tempe), c/o Aleksandra Gruzinska, Ed., Foreign Languages Department, Arizona State University, Tempe, AZ 85287-0202. TEL 602-965-6281.
FAX 602-965-0135. **Document type:** newsletter.

378 959　　　　TH　ISSN 0066-9695
A S A I H L SEMINAR REPORTS. 1963. irreg. $6. Association of Southeast Asian Institutions of Higher Learning, Ratasastra Bldg., Chulalongkorn University, Henri Dunant Rd., Bangkok 10500, Thailand. circ. 1,000.

A S C U S STAFFER. (Association for School, College and University Staffing, Inc.) see *EDUCATION — Guides To Schools And Colleges*

A S E E PRISM. (American Society for Engineering Education) see *ENGINEERING*

378　　　　　　　US　ISSN 0884-0040
A S H E - E R I C HIGHER EDUCATION REPORT SERIES.
Variant title: A S H E - E R I C Higher Education Reports. 1972. 8/yr. $98. (Association for the Study of Higher Education) A S H E - E R I C Higher Education Reports, George Washington University, One Dupont Circle, Ste. 630, Washington, DC 20036. TEL 202-296-2597. FAX 202-296-8379. Ed. Jonathan D. Fife. bibl.; charts; index. circ. 4,000. (also avail. in microfiche; back issues avail.; reprint service avail.)
—BLDSC (1742.047900); SWETS.
Former titles: A S H E - E R I C Higher Education Research Report Series; A S H E - E R I C Higher Education Research Reports; (until 1982): A A H E - E R I C Higher Education Research Report Series; E R I C - A A H E Research Reports (ISSN 0737-1292)

378　　　　　　　US
A S H E NOTES. q. membership. Association for the Study of Higher Education (College Station), c/o Stan Carpenter, Harrington Education Center, Texas A & M University, College Station, TX 77843-4426. TEL 409-845-0393. **Document type:** academic/scholarly publication.

378　　　　　　　UK　ISSN 0001-2823
A U T BULLETIN. 1962. 3/yr. membership. Association of University Teachers, United House, 9 Pembridge Rd., London W11 3JY, England.
TEL 071-221-4370. FAX 071-727-6547. Ed. David Triesman. adv.; circ. 35,000 (controlled). **Document type:** bulletin.
Description: Covers issues relevant to university academic membership, especially professional and policy matters.

378　　　　　　　UK　ISSN 0967-8859
▼**A U T UPDATE**. 1992. 9/yr. membership. Association of University Teachers, United House, 9 Pembridge Rd., London W11 3JY, England.
TEL 071-221-4370. FAX 071-727-6547. Ed. David Triesman. circ. 35,000 (controlled). **Document type:** newsletter.
Description: Lists events, covers higher education topics, and includes association news.

378 305.4 323.4　　UK
A U T WOMAN. 1984. 3/yr. membership. Association of University Teachers, United House, 9 Pembridge Rd., London W11 3JY, England.
TEL 071-221-4370. FAX 071-727-6547. Ed. David Triesman. bk.rev.; circ. 35,000 (controlled).
Document type: newsletter.
Description: Lists events and university, academic, and higher education topics, with particular emphasis on equal opportunities and related issues.

378 305.4　　　　US　ISSN 1061-768X
▼**ABOUT WOMEN ON CAMPUS**. 1992. q. $20 to individuals; institutions $28. National Association for Women in Education, 1325 18th St., N.W., Ste. 210, Washington, DC 20036-6511.
TEL 202-659-9330. FAX 202-457-0946. Ed. Bernice R. Sandler. adv.; bk.rev. (back issues avail.) **Document type:** newsletter.
Description: Publishes news about programs, issues, events and concerns on campus affecting women, for administrators, faculty and students.

378　　　　　　　US　ISSN 0190-2946
LB2301
ACADEME. 1915. bi-m. $48.50. American Association of University Professors, 1012 14th St., N.W., Ste. 500, Washington, DC 20005. TEL 202-737-5900.
FAX 202-737-5526. Ed. Eugene Arden. adv.; bk.rev.; illus.; index. circ. 43,000. (also avail. in microform from UMI,PMC; microfiche from CIS; back issues avail.) **Indexed:** Amer.Hist.& Life, ASCA, C.I.J.E., Cont.Pg.Educ., Curr.Cont., Deep Sea Res.& Oceanogr.Abstr., Educ.Admin.Abstr., Educ.Ind., Hist.Abstr., P.A.I.S., Res.High.Educ.Abstr., SRI. **Document type:** trade publication.
—BLDSC (0570.467000); Faxon; UnCover; SWETS; UMI.
Formed by the 1979 merger of: Academe (ISSN 0001-3749); A A U P Bulletin (ISSN 0001-026X)
Description: Offers features on current topics and reports on developments in higher education, and reports on the business of the AAUP.

371.2　　　　　　US　ISSN 0891-2785
ACADEMIC COLLECTIVE BARGAINING INFORMATION SERVICE. FACT SHEET. NEWSLETTER. m. $125. Academic Collective Bargaining Information Service, 1321 H St., N.W., Ste. M-1, Washington, DC 20005. TEL 202-727-2326. FAX 202-727-6998. **Document type:** newsletter.
Formerly: Academic Collective Bargaining Information Service. Monograph.
Description: Discusses topics related to labor and employer relations and fair employment practices in higher education.

ACADEMIC DIGEST. see *CHEMISTRY*

378　　　　　　　US　ISSN 8750-7730
ACADEMIC LEADER; newsletter for academic deans and department chairs. 1985. m. $73. Magna Publications, 2718 Dryden Dr., Madison, WI 53704. TEL 608-246-3580. FAX 608-249-0355. Ed. Doris Green. bk.rev.; circ. 2,000 (paid). (also avail. in diskette format; back issues avail.) **Document type:** newsletter.
—CCC.

ACADEMIC MEDICINE. see *MEDICAL SCIENCES*

ACADEMIC PSYCHIATRY. see *MEDICAL SCIENCES — Psychiatry And Neurology*

ACADEMIC TEXT REVIEW. see *PUBLISHING AND BOOK TRADE*

378　　　　　　　SZ
ACADEMICA HELVETICA. 1976. irreg., no.6, 1988. price varies. Paul Haupt AG, Falkenplatz 14, CH-3001 Bern, Switzerland. TEL 031-3012345. FAX 031-3014669. **Document type:** monographic series.

060　　　　　　　IT
ACCADEMIA NAZIONALE DI SAN LUCA. ANNUARIO. biennial. Accademia Nazionale di San Luca, Piazza dell'Accademia di San Luca 77, Rome, Italy, FAX 06-6790324.

ACCOUNTING AND FINANCE. see *BUSINESS AND ECONOMICS — Accounting*

ACCOUNTING EDUCATION. see *BUSINESS AND ECONOMICS — Accounting*

ACTA UNIVERSITATIS WRATISLAVIENSIS. STUDIA I MATERIALY Z DZIEJOW UNIWERSYTETU WROCLAWSKIEGO. see *HISTORY*

378　　　　　　　US　ISSN 0162-6620
LB1715
ACTION IN TEACHER EDUCATION. 1978. 4/yr. $75 membership. Association of Teacher Educators, 1900 Association Dr., Reston, VA 22091-1502. TEL 703-620-3110. Eds. Brenda Manning, James McLaughlin. adv.; bibl.; charts; stat. circ. 4,000. **Indexed:** C.I.J.E., Chic.Per.Ind., Educ.Ind., Mult.Ed.Abstr. **Document type:** academic/scholarly publication.
—BLDSC (0675.748000); Faxon; UnCover; SWETS; UMI.
Description: Focuses on research and practice in teacher education.

ADMINISTRATIVE COMPENSATION SURVEY. see *BUSINESS AND ECONOMICS — Labor And Industrial Relations*

ADMINISTRATOR (MADISON); the management newsletter for higher education. see *EDUCATION — School Organization And Administration*

378　　　　　　　II　ISSN 0044-6734
AGRA UNIVERSITY. BULLETIN. (Text in English and Hindi) 1970. q. Rs.6. Agra University, Agra 282004, Uttar Pradesh, India. Ed. Rajeshwar Prasad. bk.rev.; bibl.; charts; stat. **Document type:** bulletin.

AGRICULTURAL EDUCATORS DIRECTORY. see *AGRICULTURE*

378.761　　　　　US
ALABAMA. COMMISSION ON HIGHER EDUCATION. ANNUAL REPORT.* 1973. a. free. Commission on Higher Education, 3465 Norman Bridge Rd., Montgomery, AL 36105-2310.
TEL 205-269-2700. FAX 205-240-3349. Ed. Henry J. Hector. illus. (reprint service avail.) **Document type:** government publication.
Formerly (until 1978): Alabama. Commission on Higher Education. Biennial Report to the Governor and the Legislature (ISSN 0095-1285)
Description: Highlights activities of the Higher Education Commission on academic and financial aid issues.

378　　　　　　　US　ISSN 1044-3096
LA226
ALMANAC OF HIGHER EDUCATION. 1990. a. University of Chicago Press, 5801 S. Ellis Ave., Chicago, IL 60637.

ALPHA COMMUNICATIONS MONTHLY. see *COMMUNICATIONS*

378 375　　　　　US
ALVERNO MAGAZINE. 1983. 2/yr. free. Alverno College, 3401 S. 39th St., Box 343922, Milwaukee, WI 53234-3922. TEL 414-382-6166.
FAX 414-382-6167. Ed. Kathleen A. Mulvey. circ. 17,000.
Description: Explores issues of teaching and learning in higher education.

EDUCATION — HIGHER EDUCATION

370.7 US ISSN 0731-602X
AMERICAN ASSOCIATION OF COLLEGES FOR TEACHER EDUCATION. BRIEFS. 1980. 18/yr. $25. American Association of Colleges for Teacher Education, One Dupont Circle, N.W., Ste. 610, Washington, DC 20036-1186. TEL 202-293-2450.
FAX 202-457-8095. Ed. Elizabeth Foxwell. bk.rev.; illus. circ. 8,000.
Supersedes: American Association of Colleges for Teacher Education. Legislative Briefs; American Association of Colleges for Teacher Education. Bulletin (ISSN 0002-7413)

AMERICAN ASSOCIATION OF COLLEGES FOR TEACHER EDUCATION. DIRECTORY. see EDUCATION — Guides To Schools And Colleges

AMERICAN ASSOCIATION OF ENGINEERING SOCIETIES. ENGINEERING MANPOWER COMMISSION. SALARIES OF ENGINEERS IN EDUCATION (YEAR). see ENGINEERING

THE AMERICAN BIOLOGY TEACHER. see BIOLOGY

378 US
AMERICAN COLLEGE TESTING. ANNUAL REPORT. 1959. a. free. American College Testing, 2201 N. Dodge St., Box 168, Iowa City, IA 52243.
TEL 319-337-1000.
Formerly (until 1990): American College Testing Program. Annual Report (ISSN 0517-0680)

378.1 US ISSN 0065-7905
AMERICAN CONFERENCE OF ACADEMIC DEANS. PROCEEDINGS. 1946. a. $8. American Conference of Academic Deans, c/o Suzanne L. Hyers, 1818 R St., N.W., Washington, DC 20009.
TEL 202-387-3760. FAX 202-265-9532. circ. 750. (also avail. in microfilm from UMI,UNM) Document type: proceedings.

374 US
AMERICAN COUNCIL ON EDUCATION. CENTER FOR ADULT LEARNING AND EDUCATIONAL CREDENTIALS UPDATE. 1954. s-a. free. American Council on Education, One Dupont Circle, N.W., Washington, DC 20036. TEL 202-939-9470. Ed. Judith Cangialosi. circ. 25,000.
Former titles: American Council on Education. Office of Educational Credit and Credentials. News; American Council on Education. Office on Education Credit and Credentials. Newsletter; American Council on Education. Office on Educational Credit. Newsletter; Commission on Accreditation of Service Experiences. Newsletter (ISSN 0010-3209)

378.242 US ISSN 0065-809X
Z5055.U49
AMERICAN DOCTORAL DISSERTATIONS. 1956. a. $120. (Association of Research Libraries) University Microfilms International, 300 N. Zeeb Rd., Ann Arbor, MI 48106. TEL 313-761-4700;
800-521-0600. FAX 313-761-1203. (also avail. in microfiche)
●Also available online. Vendor(s): BRS Online Products, Data-Star, DIALOG Information Services, Inc. (File no. 35), STN International.
Also available on CD-ROM. Producer(s): University Microfilms International.
—BLDSC (0812.770000); UMI.
Description: Lists dissertations accepted by U.S. and Canadian universities.

AMERICAN JOURNAL OF PHARMACEUTICAL EDUCATION. see PHARMACY AND PHARMACOLOGY

378 US ISSN 0896-1018
DR201
AMERICAN ROMANIAN ACADEMY OF ARTS AND SCIENCES. JOURNAL. (Text in English, French, Rumanian) 1976. s-a. $25. A R A Publications, Department of French and Italian, University of California, Sproul Hall, Davis, CA 95616.
TEL 916-752-6442. FAX 916-752-8630. Ed. Ion Manea. bk.rev.; bibl.; illus.; stat. circ. 400. (back issues avail.) Document type: academic/scholarly publication.
Formerly: A R A Bulletin.

378.62 UA
AMERICAN UNIVERSITY IN CAIRO. NEWS. (Text in English) 1979. 3/yr. free. American University in Cairo, Box 2511, Cairo, Egypt. (In the US: 866 United Nations Plaza, Ste. 517, New York, NY 10017)
Formerly: American University in Cairo. President's Review.
Description: Provides news of the University for alumni, friends and former faculty and staff.

378 FR ISSN 0066-2771
ANNUAIRE DES CHERCHEURS FRANCAIS DU FONDS DE BOURSES DE RECHERCHE SCIENTIFIQUE ET TECHNIQUE DE L'ORGANISATION DU TRAITE DE L'ATLANTIQUE NORD. 1959. irreg. (North Atlantic Treaty Organization, Commission Francaise d'Attribution des Bourses de Recherche Scientifique) Conservatoire National des Arts et Metiers, 292 rue Saint-Martin, 75141 Paris Cedex 03, France. circ. 2,000.

378 US ISSN 0882-7133
ANNUAL DEGARMO LECTURES. 1975. a. price varies. Society of Professors of Education, c/o Richard Wisniewski, College of Education, University of Tennessee, Knoxville, TN 37996-3400.
TEL 615-974-2201. FAX 615-974-8718.
Formerly: DeGarmo Lectures.

378 379 US ISSN 0066-4049
AS911.A2
ANNUAL REGISTER OF GRANT SUPPORT; a directory of funding resources. 1967. a. 27th ed., 1994. $175. R.R Bowker, A Reed Reference Publishing Company, Part of the Reed Elsevier group, 121 Chanlon Rd., New Providence, NJ 07974. TEL 908-464-6800.
FAX 908-464-3553. TELEX 138 755. (Subscr. to: R.R. Bowker, Order Dept., Box 31, New Providence, NJ 07974-9903. TEL 800-521-8110) index.
Document type: directory.
—BLDSC (1094.400000). CCC.
Formerly: Grant Data Quarterly.
Description: Guide to over 3,000 programs offering billions of dollars in nonrepayable support. Shows how to unlock the funding potential of these sources. Organized by 11 major subject areas with 61 specific areas.

378 917.306 US ISSN 1061-2947
LC3727
ANNUAL STATUS REPORT, MINORITIES IN HIGHER EDUCATION. a. American Council on Education, Office of Minority Education, One Dupont Circle, Washington, DC 20036. TEL 202-939-9300.

378 US
ANTIOCH NEW ENGLAND NOTES. 1973. 3/yr. Antioch New England Graduate School, 40 Avon St., Keene, NH 03431-3316. TEL 603-357-3122.
FAX 603-357-0718. Ed. Sharon Krauss. bk.rev.; circ. 6,500 (controlled). (back issues avail.)
Document type: newsletter.
Description: Provides practitioner-oriented masters and doctoral programs for adult learners.

APPROVED COURSES FOR ACCOUNTANCY EDUCATION. see BUSINESS AND ECONOMICS — Accounting

378 JA ISSN 0493-4342
AREA AND CULTURE STUDIES. 1951. a. exchange basis. Tokyo University of Foreign Studies - Tokyo Gaikogugo Daigaku, 4-51-21 Nishigahara, Kitaku, Tokyo, Japan. circ. 1,000. Document type: monographic series.
Formerly: Tokyo University of Foreign Studies. Summary (ISSN 0082-4844)
Description: Faculty member's monographs on various cultures in the world, especially on languages and literatures.

378.3 US
A'S & B'S OF ACADEMIC SCHOLARSHIP. 1978. a. $6. Octameron Associates, Inc., Box 2748, Alexandria, VA 22301. TEL 703-836-5480.
Former titles: A's and B's: Your Guide to Academic Scholarship; A's and B's of Academic Scholarships (ISSN 0277-1470); A's and B's of Merit Scholarships (ISSN 0162-9883)

378.198 US ISSN 1041-2581
ASSEMBLY (WEST POINT). 1942. 6/yr. $30 to non-members; members $20 (typically set in Sep.). U.S. Military Academy, Association of Graduates, Cullum Hall, West Point, NY 10996-1780.
TEL 914-446-5800. FAX 914-446-6988. Ed. Ltc. Julian M. Olejniczak. adv.: B&W page $1100; adv. contact: Ruth Windsor. bk.rev.; circ. 23,000 (paid). (back issues avail.) Document type: consumer publication, government publication.

ASSEMBLY ON EDUCATION NETWORK. see MEDICAL SCIENCES

378 UK ISSN 0260-2938
ASSESSMENT & EVALUATION IN HIGHER EDUCATION; an international journal. 1976. 3/yr. $88 to individuals; institutions $254 (effective 1994). (University of Bath, School of Education) Carfax Publishing Co., P.O. Box 25, Abingdon, Oxon. OX14 3UE, England. TEL 44-235-555335.
FAX 44-235-553559. (U.S. subscr. to: Carfax Publishing Co., Box 2025, Dunnellon, FL 34430-2025) Ed. William A.H. Scott. adv.; bk.rev. circ. 200. (also avail. in microfiche; reprint service avail. from UMI) Indexed: Br.Educ.Ind., C.I.J.E., Cont.Pg.Educ., Educ.Tech.Abstr., ERIC, High.Educ.Curr.Aware.Bull., Mult.Ed.Abstr., Res.High.Educ.Abstr., Sp.Ed.Needs Abstr. Document type: academic/scholarly publication.
—BLDSC (1746.637000); UnCover; SWETS. CCC.
Formerly: Assessment in Higher Education.
Description: All aspects of assessment and evaluation relevant to the generalist in higher education.
Refereed Serial

378 375 US ISSN 1041-6099
ASSESSMENT UPDATE: PROGRESS, TRENDS, AND PRACTICES IN HIGHER EDUCATION. 1989. bi-m. $60. Jossey-Bass Inc., Publishers, 350 Sansome St., 5th Fl., San Francisco, CA 94104.
TEL 415-433-1767. FAX 415-433-0499. Ed. Trudy W. Banta. bk.rev. circ. 1,100. (back issues avail.)
Document type: newsletter.
—UnCover; UMI.
Description: Offers academic leaders up-to-date information and practical advice on conducting assessments in a range of areas, including student learning and outcomes, faculty instruction, academic programs and curricula, student services, and overall institutional functioning.

ASSOCIATE DEGREE EDUCATION FOR NURSING. see MEDICAL SCIENCES — Nurses And Nursing

378.1 US ISSN 0066-8729
ASSOCIATED COLLEGES OF ILLINOIS. REPORT.* a. Associated Colleges of Illinois, 150 N. Wacker Dr., Ste. 1740, Chicago, IL 60606. TEL 312-263-2391. charts; illus.; stat.

378 US
ASSOCIATED WESTERN UNIVERSITIES. PROGRAM GUIDE. biennial. Associated Western Universities, Inc., 4190 S. Highland, Ste. 211, Salt Lake City, UT 84124-2633. FAX 801-277-5632. Ed. Thomas G. Squires. Document type: corporate report.
Former titles: Associated Western Universities. Program Report; Associated Western Universities. Biennial Report; Associated Western Universities. Annual Report (ISSN 0066-877X)

378.15 US
ASSOCIATION FOR CONTINUING HIGHER EDUCATION. PROCEEDINGS. 1939 a. $15 in US, Canada, Mexico; elsewhere $17. Association for Continuing Higher Education, Inc., c/o Dr. Wayne Whelan, Exec. VP, Trident Technical College, Box 118067, CE-P, Charleston, SC 29423-8067. TEL 803-722-5570. FAX 803-722-5520. circ. 700. Document type: proceedings.
Formerly: Association of University Evening Colleges. Proceedings (ISSN 0066-9741)

ASSOCIATION FOR PROFESSIONAL EDUCATION FOR MINISTRY. REPORT OF THE BIENNIAL MEETING. see RELIGIONS AND THEOLOGY

378 296 US
ASSOCIATION OF ADVANCED RABBINICAL AND TALMUDIC SCHOOLS. ACCREDITATION COMMISSION. HANDBOOK. a. Association of Advanced Rabbinical and Talmudic Schools, 175 Fifth Ave., New York, NY 10010. TEL 212-477-0950. FAX 212-533-5335.
Description: Accreditation standards.

EDUCATION — HIGHER EDUCATION

ASSOCIATION OF AFRICAN UNIVERSITIES. NEW ACQUISITIONS LIST. see *LIBRARY AND INFORMATION SCIENCES*

378   GH
ASSOCIATION OF AFRICAN UNIVERSITIES. REPORT OF THE GENERAL CONFERENCE. 1967. irreg., 6th, 1984. Association of African Universities, Box 5744, Accra, Ghana.

ASSOCIATION OF CHRISTIANS IN HIGHER EDUCATION. FORUM. see *RELIGIONS AND THEOLOGY — Protestant*

378   US
ASSOCIATION OF COLLEGE UNIONS - INTERNATIONAL. DIRECTORY. a. $100 to non-members; members $15. Association of College Unions - International, 400 E. 7th St., Bloomington, IN 47405. TEL 812-332-8017. FAX 812-333-8050. **Document type:** directory.

378   US   ISSN 0147-1120
ASSOCIATION OF COLLEGE UNIONS - INTERNATIONAL. PROCEEDINGS OF THE ANNUAL CONFERENCE. a. $20 to non-members; members $10. Association of College Unions - International, 400 E. Seventh St., Bloomington, IN 47405. TEL 812-332-8017. FAX 812-333-8050. (also avail. in microfiche) **Document type:** proceedings.

378   UK
ASSOCIATION OF COLLEGES FOR FURTHER AND HIGHER EDUCATION. HANDBOOK. 1894. biennial. £3. Association of Colleges for Further and Higher Education, Swindon College, Regent Circus, Swindon, Wiltshire SN1 1PT, England. TEL 0793-513193. FAX 0793-641794. circ. 1,500.
Formerly: Association of Colleges for Further and Higher Education. Year Book (ISSN 0066-9539)

378   UK   ISSN 0307-2274
LA637
ASSOCIATION OF COMMONWEALTH UNIVERSITIES. ANNUAL REPORT OF THE COUNCIL TOGETHER WITH THE ACCOUNTS OF THE ASSOCIATION. 1964. a. free. Association of Commonwealth Universities, John Foster House, 36 Gordon Sq., London WC1H 0PF, England. TEL 071-387-8572. FAX 071-387-2655. **Document type:** corporate report.
Formerly: Association of Commonwealth Universities. Report of the Council Together with the Accounts of the Association (ISSN 0571-6241)

378 370.196   US
ASSOCIATION OF INTERNATIONAL COLLEGES & UNIVERSITIES DIRECTORY. 1973. a. $300. (International University Foundation) T I U Press, 1301 S. Noland Rd., Independence, MO 64055. TEL 816-461-3633. FAX 816-461-3634. Ed. John Wayne Johnston. circ. 1,000. (looseleaf format) **Document type:** directory.
Description: Lists personnels involved in higher education through the auspices of the association.

378 370.196   US
ASSOCIATION OF INTERNATIONAL COLLEGES & UNIVERSITIES NEWSLETTER. 1973. q. $300. (International University Foundation) T I U Press, 1301 S. Noland Rd., Independence, MO 64055. TEL 816-461-3633. Ed. John Wayne Johnston. circ. 1,000. (looseleaf format)
Description: Current information of interest to people involved with the association's activities.

378 282   US   ISSN 1053-8941
LC493
ASSOCIATION OF JESUIT COLLEGES AND UNIVERSITIES AND JESUIT SECONDARY EDUCATION ASSOCIATION DIRECTORY.* 1970. $7.50. Association of Jesuit Colleges and Universities, 1 Dupont Cir., N.W., Ste. 405, Washington, DC 20036-1110. TEL 202-667-3889. Ed. Paul S. Tipton. circ. 2,500. **Document type:** directory.

378   TH   ISSN 0066-9687
ASSOCIATION OF SOUTHEAST ASIAN INSTITUTIONS OF HIGHER LEARNING. HANDBOOK: SOUTHEAST ASIAN INSTITUTIONS OF HIGHER LEARNING. (Text in English) 1966. triennial. $55. Association of Southeast Asian Institutions of Higher Learning, Ratasastra Bldg., Chulalongkorn University, Henri Dunant Rd., Bangkok 10500, Thailand. Ed. Ninnat Olanvoravuth. circ. 1,500.
Description: Covers member institutions in Brunei, Hong Kong, Indonesia, Malaysia, Philippines, Singapore, Thailand, and associate members in Australia, Japan, Canada, New Zealand, Sweden and the United States. Includes name, address, phone, chief officers, faculties and deans, libraries, courses, fees, publications, and more.

378   TH   ISSN 0572-4325
ASSOCIATION OF SOUTHEAST ASIAN INSTITUTIONS OF HIGHER LEARNING. NEWSLETTER. 1969. s-a. $5. Association of Southeast Asian Institutions of Higher Learning, Ratasastra Bldg., Chulalongkorn University, Henri Dunant Road, Bangkok 10500, Thailand. circ. 1,500. **Document type:** newsletter.

378   US   ISSN 0066-975X
ASSOCIATION OF UNIVERSITY SUMMER SESSIONS. SUMMARY OF REPORTS. 1919. a. membership only. Association of University Summer Sessions, Office of Summer Sessions and Special Programs, Indiana University, Bloomington, IN 47405. TEL 812-855-5048. FAX 812-855-3815. Ed. Leslie J. Coyne. circ. 50.
Formerly: Association of Summer Session Deans and Directors. Summary of Reports.

378   IO   ISSN 0126-1584
ATMA JAYA RESEARCH CENTRE. NEWSLETTER. (Text in English) 1975. bi-m. Atma Jaya Research Centre - Pusat Penelitian Atma Jaya, Jalan Jenderal Sudirman 51, P.O. Box 2639, Jakarta 10001, Indonesia. illus. **Document type:** newsletter.

AUSTRALIA. BUREAU OF STATISTICS. RESEARCH AND EXPERIMENTAL DEVELOPMENT, HIGHER EDUCATION ORGANISATIONS, AUSTRALIA. see *EDUCATION — Abstracting, Bibliographies, Statistics*

378   AT
AUSTRALIAN AND NEW ZEALAND FACULTY DIRECTORY. 1990. triennial. Aus.$68. Auslib Press, P.O. Box 622, Blackwood, S.A. 5051, Australia. TEL 08-278-4363. FAX 08-278-4000. Ed. Alan Bundy. adv. circ. 40,000. **Document type:** directory.
Formerly: Australian Faculty Directory.
Description: Contains information on Australian and New Zealand higher education institutions, and brief details of 33,000 teaching, research and senior administrative staff.

AUSTRALIAN FEDERATION OF UNIVERSITY WOMEN. NEWSLETTER. see *WOMEN'S INTERESTS*

378 621.38   AT   ISSN 0819-2316
AUSTRALIAN FILM, TELEVISION AND RADIO SCHOOL ANNUAL REPORT. 1972. a. free. Australian Film, Television and Radio School, P.O. Box 126, North Ryde, N.S.W. 2113, Australia. TEL 612-805-6611. FAX 612-887-1030. Ed. Meredith Quinn. circ. 1,500. (back issues avail.) **Document type:** corporate report.
Former titles (until 1986): Australian Film and Television School Annual Report (ISSN 0728-6619); (until 1976): Film and Television School Annual Report (ISSN 0819-2286); Australian Film and Television School. Interim Council. Annual Report (ISSN 0310-8376).
Description: Reports on the year's activities of the school.

378 384.554   AT   ISSN 1035-1019
AUSTRALIAN FILM, TELEVISION AND RADIO SCHOOL HANDBOOK. 1978. a. free. Australian Film, Television and Radio School, P.O. Box 126, North Ryde, N.S.W. 2113, Australia. TEL 61-2-805-6111. FAX 61-2-887-1030. Ed. Meredith Quinn. circ. 1,800. (back issues avail.)
Formerly: Australian Film and Television School Handbook (ISSN 0313-8461)
Description: Description of courses, activities and resources of the school.

AUSTRALIAN HISTORICAL ASSOCIATION. BULLETIN. see *HISTORY — History Of Australasia And Other Areas*

378   AT   ISSN 0818-8068
AUSTRALIAN UNIVERSITIES' REVIEW. 1957. 2/yr. Aus.$40 (foreign Aus.$45) (effective 1993). National Tertiary Education Union, P.O. Box 1323, S. Melbourne, Vic. 3205, Australia. TEL 03-254-1880. FAX 03-254-1915. Ed. L. Johnson. adv.; bk.rev.; bibl.; charts; illus.; stat.; index. circ. 10,000. **Indexed:** Aus.P.A.I.S., C.I.J.E., Res.High.Educ.Abstr.
—BLDSC (1823.700000).
Formerly: Vestes (ISSN 0042-4560)

378   AU
AUSTRIA. BUNDESMINISTERIUM FUER WISSENSCHAFT UND FORSCHUNG. HOCHSCHULBERICHT. triennial. free. Bundesministerium fuer Wissenschaft und Forschung, Minoritenplatz 5, 1010 Vienna, Austria. TEL 0222-53120-0. FAX 0222-53120-5155. TELEX 111157. stat. **Document type:** government publication.
Description: Report by the Austrian minister for science and research about higher education.

378 370.196   GW   ISSN 0937-6569
AUSZEIT; Informationen, Berichte und Dokumentation zum Auslaenderstudium. 1964. q. DM.20($10) World University Service, German Committee, Goebenstr. 35, 65195 Wiesbaden, Germany. TEL 0611-446648. FAX 0611-446489. Ed. Kambiz Ghawami. bk.rev. (back issues avail.) **Document type:** academic/scholarly publication.

378   US   ISSN 1052-2220
LB2338
AWARDS ALMANAC; an international guide to career, research, and education funds. 1990. a. $95. St. James Press, 845 Penobscot Bldg., Detroit, MI 48226-4094. TEL 800-345-0392. FAX 313-961-6083. Ed. Miranda H. Ferrara. **Document type:** directory.

378   UK   ISSN 0967-9863
LB2337.6.G7
AWARDS FOR FIRST DEGREE STUDY AT COMMONWEALTH UNIVERSITIES. 1973. biennial. £6.50. Association of Commonwealth Universities, John Foster House, 36 Gordon Sq., London WC1H 0PF, England. TEL 071-387-8572. FAX 071-387-2655. Eds. E. Robinson, M. Hunter. **Document type:** directory.
—BLDSC (1840.558000).
Formerly (until 1989): Financial Aid for First Degree Study at Commonwealth Universities (ISSN 0260-0749)

378   UK   ISSN 0960-7986
LB2339.G7
AWARDS FOR POSTGRADUATE STUDY AT COMMONWEALTH UNIVERSITIES. 1972. biennial. £18.50. Association of Commonwealth Universities, John Foster House, 36 Gordon Sq., London WC1H 0PF, England. TEL 071-387-8572. FAX 071-387-2655. Eds. E. Robinson, M. Hunter. **Indexed:** A.I.C.P. **Document type:** directory.
—BLDSC (1840.561000).
Formerly: Scholarships Guide for Commonwealth Postgraduate Students (ISSN 0306-1736)

378   UK   ISSN 0964-2714
AWARDS FOR UNIVERSITY ADMINISTRATORS AND LIBRARIANS. 1979. biennial. £7. Association of Commonwealth Universities, John Foster House, 36 Gordon Sq., London WC1H 0PF, England. TEL 071-387-8572. FAX 071-387-2655. Ed. M. Hunter. **Document type:** directory.
Formerly: Grants for Study Visits by University Administrators and Librarians (ISSN 0144-462X)

378   UK   ISSN 0964-2706
LB2338
AWARDS FOR UNIVERSITY TEACHERS AND RESEARCH WORKERS. 1971. biennial. £19.50. Association of Commonwealth Universities, John Foster House, 36 Gordon Sq., London WC1H 0PF, England. TEL 071-387-8572. FAX 071-387-2655. Ed. M. Hunter. **Document type:** directory.
—BLDSC (1840.561500).
Former titles: Awards for Commonwealth University Academic Staff (ISSN 0144-4611); Award for Commonwealth University Staff (ISSN 0305-8697)

B C I T UPDATE. (British Columbia Institute of Technology) see *TECHNOLOGY: COMPREHENSIVE WORKS*

EDUCATION — HIGHER EDUCATION

378   SZ   ISSN 0408-6392
BASTIONS DE GENEVE.* (Text in French) no.26, 1975. s-a. Association des Universitaires de Geneve, 4 rue de Candolle, 1211 Geneva 4, Switzerland. Ed. Raymond Racine. bibl.

378   GW   ISSN 0171-645X
LB2300
BEITRAEGE ZUR HOCHSCHULFORSCHUNG. 1979. q. free. Bayerisches Staatsinstitut fuer Hochschulforschung und Hochschulplanung, Arabellastr. 1, 81925 Munich, Germany. TEL 089-92142188. FAX 089-92143175. Ed.Bd. (reprint service avail.) **Document type:** academic/scholarly publication.

378   IS
BEN GURION UNIVERSITY. BULLETIN. (Text in English) s-a. free. Ben Gurion University, Department of Public Affairs, P.O. Box 653, Beersheva 84105, Israel. TEL 972-57-39943. FAX 972-57-270656. circ. 10,000. **Document type:** bulletin.

378   US   ISSN 0742-0277
LC2781
BLACK ISSUES IN HIGHER EDUCATION. 1984. 26/yr. $40. Cox, Matthews & Associates, Inc., 10520 Warwick Ave., Ste. B-8, Fairfax, VA 22030. TEL 703-385-2981. FAX 703-385-1839. adv. —Faxon; UnCover; UMI.
Description: News, information, statistics and opinion regarding minorities in higher education.

378 374   VE
BOLETIN DE RESUMENES ANALITICOS. 1979. s-a. $20. UNESCO - C R E S A L C, Apdo. 68.394, Caracas 1062-A, Venezuela. TEL 58-2-284-5075. FAX 58-2-283-14-11. TELEX 24642 UNELC VC. circ. 1,000. (back issues avail.)

378   BL
BRAZIL. DEPARTAMENTO DE ASSUNTOS UNIVERSITARIOS. COORDENACAO DE AVAILIACAO E CONTROLE. CATALOGO GERAL DAS INSTITUICOES DE ENSINO SUPERIOR. 1973. irreg. Ministerio da Educacao e Cultura, Departamento de Assuntos Universitarios, Coordenacao de Avaliacao e Controle, Esplanada dos Ministerios, Bloco - H 7. andar, Brasilia, Brazil. **Document type:** government publication.

378   US   ISSN 1043-2833
BRICKER BULLETIN ON EXECUTIVE EDUCATION. 1982. 6/yr. $95 (foreign $115). Peterson's Guides, Inc., Bricker Executive Education Services, 202 Carnegie Center, Box 2123, Princeton, NJ 08543-2123. TEL 609-243-9111. FAX 609-243-9150. Ed. Jim Gish. bk.rev.
Description: Reports on significant events, topics and developments in executive education.

378 338.91   UK
BRITISH COUNCIL ANNUAL REPORT AND ACCOUNTS (YEAR). 1940. a. British Council, 10 Spring Gardens, London SW1A 2BN, England. TEL 071-930-8466. FAX 071-493-5035. Ed. Paul Howson. circ. 20,000. (back issues avail.)
Description: Reports on work of British Council worldwide.

378   US   ISSN 0007-4837
BULLETIN OF DENTAL EDUCATION. 1959. m. $18 to non-members (foreign $24). American Association of Dental Schools, 1625 Massachusetts Ave., N.W., Washington, DC 20036-2212. TEL 202-667-9433. Ed. Owen R. Terry. adv. circ. 3,800. (reprint service avail. from UMI) Indexed: Dent.Ind. **Document type:** bulletin.
Description: Reports on innovations and opportunities in dental education, pertinent federal legislation and regulations, and individual and institutional members.

BUSINESS EDUCATION FORUM. see *BUSINESS AND ECONOMICS*

C A L I C O. MONOGRAPH SERIES. (Computer Assisted Language & Instruction Consortium) see *COMPUTERS — Computer Assisted Instruction*

378   CN
C A U C E BULLETIN. 1969. q. Can.$80 to members. Canadian Association for University Continuing Education, c/o K. Clements, Exec. Director, 320-350 Albert St., Ottawa, ON K1R 1B1, Canada. TEL 613-563-1236. FAX 613-563-7739. circ. 475. (back issues avail.) **Document type:** bulletin.
Description: Reports current developments and noteworthy programs; includes list of regional, national and international conferences.

378   CN   ISSN 0834-9614
C A U T BULLETIN/A C P U BULLETIN. (Text in English, French) 1953. 10/yr. Can.$37.45 (in US Can.$40; elsewhere Can.$55). Canadian Association of University Teachers, 294 Albert St., Ste. 308, Ottawa, ON K1P 6E6, Canada. TEL 613-237-6885. FAX 613-232-0494. adv. contact: Stella Cosentino. bk.rev.; charts. circ. 39,000. (tabloid format; also avail. in microform from MML) Indexed: Can.Educ.Ind, CMI.
Former titles (until 1975): Canadian Association of University Teachers. Bulletin (ISSN 0834-9606); (until 1975): C A U T Bulletin (ISSN 0007-7887)
Description: Promotes the interests of teachers, professional librarians and researchers in Canadian universities and colleges; advances the standards of their profession and seeks to improve the quality of higher education in Canada.

378   US   ISSN 0146-5813
LB2341.6.T4
C B REPORT; quarterly notes from the Coordinating Board. 1966. q. free. Texas Higher Education Coordinating Board, Box 12788, Capitol Sta., Austin, TX 78711. TEL 512-483-6111. Eds. Janis Monger, Jan Friese. circ. 2,000 (controlled). **Document type:** government publication.

378   US
C C A ADVOCATE. 1966. 5/yr. membership. California Teachers Association, Community College Association, 1705 Murchison Dr., Burlingame, CA 94010. TEL 415-697-1400. FAX 415-697-0786. Ed. Jan Anderson. bk.rev. circ. 25,000.
Formerly: California Professor (ISSN 0008-1418)
Description: News articles on legislative and policy issues that affect the Community College Association chapters of the California Teachers Association.

378   US
C C D M MINORITY STUDENT RECRUITMENT GUIDE. 1973. biennial. $150. Council on Career Development for Minorities, Inc., 1341 W. Mockingbird Ln., Ste. 412E, Dallas, TX 75247. TEL 214-631-3677. FAX 214-905-2046. Ed. Elizabeth West. circ. 2,500. **Document type:** directory.
Former titles: Handbook for Recruiting Minority College Students; Handbook for Recruiting at Minority Colleges (ISSN 0163-2795); (until 1979): Handbook for Recruiting at the Historically Black Colleges (ISSN 0146-5104)

C L E JOURNAL AND REGISTER. see *LAW*

C M E - CONTINUING MEDICAL EDUCATION. see *MEDICAL SCIENCES*

378   US
C O P A CONNECTIONS. 1975. bi-m. free. Council on Postsecondary Accreditation, One Dupont Circle, N.W., Ste. 305, Washington, DC 20036. TEL 202-452-1433. FAX 202-331-9571. Ed. Morgean L. Milkofsky. circ. 7,000.
Formerly: Accreditation (ISSN 0099-0256)
Description: Addresses accreditation issues of interest to the higher education community.

C P C SALARY SURVEY; a study of beginning salary offers. (College Placement Council, Inc.) see *OCCUPATIONS AND CAREERS*

378 371.2   SZ   ISSN 1011-9019
LA628
C R E - ACTION. (Text in English and French) 1965. irreg. 20 SFr. Standing Conference of Rectors, Presidents and Vice-Chancellors of the European Universities, 10 rue du Conseil General, CH-1211 Geneva 4, Switzerland. TEL 022-3292644. FAX 022-3292821. TELEX 428380-CRE-CH. Ed. Andris Barblan. bk.rev.; bibl.; charts. circ. 2,200. (also avail. in microform from UMI; back issues avail.; reprint service avail. from UMI) Indexed: Cont.Pg.Educ., H gh.Educ.Curr.Aware.Bull., Res.High.Educ.Abstr. **Document type:** academic/scholarly publication.
—BLDSC (3487.139000); UMI.
Formerly: C R E Information (ISSN 0007-9049)

378   SZ   ISSN 1022-0216
▼**C R E - INFO.** French edition (ISSN 1022-0208) (Text in English) 1993. q. 25 SFr. Standing Conference of Rectors, Presidents and Vice-Chancellors of the European Universities, 10 rue du Conseil General, CH-1211 Geneva 4, Switzerland. TEL 022-3292644. FAX 022-3292821. TELEX 428380-CRE-CH. Eds. Andris Barblan, Catherine Fayant. bk.rev. circ. 2,200. **Document type:** newsletter.

C R L A NEWSLETTER. (College Reading and Learning Association) see *EDUCATION — Adult Education*

371   US   ISSN 0742-2121
C T A ACTION. 1962. 9/yr. $6 to non-members. California Teachers Association, 1705 Murchison Dr., Burlingame, CA 94010. TEL 415-697-1400. FAX 415-697-0786. Ed. Trudy Willis. adv.: B&W page $4089. circ. 250,000 (controlled). (tabloid format) **Document type:** newspaper.
Former titles: C T A - N E A Action (ISSN 0164-9760); C T A Action (ISSN 0007-9200)
Description: News, announcements, and articles on legislative, policy, and educational issues that affect the California Teachers Association.

C U P A JOURNAL. see *BUSINESS AND ECONOMICS — Personnel Management*

378   US
CALIFORNIA COMMUNITY COLLEGES. MASTER PLAN AND INVENTORY OF PROGRAMS. 1972. a. free. Community Colleges, Chancellor's Office, 1107 Ninth St., Sacramento, CA 95814. TEL 916-322-4656. FAX 916-323-9478. Ed. Norma Morris. charts; stat. circ. 1,200.

378   UK   ISSN 0305-764X
LB1725.G4   CODEN: CJEDEI
CAMBRIDGE JOURNAL OF EDUCATION. 1971. 3/yr. $68 to individuals; institutions $228 (effective 1994). (Cambridge Institute of Education) Carfax Publishing Co., P.O. Box 25, Abingdon, Oxon. OX14 3UE, England. TE_ 44-235-555335. FAX 44-235-553559. (U.S. subscr. to: Carfax Publishing Co., Bcx 2025, Dunnellon, FL 34430-2025) Ec. B.E. Shannon. adv.; bk.rev.; bibl. (also avail. in mic-ofiche) Indexed: Br.Educ.Ind., Cont.Pg.Educ., Educ.Admin.Abstr., Educ.Tech.Abstr., High.Educ.Curr.Aware.Bull., Mult.Ed.Abstr., Psychol.Abstr., SCMA. **Document type:** academic/scholarly publication.
—BLDSC (3015.957000); SWETS. CCC.
Refereed Serial

378   UK
CAMBRIDGE UNIVERSITY REPORTER. 1870. irreg. price varies. Cambridge University Press, Edinburgh Bldg., Shaftesbury Rd., Cambridge, CB2 2RU, England. TEL 0223-312353. FAX 0223-315052. TELEX 851817256. (N. American addr.: Cambridge University Press, Journals Dept., 40 W. 20th St., New York, NY 10011. TEL 212-924-3900. FAX 212-691-3239) **Document type:** academic/scholarly publication.

378 792   US   ISSN 0746-2328
CAMPUS ACTIVITIES PROGRAMMING. 1968. 9/yr. $20. National Association for Campus Activities, 13 Harbison Way, Columbia, SC 29212-3401. TEL 803-732-6222. FAX 803-749-1047. Ed. Glenn Farr. adv. contact: Jeff Nemens. bk.rev.; illus.; circ. 6,500 (controlled). (also avail. in microform from UMI; reprint service avail. from UMI) **Document type:** academic/scholarly publication.
—UMI.
Former titles: Student Activities Programming (ISSN 0098-1664); N E C Newsletter (ISSN 0093-3643)

EDUCATION — HIGHER EDUCATION

CAMPUS CRIME. see *CRIMINOLOGY AND LAW ENFORCEMENT — Security*

378 374.4   US   ISSN 1043-2086
LC6251
CAMPUS - FREE COLLEGE DEGREES. 1989. biennial. $16.95. Thorson Guides, Box 470886, Tulsa, OK 74147-0886. TEL 918-622-2811. FAX 918-622-2811. **Document type:** directory.
    Description: Lists accredited off-campus college degree programs for adults.

378   UK
CAMPUS REPORT. 1982. 3/yr. University of Salford, Campus Office, Maxwell Bldg., Salford M5 4WT, England. TEL 061-743-1727. FAX 061-745-5999. Ed. Anna Thornton. circ. 6,000. (back issues avail.) **Document type:** newsletter.

378 375   US   ISSN 0890-4618
CAMPUS REPORT. 1985. m. $30. Accuracy in Academia, Inc., 4455 Connecticut Ave., N.W., Ste. 330, Washington, DC 20008. TEL 202-364-4401. FAX 202-364-4098. Ed. Reed Irvine. bk.rev. circ. 176,500. (tabloid format; back issues avail.; reprint service avail.) **Document type:** newspaper.
    ●Also available online.
    Formerly (until 1986): Accuracy in Academia.
    Description: Investigates and exposes abuses of first amendment freedoms on college campuses including cases of political classroom indoctrination, discrimination, and political correctness.

CAMPUS SECURITY REPORT. see *CRIMINOLOGY AND LAW ENFORCEMENT — Security*

378   US   ISSN 1050-5644
JK468.I6
CAMPUS WATCH. 1989. 4/yr. $10. Bill of Rights Foundation, 523 S. Plymouth Ct., Ste. 800, Chicago, IL 60605. TEL 312-939-0675. FAX 312-939-7867. Eds. Deborah Crawford, Vernon Elliott. adv.; bk.rev.
    Description: Seeks to raise awareness of intelligence activities in academic community through reporting on recruitment of staff and intelligence assets, officer and scholar in residence programs, research and CIA related student activism.

378 296   CN   ISSN 0228-8397
CANADIAN ASSOCIATION OF AFRICAN STUDIES. NEWSLETTER/ASSOCIATION CANADIENNE DES ETUDES AFRICAINES. BULLETIN. (Text in English, French) 1975. 3/yr. Can.$70 membership. Canadian Association of African Studies, Centre for Urban and Community Studies, University of Toronto, 455 Spadina Ave., Ste. 426, Toronto, Ont. M5S 2G8, Canada. TEL 416-978-7067. bibl. circ. 1,000. **Document type:** newsletter.
    Description: African studies in Universities.

378 658.1   CN   ISSN 0707-7955
CANADIAN ASSOCIATION OF UNIVERSITY RESEARCH ADMINISTRATORS. BULLETIN. (Text in English, French) 1976. 3/yr. membership. Canadian Association of University Research Administrators - Association Canadienne d'Administration de Recherche Universitaire, c/o Roger Prichard, McGill University, 853 Sherbrooke St., W., Montreal, PQ H3A 2T6, Canada. TEL 514-398-3991. FAX 514-398-8257. Ed. Margaret Gardiner. bk.rev. circ. 300. **Document type:** bulletin.
    Formerly: Canadian Association of University Research Administrators. Research Bulletin.
    Description: Communicates positions and perspectives concerning current research and administrative matters to members.

CANADIAN GEMMOLOGIST. see *JEWELRY, CLOCKS AND WATCHES*

378   CN
CANADIAN JOURNAL OF CONTINUING MEDICAL EDUCATION. 1989. 10/yr. $9.50 per no. S T A Communications Inc., 955 boul. St. Jean, Ste. 306, Pointe-Claire, Que. H9R 5K3, Canada. TEL 514-695-7623. FAX 514-695-8554. Ed. Paul F. Brand. adv. circ. 30,503.

378   CN   ISSN 0316-1218
CANADIAN JOURNAL OF HIGHER EDUCATION/REVUE CANADIENNE D'ENSEIGNEMENT SUPERIEUR. (Text in English, French) 1971. 3/yr. Can.$75. Canadian Society for the Study of Higher Education, c/o Centre for Higher Education Research and Development, University of Manitoba, 220 Sinnott Bldg., 430 Dysart Rd., Canada. TEL 204-474-6211. FAX 204-275-0831. TELEX 07-587721. Ed. Lise Tremblay. adv.; bk.rev.; abstr.; bibl. circ. 750. (also avail. in microform from MML,UMI; reprint service avail. from UMI) **Indexed:** C.I.J.E., Can.Educ.Ind., Cont.Pg.Educ., Educ.Admin.Abstr., Educ.Tech.Abstr., Mult.Ed.Abstr., Res.High.Educ.Abstr., SOMA, Sp.Ed.Needs Abstr. **Document type:** academic/scholarly publication.
    —BLDSC (3031.620000); SWETS; UMI. **CCC.**
    Formerly: S T O A.
    Description: Original research in the field of higher education in Canada and abroad.

378 374   CN   ISSN 0318-9090
CANADIAN JOURNAL OF UNIVERSITY CONTINUING EDUCATION. (Text in English, French) 1972. s-a. Can.$24. Canadian Association for University Continuing Education, 320-350 Albert St., Ottawa, ON K1R 1B1, Canada. TEL 613-563-1236. FAX 613-563-7739. Ed. Katherine Seaborne. adv.; bk.rev.; index. circ. 800. **Indexed:** Cont.Pg.Educ. **Document type:** academic/scholarly publication.
    —BLDSC (3036.400000).
    Description: Devoted to the development of professional practice and scholarly research in university continuing education.
    Refereed Serial

378 370.196   US   ISSN 0734-4546
CANADIAN STUDIES UPDATE. 1982. 4/yr. $60 to individuals; institutions $105. Association for Canadian Studies in the U S, One Dupont Circle, Ste. 620, Washington, DC 20036. TEL 202-887-6375. FAX 202-296-8379. Ed. David N. Biette. circ. 1,700.
    —BLDSC (3044.897500).

378 910.03   US
CAPE OF GOOD HOPE IMVO - NEWS; encouraging American support for predominantly black universities in Namibia and South Africa. 1985. a. $4 to non-members. Cape of Good Hope Foundation, 1201 E. California Blvd., Pasadena, CA 91125. TEL 818-356-3634. FAX 818-795-1547. Ed. Ned Munger. circ. 4,500.
    Formerly (until 1986): Cape of Good Hope Foundation Newsletter.

378 378   CN   ISSN 0835-3913
CAREER OPTIONS. (Text in English, French) 1970. a. $3.95 per no. A C C I S, 1209 King St. W., Ste. 205, Toronto, Ont. M6K 1G2, Canada. TEL 416-535-8126. FAX 416-532-0934. adv. circ. 180,000 (145,000 English ed., 35,000 French ed.)
    Description: Includes current trends and market conditions, issues in the workplace, tips on the job search process, writing resumes and filling out applications, a list of employers who recruit on campus and the educational background required of new recruits.

378   US   ISSN 0069-0783
CARSON - NEWMAN COLLEGE, JEFFERSON CITY, TENNESSEE. FACULTY STUDIES. 1965. a. free. Carson - Newman College, Jefferson City, TN 37760. TEL 615-475-9061. Ed. Don H. Olive. circ. 600 (controlled). **Document type:** academic/scholarly publication.

378   BL
CATALOGO DE PESQUISAS CONCLUIDAS E EM DESENVOLVIMENTO.* 1975. irreg. Universidade Federal de Pernambuco, Cidade Universitaria, 5000 Recife, PE, Brazil.

378   BL
CATALOGO GERAL DE INSTITUICOES DE ENSINO SUPERIOR. 1973. irreg., latest 1993. Ministerio da Educacao e do Desporto, Secretaria de Educacao Superior, Esplanada dos Ministerios, Bloco L, 3o andar, 70047-903 Brasilia DF, Brazil. TEL 61-223-7965. FAX 61-224-8920. TELEX 61-1860 MBRL-BR. charts; stat. **Document type:** government publication, catalog.
    Formerly: Atividades das Instituicoes Federais de Ensino Superior.
    Description: Lists all Brazilian higher education institutions, their departments and courses, and statistical information.

378   CF
CENTRE D'ENSEIGNEMENT SUPERIEUR DE BRAZZAVILLE. ANNALES. 1965. a. Centre d'Enseignement Superieur de Brazzaville, B.P. 69, Brazzaville, Congo.

791   US   ISSN 0009-1383
LB2300
CHANGE (WASHINGTON); the magazine of higher learning. 1968. bi-m. $34 for individuals; institutions $65. (American Association of Higher Education) Heldref Publications, 1319 18th St., N.W., Washington, DC 20036-1802. TEL 202-296-6267. FAX 202-296-5149. (Co-sponsor: Helen Dwight Reid Educational Foundation) Ed. Nanette Wiese. adv. contact: Raymond Rallo. bk.rev.; illus.; index. circ. 12,000. (also avail. in microform; back issues avail.; reprint service avail.) **Indexed:** Acad.Ind., Amer.Hist.& Life (until 1990), Bk.Rev.Ind. (1978-), C.I.J.E., Child.Bk.Rev.Ind. (1978-), Cont.Pg.Educ., Educ.Admin.Abstr., Educ.Ind., G.Soc.Sci.& Rel.Per.Lit., Hist.Abstr. (until 1990), Mag.Ind., Mid.East: Abstr.& Ind., R.G., Rehabil.Lit., Res.High.Educ.Abstr., SOMA. **Document type:** academic/scholarly publication.
    —BLDSC (3129.644000); Faxon; UnCover; SWETS; UMI. **CCC.**
    Formerly: Change in Higher Education (ISSN 0363-6291)
    Refereed Serial

378   UK   ISSN 1353-3029
CHECKLIST OF UNIVERSITY INSTITUTIONS IN THE COMMONWEALTH. 1949. a. £9.25. Association of Commonwealth Universities, John Foster House, 36 Gordon Sq., London WC1H 0PF, England. TEL 071-387-8572. FAX 071-387-2655. Ed. I. Peters. **Document type:** directory.

CHEMICAL ENGINEERING EDUCATION. see *ENGINEERING — Chemical Engineering*

CHEMICAL ENGINEERING FACULTIES. see *ENGINEERING — Chemical Engineering*

CHEMICAL RESEARCH IN CHINESE UNIVERSITIES. see *CHEMISTRY*

CHEMICAL SCIENCES GRADUATE SCHOOL FINDER. see *EDUCATION — Guides To Schools And Colleges*

378   US
CHICAGO CHRONICLE. 1981. 20/yr. $20. University of Chicago, Chicago Chronicle, 5801 S. Ellis Ave., Rm. 200, Chicago, IL 60637. FAX 312-702-8324. Ed. Colleen Newquist. circ. 12,300.

378   US
THE CHIMES (COLUMBUS). w. $15. Capital University, 2199 E. Main St., Columbus, OH 43209. TEL 614-236-6716. FAX 614-236-6490. Ed. Salle Schlesselman. circ. 2,300. **Document type:** newspaper.

CHRISTOPHANY; Christ displayed. see *RELIGIONS AND THEOLOGY — Protestant*

378   UK
CHRIST'S COLLEGE MAGAZINE. 1886. a. membership. Christ's College, Cambridge CB2 3BU, England. FAX 44-334967. R.N. Barlow-Poole. adv.; bk.rev. circ. 6,500.

EDUCATION — HIGHER EDUCATION

378.3 US
LB2337.4
CHRONICLE FINANCIAL AID GUIDE. 1961. a. $28.09. Chronicle Guidance Publications, Inc., Box 1190, Moravia, NY 13118. TEL 315-497-0330. FAX 315-497-3359. circ. 6,300.
Former titles: Chronicle Student Aid Annual (ISSN 0190-339X); Student Aid Annual (ISSN 0585-4555); Student Aid Manual (ISSN 0145-8043)
Description: Lists scholarship titles.

378 US ISSN 0009-5982
CHRONICLE OF HIGHER EDUCATION. (Supplement avail.: Chronicle of Higher Education Almanac; ISSN 1043-7967) 1966. w. $75. Chronicle of Higher Education, Inc., 1255 23rd St., N.W., Ste. 700, Washington, DC 20037. TEL 202-466-1000. FAX 202-296-2691. TELEX 892505. Ed. Corbin Gwaltney. adv.; bk.rev.; charts; illus.; stat.; index. circ. 97,074. (also avail. in microfilm from UMI; microfiche from CIS; reprint service avail. from UMI) Indexed: Acad.Ind., Art & Archaeol.Tech.Abstr., Bk.Rev.Ind. (1977-), Child.Bk.Rev.Ind. (1977-), Educ.Ind., PSI, Res.High.Educ.Abstr., SRI. Document type: newspaper.
—BLDSC (3186.250000); UnCover; UMI.
Description: News reports and editorials on all facets of higher education in the United States, Canada, and abroad, with reference lists of relevant research, books, seminars, workshops, fellowships, and grants; for senior administrative, business, and academic officers.

378 US ISSN 1043-7967
LA226
THE CHRONICLE OF HIGHER EDUCATION ALMANAC. (Supplement to: Chronicle of Higher Education (ISSN 0009-5982) 1988. a. Chronicle of Higher Education, Inc., 1255 Third St., N.W., Ste. 700, Washington, DC 20037. TEL 202-466-1000. FAX 202-296-2691. Document type: newspaper.

COGITO. see *PHILOSOPHY*

378 331.8 US ISSN 0738-1913
Z5814.U7
COLLECTIVE BARGAINING IN HIGHER EDUCATION AND THE PROFESSIONS. ANNUAL BIBLIOGRAPHY. 1973. a. $50 (effective 1993). National Center for the Study of Collective Bargaining in Higher Education and the Professions, Bernard M. Baruch College, City University of New York, 17 Lexington Ave., Box 322, New York, NY 10010. TEL 212-387-1510. Ed. Beth Johnson. circ. 400. (reprint service avail. from EDR) Document type: bibliography.
Description: Annual review of books, research reports and current events in higher education collective bargaining.

COLLEGE ADMINISTRATOR AND THE COURTS; briefs of selected court cases affecting the administration of institutions of higher education. see *LAW*

378 US ISSN 0010-0889
LB2300
COLLEGE AND UNIVERSITY. 1925. q. $30 to non-members (overseas $40). American Association of Collegiate Registrars and Admissions Officers, One Dupont Circle, N.W., Ste. 330, Washington, DC 20036-1171. TEL 202-293-9161. FAX 202-872-8857. Ed. Georgeanne Porter. adv. contact: Jennifer Harrison. bk.rev.; charts; index. circ. 10,000. (also avail. in microform from UMI; back issues avail.; reprint service avail. from UMI) Indexed: Bk.Rev.Ind. (1965-), C.I.J.E., Child.Bk.Rev.Ind. (1965-), Cont.Pg.Educ., Educ.Admin.Abstr., Educ.Ind., SSCI. Document type: academic/scholarly publication.
—BLDSC (3311.017000); Faxon; UnCover; SWETS; UMI.
Description: Addresses issues relevent to the association's purposes; looks at emerging issues in higher education; and reports new techniques and technology used by members in handling their responsibilities.

378 US ISSN 0147-5894
LB2351
COLLEGE AND UNIVERSITY ADMISSIONS AND ENROLLMENT, NEW YORK STATE. 1948. a. free. Education Department, Post-Secondary Policy Analysis, Cultural Education Bldg., Rm. 5B44, Albany, NY 12230. TEL 518-474-3874. charts; stat.; circ. controlled. (back issues avail.)
Formerly: College and University Enrollment in New York State (ISSN 0077-9180)

378 US ISSN 0077-9172
COLLEGE AND UNIVERSITY DEGREES CONFERRED, NEW YORK STATE. 1950. a. free. Education Department, Post Secondary Policy Analysis, Cultural Education Bldg., Rm. 5B44, Albany, NY 12230. TEL 518-474-3874. charts; stat.; circ. controlled. (back issues avail.)

378 US ISSN 0093-3414
LB2331.7
COLLEGE AND UNIVERSITY EMPLOYEES, NEW YORK STATE. 1960. a. Education Department, Office of Post-Secondary Policy Analysis, c/o James J. Brady, Chief, Bureau of Post-Secondary Statistical Service, Rm. 5B44 CEC, Albany, NY 12230. TEL 518-474-3874. charts; stat.; circ. controlled. (back issues avail.)
Formerly: New York (State). Education Department. Employees in Colleges and Universities.

378 US
COLLEGE BOARD NEWS. 1972. 4/yr. free to qualified personnel. College Board, 45 Columbus Ave., New York, NY 10023. TEL 212-713-8000. Ed. Nancy Viggiano. film rev.; charts; illus.; stat.; tr.lit. circ. 107,000. (tabloid format; reprint service avail. from UMI)

378 US ISSN 0010-0951
LB2353
COLLEGE BOARD REVIEW. 1947. q. $25. College Board, 45 Columbus Ave., New York, NY 10023. TEL 212-713-8000. (Subscr. to: College Board Review, Box 080419, Great Kills Sta., Staten Island, NY 10308-0005) Ed. Paul Barry. illus.; cum.index every 2 yrs. circ. 15,500. (also avail. in microfilm from UMI; reprint service avail. from UMI) Indexed: C.I.J.E., Educ.Ind.
—BLDSC (3311.025000); Faxon; UnCover; UMI.
Description: Focuses on high school counseling, college admissions, financial aid, recruitment and testing.

378.0025 US
COLLEGE BOUND. 1986. m. (10/yr.). $59 (foreign $69). College Bound Publications, Inc., Box 6536, Evanston, IL 60204. TEL 312-262-5810. FAX 312-262-5806. Ed. R. Craig Sautter. bk.rev. circ. 2,500. (back issues avail.) Document type: newsletter.
Description: Covers college admissions, financial aid, issues and trends.

378.0025 US
COLLEGE BOUND ADMISSIONS SURVEY. a. $12.95 (foreign $15.95). College Bound Publications, Inc., Box 6536, Evanston, IL 60204. TEL 312-262-5810. FAX 312-262-5806.
Description: Provides current information on more than 150 colleges, including class size, tuition, available scholarships, and financial aid tips.

378 US
COLLEGE BY MAIL - ETC. NEWSLETTER. 1991. a. $6.95 (typically set in June). Sought After Publications, c/o Prosperity & Profits Unlimited, Box 416, Denver, CO 80201-0416. TEL 303-575-5676. Ed. A. Doyle. circ. 10,000. (looseleaf format) Document type: newsletter.

378 US ISSN 0733-1355
COLLEGE CATALOG COLLECTION. 1973. 3/yr. $698. Career Guidance Foundation, 8090 Engineer Rd., San Diego, CA 92111. TEL 800-854-2670. FAX 619-278-8960. Ed. Ralph Anders. (microfiche)

378 US ISSN 1045-2060
LB2342
COLLEGE CHECK MATE. 1989. a. Octameron Associates, Inc., Box 2748, Alexandria, VA 22302.

378 FR ISSN 0069-5580
COLLEGE DE FRANCE. ANNUAIRE; resume des cours et travaux. 1901. a. 100 F. College de France, 11 place Marcelin Berthelot, 75231 Paris Cedex 05, France. TEL 47-27-12-11. FAX 44-27-11-09. (Subscr. to: C I D, 131 bd. St. Michel, 75005 Paris, France) Ed.Bd. Document type: academic/scholarly publication.

378 US
COLLEGE GRANTS FROM UNCLE SAM. 1981. a. $3. Octameron Associates, Inc., Box 2748, Alexandria, VA 22301. TEL 703-836-5480.
Supersedes (1979-1980): Am I Eligible? The Easy Way to Calculate the B E O G Index.

378 615.53 US
COLLEGE INFORMATION BOOKLET. 1977. a. $2. American Association of Colleges of Osteopathic Medicine, 6110 Executive Blvd., Ste. 405, Rockville, MD 20852. TEL 301-468-0990. Ed. William P. King. Document type: directory.
Description: Contains information on the 15 fully accredited osteopathic medical colleges including a brief description of each college, admissions criteria, minimum entrance requirements, supplementary application materials required, an indication of class size or enrollment application deadlines, and tuition.

378 331.1 CN
COLLEGE INSTITUTE EDUCATORS' ASSOCIATION. PROFILE. 1989. q. College Institute Educators' Association, 301 - 555 W. Eighth Ave., Vancouver, BC V5Z 1C6, Canada. TEL 604-873-8988. FAX 604-873-8865. circ. 6,500. (back issues avail.)
Description: Offers analysis and information on policy, labor relations and professional issues affecting community college and institute educators and the higher education system in general.

378 US
COLLEGE LOANS FROM UNCLE SAM. 1981. a. $3. Octameron Associates, Inc., Box 2748, Alexandria, VA 22301. TEL 703-836-5480.
Formerly (1979-1980): Quick Help from the Governor; Directory of State Financial Aid Agencies.

378 UK ISSN 0966-6907
▼**COLLEGE MANAGEMENT TODAY.** 1993. m. £48. Longman Group UK Ltd., Westgate House, The High, Harlow, Essex CM20 1VR, England. TEL 0279-442601. FAX 0279-444501. Ed. George Low. Document type: academic/scholarly publication.
—BLDSC (3311.171000).

378 371.8 US ISSN 0010-1125
COLLEGE PRESS SERVICE.* 1962. s-w. price varies. Interrobang, Inc., 64 E. Concord St., Orlando, FL 32801-1331. Ed. Bill Sonn. bk.rev.; index every 3 years. circ. 610. (processed; also avail. in microform from UMI; reprint service avail. from UMI)
●Also available online.
Formerly: Collegiate Press Service.
Description: Covers national student, faculty, and higher education news.

378 US ISSN 1050-7159
COLLEGE PREVIEW. 1985. 4/yr. $9.60. Communications Publishing Group, Inc., 250 Mark Twain Tower, 106 W. 11th St., Ste. 250, Kansas City, MO 64105-1806. TEL 816-221-4404. FAX 816-221-1112. Ed. Georgia Lee Clarke. circ. 600,000.
Description: Focuses on continuing education, financial aid sources and survival skills for Black and Hispanic high school students who are college-bound.

COLLEGE STORE EXECUTIVE. see *BUSINESS AND ECONOMICS — Marketing And Purchasing*

COLLEGE STUDENT AND THE COURTS; briefs of selected court cases involving student-institutional relationships in higher education. see *LAW*

378 371.8 US ISSN 0146-3934
LA229 CODEN: CSJLAO
COLLEGE STUDENT JOURNAL; a journal pertaining to college students. 1967. q. $15 to individuals; institutions $20. Project Innovation of Mobile, Box 8508, Spring Hill Sta., Mobile, AL 36608. TEL 205-343-1878. Ed. George E. Uhlig. adv.; bk.rev.; index. circ. 700. (also avail. in microform from UMI) Indexed: C.I.J.E., Cont.Pg.Educ., Educ.Ind., Lang.& Lang.Behav.Abstr., Mult.Ed.Abstr., Psychol.Abstr., Res.High.Educ.Abstr., Sociol.Abstr., Stud.Wom.Abstr. Document type: academic/scholarly publication.
—BLDSC (3311.290000); Faxon; UnCover; SWETS; UMI.
Formerly: College Student Survey (ISSN 0010-1184)

EDUCATION — HIGHER EDUCATION

370.7   US   ISSN 8756-7555
L11
COLLEGE TEACHING; international quarterly journal. 1953. q. $29 to individuals; institutions $53. (Helen Dwight Reid Educational Foundation) Heldref Publications, 1319 Eighteenth St., N.W., Washington, DC 20036-1802. TEL 202-296-6267. FAX 202-296-5149. Ed. Cherie Bottum. adv. contact: Raymond Rallo. bk.rev.; index, cum.index: vols.1-10. circ. 2,500. (also avail. in microform; reprint service avail.) **Indexed:** C.I.J.E., Cont.Pg.Educ., Educ.Admin.Abstr., Educ.Ind., Educ.Tech.Abstr., Res.High.Educ.Abstr., Sociol.Educ.Abstr. **Document type:** academic/scholarly publication.
—BLDSC (3311.313000); Faxon; UnCover; SWETS; UMI. **CCC.**
    Formerly: Improving College and University Teaching (ISSN 0019-3089)
    Description: Highlights education and training of teachers.
    Refereed Serial

378   PE
COMENTARIOS REALES. Universidad Inca Garcilaso de la Vega, Escuela de Profesionalizacion Docente, Avda. Arequipa 3610, San Isidro, Lima, Peru. TEL 711421. Ed. Gustavo Armijos. **Document type:** academic/scholarly publication.
    Description: Publishes articles, essays and studies on teaching, history, literature, linguistics, geography and other areas of science and research.

COMMISSION ON PRESERVATION AND ACCESS ANNUAL REPORT. see *LIBRARY AND INFORMATION SCIENCES*

378   US   ISSN 0069-6854
LB2301.C56
COMMITTEE ON INSTITUTIONAL COOPERATION. ANNUAL REPORT. 1970. a. free. Committee on Institutional Cooperation, 302 E. John St., Ste. 1705, Champaign, IL 61820. TEL 217-333-8475. FAX 217-244-7127. Ed. Russell W. Snyder. circ. controlled.

378   UK   ISSN 0069-7745
LB2310
COMMONWEALTH UNIVERSITIES YEARBOOK. 1914. a. $265. Association of Commonwealth Universities, John Foster House, 36 Gordon Sq., London WC1H OPF, England. TEL 071-387-8572. FAX 071-387-2655. (Dist. in U.S. by: Stockton Press, 249 W. 24th St., New York, NY 10010) Ed. Alyson Barr. index. **Document type:** directory.
—BLDSC (3341.110000).

378 331   US
COMMUNITY COLLEGE COUNCIL PERSPECTIVE.* bi-m. California Federation of Teachers, Community College Council, 1200 W. Magnolia Blvd., Burbank, CA 91506. TEL 818-843-8226. Ed. Gail E. Myers. adv.; charts; illus.; stat. circ. 2,400. (tabloid format; back issues avail.)
    Description: For all community college faculty and staff who are represented by the California Federation of Teachers. Covers statewide issues including CC legislation, finances, reform, conferences and trends.

378   US   ISSN 1052-7095
LB2361.5
COMMUNITY COLLEGE EXEMPLARY INSTRUCTIONAL PROGRAMS. 1989. a. Massachusetts Bay Community College Press, 50 Oakland St., Wellesley Hills, MA 02181.

378   US   ISSN 1067-1803
LB2300
COMMUNITY COLLEGE JOURNAL. 1930. bi-m. $22. American Association of Community Colleges, One Dupont Circle, N.W., Ste. 410, Washington, DC 20036. TEL 202-728-0200. FAX 202-223-9390. Ed. Bonnie Gardner. adv.; bk.rev.; bibl.; index. circ. 24,000. (also avail. in microform from UMI; reprint service avail. from UMI) **Indexed:** C.I.J.E., Cont.Pg.Educ., Educ.Admin.Abstr., Educ.Ind.
—BLDSC (3363.606100); Faxon; UnCover; SWETS.
    Former titles (until 1991): Community, Technical, and Junior College Journal (ISSN 0884-7169); Community and Junior College Journal (ISSN 0190-3160); Junior College Journal (ISSN 0022-653X)
    Description: Essays and feature articles on a variety of topics related to faculty, staff, and administration development at community, technical, and junior colleges.

378   US   ISSN 0091-5521
LB2328
COMMUNITY COLLEGE REVIEW. 1973. q. $45 (Canada $47; elsewhere $49) (effective 1992). North Carolina State University, Department of Adult and Community College Education, Box 7801, Raleigh, NC 27695-7801. TEL 919-515-6248. FAX 919-515-4039. adv.; bk.rev.; bibl.; charts. circ. 1,470. (also avail. in microfilm from UMI) **Indexed:** C.I.J.E., Cont.Pg.Educ., Educ.Admin.Abstr., Educ.Ind., ERIC, Mult.Ed.Abstr. **Document type:** academic/scholarly publication.
—BLDSC (3363.607000); Faxon; UnCover; UMI.
    Description: Publishes scholarly articles, case studies, models, research, analyses, and literature reviews on the contemporary problems and issues that affect professionals at this educational level.

378   US   ISSN 1041-5726
COMMUNITY COLLEGE WEEK; the independent voice serving community, technical and junior colleges. 1988. bi-w. $48. Cox, Matthews & Associates, Inc., 10520 Warwick Ave., Ste. B-8, Fairfax, VA 22030. TEL 703-385-2981. FAX 703-385-1839. Ed. Robert P. Pederson. adv. **Document type:** newspaper.
    Description: Provides current information on state and national news affecting community, technical and junior colleges.

COMMUNITY JUNIOR COLLEGE JOURNAL OF RESEARCH AND PRACTICE. see *EDUCATION — Adult Education*

378   US   ISSN 0163-8475
AS30
COMMUNITY REVIEW. 1977. s-a. $24 to individuals (foreign $36); institutions $36 (foreign $48). Transaction Publishers, Transaction Periodicals Consortium, Department 3092, Rutgers University, New Brunswick, NJ 08903. TEL 908-932-2280. FAX 908-932-3138. Ed. Kenneth Peeples, Jr. bk.rev. circ. 400. (also avail. in microfilm from UMI; microfiche from UMI; reprint service avail. from UMI) **Document type:** academic/scholarly publication.
—BLDSC (3363.658000); UMI. **CCC.**
    Description: For the exchange of professional concerns and interests within the two-year college community.

378   UK
COMPENDIUM OF HIGHER EDUCATION. a. (2 vols.). £16. L A S E R Advisory Council, Chenies House, 21 Bedford Sq., London WC1B 3HH, England. TEL 071-637-3073. FAX 071-637-2733. **Document type:** directory.
    Formerly: Compendium of Advanced Courses in Colleges of Further and Higher Education.

COMPENSATION, BENEFITS AND CONDITIONS OF EMPLOYMENT FOR COLLEGE AND UNIVERSITY CHIEF EXECUTIVE OFFICERS. see *BUSINESS AND ECONOMICS — Labor And Industrial Relations*

378   II
CONFERENCE OF VICE-CHANCELLORS. PROCEEDINGS. (Text in English) 1961. irreg. University Grants Commission, 35 Ferozeshah Rd., New Delhi 110 001, India. TEL 386 365. Ed. V. Appa Rao. circ. 6,000.

378.54   II
CONFERENCE OF VICE-CHANCELLORS. REPORT. (Text in English) irreg.? University Grants Commission, 35 Ferozeshah Rd., New Delhi 110 001, India.

378   SZ
CONFERENCE UNIVERSITAIRE SUISSE. RAPPORT ANNUEL. German edition: Schweizerische Hochschulkonferenz. Jahresbericht. 1969. a. free. Conference Universitaire Suisse - Schweizerische Hochschulkonferenz, Wildhainweg 21, CH-3012 Bern, Switzerland. FAX 031-241792. circ. 660 (German ed.); 350 (French ed.). **Document type:** corporate report.

378   US   ISSN 0895-6405
LC67.65.N49
CONNECTION (BOSTON); New England's journal of higher education and economic development. 1978. q. $16. New England Board of Higher Education, 45 Temple Pl., Boston, MA 02111. TEL 617-357-9620. Ed. John O. Harney. adv. contact: Charlotte Stratton. illus.
—Faxon.
    Formerly (until 1986): Higher Education in New England (ISSN 0440-7881)
    Description: Covers issues related to higher education and its impact on economic development.

378   VE
CONSEJO NACIONAL DE INVESTIGACIONES CIENTIFICAS Y TECNOLOGICAS. DEPARTAMENTO DE EDUCACION. DIRECTORIO NACIONAL DE CURSOS DE POSTGRADO. irreg. Consejo Nacional de Investigaciones Cientificas y Tecnologicas, Departamento de Educacion, Apartado 70617 Los Ruices, Caracas, Venezuela. TEL 2390433. FAX 2398677. TELEX 25205 CONICIT.

378   CR   ISSN 0589-4301
CONSEJO SUPERIOR UNIVERSITARIO CENTROAMERICANO. ACTAS DE LA REUNION ORDINARIA. irreg. Consejo Superior Universitaria Centroamericano, Apdo. Postal 37, Cuidad Univ. R. Facio, San Jose, Costa Rica.

378   IT
CONSORZIO UNIVERSITARIO. PUBBLICAZIONI. SEZIONE MISCELLANEA. 1975. irreg. exchange basis. Consorzio per la Costituzione e lo Sviluppo degli Insegnamenti Universitari, Via T. Mantica, 5, Udine, Italy. FAX 0432-504696. **Document type:** monographic series.

378 610.73   CN   ISSN 1183-7985
CONTINUING EDUCATION IN NURSING: A DIRECTORY/FORMATION CONTINUEE EN SOINS INFIRMIERES: REPERTOIRE. 1991. a. Can.$20. Canadian Nurses Association - Association des Infirmieres et Infirmiers du Canada, 50 Driveway, Ottawa, ON K2P 1E2, Canada. TEL 613-237-2133. FAX 613-237-3520. **Document type:** directory.
    Description: Lists over 500 courses and programs, all a minimum of 12 hours and ranging from refresher programs to courses in immunology, legal issues and the psychology of patient care. Includes course name, contact address and telephone number, duration, mode of delivery and admission requirements.

378   US
CONTINUING HIGHER EDUCATION REVIEW. 1937. 3/yr. $32. National University Continuing Education Association, 1 Dupont Circle, N.W., Ste. 615, Washington, DC 20036. TEL 202-659-3130. Ed. Daniel W. Shannon. adv.; bk.rev.; index. circ. 2,000. (tabloid format) **Indexed:** C.I.J.E., Cont.Pg.Educ.
—BLDSC (3425.688210).
    Former titles (until 1986): Continuum (Washington) (ISSN 0162-4024); (until 1976): N U E A Spectator (ISSN 0027-7096)

378   UK   ISSN 0305-8441
COOMBE LODGE REPORT. 1968. 10/yr. £75. The Staff College, Coombe Lodge, Blagdon, Bristol BS18 6RG, England. TEL 0761-462503. FAX 0761-463140. index. circ. 1,000. (back issues avail.) **Indexed:** Cont.Pg.Educ., Int.Lab.Doc., SOMA. **Document type:** academic/scholarly publication.
—BLDSC (3463.881000).

378 371.42   US
CO-OP - EXPERIENCE - CO-OP MAGAZINE. 1990. q. $22 (Canada and Mexico $30; elsewhere $36). Cooperative Education Association, Inc., 11710 Beltsville Dr., Ste. 520, Beltsville, MD 20705. TEL 301-572-2329. FAX 301-572-3916. adv.: B&W page $1495, color page $1795; trim 8 1/2 x 11. circ. 3,000.

378 376   US
CORNERSTONE (ANN ARBOR). 1965. irreg. (1-2/yr.). free. University of Michigan, Center for the Education of Women, 330 E. Liberty St., Ann Arbor, MI 48104-2289. circ. 13,000.
    Formerly: University of Michigan. Center for Continuing Education of Women Newsletter.
    Description: Studies the role of women in society, with emphasis on education and careers.

378   IS
COUNCIL FOR HIGHER EDUCATION. PLANNING AND BUDGETING COMMITTEE. ANNUAL REPORT. (Text in English) 1972. a. free. Council for Higher Education, Planning and Budgeting Committee, P.O. Box 4037, Jerusalem 91040, Israel. TEL 972-2-663131. FAX 972-2-660625. Eds. Riki Madelzweig, Yael Atiyah. circ. 700. **Document type:** government publication.
    Formerly (until 1991): Council for Higher Education. Planning and Grants Committee. Annual Report.

EDUCATION — HIGHER EDUCATION

378.15   US   ISSN 0070-1076
COUNCIL OF GRADUATE SCHOOLS IN THE UNITED STATES. PROCEEDINGS OF THE ANNUAL MEETING. 1961. a. price varies. Council of Graduate Schools in the U.S., One Dupont Circle, Ste. 430, Washington, DC 20036. TEL 202-223-3791. Ed. Nancy Gaffney. circ. 750. **Indexed:** ERIC. **Document type:** proceedings.

378   US   ISSN 1072-5830
COUNCIL ON UNDERGRADUATE RESEARCH QUARTERLY. 1979. 4/yr. $70 for 4 issues. Council on Undergraduate Research, University of North Carolina, Ashville, NC 28804. TEL 704-251-6006. FAX 704-251-6002. Ed.Bd. circ. 2,500. **Document type:** newsletter.
    Formerly: Council on Undergraduate Research Newsletter (ISSN 0890-8273)
    Description: Presents articles by and for faculty members primarily at undergraduate institutions, mainly in the sciences and mathematics. Also presents news items regarding undergraduate faculty and research opportunities, conferences, and sources of funds for research.

CRACKING THE SYSTEM: THE S A T & P S A T. see *EDUCATION — Guides To Schools And Colleges*

CROSS CURRENTS. see *RELIGIONS AND THEOLOGY*

378   US   ISSN 0748-478X
LB2300
CURRENTS (WASHINGTON). 1975. m. (except Aug. and Dec.). $85 (effective Oct. 1990). Council for Advancement and Support of Education, 11 Dupont Circle, Ste. 400, Washington, DC 20036. TEL 202-328-5900. FAX 202-387-4973. Ed. Karla Taylor. adv.; bk.rev.; abstr.; illus.; index. circ. 15,000. (also avail. in microform from UMI) **Indexed:** Chic.Per.Ind., PSI.
    —BLDSC (3505.040000); Faxon; UnCover; UMI.
    Formerly (until 1983): C A S E Currents (ISSN 0360-862X)
    Description: Articles on fundraising, alumni administration, institutional relations, management, periodicals, student recruitment, government relations and general interest.

CURRICULA IN THE ATMOSPHERIC, OCEANIC, HYDROLOGIC AND RELATED SCIENCES. see *METEOROLOGY*

DAKOTA SCIENTIST. see *SCIENCES: COMPREHENSIVE WORKS*

378 070   DK   ISSN 0907-418X
DANMARKS JOURNALISTHOEJSKOLE. BERETNING. Key Title: Beretning - D J H, Danmarks Journalisthoejskole. 1972. a. DKK 35. Danmarks Journalisthoejskole, Olof Palmes Alle 11, DK-8200 Aarhus N, Denmark. TEL 86-161122. FAX 86-168910. Ed. Jens Kristian Soegaard. illus. circ. 7,000.
    Former titles (until 1992): D J H (ISSN 0108-285X); (until 1977): Danmarks Journalisthoejskole (ISSN 0904-4027)

378   US   ISSN 0098-5279
LA267.5
DATA BOOK ON ILLINOIS HIGHER EDUCATION. a. Board of Higher Education, 4 W. Old Capitol Plaza, Rm. 500, Springfield, IL 62701-1287. TEL 217-782-2551. **Document type:** directory.

371.8   CC
DAXUESHENG/UNIVERSITY STUDENT. (Text in Chinese) m. $36.80. Beijing Chubanshe - Beijing Publishing House, 6 Beisanhuan Zhonglu, Beijing 100011, People's Republic of China. TEL 2016699. (Dist. in US by: China Books & Periodicals, Inc., 2929 24th St., San Francisco, CA 94110. TEL 415-282-2994) Ed. Lin Haoji.

378 615.53   US
DEBTS AND CAREER PLANS OF OSTEOPATHIC MEDICAL STUDENTS. 1982. a. $10. American Association of Colleges of Osteopathic Medicine, 6110 Executive Blvd., Ste. 405, Rockville, MD 20852. TEL 301-468-0990. Ed. Dr. Allen M. Singer. circ. 500. (back issues avail.) **Document type:** bulletin.
    Description: Survey examining indebtedness of osteopathic medical students. The situations, characteristics and plans of students are compared at their entrance to osteopathic medical schools and just prior to their graduation.

378.41   UK
DEGREE COURSE OFFERS. 1971. a. £13.95. Trotman and Co. Ltd., 12 Hill Rise, Richmond, Surrey TW10 6UA, England. TEL 081-940-5668. FAX 081-948-9267. Ed. Brian Heap. adv. circ. 20,000. **Document type:** directory.

378   US   ISSN 0011-8044
LJ145.D5
DELTA KAPPA GAMMA BULLETIN. 1934. q. $5. Delta Kappa Gamma Society International, Box 1589, Austin, TX 78767-1589. TEL 512-478-5748. FAX 512-478-3961. Ed. Jane L. Posten. bk.rev.; abstr.; charts; illus.; index. circ. 165,000. (also avail. in microform from UMI; reprint service avail. from UMI) **Indexed:** Educ.Ind.
    —BLDSC (3548.293000); Faxon; UnCover; UMI.
    Description: Promotes professional and personal growth of members through publication of their writing.

378 330   US
DELTA PI EPSILON. SERVICE BULLETINS. 1977. irreg., no.4, 1990. price varies. Delta Pi Epsilon Graduate Business Education Society, National Office, Box 4340, Little Rock, AR 72214. TEL 501-562-1233. FAX 501-562-1293. **Document type:** bulletin.
    Description: Designed for researchers, teachers, doctoral and master's candidates interested in conducting researches in business education.

378 330   US
DELTA PI EPSILON. (YEAR) RESEARCH CONFERENCE PROCEEDINGS. 1988. biennial. $10. Delta Pi Epsilon Graduate Business Education Society, National Office, Box 4340, Little Rock, AR 72214. TEL 501-562-1233. FAX 501-562-1293. **Document type:** proceedings.
    Description: Contains selected presentations at the Delta Pi Epsilon National Research Conference.

378   US   ISSN 0011-8052
DELTA PI EPSILON JOURNAL. 1957. q. $48. Delta Pi Epsilon Graduate Business Education Society, National Office, Box 4340, Little Rock, AR 72214. TEL 501-562-1233. Ed. Marguerite Shane Joyce. bibl.; charts. circ. 10,000. (also avail. in microfilm from UMI; reprint service avail. from UMI) **Indexed:** Bus.Educ.Ind., C.I.J.E., Educ.Ind.
    —BLDSC (3548.295000); Faxon; UnCover; UMI.

THE DEPARTMENT CHAIR; a newsletter for academic administrators. see *EDUCATION — School Organization And Administration*

378   GW   ISSN 0936-4501
DEUTSCHE UNIVERSITAETS-ZEITUNG. 1945. s-m. DM.168 (students DM.126). Dr. Josef Raabe Verlag GmbH, Koenigswintererstr. 418, 53227 Bonn, Germany. TEL 0228-97020-0. FAX 0228-9702010. adv.; bk.rev.; bibl.; charts; index. circ. 8,000. **Indexed:** Amer.Hist.& Life, Can.Rev.Comp.Lit., Hist.Abstr. **Document type:** newsletter.
    —BLDSC (3633.123500).
    Former titles: Universitaetszeitung das Deutsche Hochschulmagazin; Deutsche Universitaetszeitung (ISSN 0343-5563)

378   MX   ISSN 0185-3872
DIDAC. 1970. s-a. $9 (effective 1993). Universidad Iberoamericana, Centro de Didactica, Prol. Paseo de la Reforma 880, Col. Lomas de Santa Fe, 01210 Mexico DF, Mexico. TEL 5-570-79-10. FAX 5-726-90-48. Ed. Yolanda Argudin Vazquez. bk.rev.; bibl.; illus. circ. 1,500. **Document type:** academic/scholarly publication.

378   GH
DIRECTORY OF AFRICAN UNIVERSITIES. biennial. $70. Association of African Universities, Box 5744, Accra, Ghana. **Document type:** directory.
    Description: Contains general information about African universities (principal officers, academic staff, faculties and institutes, degrees, certificates and diplomas awarded, duration of studies, admission requirements and more).

378 331.8   US   ISSN 0276-7805
LB2335.885.U5
DIRECTORY OF FACULTY CONTRACTS AND BARGAINING AGENTS IN INSTITUTIONS OF HIGHER EDUCATION. 1975. a. $50 (effective 1993). National Center for the Study of Collective Bargaining in Higher Education and the Professions, Bernard M. Baruch College, City University of New York, 17 Lexington Ave., Box 322, New York, NY 10010. TEL 212-387-1510. Ed. Frank R. Annunziato. (reprint service avail. from EDR) **Document type:** directory.
    Description: Annual compilation and statistical analysis of faculty contracts and bargaining agents in institutions of higher education.

DIRECTORY OF FELLOWSHIP PROGRAMS IN GERIATRIC MEDICINE. see *GERONTOLOGY AND GERIATRICS*

378.3   II   ISSN 0084-9936
DIRECTORY OF FULBRIGHT ALUMNI. (Text in English) 1969. triennial. free. United States Educational Foundation in India, Fulbright House, 12 Hailey Rd., New Delhi 110001, India. Ed. P.D. Sayal. cum.index 1950-1970; circ controlled.

378   UK
DIRECTORY OF FURTHER EDUCATION (D O F E). 1962. a. £46.95 (hardcover edition £51.95) (1994-1995 edition). Hobsons Publishing plc., Bateman St., Cambridge CB2 1LZ, England. TEL 0223-354551. FAX 0223-323154. TELEX 81546-HOBCAM-G. Ed. Emma Al Hudairi. adv. contact: Emma Al Hudairi. circ. 3,500. **Document type:** directory.
    Description: Examines vocational courses in colleges of higher education in the UK, including this year's NVQ, GNVQ, and general SVQs.

378 610   US
R840
DIRECTORY OF GRADUATE MEDICAL EDUCATION. 1914. a. $48 to non-members; members $36. American Medical Association, 515 N. State St., Chicago, IL 60610. TEL 312-464-5000. FAX 312-464-5834. Ed. Anne E. Crowley. (reprint service avail. from UMI) **Document type:** directory.
    —CCC.
    Former titles: Directory of Graduate Medical Education Programs Accredited by the Accreditation Council for Graduate Medical Education (ISSN 0892-0109); Directory of Residency Training Accredited by the Accreditation Council for Graduate Medical Education (ISSN 0164-1670); American Medical Association. Directory of Residency Training Programs (ISSN 0097-899X); American Medical Association. Directory of Accredited Residencies; American Medical Association. Directory of Approved Residencies; (until 1975): American Medical Association. Directory of Approved Internships and Residencies (ISSN 0419-2141).

378   US
DIRECTORY OF GRADUATE PROGRAMS. (In 4 vols.): Vol. A: Natural Sciences; Vol. B: Engineering; Vol. C: Social Sciences; Vol. D: Arts, Humanities & Other Fields) irreg., latest 14th ed. $72. Education Testing Service, Princeton, NJ 08541-0001. TEL 609-921-9000. (Subscr. to: Little Brown, 200 West St., Waltham, MA 02254. TEL 800-759-0190; Institutions subscr. to: Special Sales, Warner Book, Inc., Time & Life Bldg., 1271 Ave. of the Americas, New York, NY 10020. TEL 212-522-7381) **Document type:** directory.
    Description: Designed as a resource for individuals considering applying to graduate school. Contains 4 volumes subdivided into 50 major field areas offered at accredited institutions.

DIRECTORY OF GRANTS IN THE HUMANITIES. see *EDUCATION — Abstracting, Bibliographies, Statistics*

378   AT   ISSN 0158-9032
DIRECTORY OF HIGHER EDUCATION COURSES. 1983. a. Aus.$34.50 (diskett Aus.$29.95). New Hobsons Press Pty. Ltd., 553 Elizabeth St., Surry Hills, N.S.W. 2010, Australia. TEL 02-310-2257. FAX 02-310-2243. Ed. Melody Lord. adv.: page Aus.$1350; adv. contact: Colin Ritchie. circ. 8,500. (also avail. in diskette format) **Document type:** directory.
    Description: Lists all undergraduate and postgraduate degrees by subject. Contains advice on admission to university studies.

EDUCATION — HIGHER EDUCATION

378.761   US
DIRECTORY OF HIGHER EDUCATION IN ALABAMA.* 1972. a. Commission on Higher Education, 3465 Norman Bridge Rd., Montgomery, AL 36105-2310. TEL 205-269-2700. FAX 205-240-3349. illus. (reprint service avail.) **Document type:** government publication, directory.
Former titles: Fact Book. Higher Education in Alabama; Fact Book. Alabama Institutions of Higher Education, Universities and Colleges (ISSN 0095-0637)
Description: Overview of public and private colleges and universities in Alabama.

378   UK
DIRECTORY OF HIGHER EDUCATION INSTITUTIONS IN THE EUROPEAN COMMUNITY. a. £25. Kogan Page Ltd., 120 Pentonville Rd., London N1 9JN, England. TEL 071-278-0433. FAX 071-837-6348. TELEX 263088-KOGAN-G. **Document type:** directory.

378   US
DIRECTORY OF MINISTRIES IN HIGHER EDUCATION. 1975. a. $6. United Ministries in Education, Resource Office, 7407 Steele Creek Rd., Charlotte, NC 28217. TEL 704-588-2182. FAX 704-588-3652. Ed. Linda Freeman. circ. 2,000. **Document type:** directory.
Description: Lists more than 1,700 ministries, campus ministers, and college chaplains by state and college, including denominational affiliation.

378   US
DIRECTORY OF MINORITY PH.D. AND M.F.A. CANDIDATES AND RECIPIENTS. 1985. a. $23. Committee on Institutional Cooperation, 302 E. John St., Ste. 1705, Champaign, IL 61820. TEL 217-333-8475. FAX 217-244-7127. **Document type:** directory.

378   US   ISSN 1054-7568
LB2335.875.U6
DIRECTORY OF NON-FACULTY BARGAINING AGENTS IN INSTITUTIONS OF HIGHER EDUCATION. 1991. irreg. National Center for the Study of Collective Bargaining in Higher Education and the Professions, Bernard M. Baruch College, CUNY, 17 Lexington Ave., Box 322, New York, NY 10010. TEL 212-387-1510. **Document type:** directory.
Description: Lists all institutions of higher education in the U.S. which have collective bargaining contracts for staff members other than faculty. Includes names of agents.

DIRECTORY OF OSTEOPATHIC POSTDOCTORIAL EDUCATION. see *HOSPITALS*

378 530   US   ISSN 0361-2228
QC47.N75
DIRECTORY OF PHYSICS & ASTRONOMY STAFF (YEAR). 1959. biennial. $45 to members; non-members $60. American Institute of Physics, One Physics Ellipse, College Park, MD 20740-3843. TEL 301-209-3000. (Subscr. to: Member and Subscriber Service, 500 Sunnyside Blvd., Woodbury, NY 11797-2999. TEL 516-576-2270) stat. circ. 43,000. **Document type:** directory.
—BLDSC (3594.833000).
Formerly: Directory of Physics and Astronomy Facilities in North American Colleges and Universities (ISSN 0419-3253)

378   AT   ISSN 1035-5405
DIRECTORY OF POSTGRADUATE STUDY. 1990. a. Aus.$50. Graduate Careers Council of Australia Ltd., P.O. Box 28, Parkville, Vic. 3052, Australia. TEL 03-344-4666. FAX 03-347-7298. **Document type:** directory.
Description: Guide to postgraduate courses in Australia and awards for postgraduate study and research in Australia and overseas.

378   US
DIRECTORY OF RECOGNIZED ACCREDITING BODIES. 1975. a Council on Postsecondary Accreditation, One Dupont Circle, N.W., Ste. 305, Washington, DC 20036. TEL 202-452-1433. FAX 202-331-9571. Ed. Morgen L. Milkofsky. bibl. circ. 6,000. **Document type:** directory.
Formerly: Balance Wheel for Accreditation.
Description: Provides description of accreditation and membership, including addresses, telephone numbers and staff listings.

378   US   ISSN 0146-7336
LB2338
DIRECTORY OF RESEARCH GRANTS. 1975. a. $125 (effective 1994). Oryx Press, 4041 N. Central Ave., No. 700, Phoenix, AZ 85012-3397. TEL 602-265-2651. FAX 602-265-6250.
●Also available online. Vendor(s): DIALOG Information Services, Inc.
Also available on CD-ROM. Producer(s): DIALOG Information Services, Inc.
—BLDSC (3595.057000).
Description: Lists more than 6,000 grant programs alphabetically by grant title, providing program descriptions, requirements, restrictions, funding amounts, application deadlines, programs, and addresses.

378   AT   ISSN 0159-6306
DISCOURSE; Australian journal of educational studies. 1980. s-a. Aus.$35($50) University of Queensland, Department of Education, Brisbane, Qld. 4072, Australia. FAX 61-7-365-7199. Eds. Fazal Rizvi, Bob Lingard. adv.; bk.rev. circ. 500. (back issues avail.) **Indexed:** Cont.Pg.Educ., Educ.Tech.Abstr., Mult.Ed.Abstr., SOMA, Stud.Wom.Abstr. **Document type:** academic/scholarly publication.
—BLDSC (3595.780000).
Description: Focus on cultural, political, economic, philosophical, historical, policy studies of education.

378   IT   ISSN 0391-5018
DOC ITALIA. 1972. biennial. L.230000($143) (Istituto Nazionale Informazione) Editoriale Italiana, Via Vigliena 10, 00192 Rome, Italy. FAX 3211359. illus. circ. 5,000. **Document type:** directory.
Formerly (until 1977): Doc - Documentazione.
Description: Information on cultural and scientific centers in Italy.

378   MX   ISSN 0185-3597
DOCENCIA POSTSECUNDARIA. 1973. 4/yr. $45. (Universidad Autonoma de Guadalajara) Ediciones Educativas, Av. Patria No. 1201, Lomas del Valle, Box 1-400, 44100 Guadalajara, Jal., Mexico. FAX 36-425427. TELEX 682785 UAG PME. Ed. Oscar Soria. adv.; illus. circ. 1,000. **Indexed:** Hisp.Amer.Per.Ind.
Description: Provides an international perspective on innovation in contemporary universities, problems and possible solutions.

DOKUMENTATION ZUR GERMANISTISCHEN SPRACHWISSENSCHAFT. see *LINGUISTICS*

DOKUMENTE ZUM HOCHSCHULSPORT. see *SPORTS AND GAMES*

378   US   ISSN 0277-6987
LB2337.4
DON'T MISS OUT: THE AMBITIOUS STUDENT'S GUIDE TO FINANCIAL AID. 1976. a. $6. Octameron Associates, Inc., Box 2748, Alexandria, VA 22301. TEL 703-836-5480. Ed. Anne Leider. bibl.; illus.; stat. circ. 50,000. (back issues avail.)

378   US
E R I C CLEARINGHOUSE FOR COMMUNITY COLLEGES DIGEST. (Educational Resources Information Center) 8/yr. free. E R I C Clearinghouse for Community Colleges, 3051 Moore Hall, University of California, Los Angeles, 405 Hilgard Ave., Los Angeles, CA 90024. TEL 800-832-8256. FAX 310-206-8095. **Document type:** bulletin.
Formerly: E R I C Clearinghouse for Junior College Digest.
Description: Provides an overview of topics of current interest in community college education.

378   US
E R I C INFORMATION BULLETIN; clearinghouse for community colleges. 1966. q. free. E R I C Clearinghouse for Community Colleges, 3051 Moore Hall, University of California, Los Angeles, 405 Hilgard Ave., Los Angeles, CA 90024. TEL 800-832-8256. FAX 310-206-8095. circ. 5,000.
Former titles: E R I C Clearinghouse for Junior College & E R I C Two-Year College Information Bulletin.
Description: Includes abstracts of ERIC documents, data on clearinghouse personnel and activities and list of products currently available.

378   US   ISSN 0046-1547
LB1131
E T S DEVELOPMENTS. 1951. q. free. Educational Testing Service, Princeton, NJ 08541-0001. TEL 609-921-9000. (Dist. by: Corporate Publications, ETS, 16-D, Princeton, NJ 08541-0001) Ed. Wendy Miller Nardi. illus.; stat. circ. 85,000.
—Faxon.
Description: Reports news of ETS measurement, research, and related activities of general interest.

378   US   ISSN 0277-7002
EARN & LEARN: COOPERATIVE EDUCATION OPPORTUNITIES OFFERED BY THE FEDERAL GOVERNMENT. 1979. a. $3.50. Octameron Associates, Inc., Box 2748, Alexandria, VA 22301. TEL 703-836-5480. circ. 20,000.
Formerly: Federal Government and Cooperative Education (ISSN 0270-434X)

378   US
▼**THE EASTERN PROGRESS.** 1992. w. $30 (effective 1992). Eastern Kentucky University, Department of Mass Communications, 117 Donovan Annex, Richmond, KY 40475. TEL 606-622-1872. FAX 606-622-2354. Ed. Amy Etmans. adv. contact: Monica Keeton. circ. 10,000. **Document type:** newsletter.

ECOLE DU GRAND PARIS. see *LABOR UNIONS*

378 323   SA   ISSN 0070-8976
EDGAR BROOKES ACADEMIC AND HUMAN FREEDOM LECTURE. 1965. a. University of Natal, Students Representative Council, P.O. Box 375, Pietermaritzburg, South Africa. circ. 1,000.

EDITORS' NOTES. see *PUBLISHING AND BOOK TRADE*

378 374   UN   ISSN 0798-1228
EDUCACION SUPERIOR Y SOCIEDAD. (Text mainly in Spanish; occasionally in English, French) 1979. s-a. $18. Unesco - C R E S A L C, Apdo. 68.394, Caracas 1062-A, Venezuela. TEL 582-261-13-51. FAX 582-262-04-28. TELEX 24642 UNELC VC. circ. 1,500. (back issues avail.)
—SWETS.
Former titles (until 1990): Educacion Superior (ISSN 0251-4664); Higher Education Bulletin.

EDUCARE. see *EDUCATION — Special Education And Rehabilitation*

EDUCATION AFTER SIXTEEN. see *EDUCATION — Guides To Schools And Colleges*

378   US
EDUCATION FOR THE PEOPLE. s-a. National Coalition for Universities in the Public Interest, 1806 T St., N.W., Washington, DC 20009. TEL 202-234-0041.
Description: Covers education access, multiculturalism, corporate, military and right-wing abuses of the university and campus activism.

378   EI   ISSN 0070-9182
EDUCATION IN EUROPE. SECTION 1: HIGHER EDUCATION AND RESEARCH. 1963. irreg. price varies. Council of Europe, Council for Cultural Co-Operation, Publications Section, Strasbourg, France. FAX 33-88-41-27-81. (Dist. in U.S. by: Manhattan Publishing Co., P.O. Box 650, Croton-on-Hudson, N.Y. 10520)

EDUCATION IN KENYA; index of articles on education. see *EDUCATION — Abstracting, Bibliographies, Statistics*

378   AT   ISSN 0311-2543
LB2300
EDUCATION RESEARCH AND PERSPECTIVES. 1950. s-a. Aus.$25. University of Western Australia, Department of Education, Nedlands, W.A. 6009, Australia. FAX 09-380-1052. TELEX AA 92992. (Dist. in U.S. by: International Scholarly Book Services, Box 555, Forest Grove, OR 97116) Eds. C. Whitehead, M. O'Neill. adv.; bk.rev. circ. 800. **Indexed:** Aus.Educ.Ind., Aus.P.A.I.S., Cont.Pg.Educ., Mult.Ed.Abstr., Res.High.Educ.Abstr. **Document type:** academic/scholarly publication.
—BLDSC (3661.331000); Faxon.
Formerly: Australian Journal of Higher Education.

EDUCATION — HIGHER EDUCATION

378   US   ISSN 0013-1725
L11
EDUCATIONAL FORUM. 1936. 4/yr. $15 (foreign $18). Kappa Delta Pi International Honor Society in Education, Box A, West Lafayette, IN 47906-0576. TEL 317-743-1705. FAX 317-743-2202. Ed. Carol Bloom. bk.rev.; bibl.; index. circ. 62,000. (also avail. in microform from UMI,MIM; reprint service avail. from UMI) **Indexed:** Bk.Rev.Ind. (1977-), Bus.Educ.Ind., C.I.J.E., Child.Bk.Rev.Ind. (1977-), Cont.Pg.Educ., Educ.Admin.Abstr., Educ.Ind., Mult.Ed.Abstr. **Document type:** academic/scholarly publication.
—BLDSC (3661.414000); Faxon; UnCover; SWETS; UMI.
Description: Features scholarly analyses, and critical essays on contemporary problems and possibilities in education.
Refereed Serial

378   US   ISSN 0091-8989
LB3051
EDUCATIONAL TESTING SERVICE ANNUAL REPORT. Key Title: Annual Report - Educational Testing Service. 1949. a. free. Educational Testing Service, Princeton, NJ 08541-0001. TEL 609-921-9000. (Subscr. to: Little Brown, 200 West St., Waltham, MA 02254. TEL 800-759-0190; Institutions subscr. to: Special Sales, Warner Books, Inc., Time & Life Bldg., 1271 Ave. of the Americas, New York, NY 10020. TEL 212-522-7381) Ed. Albert Benderson. illus. circ. 65,000.
Description: An annual review of ETS research, programs, services and finances.

EDUFACTS. see *MEDICAL SCIENCES — Nurses And Nursing*

ENGINEERING GRADUATE STUDIES AND RESEARCH. DIRECTORY. see *ENGINEERING*

378   SW   ISSN 1100-181X
ENTUSIASMEN. 1979. bi-m. Laerarhoegskolan i Malmoe, Laerarhoegskolans Studentkaar, P.O. Box 23501, S-200 45 Malmoe, Sweden.

ERASMUS DIRECTORY. see *EDUCATION — Abstracting, Bibliographies, Statistics*

378   EI   ISSN 1012-9030
ERASMUS NEWSLETTER. French edition: Erasmus Bulletin d'Informations (ISSN 1012-9049); German edition: Erasmus Mitteilungsblatt (ISSN 1012-9014); Spanish edition: Erasmus Boletin (ISSN 1012-9073); Italian edition: Erasmus Bollettino (ISSN 1012-9057); Dutch edition: Erasmus Nieuwsbrief (ISSN 1012-9065) Danish edition: Erasmus Nyhedsblad (EI ISSN 1012-9006) Greek edition: Erasmus Enemerotiko Deltio (EI ISSN 1012-9022) Portuguese edition: Erasmus Boletin de Informacao (EI ISSN 1012-9081) (Text in English) 1987. 3/yr. 13 ECU. (Commission of European Communities, Task Force Human Resources) Office for the Official Publications of the European Community, 200 rue de la Loi, B-1049 Brussels, Belgium. (Dist. in US by: Unipub, 4611-F Assembly Dr., Lanham, MD 20706-4391. TEL 800-274-4888) **Document type:** newsletter.
—BLDSC (3794.910600).

378   US   ISSN 0071-1187
ERNEST BLOCH LECTURES. 1969. irreg., vol.4, 1993. price varies. University of California Press, 2120 Berkeley Way, Berkeley, CA 94720. TEL 415-642-4247. FAX 415-643-7127. (Orders to: California-Princeton Fulfillment Services, 1445 Lower Ferry Rd., Ewing, NJ 08618. TEL 800-777-4726. FAX 800-999-1958) **Document type:** monographic series.
Description: Discusses Western and Eastern musical traditions.
Refereed Serial

370.7   CL   ISSN 0716-050X
ESTUDIOS PEDAGOGICOS. (Text in Spanish; summaries in English, Spanish) 1976. a. $6 in Latin America; elsewhere $8. Universidad Austral de Chile, Facultad de Filosofia y Humanidades, Casilla 142, Valdivia, Chile. FAX 5663-212-589. Ed. Rene Novoa J. abstr.; bibl.; charts; stat. circ. 650.

378   BL   ISSN 0425-4082
ESTUDOS UNIVERSITARIOS. (Text in Portuguese; summaries in French & English) 1962. q. $12. Universidade Federal de Pernambuco, Departamento de Extensao Cultural, Recife, Pernambuco, Brazil.

378   GW
EUROMECUM; European higher education and research institutions. 1954. q. DM.295. Dr. Josef Raabe Verlag GmbH, Weberstr. 118, 53113 Bonn, Germany. TEL 0228-223071. FAX 0228-221783. **Document type:** directory.

378 630 370   US
EXCLAIMER. 1973. bi-m. free. University of Missouri System, University Relations & Extension, 806 Lewis Hall, Columbia, MO 65211. TEL 314-882-0604. FAX 314-884-4511. Ed. Eileen Bennett-Roberts. circ. 10,000. (tabloid format)
Description: Contains articles, news and information relevant to University Extension and continuing professional education throughout the state of Missouri.

378   US   ISSN 0046-3159
F A C C C BULLETIN. 1959. q. free to qualified personnel. Faculty Association of California Community Colleges, 926 J St., Ste. 211, Sacramento, CA 95814. TEL 916-447-8555. FAX 916-325-4970. Ed. Patrick McCallum. adv.; bk.rev. circ. 19,000. (tabloid format) **Indexed:** Cal.Per.Ind. (1978-), ERIC. **Document type:** bulletin.
Formerly: California Junior College Faculty Association C J C F A Bulletin.

378   US
F A C C C T S. 8/yr. membership. Faculty Association of California Community Colleges, 926 J St., Ste. 211, Sacramento, CA 95814. TEL 916-447-8555. FAX 916-325-4970. Ed. Patrick McCallum. circ. 4,500. (back issues avail.) **Document type:** newsletter.

378 331   AT
F A U S A NEWS. (Federated Australian University Staff Association) 1975. m. Aus.$12. National Tertiary Education Union, P.O. Box 1323, S. Melbourne, Vic. 3205, Australia. TEL 03-254-1880. FAX 03-254-1915. Ed. Simon Roberts. circ. 10,000. (tabloid format; back issues avail.) **Document type:** newsletter.
Description: Union newsletter for academics in higher education institutions.

378   UK   ISSN 0260-5058
F E R N JOURNAL. 1980. s-a. membership. Further Education Research Network, c/o D. G. Rogers, Centre for Postgraduate Studies, Leicester Polytechnic, Scraptoft Campus, Leicester LE7 9SU, England.

378 331.8   CN
F Q P P U UNIVERSITE. 1979. 6/yr. free. Federation Quebecoise des Professeures et Professeurs d'Universite, 4446 bd. St-Laurent, Bur. 405, Montreal, PQ H2W 1Z5, Canada. TEL 514-843-5953. FAX 514-843-6928. adv.; bk.rev. circ. 8,000. (looseleaf format; back issues avail.) **Document type:** newspaper.
Former titles (until 1991): F Q P P U Nouvelles Universitaires; F A P U Q Nouvelles Universitaires (ISSN 0709-8006); F A P U Q Information (ISSN 0709-8014)

378.73   US
FACT BOOK FOR HIGHER EDUCATION. 1958. irreg. $41.95. Oryx Press, 4041 N. Central Ave., Ste. 700, Phoenix, AZ 85012-3397. TEL 602-265-2651. stat.; cum.index. **Document type:** academic/scholarly publication.
Former titles: Fact Book for Academic Administrators (ISSN 0198-8425); Fact Book for Academic Administration; (until 1980): Fact Book on Higher Education (ISSN 0363-6720); F B; A Fact Book on Higher Education (ISSN 0014-6501)

378   US   ISSN 0191-1643
LA230.5.S6
FACT BOOK ON HIGHER EDUCATION IN THE SOUTH. 1965. biennial. price varies. Southern Regional Education Board, 592 Tenth St., Atlanta, GA 30318-5790. TEL 404-875-9211. **Document type:** academic/scholarly publication.

FACULTY PRESS REVIEW. see *PUBLISHING AND BOOK TRADE*

378   US   ISSN 1040-1288
L901
FACULTY WHITE PAGES; a subject-classified directory listing more than 510,000 names, addresses, and telephone numbers for faculty at over 3,000 U S colleges, universities, and other institutions of higher education. a. $130. Gale Research Inc., 835 Penobscot Bldg., Detroit, MI 48226. TEL 800-877-4253. FAX 313-961-6815. TELEX 810-221-7086. **Document type:** directory.

FEDERAL GRANTS & CONTRACTS WEEKLY; project opportunities in research, training and services. see *PUBLIC ADMINISTRATION*

020 378.3   US
Z668
FINANCIAL ASSISTANCE FOR LIBRARY AND INFORMATION STUDIES. a. $1 donation. American Library Association, Standing Committee on Library Education, 50 E. Huron St., Chicago, IL 60611. TEL 312-280-4277. FAX 312-280-3256. Ed. Margaret Myers. circ. 4,000.
Formerly: Financial Assistance for Library Education (ISSN 0569-6275)
Description: Lists scholarships and assistantships available from library schools, state associations and agencies, national associations and other sources.

FINANCIAL POSITION OF ONTARIO UNIVERSITIES. see *EDUCATION — School Organization And Administration*

FINANCIAL REPORT OF ONTARIO UNIVERSITIES. see *EDUCATION — School Organization And Administration*

374.013   US
FIRST OPPORTUNITY. 1985. 4/yr. $9.60. Communications Publishing Group, Inc., 106 W. 11th St., Ste. 250. Kansas City, MO 64105-1806. TEL 816-221-4404. FAX 816-221-1112. Ed. Georgia Lee Clark. adv. circ. 500,000.
Description: For young adults with a desire to pursue a vocational-technical career.

378.759   US   ISSN 0093-1071
LA258.5
FLORIDA. STATE BOARD OF INDEPENDENT COLLEGES AND UNIVERSITIES. REPORT. Key Title: Report of the State Board of Independent Colleges and Universities (Tallahassee). 1972. a. free. Florida State Board of Independent Colleges and Universities, c/o C. Wayne Freeburg, Exec. Dir. and Ed., 201 Collins Bldg., Tallahassee, FL 32399. TEL 904-488-8695. circ. 100.

371   US   ISSN 0071-5999
FLORIDA REQUIREMENTS FOR TEACHER CERTIFICATION. 1923. irreg. free. Department of Education, Knott Bldg., Tallahassee, FL 32304. TEL 904-488-1234. Ed. Ralph D. Turlington.

378   IS
FOCUS. (Text in English) 1983. q. free. University of Haifa, Department of Public Affairs and Information, Mt. Carmel, Haifa 31905, Israel. TEL 972-4-240093. FAX 972-4-342104. TELEX 46660-UNIHA-IL. Ed. A.M. Goldstein. circ. 2,000.
Former titles: Inside; Carmel: News from Haifa University.
Description: News and features about the University of Haifa.

378   US   ISSN 0276-0592
FOCUS (PRINCETON). 1976. s-a. free. Educational Testing Service, Princeton, NJ 08541-0001. TEL 609-921-9000. (Subscr. to: Little Brown, 200 West St., Waltham, MA 02254. TEL 800-759-0190; Institutions subscr. to: Special Sales, Warner Book, Inc., Time & Life Bldg., 1271 Ave. of the Americas, New York, NY 10020. TEL 212-522-7381) Ed. Carol Carlson. illus.; stat. circ. 50,000.

FOCUS ON LAW STUDIES; teaching about law in the liberal arts. see *LAW*

378   SW   ISSN 0284-7574
FOLKUNIVERSITETET; iceer och debatt om bildning och kultur. 1978. bi-m. Folkuniversitetet, Banerg. 54, S-115 26 Stockholm, Sweden.

2106 EDUCATION — HIGHER EDUCATION

378 US
FOR GRADUATES ONLY. 1979. a. free to qualified personnel. Campus Communications, Inc. (New City), 339 N. Main St., Ste. 4, New City, NY 10956. TEL 914-638-0333. circ. 100,000. **Document type:** academic/scholarly publication.
 Description: Provides guidance and planning advice to seniors of two year community and junior colleges.

378   GW
LA727.5
FORSCHUNG UND LEHRE; Mitteilungen des deutschen Hochschulverbandes. 1950. m. DM.120. Deutscher Hochschulverband, Rheinallee 18, 53173 Bonn, Germany. TEL 0228-364005. FAX 0228-353403. Ed. Felix Grigat. adv.: B&W page DM.2620; adv. contact: Felix Grigat. bk.rev. circ. 17,700. **Document type:** academic/scholarly publication.
 Formerly (until 1993): Deutscher Hochschulverband. Mitteilungen (ISSN 0437-6315)

378   AU   ISSN 0429-1573
FORSCHUNGEN ZUR INNSBRUCKER UNIVERSITAETSGESCHICHTE. (Subseries of: Universitaet Innsbruck. Veroeffentlichungen) 1962. irreg., vol.10, 1971. price varies. (Universitaet Innsbruck) Oesterreichische Kommissionsbuchhandlung, Maximilianstrasse 17, A-6020 Innsbruck, Austria. Ed. Franz Huter.

378   SW   ISSN 0348-1522
FORUM FOER DEBATT OCH INFORMATION. 1974. 8/yr. Laerarhoegskolan i Malmoe, P.O. Box 23501, S-200 45 Malmoe, Sweden.

370   AT   ISSN 0015-8542
FORUM OF EDUCATION. 1942. 2/yr. Aus.$16 to individuals; institutions and libraries Aus.$20; foreign Aus.$25. Sydney University, Faculty of Education, Institute of Education, Sydney , N.S.W. 2066, Australia. Ed. J.G. Murphy. bk.rev. circ. 1,000. **Indexed:** Aus.Educ.Ind., Aus.P.A.I.S., Res.High.Educ.Abstr.
 Description: Covers all aspects of education.

378   RM   ISSN 0015-8453
FORUM - REVISTA INVATAMINTULUI SUPERIOR. (Text in Rumanian; summaries in English, French, Rumanian and Russian) 1959. m. 180 lei to institutions; qualified personnel 96 lei. (Ministerul Educatiei si Invatamintului) Foreign Languages Press Group "Romania", Piata presei Libere 1, 71341 Bucharest, Rumania. TEL 6173836. FAX 6170487. Ed. Aurel Joltea. adv.; bk.rev.; charts; illus.; stat.; index. circ. 4,850.
 Formerly: Revista Invatamintului Superior.

FULBRIGHT ASSOCIATION NEWSLETTER. see EDUCATION — International Education Programs

378 371.42   AT
G C C A NEWSLETTER. 1969. s-a. $40 free to members. Graduate Careers Council of Australia Ltd., P.O. Box 28, Parkville, Vic. 3052, Australia. TEL 03-347-4644. FAX 03-347-7298. Ed. Bruce Guthrie. bk.rev. circ. 2,000.

378   UY
GACETA UNIVERSITARIA. 1957. q. Universidad de la Republica, 18 de Julio 1824, Montevideo, Uruguay. TEL 48-49-01. FAX 48-03-03. TELEX 26692 UDELAY UY.
 Formerly (until 1969): Gaceta de la Universidad (ISSN 0016-3759)

GAODENG XUEXIAO HUAXUE XUEBAO/CHEMICAL JOURNAL OF CHINESE UNIVERSITIES. see CHEMISTRY

378   GW   ISSN 0016-8157
GEORGIA AUGUSTA. 1964. s-a. price varies. (Universitaet Goettingen) Vandenhoeck und Ruprecht, Robert-Bosch-Breite 6, 37079 Goettingen, Germany. TEL 0551-6959-0. FAX 0551-695917. (Subscr. to: 37070 Goettingen, Germany) bk.rev.; charts; illus. **Document type:** academic/scholarly publication.
 —BLDSC (4158.295000). **CCC.**

GIJUTSU KYOIKU KENKYU RONBUNSHI/JOURNAL OF TECHNOLOGY AND EDUCATION. see ENGINEERING — Electrical Engineering

001.3 378   GW   ISSN 0085-1108
GOETTINGER UNIVERSITAETSREDEN. 1941. irreg. price varies. Vandenhoeck und Ruprecht, Robert-Bosch-Breite 6, 37079 Goettingen, Germany. TEL 0551-6959-0. FAX 0551-695917. (Subscr. to: 37070 Goettingen, Germany) **Document type:** monographic series.

378   US   ISSN 1049-717X
LB2331.63
GOURMAN REPORT. RATING OF GRADUATE AND PROFESSIONAL PROGRAMS IN AMERICAN AND INTERNATIONAL UNIVERSITIES. 1980. biennial? National Education Standards, One Wilshire Bldg., Ste. 1210, 624 S. Grand Ave., Los Angeles, CA 90017.

378   US   ISSN 1049-7188
LB2331.63
GOURMAN REPORT. RATING OF UNDERGRADUATE PROGRAMS IN AMERICAN AND INTERNATIONAL UNIVERSITIES. 1980. biennial. National Education Standards, One Wilshire Bldg., Ste. 1210, 624 S. Grand Ave., Los Angeles, CA 90017.

GRADUATE COMPUTERWORLD. see COMPUTERS

378 507   US   ISSN 0072-5250
GRADUATE FELLOWSHIP AWARDS ANNOUNCED BY NATIONAL SCIENCE FOUNDATION. a. free. U.S. National Science Foundation, Science & Technology Information System (STIS), 4201 Wilson Blvd., Ste. 245, Arlington, VA 22230. (Subscr. to: Superintendent of Documents, U.S. Government Printing Office, Box 371954, Pittsburgh, PA 15250-7954. TEL 202-783-3238. FAX 202-512-2233) **Document type:** government publication.

378 530   US   ISSN 0147-1821
QC30
GRADUATE PROGRAMS: PHYSICS, ASTRONOMY, AND RELATED FIELDS (YEAR). 1970. a. $36. American Institute of Physics, One Physics Ellipse, College Park, MD 20740-3843. TEL 301-209-3000. (Subscr. to: Member and Subscriber Service, 500 Sunnyside Blvd., Woodbury, NY 11797-2999. TEL 516-576-2270) circ. 2,300. **Document type:** academic/scholarly publication.

370   US
GRADUATE RESEARCH IN URBAN EDUCATION AND RELATED DISCIPLINES. 1965. s-a. $5. City College of New York, School of Education, Klapper Hall, 135th St. & Convent Ave., New York, NY 10031. TEL 212-690-5315. Ed.Bd. charts; stat. circ. 325. **Indexed:** Educ.Ind., Psychol.Abstr.
 Formerly (until 1979): Graduate Research in Education and Related Disciplines (ISSN 0017-2839)

GRADUATE SCHOOL JOURNAL. see EDUCATION — School Organization And Administration

378   UK
GRADUATE STUDIES (G R A S). 1972. a. £99.75. Hobsons Publishing plc., Bateman St., Cambridge CB2 1LZ, England. TEL 0223-354551. FAX 0223-323154. TELEX 81546-HOBCAM-G. Ed. Jenny Knight. adv. contact: Will Bromage. circ. 2,000. **Document type:** directory.
 Description: Covers all postgraduate study opportunities in the U.K.

378   US   ISSN 0740-5383
GRANT ADVISOR. (Supplement avail.: Grant Works) 1983. m. (except July). $138 (diskette $325) (effective Jan. 1993). c/o Robert J. Toft, Box 520, Linden, VA 22642. TEL 703-636-1529. FAX 703-636-7313. Ed. Christopher L. Watkins. bk.rev. circ. 500. (also avail. in diskette format) **Document type:** newsletter.
 Description: Comprehensive newsletter on federal, foundation, and other philanthropic grant sources available for college and university faculty and their institutions.

378   US   ISSN 1045-2761
LB2337.2
GRANTS FOR HIGHER EDUCATION. 1982. a. $65. Foundation Center, 79 Fifth Ave., New York, NY 10003. TEL 212-620-4230. FAX 212-807-3677. index.

378   UK   ISSN 0072-5471
LB2338
GRANTS REGISTER. 1968. biennial. £95. Macmillan Publishers Ltd., Houndmills, Basingstoke, Hampshire RG21 2XS, England. TEL 0256-29242. FAX 0256-810526. TELEX 858493. (Dist. in U.S. by: St. Martin's Press, 175 Fifth Ave., New York, NY 10010) **Document type:** directory.
 —BLDSC (4211.120000).

378 379   US
GRAPEVINE (NORMAL); state appropriations for higher education; state tax legislation; legislation affecting education beyond the high school. 1958. m. free. c/o Dr. Edward R. Hines, Ed., Center for Higher Education, Illinois State University, Normal, IL 61761. TEL 309-438-5405. FAX 309-438-8683. charts; stat. circ. 1,000. (looseleaf format; back issues avail.) **Document type:** newsletter.

GREAT BRITAIN. ECONOMIC & SOCIAL RESEARCH COUNCIL. BURSARY HANDBOOK. see SOCIAL SCIENCES: COMPREHENSIVE WORKS

GREAT BRITAIN. ECONOMIC & SOCIAL RESEARCH COUNCIL. STUDENTSHIP HANDBOOK. see SOCIAL SCIENCES: COMPREHENSIVE WORKS

370 711   US
GUIDE FOR NEW PLANNERS. 1984. irreg. $15. Society for College and University Planning, c/o 2026M School of Education, University of Michigan, Ann Arbor, MI 48109-1259. TEL 313-763-4776. circ. 2,400. (also avail. in microfiche)
 Description: Strategy and planning guide for higher education administrators and management personnel.

301.07   CN   ISSN 0316-1854
GUIDE TO DEPARTMENTS OF SOCIOLOGY, ANTHROPOLOGY AND ARCHAEOLOGY IN UNIVERSITIES AND MUSEUMS IN CANADA/ANNUAIRE DES DEPARTEMENTS DE SOCIOLOGIE, D'ANTHROPOLOGIE ET D'ARCHEOLOGIE DES UNIVERSITES ET DES MUSEES DU CANADA. 1974. irreg. Can.$15. Canadian Sociology and Anthropology Association, Concordia University, 1455 Bd. de Maisonneuve W., Montreal, PQ H3G 1M8, Canada. TEL 514-848-8780. FAX 514-848-8780. Ed. William Reimer.
 Formerly: Guide to Departments of Sociology and Anthropology in Canadian Universities (ISSN 0315-0895)

GUIDE TO GRADUATE DEPARTMENTS OF SOCIOLOGY. see SOCIOLOGY

378   UK   ISSN 0265-2730
GUIDE TO POSTGRADUATE DEGREES, DIPLOMAS AND COURSES IN MEDICINE. 1975. a. £13.50 (effective 1994). (British Council, National Advice Center for Postgraduate Medical Education) IntelliGene, Woodlands, Ford, Midlothian EH37 5RE, Scotland. TEL 0875-320063. FAX 0875-320276. Ed. G.M. Haddock. **Document type:** directory.
 Formerly: Summary of Postgraduate Diplomas and Courses in Medicine (ISSN 0302-3494)
 Description: Contains information on degrees and diplomas awarded by medical educational establishments in the United Kingdom, courses of study, and degree requirements. Arranged by medical specialty.

378 700   JA   ISSN 0533-6627
GUNMA UNIVERSITY, FACULTY OF EDUCATION. ANNUAL REPORT: ART, TECHNOLOGY, HEALTH & PHYSICAL EDUCATION, AND SCIENCE OF HUMAN LIVING SERIES. (Text in Japanese; summaries in English) 1966. a. exchange basis. Gunma University, Faculty of Education - Gunma Daigaku Kyoikubu, Gunma University Library, 4-2 Aramaki, Maebashi, Gunma 371, Japan. Ed.Bd. **Indexed:** Biol.Abstr.
 —UnCover.

GUOWAI YUYANXUE. see LINGUISTICS

378   DK   ISSN 0109-2111
GYDEN. 1979. 8/yr. DKK 200 (typically set in Jan.). Odense Universitet, Studenterraadet - Odense University, Students' Council, Campusvej 55, 5230 Odense M, Denmark. TEL 66-15-86-96. Ed. Birgit Martinsen. adv.; bk.rev.; illus. circ. 3,000.

EDUCATION — HIGHER EDUCATION

378 375   AT   ISSN 0813-524X
H E R D S A GREEN GUIDE. 1984. irreg. Higher Education Research and Development Society of Australasia, c/o T.E.R.C., University of New South Wales, Kensington, N.S.W. 2033, Australia. TEL 02 697 4937. (back issues avail.)
    Description: Brief, practical guides for tertiary educators.

H E R D S A NEWS. (Higher Education Research and Development Society of Australasia) see *EDUCATION*

HANDBOOK OF DEGREE AND ADVANCED COURSES IN INSTITUTES-COLLEGES OF HIGHER EDUCATION, COLLEGES OF EDUCATION, POLYTECHNICS, UNIVERSITY DEPARTMENTS OF EDUCATION. see *EDUCATION — Guides To Schools And Colleges*

HANDBOOK OF ENGINEERING EDUCATION. see *EDUCATION — Guides To Schools And Colleges*

HANDBOOK OF MEDICAL EDUCATION. see *EDUCATION — Guides To Schools And Colleges*

HARBOR BRANCH NEWS. see *EARTH SCIENCES — Oceanography*

HARVARD BUSINESS SCHOOL. BULLETIN. see *BUSINESS AND ECONOMICS*

378   FI
HELSINGIN KAUPPAKORKEAKOULU. JULKAISUSARJA A. VAEITOESKIRJOJA. (Text in English and Finnish) irreg. Helsinki School of Economics, Runeberginkatu 22-24, 00100 Helsinki, Finland.

378   GH
HI - ED NEWS; national higher education news. 6/yr. free. Ministry of Education, Higher Education Division, P.O. Box M. 45, Accra, Ghana. Ed. Irene Duncan.
    Former titles: H E News; Ghana. National Council for Higher Education. Annual Report.

378   NE   ISSN 0018-1560
LB2300   CODEN: HREDAN
HIGHER EDUCATION; the international journal of higher education and educational planning. (Text and summaries in English) 1971. 8/yr. fl.660($345) (effective 1994). Kluwer Academic Publishers, Postbus 17, 3300 AA Dordrecht, Netherlands. TEL 31-78-334911. FAX 31-78-334254. TELEX 29245 KAPG NL. (Dist. by: Kluwer Academic Publishers Group, P.O. Box 322, 3300 AH Dordrecht, Netherlands. TEL 31-78-524400. FAX 31-78-524474; N. America dist. addr.: Box 358, Accord Sta., Hingham, MA 02018-0358. TEL 617-871-6600. FAX 617-871-6528) Ed. Noel Entwistle. adv.; bk.rev.; stat.; index, cum.index every 5 yrs. (also avail. in microform from UMI; reprint service avail. from SWZ) **Indexed:** Br.Educ.Ind., C.I.J.E., Coll.Stud.Pers.Abstr., Cont.Pg.Educ., Curr.Cont., Educ.Admin.Abstr., Educ.Ind., Educ.Tech.Abstr., High.Educ.Curr.Aware.Bull., Lang.& Lang.Behav.Abstr., Lang.Teach.& Ling.Abstr., Mid.East: Abstr.& Ind., Mult.Ed.Abstr., Res.High.Educ.Abstr., Sociol.Abstr., Sociol.Educ.Abstr., SOMA, SSCI, Stud.Wom.Abstr. **Document type:** academic/scholarly publication.
—BLDSC (4307.369900); Faxon; UnCover; SWETS; UMI. **CCC.**
    Description: Serves as a forum for exhange of research results, experience and insights on education in universities, polytechnics, technical colleges, research institutes and specialist institutions throughout the world.
    Refereed Serial

378   US   ISSN 0882-4126
HIGHER EDUCATION; handbook of theory & research. 1985. a. $54 per vol. Agathon Press, 5648 Riverdale Ave., Ste. 50, Bronx, NY 10471. TEL 718-543-6207. (Subscr. to: c/o Maxway, 100 Newfield Ave., Rariton Center, Edison, NJ 08837. TEL 908-225-2727. FAX 908-225-1562) Ed. John Smart. (back issues avail.) **Document type:** academic/scholarly publication.
—BLDSC (4307.369880); UnCover. **CCC.**
    Description: Analytical reviews of history, trends and current literature on all aspects of higher education.

378 011 310   US   ISSN 0748-4364
Z5814.P8
HIGHER EDUCATION ABSTRACTS; abstracts of periodical literature, monographs and conference papers on college students, faculty and administration. 1965. q. $80 to individuals; institutions $180 (effective July 1994). Claremont Graduate School, 740 N. College Ave., Claremont, CA 91711. TEL 714-621-8555. Ed. Bonny M. McLaughlin. bk.rev.; abstr.; index. circ. 1,400. (also avail. in microform from UMI; back issues avail.) **Document type:** abstracting/indexing.
—BLDSC (4307.370400); UMI.
    Formerly (until 1984): College Student Personnel Abstracts (ISSN 0010-1168)
    Description: Synopses of current research and theory on students, faculty and administrators in higher education institutions, examining teaching, research, planning, and management, as well as the institutional environment, orientation, the role of state and federal governments, and demographic trends.

378   US   ISSN 0018-1579
D810.E3
HIGHER EDUCATION AND NATIONAL AFFAIRS. 1952. bi-w. (24/yr.). $30. American Council on Education, One Dupont Circle, N.W., Washington, DC 20036. TEL 202-939-9300. circ. 25,000. (also avail. in microform from UMI; reprint service avail. from UMI) —UMI.

378   UN   ISSN 0379-7724
LA628
HIGHER EDUCATION IN EUROPE. (Editions in English, French, Russian) 1975. q. $50. (Unesco) European Centre for Higher Education, 39 Stirbei Voda, Bucharest, Rumania. TEL 401-1-613-08-39. FAX 401-1-641-5025. TELEX 11658 CEPES R. Ed.Bd. adv.; bk.rev. circ. 1,500 English ed.; 500 French ed.; 3,000 Russian ed. (back issues avail.) **Indexed:** Cont.Pg.Educ., Educ.Tech.Abstr., ERIC, Res.High.Educ.Abstr., Stud.Wom.Abstr.
—BLDSC (4307.378500); SWETS.

378   FR   ISSN 1013-851X
HIGHER EDUCATION MANAGEMENT. (Text in English, French) 1977. 3/yr. $52. Organization for Economic Cooperation and Development, 2 rue Andre-Pascal, 75775 Paris Cedex 16, France. (U.S. orders to: O.E.C.D. Publication and Information Center, 2001 L St., N.W., Ste. 700, Washington, DC 20036-4910. TEL 202-785-6323) bk.rev. circ. 470. (also avail. in microfiche from OEC; back issues avail.) **Indexed:** C.I.J.E., Cont.Pg.Educ., Educ.Tech.Abstr., Mult.Ed.Abstr., Res.High.Educ.Abstr.
—BLDSC (4307.382500); SWETS; UMI.
    Formerly (until 1989): International Journal of Institutional Management in Higher Education.
    Description: Covers management in higher education institutions in different countries.

378 323.42   US
HIGHER EDUCATION OPPORTUNITIES FOR MINORITIES AND WOMEN: ANNOTATED SELECTIONS. a. free. U.S. Department of Education, Washington, DC 20202.

378   UK   ISSN 0952-8733
HIGHER EDUCATION POLICY. 1952. q. £50($95) to individuals; institutions £70($133). (International Association of Universities) Kogan Page Ltd., 120 Pentonville Rd., London N1 9JN, England. TEL 071-278-0433. FAX 071-837-6348. TELEX 263088 KOGAN G. (U.S. dist.: 85 Ash St., Hopkinton, MA 01748) Ed. Guy Neave. illus.; index. (also avail. in microfiche; back issues avail.) **Document type:** academic/scholarly publication.
—BLDSC (4307.385900); UnCover; SWETS. **CCC.**
    Formerly (until 1988): International Association of Universities. Bulletin (ISSN 0020-6032)
    Description: Focuses on policy issues and the role of higher education in society today; also carries reports on relevant research being carried out in various parts of the world.

378   UK
HIGHER EDUCATION POLICY SERIES. irreg., no.28. Jessica Kingsley Publishers, 116 Pentonville Rd., London N1 9JB, England. TEL 071-833-2307. FAX 071-837-2917. Ed. Maurice Kogan. **Document type:** monographic series.

HIGHER EDUCATION PRODUCT COMPANION. see *EDUCATION — Computer Applications*

378   UK   ISSN 0951-5224
LA630
HIGHER EDUCATION QUARTERLY. 1946. q. £24($54) to individuals; institutions £59 ($128). Basil Blackwell Ltd., 108 Cowley Rd., Oxford OX4 1JF, England. TEL 0865-791100. FAX 0865-791347. TELEX 837022-OXBOOK-G. Ed.Bd. adv.; bk.rev.; bibl.; index. circ. 1,000. (also avail. in microform from UMI; reprint service avail. from SWZ,UMI) **Indexed:** Br.Educ.Ind., Br.Hum.Ind., C.I.J.E., Curr.Cont., Educ.Ind., Educ.Tech.Abstr., High.Educ.Curr.Aware.Bull., Lang.& Lang.Behav.Abstr., Mid.East: Abstr.& Ind., Mult.Ed.Abstr., P.A.I.S., Res.High.Educ.Abstr., SOMA, SSCI. **Document type:** academic/scholarly publication.
—BLDSC (4307.387000); Faxon; UnCover; SWETS; UMI. **CCC.**
    Former titles: Universities Quarterly: Culture, Education and Society; New Universities Quarterly (ISSN 0307-8612); Universities Quarterly (ISSN 0041-9230)

HIGHER EDUCATION RESEARCH AND DEVELOPMENT. RESEARCH PAPERS. see *EDUCATION*

378   US   ISSN 1045-7976
LB2342
HIGHER EDUCATION REVENUES & EXPENDITURES. 1988. a. Research Associates of Washington, 2605 Klingle Rd. N.W., Washington, DC 20008. TEL 202-966-3326.

378   UK   ISSN 0018-1609
LB2300
HIGHER EDUCATION REVIEW. 1968. 3/yr. £37($75) Tyrrell Burgess Associates Ltd., 34 Sandilands, Croydon CR0 5DB, England. Ed. John Pratt. adv.; bk.rev.; bibl.; charts; illus.; cum.index every 3 yrs. circ. 1,000. (also avail. in microform from UMI; back issues avail.; reprint service avail. from UMI) **Indexed:** C.I.J.E., Cont.Pg.Educ., Educ.Tech.Abstr., ERIC, High.Educ.Curr.Aware.Bull., Mult.Ed.Abstr., Res.High.Educ.Abstr., SSCI, Stud.Wom.Abstr. **Document type:** academic/scholarly publication.
—BLDSC (4307.390000); UnCover; SWETS; UMI.

HISPANIC OUTLOOK IN HIGHER EDUCATION. see *ETHNIC INTERESTS*

378   US   ISSN 0737-2698
LB2300
HISTORY OF HIGHER EDUCATION ANNUAL. 1981. a. $12 to individuals; institutions $15 (foreign $17). Pennsylvania State University, Higher Education Program, 403 S. Allen St., Ste. 115, University Park, PA 16801-5202. TEL 814-863-3784. Ed. Roger Geiger. adv.; bk.rev. circ. 350. (also avail. in microform from EDR) **Document type:** academic/scholarly publication.
—Faxon; UnCover.
    Description: Articles on the history of higher education in America and overseas.
    Refereed Serial

378 942   UK   ISSN 0144-5138
LA173
HISTORY OF UNIVERSITIES. (Text in English, French, German, Italian and Spanish) 1981. a. Oxford University Press, Oxford Journals, Walton St., Oxford OX2 6DP, England. TEL 0865-56767. FAX 0865-267773. TELEX 837330-OXPRESS-G. (U.S. subscr. to: Oxford University Press Inc., 2001 Evans Rd., Cary, NC 27513. TEL 919-677-0977) Ed. Laurence Brockliss. adv.; bk.rev.; index. **Indexed:** Amer.Hist.& Life, Hist.Abstr., Rel.Ind.One. **Document type:** academic/scholarly publication.
—BLDSC (4318.612000).

HOCHSCHULFUHRER. see *ENGINEERING*

370   DK   ISSN 0018-3334
HOEJSKOLEBLADET. 1876. w. DKK 500 (typically set in Jan.). Hoejskolebladet, Sdr. Boulevard 1, DK-4930 Maribo, Denmark. TEL 45-53-88-41-80. FAX 45-54-75-70-77. Ed. Else-Marie Boyhus. adv.; bk.rev. circ. 1,800.
    Description: Discusses politics, literature, the arts, education and the church.

378 790.13   GW
HOFKLATSCH; Magazin fuer Schueler. 1982. bi-m. DM.25. Hofklatsch Pupil Information Service, Podbielskistr. 230 30655 Hannover, Germany. Ed. Steffen Heisterberg. adv.; bk.rev. circ. 1,000. (back issues avail.) **Document type:** academic/scholarly publication.

EDUCATION — HIGHER EDUCATION

378 UK
HOW TO COMPLETE YOUR U C A S APPLICATION FORM. 1990. a. £5.95. Trotman & Co. Ltd., 12 Hill Rise, Richmond, Surrey TW10 6AU, England. TEL 081-940-5668. FAX 081-948-9267. Eds. Tony Higgins, Stephen Lamley. circ. 15,000. **Document type:** bulletin.

378 DK ISSN 0333-3620
Z286.S37
I A S P NEWSLETTER. (Text in English) 1980. 6/yr. $60. (International Association of Scholarly Publishers) Aarhus University Press, Building 170, Aarhus University, DK-8000 Aarhus C, Denmark. TEL 45-86-197033. FAX 45-86-198433. Ed. Toennes Bekker-Nielsen. **Document type:** newsletter. —CCC.

I E E E POTENTIALS; the magazine for engineering students. see ENGINEERING — Electrical Engineering

378 II
I I A S NEWSLETTER. (Text in English) 1973. s-a. Indian Institute of Advanced Study, Rashtrapati Nivas, Summer Hill, Simla 171005, India. Ed. T. Prem Kumar. bibl.
Supersedes: Indian Institute of Advanced Study. Bulletin (ISSN 0019-4905)

378 068 II
I I A S OCCASIONAL PAPERS. (Text in English) 1974. irreg. price varies. Indian Institute of Advanced Study, Rashtrapati Nivas, Summer Hill, Simla 171005, India.

371.8 NE
I U S NEWSLETTER. (Text in English, French, Spanish) 1946. s-m. free. International Union of Students, 211 Lann Van Meerdevoort, The Hague, Netherlands. Ed. Hakaria Abdaurahman. circ. 5,000.
Formerly: New Service (ISSN 0539-1199)

I U S WOMENS NEWSLETTER. (International Union of Students) see WOMEN'S INTERESTS

378.773 US ISSN 0094-8322
L903.I3
ILLINOIS. BOARD OF HIGHER EDUCATION. DIRECTORY OF HIGHER EDUCATION. Key Title: Directory of Higher Education. a. Board of Higher Education, 4 W. Old Capitol Plaza, Rm. 500, Springfield, IL 62701-1287. TEL 217-782-2551. **Document type:** directory.

378.1 US
ILLINOIS. COMMUNITY COLLEGE BOARD. BIENNIAL REPORT. 1967. biennial. free. Community College Board, 509 S. Sixth St., Rm. 400, Springfield, IL 62701. TEL 217-785-0123. FAX 217-524-4981. stat.
Former titles: Illinois. Community College Board. Annual Report; Illinois. Community College Board. Biennial Report; Which supersedes: Illinois. Junior College Board. Annual Report (ISSN 0092-7783)

378.1 US
ILLINOIS. COMMUNITY COLLEGE BOARD. DATA AND CHARACTERISTICS. 1981. a. Community College Board, 509 S. Sixth St., Rm. 400, Springfield, IL 62701-1874. TEL 217-785-0123. FAX 217-524-4981.
Description: Contains data and characteristics of the Illinois public community college system and is designed to serve as a basic reference.

IMAGE: JOURNAL OF NURSING SCHOLARSHIP. see MEDICAL SCIENCES — Nurses And Nursing

IMPACT (OMAHA). see MEDICAL SCIENCES

378 US
INDEPENDENT (WASHINGTON, 1956). 1956. 4/yr. membership only. Council of Independent Colleges, One Dupont Cir., Ste. 320, Washington, DC 20036. TEL 202-466-7230. Ed. Stephen G. Pelletier. bk.rev. circ. 7,000. (looseleaf format) **Document type:** newsletter.
Formerly: C A S C Newsletter (Council for the Advancement of Small Colleges).

370.7 371.02 AT ISSN 0310-7175
INDEPENDENT EDUCATION. 1971. q. Aus.$35. New South Wales Independent Teachers Association, G.P.O. Box 116, Sydney, N.S.W. 2001, Australia. TEL 02-202-2600. FAX 02-261-8860. Eds. Dick Shearman, Leith Hamilton. adv.: page Aus.$660. bk.rev. circ. 27,000. (back issues avail.) **Indexed:** Aus.Educ.Ind.
Description: Examines private schools.

INDEPENDENT SCHOLAR; a newsletter for independent scholars and their organizations. see OCCUPATIONS AND CAREERS

378 II
INDIAN EDUCATION (AGRA); planning and development. 1977. q. Agra University, Agra 282004, Uttar Pradesh, India. Ed. S.B.B.B. Singh. bk.rev.

745.2 US ISSN 0091-8601
T61
INDUSTRIAL EDUCATION.* (Product Suppliers Directory avail.) 1914. m. (Sept.-May). $20. Cummins Publishing Co., 6557 Forest Park Dr., Troy, MI 48098-1954. Ed. Kelley Callaghan. adv.; bk.rev.; bibl.; charts; illus.; tr.lit.; index. circ. 46,500. (also avail. in microfilm from UMI) **Indexed:** C.I.J.E., Cont.Pg.Educ., Educ.Ind., Ind.How To Do It (1978-1983), Mag.Ind., Media Rev.Dig. —UnCover.
Formerly: Industrial Arts and Vocational Education (ISSN 0019-8005); Incorporates: Occupational Education News.
Description: Serving vocational-technical education at high school, junior college, community college, vocational school and college-university level.

370.7 600 US
INDUSTRIAL TEACHER EDUCATION DIRECTORY. 1958. a. $10. National Association of Industrial and Technical Teacher Educators, Dept. of Industrial Technology, University of Northern Iowa, Cedar Falls, IA 50615-0178. TEL 319-273-2753. FAX 319-273-5818. (Co-sponsor: Council on Technology Teacher Education) Ed. Ervin A. Dennis. circ. 3,800 (controlled). **Document type:** directory.

338 378 UK ISSN 0950-4222
LC1085
INDUSTRY AND HIGHER EDUCATION. 1987. q. $190 (elsewhere £118). In Print Publishing Ltd., c/o Mr. A. Dingwall, Dir., 9 Beaufort Terr., Brighton, BN2 2SU, England. TEL 0273-682-836. FAX 0273-620-958. (Subscr. to: Turpin Distribution Services Ltd., Blackhorse Rd., Letchworth, Herts. SG6 1HN, England. TEL 0462-672555) Eds. A. Dingwall, J. Edmondson. adv.; bk.rev.; index. (also avail. in microform from UMI; back issues avail.) **Document type:** academic/scholarly publication.
—BLDSC (4476.285000); SWETS. CCC.
Description: Explores all aspects of the collaboration between business and higher education.
Refereed Serial

378 AU ISSN 0020-0077
INFORMATION FUER AUSLAENDISCHE STUDIENBEWERBER AN OESTERREICHISCHEN HOCHSCHULEN/INFORMATION FOR FOREIGN STUDENTS INTENDING TO STUDY AT AN AUSTRIAN INSTITUTION OF HIGHER EDUCATION; fuer auslaendische Studienbewerber an oesterreichischen Universitaeten und Kunsthochschulen. 1961. irreg. Oesterreichischer Akademischer Austauschdienst, Berggasse 21, A-1090 Vienna, Austria. TEL 01-3172791. FAX 01-3172795. Ed. Ludwig Koller. circ. 12,500. **Document type:** academic/scholarly publication.

621.3 GW ISSN 0724-9616
INFORMATIONEN DEUTSCH ALS FREMDSPRACHE. 1973. 6/yr. DM.64. Iudicium Verlag, Postfach 701067, 81310 Munich, Germany. TEL 089-717868. FAX 089-7142039. **Indexed:** Bibl.Ling. **Document type:** academic/scholarly publication.
—Faxon.

378 GW
INFORMATIONEN FUER REGENSBURGER STUDENTINNEN UND STUDENTEN. 1969. a. Studentenwerk Niederbayern-Oberpfalz, Albertus-Magnus-Str. 4, 93047 Regensburg, Germany. TEL 0941-9432201. adv.: B&W page DM.600. (back issues avail.)

378 AU
INFORMATIONEN ZUR AKADEMISCHEN MOBILITAET. Short title: I A M. irreg. Oesterreichische Akademischer Austauschdienst, Berggasse 21, A-1090 Vienna, Austria. TEL 01-3172793. FAX 01-3172795. (Co-sponsor: Bundesministerium fuer Wissenschaft und Forschung) Ed. Josef Leidenfrost. **Document type:** academic/scholarly publication.

378.1 US ISSN 0363-2601
L901
INNOVATIVE GRADUATE PROGRAMS DIRECTORY. 1975. irreg., 6th ed., 1992. $25. Empire State College, Educational Materials Distribution Center, Saratoga Springs, NY 12866. TEL 518-587-2100. FAX 518-583-0801. circ. 1,000. **Document type:** directory.

378 US ISSN 0742-5627
LA227.3 CODEN: IHEDDZ
INNOVATIVE HIGHER EDUCATION. 1976. q. $135 (foreign $160) (effective 1993). Human Sciences Press, Inc. (Subsidiary of: Plenum Publishing Corp.), 233 Spring St., New York, NY 10013-1578. TEL 212-620-8000. FAX 212-463-0742. Ed. Ronald D. Simpson. adv.; bibl. (also avail. in microfilm from UMI; back issues avail.; reprint service avail. from ISI,UMI) **Indexed:** C.I.J.E., Coll.Stud.Pers.Abstr., Cont.Pg.Educ., Educ.Ind., High.Educ.Curr.Aware.Bull., Human Resour.Abstr., Lang.& Lang.Behav.Abstr., Psychol.Abstr., Res.High.Educ.Abstr., Sociol.Abstr. **Document type:** academic/scholarly publication.
—BLDSC (4515.487800); Faxon; UnCover; SWETS; UMI. **CCC.**
Formerly (until 1983): Alternative Higher Education (ISSN 0361-6851)
Description: Presents professional and scholarly information and encourages creative practices relevant to the higher education field.
Refereed Serial

378 AU
INNSBRUCKER UNIVERSITAETSREDEN. (Subseries of: Universitaet Innsbruck. Veroeffentlichungen) 1969. irreg., vol.8, 1974. price varies. (Universitaet Innsbruck) Oesterreichische Kommissionsbuchhandlung, Maximilianstrasse 17, A-6020 Innsbruck, Austria.

INSTEAD. see EDUCATION — School Organization And Administration

378 AU ISSN 0020-2320
INSTITUT FUER WISSENSCHAFT UND KUNST. MITTEILUNGEN. 1946. 4/yr. free. Institut fuer Wissenschaft und Kunst, Berggasse 17-1, A-1090 Vienna, Austria. Ed. Helga Kaschl. adv.; bk.rev.; circ. 2,000 (controlled). **Document type:** proceedings.

INSTITUTE OF EDUCATION. HANDBOOK. see EDUCATION — Guides To Schools And Colleges

378 DR
INSTITUTO TECNOLOGICO DE SANTO DOMINGO. BOLETIN. 1976. 3/yr. RD.$12($12) Instituto Tecnologico de Santo Domingo, Apdo. 249-2, Santo Domingo, Dominican Republic. circ. 4,000.

370.7 BL ISSN 0101-7136
INTER-ACAO; revista da faculdade de educacao da UFA. 1975. 2/yr. $23 or exchange basis. Universidade Federal de Goias, Faculdade de Educacao, Praca Universitaria-C.P. 131, Setor Universitario, 74000 Goiania, Goias, Brazil. Ed. Terezinha Mendonca. bk.rev.; charts. circ. 1,000.

378 FR ISSN 0579-3866
INTERNATIONAL FEDERATION OF CATHOLIC UNIVERSITIES. GENERAL ASSEMBLY. REPORT. 1963. every 3 yrs. $10. International Federation of Catholic Universities (IFCU), 51 rue Orfila, 75020 Paris, France. TEL 47-97-26-60. FAX 47-97-29-42. circ. 500.
Description: Discusses issues relevant to Catholic higher education.

EDUCATION — HIGHER EDUCATION

378 UK ISSN 0074-6215
L900
INTERNATIONAL HANDBOOK OF UNIVERSITIES AND OTHER INSTITUTIONS OF HIGHER EDUCATION. Title varies: International Handbook of Universities. (Text in English) 1959. triennial. £115. (International Association of Universities) Macmillan Press Ltd., Houndmills, Basingstoke, Hants. RG21 2XS, England. TEL 0256-817245. FAX 0256-28339. (Dist. in the U.S. by: Stockton Press, 49 E. 24th St., New York, NY 10010. TEL 212-673-4400. FAX 212-673-9842) Eds. H.M.R. Keyes, D.J. Aitken. index. **Document type:** directory.
Description: Covers more than 8,000 institutions in 116 countries. Presents information on the latest developments in higher education worldwide.

INTERNATIONAL JOURNAL OF ACCOUNTING EDUCATION AND RESEARCH. see *BUSINESS AND ECONOMICS — Accounting*

378 US ISSN 1058-1340
LC1099
INTERNATIONAL STUDIES FUNDING AND RESOURCES BOOK. biennial. Information Interface Institute, Education Interface, Box 3649, Princeton, NJ 08543.

378 370.196 US
INTERNATIONAL UNIVERSITY FOUNDATION DIRECTORY. 1973. a. $300. (International University Foundation) T I U Press, 1301 S. Noland Rd., Independence, MO 64055. TEL 816-461-3633. Ed. John Wayne Johnston. circ. 1,000. (looseleaf format) **Document type:** directory.
Description: Information on people active in higher education internationally.

378 370.196 US
INTERNATIONAL UNIVERSITY FOUNDATION REPORT. 1973. q. $300. (International University Foundation) T I U Press, 1301 S. Noland, Independence, MO 64055. TEL 816-461-3633. Ed. John Wayne Johnston. circ. 1,000. (looseleaf format)
Description: Covers major events in the Foundations's program of facilitating international higher education.

378 US
INTERNATIONAL UNIVERSITY NEWSLETTER. 1973. q. $300. T I U Press, 1301 S. Noland Rd., Independence, MO 64055. TEL 816-461-3633. Ed. John Wayne Johnston. index, cum.index. circ. 415. (looseleaf format) **Document type:** newsletter.

INTERNET WORLD. see *COMPUTERS — Computer Networks*

ISAAC PITBLADO LECTURES. see *LAW*

378 US
ISSUES IN HIGHER EDUCATION. 1970. irreg. $0.50 per no. Southern Regional Education Board, 592 Tenth St., N.W., Atlanta, GA 30318-5790. TEL 404-875-9211. **Document type:** newsletter.

ISSUES IN SOCIAL WORK EDUCATION. see *SOCIAL SERVICES AND WELFARE*

ISSUES IN WRITING; education, government, arts and humanities, business and industry, science and technology. see *JOURNALISM*

378 GW ISSN 0342-6300
JAHRBUCH DEUTSCH ALS FREMDSPRACHE. 1975. a. DM.88. Iudicium Verlag, Postfach 701067, 81310 Munich, Germany. TEL 089-717868. FAX 089-7142039. Ed. Alois Wierlacher. circ. 1,500. (back issues avail.; reprint service avail. from UMI) **Document type:** academic/scholarly publication.
Description: Deals with linguistics, the science of literature, didactics and cultural background studies; informs the reader about the present-day development of German as a foreign language at home and abroad.

378 CC
JIANGSU GAOJIAO/JIANGSU HIGHER EDUCATION. (Text in Chinese) 1985. bi-m. $10. Jiangsu Sheng Gaodeng Jiaoyu Xuehui - Jiangsu Higher Education Association, 207 Shanghai Rd., Nanjing, Jiangsu 210024, People's Republic of China. TEL 025-6638659. FAX 025-7714402. (Co-sponsor: Jiangsu Sheng Jiaowei) Ed. Ye Chunsheng. adv. contact: Gu Guanhua. bk.rev.; circ. 5,000. (controlled). **Document type:** academic/scholarly publication.
Description: Covers higher education management, research and theories.

378 CC ISSN 1001-5469
JIAOCAI TONGXUN/BULLETIN OF TEACHING MATERIAL. (Text in Chinese) bi-m. Gaodeng Jiaoyu Chubanshe - Higher Education Publishers, 55 Shatan Houjie, Beijing 100009, People's Republic of China. TEL 4016633. Ed. Jiang Liyin.

JOB PRATIQUE MAGAZINE. see *OCCUPATIONS AND CAREERS*

378 GW ISSN 0302-5926
JOHANN WOLFGANG GOETHE UNIVERSITAET. STUDIENFUEHRER. 1973. a. Johann Wolfgang Goethe Universitaet, Zentrale Studienberatung, Senckenberganlage 31, 60325 Frankfurt a.M., Germany. TEL 069-7983597. FAX 069-7988383. circ. 3,000. **Document type:** academic/scholarly publication.

378 GW
JOHANN WOLFGANG GOETHE UNIVERSITAET. VORLESUNGSVERZEICHNIS. s-a. DM.5. Universitaetsbuchhandlung Blazek und Bergmann, Goethestr. 1, 60313 Frankfurt a.M., Germany. TEL 069-288648. circ. 19,000.
Description: Provides information on the staff, courses and lectures offered by the university.

378 JO
JORDAN UNIVERSITY NEWSLETTER/ANBA AL-JAMIAH. (Text in Arabic) 1971. m. free. Jordan University, Department of Cultural and Public Relations, Box 1682, Amman, Jordan. TELEX 21629 UNVJ JO. Ed. Mohammad Khair Mamser. circ. 3,000. **Document type:** newsletter.

378 US
JOURNAL FOR HIGHER EDUCATION MANAGEMENT. 1985. s-a. $15 to non-members; institutions $20 (effective 1994). (American Association of University Administrators) Prometheus Books Incorporated, 700 E. Amherst St., Buffalo, NY 14215. TEL 716-837-2475. FAX 716-835-6901. (Subscr. to: AAUA, Box 031403, Tuscaloosa, AL 35403. TEL 205-758-0636. FAX 205-345-9778; Editorial addr.: 503 Capen Hall, SUNY Buffalo, Buffalo, NY 14260. TEL 716-645-2925) Ed. Walter C. Hobbs. circ. 950. **Indexed:** C.I.J.E., Cont.Pg.Educ., Educ.Admin.Abstr., ERIC, High.Educ.Abstr., Res.High.Educ.Abstr., Sociol.Abstr., Sociol.Educ.Abstr. **Document type:** academic/scholarly publication.
Description: Provides a forum for the discussion of current issues in higher education leadership, policy analysis and development, institutional management and professional standards.
Refereed Serial

JOURNAL OF ACCOUNTING EDUCATION. see *BUSINESS AND ECONOMICS — Accounting*

JOURNAL OF AMERICAN COLLEGE HEALTH. see *PHYSICAL FITNESS AND HYGIENE*

371.3 US ISSN 0147-1635
PE1404
JOURNAL OF BASIC WRITING. 1975. s-a. $10 to individuals; institutions $15. City University of New York, Office of Academic Affairs, Instructional Resource Center, 535 E. 80th St., New York, NY 10021. TEL 212-794-5445. FAX 212-794-5706. Eds. Karen Greenberg, Trudy Smoke. adv.: B&W page $150; adv. contact: Ruth Davis. circ. 2,000 (paid). (also avail. in microfiche; back issues avail.; reprint service avail from UMI) **Indexed:** C.I.J.E. **Document type:** academic/scholarly publication.
—BLDSC (4951.130000); Faxon; UnCover; UMI.
Description: Publishes articles on theory, research, and teaching practices related to basic writing.
Refereed Serial

JOURNAL OF BLACKS IN HIGHER EDUCATION. see *ETHNIC INTERESTS*

JOURNAL OF CAREER PLANNING & EMPLOYMENT; the international magazine of placement and recruitment. see *OCCUPATIONS AND CAREERS*

JOURNAL OF CHEMICAL EDUCATION. see *CHEMISTRY*

378 US
JOURNAL OF COLLEGE AND UNIVERSITY STUDENT HOUSING; A C U H O journal. 1971. s-a. $30 to non-members; members $20. Association of College and University Housing Officers' International, 101 Curl Dr., Ste. 140, Columbus, OH 43210-1195. TEL 614-292-0099. FAX 614-292-3205. Ed. Donald F. Whalen. adv.; bk.rev.; circ. 2,600 (controlled). (also avail. in microform from UMI; reprint service avail. from UMI) **Indexed:** C.I.J.E., Coll.Stud.Pers.Abstr., ERIC, High.Educ.Abstr. **Document type:** academic/scholarly publication.
Description: Contains current research, literature reviews and other scholarly materials related to college and university housing.

507 US ISSN 0047-231X
Q183.U6 CODEN: JSCTBN
JOURNAL OF COLLEGE SCIENCE TEACHING. 1971. 6/yr. $52. National Science Teachers Association, 1840 Wilson Blvd., Arlington, VA 22201. Ed. Michael Byrnes. adv.; bk.rev.; video rev.; abstr.; tr.lit.; index. circ. 4,500. (also avail. in microfilm from UMI; reprint service avail. from UMI) **Indexed:** Biol.Abstr., C.I.J.E., Chem.Abstr., Cont.Pg.Educ., Educ.Ind., Sci.Abstr. **Document type:** academic/scholarly publication.
—BLDSC (4958.810000); Faxon; UnCover; SWETS; UMI; CASDDS.

JOURNAL OF COLLEGE STUDENT DEVELOPMENT. see *PSYCHOLOGY*

JOURNAL OF COMPUTER INFORMATION SYSTEMS. see *COMPUTERS — Computer Systems*

JOURNAL OF COMPUTING IN HIGHER EDUCATION. see *EDUCATION — Computer Applications*

JOURNAL OF CONTINUING EDUCATION IN THE HEALTH PROFESSIONS. see *MEDICAL SCIENCES*

378 US ISSN 0894-3907
JOURNAL OF DEVELOPMENTAL EDUCATION. 1978. 3/yr. $21 to individuals; institutions $26. Appalachian State University, National Center for Developmental Education, Boone, NC 28608. TEL 704-262-2876. FAX 704-262-2128. Ed. Milton Spann. adv. contact: Barbara Calderwood. circ. 5,000. (also avail. in microfilm; reprint service avail. from UMI) **Indexed:** C.I.J.E., Cont.Pg.Educ., Educ.Ind., Mult.Ed.Abstr., Sp.Ed.Needs Abstr. **Document type:** trace publication.
—BLDSC (4969.290500); UnCover; UMI.
Formerly (until 1984): Journal of Developmental and Remedial Education (ISSN 0738-9701)
Description: Forum for educators concerned with practice, theory, research and news of postsecondary basic skills.

JOURNAL OF EDUCATION FOR BUSINESS. see *BUSINESS AND ECONOMICS*

370.71 UK ISSN 0260-7476
LB1725.G6
JOURNAL OF EDUCATION FOR TEACHING. Abbreviated title: J E T. 1975. 3/yr. $128 to individuals; institutions $298 (effective 1994). Carfax Publishing Co., P.O. Box 25, Abingdon, Oxon. OX14 3UE, England. TEL 44-235-555335. FAX 44-235-553559. (U.S. subscr. to: Carfax Publishing Co., Box 2025, Dunnellon, FL 34430-2025) Ed. Edgar Stones. adv.; bk.rev.; index. (also avail. in microfiche; back issues avail.) **Indexed:** C.I.J.E., Cont.Pg.Educ., Curr.Cont., Educ.Tech.Abstr., High.Educ.Curr.Aware.Bull., Lang.Teach.& Ling.Abstr., Mult.Ed.Abstr., Res.High.Educ.Abstr., SOMA, SSCI. **Document type:** academic/scholarly publication.
—BLDSC (4973.152500); Faxon; UnCover; SWETS. CCC.
Formerly (until 1980): British Journal of Teacher Education (ISSN 0305-8913)
Refereed Serial

JOURNAL OF FINANCIAL EDUCATION. see *BUSINESS AND ECONOMICS — Banking And Finance*

EDUCATION — HIGHER EDUCATION

370.7   UK   ISSN 0309-877X
L16
JOURNAL OF FURTHER AND HIGHER EDUCATION. 1943. 3/yr. N A T F H E - The University and College Lecturers' Union, 27 Britannia St., London WC1X 9JP, England. FAX 071-837-4403. Ed. Anne Castling. adv.; bk.rev.; bibl.; charts; illus.; stat.; index, cum.index. (also avail. in microform from UMI; reprint service avail. from UMI) **Indexed:** Br.Educ.Ind., Cont.Pg.Educ., Educ.Tech.Abstr., High.Educ.Curr.Aware.Bull., Mult.Ed.Abstr., Res.High.Educ.Abstr., SOMA, Stud.Wom.Abstr. **Document type:** academic/scholarly publication.
—BLDSC (4986.850000); SWETS.
Incorporates: Education for Teaching (ISSN 0013-1326)

JOURNAL OF GEOGRAPHY IN HIGHER EDUCATION. see *GEOGRAPHY*

JOURNAL OF GEOLOGICAL EDUCATION. see *EARTH SCIENCES — Geology*

JOURNAL OF HEALTH ADMINISTRATION EDUCATION. see *HOSPITALS*

378   US   ISSN 0022-1546
L11   CODEN: JHSBA5
JOURNAL OF HIGHER EDUCATION. 1930. bi-m. $30 to individuals (foreign $36); libraries $55 (foreign $61). Ohio State University Press, 1070 Carmack Rd., Columbus, OH 43210. TEL 614-292-6930. Ed. Robert J. Silverman. adv.; bk.rev.; index. circ. 4,800. (also avail. in microform from UMI,PMC; back issues avail.; reprint service avail. from ISI,UMI) **Indexed:** Abstr.Soc.Work., Acad.Ind., Amer.Hist.& Life, Bk.Rev.Ind. (1965-), C.I.J.E., Chem.Abstr., Chic.Per.Ind., Child.Bk.Rev.Ind. (1965-), Coll.Stud.Pers.Abstr., Cont.Pg.Educ., Educ.Admin.Abstr., Educ.Ind., Educ.Tech.Abstr., Hist.Abstr., Lang.& Lang.Behav.Abstr., Mid.East: Abstr.& Ind., Psychol.Abstr., Res.High.Educ.Abstr., Sp.Ed.Needs Abstr., SSCI, Stud.Wom.Abstr. **Document type:** academic/scholarly publication.
●Also available online. Vendor(s): Information Access Co.
Also available on CD-ROM. Producer(s): University Microfilms International.
—BLDSC (4998.600000); Faxon; UnCover; SWETS; UMI. **CCC.**
Description: Investigates issues of higher education teaching, administration, evaluation, and management.

378   II   ISSN 0252-0397
JOURNAL OF HIGHER EDUCATION. (Text in English) 4/yr. Rs.75($15) University Grants Commission, Publication Officer, 35 Ferozeshah Rd., New Delhi 110 001, India. Ed.Bd. bk.rev.; bibl. **Indexed:** Cont.Pg.Educ., High.Educ.Curr.Aware.Bull., Res.High.Educ.Abstr., Soc.Work Res.& Abstr., SSCI.

370.7   US   ISSN 0022-1864
JOURNAL OF INDUSTRIAL TEACHER EDUCATION. 1963. 4/yr. price varies. National Association of Industrial and Technical Teacher Educators, c/o Charles Linnell, Dept. of Industrial Eudcation, Clemson University, Clemson, SC 29634. Ed. Frank Pratzner. bk.rev.; illus.; stat.; index. circ. 1,400. (also avail. in microform from UMI; reprint service avail. from UMI) **Indexed:** C.I.J.E., Cont.Pg.Educ., Curr.Cont., Educ.Ind. **Document type:** academic/scholarly publication.
—BLDSC (5006.400000); Faxon; UnCover; UMI.

JOURNAL OF MARKETING FOR HIGHER EDUCATION. see *BUSINESS AND ECONOMICS — Marketing And Purchasing*

JOURNAL OF NURSING EDUCATION. see *MEDICAL SCIENCES — Nurses And Nursing*

378 371.42   US   ISSN 0163-3252
T61
JOURNAL OF STUDIES IN TECHNICAL CAREERS. 1978. q. $25 (foreign $30). Southern Illinois University, Carbondale, College of Technical Careers, Carbondale, IL 62901. TEL 618-536-6682. FAX 618-453-7286. Ed. Linda M. Grace. adv.; bk.rev.; bibl. circ. 1,500. (also avail. in microform from UMI; back issues avail.) **Indexed:** C.I.J.E., Cont.Pg.Educ., High.Educ.Abstr., SOMA, Sp.Ed.Needs Abstr., Stud.Wom.Abstr. **Document type:** academic/scholarly publication.
—BLDSC (5066.899000); UnCover; UMI.
Description: Covers occupational, technical and vocational educators manuscripts describing research work, practical applications, or commentary on topics of interest to professional educators in post-secondary institutions.

370.7   US   ISSN 0022-4871
LB1705   CODEN: JTEDA
JOURNAL OF TEACHER EDUCATION. bi-m. $15 to students (foreign $25); professionals $35 (foreign $45); institutions $45 (foreign $55). American Association of Colleges for Teacher Education, One Dupont Circle, N.W., Ste. 610, Washington, DC 20036-1186. TEL 202-293-2450. FAX 202-457-8095. (also avail. in microform from UMI; reprint service avail. from UMI,KTO) **Indexed:** Acad.Ind., Bk.Rev.Ind. (1984-), C.I.J.E., Chic.Per.Ind., Child.Bk.Rev.Ind. (1984-), Cont.Pg.Educ., Curr.Cont., Educ.Admin.Abstr., Educ.Ind., Educ.Tech.Abstr., Except.Child.Educ.Abstr., Psychol.Abstr., Res.High.Educ.Abstr., Sp.Ed.Needs Abstr., SSCI.
—BLDSC (5068.285000); Faxon; UnCover; SWETS; UMI.

378   US   ISSN 1053-203X
LB2343.32
JOURNAL OF THE FRESHMAN YEAR EXPERIENCE. 1989. s-a. $40. University of South Carolina, National Center for the Study of the Freshman Year Experience, 1728 College St., Columbia, SC 29208. TEL 803-777-6029. FAX 803-777-4699. Ed. Dorothy Fidler. bk.rev. circ. 529. **Indexed:** ERIC. **Document type:** academic/scholarly publication.
Description: Provides current research and scholarship on the freshman year.
Refereed Serial

JOURNAL OF TRANSLATION AND TEXTLINGUISTICS. see *LINGUISTICS*

JOURNAL OF VETERINARY MEDICAL EDUCATION. see *VETERINARY SCIENCE*

370.7   US   ISSN 1052-4800
JOURNAL ON EXCELLENCE IN COLLEGE TEACHING. 1990. a. $9. Miami University, O A S T, Oxford, OH 45056. TEL 513-529-6722. Ed. Laurie Richlin. circ. 1,000. (back issues avail.)
Description: Forum for faculty to share proven, innovating teaching in colleges and universities.
Refereed Serial

JOURNALISM EDUCATOR. see *JOURNALISM*

378   US   ISSN 1050-723X
JOURNEY (KANSAS CITY). 1985. s-a. $3 per no. Communications Publishing Group, Inc., 250 Mark Twain Tower, 106 W. 11th St., Ste. 250, Kansas City, MO 64105-1806. TEL 816-221-4404. FAX 816-221-1112. adv. circ. 200,000.
Description: For Asian-American high school and college students with a desire to pursue a higher education.

JURISTE. see *LAW*

378 340   CN
JUSTICE INSTITUTE OF BRITISH COLUMBIA. ANNUAL REPORT. (Text in English) 1979. a. Justice Institute of British Columbia, 4180 W. Fourth Ave., Vancouver, BC V6R 4J5, Canada. FAX 604-660-1875. Ed. Larry Goble. (back issues avail.) **Document type:** corporate report.

JUSTUF; das Juramagazin. see *LAW*

378 282   US
KAPPA GAMMA PI NEWS. 1930. 5/yr. membership. Kappa Gamma Pi, 2415 Hillcrest Dr., Stow, OH 44224. TEL 216-688-1407. Ed. Pamela W. Waitinas. circ. 7,000. (back issues avail.)

378   US
KENTUCKY COUNCIL ON HIGHER EDUCATION. COUNCIL ACTIONS. 1977. fortn. free. Kentucky Council on Higher Education, 1050 U.S. 127 S., Ste. 101, Frankfort, KY 40601-4395. TEL 502-564-3553. FAX 502-564-2063. Ed. Jean K. Ward. circ. 1,200 (controlled). **Document type:** newsletter, government publication.
Former titles: Kentucky Council on Higher Education. Executive Council Report; Kentucky Council on Higher Education. Council Report.

378   KE
KENYA EDUCATION REVIEW. 1974. s-a. Kenyatta University College, Bureau of Educational Research, P.O. Box 43844, Nairobi, Kenya. circ. 500. **Document type:** academic/scholarly publication.

378   KE
KENYATTA UNIVERSITY COLLEGE. BUREAU OF EDUCATIONAL RESEARCH. RESEARCH PROJECTS. 1973. a. Kenyatta University College, Bureau of Educational Research, P.O. Box 43844, Nairobi, Kenya. bk.rev.; stat. circ. 200. **Document type:** academic/scholarly publication.
Formerly: University of Kenya. Bureau of Educational Research. Research Projects.

378   KE
KENYATTA UNIVERSITY COLLEGE. DIRECTORY OF RESEARCH. 1975. a. supplements to base vol. free. Kenyatta University Library, Box 43844, Nairobi, Kenya. Ed. J.M. Ng'Ang'A. circ. 200. **Document type:** directory.
Description: Annual catalogue of research at Kenyatta University College.

378   SI   ISSN 0047-3383
KESATUAN BULLETIN. vol.10, 1975. irreg. free. Kesatuan Akademis Universiti Singapura, Singapore, Singapore. Ed. Tham Seong Chee. adv.; bk.rev.; charts. circ. 1,000.

KEYING IN. see *BUSINESS AND ECONOMICS*

KEYSTONE SCHOOLMASTER NEWSLETTER. see *EDUCATION — School Organization And Administration*

LAW SCHOOL RECORD. see *LAW*

LAWASIA DIRECTORY OF LAW COURSES IN THE ASIA AND WEST PACIFIC REGIONS. see *LAW*

LEARN FOR YOURSELF. see *EDUCATION — Guides To Schools And Colleges*

378   UK   ISSN 0268-2125
LEARNING RESOURCES JOURNAL. Abbreviated title: L R J. 1979. 3/yr. £29. Learning Resources Development Group, 6 St. James Ct., Piper Lane, Thirsk, N. Yorks YO7 1FN, England. TEL 0845-526749. Ed. David Bosworth. circ. 335. **Indexed:** Br.Educ.Ind., Educ.Tech.Abstr., Lib.Sci.Abstr., LISA. **Document type:** academic/scholarly publication.
—BLDSC (5179.329190).
Formerly (until 1985): L R D G Bulletin (ISSN 0143-3555)

378   UK   ISSN 0955-0631
LEARNING RESOURCES NEWS. 1985. 3/yr. £42 membership. Learning Resources Development Group, 6 St. James Ct., Piper Lane, Thirsk, N. Yorks YO7 1FN, England. TEL 0845-526749. Ed. D. Bosworth. circ. 340. **Document type:** academic/scholarly publication.
Formerly (until 1987): L R D G Newsletter.

LEGAL EDUCATION REVIEW. see *LAW*

378   BL   ISSN 0101-9635
AS80.S65
LEOPOLDIANUM; revista de estudos e comunicacoes. 1974. 3/yr. $2 per no. or exchange basis. (Sociedade Visconde de Sao Leopoldo) Editora Universitaria Leopoldinum, Rua Ceara, 70, CEP 11065 Santos, SP, Brazil. TEL 4373435. Ed. Bd. adv.; bk.rev.; illus.; index. circ. 1,000. **Document type:** academic/scholarly publication.

EDUCATION — HIGHER EDUCATION

378 340   US   ISSN 0749-9078
KF4225.A15
LEX COLLEGII. 1978. q. $36. College Legal Information Inc., Box 150541, Nashville, TN 37215. TEL 615-383-3332. Ed. Kent M. Weeks. illus.; cum.index. (back issues avail.) **Document type:** newsletter.
  Description: Legal newsletter for independent higher education.

378   US   ISSN 0024-1822
LB2301
LIBERAL EDUCATION. 1915. 5/yr. $36 to individuals, libraries, academic depts. at non-member institutions; individuals, libraries, academic depts. at member institutions $30; includes On Campus With Women. Association of American Colleges, 1818 R St., N.W., Washington, DC 20009. TEL 202-387-3760. FAX 202-265-9532. bk.rev. circ. 5,000. (also avail. in microform from UMI.) **Indexed:** Amer.Hist.& Life, C.I.J.E., Cont.Pg.Educ., Curr.Cont., Educ.Ind., High.Educ.Curr.Aware.Bull., Hist.Abstr., Lang.& Lang.Behav.Abstr., PSI, Res.High.Educ.Abstr., SSCI.
  —BLDSC (5186.600000); Faxon; UnCover; UMI.
  Incorporates: Forum for Liberal Education.
  Description: Contains insightful essays, reports of curricular developments, and information about ways in which liberal learning provides a bridge between campus and community.

378   US
LIFELONG LEARNING TRENDS; a profile of continuing higher education. 2nd ed., 1992. biennial. $20. National University Continuing Education Association, 1 Dupont Cir., N.W., Ste.615, Washington, DC 20036. TEL 202-659-3130.

378   US   ISSN 1051-3310
LA226
LINGUA FRANCA; the review of academic life. 1990. bi-m. $24.95 to individuals; Canada and Mexico $29.95; elsewhere $34.95; to institutions $40; Canada and Mexico $45; elsewhere $50. Lingua Franca, Inc., 172 E. Boston Post Rd., Mamaroneck, NY 10543. TEL 914-698-9427. FAX 914-968-9488. (Subscr. to: P.O. Box 3000, Denville, NJ 07834) Ed. David Salin. adv.: B&W page $1190, color page $1690; trim 8 3/8 x 10 7/8; adv. contact: Barbara Kimmel. bk.rev.; charts; illus. circ. 15,000.
  —Faxon; UnCover.
  Description: Covers hirings and tenurings, publishing, research topics, financial issues including retirement, academic computing, and the impact of political and social issues on academic careers. For university professors, administrators and graduate students in the humanities and social sciences.

378   US
LINZER UNIVERSITAETSSCHRIFTEN. 1969. irreg. price varies. Springer-Verlag, 175 Fifth Ave., New York, NY 10010. TEL 212-460-1500. FAX 212-473-6272. (Also: Berlin, Heidelberg, Tokyo and Vienna) (reprint service avail. from ISI) **Document type:** monographic series.
  Formerly: Linzer Hochschulschriften (ISSN 0075-9724)

378   UK
LONDON AND SOUTH EAST REGION ADVISORY COUNCIL FOR EDUCATION AND TRAINING. INDEX OF COURSES. 1965. a. L A S E R Advisory Council, Chenies House, 21 Bedford Sq., London WC1B 3HH, England. TEL 071-637-3073. FAX 071-637-2733. Ed. R. Eberhard. circ. 1,700. **Document type:** directory.
  Former titles: London and South Eastern Regional Advisory Council for Further Education. Index of Courses; London and Home Counties Regional Advisory Council for Technological Education. Index of Courses.

LOVEJOY'S GUIDANCE DIGEST. see *EDUCATION — Guides To Schools And Colleges*

M I E C SERVICO DE DOCUMENTACION. (Movimiento Internacional de Estudiantes Catolicos) see *RELIGIONS AND THEOLOGY — Roman Catholic*

378   US   ISSN 0160-5720
M L A NEWSLETTER (NEW YORK). 1969. 4/yr. $6 to non-members (effective 1993). Modern Language Association of America, 10 Astor Pl., New York, NY 10003. TEL 212-475-9500. FAX 212-477-9863. Ed. Phyllis P. Franklin. adv. circ. 32,000. (reprint service avail. from UMI) **Document type:** newsletter.
  Description: Information about the activities of the Modern Language Association, deadlines for fellowships and grants, and news of the language and literature profession.

370.73   UG
MAKERERE UNIVERSITY. FACULTY OF EDUCATION. HANDBOOK. Added title: Teacher Education in Uganda. a. Makerere University, Faculty of Education, Box 7062, Kampala, Uganda. illus.

MANCHESTER TRAINING HANDBOOKS. see *BUSINESS AND ECONOMICS — Management*

378   II   ISSN 0025-2751
MARATHWADA UNIVERSITY JOURNAL. (Text and summaries in English, Hindi and Marathi (Science no. only in English)) 1960. 3/yr. (alternating social sciences, languages and natural sciences nos.). Rs.20($2.60) Marathwada University, Shri V. K. Dhamankar, Registrar, Aurangabad, Maharashtra, India. Ed.Bd. bk.rev.; charts; illus.; stat. circ. 250. **Indexed:** Chem.Abstr.

MARKETING EDUCATION REVIEW. see *BUSINESS AND ECONOMICS — Marketing And Purchasing*

378   US   ISSN 0896-7156
MARKETING HIGHER EDUCATION NEWSLETTER. 1987. m. $94.95. Topor & Associates, 280 Easy St., No. 114, Mountain View, CA 94043-3736. TEL 415-962-1105. bk.rev.; circ. 700 (controlled). (back issues avail.) **Document type:** newsletter.

378   US
MARQUETTE. 1981. q. Marquette University, 1212 W. Wisconsin Ave., Milwaukee, WI 53233. TEL 414-288-6712. FAX 414-288-6519. Ed. Cathy J. Jakicic. illus. circ. 90,000.
  Former titles: Marquette Today; Marquette University Magazine (ISSN 0025-4002)
  Description: News of Marquette University.

378   US
MASSACHUSETTS MAGAZINE. 1975. 4/yr. free. University of Massachusetts, Massachusetts Magazine, 204 Munson Hall, Amherst, MA 01003. TEL 413-545-0155. Ed. Rachel Morton. bk.rev. circ. 100,000.
  Formerly (until vol.14, no.4, 1989): Contact (Amherst).

MASTER'S THESES IN THE ARTS AND SOCIAL SCIENCES. see *HUMANITIES: COMPREHENSIVE WORKS*

MATHEMATICS AND COMPUTER EDUCATION. see *MATHEMATICS — Computer Applications*

MATRIX NEWSLETTER. see *COMPUTERS*

MEDICAL EDUCATION. see *MEDICAL SCIENCES*

378 610.7   US   ISSN 0066-9423
R745
MEDICAL SCHOOL ADMISSION REQUIREMENTS, UNITED STATES AND CANADA. Title varies slightly. 1955. a. $10 (foreign $15). Association of American Medical Colleges, 2450 N St., Washington, DC 20037-1126. TEL 202-828-0416. FAX 202-828-1123. (also avail. in microfiche from CIS; reprint service avail. from UMI) **Indexed:** SRI.
  Formerly (until **1964**): Admission Requirements of American Medical Colleges, Including Canada (ISSN 0271-6518)

378   US   ISSN 0047-6692
MEMO: TO THE PRESIDENT. vol.13, 1973. w. $65 to non-members. American Association of State Colleges and Universities, One Dupont Circle, N.W., Ste. 700, Washington, DC 20036. TEL 202-293-7070. FAX 202-296-5819. bk.rev.; circ. controlled. (processed)

370   JO   ISSN 0040-0505
MESSAGE OF THE TEACHER/RISALAT AL-MU'ALLIM. (Text in Arabic) 1956. q. 8 din. to individuals (foreign 10 din.); institutions 10 din. (foreign 12 din.). Ministry of Education, Educational Publications Division, P.O. Box 1646, Amman, Jordan. TEL 669181. FAX 666019. TELEX 21396. Ed. Mrs. Salwa Madadha. bk.rev.; cum. index: vols. 1956-1990. circ. 42,000. (back issues avail.) **Document type:** academic/scholarly publication.

378   US   ISSN 1047-8485
LB2328.4   CODEN: METUEF
METROPOLITAN UNIVERSITIES; an international forum. 1990. q. $52 to individuals (foreign $72); institutions $90 (foreign $110). Towson State University, 7800 York Rd., Ste. 301, Towson, MD 21204-7097. TEL 410-830-3468. FAX 410-830-3456. (Co-sponsor: Coalition of Urban and Metropolitan Universities) Ed. Ernest A. Lynton; Pub. Johr Brain. bk.rev. circ. 500. (also avail. in microform from UMI) **Document type:** academic/scholarly publication.
  —UnCover; UMI.
  Description: Provides a forum for action, analysis, prognosis and prescription as well as diagnosis and evaluation.

378   US   ISSN 0047-7052
MICHIGAN ACADEMY OF SCIENCE, ARTS, AND LETTERS. ACADEMY LETTER. 1969. 3/yr. included with membership or with subscr. to Michigan Academician. Michigan Academy of Science, Arts, and Letters, 400 Fourth St., Ann Arbor, MI 48103-4816. TEL 313-936-2938. Ed. Kathleen F. Duke. bk.rev.; charts; stat. circ. 1,000. (processed)
  Description: Provides sample abstract and abstract instructions, information on the executive committee and a listing of the sections and current section chairs involved.

378   US
MIDDLE STATES ASSOCIATION OF COLLEGES AND SCHOOLS. PROCEEDINGS OF THE ANNUAL CONVENTION. 1888. a. $5. Middle States Association of Colleges and Secondary Schools, 3624 Market St., Philadelphia, PA 19104. Ed. Cecile C. Betit. circ. 3,000. (also avail. in microfilm from UMI; reprint service avail. from UMI)
  Formerly: Middle States Association of Colleges and Secondary Schools. Proceedings (ISSN 0076-8561)

378   US
MIDWESTERN ASSOCIATION OF GRADUATE SCHOOLS. PROCEEDINGS OF THE ANNUAL MEETING. 1949. a. $20. Midwestern Association of Graduate Schools, Kansas State University, Graduate School, Fairchild 102, Manhattan, KS 66506. TEL 913-532-6191. Ed. R.F. Kruh. circ. 200.
  Supersedes: Midwest Conference on Graduate Study and Research. Proceedings.

378 355   US
MILITARY EDUCATORS & COUNSELORS ASSOCIATION NEWSLETTER. 1978. q. $20. Military Educators & Counselors Association (MECA), Attn.: Newsletter Editor, Box 751386, Petaluma, CA 94975-1386. (Subscr. to: MECA, 2575 Tambridge Circle, Pensacola, FL 32503) Ed. Mary F. Koss. adv.; bk.rev.; charts; stat. circ. 800. (tabloid format) **Document type:** newsletter.
  Description: Focuses on professional counseling issues for those employed in government and the military; provides professional development and networking information for members and others; provides a forum for exploration of issues of concern to the professionals involved.

378   UK   ISSN 0026-4695
AS121
MINERVA; a review of science, learning and policy. 1962. q. £75($135) (typically set in Aug.). (International Council on the Future of the University) Minerva Quarterly Review Ltd., 19 Nottingham Rd., London SW17 7EA, England. TEL 081-682-1782. FAX 081-767-6161. Ed. Edward Shils. adv.; bk.rev.; charts; index. circ. 800. **Indexed:** Amer.Hist.& Life, Cont.Pg.Educ., Curr.Cont., Deep Sea Res.& Oceanogr.Abstr., High.Educ.Curr.Aware.Bull., Hist.Abstr., Lang.& Lang.Behav.Abstr., Mid East: Abstr.& Ind., P.A.I.S., Res.High.Educ.Abstr., Risk Abstr., SSCI. **Document type:** academic/scholarly publication.
  —BLDSC (5793.920000); Faxon; UnCover; SWETS.

EDUCATION — HIGHER EDUCATION

MINORITY STUDENT OPPORTUNITIES IN UNITED STATES MEDICAL SCHOOLS. see *MEDICAL SCIENCES*

378 FR ISSN 0247-6355
MUTU. s-a. Mutuelle Nationale des Etudiants de France, 16 Av Raspail, 94250 Gentilly, France. Eds. Jean-Michel Grosz, Jean-Pierre Alaux.
Formerly: Recherches Universitaires.

370 338 US ISSN 0148-5784
HF1101
N A B T E REVIEW. 1973. a. $15. (National Association for Business Teacher Education) National Business Education Association, 1914 Association Dr., Reston, VA 22091. TEL 703-860-8300. FAX 703-620-4483. bibl. circ. 1,200. **Indexed:** Bus.Educ.Ind.

378.2 US ISSN 1046-2929
N A C A C BULLETIN. 1963. 10/yr. $25 (foreign $27). National Association of College Admission Counselors, 1631 Prince St., Alexandria, VA 22314-2818. TEL 703-836-2222. FAX 703-836-8015. **Document type:** bulletin, newsletter.
Formerly: National Association of College Admissions Counselors. Newsletter (ISSN 0027-8416)
Description: Includes current counseling trends, research, techniques, valuable resource tips and federal legislation information.

378 US ISSN 0271-9517
LB2343
N A C A D A JOURNAL. 1981. s-a. (National Academic Advising Association) Edward-Lynne Jones & Associates, Inc., 5517 17th Ave. N.E., Seattle, Washington, WA 98105. TEL 206-543-4242. (also avail. in microform from UMI; reprint service avail. from UMI) **Indexed:** C.I.J.E., Coll.Stud.Pers.Abstr. **Document type:** academic/scholarly publication. —BLDSC (6001.781500); Faxon; UMI.

N A C C A S REVIEW. (National Accrediting Commission of Cosmetology Arts & Sciences) see *BEAUTY CULTURE*

378 US ISSN 0882-4630
N A S F A A NEWSLETTER. 1972. fortn. membership only. National Association of Student Financial Aid Administrators, 1920 L St., N.W., Ste. 200, Washington, DC 20036-5020. TEL 202-785-0453. FAX 202-785-1487. Ed. Madelein McLean. adv.; index. circ. 5,000. (looseleaf format; back issues avail.) **Document type:** newsletter.
●Also available online.
Description: Covers legislation, regulation and news to promote the effective administration of student financial aid.

378.1 658.3 US ISSN 0271-1672
N A S P A FORUM. m. National Association of Student Personnel Administrators, 1875 Connecticut Ave., N.W., Ste. 418, Washington, DC 20009-5728. TEL 202-265-7500. FAX 202-797-1157. Ed. Sybil Walker. bk.rev. circ. 6,500. **Document type:** newsletter.

371.4 US ISSN 0027-6014
LA227.3
N A S P A JOURNAL. 1963. q. $35. National Association of Student Personnel Administrators, 1875 Connecticut Ave., N.W., Ste. 418, Washington, DC 20009-5728. TEL 202-265-7500. FAX 202-797-1157. Ed. Barbara Bender. bk.rev. circ. 6,500. (also avail. in microfilm from UMI; reprint service avail. from UMI) **Indexed:** C.I.J.E., Educ.Ind. **Document type:** academic/scholarly publication.
—BLDSC (6015.605100); Faxon; UnCover; UMI.

378 US
N A S U L G C NEWSLINE. 1947. 10/yr. free. National Association of State Universities and Land-Grant Colleges, One Dupont Circle, N.W., Ste. 710, Washington, DC 20036-1191. TEL 202-293-7120. Ed. Roz Hiebert. circ. 5,500. **Document type:** newsletter.
Supersedes: National Association of State Universities and Land Grant Colleges. Circular Letter.

373.246 UK ISSN 0308-1907
N A T F H E JOURNAL. 1904. 3/yr. £8 to non-members. N A T F H E - The University and College Lecturers' Union, 27 Britannia St., London WC1X 9JP, England. FAX 071-837-4403. Ed. Dennis Gardner. adv.; bk.rev.; illus.; index. circ. 78,592. **Indexed:** Cont.Pg.Educ., High.Educ.Curr.Aware.Bull., Stud.Wom.Abstr. **Document type:** academic/scholarly publication. —BLDSC (6015.664500).
Supersedes: National Association of Teachers in Further and Higher Education. Technical Journal (ISSN 0040-0963)

N C T M NEWS BULLETIN. (National Council of Teachers of Mathematics) see *EDUCATION — Teaching Methods And Curriculum*

378 331.88 US ISSN 0198-8611
N E A ADVOCATE; a publication for NEA members in higher education. 1975. 13/yr. $30 to libraries. National Education Association of the United States, 1201 16th St., N.W., Washington, DC 20036. TEL 202-822-7207. Ed.Bd. bk.rev.; illus. circ. 88,000. (looseleaf format)
Description: Covers higher education issues of interest to NEA members.

378 331.88 US ISSN 0743-670X
LA227.3
N E A ALMANAC OF HIGHER EDUCATION. 1984. a. $30 to libraries. National Education Association of the United States, 1201 16th St., N.W., Washington, DC 20036. TEL 202-822-7207. FAX 202-822-7292. Ed. Rebecca L. Robbins. stat. circ. 85,000. (also avail. in microform from EDR) **Indexed:** Res.Educ.
Description: Surveys the status of US higher education, with special attention to the Association's role in higher education.

378 US ISSN 0028-5927
N J S D C RESEARCH BULLETIN; council schools at work. 1956. q. $2. New Jersey School Development Council, Rutgers University, Graduate School of Education, New Brunswick, NJ 08903. TEL 908-932-7533. Ed. Lawrence Kaplan. circ. 2,500. (processed)

378 US
N U C E A NEWS. 10/yr. $45. National University Continuing Education Association, 1 Dupont Circle, N.W., Ste. 615, Washington, DC 20036. TEL 202-659-3130. **Document type:** newsletter.
Formerly: National University Extension Association. N U E A Newsletter.

378 CN ISSN 1194-5958
THE NATIONAL ADVOCATE.* (Text in English, French) 1991. m. Can.$35. Association of Canadian Community Colleges, 1223 Michael St. N., Ste. 200, Ottawa, Ont. K1J 7T2, Canada. TEL 613-746-2222. FAX 613-746-6721. Ed. Peggy Robinson.
Formerly: A C C C National.

378.1 US ISSN 0090-3965
LB2343
NATIONAL ASSOCIATION OF COLLEGE ADMISSIONS COUNSELORS. MEMBERSHIP DIRECTORY. Key Title: Membership Directory - National Association of College Admissions Counselors. a. $50 to non-members; members $10. National Association of College Admission Counselors, 1631 Prince St., Alexandria, VA 22314-2818. TEL 703-836-2222. FAX 703-836-8015. **Document type:** directory.
Description: Lists NACAC members, official policy statements, state-regional leaders and annual conferences.

378.15 379 US ISSN 0077-3433
NATIONAL ASSOCIATION OF STATE UNIVERSITIES AND LAND-GRANT COLLEGES. PROCEEDINGS. 1887. a. free. National Association of State Universities and Land-Grant Colleges, One Dupont Circle, N.W., Ste. 710, Washington, DC 20036. TEL 202-293-7120. Ed. C.K. Arnold. circ. 1,000. **Document type:** proceedings.

378 331 US ISSN 0742-3667
LB2334
NATIONAL CENTER FOR THE STUDY OF COLLECTIVE BARGAINING IN HIGHER EDUCATION AND THE PROFESSIONS. ANNUAL CONFERENCE PROCEEDINGS. 1973. a. $50 (effective 1993). National Center for the Study of Collective Bargaining in Higher Education and the Professions, Bernard M. Baruch College, City University of New York, 17 Lexington Ave., Box 322, New York, NY 10010. TEL 212-387-1510. Ed. Beth Johnson. bibl. circ. 500. (reprint service avail. from EDR) **Indexed:** ERIC. **Document type:** proceedings.
Formerly: National Center for the Study of Collective Bargaining in Higher Education. Annual Conference Proceedings (ISSN 0095-9294)

331.88 US ISSN 0737-9285
LB2335.885.U6
NATIONAL CENTER FOR THE STUDY OF COLLECTIVE BARGAINING IN HIGHER EDUCATION AND THE PROFESSIONS. NEWSLETTER. 1973. 4/yr. $30 (effective 1993). National Center for the Study of Collective Bargaining in Higher Education and the Professions, Bernard M. Baruch College, City University of New York, 17 Lexington Ave., Box 322, New York, NY 10010. TEL 212-387-1510. Ed. Frank R. Annunziato. bibl. circ. 300. (reprint service avail. from EDR) **Indexed:** ERIC. **Document type:** newsletter.
Formerly: National Center for the Study of Collective Bargaining in Higher Education. Newsletter (ISSN 0738-2103)

507.2 LE
NATIONAL COUNCIL FOR SCIENTIFIC RESEARCH. ANNUAL REPORT. French edition: Conseil National de la Recherche Scientifique. Rapport Annuel. (Editions in Arabic, English and French) a. free to institutions. National Council for Scientific Research, P.O. Box 11-8281, Beirut, Lebanon.

378 US ISSN 0191-8133
L901
NATIONAL DEAN'S LIST. (In 2 vols., by region) 1978. a. $34.95. Educational Communications, Inc. (Lake Forest), 721 N. McKinley, Lake Forest, IL 60045. TEL 708-295-6650.

371.42 378 US ISSN 1044-9841
NATIONAL DIRECTORY OF INTERNSHIPS. 1984. biennial. $24. National Society for Experiential Education, 3509 Haworth Dr., Ste. 207, Raleigh, NC 27609-7229. TEL 919-787-3263. Eds. Garrett Martin, Barb Baker. **Document type:** directory.
Description: Provides information on more than 3000 internship opportunities for students from high school to graduate school, as well as for young people and adults not enrolled in school.

NATIONAL FACULTY SALARY SURVEY BY DISCIPLINE AND RANK IN PRIVATE COLLEGES AND UNIVERSITIES. see *BUSINESS AND ECONOMICS — Labor And Industrial Relations*

NATIONAL FORUM OF EDUCATION ADMINISTRATION AND SUPERVISION JOURNAL. see *EDUCATION — School Organization And Administration*

378 US
NATIONAL GUIDE TO FUNDING IN HIGHER EDUCATION. irreg. Foundation Center, 75 Fifth Ave., New York, NY 10003. TEL 212-620-4230.

378 US
NATIONAL INTRAMURAL RECREATIONAL SPORTS ASSOCIATION. PROCEEDINGS. 1968. a. $15.95. National Intramural Recreational Sports Association, 850 S.W. 15th St., Corvallis, OR 97333-4145. TEL 503-737-2088. FAX 503-737-2026. Ed.Bd. circ. 2,000. **Document type:** proceedings.
Description: Covers selected presentations from annual conferences.

NATIONAL ON-CAMPUS REPORT. see *COLLEGE AND ALUMNI*

378 371.3 US ISSN 1057-2880
LB1025.3
NATIONAL TEACHING AND LEARNING FORUM. bi-m. $39. George Washington University, ERIC - HE, One Dupont Circle, N.W., Ste. 630, Washington, DC 20036-1183. Ed. James Rhem.
Description: Provides a forum for dialogue regarding the challenge of teaching and learning in the college classroom.

EDUCATION — HIGHER EDUCATION

378 US
NATIONAL UNIVERSITY CONTINUING EDUCATION ASSOCIATION. DIRECTORY. 1974. a. $20. National University Continuing Education Association, 1 Dupont Circle, N.W., Ste. 615, Washington, DC 20036. TEL 202-659-3130. **Document type:** directory.
Former titles: National University Continuing Education Association. Handbook and Directory; National University Extension Association. Handbook and Directory (ISSN 0097-0255)

378 500 CN
NATURAL SCIENCES AND ENGINEERING RESEARCH COUNCIL OF CANADA. LIST OF SCHOLARSHIPS AND GRANTS IN AID OF RESEARCH/CONSEIL DE RECHERCHES EN SCIENCES NATURELLES ET EN GENIE DU CANADA. LISTE DES BOURSES ET SUBVENTIONS DE RECHERCHE. (Not avail. in print format) (Text and summaries in English and French) 1978. a. Natural Sciences & Engineering Research Council of Canada, 350 Albert St., Ottawa, ON K1A 1H5, Canada. TEL 613-995-5992. FAX 613-943-0742. stat. circ. 2,200. (diskette format) **Indexed:** BMT, Petrol.Abstr.
Former titles: National Research Council of Canada. Annual Report on Scholarships and Grants in Aid of Research (ISSN 0316-4047); National Research Council of Canada. Annual Report on Support of University Research.

378 500 CN
NATURAL SCIENCES AND ENGINEERING RESEARCH COUNCIL OF CANADA. REPORT OF THE PRESIDENT/CONSEIL DE RECHERCHES EN SCIENCES NATURELLES ET EN GENIE DU CANADA. RAPPORT DU PRESIDENT. (Text and summaries in English and French) 1978. a. Natural Sciences & Engineering Research Council of Canada, 350 Albert St., Ottawa, ON K1A 1H5, Canada. TEL 613-995-5992. FAX 613-943-0742. circ. 4,000.

378 IS
NEGBA. (Text in Hebrew) 1985. q. free. Ben Gurion University of the Negev, Department of Public Relations, P.O. Box 653, Beersheva 84120, Israel. FAX 972-7-270656. Ed. Chaya Galai. bk.rev. circ. 5,000. **Document type:** newsletter.

NETHERLANDS. CENTRAAL BUREAU VOOR DE STATISTIEK. STATISTIEK VAN HET BEROEPSONDERWIJS: KUNSTONDERWIJS/NETHERLANDS. CENTRAL BUREAU OF STATISTICS. STATISTICS OF PROFESSIONAL EDUCATION: ART EDUCATION. see *EDUCATION — Abstracting, Bibliographies, Statistics*

NETHERLANDS. CENTRAAL BUREAU VOOR DE STATISTIEK. STATISTIEK VAN HET WETENSCHAPPELIJK ONDERWIJS/NETHERLANDS. CENTRAL BUREAU OF STATISTICS. STATISTICS OF UNIVERSITY EDUCATION. see *EDUCATION — Abstracting, Bibliographies, Statistics*

378.1 US ISSN 0047-9616
LC2851.H83
NEW DIRECTIONS (WASHINGTON). 1973. q. Howard University, Department of Publications, Washington, DC 20008. TEL 202-806-8200. FAX 201-806-8410. Ed. Abdulkadir N. Said. adv.; bk.rev.; charts; illus. circ. 10,000. **Indexed:** A.I.P.P., Rehabil.Lit.

370 US ISSN 0194-3081
LB2328
NEW DIRECTIONS FOR COMMUNITY COLLEGES. 1973. q. $49 to individuals; institutions $72. (E R I C Clearinghouse for Junior Colleges) Jossey-Bass Inc., Publishers, 350 Sansome St., 5th Fl., San Francisco, CA 94104. TEL 415-433-1767. FAX 415-433-0499. Ed. Arthur M. Cohen. circ. 1,000. (back issues avail.; reprint service avail. from UMI) **Indexed:** C.I.J.E., Cont.Pg.Educ., Curr.Cont., Educ.Ind., Educ.Tech.Abstr., SSCI. **Document type:** monographic series.
—Faxon; UnCover; UMI.
Description: Provides expert assistance in helping community colleges meet the challenges of their distinctive and expanding educational mission.

378 US ISSN 0271-0560
LB2331.72
NEW DIRECTIONS FOR HIGHER EDUCATION. 1973. q. $47 to individuals; institutions $62. Jossey-Bass Inc., Publishers, 350 Sansome St., 5th Fl., San Francisco, CA 94104. TEL 415-433-1767. FAX 415-433-0499. Ed. Martin Kramer. circ. 1,300. (also avail. in microform from UMI; back issues avail.; reprint service avail. from UMI) **Indexed:** C.I.J.E., Cont.Pg.Educ., Curr.Cont., Educ.Ind., Educ.Tech.Abstr., Psychol.Abstr., SSCI, Stud.Wom.Abstr. **Document type:** monographic series.
—BLDSC (6083.370000); Faxon; UnCover; SWETS; UMI.
Description: Provides current information and authoritative advice about major issues and administrative problems confronting every institution of higher education.

370 US ISSN 0271-0579
LA227.3
NEW DIRECTIONS FOR INSTITUTIONAL RESEARCH. 1974. q. $47 to individuals; institutions $62. (Association for Institutional Research) Jossey-Bass Inc., Publishers, 350 Sansome St., 5th Fl., San Francisco, CA 94104. TEL 415-433-1767. FAX 415-433-0499. Ed. Patrick T. Terenzini. stat. circ. 1,100. (back issues avail.; reprint service avail. from UMI) **Indexed:** C.I.J.E., Cont.Pg.Educ., Curr.Cont., Educ.Ind., Educ.Tech.Abstr. **Document type:** monographic series.
—BLDSC (6083.390000); UnCover; SWETS; UMI.
Description: Provides planners and administrators in all types of academic institutions with guidelines in such areas as resource coordination, information analysis, program evaluation, and institutional management.

378 US ISSN 0164-7970
LB1027.5
NEW DIRECTIONS FOR STUDENT SERVICES. 1978. q. $47 to individuals; institutions $62. Jossey-Bass Inc., Publishers, 350 Sansome St., 5th Fl., San Francisco, CA 94104. TEL 415-433-1767. FAX 415-433-0499. Ed. Margaret J. Barr. circ. 1,000. (back issues avail.; reprint service avail. from UMI) **Indexed:** Cont.Pg.Educ., Educ.Ind., Mult.Ed.Abstr., Psychol.Abstr., SOMA. **Document type:** monographic series.
—UnCover; UMI.
Description: Offers guidelines and programs for aiding students in their total development: emotional, social, and physical, as well as intellectual.

378 US
NEW ENGLAND BOARD OF HIGHER EDUCATION. NEW ENGLAND REGIONAL STUDENT PROGRAM: GRADUATE LEVEL. 1955. a. $2. New England Board of Higher Education, 45 Temple Pl., Boston, MA 02111. circ. 13,000.
Description: Listing of graduate public college degree programs available to out-of-state New England students for reduced tuition.

378 US
NEW ENGLAND BOARD OF HIGHER EDUCATION. NEW ENGLAND REGIONAL STUDENT PROGRAM: UNDERGRADUATE LEVEL. 1955. a. $2. New England Board of Higher Education, 45 Temple Pl., Boston, MA 02111. circ. 13,000.
Description: Listing of undergraduate public college degree programs available to out-of-state New England students for reduced tuition.

378 US
NEW ENGLAND BOARD OF HIGHER EDUCATION. NEW ENGLAND REGIONAL STUDENT SERVICES: ENROLLMENT REPORT. 1968. a. free to qualified personnel only. New England Board of Higher Education, New England Regional Student Services, c/o Madeleine McGarrity, Dir., 45 Temple Pl., Boston, MA 02111. TEL 617-357-9620.
Description: Report of enrollment in college programs available at reduced tuition for out-of-state students under the Regional Student Program.

377.8 US ISSN 0028-5374
NEW HORIZONS (NEW YORK). 1934. 4/yr. free. United Board for Christian Higher Education in Asia, 475 Riverside Drive, New York, NY 10115. TEL 212-870-2610. FAX 212-870-2322. Ed. Anne Leo Ellisr. bk.rev.; illus. circ. 10,000.

378 US
NEW YORK STATE. EDUCATION DEPARTMENT. COLLEGE AND UNIVERSITY ENROLLMENT. 1960. a. Education Department, Office of Post-Secondary Policy Analysis, c/o James J. Brady, Chief, Bureau of Post-Secondary Statistical Service, Rm. 5B44 CEC, Albany, NY 12230. TEL 518-474-3874. stat.; charts. circ. 50C. (back issues avail.)

378 658.15 US
NEW YORK STATE. EDUCATION DEPARTMENT. COLLEGE AND UNIVERSITY REVENUES AND EXPENDITURES. 1960. a. Education Department, Office of Post-Secondary Policy Analysis, c/o James J. Brady, Chief, Bureau of Post-Secondary Statistical Service, Rm. 5B44 CEC, Albany, NY 12230. TEL 518-474-3874. charts; stat. circ. 500.

NEWSWIRE (MANHATTAN). see *JOURNALISM*

378.669 NR ISSN 1117-062X
NIGERIA. NATIONAL UNIVERSITIES COMMISSION. ANNUAL REPORT. a. free. National Universities Commission, Information and Public Relations Unit, Aja Nwachukwu House, Plot 430 Aguiyi-Ironsi St., Maitama District, P.M.B. 237 Garki G.P.O., Abuja, Nigeria. TEL 234-9-5233176. FAX 234-9-5233520. TELEX UNICOMM LAGOS. Ed. Goddy Nnadi. **Document type:** government publication, corporate report.

378.669 NR ISSN 1117-0611
NIGERIA. NATIONAL UNIVERSITIES COMMISSION. CONVOCATION SPEECHES. a. free. National Universities Commission, Information and Public Relations Unit, Aja Nwachukwu House, Plot 430 Aguiyi-Ironsi St., Maitama District, P.M.B. 237 Garki G.P.O., Abuja, Nigeria. TEL 234-9-5233176. FAX 234-9-5233520. TELEX UNICOMM LAGOS. **Document type:** government publication.

378.669 NR ISSN 1117-0638
NIGERIA. NATIONAL UNIVERSITIES COMMISSION. RESEARCH DIRECTORY. a. free. National Universities Commission, Information and Public Relations Unit, Aja Nwachukwu House, Plot 430 Aguiyi-Ironsi St., Maitama District, P.M.B. 237 Garki G.P.O., Abuja, Nigeria. TEL 234-9-5233176. FAX 234-9-5233520. TELEX UNICOMM LAGOS. **Document type:** government publication, directory.

378.669 NR ISSN 1117-0603
NIGERIA. NATIONAL UNIVERSITIES COMMISSION. STATISTICAL DIGEST. a. free. National Universities Commission, Information and Public Relations Unit, Aja Nwachukwu House, Plot 430 Aguiyi-Ironsi St., Maitama District, P.M.B. 237 Garki G.P.O., Abuja, Nigeria. TEL 234-9-5233176. FAX 234-9-5233520. TELEX UNICOMM LAGOS. stat. **Document type:** government publication.

378.669 NR ISSN 0795-9931
NIGERIA. NATIONAL UNIVERSITIES COMMISSION. UNIVERSITY SYSTEM NEWS. 1977. m. free. National Universities Commission, Information and Public Relations Unit, Aja Nwachukwu House, Plot 430 Aguiyi-Ironsi St., Maitama District, P.M.B. 237 Garki G.P.O., Abuja. TEL 234-9-5233176. FAX 234-9-5233520. TELEX UNICOMM LAGOS. Ed. Goddy Nnadi. circ. 30,000. **Document type:** government publication, bulletin.
Formerly: Nigeria. National Universities Commission. Bulletin.
Description: Covers important news from the universities in Nigeria.

NORTH AMERICAN ASSOCIATION OF SUMMER SESSIONS. ANNUAL CONFERENCE. PROCEEDINGS. see *EDUCATION — School Organization And Administration*

378.1 US
NORTH CAROLINA STATE UNIVERSITY. CHANCELLOR'S REPORT. 1958. biennial. free. North Carolina State University, Office of University Relations, Box 7508, Raleigh, NC 27695-7508. TEL 919-515-7159. FAX 919-515-7946. Ed. Beth McGee. circ. 8,000. **Document type:** corporate report.
Formerly: North Carolina State University. Chancellor's Annual Report; Incorporates (1958-1984): North Carolina State University. Development Board. Report; Which was formerly: North Carolina State University. Development Council. Report (ISSN 0078-1428); North Carolina University. State College of Agriculture and Engineering, Raleigh. Development Council. Report.

EDUCATION — HIGHER EDUCATION

378   US   ISSN 0892-2489
LB2301
NORTHWEST ASSOCIATION OF SCHOOLS AND COLLEGES. CONVENTION PROCEEDINGS. 1926. a. $7. Northwest Association of Schools and Colleges, Boise State University, Boise, ID 83725. TEL 208-334-3226. FAX 208-334-3228. Ed. David G. Steadman. circ. controlled. **Document type:** proceedings.

NORWAY. DIREKTORATET FOR ARBEIDSTILSYNET. FORSKRIFTER/REGULATIONS. see *OCCUPATIONAL HEALTH AND SAFETY*

NURSING FACULTY CENSUS. see *MEDICAL SCIENCES — Nurses And Nursing*

NURSING STUDENT CENSUS. see *MEDICAL SCIENCES — Nurses And Nursing*

O C L C NEWSLETTER. (Online Computer Library Center, Inc.) see *LIBRARY AND INFORMATION SCIENCES*

370   CN   ISSN 0316-3903
O T F - F E O INTERACTION. 1965. 4/yr. membership. Ontario Teachers' Federation, 1260 Bay St., Toronto, ON M5R 2B5, Canada. TEL 416-966-3424. Ed. Keith Fox. adv.; bk.rev. circ. 126,000. **Document type:** newsletter.
    Former titles: O T F Interaction; Interaction; (until 1974): O T F Reporter (ISSN 0029-7313)

378   US
OAK RIDGE ASSOCIATED UNIVERSITIES. ANNUAL REPORT. 1947. a. free. Oak Ridge Associated Universities, Inc., Office of Information Services, Box 117, Oak Ridge, TN 37831-0117. TEL 615-576-3146. Ed. Karen Dunham. circ. 2,500. (also avail. in microform from NTI; reprint service avail. from NTI)
    Formerly: Oak Ridge Institute for Nuclear Studies. Report (ISSN 0078-2904)

371.4   US   ISSN 0360-5434
L901   CODEN: CBBEEI
OCCUPATIONAL EDUCATION. (Included in 5-vol. College Blue Book series) 1972. biennial. $44. Macmillan Publishing Company, 866 Third Ave., New York, NY 10022.
    Formerly: Blue Book of Occupational Education (ISSN 0067-9275)

378.769   US
ODYSSEY (LEXINGTON). 1982. s-a. free. University of Kentucky, Communications and Advancement Office, 404 Kinkead Hall, Lexington, KY 40506-0057. TEL 606-257-8297. FAX 606-257-8298. Ed. Susan H. Stempel. illus.; stat. circ. 10,000. **Document type:** corporate report.
    Supersedes (in 1982): University of Kentucky Research Foundation. Annual Report (ISSN 0566-8719)

378 377.8   AU   ISSN 0029-9200
DIE OESTERREICHISCHE HOEHERE SCHULE. 1948. 5/yr. S.50. Vereinigung Christlicher Lehrerinnen und Lehrer an Hoeheren und Mittleren Schulen Oesterreichs, Kundmanngasse 22, A-1030 Vienna, Austria. TEL 0222-7123364. FAX 0222-7135103. Ed. Wolf Peschl. adv.; bk.rev.; index. circ. 5,500. **Document type:** academic/scholarly publication.

OESTERREICHISCHER KRANKENPFLEGERVERBAND. FORTBILDUNGSPROGRAMM. see *MEDICAL SCIENCES — Nurses And Nursing*

378 378   US
OFFICIAL GUIDE FOR G M A T REVIEW. (Graduate Management Admission Test) 1972. biennial. $11.95. (Graduate Management Admission Council) Educational Testing Service, Princeton, NJ 08541. TEL 609-951-1236. (Subscr. to: Little Brown, 200 West St., Waltham, MA 02254. TEL 800-759-0190; Institutions subscr. to: Special Sales, Warner Book, Inc., Time & Life Bldg., 1271 Ave. of the Americas, New York, NY 10020. TEL 212-522-7381) (back issues avail.)
    Former titles: Official Guide to G M A T; Guide to Graduate Management Education.

378   US
OFFICIAL GUIDE TO M B A PROGRAMS. (Master of Business Administration) 1972. biennial. $13.95. (Graduate Management Admission Council) Educational Testing Service, Princeton, NJ 08541. TEL 609-951-1236. (Subscr. to: Little Brown, 200 West St., Waltham, MA 02254. TEL 800-759-0190; Institutions subscr. to: Special Sales, Warner Book, Inc., Time & Life Bldg., 1271 Ave. of the Americas, New York, NY 10020. TEL 212-522-7381)
    Description: Provides information for prospective MBA students. Includes information on loans, scholarships, and work-study options, as well as specific information on financial aid at hundreds of graduate schools of management.

378 340   US   ISSN 0886-3342
KF273
OFFICIAL GUIDE TO U.S. LAW SCHOOLS. 1967. a. $13. Law School Admission Services, Inc., Box 63, Newtown, PA 18940. TEL 215-968-1136. FAX 215-968-1169. Ed.Bd. circ. 140,000. (processed)
    Former titles: Prelaw Handbook. Official Law School Guide (ISSN 0075-8264); Law Study and Practice in the United States: Pre-Law Handbook.
    Description: Contains law school profiles provided by the schools themselves.

378   US
OLD GOLD AND BLACK. 1916. w. $30. Wake Forest University, Box 7569, Reynolds Stn., Winston-Salem, NC 27109. TEL 919-759-5280. FAX 919-759-6074. Ed. Michael D. McKinley. adv.; bk.rev.; film rev.; play rev.; charts; illus. circ. 5,000. (back issues avail.)

376 305.4   US   ISSN 0734-0141
ON CAMPUS WITH WOMEN. 1971. q. $20 to qualified members; others $28. Association of American Colleges, 1818 R St., N.W., Washington, DC 20009. TEL 202-387-1300. FAX 202-265-9532. Ed. Sherry Levy-Reiner. bk.rev. circ. 6,000. (also avail. in microform from UMI; reprint service avail. from UMI) **Indexed:** ERIC, Wom.Stud.Abstr. (1971-).
    Description: Explores the ways women are changing all sectors of higher education; highlights both research and practice.

ONLINE WITH ADULT AND CONTINUING EDUCATORS. see *EDUCATION — Adult Education*

ONTARIO UNIVERSITIES BENEFITS SURVEY. see *EDUCATION — School Organization And Administration*

378.1   UK   ISSN 0268-0513
OPEN LEARNING. 1974. 3/yr. £37 (Europe £38; elsewhere £42). (Open University) Longman Group UK Ltd., Westgate House, 6th Fl., The High, Harlow, Essex CM20 1YR, England. TEL 0279-442601. FAX 0279-444501. illus. (also avail. in microform from UMI; reprint service avail. from UMI) **Indexed:** C.I.J.E., Educ.Tech.Abstr., High.Educ.Curr.Aware.Bull., Res.High.Educ.Abstr., SOMA. **Document type:** academic/scholarly publication.
    —BLDSC (6265.960600); Faxon; SWETS.
    Supersedes (in 1986): Teaching at a Distance (ISSN 0307-241X)

378.005   SZ
OPTIONS; journal d'information sur les formations et les metiers. 1970. 4/yr. 25 SFr. Office d'Orientation et de Formation Professionelle, Service d'Orientation, Case postale 457, CH-1211 Geneva 4, Switzerland. TEL 022-7050261. FAX 022-3280666. Ed. Yvonne-Marie Ruedin. bk.rev.; illus. circ. 22,000. **Indexed:** Int.Lab.Doc. **Document type:** academic/scholarly publication.
    Formerly (until 1992): Etudes et Carrieres.

378   UK
ORATORY SCHOOL MAGAZINE. 1891. a. Oratory School, Woodcote, Near Reading, England. Ed. I.C. McLean. adv. circ. 2,000.

ORIENTATION SCOLAIRE ET PROFESSIONNELLE. see *PSYCHOLOGY*

378   AU
OST-DOKUMENTATION BILDUNGS- UND WISSENSCHAFTSPOLITIK. 1987. q. S.272. Oesterreichisches Ost- und Suedosteuropa Institut, Agnerstr. 51, A-3400 Klosterneuburg, Austria. Eds. Peter Bachmaier, Werner Weilguni. abstr.; index. circ. 100. **Document type:** bulletin.
    Formerly (until 1991): Ost-Dokumentation Bildungswesen.

615.53 378   US
OSTEOPATHIC MEDICAL EDUCATION: A HANDBOOK FOR MINORITY APPLICANTS. 1978. irreg. $3. American Association of Colleges of Osteopathic Medicine, 6110 Executive Blvd., Ste. 405, Rockville, MD 20852. TEL 301-468-0990. Ed. Tamara B. Coward. circ. 5,000. **Document type:** monographic series.
    Description: Provides summary accounts of the osteopathic profession, pathways to osteopathic education, and the educational and training programs of the osteopathic colleges.
    Refereed Serial

378   US
OXFORD UNIVERSITY ALMANACK. a. price varies. Oxford University Press, 200 Madison Ave., New York, NY 10016. TEL 212-679-7300.

378   US
OXFORD UNIVERSITY CALENDAR. a. price varies. Oxford University Press, 200 Madison Ave., New York, NY 10016. TEL 212-679-7300.

331   US
P S C CLARION. 1972. 9/yr. membership. Professional Staff Congress, City University of New York, 25 W. 43 St., New York, NY 10036. TEL 212-354-1252. Ed. Carol Sims. adv.; bk.rev.; charts; illus. circ. 15,000.
    Former titles: Legislative Conference Reporter (ISSN 0024-0478); U F C T Action.

378   II
PANJAB UNIVERSITY NEWS. (Text in English) 1958. q. Rs.15. Panjab University, Publication Bureau, Chandigarh 160014, Union Territory, India. Ed. R.K. Malhotra. adv.; charts; illus. circ. 500.

378   MX
PERFIL DE ASPIRANTES Y ASIGNADOS A BACHILLERATO, TECNICO EN ENFERMERIA Y LICENCIATURA DE LA U N A M. 1989. a. Universidad Nacional Autonoma de Mexico, Direccion General de Estadistica y Sistemas de Informacion Institucionales, Ciudad Universitaria, Zona Cultural, 04510 Mexico D.F., Mexico. TEL 955-606-9686. FAX 955-665-0943. circ. 1,000.

378   MX   ISSN 0185-2698
PERFILES EDUCATIVOS. 1978; N.S. 1983. q. $20. Universidad Nacional Autonoma de Mexico, Centro de Investigaciones y Servicios Educativos, Ciudad Universitaria, Circuito Exterior de la Ciudad Universitaria, Edificio Tecnico de la Universidad Abierta, 04510 Mexico, D.F., Mexico. TEL 6228702. FAX 5501801. Ed. Fernando Vizcaino Guerra. bk.rev. circ. 2,000. **Document type:** academic/scholarly publication.

378   GW
PERSONAL- UND VORLESUNGSVERZEICHNIS. 1972. s-a. Bergische Universitaet - Gesamthochschule Wuppertal, Gausstr. 20, 42097 Wuppertal, Germany. TEL 0202-4392212. FAX 0202-4392901. TELEX 8592262-GHW. adv. circ. 8,000. **Document type:** bulletin.

378   CN   ISSN 0317-7025
PERSPECTIVES AND PLANS FOR GRADUATE STUDIES. irreg. Can.$5. Council of Ontario Universities, 444 Yonge St., Ste. 203, Toronto, Ont. M5B 2H4, Canada. TEL 416-979-2165. FAX 416-979-8635.

378   US
LB2337.2
PETERSON'S GRANTS FOR GRADUATE STUDY (YEAR). 1986. biennial. $59.95. Peterson's Guides, Inc., 202 Carnegie Center, Box 2123, Princeton, NJ 08543-2123. TEL 609-243-9111. FAX 609-243-9150. **Document type:** directory.
    Former titles: Peterson's Grants for Graduate Students (Years) (ISSN 1040-1091); Grants for Graduate Students (Year) (ISSN 0889-1613)
    Description: Covers nearly 700 broadly available grants and fellowships for graduate students.

EDUCATION — HIGHER EDUCATION

PHARMACY STUDENT. see *PHARMACY AND PHARMACOLOGY*

370.7   PH
PHILIPPINE NORMAL COLLEGE RESEARCH SERIES. 1976. irreg., no.3, 1977. price varies. Philippine Normal College, Manila 2801, Philippines. charts. circ. 500.

PHOENIX. see *OCCUPATIONS AND CAREERS*

PHYSICS EDUCATION. see *PHYSICS*

PITT MAGAZINE. see *COLLEGE AND ALUMNI*

370 711   US   ISSN 0736-0983
LA227.3
PLANNING FOR HIGHER EDUCATION. 1970. q. $40 (foreign $58). Society for College and University Planning, c/o 2026M School of Education, University of Michigan, Ann Arbor, MI 48109-1259. TEL 313-763-4776. FAX 313-747-1987. Ed. George C. Keller. bk.rev.; illus.; index. circ. 2,400. (also avail. in microform from UMI; back issues avail.; reprint service avail. from UMI) **Indexed:** C.I.J.E., Cont.Pg.Educ., Educ.Ind., High.Educ.Abstr. —BLDSC (6509.070000); UnCover; SWETS; UMI.
    Supersedes: S C U P News and Journal (ISSN 0037-9719); Society for College and University Planning Quarterly.
    Description: Provides information and ideas for the purpose of advancing the state-of-the-art of planning.

POSTEPY NAUK MEDYCZNYCH. see *MEDICAL SCIENCES*

POSTGRADUATE EDUCATION FOR GENERAL PRACTICE. see *MEDICAL SCIENCES*

POTCHEFSTROOM UNIVERSITY FOR CHRISTIAN HIGHER EDUCATION. WETENSKAPLIKE BYDRAES. REEKS B: NATUURWETENSKAPPE. SERIES. see *EDUCATION — Adult Education*

378   SA
POTCHEFSTROOM UNIVERSITY FOR CHRISTIAN HIGHER EDUCATION. WETENSKAPLIKE BYDRAES. REEKS H: INOUGURELE REDES. (Text in Afrikaans; sometimes in English) irreg. free. Potchefstroom University for Christian Higher Education - Potchefstroom Universiteit vir Christelike Hoer Onderwys, Potchefstroom, South Africa.

378   II   ISSN 0554-9884
PRAJNA. (Text in English) no.6, 1974. q. Banaras Hindu University, Varanasi 221005, Uttar Pradesh, India. Ed. R.M. Pandey. bk.rev. circ. 10,000.

378   HO
PRESENCIA UNIVERSITARIA. 1964. m. free. (Universidad Nacional Autonoma de Honduras) Editorial Universitaria U N A H, Ciudad Universitaria, Tegucigalpa, Honduras. TEL 504-32-4772. FAX 504-31-0675. illus. circ. 1,000.

378   IT   ISSN 0478-1376
PRESENZA. 1969. q. L.15000. Universita Cattolica del Sacro Cuore, Largo Gemelli 1, 20123 Milan, Italy. TEL 02-885370. FAX 8856210. Ed. Franco Monaco. adv. circ. 104,000.

378   UK
PRIOR PARK MAGAZINE. a. Prior Park College, Bath, Avon BA2 5AH, England. Ed. Angela Webster. adv. contact: B. Bane. circ. 500.

378   SP
PROFESIONES Y EMPRESAS; revista de educacion tecnologica y profesional. 1974. bi-m. 3500 ptas. (foreign 9000 ptas.). Editepsa, Gran Via, 38-9o, 28013 Madrid, Spain. TEL 5223844. Ed. Maria Cruz Mendiola. adv.; bk.rev.; illus.; pat. circ. 7,000.

378   IT   ISSN 0392-2790
PROFESSIONALITA. 1980. m. L.49000. Editrice La Scuola S.p.A., Via Cadorna 11, 25186 Brescia, Italy. TEL 030-29931. Ed. Luigi Morgano. circ. 15,000.

378 371.42   UK
PROSPECTS POSTGRAD. q. £7.50 (free to students in the UK and Ireland). C S U (Publications) Ltd., Armstrong House, Oxford Rd., Manchester M1 7ED, England. TEL 44-61-236-9816. FAX 44-61-236-8541. adv.: B&W page £1250. circ. 50,000.
    Description: Discusses options for further study and research for college and university graduates.

378   US   ISSN 1063-1771
▼**PUBLICATIONS NEWSLETTER.** 1992. m. $95.95. Topor & Associates, 280 Easy St., No. 114, Mountain View, CA 99043-3736. TEL 415-962-1105. bk.rev. circ. 500. (back issues avail.) **Document type:** newsletter.

PUBLISHING FOR THE COLLEGE MARKET: REVIEW, TRENDS & FORECAST. see *PUBLISHING AND BOOK TRADE*

378   UK
QUEEN MARY COLLEGE STUDENTS UNION HANDBOOK. 1958. a. free. University of London, Queen Mary College Students Union, 432 Bancroft Rd., London E1 4DH, England. adv. circ. 6,000. **Document type:** academic/scholarly publication.

QUERY (SUNNYVALE). see *EDUCATION — Computer Applications*

378   SA   ISSN 0033-6785
R A U - RAPPORT. (Text in Afrikaans) 1968. 2/yr. free. Rand Afrikaans University, Box 524, Auckland Park 2006, South Africa. FAX 27-11-489-2790. Ed.Bd. illus. circ. 13,000. **Document type:** newsletter.

370   SA
RANDSE AFRIKAANSE UNIVERSITEIT. JAARBOEK. 1968. a. free. Rand Afrikaans University, P.O. Box 524, Auckland Park 2006, South Africa. FAX 27-11-489-2790. circ. controlled. (processed)

378 330   US
RAPID READERS SERIES. 1977. irreg., no.7, 1985. price varies. Delta Pi Epsilon Graduate Business Education Society, National Office, Box 4340, Little Rock, AR 72214. TEL 501-562-1233. FAX 501-562-1293. **Document type:** monographic series.
    Description: Provides teachers new ideas to enliven and enrich the teaching of business subjects.

378   FR   ISSN 0988-1824
RECHERCHE ET FORMATION. 2/yr. 200 F. (foreign 255 F.). Institut National de Recherche Pedagogique, 29 rue d'Ulm, 75230 Paris Cedex 05, France. TEL 46-34-90-00.

378 800   US   ISSN 0893-889X
AS30
RECORDER (SEARCY). 1958. a. free. Alpha Chi National Honor Society, Box 773, Harding University, Searcy, AR 72149-0001. TEL 501-268-6161. Ed. Dennis M. Organ. circ. 7,500 (controlled). **Document type:** academic/scholarly publication, proceedings.

378.1   US   ISSN 0891-012X
RECRUITMENT AND RETENTION IN HIGHER EDUCATION. 1987. m. $177. Magna Publications, Inc., 2718 Dryden Dr., Madison, WI 53704-3006. TEL 608-246-3580. FAX 608-249-0355. Ed. Mary Lou Santovec; Pub. Doris Green. index. circ. 1,300. (also avail. in diskette format; back issues avail.) **Document type:** newsletter.
—CCC.
    Description: Focuses on student enrollment in colleges and universities.

378 917.306   US   ISSN 0274-8657
LA RED - THE NET. 1983. a. $54 (Includes subscr. to: La Red - The Net Hotline). Floricanto Press, 16161 Ventura Blvd., Ste. 830, Encino, CA 91436-2504. TEL 818-990-1885. bk.rev. **Indexed:** Chic.Per.Ind.
    Description: Focuses on issues, problems and discussion of current themes in education of Hispanics, with emphasis on higher education. Includes commentaries and reviews of current fiction and non-fiction humanities and social science U.S. Latino titles.

378 917.306   US   ISSN 1043-223X
LA RED - THE NET HOTLINE; the Hispanic journal of education, commentary, and reviews. 1988. m. $54 (includes subscr. to: La Red - The Net). Floricanto Press, 16161 Ventura Blvd., Ste. 830, Encino, CA 91436-2504. TEL 818-990-1885.

378   UK   ISSN 0954-2396
REFLECTIONS ON HIGHER EDUCATION. 1988. a. £20 (effective 1993-94). Higher Education Foundation, Westminster College, Oxford OX2 9AT, England. TEL 0865-247644. FAX 0865-251847. Ed. R. Ward. adv.; bk.rev. circ. 250. (back issues avail.) **Document type:** academic/scholarly publication. —BLDSC (7332.331350).
    Description: Offers a forum where the aims, organization, structures, content, and values of higher education can be probed at a fundamental level.
    Refereed Serial

378   US   ISSN 0034-3390
REGIONAL SPOTLIGHT; news of education in the South. 1974. irreg. $0.50 per no. Southern Regional Education Board, 592 Tenth St., N.W., Atlanta, GA 30318-5790. TEL 404-875-9211. Ed. Margaret Sullivan. circ. 8,500. **Document type:** newsletter.

RESEARCH DEVELOPMENT IN HIGHER EDUCATION. PUBLICATIONS. see *EDUCATION*

378   US
RESEARCH IN DEVELOPMENTAL EDUCATION. 1983. 5/yr. $11. Appalachian State University, National Center for Developmental Education, Boone, NC 28608. TEL 704-262-2876. FAX 704-262-2128. Ed. Hunter R. Boylan. (reprint service avail. from UMI) **Document type:** academic/scholarly publication.
    Former titles: Review of Research in Developmental Education; Research in Developmental Education.
    Description: Summaries and reports of research that influence the field of developmental education.

RESEARCH IN HIGHER EDUCATION. see *EDUCATION — School Organization And Administration*

378   US
RESEARCH - PENN STATE. 1980. q. free. Pennsylvania State University, Senior Vice Presicent for Research, 320 Kern Bldg., University Park, PA 16802. TEL 814-865-3477. FAX 814-863-4627. Ed. Nancy Marie Brown. bk.rev.; circ. 25,000 (controlled). **Indexed:** Ind.Free Per. **Document type:** academic/scholarly publication.

378   US   ISSN 0731-9649
RESEARCH: VIRGINIA TECH. 1981. a. free. Virginia Polytechnic Institute and State University, Research Division, 312 Sandy Hall, Blacksburg, VA 24061-0325. TEL 703-231-5646. FAX 703-231-3714. Ed. Susan Trulove. circ. 10,000. **Indexed:** Biol.Abstr., Curr.Adv.Ecol.Sci., Curr.Cont., Nutr.Abstr., Ocean.Abstr., Plant Breed Abstr.
    Description: Features articles about specific research projects conducted at the university. Most issues focus on a particular area of research, such as international affairs, arts and humanities and environmental concerns.
    Refereed Serial

378   CN   ISSN 0700-6004
RESEAU. 1969. m. free. Universite du Quebec, 2875 Bd. Laurier, Ste. Foy, PQ G1V 2M3, Canada. TEL 418-657-3551. circ. 20,500. **Document type:** academic/scholarly publication.

378   US
RESOURCE (NEW YORK). 1977. s-a. free. City University of New York, Office of Academic Affairs, Instructional Resource Center, 535 E. 80th St., Rm. 404, New York, NY 10021. TEL 212-794-5446. FAX 212-794-5706. Ed. Virginia Slaughter. circ. 2,500. **Document type:** academic/scholarly publication.
    Description: Provides news and information on instructional and support initiatives in freshman year programs at The City University of New York, as well as items of interest to CUNY basic skills faculty.

EDUCATION — HIGHER EDUCATION

REVIEW OF HIGHER EDUCATION. 378 LA226 US ISSN 0162-5748. 1977. q. $70 to individuals; students $50. Association for the Study of Higher Education (Ann Arbor), University of Michigan, 2002 School of Education, Ann Arbor, MI 48109-1259. FAX 313-746-2510. Ed. Joan S. Stark. bk.rev.; bibl.; charts. circ. 1,200. (also avail. in microform from UMI; back issues avail.; reprint service avail. from UMI) **Indexed:** C.I.J.E., Cont.Pg.Educ., High.Educ.Abstr., Mult.Ed.Abstr., Res.High.Educ.Abstr., SOMA. **Document type:** academic/scholarly publication.
—BLDSC (7790.769200); Faxon; UnCover; SWETS; UMI.
Formerly (until 1978): Higher Education Review (ISSN 0148-9585)
Description: Publishes articles, essays, and reviews that advance the study of colleges and universities.

REVISTA BRASILEIRA DE HISTORIA. see HISTORY — History Of North And South America

REVISTA CUBANA DE EDUCACION MEDICA SUPERIOR. see MEDICAL SCIENCES

REVISTA CUBANA DE EDUCACION SUPERIOR. 378 CU. 1981. q. $14 in N. and S. America; Europe $16; elsewhere $17. (Universidad de Camaguey, Carretera de Circunvalacion) Ediciones Cubanas, Obispo No. 527, Apdo. 605, Havana, Cuba. abstr.; illus.; stat. circ. 5,000.

REVISTA DE LA EDUCACION SUPERIOR.* 378 MX. 1972. q. Mex.$60($6) Asociacion Nacional de Universidades e Institutos de Ensenanza Superior, Alta Tension 80-1-A, Mexico, D.F., Mexico. Ed. Alfonso Rangel Guerra. bk.rev. circ. 5,000.

REVISTA PERSPECTIVA EDUCACIONAL. 378 CL. 1980. s-a. $40 per no. (Universidad Catolica de Valparaiso, Instituto de Educacion) Ediciones Universitarias de Valparaiso, Casilla 1415, Valparaiso, Chile. TEL 032-252900. FAX 032-212746. TELEX 230389 UCVAL CL. Dir. Karlheinz Laage. circ. 300. **Document type:** academic/scholarly publication.

REVISTA UNIMAR. 378 BL ISSN 0100-9354. (Text in Portuguese; summaries in English, Portuguese) 1974. 3/yr. exchange basis. Universidade Estadual de Maringa, Pro-Reitoria de Pesquisa e Pos-Graduacao, Av. Colombo, 3690, 87020-900 Maringa PR, Brazil. TEL 0442-224378. FAX 0442-232676. Ed. Maria Jose de Melo Vandresen. abstr.; bibl.; illus. circ. 600. **Indexed:** Ind.Med., M.L.A. **Document type:** academic/scholarly publication.
Refereed Serial

REVISTA UNIVERSITARIA. 378 CL ISSN 0250-3670. 1915. 3/yr. Esc.1900($18) to individuals; students Esc. 1500. (Pontificia Universidad Catholica de Chile) Ediciones Pontificia Universidad Catolica de Chile, Vicerrectoria Academica, Alameda 340-Oficina 212, Casilla 114-D, Santiago, Chile. FAX 56-2225515. Ed. Cecilia Garcia Huidobro. adv.; bk.rev.; illus. circ. 4,000. **Indexed:** Biol.Abstr. **Document type:** academic/scholarly publication.
Description: Scholarly articles on literature, technology, and history

RHETORIC REVIEW. 378 407 PN171.4 US ISSN 0735-0198. 1982. s-a. $12 to individuals; institutions $15. University of Arizona, Department of English, Rhetoric Review, Tuscon, AZ 85721. TEL 602-621-3371. FAX 602-621-7397. Ed. Theresa Enos. adv.; bk.rev. circ. 1,000. (back issues avail.) **Document type:** academic/scholarly publication.
—BLDSC (7960.609000); Faxon; UnCover.

RIJKSUNIVERSITEIT UTRECHT. DE UNIVERSITEIT MEDIA BULLETIN. 378 NE. 1988. s-m. free. Rijksuniversiteit te Utrecht, Afdeling Voorlichting, Heidelberglaan 8, 3584 CS Utrecht, Netherlands. TEL 030-533550. FAX 030-521818. illus.; circ. 1,700. (controlled). (looseleaf format)
Description: Provides information on new projects and activities at the university.

RIJKSUNIVERSITEIT UTRECHT. WETENSCHAPPELIJK JAAVERSLAG. 378 500 NE. 1815. a. free. Rijksuniversiteit te Utrecht, Afdeling Voorlichting, Heidelberglaan 8, 3584 CS Utrecht, Netherlands. TEL 030-533550. FAX 030-521818. circ. 1,000.
Formerly: Rijksuniversiteit Utrecht. Jaarverslag.

RIVISTA DI SCIENZE DELL'EDUCAZIONE. 370.7 IT ISSN 0393-3849. (Text in Italian; summaries in English, French, Italian, Spanish) 1963. 3/yr. L.30000 (foreign L.36000). (Pontificia Facolta di Scienze dell'Educazione "Auxilium", VC) Editrice Libreria Ateneo Salesiano, Piazza Ateneo Salesiano, 1, 00139 Rome, Italy. FAX 06-872-90-629. bk.rev.; bibl.; index. circ. 1,000. (back issues avail.)
Formerly (until 1972): Rivista di Pedagogia e Scienze Religiose (ISSN 0393-5655)
Description: Presents studies and research in the science of education with specific focus on female educational problems during the childhood and adolescent years.

S A L T EQUALIZER. (Society of American Law Teachers) see LAW

S C U P NEWS. 370 711 US. 1972. q. membership. Society for College and University Planning, c/o 2026M School of Education Bldg., University of Michigan, Ann Arbor, MI 48109-1259. TEL 313-763-4776. Ed. Mary Ann Armour. circ. 2,400. (looseleaf format; back issues avail.)

S I P E. 378 IT ISSN 0391-8599. (Servizio Stampa Educazione e Sviluppo) (Text in Italian) 1969. m. free. Istituto per la Cooperazione Universitaria - Institute for University Cooperation, Viale G. Rossini 26, 00198 Rome, Italy. TEL 06-85300722. FAX 06-8554646. Ed. Pier Giovanni Palla. adv.; bk.rev.; index. circ. 2,200. (looseleaf format; back issues avail.) **Document type:** bulletin, newsletter.
Description: Deals with the development of cooperation policies in higher education in Italy and other countries. Gives information on the activities of the institute.

S L U - E I S S I F NEWSLETTER. 378 330 PH ISSN 0115-8341. (Text in English) 1981. q. P.60($10) Saint Louis University, Extension Institute for Small-Scale Industries Foundation, C-016 Center for Culture and the Arts, S L U Campus, Baguio City 2600, Philippines. TEL 442-2193. FAX 442-2842. Ed. Ferdinand G. Fuellos. circ. 250.
Description: Features news on small business, articles that could help small entrepreneurs, and success stories of northern Luzon entrepreneurs. Includes a directory of foundation beneficiaries.

S N E S U P BULLETIN. 378 FR. 1947. bi-w. 90 F. Syndicat National de l'Enseignement Superieur, 78 rue du Faubourg Saint-Denis, 75010 Paris, France. Ed. Roger Bourderon. adv.; bk.rev.; circ. controlled.

S R H E NEWS. 378 UK. 1970. 4/yr. free to members. Society for Research into Higher Education, University of Surrey, Guildford, Surrey GU2 5XH, England. TEL 0483-39003. FAX 0483-300803. circ. 1,500.
Formerly: S R H E Bulletin (ISSN 0266-6081)

ST. AUGUSTINE'S MAGAZINE. 378 UK. 1886. a. £7. St. Augustine's Abbey, Westgate-on-Sea, Kent, England. Ed. D.A. Fligg. circ. 400. **Document type:** bulletin.

SAINT JOHN'S. see COLLEGE AND ALUMNI

ST. JOHN'S REPORTER. 378 US. 1974. 4/yr. free. St. John's College, News and Information Service Office, Box 2800, Annapolis, MD 21404. TEL 410-626-2539. FAX 410-623-4828. (Alt addr.: St. John's College, 1160 Camino de la Cruz Blanca, Santa Fe, NM 87501-4599. TEL 505-984-6104. FAX 505-989-9269) Eds. Nancy Osius, Lesli Allison. bk.rev.; illus. circ. 14,000. (tabloid format)

ST. JOHN'S REVIEW. 378 AP2 US ISSN 0277-4720. 1969. 3/yr. $15. St. John's College, Annapolis, MD 21404. TEL 410-263-2371. FAX 410-263-4828. Ed. Elliott Zuckerman. bk.rev.; charts; illus. circ. 9,000.
—UnCover.
Formerly (until Aug. 1980): College (ISSN 0010-0862)

ST. LAWRENCE. 378 US ISSN 0745-3582. 1943. q. St. Lawrence University, University Communications, Vilas Hall, Canton, NY 13617. TEL 315-379-5560. FAX 315-379-5502. Ed. Neal Burdick. bk.rev. circ. 24,500.
Description: Covers topics in education.

SAINT LOUIS CHRONICLE. 378 PH ISSN 0048-8992. (Text in English) 1969. bi-m. free. Saint Louis University, Box 71, Baguio City 2600, Philippines. TEL 0063-74-442-3043. FAX 0063-74-442-2842. Ed. Editha Somera-Salazar. bk.rev.; charts; illus. circ. 6,000.
Description: News, opinion and feature articles gathered from the elementary, high school, college and teaching hospital departments of Saint Louis University.

SALARY SURVEY (ST. LOUIS). see BUSINESS AND ECONOMICS — Labor And Industrial Relations

SAMMLUNG GROOS. 378 GW ISSN 0344-0591. 1977. irreg. price varies. Julius Groos Verlag, Hertzstr. 6, 69126 Heidelberg, Germany. TEL 06221-303621. FAX 06221-301993. circ. 500. (back issues avail.) **Document type:** academic/scholarly publication.

SCHOLARSHIPS, FELLOWSHIPS AND LOANS. 370.7 332 LB2338 US ISSN 1058-5699. biennial. $110. Gale Research Inc., 835 Penobscot Bldg., Detroit, MI 48266. TEL 313-961-2242. FAX 313-961-6083. Ed. Debra M. Kirby.
Description: Lists over 2500 financial opportunities for U.S and Canadian students and researchers.

SCHOOL LEAVER.* 378 UK. 1968. 8/yr. free. Dominion Press Ltd., Signal House, Lyon Rd., Harrow, Middx HA1 2QE, England. bibl.; illus.
Formerly: Which Course?

SELECTED SOURCES OF FINANCIAL AID FOR OSTEOPATHIC MEDICAL STUDENTS. 378 615.53 US. 1985. irreg. (every 3-4 yrs.). $8. American Association of Colleges of Osteopathic Medicine, 6110 Executive Blvd., Ste. 405, Rockville, MD 20852. TEL 301-468-0990. Ed. Bonnie McCormack. circ. 500. **Document type:** directory.
Formerly (until 1991): Guide to Sources of Financial Aid for Osteopathic Medical Students.
Description: Overview of the range of financial aid sources available to osteopathic medical students and a course guide for people to contact regarding financial aid information.

SELECTIONS (LOS ANGELES). see BUSINESS AND ECONOMICS — Management

SHANGHAI GAOJIAO YANJIU/SHANGHAI HIGHER EDUCATION RESEARCH. 378 CC ISSN 1000-4394. (Text in Chinese) q. Shanghai Gaodeng Jiaoyu Yanjiusuo - Shanghai Higher Education Research Institute, 1954 Huashan Road, Shanghai 200030, People's Republic of China. TEL 4314179. (Co-sponsor: Shanghai Gaodeng Jiaoyu Xuehui - Shanghai Higher Education Association)

SHEEPS CLOTHING. 378 US. 1985. fortn. £75 (foreign £100). Wolverhampton Polytechnic Student's Union, Wulfruna St., Wolverhampton WV1 1LY, England. TEL 0902-712-901. Ed. Terry Binns. film rev.; play rev.; illus. circ. 7,000.

SHEFFIELD UNIVERSITY ANNUAL REPORT. 378 UK. 1906. a. free. Sheffield University, Sheffield S10 2TN, England. circ. 10,000.

EDUCATION — HIGHER EDUCATION

378 UK ISSN 0307-6202
SHEFFIELD UNIVERSITY CALENDAR. 1905. a. £8.
Sheffield University, Sheffield S10 2TN, England.
circ. 1,100.
—BLDSC (3002.000000).

378 UK
SHEFFIELD UNIVERSITY POSTGRADUATE PROSPECTUS.
a. free. Sheffield University, Sheffield S10 2TN,
England. circ. 40,000.

378 UK
SHEFFIELD UNIVERSITY UNDEGRADUATE PROSPECTUS.
a. free. Sheffield University, Sheffield S10 2TN,
England. circ. 85,000.
Formerly: Sheffield University General Prospectus.

371.8 CC
SHENZHOU XUEREN/CHINA'S SCHOLARS ABROAD. (Text
in Chinese) 1988. bi-m. Y1.20($2.20) per no.
(Zhongguo Jiaoyu Guoji Jiaoliu Xiehui) Shenzhou
Xueren Zazhi She, 111, Nanheyan Jie, Beijing
100006, People's Republic of China. (Dist. outside
China by: China International Book Trading Corp.,
P.O. Box 399, Beijing, P.R.C.) (Co-sponsor: Ou-Mei
Tongxue Hui)
Description: For and about Chinese exchange
students who live or have lived abroad.

THE SHORTHORN. see COLLEGE AND ALUMNI

378 GW
SIEGENER HOCHSCHUL ZEITUNG. 1973. q. Universitaet
- Gesamthochschule Siegen, Hoelderlinstr. 3, 57076
Siegen, Germany. TEL 0271-7404864.
FAX 0271-7404899. adv.; bk.rev. circ. 5,000.
(back issues avail.)

378 AG ISSN 0326-3932
SIGNOS UNIVERSITARIOS. 1979. s-a.
Arg.$25000($40) Universidad del Salvador,
Vicerrectorado de Investigacion y Desarrollo,
Rodriguez Pena 770, 2o piso, 1020 Buenos Aires,
Argentina. TEL 42-1381. FAX 42-0631. bk.rev.;
bibl.; illus.
Description: Each issue is devoted to a scientific
discipline taught at the university. Includes research
papers and reviews.

373 NO ISSN 0804-3698
SKOLEFOKUS. 1993. fortn. NOK 300. Laererforbundet
- Teaching Association, Wergelandsveien 15,
N-0167 Oslo, Norway. TEL 47-22-03-00-00.
FAX 47-22-42-65-87. Ed. Finn Stoveland. adv.
contact: Randi Skaugrud. bk.rev.; charts; illus.; index;
circ. 36,000 (controlled).
—CCC.
Formed by the merger of (1899-1993): Skoleforum
(ISSN 0332-7167); (1947-1993): Yrke (ISSN
0049-8475); (1974-1993): Mercator (ISSN
0800-8957); Which was formerly (1939-1973):
Tidsskrift for Handelsutdannelse (ISSN 0801-7727).

378 375 US ISSN 1047-6229
SMALL COLLEGE CREATIVITY. 3/yr. $20 (foreign $30).
Human Technology Interface, Ink Press, 163 Wood
Wedge Way, Sanford, NC 27330.
TEL 919-499-9216. Ed. Lynn Veach Sadler.
Description: Publishes articles or short pieces on
innovative ideas, projects, curricula or approaches
that have been successful at institutions of ten
thousand or fewer students.

378 011 US ISSN 0739-2184
SMITH FUNDING REPORT; the quarterly guide to
research-project grant opportunities offered by
private and corporate foundations for higher
education and health institutions. 1983. q. $195. S
F R, Inc., 76 Oneil Cir., Monroe, NY 10950-3210.
TEL 914-774-4449. Ed. Melanie Smith. abstr.;
index. (looseleaf format; back issues avail.)

378 AT
SMITH'S WEEKLY. 1960. w. free. University of New
England, Publicity Office, Armidale, N.S.W. 2351,
Australia. TEL 067-723402.

SOUTHERN; the official alumni publication of Southern
Nazarene University. see COLLEGE AND ALUMNI

**STANFORD GAY AND LESBIAN AWARENESS WEEK
PROGRAM.** see HOMOSEXUALITY

378 US ISSN 0049-2108
STANFORD UNIVERSITY CAMPUS REPORT. 1968. w.
(fortn. during summer term). $25. Stanford
University, News Service, Press Courtyard, Santa
Teresa St., Stanford, CA 94305.
TEL 415-723-2558. FAX 415-321-1324. Ed. Peter
Rapalus. bk.rev.; illus.; stat. circ. 17,000. (tabloid
format; back issues avail.) Document type:
newspaper.
Description: Campus newspaper covering faculty
research, administrative issues, issues of interest to
faculty and staff.

**STATISTICAL ABSTRACT OF HIGHER EDUCATION IN
NORTH CAROLINA.** see EDUCATION — Abstracting,
Bibliographies, Statistics

**STATISTICS ON SOCIAL WORK EDUCATION IN THE
UNITED STATES.** see EDUCATION — Abstracting,
Bibliographies, Statistics

370 SA
STUDENT; monthly newspaper-maandelikse
studentekoerant. (Text in Afrikaans and English)
1970. m. free. Technikon Pretoria, Student
Representative Council, Private Bag X680, Pretoria,
South Africa. adv.; bk.rev.; charts; film rev.; illus.;
play rev.; stat. circ. 1,700. (looseleaf format)
Document type: newspaper, academic/scholarly
publication.
Formerly: Trompie (ISSN 0041-316X)

378 US ISSN 0194-2212
STUDENT AID NEWS; the independent biweekly news
service on student financial assistance programs.
1974. bi-w. $268 (foreign $294). Capitol
Publications Inc., 1101 King St., Ste. 444,
Alexandria, VA 22314. TEL 703-683-4100.
FAX 703-739-6517. (looseleaf format) Document
type: newsletter.
—CCC.
Description: Covers federal student aid programs
and the student aid community. Provides news on
federal policies affecting financial aid to
post-secondary students, including Pell Grants,
Stafford Student Loans and Perkins Loans, College
Work-Study, Supplemental Education Opportunity
Grants and State Student Incentive Grants.

378.3 US ISSN 1060-2275
LB2338
**STUDENT AID NEWSLETTER: FELLOWSHIPS, GRANTS,
LOANS, AWARDS AND SCHOLARSHIPS.** 1955. 4/yr.
$49 (foreign $55). Scovill, Paterson Inc., 141 Fifth
Ave., New York, NY 10010-7105.
TEL 212-673-6090. FAX 212-673-6603. Ed.
Archer Irby. bk.rev.; bibl.; index. (looseleaf format;
back issues avail.) Document type: newsletter.
Former titles (until 1990): Scholarships,
Fellowships and Loan News Service and Counselors
Information Services; Scholarships, Fellowships,
Loans News Service (ISSN 0036-6366)
Description: For guidance counselors, financial aid
directors, students and parents. Lists financial aid
sources.

STUDENT GUIDE TO THE S A T. see EDUCATION —
Guides To Schools And Colleges

378 DK ISSN 0108-1020
STUDENTERHAANDBOGEN. Vol.1, 1893. a. DKK 150.
Koebenhavns Universitet, Studenterraadet,
Krystalgade 16, DK-1172 Copenhagen K, Denmark.
TEL 45-35-32-38-38. FAX 45-33-13-17-47. Ed.
Tim Joergensen. adv.; illus. Document type:
academic/scholarly publication.

STUDIENFUEHRER MATHEMATIK. see MATHEMATICS

378 UK ISSN 0307-5079
LB2300
STUDIES IN HIGHER EDUCATION. 1976. 3/yr. $132 to
individuals; institutions $382 (effective 1994).
(Society for Research into Higher Education) Carfax
Publishing Co., P.O. Box 25, Abingdon, Oxon. OX14
3UE, England. TEL 44-235-555335.
FAX 44-235-553559. (U.S. subscr. to: Carfax
Publishing Co., Box 2025, Dunnellon, FL
34430-2025) Ed. Ronald Barnett. adv.; bk.rev.;
illus.; stat.; index. (also avail. in microfiche; back
issues avail.) Indexed: ASCA, C.I.J.E., Cont.Pg.Educ.,
Curr.Cont., Educ.Tech.Abstr.,
High.Educ.Curr.Aware.Bull., Psychol.Abstr.,
Res.High.Educ.Abstr., Sp.Ed.Needs Abstr., SSCI,
Stud.Wom.Abstr. Document type: academic/scholarly
publication.
—BLDSC (8490 633000); Faxon; SWETS. CCC.
Refereed Serial

370 SW ISSN 0283-7692
STUDIES OF HIGHER EDUCATION AND RESEARCH. (Text
in English) 1983. irreg. SEK 65. Research on Higher
Education Program, Box 45501, S-104 30
Stockholm, Sweden. Ed. Thorsten Nybom. circ. 850.
Indexed: Amer.Hist.& Life, ERIC, Hist.Abstr.,
Int.Polit.Sci.Abstr. Phil.Ind., Res.High.Educ.Abstr.,
Sociol.Educ.Abstr.
Former Titles: Swedish Research on Higher
Education (ISSN 0281-3408); R & D for Higher
Education (ISSN 0347-4976); Educational
Development (ISSN 0346-6175); Sweden.
Universitetskanslersaembetet. (ISSN 0082-0377)

SUM MONTHLY NEWS. see BUSINESS AND
ECONOMICS — Accounting

360 US
**SUMMARY INFORMATION ON MASTER OF SOCIAL WORK
PROGRAMS.** a. $11. Council on Social Work
Education, 1600 Duke St., Alexandria, VA
22314-3421. TEL 703-683-8080.
FAX 703-683-8099. Dir. Donald W. Beless.
Document type: directory.

SYLLABUS (SUNNYVALE). see EDUCATION —
Computer Applications

SYNERGY/SYNERGIE. see MEDICAL SCIENCES

378 340 US ISSN 1042-0169
KF4225.A15
SYNTHESIS (ASHEVILLE); law and policy in higher
education. 1988. q $104.50. College
Administration Publications, Inc., Box 15898,
Asheville, NC 28813. TEL 704-277-8777. Ed. Gary
Pavela. circ. 750.
Description: Provides an analysis and commentary
on law and policy issues of concern to higher
education administrators and faculty.

378 US
T M I FOCUS. q. $25. The Monroe Institute, Rte. 1, Box
175, Faber, VA 22938. TEL 804-361-1252.
FAX 804-361-1237. Ed.Bd. circ. 2,200. Document
type: newsletter.
Formerly: T M I Bulletin.
Description: Covers the activities, new programs
and products of the institute.

378 PH
**TARLAC COLLEGE OF TECHNOLOGY. ANNUAL REPORT
OF THE PRESIDENT.** 1966. a. Tarlac College of
Technology, Tarlac, Philippines. Ed. Lita Nicdao. circ.
105. (back issues avail.)

378 US ISSN 0890-3107
THE TARTAN. 1906. w. $30. Carnegie Mellon
University, Box 17, Pittsburgh, PA 15213.
TEL 412-268-2111. Ed. Heidi Hoover. adv.; film
rev.; play rev.; charts; illus. circ. 7,000. (back issues
avail.) Document type: newspaper.

378 US
TAYLOR; a magazine for Taylor University alumni and
friends. 1907. q. Taylor University, 500 W. Reade
Ave., Upland, IN 46989. TEL 317-998-2751.
FAX 317-998-4910. Ed. Doug Marlow. bk.rev.; circ.
23,500 (controlled).
Formerly: Taylor University Magazine.
Description: Information and continuing education
for alumni, friends, parents, faculty and staff of the
university.

EDUCATION — HIGHER EDUCATION

370   US
TEACHER EDUCATOR. 1965. 4/yr. $10. Ball State University, Teachers College, Office of Profesional Lab Experiences, Muncie, IN 47306. TEL 317-285-5480. FAX 317-285-2166. Ed. Donald W. Jones. bk.rev.; charts; illus.; cum.index: 1967-70, 1970-75. circ. 2,300. (also avail. in microform from UMI; reprint service avail. from UMI) Indexed: C.I.J.E., Educ.Ind. **Document type:** academic/scholarly publication.
    Formerly: Supervisors Quarterly (ISSN 0039-5897)
    Description: Discusses pre- and in-service education of teachers and other related matters concerning programs, personal experiences and descriptions of policies and practices.

TEACHERS' GUIDE TO OVERSEAS TEACHING; a complete and comprehensive guide of English-language schools and colleges overseas. see EDUCATION — International Education Programs

TEACHING AND LEARNING: THE JOURNAL OF NATURAL INQUIRY. see EDUCATION — Teaching Methods And Curriculum

370.7   US   ISSN 0892-2209
TEACHING PROFESSOR. 1987. 10/yr. $38. Magna Publications, 2718 Dryden Dr., Madison, WI 53704. TEL 608-246-3580. FAX 608-249-0355. Ed. Maryellen Weimer. circ. 18,000. (also avail. in diskette format; back issues avail.)
—CCC.
    Description: Offers concise information to help faculty members teach more effectively. Topics include giving lectures, testing, planning courses, student passivity and working with teaching assistants.
    Refereed Serial

378   UK
TEARS; higher education. 1950. irreg. Exeter University, Teaching Service Centre, Streatham Court, Rennes Dr., Exeter, Devon, England.

378   SA
TECHNIKON FORUM. (Text in Afrikaans and English) 1977. biennial. free. Technikon Pretoria, Private Bag X680, Pretoria, South Africa. Ed. Willa De Ruyter. illus. (also avail. in looseleaf format) **Document type:** academic/scholarly publication.
    Formerly: Kamera; Incorporates: Media News.

TECHNION - ISRAEL INSTITUTE OF TECHNOLOGY. ABSTRACTS OF RESEARCH THESES. see EDUCATION — Abstracting, Bibliographies, Statistics

378   GW
TECHNISCHE UNIVERSITAET BRAUNSCHWEIG. FORSCHUNGSBERICHT. irreg., latest 1991. Technische Universitaet Braunschweig, Postfach 3329, 38023 Braunschweig, Germany. **Document type:** monographic series.
    Formerly: Technische Universitaet Braunschweig. Berichtsband. Forschung.

378   GW
TECHNISCHE UNIVERSITAET BRAUNSCHWEIG. UNIVERSITAETSBIBLIOTHEK. VEROEFFENTLICHUNGEN. 1988. irreg. free. Technische Universitaet Braunschweig, Universitaetsbibliothek, Postfach 3329, 38023 Braunschweig, Germany. FAX 0531-3915836. Ed. Dietmar Brandes. **Document type:** academic/scholarly publication.

TECHNISCHE UNIVERSITAET MUENCHEN. JAHRBUCH. see TECHNOLOGY: COMPREHENSIVE WORKS

378   US
TENNESSEE. HIGHER EDUCATION COMMISSION. BIENNIAL REPORT. 1970. biennial. free. Higher Education Commission, Pkwy. Towers, Ste. 1900, 404 James Robertson Pkwy., Nashville, TN 37243-0830. TEL 615-741-7572. Ed. Cathy L. Cole. circ. 1,000.

378   US
TEXAS HIGHER EDUCATION COORDINATING BOARD. C B POLICY PAPER. 1968. irreg., no.9, 1970. free to qualified personnel. Texas Higher Education Coordinating Board, Box 12788, Capitol Sta., Austin, TX 78711. TEL 512-483-6111. Eds. Janis Monger, Jan Friese. circ. (controlled). **Document type:** government publication.
    Formerly: Texas College and University System. Coordinating Board. C B Policy Paper (ISSN 0082-299X)

378   US
TEXAS HIGHER EDUCATION COORDINATING BOARD. C B STUDY PAPER. 1968. irreg., no.30, 1983. free to qualified personnel. Texas Higher Education Coordinating Board, Box 12788, Capitol Sta., Austin, TX 78711. TEL 512-483-6111. Eds. Janis Monger, Jan Friese. circ. (controlled). **Document type:** government publication.
    Formerly: Texas Coordinating Board. Texas College and University System. C B Study Paper (ISSN 0082-3007)

378   US
TEXAS HIGHER EDUCATION COORDINATING BOARD. STATUS REPORT ON HIGHER EDUCATION AND STATISTICAL REPORT. 1965. a. free. Texas Higher Education Coordinating Board, Box 12788, Capitol Sta., Austin, TX 78711. TEL 512-483-6111. Eds. Janis Monger, Jan Friese. circ. 2,000 (controlled). Indexed: SRI. **Document type:** government publication.
    Former titles: Texas Higher Education Coordinating Board. C B Annual Report and Statistical Supplement; Texas College and University System. Coordinating Board. C B Annual Report and Statistical Supplement; Texas. Coordinating Board. Texas College and University System. C B Annual Report (ISSN 0082-2981)

378.669   NR
THIS IS N U C. (National Universities Commission) irreg. free. National Universities Commission, Information and Public Relations Unit, Aja Nwachukwu House, Plot 430 Aguiyi-Ironsi St., Maitama District, P.M.B. 237 Garki G.P.O., Abuja, Nigeria. TEL 234-9-5233176. FAX 234-9-5233520. TELEX UNICOMM LAGOS. **Document type:** government publication.

378   US   ISSN 0748-8475
THOUGHT & ACTION. 1984. biennial. $30 to libraries. National Education Association of the United States, 1201 16th St., N.W., Washington, DC 20036. TEL 202-822-7207. circ. 88,000.
—UnCover; UMI.
    Supersedes: Today's Education: Higher Education Edition.
    Description: Information and articles on issues of salary, part-time teaching and college level writing.

TIEMPO Y ESPACIO. see HISTORY — History Of North And South America

378.1   UK   ISSN 0049-3929
LA637
TIMES HIGHER EDUCATION SUPPLEMENT. 1971. w. $105. Times Supplements Ltd., Admiral House, 66-68 E. Smithfield, London E1 9YY, England. TEL 071-782-3000. FAX 071-782-3200. Ed. Auriol Stevens. adv.; bk.rev.; illus.; index. circ. 19,275. (tabloid format; also avail. in microform from RPI) Indexed: Br.Ceram.Abstr., Educ.Ind., High.Educ.Curr.Aware.Bull., Ind.Bus.Rep., Lang.Teach.& Ling.Abstr., Res.High.Educ.Abstr. **Document type:** academic/scholarly publication.
—BLDSC (8853.700000).
    Description: Contains news, features and commentaries about universities and colleges in Britain and abroad.

327   NE   ISSN 0929-4848
TRANSFER; vakblaad voor internationale samenwerking in hoger onderwijs en onderzoek. 1971; N.S. 1993. 10/yr. fl.98 (effective 1994). (Netherland Universities Foundation for International Cooperation - N U F F I C) Samsom H.D. Tjeenk Willink, Postbus 316, 2400 AH Alphen aan den Rijn, Netherlands. TEL 31-1720-66822. FAX 31-1720-93270. (Editorial address: Nuffic, P.O. Box 29777, 2502 LT The Hague, Netherlands. TEL 31-70-4260216. FAX 31-70-4260229) Ed. A. Hofstede. adv.; bk.rev. circ. 2,800.
    Formed by the 1993 merger of: Visum (ISSN 0925-8272); Which was formerly (until 1990): Visum Nieuws (ISSN 0920-5136) & Overzicht (ISSN 0920-5292); Which was formerly (until 1984): Overzicht Internationale Universitaire Samenwerking (ISSN 0165-148X)
    Description: Focuses on international cooperation in education and its research.

370.7   PH
TRINITY COLLEGE JOURNAL. (Text in English, Filipino, Spanish) 1974. a. P.30($2.50) Trinity College of Quezon City, E. Rodriguez Sr. Blvd., Quezon City, Philippines. FAX 70-78-79-0632. Ed. Erlinda G. Rosales. bk.rev.; abstr.; illus.; stat. circ. 300. (back issues avail.) Indexed: Ind.Phil.Per.

378 371.2   US   ISSN 0271-9746
LB2328
TRUSTEE QUARTERLY. 1977. q. $30 (free to members). Association of Community College Trustees, 1740 N St., N.W., Washington, DC 20036. TEL 202-775-4667. Ed. Sally Hutchins. adv. circ. 7,000. (also avail. in microfiche; back issues avail.)
    Description: Articles of interest to governing board members of two-year postsecondary institutions.

U C DAVIS MAGAZINE. see COLLEGE AND ALUMNI

378   CN
U - CHOOSE: A STUDENT'S GUIDE TO FINANCIAL SURVIVAL. (Editions in English, French) 1993. a. Can.$1.99. Moving Publications Ltd., 44 Upjohn Rd., Ste. 100, Don Mills, ON M3B 2W1, Canada. TEL 416-441-1168. FAX 416-441-1641. Ed. Anne Dunlop; Pub. Anita Wood. adv.

378   AT   ISSN 0156-1006
U N E CONVOCATION BULLETIN & ALUMNI NEWS. 1957. a. to graduates only. University of New England, Armidale, N.S.W. 2351, Australia. Ed. S. Bearman. bk.rev. circ. 14,000. **Document type:** bulletin.
    Former titles: U N E Bulletin; University of New England. Bulletin (ISSN 0084-6740)

378   AT
U N E NEWS; external studies newsletter. 1956. q. free. University of New England, Distance and other Learning Eduction Centre, Armidale, N.S.W. 2351, Australia. FAX 067-711644. Ed. I. Small. illus. circ. 10,000. **Document type:** newsletter.
    Former titles: Armidale News (ISSN 1036-594X) & External Studies Gazette (ISSN 0014-5459)

378   US
U S STUDENT ASSOCIATION. LEGISLATIVE UPDATE. 1947. s-m. $25 membership. U S Student Association, 815 15th St., N.W., No. 38, Washington, DC 20005-2007. TEL 202-347-8772. FAX 202-393-5886. adv. circ. 475. Indexed: ERIC. **Document type:** newsletter.
    Former titles: U S Student Association. News Update; U S National Student Association. Momentum.
    Description: Updates readers on key legislative issues affecting students in Washington DC. Focus is on educational access, financial aid and campus safety.

378   US
U: THE NATIONAL COLLEGE MAGAZINE. 1988. 9/yr. $18. American Collegiate Network, 1800 Century Park E., Ste. 820, Los Angeles, CA 90067-1511. TEL 310-551-1381. FAX 310-551-1659. Ed. Ari Cherin. adv. contact: Gayle Morris Sweetland. circ. 1,500,000. **Document type:** consumer publication.
    Formerly (until 1992): U: The National College Newspaper.
    Description: Reports on cutting-edge ideas, trends, events and issues that affect college students.

EDUCATION — HIGHER EDUCATION

378　　　　　　　　UK
THE ULTIMATE GUIDE. (Text in English, Welsh) 1972. a. free. University Union Cardiff, c/o Hermione Connon, Park Place, Cardiff CF1 3QN, Wales. TEL 0222-396421. FAX 0222-396608. Ed. Justine Griffith-Jones. adv. circ. 5,000. **Document type:** bulletin.
　Formerly (until 1993): Union Handbook.

378　　　　MX　ISSN 0188-1981
UMBRAL XXI. Variant title: Umbral Veintiuno. 1989. 3/yr. $15 (effective 1993). Universidad Iberoamericana, Direccion Investigacion y Posgrado, Prol. Paseo de la Reforma 880, Col. Lomas de Santa Fe, 01210 Mexico DF, Mexico. TEL 5-559-18-58. FAX 5-726-90-48. Ed. Ruben Lozano Herrera. bk.rev.; bibl.; illus. circ. 2,000. **Document type:** academic/scholarly publication.
　Description: Presents the advances and the results of the university's programs of research and postgraduate work.

UNI PERSPEKTIVEN FUER BERUF UND ARBEITSMARKT. see *OCCUPATIONS AND CAREERS*

UNICORN. see *EDUCATION*

378　　　　　　　　US
UNION COLLEGE. vol.64, 1973. 6/yr. free. Union College (Schenectady), Lamont House, Schenectady, NY 12308. TEL 518-370-6131. Ed. Peter E. Blankman. bk.rev. circ. 22,000.

378　　　　GW　ISSN 0937-6496
UNIPRESS. 1974. 4/yr. Universitaet Augsburg, Universitaetsstr. 2, 86159 Augsburg, Germany. TEL 0821-5982096. FAX 0821-5985288. adv.

UNISPIEGEL. see *COLLEGE AND ALUMNI*

U.S. DEPARTMENT OF EDUCATION. NATIONAL CENTER FOR EDUCATION STATISTICS. ACADEMIC LIBRARIES. see *EDUCATION — Abstracting, Bibliographies, Statistics*

U.S. DEPARTMENT OF EDUCATION. NATIONAL CENTER FOR EDUCATION STATISTICS. COMPLETIONS IN INSTITUTIONS OF HIGHER EDUCATION. see *EDUCATION — Abstracting, Bibliographies, Statistics*

U.S. DEPARTMENT OF EDUCATION. NATIONAL CENTER FOR EDUCATION STATISTICS. FALL ENROLLMENT IN HIGHER EDUCATION. see *EDUCATION — Abstracting, Bibliographies, Statistics*

U.S. DEPARTMENT OF EDUCATION. NATIONAL CENTER FOR EDUCATION STATISTICS. STATE HIGHER EDUCATION PROFILES. see *EDUCATION — Abstracting, Bibliographies, Statistics*

507　　　　US　ISSN 0094-7881
Q183.3.A1
U.S. NATIONAL SCIENCE FOUNDATION. SELECTED DATA ON STUDENTS AND POSTDOCTORALS IN SCIENCE & ENGINEERING. Key Title: Graduate Science Education Student Support and Postdoctorals. (Subseries of: N S F Surveys of Science Resources Series) a. U.S. National Science Foundation, Science & Technology Information System (STIS), 4201 Wilson Blvd., Ste. 245, Arlington, VA 22230. **Document type:** government publication.
　Formerly: U.S. National Science Foundation. Graduate Science Education Student Support and Postdoctorals.

378　　　　　　　　NQ
UNIVERSIDAD. a.? Universidad Nacional Autonoma de Nicaragua, Recinto Universitario Ruben Dario, Pabellon 7, Managua, Nicaragua. TEL 74852. Ed. Lizandro Chavez Alfaro.

378　　　　　　　　DR
UNIVERSIDAD AUTONOME DE SANTO DOMINGO. COMISION PARA EL DESARROLLO Y REFORMA UNIVERSITARIOS.* irreg. Universidad Autonoma de Santo Domingo, Comision para el Desarrollo y Reforma Universitarios, Ciudad Universitaria, Apdo. 1355, Santo Domingo, Dominican Republic.

378　　　　　　　　BO
UNIVERSIDAD BOLIVIANA JUAN MISAEL SARACHO. INFORME DE LABORES. irreg. Universidad Boliviana Juan Misael Saracho, Av. Las Americas, Casilla 51, Tarija, Bolivia. charts; illus.; stat.

378　　　　　　　　CU
UNIVERSIDAD DE LA HABANA. DIRECCION DE EXTENSION UNIVERSITARIA. REVISTA. no. 204, 1977. q. exchange basis. (Universidad de la Habana, Direccion de Extension Universitaria) Ediciones Cubanas, Obispo No. 461, Aptdo. 605, Havana, Cuba. Ed. Luisa Campuzano. **Indexed:** Amer.Hist.& Life (until 1989), Hist.Abstr. (until 1989).

378　　　　CK　ISSN 0120-5692
AS82.M4
UNIVERSIDAD DE MEDELLIN. REVISTA. 1957. irreg. Col.$1500. Universidad de Medellin, Apdo. Aereo 1983, Medellin, Colombia. FAX 890-902-9201. illus.

378.46　　　　SP　ISSN 0080-6145
UNIVERSIDAD INTERNACIONAL MENENDEZ PELAYO. PUBLICACIONES. 1947. biennial, no.43, 1974. Universidad Internacional Menendez Pelayo, Palacio de la Magdalena, Santander, Spain. circ. 1,000.

378　　　　　　　　MX
UNIVERSIDAD NACIONAL AUTONOMA DE MEXICO. CENTRO DE DOCUMENTACION LEGISLATIVA UNIVERSITARIA. CUADERNOS. (Text in Spanish; summaries in English and French) 1979. s-a. Mex.$600($20) Universidad Nacional Autonoma de Mexico, Centro de Documentacion Legislativa Universitaria, 9 Piso Torre de Rectoria, Ciudad Universitaria, Deleg. Coyocan, 04510 Mexico D.F., Mexico. bibl. circ. 2,000. (back issues avail.)

505　　　　　　　　PE
UNIVERSIDAD NACIONAL DEL CENTRO DEL PERU. ANALES CIENTIFICOS. 1971. a. price varies. Universidad Nacional del Centro del Peru, Departamento de Publicaciones e Impresiones, c/o Secretaria de Publicaciones, Calle Real 160, Huancayo, Peru. illus. circ. 1,000.

378　　　　　　　　PE
UNIVERSIDAD PERUANA CAYETANO HEREDIA. BOLETIN. 1966. Universidad Peruana Cayetano Heredia, Direccion de Biblioteca Publicaciones y Museos, Av. Honorio Delgado 932, Apdo. 2563, Lima 100, Peru.

UNIVERSIDAD TECNOLOGICA DEL CHOCO. REVISTA. see *TECHNOLOGY: COMPREHENSIVE WORKS*

800　　　　　　　　BL
UNIVERSIDADE FEDERAL DE GOIAS. PUBLICACAO. 1975. irreg., no.74, 1983. Universidade Federal de Goias, Av. Universitaria 1533, Caixa Postal 131, 74000 Goiania, Goias, Brazil. Ed.Bd. adv. circ. 1,000.

378　　　　　　　　BL
UNIVERSIDADE FEDERAL DE PERNAMBUCO. JORNAL. 1967. irreg. Universidade Federal de Pernambuco, Recife, Pernambaco, Brazil. (microfilm)

378　　　　　　　　BL
UNIVERSIDADE FEDERAL DE PERNAMBUCO. RELATORIO DES ATTIVIDADES UNIVERSITARIAS. a. Universidade Federal de Pernambuco, Biblioteca Central, Cidade Universitaria, Recife, Pernambuco, Brazil. (also avail. in microfilm)

378　　　　　　　　BL
UNIVERSIDADE FEDERAL DO PARA. RELATORIO ANUAL. a. Universidade Federal do Para, Belem, Para, Brazil.

378　　　　MX　ISSN 0041-8935
UNIVERSIDADES. 1950. s-a. $12 to non-members. Union de Universidades de America Latina, 04510 Mexico, D.F., Mexico. TEL 6220096. FAX 6220091. Eds. Luis Bernal, Martin Lopez. bk.rev.; bibl.; charts; illus.; stat.; index. circ. 2,000. **Indexed:** Bull.Signal. **Document type:** academic/scholarly publication. —BLDSC (1565.182000); Faxon.

378　　　　　　　　IT
UNIVERSITA DEGLI STUDI DI MILANO. ANNUARIO. 1924. a. Universita degli Studi di Milano, Ufficio Relazioni Pubbliche, Via Festa del Perdono 7, 20122 Milan, Italy. TEL 02-5835.1. FAX 02-58304482. circ. 1,000.

378　　　　IT　ISSN 0078-7752
UNIVERSITA DEGLI STUDI DI PADOVA. ISTITUTO PER LA STORIA. CONTRIBUTI. 1964. irreg., no.11, 1979. price varies. Editrice Antenore, Via G. Rusca 15, 35100 Padua, Italy.

378　　　　IT　ISSN 0078-7760
UNIVERSITA DEGLI STUDI DI PADOVA. ISTITUTO PER LA STORIA. QUADERNI. 1968. a., no.22-23, 1989-90. price varies. Ecitrice Antenore, Via G. Rusca 15, 35100 Padua, Italy.

378　　　　GW　ISSN 0070-7457
UNIVERSITAET DUESSELDORF. JAHRBUCH. 1969. a. DM.34. Triltsch Druck und Verlag GmbH und Co. KG, Herzstr. 53, D-4000 Dusseldorf, Germany. Ed. Hans Schadewaldt. adv.

378　　　　　　　　GW
UNIVERSITAET GOETTINGEN. JAHRESFORSCHUNGSBERICHT. 1966. biennial. Universitaet Goettingen, Wilhelmsplatz 1, 37073 Goettingen, Germany. FAX 0551-394251. adv.; stat. **Document type:** proceedings.
　Formerly: Universitaet Goettingen. Jahresbericht (ISSN 0436-1202)

378　　　　　　　　GW
UNIVERSITAET HOHENHEIM. AMTLICHE MITTEILUNGEN. 1971. irreg. (10-20/yr.). Universitaet Hohenheim, Presse und Forschungsinformation, 70593 Stuttgart, Germany. TEL 0711-4592001. FAX 0711-4593289. circ. 500. (looseleaf format) **Document type:** bulletin.
　Description: Internal administration rules for the University.

378　　　　GW　ISSN 0069-5890
LF2525
UNIVERSITAET ZU KOELN. JAHRBUCH. 1966. a. DM.8. (Freunde und Foerderer der Universitaet zu Koeln) Drei Kronen Druck, Reifferscheidt GmbH und Co. KG, Rondorfer Str. 224, 50354 Huerth, Germany. Ed. Wolfgang Mathias. adv. circ. 8,000.

378　　　　GW　ISSN 0179-7514
UNIVERSITAETSFUEHRER. 1972. a. DM.7. Universitaet Hohenheim, Presse und Forschungsinformation, 70593 Stuttgart, Germany. TEL 0711-4592001. FAX 0711-4593289. (Subscr. to: Buchhandlung Wittwer, Fruwirthstr. 24, 70599 Stuttgart, Germany) Ed. Klaus Grabowski. adv. circ. 3,700. **Document type:** directory.

378　　　　MX　ISSN 0185-4143
UNIVERSITARIOS. fortn. Mex.$20($3) Universidad Nacional Autonoma de Mexico, Direccion General de Difusion Cultural, Ciudad Universitaria, Mexico 20, D.F., Mexico.

378　　　　GH　ISSN 0049-5530
UNIVERSITAS; an inter-faculty journal. 1971. a. $20. University of Ghana, Department of English, Legon, Ghana. TEL 775381. Ed.Bd. adv.; bk.rev.; bibl.; charts. circ. 1,000. **Indexed:** Amer.Hist.& Life, Curr.Cont.Africa, Documentatieblad, Hist.Abstr. **Document type:** academic/scholarly publication.

378　　　　US　ISSN 0146-9061
UNIVERSITAS. 1970. m. $25 membership; libraries $10. (University Professors for Academic Order (UPAO)) COMCOA, Inc., Box Q, Corvallis, OR 97339. Ed. Donald Senese. adv.; bk.rev. circ. 550. (back issues avail.) **Indexed:** Res.High.Educ.Abstr.

378　　　　IT　ISSN 0393-2702
UNIVERSITAS. 1980. q. L.60000. Casa Editrice Fratelli Palombi, Via dei Gracchi 181-185, 00192 Rome, Italy. TEL 06-354456. FAX 06-319806. Dir. Piergiovanni Palla. index.
　Description: Forum covers current news, studies, research, new proposals and documents on Italian university life.

378　　　　　　　　VE
UNIVERSITAS 2000. 1979. 4/yr. $45 to individuals; institutions $50. Fondo Editorial para el Desarrollo de la Educacion Superior - Fund for the Development of Higher Education, Apdo. 62532, Caracas 1060-A, Venezuela. TEL 285-34-80. FAX 02-526387. TELEX 26111 VHA-VC. (Co-sponsor: Latin American University Group for the Reform and Improvement of Education) **Document type:** academic/scholarly publication.

378.65　　　　　　AE
L'UNIVERSITE;* revue bimestrielle de l'enseignement superieur et de la recherche scientifique. bi-m. Universite d'Alger, 2 rue Didouche Mourad, Algiers, Algeria.

EDUCATION — HIGHER EDUCATION

378   SZ
UNIVERSITE DE GENEVE. DEPARTEMENT D'HISTOIRE ECONOMIQUE. BULLETIN. (Text in French) 1970. a. free. Universite de Geneve, Departement d'Histoire Economique, CH-1211 Geneva 4, Switzerland. TEL 04122-2058192. Ed.Bd. circ. 350. **Document type:** bulletin.

378.494   SZ   ISSN 1012-4098
UNIVERSITE DE NEUCHATEL. ANNALES. 1969. a. 20 SFr. Universite de Neuchatel, Av. du Premier Mars 26, CH-2000 Neuchatel, Switzerland. illus. **Document type:** academic/scholarly publication.

378.714   CN
UNIVERSITE DU QUEBEC (PROVINCE). RAPPORT ANNUEL. 1970. a. free. Universite du Quebec, 2875 Bd. Laurier, Ste. Foy, PQ G1V 2M3, Canada. TEL 418-657-3551. circ. 3,500.

054   CF
AS659.C64
UNIVERSITE MARIEN NGOUABI. ANNALES. (Not published from 1977 to 1988) (Text in French; summaries in English) a. 2000 Fr.CFA (foreign 4000 Fr.CFA); students 1000 Fr.CFA (foreign 2000 Fr.CFA). Universite Marien Ngouabi, B.P. 69, Brazzaville, Congo. Ed. Emmanuel B. Dongala. bk.rev.; bibl.; illus. circ. 1,000. **Indexed:** Biol.Abstr., M.L.A.
Supersedes: Universite de Brazzaville. Annales (ISSN 0302-4814)
Description: Covers the academic publications of the University.

378   FR   ISSN 0751-5839
UNIVERSITE SYNDICALISTE. 1928. w. 111 F. Syndicat National des Enseignements de Second Degre, 1, Rue de Courty, 75013 Paris, France. Ed. Alain Dalancon. adv. circ. 112,225.

378   CN   ISSN 0226-7454
UNIVERSITES. 1980. q. Can.$30. Association des Universites Partiellement ou Entierement de Langue Francaise, Universite des Reseaux d'Expression Francaise, B.P. 400, succ. Cote-des-Neiges, Montreal, PQ H3C 2S7, Canada. TEL 514-343-6630. FAX 514-343-2107. TELEX 055-60955. circ. 10,000.
Supersedes: A U P E L F Bulletin de Nouvelles Breves (ISSN 0007-4373); Etudes Francaises dans le Monde (ISSN 0316-2672); Nouvelles Universitaires Africaines.

378   DK   ISSN 0106-7141
UNIVERSITETSAVISEN. 1973. fortn. DKK 30. Koebenhavns Universitet, Frue Plads, Postboks 2177, 1017 Copenhagen K, Denmark. Ed. Gitte Meyer. illus. circ. 37,000.
Supersedes: Koebenhavns Universitet. Meddelelser (ISSN 0525-6836)

378   DK   ISSN 0902-2619
UNIVERSITETSLAEREREN. BESKRIVELSE. 1985. 10/yr. DKK 175. Universitetslaererforening, Glentevej 70B, 2400 Copenhagen NV, Denmark. TEL 45-31100355. FAX 45-31100249. Ed. Cada Winteroe. adv.; bk.rev.; illus. circ. 1,500.
Formerly: Magistrenes Universitetslaererforeningen. Beskrivelse (ISSN 0900-081X)

UNIVERSITIES HANDBOOK. see *EDUCATION — Guides To Schools And Colleges*

378   CN   ISSN 0847-3536
L905
UNIVERSITIES TELEPHONE DIRECTORY (YEAR)/BOTTIN DES UNIVERSITES (YEAR). (Text in English and French) a. Can.$17.95 (US Can.$19.95, elsewhere Can.$20.95). Association of Universities and Colleges of Canada, 600-350 Albert, Ottawa, ON K1R 1B1, Canada. TEL 613-563-1236. circ. 2,500. **Document type:** directory.
Formerly: Academic and Administrative Officers at Canadian Universities (Year) (ISSN 0711-7051)

378   CN   ISSN 0041-9257
LA418.O8
UNIVERSITY AFFAIRS/AFFAIRES UNIVERSITAIRES. (Text in English and French) 1959. 10/yr. Can.$41.20 (US Can.$46.20, elsewhere Can.$74. Association of Universities and Colleges of Canada, 350 Albert St., Ste. 600, Ottawa, ON K1R 1B1, Canada. TEL 613-563-1236. FAX 613-563-9745. Ed. Christine Tausig Ford. adv.; bk.rev.; bibl. circ. 25,000. **Indexed:** Cont.Pg.Educ., Res.High.Educ.Abstr.
Description: Carries news about universities across Canada as well as advertisments of career opportunities inside and outside the universities.

UNIVERSITY BOOKMAN; a quarterly review. see *PUBLISHING AND BOOK TRADE*

378   UK
UNIVERSITY BRISTOL CALENDAR. 1910. a. £15. University of Bristol, Senate of House, Bristol BS8 1TH, England. TEL 0272-303030. FAX 0272-251424. circ. 400. **Document type:** bulletin.

378   IE
UNIVERSITY COLLEGE CORK CALENDAR. (Text in English) 1909. a. £5.50. University College, Cork, Ireland. TEL 021-276871. Ed. C. O'Brien. circ. 2,500.

378   UK   ISSN 0953-8364
UNIVERSITY COLLEGE LONDON CALENDAR. 1830. a. £10. University College London, Gower St., London WC1E 6BT, England. circ. 1,300.

378   NR
UNIVERSITY EDUCATION IN NIGERIA. 1984. irreg. free. National Universities Commission, P.M.B. 12694, Lagos, Nigeria. Ed. Chinelo 'Amaka Chizea.

378   UK   ISSN 0956-781X
LB2351
UNIVERSITY ENTRANCE.* 1963. a. £10.71. Association of Commonwealth Universities, John Foster House, 36 Gordon Square, London WC1H OPF, England. TEL 71-387-8572. FAX 71-387-2655. (Subscr. to: Sheed and Ward Ltd., 2 Creechurch Lane, London EC3A 5AQ, England) circ. 15,000.
—BLDSC (9109.396380).
Formerly (until 1987): Compendium of University Entrance Requirements for First Degree Courses in the United Kingdom (ISSN 0571-625X)

378 658.1   CN
▼**UNIVERSITY MANAGER.** 1992. q. free to members. (Canadian Association of University Business Officers) August Communications, 200-388 Donald St., Winnipeg, MB R3B 2J4, Canada. TEL 613-563-1236. FAX 613-563-7739. adv.: B&W & color, B&W page Can.$1169.50. circ. 2,500.
Description: Covers CAUBO activities and provides articles of a management nature exclusively developed for post-secondary institutions.

378   II   ISSN 0566-2257
L61
UNIVERSITY NEWS; a weekly chronicle of higher education & research. w. $70. Association of Indian Universities, A I U House, 16 Kotla Rd., New Delhi 110 002, India. TEL 11-3310059. FAX 11-3315105. TELEX 31-66180-AIU-IN. Ed. Sutinder Singh. adv.: page $250; trim 16 1/2 x 23; adv. contact: B.M. Dureja. **Document type:** newsletter.
Description: Covers higher education, campus happenings, job opportunities, and award of fellowships and scholarships.

378   UK
UNIVERSITY OF BRADFORD. ANNUAL REPORT. 1986. a. free. University of Bradford, Publications Office, Richmond Rd., Bradford, Yorks BD7 1DP, England. TEL 0274-383033. FAX 0274-305340. Ed. John Waller. stat. circ. 12,000. (back issues avail.) **Document type:** academic/scholarly publication.
Formerly (until 1993): Vice-Chancellor's Annual Report (ISSN 0305-8654)

378.794   US
UNIVERSITY OF CALIFORNIA AT BERKELEY. CAMPUS STATISTICS. 1966. a. $5. University of California at Berkeley, Office of Institutional Research, 2223 Fulton, 4th Fl., Berkeley, CA 94720. TEL 415-642-5743. FAX 415-643-6523. Ed. Paul Hoch. circ. 500 (controlled). **Indexed:** ERIC.
Formerly: University of California, Berkeley. Office of Institutional Research. Campus Statistics (ISSN 0092-0290)

378   SA
UNIVERSITY OF CAPE TOWN. RESEARCH REPORT. 1976. a. free. University of Cape Town, Research Support Services, Private Bag, Rondebosch 7700, South Africa. TEL 27-21-650-2202. FAX 27-21-650-2138. TELEX 5-22208. Dir. P.A.T. Wild. circ. 600. (back issues avail.) **Document type:** academic/scholarly publication.
Description: Reports on research in progress at the University of Cape Town.

378   US   ISSN 0362-4706
UNIVERSITY OF CHICAGO RECORD. 1967. irreg. (3-4/yr.). free. University of Chicago, 5757 Woodlawn Ave., Chicago, IL 60637. TEL 312-702-8352. FAX 312-702-8174. Ed. Ellen McGrew. charts. circ. 20,000.

UNIVERSITY OF DAYTON. SCHOOL OF EDUCATION. ABSTRACTS OF RESEARCH PROJECTS. see *EDUCATION — Abstracting, Bibliographies, Statistics*

378   UK
UNIVERSITY OF DUNDEE STUDENTS ASSOCIATION HANDBOOK. 1968. a. free to new students. University of Dundee, Students Association, Airlie Place, Dundee DD1 4HP, Scotland. adv. circ. 4,000. **Document type:** bulletin.

378   SA   ISSN 0256-7423
UNIVERSITY OF DURBAN-WESTVILLE. BULLETIN FOR ACADEMIC STAFF. 1980. 3/yr. free to qualified personnel. University of Durban-Westville, Faculty of Education, Division of Tertiary Didactics, Private Bag X54001, Durban 4000, South Africa. TEL 031-820-9111. FAX 031-8202383. TELEX 6-23328 SA. Ed. Paul Beard, Railton Loureiro. bk.rev. circ. 750.

378.669   NR   ISSN 0331-0809
UNIVERSITY OF IBADAN. STUDENT AFFAIRS OFFICE. STUDENT HANDBOOK OF INFORMATION ON UNIVERSITY POLICIES AND PRACTICES. irreg. University of Ibadan, Student Affairs Office, Ibadan, Nigeria. illus.

378.549   II
UNIVERSITY OF KASHMIR. ANNUAL REPORT. (Text in English) a. University of Kashmir, Hazratbal, Srinagar 190006, India.

378.1   UK   ISSN 0041-9737
UNIVERSITY OF LEEDS REVIEW. 1948. a. £4.80 to individuals; institutions £7.80. University of Leeds, Leeds LS2 9JT, England. FAX 0532-336017. TELEX 556473-UNILDS-G. Ed. Gwyneth Pitt. adv. circ. 1,400. **Indexed:** M.L.A. **Document type:** academic/scholarly publication.

378   UK   ISSN 0305-9227
UNIVERSITY OF LIVERPOOL CALENDAR. 1881. a. £18. University of Liverpool, Committee Secretariat, P.O. Box 147, Liverpool L69 3BX, England. TEL 051-794-2023. FAX 051-708-6502. TELEX 627095-UNILPL-G. Ed. S.M. Smitton. circ. 825. (also avail. in microfiche) **Document type:** bulletin.
Description: Yearbook of the University of Liverpool; includes statutes, ordinances, committee memberships and staff lists.

378 371   UK
UNIVERSITY OF LIVERPOOL POST GRADUATE PROSPECTUS. 1985. biennial. free. University of Liverpool, P.O. Box 147, Liverpool L69 3BX, England. TEL 051-794-2567. FAX 051-708-6502. TELEX 627095-UNILPL-G. Ed. G. Kelly. circ. 30,000. **Document type:** bulletin.
Formerly (until 1989): Postgraduate Study at the University of Liverpool (ISSN 0268-0645)
Description: Information on postgraduate degree courses, entry requirements, application procedures and general information.

EDUCATION — HIGHER EDUCATION

378 371   UK   ISSN 0268-2362
UNIVERSITY OF LIVERPOOL PROSPECTUS. 1984. a. free. University of Liverpool, P.O. Box 147, Liverpool L69 3BX, England. TEL 051-794-2567. FAX 051-708-6502. TELEX 627095-UNILPL-G. Ed. G. Kelly. circ. 70,000. **Document type:** academic/scholarly publication.
   Description: Information on first degree courses, entry requirements, application procedures and general information.

378   II   ISSN 0076-2210
UNIVERSITY OF MADRAS. ENDOWMENT LECTURES.* a. University of Madras, Chepauk, Triplicane, Madras 600005, Tamil Nadu, India.

658.15   MM
UNIVERSITY OF MALTA. ANNUAL REPORT. a. University of Malta, Msida, Malta. Ed. Lawrence Ellul. circ. 1,000. **Document type:** corporate report.

378   MM
UNIVERSITY OF MALTA. GAZETTE. q. University of Malta, Msida, Malta. Ed. Lawrence Ellul. circ. 1,000.
   Description: Information on the University of Malta, including faculty members, programs available, activities, seminars, names of students and their respective dissertation titles.

378   MF
UNIVERSITY OF MAURITIUS. ANNUAL REPORT. 1968. a. University of Mauritius, Reduit, Mauritius. stat. circ. 450. (back issues avail.)

378   AT   ISSN 0085-3275
UNIVERSITY OF MELBOURNE. GAZETTE. 1945. 3/yr. University of Melbourne, Registrar, Parkville, Vic. 3052, Australia. FAX 03-344-6895. Ed. Joanna Motion. adv.; bk.rev. circ. 65,000.

378   US   ISSN 0041-9842
UNIVERSITY OF MICHIGAN. DIVISION OF RESEARCH DEVELOPMENT AND ADMINISTRATION. RESEARCH NEWS. 1949. 5/yr. free in the US; Canada and Mexico $6; elsewhere $15. University of Michigan, Division of Research Development and Administration, 3003 S. State St., Ann Arbor, MI 48109-1274. TEL 313-763-5587. FAX 313-763-4053. TELEX 43208155. Ed. Lee Katterman. charts; illus.; stat. circ. 14,000. (also avail. in microform from UMI; back issues avail.; reprint service avail. from UMI) **Indexed:** Biol.Abstr., Ind.Free Per., Mich.Mag.Ind. **Document type:** academic/scholarly publication.
   —BLDSC (7743.883000).
   Description: Describes research from all areas and disciplines, using non-specialist language.
   Refereed Serial

378   AT   ISSN 0375-4588
UNIVERSITY OF NEW ENGLAND. ANNUAL REPORT. 1968. a. University of New England, Public Affairs Directorate, Armidale, N.S.W. 2351, Australia. Ed. John Rose. stat. circ. 250. (back issues avail.) **Indexed:** Biol.Abstr. **Document type:** corporate report.

378   AT
UNIVERSITY OF NEW ENGLAND. PUBLIC AFFAIRS SPECIALISTS LIST. 1979. a. free. University of New England, Public Affairs, Armidale, N.S.W. 2351, Australia. TEL 067-733485. FAX 067-725272.
   Formerly: University of New England. Information Office Specialists List (ISSN 0158-0604)
   Description: Provides a list of academic staff and their specialisatins.

378   US
UNIVERSITY OF NEW MEXICO. OFFICE OF RESEARCH ADMINISTRATION. RESEARCH NOTES. 1971. s-m. $15. University of New Mexico, Office of Research Administration, 102 Scholes Hall, Albuquerque, NM 87131. TEL 505-277-2256. Ed. Dir. Denise A. Wallen. circ. 1,500.

013.379   AT   ISSN 0548-6831
UNIVERSITY OF NEW SOUTH WALES, KENSINGTON. RESEARCH AND PUBLICATIONS. (Title varies slightly) a. University of New South Wales, Kensington, N.S.W. 2052, Australia. TEL 02-697-2840. FAX 02-662-2163.

378.669   NR   ISSN 0331-1686
UNIVERSITY OF NIGERIA. ANNUAL REPORT. 1958. a. University of Nigeria, Office of the Registrar, Nsukka, Enugu State, Nigeria. TEL 234-042-77-1911. FAX 234-042-770644. TELEX 51496-U-LIONS-NG. **Document type:** bulletin.

378   IO
UNIVERSITY OF NORTH SUMATRA. BULLETIN/MAJALAH UNIVERSITAS SUMATERA UTARA. (Text in Indonesian) 1975. irreg.? University of North Sumatra, Jl. Universitas No. 9, Biro Rektor, Kampus, Medan, Indonesia.

378   AT
UNIVERSITY OF QUEENSLAND. CALENDAR. VOLUME 1. THE UNIVERSITY. 1913. a. Aus.$20. University of Queensland, Secretary and Registrar, St. Lucia, Qld. 4072, Australia. TEL 617-3651111. FAX 617-365-1199. TELEX UNIVQLD AA 40315. (Subscr. to: University Bookshop, P.O. Box 86, St. Lucia, Qld. 4067, Australia) Ed. Shirley Sargeant. index. circ. 1,200. (also avail. in microfiche from UMI)
   Supersedes in part: University of Queensland. Calendar (ISSN 0157-2849)
   Description: Lists legislation, statutes, senate and other major committees, awards, senior staff and principal dates.

378   AT
UNIVERSITY OF QUEENSLAND. CALENDAR. VOLUME 2. STUDENT HANDBOOK: METROPOLITAN CAMPUSES. 1913. a. Aus.$10. University of Queensland, Secretary and Registrar, St. Lucia, Qld. 4072, Australia. TEL 617-3651111. FAX 671-3651199. TELEX UNIVQLD AA40315. (Subscr. to: University Bookshop, P.O. Box 86, St. Lucia, Qld. 4067, Australia) Ed. Shirley Sargeant. circ. 13,000. (also avail. in microfilm from UMI)
   Supersedes in part: University of Queensland. Calendar (ISSN 0157-2849); Which incorporates: University of Queensland. Student Handbook (ISSN 0819-7482); Which was formed by the 1987 merger of: University of Queensland. Higher Degree Handbook (ISSN 0157-1133); University of Queensland. Undergraduate Degree Handbook (ISSN 0157-1079)
   Description: Contains undergraduate and postgraduate courses and subjects together with the rules relating thereto; rules and procedures for admission, examinations, costs, financial assistance and student services; subject descriptions; timetables.

378   AT
UNIVERSITY OF QUEENSLAND. CALENDAR. VOLUME 3. GATTON COLLEGE HANDBOOK. 1913. a. Aus.$5. University of Queensland, Secretary and Registrar, St. Lucia, Qld.4072, Australia. TEL 617-460-1111. FAX 617-460-1499. TELEX QUCOL AA40866. circ. 3,700. (also avail. in microform) **Document type:** directory.
   Supersedes in part: University of Queensland. Calendar (ISSN 0157-2849)
   Description: Contains outlines of undergraduate and postgraduate courses and subjects; rules and procedures for admission, examinations, costs, financial assistance and student services; subject descriptions.

378   AT   ISSN 1031-8690
UNIVERSITY OF TECHNOLOGY, SYDNEY. ANNUAL REPORT. 1968. a. free. University of Technology, Sydney, P.O. Box 123, City Campus, Broadway, N.S.W. 2007, Australia. TEL 02-330-1990. FAX 02-330-1323.

378   AT   ISSN 1036-0646
UNIVERSITY OF TECHNOLOGY, SYDNEY. FACULTY OF BUSINESS HANDBOOK. 1990. a. University of Technology, Sydney, P.O. Box 123, City Campus, Broadway, N.S.W. 2007, Australia. TEL 02-330-1990. FAX 02-330-1551. circ. 3,000.
   Description: Contains detailed information about the faculty, schools, staff, courses, and includes subject synopses.

378   JM   ISSN 0799-0006
UNIVERSITY OF THE WEST INDIES. VICE-CHANCELLOR'S REPORT. (In 2 vols.) 1962. a. free. University of the West Indies, Office of University Registrar, Mona Campus, Kingston 7, Jamaica, W.I. TEL 809-927-2406. FAX 809-927-4869. TELEX 2123 JAMAICA. stat. circ. 750.
   Description: Reports on activities and major developments in the University for the report year and projected activities for the ensuing year.

378   UK
UNIVERSITY OF WARWICK NEWSLETTER. 1977. s-m. University of Warwick, Senate House, Coventry, W. Midlands CV4 7AL, England. TEL 0203-523708. FAX 0203-461606. Ed. Peter Dunn. adv. (back issues avail.) **Document type:** newsletter.

378   ZA
UNIVERSITY OF ZAMBIA. SCHOOL OF HUMANITIES AND SOCIAL SCIENCES. ANNUAL REPORT. 1968. a. School of Humanities and Social Sciences, Box 2379, Lusaka, Zambia. TELEX ZA 44370.

378   US
UNIVERSITY URBAN PROGRAMS. 1980. quadrennial. Urban Affairs Association, University of Delaware, Newark, DE 19716.

378   US
VERMONT ACADEMY OF ARTS AND SCIENCES. STUDENT SYMPOSIUM AND ANNUAL CONFERENCE. OCCASIONAL PAPERS. 1965. 2/yr. $2.50. Vermont Academy of Arts and Sciences, 2 Buxton Ave., Middletown Springs, VT 05757. TEL 802-235-2302. Ed. Frances B. Krouse. circ. 750. **Document type:** proceedings.

378   RU   ISSN 0042-4757
VESTNIK VYSSHEI SHKOLY. 1940. m. 15.60 Rub.($10 80) Izdatel'stvo Vysshaya Shkola, Prospekt Marksa 18, 103009 Moscow K-9, Russia. (Co-sponsor: Ministerstvo Vysshego i Srednego Spetsial'nogo Obrazovaniya) Ed. A.N. Yorshenev. **Indexed:** Curr.Dig Sov.Press.

378   IO
VIDYA KARYA. bi-m. Lambung Mangkurat University, Fakultas Keguruan, Jl. Veteran No. 268, Banjarmasin, Indonesia.

378 200   US
VIEWS ON EDUCATION - NEWS OF EPISCOPAL COLLEGES. Logo title: Views & News. 1986. s-a. free. Association of Episcopal Colleges, 815 Second Ave., New York, NY 10017. TEL 212-986-0989. FAX 212-986-5039. circ. 10,000. (back issues avail.) **Document type:** newsletter.
   Formerly (until 1983): News of the Episcopal Colleges.

378.776   US   ISSN 0095-5744
LD4827.S62
VIKING. Key Title: Viking (Northfield). 1904. a. $10. St. Olaf College, Northfield, MN 55057. TEL 507-663-3276. Ed. Sara Peterson. adv.; illus. circ. 2,500. **Indexed:** Avery Ind.Archit.Per.

VISIONS (KANSAS CITY). see *ETHNIC INTERESTS*

378   US
VOICE (ALBANY). 1973. m. (9/yr.). membership. United University Professions, 159 Wolf Rd., Albany, NY 12205. TEL 518-458-7935. FAX 518-459-3242. Ed. Peggy L.S. Barmore. bk.rev.; circ. 20,000 (controlled).

VOICES OF YOUTH. see *CHILDREN AND YOUTH — For*

378   US   ISSN 0511-7666
L107
W I C H E REPORTS. 1953. irreg. Western Interstate Commission for Higher Education. Drawer P, Boulder, CO 80301-9752. TEL 303-541-0200. FAX 303-541-0291. Ed. Paul Albright. circ. (controlled). **Indexed:** C.I.N.L.
   Former titles: Reports on Higher Education (ISSN 0034-4869); Higher Education in the West.

WESLEYAN UNIVERSITY ALUMNI MAGAZINE. see *COLLEGE AND ALUMNI*

378.1   US   ISSN 0511-6848
LB2371
WESTERN ASSOCIATION OF GRADUATE SCHOOLS. PROCEEDINGS OF THE ANNUAL MEETING. 19th, 1977, Albuquerque. a., 1992, Salt Lake City. membership. Western Association of Graduate Schools, University of Wyoming, The Graduate School, Box 3018, Laramie, WY 82071-3108. TEL 307-766-2287. FAX 307-766-4042. Ed. Thomas G. Dunn. circ. 500 (controlled). **Document type:** proceedings.

EDUCATION — INTERNATIONAL EDUCATION PROGRAMS

607 AT
WESTERN AUSTRALIA. OFFICE OF TECHNICAL AND FURTHER EDUCATION. HANDBOOK. 1948. a. free. Ministry of Education, Office of Technical and Further Education, 151 Royal St., East Perth, W.A. 6000, Australia. circ. 2,500.
Formerly: Western Australia. Technical Education Division. Handbook.

WHICH DEGREE IN BRITAIN. see OCCUPATIONS AND CAREERS

WHICH SCHOOL? FOR A LEVELS. see EDUCATION — Guides To Schools And Colleges

WHO'S WHO AMONG STUDENTS IN AMERICAN JUNIOR COLLEGES. see BIOGRAPHY

WHO'S WHO AMONG STUDENTS IN AMERICAN UNIVERSITIES AND COLLEGES. see BIOGRAPHY

WICAZO SA REVIEW/RED PENCIL REVIEW; a journal of Native American Studies. see ETHNIC INTERESTS

378 GW
WO GEHT'S LANG?; Tips und Infos fuer Studenten. 1976. a. free. Technische Universitaet Berlin, Universitaetsbibliothek, Str. des 17. Juni 135, 10623 Berlin, Germany. TEL 030-31423980. FAX 030-31423909. circ. 15,000. **Document type:** bulletin.
Former titles: Information Nicht nur fuer Studienanfaenger; (until 1982): Informationen fuer Studienanfaenger.

378 US ISSN 1060-8303
▼**WOMEN IN HIGHER EDUCATION.** 1992. m. $79. Wenniger Company, 1934 Monroe St., Madison, WI 53711. TEL 608-251-3232. FAX 608-284-0601. Ed. Mary See Wenniger. bk.rev. **Document type:** newsletter.
Description: Contains information to enlighten, encourage, empower, and enrich women on campus in the U.S. and Canada, students as well as faculty, administrators, and other staff.

378.3 US ISSN 0084-1145
WOODROW WILSON NATIONAL FELLOWSHIP FOUNDATION. ANNUAL REPORT. 1958. a. free. Woodrow Wilson National Fellowship Foundation, CN5281, Princeton, NJ 08543-5281. TEL 609-452-7007. FAX 609-452-0066. **Document type:** corporate report.

378.3 US ISSN 0084-1137
WOODROW WILSON NATIONAL FELLOWSHIP FOUNDATION. NEWSLETTER. 1963. irreg. (approx. 2/yr.). free. Woodrow Wilson National Fellowship Foundation, CN5281, Princeton, NJ 08543-5281. TEL 609-452-7007. FAX 609-452-0066. **Document type:** newsletter.

WORLD MANAGEMENT EDUCATION DIRECTORY - EUROPE; a practical directory to international post graduate management programmes at European business schools and management training institutes. see BUSINESS AND ECONOMICS — Management

378 CC ISSN 1001-960X
XUEWEI YU YANJIUSHENG JIAOYU/ACADEMIC DEGREES AND GRADUATE EDUCATION. (Text in Chinese) 1984. bi-m. $3.15 per no. Guowuyuan, Xuewei Weiyuanhui - State Council, Academic Degree Committee, 7 Baishiqiao Lu, Beijing 100081, People's Republic of China. TEL 8416688. (Dist. outside China by: Guoji Shudian - China International Book Trading Corp., P.O. Box 399, Beijing, P.R.C.) Ed. Zhu Hesun.

378 US ISSN 0084-344X
YALE SCENE; UNIVERSITY SERIES. 1967. irreg., no.5, 1988. price varies. Yale University Press, Box 209040, New Haven, CT 06520. TEL 203-432-0940.

378 US
YALE UNIVERSITY. BULLETIN. 12/yr. Yale University, Box 208227, New Haven, CT 06520-8227. Ed. Lois K. Jameson. **Document type:** catalog.

378 US
YESHIVA UNIVERSITY. PRESIDENT'S REPORT. 1945. a. free to qualified personnel. Yeshiva University, Department of Public Relations, 500 W. 185th St., New York, NY 10033-3201. TEL 212-960-5285. FAX 212-960-0055. TELEX 220883TAUR. Ed. Sam Hartstein.
Formerly (until 1990): Yeshiva University. Annual Report.
Description: Presidential report to the University family and the wider community on the University's progress in education, research and service.

Z V S - INFO. (Zentralstelle fuer die Vergabe von Studienplaetzen) see COLLEGE AND ALUMNI

378 CC ISSN 1002-4417
ZHONGGUO GAODENG JIAOYU/HIGHER EDUCATION IN CHINA. (Text in Chinese) 1965-1966; resumed 1982. m. Y27($21.06) (typically set in Jan.). (State Educatinal Commission) Zhongguo Jiaoyu Zazhishe, China Education Magazine House, 35 Damucang Hutong, Xidan, Beijing 100816, People's Republic of China. TEL 6015580. FAX 6022169. (Dist. in US by: China Books & Periodicals, Inc., 2929 24th St., San Francisco, CA 94110. TEL 415-282-2994) Ed. Yang Shuwang. adv.; bk.rev. circ. 24,000.
Formerly: Higher Educational Front.

EDUCATION — International Education Programs

370.196 410 US ISSN 1062-6840
PL101
A A T T NEWSLETTER. (Text in English, Turkish) 1986. s-a. $15. American Association of Teachers of Turkish, Near Eastern Studies Department, NES 110 Jones Hall, Princeton University, Princeton, NJ 08544-1008. TEL 609-424-2686. FAX 609-258-1242. Ed. E.H. Gilson. bk.rev.; charts. circ. 125. (back issues avail.) **Document type:** newsletter.
Description: To advance and improve the teaching of the Turkish language; promotes study, criticism, and research in Turkish language and literature.

370.196 UN ISSN 0253-6455
A B C HUMAN RIGHTS TEACHING. French edition: A B C Enseignement des Droits de l'Homme (ISSN 0253-6463); Russian edition: A B V Prepodavanie Prav Cheloveka. (Text in English) 1980. s-a. $5 per no. Unesco, 7-9 Place de Fontenoy, 75700 Paris, France. TEL 45-77-16-10. circ. 8,000.

370.196 UN ISSN 0251-4818
A C E I D NEWSLETTER. (Text in English) 1974. s-a. free or exchange basis. (Asian Centre of Educational Innovation for Development) Unesco, Principal Regional Office for Asia and the Pacific, P.O. Box 1425, Bangkok 10500, Thailand. FAX 391-0866. TELEX 20591 TH. circ. 1,900. **Document type:** newsletter.

A.C.F.O.A. NEWS. (Australian Council for Overseas Aid) see BUSINESS AND ECONOMICS — International Development And Assistance

370.196 US ISSN 1063-0910
A F S - U S A DIRECTIONS; a monthly newsletter for AFS volunteers. 1988. m. free to qualified personnel. A F S Intercultural Programs - U S A, 220 E. 42nd St., Third Fl., New York, NY 10017. TEL 212-949-4242. FAX 212-949-9379. TELEX AFSI UI 66379 UW (WUI). Ed. Pedro A. Velez. circ. 10,000. **Document type:** newsletter.
Description: Focuses on volunteer training, recruitment, and recognition; offers ideas for expanding AFS' student hosting and sending programs.

370.196 US ISSN 1063-0902
A F S WORLD. q. $20 includes membership. A F S Intercultural Programs - U S A, 220 E. 42nd St., Third Fl., New York, NY 10017. TEL 212-949-4242. FAX 212-949-9379. TELEX AFSI UI 66379 UW (WUI). Ed. Bill Walter. index. circ. 32,000. (back issues avail.) **Document type:** newsletter.
Formerly (until 1990): Connections.
Description: Offers a specific "AFS angle" on international and intercultural subjects, with the intent to educate towards a "global understanding," with an ultimate goal of global - cultural friendship.

370.196 336 US ISSN 1051-3639
A I P T EMPLOYER TAX GUIDE. irreg. Association for International Practical Training, 10400 Little Patuxent Pkwy., Ste. 250, Columbia, MD 21044-3510. TEL 410-992-3924. FAX 410-992-3924.

370.196 US
A I P T REPORT. 1987. q. free. Association for International Practical Training, 10400 Little Patuxent Pkwy., Ste. 250, Columbia, MD 21044-3510. TEL 410-997-2200. FAX 410-992-3924. Ed. Michael Mathes. circ. 1,500. (back issues avail.) **Document type:** newsletter.
Description: International practical training and work exchange programs for university students, young professionals, and host employers.

371.39 378.35 US ISSN 1047-2576
ACADEMIC YEAR ABROAD. 1964. a. $42.95. Institute of International Education, 809 United Nations Plaza, New York, NY 10017. TEL 212-984-5412. FAX 212-984-5358. TELEX TRT 175977. Ed. Sara Steen. index. (reprint service avail. from EDR) **Document type:** directory.
Supersedes: Learning Traveler. U S College-Sponsored Programs Abroad: Academic Year; Former titles: U S College-Sponsored Programs Abroad. Academic Year (ISSN 0082-8602); United States Academic Programs Abroad.
Description: Describes more than 2,100 semester and academic-year programs offered by U.S. and foreign universities and private organizations.

370.196 US ISSN 0895-1101
ADVISING QUARTERLY; for professionals in international education. 1987. q. $40 (foreign $50). America-Mideast Educational & Training Services, 1100 17th St., N.W., Washington, DC 20036. TEL 202-785-0022. FAX 202-822-6563. TELEX 440160. Ed. Juleann Fallgatter. adv.; bk.rev.; video rev. circ. 1,100. (back issues avail.) **Document type:** newsletter.
Formerly (until 1987): Amideast Counseling Quarterly.
Description: Contains articles, academic news, and research questions of interest to educational advisers both in the U.S. and abroad.

370.196 US
ADVISORY LIST OF INTERNATIONAL EDUCATIONAL TRAVEL AND EXCHANGE PROGRAMS. 1985. a. $8.50. Council on Standards for International Educational Travel, 3 Loudoun St., S.E., Ste. 3, Leesburg, VA 22075-3012. TEL 703-771-2040. FAX 703-771-2046. Ed. Anne Shattuck. adv.; bibl.; charts; stat. **Document type:** directory.
Description: Describes international educational exchange organizations that conduct programs for high-school-age students that have been found to be in compliance with the Council's nine standard areas.

AMERICAN O R T FEDERATION. YEARBOOK. see ETHNIC INTERESTS

AMERICANS FOR THE UNIVERSALITY OF UNESCO NEWSLETTER. see POLITICAL SCIENCE — International Relations

ASSOCIATION OF INTERNATIONAL COLLEGES & UNIVERSITIES DIRECTORY. see EDUCATION — Higher Education

ASSOCIATION OF INTERNATIONAL COLLEGES & UNIVERSITIES NEWSLETTER. see EDUCATION — Higher Education

370.196 IT
ASSOCIAZIONE PEDAGOGICA ITALIANA. BOLLETTINO; periodico d'informazione per la cultura pedagogica. 1972. q. L6000. (Associazione Pedagogica Italiana (As.Pe.I.)) Tecnodid Editrice S.R.L., Piazza Carlo 3, 42, 80127 Naples, Italy. (Subscr. to: c/o Dipartimento di Scienze dell'Educazione, Universita di Bologna, Via Zamboni, 34, 40126 Bologna, Italy) Ed. Prof. Vittorio Telmon. cum.index. (tabloid format)

AUSZEIT; Informationen, Berichte und Dokumentation zum Auslaenderstudium. see EDUCATION — Higher Education

EDUCATION — INTERNATIONAL EDUCATION PROGRAMS

370.196   SP
BANCO DE DATOS DE BECAS Y CURSOS. 1980. a. 50000 ptas.($500) Organizacion de Estados IberoAmericanos para la Educacion, la Ciencia y la Cultura (OEI), C. Bravo Murillo 38a, 28015 Madrid, Spain. TEL 34-1-594-4382. FAX 34-1-594-32-86. circ. 1,000. (also avail. in diskette format) **Document type:** directory.
    Formerly: Becas y Cursos de Educacion.
    Description: Contains information on postgraduate courses at higher education institutions in Iberoamerica. Includes financial aid information.

370.196   US
BREAKTHROUGH (NEW YORK, 1986). vol.7, 1986. q. $25. Global Education Associates, 475 Riverside Dr., Ste. 1848, New York, NY 10115. TEL 212-870-3290. FAX 212-870-2729. Ed. Patricia M. Mische. bk.rev. circ. 8,000.
    Description: Covers world peace and security, ecological responsibility, human rights, and cooperative economic development.

370.196   CN
C C U L P NEWS/NOUVELLES DU P S C J U. (Text in Chinese, English, French) 1989. 2/yrg. free. Association of Universities and Colleges of Canada, Canada - China University Linkages Program - Association des Universites et Colleges du Canada - Programme Sino-Canadien du Jumelage Universitaire, 350 Albert St., Ste. 600, Ottawa, ON K1P 1B1, Canada. TEL 613-563-1236. FAX 613-563-9745. **Document type:** newsletter.

370.196   CN
CANADIAN BUREAU FOR INTERNATIONAL EDUCATION. ANNUAL REPORT.. (Text in English and French) 1971. a. Canadian Bureau for International Education, 220 Laurier Ave., W., Ste. 1100, Ottawa, ON K1P 5Z9, Canada. TEL 613-237-4820. FAX 613-237-1300. **Document type:** corporate report.

370.196   UK   ISSN 0264-858X
COMEBACK. 1974. q. £4. Returned Volunteer Action, 1 Amwell St., London EC1R 1UL, England. TEL 071-278-0804. Ed.Bd. adv.; bk.rev. circ. 1,250. **Document type:** newsletter.
    Description: Journal on overseas volunteering and third world development issues.

COMPASSION MAGAZINE (COLORADO SPRINGS). see RELIGIONS AND THEOLOGY — Protestant

CURRICULUM AND TEACHING. see EDUCATION — Teaching Methods And Curriculum

370.196   US
DIRECTORY OF AMERICAN FULBRIGHT SCHOLARS. a. free. Council for International Exchange of Scholars, 3007 Tilden St., N.W., Ste. 5M, Washington, DC 20008-3009. TEL 202-686-7867. **Document type:** directory.
    Formerly: American Fulbright Scholars.

378.35   PK   ISSN 0070-606X
DIRECTORY OF PAKISTANI SCHOLARS ABROAD. (Text in English) 1965. a. Ministry of Education, Documentation Section, Curriculum Wing, Sector H-9, P.O. Shaigan, Industrial Area, Islamabad, Pakistan.

378.35   US
DIRECTORY OF VISITING FULBRIGHT SCHOLARS AND OCCASIONAL LECTURERS. a. free. Council for International Exchange of Scholars, 3007 Tilden St., N.W., Ste. 5M, Washington, DC 20008-3009. TEL 202-686-7867. (Affiliate: American Council of Learned Societies) **Document type:** directory.
    Former titles: Directory of Visiting Fulbright Scholars and Occasional Lecturer Program; Directory of Visiting Fulbright Scholars in the United States (ISSN 0098-1508); Directory of Visiting Lecturers and Research Scholars in the United States Under the Mutual Educational Exchange Program (the Fulbright-Hays Act); Directory of Visiting Scholars in the United States Awarded Grants Under the Mutual Educational and Cultural Exchange Act (the Fulbright-Hays Act) (ISSN 0070-6582)

370.196
E A R C O S QUARTERLY.* 1987. q. East Asia Regional Council of Overseas Schools, 2990 Telestar Ct., 314-315, Falls Church, VA 22042-1207. adv. circ. 300.

370.196   BE
E F I L DOCUMENTATION. no.3, 1979. irreg. European Federation for Intercultural Learning, 36 rue de la Montagne, B-1000 Brussels, Belgium. TEL 32-2-5145250. FAX 32-2-5142929.

370.196   BE
E F I L NEWSLETTER. s-a. $65. European Federation for Intercultural Learning, 36 rue de la Montagne, B-1000 Brussels, Belgium. TEL 32-2-5145250. FAX 32-2-5142929. Ed. Hilary Maher. circ. 1,250. **Document type:** newsletter.
    Former titles (until 1978): A F S Europa; A F S International Scholarships. European Coordination Letter.

EASTERN CHALLENGE. see RELIGIONS AND THEOLOGY — Protestant

370.196   KO
EDUCATION IN KOREA. (Text in English) 1978. a. free. Ministry of Education, National Institute of Educational Research and Training, 25, Samch'ong-dong, Chongno-gu, Seoul, S. Korea. bk.rev.; charts; stat. circ. 3,000.
    Description: Features major highlights of educational system to develop a general understanding of the Republic of Korea.

370.196   UN
EDUCATIONAL INNOVATION AND INFORMATION. Spanish edition: Informacion e Innovacion Educacionales (ISSN 1014-3548); French edition: Information et Innovation en Education (ISSN 1014-353X) 1975. q. free. Unesco, International Bureau of Education, Case Postale 199, CH-1211 Geneva 20, Switzerland. TEL 41-22-7981455. FAX 41-22-7981486. TELEX 22644. Ed. John Fox. bibl. circ. 5,000. (also avail. in microfilm from UMI; reprint service avail. from UMI) **Indexed:** PROMT.
    Incorporates: Innovation (ISSN 0251-6128); I B E D O C Information Newsletter (ISSN 0251-5792); Communication Newsletter.
    Description: Information about developments in education worldwide.

370.196   US   ISSN 1061-2343 LC6681
EDUCATIONAL TRAVEL RESOURCE GUIDE. 1977. a. $6.95. Transitions Publishing, 18 Hulst Rd., Box 1300, Amherst, MA 01004. TEL 413-256-0373. adv.; bk.rev. circ. 16,000. **Document type:** directory. —UnCover.
    Formerly: Educational Travel Directory.
    Description: Provides information on work, study, living, and responsible travel abroad.

ELDERHOSTEL CATALOG. see EDUCATION — Adult Education

370.196   FR
ENSEIGNEMENT DU FRANCAIS AUX ETRANGERS. 1949. m. Ecole de l'Alliance Francaise de Paris, 101 bd. Raspail, 75270 Paris Cedex 06, France. Dir. M.J. Degremont.

FOCUS (BURLINGTON). see RELIGIONS AND THEOLOGY — Protestant

FORUM FOCUS. see RELIGIONS AND THEOLOGY

370.196   US
FULBRIGHT ASSOCIATION NEWSLETTER. 1978. q. membership. Fulbright Association, 1307 New Hampshire Ave., N.W., Washington, DC 20036. TEL 202-331-1590. FAX 202-331-1979. Ed. Jane L. Anderson. adv. circ. 10,000. (back issues avail.) **Document type:** newsletter.
    Formerly: Fulbrighters' Newsletter.

370.196   US
FULBRIGHT SCHOLAR PROGRAM: GRANTS FOR FACULTY AND PROFESSIONALS. a. free. Council for International Exchange of Scholars, 3007 Tilden St., N.W., Ste. 5M, Washington, DC 20008-3009. TEL 202-686-7877. circ. 50,000.
    Former titles: Fulbright Scholar Program - Faculty Grants, Research and Lecturing Awards; Fulbright Scholar Program - Research Awards and Lectureships; Fulbright Awards Abroad.

370   UN   ISSN 0071-9862
FUNDAMENTALS OF EDUCATIONAL PLANNING. (Editions in English, French) 1966. irreg., no.40, 1991. price varies. International Institute for Educational Planning, 7-9 rue Eugene-Delacroix, 75116 Paris, France. TEL 33-1-45-03-77-76. FAX 33-1-40-72-83-66. TELEX 640032. (Dist. in U.S. by: Unipub, 4611-F Assembly Dr., Lanham, MD 20706-4391) **Indexed:** ERIC, Rural Recreat.Tour.Abstr., World Agri.Econ.& Rural Sociol.Abstr.

G E J - GAZETO. see LINGUISTICS

370.196   GW
G I PRISMA. 1987. s-a. free. Goethe Institut, Balanstr. 57, 81541 Munich, Germany. TEL 089-41868248. FAX 089-41868414. Ed. Horst Harnischfeger. circ. 10,000. (back issues avail.)

950   US
GHANTA. 1990. s-a free. University of Wisconsin-Madison, South Asia Center, Outreach Office, 1256 Van Hise Hall, 1220 Linden Dr., Madison, WI 53706. TEL 608-262-4884. FAX 608-262-3062. Ed. Ed Dixon. adv.; bk.rev. circ. 1,500. (tabloid format; back issues avail.) **Document type:** newsletter.
    Description: Provides information on southern Asia for K-12 teachers and on available resources. Serves as a forum for exchange of ideas on teaching about southern Asia.

GLOBAL CONNECTOR; the complete resource directory for international training. see EDUCATION — Adult Education

GLOBAL LINKS. see BUSINESS AND ECONOMICS — International Development And Assistance

370.196   CC   ISSN 1001-0114
GUOJI RENCAI JIAOLIU/INTERNATIONAL EXCHANGE OF PERSONNEL. (Text in Chinese) bi-m. Zhongguo Guoji Rencai Jiaoliu Xinxi Jiaoliu Zhongxin, No. 71615, Northeast District, Youyi Binguan (Friendship Hotel), Beijing 100873, People's Republic of China. TEL 8023586. Ed. Bi Lianggan.

370   UN   ISSN 0074-6401
I I E P OCCASIONAL PAPERS. (Some titles in English; others in French) 1968. irreg., no.79, 1990. price varies. International Institute for Educational Planning, 7-9 rue Eugene-Delacroix, 75116 Paris, France. TEL 33-1-45-03-77-76. FAX 33-1-40-72-38-66. TELEX 640032. **Indexed:** ERIC, Rural Recreat.Tour.Abstr., World Agri.Econ. & Rural Sociol.Abstr.

370.196   UN
I I E P RESEARCH REPORTS. (Text in English and French) 1975. irreg., no.92, 1991. price varies. International Institute for Educational Planning, 7-9 rue Eugene-Delacroix, 75116 Paris, France. TEL 33-1-45-03-77-76. FAX 33-1-40-72-83-66. TELEX 640032. **Indexed:** ERIC, Rural Recreat.Tour.Abstr., World Agri.Econ & Rural Sociol.Abstr.

370.196 338.91   UN
I I E P SEMINAR PAPERS. (Text in English and French) 1975. irreg., no.45, 1986. price varies. International Institute for Educational Planning, 7-9 rue Eugene-Delacroix, 75116 Paris, France. TEL 33-1-45-03-77-76. FAX 33-01-40-72-83-66. TELEX 640032. **Indexed:** ERIC.

370.196   CN
I S A BULLETIN/CONSEILLERS AUX ETUDIANTS ETRANGERS. BULLETIN. (International Student Advisers) (Text in English, French) m. membership. Canadian Bureau for International Education - Bureau Canadien de l'Education International, 220 Laurier Ave., W., Ste. 1100, Ottawa, ON K1P 5Z9, Canada. TEL 613-237-4820. FAX 613-237-1073. TELEX 053-3255. **Document type:** bulletin.
    Description: For professionals working with international students in Canada.

EDUCATION — INTERNATIONAL EDUCATION PROGRAMS

370.196 US ISSN 1040-6352
IDEAS AND INFORMATION ABOUT DEVELOPMENT EDUCATION. 1986. q. $12. International Development Conference, 1401 New York Ave., N.W., Ste. 1100, Washington, DC 20005-2160. TEL 202-638-3111. FAX 202-638-1374. Ed. Andrew E. Rice. bk.rev. circ. 1,500. (looseleaf format; back issues avail.) **Document type:** newsletter.
Description: Devoted to educating Americans about international development and global interdependence.

370.196 AU
INFORMATIONEN FUER AUSLAENDISCHE STUDIERENDE IN OESTERREICH. Short title: I A S m. Oesterreichischer Akademischer Austauschdienst, Berggasse 21, A-1090 Vienna, Austria. TEL 01-3172793. FAX 01-3172795. (Co-sponsor: Bundesministerium fuer Wissenschaft und Forschung) Ed. Josef Leidenfrost. **Document type:** academic/scholarly publication.

370.196 378 FR
INSTITUTE FOR AMERICAN UNIVERSITIES. NEWSLETTER. (Text in English, French) s.a. free. Institute for American Universities, 27 place de l'Universite, 13625 Aix-en-Provence, France. TEL 33-42-23-39-35. FAX 33-42-21-21-38. Ed. Grace Anderson.
Description: Contains news of the school, alumni and reunions.

370 NG ISSN 0534-4727
INTER-AFRICAN CONFERENCE ON INDUSTRIAL COMMERCIAL AND AGRICULTURAL EDUCATION MEETING.* Title varies slightly; some issues called reports. 1954. irreg. (Commission for Technical Co-Operation in Africa South of the Sahara) Maison de l'Afrique, B.P. 878, Niamey, Niger.

378.3 FR ISSN 0538-4427
INTERNATIONAL ASSOCIATION FOR THE EXCHANGE OF STUDENTS FOR TECHNICAL EXPERIENCE. ANNUAL REPORT. Short title: I A E S T E Annual Report. 1948. a. free. International Association for the Exchange of Students for Technical Experience, c/o A. Sfier, B.P. 3672, Nancy, France. circ. 8,000. **Document type:** corporate report.

370.196 US
INTERNATIONAL ASSOCIATION OF EDUCATORS FOR WORLD PEACE. CIRCULATION NEWSLETTER. (Text in English, French, Spanish) 1969. bi-m. Peace Progress Press, Box 3282, Mastin Lake Sta., Huntsville, AL 35810-0282. TEL 205-534-5501. FAX 205-536-1018. TELEX 4102405482. Ed. Charles Mercieca. adv.; bk.rev.; circ. 10,000 (controlled). (looseleaf format; back issues avail.) **Document type:** newsletter.
Description: Aims for the promotion of international understanding and world peace through education; the protection of the environment from man-made pollution; the safeguarding of human rights.

INTERNATIONAL ASSOCIATION OF ZOO EDUCATORS. JOURNAL. see CONSERVATION

INTERNATIONAL DIRECTIONS IN EDUCATION; an independent policy advisory service for leaders in education. see EDUCATION — School Organization And Administration

370.196 US ISSN 0160-5429
LC1090
INTERNATIONAL EDUCATION. 1971. s-a. $12. University of Tennessee at Knoxville, College of Education, 212 Claxton, Knoxville, TN 37996-3400. TEL 615-974-2272. Eds. Karl Jost, Tricia McClam. bk.rev. circ. 350. **Indexed:** Cont.Pg.Educ., Mult.Ed.Abstr., Rural Ext.Educ.& Tr.Abstr. **Document type:** academic/scholarly publication.
—BLDSC (4539.835000); Faxon; UnCover.
Description: Contains articles related to educational programs in various countries, including the U.S.
Refereed Serial

INTERNATIONAL EDUCATION FORUM. see EDUCATION — School Organization And Administration

378.35 CN ISSN 0827-0678
INTERNATIONAL EDUCATION MAGAZINE/MAGAZINE DE L'EDUCATION INTERNATIONALE. (Supplement to: Synthesis - Synthese) (Text in English and French) 1985. a. included in subscr. to Synthesis. Canadian Bureau for International Education - Bureau Canadien de l'Education Internationale, 220 Laurier Ave., W., Ste. 1100, Ottawa, ON K1P 5Z9, Canada. TEL 613-237-4820. FAX 613-237-1300. Ed. Jennifer Humphries. bk.rev. circ. 1,400.
Supersedes (1966-1985): Communications (ISSN 0319-7778); (1983-1985): International Education Forum - Forum de l'Education International (ISSN 0823-2601); Which was formerly: Canadian Bureau for International Education. Bulletin (ISSN 0068-8428); Canadian Service for Overseas Students and Trainees. Bulletin.

370 US ISSN 1059-4221
INTERNATIONAL EDUCATOR (WASHINGTON). 1991. 2/yr. $12 to nonmembers. National Association for Foreign Student Affairs, Association of International Educators, 1875 Connecticut Ave., N.W., Ste. 1000, Washington, DC 20009-5728. TEL 202-462-4811. FAX 202-667-3419. Ed. Steven B. Kennedy.
Description: Covers professional, political, administrative and social issues pertaining to international educational exchange.

370.196 371.31 US ISSN 1044-3509
L10
INTERNATIONAL EDUCATOR (WEST BRIDGEWATER). 1986. q. $25. International Educator's Institute, Box 513, Cummaquid, MA 02637. TEL 508-362-1414. FAX 508-362-1411. Ed. Cynthia Brown. adv.; bk.rev. circ. 15,000. (tabloid format; back issues avail.)
Description: Features available teaching and administrative positions in overseas schools. Includes news and developments about global education issues.

INTERNATIONAL EMPLOYMENT HOTLINE. see OCCUPATIONS AND CAREERS

370.196 US
INTERNATIONAL FOUNDATION DIRECTORY. 1974. irreg., 5th ed., 1991. $140. Gale Research Inc., 835 Penobscot Bldg., Detroit, MI 48226. TEL 313-961-2242. FAX 313-961-6083. TELEX 810-221-7086. Ed. H.V. Hodson.
Description: Guide to foundations worldwide.

370 UK ISSN 0883-0355
LB2845 CODEN: EIRSD6
INTERNATIONAL JOURNAL OF EDUCATIONAL RESEARCH. 1977. 12/yr. £270($415) includes Learning and Instruction (effective 1994). Elsevier Science Ltd., Pergamon, P.O. Box 800, Kidlington, Oxford OX5 1DX, England. TEL 44-865-843000. FAX 44-865-843010. (Subscr. in U.S. and Canada to: Elsevier Science, 660 White Plains Rd., Tarrytown, NY 10591-5153. TEL 914-524-9200. FAX 914-333-2444) Ed. Herbert J. Walberg. (also avail. in microfilm from UMI) **Indexed:** C.I.J.E., Cont.Pg.Educ., Psychol.Abstr. **Document type:** academic/scholarly publication.
—BLDSC (4542.199800); Faxon; UnCover; SWETS; UMI. **CCC**.
Former titles: Evaluation in Education; Evaluation in Education - International Progress (ISSN 0191-765X)
Refereed Serial

370.19 US ISSN 1075-2455
INTERNATIONAL JOURNAL OF VOCATIONAL EDUCATION AND TRAINING. 1993. s-a. $50. International Vocational Education and Training Association, 670-C Enterprise Dr., Westerville, OH 43081. TEL 614-847-9550. FAX 614-847-9844. Ed. Dennis R. Herschbach. bk.rev. (back issues avail.) **Document type:** trade publication.
Description: Provides a forum for the discussion of vocational education and training issues and practices.
Refereed Serial

INTERNATIONAL UNIVERSITY FOUNDATION DIRECTORY. see EDUCATION — Higher Education

INTERNATIONAL UNIVERSITY FOUNDATION REPORT. see EDUCATION — Higher Education

370.196 US
INTERNATIONAL WORKCAMP DIRECTORY. 1983. a. $10 (typically set in Apr.). V F P International Workcamps, 43 Tiffany Rd., Belmont, VT 05730. TEL 802-259-2759. FAX 802-259-2922. TELEX 401210697. Ed. Peter Coldwell. circ. 5,000. (back issues avail.) **Document type:** directory.
Description: Includes listings of 1,000 international workcamp programs in 36 countries.

370.196 US
INTERNATIONAL WORKCAMPER. 1982. a. free. V F P International Workcamps, 43 Tiffany Rd., Belmont, VT 05730. TEL 802-259-2759. FAX 802-259-2922. TELEX 401210697. Ed. Peter Coldwell.
Description: Summarizes the international workcamp program and contains information about membership.

301 US ISSN 0273-3382
LB2375
JOURNAL OF INTERNATIONAL STUDENT PERSONNEL.* 1980. 4/yr. $25. Association for International and Cultural Education, c/o Samuel B. Olorounto, Ed., Box 1127, Dublin, VA 24084. Ed. Samuel B. Olorounto. adv.; bk.rev.; charts. circ. 3,000.

JOURNAL OF MULTILINGUAL & MULTICULTURAL DEVELOPMENT. see LINGUISTICS

370.196 GW
JUGENDNACHRICHTEN. 1946. 10/yr. DM.22. Bayerischer Jugendring - Bavarian Youth Council, Herzog-Heinrich-Str. 7, 80336 Munich, Germany. TEL 089-5145820. Ed. Thomas Busch. bk.rev. circ. 3,500. **Document type:** newsletter.

370.196 US ISSN 1062-0826
KEYNOTES (GARDEN CITY). 1968. 2/yr. free. Open Door Student Exchange, 839 Stewart Ave., Ste. D, Garden City, NY 11530-4810. TEL 516-745-6232. FAX 516-745-6233. Ed. Anthony J. Lella. circ. 65,000. **Document type:** newsletter.
Description: Contains news of international high school student exchange programs bringing students from Europe, Central and South America, and Asia to the US.

370.196 US
L A S P A U INFORMATIVO. 1968. s-a. free. Latin American Scholarship Program of American Universities, Inc., 25 Mt. Auburn St., Cambridge, MA 02138. TEL 617-495-5255. FAX 617-495-8990. TELEX 325660 LASPAU. circ. 7,500. (tabloid format; back issues avail.)
Description: Reports on LASPAU's current activities, new programs, and contemporary issues in the hemisphere. It also regularly features information on scholars and alumni of LASPAU-administered programs.

L P E A HEARTBEAT. (Luis Palau Evangelistic Association) see RELIGIONS AND THEOLOGY — Protestant

LAUBACH LITERACY INTERNATIONAL ANNUAL REPORT. see EDUCATION — Adult Education

370.196 IT
MICROMEGAS; rivista di studi e confronti italiani e francesi. 1974. 3/yr. L.35000. (Universita degli Studi di Roma, Istituto di Studi Francesi) Bulzoni Editore, Via dei Liburni 14, 00185 Rome, Italy. TEL 06-4455207. FAX 06-4450355. (Co-sponsor: Services Culturels dell' Ambasciata di Francia) Ed. Massimo Colesanti.

371.3 US ISSN 0736-4660
LA203
N A F S A DIRECTORY OF INSTITUTIONS AND INDIVIDUALS IN INTERNATIONAL EDUCATIONAL EXCHANGE. 1948. biennial. $45 to non-members; members $25. National Association for Foreign Student Affairs, Association of International Educators, Publications Order Desk, 1875 Connecticut Ave., N.W., Ste. 1000, Washington, DC 20009-5728. TEL 202-462-4811. FAX 202-667-3419. adv.; index. circ. 7,200. **Document type:** directory.
Formerly: National Association for Foreign Student Affairs N A F S A Directory (ISSN 0077-3190)

EDUCATION — INTERNATIONAL EDUCATION PROGRAMS

370.196 327 US ISSN 0889-9363
N A F S A GOVERNMENT AFFAIRS BULLETIN. 1985. 8/yr. $64 to non-members (foreign $74); institutional members $36 (foreign $46). National Association for Foreign Student Affairs, Association of International Educators, 1875 Connecticut Ave., N.W., Ste. 1000, Washington, DC 20009. TEL 202-462-4811. FAX 202-667-5419. Ed. Amy Yenkin. index. circ. 1,000. (looseleaf format; back issues avail.) **Document type:** bulletin.
Description: Addresses government regulations affecting international educational exchange, immigration reform and tax legislation.

378 629.1 US
N A S A UNIVERSITY PROGRAMS REPORT. Variant title: Greenbook. a. U.S. National Aeronautics and Space Administration, Center for Aerospace Information, Box 8757, Baltimore-Washington International Airport, MD 21240. TEL 301-621-0153. charts; stat. **Document type:** government publication, directory.
Description: Compiles active projects and related statistics of the NASA University Program for the previous fiscal year.

370.196 US
N C I V NEWSLETTER. 1956. q. free. National Council for International Visitors, 1420 K St., N.W., Ste. 800, Washington, DC 20005-2401. TEL 202-842-1414. FAX 202-289-4625. TELEX 7660165 NCI UC. Ed. Claire P. Burke. bk.rev. circ. 8,000. **Document type:** newsletter.
Formerly (until 1979): C O S E R V Newsletter (National Council for Community Services to International Visitors) (ISSN 0547-5619)

370.196 338.91 US
NEWS FROM APROVECHO. 1980. 4/yr. $30. Aprovecho Institute, 80574 Hazelton Rd., Cottage Grove, OR 97424. TEL 503-942-8198. adv. circ. 2,600. (back issues avail.)
Description: Reports on research done at Aprovecho on appropriate technology, sustainable forestry, organic gardening and internship programs with an emphasis on cross-cultural learning.

370.196 US
NEWS FROM I E S - I A S. vol.10, 1988. s-a. free. Institute of European Studies - Institute of Asian Studies, 223 W. Ohio St., Chicago, IL 60610-4196. TEL 312-944-1750. FAX 312-944-1448. Ed. Karen Sokol. bk.rev. circ. 4,000. **Document type:** newsletter.
Formerly: News from I E S.

370.196 US ISSN 1043-3724
NEWSLINKS. bi-m. free. International Schools Services, Inc., Box 5910, Princeton, NJ 08543. TEL 609-452-0990. FAX 609-452-2690. TELEX 843 308 SCHOLSERV PRIN. Ed. Mea Kaemmerlen. adv. contact: Katherine English. illus. (tabloid format) **Document type:** newspaper.

NEWSMONTH. see *LABOR UNIONS*

O M S OUTREACH; official publication of O M S International. see *RELIGIONS AND THEOLOGY — Protestant*

370.196 AU
OESTERREICHISCHER AKADEMISCHER AUSTAUSCHDIENST. RECHENSCHAFTSBERICHT. 1961. a. S.200. Oesterreichischer Akademischer Austauschdienst, Berggasse 21, A-1090 Vienna, Austria. TEL 01-3172791. FAX 01-3172795. illus.; stat. circ. 350. **Document type:** academic/scholarly publication.
Formerly: Oesterreichischer Auslandsstudentendienst. Rechenschaftsbericht.

370.196 US
OHIO SLAVIC AND EAST EUROPEAN NEWSLETTER. 1973. m. free. Ohio State University, Center for Slavic and East European Studies, 303 Oxley Hall, 1712 Neil Ave., Columbus, OH 43210-1219. TEL 614-292-8770. FAX 614-292-4723. Ed. David P. Patton. circ. 800. **Document type:** newsletter.
Description: News and announcements of interest to students of the former Soviet Union and Eastern Europe, with an emphasis on activities at the University and other Ohio institutions.

378.3 US ISSN 0078-5172
LB2376
OPEN DOORS; report on international exchange. 1955. a. $39.95. Institute of International Education, 809 United Nations Plaza, New York, NY 10017. TEL 212-984-5412. FAX 212-984-5358. TELEX TRT 175977. (also avail. in microfiche from CIS; reprint service avail. from EDR) **Indexed:** SRI. **Document type:** directory.
—BLDSC (6265.953500).
Description: Reports on the IIE's annual census of international students with data on national origin, sources of financial support, fields of study, enrollments and rates of growth at virtually all accredited US colleges and universities.

OPTION. see *EDUCATION — Adult Education*

OVER THE RAINBOW. see *HANDICAPPED*

370.196 US ISSN 0857-0760
PEACE PROGRESS; I A E W P journal of education. (Text in English, French, Spanish) 1974. a. $35 (includes membership). International Association of Educators for World Peace, Box 3282, Mastin Lake Sta., Huntsville, AL 35810. TEL 205-534-5501. FAX 205-536-1018. TELEX 9102405482. (Subscr. to: 216, Laxminagar, Nagpur 440022, Maharashtra, India) Ed. Surya N. Prasad. adv.; bk.rev. circ. 5,000. (back issues avail.)
Description: Examines world peace through education, protection of the environment and the safeguard of human rights.

370.196 327 US ISSN 0031-501X
PEOPLE (KANSAS CITY). 1962. q. membership. People To People International, 501 E. Armour Blvd., Kansas City, MO 64109-2200. FAX 816-561-7502. Ed. Rosanne Kohlman. illus. circ. 24,000.
Formerly: People-to-People Newsletter.

370.196 US
PERSPECTIVE (NEW YORK, 1970). 1970. q. $12. Association of Teachers of Latin American Studies, Box 620754, Flushing, NY 11362-0754. TEL 718-428-1237. Ed. D.J. Mugan. adv.; bk.rev. circ. 1,000. **Document type:** newsletter.
Description: Provides information on conference, grants, media, employment, news from universities, and workshops.

PROGRESS OF EDUCATION IN SAUDI ARABIA; a statistical review. see *EDUCATION — Abstracting, Bibliographies, Statistics*

RELIGION FOR PEACE; newsletter on inter-religious dialogue and action for peace. see *RELIGIONS AND THEOLOGY*

ROBERT NOAH'S PARIS EN CUISINE NEWSLETTER; the insider's guide to gastronomic news of France. see *FOOD AND FOOD INDUSTRIES*

SAUDI ARABIA. MINISTRY OF EDUCATION. ANNUAL STATISTICAL REPORT. see *EDUCATION — Abstracting, Bibliographies, Statistics*

370.196 SU
SAUDI ARABIA. MINISTRY OF EDUCATION. EDUCATIONAL DOCUMENTATION. (Text in Arabic, English) 1968. s-a. Ministry of Education, Center for Statistical Data, Box 2871, Riyadh, Saudi Arabia. TEL 4768695. TELEX TATWIR 205540 SG.

371.39 US ISSN 0899-2002
L900
SCHOOLS ABROAD. Variant title: Schools Abroad of Interest to Americans. 1959. irreg., 8th ed., 1991-1992. $35. Porter Sargent Publishers, Inc., 11 Beacon St., Ste. 1400, Boston, MA 02108. TEL 617-523-1670. FAX 617-523-1021. index. circ. 2,000. **Document type:** directory.
Description: Describes 800 elementary and secondary schools in 130 countries for those seeking preparatory schooling overseas.

370.196 UK
SCHOOLS UNIT NEWS. 1984. 3/yr. Central Bureau, Seymour Mews House, Seymour Mews, London W1H 9PE, England. TEL 071-486-5101. FAX 071-935-5741.
Formerly (until 1987): Pupil Exchange News.

SERVANT LEADER. see *RELIGIONS AND THEOLOGY — Protestant*

SMITH - KETTLEWELL TECHNICAL FILE; a biannual technical journal for the blind and visually impaired. see *HANDICAPPED — Visually Impaired*

060 SP
SPAIN. MINISTERIO ASINTOS EXTERIORES. DIRECCION GENERAL DE COOPERACION TECNICA INTERNACIONAL. SINTESIS DE INFORMACION SOBRE ORGANISMOS INTERNACIONALES. m. Ministerio Asintos Exteriores, Direccion General de Cooperacion Tecnica Internacional, Madrid, Spain.
Continues: Spain. Direccion General de Cooperacion y Relaciones Economicas Internacionales. Sintesis de Informacion Sobre Organismos Internacionales.

STUDENT ACTION IN ENGINEERING. see *ENGINEERING — Mechanical Engineering*

378 US
▼**STUDENT TRAVELS.** 1992. 2/yr. free. (Council on International Educational Exchange) Marblehead Communications Inc., 376 Boylston St., Boston, MA 02116-3812. TEL 617-424-7700. FAX 617-737-7714. Ed. Robert Benchley. adv. contact: Kerri Ann Walsh. circ. 450,000.
Description: Covers student travel abroad for work and study.

STUDIES IN EDUCATIONAL ADMINISTRATION. see *EDUCATION — School Organization And Administration*

370.196 371.3 UN
STUDIES IN MATHEMATICS EDUCATION. French edition: Etudes sur l'Enseignement des Mathematiques. Spanish edition: Estudios en Educacion Matematica. (Text in English) 1980. irreg., no.8, 1992. 60 F. Unesco, 7 Place de Fontenoy, 75700 Paris, France. TEL 45-77-16-10. (Dist. in U.S. by: Unipub, 4611-F Assembly Dr., Lanham, MD 20706-4391) Ed. Robert Morris. circ. 1,500. (also avail. in microfiche; back issues avail.)
Description: Examines various ways of encouraging pupils to learn mathematics in school through activities outside the classroom or school building, such as mathematics clubs, fair and competitions.

378.391 UN ISSN 0081-895X
LB2338
STUDY ABROAD/ETUDES A L'ETRANGER/ESTUDIOS EN EL EXTRANJERO; international scholarships and courses. (Text in English, French, Spanish) 1949. biennial. $24. Unesco, 7-9 Place de Fontenoy, 75700 Paris, France. TEL 577-16-10. (Dist. in U.S. by: Unipub, 4611-F Assembly Dr., Lanham, MD 20706-4391)
—BLDSC (8501.000000); SWETS.

370.196 CN ISSN 1180-4734
SYNTHESIS. French edition: Synthese (ISSN 1180-4742) (Supplement avail.: International Education Magazine) (Editions in English, French) 1990. q. Can.$20($30) (foreign Can.$35). Canadian Bureau for International Education - Bureau Canadien de l'Education Internationale, 220 Laurier Ave., W., Ste. 1100, Ottawa, ON K1P 5Z9, Canada. TEL 613-237-4820. FAX 613-237-1073. TELEX 053-3255. Ed. Jennifer Humphries. bk.rev. circ. 1,400.

370 910.09 US
TEACHERS' GUIDE TO OVERSEAS TEACHING; a complete and comprehensive guide of English-language schools and colleges overseas. 1977. irreg. $19.95. Friends of World Teaching, Box 1049, San Diego, CA 92112-1049. TEL 619-275-4066. Ed. Louis A. Bajkai. adv.; bk.rev. circ. 5,000. **Document type:** directory.

THIRD WORLD RESOURCES; a quarterly review of resources from & about the Third World. see *BUSINESS AND ECONOMICS — International Development And Assistance*

370.196 910.09 US ISSN 0276-4717
TRANSITIONS ABROAD; the guide to learning, living, and working overseas. 1977. bi-m. $19.95. Transitions Publishing, 18 Hulst Rd., Box 1300, Amherst, MA 01004. TEL 413-256-0373. (Subscr. to: Dept., TRA, Box 3000, Denville, NJ 07834) Ed. Clayton A. Hubbs. adv.; bk.rev. circ. 15,000. (back issues avail.) **Indexed:** Curr.Lit.Fam.Plan.
Formerly (until 1985): Transitions.
Description: Resource guide for international travelers seeking work, study and special interest travel abroad.

EDUCATION — SCHOOL ORGANIZATION AND ADMINISTRATION

370.196 US
U S FOREIGN STUDENT MAGAZINE. 1990. bi-m. $3.50. International Family Company, Box 1742, Tempe, AZ 85281. TEL 602-966-0304. adv.; bk.rev. circ. 30,000.
  Description: Empasizes the forces that influence the welfare of current and potential incoming foreign students.

UNESCO. RECORDS OF THE GENERAL CONFERENCE. RESOLUTIONS. see *POLITICAL SCIENCE — International Relations*

UNESCO. REPORT OF THE DIRECTOR-GENERAL ON THE ACTIVITIES OF THE ORGANIZATION. see *POLITICAL SCIENCE — International Relations*

UNESCO AUSTRALIA. see *BUSINESS AND ECONOMICS — International Development And Assistance*

UNITED NATIONS ASSOCIATION IN CANADA. QUARTERLY BULLETIN. see *POLITICAL SCIENCE — International Relations*

370.196 II ISSN 0503-4663
UNITED SCHOOLS INTERNATIONAL. DOCUMENTS OF THE BIENNIAL CONFERENCE. 1961. irreg. free. United Schools International, c/o United Schools Organisation of India, USO House, USO Rd. 6, Special Institutional Area, New Delhi 110067, India. TEL 91-11-661103. FAX 91-11-6856283. Dir. Jiya Lal Jain. circ. 500. **Document type:** proceedings.

371.142 US
U.S. DEPARTMENT OF EDUCATION. OPPORTUNITIES FOR TEACHERS ABROAD. a. price varies. U.S. Department of Education, Washington, DC 20202. TEL 202-655-4000. (Subscr. to: Superintendent of Documents, Washington, DC 20402)
  Formerly: Opportunities Abroad for Teachers (ISSN 0078-5458)

370.196 850 IT ISSN 1121-0370
UNIVERSITA PER STRANIERI. ANNALI. 1981. s-a. L.100000 (foreign L.120000). Universita Italiana per Stranieri, Palazzo Gallenga, Piazza Fortebraccio, Perugia, Italy. TEL 075-57461. FAX 075-62014. TELEX 662079 UNSTRA I. Ed. Giorgio Spitella. **Document type:** academic/scholarly publication.

370.196 CN ISSN 1183-725X
UNIWORLD/UNIMONDE. (Text in English, French) 2/yr. free. Association of Universities and Colleges of Canada - Association des Universites et Colleges du Canada, 600-350 Albert, Ottawa, ON K1R 1B1, Canada. TEL 613-563-1236. FAX 613-563-9745.
  Description: Describes Canadian university activities in international development.

370.196 US
UP WITH PEOPLE REPORTS. 1971-1980, resumed 1988. s-a. free. Up with People, Inc., 1 International Ct., Broomfield, CO 80021-9806. TEL 303-438-7391. FAX 303-438-7302. Ed. Scott Johnson. illus.; circ. 60,000 (controlled). **Document type:** newsletter.
  Formerly (until 1980): Up with People News.
  Description: Contains news of the organization's international student program and other developments.

371.39 US ISSN 1046-2104
LB2375
VACATION STUDY ABROAD. 1947. a. $36.95. Institute of International Education, 809 United Nations Plaza, New York, NY 10017. TEL 212-984-5412. FAX 212-984-5385. TELEX TRT 175977. Ed. Sara Steen. **Document type:** directory.
  Supersedes: Learning Traveler. Vacation Study Abroad (ISSN 0271-1702); **Formerly:** Summer Study Abroad (ISSN 0081-9379)
  Description: Provides information on 1500 summer and short-term programs offered by US and foreign higher education institutions and private agencies.

VIEWS ON EDUCATION - NEWS OF EPISCOPAL COLLEGES. see *EDUCATION — Higher Education*

370.196 US ISSN 0116-5461
W C C I FORUM. 1987. s-a. $5 per no. World Council for Curriculum and Instruction, c/o School of Education, Indiana University, Bloomington, IN 47405. TEL 812-855-4702. FAX 812-855-3044. Eds. Helene Sherman, Nondita Mason. circ. 1,000. (back issues avail.)
  —BLDSC (9281.090000).
  Description: For the purpose of broadening international cooperation among educators.

370.196 CC
WENHUA JIAOLIU/CULTURAL EXCHANGE. (Text in Chinese) q. Zhejiang Sheng Waishi Bangongshi - Zhejiang Provincial Office of Foreign Affairs, 34 Tianmushan Lu, Hangzhou, Zhejiang 310007, People's Republic of China. TEL 887224. Ed. Wang Jiayang.

378 US ISSN 1043-8289
WHO'S WHO AMONG INTERNATIONAL STUDENTS IN AMERICAN UNIVERSITIES AND COLLEGES. 1988. a. $32.95. Research Services, Inc. (Norman), 1201 W. Main, Norman, OK 73069. TEL 405-329-8040. Ed. Dele T. Olasiji. circ. 5,000. (back issues avail.) **Document type:** directory.

060 US ISSN 0092-4261
AS36.W79
WOODROW WILSON INTERNATIONAL CENTER FOR SCHOLARS. ANNUAL REPORT. Key Title: Annual Report - Woodrow Wilson International Center for Scholars. 1970. a. free. Woodrow Wilson International Center for Scholars, 901 D St., S.W., Ste. 704, Washington, DC 20024-2518. illus. circ. 5,000. **Document type:** corporate report.

370.196 BA
WORKSHOP OF PEACE/MUNTADA AL-SALAAM. (Text in English) 1980. q. United Schools International, Arab Regional Office, P.O. Box 726, Bahrain. TEL 973-232576. FAX 973-272252. TELEX 9094 TARBIA BN. Eds. Rashid Sulaybikh, Jiya Lal Jain. adv.: B&W page 160 din. illus.
  Description: Dedicated to promoting peace and cooperation. Provides new of international educational issues, cooperative programs and other items of interest.

371.39 US
WORLD LEARNING. ANNUAL REPORT. 1960. a. free. World Learning, Kipling Rd., Box 676, Brattleboro, VT 05302-0676. TEL 802-257-7751. FAX 802-258-3163. circ. 8,000.
  Former titles: Experiment in International Living. Annual Report; Experiment in International Living. President's Report (ISSN 0071-3376)

WORLDVIEW MAGAZINE. see *BUSINESS AND ECONOMICS — International Development And Assistance*

370.196 US
THE YALE - CHINA REVIEW. 1979. 3/yr. $35. Yale China Association, Box 208223, Yale Sta., New Haven, CT 06520. TEL 203-432-0880. Ed. Allison Lee. adv. contact: Judith M. Collins. bk.rev. circ. 8,000. (back issues avail.)
  Formerly (until 1993): China Update.

370.196 UK ISSN 0144-7327
YOUTH EXCHANGE NEWS. 1980. 4/yr. free. Youth Exchange Centre, 10 Spring Gardens, London SW1A 2BN, England. TEL 071-389-4030. **Document type:** newsletter.
  Description: Touches on exchange programs, grants and seminars.

ZIELSPRACHE DEUTSCH; Zeitschrift fuer Unterrichtsmethodik und angewandte Sprachwissenschaft. see *LINGUISTICS*

EDUCATION — School Organization And Administration

371.2 615.53 US
A A C O M ORGANIZATIONAL GUIDE. 1980. a. $14. American Association of Colleges of Osteopathic Medicine, 6110 Executive Blvd., Ste. 405, Rockville, MD 20852. TEL 301-468-0990. Ed. Bonnie A. McCormack. circ. 110. **Document type:** directory.
  Description: Contains information on the organizational structure of the Association; including members of its councils, sections, committees, administrative staff and faculty in the 15 fully accredited US colleges of osteopathic medicine.

371.2 610 378 US ISSN 0360-7437
R712.A1
A A M C DIRECTORY OF AMERICAN MEDICAL EDUCATION. a. $50 to non-members; members $25; foreign $30. Association of American Medical Colleges, 2450 N St., Washington, DC 20037-1126. TEL 202-828-0416. FAX 202-828-1123. (reprint service avail. from UMI) **Document type:** directory.

370.193 UK ISSN 0266-6278
A C E BULLETIN. 1960. bi-m. £15 (Europe £18; elsewhere £25). Advisory Centre for Education (A C E) Ltd., 1B Aberdeen Studios, 22-24 Highbury Grove, London N5 2EA, England. TEL 44-71-354-8318. FAX 44-71-354-9069. Ed. Liz Allen. adv.; bk.rev.; abstr.; index. circ. 4,000. (back issues avail.) **Document type:** bulletin.
  —BLDSC (0573.781300).
  Former titles (until Sep. 1984): Where to Find Out More About Education; Where (ISSN 0043-4809)
  Description: Contains news, features, and guidelines for school governors and information sheets that reflect the parents' perspective on developments in education as well as digests of the latest books, pamphlets, journals, and reports on education.

A E C A RESOURCE BOOK SERIES. see *CHILDREN AND YOUTH — About*

371.2 FR ISSN 0222-674X
A F A E. 1979. 4/yr. 300 F. Association Francaise des Administrateurs de l'Education, 28 rue du General-Foy, 75008 Paris, France. TEL 42-93-12-01. FAX 42-94-11-98. Ed. Andre Lafond. bk.rev. circ. 1,500.

378 658 620 US ISSN 0736-7252
A P P A NEWSLETTER. (Association of Physical Plant Administrators) 1953. 8/yr. $40 includes Facilities Manager. A P P A: The Association of Higher Education Facilities Officers, 1446 Duke St., Alexandria, VA 22314-3492. TEL 703-684-1446. FAX 703-549-2772. Ed. Stephanie Gretchen. adv.; bk.rev.; charts; illus.; index. circ. 5,000. **Document type:** newsletter.
  —BLDSC (1568.990000).
  Description: Promotes excellence in the administration, care, operation, planning, and development of higher education facilities.

658 378 531.64 US
LB3223.3
A P P A: THE ASSOCIATION OF HIGHER EDUCATION FACILITIES OFFICERS. PROCEEDINGS OF THE ANNUAL MEETING. 1929. a. price varies. A P P A: The Association of Higher Education Facilities Officers, 1446 Duke St., Alexandria, VA 22314-3492. TEL 703-684-1446. FAX 703-549-2772. (Subscr. to: Box 1201, Alexander, VA 22313-1201) Ed. Medea Ranck. charts; illus. **Document type:** proceedings.
  Formerly (until 1992): Association of Physical Plant Administrators of Universities and Colleges. Proceedings of the Annual Meeting (ISSN 0738-3835)

371.2 US
A S B O ACCENTS. m. Association of School Business Officials, 11401 N. Shore Dr., Reston, VA 22090-4231. TEL 703-478-0405. FAX 703-478-0205. Ed. Robert L. Gluck. circ. 6,900. **Document type:** newspaper.

379.15 US ISSN 0001-2408
A S B S D BULLETIN. 1946. s-m. $25. Associated School Boards of South Dakota, Box 1211, Pierre, SD 57501. TEL 605-224-6293. FAX 605-224-6294. Ed. Gene Enck. adv.; bk.rev.; charts; film rev.; illus.; stat. circ. 2,800. **Document type:** bulletin.

371 US
A S C U S ANNUAL - A JOB SEARCH HANDBOOK FOR EDUCATORS.* 1966. a. $8 to non-members. Association for School, College and University Staffing, Inc., c/o High Shool, 1600 Dodge Ave., Ste. 5-330, Evanston, IL 60204. circ. 110,000.
  Formerly (until 1980): A S C U S Annual - Teaching Opportunities for You (ISSN 0066-9156)

EDUCATION — SCHOOL ORGANIZATION AND ADMINISTRATION

371   US   ISSN 0066-9164
A S C U S DIRECTORY OF MEMBERSHIP AND SUBJECT FIELD INDEX.* a. $20 to non-members. Association for School, College and University Staffing, Inc., c/o High School, 1600 Dodge Ave., Ste. 5-330, Evanston, IL 60204. circ. 1,500.

A S C U S STAFFER. (Association for School, College and University Staffing, Inc.) see *EDUCATION — Guides To Schools And Colleges*

371.2   US
A S S C NEWSLETTER. 1976. m. membership. Arkansas School Study Council, 255 Graduate Education Bldg., University of Arkansas, Box 428, Fayetteville, AR 72701. TEL 501-575-4207. Ed. Martin Schoppmeyer. circ. 650. (looseleaf format)
   Description: Research in school finance.

371.2   DK   ISSN 0106-0465
AARBOG FOR FOLKESKOLEN. 1978. a. DKK 275. (Danmarks Laererforening) Forlaget Kommuneinformation, Gyldenloevesgade 11, 3, DK-1600 Copenhagen V, Denmark. TEL 45-33-12-27-88. FAX 45-31-22-12-77. Ed. Lars Algreen Moeller. adv. contact: Theis Jans. bk.rev.
   Description: Presents complete information on all levels of the Danish school system, including South Schleswig, the Faroe Islands and Greenland.

ACADEMIC COLLECTIVE BARGAINING INFORMATION SERVICE. FACT SHEET. NEWSLETTER. see *EDUCATION — Higher Education*

371.2   CN   ISSN 0044-6300
ADMINISTRATIVE SCENE. 1968. m. Can.$20. (Saskatchewan Council on Educational Administration) Saskatchewan Teachers' Federation, Box 1108, 2317 Arlington Ave., Saskatoon, Sask. S7K 3N3, Canada. TEL 306-525-0368. circ. 400.
Indexed: Can.Educ.Ind.

371.2   IO   ISSN 0304-6117
ADMINISTRATOR. 1973. m. Rps.1500. Brawijaja University, Faculty of Public and Business Administation, Jalan Mayor Jendral Haryono 163, Malang, Indonesia. TEL 0341-51611. circ. 1,000. **Indexed:** E.I. **Document type:** academic/scholarly publication, bulletin.

371.2 378   US   ISSN 0744-7078
ADMINISTRATOR (MADISON); the management newsletter for higher education. 1982. s-m. $83. Magna Publications, Inc., 2718 Dryden Dr., Madison, WI 53704-3006. TEL 800-433-0499. FAX 608-249-0355. Ed. Pat Dyjak. bk.rev. circ. 1,600. (also avail. in diskette format; back issues avail.) **Document type:** newsletter.
   —CCC.
   Description: Management information for college administrators.

371.2   US
ADMINISTRATORS' COMPUTER LETTER. 1981. 12/yr. Charles Mann & Associates, Microcomputer Division, 55888 Yucca Trail, Box 2080, Yucca Valley, CA 92286-2080. TEL 619-365-9718. FAX 619-228-1567. Ed. Ray Burr. bk.rev. circ. 123,701.

371.2   US
ADMINISTRATORS NEWSLETTER. m. C M A Microcomputers, Box 2079, Yucca Valley, CA 92286-2079. TEL 619-365-9718. FAX 619-228-1567. Ed. Ray Burr. circ. 26,711. **Document type:** newsletter.

371 375   US   ISSN 0001-8430
LB3011
ADMINISTRATORS NOTEBOOK. 1952. 9/yr. $17 (Canada $19; elsewhere $21). University of Chicago, Midwest Administration Center, 5835 S. Kimbark Ave., Chicago, IL 60637. TEL 312-702-1565. Ed. Gregg Goldberg. charts. circ. 500. (also avail. in microfilm from UMI; reprint service avail. from UMI) **Indexed:** C.I.J.E., Cont.Pg.Educ., Educ.Admin.Abstr., Educ.Ind., SOMA. **Document type:** academic/scholarly publication.
   —BLDSC (0696.541000); UMI.

ADMISSIONS MARKETING REPORT. see *ADVERTISING AND PUBLIC RELATIONS*

AGENDA (NEW YORK, 1991); America's schools for the 21st century. see *EDUCATION*

371.6 658   US
AMERICAN SCHOOL AND HOSPITAL MAINTENANCE. 1978. a. Continental Communications (Bloomfield), 30 Hyde Rd., Bloomfield, NJ 07003. TEL 201-338-1315. adv. circ. 34,227.
   Description: Focuses on the renovation, maintenance, energy, and security of the physical plant and grounds.

370   US   ISSN 0003-0945
LB3205
AMERICAN SCHOOL & UNIVERSITY; facilities, purchasing and business administration. 1928. m. $65 (foreign $89). North American Publishing Co., 401 N. Broad St., Philadelphia, PA 19108. TEL 215-238-5300. FAX 215-238-5457. Ed. Joe Agron. adv.; bk.rev.; bibl.; charts; illus.; mkt.; pat.; tr.mk.; index. circ. 51,011. (also avail. in microform from UMI,PMC) **Indexed:** C.I.J.E., Consum.Ind., Cont.Pg.Educ., Educ.Ind., Mag.Ind. **Document type:** trade publication.
   —BLDSC (0856.430000); Faxon; UnCover; SWETS; UMI.
   Description: For administrators in school districts and colleges concerned with facilities operations and management.

379.15   US   ISSN 0003-0953
L11
AMERICAN SCHOOL BOARD JOURNAL. 1891. m. $48. National School Boards Association, 1680 Duke St., Alexandria, VA 22314. TEL 703-838-6722. FAX 703-683-7590. Ed. Gregg W. Downey. adv. contact: Marilee C. Rist. bk.rev. circ. 40,000. (also avail. in microform from BLH; reprint service avail. from UMI) **Indexed:** C.I.J.E., Cont.Pg.Educ., Educ.Admin.Abstr., Educ.Ind. **Document type:** trade publication.
   —BLDSC (0856.450000); Faxon; UnCover; SWETS; UMI.
   Supersedes: School Boards.

371.2   US   ISSN 0740-4565
AMERICAN UNIVERSITY STUDIES. SERIES 14. EDUCATION. 1984. irreg. Peter Lang Publishing, Inc., 62 W. 45th St., 4th Fl., New York, NY 10036. TEL 212-302-6740. Ed. Michael Flamini. **Document type:** academic/scholarly publication.
   —BLDSC (0858.078620).

379   GW
AMTLICHES SCHULBLATT FUER DEN REGIERUNGSBEZIRK MUENSTER. m. DM.24.80. Aschendorffsche Verlagsbuchhandlung, Soesterstr. 13, 48155 Muenster, Germany. TEL 0251-690-0. FAX 0251-690143. adv.; bk.rev. circ. 1,700. **Document type:** academic/scholarly publication.

370   GW   ISSN 0003-2204
AMTLICHES SCHULBLATT FUER DIE VOLKS-, REAL- UND BERUFSSCHULEN FUER DEN BEZIRKSREGIERUNG TRIER. ceased 1976. m. DM.22. Bezirks-Regierung, Schulabteilung, 5500 Trier 1, Germany.

371 379   US   ISSN 0077-9342
LB2826.N7
ANALYSIS OF SCHOOL FINANCES, NEW YORK STATE SCHOOL DISTRICTS. a. $2. Education Department, Fiscal Analysis and Services Unit, University of the State of New York, Education Bldg., Rm. 216, 89 Washington Ave., Albany, NY 12234. TEL 518-474-5213. (Co-sponsor: University of the State of New York)
   Description: Provides a perspective to staff in the Division of the Budget, the Legislature and the Education Department concerning school expenditures, state aid and local support.

ANDREANER; Schuelerzeitung am Gymnasium Andreanum. see *EDUCATION*

371.2   IT   ISSN 0391-6642
ANNALI DELLA PUBBLICA ISTRUZIONE. 1955. bi-m. L.52500 (effective 1993). Editoriale e Finanziaria Le Monnier S.P.A., Via A. Meucci 2, 50015 Grassina, Italy. (Subscr. to: Casella Postale 202, 50100 Florence, Italy) circ. 22,000.

371 379   US   ISSN 0066-8753
ASSOCIATED PUBLIC SCHOOLS SYSTEMS. YEARBOOK. 1951. a. $5. (Associated Public School Systems) Columbia University, Teachers College, 525 W. 120 St., New York, NY 10027. TEL 212-280-1754. circ. 1,000.

ASSOCIAZIONE PEDAGOGICA ITALIANA. BOLLETTINO; periodico d'informazione per la cultura pedagogica. see *EDUCATION — International Education Programs*

371.8   GW   ISSN 0076-1745
ASTA-PRESS. 1971. irreg. (Technische Universitaet Muenchen, Studentenvertretung) Asta-Tum, Tsingtauerstr. 66a, 81827 Munich, Germany. Ed. Heino Jahn. adv. circ. 10,000.
   Formerly: M S Z: Muenchener Studentenzeitung.

371.2   US   ISSN 1041-5432
ATHLETIC MANAGEMENT. 6/yr. free to qualified personnel. College Athletic Administrator, Inc., 438 W. State St., Ithaca, NY 14850-5220. TEL 607-272-0265. FAX 607-273-0701. Eleanor Frankel. adv.; circ. 25,973 (controlled). **Document type:** trade publication.
   Formerly (until 1988): College Athletic Management; Incorporates: Athletic Directory.
   Description: For key decision-makers at college and high school athletic departments. Provides information on how athletic managers can improve their operations, implement new programs and make efficient purchases with respect to equipment, training sullies, facilities and team travel.

371.2   AT   ISSN 0158-7447
AUSTRALIAN ADMINISTRATOR. 1980. bi-m. (Feb.-Dec.). Aus.$15. School of Education, Deakin University, Deakin University, Victoria 3217, Australia. TEL 052-471486. Ed. Dr. W.J. Smyth. circ. 1,000. (also avail. in microfilm from UMI) **Indexed:** Aus.Educ.Ind.

371.2   US
BECKLEY - CARDY QUARTERLY. 1988. q. Beckley - Cardy, Inc., One E. First St., Duluth, MN 55802. TEL 218-725-2234. FAX 218-725-2414. adv.: B&W or color page $3745; trim 8 1/2 x 10 7/8. circ. 200,000. **Document type:** catalog.

371   AG   ISSN 0067-7922
BIBLIOTECA DEL PLANEAMIENTO EDUCATIVO.* 1961. irreg. Ministerio de Cultura y Educacion, Departamento de Documentacion Informacion Educativa, Parera 55, Buenos Aires, Argentina.

379   SZ
BILDUNGSSTATISTIK. KLASSIFIKATIONSSCHEMA/STATISTIQUE SCOLAIRE. SCHEMA DE CLASSIFICATION. (Text in French and German) 1984. a. 6 SFr. Bundesamt fuer Statistik, Schwarztorstr. 96, CH-3003 Bern, Switzerland. TEL 031-3236011. FAX 031-3236061. **Document type:** government publication.
   Formerly: Klassifikationsschema der Schulstatistik.

379   SZ
BILDUNGSSTATISTIK DOKUMENTATION/STATISTIQUE SCOLAIRE. DOCUMENTATION. (Text in French and German) 1986. a. 5 SFr. Bundesamt fuer Statistik, Schwarztorstr. 96, CH-3003 Bern, Switzerland. TEL 031-3236011 FAX 031-3236061. **Document type:** government publication.
   Formerly: Dokumentation zu Schulstatistischen Erhebungen.

371.2   GW
BLICKPUNKT BILDUNG. 1966. 5/yr. DM.30. Deutscher Lehrerverband Hamburg, Papenstr. 18, 22089 Hamburg, Germany. TEL 040-255272. FAX 040-2505949. Ed. Helmut P. Hagge. adv.; bk.rev. circ. 4,000. (back issues avail.) **Document type:** trade publication.
   Formerly (until June 1989): Beitraege zur Schul und Bildungspolitik.

371.2 379.15   US
BOARDMEMBER.* 1947. 4/yr. $5. Louisiana School Boards Association, 7912 Summa Ave., Baton Rouge, LA 70809-3416. TEL 504-769-3191. Ed. Victor S. Hodgkins. adv.; bk.rev.; charts; illus.; stat.; index. circ. 2,800.
   Formerly (until 1984): Boardman (ISSN 0006-5358).

EDUCATION — SCHOOL ORGANIZATION AND ADMINISTRATION

370   GW   ISSN 0006-9582
BREMER SCHULBLATT. 1954. irreg. price varies. Senator fuer Bildung und Wissenschaft, Remberting 8-12, 28195 Bremen, Germany. TEL 0421-3612834. FAX 0421-3614176. TELEX 244804. abstr.; cum.index. circ. 800. (looseleaf format) **Document type:** government publication.
Description: Concerned with education in the cities of Bremen and Bremershaven. Includes decisions, regulations, laws and list of schools.

BRITISH JOURNAL OF EDUCATION AND WORK. see *EDUCATION — Teaching Methods And Curriculum*

378 371.2   US   ISSN 0147-877X
LB2341
BUSINESS OFFICER. 1967. m. membership. National Association of College and University Business Officers, 1 Dupont Circle, Ste. 500, Washington, DC 20036-1178. TEL 202-861-2500. FAX 202-861-2583. Ed. Donna J. Klinger. adv.; bk.rev. circ. 18,500. (processed) **Document type:** trade publication.
Formerly: College and University Business Officer (ISSN 0010-0919)
Description: News magazine of the association.

371.2   US
C A B E JOURNAL. 1979. bi-m. $60. Connecticut Association of Boards of Education, Inc., 309 Franklin Ave., Hartford, CT 06114-1851. TEL 203-296-8201. FAX 203-296-6719. Ed. Bonnie B. Carney. adv.; charts; illus.; stat. circ. 2,500. (tabloid format; back issues avail.)

371.2   CN
C A S E A - A C E A S NEWSLETTER. 1971. s-a. membership. Canadian Association for Studies in Educational Administration, 1 Stewart St., Ste. 205, Ottawa, ON K1N 6H7, Canada. TEL 613-230-3532. FAX 613-230-2746. Ed. W.R. Dolmage. circ. 250. **Document type:** newsletter.

371.2   AT   ISSN 0310-1878
C C E A NEWSLETTER. 1971. s-a. Aus.$10. Commonwealth Council for Educational Administration, University of New England, Armidale, N.S.W. 2351, Australia. TEL 067-73-2543. FAX 067-73-3363. TELEX 166050. Ed. Bernadette Taylor. bk.rev. circ. 6,500. (also avail. in microfiche) **Indexed:** ERIC. **Document type:** newsletter.

371.2   US
C S A NEWS. 1966. m. membership. Council of Supervisors and Administrators of the City of New York, Local 1, American Federation of School Administrators, AFL-CIO, 16 Court St., 4th Fl., Brooklyn, NY 11241. TEL 718-852-3000. FAX 718-403-0278. Ed. Charnia J. Adelman. bk.rev.; circ. 10,800 (controlled). **Document type:** newsletter.
Formerly: C S A Newsletter.

371.2   US   ISSN 0892-7855
C U P A NEWS; communications update for personnel administrators. 1973. s-m. $75 to non-members; members $50. College & University Personnel Association, 1233 20th St., N.W., Washington, DC 20036. TEL 202-429-0311. FAX 202-429-0149. Ed. David J. Uchic. circ. 5,500. **Document type:** newsletter.
Description: Keeps members current on the latest legislative, regulatory and judicial events affecting personnel management.

353.9   US   ISSN 0090-5593
LB2842.2
CALIFORNIA. TEACHERS RETIREMENT BOARD. STATE TEACHER'S RETIREMENT SYSTEM; ANNUAL REPORT TO THE GOVERNOR AND THE LEGISLATURE. Key Title: Annual Report to the Governor and Legislature - Teacher's Retirement Board. (Report Year Ends June 30.) 1963. a. Teachers Retirement Board, Box 15275-C, Sacramento, CA 95851. TEL 916-387-3700. Ed. James D. Mosman. circ. 1,500 (controlled).

371   US   ISSN 0008-1515
CALIFORNIA SCHOOL EMPLOYEE. 1932. m. (except Aug. & Sept.) $2.25 to non-members. California School Employees Association, Box 640, San Jose, CA 95106. TEL 408-263-8000. FAX 408-954-0948. Ed. Doug Crooks. adv.; bk.rev.; illus.; stat.; circ. 106,000 (controlled). (also avail. in microform from UMI; reprint service avail. from UMI) **Indexed:** Cal.Per.Ind. (1984-).

371.2 340   US   ISSN 0094-2057
KFC648.A59
CALIFORNIA SCHOOL LAW DIGEST. 1973. m. $125. Whitaker Newsletters Inc., 313 South Ave., Fanwood, NJ 07023. TEL 908-889-6336. FAX 908-889-6339. Ed. Anne Bittner. bk.rev.; cum.index. (looseleaf format; back issues avail.) **Document type:** newsletter.
—CCC.
Description: Covers news and administrative and court decisions pertaining to the law, the courts and California schools. Emphasizes decisions by the Professional Standards Review Board.

371.2   US   ISSN 1065-0857
CAMP DIRECTORS PURCHASING GUIDE. 1964. a. $42.50. Klevens Publications, Inc., 7600 Ave. V, Littlerock, CA 93543. TEL 805-944-4111. Ed. John Keller. adv.; bk.rev. circ. 14,736. (back issues avail.)
Description: Provides sources of material used in construction and operation of childrens' summer camps.

CAMPUS LAW ENFORCEMENT JOURNAL; professional publication for campus law enforcement administrators. see *CRIMINOLOGY AND LAW ENFORCEMENT*

CAMPUS SAFETY NEWSLETTER. see *PUBLIC HEALTH AND SAFETY*

371.2   CN   ISSN 0008-2813
CANADIAN ADMINISTRATOR. 1961. m. (Oct.-May). Can.$15 (typically set in Oct.). University of Alberta, Department of Educational Administration, Edmonton, Alta. T6G 2G5, Canada. TEL 403-492-5241. FAX 403-492-2024. Ed. R.G. McIntosh. bibl. circ. 1,700. (also avail. in microform from UMI; reprint service avail. from UMI) **Indexed:** C.I.J.E., Cont.Pg.Educ., Educ.Admin.Abstr. —UnCover; UMI.
Description: Aims to inform practitioners and scholars about the findings and implications of recent research, to alert them to emerging conditions and trends, and to facilitate the exchange of ideas and perspectives leading to more effective practices in the administration of schools and educational systems.
Refereed Serial

371.2   CN   ISSN 0228-0914
CANADIAN SCHOOL EXECUTIVE; magazine for leaders in education. 1981. 10/yr. Can.$39 (foreign Can.$69) (effective 1992). Xancor Canada Ltd., P.O. Box 48265 Bentall Centre, Vancouver, BC V7X 1A1, Canada. TEL 604-290-0072. FAX 604-739-8200. Ed. James Balderson. adv.; bk.rev. circ. 7,500. (also avail. in microfilm from MML; microfiche from MML)
Description: Dedicated to promoting effective leadership, management and instruction in schools.

340   US   ISSN 1059-4248
CASE CITATIONS. 1980. irreg. (2-3/yr.). $40 to non-members; members $35. National Organization on Legal Problems of Education, 3601 S.W. 29th St., Ste. 223, Topeka, KS 66614. TEL 913-273-3550. **Document type:** monographic series.

371.2 340   US
CASES IN POINT. 1990. 9/yr. free to members. National Association of Secondary School Principals, 1904 Association Dr., Reston, VA 22091. TEL 703-860-0200. FAX 703-476-5432. Ed. T.F. Koerner. circ. 43,000. **Document type:** newsletter.

371.2   US
CATALYST (CHICAGO); voices of Chicago school reform. 1990. 9/yr. Community Renewal Society, 332 S. Michigan Ave., Chicago, IL 60604-4301. TEL 312-427-4830. FAX 312-427-6130. Ed. Laura Washington; Pub. Roy Larson. circ. 15,000. **Document type:** newsletter.

CATALYST FOR CHANGE. see *EDUCATION — Teaching Methods And Curriculum*

344.07   US   ISSN 0737-2094
CHAPTER I HANDBOOK: UNDERSTANDING AND IMPLEMENTING THE PROGRAM. 1971. q. $195.50. Education Funding Research Council, 4301 Fairfax Dr. No. 875, Arlington, VA 22203-1627. TEL 703-528-1000. FAX 703-528-6060. Eds. Charles J. Edwards, Lisa Hayes-Sierra. (looseleaf format)
Former titles: Chapter I Handbook: Understanding and Implementing the New Regulations (ISSN 0275-0759); (until June 1982): Title I Handbook.
Description: Complete reference source on federal government's largest program of financial aid to educationally and economically disadvantaged children. Includes analysis of the law, amendments and all regulations.

371.2   US   ISSN 0164-8527
HV854
CHILD CARE INFORMATION EXCHANGE. 1978. bi-m. $35. Exchange Press Inc., Box 2890, Redmond, WA 98073-2890. TEL 206-883-9394. FAX 206-867-5217. Ed. Bonnie Neugebauer; Pub. Roger Neugebauer. adv. contact: Ann Warren. bk.rev.; cum.index: 1978-1993. circ. 25,000. (back issues avail.) **Indexed:** Educ.Ind., ERIC, PSI. **Document type:** trade publication.
—BLDSC (3172.927000); UnCover; UMI.

371.2 200   US
▼**CHRISTIAN SCHOOL ADMINISTRATOR.** 1993. q. Great River Publishing, Inc., 2600 Poplar Ave., Ste. 519, Memphis, TN 38112. TEL 901-324-1009. FAX 901-324-7824. Ed. David West. adv.: B&W page $1640, color page $2490; trim 8 1/2 x 11; adv. contact: Debbie Joyner. circ. 10,000. **Document type:** trade publication.

371.2 658.15   US
CITIZEN'S GUIDE TO SCHOOL DISTRICTS. a. $25. Washington Research Council, 906 S. Columbia, Ste. 350, Olympia, WA 98501. TEL 206-357-6643.
Formerly: Citizen's Guide to School District Budgeting.

371.6   FR
CLASSE. 10/yr. 12 rue Raymond-Poincare, 55800 Revigny, France. TEL 29-70-56-33. FAX 29-70-57-44. Ed. R.L. Martin. circ. 25,000.

378   US   ISSN 0195-3990
L901
COLLEGE AND UNIVERSITY ADMINISTRATORS DIRECTORY; guide to officers, deans, managers, and other administrative personnel in American colleges and universities. 1980. irreg., latest 1980. $160. Gale Research Inc., 835 Penobscot Bldg., Detroit, MI 48226. TEL 313-961-2242. FAX 3130961-6083. TELEX 810-221-7086. **Document type:** directory.
Description: Compendium of management and administrators in American colleges and universities.

642.58   US   ISSN 0738-7903
COLLEGE SERVICES ADMINISTRATION. 1978. bi-m. $35. National Association of College Auxiliary Services, Box 870, Staunton, VA 24401. TEL 703-885-8826. FAX 703-885-8355. Ed. Stan Clark. adv.; bk.rev. circ. 1,700.

371.2   AT   ISSN 0069-7087
COMMONWEALTH FOUNDATION OCCASIONAL PAPER (NO.). irreg.? Commonwealth Council for Educational Administration, University of New England, Armidale, N.S.W. 2351, Australia. TEL 067-732543. FAX 067-73-3363.

371.2   US   ISSN 0745-2233
COMMUNICATOR (ALEXANDRIA). m. $155 membership; institutions $95. National Association of Elementary School Principals, 1615 Duke St., Alexandria, VA 22314-3483. TEL 703-684-3345. FAX 703-548-6021. Ed. Betsy Berlin. circ. 29,000. (also avail. in microfilm; back issues avail.) **Document type:** newsletter.
Description: For elementary and middle school educators. Covers educational, legislative and other issues.

370.193   US
CONTACT (COLUMBIA). 1921. m. (Sep.-May). $3.50. Missouri Congress of Parents and Teachers Associations, State Office, 2101 Burlington, Columbia, MO 65202. TEL 314-474-8631. Ed. Coni Hadden. adv.; bk.rev. circ. 3,000. **Document type:** bulletin.
Formerly: Missouri Parent-Teacher.

COUNTY CARE. see *OCCUPATIONS AND CAREERS*

378 658　　　　　US
CRITICAL ISSUES IN FACILITIES MANAGEMENT. irreg., no.8, 1992. $30 to non-members; members $22. A P P A: The Association of Higher Education Facilities Officers, 1446 Duke St., Alexandria, VA 22314-3492. TEL 703-684-1446. FAX 703-549-2772. (Subscr. to: Box 1201, Alexandria, VA 22313-1201)

CURRICULUM AND TEACHING. see *EDUCATION — Teaching Methods And Curriculum*

371.2 375　　US　　ISSN 1063-3375
CURRICULUM PRODUCT NEWS; the direct response medium of the district level. 1972. m. (10/yr.) free. Educational Media, Inc. (Subsidiary of: Hanson Publishing Group, Inc.), 992 High Ridge Rd., Stamford, CT 06905. TEL 203-322-1300. FAX 203-329-9177. Ed. Jane Y. Woodward. adv.; bk.rev.; film rev.; play rev.; illus.; tr.lit. circ. 50,000. **Document type:** trade publication.
Former titles (until 1988): District Educator's Curriculum Product Review (ISSN 1052-2085); Curriculum Product Review (ISSN 0273-7418)

371.002　　DK　　ISSN 0109-3584
DEN DANSKE SKOLEHAANDBOG (YEAR). 1042. a. Kroghs Forlag AS, Chr. Hansensvej 3, DK-7100 Vejle, Denmark. TEL 45-75-82-39-00. FAX 45-75-82-32-71. adv.: B&W page DKK 3700, color page DKK 6900. circ. 5,000.

370　　GW　　ISSN 0011-8311
DIE DEMOKRATISCHE SCHULE.* 1954. m. DM.12($5) (Gewerkschaft Erziehung und Wissenschaft, Landesverband Bayern) Elwi-Verlag, Fuessener Str. 2, 8952 Marktoberdorf, Germany. Ed. Wolfgang Mischka.

371.2　　US　　ISSN 1049-3255
THE DEPARTMENT CHAIR; a newsletter for academic administrators. 1990. q. $69 (effective June 1992). Anker Publishing Company, Inc., 176 Ballville Rd., Box 249, Bolton, MA 01740-0249. TEL 508-779-6190. FAX 508-779-6296. Ed. James D. Anker. adv.; bk.rev. circ. 5,000. (back issues avail.) **Document type:** newsletter.
Description: Contains original articles, news, and resources for department chairs, division heads, and deans for any discipline at four- or two-year schools.
Refereed Serial

371.2 617.8　　US
DIRECTORY OF DENTAL EDUCATORS. 1966. biennial. $40 to non-members; members $30. American Association of Dental Schools, 1625 Massachusetts Ave., N.W., Washington, DC 20036-2212. TEL 202-667-9433. (diskette format) **Document type:** directory.
Former titles: Directory of Dental and Allied Dental Educators (ISSN 0271-8677); Directory of Dental Educators (ISSN 0090-0141); (until 1971): Directory of Dental Educators in the United States and Canada.
Description: Contains faculty names, rank, discipline, and title for full- and part-time faculty at US and Canadian, and Advanced Dental Education Institutions, and summary statistics.

371.2　　US
DIRECTORY OF MONTANA SCHOOLS. 1980. a. $6.50. Office of Public Instruction, State Capitol, Box 202501, Helena, MT 59620-2501. TEL 406-444-3095. (Orders to: Advanced Litho, 226 Ninth Ave. S., Great Falls, MT 59405-4084. TEL 406-453-0393; 406-761-1555) Ed. Sanna Kiesling. **Document type:** government publication, directory.

371.0025　　US
DIRECTORY OF NONPUBLIC SCHOOLS AND ADMINISTRATORS, NEW YORK STATE. a. $2.50. Education Department, Instruction & Program Development, Education Bldg. Annex, Rm. 381, Albany, NY 12234. TEL 518-474-7082. FAX 518-474-4351. circ. controlled. **Document type:** government publication, directory.

371　　US
DIRECTORY OF ORGANIZATIONS IN EDUCATIONAL MANAGEMENT. 1968. irreg. (approx. biennial) 8th ed., 1989. $6.50. E R I C Clearinghouse, c/o University of Oregon, 1787 Agate St., Eugene, OR 97403. TEL 503-346-5044. Ed. Stuart C. Smith. index. circ. 1,500. (also avail. in microfiche from EDR) **Document type:** directory.
Former titles: Directory of Organizations and Researchers in Educational Management; Directory of Organizations and Personnel in Educational Management (ISSN 0070-6035); Directory of Organizations and Personnel in Educational Administration.

378.1　　US
DIRECTORY OF PUBLIC SCHOOLS AND ADMINISTRATORS, NEW YORK STATE. 1977. a. $2.50. Education Department, Instruction & Program Development, Education Bldg. Annex, Rm. 381, Albany, NY 12234. TEL 518-474-7965. FAX 518-474-4351. (back issues avail.) **Document type:** government publication, directory.
Formerly: Directory of New York State Public Schools and Administrators.

371.2　　IT　　ISSN 0392-2812
DIRIGENTI SCUOLA. 1985. bi-m. L.37000. Editrice La Scuola S.p.A., Via Cadorna 11, 25186 Brescia, Italy. TEL 030-29931. Ed. Remo Bernacchia.
Formerly: Direzione e Scuola.

371.22　　US
E R S BULLETIN; a monthly summary of research, data, and information for school administrators and board members. 1973. m. price varies. Educational Research Service, 2000 Clarendon Blvd., Arlington, VA 22201-2908. FAX 703-243-1985. Ed. Deborah Gough. bk.rev.; abstr.; index. circ. 2,700. **Document type:** trade publication, bulletin.

658.15　　UK　　ISSN 0272-7757
LC65
ECONOMICS OF EDUCATION REVIEW. 1982. 4/yr. £148($230) (effective 1994). Elsevier Science Ltd., Pergamon, P.O. Box 800, Kidlington, Oxford OX5 1DX, England. TEL 44-865-843000. FAX 44-865-843010. (Subscr. in U.S. and Canada to: Elsevier Science, 660 White Plains Rd., Tarrytown, NY 10591-5153. TEL 914-524-9200. FAX 914-333-2444) Ed. Elchanan Cohn. adv.; bk.rev.; bibl.; index. circ. 525. (also avail. in microfilm from UMI; back issues avail.) **Indexed:** C.I.J.E., Cont.Pg.Educ., Curr.Cont., Educ.Tech.Abstr., J.of Econ.Lit., Mult.Ed.Abstr., Stud.Wom.Abstr. **Document type:** academic/scholarly publication.
—BLDSC (3656.990000); Faxon; SWETS; UMI. CCC.
Description: Publishes theoretical, empirical and policy-oriented research addressing the role of economic analysis in the understanding and solution of educational problems and issues.
Refereed Serial

379 610　　UK　　ISSN 0265-1602
EDUCATION AND HEALTH. 1983. 5/yr. £9.20. Schools Health Education Unit, University of Exeter, School of Education, Heavitree Rd., Exeter EX1 2LU, England. TEL 0392-264722. FAX 0392-264736. Ed. John W. Balding. adv.; bk.rev.; circ. 12,000 (controlled). **Indexed:** Cont.Pg.Educ. **Document type:** trade publication.
—BLDSC (3661.187000).
Description: For teachers and health-care professionals.

371.2　　UK　　ISSN 0964-5292
▼**EDUCATION ECONOMICS.** 1993. s-a. $88 to individuals; institutions $242 (effective 1994). Carfax Publishing Co., P.O. Box 25, Abingdon, Oxon. OX14 3UE, England. TEL 44-235-555335. FAX 44-235-553559. (N. America subscr. to: Carfax Publishing Co., Box 2025, Dunnellon, FL 34430-2025) Ed. Geraint Johnes. adv.; bk.rev.; index. (also avail. in microfiche; back issues avail.) **Document type:** academic/scholarly publication.
—BLDSC (3661.251000); SWETS.

371.2　　UK　　ISSN 0013-1296
EDUCATION EQUIPMENT. 1959. 11/yr. £33 (foreign £55). Bouverie Publishing Company Ltd., 131-135 Temple Chambers, Temple Ave., London EC4Y 0DT, England. TEL 071-583-3030. FAX 071-583-6481. Ed. Garry Parker. adv.; bk.rev.; illus.; circ. 13,394 (controlled). (also avail. in microform from UMI; reprint service avail. from UMI) **Indexed:** Educ.Tech.Abstr. **Document type:** trade publication.
Description: Geared toward those who influence and administer the purchase of equipment and services for senior education.

371.3　　UK　　ISSN 0046-1415
EDUCATION EQUIPMENT SELECTOR. 1966. 4/yr. A G B Publications Ltd., Audit House, Field End Rd., Ruislip, Middx. HA4 9LT, England. TEL 01-868-4499. FAX 01-429-3117. TELEX 926726. adv.; circ. controlled.
—CCC.

371.2　　US
EDUCATION FORWARD. 1948. m. (Aug.-May). free to Wisconsin educators and interested persons. Department of Public Instruction, 125 S. Webster St., Madison, WI 53702. TEL 608-266-4499. Ed. Mark Ibach. tr.lit.; index. circ. 17,100. (tabloid format; back issues avail.)
Former titles (until 1983): Wisconsin. Department of Public Instruction. Newsletter (ISSN 0148-5040); Wisconsin Department of Public Instruction. Administrative Newsletter.

379　　US　　ISSN 0273-4443
EDUCATION FUNDING NEWS. 1971. 50/yr. $287. Education Funding Research Council, 4301 Fairfax Dr. No. 875, Arlington, VA 22203-1627. TEL 703-528-1000. FAX 703-528-6060. Eds. Lisa Hayes, Jeanne Williams. **Document type:** newsletter.
—CCC.
Description: Details private and federal sources of financial aid and technical assistance for elementary and secondary schools and educational organizations. Provides analyses of pending legislation, funding deadlines, new program regulations, program requirements and major court decisions affecting education.

371.2　　CN　　ISSN 0843-1779
EDUCATION LEADER; news and views on education. 1967. s-m. Can.$59. British Columbia School Trustees Association, 1155 W. 8th Ave., Vancouver, BC V6H 1C5, Canada. TEL 604-734-2721. FAX 604-732-4559. Ed. Jennifer Gray-Grant. adv.; bk.rev.; index. circ. 7,000. (tabloid format; back issues avail.)
Formerly (until 1987): British Columbia School Trustees Association. Newsletter (ISSN 0381-5978)
Description: Provides information about broad curriculum and policy issues and developments, and the latest trends in research.

371.2　　US　　ISSN 1071-7420
EDUCATION PERSONNEL NEWS. m. $75. Nyper Publications, Box 662, Latham, NY 12110. TEL 518-786-1654. FAX 518-456-8582. Ed. Harvey Randall. bk.rev. (back issues avail.) **Document type:** newsletter.
Description: Reports on matters and news of concern to education administrators, teacher union leaders and attorneys representing school districts.

370　　CN
EDUCATION TODAY. 1969. 5/yr. Can.$10.70 (foreign Can.$12). Ontario Public School Board's Association, 439 University Ave., Ste. 1850, Toronto, ON M5G 1Y8, Canada. TEL 416-340-2540. FAX 416-340-7571. Ed. Heather Dion. adv.; bk.rev.; circ. 3,000 (paid); 500. (also avail. in microform from UMI; reprint service avail. from UMI) **Indexed:** Can.Educ.Ind., CM , Curr.Cont. **Document type:** academic/scholarly publication.
—UMI.
Former titles: Ontario Today (ISSN 0843-5081); Ontario Education (ISSN 0030-2902)
Description: For teachers, principals, school boards, provincial education officials, school trustees and parents who need to know the new developments in education and fresh opinions about what these mean for the school system and the education profession.

EDUCATION — SCHOOL ORGANIZATION AND ADMINISTRATION

371.2 UK ISSN 0140-0428
EDUCATIONAL ADMINISTRATION AND HISTORY MONOGRAPHS. 1973. irreg., no.18, 1990. price varies. University of Leeds, Museum of the History of Education, Parkinson Court, Leeds LS2 9JT, England. TEL 0532-431751. Eds. P.H. Gosden, W.B. Stephens. **Document type:** monographic series.

378 371.2 US ISSN 0013-161X
LB2805
EDUCATIONAL ADMINISTRATION QUARTERLY. 1964. q. $45 to individuals (foreign $51); institutions $130 (foreign $136). (University Council for Educational Administration) Corwin Press, Inc. (Subsidiary of: Sage Publications, Inc.), 2455 Teller Rd., Thousand Oaks, CA 91320. TEL 805-499-0721. FAX 805-499-0871. (And: Sage Publications, Ltd., 6 Bonhill St., London EC2A 4PU, England) Ed. James G. Cibulka. adv.: B&W page $225. bk.rev.; charts. (also avail. in microform from UMI; back issues avail.; reprint service avail. from UMI,ISI) **Indexed:** C.I.J.E., Cont.Pg.Educ., Curr.Cont., Educ.Admin.Abstr., Educ.Ind., Educ.Tech.Abstr., Mid.East: Abstr.& Ind., Mult.Ed.Abstr., Sage Pub.Admin.Abstr., SOMA, SSCI.
—BLDSC (3661.362000); Faxon; UnCover; SWETS; UMI. **CCC.**
Description: Disseminates latest knowledge about research and practice in educational administration. *Refereed Serial*

EDUCATIONAL BUILDING DIGEST. see *BUILDING AND CONSTRUCTION*

EDUCATIONAL DEALER. see *BUSINESS AND ECONOMICS — Trade And Industrial Directories*

371.2 UK ISSN 0263-211X
EDUCATIONAL MANAGEMENT & ADMINISTRATION. 1972. 4/yr. £50 (Europe £52; elsewhere £56). (British Educational Administration Society) Longman Group UK Ltd., Westgate House, 6th Fl., The High, Harlow, Essex CM20 1YR, England. TEL 0279-442601. FAX 0279-444501. Ed. Michael Locke. adv.; bk.rev.; index, cum.index: 1972-1975. circ. 2,300. (also avail. in microform from UMI; reprint service avail. from UMI) **Indexed:** C.I.J.E., Cont.Pg.Educ., Educ.Admin.Abstr., Educ.Tech.Abstr., High.Educ.Curr.Aware.Bull., SOMA. **Document type:** academic/scholarly publication.
—BLDSC (3661.442000); UnCover; SWETS. **CCC.**
Formerly (until 1982): Educational Administration (ISSN 0305-7496)
Description: Examines educational administration and management in the widest sense, especially regarding school management and administrative policy at all levels. Also provides critical discussions, accounts of new methods, developments and controversial issues as well as research reports. *Refereed Serial*

379.15 340 US
EDUCATIONEWS. 1972. s-m. $75. New York State School Boards Association, Inc., 119 Washington Ave., Albany, NY 12210. FAX 518-465-3481. circ. 7,000. **Document type:** newspaper.
Incorporates: New York State School Boards Association. Legislative Bulletin.

EINHARD INTERN; Schulzeitschrift des staedtischen Einhard-Gymnasiums Aachen. see *CHILDREN AND YOUTH — About*

371.2 US
EMPLOYERS NEGOTIATING SERVICE. 1967. s-m. $159. E F R Corp., Box 385, Pt. Richey, FL 34673-0385. Ed. Dr. Eric Rhodes. bk.rev.; index. circ. 1,000. (looseleaf format)
Formerly: Educators Negotiating Service (ISSN 0046-1571)

ENGAGEMENT; Zeitschrift fuer Erziehung und Schule. see *EDUCATION — Teaching Methods And Curriculum*

371.2 US ISSN 0882-3863
LC214.2
EQUITY AND CHOICE. 1984. 3/yr. $24 to individuals (foreign $30); institutions $60 (foreign $66). Corwin Press, Inc. (Subsidiary of: Sage Publications, Inc.), 2455 Teller Rd., Thousand Oaks, CA 91320. TEL 805-499-0721. FAX 805-499-0871. (And: Sage Publications, Ltd., 6 Bonhill St., London EC2A 4PU, England) (Co-sponsors: The Institute for Responsive Education; The Center on Families, Communities, Schools, and Children's Learning) Eds. Owen Heeleen, Scott Thompson. adv.: B&W page $225. bk.rev. (back issues avail.)
—BLDSC (3794.758000); UnCover.
Description: Forum for the exchange of ideas, insights, and practices among those working to increase educational quality. Covers developments in parent choice, desegregation, parent involvement, bilingual and multicultural education, and school-community relations.

ERWACHSENENBILDUNG IN OESTERREICH. see *EDUCATION — Adult Education*

371.2 US ISSN 0161-9500
LB2832.2 CODEN: EXEREA
EXECUTIVE EDUCATOR. 1979. m. $53. National School Boards Association, 1680 Duke St., Alexandria, VA 22314. TEL 703-838-6722. FAX 703-683-7590. Ed. Gregg W. Downey. adv. contact: Marilee C. Rist. circ. 18,000. (also avail. in microfiche from UMI; reprint service avail. from UMI) **Indexed:** C.I.J.E. **Document type:** trade publication.
—BLDSC (3836.213900); Faxon; UnCover; UMI.

378 658 US ISSN 0882-7249
FACILITIES MANAGER. 1985. q. $40 includes A P P A Newsletter. A P P A: The Association of Higher Education Facilities Officers, 1446 Duke St., Alexandria, VA 22314-3492. TEL 703-684-1446. FAX 703-549-2772. Ed. Steve Glazner. adv.; bk.rev.; charts; illus.; index. circ. 5,000.
—BLDSC (3863.455800).
Description: Promotes excellence in the administration, care, operation, planning and development of higher education facilities. Covers new products, resource management and data bases.

658.15 378 CN ISSN 0823-5872
LB2342.2.C3
FINANCIAL POSITION OF ONTARIO UNIVERSITIES. a. Council of Ontario Universities, 444 Yonge St., Ste. 203, Toronto, Ont. M5B 2H4, Canada. TEL 416-979-2165. FAX 416-979-8635.

658.15 378 CN
FINANCIAL REPORT OF ONTARIO UNIVERSITIES. a. Can.$30. Council of Ontario Universities, 444 Yonge St., Ste. 203, Toronto, Ont. M5B 2H4, Canada. TEL 416-979-2165. FAX 416-979-8635.

379 US ISSN 0733-8007
FLORIDA P T A BULLETIN. 1927. 7/yr. $5. Florida Congress of Parents and Teachers, 1747 Orlando Central Parkway, Orlando, FL 32809. TEL 407-855-7604. Ed. Marlene Carls. adv.; bk.rev. circ. 4,000. **Document type:** bulletin.

371.2 US
FORTNIGHTER. 1971. fortn. membership. Michigan Association of School Administrators, 421 W. Kalamazoo St., Lansing, MI 48933. TEL 517-371-5250. FAX 517-371-9093. Ed. Gerard E. Keidel. circ. 1,850. (looseleaf format)

379.6 GW
FRANKFURTER LEHRERZEITUNG. 1980. bi-m. membership. Gewerkschaft Erziehung und Wissenschaft, Bezirksverband Frankfurt, Bleichstr. 38A, 60313 Frankfurt, Germany. TEL 069-291818. adv.; bk.rev. circ. 4,000. (back issues avail.)
Description: Covers the activities of the teacher's union and the school board in Frankfurt.

371.2 GW ISSN 0344-2101
GANZTAGSSCHULE. 1961. q. DM.24. Ganztagsschulverband Gemeinnuetzige Gesellschaft Tagesheimschule e.V., Quellhofstr. 140, 34127 Kassel, Germany. TEL 0561-85077. adv. (back issues avail.) **Document type:** newsletter.

371 US
GEORGIA CONGRESS OF PARENTS AND TEACHERS. ANNUAL LEADERSHIP TRAINING CONFERENCE. WORKSHOP FOR P T A LEADERS. a. $3. University of Georgia, Center for Continuing Education, Athens, GA 30602. TEL 404-542-1725. circ. 700.
Formerly: Georgia Congress of Parents and Teachers. Annual Summer Institute. Handbook for P T A Leaders (ISSN 0072-1220)

GOETIKUSS. see *EDUCATION*

371.2 301 378 350 PH ISSN 0115-3110
LH7.C29
GRADUATE SCHOOL JOURNAL. (Text in English) 1976. a. P.20($3) Catanduanes State Colleges Graduate School, Virac, Catanduanes, Philippines. Ed. Susan T. Santelices. bk.rev. circ. 1,000. (back issues avail.)

371.2 340 US
GRANTS FOR SCHOOL DISTRICTS MONTHLY HOTLINE. 1989. m. $83 (effective 1993). Quinlan Publishing Co., Inc., 23 Drydock Ave., Boston, MA 02210-2387. TEL 617-542-0048; 800-229-2084. FAX 617-345-9646. index. (back issues avail.) **Document type:** newsletter.
Description: Information on available federal and foundation grants, schools programs and business partnerships throughout the country, of interest to school administrators, grants writers, district officials and superintendents.

GRAPEVINE (NORMAL); state appropriations for higher education; state tax legislation; legislation affecting education beyond the high school. see *EDUCATION — Higher Education*

371.6 UK ISSN 0260-0471
GREAT BRITAIN. DEPARTMENT OF EDUCATION AND SCIENCE. ARCHITECTS AND BUILDING BRANCH. BROADSHEETS. 1980. irreg. free. Department of Education and Science, Architects and Building Branch, Elizabeth House, York Rd., London SE1 7PH, England. Ed. J.M. Brown. circ. 2,000.
—BLDSC (2349.103200). **CCC.**

371.6 UK ISSN 0072-5870
GREAT BRITAIN. DEPARTMENT OF EDUCATION AND SCIENCE. BUILDING BULLETINS. 1955; N.S. 1964. irreg. price varies. (Department of Education and Science) H.M.S.O., P.O. Box 276, London SW8 5DT, England. **Document type:** bulletin, government publication.
—**CCC.**

371 US ISSN 0072-8101
GUIDE FOR PLANNING EDUCATIONAL FACILITIES.* 1949. triennial. $45. Council of Educational Facility Planners, 5880 Sawmill Rd., Ste. 200, Dublin, OH 43017-1592. TEL 614-442-1811. index.
Formerly: Guide for Planning School Plants.

379 US ISSN 0275-8393
LB2805
GUIDE TO FEDERAL FUNDING FOR EDUCATION. 1975. a. (plus m. supplement: Grant Updates). $248. Education Funding Research Council, 4301 Fairfax Dr., No. 875, Arlington, VA 22203-1627. TEL 703-528-1000. FAX 703-528-6060. Ed. Jeanne Williams. (looseleaf format)
—**CCC.**
Former titles: Federal Funding Guide for Education; Federal Funding Guide for Elementary and Secondary Education (ISSN 0095-3342)
Description: Details more than 230 federal aid programs available to school districts, colleges and universities, state education departments and non-profit groups. Provides specific information on eligibility requirements, outlook for funding, application deadlines, allowable uses of funds and program contacts (including telephone numbers).

EDUCATION — SCHOOL ORGANIZATION AND ADMINISTRATION

370 US ISSN 0732-3034
U408.3
GUIDE TO THE EVALUATION OF EDUCATIONAL EXPERIENCES IN THE ARMED SERVICES. (In 4 vols.) 1946. biennial (plus s-a. updates). $19.95 per vol.; 4 vol.-set $75. American Council on Education, Center for Adult Learning and Educational Credentials, One Dupont Circle, Washington, DC 20036-1193. TEL 202-939-9470. FAX 202-775-8578. (Dist. by: Oryx Press, 4041 N. Central at Indian School, Phoenix, AZ 85012-3397. TEL 800-279-6799) Ed. Eugene Sullivan. circ. 20,000. **Document type:** directory.
Description: Standard reference work for recognizing learning acquired in military life. Lists and describes courses offered by the military.

373 UK ISSN 0957-8714
HEADLINES (CAMBRIDGE). 1989. 3/yr. free. (Secondary Heads Association) Hobsons Publishing plc., Bateman St., Cambridge CB2 1LZ, England. TEL 0223-354551. FAX 0223-323154. TELEX 81546-HOBCAM-G. adv. contact: Ollie Cox. bk.rev. circ. 9,000.

HELLER REPORT ON EDUCATION TECHNOLOGY AND TELECOMMUNICATIONS MARKETS. see *BUSINESS AND ECONOMICS — Marketing And Purchasing*

371.2 US ISSN 0735-0031
HERE'S HOW. 1982. 6/yr. $155 membership; institutions $95. National Association of Elementary School Principals, 1615 Duke St., Alexandria, VA 22314-3483. TEL 703-684-3345. FAX 703-548-6021.
—BLDSC (4300.025500).

371.2 GW
HESSISCHE LEHRERZEITUNG. Short title: H L Z. 1947. m. DM.21. Landesverband Hessen, Gewerkschaft Erziehung und Wissenschaft (G E W), Zimmerweg 12, 60325 Frankfurt a.M., Germany.

371 US
HOLMES GROUP FORUM. 1987. 3/yr. free. Holmes Group, 501 Erickson Hall, Michigan State University, E. Lansing, MI 48824-1034. TEL 517-353-3874. FAX 517-353-6393. Ed. Kathleen Devaney. circ. 10,000. (back issues avail.)
Description: Promotes teacher education reform.

379.15 US ISSN 0019-0586
I S B A JOURNAL. 1955. q. $18. Indiana School Boards Association, One N. Capitol, Ste. 1215, Indianapolis, IN 46204. TEL 317-639-0330. FAX 317-639-3591. Ed. Katherine A. Hunter. adv.; charts; illus.; stat. circ. 3,000. (tabloid format) **Document type:** academic/scholarly publication.
Formerly: H S B J Journal.

371.2 US ISSN 0019-221X
ILLINOIS SCHOOL BOARD JOURNAL. 1934. bi-m. $12. Illinois Association of School Boards, 1209 S. Fifth St., Springfield, IL 62703. TEL 217-528-9688. FAX 217-528-2831. Ed. G.R. Glaub. adv. contact: Diane Cape. bk.rev.; charts; illus.; index. circ. 8,500.

INDEPENDENT EDUCATION. see *EDUCATION — Higher Education*

371 UK
INDEPENDENT SCHOOLS YEARBOOK. 1991. a. £19.99. A. & C. Black (Publishers) Ltd., Howard Rd., Eaton Socon, Huntingdon, Cambs. PE19 3EZ, England. TEL 0480-212666. FAX 0480-405014. TELEX 32524-ACBLAC-G. Ed. G. Harries. adv.; index. **Document type:** academic/scholarly publication.
—BLDSC (4375.915000). CCC.
Formed by the merger of (1986-1991): Independent Schools Yearbook. Girls' Schools (ISSN 0951-5909); Which was formerly (1906-1985): Girls' School Year Book (ISSN 0072-4564); (1986-1991): Independent Schools Yearbook. Boys' Schools, Co-educational Schools and Preparatory Schools (ISSN 0951-5917); Which was formerly (1935-1985): Public and Preparatory Schools Yearbook (ISSN 0079-7537)
Description: Contains full details of all the schools in the Headmasters' Conference, Girls' Schools Association, the Incorporated Association of Preparatory Schools, Independent Schools Association Incorporated, and the Society of Headmasters and Headmistresses of Independent Schools.

371.2 US
INDIANAGRAM. vol.8, 1978. m. membership. Indiana Association of School Principals, Box 503250, 8091 Center Run Dr., Indianapolis, IN 46250-8250. TEL 317-576-5400. FAX 317-576-5408. Dir. F. Edward Wall. bk.rev. circ. 2,000. **Document type:** newsletter.
Formerly: Indiana Secondary School Administrators. Newsletter.

658.15 US ISSN 1057-7394
LB2829.2
INFLATION MEASURES FOR SCHOOLS AND COLLEGES. a. Research Associates of Washington, 2605 Klingle Rd., N.W., Washington, DC 20008. TEL 202-966-3326.
Formed by the 1991 merger of: Elementary - Secondary School Price Indexes (ISSN 1057-9915) & Higher Education Price Indexes Update (ISSN 1051-2977); Which were formerly (until 1989): Higher Education Prices and Price Indexes. Supplement (ISSN 0148-0634)

378.3 US
INFORMATION DIGEST OF POSTSECONDARY EDUCATION IN IOWA. 1967. a. $10. College Student Aid Commission, 914 Grand Ave., Ste. 201, Des Moines, IA 50309. TEL 515-281-3501. Ed. Keith Greiner. stat. circ. 1,000.
Former titles (until 1992): Iowa. College Student Aid Commission. Annual Data Digest Report; (until 1991): Iowa. College Student Aid Commission. Annual Report; And: Iowa. College Aid Commission. Annual Report; (until 1986): Iowa. College Aid Commission. Biennium Report; (until 1978): Iowa. Higher Education Facilities Commission. Biennium Report; State of Iowa Scholarships, Tuition Grants. Biennium Report (ISSN 0091-3588).

371.2 US ISSN 1042-413X
LC1567
INITIATIVES. 1938. q. $40. National Association for Women in Education, 1325 18th St., N.W., No. 210, Washington, DC 20036-6511. TEL 202-659-9330. FAX 202-457-0946. Ed. Patricia Farrant. adv.; bk.rev.; bibl. circ. 3,000. (also avail. in microform from UMI; reprint service avail. from UMI) **Indexed:** C.I.J.E., Educ.Admin.Abstr., Educ.Ind., ERIC, Pers.Lit. **Document type:** academic/scholarly publication.
—BLDSC (4514.326000); Faxon; UnCover; UMI.
Former titles (until 1988): National Association for Women Deans, Administrators and Counselors. Journal (ISSN 0094-3460); National Association of Women Deans and Counselors. Journal (ISSN 0027-870X)
Description: Covers subjects of interest to women in higher education, with emphasis on topics not widely covered elsewhere in the professional and popular literature.
Refereed Serial

370 378 AT ISSN 0313-3249
INSTEAD. 1970. irreg. free. Western Australian Institute of Educational Administration, c/o West Ed Media, 296 Vincent St., Leederville, W.A. 6007, Australia. Ed. C.W. Rielly. circ. 500. (back issues avail.)

371.2 370.196 AT ISSN 1039-8333
▼**INTERNATIONAL DIRECTIONS IN EDUCATION;** an independent policy advisory service for leaders in education. 1992. 2/yr. Commonwealth Council for Educational Administration, University of New England, Armidale, N.S.W. 2351, Australia. TEL 067-732543. FAX 067-733363. TELEX 166050. Ed. Debra Brydon. circ. 8,500.

371.2 370.176 US ISSN 1053-1750
INTERNATIONAL EDUCATION FORUM. 1981. s-a. $16 (overseas $23.50) (effective 1994). Washington State University Press, Pullman, WA 99164-5910. TEL 509-335-3518. FAX 509-335-8568. Ed. G. Woodyard. circ. 300. (back issues avail.) **Document type:** academic/scholarly publication.
Formerly: Association of International Education Administrators. Journal.

790.1 US
INTERSCHOLASTIC ATHLETIC ADMINISTRATION. 1974. q. $12. National Federation of State High School Associations, 11724 N.W. Plaza Circle, Box 20626, Kansas City, MO 64195-0626. TEL 816-464-5400. FAX 816-464-5517. Ed. Dick Fawcett. adv. circ. 6,250. **Indexed:** Phys.Ed.Ind., Sportsearch (1980-).

INTERVARSITY. see *RELIGIONS AND THEOLOGY — Protestant*

371.2 379.15 US ISSN 0021-0668
IOWA SCHOOL BOARD DIALOGUE. 1951. bi-m. $2 to non-members. Iowa Association of School Boards, 700 Second Ave., Ste. 100, Des Moines, IA 50309-1731. FAX 515-243-4992. Ed. Lisa Bartusek. adv.; illus. circ. 4,700.
Formerly (until 1968): Iowa School Board Bulletin (ISSN 0444-4736)

379 UA
ISHRAQAH. 1989. s-a. Ministry of Higher Education, General Administration for Cultural Research, Sharia al-Falaki, Cairo, Egypt.

371.2 IS
IYUNIM B'MINHAL HACHINUCH. irreg. Haifa University, School of Education, Mt. Carmel, Haifa 31999, Israel. FAX 972-4-342101. **Document type:** academic/scholarly publication.

371.2 371.3 AT
JAMES NICHOLAS EDUCATION NEWSLETTER; education publishing news. 1986. q. Aus.$20. James Nicholas Publishers, P.O. Box 244, Albert Park, Vic. 3206, Australia. TEL 03-696-5545. FAX 613-699-2040. Ed. Joseph Zajda. adv.; bk.rev.; index. circ. 1,000. (back issues avail.) **Indexed:** Sociol.Abstr. **Document type:** academic/scholarly publication.

JAMI'AT QATAR. AL-TAQRIR AL-IHSA'I AL-SANAWI LIL-AAM AL-JAMI'I/UNIVERSITY OF QATAR. ANNUAL STATISTICAL REPORT FOR THE SCHOOL YEAR. see *EDUCATION — Abstracting, Bibliographies, Statistics*

371.2 US ISSN 0734-6670
LB2351.2
JOURNAL OF COLLEGE ADMISSIONS. 4/yr. $30 (foreign $34). National Association of College Admission Counselors, 1631 Prince St., Alexandria, VA 22314-2818. TEL 703-836-2222. FAX 703-836-8015. **Indexed:** C.I.J.E., Educ.Ind. **Document type:** trade publication.
—BLDSC (4958.799600); Faxon; UnCover; UMI.
Description: Aimed at school counselors, admission personnel and others concerned about the transition process.

371.2 UK
▼**JOURNAL OF COLLEGE MANAGEMENT.** 1993. 3/yr. £55($103) Taylor Graham Publishing, 500 Chesham House, 150 Regent St., London W1R 5FA, England. Ed. George Sweeney. **Document type:** academic/scholarly publication.

379.12 US ISSN 0098-9495
LB2825
JOURNAL OF EDUCATION FINANCE. 1975. q. $30. University of Massachusetts - Amherst, 258 Hills South, Amherst, MA 01003. TEL 413-545-3564. FAX 413-545-1523. Ed. Patricia Anthony. adv.; bk.rev. circ. 1,200. (also avail. in microfilm from WSH;PMC; reprint service avail. from WSH) **Indexed:** C.I.J.E., C.L.I., Cont.Pg.Educ., Educ.Admin.Abstr., Educ.Ind., Leg.Per.
—BLDSC (4973.130000); Faxon; UnCover.
Refereed Serial

371.2 UK ISSN 0268-0939
LC73
JOURNAL OF EDUCATION POLICY. bi-m. £126($212) Taylor & Francis Ltd., Rankine Rd., Basingstoke, Hants RG24 8PR, England. TEL 0256-840366. FAX 0256-479438. TELEX 858540. Ed.Bd. **Indexed:** Mult.Ed.Abstr., SOMA. **Document type:** academic/scholarly publication.
—BLDSC (4973.150800). CCC.
Description: Comments on current, international educational developments in a broad range of areas, as well as providing a forum for wider historical and comparative analysis of policy.
Refereed Serial

EDUCATION — SCHOOL ORGANIZATION AND ADMINISTRATION

371.2   UK   ISSN 0022-0639
LB2806
JOURNAL OF EDUCATIONAL ADMINISTRATION. 1963. 4/yr. $659.95. M C B University Press Ltd., 60-62 Toller Ln., Bradford, W. Yorks BD8 9BY, England. TEL 0274-499821. FAX 0274-547143. TELEX 51317-MCBUNI-G. Ed. Prof. A. Ross Thomas. bk.rev.; abstr.; bibl.; charts; illus.; stat.; index. (tabloid format; also avail. in microform from UMI; back issues avail.; reprint service avail. from SWZ,UMI) **Indexed:** Aus.Educ.Ind., Aus.P.A.I.S., C.I.J.E., Cont.Pg.Educ., Curr.Cont., Educ.Admin.Abstr., Educ.Tech.Abstr., Mult.Ed.Abstr., Res.High.Educ.Abstr., Sociol.Educ.Abstr., SOMA, SSCI. **Document type:** academic/scholarly publication.
—BLDSC (4973.153000); Faxon; UnCover; SWETS. CCC.
Description: Covers practice and theory of the field, oriented toward principals, inspectors, superintendents, directors, and university teachers and students.

371.2   UK   ISSN 0022-0620
L11
JOURNAL OF EDUCATIONAL ADMINISTRATION AND HISTORY. 1968. s-a. £15($25) University of Leeds, Museum of the History of Education, Parkinson Court, Leeds LS2 9JT, England. TEL 0532-431751. Ed.Bd. adv.; bk.rev.; abstr.; charts. circ. 500. (also avail. in microform from UMI; reprint service avail. from UMI) **Indexed:** Amer.Hist.& Life, Br.Educ.Ind., C.I.J.E., Child.Lit.Abstr., Cont.Pg.Educ., Educ.Admin.Abstr., High.Educ.Curr.Aware.Bull., Hist.Abstr., Mult.Ed.Abstr., Res.High.Educ.Abstr., SOMA. **Document type:** academic/scholarly publication.
—BLDSC (4973.154000); Faxon; SWETS; UMI.
Description: Presents research and literature reviews pertaining to all aspects of the administration and history of education in the nation and abroad.

379   II   ISSN 0971-3859
JOURNAL OF EDUCATIONAL PLANNING AND ADMINISTRATION. (Text in English) 1977. q. free. National Institute of Educational Planning and Administration, 17-B, Sri Aurobindo Marg., New Delhi 110 016, India. TEL 661938. FAX 011-683041. Ed. Jandhyala B.G. Tilak. bk.rev. circ. 1,500. **Document type:** academic/scholarly publication.
Formerly: E P A Bulletin.

371.2   US   ISSN 1058-2622
LB2826.I3
JOURNAL OF SCHOOL BUSINESS MANAGEMENT. 1989. q. $16.05. Illinois A S B O, Northern Illinois Univ., Graham Hall 244, DeKalb, IL 60115. TEL 815-753-1276. FAX 815-753-9367. Ed. Thomas E. Glass; Pub. Ronald E. Everett. adv. **Document type:** trade publication.

371.2   US   ISSN 1052-6846
LB2805
JOURNAL OF SCHOOL LEADERSHIP. 1991. bi-m. $95. Technomic Publishing Co., Inc., 851 New Holland Ave., Box 3535, Lancaster, PA 17604. TEL 717-291-5609. FAX 717-295-4538. TELEX 230 753565 TECHNOMIC UD. Ed. Paula M. Short. circ. 350. **Document type:** academic/scholarly publication.
—BLDSC (5052.660000); UMI. CCC.
Description: Presents information on concepts, research, theories, and practical applications related to school leadership.
Refereed Serial

371.2   US
KEYSTONE SCHOOLMASTER NEWSLETTER. 1961. m. membership. Pennsylvania Association of Secondary School Principals, 801 N. Second St., Harrisburg, PA 17102-3297. TEL 717-233-3001. Ed. Joseph Mamana. bk.rev. circ. 2,200. (back issues avail.) **Document type:** newsletter.

379   GW   ISSN 0933-7776
KULTUS UND UNTERRICHT. s-m. DM.110.40. (Ministerium fuer Kultus und Sport) Neckar Verlag GmbH, Postfach 1820, 78008 Villingen-Schwenningen, Germany. TEL 07721-8987-0. FAX 07721-898750. adv.; bk.rev. circ. 7,800. **Document type:** academic/scholarly publication.

371   DK   ISSN 0108-836X
L U INFORMATION.* 1978. irreg. DKK 12.20 per no. Landsforeningen af Ungdomsskoleledere, Mitchellsgade 23-5, DK-1568 Copenhagen, Denmark.

LEGAL NOTES FOR EDUCATION. see *LAW*

371.2   GW
LEHRMITTEL AKTUELL - LEHRMITTEL COMPUTER; Informationen fuer die Unterrichtspraxis. 1969. 4/yr. DM.26. Westermann Schulbuchverlag GmbH, Postfach 4938, 38039 Braunschweig, Germany. TEL 0531-708375. FAX 0531-708127. Ed. Michael Junga. adv.: B&W page DM.6900, color page DM.11040; trim 187 x 258. bk.rev.; circ. 40,908 (controlled). **Document type:** academic/scholarly publication.
—CCC.
Formerly: Lehrmittel Aktuell (ISSN 0341-8243)

379.15   US   ISSN 0026-2439
M A S B JOURNAL. 1949. bi-m. $24. Michigan Association of School Boards, Inc., 421 W. Kalamazoo, Lansing, MI 48933. TEL 517-371-5700. FAX 517-371-5338. Ed. Gail M. Braverman. adv.; bk.rev.; illus. circ. 9,100. (tabloid format; reprint service avail. from UMI) **Indexed:** Mich.Mag.Ind.
—UMI.

371.2   US   ISSN 0024-8444
M S S C EXCHANGE. 1943. m. (Sep.-June). $5. (Metropolitan School Study Council) Columbia University, Teachers College, 525 W. 120th St., New York, NY 10027. TEL 212-854-1754. Ed. Jane Przybysz. bk.rev.; abstr.; charts; stat. circ. 5,000.

371.2   US
MAINE APPRISE. vol.41, 1970. m. (10/yr.). $20. Maine Secondary School Principals' Association, Box 2468, Augusta, ME 04338-2468. FAX 207-622-1513. Ed. Heidi Shott. adv.; circ. 480 (controlled). (processed)
Former titles (until 1992): Maine Principal; Maine Secondary School Principals' Association. Newsletter; Maine Secondary School Principals' Association. Bulletin; State Principals Association. Bulletin (ISSN 0039-0143)

371.2   UK
MANAGEMENT AND LEADERSHIP IN EDUCATION SERIES. irreg. £14.95. Kogan Page Ltd., 120 Pentonville Rd., London N1 9JN, England. TEL 071-278-0433. FAX 071-837-6348. TELEX 263088-KOGAN-G. Ed. Howard Green. **Document type:** monographic series.

371.2   UK
MANAGING SCHOOLS TODAY. q. Questions Publishing Company Ltd., 6-7 Hockley Hill, Birmingham B18 5AA, England. TEL 021-507-0850. FAX 021-554-7513. Ed. Howard Sharron.
Incorporates: School Governor.

379.15   US
MASSACHUSETTS ASSOCIATION OF SCHOOL COMMITTEES BULLETIN. 6/yr. $10. Massachusetts Association of School Committees, 179 South St., Boston, MA 02111. TEL 617-542-3225. Ed. Jenifer Penfield Handy. circ. 2,800. (tabloid format; back issues avail.) **Document type:** bulletin.

MEGAPHON. see *CHILDREN AND YOUTH — For*

371.2   US
MILWAUKEE PUBLIC SCHOOLS STAFF BULLETIN. 1952. w. (Sep.-June). $6.50. Milwaukee Public Schools, Public Information-Community Relations, Board of School Directors, Drawer 10K, Milwaukee, WI 53201. TEL 414-475-8277. Ed. Robin L. Nehring Brodie. circ. 10,000.
Supersedes: Teaching Progress; **Formerly:** Milwaukee Public Schools Superintendent's Bulletin (ISSN 0040-0661)

379   US   ISSN 1047-3300
MINORITY FUNDING REPORT. 1989. m. $128 (effective Jan. 1992). Government Information Services, 4301 Fairfax Dr., Ste. 875, Arlington, VA 22203-1627. TEL 703-528-1000. FAX 703-528-6060. Ed. David Lytle. (looseleaf format; back issues avail.)
—CCC.
Description: Reports on federal and private financial aid opportunities for disadvantaged minority groups.

371   US   ISSN 0076-9460
MISSISSIPPI CONGRESS OF PARENTS AND TEACHERS. PROCEEDINGS. a. Mississippi Congress of Parents and Teachers, Box 1937, Jackson, MS 39215-1937. TEL 601-352-7383. circ. controlled.

371   US   ISSN 0076-9479
MISSISSIPPI CONGRESS OF PARENTS AND TEACHERS. YEARBOOK. a. Mississippi Congress of Parents and Teachers, Box 1937, Jackson, MS 39215-1937. TEL 601-352-7383. circ. controlled.

379.15 371.2   US   ISSN 0026-6698
MISSOURI SCHOOL BOARD.* vol.17, 1970. m. (except July & Aug.). $15. Missouri School Boards Association, 2100 Interstate 70 Dr., S.W., Columbia, MO 65203. TEL 314-445-9920. Ed. Diana Ranly Juergens. adv.; bk.rev. circ. 3,500.

371.2   US   ISSN 0270-6881
L13
N A E N BULLETIN.* 1970. m. $40. National Association of Educational Negotiators, 104 11th Ave., Windermere, FL 32786. circ. 500.
Formerly: A E N Bulletin (ISSN 0044-958X)

371.2 373   US   ISSN 0192-6365
L13
N A S S P BULLETIN. 1917. m. (Sep.-May). $10 membership. National Association of Secondary School Principals, 1904 Association Dr., Reston, VA 22091-1598. TEL 703-860-0200. FAX 703-476-5432. Ed. Robert Mahaffey. bk.rev.; bibl.; charts; illus.; index. circ. 42,000. (also avail. in microform from UMI; reprint service avail. from UMI,KTO) **Indexed:** Acad.Ind., Bk.Rev.Ind. (1965-), C.I.J.E., Child.Bk.Rev.Ind. (1965-), Cont.Pg.Educ., Educ.Ind., Except.Child.Educ.Abstr., Mult.Ed.Abstr., SOMA, Stud.Wom.Abstr. **Document type:** academic/scholarly publication, bulletin.
—BLDSC (6015.613000); Faxon; UnCover; SWETS; UMI.
Formerly: National Association of Secondary School Principals. Bulletin (ISSN 0027-8653)
Description: Publishes articles for administrators dealing with all aspects of education.

373   US
KF4102
N A S S P LEGAL MEMORANDUM. 1969. bi-m. $4 membership. National Association of Secondary School Principals, 1904 Association Dr., Reston, VA 22091-1598. TEL 703-860-0200. FAX 703-476-5432. Ed. Patricia George. circ. 42,000. (reprint service avail. from UMI) **Document type:** newsletter.
—SWETS.
Formerly: Legal Memorandum (ISSN 0192-6152)
Description: Addresses current legal issues of interest to educators.

373   US   ISSN 0278-0569
N A S S P NEWSLEADER. m. (Sep.-May). membership. National Association of Secondary School Principals, 1904 Association Dr., Reston, VA 22091-1598. TEL 703-860-0200. FAX 703-476-5432. Ed. Carol A. Bruce. circ. 42,000. (reprint service avail. from UMI) **Document type:** newspaper.
Formerly: N A S S P Newsletter (ISSN 0547-034X)
Description: News of special interest to members of the association.

371.2   US
N A S S P TIPS FOR PRINCIPALS. m. National Association of Secondary School Principals, 1904 Association Dr., Reston, VA 22091. TEL 703-860-0200. FAX 703-476-5432. (Subscr. to: Box 3250, Reston, VA 22090) Ed. Patricia George. circ. 42,000. (back issues avail.) **Document type:** newsletter.
Formerly: Tips for Principals.
Description: Tips for administrators on a variety of topics.

371.2   US   ISSN 0027-6227
N C A W E NEWS.* 1951. q. membership. National Council of Administrative Women in Education, c/o Mary Walsh, 17 Forsythe Rd., Pittsburgh, PA 15220. adv.; bk.rev. circ. 2,300.

N C R T L SPECIAL REPORT. (National Center for Research on Teacher Learning) see *EDUCATION — Teaching Methods And Curriculum*

EDUCATION — SCHOOL ORGANIZATION AND ADMINISTRATION

379 US
N E A TODAY: EDUCATIONAL SUPPORT EDITION. (Special edition of N E A Today) a. National Education Association of the United States, 1201 16th St., N.W., Washington, DC 20036. TEL 202-822-7207. FAX 202-822-7206.
Formerly: Today's Education - Educational Support Edition (ISSN 0737-187X)

374.4 US ISSN 0027-6596
N H S C NEWS. 1971. s-a. free. National Home Study Council, 1601 18th St., N.W., Washington, DC 20009. TEL 202-234-5100. Ed. Sally Welch. bk.rev.; illus.; stat. circ. 1,500. **Document type:** newsletter.
Description: Describes the council's activities and provides articles on the home home study industry.

344.07 US ISSN 0047-8997
N O L P E NOTES. 1954. m. $95 includes N O L P E School Law Reporter (Canada $105; elsewhere $115). National Organization on Legal Problems of Education, 3601 S.W. 29th St., Ste. 223, Topeka, KS 66614. TEL 913-273-3550. bk.rev. circ. 2,800. (looseleaf format; also avail. in microform from UMI) **Document type:** newsletter.

379.15 US
N Y SCHOOL BOARDS. 1929. 10/yr. $75. New York State School Boards Association, Inc., 119 Washington Ave., Albany, NY 12210. FAX 518-465-3481. Ed. William J. Pape. adv.; illus. circ. 8,500.
Formerly (until 1991): New York State School Boards Association Journal (ISSN 0028-7709)

374.013 UK
NATIONAL ASSOCIATION OF CAREER & GUIDANCE TEACHERS. JOURNAL. 1979. 5/yr. £15. National Association of Careers & Guidance Teachers, Stonesfield House, Overthorpe, Banbury, Oxon OX17 2AF, England. Ed. G. Robb. adv.; bk.rev. circ. 1,000. (back issues avail.) **Indexed:** Cont.Pg.Educ.
Formerly: Careers and Guidance Teacher.

379.15 US
NATIONAL ASSOCIATION OF STATE BOARDS OF EDUCATION. STATE BOARD CONNECTION. 1982. m. membership. National Association of State Boards of Education, Inc., 1012 Cameron St., Alexandria, VA 22314. TEL 703-684-4000. FAX 703-836-2313. Ed. David Kysilko. bk.rev.; illus.; stat. circ. 850. **Document type:** newsletter.
Supersedes (in 1980): National Association of State Boards of Education. Focus (ISSN 0015-4962)

371 US ISSN 0077-4472
L901
NATIONAL FACULTY DIRECTORY. 1971. a. $585 for 3 vols. Gale Research Inc., 835 Penobscot Bldg., Detroit, MI 48226. TEL 313-961-2242. FAX 313-961-6083. TELEX 810-221-7086. **Document type:** directory.
—BLDSC (6022.690000).
Description: Cumulation of American faculty members.

790.1 US ISSN 0737-5204
NATIONAL FEDERATION NEWS. 1983. m. (10/yr.). $10 (foreign $18). National Federation of State High School Associations, 11724 N.W. Plaza Circle, Box 20626, Kansas City, MO 64195-0626. TEL 816-464-5400. FAX 816-464-5571. Ed. Bruce Howard. circ. 130,000. **Indexed:** Sports Per.Ind., Sportsearch (1985-).

371.2 US ISSN 0888-8132
NATIONAL FORUM OF EDUCATION ADMINISTRATION AND SUPERVISION JOURNAL. Short title: N F E A S Journal. 1983. 3/yr. $30 to individuals; institutions $60. (Wright State University) National Forum Journals, 1930 Nicholas St., Lake Charles, LA 70605. TEL 318-474-6976. Ed. William Allan Kritsonis. adv.; bk.rev. circ. 10,000. (back issues avail.) **Document type:** academic/scholarly publication.
—UnCover. CCC.
Formerly: National Forum of Educational Administration and Supervision (ISSN 0882-9047)
Refereed Serial

370 US ISSN 0275-4142
NATIONAL GUIDE TO EDUCATIONAL CREDIT FOR TRAINING PROGRAMS. 1976. a. $49.95 (foreign $59.95). (American Council on Education, Office on Educational Credit) Oryx Press, 4041 N. Central Ave., No. 700, Phoenix, AZ 85012-3397. TEL 602-265-2651. FAX 602-265-6250. adv. circ. 3,000. (also avail. in microfiche) **Indexed:** ERIC.
Formerly: National Guide to Credit Recommendations for Noncollegiate Courses.
Description: Describes more than 2000 educational programs conducted by businesses, labor uniuons, professional and voluntary associations and gfovernment agencies, listing course titles, dates and locations, objectives and methods of instruction.

NATIONAL PEDICULOSIS ASSOCIATION. PROGRESS. see *PUBLIC HEALTH AND SAFETY*

NETHERLANDS. CENTRAAL BUREAU VOOR DE STATISTIEK. STATISTIEK VAN DE UITGAVEN DER OVERHEID VOOR ONDERWIJS/NETEHRLANDS. CENTRAL BUREAU OF STATISTICS. STATISTICS OF THE EXPENDITURE OF THE STATE, THE PROVINCES AND THE MUNICIPALITIES ON EDUCATION. see *EDUCATION — Abstracting, Bibliographies, Statistics*

NETHERLANDS. CENTRAAL BUREAU VOOR DE STATISTIEK. STATISTIEK VAN HET W V O, H A V O EN M A V O: SCHOLEN EN LEERLINGEN. see *EDUCATION — Abstracting, Bibliographies, Statistics*

379.15 US ISSN 0039-0070
NEW JERSEY SCHOOL BOARDS ASSOCIATION. SCHOOL BOARD NOTES. 1969. w. $80 includes School Leader. New Jersey School Boards Association, 413 W. State St., Box 909, Trenton, NJ 08605. TEL 609-695-7600. FAX 609-695-0413. adv.; illus.; stat.; index. circ. 8,000.
Supersedes: School Boards Newsletter (ISSN 0036-648X)

379.15 US
NEW JERSEY SCHOOL BOARDS ASSOCIATION. SCHOOL LEADER. 1954. 6/yr. $80 includes School Board Notes. New Jersey School Boards Association, 413 W. State St., Box 909, Trenton, NJ 08605. TEL 609-695-7600. FAX 609-695-0413. adv.; bk.rev.; abstr.; charts; illus.; stat.; index. circ. 8,000.
Incorporates: New Jersey School Boards Association. Legislative Bulletin (ISSN 0024-046X); New Jersey School Boards Association. Legislation News; New Jersey School Boards Association. Negotiations News and School Law Reporter; Which was formerly titled: Negotiations News (ISSN 0028-2472)

NEW YORK STATE. EDUCATION DEPARTMENT. COLLEGE AND UNIVERSITY REVENUES AND EXPENDITURES. see *EDUCATION — Higher Education*

379.15 371 US
NEW YORK STATE SCHOOL BOARDS ASSOCIATION. EMPLOYEE RELATIONS NEWS. m. $80 to non-members; members $40. New York State School Boards Association, Inc., 119 Washington Ave., Albany, NY 12210. FAX 518-465-3481. **Document type:** newsletter.

371.2 US
NEW YORK SUPERVISOR. 1945. s-a. $1 per no. New York City Elementary School Principals Association, c/o Thomas J. Hiler, Ed., Public School 48, 6015 18th Ave., Brooklyn, NY 11204. adv.; bk.rev.; illus. circ. 2,000.

371.2 US
NORTH AMERICAN ASSOCIATION OF SUMMER SESSIONS. ANNUAL CONFERENCE. PROCEEDINGS. 1964. a. $6. North American Association of Summer Sessions, 11728 Summerhaven Drive, St. Louis, MO 63146-5444. TEL 314-872-8406. Ed. Michael U. Nelson. abstr. circ. 475. (back issues avail.) **Document type:** proceedings.
Description: Deals with the administration of problems in and solutions for directors of higher education summer session programs.

378.1 US
NORTH AMERICAN ASSOCIATION OF SUMMER SESSIONS. NEWSLETTER. 1965. q. membership. North American Association of Summer Sessions, 11728 Summerhaven Dr., St. Louis, MO 63146-5444. Ed. Michael U. Nelson. circ. controlled. **Document type:** newsletter.
Former titles: National Association of Summer Sessions. Newsletter (ISSN 0027-867X); National Association of College and University Summer Sessions. Newsletter.

379.15 CN ISSN 0702-9292
NOVA SCOTIA SCHOOL BOARDS ASSOCIATION NEWSLETTER. Abbreviated title: N S S B A Newsletter. 1971. m. Can.$10. Nova Scotia School Boards Association, P.O. Box 605, Sta. "M", Halifax, NS B3J 2R7, Canada. TEL 902-420-9191. FAX 902-429-7405. Ed. Sharon Findlay. adv.: page Can.$100. bk.rev. circ. 700. (looseleaf format; back issues avail.) **Document type:** newsletter.
Description: Focuses on educational issues.

379.15 US ISSN 0893-5289
OHIO SCHOOL BOARDS ASSOCIATION. JOURNAL. Key Title: Journal - Ohio School Boards Association. 1956. 10/yr. $35. Ohio School Boards Association, 700 Brooksedge Blvd., Box 6100, Westerville, OH 43081-6100. TEL 614-891-6466. FAX 614-891-2834. Ed. Scott Ebright. adv.; charts; illus.; stat. circ. 5,800. (processed) **Document type:** trade publication.
Formerly (until 1982): Ohio School Boards Journal (ISSN 0030-1078)

371.2 378 CN ISSN 0711-6896
LB2335.C3
ONTARIO UNIVERSITIES BENEFITS SURVEY. (In 2 parts: I - Benefits; II - Pensions) a. Can.$6.55. Council of Ontario Universities, 444 Yonge St., Ste. 203, Toronto, Ont. M5B 2H4, Canada. TEL 416-979-2165. FAX 416-979-8635.

379.15 US ISSN 0162-3559
P S B A BULLETIN. 1937. bi-m. $50 ($25 to affiliates). Pennsylvania School Boards Association, 774 Limekiln Rd., New Cumberland, PA 17070-2398. TEL 717-774-2331. FAX 717-774-0718. Ed. Lynn H. Mannion. adv; bk.rev.; charts; illus.; stat. circ. 11,300. **Document type:** bulletin.
—Faxon.
Formerly: Pennsylvania School Boards Association. Bulletin (ISSN 0031-4668)

370.193 US
P T A COMMUNICATOR. 1922. 9/yr. $5. Texas Congress of Parents and Teachers, 408 W. 11th St., Austin, TX 78701. TEL 512-476-6769. FAX 512-476-8152. Ed. Bernice Schnerr. adv.; index. circ. 8,000.
Former titles: Texas P T A Communicator; Texas P T A; Texas Parent-Teacher (ISSN 0040-4578)
Description: Contains organization news and educational and parental instruction material.

371.2 US ISSN 0032-0684
LA210
PLANNING & CHANGING; an educational leadership and policy journal. 1970. q. $18 (foreign $24). Illinois State University, Department of Educational Administration and Foundations, 331 DeGarmo Hall, Normal, IL 61761. TEL 309-438-5422. FAX 309-438-8683. Ed. Chris Eisele. bk.rev. circ. 1,000. (also avail. in microform from UMI; reprint service avail. from UMI) **Indexed:** C.I.J.E., Cont.Pg.Educ., Educ.Admin.Abstr., Educ.Ind., SOMA.
—BLDSC (6508.990000); Faxon; UnCover; SWETS; UMI.

POLITICA MERIDIONALISTA; rivista mensile di cultura, economia e attualita. see *BUSINESS AND ECONOMICS — Economic Situation And Conditions*

373 US ISSN 0192-6160
THE PRACTITIONER; a newsletter for the on-line administrator. 1976. bi-m. $4 membership. National Association of Secondary School Principals, Research Department, 1904 Association Dr., Reston, VA 22091-1537. TEL 703-860-0200. FAX 703-476-5432. Ed. Patricia George. circ. 37,000. (also avail. in microfilm; reprint service avail. from UMI; back issues avail.) **Indexed:** C.I.J.E., C.L.I., L.R.I. **Document type:** newsletter.
—BLDSC (6598.050000).
Description: Addresses administrative issues in secondary school education.

EDUCATION — SCHOOL ORGANIZATION AND ADMINISTRATION

371.2   CN
PRESIDENT REPORTS.* (Text in English, French) q. membership. Canadian Association of School Administrators - Association Canadienne des Administrateurs et des Administratrices Scolaires, 160 A St., White Rock, BC V4A 7G9, Canada. circ. 2,000. (looseleaf format; back issues avail.)

371.2 372   US   ISSN 0271-6062
L13
PRINCIPAL (ALEXANDRIA). 1921. 5/yr. $155 membership; institutions $155. National Association of Elementary School Principals, 1615 Duke St., Alexandria, VA 22314. TEL 703-684-3345. FAX 703-548-6021. Ed Leon E. Greene. adv.; bk.rev.; illus.; index. circ. 26,000. (also avail. in microform from UMI; reprint service avail. from UMI) **Indexed:** C.I.J.E., Cont.Pg.Educ., Educ.Ind., Except.Child.Educ.Abstr. **Document type:** academic/scholarly publication.
—BLDSC (6612.967800); Faxon; UnCover; UMI.
Formerly (until Sep. 1980): National Elementary Principal (ISSN 0027-920X)

658.15   CN
QUEBEC (PROVINCE). MINISTERE DE L'EDUCATION. DIRECTION GENERALE DU FINANCEMENT. REGLES BUDGETAIRES DES COMMISSION SCOLAIRES.. 1965. a. Direction Generale du Financement, 1035 rue de la Chevrotiere, Quebec, Que. G1R 5A5, Canada. TEL 418-643-3108. FAX 418-643-9224.
Former titles: Quebec (Province). Direction Generale des Ressources Materielles et Financieres. Regles Budgetaires des Commission Scolaires et des Commissions Regionales & Quebec (Province). Ministere de l'Education. Regles Budgetaires des Commissions Scolaires et des Commissions Regionales; Quebec (Province). Ministere de l'Education. Direction du Financement. Regles Budgetaires des Commissions Scolaires et des Commissions Regionales.

344.07   FR   ISSN 0758-9867
RECUEIL DES LOIS ET REGLEMENTS DU MINISTERE DE L'EDUCATION NATIONAL. 1963. 10 base vols. (plus m. updates). 1480 F. (Ministere de l'Education National) Centre National de Documentation Pedagogique, 29 rue d'Ulm, 75230 Paris Cedex 05, France. TEL 46-34-92-97. FAX 46-34-55-44.

371.2   CN
RECUEIL DES SENTENCES DE L'EDUCATION. 40/yr. Can.$290. Ministere des Communications, P.O. Box 1005, Quebec, PQ G1K 7B5, Canada. TEL 418-643-5150. (Subscr. to: Publications du Quebec, Service des Abonnements, CP 1190, Outremont, PQ H2V 4S7, Canada. TEL 514-948-1222) cum.index. **Document type:** government publication.

330   US
▼**REPORT ON CORPORATE EDUCATIONAL SUPPORT.** 1992. m. $273. Business Publishers, Inc., 951 Pershing Dr., Silver Spring, MD 20910-4464. TEL 301-587-6300. FAX 301-585-9075. Ed. Rosemary Lally. (back issues avail.) **Document type:** newsletter.
●Also available online. Vendor(s): NewsNet.
Description: Issues in improving America's workforce capability, including corporate support for public education.

371.2   US   ISSN 1041-6757
THE REPORTER (LITTLE ROCK). 1982. 10/yr. Arkansas School Boards Association, 808 Dr. M.L. King Dr., Little Rock, AR 72201-3646. TEL 501-372-1415. FAX 501-375-2454. Ed. Dan Farley. circ. 3,500 (controlled). (tabloid format)
Description: News and features pertinent to Arkansas School Board members.

371 372   US   ISSN 0080-1429
LB1771
REQUIREMENTS FOR CERTIFICATION OF TEACHERS, COUNSELORS, LIBRARIANS, ADMINISTRATORS FOR ELEMENTARY SCHOOLS, SECONDARY SCHOOLS, JUNIOR COLLEGES. 1935. a. price varies. University of Chicago Press, 5801 S. Ellis Ave., Chicago, IL 60637. TEL 312-702-7899. Ed. Mary P. Burks. (reprint service avail. from UMI,ISI)
Refereed Serial

371.2 378   US   ISSN 0361-0365
LB2331.63   CODEN: RHEDAT
RESEARCH IN HIGHER EDUCATION. 1973. bi-m. $195 (foreign $230) (effective 1993). Human Sciences Press, Inc. (Subsidiary of: Plenum Publishing Corp.), 233 Spring St., New York, NY 10013. TEL 212-620-8000. FAX 212-463-0742. TELEX 23-421139. (Co-sponsor: Association for Institutional Research) Ed. John C. Smart. adv.; bibl.; charts; illus.; stat.; index. (processed; also avail. in microform from UMI; reprint service avail. from UMI) **Indexed:** C.I.J.E., Cont.Pg.Educ., Curr.Cont., Educ.Admin.Abstr., Educ.Ind., Educ.Tech.Abstr., High.Educ.Abstr., Mult.Ed.Abstr., Psychol.Abstr., Res.High.Educ.Abstr., Sociol.Abstr., SOMA, SSCI, Stud.Wom.Abstr. **Document type:** academic/scholarly publication.
—BLDSC (7741.245000); Faxon; UnCover; SWETS; UMI. **CCC.**
Description: Features original theoretical and in-depth empirical research about the functioning of post-secondary educational institutions.
Refereed Serial

371.2   US
RESEARCH ROUNDUP. 1984. 3/yr. $155 membership; institutions $95. National Association of Elementary School Principals, 1615 Duke St., Alexandria, VA 22314-3483. TEL 703-684-3345. FAX 703-548-6021.

379.15 340   US
RESOLUTIONS, BELIEFS & POLICIES, CONSTITUTION AND BYLAWS. 1940. a. free. National School Boards Association, 1680 Duke St., Alexandria, VA 22314. TEL 703-838-6722. FAX 703-683-7590. Ed. Thomas A. Shannon. circ. 2,000. (tabloid format)
Description: Official policy positions of the association passed annually by the Delegate Assembly.

370   FR
REVIEWS OF NATIONAL POLICIES FOR EDUCATION. irreg. price varies. Organization for Economic Cooperation and Development, 2 rue Andre-Pascal, 75775 Paris Cedex 16, France. (U.S. orders to: O.E.C.D. Publications and Information Center, 2001 L St., N.W., Ste. 700, Washington, DC 20036-4910. TEL 202-785-6323) (also avail. in microfiche from CIS) **Indexed:** IIS.

371.2 371.3   GW
RHEINLAND PFALZ. KULTUSMINISTERIUM. AMTSBLATT. 1948. s-m. DM.45. (Kultusministerium Rheinland-Pfalz) Neuwieder Verlagsgesellschaft m.b.H., Postfach 1869, 5450 Neuwied 1, Germany. Ed. Konrad Mohr. adv.; bk.rev. circ. 5,200.

371.2   IT   ISSN 1121-0761
RIVISTA DELLA SCUOLA. 1979. fortn. L.54000. Girgenti Editore s.r.l., Via A. Doria 10, Casella Postale 10016, 20124 Milan, Italy. TEL 02-6692195. FAX 02-66983333. Ed. Salvatore Girgenti. adv. circ. 70,000.

370   AT
S A I T JOURNAL. 1915; N.S. 1969. every 3 weeks. Aus.$15. South Australian Institute of Teachers, 163A Greenhill Rd., 5063 Parkside, S.A., Australia. TEL 08-272-1399. FAX 08-373-1254. TELEX 89144. Ed. Andrew Macfarlane. adv.; bk.rev.; stat.; index. circ. 21,500. **Indexed:** Aus.Educ.Ind., C.I.J.E. **Document type:** newspaper.
Formerly (until Nov., 1990): South Australian Teachers Journal (ISSN 0038-3015)

371.2   CN
S A S C A JOURNAL - NEWSLETTER. irreg. (1-2/yr.). Can.$15. (Saskatchewan Association of Student Council Advisors) Saskatchewan Teachers' Federation, Box 1108, Saskatoon, SK S7K 3N3, Canada. Eds. Dorothy Karlson, Shannon Ferguson. adv.

371.2   US   ISSN 0048-9441
S M S G NEWSLETTER. 1970. 8/yr. $25. School Management Study Group, 860 18th Ave., Salt Lake City, UT 84103. TEL 801-532-5340. FAX 801-484-2089. Ed. Donald Thomas. bk.rev. circ. 200. **Document type:** newsletter.

371.2   CN   ISSN 0709-8146
SASKATCHEWAN EDUCATIONAL ADMINISTRATOR. 1967. s-a. Can.$20 to non-members. (Saskatchewan Council on Educational Administration) Saskatchewan Teachers' Federation, Box 1108, Saskatoon, SK S7K 3N3, Canada. TEL 306-525-0368. Ed. Keith Walker. adv. **Indexed:** Can.Educ.Ind.
Formerly: Saskatchewan Administrator (ISSN 0048-914X)

371.2   US   ISSN 0036-6439
LB2805
SCHOOL ADMINISTRATOR. 1943. m. (11/yr.). membership. American Association of School Administrators, 1801 North Moore St., Arlington, VA 22209. TEL 703-528-0700. FAX 703-528-2146. Ed. Jay P. Goldman. adv. contact: Bob Solomon. circ. controlled. **Indexed:** C.I.J.E., PSI, SOMA. **Document type:** trade publication.
—BLDSC (8092.570000); UnCover.
Incorporates: D C Dateline.

371.2   AT   ISSN 0048-9387
SCHOOL BELL. 1946. 10/yr. Aus.$23. Victorian Council of School Organisation, 270 Highett St., Richmond, Vic. 3121, Australia. TEL 03 429 5900. FAX 03-428-5897. Ed. Ruth Crichton. adv.; bk.rev. circ. 6,000. (back issues avail.)

371.2   US   ISSN 1045-8115
SCHOOL BOARD NEWS. 1981. fortn. $36. National School Boards Association, 1680 Duke St., Alexandria, VA 22314. TEL 703-838-6722. FAX 703-683-7590. Ed. Ellie Ashford. circ. 24,000. (reprint service avail. from UMI) **Document type:** newspaper.

SCHOOL BUS BRIEFS. see *TRANSPORTATION*

371.2   CN   ISSN 1192-4357
▼**SCHOOL BUSINESS.** 1992. bi-m. Momentum Magazines, 4040 Creditview Rd., Unit 11, Box 6900, Mississauga, Ont. L5C 3Y8, Canada. TEL 416-569-6900. FAX 416-569-6915. Ed. Jerry Hymshyn. adv.: B&W page Can.$1915, color page Can.$2750; trim 8 x 11; adv. contact: Hugh Parkinson. circ. 10,095. **Document type:** trade publication.
Description: Business and administrative issues for officials and university administrative executives.

371.2   US   ISSN 0036-651X
LB2804
SCHOOL BUSINESS AFFAIRS. 1936. m. $68 to non-members. Association of School Business Officials, 11401 N. Shore Dr., Reston, VA 22090-4232. TEL 703-478-0405. FAX 703-478-0205. Ed. P.D. Kirkpatrick. adv.; bk.rev.; bibl.; charts; illus.; stat.; index. (also avail. in microform from UMI; reprint service avail. from UMI) **Indexed:** Account.Ind. (1990-), C.I.J.E., Cont.Pg.Educ., Educ.Admin.Abstr., Educ.Ind. **Document type:** trade publication.
—BLDSC (8092.700000); UnCover; UMI.
Description: Supplies management information to school administrators in charge of school operations.

371.2   NE
SCHOOL EN BESTUREN. bi-m. fl.33. Centraal Bureau Katholiek Onderwijs, Stadhouderslaan 9, 2517 HV The Hague, Netherlands. adv.; bk.rev. circ. 12,250.

SCHOOL FOOD SERVICE JOURNAL. see *FOOD AND FOOD INDUSTRIES*

SCHOOL FOOD SERVICE NEWS. see *HOTELS AND RESTAURANTS*

SCHOOL FOOD SERVICE RESEARCH REVIEW. see *FOOD AND FOOD INDUSTRIES*

371.2   US   ISSN 8755-8297
KF4114
SCHOOL LAW BULLETIN (BOSTON). 1974. m. $60. Quinlan Publishing Co., Inc., 23 Drydock Ave., 2nd Fl., Boston, MA 02210-2387. TEL 617-542-0048; 800-229-2084. FAX 617-345-9646. index. (looseleaf format; also avail. in microform from UMI; reprint service avail. from UMI) **Indexed:** C.L.I., L.R.I. **Document type:** newsletter.
—UMI. **CCC.**
Description: Summarizes current cases concerning labor relations, tort liability, student searches, student injuries, special education and other issues facing schools and school districts.

EDUCATION — SCHOOL ORGANIZATION AND ADMINISTRATION

344.7 US ISSN 0194-2271
SCHOOL LAW NEWS; the independent bi-weekly news service on legal developments affecting education. 1973. bi-w. $267 (foreign $293). Capitol Publications Inc., 1101 King St., Ste. 444, Alexandria, VA 22314. TEL 703-683-4100. FAX 703-739-6517. Ed. Douglas Onley. s-a. index. (looseleaf format) **Document type:** newsletter.
—CCC.
   Incorporates (in Sep. 1987): Equal Opportunity in Higher Education (ISSN 0194-2344)
   Description: Keeps school administrators and legal advisors informed of legal decisions, pending court cases and issues that affect schools. Covers the federal judiciary, the US Supreme Court, state courts, and legal developments in federal agencies and Congress.

SCHOOL LIBRARIAN. see *LIBRARY AND INFORMATION SCIENCES*

371.2 UK ISSN 1351-4660
SCHOOL MANAGEMENT HANDBOOK (YEAR). a. £16.95. Kogan Page Ltd., 120 Pentonville Rd., London N1 9JN, England. TEL 071-278-0433. FAX 071-837-6348. TELEX 263088-KOGAN-G. Ed. Howard Green. **Document type:** directory.

371.2 658.8
SCHOOL MARKETING NEWSLETTER. 1981. m. $119. School Market Research Institute, Box 10, Haddam, CT 06438. TEL 203-345-8183. FAX 203-345-3985. Ed. Lynn O. Vosburgh. circ. 500. **Document type:** newsletter.
   Formerly (until Dec. 1987): Direct Response Marketing to Schools Newsletter (ISSN 0882-701X)

344.07 US ISSN 1045-4128
KF4114
SCHOOL OFFICIALS AND THE COURTS. 1979. a. Educational Research Service, 2000 Claredon Blvd., Arlington, VA 22201-2908. FAX 703-243-1985.

371.2 UK ISSN 0260-1362
SCHOOL ORGANISATION. 1981. 3/yr. $84 to individuals; institutions $232 (effective 1994). Carfax Publishing Co., P.O. Box 25, Abingdon, Oxon. OX14 3UE, England. TEL 44-235-555335. FAX 44-235-553559. (U.S. subscr. to: Carfax Publishing Co. Box 2025, Dunnellon, FL 34430-2025) Ed. David Smetherham. adv.; bk.rev.; index. (also avail. in microfiche; back issues avail.) **Indexed:** Cont.Pg.Educ., Educ.Admin.Abstr., Educ.Tech.Abstr., SOMA, Stud.Wom.Abstr. **Document type:** academic/scholarly publication.
—BLDSC (8092.923400); Faxon; SWETS. **CCC.**
   Description: Discusses the management and organizational problems faced in primary and secondary schools.
   Refereed Serial

SCHOOL PHOTOGRAPHER. see *PHOTOGRAPHY*

371.77 US
SCHOOL SAFETY WORLD. q. $19 to non-members; members $15. National Safety Council, Periodicals Department, 1121 Spring Lake Dr., Itasca, IL 60143. TEL 708-285-1121. Ed. Kathy Henderson; Pub. Kevin H. Axe. (also avail. in microfilm from UMI; reprint service avail. from UMI)
   Supersedes: School Safety (ISSN 0036-6781)
   Description: Information and recommendations on safety issues pertaining to school safety.

370 CN ISSN 0036-6854
SCHOOL TRUSTEE. 1934. 5/yr. Can.$10. Saskatchewan School Trustees Association, 400-2222 13th Ave., Regina, Sask. S4P 3M7, Canada. TEL 306-569-0750. Ed. L. Anderson. adv.; bk.rev.; abstr.; stat. circ. 4,000. **Indexed:** Can.Educ.Ind., Can.Per.Ind., CMI.

371.2 GW ISSN 0341-8235
SCHUL-MANAGEMENT. 1970. bi-m. DM.60. S L Verlag GmbH, Helmstedter Str. 84, Postfach 4250, 38126 Braunschweig, Germany. TEL 0531-791026. Ed. Burkhard Hitz. adv.; bk.rev. circ. 4,000.
—CCC.

371 GW ISSN 0170-7922
SCHULLEITER HANDBUCH. 1977. q. DM.80. S L - Verlag GmbH, Helmstedter Str. 84, 38126 Braunschweig, Germany. TEL 0531-791026. Ed. Burkhard Hitz. adv.; bk.rev.; index. circ. 3,500.
—CCC.

SCHULPRAXIS; Zeitschrift fuer Unterricht und Schulorganisation. see *EDUCATION — Teaching Methods And Curriculum*

371 GW ISSN 0048-9484
SCHULVERWALTUNGSBLATT FUER NIEDERSACHSEN. 1949. m. DM.60. (Kultusministerium Niedersachsen) Verlag Hahnsche Buchhandlung, Postfach 2460, 30024 Hannover, Germany. TEL 0511-322294. FAX 0511-363698. adv.; bk.rev. circ. 7,700. **Document type:** bulletin.

371 IT
SCUOLA MATERNA. 1945. fortn. L.59000. Editrice La Scuola S.p.A., Via Cadorna 11, 25186 Brescia, Italy. TEL 030-29931. Ed. Giovanni Cattanei. bk.rev.

371.2 US
SIGNAL (OLYMPIA). 1948. 12/yr. $12. Washington State School Directors Association, 221 College St., N.E., Olympia, WA 98516. TEL 206-493-9237. Ed. Susan Kerber. bk.rev. circ. 3,800. **Indexed:** Tel.Abstr.
   Formerly: Washington State School Directors Association Newsletter (ISSN 0043-0811)

370 US ISSN 8755-4054
LA244.S6
SOUTHERN CALIFORNIA COUNTIES PUBLIC SCHOOLS. SURVEY. 1985. a. California School Surveys, 110 La Bolsa Rd., Walnut Creek, CA 94598.

371.2 SP
SPAIN. MINISTERIO DE EDUCACION Y CIENCIA. BOLETIN OFICIAL: ACTOS ADMINISTRATIVOS. w. 5500 ptas. (foreign 6950 ptas.). Ministerio de Educacion y Ciencia, Centro de Publicaciones, Ciudad Universitaria, 28040 Madrid, Spain. TEL 549 77 00. **Document type:** government publication, bulletin.

371.2 GW ISSN 0931-0029
STADT DUISBURG. BERUFSBILDUNGSBERICHT (YEAR). 1984. a. DM.19. Amt fuer Statistik, Stadtforschung und Europaangelegenheiten, Der Oberstadtdirektor, 47049 Duisburg, Germany. TEL 0203-283-3085. FAX 0203-2834404. TELEX 203314. circ. 600. (back issues avail.) **Document type:** government publication.

371.2 US ISSN 0735-0023
STREAMLINED SEMINAR. 1982. 6/yr. $155 membership; institutions $95. National Association of Elementary School Principals, 1615 Duke St., Alexandria, VA 22314-3483. TEL 703-684-3345. FAX 703-548-6021.
—BLDSC (8474.052700).

371.2 370.196 AT
STUDIES IN EDUCATIONAL ADMINISTRATION. 1972. s-a. Aus.$10. Commonwealth Council for Educational Administration, University of New England, Armidale, N.S.W. 2351, Australia. TEL 067-732543. FAX 067-733363. TELEX 166050. Ed. Bernadette Taylor. adv.; bk.rev. circ. 6,500. (also avail. in microfiche; back issues avail.) **Indexed:** ERIC, Mult.Ed.Abstr., SOMA.

371.2 IS ISSN 0334-4770
STUDIES IN EDUCATIONAL ADMINISTRATION AND ORGANIZATION. (Text in Hebrew; summaries in English) 1973. a. $7. Haifa University, School of Education, Center for Educational Administration, Mt. Carmel, Haifa 31999, Israel. FAX 972-4-342101. Ed. Lya Kremer-Hayon. bk.rev. **Document type:** academic/scholarly publication.

371.2 US ISSN 0300-6433
T E P S A JOURNAL. 1970. s-a. $5. Texas Elementary Principals and Supervisors Association, 501 E. 10th St., Austin, TX 78701-2697. TEL 512-478-5268. FAX 512-478-1502. Ed. Sarah Jane Hubert. adv. circ. 5,500.
   Description: Contains current, timely articles by principals and professors on education practices.

370 CN ISSN 0382-408X
TEACHER (ARMDALE). (Text in English, French) 1971. bi-w. Can.$18 (foreign Can.$22). Nova Scotia Teachers Union, 3106 Dutch Village Rd., Halifax, NS B3L 4L7, Canada. TEL 902-477-5621. FAX 902-477-3517. Ed. Paul McCormick. adv.; bk.rev. circ. 16,000. (tabloid format; also avail. in microfiche) **Indexed:** CMI.
   Formerly: Nova Scotia Teachers Union Newsletter (ISSN 0029-5108)

371.2 331.1 US
TEACHER SUPPLY - DEMAND. a. $10. Association for School, College and University Staffing, Inc., c/o High School, 1600 Dodge Ave., Ste. 5-330, Evanston, IL 60204. (also avail. in microfiche from CIS) **Indexed:** SRI.

TEACHERS' MONEY MATTERS. see *BUSINESS AND ECONOMICS — Banking And Finance*

371 IT
TECNICA DELLA SCUOLA. 1949. 24/yr. L.48000 (effective Sep. 1993). Edizione la Tecnica della Scuola, Via Tripolitania 12, 95127 Catania, Italy. TEL 095-446580. FAX 095-503256. TELEX 972294. Ed. Venero Girgenti. adv.; bk.rev.; charts; illus.; stat. circ. 70,000.

379.14 US ISSN 0049-3406
TENNESSEE SCHOOL BOARD BULLETIN. Variant title: Tennessee School Boards Association Bulletin. 1950. 8/yr. $10. Tennessee School Boards Association, 500 13th Ave. North, Nashville, TN 37203-2830. FAX 615-741-2824. Ed. Holly Hewitt. adv.; bk.rev.; charts; stat.; circ. 1,800 (controlled). **Document type:** bulletin.

TENNESSEE SCHOOL BOARDS JOURNAL. see *EDUCATION*

371.2 US ISSN 0749-9310
TEXAS LONE STAR. 1982. m. $30. Texas Association of School Boards, Box 400, Austin, TX 78767-0400. TEL 512-467-0222. Ed. Roger White. bk.rev.; index. circ. 13,500. (back issues avail.)
   Formerly: Texas School Board Journal.

370 US ISSN 0040-4551
L11
TEXAS OUTLOOK. 1917. q. $15 to non-members. Texas State Teachers Association, 316 W. 12th St., Austin, TX 78701. TEL 512-476-5355. Ed. Debbie Turner. adv.; bk.rev.; charts; illus.; index. circ. 100,000. (also avail. in microform from UMI) **Indexed:** Educ.Ind.

344.07 US
TEXAS SCHOOL LAW BULLETIN. irreg. $15. Texas Education Agency, Resource Center Library, 1701 N. Congress Ave., Austin, TX 78701-1494. TEL 512-463-9744. index. **Document type:** bulletin.

TRUSTEE QUARTERLY. see *EDUCATION — Higher Education*

371 US ISSN 1041-3502
U C E A MONOGRAPH SERIES. 1986. irreg. price varies. University Council for Educational Administration, 212 Rackley Bldg. University Park, PA 16802. TEL 814-863-7916. FAX 814-863-7918. **Document type:** monographic series.

378 US ISSN 0734-5798
U C E A REVIEW. 1959. 4/yr. $7. University Council for Educational Administration, 212 Rackley Bldg., University Park, PA 16802-3200. TEL 814-863-7915. FAX 814-863-7918. adv.; bk.rev. circ. 4,000. (tabloid format)
   Description: List for professional administrative personnel in continuing education and pre-service programs.

370 SA
U.T.A.S.A. ANNUAL. (Text in English; occasionally in Afrikaans) 1979. a. free. Union of Teachers' Associations of South Africa, P.O. Box 239, Durban 4000, South Africa. Ed. A.R. Pierce. adv.; bk.rev. circ. 20,000.

379 TS
UNITED ARAB EMIRATES. WIZARAT AL-TARBIYYAH WAL-TA'LIM. AL-TAQRIR AL-SANAWI/UNITED ARAB EMIRATES. MINISTRY OF EDUCATION. ANNUAL REPORT. (Text in Arabic) 1977. a. Wizarat al-Tarbiyyah wal-Ta'lim, Idarat al-I'lam al-Tarbawi - Ministry of Education, Educational Information Department, P.O. Box 259, Abu Dhabi, United Arab Emirates. TEL 213800. stat.; circ. 1,000 (controlled). **Document type:** government publication.
   Description: Provides a comprehensive overview of the activities of the departments of the ministry and the educational climate in the U.A.E.

EDUCATION — SPECIAL EDUCATION AND REHABILITATION

379 500   US
U.S. NATIONAL SCIENCE FOUNDATION. GUIDE TO PROGRAMS. 1966. a. $8. U.S. National Science Foundation, Science & Technology Information System (STIS), 4201 Wilson Blvd., Ste. 245, Arlington, VA 22230. circ. 35,000. **Document type:** government publication.

371.2   US
UPDATING SCHOOL BOARD POLICIES. 1970. bi-m. $250. National School Boards Association, 1680 Duke St., Alexandria, VA 22314. TEL 703-838-6722. FAX 703-683-7590. Ed. Karen Powe. index. circ. 20,000. (back issues avail.) **Document type:** newsletter.
   Description: Includes articles, trends, tips and legal analyses on subjects relating to school policies and issues of concern to school boards and superintendents.

379.792   US   ISSN 0094-8314
L206
UTAH. STATE OFFICE OF EDUCATION. ANNUAL REPORT OF THE STATE SUPERINTENDENT OF PUBLIC INSTRUCTION. Key Title: Annual Report of the State Superintendent of Public Instruction Utah Public School System. At head of title: Utah Public School System. a. State Office of Education, Publications Secretary, 250 E. Fifth S., Salt Lake City, UT 84111. TEL 801-533-5431. illus. **Document type:** government publication.

371.2   US   ISSN 0093-0040
LB2809.U8
UTAH. STATE OFFICE OF EDUCATION. OPINIONS OF THE UTAH STATE SUPERINTENDENT OF PUBLIC INSTRUCTION. Key Title: Opinions of the Utah State Superintendent of Public Instruction. 1963. irreg., latest issue 1972. State Board of Education, Publications Secretary, 250 E. Fifth S., Salt Lake City, UT 84111. TEL 801-533-5431. **Document type:** government publication.

V S T A NEWS. (Victorian Secondary Teachers Association) see EDUCATION — Teaching Methods And Curriculum

379.15   US   ISSN 0042-6776
VIRGINIA SCHOOL BOARDS ASSOCIATION NEWSLETTER. 1953. 9/yr. membership. Virginia School Boards Association, 2320 Hunters Way, Ste. B, Charlottesville, VA 22901-7931. TEL 804-295-8722. FAX 804-295-8785. Ed. Cass Cannon. bk.rev.; illus.; circ. 2,000. (controlled). (processed) **Document type:** newsletter.

379.15   US   ISSN 0744-4583
VOICE OF NORTH CAROLINA SCHOOL BOARDS ASSOCIATION. 1953. q. $15 (foreign $20). North Carolina School Boards Association, 311 E. Edenton St., Box 27963, Raleigh, NC 27611-7963. TEL 919-832-7024. FAX 919-829-5810. Ed. M. Thomasine Hardy. adv.; bk.rev.; illus. circ. 7,500. (reprint service avail.)
   Formerly: North Carolina School Boards Association Bulletin (ISSN 0029-2613)
   Description: Covers schools, school systems, education techniques and various topics related to education and school boards.

371 370   SZ
W C O T P BIENNIAL REPORT. (Editions in English, French and Spanish) 1952. biennial. 8 Fr. World Confederation of Organizations of the Teaching Profession, 5 Ave. du Moulin, CH-1110 Morges, Switzerland. TEL 021-8017467. FAX 021-8017469. TELEX 458219 WCTP CH. Ed. Nick Grisewood. circ. 1,400 (combined).
   Former titles: W C O T P Report; W C O T P Annual Report (ISSN 0084-1528)

371.1   US
WAGES AND BENEFITS. 1965. m. $95. Employee Futures Research, Box 385, Pt. Richey, FL 34673-0385. Ed. Eric Rhodes. bk.rev.; circ. 700.
   Formed by the merger of: Salary and Merit (ISSN 0048-9026) & Personnel News for School Systems (ISSN 0048-3478)

WEST'S EDUCATION LAW REPORTER. see LAW

371.2   US
WISCONSIN CENTER FOR EDUCATION RESEARCH HIGHLIGHTS. 1970. q. free. Wisconsin Center for Education Research, 1025 W. Johnson St., Madison, WI 53706. TEL 608-263-8814. FAX 808-263-6448. Ed. Paul Baker. circ. 7,000. **Document type:** newsletter.
   Formerly (until 1989): Wisconsin Center for Education Research News.
   Description: Examines university research on teaching methods and curriculum, organization and administration, higher education, special education and rehabilitation.

370.193   US
WISCONSIN PARENT TEACHER. 1938. 9/yr. (Sep.-May). $5. Wisconsin Congress of Parents and Teachers Inc., 4797 Hayes Rd., No. 2, Madison, WI 53704. TEL 608-244-1455. Ed. Bonny Buran. illus. circ. 3,000. **Document type:** newsletter.
   Formerly: Wisconsin Parent Teacher Bulletin (ISSN 0043-6577)

379.15   US
WISCONSIN SCHOOL NEWS. 1945. m. $30. Wisconsin Association of School Boards, 122 W. Washington Ave., Madison, WI 53703. TEL 608-257-2622. FAX 608-257-8386. Ed. Kathryn Derene. adv.; bk.rev.; mkt.; stat.; index; circ. 5,500 (controlled).
   Formerly: Wisconsin School Board News (ISSN 0043-664X)
   Description: Covers Wisconsin educational issues for school boards and educators.

379.15 340   US
A WORD ON.... q. $75. National School Boards Association, 1680 Duke St., Alexandria, VA 22314. TEL 703-838-6722. FAX 703-683-7590. circ. 3,500. (looseleaf format; back issues avail.) **Document type:** newsletter.
   Description: Covers both legal and legislative issues affecting education.

371.2   US
YEAR-ROUNDER. 1972. q. $35. National Association for Year-Round Education, Box 711386, San Diego, CA 92171-1386. TEL 619-276-5296. FAX 619-571-5754. Ed. Thomas Balakas. adv. circ. 4,000. **Document type:** newsletter.
   Description: Articles and comment regarding the year-round education movement in the U.S. and Canada.

344.07   US   ISSN 0094-0399
KF4102
YOUR SCHOOL AND THE LAW. 1971. m. $155 (Canada $177; elsewhere $199) (effective June 1994). Axon Group, 747 Dresher Rd., Horsham, PA 19044-0980. TEL 800-341-7874. FAX 215-784-9014. Ed. Rae Theodore; Pub. Kenneth F. Kahn. (looseleaf format) **Document type:** newsletter.
   Incorporates (in 1990): Athletic Director and Coach; Which was formerly: Coach's Legal Report (ISSN 8750-9261); Your School District and the Law; School Board Advisor.
   Description: Aims to provide school administrators, athletic directors, coaches and their legal counsel with up-to-date information on court decisions that affect educational institutions and their athletic programs.

371   ISSN 0044-1112
YOUR SCHOOLS. 1957. 10/yr. free to school district residents. Sweet Home Central School District - Towns of Amherst and Tonawanda, 1901 Sweet Home Rd., Amherst, NY 14228. TEL 716-689-5227. FAX 716-689-5229. Ed. Vicki Mastorides. circ. 13,500. **Document type:** newsletter.

371.2   CC   ISSN 1002-2384
CODEN: BM4238
ZHONGXIAOXUE GUANLI/ADMINISTRATION OF ELEMENTARY AND SECONDARY SCHOOL. (Text in Chinese) 1987. m. Y21.50. Zhongxiaoxue Guanli Zazhishe, A-24 Huangsi Dajie, Dewai, Beijing 100011, People's Republic of China. TEL 2019993. (Dist. overseas by: China International Books Trading Corp., P.O. Box 399, Beijing, P.R.C.) Ed. Tao Xiping. adv. circ. 61,050. **Document type:** academic/scholarly publication.
   Description: Covers the latest development in educational policies, researches, and administrations of elementary and secondary schools in China.

EDUCATION — Special Education And Rehabilitation

see also Criminology and Law Enforcement; Handicapped; Social Services and Welfare

A A C R C NEWSLETTER. (American Association of Children's Residential Centers) see PSYCHOLOGY

A C C H NETWORK; family centered care for children with special health care needs and their families. (Association for the Care of Children's Health) see MEDICAL SCIENCES — Pediatrics

A C E H I JOURNAL/ASSOCIATION CANADIENNE DES EDUCATEURS DES DEFICIENTS AUDITIFS. REVUE. (Association of Canadian Educators of the Hearing Impaired) see HANDICAPPED — Hearing Impaired

371.9   US
A C R M D ON THE RECORD. (Association for Children with Retarded Mental Development) 1960. s-a. free. Association for C R M D, Inc., 162 Fifth Ave., New York, NY 10010. TEL 212-741-0100. Ed. Philip Vassallo. circ. 3,500.

A F E T - MITGLIEDER - RUNDBRIEF. (Arbeitsgemeinschaft fuer Erziehungshilfe (AFET) e.V.) see SOCIAL SCIENCES: COMPREHENSIVE WORKS

371.4   US
A S C A COUNSELOR. 1963. 5/yr. membership. American Counseling Association, American School Counselor Association, 5999 Stevenson Ave., Alexandria, VA 22304. TEL 703-823-9800. FAX 703-823-0252. Ed. Patricia Ferris. illus. circ. 15,000. (looseleaf format; also avail. in microform from UMI; reprint service avail. from UMI)
   Formerly: A S C A Newsletter (ISSN 0001-2416)

A V K O NEWSLETTER. see EDUCATION — Adult Education

371.9   CN   ISSN 0380-4194
ADAPTATION; revue d'education specialisee. 1974. q. Association des Educateurs Specialises pour Inadaptes du Quebec, 8147 Est, rue Sherbrooke, Montreal, Que. H1L 1A7, Canada. Ed. Gilles Beaulieu.

613.7   US   ISSN 0736-5829
GV445
ADAPTED PHYSICAL ACTIVITY QUARTERLY. Short title: A P A Q. 1984. q. $36 to individuals (foreign $40); institutions $80 (foreign $84); students $24 (foreign $28). (International Federation for Adapted Physical Activity) Human Kinetics Publishers, Inc., Box 5076, Champaign, IL 61825-5076. TEL 217-351-5076. FAX 217-351-2674. Ed. Dr. Greg Reid. adv. contact: Michele Watson. bk.rev.; abstr.; bibl.; charts; stat.; index. circ. 820. (back issues avail.) **Indexed:** Excerp.Med., Phys.Ed.Ind., Psychol.Abstr., Sportsearch (1984-). **Document type:** academic/scholarly publication.
—BLDSC (0678.308000); Faxon; UnCover; SWETS. CCC.
   Description: Communicates scholarly inquiries related to physical activity for at-risk infants; pre-schoolers; and students who receive special educations.
Refereed Serial

155.4 371.9   US   ISSN 0735-004X
ADVANCES IN LEARNING AND BEHAVIORAL DISABILITIES. 1982. a. $63.50 to institutions. J A I Press Inc., 55 Old Post Rd., No. 2, Box 1678, Greenwich, CT 06836-1678. TEL 203-661-7602. FAX 203-661-0792. (Addr. in the U.K. and Europe: J A I Press Ltd., The Courtyard, 28 High St., Hampton Hill, Mddx. TW12 1PD, England. TEL 44-81-943-9296. FAX 44-81-943-9317) Ed. Kenneth D. Gadow. **Indexed:** Lang.& Lang.Behav.Abstr., Psychol.Abstr.
—Faxon. CCC.
Refereed Serial

EDUCATION — SPECIAL EDUCATION AND REHABILITATION

371.9 US ISSN 0270-4013
LC3950 CODEN: ASEDEP
ADVANCES IN SPECIAL EDUCATION; a research annual. 1980. a. $58.50 to institutions. J A I Press Inc., 55 Old Post Rd., No. 2, Box 1678, Greenwich, CT 06836-1678. TEL 203-661-7602. Ed. Jay Gottlieb. **Indexed:** Psychol.Abstr.
—BLDSC (0711.530000); Faxon. **CCC.**

371.9 US
ADVOCATE (BETHESDA). 1968. 6/yr. $20. Autism Society of America, 7910 Woodmont Ave., Ste. 650, Bethesda, MD 20814-3015. TEL 301-657-0881; 800-348-8476. FAX 301-657-0869. Ed. Beth Sposato. adv.; bk.rev. circ. 14,000. (processed) **Document type:** newsletter.
Formerly (until vol.11, 1979): N S A C Newsletter (ISSN 0047-9101)

ALL INDIA INSTITUTE OF SPEECH AND HEARING. JOURNAL. see HANDICAPPED — Hearing Impaired

AMERICAN ANNALS OF THE DEAF. see HANDICAPPED — Hearing Impaired

700 150 US ISSN 1066-4076
AMERICAN ART THERAPY ASSOCIATION NEWSLETTER. q. $16 (foreign $28). American Art Therapy Association, Inc., 1202 Allanson Rd., Mundelin, IL 60060. TEL 708-949-6064. FAX 708-566-4580. Ed. Debra Paskind. adv. contact: Christine Fryer. circ. 4,000. **Document type:** newsletter.

616.89 700 US ISSN 0007-4764
RC489.A7 CODEN: AJATA
AMERICAN JOURNAL OF ART THERAPY; art in psychotherapy, education, and rehabilitation. 1961. q. $27 to individuals; institutions $48 (foreign $32). Vermont College of Norwich University, Montpelier, VT 05602. TEL 802-828-8810. FAX 802-828-8855. Ed. Gladys Agell. adv.; bk.rev.; bibl.; illus.; index. circ. 1,800. (also avail. in microform from UMI; reprint service avail. from UMI) **Indexed:** Artbibl.Mod., CLOA, Cont.Pg.Educ., Curr.Cont., Educ.Ind., Except.Child Educ.Abstr., Excerp.Med., Hosp.Lit.Ind., Ind.Med., Ment.Retard.Abstr., Mid.East: Abstr.& Ind., Psychol.Abstr., Rehabil.Lit., SSCI. **Document type:** academic/scholarly publication.
—BLDSC (0821.500000); Faxon; UnCover; SWETS; UMI. **CCC.**
Formerly: Bulletin of Art Therapy.
Description: Deals with graphic and plastic arts as they contribute to human understanding and mental health. Includes new theoretical formulations, research, and description of programs.

AMERICAN PRINTING HOUSE FOR THE BLIND. DEPARTMENT OF EDUCATIONAL AND TECHNICAL RESEARCH. REPORT OF RESEARCH AND DEVELOPMENT ACTIVITIES. see HANDICAPPED — Visually Impaired

371.9 US ISSN 0474-7534
RJ496.A5 CODEN: ORSBBT
ANNALS OF DYSLEXIA; an interdisciplinary journal of specific language disability. 1951. a. price varies. Orton Dyslexia Society, 8600 LaSalle Rd., Ste. 382, Baltimore, MD 21286-2044. TEL 301-296-0232. Ed. Ann Fowler. circ. 10,000. (also avail. in microform from UMI; reprint service avail. from UMI) **Indexed:** C.I.J.E., Child Devel.Abstr., DSH Abstr., Educ.Ind., Except.Child.Educ.Abstr., Lang.& Lang.Behav.Abstr., Psychol.Abstr., SSCI. **Document type:** academic/scholarly publication.
Former titles: Orton Society. Bulletin. (ISSN 0078-6624); Orton Society. Monograph.
Refereed Serial

371.9 US ISSN 0198-7518
LC4031
ANNUAL EDITIONS: EDUCATING EXCEPTIONAL CHILDREN. Key Title: Educating Exceptional Children. 1979. a. $11.95. Dushkin Publishing Group, Inc., Sluice Dock, Guilford, CT 06437-9989. TEL 203-453-4351. FAX 203-453-6000. Ed. Karen Freiberg; Pub. Lan Nielsen. illus. **Document type:** academic/scholarly publication.
Refereed Serial

371.9 362.7 CN ISSN 1189-3958
APPRENTISSAGE ET SOCIALISATION. (Text in French, summaries in English) 1965. q. Can.$27 to individuals; institutions Can.$38. Universite du Quebec a Hull, C.P. 1250, succ. B, Hull, PQ J8X 3X7, Canada. TEL 819-595-2233. FAX 819-595-2384. Ed. Lucie Frechette. adv.; bk.rev. circ. 1,500. **Indexed:** Bull.Signal., Psychol.Abstr., Pt.de Rep. (1991-). **Document type:** academic/scholarly publication.
—BLDSC (1580.166000).
Former titles (until 1991): Apprentissage et Socialisation en Piste (ISSN 0827-1844); (until 1985): Apprentissage et Socialisation (ISSN 0704-7517); (until 1978): Enfant Exceptionnel (ISSN 0046-1970)

371.9 353.9 US
ARKANSAS. DIVISION OF REHABILITATION SERVICES. ANNUAL REPORT. 1940. a. free. Division of Rehabilitation Services, Box 3781, Little Rock, AR 72203. TEL 501-628-8168. illus.; stat. circ. 1,000.

700 150 US ISSN 0742-1656
ART THERAPY. 1983. q. $40 to individuals (foreign $64); institutions $57 (foreign $80). American Art Therapy Association, Inc., 1202 Allanson Rd., Mundelein, IL 60060. TEL 708-949-6064. FAX 708-566-4580. Ed. Cathy Malchiodi. adv. contact: Christine Fryer. bk.rev. circ. 4,000. **Indexed:** Artbibl., Artbibl.Mod., Psychol.Abstr.
—BLDSC (1733.473800); Faxon; UnCover.

610 US ISSN 1040-0435
RM698
ASSISTIVE TECHNOLOGY. 1989. s-a. $49.95 to individuals (foreign $59.95); institutions $62 (foreign $75). R E S N A, 1700 N. Moore St., Ste. 1540, Arlington, VA 22209-1903. TEL 703-524-6686. FAX 703-524-6630. Ed. Lawrence Trachtman.
—UnCover.

AUSTRALIA AND NEW ZEALAND JOURNAL OF DEVELOPMENTAL DISABILITIES. see MEDICAL SCIENCES — Psychiatry And Neurology

371.394 AT ISSN 0311-1954
AUSTRALIAN JOURNAL OF REMEDIAL EDUCATION. 1969. 4/yr. Aus.$55 (foreign Aus.$67). Australian Remedial Education Association, 4 Canterbury Rd., Toorak, Vic. 3142, Australia. TEL 03-826-2929. FAX 03-826-2829. Ed. Christopher Davidson. adv.; bk.rev.; index. circ. 1,900. **Indexed:** Aus.Educ.Ind., Aus.P.A.I.S., Cont.Pg.Educ., Except.Child.Educ.Abstr., Sp.Ed.Needs Abstr. **Document type:** academic/scholarly publication.
Formerly: Remedial Education (ISSN 0048-7236)
Description: Covers all aspects of special education. Looks at learning disabilities and the intelligent underachiever.

371.9 CN ISSN 0704-7509
B C JOURNAL OF SPECIAL EDUCATION. 1976. 3/yr. Can.$25 to non-members; institutions $30. Special Education Association, Dept. of Special Education, University of British Columbia, 2075 Wesbrook Mall, Vancouver, B.C. V6T 1W5, Canada. TEL 604-228-6361. FAX 604-822-3302. Ed. Marg Csapo. adv.; bk.rev. circ. 1,500. **Indexed:** C.I.J.E., Can.Educ.Ind., Educ.Admin.Abstr., ERIC, Except.Child Educ.Abstr.
—BLDSC (1871.370700).
Description: Devoted to reviews of research, case studies, surveys, and reports on the effectiveness of innovative programs.

DAS BAND. see HANDICAPPED

BAUSTEINE KINDERGARTEN. see EDUCATION — Teaching Methods And Curriculum

371.4 US ISSN 0198-7429
RJ506.B44
BEHAVIORAL DISORDERS. 1976. 4/yr. $20 to individuals; institutions $50; foreign $54. (Council for Children with Behavioral Disorders) Council for Exceptional Children, 1920 Association Dr., Reston, VA 22091. TEL 703-620-3660. FAX 703-264-9494. Ed. Frank Wood. adv.; bk.rev. circ. 9,700. (also avail. in microform from UMI; reprint service avail. from UMI) **Indexed:** C.I.J.E., Educ.Ind., Mult.Ed.Abstr., Psychol.Abstr., Sp.Ed.Needs Abstr. **Document type:** academic/scholarly publication, trade publication.
—BLDSC (1877.370000); Faxon; UnCover; UMI.
Description: Directed to educators, parents, mental health personnel and others concerned with the education and well-being of children and youth with behavioral and emotional disorders.

371 GW ISSN 0171-9718
BEHINDERTENHILFE DURCH ERZIEHUNG, UNTERRICHT UND THERAPIE. 1977. irreg., no.18, 1993. price varies. Ernst Reinhardt Verlag, Kemnatenstr. 46, 80639 Munich, Germany. TEL 089-1783005. FAX 089-1781827. Ed. Otto Speck. **Document type:** monographic series.

371.9 GW ISSN 0341-7301
BEHINDERTENPAEDAGOGIK; Vierteljahresschrift fuer Behindertenpaedagogik in Praxis, Forschung und Lehre und Integration Behinderter. 1971. q. DM.49.50. Jarick Oberbiel Verlag GmbH & Co. KG, Roethweg 1, 35606 Solms, Germany. TEL 06441-5868. Ed. Georg Feuser. adv.; bk.rev.; bibl.; index. circ. 2,500. **Indexed:** Psychol.Abstr. **Document type:** academic/scholarly publication.

371.9 GW ISSN 0723-4511
BEHINDERTENPAEDAGOGIK IN BAYERN. 1957. q. DM.20. Verband Deutscher Sonderschulen e.V., Neue Bergstr. 14, 91085 Weisendorf, Germany. TEL 09131-44493. Ed. Bernd Urlaub. adv.; bk.rev. circ. 3,000. (back issues avail.) **Document type:** academic/scholarly publication.
Formerly (until 1981): Sonderschule in Bayern (ISSN 0723-4503)

362.3 US
BETHPHAGE MESSENGER. q. Lancaster House Publishing Co., 1620 N. St., Lincoln, NE 68508. TEL 402-474-2200. Ed. Jane Medinger. circ. 100,000.

BIBLIOGRAFIA ERITYSIRYHMIEN LIIKUNNAN TUTKIMUKSESTA/BIBLIOGRAPHY ON RESEARCH IN PHYSICAL EDUCATION AND SPORT FOR THE HANDICAPPED. see EDUCATION — Abstracting, Bibliographies, Statistics

BRITISH ASSOCIATION OF TEACHERS OF THE DEAF. JOURNAL. see HANDICAPPED — Hearing Impaired

BRITISH INSTITUTE OF LEARNING DISABILITIES. CURRENT AWARENESS SERVICE. see EDUCATION — Abstracting, Bibliographies, Statistics

371.9 150 UK
CODEN: BJMSBL
BRITISH JOURNAL OF DEVELOPMENTAL DISABILITIES. 1952. s-a. £15($34) (British Society for Developmental Disabilities) S E F A (Publications) Ltd., The Globe, 4 Great William St., Stratford-upon-Avon CV37 6RY, England. Ed. H.C. Gunzburg. adv.; bk.rev.; charts; illus.; cum.index every 2 yrs. circ. 1,500. (reprint service avail. from SWZ) **Indexed:** Adol.Ment.Hlth.Abstr., ASSIA, Bibl.Dev.Med.& Child Neur., Biol.Abstr., Curr.Cont., Except.Child.Educ.Abstr., Excerp.Med., Mid.East: Abstr.& Ind., Psychol.Abstr., Sp.Ed.Needs Abstr., SSCI. **Document type:** academic/scholarly publication.
—UnCover.
Former titles (until 1992): British Journal of Mental Subnormality (ISSN 0374-633X); Journal of Mental Subnormality (ISSN 0022-2666)
Description: Provides an international forum for a multidisciplinary approach to the problems posed by mental handicaps and learning disabilities.

EDUCATION — SPECIAL EDUCATION AND REHABILITATION

371.9 UK ISSN 0952-3383
LC3986.G7 CODEN: BJSPEB
BRITISH JOURNAL OF SPECIAL EDUCATION. 1974. q. £25($65) to individuals; institutions £50($130). (National Association for Special Education Needs) Basil Blackwell Ltd., 108 Cowley Rd., Oxford, OX4 1JF, England. TEL 0865-791100. Ed. Margaret Peter. adv.; bk.rev.; cum.index: 1974-1983. (also avail. in microfilm; microfiche; back issues avail.) **Indexed:** ASSIA, C.I.J.E., Cont.Pg.Educ., Curr.Adv.Ecol.Sci., Educ.Tech.Abstr., Except.Child.Educ.Abstr., High.Educ.Curr.Aware.Bull., Ind.Med., Sp.Ed.Needs Abstr.
—Faxon; SWETS; UMI. **CCC.**
Formerly (until 1985): Special Education - Forward Trends (ISSN 0015-8658)

371.9 GW
DAS BRUDERHAUS. 1949. s-a. free. Gustav Werner Stiftung, Ringelbachstr. 211, 72762 Reutlingen, Germany. FAX 07121-278300. Ed. I. Steudle. circ. 20,000.

DAS BUERO. see HANDICAPPED — Visually Impaired

371.9 GW
BUNDESARBEITSGEMEINSCHAFT HILFE FUER BEHINDERTE. BERICHTE. JAHRESSPIEGEL. a. free. (Bundesarbeitsgemeinschaft Hilfe fuer Behinderte e.V.) Verlag fuer Medizin Dr. Ewald Fischer GmbH, Postfach 105767, 69047 Heidelberg, Germany. TEL 06221-4062-0. Ed. Elfriede Loebel. **Document type:** academic/scholarly publication.
Formerly: Bundesarbeitsgemeinschaft Hilfe fuer Behinderte. Jahrespiegel.

371.9 US
C C B D NEWSLETTER. 1987. 4/yr. membership only. (Council for Children with Behavioral Disorders) Council for Exceptional Children, 1920 Association Dr., Reston, VA 22091-1589. TEL 703-620-3660. FAX 703-264-9494. Ed. Dr. Cynthia Warger. circ. 8,800. **Document type:** newsletter.
Description: Gives information on the council and its activities; includes news legislation and other developments in the field.

C R L A NEWSLETTER. (College Reading and Learning Association) see EDUCATION — Adult Education

371.9 FR
CAHIERS DE L'ADAPT. 1929. q. Ligue pour l'Adaptation du Diminue Physique au Travail, 185 bis rue Ordener, 75882 Paris Cedex 1, France. Ed. Andre Dessertine.

371.9 CN
CANADIAN JOURNAL OF SPECIAL EDUCATION. 1984. s-a. Can.$25. Center for Human Development and Research, c/o Dr. Marg Csapo, Dept. of Special Education, University of British Columbia, 2125 Main Mall, Vancouver, B.C. V6T 1Z4, Canada. TEL 604-822-5351.

371.9 362.4 CN
CANADIAN REHABILITATION COUNCIL. ANNUAL REPORT/CONSEIL CANADIEN DE READAPTATION. RAPPORT ANNUEL. 1963. a. free. Canadian Rehabilitation Council - Conseil Canadien de Readaptation, 45 Sheppard Ave. E., Ste. 801, Toronto, ON M3N 5W9, Canada. TEL 416-250-7490. FAX 416-229-1371. Ed. Heather Ney. circ. 2,000.
Formerly: Canadian Rehabilitation Council for the Disabled. Annual Report (ISSN 0068-9580)
Description: Information on rehabilitation, fund raising services and the network of organizations improving the quality of life for the disabled.

CAPTION. see COMMUNICATIONS — Television And Cable

CAREER DEVELOPMENT FOR EXCEPTIONAL INDIVIDUALS. see OCCUPATIONS AND CAREERS

CATALYST (MENLO PARK). see COMPUTERS — Computer Assisted Instruction

371.9 US ISSN 0745-6298
LC3991
CHALLENGE (CARTHAGE); reaching and teaching the gifted child. 1982. 5/yr. $21.95 (effective 1992). Good Apple, 1204 Buchanan St., Box 299, Carthage, IL 62321-0299. TEL 217-357-3981. FAX 217-357-3987. Ed. Sharon Thompson. bk.rev. circ. 14,000. (back issues avail.)
Description: Contains articles and reproducible activity worksheets to be used by teachers and parents educating gifted children.

371.9 UK ISSN 0265-6590
LC4704.5
CHILD LANGUAGE TEACHING AND THERAPY. 1985. 3/yr. £36($66) to individuals; institutions £57.50 (effective 1994). Edward Arnold (Subsidiary of: Hodder Headline plc), Mill Rd., Dunton Green, Sevenoaks, Kent TN13 2YA, England. TEL 0732-450111. FAX 0732-461321. (Subscr. to: Turpin Distribution Services Ltd., Blackhorse Rd., Letchworth, Herts. SG6 1HN, England) adv.; bk.rev. **Indexed:** Cont.Pg.Educ., Lang.& Lang.Behav.Abstr. (1985-). **Document type:** academic/scholarly publication.
—BLDSC (3172.944690); UnCover; SWETS. **CCC.**
Description: Helps those involved with children handicapped by an inadequate command of the spoken or written language.

371.9 JA ISSN 0916-2682
CHIRYO KYOIKU KENKYU KIYO/GIFU UNIVERSITY. DEPARTMENT OF REMEDIAL EDUCATION. REPORT. (Text in Japanese) 1979. a. Gifu Daigaku, Kyoikugakubu, Chiryo Kyoikugaku Kenkyushitsu - Gifu University, Faculty of Education, Department of Remedial Education, 1-1, Yanagito, Gifu-shi, Gifu-ken 501-11, Japan.

420 US ISSN 0890-409X
RJ496.C67
CLINICAL CONNECTION; idea source for the speech and language specialist working with the young communicator. 1986. q. $39. A A D of Northern Virginia, 708 Pendleton St., Alexandria, VA 22314-1819. TEL 703-549-5126. FAX 703-548-5563. Ed. Georgina Ruley Parks. bk.rev. circ. 6,000. (back issues avail.)
Description: Forum for speech and language pathologists to share practical clinical ideas.

CLINICAL LINGUISTICS & PHONETICS. see MEDICAL SCIENCES — Psychiatry And Neurology

371.9 US ISSN 1054-8505
RC423.A1
CLINICS IN COMMUNICATION DISORDERS. 1991. q. $60 to individuals (foreign $75); institutions $95 (foreign $110). Butterworth - Heinemann, Part of the Reed Elsevier group, 313 Washington St., Newton, MA 02158. TEL 617-928-2500; 800-366-2665. FAX 617-928-2610. Ed. Betty Jane Philips. (back issues avail.) **Document type:** academic/scholarly publication.
—BLDSC (3286.545500); UMI. **CCC.**
Description: Provides speech and language pathologists with clinical information on the assessment, diagnosis and treatment of communication disorders.

CLOSING THE GAP. see EDUCATION — Computer Applications

420 UK ISSN 0953-6086
COLLEGE OF SPEECH AND LANGUAGE THERAPISTS. BULLETIN. 1945. m. £35 (overseas £40) (membership). College of Speech and Language Therapists, 7 Bath Place, London EC2, England. TEL 071-613-3855. FAX 071-613-3854. Ed. Sally Heath. adv.; bk.rev. circ. 6,000. **Document type:** academic/scholarly publication, bulletin.
Formerly: College of Speech Therapists. Bulletin.
Description: Contains research papers, practice reports, correspondence and college news of interest to students and professionals in speech-language pathology and audiology.

COMMUNICATING TOGETHER. see EDUCATION — Computer Applications

371.9 UK ISSN 0045-7663
COMMUNICATION (LONDON, 1967). 1967. 3/yr. £10 (foreign £15). National Autistic Society, 276 Willesden Ln., London NW2 5RB, England. TEL 081-451-1114. FAX 081-451-5865. Ed. Christine Nickles. adv.; bk.rev. circ. 2,500. **Indexed:** Curr.Cont., Lang.& Lang.Behav.Abstr., SSCI. **Document type:** academic/scholarly publication.
—BLDSC (3354.818000).

371.9 US
CONTEMPORARY PERSPECTIVES IN REHABILITATION. 1986. irreg. price varies. F.A. Davis Company, 1915 Arch St., Philadelphia, PA 19103. TEL 800-523-4049. TELEX 83-4837. Ed. Steven L. Wolf. **Document type:** monographic series.

CONTRIBUTIONS TO RESIDENTIAL TREATMENT. see PSYCHOLOGY

COUNSELING AND VALUES. see RELIGIONS AND THEOLOGY — Roman Catholic

371.9 362.42 US
COURAGE NEWS. q. A H A Stroke Connection, 7272 Greenville Ave., Dallas, TX 75231. TEL 214-706-1556. FAX 214-696-5211. (back issues avail.)

CUED SPEECH CENTER LINES. see HANDICAPPED — Hearing Impaired

CUED SPEECH JOURNAL. see HANDICAPPED — Hearing Impaired

371.9 US
D E C COMMUNICATOR. 1974. q. membership only. Council for Exceptional Children, Division for Early Childhood, 1920 Association Dr., Reston, VA 22091-1589. TEL 703-620-3660. FAX 703-264-9494. Ed. Sarah Rule. circ. 8,000. **Document type:** newsletter.
Description: Information on the division and its activities. Includes news in the field of early childhood education.

371.9 US
D L D TIMES. 1984. 3/yr. membership only. Council for Exceptional Children, Division of Learning Disabilities, 1920 Association Dr., Reston, VA 22091. TEL 703-620-3660. FAX 703-264-9494. Ed. Dr. Kate Garnett. circ. 14,000.
Description: Provides business information and news in the field of learning disabilities.

D P H D NEWSLETTER. (Division for Physical & Health Disabilities) see HANDICAPPED — Physically Impaired

371.9 362.4 DK ISSN 0905-0221
DATCH INFORMATION. 1989. 4/yr. free. Danish Centre for Rehabilitation and Special Education, Graham Bells Vej 1 A, DK-8200 Aarhus N, Denmark. TEL 45-86-783700. FAX 45-86-783730. Ed. Maiken Hansen. bk.rev. **Document type:** newsletter.

DEUTSCHE BEHINDERTENZEITSCHRIFT. see MEDICAL SCIENCES — Psychiatry And Neurology

371.9 UK
DEVELOPING HORIZONS IN SPECIAL EDUCATION SERIES.* 1982. irreg. £2.50 per no. National Council for Special Education, York House, Exhall Grange, Wheelwright Lane, Coventry CV7 9HP, England. Ed. Richard Rose.

DEVELOPMENT DISABILITIES BULLETIN. see MEDICAL SCIENCES — Psychiatry And Neurology

371.9 US ISSN 1046-6657
HD77
DEVELOPMENT EDUCATION ANNUAL. 1989. a. National Clearinghouse on Development Education, 45 John St., Ste. 1200, New York, NY 10038.

EDUCATION — SPECIAL EDUCATION AND REHABILITATION

362.7 US ISSN 0737-2477
LB3050
DIAGNOSTIQUE. 1976. 4/yr. $28 (foreign $32). (Council for Educational Diagnostic Services) Council for Exceptional Children, 1920 Association Dr., Reston, VA 22091. TEL 703-620-3660. FAX 703-264-9494. Ed. Ronald Taylor. adv.; bk.rev. circ. 2,000. (also avail. in microform from UMI; back issues avail.) Indexed: C.I.J.E., Cont.Pg.Educ.
—BLDSC (3579.671900); Faxon; UMI.
  Description: Directed to psychologists, diagnosticians, and special educators who use methods of educational measurement in evaluating exceptional individuals.

371.9 US
DIRECT LINK. q. $5. Center for Computer Assistance to the Disabled, 1950 Stemmons Frwy., Ste. 4041, Dallas, TX 75207-3109. TEL 214-746-4217. FAX 214-746-4203. Ed. David Green. circ. 5,000. **Document type:** newsletter.

371.9 136.7 US ISSN 0070-5012
LC4007
DIRECTORY FOR EXCEPTIONAL CHILDREN; a listing of educational and training facilities. 1950. irreg., 13th ed., 1994-1995. $60. Porter Sargent Publishers, Inc., 11 Beacon St., Ste. 1400, Boston, MA 02108. TEL 617-523-1670. FAX 617-523-1021. adv.; illus.; stat.; index. circ. 4,000. **Document type:** directory.
  Description: Surveys more than 3,000 U.S. schools and organizations serving children and young adults with all types of developmental, physical, and emotional handicaps.

DIRECTORY OF COLLEGE FACILITIES AND SERVICES FOR PEOPLE WITH DISABILITIES. see EDUCATION — Guides To Schools And Colleges

DIRECTORY OF GRANTS FOR ORGANIZATIONS SERVING PEOPLE WITH DISABILITIES; a guide to sources of funding in the United States for handicapped programs & services. see HANDICAPPED

371.9 US
DIRECTORY OF SERVICES AND FACILITIES FOR THE LEARNING DISABLED. 1968. biennial. free. Academic Therapy Publications, Inc., 20 Commercial Blvd., Novato, CA 94949. TEL 415-883-3314. FAX 415-883-3720. Ed. Betty Lou Kratoville. adv. circ. 20,000. **Document type:** directory.
  Former titles: Directory of Educational Facilities for the Learning Disabled (ISSN 0093-7703); Directory of Facilities for the Learning Disabled (ISSN 0092-3257)

371.9 362.4 UK
▼**DISABILITY AND REHABILITATION SERIES.** 1992. irreg., vol.6, 1994. $42. (Rehabilitation Resource Center) Jessica Kingsley Publishers, 116 Pentonville Rd., London N1 9JB, England. TEL 071-833-2307. FAX 071-837-2917. (U.S. subscr. to: Taylor & Francis, 1900 Frost Rd., Ste. 101, Bristol, PA 19007-1598. TEL 800-821-8312. FAX 215-785-5515) Eds. Michael Floyd, Elizabeth Blair. **Document type:** monographic series.

DIVISION ON VISUAL HANDICAPS QUARTERLY. see HANDICAPPED — Visually Impaired

DOEVES TIDSSKRIFT. see HANDICAPPED — Hearing Impaired

DOWN SYNDROME NEWS. see MEDICAL SCIENCES — Psychiatry And Neurology

EARLY CHILDHOOD REPORTER. see LAW

371 618 US ISSN 1058-8396
EARLY INTERVENTION. 1986. q. free. (Illinois Early Childhood Intervention Clearinghouse) Illinois Public Health Association, 428 W. Jefferson, Springfield, IL 62702. TEL 217-522-5687. (Subscr. to: 830 S. Spring St., Springfield, IL 62704. TEL 217-785-1364) Ed. Chet Brandt. bk.rev.; circ. 3,500 (controlled). (back issues avail.) **Document type:** newsletter.

371 VE ISSN 0252-998X
EDUCACION ESPECIAL. 1980. 3/yr. Bs.60($12) Ministerio de Educacion, Fundacion para el Desarrollo de la Educacion Especial, Esquina de Salas, Piso 12, Caracas 1010, Venezuela. Ed. Estela Falicov. bk.rev.; illus. circ. 4,000. (back issues avail.)

371.9 378 UK ISSN 0141-7282
EDUCARE. 1976. 3/yr. membership. Skill: National Bureau for Students with Disabilities, 336 Brixton Rd., London SW9 7AA, England. TEL 071-274-0565. FAX 071-274-7840. Ed. Deborah Cooper. bk.rev.; bibl.; cum.index. circ. 1,500. Indexed: Cont.Pg.Educ., Sp.Ed.Needs Abstr. **Document type:** academic/scholarly publication.
—BLDSC (3661.155500).

371.9 US
EDUCATION AND TRAINING IN MENTAL RETARDATION. 1966. q. $30 to individuals; institutions $55; foreign $59.50. Council for Exceptional Children, Division on Mental Retardation and Developmental Disabilities, 1920 Association Dr., Reston, VA 22091. TEL 703-620-3660. FAX 703-264-9494. Ed. Stanley Zucker. adv.; bk.rev.; index. circ. 9,100. (also avail. in microform from UMI; reprint service avail. from UMI) Indexed: Adol.Ment.Hlth.Abstr., Behav.Med.Abstr., C.I.J.E., Cont.Pg.Educ., Curr.Cont., Educ.Admin.Abstr., Educ.Ind., Except.Child Educ.Abstr., Excerp.Med., Lang.& Lang.Behav.Abstr., Mid.East: Abstr.& Ind., Psychol.Abstr., Rehabil.Lit., Soc.Work Res.& Abstr., Sp.Ed.Needs Abstr., SSCI.
—BLDSC (3661.200000); UnCover.
  Formerly (until Dec. 1986): Education and Training of the Mentally Retarded (ISSN 0013-1237)

EDUCAZIONE DEI SORDOMUTI. see HANDICAPPED — Hearing Impaired

EFFECTIVE SCHOOL PRACTICES. see EDUCATION — Teaching Methods And Curriculum

ENTOURAGE. see HANDICAPPED

362.7 FR
EPANOUIR. 1962. bi-m. 90 F.($14) Union Nationale des Associations de Parents d'Enfants Inadaptes, 15 rue Coysevox, 75018 Paris, France. Ed. Jean-Marie Brun. adv.; bk.rev.; film rev.; bibl.; stat. circ. 68,000.

420 UK ISSN 0963-7273
RC423.A1 CODEN: EJDCEW
EUROPEAN JOURNAL OF DISORDERS OF COMMUNICATION. 1966. 4/yr. £49($89) to individuals; institutions £75($135). Whurr Publishers Ltd., 19b Compton Terrace, London N1 2UN, England. TEL 071-359-5979. FAX 071-226-5290. (U.S. subscr. to: Whurr Publishers Ltd., Box 1897, Lawrence, KS 66044-8897) Ed. Evelyn Abberton. adv.; bk.rev.; abstr.; bibl.; charts; illus.; stat.; index. circ. 6,000. Indexed: ASSIA, Bibl.Dev.Med.& Child Neur., Curr.Adv.Ecol.Sci., Dent.Ind., Except.Child.Educ.Abstr., Excerp.Med., Ind.Med., Lang.& Lang.Behav.Abstr., Lang.Teach.& Ling.Abstr., Psychol.Abstr., Rehabil.Lit., SSCI. **Document type:** academic/scholarly publication.
—BLDSC (3829.728290); ADONIS; Faxon; UnCover; SWETS; UMI.
  Formerly: British Journal of Disorders of Communication (ISSN 0007-098X); Incorporates: Speech Pathology and Therapy.
  Description: Covers all aspects of disorders of human communication.

371 UK ISSN 0885-6257
LC3986.A2 CODEN: EJSEEB
EUROPEAN JOURNAL OF SPECIAL NEEDS EDUCATION. 1986. 3/yr. £32 (foreign £36) to individuals; institutions £68 (foreign £74). (National Foundation for Educational Research) Routledge, 11 New Fetter Ln., London EC4P 4EE, England. TEL 071-583-9855. FAX 071-583-0701. TELEX 263398-ROUT-G. (Subscr. to: ITPS Ltd., Cheriton House, Andover, Hants SP10 5BE, England. TEL 0264-342919. FAX 0264-342807) Ed. Seamus Hegarty. Indexed: ASSIA, Curr.Cont., Mult.Ed.Abstr., Sp.Ed.Needs Abstr. **Document type:** academic/scholarly publication.
—BLDSC (3829.744000); SWETS; UMI.

371.9 US
EXCEPTIONAL NEWS. vol.15, no.2, 1992. q. free. Center for Persons with Disabilities, Outreach, Development & Dissemination Division, Department of Special Education, Utah State University, Logan, UT 84322-6845. TEL 801-750-1991. FAX 801-750-2044. Ed. Amy Santos. circ. 2,500. **Document type:** trade publication.
  Description: Designed for professionals and paraprofessionals.

371.9 CN ISSN 1183-322X
EXCEPTIONALITY EDUCATION CANADA. 1991. q. Can.$30 to individuals; institutions Can.$50 (foreign $50); students Can.$20 (foreign $20). University of Calgary Press, 2500 University Dr., N.W., Calgary, AB T2N 1N4, Canada. TEL 403-220-7578. FAX 403-282-0085. TELEX 03-821545. Ed. Judy Lupart. circ. 400.
—BLDSC (3835.570000).
  Description: Provides a forum for scholarly exchange among Canadian professionals in education and related disciplines who are involved with students across the spectrum of exceptionality.
  Refereed Serial

362 US ISSN 1066-7032
FAMILY COUNSELING AND THERAPY. 1993. 6/yr. $30. Love Publishing Co., 1777 S. Bellaire St., Denver, CO 80222. TEL 303-757-2579. FAX 303-782-5683. circ. 1,000.

FOCUS ON AUTISTIC BEHAVIOR. see MEDICAL SCIENCES — Psychiatry And Neurology

371.9 US ISSN 0015-511X
FOCUS ON EXCEPTIONAL CHILDREN. 1969. m. (Sep.-May). $30 (effective 1994). Love Publishing Co., 1777 S. Bellaire St., Denver, CO 80222. TEL 303-757-2579. FAX 303-782-5683. Ed. Stanley F. Love. bk.rev.; index, cum.index. circ. 3,000. (also avail. in microform from UMI; reprint service avail. from UMI) Indexed: C.I.J.E., Cont.Pg.Educ., Curr.Cont., Educ.Ind., Except.Child Educ.Abstr., Rehabil.Lit., SSCI.
—BLDSC (3964.215000); Faxon; UnCover; UMI.

FOCUS ON LEARNING PROBLEMS IN MATHEMATICS. see MATHEMATICS

FUTURE REFLECTIONS. see HANDICAPPED — Visually Impaired

G L A D NEWS. (Greater Los Angeles Council on Deafness, Inc.) see HANDICAPPED — Hearing Impaired

420 GW ISSN 0932-934X
G W G - ZEITSCHRIFT. 1971. q. DM.40. Gesellschaft fuer Wissenschaftliche Gesprachspsychotherapie e.V., Richard-Wagner-Str. 12, 5000 Cologne 1, Germany. TEL 0221-252917. Ed. Michael Behr. adv.; bk.rev. circ. 3,000. (back issues avail.)
  Formerly: G W G-Info.

371.9 GW ISSN 0173-9573
GEISTIGE BEHINDERUNG; Fachzeitschrift der Lebenshilfe fuer geistig Behinderte. 1962. q. DM.38. Bundesvereinigung Lebenshilfe fuer geistig Behinderte e.V, Postfach 701163, 35020 Marburg, Germany. TEL 06421-491-0. FAX 06421-491167. Ed. Regina Humbert. adv.; bk.rev.; illus.; index. circ. 9,500. **Document type:** academic/scholarly publication.
—BLDSC (4096.150000).
  Formerly (until 1980): Lebenshilfe (ISSN 0023-995X)
  Description: Directed to specialists working with the mentally retarded. Focus is on development, education, social adaptation, special problems. Also lists available positions.

GERIATRIC CARE. see GERONTOLOGY AND GERIATRICS

371.9 UK ISSN 0261-4294
GIFTED EDUCATION INTERNATIONAL. 1982. 3/yr. £49($99) A B Academic Publishers, P.O. Box 42, Bicester, Oxon. OX6 7NW, England. TEL 0869-320949. Ed. Belle Wallace. adv.; bk.rev.; bibl.; illus. (also avail. in microform) Indexed: ASSIA, C.I.J.E., Cont.Pg.Educ., ERIC, Psychol.Abstr., SOMA. **Document type:** academic/scholarly publication.
—BLDSC (4175.320000); Faxon; UnCover; SWETS. CCC.

371.3 028.5 US ISSN 1064-0053
GIFTED EDUCATION PRESS QUARTERLY. 1987. q. $12. Gifted Education Press, 10201 Yuma Court, Box 1586, Manassas, VA 22110. TEL 703-369-5017. Ed. Maurice D. Fisher. bk.rev. circ. 1,000. **Document type:** academic/scholarly publication.
  Formerly: Gifted Education Press Newsletter.
  Description: Covers current problems and issues concerned with educating the gifted, and using the humanities and sciences with the gifted.

EDUCATION — SPECIAL EDUCATION AND REHABILITATION

371.9 US ISSN 1060-3166
GIFTED EDUCATION REVIEW. 1991. 4/yr. $45. Box 2278, Evergreen, CO 80439-2278. TEL 303-674-5489. Ed. Carol Fertig. adv. **Document type:** academic/scholarly publication.
 Description: Summarizes current research, trends, teaching units, and other information available in the field of gifted education.

371.9 US
GIFTED UNLIMITED. m. $25 includes membership. Northwest Gifted Child Association, Box 1226, Bellevue, WA 98009. TEL 206-649-8546; 800-864-2073. Ed. Charlotte Kanemori. circ. 375.

GONG. see HANDICAPPED — Hearing Impaired

371.4 CN
GOODWILL DIMENSIONS. 195? s-a. free. Goodwill Industries of Toronto, 234 Adelaide St. E., Toronto, Ont. M5A 1M9, Canada. TEL 416-362-4711. FAX 416-362-0720. Ed. MaryLou Frazer. (tabloid format; back issues avail.)
 Description: Informs clients, customers, donors, corporations about job training programs, retail news, donation needs.

371.9 US
THE GRAM. 1968. bi-m. $10. L D A - California, 655 Lewelling Blvd., Ste. 355, San Leandro, CA 94571-1840. Ed. Polly Tyner. adv.; bk.rev.; film rev.; bibl. circ. 5,700.
 Formerly: C A N H C - Gram (California Association for Neurologically Handicapped Children).

H K N C - T A C NEWS. (Helen Keller National Center, Technical Assistance Center) see HANDICAPPED — Visually Impaired

HABILITATIVE MENTAL HEALTHCARE NEWSLETTER. see MEDICAL SCIENCES — Psychiatry And Neurology

HANDICAP IDRETT. see HANDICAPPED

371.9 CN
HEAR OUR WINGS. irreg. Can.$15. (Saskatchewan Council for the Education of Gifted Learners) Saskatchewan Teachers' Federation, Box 1108, Saskatoon, SK S7K 3N3, Canada. Ed. Carol Casswell.

HEILPAEDAGOGISCHE FORSCHUNG; Zeitschrift fuer Paedagogik und Psychologie Behinderter. see MEDICAL SCIENCES — Psychiatry And Neurology

HOERGESCHAEDIGTE KINDER. see HANDICAPPED — Hearing Impaired

371.9 410 US ISSN 1046-7599
RC423.A1
HUMAN COMMUNICATION AND ITS DISORDERS; a review. 1987. irreg., vol.3, 1991. price varies. Ablex Publishing Corporation, 355 Chestnut St., Norwood, NJ 07648. TEL 201-767-8450. FAX 201-767-6717. TELEX 135-393. Ed. Harris Winitz.

371.9 AT ISSN 0810-6398
HYPER ACTIVITIES. 1976. 8/yr. Aus.$15. Hyperactivity Association, 15-29 Bertram St., Chatswood, N.S.W. 2067, Australia. TEL 4112186. Ed. Roslyn Mitchell. bk.rev.; index. circ. 700. (back issues avail.) **Document type:** newsletter.
 Description: Discusses diet behavior management, medication, hyperactivity, attention deficit disorder.

371.9 US ISSN 0300-6883
I A L NEWS. 1955. 3/yr. free. International Association of Laryngectomees, c/o American Cancer Society, 1599 Clifton Rd. N.E., Atlanta, GA 30329. TEL 404-320-3333. Ed. Jane Del Vecchio. bk.rev.; illus. circ. 15,000. Indexed: Rehabil.Lit. **Document type:** newsletter.

371.9 362.4 US
I C E V H EDUCATOR. 1952. s-a. membership. International Council for Education of the Visually Handicapped, c/o Perkins School for the Blind, 175 N. Beacon St., Watertown, MA 02172. FAX 617-926-2027. TELEX 910-240-9886. Ed. Kevin J. Lessard. bk.rev. circ. 2,200.
 Formerly: International Conference of Educators of Blind Youth. Proceedings (ISSN 0074-2937)

I F H O H JOURNAL. (International Federation of the Hard of Hearing) see HANDICAPPED — Hearing Impaired

371.9 362.4 NE ISSN 0925-8396
I R V SERIES IN REHABILITATION RESEARCH. 1991. irreg. fl.57.50($42) Swets & Zeitlinger bv, Heereweg 347, 2161 CA Lisse, Netherlands. TEL 31-2521-35111. FAX 31-2521-15888. TELEX 41325. (Dist. in N. America by: Swets & Zeitlinger, 440 Creamery Way, Ste. A, Exton, PA 19341. TEL 800-447-9387. FAX 610-524-5366) (Co-sponsors: Institute for Rehabilitation, Hoensbroek; University of Limburg, Department of Medical Psychology) **Document type:** monographic series.
 Refereed Serial

371.9 360 US
▼**INCLUSION TIMES.** 1993. 4/yr. $29.95. National Professional Resources, Inc., 25 S. Regent St., Port Chester, NY 10573. TEL 914-937-8879; 800-453-7461. FAX 914-937-9327. Ed. Daniel Sage. **Document type:** newsletter.
 Description: Focuses on issues relating to eudcating children and youth with disabilities in reguIar education and other inclusive leraning environments.

371.9 340 US ISSN 1055-520X
INDIVIDUALS WITH DISABILITIES EDUCATION LAW REPORTER. 1978. 24/yr. $855. L R P Publications, 747 Dresher Rd., Box 980, Horsham, PA 19044-0980. FAX 215-784-9639. Ed. Melinda H. Maloney. cum.index. circ. 1,250. (back issues avail.)
●Also available online.
Also available on CD-ROM.
 —CCC.
 Formerly: Education for the Handicapped Law Report (ISSN 0744-4117)

INSTITUTO INTERAMERICANO DEL NINO. EDUCACION ESPECIAL. INFORMES TECNICOS. see SOCIAL SERVICES AND WELFARE

INTERFACE (CHICAGO, 1978). see LIBRARY AND INFORMATION SCIENCES

371.9 FR
INTERNATIONAL ASSOCIATION OF WORKERS FOR TROUBLED CHILDREN AND YOUTH. CONGRESS REPORTS. (Text in English, French) 1955. quadrennial. $20. International Association of Workers for Troubled Children and Youth, 3 rue Pierre Brossolette, 64000 Pau, France. **Document type:** proceedings, bulletin.
 Formerly: International Association of Workers for Maladjusted Children. Congress Report (ISSN 0074-1787)

INTERNATIONAL CONFERENCE ON PIAGETIAN THEORY AND THE HELPING PROFESSIONS. PROCEEDINGS. see EDUCATION

371.9 236.4 AT ISSN 1034-912X
LC4661
INTERNATIONAL JOURNAL OF DISABILITY, DEVELOPMENT AND EDUCATION; the Australian journal on the education of handicapped children. 1954. 3/yr. Aus.$42. (Fred and Eleanor Schonell Educational Research Centre) University of Queensland Press, Box 42, St. Lucia, Qld. 4067, Australia. TEL 07-365-2740. FAX 07-365-1988. Ed.Bd. adv.; bk.rev.; bibl.; charts. circ. 1,400. (also avail. in microfilm from KTO; reprint service avail. from KTO) Indexed: ASSIA, C.I.J.E., Cont.Pg.Educ., Curr.Cont., Except.Child.Educ.Abstr., Mid.East Abstr.& Ind., Mult.Ed.Abstr., Psychol.Abstr., SSCI.
 —BLDSC (4542.185450); Faxon; UnCover; SWETS.
 Former titles (until 1990): Exceptional Child (ISSN 0156-6555); Slow Learning Child (ISSN 0037-704X)

INTERNATIONAL JOURNAL OF REHABILITATION RESEARCH. see HANDICAPPED

371.9 CN
INTERNATIONAL JOURNAL OF SPECIAL EDUCATION. 1985. s-a. Can.$30. Center for Human Development and Research, c/o Dr. Marg Csapo, Dept. of Ed. Psych. & Special Education, University of British Columbia, 2125 Main Mall, Vancouver, B.C. V6T 1Z4, Canada. TEL 604-822-5351. Ed. Marg Csapo.
 Description: Descriptive research articles on special education worldwide.

INTERNATIONAL REVIEW OF RESEARCH IN MENTAL RETARDATION. see MEDICAL SCIENCES — Psychiatry And Neurology

371.9 US ISSN 1053-4512
LC4001 CODEN: ISCLEP
INTERVENTION IN SCHOOL AND CLINIC; an interdisciplinary journal directed to an international audience of teachers and specialists working with capable but underachieving children and youth. 1965. 5/yr. $35 to individuals; institutions $80 (foreign $105) (effective 1994). Pro-Ed Inc., 8700 Shoal Creek Blvd., Austin, TX 78757-6897. TEL 512-451-3246. FAX 512-451-8542. Ed. Gerald Wallace; Pub. Donald D. Hammill. adv.; bk.rev.; bibl.; charts. circ. 4,000. (also avail. in microfilm from UMI.) Indexed: ASCA, Bull.Signal., C.I.J.E., Cont.Pg.Educ., Curr.Cont., DSH Abstr., Educ.Ind., Except.Child.Educ.Abstr., Lang.& Lang.Behav.Abstr., Psychol.Abstr., Rehabil.Lit., Sociol.Abstr., Sp.Ed.Needs Abstr., SSCI. **Document type:** academic/scholarly publication.
 —BLDSC (4557.471850); Faxon; UnCover; SWETS; UMI. **CCC.**
 Formerly: Academic Therapy (ISSN 0001-396X)
 Description: Interdisciplinary journal directed to an international audience of teachers, parents, educational therapists and specialists in all fields who deal with the day to day aspects of special and remedial education.
 Refereed Serial

420 301.16 US
IOWA JOURNAL OF COMMUNICATION. 1968. s-a. $15 (students $7). Iowa Communication Association, c/o Marvin D. Jensen, Dept. of Communication Studies, University of Northern Iowa, Cedar Falls, IA 50614. TEL 319-273-2593. Ed. Fred Antczak. adv. circ. 200. Indexed: Commun.Abstr.
 —UnCover. **CCC.**
 Formerly: Iowa Journal of Speech Communication (ISSN 0886-1943)

JAHRBUCH FUER BLINDENFREUNDE. see HANDICAPPED — Visually Impaired

JIAOYU YANJIU/EDUCATIONAL RESEARCH. see EDUCATION

371.9 US ISSN 0162-3532
LC3993.9
JOURNAL FOR THE EDUCATION OF THE GIFTED. q. $36 to individuals (foreign $42); institutions $48 (foreign $54). (Association for the Gifted) University of North Carolina Press, Box 2288, Chapel Hill, NC 27515-2288. TEL 919-966-3561. FAX 919-966-3829. Ed. Laurence J. Coleman. adv.; bk.rev. circ. 2,700. Indexed: C.I.J.E., Cont.Pg.Educ., Mult.Ed.Abstr., Psychol.Abstr.
 —BLDSC (4973.140000); UnCover; UMI.
 Refereed Serial

371.9 US ISSN 0195-7597
JOURNAL FOR VOCATIONAL SPECIAL NEEDS EDUCATION. 1978. 3/yr. $24 (foreign $30). National Association of Vocational Education Special Needs Personnel, 518 E. Nebraska Hall, University of Nebraska, Lincoln, NE 68508-0515. TEL 402-472-2365. FAX 402-472-5907. Ed. Gary D. Meers. adv.; bk.rev.; charts; stat. circ. 2,500. (also avail. in microfilm from UMI; back issues avail.) Indexed: C.I.J.E., Cont.Pg.Educ., Mult.Ed.Abstr. **Document type:** academic/scholarly publication.
 —BLDSC (5072.512500); UnCover; UMI.

780 UK ISSN 0951-5038
ML3919
JOURNAL OF BRITISH MUSIC THERAPY. 1968. 2/yr. £30($36) British Society for Music Therapy, 69 Avondale Ave., E. Barnet, Herts. EN4 8NB, England. Ed. Nicky Barber. bk.rev.; index. circ. 700. Indexed: Sp.Ed.Needs Abstr.
 —BLDSC (4954.450000); UnCover.
 Formerly: British Journal of Music Therapy (ISSN 0308-244X)

EDUCATION — SPECIAL EDUCATION AND REHABILITATION

371 US ISSN 0735-3170
RJ496.C67 CODEN: JCCDE2
JOURNAL OF CHILDHOOD COMMUNICATION DISORDERS.
1977. 2/yr. $16 (foreign $19). Council for Exceptional Children, Division for Children with Communication Disorders, 1920 Association Dr., Reston, VA 22091-1589. TEL 703-620-3660. FAX 703-264-9494. Ed. Brian Shulman. adv.; bk.rev. circ. 3,200. **Indexed:** C.I.J.E., Lang.& Lang.Behav.Abstr. (1988-).
—BLDSC (4957.910000); UnCover; UMI.
Description: Discusses many aspects of communication disorders: speech, hearing, language, and learning disabilities.

371.9 US ISSN 1062-2969
RC387.5
JOURNAL OF COGNITIVE REHABILITATION; a publication for the therapist, family and patient. 1983. bi-m. $35 (in Canada $40; elsewhere $50). NeuroScience Publishers, 6555 Carrollton Ave., Indianapolis, IN 46220. TEL 317-257-9672. Ed. Odie L. Bracy. adv. contact: Nancy Bracy. circ. 1,547. (back issues avail.) **Indexed:** CINAHL, Psychol.Abstr.
—BLDSC (4958.799300); Faxon; UnCover.
Formerly: Cognitive Rehabilitation (ISSN 0738-1069)

362.7 371.9 US ISSN 1053-8151
LC4019.2
JOURNAL OF EARLY INTERVENTION. 1979. q. $28 (foreign $232). (Council for Exceptional Children, Division for Early Childhood) Special Press, 474 N. Lake Shore Dr., No. 3910, Chicago, IL 60611-3400. TEL 703-446-0500. (Subscr. to: 1920 Association Dr., Reston, VA 22091) Ed. Samuel Odom. adv.; bk.rev. circ. 4,800. (back issues avail.) **Indexed:** C.I.J.E., Mult.Ed.Abstr., Psychol.Abstr.
—BLDSC (4970.705000); Faxon; UnCover.
Formerly: Council of Exceptional Children. Division for Early Childhood. Journal (ISSN 0885-3460)
Description: Features current research, exemplary practices, family involvement, personnel preparation, collaborative efforts, legislation and technology for professionals.

371.9 UK
JOURNAL OF EDUCATIONAL THERAPY & THERAPEUTIC TEACHING. 1985. a. £13 (foreign £14.20). Forum for the Advancement of Educational Therapy & Therapeutic Teaching, 46 Pepys Rd., London SE14 5SB, England. TEL 071-639-3062. Ed.Bd. adv.; bk.rev.; index. (back issues avail.)
—BLDSC (3662.570000).
Former titles (until 1992): Educational Therapy and Therapeutic Education (ISSN 0964-8690); (until 1991): Journal of Educational Therapy (ISSN 0952-4339)

JOURNAL OF EMOTIONAL AND BEHAVIORAL DISORDERS. see *MEDICAL SCIENCES — Psychiatry And Neurology*

371.9 370.15 US ISSN 0022-2194
LB1134 CODEN: JLDIAD
JOURNAL OF LEARNING DISABILITIES. 1968. 10/yr. $45 to individuals; institutions $90 (foreign $115) (effective 1994). Pro-Ed Inc., 8700 Shoal Creek Blvd., Austin, TX 78757-6897. TEL 512-451-3246. FAX 512-451-8542. Ed. J. Lee Wiederholt; Pub. Donald D. Hammill. adv.; bibl.; charts; illus.; index. circ. 9,000. (also avail. in microform from KTO,UMI) **Indexed:** Adol.Ment.Hlth.Abstr., ASSIA, Bibl.Dev.Med.& Child Neur., Biol.Abstr., Bk.Rev.Ind. (1975-1990), C.I.J.E., Child.Bk.Rev.Ind. (1975-1990), Child Devel.Abstr., CINAHL, Cont.Pg.Educ., Curr.Cont., Educ.Admin.Abstr., Educ.Ind., Except.Child.Educ.Abstr., Excerp.Med., High.Educ.Curr.Aware.Bull., Lang.& Lang.Behav.Abstr., Mid.East: Abstr.& Ind., Psychol.Abstr., Psycscan D.P., Rehabil.Lit., SSCI, Yrbk.Assoc.Educ.& Rehab.Blind. **Document type:** academic/scholarly publication.
—BLDSC (5010.230000); Faxon; UnCover; SWETS; UMI. **CCC.**
Description: Contains articles on practice, research, and theory related to learning disabilities.
Refereed Serial

JOURNAL OF LEISURABILITY. see *LEISURE AND RECREATION*

JOURNAL OF MUSIC THERAPY. see *MUSIC*

371.9 CN ISSN 0707-7807
JOURNAL OF PRACTICAL APPROACHES TO DEVELOPMENTAL HANDICAP. 1977. 2/yr. Can.$11 to individuals; institutions Can.$14 (foreign Can.$16). University of Calgary, Rehabilitation Studies, c/o Rehabilitation Studies, Education Tower 4th fl., University of Calgary, 2500 University Dr., N.W., Calgary, Alta. T2N 1N4, Canada. TEL 403-220-7429. (Co-sponsor: Vocational and Rehabilitation Research Institute) Ed. Roy I. Brown. adv.; bk.rev.; abstr.; illus.; stat. circ. 450. (back issues avail.) **Indexed:** ASSIA, Sp.Ed.Needs Abstr.
—BLDSC (5041.500000).
Description: Concerned with disability, practice and applied research in the field of rehabilitation.

JOURNAL OF PSYCHOEDUCATIONAL ASSESSMENT. see *PSYCHOLOGY*

371.9 US ISSN 0022-4669
LC4001 CODEN: JSPEB9
THE JOURNAL OF SPECIAL EDUCATION. 1966. q. $35 to individuals; institutions $70 (foreign $95) (effective 1994). Pro-Ed Inc., 8700 Shoal Creek Blvd., Austin, TX 78757-6897. TEL 512-451-3246. FAX 512-451-8542. Eds. Lynn & Douglas Fuchs; Pub. Donald D. Hammill. adv.; abstr.; bibl.; charts; illus.; stat.; index. circ. 3,500. (also avail. in microform from KTO,UMI) **Indexed:** Adol.Ment.Hlth.Abstr., ASSIA, C.I.J.E., Child Devel.Abstr., Cont.Pg.Educ., Curr.Cont., Curr.Lit.Fam.Plan., Educ.Admin.Abstr., Educ.Ind., Educ.Tech.Abstr., Except.Child.Educ.Abstr., Excerp.Med., High.Educ.Curr.Aware.Bull., Lang.& Lang.Behav.Abstr., Ment.Retard.Abstr., Psychol.Abstr., Rehabil.Lit., SSCI, Yrbk.Assoc.Educ.& Rehab.Blind. **Document type:** academic/scholarly publication.
—BLDSC (5066.120000); Faxon; UnCover; SWETS; UMI. **CCC.**
Refereed Serial

371.9 371.394 US ISSN 0162-6434
LC4023
JOURNAL OF SPECIAL EDUCATION TECHNOLOGY. 1978. q. $40 (foreign $42). Council for Exceptional Children, Technology and Media Division, c/o Herbert Rielf, Ed., Box 328, Peabody College, Nashville, TN 37203. TEL 615-322-8165. FAX 615-343-1570. adv.; bk.rev.; charts; illus. circ. 2,000. (also avail. in microform from UMI; back issues avail.; reprint service avail. from UMI) **Indexed:** C.I.J.E., Cont.Pg.Educ., Educ.Ind., Sp.Ed.Needs Abstr. **Document type:** academic/scholarly publication.
—BLDSC (5066.120500); Faxon; UnCover; UMI.
Description: Features articles on theory and research in the applications of computer-assisted instruction in special education.
Refereed Serial

420 CN ISSN 0848-1970
CODEN: JSLAEE
JOURNAL OF SPEECH LANGUAGE PATHOLOGY AND AUDIOLOGY/REVUE D'ORTHOPHONIE ET D'AUDIOLOGIE. Short title: J S L P A - R O A. (Text in English and French) 1973. 4/yr. Can.$45 to individuals; institutions Can.$55; students Can.$30. Canadian Association of Speech Language Pathologists and Audiologists - Association Canadienne des Orthophonistes et Audiologistes, 25 Main St. W., Ste. 1215, Hamilton, Ont. L8P 1H1, Canada. TEL 416-523-5790. Ed. Christine Sloan. adv.; bk.rev.; abstr. circ. 3,800. **Indexed:** DSH Abstr.
—BLDSC (5066.175000); Faxon.
Former titles: Journal of Speech Language Pathologists and Audiologists; (until 1989): Human Communication Canada (ISSN 0822-5486); Which was formed by the 1983 merger of: Human Communication; Hear Here.
Description: Aims to disseminate knowledge pertaining to human communication and its disorders.

371.9 KO
KOREA SOCIAL WORK COLLEGE. RESEARCH INSTITUTE FOR SPECIAL EDUCATION. JOURNAL/KWANG-EUNG YEO. (Text in Korean) vol.6, 1978. a. Korea Social Work College, Research Institute for Special Education, 2288 Daemyung-dong Nam Gu, Daegu 634-00, S. Korea.

371.9 US
L D A NEWSBRIEFS; items of interest on learning disabilities. no.118, 1978. 6/yr. $13.50. Learning Disabilities Association of America, 4156 Library Rd., Pittsburgh, PA 15234. FAX 412-344-0224. Ed. Lynne Cannon. adv.; bk.rev. circ. 50,000.
Formerly: A C L D Newsbriefs (Association for Children and Adults with Learning Disabilities).

371.9 US
L D FORUM. (Learning Disabilities) q. (Council for Learning Disabilities) C L D, Box 40303, Overland Park, KS 66204. TEL 913-492-8755. FAX 913-492-2546. Ed. Rich Wilson. circ. 4,000. **Document type:** academic/scholarly publication.
Description: Teacher-oriented classroom ideas for teachers of students with learning disabilities.

362.16 US ISSN 0163-2205
L I N K S. (Living in New Kinds of Situations) 1970. m. $45. (National Association for Private Residential Resources) A N C O R, Box 163270, Sacramento, CA 95816. TEL 916-455-0723. Ed. Charles W. Skoien, Jr. adv.; bk.rev. circ. 7,000. **Document type:** newspaper, trade publication.

771.912 US ISSN 0161-1461
LB3454 CODEN: LGSHA4
LANGUAGE, SPEECH AND HEARING SERVICES IN SCHOOLS. 1970. q. $24 to individuals (foreign $36); institutions $36 (foreign $48); members $18. American Speech - Language - Hearing Association, 10801 Rockville Pike, Rockville, MD 20852. TEL 301-897-5700. FAX 301-571-0457. Ed. Alan Kamhi. circ. 73,000. (also avail. in microform from UMI; reprint service avail. from UMI) **Indexed:** C.I.J.E., Child Devel.Abstr., Educ.Ind., Except.Child.Educ.Abstr., Lang.& Lang.Behav.Abstr., Psychol.Abstr. **Document type:** bulletin.
—BLDSC (5155.711900); Faxon; UnCover; SWETS; UMI. **CCC.**
Description: Presents up-to-date information dealing with all aspects of clinical speech, language and hearing services to children.

371.9 360 US
LEADERSHIP TIMES FOR SPECIAL SERVICES PERSONNEL. 5/yr. $49.95 (effective 1994). National Professional Resources, Inc., 25 S. Regent St., Port Chester, NY 10573. TEL 914-937-8879; 800-453-7461. FAX 914-937-9327. **Document type:** newsletter.
Formerly (until 1994): Effective Special Services Management.
Description: Publishes news and information of interest to special services and special education personnel.

362.7 371.9 US ISSN 0938-8982
LC4704 CODEN: LDRPE6
LEARNING DISABILITIES RESEARCH AND PRACTICE. 1985. s-a. $39 to individuals (foreign $64); institutions $145 (foreign $170). (Council for Exceptional Children, Division for Learning Disabilities) Lawrence Erlbaum Associates, Inc., 365 Broadway, Hillsdale. NJ 07642. TEL 201-666-4110. FAX 201-666-2394. Eds. Marga A. Mastropier, Thomas E. Scruggs. adv.; bk.rev. circ. 14,000. **Indexed:** Psychol.Abstr. **Document type:** academic/scholarly publication.
—Faxon; UnCover; SWETS.
Incorporates (1985-1991): Learning Disabilities Research (ISSN 0892-502X); (1985-1991): Learning Disabilities Focus (ISSN 0892-5011)
Description: Covers current research of interest to teachers, teacher educators and researchers.

371 US ISSN 0731-9487
LC4704
LEARNING DISABILITY QUARTERLY. 1978. q. $50 (foreign $55). (Council for Learning Disabilities) C L D, Box 40303, Overland Park, KS 66204. TEL 913-492-8755 Ed. H. Lee Swanson. adv.; bk.rev.; index. circ. 5,500. (also avail. in microform; back issues avail.) **Indexed:** Behav.Abstr., C.I.J.E., Chic.Per.Ind., Curr.Cont., Educ.Ind., Except.Child Educ.Abstr., Psychol.Abstr., Soc.Sci.Ind., Sp.Ed.Needs Abstr. **Document type:** academic/scholarly publication.
—BLDSC (5179.326490); Faxon; UnCover; SWETS; UMI.
Description: Reports on techniques in identification, assessment, remediation and programming, advanced theories, research and personnel preparation.

EDUCATION — SPECIAL EDUCATION AND REHABILITATION

371.9 GW
LEBENSHILFE AKTUELL. 1975. bi-m. Bundesvereinigung Lebenshilfe fuer Geistig Behinderte e.V., Postfach 701163, 35020 Marburg, Germany. TEL 06421-491-0. FAX 06421-491167. circ. 200,000. (back issues avail.) **Document type:** academic/scholarly publication.
Description: Provides information about mental handicaps.

371.9 GW
LEBENSHILFE ZEITUNG. 1980. bi-m. DM.12. Bundesvereinigung Lebenshilfe fuer geistig Behinderte e.V., Postfach 701163, 35020 Marburg, Germany. TEL 06421-491-0. FAX 06421-491167. Ed. Dr. Bernhard Conrads. circ. 130,000. **Document type:** academic/scholarly publication.

371.9 GW ISSN 0720-8316
LERNEN FOERDERN; Zeitung fuer Eltern, Lehrer und Erzieher. 1981. q. DM.17.50. Bundesverband zur Foerderung Lernbehinderter e.V., Rolandstr. 61, 50677 Cologne, Germany. TEL 0221-374828. Eds. P. Hass, R.C. Zelfel. circ. 5,000. (back issues avail.) **Document type:** newsletter.

LIFE-LINE. see *MEDICAL SCIENCES — Psychiatry And Neurology*

LIGHT (WHEATON). see *HANDICAPPED — Visually Impaired*

371.9 US
M R D D EXPRESS. (Mental Retardation and Developmental Disabilities) 1984. s-a. membership only. Council for Exceptional Children, Division on Mental Retardation and Developmental Disabilities, 1920 Association Dr., Reston, VA 22091-1589. TEL 703-620-3660. FAX 703-264-9494. Ed. Dr. Greg Robinson. circ. 7,900. **Document type:** newsletter.
Former titles: C E C - M R Newsletter; C E C - M Report.
Description: Information on the division and its activities. Includes news in the field of mental retardation.

MARBURGER BUECHERLISTEN. see *HANDICAPPED — Visually Impaired*

371.9 GW
MARIABERGER BRIEF; Berichte aus unserer Arbeit. 1968. 2/yr. Mariaberger Heime, Klosterhof 1, 72501 Gammertingen, Germany. TEL 07124-290. Ed. K.R. Eder. circ. 20,000. **Document type:** bulletin.

371.9 GW
MARIABERGER HEIME; Berichte aus unserer Arbeit. 1847. a. Mariaberger Heime, Klosterhof 1, 72501 Gammertingen, Germany. TEL 07124-290. FAX 07124-29500. Ed. K.R. Eder. circ. 20,000. **Document type:** bulletin.

MATERIALIEN ZUR HEIMERZIEHUNG. see *SOCIAL SERVICES AND WELFARE*

MATH NOTEBOOK. see *MATHEMATICS*

371.9 616.8 US ISSN 0047-6765
RC569.7 CODEN: MRTDAH
MENTAL RETARDATION (WASHINGTON). 1963. bi-m. $75. American Association on Mental Retardation, 1719 Kalorama Rd., N.W., Washington, DC 20009. TEL 202-387-1968. FAX 202-387-2193. Ed. Steven Taylor. adv.; bk.rev.; illus.; index. circ. 11,500. (also avail. in microfilm) **Indexed:** Adol.Ment.Hlth.Abstr., Bibl.Dev.Med.& Child Neur., Biol.Abstr., C.I.J.E., Curr.Lit.Fam.Plan., Dent.Ind., Educ.Ind., Excerp.Med., Hosp.Lit.Ind., Ind.Med., Psychol.Abstr., Rehabil.Lit., Sp.Ed.Needs Abstr., SSCI. —Faxon; UnCover; SWETS; UMI. **CCC.**

420 US
MICHIGAN ASSOCIATION OF SPEECH COMMUNICATION JOURNAL. 1964. a. $3. Michigan Association of Speech Communication, Dept. of Speech Communications, Central Michigan Univ., Mt. Pleasant, MI 48859. TEL 517-774-7896. Ed. David A. Ling. circ. 250. (back issues avail.)
Formerly (until 1984): Michigan Speech Association Journal.

MILL NECK MANOR BULLETIN. see *HANDICAPPED — Hearing Impaired*

MINNESOTA SPEECH - LANGUAGE - HEARING ASSOCIATION. NEWSLETTER. see *MEDICAL SCIENCES — Otorhinolaryngology*

MISSOURI RECORD. see *HANDICAPPED — Hearing Impaired*

371.9 US
N A P M R QUARTERLY. (Former name of issuing body: National Apostolate with Mentally Retarded Persons) 1968. q. $25 (includes Newsletter). National Apostolate with People with Mental Retardation, Box 4711, Columbia, SC 29240. TEL 800-736-1280. Ed. Marilyn Bishop. illus.
Formerly: N A M R P Quarterly Publication (ISSN 0273-9178)
Description: Covers current news, issues and concerns of parents and those affected by mental retardation.

371.9 US
N A P S E C MEMBERSHIP DIRECTORY. 1980. biennial. $28. National Association of Private Schools for Exceptional Children, 1522 K St., N.W., Ste. 1032, Washington, DC 20005. TEL 202-408-3338. FAX 202-408-3340. Ed. Mara S. Miller. circ. 500. **Document type:** directory.
Description: Lists and describes approximately 200 member schools that have populations of students with disabilities, including day, residential, summer clinical programs, and hospital affiliated programs.

371.9 US
N H S A JOURNAL. 1989. q. $60. National Head Start Association, 201 N. Union St., Ste. 320, Alexandria, VA 22314. TEL 703-739-0875. FAX 703-739-0878. Ed. Marlene Karwowski. adv. circ. 7,000.
Description: Features activities and projects on behalf of at-risk families and children, updates on legislation, and interviews with leaders in the child care field.

371.9 AT
N S W JOURNAL OF SPECIAL EDUCATION. 1975. 2/yr. Aus.$25. Australian Association of Special Education, Inc., New South Wales Chapter, P.O. Box 282, Strathfield, N.S.W. 2135, Australia. Ed. K.F. Mitchell. adv.; bk.rev.; illus. circ. 500. (tabloid format) **Indexed:** Sp.Ed.Needs Abstr.
Former titles: A S E T Journal; O A Journal.

371.9 CN ISSN 0709-1370
NATIONAL (OTTAWA, 1970). (Editions in English and French) 1970. q. Can.$14. Learning Disabilities Association of Canada, Kildare House, 323 Chapel St., Ottawa, ON K1N 7Z2, Canada. TEL 613-238-5721. FAX 613-235-5391. Ed. Juli Voyer. adv.; bk.rev. circ. 8,000. **Document type:** newsletter.
Former titles: Post (ISSN 0380-7967); Perceptual Post (ISSN 0380-7975)
Description: Covers the Association's national activities: projects, federal government liasion; reports on provincial, territorial associations' initiatives; includes articles and resources about learning disabilities

371.9 US
NATIONAL APOSTOLATE WITH PEOPLE WITH MENTAL RETARDATION. NEWSLETTER. (Former name of issuing body: National Apostolate with Mentally Retarded Persons) 1971. bi-m. $25 (includes N A P M R Quarterly). National Apostolate with People with Mental Retardation, Box 4711, Columbia, SC 29240. TEL 800-736-1280. Ed. Jill Johnson. film rev. circ. 1,000. **Document type:** newsletter.
Formerly: National Apostolate with Mentally Retarded Persons. Newsletter (ISSN 0889-9592)
Description: Covers current news, issues and concerns of parents or those affected by mental retardation.

NATIONAL ASSOCIATION OF TRAINING SCHOOLS AND JUVENILE AGENCIES. PROCEEDINGS. see *CRIMINOLOGY AND LAW ENFORCEMENT*

371.9 UK
NATIONAL COUNCIL FOR SPECIAL EDUCATION. CONFERENCE REPORTS.* irreg. price varies. National Council for Special Education, York House, Exhall Grange, Wheelwright Lane, Coventry CV7 9HP, England.

371.9 UK
NATIONAL COUNCIL FOR SPECIAL EDUCATION. OCCASIONAL PUBLICATIONS.* 1983. irreg. £2.50 per issue. National Council for Special Education, York House, Exhall Grange, Wheelwright Lane, Coventry CV7 9HP, England. Ed. Richard Rose.

371.9 US ISSN 1043-2167
LC3981
NATIONAL FORUM OF SPECIAL EDUCATION JOURNAL. Short title: N F S E Journal. 1989. 2/yr. $80. (University of Mississippi) National Forum Journals, 1930 Nicholas St., Lake Charles, LA 70605. TEL 318-474-6976. Ed. William Allan Kritsonis. index. circ. 7,500. (back issues avail.) **Document type:** academic/scholarly publication.
—BLDSC (6023.646100).
Refereed Serial

371.9 JA ISSN 0387-3528
NATIONAL INSTITUTE OF SPECIAL EDUCATION. BULLETIN/KOKURITSU TOKUSHU KYOIKU SOGO KENKYUJO KENKYU KIYO. (Text in Japanese; summaries in English) 1974. a. free. National Institute of Special Education - Kokuritsu Tokushu Kyoiku Sogo Kenkyusho, 5-1-1 Nobi, Yokosuka 239, Japan. TEL 0469-48-4121. Ed.Bd. circ. 1,480. **Document type:** bulletin.

371.9 JA
NATIONAL INSTITUTE OF SPECIAL EDUCATION. NEWSLETTER. (Text in Japanese) q.? National Institute of Special Education - Kokuritsu Tokushu Kyoiku Sogo Kenkyusho, 5-1-1 Nobi, Yokosuka 239, Japan. TEL 0469-48-4121. **Document type:** newsletter.

371.9 JA
NATIONAL INSTITUTE OF SPECIAL EDUCATION SEMINAR. FINAL REPORT. (Text in Japanese) a.? National Institute of Special Education - Kokuritsu Tokushu Kyoiku Sogo Kenkyusho, 5-1-1 Nobi, Yokosuka 239, Japan. TEL 0469-48-4121. **Document type:** corporate report.

372 UK ISSN 0952-9705
NATIONAL LIBRARY FOR THE HANDICAPPED CHILD. NEWSLETTER. 1985. 3/yr. £15. National Library for the Handicapped Child, Reach Resource Centre, Wellington House, Wellington Rd., Wokingham, Berkshire RG11 2AG, England. TEL 0734-891101. FAX 0734-790989. bk.rev. circ. 1,500. **Document type:** newsletter.
Formerly: Blyton Handi Read Centre Newsletter.
Description: Contains articles for people who work with children who have reading disabilities.

NATIONAL REHABILITATION CENTER FOR THE DISABLED. RESEARCH BULLETIN. see *HANDICAPPED*

NEW MEXICO PROGRESS. see *HANDICAPPED — Hearing Impaired*

NORDISK TIDSKRIFT FOER DOEVUNDERVISNINGEN. see *HANDICAPPED — Hearing Impaired*

371.9 NO ISSN 0048-0509
NORDISK TIDSSKRIFT FOR SPESIALPEDAGOGIKK/POHJOISMAINEN ERTYISKASVATUKSEN AIKAKAUSLEHTI. (Text in Danish, Norwegian, Swedish; summaries in English, Finnish) 1923. q. NOK 3660 in the Nordic countries; elsewhere NOK 410. Scandinavian University Press, P.O. Box 2959-Toeyen, N-0608 Oslo, Norway. TEL 472-67-7600. FAX 472-67-7575. Ed. Hans Arte. adv.; bk.rev.; illus.; index. circ. 2,000.
Description: Provides information on current research and development within special education.

362.8 US ISSN 0093-7843
HD7256.U6
NORTH DAKOTA STATE PLAN FOR REHABILITATION FACILITIES AND WORKSHOPS; annual modification. a. free. Division of Vocational Rehabilitation, State Capitol Bldg., Bismarck, ND 58505. TEL 701-224-2907. stat.

NURSING AND HEALTH SCIENCE EDUCATION. see *MEDICAL SCIENCES — Nurses And Nursing*

EDUCATION — SPECIAL EDUCATION AND REHABILITATION

371.9 614   CN   ISSN 0836-4362
O S L A NEWSLETTER. 1960. 4/yr. free. Ontario Association of Speech - Language Pathologists and Audiologists, 410 Jarvis St., Toronto, ON M4Y 2G6, Canada. Ed. Liz Brady. circ. 1,700 (controlled). **Document type:** newsletter.
    Former titles (until 1987): O.S.H.A. Ontario Speech and Hearing Association (ISSN 0705-8713); (until 1976): Ontario Speech and Hearing Association. Journal (ISSN 0705-8888)

379   US   ISSN 0098-5139
LC1046.O3
OHIO. COUNCIL ON VOCATIONAL EDUCATION. ANNUAL REPORT. Key Title: Annual Report, Ohio Advisory Council on Vocational Education. 1970. a. Council on Vocational Education, 750 Brooksedge Blvd., Ste. 105, Westerville, OH 43081. TEL 614-891-4764. FAX 614-891-2834. illus.; stat.

ON CUE. see *HANDICAPPED — Hearing Impaired*

OREGON OUTLOOK. see *HANDICAPPED — Hearing Impaired*

371.4   IT
ORIENTAMENTO SCOLASTICO PROFESSIONALE. vol.16, 1976. q. L.4300. Associazione Italiana di Orientamento Scolastico e Professionale, Viale Trastevere 82, 00153 Rome, Italy. Ed. Mario Baldini. abstr.; bibl.; charts. **Indexed:** Int.Lab.Doc.

371.9   US   ISSN 0732-5258
P I P COLLEGE "H E L P S" NEWSLETTER. (Handicapped and Exceptional Learners Programs and Services); college - handicapped and exceptional learners programs and services. 1976. m. (13/yr.). $33 (foreign $38). Partners in Publishing, Box 50347, Tulsa, OK 74150. TEL 918-835-8258. FAX 918-835-8258. Ed. P.M. Fielding. bk.rev.; index. circ. 1,000. (looseleaf format; back issues avail.) **Document type:** newsletter.
    Description: Provides news of products and programs for college-level learning-disabled youth and adults and the professionals who work with them.

371.9   US   ISSN 0737-514X
PAEDOPERISSE; an international journal of comparative special education. 1984. q. Eterna International, Inc., Box 6558, Flushing, NY 11365-6558. Ed. Stephen B. Parrish. adv.; bk.rev.; abstr.; charts; illus.; index.

PALAESTRA; the forum of sport, physical education and recreation for the disabled. see *HANDICAPPED*

PARAGRAPHIC. see *HANDICAPPED*

PARAPLEGIA NEWS. see *HANDICAPPED — Physically Impaired*

PAREGIAN DIRECTORY OF INDEPENDENT - PRIVATE SCHOOLS. see *EDUCATION — Guides To Schools And Colleges*

362.3   US   ISSN 0031-4609
PENNSYLVANIA MESSAGE. 1965. q. $20. Pennsylvania Association for Retarded Citizens, Inc., 123 Forster St., Harrisburg, PA 17102-3498. FAX 717-234-7615. Ed. Linda Drummond. adv.; bk.rev.; abstr.; circ. 8,500 (controlled). (tabloid format)

371.9   US   ISSN 0731-566X
PEOPLE WITH SPECIAL NEEDS - DOWN SYNDROME REPORT. 1985. 3/yr. $5. Northern State University, Department of Special Education, Box 635, Aberdeen, SD 57401. TEL 605-622-2621. Ed. Lois Sollie. bk.rev.; film rev.; bibl.; charts; stat. circ. 6,000. (tabloid format)

051   US
PEOPLENET. 1987. 3/yr. $26 membership only. (Peoplenet, Inc.) Robert Mauro, Ed. & Pub., Box 897, Levittown, NY 11756. TEL 516-579-4043. adv.; bk.rev. circ. 200. **Document type:** newsletter.

371.9   US   ISSN 1051-6204
HV2510
PERSPECTIVES IN EDUCATION AND DEAFNESS. 1982. bi-m. (5/yr.) $15 (foreign $21). Gallaudet University, Pre-College Programs, KDES PAS-6, 800 Florida Ave., N.E., Washington, DC 20002-3695. TEL 202-651-5340. FAX 202-651-5708. Ed. Mary E. Abrams. adv.; bk.rev.; film rev.; index. circ. 4,000. (back issues avail.) **Indexed:** C.I.J.E., Comput.Lit.Ind., Soc.Sci.Ind.
    —BLDSC (6428.142310); UnCover.
    Formerly (until 1989): Perspectives for Teachers of the Hearing Impaired (ISSN 0735-6315)
    Description: Directed to professionals and families involved with educating deaf and hard-of-hearing students. Provides a forum for exchange of creative approaches to classroom teaching; gives views about current issues in deafness and education.

PERSPECTIVES ON DYSLEXIA. see *MEDICAL SCIENCES — Psychiatry And Neurology*

PHYSICAL DISABILITIES - EDUCATION & RELATED SERVICES. see *HANDICAPPED — Physically Impaired*

PINE CONE. see *MEDICAL SCIENCES — Psychiatry And Neurology*

A POSITIVE APPROACH; a national magazine for the physically challenged. see *HANDICAPPED — Physically Impaired*

371.9   JA
PRACTICAL EDUCATION FOR THE HANDICAPPED/JISSEN SHOGAIJI KYOIKU. (Text in Japanese) 1973. m. 4800 Yen. Gakken Co. Ltd., 40-5, 4-chome, Kamiikedai, Ohta-ku, Tokyo 145, Japan. Ed. Yukio Nakayama.
    Formerly: Education for the Handicapped.

DIE PRAXIS; soziolpolitische Vierteljahresschrift. see *SOCIAL SERVICES AND WELFARE*

371.9   US   ISSN 1045-988X
HV888
PREVENTING SCHOOL FAILURE; for special class teachers and parents of the handicapped. 1976. q. $36 to individuals; institutions $67. (Helen Dwight Reid Educational Foundation) Heldref Publications, 1319 Eighteenth St., N.W., Washington, DC 20036-1802. TEL 202-296-6267. FAX 202-296-5149. Ed. Isabella Owen. adv. contact: Raymond Rallo. bk.rev.; charts; illus.; index. circ. 800. (also avail. in microform; back issues avail.; reprint service avail. from UMI) **Indexed:** Behav.Abstr., C.I.J.E., Cont.Pg.Educ., Educ.Ind., Except.Child Educ.Abstr., Psychol.Abstr., Rehabil.Lit., Sp.Ed.Needs Abstr. **Document type:** academic/scholarly publication.
    —BLDSC (6612.727400); UnCover; UMI. **CCC.**
    Formerly: Pointer (Washington) (ISSN 0554-4246)
    Refereed Serial

PREVENTION PIPELINE; an alcohol and drug awareness service. see *DRUG ABUSE AND ALCOHOLISM — Abstracting, Bibliographies, Statistics*

371.4   US
PROGRAMMING TRENDS IN THERAPEUTIC RECREATION. 1980. bi-m. $25 to individuals; institutions $45. Leisure Learning Systems, Inc., 9843 Logans Ridge Dr., Converse, TX 78109-2761. TEL 817-382-0000. Ed. Jean R. Tague. bk.rev. circ. 500.

PSYCSCAN: LEARNING DISORDERS AND MENTAL RETARDATION. see *PSYCHOLOGY — Abstracting, Bibliographies, Statistics*

PURE FACTS. see *MEDICAL SCIENCES — Psychiatry And Neurology*

QUALITY OF CARE. see *MEDICAL SCIENCES — Psychiatry And Neurology*

371.9   US
R E S N A NEWS. 1982. bi-m. $25. R E S N A, 1700 N. Moore St., Ste. 1540, Arlington, VA 22209-1903. TEL 703-524-6686. FAX 703-524-6630. Ed. Marian Hall. adv.; bk.rev. circ. 1,500. (back issues avail.)
    Formerly (until 1990): Rehabilitation Technology Review (ISSN 0882-2476)
    Description: Aims for the dissemination and utilization of knowledge of rehabilitative and assistive technology.

371.9 370   FR   ISSN 0484-0305
READAPTATION. 1954. m. (10/yr.). 250 F. (foreign 305 F.). Centre National d'Information pour la Readaptation, 10 rue de Sevres, 75007 Paris, France. TEL 42-22-22-73. FAX 42-22-65-12. (Co-sponsor: Office National d'Information sur les Enseignements et les Professions) adv.; bk.rev. circ. 5,600. **Indexed:** Excerp.Med., Pt.de Rep.
    —BLDSC (7300.600000).

371.9 028.5 420
375.4   US   ISSN 1057-3569
LB1050.5   CODEN: RWQUEB
READING AND WRITING QUARTERLY: OVERCOMING LEARNING DIFFICULTIES. 1984. q. $134. Taylor & Francis, 1900 Frost Rd., Ste. 101, Bristol, PA 19007-1598. TEL 800-821-8312. Ed. Howard Margolis. film rev.; abstr.; bibl.; charts; tr.lit. (also avail. in microform from UMI; back issues avail.; reprint service avail. from UMI) **Indexed:** Child Devel.Abstr., Except.Child Educ.Abstr., IRA, Lang.& Lang.Behav.Abstr., Psychol.Abstr., Rehabil.Lit., Sociol.Abstr., Sp.Ed.Needs Abstr. **Document type:** academic/scholarly publication.
    —BLDSC (7300.877000); Faxon; UnCover. **CCC.**
    Former titles: Journal of Reading, Writing, and Learning Disabilities International (ISSN 0748-7630); Chicorel Abstracts to Reading and Learning Disabilities.
    Description: Covers reading, writing, and learning disabilities.
    Refereed Serial

372   US   ISSN 0034-0502
READING HORIZONS. 1960. 5/yr. $18. Western Michigan University, College of Education, Kalamazoo, MI 49008. TEL 616-387-3470. FAX 616-387-2882. Ed. Jeanne M. Jacobson. adv.; bk.rev.; abstr.; bibl. circ. 1,000. (also avail. in microform from UMI; reprint service avail. from UMI) **Indexed:** C.I.J.E., Cont.Pg.Educ.
    —BLDSC (7300.990000); Faxon; UnCover; UMI.
    Description: Shares reports, research, and ideas about teaching reading at all levels.

372   US   ISSN 0034-0510
LB1050.5
READING IMPROVEMENT; a journal for the improvement of reading teaching. 1963. q. $15 to individuals; institutions $20. Project Innovation of Mobile, Box 8508, Spring Hill Sta., Mobile, AL 36608. TEL 205-343-7802. Ed. Phil Feldman. adv.; bk.rev.; abstr.; index, cum.index. circ. 2,500. (also avail. in microform from UMI; reprint service avail. from UMI) **Indexed:** C.I.J.E., Cont.Pg.Educ., Educ.Ind., Lang.& Lang.Behav.Abstr. **Document type:** academic/scholarly publication.
    —BLDSC (7301.050000); Faxon; UnCover; SWETS; UMI.
    Formerly: Reading in High School.

372   US
READING IN VIRGINIA.* 1972. s-a. $4. Virginia State Reading Association, Reading Center, James Madison University, Harrisonburg, VA 22801. Eds. James L. Laffey, Donna G. Kelly. bk.rev. circ. 5,000. **Indexed:** ERIC.

READING PSYCHOLOGY; an international quarterly. see *EDUCATION — Teaching Methods And Curriculum*

371.9   US   ISSN 0270-1448
LC4091
READINGS ON EQUAL EDUCATION. 1970. a. $47.50. A M S Press, Inc., 56 E. 13th St., New York, NY 10003. TEL 212-777-4700. FAX 212-995-5413. Ed.Bd. bibl.; charts; stat.; index. (back issues avail.)
    —BLDSC (7301.900000).
    Formerly: Educating the Disadvantaged (ISSN 0531-8327)
    Description: Contains articles on education policy toward minorities in the United States.

EDUCATION — SPECIAL EDUCATION AND REHABILITATION

371.9   CN   ISSN 0048-7139
REHABILITATION DIGEST. 1969. q. Can.$17.50 (foreign $20). Canadian Rehabilitation Council, 45 Sheppard Ave. E., Ste. 801, Willowdale, Ont. M2N 5W9, Canada. TEL 416-250-7490. FAX 416-229-1371. Ed. Heather Ney. adv.; bk.rev.; film rev. circ. 2,200. (back issues avail.) **Indexed:** Can.Per.Ind., Sportsearch (1979-).
—BLDSC (7350.234000); UnCover.

371.9   US   ISSN 0889-7018
HD7255.5
REHABILITATION EDUCATION; official journal of the National Council on Rehabilitation Education. 1987. q. $75 (foreign $85). Elliot & Fitzpatrick Inc., Box 1945, Athens, GA 30603. TEL 706-548-8161; 800-843-4977. FAX 706-546-8417. Ed. Dr. Douglas Strohmer. circ. 500. **Document type:** academic/scholarly publication.
—BLDSC (7350.236200); Faxon; UnCover; UMI. **CCC.**
Refereed Serial

REHABILITATION INDEX. see *MEDICAL SCIENCES — Abstracting, Bibliographies, Statistics*

338   II   ISSN 0080-0724
REHABILITATION INDUSTRIES CORPORATION. ANNUAL REPORT.* (Report year ends Mar. 31) (Text in English) 1959. a. Rehabilitation Industries Corporation Ltd., 25 Free School St., Calcutta 16, India.

371.9 615.82   US
REHABILITATION INTERNATIONAL. WORLD CONGRESS. PROCEEDINGS. 1921. quadrennial, 17th, 1992, Nairobi. Rehabilitation International, 25 E. 21st St., 4th Fl., New York, NY 10010. TEL 212-420-1500. FAX 212-505-0871. TELEX 446412. (Orders to: Association for the Physically Disabled of kenya, APDK House, P.O. Box 56643, Nairobi, Kenya. TEL 254-2-332227. FAX 254-2-219541) circ. 3,000. **Document type:** proceedings.
Description: Contains compendia of main papers presented at the world congress.

REHABILITATION PSYCHOLOGY. see *PSYCHOLOGY*

371.9   CN
REHABINFO. bi-m. free to members. Canadian Rehabilitation Council - Conseil Canadien de Readaptation, 45 Sheppard Ave. E., Ste. 801, Toronto, Ont. M2N 5W9, Canada.
TEL 416-250-7490. FAX 416-229-1371.
Description: Provides a comprehensive package of the latest information on rehabilitation.

371.9   US   ISSN 0741-9325
LC3950
REMEDIAL AND SPECIAL EDUCATION. Short title: R A S E. 1984. 6/yr. $35 to individuals; institutions $80; foreign $105 (effective 1994). Pro-Ed Inc., 8700 Shoal Creek Blvd., Austin, TX 78757-6897.
TEL 512-451-3246. FAX 512-451-8542. Ed. Lorna Idol; Pub. Donald D. Hammill. adv.; bk.rev. circ. 2,700. (also avail. in microfilm from UMI; back issues avail.) **Indexed:** C.I.J.E., Cont.Pg.Educ., Curr.Lit.Fam.Plan., Educ.Ind., Except.Child.Educ.Abstr., Psychol.Abstr., Sp.Ed.Needs Abstr. **Document type:** academic/scholarly publication.
—BLDSC (7356.760000); Faxon; UnCover; SWETS; UMI. **CCC.**
Formed by the merger of (1981-1984): Topics in Learning and Learning Disabilities (ISSN 0271-1494); (1980-1984): Exceptional Education Quarterly (ISSN 0196-6960); (1978-1983): Journal for Special Educators (ISSN 0197-5323); Which was formed by the 1978 merger of: Special Children (ISSN 0160-3248); Journal for Special Educators of the Mentally Retarded (ISSN 0012-2807); Which was formerly (1964-19??): Digest of the Mentally Retarded; Incorporates: Retarded Adult.
Description: Features articles on a wide spectrum of subjects, bridging the gap between theory and practice. Two special issues per year provide in-depth coverage of a single topic.
Refereed Serial

370   US   ISSN 0034-4680
REPORT ON EDUCATION OF THE DISADVANTAGED; the biweekly newsletter on Title I and other federal programs for disadvantaged children. 1967. bi-w. $260 (effective Sep. 1992). Business Publishers, Inc., 951 Pershing Dr., Silver Spring, MD 20910-4464. TEL 301-587-6300.
FAX 301-585-9075. Ed. Rosemary Lally. (looseleaf format) **Document type:** newsletter.
•Also available online. Vendor(s): NewsNet.
—**CCC.**
Description: Advice and funding info for managers of programs to assist disadvantaged youth, with an emphasis on Head Start and other programs.

RESEARCH IN DEVELOPMENTAL DISABILITIES; a multidisciplinary journal. see *MEDICAL SCIENCES — Psychiatry And Neurology*

REVUE CANADIENNE DE PSYCHO-EDUCATION. see *PSYCHOLOGY*

RIABILITAZIONE E APPRENDIMENTO. see *MEDICAL SCIENCES — Physical Medicine And Rehabilitation*

ROLLSTUHLSPORT. see *SPORTS AND GAMES*

371.9   US   ISSN 8756-8705
RURAL SPECIAL EDUCATION QUARTERLY. 1984. q. $30 to individuals; libraries $50. American Council on Rural Special Education, RSEQ Offices, University Affiliated Programs, Box 30001 - 3 SPE, NMSU, Las Cruces, NM 88003-0001. TEL 505-646-6810. Ed. Jack Cole. circ. 600. (back issues avail.)
—BLDSC (8052.631000); UnCover.
Description: Covers pre-service training, administration and curriculum for pre-service educators and direct service providers.

371.9   US
RURALINK. 6/yr. membership. American Council on Rural Special Education, RSEQ Offices, University Affiliated Programs, Box 30001 - 3 SPE, NMSU, Las Cruces, NM 88003-0001. TEL 505-646-6810. Ed. Jack Cole. circ. 800. **Document type:** newsletter.
Description: Covers resources and information on rural special education.

362.4   JA   ISSN 0036-0538
RYOIKU/REHABILITATION. (Text in Japanese) 1951. a. 2060 Yen. Japanese Society for Disabled Children - Nihon Shitai Fujiyuuji Kyokai, 1-7, 1-chome, Komone, Itabashi-ku, Tokyo 173, Japan. Ed.Bd. circ. 2,000.

375   AT
S P E L D BULLETIN. 1970. 3/yr. Aus.$20 membership. Specific Learning Difficulties Association of Victoria, 494 Brunswick St., North Fitzroy, Vic. 3068, Australia. TEL 03-489-4344. Ed. Margaret Roberts. adv.; bk.rev. circ. 500. **Document type:** bulletin.
Formerly: D.A.W.A. Bulletin.

375   AT
S P E L D NEWS. 1969. q. Aus.$15. Specific Learning Difficulties Association of New South Wales, 129 Greenwich Rd., Greenwich, N.S.W. 2065, Australia. FAX 02-906-5657. Ed. Yvonne Stewart. bk.rev. circ. 2,500.

SAGGI; neuropsicologia infantile psicopedagogia riabilitazione. see *MEDICAL SCIENCES — Psychiatry And Neurology*

371.9   NE
SAMENWIJS. 1980. 10/yr. fl.65. Stichting Activering Minderheden Educatie Nederland, Postbus 9011, 3007 AA Rotterdam, Netherlands. A.J.M. Triesscheijm. adv.; bk.rev. circ. 3,500.

371.4   US   ISSN 0161-5653
LB3013.4
SCHOOL SOCIAL WORK JOURNAL. 1976. s-a. $12 to individuals; institutions $20 (foreign $28). Illinois Association of School Social Workers, Box 2072, Northlake, IL 60164-0072. Ed. Joan M. Fedota. adv.; bk.rev. circ. 1,000. (also avail. in microform from UMI; reprint service avail. from UMI) **Indexed:** Adol.Ment.Hlth.Abstr., Soc.Work.Res.& Abstr.
—BLDSC (8093.508000); Faxon; UMI. **CCC.**

SEE HEAR!. see *HANDICAPPED — Hearing Impaired*

SENSORY INTEGRATION SPECIAL INTEREST SECTION NEWSLETTER. see *OCCUPATIONAL HEALTH AND SAFETY*

371.9   JA   ISSN 0037-3990
SHITAI FUJIYU KYOIKU/JAPANESE JOURNAL OF EDUCATION OF THE HANDICAPPED. 1970. 5/yr. 3100 Yen. Japanese Society for Disabled Children - Nihon Shitai Fujiyuji Kyokai, 1-7, 1-chome, Komone, Itabashi-ku, Tokyo 173, Japan. circ. 4,500.
Description: Includes rehabilitation techniques.

SIGHTS AND SOUNDS. see *HANDICAPPED — Hearing Impaired*

SILENT ADVOCATE. see *HANDICAPPED — Hearing Impaired*

SMITH - KETTLEWELL TECHNICAL FILE; a biannual technical journal for the blind and visually impaired. see *HANDICAPPED — Visually Impaired*

SOGO REHABILITATION. see *MEDICAL SCIENCES*

371.9   GW   ISSN 0342-7366
SONDERPAEDAGOGIK; Vierteljahresschrift ueber aktuelle Probleme der Behinderten in Schule und Gesellschaft. 1964. q. DM.48 (students DM.38.40). Wissenschaftsverlag Volker Spiess GmbH, Postfach 303046, 10730 Berlin, Germany.
TEL 030-2165061. FAX 030-2165064. Eds. Heinz Neukaeter, Herbert Goetze. adv.; bk.rev. **Document type:** academic/scholarly publication.
—**CCC.**

371.9   US
SOURCE (ST. CHARLES). 1987. m. $12. J A G Enterprises, Box 1439, St. Charles, MO 63302. TEL 314-949-9456. FAX 314-724-8082. Ed. Julie Ann Groog. adv.; bk.rev. circ. 10,000. **Document type:** newspaper.

371.4   US
SOWER. 1981. q. free. Beatrice State Development Center, Department of Public Institutions, 3000 Lincoln Blvd., Beatrice, NE 68310.
TEL 402-223-2302. Ed. Jerry Crisp. circ. 2,500. (tabloid format; back issues avail.) **Document type:** newsletter.
Formerly: Broadcaster.

371.9   IS   ISSN 0334-7613
SPECIAL EDUCATION AND REHABILITATION. (Text in English) q. Freund Publishing House Ltd., P.O. Box 35010, 61 Nachmani St., Tel Aviv 61 350, Israel. Ed. S. Reiter.

371.9   US
SPECIAL EDUCATION BULLETIN AND REVIEW.* 1980. m. Eterna International, Inc., Box 6558, Flushing, NY 11365-6558. Ed. Stephen B. Parrish.

371.9   US
SPECIAL EDUCATION REPORT; the independent bi-weekly news service on legislation, programs and funding for special education. 1975. bi-w. $266 (foreign $292). Capitol Publications Inc., 1101 King St., Ste. 444, Alexandria, VA 22314.
TEL 703-683-4100. FAX 703-739-6517. s-a. index. (looseleaf format) **Indexed:** Rehabil.Lit. **Document type:** newsletter.
—UnCover. **CCC.**
Formerly (until 1992): Education of the Handicapped (ISSN 0194-2255)
Description: Covers federal and state legislation on the Education for All Handicapped Children Act and other relevant laws. Looks at innovations and research in the field.

371.9 340   US
SPECIAL EDUCATION UPDATE. 1983. m. $107. Data Research, Inc., 4635 Nicols Rd., Ste. 100, Eagan, MN 55122. TEL 612-452-8267.
FAX 612-452-8694. (Subscr. to: Box 409, Rosemount, MN 55068. TEL 800-365-4900) Ed. Warren Cody. (looseleaf format; back issues avail.) **Document type:** newsletter.
Formerly: Special Education and the Handicapped (ISSN 8756-3746)

371.9 340   US   ISSN 1047-1618
KF4031.S74
THE SPECIAL EDUCATOR. 1982. 18/yr. $215. L R P Publications, 747 Dresher Rd., Horsham, PA 19044. TEL 215-628-3113. FAX 215-784-0870. Ed. Melinda Maloney. circ. 2,000. (looseleaf format; back issues avail.) **Document type:** newsletter.
•Also available online.
—**CCC.**

EDUCATION — SPECIAL EDUCATION AND REHABILITATION

371.4 616.89 US ISSN 0739-9820
SPECIAL SERVICES IN THE SCHOOLS. 1984. q. $34 to individuals; institutions $60; libraries $75. Haworth Press, Inc., 10 Alice St., Binghamton, NY 13904. TEL 607-722-5857; 800-342-9678. FAX 607-722-1424. TELEX 4932599. Ed. Charles A. Maher. adv.; bk.rev. circ. 243. (also avail. in microfiche from UMI; back issues avail.; reprint service avail. from HAW) Indexed: Cont.Pg.Educ., Educ.Tech.Abstr., Psychol.Abstr., Soc.Work Res.& Abstr., Sp.Ed.Needs Abstr.
—BLDSC (8404.023000).
   Description: Disseminates state-of-the-art material to education professionals of children with special needs in public schools and related educational settings.
   Refereed Serial

371.9 US
SPECIAL TEACHER. 1973. s-a. $10. New York State Association of Teachers of the Handicapped, Inc., New York City Chapter, 1721 E. 54th St., Brooklyn, NY 11234. TEL 718-949-1155. Ed. Stanley Scher. adv.; bk.rev.; bibl.; illus. circ. 3,000.

371.9 DK ISSN 0907-6069
SPECIALUNDERVISNING. 1976. biennial. DKK 19.80. Landsforeningen for Laesepaedagoger, Oernevej 30, 2400 Copenhagen NV, Denmark.
   Former titles (until 1992): Undervisningsmidler til Specialundervisning (ISSN 0106-7745); (until 1980): Materialer til Specialundervisning (ISSN 0107-1505)

SPEECH COMMUNICATION DIRECTORY. see EDUCATION — *Abstracting, Bibliographies, Statistics*

613.7 796 370 NE ISSN 0038-8130
SPORTPARADE. 1952. s-m. fl.21. Nederlandse Katholieke Sportfederatie, Postbus 90124, 5200 MA 's-Hertogenbosch, Netherlands. TEL 073-138884. FAX 073-145705. Ed. Hans Van Bovene. adv.; bk.rev.; illus. circ. 2,500.

SPRACHE - STIMME - GEHOER; Zeitschrift fuer Kommunikationsstoerungen. see *MEDICAL SCIENCES — Otorhinolaryngology*

420 DK ISSN 0907-5364
STAMMEBLADET. 1977. bi-m. DKK 120. Foreningen for Stammere i Danmark - Association for Stutterers in Denmark, c/o D.S.I., Landskronagade 66, DK-2100 Copenhagen Oe, Denmark. TEL 45-86-86-26-96. FAX 45-86-86-27-96. Ed.Bd. adv.; bk.rev. circ. 350.
   Formerly: P P P (ISSN 0108-7207)

STUDENT ASSISTANCE JOURNAL. see *DRUG ABUSE AND ALCOHOLISM*

371.9 378 GW
STUDIENSTIFTUNG. JAHRESBERICHT. 1970. a. free. Studienstiftung des Deutschen Volkes, Mirbachstr. 7, 53173 Bonn, Germany. Ed. Klaus H. Kohrs. illus.; stat. circ. 32,000. **Document type:** corporate report.
   Description: Report of a society which enables specially gifted students to further their education and receive scholarships. Includes report on activities and statistics.

371.9 UK ISSN 0268-2141
LB1029.R4
SUPPORT FOR LEARNING. 1967. q. £32($67) (National Association for Remedial Education) Basil Blackwell Ltd., 108 Cowley Rd., Oxford OX4 1JF, England. TEL 0865-791100. (Subscr. to.: c/o Marston Book Services, P.O. Box 87, Oxford OX2 0DT, England) Ed. C. Gains. circ. 5,500. (also avail. in microform from SWZ) **Indexed:** Educ.Tech.Abstr., High.Educ.Curr.Aware.Bull., Psychol.Abstr., Sp.Ed.Needs Abstr.
—BLDSC (8547.638300); UMI. **CCC.**
   Formerly (until 1986): Remedial Education (ISSN 0034-4214)

371.9 362.4 PL ISSN 0137-818X
SZKOLA SPECJALNA. 1924. bi-m. $18. (Ministerstwo Edukacji Narodowej) Wydawnictwa Szkolne i Pedagogiczne, Pl. Dabrowskiego 8, 00-950 Warsaw, Poland. TEL 48-22-265451. (Dist. by: Ars Polona-Ruch, Krakowskie Przedmiescie 7, Warsaw, Poland) Ed. Ewa Zabczynska. circ. 2,000.
   Description: Discusses problems of children who are mentally handicapped, or with impaired hearing, speech, or sight, as well as children suffering from chronic illness or who are socially maladjusted. Publishes articles on teaching and care in special schools and institutions. Reports the progress of special education in other countries.

371.9 AT ISSN 0815-8150
TALENTED. 1983. 4/yr. Aus.$40($28) (typically set in Jan.). University of New England, Department of Learning, Development and Communication, Armidale, N.S.W. 2351, Australia. TEL 067-734-298. FAX 067-729702. Ed. Stan Bailey. bk.rev.; circ. 600 (paid). (back issues avail.) **Document type:** newsletter.
   Description: For teachers and parents on the education of the gifted and talented.

362.7 US
TEACHER EDUCATION AND SPECIAL EDUCATION. 1977. q. $18 to individuals (foreign $23); institutions $35 (foreign $40). Council for Exceptional Children, Teacher Education Division, 1920 Association Dr., Reston, VA 22091. TEL 703-620-3660. FAX 703-264-9494. (Subscr. to: Boyd Printing Co., Inc., 49 Sheridan Ave., Albany, NY 12210) Eds. Vivian Correa, Paul Sindelar. adv.; bk.rev. circ. 2,700. (also avail. in microform from UMI; back issues avail.) **Indexed:** C.I.J.E.
   Description: Contains reports of original research, evaluations of personnel preparation programs or components thereof, and theoretically based discussions of personnel preparation practices.

TEACHER'S PROFESSIONAL UPDATE; personal, financial, and career development. see *EDUCATION*

371.9 UK ISSN 0040-0572
TEACHING & TRAINING. 1962. q. £1.65. National Association of Teachers of the Mentally Handicapped, c/o Edward R.D. Myer, 77 Highfield Bromham, Chippenham, Wilts. SN15 2HT, England. adv.; bk.rev.; film rev.; illus. circ. 1,600. **Indexed:** High.Educ.Curr.Aware.Bull.

371.9 420 US
TEACHING ENGLISH TO DEAF AND SECOND LANGUAGE STUDENTS. 1974. 2/yr. $10 to individuals; institutions $15. Gallaudet University, Department of English, Kendall Green, Washington, DC 20002. TEL 202-651-5580. Ed. Nancy E. Kensicki. adv.; bk.rev.; abstr. circ. 1,000. (back issues avail.) **Indexed:** C.I.J.E., DSH Abstr.
—BLDSC (8614.107000).
   Formerly: Teaching English to the Deaf (ISSN 0093-8874)
   Description: Examines problems and possible solutions for teaching English to deaf and second-language students, with emphasis on practical methods.

371.9 US ISSN 0040-0599
LC3950
TEACHING EXCEPTIONAL CHILDREN. 1968. 4/yr. $48 to non-members (foreign $54). Council for Exceptional Children, 1920 Association Dr., Reston, VA 22091. TEL 703-620-3660. FAX 703-264-9494. Eds. Harold W. Heller, Fred Spooner. adv.; charts; illus. circ. 55,000. (also avail. in microform from UMI; reprint service avail. from UMI) **Indexed:** Adol.Ment.Hlth.Abstr., C.I.J.E., Child Devel.Abstr., Cont.Pg.Educ., Educ.Ind., Except.Child.Educ.Abstr., Rehabil.Lit., Sp.Ed.Needs Abstr.
—BLDSC (8614.120000); Faxon; UnCover; SWETS; UMI.
   Description: Designed specifically for teachers of handicapped and gifted children, including therapists, related service personnel, special-education teachers, and teachers who have exceptional children in regular classes. Articles deal with practical methods and materials for classroom use.

TEAM OF ADVOCATES FOR SPECIAL KIDS NEWSLETTER. see *HANDICAPPED*

TECHNOLOGY AND DISABILITY. see *HANDICAPPED*

373.2 US ISSN 0093-9889
LC1046.T4
TENNESSEE. STATE BOARD FOR VOCATIONAL EDUCATION. INFORMATION SERIES. Key Title: Information Series - Tennessee State Board of Vocational Education. irreg. State Board for Vocational Education, Nashville, TN 37219. TEL 615-741-3446.

371.9 US
THEIR WORLD. 1970. a. $10. National Center for Children with Learning Disabilities, 381 Park Ave. S., No. 1420, New York, NY 10016-8806. TEL 212-687-7211. Ed. William Ellis. adv.; bk.rev.; abstr. circ. 70,000.

371.9 UK ISSN 0968-1728
THERAPEUTIC CARE AND EDUCATION. (Former name of issuing body: Association of Workers for Maladjusted Children) 1959. 3/yr. £34 to individuals (foreign £30); U.K. libraries £30 (effective 1994). Association of Workers for Children with EBD, c/o Mr. A. Fox, Longview, Lodge Rd., Caerleon, Newport, Gwent NP6 1QS, Wales. TEL 0633-421209. Ed. Paul Cooper. adv.; bk.rev. circ. 2,000. **Indexed:** ASSIA, Br.Educ.Ind., Psychol.Abstr., Sp.Ed.Needs Abstr. **Document type:** academic/scholarly publication.
—BLDSC (8814.642700).
   Former titles: Maladjustment and Therapeutic Education (ISSN 0264-4614); New Growth (ISSN 0261-0477); Therapeutic Education (ISSN 0305-7860); Association of Workers for Maladjusted Children. Journal.
   Description: Covers interests of disturbed children and promotes communication between professional workers involved with them. Regional and national events; monographs on specific topics.

TIJDSCHRIFT VOOR REVALIDATIEWETENSCHAPPEN/JOURNAL OF REHABILITATION SCIENCES. see *MEDICAL SCIENCES — Physical Medicine And Rehabilitation*

372 US ISSN 0271-1214
LC4019.2 CODEN: TECEER
TOPICS IN EARLY CHILDHOOD SPECIAL EDUCATION. 1981. q. $35 to individuals; institutions $70 (foreign $95) (effective 1994). Pro-Ed Inc., 8700 Shoal Creek Blvd., Austin, TX 78757-6897. TEL 512-451-3246. FAX 512-451-8542. Ed. Mark Wolery; Pub. Donald D. Hammill. adv.; charts; illus. circ. 2,500. (also avail. in microform from UMI; back issues avail.; reprint service avail. from UMI) **Indexed:** C.I.J.E., Psychol.Abstr., Sp.Ed.Needs Abstr., Stud.Wom.Abstr. **Document type:** academic/scholarly publication.
—BLDSC (8867.437300); Faxon; UnCover; UMI. **CCC.**
   Description: Presents comprehensive discussion of timely and important issues in the field of early childhood special education.
   Refereed Serial

371.912 US ISSN 0271-8294
RC423.A1
TOPICS IN LANGUAGE DISORDERS. 1981. q. $63 (foreign $76). Aspen Publishers, Inc., 200 Orchard Ridge Dr., Gaithersburg, MD 20878. TEL 301-417-7500. FAX 301-417-7550. **Indexed:** C.I.J.E., Educ.Ind., Lang.& Lang.Behav.Abstr., Psychol.Abstr.
—BLDSC (8867.458500); Faxon; UnCover; UMI. **CCC.**

371.9 CN ISSN 0381-9612
TRUST. 1967. q. membership. Regina and District Association for Community Living Inc., Regina and District Branch, 4052 631 28th Ave., Regina, SK S4S 6X3, Canada. TEL 306-586-7988. bk.rev. circ. 200 (controlled). **Document type:** newsletter.

371.9 UK
U K SPECIAL EDUCATION DIRECTORY. 1991. a. School Government Publishing Co. Ltd., Darby House, Bletchingley Rd., Merstham, Redhill, Surrey RH1 3DN, England. TEL 0737-642223. FAX 0737-644283. Ed. P.J. Swaine. adv.: page £200; trim 178 x 105. circ. 2,000. **Document type:** directory.
   Formerly: U K Special Learning Needs Directory.
   Description: Details the provision of special education throughout England, Wales, Scotland and Northern Ireland.

EDUCATION — TEACHING METHODS AND CURRICULUM

371.9 US ISSN 0070-6736
LC4019
U S C ANNUAL DISTINGUISHED LECTURE SERIES MONOGRAPHS IN SPECIAL EDUCATION AND REHABILITATION. 1962. a. price varies. (University of Southern California, School of Education) University of Southern California Press, c/o Bookstore, University Park, Los Angeles, CA 90007. TEL 213-743-5371. Ed. James F. Magary. circ. 3,000. **Indexed:** ERIC, Except.Child Educ.Abstr., Rehabil.Lit. **Document type:** monographic series.

371.9 DK ISSN 0107-377X
UNDERVISNINGSMATERIALER TIL BEGYNDER- OG SPECIALUNDERVISNING. 1980. a. free. Special Paedagogisk Forlag, Herning, Denmark. illus.
Formerly: Test- og Undervisningsmaterialer.

371.9 XO
UNIVERZITA KOMENSKEHO. PEDAGOGICKA FAKULTA. KATEDRA SPECIALNEJ PEDAGOGIKY. ZBORNIK. PAEDAGOGICA SPECIALIS. (Text in Slovak; summaries in English, German and Russian) 1969. a. exchange basis. Univerzita Komenskeho, Pedagogicka Fakulta, Katedra Specialnej Pedagogiky, Moskovska ul. 3, 813 34 Bratislava, Slovakia. TEL 07-254-874. Ed. Stefan Vasek. circ. 500. (also avail. in microfilm) **Indexed:** Bibl.Ling. **Document type:** academic/scholarly publication, monographic series.
Formerly: Univerzita Komeskeho. Oddelenie Liecebnej a Specialnej Pedagogiky. Zbornik. Paedagogica Specialis (ISSN 0083-4211)
Description: Forum for the theory, practice and research of special education for handicapped children.

371.9 DK ISSN 0903-9821
VIA DATCH. 1988. 9/yr. DKK 255. Danish Centre for Rehabilitation and Special Education, Graham Bells Vej 1 A, DK-8200 Aarhus N, Denmark. TEL 45-86-783700. FAX 45-86-783730. Ed. Maiken Hansen. adv.; bk.rev.
Formerly (until 1988): Mikronyt i Specialundervisningen (ISSN 0900-6230)

371.9 SZ ISSN 0017-9655
VIERTELJAHRESSCHRIFT FUER HEILPAEDAGOGIK UND IHRE NACHBARGEBIETE. 1932. q. 42 SFr. Heilpaedagogisches Institut der Universitaet Freiburg, Petrus-Kanisius-Gasse 21, CH-1700 Freiburg, Switzerland. TEL 037-219740. FAX 037-219743. Ed. Christina Amrein. adv.; bk.rev. **Indexed:** Psychol.Abstr. **Document type:** academic/scholarly publication.
Formerly: Heilpaedagogische Werkblaetter.

371 US
VOCATIONAL REHABILITATION REVIEW. 1982. w. membership. National Association of Rehabilitation Facilities, Box 17675, Washington, DC 20041. (Subscr. to: Box 17675, Washington, DC 20041) Ed. Charles W. Harles. circ. 545.

VOLTA REVIEW. see *HANDICAPPED — Hearing Impaired*

362.8 US
WASHINGTON (STATE). DIVISION OF VOCATIONAL REHABILITATION. STATE FACILITIES DEVELOPMENT PLAN. 1969. every 3 yrs. free. Department of Social and Health Services, Division of Vocational Rehabilitation, OB 2, Olympia, WA 98504. TEL 206-753-0767. FAX 206-586-6505. circ. 1,000.
Former titles: Washington (State). Vocational Rehabilitation Services Division. State Facilities Development Plan; Washington (State). Vocational Rehabilitation Services Division. State Facilities Plan (ISSN 0092-5543)

371.9 371.3 UK ISSN 0144-5359
WESSEX STUDIES IN SPECIAL EDUCATION. 1981. biennial. £5. King Alfred's College, Winchester SO22 4NR, England. Ed. Barny Gray. bk.rev. circ. 400. (looseleaf format; also avail. in microfiche) **Indexed:** Br.Educ.Ind, Except.Child.Educ.Abstr.

WHICH SCHOOL? FOR SPECIAL NEEDS. see *EDUCATION — Guides To Schools And Colleges*

420 US ISSN 1048-3950
WORD OF MOUTH (SAN ANTONIO). 1989. 6/yr. $20. Box 13716, San Antonio, TX 78213-0716. TEL 210-340-4059. Ed. Lauren Newton. index. (back issues avail.) **Document type:** newsletter.
Description: Addresses the needs of the school speech pathologist interested in keeping up with trends in working with school-age children.

371.9 155.4 US
WORLD COUNCIL FOR GIFTED AND TALENTED CHILDREN. YEARBOOK. 1981. biennial. $15. World Council for Gifted and Talented Children, Box 10034, Beaumont, TX 77710. TEL 409-880-8046. FAX 409-880-8685. (back issues avail.) **Document type:** proceedings.
Description: Describes the proceedings of the world conferences held by the council.

371.9 UK
WORLD O R T UNION. YEARBOOK. (Organization for Educational Resources and Technological Training) 1971. a. World O R T Union, 3 Sumpter Close, Finchley Rd., London NW3 5HR, England. TEL 071-431-1333. FAX 071-435-4784. charts; illus.; stat. circ. 10,000. **Document type:** academic/scholarly publication.
Formerly: O R T Yearbook.

YOU'ER ZHILI SHIJIE/TODDLERS' INTELLIGENCE WORLD. see *CHILDREN AND YOUTH — About*

371.9 GW
ZEITSCHRIFT FUER HEILPAEDAGOGIK. (Text in German; summaries in English, German) 1949. m. DM.175. Verband Deutscher Sonderschulen e.V., c/o Bernd Schulze, Postfach 1666, 31566 Nienburg, Germany. Eds. Ulrich Bleidick, P. Wachtel. adv.; bk.rev.; cum.index: 1959-1976. circ. 10,500. (back issues avail.)

EDUCATION — Teaching Methods And Curriculum
see also specific subjects

610.7 US ISSN 0092-0371
R745
A A M C CURRICULUM DIRECTORY. 1972. a. $15 (foreign $20). Association of American Medical Colleges, 2450 N St., Washington, DC 20037-1126. TEL 202-828-0416. FAX 202-828-1123. (reprint service avail. from UMI) **Document type:** directory.

A A P T ANNOUNCER. (American Association of Physics Teachers) see *PHYSICS*

375 US
A A T A NEWSLETTER. 3/yr. $20 to individuals; institutions $200; students $10 (includes Al-Arabiyya journal). American Association of Teachers of Arabic, 280 HRCB, Brigham Young University, Provo, UT 84602. TEL 801-378-6528. FAX 801-378-7075. Ed. Mushira Eid. adv. circ. 200.
Description: Contains letters of the association and articles of interest. Lists Arabic teaching positions.

A A T F NATIONAL BULLETIN. (American Association of Teachers of French) see *LINGUISTICS*

371.3 700 AT ISSN 0155-722X
A C T A NEWS. q. Aus.$40 membership. Art Craft Teachers Association of Victoria, 217 Church St., Richmond, Vic. 3121, Australia. Ed. Sandra Taylor. adv.; bk.rev. circ. 1,000. **Document type:** newsletter.
Description: Provides news about forthcoming art education activities for teachers.

375 US ISSN 0147-1236
P10
A C T F L FOREIGN LANGUAGE EDUCATION SERIES. 1969. a., vol.5, no.1, 1992. $14.60 to non-members; members $10.95. American Council on the Teaching of Foreign Languages, Inc., 6 Executive Plaza, Yonkers, NY 10701-6801. TEL 914-963-8830. FAX 914-963-1275. **Document type:** academic/scholarly publication.
Former titles: A C T F L Review of Foreign Languages Education (ISSN 0091-2476); A C T F L Annual Review of Foreign Language Education (ISSN 0068-1180); Britannica Review of Foreign Language Education.

A C T F L NEWSLETTER. (American Council on the Teaching of Foreign Languages, Inc.) see *LINGUISTICS*

A E C A RESOURCE BOOK SERIES. see *CHILDREN AND YOUTH — About*

371.3 UK
A E T T JOURNAL - E T T I. 1962. q. £45. Association for Educational and Training Technology, Educational and Training Technology International, c/o Centre for Continuing Education, City University, Northampton Square, London EC1V 0HB, England. FAX 0752-232375. Ed. C. Bell. bk.rev. circ. 1,300.
Incorporates (1966-1990): Ed.Tech.News; Former titles (until 1989): A E T T Journal - P L E T; A E T T Journal; A P L E T Journal.

791.43 US ISSN 1051-5925
LB1044
A F V A EVALUATIONS.* 1946. a. membership. American Film & Video Association, Inc., Box 6467, Jersey City, NJ 07306-0457. TEL 708-698-6440. FAX 708-823-1561. TELEX 403681 AFVA. film rev.; index. circ. 1,000. (also avail. in microform from UMI; reprint service avail. from UMI)
Formerly (until 1987) E F L A Evaluations.

028.5 US ISSN 0882-2840
A L A N REVIEW. 1972. 3/yr. $15. National Council of Teachers of English, Assembly on Literature for Adolescents, Office of the Dean, College of Education & Human Development, Radford University, VA 24142. TEL 703-831-5439. FAX 703-831-6053. (Subscr. to: 1111 Kenyon Rd., Urbana, IL 61801) Eds. Robert C. Small, Jr., Patricia Kelly. adv.; bk.rev. circ. 3,000. (also avail. in microfiche) **Indexed:** ERIC. **Document type:** academic/scholarly publication.
—BLDSC (0786.525117); UnCover.
Formerly: A L A N Newsletter.
Description: Features interviews with authors and provides techniques for intergrating young adult literature into the classroom.

A L A NEWS. (American Lawyers Auxiliary) see *LAW*

A M A T Y C REVIEW. (American Mathematical Association of Two-Year Colleges) see *EDUCATION — Higher Education*

372 US ISSN 1054-0040
A M S MONTESSORI LIFE. 1981. q. $29.50 to non-members (effective Sep. 1993). American Montessori Society, 150 Fifth Ave., Ste. 203, New York, NY 10011. TEL 212-924-3209. Ed. Joy S. Turner. adv.; bk.rev. circ. 13,000.
Formerly (until 1989): A M S Constructive Triangle; Which was formed by the merger of (1960-1981): A M S Bulletin (New York); (1965-1981): Constructive Triangle (ISSN 0010-700X); (1980-1981): A M S Newsletter; Which was formerly titled (1970-1979): A M S News; A M S News Notes (ISSN 0065-9444); A M S Board Briefs.
Description: Provides a forum for educational issues and advances and for the promotion of professional development and parent education.

373.246 630 US
A N R EDUCATOR. (Agricultural and Natural Resources) vol. 38, 1974. bi-m. free to qualified personnel. Michigan State University, Agricultural and Extension Education, 410 Agriculture Hall, East Lansing, MI 48824-1039. TEL 517-355-6580. FAX 517-353-4981. Ed. Carroll H. Wamhoff. adv.; bk.rev. circ. 550. **Document type:** newsletter.
Former titles: A N R E I Gram; Michigan State University. Agricultural and Natural Resources Education Institute. Newsletter; Michigan State University. College of Education. Service Letter to Teachers of Vocational Agribusiness and Natural Resources.

A S W E A JOURNAL FOR SOCIAL WORK EDUCATION IN AFRICA. (Association for Social Work Education in Africa) see *SOCIAL SERVICES AND WELFARE*

A T S S BULLETIN. (Association of Teachers of Social Studies in the City of New York) see *SOCIAL SCIENCES: COMPREHENSIVE WORKS*

371.33 JA ISSN 0065-0102
A V E IN JAPAN. (Audio-Visual Education) (Text in English) 1963. a. 1220 Yen. Japan Audio-Visual Education Association - Nihon Shichokaku Kyoiku Kyokai, 1-17-1 Toranomon, Minato-ku, Tokyo 105, Japan. FAX 81-3-3597-0564. Ed. Kenji Fujii. circ. 1,000.

EDUCATION — TEACHING METHODS AND CURRICULUM

371.3 791.43   US   ISSN 0091-360X
LB1044.A2
A V GUIDE; the learning media newsletter. 1922. m. $15. Educational Screen, Inc., 380 E. Northwest Highway, Des Plaines, IL 60016-2282. TEL 708-298-6622. FAX 708-390-0408. TELEX 206041 MSG RLY CARY. Ed. Natalie Ferguson. adv.; bk.rev.; film rev.; rec.rev.; charts; illus.; tr.lit.; index. circ. 600. (also avail. in microfilm (ISSN 0364-9946) from UMI; reprint service avail. from UMI) **Indexed:** Educ.Ind. **Document type:** trade publication.
—UMI. **CCC.**
  Former titles: A V Guide Newsletter; Educational Screen and Audio Visual Guide (ISSN 0013-1938)

A V K O NEWSLETTER. see EDUCATION — Adult Education

371.3   US   ISSN 1044-0445
LB1043
A V MARKET PLACE; the complete business directory of: audio, audio visual, computer systems, film, video, programming - with industry yellow pages. 1969. a. since 1976; previously biennial. $139.95. R.R. Bowker, A Reed Reference Publishing Company, Part of the Reed Elsevier group, 121 Chanlon Rd., New Providence, NJ 07974. TEL 908-665-3576. FAX 908-665-6688. TELEX 138 755. (Subscr. to: Order Dept., Box 31, New Providence, NJ 07974-9903. TEL 800-521-8110) **Document type:** directory.
  Former titles (until 1988): Audio Video Market Place (ISSN 0000-1112); (until 1984): Audiovisual Market Place (ISSN 0067-0553)
  Description: Lists companies that create, supply or distribute audiovisual equipment and services for business, education, science, government, and libraries.

A W P CHRONICLE. (Associated Writing Programs) see JOURNALISM

ACADEMIA VENEZOLANA DE LA LENGUA. BOLETIN. see LINGUISTICS

371.3 700   AT
ACTION (POTTS POINT). 1970. q. free. A B B Marketing Services, ABB EPT House, 166 William St., Potts Point, N.S.W., Australia. TEL 02-389-6688. FAX 02-389-2641. Ed. Susan Tennant. circ. 4,000. **Document type:** newsletter.
  Formerly (until Nov. 1987): A S E A Action.
  Description: Contains information on campany activities, projects.

658 370   FR   ISSN 0397-331X
ACTUALITE DE LA FORMATION PERMANENTE. 1972. 6/yr. 465 F. (foreign 575 F.). Centre I N F F O, Tour Europe, 92049 Paris Cedex 7 (La Defense), France. TEL 47-78-13-50. FAX 47-73-74-20. TELEX 615 383. bk.rev.; bibl. circ. 4,400.

ADMINISTRATORS NOTEBOOK. see EDUCATION — School Organization And Administration

613.7 370.15   US   ISSN 0890-4073
RA440.A1
ADVANCES IN HEALTH EDUCATION: CURRENT RESEARCH. 1988. a. $37.50. A M S Press, Inc., 56 E. 13th St., New York, NY 10003. TEL 212-777-4700. FAX 212-995-5413. Ed. James H. Humphrey. bk.rev.; index. (back issues avail.)
—BLDSC (0709.008200).
  Description: Contains original research on current issues, both biological and behavioral, in the field of health education.
  Refereed Serial

371.3   US   ISSN 0748-0067
LB1715
ADVANCES IN TEACHER EDUCATION. 1984. irreg., vol.4, 1991. price varies. Ablex Publishing Corporation, 355 Chestnut St., Norwood, NJ 07648. TEL 201-767-8450. FAX 201-767-6717. TELEX 135-393. Eds. Lilian Katz, James Raths.
—BLDSC (0711.595800).

ADVANCES IN THE PSYCHOLOGY OF HUMAN INTELLIGENCE. see PSYCHOLOGY

371.3   KE
AFRICAN ASSOCIATION FOR LITERACY AND ADULT EDUCATION. NEWSLETTER. (Text in English, French) 1977. a. free. African Association for Literacy and Adult Education, P.O. Box 50768, Nairobi, Kenya. TEL 331512. FAX 340849. Ed. Paul Wangoola. adv.; bk.rev. circ. 1,200. (back issues avail.) **Document type:** newsletter.
  Formerly: Afrolit News.

AIR & SPACE - SMITHSONIAN. see AERONAUTICS AND SPACE FLIGHT

370   YU
AKTUELNOSTI U VASPITANJU I OBRAZOVANJU. 1971-1983; resumed 198? 10/yr. 10000 din.($50) Republicki Zavod za Unapredjivanje Vaspitanja i Obrazovanja SR Srbije, Sector za Pedagosku Dokumentaciju, Draze Pavlovica 15, 11124 Belgrade, Yugoslavia. TEL 765-366. Ed. Iskra Maksimovic. circ. 1,000.

373.246   CN   ISSN 0709-0528
ALBERTA TEACHERS' ASSOCIATION. INDUSTRIAL EDUCATION COUNCIL. NEWS & NOTES. (Supplement to: I N D E C Communicator) 1963. 2/yr. Alberta Teachers' Association, Industrial Education Council, 11010 142nd St., Edmonton, Alta. T5N 2R1, Canada. TEL 403-453-2411. FAX 403-455-6481. Ed. Gerry Bawford. software rev.; bibl. circ. 500. (looseleaf format; back issues avail.)
  Formerly: I A V E C Newsletter.
  Description: Provides curriculum information, teaching hints and professional activities for industrial and vocational teachers in Alberta.

ALHAPEREK. see RELIGIONS AND THEOLOGY — Judaic

ALLIANCE UPDATE. see PHYSICAL FITNESS AND HYGIENE

DER ALTSPRACHLICHE UNTERRICHT; Arbeitshefte zu seiner wissenschaftlichen Begruendung und praktischen Gestalt. see LINGUISTICS

ALVERNO MAGAZINE. see EDUCATION — Higher Education

499.992 370   US   ISSN 0002-7499
AMERICAN ASSOCIATION OF TEACHERS OF ESPERANTO QUARTERLY BULLETIN/AMERIKA ASOCIO DE INSTRUISTOJ DE ESPERANTO KVARONJARA BULTENO. (Text in English and Esperanto) 1963. q. $20 to members only. American Association of Teachers of Esperanto, c/o Sally Lawton, 12 Stage Rd., Westhampton, MA 01027. TEL 805-967-5241. Ed. Dorothy Holland-Kaupp. bk.rev. circ. 100. (processed) **Document type:** bulletin.

613.7   US   ISSN 0003-1259
AMERICAN SOKOL. (Text mainly in English; occasionally in Czech) 1879. m. $4. American Sokol Organization, 6424 W. Cermak Rd., Berwyn, IL 60402. TEL 708-795-6671. Ed. Patricia Satek. adv.; illus. circ. 5,000. **Document type:** newsletter.
  Description: Focuses on physical education and cultural activities of members.

L'AMITIE/FRIENDSHIP. see LINGUISTICS

ANNUAL REPORT ON ADVANCED DENTAL EDUCATION. see MEDICAL SCIENCES — Dentistry

371   GW   ISSN 0402-5563
ANREGUNG (MUNICH); Zeitschrift fuer Gymnasialpaedagogik. 1954. bi-m. DM.54. Bayerischer Schulbuch-Verlag, Hubertusstr. 4, 80639 Munich, Germany. Ed. Alfons Staedele. **Document type:** academic/scholarly publication.
—CCC.

ARAB JOURNAL OF LANGUAGE STUDIES/AL-MAJALLAH AL-'ARABIYYAH LIL-DIRASAT AL-LUGHAWIYYAH. see LINGUISTICS

375 956   US   ISSN 1047-711X
DS36
ARAB WORLD ALMANAC. 1989. a. AMIDEAST, 1100 17th St., N.W., Washington, DC 20036-4601. TEL 202-785-0022. FAX 202-822-6563. TELEX 440160. Ed.Bd adv.; bk.rev. circ. 300. (also avail. in microform from EDR; back issues avail.) **Indexed:** Per.Islam. (1991-).
  Formerly (until no.65, 1989): Human Resource Developments in the Middle East and North Africa (ISSN 0747-8941)
  Description: Contains complete lesson plans, including background essays, classroom exercises and supplementary materials to help high school teachers incorporate regional studies into the curriculum.

371.3   GW
ARBEITEN & LERNEN: TECHNIK UND WIRTSCHAFT; Zeitschrift fuer Arbeit, Beruf, Wirtschaft und Technik in der Unterrichts praxis. 1969. 8/yr. DM.119.90. Erhard Friedrich Verlag GmbH, Im Brande 17, 30926 Seelze, Germany. TEL 0511-40004-0. FAX 0511-40004-19. (Subscr. to: Postfach 100150, 30917 Seelze, Germany) Eds. E.A. Grunert, K. Schnedewind. adv.; index. circ. 7,000. (back issues avail.) **Document type:** trade publication.
—CCC.
  Former titles: Arbeiten und Lernen (ISSN 0176-3717); Arbeitslehre; Dortmunder Hefte fuer Arbeitslehre und Sachunterricht.

379   US
ARIZONA. STATE COUNCIL FOR VOCATIONAL EDUCATION. BIENNIAL REPORT. 1970. biennial. free. Council for Vocational Education, 4725 N. 19th Ave., Ste. 2, Phoenix, AZ 85015. TEL 602-255-5040. Ed. Dr. Richard Froese. circ. 2,500.
  Former titles: Arizona. State Advisory Council for Vocational Technical Education. Annual Report; Arizona. State Advisory Council for Vocational Education. Annual Report (ISSN 0091-8792)

370 420.07   US   ISSN 0004-1483
ARIZONA ENGLISH BULLETIN. 1958. 3/yr. (Sep.-June). $20 to individuals; institutions $25. Arizona English Teachers Association, Arizona State University, Tempe, AZ 85287-0302. TEL 602-965-3105. Eds. Ken Donelson, Caro Williams. adv.; bk.rev.; bibl. circ. 500. (processed) **Indexed:** ERIC. **Document type:** academic/scholarly publication.
—UnCover.
  Description: Focuses on methods of studying and teaching English.

371.3   US   ISSN 0004-3931
ARTS AND ACTIVITIES; the nation's leading arts education magazine. 1932. m. (Sep.-June). $24.95. Publishers Development Corp., 591 Camino de la Reina, Ste. 200, San Diego, CA 92108. TEL 619-297-8032. FAX 619-297-5353. Ed. Maryellen Bridge; Pub. George V. Von Rosen. adv. contact: Steve Polite. bk.rev.; video rev.; illus.; tr.lit.; s-a. index. circ. 22,000. (also avail. in microform from UMI) **Indexed:** Biog.Ind., Educ.Ind., Ind.Child.Mag., Jun.High.Mag.Abstr. **Document type:** consumer publication.
—BLDSC (1735.400000); Faxon; UnCover; UMI.
  Description: Publishes articles dealing with the theory and practice of art education at the elementary and secondary levels, as well as teacher education and related issues. Reviews useful products, materials and supplies.

ARTS EDUCATION POLICY REVIEW. see ART

371.3   UK   ISSN 1350-1933
ASPECTS OF EDUCATIONAL AND TRAINING TECHNOLOGY SERIES. a. £32. (Association for Educational and Training Technology) Kogan Page Ltd., 120 Pentonville Rd., London N1 9JN, England. TEL 071-278-0433. FAX 071-837-6348. TELEX 263088 KOGAN G. Ed.Bd. **Indexed:** C.I.J.E., Cont.Pg.Educ., Educ.Tech.Abstr., SOMA. **Document type:** proceedings.
—BLDSC (8285.163600).
  Former titles: Aspects of Educational Technology Series (ISSN 0141-5956); Perspectives on Academic Gaming and Simulation; Simulation - Games for Learning (ISSN 0142-9361)
  Description: Covers the proceedings of the association's conference.

EDUCATION — TEACHING METHODS AND CURRICULUM

ASSESSMENT UPDATE: PROGRESS, TRENDS, AND PRACTICES IN HIGHER EDUCATION. see *EDUCATION — Higher Education*

375   US   ISSN 0066-9199
LB2804
ASSOCIATION FOR SUPERVISION AND CURRICULUM DEVELOPMENT. YEARBOOK. 1944. a. membership. Association for Supervision and Curriculum Development, 1250 N. Pitt St., Alexandria, VA 22314-1453. TEL 703-549-9110. FAX 703-549-3891. Ed. Ron Brandt. **Indexed:** Educ.Ind. **Document type:** bulletin.

375 960   NR
ASSOCIATION OF HISTORY TEACHERS IN NIGERIA. 1971. a. S.10. Educational Research Institute, Box 277, Ibadan, Nigeria. Ed. Od Olusola Akintagy.

420   AT   ISSN 0310-608X
ASSOCIATION OF TEACHERS OF ENGLISH AS A FOREIGN LANGUAGE. BULLETIN.* 1972. 3/yr. Aus.$3. Association of Teachers of English as a Foreign Language, P.O. Box 187, Rozelle, N.S.W. 2039, Australia. Ed. Patricia Smith. **Document type:** bulletin.

ASSOCIATION OF TEACHERS OF JAPANESE. JOURNAL. see *LINGUISTICS*

613.7 370   US   ISSN 0004-6647
ATHLETIC DIRECTOR. 1969. 2/yr. free to members. National Council of Secondary School Athletic Directors, 1900 Association Dr., Reston, VA 22091. TEL 703-476-3400. FAX 703-476-9527. Ed. Kathy Taves. bk.rev.; bibl.; charts; illus.; circ. controlled. (also avail. in microfilm from UMI; reprint service avail. from ISI,UMI) **Indexed:** Sportsearch.
    Description: Discusses physical education.

371.3   IO
ATMA JAYA RESEARCH CENTRE. ANNUAL REPORT. (Text in English) 1973. a. Atma Jaya Research Centre - Pusat Penelitian Atma Jaya, Jalan Jenderal Sudirman 51, Box 2639, Jakarta 10001, Indonesia. illus. (also avail. in microfiche)

371.3 791.43   UK   ISSN 0305-2249
TS2301.A7
AUDIO VISUAL. 1972. m. £50. E M A P Vision Ltd., 19 Scarbrook Rd., Croydon, Surrey, CR9 1QH, England. TEL 081-760-9690. FAX 081-681-1672. TELEX 946665. Ed. Peter Lloyd. adv.; bk.rev.; film rev.; illus.; tr.lit.; index. circ. 20,000. (also avail. in microfilm from UMI; reprint service avail. from UMI) **Indexed:** Account.& Data Proc.Abstr., Build.Manage.Abstr., Educ.Tech.Abstr., Fluidex, High.Educ.Curr.Aware.Bull., Info.Media & Tech., Media Rev.Dig., Sci.Abstr.
—BLDSC (1788.500000); SWETS; UMI. **CCC.**
    Supersedes: Film User (ISSN 0015-1459)

371.33   NE
AUDIO VISUEEL MAGAZINE. 1980. 12/yr. fl.150. A V Press B.V., Postbus 1249, 6501 BE Nijmegen, Netherlands. TEL 080-600611. FAX 080-230800. TELEX 48579 NL. Ed. Leo Koomen. adv.; bk.rev.; illus. circ. 12,600.

371.33 791.43   IT   ISSN 0004-7627
AUDIOVISIVI. 1961. m. L.6000. Via Taranto 21, 00182 Rome, Italy. adv.; bk.rev.; film rev.; music rev.; play rev.; rec.rev.; abstr.; charts; illus.; stat.; index. circ. 15,000.

778.5   US   ISSN 0738-7954
AUGSBURG MEDIA MESSENGER. 1956. a. free. Augsburg Fortress, 426 S. Fifth St., Box 1209, Minneapolis, MN 55440. TEL 612-330-3300. Ed. Susan Nauha. adv.; film rev.; abstr.; bibl.; index, cum.index. circ. 15,000.
    Formerly: Augsburg Audiovisual Newsletter.

375.38   AT   ISSN 0084-6961
AUSTRALASIAN COMMERCIAL TEACHERS' ASSOCIATION. JOURNAL.* 1968. a. $1. Australasian Commercial Teachers' Association, 20 Napoleon St., Roseberry, N.S.W. 2018, Australia.

AUSTRALASIAN SCIENCE MAGAZINE. see *SCIENCES: COMPREHENSIVE WORKS*

AUSTRALIAN ART EDUCATION. see *ART*

AUSTRALIAN EARLY CHILDHOOD NEWSLETTER. see *CHILDREN AND YOUTH — About*

371.3   AT   ISSN 0814-673X
AUSTRALIAN JOURNAL OF EDUCATIONAL TECHNOLOGY. 1985. s-a. Aus.$40 (New Zealand & S.E. Asia Aus.$45; elsewhere Aus.$55). A J E T Publications Ltd., P.O. Box 772, Belconnen, A.C.T. 2616, Australia. TEL 61-6-2735405. FAX 61-6-2735403. Ed. John G. Heoberg. adv.; bk.rev. circ. 800. **Indexed:** Aus.Educ.Ind. **Document type:** academic/scholarly publication.
—BLDSC (1807.620000).
    Description: Publishes research, development and practical articles on all aspects of learning with technology.

371.3   AT   ISSN 1038-1562
LB1049.9   CODEN: AJLLEL
AUSTRALIAN JOURNAL OF LANGUAGE AND LITERACY. 1978. q. membership. Australian Reading Association, P.O. Box 78, Carlton South, Vic. 3053, Australia. TEL 03-347-2555. FAX 03-347-8971. Ed. Bruce Shortland-Jones. adv.; B&W page Aus.$300; trim 250 x 180. bk.rev.; tr.lit.; cum.index. circ. 6,000. (back issues avail.) **Indexed:** C.I.J.E.
—BLDSC (1809.130000); UnCover; UMI.
    Formerly: Australian Journal of Reading (ISSN 0156-0301)

507   AT   ISSN 0045-0855
Q183.43.A8
AUSTRALIAN SCIENCE TEACHERS' JOURNAL. 1955. 4/yr. Aus.$32 to individuals; institutions Aus.$36. Australian Science Teachers Association, University of South Australia (Salisbury Campus), Smith Rd., Salisbury E., S.A. 5109, Australia. TEL 08-302-5137. FAX 08-302-5101. Ed. Mark Hackling. adv.; bk.rev.; index, cum.index: 1955-1971; circ. 5,500 (controlled). (also avail. in microfrom from UMI) **Indexed:** Aus.Educ.Ind., C.I.J.E., Chem.Abstr., Cont.Pg.Educ.
—UnCover; UMI.

607   AT   ISSN 0815-3701
AUSTRALIAN T A F E TEACHER. 1969. q. Aus.$10. (Technical and Further Education Teacher's Association) Percival Publishing Co. Pty. Ltd., 862-870 Elizabeth St., Waterloo, N.S.W. 2017, Australia. **Indexed:** Aus.Educ.Ind., Cont.Pg.Educ., Mult.Ed.Abstr.
    Formerly: Australian Technical Teacher (ISSN 0045-0928)

AWASIS JOURNAL. see *ETHNIC INTERESTS*

AWASIS NEWSLETTER. see *ETHNIC INTERESTS*

707   GW   ISSN 0005-2981
B D K MITTEILUNGEN. 1964. q. DM.36. Bund Deutscher Kunsterzieher, Jakobistr. 40, 30163 Hannover, Germany. TEL 0511-662229. Ed. Raimund Lehmann. adv.; bibl.; illus. circ. 4,200. **Document type:** academic/scholarly publication.
    Formerly: B D K Mitteilungen und Werkdidaktische Studien.

B S C S: THE NATURAL SELECTION; innovative science education. (Biological Sciences Curriculum Study) see *BIOLOGY*

375   UK
B T A DIRECTIONS SERIES. 1989. a. free to U.K. senior schools. British Trades Alphabet, Thames View Business Centre, Thames View Industrial Park, Abingdon, Oxon., OX14 3LF, England. TEL 0235-553233. FAX 0235-553356. Ed. Alan Rothery. circ. 7,500. (looseleaf format; back issues avail.)
    Description: Contains information on a variety of subjects for national curriculum sponsored by national companies.

808.5 370   AT   ISSN 0005-3503
BABEL. 1950. 3/yr. Aus.$45 to individuals (foreign Aus.$50); institutions Aus.$50 (foreign Aus.$55). Australian Federation of Modern Languages Teachers Associations, c/o Angela Scarino, Ed., 9 Stanley St., N. Adelaide, S.A. 5006, Australia. TEL 08-3022726. FAX 08-3022040. adv.; bk.rev.; bibl.; cum.index. circ. 2,600. (tabloid format; also avail. in microform; back issues avail.) **Indexed:** Aus.P.A.I.S., Educ.Ind., Lang.& Lang.Behav.Abstr., Lang.Teach.& Ling.Abstr., M.L.A., Mid.East: Abstr.& Ind. **Document type:** academic/scholarly publication.
—BLDSC (1854.600000); UnCover. **CCC.**

286   US   ISSN 0005-5727
BAPTIST LEADER. 1939. q. $8. American Baptist Churches in the U S A, Educational Ministries, Box 851, Valley Forge, PA 19482-0851. TEL 215-768-2000. FAX 215-768-2056. Ed. Linda Isham. illus.; index. circ. 7,000.

371.9   GW   ISSN 0173-8585
BAUSTEINE KINDERGARTEN. 1980. q. DM.56. Bergmoser und Hoeller Verlag GmbH, Karl-Friedrich-Str. 76, 52072 Aachen, Germany. TEL 0241-1730922. FAX 0241-1730934. circ. 29,000. (looseleaf format; back issues avail.) **Document type:** academic/scholarly publication.
    Description: Written for educators of kindergartens and nursery schools. Provides ideas for projects and activites; learning materials for the classroom.

375 371.3   GW
DIE BAYERISCHE REALSCHULE. 1954. m. DM.50 to non-members. (Bayerischer Realschullehrerverband e.V.) Verlag Gebr. Geiselberger, Postfach 69, 8262 Altoetting, Germany. TEL 08671-5065-0. FAX 08671-506568. (Subscr. to: BRLV Geschaeftsstelle, Dachauer Str. 44b, 8000 Munich 2, Germany. TEL 089-553876) Ed. Martha Haertl. adv.; bk.rev. circ. 8,000. **Document type:** academic/scholarly publication.

375 370.15   US
BEHAVIORAL EDUCATOR. 1980. q. $5 to individuals; students $3. Special Interest Group in Education, c/o Deborah A. Shanley, Ed., 330 E. 71st St., New York, NY 10021. TEL 212-734-8401. (Subscr. to: Theodore A. Hoch, 509 Allen Hall, West Virginia University, Box 6122, Morgantown, WV 26506-6122) (Co-sponsor: Association for Behavior Analysis in Education) adv.; bk.rev. circ. 110. (back issues avail.)

371.3   GW   ISSN 0175-2723
BEISPIELE; in Niedersachsen Schule Machen. 1983. q. DM.28. (Niedersaechsisches Kulturministerium) Kallmeyer'sche Verlagsbuchhandlung GmbH, Im Brande 19, 30926 Seelze, Germany. TEL 0511-4000475. FAX 0511-4000476. Ed. Jochen Elies. bk.rev. circ. 17,000. (back issues avail.) **Document type:** academic/scholarly publication.
—**CCC.**

BEITRAEGE ZUR PAEDAGOGISCHEN ARBEIT. see *PHILOSOPHY*

371   US   ISSN 1061-1495
BETTER TEACHING; tips and techniques to improve student learning. 1987. s-m. (Sep.-June). $79 (effective 1994). Teacher Institute, Box 397, Fairfax Station, VA 22039-0397. TEL 703-323-9170; 800-333-0776. FAX 703-323-9173. Ed. John H. Wherry. bk.rev.; charts; illus. (back issues avail.) **Document type:** newsletter.
    Description: Practical ideas to help teachers improve student learning.

BIG PICTURE. see *CHILDREN AND YOUTH — For*

BITON LEMORIM LE'ARAVIT. see *LINGUISTICS*

371.3   SZ
BLAETTER - REVUE - RIVISTA. 10/yr. 61 SFr. (foreign 79 SFr.). (Schweizerischer Verband fuer Beruflichen Unterricht) Sauerlaender AG, Laurenzenvorstadt 89, CH-5001 Aarau, Switzerland. TEL 064-268626. FAX 064-245780. TELEX 981195-SAG-CH. Ed.Bd. adv.: B&W page 1533 SFr.; trim 185 x 264. **Document type:** trade publication.
—**CCC.**
    Formerly: Schweizerischer Verband fuer Beruflichen Unterricht. Blaetter (ISSN 0378-7664)

BLUEGRASS BULLETIN. see *LINGUISTICS*

BLUEGRASS MUSIC NEWS. see *MUSIC*

375   US
BLUMENFELD EDUCATION LETTER. 1986. m. $36. Paradigm Co., Box 45161, Boise, ID 83711. TEL 208-343-3790. Ed. Samuel L. Blumenfeld. cum.index: 1986-1991. (back issues avail.) **Document type:** newsletter.

BOOK MARK; children's literature in review with related activities for preschoolers through young adults. see *CHILDREN AND YOUTH — About*

EDUCATION — TEACHING METHODS AND CURRICULUM

370 796 BL
BRAZIL. MINISTERIO DE EDUCACAO. DEPARTAMENTO DE EDUCACAO FISICA E DESPORTOS. CADERNO CULTURAL. q. Cr.$56($48) for 2 yrs. Ministerio da Educacao, Departamento de Educacao Fisica e Desportos, Brasilia, Brazil. illus.; charts; bibl. **Document type:** government publication.

370.1 707 CN ISSN 0316-1544
BRITISH COLUMBIA ART TEACHERS' ASSOCIATION. JOURNAL. 1960. irreg. Can.$37 to non-members; members Can.$25; students Can.$15. (B.C. Art Teachers' Association) B.C. Teachers' Federation, 2235 Burrard St., Vancouver, B.C. V6J 3H9, Canada. TEL 604-731-8121. adv. circ. 375. **Indexed:** Can.Educ.Ind.
Formerly: British Columbia Art Teachers' Association. Newsletter (ISSN 0045-2904)

420 820 CN ISSN 0316-0173
BRITISH COLUMBIA ENGLISH TEACHERS' ASSOCIATION. JOURNAL. (Supplement a.: Update) 1960. a. Can.$45 to non-members; members Can.$35; students Can.$15. (B.C. English Teachers' Association) B.C. Teachers' Federation, 2235 Burrard St., Vancouver, B.C. V6J 3H9, Canada. TEL 604-731-8121. adv.; bk.rev. circ. 450. **Indexed:** Can.Educ.Ind.
Formerly (1966-1971): British Columbia English Teacher (ISSN 0045-2955)

375.5 UK ISSN 0960-796X
BRITISH JOURNAL OF CURRICULUM & ASSESSMENT. 1990. 3/yr. £23 in EC nations; elsewhere £32. Hodder & Stoughton (Subsidiary of: Hodder Headline plc), Charles Knight, Pub., 338 Euston Rd., London NW1 3BHP, England. TEL 071-873-6000. FAX 071-873-6024. Ed. David Hanson. bk.rev. **Document type:** academic/scholarly publication.
—BLDSC (2307.310000).
Description: Bridges the gap between topical reporting and erudite papers about technical issues.

371.3 658.3 UK ISSN 0269-0004
BRITISH JOURNAL OF EDUCATION AND WORK. 1987. 3/yr. £60 (foreign £67). Trentham Books Ltd., Westview House, 734 London Rd., Oakhill, Stoke-on-Trent, Staffs. ST4 5NP, England. TEL 0782-745567. FAX 0782-745553. Ed. Ian Jamieson. adv.; bk.rev.; cum.index every 5 yrs. circ. 750. (back issues avail.) **Indexed:** SOMA. **Document type:** academic/scholarly publication.
—BLDSC (2307.630000).
Description: Incorporates the curriculum, teaching methods and research about school and college programs linking industry, careers, employment and education.

371.3 UK ISSN 0007-1013
LB1043 CODEN: BJETDK
BRITISH JOURNAL OF EDUCATIONAL TECHNOLOGY. 1970. 3/yr. £60 (foreign £70). National Council for Educational Technology, Millburn Hill Rd., Science Park, Coventry CV4 7JJ, England. TEL 0203-416994. FAX 0203-411418. TELEX 9312132335-ET-G. Ed. Nick Rushby. bk.rev. circ. 1,200. (also avail. in microform from UMI; reprint service avail. from UMI) **Indexed:** C.I.J.E., Cont.Pg.Educ., Curr.Cont., Educ.Admin.Abstr., Educ.Ind., Educ.Tech.Abstr., High.Educ.Curr.Aware.Bull., Res.High.Educ.Abstr., Sociol.Abstr., SOMA, SSCI. **Document type:** academic/scholarly publication.
—BLDSC (2307.750000); Faxon; UnCover; SWETS; UMI.
Formerly: Journal of Eductional Technology (ISSN 0022-0698)

375 UK ISSN 0305-7631
BRITISH JOURNAL OF IN-SERVICE EDUCATION. 1974. 3/yr. £24 to individuals; institutions £36. (National Association of Teachers in Further and Higher Education) Triangle Journals Ltd., P.O. Box 65, Wallingford, Oxfordshire OX10 0YG, England. TEL 0491-838013. FAX 0491-834968. (back issues avail.) **Indexed:** Cont.Pg.Educ., High.Educ.Curr.Aware.Bull., Mult.Ed.Abstr., Res.High.Educ.Abstr., SOMA. **Document type:** academic/scholarly publication.
—BLDSC (2309.800000).

613.7 370 UK ISSN 0954-6693
CODEN: BJPEBS
BRITISH JOURNAL OF PHYSICAL EDUCATION. 1970. q. membership. Physical Education Association of Great Britain and Northern Ireland, Ling House, 5 Western Court, Bromley St., Digbeth, Birmingham B9 4AN, England. TEL 021-753-0909. FAX 021-753-0170. Ed. Alan Gibbon. adv.; bk.rev.; bibl.; charts; illus. circ. 6,000. **Indexed:** Biol.Abstr., Br.Educ.Ind., C.I.J.E., Cont.Pg.Educ., Except.Child.Educ.Abstr., Phys.Ed.Ind., Sportsearch (1983-).
—BLDSC (2317.500000); UnCover; SWETS.
Former titles (until 1983): Action (ISSN 0144-3569); (until 1980): British Journal of Physical Education (ISSN 0007-120X); Which incorporates: Outdoors (ISSN 0306-5723); Research in Physical Education; Physical Education.
Description: Includes research articles; lists of resources; announcements of conferences and seminars pertaining to all aspects of physical and health education; outdoor activities, sports, and dance in the UK.

613.7 370 UK ISSN 0007-5043
BULLETIN OF PHYSICAL EDUCATION. 1946. q. $36. British Association of Advisers and Lecturers in Physical Education, c/o Studies in Education Ltd., Nafferton, Driffield, E. Yorks YO25 0JL, England. FAX 0377-46861. Ed. B. Chappell. adv.; bk.rev.; charts; illus.; stat. circ. 1,500. (also avail. in microform) **Indexed:** Phys.Ed.Ind., Sportsearch (1971-). **Document type:** bulletin.
—BLDSC (2882.840000).

BUROS - NEBRASKA SERIES ON MEASUREMENT AND TESTING. see PSYCHOLOGY

BUSINESS - EDUCATION INSIDER; how business can reform education. see BUSINESS AND ECONOMICS — Economic Situation And Conditions

650.07 373.246 UK ISSN 0951-1512
BUSINESS EDUCATION TODAY. 1970. bi-m. £37.50. Pitman Publishing, 128 Long Acre, London WC2E 9AN, England. TEL 071-379-7383. FAX 071-240-5771. Ed. Jill Priest. adv.: B&W page £370; trim 264 x 190. bk.rev. circ. 6,000. **Document type:** consumer publication.
—BLDSC (2933.568000).
Incorporates: Office Skills for the Business Studies Teacher; Which was formerly: Office Skills; Memo Key (ISSN 0025-9101)
Description: Resource magazine for teachers, lecturers and trainers of business courses.

650.07 370 US ISSN 0007-6694
BUSINESS EDUCATION WORLD. 1919. 2/yr. free to business educators. McGraw-Hill, Inc., 1221 Ave. of the Americas, New York, NY 10020. TEL 212-512-4736. FAX 212-512-6904. Ed. Wendy K. Spiegel. charts; illus.; index, cum.index. circ. 104,000. (also avail. in microform from UMI,MIM; reprint service avail. from UMI) **Indexed:** Bus.Educ.Ind., C.I.J.E., Cont.Pg.Educ.

C A L I C O. MONOGRAPH SERIES. (Computer Assisted Language & Instruction Consortium) see COMPUTERS — Computer Assisted Instruction

371.33 282 US
C A V E NEWSLETTER. 1974. q. free. Catholic Audio-Visual Educators, Box 9257, Pittsburgh, PA 15224. TEL 412-683-9996. Ed. John Manear. adv.; bk.rev.; film rev. circ. 1,000. (looseleaf format) **Document type:** newsletter.

375 US
C C - P A L S COMMUNICATIONS NETWORK. 1983. q. $10 to non-members; members $6. California Coalition of People for Alternative Learning Situations, Box 92, Escondido, CA 92033. TEL 619-279-7072. Ed. Marie Hartwell. adv.; bk.rev. circ. 500. **Document type:** newsletter.
Description: Supports alternative schools and home-centered learning situations.

791.43 US
C C U M C LEADER. 1972. s-a. membership. Consortium of College and University Media Centers, Iowa State University, Media Resource Center, 121 Pearson Hall, Ames, IA 50011. TEL 515-294-1811. FAX 515-294-8089. Ed. Beverly Teach. bk.rev. circ. 400. **Document type:** newsletter.
Formerly: C U F C Leader.

C E A CRITIC. (College English Association) see LITERATURE

378.1 US ISSN 0007-8034
PE11
C E A FORUM. (Includes: C E A Critic) 1970. 2/yr. $25 to individuals; libraries $30. College English Association, c/o Bege K. Bowers and Patricia Kelvin, Eds., Dept. of English, Youngstown State University, Youngstown, OH 44555. TEL 216-742-3414. FAX 216-742-1998. adv.; cum.index. circ. 1,200. (also avail. in microform from UMI; reprint service avail. from UMI) **Indexed:** Amer.Hum.Ind., C.I.J.E. —UnCover; UMI.
Description: Gives information and opinions about innovations, changes, and advancements regarding teaching English literature and language in the college and university classroom.

C I I L ADULT LITERACY SERIES. (Central Institute of Indian Languages) see EDUCATION — Adult Education

C I I L BILINGUAL EDUCATION SERIES. (Central Institute of Indian Languages) see LINGUISTICS

C I I L BILINGUAL HINDI SERIES. (Central Institute of Indian Languages) see LINGUISTICS

C I I L BORDER AND TRIBAL LANGUAGES. ADULT LITERACY SERIES. (Central Institute of Indian Languages) see EDUCATION — Adult Education

C I I L COMMON VOCABULARY SERIES. see LINGUISTICS

C I I L DOCUMENTATION SERIES. see LINGUISTICS

C I I L GRAMMAR SERIES. see LINGUISTICS

C I I L INTENSIVE COURSE SERIES. see LINGUISTICS

C I I L - K V S. MOTHER TONGUE SERIES - APNI BOLI. see LINGUISTICS

C I I L OCCASIONAL BULLETIN SERIES. see LINGUISTICS

C I I L OCCASIONAL MONOGRAPH SERIES. see LINGUISTICS

C I I L PHONETIC READER SERIES. see LINGUISTICS

C I I L PICTORIAL GLOSSARY SERIES. see LINGUISTICS

C I I L READING SERIES. see LINGUISTICS

C I I L SECOND LANGUAGE TEXTBOOK SERIES. see LINGUISTICS

C I I L SOCIOLINGUISTICS SERIES. see LINGUISTICS

C R L A NEWSLETTER. (College Reading and Learning Association) see EDUCATION — Adult Education

371.3 US
C S E MONOGRAPH SERIES IN EVALUATION. 1973. a. University of Californa, Los Angeles, Center for the Study of Evaluation, 405 Hilgard Ave., 145 Moore Hall, Los Angeles, CA 90024-1522. TEL 213-206-1512. **Indexed:** ERIC. **Document type:** monographic series.
●Also available online

371.33 US ISSN 1054-5409
LB1044.7
CABLE IN THE CLASSROOM; teaching with television. 1989. m. $18. Connell Communications (Subsidiary of: International Data Group), 86 Elm St., Peterborough, NH 03458. TEL 800-216-2225. FAX 603-924-6838. Ed. Al Race. circ. 90,000. **Document type:** consumer publication.
Formerly (until 1991): Connect (Boston) (ISSN 1047-7268)
Description: Directed to teachers interested in bringing television into the classroom as an educational medium.

CADENZA. see MUSIC

CAHIERS DE LINGUISTIQUE FRANCAISE. see LINGUISTICS

371.3 375 410 US
CALIFORNIA ENGLISH. 1950. bi-m. $35. California Association of Teachers of English, 14401 McDonough Hts. Rd., Healdsburg, CA 95448. Ed. Wanda Burzycki. adv.; bk.rev.; charts. circ. 3,500. **Indexed:** Abstr.Engl.Stud.

EDUCATION — TEACHING METHODS AND CURRICULUM

372 US
CALIFORNIA READER. vol.6, 1972. q. $15 to non-members. California Reading Association, 2790 Harbor Blvd., Ste. 204, Costa Mesa, CA 92626-5156. TEL 714-880-5605. FAX 714-435-0269. Ed. Lisbeth Ceaser. adv.; bk.rev. circ. 18,000. **Document type:** academic/scholarly publication.
Refereed Serial

375 SP ISSN 0213-9529
CAMPO ABIERTO. 1982. a. 800 ptas. Universidad de Extremadura, Escuela de Formacion del Profesorado, Av. de Elvas s-n, 06071 Badajoz, Spain. TEL 924-238800. Ed. Jose Maria de Peralta y Sosa. adv.; bk.rev. circ. 1,000.

CAMPUS REPORT. see *EDUCATION — Higher Education*

CANADIAN ASSOCIATION FOR HEALTH, PHYSICAL EDUCATION AND RECREATION. JOURNAL. see *PHYSICAL FITNESS AND HYGIENE*

420 820 CN ISSN 0705-386X
CANADIAN COUNCIL OF TEACHERS OF ENGLISH. NEWSLETTER. 1968. 4/yr. membership. Canadian Council of Teachers of English, Box 4520, Sta. C, Calgary, AB T2T 5N3, Canada. TEL 403-244-4487. FAX 403-244-2340. Ed. Marjorie Zingle. circ. 1,000. **Document type:** newsletter.
Description: Forum for opinions and concerns of membership presents practical teaching ideas on composition and techniques.

CANADIAN FEDERATION OF MUSIC TEACHERS' ASSOCIATIONS. NEWSLETTER. see *MUSIC*

CANADIAN INTRAMURAL RECREATION ASSOCIATION. BULLETIN; the voice of intramurals in Canada. see *PHYSICAL FITNESS AND HYGIENE*

371.3 CN ISSN 0710-4340
CANADIAN JOURNAL OF EDUCATIONAL COMMUNICATION. 1972. 3/yr. Can.$45 (foreign $45). Association for Media and Technology in Education in Canada (AMTEC), 3 - 1750 The Queensway, Ste. 1318, Etobicoke, ON M9C 5H5, Canada. Ed. Mary Kennedy. adv.; bk.rev.; film rev.; illus.; charts; bibl.; index. circ. 500. **Indexed:** Cont.Pg.Educ.
—BLDSC (3031.275000).
Formerly: Media Message (ISSN 0380-0199)
Description: Provides Canadian and international focus on educational communication through the application of media and technology.

371.3 900 300 CN ISSN 1191-162X
D16.4.C3
CANADIAN SOCIAL STUDIES. 1965-1990 (vol.25, no.4); resumed 1991. q. Can.$18 to individuals; institutions Can.$21. University of Alberta, Publication Services, Faculty of Education, 4-116 Education N., Edmonton, AB T6G 2G5, Canada. FAX 403-492-0390. Ed. Joseph M. Kirman. adv.; bk.rev.; illus. circ. 700. (also avail. in microform from UMI,MMI) **Indexed:** C.I.J.E., Can.Educ.Ind., Cont.Pg.Educ.
—BLDSC (3044.740700); Faxon; UnCover; UMI.
Former titles: History and Social Science Teacher (ISSN 0316-4969); Canadian Journal of History and Social Science.

CANADIAN UNIVERSITY MUSIC REVIEW/REVUE DE MUSIQUE DES UNIVERSITES CANADIENNES. see *MUSIC*

373.246 CN ISSN 0045-5520
CANADIAN VOCATIONAL JOURNAL. 1965. q. Can.$50 (in U.S. Can.$60; elsewhere Can.$70). Canadian Vocational Association, P.O. Box 3435, Sta. "D", Ottawa, ON K1P 6L4, Canada. TEL 613-596-2515. FAX 613-596-2515. Ed. Bob Louks. adv.; bk.rev.; index. circ. 1,000. (also avail. in microform from MIM,MML; reprint service avail. from UMI) **Indexed:** C.I.J.E., Can.Educ.Ind., CMI, Cont.Pg.Educ., Res.High.Educ.Abstr.
—BLDSC (3046.120000); UMI.

CARLETON PAPERS IN APPLIED LANGUAGE STUDIES. see *LINGUISTICS*

CAROLINA TIPS. see *BIOLOGY*

507 CN ISSN 0834-2466
CATALYST (VANCOUVER). 1959. irreg. Can.$40 to non-members; members Can.$25; students Can.$10. (B.C. Science Teachers' Association) B.C. Teachers' Federation, 2235 Burrard St., Vancouver, B.C. V6J 3H9, Canada. TEL 604-731-8121. adv.; bk.rev.; charts; illus. circ. 600. **Indexed:** Aus.Rd.Ind., Can.Educ.Ind.
Former titles: B.C. Science Teacher (ISSN 0381-6036) & S T A News (ISSN 0048-9719); British Columbia Science Teachers' Association. Newsletter.

371 US ISSN 0739-2532
CATALYST FOR CHANGE. 1971. 3/yr. $6. (National School Development Council) East Texas School Study Council, East Texas State University, Commerce, TX 75428. TEL 903-886-5521. FAX 903-886-5507. Ed. Mike McGrew. bk.rev. circ. 3,200. (also avail. in microform from UMI; reprint service avail. from UMI) **Indexed:** C.I.J.E., Educ.Admin.Abstr.

028.5 US
CELEBRATIONS.* 1976. q. membership. Association for Humanistic Education, 1300 26th Ave., Ste. 502, San Francisco, CA 94122-1549. Ed. Mary Blankenship. adv.; bk.rev. circ. 300.
Description: For parents, teachers, students; communication and dissemination of information on humanistic education.

CENTRAL STATES CONFERENCE ON THE TEACHING OF FOREIGN LANGUAGES. EDUCATION SERIES. see *LINGUISTICS*

CHALLENGE (CARTHAGE); reaching and teaching the gifted child. see *EDUCATION — Special Education And Rehabilitation*

370 510 FR ISSN 0395-7837
CHANTIERS DE PEDAGOGIE MATHEMATIQUE. 1970. 4/yr. 30 F. Association des Professeurs de Mathematiques de l'Enseignement Public, Regionale Ile de France, 26, rue Dumeril, 75013 Paris, France. TEL 45-35-43-05. FAX 43-31-07-32. adv.; bk.rev. circ. 1,600. **Document type:** bulletin.
Description: Covers meetings, appointments, opinions and experiences of the members of the Association.

CHILD CARE FOCUS. see *CHILDREN AND YOUTH — About*

CHILD LANGUAGE TEACHING AND THERAPY. see *EDUCATION — Special Education And Rehabilitation*

CHILD NETWORK. see *CHILDREN AND YOUTH — About*

CHILDBIRTH INSTRUCTOR. see *MEDICAL SCIENCES — Obstetrics And Gynecology*

CHILDREN'S CHOIR NEWSLETTER. see *MUSIC*

CHILDREN'S SOFTWARE REVIEW. see *COMPUTERS — Software*

371 377 US
CHRISTIAN SCHOOL BUILDER. m. $8.50. Rod and Staff Publishers, Inc., State Rte. 172, Crockett, KY 41413. TEL 606-522-4348. FAX 606-522-4896.

375 US ISSN 0886-6880
LB1049.95
CLAREMONT READING CONFERENCE. YEARBOOK. 1932. a. $20. (Claremont Reading Conference) Claremont Graduate School, Institute for Development Studies, Harper 200, CGS, 150 E. 10th St., Claremont, CA 91711-6160. TEL 714-621-8000. Ed. Philip H. Dreyerass. circ. 1,200. (also avail. in microfilm from UMI; reprint service avail. from EDR,UMI) **Indexed:** Educ.Ind., ERIC.
—UMI.

371.3 US
CLASS ACT. 1987. m. (Sep.-May). $20. Class Act, Box 802, Henderson, KY 42420. Ed. Susan Thurman. bk.rev. circ. 300. (back issues avail.) **Document type:** newsletter.
Formerly (until May, 1993): Cottonwood Monthly.
Description: Includes practical ideas, activities, lessons, games and assignments for language arts teachers, grades 6-12.

370 CN ISSN 0315-906X
CLASSMATE. 3/yr. Can.$20. Manitoba Association of Teachers of English, 191 Harcourt St., Winnipeg, MB R3J 3H2, Canada. TEL 204-888-7961. FAX 204-831-0877. Eds. Marita Watson, Raymond Lavery. bk.rev. circ. 600.
Description: Presents study and teaching techniques by teachers to teachers.

371.3 AT ISSN 0727-1255
CLASSROOM; the magazine for teachers. 1981. 10/yr. Aus.$38 (foreign Aus.$49). Ashton Scholastic Pty. Ltd., Railway Crescent, Lisarow, N.S.W. 2250, Australia. TEL 043-28-3555. FAX 043-23-3827. (Subscr. to: P.O. Box 579, Gosford, N.S.W. 2250, Australia. TEL 02-4164000) Ed. Mark Butler. adv.; bk.rev. circ. 15,000. (back issues avail.) **Indexed:** Aus.Educ.Ind.
—CCC.
Incorporates: Classroom Computing.

CLINICS IN COMMUNICATION DISORDERS. see *EDUCATION — Special Education And Rehabilitation*

378 420.07 US ISSN 0010-096X
PE1001
COLLEGE COMPOSITION AND COMMUNICATION. 1950. 4/yr. $52 membership. (Conference on College Composition and Communication) National Council of Teachers of English, 1111 W. Kenyon Rd., Urbana, IL 61801-1096. TEL 217-328-3870. FAX 217-323-9645. Ed. Joseph Harris. adv.; bk.rev.; index. circ. 8,500. (also avail. in microform from UMI; reprint service avail. from KTO) **Indexed:** Bk.Rev.Ind. (1984-), C.I.J.E., Child.Bk.Rev.Ind. (1984-), Curr.Cont., Educ.Ind., Ind.Bk.Rev.Hum., Lang.& Lang.Behav.Abstr., M.L.A. **Document type:** academic/scholarly publication.
—BLDSC (3311.050000); Faxon; UnCover; SWETS; UMI.
Description: Contains articles dealing with the theory, practice, research of composition, and the preparation of writing teachers.

375 US
COLLEGE E S L. 1991. s-a. City University of New York, Office of Academic Affairs, Instructional Resource Center, 535 E. 80th St., New York, NY 10021. TEL 212-794-5444. **Document type:** academic/scholarly publication.
Description: Journal of theory and practice in the teaching of English as a second language to students, specifically urban immigration and refugee adults in college.
Refereed Serial

420.07 378 US ISSN 0010-0994
PE1
COLLEGE ENGLISH. 1939. m. (Sep.-Apr.). $40 to individuals; institutions $50. National Council of Teachers of English, 1111 W. Kenyon Rd., Urbana, IL 61801-1096. TEL 217-328-3870. FAX 217-328-9645. Ed. Louise Smith. adv.; bk.rev.; index. circ. 16,200. (also avail. in microform from PMC,UMI; back issues avail.) **Indexed:** A.I.P.P., Acad.Ind., Arts & Hum.Cit.Ind., Bk.Rev.Ind., C.I.J.E., Cont.Pg.Educ., Curr.Cont., Educ.Ind., ERIC, Except.Child Educ.Abstr., Ind.Bk.Rev.Hum., Lang.& Lang.Behav.Abstr., Lang.Teach.& Ling.Abstr., M.L.A. **Document type:** academic/scholarly publication.
—BLDSC (3311.060000); Faxon; UnCover; SWETS; UMI.
Description: Examines different study and teaching methods.

375 001.3 US
COLLOQUY (SAN FRANCISCO). 1980. q. $2 outside California. World Affairs Council, 312 Sutter St., Ste. 200, San Francisco, CA 94108. TEL 415-982-3263. FAX 415-982-5028. Diana M. Wolf. circ. 3,000. (back issues avail.) **Document type:** academic/scholarly publication, newsletter.
Description: Examines international studies of teaching, teaching methods and curriculum, the humanities, history, and social studies.

COME LEARN BEGINNERS. see *RELIGIONS AND THEOLOGY*

COME LEARN JUNIORS. see *RELIGIONS AND THEOLOGY*

COME LEARN PRIMARIES. see *RELIGIONS AND THEOLOGY*

COMMUNIQUE (COLUMBUS, 1967). see *BUSINESS AND ECONOMICS — Office Equipment And Services*

EDUCATION — TEACHING METHODS AND CURRICULUM

375 360   US   ISSN 1046-0780
HD2769.2.U6
COMPENDIUM OF RESOURCES FOR TEACHING ABOUT THE NONPROFIT SECTOR, VOLUNTARISM AND PHILANTHROPY. 1989. a. Independent Sector, 1828 L St. N.W., Washington, DC 20036. TEL 202-223-8100.

374   II
COMPETITION MASTER. (Text in English) 1959. m. Rs.144. D.D. Khanna, 126 Industrial Area, Phase I, Chandigarh 160 002, India. TEL 0172-26517. FAX 91-172-44398. Ed. O.P. Khanna. adv. contact: K.D. Khanna. index. circ. 115,000. **Document type:** academic/scholarly publication.
   Description: Featrues current affairs and competition aids.

375   US
COMPOSITION STUDIES - FRESHMAN ENGLISH NEWS. 1972. 2/yr. $8 to individuals; libraries $20. Texas Christian University, Department of English, Box 32875, Ft. Worth, TX 76129. TEL 817-921-7221. Ed. Christina Murphy. adv.; bk.rev. circ. 900. (also avail. in microform from UMI; back issues avail.; reprint service avail. from UMI) **Indexed:** C.I.J.E. **Document type:** academic/scholarly publication.
—Faxon; UnCover.
   Formerly: Freshman English News (ISSN 0739-4713)

COMPUTER SCIENCE EDUCATION. see *COMPUTERS*

COMPUTING TEACHER. see *COMPUTERS*

371.3 510 500   US   ISSN 1041-682X
CONNECT (BRATTLEBORO); the newsletter of practical science and math for K-8 teachers. 1987. m. (5/yr.). $18. Teachers' Laboratory, Inc., 28 Birge St., Box 6480, Brattleboro, VT 05301. TEL 802-254-3457. FAX 802-254-5233. Ed. Casey Murrow. bk.rev.; index. circ. 1,600. (looseleaf format; back issues avail.) **Document type:** newsletter.

371.3   AT
CONTACT (PARKVILLE). m. Science Teachers' Association of Victoria, Clunies Ross House, 191 Royal Parade, Parkville, Vic. 3052, Australia. TEL 03-347-2211. FAX 03-349-1319.

375   US   ISSN 0886-5612
COPYCAT MAGAZINE. 1985. bi-m. $16.95. Copycat Press, Inc., 2625 Lathrop Ave., Racine, WI 53405. TEL 414-634-0146. FAX 414-634-0717. (Subscr. to: Box 081546, Racine, WI 53408-1546) Eds. Jo Anne Wood, Sharon Tuttle. circ. 45,000. (back issues avail.)
   Description: Provides enrichment materials for K-3 teachers.

373   US   ISSN 0045-8538
CORE TEACHER. 1950. q. $10. National Association for Core Curriculum, Inc., 404 R.I. White Hall, Kent State Univ., Kent, OH 44242. TEL 216-672-2580. Ed. Gordon F. Vars. bk.rev.; film rev.; abstr.; bibl.; stat. circ. 200. **Document type:** newsletter.
   Description: Describes interdisciplinary programs in elementary, middle, high schools and colleges.

371.3   US   ISSN 0887-042X
CREATIVE CLASSROOM. 1986. 6/yr. $19.97. Children's Television Workshop, One Lincoln Plaza, New York, NY 10023. TEL 212-595-3456. FAX 212-595-3650. (Subscr. to: Box 53148, Boulder, CO 80322-3149. TEL 800-274-1364) Ed. Elaine Israel. adv.; bk.rev.; film rev.; bibl.; charts; illus. circ. 172,000. (back issues avail.)
   Description: Presents hands-on teaching techniques for teachers of grades pre-K through 6.

371.3   US
CRITICAL ISSUES IN TEACHER EDUCATION. 1991. a. $25. Illinois Association of Teacher Education, Dept. of Secondary Education and Foundations, Eastern Illinois University, Charleston, IL 61920. TEL 618-242-3454. Ed. Jerry A. Ligon. bk.rev. circ. 300. **Document type:** academic/scholarly publication.
   Description: Focuses on issues related to teacher education, including preservice and inservice teacher education, curriculum and instruction, and policies related to teacher education.

371.3 410   JA   ISSN 0289-1239
P51
CROSS CURRENTS; a journal of language teaching and cross-cultural communication. 1972. 2/yr. 2600 Yen($48) to individuals; institutions $19.50. Language Institute of Japan, Asia Center, 14-1 Shiroyama 4-chome, Odawara-shi, Kanagawa-ken 250, Japan. TEL 0465-23-1677. FAX 0465-22-1688. (Co-sponsor: M R A Foundation) Ed. T. Clayton. adv.; bk.rev. circ. 1,000. (also avail. in microfiche; back issues avail.) **Indexed:** G.Soc.Sci.& Rel.Per.Lit., Lang.& Lang.Behav.Abstr.
—BLDSC (3488.854000).

CROSS SECTION. see *MATHEMATICS*

371.3   SP   ISSN 0213-1269
CUESTIONES PEDAGOGICAS. 1984. a. price varies. Universidad de Sevilla, Instituto de Ciencias de la Educacion, Servicio de Publicaciones, Valparaiso 5, 41013 Seville, Spain. TEL 954-231958. FAX 954-232245.

CURRENT HEALTH 1; the beginning guide to health education. see *PHYSICAL FITNESS AND HYGIENE*

CURRENT HEALTH 2; the continuing guide to health education. see *PHYSICAL FITNESS AND HYGIENE*

375 780   US   ISSN 0070-198X
CURRENT ISSUES IN MUSIC EDUCATION. 1963. irreg., no.5, 1970. price varies. Ohio State University, School of Music, Div. of Music Education, Columbus, OH 43210. TEL 615-422-6511.

375   UK   ISSN 0143-8689
CURRICULUM. 1980. 3/yr. $36. Studies in Education Ltd., Lloyds Bank Chambers, Market Place, Driffield, Humberside, England. Eds. M. Bottamly, P. Costello. adv.; bk.rev. circ. 1,500. (also avail. in microform from UMI; reprint service avail. from UMI) **Indexed:** Cont.Pg.Educ., Educ.Tech.Abstr., Mult.Ed.Abstr., SOMA. **Document type:** academic/scholarly publication.
—BLDSC (3505.215000); UMI.

370 370.196   AT   ISSN 0726-416X
LB1570
CURRICULUM AND TEACHING. 1986. s-a. $48 to individuals; institutions $95. James Nicholas Publishers, P.O. Box 244, Albert Park, Vic. 3206, Australia. TEL 03-696-5545. FAX 613-699-2040. Ed. Joseph Zajda. index. **Indexed:** Mult.Ed.Abstr., SOMA, Sp.Ed.Needs Abstr. **Document type:** academic/scholarly publication.
—BLDSC (3505.230000); SWETS. **CCC.**
   Description: Explores current issues in curriculum theory, design, evaluation and devolopment of elementary and secondary schooling. Includes information on instruction, innovation, policy planning and educational administration.

375   US   ISSN 0362-6784
LB1570
CURRICULUM INQUIRY. 1971. 4/yr. $27 to individuals in N. America (elsewhere $37.50); institutions in N. America $88.50 (elsewhere $100). (University of Toronto, Ontario Institute for Studies in Education, CN) Basil Blackwell Inc., 238 Main St., Cambridge, MA 02142. TEL 617-547-7110. FAX 617-547-0789. Ed. F. Michael Connelly. adv.: page $300; trim 4 1/2 x 8 1/2; adv. contact: Roberta Frederick. bk.rev.; bibl.; illus.; index. circ. 1,700. (also avail. in microform; back issues avail.; reprint service avail. from UMI) **Indexed:** C.I.J.E., Can.Educ.Ind., Cont.Pg.Educ., Curr.Cont., Educ.Ind., Educ.Tech.Abstr., Mult.Ed.Abstr., Res.High.Educ.Abstr., SOMA, SSCI.
—BLDSC (3505.276000); Faxon; UnCover; SWETS; UMI. **CCC.**
   Formerly: Curriculum Theory Network (ISSN 0011-4049)
   Description: Studies curriculum research, development and evaluation. Also covers school reform, educational theory and practice, and classrooms and teaching.
   Refereed Serial

375   UK   ISSN 0960-8567
CURRICULUM JOURNAL. 1990. 3/yr. £32 (foreign £35) to individuals; institutions £52(foreign £65). (Curriculum Association) Routledge, 11 New Fetter Ln., London EC4P 4EE, England. TEL 071-583-9855. FAX 071-583-0701. (Subscr. to: ITPS Ltd., Cheriton House, Andover, Hants SP10 5BE, England. TEL 0264-342919. FAX 0264-342807) Ed. Mary James. **Document type:** academic/scholarly publication.
—**CCC.**
   Description: Concerned with vital issues of curriculum structure, organization, and development.

CURRICULUM PRODUCT NEWS; the direct response medium of the district level. see *EDUCATION — School Organization And Administration*

375   US   ISSN 0147-2453
Z1035.A1
CURRICULUM REVIEW. 1960. m. $59. Curriculum Review Company, 212 W. Superior St., Ste. 200, Chicago, IL 60610-3533. TEL 312-922-8245. FAX 312-922-3336. Ed. Janine Ragan; Pub. Larry Ragan. adv.; bk.rev. circ. 4,800. (also avail. in microform from UMI; reprint service avail. from UMI) **Indexed:** Bk.Rev.Ind. (1977-), Chic.Per.Ind., Child.Bk.Rev.Ind. (1977-), Cont.Pg.Educ., Educ.Ind., Media Rev.Dig. **Document type:** newsletter.
—BLDSC (3505.283000); Faxon; UnCover; SWETS; UMI.
   Former titles (until Dec. 1975): C A S Review; C S Review.
   Description: For teachers of grades K-12. Each issue contains articles, columns, and reports on current trends in curriculum development. Provides analytical reviews of textbooks, supplement materials, multimedia kits, and software.

375   UK   ISSN 0965-9757
▼**CURRICULUM STUDIES;** a journal of educational discussion and debate. 1993. 3/yr. £30 to individuals; institutions £64. Triangle Journals Ltd., P.O. Box 65, Wallingford, Oxfordshire OX10 0YG, England. TEL 0491-838013. FAX 0491-834968. Ed.Bd. **Document type:** academic/scholarly publication.
—BLDSC (3505.236900).
   Description: Provides an international forum for curriculum discussion and debate.

D O E. see *THEATER*

DANCE TEACHER. see *DANCE*

650   US   ISSN 0416-9336
DELTA PI EPSILON. RESEARCH BULLETIN. 1962. irreg. price varies. Delta P Epsilon Graduate Business Education Society, National Office, Box 4340, Little Rock, AR 72214. TEL 501-562-1233. circ. 10,000. (reprint service avail. from UMI) **Indexed:** Bus.Educ.Ind. **Document type:** bulletin.

375 600   UK   ISSN 0958-9295
DESIGN & TECHNOLOGY FILE. 1990. 3/yr. £36. Stanley Thornes, Old Station Dr., Leckhampton, Cheltenham GL53 0DN, England. TEL 0242-228888. FAX 0242-221914. Ed. Liz Galley. circ. 1,000. (looseleaf format; back issues avail.) **Document type:** academic/scholarly publication.

745 375   UK   ISSN 0958-3017
DESIGN & TECHNOLOGY TEACHING. 1968. 3/yr. £18 (foreign £21). Trentham Books Ltd., Westview House, 734 London Rd., Oakhill, Stoke-on-Trent, Staffs. ST4 5NP, England. TEL 0782-745567. FAX 0782-745553. Ed. John Eggleston. adv. contact: Christine Foulkes. bk.rev. circ. 4,500. (also avail. in microform from UMI; back issues avail.; reprint service avail. from UMI) **Indexed:** Cont.Pg.Educ., High.Educ.Curr.Aware.Bull., Mult.Ed.Abstr., Tech.Educ.Abstr. **Document type:** academic/scholarly publication.
—BLDSC (3559.917000).
   Formerly: Studies in Design, Education Craft and Technology (ISSN 0142-4807)
   Description: News of new curriculum, teaching methods and research in technology, design and craft teaching.

EDUCATION — TEACHING METHODS AND CURRICULUM

371.3 745.5   UK
DESIGNING. 1982. 6/yr. £15($34) (typically set in Fall). Design Council, 28 Haymarket, London SW1Y 4SU, England. TEL 071-839-8000. FAX 071-925-2130. (Subscr. to: Designing, Subscr., P.O. Box 167, Sittingbone, Kent ME10 1BR, England) Ed. Laurie Johnston. adv.; bk.rev. circ. 7,000. (back issues avail.) Document type: trade publication.
   Description: Intended for secondary school teachers and students of design and technology. Includes school project work, reports about a wide variety of design-related topics, posters, advice on careers, news, events and reviews.

DEUTSCH - BETRIFFT UNS. see *LINGUISTICS*

DER DEUTSCHE LEHRER IM AUSLAND. see *LINGUISTICS*

370   GW   ISSN 0012-0421
DEUTSCHE LEHRERZEITUNG. 1954. w. Verlag Deutsche Lehrerzeitung GmbH, Lindenstr. 54A, 10117 Berlin, Germany. TEL 030-238094-0. FAX 030-20343645. Ed. Wolfgang Bergmann; Pub. Erhard Friedrich. adv. contact: Ingrid Ebert. bk.rev.; film rev.; illus. circ. 30,000. Document type: newspaper.

430.07 378   AU   ISSN 0012-1398
DEUTSCHKURSE/GERMAN LANGUAGE COURSES. 1961. a. Oesterreichischer Akademischer Austauschdienst, Berggasse 21, A-1090 Vienna, Austria. TEL 01-3172791. FAX 01-3172795. Ed. Ludwig Koller. adv. circ. 10,000. Document type: academic/scholarly publication.

942 373   UK
DEVELOPMENT EDUCATION. 1980. 3/yr. 1 St. Paul's Close, Clitheroe, Lancashire BB7 2NB, England. TEL 0200 24719. Ed. Colin Scott. bk.rev.
   Description: Covers human rights, world development, women's issues, sexism, racism and the environment.

DEYU XUEXI/LEARNING GERMAN. see *LINGUISTICS*

DIAGNOSTIQUE. see *EDUCATION — Special Education And Rehabilitation*

DIALOGO. see *SOCIOLOGY*

780.7   US   ISSN 0147-7544
ML1
DIALOGUE IN INSTRUMENTAL MUSIC EDUCATION. 1977. s-a. $8 (foreign $10). D I M E, c/o Gerald B. Olson, Ed., 5557 Humanities Bldg., 455 N. Park St., University of Wisconsin, Madison, WI 53706-1483. TEL 608-263-3220. bk.rev.; cum.index every 5 yrs. circ. 300. Indexed: Music Ind., RILM. Document type: academic/scholarly publication.
—Faxon; UnCover.

DIALOGUES ET CULTURES. see *LINGUISTICS*

371 510   GW   ISSN 0343-5334
DIDAKTIK DER MATHEMATIK. 1973. q. DM.58. Bayerischer Schulbuch-Verlag, Hubertusstr. 4, 80639 Munich, Germany. Ed. Franz Hager. Document type: academic/scholarly publication.
—CCC.

500 510   IT   ISSN 0419-1218
DIDATTICA DELLE SCIENZE E INFORMATICA NELLA SCUOLA. 1965. bi-m. L.50000. Editrice La Scuola S.p.A., Via Cadorna 11, 25186 Brescia, Italy. TEL C30-29931. Ed. Remo Bernacchia.

371.3   IT
DIDATTICA NUOVA. q. Tecnodatta S.p.A., Piazza Quattro Novembre 3, 20124 Milan, Italy. Ed. Umberto Domina.

371.3 910   CC   ISSN 1000-078X
DILI JIAOXUE/GEOGRAPHY TEACHING. (Text in Chinese) 1959-1966; resumed 1980. bi-m. Y1.60 per no. Huadong Shifan Daxue, DiJi Xi - East China Normal University, Department of Geography, 3663 Zhongshan Beilu, Shanghai 200062, People's Republic of China. TEL 2577577. circ. 18,818. Document type: academic/scholarly publication.

371.3   US   ISSN 0070-4881
DIMENSION: LANGUAGES (YEAR); proceedings of the Southern Conference on Language Teaching. 1966. a. $9.50 (typically set in Aug.). (Southern Conference on Language Teaching) S C O L T Publications, c/o Dept. of Italian, Portuguese, Spanish, University of South Carolina, Columbia, SC 29208. TEL 803-777-4881. FAX 803-777-8021. Eds. T. Bruce Fryer, Frank W. Medley, Jr. circ. 1,000. Document type: proceedings.

DIRECTORY OF EDUCATIONAL SOFTWARE FOR NURSING. see *COMPUTERS — Software*

DISKUSSION DEUTSCH; Zeitschrift fuer Deutschlehrer aller Schulformen in Ausbildung und Praxis. see *LINGUISTICS*

DRAMA - THEATRE TEACHER. see *THEATER*

DRAMATICS; devoted to the advancement of theatre arts in the secondary schools. see *THEATER*

371.33   IT   ISSN 0393-098X
E D A V. (Educazione Audiovisiva) 1972. m. (10/yr.). L.60000 (foreign L.85000) (effective 1994). Centro Internazionale dello Spettacolo e della Comunicazione Sociale (C.I.S.C.S.), Via Giolitti 208, 00185 Rome, Italy. TEL 06-7027212. (Subscr. to: CISCS, Via Settembre 78, 19121 La Spezia, Italy. TEL 0871-778147) Ed. Nazareno Taddei. (also avail. in video cassette; back issues avail.) Document type: academic/scholarly publication.
   Description: Covers current news in the field of education and problems that mass media create related to education.

613.7 790   FR   ISSN 0245-8969
E P S. Cover title: Revue E P S. (Text in French; summaries in English, French, German and Spanish) 1950. bi-m. 280 F. (foreign 350 F.). (Comite d'Etudes et d'Informations Pedagogiques de l'Education Physique et du Sport) Éditions Revue E P S, 11 av. du Tremblay, 75012 Paris, France. TEL 1-48-08-30-87. FAX 1-43-98-37-38. adv.; bk.rev.; bibl.; charts; illus.; index. circ. 26,000. Indexed: Cont.Pg.Educ., Pt.de Rep. (1979-), Sportsearch (1971-).
—SWETS.
   Formerly (until 1976): Education Physique et Sport (ISSN 0013-1474)
   Description: Addresses topics in sports medicine.

371.33   US   ISSN 0012-8023
E T V NEWSLETTER. (Educational Television); biweekly news report of educational & instructional television. 1967. fortn. $185 (foreign $210) (effective 1992). Box 597, Ridgefield, CT 06877. TEL 203-454-2618. FAX 203-454-2618. adv.; bibl.; charts; stat.; index. (looseleaf format)

EARLY KEYBOARD STUDIES NEWSLETTER. see *MUSIC*

375   UK   ISSN 0957-5146
EARLY YEARS. 1980. s-a. £14.50 (foreign £16.50). (Association of Tutors of Advanced Courses for Teachers of Young Children) Trentham Books Ltd., Westview House, 734 London Rd., Oakhill, Stoke-on-Trent, Staffs. ST4 5NP, England. TEL 0782-745567. FAX 0782-745553. Ed.Bd. Document type: academic/scholarly publication.
—BLDSC (3643.002200).

371.3   BB
EASTERN CARIBBEAN STANDING CONFERENCE ON TEACHER EDUCATION. REPORT. 1957. biennial. B.$30. University of the West Indies, Faculty of Education, Research & Development Section, Cave Hill, Barbados, W.I. FAX 809-425-1327. TELEX UNIVADOS WB2257. Ed. W.K. King. circ. 800.
   Formerly: Conference on Teacher Education in the Eastern Caribbean. Report (ISSN 0069-8695)

370   FR   ISSN 0761-3903
ECOLE DES LETTRES DES COLLEGES. 1908. 14/yr. 285 F. (foreign 343 F.). Ecole des Loisirs, 11 rue de Sevres, 75278 Paris Cedex 06, France. TEL 42-22-94-10. FAX 45-48-04-99. TELEX 205 735 F. (Subscr. to: Ecole des Lettres, 99 rue d'Amsterdam, 75385 Paris Cedex 08, France. TEL 42-80-68-55) Ed. Michele Filatoff.
   Former titles (until 1964): Ecole. Cycle d'Observation et Classes de 4e et 3e Enseignement Litteraire (ISSN 1153-1622); (until 1960): Ecole. Classes du 1er Cycle Enseignement Litteraire (ISSN 1153-1630)
   Description: Serves as a professional review of French language, history and geography.

370   FR   ISSN 0765-6017
ECOLES DES LETTRES. SECOND CYCLE. 1908. 14/yr. 335 F. (foreign 392 F.). Ecole des Loisirs, 11 rue de Sevres, 75006 Paris, France. TEL 42-22-94-10. FAX 45-48-04-99. TELEX 205 735 F. (Subscr. to: 99 rue d'Amsterdam, 75008 Paris, France. TEL 42-80-68-55) Ed. Claude Riva.
—BLDSC (3648.681800).
   Former titles: Ecole. Classes du Second Cycle Enseignement Litteraire (ISSN 1153-1649); Revue Pedagogique et Litteraire (ISSN 0070-7139)
   Description: Acts as a forum for the methods and contents for teaching.

ECONOMICS. see *BUSINESS AND ECONOMICS*

371.3   US   ISSN 0748-8491
LA217   CODEN: ETRCE2
EDUCATION AND TREATMENT OF CHILDREN. 1978. q. $35 to individuals; institutions $70 (foreign $85) (effective 1994). Pressley Ridge Schools, 530 Marshall Ave., Pittsburgh, PA 15214. TEL 412-321-6995. FAX 412-321-5313. (Co-sponsors: West Virginia University; California University of Pennsylvania) Ed. Andy Reitz. adv.; bk.rev.; charts; illus.; stat.; index; circ. 600 (paid). (also avail. in microform from UMI; back issues avail.) Indexed: C.I.J.E., Child Devel.Abstr., Educ.Ind., Except.Child.Educ.Abstr., Psychol.Abstr. Document type: academic/scholarly publication.
—BLDSC (3661.203500); Faxon; UnCover; UMI.
   Formerly: School Applications of Learning Theory. *Refereed Serial*

EDUCATION IN CHEMISTRY. see *CHEMISTRY*

371.3   KO
EDUCATION MANAGEMENT TECHNOLOGY. (Text in Korean) 1954. m. 27600 Won. Kyoyuk Publishing Co., 448-17 Seokyo-dong, Mapo-ku, Seoul 121, S. Korea. Ed. Choi Won Sik. adv. circ. 95,000. (also avail. in microfiche)

371.3   IE
EDUCATION TODAY. 3/yr. I£12 (foreign I£15). 35 Panell Sq., Dublin 1, Ireland. TEL 01-8722533. FAX 01-8722462. Ed. Sinead Shannon. adv.; bk.rev. circ. 21,000. Document type: academic/scholarly publication.
   Formerly (until 1993): Irish Teachers Journal.

371.33   FR
EDUCATION 2000. 1971. q. 100 F. Institut Superieur de Paris, 3 rue de l'Abbaye, 75006 Paris, France. Ed. Gilles Delavaud.
   Description: Discusses audio-visual aids.

375   UK   ISSN 0965-0792
LB1028.24
▼**EDUCATIONAL ACTION RESEARCH.** 1993. 3/yr. £30 to individuals; institutions £64. Triangle Journals Ltd., P.O. Box 65, Wallingford, Oxfordshire OX10 0YG, England. TEL 0491-838013. FAX 0491-834968. Ed.Bd. Indexed: SOMA. Document type: academic/scholarly publication.
—BLDSC (3661.356500).
   Description: Explores the unity between educational research and practice.

EDUCATION — TEACHING METHODS AND CURRICULUM

371.3   UK   ISSN 0954-7304
LB1028.5   CODEN: ETTIEU
EDUCATIONAL AND TRAINING TECHNOLOGY INTERNATIONAL. Short title: E T T I. 1964. q. £52($98) (Association for Educational and Training Technology) Kogan Page Ltd., 120 Pentonville Rd., London N1 9JN, England. TEL 071-278-0433. FAX 071-837-6348. TELEX 263088 KOGAN G. Ed. Chris Bell. adv.; bk.rev.; film rev.; abstr.; charts; illus. circ. 1,200. (also avail. in microform from UMI; reprint service avail. from UMI,KTO; back issues avail.) **Indexed:** Abstr.Hum.Comp.Inter., C.I.J.E., Comput.Abstr., Comput.Cont., Cont.Pg.Educ., Curr.Cont., Educ.Tech.Abstr., High.Educ.Curr.Aware.Bull., Res.High.Educ.Abstr., Sci.Abstr., SSCI. **Document type:** academic/scholarly publication.
—BLDSC (3661.366600); Faxon; UnCover; SWETS; UMI. **CCC.**
   Former titles (until 1989): Programmed Learning and Educational Technology (ISSN 0951-0907); Programmed Learning (ISSN 0033-0396)
   Description: Presents topics and issues relevant to educational and training technology.

375   UK   ISSN 0141-1160
EDUCATIONAL CHANGE AND DEVELOPMENT. 2/yr. £12 (foreign £16). Trentham Books Ltd., Westview House, 734 London Rd., Oakhill, Stoke-on-Trent, Staffs. ST4 5NP, England. TEL 0782-745567. FAX 0782-745553. **Indexed:** Mult.Ed.Abstr., SOMA. **Document type:** academic/scholarly publication.
—BLDSC (3661.381000).

EDUCATIONAL FILM & VIDEO LOCATOR. see MOTION PICTURES — Abstracting, Bibliographies, Statistics

371   US   ISSN 1047-8248
LA217
EDUCATIONAL FOUNDATIONS. 1986. 4/yr. $40 to individuals; institutions $50. (American Educational Studies Association) Caddo Gap Press, 3145 Geary Blvd., Ste. 275, San Francisco, CA 94118. TEL 415-750-9978. FAX 415-668-5450. Ed.Bd. circ. 800. **Document type:** academic/scholarly publication.
—BLDSC (3661.414200); UnCover; UMI.
   Description: Features the social foundations of education.

371.3 370   US
EDUCATIONAL I R M QUARTERLY. (Information Resource Manager) 1991. q. $29. International Society for Technology in Education, University of Oregon, 1787 Agate St., Eugene, OR 97403-1923. TEL 503-346-4414. FAX 503-346-5890. Ed. Dennis Bybee. adv.: B&W page $1500, color page $2250. circ. 10,000 (controlled). **Document type:** academic/scholarly publication.
   Description: Designed for educators who use technology for decision-making.

371 375   US   ISSN 0013-1784
L11
EDUCATIONAL LEADERSHIP. 1943. m. (8/yr.). $32. Association for Supervision and Curriculum Development, 1250 N. Pitt St., Alexandria, VA 22314-1453. TEL 703-549-9110. FAX 703-549-3891. Ed. Ronald S. Brandt. adv.; bk.rev.; charts; illus.; index. circ. 165,000. (also avail. in microform from UMI; reprint service avail. from UMI) **Indexed:** Acad.Ind., Bk.Rev.Ind. (1965-), C.I.J.E., Child.Bk.Rev.Ind. (1965-), Cont.Pg.Educ., Educ.Ind., Except.Child.Educ.Abstr., Lang.& Lang.Behav.Abstr., Mult.Ed.Abstr., SOMA, Sp.Ed.Needs Abstr., SSCI. **Document type:** academic/scholarly publication.
—BLDSC (3661.427000); Faxon; UnCover; SWETS; UMI.

371.33   US   ISSN 8755-2094
LB1028.3
EDUCATIONAL MEDIA AND TECHNOLOGY YEARBOOK. 1973. a. $60. (Association for Educational Communications and Technology) Libraries Unlimited, Inc., Box 6633, Englewood, CO 80155-6633. TEL 800-237-6124. FAX 303-220-8843. Eds. Donald P. Ely, Barbara B. Minor.
—BLDSC (3661.452000); UnCover.
   Formerly (until 1985): Educational Media Yearbook (ISSN 0000-037X)
   Description: Provides an up-to-date overview of educational media, technology, and communications; includes information on professional associations, graduate programs, foundations, and funding sources.

375   US
EDUCATIONAL MEDIA LOCATOR. 1975. a. $68. Olympic Media Information, Box 190, West Park, NY 12493. TEL 914-384-6563. Ed. Walter J. Carroll. circ. 1,000. (diskette format) **Document type:** directory.
   Supersedes (in 1992): Educational Media Catalogs on Microfiche.
   Description: Presents information on materials from audiovisual producers and distributors who sell, rent or lend educational and teaching materials. Includes 7000 entries, including a complete supplier directory.

371.3   US   ISSN 0892-2853
LA201
EDUCATIONAL OASIS. 1985. 5/yr. $21.95 (effective 1992). Good Apple, 1204 Buchanan St., Box 299, Carthage, IL 62321. TEL 217-357-3981. FAX 217-357-3987. Ed. Kim Rankin. adv.; bk.rev. circ. 15,000.
—UnCover.
   Formerly: Oasis (Carthage).

371.33   US   ISSN 1042-1629
LB1028.3   CODEN: ETRDE5
EDUCATIONAL TECHNOLOGY RESEARCH & DEVELOPMENT. Short title: E T R and D. 1953. 4/yr. $45 (foreign $53). Association for Educational Communications and Technology, 1025 Vermont Ave. N.W., Ste. 820, Washington, DC 20005-3516. TEL 202-347-7834. FAX 202-347-7839. Eds. Norman Higgins, Howard Sullivan. adv.; bk.rev.; abstr.; charts; index. circ. 5,000. (also avail. in microform from UMI; back issues avail.; reprint service avail. from UMI) **Indexed:** C.I.J.E., Commun.Abstr., Cont.Pg.Educ., Curr.Cont., Educ.Ind., Educ.Tech.Abstr., Lang.& Lang.Behav.Abstr., Psychol.Abstr., SSCI, Tr.& Dev.Alert.
—BLDSC (3662.531500); Faxon; UnCover; SWETS; UMI.
   Incorporates (1977-1989): Journal of Instructional Development (ISSN 0162-2641); (1953-1989): Educational Communications and Technology Journal (ISSN 0148-5806); **Formerly:** A V Communication Review (ISSN 0001-2890)
   Description: Focuses entirely on research and instructional development in the ever-changing field of educational technology.
   Refereed Serial

371.3   US   ISSN 0070-9387
AG600
EDUCATORS GRADE GUIDE TO FREE TEACHING AIDS. 1955. a. $44.95 (typically set in Mar.). Educators Progress Service, Inc., 214 Center St., Randolph, WI 53956. TEL 414-326-3126. FAX 414-326-3127. Ed. Thomas John Haider. index. (looseleaf format)

371.3   US   ISSN 0070-9395
LB1044
EDUCATORS GUIDE TO FREE FILMS. 1941. a. $23.95 (effective July 1993). Educators Progress Service, Inc., 214 Center St., Randolph, WI 53956. TEL 414-326-3126. FAX 414-326-3127. Eds. John Diffor, Elaine Diffor. index.
—BLDSC (3662.735000).

371.3   US
EDUCATORS GUIDE TO FREE FILMSTRIPS AND SLIDES. 1949. a. $21.95 (effective July 1992). Educators Progress Service, Inc., 214 Center St., Randolph, WI 53956. TEL 414-326-3126. FAX 414-326-3127. Eds. John Diffor, Elaine Diffor. index.
   Formerly: Educators Guide to Free Filmstrips, Slides, and Audiotapes (ISSN 0070-9409)

371.42   US   ISSN 0070-9417
HF5381.A1
EDUCATORS GUIDE TO FREE GUIDANCE MATERIALS. 1962. a. $27.95 (effective Aug. 1993). Educators Progress Service, Inc., 214 Center St., Randolph, WI 53956. TEL 414-326-3126. FAX 414-326-3127. Ed. Mary Horkheimer Saterstrom.
   Description: Lists free films, filmstrips, slides, tapes, records and printed materials.

371.3   US   ISSN 0424-6241
EDUCATORS GUIDE TO FREE HEALTH, PHYSICAL EDUCATION & RECREATION MATERIALS. 1968. a. $27.95 (typically set in Mar.). Educators Progress Service, Inc., 214 Center St., Randolph, WI 53956. TEL 414-326-3126. FAX 414-326-3127. Eds. John H. Wiersma, Tina M. Wiersma.
   Description: Lists free films, filmstrips, slides, tapes and printed materials.

371.3   US   ISSN 0070-9425
Q181.A1
EDUCATORS GUIDE TO FREE SCIENCE MATERIALS. 1960. a. $26.95. Educators Progress Service, Inc., 214 Center St., Randolph, WI 53956. TEL 414-326-3126. FAX 414-326-3127. Ed. Mary Horkheimer Saterstrom. index.
   Description: Lists free films, filmstrips, slides, tapes and printed materials.

371.3   US   ISSN 0070-9433
EDUCATORS GUIDE TO FREE SOCIAL STUDIES MATERIALS. 1961. a. $28.95 (typically set in Mar.). Educators Progress Service, Inc., 214 Center St., Randolph, WI 53956. TEL 414-326-3126. FAX 414-326-3127. Eds. Steven A. Suttles, Sharon F. Suttles.
   Description: Covers free films, filmstrips, slides, tapes and printed materials.

371.3 884.55   US
LB1043.Z9
EDUCATORS GUIDE TO FREE VIDEOTAPES. 1954. a. $25.95 (typically set in Mar.). Educators Progress Service, Inc., 214 Center St., Randolph, WI 53956. TEL 414-326-3126. FAX 414-326-3127. Eds. James L. Berger.
   Former titles (until 1992): Educators Guide to Free Audio and Video Materials (ISSN 0160-1296); (until 1977): Educators Guide to Free Tapes, Scripts, and Transcriptions (ISSN 0070-9441)

371.3   US
EDUCATORS INDEX OF FREE MATERIALS. 1934. a. $46.95. Educators Progress Service, Inc., 214 Center St., Randolph, WI 53956. TEL 414-326-3126. FAX 414-326-3127. Ed. Mary P. Parent. (looseleaf format)
   Description: Lists free pamphlets, pictures and chart materials for high school and college levels.

371.3   US   ISSN 1068-7378
EFFECTIVE SCHOOL PRACTICES. 1981. a. $10. Association for Direct Instruction, Box 10252, Eugene, OR 97440. TEL 503-485-1293. FAX 503-683-7543. Ed. Bonnie Grossen. adv.; bk.rev. circ. 3,000. **Document type:** newsletter.
   Formerly (until 1992): A D I News.
   Description: Publishes research, training methods, and experiences of teachers on research-based effective technology practices.

EICHSTAETTER HOCHSCHULREDEN. see RELIGIONS AND THEOLOGY — Roman Catholic

EICHSTAETTER MATERIALIEN. see RELIGIONS AND THEOLOGY — Roman Catholic

ELECTRONIC LEARNING. see EDUCATION — Computer Applications

ELEMENTARY MATHEMATICIAN; a mathematics - multidisciplinary teaching unit for grades K-3. see MATHEMATICS

375   US   ISSN 0070-9980
ELEMENTARY TEACHERS GUIDE TO FREE CURRICULUM MATERIALS. 1944. a. $24.95. Educators Progress Service, Inc., 214 Center St., Randolph, WI 53956. TEL 414-326-3126. FAX 414-326-3127. Ed. Thomas John Haider.
   Description: Lists free pamphlets, pictures and chart materials.

371.3   GW   ISSN 0931-5020
EMPIRISCHE PAEDAGOGIK; Zeitschrift zu Theorie und Praxis erziehungswissenschaftlicher Forschung. 1987. q. DM.70($43) Empirische Paedagogik e.V., Friedrich-Ebert-Str. 12, 76829 Landau, Germany. TEL 06341-906-0. FAX 06341-906200. adv.; bk.rev. circ. 250. (back issues avail.) **Document type:** academic/scholarly publication.
   Description: Presents papers on empirical education.

371.3   GW
ENGAGEMENT; Zeitschrift fuer Erziehung und Schule. 1983. q. DM.36. (Zentralstelle Bildung der Deutschen Bischofskonferenz) Aschendorffsche Verlagsbuchhandlung, Soesterstr. 13. 48155 Muenster, Germany. TEL 0251-690-0. FAX 0251-690143. Ed. Rainer Ilgner. adv.; bk.rev. circ. 1,900. (back issues avail.) **Document type:** academic/scholarly publication.

ENGLISH AND MEDIA MAGAZINE. see LITERATURE

EDUCATION — TEACHING METHODS AND CURRICULUM

ENGLISH FOR SPECIFIC PURPOSES; an international journal of English for specific purposes. see *LINGUISTICS*

420 375.4   UK   ISSN 0425-0494
ENGLISH IN EDUCATION. 1963. 3/yr. £35 (£20 for library membership). National Association for the Teaching of English, Broadfield Business Centre, 50 Broadfield Rd., Sheffield S8 0XJ, England. TEL 0742-555419. FAX 0742-555296. Ed. Richard Andrews. circ. 5,500. (also avail. in microform from UMI; reprint service avail. from UMI). **Indexed:** Child.Lit.Abstr., Cont.Pg.Educ., High.Educ.Curr.Aware.Bull., Lang.Teach.& Ling.Abstr. **Document type:** academic/scholarly publication.
—BLDSC (3773.500000); UnCover; UMI.
   Description: Presents study and teaching methods.

371.3 407   US   ISSN 0071-0601
PE1068.U5
ENGLISH LANGUAGE AND ORIENTATION PROGRAMS IN THE UNITED STATES; including a list of summer programs for training teachers of English as a second language. 1960. irreg. $42.95. Institute of International Education, 809 United Nations Plaza, New York, NY 10017. TEL 212-984-5412. FAX 212-984-5358. TELEX TRT 175977. (reprint service avail. from EDR) **Document type:** directory.
   Description: Describes 1100 intensive ESL programs and courses at accredited US higher educational institutions, language schools and private secondary schools nationwide.

ENGLISH LANGUAGE JOURNAL/REVISTA DE LA LENGUA INGLESA; for the Latin American teacher of English. see *LINGUISTICS*

ENGLISH LANGUAGE TEACHING JOURNAL. see *LINGUISTICS*

420   US   ISSN 1054-1578
LB1620 5
ENGLISH LEADERSHIP QUARTERLY. (Former name of sponsoring body: Conference for Secondary School English Department Chairpersons) vol.3, 1972. 4/yr. $55 membership. (Conference on English Leadership) National Council of Teachers of English, 1111 W. Kenyon Rd., Urbana, IL 61801-1096. TEL 217-328-3870. FAX 217-328-9645. Ed. Henry Kiernan. circ. 2,000. **Document type:** newsletter.
   Former titles (until 1991): C S S E D C Quarterly (ISSN 0738-1409); (until 1979): C S S E D C Newsletter.

420 370   CN   ISSN 0013-8355
PR31
ENGLISH QUARTERLY. 1968. q. membership. Canadian Council of Teachers of English, Box 4520, Sta. C, Calgary, AB T2T 5N3, Canada. TEL 403-244-4487. FAX 403-244-2340. Ed. David Dillon. adv.; bk.rev.; illus.; index. circ. 1,000. (also avail. in microform from MIM,UMI) **Indexed:** C.I.J.E., Cont.Pg.Educ., Mult.Ed.Abstr.
—BLDSC (3775.113000); Faxon.
   Description: Dedicated to scholarship levels and theory at all levels of English education.
   Refereed Serial

ENGLISH REVIEW. see *LINGUISTICS*

375   IS   ISSN 0333-533X
PE1068.I8
ENGLISH TEACHERS' JOURNAL (ISRAEL). (Text in English; summaries in Hebrew) 1968. s-a. Ministry of Education and Culture, English Inspectorate, Box 292, Jerusalem 91911, Israel. (Subscr. to: Eric Cohen, Ltd., 5 Hankin St., Raanana, Israel) Ed. Raphael Gefen. bk.rev. circ. 2,000. **Indexed:** Lang.& Lang.Behav.Abstr., Lang.Teach.& Ling.Abstr.
—BLDSC (3775.147000).
   Incorporates: English Teaching Guidance.

370   SP   ISSN 0212-5374
L41
ENSENANZA; anuario interuniversitario de didactica. 1983. a. 1800 ptas. Ediciones Universidad de Salamanca, Apdo. 325, 37080 Salamanca, Spain. TEL 923-26-14-54. Dir. Jose Luis Rodriguez Dieguez. **Document type:** academic/scholarly publication.

ENTWURF; religionspaedagogische Mitteilungen. see *RELIGIONS AND THEOLOGY — Protestant*

EQUINE VETERINARY EDUCATION. see *VETERINARY SCIENCE*

ESPERANTO - NYTT. see *LINGUISTICS*

371.3 790.13   US
ESTES EDUCATOR NEWS. 1973. irreg. (3-4/yr.). free to qualified personnel. Estes Industries, 1295 H St., Penrose, CO 81240. TEL 719-372-6565. FAX 719-372-3419. Ed. Jim Kranich. adv. circ. 50,000.

ETHICS & INTERNATIONAL AFFAIRS (JOURNAL). see *POLITICAL SCIENCE — International Relations*

ETHICS AND INTERNATIONAL AFFAIRS (NEWSLETTER); a college-level curriculum development program. see *POLITICAL SCIENCE — International Relations*

375   AT
▼**ETHOS P - 6**; ideas for the classroom, discussions & reviews for primary teachers of social education. 1993. 2/yr. Victorian Association of Social Studies Teachers Inc., 217-225 Church St., Richmond, Vic. 3121, Australia. TEL 428-7400.

375   AT
ETHOS 7-12; ideas for the classroom discussions & reviews. (Supplement avail.: Ethos Annual) 1982. 3/yr. Aus.$50 to individuals; corporations $90. Victorian Association of Social Studies Teachers Inc., 217-225 Church St., Richmond, Vic. 3121, Australia. TEL 428-7400. FAX 428-0313. adv.; bk.rev. circ. 1,500.
   Formerly: Ethos Papers; Supersedes in part: Ethos.

EUCLIDES; maandblad voor de didactiek van de wiskunde. see *MATHEMATICS*

375   UK
EUROPEAN VOCATIONAL EDUCATION SYSTEMS. a. £22.50. Kogan Page Ltd., 120 Pentonville Rd., London N1 9JN, England. TEL 071-278-0433. FAX 071-837-6348. TELEX 263088-KOGAN-G. Ed. Hellen Collins. **Document type:** directory.

EVANGELIZING TODAY'S CHILD. see *RELIGIONS AND THEOLOGY — Protestant*

371   US   ISSN 0740-9893
LB1027
EXCELLENCE IN TEACHING. 1984. 4/yr. $10 to individuals; institutions $15. Northern Arizona University, Center for Excellence in Education, Box 5774, Flagstaff, AZ 86011-5774. TEL 602-523-3480. FAX 602-523-1929. Ed. Stephen D. Lapan. bk.rev.; film rev.; bibl. circ. 800.
   Description: Contains articles on teaching and the teaching profession, including those describing exemplary programs, projects, and research activities in primary and secondary schools.

375   US   ISSN 0531-531X
EXERCISE EXCHANGE; a journal for teachers of English in high schools and colleges. 1953. s-a. $5 to individuals; institutions $6. c/o Charles R. Duke, Ed., Clarion Univ., Clarion, PA 16214. TEL 814-226-2146. FAX 814-226-2039. adv.; illus. circ. 1,000. (also avail. in microform from UMI; reprint service avail. from UMI) **Indexed:** C.I.J.E., Lang.& Lang.Behav.Abstr., Sociol.Abstr.
—BLDSC (3836.235600); UMI.

EYU XUEXI/LEARNING RUSSIAN. see *LINGUISTICS*

373.246   GW   ISSN 0014-6390
DIE FACHSCHULE; Zeitschrift fuer das Fachschulwesen. 1953. m. DM.81. (Ministerium fuer Hoch- und Fachschulwesen) Deutscher Verlag der Wissenschaften, Johannes-Dieckmann-Str. 10, 1080 Berlin, Germany. Ed.Bd. adv.; bk.rev.; bibl.; charts; illus.; index.

FAST FOREWORD. see *MOTION PICTURES*

FAYU XUEXI/LEARNING FRENCH/APPRENONS LE FRANCAIS. see *LINGUISTICS*

FEDERATION OF STATE MEDICAL BOARDS OF THE UNITED STATES. FEDERATION BULLETIN. see *MEDICAL SCIENCES*

FEMINIST TEACHER. see *WOMEN'S STUDIES*

FIVE OWLS; a publication for readers, personally and professionally involved in children's literature. see *CHILDREN AND YOUTH — About*

FLORIDA COMMUNICATION JOURNAL. see *COMMUNICATIONS*

371.33   US
FLORIDA MEDIA QUARTERLY. 1973. q. $40. Florida Association for Media in Education, Box 131119, Tallahassee, FL 32317-3119. TEL 305-754-9345. Ed. Pat Conlon. adv. contact: Nancy Jackson. bk.rev.; film rev.; charts; illus. circ. 1,800. **Indexed:** ERIC, Lib.Lit. **Document type:** newsletter.
   Supersedes (in Sep. 1975): F A M E Newsletter; Which supersedes in part: Florida Audiovisual Association. A V A News (ISSN 0046-4090)

375   US
FOCUS MAGAZINE (DETROIT).* 1976. 4/yr. membership. Michigan Association for Supervision and Curriculum Development, 1121 E. McNichols, MI 48203. Ed. Harold Karbal. adv.; bk.rev. circ. 1,000.
   Formerly: M A S C D Newsletter (ISSN 0300-7707)

370 370   UK
FOCUS ON BUSINESS EDUCATION. 1907. 3/yr. £17.50. Society of Teachers in Business Education, Saffron Hill, Uplands Rd., Totland, Isle of Wight PO39 0DY, England. Ed. A.G.H. Elsegood. adv.; bk.rev. circ. 1,800. **Document type:** academic/scholarly publication.
   Formerly (until 1986): Commercial Teacher (ISSN 0010-311X)

371.3 500   US
FOCUS ON SCIENCE EDUCATION. q. $7.50. California Academy of Sciences, Golden Gate Park, San Francisco, CA 94118. TEL 415-750-7114. Ed. Mary Marcussen.

371.3 420 375.4   US   ISSN 0163-5425
LB1576
FOCUS: TEACHING ENGLISH LANGUAGE ARTS. 1974. 2/yr. $12. Southeastern Ohio Council of Teachers of English, 14 Briarwood Dr., Athens, OH 45701-1301. TEL 614-592-2632. Ed. Ron Luce. bk.rev. circ. 250. **Document type:** academic/scholarly publication.

371.3   US   ISSN 1040-3205
FOCUSES. 1988. s-a. $10 to individuals; institutions $15. Appalachian State University, Department of English, Boone, NC 28608. TEL 704-262-3098. Ed. William C. Wolff. adv.; bk.rev. (back issues avail.)
   Description: Rhetorical theory and its practice in classrooms and writing centers. For college teachers of writing, and writing center personnel.

FOREIGN LANGUAGE ANNALS. see *LINGUISTICS*

FORMING I SKOLEN. see *ART*

371.3   UK   ISSN 0963-8253
L16
FORUM; for promoting 3-19 comprehensive education. 1958. 3/yr. £12 to individuals; institutions £24. Triangle Journals Ltd., P.O. Box 65, Wallingford, Oxfordshire OX10 0YG, England. TEL 0491-838013. FAX 0491-834968. adv.; bk.rev.; cum.index. circ. 2,000. **Indexed:** C.I.J.E., Cont.Pg.Educ., Educ.Ind., Educ.Tech.Abstr., High.Educ.Curr.Aware.Bull., Mid.East: Abstr.& Ind., Mult.Ed.Abstr. **Document type:** academic/scholarly publication.
—BLDSC (4024.095550); Faxon; UnCover.
   Formerly (until 1991): Forum for the Discussion of New Trends in Education (ISSN 0046-4708)

371.3 407   US   ISSN 1072-2076
FORUM (WASHINGTON, 1978). 1978. bi-m. free. National Clearinghouse for Bilingual Education, 1118 22nd St. N.W., Washington, DC 20037-1214. TEL 800-321-6223. FAX 202-429-9766. Ed. Omar Shabka. bk.rev.; bibl.; charts; stat.; index. circ. 30,000. **Indexed:** Lang.Teach.& Ling.Abstr. **Document type:** newsletter.
   Description: Contains research articles and news of instructional materials for bilingual educators.

FORUM (WASHINGTON, 1980). see *LINGUISTICS*

FORUM DEUTSCH. see *LINGUISTICS*

EDUCATION — TEACHING METHODS AND CURRICULUM

371.3 US ISSN 0738-9523
FORUM FOR READING; the journal of college reading improvement. 1983. a. $9. (International Reading Association, College Reading Improvement) University of Pittsburgh, School of Education, 5T01 Forbes Quadrangle, Pittsburgh, PA 15260. Ed. Shirley A. Biggs. adv.; bk.rev. circ. 650. **Indexed:** ERIC, Psychol.Abstr. **Document type:** academic/scholarly publication.
—Faxon; UnCover.
Description: Publishes materials related to the teaching of reading and study skills at the college and postsecondary levels. Provides a forum for the exchange of information regarding research, theory, and practice.
Refereed Serial

375 GW ISSN 0934-0939
FORUM POLITISCHE BILDUNG. s-a. DM.10. (Deutsche Vereinigung fuer Politische Bildung - Landesverband Hessen) Schueren Presseverlag GmbH, Deutschhausstr. 31, 35037 Marburg, Germany. TEL 06421-63084. FAX 06421-681190. circ. 750. (back issues avail.) **Document type:** academic/scholarly publication.

FRANCAIS AU NIGERIA. see *LINGUISTICS*

440 375.4 GW ISSN 0342-2895
FRANZOESISCH HEUTE; Informationsblaetter fuer Franzoesischlehrer in Schule und Hochschule. (Text in French and German) 1972. q. DM.36. (Vereinigung der Franzoesischlehrer e.V.) Verlag Moritz Diesterweg GmbH, Waechtersbacher Str. 89, 60386 Frankfurt a.M., Germany. TEL 069-42081-0. FAX 069-1301-100. TELEX 413234-MDD. adv.; bk.rev. circ. 3,500. **Indexed:** M.L.A. **Document type:** academic/scholarly publication.
—BLDSC (4033.020700). **CCC.**

DER FREMDSPRACHLICHE UNTERRICHT; textarbeit, landeskunde, sprachpraxis und methodenfragen. see *LINGUISTICS*

FRENCH REVIEW. see *LINGUISTICS*

613 JA
FUKUI UNIVERSITY. FACULTY OF EDUCATION. MEMOIRS. SERIES 6: PHYSICAL EDUCATION. (Text in Japanese) a. Fukui University, Faculty of Education, 9-1, 3-chome, Bunkyo, Fukui 910, Japan.

371 US
G P N EDUCATIONAL VIDEO CATALOG. ELEMENTARY - SECONDARY. 1967. a. free. Great Plains National Instructional Television Library, Box 80669, Lincoln, NE 68501. TEL 402-472-2007. FAX 402-472-1785. TELEX 484340. (Affiliate: University of Nebraska) Eds. Richard L. Spence, Thomas Henderson. circ. 28,000. (also avail. in video cassette; also avail. on video disc and video tape)
Formerly: G P N Educational Media. Elementary - Secondary; Superseded in part: Great Plains National Instructional Television Library. Recorded Visual Instruction (ISSN 0740-2732); Which was formerly (until 1973): Catalog of Recorded Instruction for Television.
Description: Lists series and singles available for lease or purchase on video-tape, videocassette, and videodisc.

G. STANLEY HALL LECTURE SERIES. see *PSYCHOLOGY*

GANZTAGSSCHULE. see *EDUCATION — School Organization And Administration*

GENERAL COUNCIL OF THE ASSEMBLIES OF GOD. MEMOS; leadership magazine for Women's Ministries Auxiliary. see *RELIGIONS AND THEOLOGY — Other Denominations And Sects*

375 JA ISSN 0912-6015
LB1577.J3
GENGO TO KYOIKU NO KENKYU. (Text in Japanese) 1986. biennial. 6000 Yen. Saitama Daigaku Kyoiku Gakubu, Kyoiku Gakubu, Kokugo Kyoiku Kenkyushitsu, Takenaga Laboratory, 255, Shimo Okubo, Urawa-shi 338, Japan. TEL 048-852-2111. FAX 048-855-7196. Ed. Yoshimasa Takenaga. adv.: page 10000 Yen. **Document type:** academic/scholarly publication.
●Also available online.
Refereed Serial

GEOACTIVE. see *GEOGRAPHY*

GEOGRAFIA. see *GEOGRAPHY*

GEOGRAFIA NELLE SCUOLE. see *GEOGRAPHY*

GEOGRAFISKA NOTISER. see *GEOGRAPHY*

910 AT ISSN 0085-0969
GEOGRAPHICAL EDUCATION. 1969. a. Aus.$15. Australian Geography Teachers' Association, c/o John Fien, Ed., Faculty of Environmental Science, Griffith University, Nathan, Bribane, Qld. 4111, Australia. FAX 61-7-874759. adv.; bk.rev. circ. 2,600. **Indexed:** Aus.Educ.Ind., Aus.P.A.I.S., ERIC, Geo.Abstr. **Document type:** academic/scholarly publication.
—UnCover.

GEOGRAPHIE UND IHRE DIDAKTIK. see *GEOGRAPHY*

GERMAN TEACHING. see *LINGUISTICS*

375 GW
GERMANY (FEDERAL REPUBLIC, 1949-). BUNDESANSTALT FUER ARBEIT. FOERDERUNG DER BERUFLICHEN WEITERBILDUNG; ERGEBNISSE DER TEILNEHMERSTATISTIK.. (Supplement to the Amtliche Nachrichten of the Bundesanstalt fuer Arbeit) 1970. a. DM.7. Bundesanstalt fuer Arbeit, Regensburgerstr. 104, 90327 Nuernberg, Germany. TEL 0911-1795034. FAX 0911-1792123. **Document type:** government publication.

371.3 GW
GESTALTUNGS-STUNDE; Lehrblaetter fuer bild- und werkhaftes Gestalten in der Grundschule. 1971. 3/yr. DM.19. A L S Verlag GmbH, Voltastr. 3, 63128 Dietzenbach, Germany. TEL 06074-25051. FAX 06074-27322. Ed. Ingrid Kreide. cum.index: 1990-1993. circ. 37,000. (looseleaf format; back issues avail.) **Document type:** academic/scholarly publication.

GO TEACH BEGINNERS. see *RELIGIONS AND THEOLOGY*

GO TEACH JUNIORS. see *RELIGIONS AND THEOLOGY*

GO TEACH PRIMARIES. see *RELIGIONS AND THEOLOGY*

GO TEACH YOUNG TEENS. see *RELIGIONS AND THEOLOGY*

370 SW ISSN 0348-2219
GOETEBORGS UNIVERSITET. INSTITUTIONEN FOER PRAKTISK PEDAGOGIK. RAPPORT. 1966. irreg., no.91, 1979. free. Goeteborgs Universitet, Institutionen foer Praktisk Pedagogisk, Box 1010, S-431 26 Moelndal, Sweden. Ed. K.G. Stukat.
Former titles: Laerarhoegskolan i Moelndal. Pedagogiska Institutionen. Rapport; Laerarhoegskolan i Goeteborg. Pedagogiska Institutionen. Rapport (ISSN 0534-042X)

GOULD LEAGUE OF VICTORIA. GREENPRINT. see *ENVIRONMENTAL STUDIES*

375 UK ISSN 0072-7113
GREAT BRITAIN. SCHOOLS COUNCIL PUBLICATIONS. CURRICULUM BULLETINS. 1965. irreg. price varies. Routledge, 11 New Fetter Ln., London EC4P 4EE, England. TEL 071-583-9855. FAX 071-583-0701. **Document type:** bulletin.

375 614 CN ISSN 1192-1285
GREEN TEACHER. 1991. 5/yr. Can.$27($27) Green Teacher, 95 Robert St., Toronto, ON M5S 2K5, Canada. TEL 416-960-1244. FAX 416-925-3474. Ed. Tim Grant. adv.: page Can.$350; 9 11/16 x 7 3/16. bk.rev.; film rev.; charts; illus. circ. 4,000. (back issues avail.) **Document type:** academic/scholarly publication.
Description: Covers teaching methods, philosophy, resources in the areas of environmental and global education for elementary and secondary teachers.

371 GW
GROSS UND KLEIN. 1948. m. DM.24.60. Luchterhand Verlag, Lindenstr. 54A, 1086 Berlin, Germany. TEL 030-20343431.
Formerly: Neue Erziehung im Kindergarten (ISSN 0323-3022)

371.3 GW ISSN 0533-3431
GRUNDSCHULE. (Supplement avail.: Arbeitskreis Aktuell) 1969. 11/yr. DM.117.60. Westermann Schulbuchverlag GmbH, Postfach 4938, 38039 Braunschweig, Germany. TEL 0531-708373. FAX 0531-708127. Ed. D.H. Heckt. adv.: B&W page DM.3650, color page DM.5840; trim 187 x 258. bk.rev. circ. 21,362. **Document type:** academic/scholarly publication.
—CCC.

371.3 GW
GRUNDSCHULMAGAZIN; Zeitschrift fuer die Unterrichtspraxis. 1926. m. DM.106.80. Ehrenwirth Verlag GmbH, Schwanthalerstr. 91, 80336 Munich, Germany. TEL 039-544335-0. FAX 089-534739. (Co-publisher: R. Oldenbourg Verlag) Ed. Gertrud Langhammer. **Document type:** academic/scholarly publication.
—CCC.
Formerly: Lehrerjournal Grundschulmagazin (ISSN 0930-6943); Supersedes in part (in 1986): Lehrer Journal (ISSN 0722-8600); Which was formed by the merger of: Hauptschulmagazin (ISSN 0724-3502); Which was formerly: Ehrenwirth Hauptschulmagazin (ISSN 0340-580X); Grundschulmagazin (ISSN 0724-3499); Which was formerly: Ehrenwirth Grundschulmagazin (ISSN 0340-5842).

375 GW
DIE GRUNDSCHULZEITSCHRIFT. 1985. 10/yr. DM.128.10. Erhard Friedrich Verlag GmbH, Im Brande 17, 30926 Seelze, Germany. TEL 0511-40004-0. (Subscr. to: Postfach 100150, 30917 Seelze, Germany) Ed. Anneli Kessler. **Document type:** academic/scholarly publication.

808.5 GW ISSN 0341-6879
GRUPPE UND SPIEL; Zeitschrift fuer kreative Gruppenarbeit. 1983. q. DM.30.60. Kallmeyer'sche Verlagsbuchhandlung GmbH, Im Brande 19, 30926 Seelze, Germany. Eds. Ulrich Baer, Andreas Knapp. adv.; bk.rev. **Document type:** bulletin.

371.3 UK ISSN 0072-8918
GUIDELINES FOR TEACHERS.* 1971. irreg. price varies. National Council for Special Education, York House, Exhall Grange, Wheelwright Lane, Coventry CV7 9HP, England.

GUINIGUADA. see *EDUCATION — Adult Education*

GUYANA SCIENCE TEACHERS' ASSOCIATION. NEWSLETTER. see *SCIENCES: COMPREHENSIVE WORKS*

H E R D S A GREEN GUIDE. (Higher Education Research and Development Society of Australasia) see *EDUCATION — Higher Education*

377.9 296 FR ISSN 0046-676X
HAMORE; revue trimestrielle des enseignants juifs. (Text in French and Hebrew) 1957. q. 80 F. European Council of Jewish Community Services, 19 rue de Teheran, 75008 Paris, France. (Co-sponsor: F S J U) Ed. Prosper Elkonby. bk.rev.; bibl.; cum.index.

HANDELSSKOLEN. see *BUSINESS AND ECONOMICS*

371.3 US
HANDS ON (RABUN GAP); a journal for teachers. q. $20 (foreign $30). Foxfire Fund, Inc., Box 541, Mountain City, GA 30562. TEL 706-746-5828.

HANYU XUEXI/CHINESE LANGUAGE LEARNING. see *LINGUISTICS*

HEALTHCARE MEDIA LOCATOR. see *MEDICAL SCIENCES*

HEAR OUR WINGS. see *EDUCATION — Special Education And Rehabilitation*

371.3 UK ISSN 0073-1714
HELPS FOR STUDENTS OF HISTORY. 1950. irreg. Historical Association, 59a Kennington Park Rd., London SE11 4JH, England. TEL 071-735-3901. (reprint service avail. from UMI) **Document type:** monographic series.

HI HELLO SALUT. see *LINGUISTICS*

EDUCATION — TEACHING METHODS AND CURRICULUM

375   US   ISSN 0892-5135
HIGH-SCOPE EXTENSIONS; the newsletter of the high-scope curriculum. 1986. 6/yr. $30 (foreign $33). (High-Scope Educational Research Foundation) High-Scope Press, 600 N. River St., Ypsilanti, MI 48198-2898. TEL 313-485-2000. FAX 313-485-0704. TELEX 650-2530989 WUI. Eds. Lynn Spencer Taylor, Nancy Altman Brickman. abstr.; charts. circ. 2,500. (looseleaf format; back issues avail.)
    Description: Designed for early childhood education teachers and caregivers, providing information and activity ideas.

375   US   ISSN 0887-2007
HIGH-SCOPE RESOURCE; a magazine for educators. 1981. 4/yr. free. (High-Scope Educational Research Foundation) High-Scope Press, 600 N. River St., Ypsilanti, MI 48198-2898. TEL 313-485-2000. FAX 313-485-0704. TELEX 650-2530989. Ed. Lynn Spencer Taylor. adv.; bk.rev.; tr.lit. circ. 145,000. (tabloid format)
    Description: Explores issues, research primarily in early childhood education, focusing on the High-Scope curricula and publications.

371.3   UK
HILLCOLE GROUP PAPERS. 1989. irreg., no.6, 1991. Tufnell Press, 47 Dalmeny Rd., London N7 0DY, England. Ed.Bd.
    Description: Intends to influence and improve the quality of schooling based on the ideological principles of the Radical Left.

HISTORIE OG SAMTIDSORIENTERING. see *HISTORY*

907   AT   ISSN 0085-1558
HISTORY TEACHERS ASSOCIATION OF NEW SOUTH WALES. NEWSLETTER. 1965. 4/yr. History Teachers' Association of New South Wales, Box 87, Rozelle, N.S.W. 2039, Australia. Eds. D. Anderson, L. Goodwin. **Document type:** newsletter.

HJEMKUNDSKAB (HVALSOE). see *HOME ECONOMICS*

371.3 778.534 792   US   ISSN 1069-3874
HOLLYWOOD ACTING COACHES AND TEACHERS DIRECTORY. 1984. q. Acting World Books, Box 3044, Hollywood, CA 90078. TEL 818-905-1345. Ed. Lawrence Parke. tr.lit. circ. 2,000. **Document type:** directory.
    Description: Contains a directory of all Hollywood acting instruction programs; includes biographies of instructors, articles about studying acting.

HOLMES GROUP FORUM. see *EDUCATION — School Organization And Administration*

375 100   US
HOME EDITION.* 1989. m. $15. Crowley's Ridge Christian Parent Education Association, 3201 Creekwood Dr., Jonesboro, AR 72401-7757. Ed. Jerry Schaeffer. adv. circ. 100.
● Also available online.
Also available on CD-ROM.
    Description: Assists parents interested in home schooling.

375   US   ISSN 0888-4633
HOME EDUCATION MAGAZINE. 1984. bi-m. $24. Home Education Press, Box 1083, Tonasket, WA 98855. TEL 509-486-1351. Eds. Helen E. Hegener, Mark J. Hegener. adv.; bk.rev. circ. 5,200. (back issues avail.) **Document type:** consumer publication.
    Description: Contains articles, news, resources and reviews for home schooling families.

HOME SCHOOL RESEARCHER. see *EDUCATION*

372.83   CN   ISSN 0315-8527
HORIZON (VANCOUVER). 1961. a. Can.$30 to non-members; members Can.$25; students Can.$10. (B.C. Social Studies Teachers Association) B.C. Teachers' Federation, 2235 Burrard St., Vancouver, B.C. V6J 3H9, Canada. TEL 604-731-8121. bk.rev. circ. 500. **Indexed:** Acad.Ind., Can.Educ.Ind., CMI.
    Formerly: British Columbia Social Studies Teachers' Association. Newsletter (ISSN 0045-3048)

HYOGO KYOIKU DAIGAKU KENKYU KIYO. DAI-3-BUNSATSU. SHIZENKEI KYOIKU, SEIKATSU KENKOKEI KYOIKU/HYOGO UNIVERSITY OF TEACHER EDUCATION JOURNAL. SERIES 3: NATURAL SCIENCE, PRACTICAL LIFE STUDIES. see *SCIENCES: COMPREHENSIVE WORKS*

THE I A L L JOURNAL OF LANGUAGE LEARNING TECHNOLOGIES. (International Association of Learning Laboratories) see *LINGUISTICS*

I A M H I S T NEWSLETTER. (International Association of Audio-Visual Media in Historical Research and Education) see *HISTORY*

371.3   US
I D R A NEWSLETTER. 1973. m. free. Intercultural Development Research Association, 5835 Callaghan Rd., Ste. 350, San Antonio, TX 78228. TEL 210-684-8180. FAX 210-684-5389. Ed. Maria Robledo Montecel. bk.rev. circ. 6,000. (tabloid format; back issues avail.) **Document type:** newsletter.
    Description: Addresses various educational topics. Disseminates IDRA's research and information.

I P N - BLAETTER. (Institut fuer die Paedagogik der Naturwissenschaften) see *SCIENCES: COMPREHENSIVE WORKS*

I R A L. (International Review of Applied Linguistics in Language Teaching) see *LINGUISTICS*

375   US   ISSN 0891-3978
IDEA FACTORY. 1976. q. $10. National Council of Teachers of English, Junior High - Middle School Assembly, 1111 Kenyon Rd., Urbana, IL 61801. Ed. Joel Turvey. bk.rev. circ. 700.

420   AT   ISSN 0046-8568
IDIOM. 1963. 7/yr. Aus.$45. Victorian Association for the Teaching of English, c/o Amanda McGraw, 185 Lygon St., Carlton South, Vic. 3053, Australia. FAX 03-347-3918. Ed. Philip Gardner. adv.; bk.rev. circ. 1,400. **Indexed:** Aus.Educ.Ind., Child.Lit.Abstr.

375   US   ISSN 0019-2023
PE11
ILLINOIS ENGLISH BULLETIN. 1907. bi-m. (Oct.-May). $15 membership. University of Illinois at Urbana-Champaign, English Department, 608 Wright St., Urbana, IL 61801. TEL 217-333-2392. FAX 217-333-4321. (Co-sponsor: Illinois Association of Teachers) Ed. J.F. Stottlar. circ. 2,100. (also avail. in microfiche) **Indexed:** ERIC. **Document type:** abstracting/indexing, bulletin.

375   US   ISSN 0163-822X
LA267
ILLINOIS SCHOOL RESEARCH AND DEVELOPMENT. 1964. 2/yr. $11. Illinois Association for Supervision and Curriculum Development, College of Education 5300, Illinois State University, Normal, IL 61790-5300. TEL 309-438-8294. FAX 309-438-3813. Ed. Susan Bisinger. adv.; bk.rev.; charts; stat.; index; circ. 2,500 (paid). (also avail. in microfilm from UMI; reprint service avail. from UMI) **Indexed:** C.I.J.E., Educ.Ind.
—BLDSC (4365.521000); Faxon; UnCover; UMI.
    Formerly: Illinois School Research (ISSN 0019-2228)

ILLINOIS SPEECH AND THEATRE ASSOCIATION. JOURNAL. see *COMMUNICATIONS*

INDEPENDENT EDUCATION. see *EDUCATION — Higher Education*

INDIANA ENGLISH. see *LITERATURE*

379   US
INDIANA FEDERAL PLAN FOR VOCATIONAL - TECHNICAL EDUCATION. 1970. irreg. Indiana Commission on Vocational and Technical Education, I G C S - E 204, 10 N. Senate St., Indianapolis, IN 46204-2277. TEL 317-232-1981. Ed. Pamela B. Peterson. illus.
    Former titles: Indiana. Indiana Commission on Vocational and Technical Education; Indiana. Council on Vocational Education. Annual Report; Indiana. State Advisory Council for Vocational Technical Education. Annual Report (ISSN 0091-8970)

INDIANA MUSICATOR. see *MUSIC*

372   US   ISSN 0019-672X
INDIANA READING QUARTERLY. 1968. q. $5 to non-members; members $5. International Reading Association, Inc., Indiana State Reading Association, 314 Teachers College, Ball State Univ., Muncie, IN 47306. TEL 317-285-1861. FAX 317-285-8793. Ed.Bd. adv.; bk.rev. circ. 12,000.
    Description: Directed to teachers, administrators, and parents; covers new knowledge, practical teaching strategies and organizational information.

INFO-LINE. see *EDUCATION — Adult Education*

INFORM-ACTION; educateurs franco-manitobains. see *LINGUISTICS*

INNOVATING. see *BUSINESS AND ECONOMICS — Management*

INSEGNAMENTO DELLA MATEMATICA E DELLE SCIENZE INTEGRATE. see *MATHEMATICS*

INSEGNARE RELIGIONE. see *RELIGIONS AND THEOLOGY — Roman Catholic*

371.3   US   ISSN 0740-5596
INSIGHTS INTO OPEN EDUCATION. 1968. m. (8/yr.). $7. Center for Teaching & Learning, Box 7189, University Sta., Grand Forks, ND 58202-7189. TEL 701-777-4421. FAX 701-777-4365. Ed. Sara Hanhan. circ. 500. (back issues avail.)
—BLDSC (4518.195000).
    Description: Primarily for elementary and early childhood education teachers and administrators.

375 330   US
INSTRUCTIONAL STRATEGIES: AN APPLIED RESEARCH SERIES. q. $15. Delta Pi Epsilon Graduate Business Education Society, National Office, Box 4340, Little Rock, AR 72214. TEL 501-562-1233. FAX 501-562-1293. **Document type:** trade publication.
    Description: Provides information, especially teaching tips for business educators on current topics in the business field.
    Refereed Serial

707   AT
INTERACTA. (Supplement avail.) 1968. 4/yr. Aus.$40 membership. Art Craft Teachers Association of Victoria, 217 Church St., Richmond, Vic. 3121, Australia. Ed. Sandra Taylor. adv.; bk.rev. circ. 1,000. **Indexed:** Aus.Educ.Ind. **Document type:** academic/scholarly publication.
    Former titles: A C T A Magazine; Art Teachers Association of Victoria. Journal (ISSN 0044-9059)
    Description: For art teachers: curriculum development and educational issues.

INTERCOM (SASKATOON). see *BUSINESS AND ECONOMICS*

INTERDISCIPLINARY HUMANITIES. see *HUMANITIES: COMPREHENSIVE WORKS*

371.3   SZ   ISSN 0257-3849
INTERFACE. 4/yr. 30 SFr. Schweizerischer Informatik Lehrer Verein, Postfach 126, CH-5600 Lenzburg, Switzerland. Ed.Bd. index. **Document type:** academic/scholarly publication.
—CCC.

INTERNATIONAL ASSOCIATION OF EDUCATORS FOR WORLD PEACE. CIRCULATION NEWSLETTER. see *EDUCATION — International Education Programs*

INTERNATIONAL EDUCATOR (WASHINGTON). see *EDUCATION — International Education Programs*

INTERNATIONAL EDUCATOR (WEST BRIDGEWATER). see *EDUCATION — International Education Programs*

INTERNATIONAL JOURNAL OF ELECTRICAL ENGINEERING EDUCATION. see *ENGINEERING — Electrical Engineering*

370 600   US   ISSN 0092-1815
LB1043
INTERNATIONAL JOURNAL OF INSTRUCTIONAL MEDIA. 1973. q. $105 per vol. Westwood Press, Inc., 23 E. 22nd St., 4th Fl., New York, NY 10010. TEL 212-420-8008. FAX 212-353-8291. Ed. Phillip J. Sleeman. bk.rev.; abstr.; bibl.; charts; illus.; index. circ. 500. **Indexed:** Cont.Pg.Educ., Educ.Ind.
—BLDSC (4542.310000); Faxon; UnCover; SWETS; UMI.

EDUCATION — TEACHING METHODS AND CURRICULUM

613.7 796   GW   ISSN 0341-8685
GV201
INTERNATIONAL JOURNAL OF PHYSICAL EDUCATION/INTERNATIONALE ZEITSCHRIFT FUER SPORTPAEDAGOGIK. (Text in English and German; summaries in French and Spanish) 1963. q. DM.44 (students DM.36). Verlag Karl Hofmann, Postfach 1360, 73603 Schorndorf, Germany. TEL 07181-402-0. FAX 07181-402111. Ed. Herbert Haag. adv.; bk.rev.; charts; illus.; index. circ. 2,500. **Indexed:** Cont.Pg.Educ., Educ.Ind., Phys.Ed.Ind., Sportsearch (1973-). **Document type:** academic/scholarly publication.
—BLDSC (4542.466000); UnCover; SWETS. **CCC.**
   Formerly: Gymnasion.

375 600   NE   ISSN 0957-7572
INTERNATIONAL JOURNAL OF TECHNOLOGY AND DESIGN EDUCATION. 1989. 3/yr. fl.212($126) (effective 1994). Kluwer Academic Publishers, Postbus 17, 3300 AA Dordrecht, Netherlands. TEL 31-78-334911. FAX 31-78-334254. (Dist by: Kluwer Academic Publishers Group, P.O. Box 322, 3300 AH Dordrecht, Netherlands. TEL 31-78-524400. FAX 31-78-524474; N. America dist addr.: Box 358, Accord Sta., Hingham, MA 02018-0358. TEL 617-871-6600. FAX 617-871-6528) Ed. Edgar W. Jenkins. **Document type:** academic/scholarly publication.
—BLDSC (4542.693250).
   Description: International review of research and development in technology education with features on new curriculum, methodology, resources and evaluation.
   Refereed Serial

INTERNATIONAL JOURNAL OF VOCATIONAL EDUCATION AND TRAINING. see *EDUCATION — International Education Programs*

INTERNATIONAL REVIEW FOR BUSINESS EDUCATION/REVUE INTERNATIONALE POUR L'ENSEIGNEMENT COMMERCIAL/INTERNATIONALE ZEITSCHRIFT FUER KAUFMAENNISCHES BILDUNGSWESEN/RIVISTA INTERNAZIONALE PER LA CULTURA COMMERCIALE/REVISTA INTERNACIONAL PARA LA ENSENANZA COMERCIAL. see *BUSINESS AND ECONOMICS*

371.3   UK   ISSN 0962-0214
             CODEN: ISSDED
INTERNATIONAL STUDIES IN SOCIOLOGY OF EDUCATION. 1991. s-a. £24 to individuals; institutions £48. Triangle Journals Ltd., P.O. Box 65, Wallingford, Oxfordshire OX10 0YG, England. TEL 0491-838013. FAX 0491-834968. **Indexed:** Mult.Ed.Abstr., SOMA. **Document type:** academic/scholarly publication.
—BLDSC (4549.822000).
   Description: Contains material from current research projects and offers insights and ideas on their respective topics.

371.3 370   US
INTERNATIONAL VISUAL LITERACY ASSOCIATION. ANNUAL CONFERENCE READINGS. 1978. a. $25. International Visual Literacy Association (Blacksburg), c/o Alice D. Walker, Educational Technologies - LRC, Virginia Tech, Blacksburg, VA 24061-0232. TEL 703-231-8992. Ed. Roberts A. Braden. bk.rev.; bibl.; charts; illus. circ. 300.

371.3   UK   ISSN 1351-4652
LB1028.3
INTERNATIONAL YEARBOOK OF EDUCATIONAL & TRAINING TECHNOLOGY. 1976. biennial. £47.50. Kogan Page Ltd., 120 Pentonville Rd., London N1 9JN, England. TEL 071-278-0433. FAX 071-837-6348. TELEX 263088 KOGAN G. Ed. Chris Osborne. **Document type:** academic/scholarly publication.
—BLDSC (4552.325500).
   Formerly (until 1989): International Yearbook of Educational and International Technology (ISSN 0307-9732).
   Description: News about the Association; includes directory of over 2000 research centers, current research, and personnel worldwide.

371.3 900   GW   ISSN 0172-8237
LB3045
INTERNATIONALE SCHULBUCHFORSCHUNG. (Text in English, French, German) 1951. 3/yr. $40. Georg-Eckert-Institut fuer Internationale Schulbuchforschung, Celler Str. 3, 38114 Braunschweig, Germany. (Distr. by: Verlag Diesterweg, Postfach 630180, 60351 Frankfurt a.M., Germany. TEL 069-42081-0) Ed.Bd. bk.rev. circ. 2,500. **Indexed:** Amer.Hist.& Life, Hist.Abstr. **Document type:** academic/scholarly publication.
—BLDSC (4554.695500). **CCC.**
   Former titles: Internationales Jahrbuch fuer Geschichts und Geographieunterricht (ISSN 0074-9834); Internationales Jahrbuch fuer Geschichtsunterricht.

375   US
IOWA EDUCATIONAL LEADERSHIP. 1977. s-a. $3 to non-members. (Iowa Association for Supervision and Curriculum Development) University of Northern Iowa, College of Education, Cedar Falls, IA 50614. TEL 319-273-2167. Ed. Charles R. May.
   Formerly: Iowa Curriculum Bulletin.
   Description: Articles dealing with all aspects of curriculum, instruction and supervision.

371.3 407   US   ISSN 0444-4663
IOWA ENGLISH BULLETIN. 1956. a. $5. Iowa Council of Teachers of English Language Arts, 130 Baker Hall, English Dept., University of Northern Iowa, Cedar Falls, IA 50614. TEL 319-273-2729. FAX 319-273-5807. Eds. Rich Fehlman, Kay Butler-Nalin. adv.; bk.rev. circ. 1,200. **Indexed:** Abstr.Engl.Stud., M.L.A. **Document type:** bulletin.
—UnCover.
   Former titles: Iowa English Bulletin - Yearbook; Iowa English Yearbook (ISSN 0075-0352).
   Description: Covers pedagogical and curricular issues judged to have an impact on critical and educational theory as well as on practical affairs in the English profession from preschool through college.
   Refereed Serial

371.3   US
IOWA MIDDLE LEVEL EDUCATORS BULLETIN. a. $2 to non-members. (Iowa Association for Middle Level Educators) University of Northern Iowa, College of Education, Cedar Falls, IA 50614. TEL 319-273-2167. Ed. Mary Nan Aldrige. **Document type:** bulletin.

IOWA SCIENCE TEACHERS JOURNAL. see *SCIENCES: COMPREHENSIVE WORKS*

371.3 745.5   US
ITALIC HANDWRITING NEWSLETTER; a newsletter for people who care about legibility. 1988. s-a. free. (Portland State University) Continuing Education Press, 1633 S.W. Park, Box 1491, Portland, OR 97207. TEL 503-725-4846. FAX 503-725-4840. Ed. Tena Spears. bk.rev.; bibl.illus.; circ. 15,000 (controlled). (looseleaf format) **Document type:** newsletter.
   Description: Handwriting, penmanship using italic method which produces a more legible, rapidly written hand than other commercially available programs.

IWATE UNIVERSITY. FACULTY OF EDUCATION. ANNUAL REPORT/IWATE DAIGAKU KYOIKUGAKUBU KENKYU NENPO. see *SOCIAL SCIENCES: COMPREHENSIVE WORKS*

J A C T REVIEW. (Joint Association of Classical Teachers) see *CLASSICAL STUDIES*

375   US   ISSN 1057-896X
LB1570
J C T. 1978. s-a. $45 to individuals; institutions $75. Corporation for Curriculum Research, 53 Falstaff Rd., Rochester, NY 14609. TEL 716-654-8010. Ed. Joanne Pagano. adv.; bk.rev. circ. 800. **Document type:** academic/scholarly publication.
—Faxon; UnCover; SWETS.
   Formerly: Journal of Curriculum Theorizing (ISSN 0162-8453).
   Description: Provides an interdisciplinary forum for curriculum studies.

J E T S REPORT; promoting interest in engineering, technology, mathematics and science in high school. (Junior Engineering Technical Society) see *ENGINEERING*

JAMES NICHOLAS EDUCATION NEWSLETTER; education publishing news. see *EDUCATION — School Organization And Administration*

371.3   JA
JAPANESE SOCIETY OF INDUSTRIAL AND TECHNOLOGY EDUCATION. JOURNAL. 1954. q. 7000 Yen. Japanese Society of Industrial and Technology Education, c/o Faculty of Education, Shiga University, Hiratsu 2-5-1, Otsu 520, Japan. TEL 0775-33-2774. Ed.Bd. circ. 800.
   Formerly: Japan Society of Industrial and Technical Education. Bulletin.
   Description: Covers curriculum developoment and evaluation, teaching methodology and materials, philosophy and history.

JEZIK IN SLOVSTVO see *LINGUISTICS*

371.3   CC   ISSN 0257-2826
JIAOXUE YU YANJIU/TEACHING AND RESEARCH. (Text in Chinese) 1972. bi-m. Y11.40($35.10) (Zhongguo Renmn Daxue - China People's University) Zhongguo Renmin Daxue Chubanshe - People's University Press, Haidian Lu 39, Haidian Qu, Beijing 100872, People's Republic of China. TEL 285431-2429. (Dist. in China by: China International Book Trading Corp., P.O. Box 399, Beijing, P.R.C.; Dist. in US by: China Books & Periodicals, Inc., 2929 24th St., San Francisco, CA 94110. TEL 415-282-2994)
   Description: Contains papers on teaching and research.

371.42   US
JOBS CLEARINGHOUSE. m. $25 to members; non-members $40. Association for Experiential Education, 2885 Aurora Ave., Ste. 28, Boulder, CO 80303-2252. TEL 303-440-8844. FAX 303-440-9581. adv. circ. 1,500. **Document type:** newsletter.
   Description: Lists jobs available nationwide in the experimental and outdoor education fields.

JOINT ASSOCIATION OF CLASSICAL TEACHERS. BULLETIN. see *CLASSICAL STUDIES*

JOURNAL FOR RESEARCH IN MATHEMATICS EDUCATION. see *MATHEMATICS*

JOURNAL FOR VOCATIONAL SPECIAL NEEDS EDUCATION. see *EDUCATION — Special Education And Rehabilitation*

JOURNAL OF BASIC WRITING. see *EDUCATION — Higher Education*

371.3   US
JOURNAL OF CLINICAL READING: RESEARCH AND PROGRAMS. 1984. a. $12.50 for 3 issues. (College Reading Association, Clinical Division) Cleveland State University (Cleveland), Rhodes Tower, 1319, E. 22nd St., Cleveland, OH 44115. TEL 216-687-4600. Ed. Lillian R. Hinds. bk.rev.; bibl.; stat. circ. 100. (back issues avail.) **Document type:** academic/scholarly publication.

JOURNAL OF COMPUTER SCIENCE EDUCATION. see *COMPUTERS*

371.3   US   ISSN 0882-1232
JOURNAL OF CURRICULUM AND SUPERVISION. q. $35 to non-members; members $25. Association for Supervision and Curriculum Development, 1250 N. Pitt St., Alexandria, VA 22314-1453. TEL 703-549-9110. FAX 703-549-3891. Ed. O.L. Davis, Jr. charts; index. **Indexed:** SOMA. **Document type:** academic/scholarly publication.
—BLDSC (4965.935C00); Faxon; UnCover; SWETS; UMI.
   Description: Provides information on what your school should teach, how to teach it, and why.

EDUCATION — TEACHING METHODS AND CURRICULUM

375 UK ISSN 0022-0272
L16
JOURNAL OF CURRICULUM STUDIES. 1968. bi-m. £124($208) to institutions. Taylor & Francis Ltd., Rankine Rd., Basingstoke, Hants RG24 8PR, England. TEL 0256-840366. FAX 0256-479438. TELEX 858540. Ed. Ian Westbury. adv.; bk.rev. (back issues avail.) **Indexed:** C.I.J.E., Cont.Pg.Educ., Curr.Cont., Educ.Admin.Abstr., Educ.Tech.Abstr., High.Educ.Curr.Aware.Bull., Lang.Teach.& Ling.Abstr., Mult.Ed.Abstr., Res.High.Educ.Abstr., Sociol.Educ.Abstr., SOMA, SSCI, Stud.Wom.Abstr. **Document type:** academic/scholarly publication.
—BLDSC (4965.950000); Faxon; UnCover; SWETS. CCC.
Description: Contains original contributions to the theory and practice of curriculum and teaching at the national level. Primary focus is on school experience, but the scope extends to any area where the curriculum is researched and debated.
Refereed Serial

375 US ISSN 0022-0337
RK71
JOURNAL OF DENTAL EDUCATION. 1936. m. $75 (foreign $125). American Association of Dental Schools, 1625 Massachusetts Ave., N.W., Washington, DC 20036-2212. TEL 202-667-9433. Ed. Dr. James D. Bader. adv.; bk.rev.; charts; illus.; stat.; index. circ. 4,300. (also avail. in microform; reprint service avail.) **Indexed:** Biol.Abstr., C.I.J.E., Cont.Pg.Educ., Curr.Tit.Dent., Dent.Abstr., Dent.Ind., Ind.Med., Res.High.Educ.Abstr. **Document type:** academic/scholarly publication.
—BLDSC (4968.450000); Faxon; UnCover; SWETS; UMI.
Description: Contains articles on educational research, teaching methods and materials, curriculum, and administration of educational programs.

JOURNAL OF DISTANCE EDUCATION. see EDUCATION — Adult Education

JOURNAL OF EARLY INTERVENTION. see EDUCATION — Special Education And Rehabilitation

THE JOURNAL OF ECONOMIC EDUCATION. see BUSINESS AND ECONOMICS

JOURNAL OF EDUCATION FOR LIBRARY AND INFORMATION SCIENCE. see LIBRARY AND INFORMATION SCIENCES

JOURNAL OF EDUCATIONAL TELEVISION. see COMMUNICATIONS — Television And Cable

JOURNAL OF ENGLISH AND FOREIGN LANGUAGES. see LINGUISTICS

371.3 US ISSN 1053-8259
L11
JOURNAL OF EXPERIENTIAL EDUCATION (BOULDER). 1978. 3/yr. $25 to non-members. Association for Experiential Education, 2885 Aurora Ave., Ste. 28, Boulder, CO 80303-2252. TEL 303-440-8844. FAX 303-440-9581. Ed. Chuck Luckmann. bk.rev. circ. 2,100. (also avail. in microfilm) **Indexed:** C.I.J.E., ERIC. **Document type:** academic/scholarly publication.
—BLDSC (4979.686000); UnCover; SWETS.
Description: Provides a vehicle to disseminate valuable ideas, practices, and research in the field of experiential education.

371.3 375 US ISSN 0022-0973
L11 CODEN: JEXEAI
JOURNAL OF EXPERIMENTAL EDUCATION. 1932. q. $31 to individuals; institutions $62. (Helen Dwight Reid Educational Foundation) Heldref Publications, 1319 Eighteenth St., N.W., Washington DC 20036-1802. TEL 202-296-6267. FAX 202-296-5149. Ed. Paige W. Jackson. adv. contact: Raymond Rallo. abstr.; charts; illus.; stat.; index. circ. 1,700. (also avail. in microform from PMC; reprint service avail.) **Indexed:** Adol.Ment.Hlth.Abstr., C.I.J.E., Child Devel.Abstr., Cont.Pg.Educ., Curr.Cont., Educ.Admin.Abstr., Educ.Ind., High.Educ.Curr.Aware.Bull., Lang.& Lang.Behav.Abstr., Mult.Ed.Abstr., Psychol.Abstr., Res.High.Educ.Abstr., Sociol.Abstr., Sociol.Educ.Abstr., SSCI. **Document type:** academic/scholarly publication.
—BLDSC (4981.500000); Faxon; UnCover; SWETS; UMI. CCC.
Refereed Serial

JOURNAL OF FRENCH LANGUAGE STUDIES. see LINGUISTICS

613 613.7 US ISSN 1055-6699
LB3401 CODEN: HEEDE4
JOURNAL OF HEALTH EDUCATION. 1970. bi-m. $70 to institutions. American Alliance for Health, Physical Education, Recreation, and Dance, 1900 Association Dr., Reston, VA 22091. TEL 703-476-3400. FAX 703-476-9527. Eds. Becky J. Smith, Patricia Lyle. adv.; bk.rev.; charts; stat.; index. circ. 10,000. (also avail. in microform from ISI,UMI; back issues avail.) **Indexed:** C.I.J.E., C.I.N.L., Cont.Pg.Educ., Educ.Ind., Except.Child.Educ.Abstr., Media Rev.Dig., Phys.Ed.Ind., Sportsearch. **Document type:** academic/scholarly publication.
—BLDSC (4996.770000); Faxon; UnCover; SWETS; UMI.
Formerly: School Health Review (ISSN 0097-0050)
Description: Provides articles and thought-provoking features on a spectrum of issues and topics related to teaching and promoting health.
Refereed Serial

371.3 UK ISSN 0962-029X
JOURNAL OF INFORMATION TECHNOLOGY FOR TEACHER EDUCATION. s-a. £24 to individuals; institutions £48. Triangle Journals Ltd., P.O. Box 65, Wallingford, Oxfordshire OX10 0YG, England. TEL 0491-838013. FAX 0491-834968. **Document type:** academic/scholarly publication.
—BLDSC (5006.797000).
Description: Focuses on the implications of teacher education, both pre-service and in-service, and of all aspects of information technology.

JOURNAL OF INTENSIVE ENGLISH STUDIES. see LINGUISTICS

JOURNAL OF INTERACTIVE INSTRUCTION DEVELOPMENT. see EDUCATION — Computer Applications

JOURNAL OF INTERIOR DESIGN. see INTERIOR DESIGN AND DECORATION

JOURNAL OF JAPANESE LINGUISTICS. see LINGUISTICS

JOURNAL OF MANAGEMENT EDUCATION. see BUSINESS AND ECONOMICS — Management

JOURNAL OF MARKETING EDUCATION. see BUSINESS AND ECONOMICS — Marketing And Purchasing

JOURNAL OF MUSIC THEORY PEDAGOGY. see MUSIC

JOURNAL OF NATURAL RESOURCES AND LIFE SCIENCES EDUCATION. see AGRICULTURE — Crop Production And Soil

JOURNAL OF PHARMACY TEACHING. see PHARMACY AND PHARMACOLOGY

JOURNAL OF PHYSICAL EDUCATION, RECREATION AND DANCE. see SPORTS AND GAMES

JOURNAL OF RESEARCH IN MUSIC EDUCATION. see MUSIC

371.3 500 510 MY ISSN 0126-7663
JOURNAL OF SCIENCE AND MATHEMATICS EDUCATION IN SOUTHEAST ASIA. (Text in English) 1978. s-a. M.$19($38) Southeast Asian Ministers of Education Organisation, Regional Centre for Education in Science and Mathematics, 11700 Glugor, Penang, Malaysia. TEL 883266. Ed. Mrs. Perla S. Roxas. bk.rev. circ. 650. (reprint service avail. from UMI) **Indexed:** C.I.J.E., Cont.Pg.Educ.
—BLDSC (5054.830000).
Description: Contains articles related to teaching and learning science and math in Southeast Asia.

375 US ISSN 0885-985X
JOURNAL OF SOCIAL STUDIES RESEARCH. 1977. s-a. $10 (foreign $12). Kansas State University, College of Education, Bluemont Hall, Manhattan, KS 66506-5301. TEL 404-542-6479. Ed. Ben Smith. circ. 200. (also avail. in microfilm; back issues avail.) **Indexed:** C.I.J.E.
—BLDSC (5064.914000).

JOURNAL OF SOCIAL THEORY IN ART EDUCATION. see ART

371.3 US ISSN 0276-928X
LC5251
JOURNAL OF STAFF DEVELOPMENT. 1980. 4/yr. $32 to libraries; members free. National Staff Development Council, Box 240, Oxford, Oxford, OH 45056. TEL 513-523-6029. FAX 513-523-0638. Ed. Paul Burden. adv.; bk.rev. circ. 6,000. (also avail. in microfilm; back issues avail.) **Indexed:** C.I.J.E. **Document type:** academic/scholarly publication.
—BLDSC (5066.500000); Faxon; UnCover; SWETS; UMI.

JOURNAL OF STRUCTURAL LEARNING. see PSYCHOLOGY

613.7 790.1 US ISSN 0273-5024
GV363
JOURNAL OF TEACHING IN PHYSICAL EDUCATION. 1981. q. $36 to individuals (foreign $40); institutions $80 (foreign $84); students $24 (foreign $28). Human Kinetics Publishers, Inc., Box 5076, Champaign, IL 61825-5076. TEL 217-351-5076. FAX 217-351-2674. Eds. Drs. Stephen Silverman, Mary O'Sullivan. adv. contact: Michele Watson. bk.rev.; bibl.; charts; stat.; index. circ. 910. (back issues avail.) **Indexed:** ASCA, C.I.J.E., Curr.Cont., Phys.Ed.Ind., SOMA, Sp.Ed.Needs Abstr., Sportsearch (1982-), SSCI. **Document type:** academic/scholarly publication.
—BLDSC (5068.285700); Faxon; UnCover; SWETS. CCC.
Description: Designed to stimulate and communicate research and practical applications in the field of physical education. Offers new teaching methods and ideas to help students, teachers, teacher educators, and administrators at all levels.
Refereed Serial

371.3 360 US ISSN 0884-1233
HV11
JOURNAL OF TEACHING IN SOCIAL WORK. 1987. s-a. $36 to individuals; institutions $60; libraries $80. Haworth Press, Inc., 10 Alice St., Binghamton, NY 13904. TEL 607-722-5857; 800-342-9678. FAX 607-722-1424. TELEX 4932599. Eds. Florence Vigilante, Harold Lewis. adv.; bk.rev. circ. 278. (also avail. in microfiche from UMI; reprint service avail. from HAW) **Indexed:** ASSIA, Cont.Pg.Educ., P.A.I.S., Ref.Zh., Sage Fam.Stud.Abstr., Soc.Work Res.& Abstr., Sociol.Abstr., Sp.Ed.Needs Abstr., Stud.Wom.Abstr. —BLDSC (5068.285750); Faxon; UnCover.
Description: Addresses qualitative as well as quantitative studies, philosophical and historical insights; focuses on the educational process in social work.
Refereed Serial

370.7 370 AT ISSN 1030-407X
JOURNAL OF TEACHING PRACTICE. 1981. s-a. Aus.$25 to individuals; institutions Aus.$30. Monash University College Gippsland, School of Education, Switchback Rd., Churchill, Vic. 3842, Australia. TEL 051-226375. FAX 051-226361. Eds. Len Cairns, Les Regan. adv.; bk.rev. circ. 180. (tabloid format; back issues avail.)
Formerly (until 1984): Australian Journal of Teaching Practice.
Description: Provides a forum for people interested in the school-experience programs for student teachers in Australia.

371.3 370 US ISSN 1051-144X
LB1068
JOURNAL OF VISUAL LITERACY. 1981. s-a. $12 to individuals; libraries $18. International Visual Literacy Association, c/o John C. Belland, 122 Ramseyer Hall, 29 West Woodruff Ave., Ohio State University, Columbus, OH 43210. bk.rev.; bibl.; illus. **Document type:** academic/scholarly publication.
—UnCover.
Formerly: Journal of Visual-Verbal Languaging.

EDUCATION — TEACHING METHODS AND CURRICULUM

375 US ISSN 0739-3369
JOURNAL OF VOCATIONAL EDUCATION RESEARCH. 1976. q. $52 (foreign $62). American Vocational Education Research Association, c/o Natalie Wysong, Center on Education & Work, 964 Educational Sciences Bldg., 1025 W. Johnson, Madison, WI 53706. TEL 608-262-8415. FAX 608-262-9197. Ed. Brian Cobb. bk.rev.; bibl.; charts. circ. 800. **Indexed:** C.I.J.E., Cont.Pg.Educ., Educ.Ind., ERIC. **Document type:** academic/scholarly publication.
—BLDSC (5072.512000); UnCover; UMI.
  Description: Publishes articles dealing with research and research-related topics in vocational education.
  Refereed Serial

371.3 621.38 GW
DER JUNGE ELEKTRO-TECHNIKER. 1949. m. DM.70.80. Frankfurter Fachverlag, Emil-Sulzbach-Str. 12, 60486 Frankfurt a.M., Germany. FAX 069-702003. Ed. Heinz O. Haeberle. adv.; bk.rev.; illus.; index. circ. 35,000. **Document type:** trade publication.
—CCC.
  Formerly: Junge Elektrohandwerk (ISSN 0022-6246)

371.3 375 500 II
JUNIOR SCIENTIST. (Text in English) 1963. m. Rs.45 for 10 nos. Association for the Promotion of Science Education, 3, First Trust Link St., Mandavelipakkam, Madras 600028, India. Ed. G. Venkataraman. adv.; bk.rev. circ. 1,500.

KANSAS MUSIC REVIEW. see *MUSIC*

375 US ISSN 0022-8958
LJ75
KAPPA DELTA PI RECORD. 1964. 4/yr. $7 (foreign $9). Kappa Delta Pi International Honor Society in Education, Box A, West Lafayette, IN 47906-0576. TEL 317-743-1705. FAX 317-743-2202. Ed. Carol Bloom. bk.rev.; charts; illus.; index. circ. 60,000. (also avail. in microform from UMI; reprint service avail. from UMI) **Indexed:** C.I.J.E., Educ.Admin.Abstr., ERIC. **Document type:** trade publication.
—Faxon; UnCover; UMI.
  Description: Practitioner-oriented articles featuring implementation strategies of the latest theories in elementary and secondary education.
  Refereed Serial

KATECHETISCHE BLAETTER; Zeitschrift fuer Religionsunterricht, Gemeindekatechese, Kirchliche Jugendarbeit. see *RELIGIONS AND THEOLOGY — Roman Catholic*

371.3 375 CC ISSN 1000-0186
KECHENG - JIAOCAI - JIAOFA/CURRICULUM, TEACHING MATERIALS, AND METHOD. (Text in Chinese) 1981. m. $35.90. Renmin Jiaoyu Chubanshe, 55, Shatan Houjie, Beijing 100009, People's Republic of China. TEL 4035745. FAX 4010370. (Dist. overseas by: China International Book Trading Corporation, P.O. Box 399, P.R. China; Dist. in US by: China Books & Periodicals, Inc., 2929 24th St., San Francisco, CA 94110. TEL 415-282-2994) Ed. Ye Liqun. adv.; bk.rev. **Document type:** academic/scholarly publication.
  Description: Contains domestic and international news about curriculum, teaching materials, research results, reform trends and educational experiences in the fields of normal education, vocational education, adult education and pre-school education.
  Refereed Serial

KEJI YINGYU XUEXI/LEARNING ENGLISH FOR SCIENCE & TECHNOLOGY. see *LINGUISTICS*

DAS KIND. see *CHILDREN AND YOUTH — About*

KINESIOLOGY AND MEDICINE FOR DANCE. see *DANCE*

KUNSTSTUNDE; Unterrichtsbeispiele zur aesthetischen Erziehung. see *ART*

KYOIKU ONGAKU, CHUGAKU KOKO-BAN/EDUCATIONAL MUSIC, JUNIOR HIGH AND HIGH SCHOOL. see *MUSIC*

KYOIKU ONGAKU, SHOGAKU-BAN/EDUCATIONAL MUSIC, ELEMENTARY SCHOOL. see *MUSIC*

371.3 JA
KYOKA KYOIKU KENKYU.* 1968. a. Kanazawa Daigaku, Kyoikugakubu - Kanazawa University, Faculty of Education, 1-1 Marunouchi, Kanazawa-shi, Ishikawa-ken 920, Japan. illus. **Indexed:** Lang.& Lang.Behav.Abstr.

371.3 KO
KYOYUK TARJO/EDUCATIONAL MATERIALS. (Text in Korean) 1954. m. 27600 Won. Kyoyuk Publishing Co., 448-17 Seokyodong, Mapo Ku, Seoul 121, S. Korea. Ed. Choi Won Sik. adv. circ. 95,000. (also avail. in microfiche)

371.3 DK ISSN 0904-2180
L L - NYT.* 1972. 8/yr. Laererstuderendes Landsraad, Vesterbrogade 41D, 1620 Copenhagen, Denmark. Ed. Per Djervig. adv. circ. 17,000.

371.3 AT
LAB LINES. q. Science Teachers' Association of Victoria, Clunies Ross House, 191 Royal Parade, Parkville, Vic. 3052, Australia. TEL 03-347-2211. FAX 03-349-1319.

507 AT ISSN 0159-2033
LAB TALK. 1957. bi-m. Aus.$75 (includes monthly newsletter "Contact"). Science Teachers' Association of Victoria, Clunies Ross House, 191 Royal Pde., Parkville, Vic. 3052, Australia. TEL 03-347-2211. FAX 03-349-1319. Ed. E. Gregory. adv.; bk.rev. circ. 1,700. **Indexed:** Aus.Educ.Ind., Aus.P.A.I.S.
  Description: Provides teachers and educators with latest trends in science education.

LANGUAGE AND EDUCATION; an international journal. see *LINGUISTICS*

371.3 US
LANGUAGE AND EDUCATIONAL PROCESSES. 1990. irreg. price varies. Ablex Publishing Corporation, 355 Chestnut St., Norwood, NJ 07648. TEL 201-767-8450. FAX 201-767-6717. TELEX 135-393. Ed. Judith L. Green.

371.3 US
LANGUAGE AND LEARNING FOR HUMAN SERVICE PROFESSIONS. 1984. irreg., vol.6, 1990. price varies. Ablex Publishing Corporation, 355 Chestnut St., Norwood, NJ 07648. TEL 201-767-8450. FAX 201-767-6717. TELEX 135-393. Ed. Cynthia Wallat.

LATEIN UND GRIECHISCH IN BERLIN. see *CLASSICAL STUDIES*

LAW TEACHER. see *LAW*

LEAFLET (LEXINGTON). see *LINGUISTICS*

LEARNING DISABILITIES RESEARCH AND PRACTICE. see *EDUCATION — Special Education And Rehabilitation*

371.3 028.5 US ISSN 0896-8756
LEARNING EDGE; home based education program news. 1984. 6/yr. $15 (foreign $20). Clonlara Publications, 1289 Jewett, Ann Arbor, MI 48104. TEL 313-769-4515. Ed. Jo Hinsdale. adv.: B&W page $50. bk.rev. circ. 2,000. **Document type:** newsletter.
  Description: Features information for families enrolled in a home-based education program, including articles of general interest to home educators. Covers teaching, learning methods and materials.

375 US
LEARNING EXCHANGE NEWS.* 1974. q. $15. Learning Exchange, 2940 N. Lincoln Ave., Chicago, IL 60657. Ed. Diane Kinishi. circ. 8,000.

LECTURA Y VIDA; revista latinoamericana de lectura. see *LINGUISTICS*

613.7 GW ISSN 0342-2461
LEHRHILFEN FUER DEN SPORTUNTERRICHT. m. DM.27.60. Verlag Karl Hofmann, Postfach 1360, 73603 Schorndorf, Germany. TEL 07181-402-0. FAX 07181-402111. Ed. Heinz Lang. **Document type:** academic/scholarly publication.
—CCC.

371.3 AT
LET'S FIND OUT. q. Aus.$4.75. Science Teachers' Association of Victoria, Clunies Ross House, 191 Royal Parade, Parkville, Vic. 3052, Australia. TEL 03-347-2211. FAX 03-349-1319.

613.7 370 NE ISSN 0024-2810
LICHAMELIJKE OPVOEDING. 1912. 18/yr. fl.115. Koninklijke Vereniging van Leraren Lichamelijke Opvoeding, Postbus 398, 4000 AJ Zeist, Netherlands. FAX 31-3404-12810. Ed. Harry Stegeman. adv.; bk.rev.; illus. circ. 10,000.

LIFELINES (SASKATOON). see *PHYSICAL FITNESS AND HYGIENE*

LIIKUNTAKASVATUS. see *PHYSICAL FITNESS AND HYGIENE*

LINGUISTIQUE ET ENSEIGNEMENT. see *LINGUISTICS*

LISHI JIAOXUE/HISTORY TEACHING. see *HISTORY*

LISHI JIAOXUE WENTI. see *HISTORY*

LITERATURA V SHKOLE. see *LITERATURE*

371.3 US ISSN 0890-3557
LOLLIPOPS; the magazine for preschool and early childhood educators. 1981. 5/yr. $16.95 (effective 1992). Good Apple, 1204 Buchanan St., Box 299, Carthage, IL 62321-0299. TEL 217-357-3981. FAX 217-357-3987. Ed. Donna Borst. adv.; bk.rev. circ. 18,000. (back issues avail.)
  Description: Focuses on social studies, sciences, music and art for teachers of preschool to second grade.

371.33 UK ISSN 0954-5611
LOOK HEAR; the resource magazine for religious and social education in church and school. 1960. 3/yr. £3.25 (foreign £5.50). United Reformed Church, 86 Tavistock Place, London WC1H 9RT, England. Ed. Wendy Cooper. adv.; bk.rev. circ. 12,500. **Document type:** academic/scholarly publication.
—BLDSC (5294.507400).
  Formerly (until 1988): A V A Magazine (ISSN 0001-2858)
  Description: Highlights audio-visual aides.

LOUISIANA ENGLISH JOURNAL. see *LINGUISTICS*

M L T A V NEWSLETTER. (Modern Language Teachers' Association of Victoria) see *LINGUISTICS*

027.8 CN ISSN 0315-9124
M S L A V A JOURNAL. (Includes supplement: M S L A V A Newsletter) 1963. 4/yr. (plus 2 supplements). $20 to members. Manitoba School Library Audio Visual Association, c/o Manitoba Teachers' Society, 191 Harcourt St., Winnipeg, Man. R3J 3H2, Canada. TEL 204-888-7961. adv.; bk.rev.; illus.; index; circ. 250 (controlled). **Indexed:** Can.Per.Ind. **Document type:** academic/scholarly publication.
  Formerly: Manitoba Association of School Librarians Newsletter (ISSN 0025-2204)

420 PH ISSN 0047-5289
M S T ENGLISH QUARTERLY. 1950. a. price varies. D C S Manila Teachers of Secondary English, Office of the Supervisors of Secondary English, Manila Science High School, Taft Ave., Manila, Philippines. Ed.Bd. bk.rev. circ. 700. **Indexed:** Ind.Phil.Per., Lang.Teach.& Ling.Abstr.

M SCOPE REVUE. see *COMMUNICATIONS*

371.42 US
M V A VIEWPOINTS. 1947. 4/yr. $2. Minnesota Vocational Association, 6016 Oakland Ave., Minneapolis, MN 55417. TEL 612-866-6574. Ed. James Lee. adv.; bk.rev.; charts; illus.; stat.; tr.lit. circ. 3,200.

MA F L A NEWSLETTER. (Massachusetts Foreign Language Association) see *LINGUISTICS*

MACHINE-MEDIATED LEARNING. see *COMPUTERS — Computer Assisted Instruction*

MAJALLAH-I FIZIK/IRANIAN JOURNAL OF PHYSICS. see *PHYSICS*

371.3 CN ISSN 0315-9116
MANITOBA SOCIAL SCIENCE TEACHER. 1973. 4/yr. Can.$10 to members. Manitoba Social Science Teachers' Association, 191 Harcourt St., Winnipeg, MB R3J 3H2, Canada. TEL 204-888-7961. Ed. Ken Osborne. adv.; bk.rev. circ. 700.

371.3 CN ISSN 0318-2118
MANITOBA SPECTRA. 1960. 2/yr. Can.$14. Manitoba Business Education Teachers' Association, 191 Harcourt St., Winnipeg, Man. R3J 3H2, Canada. TEL 204-888-7961. adv.; bk.rev.

2160 EDUCATION — TEACHING METHODS AND CURRICULUM

371.3 375 810 US ISSN 0542-8343
MARYLAND ENGLISH JOURNAL. 1960. s-a. $10. Maryland Council of Teachers of English Language Arts, Frostburg State University, Dept. of English, Frostburg, MD 21532. TEL 301-689-4221. FAX 301-689-4495. Ed. Judith J. Pula. adv.; bk.rev.; bibl. circ. 500. (back issues avail.) **Document type:** academic/scholarly publication.
Description: Publishes theoretical, practical and pedagogical essays of interest to English and language arts teachers; also creative writing by teachers.

371.3 792 AT ISSN 0726-9072
MASK. 1977. q. Aus.$35 (foreign Aus.$50) (effective 1994). Victorian Association for Drama in Education, P.O. Box 1114, North Fitzroy, Vic. 3068, Australia. TEL 03-489-9744. FAX 03-489-9771. Ed. Domm Camenzuli. adv.; bk.rev. circ. 350. (back issues avail.) **Document type:** academic/scholarly publication.

MATEMATIKA V SHKOLE. see *MATHEMATICS*

MATHEMATICAL EDUCATION. see *MATHEMATICS*

371.3 510 AT ISSN 1033-2170
MATHEMATICS EDUCATION RESEARCH JOURNAL. 1977. 2/yr. Aus.$75 to institutions. Mathematics Education Research Group of Australasia, c/o Dr. M. Mitchelmore, School of Education, Macquarie University, North Ryde, N.S.W. 2109, Australia. TEL 02-805-8654. FAX 02-805-8674. Ed. N. Ellerton. bk.rev. circ. 350. (back issues avail.) **Indexed:** Aus.Educ.Ind. **Document type:** academic/scholarly publication.
—BLDSC (5405.917000).
Formerly (until 1989): Research in Mathematics Education in Australia (ISSN 0812-7859)
Description: For academics, students, and teachers involved in mathematics education.
Refereed Serial

MATHEMATICS IN SCHOOL. see *MATHEMATICS*

MATHEMATICS TEACHER. see *MATHEMATICS*

MATHEMATICS TEACHING. see *MATHEMATICS*

MATHEMATIK IN DER SCHULE. see *MATHEMATICS*

375 510 GW
MATHEMATIK LEHREN. bi-m. DM.110.10. Erhard Friedrich Verlag GmbH, Im Brande 17, 30926 Seelze, Germany. TEL 0511-40004-0. (Subscr. to: Postfach 100150, 30917 Seelze, Germany) **Document type:** academic/scholarly publication.

DER MATHEMATIKUNTERRICHT; Beitraege zu seiner wissenchaftlichen und methodischen Gestaltung. see *MATHEMATICS*

MATHEMATISCHE LEHRBUECHER UND MONOGRAPHIEN. ABTEILUNG 1: MATHEMATISCHE LEHRBUECHER. see *MATHEMATICS*

371.3 370 US ISSN 0025-6897
LB1043
MEDIA & METHODS; educational products, technologies & programs for schools & universities. 1964. 5/yr. $29 (foreign $47). American Society of Educators, 1429 Walnut St., Philadelphia, PA 19102. TEL 215-563-3501. FAX 215-563-1588. Ed. Diane Falten; Pub. Michele Sokoloff. adv. contact: Caliann Mitoulis. bk.rev.; illus. circ. 42,000. (also avail. in microform from UMI) **Indexed:** Comput.Cont., Consum.Ind., Cont.Pg.Educ., Educ.Ind., Educ.Tech.Abstr., LAMP, LHTN, Media Rev.Dig., Microcomp.Ind., R.G. **Document type:** academic/scholarly publication, trade publication.
—BLDSC (5525.250000); Faxon; UnCover; SWETS; UMI.
Formerly: Teachers Guide to Media and Methods.
Description: Educational magazine devoted to the practical applications of instructional technologies.Readers include those who influence the practical uses of multimedia equipment, computers, laserdiscs, audiovisual media and library automation systems in K-12 school districts.

371.33 US ISSN 0146-2091
MEDIA DIGEST;* a bi-monthly media resource for education. 1971. bi-m. $10 to individuals; students $8. National Film & Video Center, Inc., c/o Charles H. Slingluff, 201 Broadway St., Frederick, MD 21701-6501. Ed. George M. Ulysses. adv.; bk.rev.; film rev.; illus. circ. 40,000. (tabloid format; also avail. in microform from UMI; reprint service avail. from UMI)
Formerly: Sneak Preview.

MEDIA PROFILES: HEALTH SCIENCES EDITION. see *MEDICAL SCIENCES*

371.3 US ISSN 0731-3675
MEDIA SPECTRUM. 1974. q. $25 (foreign $30). Michigan Association for Media in Education, 6810 South Cedar, Ste. 8, Lansing, MI 48911. TEL 517-699-1717. Eds. Freda Richards, Marion West. adv.; bk.rev. circ. 1,500. **Indexed:** LHTN.
Supersedes: Forward (ISSN 0015-8593)

375 UK ISSN 0954-3473
MEDIAFILE. 1988. 3/yr. £32.95. Stanley Thornes, Ellenborough House, Wellington St., Cheltenham, Glos. GL50 1YD, England. TEL 0242-228888. FAX 0242-221914. illus. circ. 800. (looseleaf format)
Description: Provides information for English and media study teachers.

MEDIUM. see *LIBRARY AND INFORMATION SCIENCES*

375 US
MEMBERANDA.* 1983. q. Secondary School Admission Test Board, 12 Stockton St., Princeton, NJ 08540-6813. TEL 609-683-4440. Ed. Regan Kenyon. circ. 1,000. (back issues avail.)
Description: Directed to educators of independent school admission; features articles about marketing, demographics, applicant pool and leadership.

MENTAL MEASUREMENTS YEARBOOK. see *PSYCHOLOGY*

371.33 778 384 AT ISSN 0312-2654
METRO; media and education magazine. 1964. q. Aus.$70. Australian Teachers of Media, P.O. Box 222, Carlton South, Vic. 3053, Australia. TEL 03-482-2393. Ed. Sheila Allison. adv.; bk.rev. circ. 18,000. (back issues avail.) **Indexed:** Film Lit.Ind. (1976-).

MICROMATH. see *MATHEMATICS*

373 US ISSN 0094-0771
L11
MIDDLE SCHOOL JOURNAL. 1970. 5/yr. $35 (foreign $50) (effective 1993). National Middle School Association, 4807 Evanswood Dr., Columbus, OH 43229-6292. TEL 614-848-8211. FAX 614-848-4301. adv.; charts; illus.; circ. 19,000 (paid). (also avail. in microform from UMI; back issues avail.; reprint service avail. from UMI) **Indexed:** C.I.J.E., Cont.Pg.Educ., Educ.Ind. **Document type:** academic/scholarly publication.
—BLDSC (5761.406560); Faxon; UnCover; UMI.
Formerly: Midwest Middle School Journal.
Description: Seeks to further the understanding and the implementation of effective practices at the middle school level.

371.3 375 US
MINNESOTA ENGLISH JOURNAL. 1973. 2/yr. membership. Minnesota Council of Teachers of English, c/o Terrance Flaherty, Mankato State University, Mankato, MN 56001. TEL 507-389-1821. Ed. Eleanor M. Hoffman.

371.3 US ISSN 0544-3520
MINNESOTA ENGLISH NEWSLETTER. 6/yr. membership. Minnesota Council of Teachers of English, c/o Terrance Flaherty, Mankato State University, Mankato, MN 56001. TEL 507-389-1821. **Document type:** newsletter.

371.3 US
MISSOURI ENGLISH BULLETIN. 1943. 6/yr. $10 to non-members. Missouri Association of Teachers of English, c/o 10500 E. 60th Terr., Raytown, MO 64133. TEL 816-737-6200. (Subscr. to: Peter Hasselriis, 207 Education Bldg., Univ. of Missouri, Columbia, MO 65211) Eds. Barry Kincaid, Sally Frederick. bk.rev. circ. 650. (also avail. in microfiche from EDR) **Indexed:** ERIC. **Document type:** bulletin, academic/scholarly publication.

MISSOURI JOURNAL OF RESEARCH IN MUSIC EDUCATION. see *MUSIC*

MODERN ENGLISH TEACHER; a magazine of practical suggestions for improving the teaching of English as a foreign language. see *LINGUISTICS*

MODERN LANGUAGE JOURNAL. see *LINGUISTICS*

MONATSHEFTE. see *LINGUISTICS*

371.3 PL ISSN 0077-0558
MONOGRAFIE Z DZIEJOW OSWIATY. (Text in Polish; summaries in English, French, Russian) 1957. irreg., vol.35, 1991. price varies. (Polska Akademia Nauk, Instytut Historii Nauki, Oswiaty i Techniki, Pracownia Dziejow Oswiaty) Ossolineum, Publishing House of the Polish Academy of Sciences, Rynek 9, 50-106 Wroclaw, Poland. TEL 48-71-386-25. FAX 48-71-448-103. TELEX 0712771 OSS PL. Ed. Jozef Miaso. **Document type:** monographic series.

379.155 US
MONTANA COUNCIL ON VOCATIONAL EDUCATION. ANNUAL REPORT. 1970. a. free. Montana Advisory Council on Vocational Education, 1228 11th Ave., Helena, MT 59620. TEL 406-444-2964. FAX 406-444-1523. Ed. James W. Fitzpatrick. circ. 100.
Formerly: Montana Advisory Council for Vocational Education. Annual Report (ISSN 0093-6472)

MOTORIK. see *PHYSICAL FITNESS AND HYGIENE*

375 AT ISSN 0818-6197
MOUTHPIECE. 1984. q. Aus.$12 (free to qualified personnel). Christian Parent Controlled Schools Ltd., 58 Douglas Rd., Blacktown, N.S.W. 2148, Australia. TEL 02-671-3311. FAX 02-671-5968. Ed. Andrew White. adv.; bk.rev. circ. 1,500.
Formerly (until 1985): Curriculum News (ISSN 0818-6227)
Description: Provides a vehicle for exchange of curriculum and staff development information among teachers in Christian schools.

375 917.306 US ISSN 1058-9236
Z711.8
▼**MULTICULTURAL REVIEW;** dedicated to a better understanding of ethnic, racial and religious diversity. 1992. q. $59 (foreign $79). G P Subscription Publications (Subsidiary of: Greenwood Publishing Group Inc.), 88 Post Rd., W., Box 5007, Westport, CT 06881. TEL 203-226-3571. FAX 203-222-1502. Ed. Brenda Mitchell-Powell. adv.; bk.rev. (reprint service avail.) **Indexed:** Bk.Rev.Ind. (1992-), Child.Bk.Rev.Ind. (1992-).
—BLDSC (5983.084420); Faxon; UnCover.
Incorporates (in 1992): Journal of Multicultural Librarianship (ISSN 0950-1649)
Description: Reviews multicultural books and educational curriculum materials.

375 UK ISSN 0263-0869
MULTICULTURAL TEACHING. 1982. 3/yr. £18 (foreign £21). Trentham Books Ltd., Westview House, 734 London Rd., Oakhill, Stoke-on-Trent, Staffs. ST4 5NP, England. TEL 0782-745567. FAX 0782-745553. Ed. Gillian Klein. adv.; bk.rev.; index. circ. 2,100. (also avail. in microform; back issues avail.) **Indexed:** Child.Lit.Abstr., Cont.Pg.Educ., Mult.Ed.Abstr., SOMA. **Document type:** academic/scholarly publication.
—BLDSC (5983.084450).
Description: Serves all teachers preparing students for life in a multi-ethnic society.

MUNHWAO HAKSUP/STUDY OF KOREAN LANGUAGE. see *LINGUISTICS*

MURDER IS ACADEMIC; the teaching and criticism of crime fiction on campus. see *LITERATURE — Mystery And Detective*

780.7 AT ISSN 0047-8431
MUSIC AND THE TEACHER. 1965. q. $18 to members and educational institutions only. Victorian Music Teachers Association, 49 Earl St., Kew, Vic. 3101, Australia. TEL 03-853-7861. Ed. Vera Jeppeson. adv.; bk.rev. circ. 1,200. **Indexed:** Aus.Educ.Ind. **Document type:** academic/scholarly publication.

MUSIC EDUCATORS JOURNAL. see *MUSIC*

EDUCATION — TEACHING METHODS AND CURRICULUM

375 780   UK   ISSN 0954-0377
MUSIC FILE. 1988. 3/yr. £49.95. Stanley Thornes, Old Station Dr., Leckhampton, Cheltenham GL53 ODN, England. TEL 0242-2288888. FAX 071-602-5197.
 Description: Serves as a resource for music teachers.

780.7   AT   ISSN 0727-8683
MUSIC TEACHERS' ASSOCIATION OF N.S.W. QUARTERLY MAGAZINE. 1936. q. Aus.$50 includes membership. Music Teachers' Association of N.S.W. Ltd., P.O. Box 491, Burwood, N.S.W. 2134, Australia. TEL 747-1676. Ed. Warren Thomson. adv. circ. 1,000. (back issues avail.) **Document type:** trade publication.

658.13   US   ISSN 0161-7990
N A E B BULLETIN. 1940. m. $40 to non-members; members $20. National Association of Educational Buyers, 450 Wireless Blvd., Hauppauge, NY 11788-3934. TEL 516-273-2600. FAX 516-273-2305. Ed. Neil D. Markee. bk.rev.; abstr.; tr.lit.; circ. controlled. **Document type:** bulletin.
 Formerly: Buying for Higher Education.

N A S A EDUCATIONAL HORIZONS. (U.S. National Aeronautics and Space Administration) see AERONAUTICS AND SPACE FLIGHT

375   US
N A S S P CURRICULUM REPORT. 1964. bi-m. $4 membership. National Association of Secondary School Principals, 1904 Association Dr., Reston, VA 22091. TEL 703-860-0200. Ed. Patricia George. charts; illus. circ. 42,000. (back issues avail.; reprint service avail. from UMI) **Document type:** newsletter.
 Formerly: National Association of Secondary School Principals. Curriculum Report. (ISSN 0547-4205)
 Description: Curriculum-related issues in secondary school education.

371.2 371.3   US   ISSN 1054-7673
N C R T L SPECIAL REPORT. (Former name of issuing body: National Center for Research on Teacher Education) 1988. irreg. price varies. National Center for Research on Teacher Learning, Michigan State University, 116 Erickson Hall, E. Lansing, MI 48824-1034. TEL 517-355-9302. FAX 517-336-2795. Ed. Sandra Gross. **Document type:** monographic series.
 Formerly (until 1991): N C R T E Colloquy (ISSN 0896-3932)
 Description: Research on teacher education, with a focus on teacher learning.

371.3 510   US   ISSN 0277-1365
N C T M NEWS BULLETIN. 1964. 6/yr. $3. National Council of Teachers of Mathematics, 1906 Association Dr., Reston, VA 22091. TEL 703-620-9840. FAX 703-476-2970. Ed. Cynthia C. Rosso. illus. circ. 85,000. **Document type:** bulletin.
 —SWETS.
 Description: Directed to math teachers in grades K-12 and two-year colleges.

N E A T E NEWSLETTER. (New England Association of Teachers of English) see LINGUISTICS

371.3   US
N H S C REPORT. 1974. s-a. free. National Home Study Council, 1601 18th St., N.W., Washington, DC 20009. TEL 202-234-5100. Ed. Sally R. Welch. circ. 1,500. **Document type:** proceedings.
 Description: Reports about NHSC conference workshops.

371 917.402   US   ISSN 0027-6758
L11
N J E A REVIEW. 1927. m (Sep.-May). $25. New Jersey Education Association, 180 W. State St., Box 1211, Trenton, NJ 08607-1211. TEL 609-599-4561. Ed. Martha O. DeBlieu. adv.; bk.rev.; circ. 144,000 (paid). (also avail. in microform from UMI) **Indexed:** C.I.J.E.
 —UnCover; UMI.
 Description: Educational journal for active and retired New Jersey public school employees.

375   US
N R C YEARBOOK. a. $55 (foreign $65). National Reading Conference, Inc., 200 N. Michigan Ave., 3rd Fl., Chicago, IL 60601-5909. TEL 312-541-1272. **Indexed:** Psychol.Abstr.

N S B E MAGAZINE. (National Society of Black Engineers) see ENGINEERING

N S S A NEWSLETTER. (National Science Supervisors Association) see SCIENCES: COMPREHENSIVE WORKS

NAEMNAREN; tidskrift foer matematikundervisning. see MATHEMATICS

NASTAVA I VASPITANJE. see EDUCATION

370   US
NATIONAL ASSESSMENT OF EDUCATIONAL PROGRESS. ASSESSMENT REPORTS. 1970. irreg. (approx. 10-25/yr.). price varies. (Educational Testing Service) National Assessment of Educational Progress, CN 6710, Princeton, NJ 08541-6710. (Subscr. to: Supt. of Documents, Govt. Printing Office, Washington, DC 20402) bibl.; charts; stat. circ. 10,000. (also avail. in microfiche from EDR) **Indexed:** ERIC.
 Formerly: Education Commission of the States. National Assessment of Educational Progress. Assessment Reports.

420 375.4   UK   ISSN 0143-4136
NATIONAL ASSOCIATION FOR THE TEACHING OF ENGLISH. NEWSLETTER. 3/yr. £35 (£20 for library membership). National Association for the Teaching of English, Broadfield Business Centre, 50 Broadfield Rd., Sheffield S8 0XJ, England. TEL 0742-555419. FAX 0742-555296. Ed. Andrew Burn. adv. **Document type:** newsletter.

NATIONAL ASSOCIATION OF BIOLOGY TEACHERS. NEWS AND VIEWS; issues, events, professional development for biology teachers. see BIOLOGY

NATIONAL ASSOCIATION OF SCHOOLS OF MUSIC. DIRECTORY. see MUSIC

NATIONAL ASSOCIATION OF SCHOOLS OF MUSIC. HANDBOOK. see MUSIC

650 338   US   ISSN 1049-0256
HF1101
NATIONAL BUSINESS EDUCATION YEARBOOK. (Published 1984-1987 as special issue of Business Education Forum) 1963. a. $12. National Business Education Association, 1914 Association Dr., Reston, VA 22091. TEL 703-860-8300. FAX 703-620-4483. bibl. circ. 15,000. (also avail. in microform from UMI; reprint service avail. from UMI) **Indexed:** Bus.Educ.Ind.; Educ.Ind.
 —UMI.
 Description: In-depth coverage of a single topic relating to business education.

371.3   US
NATIONAL MONITOR OF EDUCATION. 1977. 10/yr. $20. Box 402, Alamo, CA 94507. TEL 510-945-6745. Ed. Betty Arras. adv.; bk.rev.; charts; stat. circ. 2,000. (looseleaf format; back issues avail.)
 Formerly: California Monitor of Education.

NATIONAL TEACHING AND LEARNING FORUM. see EDUCATION — Higher Education

371.3   UK   ISSN 0077-5940
NATIONAL UNION OF TEACHERS. ANNUAL REPORT. 1871. a. free. National Union of Teachers, Hamilton House, Mabledon Pl., London WC1H 9BD, England. TEL 071-388-6191. FAX 071-387-8458. **Document type:** corporate report.
 Formerly (until 1887): National Union of Elementary Teachers. Annual Report.

371.3   US   ISSN 0896-3592
NATIONAL WRITING PROJECT. CENTER FOR THE STUDY OF WRITING QUARTERLY. q. $10 to N. America; elsewhere $16. National Writing Project, Center for the Study of Writing, Tolman Hall, University of California, Berkeley, CA 94720. TEL 510-642-0976. Ed. Miriam Ylvisaker. bk.rev. circ. 4,000. (back issues avail.) **Document type:** academic/scholarly publication.
 ●Also available online.
 —UnCover.
 Description: Covers issues in writing and the teaching and learning of writing, literacy and research in writing.

NATURWISSENSCHAFTEN IM UNTERRICHT. BIOLOGIE. see SCIENCES: COMPREHENSIVE WORKS

371 530 540   GW
NATURWISSENSCHAFTEN IM UNTERRICHT. PHYSIK-CHEMIE. 1952. m. DM.101.50 (foreign DM.108). Erhard Friedrich Verlag GmbH, Im Brande 15, 30926 Seelze, Germany. (Subscr. to: Postfach 100150, 30917 Seelze, Germany) Ed.Bd.
 Supersedes in part: Naturwissenschaften im Unterricht.

NATURWISSENSCHAFTEN IM UNTERRICHT PHYSIK; Beitraege zu seinen fachlichen, methodischen und didaktischen Problemen. see PHYSICS

371.3   PL   ISSN 0077-653X
LB1043.2.P6
NEODIDAGMATA. (Text in Polish, occasionally in English, French or German; summaries in English, French and Russian) 1970. irreg., vol.21, 1993. price varies. Adam Mickiewicz University Press, Nowowiejskiego 55, 61-734 Poznan, Poland. TEL 527-380. FAX 61-526425. TELEX 413260 UAMPL. Ed. Wadaw Strykowski. circ. 400. **Indexed:** Psychol.Abstr. **Document type:** academic/scholarly publication.
 —BLDSC (6075 606000).
 Description: Contains papers of the university's specialists in the field of psychology, pedagogics and sociology.

375   NE   ISSN 0168-4906
NETHERLANDS. CENTRAAL BUREAU VOOR DE STATISTIEK. STATISTIEK VAN HET ERKENDE SCHRIFTELIJK ONDERWIJS/NETHERLANDS. CENTRAL BUREAU OF STATISTICS. STATISTICS ON CORRESPONDENCE COURSES. (Text in Dutch and English) 1947. a Centraal Bureau voor de Statistiek, Prinses Beatrixlaan 428, Voorburg, Netherlands. (Dist. by: SDU - Publishers, Christoffel Plantijnstraat 2, Postbus 20014, 2500 EA The Hague, Netherlands) **Document type:** government publication.
 Formerly: Netherlands. Centraal Bureau voor de Statistiek. Statistiek van het Schriftelijk Onderwijs (ISSN 0077-7366)

371.3   SZ
NEUE SCHULPRAXIS. 1931. m. (11/yr.). 75 SFr. to individuals (foreign 81 SFr.); institutions 112 SFr. (foreign 118 SFr.). Zollikofer AG, Fuerstenlandstr. 122, CH-9001 St. Gallen, Switzerland. TEL 071-297777. FAX 071-297384. TELEX 77537. circ. 11,000. (back issues avail.) **Document type:** academic/scholarly publication.

THE NEW ADVOCATE. see LITERATURE

NEW ENGLAND JOURNAL OF HISTORY. see HISTORY — History Of North And South America

375   US   ISSN 0884-688X
THE NEW GOOD APPLE NEWSPAPER. 1973. 5/yr. $16.95 (effective 1993). Good Apple, 1204 Buchanan St., Box 299, Carthage, IL 62321-0299. TEL 217-357-3981. FAX 217-357-3987. Ed. Donna L. Borst. adv.; bk.rev. circ. 30,000. (back issues avail.) **Indexed:** Ind.Child.Mag.
 Formerly (until Jan. 1994): Good Apple Newspaper.
 Description: Focus on educational ideas and activities for teachers of grades 2-8.

NEW HAMPSHIRE POLYGLOT. see LINGUISTICS

371 500   UN
NEW TRENDS IN INTEGRATED SCIENCE TEACHING. (Text in English) 1971. irreg. price varies. Unesco, 7-9 Place de Fontenoy, 75700 Paris, France. TEL 45-77-16-10. (Dist. in U.S. by: Unipub, 4611-F Assembly Dr., Lanham, MD 20706-4391) Ed. P.E. Richmond.

371.39   US   ISSN 1044-9752
NEWS & NOTES (WASHINGTON). 1988. 10/yr. $10 to non-members. National Society for Performance and Instruction, 1300 L St. N.W., Ste. 1250, Washington, DC 20005. TEL 202-408-7969. FAX 202-408-7972. **Document type:** bulletin.

NEWS & VIEWS (MAYS LANDING). see AGRICULTURE

375   US
NEWSCOPE - ELEMENTARY EDITION;* weekly news summary and teaching quiz. 1974. w. (34/yr.). $74.80. Essex Editors, 2323 Pebble Fork Ln., Northfield, IL 60093.

EDUCATION — TEACHING METHODS AND CURRICULUM

373   US
NEWSCOPE - HIGH SCHOOL-COLLEGE EDITION;* a weekly news summary and teaching quiz. 1966. w. (34/yr.). $74.80. Essex Editors, 2323 Pebble Fork Ln., Northfield, IL 60093.
Formerly: Newscope - Secondary Current Events Edition (ISSN 0048-0266)

372.8
NEWSCOPE - MIDDLE-INTERMEDIATE-JUNIOR HIGH SCHOOL EDITION;* a weekly news summary and teaching quiz. 1966. w. (34/yr.). $74.80. Essex Editors, 2323 Pebble Fork Ln., Northfield, IL 60093. TEL 312-441-5880.
Formerly: Newscope - Current Events Edition (ISSN 0048-024X)

371.3 507   US
NEWSCOPE - SCIENCE EDITION;* a weekly science news summary and teaching quiz. 1966. w. (34/yr.). $74.80. Essex Editors, 2323 Pebble Fork Ln., Northfield, IL 60093.
Former titles: ScienceCope; Newscope - Science Edition (ISSN 0048-0258)

375   US
NEWSNAMES - CURRENT EVENTS.* 1975. w. (34/yr.). $38. Essex Editors, 2323 Pebble Fork Ln., Northfield, IL 60093.
Supersedes: Newsnames - Wordsearch.

375   US
NEWSPUZZLER: CURRENT EVENTS.* 1975. w. (34/yr.). $38. Essex Editors, 2323 Pebble Fork Ln., Northfield, IL 60093.
Supersedes in part: Newspuzzler and Newsquestionnaire.

375   US
NEWSQUESTIONNAIRE: CURRENT EVENTS.* w. (34/yr.). $38. Essex Editors, 2323 Pebble Fork Ln., Northfield, IL 60093.
Supersedes in part: Newspuzzler and Newsquestionnaire.

NIGERIA ENGLISH STUDIES ASSOCIATION JOURNAL. see *LINGUISTICS*

NIHON RIKAGAKU KYOKAI. KENKYU KIYO. see *PHYSICS*

371.3 375   US
NORTH CAROLINA ENGLISH TEACHER. 1938. q. $20. North Carolina English Teachers Association, c/o Chris Gould, Ed., English Department, U N C - Wilmington, Wilmington, NC 28403. TEL 919-757-6041. FAX 919-759-6074. adv.; bk.rev.; circ. 650 (paid). **Indexed:** Lang.& Lang.Behav.Abstr., Sociol.Abstr. **Document type:** academic/scholarly publication.

379.155   US
NORTH DAKOTA. COUNCIL ON VOCATIONAL EDUCATION. BIENNIAL EVALUATION REPORT. 1987. biennial. Council on Vocational Education, Box 1373, Bismarck, ND 58502-1373. FAX 701-258-9826. Ed. Alan Austad. illus. circ. 2,000. **Document type:** government publication.
Formerly: North Dakota. State Advisory Council for Vocational Education. Annual Evaluation Report (ISSN 0094-8306)
Description: Highlights recommendations of North Dakota vocational education delivery system and coordination between vocational education and Job Training Partnership Act.

NOTES A TEMPO. see *MUSIC*

NOTES ON TEACHING ENGLISH. see *LINGUISTICS*

371.3 420   US   ISSN 0738-8624
LB1576
NOTES PLUS; a quarterly of practical teaching ideas. 1983. q. $55 membership; includes subscr. to English Journal. National Council of Teachers of English, 1111 W. Kenyon Rd., Urbana, IL 61801-1096. TEL 217-328-3870. FAX 217-328-9645. Ed. Felice A. Kaufmann. circ. 27,500.
—UnCover.
Description: Contains teachers' ideas for teaching English at junior high and high school levels.

NURSE EDUCATOR. see *MEDICAL SCIENCES — Nurses And Nursing*

375   AT
NURTURE; journal for home and school. 1981. q. Aus.$11. Christian Parent Controlled Schools Ltd., P.O. Box 78, Doonside, N.S.W. 2767, Australia. TEL 02-671-3311. FAX 02-671-5968. Ed. Bill Salier. adv.; bk.rev.; circ. 6,500 (paid).

370   UK   ISSN 0269-9729
O L S NEWS. (Open Learning Systems) 1980. q. £25 (foreign £33). (G S S E) David P. Bosworth, Ed. & Pub., 11 Malford Grove, Gilwern, Abergavenny, Gwent NP7 0RN, England. TEL 0873-830872. adv.; bk.rev. circ. 800. **Document type:** newsletter.
—BLDSC (6256.400900).
Description: Contians news about the organization of open access learning, flexible learning and supported self study, and information about the application of educational technology and education consultancy.

O R T E S O L JOURNAL. (Oregon Teachers of English to Speakers of Other Languages) see *LINGUISTICS*

OKLAHOMA COUNCIL ON ECONOMIC EDUCATION NEWSLETTER. see *BUSINESS AND ECONOMICS*

370.193   US   ISSN 0030-1833
OKLAHOMA READER. 1966. 3/yr. $10. Oklahoma Reading Association, School of Education, East Central University, OK 74820. TEL 405-332-8000. FAX 405-332-1623. Ed. Tim Green. adv.; bk.rev. circ. 2,500.

650.07 370   UK   ISSN 0968-154X
ON COURSE. 1978. 3/yr. free. Scottish Vocational Education Council, Hanover House, 24 Douglas St., Glasgow G2 7NG, Scotland. TEL 041-248-7900. FAX 041-242-2244. Ed. Stephanie Wilson. adv. circ. 15,000. **Indexed:** Lang.& Lang.Behav.Abstr. **Document type:** newsletter.
Former titles (until 1991): Scotvec Journal (ISSN 0967-3709); (until 1985): Scottish Vocational Education Council. Handbook; Scottish Business Education Council. Business Education Guide (ISSN 0144-0101)

ON THE MOVE. see *PHYSICAL FITNESS AND HYGIENE*

ONGAKU KYOIKU KENKYU/STUDY OF MUSICAL EDUCATION. see *MUSIC*

375   US   ISSN 1066-2855
OPTIONS IN LEARNING; public, home, private. 1990. q. $20. Alliance for Parental Involvement in Education, Inc., Box 59, E. Chatham, NY 12060-0059. TEL 518-392-6900. Eds. Katharine Houk, Seth Rockmuller. bk.rev. circ. 2,000. (back issues avail.) **Document type:** newsletter.
Description: Offers parents information about educational options (public, private, and homeschooling), resources, and encouragement.

ORA DI RELIGIONE. see *RELIGIONS AND THEOLOGY — Roman Catholic*

OREGON MUSIC EDUCATOR. see *MUSIC*

OSAKA UNIVERSITY. COLLEGE OF GENERAL EDUCATION. SCIENCE REPORTS. see *SCIENCES: COMPREHENSIVE WORKS*

371.3 420   TH   ISSN 0125-2488
PE1068.T5
P A S A A JOURNAL. (Text in English and Thai) 1970. s-a. B.30($15) Chulalongkorn University, Phyathai Rd., Bangkok 10500, Thailand. FAX 010-662-2554441. Ed. Supanee Tiancharoen. bk.rev.; illus. circ. 500. **Indexed:** Lang.& Lang.Behav.Abstr., Lang.Teach.& Ling.Abstr., M.L.A.
—UnCover.
Formerly (until 1973): Bangkok English Language Center. Bulletin.
Description: Examines language instruction and education in Thailand.

371.3   GW
P H - F R. 1976. s-a. Paedagogische Hochschule Freiburg, Kunzenweg 21, 79117 Freiburg, Germany. TEL 0761-682-380. FAX 0761-682-402. Ed. Reinhold Voss. illus. circ. 1,000. **Document type:** academic/scholarly publication.

375   AT   ISSN 1019-8725
PACIFIC-ASIAN EDUCATION. 1990. s-a. Aus.$30. (Pacific Circle Consortium) Curriculum Corporation, St. Nicholas Pl., 141 Rathdowne St., Carlton, Vic. 3053, Australia. **Document type:** academic/scholarly publication.
Description: For curriculum and general education studies within the Pacific Rim educational community.

371.3   GW   ISSN 0342-8257
PAEDAGOGISCHE WELT. 1946. m. DM.58.80. (Paedagogische Stiftung Cassianeum) Verlag Ludwig Auer GmbH, Postfach 1152, 86609 Donauwoerth, Germany. TEL 0906-73-0. FAX 0906-73177. Ed. Peter Franke. adv.; bk.rev.; index. **Document type:** academic/scholarly publication.

371.3   US
PAPERS AND RECORDINGS IN EDUCATION. 1971. a. $5 paper; recording $10. Arizona State University, College of Education, Tempe, AZ 85287-1911. TEL 602-965-3306. Ed. James John Jelinek. circ. 1,000. (looseleaf format; also avail. in audio cassette; back issues avail.) **Indexed:** ERIC.

371.3 028.5   US
PARENTS EXPRESS; the community service newspaper for schools, kids, involved parents. 1986. 10/yr. $15. Parents Express, Box 12900, Philadelphia, PA 19108. TEL 215-629-1774. FAX 215-629-4853. Eds. Cynthia Roberts; Pub. Sharon Sexton. adv. contact: Laurie Grant. bk.rev. circ. 65,000. (back issues avail.) **Document type:** newspaper.
Formerly: Skip Magazine.
Description: Deals with family, child-raising, health, emotional health, education, and activities for families of children ages 1-16.

375   US
PATHWAYS (GRAND FORKS). 3/yr. $10 to individuals; institutions $40. Center for Teaching & Learning, Box 7189, University Sta., Grand Forks, ND 58202-7189. TEL 701-777-4421. FAX 701-777-4365. Ed. Carol Montag.

PEACE PROGRESS; I A E W P journal of education. see *EDUCATION — International Education Programs*

PEER COUNSELLOR JOURNAL. see *SOCIAL SERVICES AND WELFARE*

371.3 959   AT   ISSN 0815-6816
PELANGI; Indonesian-English bilingual magazine. (Text and summaries in English, Indonesian) 1985. q. Aus.$20. (University of Southern Queensland) U S Q Press, P.O. Box 58, Darling Heights, Toowoomba, Qld. 4350, Australia. TEL 076-31-2768. FAX 076-35-5550. TELEX 40010. Ed. Lesley Harbon. adv.; bk.rev.; film rev.; play rev.; bibl.; illus. circ. 1,000. (back issues avail.)
—CCC.
Formerly: Pelangi Rainbow.
Description: Features articles on Indonesia with emphasis on current use of the Indonesian language in a cultural context.

375   US
PENNSYLVANIA JOURNAL OF HEALTH, PHYSICAL EDUCATION, RECREATION AND DANCE. 1940? q. $30. Pennsylvania Association for Health, Physical Education, Recreation and Dance, Inc., Pennsylvania State University, Beaver Campus, Brodhead Rd., Monaca, PA 15061. TEL 814-865-4700. (Subscr. to: Linda Huber, 202 E. Third Ave., Lititz, PA 17543) Eds. Donna J. Kuga, William G. Meacci. adv.; bk.rev. circ. 3,500. **Indexed:** Phys.Ed.Ind. **Document type:** academic/scholarly publication.
Formerly: Pennsylvania Journal of Health, Physical Education and Recreation.

PEP TALK. see *POLITICAL SCIENCE*

EDUCATION — TEACHING METHODS AND CURRICULUM

371.39 US ISSN 0884-1985
LB1028.5
PERFORMANCE & INSTRUCTION. 1962. m. (10/yr.). $69 to non-members. National Society for Performance and Instruction, 1300 L St., N.W., Ste. 1250, Washington, DC 20005. TEL 202-408-7969. FAX 202-408-7972. adv.; bk.rev. circ. 6,000. (also avail. in microform from UMI; reprint service avail. from ISI,UMI) **Indexed:** C.I.J.E., Cont.Pg.Educ., ERIC, Pers.Lit., Psychol.Abstr., Q.Abstr., Tr.& Dev.Alert. **Document type:** academic/scholarly publication.
—BLDSC (6423.745000); Faxon; UnCover; SWETS; UMI.
Former titles (until 1985): Performance and Instruction Journal (ISSN 8750-0191); (until 1983): Performance and Instruction (ISSN 0273-5326); (until 1980): N S P I Journal (Year) (ISSN 0147-2747); Incorporates (in Feb. 1980): Improving Human Performance Quarterly (ISSN 0146-3756); National Society for Programmed Instruction. Journal (ISSN 0027-7002); National Society for Programmed Instruction. Newsletter (ISSN 0090-8118).
Description: Addresses improving human performance through a wide range of techniques, including incentives and feedback, effective management, performance aids, organizational development, job design and instruction.

371.39 US ISSN 0898-5952
PERFORMANCE IMPROVEMENT QUARTERLY. q. $20 to non-members. National Society for Performance and Instruction, 1300 L St. N.W., Ste. 1250, Washington, DC 20005. TEL 202-408-7969. FAX 202-408-7972. **Indexed:** Psychol.Abstr., Tr.& Dev.Alert. **Document type:** academic/scholarly publication.
—BLDSC (6423.805000); Faxon; UnCover; SWETS.
Description: Represents the cutting edge in research and theory in performance technology.

PERSPECTIVE (NEW YORK, 1970). see EDUCATION — International Education Programs

371.3 375 CN ISSN 0316-3334
PERSPECTIVES (SASKATOON). 1965. q. Can.$20 to non-members. (Saskatchewan Council of Social Sciences) Saskatchewan Teachers' Federation, Box 1108, Saskatoon, SK S7K 3N3, Canada. TEL 306-373-1660. Ed. John Schaller. adv.: B&W page Can.$100. bk.rev.; bibl.; charts; illus. circ. 200. **Indexed:** Can.Educ.Ind.

LE PHARE. see LINGUISTICS

PHYSICAL EDUCATION INDEX. see PHYSICAL FITNESS AND HYGIENE — Abstracting, Bibliographies, Statistics

613.7 790 370 NZ ISSN 1172-5958
PHYSICAL EDUCATION NEW ZEALAND. JOURNAL. 1953. 4/yr. $30. Physical Education New Zealand, P.O. Box 6203, Te Aro, Wellington, New Zealand. TEL 04-382-9439. FAX 04-382-9927. adv.; bk.rev.; cum.index: 1953-1967. circ. 800. (also avail. in microform from UMI; reprint service avail. from UMI) **Indexed:** Cont.Pg.Educ., Phys.Ed.Ind., Sportsearch (1973-). **Document type:** academic/scholarly publication.
—UnCover; UMI. CCC.
Formerly: New Zealand Journal of Health, Physical Education and Recreation (ISSN 0028-8314)

PHYSICS EDUCATION. see PHYSICS

PHYSICS TEACHER. see PHYSICS

PHYSICS TEACHER. see PHYSICS

371 530 GW ISSN 0340-8515
PHYSIK UND DIDAKTIK. 1973. q. DM.58. Bayerischer Schulbuch-Verlag, Hubertusstr. 4, 80639 Munich, Germany. Ed. Hansjoerg Jodl. **Document type:** academic/scholarly publication.
—CCC.

PIANO JOURNAL. see MUSIC

PLAYS; the drama magazine for young people. see THEATER

PO SVETU/PO SWIECIE/PO SVETE. see LINGUISTICS

371.3 GW ISSN 0176-9448
POLITIK BETRIFFT UNS. 1977. 11/yr. DM.118.80. Bergmoser und Hoeller Verlag GmbH, Karl-Friedrich-Str. 76, 52072 Aachen, Germany. TEL 0241-1730925. FAX 0241-1730934. Ed. Frank Dippel. circ. 5,200. (looseleaf format; back issues avail.) **Document type:** academic/scholarly publication.
Description: Intended for instructional purposes. Covers current political, social, economic and health issues. Each issue is devoted to a single topic.

371.3 GW ISSN 0344-3531
POLITIK UND UNTERRICHT; Zeitschrift zur Gestaltung des politischen Unterrichts. 1975. q. DM.16. (Landeszentrale fuer Politische Bildung Baden-Wuerttemberg) Neckar Verlag Herbert Holtzhauer GmbH, Klosterring 1, 78050 Villingen-Schwenningen, Germany. TEL 07721-89870. FAX 07721-898750. circ. 26,000. (back issues avail.) **Document type:** academic/scholarly publication.
Description: Discusses political education in schools, lessons for social science, history and political science.

375 US
PORTFOLIO NEWS. 1990. q. $25. Portfolio Assessment Clearinghouse, Teacher Education Program - 0070, Univ. of California, San Diego, 9500 Gilman Dr., La Jolla, CA 92093-0070. TEL 619-534-1681. FAX 619-534-2462. Ed. Winfield Cooper. bk.rev. circ. 3,000. **Document type:** newsletter.
Description: Includes articles and news from educators involved in portfolio assessment, and provides a forum for the exchange of information and ideas about the use of portfolios in schools.

POSTGRADUATE INSTITUTE OF MEDICAL EDUCATION AND RESEARCH, CHANDIGARH. BULLETIN. see MEDICAL SCIENCES

PRACTICAL ENGLISH TEACHING; for teachers of English as a foreign language to secondary level. see LINGUISTICS

PRAXIS DER MATHEMATIK. see MATHEMATICS

PRAXIS DER NATURWISSENSCHAFTEN. BIOLOGIE; im Unterricht der Schulen. see BIOLOGY

PRAXIS DER NATURWISSENSCHAFTEN. CHEMIE; im Unterricht der Schulen. see CHEMISTRY

PRAXIS DER NATURWISSENSCHAFTEN. PHYSIK; im Unterricht der Schulen. see PHYSICS

PRAXIS DES NEUSPRACHLICHEN UNTERRICHTS. see LINGUISTICS

PRAXIS DEUTSCH. see LINGUISTICS

PRAXIS GEOGRAPHIE. see GEOGRAPHY

371.3 GW ISSN 0933-5374
PRAXIS GESCHICHTE. 1988. 6/yr. DM.62.40. Westermann Schulbuchverlag GmbH, Postfach 4938, 38039 Braunschweig, Germany. TEL 0531-708373. FAX 0531-708127. Ed. Bernd Bredemeyer. adv.: B&W page DM.2100, color page DM.3360; trim 187 x 258. bibl.; charts; illus. circ. 12,758. **Document type:** academic/scholarly publication.

371.3 GW ISSN 0170-3722
PRAXIS GRUNDSCHULE. 1976. 6/yr. DM.81. Westermann Schulbuchverlag GmbH, Postfach 4938, 38039 Braunschweig, Germany. TEL 0531-708373. FAX 0531-708127. Ed. D.H. Heckt. adv.: B&W page DM.4400, color page DM.7040; trim 187 x 258. charts; illus. circ. 46,019. **Document type:** academic/scholarly publication.

375 GW ISSN 0936-6970
PRAXIS SCHULE 5-10. 1990. 6/yr. DM.62.40. Westermann Schulbuchverlag GmbH, Postfach 4938, 38039 Braunschweig, Germany. TEL 0531-708372. FAX 0531-708248. Ed. B. Burgtorf. adv.: B&W page DM.1500, color page DM.2400; trim 187 x 258. bk.rev.; charts; illus. circ. 7,548. **Document type:** academic/scholarly publication.

PREPODAVANIE ISTORII V SHKOLE. see HISTORY

375 600 UK ISSN 0964-8941
PRIMARY D A T A. 1991. 3/yr. £15 (foreign £18). (Design and Technology Association) Trentham Books Ltd., Westview House, 734 London Rd., Oakhill, Stoke-on-Trent, Staffs. ST4 5NP, England. TEL 0782-745567. FAX 0782-745553. **Document type:** academic/scholarly publication.
Description: Contains practical ideas, support and news for all primary school teachers of design and technology.

375 UK ISSN 0952-2921
PRIMARY FILE. 1987. 3/yr. £43.50. Primary File Publishing, 61 Gray's Inn Rd., London WC1X 8TZ, England. TEL 071-404-2776. FAX 071-404-2766. Ed. Helen Skelton; Pub. Nick Hutchins. (looseleaf format) **Document type:** academic/scholarly publication.

370 US ISSN 1068-073X
LB1576.A1
▼**PRIMARY VOICES K - 6**. 1993. q. $55 membership includes subscr. to Language Arts. National Council of Teachers of English, 1111 W. Kenyon Rd., Urbana, IL 61801-1096. TEL 217-328-3870. FAX 217-328-9645. Ed.Bd.
Description: For English language arts educators in the K-6 classroom. Each issue highlights a specific topic, and provides theoretical and practical guidance.

PRINT PUBLISHING FOR THE SCHOOL MARKET: REVIEW, TRENDS & FORECAST. see PUBLISHING AND BOOK TRADE

PRISMA CANADA. see LINGUISTICS

613.7 CN ISSN 0048-5381
PRO MOTION. 1960. ir-eg. Can.$30 to non-members; members Can.$25; students Can.$15. (B.C. Physical Education Teachers' Association) B.C. Teachers' Federation, 2235 Burrard St., Vancouver, B.C. V6J 3H9, Canada. TEL 604-731-8121. circ. 275. **Indexed:** Can.Educ.Ind., Sportsearch.

375 UK ISSN 0260-5554
PROBLEM-SOLVING NEWS. 1980. 3/yr. £2($3.15) K.F. Jackson, Ed., 16 Campbell Drive, Beaconsfield, Bucks HP9 1TF, England. adv.; bk.rev. circ. 500. (back issues avail.)

375 US ISSN 0740-6959
P57.U7
PROFESSION. 1977. a. $7.50. Modern Language Association of America, 10 Astor Pl., New York, NY 10003. TEL 212-475-9500. FAX 212-477-9863. Ed. Phyllis Franklin. circ. 36,000. (back issues avail.; reprint service avail. from UMI) **Document type:** academic/scholarly publication.
Description: Essays on the current state of the modern language profession and on aspects of the study of teaching of the modern languages and their literatures.

370 US ISSN 0196-786X
PROFESSIONAL EDUCATOR. 1978. s-a. $12. Auburn University, College of Education, 3084 Haley Ctr., AL 36849-5218. TEL 205-844-5979. FAX 205-844-5785. (Co-sponsors: Alabama Association of Teacher Educators; Turman Pierce Institute) Ed. Jeffrey Gorrell. bk.rev.; charts; illus.; stat. circ. 500. **Document type:** academic/scholarly publication.
—Faxon.

PROFESSIONAL SPEAKER. see LINGUISTICS

PROFESSIONAL THEATRE FOR YOUNG AUDIENCES. see THEATER

PROFILE (WHEATON). see EDUCATION — Adult Education

PSYCHOLOGIA A PATOPSYCHOLOGIA DIETATA. see PSYCHOLOGY

PSYCHOLOGY IN THE SCHOOLS. see PSYCHOLOGY

EDUCATION — TEACHING METHODS AND CURRICULUM

613.7 617.1   US   ISSN 0033-6297
GV201
QUEST (CHAMPAIGN). 1963. q. $36 to individuals (foreign $40); institutions $80 (foreign $84); students $24 (foreign $28). (National Association for Physical Education in Higher Education) Human Kinetics Publishers, Inc., Box 5076, Champaign, IL 61825-5076. TEL 217-351-5076. FAX 217-351-2674. (Co-sponsor: American Academy of Physical Education) Ed. Dr. Charles B. Corbin. adv. contact: Michele Watson. bk.rev.; bibl.; charts; illus.; stat. circ. 1,370. (also avail. in microform from UMI; back issues avail.) **Indexed:** CERDIC, Cont.Pg.Educ., Curr.Cont., Educ.Ind., Phys.Ed.Ind., Sportsearch (1975-), SSCI. **Document type:** academic/scholarly publication.
—BLDSC (7216.146400); Faxon; UnCover; SWETS; UMI. **CCC**.
  Description: Examines issues facing today's physical education faculty and students. Synthesizes research in the sports sciences and other subdisciplines of human movement.
  Refereed Serial

375   US
R & D PREVIEW. 1987. 6/yr. free. Council for Educational Development and Research, 2000 L St., N.W., Ste. 601, Washington, DC 20036. TEL 202-223-1593. Ed. Ullik Rouk. **Document type:** trade publication.

R E C S A M ANNUAL REPORT. (Regional Centre for Education in Science and Mathematics) see *EDUCATION*

507   MY   ISSN 0126-7612
R E C S A M NEWS. (Text in English) 1967. q. M.$3. Southeast Asian Ministers of Education Organisation, Regional Centre for Education in Science and Mathematics, 11700 Glugor, Penang, Malaysia. TEL 883266. Ed. Wong Wai Yi. illus. circ. 2,450. (reprint service avail. from UMI)
  Formerly: R E C S A M Newsletter.
  Description: Reports on the activities of the center: seminars, workshops, colloquia and research.

R S G RICHTING - SPORT-GERICHT; vakblad voor training, onderwijs en wetenschap. see *SPORTS AND GAMES*

R U; oekumenische Zeitschrift fuer die Praxis des Religionsunterrichts. (Religionsunterricht) see *RELIGIONS AND THEOLOGY* — Roman Catholic

371 500   US
RANGER RICK'S NATURESCOPE. 1984. 18/yr. National Wildlife Federation, 1400 16th St., N.W., Washington, DC 20036-2266. TEL 202-797-6800. (Subscr. to: 8925 Leesburg Pike, Vienna, VA 22184-0001. TEL 800-432-6564. FAX 703-790-4039) illus.
  Description: Provides elementary and middle school educators with science and environmental education information.

371.3 539.7   US
RE-ACTIONS. 1985. 5/yr. free to qualified personnel. American Nuclear Society, 555 N. Kensington Ave., La Grange, IL 60525. TEL 708-352-6611. Ed. Sharon Kerrick. bibl.; charts; illus. circ. 6,484. **Document type:** newsletter.
  Description: For educators interested in learning and teaching about the various peaceful uses of nuclear science, and related careers.

371   US   ISSN 0891-4214
READ, AMERICA!; a quarterly newsletter for reading coordinators. 1983. q. $25. Place in the Woods, 3900 Glenwood Ave., Golden Valley, MN 55422-5302. TEL 612-374-2120. FAX 612-593-5593. Ed. Roger A. Hammer. adv.; bk.rev. circ. 10,000. (tabloid format; back issues avail.) **Document type:** newsletter.
  Formerly (until vol.4, no.4, 1986): Supply Side.
  Description: Covers activities and ideas promoting reading. Serves to instruct and inform adult teachers, librarians and literacy program leaders.

371.3 410   AT   ISSN 0812-1710
READING AROUND SERIES. 1984. q. membership. Australian Reading Association, P.O. Box 78, Carlton South, Vic. 3053, Australia. TEL 03-347-2555. FAX 03-347-8971. (Subscr. to: P.O. Box 78, Carlton South, Vic. 3053, Australia) Ed. Jennie Bickmore-Brand. circ. 6,000. (back issues avail.)
  Description: Focuses on literacy programs for children. Includes teaching methods, curriculum and linguistics.

READING IN A FOREIGN LANGUAGE. see *LINGUISTICS*

028   II   ISSN 0377-3426
LB1049.9
READING JOURNAL. (Text in English and Hindi) 1973. a. Rs.3($0.50) Indian Reading Association, J-15 Haus Khas Enclave, Mehrauli Road, New Delhi 16, India. Ed. K. Bose. bk.rev.

371 370   US   ISSN 0270-2711
BF456.R2   CODEN: RRPSDW
READING PSYCHOLOGY; an international quarterly. 1979. q. $115. (University of North Texas, College of Education, Pupil Appraisal Center) Taylor & Francis, 1900 Frost Rd., Ste. 101, Bristol, PA 19007-1598. TEL 800-821-8312. FAX 215-785-5515. Ed. Lance M. Gentile. adv.; bk.rev.; bibl.; charts; stat.; index. circ. 275. (back issues avail.; reprint service avail. from UMI) **Indexed:** C.I.J.E., Child Devel.Abstr., Cont.Pg.Educ., ERIC, Lang.& Lang.Behav.Abstr., M.L.A., Psychol.Abstr., Sociol.Abstr., Sp.Ed.Needs Abstr. **Document type:** academic/scholarly publication.
—BLDSC (7301.260000); Faxon; UnCover; SWETS. **CCC**.
  Description: Offers material covering all levels - elementary, secondary and adult.
  Refereed Serial

428   US   ISSN 0886-0246
LB1050
READING RESEARCH AND INSTRUCTION. 1961. q. $50 (Canada $55; elsewhere $58). College Reading Association, c/o Dr. E. Sutton Flynt, Dept. Curriculum and Instruction, Pittsburg State University, Pittsburg, KS 66762. TEL 316-235-4494. FAX 316-232-7515. Ed. Robert Cooter. adv. contact: E. Suttan Flynt. bk.rev.; abstr. circ. 1,200. (also avail. in microform from UMI; reprint service avail. from UMI) **Indexed:** C.I.J.E., Cont.Pg.Educ., Educ.Ind., Psychol.Abstr. **Document type:** academic/scholarly publication.
—Faxon; UnCover; SWETS; UMI.
  Former titles (until vol.25): Reading World; Journal of the Reading Specialist (ISSN 0022-5126)

372   US   ISSN 0034-0561
LB1573   CODEN: REDTAH
READING TEACHER. 1957. 8/yr. (Sep.-May; except Dec.-Jan. combined). $38 in developed countries; developing countries $19. International Reading Association, Inc., 800 Barksdale Rd., Box 8139, Newark, DE 19714-8139. TEL 302-731-1600. FAX 301-731-1057. TELEX 5106002813READING. Eds. Nancy Padak, Tim Rasinski. adv. contact: Linda Hunter. bk.rev.; charts; illus.; index. circ. 65,000. (also avail. in microform from UMI; reprint service avail. from UMI) **Indexed:** Acad.Ind., Bk.Rev Ind. (1976-), C.I.J.E., Child.Bk.Rev.Ind. (1976-), Child.Lit.Abstr., Cont.Pg.Educ., Curr.Cont., Educ.Ind., Except.Child.Educ.Abstr., Jun.High.Mag.Abstr., Lang.& Lang.Behav.Abstr., Mid.East: Abstr.& Ind., Psychol.Abstr., Sp.Ed.Needs Abstr, SSCI. **Document type:** academic/scholarly publication.
—BLDSC (7301.400000); Faxon; UnCover; SWETS; UMI. **CCC**.
  Description: Directed to preschool, primary and elementary school educators.
  Refereed Serial

371.3   AT   ISSN 0156-7799
REFLECTIONS. 1976. q. Aus.$25. Mathematical Association of New South Wales, P.O. Box 536, Darlinghurst, N.S.W. 2010, Australia. Ed. Mia Kumar. adv.; bk.rev. circ. 1,000. (back issues avail.)

REHOVOT. see *SCIENCES: COMPREHENSIVE WORKS*

RELIGIONSLAEREREN. see *RELIGIONS AND THEOLOGY*

REPERES (PARIS, 1970); recherches en didactique du francais langue maternelle. see *LINGUISTICS*

507 375   AT   ISSN 0157-244X
RESEARCH IN SCIENCE EDUCATION. 1971. a. Aus.$40. Australasian Science Education Research Association, c/o Richard T. White, Faculty of Education, Monash University, Melbourne, Vic. 3168, Australia. TEL 61-3-905-1096. FAX 61-3-905-2779. TELEX AA32691. Ed. Paul Gardner. adv. circ. 300. **Indexed:** Aus.Educ.Ind., Aus.Educ.Ind., ERIC. **Document type:** academic/scholarly publication.
—BLDSC (7769.693000).
  Description: Publishes refereed and edited versions of research papers presented at association meetings.
  Refereed Serial

420.07 370   US   ISSN 0034-527X
PE1066
RESEARCH IN THE TEACHING OF ENGLISH. 1967. 4/yr. $15. National Council of Teachers of English, 1111 W. Kenyon Rd., Urbana, IL 61801-1096. TEL 217-328-3870. FAX 217-328-9645. Ed. Sandra Stotsky. bk.rev.; bibl.; stat. circ. 4,600. (also avail. in microform from UMI; reprint service avail. from UMI) **Indexed:** C.I.J.E., Cont.Pg.Educ., Curr.Cont., Educ.Ind., Lang.& Lang.Behav.Abstr., Lang.Teach.& Ling.Abstr., SSCI. **Document type:** academic/scholarly publication.
—BLDSC (7773.707000); Faxon; UnCover; SWETS; UMI.

371.3   JA   ISSN 0385-9746
RESEARCH JOURNAL OF EDUCATIONAL METHODS. 1975. a. 1200 Yen. National Association for the Study of Educational Methods, 1-1-89 Higashisendamachi Nakaku, Hiroshima 730, Japan. TEL 082-241-1221. Ed.Bd.

RESEARCH QUARTERLY FOR EXERCISE AND SPORT. see *PHYSICAL FITNESS AND HYGIENE*

370.78   US   ISSN 0091-732X
LB1028
REVIEW OF RESEARCH IN EDUCATION. 1973. a. $37 to individuals; institutions $46. American Educational Research Association, 1230 17th St., N.W., Washington, DC 20036-3078. TEL 202-223-9485. FAX 202-775-1824. Ed. Linda Darling-Hammond. index. circ. 8,000. **Indexed:** SSCI.
—BLDSC (7794.530000); UnCover; SWETS; UMI.
  Description: Surveys research, development, and theory in education through critical synthesizing essays.

REVISTA DE HISTORIA. see *HISTORY*

613.7 370   BE   ISSN 0035-1377
REVUE DE L'EDUCATION PHYSIQUE. 1960. q. 1300 Fr. Federation d'Education Physique, 33 Bd. de la Sauveniere 33, 4000 Liege, Belgium. (Co-sponsor: Groupement de Professeurs d'Education Physique) Ed. Maurice Pieron. adv.; bk.rev.; charts; stat. circ. 2,300. **Indexed:** Sportsearch (1973-).
—BLDSC (7898.876500).

370   FR   ISSN 0556-7807
REVUE FRANCAISE DE PEDAGOGIE. (Text in French; summaries in English) 1967. q. 210 F. (foreign 270 F.). Institut National de Recherche Pedagogique, 29 rue d'Ulm, 75230 Paris cedex 05, France. TEL 46-34-90-49. FAX 43-54-32-01. Ed. Jean Hassenforder. bk.rev.; abstr.; bibl.; index. circ. 2,500. (back issues avail.) **Indexed:** Cont.Pg.Educ., Educ.Tech.Abstr., Sp.Ed.Needs Abstr.
—BLDSC (7904.215000); SWETS.

RHEINLAND PFALZ. KULTUSMINISTERIUM. AMTSBLATT. see *EDUCATION* — School Organization And Administration

808.5   GW   ISSN 0720-5775
PN171.4
RHETORIK; ein internationales Jahrbuch. 1980. a. price varies. Max Niemeyer Verlag, Postfach 2140, 72011 Tuebingen, Germany. TEL 07071-98940. FAX 07071-989450. Ed. Joachim Dyck. adv.; bk.rev. circ. 800. **Indexed:** Bibl.Ling. **Document type:** academic/scholarly publication.

371.3   IT
RICERCHE PEDAGOGICHE. 1966. q. L.60000 (foreign L.100000) (effective Jan. 1993). Casella Postale 201, Parma, Italy. Ed. G. Genovesi.

ROUNDALAB JOURNAL. see *DANCE*

EDUCATION — TEACHING METHODS AND CURRICULUM

RUSSKII YAZYK V SHKOLE. see *LINGUISTICS*

RUSTINAR. see *LINGUISTICS*

S A S C A JOURNAL - NEWSLETTER. (Saskatchewan Association of Student Council Advisors) see *EDUCATION — School Organization And Administration*

371.3 II
S C E R T JOURNAL.* (Text in English) 1970. s-a. State Council of Educational Research and Training, Dept. of Public Instruction, Hyderabad, Andhra Pradesh, India. Ed.Bd. charts.

373 AT ISSN 0157-6488
S C I O S. 1965. q. Aus.$2 per no. Science Teachers Association of Western Australia, Unit 9, 25 Walters Dr., Osborne Park, W.A. 6017, Australia. Ed. R. Thiele. bk.rev. circ. 700. **Document type:** academic/scholarly publication.

S C W E A NEWSLETTER. (Saskatchewan Career - Work Education Association) see *OCCUPATIONS AND CAREERS*

S D A JOURNAL - NEWSLETTER. (Saskatchewan Drama Association) see *THEATER*

371.3 UK
S E A C ASSESSMENT MATTERS. irreg. School Examinations and Assessment Council, Newcombe House, 45 Notting Hill Gate, London W11 3JB, England. TEL 071-229-1234.

S I E C U S REPORT. (Sex Information and Education Council of the U S) see *PHYSICAL FITNESS AND HYGIENE*

S I L - A A I B OCCASIONAL PAPERS. (Summer Institute of Linguistics, Australian Aborigines and Islanders Branch) see *LINGUISTICS*

375 US
S L A T E NEWSLETTER. (Support for the Learning and Teaching of English) 1975. irreg. $15. National Council of Teachers of English, 1111 W. Kenyon Rd., Urbana, IL 61801-1096. TEL 217-328-3870. FAX 217-328-9645. Ed. Charles Suhor. circ. 2,000. **Document type:** newsletter.
  Description: Directed to K-6 English language art teachers about censorship, writing centers, and composition.

S M T S JOURNAL - NEWSLETTER. (Saskatchewan Mathematics Teachers' Society) see *MATHEMATICS*

371.3 500 510 US
S S M A CLASSROOM ACTIVITIES MONOGRAPH SERIES. 1987. irreg., vol. 3, 1992. price varies. School Science and Mathematics Association, c/o Donald L. Pratt, Curriculum and Foundations, Bloomsburg University, Bloomsburg, PA 17815. TEL 717-389-4915. FAX 717-389-3894. **Document type:** monographic series.
  Description: Covers various topics on developing mathematics and science curricula in elementary schools.

371.3 500 510 US
S S M A TOPICS FOR TEACHERS MONOGRAPH SERIES. 1979. irreg., vol. 5, 1990. price varies. School Science and Mathematics Association, c/o Donald L. Pratt, Curriculum and Foundations, Bloomsburg University, Bloomsburg, PA 17815. TEL 717-389-4915. FAX 717-389-3894. **Document type:** monographic series.
  Description: Covers teaching techniques and curriculum development for elementary school teachers of science and mathematics.

507 US
S S M ARRT. 1971. q. membership. School Science & Mathematics Association, Inc., 126 Life Science Bldg., Bowling Green State University, Bowling Green, OH 43403. TEL 419-372-7393. Ed. Norma Hernandez. circ. 1,200. (looseleaf format)

S T F M MESSENGER. (Society of Teachers of Family Medicine) see *MEDICAL SCIENCES*

S U T BULLETIN. (Science University of Tokyo) see *TECHNOLOGY: COMPREHENSIVE WORKS*

372 510 GW ISSN 0170-0944
SACHUNTERRICHT UND MATHEMATIK IN DER GRUNDSCHULE. 1972. m. DM.91.20 (foreign DM.103.20). Aulis-Verlag Deubner und Co. KG, Antwerpener Str. 6-12, 50672 Cologne, Germany. TEL 0221-518051. FAX 0221-518443. TELEX 8883068-AVD. Ed. V. Zenker. **Document type:** academic/scholarly publication.

SASKATCHEWAN ASSOCIATION OF TEACHERS OF FRENCH. BULLETIN DE SERVICE. see *LINGUISTICS*

SBORNIK STATEI PO FRANTSUZSKOI LINGVISTIKE I METODIKE PREPODAVANIYA INOSTRANNOGO YAZIKA V V U ZE. see *LINGUISTICS*

SCHATZKAMMER; der deutschen Sprache, Dichtung und Geschichte. see *LINGUISTICS*

370 US ISSN 0163-3570
SCHOLASTIC ACTION. 1977. 14/yr. (Sep.-May). $6.95. Scholastic Inc., 555 Broadway, New York, NY 10012-3999. TEL 212-343-6100. Ed. Denise Willi. circ. 230,000. (also avail. in microform from UMI; reprint service avail. from UMI) **Indexed:** Ind.Child.Mag.
  —UMI.
  Description: Helps develop basic English skills for remedial and special students of grades 7-12 with reading levels of grades 4-5.

SCHOLASTIC ART. see *ART*

SCHOLASTIC CHOICES; personal development & living skills. see *HOME ECONOMICS*

SCHOLASTIC COACH. see *PHYSICAL FITNESS AND HYGIENE*

SCHOLASTIC MATH. see *MATHEMATICS*

SCHOOL AGE NOTES; the newsletter for school-age care professionals. see *CHILDREN AND YOUTH — About*

701 US ISSN 0036-6463
N81
SCHOOL ARTS; the art education magazine for teachers. 1901. m. (Sep.-May). $23. Davis Publications, Inc. (Worcester), 50 Portland St., Printers Bldg., Worcester, MA 01608. TEL 508-754-7201. FAX 508-753-3834. Ed. Kent Anderson. adv.; bk.rev.; film rev.; bibl.; illus.; stat.; tr.lit.; index. circ. 22,422. (also avail. in microform from UMI; microfilm; back issues avail.; reprint service avail. from UMI,BLH,MCE) **Indexed:** Access (1980-1987), Bk.Rev.Ind. (1980-), Bus.Ind., C.I.J.E., Child.Bk.Rev.Ind. (1980-), Educ.Ind., Jun.High.Mag.Abstr., Mag.Ind., Media Rev.Dig., PMR, TOM, Tr.& Indus.Ind. **Document type:** trade publication.
  —BLDSC (8092.629000); Faxon; UnCover; SWETS; UMI.

377.8 NE ISSN 0036-6544
SCHOOL EN GODSDIENST; catechetical periodical for elementary school teachers. 1947. 8/yr. fl.45. Katholiek Pedagogisch Centrum, Postbus 482, 5201 AL Den Bosch, Netherlands. adv.; bk.rev.; bibl.; illus.; index. circ. 2,400. **Indexed:** CERDIC.

SCHOOL LIBRARY MEDIA ACTIVITIES MONTHLY. see *LIBRARY AND INFORMATION SCIENCES*

SCHOOL LIBRARY MEDIA FOLDERS OF IDEAS FOR LIBRARY EXCELLENCE. see *LIBRARY AND INFORMATION SCIENCES*

SCHOOL MUSIC NEWS. see *MUSIC*

SCHOOL OF CELTIC STUDIES. NEWSLETTER/SCEALA SCOIL AN LEINN CHEILTIGH. see *LINGUISTICS*

370.15 150 UK ISSN 0143-0343
LB1051
SCHOOL PSYCHOLOGY INTERNATIONAL. 1979. q. £35 to individuals; institutions £120. Sage Publications Ltd., 6 Bonhill St., London EC2A 4PU, England. TEL 071-374-0645. FAX 071-374-8741. Eds. R.L. Burden, C.S. Mcloughlin. adv.: color page £170; trim 193 x 114; adv. contact: Bernie Folan. bk.rev.; illus. **Indexed:** Br.Educ.Ind., Child Devel.Abstr., Cont.Pg.Educ., Psychol.Abstr., Sociol.Abstr., Sociol.Educ.Abstr. **Document type:** academic/scholarly publication.
  —BLDSC (8092.926300); Faxon; UnCover; SWETS. CCC.
  Description: Highlights the concerns of those who provide quality mental health, educational, therapeutic and support services to schools and communities throughout the world.
  Refereed Serial

SCHOOL SCIENCE REVIEW. see *SCIENCES: COMPREHENSIVE WORKS*

371.3 GW
SCHULFERNSEHEN (BERLIN). 1973. irreg. price varies. (Landesbildstelle Berlin, Zentrum fuer Audiovisuelle Medien) Colloquium Verlag, Luetzowstr. 105, 10785 Berlin, Germany. circ. 300.

371.3 GW ISSN 0172-5408
DER SCHULGEOGRAPH. 1968. 4/yr. membership. Verband Deutscher Schulgeographen, Landesverband Hessen, Karl-Gloeckner-Str. 21, 35394 Giessen, Germany. TEL 069-1301-0. bk.rev. circ. 400.

371.3 GW ISSN 0720-8634
SCHULPRAXIS; Zeitschrift fuer Unterricht und Schulorganisation 1980. 6/yr. DM.49. B und B Verlagsgesellschaft mbH, Rathenaustr. 16, 33102 Paderborn, Germany. TEL 05251-34024. FAX 05251-31414. Ed. Gerhard E. Ortner. adv.; bk.rev. circ. 5,000.

507 AT ISSN 0048-9603
SCIENCE EDUCATION NEWS. 1952. 4/yr. Aus.$42 (foreign Aus.$52) (effective Jan. 1992). Science Teachers Association of New South Wales, P.O. Box 1060, Leichhardt, N.S.W. 2040, Australia. TEL 02-939-6107 Ed. Catherine Odlum. adv.; bk.rev. circ. 1,800. **Indexed:** Aus.Educ.Ind. **Document type:** academic/scholarly publication.

SCIENCE LEADERSHIP TREND NOTES. see *SCIENCES: COMPREHENSIVE WORKS*

SCIENCE NOTES AND NEWS. see *SCIENCES: COMPREHENSIVE WORKS*

SCIENCE SCOPE; a journal for middle-junior high science teachers. see *SCIENCES: COMPREHENSIVE WORKS*

SCIENCE TEACHER/VIGYAN SHIKSHAK. see *SCIENCES: COMPREHENSIVE WORKS*

SCIENCE WORLD. see *SCIENCES: COMPREHENSIVE WORKS*

SCIENCELAND; to nurture scientific thinking. see *CHILDREN AND YOUTH — For*

371.3 791.43 UK ISSN 0036-9543
PN1993
SCREEN. 1959. q. £48($92) (effective 1994). (John Logie Baird Centre) Oxford University Press, Oxford Journals, Walton St., Oxford OX2 6DF, England. TEL 0865-56767. FAX 0865-56646. TELEX 837330-OXPRES-G. (U.S. subscr. to: Oxford University Press Inc., 2001 Evans Rd. Cary, NC 27513. TEL 919-677-0977) Ed.Bd. adv. contact: Jane Parker. bk.rev.; film rev.; illus.; index. circ. 1,850. (also avail. in microform from JMI; reprint service avail. from UMI) **Indexed:** Film Lit.Ind. (1973-), Intl.Ind.TV, Media Rev.Dig., Stud.Wom.Abstr. **Document type:** academic/scholarly publication.
  —BLDSC (8211.754800); Faxon; UnCover; SWETS; UMI. CCC.

EDUCATION — TEACHING METHODS AND CURRICULUM

371.33   AU
SEHEN - HOEREN - BILDEN/SEE & LISTEN; Beitraege zur Medienpaedagogik. 1962. 5/yr. $15. S H B - Medienzentrum des Bundesministeriums fuer Unterricht, Kunst und Sport, Plunkergasse 3-5, A-1152 Vienna, Austria. FAX 0222-951322. Ed. Dr. Karin Hofbauer. adv.; bk.rev.; film rev.; illus.; mkt.; cum.index. circ. 6,500. (tabloid format)
    Formerly: Sehen und Hoeren (ISSN 0037-0975)

SHIJIE HANYU JIAOXUE/CHINESE TEACHING IN THE WORLD. see *LINGUISTICS*

SHORT COURSES AND SEMINARS; a compendium of short management & business courses. see *BUSINESS AND ECONOMICS — Management*

371.3 510   CC   ISSN 0488-7387
SHUXUE JIAOXUE/MATHEMATICS TEACHING. (Text in Chinese) 1956. bi-m. Y9 (effective 1994). Huadong Shifan Daxue, Shuxue Xi - East China Normal University, Department of Mathematics, 3663 Zhongshan Beilu, Shanghai 200062, People's Republic of China. TEL 2577577. FAX 86-21-2578367. Ed. Zhang Dianzhou. adv.; bk.rev. circ. 30,000. **Document type:** academic/scholarly publication.

SIGNAL (STREAMWOOD). see *CHILDREN AND YOUTH — About*

SKYLARK (SASKATOON). see *LINGUISTICS*

SLAVIC AND EAST EUROPEAN JOURNAL. see *LINGUISTICS*

SLOVENSKY JAZYK A LITERATURA V SKOLE. see *LINGUISTICS*

SLUR; a smooth connection between notes. see *MUSIC*

SMALL COLLEGE CREATIVITY. see *EDUCATION — Higher Education*

375   US   ISSN 1056-0300
LB1584
SOCIAL STUDIES AND THE YOUNG LEARNER. 1988. q. National Council for the Social Studies, 3501 Newark St., N.W., Washington, DC 20016. TEL 202-966-7840. **Document type:** academic/scholarly publication.
    Description: Provides creative teaching ideas for grades K-6.

SOCIAL STUDIES PROFESSIONAL. see *SOCIAL SCIENCES: COMPREHENSIVE WORKS*

375   GW
SONDERSCHULMAGAZIN. 1979. m. DM.109.80. Ehrenwirth Verlag GmbH, Schwanthalerstr. 91, 80336 Munich, Germany. TEL 089-544335-0. FAX 089-534739. Ed. Ortwin Krieg. **Document type:** academic/scholarly publication.
—CCC.
    Former titles: Lehrermagazin Sonderschulmagazin (ISSN 0930-696X); Sonderschulmagazin (ISSN 0171-9629)
    Description: Aimed at teachers working with educationally subnormal children. Includes instructional models.

SOUTH AUSTRALIAN GEOGRAPHER. see *GEOGRAPHY*

371.3   UK   ISSN 0311-2136
SOUTH PACIFIC JOURNAL OF TEACHER EDUCATION. 1972. s-a. $84 to individuals; institutions $212 (effective 1994). (Curtin University, Faculty of Education) Carfax Publishing Co., P.O. Box 25, Abingdon, Oxon. OX14 3UE, England. TEL 44-235-555335. FAX 44-235-553559. (U.S. subscr. to: Carfax Publishing Co., Box 2025, Dunnellon, FL 34430-2025) (Co-sponsor: Australian Teacher Education Association, Inc.) Eds. John Williamson, Barry Fraser. bk.rev. (back issues avail.) Indexed: Rural Ext.Educ.& Tr.Abstr. **Document type:** academic/scholarly publication.
—BLDSC (8352.122000). **CCC.**
    Refereed Serial

370   MY   ISSN 0126-8155
SOUTHEAST ASIAN-MINISTERS OF EDUCATION ORGANISATION. REGIONAL CENTRE FOR EDUCATION IN SCIENCE AND MATHEMATICS. GOVERNING BOARD MEETING. FINAL REPORT. (Text in English) a. free. Southeast Asian Ministers of Education Organisation, Regional Centre for Education in Science and Mathematics, 11700 Glugor, Penang, Malaysia. TEL 833266. circ. 150. (reprint service avail. from UMI)

SOUTHEAST ASIAN MINISTERS OF EDUCATION ORGANISATION. REGIONAL CENTRE FOR EDUCATION IN SCIENCE AND MATHEMATICS. LIBRARY ACCESSION LIST. see *BIBLIOGRAPHIES*

371.3 800   US
SOUTHEASTERN WRITING CENTER ASSOCIATION. SELECTED PAPERS. 1984. $8 to individuals; libraries $14.95. Appalachian State University, Department of English, Boone, NC 28608. TEL 704-262-3098. Ed. William C. Wolff.

SOUTHERN SOCIAL STUDIES JOURNAL. see *SOCIAL SCIENCES: COMPREHENSIVE WORKS*

SOUTHWESTERN MUSICIAN COMBINED WITH THE TEXAS MUSIC EDUCATOR. see *MUSIC*

SPOKEN ENGLISH; ideas and developments in oral education. see *LINGUISTICS*

371 796   GW
SPORTPAEDAGOGIK; zeitschrift fuer Sport- Spiel- und Bewegungserziehung. 1977. 6/yr. DM.108.30. Erhard Friedrich Verlag GmbH, Im Brande 17, 30926 Seelze, Germany. TEL 0511-40004-0. (Subscr. to: Postfach 100150, 30917 Seelze, Germany) Ed. Knut Dietrich. **Document type:** academic/scholarly publication.
    Formerly (until Jan. 1979): Zeitschrift fuer Sportpaedagogik (ISSN 0340-9058)

SPORTPRAXIS; die Fachzeitschrift fuer den Sportlehrer und Uebungsleiter. see *SPORTS AND GAMES*

371.7   GW   ISSN 0342-2402
SPORTUNTERRICHT. (Supplement avail.: Lehrhilfen fuer den Sportunterricht) 1951. m. DM.73.80 (students DM.65.40). (Deutscher Sportlehrerverband e.V.) Verlag Karl Hofmann, Postfach 1360, 73603 Schorndorf, Germany. TEL 07181-402-0. FAX 07181-402111. Ed. Ulrich Goehner. adv.; bk.rev.; illus.; index. circ. 14,000. Indexed: Sportsearch (1980-). **Document type:** newsletter.
—SWETS. **CCC.**
    Formerly: Leibeserziehung.

SPROUT/ME. see *EDUCATION*

STADION; Internationale Zeitschrift fuer Geschichte des Sports. see *SPORTS AND GAMES*

371.3   FR   ISSN 0987-7622
STANDPOINTS. 1988. 5/yr. (2 with audio cassettes). 250 F. (foreign 290 F.). Centre National de Documentation Pedagogique, 29 rue d'Ulm, 75230 Paris, France. (Subscr. to: CNDP, Abonnements, B.P. 7, 21 Square St. Charles, 75012 Paris, France) (Co-sponsor: Mission Laique Francaise) Ed. Elyane Conarteau. bk.rev.
    Description: Covers current events and daily life language, literature, cinema and the arts. Ideas for teaching young beginners to advanced students. Includes student worksheets and teacher guidelines.

371.3 375   US
STATEMENT (FORT COLLINS). 1970. 3/yr. $10. (Colorado Language Arts Society) Colorado State University, English Department, Eddy Bldg., Fort Collins, CO 80523. TEL 303-491-5264. FAX 303-491-5601. Ed. Louann Reid. bk.rev.; bibl. circ. 800. **Document type:** academic/scholarly publication.

STEPPING STONES. see *EDUCATION — Adult Education*

STOCHASTIK IN DER SCHULE. see *STATISTICS*

617.1   US   ISSN 0892-4562
GV223
STRATEGIES (RESTON); a journal for physical and sport educators. 8/yr. $40 to individuals; institutions $50. (National Association for Girls and Women in Sport) American Alliance for Health, Physical Education, Recreation, and Dance, 1900 Association Dr., Reston, VA 22091. TEL 703-476-3400. FAX 703-476-9527. (Co-sponsor: National Association for Sport and Physical Education) Ed. Gretchen O'Brien. circ. 10,000. **Document type:** newsletter.
—BLDSC (8474.034210); UnCover; UMI.
    Description: Geared towards physical and sports educators including teachers, coaches, administrators, and athletic directors. Emphasis is placed on applying research to daily practice and on collaboration between practitioners in the field and university-based educators.

370   US
STREET SCENES. 1964. q. free. Bank Street College of Education, 610 W. 112th St., New York, NY 10025. TEL 212-875-4400. FAX 212-875-4761. Ed. Renee Creange. circ. 10,000.
    Former titles (until 1989): Bank Street News - Reviews - Reporting; Report from Bank Street; Bank Street Reporting (ISSN 0045-1509)

STREETWISE; magazine of urban studies and environmental education. see *ENVIRONMENTAL STUDIES*

371.3   US
STUDENT ACCELERATION IN FLORIDA PUBLIC EDUCATION. 1975. a. Department of Education, Knott Building, Tallahassee, FL 32301. TEL 904-487-1630.

375   US
STUDENT SUCCESS TUTOR DIRECTORY - SARASOTA AND MANATEE COUNTY. 1989. a. free. Student Success Consultants, 2911 8th Ave., Bradenton, FL 34205. TEL 813-748-4237. FAX 813-748-8883. Ed. Andrea Page. adv.; illus.; stat.; tr.lit. circ. 5,000. **Document type:** directory.
    Formerly: Student Success Tutor Directory - Sarasota County (ISSN 0899-2355)
    Description: Lists tutors, counselors, teachers, and other support resources for students (kindergarten through post-secondary) in Sarasota and Manatee counties, Florida.

STUDENT UND PRAKTIKANT; Forum fuer die Pharmazeutische Ausbildung. see *PHARMACY AND PHARMACOLOGY*

373.246   GW
STUDIENFUEHRER UND PERSONAL VERZEICHNIS. 1976. a. DM.4. Fachhochschule Kiel, Breiter Weg 10, 24105 Kiel, Germany. circ. 3,000.

STUDIES IN EDUCATION AND TEACHING TECHNIQUES. see *EDUCATION*

STUDIES IN MATHEMATICS EDUCATION. see *EDUCATION — International Education Programs*

371.3   US
SUNSHINE CLASSROOM. 1985. 5/yr. $11. Sunshine Classroom, Inc., 1222 S. Dale Mabry, Ste. 637, Tampa, FL 33629. Ed. Shirley Jovanovic. adv. circ. 5,000. (back issues avail.)
    Description: Provides a forum for the exchange of ideas for teachers of pre-kindergarten to high school.

375 200   US
SYCAMORE TREE NEWSLETTER. m. membership. Sycamore Tree, 2179 Meyer Place, Costa Mesa, CA 92627. TEL 714-650-4466.
    Description: Provides Bible-centered alternative education programs and curricular materials for home and school teaching.

SYLLABUS (CHICAGO). see *LAW*

SYMBOLAE. SERIES C. LINGUISTICA. see *LINGUISTICS*

375   US   ISSN 1042-6655
SYNTAX IN THE SCHOOLS. 1984. q. $7.50. Pennsylvania College of Technology, One College Ave., Williamsport, PA 17701. TEL 717-326-3761. Ed. Edward Vavra. bk.rev. circ. 450. **Document type:** newsletter.
    Refereed Serial

EDUCATION — TEACHING METHODS AND CURRICULUM

371.3 407   UK   ISSN 0346-251X
P51
SYSTEM; an international journal of educational technology and applied linguistics. 1979. 4/yr. £121($185) (effective 1994). Elsevier Science Ltd., Pergamon, P.O. Box 800, Kidlington, Oxford OX5 1DX, England. TEL 44-865-843000. FAX 44-865-843010. (Subscr. in U.S. and Canada to: Elsevier Science, 660 White Plains Rd., Tarrytown, NY 10591-5153. TEL 914-524-9200. FAX 914-333-2444) Ed. Norman Davies. adv.; bk.rev. circ. 1,000. (also avail. in microfilm from UMI) **Indexed:** ASCA, C.I.J.E., Cont.Pg.Educ., Educ.Tech.Abstr., Lang.& Lang.Behav.Abstr., Lang.Teach.& Ling.Abstr. **Document type:** academic/scholarly publication.
—BLDSC (8589.095000); Faxon; UnCover; SWETS; UMI. **CCC**.
    Description: Features articles on educational technology applications and systems developments for teaching foreign languages.
    Refereed Serial

SZOCIALISTA NEVELES. see *LINGUISTICS*

T E S O L JOURNAL. (Teachers of English to Speakers of Other Languages) see *LINGUISTICS*

T E S O L MATTERS. (Teachers of English to Speakers of Other Languages) see *LINGUISTICS*

T E S O L QUARTERLY; a journal for teachers of English to speakers of other languages and of standard English as a second dialect. (Teachers of English to Speakers of Other Languages) see *LINGUISTICS*

T R A C E. (Teachers of Religion and Christian Ethics) see *RELIGIONS AND THEOLOGY*

613.7 370   JA
TAIIKU NO KAGAKU/JOURNAL OF HEALTH, PHYSICAL EDUCATION AND RECREATION. (Text in Japanese) 1951. m. 4800 Yen($16) Japanese Society of Physical Education - Nihon Taiiku Gakkai, Kyorin Shoin, 4-2-1 Yushima, Bunkyo-ku, Tokyo 113, Japan. Ed. Shinshiro Ebashi. circ. 4,000.
    Formerly: Journal of Health and Physical Education (ISSN 0022-1457)

375 614.7   US   ISSN 0894-833X
TALKING LEAVES. 1981. q. $25 (Canada Can.$35). Institute for Earth Education, Cedar Cove, Greenville, WV 24945-0115. TEL 304-832-6404. Ed. Laurie Farber. bk.rev.; illus. circ. 1,300. **Document type:** newsletter.
    Description: Directed to people interested in learning to live harmoniously with the earth.

TANZANIAN MATHEMATICAL BULLETIN. see *MATHEMATICS*

371.3   US   ISSN 1046-6193
TEACHER. 1989. 9/yr. $17.94 (foreign $44.31). Editorial Projects in Education, Inc., 4301 Connecticut Ave. N.W., Ste. 250, Washington, DC 20008. TEL 202-364-4114. (Subscr. to: Box 2090, Marion, OH 43306) Ed. Ronald Wolk. adv. circ. 100,000. (also avail. in microfiche)
●Also available online.
—BLDSC (8613.510000); UnCover; UMI. **CCC**.
    Description: Provides a national communications network for teachers, enabling them to be better teachers and effective leaders.

371.3   GH
THE TEACHER. 1931. q. free. Ghana National Association of Teachers, P.O. Box 209, Accra, Ghana. TEL 021-221515. adv.; bk.rev. circ. 20,000. **Document type:** academic/scholarly publication.
    Description: Informs members and the general public about developments in the field of education, pedagogy, and curriculum, as well as news about the association.

TEACHER EDUCATION AND SPECIAL EDUCATION. see *EDUCATION — Special Education And Rehabilitation*

371.3 375   US   ISSN 0737-5328
LB1705
TEACHER EDUCATION QUARTERLY. 1972. 4/yr. $40 to individuals; institutions $50. (California Council on the Education of Teachers) Caddo Gap Press, 3145 Geary Blvd., Ste. 275, San Francisco, CA 94118. TEL 415-750-9978. FAX 415-668-5450. Ed. Alan H. Jones. adv.; bk.rev. circ. 650. (also avail. in microform from EDR,UMI; reprint service avail. from UMI) **Indexed:** C.I.J.E., Cont.Pg.Educ., ERIC, Sp.Ed.Needs Abstr. **Document type:** academic/scholarly publication.
—BLDSC (8613.465000); UnCover; UMI.
    Formerly (until 1983): California Journal of Teacher Education (ISSN 0278-6052)
    Description: Features articles on all aspects of teacher education, with focus on research and practice with attention to major themes in the field.

TEACHER EDUCATOR. see *EDUCATION — Higher Education*

375   UK   ISSN 0951-7626
THE TEACHER TRAINER; a practical journal mainly for modern language teacher trainers. 3/yr. £15 to individuals; institutions £20. Pilgrims Language Courses, 8 Vernon Pl., Canterbury, Kent CT1 3HG, England. TEL 0227-762111. FAX 0227-459027. Ed. Tessa Woodward. **Document type:** academic/scholarly publication.
—BLDSC (8613.560000).

371.3   US   ISSN 0194-2859
TEACHER UPDATE; ideas for teachers. 1977-1989; resumed 1990. q. $25. N A R Publications, Box 233, Barryville, NY 12719. TEL 914-557-8713. FAX 914-557-6770. Ed. Nicholas A. Roes. bk.rev. circ. 7,500. **Document type:** newsletter.
    Description: Contains suggestions for art projects, unit ideas, math and science games, and other projects of interest to teachers of younger children.

371.3 375 800 700   US   ISSN 0146-3381
LB1576
TEACHERS & WRITERS MAGAZINE. 1967. 5/yr. $16. Teachers & Writers Collaborative, 5 Union Sq. W., New York, NY 10003-3306. TEL 212-691-6590. FAX 212-675-0171. Ed. Ron Padgett. bk.rev.; cum.index: 1967-1992. circ. 2,200. (also avail. in microform from UMI; reprint service avail. from UMI) **Indexed:** C.I.J.E.
    Former titles (until Fall 1976): T and W Newsletter; Teachers and Writers Collaborative Newsletter (ISSN 0496-9936)
    Description: Provides ideas and strategies for the teaching of writing. Includes practical classroom activities, new resources and articles that emphasize a how-to approach usable in the classroom, from first grade through college level.

375   US   ISSN 1068-378X
▼**TEACHING AND CHANGE**. 1993. q. $30 to individuals (foreign $36); institutions $75 (foreign $81). (N E A Professional Library) Corwin Press, Inc. (Subsidiary of: Sage Publications, Inc.), 2455 Teller Rd., Thousand Oaks, CA 91320. TEL 805-499-0721. FAX 805-499-0871. (And: Sage Publications, Ltd., 6 Bonhill St., London EC2A 4PU, England) Ed. Karen Zauber. adv.; B&W page $225. bk.rev.; index.
—BLDSC (8614.001000).
    Description: A forum for reporting the experiences of classroom teachers as they learn how schools must change to make good practice possible.

378 371.3   US   ISSN 0887-9486
LB1025.3
TEACHING AND LEARNING: THE JOURNAL OF NATURAL INQUIRY. 1915. 3/yr. $12 (foreign $22) (effective 1993-1994). University of North Dakota, Box 7189, Grand Forks, ND 58202-7189. TEL 701-777-3146. FAX 701-777-4393. Ed. Mary Laycock. bk.rev.; abstr.; bibl. circ. 2,600. (tabloid format) **Indexed:** C.I.J.E., Psychol.Abstr. **Document type:** academic/scholarly publication.
—BLDSC (8614.003400); Faxon.
    Former titles (until vol.10, no.16 1986): Journal of Teaching and Learning (ISSN 0360-5027); University of North Dakota. College of Education. Record (ISSN 0010-1052)
    Description: Qualitative research, naturalistic inquiry, and experiential thought.
    Refereed Serial

371.3   UK   ISSN 0742-051X
LB1025.2
TEACHING & TEACHER EDUCATION. 1985. 6/yr. £182($280) (effective 1994). Elsevier Science Ltd., Pergamon, P.O. Box 800, Kidlington, Oxford OX5 1DX, England. TEL 44-865-843000. FAX 44-865-843010. (Subscr. in U.S. and Canada to: Elsevier Science, 660 White Plains Rd., Tarrytown, NY 10591-5153. TEL 914-524-9200. FAX 914-333-2444) Ed. Michael J. Dunkin. abstr.; bibl. (also avail. in microfilm from UMI; back issues avail.) **Indexed:** Cont.Pg.Educ., Curr.Cont., Psychol.Abstr. **Document type:** academic/scholarly publication.
—BLDSC (8614.014000); Faxon; UnCover; SWETS; UMI. **CCC**.
    Description: Devoted to the description and analysis of cognitive, affective and behavioral components of teaching, teacher effectiveness, teacher education, teacher thinking, and social policies affecting teachers.
    Refereed Serial

TEACHING CHILDREN MATHEMATICS. see *MATHEMATICS*

TEACHING EARTH SCIENCES. see *EARTH SCIENCES — Geology*

613.7   US   ISSN 1045-4853
TEACHING ELEMENTARY PHYSICAL EDUCATION. Short title: T E P E. 1990. 6/yr. $18 to individuals (foreign $24); institutions $36 (foreign $42); students $12 (foreign $18). Human Kinetics Publishers, Inc., Box 5076, Champaign, IL 61825-5076. TEL 217-351-5076. FAX 217-351-2674. Ed. Christine Hopple. adv. contact: Michele Watson. bk.rev. circ. 4,000. (back issues avail.) **Indexed:** Phys.Ed.Ind. **Document type:** newsletter.
    Description: Provides elementary physical educators an exchange of information. Bridges the gap between theory and the demands of the real world in elementary physical education.
    Refereed Serial

420 375.4   UK   ISSN 0305-7755
TEACHING ENGLISH. 1967. 3/yr. £5.40 (foreign £10.80). MacDonald Publishers (Edinburgh), Edgefield Rd., Loanhead, Midlothian EH20 9SY, Scotland. TEL 031 440-0246. Ed. Tom Sommervielle. adv.; bk.rev.; index. circ. 3,000. (also avail. in microfilm from UMI; reprint service avail. from UMI) **Indexed:** Br.Educ.Ind., Cont.Pg.Educ., Lang.Teach.& Ling.Abstr.
    Formerly: Cite Newsletter.
    Description: Education teaching methods curriculum explained.

TEACHING ENGLISH FOR SPECIFIC PURPOSES JOURNAL. see *LINGUISTICS*

807   US   ISSN 0098-6291
PE1065
TEACHING ENGLISH IN THE TWO-YEAR COLLEGE. 1974. 4/yr. $15. National Council of Teachers of English, 1111 W. Kenyon Rd., Urbana, IL 61801-1096. TEL 217-328-3870. FAX 217-328-9645. Ed. Mark Reynolds. adv.; bk.rev.; index. circ. 3,400. (also avail. in microform from UMI; reprint service avail. from UMI) **Indexed:** C.I.J.E., Educ.Ind. **Document type:** academic/scholarly publication.
—BLDSC (8614.108000); UnCover; UMI.

TEACHING GEORGIA GOVERNMENT. see *PUBLIC ADMINISTRATION*

907 371   AT   ISSN 0040-0602
TEACHING HISTORY. 1960; N.S. 1967. 4/yr. Aus.$42. History Teachers' Association of New South Wales, P.O. Box 87, Rozelle, N.S.W. 2039, Australia. Ed.Bd. adv.; bk.rev.; bibl.; index. circ. 1,300. (also avail. in microform from UMI; reprint service avail. from UMI) —UMI.

907 371   UK   ISSN 0040-0610
D16.4.G7
TEACHING HISTORY. 1969. 4/yr. £40($85) (Historical Association) Basil Blackwell Ltd., 108 Cowley Rd., Oxford OX4 1JF, England. TEL 0865-791100. (Subscr. to: c/o Marston Book Services, P.O. Box 87, Oxford OX2 ODT, England) Eds. Hilary Cooper, Richard Brown. adv.; bk.rev.; bibl.; illus. circ. 3,200. (also avail. in microform from MIM,UMI; reprint service avail. from UMI) **Indexed:** Cont.Pg.Educ.
—BLDSC (8614.210000); Faxon; UnCover; SWETS; UMI.

EDUCATION — TEACHING METHODS AND CURRICULUM

900 371   US   ISSN 0730-1383
TEACHING HISTORY: A JOURNAL OF METHODS. 1976. s-a. $5 to individuals; institutions $10. Emporia State University, Division of Social Sciences, C B 4032, Emporia, KS 66801. TEL 316-341-5579. Ed. Stephen Kneeshaw. adv.; bk.rev. circ. 750. **Indexed:** Amer.Hist.& Life, Hist.Abstr.

372.2   US
TEACHING K-8; a magazine for teachers of preschool through grade eight. 1971. m. (8/yr.). $19.77. Early Years, Inc., 40 Richards Ave., Norwalk, CT 06854-2309. TEL 203-855-2650. FAX 203-855-2656. (Subscr. to: Box 54805, Boulder, CO 80323-4805) Ed. Allen A. Raymond. adv.; bk.rev. circ. 132,986. (also avail. in microform from UMI; reprint service avail. from UMI) **Indexed:** Educ.Ind., Except.Child.Educ.Abstr., Ind.Child.Mag., Rehabil.L t.
—BLDSC (8614.322000).
   Former titles: Early Years - K-8; Early Years (ISSN 0094-6532)
   Description: Articles cover innovation and techniques of individualized instruction.

TEACHING MATHEMATICS AND ITS APPLICATIONS. see MATHEMATICS

420.7   AT   ISSN 0049-3147
TEACHING OF ENGLISH. 1962. 2/yr. Aus.$8. English Teachers Association of N.S.W., Sydney Teachers' College, P.O. Box 63, Camperdown, N.S.W. 2050, Australia. (Subscr. to: Mrs. J. Moore, Business Sec., 14/44 Milton St., Ashfield, N.S.W. 2131, Australia) Ed. Dennis Robinson. adv.; bk.rev. circ. 1,500. **Indexed:** Aus.Educ.Ind.

371.3   UK   ISSN 0073-2605
TEACHING OF HISTORY. 1961. irreg. Historical Association, 59a Kennington Park Rd., London SE11 4JH, England. TEL 071-735-3901. (reprint service avail. from UMI) **Document type:** monographic series.

TEACHING OF PSYCHOLOGY. see PSYCHOLOGY

TEACHING PHILOSOPHY. see PHILOSOPHY

375 350   UK   ISSN 0144-7394
TEACHING PUBLIC ADMINISTRATION. 1979. 2/yr. £13.50($27) to individuals; institutions £20($40). Sheffield Business School, Policy Research Centre, 113 Arundel St., Sheffield S1 2NT, England. Ed. Lloyd Edmonds. bk.rev. circ. 250. **Document type:** academic/scholarly publication.
—BLDSC (8614.332000).
   Formerly: Public Administration Teacher.
   Description: Covers conceptions, approaches, and practices in public administration education, teaching and training.

TEACHING SOCIOLOGY. see SOCIOLOGY

371.3   CN   ISSN 0827-3049
TEACHING TODAY. 1983. 5/yr. Can.$15($17) (group rates avail.). Teaching Today, Inc., Box 68149, 70 Bonnie Doon Mall, Edmonton, AB T6C 4N6, Canada. TEL 403-462-0585. FAX 403-468-0099. Ed. Andrea Carter. adv.: B&W page Can.$900. bk.rev.; illus. circ. 10,000. (back issues avail.) **Document type:** trade publication.
   Description: Written for teachers by teachers. Provides practical information as well as a resource network for teachers.

373.246   US   ISSN 1062-9351
T61
TECH DIRECTIONS; the magazine linking education to industry. (Directory number avail.) 1941. m. (Aug.-May). $25. Prakken Publications, Inc., Box 8623, Ann Arbor, MI 48107. TEL 313-769-1211. FAX 313-769-8383. Ed. Paul Bamford. adv.; bk.rev.; charts; illus.; tr.lit.; index; circ. 44,000 (controlled). (also avail. in microform from UMI; back issues avail.; reprint service avail. from UMI,BLH) **Indexed:** Educ.Ind., Media Rev.Dig.
—BLDSC (8614.690000); Faxon; UnCover; UMI.
   Former titles (until 1992): School Shop - Tech Directions (ISSN 1050-3749); (until 1990): New School Shop, Tech Directions (ISSN 1049-8818); (until 1989): School Shop (ISSN 0036-682X)

371.3   US   ISSN 1057-2252
T11
TECHNICAL COMMUNICATION QUARTERLY. 1973. 4/yr. $30 to individuals (foreign $35); institutions $50 (effective 1994). (Association of Teachers of Technical Writing) University of Minnesota, Rhetoric Department, 202 Haecker Hall, St. Paul, MN 55108. TEL 612-624-9729. FAX 612-624-3167. Eds. Billie J. Wahlstrom, Mary M. Lay. adv.; bk.rev.; software rev.; bibl. circ. 1,000. (also avail. in microform from UMI; back issues avail.; reprint service avail.) **Indexed:** C.I.J.E., Educ.Ind.
—BLDSC (8655.150000); Faxon; UnCover; UMI.
   Formerly (until 1992): Technical Writing Teacher (ISSN 0888-4323)
   Description: Includes articles on research, theory, and teaching methods, approaches to teaching, and news items of interest.

374.013   US   ISSN 0146-0137
T61
TECHNICAL EDUCATION NEWS. 1941. 2/yr. free to qualified personnel. Glencoe - McGraw-Hill (Subsidiary of: McGraw-Hill, Inc.), 1221 Ave. of the Americas, New York, NY 10020. TEL 212-512-4736. FAX 212-512-6904. Ed. Wendy K. Spiegel. adv. circ. 47,000. (also avail. in microform from UMI; reprint service avail. from UMI) **Indexed:** C.I.J.E.

373.246   FR   ISSN 0768-9454
TECHNOLOGIE. 1950. 9/yr. 230 F. (foreign 275 F.). Centre National de Documentation Pedagogique, 29 rue d'Ulm, 75230 Paris Cedex 05, France. (Subscr. to: C.N.D.P., Abonnements, B.P. 21, Square St. Charles, 75012 Paris, France) Ed. Christian Patoz. bk.rev.; charts; illus.; mkt. circ. 5,000. (looseleaf format)
   Former titles: Techniques Industrielles (ISSN 0013-8576); Enseignement des Techniques Industrielles.

371.3   AT   ISSN 1034-6902
TECHNOLOGY DESIGN EDUCATION. 1960. q. Aus.$33($30) Institute of Industrial Arts, P.O. Box 180, Chartswood, N.S.W. 2067, Australia. Ed. John Barlow. adv.; bk.rev. circ. 1,200. (back issues avail.)
   Supersedes (in Mar. 1990): Industrial Arts Education (ISSN 0312-9152)

TECHNOS; quarterly for education and technology. see EDUCATION — Computer Applications

371.33 370   US   ISSN 8756-3894
LB1043   CODEN: TETREF
TECHTRENDS; for leaders in education and training. 1956. 6/yr. $36 (foreign $40). Association for Educational Communications and Technology, 1025 Vermont Ave., N.W., Ste. 820, Washington, DC 20005-3516. TEL 202-347-7834. FAX 202-347-7839. Ed. Nancy A. Klinck. adv.; bk.rev.; charts; illus.; index. circ. 9,000. (back issues avail.; reprint service avail. from UMI) **Indexed:** C.I.J.E., Curr.Cont., Educ.Ind., Educ.Tech.Abstr., Lang.& Lang.Behav.Abstr., LHTN, Media Rev.Dig., Microcomp.Ind., Sci.Abstr.
—BLDSC (8614.727000); Faxon; UnCover; SWETS; UMI.
   Former titles (until 1985): Instructional Innovator (ISSN 0196-6979); Audiovisual Instruction with Instructional Resources (ISSN 0191-3417); Audiovisual Instruction (ISSN 0004-7635)
   Description: Features authoritative, practical articles about technology and its integration into the learning environment.
   Refereed Serial

TEEN-SEARCH. see RELIGIONS AND THEOLOGY

371.33   FR   ISSN 1164-5679
▼**TELESCOPE;** l'hebdomadaire de television pour les enseignants, les parents et les educateurs. 1992. 30/yr. 250 F. (Ministere de l'Education) Centre National de Documentation Pedagogique, 29 rue d'Ulm, 75230 Paris Cedex 05, France. TEL 46-34-90-00. (Subscr. to: CNDP Abonnement, B.P. 7, 21 Square St. Charles, 75012 Paris, France) Ed. Tania Agopian.
   Description: Presents comments, reviews and analysis of a selection of educational programs on French TV, including CNDP "Parole d'Ecole" on FR3.

613.7 370   XR   ISSN 0040-2850
TELOVYCHOVNY PRACOVNIK. (Supplement avail.) 1957. s-m. 96 Kcs.($50.6) (Cesky Svaz Talesne Vychovy) Olympia a.s., Klimentska 1, 115 88 Prague 1, Czech Republic..(Dist. by: Artia, Ve Smeckach 30, 111 27 Prague 1, Czech Republic) Ed. Jaroslav Loncak. illus.

TEMA. see LINGUISTICS

TENNISPRO. see SPORTS AND GAMES — Ball Games

613.7 370   RU   ISSN 0040-3601
                               CODEN: TPFKAV
TEORIYA I PRAKTIKA FIZICHESKOI KUL'TURY. 1925. m. $39. Izdatel'stvo Fizkul'tura i Sport, Kalyaevskaya ul., 27, 101421 Moscow, Russia. TEL 095-258-2690. FAX 095-220-1217. (Dist. in U.S. by: Victor Kamkin Inc., 4956 Boiling Brook Pkwy., Rockville, MD 20852. TEL 301-881-5973. FAX 301-881-1637) Ed. A.V. Sedov. bk.rev.; bibl.; charts; illus.; stat.; index. circ. 16,200. **Indexed:** Biol.Abstr., Int.Aerosp.Abstr.
—BLDSC (0178.100000).

TESTS IN PRINT. see PSYCHOLOGY

375   US
TEXTBOOK LETTER. 1990. bi-m. $36. California Textbook League, Box 51, Sausalito, CA 94966. Ed. William J. Bennetta. bk.rev. circ. 1,000. **Document type:** newsletter.
   Description: Focuses on evaluative reviews of textbooks sold nationally for use in public schools.

THEORY AND RESEARCH IN SOCIAL EDUCATION. see SOCIAL SCIENCES: COMPREHENSIVE WORKS

THINGS OF SCIENCE. see SCIENCES: COMPREHENSIVE WORKS

THINKING; the journal of philosophy for children. see PHILOSOPHY

370   NE   ISSN 0049-3805
THOMAS;* maandblad voor lichamelijke opvoeding. 1960. m. fl.45 to individuals; students fl.40. Katholieke Vereniging van Leerkrachten in de Lichamelijke Opvoeding "Thomas van Aquino", Willem van Oranjelaan 33, 5211 CP den Bosch, Netherlands. Ed. H.M.P.G. van der Loo. adv.; bk.rev.; film rev.; illus. circ. 6,000.

371.3   NE   ISSN 0165-0947
TIJDSCHRIFT VOOR ORTHOPEDAGOGIEK. 1962. 11/yr. fl.125. (Vereniging Ter Bevordering van Ortho-Agogische Aktiviteiten) WoltersgroepGroningen b.v. (Subsidiary of: Wolters Kluwer N.V.), Postbus 58, 9700 MB Groningen, Netherlands. TEL 31-50-226922. FAX 31-50-264866. **Indexed:** Psychol.Abstr. **Document type:** academic/scholarly publication.
—SWETS.

TIRO. see LINGUISTICS

TITO; locosa, lucunda, Seria. see LINGUISTICS

TOHOKU - HOKURIKU SUGAKU KYOIKU KISOTEKI KENKYU HOKOKU. see MATHEMATICS

TRAINING; the magazine covering the human side of business. see BUSINESS AND ECONOMICS — Management

U S B L NYTT. (Ungdomen Selvbyggerlag) see BUILDING AND CONSTRUCTION

UCITELJ/TEACHER. see CHILDREN AND YOUTH — For

UCITELSKE VZDELANI. see HISTORY — History Of Europe

DER UEBUNGSLEITER; Arbeitshilfen fuer Uebungsleiter im Deutschen Sportbund. see SPORTS AND GAMES

UKRAINS'KA MOVA I LITERATURA V SHKOLI; metodychnyi zhurnal. see LINGUISTICS

UNITED NATIONS ECONOMIC AND SOCIAL COMMISSION FOR ASIA AND THE PACIFIC. SOCIAL DEVELOPMENT DIVISION. SOCIAL WORK EDUCATION AND DEVELOPMENT. see SOCIAL SERVICES AND WELFARE

EDUCATION — TEACHING METHODS AND CURRICULUM

371.3   FR   ISSN 0077-2712
UNIVERSITE DE NANCY II. CENTRE DE RECHERCHES ET D'APPLICATIONS PEDAGOGIQUES EN LANGUES. MELANGES. Spine title: Melanges CRAPEL. (Text in French; occasionally in English) 1970. a. 175 F. to individuals (foreign 215 F.); institutions 340 F.(foreign 395 F.) (for 3 years). Universite de Nancy II, Centre de Recherches et d'Applications Pedagogiques en Langues, B.P. 33-97, 54015 Nancy, France. TEL 83-98-34-12. FAX 83-98-04-99. Eds. F. Carton, P. Riley. circ. 1,000. **Indexed:** Lang.& Lang.Behav.Abstr. —BLDSC (5536.803900).

UNIVERSITY OF TECHNOLOGY, SYDNEY. FACULTY OF DESIGN ARCHITECTURE AND BUILDING HANDBOOK. see ARCHITECTURE

375   AT   ISSN 1036-0662
UNIVERSITY OF TECHNOLOGY, SYDNEY. FACULTY OF EDUCATION HANDBOOK. 1990. a. Aus.$5 (foreign Aus.$10). University of Technology, Sydney, P.O. Box 123, City Camp, Broadway, N.S.W. 2007, Australia. TEL 02-330-1990. FAX 02-330-1551. circ. 3,000.

UNIVERSITY OF TECHNOLOGY, SYDNEY. FACULTY OF ENGINEERING HANDBOOK. see ENGINEERING

UNIVERSITY OF TECHNOLOGY, SYDNEY. FACULTY OF MATHEMATICAL & COMPUTING SCIENCES HANDBOOK. see MATHEMATICS

UNIVERSITY OF TECHNOLOGY, SYDNEY. FACULTY OF NURSING HANDBOOK. see MEDICAL SCIENCES — Nurses And Nursing

UNIVERSITY OF TECHNOLOGY, SYDNEY. FACULTY OF SCIENCE HANDBOOK. see SCIENCES: COMPREHENSIVE WORKS

UNIVERSITY OF TECHNOLOGY, SYDNEY. FACULTY OF SOCIAL SCIENCES HANDBOOK. see SOCIAL SCIENCES: COMPREHENSIVE WORKS

375   AT   ISSN 1031-8720
UNIVERSITY OF TECHNOLOGY, SYDNEY. GENERAL INFORMATION OF POSTGRADUATE STUDIES. 1977. a. free. University of Technology, Sydney, P.O. Box 123, City Campus, Broadway, N.S.W. 2007, Australia. TEL 02-330-1990. FAX 02-330-1200. circ. 3,000.
Description: Information on courses, admission requirements, and application procedures.

375   AT
UNIVERSITY OF TECHNOLOGY, SYDNEY. UNDERGRADUATE STUDIES GUIDE. 1977. a. free. University of Technology, Sydney, P.O. Box 123, City Campus, Broadway, N.S.W. 2007, Australia. TEL 02-330-1558. FAX 02-330-1200. circ. 35,000.
Formerly (until 1991): University of Technology, Sydney. Undergraduate Studies (ISSN 1031-1866)
Description: Includes courses, admission requirements, and applications procedures.

UNIWERSYTET GDANSKI. WYDZIAL HUMANISTYCZNY. STUDIUM JEZYKOW OBCYCH. ZESZYTY NAUKOWE. see LINGUISTICS

UNIWERSYTET GDANSKI. WYDZIAL MATEMATYKI, FIZYKI I CHEMII. ZESZYTY NAUKOWE. PROBLEMY DYDAKTYKI FIZYKI. see PHYSICS

373.246 362.7   US   ISSN 1057-1043
UNSCHOOLERS NETWORK. 1977. irreg. (4-6/yr.) $12 (typically set in Jan.). 2 Smith St., Farmingdale, NJ 07727. TEL 908-938-2473. Ed. Nancy Plent. adv.; bk.rev. circ. 350. (looseleaf format)

UNTERRICHT BIOLOGIE; Beitraege zu seiner Gestaltung. see BIOLOGY

UPDATE (RESTON); applications of research in music education. see MUSIC

UPDATE ON LAW-RELATED EDUCATION. see LAW

373.246   AT
V S T A NEWS. 1980. w. Aus.$50. Victorian Secondary Teachers Association, 112 Trenerry Crescent, Abbotsford, Vic. 3067, Australia. TEL 03-417-2822. FAX 03-417-6198. Ed. Grant McMundo. adv.; circ. 14,000. (controlled). (also avail. in microform; back issues avail.)
Description: Covers events in the education field with emphasis on teacher unionism.

377.8   NE   ISSN 0166-6002
VERBUM; tijdschrift voor jongerkatechese. 1930. 8/yr. fl.45. Katholiek Pedagogisch Centrum, Postbus 482, 5201 AL Den Bosch, Netherlands. illus. circ. 1,000. **Indexed:** CERDIC.
—SWETS.

VERPLEEGKUNDE; nederlandse-vlaams tijdschrift voor verpleegkundigen. see MEDICAL SCIENCES — Nurses And Nursing

VIDEOS FOR BUSINESS AND TRAINING; professional and vocational videos and how to get them. see COMMUNICATIONS — Video

371.3   CN   ISSN 0707-2511
LA418.Q7
VIE PEDAGOGIQUE. 1979. 5/yr. free. Ministere de l'Education, 1035 rue de la Chevrotiere, 6e etage, Quebec, PQ G1R 5A5, Canada. bk.rev. circ. 65,000. **Indexed:** Pt.de Rep. (1979-). **Document type:** government publication.

778.5 371.33   UK   ISSN 0952-4444
VIEWFINDER. 1967. 3/yr. £9 (rest of Europe £13; elsewhere £15) (effective 1994). British Universities Film and Video Council, 55 Greek St., London W1V 5LR, England. TEL 071-734-3687. FAX 071-287-3914. Ed. Nick Wray. adv.; bk.rev.; abstr.; film rev.; cum. index. circ. 5,800. **Indexed:** A.I.C.P., Educ.Tech.Abstr., High.Educ.Curr.Aware.Bull., Int.Ind.Film Per., Media Rev.Dig. **Document type:** newsletter.
—BLDSC (9236.046070).
Former titles: B U F V C Newsletter (ISSN 0265-6817); B U F C Newsletter (ISSN 0308-5376)

VINCULUM. see MATHEMATICS

420 375.4   US   ISSN 0504-426X
PE65
VIRGINIA ENGLISH BULLETIN. 1951. s-a. $15. Virginia Association of Teachers of English, College of Education, Virginia Tech, Blacksburg, VA 24061-0313. TEL 804-231-9075. FAX 703-231-3717. (Subscr. to: Patricia P. Kelly, C & I, Virginia Tech., Blacksburgh, VA 24061-0313) Ed. Patricia P. Kelly. adv.; bk.rev.; bibl. circ. 2,500. **Document type:** academic/scholarly publication.

371.33   FI   ISSN 0780-4199
VISIO. 1971. 8/yr. FIM 364. Tapiolan Viestintasuunnittelu Oy, P.O. Box 84, SF-02101 Espoo, Finland. TEL 358-0-455-5088. FAX 358-0-455-4084. Ed. Timo M. Rinta. adv.; bk.rev. circ. 9,000. **Document type:** trade publication.
Formerly: Kuva ja Aani (ISSN 0357-2943)
Description: For A-V, video and new media professionals and users in Finland.

371.33   US   ISSN 0736-0770
N81
VISUAL ARTS RESEARCH; educational, historical, philosophical and psychological perspectives. 1973. s-a. $16 to individuals (foreign $43); institutions $27 (foreign $62). University of Illinois at Urbana-Champaign, School of Art and Design, 143 Art and Design Bldg., 408 E. Peabody Dr., Champaign, IL 61802. circ. 400. **Indexed:** Psychol.Abstr.
—BLDSC (9241.230000); Faxon; UnCover; SWETS.
Formerly: Review of Research in Visual Arts Education.

371.3   US
VISUAL LITERACY NEWSLETTER. 1971. bi-m. $25. International Visual Literacy Association (Tempe), c/o Marina McIsaac, Arizona State University, Tempe, AZ 85287. bk.rev. circ. 250.

VOCATIONAL TRAINING. see OCCUPATIONS AND CAREERS

VOCATIONAL TRAINING NEWS; the independent weekly report on employment, training & vocational education. see OCCUPATIONS AND CAREERS

370   RU   ISSN 0042-8957
VOSPITANIE SHKOL'NIKOV. bi-m. 7.20 Rub. Pavla Korchagena 7, Moscow, Russia.

371.33   CC   ISSN 1001-5795
WAIYU DIANHUA JIAOXUE/AUDIO-VISUAL TEACHING OF FOREIGN LANGUAGES. (Text in Chinese, summaries in English) 1981. q. Y0.90. Shanghai Waiyu Dianhua Jiaoxue Guan - Shanghai Foreign Language Audiovisual Publishing House, 550 Dalian Xilu, Shanghai 200083, People's Republic of China. TEL 86-21-5420787. FAX 86-21-5427900. (Subscr. to: China International Book Trading Corporation, P.O. Box 399, Beijing, P.R. China.) Eds. Sun Congyang, Shi Xin. circ. 50,005. **Document type:** academic/scholarly publication.

WAIYU JIAOXUE YU YANJIU/FOREIGN LANGUAGE TEACHING & RESEARCH. see LINGUISTICS

WEEKLY READER, EDITION 1. see CHILDREN AND YOUTH — For

WEEKLY READER, EDITION 2. see CHILDREN AND YOUTH — For

WEEKLY READER, EDITION 3. see CHILDREN AND YOUTH — For

WEEKLY READER, EDITION 4. see CHILDREN AND YOUTH — For

WEEKLY READER, EDITION 5. see CHILDREN AND YOUTH — For

WEEKLY READER, PRE-K EDITION. see CHILDREN AND YOUTH — For

WEEKLY READER, SENIOR EDITION. see CHILDREN AND YOUTH — For

WESSEX STUDIES IN SPECIAL EDUCATION. see EDUCATION — Special Education And Rehabilitation

371.3   US   ISSN 0083-9116
L11
WHAT RESEARCH SAYS TO THE TEACHER SERIES. 1953. irreg. price varies. National Education Association of the United States, 1201 16th St., N.W., Washington, DC 20036. TEL 800-229-4200. (Subscr. to: NEA Professional Library, Box 509, West Haven, CT 06515)

650 330   GW
WIRTSCHAFT UND GESELLSCHAFT IM BERUF. 1976. bi-m. DM.39.80. Verlag Dr. Max Gehlen GmbH und Co. KG, Daimlerstr. 12, 61352 Bad Homburg, Germany. TEL 06272-1804-0. FAX 06272-23055. **Document type:** academic/scholarly publication.
—CCC.
Formerly: Wirtschaft und Gesellschaft im Unterricht (ISSN 0342-6017)

371.3 800   US   ISSN 0512-1213
WISCONSIN ENGLISH JOURNAL. 1959. 3/yr. $10. Wisconsin Council of Teachers of English, c/o Mary Ellen Alea, Department of English, University of Wisconsin, Eau Claire, WI 54702. TEL 715-836-5848. FAX 715-8362026. adv.; bk.rev.; cum.index. circ. 1,200. (back issues avail.) **Document type:** academic/scholarly publication.

WISCONSIN SCHOOL MUSICIAN. see MUSIC

WORLD EAGLE; the monthly social studies resource. see SOCIAL SCIENCES: COMPREHENSIVE WORKS

375   US   ISSN 1040-3779
WRITING LAB NEWSLETTER. 1976. 10/yr. $15. Purdue University, Department of English, 1356 Heavelon, West Lafayette, IN 47907-1356. TEL 317-494-3723. FAX 317-494-3780. Ed. Muriel Harris. bk.rev. circ. 800. (back issues avail.) **Document type:** academic/scholarly publication, newsletter.

WULI JIAOXUE/PHYSICS TEACHING. see PHYSICS

613.7   PL   ISSN 0510-9868
WYCHOWANIE FIZYCZNE I HIGIENA SZKOLNA.* 1953. 10/yr. $28. (Ministerstwo Edukacji Narodowej) Spodzielcza Agencja Reklamowa "SPAR", c/o Ars Polona-Ruch, Krakowskie Przedmiescie 7, Warsaw, Poland.

ELECTRICAL ENERGY

613.7   PL   ISSN 0043-9630
WYCHOWANIE FIZYCZNE I SPORT. STUDIA I MATERIALY. (Text in Polish; summaries in English) 1957. q. $32. (Polska Akademia Nauk, Komitet Nauk o Kulturze Fizycznej) Wydawnictwo Naukowe P W N, Miodowa 10, 00-251 Warsaw, Poland. (Co-sponsor: Akademia Wychowania Fizycznego w Warszawie) Ed. K. Hadzelek. charts; illus.; index. circ. 1,950.
—BLDSC (9365.410000).

WYCHOWANIE FIZYCZNE I ZDROWOTNE. see *PHYSICAL FITNESS AND HYGIENE*

WYZSZA SZKOLA PEDAGOGICZNA IM. KOMISJI EDUKACJI NARODOWEJ W KRAKOWIE. ROCZNI NAUKOWO-DYDAKTYCZNY. PRACE EKONOMICZNO-SPOLECZNE. see *BUSINESS AND ECONOMICS*

WYZSZA SZKOLA PEDAGOGICZNA IM. KOMISJI EDUKACJI NARODOWEJ W KRAKOWIE. ROCZNIK NAUKOWO-DYDAKTYCZNY. PRACE FILOZOFICZNE. see *PHILOSOPHY*

WYZSZA SZKOLA PEDAGOGICZNA IM. KOMISJI EDUKACJI NARODOWEJ W KRAKOWIE. ROCZNIK NAUKOWO-DYDAKTYCZNY. PRACE FIZYCZNE. see *PHILOSOPHY*

WYZSZA SZKOLA PEDAGOGICZNA IM. KOMISJI EDUKACJI NARODOWEJ W KRAKOWIE. ROCZNIK NUKOWO-DYDAKTYCZNY. PRACE GEOGRAFICZNE. see *GEOGRAPHY*

WYZSZA SZKOLA PEDAGOGICZNA IM. KOMISJI EDUKACJI NARODOWEJ W KRAKOWIE. ROCZNIK NAUKOWO-DYDAKTYCZNY. PRACE HISTORYCZNE. see *HISTORY*

WYZSZA SZKOLA PEDAGOGICZNA IM. KOMISJI EDUKACJI NARODOWEJ W KRAKOWIE. ROCZNIK NAUKOWO-DYDAKTYCZNY. PRACE HISTORYCZNOLITERACKIE. see *LITERATURE*

WYZSZA SZKOLA PEDAGOGICZNA IM. KOMISJI EDUKACJI NARODOWEJ W KRAKOWIE. ROCZNIK NAUKOWO-DYDAKTYCZNY. PRACE MATEMATYCZNE. see *MATHEMATICS*

WYZSZA SZKOLA PEDAGOGICZNA IM. KOMISJI EDUKACJI NARODOWEJ W KRAKOWIE. ROCZNIK NAUKOWO-DYDAKTYCZNY. PRACE PSYCHOLOGICZNE. see *PSYCHOLOGY*

WYZSZA SZKOLA PEDAGOGICZNA IM. KOMISJI EDUKACJI NARODOWEJ W KRAKOWIE. ROCZNIK NAUKOWO-DYDAKTYCZNY. PRACE ROMANISTYCZNE. see *LINGUISTICS*

WYZSZA SZKOLA PEDAGOGICZNA IM. KOMISJI EDUKACJI NARODOWEJ W KRAKOWIE. ROCZNIK NAUKOWE-DYDAKTYCZNY. PRACE TECHNICZNE. see *TECHNOLOGY: COMPREHENSIVE WORKS*

WYZSZA SZKOLA PEDAGOGICZNA IM. KOMISJI EDUKACJI NARODOWEJ W KRAKOWIE. ROCZNIK NAUKOWO-DYDAKTYCZNY. PRACE Z DYDAKTYKI BIOLOGII. see *BIOLOGY*

WYZSZA SZKOLA PEDAGOGICZNA IM. KOMISJI EDUKACJI NARODOWEJ W KRAKOWIE. ROCZNIK NAUKOWO-DYDAKTYCZNY. PRACE Z DYDAKTYKI LITERATURY I JEZYKA POLSKIEGO. see *LINGUISTICS*

WYZSZA SZKOLA PEDAGOGICZNA IM. KOMISJI EDUKACJI NARODOWEJ W KRAKOWIE. ROCZNIK NAUKOWO-DYDAKTYCZNY. PRACE Z DYDAKTYKI MATEMATYKI. see *MATHEMATICS*

WYZSZA SZKOLA PEDAGOGICZNA IM. KOMISJI EDUKACJI NARODOWEJ W KRAKOWIE. ROCZNIK NAUKOWO-DYDAKTYCZNY. PRACE Z RACHUNKU PRAWDOPODOBIENSTWA I JEGO DYDAKTYKI. see *MATHEMATICS*

WYZSZA SZKOLA PEDAGOGICZNA IM. KOMISJI EDUKACJI NARODOWEJ W KRAKOWIE. ROCZNIK NAUKOWO-DYDAKTYCZNY. PRACE Z WYCHOWANIA PLASTYCZNEGO. see *ART*

371.3   PL   ISSN 0324-8968
WYZSZA SZKOLA PEDAGOGICZNA, OPOLE. ZESZYTY NAUKOWE. SERIA A. DYDAKTYKA. 1969. irreg., vol.14, 1984. price varies; avail. on exchange basis. Wyzsza Szkola Pedagogiczna, Opole, Oleska 48, 45-951 Opole, Poland. TEL 48 77 383-87. (Dist. by: Ars Polona-Ruch, Krakowskie Przedmiescie 7, Warsaw, Poland) Ed. Adam Suchonski. **Document type:** academic/scholarly publication.

371.3   PL   ISSN 0474-2982
WYZSZA SZKOLA PEDAGOGICZNA, OPOLE. ZESZYTY NAUKOWE. SERIA A. PEDAGOGIKA. (Text in Polish; summaries in English) 1956. irreg., vol.29, 1993. price varies; avail. on exchange basis. Wyzsza Szkola Pedagogiczna, Opole, Oleska 48, 45-951 Opole, Poland. TEL 48-77-383-87. (Dist. by: Ars Polona-Ruch, Krakowskie Przedmiescie 7, Warsaw, Poland) Eds. Zygmunt Lomny, Tadeusz Gospodarek. **Document type:** academic/scholarly publication.
—BLDSC (9512.478494).

XIAOXUE SHUXUE JIAOSHI/ARITHMETIC TEACHER. see *MATHEMATICS*

XIAOXUE YUWEN JIAOSHI/ELEMENTARY SCHOOL CHINESE LANGUAGE TEACHER. see *LINGUISTICS*

371.3 410   CC   ISSN 1004-6720
XIAOXUE YUWEN JIAOXUE/ELEMENTARY SCHOOL CHINESE TEACHING. (Text in Chinese) 1980. m. Y1.50 per no. Zhongguo Jiaoyu Xuehui, Quanguo Xiaoxue Yuwen Jiaoxue Yanjiuhui - Chinese Education Society, National Association of Elementary Chinese Teaching, 8, Jiefang Lu, Dongtou Daoxiang, Taiyuan, Shanxi 030009, People's Republic of China. TEL 382166. Ed. Zhang Kuanming. circ. 100,000 (paid). **Document type:** academic/scholarly publication.

XIUCI XUEXI/RHETORIC STUDY. see *LITERATURE*

XUE HANYU/LEARNING CHINESE. see *LINGUISTICS*

371.3   US   ISSN 0044-0728
LB1140.A1   CODEN: YNGCAJ
YOUNG CHILDREN. 1944. 6/yr. $30 to non-members. National Association for the Education of Young Children, 1509 16th St., N.W., Washington, DC 20036-1426. TEL 202-232-8777. FAX 202-328-1846. Ed. Polly Greenberg. adv.; bk.rev.; bibl.; charts; illus.; index. circ. 83,000. (also avail. in microform from KTO,UMI; reprint service avail. from UMI) **Indexed:** Biog.Ind., C.I.J.E., Child Devel.Abstr., Cont.Pg.Educ., Curr.Cont., DSH Abstr., Educ.Ind., ERIC, Except.Child.Educ.Abstr., Lang.& Lang.Behav.Abstr., Psychol.Abstr., SSCI.
—BLDSC (9421.410000); Faxon; UnCover; SWETS; UMI.
Description: Directed to early childhood educators who use research and theory for classroom practice.

YOUTH THEATRE JOURNAL. see *THEATER*

YUWEN JIAOXUE TONGXUN/BULLETIN OF CHINESE LANGUAGE TEACHING. see *LINGUISTICS*

YUYAN JIAOXUE YU YANJIU/LANGUAGE TEACHING & STUDIES. see *LINGUISTICS*

371.3   GW   ISSN 0172-2875
ZEITSCHRIFT FUER BERUFS- UND WIRTSCHAFTSPAEDAGOGIK. 1892. 6/yr. DM.124 (supplements priced individually). Franz Steiner Verlag Stuttgart GmbH, Birkenwaldstr. 44, 70191 Stuttgart, Germany. TEL 0711-2582-0. FAX 0711-2582290. TELEX 723636-DAZ-D. (Subscr. to: Postfach 101061, 70009 Stuttgart, Germany) Ed. Gerhard Hauptmeier. adv.; bk.rev.; index. circ. 2,500. (back issues avail.) **Document type:** academic/scholarly publication.
—CCC.
Formerly: Deutsche Berufs- und Fachschule (ISSN 0011-9946).

371.3   GW   ISSN 0174-0830
ZEITSCHRIFT FUER BERUFS- UND WIRTSCHAFTSPAEDAGOGIK. BEIHEFTE. irreg., vol.11, 1993. price varies. Franz Steiner Verlag Wiesbaden GmbH, Birkenwaldstr. 44, 70191 Stuttgart, Germany. TEL 0711-2582-0. FAX 0711-2582290. TELEX 723636-DAZ-D. (Subscr. to: Postfach 101061, 70009 Stuttgart, Germany) Ed.Bd. **Document type:** monographic series.

ZEITSCHRIFT FUER DIDAKTIK DER PHILOSOPHIE. see *PHILOSOPHY*

ZEITSCHRIFT FUER MUSIKPAEDAGOGIK. see *MUSIC*

ZENTRALBLATT FUER DIDAKTIK DER MATHEMATIK. see *MATHEMATICS*

ZHONGXUE YUWEN JIAOXUE/LANGUAGE TEACHING IN MIDDLE SCHOOL. see *LINGUISTICS*

373 500   CC   ISSN 1001-6953
ZHONGXUESHENG SHU-LI-HUA (GAOZHONG BAN). (Text in Chinese) m. $24.20. Henan Jiaoyu She, 11, Shunhe Lu, Zhengzhou, Henan 450004, People's Republic of China. TEL 29013. (Dist. in US by: China Books & Periodicals, Inc., 2929 24th St., San Francisco, CA 94110. TEL 415-282-2994) Ed. Yang Zhongxing.
Description: Covers mathematics, physics, and chemistry for high school students.

ZHONGXUESHENG WULI YUANDI/PHYSICS FOR MIDDLE SCHOOL STUDENTS. see *PHYSICS*

ZI XUE/SELF-TEACHING. see *EDUCATION — Adult Education*

375   GW   ISSN 0939-8376
5 - 10 SCHULMAGAZIN. 1976. m. DM.121.20. Ehrenwirth Verlag GmbH, Schwanthalerstr. 91, 80336 Munich, Germany. TEL 089-544335-0. FAX 089-534739. (Co-publisher: R. Oldenbourg Verlag) Ed. Siegfried Baumann. **Document type:** academic/scholarly publication.
—CCC.
Formerly (until 1991): Lehrerjournal Hauptschulmagazin (ISSN 0930-6951); Supersedes in part (in 1986): Lehrer Journal (ISSN 0722-8600); Which was formed by the merger of: Grundschulmagazin (ISSN 0724-3499); Which was formerly: Ehrenwirth Grundschulmagazin (ISSN 0340-5842); Hauptschulmagazin (ISSN 0724-3502); Which was formerly: Ehrenwirth Hauptschulmagazin (ISSN 0340-580X).

ELECTRICAL ENERGY

see *Energy–Electrical Energy*

ELECTRICAL ENGINEERING

see *Engineering–Electrical Engineering*

ELECTRICITY

see *Physics–Electricity*

ELECTROCHEMISTRY

see *Chemistry–Electrochemistry*

ELECTRONIC DATA PROCESSING

see *Computers–Electronic Data Processing*

ELECTRONICS

621.381   US   ISSN 1065-0555
TK7874
ADVANCED PACKAGING. 1984. 6/yr. $45 (Canada $60; elsewhere $110). I H S Publishing Group, Inc., Box 159, 17730 W. Peterson Rd., Libertyville, IL 60048-0159. TEL 708-362-8711. FAX 708-362-3484. Ed. Thomas A. Williams. adv. circ. 26,500.
—EI; Faxon. **CCC.**
Supersedes (in 1992): Hybrid Circuit Technology (ISSN 0747-1599)
Description: Reports on the design, assembly, and testing of electronic components such as multi-chip module, hybrid circuits, and other advanced electronic devices.

537 SW ISSN 0280-8765
ALLT OM ELEKTRONIK; Sveriges stoersta specialtidning foer tillaempad elektronik. 1982. 11/yr. SEK 285 (effective 1991). Electronic Press, P.O. Box 5505, S-141 05 Huddinge, Sweden.

AMATERSKE RADIO. see *COMMUNICATIONS — Radio*

AMATERSKE RADIO PRO KONSTRUKTERY. see *COMMUNICATIONS — Radio*

ANTENNA - ELETRONICA POPULAR. see *COMMUNICATIONS — Television And Cable*

643 658.8 UK
AUDIO: THE INTERNATIONAL MARKET. a. £1375($2750) Euromonitor, 87-88 Turnmill St., London EC1M 5QU, England. TEL 071-251-8024. FAX 071-608-3149. (Addr. in N. America: Euromonitor International, 111 W. Washington St., Ste. 290, Chicago, IL 60602. TEL 312-541-8024. FAX 312-541-1567) (looseleaf format) **Document type**: trade publication.
●Also available online. Vendor(s): Data-Star, DIALOG Information Services, Inc.
Description: Analyzes the market for high-fidelity audio equipment in France, Germany, Italy, Spain, the U.K., the U.S., and Japan.

AUDIO, VIDEO. see *SOUND RECORDING AND REPRODUCTION*

643.3 US ISSN 1041-5378
TK7881.8
AUDIO - VIDEO INTERIORS. 1989. m. $23.95. A V C O M Publishing, 21700 Oxnard St., Ste. 1600, Woodland Hills, CA 91367. TEL 818-593-3900. FAX 818-593-2274. Ed. Maureen Jenson. circ. 57,285 (paid). **Document type**: consumer publication.
Description: For consumers who want to know how audio and video products best integrate with fine interior design and decor.

643 658 382 US ISSN 0362-1162
TK7800
AUDIOVIDEO INTERNATIONAL. 1973. m. $30. Dempa Publications, Inc., 275 Madison Ave., 32nd Fl., New York, NY 10016-1101. TEL 212-682-3755. FAX 212-682-2730. Ed. Nancy Klosek. adv.; illus. circ. 40,000. (back issues avail.) **Indexed**: PROMT.
Document type: trade publication.
Formerly: Audio Video News.
Description: Articles for retailers and distributors of consumer electronics products.

AUDIOVISUELLA MEDIER. see *SOUND RECORDING AND REPRODUCTION*

643 AT ISSN 1035-9346
AUSTRALIA. BUREAU OF STATISTICS. MANUFACTURING PRODUCTION, AUSTRALIA: HOUSEHOLD APPLIANCES AND ELECTRICAL EQUIPMENT. 1977. m. Aus.$8 per no. Australian Bureau of Statistics, P.O. Box 10, Belconnen, A.C.T. 2616, Australia. **Document type**: government publication.
Formerly: Australia. Bureau of Statistics. Production of Household Appliances and Electrical Equipment, Australia.
Description: Provides production statistics for water heaters, space heaters, solar collectors, electrical appliances, air conditioners, electric motors and lawn mowers.

643 AT ISSN 0159-2947
AUSTRALIAN ELECTRONICS DIRECTORY. a. Aus.$95. Technical Indexes Pty. Ltd., 4 Kembla St., East Cheltenham, Vic. 3192, Australia. FAX 03-584-6871. TELEX 34007. (Subscr. to: Technical Indexes Pty. Ltd., P.O. Box 98, Cheltenham, Vic. 3192, Australia) Ed. Ross MacKay. adv. circ. 5,000.

621.381 AT ISSN 0004-9042
TK7800 CODEN: AUEEB5
AUSTRALIAN ELECTRONICS ENGINEERING. 1967. m. Aus.$72. Thomson Business Publishing, 47 Chippen St., Chippendale, N.S.W. 2008, Australia. TEL 02-699-2411. FAX 02-698-3920. Ed. Jennifer Liston. adv.; bk.rev.; charts; illus.; stat.; index. circ. 10,158. **Indexed**: Aus.Rd.Ind., Sci.Abstr.
—BLDSC (1798.850000); EI.

621.38 IT
AUTOMAZIONE ENERGIA INFORMAZIONE; rivista generale di automazione, energia, informazione. Short title: A E I. 1914. m. L.120000($90) Associazione Elettrotecnica ed Elettronica Italiana, Viale Monza 259, 20126 Milan, Italy. TEL 02-257791. FAX 02-2570512. Ed. Andrea Silvestri. adv.; abstr.; bibl.; charts; illus.; index. circ. 11,600. **Indexed**: C.I.S. Abstr., Chem.Abstr., Curr.Cont., Eng.Ind., Excerp.Med., Risk Abstr., Sci.Abstr.
—EI. CCC.
Formerly: Elettrotecnica (ISSN 0013-6131)
Description: Contains articles on various topics of electrotechnics and electronics.

643 AU
A3 VOLT. 8/yr. S.480 (foreign S.680). A3 Zeitschriftenverlags GmbH, Hagenauertalstr. 40, A-2372 Giesshuebl, Austria. TEL 02236-42528. FAX 02236-26311. circ. 18,000. **Document type**: bulletin.

537.5 CC ISSN 0253-4177
QC610.9 CODEN: PTTPDZ
BANDAOTI XUEBAO. English translation: Chinese Journal of Semiconductors (US ISSN 0899-9988) (Text in Chinese; summaries in English) 1980. m. $164.80. (Chinese Academy of Sciences, Institute of Semiconductors) Science Press, Marketing and Sales Department, 16 Donghuangchenggen Beijie, Beijing 100707, People's Republic of China. TEL 4010642. FAX 4012180. TELEX 210247-SPBJ-CN. adv. circ. 11,000. **Indexed**: Chem.Abstr., Sci.Abstr.
—BLDSC (3180.676400); CASDDS.
Description: Covers semiconductor research in China, including semiconductor materials, integrated circuits, and devices. Includes papers, research notes, and letters.
Refereed Serial

BERNARDS AND BABANI PRESS RADIO & ELECTRONICS & COMPUTER BOOKS. see *COMMUNICATIONS — Radio*

643 IT
BIANCO E BRUNO. 12/yr. E.T.A. Edizioni Tecniche Associate, Via Michelino 65, 40127 Bologna, Italy. TEL 51-50-25-39. FAX 51-50-84-14. Ed. Fausto Zaccarini. circ. 12,000.

BILTEN DOKUMENTACIJE. ELEKTROTEHNIKA I ELEKTRONIKA. PROIZVODNJA ELEKTRICNIH MASINA I APARATA. PTT USLUGE/BULLETIN OF DOCUMENTATION. ELECTROTECHNICS AND ELECTRONICS. MANUFACTURE OF ELECTRICAL MACHINERY AND APPARATUS. POSTAL SERVICES. see *ENGINEERING — Electrical Engineering*

621.381 US
BIPOLAR CIRCUITS AND TECHNOLOGY MEETING. PROCEEDINGS. Short title: B C T M. 1986. a. price varies. (I E E E, Electron Devices Society) Institute of Electrical and Electronics Engineers, Inc., 345 E. 47th St., New York, NY 10017-2394. TEL 212-705-7900. FAX 212-705-7682. (Subscr. to: 445 Hoes Ln., Box 1331, Piscataway, NJ 08855-1331) **Indexed**: Sci.Abstr. **Document type**: proceedings.
Formerly (until 1987): I E E E Bipolar Circuits and Technology Meeting.
Description: Focuses on the needs and interests of the bipolar community. Covers the design, performance, fabrication, testing, and application of bipolar and bipolar-FET ICs and discrete devices.

BUSINESS, VIDEO & ELECTRONICS. see *COMMUNICATIONS — Video*

621.381 JA ISSN 0285-418X
C E C INFORMATION/C E C JOHO. (Text in Japanese) 1964. a. Chubu Electronics Center - Chubu Denshi Kogyo Gijutsu Senta, 9959, Okaya-shi, Nagano-ken 394, Japan.

643 UK
C E M A CONSUMER ELECTRONICS. 1986. m. £2000. (Cores European Market Analysis) Portman Communications Ltd., 2 Dunollie Pl., London NW5 2XR, England. TEL 071-837-0815. FAX 071-278-9917. Ed. Philip Gallagher. circ. 550. **Document type**: newsletter.

621.381 US
C E S TRADE NEWS DAILY. (Consumer Electronics Shows) 1982. 2/yr. Argus Inc., 6151 Powers Ferry Rd., N.W., Atlanta, GA 30339-2941. TEL 404-955-2500. FAX 404-955-0400. Ed. Ben Johnson. (tabloid format) **Document type**: trade publication.

621.381 CU
C I D: ELECTRONICA Y PROCESAMIENTO DE DATOS. q. $22 in N. America; S. America $24; Europe $28. (Instituto Nacional de Sistemas Automatizados y Tecnicas de Computacion) Ediciones Cubanas, Obispo No. 527, Apdo. 605, Havana, Cuba. (Alt. addr.: 58-B No. 3118, Apdo. 3, Playa, Havana, Cuba)

643 SZ
C T BUSINESS.* 11/yr. Graf und Neuhaus AG, Moehrlistr. 69, CH-8033 Zurich, Switzerland. Ed. Martin Freund. circ. 3,500.

643 621.388 UK ISSN 0954-2108
CAMCORDER USER. 1988. m. £24. W V Publications & Exhibitions Ltd., 57-59 Rochester Pl., London NW1 9JU, England. TEL 071-485-0011. FAX 071-284-2145. (Subscr. to: Select Subscriptions, Northbridge Rd., Berkhamstead, Herts HP4 1ST, England) Ed. Robert Uhlig. circ. 31,868. **Document type**: consumer publication.

621.381 JA
CASIO DISCLOSURE JOURNAL. (Text in Japanese) 1984. irreg. Tesuko K.K., 2-2, Toranomon 3-chome, Minato-ku, Tokyo 105, Japan.

CHILTON MOTOR - AGE PROFESSIONAL ELECTRONIC ENGINE CONTROLS MANUAL. ASIAN. see *TRANSPORTATION — Automobiles*

621.381 US ISSN 0193-614X
CHILTON'S E C N - ELECTRONIC COMPONENT NEWS. 1957. m. $60 (foreign $75; free to qualified personnel). Chilton Co. (Subsidiary of: Capital Cities), Chilton Way, Radnor, PA 19089. TEL 215-964-4343. (Subscr. to: Box 2010, Radnor, PA 19089) Ed. Hy Natkin. adv.; illus.; tr.lit. circ. 125,000. (tabloid format; reprint service avail. from UMI)
—UMI. CCC.
Formerly: Electronic Component News.
Description: Provides new product information to design engineers and engineering management.

643 621.9 CH
CHINA, REPUBLIC. MACHINERY AND ELECTRICAL APPARATUS INDUSTRY YEARBOOK/CHUNG HUA MIN KUO CHI CH'I YU TIEN KUNG CH'I TS'AI NIEN CHIEN. (Text in Chinese and English) a. World Enterprise, 247 San Min Rd., Taichung, Taiwan, Republic of China.

621.381 US
CIRCUITREE MAGAZINE.* 1987. m. $48 (foreign $128). 700 Gale Dr., Ste. 200, Campbell, CA 95008-0938. TEL 408-986-1292. FAX 408-986-1873. Ed. Raymond Rasmussen. adv.; bk.rev. circ. 8,000. (back issues avail.) **Document type**: trade publication.
Formerly: Circuitree International.
Description: For owners and operators of printed circuit board facilities worldwide.

621.381 US ISSN 1054-0407
TK7868.P7 CODEN: CIATE5
CIRCUITS ASSEMBLY; the magazine for surface-mount and board-level assembly. 1961. m. $80 (free to qualified personnel). Miller Freeman, Inc. (Subsidiary of: United Newspapers), 600 Harrison St., San Francisco, CA 94107. TEL 415-905-2200. FAX 415-905-2232. TELEX 278273. Ed. Ron Daniels. adv.; index; circ. 40,000 (controlled). (also avail. in microform from UMI) **Indexed**: Excerp.Med., Int.Aerosp.Abstr., ISMEC, Sci.Abstr.
—BLDSC (3198.839350); Faxon; SWETS; UMI. CCC.
Formed by the merger of (1964-1990): Circuits Manufacturing (ISSN 0009-7306); (1987-1990): Printed Circuit Assembly (ISSN 0896-8489);
Formerly: Electronic Production.
Description: Addresses innovations in the electronics industry

ELECTRONICS

621.381 — **FR**
CIRCUITS F A B GALVANO ORGANO. 26/yr. S.A.R.L. Galvano, 22-24 rue du President Wilson, 92532 Levallois-Perret Cedex, France. TEL 47-39-34-81. FAX 47-39-34-79. Ed. M. Gaultier.
Description: Covers the study and review of printed circuits.

643 658.3 — **UK**
CLEANING APPLIANCES: THE INTERNATIONAL MARKET. a. £1375($2750) Euromonitor, 87-88 Turnmill St., London EC1M 5QU, England. TEL 071-251-8024. FAX 071-608-3149. (Addr. in N. America: Euromonitor International, 111 W. Washington St., Ste. 920, Chicago, IL 60602. TEL 312-541-8024. FAX 312-541-1567) (looseleaf format) Document type: trade publication.
●Also available online. Vendor(s): Data-Star, DIALOG Information Services, Inc.
Description: Analyzes the household cleaning appliances market for France, Germany, Italy, Spain, the U.K., the U.S., and Japan.

643 — **US**
COMPANY-STATS SEMICONDUCTOR PROFILE SERVICE. (In 2 vols.) 4/yr. $1395 (foreign $1595). H T E Research, Inc., 400 Oyster Point Blvd., Ste. 220, S. San Francisco, CA 94080. TEL 415-871-4377. FAX 415-871-0513.
Description: Provides mini-profiles of companies, containing general information, plants and facilities, product families and technologies, technology and licensing agreements, financial information, and key executives and officers.

643 — **UK**
COMPONENTS IN ELECTRONICS. 1986. 11/yr. £85. T A S Publishing Ltd., 80 Highgate Rd., London NW5 1PB, England. TEL 071-267-9521. FAX 071-485-9030. Ed. Nick Foot. adv. contact: Sean Stewart. circ. 18,292. Document type: trade publication.
Description: Contains information for those with an interest in the design-in, specification and purchasing of electronic components and related products and services.

621.381 658 — **FR** ISSN 1155-2093
COMPOSANTS INSTRUMENTATION ELECTRONIQUES. 1990. m. 400 F. Elsevier - Thomas, 128 rue d'Aguesseau, 92100 Boulogne Billancourt, France. TEL 46-03-44-99. FAX 48-25-14-00. Ed. Alain Dieul. circ. 35,010 (controlled). (tabloid format)
Description: Helps R&D and product engineers in their purchasing and sourcing decisions.

643 — **FR**
CONFORT MENAGER. 10/yr. S.E.P., 106 bd. Malesherbes, 75017 Paris, France. TEL 47-66-04-60. FAX 46-22-98-79. Ed. Monique Coralli. adv. circ. 8,000.

643 — **FR**
CONFORTIQUE MAGAZINE. 9/yr. 72 rue du Dr. Decorse, 94410 Saint-Maurice, France. TEL 43-76-65-29. FAX 43-76-54-68. TELEX 699 559. Ed. Marie Jose Nicol. circ. 14,000.

621.381 643 — **US**
THE CONSUMER ELECTRONICS INDUSTRY: AN OVERVIEW. 1991. a. $395. Dun & Bradstreet Information Services (Murray Hill) (Subsidiary of: Dun & Bradstreet, Inc.), One Diamond Hill Rd., Murray Hill, NJ 07974. TEL 908-665-5224. FAX 908-771-7599. Ed. John Virgone.
Description: Examines electronic products like high definition television. Also studies the origins and evolution of the industry, the consumer electronics trade deficit, the influence of the FCC and questionable trade practices.

CORREO C B. see *COMMUNICATIONS*

643 — **AT**
COUNTERPOINT. 1984. m. Aus.$48 free to qualified personnel. Reed Business Publishing Pty. Ltd. (Subs.diary of: Reed International PLC), 1-5 Railway St., Chatswood, N.S.W. 2067, Australia. TEL 02-372-5222. FAX 02-491-7399. Ed. S. Hawthorn. adv. circ. 5,074. (tabloid format)
Description: Provides information on consumer electrical goods such as TVs, videos, washing machines, and dishwashers.

016 621.3 — **KO**
CURRENT BIBLIOGRAPHIES ON SCIENCE & TECHNOLOGY: ELECTRICAL ENGINEERING AND ELECTRONICS. 1962. m. $92. Korea Institute for Economics and Technology, P.O.B. 250, Seoul, S. Korea. circ. 350. (reprint service avail. from UMI)
Formerly: Current Index to Journals in Science and Technology: Electrical Engineering and Electronics; Supersedes in part: Current Bibliography on Science and Technology.

CURRENT BIBLIOGRAPHY ON SCIENCE AND TECHNOLOGY: ELECTRONICS AND ELECTRICAL ENGINEERING/KAGAKU GIJUTSU BUNKEN SOKUHO. DENKI KOGAKU HEN. see *ENGINEERING — Abstracting, Bibliographies, Statistics*

643 — **US** ISSN 1049-1236
C2C CURRENTS: JAPAN - ELECTRONICS.* 1990. m. $100. Scan C2C, 1001 Pennsylvania Ave., N.W., No.1300, Washington, DC 20024-2024. TEL 800-525-3865. FAX 202-863-3855.
●Also available online. Vendor(s): Data-Star (JPTC), DIALOG Information Services, Inc. (File no.582), European Space Agency (File no.241), Orbit Search Service (JTEC).
Also available on CD-ROM. Producer(s): DIALOG Information Services, Inc.
Description: Provides a summary of the contents of leading Japanese scientific and business journals. Contains a table of contents for selected journals. Lists title, author, date of publication, number of pages, and source journal.

621.381 — **US** ISSN 1069-353X
▼**D S P APPLICATIONS.** (Digital Signal Processing) 1992. m. $75 (free to qualified personnel). Golden Gate Enterprises, Inc., Box 428, Los Altos, CA 94023. TEL 415-969-6920. FAX 415-969-0222. adv.: B&W page $2600, color page $3400; trim 8 1/8 x 10 7/8. circ. 16,000. (back issues avail.) Document type: trade publication.

643 — **US** ISSN 0888-4501
HD9971.U6
DEALERSCOPE MERCHANDISING; the marketing magazine for consumer electronics and major appliance retailing. 1986. m. $65 (foreign $132) (free to qualified personnel). North American Publishing Co., 401 N. Broad St., Philadelphia, PA 19108. TEL 215-238-5300. FAX 215-238-5457. Ed. Richard Sherwin. adv.; bk.rev.; charts; illus.; stat.; index. Indexed: B.P.I., Fuel & Energy Abstr., Tr.& Indus.Ind. Document type: trade publication.
●Also available online. Vendor(s): DIALOG Information Services, Inc.
—BLDSC (3535.960125); UnCover; UMI.
Formed by the merger of (1958-1986): Dealerscope (ISSN 0011-7218); Merchandising (ISSN 0362-3920); Which was formerly: Merchandising Week (ISSN 0025-9888); Electrical Merchandising Week.
Description: Tells retailers how to market and merchandise appliances, video equipment, TVs, radios and home office equipment for maximum sales. Covers advertising tips, management suggestions, marketing and merchandising trends and new product news.

643 — **US** ISSN 0278-3479
UG485 CODEN: DEELDH
DEFENSE ELECTRONICS. 1969. m. $39 (Canada and Mexico $59; elsewhere $99). Argus Inc., 6151 Powers Ferry Rd., N.W., Atlanta, GA 30339-2491. TEL 404-955-2500. FAX 404-955-0400. (Subscr. to: Box 41528, Nashville, TN 37204. TEL 615-377-3322) Ed. George A. Neranchi. adv. circ. 45,830. (also avail. in microfilm from UMI; reprint service avail. from UMI) Indexed: Abstr.Mil.Bibl., Air Un.Lib.Ind., Bus.Ind., DM & T, PROMT, Sci.Abstr., Tr.& Indus.Ind. Document type: trade publication.
●Also available online. Vendor(s): DIALOG Information Services, Inc., Mead Data Central, Inc.
—BLDSC (3546.214000); Faxon; SWETS; UMI.
CCC.
Incorporates (1988-1989): Defense Computing (ISSN 0896-839X); Former titles (1977-1979): Electronic Warfare - Defense Electronics (ISSN 0194-7885); Electronic Warfare (ISSN 0363-258X)
Description: Serves government and industrial users, designers, and OEM's of military electronic systems, sub-systems and specialized components.

621.381 — **SP** ISSN 1132-2098
DELEK ELEKTOR ELECTRONICS ESPANA. Key Title: Delek. 1990. 13/yr. Editorial Resistor, S.A., C. Maudes 15, entlo. C, 28003 Madrid, Spain. TEL 1-53-44-666. FAX 1-53-44-751. Ed. A. Gonzalez Buelta. adv.: B&W page 100000 ptas., color page 150000 ptas.; 210 x 280. circ. 16,000.

643 — **JA** ISSN 0288-6103
DEMPA DIGEST. (Text in English) 1983. w. 55000 Yen($350) Dempa Publications, Inc., 1-11-15, Higashi Gotanda, Shinagawa-ku, Tokyo 141, Japan. TEL 81-3-3345-6111. FAX 81-3-3445-6890. (US addr.: 275 Madison Ave., New York, NY 10016. TEL 212-682-4755) charts; illus.; stat. (back issues avail.)
Description: Summarizes significant events shaping Japan's electronics market.

643 — **JA**
DEMPA SHIMBUN DAILY. 1950. d. Dempa Publications, Inc., 1-11-15 Higashi-Gotanda, Shingawa-ku, Tokyo 141, Japan. TEL 81-3-3445-6111. FAX 81-3-3445-6890. (US addr.: 275 Madison Ave., New York, NY 10016. TEL 212-682-4755) adv. circ. 225,000. Document type: newspaper.

DENKI GAKKAI RONBUNSHI. C, DENSHI JOHO SHISUTEMU BUMONSHI/INSTITUTE OF ELECTRICAL ENGINEERS OF JAPAN. TRANSACTIONS. C; ELECTRONICS, INFORMATION AND SYSTEMS SOCIETY PUBLICATION. see *ENGINEERING — Electrical Engineering*

621.381 — **JA** ISSN 0285-8088
DENKI GENBA GIJUTSU/SITE ELECTROTECHNICS. (Text in Japanese) 1962. m. 927 Yen per no. Denki Johosha, 7-9, Iidabashi 1-chome, Chiyoda-ku, Tokyo 102, Japan.

621.3 — **JA** ISSN 0913-106X
DENKI GIJUTSUSHA/ELECTRONIC ENGINEERS. (Text in Japanese) 1955. m. 600 Yen per no. Nihon Denki Gijutsusha Kyokai - Japan Electrical Engineers Association, 5-3, Koraku 1-chome, Bunkyo-ku, Tokyo 112, Japan.

DENKITEN/ELECTRONICS RETAILER. see *BUSINESS AND ECONOMICS — Marketing And Purchasing*

621.38 — **JA** ISSN 0910-593X
DENPA GIJUTSU KYOKAIHO/RADIO ENGINEERING AND ELECTRONICS ASSOCIATION. JOURNAL. (Text in Japanese) 1963. bi-m. Denpa Gijutsu Kyokai - Radio Engineering and Electronics Association, 12-1, Yuraku-cho 1-chome, Chiyoda-ku, Tokyo 100, Japan.

621.381 — **JA** ISSN 0417-0318
DENSHI/ELECTRONICS. (Text in Japanese) 1961. m. 1030 Yen per no. Nihon Denshi Kikai Kogyokai - Electronic Industries Association of Japan, 2-2, Marunouchi 3-chome, Chiyoda-ku, Tokyo 100, Japan.
—BLDSC (3703.005000).

621.3 — **JA**
DENSHI JOHO TSUSHIN GAKKAI TAIKAI KOEN RONBUNSHU/INSTITUTE OF ELECTRONICS, INFORMATION AND COMMUNICATION ENGINEERS. NATIONAL CONVENTION RECORD. (Text in Japanese) s-a. Denshi Joho Tsushin Gakkai - Institute of Electronics, Information and Communication Engineers, Kikai Shinko Kaikan, 5-8, Shiba Koen 3-chome, Minato-ku, Tokyo 105, Japan.

621.381 — **JA** ISSN 0913-6940
DENSHI KOGYO GEPPO/JOURNAL OF ELECTRONIC INDUSTRY. (Text in Japanese) 1959. m. $159.50. Nihon Denshi Kogyo Shinko Kyokai - Japan Electric Indutry Development Association, 5-8, Shiba Koen 3-chome, Minato-ku, Tokyo 105, Japan. (Dist. by: Intercontinental Marketing Corp., I.P.O. Box 5056, Tokyo 100-30, Japan. TEL 81-3-3661-7458. FAX 81-3-3667-9646)

621.3 — **JA** ISSN 0285-1903
DENSHI TOKYO/I E E E TOKYO SECTION. BULLETIN. (Text in English; summaries in English, Japanese) 1973. a. 2000 Yen. I E E E Tokyo Section, c/o Hitachi Central Research Lab, 1-280 Higashi-Koigakubo, Kokubunji-shi, Tokyo 185, Japan. TEL 81-423-27-7642. FAX 81-423-27-7643. adv. circ. 8,550. Indexed: Eng.Ind. Document type: bulletin.

ELECTRONICS 2173

621.381   JA   ISSN 0387-0774
CODEN: DEZADL
DENSHI ZAIRYO/ELECTRONIC PARTS AND MATERIALS. (Text in Japanese) 1962. m. 940 Yen per no. Kogyo Chosakai Publishing Co., Ltd., 14-7, Hongo 2-chome, Bunkyo-ku, Tokyo 113, Japan. **Indexed:** Chem.Abstr.
—BLDSC (3702.684000); CASDDS.

621.381   JA   ISSN 0911-2626
CODEN: DEGIEJ
DENSHI ZAIRYO KENKYUJO DENZAIKEN GIHO/ELECTRONICS MATERIALS LABORATORY. TECHNICAL REPORTS. (Text in Japanese; summaries in English) 1983. s-a. Sumitomo Kinzoku Kozan K.K., Denshi Zairyo Kenkyujo - Sumitomo Metal Mining Co., Ltd., Electronics Materials Laboratory, 6-1, Suehiro-cho 1-chome, Ome-shi, Tokyo 198, Japan.
—CASDDS.

643   UK   ISSN 0953-6949
DIAL ELECTRICAL - ELECTRONICS. 1982. a. free to qualified personnel. Dial Industry Publications (Subsidiary of: Reed Information Services), Windsor Court, Grinstead House, E. Grinstead, W. Sussex RH19 1XA, England. TEL 0342-326972. FAX 0342-335612. TELEX 95127-INFSER-G. Ed. Jan Brazier. circ. 15,000 (controlled). **Document type:** trade publication.
●Also available online. Vendor(s): Reed Information Services Ltd.
Formerly (until 1983): Dial Industry. Electrical, Electronic Equipment and Products (ISSN 0263-5305)
Description: For buyers and specifiers of electrical, electronics, and computing instrumentation; lists 12,000 companies.

621.381   CC   ISSN 1000-0755
DIANZI JISHU/ELECTRONIC TECHNOLOGY. (Text in Chinese) m. Shanghai Dianzi Xuehui - Shanghai Electronics Society, P.O. Box 085-253, Shanghai 200009, People's Republic of China. TEL 3242671. (Co-sponsor: Shanghai Tongxin Xuehui) Ed. Cheng Weiyu.
—BLDSC (3702.798000).

621.381   CC
DIANZI JISHU YINGYONG/APPLICATIONS OF ELECTRONIC TECHNIQUE. (Text in Chinese) m. $0.80 per no. Guoji Shudian, Qikan Bu - China International Book Trading Corp., P.O. Box 399, Beijing 100044, People's Republic of China.

621.38   CC   ISSN 1001-7194
DIANZI JISHU ZAZHI/JOURNAL OF ELECTRONICS TECHNOLOGY. (Text in Chinese) 1982. bi-m. Y24. (Jixie Dianzi Bu, Jixie Kexue Jishu Yanjiusuo) China Machine Press, 1 Baiwanzhuang Nanjie, Beijing 100037, People's Republic of China. TEL 861-8316677. FAX 861-8326337. TELEX 222557 STIP CN. Ed. Yang Yingqiu. index. circ. 20,000.
Description: Covers the latest technical developments in the field of electrical engineering.

621.381   CC
DIANZI KEXUE JISHU/ELECTRONIC SCIENCE AND TECHNOLOGY. (Text in Chinese) m. $0.60 per no. Guoji Shudian, Qikan Bu - China International Book Trading Corp., Chegongzhuang Xilu 21, P.O. Box 399, Beijing 100044, People's Republic of China.

621.3   CC   ISSN 0258-798X
TK7800   CODEN: DKXUEC
DIANZI KEXUE XUEKAN. English edition: Journal of Electronics (ISSN 0217-9822) (Text in Chinese; summaries in English) 1978. bi-m. $114.60. (Chinese Academy of Sciences, Institute of Electronics) Science Press, Marketing and Sales Department, 16 Donghuangchenggen Beijie, Beijing 100707, People's Republic of China. TEL 4010642. FAX 4012180. TELEX 210247-SPBJ-CN. adv. circ. 11,000.
—CASDDS.
Formerly: Electronics Bulletin.
Description: Covers the broad field of electronics in mainland China; includes electrical circuits, devices, and power, theory, new technology, new materials and their applications. For specialists, teachers, engineers, technicians, and students.
Refereed Serial

621.381   CC
DIANZI SHIJIE/ELECTRONIC WORLD. (Text in Chinese) m. $0.40 per no. (Zhongguo Dianzi Xuehui - China Electronics Society) Dianzi Shijie Zazhishe, 14 Wanshoulu Xijie, Beijing 100036, People's Republic of China. TEL 813159. Ed. Zhang Daoyuan. illus.

621.381   CC   ISSN 0372-2112
DIANZI XUEBAO/ACTA ELECTRONICA SINICA. (Text in Chinese) bi-m. $2 per no. Guoji Shudian, Qikan Bu - China International Book Trading Corp., P.O. Box 399, Beijing 100044, People's Republic of China. **Indexed:** Sci.Abstr.
—BLDSC (0612.520000).

001.6 629.8   CC   ISSN 1004-2792
DIANZI YU ZIDONGHUA/ELECTRONICS AND AUTOMATION. (Text in Chinese) 1972. bi-m. $9.78 (effective 1994). Shanghai Kexue Jishu Qingbao Yanjiusuo - Institute of Scientific and Technical Information of Shanghai, 1634 Huaihai Zhonglu, Shanghai 200031, People's Republic of China. TEL 86-21-4374599. FAX 86-21-4335311. (Dist. outside China by: China International Book Trading Corp., P.O. Box 399, Beijing, P.R. China. TEL 86-1-8412255) Ed. Ma Hongchu. adv. **Document type:** academic/scholarly publication.

621.381   US   ISSN 1051-2004
TK5102.5   CODEN: DSPREJ
DIGITAL SIGNAL PROCESSING; a review journal. 1991. q. $140 (foreign $160). Academic Press, Inc., Journal Division, 525 B St., Ste. 1900, San Diego, CA 92101-4495. TEL 619-230-1840. FAX 619-699-6800. (Subscr. to: Box 620000, Orlando, FL 32891-8340. TEL 800-542-9534) Eds. Rao Yarlagadda, James Schroeder. **Document type:** academic/scholarly publication.
—BLDSC (3588.397490); SWETS. **CCC.**
Description: Illuminates and explores the path of creativity in the field of signal processing.

621.381   US   ISSN 1040-0249
TK7871.86
DIODE D.A.T.A. DIGEST. Key Title: Discrete Semiconductors. Diodes. 1957. s-a. $205. D.A.T.A. Business Publishing (Subsidiary of: Information Handling Services), 15 Inverness Way E., Box 6510, Englewood, CO 80155-6510. TEL 800-447-4666. FAX 303-799-4082. TELEX 4322083 IHS UI. adv. contact: Peggy Anderson.
●Also available on CD-ROM.
Former titles (until 1988): Diode (ISSN 0732-0353); (until 1982): Diode Semiconductor (ISSN 0271-0803); Which was formerly (until 1980): Diode D.A.T.A. Digest (ISSN 0193-2934); (until 1979): Semiconductor Diodes (ISSN 0732-0361); (until 1978): Semiconductor Diode D.A.T.A. Book (ISSN 0091-9675); (until 1973): Semiconductor Diode and S C R D.A.T.A. Book (ISSN 0037-1904).
Description: Reference guide covering up to 20 technical parameters on over 220,400 devices from more than 240 manufacturers.

621.3   US   ISSN 1046-395X
TK7871.85
DISCONTINUED DISCRETE SEMICONDUCTORS D.A.T.A. DIGEST. 1989. biennial. $195. D.A.T.A. Business Publishing (Subsidiary of: Information Handling Services), 15 Inverness Way E., Box 6510, Englewood, CO 80155-6510. TEL 800-447-4666. FAX 303-799-4082. TELEX 4322083 IHS UI. adv. contact: Peggy Anderson.
●Also available on CD-ROM.
Description: Reference guide to discontinued discrete semiconductors. Lists over 320,540 devices from more than 325 manufacturers.

621.381   US   ISSN 1046-3941
TK7874.5
DISCONTINUED I CS D.A.T.A. DIGEST. (Integrated Circuits) 1989. biennial. $125. D.A.T.A. Business Publishing (Subsidiary of: Information Handling Services), 15 Inverness Way E., Box 6510, Englewood, CO 80155-6510. TEL 800-447-4666. FAX 303-799-4082. TELEX 4322083 IHS UI. adv. contact: Peggy Anderson.
●Also available on CD-ROM.
Description: Reference guide to discontinued integrated circuits. Lists over 106,770 devices from more than 300 manufacturers.

643   US
DISCRETE SEMICONDUCTORS DIRECT ALTERNATE SOURCES & REPLACEMENTS. (Subseries of D.A.T.A. Digest Electronic Information Series) 1986. s-a. $133. D.A.T.A. Business Publishing (Subsidiary of: Information Handling Services), 15 Inverness Way E., Box 6510, Englewood, CO 80155-6510. TEL 800-447-4666. FAX 303-799-0381. TELEX 4322083 IHS UI. Ed. Paul Magin. adv. contact: Peggy Anderson.
Former titles: Discrete Semiconductors Direct Alternate Sources (ISSN 1043-6367); Direct Replacement Guide; Which supersedes in part (in 1988): Suggested Replacement - Alternative Source Guide, Discrete Semiconductors (ISSN 0887-0047).
Description: Reference guide to discrete semiconductor direct alternate sources. Covers about 600,000 devices from more than 474 manufacturers.

621.381 658.8   US
DISTRIBUTOR MANAGEMENT DIGEST. vol.7, 1994. q. $19.50. Business Marketing & Publishing Inc., Box 7457, Wilton, CT 06897. TEL 203-834-9959. FAX 203-762-5664. Ed. George B. Young. adv.

643   US
E C N LITERATURE NEWS. (Electronic Component News) 1979. bi-m. Chilton Co., 201 King of Prussia Rd., Radnor, PA 19089. TEL 215-964-4000. FAX 215-964-4273. adv. circ. 125,000.
Description: Provides information on electronics industry manufacturer's catalogs, technical literature, booklets, handbooks, and reference material.

621.381   UK   ISSN 0951-5690
E D A. 1986. m. £35. Electronic Design Automation Ltd., 31-33 High Holborn, London WC1V 6BD, England. TEL 071-404-0564. FAX 071-831-2057. (Subscr. to: 93 Chancery Ln., London WC2A 1DJ) Ed. J. Kenyon. circ. 9,637. (back issues avail.)
Document type: trade publication.
Incorporates: Silicon Design.

621.381   US
▼**E D N ASIA.** (Electronics Design News) 1992. m. $99. Cahners Publishing Company (Newton), Division of Reed Elsevier Inc., 275 Washington St., Newton, MA 02158-1630. TEL 617-964-3030. FAX 617-558-4506. (US subscr. to: 44 Cook St., Denver, CO 80206. TEL 303-388-4511; Asian addr.: Cahners Asia Ltd., 19th Fl., Centre Point, 181-185 Gloucester Rd., Wanchai, Hong Kong. TEL 852-838-2666. FAX 852-575-1690) Ed. Michael C. Markowitz. adv.: B&W page $4490, color page $5790; trim 8 x 10 3/4. circ. 28,000. **Document type:** trade publication.
Description: Focuses on the interests of the Asian electronics industry. Provides technical data on new electronics designs, products and applications, plus special news and reports on design developments throughout the Asia-Pacific Rim.

621.381   US
E D N MAGAZINE. (Electronics Design News); electronic technology for engineers and engineering managers. (Special edition avail.: E D N Products & Careers) 1956. 26/yr. $120 (Canada $182; Mexico $170; elsewhere $210); free to qualified personnel. Cahners Publishing Company (Newton), Division of Reed Elsevier Inc., 275 Washington St., Newton, MA 02158-1630. TEL 617-964-3030. FAX 617-558-4470. (Subscr. to: 44 Cook St., Denver, CO 80206. TEL 800-662-7776) Ed. Jonathan Titus. adv.; bk.rev.; charts; illus.; stat.; tr.lit.; index; circ. 161,500 (controlled). (also avail. in microform) **Indexed:** A.I.Abstr., A.S.& T.Ind., Bus.Ind., Comput.Cont., Comput.Dtbs., Eng.Ind., Sci.Abstr., Tel.Abstr., Tr.& Indus.Ind. **Document type:** trade publication.
●Also available online. Vendor(s): DIALOG Information Services, Inc.
—BLDSC (3661.094000); EI; Faxon; UnCover; SWETS; UMI. **CCC.**
Formerly: E E E - Magazine of Circuit Design Engineering (ISSN 0012-7515)
Description: For designers and design managers in electronics. Features products, technology and applications, with detailed samplings of the best design from all over the world. Covers computers and peripherals, test and measurement equipment, data communications, semiconductor technology and semicustom ICs.

2174 ELECTRONICS

621.381 US
E D N PRODUCTS & CAREERS. (Electronics Design News) (Special edition of: E D N Magazine) 1986. 22/yr. $79.95 (Canada $117.65; Mexico $109.95; elsewhere $124.95) avail. only to qualified subscribers of E D N Magazine. Cahners Publishing Company (Newton), Division of Reed Elsevier Inc., 275 Washington St., Newton, MA 02158-1630. TEL 617-964-3030. FAX 617-558-4470. (Subscr. to: 44 Cook St., Denver, CO 80206. TEL 800-662-7776) Ed. John Whitmarsh. circ. 131,000. **Indexed:** Tel.Abstr., Tr.& Indus.Ind. **Document type:** trade publication.
  Former titles: E D N News; E D N Product News; Incorporating: E D N Career News.
  Description: For design engineers and managers in electronics. Provides news of products and technology; includes a career news section.

621.381 US ISSN 0149-0370
TK7869 CODEN: EVENAE
E E: EVALUATION ENGINEERING; the magazine of electronic evaluation and test. 1962. 12/yr. $95 (foreign $135). Nelson Publishing Co., 2504 N. Tamiami Trail, Nokomis, FL 34275-3476. TEL 813-966-9521. FAX 813-966-2590. Ed. A. Verner Nelson. adv.; bk.rev.; charts; illus.; stat.; tr.lit. circ. 75,526. **Indexed:** Comput.Cont., Sci.Abstr. **Document type:** trade publication.
  —BLDSC (3830.600000); EI; Faxon; SWETS. **CCC.**
  Continues: Evaluation Engineering (ISSN 0014-3316)
  Refereed Serial

621.381 US ISSN 0732-9016
TK7870.3
E E M. (Electronic Engineers Master) 1957. a. $90 free to qualified personnel. Hearst Business Communications, Inc., 645 Stewart Ave., Garden City, NY 11530. TEL 516-227-1300. Ed. Tom Mays. adv. circ. 102,500. **Document type:** catalog.
  Description: Four volume catalog of electronic products including manufacturers' technical data pages and complete manufacturers and distributors directory.

621.381 US ISSN 0899-952X
E E PRODUCT NEWS. (Electronics - Electrical) 1941. m. free to qualified personnel. Intertec Publishing Corp. (White Plains), 707 Westchester Ave., White Plains, NY 10604. TEL 914-949-8500. FAX 914-682-0922. Ed. Joseph Del Gatto. adv.; illus.; tr.lit.; index. circ. 103,000. (tabloid format) **Document type:** trade publication.
  —**CCC.**
  Former titles: E E-Electrical Equipment (ISSN 0364-9369); Electrical Equipment (ISSN 0013-4325)
  Description: Reports on new products for the prototype design engineer.

E F Y DIRECTORY. (Electronics For You) see BUSINESS AND ECONOMICS — Trade And Industrial Directories

643 JA
E I A J NEWSLETTER. q. Electronics Industries Association Japan, Tosho Bldg., 3-2-2 Marunouchi, Chiyoda-ku, Tokyo 100, Japan. TEL 03-2131073. FAX 03-2871712.
  Description: News of the association and the industry.

621.381 JA
E I A J REVIEW. (Text in English) 1987. q. Electronic Industries Association of Japan - Nihon Denshi Kikai Kogyokai, 2-2, Marunouchi 3-chome, Chiyoda-ku, Tokyo 100, Japan.

643 CN ISSN 0226-7748
E I C. (Electronique Industrielle & Commerciale) 1980. 5/yr. Can.$25. Serpro International Inc., 8735 Lucien Plante, Montreal, PQ H2M 2M7, Canada. TEL 514-383-7700. FAX 514-383-7691. Ed. Ernest Bourgault. adv.; B&W page Can.$2460, color page Can.$3255; trim 11 x 15 3/4. bk.rev. circ. 10,000. (tabloid format; back issues avail.) **Document type:** trade publication.
  Description: Covers commercial and industrial electronics.

643 GW ISSN 0174-5522
E I - ELEKTRONIK INDUSTRIE. 1969. m. DM.211.50 (foreign DM.228). Huethig GmbH, Postfach 102869, 69018 Heidelberg, Germany. TEL 06221-489281. FAX 06221-489205. TELEX 461727-HUEHDD. Ed. Curt Rint. adv.: B&W page DM.6460; trim 210 x 297; adv. contact: Heidrun Dangl. bk.rev.; bibl.; illus.; tr.lit.; circ. 16,991. **Indexed:** PROMT, Sci.Abstr. **Document type:** trade publication.
  —BLDSC (3717.635000).
  Description: Specialist journal for components and boards, SICs, development tools and CAE/CAD, system integration components and software, and measuring techniques.

643 IT
E I - ELETTRORADIO INFORMAZIONI; the magazine for manufacturers, retailers, dealers and technicians of consumer electronic goods. 1960. every 20 days. L.200000. Publiedim s.r.l., Via Matteo Civitali 51, 20148 Milan, Italy. TEL 392-48703201. FAX 392-48703614. TELEX 322291 PUBIEM I. Ed. Carlo Moradei. adv.; bk.rev.; index. circ. 30,000. (back issues avail.) **Document type:** trade publication.
  Description: Covers new products, equipment and methods in the field of consumer electronics.

643 IT
E I - ELETTRORADIO INFORMAZIONI INTERNATIONAL. (Text in English, French, German, Spanish) 1989. m. Publiedim s.r.l., Via Matteo Civitali 51, 20148 Milan, Italy. TEL 392-48703201. FAX 392-48703614. TELEX 322291 PUBIEM I. Ed. Fiorenza Moradei. circ. 7,000. **Document type:** trade publication.
  Description: For buyers, store managers, importers, exporters, manufacturers in electronic consumer goods field.

621.381 IT
E O NEWS SETTIMANALE; il settimanale Jackson di elettronica automazione & strumentazione. 26/yr. L.16800 (foreign L.33600). Gruppo Editoriale Jackson S.p.A., Via M. Gorki 69, 20092 Cinisello B. (MI), Italy. TEL 39-2-66034247. FAX 39-2-66034238. Ed. Enzo Pavese. adv.; B&W page L.2500000, color page L.3700000; trim 210 x 280. circ. 18,594 (controlled).
  Description: For commercial operators and design engineers working in the field of new electronic technologies. Dedicated to new product information.

621.381 CN ISSN 0708-4366
E P & T. (Electronic Products and Technology) 1979. 7/yr. Can.$36($60) Lakeview Publications Inc., 1200 Aerowood Dr., 27, Mississauga, ON L4W 2S7, Canada. TEL 905-624-8100. FAX 905-624-1760. Ed. E. David Kerfoot. adv.; charts; illus.; stat.; tr.lit.; circ. 23,000 (controlled). (tabloid format)

643 CN
E P & T'S ELECTROSOURCE PRODUCT REFERENCE GUIDE & TELEPHONE DIRECTORY. 1984. a. Can.$40($50) Lakeview Publications Inc., 1200 Aerowood Dr., 27, Mississauga, ON L4W 2S7, Canada. TEL 905-624-8100. FAX 905-624-1760. Ed. E. David Kerfoot. adv.; circ. 23,000 (controlled).

621.381 BE ISSN 0939-8368
E P E JOURNAL. (Text in English) 1991. q. DM.200. E P E Association, Secretariat S R B E, Av. de la Plaine 2, B-1050 Brussels, Belgium.
  —BLDSC (3793.410000).

E R M; het vakblad voor de elektrodetailhandel. see BUSINESS AND ECONOMICS — Marketing And Purchasing

643 AU
E S KONTAKT.* q. Erb Verlag GmbH, Eichenstr. 38, A-1120 Vienna, Austria. TEL 01-5871381. FAX 01-58713816. circ. 16,000.

643 AU
E S SPECIAL.* bi-m. Erb Verlag GmbH, Eichenstr. 38, A-1120 Vienna, Austria. TEL 01-5871381. FAX 01-58713816. Ed. Wolfgang Stabauer. circ. 24,000.

621.381 US
E T A TECHNICIAN ASSOCIATION NEWS. 1978. m. $15. Electronics Technicians Association, 602 N. Jackson St., Greencastle, IN 46135. TEL 317-653-8262. FAX 317-653-8262. Ed. Dick Glass. adv.; bk.rev. circ. 2,500.
  Former titles: E T A Association Newsletter; E E A Training Program.

621.381 FR ISSN 0760-0909
E T I. (Electronique Techniques et Industries) 1983. 8/yr. $170 (typically set in Jan.). Masson - Periodiques, Villa Laromiguiere, 75005 Paris, France. TEL 1-40-46-62-00. FAX 1-40-46-62-01. adv.
  —BLDSC (3706.160000).
  Description: Covers the businesses, climate, trends, and new products of the industry.

643 UK ISSN 0957-0438
E T I: ELECTRONICS TODAY INTERNATIONAL. 1972. m. £25.80. Argus Specialist Publications Ltd., Argus House, Boundary Way, Hemel Hempstead, Herts. HP2 7ST, England. TEL 0442-66551. FAX 0442-66998. (Subscr. to: Argus Subscription Services, Queensway House, 2 Queensway, Redhill, Surrey, England. TEL 0737-768611) Ed. Paul Freeman. adv. **Document type:** consumer publication.
  —BLDSC (3705.460000); SWETS.
  Former titles: Electronics Today International (ISSN 0142-7229); Electronics Today (ISSN 0013-5216)
  Description: Emphasizes the practical application of electronics.

621.38 016 RU ISSN 0131-0747
EKSPRESS-INFORMATSIYA. ELEKTRONIKA. 1961. 48/yr. 40.60 Rub. Vsesoyuznyi Institut Nauchno-Tekhnicheskoi Informatsii (VINITI), Baltiiskaya ul., 14, Moscow A-219, Russia. (Mezhdunarodnaya Kniga, Dimitrova ul. 39, 113095 Moscow, Russia)

643 SP
EL. 12/yr. Cadi 47, bajos 2a, 08031 Barcelona, Spain. TEL 3-42-06-407. FAX 3-42-06-409. Ed. J.M. Olaya. circ. 120,000.

ELECTRICAL & ELECTRONICS ABSTRACTS. see ENGINEERING — Abstracting, Bibliographies, Statistics

ELECTRICAL AND RADIO TRADING. see COMMUNICATIONS — Radio

621.381 US ISSN 0070-9697
ELECTRICAL - ELECTRONICS INSULATION CONFERENCE. RECORD. 1958. biennial. price varies. National Electrical Manufacturers Association, 2101 L St. N.W., Washington, DC 20037. TEL 202-457-8400. (Co-sponsor: Institute of Electrical and Electronic Engineers) **Indexed:** Chem.Abstr.
  Formerly: Electrical Insulation Technical Conference. Record.

621.38 II ISSN 0013-4538
ELECTRICITY AND ELECTRONICS. (Text in English) 1968. m. Rs.40. L. K. Pandeya, Ed. & Pub., Block F, 105C New Alipore, Calcutta 700053, India. circ. 6,282.

621.381 FR
ELECTRO. ANNUAIRE; electricite, electronique, electromenager. a. 55 F. Societe Nouvelle d'Editions Publicitaires, 16, Av. de Verdun, 75010 Paris, France. adv.; illus.; index.

621.381 SP
ELECTRO ARAGON. 4/yr. Ayala 71, 2o L, 28001 Madrid, Spain. TEL 1-401-46-27. FAX 1-402-97-07. Ed. Oscar Gonzalbo.

643 SP
ELECTRO MARKET.* 12/yr. Publimicros S.L., Avda. Meridiana 322, Bajos 2a, 08027 Barcelona, Spain. TEL 3-340-07-09. FAX 3-351-59-02. Ed. Angel Salada.

621.381   FR   ISSN 0153-9396
ELECTRO-NEGOCE. 1953. m. (10/yr.). 270 F. (foreign 350 F.). (Federation Nationale des Syndicats de Grossistes en Materiel Electrique et Electronique) Societe des Editions Electro Negoce, 13, rue Marivaux, 75002 Paris, France.
TEL 1-42-97-46-25. FAX 1-42-86-01-74. Ed. Pierre Allias. adv.: B&W page 18750 F., color page 27000 F.; 275 X 380. bk.rev. circ. 17,300.
Description: Provides a link between the producers and professional consumers of materials.

621.381   SP
ELECTRO NOTICIAS. 6/yr. Ayala 71, 2o L, 28001 Madrid, Spain. TEL 1-410-46-27. FAX 1-402-97-07. Ed. Oscar Gonzalbo.

621.381   US   ISSN 0740-1922
THE ELECTRON; electronics news for those still learning. 1974. bi-m. $12. Cie Publishing, 1776 E. 17th St., Cleveland, OH 44114. TEL 216-781-9400. FAX 216-781-0331. (Subscr. to: 4781 E. 355th St., Willoughby, OH 44094) Ed. Denise M. Zakrajsek. adv.; bk.rev.; charts; illus.; pat.; tr.lit. circ. 30,000. (tabloid format) **Document type:** newspaper.
Description: Covers breakthroughs and trends in electronics technology.

621.381   US
ELECTRON OPTICS BULLETIN. 1954. q. Philips Electronic Instruments, Inc., 85 McKee Dr., Mahwah, NJ 07430. TEL 201-529-6168. (Affiliate: North American Philips Company) illus.; index. circ. 10,000. **Indexed:** Biol.Abstr., Br.Ceram.Abstr., Chem.Abstr., Met.Abstr., Sci.Abstr., World Alum.Abstr.
Former titles: Electron Optics Reporter; Norelco Reporter (ISSN 0029-1625)

621.381   PL   ISSN 0070-9816
TK7800   CODEN: ETNTAT
ELECTRON TECHNOLOGY. (Text in English; summaries in Polish) 1968. irreg., vol.26, 1993. price varies. (Instytut Technologii Elektronowej) Wydawnictwo Naukowe P W N, Ul. Miodowa 10, 00-251 Warsaw, Poland. (Dist. by: Ars Polona, Krakowskie Przedmiescie 7, 00-068 Warsaw, Poland) Ed. C.A. Ambroziak. **Indexed:** Chem.Abstr., Eng.Ind., INIS Atomind., Met.Abstr., Phys.Abstr., Sci.Abstr., Solid St.Abstr., World Alum.Abstr.
—BLDSC (3699.765000); EI; CASDDS.
Description: Covers theoretical and experimental problems of electron technology.

621.381   II   ISSN 0013-4813
ELECTRONIC APPLICATION NEWS. (Text in English) 1964. bi-m. Rs.30($9) Peico Electronics and Electricals Ltd. (Subsidiary of: Philips India Ltd.), Band Box Building, 254-D, Dr. Annie Besant Road, Bombay 400 025, India. Ed. K. Sharma. bk.rev.; index. circ. 1,500.

643
ELECTRONIC BUSINESS ASIA. (Editions in Chinese, English, Japanese, Korean) 1990. m. $90. Cahners Publishing Company (Newton), Division of Reed Elsevier Inc., 275 Washington St., Newton, MA 02158-1630. TEL 617-964-3030. FAX 617-558-4506. (Subscr. to: 44 Cook St., Denver, CO 80206) Ed. Tom McHale. adv.; circ. 41,087 (controlled). **Document type:** trade publication.
Description: For management in electronics, computer, and systems companies in Asia and the Pacific Rim.

643   US   ISSN 1073-1059
HD9696.A3   CODEN: ELBUDL
ELECTRONIC BUSINESS BUYER. 1961. 12/yr. $65 (Canada $96; Mexico $90; elsewhere $120). Cahners Publishing Company (Newton), Division of Reed Elsevier Inc., 275 Washington St., Newton, MA 02158-1630. TEL 617-558-4250. FAX 617-558-4470. (Subscr. to: 44 Cook St., Denver, CO 80206. TEL 800-662-7776) Ed. John Russell. adv.; charts; illus.; mkt.; tr.lit.; circ. 77,331 (controlled). (also avail. in microform; microfiche from CIS) **Indexed:** A.I.Abstr. (until 1992), B.P.I., BPIA, CAD CAM Abstr. (until 1992), Comput.Bus., Comput.Cont., Comput.Dtbs., Comput.Indus.Up., Energy Ind., Energy Info.Abstr., Key to Econ.Sci., Manage.Cont., PROMT, Robomat. (until 1992), SRI, Tel.Abstr., Tr.& Indus.Ind. **Document type:** trade publication.
●Also available online. Vendor(s): DIALOG Information Services, Inc.
—Faxon; UnCover; SWETS; UMI. **CCC.**
Former titles (until 1993): Electronic Business (ISSN 0163-6197); (until 1975): Electronic Purchasing; Electro-Procurement (ISSN 0013-4600)
Description: For the management team in the electronics, computer and systems companies; offers analysis, trends, figures, and forecasts. Examines successful firms and managers and evaluates marketing strategies and manufacturing methods.

643   US   ISSN 0736-5705
ELECTRONIC BUSINESS FORECAST; the early warning forecast for the electronics industry. 1982. s-m. $337 (foreign $387). Cahners Publishing Company (Newton), Business Research Group, Part of the Reed Elsevier group, 275 Washington St., Newton, MA 02158-1630. TEL 617-558-4511. FAX 617-630-2100. Ed. John Farrell. circ. 500. **Document type:** newsletter.

643   US
ELECTRONIC BUYERS' NEWS;* the electronic industry's purchasing newsweekly. 1971. w. $149 (free to qualified personnel). C M P Publications, Inc., 600 Community Dr., Manhasset, NY 11030. TEL 516-562-5000. FAX 516-562-5123. TELEX 647035 CMP PUB MAHA. Ed. Jeremy Young. adv. circ. 65,000. **Indexed:** Comput.Indus.Up.
●Also available online. Vendor(s): NewsNet (EC12).

643 540   US   ISSN 0886-5671
ELECTRONIC CHEMICALS NEWS. 1986. s-m. $452. Chemical Week Associates, 888 Seventh Ave., New York, NY 10106. TEL 212-621-4900. FAX 212-621-4949. Ed. Maurice Marporella.
—CCC.
Description: Covers market developments in the electronic chemicals, materials and processes used in computer and electronics manufacture.

621.381   US   ISSN 0569-5503
TK7801   CODEN: PECCA7
ELECTRONIC COMPONENTS CONFERENCE. PROCEEDINGS. irreg. (approx. a., latest 1986). price varies. (I E E E, Components, Hybrids, and Manufacturing Technology Society) Institute of Electrical and Electronics Engineers, Inc., 345 E. 47th St., New York, NY 10017. TEL 212-705-7900. FAX 212-705-7682. (Subscr. to: Box 1331, 445 Hoes Lane, Piscataway, NJ 08855-1331) **Indexed:** Chem.Abstr. **Document type:** proceedings.
—EI. **CCC.**
Formerly (until 1958): Electronic Components Symposium. Proceedings.
Description: Progress in research, design, development, manufacturing, technology, applications and reliability.

621.381   US   ISSN 0013-4872
TK7800   CODEN: ELODAW
ELECTRONIC DESIGN. 1952. fortn. $95 (foreign $255). Penton Publishing (San Jose) (Subsidiary of: Pittway Company), San Jose Gateway, Ste. 354, 2025 Gateway Pl., San Jose, CA 95110.
TEL 408-441-0550. Ed. Stephen Scrupski. adv.; bk.rev.; abstr.; charts; illus.; pat.; stat.; tr.lit. circ. 165,090. (also avail. in microfilm from UMI; reprint service avail. from UMI) **Indexed:** A.S.& T.Ind., Abstr.Bull.Inst.Pap.Chem., Bus.Ind., Cadscan, Comput.Cont., Comput.Dtbs., Curr.Cont., Eng.Ind., INIS Atomind., Lead Abstr., Sci.Abstr., Tr.& Indus.Ind., Zincscan. **Document type:** trade publication.
●Also available online. Vendor(s): DIALOG Information Services, Inc., Mead Data Central, Inc.
—BLDSC (3700.700000); Faxon; UnCover; SWETS; UMI. **CCC.**
Description: Provides international technical information for design engineers, engineering managers and corporate managers.

643   US   ISSN 0742-1532
ELECTRONIC DISPLAY WORLD. 1980. m. $440. Stanford Resources, Inc., Box 20324, San Jose, CA 95160. TEL 408-448-4440. FAX 408-448-4445. (Dist. in U.S. by: Information Associates, 1259 El Camino Real, Ste. 231, Menlo Park, CA 94025; in Europe by: IPI Rugvaenget 19-21, DK-2630 Taastrup, Denmark; in Japan by: ODS Corporation, Dai-ni Kuyo Bldg., 5-10-2 Minami-Aoyama, Minato-ku, Tokyo 107, Japan. TEL 415-322-0247) Ed. Joseph A. Castellano. index. circ. 400. (looseleaf format; back issues avail.) **Document type:** newsletter.
—CCC.
Description: Covers developments and provides in-depth analyses and forecasts of the worldwide electronic display industry.

643   US   ISSN 1066-5773
ELECTRONIC DISTRIBUTION TODAY. 1991. bi-m. $30. Custom Media, Inc., 7912 Country Ln., Chagrin Falls, OH 44023. TEL 216-543-9451. FAX 216-543-9764. Ed. Edward J. Walter. adv.; circ. 6,495 (controlled). **Document type:** trade publication.
Description: Covers management, sales and marketing, industry trends, purchasing, trade association news and new product information for electronics distributors.

621.381   UK   ISSN 0013-4902
TK6630.A1   CODEN: ELCEA9
ELECTRONIC ENGINEERING. 1928. m. Morgan-Grampian Technical Press Ltd. (Subsidiary of: Morgan-Grampian plc), Morgan-Grampain House, 30 Calderwood St., London SE18 6QH, England. TEL 081-855-7777. FAX 081-854-8814. Ed. Ron Neale. adv. contact: Steve Diprose. charts; illus.; tr.lit.; index. circ. 25,444. (also avail. in microform from UMI,PMC; reprint service avail. from UMI) **Indexed:** A.S.& T.Ind., BMT, Br.Tech.Ind., C.I.S. Abstr., Cadscan, Chem.Abstr., Chem.Eng.Abstr., Curr.Cont., Eng.Ind., Excerp.Med., Lead Abstr., Met.Abstr., PROMT, Sci.Abstr., Zincscan. **Document type:** trade publication.
—BLDSC (3701.000000); Faxon; UnCover; SWETS. **CCC.**

621.381   JA   ISSN 0366-8819
ELECTRONIC ENGINEERING/DENSHI GIJUTSU. (Text in Japanese) 1959. m. 890 Yen per no. Industrial Daily News Ltd. - Nikkan Kogyo Shinbunsha, 8-10, Kudan Kita 1-chome, Chiyoda-ku, Tokyo 102, Japan. TEL 03-3263-2311. FAX 13-3262-4603. TELEX NIKKANKO J29687. Ed. Tatsuo Ohishi. circ. 30,000. **Indexed:** Chem.Abstr., JCT, JTA.
Description: Informat on on software and hardware, new materials, electronic device information, method of designing the latest electronic circuits, and examples of designs of electronic machinery and equipment.

621.381   UK   ISSN 0308-8375
ELECTRONIC ENGINEERING INDEX. 1965. 3/yr. Technical Indexes Ltd., Willoughby Rd., Bracknell, Berks RG12 8DW, England. TEL 0344-426311. FAX 0344-424971. Ed. Tim Mullick. circ. 11,124. **Document type:** abstracting/indexing.
●Also available on CD-ROM.

2176 ELECTRONICS

621.381 US ISSN 0192-1541
TK7800
ELECTRONIC ENGINEERING TIMES;* the industry newspaper for engineers and technical management. 1972. w. $159 in U.S. and Canada; Mexico, S. America, Europe $210; elsewhere $240 (free to qualified personnel). C M P Publications, Inc., 600 Community Dr., Manhasset, NY 11030. TEL 516-562-5000. FAX 516-562-5325. TELEX 647035 CMP PUB MAHA. Ed. Richard Wallace. adv.; circ. 125,000 (controlled). (also avail. in microfiche from UMI) Indexed: A.I.Abstr., CAD CAM Abstr., Comput.Cont., Comput.Dtbs., PROMT, Robomat., Tel.Abstr.
●Also available online. Vendor(s): NewsNet (EC14).
—BLDSC (3701.300000); UMI. **CCC**.

643 KO
ELECTRONIC EQUIPMENT MONTHLY. 1988. m. Electronic Sources International, 498-5 Dapsimri-Dong, Dongdaemun-ku, Seoul, South Korea. TEL 82-2-243-4658. FAX 82-2-249-4279. adv. circ. 9,020.
Description: Reports on equipment, testers, instruments, and related materials in semi-conductor design and manufacture.

ELECTRONIC INDUSTRIES ASSOCIATION. TRADE DIRECTORY AND MEMBERSHIP LIST. see *BUSINESS AND ECONOMICS — Trade And Industrial Directories*

643 US
ELECTRONIC INDUSTRIES ASSOCIATION'S EXECUTIVE REPORT. bi-m. $50 to non-members. Electronic Industries Association, 2001 Pennsylvania Ave. N.W., Washington, DC 20006. TEL 202-457-4950. Ed. Mark V. Rosenker. circ. 5,000. (back issues avail.)

ELECTRONIC INDUSTRY TELEPHONE DIRECTORY (YEAR). see *BUSINESS AND ECONOMICS — Trade And Industrial Directories*

643 US ISSN 0070-9867
ELECTRONIC MARKET DATA BOOK. 1951. a. $75 to members (foreign $87); non-members $125 (foreign $137). Electronic Industries Association, 2001 Pennsylvania Ave. N.W., Washington, DC 20006. TEL 202-457-4950. cum.index. **Indexed:** SRI.
Formerly: Electronic Industries Review; Supersedes: Electronic Industries Yearbook.
Description: Encyclopedia on the US electronic industries, covering the full range of products and technologies with comprehensive sales, production, and background information.

643 US
ELECTRONIC MARKET TRENDS. 1964. m. $100 to members (foreign $136); non-members $150 (foreign $186). Electronic Industries Association, Marketing Services Dept., 2001 Pennsylvania Ave. N.W., Washington, DC 20006. TEL 202-457-4950. abstr.; charts; mkt.; pat.; stat.; index. circ. 350. (also avail. in microfiche from CIS) **Indexed:** PROMT, SRI.
Formerly: Electronics Trends (Washington) (ISSN 0013-4996).
Description: Provides economic information and analysis on the US electronics industry, including coverage of shipments, trade, employment, imports, exports, key economic indicators, and producers and consumer price indices.

ELECTRONIC MARKETING DIRECTORY. see *BUSINESS AND ECONOMICS — Trade And Industrial Directories*

621.381 535 UK ISSN 0957-9737
ELECTRONIC MATERIALS AND PROCESSING. 1990. 6/yr. £247($380) (effective 1994). Elsevier Science Ltd., Oxford Fulfilment Centre, P.O. Box 800, Kidlington, Oxford OX5 1DX, England. TEL 44-865-843000. FAX 44-865-843010. (Subscr. in U.S. and Canada to: Elsevier Science, 660 White Plains Rd., Tarrytown, NY 10591-5153. TEL 914-524-9200. FAX 914-333-2444) Ed. R. Szweda. adv. **Document type:** newsletter.
Formerly: Optoelectronics.
Description: Covers developments in the field of electronics and optoelectronic materials, manufacturing techniques and equipment, and new devices and applications. Concentrates on semiconductors and optically nonlinear materials.

621.381 US ISSN 1045-0955
ELECTRONIC MATERIALS TECHNOLOGY NEWS. 1986. m. $305. Business Communications Co., Inc. (Norwalk), 25 Van Zant St., Ste. 13, Norwalk, CT 06855. TEL 203-853-4266. FAX 203-853-0348. TELEX 6502934929 WUI. Ed. Kurt Miska.
●Also available online. Vendor(s): NewsNet (ML04).

621.381 JA
ELECTRONIC MONTHLY. (Text in Japanese) 1966. m. 200 Yen per no. Shinko Shoji K.K., 1-5, Meguro 1-chome, Meguro-ku, Tokyo 153, Japan.

621.381 US ISSN 1061-6624
HD9696.U5 CODEN: ELNEAU
ELECTRONIC NEWS. 1957. w. $59 (Canada $139; elsewhere $239). International Publishing Corporation (New York), 488 Madison Ave., New York, NY 10022. TEL 212-909-5924. FAX 212-755-2801. Ed. Frank Barbetta. adv.; charts; illus.; mkt.; pat.; tr.lit. circ. 24,000. (also avail. in microform from FCM,MIM,UMI; reprint service avail. from UMI) **Indexed:** B.P.I., Bus.Ind., CAD CAM Abstr., Comput.Bus., Comput.Cont., Comput.Dtbs., Comput.Indus.Up., Comput.Lit.Ind., PROMT, Tr.& Indus.Ind. **Document type:** trade publication.
●Also available online. Vendor(s): DIALOG Information Services, Inc.
—BLDSC (3702.650000);
Former titles (until 1991): Chilton's Electronic News (ISSN 1054-6847); Electronic News (ISSN 0013-4937)

643 UK
ELECTRONIC NEWS. w. 121 Kingsway, London WC2B 6PA, England. TEL 071-831-3607. FAX 071-831-6485. Ed. James Fallon. circ. 75,000.

621.38 HK ISSN 0259-1235
ELECTRONIC NEWS FOR CHINA. Key Title: Guoji Dianzi Shangqing. (Text in Chinese and English) 1985. m. Y160 (effective 1991). Asian Sources Media Group, 20/F, Vita Tower, 29, Wong Chuk Hang Rd., Hong Kong. TEL 852-555-4777. FAX 852-870-0816. (Subscr. to: China Media Ltd., G.P.O. Box 11112, Hong Kong) Ed. Stephanie Chin. circ. 17,350.
Formerly: Electronics for China.
Description: For Chinese managers and government officials, who are involved the development, purchasing and marketing of electronic compenents, materials, equipments and telecommunications products.

643 UK
ELECTRONIC OFFICE. s-m. £399. Financial Times Business Information Ltd., Tower House, Southampton St., London WC2E 7HA, England. TEL 071-240 9391. FAX 071-240-7946. TELEX 296926-BUSINF-G. (Subscr. to: Tessa Edgecombe, Financial Times Business Information, Tower House, Southampton St., London WC2E 7HA, England)
●Also available online. Vendor(s): Data-Star, Mead Data Central, Inc.
Description: Covers office technology, vendors, equipment, systems, international standards, attitudes. Case studies on automation successes and failures.

621.381 US ISSN 0013-4945
TK7870 CODEN: ELPPA5
ELECTRONIC PACKAGING & PRODUCTION. 1961. m. $79.95 (Canada $117.65; Mexico $109.95; elsewhere $144.95). Cahners Publishing Company (Des Plaines), Division of Reed Elsevier Inc., 1350 E. Touhy Ave., Box 5080, Des Plaines, IL 60017-5080. TEL 708-635-8800. FAX 708-299-8622. (Subscr. to: 44 Cook St., Denver, CO 80206. TEL 800-662-7776) Ed. Don Swanson. adv.; tr.lit.; index. circ. 40,000. (also avail. in microform from UMI) **Indexed:** CAD CAM Abstr. (until 1992), Comput.Cont., Eng.Ind., Robomat. (until 1992), Sci.Abstr. **Document type:** trade publication.
—BLDSC (3702.680000); EI; UnCover; SWETS; UMI. **CCC**.
Description: For engineers and managers involved in printed circuit (including hybrid circuit) board design, and in the packaging, production and testing of electronic products and equipment.

643 BE
ELECTRONIC PRODUCT NEWS. 1972. 11/yr. Pan European Publishing Co. (Subsidiary of: Reed Elsevier plc), Rue Verte 216, B-1210 Brussels, Belgium. TEL 32-2-2402611. FAX 32-2-2427111. TELEX 25828. Ed. J.P. Joosting. adv.; circ. 60,000 (controlled).
Description: Reports exclusively on what is new and improved in electronic components, instruments and services from manufacturers worldwide.

643 UK
ELECTRONIC PRODUCT NEWS. 11/yr. 85 Carlton Rd., Redhill, Surrey RH1 2BZ, England. TEL 0737-761788. FAX 0737-779503. Ed. Ian Hemsworth. circ. 7,723.

643 UK
ELECTRONIC PRODUCT REVIEW. 1984. 10/yr. £35($159) Wilmington Publishing, Wilmington House, Church Hill, Dartford, Kent UA2 7EF, England. TEL 0322-277788. FAX 0322-276474. (Subscr. to: Ferrari House, 258 Field End Rd., Ruislip, Middx HA4 9AU. TEL 081-868-4499) Ed. Phil Brown. circ. 40,000.

621.381 UK ISSN 0306-333X
CODEN: ELPDB4
ELECTRONIC PRODUCTION. 1972. m. £46($174) in Europe; elsewhere £58 (effective 1994) (free to qualified personnel). Angel Publishing Ltd., Kingsland House, 361 City Rd., London EC1V 1LR, England. TEL 071-417-7400. FAX 071-417-7500. Ed. Steven Keeping. adv. contact: Steve Wyper. bk.rev.; charts; illus.; pat.; stat.; tr.lit.; circ. 13,000 (controlled). (back issues avail.) **Indexed:** Sci.Abstr. **Document type:** trade publication.
—BLDSC (3702.688000); Faxon; SWETS; CASDDS. **CCC**.
Description: For production engineers concerned with the manufacture of electronic products and equipment.
Refereed Serial

643 US ISSN 0013-4953
TK7870
ELECTRONIC PRODUCTS. 1958. 12/yr. $50 (free to qualified engineers). Hearst Business Communications, Inc., 645 Stewart Ave., Garden City, NY 11530. TEL 516-227-1300. FAX 516-227-1444. Ed. Frank Egan. adv.; bk.rev.; illus.; mkt.; tr.lit.; circ. 124,126 (controlled). (also avail. in microfilm from UMI; reprint service avail. from UMI) **Indexed:** Curr.Cont., Eng.Ind., Sh.& Vib.Dig. **Document type:** trade publication.
—BLDSC (3702.694000); EI; Faxon; SWETS; UMI.
Description: Developments in products and technology for electronic design engineers.

ELECTRONIC PRODUCTS FINDER. see *BUSINESS AND ECONOMICS — Production Of Goods And Services*

621.381 US ISSN 0013-4961
TK7800 CODEN: ELTPAP
ELECTRONIC PROGRESS. 1956. q. free to qualified personnel. Raytheon Co., Lexington, MA 02173. TEL 617-862-6600. Ed. John E. Severance. adv.; bibl.; charts; illus.; stat.; index. circ. 15,000. (also avail. in microfilm from UMI; reprint service avail. from UMI) **Indexed:** Phys.Abstr., PROMT, Sci.Abstr.
—BLDSC (3702.700000); UMI.

621.381 UK
ELECTRONIC QUALITY ASSURANCE DOCUMENTS. Short title: E Q A D. 1980. bi-m. Technical Indexes Ltd., Willoughby Rd., Bracknell, Berkshire RG12 8DW, England. TEL 0344-426311. FAX 0344-424971. **Document type:** abstracting/indexing.
●Also available on CD-ROM.
Former titles: Electronic Quality Assurance Microfile; Electronic Components of Assessed Quality Microfile.

ELECTRONIC REPRESENTATIVES DIRECTORY (YEAR). see *BUSINESS AND ECONOMICS — Trade And Industrial Directories*

ELECTRONICS

621.381　　　US　ISSN 0278-9922
TK7870
ELECTRONIC SERVICING & TECHNOLOGY; the how-to magazine of electronics. 1951. m. $24.50 to qualified personnel. C Q Communications, Inc., 76 N. Broadway, Hicksville, NY 11801. TEL 516-681-2922. FAX 516-681-2926. Ed. Conrad Persson. adv.; bk.rev.; charts; illus.; tr.lit.; index. circ. 28,528. (also avail. in microform from UMI; reprint service avail. from UMI) **Document type:** trade publication.
—UMI.
Formerly: Electronic Servicing (ISSN 0013-497X); Incorporates: P F Reporter; (1953-1982): Electronic Technician-Dealer (ISSN 0192-7175); Which was formerly: Electronic Technician (ISSN 0013-4988)
Description: The how-to magazine for professional servicers of consumer electronics and computer equipment.

621.38 001.64　　　HK
ELECTRONIC TECHNOLOGY. (Text in Chinese) 1969. m. HK.$480($80) (effective 1993). Electronic Technology Publishing Co., 15 Shing Yip St., 9th Fl., Block 1, Kwun Tong, Kowloon, Hong Kong. TEL 342-8298. FAX 341-4247. Ed. Peter Luk. adv. circ. 35,000. (also avail. in microfilm from PMC) **Document type:** trade publication.

643　　　US
ELECTRONIC WORLD NEWS.* 1989. m. C M P Publications, Inc., 600 Community Dr., Manhasset, NY 11030. TEL 516-562-5000. Ed. Eric Lundquist. adv.; circ. 32,000 (controlled). **Indexed:** Abstr.Hum.Comp.Inter.
●Also available online. Vendor(s): NewsNet (EC13).
Description: For corporate and managing engineers. Covers the buying and selling of electronics on a global scale.

621.381　　　SP
ELECTRONICA HOY.* 11/yr. V N U Business Publications Espana, S.A., C. Cinca 13, 28020 Madrid, Spain. TEL 1-355-82-02. FAX 1-245-95-62. circ. 10,000.

621.38　　　SP　ISSN 1130-6971
ELECTRONICA Y COMUNICACIONES MAGAZINE. 1974. 11/yr. 7000 ptas. (foreign 16000 ptas.). Editorial Cypsela, Apdo. 8054, 08080 Barcelona, Spain. TEL 3-412-38-99. FAX 3-318-29-71. Ed. Llorenc Aulesa. adv.: B&W page 80000 ptas., color page 125000 ptas.; 265 x 190. circ. 12,000. **Document type:** consumer publication.

621.38　　　US　ISSN 0883-4989
TK7800
ELECTRONICS. 1930. s-w. $98 in U.S.; Canada & Latin America $120; elsewhere $190. Penton Publishing (San Jose) (Subsidiary of: Pittway Company), San Jose Gateway, Ste. 354, 2025 Gateway Pl., San Jose, CA 95110. TEL 408-441-0550. Ed. Jonah McLeod. adv.; bk.rev.; charts; illus.; stat.; tr.lit. circ. 85,061. (also avail. in microfilm from UMI,PMC; reprint service avail. from UMI) **Indexed:** A.I.Abstr., A.S.& T.Ind., Acad.Ind., Appl.Mech.Rev., ASCA, Biol.Abstr., BMT, CAD CAM Abstr. (until 1992), Chem.Abstr., Comput.Bus., Comput.Cont., Comput.Indus.Up., Curr.Cont., Deep Sea Res.& Oceanogr.Abstr., Eng.Ind., Excerp.Med., Graph.Arts Lit.Abstr., Ind.Sci.Rev., INIS Atomind., Mag.Ind., Met.Abstr., Photo.Abstr., PROMT, Risk Abstr., Robomat. (until 1992), Sci.Abstr., Sci.Cit.Ind., SRI, Tel.Abstr., Tr.& Indus.Ind., World Text.Abstr.
Document type: trade publication.
●Also available online. Vendor(s): DIALOG Information Services, Inc. (File no.624/McGRAW-HILL PUBLICATIONS ONLINE), Mead Data Central, Inc.
—BLDSC (3703.000000); Faxon; UnCover; SWETS; UMI. **CCC.**
Former titles (until 1985): Electronics Week (ISSN 0748-3252); (until 1984): Electronics (ISSN 0013-5070)
Description: Reports on worldwide technical and industry developments of interest to corporate and engineering management in the electronics industry.

643　　　UK
ELECTRONICS. m. 16 Malyons Rd., Hextable, Kent BR8 7RE, England. TEL 0322-664355. FAX 0322-669829. TELEX 94017788-FLET-G. Ed. Peter Fletcher. circ. 150,427.

621.381　　　UK　ISSN 0954-0695
TK6540　　　CODEN: ECEJE9
ELECTRONICS & COMMUNICATION ENGINEERING JOURNAL. 1939. bi-m. £77 in EC nations; elsewhere £85. I.E.E, Michael Faraday House, Six Hills Way, Stevenage, Herts. SG1 2AY, England. TEL 0438-313311. FAX 0438-742840. TELEX 825578-IEESTV-G. (Subscr. to: Publications Sales Dept., P.O. Box 96, Stevenage, Herts. SG1 2SD, England; U.S. Addr.: INSPEC/IEEE, Box 1331, 445 Hoes Ln., Piscataway, NJ 08855-1331. TEL 908-562-5549) Ed.Bd. adv.; bk.rev.; bibl.; charts; illus.; index. circ. 25,000. **Indexed:** A.S.& T.Ind., Br.Tech.Ind., Chem.Abstr., Curr.Cont., Eng.Ind., Excerp.Med., Fuel & Energy Abstr., Int.Aerosp.Abstr., Met.Abstr., Ref.Zh., Sci.Abstr., Sci.Cit.Ind., World Text.Abstr. **Document type:** academic/scholarly publication.
—BLDSC (3703.127000); EI; Faxon; UnCover; SWETS. **CCC.**
Former titles: Institution of Electronic and Radio Engineers. Journal (ISSN 0267-1689); Radio and Electronic Engineer (ISSN 0033-7722); British Institution of Radio Engineers. Journal (ISSN 0538-0022); Incorporates: Institution of Electronic and Radio Engineers. Proceedings.
Description: Provides in-depth coverage of new work for practicing engineers.

ELECTRONICS AND COMMUNICATIONS ABSTRACTS. see COMMUNICATIONS — Abstracting, Bibliographies, Statistics

ELECTRONICS AND COMMUNICATIONS ABSTRACTS JOURNAL. see COMMUNICATIONS — Abstracting, Bibliographies, Statistics

621.381　　　US　ISSN 0424-8368
TK7800　　　CODEN: ECOJAL
ELECTRONICS AND COMMUNICATIONS IN JAPAN. (Selected English translation of transactions of the institute; Published in 3 parts: Part I - Communications; Part II - Electronic and Electronic Devices; Part III - Fundamental Electronics Science) 1963. 36/yr. (each part published m.). $2460 (Canada & Mexico $2820; elsewhere $2955). (Institute of Electronics, Information and Communication Engineers, JA - Denshi Joho Tsushin Gakkai)˙Scripta Technica, Inc. (Subsidiary of: John Wiley & Sons, Inc.), 7961 Eastern Ave., Silver Spring, MD 20910. TEL 301-588-0484. FAX 301-588-5278. (Dist. by: John Wiley & Sons, Inc. Periodicals Division, 650 Third Ave., New York, NY 10158. TEL 212-692-6000) Ed. Tatsuo Itoh. adv.; charts; illus.; pat.; index. circ. 425. (also avail. in microform from UMI) **Indexed:** CAD CAM Abstr., Eng.Ind., INSPEC, Math.R., Tel.Abstr. **Document type:** academic/scholarly publication.
—**CCC.**

621.381　　　UK　ISSN 0965-030X
ELECTRONICS AND ELECTRICAL ENGINEERING. 1968. m. £6 to non-members. Institution of Electronics & Electrical Incorporated Engineers, Savoy Hill House, Savoy Hill, London WC2R OBS, England. TEL 071-836-3357. FAX 071-497-9006. Ed. P.R. Bennett. adv.; bk.rev.; bibl. circ. 28,000. (tabloid format) **Document type:** bulletin.
Formerly (until 1990): Electrical and Electronics Incorporated Engineer; (until 1983): Incorporated Engineer; I E E I E Bulletin; (until 1982): I E E T E Bulletin (ISSN 0018-9561)
Description: Carries news of the institution and reports on events, courses, and lectures. Also covers electrical and electronics developments.

621.38　　　AT　ISSN 1036-0212
ELECTRONICS AUSTRALIA WITH E T I. 1990. m. Aus.$47. Federal Publishing Company, 180 Bourke Rd., Alexandria, N.S.W. 2015, Australia. Ed. Jim Rowe. adv.; bk.rev.; charts; illus.; record rev.; tr.lit.; index. circ. 23,315. **Indexed:** Aus.Rd.Ind., Gdlns., Pinpointer, Sci.Abstr.
—UMI.
Formed by the merger of (1966-1990): Electronics Today (ISSN 0313-0150); (1972-1990): Electronics Today International (ISSN 0811-0727)

643　　　CN　ISSN 0046-1733
ELECTRONICS COMMUNICATOR. 1970. 40/yr. Can.$575. Evert Communications Ltd., 1296 Carling Ave., Ottawa, ON K1Z 7K8, Canada. TEL 613-728-4621. FAX 613-728-0385. Ed. Gordon Hutchison. **Document type:** newsletter.
Description: Deals with the market for electronic products, in particular Canadian-based manufacture.

643　　　UK　ISSN 0960-7897
ELECTRONICS EUROPE; analysing strategies of electronics companies in europe. 1989. 18/yr. £465($700) Portman Communications Ltd., 52 Foundling Ct. London WC1N 1AN, England. TEL 071-877-0815. FAX 071-278-9917. Ed. Philip Gallagher. circ. 10,000. **Document type:** newsletter.
Description: Concerned with regulatory issues and corporate strategies in Europe's computer, semiconductor, and consumer electronics sectors.

621.381 621.384　　　US
ELECTRONICS EXPERIMENTERS HANDBOOK (YEAR). 1983. s-a. $3 95. Gernsback Publications, Inc., 500-B Bi-County Blvd., Farmingdale, NY 11735. TEL 516-293-3000. FAX 516-293-3115. Ed. Brian Fenton. adv.; bk.rev.; charts; illus. circ. 135,000. (back issues avail.; reprint service avail. from UMI) **Indexed:** Sci.Abstr.
Former titles: Radio Electronics Electronics Experimenters Handbook (Year); (until 1987): Radio - Electronics Annual.
Description: Collection of reprinted articles from Electronics Now magazine. Feature articles include coverage on microcomputers, hardware and peripherals, as well as new product reviews.

643　　　US
ELECTRONICS FOR KIDS OF ALL AGES.* Issued with: Toy & Hobby World (ISSN 0041-011X) s-a. Toy & Hobby World (Subsidiary of: V S D Communications), 41 Madison Ave., New York, NY 10010-2202. TEL 212-594-4237. adv. circ. 17,777.

643　　　II　ISSN 0013-516X
ELECTRONICS FOR YOU. (Text in English) 1969. m. $62 includes EFY Directory. E F Y Enterprises Pvt. Ltd., D-87-1 Okhla Industrial Area, Phase-1, New Delhi 110 020, India. TEL 11-6812312. FAX 11-6817563. TELEX 31-75147 BOND IN. Ed. Ramesh Chopra. adv.: B&W page $500, color page $1000; trim 23 x 17. bk.rev.; charts; illus.; stat. circ. 80,000.

382 643　　　US
ELECTRONICS FOREIGN TRADE. 1977. m. $100 to members (foreign $160); non-members $150 (foreign $210). Electronic Industries Association, Marketing Services Dept., 2001 Pennsylvania Ave. N.W., Washington, DC 20006. TEL 202-457-4950. stat. (also avail. in microfiche from CIS) **Indexed:** SRI.
Formerly: E I A International Report.
Description: Provides statistical guide to US imports, exports, and balance-of-trade information, with the top ten foreign markets, top ten foreign suppliers, and bilateral trade data on the electronic industries.

643 332.6　　　US
ELECTRONICS INDUSTRY OUTLOOK. 1986. m. $365. Rolander Financial Services, 126 Ponderosa Dr., Box 616, Santa Cruz, CA 95061. TEL 408-439-8510. FAX 408-438-0542. Ed. Charles Rolander.

643　　　CC
ELECTRONICS INTERNATIONAL - CHINA REPORT. (Text in English) 1987. s-m. $265. Electronics International Publishing House, P.O. Box 750, Beijing, People's Republic of China. TEL 8214356. Ed. Liu Xiaofeng. (back issues avail.)
Description: Reports the latest developments in policies, investment environment, market trends and forecasts of China's electronics industry.

643　　　US
ELECTRONICS: LATIN AMERICAN INDUSTRIAL REPORT. (Avail. for each of 22 Latin American countries) 1985. a. $435 per country report. Aquino Productions, Box 15760, Stamford, CT 06901. TEL 203-325-3138. Ed. Andres C. Aquino.

ELECTRONICS

643 — UK — ISSN 0013-5194
TK7800 — CODEN: ELLEAK
ELECTRONICS LETTERS. 1965. fortn. £435. I.E.E, Michael Faraday House, Six Hills Way, Stevenage, Herts. SG1 2AY, England. TEL 0438-313311. FAX 0438-742840. TELEX 825578-IEESTV-G. (Subscr. to: Publications Sales Dept., P.O. Box 96, Stevenage, Herts. SG1 2SD, England; U.S. Addr.: INSPEC/IEEE, Box 1331, 445 Hoes Ln., Piscataway, NJ 08855-1331. TEL 908-562-5549) Ed. M. Fox. adv.; charts; illus.; index. circ. 2,200. **Indexed:** Cadscan, Ceram.Abstr., Chem.Abstr., Curr.Cont., Deep Sea Res.& Oceanogr.Abstr., Eng.Ind., Excerp.Med., Ind.Sci.Rev., INIS Atomind., Int.Aerosp.Abstr., Lead Abstr., Met.Abstr., Sci.Abstr., Sci.Cit.Ind., World Alum.Abstr., Zincscan. **Document type:** academic/scholarly publication.
● Also available online.
— BLDSC (3705.060000); Faxon; UnCover; SWETS; UMI; CASDDS. **CCC.**
Description: Offers speedy dissemination of research and development results in electronics, control, communication, and allied subjects.

621.381 — UK
▼**ELECTRONICS LETTERS ONLINE.** 1993. d. I.E.E., Michael Faraday House, Six Hills Way, Stevenage, Herts. SG1 2AY, England. TEL 0438-313311. FAX 0438-742840. TELEX 825578-IEESTV-G.
● Available only online.

621.381 — UK — ISSN 0265-301X
ELECTRONICS MANUFACTURE AND TEST. 1982. m. £55 in the UK; Europe £75; elsewhere £100. I M L Group plc, Blair House, High St., Tonbridge, Kent TN9 1BQ, England. TEL 0732-359990. FAX 0732-770049. Ed. Gordon Wong. circ. 11,891. (back issues avail.)
— BLDSC (3705.092500).

621.381 — US
ELECTRONICS MANUFACTURING. q. $45 to individuals; institutions $60. Society of Manufacturing Engineers, One SME Dr., Box 930, Dearborn, MI 48121-0930. TEL 313-271-1500. FAX 313-271-2861. TELEX 297742 SME UR (VIA RCA).

621.381 — UK
ELECTRONICS MATERIALS INFORMATION SERVICE DATAREVIEWS. irreg., vol.9, 1994. Institution of Electrical Engineers, Michael Faraday House, Six Hills Way, Stevenage, Herts. SG1 2AY, England. TEL 0438-313311. FAX 0438-313465. TELEX 825578-IEESTV-G. Ed. B.L. Weiss. **Document type:** monographic series.

537 643 — AT — ISSN 0311-0230
ELECTRONICS NEWS. 1973. m. Aus.$60. Reed Business Publishing Pty. Ltd. (Subsidiary of: Reed International PLC), 1-5 Railway St., Chatswood, N.S.W. 2067, Australia. TEL 02-372-5222. FAX 02-419-7599. Ed. R. Chirgwin. circ. 10,967. (tabloid format) **Indexed:** CAD CAM Abstr.

621.381 — JA — ISSN 0913-199X
ELECTRONICS NEWS FROM FUJITSU. (Text in English) m. Fujitsu Ltd., Public Relations Department - Fujitsu K.K. Kohoshitsu, 6-1, Marunouchi 1-chome, Chiyoda-ku, Tokyo 100, Japan.

621.381 — US
TK6540 — CODEN: RAECAB
ELECTRONICS NOW; technology, audio, video, computers, projects. 1929. m. $19.97. Gernsback Publications, Inc., 500-B Bi-County Blvd., Farmingdale, NY 11735. TEL 516-293-3000. FAX 516-293-3115. (Subscr. to: Box 51866, Boulder, CO 80322) Ed. Brian Fenton. adv.: B&W page $6440, color page $8435. bk.rev.; charts; illus.; tr.lit.; index. circ. 171,679. (also avail. in microfilm from UMI; microfiche from UMI,MCE; reprint service avail. from UMI) **Indexed:** A.S.& T.Ind., Consum.Ind., Ind.How To Do It (1977-), Mag.Ind., Microcomp.Ind., PROMT, R.G.
— Faxon; UnCover; SWETS. **CCC.**
Incorporates: Radio-Electronics (ISSN 0033-7862)
Description: Reports on microcomputers, the electronics industry, technology, and service. Coverage includes feature articles, building projects, products reviews.

621.381 — US
ELECTRONICS PACKAGING FORUM. a. Van Nostrand Reinhold Co., 115 Fifth Ave., New York, NY 10003. TEL 212-254-3232.

621.9 — HK
ELECTRONICS PRODUCTION EQUIPMENT NEWS. Short title: E P E. (Text in English) bi-m. B & I Publication Co., Ltd., 18-F, First Pacific Bank Centre, 51-57 Gloucester Rd., Wanchai, Hong Kong. TEL 852-865-2633. FAX 852-866-1770.
Description: Covers production machinery, materials and products for the electronics industry.

621.3 — CC
ELECTRONICS SCIENCE. (Text in Chinese) m. Shanghai Advertising Corp., 97 Yuanmingyuan Lu, Shanghai, People's Republic of China. Ed. C.P. Ho. adv. circ. 100,000.

621.381 — UK
ELECTRONICS TECHNOLOGY INTERNATIONAL. q. Essex House, Regent St., Cambridge CB2 3AB, England. TEL 0223-324330. FAX 0223-355470. Ed. David Manners.

621.381 — UK
▼**ELECTRONICS TESTING REVIEW.** 1993. a. Warwick House, Azalea Dr., Swanley, Kent BR8 8HY, England. TEL 0322-660070. FAX 0322-667633. Ed. Tony Doran. circ. 10,000. **Document type:** trade publication.

621.381 — UK — ISSN 0957-5456
ELECTRONICS - THE MAPLIN MAGAZINE. 1981. m. £19.92 (foreign £41). Maplin Electronics Plc., Maplin House, 274-288 London Rd., Hadleigh, Benfleet, Essex SS7 2DE. TEL 0702-554155. FAX 0702-553935. (Subscr. to: P.O. Box 3, Rayleigh, Essex SS6 8LR, England. TEL 0702-554161) Ed. Robert Ball. adv. contact: Eric Richardson. bk.rev. circ. 23,600. **Document type:** consumer publication.

643 — UK
ELECTRONICS TIMES. 1978. w. $215. Morgan-Grampian Technical Press Ltd. (Subsidiary of: Morgan-Grampian plc), Morgan-Grampian House, 30 Calderwood St., London SE18 6QH, England. TEL 081-855-7777. FAX 081-854-1793. Ed. John Walko. adv. contact: Stuart Baker. circ. 29,016. **Indexed:** Sci.Abstr. **Document type:** trade publication.

621.381 — JA — ISSN 0914-353X
ELECTRONICS UPDATE. (Text in Japanese) m. 250 Yen per no. Japan Tech Co., Ltd. - Nihon Tekku K.K., 2-5, Tsukudo Hachiman-cho, Shinjuku-ku, Tokyo 162, Japan.

643 — UK — ISSN 0013-5224
ELECTRONICS WEEKLY. 1960. w. £73 (foreign £93). Reed Business Publishing Ltd. (Subsidiary of: Reed Elsevier group), Quadrant House, The Quadrant, Sutton, Surrey SM2 5AS, England. TEL 081-652-3142. FAX 081-652-8956. Ed. Mick Elliott. adv. contact: Richard Napier. bk.rev.; charts; illus.; mkt.; tr.lit. circ. 31,765. (also avail. in microform from UMI; reprint service avail. from UMI) **Indexed:** Br.Tech.Ind., Comput.Dtbs., F.A.C.T., PROMT, Sci.Abstr. **Document type:** newspaper.
— BLDSC (3705.475000); EI; SWETS; UMI. **CCC.**

621.381 — UK — ISSN 0266-3244
TK5700 — CODEN: EWWOEG
ELECTRONICS WORLD & WIRELESS WORLD. 1911. m. £30 (foreign £35). Reed Business Publishing Ltd. (Subsidiary of: Reed Elsevier group), Quadrant House, The Quadrant, Sutton, Surrey SM2 5AS, England. TEL 081-652-3128. FAX 081-652-8956. TELEX 892082-REEDBP-G. (Subscr. to: Reed Business Publishing, Stuart House, Perrymount Rd., Haywards Heath, W. Sussex RH16 3DH, England. TEL 0444-445566) Ed. Frank Ogden. adv.; bk.rev.; charts; illus. circ. 20,000. (also avail. in microform from UMI,PMC) **Indexed:** A.I.Abstr., A.S.& T.Ind., Agri.Eng.Abstr., ASCA, BMT, Br.Tech.Ind., Curr.Cont., Eng.Ind., Fluidex, Sci.Abstr., Tel.Abstr., World Text.Abstr. **Document type:** trade publication.
— UnCover. **CCC.**
Formerly (until 1983): Wireless World (ISSN 0043-6062)

621.381 — SZ
ELECTRONIQUE. 10/yr. 60 SFr. Verlag Aargauer Tagblatt AG, Bahnhofstrasse 39-43, 5001 Aarau, Switzerland. adv.

643 — FR
ELECTRONIQUE EUROPE 2000. 6/yr. Kathya de Brinon Edition, 18 bis, rue Violet, 75015 Paris, France. TEL 47-05-58-11. Ed. Kathya de Brinon. circ. 20,000.
Description: Provides technical and professional information in the electronics field.

621.38 — FR
ELECTRONIQUE PRATIQUE. 11/yr. 335 F. Publications George Ventillard, 2-12 rue de Bellevue, 75940 Paris Cedex 19, France. Ed. Bernard Fighiera.

621.38 — UK — ISSN 0306-8552
CODEN: ETNYBB
ELECTROTECHNOLOGY. 1965. bi-m. £30 to non-members. Institution of Electronics & Electrical Incorporated Engineers, Savoy Hill House, Savoy Hill, London WC2R 0BS, England. TEL 071-836-3357. FAX 071-447-9006. Ed. B. Dunkley. adv.; bk.rev. circ. 28,000. **Indexed:** Br.Tech.Ind., Sci.Abstr.
— BLDSC (3709.545000).
Formerly: Electrical and Electronics Technician Engineers (ISSN 0013-421X)
Description: Keeps its readers up-to-date with industrial and technological developments, trends in electrical and electronics technology, and selected application notes.

ELECTROTECNIA POPULAR. see *ENGINEERING — Electrical Engineering*

621.381 — RM
ELECTROTEHNICA, ELECTRONICA SI AUTOMATICA. ELECTROTEHNICA. (Text in Romanian; summaries in English, French, German and Russian) 1952. 8/yr. 30 lei($15) Ministerul Industriei Constructiilor de Masini, Str. Jon Ghica Nr. 3, Bucharest, Rumania. (Subscr. to: Il xim, Str. 13 Decembrie Nr. 3,P.O. Box 136-137, Bucharest, Rumania) Ed. Dr. Aurel Avramescu. adv.; bk.rev.; abstr.; bibl.; charts; illus.; index. circ. 2,400. **Indexed:** Chem.Abstr., Eng.Ind., Sci.Abstr.
Formerly: Electrotehnica (ISSN 0013-5321)

621.381 — PO
ELEKTOR. 11/yr. Rua D. Estefania 32-1o, 1000 Lisbon, Portugal. TEL 572763. FAX 522643. TELEX 64198 FERBEN P. Ed. Antonio Pancianelli. circ. 5,500.

621.381 — UK — ISSN 0268-4519
ELEKTOR ELECTRONICS. (Editions in Dutch, French, German, Greek, Hungarian, Italian, Polish, Portuguese, Spanish) 1960. m. (11/yr.). £25 (Europe £34; elsewhere £43). Elektor Electronics (Publishing), P.O. Box 1414, Dorchester, Dorset DT2 8YH, England. TEL 44-305-250996. FAX 44-305-250996. (Subscr. to: Worldwide Subscription Service, Unit 4, Gibbs Reed Farm, Ticehurst TN5 7HE, England. TEL 44-580-200657) Ed. L. Seymour. adv.; bk.rev.; abstr.; illus.; index. circ. 19,300. **Indexed:** Comput.Dtbs., Tr.& Indus.Ind. **Document type:** consumer publication.
— BLDSC (3710.550000); SWETS.
Formerly (until 1984): Elektor (ISSN 0308-308X)
Description: Features articles on electronics technology and projects under way in the electronics industry geared for those working in the industry; also discusses new products and contains a Buyer's Guide.

643 — FR — ISSN 0181-7450
ELEKTOR - ELECTRONIQUE. 1978. m. 250 F. (foreign 480 F.) (effective Sep. 1992). Publitronic, Les Trois Tilleuls, B.P. 59, F-59850 Nieppe, France. TEL 20-48-64-64. FAX 20-48-69-64. circ. 32,995. (back issues avail.)
— SWETS.
Description: Building descriptions of do-it-yourself electronic circuits.

643 — GW
DIE ELEKTRO-INDUSTRIE, ELEKTRONIK UND IHRE HELFER. 1952. a. $47. Industrieschau-Verlagsgesellschaft mbH, Postfach 100262, 64202 Darmstadt, Germany. TEL 06151-3892-0. FAX 06151-33164. (U.S. subscr. to: Western Hemisphere Publishing Corp., Box 847, Hillsboro, OR 97123-0847. TEL 503-640-3736. FAX 503-640-2748) Ed. Margit Selka. adv.; charts; illus. circ. 8,000. **Document type:** directory.
● Also available online.
Also available on CD-ROM.

ELECTRONICS

643 GW ISSN 0013-5577
ELEKTROMARKT. 1918. 10/yr. DM.99. Vogel Verlag und Druck KG, Max-Planck-Str. 7-9, 97082 Wuerzburg, Germany. TEL 0931-4182145. FAX 0931-4182640. (Subscr. to: Vogel Verlag, 97064 Wuerzburg, Germany; Dist. in U.S. by: Vogel Europublishing, Inc., 20092 Gibbs Dr., Sonora, CA 95370. TEL 209-533-3555. FAX 209-533-9555) Ed. Elmo Schwandke. adv.: B&W page DM.5760, color page DM.8037; trim 270 x 190. illus.; circ. 20,000. (controlled). (processed) **Document type:** trade publication.
—CCC.

537 GR ISSN 1105-1930
HD9685.G84
ELEKTRON. (Text in Greek) 1988. m. Demosia Epiheirese Elektrismou, Chalkokondyle 30, 4 Orophos, Athens, Greece.

621.381 NE ISSN 0168-7840
ELEKTRONICA. 1951. fortn. fl.140. Kluwer Technische Tijdshcriften, Postbus 23, 7400 GA Deventer, Netherlands. TEL 05700-48699. FAX 05700-43015. Ed. H. de Vries. adv.; bk.rev.; charts; illus.; index. circ. 10,181. **Indexed:** Sci.Abstr.
—BLDSC (3717.453000); SWETS. **CCC.**
Former titles: R E - Radio Electronica; Radio Electronica (ISSN 0033-7854)

621.381 NE
ELEKTRONICA REVUE. (Supplement to: Technische Revue (ISSN 0165-3202)) 8/yr. C. Misset B.V., Hanzestr. 1, 7006 RH Doetinchem, Netherlands. TEL 31-8340-49911. FAX 31-8340-43839. TELEX 45481. (Subscr. to: Postbus 4, 7000 BA Doetinchem, Netherlands) Ed. J.F.F. van Bruggen. adv. contact: Cor van Nek. circ. controlled. **Document type:** trade publication.
Formerly: T.R. Elektronika.
Description: Product information on the complete electronics market.

621.381 GW ISSN 0013-5658
CODEN: EKRKAR
ELEKTRONIK; Fachzeitschrift fuer Entwickler und industrielle Anwender. 1954. bi-w. DM.164 (foreign DM.175). Franzis Verlag GmbH, Karlstr. 41, Postfach 370280, 80333 Munich, Germany. TEL 089-5117-284. FAX 089-5117363. Ed. Wolfgang Hascher. adv.; bk.rev.; abstr.; illus.; upd. 27 92165. circ. 25,823. **Indexed:** Cyb.Abstr., Eng.Ind., Excerp.Med., INIS Atomind., Sci.Abstr., VITIS.
—BLDSC (3717.500000); SWETS; UMI. **CCC.**
Description: Trade magazine for the electronics industry. Covers current developments, industrial applications, microcomputers, software engineering, and new products.

643 AU
ELEKTRONIK AKTUELL. m. S.350. Poetzleinsdorferstr. 164-6, A-1180 Vienna, Austria. TEL 01-443376. FAX 01-44337622. Ed. Franz Maderbacher.
Document type: consumer publication.

621.381 DK ISSN 0108-8149
ELEKTRONIK INDKOEBSBOGEN. 1979. a. DKK 235. Teknisk Forlag A-S, Skelbaekgade 4, DK-1780 Copenhagen V, Denmark. TEL 45-31-21-68-01. FAX 45-31-21-04-01. illus.

643 AU
ELEKTRONIK INDUSTRIELL. m. Dialog Verlag GmbH, Marschallplatz 23-1-21, A-1125 Vienna, Austria. TEL 01-8040474. FAX 01-8044439. Ed. Gerhard Buchenberger. circ. 17,700.

621.381 GW ISSN 0343-6675
ELEKTRONIK INFORMATIONEN. 1968. 12/yr. DM.120. A T Fachverlag GmbH, Postfach 500180, 70331 Stuttgart, Germany. TEL 0711-952951-0. FAX 0711-952951-99. Ed. Ralf-P. Hazebrouck. circ. 19,443. **Document type:** trade publication.

621.381 GW ISSN 0013-5674
ELEKTRONIK JOURNAL. 1966. m. DM.158 (foreign DM.170). Verlag Moderne Industrie, Justus-von-Liebig-Str. 1, 86899 Landsberg, Germany. TEL 08191-125-0. FAX 08191-125483. Ed. Michael Himmelstoss. adv.: B&W page DM.6700; trim 257 x 178; adv. contact: Hermann Kleiner. bk.rev.; charts. circ. 19,190. **Indexed:** Sci.Abstr. **Document type:** trade publication.
—BLDSC (3717.650000). **CCC.**

621.381 DK ISSN 0106-164X
ELEKTRONIK NYT. 1972. 17/yr. free to qualified personnel. Teknisk Forlag A - S, Skelbaekgade 4, DK-1717 Copenhagen V, Denmark. TEL 45-31-21-68-01. FAX 45-31-21-04-01. TELEX 16368 TEKFO DK. Eds. Jesper Koefoed, Erik Kuhlman. adv.: B&W page DKK 12320, color page DKK 18200; trim 257 x 175. bk.rev.; charts; illus.; circ. 14,288 (controlled).
Description: Provides information to engineers and technicians in the electronics industry through articles about new products in EDP, electronic components, instruments, production and testing equipment.

621.381 DK
ELEKTRONIK NYTS LEVERANDOERREGISTER. a. DKK 175. Teknisk Forlag A - S, Skelbaekgade 4, DK-1717 Copenhagen V, Denmark. TEL 45-31-21-68-01. FAX 45-31-21-23-96. TELEX 16368 TEKFO DK. adv. circ. 3,500.

621.38 338 GW ISSN 0172-6250
ELEKTRONIK PRODUKTION UND PRUEFTECHNIK. 10/yr. Konradin-Verlag Robert Kohlhammer GmbH, Ernst-Mey-Str. 8, 70771 Leinfelden-Echterdingen, Germany. TEL 0711-7594-0. FAX 0711-7594-390. Ed. J. Schubert. adv.: B&W page DM.5740, color page DM.7510; trim 190 x 270. charts; illus.; stat.; tr.lit. circ. 14,896. (back issues avail.) **Document type:** trade publication.
—BLDSC (3717.654200).
Formerly: Elektronik Packaging und Produktion.
Description: Details production processes, equipment, machinery and tools and testing techniques.

621.38 PL ISSN 0033-2089
TK7850.A1P7 CODEN: EKNTBZ
ELEKTRONIKA. (Text in Polish; summaries in English, Russian) 1960. m. $61. (Polska Akademia Nauk, Komitet Elektroniki i Telekomunikacji) Wydawnictwo Czasopism i Ksiazek Technicznych SIGMA - NOT, Ul. Ratuszowa 11, P.O. Box 1004, 00-950 Warsaw, Poland. TEL 48-22-180918. FAX 48-22-192187. TELEX 814550 SIGMA PL. (Dist. by: SIGMA NOT Ltd., Ul. Bartycka 20, 00-716 Warsaw, Poland) (Co-sponsor: Stowarzyszenia Elektrykow Polskich) adv.; bk.rev.; abstr.; bibl.; illus.; index. circ. 3,100. **Indexed:** Chem.Abstr., Eng.Ind., INIS Atomind., Sci.Abstr.
—BLDSC (3717.700000); CASDDS.
Formerly: Przeglad Elektroniki.

ELEKTRONIKAI ES HIRADASTECHNIKAI SZAKIRODALMI/ELECTRONICS & COMMUNICATIONS ABSTRACTS. see *COMMUNICATIONS — Abstracting, Bibliographies, Statistics*

621.381 NO ISSN 0013-5690
ELEKTRONIKK. 1967. 11/yr. NOK 245. Teknisk Presse A.S, Hovfaret 17, P.O. Box 235 Skoeyen, N-0212 Oslo 2, Norway. TEL 47-2-52-10-40. FAX 47-2-50-66-48. Ed. Kristin Moe Krohn. adv. circ. 9,158. **Indexed:** INIS Atomind.
—CCC.
Description: Covers a wide range of professional electronics; components, design, manufacture and instrumentation, as well as computer technology.

621.381 384.55 NO ISSN 0802-8559
ELEKTRONIKK BRANSJEN. 1936. 10/yr. NOK 350. Elektronikkforbundet, Karoline Kristiansens vei 1A, P.O. Box 6322, Etterstad, N-0604 Oslo, Norway. TEL 47-22-67-12-50. FAX 47-22-67-06-02. Ed. Erik Andersen. adv.: B&W page NOK 8500, color page NOK 10900. circ. 3,100. **Document type:** trade publication.
Formerly: Radiobransjen.

621.38 GW ISSN 0341-5589
ELEKTRONIKPRAXIS. 1966. 24/yr. DM.245. Vogel Verlag und Druck KG, Max-Planck-Str. 7-9, 97082 Wuerzburg, Germany. TEL 0931-4182145. FAX 0931-4182640. (Subscr. to: Vogel Verlag, 97064 Wuerzburg, Germany; Dist. in U.S. by: Vogel Europublishing, Inc., 20092 Gibbs Dr., Sonora, CA 95370. TEL 209-533-3555. FAX 209-533-9555) Ed. Guenter Weeth. adv.: B&W page DM.9064, color page DM.11849; trim 270 x 190. bk.rev.; charts; circ. 40,000 (controlled). **Indexed:** Eng.Ind. **Document type:** trade publication.
—BLDSC (3717.653000).

621.381 PL ISSN 0138-0826
ELEKTRONIZACJA. 1980. m. Wydawnictwo Czasopism i Ksiazek Technicznych SIGMA - NOT, Ul. Ratuszowa 11, P.O. Box 1004, 00-950 Warsaw, Poland. TEL 48-22-180918. FAX 48-22-192187. Ed. Jan Grzybowski. circ. 3,100.
Description: Presents developments in the fields of informatics and electronics.

621.38 MV ISSN 0013-5739
CODEN: EOBMAF
ELEKTRONNAYA OBRABOTKA MATERIALOV. English translation: Surface Engineering and Applied Electrochemistry (US ISSN 1068-3755) 1965. bi-m. 25.20 Rub. Academia de Stiinte a Republica Moldova - Akademiya Nauk Moldovskoi Respubliki, Bd. Stefan cel Mare, 1, Kishinev 277001, Moldova. **Indexed:** Biodet.Abstr., Biol.Abstr., Chem.Abstr., Eng.Ind., INIS Atomind., Met.Abstr., Sci.Abstr., Sugar Ind.Abstr., World Alum.Abstr.
—BLDSC (0398 930000).

621.3 KR ISSN 0204-3572
QA75.5 CODEN: ELMODO
ELEKTRONNOE MODELIROVANIE; mezhdunarodni naucho-teoretichesii zhurnal. English translation: Engineering Simulation (US ISSN 1063-1100) (Text in Russian; summaries in English, Russian, Ukrainian) 1979. bi-m. 15000 Rub. to individuals; institutions 45000 Rub. Akademiya Nauk Ukrainy, Institut Problem Modelirovaniya v Energetike, Ul. Generala Naumova, 15, Kiev 252680, Ukraine. TEL 044-444-1414. FAX 044-444-0586. E-mail: evf@ipme.kiev.ua. Ed. G.E. Pukhov. circ. 1,020. **Indexed:** Cyb.Abstr., Sci.Abstr. **Document type:** academic/scholarly publication.
—BLDSC (0398.975000); CASDDS. **CCC.**
Formerly: Matematicheskoe Modelirovanie i Teoriya Elektricheskikh Tsepei.

621.381 SW ISSN 1102-7495
TK4 CODEN: ETAEBM
ELEKTRONTIDNINGEN. 1992. 20/yr. SEK 470 (effective 1990). (Svenska Elektro- och Dataingenjorers Riksfoerening (SER)) Ekonomi och Teknik Foerlag AB, Klara S. Kyrkogata 1, S-106 12 Stockholm, Sweden. TEL 46-8-796-66-50. TELEX 17191-TECNEWS-S. Ed. Ulla Skiden. adv.: B&W page SEK 20979, color page SEK 26176; trim 255 x 350. bk.rev. charts; illus.; tr.lit.; index. circ. 15,000. **Indexed:** INIS Atomind., Sci.Abstr.
Formed by the merger of (1970-1992): Modern Elektronik (ISSN 0345-7656); (1989-1992): Eltcknik (ISSN 1101-6965); Which was formerly (1972-1989): Elteknik med Aktuell Elektronik (ISSN 0346-6310); (1953-1972): Elteknik (ISSN 0013-6425).
Description: Focuses on components, tests and measurements, production, automation, telecommunication, design, industrial electronics and power electronics.

643 AU
ELEKTROTECHNIK UND INFORMATIONSTECHNIK. m. Moelkerbastei 5, Postfach 367, A-1011 Vienna, Austria. TEL 01-5339614. FAX 01-638158. TELEX 114506. Ed. Rudolf Siegle. circ. 3,000.

621.381 CI ISSN 0013-5828
ELEKTROTEHNICAR; casopis za elektro, radio, TV i kinotehniku. 1950. bi-m. 120 din. Tehnicka Knjiga (Zagreb), Jurisiceva 10, Zagreb, Croatia. Ed. Zvonimir Vistricka. adv.; charts; illus.; tr.lit.

621.3 NE ISSN 0013-5895
ELEKTUUR; maandblad voor electronica. 1983. m. (11/yr.) fl.89.50($85) Uitgeversmaatschappij Elektuur B.V., Postbus 75, 6190 AB Beek, Netherlands. TEL 31-46-3894444. FAX 31-46-3701611. Ed. P.E.L. Kersemakers; Pub. M.M.J. Landman. adv.: B&W page fl.3395, color page fl.5220; trim 210 x 297; adv. contact: Peter Kunkels. bk.rev.; circ. 38,567 (paid).
—SWETS.
Incorporates (1983-1993): Elex (ISSN 0167-7349); Which incorporated in (1984): Hobbit (ISSN 0166-5642); Which was formed by the 1980 merger of: E L O (ISSN 0165-375X); Elektronika Hobbie (ISSN 0166-4042)
Description: Covers news and developments in the electronics field.

ELECTRONICS

621.381 BL ISSN 0046-1814
ELETRONICA EM FOCO. 1961. m. $20. Amplie Editora S-C Ltda., Rua Tavares Bastos 702, 05012-020 Sao Paulo SP, Brazil. Ed. Desdir Herivelto Amaral. adv.; bk.rev. circ. 30,000. (tabloid format) Document type: newspaper.

621.381 IT ISSN 0013-6123
TK7800 CODEN: ETTCB9
ELETTRONICA E TELECOMUNICAZIONI. (Text in Italian; summaries in English and Italian) 1952. 3/yr. L.20000 (foreign L.40000). E R I Edizioni R A I, Via Arsenale 41, 10121 Turin, Italy. TEL 11-8800. FAX 011-534732. bibl.; charts; illus.; index. circ. 20,000. Indexed: Chem.Abstr., Eng.Ind., Sci.Abstr. —BLDSC (3729.930000).

621.381
ELETTRONICA FLASH. 12/yr. Via Fattori 3, 40133 Bologna, Italy. TEL 51-38-29-72. Ed. Giacomo Marafioti. circ. 25,000.

621.381 IT
ELETTRONICA INTEGRATA. 12/yr. Via Ciro Menotti 14, 20129 Milan, Italy. TEL 2-75-701. FAX 2-76-10-351. Ed. G. Nardella.

643 IT ISSN 0391-6391
CODEN: ELOGDA
ELETTRONICA OGGI. 1978. 20/yr. L.112000 (foreign L.224000). Gruppo Editoriale Jackson S.p.A., Via M. Corki 69, 20092 Cinisello B. (MI), Italy. TEL 39-2-660341. FAX 39-2-66034238. TELEX 316213 GEJIT 1. Ed. Cecilia de Serio. adv.: B&W page L.2800000, color page L.4000000; 210 x 280. circ. 11,223 (controlled). Indexed: Sci.Abstr.
—BLDSC (3729.990000).
Description: Features special reports on the emerging technology and its applications, providing full information on the new products, new technologies and market facts of the field.

621.3 623.820
ELETTRONICA 2000 MISTER KIT. 1979. m. L.19500($30) Agora s.r.l., Corso Vittorio Emanuele 15, 20122 Milan, Italy. Ed. Mario Magronei. adv. circ. 50,000.

621.381 US ISSN 1063-1100
QA75.5 CODEN: ENSIEH
ENGINEERING SIMULATION. English translation of: Elektronnoe Modelirovanie (KR ISSN 0204-3572) 1982. 12/yr. (in 2 vol.; 6 nos./vol.). 358 ECU per vol. (effective 1993). (Akademiya Nauk Ukrainy, Institut Problem Modelirovaniya v Energetike, KR) Gordon and Breach Science Publishers, 820 Town Center Dr., Langhorne, PA 19047. TEL 215-750-2642. FAX 215-750-6343. (UK subscr. to: P.O. Box 90, Reading, Berkshire RG1 8JL, England. TEL 0734-560-080) Ed. G.E. Pukhov. (also avail. in microform)
—BLDSC (0411.718000). CCC.
Formerly (until vol.9): Electronic Modeling (ISSN 0275-9136)
Description: Elucidates current problems in various fields of engineering and mathematical simulation, application of mathematical methods and means of computer science in various fields of activity.
Refereed Serial

621.381 SP
EQUIPOS Y PRODUCTOS ELECTRONICOS. 6/yr. Elsevier Prensa S.A., Avda. Paral.lel 180, 08015 Barcelona, Spain. TEL 325-53-50. FAX 425-28-80. Ed. Lluis Lahoz. circ. 21,000. Document type: trade publication.
Description: New products for the electronic industry.

621.381 JA ISSN 0387-7337
EREKUTORONIKU SERAMIKUSU/ELECTRONIC CERAMICS. (Text in English, Japanese) 1970. bi-m. 1500 Yen per no. Gakkensha, 3-6, Zoshigaya 2-chome, Toshima-ku, Tokyo 171, Japan.
—BLDSC (3700.270000).

621.381 JA ISSN 0421-3513
EREKUTORONIKUSU/ELECTRONICS MAGAZINE. (Text in Japanese) 1956. m. 1100 Yen per no. Ohm-sha, 3-1, Kanda Nishiki-cho, Chiyoda-ku, Tokyo 101, Japan. Indexed: Chem.Abstr., INIS Atomind.

621.381 688.8 JA
EREKUTORONIKUSU JISSO GIJUTSU/ELECTRONIC PACKAGING TECHNOLOGY. (Text in Japanese) 1985. m. 1030 Yen per no. Joho Chosakai - Information Research Center, 8-1, Kudan Kita 1-chome, Chiyoda-ku, Tokyo 102, Japan.

621.381 JA ISSN 0911-0038
EREKUTORONIKUSU RAIFU/ELECTRONICS LIFE. (Text in Japanese) 1933. m. 750 Yen per no. Nihon Hoso Shuppan Kyokai, 41-1, Udagawa-cho, Shibuya-ku, Tokyo 150, Japan.

621.381 SP
EUROFACH ELECTRONICA; actualidad y tecnologia de la industria electronica. 12/yr. 6000 ptas. Pedeca Sociedad Cooperativa, Ltda., Maria Auxiliadora 5, 28040 Madrid, Spain. TEL 450-88-37. FAX 450-88-37. Ed. A Hennequet. circ. 8,500.

643 658.8 UK ISSN 0952-9551
EUROPEAN CONSUMER ELECTRONICS MARKETING DIRECTORY. 1988. irreg. £135($270) Euromonitor, 87-88 Turnmill St., London EC1M 5QU, England. TEL 071-251-8024. FAX 071-608-3149. (Addr. in N. America: Euromonitor International, 111 W. Washington St., Ste. 920, Chicago, IL 60602. TEL 312-541-8024. FAX 312-541-1567) Document type: directory.
Description: Examines the European market for consumer electronics.

EUROPEAN ELECTRICAL APPLIANCES MARKETING DIRECTORY. see BUSINESS AND ECONOMICS — Trade And Industrial Directories

537.5 US
TA1501 CODEN: EEOPEN
EUROPEAN ELECTRO-OPTICS. 1990. q. PennWell Publishing Co., 1421 S. Sheridan, Tulsa, OK 74112. TEL 800-331-4463. FAX 918-831-9497. adv.: B&W page $2180, color page $3045; trim 8 x 10 3/4. circ. 12,960.
Description: Covers the European marketplace and technical developments.

621.38 338.4 UK ISSN 0143-2958
EUROPEAN ELECTRONIC COMPONENT DISTRIBUTOR DIRECTORY. 1979. biennial. £195. Elsevier Science Ltd., Books Division, P.O. Box 800, Kidlington, Oxford OX5 1DX, England. TEL 44-865-843000. FAX 44-865-843010. (Subscr. in U.S. and Canada to: Elsevier Science, 660 White Plains Rd., Tarrytown, NY 10591-5153. TEL 914-524-9200) adv. circ. 5,000. (back issues avail.) Document type: trade publication, directory.
—CCC.
Description: Details over 3,000 active and passive component distribution outlets internationally.

621.381 UK
EUROPEAN ELECTRONIC PRODUCTION DIRECTORY - SMART GROUP YEARBOOK. 1990. a. Angel Publishing Ltd., Kingsland House, 361 City Rd., London EC1V 1LR, England. TEL 071-417-7400. FAX 071-417-7500. Document type: directory.
Formerly: Electronic Production - The Industry Directory (ISSN 0959-2628)

EUROPEAN ELECTRONICS DIRECTORY (YEAR) - COMPONENTS & SUB-ASSEMBLIES; guide to manufacturers, distributors and agents. see BUSINESS AND ECONOMICS — Trade And Industrial Directories

621.381 UK ISSN 0957-5685
EUROPEAN SEMICONDUCTOR; design production assembly. 1979. 10/yr. £46($162) in Europe; elsewhere £58 (effective 1994) (free to qualified personnel). Angel Publishing Ltd., Kingsland House, 5th Fl., 361 City Rd., London EC1V 1LR, England. TEL 071-417-7400. FAX 071-417-7500. Ed. Rowland McDonnell. adv.; bk.rev.; charts; illus.; tr.lit.; circ. 9,350 (controlled). Indexed: Sci.Abstr. Document type: trade publication.
—BLDSC (3829.970380). CCC.
Former titles (until 1987): European Semiconductor Design and Production (ISSN 0265-6027); (until 1983): European Semiconductor Production.
Description: Addresses innovations in the semiconductor industry.

621.381 UK
EUROPEAN SEMICONDUCTOR BULLETIN; developments in the European semiconductor manufacturing industry. 24/yr. £119($210) (effective 1993). Angel Publishing Ltd., Kingsland House, 361 City Rd., London EC1V 1LR, England. TEL 071-417-7400. FAX 071-417-7500. Document type: newsletter.

621.381 UK
EVERYDAY WITH PRACTICAL ELECTRONICS. 1992. m. £22 (foreign £28). Wimborne Publishing Ltd., 6 Church St., Wimborne, Dorset BH21 1JH, England. TEL 0202-881749. FAX 0202-841692. Ed. Michael Kenward. adv.: B&W page £475. illus.; index; circ. 23,358 (paid). (back issues avail.) Indexed: Pinpointer. Document type: consumer publication.
—SWETS. CCC.
Formed by the merger of (1971-1992): Everyday Electronics (ISSN 0262-3617); (1964-1992): Practical Electronics (ISSN 0032-6372)

621.3 GW
EXTRAKTE: ELEKTRO UND UNTERHALTUNGS-ELEKTRONIK. 1966. w. DM.498 (foreign DM.560). Extrakte-Team-Verlag GmbH, Wolfgang-Doering-Str. 2-4, 40595 Duesseldorf, Germany. TEL 0211-701011. FAX 0211-701013. TELEX 8582866. Ed. Dietmar Cloos. adv.; stat.; tr.lit. circ. 4,100. (back issues avail.)

621.381 JA ISSN 0918-2772
F E D JOURNAL. (Future Electron Devices) (Text in English, Japanese) 1990. s-a. Research & Development Association for Future Electron Devices - Shin Kono Soshi Kenkyu Kaihatsu Kyokai, 1-21, Toranomon 4-chome, Minato-ku, Tokyo 105, Japan.
—BLDSC (3901.667000).

643 AU
F Z JOURNAL. 6/yr. Helgu Verlag, Sigmundstadl 9, A-8020 Graz, Austria. TEL 0316-911540. FAX 0316-918611. Ed. Helmuth Gugl.

621.3 GW ISSN 0343-642X
FACHBUCHVERZEICHNIS ELEKTROTECHNIK - ELEKTRONIK (YEAR). 1900. a. DM.4. Fr. Weidemanns Buchhandlung (H.Witt), Postfach 6406, 30064 Hannover, Germany. TEL 0511-16382-0. FAX 0511-1638266. Ed. Renate Boehm. circ. 20,000. Document type: trade publication.

643 338 US ISSN 1061-9577
HD9696.A1
FAIRCHILD'S ELECTRONICS INDUSTRY FINANCIAL DIRECTORY.* 1962. a. $135 (effective Sep. 1990). Fairchild Books (Subsidiary of: Fairchild Publications Inc.), 7 W. 34th St., New York, NY 10001. TEL 212-630-4000. FAX 212-887-1946. TELEX 232666 FAPB. Ed. Robert Benjamin. circ. 2,000. (also avail. in microfiche from CIS; back issues avail.) Indexed: SRI. Document type: directory.
—CCC.
Formerly (until 1991): Electronic News Financial Fact Book and Directory (ISSN 0070-9875)

643 IT
FARE ELETTRONICA. m. (11/yr.). Gruppo Editoriale Jackson S.p.A., Via M. Gorki 69, 20092 Cinisello B. (MI), Italy. TEL 02-66034258. FAX 02-66034238. adv.: B&W page L.2800000, color page L.3700000; trim 185 x 250. circ. 15,151.

FOCUS ON ELECTRONICS CHEMICALS. see CHEMISTRY — Electrochemistry

621.38 534   US
FREQUENCY CONTROL SYMPOSIUM. Variant titles: Symposium on Frequency Control. Proceedings. Also: Frequency Symposium. 10th, 1956. a. price varies. (I E E E, Sonics and Ultrasonics Group) Institute of Electrical and Electronics Engineers, Inc., 345 E. 47th St., New York, NY 10017.
TEL 212-705-7900. FAX 212-705-7682. (Subscr. to: Box 1331, 445 Hoes Lane, Piscataway, NJ 08855-1331; 1956-1977 avail. from NTIS, Sills Bldg., 5285 Port Royal Rd., Springfield, VA 22161; 1978-1981 avail. from Electronic Industries Association, 2001 Eye St., Washington, DC 20006; 1982 avail. from Systematics General Corp., Brinley Plaza, Rte. 38, Wall Township, NJ 07719) (Co-sponsor: U.S. Army Electronics Research and Development Command, Electronics Technology and Devices Laboratory) **Indexed:** Chem.Abstr.
Formerly: Annual Frequency Control Symposium.
Description: Explores piezoelectricity, resonators, SAW devices, frequency standards, filters and signal processing.

621.381   JA   ISSN 0911-050X
CODEN: FKDSEU
FUKUOKA KOGYO DAIGAKU EREKUTORONIKUSU KENKYUJO SHOHO/FUKUOKA INSTITUTE OF TECHNOLOGY, ELECTRONICS RESEARCH LABORATORY. REPORTS. (Text in English, Japanese) 1984. a. Fukuoka Kogyo Daigaku, Erekutoronikusu Kenkyujo, 30-1, Wajiro Higashi 3-chome, Higashi-ku, Fukuoka-shi, Fukuoka-ken 811-02, Japan. **Indexed:** Chem.Abstr.
—BLDSC (7460.325000); CASDDS.

621.381   US   ISSN 1064-7775
TK7871.15.G3
GA AS I C SYMPOSIUM. Represents: I E E E Gallium Arsenide Integrated Circuit Symposium. Technical Digest. (Symposia prior to 1982 not published) 1982. a. (I E E E, Electron Devices Society) Institute of Electrical and Electronics Engineers, Inc., 345 E. 47th St., New York, NY 10017.
TEL 212-705-7900. FAX 212-705-7682. (Subscr. to: 445 Hoes Ln., Box 1331, Piscataway, NJ 08855-1331) (Co-sponsor: I E E E, Microwave Theory and Techniques Society)
—BLDSC (4065.300000). **CCC.**

621.381   JA   ISSN 0285-9831
GAZO DENSHI GAKKAISHI/INSTITUTE OF IMAGE ELECTRONICS ENGINEERS OF JAPAN. JOURNAL. (Text in Japanese; summaries in English, Japanese) 1972. bi-m. Gazo Denshi Gakkai, 21-27-505 Shinmomeguro 2-chome, Meguro-ku, Tokyo 153, Japan.
—BLDSC (4776.250000).

621.3   JA   ISSN 0286-5025
GEKKAN SEMICONDUCTOR WORLD. (Text in Japanese) 1982. m. 1000 Yen per no. Press Journal Inc., 2-6, Kudan Kita 1-chome, Chiyoda-ku, Tokyo 102, Japan.

643   IT   ISSN 0392-3614
GIORNALE DEGLI APPARECCHI DOMESTICI. 1975. 6/yr. L.75000($104) (foreign L.120000). Stammer S.p.A., Via della Liberazione 1, 20068 Peschiera Borromeo (MI), Italy. TEL 02-55302606. FAX 02-55302700. Ed. Girolamo Bellina. adv. circ. 9,000.

621.381   US
GIZMO. Issued with: Popular Electronics. 1988. m. Gernsback Publications, Inc., 500-B Bi-County Blvd., Farmingdale, NY 11735. TEL 516-293-3000. FAX 516-293-3115. (Subscr. to: Box 338, Mt. Morris, IL 61504-9932) Ed. Carl Laron. adv. circ. 87,824. (back issues avail.)
Description: Covers the latest consumer electronic products on the market.

621.381   US
GLOBAL ELECTRONICS. 1980. m. $12. Pacific Studies Center, 222B View St., Mountain View, CA 94041. TEL 415-969-1545. FAX 415-968-1126. Ed. Lenny Siegel. bk.rev.; charts; stat. circ. 350. (also avail. in microform from UMI; back issues avail.) **Indexed:** Alt.Press Ind. **Document type:** newsletter.
Formerly (until 1985): Global Electronics Information Newsletter (ISSN 0739-0416)
Description: Covers current trends in the computer and semiconductor industries, emphasizing the impact on the workforce and environment.

683.88   GW
GROSSE ELEKTRONIK ATLAS; der Branchenfuehrer fuer Entscheidungstraeger in der industr. Elektronik. 1982. a. DM.100. Europa-Fachpresse-Verlag GmbH (Subsidiary of: Sueddeutscher Verlag), Thomas-Dehler-Str. 27, 81737 Munich, Germany. TEL 089-67804-243. circ. 15,000.
Formerly (until 1987): Produkt Atlas: Industrielle Elektronik.

338.4   FR
GROUPEMENT DES INDUSTRIES ELECTRONIQUES. RAPPORT D'ACTIVITES. 1971. a. free. Groupement des Industries Electroniques, 11 rue Hamelin, 75783 Paris 16, France. stat. circ. 200.
Formerly: Electronique Francaise.

643 011   FR
GROUPEMENT DES INDUSTRIES ELECTRONIQUES. STATISTIQUES ANNUELLES. a. free. Groupement des Industries Electroniques, 11 rue Hamelin, 75783 Paris 16, France. stat.
Formerly: Industrie Electronique Francaise.

643   II
GUIDE TO ELECTRONICS INDUSTRY IN INDIA. (Text in English) no.2, 1974. irreg. Rs.50($10) per no. Statistics Investigations Bureau, 4-A Naaz Bldg., Lamington Rd., Bombay 400004, India. Ed. S. Swarn. illus.
Supersedes: Guide to Radio Electronics and Components Trade and Industry in India (ISSN 0533-540X)

621.381   CC   ISSN 1001-7437
GUILIN DIANZI GONGYE XUEYUAN XUEBAO/GUILIN INSTITUTE OF ELECTRONIC INDUSTRY. JOURNAL. (Text in Chinese) q. Guilin Dianzi Gongye Xueyuan, Xuebao Bianjibu, Liuhe Lu, Guilin, Guangxi 541004, People's Republic of China. TEL 443343. Ed. Ye Xiuhua.

621.38   CC   ISSN 1000-3819
CODEN: GDYJE2
GUTI DIANZIXUE YANJIU YU JINZHAN/RESEARCH & PROGRESS OF SOLID STATE ELECTRONICS. (Text in Chinese; abstracts in Chinese, English) 1981. q. $60. Nanjing Dianzi Qijian Yanjiusuo - Nanjing Electronic Devices Institute, 524 Zhongshan Donglu, P.O. Box 1601, Nanjing, Jiangsu 210016, People's Republic of China. TEL 86-25-4414155. FAX 86-25-4407126. Ed. Lin Jinting. circ. 1,300. **Document type:** academic/scholarly publication.
—BLDSC (7715.701000); CASDDS.
Description: Covers solid state electronics, integrated circuits, microelectronics, optoelectronics, and semiconductor materials.
Refereed Serial

621.38   HK
H K P C ELECTRONICS BULLETIN. m. Hong Kong Productivity Council, H K P C Bldg., 78 Tat Chee Ave., Kowloon, Hong Kong. TEL 852-788-5960. FAX 852-788-5959. Ed. Simon Yu. adv.: B&W page HK$2100, color page HK$3800. circ. 5,500.
Description: For designers, engineers, researchers, technical management and approved authorities in industrial and scientific establishments involving electronics.

621.381   NE
HANDBOOK OF SEMICONDUCTORS. 1980. irreg., vol.4, 1993. price varies. Elsevier Science B.V., Books Division, P.O. Box 211, 1000 AE Amsterdam, Netherlands. TEL 31-20-5803911. FAX 31-20-5803705. TELEX 18582 ESPA NL. (Subscr. in U.S. and Canada to: Elsevier Science Inc., Box 882, Madison Sq. Sta., New York, NY 10159. TEL 212-989-5800) **Document type:** monographic series.
Refereed Serial

621.381   JA
HANDOTAI KENKYU/SEMICONDUCTOR RESEARCH. (Text in Japanese) 1964. a. 17000 Yen. (Handotai Kenkyu Shinkokai - Semiconductor Research Foundation) Kogyo Chosakai Publishing Co., Ltd., 14-7, Hongo 2-chome, Bunkyo-ku, Tokyo 113, Japan.

621.381   JA   ISSN 0385-7131
HANDOTAI KENKYUJO HOKOKU/SEMICONDUCTOR RESEARCH INSTITUTE. REPORT. (Text in Japanese) 1963. q. Handotai Kenkyu Shinkokai - Semiconductor Research Foundation, Kawauchi, Aoba-ku, Sencai-shi, Miyagi-ken 980, Japan. **Indexed:** INIS Atomind.
—BLDSC (4262.045000).

621.3   JA
HANDOTAI SANGYO SHINBUN/SEMICONDUCTOR INDUSTRY NEWS. (Text in Japanese) 1990. w. 57000 Yen. Sangyo Times, Inc., 5-4, Sotokanda 5-chome, Chiyoda-ku, Tokyo 101, Japan.

621.3   JA
HANDOTAI SHUSEKI KAIRO GIJUTSU SHINPOJUMU KOEN RONBUNSHU/PROCEEDINGS OF THE SYMPOSIUM ON SEMICONDUCTORS AND INTEGRATED CIRCUITS TECHNOLOGY. (Text in Japanese; summaries in English) 1971. s-a. 6000 Yen per no. Denki Kagaku Kyokai, Denshi Zairyo Iinkai - Electrochemical Society of Japan, Electro Materials Committee, 12-1, Yuraku-cho 1-chome, Chiyoda-ku, Tokyo 100, Japan. **Document type:** proceedings.

643   SZ
HI-FI VIDEO TEST; schweizer Testzeitschrift fuer Audio, Video, Heimelektronik. 10/yr. 45 SFr. (foreign 55 SFr.). Graf und Neuhaus AG, Moehrlistr. 69, CH-8033 Zurich, Switzerland. TEL 01-3615600. FAX 01-3617715. Ed. Martin Freund. adv. contact: Walter Keller. circ. 14,000. **Document type:** consumer publication.

643   GW
HIFI TEST. 1991. bi-m. DM.22.80. Michael E. Brieden Verlag GmbH, Ruhrorterstr. 9, 46049 Oberhausen, Germany. TEL 0208-85976-0. FAX 0208-8597649. **Document type:** consumer publication.
Description: Provides information and reviews about consumer electronics.

643   SZ
HIFI VISION. 10/yr. Fachpresse Goldach, Sulzstr. 12, CH-9403 Goldach, Switzerland. TEL 071-416611. FAX 071-413881. Ed. Sonja Noger. circ. 11,000.

621.381   US
HIGH TC INFORMATION SERVICE. 1988. m. $248. Atlantic Information Services, Inc., 1050 17th St., N.W., Ste. 480, Washington, DC 20036-5500. TEL 202-775-9008. FAX 202-331-9542. (looseleaf format)
Description: Provides a wide range of original documents in the field of superconductivity.

621.381   JA   ISSN 0913-932X
HIKARI SHIN JIDAI/OPTOELECTRONICS MAGAZINE NEW ERA. 1987. q. 1330 Yen per no. Press Kogyo Tsusin Co., Ltd., 14-9, Nihonbashi Ningyo-cho 2-chome, Chuo-ku, Tokyo 103, Japan.

621.3   JA   ISSN 0917-4346
HITACHI DENSHI ENJINIARINGU GIHO/HITACHI ELECTRONICS ENGINEERING CO. TECHNICAL REPORT. (Text in Japanese) 1991. 2/yr. Hitachi Denshi Enjiniaringu K.K. - Hitachi Electronics Engineering Co., Ltd., 15-2, Uchikanda 2-chome, Chiyoda-ku, Tokyo 101, Japan.

621   JA   ISSN 0914-1413
HITACHI MAIKON GIHO/HITACHI MAIKON TECHNICAL JOURNAL. (Text in Japanese; summaries in English, Japanese) 1987. s-a. Fukuokaken Kogyo Gijutsu Senta, Kikai Denshi Kenkyujo - Fukuoka Industrial Technology Center, Mechanics and Electronics Research Institute, 6-1, Norimatsu 3-chome, Yahata Nishi-ku, Kitakyushu-shi, Fukuoka-ken 807, Japan.

621.381   JA   ISSN 0018-277X
T1   CODEN: HITAAQ
HITACHI REVIEW. 1952. bi-m. 1000 Yen. Hitachi, Ltd., Advertising Dept., 6, Kanda-Surugadai 4 chome, Chiyoda-ku, Tokyo, Japan. Ed. Shozaburo Kobayashi. abstr.; charts; illus. circ. 8,000. **Indexed:** A.I.Abstr. (until 1992), Acid Rain Abstr., Acid Rain Ind., CAD CAM Abstr. (until 1992), Cadscan, Chem.Abstr., Cyb.Abstr., Eng.Ind., Excerpt.Med., Fluidex, INIS Atomind., JCT, JTA, Lead Abstr., Met.Abstr., Robomat. (until 1992), Sci.Abstr., Tel.Abstr., World Alum.Abstr., Zincscan.
—BLDSC (4318.770000); EI; Faxon; UnCover; SWETS; CASDDS.

ELECTRONICS

643   AU
HOBBY UND ELEKTRONIK. 11/yr. Marschallplatz 23-1-21, A-1125 Vienna, Austria. TEL 01-8040474. FAX 01-8044439. Ed. G.K. Buchberger. circ. 11,200.

643 697   US
HOME AUTOMATION NEWS. 1988. m. $125. Home Automation Association, 808 17th St., N.W., Ste. 200, Washington, DC 20006. TEL 202-333-8579. FAX 202-223-9569. Ed. Charles McGrath. adv.; tr.lit.; circ. 500 (paid). **Document type:** newsletter.
Description: Covers current developments on the integration of home systems including electronics, security, lighting, audio, video, computers, home control.

643   HK
HONG KONG ELECTRONICS. (Text in English) 1985. q. $100 (free to qualified personnel). Hong Kong Trade Development Council, 36-39th Fl., Office Tower, Convention Plaza, 1 Harbour Rd., Wanchai, Hong Kong. TEL 584-4333. FAX 824-0249. Ed. Saul Lockhart. circ. 40,000.

621.381   UK   ISSN 0265-3028
CODEN: HYCRD5
HYBRID CIRCUITS. 1982. 3/yr. (International Hybrid Microelectronics Society - Europe) Wela Publications Ltd., Asani House, 10 Church Rd., Port Erin IM99 8HD, Isle of Man. TEL 0624-836044. FAX 0624-835400. Ed. William Goldie. **Document type:** academic/scholarly publication.
—BLDSC (4340.345000); Faxon; SWETS; CASDDS. **CCC.**

621.38   UK   ISSN 0073-4136
HYBRID MICROELECTRONICS SYMPOSIUM. (PAPERS). * Variant title: Symposium on Hybrid Microelectronics. irreg., 3rd, 1968. price varies. International Society for Hybrid Microelectronics, c/o David Boswell, 20 Hale Lane, London NW 7, England.

621.381   JA   ISSN 0914-2568
HYBRIDS. Variant title: S H M Journal. (Text in Japanese) 1985. bi-m. 1500 Yen per no. Society for Hybrid Microelectronics - Haiburiddo Maikuro Erekutoronikusu Kyokai, 20-4, Hanakoganei 6-chome, Kodaira-shi, Tokyo 187, Japan. **Indexed:** Chem.Abstr.
—BLDSC (4340.390000).

643 670   US   ISSN 1049-2682
TK7874.5
I C ALTERNATE SOURCES & REPLACEMENTS D.A.T.A. DIGEST. (Subseries of: D.A.T.A. Digest Electronic Information Series) 1986. s-a. $135. D.A.T.A. Business Publishing (Subsidiary of: Information Handling Services) m. $445, Box 6510, Englewood, CO 80155-6510. TEL 800-447-4666. FAX 303-799-4082. TELEX 4322083 IHS UI. Ed. Paul Magin. adv. contact: Peggy Anderson.
Formerly: I C Alternate Sources (ISSN 1040-0923).
Description: Reference guide to alternate sources and replacements for ICs. Covers over 210,000 devices from more than 600 manufaturers.

621.381   US
I C E C A P REPORT; semiconductor industry newsletter. Short title: Icecap. (Supplement avail. quarterly: I C E Breaker Reports) m. $445 (foreign $465). Integrated Circuit Engineering Corporation, 15022 N. 75th St., Scottsdale, AZ 85260-2476. TEL 602-998-9780. FAX 602-948-1925. Ed. Bill McClean. **Document type:** newsletter.
Description: Disseminates information on issues confronting the semiconductor industry. Emphasis is placed on advanced semiconductor processing as well as technological and market trends.

537   US   ISSN 0894-6809
TK7874
I C MASTER. (Integrated Circuits) (S-a supplement avail.: I C Master Update) 1975. a. $170. Hearst Business Communications, Inc., 645 Stewart Ave., Garden City, NY 11530. TEL 516-227-1300. Ed. Dave Howell. adv.; illus. circ. 30,000. **Document type:** catalog.
Description: Catalog of parameter search data on commercially available integrated circuits.

621.3 016   SZ
I E C CATALOGUE OF PUBLICATIONS. (Editions in English, French) 1960. a. (plus bi-m. supplements). 20 SFr. International Electrotechnical Commission, 3 rue de Varembe, CH-1211 Geneva 20, Switzerland. TEL 022-9190266. FAX 022-9190300. (Dist. in U.S. by: American National Standards Institute, 1430 Broadway, Nrew York, NY 10018) adv.; index. **Document type:** bibliography.

621.2 629   US   ISSN 0885-8985
TL693   CODEN: IESMEA
I E E E AEROSPACE AND ELECTRONIC SYSTEMS MAGAZINE. 1961. m. $84 to non-members. Institute of Electrical and Electronics Engineers, Inc., 345 E. 47th St., New York, NY 10017. TEL 908-981-0060. FAX 908-981-9667. (Subscr. to: Box 1331, 445 Hoes Lane, Piscataway, NJ 08855-1331) Ed. H. Warren Cooper. bk.rev. (also avail. in microform from UMI,EEE) **Indexed:** Tel.Abstr.
—BLDSC (4362.787680); EI; Faxon; UnCover; SWETS; UMI. **CCC.**
Supersedes (in 1986): I E E E Aerospace and Electronic Systems Society Newsletter.
Description: Deals with aspects of earth and space systems. Includes reviews and patent announcements.

537   US   ISSN 1048-2334
TK7881.15
I E E E APPLIED POWER ELECTRONICS CONFERENCE AND EXPOSITION. CONFERENCE PROCEEDINGS.. Short title: A P E C. 1986. a. price varies. (I E E E, Power Electronics Council) Institute of Electrical and Electronics Engineers, Inc., 345 E. 47th St., New York, NY 10017-2394. TEL 212-705-7900. FAX 212-705-7682. (Subscr. to: I E E E Service Center, Box 1331, 445 Hoes Lane, Piscataway, NJ 08855-1331) (microfiche)
—UMI. **CCC.**
Description: Application-oriented data on power electronics.

621.381   US   ISSN 8755-3996
TK1   CODEN: ICDMEN
I E E E CIRCUITS AND DEVICES MAGAZINE. 1985. bi-m. $120 to non-members. Institute of Electrical and Electronics Engineers, Inc., 345 E. 47th St., New York, NY 10017-2349. FAX 908-981-9667. (Subscr. to: IEEE Service Center, 445 Hoes Lane, Box 1331, Piscataway, NJ 08855-1331. TEL 908-981-1393) Ed. Ronald W. Waynant. adv. circ. 30,725. (also avail. in microform from UMI,EEE) **Indexed:** Tel.Abstr.
—BLDSC (4362.811500); EI; UnCover; SWETS; UMI. **CCC.**
Description: In-depth assessments of emerging technologies and their continued impact on the human-machine interface. Includes information on new products and inventions.

621.381   US   ISSN 0741-3106
TK7869   CODEN: EDLEDZ
I E E E ELECTRON DEVICE LETTERS. 1980. m. $160 to non-members. (I E E E, Electron Devices Society) Institute of Electrical and Electronics Engineers, Inc., 345 E. 47th St., New York, NY 10017-2394. FAX 908-981-9667. (Subscr. to: Box 1331, 445 Hoes Lane, Piscataway, NJ 08855-1331. TEL 908-981-0060) Ed. John R. Brews. (also avail. in microform) **Indexed:** Chem.Abstr., Curr.Cont., Ind.Sci.Rev., INIS Atomind., Int.Aerosp.Abstr., Sci.Abstr., Sci.Cit.Ind.
—BLDSC (4362.922800); EI; Faxon; UnCover; SWETS; UMI; CASDDS. **CCC.**
Formerly (until Jan. 1980): Electron Device Letters (ISSN 0193-8576)

643   US
I E E E INTERNATIONAL CONFERENCE ON CONSUMER ELECTRONICS. DIGEST OF TECHNICAL PAPERS. Short title: I C C E. 1982. a. (I E E E, Consumer Electronics Society) Institute of Electrical and Electronics Engineers, Inc., 345 E. 47th St., New York, NY 10017-2394. TEL 212-705-7900. FAX 212-705-7682. (Subscr. to: 445 Hoes La., Box 1331, Piscataway, NJ 08854)

621.38   US   ISSN 0193-6530
TK7870   CODEN: DTPCDE
I E E E INTERNATIONAL SOLID STATE CIRCUITS CONFERENCE. DIGEST OF TECHNICAL PAPERS. 1958. a. price varies. (I E E E, Solid-State Circuits Society) Institute of Electrical and Electronics Engineers, Inc., 345 E. 47th St., New York, NY 10017-2394. TEL 212-706-7900. FAX 212-705-7682. (Subscr. to: Box 1331, 445 Hoes Lane, Piscataway, NJ 08855-1331)
—BLDSC (3588.320000); UMI. **CCC.**
Supersedes: International Solid State Circuits Conference. Digest (ISSN 0074-8587); Solid-State Circuits Conference. Digest of Technical Papers (ISSN 0277-7983)
Description: Examines innovative chip design developments.

621.381   US   ISSN 0277-674X
I E E E INTERNATIONAL SYMPOSIUM ON CIRCUITS AND SYSTEMS. PROCEEDINGS. Variant title: International Symposium on Circuits and Systems. a. price varies. (I E E E, Circuits and Systems Society) Institute of Electrical and Electronics Engineers, Inc., 345 E. 47th St., New York, NY 10017-2394. TEL 212-705-7900. FAX 212-705-7682. (Subscr. to: Box 1331, 445 Hoes Lane, Piscataway, NJ 08855-1331)
—CCC.
Supersedes: I E E E International Symposium on Circuit Theory. Symposium Digest. Summaries of Papers (ISSN 0579-4234)

621.381 535   US   ISSN 0018-9197
TK7800   CODEN: IEJQA7
I E E E JOURNAL OF QUANTUM ELECTRONICS. 1965. m. $535 to non-members. (I E E E, Lasers and Electro-Optics Society) Institute of Electrical and Electronics Engineers, Inc., 345 E. 47th St., New York, NY 10017-2394. FAX 908-981-9667. (Subscr. to: Box 1331, 445 Hoes Lane, Piscataway, NJ 08855-1331. TEL 908-981-0060) Ed. Steven R.J. Brueck. charts; illus.; index. (microfiche; also avail. in microform) **Indexed:** A.S.& T.Ind., Chem.Abstr., Curr.Cont., Eng.Ind., Ind.Sci.Rev., INIS Atomind., Int.Aerosp.Abstr., Phys.Ber., Sci.Abstr.
—BLDSC (4362.981000); EI; Faxon; UnCover; SWETS; UMI; CASDDS. **CCC.**
Description: Opto-electronic theory and techniques, lasers, fiber optics, and development and manufacture of systems and subsystems.

I E E E PUBLICATIONS BULLETIN. see *ENGINEERING — Abstracting, Bibliographies, Statistics*

621.381   US   ISSN 1051-8223
TK7872.S8   CODEN: ITASE9
I E E E TRANSACTIONS ON APPLIED SUPERCONDUCTIVITY. 1991. q. $115 to non-members. Institute of Electrical and Electronics Engineers, Inc., 345 E. 47th St., New York, NY 10017-2394. TEL 908-981-0060. FAX 908-981-9667. (Subscr. to: 445 Hoes Lane, Box 1331, Piscataway, NJ 08855-1331) Ed. Theodore Van Duzer.
—BLDSC (4363.131000); EI; UnCover; SWETS; UMI. **CCC.**
Description: Contains articles on the applications of superconductivity and on the relevant technology, analog and digital circuits employing thin films and active devices such as Josephson junctions.

621.381   US   ISSN 1051-8215
CODEN: ITCTEM
I E E E TRANSACTIONS ON CIRCUITS AND SYSTEMS FOR VIDEO TECHNOLOGY. 1991. bi-m. $137 to non-members. Institute of Electrical and Electronics Engineers, Inc., 345 E. 47th St., New York, NY 10017-2394. TEL 908-981-0060. FAX 908-981-9667. (Subscr. to: 445 Hoes Lane, Box 1331, Piscataway, NJ 08855-1331) Ed. Ming Liou. (also avail. in microform)
—BLDSC (4363.166500); EI; Faxon; UnCover; SWETS; UMI. **CCC.**
Description: Covers video processing algorithms, real-time implementation, VLSI architecture and technology, and related topics.

621.38　　　　　US　　ISSN 1057-7122
TK7867 b .I373　　　　CODEN: ITCAEX
I E E E TRANSACTIONS ON CIRCUITS AND SYSTEMS PART 1: FUNDAMENTAL THEORY AND APPLICATIONS. 1952. m. $241 to non-members. (I E E E, Circuits and Systems Society) Institute of Electrical and Electronics Engineers, Inc., 345 E. 47th St., New York, NY 10017-2394. TEL 908-981-0060. FAX 908-981-9667. (Subscr. to: 445 Hoes Lane, Box 1331, Piscataway, NJ 08855-1331) Ed. Martin Hasler. bk.rev.; abstr.; illus.; index. (also avail. in microform) **Indexed:** A.S.& T.Ind., Chem.Abstr., Comput.Abstr., Curr.Cont., Eng.Ind., Ind.Sci.Rev., Math.R., Sci.Abstr., Sci.Cit.Ind., Tel.Abstr.
—BLDSC (4363.166100); El; Faxon; UnCover; SWETS; UMI. **CCC.**

Supersedes in part (in 1992): I E E E Transactions on Circuits and Systems (ISSN 0098-4094); Former titles (until 1973): I E E E Transactions on Circuit Theory (ISSN 0018-9324); (until 1962): I R E Transactions on Circuit Theory; (until 1954): Professional Group on Circuit Theory. Transactions.

Description: Design and theory of circuits operations for use in radio and electronic equipment.

621.38　　　　　US　　ISSN 1057-7130
TK7867　　　　　CODEN: ICSPE5
I E E E TRANSACTIONS ON CIRCUITS AND SYSTEMS PART 2: ANALOG AND DIGITAL SIGNAL PROCESSING. 1952. m. $218 to non-members. (I E E E, Circuits and Systems Society) Institute of Electrical and Electronics Engineers, Inc., 345 E. 47th St., New York, NY 10017. TEL 908-981-0060. (Subscr. to: Box 1331, 445 Hoes La., Piscataway, NJ 08855-1331) Ed. David Allstot. bk.rev.; abstr.; illus.; index. (also avail. in microform) **Indexed:** Comput.Abstr.
—BLDSC (4363.166200); El; Faxon; UnCover; SWETS; UMI. **CCC.**

Supersedes in part (in 1992): I E E E Transactions on Circuits and Systems (ISSN 0098-4094); Former titles (until 1973): I E E E Transactions on Circuit Theory (ISSN 0018-9324); (until 1962): I R E Transactions on Circuit Theory; (until 1954): Professional Group on Circuit Theory Transactions.

643　　　　　US　　ISSN 0098-3063
TK6563　　　　CODEN: ITCEDA
I E E E TRANSACTIONS ON CONSUMER ELECTRONICS. 1952. q. $135 to non-members. (I E E E, Consumer Electronics Society) Institute of Electrical and Electronics Engineers, Inc., 345 E. 47th St., New York, NY 10017-2394. TEL 908-981-0060. FAX 908-981-9667. (Subscr. to: 445 Hoes Lane, Box 1331, Piscataway, NJ 08855-1331) Ed. Wayne C. Luplow. bk.rev.; abstr.; illus.; index. (also avail. in microform) **Indexed:** A.S.& T.Ind., Cadscan, Chem.Abstr., Comput.Abstr., Comput.Cont., Curr.Cont., Eng.Ind., Ergon.Abstr., Ind.Sci.Rev., Lead Abstr., Math.R., Sci.Abstr., Sci.Cit.Ind., SSCI, Zincscan.
—BLDSC (4363.176500); El; Faxon; UnCover; SWETS; UMI. **CCC.**

Former titles (until 1974): I E E E Transactions on Broadcast and Television Receivers (ISSN 0018-9308); (until 1962): I R E Transactions on Broadcast and Television Receivers; (until 1954): I R E Professional Group on Broadcast and Television Receivers. Transactions.

Description: Design and manufacture of products, components and related activities, used for entertainment, leisure and educational purposes.

621.38　　　　　US　　ISSN 0018-9375
　　　　　　　　　CODEN: IEMCAE
I E E E TRANSACTIONS ON ELECTROMAGNETIC COMPATIBILITY. 1959. q. $93 to non-members. (I E E E, Electromagnetic Compatibility Society) Institute of Electrical and Electronics Engineers, Inc., 345 E. 47th St., New York, NY 10017-2394. TEL 908-981-1393. FAX 908-981-9667. (Subscr. to: Box 1331, 445 Hoes Lane, Piscataway, NJ 08855-1331) Ed. Motohisa Kanda. abstr.; illus.; index. (also avail. in microform) **Indexed:** A.S.& T.Ind., BMT, Chem.Abstr., Curr.Cont., Eng.Ind., Ind.Sci.Rev., Int.Aerosp.Abstr., Math.R., Sci.Abstr.
—BLDSC (4363.181100); El; Faxon; UnCover; SWETS; UMI. **CCC.**

Description: Presents the origin, control and measurement of effects on electronic and biological systems.

621.38　　　　　US　　ISSN 0018-9383
　　　　　　　　　CODEN: IETDAI
I E E E TRANSACTIONS ON ELECTRON DEVICES. 1952. m. $395 to non-members. (I E E E, Electronic Devices Society) Institute of Electrical and Electronics Engineers, Inc., 345 E. 47th St., New York, NY 10017-2394. TEL 908-981-1393. FAX 908-981-9667. (Subscr. to: 445 Hoes Lane, Box 1331, Piscataway, NJ 08855-1331) Ed. Renuka Jindal. bk.rev.; abstr.; illus.; index. (also avail. in microform from MIM,UMI,EEE) **Indexed:** A.S.& T.Ind., Cadscan, Chem.Abstr., Comput.Abstr., Curr.Cont., Cyb.Abstr., Eng.Ind., Excerp.Med., Ind.Sci.Rev., INIS Atomind., Int.Aerosp.Abstr., Lead Abstr., Math.R., Sci.Abstr., Sci.Cit.Ind.
—BLDSC (4363.182500); El; Faxon; UnCover; SWETS; UMI; CASDDS. **CCC.**

Former titles (until 1962): I R E Transactions on Electron Devices; (until 1954): I R E Professional Group on Electron Devices. Transactions.

Description: Theory, design and performance of devices, including electron tubes, solid-state devices, energy sources, displays and device reliability.

621.38　　　　　US　　ISSN 0278-0046
TK7800　　　　　CODEN: ITIED6
I E E E TRANSACTIONS ON INDUSTRIAL ELECTRONICS. 1953. bi-m. $140 to non-members. (I E E E, Industrial Electronics Society) Institute of Electrical and Electronics Engineers, Inc., 345 E. 47th St., New York, NY 10017-2394. TEL 908-981-0060. FAX 908-981-9667. (Subscr. to: 445 Hoes Lane, Box 1331, Piscataway, NJ 08855-1331) Ed. James C. Hung. bk.rev.; charts; illus.; index. (also avail. in microform; back issues avail.) **Indexed:** A.S.& T.Ind., Appl.Mech.Rev., Cadscan, Chem.Abstr., Comput.Abstr., Curr.Cont., Cyb.Abstr., Eng.Ind., Fuel & Energy Abstr., Ind.Sci.Rev., Int.Aerosp.Abstr., Lead Abstr., Math.R., Sci.Abstr., Sh.& Vib.Dig., Zincscan.
—BLDSC (4363.191500); El; Faxon; UnCover; SWETS; UMI. **CCC.**

Former titles (until 1981): I E E E Transactions on Industrial Electronics and Control Instrumentation (ISSN 0018-9421); (until 1963): I E E E Transactions on Industrial Electronics; (until 1962): I R E Transactions on Industrial Electronics; (until 1959): I R E Professional Group on Industrial Electronics. Transactions.

Description: Provides papers on the application of electronics and electrical sciences on the control of industrial processes. Special issues are dedicated to a specific topic.

621.381　　　　　US　　ISSN 0885-8993
TK7881.15　　　　　CODEN: ITPEE8
I E E E TRANSACTIONS ON POWER ELECTRONICS. 1986. q. $140 to non-members. (I E E E, Power Electronics Council) Institute of Electrical and Electronics Engineers, Inc., 345 E. 47th St., New York, NY 10017-2394. TEL 908-981-0060. FAX 908-981-9667. (Subscr. to: IEEE Service Center, 445 Hoes Lane, Box 1331, Piscataway, NJ 08855-1331) Ed. Richard Hoft. (also avail. in microform) **Indexed:** INIS Atomind.
—BLDSC (4363.213600); El; Faxon; UnCover; SWETS; UMI. **CCC.**

I E I C E TRANSACTIONS ON COMMUNICATIONS. (Institute of Electronics, Information and Communication Engineers) see *COMMUNICATIONS — Television And Cable*

621.38　　　　　JA　　ISSN 0916-8524
　　　　　　　　　CODEN: IELEEJ
I E I C E TRANSACTIONS ON ELECTRONICS. (Text in English) 1962. m. 2060 Yen. Institute of Electronics, Information and Communication Engineers - Denshi Joho Tsushin Gakkai, c/o Kikai Shinko Kaikan, 5-8 Shiba Koen, 3-chome, Minato-ku, Tokyo 105, Japan.
—BLDSC (4363.240668); El; UnCover. **CCC.**

Supersedes in part (in 1991): I E I C E Transactions on Communications Electronics Information and Systems (ISSN 0917-1673); Former titles (until 1991): Transactions of the Institute of Electronics, Information and Communication Engineers (ISSN 0913-574X); (until 1987): Transactions of the Institute of Electronics and Communication Engineers of Japan. Section E (ISSN 0387-236X); (until 1976): Transactions of the Institute of Electronics and Communication Engineers of Japan. Abstracts (ISSN 0418-6869); (until 1968): Journal of the Institute of Electrical Communication Engineers of Japan. Abstracts (ISSN 0914-5273).

235 621.38　　　　　JA　　ISSN 0916-8508
TK7800　　　　　CODEN: IFESEX
I E I C E TRANSACTIONS ON FUNDAMENTALS OF ELECTRONICS, COMMUNICATIONS AND COMPUTER SCIENCES. (Text in English) 1962. m. 2060 Yen. Institute of Electronics, Information and Communication Engineers - Denshi Joho Tsushin Gakkai, c/o Kikai Shinko Kaikan, 5-8 Shiba Koen, 3-chome, Minato-ku, Tokyo 105, Japan.
—BLDSC (4363.240672); El; UnCover. **CCC.**

Supersedes in part (in 1991): I E I C E Transactions on Communications Electronics Information and Systems (ISSN 0917-1673); Former titles (until 1991): Transactions of the Institute of Electronics, Information and Communication Engineers (ISSN 0913-574X); (until 1987): Transactions of the Institute of Electronics and Communication Engineers of Japan. Section E (ISSN 0387-236X); (until 1976): Transactions of the Institute of Electronics and Communication Engineers of Japan. Abstracts (ISSN 0418-6869); (until 1968): Journal of the Institute of Electrical Communication Engineers of Japan. Abstracts (ISSN 0914-5273).

I E I C E TRANSACTIONS ON INFORMATION AND SYSTEMS. (Institute of Electronics, Information and Communication Engineers) see *COMPUTERS — Information Science And Information Theory*

621.38　　　　　IT　　ISSN 0018-957X
I E N PUBBLICAZIONI. (Text in English) 1935. 50/yr. price varies. Istituto Elettrotecnico Nazionale Galileo Ferraris, Corso Massimo d'Azeglio 42, Turin, Italy. TEL 011-3488933. FAX 6507611. TELEX 211553 IENGF. charts; illus.; stat.; index, cum.index.

Formerly (in 1990 only): I E N Annual Report.

Description: Covers applied research in the electrotechnic world. Includes electromagnetic and electrical metrology, photometry, acoustics and electromechanics, materials and systems engineering.

621.38　　　　　US
I I C I T NEWS. q. International Institute of Connector and Interconnection Technology, Inc., Box 880, Westfield, NJ 07091-0880. TEL 908-233-7278. Ed. S. Parker.

Formerly: E C S G News.

Description: Provides technical data and news from the electrical engineering field and information on the activities of the institute.

621.381　　　　　US
I S C E T UPDATE. 1980. q. membership. International Society of Certified Electronics Technicians, 2708 W. Berry, Ste. 3, Ft. Worth, TX 76109. TEL 817-921-9101. FAX 817-921-3741. Ed. Barbara Rubin. bk.rev. circ. 1,800.

Description: Information for industrial and consumer electronics technicians.

621.381 539.7　　　　　JA　　ISSN 0915-0609
I S T E C JOURNAL. (Editions in English and Japanese) 1988. q. International Superconductivity Technology Center - Kokusai Chodendo Sangyo Gijutsu Kenkyu Senta, 34-3, Shinbashi 5-chome, Minato-ku, Tokyo 105, Japan.

537.5　　　　　UK　　ISSN 0961-1290
3 - 5S REVIEW; the journal of compound semiconductor technology. Variant title: Three - Fives Review. 1988. 6/yr. £70($110) (effective 1994). Elsevier Science Ltd., Oxford Fulfilment Centre, P.O. Box 800, Kidlington, Oxford OX5 1 DX, England. TEL 44-865-843000. FAX 44-865-843010. (Subscr. in U.S. and Canada to: Elsevier Science, 660 White Plains Rd., Tarrytown, NY 10591-5153. TEL 914-524-9200. FAX 914-333-2444) Ed. Roy Szweda. adv. **Document type:** academic/scholarly publication, trade publication.
—El. **CCC.**

Formerly (until 1991): Euro III - Vs (ISSN 0959-3527)

Description: For those involved in the international compound semiconductor industry and senior staff in all relevant compound semiconductor companies and institutions.

ELECTRONICS

643 658.8 UK
IN-CAR ENTERTAINMENT: THE INTERNATIONAL MARKET. a. £1375($2750) Euromonitor, 87-88 Turnmill St., London EC1M 5QU, England. TEL 071-251-8024. FAX 071-608-3149. (Addr. in N. America: Euromonitor International, 111 W. Washington St., Ste. 920, Chicago, IL 60602. TEL 312-541-8024. FAX 312-541-1567) **Document type:** trade publication.
●Also available online. Vendor(s): Data-Star, DIALOG Information Services, Inc.
Description: Analyzes the automobile high-fidelity audio equipment market for France, Germany, Italy, Spain, the U.K., the U.S., and Japan.

621.38 US ISSN 0888-9406
IN-STAT ELECTRONICS REPORT.* 1981. m. $795 (foreign $870). In-Stat, Inc., Box 14667, Scottsdale, AZ 85267-4667. TEL 602-483-4440. FAX 602-483-4479. Ed. Jack Beedle. charts; stat. **Document type:** newsletter.
Description: Keeps readers abreast of current semiconductor and end-use market conditions as well as providing forecasts.

643 II ISSN 0377-7340
TK7805
INDIAN ELECTRONICS DIRECTORY. (Text in English) 1974. biennial. Rs.200 per no. Electronic Component Industries Association, 408 & 707 Sahyog, 58 Nehru Place, New Delhi 110019, India. adv. circ. 1,000. **Document type:** directory.
Description: Lists manufacturers of all kinds of electronic products in India.

643 SP
INFORMACIONES ACEMA. 1980. 6/yr. membership. Association of Electrical Appliances, C. Abtao 11, 1o C, 28007 Madrid, Spain. TEL 1-551-32-06. FAX 1-501-22-40. Ed. Juan Zurita Lopez. adv. contact: Rosa Maria Hernanz de Antonio. bk.rev. circ. 6,000. **Document type:** trade publication.

537.5 IT ISSN 0390-2455
INFORMAZIONE ELETTRONICA. 1973. m. L.15000. Editrice Il Rostro, Via Monte Generoso 6-A, 20155 Milano, Italy. Ed. Patrizio Giovene. adv. circ. 14,000. **Indexed:** Sci.Abstr.

621.381 IT
INGEGNERIA ELETTRONICA. 1963. m. (11/yr.). L.100000. Edizioni Gammatrol, Via Bitti 28, 20125 Milan, Italy. TEL 02-6473123. Ed. Alfredo Casieri. adv.; bk.rev. circ. 9,000.
Description: Forum specialized in electronic components, instrumentation and equipment for automation in the industrial field.

537.5 CU ISSN 0258-5944
INGENIERIA ELECTRONICA, AUTOMATICA Y COMUNICACIONES. 1977. 3/yr. $24 in N. America; S. America $25; Europe $26. (Ministerio de Educacion Superior, Instituto Superior Politecnico) Ediciones Cubanas, Obispo No. 527, Apdo. 605, Havana, Cuba.

INSTELEC. see COMMUNICATIONS

621.38 SZ ISSN 0153-9930
INSTITUT EUROPEEN DE FORMATION DES TECHNICIENS DES CIRCUITS IMPRIMES. INFORMATIONS. Cover title: I F T E C Informations, (Text in English, French, German) 1968. q. 96.60 SFr. Institut Europeen de Formation des Techniciens des Circuits Imprimes, Via Maraini 17, CH-6900 Lugano, Switzerland. Ed. L. Duriez. adv.; charts; illus.

INSTITUTE OF ELECTRONICS, INFORMATION AND COMMUNICATION ENGINEERS. TRANSACTIONS (SECTION A)/DENSHI JOHO TSUSHIN GAKKAI RONBUNSHI (A). see ENGINEERING

621.38 JA ISSN 0915-1877
TK5101.A1 CODEN: DJBTES
INSTITUTE OF ELECTRONICS, INFORMATION AND COMMUNICATION ENGINEERS. TRANSACTIONS (SECTION B-I)/DENSHI JOHO TSUSHIN GAKKAI RONBUNSHI (B-I). English translation (in part): Electronics and Communications in Japan - Part 1: Communications (US ISSN 8756-6621) (Text in Japanese) 1968. m. 1030 Yen. Institute of Electronics, Information and Communication Engineers - Denshi Joho Tsushin Gakkai, c/o Kikai Shinko Kaikan, 5-8 Shiba Koen, 3-chome, Minato-ku, Tokyo 105, Japan. Ed. Michiyuki Uenohara. **Indexed:** Cyb.Abstr., Int.Abstr.Oper.Res., JCT, Sci.Abstr., Tel.Abstr.
—BLDSC (8939.441100). **CCC.**
Supersedes in part in (1989): Institute of Electronics, Information and Communication Engineers. Transactions. Section B (ISSN 0913-5715)

INSTITUTE OF ELECTRONICS, INFORMATION AND COMMUNICATION ENGINEERS. TRANSACTIONS (SECTION B-II)/DENSHI JOHO TSUSHIN GAKKAI RONBUNSHI (B-II). see COMMUNICATIONS — Television And Cable

621.38 JA ISSN 0915-1893
TK7800 CODEN: DTGEEA
INSTITUTE OF ELECTRONICS, INFORMATION AND COMMUNICATION ENGINEERS. TRANSACTIONS (SECTION C-I)/DENSHI JOHO TSUSHIN GAKKAI RONBUNSHI (C-I). English translation (in part): Electronics and Communications in Japan - Part 2: Electronics (US ISSN 8756-663X) (Text in Japanese) 1968. m. 1030 Yen. Institute of Electronics, Information and Communication Engineers - Denshi Joho Tsushin Gakkai, c/o Kikai Shinko Kaikan, 5-8 Shiba Koen, 3-chome, Minato-ku, Tokyo 105, Japan. Ed. Michiyuki Uenohara. **Indexed:** Cyb.Abstr., Int.Abstr.Oper.Res., JCT, Sci.Abstr., Tel.Abstr.
—BLDSC (8939.441510). **CCC.**
Supersedes in part (in 1989): Institute of Electronics, Information and Communication Engineers. Transactions. Section J - C (ISSN 0913-5723)

621.38 JA ISSN 0915-1907
TK7800 CODEN: DCSOEF
INSTITUTE OF ELECTRONICS, INFORMATION AND COMMUNICATION ENGINEERS. TRANSACTIONS (SECTION C-II)/DENSHI JOHO TSUSHIN GAKKAI RONBUNSHI (C-II). English translation (in part): Electronics and Communications in Japan - Part 2: Electronics (US ISSN 8756-663X) (Text in Japanese) 1968. m. 1030 Yen. Institute of Electronics, Information and Communication Engineers - Denshi Joho Tsushin Gakkai, c/o Kikai Shinko Kaikan, 5-8 Shiba Koen, 3-chome, Minato-ku, Tokyo 105, Japan. Ed. Michiyuki Uenohara. **Indexed:** Int.Abstr.Oper.Res., JCT, Sci.Abstr.
—BLDSC (8939.441520). **CCC.**
Supersedes in part (in 1989): Institute of Electronics, Information and Communication Engineers. Transactions. Section J - C (ISSN 0913-5723)

621.38 JA ISSN 0913-5693
TK5101.A1 CODEN: DJTGEB
INSTITUTE OF ELECTRONICS, INFORMATION AND COMMUNICATIONS ENGINEERS. JOURNAL/DENSHI JOHO TSUSHIN GAKKAISHI. (Text in Japanese) 1917. m. 2060 Yen. Institute of Electronics, Information and Communication Engineers - Denshi Joho Tsushin Gakkai, c/o Kikai Shinko Kaikan, 3-5-8 Shiba Koen, Minato-ku, Tokyo 105, Japan. Ed. Toshio Sekiguchi. adv.; index. circ. 40,000. **Indexed:** Chem.Abstr., Cyb.Abstr., Eng.Ind., JCT, JTA, Sci.Abstr.
—BLDSC (4775.540000). **CCC.**
Former titles (until 1987): Institute of Electronics and Communication Engineers of Japan. Journal (ISSN 0373-6121); (Until 1967): Institute of Electrical Communication Engineers of Japan. Journal (ISSN 0020-286X)

621.381 II ISSN 0020-3378
INSTITUTION OF ENGINEERS (INDIA). ELECTRONICS AND TELECOMMUNICATION ENGINEERING DIVISION. JOURNAL. (Text in English) 1920. 4/yr. Rs.80($10) Institution of Engineers (India), Electronics and Telecommunication Engineering Division, 8 Gokhale Rd., Calcutta 700 020, India. TEL 033-288334. FAX 033-288345. TELEX 0217885 IEIC IN. Ed. K.N. Majumdar. adv.; charts; illus.; index. circ. 6,000. **Indexed:** Sci.Abstr.

621.381 SP
INSTRUMENTACION, COMPONENTES Y EQUIPOS ELECTRONICOS. 11/yr. Extra Editorial S.L., C. Ibiza 35, bajo A, 28009 Madrid, Spain. TEL 1-504-16-95. FAX 1-504-17-72. Ed. Ana Heredia. circ. 15,000.

621.381 US ISSN 1057-4530
INTEGRATED CIRCUITS. DIGITAL. 1969. s-a. $205. D.A.T.A. Business Publishing (Subsidiary of: Information Handling Services), 15 Inverness Way E., Box 6510, Englewood, CO 80155-6510. TEL 800-447-4666. FAX 303-799-4082. TELEX 4322083 IHS UI. adv. contact: Peggy Anderson.
●Also available on CD-ROM.
Former titles (until 1988): Integrated Circuits. Digital Integrated Circuits (ISSN 0899-8523); (until 1981): Digital Integrated Circuits (ISSN 8755-8424); (until 1979): Digital Integrated Circuit D.A.T.A. Book (ISSN 0193-4295); Digital Logic-Computational Integrated Circuit D.A.T.A. Book.
Description: Reference guide covering up to 20 technical parameters on over 66,000 digital ICs from more than 196 manufacturers.

INTELLIGENT DECISIONS. see CONSUMER EDUCATION AND PROTECTION

621.381 US ISSN 1065-0415
INTERCONNECTION TECHNOLOGY. 1985. m. $60 (Canada & Mexico $90, elsewhere $160). I H S Publishing Group, Inc., 17730 W. Peterson Rd., Box 159, Libertyville, IL 60048-0159. TEL 708-362-8711. FAX 708-362-3484. Ed. Jim Fulcher. adv.; bk.rev.; stat.; tr.lit.; index. circ. 31,500. (back issues avail.)
—EI; Faxon; SWETS. **CCC.**
Formerly: Connection Technology (ISSN 8756-4076)
Description: Deals with all levels of electrical and electronic interconnection and connecting devices in the manufacture of electrical and electronic equipment.

621.381 IT
INTERCONNECTIONS & CABLES. 9/yr. Gruppo Editoriale J C E, Via Ferri 6, 20092 Cinisello Balsamo (MI), Italy. TEL 02-66051. FAX 02-6127620. TELEX 352376 JCE MIL I. adv.: B&W page L.2500000, color page L.4000000; trim 184 x 250. circ. 10,889.

621.38 US ISSN 1057-4522
TK7868.I58
INTERFACE I CS D.A.T.A. DIGEST. (Integrated Circuits) 1977. s-a. $205. D.A.T.A. Business Publishing (Subsidiary of: Information Handling Services), 15 Inverness Way E., Box 6510, Englewood, CO 80155-6510. TEL 800-447-4666. FAX 303-799-4082. TELEX 4322083 IHS UI. Ed. Paul Magin. adv. contact: Peggy Anderson.
●Also available on CD-ROM.
Formerly: Interface I Cs D.A.T.A. Book (ISSN 0164-0119)
Description: Reference guide to interface integrated circuits. Covers up to 20 technical parameters on over 60,900 devices from more than 240 manufactureres.

621.38 US ISSN 0163-1918
TK7801 CODEN: TDIMD5
INTERNATIONAL ELECTRON DEVICES MEETING. I E D M TECHNICAL DIGEST. a. (I E E E, Electron Devices Society) Institute of Electrical and Electronics Engineers, Inc., 345 E. 47th St., New York, NY 10017-2394. TEL 212-705-7900. FAX 212-705-7682. (Subscr. to: Box 1331, 445 Hoes Lane, Piscataway, NJ 08855-1331)
—BLDSC (4539.899000); Faxon; UMI; CASDDS. **CCC.**
Formerly (until 1973): International Electron Devices Meeting. Abstracts (ISSN 0074-4670)

621.38 US
INTERNATIONAL ELECTRONICS PACKAGING SOCIETY. (PUBLICATION). 1981. 4/yr. $115. International Electronics Packaging Society, 114 N. Hale St., Wheaton, IL 60187-5113. FAX 708-260-0867. Ed. Rick McMasters. bk.rev. circ. 1,200. **Document type:** proceedings.

ELECTRONICS

537.5   US   ISSN 1063-1674
TK7870.15   CODEN: IMEPE5
INTERNATIONAL JOURNAL FOR MICROCIRCUITS AND ELECTRONIC PACKAGING. 1978. q. $60. International Society for Hybrid Microelectronics, Box 2698, Reston, VA 22090-0698. TEL 703-471-0066. FAX 703-471-1937. Ed. Robert Lagou. circ. 5,600. **Indexed:** Ceram.Abstr., Chem.Abstr., Comput.Cont., Elec.& Electron.Abstr., Sci.Abstr.
—BLDSC (4542.353500); El; Faxon; SWETS; CASDDS.
Formerly (until 1994): International Journal for Hybrid Microelectronics (ISSN 0277-8270)

621.38   UK   ISSN 0020-7217
TK7800   CODEN: IJELA2
INTERNATIONAL JOURNAL OF ELECTRONICS. 1965. m. £583($980) Taylor & Francis Ltd., Rankine Rd., Basingstoke, Hants RG24 8PR, England. TEL 0256-840366. FAX 0256-479438. TELEX 858540. Ed. D.J. Jefferies. adv.; bk.rev. (also avail. in microfiche) **Indexed:** Appl.Mech.Rev., Cadscan, Chem.Abstr., Curr.Cont., Eng.Ind., Excerp.Med., Ind.Sci.Rev., Lead Abstr., Math.R., Sci.Abstr., Sci.Cit.Ind., Zincscan. **Document type:** academic/scholarly publication.
—BLDSC (4542.232000); El; Faxon; UnCover; SWETS; CASDDS. **CCC**.
Description: Coverage ranges from fundamental conduction processes in vacuum, gases, vapours and semiconductors to the applications of electronic devices and techniques to engineering requirements in communications, digital processing and computing, power regulation and measurement.
Refereed Serial

621.381   SI   ISSN 0129-1564
    CODEN: IHSEE7
INTERNATIONAL JOURNAL OF HIGH SPEED ELECTRONICS. 1990. q. $125 for developing countries; developed countries $270. World Scientific Publishing Co. Pte. Ltd., Farrer Rd., P.O. Box 128, Singapore 9128, Singapore. TEL 3825663. FAX 3825919. TELEX RS-28561-WSPC. (UK addr.: 73 Lynton Mead, Totteridge, London N20 8DH, England. TEL 44-81-4462461; US addr.: 1060 Main St., Ste. 1B, River Edge, NJ 07661. TEL 800-227-7562) Ed.Bd. **Document type:** academic/scholarly publication.
—**CCC**.
Description: Covers new milestones in research and development, new materials, device structures, processing technologies, circuit and system architecture that lead to speed and performance. Also includes critical evaluation of pertinent topics, tutorial, review papers and technical reports.

621.3   II   ISSN 0047-0937
INTERNATIONAL PRESS CUTTING SERVICE: ELECTRONICS AND ELECTRICALS INDUSTRY. 1967. w. $65. International Press Cutting Service, Box 63, Allahabad 211001, India. Ed. N. Khanna. bk.rev.; index. circ. 1,200. (processed)

621.38   US
INTERNATIONAL SEMICONDUCTOR DIRECTORY D.A.T.A. DIGEST: MASTER TYPE LOCATOR. (Subseries of D.A.T.A. Digest Electronic Information Series.) 1979. s-a. $130. D.A.T.A. Business Publishing (Subsidiary of: Information Handling Services), 15 Inverness Way E., Box 6510, Englewood, CO 80155-6510. TEL 800-447-4666. FAX 303-799-0381. TELEX 4322083 IHS UI. Ed. Paul Magin. adv. contact: Peggy Anderson.
●Also available on CD-ROM.
Former titles (until 1992): International Semiconductor Directory I Cs and Discrete Semiconductors D.A.T.A. Digest: Master Type Locator (ISSN 1048-6607); International Directory I Cs and Discrete Semiconductors D.A.T.A. Digest; International Directory I Cs and Semiconductors D.A.T.A. Book; D.A.T.A. Books Master Type Locator (ISSN 0271-079X); Master Type Locator D.A.T.A. Book (ISSN 0730-6776).
Description: Lists over 601,300 integrated circuits and discrete semiconductor part numbers from more than 900 manufacturers.

621.38   RU
ITOGI NAUKI I TEKHNIKI: ELEKTRONIKA. irreg., vols.23-25, 1989. 6.60 Rub. Vsesoyuznyi Institut Nauchno-Tekhnicheskoi Informatsii (VINITI), Baltiiskaya ul. 14, Moscow A-219, Russia. (Subscr. to: Mezdunarodnaya Kniga, Dimitrova ul. 39, 113095 Moscow, Russia)

IZVESTIYA VYSSHIKH UCHEBNYKH ZAVEDENII. SERIYA RADIOELEKTRONIKA. see *COMMUNICATIONS — Radio*

621.3   GW   ISSN 0344-6581
JAHRBUCH FUER DAS ELEKTROHANDWERK (YEAR). 1955. a. DM.21.80. Huethig und Pflaum Verlag, Lazarettstr. 4, 80636 Munich, Germany. TEL 089-12607240. FAX 089-12607200. (Subscr. addr.: Im Weiher 10, 6900 Heidelberg 1, Germany) Eds. G. Lehwald, J. Eiselt, G. Dusch. circ. 35,000.

621.38 380.3   JA   ISSN 0167-5036
TK5101.A1   CODEN: JATED7
JAPAN ANNUAL REVIEWS IN ELECTRONICS, COMPUTERS & TELECOMMUNICATIONS. AMORPHOUS SEMICONDUCTOR TECHNOLOGIES & DEVICES. 1982. a. 16000 Yen. Ohmsha, Ltd., 3-1 Kanda Nishiki-cho, Chiyoda-ku, Tokyo 101, Japan. FAX 3-3293-2824. TELEX 222-3125 OHMSHAJ. Ed. Y. Hamakawa. circ. 1,500. **Indexed:** Chem.Abstr., Compumath.
—CASDDS.
Description: Covers the progress and results of recent Japanese studies in amorphous semi-conductors.

643 382   JA
JAPAN ELECTRONICS ALMANAC. (Text in English) a. $98. Dempa Publications, Inc., 11-15, Higashi Gotanda 1-chome, Shinagawa-ku, Tokyo 141, Japan. TEL 81-3-3445-6111. FAX 81-3-33445-6101. (Dist. by Intercontinental Marketing Corp., I.P.O. Box 5056, Tokyo 100-30, Japan. TEL 81-3-3661-7458. FAX 81-3-3667-9646; US addr.: 400 Madison Ave., New York, NY 10017. TEL 212-752-3003) Ed. Hideo Hirayama. adv.
Former titles: Japan's Electronics Almanac and Leading Firms; Japan Fact Book.
Description: Contains profiles of companies, as well as comprehensive forecasts of their anticipated performance.

621.38   US   ISSN 1058-7292
JAPANESE TECHNOLOGY REVIEWS: ELECTRONICS (SECTION A). 1989. 4/yr. (in 2 vols., 2 nos./vol.). 60 ECU per vol. (effective 1993). Gordon & Breach Science Publishers, 820 Town Center Dr., Langhorne, PA 19047. TEL 215-750-2642. FAX 215-750-6343. (UK subscr. to: P.O. Box 90, Reading, Berkshire RG1 8JL, England. TEL 0734-560-080) Ed. Toshiaki Ikoma. (also avail. in microform)
—BLDSC (4662.120440). **CCC**.
Supersedes in part: Japanese Technology Review (ISSN 0898-5693)
Refereed Serial

621.38   JA   ISSN 0385-0447
TK7800   CODEN: AEUNAX
JOURNAL OF ASIA ELECTRONICS UNION. Short title: A E U. (Text in English) 1968. bi-m. $60 for Asia & Oceania; N. & C. America $65; elsewhere $70. (Asia Electronics Union) Dempa Publications, Inc., 1-11-15 Higashi Gotanda, Shinagawa-ku, Tokyo 141, Japan. TEL 81-3-3445-6111. FAX 81-3-3445-6890. (U.S. addr.: 275 Madison Ave., New York, NY 10016. TEL 212-682-4755) Pub. Tetso Hirayama. adv. circ. 40,000. **Indexed:** Chem.Abstr., Comput.Cont., JCT, JTA, Sci.Abstr.
—BLDSC (0730.610000).
Description: Treats telecom and electronics separately, introducing the latest Asian developments.

JOURNAL OF COMMUNICATIONS TECHNOLOGY AND ELECTRONICS. see *COMMUNICATIONS*

621.38   US   ISSN 0361-5235
TK7871   CODEN: JECMA5
JOURNAL OF ELECTRONIC MATERIALS. 1971. 12/yr. $83 to individuals; intstitutions $198. Minerals, Metals and Materials Society, 420 Commonwealth Dr., Warrendale, PA 15086. TEL 412-776-9080. FAX 412-776-3770. Ed. Theodore E. Harman. index. circ. 1,800. (also avail. in microfilm from JSC; back issues avail.; reprint service avail. from UMI) **Indexed:** Cadscan, Chem.Abstr., Curr.Cont., Elec.& Electron.Abstr., Electron.& Communic.Abstr.J, Eng.Ind., Ind.Sci.Rev., Int.Aerosp.Abstr., Lead Abstr., Met.Abstr., Phys.Abstr., Sci.Abstr., Sci.Cit.Ind., Sci.Res.Abstr., Solid St.Abstr., World Alum.Abstr., Zincscan. **Document type:** proceedings.
—BLDSC (4974.950000); El; Faxon; UnCover; SWETS; UMI; CASDDS. **CCC**.
Description: Thoroughly covers all technical aspects of electronic materials.

621.381   US   ISSN 1043-7398
TK7870   CODEN: JEPAE4
JOURNAL OF ELECTRONIC PACKAGING. q. American Society of Mechanical Engineers, 345 E. 47th St., New York, NY 10017. illus. **Indexed:** Comput.& Contr.Abstr., Elec.& Electron.Abstr., Phys.Abstr.
—BLDSC (8896.760000); El; Faxon; UnCover; SWETS; UMI. **CCC**.
Refereed Serial

621.38   CC   ISSN 0217-9822
JOURNAL OF ELECTRONICS. Chinese edition: Dianzi Kexue Xuekan (ISSN 0258-798X) (Text in English) 1984. q. $120 to individuals (foreign $140); institutions $186.50 (foreign $206.50). (Chinese Academy of Sciences, Institute of Electronics) Science Press, Marketing and Sales Department, 16 Donghuangchenggen Beijie, Beijing 100707, People's Republic of China. TEL 4010642. FAX 4012180. TELEX 210247-SPBJ-CN. (Overseas dist. by: Science Press New York, Ltd., 63-117 Alderton St., Rego Park, NY11374. TEL 718-459-4633) Ed. Richard P. Bain. adv. circ. 6,000. (back issues avail.)
—UnCover. **CCC**.
Description: Covers the broad field of electronics in China, including electrical circuits, devices, and power.
Refereed Serial

621.38 001.6   IQ   ISSN 1012-3385
JOURNAL OF ELECTRONICS AND COMPUTER RESEARCH. (Text in Arabic, English) s-a. ID.5($15) to individuals; institutions $50. Scientific Research Council, Electronics and Computer Center, Jadiriyah P.O. Box 2441, Baghdad, Iraq. TELEX 213976 SR IK. Ed. Munther N.B. Al-Tikriti. circ. 500. **Indexed:** Comput.& Contr.Abstr., Elec.& Electron.Abstr., Phys.Abstr.

621.381   UK   ISSN 0960-3131
    CODEN: JELMEK
JOURNAL OF ELECTRONICS MANUFACTURING. 1991. q. £110 to institutions in EC nations (North America $190; elsewhere £120). Chapman & Hall, 2-6 Boundary Row, London SE1 8HN, England. TEL 071-865-0066. FAX 071-522-9623. TELEX 290164-CHAPMAG. (Dist. by: International Thomson Publishing, Ltd., N. Way, Andover, Hants. SP10 5BE, England. TEL 0263-342919; US subscr. to: Chapman & Hall, Journals Promotion Department, One Penn Plaza, 41st Fl., New York, NY 10019. TEL 212-564-1060. FAX 212-564-1505) Ed.Bd. bk.rev. **Document type:** academic/scholarly publication.
—BLDSC (4975.800000); CASDDS. **CCC**.
Description: Presents application-oriented papers covering all aspects of electronics manufacturing.
Refereed Serial

621.38   JA   ISSN 0385-4515
HD9696.A3   CODEN: JJEID7
JOURNAL OF THE ELECTRONICS INDUSTRY. Short title: J E I. (Text in English) 1954. m. $135 for Asia & Oceania; N. and C. America $150; elsewhere $165. Dempa Publications Inc., 1-11-15, Higashi Gotanda, Shinagawa-ku, Tokyo 141, Japan. TEL 81-3-3445-6111. FAX 81-3-3445-6890. (U.S. addr.: 275 Madison Ave., New York, NY 10016. TEL 212-682-4755) Pub. Hideo Hirayama. adv.; charts; illus.; index. circ. 108,500. **Indexed:** JTA, PROMT, Sci.Abstr.
—BLDSC (4975.600000); SWETS.
Formerly: J E I: Japan Electronic Industry (ISSN 0021-3616)
Description: Reports on developments in consumer electronics.

JUNGE RADIO-, FERNSEH- UND INDUSTRIE-ELEKTRONIKER. see *COMMUNICATIONS — Radio*

621.381   JA
K E C JOHO/KANSAI ELECTRONIC INDUSTRY DEVELOPMENT CENTER. BULLETIN. (Text in Japanese) 1961. q. Kansai Denshi Kogyo Shinko Senta - Kansai Electronic Industry Development Center, Denshi Kaikan, 8-7, Nishitenma 6-chome, Kita-ku, Osaka-shi, Osaka 530.

621.381   JA
KADEN SHINBUN/HOUSEHOLD APPLIANCES NEWS. (Text in Japanese) m. 500 Yen per no. Kaden Shinbunsha, 50-22, Wakahisa 3-chome, Minami-ku, Fukuoka-shi, Fukuoka-ken 815, Japan.

ELECTRONICS

KEISAN DENKI DENSHI KOGAKU SHINPOJUMU RONBUNSHU/J S S T SYMPOSIUM ON CALCULATIONS IN ELECTRICAL AND ELECTRONICS ENGINEERING. PROCEEDINGS. see *ENGINEERING — Electrical Engineering*

621.3   UK   ISSN 0306-557X
TK7800
KEY ABSTRACTS - ELECTRONIC CIRCUITS. 1975. m. £90($160) INSPEC, I.E.E., Michael Faraday House, Six Hills Way, Stevenage, Herts. SG1 2AY, England. TEL 0438-313311. FAX 0438-742840. TELEX 825578-IEESTV-G. (Subscr. to: Publication Sales Dept., P.O. Box 96, Stevenage, Herts. SG1 2SD, England; U.S. addr.: INSPEC/IEEE, Box 1331, 445 Hoes Ln., Piscataway, NJ 08855-1331. TEL 908-562-5549) Indexed: Agri.Eng.Abstr. **Document type:** abstracting/indexing.
   Description: Covers power electronics, amplifiers, signal generators, modulators, pulse circuits, digital electronics, and filters.

621.3 016   UK   ISSN 0950-480X
TK7869
KEY ABSTRACTS - ELECTRONIC INSTRUMENTATION. 1976. m. £90($160) INSPEC, I.E.E., Michael Faraday House, Six Hills Way, Stevenage, Herts. SG1 2AY, England. TEL 0483-313311. FAX 0438-742840. TELEX 825578-IEESTV-G. (Subscr. to: Publication Sales Dept., P.O. Box 96, Stevenage, Herts. SG1 2SD, England; U.S. addr.: INSPEC/IEEE, Box 1331, 445 Hoes Ln., Piscataway, NJ 08855-1331. TEL 908-562-5549) index. Indexed: Agri.Eng.Abstr. **Document type:** abstracting/indexing.
   Formerly (until 1987): Key Abstracts - Electrical Measurements and Instrumentation (ISSN 0307-7977)
   Description: Covers instrumentation and measurement systems, signal processing circuits and devices, transducers, bench instruments, display technology, measurement of electrical, and magnetic variables.

621.38   UK   ISSN 0952-7060
KEY ABSTRACTS - MICROELECTRONICS & PRINTED CIRCUITS. 1989. m. £90($160) INSPEC, I.E.E., Michael Faraday House, Six Hills Way, Stevenage, Herts. SG1 2AY, England. TEL 0438-313311. FAX 0438-742840. TELEX 825578-IEESTV-G. (Subscr. to: Publication Sales Dept., P.O. Box 96, Stevenage, Herts. SG1 2SD, England; U.S. addr.: INSPEC/EEE, Box 1331, 445 Hoes Ln., Piscataway, NJ 08855-1331. TEL 908-562-5549) Ed. John Deaves. **Document type:** abstracting/indexing.

621.38 011   UK   ISSN 0952-7079
KEY ABSTRACTS - MICROWAVE TECHNOLOGY. 1989. m. £90($160) INSPEC, I.E.E., Michael Faraday House, Six Hills Way, Stevenage, Herts. SG1 2AY, England. TEL 0438-313311. FAX 0438-742840. TELEX 825578-IEESTV-G. (Subscr. to: Publication Sales Dept., P.O. Box 96, Stevenage, Herts. SG1 2SD, England. U.S. addr.: INSPEC/IEEE, Box 1331, 445 Hoes Ln., Piscataway, NJ 08855-1331. TEL 908-562-5549) Ed. John Deaves. **Document type:** abstracting/indexing.
—CCC.

621.38 016   UK   ISSN 0950-4850
TK7871.85
KEY ABSTRACTS - SEMICONDUCTOR DEVICES. 1975. m. £60($160) INSPEC, I.E.E., Michael Faraday House, Six Hills Way, Stevenage, Herts. SG1 2AY, England. TEL 0438-313311. FAX 0438-742840. TELEX 825578-IEESTV-G. (Subscr. to: Publication Sales Dept., P.O. Box 96, Stevenage, Herts. SG1 2SD, England; U.S. addr.: INSPEC/IEEE, Box 1331, 445 Hoes Ln., Piscataway, NJ 08855-1331. TEL 908-562-5549) index. **Document type:** abstracting/indexing.
   Formerly (until 1987): Key Abstracts - Solid State Devices (ISSN 0306-5537)
   Description: Covers semiconductor devices and device technology and semiconductor integrated circuits.

621.3   JA
KINO EREKUTORONIKUSU KENKYU SENTA. KENKYU SEIKA RONBUNSHU/CENTER FOR FUNCTION-ORIENTED ELECTRONICS. ANNUAL REPORT. (Text in English, Japanese) a. Tokyo Daigaku, Seisan Gijyutsu Kenkyujo, Kino Erekutoronikusu Kenkyu Senta - University of Tokyo, Institute of Industrial Science, Center for Function-Oriented Electronics, 22-1, Roppongi 7-chome, Minato-ku, Tokyo 106, Japan.

KOKU DENSHI GIHO/JAPAN AVIATION ELECTRONICS TECHNICAL REPORT. see *AERONAUTICS AND SPACE FLIGHT*

KOMPASS PROFESSIONNEL. ELECTRICITE, ELECTRONIQUE, INFORMATIQUE. see *BUSINESS AND ECONOMICS — Trade And Industrial Directories*

621.38   JA   ISSN 0387-6195
KONDENSA HYORON/CONDENSER REVIEW. (Text in Japanese) 1947. irreg. Kondensa Kenkyukai - Capacitors Engineering Committee, Nihon Denshi Kikai Kogyokai, Tosho Biru, 2-2, Marunouchi 3-chome, Chiyoda-ku, Tokyo 100.

621.38   PL   ISSN 0867-6747
KWARTALNIK ELEKTRONIKI I TELEKOMUNIKACJI/ELECTRONICS AND TELECOMMUNICATIONS QUARTERLY. (Text and summaries in English, Polish) 1955. q. $80. (Polska Akademia Nauk, Komitet Elektroniki i Telekomminikacji) Wydawnictwo Naukowe P W N, Miodowa 10, 00-251 Warsaw, Poland. Ed. Wieslaw Wolinski. bibl.; charts; index. circ. 550. Indexed: Chem.Abstr., Eng.Ind., Sci.Abstr.
   Formerly (until 1990): Rozprawy Elektrotechniczne (ISSN 0035-9386)

643 658.8   UK
LARGE KITCHEN APPLIANCES: THE INTERNATIONAL MARKET. a. £1375($2750) Euromonitor, 87-88 Turnmill St., London EC1M 5QU, England. TEL 071-251-8024. FAX 071-608-3149. (Addr. in N. America: Euromonitor International, 111 W. Washington St., Ste. 920, Chicago, IL 60602. TEL 312-541-8024. FAX 312-541-1567) (looseleaf format) **Document type:** trade publication.
● Also available online. Vendor(s): Data-Star, DIALOG Information Services, Inc.
   Description: Analyzes the market for large domestic kitchen appliances for France, Germany, Italy, Spain, the U.K., the U.S., and Japan.

537.5   US   ISSN 0896-4130
T1   CODEN: LLJOEJ
LINCOLN LABORATORY JOURNAL. 1988. 2/yr. free to qualified personnel. Massachusetts Institute of Technology, Lincoln Laboratory, 244 Wood St., Lexington, MA 02173-9108. TEL 617-981-2342. Ed. Jack Nolan. (back issues avail.)
—BLDSC (5220.237000); UnCover.
Refereed Serial

621.38   US   ISSN 0899-854X
TK7874
LINEAR I CS D.A.T.A. DIGEST. 1968. s-a. $205. D.A.T.A. Business Publishing (Subsidiary of: Information Handling Services), 15 Inverness Way E., Box 6510, Englewood, CO 80155-6510. TEL 800-447-4666. FAX 303-799-4082. TELEX 4322083 IHS UI. Ed. Paul Magin. adv. contact: Peggy Anderson.
● Also available on CD-ROM.
   Former titles: Linear I Cs D.A.T.A. Book (ISSN 0270-9988); Linear Integrated Circuit D.A.T.A. Book (ISSN 0024-3809)
   Description: Covers up to 20 technical parameters on over 56,000 devices from more than 320 manufacturers.

621.381   JA
MAIKURO EREKUTORONIKUSU SHINPOJUMU RONBUNSHU/PROCEEDINGS OF MICROELECTRONICS SYMPOSIUM. (Text in Japanese) 1985. biennial. Haiburiddo Maikuro Erekutoronikusu Kyokai - Society for Hybrid Microelectronics, 20-4, Hanakoganei 6-chome, Kodaira-shi, Tokyo 187, Japan. **Document type:** proceedings.

MARINE ELECTRONICS DIRECTORY (YEAR). see *TRANSPORTATION — Ships And Shipping*

643   SP
MARKET VISION MONOGRAFIAS. SERIE EQUIPO DOMESTICO. 1985. 4/yr. Aramo Editorial, S.A., Muntaner 60 2o 2a, 08011 Barcelona, Spain. TEL 3-453-79-38. FAX 3-323-79-26. Ed. Humberto Martinez. adv.; circ. 5,500 (controlled). **Document type:** monographic series, trade publication.

643   SP
MARKET VISION NOTICIAS. (Supplement avail.) 1985. 20/yr. 15000 ptas. (effective 1993). Aramo Editorial, S.A., Muntaner 60 2o 2a, 08011 Barcelona, Spain. TEL 3-453-79-38. FAX 3-323-79-26. Ed. Humberto Martinez. circ. 2,000. **Document type:** bulletin.

643   SP
MARKET VISION SUPLEMENTOS. (Supplement to: Market Vision Noticias) 1985. 5/yr. Aramo Editorial, S.A., Muntaner 60 2o 2a, 08011 Barcelona, Spain. TEL 3-453-79-38. FAX 3-323-79-26. Ed. Humberto Martinez. adv.; circ. 5,500 (controlled). **Document type:** trade publication.

643   SP
MARRON Y BLANCO. 11/yr. Mallorca 370, 08013 Barcelona, Spain. TEL 93-207-04-46. FAX 93-4582370. Ed. Pilar Eneriz Torres. adv. circ. 65,000.
   Description: Covers consumer electronics and home appliances.

MEDIA NETWORK RECEIVER SHOPPING LIST; consumer survey of shortwave portable radios for international radio listening. see *COMMUNICATIONS — Radio*

643   SZ
MEGALINK. 50/yr. A T Zeitschriftenverlag, Bahnhofstr. 39-43, CH-5001 Aarau, Switzerland. TEL 064-266310. FAX 064-266213. Ed. Ruedi Bolliger. adv. contact: Hans-Peter Christ. circ. 18,000. **Document type:** trade publication.
   Formed by the 1994 merger of: E C Woche & Elektroniker.

621.38   US   ISSN 1048-2598
TK7895.M4
MEMORY I CS D.A.T.A. DIGEST. 1971. a. $205. D.A.T.A. Business Publishing (Subsidiary of: Information Handling Services), 15 Inverness Way E., Box 6510, Englewood, CO 80155-6510. TEL 800-447-4666. FAX 303-799-4082. TELEX 4322083 IHS UI. adv. contact: Peggy Anderson.
● Also available on CD-ROM.
   Former titles: Memory I Cs D.A.T.A. Book (ISSN 0195-5853); M S I - L S I Memory D.A.T.A. Book (ISSN 0163-9226)
   Description: Covers up to 20 technical parameters on over 105,450 devices from more than 170 manufacturers.

537.5   US   ISSN 0738-713X
TK7870.27   CODEN: MCRCE5
MICROCONTAMINATION. 1983. m. Canon Communications, Inc., 3340 Ocean Park Blvd., Ste. 1000, Santa Monica, CA 90405-3207. TEL 310-392-5509. FAX 310-392-4920. Ed. Tom Cheyney. adv.; tr.lit. circ. 35,000. (reprint service avail.) **Document type:** trade publication.
—BLDSC (5758.570000); EI; SWETS.
   Description: Covers contamination analysis and control for advanced technology manufacturing industries, includes semiconductors, disk drive, aerospace, computer and computer peripherals, medical and pharmaceutical.

621.3   NE   ISSN 0167-9317
TK7871.85   CODEN: MIENEF
MICROELECTRONIC ENGINEERING; an interdisciplinary journal of semiconductor manufacturing technology. 1983. 16/yr. (in 4 vols.; 4 nos./vol.). fl.1564($845) (effective 1994). North-Holland (Subsidiary of: Elsevier Science B.V.), P.O. Box 211, 1000 AE Amsterdam, Netherlands. TEL 31-20-5803911. FAX 31-20-5803598. TELEX 18582 ESPA NL. (Subscr. in U.S. and Canada to: Elsevier Science Inc., Box 882, Madison Sq. Sta., New York, NY 10159. TEL 212-989-5800. FAX 212-633-3990) Ed.Bd. (back issues avail.) Indexed: Curr.Cont., Eng.Ind., INSPEC, Sci.Cit.Ind. **Document type:** academic/scholarly publication.
—BLDSC (5758.810000); EI; Faxon; SWETS; CASDDS. CCC.
   Description: Brings together the results of Japanese, American and European work in the field of microelectronic devices. Includes materials, methods and designs for microfabrication, processing and inspection for microelectronic elements from centimeters to nanometers.
Refereed Serial

ELECTRONICS

621.38 UK ISSN 0026-2714
TK7870 CODEN: MCRLAS
MICROELECTRONICS AND RELIABILITY; an international journal and world abstracting service. 1962. 15/yr. £745($1145) (effective 1994). Elsevier Science Ltd., Pergamon, P.O. Box 800, Kidlington, Oxford OX5 1DX, England. TEL 44-865-843000. FAX 44-865-843010. (Subscr. in U.S. and Canada to: Elsevier Science, 660 White Plains Rd., Tarrytown, NY 10591-5153. TEL 914-524-9200. FAX 914-333-2444) Ed. G.W.A. Dummer. adv.; bk.rev.; charts; illus.; index. circ. 1,600. (also avail. in microfilm from UMI; back issues avail.) **Indexed:** Chem.Abstr., Comput.Cont., Curr.Cont., Cyb.Abstr., Eng.Ind., Excerp.Med., Ind.Sci.Rev., Intl.Civil Eng.Abstr., Oper.Res.Manage.Sci., Qual.Contr.Appl.Stat., Risk Abstr., Sci.Abstr., Soft.Abstr.Eng., Sugar Ind.Abstr. **Document type:** academic/scholarly publication, abstracting/indexing. —BLDSC (5758.900000); El; Faxon; UnCover; SWETS; UMI; CASDDS. **CCC.**
Description: Combines the practical, theoretical and statistical aspects of reliability research with design, construction, engineering and testing of microelectronic systems.
Refereed Serial

621.381 US
MICROELECTRONICS AND SIGNAL PROCESSING. 1982. irreg., vol.7, 1990. Academic Press, Inc., 525 B St., Ste. 1900, San Diego, CA 92101-4495. TEL 619-231-6616. FAX 619-699-6715. (Subscr. to: Order Dept., 6277 Sea Harbor Dr., 4th Fl., Orlando, FL 32887. TEL 800-321-5068) Eds. P.G. Farrell, J.R. Forrest. (back issues avail.)
Description: Provides information about microelectronic technology and its applications.

621.38 UK ISSN 0026-2692
TK7874 CODEN: MICEB9
MICROELECTRONICS JOURNAL. 1967. 8/yr. £295($455) (effective 1994). Elsevier Science Ltd., Oxford Fulfilment Centre, P.O. Box 800, Kidlington, Oxford OX5 1DX, England. TEL 44-865-843000. FAX 44-865-843010. (Subscr. in U.S. and Canada to: Elsevier Science, 660 White Plains Rd., Tarrytown, NY 10591-5153. TEL 914-524-9200. FAX 914-333-2444) Ed. J.B. Butcher. adv.; bk.rev.; index. circ. 700. (back issues avail.) **Indexed:** Chem.Abstr., Comput.Cont., Intl.Civil Eng.Abstr., Sci.Abstr., Soft.Abstr.Eng. **Document type:** academic/scholarly publication. —BLDSC (5758.973000); El; Faxon; UnCover; SWETS; CASDDS. **CCC.**
Incorporates (1983-1991): Journal of Semi-Custom I Cs (ISSN 0264-3375); (1983-1991): Semi-Custom I C Yearbook (ISSN 0264-908X)
Description: Source of original research on solid-state technology.
Refereed Serial

621.381 IT
MICROELETTRONICA E IMPRESE. 6/yr. Via Alghero 20, 20128 Milan, Italy. TEL 2-255-26-00. Ed. Giovanni Landi. circ. 10,000.

621.39 US
▼**MICROLITHOGRAPHY WORLD.** 1992. q. (International Society for Optical Engineering) PennWell Publishing Co. (Nashua), 10 Tara Blvd., 5th Fl., Nashua, NH 03062-2801. TEL 603-891-0123. FAX 603-891-0574. Ed. Sidney Marshall. adv.: B&W page $2475. circ. 5,000.
Description: Microlithography in the science of imaging and generating geometrical patterns having microscopic dimensions. Focuses on high-level engineering, scientific and corporate management issues, as well as worldwide news of the microlithography industry.

621.38 GW ISSN 0931-2714
MIKROELEKTRONIK; Fachzeitschrift fuer Hersteller und Anwender. bi-m. DM.174 (foreign DM.183). V D E-Verlag GmbH, Bismarckstr. 33, 10625 Berlin, Germany. TEL 030-348001-0. FAX 030-3417093. Ed. Juergen Gabel. circ. 1,700. **Document type:** trade publication.
—El.

643 AT
MINGAY'S RETAIL GUIDE. 1948. s-a. Aus.$150. Thomson Business Publishing, 47 Chippen St., Chippendale, N.S.W. 2008, Australia. TEL 02-699-2411. FAX 02-698-3920. Ed. Brenda McLean. adv. circ. 3,000.
Incorporates: Mingay's Product Service - Home Entertainment (ISSN 0812-6461) & Mingay's Product Service - Appliances (ISSN 0812-6453); Formerly: Mingay's Price Service (ISSN 0026-5101)

621.38 GW
MODELL ELEKTRONIK. 1975. bi-m. DM.46.80 (foreign DM.56.40). Heinrich Mueller Verlag, Seitenstr. 28, 71409 Schwaikheim, Germany. TEL 07195-52222. **Document type:** consumer publication.

621.38 IT
MODEM & TELECOMUNICAZIONI.* 12/yr. Editore Edicomp s.r.l., Via Sannio 79, 00183 Rome, Italy. TEL 6-70-92-444. FAX 6-77-51-50. Ed. Renzo Rubeo. circ. 36,000.

643 SP
MUNDO DEL MAYORISTA ELECTRICO. 6/yr. Santo Angel 76, 28043 Madrid, Spain. TEL 1-200-56-31. FAX 1-759-75-84. Ed. Antonio Cabello. circ. 60,000.

621.3 SP ISSN 0300-3787
TK7800 CODEN: MUELCN
MUNDO ELECTRONICO; revista tecnica iberoamericana. 1971. m. (except Aug.). 13490 ptas. (effective 1994). Cetisa - Boixareu S.A., Concepcion Arenal 5, 08027 Barcelona, Spain. TEL 93-3527061. FAX 93-3492350. Ed. Eugenio Rey Veiga. circ. 4,000. (back issues avail.)
—BLDSC (5983.840000); SWETS. **CCC.**

621.381 BL
MUNDO ELETRONICO. 1973. m. $300. Editora Signo Ltda, Caixa Postal 2483, 20001 Rio de Janeiro, Brazil. Ed. Apollon Fanzeres. bk.rev. circ. 50,000.

621.381 JA ISSN 0916-0345
N I NEWS. (Text in Japanese) 1964. s-a. Nihon Inter Electronics Corp. - Nihon Inta K.K., 1204, Soya, Hatano-shi, Kanagawa-ken 257, Japan.
Formerly (until 1988): I R News (ISSN 0910-5697)

621.3 016 US
N T I S ALERTS: ELECTROTECHNOLOGY. w. $135 (foreign $195). U.S. National Technical Information Service, 5285 Port Royal Rd., Springfield, VA 22161. TEL 703-487-4630. FAX 703-321-8547. TELEX 64617. index. (back issues avail.) **Document type:** abstracting/indexing.
Former titles: Abstract Newsletter: Electrotechnology (ISSN 0163-1462); Weekly Abstract Newsletter: Electrotechnology; Weekly Government Abstracts. Electrotechnology.

621.381 JA ISSN 0914-2487
NAKATANI DENSHI KEISOKU GIJUTSU SHINKO ZAIDAN NENPO/NAKATANI ELECTRONIC MEASURING TECHNOLOGY ASSOCIATION OF JAPAN. ANNUAL REPORT. (Text in Japanese) 1987. a. Nakatani Denshi Keisoku Gijutsu Shinko Zaidan, 9-17, Shibadaimon 2-chome, Minato-ku, Tokyo 105, Japan.

621.381 UK ISSN 0047-9624
CODEN: NWELAC
NEW ELECTRONICS. 1968. m. £65. International Thomson Business Publishing Ltd., 100 Avenue Rd., London NW3 3TP, England. Ed. Peter Mitchell. adv.; illus.; circ. controlled. **Indexed:** CLOSS, Fluidex, Sci.Abstr., World Surf.Coat.
—El; Faxon; SWETS. **CCC.**
Incorporating: Electronics Today (ISSN 0013-483X); Which was formerly: Electronic Appointments Service.

643 NZ ISSN 0110-8034
NEW ELECTRONICS. 1979. 11/yr. NZ.$44.55 plus postage. Matrix Publishing Ltd., P.O. Box 99-731, Auckland, New Zealand. TEL 09-357-6006. FAX 09-358-0606. Ed. Graham Hawkes. adv. contact: John Emmanuel. bk.rev.; charts; illus.; tr.lit. circ. 7,000. **Document type:** trade publication.
Description: Contains national and international news of the electronics industry. Covers electronics equipment and components, instrumentation, and computer hardware and software.

621.381 JA ISSN 0386-6572
NIHON DENSHI NEWS. (Text in Japanese) 1961. q. Nihon Denshi K.K., 1-2, Musashino 3-chome, Akishima-shi, Tokyo 196, Japan.

621.381 JA
NIHON HANDOTAI NENKAN/YEARBOOK OF SEMICONDUCTORS IN JAPAN. (Text in Japanese) a. 40000 Yen. Press Journal Inc., 2-6, Kudan Kita 1-chome, Chiyoda-ku, Tokyo 102, Japan.

621.381 JA
NIHON NO DENSHI KOGYO/ELECTRONICS INDUSTRY IN JAPAN. (Text in Japanese) 1965. a. Nihon Denshi Kikai Kogyokai - Electronic Industries Association of Japan, 2-2, Marunouchi 3-chome, Chiyoda-ku, Tokyo 100, Japan.

621.381 JA ISSN 0385-1680
NIKKEI ELECTRONICS. (Text in Japanese) 1971. 27/yr. 16300 Yen. Nikkei Business Publications, Inc. (Subsidiary of: Nihon Keizai Shimbun, Inc.), 2-7-6 Hirakawa-cho, Chiyoda-ku, Tokyo 102, Japan. TEL 03-5210-8502. FAX 03-5210-8119. Ed. Yoshiyuki Furusawa. adv. contact: Tomoe Nishimura. circ. 50,921. **Indexed:** JCT, JTA. **Document type:** trade publication.
—BLDSC (6113.178000).
Description: Provides detailed coverage of electronics technologies from devices to complete systems, with emphasis on R & D and marketing activities.

621.381 JA ISSN 0917-429X
▼**NIKKEI ELECTRONICS ASIA.** (Text in Chinese) 1992. m. free to qualified personnel. Nikkei Business Publications, Inc. (Subsidiary of: Nihon Keizai Shimbun, Inc.), 2-7-6 Hirakawa-cho, Chiyoda-ku, Tokyo 102, Japan. TEL 03-5210-8502. FAX 03-5210-8119. Ed. Minoru Inaba. adv. contact: Ritsuya Kaminaga. circ. 23,000 (controlled). **Document type:** trade publication.
Description: Contains the latest development of electronics industries around the world, with emphasis on news from Japan.

621.381 JA ISSN 0910-7207
NIKKEI MICRODEVICES. (Text in Japanese) 1985. m. 15700 Yen. Nikkei Business Publications, Inc. (Subsidiary of: Nihon Keizai Shimbun, Inc.), 2-7-6 Hirakawa-cho, Chiyoda-ku, Tokyo 102, Japan. TEL 03-5210-8502. FAX 03-5210-8119. Ed. Ken Nakamura. adv. contact: Yasuhiro Gonda. circ. 15,575. **Document type:** trade publication.
—BLDSC (6113.178350).
Description: Provides specialized technical information on electronic devices and materials, detailing new trends and technologies.

NORTH AMERICAN DIRECTORY OF CONTRACT MANUFACTURERS IN ELECTRONICS. see *BUSINESS AND ECONOMICS — Trade And Industrial Directories*

621.38 US
NOTICIARIO DE PRODUCTOS ELETRO- ELECTRONICOS. (Text in Portuguese) 1991. 3/yr. Thomas Publishing Company, 5 Penn Plaza, 8th fl., New York, NY 10001. TEL 212-629-1549. FAX 212-629-1542. adv. circ. 16,000. (tabloid format)
Description: Covers the Brazilian electronic market for engineering management, design engineers and manufacturing and production managers.

621.3 RU
NOVYE ISSLEDOVANIYA V GORNOI ELEKTROMEKHANIKE. (Subseries of: Gornyi Institut, Leningrad. Nauchnye Trudy) irreg. 0.45 Rub. Leningradskii Gornyi Institut, St. Petersburg, Russia. illus.

621.381 PL
NOWY ELEKTRONIK. 1990. m. Wydawnictwo Articon, P.O. Box 100, 82-300 Elblag, Poland. TEL 418-84. Ed. Ryszard Swiatkowski. circ. 40,000.
Description: Covers electronics novelties.

621.381 SP
NUEVA ELECTRONICA. 12/yr. Ctra. de Irun 12400, 28049 Madrid, Spain. TEL 734-70-12. circ. 19,000.

621.381 SP
NUEVOS PRODUCTOS ELECTRONICOS. 12/yr. N P E S.A., P. Alameda de Osuna 82 1o, 28042 Madrid, Spain. TEL 1-747-91-91. FAX 1-747-93-41. Ed. C. Alberto Dominquez. circ. 10,000.

ELECTRONICS

621.381 IT
NUOVA ELETTRONICA. 1969. m. L.50000. Centro Ricerche Elettroniche, Via Cracovia 19, 40139 Bologna, Italy. TEL 51-464-320. FAX 51-45-03-87. Ed. Giuseppe Montuschi. adv. circ. 162,000.

651.2 JA ISSN 0387-5245
CODEN: OEPRA4
OFFICE EQUIPMENT AND PRODUCTS. Short title: O E P. (Text in English) 1972. m. $130 for Asia & Oceania; N. & C. America $176. Dempa Publications, Inc., 11-15 Higashi Gotanda 1-chome, Shinagawa-ku, Tokyo 141, Japan. TEL 81-3-3445-6111. FAX 81-3-3445-6101. (Dist. by: Intercontinental Marketing Corp., I.P.O. Box 5056, Tokyo 100-30, Japan. TEL 81-3-3661-7458. FAX 81-3-3667-9646; US addr.: 400 Madison Ave., New York, NY 10017. TEL 212-752-3003) Ed. Tetsuo Hirayama. **Indexed:** ABI Inform., Comput.Cont., JTA, PROMT, Sci.Abstr. **Document type:** trade publication.
—BLDSC (6237.429200); SWETS.
Description: Presents new products, market trends and industry issues in office automation.

621.381 IT ISSN 0390-3087
ONDA QUADRA. 1973. m. L.75000. Editor Iniziative Editoriali sas, Via Mazzini 14, 24034 Cisano Bsco. (BG), Italy. TEL 035-78-25-11. Ed. Antonio Marizzoli. adv.; charts; illus. circ. 8,700.

621.38 FR ISSN 0030-2430
CODEN: ONELAS
ONDE ELECTRIQUE. (Summaries in English, French) 1922. 6/yr. 865 F. to individuals; libraries 778.50 F. (Societe des Electriciens et des Electronicines) Revue Generale de l'Electricite S.A., 48 rue de la Procession, 75015 Paris, France. FAX 44-49-60-35. TELEX SEE 200565F. Ed. Lucien Boithias. adv.; bk.rev.; charts; illus.; index. circ. 3,812. (also avail. in microform from PMC; reprint service avail. from ISI) **Indexed:** Chem.Abstr., Curr.Cont., Eng.Ind., Int.Aerosp.Abstr., Risk Abstr., Sci.Abstr.
—BLDSC (6257.000000); EI; SWETS; CASDDS. **CCC.**
Description: Covers components, micro-electronics, telecommunications, measurement, radio-broadcasting, television, navigation and signal processing.

ONDENEMINGSANALYSES METAAL- EN ELEKTRO-INDUSTRIE. see *METALLURGY*

537.5 UK ISSN 0306-8919
TA1671 CODEN: OQELDI
OPTICAL AND QUANTUM ELECTRONICS. Variant title: O Q E. (Text in English, French and German; summaries in English) 1969. 12/yr. £380 to institutions in EC nations (North America $657; elsewhere £410). Chapman & Hall, 2-6 Boundary Row, London SE1 8HN, England. TEL 071-865-0066. FAX 071-522-9623. TELEX 290164-CHAPMAG. (Dist. by: International Thomson Publishing Services, Ltd., N. Way, Andover, Hants. SP10 5BE, England. TEL 0264-342919; US addr.: Chapman & Hall, Journals Promotion Department, One Penn Plaza, 41st Fl., New York, NY 10019. TEL 212-564-1060. FAX 564-1505) Ed. G. Parry. adv.; bk.rev.; charts; illus.; index. (reprint service avail. from ISI, UMI) **Indexed:** Chem.Abstr., Curr.Cont., Int.Aerosp.Abstr., Phys.Ber., Sci.Abstr. **Document type:** academic/scholarly publication.
—BLDSC (6273.170000); EI; Faxon; UnCover; SWETS; UMI; CASDDS. **CCC.**
Formerly: Opto-Electronics (ISSN 0030-4077)
Description: Provides an international forum for research papers, tutorial reviews, and letters in such fields as optical physics, optical engineering, and optoelectronics.

621.381 535 SP
OPTO. 6/yr. Extra Editorial S.L., C. Ibiza 35, Bajo A, 28009 Madrid, Spain. TEL 1-504-16-95. FAX 1-504-17-72. circ. 5,000.

621.3 FR ISSN 0247-4808
TA1671
OPTO ELECTRONIQUE. 1980. 5/yr. $113 (typically set in Jan.). E S I Publications, Villa Laromiguiere, 75005 Paris, France. TEL 1-40-46-62-00. FAX 1-40-46-62-01. Ed. A. Baudevin. (also avail. in microform from UMI)
—UMI.

537.5 GW
OPTO ELEKTRONIK MAGAZIN. 1985. bi-m. DM.545. Sprechsaal Publishing Group, Mauer 2, 96450 Coburg, Germany. TEL 09561-76773. FAX 09561-90009. TELEX 663226-SPRECH-D. Ed. Christoph Mueller. adv.; B&W page DM.5775; trim 270 x 185. bk.rev. circ. 12,000. **Document type:** trade publication.

621.38 JA ISSN 0912-5434
TA1750 CODEN: ODTEEG
OPTOELECTRONICS; devices and technologies. (Text and summaries in English) 1986. q. 18540 Yen($65) to individuals; institutions and libraries 30900 Yen ($125). Mita Press, Ochanomizu Center Bldg. 8F, 2-12, Hongo-3, Bunkyo-ku, Tokyo 113, Japan. TEL 03-3818-1011. FAX 03-3818-1016. TELEX 2722813-MITA-PS. Eds. Makoto Kikuchi, Yoshihiro Hamakawa. circ. 1,100. (back issues avail.)
—BLDSC (6275.551000); EI; Faxon; SWETS; UMI; CASDDS.
Description: Technical papers about the subatomic interactions and related devices and technologies.

621.38 JA
OPTOELECTRONICS CONFERENCE. TECHNICAL DIGEST. (Text in English) 1986. biennial. (Institute of Electronics, Information and Communication Engineers - Denshi Joho Tsushin Gakkai) Business Center for Academic Societies Japan - Nihon Gakkai Jimu Senta, 5-16-9 Honkomagome, Bunkyo-ku, Tokyo 100, Japan.

621.38 US ISSN 1040-0907
TK8300
OPTOELECTRONICS D.A.T.A. DIGEST. 1975. s-a. $205. D.A.T.A. Business Publishing (Subsidiary of: Information Handling Services), 15 Inverness Way E., Box 6510, Englewood, CO 80155-6510. TEL 800-447-4666. FAX 303-799-4082. TELEX 4322083 IHS UI. adv. contact: Peggy Anderson.
●Also available on CD-ROM.
Formerly: Optoelectronics D.A.T.A. Book (ISSN 0164-002X)
Description: Reference guide covering up to 20 technical parameters on over 72,650 devices from more than 225 manufacturers.

537.5 US ISSN 8756-6990
TK7878 CODEN: OIDPE4
OPTOELECTRONICS, INSTRUMENTATION AND DATA PROCESSING. English translation of: Avtometriya (RU ISSN 0320-7102) 1984. bi-m. $920. (Rossiiskaya Academiya Nauk, Sibirskoe Otdelenie, RU) Allerton Press, Inc., 150 Fifth Ave., New York, NY 10011. TEL 212-924-3950. FAX 212-463-9684. Ed. P.E. Tverdokhleb. **Document type:** academic/scholarly publication.
—BLDSC (0416.661000); UnCover. **CCC.**

537.5 KR ISSN 1011-6559
CODEN: OPTEDV
OPTOELEKTRONIKA I POLUPROVODNIKOVAYA TEKHNIKA; republikanskii mezhvedomstvennyi sbornik nauchnykh trudov. (Text in Russian) 1966. s-a. (Akademiya Nauk Ukrainy, Institut Poluprovodnikov, Otdelenie Optoelektroniki) Vidavnitstvo Naukova Dumka, Vul. Tereshchenkivska 3, 252601 Kiev, Ukraine. (Dist. by: Mezhdunarodnaya Kniga, B. Yakimanka 39, 117049 Moscow, Russia) Ed. S.V. Svechnikov. **Indexed:** Int.Aerosp.Abstr., Sci.Abstr.
—CASDDS.
Formerly (until 1982): Poluprovonikvaya Tekhnika i Mikroelektronika (ISSN 0554-6222)

621.381 UK
OUTPUT. q. 29 Forth St., Edinburgh EH1 3LE, Scotland. TEL 031-557-5793. FAX 031-554-5665. Ed. John Hunter.

621.3 016 FR ISSN 1146-5352
P A S C A L. E 20: ELECTRONIQUE ET TELECOMMUNICATIONS. (Text in French, English) 1984. 10/yr. 1220 F. (outside EC 1295 F.). Centre National de la Recherche Scientifique, Institut de l'Information Scientifique et Technique, 2 allee du Parc de Brabois, 54514 Vandoeuvre-Les-Nancy Cedex, France. TEL 83-50-46-00. FAX 83-50-46-50. adv. contact: Veronique Guinvarc'h. abstr.; index, cum.index. (also avail. in microfiche) **Document type:** bibliography.
●Also available online. **Vendor(s):** DIALOG Information Services, Inc. (File no.144), European Space Agency (File no.14), Telesystemes - Questel. Also available on CD-ROM.
Former titles: P A S C A L Explore. E 20: Electronique et Telecommunications (ISSN 0246-1161); P A S C A L Explore. Part 20: Electronique et Telecommunications; Which supersedes: Bulletin Signaletique. Part 145: Electronique; Bulletin Signaletique. Part 145: Eldoc-Electronique (ISSN 0240-8554); Bulletin Signaletique. Part 145: Electronique (ISSN 0301-3316); Which supersedes in part: Bulletin Signaletique. Part 140: Electricite - Electronique (ISSN 0007-5353).

621.381 IT
P C B MAGAZINE. m. (9/yr.). Gruppo Editoriale J C E, Via Ferri 6, 20092 Cinisello Balsamo (MI), Italy. TEL 02-660251. FAX 02-6127620. TELEX 352376 JCE MIL I. adv.; B&W page L.2300000, color page L.3600000; trim 184 x 250. circ. 6,720.

621.381 JA
PAIONIA GIHO/PIONEER TECHNICAL REPORT. (Text in Japanese; summaries in English, Japanese) 1990. 2/yr. Paionia K.K., Sogo Kenkyujo - Pineer Electronic Corp., Corporate Research and Development Laboratory, 1-1, Fujimi 6-chome, Tsurugashima-machi, Iruma-gun, Saitama-ken 350-02, Japan.

790.068 US ISSN 0031-2215
SB481.A1
PARKS AND RECREATION; journal of park and recreation management. (Buyer's Guide Number avail.) 1903. m. $18 to individuals; libraries $25. National Recreation and Park Association, 3101 Park Center Dr., Alexandria, VA 22302. TEL 703-820-4940. FAX 703-671-6772. Ed. Pamela Leigh. adv.; B&W page $1165; 8 3/8 x 11. bk.rev.; bibl.; illus.; index. circ. 24,000. (also avail. in microform from UMI; reprint service avail. from UMI) **Indexed:** Avery Ind.Archit.Per., Bk.Rev.Ind. (1966-), C.I.J.E., Child.Bk.Rev.Ind. (1966-), Curr.Adv.Ecol.Sci., Geo.Abstr., Hlth.Ind., Mag.Ind., P.A.I.S, Phys.Ed.Ind., R.G., Rehabil.Lit., Rural Recreat.Tour.Abstr., Sports Per.Ind., Sportsearch (1977-), World Agri.Econ.& Rural Sociol.Abstr.
—BLDSC (6406.800000); Faxon; UnCover; UMI.

621.381 JA ISSN 0916-7269
PAWA EREKUTORONIKUSU KENKYUKAI RONBUNSHI/JAPAN SOCIETY FOR POWER ELECTRONICS. JOURNAL. (Text in Japanese) 1976. a. Pawa Erekutoronikusu Kenkyukai - Japan Society for Power Electronics, Shapu K.K. Gijutsu Honbu, Enerugi Henkan Kenkyujo Dai 3 Kenkyubu, 282-1, Hajikami, Shinjo-cho, Kitakatsuragi-gun, Nara-ken 639-21, Japan. **Document type:** academic/scholarly publication.

643 658.8 UK
PERSONAL CARE APPLIANCES: THE INTERNATIONAL MARKET. a. £1375($2750) Euromonitor, 87-88 Turnmill St., London EC1M 5QU, England. TEL 071-251-8024. FAX 071-608-3149. (Addr. in N. America: Euromonitor International, 111 W. Washington St., Ste. 920, Chicago, IL 60602. TEL 312-541-8024. FAX 312-541-1567) (looseleaf format) **Document type:** trade publication.
●Also available online. **Vendor(s):** Data-Star, DIALOG Information Services, Inc.
Description: Analyzes the market for personal-care appliances for France, Germany, Italy, Spain, the U.K., the U.S., and Japan.

PHOTONICS AND OPTOELECTRONICS. see *PHYSICS — Optics*

ELECTRONICS

621.381 US ISSN 1042-170X
TK7800
POPULAR ELECTRONICS. (Includes: Gizmo) m. $18.95. Gernsback Publications, Inc., 500-B Bi-County Blvd., Farmingdale, NY 11735. TEL 516-293-3000. FAX 516-293-3115. (Subscr. to: Box 338, Mt. Morris, IL 61054-9932) Ed. Carl Laron. adv.; bk.rev.; illus.; index. circ. 87,824. (back issues avail.; reprint service avail. from UMI) **Indexed:** Ind.How To Do It (1984-).
—Faxon; SWETS; UMI. **CCC.**
Former titles (until 1989): Hands On Electronics (ISSN 0743-2968); Radio-Electronics Hands-On Electronics; Radio Electronics Special Projects (ISSN 0730-7616)
Description: For the electronics activist.

621.381 II ISSN 0970-9223
POPULAR ELECTRONICS; trends & ideas in electronics. 1983. m. Rs.120. Popular Electronics India, 23-354 Azadnagar, Jaiprakash Rd., Andheri, Bombay 400 058, India. TEL 6263974. Ed. Randhir M. Sinha. adv.; bk.rev.; charts; index. circ. 15,000. **Indexed:** Ind.How To Do It, MELSA. **Document type:** consumer publication.

POPULAR ELECTRONICS HOBBYISTS HANDBOOK. see HOBBIES

621.38 US ISSN 1040-0214
TK7871.85
POWER SEMICONDUCTORS D.A.T.A. DIGEST. 1974. s-a. $205. D.A.T.A. Business Publishing (Subsidiary of: Information Handling Services), 15 Inverness Way E., Box 6510, Englewood, CO 80155-6510. TEL 800-447-4666. FAX 303-799-4082. TELEX 4322083 IHS UI. Ed. Paul Magin. adv. contact: Peggy Anderson. **Document type:** directory.
Former titles: Power Semiconductors D.A.T.A. Book (ISSN 0164-0038); Power Semiconductors (ISSN 0095-4225)
Description: Reference guide covering technical parameters on over 75,000 devices from more than 200 manufacturers.

621.042 US ISSN 0885-0259
CODEN: PIMOEN
POWERCONVERSION & INTELLIGENT MOTION. Abbreviated title: P C I M. 1975. 12/yr. free to qualified personnel. Intertec International Inc., 2472 Eastman Ave., Bldg. 33-34, Ventura, CA 93003-5792. TEL 805-650-7070. FAX 805-650-7079. (Subscr. to: DirectLink Inc., 200 Kingston Dr., W. Lafayette, IN 47906-2046. TEL 800-227-2914. FAX 317-743-3545) Ed. Sam Davis; Pub. Myron Miller. adv.; bk.rev. circ. 36,000. **Indexed:** Sci.Abstr. **Document type:** trade publication.
—El; SWETS. **CCC.**
Former titles (until Aug. 1985): Power Conversion International (ISSN 0199-1884); Incorporates (in 1983): Drives and Controls International (ISSN 0744-351X); Solid State Power Conversion (ISSN 0192-1746)
Description: Assists power, motion control and linear electronics engineers to maintain their professional proficiency in subsystems designs.

621.381 US
CODEN: PCIDEU
PRINTED CIRCUIT DESIGN. 1984. m. $55 (free to qualified personnel). Miller Freeman, Inc. (Subsidiary of: United Newspapers), 600 Harrison St., San Francisco, CA 94107. TEL 415-905-2200. FAX 415-905-2232. TELEX 278273. Ed. Pete Waddell. bk.rev. circ. 25,000. (back issues avail.) **Indexed:** ABI Inform.
—BLDSC (6613.235180); UnCover; SWETS. **CCC.**
Former titles (until 1990): Circuit Design (ISSN 1047-5567); (until Oct. 1989): Printed Circuit Design (ISSN 0884-9862)
Description: For printed circuit board design professionals.

621.381 US ISSN 0274-8096
CODEN: PCFAE6
PRINTED CIRCUIT FABRICATION. 1978. m. $60 (free to qualified personnel). Miller Freeman, Inc. (Subsidiary of: United Newspapers), 600 Harrison St., San Francisco, CA 94107. TEL 415-905-2200. FAX 415-905-2232. TELEX 278273. Ed. Donna Esposito. adv.; bk.rev. circ. 22,300. **Indexed:** Copper Abstr., Sci.Abstr.
—BLDSC (6613.235200); El; Faxon; UnCover; SWETS; UMI. **CCC.**
Description: For key personnel of printed circuit board manufacturers, both at independent and captive operations.

621.38 US
PRINTED CIRCUIT NETWORK. 1987. 6/yr. P C N Publishing, 91 Ryerson Ave., Box 457, Newton, NJ 07860. TEL 201-383-2296.

621.381 GW ISSN 0930-1100
PRODUCTRONIC; Kennziffer-Fachzeitschrift fuer Elektronik-Fertigung und Test. 1980. 9/yr. DM.205.50 (foreign DM.222). Huethig GmbH, Postfach 102869, 69018 Heidelberg, Germany. TEL 06221-489281. FAX 06221-489205. TELEX 5215498-HUEMD. Ed. Hilmar Beine. adv.: B&W page DM.5700; trim 210 x 297; adv. contact: Christine Neumair. bk.rev.; circ. 14,546 (controlled). (back issues avail.) **Document type:** trade publication.
Description: Covers electronic industry production techniques and machines, including testing and control systems. Features semiconductor production and circuit boards.

643 FR
PRODUITS ET COMMUNICATION. 9/yr. 54 rue Etienne Marcel, 75002 Paris, France. TEL 42-36-73-84. FAX 40-26-37-11. TELEX 216 974 F. Ed. Eric Duval. circ. 6,000.
Description: For professionals in the sound and industry trade.

380 643 US
PROFESSIONAL ELECTRONICS YEARBOOK. 1970. a. $12. National Electronics Service Dealers Association, 2708 W. Berry St., Ft. Worth, TX 76109. TEL 817-921-9061. Ed. Wallace Harrison. adv.; tr.lit. circ. 5,000. **Document type:** trade publication.

621.38 UK ISSN 0951-5631
PROFILE OF THE WORLDWIDE SEMICONDUCTOR INDUSTRY. 1982. irreg., latest 1991. £495. Elsevier Science Ltd., Books Division, P.O. Box 800, Kidlington, Oxford OX5 1DX, England. TEL 44-865-843000. FAX 44-865-843010. (Subscr. in U.S. and Canada to: Elsevier Science, 660 White Plains Rd., Tarrytown, NY 10591-5153. TEL 914-524-9200) Ed. A. Fletcher. **Document type:** trade publication.
—BLDSC (6864.300840).
Description: Forecasts worldwide semiconductor markets.
Refereed Serial

621.381 IT
PROGETTO ELEKTOR. 11/yr. Gruppo Editoriale J C E, Via Ferri 6, 20092 Cinisello Balsamo (MI), Italy. TEL 2-66-02-51. FAX 2-612-76-20. TELEX 352376 JCE MIL I. Ed. Amedeo Bozzoni. adv.: B&W page L.1400000, color page L.2300000; trim 180 x 256. circ. 10,686.

537.05 NE ISSN 1043-626X
QC759.6 CODEN: PELREX
PROGRESS IN ELECTROMAGNETICS RESEARCH. (Text in English) 1989. irreg., vol.6, 1991. Elsevier Science B.V., P.O. Box 211, 1000 AE Amsterdam, Netherlands. TEL 31-20-5803911. FAX 31-20-5803705. TELEX 18582 ESPA NL. (Subscr. in U.S. and Canada to: Elsevier Science Inc., Box 882, Madison Sq. Sta., New York, NY 10159. TEL 212-989-5800) **Document type:** monographic series.
—BLDSC (6868.280000); CASDDS.

537.5 UK ISSN 0079-6727
QC680 CODEN: PQUEAH
PROGRESS IN QUANTUM ELECTRONICS; an international review journal. 1969. 5/yr. £255($395) (effective 1994). Elsevier Science Ltd., Pergamon, P.O. Box 800, Kidlington, Oxford OX5 1DX, England. TEL 44-865-843000. FAX 44-865-843010. (Subscr. in U.S. and Canada to: Elsevier Science, 660 White Plains Rd., Tarrytown, NY 10591-5153. TEL 914-524-9200. FAX 914-333-2444) Eds. P.T. Landsberg, M. Osinski. (also avail. in microfilm from UMI) **Indexed:** Chem.Abstr., Phys.Ber., Sci.Abstr. **Document type:** academic/scholarly publication.
—BLDSC (6873.670000); El; Faxon; UnCover; UMI; CASDDS. **CCC.**
Description: Chiefly concerned with the interaction of radiation and matter, with additional emphasis on superconductivity and quantum effects in semiconductors.
Refereed Serial

621.38 001.6 PL ISSN 0509-7053
TK7800 CODEN: PPIEAI
PRZEMYSLOWY INSTYTUT ELEKTRONIKI. PRACE/INDUSTRIAL INSTITUTE OF ELECTRONICS. PROCEEDINGS. (Text in Polish, occasionally English; summaries in English and Russian) 1959. q. 50000 Zl. Przemyslowy Instytut Elektroniki, Ul. Dluga 44-50, 00-241 Warsaw, Poland. TEL 48-22-313014. FAX 48-22-313014. TELEX 813260 PIE PL. Ed. Krzysztof Badzmirowski. circ. 300 (controlled). (also avail. in diskette format) **Indexed:** Sci.Abstr. **Document type:** proceedings.
—CASDDS.
Description: Contains articles covering the different aspects of industrial electronics.

621.381 PL ISSN 0032-6283
PRZEMYSLOWY INSTYTUT TELEKOMUNIKACJI. PRACE. (Supplement avail.) (Text in Polish; summaries in English and Russian) 1950. q. $32. Przemyslowy Instytut Telekomunikacji - Telecommunications Research Institute, Poligonowa 30, 00-991 Warsaw, Poland. TEL 48-22-102699. FAX 48-22-102571. TELEX 813231 PL. (Dist. by: Ars Polona-Ruch, Krakowskie Przedmiescie 7, Warsaw, Poland) Ed.Bd. illus.; index. circ. 350. **Indexed:** Sci.Abstr.
—BLDSC (6588.500000).

621.381 SA
PULSE ELECTRONICS IN SOUTH AFRICA. (Text in English) 1973. m. Pulse Publications (Pty) Ltd., P.O. Box 1884, Johannesburg 2000, South Africa. TEL 27-11-835-2221. FAX 27-11-835-1943. Ed. Georgina Hatch. adv.: B&W page R.2730; trim 180 x 260; adv. contact: Shelley Wolstenholme. circ. 4,045. **Document type:** trade publication.

PURAZUMA PUROSESHINGU KENKYUKAI PUROSHIDINGUSL/PLASMA PROCESSING. see PHYSICS

621.381 NE ISSN 0928-5008
R B ELEKTRONICA. (Radio Bulletin); praktijkblad voor de elektronicus. 1929. m. fl.75 (effective 1993). Uitgeverij De Muiderkring B.V., Hogeweyselaan 227, 1382 JL Weesp, Netherlands. TEL 31-2940-15210. FAX 31-2940-12782. Ed. D.F.J. Scheper; Pub. A. van Lidth de Jeude. adv. contact: H.J. Olden. bk.rev.; abstr.; bibl.; charts; illus.; stat.; circ. 20,000 (controlled). **Document type:** trade publication.
—SWETS.
Former titles (until 1992): R B Elektronica Magazine (ISSN 0928-4990); (until 1988): R B Elektronica Computers (ISSN 0928-4982); (until 1985): Radio Bulletin (ISSN 0165-6104)
Description: Details developments in the electronics and engineering industries in a practical manner for technicians and engineers.

643 CN
R C C SERVICE MANUALS. 1937. a. Can.$240. (Radio College of Canada) Lewcor Communications, 243 College St., Ste. 305, Toronto, ON M5T 2Y1, Canada. TEL 416-971-4170. FAX 416-971-4173. cum.index; circ. 500 (paid). (looseleaf format; back issues avail.) **Document type:** trade publication.

621.381 JA ISSN 0910-2787
R C J JOURNAL/R C J KAIHO. (Text in Japanese) bi-m. Reliability Center for Electronic Components of Japan - Nihon Densni Buhin Shinraisei Senta, 4-13, Nihonbashi 3-chome, Chuo-ku, Tokyo 103, Japan.

621.381 US ISSN 0163-321X
TK6540 CODEN: RFDEDG
R F DESIGN. (Radio Frequency) 1978. m. $59 (Canada and Mexico $59; elsewhre $99). Argus Inc., 6151 Powers Ferry Rd., N.W., Atlanta, GA 30339-2491. TEL 404-955-2500. FAX 404-955-0400. (Subscr. to: 1 E. First St., Duluth, MN 55802) Ed. James N. MacDonald. circ. 41,810. (also avail. in microform from UMI; back issues avail.; reprint service avail. from UMI) **Indexed:** Sci.Abstr. **Document type:** trade publication.
—BLDSC (7960.039300); Faxon; SWETS; UMI. **CCC.**
Description: Serves engineers, managers and other personnel responsible for the design and development of electronic systems and equipment using radio frequencies.

ELECTRONICS

621.38 US ISSN 1040-2012
CODEN: RLECEO
R L E CURRENTS. (Research Laboratory of Electronics) 1987. biennial. Massachusetts Institute of Technology, 36-412, Research Laboratory of Electronics, 77 Massachusetts Ave., Cambridge, MA 02139. FAX 617-258-7864. Ed. Dorothy A. Fleischer. circ. 6,300.
Description: Describes the intellectual concerns and activities of RLE investigators. Each issue focuses on a specific area of research, includes historical photographs, information on the RLE collegium, and lists RLE publications.

R T E GUIDE. (Radio Telefis Eireann) see COMMUNICATIONS — Radio

RADIO AND ELECTRICAL RETAILING. see BUSINESS AND ECONOMICS — Marketing And Purchasing

RADIO ELECTRONICA PRACTICA. see COMMUNICATIONS — Radio

RADIO ELETTRONICA AND COMPUTER. see COMMUNICATIONS — Radio

621.38 GW ISSN 0033-7900
TK7800
RADIO FERNSEHEN ELEKTRONIK; Zeitschrift fuer Theorie und Praxis der Elektronik. 1952. m. DM.60. Verlag Technik GmbH, Am Friedrichshain 22, 10407 Berlin, Germany. TEL 030-4287-0. FAX 030-4261249. Ed. Wolfgang E. Schlegel. adv.: B&W page DM.6200; trim 185 x 265; adv. contact: Matthias Thiel. bk.rev.; charts; illus.; tr.lit.; index. circ. 24,282. **Indexed:** Sci.Abstr. **Document type:** trade publication.
—BLDSC (7232.223000).
Description: Covers theory and practice of electronics, including bases and applications of microelectronics.

621.38 US ISSN 0735-2727
RADIOELECTRONICS AND COMMUNICATIONS SYSTEMS. English translation of: Izvestiya Vysshikh Uchebnykh Zavedeni . Seriya Radioelektronika (UR ISSN 0021-3470) 1977. m. $950. (Politekhnichnyi Instytut, KR) Allerton Press, Inc., 150 Fifth Ave., New York, NY 10011. TEL 212-924-3950. FAX 212-463-9684. Ed. Ya.K. Trokhimenko.
Indexed: Int.Aerosp.Abstr.; Sci.Abstr. **Document type:** academic/scholarly publication.
—BLDSC (0420.580000); UnCover. **CCC.**

537.5 US ISSN 0033-8443
QC661 CODEN: RPQEAC
RADIOPHYSICS AND QUANTUM ELECTRONICS. English translation of: Izvestiya Vysshikh Uchebnykh Zavedenii. Seriya Radiofizika (RU ISSN 0021-3462) 1965. m. $1215 (foreign $1425) (effective 1994). (Vysshie Uchebnye Zavedeniya, RU) Plenum Publishing Corp., Consultants Bureau, 233 Spring St., New York, NY 10013-1578. TEL 212-620-8468. FAX 212-463-0742. TELEX 23-421139. Ed. V.L. Ginzburg. (also avail. in microfilm from JSC; back issues avail.) **Indexed:** Appl.Mech.Rev., Eng.Ind., Math.R., Sci.Abstr., Solid St.Abstr. **Document type:** academic/scholarly publication.
—BLDSC (0420.718500); UnCover; UMI. **CCC.**
Formerly: Soviet Radiophysics.
Refereed Serial

RADIOTEKHNIKA I ELEKTRONIKA. see COMMUNICATIONS — Radio

621.381 JA ISSN 0485-9642
RAJIO NO SEISAKU/ELECTRONICS HOBBY MAGAZINE. (Text in Japanese) 1954. m. 680 Yen per no. Dempa Publications Inc., 1-11-15, Higashi Gotanda, Shinagawa-ku, Tokyo 141, Japan. TEL 81-3-3445-6111. FAX 81-3-3445-6890. (US addr.: 275 Madison Ave., New York, NY 10016. TEL 212-682-4775)

621.38 016 RU ISSN 0206-5452
REFERATIVNYI ZHURNAL. ELEKTRONIKA. 1963. m. 136 Rub. (162.80 Rub. including index). Vsesoyuznyi Institut Nauchno-Tekhnicheskoi Informatsii (VINITI), Baltiiskaya ul., 14, Moscow A-219, Russia. (Subscr. to: Mezhdunarodnaya Kniga, Dimitrova ul. 39, 113095 Moscow, Russia) **Document type:** abstracting/indexing.
—BLDSC (0152.600000).
Formerly: Referativnyi Zhurnal. Elektronika i ee Primenenie (ISSN 0486-2287).

621.38 016 RU ISSN 0203-5316
REFERATIVNYI ZHURNAL. ELEKTROTEKHNIKA. m. 189.90 Rub. (210.40 Rub. including index). Vsesoyuznyi Institut Nauchno-Tekhnicheskoi Informatsii (VINITI), Baltiiskaya ul., 14, Moscow A-219, Russia. (Subscr. to: Mezhdunarodnaya Kniga, Dimitrova ul. 39, 113095 Moscow, Russia) **Indexed:** Agri.Eng.Abstr. **Document type:** abstracting/indexing.
Former titles: Referativnyi Zhurnal. Elektrotekhnika i Elektroenergetika (ISSN 0203-5189); (until Dec. 1980): Referativny Zhurnal. Elektrotekhnika i Energetika (ISSN 0034-2327)

REFERENCE DATA FOR ENGINEERS; radio, electronics, computer and communications. see COMMUNICATIONS

621.381 SP ISSN 0211-0830
RESISTOR. 1980. 11/yr. 4500 ptas. (effective 1993). Editorial Resistor, S.A., Maudes 15 entlo. C, 28003 Madrid, Spain. TEL 1-534-29-67. FAX 1-534-47-51. Ed. Agustin Gonzalez Buelta. adv.: B&W page 65000 ptas., color page 100000 ptas.; 210 x 280; adv. contact: Maria Martin. circ. 14,000.

621.381 SP ISSN 0482-6396
REVISTA ESPANOLA DE ELECTRONICA. 1954. m. 14160 ptas.($160) (for 2 yrs.) (typically set in Jan.). Ediciones Tecnicas Rede, S.A., Ecuador, 91-1, 08029 Barcelona, Spain. TEL 93-4302872. FAX 439-28-13. Ed. Pascual Gomez Apricio. adv.; index. circ. 15,000. (back issues avail.)
—BLDSC (7853.950000).
Description: Covers news on equipment and electronics applications.

537.5 US ISSN 1063-7397
TK7874 CODEN: RUICE5
RUSSIAN MICROELECTRONICS. English translation of: Mikroelektronika (RU ISSN 0544-1269) 1974. bi-m. $750 (foreign $880) (effective 1994). (Russian Academy of Sciences, RU) Plenum Publishing Corp., Consultants Bureau, 233 Spring St., New York, NY 10013-1578. TEL 212-620-8468. FAX 212-463-0742. TELEX 23-421139. Ed. K.A. Valiev. (also avail. in microfilm from JSC; back issues avail.) **Indexed:** Chem.Abstr., Comput.& Info.Sys., Electron.& Communic.Abstr.J., Eng.Ind., INSPEC. **Document type:** academic/scholarly publication.
—BLDSC (0420.772500); Faxon; UnCover; SWETS; UMI. **CCC.**
Former titles (until Nov. 1992): Soviet Microelectronics (ISSN 0363-8529); (until 1975): Microelectronics (ISSN 0098-6658)
Refereed Serial

621.381 JA
S E M I GIJUTSU KENSHU SEMINA/S E M I TECHNICAL EDUCATION PROGRAM. (Text in English, Japanese) irreg. Semiconductor Equipment & Material International Japan, 7-18, Motoakasaka 1-chome, Minato-ku, Tokyo 107, Japan.

621.381 JA
S E M I TEKUNOROJI SHINPOJUMU KOEN YOKOSHU. (Text in English, Japanese) a. 10000 Yen. Semiconductor Equipment & Material International Japan, 7-18, Motoakasaka 1-chome, Minato-ku, Tokyo 107, Japan.

621.381 JA
S H M GIJUTSU KOENKAI KOEN YOKOSHU/SOCIETY FOR HYBRID MICROELECTRONICS. PREPRINTS OF TECHNICAL MEETING. (Text in English, Japanese) 1981. s-a. Haiburiddo Maikuro Erekutoronikusu Kyokai - Society for Hybrid Microelectronics, 2-4, Hanakoganei 6-chome, Kodaira-shi, Tokyo 187, Japan.

621.381 US ISSN 0890-7900
S M T TRENDS. (Surface Mount Technology) m. $325 (overseas $345) (Effective Jan. 1994). Vital Information Publications, 321 Carrera Dr., Mill Valley, CA 94941-3995. TEL 415-389-8671. FAX 415-345-7018. Ed. Sarah Collings. circ. 300.
●Also available online. Vendor(s): Data-Star, DIALOG Information Services, Inc., Information Access Co., NewsNet (MG18).
Description: Covers surface mount technology and electronic assembly, trends in manufacturing processes and equipment, component packaging, printed circuit board inspection and testing, and application markets.

621.38 629 FR
S P E R ANNUAIRE. 1962. a. free. Syndicat des Industries de Materiel Professionnel Electronique et Radioelectrique, 11 rue Hamelin, 75783 Paris Cedex 16, France. Ed.Bd. circ. 2,000.
Formerly: Syndicat des Industries de Materiel Professionnel Electronique et Radioelectrique. Annuaire (ISSN 0082-1020)

SAFETY AND E M C. see ENGINEERING — Electrical Engineering

621.381 IT
SELEZIONE DI ELETTRONICA. m. (11/yr.). Gruppo Editoriale J C E, Via Ferri 6, 20092 Cinisello Balsamo (MI), Italy. TEL 02-660251. FAX 02-6127620. TELEX 352376 JCE MIL I. adv.: B&W page L. 2500000, color page L.4000000; trim 184 x 250. circ. 10,670.

621.38 US
SEMI - STANDARDS INFO ALERT. q. Semiconductor Equipment & Materials, International, 805 E. Middlefield Rd., Mountainview, CA 94043. TEL 415-964-5111. FAX 415-967-5375. Ed. Lisa Altera. (back issues avail.)
Formerly: Semi - Outlook.
Description: Non-profit standards and trade show organization publication for the semiconductor industry.

621.381 US ISSN 0730-1014
SEMICONDUCTOR INDUSTRY & BUSINESS SURVEY NEWSLETTER. 1979. 18/yr. $495 (foreign $595). H T E Research, Inc., 400 Oyster Point Blvd., Ste. 220, S. San Francisco, CA 94080. TEL 415-871-4377. FAX 415-871-0513. Ed. Steve Z. Szirom. bk.rev.; stat.; index. circ. 2,000. (back issues avail.) **Document type:** newsletter.
●Also available online. Vendor(s): NewsNet (EC35).
Description: Presents business analyses, company profiles, growth market trends, and a survey of the semiconductor industry's developments.

621.381 US
SEMICONDUCTOR INDUSTRY ASSOCIATION. YEARBOOK AND DIRECTORY (YEAR). 1981. a. $75. S I A, 4300 Stevens Creek Blvd., Ste. 271, San Jose, CA 95129. TEL 408-246-2711. FAX 408-246-2830. Ed. Thomas G. Beermann. charts. **Document type:** directory.
Description: Chronicles the past year's events, including the public policy and trade issues in the semiconductor industry; features a directory of 250 firms in the U.S.

620 US
SEMICONDUCTOR INDUSTRY PLANT SITE DATABASE DIRECTORY. a. $395 (foreign $425). H T E Research, Inc., 400 Oyster Point Blvd., Ste. 220, S. San Francisco, CA 94080. TEL 415-871-4377. FAX 415-871-0513.
Formerly: Semiconductor Industry Plant Site Database Service.
Description: Provides data on over 950 semiconductor plant site locations worldwide, including foundries, design houses, start-ups, and overseas firms.

621.381 US ISSN 0163-3767
TK7871.85 CODEN: SITLDD
SEMICONDUCTOR INTERNATIONAL. 1978. 13/yr. $84.95 (Canada $123.95; Mexico $114.95; elsewhere $144.95). Cahners Publishing Company (Des Plaines), Division of Reed Elsevier Inc., 1350 E. Touhy Ave., Box 5080, Des Plaines, IL 60017-5080. TEL 708-635-8800. FAX 708-390-2770. (Subscr. to: 44 Cook St., Denver, CO 80206. TEL 800-662-7776) Ed. Betty Newbboe. circ. 48,100. (also avail. in microform from UMI; reprint service avail. from UMI) **Indexed:** Sci.Abstr. **Document type:** trade publication.
—BLDSC (8238.774000); Faxon; SWETS; UMI; CASDDS. **CCC.**
Description: Coverage includes wafer fabrication, circuit and mask design, wafer processing, assembly and testing, plus equipment trends, chemicals, materials, assembly techniques, quality control and testing, industry news and forecasts.

ELECTRONICS 2191

621.381 US
SEMICONDUCTOR INTERNATIONAL TECHNICAL PRODUCTS REFERENCE SOURCE. (Published as an issue of: Semiconductor International (ISSN 0163-3767)) a. $50 (or included in subscr. to: Semiconductor International). Cahners Publishing Company (Des Plaines), Division of Reed Elsevier Inc., 1350 E. Touhy Ave., Box 5080, Des Plaines, IL 60017-5080. TEL 708-635-8800. FAX 708-390-2770. (Subscr. to: 44 Cook St., Denver, CO 80206. TEL 800-662-7776) Ed. Betty Newboe. adv.; tr.lit. circ. 48,093. (reprint service avail.) **Document type:** directory.
Former titles: Semiconductor International Telephone - Fax and Source Guide (Year); Semiconductor International Telephone and Source Directory (Year); Semiconductor International Master Buying Guide.

621.38 US
SEMICONDUCTOR RELIABILITY NEWS. 1989. m. $195 (foreign $275). D M Data, Inc., 10170 E. Jenan Dr., Bldg. 2, Scottsdale, AZ 85260. TEL 602-451-7449. FAX 602-451-1890. Ed. Howard K. Dicken.
Description: Discusses hard facts, early warnings, and case histories of semiconductor failures. Essential to designers, component engineers, and failure analysis personnel.

530 621.38 UK ISSN 0268-1242
QC610.9 CODEN: SSTEET
SEMICONDUCTOR SCIENCE AND TECHNOLOGY. 1986. m. £604($1238) (effective 1994). (Institute of Physics) I O P Publishing, Techno House, Redcliffe Way, Bristol BS1 6NX, England. TEL 0272-297481. FAX 0272-294318. TELEX 449149-INSRTP-G. (Subscr. to: I O P Circulation Centre, Readerlink, Audit House, 260 Field End Rd., Eastcote, Ruislip, Mddx. HA4 9LT, England. TEL 081-868-4499. FAX 081-428-3117; U.S. addr.: American Institute of Physics, Member and Subscriber Services, 500 Sunnyside Blvd., Woodbury, NY 11797-2999. TEL 516-576-2200) Ed. R.A. Stradling. circ. 799. (also avail. in microfiche from AIP; microfilm from AIP; back issues avail.) **Document type:** academic/scholarly publication.
—BLDSC (8238.817000); EI; Faxon; UnCover; SWETS; CASDDS. **CCC.**
Description: Experimental and theoretical studies of the electrical, optical and acoustic properties of bulk, low-dimensional, amorphous and layered semiconductors.

530 621.3 US ISSN 0309-5991
QC610.9 CODEN: SINSD4
SEMICONDUCTORS AND INSULATORS; a journal of ionic and covalent solids. 1972. 8/yr. (in 2 vols., 4 nos./vol.). 215 ECU per vol. (effective 1993). Gordon and Breach Science Publishers, 820 Town Center Dr., Langhorne, PA 19047. TEL 215-750-2642. FAX 215-750-6343. (UK subscr. to: P.O. Box 90, Reading, Berkshire RG1 8JL, England. TEL 0734-560-808) Ed. R. Smoluchowski. adv.; index. (also avail. in microform) **Indexed:** Chem.Abstr., Phys.Ber., Sci.Abstr.
—CASDDS. **CCC.**
Former titles: Journal of Nonmetals and Semiconductors; Journal of Non-Metals (ISSN 0090-3477)
Refereed Serial

621.381 CC ISSN 1001-1374
SHANGHAI DIANQI JISHU/SHANGHAI ELECTRONIC TECHNOLOGY. (Text in Chinese) q. Shanghai Dianqi Jishu Yanjiusuo - Shanghai Institute of Electrical Appliance Technology, 85 Anhua Lu, Shanghai 200050, People's Republic of China. TEL 2520175. Ed. Zhu Gui.

621.381 JA ISSN 0285-0362
CODEN: STEJD9
SHAPU GIHO/SHARP TECHNICAL JOURNAL. (Text in Japanese; summaries in English, Japanese) 1962. q. Shapu K.K., Gijutsu Honbu - Sharp Co., Ltd., Technical Headquarters, 2613-1 Ichinomoto-cho, Tenri-shi, Nara-ken 632, Japan. **Indexed:** Chem.Abstr., Curr.Cont., Eng.Ind., Sci.Abstr.
—BLDSC (8254.650000); EI; CASDDS.

621.381 JA ISSN 0388-5070
SHIZUOKA DAIGAKU DAIGAKUIN DENSHI KAGAKU KENKYUKA KENKYU HOKOKU/SHIZUOKA UNIVERSITY. GRADUATE SCHOOL OF ELECTRONIC SCIENCE AND TECHNOLOGY. REPORTS. (Text in English, Japanese) 1980. a. Shizuoku Daigaku, Daigakuin Denshi Kagaku Kenkyuka, 5-1, Johoku 3-chome, Hamamatsu-shi, Shizuoka-ken 432, Japan. **Indexed:** Sci.Abstr.

621.38 JA ISSN 0286-3383
CODEN: SDDHDM
SHIZUOKA DAIGAKU DENSHI KOGAKU KENKYUJO KENKYU HOKOKU/SHIZUOKA UNIVERSITY. RESEARCH INSTITUTE OF ELECTRONICS. BULLETIN. (Text in Japanese; summaries in English) 1966. s-a. free. Shizuoka Daigaku, Denshi Kogaku Kenkyujo - Shizuoka University, Research Institute of Electronics, 5-1, Johoku 3-chome, Hamamatsu-shi, Shizuoka-ken 432, Japan. TEL 053-471-1171. FAX 053-474-0630. circ. 500. **Indexed:** Chem.Abstr., Sci.Abstr. **Document type:** academic/scholarly publication.
—BLDSC (2694.877000); CASDDS.

621.38 GW ISSN 0173-1726
SIEMENS COMPONENTS. English edition (ISSN 0173-1734) 1906. bi-m. DM.84 (Ger. ed. DM.74). Siemens Verlag AG, Postfach 3240, 91050 Erlangen, Germany. TEL 09131-723004. FAX 09131-725022. bibl.; charts; illus. **Indexed:** Cyb.Abstr., Sci.Abstr. **Document type:** bulletin.
Former titles: Components Report (ISSN 0341-6569); Siemens Electronic Components Bulletin (ISSN 0037-4679)

621.38 IT
SISTEMI DI TELECOMUNICAZIONI. 12/yr. Via Taramelli 19, Milan, Italy. TEL 2-689-0-890. FAX 2-607-20-78. Ed. M. Bufalini. circ. 11,000.

643 658.8 UK
SMALL KITCHEN APPLIANCES: THE INTERNATIONAL MARKET. a. £1375($2750) Euromonitor, 87-88 Turnmill St., London EC1M 5QU, England. TEL 071-251-8024. FAX 071-608-3149. (Addr. in N. America: Euromonitor International, 111 W. Washington St., Ste. 920, Chicago, IL 60602. TEL 312-541-8024. FAX 312-541-1567) (looseleaf format) **Document type:** trade publication.
●Also available online. Vendor(s): Data-Star, DIALOG Information Services, Inc.
Description: Analyzes the market for small household kitchen appliances for France, Germany, Italy, Spain, the U.K., the U.S., and Japan.

537.58 UK ISSN 0038-1101
TK7872.S4 CODEN: SSELA5
SOLID-STATE ELECTRONICS; an international journal. (Text in English, French and German) 1960. 12/yr. £667($1025) (effective 1994). Elsevier Science Ltd., Pergamon, P.O. Box 800, Kidlington, Oxford OX5 1DX, England. TEL 44-865-843000. FAX 44-865-843010. (Subscr. in U.S. and Canada to: Elsevier Science, 660 White Plains Rd., Tarrytown, NY 10591-5153. TEL 914-524-9200. FAX 914-333-2444) Ed. W. Crawford Dunlap. adv.: B&W page $550, color page $1350. bk.rev.; bibl.; illus.; index. circ. 2,400. (also avail. in microfiche from MIM; microfilm from UMI) **Indexed:** A.S.& T.Ind., ASCA, Chem.Abstr., Curr.Cont., Eng.Ind., Excerp.Med., Int.Aerosp.Abstr., Met.Abstr., Sci.Abstr. **Document type:** academic/scholarly publication.
—BLDSC (8327.385000); EI; Faxon; UnCover; SWETS; UMI; CASDDS. **CCC.**
Description: Research in the areas of solid state physics, transistor technology, theory and design, crystal growth, semiconductors and circuit engineering
Refereed Serial

537.5 US ISSN 0038-111X
TK7872.S4 CODEN: SSTEAP
SOLID STATE TECHNOLOGY. 1958. m. $110 (foreign $157). PennWell Publishing Co. (Nashua), 10 Tara Blvd., 5th Fl., Nashua, NH 03062-2801. TEL 603-891-0123. FAX 609-891-0597. Ed. Robert Haavind. adv.: B&W page $5025, color page $6295; trim 178 x 254. bk.rev.; bibl.; charts; illus.; mkt.; pat.; tr.lit.; index. circ. 45,000. (also avail. in microform from UMI; reprint service avail. from UMI) **Indexed:** A.S.& T.Ind., ASCA, Ceram.Abstr., Chem.Abstr., Curr.Cont., Eng.Ind., Int.Aerosp.Abstr., Met.Abstr., PROMT, Risk Abstr., Sci.Abstr., World Alum.Abstr. **Document type:** trade publication.
—BLDSC (8327.500000); CIS; Faxon; UnCover; SWETS; UMI; CASDDS. **CCC.**
Former titles (until 1968): Semiconductor Products and Solid State Technology (ISSN 0096-3631); (Until 1962): Semiconductor Products (ISSN 0096-4034)
Description: Serves firms manufacturing and testing semiconductor materials, equipment, device and circuits, and OEM with in-house IC manufacturing facilities.
Refereed Serial

621.3 JA ISSN 0286-598X
SOLID STATE TECHNOLOGY, JAPANESE EDITION. (Text in Japanese) 1978. m. 8240 Yen. Solid State Technology Japan Inc. - Nihon Esu Esu Ti K.K., 4-5, Sarugaku-cho 1-chome, Chiyoda-ku, Tokyo 101, Japan.

643 SP
SONITRON. 11/yr. Ediciones Tecnicas Doria, Avda. Puerta del Angel 7, sobreatico A y B, 08002 Barcelona, Spain TEL 3-318-74-89. FAX 3-301-11-05. Ed. Javier Bolufer. circ. 5,500. **Document type:** trade publication.

621.381 JA
SONY TECHNICAL REPORTS. (Text in English, Japanese) a. Sony Corporation, Technical Information Center - Soni K.K. Gijutsu Joho Senta, 7-35, Kitashinagawa 6-chome, Shinagawa-ku, Tokyo 141, Japan.

621.38 CN ISSN 0829-3678
SOUND & VISION. 1970. 6/yr. Can.$11.95 (foreign Can.$21.95). Sound & Vision, 99 Atlantic Ave., Ste.302, Toronto, ON M6K 3J8, Canada. TEL 416-535-7611. FAX 416-535-6325. Ed. Alan Lofft. adv. circ. 45,000. (also avail. in microform) **Indexed:** Can.Per.Ind., CMI, Sci.Abstr. **Document type:** consumer publication.
●Also available on-line.
Formerly: Sound Canada (ISSN 0383-6908); Incorporates: Audio Canada & AudioScene Canada (ISSN 0315-1182); Which was formerly: Electron (ISSN 0013-475X)
Description: The latest on consumer entertainment electronics including home and car equipment.

621.381 US ISSN 1041-2379
SOUTHWEST TECHNOLOGY REPORT. 1986. s-m. $69. C - S Communications Inc., Box 23899, Tempe, AZ 85285. TEL 602-345-1118. FAX 602-345-1119. Ed. Walter J. Schuch. (looseleaf format; back issues avail.) **Document type:** newsletter.
Description: Focuses on electronics industry business news.

643 IT
SPECIALE ELETTRORADIO INFORMAZIONI. 2/yr. Publiedim s.r.l., Via Matteo Civitali 51, 20148 Milan, Italy. TEL 2-48-70-32-01. FAX 2-48-70-36-14. TELEX 322291 PUBIEM I. Ed. Carlo Moradei. **Document type:** monographic series.
Description: Each issue is dedicated to a specific product line and its updated style in the consumer electronics business.

621.38 JA
STRUCTURE OF THE JAPANESE ELECTRONICS INDUSTRY. (Text in English) 1985. irreg., latest Feb. 1993. $700. Dodwell Marketing Consultants, Kowa no.35, Bldg. 3F, 14-14 Akasaka, 1-chome, Minato-ku, Tokyo 107, Japan. TEL 03-3589-0207. FAX 03-5570-7132. TELEX J22274 DODWELL J. **Document type:** directory.
Formerly: Key Players in the Japanese Electronics Industry.
Description: Features profiles of major companies, market trends and market share analysis. Includes a directory of major companies.

ELECTRONICS

537.5   GW
SUPER ELECTRONICS JAHRBUCH; ein Nachschlagewerk fuer die gesamte Elektrotechnik - Elektronik. 1957. a. DM.48. Vogel Verlag und Druck KG, Max-Planck-Str. 7-9, 97082 Wuerzburg, Germany. TEL 0931-4182145. FAX 0931-4182640. (Subscr. to: Vogel Verlag, 97064 Wuerzburg, Germany; Dist. in U.S. by: Vogel Europublishing, Inc., 20092 Gibbs Dr., Sonora, CA 95370. TEL 209-533-3555. FAX 209-533-9555) Ed. Ernst Pohl. adv.: B&W page DM.8620, color page DM.11350; trim 270 x 190. circ. 50,000. **Indexed:** Sci.Abstr. **Document type:** trade publication.
Formerly: Elektro-Jahr (ISSN 0070-9956)

621.38   US   ISSN 0897-2427
SUPERCONDUCTIVITY NEWS. 1987. w. (48/yr., plus m. technical issues and q. patent issues). $277 in N. America (overseas $327). Superconductivity Publishers, 710 Easton Ave., Ste. C, Somerset, NJ 08873-1855. TEL 908-846-2002. FAX 908-846-2050. E-mail: 74130.650@COMPUSERVE.COM. Ed. Sean Keating. adv.: B&W page $300. illus.; pat.; index. (back issues avail.)
Description: Covers topics in superconductivity and magnetic resonance imaging, both business and research and development news.

621.5   US   ISSN 1054-2698
QC611.9   CODEN: SPCREU
SUPERCONDUCTIVITY REVIEWS. 1991. q. 82 ECU (effective 1993). Gordon and Breach Science Publishers, 820 Town Center Dr., Langhorne, PA 19047. TEL 215-750-2642. FAX 215-750-6343. (UK subscr. to: P.O. Box 90, Reading, Berkshire RG1 8JL, England. TEL 0734-560-080) Ed. Charles P. Poole. (also avail. in microform)
—CCC.
Description: Compiles literature on superconductivity.

537   US   ISSN 0893-3588
TK7868.P7
SURFACE MOUNT TECHNOLOGY. 1987. m. $60 (Canada & Mexico $90, elsewhere $160). I H S Publishing Group, Inc., 17730 W. Peterson Rd., Box 159, Libertyville, IL 60048-0159. TEL 708-362-8711. FAX 708-362-3484. Ed. Thomas A. Williams. circ. 58,000.
—BLDSC (8547.910000); EI; UnCover; SWETS. CCC.
Description: Reports on the design, fabrication, manufacturing, assembly, packaging and testing of surface mounted printed circuit boards adn bybrid circuits.

621.38   HU
SYMPOSIUM ON RELIABILITY IN ELECTRONICS. (Text in English and Russian) 1962. quinquennial, latest 6th, Budapest, Hungary, 1985. $38. Orszagos Muszaki Informacios Kozpont es Konyvtar (O.M.I.K.K.) - National Technical Information Centre and Library, Muzeum u.17, Box 12, 1428 Budapest, Hungary. (Co-sponsor: Scientific Society for Telecommunication) Ed. Merey.

621.381   JA
SYMPOSIUM RECORD OF ALLOY SEMICONDUCTOR PHYSICS AND ELECTRONICS/KONSHO EREKUTORONIKUSU SHINPOJUMU RONBUNSHU. (Text in English) 1982. a. Organizing Committee of Alloy Semiconductor Physics and Electronics - Konsho Erekutronikusu Shinpojumu Soshiki Iinkai, Kyoto Daigaku Kogakubu Denki Oyo Kogaku Koza, Yoshida Hon-machi, Sakyo-ku, Kyoto-shi, Kyoto 606, Japan.

621.381 384.55   FR
SYNDICAT DES INDUSTRIES DE MATERIEL PROFESSIONNEL ELECTRONIQUE ET RADIOELECTRIQUE. RAPPORT D'ACTIVITE. a. free. Syndicat des Industries de Materiel Professionnel Electronique et Radioelectrique, 11 Rue Hamelin, 75783 Paris Cedex 16, France. TEL 1-45-05-70-70. FAX 1-45-53-09-23. TELEX 611045.

683.83 001.642   US   ISSN 0892-7278
T W I C E. (This Week in Consumer Electronics) 1986. 28/yr. $85 (Canada $150; Mexico $139; elsewhere $185). Cahners Publishing Company (New York), Division of Reed Elsevier Inc., 249 W. 17th St., New York, NY 10011. TEL 212-645-0067. FAX 212-337-7066. (Subscr. to: 44 Cook St., Denver, CO 80206) Ed. Robert E. Gerson. adv.; charts; illus.; stat.; circ. 31,385 (controlled). (tabloid format; back issues avail.) **Document type:** consumer publication.
—CCC.
Description: Covers the consumer electronics, major appliance, and video software business for retailers.

621.38 658   CH
TAIWAN ELECTRONICS INDUSTRY. Cover title: T E I. m. $65 in Asia, Oceania, Middle East; elsewhere $75. United Pacific International Inc., P.O. Box 81-417, Taipei, Taiwan, Republic of China. TEL 02-7150751. FAX 886-2-7125591. TELEX 28784-UNIPAINC. (Or: 4th Fl., 311 Nanking E. Rd. Sec. 3, Taipei, Taiwan, R.O.C.) adv.
Formerly: Target Electronics Industry (ISSN 0257-8166)
Description: Information on the consumer electronics industry, including electronic products, components and accessories.

621.38   AT   ISSN 0811-3742
TALKING ELECTRONICS. 1981. q. Aus.$17. 35 Rosewarne Ave., Cheltenham, Victoria 3192, Australia. Ed. Colin Mitchell. circ. 15,000. (back issues avail.)
Description: For beginners in electronics.

621.381   JA
TECHNICAL DIGEST OF THE SENSOR SYMPOSIUM. (Text in English) 1988. a. Institute of Electrical Engineers of Japan, Technical Committee on Electronic Devices - Denki Gakkai Denshi Debaisu Gijutsu Iinkai, 12-1 Yuraku-cho 1-chome, Chiyoda-ku, Tokyo 100, Japan.

621.381   JA
TECHNOLOGY DEVELOPMENT REPORT/T D REPOTO. (Text in Japanese) 1986. a. Toenec Corporation, Technology Development Department - Toenekku Gijutsu Kaihatsushitsu, 20-31, Sakae 1-chome, Naka-ku, Nagoya-shi, Aichi-ken 460, Japan. TEL 052-221-1111. (Subscr. to: Toenec Corporation F S Laboratory, 1-79, Takiharu-cho, Minami-ku, Nagoya 457, Japan. TEL 052-619-1707. FAX 052-619-1705) Ed. Yoshikazu Kobayasi. circ. 1,750. **Document type:** corporate report.
Description: Covers new technology relating to electrical construction, power source, and telecommunication.

621.381   JA   ISSN 0918-6840
TEKUNO INTEGURESHON/TECHNO INTEGRATION. (Text in Japanese) 1985. m. 1100 Yen per no. Nihon Kogyo Shuppan K.K., 3-26, Honkomagome 6-chome, Bunkyo-ku, Tokyo 113, Japan.

TELEFONO. see COMMUNICATIONS — Telephone And Telegraph

643 658.8   UK
TELEVISION AND VIDEO: THE INTERNATIONAL MARKET. a. £1375($2750) Euromonitor, 87-88 Turnmill St., London EC1M 5QU, England. TEL 071-251-8024. FAX 071-608-3149. (Addr. in N. America: Euromonitor International, 111 W. Washington St., Ste. 920, Chicago, IL 60602. TEL 312-841-8024. FAX 312-608-3149) (looseleaf format) **Document type:** trade publication.
●Also available online. Vendor(s): Data-Star, DIALOG Information Services, Inc.
Description: Analyzes the markets for televisions and video recorders in France, Germany, Italy, Spain, the U.K., the U.S., and Japan.

TELEVISION DIGEST WITH CONSUMER ELECTRONICS. see COMMUNICATIONS — Television And Cable

621.38   JA   ISSN 0497-2791
TEREBI GIJUTSU/TELEVISION TECHNICS & ELECTRONICS. (Text in Japanese) 1953. m. 1200 Yen per no. Denshi Gijutsu Shuppan K.K. - Electronics Technique Publication Co., 26-3, Hongo 2-chome, Bunkyo-ku, Tokyo 113, Japan.

TEREMATIKUSU SHINPOJUMU/TELEMATICS SYMPOSIUM. see COMMUNICATIONS

537.5   US
TEXAS ANNUAL OF ELECTRONICS RESEARCH. 1964. a. $6 per no. University of Texas at Austin, Electronics Research Center, Austin, TX 78712. TEL 512-471-3954. Ed. Edward J. Powers. abstr.; bibl.; illus.
Formerly: Texas Biannual of Electronics Research (ISSN 0563-2625)

621.381   JA   ISSN 0287-3672
TOA NYUSU/TOA NEWS. (Text in Japanese) 1954. irreg. Toa Denpa Kogyo K.K. - Toa Electronics Ltd., 29-10, Takadanobaba 1-chome, Shinjuku-ku, Tokyo 160, Japan.

621.381   JA   ISSN 0917-8600
TOHOKU DAIGAKU DENKI TSUSHIN KENKYUJO CHOBISAI DENSHI KAIRO JIKKEN SHISETSU KENKYU HOKOKU/TOHOKU UNIVERSTIY. RESEARCH INSTITUTE OF ELECTRICAL COMMUNICATION. LABORATORY FOR MICROELECTRONICS. ANNUAL REPORT. (Text in English, Japanese; summaries in English) 1988. a. Tohoku Daigaku, Denki Tsushin Kenkyujo, 1-1, Hatahira 2-chome, Aoba-ku, Sendai-shi, Miyagi-ken 980, Japan.

621.381   JA
TOKIN EREKUTORONIKUSU/TOKIN ELECTRONICS. (Text in Japanese) 1985. q. Tokin Corporation, 7-1, Koriyama 6-chome, Taihaku-ku, Sendai-shi, Miyagi-ken 982, Japan.

621.381   JA   ISSN 0914-126X
TOKYO EREKUTORON NYUSU. HANDOTAI SEIZO SOCHI HEN. (Text in Japanese) 1983. 3/yr. Tokyo Erekutoron K.K. - Tokyo Electron Ltd., 3-1, Nishishinjuku 2-chome, Shinjuku-ku, Tokyo 163, Japan.

621.38   JA   ISSN 0040-9413
TORANJISUTA GIJUTSU/TRANSISTOR ELECTRONICS. (Text in Japanese) 1964. m. 13560 Yen. C Q Publishing Co., 14-2, Sugamo 1-chome, Toshima-ku, Tokyo 170, Japan. TEL 81-3-5395-2123. FAX 81-3-5395-2103. (Dist. outside Japan by: Nippon IPS Co., Ltd., 11-6, 3-chome, Iidabashi, Chiyoda-ku, Tokyo 102, Japan. TEL 03-3238-0700. FAX 03-3238-0707) Ed. Hisaki Masuda. adv.: B&W page $2400, color page $5600; trim 10 1/8 x 7 3/16. charts; illus.; pat. circ. 70,809. **Indexed:** JTA.
Description: Provides reports on the latest technical and development of semiconductor electronics.

621.381   JA   ISSN 0288-2701
TOSHIBA GIJUTSU KOKAISHU/TOSHIBA TECHNICAL DISCLOSURE BULLETIN. (Text in Japanese) 1983. 84/yr. Toshiba Chiteki Zaisanbu - Toshiba Corp., Patent Division, 72, Horikawa-cho, Saiwai-ku, Kawasaki-shi, Kanagawa-ken 210, Japan.

621.381   JA   ISSN 0372-0462
TOSHIBA REBYU/TOSHIBA REVIEW. JAPANESE EDITION. (Text in Japanese; summaries in English, Japanese) 1946. m. 720 Yen per no. (Toshiba K.K., Gijutsu Kikakubu - Toshiba Corp., Technology Planning and Coordination Division) Toshiba Rebyu Hakkojo, 72, Horikawa-cho, Saiwai-ku, Kawasaki-shi, Kanagawa-ken 210, Japan. **Indexed:** INIS Atomind.
—BLDSC (8869.795000); Faxon.

621.381   JA   ISSN 0916-1465
TOSHIBA'S SELECTED PAPERS ON SCIENCE & TECHNOLOGY. (Text in English) 1989. s-a. Toshiba Corp., 1-1, Shibaura 1-chome, Minato-ku, Tokyo 105, Japan.

621.38   JA
TRANSISTOR TECHNOLOGY. (Text in Japanese) m. $250. Intercontinental Marketing Corp., I.P.O. Box 5056, Tokyo 100-31, Japan. TEL 81-3-3661-7458. FAX 81-3-3667-9646.

643   US
U S TECH. 1986. m. Mid-Atlantic Tech Publications, Inc., Box 957, Valley Forge, PA 19482. TEL 610-783-6100. FAX 610-783-0317. Ed. Walter Salm. adv.; bk.rev.; circ. 50,000 (controlled). **Document type:** newspaper, trade publication.
Description: Covers electronics manufacturing, and related technologies for the electronics industry, engineering and design segments.

ELECTRONICS — ABSTRACTING, BIBLIOGRAPHIES, STATISTICS

621.381 620.40   JA   ISSN 0917-0375
ULTRA CLEAN TECHNOLOGY. ENGLISH EDITION. 1990. q. Ultra Clean Society - Handotai Kiban Gijutsu Kenkyukai, 16-13, Yushima 2-chome, Bunkyo-ku, Tokyo 113, Japan.

621.381 620.40   JA   ISSN 0917-0367
ULTRA CLEAN TECHNOLOGY. JAPANESE EDITION/URUTORA KURIN TEKUNOROJI. NIHONGO BAN. (Text in English, Japanese; summaries in English) 1989. q. 3500 Yen. Ultra Clean Society - Handotai Kiban Gijutsu Kenkyukai, 16-13, Yushima 2-chome, Bunkyo-ku, Tokyo 113, Japan.
—BLDSC (9082.780621).

621.381 537   RM
TK4
UNIVERSITATEA POLITEHNICA BUCURESTI. BULETIN STIINTIFIC. INGINERIE ELECTROTEHNICA/POLYTECHNICAL UNIVERSITY OF BUCHAREST. SCIENTIFIC BULLETIN. ELECTRICAL ENGINEERING. (Text in English, French or German) 1929. q. $195. Universitatea Politehnica Bucuresti, Splaiul Independentei 313, 77206 Bucharest 16, Rumania. FAX 401-312-01-88. TELEX IPOLB R 10252. bk.rev.; abstr.; bibl.; charts. circ. 1,300. **Document type:** academic/scholarly publication, bulletin.
—BLDSC (8177.823000); EI.
Formerly: Institutul Politehnic Bucuresti. Buletin Stiintific. Inginerie Electrotehnica (ISSN 1220-3033); Formed by the 1990 merger of: Institutul Politehnic Bucuresti. Buletin. Seria Electronica (ISSN 1012-3180) & Institutul Politehnic Bucuresti. Buletin. Seria Electrotehnica (ISSN 1010-4186) & Institutul Politehnic Bucuresti. Buletin. Seria Energetica (ISSN 1012-3202) & Institutul Politehnic Bucuresti. Buletin. Seria Automatica - Calculatoare (ISSN 1012-3245); Seria Electronica was formerly: Institutul Politehnic Gheorghe Gheorghiu-Dej Bucuresti. Buletin. Serie Electronica (1983) (ISSN 1010-9404); Seria Electrotehnica was formerly (until 1983): Institutul Politehnic Gheorghe Gheorghiu-Dej Bucuresti. Seria Electrotehnica (ISSN 1010-9390); Seria Energetica was formerly (until 1983): Institutul Politehnic Gheorghe Gheorghiu-Dej Bucuresti. Seria Energetica (ISSN 0256-7938); Seria Automatica-Calculatoare was formerly: Institutul Politehnic Gheorghe Gheorghiu-Di. Buletin. Seria Automatica (ISSN 0256-4564); All four superseded in part (in 1982): Institutul Politehnic Gheorghe Gheorghiu-Dej Bucuresti. Buletin. Seria Electrotehnica, Energetica, Automatica, Calculatoare, Electronica (ISSN 1010-9382); Which was formerly (until 1983): Institutul Politehnic Gheorghe Gheorghiu-Dej Bucuresti. Buletin. Seria Electrotehnica (ISSN 0378-9624); (until 1965): Institutul Politehnic Gheorghe Gheorghiu-Dej Bucuresti. Buletin.

621.38   US   ISSN 0195-9751
TK7874
UNIVERSITY - GOVERNMENT - INDUSTRY MICROELECTRONICS SYMPOSIUM. PROCEEDINGS. Title varies: Conference Record. 1975. biennial. Institute of Electrical and Electronics Engineers, Inc., 345 E. 47th St., New York, NY 10017-2394. TEL 212-705-7900. FAX 212-705-7682. (Subscr. to: Box 1331, 445 Hoes Lane, Piscataway, NJ 08855-1331) **Document type:** proceedings.

537.5   US   ISSN 0026-2870
UNIVERSITY OF UTAH. MICROWAVE DEVICE AND PHYSICAL ELECTRONICS LABORATORY QUARTERLY REPORT. 1962. q. free. University of Utah, Electrical Engineering Department, Microwave Device and Physical Electronics Lab, 3054 Merrill Engineering Bldg., Salt Lake City, UT 84112. TEL 801-581-6941. Ed. Richard W. Grow. circ. 140. (processed; also avail. in microfiche)

621.381   YU   ISSN 0351-2177
TK4
UNIVERZITET U BEOGRADU. ELEKTROTEHNICKI FAKULTET. PUBLIKACIJE. SERIJA: ELEKTRONIKA, TELEKOMUNIKACIJE, AUTOMATIKA. (Text in English) no.53, 1970. irreg. free or exchange basis. Univerzitet u Beogradu, Elektrotehnicki Fakultet, Studentski trg 1, Belgrade, Serbia, Yugoslavia. Ed. Milic Stojic. bk.rev.; illus. circ. 1,000. **Indexed:** Elec. & Electron.Abstr., Ref.Zh.
Formerly: Univerzitet u Beogradu. Elektrotehnicki Fakultet. Publikacije. Serija: Telekomunikacije i Elektronika (ISSN 0353-7641)

621.381   US
UPDATE (SANTA CLARA). 1978. m. (11/yr.). $72. American Electronics Association, 5201 Great America Pkwy., Santa Clara, CA 95054. TEL 408-987-4200. FAX 408-970-8565. Ed. April Neilson. adv. circ. 30,742.
Description: For executives and upper-level managers in the high-tech electronics industry. Focuses on trends and issues impacting electronics companies in the U.S.

V R F INFO. (Verband des Radio-, Fernseh-, und Elektro-Fachhandels und Gewerbes Oesterreichs) see COMMUNICATIONS — Television And Cable

643 658   FR   ISSN 1156-1874
VENTE EQUIPEMENTS MENAGERS. 11/yr. Distripresse, 32 rue St.-Marc, 75002 Paris, France. TEL 45-65-44-00. FAX 45-89-72-85. TELEX 202 548 F. Ed. Catherine Poterlot. circ. 12,500.

621.381   US
VOICE COIL. 1987. m. $50. Audio Amateur Publications, Box 176, Peterborough, NH 03458-0576. TEL 603-924-9464. FAX 603-924-9467. Ed. Vance Dickason. adv. contact: Martha Povey. **Document type:** newsletter.

W E S A NEWSLETTER. (Wisconsin Electronic Sales and Service Association) see BUSINESS AND ECONOMICS — Small Business

621.38   CC
WEIBO XUEBAO/JOURNAL OF MICROWAVES. (Text in Chinese; abstracts in English) q. $4 per no. Zhongguo Dianzi Xuehui, Weibo Xuehui, 525 Longhua Xilu, Shanghai 200232, People's Republic of China. TEL 86-21-4384041. FAX 86-21-4390998. Ed. Wang Zuqi.

621.38   AT   ISSN 0728-3873
WHAT'S NEW IN ELECTRONICS. 1981. m. Aus.$48. Westwick-Farrow Pty. Ltd., Cnr. Fox Valley Rd. and Kiogle St., Wahroonga, N.S.W. 2076, Australia. Ed. Janny Hauden. adv.; circ. 7,200 (controlled). (back issues avail.) **Document type:** trade publication.
Description: Contains new product information for the electronics professional.

621.38   PL   ISSN 0043-5112
WIADOMOSCI ELEKTROTECHNICZNE. 1933. m. $71. (Stowarzyszenie Elektrykow Polskich) Wydawnictwo Czasopism i Ksiazek Technicznych SIGMA - NOT, Ul. Ratuszowa 11, P.O. Box 1004, 00-950 Warsaw, Poland. TEL 48-22-180918. FAX 48-22192187. TELEX 814550 SIGMA PL. (Dist. by: SIGMA NOT Ltd., Bartycka 20, 00-716 Warsaw, Poland) adv.; bk.rev.; bibl.; charts; illus.; pat.; index. circ. 3,650. **Indexed:** C.I.S. Abstr., Sci.Abstr.

384.55   US
THE WORD (CHICAGO). 1950. m. $12. Electronic Service Dealers Association, 4621 N. Kedzie Ave., Chicago, IL 60625. TEL 312-463-2499. Ed. George J. Weiss. adv.; bk.rev. circ. 3,000.
Formerly: Illinois Word.

621.38   US   ISSN 0740-3585
WORLD ELECTRONIC DEVELOPMENTS; research advisory service on electronic developments in the U S, Japan and Western Europe. 1981. m. $195. Prestwick Publications, Inc., 390 N. Federal Hwy., Ste. 401, Deerfield Beach, FL 33441-2209. TEL 305-427-2924. Ed. R. Roecker. bk.rev. circ. 1,200. (back issues avail.)

WORLD ELECTRONICS COMPANIES FILE. see BUSINESS AND ECONOMICS — Trade And Industrial Directories

621.3   CH   ISSN 1022-2928
XING DIANZI KEJI/MICRO ELECTRONICS. (Text in Chinese) 1986. m. NT.$1080 (foreign NT.$2800). Third Wave Publishing Corp., 19-1, Lane 231, Fu-Hsing N. Rd., Taipei, Taiwan, Republic of China. TEL 886-2-7136959. FAX 886-2-7189467. Ed. Angel Chen. adv.: color page NT.$1600. circ. 10,000.

338.4 621.38   UK
YEARBOOK OF WORLD ELECTRONICS DATA VOL. 1: WEST EUROPE. 1973. a. £495 (diskette £803) (effective 1993). Elsevier Science Ltd., Books Division, P.O. Box 800, Kidlington, Oxford OX5 1DX, England. TEL 44-865-843000. FAX 44-865-843010. (Subscr. in U.S. and Canada to: Elsevier Science, 660 White Plains Rd., Tarrytown, NY 10591-5153. TEL 914-524-9200. FAX 914-333-2444) adv.; illus.; stat. circ. 450. (also avail. in diskette format; back issues avail.)
—BLDSC (9417.653250). **CCC.**
Formerly: Mackintosh Yearbook of West European Electronics Data (ISSN 0306-5774)
Description: Production and markets statistics for electronics products in Western European countries.

621.38 338.4   UK   ISSN 0954-0172
HD9696.A1
YEARBOOK OF WORLD ELECTRONICS DATA VOL. 2: AMERICA, JAPAN ASIA-PACIFIC. 1983. a. £495 (diskette £1204) (effective 1993). Elsevier Science Ltd., Books Division, P.O. Box 800, Kidlington, Oxford OX5 1DX, England. TEL 44-865-843000. FAX 44-865-843010. (Subscr. in U.S. and Canada to: Elsevier Science, 660 White Plains Rd., Tarrytown, NY 10591-5153. TEL 914-524-9200) Ed. Ken Wilson. adv.; charts; illus.; stat. (also avail. in diskette format)
—CCC.
Formerly: Mackintosh Yearbook of International Electronics Data (ISSN 0264-0721)
Description: Production and markets statistics for electronics products worldwide.

621.38   UK
YEARBOOK OF WORLD ELECTRONICS DATA VOL. 4: EAST EUROPE & WORLD SUMMARY. a. £495 (effective 1993). Elsevier Science Ltd., Books Division, P.O. Box 800, Kidlington, Oxford OX5 1DX, England. TEL 44-865-843000. FAX 44-865-843010. (Subscr. in U.S. and Canada to: Elsevier Science, 660 White Plains Rd., Tarrytown, NY 10591-5153. TEL 914-524-9200) Ed. Ken Wilson.
Description: Production and market statistics for electronics products in Eastern Europe and the World.

ELECTRONICS — Abstracting, Bibliographies, Statistics

BEIKOKU TOKKYO SHOROKU. DENSHI, TSUSHIN HEN/U.S. PATENT ABSTRACTS. ELECTRONICS, COMMUNICATIONS. see PATENTS, TRADEMARKS AND COPYRIGHTS — Abstracting, Bibliographies, Statistics

COMBINED INDEX FOR I E E E TRANSACTIONS ON POWER DELIVERY, I E E E TRANSACTIONS ON POWER SYSTEMS, I E E E TRANSACTIONS ON ENERGY CONVERSION. see ENGINEERING — Abstracting, Bibliographies, Statistics

CURRENT PAPERS IN ELECTRICAL & ELECTRONICS ENGINEERING. see ENGINEERING — Abstracting, Bibliographies, Statistics

621.38   UK   ISSN 0953-0509
PRINTED CIRCUITS AND ELECTRONICS COATINGS ABSTRACTS. (Supplement to: Surface Treatment Technology Abstracts (ISSN 0950-5199) 1985. bi-m. £100($255) (overseas £130) (effective 1992). Finishing Publications Ltd., 105 Whitney Dr., Stevenage, Herts. SG1 4DF, England. TEL 0438-745115. FAX 0438-364536. Ed. R. Pinner. adv.; bk.rev.; abstr.; pat.; index. circ. 1,000. **Document type:** abstracting/indexing.
—SWETS.
Description: Summarizes patpers, patent and standards reports, and translations covering printed circuit boards, electrical connectors, and surface treatment of semiconductor devices.

384.5 016   FU   ISSN 0135-0633
SIGNAL'NAYA INFORMATSIYA. RADIOFIZIKA I FIZICHESKIE OSNOVY ELEKTRONIKI. s-m. 47.80 Rub. Vsesoyuznyi Institut Nauchno-Tekhnicheskoi Informatsii (VINITI), Baltiiskaya ul. 14, Moscow A-219, Russia. **Document type:** abstracting/indexing.

ELECTRONICS — COMPUTER APPLICATIONS

621.381   JA
SYMPOSIUM ON FUTURE ELECTRON DEVICES. EXTENDED ABSTRACTS/SHIN KONO SOSHI GIJUTSU SHINPOJUMU YOKOSHU. (Text in English) 1982. a. 5000 Yen. Research & Development Association for Future Electron Devices - Shin Kono Soshi Kenkyu Kaihatsu Kyokai, 1-21, Toranomon 4-chome, Minato-ku, Tokyo 105, Japan. **Document type:** abstracting/indexing.

ELECTRONICS — Computer Applications

621.381   US   ISSN 0278-0070
TK7874   CODEN: ITCSDI
I E E E TRANSACTIONS ON COMPUTER-AIDED DESIGN OF INTEGRATED CIRCUITS AND SYSTEMS. 1982. m. $312 to non-members. (I E E E, Circuits and Systems Society) Institute of Electrical and Electronics Engineers, Inc., 345 E. 47th St., New York, NY 10017-2394. TEL 908-981-0060. FAX 908-981-9667. (Subscr. to: Box 1331, 445 Hoes Lane, Piscataway, NJ 08855-1331) Ed. Malgorzata Marek-Sadowska. (also avail. in microform) **Indexed:** ASCA, CAD CAM Abstr., Compumath, Comput.Abstr., Comput.Dtbs., Cyb.Abstr., Ergon.Abstr., Ind.Sci.Rev., Int.Aerosp.Abstr., Sci.Abstr.
—BLDSC (4363.174500); EI; Faxon; UnCover; SWETS; UMI. **CCC.**

ENCYCLOPEDIAS AND GENERAL ALMANACS

031   US   ISSN 1056-2168
F321
ALABAMA FACTS; a comprehensive look at Alabama today, county by county. (Subseries of: Flying Colors Series) 1991. irreg. $59.50. Clements Research (Subsidiary of: Political Research, Inc.), 16850 Dallas Pkwy., Dallas, TX 75248. TEL 214-931-8827. FAX 214-248-7159. Ed. John Clements.
Description: Examination of the land, people, economy, government, history, community services and attractions of Alabama in a county-by-county format.

031 917.98   US
F902.3
ALASKA ALMANAC: FACTS ABOUT ALASKA. 1976. a. $9.95. Alaska Northwest Books (Subsidiary of: Graphic Arts Center Publishing Co.), Box 10306, Portland, OR 97210. TEL 800-452-3032. FAX 503-223-1410. Pub. Doug Pfeiffer. charts; illus.
Former titles: Facts about Alaska - Alaska Almanac (ISSN 1051-5623); Alaska Almanac - Facts about Alaska (ISSN 0270-5370); Facts about Alaska (ISSN 0361-7823)
Description: General facts on and pertaining to Alaska and the Arctic Circle.

031 631   US
ALBEMARLE ALMANAC. 1984. a. $4. Virginia Almanacs, Box 39, Crozet, VA 22932. TEL 804-823-4936. Ed. Steven G. Meeks. adv.; bk.rev. circ. 25,000. (back issues avail.) **Document type:** bulletin.
Description: Regional "old farmers" style almanac for central Virginia. Includes natural and local history articles.

030 630   US   ISSN 0739-6961
ALMANAC FOR FARMERS AND CITY FOLK. 1984. a. $2.95. Greentree Publishing, Inc., 515 S. Seventh St., Las Vegas, NV 89101-6907. TEL 702-387-6777. FAX 702-385-1370. Ed. Lucas McFadden. adv. circ. 1,000,000.
Description: Includes weather forecasts, fishing, planting and tide tables, anecdotes, recipes, and astronomical data.

035   IT
ALMANACCO REPUBBLICANO. a. L.3000. Edizioni della Voce s.r.l., Via Tomacelli 146, 00186 Rome, Italy. Ed. Giuseppe Ciranna. adv.; illus. circ. 15,000.

031 920   CN   ISSN 0065-650X
ALMANACH DU PEUPLE. 1869. a. Can.$5.99. Groupe Polygone Editeurs, Inc., 11450 Blvd. Albert-Hudon, Montreal, PQ H1G 3J9, Canada. TEL 514-327-4464. FAX 514-327-0514. adv.; bk.rev. circ. 100,000.

ALMANAKH GOMONU UKRAINY. see *ETHNIC INTERESTS*

056.9   BL   ISSN 0104-4788
ALMANAQUE ABRIL. 1974. a. price varies. Editora Abril, S.A., Rua do Curtume, 769, Bl. G, 10o andar, 05066-900 Sao Paulo, SP, Brazil. TEL 011-831-0599. FAX 011-831-0599. Ed. Lucila Camargo. adv.; charts; illus.; stat. circ. 190,000. **Document type:** consumer publication.
●Also available on CD-ROM.
Formerly: Almanaque Brazil.

ALMANAQUE NAUTICO REDUCIDO PARA USO CON MAQUINAS DE CALCULAR. see *ASTRONOMY*

036   PR
ALMANAQUE PUERTORRIQUENO (YEAR). 1978. a. $11.95. Editorial Edil, Inc., P.O. Box 23088, U.P.R. Sta., Rio Piedras, PR 00931. TEL 809-763-2958. FAX 809-250-1407. Ed. Jose A. Toro Sugranes. circ. 3,000. **Document type:** academic/scholarly publication.
Description: Includes information on Puerto Rico: statistics, general information, population, election results and government agencies.

032   UK
ALTERNATIVE ENGLAND AND WALES. 1970. biennial (with quarterly supplements). £2.50. 65 Edith Grove, London SW10, England. Ed. Nicholas Saunders. bk.rev.; charts; illus.; index. circ. 30,000. (back issues avail.)
Formerly: Alternative London.

030 917.3   US   ISSN 0196-0180
AE5
AMERICANA ANNUAL. 1923. a. $21.75. Grolier Incorporated, Sherman Turnpike, Danbury, CT 06816. TEL 203-797-3500. Ed. James E. Churchill, Jr.
Description: Includes feature items, special reports and summaries of the year's major events and trends in all fields.

039   CC   ISSN 1004-5252
ANHUI NIANJIAN/ANHUI YEARBOOK. (Text in Chinese) 1983. a. $35. Anhui Shehui Kexueyuan - Anhui Academy of Social Sciences, Shehui Kexueyuan Dalou, Weigang, Hefei, Anhui, People's Republic of China. TEL 331838. adv. circ. 7,000.
Formerly (until 1987): Anhui Economic Yearbook.
Description: An encyclopaedia about Anhui Province in China.

036.9   BL
ANUARIO DELTA LAROUSSE. 1972. a. $13. Editora Delta S.A., Avda. Almirante Barroso 63-26, 20036 Rio de Janeiro, Brazil. Ed. Paulo Geiger. illus.
Description: Covers the events of the previous year.

033   GW   ISSN 0944-5668
ARBEITSMAPPE SOZIAL- UND WIRTSCHAFTSKUNDE. 1955. m. DM.168. Erich Schmidt Verlag GmbH & Co., Genthinerstr. 30G, 10785 Berlin, Germany. TEL 030-250085-0. FAX 030-25008521. Ed. Gerhard Huck. charts. (looseleaf format; back issues avail.) **Document type:** academic/scholarly publication.

031 917.91   US   ISSN 1043-1659
F806
ARIZONA FACTS; a comprehensive look at Arizona today, county by county. (Subseries of: Flying the Colors Series) 1989. irreg. $59.50. Clements Research (Subsidiary of: Political Research, Inc.), 16850 Dallas Pkwy., Dallas, TX 75248. TEL 214-931-8827. FAX 214-248-7159. Ed. John Clements.
Description: Examination of the land, people, economy, government, history, community services and attractions of Arizona in a county-by-county format.

007   US   ISSN 0196-6316
AS8
AWARDS, HONORS AND PRIZES. (Vol.1: U.S. and Canada; Vol.2: International and Foreign) 1969. biennial. $390 (vol.1 $180; vol.2 $210). Gale Research Inc., 835 Penobscot Bldg., Detroit, MI 48226. TEL 313-961-2242. FAX 313-961-6083. TELEX 810-221-7086. Ed. Gita Siegman. index.
Description: Covers all prizes in every field of human endeavor, with information on the administration and awards given.

031   US   ISSN 0068-1156
AE5   CODEN: BBYEDJ
BRITANNICA BOOK OF THE YEAR. Variant Title: Britannica World Data Annual. 1938. a. $37.95. Encyclopaedia Britannica, Inc., 310 S. Michigan Ave., Chicago, IL 60604. TEL 312-347-7000. FAX 312-347-7914. TELEX 190203. Ed. Daphne Daume. index.
●Also available online.
Also available on CD-ROM.
—BLDSC (2286.400000); CASDDS.

031 917.94   US   ISSN 0883-6264
F856
CALIFORNIA FACTS; a comprehensive look at California today, county by county. (Subseries of: Flying the Colors Series) 1985. irreg., latest 1989. $59.50. Clements Research (Subsidiary of: Political Research, Inc.), 16850 Dallas Pkwy., Dallas, TX 75248. TEL 214-931-8827. FAX 214-248-7159. Ed. John Clements.
Description: Examination of the land, economy, people, government, history, community services and attractions of California in a county-by-county format.

CALIFORNIA HANDBOOK; a comprehensive guide to sources of current information and action. see *PUBLIC ADMINISTRATION*

CANADA YEARBOOK. see *STATISTICS*

CARITAS-KALENDER. see *RELIGIONS AND THEOLOGY*

030   US
GT4803
CHASE'S CALENDAR OF EVENTS. 1958. a. $45.95. Contemporary Books, Inc., 2 Prudential Plaza, Chicago, IL 60601. TEL 312-540-4500. FAX 312-540-4687. Ed. Mary M. Eley. bk.rev.; index. circ. 22,000. **Document type:** directory.
Former titles: Chase's Annual Events (ISSN 0740-5286); (until 1984): Chase's Calendar of Annual Events (ISSN 0577-5728)
Description: Day-by-day listing of celebrations, fairs, festivals, holidays and other special observances throughout the US and world.

031   US   ISSN 0069-5793
AE5
COLLIER'S YEARBOOK. (Supplement to: Collier's Encyclopedia and Merit Students Encyclopedia) 1939. a. $30.95. P.F. Collier, Inc., 866 Third Ave., 11th Fl., New York, NY 10022-6221. Ed. Richard Hantula. index.

031   US
COMPTON'S YEARBOOK. 1958. a. $33.90. Compton's Multimedia Publishing Group, Inc., Compton's Learning Co. (Subsidiary of: Tribune Company), 310 S. Michigan Ave., Chicago, IL 60604. TEL 312-347-7000. FAX 312-347-7914. Dir. Dale Good. adv.; bibl.; index. **Document type:** consumer publication.
Formerly: Compton Yearbook (ISSN 0069-8091)
Description: Supplement updating entries in Compton's Encyclopedia; includes encyclopedia update, feature articles, pictured highlights and chronology, events of the year and special reports.

031 017.4   US   ISSN 1050-4613
F91
CONNECTICUT FACTS - RHODE ISLAND FACTS; a comprehensive look at Connecticut and Rhode Island today, county-by-county. (Subseries of: Flying the Colors Series) 1990. irreg. $59.50. Clements Research (Subsidiary of: Political Research, Inc.), 16850 Dallas Pkwy., Dallas, TX 75248. TEL 214-931-8827. FAX 214-248-7159. Ed. John Clements.
Description: Examination of the land, people, economy, government, history, community services and attractions of Connecticut and Rhode Island in a county-by-county format.

ENCYCLOPEDIAS AND GENERAL ALMANACS

032　　　　　CN　　ISSN 0823-1133
F1004.7
CORPUS ALMANAC & CANADIAN SOURCEBOOK. 1966. a. Can.$157.50. Southam Information and Technology Group, 1450 Don Mills Rd., Don Mills, ON M3B 2X7, Canada. TEL 416-445-6641. FAX 416-442-2200. Ed. Mary Mancini. bibl.; charts; illus.; index. circ. 4,500. (back issues avail.)
Formerly (until 1983): Corpus Almanac (ISSN 0315-7083)
Description: Statistical and government jurisdictional information providing names and addresses.

DICTIONNAIRE DES COMMUNES (LAVAUZELLE ET CIE). see PUBLIC ADMINISTRATION

010　　　　　　　US
E A SUPPLEMENT. (Encyclopedia of Associations) 1964. s-a. $320 (effective Nov. 1993). Gale Research Inc., 835 Penobscot Bldg., Detroit, MI 48226. TEL 313-961-2242; 800-877-4253. FAX 313-961-6083. TELEX 810-221-7086. Ed. Deborah Burek. cum.index in each issue.
Former titles: New Associations and Projects (ISSN 0028-4238); New Associations; Incorporates: Programs-in-Progress Encyclopedia.

309.23　　　　　UV
ECHO DU S P O N G. 1991. q. Secretariat Permanent des Organisations Non Gouvernementales, 01 B.P. 131, Ouagadougou 01, Burkina Faso. TEL 226-30-62-63. FAX 226-31-18-85. **Document type:** bulletin.

030 338.025　　　　　HK
ENCYCLOPAEDIA OF HONG KONG TRADE & INDUSTRY (YEAR). (In 4 vols.) a. $120 per vol. Worldwide Credit Information Estate, P.O. Box 96032, Tsim Sha Tsui Post Office, Kowloon, Hong Kong. TEL 852-384-1202. FAX 852-384-1192. adv. **Document type:** directory.
Description: Provides a listing of over 40,000 Hong Kong firms and organizations with names, addresses, telephone numbers, products, and services.

034　　　　　FR
ENCYCLOPEDIA AZ. 1978. w. Editions Atlas, 33 av. du Maine, Tour Maine-Montparnasse, 75015 Paris, France. Ed. Bernard Bosc.

ENCYCLOPEDIA OF AMERICAN RELIGIONS. see RELIGIONS AND THEOLOGY

ENCYCLOPEDIA OF AMERICAN RELIGIONS: RELIGIOUS CREEDS. see RELIGIONS AND THEOLOGY

030 366　　　　US　　ISSN 0071-0202
AS22
ENCYCLOPEDIA OF ASSOCIATIONS. (In 3 vols: Vol.1: National Organizations of the U.S.; Vol.2: Geographic-Executive Index; Vol.3: Supplement) 1956. a. $375 for vol.1; vol.2 $295; vol.3 $320 (effective July 1993). Gale Research Inc., 835 Penobscot Bldg., Detroit, MI 48226. TEL 313-961-2242; 800-877-4253. FAX 313-961-6083. TELEX 810-221-7086. Ed. Carol A. Schwartz. (also avail. in diskette format; magnetic tape) **Document type:** directory.
●Also available online. Vendor(s): DIALOG Information Services, Inc. (File no.114). Also available on CD-ROM.
—BLDSC (3738.560000).
Formerly: Encyclopedia of American Associations (ISSN 0190-3071)
Description: Bibliographic directory of American associations and organizations.

030 366　　　　US　　ISSN 1041-0023
AS8
ENCYCLOPEDIA OF ASSOCIATIONS. INTERNATIONAL ORGANIZATIONS. 1989. a. Gale Research Inc., 835 Penobscot Bldg., Detroit, MI 48226-9948. TEL 313-961-2242. FAX 313-961-6083. **Document type:** directory.
—BLDSC (3738.561000).
Supersedes in part: Encyclopedia of Associations (ISSN 0071-0202); Which was formerly (1956-1959): Encyclopedia of American Associations (ISSN 0190-3071)

ENCYCLOPEDIA OF PHYSICAL SCIENCE & TECHNOLOGY YEARBOOK. see SCIENCES: COMPREHENSIVE WORKS

031　　　　US　　ISSN 0196-0172
ENCYCLOPEDIA YEAR BOOK. 1947. a. $21.75. Grolier Incorporated, Sherman Turnpike, Danbury, CT 06816. TEL 203-797-3500. Eds. James E. Churchill, Jr. charts; illus.; stat.; index.
Description: Includes feature items, special reports and summaries of the year's major events and trends in all fields.

ENCYCLOPEDIC DICTIONARY OF ECONOMICS. see BUSINESS AND ECONOMICS — Management

ENCYCLOPEDIE BERBERE. see RELIGIONS AND THEOLOGY — Islamic

ETUDES ET DOCUMENTS BERBERES. see RELIGIONS AND THEOLOGY — Islamic

940　　　　UK　　ISSN 0956-2273
JN1　　　　　　CODEN: EWYBEL
EUROPA WORLD YEAR BOOK. (In 2 vols.) 1926. a. $580. Europa Publications Ltd., 18 Bedford Sq., London WC1B 3JN, England. TEL 071-580-8236. FAX 071-636-1664. TELEX 21540-EUROPA-G. (Dist in U.S. by: Gale Research, Inc., 835 Penobscot Bldg., Detroit, MI 48226-4094. TEL 313-961-2242) **Document type:** directory.
—BLDSC (3829.339000); SWETS. **CCC.**
Formerly: Europa Year Book: A World Survey (ISSN 0071-2302)
Description: Surveys world politics, economics, religion, commerce, diplomacy, and transport country by country.

327 338.025　　　UK　　ISSN 0962-1032
THE EUROPEAN COMMUNITIES ENCYCLOPEDIA AND DIRECTORY (YEAR). 1991. a. $325. Europa Publications Ltd., 18 Bedford Sq., London WC1B 3JN, England. TEL 071-580-8236. FAX 071-636-1664. TELEX 21540-EUROPA-G. **Document type:** directory.
Description: Provides comprehensive details on the separate European Communities as they approach the Single Market how this will affect the rest of the world.

031　　　　US　　ISSN 0737-6731
FARMER'S ALMANAC. 1817. a. $2.95 (effective 1994). Geiger Brothers, Mt. Hope Ave., Box 1609, Lewiston, ME 04241. TEL 207-783-2001. FAX 207-777-7083. Ed. Peter Geiger. adv.: B&W page $1500; trim 5 1/4 x 8; adv. contact: Roy Park. circ. 300,000 (paid). **Document type:** consumer publication.
Description: Includes Americana, folk sayings, folklore, and information on weather, planting dates, the moon and stars, and holidays.

031 917.59　　　US　　ISSN 0895-8084
F306
FLORIDA FACTS; a comprehensive look at Florida today, county by county. (Subseries of: Flying the Colors Series) 1987. irreg. $59.50. Clements Research (Subsidiary of: Political Research, Inc.), 16850 Dallas Pkwy., Dallas, TX 75248. TEL 214-931-8827. FAX 214-248-7159. Ed. John Clements.
Description: Examination of the land, people, economy, government, history, community services and attractions of Florida in a county-by-county format.

030　　　　　US
FLYING THE COLORS SERIES; state fact books. irreg., latest 1991. $59.50 per vol. Political Research, Inc., Tegoland at Bent Tree, 16850 Dallas Pkwy., Dallas, TX 75248. TEL 214-931-8827. FAX 214-248-7159. **Document type:** monographic series.
Description: Provides statistical, historical and current information on individual states in the U.S. Each state is profiled county by county, including demographics, business, government and other types of information.

030　　　　　US
FORD ALMANAC;* for farm and home. 1954. a. $1.25. Almanac Co., Box 789, Woodstock, IL 60098. TEL 815-338-2053. Ed. Cliff Granschow. adv.; illus. circ. 100,000.

030　　　　　IE　　ISSN 0072-0887
GENUINE IRISH OLD MOORE'S ALMANAC. 1764. a. £0.76 per no. John Arigho & Sons (1964) Ltd., 16 Knocklyon Park, Templeogue, Dublin 16, Ireland. Ed. K. Ryan. adv.; index. circ. 90,000.

031 917.58　　　US　　ISSN 1044-9086
F281
GEORGIA FACTS; a comprehensive look at Georgia today, county by county. (Subseries of: Flying the Colors Series) 1989. irreg. $59.50. Clements Research (Subsidiary of: Political Research, Inc.), 16850 Dallas Pkwy., Dallas, TX 75248. TEL 214-931-8827. FAX 214-248-7159. Ed. John Clements.
Description: Examination of the land, people, economy, government, history, community services and attractions of Georgia in a county-by-county format.

039　　　　　CC
GUANGXI NIANJIAN/GUANGXI YEARBOOK. (Text in Chinese) a. (Guangxi Zhuangzu Zhiziqu Renmin Zhengfu - People's Government of Guangxi Zhuang Nationality Autonomous Region) Guangxi Nianjian Bianjibu, 30 Xinzhu Lu, Nanning, Guangxi 530022, People's Republic of China. TEL 27475.

032 916.897　　　MW
GUIDE TO PROFESSIONAL BODIES IN MALAWI. a. Centraf Associates Ltd., P.O. Box 3046, Chichiri, Blantyre 3, Malawi.

001.9　　　　US　　ISSN 1057-4557
AG243
GUINNESS BOOK OF RECORDS. (Editions in 36 languages) 1955. a. $22.95. Facts on File, Inc., 460 Park Ave. S., New York, NY 10016. TEL 212-683-2244. FAX 212-683-3633. TELEX 238552. Ed. Mark Young. bk.rev.; illus. circ. 450,000.
Former titles (until 1991): Guinness Book of World Records (ISSN 0072-9000); Guinness Book of Records (ISSN 0300-1679)
Description: Lists all the most important records and feats in science, entertainment, politics, business, sports, and the animal, vegetable and mineral worlds.

001.9 790.1　　　US　　ISSN 1054-4178
GV741
THE GUINNESS BOOK OF SPORTS RECORDS. 1972. a. Facts on File, Inc., 460 Park Ave. S., New York, NY 10016. TEL 212-683-2244. FAX 212-683-3633. Ed. Mark Young.
Former titles (until 1991): Guinness Sports Record Book (ISSN 1054-4542); (until 1985): Guinness Book of Sports Records, Winners and Champions (ISSN 1054-4534); (until 1980): Guinness Sports Record Book (1972) (ISSN 1054-4526)
Description: Lists all the up-to-date records in every sport, with thumbnail sketches of the sports' histories.

HISPANIC - AMERICAN ALMANAC. see ETHNIC INTERESTS

031 917.73　　　US　　ISSN 1041-2778
F536
ILLINOIS FACTS; a comprehensive look at Illinois today, county by county. (Subseries of: Flying the Colors Series) 1989. irreg. $59.50. Clements Research (Subsidiary of: Political Research, Inc.), 16850 Dallas Parkway, Dallas, TX 75248. TEL 214-931-8827. FAX 214-248-7159. Ed. John Clements.
Description: Examination of the land, people, economy, government, history, community services and attractions of Illinois in a county-by-county format.

031 917.72　　　US　　ISSN 0893-2298
F521
INDIANA FACTS; a comprehensive look at Indiana today, county by county. (Subseries of: Flying the Colors Series) 1987. irreg. $59.50. Clements Research (Subsidiary of: Political Research, Inc.), 16850 Dallas Pkwy., Dallas, TX 75248. TEL 214-931-8827. FAX 214-248-7159. Ed. John Clements.
Description: Examination of the land, people, economy, government, history, community services and attractions of Indiana in a county-by-county format.

ENCYCLOPEDIAS AND GENERAL ALMANACS

031 917.77 US ISSN 0895-8092
F616
IOWA FACTS; a comprehensive look at Iowa today, county by county. (Subseries of: Flying the Colors Series) 1988. irreg. $59.50. Clements Research (Subsidiary of: Political Research, Inc.), 16850 Dallas Pkwy., Dallas, TX 75248. TEL 214-931-8827. FAX 214-248-7159. Ed. John Clements.
  Description: Examination of the land, people, economy, government, history, community services and attractions of Iowa in a county-by-county format.

,630 133.5 US
J. GRUBER'S HAGERS-TOWN TOWN AND COUNTRY ALMANACK. 1797. a. $1.95 (effective Sep. 1993). Gruber Almanack Company, 1120 Professional Court, Box 609, Hagerstown, MD 21741-0609. TEL 301-733-2530. FAX 301-791-1478. Ed. Charles W. Fisher. adv. circ. 175,000. **Document type:** directory.
  Description: Provides the rising, setting and eclipses of the sun, moon, and most conspicuous planets and fixed stars; the conjecture of the weather by month.

034 FR ISSN 0449-4733
D410
JOURNAL DE L'ANNEE. 1966. a. Larousse, 17 rue de Montparnasse, 75280 Paris Cedex 06, France. illus. —CCC.

031 US ISSN 1051-7138
F676
KANSAS FACTS; a comprehensive look at Kansas today, county by county. (Subseries of: Flying the Colors Series) 1990. irreg. $59.50. Clements Research (Subsidiary of: Political Research, Inc.), 16850 Dallas Pkwy., Dallas, TX 75248. TEL 214-931-8827. FAX 214-248-7159. Ed. John Clements.
  Description: Examination of the land, people, economy, government, history, community services and attractions of Kansas in a county-by-county format.

031 917.6 US ISSN 1046-834X
F446
KENTUCKY FACTS; a comprehensive look at Kentucky today, county by county. (Subseries of: Flying the Colors Series) 1990. irreg. $59.50. Clements Research (Subsidiary of: Political Research, Inc.), 16850 Dallas Pkwy., Dallas, TX 75248. TEL 214-931-8827. FAX 214-248-7159. Ed. John Clements.
  Description: Examination of the land, people, economy, government, history, community services and attractions of Kentucky in a county-by-county format.

039 YU ISSN 0541-9344
MAGYAR SZO NAPTARA. (Text in Hungarian) 1969. a. 60 din. Forum, Novi Sad, Vojvode Misica 1, Novi Sad, Yugoslavia. illus.

030 JA
MAINICHI DAILY NEWS. (Text in English) 1972. a. 3200 Yen($17.50) Mainichi Newspapers, 1-1-1, Hitotsubashi, Chiyoda-ku, Tokyo 100-51, Japan. TEL 03-3212-0321. FAX 03-3211-0895. TELEX 22324. adv.; charts; stat.
  Formerly: Japan Almanach.
  Description: General interest publication covering domestic and world events affecting Japan.

031 917.44 US ISSN 0894-3427
F61
MASSACHUSETTS FACTS; a comprehensive look at Massachusetts today, county by county. (Subseries of: Flying the Colors Series) 1987. irreg. $59.50. Clements Research (Subsidiary of: Political Research, Inc.), 16850 Dallas Pkwy., Dallas, TX 75248. TEL 214-931-8827. FAX 214-248-7159. Ed. John Clements.
  Description: Examination of the land, people, economy, government, history, community services and attractions of Massachusetts in a county-by-county format.

031 917.7 US ISSN 1051-7146
F561
MICHIGAN FACTS; a comprehensive look at Michigan today, county by county. (Subseries of: Flying the Colors Series) 1990. irreg. $59.50. Clements Research (Subsidiary of: Political Research, Inc.), 16850 Dallas Pkwy., Dallas, TX 75248. TEL 214-931-8827. FAX 214-248-7159. Ed. John Clements.
  Description: Examination of the land, people, economy, government, history, community services and attractions of Michigan in a county-by-county format.

MILLENNIUM WHOLE EARTH CATALOG; access to tools & ideas for the twenty-first century. see *NEW AGE PUBLICATIONS*

031 US ISSN 1056-9596
F461
MISSOURI FACTS; a comprehensive look at Missouri today, county by county. (Subseries of: Flying the Colors Series) 1991. irreg. $59.50. Clements Research (Subsidiary of: Political Research, Inc.), 16850 Dallas Pkwy., Dallas, TX 75248. TEL 214-931-8827. FAX 214-248-7159. Ed. John Clements. **Document type:** consumer publication.
  Description: Examines the land, people, economy, government, history, community services and attractions of Missouri in a county-by-county format.

NEGRO ALMANAC: A REFERENCE WORK ON THE AFRICAN AMERICAN. see *ETHNIC INTERESTS*

NEW AGE ENCYCLOPEDIA. see *NEW AGE PUBLICATIONS*

030 US ISSN 0196-0148
NEW BOOK OF KNOWLEDGE ANNUAL; the young people's book of the year. 1940. a. $21.75. Grolier Incorporated, Sherman Turnpike, Danbury, CT 06816. TEL 203-797-3500. Ed. Fern Mamberg. (back issues avail.)
  Description: Heavily illustrated and topically organized. Emphasizes high-interest articles and trends, projects and activities, and social studies.

031 917.42 US ISSN 0895-8114
F31
NEW HAMPSHIRE FACTS; a comprehensive look at New Hampshire today, county by county. (Subseries of: Flying the Colors Series) 1987. irreg. $59.50. Clements Research (Subsidiary of: Political Research, Inc.), 16850 Dallas Pkwy., Dallas, TX 75248. TEL 214-931-8827. FAX 214-248-7159. Ed. John Clements.
  Description: Examination of the land, people, economy, government, history, community services and attractions of New Hampshire in a county-by-county format.

031 917.49 US ISSN 0898-5405
F131
NEW JERSEY FACTS; a comprehensive look at New Jersey today, county by county. (Subseries of: Flying the Colors Series) 1988. irreg. $59.50. Clements Research (Subsidiary of: Political Research, Inc.), 16850 Dallas Pkwy., Dallas, TX 75248. TEL 214-931-8827. FAX 214-248-7159. Ed. John Clements.
  Description: Examination of the land, people, economy, government, history, community services and attractions of New Jersey in a county-by-county format.

031 917.47 US ISSN 0888-4285
F116
NEW YORK FACTS; a comprehensive look at New York today, county by county. (Subseries of: Flying the Colors Series) 1986. irreg., latest 1989. $59.50. Clements Research (Subsidiary of: Political Research, Inc.), 16850 Dallas Pkwy., Dallas, TX 75248. TEL 214-931-8827. FAX 214-248-7159. Ed. John Clements.
  Description: Examination of the land, economy, people, government, history, community services and attractions of New York State, presented in a county-by-county format.

031 917.56 US ISSN 0895-8106
F251
NORTH CAROLINA FACTS; a comprehensive look at North Carolina today, county by county. (Subseries of: Flying the Colors Series) 1988. irreg. $59.50. Clements Research (Subsidiary of: Political Research, Inc.), 16850 Dallas Pkwy., Dallas, TX 75248. TEL 214-931-8827. FAX 214-248-7159. Ed. John Clements.
  Description: Examination of the land, people, economy, government, history, community services and attractions of North Carolina in a county-by-county format.

031 917.71 US ISSN 1040-4872
F486
OHIO FACTS; a comprehensive look at Ohio today, county by county. (Subseries of: Flying the Colors Series) 1988. irreg. $59.50. Clements Research (Subsidiary of: Political Research, Inc.), 16850 Dallas Pkwy., Dallas, TX 75248. TEL 214-931-8827. FAX 214-248-7159. Ed. John Clements.
  Description: Examination of the land, people, economy, government, history, community services and attractions of Ohio in a county-by-county format.

031 631 US ISSN 0078-4516
AY81
OLD FARMER'S ALMANAC. 1792. a. $2.95 (effective 1992). Yankee Publishing, Inc., Box 520, Dublin, NH 03444-0520. TEL 603-563-8111. FAX 603-563-8252. Ed. Judson D. Hale, Sr. adv. circ. 4,500,000. (reprint service avail. from UMI)

ONE TO ONE (FRESNO); the journal of creative broadcasting. see *COMMUNICATIONS — Radio*

ONE TO ONE II. see *COMMUNICATIONS — Radio*

032 UK ISSN 0079-0362
PEARS CYCLOPAEDIA. 1897. a. £14.99. Pelham Books Ltd., 27 Wrights Lane, London W8 5TZ, England. TEL 071-416-3200. FAX 071-416-3293. Ed. Dr. Chris Cook. circ. 50,000. **Document type:** consumer publication.
  Description: Explores world politics, economics, science, sports, prominent people, literature and music. Family orientated.

032 028.5 UK
PEARS JUNIOR ENCYCLOPAEDIA. 1961. biennial. £12.99. Pelham Books Ltd., 27 Wrights Lane, London W8 5TZ, England. TEL 071-416-3200. FAX 071-416-3293. Ed. Edward Blishen. **Document type:** academic/scholarly publication.
  Description: Teaches children about history, geography, science, mathematics, computers, cars, sports, radio and television.

031 917.48 US ISSN 0894-3850
F146
PENNSYLVANIA FACTS; a comprehensive look at Pennsylvania today, county by county. (Subseries of: Flying the Colors Series) 1987. irreg. $59.50. Clements Research (Subsidiary of: Political Research, Inc.), 16850 Dallas Pkwy., Dallas, TX 75248. TEL 214-931-8827. FAX 214-248-7159. Ed. John Clements.
  Description: Examination of the land, people, economy, government, history, community services and attractions of Pennsylvania in a county-by-county format.

039 CC ISSN 1000-9396
PEOPLE'S REPUBLIC OF CHINA YEAR BOOK. Chinese edition: Zhongguo Nianjian (ISSN 1000-9647) 1989. a. HK.$76 (foreign $115). Zhongguo Nianjian She - China Year Book Publishing House, 57 Xuanwumen Xidajie, Beijing 100803, People's Republic of China, Hong Kong. TEL 307-4562. FAX 307-4973. (back issues avail.)
  Description: Covers politics, the economy, legislation, military affairs, foreign relations, science and technology, education, public health, culture and arts, sports, society and people' life, religious affairs, and people in the news.

948 038 NE ISSN 0079-8223
PYTTERSEN'S NEDERLANDSE ALMANAK; jaarlijks verschijnend handboek van personen en instellingen in Nederland en de Nederlandse Antillen. 1901. a. fl.169 for 1993-1994 edition. Bohn Stafleu van Loghum B.V., P.O. Box 246, 3990 GA Houten, Netherlands. TEL 31-3403-95711. FAX 31-3403-50903. Ed. Alice Garritsen. index. circ. 5,000. **Document type:** directory.

REFERENCE ENCYCLOPEDIA OF THE AMERICAN INDIAN.
see *ETHNIC INTERESTS*

039 059.951   CH   ISSN 1013-0942
DS798.92
REPUBLIC OF CHINA YEARBOOK (YEAR). (Text in English) 1874. a. $45. Kwang Hwa Publishing Co., 2 Tientsin St., Taipei, Taiwan 10041, Republic of China. (Dist. in US by: Kwang Hwa Publishing (USA) Inc., 900 N. Western Ave., Ste. 101, Los Angeles, CA 90029. TEL 213-461-4918)
   Formerly: Republic of China: A Reference Guide.
   Description: Reports on the development and current state of the nation in politics, economics, culture, foreign affairs, education, art, science. Includes a Who's Who.

500   US   ISSN 0080-7621
Q9
SCIENCE YEAR. 1965. a. price varies. World Book, Inc., 525 W. Monroe, Chicago, IL 60661. TEL 312-258-3874; 800-874-0520. FAX 312-258-3950. (Subscr. to: World Book Encyclopedia, Inc., Box 3073, Evanston, IL 60204) Ed. Darlene R. Stille. cum.index. **Document type:** consumer publication.

309.23   UV
SECRETARIAT PERMANENT DES ORGANISATIONS NON GOUVERNEMENTALES. RAPPORT D'ACTIVITIES. 1976. a. Secretariat Permanent des Organisations Non Gouvernementales, 01 B.P. 131, Ouagadougou 01, Burkina Faso. TEL 226-30-62-63. FAX 226-31-18-85. **Document type:** corporate report.

031   US   ISSN 1056-960X
F266
SOUTH CAROLINA FACTS; a comprehensive look at South Carolina today, county by county. (Subseries of: Flying the Colors Series) 1991. irreg. $59.50. Clements Research (Subsidiary of: Political Research, Inc.), 16850 Dallas Pkwy., Dallas, TX 75248. TEL 214-931-8827. FAX 214-248-7159. Ed. John Clements.
   Description: Examination of the land, people, economy, government, history, community services and attractions of South Carolina in a county-by-county format.

031 917.64   US   ISSN 0899-7349
HC107.T4
TEXAS FACTS; a comprehensive look at Texas today, county by county. (Subseries of: Flying the Colors Series) 1984. irreg. latest 1988. $59.50. Clements Research (Subsidiary of: Political Research, Inc.), 16850 Dallas Pkwy., Dallas, TX 75248. TEL 214-931-8827. FAX 214-248-7159. Ed. John Clements.
   Description: Examination of the land, economy, people, government, history, community services and attractions of Texas presented in a county-by-county format.

031   US   ISSN 1054-8351
F221
VIRGINIA FACTS; a comprehensive look at Virginia today, county by county. (Subseries of: Flying the Colors Series) 1991. irreg. $59.50. Clements Research (Subsidiary of: Political Research, Inc.), 16850 Dallas Pkwy., Dallas, TX 75248. TEL 214-931-8827. FAX 214-248-7159. Ed. John Clements.
   Description: Examination of the land, people, economy, government, history, community services and attractions of Virginia in a county-by-county format.

030   UK   ISSN 0083-7067
WALKER'S OLD MOORE'S ALMANAC. 1844. a. 10p. W. Foulsam & Co. Ltd., Yeovil Rd., Slough SL1 4JH, England. FAX 0753-811409. adv.

031 917.97   US   ISSN 1044-9078
F886
WASHINGTON FACTS; a comprehensive look at Washington today, county by county. (Subseries of: Flying the Colors Series) 1989. irreg. $59.50. Clements Research (Subsidiary of: Political Research, Inc.), 16850 Dallas Pkwy., Dallas, TX 75248. TEL 214-931-8827. FAX 214-248-7159. Ed. John Clements.
   Description: Examination of the land, people, economy, government, history, community services and attractions of Washington State in a county-by-county format.

032   UK   ISSN 0083-9256
AY754
WHITAKER'S ALMANACK. 1869. a. £25. J. Whitaker & Sons Ltd., 12 Dyott St., London WC1A 1DF, England. TEL 071-836-8911. FAX 071-836-2909. (Dist. in U.S. by: Gale Research Co., Book Tower, Detroit, MI 48226) adv. **Document type:** academic/scholarly publication.

910   US   ISSN 0743-6122
TX907
WHO'S WHO IN AMERICA'S RESTAURANTS; encyclopedia of America's dining establishments. Variant title: Landwehr's Who's Who in America's Restaurants. 1982. a. $14.95. Who's Who in Restaurants, Inc., 345 W. 58th St., No. 8A, New York, NY 10019. FAX 212-489-1973. Ed. Sheldon Landwehr. circ. 50,000. **Document type:** directory.
   Incorporates: Who's Who in America's Caterers.
   Description: Lists and reviews American restaurants.

031 917.7   US   ISSN 1046-8331
WISCONSIN FACTS; a comprehensive look at Wisconsin today, county by county. (Subseries of: Flying the Colors Series) 1990. irreg. $59.50. Clements Research (Subsidiary of: Political Research, Inc.), 16850 Dallas Pkwy., Dallas, TX 75248. TEL 214-931-8827. FAX 214-248-7159. Ed. John Clements.
   Description: Examination of the land, people, economy, government, history, community services and attractions of Wisconsin in a county-by-county format.

031   US   ISSN 0084-1382
AY67.N5   CODEN: WABFDT
WORLD ALMANAC AND BOOK OF FACTS. 1868. a. $8.95 paperback; $24.95 hardcover. World Almanac Books (Subsidiary of: Funk & Wagnalls), 1 International Blvd., Mahwah, NJ 07495. TEL 201-529-6900. Ed. Robert Famighetti. charts; stat. circ. 2,000,000. (also avail. in microform from UMI,BHP) **Document type:** consumer publication, directory.
—BLDSC (9352.910000); UMI; CASDDS.
   Formerly: World Almanac and Encyclopedia.
   Description: Compiles the major events of the past year and provides demographic, geographic, socioeconomic, political, and historical information on each country and each state in the U.S. Lists major sports, science, and entertainment figures and contains the addresses of federal and state government agencies and the people who run them.

613.7 610   US   ISSN 0890-4480
RA431
WORLD BOOK HEALTH AND MEDICAL ANNUAL. 1987. a. price varies. World Book, Inc., 525 W. W. Monroe, Chicago, IL 60661. TEL 312-258-3874; 800-874-0520. FAX 312-258-3950. (Subscr. to: World Book Encyclopedia, Inc., Box 3073, Evanston, IL 60204) Ed.Darlene R. Stille. cum.index. **Document type:** consumer publication.

031   US   ISSN 0084-1439
AE5
WORLD BOOK YEAR BOOK. (Supplement to: World Book Encyclopedia) 1962. a. World Book, Inc., 525 W. Monroe, Chicago, IL 60661. TEL 312-258-3874; 800-874-0520. FAX 312-258-3950. (Subscr. to: World Book Encyclopedia, Inc., Box 3073, Evanston, IL 60204) Ed. Darlene R. Stille. cum.index.

039   CC   ISSN 1000-9647
ZHONGGUO NIANJIAN. English edition: People's Republic of China Year Book (ISSN 1000-9396) (Text in Chinese) a. Zhongguo Nianjian She - China Year Book Publishing House, 57 Xuanwumen Xidajie, Beijing 100803, People's Republic of China. TEL 3074562. FAX 307-4973. Ed. Song Jichao.

ENDOCRINOLOGY

see *Medical Sciences–Endocrinology*

ENERGY

see also *Energy–Electrical Energy; Energy–Geothermal Energy; Energy–Hydroelectrical Energy; Energy–Nuclear Energy; Energy–Solar Energy; Energy–Wind Energy*

A A P G EXPLORER. (American Association of Petroleum Geologists) see *PETROLEUM AND GAS*

A D A TODAY; a newsletter for liberal activists. (Americans for Democratic Action) see *POLITICAL SCIENCE*

A E C L REPORT SERIES. (Atomic Energy of Canada Ltd.) see *ENERGY — Nuclear Energy*

621.042   US
A E E ENERGY INSIGHT. 3/yr. Association of Energy Engineers, 4025 Pleasantdale Rd., No.420, Atlanta, GA 30340-4264. TEL 404-447-5083. Ed. Ruth Bennett. circ. 15,000.

333.79   US   ISSN 1046-0993
A E R O SUN TIMES.* 1973. q. $15. Alternative Energy Resource Organization, 25 S. Ewing St., Ste. 214, Helena, MT 59601-5732. TEL 406-443-7272. FAX 406-442-9120. Ed. Sally Hilander. adv.; bk.rev.; bibl.; charts; illus. circ. 700. (back issues avail.) **Indexed:** Energy Info.Abstr., New Per.Ind. **Document type:** newsletter.
   Description: Information on sustainable energy resources, agriculture and community-based economic development.

333.79   US
A G A FINANCIAL QUARTERLY REVIEW. 1950. q. $20 to non-members; members $16. American Gas Association, 1515 Wilson Blvd., Arlington, VA 22209. TEL 703-841-8400. FAX 703-841-8406. (Subscr. to: Dept. 0765, McLean, VA 22109-0765) Ed. Karen S. Ryan. circ. 3,100. (back issues avail.) **Indexed:** Energy Info.Abstr.

333.79   US   ISSN 1045-2311
A G A FORECASTING REVIEW. 1988. biennial. American Gas Association, 1515 Wilson Blvd., Arlington, VA 22109. TEL 703-841-8400. FAX 703-841-8406. (Subscr. to: Dept. 0765, McLean, VA 22109-0765) **Document type:** trade publication.

A I P E NEWSLINE. (American Institute of Plant Engineers) see *ENGINEERING*

A P P A: THE ASSOCIATION OF HIGHER EDUCATION FACILITIES OFFICERS. PROCEEDINGS OF THE ANNUAL MEETING. see *EDUCATION — School Organization And Administration*

333.79 327   CY
A P S NEWS SERVICE. 1972. w. $800 (includes subscr. to Strategic Balance in the Middle East, Fate of the Arab Peninsula, Operations in Oil Diplomacy, Re-Drawing the Islamic Map) (effective 1994). Arab Press Service, P.O. Box 3896, Nicosia, Cyprus. FAX 357-2-350265. s-a. index. **Document type:** bulletin.
   Description: Provides a condensation of exclusive information gathered by A.P.S. correspondents and contributors.

333.79   US   ISSN 0890-8265
ACCESS TO ENERGY; pro-science, pro-technology, pro-free enterprise monthly newsletter. 1973. m. $25 to individuals; corporations $50. Box 1250, Cave Junction, OR 97523. Ed. Arthur Robinson. bk.rev.; index, cum.index: 1973-1987. circ. 3,350. **Indexed:** Energy Info.Abstr. **Document type:** newsletter.

621.31   US   ISSN 0896-520X
ADVANCED FOSSIL ENERGY TECHNOLOGIES. s-m. $175 in U.S., Canada, Mexico; elsewhere $350. (Department of Energy) U.S. National Technical Information Service, 3285 Port Royal Rd., Springfield, VA 22161. TEL 703-487-4630. abstr. **Document type:** government publication, academic/scholarly publication.

ENERGY

ADVANCED OIL AND GAS RECOVERY TECHNOLOGIES. see *PETROLEUM AND GAS*

333.79   US   ISSN 0192-558X
HD9502.A1
ADVANCES IN THE ECONOMICS OF ENERGY AND RESOURCES. 1979. a. $63.50 to institutions. J A I Press Inc., 55 Old Post Rd., No. 2, Box 1678, Greenwich, CT 06836-1678. TEL 203-661-7602. Ed. John R. Moroney. stat. **Indexed:** AESIS. —BLDSC (0704.570000). **CCC.**

AFRIQUE INDUSTRIE. see *MINES AND MINING INDUSTRY*

AIR INFILTRATION REVIEW. see *HEATING, PLUMBING AND REFRIGERATION*

ALBERTA'S RESERVE OF GAS: COMPLETE LISTING. see *PETROLEUM AND GAS*

621.042   US
ALTERNATIVE ENERGY. 1979. m. $90 (outside U.S. $104). 205 S. Beverly Dr., Ste. 208, Beverly Hills, CA 90212-3873. TEL 310-273-3486. Ed. Irwin Stambler. **Document type:** newsletter.

333.79   US   ISSN 0273-8163
ALTERNATIVE ENERGY RETAILER. 1980. m. $32. Zackin Publications, Inc., Box 2180, Waterbury, CT 06722. TEL 203-755-0158. Ed. John Florian. adv. circ. 9,500. **Document type:** trade publication.
    Description: Aimed at retailers of wood, coal and gas burning appliances and hearth accessories across the United States.

621.47   US
ALTERNATIVE ENERGY SOURCEBOOK. a. $16 (foreign $25). Real Goods, 966-A Mazzoni St., Ukiah, CA 95482. TEL 800-762-7325. charts; illus. **Document type:** catalog.
    Description: Information resource for solar and other methods of generating electricity for household consumption. Includes coverage of products and technology available, electromagnetic radiation safety issues, electric vehicles, non-toxic and recycled products, air and water purification, lighting efficiency, and more.

621.042   UK   ISSN 0261-6033
ALTERNATIVE TIMES; rundown of alternative energy news and views--plus items on nuclear power. 1981. q. £3. R. Stevens, 35 Wedmore St., London N19 4RU, England.

621.31   US   ISSN 0097-2126
TJ5   CODEN: PAPWA2
AMERICAN POWER CONFERENCE. PROCEEDINGS. 1952. a. $160. American Power Conference, Illinois Institute of Technology, Chicago, IL 60616. TEL 312-567-3406. Ed. Patricia Dawkins. index, cum.index: 1938-1963, 1964-1988. circ. 3,400. **Indexed:** Chem.Abstr. **Document type:** proceedings. —BLDSC (6837.000000); Faxon; CASDDS. **CCC.**

622 350   FR   ISSN 1140-7123
ANNUAIRE DE L'ADMINISTRATION DES D.R.I.R.E. 1852. a. 335 F. Annales des Mines, 22, rue Monge, 75005 Paris, France. TEL 44-06-80-40. (Subscr. to: ESKA, 30 rue de Domremy, 75013 Paris, France) Ed. Francois Baratin. adv. circ. 3,000. (back issues avail.) **Document type:** directory.
    Former titles: Annuaire de l'Administration des Mines; Annuaire de l'Administration et du Corps des Mines (ISSN 0071-822X)
    Description: Directory of the public agencies dealing with energy, industry, research and environment.

ANNUAL BOOK OF A S T M STANDARDS. VOLUME 12.02. NUCLEAR ENERGY (2), SOLAR, AND GEOTHERMAL ENERGY. see *ENGINEERING — Engineering Mechanics And Materials*

333.79   US   ISSN 0740-4190
TJ163.25.U6
ANNUAL ENERGY OUTLOOK. (Supplements avail.: Annual Energy Outlook. Supplement (ISSN 0742-7328); Annual Energy Review and Outlook. Synopsis (ISSN 0740-4786)) a. (U.S. Office of Energy Markets and End Use) Government Printing Office, Superintendent of Documents, Washington, DC 20402. **Document type:** government publication.
    Supersedes in part (in 1982): U.S. Department of Energy. Energy Information Administration. Annual Report to Congress (ISSN 0161-5807)

333.79   US   ISSN 0742-7328
TJ163.25.U6
ANNUAL ENERGY OUTLOOK. SUPPLEMENT. (Supplement to: Annual Energy Outlook (ISSN 0742-7328)) a.? (U.S. Office of Energy Markets and End Use) Government Printing Office, Superintendent of Documents, Washington, DC 20402.

333.79   US   ISSN 0740-4786
ANNUAL ENERGY REVIEW AND OUTLOOK. SYNOPSIS. (Supplement to: Annual Energy Outlook (ISSN 0740-4190)) a.? (U.S. Office of Energy Markets and End Use) Government Printing Office, Superintendent of Documents, Washington, DC 20402.

531.6   US
ANNUAL OUTLOOK FOR U.S. COAL. a. U.S. Department of Energy, Energy Information Administration, National Energy Information Center, EI-231, Forrestal Bldg., Rm. 1F-048, 1000 Independence Ave., S.W., Washington, DC 20585. (Avail. from: Superintendent of Documents, U.S. Government Printing Office, Box 371954, Pittsburgh, PA 15250-7954. TEL 202-783-3238. FAX 202-512-2233) charts; stat. **Indexed:** Energy Info.Abstr. (until 1994). **Document type:** government publication.
    Description: Analyzes production, consumption, import, and export trends for all types of U.S. coal.

531.6   US
ANNUAL REVIEW OF ENERGY. a. U.S. Department of Energy, Energy Information Administration, National Energy Information Center, EI-231, Forrestal Bldg., Rm. 1F-048, 1000 Independence Ave., S.W., Washington, DC 20585. TEL 202-586-8800. (Subscr. to: Superintendent of Documents, U.S. Government Printing Office, Box 371954, Pittsburgh, PA 15250-7954. TEL 202-783-3238. FAX 202-512-2233) charts; stat. **Indexed:** Energy Info.Abstr. (until 1994). **Document type:** government publication.
    •Also available online.
    Description: Analyzes production, consumption, import, and export trends for all forms of U.S. energy.

333.79   US   ISSN 1056-3466
TJ163.2   CODEN: ANEEER
ANNUAL REVIEW OF ENERGY AND THE ENVIRONMENT. 1976. a. $71 (foreign $76) (effective Jan. 1994). Annual Reviews Inc., 4139 El Camino Way, Box 10139, Palo Alto, CA 94303-0139. TEL 415-493-4400; 800-523-8635. FAX 415-855-9815. Ed. Robert H. Socolow. adv. contact: Elizabeth Kao. bibl.; index, cum.index every 5 yrs. (also avail. in microfilm from UMI; back issues avail.; reprint service avail.) **Indexed:** AESIS, Chem.Abstr., Curr.Cont., Deep Sea Res.& Oceanogr.Abstr., Energy Info.Abstr., Energy Rev., GeoRef., Ind.Sci.Rev., INIS Atomind., Sci.Cit.Ind., So.Pac.Per.Ind. **Document type:** academic/scholarly publication.
—BLDSC (1522.475000); EI; Faxon; UnCover; UMI. **CCC.**
    Formerly (until vol.16, 1991): Annual Review of Energy (ISSN 0362-1626)
    Description: Original reviews of critical literature and current developments in energy.

333.79   CL   ISSN 0211-5786
ANUARIO DE ENERGIA. 1975. a. Instituto Nacional de Estadisticas, Av. Bulnes 418, Casilla 498, Correo 3 Santiago, Chile.

665.5   UK   ISSN 0306-2619
TJ1   CODEN: APENDX
APPLIED ENERGY. 1975. 12/yr. (in 3 vols., 4 nos./vol.). £616($950) (effective 1994). Elsevier Science Ltd., Oxford Fulfilment Centre, P.O. Box 800, Kidlington, Oxford OX5 1DX, England. TEL 44-865-843000. FAX 44-865-843010. (Subscr. in U.S. and Canada to: Elsevier Science, 660 White Plains Rd., Tarrytown, NY 10591-5153. TEL 914-524-9200. FAX 914-333-2444) Ed. S.D. Probert. adv.; bk.rev.; illus.; index. (also avail. in microform from UMI; back issues avail.) **Indexed:** AESIS, AIT Reports, Appl.Mech.Rev., Chem.Abstr., Curr.Cont., Energy Rev., Eng.Ind., Environ.Abstr., Environ.Per.Bibl. (1989-), Excerp.Med., Fuel & Energy Abstr., Gas Abstr., GeoRef., Ind.Sci.Rev., INIS Atomind., Int.Build.Serv.Abstr., Sci.Abstr., Sci.Cit.Ind. **Document type:** academic/scholarly publication.
—BLDSC (1572.300000); EI; UnCover; SWETS; CASDDS. **CCC.**
    Description: Covers energy conversion, conservation, and the optimal management and use of energy and power sources.
    Refereed Serial

ARIZONA GEOLOGY; investigation, service, information. see *EARTH SCIENCES — Geology*

621.042   II   ISSN 0379-573X
ASSET. (Text in English) 1987. 4/yr. Rs.200($80) Tata Energy Research Institute, 9 Jor Bagh, New Delhi 110 003, India. TEL 4625296. FAX 91-11-4621770. TELEX 31-61593 TERI IN. Ed. Nalini Rangnathan. abstr. circ. 1,800. **Document type:** academic/scholarly publication.
    Description: Provides scientists and engineers working in developing countries with articles, reports, and conference papers about solar, bioconversion, and wind energy technologies.

ATOMIC ENERGY CLEARINGHOUSE. see *ENERGY — Nuclear Energy*

ATOMIC ENERGY POCKETBOOK. see *ENERGY — Nuclear Energy*

333.79   IT   ISSN 0004-718X
ATOMO PETROLIO ELETTRICITA. bi-m. Piazza Borghese, 3, 00186 Rome, Italy. Ed. Giuseppe Guarino.

531.6   AT   ISSN 0815-6115
AUSTRALIA. BUREAU OF AGRICULTURAL AND RESOURCE ECONOMICS. PROJECTIONS OF ENERGY DEMAND AND SUPPLY, AUSTRALIA. a. Aus.$25. Australian Bureau of Agricultural and Resource Economics, G.P.O. Box 1563, Canberra, A.C.T. 2601, Australia. TEL 06-272-2211. FAX 06-272-2001. **Document type:** government publication.
    Description: Presents an outlook for Australian energy by discussing government policies, industry intentions, observed trends and assumptions about future economics.

AUSTRALIAN COAL REPORT. see *MINES AND MINING INDUSTRY*

AVIATION FACILITIES ENERGY ASSOCIATION. ANNUAL REPORT. see *AERONAUTICS AND SPACE FLIGHT*

AVIATION FACILITIES ENERGY ASSOCIATION. ENERGY CONSUMPTION ANALYSIS REPORT. see *AERONAUTICS AND SPACE FLIGHT*

333.79 574   UK
B A B A TRADE ASSOCIATION FOR THE BRITISH BIOMASS INDUSTRIES. THE DIGEST. 1980. 2-4/yr. free. B A B A, P.O. Box 7, Southend Reading RG7 6AZ, England. Ed. Y.R. Alston. adv.; bk.rev. circ. 300.

B H E L JOURNAL. (Bharat Heavy Electricals Ltd.) see *ENGINEERING — Electrical Engineering*

B N F L NEWS. see *ENERGY — Nuclear Energy*

333.79   US   ISSN 1055-6168
KF5701
B O C A NATIONAL ENERGY CONSERVATION CODE. 1987. triennial, plus a. supplements. Building Officials and Code Administrators International, 4051 W. Flossmoor Rd., Country Club Hills, IL 60477-5795.

ENERGY

621.042   GW   ISSN 0006-9612
TJ260.A1   CODEN: BRWKAY
B W K. (Brennstoff-Waerme-Kraft); Zeitschrift des Vereins Deutscher Ingenieure fuer Energietechnik und Energiewirtschaft. (Text in German; summaries in English) 1949. 10/yr. (plus special editions). DM.388($157.50) (Verein Deutscher Ingenieure - Society of German Engineers) V D I Verlag GmbH, Heinrichstr. 24, 40239 Duesseldorf, Germany. TEL 0211-6188-0. FAX 0211-6188-112. TELEX 85787743. (Subscr. to: Postfach 101054, 40001 Duesseldorf, Germany) Ed. W. Pohl. adv.; bk.rev.; abstr.; bibl.; charts; illus.; pat.; stat.; index. **Indexed:** API Abstr., C.I.S. Abstr., Chem.Abstr., Chem.Eng.Abstr., Curr.Cont., Energy Ind., Energy Info.Abstr., Excerp.Med., Fluidex, Foul.Prev.Res.Dig., Fuel & Energy Abstr., Ind.Sci.Rev., INIS Atomind., ISMEC, Met.Abstr., Petrol.Abstr., Risk Abstr., Sci.Abstr., Sci.Cit.Ind., T.C.E.A., World Alum.Abstr. **Document type:** trade publication.
—BLDSC (2279.000000); EI; SWETS; CASDDS. **CCC**.

333.79   BL   ISSN 0101-6636
TJ163.25.B6
BALANCO ENERGETICO NACIONAL. 1976. a. free. Ministerio de Minas e Energia, Secretaria Executiva - Divisao de Informacoes Energeticas, Esplanada dos Ministerios, Bloco U, 5o andar, 70065-900 Brasilia DF, Brazil. TEL 061-2253417. FAX 061-2248857. TELEX 061-1453. circ. 3,000. (also avail. in diskette format) **Document type:** government publication.
Description: Contains data on energy industry fields, energy sources and sectors of energy use.

BALLAST (ATLANTA). see AERONAUTICS AND SPACE FLIGHT

BERGBAU; Zeitschrift fuer Bergbau und Energiewirtschaft. see MINES AND MINING INDUSTRY

333.79   GW
BETRIEB UND BELEGSCHAFT. 1969. a. Ueberlandwerk Nord-Hannover AG, Stresemannstr. 48, 28207 Bremen, Germany. TEL 0421-4493462. FAX 0421-4493908. illus.

333.79   GW   ISSN 0931-9344
BETRIEB UND ENERGIE. q. Resch Media Mail Verlag GmbH, Geigerstr. 13, 82166 Graefelfing, Germany. TEL 089-8580746. FAX 089-85807-62. Ed. Jan Muehlstein. adv.; bk.rev. circ. 46,000. (back issues avail.) **Document type:** academic/scholarly publication.

333.79 338.2   UK   ISSN 0264-4126
BIBLIOGRAPHY OF ECONOMIC GEOLOGY. 1968. bi-m. £85($170) Geosystems, P.O. Box 40, Didcot, Oxon. OX11 9BX, England. TEL 44-235-813913. Ed. Rosalind Templeman. adv.; bk.rev.; index. **Document type:** bibliography.
●Also available online. Vendor(s): DIALOG Information Services, Inc.
Also available on CD-ROM. Producer(s): NISC (GeoArchive).
Formerly (until 1982): Geocom Bulletin (ISSN 0016-7053)

621.042   UK   ISSN 0961-9534
TP360   CODEN: BMSBEO
BIOMASS & BIOENERGY. 1991. 12/yr. £340($525) (effective 1994). Elsevier Science Ltd., Pergamon, P.O. Box 800, Kidlington, Oxford OX5 1DX, England. TEL 44-865-843000. FAX 44-865-843010. (Subscr. in U.S. and Canada to: Elsevier Science, 660 White Plains Rd., Tarrytown, NY 10591-5153. TEL 914-524-9200. FAX 914-333-2444) index. (also avail. in microfilm from UMI; back issues avail.) **Indexed:** Energy Info.Abstr., Environ.Per.Bibl. (1992-). **Document type:** academic/scholarly publication.
—BLDSC (2087.706500); UMI; CASDDS. **CCC**.
Description: Presents research papers, shorter technical articles, notes, communications, technical reports, and reviews on all aspects of biomass and bioenergy research, including biological residues and bioenergy process and use.
Refereed Serial

621.042   UK   ISSN 0262-7183
BIOMASS BULLETIN. 1982. 4/yr. £114 (foreign £126). Multi-Science Publishing Co. Ltd., 107 High St., Brentwood, Essex CM14 4RX, England. TEL 0277-224632. FAX 0277-224632. (U.S. subscr. to: Box 176, Avenel, NJ 07001) Ed. W.O. Hughes. index. (also avail. in microform) **Indexed:** Curr.Biotech.Abstr., Environ.Abstr. **Document type:** abstracting/indexing.
—BLDSC (2087.707000). **CCC**.
Description: Contains news items, article summaries, and abstracts of conference proceedings, on both the fuel potential and recycling aspects of biomass.

BIORESOURCE TECHNOLOGY. see BIOLOGY — Biotechnology

333.8   GW
KK3
BONNER UMWELT UND ENERGIE REPORT; das unabhaengige kritische Umwelt- und Energiemagazin. 1979. s-m. DM.150. Bonner Energie-Report Verlags GmbH, Hans-Boeckler-Str. 19, 53225 Bonn, Germany. TEL 0228-470036. FAX 0228-469001. Ed. Dieter Kassing. adv.; index. circ. 15,000. (back issues avail.) **Indexed:** INIS Atomind.
Formerly: Bonner Energie-Report (ISSN 0340-3718)

333.79   CN
BRITISH COLUMBIA. UTILITIES COMMISSION. ANNUAL REPORT. 1973. a. free. Utilities Commission, Box 250, 900 Howe St., 6th Fl., Vancouver, BC V6Z 2N3, Canada. TEL 604-660-4700. stat. circ. 2,000. **Document type:** government publication.
Formerly (until 1980): British Columbia. Energy Commission. Annual Report (ISSN 0703-086X); **Supersedes:** British Columbia Energy Board. Annual Report (ISSN 0524-5672)

333.79   CN   ISSN 0832-820X
BRITISH COLUMBIA ENERGY SUPPLY AND REQUIREMENTS FORECAST UPDATE. 1986. a. Can.$5.90. Ministry of Energy, Mines and Petroleum Resources, Energy Resources Division, 7th Fl., 1810 Blanshard St., Victoria, BC V8V 1X4, Canada. (Subscr. to: Crown Publications, 546 Yates St., Victoria, BC V8W 1K8, Canada. TEL 604-386-4636) **Document type:** government publication.
Formed by the merger of: British Columbia Energy Supply and Requirements Forecast Summary Report (ISSN 0827-0333) & British Columbia Energy Supply and Requirements Forecast Technical Report (ISSN 0827-0325)

BRITISH GAS. MONITOR. see PETROLEUM AND GAS

BUILDINGS ENERGY TECHNOLOGY; a current awareness bulletin. see BUILDING AND CONSTRUCTION

333.79   US
CALIFORNIA. ENERGY COMMISSION. BIENNIAL FUELS REPORT. 1986. biennial. Energy Commission, 1516 Ninth St., Sacramento, CA 95814. TEL 916-324-3009. **Document type:** government publication.

333.79   US
CALIFORNIA. ENERGY COMMISSION. BIENNIAL REPORT. 1977. biennial. free. Energy Commission, 1516 Ninth St., Sacramento, CA 95814. TEL 916-324-3009. **Document type:** government publication.

531.6   US   ISSN 1044-2022
CALIFORNIA ENERGY MARKETS. Key Title: Clearing Up: California Energy Markets. 1989. w. $989. NewsData Corporation, Box C-900928, Seattle, WA 98109-9228. TEL 206-285-4848. FAX 206-281-8035. Ed. Arthur O'Donnell. **Document type:** newsletter.
Description: Covers energy policy and resource development, public utility and energy litigation, and utility capital financing in California, Nevada, Arizona and New Mexico.

333.79   CN   ISSN 0068-7901
HD9502.C3
CANADA. NATIONAL ENERGY BOARD. ANNUAL REPORT. a. National Energy Board, 311-6th Ave. S.W., Calgary, AB T2P 3H2, Canada. TEL 403-292-4800. FAX 403-292-5503. **Document type:** government publication.

333.79   CN
CANADA. NATIONAL ENERGY BOARD. REASONS FOR DECISION. irreg. National Energy Board, 311-6th Ave. S.W., Calgary, AB T2P 3H2, Canada. TEL 403-292-4800. FAX 403-292-5503. **Document type:** government publication.

333.79   CN   ISSN 0319-3403
CANADIAN ENERGY NEWS. 1972. 24/yr. Can.$335. Intratech (Subsidiary of: E L LittleJohn and Associates), Minto Place Postal Outlet, Box 56067, Ottawa, ON K1R 7Z1, Canada. TEL 613-235-9183. FAX 613-594-3857. Ed. E.L. LittleJohn. circ. 150. **Indexed:** INIS Atomind. **Document type:** newsletter.
Description: Covers energy developments in Canada and elsewhere.

CANADIAN GAS FACTS. see PETROLEUM AND GAS

333.79   CN
CANADIAN NATIONAL ENERGY FORUM PROCEEDINGS. 1974. irreg. price varies. Energy Council of Canada, 30 Colonnade Rd., Ste. 400, Nepean, ON K2E 7J6, Canada. TEL 613-952-6469. FAX 613-952-6470. **Document type:** proceedings.

333.79   TR   ISSN 0253-0538
HD9502.C37
CARIB-LATIN ENERGY CONSULTANT. Short title: C L E C. 1977. bi-m. $195. Carib-Latin Energy Consultants Ltd., P.O. Box 3074, St. James P.O., Trinidad & Tobago, W.I. TEL 809-637-9038. FAX 809-637-9038. Ed. Rodney C.L. Appleton. adv.; charts; stat. circ. 12,500. (also avail. in microfilm) **Indexed:** Petrol.Abstr.
Description: Provides current technical, economic and political analyses of the oil, gas, petrochemical and other energy forms in all Latin American and Caribbean countries; includes the banking, financial, debt-related aspects of energy developments.

CATALYST FOR ENVIRONMENT - ENERGY. see ENVIRONMENTAL STUDIES

CHOCS. see ENERGY — Nuclear Energy

531.6 340   US   ISSN 0738-2332
HD2763.A2C552
CLEARING UP: NORTHWEST ENERGY MARKETS. 1982. w. NewsData Corporation, Box C-900928, Seattle, WA 98109-9228. TEL 206-285-4848. FAX 206-281-8035. Ed. Pamela Russell. (back issues avail.) **Document type:** newsletter.
Description: Covers public utility and energy litigation, energy policy, resource development and utility capital financing in the Pacific Northwestern U.S. and Western Canada.

CLINCH RIVER BREEDER REACTOR PLANT. TECHNICAL REVIEW. see ENERGY — Nuclear Energy

621.042 011   UK   ISSN 0309-4979
TP325
COAL ABSTRACTS. 1977. m. £510($765) to non-members; members £170 ($255). I.E.A. Coal Research, Gemini House, 10-18 Putney Hill, London SW15 6AA, England. TEL 081-780-2111. FAX 081-780-1746. index. circ. 750. (also avail. in microfiche) **Indexed:** AESIS. **Document type:** abstracting/indexing.
●Also available online. Vendor(s): BELINDIS, CISTI, FIZ Technik (COAL), NKA, JICST, QL Systems Ltd., STN International.
Also available on CD-ROM.
—BLDSC (3287.970000).
Description: Provides details of the most recent and relevant items from the world's literature on coal.

665.5   US   ISSN 0883-9735
COAL & SYNFUELS TECHNOLOGY. 1979. w. $790 (foreign $820). Pasha Publications Inc., 1616 N. Ft. Myer Dr., Ste. 1000, Arlington, VA 22209-3107. TEL 703-528-1244. FAX 703-528-1253. Ed. Elizabeth Hinkle. **Indexed:** Br.Ceram.Abstr., Energy Rev. **Document type:** newsletter.
●Also available online. Vendor(s): Data-Star, DIALOG Information Services, Inc., NewsNet (EY49).
—**CCC**.
Formerly: Synfuels Week (ISSN 0196-6693); **Incorporates (1975-1984):** Energy Research Digest (ISSN 0270-823X)
Description: Reports on coal technology project financing, environmental issues, oil shale, coal liquefaction and gasification, and synfuels projects.

ENERGY

333.8   US
COAL-ENERGY NEWS. 1974. m. 56630 Overlook Ct., Bellaire, OH 43906. TEL 614-676-4424. adv. circ. 13,104.
Formerly (until Sep. 1979): Coal Monthly and Energy News.

COAL OUTLOOK. see *MINES AND MINING INDUSTRY*

621.042   UK
COAL RESEARCH PROJECTS. 1981. a. price varies. I.E.A. Coal Research, Gemini House, 10-18 Putney Hill, London SW1S 6AA, England. TEL 081-780-2111. FAX 081-780-1746. (also avail. in microfiche) **Document type:** academic/scholarly publication.
●Also available online. Vendor(s): FIZ Technik (COALRIP), STN International.
Also available on CD-ROM.
Formerly: Coal Research Projects. Coal Research Database.

COAL SCIENCE AND TECHNOLOGY. see *MINES AND MINING INDUSTRY*

665   US
COAL TECH INTERNATIONAL. 1979. w. $840 (foreign $875). McGraw-Hill, Inc., Energy & Business Newsletters, 1221 Ave. of the Americas, 36th Fl., New York, NY 10020. Ed. John Higgins. charts; stat. (looseleaf format; reprint service avail. from UMI)
●Also available online. Vendor(s): DIALOG Information Services, Inc. (File no.624/McGRAW-HILL PUBLICATIONS ONLINE), Dow Jones News Retrieval (CSL), Mead Data Central, Inc. (SYNFLS), NewsNet (EY76).
Former titles: Clean Coal - Synfuels Letter; Synfuels.

COAL TRANSPORTATION REPORT. see *TRANSPORTATION — Railroads*

333.79   UK   ISSN 0965-9579
COAL U.K.. m. £398($664) (foreign £415) (effective 1993). Financial Times Business Information Ltd., 126 Jermyn St., London SW1Y 4UJ, England. TEL 071-411-4414. FAX 071-411-4415. charts; stat. **Document type:** newsletter.
Description: Covers the U.K. import market for coal

333.79   US
COAL UNIT PERFORMANCE DATA BASE. a. $495. Utility Data Institute (Subsidiary of: McGraw-Hill), 1200 G St., N.W., Ste. 250, Washington, DC 20005. TEL 202-942-8788; 800-486-3660. FAX 202-942-8789. (diskette format) **Document type:** trade publication.
Description: Provides technical information on more than 850 coal-fired generating units in the US.

COALDAT MONTHLY (PRODUCING DISTRICT FORMAT). see *BUSINESS AND ECONOMICS — Marketing And Purchasing*

COALDAT MONTHLY (SUPPLIERS FORMAT). see *BUSINESS AND ECONOMICS — Marketing And Purchasing*

COALDAT MONTHLY (UTILITY FORMAT). see *BUSINESS AND ECONOMICS — Marketing And Purchasing*

COALDAT QUARTERLY. see *BUSINESS AND ECONOMICS — Marketing And Purchasing*

621.042 333.8   US
COGENERATION; the magazine for cogeneration management. 1984. bi-m. $48. Pequot Publishing, Inc., Box 447, Southport, CT 06490. TEL 203-259-1812. Ed. Lee Harrison. adv.; illus. circ. 12,000. **Indexed:** INIS Atomind. **Document type:** trade publication.

621.042 333.8   US
COGENERATION AND COMPETITIVE POWER JOURNAL. 1985. q. $99 in US and Canada; elsewhere $125 (effective 1992). (Association of Energy Engineers, Cogeneration Institute) Fairmont Press, Inc., 700 Indian Trail, Lilburn, GA 30247. TEL 404-925-9388. FAX 404-381-9865. Ed. F. William Payne. adv. circ. 2,074. (back issues avail.) **Indexed:** Energy Info.Abstr., Energy Rev. —Faxon.
Formerly (until 1993): Cogeneration Journal (ISSN 0883-5985)

665.5   FR   ISSN 0180-6734
COMBUSTIBLES ET CARBURANTS.* 11/yr. 220 F.($55) Federation Nationale des Syndicats de Negociants en Combustibles et Carburants de France, 114 av. de Wagram, 75017 Paris, France. TEL 47-63-46-50. FAX 42-27-14-01. TELEX 649 487. Ed. Andre Amalbert. adv.; stat. circ. 5,500. (tabloid format)
Formed by the 1977 merger of: Commerce des Combustibles. Journal des Charbonnages (ISSN 0180-7854); Commerce des Combustibles. Revue des Combustibles Solides Liquides et Gazeux (ISSN 0010-2806)

COMMONWEALTH SCIENTIFIC AND INDUSTRIAL RESEARCH ORGANIZATION. DIVISION OF COAL AND ENERGY TECHNOLOGY. ANNUAL REPORT. see *ENVIRONMENTAL STUDIES*

COMMUNICATOR (SCOTTSDALE). see *ADVERTISING AND PUBLIC RELATIONS*

621.042 333.791   US
CONSERVATION AND RENEWABLE ENERGY TECHNOLOGIES FOR UTILITY TECHNOLOGIES. a. free to qualified personnel. (U.S. Department of Energy, Conservation and Renewable Energy Office) Solar Energy Research Institute, Technical Inquiry Service, 1617 Cole Blvd., Golden, CO 80401-3393. TEL 303-231-1000. circ. controlled. **Document type:** government publication.
Supersedes in part (in 1991): Energy Storage and Distribution Program Summary; Incorporates (in 1991): Geothermal Energy Program Summary & Ocean Energy Program Summary & Photovoltaic Energy Progam Summary; Wind Energy Program Summary; Solar Thermal Energy Program Summary; Which supersedes: Solar Thermal Technology Annual Evaluation Report.

COUNCIL FOR A LIVABLE WORLD. NEWSLETTER. see *MILITARY*

531.64   US
CRITICAL MASS. 1985. q. $40. Public Citizen's Critical Mass Energy Project, 215 Pennsylvania Ave., S.E., Washington, DC 20003. TEL 202-546-4996. FAX 202-547-7392. (Subscr. to: Public Citizen Publications Department, 2000 P St., N.W., Washington, DC 20036. TEL 202-833-3000) Ed. Sam Totten. **Document type:** newsletter.
Formerly: Connections (Washington); Supersedes: Critical Mass Bulletin; Which superseded (1975-1983): Critical Mass Energy Journal (ISSN 0194-4185); Which was formerly: Critical Mass Journal.

621.31   US   ISSN 1053-122X
TK2960   CODEN: CTPHEJ
CURRENT TOPICS IN PHOTOVOLTAICS. 1985. a. Academic Press, Inc., 525 B St., Ste. 1900, San Diego, CA 92101-4495. TEL 619-231-0926. FAX 619-699-6715. Eds. T.J. Coutts, J.D. Meakin. —BLDSC (3504.898100); CASDDS.

333.79 614.7   US   ISSN 0739-7828
CURRENTS (DES MOINES); news and views on Iowa's energy and environment. 1974. q. $15. Energy and Self-Reliance Center, 3500 Kingman Blvd., Des Moines, IA 50311. TEL 515-277-0253. Ed. Linda Nicholson. adv.; bk.rev.; illus.; tr.lit. circ. 3,500. (tabloid format; back issues avail.)

CUSTOM BUILDER; the business magazine for builders of premier homes. see *BUILDING AND CONSTRUCTION*

333.79   US   ISSN 1057-5782
D O E THIS MONTH. 1977. s-m. $21 (foreign $26.25). U.S. Department of Energy, 1000 Independence Ave., S.W., PA-5, Washington, DC 20585. TEL 202-586-2050. FAX 5202-586-7303. (Subscr. to: Superintendent of Documents, U.S. Government Printing Office, Box 371954, Pittsburgh, PA 15250-7954. TEL 202-783-3238. FAX 202-512-2233) Ed. Martin Moon. circ. 29,500. (back issues avail.) **Indexed:** Energy Info.Abstr. (until 1994), Ind.U.S.Gov.Per. **Document type:** government publication.
Formerly (until 1984): Energy Insider (ISSN 0886-3539)

333.79   US
D R I - McGRAW-HILL ENERGY REVIEW. s-a. D R I - McGraw-Hill, 24 Hartwell Ave., Lexington, MA 02173. TEL 617-863-5100. FAX 617-860-6332. TELEX 200 284.

333.79   US
D R I - McGRAW-HILL ENERGY REVIEW: CANADIAN INDUSTRY FOCUS. s-a. D R I - McGraw-Hill, 24 Hartwell Ave., Lexington, MA 02173. TEL 617-863-5100. FAX 617-860-6332. TELEX 200 284.

D R I - McGRAW-HILL ENERGY REVIEW: COAL INDUSTRY FOCUS. see *PETROLEUM AND GAS*

D R I - McGRAW-HILL ENERGY REVIEW: NATURAL GAS REVIEW. see *PETROLEUM AND GAS*

333.8   US
DAKOTA COUNSEL. 1978. 6/yr. $20. Dakota Resource Council, Box 1095, Dickinson, ND 58602-1095. TEL 701-227-1851. Ed. Aleta Hendricks. bk.rev. circ. 600. (back issues avail.) **Document type:** newsletter.

621.3 330   DK   ISSN 0108-8068
DANSK ENERGI TIDSSKRIFT; energibladet for erhverv og industri. 1983. 10/yr. DKK 490. Forlaget Beilin og Johansen ApS, 1, Rosenborggade, 1130 Copenhagen K, Denmark. TEL 33 15 22 77. FAX 33-15-93-43. Ed. Stig Juul Hesselaa. illus. circ. 4,725.
Description: Focuses on Danish trade and industry.

DENGEN KAIHATSU K.K. CHOSA SHIRYO/ELECTRIC POWER DEVELOPMENT CO., LTD. STUDY REPORT. see *ENGINEERING — Electrical Engineering*

621.3   DK   ISSN 0108-4011
DENMARK. ENERGIMINISTERIET. ENERGIFORSKNINGSPROGRAM; program for udbygning af Dansk energiforskning og udvikling. 1980. a. free. Energistyrelsen - Danish Energy Agency, Landemoerket 11, DK-1119 Copenhagen K, Denmark. circ. 2,000.

333.79 621.042   DK   ISSN 0905-6416
     CODEN: ENNYE6
DENMARK. ENERGISTYRELSEN. ENERGINYT. 1983. q. free. Energistyrelsen - Danish Energy Agency, Landemoerket 11, DK-1119 Copenhagen K, Denmark. illus.
Formed by the 1990 merger of: Denmark. Energistyrelsen. Nyt fra Energistyrelsen (ISSN 0108-7495) & Denmark. Energistyrelsen. Nyt fra Energiforskningen (ISSN 0901-8506) & Denmark. Energistyrelsen. Nyt om Energi-Eksport (ISSN 0904-0986)

DENMARK. FORSKNINGSCENTER RISOE. RISOE-R. see *ENERGY — Nuclear Energy*

333.79   US
DETROIT EDISON TODAY. 1973. bi-w. free. Detroit Edison Company, 2000 Second Ave., Detroit, MI 48226. TEL 313-237-9210. FAX 313-596-6622. Ed. Daniel J. Vecchioni. circ. 15,500. (tabloid format) **Document type:** newsletter.
Description: Keeps the Detroit Edison community informed about the company's goals and accomplishments, problems, issues and concerns.

333.79   SW   ISSN 0281-2517
DIALOGEN; forum foer information, rapporter, debatt inom S A F E. 1978. s-a. SEK 30 membership (effective 1990). Socialdemokratiska Arbetsgruppen foer en Alternativ Energipolitik (SAFE), Sekretariatet, Vaestanbogatan 1 B, S-571 33 Naessjoe, Sweden. TEL 0380-114-42. **Document type:** newsletter.

531.64   IT
DIMENSIONE ENERGIA. (Text in Italian; summaries in English) 1983. bi-m. L.40000. E.N.E.L.-E.N.T.E. Nazionale per L'Energia Elettrica, Via G.B. Martini, 3, 00198 Rome, Italy. TEL 06-850 92465. adv. circ. 5,000. (back issues avail.)

DIRECTORY OF CERTIFIED APPLIANCES AND ACCESSORIES. see *PETROLEUM AND GAS*

DIRECTORY OF NATURAL GAS COMPANY OPERATIONS. see *PETROLEUM AND GAS*

333.79   IT
DIRIGENTE E.N.E.L. 1980. bi-m. Ente Nazionale per l'Energia Elettrica (ENEL), Via G.B. Martini, 3, 00198 Rome, Italy. Ed. Ermete Giorgio Tamberlani. adv.; bk.rev. circ. 2,800. (back issues avail.)

ENERGY

333.79 CY
DOWNSTREAM TRENDS. 1972. w. $600 (includes subscr. to Oil Market Trends and Gas Market Trends) (effective 1994). Arab Press Service, Box 3896, Nicosia, Cyprus. FAX 357-2-350265. s-a. index. **Document type:** newsletter.
Description: Focuses on oil refineries, petrochemical industries, and other downstream investments in Cyprus and abroad.

DRILLING - THE WELLSITE MAGAZINE. see *PETROLEUM AND GAS*

333.79 UK ISSN 0957-3666
E C ENERGY MONTHLY. (European Community) m. £354($606) (overseas £379) (effective 1993). Financial Times Business Information Ltd., 126 Jermyn St., London SW1Y 4UJ, England. TEL 071-411-4414. FAX 071-411-4415.
●Also available online. Vendor(s): Data-Star, Mead Data Central, Inc.
—BLDSC (3647.255100).
Description: Reports on energy-related developments within the European Community.

E C O L NEWS. (Environmental Conservation Library) see *ENVIRONMENTAL STUDIES*

333.79 US
E I A PUBLICATIONS DIRECTORY: A USER'S GUIDE. a. free. U.S. Department of Energy, Energy Information Administration, National Energy Information Center, EI-231, Rm. 1F-048, Forrestal Bldg., 1000 Independence Ave., S.W., Washington, DC 20585. TEL 202-586-8800. **Document type:** directory, government publication.

E L F AQUITAINE; bulletin mensuel d'informations. see *PETROLEUM AND GAS*

E L F - AQUITAINE NEWS. see *PETROLEUM AND GAS*

333.79 US
E M F KEEPTRACK. (Electromagnetic Fields) s-m. $400. (Central Maine Power Company, Center for Energy Information) Utility Data Institute (Subsidiary of: McGraw-Hill), 1200 G St., N.W., Ste. 250, Washington, DC 20005. TEL 202-942-8788; 800-486-3660. FAX 202-942-8789. **Document type:** newsletter.
Description: Focuses on current research on the effects of electromagnetic fields.

E M F LITIGATION NEWS. see *LAW*

531.6 628.4 US
E M PROGRESS. q. free. U.S. Department of Energy, Office of Environmental Restoration and Waste Management, EM-14, Washington, DC 20585. Ed. Beverly C. Heffernan. **Document type:** government publication.

621.042 IT ISSN 0393-716X
QC770
E N E A NOTIZIARIO - ENERGIA E INNOVAZIONE; mensile di informazione sulle nuove tecnologie, l'energia, e l'ambiente. 1955. m. (foreign L.70000). Ente per le Nuove Tecnologie, l'Energie e l'Ambiente, Viale Regina Margherita 125, 00198 Rome, Italy. TEL 06-85282401. FAX 06-85285875. TELEX 610183 ENEA I. (And: Via Martiri di Monte Sole 4, 40136 Bologna, Italy. TEL 051-498111) Eds. Ferrante Pierantoni, Angiolo Ceroni. adv.; bk.rev. circ. 10,000. **Indexed:** C.I.S. Abstr., Chem.Abstr., ELLIS, GeoRef., INIS Atomind.
Former titles: Energia e Innovazione; E N E A Notiziario; C N E N Notiziario (ISSN 0007-8751)
Refereed Serial

333.79 665.5 IT
E N I ANNUAL REPORT. a. Ente Nazionale Idrocarburi, Piazzale Enrico Mattei 1, 00144 Rome, Italy. illus.

333.79 UN
E S C A P ENERGY NEWS. (Text and summaries in English) 1983. s-a. free. United Nations Economic and Social Commission for Asia and the Pacific, Environment & Natural Resources Management Division, United Nations Bldg., Rajadamnern Ave., Bangkok 10200, Thailand. TEL 282-9161-200. FAX 282-9602. TELEX 82392 ESCAP TH. Ed. Steven J. Torok. bk.rev. circ. 1,000. **Document type:** newsletter.

333.79 US
EARTHMIND NEWSLETTER. 1975. a. $2. Earthmind, Box 743, Mariposa, CA 95338-0743. Ed. Michael Hackleman. bk.rev. circ. 500. **Document type:** newsletter.
Description: Works with natural energy sources, organic gardening, and other aspects of a more self-reliant living.

333.79 UK ISSN 0965-3503
EAST EUROPEAN ENERGY REPORT. 1991. m. £364($624) (foreign £390) (effective 1993). Financial Times Business Information Ltd., 126 Jermyn St., London SW1Y 4UJ, England. TEL 071-411-4414. FAX 071-411-4415. **Document type:** newsletter.
—SWETS.
Description: Covers developments in the East European energy markets.

ECOALERT. see *ENVIRONMENTAL STUDIES*

333.79 IT
ECONOMIA DELLE FONTI DI ENERGIA. 1957. 3/yr. L.75000 (foreign L.95000) (effective 1993). (Universita Commerciale Luigi Bocconi, Istituto di Economia delle Fonti di Energia) Franco Angeli Editore, Viale Monza 106, 20127 Milan, Italy. TEL 02-28-27-651. Ed. S. Vacca. adv.; charts; stat. **Indexed:** ELLIS.

331 333.8 EC
ECUADOR. MINISTERIO DE ENERGIA Y MINAS. INFORME DE LABORES. 1960. a. free. Ministerio de Energia y Minas, Oficio 504, Director de Planificacion, Quito, Ecuador. FAX 580724. TELEX 2271 MINREC ED. illus.; stat. circ. 200. **Document type:** government publication.
Formerly: Ecuador. Ministerio de Recursos Naturales y Energeticos. Informe de Labores.

THE EFFICIENT HOUSE SOURCEBOOK; an annotated bibliography and directory of helpful organizations. see *BUILDING AND CONSTRUCTION*

621.3 RU ISSN 0207-5032
EKSPRESS-INFORMATSIYA. PRYAMOE PREOBRAZOVANIE TEPLOVOI I KHIMICHESKOI ENERGII V ELEKTRICHESKUYU. 1975. w. 38 Rub. Vsesoyuznyi Institut Nauchno-Tekhnicheskoi Informatsii (VINITI), Baltiiskaya ul. 14, Moscow A-219, Russia. (Subscr. to: Mezhdunarodnaya Kniga, Dimitrova ul. 39, 113095 Moscow, Russia)

ELECTRIC UTILITY POWER PLANT CONSTRUCTION COST. see *ENGINEERING — Electrical Engineering*

EMOTION; Wilhelm-Reich-Zeitschrift ueber Triebenergie, Charakterstruktur, Krankheit, Natur und Gesellschaft. see *PSYCHOLOGY*

333.79 US
ENERCOM. 1983. q. free. Energy Office, Office of Communications, 2 Rockefeller Plaza, Albany, NY 12223. Ed. Gary Sheffer. circ. 5,500. **Indexed:** Energy Info.Abstr. **Document type:** government publication.

621.31 333.79 RM ISSN 1220-5133
CODEN: EGTAAD
ENERGETICA. SERIES A. (Text mainly in Rumanian; occasionally in English, French or German; summaries in English, French, German and Russian) 1953. m. 9600 lei to individuals; institutions 19200 lei; foreign $100. Icemenerg, Bd. Energeticienilor Nr. 8, Sector 3, 79619 Bucharest, Rumania. TEL 401-3220692. FAX 410-3129315. TELEX 10783 ICCER. Ed. Eugeniu Pavel. adv.; bk.rev. circ. 2,500. (back issues avail.) **Indexed:** Chem.Abstr., Sci.Abstr. **Document type:** proceedings.
Supersedes in part (in 1990): Energetica (ISSN 0423-1082); Which superseded in part (in 1956): Energetica si Hidrotehnica (ISSN 0367-0414); Which was formed by the 1954 merger of: Energetica (ISSN 1220-5125); And: Hidrotehnica (ISSN 1220-0794).
Description: Covers technical, scientific and related economical and ecological problems stemming from the utilization of all forms of energy.

621.31 333.79 RM ISSN 1220-5141
CODEN: EGTAAD
ENERGETICA. SERIES B. (Text mainly in Rumanian; occasionally in English, French or German; summaries in English, French, German and Russian) 1953. m. 9600 lei to individuals; institutions 19200 lei; foreign $100. Icemenerg, Bd. Energeticienilor Nr. 8, Sec. 3, 79619 Bucharest, Rumania. TEL 401-3220692. FAX 410-3129315. TELEX 10783 ICCER. Ed. Eugeniu Pavel. adv.; bk.rev. circ. 2,500. (back issues avail.) **Indexed:** Chem.Abstr., Sci.Abstr. **Document type:** proceedings.
Supersedes in part (in 1990): Energetica (ISSN 0423-1082); Which superseded in part (in 1956): Energetica si Hidrotehnica (ISSN 0367-0414); Which was formed by the 1954 merger of: Energetica (ISSN 1220-5125); And: Hidrotehnica (ISSN 1220-0794).

333.79 CI ISSN 0350-3771
ENERGETICAR. 1960. q. 5000 din. Savez Energeticara SR Hrvatske, Ilica 34-1, Zagreb, Croatia. Ed. Z. Prelec. adv.; bk.rev.; charts; illus. circ. 2,500.

333.79 MX
ENERGETICOS.* 1977. m. (Direccion General de Informacion, Secretaria de Patrimonio y Fomento Industrial) Secretariat for Energy, Mines and Federal Industry, Insurgentes Sur 552, 30, 06769 Mexico D.F., Mexico.

621.3 RU ISSN 0013-7278
TK4 CODEN: EGTKA9
ENERGETIK. 1953. m. 28.80 Rub. Izdatel'stvo Energiya, Slyuzovaya Nab., 10, Moscow Z-114, Russia. (Subscr. to: Mezhdunarodnaya Kniga, Moscow G-200, Russia) Ed. L.A. Gvozdetzki. bk.rev.; charts; illus. circ. 53,063. **Indexed:** C.I.S. Abstr., Chem.Abstr., INIS Atomind., Sci.Abstr., W.R.C.Inf.
—CASDDS.

621.3 PL ISSN 0013-7294
CODEN: EGYAA4
ENERGETYKA. (Text in Polish; summaries in English and Russian) 1947. m. $61. (Stowarzyszenie Elektrykow Polskich) Wydawnictwo Czasopism i Ksiazek Technicznych SIGMA - NOT, Ul. Ratuszowa 11, P.O. Box 1004, 00-950 Warsaw, Poland. TEL 48-22-180918. FAX 48-22-192187. TELEX 814550 SIGMA PL (Dist. by: SIGMA NOT Ltd., Ul. Bartycka 20, 00-716, Warsaw, Poland) Ed. Br. Lis. bibl.; charts; illus.; index. circ. 3,500. **Indexed:** Ceram.Abstr., Chem.Abstr., Fuel & Energy Abstr., INIS Atomind., Sci.Abstr.
—BLDSC (3744.350000); CASDDS.

333.79 FR ISSN 0222-6650
ENERG'HIC. m. 895 F. 44 rue de l'Etang, 78960 Voisins le Bretonneux, France. TEL 30-43-47-48. FAX 30-57-02-88. Ed. J. Provost. circ. 4,000.

333.79 DK ISSN 0900-8063
ENERGI OG PLANLAEGNING. 1985. 6/yr. DKK 140 in Denmark; elsewhere $35. Sun Media, Ryesgade 19, 2200 Copenhagen N, Denmark. TEL 31-352211. FAX 45-31-35-65-45. Ed. Jette Johnsen. adv. circ. 5,300. (back issues avail.)

621.042 SP ISSN 0210-2056
CODEN: ENMAEV
ENERGIA; revista de ingenieria energetica. 1975. bi-m. 10600 ptas.($164) (effective 1993). Ingenieria Quimica, S.A., Triana 51-53, 28016 Madrid, Spain. TEL 341-3456400. FAX 341-3453945. Ed. Pedro de la Pezuela. adv.; bk.rev.; bibl.; charts; illus.; stat.; tr.lit.; index, cum.index: 1975-1977. circ. 5,000. (back issues avail.) **Indexed:** Chem.Abstr., Ind.SST.
—CASDDS. **CCC**.

333.79 IT ISSN 0392-7911
ENERGIA; rivista trimestrale sui problemi dell'energia. 1980. q. L.200000($200) (Automobile Club d'Italia) Editrice dell' Automobile s.r.l., Viale Regina Margherita, 290, 00198 Rome, Italy. TEL 06-4402061. FAX 06-8840926. Ed. Alberto Clo. adv.; bk.rev. circ. 5,000.

333.79 CU
ENERGIA. s-a. $24 in S. America; N. America $26; elsewhere $30. (Comison Nacional de Energia) Ediciones Cubanas, Obispo No. 527, Apdo. 605, Havana, Cuba.

333.79 IS
ENERGIA. (Text in Hebrew) 1987. bi-m. IS.40. R B S Ltd., P.O. Box 3039, Herziliyah B 46 103, Israel. TEL 052-555912.

ENERGY

333.79   **PO**
▼**ENERGIA DIRECTORIO.** 1994. a. Energia Press Lda., Av. Infante Santo 21 2o Dto., 1600 Lisbon, Portugal. TEL 3963225. FAX 3966043. Ed. Ana Xavier. adv. contact: Manuela Colaco. circ. 5,000. **Document type:** directory.

ENERGIA ELETTRICA. see *ENGINEERING — Electrical Engineering*

620   **HU**
   CODEN: ENGGAF
ENERGIAGAZDALKODAS. (Text in Hungarian; contents page in English, German and Russian) 1960. m. $50. (Energiagazdalkodasi Tudomanyos Egyesulet - Scientific Society for Energetics) Lapkiado Vallalat, Lenin korut 9-11, 1072 Budapest 7, Hungary. TEL 222-408. (Subscr. to: Kultura, P.O. Box 149, H-1389 Budapest 62, Hungary) Ed. Tomas Rapp. adv.; bk.rev.; charts; circ. 1,100. **Indexed:** Chem.Abstr., Hung.Build.Bull., INIS Atomind.
—BLDSC (3744.830000); CASDDS.
   Formerly: Ipari Energiagazdalkodas (ISSN 0021-0757)

333.79   **GW**   **ISSN 0013-7359**
TJ3   **CODEN: ENERA4**
ENERGIE; das Magazin fuer Wirtschaft, Forschung, Technik, Umwelt. 1949. m. DM.209. P M S GmbH und Co. KG, Postfach 290180, 47261 Duisburg, Germany. TEL 0203-76908-0. FAX 0203-7690830. Ed. Karl H. Schwarz. **Indexed:** INIS Atomind. **Document type:** academic/scholarly publication.
—BLDSC (3745.025000); SWETS; CASDDS. **CCC.**

621.042   **IT**   **ISSN 0391-5360**
TJ163.13   **CODEN: EHTEDZ**
ENERGIE ALTERNATIVE: HABITAT, TERRITORIO, ENERGIA. 1979. bi-m. L.55000($90) Editoriale P E G SpA, Via Fratelli Bressan 2, 20126 Milan, Italy. TEL 02-25-79-841. FAX 02-25-52-779. TELEX 323088 PEGMOS I. Ed. Mara Portoso. adv.: B&W page L.1850000, color page L.2960000; trim 185 x 260. bk.rev.; abstr.; charts; stat.; tr.lit.; index. circ. 3.000. **Indexed:** Int.Build.Serv.Abstr.
—BLDSC (3745.280000); EI.
   Description: Covers renewable energies and rational use of conventional ones. Also considers environmental problems.

531.6   **GW**   **ISSN 0175-0968**
ENERGIE DATEN. 1983. irreg., no.4, 1991. DM.30. Fachinformationszentrum Karlsruhe, Gesellschaft fuer Wissenschaftliche-Technische Information mbH, 76344 Eggenstein-Leopoldshafen, Germany. TEL 07247-808333. FAX 07247-808135. TELEX 724710-FIZKA. **Document type:** monographic series.

333.79   **FR**
ENERGIE EN ALGERIE. 1987. irreg. 1390 F. I C Publications, 10 rue Vineuse, 75116 Paris, France. TEL 44-30-81-11. FAX 44-30-81-11.

333.79   **NE**
ENERGIE & MILIEUSPECTRUM. 1980. 8/yr. fl.123 (foreign fl.185). (Energieonderzoek Centrum Necerland) Ten Hagen & Stam b.v., Postbus 235, 2280 AE Rijswijk, Netherlands. TEL 31-70-3988100. FAX 31-70-3988276. (Co-sponsor: Nederlandse Maatschappij voor Energie en Milieu) Ed.Bd. adv. contact: Herman Voois. bk.rev.; illus. circ. 4,874. **Indexed:** ELLIS, Key to Econ.Sci. **Document type:** trade publication.
—SWETS.
   Formerly (until 1992): E M - Energie en Milieutechnologie (ISSN 0925-2924); (until 1990): P T - Energiebeheer en Afvalbeheer (ISSN 0921-5182); Energiebeheer en Afvalbeheer (ISSN 0920-5756); Which was formed by the 1986 merger of: Afvalbeheer (ISSN 0920-6345); Energiebeheer (ISSN 0920-5985)

333.79   **FR**
ENERGIE PLUS. m. 47 av. Laplace, 94117 Arceuil Cedex, France. TEL 49-85-15-08. Ed. Michel Hoez. circ. 5,890.

333.791   **GW**   **ISSN 0179-9932**
TJ163.13   **CODEN: ENSPE4**
ENERGIE SPEKTRUM; Magazin fuer Energiemanagement. 1949. m. DM.198. Resch Media Mail Verlag GmbH, Geigerstr. 13, 82166 Graefelfing, Germany. TEL 089-858070. FAX 089-85807-64. Ed. Helmut Sendner. adv.; bk.rev.; charts; illus.; stat.; index. circ. 9,000. **Indexed:** Chem.Abstr., Eng.Ind., Excerp.Med., Sci.Abstr. **Document type:** trade publication.
—BLDSC (3745.790000).
   Description: Trade publication covering various aspects of the energy industry: environmental protection, solar energy, measurement of emissions, market, and ethics. Includes new products, list of events.

621.3   **NE**
ENERGIE TECHNOLOGIE; vakblad voor de technische professional. 11/yr. fl.142.50 (foreign fl.192.50). (Nederlandse Ingenieurs Vereniging (NIRIA)) V N U Business Publications B.V., Postbus 90162, 1006 BD Amsterdam, Netherlands. TEL 31-20-5102911. FAX 31-20-6174121. (Co-sponsor: Koninklijk Instituut van Ingenieurs) Ed. Ruud Plaizier. adv.: B&W page fl.2860, color page fl.4855; trim 205 x 285; adv. contact: Erna Oonk. circ. 8,422. **Document type:** trade publication.

621.042   **GW**   **ISSN 0944-3169**
TJ3   **CODEN: ENAEEH**
ENERGIEANWENDUNG, ENERGIE- UND UMWELTTECHNIK; technisch-wissenschaftliche Zeitschrift fuer effiziente Energienuetzung, Energie- und Umwelttechnik. 1952. m. DM.180. Deutscher Verlag fuer Grundstoffindustrie GmbH, Karl-Heine-Str. 27b, 04229 Leipzig, Germany. TEL 0341-49057-0. FAX 0341-4905720. adv.; bk.rev. **Indexed:** Excerp.Med., INIS Atomind. **Document type:** academic/scholarly publication.
—EI.
   Formerly: Energieanwendung und Energietechnik; Which was formed by the merger of: Energieanwendung (ISSN 0013-7405); Energietechnik (ISSN 0013-7421)
   Description: Covers the technology of energy and energy economization in industry, agriculture, and transportation. Covers design and construction of power plants. Includes reports of events and list of university courses.

333.79   **GW**   **ISSN 0933-8055**
ENERGIEDEPESCHE. 1987. q. DM.24. Bund der Energie Verbraucher e.V., Josefstr. 24, 53619 Rheinbreitbach, Germany. TEL 02224-78475. adv.; bk.rev. circ. 25,000. (back issues avail.)

621.042 333.79   **NE**
ENERGIEONDERZOEK CENTRUM NEDERLAND. JAARVERSLAG/NETHERLANDS ENERGY RESEARCH FOUNDATION. ACTIVITIES REPORT. (Editions in Dutch and English) 1955. a. Energieonderzoek Centrum Nederland - Netherlands Energy Research Foundation, Postbus 1, 1755 ZG Petten, Netherlands. TEL 32-2246-4412. FAX 32-2246-3053. TELEX 57211 REACP NL. circ. 4,000 (controlled). **Document type:** corporate report.
   Description: Covers renewable energy sources (solar and wind), nuclear energy, energy from fossil fuels and energy policy studies.

ENERGIETECHNIEK. see *ENGINEERING — Electrical Engineering*

333.79   **GW**   **ISSN 0720-6240**
ENERGIEWIRTSCHAFTLICHE TAGESFRAGEN; Zeitschrift fuer Energie-Wirtschaft, Recht und Technik, und Umwelt. 1950. m. DM.220. P M S GmbH und Co. KG, Postfach 290180, 47261 Duisburg, Germany. TEL 0203-76908-0. FAX 0203-7690830. Ed. Martin Czakainski. adv.; bk.rev.; bibl.; charts; illus.; mkt.; pat.; stat.; index. circ. 5,200. **Indexed:** ELLIS, Excerp.Med., INIS Atomind., Sci.Abstr. **Document type:** academic/scholarly publication.
—BLDSC (3746.080000); SWETS.

621.3   **CI**   **ISSN 0013-7448**
   CODEN: ENJAAC
ENERGIJA; casopis hrvatske elektroprivrede. (Text in Croation) 1951. 6/yr. 6000 din.($90) (effective 1991). Institut za Elektroprivredu, Avenija Vukovar 37, Zagreb, Croatia. FAX 38-41-530604. Ed. Zorko Cvetkovic. adv.; bk.rev. circ. 1,700. **Indexed:** Chem.Abstr., Sci.Abstr.
—BLDSC (3746.200000); EI; CASDDS.

333.79   **UK**   **ISSN 0360-5442**
HD9502.A1   **CODEN: ENEYDS**
ENERGY; the international journal. 1976. m. £474($730) (effective 1994). Elsevier Science Ltd., Pergamon, P.O. Box 800, Kidlington, Oxford OX5 1DX, England. TEL 44-865-843000. FAX 44-865-843010. (Subscr. in U.S. and Canada to: Elsevier Science, 660 White Plains Rd., Tarrytown, NY 10591-5153. TEL 914-524-9200. FAX 914-333-2444) Ed. S.S. Penner. adv.; bk.rev.; abstr.; illus.; stat.; index. circ. 1,100. (also avail. in microfilm from UMI) **Indexed:** A.S.& T.Ind., Biodet.Abstr., Chem.Abstr., Curr.Adv.Ecol.Sci., Energy Info.Abstr., Energy Rev., Environ.Abstr., Environ.Per.Bibl. (1976-), Excerp.Med., INIS Atomind., Key to Econ.Sci., Sci.Abstr. **Document type:** academic/scholarly publication.
—BLDSC (3747.445000); EI; Faxon; UnCover; SWETS; UMI; CASDDS. **CCC.**
   Description: Covers economic and environmental aspects of energy research, energy conservation measures, evaluation of energy systems, policy alternatives, design, applications, cost and management.
Refereed Serial

333.79   **US**   **ISSN 0272-9857**
ENERGY (BOCA RATON). (Subseries to: S I R S Social Issues (ISSN 0740-3127)) 1971. a. price varies; a. supplement $17. Social Issues Resources Series, Box 2348, Boca Raton, FL 33427-2348. TEL 407-994-0079; 800-232-7477. FAX 407-994-4704. (looseleaf format; also avail. in microfiche; back issues avail.)
   Description: Reprints articles that address all sociopolitical aspects of energy supply and demand.

333.79   **UK**
ENERGY ACTION. 1981. q. £15. Neighbourhood Energy Action, St. Andrew's House, 90-92 Pilgrim St., Newcastle-upon-Tyne NE1 6SG, England. TEL 091-261-5677. FAX 091-261-6496. Ed. Neil Ritchie. bk.rev.; illus. circ. 1,000. (back issues avail.) **Document type:** bulletin.
   Formerly: Energy Action Bulletin (ISSN 0262-5296)

696   **SZ**   **ISSN 0378-7788**
TJ163.5.B84   **CODEN: ENEBDR**
ENERGY AND BUILDINGS; an international journal of research applied to energy efficiency in the built environment. (Text in English) 1977. 3/yr. 375 SFr. (effective 1994). Elsevier Science S.A., P.O. Box 564, CH-1001 Lausanne 1, Switzerland. TEL 41-21-3207381. FAX 41-21-3235444. TELEX 450620-ELSA-CH. (Subscr. in U.S. and Canada to: Elsevier Science Inc., Box 882, Madison Sq. Sta., New York, NY 10159. TEL 212-989-5800) Eds. A. Meier, B.B. Todorovic. adv.; bk.rev.; illus.; index. (also avail. in microform from UMI) **Indexed:** AESIS, Br.Ceram.Abstr., Br.Tech.Ind., Curr.Cont., Energy Ind., Energy Info.Abstr., Energy Rev., Environ.Abstr., Environ.Per.Bibl. (1977-), Excerp.Med., Fuel & Energy Abstr., Gas Abstr., Int.Build.Serv.Abstr., Sage Pub.Admin.Abstr., Sage Urb.Stud.Abstr., Sci.Abstr., Sci.Cit.Ind. **Document type:** academic/scholarly publication.
—BLDSC (3747.493000); EI; Faxon; UnCover; SWETS. **CCC.**
   Description: Presents the results of research activities conducted by the building science community concerned with energy use, quality of the indoor environment and climatology.
Refereed Serial

621.042   **US**   **ISSN 1042-1939**
ENERGY AND ENGINEERING SCIENCE. (Subseries of Abacus Press Series) 1984. irreg., vol.10, 1987. Gordon & Breach Science Publishers, 820 Town Center Dr., Langhorne, PA 19047. TEL 215-750-2642. FAX 215-750-6343. (UK subscr. to: P.O. Box 90, Reading, Berkshire RG1 8JL, England. TEL 0734-560-080) Eds. A.K. Gupta, D.G. Lilley. **Document type:** monographic series.
Refereed Serial

321.042 613.1   **UK**   **ISSN 0958-305X**
ENERGY & ENVIRONMENT. 1990. q. £87 (outside Europe $162). Multi-Science Publishing Co. Ltd., 107 High St., Brentwood, Essex CM14 4RX, England. TEL 0277-224632. (U.S. subscr. to: Box 176, Avenel, NJ 07001) **Indexed:** Environ.Per.Bibl. **Document type:** academic/scholarly publication.
—BLDSC (3747.509500).

333.79 US
ENERGY AND ENVIRONMENT ALERT; brief notes by and about N.C.E.B. and N.C.E.B. associates. 1978. q. $20 to individuals; institutions $25. National Council for Environmental Balance, 4169 Westport Rd., Box 7732, Louisville, KY 40257-0732.
TEL 502-896-8731. Ed. Irwin W. Tucker. bk.rev. circ. 1,000. (looseleaf format; back issues avail.)
Document type: newsletter.
Formerly: Enviraction.

662 US ISSN 0887-0624
TP315 CODEN: ENFUEM
ENERGY & FUELS. 1987. bi-m. $345 to non-members (foreign $365); members $48 (foreign $68). American Chemical Society, 1155 16th St., N.W., Washington, DC 20036. TEL 800-333-9511. FAX 614-447-3671. (Subscr. to: Membership and Subscription Services, Box 3337, Columbus, OH 43210. TEL 614-447-3774) Ed. John W. Larsen. (back issues avail.) **Indexed:** Chem.Abstr., Energy Info.Abstr., Environ.Per.Bibl., Excerp.Med., Sugar Ind.Abstr. **Document type:** academic/scholarly publication.
●Also available online. Vendor(s): STN International (CJACS).
—BLDSC (3747.513000); EI; Faxon; UnCover; SWETS; CASDDS. **CCC**.
Description: Interdisciplinary journal, focusing on a broad range of chemical specialties from geochemistry to catalysis. Features reports on all aspects of the chemistry of non-nuclear energy sources.

696 333.79 US ISSN 0731-6313
ENERGY AND HOUSING REPORT; the national newsletter on residential energy conservation and consumption trends. 1981. m. $156 (foreign $168. A L F A Publishing, 9124 Bradford Rd., Silver Spring, MD 20901-4918. TEL 301-565-2532. FAX 301-565-3298. Ed. Allan F. Frank. bk.rev. **Document type:** newsletter.
Description: Covers new technologies and marketing techniques; local, state and federal energy conservation programs; current news on corporate activities; updates on recent laboratory research findings; and before-implementation details on consensus standards.

333.79 UK
ENERGY AND NUCLEAR SCIENCES INTERNATIONAL WHO'S WHO. 1983. irreg., 4th ed., 1992. £225. Longman Group UK Ltd., Westgate House, 6th Fl., The High, Harlow, Essex CM20 1YR, England. TEL 0279-442601. FAX 0279-444501. (Dist. in U.S. and Canada by: Gale Research Co. Inc., 835 Penobscot Bldg., Detroit, MI 48226) **Document type:** directory.
Formerly: International Who's Who in Energy and Nuclear Sciences.

ENERGY ASIA; weekly newsletter on Asia's energy industry. see *PETROLEUM AND GAS*

333.79 FR
ENERGY BALANCES OF O E C D COUNTRIES. (Text in English, French) 1976. a. price varies. Organization for Economic Cooperation and Development, International Energy Agency, 2 rue Andre-Pascal, 75775 Paris Cedex 16, France.
TEL 33-1-45-24-82-00. FAX 33-1-45-24-85-00. (U.S. orders to: O.E.C.D. Publications and Information Office, 2001 L St., N.W., Ste. 700, Washington DC 20036-4910. TEL 202-785-6323) (also avail. in microfiche from OEC,CIS; magnetic tape; diskette format) **Indexed:** IIS.

333.79 CY ISSN 0959-0072
ENERGY BUSINESS REVIEW. 1990. q. $240 (effective 1994-1995). Arab Press Service, P.O. Box 3896, Nicosia, Cyprus. FAX 357-2-350265. Ed. Gilbert Jenkins. adv. **Document type:** academic/scholarly publication.
—BLDSC (3747.534700).
Description: Covers the economic aspects of oil and other energy sources.

531.6 US ISSN 0897-9138
ENERGY CONFERENCES AND SYMPOSIA. 1978. m. $90. U.S. Department of Energy, Office of Scientific and Technical Information, Box 62, Oak Ridge, TN 37831. TEL 615-574-0733. (Subscr. to: National Technical Information Service, 5285 Port Royal Rd., Springfield, VA 22161. TEL 703-487-4630. FAX 703-321-8547) Ed. Judith H. Osborne. **Document type:** government publication, directory.
Description: Lists forthcoming energy and energy-related conferences worldwide.

333.791 US ISSN 0161-6595
ENERGY CONSERVATION NEWS. 1978. m. $295. Business Communications Co., Inc. (Norwalk), 25 Van Zant St., Ste. 13, Norwalk, CT 06855. TEL 203-853-4266. FAX 203-853-0348. TELEX 6502934929 WUI. Ed. Gail Greenberg.
●Also available online. Vendor(s): Data-Star, DIALOG Information Services, Inc., NewsNet (EY59).

621.042 UK ISSN 0196-8904
TK2896 CODEN: ECMADL
ENERGY CONVERSION AND MANAGEMENT. (Text in English, French, German) 1961. 12/yr. £673($1035) (effective 1994). Elsevier Science Ltd., Pergamon, P.O. Box 800, Kidlington, Oxford OX5 1DX, England. TEL 44-865-843000. FAX 44-865-843010. (Subscr. in U.S. and Canada to: Elsevier Science, 660 White Plains Rd., Tarrytown, NY 10591-5153. TEL 914-524-9200. FAX 914-333-2444) Ed. Jesse Denton. adv.; bk.rev.; charts; illus.; index. circ. 1,300. (also avail. in microform from UMI; reprint service avail. from UMI) **Indexed:** A.S.& T.Ind., Agri.Eng.Abstr., Appl.Mech.Rev., Chem.Abstr., Chem.Eng.Abstr., Curr.Cont., Energy Info.Abstr., Energy Rev., Eng.Ind., Environ.Per.Bibl. (1977-), Excerp.Med., Fluidex, Fuel & Energy Abstr., Gas Abstr., INIS Atomind., Sci.Abstr., T.C.E.A. **Document type:** academic/scholarly publication.
—BLDSC (3747.547000); EI; Faxon; UnCover; SWETS; UMI; CASDDS. **CCC**.
Former titles: Energy Conversion (ISSN 0013-7480); Advanced Energy Conversion (ISSN 0365-1789)
Description: Covers magnohydrodynamics, nuclear and geothermal design principles, solar collection, energy storage, applications of fossil fuel technologies, and alternative energy.
Refereed Serial

333.79 US ISSN 0364-5274
ENERGY DAILY. 1973. d. $1395. King Publishing Group, Inc., 627 National Press Bldg., Washington, DC 20045. TEL 202-638-4260. FAX 202-662-9744. Ed. Dennis Wamsted. adv.; bk.rev. **Indexed:** INIS Atomind.
●Also available online. Vendor(s): Data-Star, DIALOG Information Services, Inc., Mead Data Central, Inc., NewsNet (EY57).
—**CCC**.
Formerly: Weekly Energy Report.
Description: Provides information on the energy industry worldwide, including natural gas, nuclear power, electric utilities, oil, energy technology, financial and legislative developments, alternate fuels, environmental issues and regulators.

621.042 US
ENERGY DATA BASE. Short title: E D B. s-m. price varies. (U.S. Department of Energy) U.S. National Technical Information Service, 5285 Port Royal Rd., Springfield, VA 22161. TEL 703-487-4630.
●Available only online. Vendor(s): DIALOG Information Services, Inc., STN International.
Description: Provides international coverage of scientific and technical information on energy.

696 UK ISSN 0367-1119
TJ153 CODEN: ENDGBZ
ENERGY DIGEST. 1952. bi-m. £35. Comprint Ltd., 177 Hagden Lane, Watford, Herts. WD1 8LW, England. Ed. John Perkins. adv.; illus. circ. 2,800. (also avail. in microform from UMI; reprint service avail. from UMI) **Indexed:** Br.Tech.Ind., Energy Info.Abstr., Environ.Abstr., Fuel & Energy Abstr., Gas Abstr., INIS Atomind.
—BLDSC (3747.569000); CIS; UMI.
Incorporates: Journal of Fuel and Heat Technology (ISSN 0022-121X)

ENERGY DIRECTORY. see *HOUSING AND URBAN PLANNING*

333.79 UK ISSN 0140-9883
HD9502.A1 CODEN: EECODR
ENERGY ECONOMICS; for professionals concerned with economic analysis of energy issues. 1979. q. £185 in UK and Europe; elsewhere £195. Butterworth - Heinemann (Subsidiary of: Reed International PLC), Linacre House Jordan Hill, Oxford OX2 8DP, England. TEL 0865-310366. FAX 0865-310898. TELEX 83111 BHPOXF G. (Subscr. to: Turpin Transactions Ltd., Distribution Centre, Blackhorse Rd., Letchworth, Herts SG6 1HN, England. TEL 0462-672555) Ed. Homa Motamen. adv.; bk.rev.; abstr.; charts; index. (also avail. in microform from UMI; back issues avail.) **Indexed:** Acid Rain Abstr., Acid Rain Ind., AESIS, C.R.E.J., Curr.Cont., Energy Ind., Energy Info.Abstr., Energy Rev., Excerp.Med., Gas Abstr., HRIS, I D A, INIS Atomind., J.of Econ.Lit., Key to Econ.Sc., P.A.I.S., Risk Abstr., Rural Devel.Abstr., SCIMP (1982-), SSCI. **Document type:** academic/scholarly publication.
—BLDSC (3747.585000); CIS; Faxon; UnCover; SWETS; UMI. **CCC**.
Description: Covers applications of economic theory, statistical analysis and mathematical modelling to such problems as energy pricing, energy-GDP relationships, sector substitution, and the nuclear fuel cycle.
Refereed Serial

333.79 UK ISSN 0262-7108
ENERGY ECONOMIST; an international analysis. 1981. m. £511($867) (overseas £542) (effective 1993). Financial Times Business Information Ltd., 126 Jermyn St., London SW1Y 4UJ, England. TEL 071-411-4414. FAX 071-411-4415. charts; stat. **Indexed:** BP A, INIS Atomind. **Document type:** newsletter.
●Also available online.
—BLDSC (3747.586000); UMI.
Description: Contains international energy news, statistics, prices, and market commentary on all major energy sources: oil, refined products, natural gas, coal, and uranium. Includes a monthly in-depth examination of a particular energy subject with up-to-date data and forecasts.

333.79 US
▼**ENERGY EFFICIENCY JOURNAL.** 1993. bi-m. (National Association of Energy Service Companies) C M A Publications, Creative Marketing Alliance, Inc., 34-C Washington Rd., Princeton Junction, NJ 08550. TEL 609-799-4900. FAX 609-799-7032. Ed. Terry Singer. adv.; illus.; tr.lit. **Document type:** trade publication.
Description: Provides a forum for the evolving energy efficiency industry to discuss issues such as finance, technology and applications, marketing, business management, legal and legislative issues.

696 621.042 US ISSN 0199-8595
TJ163.6 CODEN: EENGDO
ENERGY ENGINEERING. 1904. bi-m. $99 in US & Canada; elsewhere $125 (effective 1992). (Association of Energy Engineers) Fairmont Press, Inc., 700 Indian Trail, Lilburn, GA 30247. TEL 404-925-9383. FAX 404-381-9865. Ed. Randall Sumpter. adv.; bk.rev.; charts; illus.; tr.lit.; index. circ. 8,500. (also avail. in microform from UMI,PMC; reprint service avail. from UMI) **Indexed:** A.S.& T.Ind., C.I.S. Abstr., Cadscan, Chem.Abstr., Curr.Cont., Energy Info.Abstr., Energy Rev., Eng.Ind., Environ.Per.Bibl (1991-), Excerp.Med., Fuel & Energy Abstr., Gas Abstr., INIS Atomind., Int.Build.Serv.Abstr., Lead Abstr., Sci.Abstr., Zincscan.
—BLDSC (3747.587000); EI; Faxon; UnCover; SWETS; UMI. **CCC**.
Former titles (until 1979): Building Systems Design (ISSN 0002-2284); Air Conditioning, Heating and Ventilating.

333.79 614.7 II ISSN 0970-3446
ENERGY ENVIRONMENT MONITOR. (Text in English) 1985. s-a. Rs.200 (foreign $25). Tata Energy Research Institute, 9 Jor Bagh, New Delhi 110 003, India. TEL 462-3983. FAX 91-11-4621770. TELEX 31-61593 TERI IN. Ed. P.V. Sridharan. circ. 1,000. **Indexed:** Energy Info.Abstr., Environ.Abstr. **Document type:** academic/scholarly publication.
—EI.
Description: Contains abstracts, reviews and current literature survey as well as original papers, concentrating mainly on energy-environment issues.

ENERGY

333.79 614.7   CN
ENERGY ENVIRONMENT REPORT. 1990. 6/yr. free. Maclean-Hunter Ltd. (Calgary), Ste. 2450, 101-6th Ave. S.W., Calgary, AB T2P 3P4, Canada. TEL 403-266-8700; 800-561-1294. FAX 403-266-6634. Ed. Jeffery Jones. circ. 12,588.

333.8 551   UK   ISSN 0144-5987
TJ163.13   CODEN: EEEXDU
ENERGY EXPLORATION AND EXPLOITATION. 1982. bi-m. £129 (foreign £141). Multi-Science Publishing Co. Ltd., 107 High St., Brentwood, Essex CM14 4RX, England. TEL 0277-224632. FAX 0277-224632. (U.S. subscr. to: Box 176, Avenel, NJ 07001) Eds. D. Abbott, G. Jenkins. (also avail. in microform) **Indexed:** AESIS, Chem.Abstr., E&P Hlth. (1993-), Excerp.Med., Gas Abstr., Gas Process.& Ppl. (1993-), Off.Tech. (1993-), Petrol.Abstr. (1984-). **Document type:** academic/scholarly publication.
—BLDSC (3747.589000); SWETS; CASDDS. **CCC.**
Description: Contains reviews and original articles on important issues in the exploration, exploitation, use and economics of the world's energies.

531.64   UK   ISSN 0265-1734
ENERGY FOCUS. 1984. 3/yr. £25($50) Parliamentary Group for Energy Studies, 90 Jarmyn St., London SW1Y 6JD, England. Ed. C. Stewart Munro. **Indexed:** INIS Atomind.
—BLDSC (3747.589650). **CCC.**

696   US
ENERGY FOCUS. 1991. bi-m. $15. Palmer Publishing Co., 651 W. Washington, Ste. 300, Chicago, IL 60661. TEL 312-993-0929. FAX 312-993-0960. Ed. Chuck Ross. adv. circ. 25,000. **Document type:** trade publication.
Description: Addresses efficient commercial and industrial construction, and energy efficiency as related to environmental standards and building operating codes.

333.79   JA   ISSN 0388-5267
ENERGY FORUM. Key Title: Enerugi Foramu. 1955. m. 10120 Yen($77.80) Denryoku Shinposha Co. Ltd., 10-13, 5-chome, Ginza, Chuo-ku, Tokyo, Japan. FAX 03-574-1649. Ed. Setsuo Sakai. adv.; bk.rev. circ. 40,000. (back issues avail.) **Indexed:** AESIS.
Formerly (until 1980): Denryoku Shinpo (ISSN 0388-5259)

333.79   DK   ISSN 0901-3768
ENERGY IN DENMARK; a report on energy planning. 1983. a. free. Ministry of Energy, Strandgade 29, DK-1901 Copenhagen, Denmark. **Document type:** government publication.

333.79   EI   ISSN 0256-6141
TJ163.25.E86
ENERGY IN EUROPE; energy policies and trends in the European community. (Text in English, French, German, Spanish) 1986. 3/yr. $65. Office for Official Publications of the European Communities, L-2985 Luxembourg, Luxembourg. (Dist. in U.S. by: Unipub, 4611-F Assembly Dr., Lanham, MD 20706-4391. TEL 800-274-4888. FAX 301-459-0056) (also avail. in microfiche from CIS) **Indexed:** IIS.
Description: Concerned with management of the energy sector in Europe.

333.79   JA   ISSN 0919-6080
ENERGY IN JAPAN. (Text in English) 1966. bi-m. $200. Institute of Energy Economics, Japan - Nippon Enerugi Keizai Kenkyujo, Shuwa Kamiyacho Bldg., 3-13 Toranomon 4-chome, Minato-ku, Tokyo 105, Japan. TEL 03-5401-4322. FAX 03-5401-4310. TELEX 2225457 IEETKJ. Ed. Toshiaki Yuasa. charts; stat. circ. 800. **Indexed:** Asian-Pac.Econ.Lit. **Document type:** academic/scholarly publication.
Formerly: Energy in Japan Quarterly Report.

333.79 631   NE   ISSN 0921-9757
ENERGY IN WORLD AGRICULTURE. (Text in English) 1986. irreg., vol.6, 1992. price varies. Elsevier Science B.V., Books Division, P.O. Box 211, 1000 AE Amsterdam, Netherlands. TEL 31-20-5803911. FAX 31-20-5803705. TELEX 18582 ESPA NL. (Subscr. in U.S. and Canada to: Elsevier Science Inc., Box 882, Madison Sq. Sta., New York, NY 10159. TEL 212-989-5800) (back issues avail.) **Document type:** monographic series.
Refereed Serial

333.79   UK
ENERGY INDUSTRIES COUNCIL CATALOGUE (YEAR). biennial. £50 (foreign £50). C.H.W. Roles & Associates Ltd., P.O. Box 25, Sunbury-on-Thames, Mddx. TW16 5QB, England. TEL 081-783 0088. adv. circ. 5,000. **Document type:** directory.
Description: Product information and buyers guide on the energy industries, covering oil, gas, petrochemical, nuclear, solar and coal processing, and power generation.

333.8 340   US
ENERGY INFORMATION BULLETIN. 1985. 2/yr. $6. American Bar Association, Coordinating Group on Energy Law, 1800 M St., N.W., Washington, DC 20036. TEL 202-331-2277. FAX 202-331-2220. Ed. Richard Cohen. **Document type:** newsletter.

333.79   US
ENERGY INFORMATION DIRECTORY. 1980. a. free. U.S. Department of Energy, Energy Information Administration, National Energy Information Center, EI-231, Rm. 1F-048, Forrestal Bldg., 1000 Independence Ave., S.W., Washington, DC 20585. TEL 202-586-8800. FAX 202-586-0727. charts; index. circ. 1,474. **Document type:** directory.
Formerly (until 1981): Energy Information Referral Directory.
Description: Lists various information offices within the D O E and other federal agencies arranged by subject.

333.79   US   ISSN 0195-6574
HD9502.A1
ENERGY JOURNAL. 1980. q. $175 in US & Canada; elsewhere $200. International Association of Energy Economics, 28790 Chagrin Blvd., Ste. 210, Cleveland, OH 44122. TEL 216-464-5365. (Co-sponsor: Energy Economics Educational Foundation Inc.) Ed. Leonard Waverman. adv.; bk.rev.; charts; index. circ. 2,500. (also avail. in microform from UMI; back issues avail.) **Indexed:** ABI Inform., AESIS; Energy Info.Abstr., Energy Rev., Environ.Per.Bibl. (1980-), Gas Abstr., INIS Atomind., J.of Econ.Lit., P.A.I.S., Tr.& Indus.Ind., World Alum.Abstr.
—BLDSC (3747.670500); Faxon; UnCover; SWETS; UMI. **CCC.**
Description: Contains articles on a wide range of energy economics issues, notes and special notices to members.
Refereed Serial

333.79   US
ENERGY: LATIN AMERICAN INDUSTRIAL REPORT. (Avail. for each of 22 Latin American countries) 1985. a. $435 per country report. Aquino Productions, Box 15760, Stamford, CT 06901. TEL 203-325-3138. Ed. Andres C. Aquino.

ENERGY LAW JOURNAL. see *LAW*

333.7   US   ISSN 0149-9386
TJ163.2   CODEN: ENGYD4
ENERGY MAGAZINE. 1975. 5/yr. $185. Business Communications Co., Inc. (Norwalk), 25 Van Zant St., Ste. 13, Norwalk, CT 06855. TEL 203-853-4266. FAX 203-853-0348. TELEX 6502934929 WUI. Ed. Gail Greenberg. circ. 2,500. (also avail. in microform from UMI; reprint service avail. from UMI) **Indexed:** Fluidex, GeoRef., HRIS, INIS Atomind., Int.Aerosp.Abstr., Met.Abstr., Ocean.Abstr., Petrol.Abstr., Sci.Cit.Ind., World Alum.Abstr.
—BLDSC (3747.456000); CIS; EI; Faxon; SWETS; UMI. **CCC.**

333.79   II
ENERGY MANAGEMENT. (Text in English) 1977. q. Rs.150($60) National Productivity Council, Business Management Section, Utpadakta Bhawan, Lodi Rd., New Delhi 110003, India. Ed. V. Raghuraman. circ. 1,500. **Indexed:** CLOSS, Energy Info.Abstr., Environ.Abstr., INIS Atomind., Mgmt.& Market.Abstr.
Description: Covers interdisciplinary reporting on all facets of energy, dealing with conventional and alternate sources in a realistic way.

333.79   US
ENERGY MANAGEMENT AND FEDERAL ENERGY GUIDELINES. 1973. bi-w. $1300. Commerce Clearing House, Inc., 4025 W. Peterson Ave., Chicago, IL 60646. TEL 312-583-8500. index. (looseleaf format) **Indexed:** World Alum.Abstr., World Surf.Coat.
Formerly: Energy Management.

333.79   IT
ENERGY MANAGER. 4/yr. Systems Comunicazioni, Via Olanda, 6, 20083 Gaggiano (MI), Italy. TEL 02-90841814. FAX 02-90841682. Ed. Michele di Pisa. circ. 15,000.

051   US
ENERGY NEWS EXCHANGE. 1982. bi-m. free. Kentucky Utilities Company, One Quality St., Lexington, KY 40507. TEL 606-255-2100. FAX 606-288-1165. Ed. Joyce C. Barr. circ. 3,000 (controlled). (back issues avail.)

333.79 614.7   US   ISSN 1059-289X
THE ENERGY NEWSBRIEF. 1986. w. (35/yr.). $295 to individuals; non-profit institutions $195. I R T Environment, Inc., Box 10990, Aspen, CO 81612-9689. TEL 303-927-3155. FAX 303-927-9428. Ed. Ted Flanigan. bk.rev.; index. circ. 1,000. **Document type:** newsletter.
Formerly (until 1991): I R T.
Description: Energy and environment newsbrief that covers strategic issues and international developments.

531.6 510   US
▼**ENERGY: PHYSICAL PROCESSES AND MATHEMATICAL MODELLING.** 1993. irreg. price varies. Nova Science Publishers, Inc., 6080 Jericho Tpke., Ste. 207, Commack, NY 11725-2808. TEL 516-499-3103. **Document type:** academic/scholarly publication.

333.79   FR
ENERGY POLICIES OF I E A COUNTRIES. a. price varies. Organization for Economic Cooperation and Development, International Energy Agency, 2 rue Andre-Pascal, 75775 Paris Cedex 16, France. (U.S. orders to: O.E.C.D. Publications and Information Center, 2001 L St., N.W., Ste. 700, Washington, DC 20036-4910. TEL 202-785-6323) (also avail. in microfiche from OEC,CIS) **Indexed:** IIS.
Formerly: Energy Policies and Programs of I E A Countries.

333.79   UK   ISSN 0301-4215
HD9502.A1   CODEN: ENPYAC
ENERGY POLICY; international journal of the political, economic, planning and social aspects of energy. 1973. 12/yr. £285 in UK and Europe; elsewhere £305. Butterworth - Heinemann (Subsidiary of: Reed International plc), Linacre House, Jordan Hill, Oxford OX2 8DP, England. TEL 0865-310366. FAX 0865-310898. TELEX 83111 BHPOXF G. (Subscr. to: Turpin Transactions Ltd., Distribution Centre, Blackhorse Rd., Letchworth, Herts. SG6 1HN, England. TEL 0462-672555) Ed. Nicky France. adv.; bk.rev.; charts; illus.; stat.; index. (also avail. in microform from UMI; back issues avail.) **Indexed:** ABI Inform, AESIS, Asian-Pac.Econ.Lit., BPIA, Br.Ceram.Abstr., C.R.E.J., CLOSS, Cont.Pg.Manage., Curr.Cont., Energy Ind., Energy Info.Abstr., Energy Rev., Environ.Abstr., Environ.Ind., Environ.Per.Bibl. (1989-), Excerp.Med., Fuel & Energy Abstr., Fut.Surv., Gas Abstr., GeoRef., HRIS, I D A, INIS Atomind., Key to Econ.Sci., P.A.I.S., Risk Abstr., Rural Devel.Abstr., Sci.Abstr., SCIMP (1982-), SSCI. **Document type:** academic/scholarly publication.
—BLDSC (3747.720000); CIS; Faxon; UnCover; SWETS; UMI. **CCC.**
Description: Addresses the issues of energy supply, demand, and utilization that confront managers, consultants, researchers, planners and politicians.
Refereed Serial

333.79   US   ISSN 0882-3537
ENERGY POLICY STUDIES. a. $21.95. Transaction Publishers, Transaction Periodicals Consortium, Department 3092, Rutgers University, Brunswick, NJ 08903. TEL 908-932-2280. FAX 908-932-3138. Eds. John Byrne, Daniel Rich. **Document type:** academic/scholarly publication.
Description: Examines social, political, and economic dimensions of energy technology, resources, and use. Covers issues of technological scale, resource allocation, environmental quality, and international relations.

ENERGY 2205

665.7   CN   ISSN 0319-5759
CODEN: EPCADS
ENERGY PROCESSING - CANADA. 1908. 6/yr. Can.$30($35) Northern Star Communications, 1600 - 700 4 Ave. W., Calgary, AB T2P 3J4, Canada. TEL 403-263-6881. FAX 403-263-6886. Ed. Scott Jeffrey. adv.; abstr.; charts; illus.; stat.; tr.lit. circ. 6,000. (processed) **Indexed:** API Abstr., Can.B.P.I., Chem.Abstr., E&P Hlth. (1993-), Fuel & Energy Abstr., Gas Process.& Ppl. (1993-), Off.Tech. (1993-), Petrol.Abstr. (1972-). **Document type:** trade publication.
—BLDSC (3747.730000); CASDDS. **CCC.**
Formerly: Gas Processing - Canada (ISSN 0016-4968)

333.79   UK   ISSN 0144-4247
ENERGY R & D SUMMARY AND SOURCES. 1979. m. £140($260) Ferndown Publications, 302 Bramhall Ln. S., Bramhall, Stockport SK7 3DL, England. TEL 061-439-4926. Ed. P. Smith.
Description: News about renewable energy, conservation, management systems.

333.7   US   ISSN 0888-8183
TJ153   CODEN: ENRPEX
ENERGY REPORT. 1973. w. $695 (foreign $769). Pasha Publications Inc., 1616 N. Fort Myer Dr., Ste. 1000, Arlington, VA 22209-3107. TEL 703-528-1244. FAX 703-528-1253. Ed. Gary Darst. bk.rev.; stat.; index. (looseleaf format) **Document type:** newsletter.
●Also available online. Vendor(s): Data-Star, DIALOG Information Services, Inc., Mead Data Central, Inc., NewsNet (EY50).
—**CCC.**
Former titles (until 1986): B N A's Energy Report; (until 1985): Energy Users Report (ISSN 0093-0261)
Description: Reports on law and policy for the oil, gas, coal, nuclear, solar and alternative energy industries as well as major energy consumers.

333.79 621.042   UK   ISSN 0093-7657
HV8131
ENERGY REPORT; energy policy and technology news bulletin. 1974. m. £82.50 (foreign £87.50). Springfield Information Services, P.O. Box 31, Peterborough, Cambs. PE1 1SD, England. TEL 0733-267272. Ed. John Franks. bk.rev.; bibl. (back issues avail.) **Document type:** newsletter.
—BLDSC (3747.740000).

621.042   NE   ISSN 0167-692X
CODEN: ENRSD7
ENERGY RESEARCH. 1980. irreg., no.8, 1990. price varies. Elsevier Science B.V., Books Division, P.O. Box 211, 1000 AE Amsterdam, Netherlands. TEL 31-20-5803911. FAX 31-20-5803705. TELEX 18582 ESPA NL. (Subscr. in U.S. and Canada to: Elsevier Science Inc., Box 882, Madison Sq. Sta., New York, NY 10159. TEL 212-989-5800) bibl. (back issues avail.) **Indexed:** Acid Rain Abstr., Acid Rain Ind. **Document type:** monographic series.
—CASDDS.
Refereed Serial

621.042   US   ISSN 0090-8312
TJ153   CODEN: EGYSAO
ENERGY SOURCES; an international interdisciplinary journal of science and technology. 1973. q. $95 to individuals; institutions $226. Taylor & Francis, 1900 Frost Rd., Ste. 101, Bristol, PA 19007-1598. TEL 215-785-5800. FAX 215-785-5515. Ed. G. Ali Mansoori. adv.; bk.rev.; abstr.; index. **Indexed:** API Abstr, API Catal., API Hlth.& Environ., API Oil., API Pet.Ref., API Pet.Subst., API Transport., Biodet.Abstr., Chem.Abstr., E&P Hlth. (1993-), Ecol.Abstr., Econ.Abstr., Elec.& Electron.Abstr., Energy Abstr., Energy Ind., Energy Info.Abstr., Energy Rev., Eng.Ind., Environ.Abstr., Environ.Per.Bibl., Fuel & Energy Abstr., Gas Process.& Ppl. (1993-), GeoRef., Ind.Sci.Rev., INIS Atomind., Int.Abstr.Oper.Res., ISMEC, Off.Tech. (1993-), Oper.Res.Manage.Sci., Petrol.Abstr. (1976-), Phys.Ber., Sci.Abstr., Sci.Cit.Ind. **Document type:** academic/scholarly publication.
—BLDSC (3747.790000); CIS; EI; Faxon; UnCover; SWETS; CASDDS. **CCC.**
Description: Forum for scientists, engineers and researchers studying conventional and new sources of energy and developing these sources into practical fuels.
Refereed Serial

333.79   CN   ISSN 1188-665X
▼**ENERGY STATISTICS HANDBOOK/GUIDE STATISTIQUE SUR L'ENERGIE.** (Catalogue 57-601) 1992. m. $360. Statistics Canada, Publications Division, Ottawa, ON K1A 0T6, Canada. TEL 800-267-6677. FAX 613-951-1582. (looseleaf format) **Document type:** government publication.
Description: Detailed information on the energy field, organized by energy type: total energy, petroleum, natural gas, electricity, uranium and coal. Sections on prices and conversion factors.

333.79   CN   ISSN 0843-4379
ENERGY STUDIES REVIEW. 1980. 3/yr. Can.$33($27) to individuals; institutions Can.$55 ($45). McMaster University, Institute for Energy Studies, Hamilton, ON L8S 4M4, Canada. TEL 905-525-9140. FAX 905-521-8232. Ed. M.L. Kliman. bk.rev. circ. 700. (back issues avail.) **Indexed:** Energy Info.Abstr., Environ.Abstr., Environ.Per.Bibl. (1991-), INIS Atomind.
—BLDSC (3747.806500); CIS; Faxon.
Formerly (until vol.9, no.2): Energy Newsletter (ISSN 0711-3366)
Description: An interdisciplinary journal for energy analysts concerned with energy policy, energy and the environment, technology, social impacts of energy utilization and experimental and theoretical research on energy.
Refereed Serial

333.79 621.042   US   ISSN 0090-8347
HD9502.A2   CODEN: ESYPBW
ENERGY SYSTEMS AND POLICY; an international interdisciplinary journal. 1973. q. $75 to individuals; institutions $160. Taylor & Francis, 1900 Frost Rd., Ste. 101, Bristol, PA 19007-1598. TEL 215-785-5800. FAX 215-785-5515. Ed. S. William Gouse, Jr. adv.; abstr.; index. **Indexed:** ABI Inform., Acid Rain Abstr., Acid Rain Ind., AESIS, BPIA, CAD CAM Abstr., Econ.Abstr., Elec.& Electron.Abstr., Electron.& Communic.Abstr.J., Energy Ind., Energy Info.Abstr., Energy Rev., Eng.Ind., Environ.Per.Bibl. (1981-), Gas Abstr., GeoRef., INIS Atomind., Int.Abstr.Oper.Res., Int.Polit.Sci.Abstr., Key to Econ.Sci., Nucl.Sci.Abstr., Oper.Res.Manage.Sci., P.A.I.S., Phys.Ber., Pollut.Abstr., Qual.Contr.Appl.Stat., Sci.Abstr. **Document type:** academic/scholarly publication.
—Faxon; UnCover; UMI. **CCC.**
Description: Deals with energy systems problems from resource assessment to final consumption.
Refereed Serial

333.79   US   ISSN 0093-500X
HD9502.A1
ENERGY TODAY. 1973. m. $795. Trends Publishing Inc., National Press Bldg., Washington, DC 20045. TEL 202-393-0031. FAX 202-393-1732. Ed. A. Kranish. bk.rev.; index. (looseleaf format) **Document type:** academic/scholarly publication.
Description: Examines energy problems, policy, regulation and conservation.

333.79   UK   ISSN 0308-1222
ENERGY TRENDS. 1974. m. price varies. Department of Trade & Industry, Rm. 3-3-26, 1 Palace St., London SW1E 5HE, England. TEL 071-238-3606. FAX 071-238-3121. charts; stat. **Indexed:** Br.Ceram.Abstr., Mgmt.& Market.Abstr. **Document type:** government publication.
—BLDSC (3747.832000). **CCC.**
Description: Discusses production, consumption and foreign trade of energy.

333.79   EC
ENERGY UPDATE. q. $50 includes Revista Energetica. Organizacion Latinoamericana de Energia - Latin-American Energy Organization, Casilla 17-11-6413, Quito, Ecuador. TEL 593-2-538122. FAX 593-2-539684. TELEX 2-2728 OLADE ED.

333.79   US   ISSN 0162-9131
ENERGY USER NEWS. 1976. m. $69.50. Chilton Co. (Subsidiary of: Capital Cities - A B C), Chilton Way, Radnor, PA 19089. TEL 215-964-4028. (Subscr. to: Box 2165, Radnor, PA 19080-9231) Ed. Virginia Hines. adv.: B&W page $4785. bk.rev.; charts; stat. circ. 40,000. (tabloid format; also avail. in microform; back issues avail.) **Indexed:** Bus.Ind., Energy Rev., Hlth.Ind., INIS Atomind., PROMT, Tr.& Indus.Ind. **Document type:** trade publication.
●Also available online. Vendor(s): DIALOG Information Services, Inc., Mead Data Central, Inc.
—BLDSC (3747.832000); UnCover. **CCC.**
Description: Serves professional energy managers, facility managers and building owners.

333.79   UK   ISSN 0959-0196
▼**ENERGY UTILITIES.** 1990. m. £385. Oxford Economic Research Associates, Blue Boar Ct., Alfred St., Oxford OX1 4EH, England. TEL 0865-251142. FAX 0865-251172. Eds. Dieter Helm, Patrick Lane. adv.; bk.rev. **Document type:** academic/scholarly publication, trade publication.
Description: Comments on all the major developments in the energy industry.

333.79   UK   ISSN 0307-7942
TP315   CODEN: EGYWA2
ENERGY WORLD. 1973. 10/yr. £60 (overseas £70) (effective 1994). (Institute of Energy) H. Howland Associates, The Martins, East St., Harrietsham, Kent ME17 1HH, England. TEL 0622-850100. Ed. Johanna Fender. adv.; bk.rev.; illus. circ. 6,000. **Indexed:** Anal.Abstr., Br.Ceram.Abstr., Br.Tech.Ind., Chem.Eng.Abstr., Energy Info.Abstr., Excerp.Med., Fuel & Energy Abstr., Gas Abstr., GeoRef., INIS Atomind., Int.Build.Serv.Abstr., T.C.E.A. **Document type:** trade publication.
—BLDSC (3747.840000); EI; UnCover; SWETS.

333.79   UK
ENERGY WORLD YEARBOOK. 1985. a. £50. (Institute of Energy) H. Howland Associates, The Martin, East St., Harrietsham, Kent ME17 1HH, England. TEL 0622-850100. Ed. Johanna Fender. adv. circ. 5,100. **Document type:** directory.

333.79   FR   ISSN 0153-9442
ENERPRESSE. 1970. d. 12300 F. (foreign 12650 F.). Societe d' Information et de Documentation, Bureau d'Informations Professionnelles, 142 rue Montmartre, 75002 Paris, France. FAX 40-39-97-52. TELEX 220528F. Ed. Patrick Lavilleon.
Description: News and comments in the energy field.

333.8   JA   ISSN 0285-0494
ENERUGI SHIGEN/ENERGY AND RESOURCES. (Text in Japanese) 1980. bi-m. 10000 Yen. Japan Society of Energy and Resources - Nippon Enerugi Shigen Gakkai, Boshi-kaikan 9-10, Kyomachi-bori 1-chome, Nishi-ku, Osaka 550, Japan. TEL 81-6-446-0537. FAX 81-6-446-0559. Ed. R. Echigo. adv.; bk.rev.; abstr.; charts; tr.lit.; illus.; index. circ. 55,000. **Document type:** academic/scholarly publication.
—BLDSC (3747.522000).
Description: Studies on energy and resources; education of energy-saving and resources management.

ENGENHARIA AGRICOLA. see *AGRICULTURE*

333.79   US   ISSN 0271-7085
ENHANCED ENERGY RECOVERY NEWS. 1980. m. $305. Business Communications Co., Inc. (Norwalk), 25 Van Zant St., Ste. 13, Norwalk, CT 06855. TEL 203-853-4265. FAX 203-853-0348. TELEX 6502934929 WU. Ed. Donald Saxman.
●Also available online. Vendor(s): NewsNet (EY60).

536.7 621.4   FR   ISSN 0013-9084
TJ260   CODEN: ENTPA5
ENTROPIE; revue internationale d'energetique, genie chimique, genie biologique. (Supplements avail.) 1965. 7/yr. 1580 F. Entropie, B.P. 63, 94002 Creteil Cedex, France. TEL 48-99-10-58. FAX 45-17-17-21. Eds. J.C. Charpentier, G. Piar. adv.; bk.rev.; abstr.; bibl.; charts; illus.; mkt.; pat.; stat.; tr.mk.; index. circ. 3,000. **Indexed:** Appl.Mech.Rev., Biol.Abstr., Chem.Abstr., Chem.Eng.Abstr., Curr.Biotech.Abstr., Dairy Sci.Abstr., Eng.Ind., Excerp.Med., Fluidex, Fuel & Energy Abstr., INIS Atomind., Int.Aerosp.Abstr., Nucl.Sci.Abstr., Sci.Abstr., T.C.E.A.
—BLDSC (3790.900000); Faxon; SWETS; CASDDS. **CCC.**

ENVEST; the business and investment newsletter for energy and the environment. see *BUSINESS AND ECONOMICS — Investments*

ENVIRONMENT; exploring the social and physical environments of W.A. see *ENVIRONMENTAL STUDIES*

ENVIRONMENTAL BIOLOGY. see *ENVIRONMENTAL STUDIES*

ENERGY

621.48 333.792 US
ENVIRONMENTAL COALITION ON NUCLEAR POWER NEWSLETTER. 1970. irreg. $10. Environmental Coalition on Nuclear Power, 433 Orlando Ave., State College, PA 16803. Ed. J.H. Johnsrud. bk.rev.; illus. circ. 600. **Document type:** newsletter.

333.8 340 US
▼**ENVIRONMENTAL LAW AND ENERGY JOURNAL.** 1992. 4/yr. membership. Missouri Bar, Environmental Law and Energy Committee, 326 Monroe St., Box 119, Jefferson City, MO 65102. TEL 314-635-4128. FAX 314-635-2811. Ed. Terry Satterlee. (looseleaf format) **Document type:** newsletter.

665 GW ISSN 0343-6705
ERDOEL-INFORMATIONSDIENST. 1947. w. DM.642. Verlagsgruppe Handelsblatt GmbH, Kasernenstr. 67, 40213 Duesseldorf, Germany. (Subscr. to: Postfach 102717, 40018 Duesseldorf, Germany) Ed. Heino Elfert. **Document type:** trade publication.

333.79 BE ISSN 1021-4259
EUROPE ENERGY. French edition: Europe Energie (ISSN 0772-1528) (Text in English) 1978. fortn. 22950 BEF (effective 1994). Europe Information Service, Rue de Geneve, 6, 1140 Brussels, Belgium. TEL 32-2-242-6020. FAX 32-2-242-9410.
●Also available online. Vendor(s): Mead Data Central, Inc.

EUROPEAN DIRECTORY OF ENERGY EFFICIENT BUILDING - COMPONENTS SERVICES MATERIALS. see BUILDING AND CONSTRUCTION — Hardware

621.042 UK ISSN 0957-8595
EUROPEAN DIRECTORY OF RENEWABLE ENERGY SUPPLIERS AND SERVICES. 1991. a. £49.50($75) James & James (Science Publishers) Ltd., 5 Castle Rd., London NW1 8PR, England. TEL 071-284-3833. FAX 071-284-3737. (Dist. in N. America by: Books International, Box 605, Herndon, VA 22070. TEL 703-435-7064. FAX 703-689-0660) Ed. Bruce Cross. **Document type:** directory.
—BLDSC (3829.689568).

333.79 UK ISSN 0261-2259
EUROPEAN ENERGY REPORT. fortn. £449($824) (foreign £495). Financial Times Business Information Ltd., 126 Jermyn St., London SW1Y 4UJ, England. TEL 071-411-4414. FAX 071-411-4415. stat.; q. index. **Document type:** newsletter.
●Also available online.
—SWETS.
Formerly: Financial Times Energy Report (ISSN 0141-3570)
Description: Provides news and analysis from the European energy industries: oil, gas, coal, nuclear, hydroelectricity, renewables. Includes prices, supply-and-demand statistics, and market reports.

EUROPEAN POWER NEWS. see ENGINEERING — Electrical Engineering

333.79 UK
EXECUTIVE ENERGY AND ENVIRONMENT. 1976. q. £48. Energy Information Centre, P.O. Box 147, Grosvenor House, High St., Newmarket, Suffolk CB8 9AL, England. TEL 0638-663030. FAX 0638-666049. adv.; stat.
Formerly (until 1992): Energy for Industry and Commerce.
Description: Provides informed, independent commentary about energy and environmental trends and developments.

333.79 665.5 AU
FACTS & FIGURES; a graphical analysis of world energy. (Text in English) 1979. a. free. Organization of the Petroleum Exporting Countries, Obere Donaustr. 93, A-1020 Vienna, Austria. TEL 01-21112. FAX 01-2149827. TELEX 134474. Ed.Bd. bk.rev.; circ. 10,000 (controlled). (also avail. in microfiche from CIS) Indexed: IIS. **Document type:** corporate report.
Description: Includes graphs which examine energy issues on a global scale, which concentrate on OPEC, and which make broad economic comparisons between different world groupings.

333.79 GW ISSN 0343-8449
FAKTEN; Energiewirtschaft heute und morgen. 1968. m. DM.48. Energie-Verlag GmbH, Haeusserstr. 36, 69115 Heidelberg, Germany. TEL 06221-90130. FAX 06221-901341. Eds. Klaus-Dieter Hilbert, Werner Idstein. circ. 34,000. **Document type:** trade publication.

333.79 327 CY
THE FATE OF THE ARABIAN PENINSULA. 1972. m. $800 (includes subscr. to A P S News Service, Strategic Balance in the Middle East, Operations in Oil Diplomacy, Re-Drawing the Islamic Map) (effective 1994). Arab Press Service, P.O. Box 3896, Nicosia, Cyprus. FAX 357-2-350265. s-a. index. **Document type:** bulletin.
Description: Surveys Arab government structures, their opposition, and detailed profiles of decision-makers.

333.79 US
FEDERAL ENERGY REGULATORY COMMISSION REPORTS. 1979. irreg. $1060. Commerce Clearing House, Inc., 4025 W. Peterson Ave., Chicago, IL 60646. TEL 312-583-8500. Ed. D. Newquist.

FEDERAL TAXATION OF OIL AND GAS TRANSACTIONS. see PETROLEUM AND GAS

333.79 US
FEDERAL TECHNOLOGY REPORT. bi-w. $495.(foreign $520). McGraw-Hill, Inc., Energy & Business Newsletters, 1221 Ave. of the Americas, 36th Fl., New York, NY 10020. TEL 212-512-6410. Ed. Bill Loveless. (reprint service avail. from UMI)
Formerly: Tech Transfer Report.

FINLAND. TILASTOKESKUS. ENERGIATILASTOT/FINLAND. STATISTIKCENTRALEN. ENERGISTATISTIK. see ENERGY — Abstracting, Bibliographies, Statistics

333.79 US
FIVE YEAR COMPARISON OF UTILITY POWER PRODUCTION AND ELECTRIC O & M EXPENSES. (Operating & Maintenance) 1990. a. $395. Utility Data Institute (Subsidiary of: McGraw-Hill), 1200 G St., N.W., Ste. 250, Washington, DC 20005. TEL 202-942-8788; 800-486-3660. FAX 202-942-8789. **Document type:** trade publication.
Description: Provides comparative financial, sales, operating and maintenance information for 150 U.S. electric utilities over a five-year period.

FLAME. see PETROLEUM AND GAS

665.5 GW ISSN 0721-5894
FLUESSIGGAS. 1954. 6/yr. DM.67. (Deutscher Verband Fluessiggas e.V.) Verlag A. Strobel KG, Postfach 5654, 59806 Arnsberg, Germany. TEL 02931-8900-0. FAX 02931-890038. Ed. Ekkehard Strobel. index. circ. 5,000. **Document type:** trade publication.
Description: Trade journal in the liquid propane gas field of Germany.

621.48 DK ISSN 0106-2557
FORSKNINGSCENTER RISOE. AARSBERETNING/RISOE ANNUAL REPORT. (Text in Danish, English) 1977. a. free. Forskningscenter Risoe, Roskilde, Denmark.
Indexed: Potato Abstr.
Former titles: Forsoegsanlaeg Risoe. Aarsberetning (ISSN 0106-2557); Beretning om Atomenergikommissionens Virksomhed.

621.3 DK
FORSKNINGSCENTER RISOE. SYSTEMS ANALYSIS DEPARTMENT. ANNUAL PROGRESS REPORT. 1980. a. DKK 24.40. Forskningscenter Risoe, Roskilde, Denmark.
Former titles: Forskningscenter Risoe. Energi Systems Gruppen. Annual Progress Report & Forsoegsanlaeg Risoe. (ISSN 0107-9077)

333.79 NE
FORUM; personeelsblad energieonderzoek centrum nederland. 1961. m. Energieonderzoek Centrum Nederland - Netherlands Energy Research Foundation, Postbus 1, 1755 ZG Petten, Netherlands. TEL 31-2246-4412. FAX 31-2246-3053. TELEX 57211 REACP NL. Ed. Jan Worst. circ. 1,500 (controlled).
Description: Reviews current improvements and developments in the working area of ECN.

FORUM FOR APPLIED RESEARCH AND PUBLIC POLICY. see ENVIRONMENTAL STUDIES

333.79 US
FOSSIL UNIT PERFORMANCE DATA BASE. base vol. and a. updates. $495 for base vol.; a. updates $250. Utility Data Institute (Subsidiary of: McGraw-Hill), 1200 G St., N.W., Ste. 250, Washington, DC 20005. TEL 202-942-8788; 800-486-3660. FAX 202-942-8789. stat. (diskette format) **Document type:** trade publication.
Description: Compils coal-fired unit heat rate data for approximately 850 U.S. coal-fired units each year.

FRANCE. COMMISSARIAT A L'ENERGIE ATOMIQUE. ANNUAL REPORT. see ENERGY — Nuclear Energy

FRANCE. COMMISSARIAT A L'ENERGIE ATOMIQUE. NOTES D'INFORMATION. see ENERGY — Nuclear Energy

621.31 US
FRONTIERS OF POWER CONFERENCE. PROCEEDINGS. 6th, 1973. a. price varies. Oklahoma State University, College of Engineering, Engineering Extension, 512 Engineering North, Stillwater, OK 74078. TEL 405-744-5033. **Document type:** proceedings.
Formerly: Frontiers of Power Technology Conference. Proceedings (ISSN 0161-5319)

FUEL; science and technology of fuel and energy. see PETROLEUM AND GAS

333 AG
FUNDACION BARILOCHE. INSTITUTO DE ECONOMIA DE LA ENERGIA. PUBLICACIONES. irreg. price varies. Fundacion Bariloche, Instituto de Economia de la Energia, Casilla de Correo 138, 8400 San Carlos de Bariloche - Rio Negro, Argentina.
Supersedes in part: Fundacion Bariloche. Departamento de Recursos Naturales y Energia. Publicaciones; Which superseded in part: Fundacion Bariloche. Departamento de Recursos Naturales y Energia. Publicaciones (ISSN 0071-9846)

531 SZ ISSN 0173-9387
FUSION;* Wissenschaft - Technik fuer das 21. Jahrhundert. 1980. q. DM.35. (Fusion Energy Foundation e.V.) Azed AG, Dornacherstr. 60-62, CH-4002 Basel, Switzerland. circ. 14,000.

FUSION POWER REPORT; complete monthly coverage of worldwide fusion developments. see ENERGY — Nuclear Energy

GAS. see PETROLEUM AND GAS

GAS; internationale Zeitschrift fuer wirtschaftliche und umweltfreudliche Energieanwendung. see PETROLEUM AND GAS

333.79 CY
GAS MARKET TRENDS. 1972. w. $600 (includes subscr. to Oil Market Trends and Downstream Trends) (effective 1994). Arab Press Service, P.O. Box 3896, Nicosia, Cyprus. FAX 357-2-350265. s-a. index. **Document type:** newsletter.
Description: Discusses liquid natural gas, liquid petroleum gas, and natural gas liquids, along with pipeline gas trade and pricing trends in the Middle East and other major export centers.

GAS SUPPLY AND DEMAND STUDY. see PETROLEUM AND GAS

620.11 333.9 US ISSN 0746-4134
TJ778
GAS TURBINE WORLD. 1971. bi-m. $60. Pequot Publishing, Inc., Box 447, Southport, CT 06490. Ed. Robert Farmer. adv.; tr.lit. circ. 8,561. **Indexed:** Fuel & Energy Abstr., Gas Abstr., Sci.Abstr. **Document type:** trade publication.

GENERATOR'S JOURNAL. see ENVIRONMENTAL STUDIES — Waste Management

GENSHIRYOKU CHOSA JIHO/NUCLEAR INDUSTRIAL SURVEY. see ENERGY — Nuclear Energy

GENSHIRYOKU NENKAN/NUCLEAR ALMANAC. see ENERGY — Nuclear Energy

GOOD CENTS. see BUILDING AND CONSTRUCTION

333.79 PL ISSN 0017-2413
CODEN: GPENAS
GOSPODARKA PALIWAMI I ENERGIA/FUEL AND ENERGY MANAGEMENT. (Text in Polish; summaries in English and Russian; contents page in German) 1953. m. $51. (Ministerstwo Przemyslu) Wydawnictwo Czasopism i Ksiazek Technicznych SIGMA - NOT, Ul. Ratuszowa 11, P.O. Box 1004, 00-950 Warsaw, Poland. TEL 48-22-180918. FAX 48-22-192187. TELEX 814550 SIGMA PL. (Dist. by: SIGMA - NOT Ltd., Ul. Bartycka 20, 00-716 Warsaw, Poland) (Co-sponsors: Stowarzyszenie Elektrykow Polskich; Polski Komitet Gospodarki Energetycznej) Ed. Jozef Michejda. adv.: Page $1260. circ. 2,850. **Indexed:** Chem.Abstr., INIS Atomind.
—CASDDS.

GREAT BRITAIN. DEPARTMENT OF TRADE & INDUSTRY. DEVELOPMENT OF THE OIL AND GAS RESOURCES OF THE UNITED KINGDOM. see *PETROLEUM AND GAS*

621.4 US ISSN 1059-6143
▼**GREEN CAR JOURNAL.** 1992. m. $320 (foreign $360) (effective 1994). Green Car Media, 1334-D N. Benson Ave., Upland, CA 91786. TEL 909-985-9700. FAX 909-946-0664. Ed. R.J. Cogan. bk.rev. **Document type:** newsletter. **Incorporates:** Environmental Vehicles Review. **Description:** Covers alternative fuel automobiles.

GUIDE TO U S G S GEOLOGIC AND HYDROLOGIC MAPS. see *EARTH SCIENCES*

HARBINGER FILE; a descriptive directory of organizations concerned with environmental issues in California. see *ENVIRONMENTAL STUDIES*

HEALTH FACILITIES ENERGY REPORT. see *HOSPITALS*

333.79 US
HEARTH & HOME; the magazine of specialty retailing. 1976. m. $30 (Canada $42; overseas $84 (includes a. Buyer's Guide). Village West Publishing, Box 2008, Laconia, NH 03247-2008. TEL 603-528-4285. FAX 603-524-0643. Ed. Richard Wright. adv. contact: Jackie Avignone. bk.rev.; bibl.; charts; illus.; stat.; tr.lit.; circ. 100 (paid); 19,000 (controlled). (back issues avail.) **Document type:** trade publication.
Formerly (until 1989): Wood 'n Energy (ISSN 0273-5695)
Description: Geared towards the solid fuel industry, as well as the casual furnishings industry.

HENONG XUEBAO/ACTA AGRICULTURAE NUCLEATAE SINICA. see *AGRICULTURE*

696 US ISSN 0896-9442
TJ163.5.D86
HOME ENERGY; magazine of residential energy conservation. 1984. bi-m. $49 (Canada $54; elsewhere $59) (effective Nov. 1991). Energy Auditor and Retrofitter, Inc., 2124 Kittredge St., No. 95, Berkeley, CA 94704. TEL 510-524-5405. Ed. Alan Meier. adv.; bk.rev.; illus.; index. circ. 4,300. **Indexed:** Energy Info.Abstr., Energy Rev., Environ.Abstr., Environ.Per.Bibl. (1989-), INIS Atomind. **Document type:** trade publication.
—UnCover.
Formerly (until 1987): Energy Auditor and Retrofitter.
Description: Covers every aspect of energy conservation in the home, from super-efficient appliances to indoor air quality.

621.042 696 US ISSN 1050-2416
HOME POWER; the hands-on journal of home-made power. 1987. bi-m. $15. Home Power, Inc., Box 520, Ashland, OR 97520-0520. TEL 916-475-3179. FAX 916-475-3179. adv.: B&W page $1200. illus. circ. 15,100. **Document type:** consumer publication.
Description: Practical, do-it-yourself information for people who want to use solar, wind, water, hydrogen, methane and other renewable energy sources.

HUDSON VALLEY G R E E N TIMES. see *ENVIRONMENTAL STUDIES*

333.79 US
HUTTLINGER'S ENERGY REPORTS. w. $360. Huttlinger's Energy News, Box 409, Poolesville, MD 20837. TEL 301-972-8100. Ed. Stan Janet. bibl.; stat. (looseleaf format; back issues avail.) **Document type:** newspaper.

333.79 US
I A E E NEWSLETTER. 1977. q. $60 membership. International Association for Energy Economics, 28790 Chagrin Blvd., Ste. 210, Cleveland, OH 44122. TEL 216-464-5365. Ed. Dave Williams. adv. circ. 3,200. **Document type:** newsletter.
Description: Announces upcoming events, conferences and workshops, details chapter and affiliate news and provides special reports and information on an international basis.

622 UK
I E A COAL RESEARCH NEWSLETTER. 1990. q. free. (International Energy Agency) I E A Coal Research, Gemini House, 10-18 Putney Hill, London SW15 6AA, England. TEL 071-780-2111. FAX 071-780-1746. **Document type:** newsletter.
Description: Provides information and assessment service concerning coal-related technologies and economics

621.042 UK
I E A COAL RESEARCH PROFILES. irreg. (approx. 10/yr.). £30($55) no member countries; non-member countries £90 ($165). (International Energy Agency) I E A Coal Research, Gemini House, 10-18 Putney Hill, London SW15 6AA, England. TEL 081-780-2111. FAX 081-780-1746. **Document type:** trade publication.
Description: Provides information on coal technology, supply, use and the environment.

I E E E ELECTRON DEVICE LETTERS. see *ELECTRONICS*

I E E E PULSED POWER CONFERENCE. DIGEST OF TECHNICAL PAPERS. see *ENERGY — Electrical Energy*

I E E E TRANSACTIONS ON POWER SYSTEMS. see *ENERGY — Electrical Energy*

621.3 UK
I E E ENERGY SERIES. 1981. irreg., vol.7, 1994. Institution of Electrical Engineers, Michael Faraday House, Six Hills Way, Stevenage, Herts SG1 2AY, England. TEL 0438-313311. FAX 0438-313465. TELEX 825578-IEESTV-G. Eds. D. Swift-Hook, L. Divone. **Document type:** monographic series.

621.31 CN ISSN 0847-1460
CODEN: IPFCEQ
I P P S O FACTO. 1988. bi-m. Can.$100. Independent Power Producers' Society of Ontario, P.O. Box 1084, Sta. F, Toronto, ON M4Y 2T7, Canada. Ed. Jake Brooks. adv.; bk.rev. circ. 2,000. **Document type:** trade publication.
Description: Covers business, financial, regulatory and technical developments in the field of cogeneration, small hydro, energy from waste, biomass, peat, wind and solar energy. Provides extensive coverage of Canadian utility policy and practice particularly of Ontario Hydro.

531.6 UN ISSN 0250-4227
I R P T C BULLETIN. Variant title: International Register of Potentially Toxic Chemicals Bulletin. 1978. a. United Nations, Environment Programme, Palais des Nations, CH-1211 Geneva 10, Switzerland. **Indexed:** Environ.Abstr.
—BLDSC (4580.580000); SWETS.

I S G E TRANSACTIONS. (International Society for Geothermal Engineering, Inc.) see *ENERGY — Geothermal Energy*

IMPORTED CRUDE OIL AND PETROLEUM PRODUCTS. see *PETROLEUM AND GAS*

333.8 622 US ISSN 1061-3692
IMPROVED RECOVERY WEEK. 1980. w. $495 (foreign $525). Pasha Publications Inc., 1616 N. Ft. Myer Dr., Ste. 1000, Arlington, VA 22209-3107. TEL 703-528-1244. FAX 703-528-1253. Ed. F. Jay Schempf. index. **Document type:** newsletter.
●Also available online. Vendor(s): Data-Star, DIALOG Information Services, Inc., Mead Data Central, Inc.
—CCC.
Former titles (until 1992): Advanced Recovery Week (ISSN 1050-1347); (until 1990): Enhanced Recovery Week (ISSN 0277-9137); Incorporates (in Nov. 1983): Petro Engineering News; Biofuels Report (ISSN 0273-2904)
Description: Updates economic analyses of improved oil and gas recovery projects such as horizontal drilling, tertiary oil recovery, profile modification and more.

333.79 US ISSN 1043-7320
TJ163.2 CODEN: IDPEEW
INDEPENDENT ENERGY; the industry's business magazine. 1971. 10/yr. $81 (effective Jan. 1994). Marier Communications Inc., 620 Central Ave., N., Milaca, MN 56363-1788. TEL 612-983-6892. FAX 612-983-6893. TELEX 6503306729. Ed. Donald Marier. adv.: B&W page $2410, trim 8 1/4 x 11 1/4; adv. contact: Rick Huntzicker. bk.rev.; film rev. circ. 4,777. (also avail. in microfilm from UMI; back issues avail.) **Indexed:** A.S.& T.Ind., Alt.Press Ind., Energy Ind., Energy Info.Abstr., Energy Rev., Environ.Abstr., Environ.Per.Bibl. (1978-), Fuel & Energy Abstr., Gas Abstr., Ind.How To Do It (1978-1980), Ind.Sci.Rev., INIS Atomind., MELSA, New Per.Ind., Sci.Abstr. **Document type:** trade publication.
—BLDSC (4375.881500); CIS; Faxon; UnCover; SWETS; UMI.
Former titles: Independent Power; Alternative Sources of Energy (ISSN 0146-1001)
Description: Provides senior executives at companies that develop, own and operate independent power production facilities with news and critical insights that help them better manage their growing businesses; also companies that service the industry with information and analysis which is vital to their marketing plans.

333.79 US
INDEPENDENT POWER REPORT. 1985. fortn. $815 (foreign $840). McGraw-Hill, Inc., Energy & Business Newsletters, 1221 Ave. of the Americas, 36th Fl., New York, NY 10020. TEL 212-512-6410. Ed. Richard Schwartz. (looseleaf format; back issues avail.; reprint service avail. from UMI) **Document type:** newsletter.
●Also available online. Vendor(s): DIALOG Information Services, Inc. (File no.624/McGRAW-HILL PUBLICATIONS ONLINE), Dow Jones News Retrieval (COG), Mead Data Central, Inc. (IPR), NewsNet (EY67).
Formerly (until 1988): Cogeneration Report.

363.6 II
INDIA. DEPARTMENT OF POWER. REPORT. (Text in English) 1975. a. Department of Power, Ministry of Energy, New Delhi, India.

621.042 II
INDIAN ENERGY AND POWER UPDATE. 1988. biennial. $55. Technical Press Publications, 5-1 Convent Str., Colaba, Bombay 400 039, India. TEL 2021446. TELEX 11-83479 CHEM IN. Ed. J.P. de Sousa. adv.; bk.rev.; abstr.; charts; illus. circ. 6,400. (also avail. in microform from UMI; reprint service avail. from UMI)

INDUSTRIAL BIOPROCESSING; a monthly intelligence service. see *CHEMISTRY — Organic Chemistry*

333.79 US ISSN 0894-5764
INDUSTRIAL ENERGY BULLETIN. fortn. $685 (foreign $710). McGraw-Hill, Inc., Energy & Business Newsletters, 1221 Ave. of the Americas, 36th Fl., New York, NY 10020. TEL 212-512-2000. (reprint service avail. from UMI)
●Also available online. Vendor(s): DIALOG Information Services Inc. (File no.624/McGRAW-HILL PUBLICATIONS ONLINE), Dow Jones News Retrieval, Mead Data Central, Inc., NewsNet (EY68).
Description: Covers competitive new market forces reshaping the relationship between industrial energy consumers and their utility and fuel suppliers.

DIE INDUSTRIEFEUERUNG. see *PETROLEUM AND GAS*

621.042 CU ISSN 0253-5645
CODEN: INEEDC
INGENIERIA ENERGETICA. 1980. 3/yr. $24 in N. America; S. America $25; Europe $26. (Ministerio de Educacion Superior, Instituto Superior Politecnico) Ediciones Cubanas, Obispo No. 527, Apdo. 605, Havana, Cuba. **Indexed:** Sugar Ind.Abstr.
—CASDDS.

ENERGY

333.79 — US — ISSN 0278-2227
INSIDE ENERGY WITH FEDERAL LANDS. 1978. w. $1065 (foreign $1090). McGraw-Hill, Inc., Energy & Business Newsletters, 1221 Ave. of the Americas, 36th Fl., New York, NY 10020. TEL 212-512-6410. Ed. William Loveless. (back issues avail.; reprint service avail. from UMI)
● Also available online. Vendor(s): DIALOG Information Services, Inc. (File no.624/McGRAW-HILL PUBLICATIONS ONLINE), Dow Jones News Retrieval (IE), Mead Data Central, Inc. (INERGY), NewsNet (EY69).
Formerly: Inside D.O.E. (Department of Energy) (ISSN 0149-5798); Incorporates: Platt's Oil Policy Report; Which was formerly: Platt's Oil Policy Letter; Platt's Oil Policy and Regulation Report; Platt's Oil Regulation Report (ISSN 0190-4124); Regulatory Insight.
Description: Examines federal energy policy, especially as it relates to the Departments of Energy and the Interior.

333.79 — US — ISSN 0163-948X
HD9502.U5
INSIDE F E R C. 1979. w. $975 (foreign $1025). (Federal Energy Regulatory Commission) McGraw-Hill, Inc., 1221 Ave. of the Americas, New York, NY 10020. Ed. Larry Foster. (reprint service avail. from UMI)
● Also available online. Vendor(s): DIALOG Information Services, Inc. (File no.624/McGRAW-HILL PUBLICATIONS ONLINE), Dow Jones News Retrieval (FERC), Mead Data Central, Inc. (INFERC), NewsNet (EY70).

621.042 665.5 — UK — ISSN 0144-2600
TP315 — CODEN: JINEDX
INSTITUTE OF ENERGY. JOURNAL. 1927. q. £150. Institute of Energy, 18 Devonshire St., London W1N 2AU, England. TEL 071-580-0008. FAX 071-580-4420. Ed. T. Atkinson. adv.; bibl.; illus.; index, cum.index; circ. 2,500 (controlled). **Indexed:** A.S.& T.Ind., Appl.Mech.Rev., Br.Ceram.Abstr., Br.Tech.Ind., C.I.S. Abstr., Chem.Abstr., Chem.Eng.Abstr., Curr.Cont., Eng.Ind., Environ.Per.Bibl. (1991-), Excerp.Med., Foul.Prev.Res.Dig., Fuel & Energy Abstr., Geo.Abstr., GeoRef., INIS Atomind., Int.Build.Serv.Abstr., Met.Abstr., Sci.Abstr., T.C.E.A., World Alum.Abstr. **Document type:** academic/scholarly publication.
—BLDSC (4775.600000); Faxon; UnCover; SWETS; CASDDS.
Incorporates: Institute of Energy. Report and Accounts; **Formerly:** Institute of Fuel. Journal (ISSN 0020-2886)

621.042 — RM — ISSN 1220-4145
TK1
INSTITUTUL DE STUDII SI PROIECTARI ENERGETICE. BULETINUL. (Text in English, French, German and Spanish; summaries in English, French, Rumanian, Russian, Spanish) 1957. q. exchange basis. Institutul de Studii si Proiectari Energetice, Bd. Lacul Tei nr. 1, Sector 2, 72301 Bucarest 30, Rumania. TEL 400-107080. FAX 400-122620. TELEX 10978 ISPE R. circ. 200. (back issues avail.) **Indexed:** Sci.Abstr.

INTEGRATED WASTE MANAGEMENT. see ENVIRONMENTAL STUDIES — Waste Management

621.042 — US
INTERAGENCY POWER GROUP BRIEFS. (Subseries of: Chemical, Electrical, Mechanical, Nuclear, Solar, Magneto-Hydrodynamic, Systems, All Categories) m. price varies. (Interagency Advanced Power Group) U.S. National Technical Information Service, 5825 Port Royal Rd., Springfield, VA 22161. TEL 703-487-4630.
Description: Members of the IAPG include the U.S. Army, Navy, and Air Force; Department of Energy; and National Aeronautics and Space Administration. Their cooperative effort monitors government-funded research and development producing project briefs in the listed categories.

622.33 333.8 — BE
INTERNATIONAL COAL LETTER. 1979. fortn. 20500 BEF. International Coal Letter s.p.r.l., 19 Rue Capouillet, Box 1, B-1060 Brussels, Belgium. TEL 32-2-536-8611. FAX 32-2-536-8600. TELEX 24672. Ed. Dr. Peter E. Doerell. bk.rev. **Document type:** newsletter.
Formerly: World Coal Letter.

333.79 — FR — ISSN 0256-2332
HD9502.A1 — CODEN: EPRTEP
INTERNATIONAL ENERGY AGENCY. ENERGY PRICES AND TAXES. 1984. a. 750 F.($170) Organization for Economic Cooperation and Development, International Energy Agency, 2 rue Andre-Pascal, 75775 Paris Cedex 16, France. (U.S. subscr. to: O.E.C.D. Publications and Information Center, 2001 L St., Ste. 700, N.W., Washington, D.C. 20036-4910. TEL 202-785-6323) circ. 1,950. (also avail. in microfiche from OEC,CIC; magnetic tape; diskette format) **Indexed:** IIS.
—BLDSC (3747.728500); SWETS.
Description: Contains a major international compilation of energy prices at all market levels: import prices, industry prices and consumer prices.

621.042 — US — ISSN 0731-5341
INTERNATIONAL ENERGY ANNUAL. 1976. a., latest 1990. $11. U.S. Department of Energy, Energy Information Administration, National Energy Information Center, EI-231, Rm. 1F-048, Forrestal Bldg., 1000 Independence Ave., S.W., Washington, DC 20585. TEL 202-586-8800. (Dist. by: Supt. of Documents, Washington, DC 20402) charts. **Indexed:** Energy Info.Abstr., PROMT. **Document type:** government publication.
● Also available online.

621.042 — US — ISSN 1051-6360
HD9502.A1
INTERNATIONAL ENERGY OUTLOOK. a., latest 1991. free. U.S. Department of Energy, Energy Information Administration, National Energy Information Center, EI-231, Rm. 1F-048, Forrestal Bldg., 1000 Independence Ave., S.W., Washington, DC 20585. TEL 202-586-8800. **Document type:** government publication.
Supersedes in part (in 1982): U.S. Department of Energy. Energy Information Administration. Annual Report to Congress (ISSN 0161-5807)

INTERNATIONAL GAS RESEARCH CONFERENCE. PROCEEDINGS. see PETROLEUM AND GAS

333.8 — UK — ISSN 0143-0750
TJ163.13 — CODEN: IJAEDW
INTERNATIONAL JOURNAL OF AMBIENT ENERGY. 1980. q. £160($268) Ambient Press Ltd., P.O. Box 25, Lutterworth, Leics. LE17 4FF, England. Ed. J.C. McVeigh. bk.rev.; index. (also avail. in microfiche) **Indexed:** Br.Tech.Ind., Energy Info.Abstr., Environ.Abstr., Excerp.Med., Fluidex, Int.Build.Serv.Abstr., Sci.Abstr. **Document type:** academic/scholarly publication.
—BLDSC (4542.025000); EI; Faxon; UnCover; SWETS; CASDDS. CCC.
Description: Contains information on renewable energy: solar, wind, wave, tidal, geothermal and biomass, with emphasis on application in buildings.

INTERNATIONAL JOURNAL OF ELECTRICAL POWER AND ENERGY SYSTEMS. see ENGINEERING — Electrical Engineering

333.8 — US — ISSN 1054-853X
TD195.E49 — CODEN: IJEEEJ
INTERNATIONAL JOURNAL OF ENERGY - ENVIRONMENT - ECONOMICS. 1991. bi-m. $195 (effective 1994). Nova Science Publishers, Inc., 6080 Jericho Tpke., Ste. 207, Commack, NY 11725-2808. TEL 516-499-3103. Ed. T. Nejat Veziroglu. **Indexed:** Energy Info.Abstr. **Document type:** academic/scholarly publication.
—BLDSC (4542.234000).
Description: Focuses on the interrelationship of energy, environment and economics, especially as they impact on major global environmental problems, including the greenhouse effect.

621.042 333.7 — UK — ISSN 0363-907X
TJ163.13 — CODEN: IJERDN
INTERNATIONAL JOURNAL OF ENERGY RESEARCH. 1976. 9/yr. $995 (effective 1994). John Wiley & Sons Ltd., Journals, Baffins Ln., Chichester, Sussex PO19 1UD, England. TEL 0243-779777. FAX 0243-775878. TELEX 86290-WIBOOK-G. Ed. J.T. McMullan. (reprint service avail. from ISI,SWZ,UMI) **Indexed:** AESIS, AIT Reports, API Abstr., API Catal., API Hlth.& Environ., API Oil., API Pet.Ref., API Pet.Subst., API Transport., Appl.Mech.Rev., Br.Tech.Ind., Cadscan, Chem.Abstr., Curr.Cont., Energy Info.Abstr., Energy Rev., Environ.Per.Bibl. (1979-), Excerp.Med., Fluidex, Gas Abstr., Geo Abstr., INIS Atomind., Int.Aerosp.Abstr., Int.Build.Serv.Abstr., Lead Abstr., Sci.Abstr., Sci.Cit.Ind., Zincscan. **Document type:** academic/scholarly publication.
—BLDSC (4542.236000); EI; Faxon; UnCover; SWETS; UMI; CASDDS. CCC.
Description: Provides a broad platform on which research results and issues in energy research and development can be discussed.

INTERNATIONAL JOURNAL OF ENVIRONMENTAL ISSUES IN MINERALS & ENERGY INDUSTRY. see MINES AND MINING INDUSTRY

333.79 621.042 — SZ — ISSN 0954-7118
TJ163.13 — CODEN: IJGIE7
INTERNATIONAL JOURNAL OF GLOBAL ENERGY ISSUES. (Text in English) 1989. q. $155 in N. America; elsewhere £100. (Unesco, UN) Inderscience Enterprises Ltd., World Trade Centre Bldg., 110 Ave. Louis Casai, Case Postale 306, CH-1215 Geneva-Aeroport, Switzerland. FAX 22-7910885. TELEX 289950. Ed.Bd. (back issues avail.) **Indexed:** Energy Info.Abstr., Environ.Abstr., Environ.Ind., Environ.Per.Bibl. (1991-).
—BLDSC (4542.267000); EI; Faxon; SWETS.
Description: Covers energy policy, management and planning as well as conservation, development of alternate energy and economic control.

539.7 — UK — ISSN 0360-3199
TP360 — CODEN: IJHEDX
INTERNATIONAL JOURNAL OF HYDROGEN ENERGY. 1976. 12/yr. £510($785) (effective 1994). (International Association for Hydrogen Energy) Elsevier Science Ltd., Pergamon, P.O. Box 800, Kidlington, Oxford OX5 1DX, England. TEL 44-865-843000. FAX 44-865-843010. (Subscr. in U.S. and Canada to: Elsevier Science, 660 White Plains Rd., Tarrytown, NY 10591-5153. TEL 914-524-9200. FAX 914-333-2444) Ed. T.N. Veziroglu. adv.; bk.rev.; bibl.; abstr.; illus.; stat.; index. circ. 2,250. (also avail. in microform from UMI,PMC; reprint service avail. from UMI) **Indexed:** Cadscan, Chem.Abstr., Curr.Cont., Energy Info.Abstr., Energy Rev., Environ.Abstr., Environ.Per.Bibl. (1981-), Gas Abstr., Ind.Sci.Rev., INIS Atomind., Int.Aerosp.Abstr., Int.Build.Serv.Abstr., Lead Abstr., Meteor.& Geoastrophys.Abstr., Risk Abstr., Sci.Abstr., Sci.Cit.Ind., Sugar Ind.Abstr., Zincscan. **Document type:** academic/scholarly publication.
—BLDSC (4542.290000); EI; Faxon; UnCover; SWETS; UMI; CASDDS. CCC.
Description: Covers all areas of hydrogen energy.
Refereed Serial

621.042 — CN — CODEN: IJSYDC
TJ163.13
INTERNATIONAL JOURNAL OF POWER AND ENERGY SYSTEMS. (Text in English, French) 1981. 3/yr. $183.50. International Association of Science and Technology for Development, 4500 16th Ave., N.W., Ste. 80, Calgary, AB T3B 0M6, Canada. TEL 403-288-1195. FAX 403-247-6851. (In Europe: P.O. Box 354, CH-8053 Zurich, Switzerland; In U.S.: Box 2481, Anaheim, CA 92814) Ed. C. Wu. adv.; bk.rev.; index. **Indexed:** Chem.Abstr., Cyb.Abstr.
—BLDSC (4542.237000); Faxon.
Former titles: International Journal of Energy Systems (ISSN 0226-1472); Energy Systems - Modelling, Planning and Decision.
Description: Policy planning, economics, simulation, modelling, decision, technology, alternative energy sources, energy and power systems.

621.042 — II
INTERNATIONAL PRESS CUTTING SERVICE: WEEKLY ENERGY - ECOLOGY - POLLUTION REPORT. 1977. w. $95. International Press Cutting Service, Box 63, Allahabad 211001, India. Ed. Nandi Khanna. bk.rev.; index. circ. 1,200. (looseleaf format)

ENERGY

333.79   US   ISSN 1070-2989
▼**INTERNATIONAL PRIVATE POWER QUARTERLY**; a country-by-country update of markets outside the U.S. and Canada. 1993. q. $745. McGraw-Hill, Inc., 1221 Ave. of the Americas, New York, NY 10020. TEL 212-512-2904. FAX 212-512-2723. Ed. Richard Schwartz. (back issues avail.)

333.79   US
INTERNATIONAL RESEARCH CENTER FOR ENERGY AND ECONOMIC DEVELOPMENT. ANNUAL CONFERENCE. PROCEEDINGS. a. International Research Center for Energy and Economic Development, 909 14th St., Ste. 201, Boulder, CO 80302. TEL 303-492-7667. FAX 303-442-5042. **Document type:** proceedings.

333.79   US
INTERNATIONAL RESEARCH CENTER FOR ENERGY AND ECONOMIC DEVELOPMENT. OCCASIONAL PAPERS. irreg., no.21, 1993. $10. International Research Center for Energy and Economic Development, 909 14th St., Ste. 201, Boulder, CO 80302. TEL 303-492-7667. FAX 303-442-5042. **Document type:** academic/scholarly publication.
 Description: Deals with current energy, development and environmental issues.

333.8   US   ISSN 0277-870X
HD9971.5.S76
INTERNATIONAL SOLID FUEL BUYER'S GUIDE DIRECTORY.* a. National Wood Stove & Fireplace Journal, Inc., c/o J.P. Dunleavy, 7873 E Via Costa, Scottsdale, AZ 85258-2822.

333.79   GW   ISSN 0170-6640
INTERNATIONALES ENERGIE FORUM; Magazin zur energiepolitischen Meinungsbildung. (Text in German) 1978. q. Suedwestdeutsche Verlagsanstalt, Postfach 121863, 68161 Mannheim, Germany. TEL 0621-3922803. FAX 0621-3922800. circ. 10,000. **Indexed:** INIS Atomind. **Document type:** bulletin.

333.79   IT
ITALIA ENERGIA. 2/yr. L' Annuario s.r.l., Via Giulia 4, 14049 Nizza Monferrato - Asti, Italy. TEL 141-70-22-77. Ed. Carlo Ricci. circ. 10,000.

621 536   BW   ISSN 0579-2983
CODEN: IVZEAY
IZVESTIYA VYSSHIKH UCHEBNYKH ZAVEDENII. SERIYA ENERGETIKA. 1958. m. 43.20 Rub. Belorusskii Politekhnicheskii Institut, Leninskii prosp. 65, 220027 Minsk, Belarus. (Co-sponsor: Ministerstvo Vysshego i Srednego Spetsial'nogo Obrazovaniya) Ed. M.I. Streliuk. bk.rev. circ. 2,500. **Indexed:** Chem.Abstr., Sci.Abstr.
—CCC.

JOBSON'S QUARTERLY. see BUSINESS AND ECONOMICS — Investments

333.79   US   ISSN 0361-4476
HD9502.A1
JOURNAL OF ENERGY AND DEVELOPMENT. 1975. s-a. $38 to institutions; libraries $30; individuals $20. International Research Center for Energy and Economic Development, 909 14th St., Ste. 201, Boulder, CO 80302. TEL 303-492-7667. FAX 303-442-5042. Ed. Dorothea H. El Mallakh. adv.; bk.rev.; charts; stat. circ. 2,000. (also avail. in microform from WSH; reprint service avail. from WSH) **Indexed:** A.B.C.Pol.Sci., Acid Rain Abstr., Acid Rain Ind., AESIS, C.L.I., C.R.E.J., Curr.Cont., Energy Info.Abstr., Energy Rev., Environ.Abstr., Environ.Per.Bibl. (1975-), INIS Atomind., J.of Econ.Lit., Key to Econ.Sci., Leg.Per., Mid.East: Abstr.& Ind., P.A.I.S., Petrol.Abstr., PROMT, SSCI. **Document type:** academic/scholarly publication.
—BLDSC (4978.300000); CIS; Faxon; UnCover; SWETS.
 Description: For professionals, the business and industry community, government officials, and scholars in a broad area of energy and development topics.

JOURNAL OF ENERGY AND NATURAL RESOURCES LAW. see LAW

621.042 536   II   ISSN 0970-9991
CODEN: JEHTEL
JOURNAL OF ENERGY, HEAT AND MASS TRANSFER. q. Rs.600($40) Regional Centre for Energy, Heat and Mass Transfer for Asia and the Pacific, Madras 60036, India. Eds. V.M.K. Sastri, A.R. Balakrishnan. bk.rev. **Indexed:** Agri.Eng.Abstr. **Document type:** academic/scholarly publication.
—BLDSC (4978.314000); CASDDS.
 Formerly (until 1990): Regional Journal of Energy, Heat and Mass Transfer (ISSN 0253-6854)
 Description: Provides a forum for the presentation of original work, reviews and discussion of latest developments in the fields of energy, heat and mass transfer.

333.79 621.042   SA   ISSN 1021-447X
JOURNAL OF ENERGY IN SOUTHERN AFRICA. 1990. q. R.91.20($65) to individuals; instituitons R.176.70($130). Energy Research Institute, Information Service, P.O. Box 33, Plumstead 7800, South Africa. TEL 27-21-705-0120. FAX 27-21-705-6266.
 Formerly: Journal of Energy R and D in Southern Africa (ISSN 1016-1686)
 Description: Covers the technical, economic, environmental and techno-social aspects of energy research in Southern Africa.

333.79 340   US   ISSN 1053-377X
K10
JOURNAL OF ENERGY, NATURAL RESOURCES AND ENVIRONMENTAL LAW. 1980. s-a. $10. University of Utah, College of Law, Salt Lake City, UT 84112. TEL 801-581-6833. Ed.Bd. bk.rev.; index. circ. 350. (back issues avail.; reprint service avail. from RRI) **Indexed:** BPIA, C.L.I., Energy Info.Abstr., Environ.Abstr., INIS Atomind., L.R.I., Leg.Cont., Leg.Per., P.A.I.S. **Document type:** academic/scholarly publication.
●Also available online. Vendor(s): West Services, Inc. —Faxon; UnCover.
 Formerly (until 1990): Journal of Energy Law and Policy (ISSN 0275-9926)

621   US   ISSN 0195-0738
TJ163.13   CODEN: JERTD2
JOURNAL OF ENERGY RESOURCES TECHNOLOGY. 1979. q. $100 to non-members; members $29. American Society of Mechanical Engineers, 345 E. 47th St., New York, NY 10017. TEL 212-705-7703. Ed. J.S. Chung. (also avail. in microfiche from UMI; reprint service avail. from UMI) **Indexed:** A.I.Abstr., A.S.& T.Ind., Acid Rain Abstr., Acid Rain Ind., AESIS, API Abstr., API Catal., API Hlth.& Environ., API Oil., API Pet.Ref., API Pet.Subst., API Transport., Appl.Mech.Rev., Chem.Eng.Abstr., Curr.Biotech.Abstr., Curr.Cont., E&P Hlth. (1993-), Energy Info.Abstr., Environ.Abstr., Excerp.Med., Fluidex, Gas Process.& Ppl. (1993-), Ind.Sci.Rev., INIS Atomind., Met.Abstr., Off.Tech. (1993-), Petrol.Abstr. (1981-), Risk Abstr., Sci.Abstr., Sci.Cit.Ind., Sh.& Vib.Dig., T.C.E.A., World Alum.Abstr. —BLDSC (8896.780000); CIS; EI; Faxon; UnCover; SWETS; UMI. CCC.
Refereed Serial

JOURNAL OF MATERIALS ENGINEERING. see METALLURGY

KING'S COAL EXPORT REPORT. see MINES AND MINING INDUSTRY

KING'S COALSTATS. see MINES AND MINING INDUSTRY

KING'S INTERNATIONAL COAL TRADE. see MINES AND MINING INDUSTRY

KING'S NORTHERN COAL. see MINES AND MINING INDUSTRY

KING'S SOUTHERN COAL. see MINES AND MINING INDUSTRY

KING'S WESTERN COAL. see MINES AND MINING INDUSTRY

LAMP (NEW YORK). see PETROLEUM AND GAS

621.042 360   IT
IL LAVORATORE ELETTRICO. 1950. w. L.3000. F.L.A.E.I.-C.I.S.L., Via Salaria 83, 00198 Rome, Italy. TEL (06) 862.352. circ. 50,000.

333.79 659 2   US
LEWIS LETTER ON ENERGY COMMUNICATION. 1979. s-m. $135. Lewis Associates, Inc., 292 Main St., Great Barrington, MA 01230. TEL 413-528-9445. (Subscr. to: Box 567, Housatonic, MA 01236) Ed. Eilenn Willner. (back issues avail.)
 Description: Information on effective communication techniques used by various utilities, with tips on effective community, media and governmental relations.

LIGHT (WASHINGTON). see BUSINESS AND ECONOMICS — Labor And Industrial Relations

LLOYD'S LIST INTERNATIONAL. see TRANSPORTATION — Ships And Shipping

333.79   UK   ISSN 0267-1263
LONDON ENERGY NEWS. 1985. q. £25($50) (London Energy Group) Ambient Press Ltd., P.O. Box 25, Lutterworth, Leics. LE17 4FF, England. Ed. Colin Gomez.
—CCC.
 Description: Information on energy as it relates to buildings.

333.79   TZ
MAJI REVIEW. (Text in English) 1974. irreg., approx. a. Ministry of Water, Energy and Minerals, Research and Training Division, P.O. Box 35066, Dar es Salaam, Tanzan a. illus. **Indexed:** GeoRef. **Document type:** government publication.

MAJOR ENERGY COMPANIES OF EUROPE. see BUSINESS AND ECONOMICS — Trade And Industrial Directories

333.79 622   CN
MANITOBA. ENERGY AND MINES. ANNUAL REPORT SERIES. 1980. a. Manitoba Energy and Mines, 555-330 Graham Ave., Winnipeg, MB R3C 4E3, Canada. TEL 204-945-6541. FAX 204-945-0586. circ. 1,000. **Document type:** government publication.
 Formerly: Manitoba. Mineral Resources Division. Annual Report Series.
 Description: Covers activities of the Department and the mining industry in Manitoba.

621.042   US
MATERIALS AND COMPONENTS IN FOSSIL ENERGY APPLICATIONS. bi-m. U.S. Department of Energy, Department of Fossil Energy, 1000 Independence Ave., S.W., Washington, DC 20585. TEL 202-586-4695. **Indexed:** Ind.U.S.Gov.Per., INIS Atomind. **Document type:** government publication.
—BLDSC (5393.972000).
 Formerly: Materials and Components in Fossil Energy Applications and E R D A Newsletter (ISSN 0145-9244)

MESTNYI PROIZVODSTVENNYI OPYT V PROMYSHLENNOSTI/LOCAL LEVEL EXPERIENCE IN THE MANUFACTURING INDUSTRY; nauchno-tekhnicheskii referativnyi sbornik. see ENGINEERING — Mechanical Engineering

METHANE RECOVERY FROM LANDFILL YEARBOOK. see ENVIRONMENTAL STUDIES — Waste Management

621.042   IS
MICHERON BINIYA, ENERGIA VESHERUTIM NIVCHARIM. 3/yr. Cheshev Ltd., P.O. Box 40021, Tel Aviv 61 400, Israel. TEL 03-216291.

621.042   UK   ISSN 0260-7840
TJ1   CODEN: MPSYDU
MODERN POWER SYSTEMS. 1963. m. £69($160) (foreign £120). Wilmington Publishing, Wilmington House, Church Hill, Dartford, Kent UA1 7EF, England. TEL 0322-277788. FAX 0322-276476. (Subscr. to: Ferrari House, 258 Field End Rd., Ruislip, Middx HA4 9UX. TEL 081-868-4499) Ed. L. David Smith. adv.; bk.rev. circ. 11,050. (back issues avail.) **Indexed:** Acid Rain Abstr., Acid Rain Ind., AESIS, B.P.I, Bus.Ind. Energy Info.Abstr., Environ.Abstr., Excerp.Med., Fuel & Energy Abstr., Key to Econ.Sci., Sci.Abstr., Tr.& Indus.Ind. —BLDSC (5893.10C000); CIS; Faxon; UnCover; SWETS. CCC.
 Incorporates (in 1931): Energy International (ISSN 0013-7529)

MONTHLY ENERGY REVIEW. see ENERGY — Abstracting, Bibliographies, Statistics

2210 ENERGY

621.042 333.79 GW ISSN 0580-3403
MUSTERANLAGEN DER ENERGIEWIRTSCHAFT. 1966. irreg. price varies. Energiewirtschaft und Technik Verlagsgesellschaft mbH, Oberratherstr. 2, 40472 Duesseldorf, Germany. TEL 0211-96509-0. FAX 0211-9550960. Ed. Klaus Schneider. bk.rev. **Document type:** academic/scholarly publication.

MYERS' FINANCE REVIEW (1993). see *BUSINESS AND ECONOMICS — Investments*

N P G A REPORTS. (National Propane Gas Association) see *PETROLEUM AND GAS*

333.79 US
N S P NEWS. 1958. m. Northern States Power Company, 414 Nicollet Mall, Minneapolis, MN 55401. TEL 612-330-6381. Ed. Nancy Kluver. bk.rev.; index. circ. 10,000.

NATIONAL ASSOCIATION OF REGULATORY UTILITY COMMISSIONERS. BULLETIN. see *PUBLIC ADMINISTRATION*

NATIONAL ASSOCIATION OF REGULATORY UTILITY COMMISSIONERS. PROCEEDINGS. see *PUBLIC ADMINISTRATION*

333.8 US ISSN 0279-4357
TH7438
NATIONAL ENERGY JOURNAL.* 1978. m. $21 (free to qualified personnel). National Wood Stove & Fireplace Journal, Inc., c/o J.P. Dunlavey, 7873 E Via Costa, Scottsdale, AZ 85258-2822. Ed. Harold Illingworth. circ. 33,696.
Formerly: National Wood Stove and Fireplace Journal (ISSN 0164-8241)

NATIONAL STRIPPER WELL SURVEY. see *PETROLEUM AND GAS*

NATURAL GAS ANNUAL. see *PETROLEUM AND GAS*

333.79 340 US ISSN 1052-3413
NATURAL GAS LAWYER'S JOURNAL. irreg. American Gas Association, 1515 Wilson Blvd., Arlington, VA 22209. TEL 703-841-8400. FAX 703-841-8406. (Subscr. to: Dept. 0765, McLean, VA 22109) **Document type:** trade publication.

NATURAL GAS MONTHLY. see *PETROLEUM AND GAS*

NATURAL GAS POLICY ACT NOTICES OF DETERMINATION (F E R C FORM 121). see *PETROLEUM AND GAS*

NATURAL RESOURCES FORUM. see *GEOGRAPHY*

NEIGHBORHOOD WORKS. see *HOUSING AND URBAN PLANNING*

333.79 CC ISSN 0258-1469
NENG YUAN/ENERGY SOURCES. English title varies. (Text in Chinese) bi-m. $1.90 per no. Guoji Shudian, Qikan Bu - China International Book Trading Corp., Chegongzhuang Xilu 21, P.O. Box 399, Beijing 100044, People's Republic of China.

333.79 CC
NENGYUAN GONGCHENG. (Text in Chinese) q. Zhejiang Nengyuan Yanjiusuo - Zhejiang Energy Institute, 33 Tianmushan Lu, Hangzhou, Zhejiang 310007, People's Republic of China. TEL 881910.

333.79 CC ISSN 1001-5523
NENGYUAN YANJIU YU LIYONG. (Text in Chinese) bi-m. Nanjing Jieneng Jishu Fuwu Zhongxin, Muxuyuan South No.52, Zhongshan Menwai, Nanjing, Jiangsu 210014, People's Republic of China. TEL 432001. Ed. Zhang Xiaodan.

NETWORKER. see *BUSINESS AND ECONOMICS — Small Business*

333.79 GW ISSN 0341-0323
CODEN: NEUDAA
NEUE D E L I W A - ZEITSCHRIFT; Fachzeitschrift fuer die Energie- und Wasserversorgung. Short title: N D Z. m. DM.96 (foreign DM.140). D E L I W A Berufsvereinigung fuer das Energie- und Wasserfach e.V., Am Listholze 78, 30177 Hannover, Germany. TEL 0511-39078-0. **Document type:** trade publication.
—CASDDS.

333.8 663 US
NEW FUELS REPORT. w. $610 (foreign $660). Inside Washington Publishers, Box 7167, Benjamin Franklin Sta., Washington, DC 20044. TEL 703-892-8500. FAX 703-685-2606. **Document type:** newsletter.
Formerly: Alcohol Week.

333.79 US ISSN 1058-3394
NEW PIPELINE CONSTRUCTION REPORT. a. American Gas Association, 1515 Wilson Blvd., Arlington, VA 22209. TEL 703-841-8400. FAX 703-841-8406. (Subscr. to: Dept. 0765, McLean, VA 22109-0765) **Document type:** newsletter.

333.79 US
NEW YORK (STATE). ENERGY OFFICE. ANNUAL REPORT. 1980. a. Energy Office, Office of Communications, 2 Rockefeller Plaza, Albany, NY 12223. **Document type:** government publication.

NEWFOUNDLAND. DEPARTMENT OF MINES AND ENERGY. GEOLOGICAL SURVEY BRANCH. CURRENT RESEARCH. see *MINES AND MINING INDUSTRY*

NORSK ENERGI. see *ENGINEERING*

621.47 US
NORTHEAST SUN (GREENFIELD). 1974. 4/yr. $35. Northeast Sustainable Energy Association, 23 Ames St., Greenfield, MA 01301-2444. TEL 413-774-6051. adv.; bk.rev. circ. 3,000. Indexed: Energy Rev.
Formerly (until 1983): N E S E A Newsletter.

333.79 US ISSN 0278-4408
NORTHERN SUN NEWS;* alternatives for the North Country in energy and politics. 1978. 10/yr. $15. Northern Sun Alliance, Box 581487, Minneapolis, MN 55458-1487. TEL 612-874-1540. Ed. Mordecai Specktor. adv.; bk.rev. circ. 25,000. (tabloid format; also avail. in microfiche) **Indexed:** Alt.Press Ind.

NORTHROP UNIVERSITY LAW JOURNAL OF AEROSPACE, BUSINESS AND TAXATION. see *AERONAUTICS AND SPACE FLIGHT*

333.79 US ISSN 0885-5870
NORTHWEST ENERGY NEWS. bi-m. free. Northwest Power Planning Council, 851 S.W. Sixth Ave., Ste. 1100, Portland, OR 97204. TEL 503-222-5161. FAX 503-745-3370. Ed. Carlotta Collette. **Indexed:** Energy Info.Abstr., Environ.Abstr. **Document type:** government publication.

333.7 350 US
NORTHWEST PUBLIC POWER BULLETIN. 1946. m. $25. Northwest Public Power Association, Box 4576, Vancouver, WA 98662-0576. TEL 206-254-0109. FAX 206-254-5731. Ed. Don Noel. adv.; B&W page $615. charts; illus.; stat. circ. 4,309. **Document type:** bulletin.

621.3 CN
NOVA SCOTIA POWER INC. ANNUAL REPORT. 1913. a. free. Nova Scotia Power Inc., P.O. Box 910, Halifax, N.S. B3J 2W5, Canada. TEL 902-428-6230. circ. 4,500.
Formerly (until 1992): Nova Scotia Power Corporation. Annual Report (ISSN 0078-2459)

NUCLEAR LEMONS; an assessment of America's worst commercial nuclear reactors. see *ENERGY — Nuclear Energy*

NUCLEAR MONITOR. see *ENERGY — Nuclear Energy*

NUCLEAR PLANT JOURNAL. see *ENERGY — Nuclear Energy*

NUCLEAR POWER PLANTS IN THE WORLD/GENSHIRYOKU HATSUDENSHO. see *ENERGY — Nuclear Energy*

539 US ISSN 0048-105X
HD9698.A1
NUCLEONICS WEEK. 1960. w. $1395 (foreign $1495). McGraw-Hill, Inc., Energy & Business Newsletters, 1221 Ave. of the Americas, 36th Fl., New York, NY 10020. TEL 212-512-6410. Ed. Margaret Ryan. charts; stat. (looseleaf format; back issues avail.; reprint service avail. from UMI)
●Also available online. Vendor(s): DIALOG Information Services, Inc. (File no.624/McGRAW-HILL PUBLICATIONS ONLINE), Dow Jones News Retrieval (NUC), Mead Data Central, Inc. (NUWEEK), NewsNet (EY73).

333.79 628 US ISSN 0888-5729
NUCLEUS (CAMBRIDGE). 1976. q. donation; libraries $15. Union of Concerned Scientists, 26 Church St., Cambridge, MA 02238. TEL 617-547-5552. FAX 617-864-9405. Ed. Janet S. Wager. circ. 90,000. (back issues avail.) **Document type:** academic/scholarly publication.
Description: Examines energy policy, world and national security, nuclear power safety, and global environmental problems.

O E C D NUCLEAR ENERGY AGENCY. NUCLEAR ENERGY DATA. see *ENERGY — Nuclear Energy*

O E C D NUCLEAR ENERGY AGENCY ACTIVITIES IN (YEAR). see *ENERGY — Nuclear Energy*

333.79 UK
O I E S PAPERS. irreg. Oxford Institute for Energy Studies, 57 Woodstock Rd., Oxford OX2 6FA, England. TEL 0865-311377. FAX 0865-310527. **Document type:** academic/scholarly publication.

O P E C BULLETIN. (Organization of the Petroleum Exporting Countries) see *PETROLEUM AND GAS*

O P E C REVIEW; an energy and development forum. (Organization of the Petroleum Exporting Countries) see *PETROLEUM AND GAS*

539.7 600 US ISSN 0048-1262
OAK RIDGE NATIONAL LABORATORY REVIEW. 1967. q. free. Oak Ridge National Laboratory, Box 2008, Oak Ridge, TN 37831-6144. TEL 615-574-7183. FAX 615-574-1001. Ed. Carolyn Krause. bk.rev.; charts; illus.; cum.index every 5 yrs. circ. 6,700. **Indexed:** CAD CAM Abstr., Chem.Abstr., Energy Res.Abstr. **Document type:** government publication. —BLDSC (7786.420000).
Description: Communicates ORNL research results and technological developments to ORNL employees, industry, laboratories, government agencies, the press, and universities in the U.S. and abroad.

OIL AND ARAB COOPERATION. see *PETROLEUM AND GAS*

OIL AND ENERGY TRENDS: ANNUAL STATISTICAL REVIEW. see *PETROLEUM AND GAS*

OIL AND GAS DEVELOPMENTS IN PENNSYLVANIA. see *PETROLEUM AND GAS*

OIL AND GAS REPORTER. see *PETROLEUM AND GAS*

333.79 CY
OIL MARKET TRENDS. 1972. w. $600 (includes subscr. to Downstream Trends and Gas Market Trends) (effective 1994). Arab Press Service, P.O. Box 3896, Nicosia, Cyprus. FAX 357-2-350265. s-a. index. **Document type:** newsletter.
Description: Covers crude oil supply and pricing trends within OPEC and in the Middle East. Provides surveys of oil decisions in major exporting nations.

333.79 US ISSN 0733-0219
OLIPHANT WASHINGTON SERVICE. ENERGY SUMMARY. 1972. w. $350. Oliphant Washington Service, Box 9808, Friendship Sta., Washington, DC 20016. TEL 202-338-3616. FAX 202-333-5006. Ed. Cortright Oliphant. circ. 200. (back issues avail.) **Document type:** newspaper.

OPERATIONS IN OIL DIPLOMACY. see *POLITICAL SCIENCE — International Relations*

333.79 US
OXY-FUEL NEWS. 1984. w. $695 (foreign $795). Information Resources, Inc., 1925 N. Lynn St., Ste. 1000, Arlington, VA 22204-1707. TEL 703-528-2500. FAX 703-528-1483. Ed. Shannon Schaffer. (back issues avail.) **Document type:** newsletter.
●Also available online. Vendor(s): NewsNet.
Formerly: Alcohol Update.
Description: Covers the international oxygenate market and the latest regulatory developments.

P A S C A L. T 230: ENERGIE. see PHYSICS — Abstracting, Bibliographies, Statistics

P I D S MONOGRAPH SERIES. (Philippine Institute for Development Studies) see BUSINESS AND ECONOMICS — International Development And Assistance

333.79 II ISSN 0970-3888
HD9502.P16
PACIFIC AND ASIAN JOURNAL OF ENERGY. (Text in English) 1987. s-a. Rs.250 (foreign $60). Tata Energy Research Institute, 9 Jor Bagh, New Delhi 110 003, India. TEL 11-462-3983. FAX 11-4621770. TELEX 31-61593-TERI-IN. Ed. R.K. Pachauri. adv. contact: Rashmi Kaistha. circ. 500. **Document type:** academic/scholarly publication.
Description: Latest developments in energy policy and resource planning with an emphasis on issues facing developing countries.

333.79 UK ISSN 0961-1347
PERSPECTIVES IN ENERGY. 1991. q. $200. Pion Ltd., 207 Brondesbury Park, London NW2 5JN, England. TEL 081-459-0066. FAX 081-451-6454. (Co-publisher: Moscow International Energy Club) Ed. A. Sheindlin. **Document type:** trade publication.
—BLDSC (6428.142315).
Description: Promotes international and interdisciplinary analysis of energy problems and developments, from both technological and developmental standpoint, advanced energy technologies, ecology challenges, and social implications of energy development.
Refereed Serial

PETRO ASIAN BUSINESS REPORTS. see PETROLEUM AND GAS

PETROMIN. see PETROLEUM AND GAS

PIPELINE DIGEST. see PETROLEUM AND GAS

333.8 CN ISSN 0708-918X
PLANETARY ASSOCIATION FOR CLEAN ENERGY. NEWSLETTER. (Text in English) 1979. irreg. (4-6/yr.) Can.$45. Planetary Association for Clean Energy, Inc., 100 Bronson Ave., Ste. 1001, Ottawa, Ont. K1R 6G8, Canada. TEL 613-236-6265. FAX 613-235-5876. Ed. Monique Michaud Michrowski. adv.; bk.rev. circ. 5,000. (back issues avail.) **Document type:** newsletter.

PLATT'S ASIA - PACIFIC - ARAB GULF MARKETSCAN. see PETROLEUM AND GAS

PLATT'S CRUDE OIL MARKET WIRE. see PETROLEUM AND GAS

PLATT'S CRUDE TANKERWIRE. see PETROLEUM AND GAS

PLATT'S EUROPEAN PETROCHEMICALSCAN. see PETROLEUM AND GAS

PLATT'S FAR EASTERN PETROCHEMICAL SCAN. see PETROLEUM AND GAS

PLATT'S L P GASWIRE. see PETROLEUM AND GAS

PLATT'S OILGRAM BUNKERWIRE. see PETROLEUM AND GAS

PLATT'S OILGRAM MARKETSCAN. EUROPEAN EDITION. see PETROLEUM AND GAS

PLATT'S OILGRAM MARKETSCAN. U S EDITION. see PETROLEUM AND GAS

PLATT'S OILGRAM NEWS - WIRE. see PETROLEUM AND GAS

PLATT'S OLEFINSCAN. see PETROLEUM AND GAS

PLATT'S PETROCHEMICALSCAN. see PETROLEUM AND GAS

PLATT'S PRODUCT TANKERWIRE. see PETROLEUM AND GAS

621 PL ISSN 0372-9796
TJ4 CODEN: ZPSEA8
POLITECHNIKA SLASKA. ZESZYTY NAUKOWE. ENERGETYKA. (Text in Polish; summaries in English, German, Russian) 1957. irreg. price varies. Politechnika Slaska, Katowicka 7, 44-100 Gliwice, Poland. FAX 371655. TELEX 036304. (Dist. by: Ars Polona, Krakowskie Przedmiescie 7, 00-068 Warsaw, Poland) Ed. Zbigniew Rudnicki. circ. 205. **Indexed:** Chem.Abstr. **Document type:** academic/scholarly publication.
—CASDDS.

333.79 US
POWER AUTHORITY OF THE STATE OF NEW YORK. ANNUAL REPORT. 1931. a. free. New York Power Authority, 1633 Broadway, New York, NY 10019. TEL 212-468-6000. FAX 212-468-6259. Ed. Susan Gessner. circ. 20,000. **Document type:** corporate report.

POWER ENGINEERING (TULSA). see ENGINEERING — Electrical Engineering

333.79 621.042 US
POWER LETTER. 1986. s-m. $395 (effective Jan. 1992). Forecast International Inc. - D M S, 22 Commerce Rd., Newtown, CT 06470-1643. TEL 203-426-0800. FAX 203-426-4262. Ed. David J. Francus. circ. 475. (looseleaf format; back issues avail.) **Document type:** newsletter.
●Also available online. Vendor(s): DIALOG Information Services, Inc.
Description: Covers combustion systems, R & D, contracts, maintenance, overhaul, marketing, business development, engineering.

333.79 US ISSN 0738-5676
POWER LINE. 1975. bi-m. $20 to individuals; institutions $35. Environmental Action Foundation, 6930 Carroll Ave., Ste. 600, Takoma Park, MD 20912. TEL 301-891-1100. FAX 301-891-2218. Ed. Lynne Capehart. adv.; bk.rev.; illus. circ. 2,300. (back issues avail.) **Indexed:** Alt.Press Ind.
Description: Studies energy issues from a consumer activist perspective; including conservation, utilities, nuclear and renewable energy.

333.79 US ISSN 1072-9569
POWER SOURCE; independent energy business news. 1985. bi-w. $295 (foreign $375). H C I Publications, 410 Archibald St., Kansas City, MO 64111-3046. TEL 816-931-1311. FAX 816-931-2015. Ed. John Braden; Pub. Leslie Eden. cum.index: 1985-1990. (looseleaf format; back issues avail.) **Document type:** newsletter.
●Also available online. Vendor(s): NewsNet (EY54).
Formerly: Purpa Lines.
Description: Covers the cogeneration and independent power industry; including relevant business, finance, project, fuel and tax news.

621.042 US ISSN 0079-4457
TK2921 CODEN: PSSYAD
POWER SOURCES SYMPOSIUM. PROCEEDINGS. 1956. biennial. $60. (I E E E) Institute of Electrical and Electronics Engineers, Inc., 345 E. 47th St., New York, NY 10017-2394. TEL 212-705-7900. FAX 212-705-7682. (Subscr. to: 445 Hoes Ln., Box 1331, Piscataway, NJ 08855-1331) circ. 700. **Indexed:** Chem.Abstr. **Document type:** proceedings.
—CCC.

PREVISIONS GLISSANTES DETAILLEES EN PERSPECTIVES SECTORIELLES (VOL.17): ENERGIE. see BUSINESS AND ECONOMICS — Economic Situation And Conditions

PROGRESS IN ENERGY AND COMBUSTION SCIENCE; an international review journal. see ENGINEERING — Chemical Engineering

ENERGY 2211

621.042 US ISSN 1062-7995
TK2960 CODEN: PPHOED
▼**PROGRESS IN PHOTOVOLTAICS;** research and applications. 1993. q. $195 to institutions. John Wiley & Sons, Inc., 605 Third Ave., New York, NY 10158-0012. TEL 212-850-6000. FAX 212-850-6088. Ed. P.A. Lynn. **Indexed:** Environ.Per.Bibl. **Document type:** academic/scholarly publication.
—BLDSC (6873.060000); EI; SWETS; CASDDS.
Description: Provides timely information about this alternative energy resource including the applications, materials, and improvements in efficiency techniques.

621.3 RU ISSN 0033-1155
TK4 CODEN: PREGAI
PROMYSHLENNAYA ENERGETIKA. 1944. m. $150. Ministerstvo Goryuchego i Energetiki Rosii - Ministry of Fuel and Energetics of Russia, Bol'shoi Cherkasskii Per., 2-10, 103012 Moscow, Russia. TEL 921-66-04 Ed. V.A. Lukin. bk.rev.; bibl.; charts; stat. circ. 10,000. **Indexed:** C.I.S. Abstr., Chem.Abstr, Pollut.Abstr., Sci Abstr.
—BLDSC (0134.240000); CASDDS.

333.79 US ISSN 0196-7843
PUBLIC UTILITIES REPORTS. (Supplement avail.: Annual Digest (ISSN 0895-1713)) 1915; 3rd Series 1953; 4th Series 1974 10/yr. $890 ($979 with Annual Digest) (effective 1994). Public Utilities Reports, Inc., 2111 Wilson Blvd., Ste., 200, Arlington, VA 22201. TEL 703-243-7000; 800-368-5001. FAX 703-527-5829.
●Also available online. Vendor(s): Mead Data Central, Inc., West Services, Inc.
Also available on CD-ROM.
Description: Covers the entire field of public utilities regulation including state and federal regulatory commission decisions and relevant court decisions.

PULSE OF THE PLANET. see ENVIRONMENTAL STUDIES

THE QUAD REPORT; covering efficiency, demand-side management, and energy policy. see CONSUMER EDUCATION AND PROTECTION

QUAD REPORT CASE STUDIES. see CONSUMER EDUCATION AND PROTECTION

333.79 622.33 US ISSN 0736-4598
CODEN: QCREDK
QUARTERLY COAL REPORT. q. $20. U.S. Department of Energy, Energy Information Administration, c/o Paulette Young, Coal Division, 1000 Independence Ave., S.W., EI-522, DC 20585. TEL 202-586-8800. FAX 202-586-0727. Ed. Mary Paull. (also avail. in microfiche from CIS diskette format; reprint service avail. from CIS) **Indexed:** Amer.Stat.Ind. (1982-). **Document type:** government publication.
●Also available online. Vendor(s): DIALOG Information Services, Inc.
—CASDDS.
Incorporates in part (1980-1991): Coal Distribution (ISSN 0737-4399); Formerly (until 1982): Coke Plant Report (ISSN 0730-7543); Which incorporated (in 1980) Coke and Coal Chemicals (Annual) (ISSN 0162-6175); Which was formerly: Coke and Coal Chemicals Monthly; Monthly Coke Report; Coal Distribution was formerly (until 1980): Bituminous and Subbituminous Coal and Lignite Distribution; (until 1979): Bituminous Coal and Lignite Distribution.

338.2 621.042 US ISSN 8756-9655
TN844 CODEN: QRMTEA
QUARTERLY REVIEW OF METHANE FROM COAL SEAMS TECHNOLOGY. 1983. q. Gas Research Institute, 8600 W. Bryn Mawr Ave., Chicago, IL 60631.
—BLDSC (7207.550000); UnCover.

333.79 622 CN ISSN 0228-9113
QUEBEC (PROVINCE). MINISTERE DE L'ENERGIE ET DES RESSOURCES. RAPPORT ANNUEL. a. Can.$4. Ministere de l'Energie et des Ressources, Renseignements, 5700 4e Ave., Ouest, Charlesbourg, PQ G1H 6R1, Canada. TEL 418-643-5150. (Dist. by: Publications du Quebec, C.P. 1005, Quebec, PQ G1K 7B5, Canada) illus.; stat. **Document type:** government publication.
Formed by the merger of: Quebec (Province). Ministere des Terres et Forets. Rapport Annuel (ISSN 0703-4938) & Quebec (Province). Ministere des Richesses Naturelles. Rapport Annuel (ISSN 0703-0940)

ENERGY

QUEBEC (PROVINCE). MINISTERE DES FORETS. DIRECTION DE LA RECHERCHE. GUIDE. see *FORESTS AND FORESTRY*

QUEBEC (PROVINCE). MINISTERE DES FORETS. DIRECTION DE LA RECHERCHE. MEMOIRE DE RECHERCHE FORESTIERE. see *FORESTS AND FORESTRY*

621.042 540   UK   ISSN 0268-330X
R & D DIGEST. (Research & Development) 1977. a. free. British Gas Plc., Rivermill House, 152 Grosvenor Rd., London SW1V 3JL, England. TEL 071-821-1444. FAX 071-630-7538. TELEX 938529. Ed. B. Bellwood. charts; illus. circ. 20,000. (back issues avail.) **Indexed:** Energy Info.Abstr.
—BLDSC (7218.330000).

333.7   GW
KK6852.A13
R D E - RECHT DER ENERGIEWIRTSCHAFT. m. DM.138. (Vereinigung Deutscher Elektrizitaetswerke) Carl Heymanns Verlag KG, Luxemburgerstr. 449, 50939 Cologne, Germany. TEL 0221-46010-0. FAX 0221-4601069. **Document type:** trade publication.
—CCC.
Formerly (until 1993): Recht der Elektrizitaetswirtschaft (ISSN 0171-712X)

333.79   TH   ISSN 0857-6173
R E R I C INTERNATIONAL ENERGY JOURNAL. (Text in English) 1979. s-a. $75 membership; institutions $120. Asian Institute of Technology, Regional Energy Resources Information Center, G.P.O. Box 2754, Bangkok 10501, Thailand. TEL 66-2-5245866. FAX 66-2-5245870. TELEX 84276 AITTH. Ed. On-Anong Suramranat. adv.; bk.rev. circ. 600. (back issues avail.) **Indexed:** AIT Reports, Energy Info.Abstr., Energy Rev., Environ.Abstr., Environ.Per.Bibl. (1985-). **Document type:** academic/scholarly publication.
—BLDSC (7713.846270); EI.
Formerly: Renewable Energy Review Journal (ISSN 0125-3719)
Description: Reviews and research papers on energy planning, energy conservation and renewable energy.

333.8   TH   ISSN 0125-1775
R E R I C NEWS. 1978. q. membership. Asian Institute of Technology, Regional Energy Resources Information Center, P.O. Box 2754, Bangkok 10501, Thailand. TEL 66-2-5245866. FAX 66-2-5245870. TELEX 84276 AITTH. (back issues avail.) **Indexed:** Energy Info.Abstr., Energy Rev., Environ.Abstr. **Document type:** newsletter.
—BLDSC (7713.846300).
Description: Information on energy planning and conservation, solar and bio-mass energy and small-scale hydropower and wind energy.

333.8   UK   ISSN 0955-5188
R E VIEW. (Renewable Energy) 1979. q. free. Department of Trade & Industry, Rm. 3-3-26, 1 Palace St., London SW1E 5HE, England. TEL 071-238-3037. illus. circ. 7,000. **Indexed:** Br.Ceram.Abstr., Fluidex. **Document type:** government publication.
—BLDSC (7785.898400).
Formerly (until 1987): R E News (ISSN 0262-2556)

333.79 327   CY
RE-DRAWING THE ISLAMIC MAP. 1972. m. $800 (includes subscr. to A P S News Service, Strategic Balance in the Middle East, Fate of the Arabian Peninsula, Operations in Oil Diplomacy) (effective 1994). Arab Press Service, P.O. Box 3896, Nicosia, Cyprus. FAX 357-2-350265. s-a. index. **Document type:** bulletin.
Description: Surveys Islamic states and political activities.

333.79   UY
RECURSOS ENERGETICOS DE LOS PAISES DE LA C I E R. (Text in Portuguese, Spanish) 1968. irreg. Comision de Integracion Electrica Regional, Bulevar Artigas 1040, 11300 Montevideo, Uruguay. TEL 79-53-59. FAX 5982-783193. TELEX 26609 CIER UY. index.

333.8 621.042   UK
RENEW NEWSLETTER. 1979. bi-m. £12 to individuals; institutions, libraries £30. Network for Alternative Technology and Technology Assessment, c/o Energy and Environment Research Unit, Faculty of Technology, Open University, Walton Hall, Milton Keynes, Bucks. MK7 6AA, England. TEL 0908-653197. FAX 0908-653744. Ed. Dave Elliott. bk.rev. circ. 500. (looseleaf format; back issues avail.) **Document type:** newsletter.
Formerly (until 1991): N A T T A Newsletter (ISSN 0262-7221)
Description: Features news about renewable energy and allied topics, such as the development of solar, wind, wave, and tidal power.

621.042   UK   ISSN 0960-1481
TJ809   CODEN: RNENE3
RENEWABLE ENERGY. 1991. 10/yr. £535($825) (effective 1994). Elsevier Science Ltd., Pergamon, P.O. Box 800, Kidlington, Oxford OX5 1DX, England. TEL 44-865-843000. FAX 44-865-843010. (Subscr. in U.S. and Canada to: Elsevier Science, 660 White Plains Rd., Tarrytown, NY 10591-5153. TEL 914-524-9200. FAX 914-333-2444) Ed. A.A.M. Sayigh. adv.; index. (also avail. in microfilm from UMI; back issues avail.) **Indexed:** AESIS, Curr.Cont., Energy Info.Abstr., Energy Rev., Environ.Per.Bibl. (1990-), Excerp.Med., Sci.Abstr. **Document type:** academic/scholarly publication.
—BLDSC (7364.187000); EI; SWETS; UMI; CASDDS. **CCC**.
Incorporates (1984-1990): Solar and Wind Technology (ISSN 0741-983X)
Description: Covers all aspects of renewable energy.
Refereed Serial

333.79 621.042   UK   ISSN 0306-364X
Z5853.P83
RENEWABLE ENERGY BULLETIN. (Issued in two parts) 1974. bi-m. £186 for Parts A & B (foreign £197). Multi-Science Publishing Co. Ltd., 107 High St., Brentwood, Essex CM14 4RX, England. TEL 0277-224632. FAX 0277-224632. (U.S. subscr. to: Box 176, Avenel, NJ 07001) Ed. J. Wilson. index. **Indexed:** Energy Info.Abstr. **Document type:** abstracting/indexing.
—CCC.
Description: Provides information on non-fossil sources of energy.

621.042   US
RENEWABLE ENERGY MANUFACTURERS LISTS: BIOMASS FUELS. a. $5. Synerjy, Box 1854, Cathedral Sta., New York, NY 10025. index. (also avail. in diskette format)
Description: Covers wood, alcohol and methane and refuse-derived fuels. Organized by geographic area and subject.

RESEARCH & DEVELOPMENT. see *EARTH SCIENCES*

333.7 622   CN   ISSN 0380-4275
TN873.C22
RESERVES OF COAL, PROVINCE OF ALBERTA. 1972. a. Can.$110. Energy Resources Conservation Board, 640 5th Ave. S.W., Calgary, Alta. T2P 3G4, Canada. TEL 403-297-8311. FAX 403-297-7040. TELEX 03-821717. illus. **Indexed:** CS Ind.
Description: Data on established coal reserves in the province of Alberta.

333.79   US   ISSN 0145-1901
RESERVES OF CRUDE OIL, NATURAL GAS LIQUIDS AND NATURAL GAS IN THE UNITED STATES AND CANADA AND UNITED STATES PRODUCTIVE CAPACITY. 1966. a. American Gas Association, 1515 Wilson Blvd., Arlington, VA 22209. TEL 703-841-8400. FAX 703-841-8406. (Subscr. to: Dept. 0765, McLean, VA 22109-0765) stat. **Document type:** trade publication.

333.79   NE   ISSN 0928-7655
HD9502.A1   CODEN: REEEEF
RESOURCE AND ENERGY ECONOMICS; a journal devoted to interdisciplinary studies in the allocation of natural resources. (Text in English) 1978. 4/yr. fl.501($271) (effective 1994). North-Holland (Subsidiary of: Elsevier Science B.V.), P.O. Box 211, 1000 AE Amsterdam, Netherlands. TEL 31-20-5803911. FAX 31-20-5803598. TELEX 18582 ESPA NL. (Subscr. in U.S. and Canada to: Elsevier Science Inc., Box 882, Madison Sq. Sta., New York, NY 10159. TEL 212-989-5800. FAX 212-633-3990) Eds. G.S. Tolley, J.L. Sweeney. adv.; bk.rev.; index. (also avail. in microfilm from UMI; back issues avail.) **Indexed:** ABI Inform., AESIS, AIT Reports, Asian-Pac.Econ.Lit., Biol.Abstr., C.R.E.J., Energy Ind., Energy Info.Abstr., Environ.Abstr., GeoRef., J.of Econ.Lit., Risk Abstr., Sci.Abstr. **Document type:** academic/scholarly publication.
—BLDSC (7777.601530); EI; Faxon; UnCover; SWETS; UMI. **CCC**.
Formerly (until 1993): Resources and Energy (ISSN 0165-0572)
Description: Presents empirical studies, theoretical models and applications of specific techniques and methods, such as systems analysis, econometrics, growth models and energy and resource analysis.
Refereed Serial

RESOURCE RECOVERY YEARBOOK. see *ENVIRONMENTAL STUDIES — Waste Management*

RESOURCES. see *LAW*

333.8   KE
RESOURCES. 1989. q. Kenya Energy and Environment Organizations, P.O. Box 48197, Nairobi, Kenya. **Indexed:** P.L.E.S.A. (1989-).

333.79   UK   ISSN 0301-4207
TN1   CODEN: RSPCAM
RESOURCES POLICY. 1975. q. £175 in UK and Europe; elsewhere £185. Butterworth - Heinemann (Subsidiary of: Reed International PLC), Linacre House, Jordan Hill, Oxford OX2 8DP, England. TEL 0865-310366. FAX 0865-310898. TELEX 83111 BHPOXF G. (Subscr. to: Turpin Transactions Ltd., Distribution Centre, Blackhorse Rd., Letchworth, Herts SG6 1HN, England. TEL 0462-672555) Ed. Roderick G. Eggert. bk.rev.; abstr.; illus. (also avail. in microform from UMI; back issues avail.) **Indexed:** AESIS, Asian-Pac.Econ.Lit., Br.Ceram.Abstr., Br.Rail.Bd., C.R.E.J., Cadscan, Cont.Pg.Manage., Copper Abstr., Curr.Cont., Deep Sea Res.& Oceanogr.Abstr., Energy Ind., Energy Info.Abstr., Environ.Abstr., Environ.Ind., Excerp.Med., Fuel & Energy Abstr., Gas Abstr., Geo.Abstr., GeoRef., I D A, Key to Econ.Sci., Lead Abstr., Met.Abstr., P.A.I.S., Risk Abstr., Rural Devel.Abstr., SSCI, Zincscan.
—BLDSC (7777.608600); CIS; Faxon; UnCover; SWETS; UMI. **CCC**.
Description: Devoted to minerals policy and economics. Topics include minerals availability, exploration and development, production, international trade, taxation, investment and finance. Aimed at economists and decisionmakers in academia, government, commerce and industry worldwide.
Refereed Serial

333.79   EC   ISSN 0254-8445
REVISTA ENERGETICA/ENERGY MAGAZINE. (Text in English and Spanish) 1977. 3/yr. $50 includes: Energy Update. Organizacion Latinoamericana de Energia - Latin-American Energy Organization, Casilla 17-11-6413, Quito, Ecuador. TEL 593-2-538122. FAX 593-2-539684. TELEX 2-2728 OLADE ED. Ed. Francisco J. Gutierrez. bk.rev. circ. 1,300.
Formerly (until 1981): Organizacion Latinoamericana de Energia. Energy Bulletin.

ENERGY

333.79   FR   ISSN 0303-240X
TJ2   CODEN: REEND7
REVUE DE L'ENERGIE. (Text in French; summaries in English, French) 1949. m. 892.50 F. (foreign 1050 F.). Editions Techniques et Economiques, 3 rue Soufflot, 75005 Paris, France. TEL 46-34-10-30. FAX 46-34-55-83. TELEX 260 717 F. Ed. Genevieve Epstein. adv.; charts; illus.; stat. **Indexed:** C.I.S.Abstr., Chem.Abstr., Eng.Ind., Fuel & Energy Abstr., Gas Abstr., Geo.Abstr., I D A, Key to Econ.Sci., P.A.I.S.For.Lang.Ind., Sci.Abstr.
—BLDSC (7900.060000); Faxon; SWETS; CASDDS.
     Formerly (until 1974): Revue Francaise de l'Energie (ISSN 0035-2934)
     Description: Covers petroleum, carbon, gas, and electricity.

333.79   TI
REVUE TUNISIENNE DE L'ENERGIE. 1985. q. TL.20($22.50) Ministere de l'Economie Nationale, Avenue Mohamed 5, 1002 Tunis, Tunisia. TELEX 14652 DGE. Ed. M. Haddad. adv.; bk.rev. circ. 1,500. **Document type:** government publication.
     Description: Covers maintenance, productivity, innovations and modernization in the energy sector of Tunisia.

333.79   IT
RISPARMIO ENERGETICO. 4/yr. Viale Regina Margherita 125, 00198 Rome, Italy. TEL 6-85-281. Ed. Ferrante Pierantoni. circ. 15,000.

333.79 621.042   US
ROCKY MOUNTAIN INSTITUTE NEWSLETTER. 1985. 3/yr. $10 donation. Rocky Mountain Institute, 1739 Snowmass Creek Rd., Snowmass, CO 81654-9199. TEL 303-927-3851. FAX 303-927-4178. E-mail: mhenson@rmi.org. Ed. Randy Udall. illus.; stat. circ. 26,000. (back issues avail.) **Document type:** newsletter.
     Description: Discusses policy and issues relating to energy and natural resource use reduction in all sectors, the development of sustainable technologies, international projects, and activities, projects and publications of the institute.

RUSSIAN JOURNAL OF HEAVY MACHINERY. see *MACHINERY*

333.79   AO
S A D C C ENERGY BULLETIN. (Editions in English, Portuguese) 1983. q. $12 (outside Africa $24). Southern African Development Coordination Conference, Energy Sector, Technical & Administrative Unit, P.O. Box 2876, Luanda, Angola. TEL 244-2-345288. FAX 244-2-343003. TELEX 4090 TAUANG AN. (Subscr. to: P.O. Box 3217, Luanda, Angola) Ed. Gabriel Musole. adv.; illus. circ. 14,000. (back issues avail.)
     Description: Technical publication which specializes in energy problems of the Southern part of Africa.

333.792   UK
S C R A M SAFE ENERGY JOURNAL. 1977. bi-m. £10 to individuals; institutions £25. Scottish Campaign to Resist the Atomic Menace, 11 Forth St., Edinburgh EH1 3LE, Scotland. TEL 031-557-4283. FAX 031-557-4284. Ed. Dave Spence. adv.; bk.rev. circ. 1,000.
     Former titles: S C R A M Journal; (until: 1983): S C R A M Energy Bulletin.

S E B E S. (Strategies Energetiques Biosphere et Societe) see *ENVIRONMENTAL STUDIES*

621.042   US
S E R I ETHANOL ANNUAL REPORT. 1985. a. free to qualified personnel. (U.S. Department of Energy, Conservation and Renewable Energy Office) Solar Energy Research Institute, Technical Inquiry Service, 1617 Cole Blvd., Golden, CO 80401-3393. TEL 303-231-1000. circ. controlled. **Document type:** government publication.
     Former titles: Alcohol Fuels Program. Annual Report; Alcohol Fuels Process R - D Newsletter.
     Refereed Serial

S O N R E E L MONOGRAPH SERIES. (Section of Natural Resources, Energy, and Environmental Law) see *LAW*

SAARBERG. see *MINES AND MINING INDUSTRY*

333.79   US   ISSN 0279-2338
SAVING ENERGY. 1977. m. $75 (foreign $100). Saving Energy, 5411-117th Ave., S.E., Bellevue, WA 98006. TEL 206-643-4248. Pub. Larry Liebman. (back issues avail.) **Document type:** newsletter.
     Description: Describes what business, industry, and institutions can and are doing to save energy.

333.8   GW
SCHRIFTENREIHE AKTUELLE FRAGEN DER ENERGIEWIRTSCHAFT. irreg., vol.29, 1986. price varies. R. Oldenbourg Verlag GmbH, Rosenheimerstr. 145, 81671 Munich, Germany. TEL 089-4112-0. FAX 089-4112207. (Subscr. to: Postfach 801360, 81613 Munich, Germany) **Document type:** monographic series.

333.79   US
SCIENCE AND TECHNOLOGY SERIAL REPORTS: CHINA: ENERGY. irreg. $696 in U.S., Canada, Mexico; elsewhere $1392. (Joint Publications Research Service) U.S. National Technical Information Service, 5285 Port Royal Rd., Springfield, VA 22161. TEL 703-487-4630. **Document type:** government publication.

SECTOR ENERGIA E INDUSTRIA. see *ENGINEERING*

333.79 640.73   US
SENIOR SUN. 1980. a. free. New York State Electric & Gas Corp., 4500 Vestal Parkway E., Binghamton, NY 13902. TEL 607-762-4822. FAX 607-762-4189. Ed. Stacey L. Lovett. tr.lit.; circ. 65,000 (controlled). (tabloid format) **Document type:** newsletter.
     Description: Provides news and articles about energy and cost saving ideas for consumers.

621 333.8   JA
SHIGEN ENERUGI KENKYUKAI KOENSHU/PROCEEDINGS ON STUDY OF RESOURCES AND ENERGY. (Text in Japanese; summaries in English) 1983. a. Kansai Daigaku, Kogyo Gijutsu Kenkyujo - Kansai University, Research Institute of Industrial Technology, 3-35, Yamatecho 3-chome, Suitas-shi, Osaka 564, Japan.

333.8 628.4   US
TD796.2
SOLID WASTE TECHNOLOGIES; a magazine of waste management solutions. (Supplement avail.: Industry Directory) 1987. bi-m. $49 (foreign $60). H C I Publications, 410 Archibald St., Kansas City, MO 64111-3046. TEL 816-931-1311. FAX 816-931-2015. Ed. Michael Hilts. adv.; cum.index: 1987-1990. (back issues avail.) **Indexed:** Energy Info.Abstr., Environ.Abstr., Environ.Per.Bibl. (1989-). **Document type:** trade publication.
—BLDSC (8327.507000); EI.
     Formerly: Solid Waste and Power (ISSN 1058-9074)
     Description: Covers all aspects of the municipal solid waste - recycling, landfills and energy-from-waste, including operations, equipment and systems, technical briefs, and industry news.

621.042   US   ISSN 0275-7893
TJ163.25.S68
SOVIET TECHNOLOGY REVIEWS. SECTION A: ENERGY REVIEWS. 1982. a. 108 ECU (effective 1993). Harwood Academic Publishers, 820 Town Center Dr., Langhorne, PA 19047. TEL 215-750-2642. FAX 216-750-6343. (UK subscr. to: P.O. Box 90, Reading, Berkshire RG1 8JL, England. TEL 0734-560-080) Ed. Yu.N. Rudenko. index. (also avail. in microform; back issues avail.)
—EI; Faxon. **CCC.**
     Refereed Serial

SPACE POWER; resources, manufacturing and development. see *AERONAUTICS AND SPACE FLIGHT*

333.8 622   CN   ISSN 0834-9886
HC113.5
STANDING COMMITTEE ON ENERGY, MINES AND RESOURCES. MINUTES OF PROCEEDINGS AND EVIDENCE. 1986. irreg. Canadian Government Publishing Centre, Publicity and Promotion, Supply and Services Canada, Ottawa, Ont. K1A 0S9, Canada. **Document type:** government publication, proceedings.

621.1   II   ISSN 0039-0828
TJ275   CODEN: SFUJAM
STEAM & FUEL USERS' JOURNAL. (Text in English) 1950. q. Rs.60. Steam & Fuel Users' Association of India, Technical Advisory Committee, 4B1 J.P. Tower, 1 Thirumurthy Rd., Nungambakkam, Madras 600 034, India. Ed. L. Subramanian. adv.; bk.rev.; abstr.; charts; illus. circ. 450.
—CASDDS.

STRATEGIC BALANCE IN THE MIDDLE EAST. see *POLITICAL SCIENCE — International Relations*

333.79   US   ISSN 1048-5236
HD9502.A1   CODEN: SEENEJ
STRATEGIC PLANNING FOR ENERGY AND THE ENVIRONMENT. 1981. q. $99 (foreign $125) (effective 1992). (Association of Energy Engineers) Fairmont Press, Inc., 700 Indian Trail, Lilburn, GA 30247. TEL 404-925-9388. FAX 404-381-9865. Ed. F. William Payne. **Indexed:** Energy Ind., Energy Info.Abstr., Energy Rev., Environ.Abstr., Environ.Ind., Environ.Per.Bibl. (1990-).
—BLDSC (8474.031545); EI; UMI. **CCC.**
     Former titles (until 1990): Strategic Planning and Energy Management (ISSN 8750-3204); (until 1984): Energy Economics, Policy and Management (ISSN 0275-7966)

333.79   GW   ISSN 0170-7779
STUDIEN ZUR ENERGIEWIRTSCHAFT. 1978. irreg. price varies. I F O Institut fuer Wirtschaftsforschung, Poschingerstr. 5, 8000 Munich 86, Germany. TEL 089-9224-0. circ. 400.
     Description: Research results of the FRG's Department of Energy, Raw Materials and Technology.

SURVEY OF MINES AND ENERGY RESOURCES. see *MINES AND MINING INDUSTRY*

621.042   US   ISSN 0163-2183
TJ163.2
SYNERJY; a directory of renewable energy. 1974. s-a. $50. Box 1854, Cathedral Sta., New York, NY 10025. TEL 212-865-9595. Ed. Jeffrey M. Twine. pat. circ. 300. (also avail. in diskette format; back issues avail.) **Document type:** directory.
     Description: Solar, wind, biomass and hydropowers; energy storage books, government publications, research groups as well as facilities are listed.

621.042   II   ISSN 0971-085X
TJ163.13
T I D E. (Teri Information Digest on Energy) (Text in English) 1991. q. Rs.150($25) Tata Energy Research Institute, 9 Jor Bagh, New Delhi 110 003, India. TEL 462-3983. TELEX 31-61593 TERI IN. Ed. Nalini Ranganathan. adv. contact: Rashmi Kaistha. bk.rev.; abstr. circ. 800. (back issues avail.) **Document type:** academic/scholarly publication.
     Formed by the 1991 merger of: Energy Digest (ISSN 0970-3454) & Indian Energy Abstracts (ISSN 0970-3853)
     Description: Covers conventional energy sources such as coal, oil, water power as well as emerging renewable technologies such as solar, wind, and biomass.

621.3   YU   ISSN 0350-218X
TERMOTEHNIKA. (Text in Serbo-Croatian; summaries in English) 1968. q. $45. Savez Drustava Termicara Jugoslavije - Yugoslav Society for Thermal Sciences, c/o Institut za Nuklearne Nauke "Boris Kidric", P.O. Box 522, 11001 Belgrade, Serbia, Yugoslavia. TEL 38-11-458-222. FAX 38-11-453-670. TELEX 11563 YU. Ed. Jovica. R. Riznic. adv.; bk.rev.; software rev. circ. 1,000.
     Description: Publishes scientific and professional papers on energy, energy engineering, thermal sciences and related topics.

333.8 622   US
TEXAS ENERGY. 1974. bi-m. free. Texas A & M University, Center for Energy and Mineral Resources, College Station, TX 77843-1243. TEL 409-845-8025. Ed. Mary Ann Williams. bk.rev.; illus. circ. 12,000. **Indexed:** Energy Info.Abstr.
     Formerly: Texas Energy and Mineral Resources.

333.79   US
TEXAS ENERGY REPORTER. 1983. q. $85. 5926 Balcones Dr., Ste. 220, Austin, TX 78731. TEL 512-452-9872. FAX 512-452-9007. Ed. Edward Selig. stat.

ENERGY

TEXAS NATURAL RESOURCES REPORTER. see *WATER RESOURCES*

363.6   US   ISSN 0744-7981
TEXAS PUBLIC UTILITY NEWS.* 1978. s-m. $495. Research & Planning Consultants, Inc., 7600 Chevy Chase Dr., Ste. 500, Austin, TX 78752-1568. TEL 512-472-7765. Ed. Gaylon Finklea. cum.index: 1980-1989. circ. 150. (looseleaf format; back issues avail.)

333.79   US
TOPICS IN ENERGY. 1982. irreg. price varies. Springer-Verlag, 175 Fifth Ave., New York, NY 10010. TEL 212-460-1500. FAX 212-473-6272. (Also: Berlin, Heidelberg, Tokyo and Vienna) **Document type:** monographic series.

TYAZHELOE MASHINOSTROENIE. see *MACHINERY*

333.79   US
U S COAL PLANT STATISTICS. 1986. a. $225. Utility Data Institute (Subsidiary of: McGraw-Hill), 1200 G St., N.W., Ste. 250, Washington, DC 20005. TEL 202-942-8788; 800-486-3660. FAX 202-942-8789. stat. (back issues avail.) **Document type:** trade publication.
 Description: Provides operating and pollution-control statistics for all U.S. coal-powered electric plants, including technical and financial information.

333.79   GW   ISSN 0173-8720
UMWELT UND ENERGIE. 1980. bi-m. DM.178. Rudolf Haufe Verlag GmbH & Co. KG, Hindenburgstr. 64, 79102 Freiburg, Germany. TEL 0761-3683-0. FAX 0761-3683-195. **Document type:** academic/scholarly publication.

333.79   UN
UNITED NATIONS. ECONOMIC COMMISSION FOR ASIA AND THE PACIFIC. ENERGY RESOURCES DEVELOPMENT SERIES. 1954. irreg., no.31, 1988. price varies. United Nations Economic and Social Commission for Asia and the Pacific (ESCAP), United Nations Bldg., Rajadamnern Ave., Bangkok 10200, Thailand. (Dist. by: United Nations Publications, Room DC2-0853, New York, NY 10017; or Distribution and Sales Section, Palais des Nations, CH-1211 Geneva 10, Switzerland) (also avail. in microfiche from CIS) **Indexed:** IIS.

621.3   US
U.S. DEPARTMENT OF ENERGY REPORTS. s-m. $16 per no. in U.S., Canada, Mexico; elsewhere $32. U.S. National Technical Information Service, 5825 Port Royal Rd., Springfield, VA 22161. TEL 703-487-4630. (microfiche)
 Description: Unclassified technical reports, critical reviews, conference papers, symposia produced by DOE.

333.79   US   ISSN 0270-8205
U.S. ENERGY INFORMATION ADMINISTRATION. SHORT-TERM ENERGY OUTLOOK. 1979. q. $16. U.S. Department of Energy, Energy Information Administration, National Energy Information Center, EI-231, Rm. 1F-048, Forrestal Bldg., 1000 Independence Ave., S.W., Washington, DC 20585. TEL 202-586-8800. (Dist. by: Supt. of Documents, Washington, DC 20402) charts; stat. (also avail. in microfiche from CIS; reprint service avail. from CIS) **Indexed:** Amer.Stat.Ind. (1979-), Energy Info.Abstr. **Document type:** government publication.

333.79   US
U.S. GAS TURBINE HISTORICAL ANNUAL DATA BASE. (Includes: Production on Costs: U.S. Gas Turbine and Combined-Cycle Power Plants) a. $495 (updates $295). Utility Data Institute (Subsidiary of: McGraw-Hill), 1200 G St., N.W., Ste. 250, Washington, DC 20005. TEL 202-942-8788; 800-486-3660. FAX 202-942-8789. (diskette format) **Document type:** trade publication.
 Description: Compiles gas turbine production and running costs.

U.S. NUCLEAR ENERGY INSTITUTE. NUCLEAR ENERGY INFO. see *ENERGY — Nuclear Energy*

U.S. NUCLEAR REGULATORY COMMISSION. REPORT TO CONGRESS ON ABNORMAL OCCURRENCES. see *ENERGY — Nuclear Energy*

U.S. NUCLEAR REGULATORY COMMISSION. WEEKLY INFORMATION REPORT. see *ENERGY — Nuclear Energy*

621.042 620.1   US
U.S. OFFICE OF TECHNOLOGY ASSESSMENT. REPORTS. ENERGY AND MATERIALS PROGRAM. irreg. price varies. U.S. Office of Technology Assessment, Publication Distribution, U.S. Congress, 600 Pennsylvania Ave., S.E., Washington, DC 20510-8025. TEL 202-224-8996. FAX 202-228-6098. E-mail: PUBSREQUEST@OTA.GOV. (Dist. by: Superintendent of Documents, U.S. Government Printing Office, Box 371954, Pittsburgh, PA 15250-7954. TEL 202-783-3238. FAX 202-512-2250; And: National Technical Information Service, 5285 Port Royal Rd., Springfield, VA 22161. TEL 703-487-7650. FAX 703-321-8547) (also avail. in microfiche from CIS; back issues avail.; reprint service avail. from CIS) **Document type:** monographic series, government publication.
 Formerly: U.S. Office of Technology Assessment. Reports. Energy Program.
 Description: Reports provide technical information on various energy and energy technology issues.

UNIVERSITY OF TASMANIA. CENTRE FOR ENVIRONMENTAL STUDIES. WORKING PAPERS. see *CONSERVATION*

333.8   II   ISSN 0378-9535
TJ163.2   CODEN: URJADF
URJA. (Text in English) 1977. m. Rs.200($75) Urja, P.O. Box 3008, G-82 Sujan Singh Park, New Delhi 110 003, India. TEL 11-611536. FAX 11-4628251. TELEX 31-7411-URJA-IN. Ed. Dipak B.R. Chaudhuri. adv.; bk.rev. circ. 6,357. **Indexed:** Acid Rain Abstr., Acid Rain Ind., Agri.Eng.Abstr., C.R.I. Abstr., Chem.Abstr., Energy Info.Abstr., Environ.Abstr.
 —BLDSC (9124.330000); CIS; EI; CASDDS. **CCC**.
 Description: Promotes utilization of the untapped natural resources of India.

333.79   UY   ISSN 0797-4264
URUGUAY. UNIDAD ASESORA DE PROMOCION INDUSTRIAL. MEMORIA DE ACTIVIDADES. 1980. a. Ministerio de Industria y Energia, Montevideo, Uruguay.

UTILITIES LAW REVIEW. see *LAW*

UTILITY COMMUNICATORS INTERNATIONAL. NEWSLETTER. see *ADVERTISING AND PUBLIC RELATIONS*

UTILITY FORECASTER. see *BUSINESS AND ECONOMICS — Investments*

333.79 621.042   US   ISSN 0890-2984
UTILITY REPORTER - FUELS ENERGY & POWER. m. $269 (Canada $289; elsewhere $319). Merton Allen Associates, InfoTeam Inc., Box 15640, Plantation, FL 33318-5640. TEL 305-473-9560. FAX 305-473-0544. **Document type:** newsletter.
 ●Also available online. Vendor(s): Data-Star, DIALOG Information Services, Inc., NewsNet (EY12).
 —CCC.
 Description: Covers the energy arena: fuels, energy power, utilities, exploration and production, research and development, transmission, equipment, systems, exotic and alternative energy, conservation, cogeneration and regulation.

363.6   US
UTILITY WEEKLY. 1934. w. $459 in U.S. and Canada; elsewhere $489. Public Utilities Reports, Inc., 2111 Wilson Blvd., Ste. 2100, Arlington, VA 22201. TEL 703-243-7000. FAX 703-527-5829. Ed. Marshall Yates. circ. 700. (looseleaf format) **Document type:** newsletter.
 Former titles (until 1994): P.U.R. Letter; P.U.R. Executive Information Service (ISSN 0030-8420)

V W D - ENERGIE. see *BUSINESS AND ECONOMICS — Investments*

333.79   US
WASHINGTON STATE ENERGY OFFICE. BIENNIAL ENERGY REPORT. biennial. Washington State Energy Office, 925 Plum St., S.E., Olympia, WA 98504-3169. TEL 206-956-2000. FAX 206-956-2217. **Document type:** government publication.

333.79   US
WASHINGTON STATE ENERGY OFFICE DISPATCH; a bi-monthly newsletter of Washington's energy and environmental issues and programs. bi-m. Washington State Energy Office, 925 Plum St., S.E., Olympia, WA 98504-3169. TEL 206-956-2000. FAX 206-956-2217. Ed. Jim Erickson. illus. **Indexed:** Energy Info.Abstr., Environ.Abstr. **Document type:** government publication, newsletter.

WASSER, ENERGIE, LUFT/EAU, ENERGIE, AIR. see *WATER RESOURCES*

333.8 622.33   US   ISSN 0733-0545
  CODEN: WCOPD2
WEEKLY COAL PRODUCTION. w. $95. U.S. Department of Energy, Energy Information Administration, National Energy Information Center, EI-231, Rm. 1F-048, Forrestal Bldg., 1000 Independence Ave., S.W., Washington, DC 20585. TEL 202-586-8800. (also avail. in microfiche from CIS; reprint service avail. from CIS) **Indexed:** Amer.Stat.Ind. (1977-), Chem.Abstr., Energy Info.Abstr., PROMT. **Document type:** government publication.
 —CASDDS.
 Former titles: Weekly Coal Production: Bituminous and Lignite, Pennsylvania Anthracite; Weekly Coal Report (ISSN 0191-4367); Which incorporated (as of 1980): Pennsylvania Anthracite Weekly.

354.941   AT
WESTERN AUSTRALIA. STATE ENERGY COMMISSION. ANNUAL REPORT. 1976. a. State Energy Commission, Perth, W.A., Australia. TEL 09-325-4597. FAX 09-326-4984. Ed. Peter Winner. illus.; circ. 6,000 (controlled). **Document type:** corporate report.

WHO'S DRILLING. see *PETROLEUM AND GAS*

333.79   GW
WIR VON MAINGAS. 1950. q. Maingas Aktiengesellschaft, Solmsstr. 38, 60486 Frankfurt a.M. TEL 069-79110. Ed. Ernst Krieges.

333.79 621.042   US   ISSN 1053-5802
WORLD COGENERATION; a power source for partnering in the '90's. 1988. 5/yr. $36. Dick Flanagan, Ed. & Pub., 84-54 118th St., Kew Gardens, NY 11415. TEL 718-847-0230. FAX 718-847-5599. adv.: B&W page $2960; color page $3910. circ. 12,020. (tabloid format) **Document type:** trade publication.
 Description: Covers news, features and announcements on how industrial facilities and utilities provide electricity and broker power.

WORLD ENERGY CONFERENCE. DIRECTORY OF ENERGY INFORMATION CENTRES IN THE WORLD. see *BUSINESS AND ECONOMICS — Trade And Industrial Directories*

363.6   FR   ISSN 0084-1722
WORLD ENERGY CONFERENCE. PLENARY CONFERENCES. TRANSACTIONS. triennial. $155. French National Committee of the W E C, 89 blvd. Haussmann, 75008 Paris, France.

621.3   UK   ISSN 0084-1730
WORLD ENERGY CONFERENCE. SURVEY OF ENERGY RESOURCES. 1962. base vol. every 6 yrs (statistical tables triennially). £40. Longman Group UK Ltd., Westgate House, 6th Fl., The High, Harlow, Essex CM20 1YR, England. TEL 0279-442601. FAX 0279-444501.

333.79   US
WORLDWIDE ENERGY. 1990. m. $150. Worldwide Videotex, Box 3273, Boynton Beach, FL 33424-3273. TEL 407-738-2276. Ed. Mark Wright. bk.rev. **Document type:** newsletter.
 ●Also available online. Vendor(s): NewsNet (EY63).
 Description: Provides information about all types of energy sources and applications with exploration, operation, research and development, energy production, and conservation news.

621.042   UK   ISSN 1352-5530
▼**YEARBOOK OF RENEWABLE ENERGIES.** 1993. a. £29.50($45) James & James (Science Publishers) Ltd., 5 Castle Rd., London NW1 8PR, England. TEL 071-284-3833. FAX 071-284-3737. (Dist. in N. America by: Books International, Box 605, Herndon, VA 22070. TEL 703-435-7064. FAX 703-689-0660) Ed.Bd. **Document type:** academic/scholarly publication.

333.79   GW   ISSN 0343-5377
HD9502.A1
ZEITSCHRIFT FUER ENERGIEWIRTSCHAFT. 1978. q. DM.272. Friedr. Vieweg und Sohn Verlagsgesellschaft mbH, Postfach 5829, 65048 Wiesbaden, Germany. TEL 0611-160230. FAX 0611-160229. Eds. Hans Schneider, Christian von Weizsaecker. **Document type:** academic/scholarly publication.
—BLDSC (9458.500000); SWETS. **CCC.**

ENERGY — Abstracting, Bibliographies, Statistics

333.79   TH   ISSN 0857-6181
A I T REPORTS AND PUBLICATIONS ON ENERGY. ABSTRACTS. (Text in English) 1979. a. $75 to individuals; institutions $120. Asian Institute of Technology, Regional Energy Resources Information Center, G.P.O. Box 2754, Bangkok 10501, Thailand. TEL 66-2-5245866. FAX 66-2-5245870. TELEX 84276 AITTH. Ed. On-Anong Suraniranat. adv.; cum.index. circ. 600. (back issues avail.) **Indexed:** Geotech.Abstr. **Document type:** abstracting/indexing.
—BLDSC (0553.803200).
    Formerly: A I T Reports and Publications on Renewable Energy Resources. Abstracts (ISSN 0857-4499)
    Description: Compilation of all research carried out at the Asian Institute of Technology in the field of energy and renewable energy resources.

363.6   CN   ISSN 0710-6874
ALBERTA ENERGY RESOURCE INDUSTRIES. MONTHLY STATISTICS. Title varies. 1938. m. Can.$50. Energy Resources Conservation Board, 640 5th Ave. S.W., Calgary, Alta. T2P 3G4, Canada. TEL 403-297-8311. FAX 403-297-7040. TELEX 03-821717. (back issues avail.) **Indexed:** CS Ind.
    Former titles: Alberta Energy Resource Industries. Summary of Monthly Statistics; Alberta Oil and Gas Industry. Monthly Statistics (ISSN 0002-4872)
    Description: Statistical data on supply and disposition of crude oil, natural gas, coal and electric energy in the province of Alberta.

621.042   US   ISSN 1050-3145
ALTERNATIVE ENERGY DIGESTS. 1990. m. $240. International Academy at Santa Barbara, Environmental Studies Institute, 800 Garden St., Ste. D, Santa Barbara, CA 93101. TEL 805-965-5010. FAX 805-965-6071. Ed. Mary Ann Short. **Document type:** abstracting/indexing.
●Also available online. Vendor(s): Data-Star, DIALOG Information Services, Inc.
—**CCC.**
    Description: Summarizes articles, books, news releases, documents, and reports relating to alternative energy sources.

621.3 314   UN   ISSN 0066-3816
HD9685.A1
ANNUAL BULLETIN OF ELECTRIC ENERGY STATISTICS FOR EUROPE. (Text in English, French and Russian) 1956 (covering 1955). a. price varies. Economic Commission for Europe (ECE), Palais des Nations, 1211 Geneva 10, Switzerland. TEL 22-917-2609. FAX 22-917-0036. TELEX 412962. (Or United Nations Publications, Rm. DC2-853, New York, NY 10017) (also avail. in microfiche from CIS) **Indexed:** IIS.

338 314   UN   ISSN 0377-9165
ANNUAL BULLETIN OF GENERAL ENERGY STATISTICS FOR EUROPE. (Text in English, French and Russian) 1970. a. price varies. Economic Commission for Europe (ECE), Palais des Nations, 1211 Geneva 10, Switzerland. TEL 22-917-1234. FAX 917-01-23. TELEX 412962. (Or: United Nations Publications, Rm. DC2-853, New York, NY 10017) (also avail. in microfiche) **Indexed:** IIS.
—BLDSC (1077.820000).

333.79   US   ISSN 0895-1713
ANNUAL DIGEST OF THE PUBLIC UTILITIES REPORTS. 1934. a. $95 (effective 1994). Public Utilities Reports, Inc., 2111 Wilson Blvd., Ste. 200, Arlington, VA 22201. TEL 703-243-7000. FAX 703-527-5829. **Document type:** abstracting/indexing.
    Description: Provides access to decisions reported in the Public Utilities Reports.

333.79   CL
ANUARIO DE ESTADISTICAS DEL MEDIO AMBIENTE. 1986. a. Instituto Nacional de Estadisticas, Ave. Bulnes 418, Casilla 498, Correo 3 Santiago, Chile. (Co-sponsor: Departamento de Energia y Ambiente de Chile) **Document type:** government publication.

333.79   BL   ISSN 0102-1028
ANUARIO ESTATISTICO DE ENERGIA ELECTRICA. AUTOPRODUTORES NO ESTADO DE SAO PAULO. 1970. a. Cr.$5000. Companhia Energetica de Sao Paulo, Divisao de Estudos do Mercado de Energia Eletrica, Av. Angelica, 2565, 15 Andar, 01227 Sao Paulo, Brazil. circ. 1,000.

333.8   CN
ASSESSMENT REPORT INDEX. a. (Ministry of Energy, Mines and Petroleum Resources, Publications Distribution Section) Queen's Printer, Victoria, 563 Superior St., Victoria, B.C. V8V 1X4, Canada. FAX 604-386-0221. (Dist. by: Crown Publications, 546 Yates St., Victoria, B.C. V8W 1K8, Canada. TEL 604-386-4636) **Document type:** government publication.
    Description: Presents a summary of assessments reports filed with the ministry.

539 016   CN   ISSN 0067-0405
ATOMIC ENERGY OF CANADA. LIST OF PUBLICATIONS. Title varies: Publications of A E C L. 1952. irreg. free. Atomic Energy of Canada Ltd., Chalk River Nuclear Laboratories, Technical Information Services, S.D.D.O., Sta. 14, Chalk River, Ont. K0J 1J0, Canada. TEL 613-584-3311. **Document type:** catalog.

333   AT   ISSN 1037-9886
AUSTRALIA. BUREAU OF STATISTICS. ELECTRICITY AND GAS OPERATIONS, AUSTRALIA. 1968. a. Aus.$10.50. Australian Bureau of Statistics, P.O. Box 10, Belconnen, A.C.T. 2616, Australia. **Document type:** government publication.
    Formerly: Australia. Bureau of Statistics. Electricity and Gas Establishments: Details of Operations, Australia.

333.79   AT   ISSN 1035-9133
AUSTRALIA. BUREAU OF STATISTICS. MANUFACTURING PRODUCTION, AUSTRALIA: ENERGY PRODUCTS. 1977. m. Aus.$6 per no. Australian Bureau of Statistics, P.O. Box 10, Belconnen, A.C.T. 2616, Australia. **Document type:** government publication.
    Supersedes in part (in 1989): Australia. Bureau of Statistics. Production of Energy and Metal Products, Australia (ISSN 1033-4378); Formerly: Australia. Bureau of Statistics. Production of Energy Products, Australia.
    Description: Provides production statistics for electricity, gas, and petroleum refinery input and products.

333.8 011   UK   ISSN 1350-7397
B C R A QUARTERLY; a review of published literature on coal, coke and allied topics. 1983. q. £85. B C R A Scientific and Technical Services Ltd., Mill Ln. Wingerworth, Chesterfield, Derbys. S42 6NG, England. TEL 0246-209654. FAX 0246-272247. TELEX 547061-CB-WING-G. Ed. D.G. Edwards. circ. 150. (back issues avail.) **Document type:** abstracting/indexing.
—BLDSC (1871.391400).

621.32   BL
BAHIA, BRAZIL (STATE). SECRETARIA DAS MINAS E ENERGIA. BOLETIM ESTATISTICO MENSAL DE ENERGIA ELETRICA. 1974. m. free. Secretaria das Minas e Energia, Coordenacao de Energia, Av. Centro Administrativo da Bahia, Av. Luiz Viana Filho, 40000 Salvador - Bahia, Brazil. stat. **Document type:** government publication.

333.792   BL   ISSN 0102-3500
BIBLIOGRAFIA BRASILEIRA DE ENERGIA NUCLEAR. (Print format ceased in 1988.) 1981. a. Comissao Nacional de Energia Nuclear, Centro de Informacoes Nucleares, Rio de Janeiro, Brazil. TEL 021-5462440. FAX 021-5462447. TELEX 21-21280. circ. 150.
●Available only online.

621.3 016   YU   ISSN 0351-238X
BILTEN DOKUMENTACIJE. ELEKTROPRIVREDA/BULLETIN OF DOCUMENTATION. ELECTRICAL ENERGY. 1950. bi-m. $264. Jugoslovenski Centar za Tehnicku i Naucnu Dokumentaciju - Yugoslav Center for Technical and Scientific Documentation (YCTSD), Sl. Penezica-Krcuna 29-31, PO Box 724, 11000 Belgrade, Yugoslavia. Ed. Ljiljana Kojic-Bogdanovic.
    Supersedes in part (in 1980): Bilten Dokumentacije. Elektrotehnika (ISSN 0006-2588)

621.4 624   US   ISSN 1069-112X
▼**BUILDINGS ENERGY TECHNOLOGY ABSTRACTS.** 1993. bi-m. $195 (overseas $215). WindBooks, Inc., Box 4008, St. Johnsbury, VT 05819-4008. TEL 802-748-5148. FAX 802-748-3286. Ed. Farrell Smith Seiler. adv.; bk.rev. (looseleaf format; back issues avail.) **Document type:** abstracting/indexing.
    Description: Summarizes proceedings on energy conservation and technology in building design and construction.

541.3   US   ISSN 0162-7791
                              CODEN: CSEBD6
C A SELECTS. ENERGY REVIEWS & BOOKS. s-w. $210 (effective Jan. 1994). Chemical Abstracts Service (Subsidiary of: American Chemical Society), 2540 Olentangy River Rd., Box 3012, Columbus, OH 43210-0012. TEL 614-447-3600. FAX 614-447-3713. TELEX 6842086. **Document type:** abstracting/indexing.
    Description: Covers the chemical aspects of energy and heat, primarily commercial and industrial applications.

621.47 011   US   ISSN 0148-236X
                              CODEN: CASEDR
C A SELECTS. SOLAR ENERGY. s-w. $210 (effective Jan. 1994). Chemical Abstracts Service (Subsidiary of: American Chemical Society), 2540 Olentangy River Rd., Box 3012, Columbus, OH 43210-0012. TEL 614-447-3600. FAX 614-447-3713. TELEX 68420866. **Document type:** abstracting/indexing.
    Description: Covers solar-energy conversion devices, materials, and processes; biosolar energy processes and solar sea thermal energy conversion systems; photoelectric solar cells, photoelectrochemical cells, photogalvanic cells.

C S I CONGRESSIONAL RECORD ABSTRACTS: ENERGY EDITION. (Capitol Services, Inc.) see *PUBLIC ADMINISTRATION — Abstracting, Bibliographies, Statistics*

621.31   CN   ISSN 0380-951X
TK26
CANADA. STATISTICS CANADA. ELECTRIC POWER STATISTICS VOLUME 1: ANNUAL ELECTRIC POWER SURVEY OF CAPABILITY AND LOAD. (Catalogue 57-204) 1955. a. Can.$27($32) (foreign $38). Statistics Canada, Publications Sales and Services, Ottawa, Ont. K1A 0T6, Canada. TEL 613-951-7277. FAX 613-951-1584. (also avail. in microform from MML) **Document type:** government publication.
    Description: Provides current and projected data of capability and load of producers of electric energy by province.

621.3 690   CN   ISSN 0835-104X
HD9695.C2
CANADA. STATISTICS CANADA. ELECTRICAL TRADE CONTRACTORS. (Catalogue 64-205) (Text in English and French) 1969. a. Can.$22($26) (foreign $31). Statistics Canada, Publications Sales and Services, Ottawa, Ont. K1A 0T6, Canada. TEL 613-951-7277. FAX 613-951-1584. (also avail. in microform from MML) **Document type:** government publication.
    Formerly: Canada. Statistics Canada. Electrical Contracting Industry (ISSN 0702-8083)
    Description: Covers the aggregate activity of electrical trade contractors, input and output dollar volumes, labor hours and person years, listed by province and size group.

ENERGY — ABSTRACTING, BIBLIOGRAPHIES, STATISTICS

333.79 CN ISSN 0702-0465
TJ163.25.C3
CANADA. STATISTICS CANADA. QUARTERLY REPORT ON ENERGY SUPPLY. DEMAND IN CANADA. (Catalogue 57-003) (Text in English, French) 1976. q. Can.$127($152) (foreign $178). Statistics Canada, Publications Sales and Services, Ottawa, Ont. K1A 0T6, Canada. TEL 613-951-7277. FAX 613-951-1584. **Document type:** government publication.
   Description: Covers energy balance sheets in natural units and heat equivalents in primary and secondary forms, by province, each showing data on production, trade, interprovincial movements, conversion and consumption by sector.

333.8 US
CLEAN COAL TECHNOLOGIES. m. $145 in US, Canada, Mexico; elsewhere $290. (U.S. Department of Energy) U.S. National Technical Information Service, 5825 Port Royal Rd., Springfield, VA 22161. TEL 703-487-4630. **Document type:** government publication.
   Description: Abstracts international information on all aspects of clean coal, including mechanical coal cleaning, desulfurization, coal gasefication and liquefication, flue gas cleanup, and advanced coal combustion.

333.79 BL
COMPANHIA PARANAENSE DE ENERGIA. BOLETIM ESTATISTICO MENSAL. (Former name of issuing body: Companhia Paranaense de Energia Eletrica) 1970. m. free. Companhia Paranaense de Energia, Superintendencia de Planejamento e Estudos, Departamento de Mercado, Rua Treze de Maio, 616 6o Andar, 80510-030 Curitiba, Parana, Brazil. TEL 041-3224224. charts; stat. circ. 100. **Document type:** bulletin.
   Formerly: C O P E L. Boletim Estatistico Mensal.

333.79 BL
COMPANHIA PARANAENSE DE ENERGIA. INFORME ESTATISTICO ANUAL. 1971. a. free. Companhia Paranaense de Energia, Superintendencia de Planejamento e Estudos, Rua Treze de Maio, 616 6o Andar, 80510-030 Curitiba, Parana, Brazil. TEL 041-322-4224. stat.; charts. circ. 1,500. (back issues avail.) **Document type:** corporate report.

333.79 US
COST AND QUALITY OF FUELS FOR ELECTRIC UTILITIES (F E R C 423). m. $240 per no. in U.S., Canada, Mexico; elsewhere $480. (U.S. Department of Energy, Energy Information Administration) U.S. National Technical Information Service, 5285 Port Royal Rd., Springfield, VA 22161. TEL 703-487-4630. (magnetic tape; also avail. in diskette format) **Document type:** government publication.
   Description: Contains the cost and quality of fossil fuels delivered to steam-electric plants with a rated generating capacity of 50 megawatts or larger. Includes country of origin of imported coal deliveries.

CURRENT BIBLIOGRAPHIES ON SCIENCE AND TECHNOLOGY: METALLURGY, NATURAL RESOURCES & ENERGY. see *METALLURGY — Abstracting, Bibliographies, Statistics*

621.042 JA ISSN 0387-4001
CURRENT BIBLIOGRAPHY ON SCIENCE AND TECHNOLOGY: ENERGY/KAGAKU GIJUTSU BUNKEN SOKUHO. ENERUGI-HEN. (Text in Japanese) 1979. m. $1240. Japan Information Center of Science and Technology - Nihon Kagaku Gijutsu Joho Senta, 5-2 Nagata-cho, 2-chome, Chiyoda-ku, Tokyo 100, Japan. TEL 03-3581-6411. FAX 03-3581-6446. index. circ. 300. **Document type:** bibliography.
   ●Also available online. Vendor(s): JICST.

333.79 UY
DATOS ESTADISTICOS DE LAS EMPRESAS ELECTRICAS. a. Comision de Integracion Electrica Regional, Boulevar Artigas 1040, 11300 Montevideo, Uruguay. TEL 79-53-59. FAX 5982-783193. TELEX 26609 CIER UY.

333.8 UK ISSN 0307-0603
HD9551.4
DIGEST OF UNITED KINGDOM ENERGY STATISTICS. 1974. a. price varies. Department of Trade & Industry, c/o M.F. Ward, ES8 Rm. 3-3-26, London SW1E 5HE, England. TEL 071-873-0011. (Avail. from H.M.S.O., P.O. Box 276, London SW8 5DT, England) illus. **Document type:** government publication.
   —BLDSC (3588.326000). **CCC.**
   Formerly: Great Britain. Department of Trade and Industry. Digest of Energy Statistics.
   Description: Discusses production, consumption and foreign trade in energy, renewable energy, and emissions.

E E I STATISTICAL RELEASES. ELECTRIC OUTPUT. (Edison Electric Institute) see *ENGINEERING — Abstracting, Bibliographies, Statistics*

621.3 333.79 US
ELECTRIC ENERGY SYSTEMS. bi-m. $145 in U.S., Canada, Mexico; elsewhere $290. (U.S. Department of Energy) U.S. National Technical Information Service, 5285 Port Royal Rd., Springfield, VA 22161. TEL 703-487-4630. **Document type:** government publication.
   Description: Abstracts global information on all aspects of electric power including fossil and hydroelectric power generation, transmission, environmental control technology, and policy.

333.79 US
ELECTRIC POWER USE BY INDUSTRIES. m. $200 per no. in U.S., Canada, Mexico; elsewhere $400. (Federal Reserve System) U.S. National Technical Information Service, 5825 Port Royal Rd., Springfield, VA 22161. TEL 703-487-4630. index. (magnetic tape)
   Description: Statistics based on reports of power sold by the electric utilities, and of power generated by industrial plants.

363.6 US
ELECTRIC RATE BOOK. 1986. a. $695 (effective 1994). (Casazza, Schultz and Associates, Inc.) C S A Energy Consultants, Inc., 1901 N. Fort Myer Dr., Ste. 503, Arlington, VA 22209. TEL 703-841-9644. FAX 703-841-9649. Ed. Lynda J. White. circ. 300.
   Description: Current abstracts of the rate structures and schedules of 119 investor-owned U.S. electric utilities that provide residential, commercial, and industrial service to 96 percent of all customers of this segment of the industry.

333.79 011 HO
EMPRESA NACIONAL DE ENERGIA ELECTRICA. DATOS ESTADISTICOS. 1960. a. free. Empresa Nacional de Energia Electrica, Departamento de Planificacion Economica, Tegucigalpa, Honduras. TEL 328470. FAX 378473. adv.; stat. circ. 180. (also avail. in microform)

333.79 BL ISSN 0102-3519
Z5853.P83
ENERGIA: BIBLIOGRAFIA SELETIVA. (Print format ceased in 1988.) 1984. a. Comissao Nacional de Energia Nuclear, Centro de Informacoes Nucleares, R. General Severiano, 90, Botafogo, Rio de Janeiro, Brazil. TEL 021-5462440. FAX 021-5462447. TELEX 21-21280.
   ●Available only online.

621.31 011 HU ISSN 0231-0678
ENERGIAIPARI ES ENERGIAGAZDALKODASI TAJEKOZTATO/POWER ENGINEERING ABSTRACTS. 1949. m. 9900 Ft. Orszagos Muszaki Informacios Kozpont es Konyvtar (O.M.I.K.K.) - National Technical Information Centre and Library, Muzeum u. 17, Box 12, 1428 Budapest, Hungary. (Subscr. to: Kultura, Box 149, 1389 Budapest, Hungary) Ed. Rezso Folkl. index. circ. 400. **Document type:** abstracting/indexing.
   Supersedes (as from 1982): Muszaki Lapszemle. Energia - Technical Abstracts. Energy (ISSN 0027-4984)

531.64 AU
ENERGIEVERSORGUNG OESTERREICHS. 1975. 15/yr. S.780. Oesterreichisches Statistisches Zentralamt, Hintere Zollamtsstr. 2b, A-1033 Vienna, Austria. TEL 0222-71128-7624. FAX 0222-7156828. (Co-sponsor: Bundesministerium fuer Wirtschaftliche Angelegenheiten) stat. circ. 380. **Document type:** government publication.
   Description: Provides information on energy consumption by fuels.

621.3 025.4 US ISSN 0093-8408
TJ163.13 CODEN: EIEAAK
ENERGY ABSTRACTS. 1974. m. $975 in N. America; elsewhere $1075. Engineering Information, Inc., Castle Point on the Hudson, Hoboken, NJ 07030. TEL 201-216-8500. FAX 201-216-8532. (Subscr. in U.K. and Western Europe to: Thompson, Henry Ltd., London Rd., Sunningdale, Berks. SL5 OEP, England) (back issues avail.; reprint service avail.) **Document type:** abstracting/indexing.
   —CCC.
   Incorporates: Energy Conversion Abstracts (ISSN 0093-8416)
   Description: Abstracts of the world's literature in the field of energy.

333.79 US ISSN 0892-5461
ENERGY BOOKS QUARTERLY. 1987. 4/yr. $120. International Academy at Santa Barbara, 800 Garden St., Ste. D, Santa Barbara, CA 93101. TEL 805-965-5010. Ed. Mary Ann Short. bk.rev. (back issues avail.) **Document type:** bibliography.
   ●Also available online. Vendor(s): Data-Star, DIALOG Information Services, Inc.
   —CCC.
   Description: Cites 200 new books, conference volumes, and reports on energy each year.

333.79 US ISSN 0195-4474
ENERGY CONSERVATION DIGEST. Short title: E C D. 1977. 24/yr. $176. Editorial Resources, Inc., Box 21133, Washington, DC 20009. TEL 202-783-2929. (Subscr. to: Box 20754, Seattle, WA 98102-1754) Ed. D.L. Howell. bk.rev.; charts.
   Incorporates: Facilities Energy Report.

621.4 011 US ISSN 1069-2223
▼**ENERGY MEETINGS, CONFERENCES AND SYMPOSIA.** 1993. bi-m. $195 (overseas $215). WindBooks, Inc., Box 4008, St. Johnsbury, VT 05819-4008. TEL 802-748-5148. FAX 802-748-3286. Ed. Farrell Smith Seiler. adv.; bk.rev. (looseleaf format; back issues avail.) **Document type:** directory.
   Description: Lists forthcoming meetings, conferences, and symposia that deal with energy topics.

333.79 016 US ISSN 0160-3604
Z5853.P83 CODEN: ERABDZ
ENERGY RESEARCH ABSTRACTS. (Catalog ID: ERDA) 1976. m. $164 (foreign $205). U.S. Department of Energy, Office of Scientific and Technical Information, Box 62, Oak Ridge, TN 37831. TEL 615-574-0733. (Subscr. to: Superintendent of Documents, U.S. Government Printing Office, Box 371954, Pittsburgh, PA 15250-7954. TEL 202-783-3238. FAX 202-512-2233) Ed. Milton O. Whitson. index, cum.index. (also avail. in microform from UMI,PMC; reprint service avail. from UMI) **Indexed:** Anal.Abstr., Chem.Abstr., Corros.Abstr., MEDOC, Petrol.Abstr. **Document type:** abstracting/indexing, government publication.
   ●Also available online. Vendor(s): DIALOG Information Services, Inc., STN International (ENERGY).
   —UMI; CASDDS.
   Formerly: E R D A Energy Research Abstracts (ISSN 0360-3571)
   Description: Abstracts all the scientific and technical reports, journal articles, conference prodeedings, books, patents, theses, and monographs sponsored by the U.S. Energy Research and Development Administration.

ENERGY — ABSTRACTING, BIBLIOGRAPHIES, STATISTICS

333.79 US ISSN 0094-8063
TJ153 CODEN: EGYRBM
ENERGY REVIEW (SANTA BARBARA). 1973. m. $360 to individuals; $455 to colleges. International Academy at Santa Barbara, 800 Garden St., Ste. D, Santa Barbara, CA 93101. TEL 805-965-5010. FAX 805-965-6071. Ed. Mary Ann Short. bk.rev.; abstr.; pat.; stat.; cum.index. circ. 500. (also avail. in microfiche) **Document type:** abstracting/indexing.
—CCC.
Description: Summarizes technical reports, journal articles and books concerned with all facets of energy.

621 FR
ENERGY STATISTICS OF O E C D COUNTRIES. (Text in English, French) 1961. a. price varies. Organization for Economic Cooperation and Development, 2 rue Andre-Pascal, 75775 Paris Cedex 16, France. (U.S. orders to: O.E.C.D. Publications and Information Center, 2001 L St., N.W., Ste. 700, Washington, D.C. 20036-4910. TEL 202-785-6323) (also avail. in microfiche from OEC,CIS) **Indexed:** IIS.
Formerly: Organization for Economic Cooperation and Development. Statistics of Energy.

621.3 UN ISSN 0256-6400
ENERGY STATISTICS YEARBOOK. (Text in English and French) 1952. a. price varies. (United Nations, Department of Economic and Social Affairs) United Nations Publications, Room DC2-853, New York, NY 10017. TEL 212-963-9300. FAX 212-963-3489. (Dist. by: United Nations Sales Section, Room DC2-853, New York, NY; or Palais des Nations, CH-1211 Geneva 10, Switzerland) (also avail. in microfiche from CIS; reprint service avail. from KTO) **Indexed:** IIS.
Former titles (until 1981): Yearbook of World Energy Statistics (ISSN 0255-5085); (until 1978): World Energy Supplies (ISSN 0084-1749)

621.042 US
ENERGY STORAGE SYSTEMS. bi-m. $140 in US, Canada, Mexico; elsewhere $280. (U.S. Department of Energy) U.S. National Technical Information Service, 5825 Port Royal Rd., Springfield, VA 22161. TEL 703-487-4630.
Description: Abstracts current international information on all aspects of energy storage.

621.4 621.31 US ISSN 1069-1146
▼**ENERGY STORAGE SYSTEMS ABSTRACTS.** 1993. bi-m. $195 (overseas $215). WindBooks, Inc., Box 4008, St. Johnsbury, VT 05819-4008. TEL 802-748-5148. FAX 802-748-3286. Ed. Farrell Smith Seiler. adv.; bk.rev. (looseleaf format; back issues avail.) **Document type:** abstracting/indexing.
Description: Summarizes proceedings on dry cells and other energy-storage technologies and applications.

621.34 SP
ESTADISTICA DE ENERGIA ELECTRICA. a. 2,000 ptas. Ministerio de Industria, Paseo de la Castellana 160, Madrid 28046, Spain. FAX 259-84-80.

333.79 BL ISSN 0512-350X
ESTATISTICA BRASILEIRA DE ENERGIA/BRAZILIAN ENERGY STATISTICS. (Text in Portuguese and English; summaries in English) 1965. a. free. Conselho Mundial da Energia, Comite Nacional Brasileiro - World Energy Council, Brazilian National Committee, Rua Real Grandeza, 219, 22283-900 Rio de Janeiro RJ, Brazil. TEL 5521-246-8593. FAX 5521-226-0508. TELEX 2121166 FURN BR. Ed. Jose Malhaes da Silva. charts; stat.; circ. 1,000 (controlled). (back issues avail.) **Document type:** bulletin.

333.79 016 FR ISSN 1157-3848
F R A N C I S. 731: ECONOMIE DE L'ENERGIE. (Text in English, French) 1971. q. 990 F. (outside EEC 1050 F.). Centre National de la Recherche Scientifique, Institut de l'Information Scientifique et Technique, 2 allee du Parc de Brabois, 54514 Vandoeuvre-les-Nancy Cedex, France. TEL 83-50-46-00. FAX 83-50-46-50. Ed.Bd. adv. contact: Veronique Guinvarc'h. abstr. **Document type:** bibliography.
●Also available online. Vendor(s): Telesystemes - Questel.
—CCC.
Formerly: Economie de l'Energie (ISSN 0046-1202)
Description: Comprehensive bibliographic report reprinting information on energetics from private and government organizations in France and other countries.

333.79 BE ISSN 0773-090X
FEDERATION PROFESSIONNELLE DES PRODUCTEURS ET DISTRIBUTEURS D'ELECTRICITE DE BELGIQUE. ANNUAIRE STATISTIQUE. Dutch edition: Bedrijfsfederatie van de Voortbrengers en Verdelers van Elekticiteit in Belgie. Statistisch Jaarboek (ISSN 0778-6298) (Text in French) 1952. a. 900 BEF. Federation Professionnelle des Producteurs et Distributeurs d'Electricite de Belgique - Bedrijfsfederatie der Voortbrengers en Verdelers van Elektriciteit in Belgie, Avenue de Tervueren 34, Boite Postale 38, B-1040 Brussels, Belgium. TEL 32-2-733-96-07. FAX 32-2-733-95-65. Ed. M.C. Oz. circ. 4,000.
Description: Statistics on the Belgian electricity sector.

333.79 US
FINANCIAL STATISTICS OF MAJOR INVESTOR-OWNED ELECTRIC UTILITIES (YEAR). a. (U.S. Department of Energy, Energy Information Administration, Office of Coal, Nuclear, Electric and Alternate Fuels) U.S. Government Printing Office, Superintendent of Documents, Washington, DC 20402-9341. TEL 202-783-3238. FAX 202-512-2233. (Subscr. to: U.S. Government Printing office, c/o Mellon Bank, Box 371954, Pittsburgh, PA 15250-7954) **Document type:** government publication.

333.79 US ISSN 0747-7635
FINANCIAL STATISTICS OF SELECTED ELECTRIC UTILITIES. 1938. a. $35. U.S. Department of Energy, Energy Information Administration, National Energy Information Center, EI-231, Rm. 1F-048, Forrestal Bldg., 1000 Independence Ave., S.W., Washington, DC 20585. TEL 202-586-8800. (Orders to: Supt. of Documents, Washington, DC 20402) (also avail. in microfiche from NTI) **Document type:** government publication.
Former titles: Statistics of Privately Owned Electric Utilities in the United States (ISSN 0161-9004); Statistics of Electric Utilities in the United States. Classes A and B Privately Owned Companies (ISSN 0083-0828)

333.79 011 FI
HD9502.F5
FINLAND. TILASTOKESKUS. ENERGIATILASTOT/FINLAND. STATISTIKCENTRALEN. ENERGISTATISTIK. (Text in English, Finnish, Swedish) 1982. a. FIM 270. Statistics Finland, P.O. Box 504, SF-00101 Helsinki, Finland. FAX 0-1734-2474. Ed. Olli Pirinen. circ. 530. **Document type:** government publication.
Former titles: Finland. Kauuppa- ja Teollisuusministerioe. Energiatilastot (ISSN 0785-3165); Finland. Tilastokeskus. Energiatilastot (ISSN 0358-2019)

333.79 FR
FRANCE. SERVICE D'ETUDE DES STRATEGIES ET DES STATISTIQUES INDUSTRIELLES. LES CONSOMMATIONS D'ENERGIE DANS L'INDUSTRIE. a. 85 F. (foreign 110 F.) (effective 1991). Service d'Etude des Strategies et des Statistiques Industrielles (SESSI), 85 Bd. du Montparnasse, 75270 Paris Cedex 06, France. TEL 45-56-42-34. FAX 45-56-40-71. stat. **Document type:** government publication.
Description: Analyzes the purchase, consumption, production and usage of fuel and electricity by region and size of industrial operation.

GAS INDUSTRY STATISTICS (YEAR). see *PETROLEUM AND GAS — Abstracting, Bibliographies, Statistics*

621.44 US
Z5853.G4
GEOTHERMAL ENERGY. 1977. bi-m. $145 (foreign $290). (U.S. Department of Energy, Office of Scientific and Technical Information) U.S. National Technical Information Service, 5825 Port Royal Rd., Springfield, VA 22161. TEL 703-487-4630. FAX 703-321-8547. TELEX 64617. **Indexed:** Energy Rev. **Document type:** government publication, abstracting/indexing.
Former titles: Geothermal Energy Technology (ISSN 0736-6620); Geothermal Energy Update (ISSN 0146-194X)
Description: Abstracts current international information on the technology required for economic recovery of geothermal energy and its eventual utilization either directly or for the production of electric power.

621.44 US ISSN 1069-1154
▼**GEOTHERMAL ENERGY ABSTRACTS.** 1993. bi-m. $195 (overseas $215). WindBooks, Inc., Box 4008, St. Johnsbury, VT 05819-4008. TEL 802-748-5148. FAX 802-748-3286. Ed. Farrell Smith Seiler. adv.; bk.rev. (looseleaf format; back issues avail.) **Document type:** abstracting/indexing.
Description: Summarizes proceedings on geothermal energy developments, resources, and technology

621.3 JA
HOKURIKU NO DENKI TO KOGYO/ELECTRICITY AND INDUSTRY IN HOKURIKU. (Text in Japanese) 1955. a. Hokuriku Denki Kyokai - Hokuriku Electric Association, 13-15 Ushijimamachi, Toyama-shi, Toyama-ken 930 Japan. Ed.Bd. circ. 180.

333.79 HK
HONG KONG. CENSUS AND STATISTICS DEPARTMENT. ENERGY STATISTICS (TEN YEAR SPAN). (Text in English) 1975. a. HK.$18. (Census and Statistics Department) Government Publication Centre, G.P.O. Bldg., Ground Fl., Connaught Pl., Hong Kong, Hong Kong. (Subscr. to: Director of Information Services, Information Services Dept., 1 Battery Path, G-F, Central, Hong Kong) Ed.Bd. **Document type:** government publication.

333.791 US ISSN 0896-5161
INDUSTRIAL ENERGY CONSERVATION. 1988. m. $155 in US, Canada, Mexico; elsewhere $310. (U.S. Department of Energy) U.S. National Technical Information Service. 5825 Port Royal Rd., Springfield, VA 22161. TEL 703-487-4630. **Document type:** abstracting/indexing.
Description: Abstracts global information on all aspects of energy conservation in industry including alternate energy sources, improved materials, equipment and processes, waste heat recovery, and industrial waste management.

621.4 628.5 US ISSN 1069-1138
▼**INDUSTRIAL ENERGY TECHNOLOGY ABSTRACTS.** 1993. bi-m. $195 (foreign $215). WindBooks, Inc., Box 4008, St. Johnsbury, VT 05819-4008. TEL 802-748-5148 FAX 802-748-3286. Ed. Farrell Smith Seiler. adv.; bk.rev. (looseleaf format; back issues avail.) **Document type:** abstracting/indexing
Description: Summarizes proceedings on energy research and development in industrial applications.

INSTITUTE FOR THE STUDY OF EARTH AND MAN NEWSLETTER. see *ARCHAEOLOGY*

539.7 011 JA ISSN 0385-6437
J A E R I REPORTS ABSTRACTS/GENKEN KENKYU SEIKA SHOROKUSYU. (Text in English or Japanese) 1964. m. exchange basis. Japan Atomic Energy Research Institute, Tokai Research Establishment - Nihon Genshiryoku Kenkyujo, Tokai Kenkyujo Gijutsu Johobu, Tokai-mura, Naka-gun, Ibaraki-ken 319-11, Japan. index. **Document type:** abstracting/indexing.
—BLDSC (4616.640000).
Former titles: Kenkyuseika Yoshisyu (ISSN 0022-9954); Genken Biburio.

ENERGY — ABSTRACTING, BIBLIOGRAPHIES, STATISTICS

621.48   JA   ISSN 0917-1746
CODEN: KDGHEI
KYOTO DAIGAKU GENSHIRO JIKKENSHO GAKUJUTSU KOENKAI HOUBUNSHU/KYOTO UNIVERSITY. RESEARCH REACTOR INSTITUTE. PROCEEDINGS OF THE SCIENTIFIC MEETING. (Text in Japanese; summaries in English) 1967. a. free. Kyoto Daigaku, Genshiro Jikkensho Gakujutsu Kokai Iinkai, Kumatori-cho, Sennani-gun, Osaka 590-04, Japan. Ed. Mitsuo Mizuma. **Document type:** proceedings.
—CASDDS.

333.79   MH
MACAO. DIRECCAO DOS SERVICOS DE ESTATISTICA E CENSOS. BALANCO ENERGETICO (ANUAL)/MACAO. CENSUS AND STATISTICS DEPARTMENT. BALANCE OF ENERGY (ANNUAL). (Text in Chinese, Portuguese) 1988. a. free. Direccao dos Servicos de Estatistica e Censos, Rua Inacio Baptista, No. 4-6, P.O. Box 3022, Macao. TEL 3995311. FAX 307825. **Document type:** government publication.

333.79   MH
MACAO. DIRECCAO DOS SERVICOS DE ESTATISTICA E CENSOS. ESTATISTICAS DE ENERGIA/MACAO. CENSUS AND STATISTICS DEPARTMENT. ENERGY STATISTICS. (Text in Chinese, Portuguese) 1988. q. free. Direccao dos Servicos de Estatistica e Censos, Rua Inacio Baptista, No. 4-6, P.O. Box 3022, Macao. TEL 3995311. FAX 307825. **Document type:** government publication.
Formerly: Macao. Direccao dos Servicos de Estadistica e Censos. Balanco Energetico - Balance of Energy.
Description: Provides statistics on supplies and consumption of oil products, electricity in terms of volume, prices, sources and storage capacity.

MANITOBA. DEPARTMENT OF ENERGY AND MINES. PRODUCTION STATISTICS REPORT.. see *PETROLEUM AND GAS — Abstracting, Bibliographies, Statistics*

333.79   US
MONTHLY ELECTRIC UTILITIES SALES AND REVENUE REPORT (E I A - 826). m. $240 per no. in U.S., Canada, Mexico; elsewhere $480. (U.S. Department of Energy, Energy Information Administration) U.S. National Technical Information Service, 5825 Port Royal Rd., Springfield, VA 22161. TEL 703-487-4630. (magnetic tape) **Document type:** government publication.
Description: Collects the data necessary to fulfill regulatory responsibility, identify near-term trends in energy use, and contingency analysis. Includes data on depreciation, construction, net income before taxes, and extraordinary items.

333.79   US   ISSN 0095-7356
HD9564
MONTHLY ENERGY REVIEW. 1974. m. $77 (foreign $96.25). U.S. Department of Energy, Energy Information Administration, National Energy Information Center, EI-231, Rm. 1F-048, Forrestal Bldg., 1000 Independence Ave., S.W., Washington, DC 20585. TEL 202-586-8800. (Subscr. to: Superintendent of Documents, U.S. Government Printing Office, Box 371954, Pittsburgh, PA 15250-7954. TEL 202-783-3238. FAX 202-512-2233) charts. (also avail. in microfiche from CIS; back issues avail.; reprint service avail. from CIS) **Indexed:** Amer.Stat.Ind. (1979-), Energy Info.Abstr., Fuel & Energy Abstr., GeoRef., Ind.U.S.Gov.Per., Key to Econ.Sci., Mid.East: Abstr.& Ind., PROMT. **Document type:** government publication.
—UMI.
Incorporates: P I M S Monthly Petroleum Report (ISSN 0099-0914); Monthly Energy Indicators (ISSN 0095-1897)
Description: Presents current data on production, consumption, stocks, imports, exports, and prices of principal energy commodities in the United States.

621.042 333.79   US
N T I S ALERTS: ENERGY. w. $160 (foreign $225). U.S. National Technical Information Service, 5285 Port Royal Rd., Springfield, VA 22161. TEL 703-487-4630. FAX 703-321-8547. TELEX 64617. index. (back issues avail.) **Document type:** abstracting/indexing.
Former titles: Abstract Newsletter: Energy (ISSN 0148-446X); Weekly Abstract Newsletter: Energy; Weekly Government Abstracts. Energy.

NETHERLANDS. CENTRAAL BUREAU VOOR DE STATISTIEK. NEDERLANDSE ENERGIEHUISHOUDING.
see *ENVIRONMENTAL STUDIES — Abstracting, Bibliographies, Statistics*

333.79   NO
NORWAY. STATISTISK SENTRALBYRAA. ELEKTRISITESSTATISTIKK/ELECTRICITY STATISTICS. (Subseries of: Norges Offisielle Statistikk) 1937. a. NOK 60. Statistisk Sentralbyraa, Box 8131 Dep., 0033 Oslo 1, Norway. TEL 47-22-864500. FAX 47-22-864973. circ. 750. **Document type:** government publication.

621.3   IT
NOTIZIE STATISTICHE SULL'ENERGIA ELETTRICA. 1978. m. E.N.E.L.-E.N.T.E. Nazionale per L'Energia Elettrica, 3, Via G.B. Martini, 00198 Rome, Italy. Ed. Calogero Rizzo. circ. 3,500. (back issues avail.)

333.792   US   ISSN 0271-0706
NUCLEAR INDEX. 1980. m. $350. (National Energy Researchers) McGraw-Hill, Inc., 1221 Ave. of the Americas, New York, NY 10020. TEL 212-512-2000. Ed. Margaret Ryan. (back issues avail.)

621   FR
O E C D WORLD ENERGY STATISTICS. a. price varies. Organization for Economic Cooperation and Development, 2 rue Andre-Pascal, 75775 Paris Cedex 16, France. (U.S. orders to: O.E.C.D. Publications and Information Center, 2001 L St., N.W., Ste. 700, Washington, DC 20036-4910. TEL 202-785-6323) (also avail. in microfiche from OEC)

333.79 310   AQ   ISSN 1021-7347
O E C S ENERGY REVIEW. 1983. irreg. EC$25($10) Organisation of Eastern Caribbean States, Economic Affairs Secretariat, P.O. Box 822, St. John's, Antigua, W.I. TEL 809-462-3500. FAX 809-462-1537. charts; stat. circ. 350. **Document type:** government publication.
Formerly (until 1990): O E C S Energy Bulletin.
Description: Reviews energy situation in member countries, analyzes international energy developments.

621.47   US
PHOTOVALTIC ENERGY. bi-m. $90 in US, Canada, Mexico; elsewhere $180. (Department of Energy) U.S. National Technical Information Service, 5825 Port Royal Rd., Springfield, VA 22161. TEL 703-487-4630.
Description: Abstracts current international information on all aspects of solar cells and photovaltic power supplies.

621.47   US   ISSN 1069-0786
▼**PHOTOVOLTAIC ENERGY ABSTRACTS.** 1993. bi-m. $195 (overseas $215). WindBooks, Inc., Box 4008, St. Johnsbury, VT 05819-4008. TEL 802-748-5148. FAX 802-748-3286. Ed. Farrell Smith Seiler. adv.; bk.rev. (looseleaf format; back issues avail.) **Document type:** abstracting/indexing.
Description: Summarizes proceedings on photovoltaic energy technology and applications.

621.3   NP
POWER STATISTICS JOURNAL OF NEPAL.* (Text in English) 1971. irreg. Department of Electricity, Kathmandu, Nepal. illus.; stat.

333.79   US
PRODUCTION COSTS: OPERATING STEAM ELECTRIC PLANTS. 1983. a. $225 (diskette version $495). Utility Data Institute (Subsidiary of: McGraw-Hill), 1200 G St., N.W., Ste. 250, Washington, DC 20005. TEL 202-942-8788; 800-486-3660. FAX 202-942-8789. stat.; index. (also avail. in diskette format; back issues avail.) **Document type:** trade publication.
Description: Supplies production- and fuel-expense data for U.S. steam electric plants.

621.3   IT
PRODUZIONE E CONSUMO DI ENERGIA ELETTRICA IN ITALIA. English edition: Production and Consumption of Electricity in Italy. 1975. a. free. Ente Nazionale per l'Energia Elettrica (ENEL), Direzione della Programmazione, Via G.B. Martini 3, 00198 Rome, Italy. TEL 06-85091. FAX 06-85092162. stat.
Description: Provides statistical data on the electricity production and distribution in Italy related to the four categories of domestic producers: ENEL, municipal utilities, autoproducers and small non-nationalized utilities.

PUBLIC USE ENERGY STATISTICAL DATA BASE. see *PUBLIC HEALTH AND SAFETY — Abstracting, Bibliographies, Statistics*

531.64   RU   ISSN 0203-5308
TK4
REFERATIVNYI ZHURNAL. ENERGETIKA. 1955. m. 181.60 Rub. (206.60 Rub. with index). Vsesoyuznyi Institut Nauchno-Tekhnicheskoi Informatsii (VINITI), Baltiiskaya ul. 14, Moscow A-219, Russia. (Subscr. to: Mezhdunarodnaya Kniga, Dimitrova ul. 39, 113095 Moscow, Russia) **Document type:** abstracting/indexing.
—BLDSC (0153.040000).

REFERATIVNYI ZHURNAL. KOTLOSTROENIE. see *ENGINEERING — Abstracting, Bibliographies, Statistics*

531.64 016   RU   ISSN 0203-6436
REFERATIVNYI ZHURNAL. TEPLO I MASSOBMEN. 1976. m. 34.60 Rub. (37 Rub. with index). Vsesoyuznyi Institut Nauchno-Tekhnicheskoi Informatsii (VINITI), Baltiiskaya ul. 14, Moscow A-219, Russia. (Subscr. to: Mezhdunarodnaya Kniga, Dimitrova ul. 39, 113095 Moscow, Russia) **Document type:** abstracting/indexing.

333.79   SA
SELECTED ENERGY STATISTICS: SOUTH AFRICA. (Text in English) 1988. q. R.490($270) Energy Research Institute, Information Service, P.O. Box 33, Plumstead 7800, South Africa. TEL 27-21-705-0120. FAX 27-21-705-6266. Ed. Yvonne Blomkamp. circ. 75.

621.4   JA
SHIN GIJUTSU HAPPYO GAIYO/ABSTRACTS OF MEETING ON THERMAL AND NUCLEAR POWER ENGINEERING. (Text in Japanese) a. Karyoku Genshiryoku Hatsuden Gijutsu Kyokai, Kanto Shibu - Thermal and Nuclear Power Engineering Society of Japan, Kanto Branch, 23-11, Toranomon 1-chome, Minato-ku, Tokyo 105, Japan. **Document type:** abstracting/indexing.

621.47   US
SOLAR BUILDINGS TECHNOLOGY. bi-m. $145 in US, Canada, Mexico; elsewhere $290. (U.S. Department of Energy) U.S. National Technical Information Service, 5825 Port Royal Rd., Springfield, VA 22161. TEL 703-487-4630. **Document type:** government publication, abstracting/indexing.
Description: Abstracts current international information on all aspects of solar energy use in buildings including desulfurization, photovaltic systems, solar thermal, solar collectors, and heat storage.

621.47   US   ISSN 1069-1111
▼**SOLAR THERMAL ENERGY TECHNOLOGY ABSTRACTS.** 1993. bi-m. $195 (overseas $215). WindBooks, Inc., Box 4008, St. Johnsbury, VT 05819-4008. TEL 802-748-5148. FAX 802-748-3286. Ed. Farrell Smith Seiler. adv.; bk.rev. (looseleaf format; back issues avail.) **Document type:** abstracting/indexing.
Description: Summarizes proceedings dealing with solar energy research, developments, and applications.

333.79 316.8   SA
SOUTH AFRICA. CENTRAL STATISTICAL SERVICE. CENSUS OF ELECTRICITY, GAS AND STEAM. (Report No. 41-01-01) 1963. triennial, latest 1989. R.6 (foreign R.7.50). Central Statistical Service - Sentrale Statistiekdiens, Private Bag X44, Pretoria 0001, South Africa. TEL 27-12-310-8911. FAX 27-12-310-8500. (Orders to: Government Printing Works, Private Bag X85, Pretoria 0001, South Africa) **Document type:** government publication.
Formerly: South Africa. Department of Statistics. Census of Electricity, Gas and Steam (ISSN 0301-8105)

333.79 316.8   SA
SOUTH AFRICA. CENTRAL STATISTICAL SERVICE. STATISTICAL RELEASE. CENSUS OF ELECTRICITY, GAS AND STEAM. (No. P4101) irreg., latest 1989. free. Central Statistical Service - Sentrale Statistiekdiens, Private Bag X44, Pretoria 0001, South Africa. TEL 27-12-310-8911. FAX 27-12-310-8500. **Document type:** government publication.

333.79 316.8 SA
SOUTH AFRICA. CENTRAL STATISTICAL SERVICE. STATISTICAL RELEASE. ELECTRICITY AVAILABLE FOR DISTRIBUTION. (No. P4141) m. free. Central Statistical Service - Sentrale Statistiekdiens, Private Bag X44, Pretoria 0001, South Africa. TEL 27-12-310-8911. FAX 27-12-310-8500. **Document type:** government publication.

333.79 EI
STATISTICAL OFFICE OF THE EUROPEAN COMMUNITIES. BULLETIN OF ENERGY PRICES. s-a. Office of Official Publications of the European Communities, 2, rue Mercier, L-2985 Luxembourg, Luxembourg. (also avail. in microfiche from CIS) **Indexed:** IIS.
Description: Features various examples of prices, comparisons of prices between member states, and comparisons between energy sources.

333.79 EI ISSN 0081-489X
STATISTICAL OFFICE OF THE EUROPEAN COMMUNITIES. ENERGY STATISTICS. YEARBOOK. (Text in English) a. $40. Statistical Office of the European Communities, L- 2985 Luxembourg, Luxembourg. (Dist. in the U.S. by: Unipub, 4611-F Assembly Dr., Lanham, MD 20706-4391. TEL 800-274-4888. FAX 301-459-0056) (also avail. in microfiche from CIS) **Indexed:** IIS.

333.79 EI
HD9502.E862
STATISTICAL OFFICE OF THE EUROPEAN COMMUNITIES. ENERGY STATISTICS MONTHLY BULLETIN. (Text in English, French, German) m. $115. Statistical Office of the European Communities, L-2985 Luxembourg, Luxembourg. (Dist. in the U.S. by: Unipub, 4611-F Assembly Dr., Lanham, MD 20706-4391. TEL 800-274-4888. FAX 301-459-0056) (also avail. in microfiche from CIS) **Indexed:** IIS.
●Also available online. Vendor(s): GSI-ECO.
—BLDSC (3747.690200).
Former titles: Statistical Office of the European Communities. Energy (ISSN 0258-3569); Statistical Office of the European Communities. Quarterly Bulletin of Energy Statistics. (ISSN 0585-1580)

333.79 EI
STATISTICAL OFFICE OF THE EUROPEAN COMMUNITIES. GAS PRICES. (Text in English) 1971. a. $12. Statistical Office of the European Communities, L-2985 Luxembourg, Luxembourg. (Dist. in the U.S. by: Unipub, 4611-F Assembly Dr., Lanham, MD 20706-4391. TEL 800-274-4888. FAX 301-459-0056) Ed.Bd. circ. 2,000. (also avail. in microfiche from CIS; back issues avail.) **Indexed:** IIS.

665.7 US
SUMMARY OF RATE SCHEDULES OF NATURAL GAS PIPELINE COMPANIES. 1952. q. $375 (effective Jan. 1991). H. Zinder and Associates, Inc., 1828 L St., N.W., Washington, DC 20036. TEL 202-862-3400. Ed. Joseph Blackburn. circ. 250.
Former titles: Summary of Rate Schedules of Natural Gas Pipeline Companies as Filed with the Federal Energy Regulatory Commission and the National Energy Board of Canada (ISSN 0190-2997); Summary of Rate Schedules of Natural Gas Pipeline Companies as Filed with the Federal Power Commission (ISSN 0146-1907)

333.79 SW ISSN 0349-5299
HD9502.S8
SWEDEN. STATISTISKA CENTRALBYRAAN. STATISTISKA MEDDELANDEN. SERIE E, ENERGI. 1981. irreg. SEK 700 (effective 1992). Statistiska Centralbyraan, Publishing Unit, S-701 89 Oerebro, Sweden. **Document type:** government publication.

333.79 380.4 US ISSN 0885-8330
TRANSPORTATION ENERGY RESEARCH. m. $150 in US, Canada, Mexico; elsewhere $300. (U.S. Department of Energy) U.S. National Technical Information Service, 5825 Port Royal Rd., Springfield, VA 22161. TEL 703-487-4630. **Document type:** abstracting/indexing.
Description: Abstracts current international information on the engineering and design of energy-efficient advanced automotive propulsion systems and all aspects of energy conservation measures involving transportation.

621.4 380.5 US ISSN 1069-0719
▼**TRANSPORTATION ENERGY RESEARCH ABSTRACTS.** 1993. bi-m. $195 (overseas $215). WindBooks, Inc., Box 4008, St. Johnsbury, VT 05819-4008. TEL 802-748-5148. FAX 802-748-3286. Ed. Farrell Smith Seiler. adv.; bk.rev. (looseleaf format; back issues avail.) **Document type:** abstracting/indexing.
Description: Summarizes proceedings on energy research and development in the transporation sector.

315.61 TU
TURKEY. DEVLET ISTATISTIK ENSTITUSU. GAZ VE SU ISTATISTIKLERI/TURKEY. STATE INSTITUTE OF STATISTICS. GAS AND WATER STATISTICS. (Text in English, Turkish) 1986. a., latest 1990. $25. Devlet Istatistik Enstitusu - State Institute of Statistics, Necatibey Caddesi No. 114, 06100 Ankara, Turkey. TEL 90-312-4185027. FAX 90-312-4170432. **Document type:** government publication.
Description: Provdes statistical data for the gas and water sub-sectors of the energy sector in Turkey.

016 US ISSN 1054-2914
Z5162.R42
U.S. NUCLEAR REGULATORY COMMISSION. TITLE LIST OF DOCUMENTS MADE PUBLICLY AVAILABLE. Key Title: Title List of Documents Made Publicly Available. m. U.S. Nuclear Regulatory Commission, Division of Technical Information and Documents, Washington, DC 20555. (Dist. by: Superintendent of Documents, Box 37082, Washington, DC 20402-7082) **Document type:** government publication, bibliography.
Formerly (until 1979): Power Reactor Docket Information (ISSN 0363-5856)

318 333.8 VE
VENEZUELA. MINISTERIO DE ENERGIA Y MINAS. APENDICE ESTADISTICO. (Supplement to: Venezuela. Ministerio de Energia y Minas. Memoria.) a. Ministerio de Energia y Minas, Oficina de Estudios Economicos Energeticos, Torre Norte, Centro Simon Bolivar, Caracas, Venezuela. charts. **Document type:** government publication.

318 333.8 VE
VENEZUELA. MINISTERIO DE ENERGIA Y MINAS. MEMORIA. a. Ministerio de Energia y Minas, Oficina de Estudios Economicos Energeticos, Torre Norte, Centro Simon Bolivar, Caracas, Venezuela. (Subscr. to: Ministerio de Energia y Minas, Biblioteca, Torre Oeste, Parque Central piso 16, Caracas, Venezuela) **Document type:** government publication.

621.4 333.9 US ISSN 0277-2140
WIND ENERGY ABSTRACTS; the international wind power abstracts journal. 1983. bi-m. $195. WindBooks, Inc., Box 4008, St. Johnsbury, VT 05819-4008. TEL 802-748-5148. FAX 802-748-3286. Ed. Farrell Smith Seiler. adv.; bk.rev. circ. 1,250. (looseleaf format; back issues avail.) **Document type:** abstracting/indexing.
—CCC.
Incorporates (1988-199?): Journal of Wind Energy Technology (ISSN 0884-0318); (1978-199?): Wind Energy Report (ISSN 0162-8623)
Description: Reports on energy engineering, technology, economics, politics, and meteorology projects throughout the world.

621.4 US
WIND ENERGY TECHNOLOGY. bi-m. $135 in US, Canada, Mexico; elsewhere $270. (U.S. Department of Energy) U.S. National Technical Information Service, 5825 Port Royal Rd., Springfield, VA 22161. TEL 703-487-4630. **Document type:** abstracting/indexing.
Description: Abstracts current international information on all aspects of energy from the wind.

621.4 UK ISSN 0263-0915
WIND ENGINEERING ABSTRACTS. 1982. 4/yr. £95 (foreign £102). Multi-Science Publishing Co. Ltd., 107 High St., Brentwood, Essex CM14 4RX, England. TEL 0277-224632. FAX 0277-224632. (U.S. subscr. to: Box 176, Avenel, NJ 07001) index. **Document type:** abstracting/indexing.
—CCC.
Description: Summarizes articles, reports and proceedings on the advancement of wind energy.

ENERGY — Computer Applications

621.3 US
BUFFER. 1977. m. free. National Energy Research Supercomputer Center, Lawrence Livermore National Laboratory, Box 5509, L-560, Livermore, CA 94551. TEL 510-423-0790. FAX 510-422-0425. Ed. Stephanie P. Shang. cum.index: 1985-1992. (back issues avail.)
●Also available online.
Description: Provides information about computer hardware and software at the center.

333.79 US
CO-OP POWER. 1944. m. Association of Texas Electric Cooperatives, Box 9589, Austin, TX 78766. TEL 512-454-0311. Ed. George Macias. adv. circ. 416,000. **Document type:** consumer publication.
Description: Keeps the consumers of Texas electric cooperatives abreast of developments affecting electric cooperatives.

621.3 005.3 US ISSN 1051-3981
HD9696.C6
ELECTRICAL INDUSTRY SOFTWARE DIRECTORY. 1991. a. PennWell Publishing Co., Box 1260, Tulsa, OK 74101. TEL 918-835-3161. FAX 918-831-9497. TELEX 211012. **Document type:** directory.

ENERGY — Electrical Energy

333.79 363.6 CN ISSN 0706-1420
TN873.C22
ALBERTA ELECTRIC INDUSTRY, ANNUAL STATISTICS. 1972. a. Can.$40. Energy Resources Conservation Board, 640 5th Ave. S.W., Calgary, Alta. T2P 3G4, Canada. TEL 403-297-8311. FAX 403-297-7040. TELEX 03-821717. illus.; stat. **Indexed:** CS Ind.
Formerly (until 1979): Alberta Electric Industry, Cumulative Annual Statistics.
Description: Statistical data on electric power in Alberta.

ANNUAL BULLETIN OF ELECTRIC ENERGY STATISTICS FOR EUROPE. see *ENERGY — Abstracting, Bibliographies, Statistics*

ANUARIO ESTATISTICO DE ENERGIA ELECTRICA. AUTOPRODUTORES NO ESTADO DE SAO PAULO. see *ENERGY — Abstracting, Bibliographies, Statistics*

333.79 US
AROUND THE SYSTEM. 1936. 10/yr. Consolidated Edison Company, 4 Irving Pl., No. 1627, New York, NY 10003-3598. TEL 212-460-4106. Ed. Allen Pinto. circ. 37,000.

621.31 IT
ATTIVITA COSTRUTTIVA NEL (YEAR). a. Ente Nazionale per l'Energia Elettrica (ENEL), Via G.B. Martini 3, 00198 Rome, Italy. TEL 06-85091. FAX 06-85092162.

AUSTRALIA. BUREAU OF STATISTICS. ELECTRICITY AND GAS OPERATIONS, AUSTRALIA. see *ENERGY — Abstracting, Bibliographies, Statistics*

BAHIA, BRAZIL (STATE). SECRETARIA DAS MINAS E ENERGIA. BOLETIM ESTATISTICO MENSAL DE ENERGIA ELETRICA. see *ENERGY — Abstracting, Bibliographies, Statistics*

BILTEN DOKUMENTACIJE. ELEKTROPRIVREDA/BULLETIN OF DOCUMENTATION. ELECTRICAL ENERGY. see *ENERGY — Abstracting, Bibliographies, Statistics*

CANADA. STATISTICS CANADA. ELECTRIC POWER STATISTICS VOLUME 1: ANNUAL ELECTRIC POWER SURVEY OF CAPABILITY AND LOAD. see *ENERGY — Abstracting, Bibliographies, Statistics*

CANADA. STATISTICS CANADA. ELECTRICAL TRADE CONTRACTORS. see *ENERGY — Abstracting, Bibliographies, Statistics*

333.79 CN
CANADIAN ELECTRICAL ASSOCIATION. CONNECTIONS. (Text in English, French) 1929. bi-m. $35 (foreign $65). Canadian Electrical Association - Association Canadienne de l'Electricite, 1 Westmount Sq., Ste. 1600, Montreal, Que. H3Z 2P9, Canada. TEL 514-937-6181. FAX 514-937-6498. Ed. Beverley Gard. charts; illus.; stat. circ. 3,500. (back issues avail.)
Formerly: Canadian Electrical Association. Bulletin.

ENERGY — ELECTRICAL ENERGY

051 US ISSN 0008-6746
CAROLINA COUNTRY. 1946. m. $4 to non-members. Carolina Electric Cooperatives, Box 27306, Raleigh, NC 27611. TEL 919-872-0800. FAX 919-878-3970. Ed. Michael E.C. Gery. adv. contact: Monica Russell. bk.rev. circ. 340,000. (also avail. in microfiche) **Document type:** consumer publication.
Formerly: Carolina Farmer.
Description: Directed to consumer-members of electric cooperatives in North Carolina. Focuses on developments within the rural electric program, and on issues and events which have implications for the state's rural people.

333.79 US
COGENERATION & I P P POWER SALES. a. $395 (with diskette $750). Utility Data Institute (Subsidiary of: McGraw-Hill), 1200 G St., N.W., Ste. 250, Washington, DC 20005. TEL 202-942-8788; 800-486-3660. FAX 202-942-8789. charts; stat. (also avail. in diskette format) **Document type:** trade publication.
Description: Reports on who is buying power and how much they are paying for it.

333.79 US
COGENERATION AND INDEPENDENT POWER PRODUCERS. 1990. a. $1250 (s-a. updates $595). Utility Data Institute (Subsidiary of: McGraw-Hill), 1200 G St., N.W., Ste. 250, Washington, DC 20005. TEL 202-942-8788; 800-486-3660. FAX 202-942-9789. stat. (diskette format) **Document type:** trade publication.
Formerly: Multi-Year Comparison of Utility Power Purchases from Cogenerators and Independent Power Producers.
Description: Provides financial and technical information on purchases by U.S. utilities from 4,000 cogenerators and independent power producers, as reported to the Federal Energy Regulatory Commission.

333.8 US
COGENERATION AND RESOURCE RECOVERY. 1983. bi-m. $50. Cogeneration and Small Power, 747 Leigh Mill Rd., Great Falls, VA 22066. TEL 703-759-5060. FAX 703-759-0232. adv.: B&W page $1700, color page $2475; trim 8 1/2 x 11. circ. 3,000 (paid); 1,500 (controlled).

051 US
COLORADO COUNTRY LIFE. 1952. m. $12. Colorado Rural Electric Association, 1313 W. 46th Ave., Denver, CO 80211-2350. TEL 303-455-2700. Ed. Frank McCrea. adv. circ. 90,000. **Document type:** consumer publication.
Formerly: Rocky Mountain Rural Electric News.

COMPANHIA PARANAENSE DE ENERGIA. BOLETIM ESTATISTICO MENSAL. see ENERGY — Abstracting, Bibliographies, Statistics

333.79 IT
COMPOLUX. 6/yr. Via Rosetti 9, 20145 Milan, Italy. TEL 2-480-07-449. FAX 2-480-07-493. Ed. Renato Pisaniello. circ. 6,000.

333.79 IT
CONTATTO ELETTRICO. 9/yr. Via del Fusaro 8, 20146 Milan, Italy. TEL 2-48-19-086. FAX 2-481-90-91. Ed. Filippo di Gregorio. circ. 75,000.

COST AND QUALITY OF FUELS FOR ELECTRIC UTILITIES (F E R C 423). see ENERGY — Abstracting, Bibliographies, Statistics

333.79 US
D E E D DIGEST. (Demonstrate Energy Efficient Developments) 1980. q. $150. American Public Power Association, 2301 M St., N.W., Washington, DC 20037. TEL 202-467-2900. FAX 202-467-2910. Ed. Stacey Hobart. charts; illus. circ. 1,300. (back issues avail.)

621.3 US
D R I - MCGRAW-HILL ENERGY REVIEW: ELECTRICITY INDUSTRY FOCUS. s-a. D R I - McGraw-Hill, 24 Hartwell Ave., Lexington, MA 02173. TEL 617-863-5100. FAX 617-860-6332.

333.79 US
▼**D S M QUARTERLY.** 1992. q. (Demand-Side Management Society) Cogeneration and Small Power, 747 Leigh Mill Rd., Great Falls, VA 22066. TEL 703-759-5060. FAX 703-759-0232. adv.: B&W page $1700, color page $2475; trim 8 1/2 x 11. circ. 1,250.

DATOS ESTADISTICOS DE LAS EMPRESAS ELECTRICAS. see ENERGY — Abstracting, Bibliographies, Statistics

DENKI GAKKAI RONBUNSHI. B, DENRYOKU ENERUGI BUMONSHI/INSTITUTE OF ELECTRICAL ENGINEERS OF JAPAN. TRANSACTIONS. B; POWER AND ENERGY SOCIETY PUBLICATION. see ENGINEERING — Electrical Engineering

333.79 UY
DIRECTORIO DEL SECTOR ELECTRICO. 1968. irreg., no.6, 1978. price varies. Comision de Integracion Electrica Regional, Bulevar Artigas 1040, 11300 Montevideo, Uruguay. TEL 79-53-59. FAX 5982-783193. TELEX 26609 CIER UY. **Document type:** directory.

333.79 US
DIRECTORY OF POWER PLANTS IN ASIA AND AUSTRALIA. 1990. a. $395. Utility Data Institute (Subsidiary of: McGraw-Hill), 1200 G St., N.W., Ste. 250, Washington, DC 20005. TEL 202-942-8788; 800-486-3660. FAX 202-942-8789. (also avail. in diskette format) **Document type:** directory.
Formerly (until 1992): Directory of Power Plants in Japan.
Description: Provides power plant design data on more than 650 utility and industrial companies in 34 countries.

333.79 US
DIRECTORY OF POWER PLANTS IN CANADA. base vol. with a. updates. $225 (with diskette $495; updates $395). Utility Data Institute (Subsidiary of: McGraw-Hill), 1200 G St., N.W., Ste. 250, Washington, DC 20005. TEL 202-942-8788; 800-486-3660. FAX 202-942-2789. (also avail. in diskette format) **Document type:** directory.
Description: Compiles key design data for every generating unit in Canada.

333.79 US
DIRECTORY OF POWER PLANTS IN THE EUROPEAN COMMUNITY. 1989. a. $395. Utility Data Institute (Subsidiary of: McGraw-Hill), 1200 G St., N.W., Ste. 250, Washington, DC 20005. TEL 202-942-8788; 800-486-3660. FAX 202-942-8789. (also avail. in diskette format) **Document type:** directory.
Description: Provides comprehensive information on more than 2,500 electric power plants in European Community nations.

621.3 333.79 US
DIRECTORY OF SELECTED U S COGENERATION, SMALL POWER AND INDUSTRIAL POWER PLANTS. 8th ed., 1988. a. (in 2 vols./yr.). $395 per no. Utility Data Institute (Subsidiary of: McGraw-Hill), 1200 G St., N.W., Ste. 250, Washington, DC 20005. TEL 202-942-8766; 800-486-3660. FAX 202-942-8789. **Document type:** directory.
Description: Provides information on more than 4,700 power projects, including wood-fired, geothermal, refuse-to-energy, wind, and solar generating units.

333.79 US
DIRECTORY OF SELECTED U S COGENERATION, SMALL POWER & INDUSTRIAL POWER PLANTS. a. (in 2 vols.). $395. Utility Data Institute (Subsidiary of: McGraw-Hill), 1200 G St., N.W., Ste. 250, Washington, DC 20005. TEL 202-942-8788; 800-486-3660. FAX 202-942-8789. **Document type:** directory.
Description: Lists more than 4,000 U.S. cogeneration, small power, and industrial power projects. Also covers refuse-to-energy, gas turbine and combined-cycle facilities, geothermal units, coal- and wood-fired plants, and wind and solar installations.

621.3 US
E E I SUPERDIRECTORY OF POWER PLANT ENVIRONMENTAL DATA. a. $495 includes: E E I Environmental Directory. (Edison Electric Institute) Utility Data Institute (Subsidiary of: McGraw-Hill), 1200 K St., N.W., Ste. 250, Washington, DC 20005. TEL 202-942-8788; 800-486-3660. FAX 202-942-8789. **Document type:** directory.
Description: Provides information on pollution-control equipment and waste disposal systems for more than 950 U.S. electric power plants.

333.79 SP
ELECTRA. 6/yr. Navaleno 9, Residencia el Bosque de Charmarti, 28033 Madrid, Spain. TEL 1-302-81-46. FAX 1-766-16-64. Ed. Carlos Garcia Ocejo. circ. 42,000.

051 US ISSN 0745-4651
ELECTRIC CONSUMER. 1951. m. $4 to non-members. Indiana Statewide Association of Rural Electric Cooperatives Inc., 720 N. High School Rd., Indianapolis, IN 46214. TEL 317-248-9453. FAX 317-247-5220. Ed. Emily Born. adv.: B&W page $2450, color page $2900. bk.rev.; illus.; circ. 265,502 (paid); 186 (controlled). (tabloid format) **Document type:** consumer publication.
Former titles: Indiana Rural News - Electric Consumer (ISSN 0279-9952); Indiana Rural News (ISSN 0442-8102)
Description: Publication serving electric cooperative members in Indiana.

ELECTRIC ENERGY SYSTEMS. see ENERGY — Abstracting, Bibliographies, Statistics

333.79 US
ELECTRIC PLANT DATAPAK; computerized directory of utility plants equipment and owners. 1990. a. $495. Utility Data Institute (Subsidiary of: McGraw-Hill), 1200 K St., N.W., Ste. 250, Washington, DC 20005. TEL 202-942-8788; 800-486-3660. FAX 202-942-8789. (diskette format) **Document type:** directory.
Incorporates (in 1993): Hydroelectric Plants Data Base; Formerly: Electric Plant Ownerpak.
Description: Provides data about ownership and operation of equipment in more than 7,700 electric generating units in the U.S.

333.79 CN ISSN 0070-962X
TK26
ELECTRIC POWER IN CANADA. French edition: Energie Electrique au Canada (ISSN 0821-8218) (Text and summaries in English and French) 1979. a. free. Department of Natural Resources, Energy Sector, 580 Booth St., Ottawa, ON K1A 0E4, Canada. TEL 613-996-4779. FAX 613-995-0087. Ed. Po-Chih Lee. circ. 6,000. **Document type:** government publication.
Description: Includes qualitative and statistical information on electrical energy in Canada: electrical generation and consumption, trade, transmission, costing and pricing, and federal and provincial regulatory and environmental reports.

333.79 US ISSN 0732-2305
TK23
ELECTRIC POWER MONTHLY. 1980. m. $87 (foreign $108.75). U.S. Department of Energy, Energy Information Administration, National Energy Information Center, EI-231, Rm. 1F-048, Forrestal Bldg., 1000 Independence Ave., S.W., Washington, DC 20585. TEL 202-586-8800. (Subscr. to: Superintendent of Documents, U.S. Government Printing Office, Box 371954, Pittsburgh, PA 15250-7954. TEL 202-783-3238. FAX 202-512-2233) charts. (also avail. in microfiche from CIS; back issues avail.; reprint service avail. from CIS) **Indexed:** Amer.Stat.Ind. (1980-), Energy Info.Abstr. (until 1994), PROMT. **Document type:** trade publication, government publication.
Incorporates (1983-1988): Electric Power Quarterly (ISSN 0742-1885); Which supersedes in part: Cost and Quality of Fuels for Electric Utility Plants (Monthly) (ISSN 0743-7145); Which was formerly (1978-1981): Monthly Report, Cost and Quality of Fuels for Electric Utility Plants (ISSN 0740-056X)
Description: Compiles electric utility statistics on net energy for load; peak load and net capability; and fuel consumption, stocks, deliveries, and prices.

ELECTRIC POWER USE BY INDUSTRIES. see ENERGY — Abstracting, Bibliographies, Statistics

ENERGY — ELECTRICAL ENERGY

ELECTRIC RATE BOOK. see *ENERGY — Abstracting, Bibliographies, Statistics*

333.79   US
ELECTRIC UTILITY ADDRESS DATA BASE. s-a. $250. Utility Data Institute (Subsidiary of: McGraw-Hill), 1200 G St., N.W., Ste. 250, Washington, DC 20005. TEL 202-942-8788; 800-486-3660. FAX 202-942-8789. (diskette format) **Document type:** directory.
  Description: Lists the addresses and company type for 3,000 electric utilities.

333.79   US
ELECTRIC UTILITY C E O DATA BASE. q. $125. Utility Data Institute (Subsidiary of: McGraw-Hill), 1200 G St., N.W., Ste. 250, Washington, DC 20005. TEL 202-942-8788; 800-486-3660. FAX 202-942-8789. (diskette format) **Document type:** directory.
  Description: Lists the chief executive officers of investor-owned utilities and holding companies

333.79   US   ISSN 1065-8696
▼**ELECTRIC UTILITY WEEK'S DEMAND-SIDE REPORT.** 1992. fortn. $445 in N. America; overseas $490. McGraw-Hill, Inc., 1221 Ave. of the Americas, New York, NY 10020. TEL 212-512-6410. (Subscr. to: Box 513, Hightstown, NJ 08520) **Document type:** newsletter.
  Description: Provides in-depth coverage of demand-side management as it applies to utility companies and to policymakers.

333.79   621.3   US
ELECTRICAL ADVERTISER. m. $34 (foreign $45). Electrical Advertiser, 6500 Brooklyn Blvd., Minneapolis, MN 55429. TEL 800-328-0328. FAX 612-566-4826. adv.: B&W page $685; trim 10 x 12. circ. 21,000.
  Description: Source for buyers and sellers of new, used and surplus electrical equipment.

ELECTRICAL INDUSTRY SOFTWARE DIRECTORY. see *ENERGY — Computer Applications*

621.3   UK
ELECTRICITY INTERNATIONAL. 10/yr. 17A Woodcote Rd., Wallington, Surrey SM6 0LH, England. TEL 081-773-3773. FAX 081-773-2019. Ed. Richard Hooper. circ. 11,500.

333.79   US   ISSN 1040-6190
HD9685.U4   CODEN: ELEJE4
ELECTRICITY JOURNAL. 1988. 10/yr. $395 to individuals; libraries $125; government agencies $275. Robert O. Marritz, Ed. & Pub., 1932 First Ave., Ste. 809, Seattle, WA 98101-1040. TEL 206-448-4078; 800-326-1676. bk.rev. **Indexed:** Energy Info.Abstr., P.A.I.S. **Document type:** trade publication.
—BLDSC (3698.105400).
  Description: Focuses on policy issues in America's electric utility industry.

333.79   US
ELECTRICITY SUPPLY & DEMAND (YEAR). (Supplement to: Reliability Assessment) a. free. North American Electric Reliability Council, Princeton Forrestal Village, 116-390 Village Blvd., Princeton, NJ 08540-5731. TEL 609-452-8060. charts; stat.
  Description: Covers resources, demands, net energy for load, transmission facilities and other related electricity parameters.

EMPRESA NACIONAL DE ENERGIA ELECTRICA. DATOS ESTADISTICOS. see *ENERGY — Abstracting, Bibliographies, Statistics*

621.3   XR   ISSN 0013-7286
ENERGETIKA/POWER ENGINEERING; technical monthly for electric power engineering, thermal power stations and utilizations of power. (Supplement avail.) (Text in Czech; summaries in English, German, Russian) 1950. m. $54.50. (Federalni Ministerstvo Paliv a Energetiky) Nakladatelstvi Technicke Literatury, Spalena 51, 113 02 Prague 1, Czech Republic. (Dist. by: Artia, Ve Smeckach 30, 111 27 Prague 1, Czech Republic) Ed. Vladimir Prusa. adv.; bk.rev.; charts; illus.; pat. circ. 6,000. **Indexed:** BSL Indus., C.I.S. Abstr., INIS Atomind., Int.Aerosp.Abstr., PROMT, Risk Abstr., Sci.Abstr.

ENERGY STORAGE SYSTEMS ABSTRACTS. see *ENERGY — Abstracting, Bibliographies, Statistics*

ESTADISTICA DE ENERGIA ELECTRICA. see *ENERGY — Abstracting, Bibliographies, Statistics*

FEDERATION PROFESSIONNELLE DES PRODUCTEURS ET DISTRIBUTEURS D'ELECTRICITE DE BELGIQUE. ANNUAIRE STATISTIQUE. see *ENERGY — Abstracting, Bibliographies, Statistics*

FINANCIAL STATISTICS OF MAJOR INVESTOR-OWNED ELECTRIC UTILITIES (YEAR). see *ENERGY — Abstracting, Bibliographies, Statistics*

FINANCIAL STATISTICS OF SELECTED ELECTRIC UTILITIES. see *ENERGY — Abstracting, Bibliographies, Statistics*

FRANCE. SERVICE D'ETUDE DES STRATEGIES ET DES STATISTIQUES INDUSTRIELLES. LES CONSOMMATIONS D'ENERGIE DANS L'INDUSTRIE. see *ENERGY — Abstracting, Bibliographies, Statistics*

621.3   UK
THE GEN. 1989. m. PowerGen plc, Haslucks Green Rd., Shirley, Solihull B90 4PD, England. TEL 021-701-2291. FAX 021-701-2859. Ed. Ralph Webster. circ. 18,000. **Document type:** newsletter.

333.79   US
GENERATING AVAILABILITY REPORT (YEAR). a. $40 to non-utilities (foreign $50). North American Electric Reliability Council, Princeton Forrestal Village, 116-390 Village Blvd., Princeton, NJ 08540-5731. TEL 609-452-8060.
  Description: Presents historical statistics on the performance of electric generating units and their major components. Serves as a statistical basis for exploring areas of equipment availability improvements.

333.79   US
GENERATING UNIT STATISTICS (YEAR). a. free. North American Electric Reliability Council, Princeton Forrestal Village, 116-390 Village Blvd., Princeton, NJ 08540-5731. TEL 609-452-8060.
  Description: Brochure presenting generating unit availability statistics for the most recent year and the latest five-year period.

333.79   UK
THE GRID. 1989. m. The National Grid Company plc, National Grid House, Kirby Corner Rd., Coventry CV4 8JY, England. TEL 0203-423610. FAX 0203-423613. Ed. Trevor Seeley. circ. 14,000. **Document type:** newsletter.

621.31   US
I E E E PULSED POWER CONFERENCE. DIGEST OF TECHNICAL PAPERS.. 1976. biennial. Institute of Electrical and Electronics Engineers, Inc., 345 E. 47th St., New York, NY 10017-2394. TEL 212-705-7900. FAX 212-705-7682. (Subscr. to: Box 1331, 445 Hoes Lane, Piscataway, NJ 08855-1331) Ed. A.H. Guenther. (reprint service avail. from ISI)
  Former titles (until 1981): I E E E International Pulsed Power Conference. Digest of Technical Papers; (until 1979): I E E E International Pulsed Power Conference. Proceedings.

621.31   US   ISSN 0885-8969
TK1001   CODEN: ITCNE4
I E E E TRANSACTIONS ON ENERGY CONVERSION. 1986. q. $150 to non-members. (I E E E, Power Engineering Society) Institute of Electrical and Electronics Engineers, Inc., 345 E. 47th St., New York, NY 10017-2394. TEL 908-981-0060. FAX 908-981-9667. (Subscr. to: IEEE Service Center, 445 Hoes Ln., Piscataway, NJ 08854) Ed. Harold Gold. (also avail. in microform from UMI,EEE) **Indexed:** A.S.& T.Ind., Comput.Abstr., Energy Info.Abstr., INIS Atomind.
—BLDSC (4363.185000); EI; Faxon; UnCover; SWETS; UMI. **CCC.**
  Supersedes in part: I E E E Transactions on Power Apparatus and Systems (ISSN 0018-9510)

621.31   US   ISSN 0885-8950
TK1005   CODEN: ITPSEG
I E E E TRANSACTIONS ON POWER SYSTEMS. 1986. q. $180 to non-members. (I E E E, Power Engineering Society) Institute of Electrical and Electronics Engineers, Inc., 345 E. 47th St., New York, NY 10017-2394. TEL 908-981-0060. FAX 908-981-9667. (Subscr. to: IEEE Service Center, 445 Hoes Lane, Box 1331, Piscataway, NJ 08855-1331) Ed. S.H. Gold. (also avail. in microform) **Indexed:** A.S.& T.Ind., Comput.Abstr., Energy Info.Abstr., INIS Atomind.
—BLDSC (4353.214000); EI; Faxon; UnCover; SWETS; UMI. **CCC.**
  Supersedes in part: I E E E Transactions on Power Apparatus and Systems (ISSN 0018-9510)

333.79   SZ
I N F E L INFO. q. Informationsstelle fuer Elektrizitaetsanwendung (INFEL), Lagerstr. 1, CH-8021 Zurich, Switzerland. TEL 01-2910102. FAX 01-2910903. Ed. Ruedi Spalinger. circ. 1,000.

333.79   UK
INDEPENDENT POWER NEWS. 6/yr. South West One Ltd., Herodsfoot, Liskeard, Cornwall PL14 4QX, England. TEL 0579-21300. FAX 0579-20586. Ed. David Porter. circ. 3,000.

333.79   UK
INSIDE ENERGY. 1990. fortn. £325 (foreign £345). Reed Business Publishing Ltd. (Subsidiary of: Reed Elsevier group), Quadrant House, The Quadrant, Sutton, Surrey SM2 5AS, England. TEL 081-652-3113. FAX 081-652-8951. Ed. Tim Tunbridge. **Document type:** trade publication.

333.79   US
INTERNATIONAL DIRECTORY OF ELECTRIC UTILITIES. bi-a. $295. McGraw-Hill, Inc., 1221 Avenue of the Americas, New York, NY 10020. TEL 212-512-6410. (Subscr. to: Box 513, Hightstown, NJ 08520) **Document type:** directory.
  Description: Covers utility companies and executives in 162 countries in Europe, Africa, the Middle East, and Latin America.

KEY ABSTRACTS - POWER SYSTEMS & APPLICATIONS. see *ENGINEERING — Abstracting, Bibliographies, Statistics*

333.79   US
L M & M: LIGHTING MANAGEMENT & MAINTENANCE. 1953. m. $110. (International Association of Lighting Management Companies) C M A Publications, Creative Marketing Alliance, Inc., 34-C Washington Rd., Princeton Junction, NJ 08550. TEL 609-799-5501. FAX 609-799-7032. Ed. Jeff Barnhart. illus.; tr.lit. circ. 1,000. **Document type:** trade publication.
  Description: Promotes and encourages the success and growth of companies and organizations which participate in the strategic management of lighting systems.

333.79   UK
LIVE WIRE. 13/yr. The Smokehouse, Smokehouse Yard, 44-46 St. Johns St., London EC1M 4DT, England. TEL 071-253-1514. FAX 071-253-4740. Ed. Sarah Johnson. circ. 14,000.

333.79   US
LIVE WIRES. fortn. South Carolina Electric, Box 764, Columbia, SC 29218-0001. TEL 803-748-3088. Ed. Wanda Martin. circ. 5,500.

333.79   UK
M A N W E B REPORT AND ACCOUNTS. a. Merseyside and North Wales Electricity Board plc, Sealand Rd., Chester CH1 4LR, England. TEL 0244-652091. FAX 0244-652119. TELEX 61277. **Document type:** corporate report.

621.3   UK
MICROWAVE ENGINEERING EUROPE. 8/yr. $130. Morgan-Grampian Technical Press Ltd. (Subsidiary of: Morgan-Grampian plc), Morgan-Grampian House, 30 Calderwood St., London SE18 6QH, England. TEL 081-855-7777. FAX 081-316-3102. Ed. Paul Jackson. adv. contact: Jason Saywood. circ. 12,759. **Document type:** trade publication.

MONTHLY ELECTRIC UTILITIES SALES AND REVENUE REPORT (E I A - 826). (Energy Information Administration) see *ENERGY — Abstracting, Bibliographies, Statistics*

ENERGY — ELECTRICAL ENERGY

333.79 SP
MUNDO COOPERATIVO. 4/yr. Valverde 13, 4o, 28004 Madrid, Spain. TEL 1-231-53-08. Ed. F. de la Caballeria.

333.79 NR
NIGERIA. NATIONAL ELECTRIC POWER AUTHORITY. ANNUAL REPORT AND ACCOUNTS.* 1972. a. National Electric Power Authority, Electricity Headquarters, 24-25 Marina, PMB 12030, Lagos, Nigeria. Ed.Bd. charts; illus.; stat. circ. 5,000. **Document type:** government publication.

333.79 US
NODAK NEIGHBOR. 1953. m. $1. Nodak Rural Electric Coop., Inc., Box 13000, Grand Forks, ND 58208-3000. TEL 701-746-4461. FAX 701-746-7431. Ed. Carol Ackerman.

333.79 US
NORTH AMERICAN ELECTRIC RELIABILITY COUNCIL. ANNUAL REPORT. 1969. a. North American Electric Reliability Council, Princeton Forrestal Village, 116-390 Village Blvd., Princeton, NJ 08540-5731. TEL 609-452-8060. circ. 5,000. **Document type:** corporate report.
 Formerly: National Electric Reliability Council. Annual Report.

333.79 US
NORTH AMERICAN LIGHTING DISTRIBUTOR. 1979. 8/yr. $110. (Lighting Distributors of North America) C M A Publications, Creative Marketing Alliance, Inc., 34-C Washington Rd., Princeton Junction, NJ 08550. TEL 609-799-6253. FAX 609-799-7032. Ed. Russ Mykytyn. adv.; illus.; tr.lit. circ. 1,000. **Document type:** trade publication.
 Formerly: (until 1994): Today's Lighting Distributor.
 Description: Provides a forum for all distributors of lighting products. Covers feature stories, industry news, legislative and environmental information, general business management, trends, people, new products, and activities and services of LDNA.

333.79 US
NORTHEAST POWER REPORT; covering the New England, New York and PJM power pools. 1990. fortn. $795 (foreign $845). McGraw-Hill, Inc., Energy & Business Newsletters, 1221 Ave. of the Americas, 36th Fl., New York, NY 10020. TEL 212-512-6410. FAX 212-512-2723. Ed. Ron Dionne. stat. (looseleaf format; back issues avail.; reprint service avail. from UMI)
 Description: Covers electric power planning and development in New England, New York and Mid-Atlantic states.

333.79 US
NORTHWEST ELECTRIC UTILITY DIRECTORY. 1948. a. $45. Northwest Public Power Association, Box 4576, Vancouver, WA 98662-0576. TEL 206-254-0109. FAX 206-254-5731. Ed. Don Noel. adv. circ. 5,000. **Document type:** trade publication, directory.

NORWAY. STATISTISK SENTRALBYRAA. ELEKTRISITESSTATISTIKK/ELECTRICITY STATISTICS. see *ENERGY — Abstracting, Bibliographies, Statistics*

333.79 IT
NOTIZIARIO ELETTRICO. 2/yr. Edizioni Pubblicita Editoriale, Via La Spezia 33, 20142 Milan, Italy. TEL 2-89-50-06-73. FAX 2-84-63-045. Ed. Vincenzo Casolaro. circ. 27,000.

NOTIZIE STATISTICHE SULL'ENERGIA ELETTRICA. see *ENERGY — Abstracting, Bibliographies, Statistics*

333.79 US
OFFICIAL GUIDE TO D S M PROGRAMS & RESEARCH. (Demand-Side Management) a. $145 (with diskette $495). Utility Data Institute (Subsidiary of: McGraw-Hill), 1200 G St., N.W., Ste. 250, Washington, DC 20005. TEL 202-942-8788; 800-486-3660. (also avail. in diskette format) **Document type:** trade publication.
 Description: Reports on utility companies participating in demand-side management.

P V NEWS. see *ENERGY — Solar Energy*

333.79 US
▼**POCKET GUIDE TO U S ELECTRIC UTILITIES.** 1992. a. $110. Utility Data Institute (Subsidiary of: McGraw-Hill), 1200 G St., N.W., Ste. 250, Washington, DC 20005. TEL 202-942-8788; 800-486-3660. FAX 202-942-8789. stat. **Document type:** directory.
 Description: Profiles every major U.S. electric utility.

POWER STATISTICS JOURNAL OF NEPAL. see *ENERGY — Abstracting, Bibliographies, Statistics*

PRODUCTION COSTS: OPERATING STEAM ELECTRIC PLANTS. see *ENERGY — Abstracting, Bibliographies, Statistics*

333.79
PRODUCTION COSTS: U S GAS TURBINE AND COMBINED-CYCLE POWER PLANTS. 1988. a. $225. Utility Data Institute (Subsidiary of: McGraw-Hill), 1200 G St., N.W., Ste. 250, Washington, DC 20005. TEL 202-942-8788; 800-486-3660. FAX 202-942-8789. (also avail. in diskette format) **Document type:** directory.
 Formerly: Directory of U S Utility Gas Turbine and Combined-Cycle Power Plants.
 Description: Provides information on more than 1,500 power-generating plants in the U.S.

PRODUZIONE E CONSUMO DI ENERGIA ELETTRICA IN ITALIA. see *ENERGY — Abstracting, Bibliographies, Statistics*

333.79 US ISSN 0033-3654
HD9685.U4
PUBLIC POWER. 1942. bi-m. $35. American Public Power Association, 2301 M St., N.W., Washington, DC 20037. TEL 202-467-2948. FAX 202-467-2910. Ed. Jeanne Wickline LaBella. adv.: B&W page $1575, color page $2875. bk.rev.; illus.; stat.; tr.lit.; index. circ. 12,000. (also avail. in microfiche from CIS) **Indexed:** C.I.S. Ind., Energy Info.Abstr., Energy Rev., Environ.Abstr., SRI.—BLDSC (6968.390000); Faxon; UnCover.
 Description: Provides legislative and regulatory monitoring, coverage of technical and statistical research, educational and informational services for America's publicly owned electric utilities.

333.79 621.3 US
PUBLIC POWER WEEKLY. w. $250. American Public Power Association, 2301 M St., N.W., Washington, DC 20037. TEL 202-467-2947. Ed. Robert Varela. circ. 10,000.

333.79 US
RELAY MAGAZINE. 1957. m. membership. Florida Municipal Electric Association, Inc., Box 10114, 417 E. College Ave., Tallahassee, FL 32302-2114. TEL 904-224-3314. Ed. Stephanie Wolanski. adv.; circ. 1,800 (controlled). (back issues avail.) **Document type:** trade publication.
 Description: Covers the state's municipal electric utility industry.

339.79 US
RELIABILITY ASSESSMENT. 1970. a. North American Electric Reliability Council, Princeton Forrestal Village, 116-290 Village Blvd., Princeton, NJ 08540-5731. TEL 609-452-8060. circ. 6,000. (also avail. in microfiche from CIS) **Indexed:** Oper.Res.Manage.Sci., Qual.Contr.Appl.Stat., SRI.
 Former titles: Reliability Review; (until 1985): Overall Reliability and Adequacy of the North American Bulk Power Systems. Annual Review.
 Description: Covers overall reliability of generation and transmission systems--both existing and for ten year projections--of the nine regional reliability councils in North America.
 Refereed Serial

051 US ISSN 0193-4937
RURAL ELECTRIC NEBRASKAN. 1947. m. $7. Nebraska Rural Electric Association, 800 S. 13th St., Lincoln, NE 68501. TEL 402-475-4988. Ed. Jack Merritt. adv.: B&W page $915, color page $1160. bk.rev.; charts; illus.; circ. 58,000 (controlled). **Document type:** consumer publication.
 Formerly: Nebraska Electric Farmer.

333.79 US ISSN 0747-4784
RURAL ELECTRIC NEWS LETTER; a roundup of legislative, regulatory, and political news affecting rural electrification. bi-w. $26. National Rural Electric Cooperative Association, 1800 Massachusetts Ave., N.W., Washington, DC 20036. TEL 202-857-9585. FAX 202-857-9791. Ed. J.C. Brown. circ. 16,000. **Document type:** newsletter.

333.79 MX ISSN 0186-050X
HD9685.M58
SECTOR ELECTRICO EN MEXICO. 1981. irreg., latest 1990. Mex.$26500($23) Instituto Nacional de Estadistica, Geografia e Informatica, Secretaria de Programacion y Presupuesto, Prol. Heroe de Nacozari, 2301, Sur, Puerta 11, Acceso, 20270 Aguascalientes, Ags., Mexico. TEL 91-49-18-19-48. FAX 91-491-80739. circ. 500.

333.79 US
STATE DIRECTORY OF NEW ELECTRIC POWER PLANTS. a. $145 (with diskette $495). Utility Data Institute (Subsidiary of: McGraw-Hill), 1200 G St., N.W., Ste. 250, Washington, DC 20005. TEL 202-942-8788; 800-486-3660. FAX 202-942-8789. (also avail. in diskette format) **Document type:** directory.
 Description: Lists new plants planned by cogenerators, independent power producers, and regulated electric utilities, along with the names and addresses of key personnel.

333.79 US
SUMMER ASSESSMENT (YEAR). a. free. North American Electric Reliability Council, Princeton Forrestal Village, 116-390 Village Blvd., Princeton, NJ 08540-5731. TEL 609-452-8060.
 Description: Assesses the electricity supply conditions for the upcoming summer peak demand period.

537 US ISSN 1062-1776
SUPERCONDUCTIVITY BULLETIN. 1991. q. free. (U.S. Department of Energy) Argonne National Laboratory, 9700 S. Cass Ave., Bldg. 900, Argonne, IL 60439. TEL 708-252-6393. FAX 708-252-5230. Ed. M. Margaret Hanley. circ. 900. (back issues avail.) **Document type:** newsletter.
 Description: Describes the activities of the Department of Energy program for superconductivity; progress in HTS electric power applications.

333.79 US
SYSTEM DISTURBANCES (YEAR). a. free. North American Electric Reliability Council, Princeton Forrestal Village, 116-390 Village Blvd., Princeton, NY 08540-5731. TEL 609-452-8060.
 Description: Covers electric system disturbances and unusual occurrences.

621.3 JA
TOHOKU NO DENGEN/ELECTRIC POWER RESOURCES IN TOHOKU DISTRICT. (Text in Japanese) a. Tsusho Sangyosho, Tohoku Tsusho Sangyokyoku - Ministry of International Trade and Industry, Tohoku Bureau, 3-1, Hon-cho 3-chome, Aoba-ku, Sendai-shi, Miyagi-ken 980, Japan.

333.79 US
U D I DATAGRAM. 1989. 3/yr. free to qualified personnel. Utility Data Institute (Subsidiary of: McGraw-Hill), 1200 G St., N.W., Ste. 250, Washington, DC 20005. TEL 202-942-8788; 800-486-3660. FAX 202-942-8789. circ. (controlled). **Document type:** newsletter.
 Description: Covers news from U.D.I. on industry-related publications and developments.

333.79 US
U D I UTILITY DATAPAK. a. $2,500. Utility Data Institute (Subsidiary of: McGraw-Hill), 1200 G St., N.W., Ste. 250, Washington, DC 20005. TEL 202-942-8788; 800-486-3660. FAX 202-927-8789. (diskette format) **Document type:** trade publication.
 Description: Provides comparative financial, operating, and sales information for 150 U.S. electric utilities.

333.79 US
U D I WHO'S WHO AT ELECTRIC POWER PLANTS. 1990. a. $150. Utility Data Institute (Subsidiary of: McGraw-Hill), 1200 G St., N.W., Ste. 250, Washington, DC 20005. TEL 202-466-3660; 800-486-3660. FAX 202-466-3667. (also avail. in diskette format) Document type: directory.
  Description: Lists 6,000 managers at more than 1,200 electric generating plants of all types throughout the U.S.

333.79 US
U D I WHO'S WHO IN COGENERATION AND INDEPENDENT POWER. a. $150 (with diskette $495). Utility Data Institute (Subsidiary of: McGraw-Hill), 1200 G St., N.W., Ste 250, Washington, DC 20005. TEL 202-942-8788; 800-486-3660. FAX 202-942-8789. (also avail. in diskette format) Document type: directory.
  Description: Profiles the nonutility generation involvement of 1,000 power companies and lists key personnel.

333.79 US
U S STEAM ELECTRIC PLANTS: FIVE YEAR PRODUCTION COSTS. 1986. a. $395. Utility Data Institute (Subsidiary of: McGraw-Hill), 1200 G St., N.W., Ste. 250, Washington, DC 20005. TEL 202-942-8788; 800-486-3660. FAX 202-942-8789. (also avail. in diskette format) Document type: trade publication.
  Formerly: Five Year Comparison of Production Expenses for Selected Steam Electric Plants.
  Description: Provides line-item, variable operating, and maintenance expense data for more than 550 active steam-electric plants.

051 US
UNION ELECTRIC NEWS. 1904. m. Union Electric Company, 1901 Chouteau Ave, Box 149, St. Louis, MO 63166. TEL 314-554-3120. Ed. D. Walther. cum.index: 1950-1992; circ. 10,100 (controlled). (tabloid format)

UNIVERSITATEA POLITEHNICA BUCURESTI. BULETIN STIINTIFIC. INGINERIE ELECTROTEHNICA/POLYTECHNICAL UNIVERSITY OF BUCHAREST. SCIENTIFIC BULLETIN. ELECTRICAL ENGINEERING. see ELECTRONICS

333.79 US ISSN 1065-6480
UTILITY SPOTLIGHT. 1947. w. $547. Utility Spotlight LP, Box 819, McLean, VA 22101. TEL 703-847-6344. FAX 703-847-0544. Ed. Gene Smith. (back issues avail.) Document type: newsletter.
—CCC.
  Description: Features current information for upper and middle-management about the utility industry, especially as it pertains to Washington and Wall Street.

333.79 US
WINTER ASSESSMENT (YEAR). a. free. North American Electric Reliability Council, Princeton Forrestal Village, 116-390 Village Blvd., Princeton, NJ 08540-5731. TEL 609-452-8060.
  Description: Assesses the electricity supply conditions for the upcoming winter peak demand period.

333.79 US
WORLD DIRECTORY OF NEW ELECTRICAL POWER PLANTS. 1994. a. $395 (with data diskette $595). Utility Data Institute (Subsidiary of: McGraw-Hill), 1200 G St., N.W., Ste. 250, Washington, DC 20005. TEL 202-942-8788. FAX 202-942-8789. stat. (also avail. in diskette format) Document type: trade publication, directory.
  Description: Lists all electric power plants planned or under construction.

333.79 US ISSN 0043-9770
WYOMING RURAL ELECTRIC NEWS. 1955. m. $4.50 (effective Jan. 1993). Wyoming Rural Electric Association, Box 380, Casper, WY 82602. TEL 307-234-6152. FAX 307-234-4115. Ed. Patty Bratton. adv.; pat.; stat.; circ. 30,000 (controlled). Document type: consumer publication.
—UnCover.
  Description: For rural electric customers in the state: farmers, town residents, and vacation homeowners. Celebrates Wyoming culture, natural resources, energy, and agriculture.

ENERGY — Geothermal Energy

AUSTRALIA. BUREAU OF STATISTICS. ELECTRICITY AND GAS OPERATIONS, AUSTRALIA. see ENERGY — Abstracting, Bibliographies, Statistics

621.44 551 JA ISSN 0385-7034
CODEN: JJGTAD
CHINETSU/JAPAN GEOTHERMAL ENERGY ASSOCIATION. JOURNAL. (Text in Japanese; summaries in English, Japanese) 1963. 5/yr. Nihon Chinetsu Chosakai - Japan Geothermal Energy Association, 7-1, Yurakucho 1-chome, Chiyoda-ku, Tokyo 100, Japan. Indexed: Chem.Abstr., Jap.Per.Ind.
—CASDDS.

621.44 551 JA ISSN 0285-1717
CODEN: CGIJDY
CHINETSU GIJUTSU/GEOTHERMAL ENERGY RESEARCH AND DEVELOPMENT CO., LTD. JOURNAL. (Text in Japanese) s-a. Chinetsu Gijutsu Kaihatsu K.K. - Geothermal Energy Research and Development Co., Ltd., 11-7, Nihonbashi Kabutocho, Chuo-ku, Tokyo 103, Japan.
—CASDDS.

621.44 II
ENERGY & FUEL USERS' JOURNAL. (Text in English) q. Rs.100 (foreign Rs.300). Energy & Fuel Users' Association of India, 4 B-1, J.P. Tower, 7-2, Nungambakkam High Rd., Madras 600 034, India. TEL 8278604. Ed. L. Subramanian.

GENSHIRYOKU HATSUDENJO UNTEN KANRI NENPO/ANNUAL REPORT OF OPERATION CONTROL IN THE NUCLEAR POWER PLANTS. see ENERGY — Nuclear Energy

GEOTHERMAL ENERGY. see ENERGY — Abstracting, Bibliographies, Statistics

GEOTHERMAL ENERGY ABSTRACTS. see ENERGY — Abstracting, Bibliographies, Statistics

621.44 551 US ISSN 0735-0503
GEOTHERMAL HOTLINE. 1972. 2/yr. free. Division of Oil, Gas, and Geothermal Resources, 801 K St., MS 20-20, Sacramento, CA 95814-3530. FAX 916-323-0424. Ed. Susan F. Hodgson. bk.rev.; bibl. circ. 1,300. Indexed: Energy Rev.

333.8 US ISSN 0160-7782
GB1199.6 CODEN: BGRCDD
GEOTHERMAL RESOURCES COUNCIL. BULLETIN. 1980. 11/yr. $80 to non-members. Geothermal Resources Council, Box 1350, Davis, CA 95617-1350. TEL 916-758-2360. FAX 916-758-2839. (Street addr.: 2001 Second St., Ste. 5, Davis, CA 95616) Ed. David N. Anderson. adv.; bk.rev. circ. 1,500. (back issues avail.) Indexed: AESIS, GeoRef. Document type: bulletin.
—EI.

333.8 US
GEOTHERMAL WORLD JOURNAL.* (Text in English and Spanish) 1974. q. membership. International Society for Geothermal Engineering, Inc., 10707 Orange Dr., Whittier, CA 90606-1116. Ed. Edward F. Wehlage.

621.44 531.64 US
I S G E TRANSACTIONS.* (Text in English and Spanish) 1974. q. membership. International Society for Geothermal Engineering, Inc., 10707 Orange Dr., Whittier, CA 90606-1116. Ed. Edward F. Wehlage.

ENERGY — Hydroelectrical Energy

621.3 US ISSN 1048-6291
TK23.7
BONNEVILLE POWER ADMINISTRATION. RESEARCH AND DEVELOPMENT REPORT. biennial. U.S. Department of Energy, Bonneville Power Administration, Box 3621, Portland, OR 97208.
  Formerly (until 1988): Research and Development Yearbook (ISSN 8756-9884)

621.31 US ISSN 0884-0385
HYDRO REVIEW; a magazine covering the North American hydroelectric industry. (Supplement avail.: Industry Directory) 1982. 8/yr. $56 (foreign $68). H C I Publications, 410 Archibald St., Kansas City, MO 64111-3046. TEL 816-931-1311. FAX 816-931-2015. Ed. Marla Barnes. adv.: B&W page $1557, color page $2216; 8 1/2 x 11. cum.index: 1982-1991. (back issues avail.) Indexed: Energy Info.Abstr., Environ.Abstr. Document type: trade publication.
—BLDSC (4342.950000); CIS.
  Description: Covers all aspects of the North American hydroelectric industry, including plant operations and maintenance, equipment, and rehabilitation.

621.31 333.91 US
▼HYDRO REVIEW WORLDWIDE; a quarterly magazine covering hydroelectric development and generation outside North America. 1993. 4/yr. $37. H C I Publications, 410 Archibald St., Kansas City, MO 64111-3046. TEL 816-931-1311. FAX 816-931-2015. Ed. Marla Barnes. adv.: B&W page $2372, color page $3009; 8 1/2 x 11. Document type: trade publication.
  Description: Covers the practical aspects of designing, building and maintaining small to large scale hydroelectric facilities. Also covers dam safety issues.

HYDROCARBON ASIA. see PETROLEUM AND GAS

HYDROCARBON ASIAN BUSINESS REPORTS. see PETROLEUM AND GAS

333.91 FR ISSN 1147-9213
HYDROECOLOGIE APPLIQUEE. (Text in English, French) 1989. q. Electricite de France, Direction de l'Equipement, Departement S.E.I., 22-30 av. de Wagram, 75382 Paris Cedex 08, France. Ed. A. Gregoire. illus.
  Formerly: Cahiers du Laboratoire d'Hydrobiologie de Montereau (ISSN 0396-132X)

621.31 US
HYDROWIRE; nationa hydroelectric energy news. 1980. bi-w. $295 (foreign $375). H C I Publications, 410 Archibald St., Kansas City, MO 64111-3046. TEL 816-931-1311. FAX 816-931-2015. Ed. John Braden. cum.index 1980-1992. (looseleaf format; back issues avail.) Document type: newsletter.
●Also available online. Vendor(s): NewsNet (EY53).
  Description: Covers the hydroelectric market including business, finance and regulatory news in both the US and Canada.

333.91 II
NATIONAL HYDRO ELECTRIC POWER CORPORATION. ANNUAL REPORT.* (Text in English) 1976. a. National Hydro Electric Power Corporation Ltd., Manjusha, 57 Nehru Place, New Delhi 110019, India. Document type: corporate report.

333.91 621.31 US
PRODUCTION COSTS: U S HYDROELECTRIC POWER PLANTS. a. $225 (with diskette $495). Utility Data Institute (Subsidiary of: McGraw-Hill), 1200 G St., N.W., Ste. 250, Washington, DC 20005. TEL 202-942-8788; 800-486-3660. FAX 202-942-8789. stat. Document type: trade publication.
  Description: Compiles operation and maintenance expenses for more than 800 conventional and pumped-storage hydroelectric power plants.

RENEWABLE ENERGY MANUFACTURERS LISTS: WIND AND HYDRO POWER. see ENERGY — Wind Energy

333.91 GW ISSN 0509-8858
DAS WASSERTRIEBWERK. 1951. m. DM.62.50. (Bundesverband Deutscher Kraftwerke) Verlag Moritz Schaefer, Postfach 2254, 32712 Detmold, Germany. TEL 05231-24637. FAX 05231-35896. Ed.Bd. adv.; bk.rev.; illus.; stat. circ. 5,600. (back issues avail.) Document type: trade publication.

ENERGY — Nuclear Energy

621.48 UK
A E A TIMES. 1962. m. free. United Kingdom Atomic Energy Authority, Corporate Communication Service, Harwell Laboratory, Didcot, Oxon. OX11 0RA, England. FAX 0235-433101. Ed. Lindsay Chandler. adv.; bk.rev.; film rev.; illus. circ. 15,000.
  Formerly: Atom News (ISSN 0004-7058)

ENERGY — NUCLEAR ENERGY

621.48   CN   ISSN 0067-0367
CODEN: AECRAN
A E C L REPORT SERIES. (Text in English; abstracts in English and French) 1952. irreg. price varies. Atomic Energy of Canada Ltd., Chalk River Nuclear Laboratories, Technical Information Services, S.D.D.O., Sta. 14, Chalk River, Ont. K0J 1J0, Canada. TEL 613-584-3311. cum.index. **Indexed:** Chem.Abstr., INIS Atomind.
—EI; CASDDS.
Description: Discusses basic and applied nuclear research and development results.

621.48   US   ISSN 0737-6812
A N S NEWS. 1983. m. $88. American Nuclear Society, 555 N. Kensington Ave., La Grange Park, IL 60525. TEL 708-352-6611. circ. 16,000. (tabloid format; back issues avail.) **Document type:** newsletter.

621.48   AT   ISSN 1031-8216
A N S T O TECHNOLOGY. 4/yr. Australian Nuclear Science and Technology Organisation, Menai, N.S.W. 2234, Australia. FAX 02-543-9274. Ed. G. Carrard. illus. circ. 6,000.
Former titles (until 1988): A N S T O Nuclear News; (until 1979): A A E C Nuclear News (Australian Atomic Energy Commission) (ISSN 0157-6224)
Description: Covers work done by A N S T O.

621.48   JA   ISSN 0916-3743
AISOTOPU SENTA NYUSU/RAIDIOISOTOPE CENTER NEWS. (Text in Japanese) 1978. irreg. Tusukuba Daigaku, Aisotopu Senta - University of Tsukuba, Raidioisotope Center, 1-1, Tennodai 1-chome, Tsukuba-shi, Ibaraki-ken 305, Japan.

621.48   NE   ISSN 0168-3748
ALLICHT. 1981. 4/yr. fl.15 to individuals; institutions fl.30. (Gezamelijke Energie Komitee's Zuid-Nederland) Stichting Allicht, Postbus 8107, 5004 GC Tilburg, Netherlands. TEL 31-13-351535. FAX 31-13-358169. Ed.Bd. adv.; bk.rev. cir. 750. (also avail. in diskette format) **Document type:** bulletin.
—SWETS.

539 621.48   US   ISSN 0003-018X
QC770   CODEN: TANSAO
AMERICAN NUCLEAR SOCIETY TRANSACTIONS. (Supplement avail.) 1958. 3/yr. $340. American Nuclear Society, 555 N. Kensington Ave., La Grange Park, IL 60525. TEL 708-352-6611. FAX 708-352-0499. Ed. I. Macke. charts; illus.; index. circ. 2,000. (back issues avail.) **Indexed:** Biol.Abstr., Chem.Abstr., Curr.Cont., Energy Info.Abstr., Eng.Ind., Environ.Abstr., Fuel & Energy Abstr., Met.Abstr., Pollut.Abstr., Risk Abstr., Sci.Abstr., World Alum.Abstr. **Document type:** academic/scholarly publication.
—BLDSC (8893.500000); Faxon; SWETS.
Description: Publishes summaries of papers reviewed and accepted for presentation at the ANS annual and winter meetings.
Refereed Serial

621.48   UK   ISSN 0306-4549
TK9001   CODEN: ANENDJ
ANNALS OF NUCLEAR ENERGY. (Contains section: English translations from "Atomnaya Energiya") (Text and summaries in English, French and German) 1974. 12/yr. £530($815) (effective 1994). Elsevier Science Ltd., Pergamon, P.O. Box 800, Kidlington, Oxford OX5 1DX, England. TEL 44-865-843000. FAX 44-865-843010. (Subscr. in U.S. and Canada to: Elsevier Science, 660 White Plains Rd., Tarrytown, NY 10591-5153. TEL 914-524-9200. FAX 914-333-2444) Eds. M.M.R. Williams, L.E. Weaver. adv.; bk.rev.; abstr.; bibl.; charts; illus. circ. 1,100. (also avail. in microfilm from UMI) **Indexed:** Chem.Abstr., Curr.Cont., Energy Info.Abstr., Energy Rev., Eng.Ind., Environ.Per.Bibl. (1981-), Excerp.Med., Fluidex, Ind.Sci.Rev., INIS Atomind., Risk Abstr., Sci.Abstr., Sci.Cit.Ind. **Document type:** academic/scholarly publication.
—BLDSC (1043.150000); EI; Faxon; UnCover; SWETS; UMI; CASDDS. **CCC.**
Formerly (until 1975): Annals of Nuclear Science and Engineering (ISSN 0302-2927); Incorporates: Journal of Nuclear Energy (ISSN 0022-3107)
Description: Provides an international medium for the communication of original research in all areas of the field of nuclear science and technology.
Refereed Serial

621.48   US
ARIZONA RADIATION REGULATORY AGENCY. ANNUAL REPORT. 1965. a. Radiation Regulatory Agency, 4814 S. 40th St., Phoenix, AZ 85040. TEL 602-255-4845. **Document type:** government publication.
Description: Annual summary of agency program activities.

621.48   US
ARIZONA RADIATION REVIEW. 1970. s-a. Radiation Regulatory Agency, 4814 S. 40th St., Phoenix, AZ 85040. TEL 602-255-4845. Ed. John T. O'Neill. circ. 1,000. (tabloid format; back issues avail.) **Document type:** government publication.
Formerly: Radiation Review.
Description: Current topics in radiation, radiology and agency program activities.

621.48 333.792   UK   ISSN 0004-7015
HD9698.G7   CODEN: ATMMAR
ATOM. 1956. m. free. United Kingdom Atomic Energy Authority, Corporate Communication Service, Harwell Laboratory, Didcot, Oxon. OX11 0RA, England. FAX 0235-433101. Ed. Lindsay Chandler. adv.; bk.rev.; charts; index. circ. 16,000. (also avail. in microfiche) **Indexed:** Biol.Abstr., BMT, Br.Tech.Ind., Chem.Abstr., Excerp.Med., Fluidex, Fuel & Energy Abstr., INIS Atomind., Met.Abstr., P.A.I.S., Risk Abstr., Sci.Abstr.
—BLDSC (1768.500000); EI; UnCover.

621.48   IO   ISSN 0126-1568
QC791.9   CODEN: ATINDD
ATOM INDONESIA; a medium for the publication of results of research and development of atomic energy in Indonesia. (Text and summaries in English) 1975. s-a. free. National Atomic Energy Agency - Badan Tenaga Atom Nasional, Puspiptek - Serpong - Tangerang, P.O. Box 4274, Jakarta 12042, Indonesia. TEL 2104-7560905. FAX 021-750923. (Alt. addr.: Puspitek Serpong, P.O. Box 4437, Jakarta 12044, Indonesia) Ed. Pratiwi Sapto Sutarno. abstr.; bibl.; charts; illus.; stat. **Indexed:** Biol.Abstr., INIS Atomind.
—BLDSC (1768.650000); CASDDS.

539 621.48   US   ISSN 1063-4258
QC770
ATOMIC ENERGY. English translation of: Atomnaya Energiya (RU ISSN 0004-7163) 1956. m. (2 vols./yr.) $1215 (foreign $1425) (effective 1994). (Russian Academy of Sciences, RU) Plenum Publishing Corp., Consultants Bureau, 233 Spring St., New York, NY 10013-1578. TEL 212-620-8468. FAX 212-463-0742. TELEX 23-421139. Ed. N.N. Ponomarev-Stepnoi. (also avail. in microfilm from JSC; back issues avail.) **Indexed:** Appl.Mech.Rev., Chem.Titles, Curr.Cont., Energy Res.Abstr., Eng.Ind., Pollut.Abstr., Risk Abstr., Saf.Sci.Abstr., Sci.Res.Abstr. **Document type:** academic/scholarly publication.
—BLDSC (0404.814000); Faxon; UMI. **CCC.**
Formerly (until 1992): Soviet Atomic Energy (ISSN 0038-531X)
Refereed Serial

333.792   US   ISSN 0519-3389
ATOMIC ENERGY CLEARINGHOUSE. 1955. w. $525 (foreign $650). Congressional Information Bureau, Inc., 1325 G St., N.W., Ste. 1005, Washington, DC 20005. TEL 202-347-2275. FAX 202-347-2278. Ed. Pamela Lessard. circ. 500. (looseleaf format; back issues avail.)
—BLDSC (1769.626000). **CCC.**
Description: Covers commercial nuclear energy: international and U.S. nuclear plants, NRC, DOE, Congress and courts.

621.48   US   ISSN 0004-7104
LAW
ATOMIC ENERGY LAW JOURNAL.* 1959. q. $59. Invictus Publishing Co., 29 Top of Ridge Dr., Scarsdale, NY 10583-6715. TEL 914-949-6550. bk.rev.; index. circ. 500. (also avail. in microfilm; reprint service avail. from RRI) **Indexed:** C.L.I., INIS Atomind., L.R.I., Leg.Per.

621.48   JA
ATOMIC ENERGY POCKETBOOK. (Text in Japanese) 1964. a. 4800 Yen. Japan Atomic Industrial Forum, Inc. - Nihon Genshiryoku Sangyo Kaigi, Toshin Bldg., 1-1-13 Shinbashi, Minato-ku, Tokyo 105, Japan. TEL 03-3508-2411. FAX 03-3508-2094. TELEX 2226623-JAIFRM-J.

621.48   JA   ISSN 0004-7120
CODEN: NGEGAL
ATOMIC ENERGY SOCIETY OF JAPAN. JOURNAL/NIHON GENSHIRYOKU GAKKAI SHI. (Text in Japanese; summaries in English) 1959. m. 18000 Yen($150) Atomic Energy Society of Japan - Nihon Genshiroku Gakkai, 1-1-13, Shinbashi, Minato-ku, Tokyo 105, Japan. TEL 03-3508-1261. FAX 03-3581-6128. Ed. Genki Yagawa. adv.; bk.rev.; abstr.; charts; illus.; index. cum.index. circ. 8,200. (also avail. in microfiche) **Indexed:** Cadscan, Chem.Abstr., Curr.Cont., Energy Ind., Energy Info.Abstr., INIS Atomind., JTA, Lead Abstr., Met.Abstr., Risk Abstr., Sci.Abstr., World Alum.Abstr., Zincscan. **Document type:** academic/scholarly publication.
—BLDSC (4705.850000); EI; UMI; CASDDS.

333.792   US
ATOMIC INDUSTRIAL FORUM REPORT.* a. U.S. Council for Energy Awareness, 1776 Eye St., N.W., Ste. 400, Washington, DC 20006-3708. **Indexed:** Energy Info.Abstr.

621.48   RU   ISSN 0004-7163
QC770   CODEN: AENGAB
ATOMNAYA ENERGIYA. English translation: Atomic Energy (US ISSN 1063-4258) (Text in Russian; contents page in English) 1956. m. $360 (effective 1994). (Ministry of Russian Federation on Atomic Energy) Redaktsiya Zhurnala Atomnaya Energiya, Ul. Miasnitskaya 18, 101000 Moscow, Russia. TEL 095-9258670. FAX 095-9235189. TELEX 411594 SHUGA UR. (Co-sponsors: Nuclear Society, Russian Academy of Sciences) Ed. N.N. Ponomarev-Stepnoi. adv. contact: V.S. Yuzgin. bk.rev.; bibl.; charts; illus.; index. circ. 800. **Indexed:** Biol.Abstr., Chem.Abstr., Eng.Ind., GeoRef, INIS Atomind., Sci.Abstr. **Document type:** academic/scholarly publication.
—BLDSC (0014.000000); CASDDS. **CCC.**

ATOMO PETROLIO ELETTRICITA. see *ENERGY*

621.48   JA   ISSN 0403-9319
ATOMS IN JAPAN. (Text in English) 1956. m. 58000 Yen($300) membership. Japan Atomic Industrial Forum - Nihon Genshiryoku Sangyo Kaigi, Toshin Bldg., 1-1-13 Shinbishi, Minato-ku, Tokyo 105, Japan. FAX 03-3508-2411. TELEX 2226623-JAIFRM-J. **Indexed:** Excerp.Med., INIS Atomind.

621.48   JA   ISSN 0386-1430
ATOMU FUKUSHIMA. 1974. bi-m. free. Fukushimaken Genshiryoku Koho Kyokai - Fukushima Prefectural Atomic Power Public Information Association, 199, Ono, Shimonogami, Okuma-machi, Futaba-gun, Fukushima-ken 979-13, Japan. circ. 28,000.

621.48 333.792   GW   ISSN 0365-8414
TK9001   CODEN: AWAKAG
ATOMWIRTSCHAFT - ATOMTECHNIK. (Summaries in English, French) 1956. m. DM.252. (Kerntechnische Gesellschaft) Verlagsgruppe Handelsblatt GmbH, Kasernenstr. 67, 40213 Duesseldorf, Germany. TEL 0211-8870. (Subscr. to: Postfach 102717, 40018 Duesseldorf, Germany) Ed. Wolf Liebholz. adv.; bk.rev.; bibl.; charts; illus.; mkt.; pat.; index. circ. 4,100. (reprint service avail. from UMI) **Indexed:** C.I.S. Abstr., Chem.Abstr., Curr.Cont., Dok.Arbeitsmed., Energy Info.Abstr., Environ.Abstr., Excerp.Med., Fuel & Energy Abstr., Ind.Sci.Rev., INIS Atomind., Key to Econ.Sci., Nucl.Sci.Abstr., Risk Abstr., Robomat. (until 1992) Sci.Abstr., Sci.Cit.Ind. **Document type:** academic/scholarly publication.
—BLDSC (1772.702000); CIS; EI; SWETS; UMI; CASDDS. **CCC.**
Formerly: Atomwirtschaft (ISSN 0004-721X)

539.7 621.48   AT   ISSN 1030-7745
CODEN: ANSAEH
AUSTRALIA. NUCLEAR SCIENCE AND TECHNOLOGY ORGANISATION. A N S T O - E. (Technical report series) 1958. irreg. price varies. Australian Nuclear Science and Technology Organisation, Private Bag 1, Menai, N.S.W. 2234, Australia. index. cum.index: 1958-1981. (also avail. in microfiche) **Indexed:** INIS Atomind., Nucl.Sci.Abstr. **Document type:** government publication.
—CASDDS.
Formerly: Australia. Atomic Energy Commission. Research Establishment. A A E C - E (ISSN 0067-1657)

ENERGY — NUCLEAR ENERGY

539.7 621.48   AT   ISSN 1031-6655
AUSTRALIAN NUCLEAR SCIENCE AND TECHNOLOGY ORGANISATION. ANNUAL REPORT. a. Australian Nuclear Science and Technology Organisation, Private Bag 1, Menai, N.S.W. 2234, Australia. FAX 02-543-9274. **Document type:** government publication.
—BLDSC (1112.300000).
Formerly (until 1987): Australian Atomic Energy Commission. Annual Report (ISSN 0519-4849)

539.7 621.48   AT   ISSN 1031-6515
AUSTRALIAN NUCLEAR SCIENCE AND TECHNOLOGY ORGANISATION - M. Key Title: A N S T O - M. (Technical Report Series) 195? irreg. price varies. Australian Nuclear Science and Technology Organisation, Private Bag 1, Menai, N.S.W. 2234, Australia. FAX 02-543-9274. index, cum.index. (also avail. in microfiche) **Indexed:** INIS Atomind., Nucl.Sci.Abstr. **Document type:** government publication.
Formerly (until 1987): Australian Atomic Energy Commission. Research Establishment. A A E C - M (ISSN 0067-1665)

333.792 614.7   US
B A N NEWSLETTER.* 1981. bi-m. contributions. Blacks Against Nukes, c/o Brenda Johnson, Ed., RR 3, Box 260, Heathsville, VA 22473-9365. bk.rev. circ. 450. (back issues avail.) **Document type:** newsletter.

333.792   UK
B N F L NEWS. 1973. m. free. British Nuclear Fuels plc, Head Office, Risley, Warrington, Ches. WA3 6AS, England. Ed. Steve Howarth. adv. contact: Julie Anne Heath. circ. 18,500. (tabloid format) **Document type:** newspaper.
Description: For employees of British Nuclear Fuels, dealing with all aspects of the nuclear industry, particularly those relating to BNF and its employees.

539.7 621.48   BE   ISSN 0005-8408
BELGICATOM;* atomic space age & electronics. (Text in Dutch, English, French; summaries in Dutch, English, French, German) 1956. bi-m. 200 BEF. 1 Heiken, 2840 Haacht, Belgium. Ed. A. Van Goethem. adv.; bk.rev.; film rev.; bibl.; charts; illus.; stat.; tr.lit.; tr.mk. circ. 5,463. (processed)

BEZPIECZENSTWO JADROWE I OCHRONA RADIOLOGICZNA. see *PUBLIC HEALTH AND SAFETY*

BIBLIOGRAFIA BRASILEIRA DE ENERGIA NUCLEAR. see *ENERGY — Abstracting, Bibliographies, Statistics*

539.7   US
BROOKHAVEN BULLETIN. q. Brookhaven National Laboratory, Upton, NY 11973. TEL 516-282-2345. (Dist. by: National Technical Information Service, 5285 Port Royal Rd., Springfield, VA 22151) **Document type:** bulletin.

621.48   US   ISSN 0092-1548
QC789.U62
BROOKHAVEN HIGHLIGHTS. 1971. a. Brookhaven National Laboratory, Upton, NY 11973. TEL 516-282-2345. (Dist. by: National Technical Information Service, 5285 Port Royal Rd., Springfield, VA 22151) Ed. Mona S. Rowe. illus. (also avail. in microfiche)

621.48   US
BROOKHAVEN LECTURE SERIES. no.83, 1969. irreg., no.145, 1977. Brookhaven National Laboratory, Upton, NY 11973. TEL 516-282-3484. (Dist. by: National Technical Information Service, 5285 Port Royal Rd., Springfield, VA 22151) (back issues avail.) **Indexed:** Biol.Abstr. **Document type:** monographic series.

333.792   JA
BUYERS' GUIDE: NUCLEAR INDUSTRY IN JAPAN. (Text in English) 1961. irreg. 2500 Yen. Japan Atomic Industrial Forum, Inc. - Nihon Genshiryoku Sangyo Kaigi, Toshin Bldg., 1-1-13 Shinbashi, Minato-ku, Tokyo 105, Japan. TEL 03-3503-2411. FAX 03-3508-2094. TELEX 2226623-JAIFRM-J.

C E A S E NEWS. (Concerned Educators Allied for a Safe Environment) see *CONSERVATION*

621.48   US
▼**C I S - EASTERN EUROPE NUCLEAR SAFETY & CLEANUP REPORT.** 1992. m. $558. Business Publishers, Inc., 951 Pershing Dr., Silver Spring, MD 20910-4464. TEL 301-587-6300. FAX 301-585-9075. **Document type:** newsletter.
Formerly (until 1993): C I S - Nuclear Safety Report.

621.48   CN   ISSN 0714-7074
QC770   CODEN: BCSCEP
C N S BULLETIN. 1980. 6/yr. membership. Canadian Nuclear Society, c/o K. Murphy, 144 Front St. W., Ste. 725, Toronto, ON M5J 2L7, Canada. TEL 416-977-6152. FAX 416-979-8356. Ed. Frederick C. Boyd. circ. 700. **Document type:** bulletin.
Description: Newsletter for members of the Canadian Nuclear Society.

539.7   JA
C Y R I C ANNUAL REPORT. (Text in English) 1980. a. Tohoku University, Cyclotron Radioisotope Center - Tohoku Daigaku Saikurotoron Rajio Aisotopu Senta, Aoba, Aramaki, Aoba-ku, Sendai-shi, Miyagi-ken 980, Japan. **Document type:** academic/scholarly publication.

539.7   JA   ISSN 0916-3751
C Y R I C NEWS/C Y R I C NYUSU. (Text in Japanese) s-a. Tohoku University, Cyclotron Radioisotope Center - Tohoku Daigaku Saikurotoron Rajio Aisotopu Senta, Aoba, Aramaki, Aoba-ku, Sendai-shi, Miyagi-ken 980, Japan.

621.48   CN
CANADIAN NUCLEAR ASSOCIATION. ANNUAL INTERNATIONAL CONFERENCE PROCEEDINGS. 1961. a. Canadian Nuclear Association, 144 Front St., Ste. 725, Toronto, ON M5J 2L7, Canada. TEL 416-977-6152. FAX 416-979-8356. circ. 150. **Document type:** proceedings.
—BLDSC (1082.275000).
Former titles (until 1984): Canadian Nuclear Association. Annual International Conference. Summaries (ISSN 0706-1293); Canadian Nuclear Association. Annual Meeting; Canadian Conference on Uranium and Atomic Energy. Proceedings (ISSN 0068-8517)

621.48   CN   ISSN 0227-1907
TK9006   CODEN: CCSCDZ
CANADIAN NUCLEAR SOCIETY. ANNUAL CONFERENCE PROCEEDINGS. (Text in English) 1980. a. Canadian Nuclear Society, c/o K. Murphy, 144 Front St. W., Ste. 725, Toronto, ON M5J 2L7, Canada. TEL 416-977-6152. FAX 416-979-8356. **Indexed:** Chem.Abstr. **Document type:** proceedings.
—BLDSC (6840.265000); CASDDS.

621.48   CN   ISSN 0227-0129
TK9006
CANADIAN NUCLEAR SOCIETY. ANNUAL CONFERENCE SUMMARIES. French edition: Societe Nucleaire Canadienne. Sommaires du Congres. (Text in English) 1981. a. Canadian Nuclear Society, c/o K. Murphy, 144 Front St. W., Ste. 725, Toronto, ON M5J 2L7, Canada. TEL 416-977-6152. FAX 416-979-8356. **Document type:** proceedings.
Formerly: Canadian Nuclear Society. Transactions (ISSN 0226-7470)

621.48   CC
CHINA INSTITUTE OF ATOMIC ENERGY. ANNUAL REPORT (YEAR). (Text in English) a. $49. China Ocean Press, International Department, Haimao Dalou, 1 Fuxingmenwai Dajie, Beijing 100860, People's Republic of China. TEL 8032211. FAX 8033515. TELEX 22536 NBO CN. Ed. Sun Zuxun.

539 621.48   FR   ISSN 1157-741X
TK9001   CODEN: CHCSE5
CHOCS. 1991. 3/yr. free. Commissariat a l'Energie Atomique, Direction des Applications Militaires, Centre d'Etudes de Limeil-Valenton, 94195 Villeneuve-Saint-Georges Cedex. TEL 45-95-61-46. FAX 45-95-95-55. Ed. Jacques Salvy. **Document type:** government publication.
—BLDSC (3181.530600); CASDDS.
Description: Studies the military applications of atomic energy.

621.48   US
CLINCH RIVER BREEDER REACTOR PLANT. TECHNICAL REVIEW.* 1979. q. Breeder Reactor Corp., Box U, Oak Ridge, TN 37830.

621.48   EI   ISSN 0255-4003
COMMISSION OF THE EUROPEAN COMMUNITIES. OPERATION OF NUCLEAR POWER STATIONS. (Text in English) 1982. a. $17. Office for Official Publications of the European Communities, L-2985 Luxembourg, Luxembourg. (Dist. in the U.S. by: Unipub, 4611-F Assembly Dr., Lanham, MD 20706-4391. TEL 800-274-4888. FAX 301-459-0056) (also avail. in microfiche from CIS) **Indexed:** IIS.

621.48   US
THE COMMUNICATOR (MISHICOT). 1981. q. $35. Professional Reactor Operator Society, Box 181, Mishicot, WI 54228-0181. TEL 414-755-2725; 800-422-2725. Ed. Gregory Veith. adv. circ. 900. (reprint service avail.) **Document type:** newsletter.

CONFERENCE ON REMOTE SYSTEMS TECHNOLOGY. PROCEEDINGS. see *COMPUTERS — Robotics*

COUNCIL FOR A LIVABLE WORLD. NEWSLETTER. see *MILITARY*

DEFECT AND DIFFUSION FORUM. see *METALLURGY*

539.7   JA
DEKOMISSHONINGU GIHO/RESEARCH ASSOCIATION FOR NUCLEAR FACILITY DECOMMISSIONING. JOURNAL. (Text in Japanese) 1989. 2/yr. Genshiryoku Shisetsu Dekomisshoningu Kenkyu Kyokai, 821-100, Funashikawa, Tokaimura, Naka-gun, Ibaraki-ken 319-11, Japan.

539 621.48   DK
    CODEN: RNLRDF
DENMARK. FORSKNINGSCENTER RISOE. RISOE-R. (Text in English) 1957. irreg., no.618, 1992. free. Forskningscenter Risoe - Risoe National Laboratory, DK-4000 Roskilde, Denmark. TEL 45-42-37-12-12. FAX 45-75-56-27. circ. 300. **Document type:** government publication.
—BLDSC (7973.500000); CASDDS.
Former titles: Denmark. Forsoegsanslaeg Risoe. Risoe-R (ISSN 0106-2840); Denmark. Atomenergikommissionens Forsoegsanslaeg, Risoe. Risoe Report (ISSN 0418-6443)

DIFFUSION AND DEFECT DATA; reviews and original contributions in solid state physics. see *METALLURGY*

621.48   FR   ISSN 0066-2593
DIRECTORY OF THE FRENCH NUCLEAR INDUSTRY. 1962. irreg. 150 F. Groupe Intersyndical de l'Industrie Nucleaire (GIIN), Forum Atomique Francais, 39-41, rue Louis Blanc, 92400 Courbevoie Cedex 72, 92038 Paris La Defense. TEL 1-47-17-62-78. FAX 1-47-17-62-82. circ. 3,000. **Document type:** directory.
Formerly: Annuaire Bilingue de l'Industrie Nucleaire Francaise.
Description: Reference guide providing a complete picture of the entire French nuclear industry including organizations, facilities, plants, services, and suppliers.

621.48   JA   ISSN 0912-7291
DORYOKURO KAKU NENRYO KAIHATSU JIGYODAN. HOKOKU TO KOEN NO KAI YOKOSHU/POWER REACTOR AND NUCLEAR FUEL DEVELOPMENT CORPORATION. PREPRINTS OF MEETING. (Text in Japanese) 1968. a. Doryokuro Kaku Nenryo Kaihatsu Jigyodan, 9-13, Akasaka 1-chome, Minato-ku, Tokyo 107, Japan.

539.7   JA
DORYOKURO KAKU NENRYO KAIHATSU JIGYODAN NENPO/POWER REACTOR AND NUCLEAR FUEL DEVELOPMENT CORPORATION. ANNUAL REPORT. (Text in Japanese) 1968. a. Doryokuro Kaku Nenryo Kaihatsu Jigyodan, 9-13, Akasaka 1-chome, Minato-ku, Tokyo 107, Japan. **Document type:** corporate report.

ENERGY — NUCLEAR ENERGY

333.792 340   FR   ISSN 1016-4995
DROIT NUCLEAIRE. English edition: Nuclear Law Bulletin (ISSN 0304-341X) (Includes supplements) (Text in French) 1968. s-a. 170 F.($36) (effective 1992). Organization for Economic Cooperation and Development, Nuclear Energy Agency, 12 bd. des Iles, 92130 Issy-les-Moulineaux, France. TEL 45-24-10-15. (U.S. orders to: O.E.C.D. Publications and Information Center, 2001 L St., N.W., Ste. 700, Washington, DC 20036-4910. TEL 202-785-6323) index, cum.index every 5 yrs. (also avail. in microfiche from OEC)
   Formerly (until 1988): Bulletin de Droit Nucleaire (ISSN 0304-3428)
   Description: Covers legislative and regulatory developments, agreements and case law in the nuclear field throughout the world, with reports on regulatory initiatives of international organizations with jurisdiction in nuclear affairs.

621.48   IT   ISSN 1120-5563
E N E A (RAPPORTI TECNICI) R T - AREA ENERGETICA. 1990. irreg. Ente per le Nuove Tecnologie, l'Energia e l'Ambiente, Viale Regina Margherita 125, 00198 Rome, Italy. TEL 06-85282401. FAX 06-85285875.

621.48   IT   ISSN 1120-5555
E N E A (RAPPORTI TECNICI) R T - AREA ENERGIA, AMBIENTE E SALUTE. irreg. Ente per le Nuove Tecnologie, l'Energia e l'Ambiente, Viale Regina Margherita 125, 00198 Rome, Italy. TEL 06-85282401. FAX 06-85285875.
—BLDSC (3776.422505).
   Formerly (until 1989): E N E A (Rapporti Tecnici) R T - P A S (ISSN 0393-6309)

621.48   IT   ISSN 1120-5598
E N E A (RAPPORTI TECNICI) R T - AREA NUCLEARE. 1990. irreg. Ente per le Nuove Tecnologie, l'Energia e l'Ambiente, Viale Regina Margherita 125, 00198 Rome, Italy. TEL 06-85282401. FAX 06-85285875.

621.48   IT   ISSN 0393-6317
E N E A (RAPPORTI TECNICI) R T - DIREZIONI CENTRALE STUDI. 1984. irreg. Ente Per le Nuove Tecnologie, l'Energia e l'Ambiente, Viale Regina Margherita 125, 00198 Rome, Italy. TEL 096-85282401. FAX 06-85285875.

621.48   IT   ISSN 1120-5571
E N E A (RAPPORTI TECNICI) R T - GEN. 1990. irreg. Ente per le Nuove Tecnologie, l'Energia e l'Ambiente, Viale Regina Margherita 125, 00198 Rome, Italy. TEL 06-85282401. FAX 06-85285875.
—BLDSC (3776.422515).

621.48   IT   ISSN 1120-558X
E N E A (RAPPORTI TECNICI) R T - I N N. irreg. Ente per le Nuove Tecnologie, l'Energia e l'Ambiente, Via Regina Margherita, 125, 00198 Rome, Italy. TEL 06-85282778.
—BLDSC (3776.422520).
   Formerly (until 1989): E N E A (Rapporti Tecnici) R T - T I B (ISSN 0393-6333)

EMERGENCY PREPAREDNESS DIGEST/REVUE PROTECTION CIVILE. see *CIVIL DEFENSE*

ENERGIA: BIBLIOGRAFIA SELETIVA. see *ENERGY — Abstracting, Bibliographies, Statistics*

333.792   HU   ISSN 0013-7316
TJ4   CODEN: ENATAO
ENERGIA ES ATOMTECHNIKA. (Text in Hungarian; summaries in English, German) 1948. bi-m. $34.50. (Energiagazdalkodasi Tudomanyos Egyesulet - Scientific Society for Energy Economics) Leanyvallalat, Kossuth Lajos ter.6-8, 1073 Budapest 5, Hungary. TEL 117-0011. (Subscr. to: Kultura, P.O. Box 149, H-1389 Budapest, Hungary) Ed. Buki Gergely. adv.; bk.rev.; bibl.; charts; illus.; index. circ. 800. **Indexed:** Appl.Mech.Rev., Cadscan, Chem.Abstr., Curr.Cont., Energy Info.Abstr., Lead Abstr., Met.Abstr., Risk Abstr., Sci.Abstr., World Alum.Abstr., Zincscan.
—BLDSC (3744.500000).

333.792   AG
ENERGIA NUCLEAR. 1980. 6/yr. Indupress s.r.l., Piedras 930, Piso 1o, 1070 Buenos Aires, Argentina. TEL 23-2098. Ed. Julio C. Di Pietro Paolo. circ. 5,000.

ENERGIA NUCLEAR E AGRICULTURA. see *AGRICULTURE*

621.48   NE   ISSN 0165-2117
TJ163.2   CODEN: NRGSDB
ENERGIESPECTRUM. 1959. m. fl.77 (foreign fl.103). (Energieonderzoek Centrum Nederland) Insert B.V., P.B. 90053, 1006 BB Amsterdam, Netherlands. TEL 020-5182882. FAX 020-170350. Ed. R.C.J. de Vos. adv.; bk.rev.; abstr.; bibl.; charts; illus. circ. 3,500. **Indexed:** Chem.Abstr., Excerp.Med., Key to Econ.Sci., Met.Abstr.
   Formerly: Atoomenergie en Haar Toepassingen (ISSN 0004-7228)

ENERGY AND NUCLEAR SCIENCES INTERNATIONAL WHO'S WHO. see *ENERGY*

ENERGY CONVERSION AND MANAGEMENT. see *ENERGY*

ENERGY POLICY; international journal of the political, economic, planning and social aspects of energy. see *ENERGY*

ENERGY TODAY. see *ENERGY*

ENVIRONMENTAL COALITION ON NUCLEAR POWER NEWSLETTER. see *ENERGY*

621.48   JA   ISSN 0014-5645
F A P I G. (Text in Japanese) 1957. 3/yr. free. First Atomic Power Industry Group - Daiichi Genshiryoku Sangyo Gurupu Jimukyoku, Nissho-Iwai Bldg. 3rd Fl., 2-4-5 Akasaka, Minato-ku, Tokyo 107, Japan. TEL 03-3588-4231. FAX 03-3588-4232. Ed. H. Ishiwatari. circ. 2,000 (controlled). **Indexed:** INIS Atomind.
—BLDSC (3865.750000).

FEDERAL REGULATION OF ENERGY. see *LAW*

333.792   FR   ISSN 0071-8467
HD9698.F7
FRANCE. COMMISSARIAT A L'ENERGIE ATOMIQUE. ANNUAL REPORT. 1945. a. free. Commissariat a l'Energie Atomique, 29-33 rue de la Federation, 75015 Paris, France. circ. 20,000. **Indexed:** AESIS, GeoRef. **Document type:** government publication.

333.792   FR   ISSN 0029-3997
FRANCE. COMMISSARIAT A L'ENERGIE ATOMIQUE. NOTES D'INFORMATION. 1962. 2/yr. free. Commissariat a l'Energie Atomique, 29-33 rue de la Federation, 75015 Paris, France. Dir. Pascale Antoni. circ. 10,000. **Indexed:** AESIS, Met.Abstr. **Document type:** government publication.

539.2 628   JA
FUKUSHIMAKEN GENSHIRYOKU SENTA. GYOMU NENPO/FUKUSHIMA ENVIRONMENTAL RADIOACTIVITY RESEARCH CENTER. ANNUAL REPORT. (Text in Japanese) a. Fushimaken Genshiryoku Senta, 199, Ono, Shimonogami, Okumamachi, Futaba-gun, Fukushima-ken 979-13, Japan.

621.48   CC   ISSN 1000-3436
R895   CODEN: FYYXEA
FUSHE YANJIU YU FUSHE GONGYI XUEBAO. (Text in Chinese; abstracts in English) q. $64. Zhongguo Kexueyuan, Shanghai Yuanzihe Yanjiusuo - Chinese Academy of Sciences, Shanghai Institute of Nuclear Research, P.O. Box 800-204, Shanghai 201800, People's Republic of China. TEL 9530998. Ed. Lin Nianyun. **Document type:** academic/scholarly publication.

FUSION; Wissenschaft - Technik fuer das 21. Jahrhundert. see *ENERGY*

333.792   US
FUSION FACILITIES DIRECTORY. 1983. biennial. $20. Fusion Power Associates, 2 Professional Dr., Ste. 248, Gaithersburg, MD 20879. TEL 301-258-0545. FAX 301-975-9869. Ed. R. Watkins. circ. 500. **Document type:** directory.
   Description: Gives phone listings of major participants in the U.S. fusion program as well as travel information.

621.48   US
FUSION POWER ASSOCIATES EXECUTIVE NEWSLETTER. 1979. m. $40 to individuals; libraries $150. Fusion Power Associates, 2 Professional Dr., Ste. 248, Gaithersburg, MD 20879. TEL 301-258-0545. FAX 301-975-9869. Ed. Stephen O. Dean. circ. 1,600. **Document type:** newsletter.
   Description: Contains information on the latest developments occurring in fusion energy R & D.

621.48   US   ISSN 0276-2919
FUSION POWER REPORT; complete monthly coverage of worldwide fusion developments. 1980. m. $666. Business Publishers, Inc., 951 Pershing Dr., Silver Spring, MD 20910-4464. TEL 301-587-6300. FAX 301-585-9075. Ed. Thecla Fabian. (looseleaf format; back issues avail.) **Document type:** newsletter.
●Also available online. Vendor(s): DIALOG Information Services, Inc., NewsNet (EY46).
—CCC.
   Description: Covers worldwide new technology and government support of fusion power research.

621.48   US   ISSN 0748-1896
TK9204   CODEN: FUSTE8
FUSION TECHNOLOGY. 1981. 8/yr. (plus supplements). $485. American Nuclear Society, 555 N. Kensington Ave., La Grange Park, IL 60525. TEL 708-352-6611. (Co-sponsor: European Nuclear Society) Ed. George H. Miley. bk.rev.; charts. (reprint service avail.) **Indexed:** A.S.& T.Ind., ASCA, Chem.Abstr., Curr.Cont., Energy Ind., Energy Info.Abstr., Environ.Abstr., Ind.Sci.Rev., INIS Atomind., Met.Abstr., Risk Abstr., Sci.Abstr., World Alum.Abstr.
—BLDSC (4059.695400); EI; UnCover; SWETS; CASDDS. **CCC.**
   Formerly: Nuclear Technology - Fusion (ISSN 0272-3921)
   Refereed Serial

539.7   JA
GENDEN NO GENKYO/JAPAN ATOMIC POWER COMPANY. ANNUAL REPORT. (Text in Japanese) a. Nihon Genshiryoku Hatsuden K.K. - Japan Atomic Power Co., Ltd., 6-1, Otemachi 1-chome, Chiyoda-ku, Tokyo 100, Japan.

539.7   JA   ISSN 0911-4068
GENDEN REPOTO/JAPAN ATOMIC POWER COMPANY. REPORT. (Text in Japanese) 1985. irreg. Nihon Genshiryoku Hatsuden K.K. - Japan Atomic Power Co., Ltd., 6-1, Otemachi 1-chome, Chiyoda-ku, Tokyo 100, Japan.

539.7   JA
GENSAN NENJI TAIKAI GAIYO HOKOKU/JAPAN ATOMIC INDUSTRIAL FORUM. REPORTS OF ANNUAL MEETING. (Text in Japanese) a. Nihon Genshiryoku Sangyo Kaigi - Japan Atomic Industrial Forum, 1-13, Shinbashi 1-chome, Minato-ku, Tokyo 105, Japan.

539.7   JA
GENSAN NENJI TAIKAI HOBUNSHU/JAPAN ATOMIC INDUSTRIAL FORUM. PROCEEDINGS OF ANNUAL MEETING. (Text in English, Japanese) 1968. a. 25000 Yen. Nihon Genshiryoku Sangyo Kaigi - Japan Atomic Industrial Forum, 1-13, Shinbashi 1-chome, Minato-ku, Tokyo 105, Japan. **Document type:** proceedings.

539.7   JA
GENSHI DORYOKU KENKYUKAI NENKAI HOKOKUSHO/NUCLEAR POWER ENGINEERING WORKSHOP. ANNUAL MEETING REPORT. (Text in Japanese) a. Nihon Genshiryoku Sangyo Kaigi, Genshi Doryoku Kenkyukai - Japan Atomic Industrial Forum, Nuclear Power Engineering Workshop, 1-13, Shinbashi 1-chome, Minato-ku, Tokyo 105, Japan.

621.48   JA   ISSN 0387-088X
GENSHIRYOKU CHOSA JIHO/NUCLEAR INDUSTRIAL SURVEY. 1961. q. 3000 Yen. Japan Atomic Industrial Forum - Nihon Genshiryoku Sangyo Kaigi, Toshin Bldg., 1-1-13 Shinbashi, Minato-ku, Tokyo 105, Japan. TEL 03-3508-2094. FAX 03-3508-2094. TELEX 2226623-JAIFRM-J. **Indexed:** INIS Atomind.

621.48   JA
GENSHIRYOKU DAYORI KAGOSHIMA/KAGOSHIMA NUCLEAR POWER NEWS. (Text in Japanese) q. Kagoshimaken Hoken Kankyobu - Kagoshima Prefectural Government, Health and Environment Department, 14-50, Yamashita-cho, Kagoshima-shi, Kagoshima-ken 892, Japan.

621.48   JA
GENSHIRYOKU DAYORI MIYAGI/MIYAGI NUCLEAR POWER NEWS. (Text in Japanese) 1982. q. Miyagiken Hoken Kankyobu - Miyagi Prefectural Government, Health and Environment Division, 8-1, Hancho 3-chome, Aoba-ku, Sendai-shi, Miyagi-ken 980, Japan.

ENERGY — NUCLEAR ENERGY

621.48 — JA
GENSHIRYOKU HAKUSHO/WHITE PAPER OF ATOMIC ENERGY. (Text in Japanese) a. 2300 Yen. (Sorifu Genshiryoku Iinkai - Prime Minister's Office, Atomic Energy Commission) Okurasho Insatsukyoku - Ministry of Finance, Printing Bureau, 2-4, Toranomon 2-chome, Minato-ku, Tokyo 105, Japan.

621.48 — JA
GENSHIRYOKU HATSUDEN. (Text in Japanese) 1978. a. Hokkaido Shoko Rodo Kankobu - Hokkaido Prefectural Government, Department of Commerce, Industry, Labor and Tourism, Nishi 6-chome, Kita 3-jo, Chuo-ku, Sapporo-shi, Hokkaido 060, Japan.

621.4
GENSHIRYOKU HATSUDENJO UNTEN KANRI NENPO/ANNUAL REPORT OF OPERATION CONTROL IN THE NUCLEAR POWER PLANTS. (Text in Japanese) 1981. a. 4700 Yen. Shigen Enerugicho - Agency of Natural Resources and Energy, 23-11, Toranomon 1-chome, Minato-ku, Tokyo 105, Japan. (Co-sponsor: Karyoku Genshiryoku Hatsuden Gijutsu Kyokai - Thermal and Nuclear Power Engineering Society of Japan)

621.48 — JA — ISSN 0433-4019
GENSHIRYOKU IINKAI GEPPO/ATOMIC ENERGY COMMISSION. JOURNAL. (Text in Japanese) 1956. m. 500 Yen per no. (Kagaku Gijutsucho Genshiryokukyoku - Science and Technology Agency, Atomic Energy Bureau) Okurasho Insatsukyoku - Ministry of Finance, Printing Bureau, 2-4, Toranomon 2-chome, Minato-ku, Tokyo 105, Japan.

621.48 — JA
GENSHIRYOKU KAIHATSU RIYO KIHON KEIKAKU/FUNDAMENTAL PLAN OF DEVELOPMENT AND UTILIZATION OF NUCLEAR POWER. (Text in Japanese) a. Sorifu - Prime Minister's Office, 6-1, Nagata-cho 1-chome, Chiyoda-ku, Tokyo 100, Japan.

621.48 — JA
GENSHIRYOKU KOGAKU KENKYU SHISETSU NENPO/NUCLEAR ENGINEERING RESEARCH LABORATORY. ANNUAL REPORT. (Text in Japanese) a. Tokyo Daigaku, Kogakubu, Fuzoku Genshiryoku Kogaku Kenkyu Shisetsu - University of Tokyo, Faculty of Engineering, Nuclear Engineering Research Laboratory, 2-22, Shirane, Shirakata, Tokaimura, Naka-gun, Ibaraki-ken 319-11, Japan.

621.48 — JA
GENSHIRYOKU KOHO SENDAI/SENDAI NUCLEAR POWER NEWS. (Text in Japanese) irreg. 3-22, Kanda-cho, Sendai-shi, Kogoshima-ken 895, Japan.

621.48 — JA
GENSHIRYOKU NENKAN/NUCLEAR ALMANAC. 1957. a. 7100 Yen. Japan Atomic Industrial Forum - Nihon Genshiryoku Sangyo Kaigi, Toshin Bldg., 1-1-13 Shinbashi, Minato-ku, Tokyo 105, Japan. TEL 03-3508-2411. FAX 03-3508-2094. TELEX 2226623-JAIFRM-J.

539.7 — JA
GENSHIRYOKU NYUSU/ATOMIC ENERGY NEWS. (Text in Japanese) 1980. m. Genshiryoku Mondai Joho Senta - Atomic Energy Problems Information Center, c/o Nakajima Kenkyushitsu, Chuo Daigaku Shogakubu, 724-1, Higashinakano, Hachioji-shi, Tokyo 192-03, Japan.

621.48 — JA — ISSN 0913-8609
GENSHIRYOKU SEISAKU. JOHO FAIRU CIRCULAR. (Text in Japanese) 1987. m. 61800 Yen. Nihon Genshiryoku Joho Senta - Japan Nuclear - Energy Information Center, 6-10, Toranomon 2-chome, Minato-ku, Tokyo 105, Japan. TEL 81-3-3580-8851. FAX 81-3-3480-1305. Pub. Hiroshi Waragai. **Document type:** government publication.
Description: Contains accurate nuclear information

539.7 — JA — ISSN 0387-0928
GENSHIRYOKU SHIRYO/NUCLEAR POWER INFORMATION. (Text in Japanese) 1967. m. Nihon Genshiryoku Sangyo Kaigi - Japan Atomic Industrial Forum, 1-13, Shinbashi 1-chome, Minato-ku, Tokyo 105, Japan.
Indexed: INIS Atomind.

539.7 — JA
GENSHIRYOKU SHIRYO JOHOSHITSU TSUSHIN/CITIZENS' NUCLEAR INFORMATION CENTER. NEWS. (Text in Japanese) m. 300 Yen per no. Genshiryoku Shiryo Johoshitsu, 10-11, Motoasakusa 2-chome, Taito-ku, Tokyo 111, Japan.

539.7 — JA
GENSHIRYOKU SOGO SHINPOJUMU YOKOSHU/NATIONAL SYMPOSIUM ON ATOMIC ENERGY. PROCEEDINGS. (Text in Japanese) 1963. a. 2000 Yen. Nihon Genshiryoku Gakkai - Atomic Energy Society of Japan, 1-13, Shinbashi 1-chome, Minato-ku, Tokyo 105, Japan. TEL 03-3508-1261. FAX 03-3581-6128. Ed. Genki Yagawa. **Document type:** proceedings.

539.7 — JA
GENTSU/ATOMIC PRESS. (Text in Japanese) 1954. w. 170000 Yen. Gentsu Co., Ltd., 18-2, Shinbashi 1-chome, Minato-ku, Tokyo 105, Japan.

621.48 — JA
HANDBOOK OF NUCLEAR SAFEGUARDS. (Text in Japanese) 1984. a. 6386 Yen. Japan Atomic Industrial Forum, Inc. - Nihon Genshiryoku Sangyo Kaigi, Toshin Bldg., 1-1-13 Shinbashi, Minato-ku, Tokyo 105, Japan. TEL 03-3508-2411. FAX 03-3508-2094. TELEX 2226623-JAIFRM-J.

539.7 — JA
HATSUDENJO NO UNTEN KENSETSU NENPO/ANNUAL REPORT ON OPERATION AND CONSTRUCTION OF POWER PLANT. (Text in Japanese) a. Fukuiken Genshiryoku Kankyo Anzen Kanri Kyogikai - Fukui Prefectural Confirmation Council for Nuclear Environment Safety, Fukuiken Genshiryoku Anzen Taisakuka, 17-1, Ote 3-chome, Fukui-shi, Fukui-ken 910, Japan.

539.7 — JA
HATSUDENJO NO UNTEN OYOBI KENSETSU JOKYO/OPERATION AND CONSTRUCTION OF NUCLEAR POWER PLANTS. (Text in Japanese) q. Fukuiken Genshiryoku Kankyo Anzen Kanri Kyogikai - Fukui Prefectural Confirmation Council for Nuclear Environment Safety, Fukuiken Genshiryoku Anzen Taisakuka, 17-1, Ote 3-chome, Fukui-shi, Fukui-ken 910, Japan.

621.48 — CC — ISSN 0253-3219
TK9001 — CODEN: NUTEDL
HE JISHU. English edition: Nuclear Science and Techniques (ISSN 1001-8042) (Text in Chinese; summaries in English) 1978. m. $94.80. Science Press, Marketing and Sales Department, 16 Donghuangchenggen Beijie, Beijing 100717, People's Republic of China. TEL 4010642. FAX 4012180. TELEX 210247-SPBJ-CN. adv. circ. 10,000. **Indexed:** Chem.Abstr., Sci.Abstr. **Document type:** academic/scholarly publication.
—BLDSC (6183.515000); CASDDS.
Description: Carries articles on research results in nuclear techniques and their applications in industry, agriculture, and medicine. Also covers radiochemistry and radiation chemistry, use of nuclear measuring devices, radiation protection and radioactive waste treatment.
Refereed Serial

621.48 — CC — ISSN 0258-0918
HE KEXUE YU GONGCHENG/CHINESE JOURNAL OF NUCLEAR SCIENCE AND ENGINEERING. (Text in Chinese; abstracts in English) 1981. q. $20 per no. Zhongguo He Xuehui - China Nuclear Society, P.O. Box 2125, Beijing 100822, People's Republic of China. TEL 8012211.
—BLDSC (3180.438300).

539.7 — JA
HOKKAIDO DAIGAKU. AISOTOPU SOGO SENTA NYUSU/HOKKAIDO UNIVERSITY. CENTRAL INSTITUTE OF ISOTOPE SCIENCE. NEWS. (Text in Japanese) 1983. a. Hokkaido Daigaku, Aisotopu Sogo Senta - Hokkaido University, Central Institute of Isotope Science, Nishi 7-chome, Kita 15-jo, Kita-ku, Sapporo-shi, Hokkaido 060, Japan.

539.7 — JA — ISSN 0913-1760
HOKKAIDO GENSHIRYOKU KANKYO DAYORI/HOKKAIDO NUCLEAR ENERGY ENVIRONMENTAL RESEARCH CENTER. NEWS. (Text in Japanese) 1986. q. free. Hokkaido Genshiryoku Kankyo Senta, 261, Kyowacho Miyaoka, Iwanai-gun, Hokkaido 045-01, Japan. TEL 0135-74-3131. FAX 0135-74-3135. Ed. Yoichi Saito. circ. 16,000. **Document type:** government publication.
Description: Provides information about the Center's researches on the environment of nuclear energy.

539.7 621.48 — UN — ISSN 0020-6067
QC770 — CODEN: IAEBAB
I A E A BULLETIN. Chinese edition: Guoji Yuanzineng Jigou Tongbao (ISSN 1011-257X); French edition: Agence Internacional du l'Energie Atomique Bulletin (ISSN 0251-4044); Spanish edition: Organismo International de Energia Atomica Boletin (ISSN 0534-7297) 1959. 4/yr. free. International Atomic Energy Agency, Wagramerstr. 5, P.O. Box 100, A-1400 Vienna Austria. TEL 01-23601286. FAX 01-234564. Ed. Lothar Wedekind. adv.: color page $2690. illus. circ. 20,000. (also avail. in microfiche from CIS; back issues avail.) **Indexed:** AESIS, Biol.Abstr., Chem.Abstr., Energy Info.Abstr., Energy Rev., Environ.Abstr., Environ.Per.Bibl. (1980-), Excerp.Med., Food Sci.& Tech.Abstr., Fuel & Energy Abstr., IIS, INIS Atomind., Key to Econ.Sci., Mid.East: Abstr.& Ind., Pollut.Abstr., Sci.Abstr. **Document type:** government publication.
—BLDSC (4359.070000); EI; Faxon; UnCover; CASDDS.

333.792 — UN
I A E A NEWSBRIEFS. 1986. bi-m. free. International Atomic Energy Agency, Division of Public Information, Wagramstr. 5, Postfach 100, A-1400 Vienna, Austria. TEL 01-23601270. FAX 01-234564. Ed. Lothar Wedekind. **Indexed:** Energy Info.Abstr. **Document type:** newsletter.
Formerly (until 1988): I A E A News Features.

621.48 — UN — ISSN 1011-4289
I A E A TECHNICAL DOCUMENTS SERIES. Key Title: IAEA Tecdoc. (Text in English) 1966. irreg. free. International Atomic Energy Agency, Wagramerstr. 5, P.O. Box 100, A-1400 Vienna, Austria. circ. 200. (also avail. in microfiche)

I E E E TRANSACTIONS ON NUCLEAR SCIENCE. see *ENGINEERING — Electrical Engineering*

621.48 530 — US
I F S NEWSLETTER. 1981. s-a. free. Institute for Fusion Studies, University of Texas, Austin, TX 78712. TEL 512-471-4378. Ed. F.L. Waelbroeck. charts; illus.; circ. 400 (controlled). (back issues avail.) **Document type:** newsletter.
Description: Discusses results in fusion theory research.

539.7 — JA — ISSN 0915-6631
I N C C NEWSLETTER. (Text in English) 1987. q. Japan Atomic Industrial Forum, International Nuclear Cooperation Center - Nihon Genshiryoku Sangyo Kaigi, Kokusai Kyoryoku Senta, 1-13, Shinbashi 1-chome, Minato-ku, Tokyo 105, Japan. **Document type:** newsletter.

I N I S REFERENCE SERIES. see *LIBRARY AND INFORMATION SCIENCES*

621.48 — JA
I N S INTERNATIONAL SYMPOSIUM. PROCEEDINGS. (Text in English) 1973. a. University of Tokyo, Institute for Nuclear Study - Tokyo Daigaku Genshirkaku Kenkyujo, 2-1, Midori-cho 3-chome, Tanashi-shi, Tokyo 188, Japan. **Document type:** proceedings.

539.7 621.48 — BU — ISSN 0204-6989
QC791.9 — CODEN: YAENEN
IADERNA ENERGIIA/NUCLEAR ENERGY. (Text in various languages; summaries in Bulgarian, English, Russian) 1975. bi-m. 1.35 lv. per no. (Bulgarska Akademiia na Naukite) Publishing House of the Bulgarian Academy of Sciences, Acad. G. Bonchev St., Bldg. 6, 1113 Sofia, Bulgaria. Ed. V. Khristov. circ. 600. (reprint service avail. from IRC) **Indexed:** BSL Math.
—BLDSC (0399.795000).

ENERGY — NUCLEAR ENERGY

621.48   II   ISSN 0073-618X
INDIA. DEPARTMENT OF ATOMIC ENERGY. ANNUAL REPORT. Title varies: Brief Report. (Text in English and Hindi) 1963. a. free. Department of Atomic Energy, Publications Officer, Chhatrapati Shivaji Maharaj Marg, Bombay 400039, India. circ. 4,100. **Document type:** government publication.

621.48   US   ISSN 0194-0252
INSIDE N R C. (U.S. Nuclear Regulatory Commission) 1979. fortn. $1415 (foreign $1510). McGraw-Hill, Inc., Energy and Business Newsletters, 1221 Ave. of the Americas, New York, NY 10020. Ed. Michael Knapik. (looseleaf format; reprint service avail. from UMI) **Document type:** newsletter.
●Also available online. Vendor(s): DIALOG Information Services, Inc. (File no.624/McGRAW-HILL PUBLICATIONS ONLINE), Dow Jones News Retrieval (NRC), Mead Data Central, Inc. (INNRC), NewsNet (EY71).

604.7   US   ISSN 0073-9472
INSTITUTE OF NUCLEAR MATERIALS MANAGEMENT. PROCEEDINGS OF ANNUAL MEETING. 1960. a. $65. Institute of Nuclear Materials Management, Inc., 60 Revere Dr., Ste. 500, Northbrook, IL 60062-1563. TEL 708-480-9573. **Document type:** proceedings.

539.7 621.48   UN   ISSN 0085-2023
INTERNATIONAL ATOMIC ENERGY AGENCY. ANNUAL REPORT. (Report of Board of Governors to General Conference) (Editions in English, French, Russian, Spanish) 1958. a. free. International Atomic Energy Agency, Wagramerstr. 5, P.O. Box 100, A-1400 Vienna, Austria. circ. 4,600. (also avail. in microfiche from CIS) **Indexed:** IIS.

INTERNATIONAL ATOMIC ENERGY AGENCY. LEGAL SERIES. see *LAW*

539 621.48   UN
INTERNATIONAL ATOMIC ENERGY AGENCY. NUCLEAR POWER REACTORS IN THE WORLD. (Text in English) a. S.120. International Atomic Energy Agency, Wagramerstr. 5, P.O. Box 100, A-1400 Vienna, Austria. (Dist. by: Unipub, 4611-F Assembly Dr., Lanham, MD 20706-4391) (also avail. in microfiche from CIS) **Indexed:** IIS.
Formerly: International Atomic Energy Agency. Power Reactors in Member States.

539 621.48   UN   ISSN 0074-1876
     CODEN: PNEXDA
INTERNATIONAL ATOMIC ENERGY AGENCY. PANEL PROCEEDINGS SERIES. (Text in English, French or Spanish) 1960. irreg. price varies. International Atomic Energy Agency, Wagramerstr. 5, P.O. Box 100, A-1400 Vienna, Austria. (Dist. in U.S. by: Unipub, 4611-F Assembly Dr., Lanham, MD 20706-4391) **Indexed:** Excerp.Med. **Document type:** proceedings.

539 621.48   UN   ISSN 0074-1884
INTERNATIONAL ATOMIC ENERGY AGENCY. PROCEEDINGS SERIES. (Text in English, French, Russian and Spanish) 1959. irreg. price varies. International Atomic Energy Agency, Wagramerstr. 5, P.O. Box 100, A-1400 Vienna, Austria. (Dist. in U.S. by: Unipub, 4611-F Assembly Dr., Lanham, MD 20706-4391) **Indexed:** Biol.Abstr., Excerp.Med. **Document type:** proceedings.

539 621.48   UN   ISSN 0074-1906
QC786.45
INTERNATIONAL ATOMIC ENERGY AGENCY. TECHNICAL DIRECTORIES. (Text in English) 1959. irreg. price varies. International Atomic Energy Agency, Wagramerstr. 5, P.O. Box 100, A-1400 Vienna, Austria. (Dist. in U.S. by: Unipub, 4611-F Assembly Dr., Lanham, MD 20706-4391) **Document type:** directory.

539 621.48   UN   ISSN 0074-1914
HD9698.A1   CODEN: TRAEA2
INTERNATIONAL ATOMIC ENERGY AGENCY. TECHNICAL REPORT SERIES. (Text mainly in English; some in French, Russian or Spanish) 1960. irreg. price varies. International Atomic Energy Agency, Wagramerstr. 5, P.O. Box 100, A-1400 Vienna, Austria. (Dist. in U.S. by: Unipub, 4611-F Assembly Dr., Lanham, MD 20706-4391) **Indexed:** Biol.Abstr., Ocean.Abstr., Pollut.Abstr., Soils & Fert.
—BLDSC (8724.800000); CASDDS.

539.7   UN   ISSN 0258-8048
INTERNATIONAL BULLETIN ON ATOMIC AND MOLECULAR DATA FOR FUSION. (Text in English) 1977. q. free. International Atomic Energy Agency, Wagramerstr. 5, P.O. Box 100, A-1400 Vienna, Austria. circ. 750.

333.792   US   ISSN 0742-5821
TK9012
INTERNATIONAL DIRECTORY OF NUCLEAR UTILITIES. 1983. a. $220. Nuexco, 1515 Arapahoe St., Ste. 1000, Denver, CO 80202. TEL 303-899-4500. FAX 303-899-4555. TELEX 450202-NUEXCODVR. Ed. Carolyn B. McCants. **Document type:** directory.
—BLDSC (4539.685500).
   Description: Covers over 125 utilities in 35 countries that operate nuclear plants or that have plants under construction. Provides information on reactors and key personnel.

INTERNATIONAL SIMULATORS CONFERENCE. PROCEEDINGS. see *COMPUTERS — Computer Simulation*

INVENTIVA; periodico tecnico - scientifico - sociale. see *TECHNOLOGY: COMPREHENSIVE WORKS*

621.48   US   ISSN 0275-7575
ISPRA COURSES ON NUCLEAR ENGINEERING AND TECHNOLOGY SERIES. irreg. Harwood Academic Publishers, 820 Town Center Dr., Langhorne, PA 19047. TEL 215-750-2642. FAX 215-750-6343. (UK subscr. to: Box 90, Reading, Berkshire RG1 8JL, England. TEL 0734-560-080) (also avail. in microform) **Document type:** monographic series.
Refereed Serial

621.48   IS   ISSN 0333-5771
ISRAEL. ATOMIC ENERGY COMMISSION. ANNUAL REPORT. a. exchange basis. Israel Atomic Energy Commission, Soreq Nuclear Research Centre, Yavne 70600, Israel. **Document type:** government publication.
   Description: Includes abstracts of papers on research in progress at the laboratories of the IAEC.

621.48   IS   ISSN 0075-0980
ISRAEL. ATOMIC ENERGY COMMISSION. I A - REPORTS. (Text in English or Hebrew; abstracts in English) 1958. irreg., latest 1989. exchange basis. Israel Atomic Energy Commission, Soreq Nuclear Research Centre, Yavne 70600, Israel. **Indexed:** Chem.Abstr. **Document type:** government publication.
   Description: Contains research results in various subjects, carried out at the laboratories of the IAEC.

621.48 011   JA
J A E R I REPORT. (Text in English or Japanese) 1957. irreg. exchange basis. Japan Atomic Energy Research Institute, Tokai Research Establishment - Nihon Genshiryoku Kenkyujo, Tokai Kenkyujo Gijutsu Johobu, Tokai-mura, Naka-gun, Ibaraki-ken 319-11, Japan. **Indexed:** INIS Atomind.

621.48   JA
J A E R I REPORTS. LIST. (Text in English, Japanese) a. exchange basis. Japan Atomic Energy Research Institute, Tokai Research Establishment - Nihon Genshiryoku Kenkyujo, Tokai Kenkyujo Gijutsu Johobu, Tokai-mura, Naka-gun, Ibaraki-ken 319-11, Japan. **Document type:** bibliography.

J A E R I REPORTS ABSTRACTS/GENKEN KENKYU SEIKA SHOROKUSYU. (Japan Atomic Energy Research Institute) see *ENERGY — Abstracting, Bibliographies, Statistics*

333.792   XR   ISSN 0448-116X
     CODEN: JADEAQ
JADERNA ENERGIE/NUCLEAR ENERGY. (Text in Czech or Slovak; summaries in English, French, German, Russian) 1955. m. $65.70. (Ceskoslovenska Atomova Komise) Nakladatelstvi Technicke Literatury, Spalena 51, 113 02 Prague 1, Czech Republic. (Dist. by: Artia, Ve Smeckach 30, 111 27 Prague 1, Czech Republic) Ed. Milos Drahny. abstr. circ. 1,250. **Indexed:** C.I.S. Abstr., Chem.Abstr., Curr.Cont., Fuel & Energy Abstr., INIS Atomind., Risk Abstr., Sci.Abstr.
—BLDSC (4616.500000); CASDDS.

621.48   EI
JOINT NUCLEAR RESEARCH CENTER, ISPRA, ITALY. ANNUAL REPORT. a. Commission of the European Communities, Joint Research Centre, I-21020 Ispra, Italy. (Dist. in the U.S. by: European Community Information Service, 2100 M St., N.W., Ste. 707 Washington, DC 20037)

JOURNAL OF EDUCATIONAL RESEARCH AND EXTENSION. see *EDUCATION*

621.48   US   ISSN 0164-0313
TK9001   CODEN: JFENDS
JOURNAL OF FUSION ENERGY. 1981. q. $315 (foreign $370) (effective 1994). Plenum Publishing Corp., 233 Spring St., New York, NY 10013-1578. TEL 212-620-8000. FAX 212-463-0742. TELEX 23-421139. Ed. Daniel Cohn. adv. (also avail. in microfilm from JSC; back issues avail.) **Indexed:** Chem.Abstr., Energy Ind., Energy Info.Abstr., INIS Atomind., Phys.Ber., Sci.Abstr. **Document type:** academic/scholarly publication.
—BLDSC (4986.890000); EI; Faxon; UnCover; SWETS; UMI; CASDDS. CCC.
Refereed Serial

JOURNAL OF NUCLEAR AGRICULTURE AND BIOLOGY. see *AGRICULTURE — Crop Production And Soil*

621.48   US   ISSN 0893-6188
TK9185.A1   CODEN: JNMMEK
JOURNAL OF NUCLEAR MATERIALS MANAGEMENT. Short title: J N M M. (Summaries in English and Japanese) 1972. q. $100 (foreign $135). Institute of Nuclear Materials Management, Inc., 60 Revere Dr., Ste. 500, Northbrook, IL 60062-1563. TEL 708-480-9573. FAX 708-480-9282. Ed. William A. Higinbotham. adv.; bk.rev.; bibl.; charts; illus.; tr.lit. circ. 7,000. (back issues avail.) **Indexed:** Chem.Abstr., Excerp.Med., Fuel & Energy Abstr., Sci.Abstr.
—BLDSC (5023.250000); EI; UnCover; CASDDS.
Former titles: Nuclear Materials Management (ISSN 0362-0034); I N M M Journal (Institute of Nuclear Materials Management).
   Description: Covers nuclear materials safeguards including physical protection, waste management, materials control and excavating.
Refereed Serial

539.7 614.7   UK   ISSN 0952-4746
     CODEN: JRPREA
JOURNAL OF RADIOLOGICAL PROTECTION. 1981. q. £122($250) (effective 1994). (Society for Radiological Protection) I O P Publishing, Techno House, Redcliffe Way, Bristol BS1 6NX, England. TEL 0272-297481. FAX 0272-294318. TELEX 449149-INSTP-G. (Subscr. to: I O P Circulation Centre, Readerlink, Audit House, 260 Field End Rd., Eastcote, Ruislip, Mddx. HA4 9LT, England. TEL 081-868-4499. FAX 081-428-3117; U.S. addr.: American Institute of Physics, Member and Subscriber Service, 500 Sunnyside Blvd., Woodbury, NY 11797-2999. TEL 516-576-2200) Ed. G. Meggit. adv.; bk.rev. circ. 254. (also avail. in microform) **Indexed:** Bioeng.Abstr., Biol.Abstr., Chem.Abstr., Excerp.Med., Sci.Abstr. **Document type:** academic/scholarly publication.
—BLDSC (5043.950000); Faxon; SWETS; CASDDS. CCC.
Formerly: Society for Radiological Protection. Journal (ISSN 0260-2814)
   Description: Covers dosimetry, instrument development, specialized measuring techniques, biological effects, environmental impact assessment.

621.48   JA   ISSN 0385-4876
     CODEN: KDNYDZ
KAKU DETA NYUSU/NUCLEAR DATA NEWS. (Text in Japanese, sometimes in English) 1966. 3/yr. Nihon Genshiryoku Kenkyujo, Tokai Kenkyujo, Kaku Deta Senta - Japan Atomic Energy Research Institute, Tokai Research Establishment, Nuclear Data Center, 2-4, Shirane, Shirakata, Tokaimura, Naka-gun, Ibaraki-ken 319-11, Japan. TEL 81-292-82-5482. FAX 81-292-82-6122. Ed. Tsuneo Nakagawa. circ. 500. **Document type:** newsletter.
—CASDDS.
Formerly (until 1976): Nuclear Data Center Newsletter.

KARYOKU GENSHIRYOKU HATSUDEN/THERMAL AND NUCLEAR POWER. see *ENERGY — Solar Energy*

ENERGY — NUCLEAR ENERGY 2229

539 621.48 GW ISSN 0171-3191
KERNFORSCHUNGSZENTRUM KARLSRUHE. ERGEBNISBERICHT UEBER FORSCHUNG UND ENTWICKLUNG. 1970. a. DM.50. Kernforschungszentrum Karlsruhe GmbH, Postfach 3640, 76021 Karlsruhe, Germany. FAX 07247-825802. TELEX 724716 KFK. illus. circ. 1,000. **Indexed:** Chem.Abstr. **Document type:** corporate report.
—BLDSC (3802.177000).
Formerly: Gesellschaft fuer Kernforschung. Bericht ueber Forschungs- und Entwicklungsarbeiten.

621.48 GW ISSN 0932-3902
TK9001 CODEN: KERNEU
KERNTECHNIK; independent journal for nuclear engineering, energy systems, radiation and radiological protection. 1956. q. DM.468. Carl Hanser Verlag, Kolbergerstr. 22, 81679 Munich, Germany. TEL 089-998300. FAX 089-984809. (Subscr. to: Postfach 860420, 81631 Munich, Germany) Ed. Alfred Kraut. adv.; bk.rev.; abstr.; charts; illus.; stat.; index. circ. 1,100. **Indexed:** Biol.Abstr., C.I.S. Abstr., Chem.Abstr., Curr.Cont., Dairy Sci.Abstr., Energy Ind., Energy Info.Abstr., Excerp.Med., Food Sci.& Tech.Abstr., Fuel & Energy Abstr., Ind.Sci.Rev., INIS Atomind., Risk Abstr., Sci.Abstr., Sci.Cit.Ind. **Document type:** trade publication.
—BLDSC (5089.901000); El; SWETS; CASDDS. CCC.
Formerly: Atomkernenergie - Kerntechnik (ISSN 0171-5747); Formed by the merger of: Atomkernenergie (ISSN 0004-7117); Kerntechnik (ISSN 0004-7198)

539.7 JA ISSN 0374-8715
CODEN: KDGNBX
KINKI DAIGAKU GENSHIRYOKU KENKYUJO NENPO/KINKI UNIVERSITY. ATOMIC ENERGY RESEARCH INSTITUTE. ANNUAL REPORT. (Text in English, Japanese; summaries in English) 1963. a. Kinki Daigaku, Genshiryoku Kenkyujo, 4-1, Kowakae 3-chome, Higashiosaka-shi, Osaka 577, Japan. TEL 06-721-2332. FAX 06-723-3723. Ed. S. Morishima. **Indexed:** Chem.Abstr., INIS Atomind. **Document type:** academic/scholarly publication.
—BLDSC (1318.550000); CASDDS.

539.7 JA
KISOKAN/PNEUMATIC TUBE. (Text in Japanese; summaries in English, Japanese) s-a. membership. Tokyo Daigaku, Genshiryoku Kenkyu Sogo Senta - University of Tokyo, Research Center for Nuclear Science and Technology, Nihon Genshiryoku Kenkyujo Tokai Kenkyujo, Tokaimura, Naka-gun, Ibaraki-ken 319-11, Japan.

539.7 JA ISSN 0288-8874
KOKURITSU KIKAN GENSHIRYOKU SHIKEN KENKYU SEIKA HOKOKUSHO/ATOMIC ENERGY RESEARCH REPORT OF NATIONAL LABORATORIES. (Text in Japanese) 1960. a. Kagaku Gijutsucho, Genshiryokukyoku - Science and Technology Agency, Atomic Energy Bureau, 2-1, Kasumigaseki 2-chome, Chiyoda-ku, Tokyo 100, Japan.
—BLDSC (5101.783750).

539.7 JA ISSN 0914-708X
KOKUSAI GENSHIRYOKU KIKAN KIHO. NIHONGOBAN/INTERNATIONAL ATOMIC ENGERGY AGENCY. BULLETIN. JAPANESE EDITION. 1987. q. Nihon Genshiryoku Sangyo Kaigi - Japan Atomic Industrial Forum, 1-13, Shinbashi 1-chome, Minato-ku, Tokyo 105, Japan.

621.48 JA
KOON KOGAKU SHIKEN KENKYU NO GENJO/PRESENT SITUATION OF HIGH TEMPERATURE ENGINEERING RESEARCH. (Text in Japanese) 1972. a. Nihon Genshiryoku Kenkyujo, Tokai Kenkyujo, Doryokuro Kaihatsu Anzensei Kenkyu Kanribu - Japan Atomic Energy Research Institute, Tokai Research Establishment, Department of Power Reactor Projects, Tokaimura, Naka-gun, Ibaraki-ken 319-11, Japan.

539.7 JA
KOSOKU ZOSHOKURO KENKYU KAIHATSU NO GENJO/CURRENT STATUS OF DEVELOPMENT OF FAST NUCLEAR BREEDER REACTOR. (Text in Japanese) a. Doryokuro Kaku Nenryo Kaihatsu Jigyodan - Power Reactor and Nuclear Fuel Development Corporation, 9-13, Akasaka 1-chome, Minato-ku, Tokyo 107, Japan.

621.48 JA
KYODO KENKYU SEIKA HOKOKUSHO/ANNUAL COLLABORATION REPORT. (Text in English, Japanese) a. Osaka University, Institute of Laser Engineering - Osaka Daigaku Reza Kaku Yugo Kenkyu Senta, 2-6, Yamadaoka, Suita-shi, Osaka 565, Japan.

621.48 JA ISSN 0368-5039
CODEN: KDGEA5
KYOTO DAIGAKU GENSHI ENERUGI KENKYUJO IHO/KYOTO UNIVERSITY. INSTITUTE OF ATOMIC ENERGY. BULLETIN. 1952. s-a. Kyoto Daigaku, Genshi Enerugi Kenkyujo, Gokasho, Uji-shi, Kyoto 611, Japan. **Indexed:** Chem.Abstr., Eng.Ind., INIS Atomind., Sci.Abstr.
—BLDSC (2578.400000); CASDDS.

KYOTO DAIGAKU GENSHIRO JIKKENSHO GAKUJUTSU KOENKAI HOUBUNSHU/KYOTO UNIVERSITY. RESEARCH REACTOR INSTITUTE. PROCEEDINGS OF THE SCIENTIFIC MEETING. see ENERGY — Abstracting, Bibliographies, Statistics

621.48 JA ISSN 0386-0752
TA1
KYOTO UNIVERSITY. INSTITUTE OF ATOMIC ENERGY. RESEARCH ACTIVITIES. (Text in English) 1968. a. Kyoto University, Institute of Atomic Energy - Kyoto Daigaku Genshi Enerugi Kenkyusho, Gokasho, Uji-shi, Kyoto 611, Japan. Ed.Bd.

621.48 JA ISSN 0372-1043
KYOTO UNIVERSITY. INSTITUTE OF ATOMIC ENERGY. TECHNICAL REPORTS/KYOTO DAIGAKU GENSHI ENERUGI KENKYUJO KENKYU HOKOKU. (Text in English) 1951. irreg. Kyoto University, Institute of Atomic Energy - Kyoto Daigaku Genshi Enerugi Kenkyujo, Gokasho, Uji-shi, Kyoto 611, Japan. **Indexed:** Eng.Ind., INIS Atomind. **Document type:** academic/scholarly publication.
—BLDSC (8715.874000).

546 621.48 JA ISSN 0454-9244
QC770 CODEN: KURAAV
KYOTO UNIVERSITY. RESEARCH REACTOR INSTITUTE. ANNUAL REPORTS. (Text and summaries in English) 1968. a. donation or exchange basis. Kyoto University, Research Reactor Institute, Kumatori-cho, Sennan-gun, Osaka 590-04, Japan. TEL 0724-52-0901. FAX 0724-53-5810. Ed. Keiji Kanda. circ. 1,000 (controlled). (back issues avail.) **Indexed:** Biol.Abstr., Chem.Abstr., Eng.Ind., INIS Atomind. **Document type:** academic/scholarly publication.
—BLDSC (1411.130000); El; UnCover; CASDDS.

621.48 JA ISSN 0287-9808
CODEN: KDGHDH
KYOTO UNIVERSITY. RESEARCH REACTOR INSTITUTE. TECHNICAL REPORT. (Text in English, Japanese) 1964. irreg. Kyoto University, Research Reactor Institute - Kyoto Daigaku Genshiro Jikkenjo, Kumatori-cho, Sennami-gun, Osaka 590-04, Japan.
—BLDSC (8717.743000); CASDDS.

333.792 FR
LETTRE DE L'ENERGIE; hebdomadaire d'information et de documentation professionnelles. w. 4900 F. (foreign 5180 F.). Societe Generale de Presse et d'Editions, 13 av. de l'Opera, 75001 Paris, France. TEL 40-15-17-89. FAX 40-15-17-15. TELEX SOGPRES 230023.

621.48 US
LICENSED FUEL FACILITY STATUS REPORT. s-a. U.S. Nuclear Regulatory Commission, Office of Nuclear Regulatory Research, Washington, DC 20555. TEL 301-492-7000. **Indexed:** Energy Info.Abstr. **Document type:** government publication.

333.792 US
LIFETIME NUCLEAR PLANT CAPITALIZATION AND O & M SUMMARY DATA. (Operating & Maintenance) a. $495 includes U S Nuclear Plant Statistics. Utility Data Institute (Subsidiary of: McGraw-Hill), 1200 G St., N.W., Ste. 250, Washington, DC 20005. TEL 202-942-8788; 800-486-3660. FAX 202-942-8789. stat. (diskette format) **Document type:** trade publication.
Description: Provides operating and maintenance expenses for all U.S. nuclear plants, including changes in plant capitalization.

621.48 IO ISSN 0303-2876
QC792 CODEN: MBTNA3
MAJALAH B A T A N. (Text in Indonesian; summaries in English, Indonesian) q. free. National Atomic Energy Agency - Badan Tenaga Atom Nasional, Puspiptek - Serpong - Tangerang, P.O. Box 4274, Jakarta 12042, Indonesia. TEL 2104-7560905. FAX 021-7560923. (Alt. addr.: Puspitek Serpong, P.O. Box 4437, Jakarta 12044, Indonesia) illus. **Indexed:** Biol.Abstr., Chem.Abstr., INIS Atomind.
—BLDSC (5352.850000); CASDDS.
Formerly: Indonesia. Badan Tenaga Atom Nasional. Majalah B A T A N (ISSN 0125-9555)

MEETINGS ON ATOMIC ENERGY. see MEETINGS AND CONGRESSES

THE MESSENGER (HEWITT); environment, nuclear hazards and alternative energies. see ENVIRONMENTAL STUDIES

621.48 JA ISSN 0388-3396
MITSUBISHI GENSHIRYOKU GIHO/TECHNICAL INFORMATION OF MITSUBISHI NUCLEAR SCIENCE. (Text in Japanese) 1975. q. Mitsubishi Jukogyo K.K., Keisuiro Gijutsubu - Mitsubishi Heavy Industries, Ltd., Nuclear System Engineering Department, 4-1, Shiba Koen 2-chome, Minato-ku, Tokyo 105, Japan.

621.48 JA ISSN 0285-0354
CODEN: MKGSEK
MUSASHI KOGYO DAIGAKU. GENSHIRYOKU KENKYUJO. KENKYUJOHO/MUSASHI INSTITUTE OF TECHNOLOGY. ATOMIC ENERGY RESEARCH LABORATORY. BULLETIN. Key Title: Kenkyujoho - Musashi Kogyo Daigaku Genshiryoku Kenkyujo. 1979. a. free. Musashi Kogyo Daigaku, Genshiryoku Kenkyujo - Musashi Institute of Technology, Atomic Energy Research Laboratory, 971 Ozenji, Asao-ku, Kawasaki 215, Japan. TEL 044-966-6131. FAX 044-955-6071. **Indexed:** Chem.Abstr.

333.792 US
N A C - FOCUS; quarterly review of the nuclear industry. 1973; N.S. 1980. q. $4000. Nuclear Assurance Corporation, 655 Engineering Dr., Ste. 200, Norcross, GA 30092-2843. TEL 404-447-1144. FAX 404-447-1797.
Former titles: N A C - Update; Nuclear Fuel Status and Forecast (ISSN 0092-993X)

333.792 FR
N E A ISSUE BRIEF; an analysis of principal nuclear energy issues. irreg. free. Organization for Economic Cooperation and Development, Nuclear Energy Agency, 12 bd. des Iles, 92130 Issy-les-Moulineaux, France. TEL 45-24-10-15. (U.S. orders to: O.E.C.D. Publications and Information Center, 2001 L St., N.W., Ste. 700, Washington, DC 20036-4910. TEL 202-785-6323) illus.

333.792 FR ISSN 1016-5398
N E A NEWSLETTER. French edition: A E N Bulletin (ISSN 0255-7495) (Text in English) 1983. s-a. 120 F.($28) Organization for Economic Cooperation and Development, Nuclear Energy Agency - Organisation de Cooperation et de Developpement Economiques. Agence pour l'Energie Nucleaire, 12 bd. des Iles, 92130 Issy-les-Moulineaux, France. TEL 45-24-10-15. (U.S. subscr. to: O E C D Publications and Information Center, 2001 L St., N.W., Ste. 700, Washington, DC 20036-4910. TEL 202-785-6323) (also avail. in microfiche from CIS) **Indexed:** IIS. **Document type:** newsletter.
Description: Furthers the development of the peaceful uses of nuclear energy by sponsoring economic, technical and scientific studies and projects as well as contributing to the optimization of safety, regulatory policies and practices.

621.48 JA ISSN 0917-7620
N G K GENSHIRYOKU GIHO/N G K TECHNICAL REPORT ON NUCLEAR ENGINEERING. (Text in Japanese; summaries in English) 1987. irreg. Nippon Gaishi K.K., 2-56, Suda-cho, Mizuho-ku, Nagoya-shi, Aichi-ken 467, Japan.

621.48 JA
N S R A NEWS. (Text in Japanese) 1966. bi-m. free. Nuclear Safety Research Association - Genshiryoku Anzen Kenkyu Kyokai, 1-2-2 Uchisaiwai-cho, Chiyoda-ku, Tokyo 107, Japan. TEL 03-3503-5785. Ed. Motohiro Otaka. bk.rev.; abstr.; circ. 1,500 (controlled).
Formerly (until 1969): N S R A Memo.

ULRICH'S INTERNATIONAL PERIODICALS DIRECTORY 1994-95

ENERGY — NUCLEAR ENERGY

333.792   **GW**
NACHBAR G K N. 1978. bi-m.
Gemeinschaftskernkraftwerk Neckar GmbH,
Postfach, 74380 Neckarwestheim, Germany.
TEL 07133-133296. FAX 07133-17645. Ed. Uwe
H. Mundt. circ. 35,000. **Document type:** trade
publication.

NIELS BOHR - COLLECTED WORKS. see *PHYSICS*

621.48   **JA**   ISSN 0285-4066
**NIHON DAIGAKU GENSHIRYOKU KENKYUJO
HOKOKU/NIHON UNIVERSITY. ATOMIC ENERGY
RESEARCH INSTITUTE. ANNUAL REPORT. JAPANESE
EDITION.** 1962. a. Nihon Daigaku, Genshiryoku
Kenkyujo, 1-8, Kanda Surugadai, Chiyoda-ku, Tokyo
101, Japan.

621.48   **JA**
**NIHON GENSHIRYOKU KENKYUJO. TOKAI KENKYUJO
GIJUTSU JOHOBU. SHIRYO JOHO/JAPAN ATOMIC
ENERGY RESEARCH INSTITUTE. TOKAI RESEARCH
ESTABLISHMENT. INFORMATION SERVICE.** (Text in
English, Japanese) 1958. w. Nihon Genshiryoku
Kenkyujo, Tokai Kenkyujo Gijutsu Johobu,
Tokaimura, Naka-gun, Ibaraki-ken 319-11, Japan.

621.48   **JA**   ISSN 0285-1989
**NIHON UNIVERSITY. ATOMIC ENERGY RESEARCH
INSTITUTE. ANNUAL REPORT.** (Text in English) 1962.
a. exchange basis. Nihon University, Atomic Energy
Research Institute - Nihon Daigaku Genshiryoku
Kenkyujo, 1-8 Kanda Surugadai, Chiyoda-ku, Tokyo
101, Japan. circ. 280.

621.48   **JA**   ISSN 0285-6360
NIKKI GENSHIRYOKU GIHO/J G C NUCLEAR REVIEW.
(Text in Japanese; summaries in English) 1981.
irreg. Nikki K.K., Genshiryoku Kodo Gijutsu Jigyo
Honbu - J G C Corporation, Nuclear and Advanced
Technology Division, 14-1, Bessho 1-chome,
Minami-ku, Yokohama-shi, Kanagawa-ken 232,
Japan.

539.7 614   **CN**
NUCLEAR AWARENESS NEWS. 1982. irreg. (2-4/yr.).
Can.$30. Nuclear Awareness Project, Box 2331,
Oshawa, Ont. L1H 7V4, Canada.
TEL 416-725-1565. FAX 416-725-1565. Ed. David
Martin. bk.rev. circ. 1,000. (back issues avail.)
●Also available online.

333.792   **CN**   ISSN 0029-5469
NUCLEAR CANADA/CANADA NUCLEAIRE. (Text in
English and French) 1962. m. (10/yr.).
membership. Canadian Nuclear Association, 144
Front St., Ste. 725, Toronto, ON M5J 2L7, Canada.
TEL 416-977-6152. FAX 416-979-8356. Ed.
James Weller. circ. 800. **Document type:** newsletter.
Formerly: C N A Newsletter.
Description: Reports on the peaceful use of nuclear
energy in Canada.

333.792   **CN**   ISSN 0383-8536
TK9026
NUCLEAR CANADA. YEARBOOK. (Includes: Canadian
Nuclear Industry Buyer's Guide) 1976. a. Canadian
Nuclear Association, 144 Front St., Ste. 725,
Toronto, ON M5G 2L7, Canada.
TEL 416-977-6152. FAX 416-979-8356. circ.
3,000.
—BLDSC (6180.621100).

333.792   **UN**   ISSN 0257-6376
NUCLEAR DATA NEWSLETTER. (Text in English) 1979.
irreg. free. International Atomic Energy Agency,
Wagramerstr. 5, P.O. Box 100, A-1400 Vienna,
Austria. circ. 2,300. **Document type:** newsletter.

621.48   **US**   ISSN 0090-3752
QC783   CODEN: NDTSBA
NUCLEAR DATA SHEETS. 1966. m. $528 (foreign
$628). (U.S. Department of Energy) Academic
Press, Inc., Journal Division, 525 B St., Ste. 1900,
San Diego, CA 92101-4495. TEL 619-230-1840.
FAX 619-699-6800. (Subscr. to: Box 620000,
Orlando, FL 32891-8340. TEL 800-543-9534)
Eds. M.J. Martin, J.K. Tuli. adv.; bibl.; charts. (back
issues avail.) Indexed: Chem.Abstr., Excerp.Med.,
Phys.Ber., Sci.Abstr. **Document type:**
academic/scholarly publication.
●Also available online.
—BLDSC (6180.622800); SWETS; CASDDS. **CCC.**
Supersedes in part: Nuclear Data (ISSN
0029-5477)
Description: Covers nuclear structure data
evaluations and nuclear structure bibliographies.

621.48   **UK**   ISSN 0140-4067
TK9001.B7   CODEN: NEBSDV
NUCLEAR ENERGY. 1962. bi-m. £98 (foreign £134).
(British Nuclear Energy Society) Thomas Telford
Services Ltd., Thomas Telford House, 1 Heron Quay,
London E14 4JD, England. TEL 071-987-6999.
FAX 071-538-4101. Ed. V.S. Crocker. adv.; bk.rev.;
charts; illus.; index. circ. 1,800. Indexed: Br.Tech.Ind.,
CAD CAM Abstr., Chem.Abstr., Curr.Cont., Energy
Ind., Energy Info.Abstr., Eng.Ind., Environ.Abstr.,
Environ.Per.Bibl., Excerp.Med., Fluidex, Fuel & Energy
Abstr., Geo.Abstr., Intl.Civil Eng.Abstr., Met.Abstr.,
P.A.I.S., Risk Abstr., Sci.Abstr., Soft.Abstr.Eng., World
Alum.Abstr. **Document type:** trade publication.
—BLDSC (6180.635000); CIS; EI; Faxon; UnCover;
SWETS; CASDDS. **CCC.**
Formerly: British Nuclear Energy Society. Journal
(ISSN 0007-1587)
Description: Covers practical and theoretical
aspects of nuclear energy.

621.48   **US**
HD9698.A1   CODEN: NUIDA
NUCLEAR ENERGY. 1954. q. membership. U.S. Nuclear
Energy Institute, 1776 Eye St., N.W., Ste. 400,
Washington, DC 20006-3708. TEL 202-739-8000.
Ed. Richard Myers. index; circ. 10,000. (controlled).
Document type: trade publication.
—UnCover.
Former titles (until 1994): Nuclear Industry (ISSN
0029-5531); (until 1964): Forum Memo to
Members.

NUCLEAR ENGINEER. see *ENGINEERING*

621.48   **JA**   ISSN 0433-4035
TK9145   CODEN: GKOGAM
NUCLEAR ENGINEERING/GENSHIRYOKU KOGYO. 1955.
m. 1340 Yen per no. Industrial Daily News Ltd. -
Nikkan Kogyo Shinbunsha, 1-8-10 Kudan Kita,
Chiyoda-ku, Tokyo 102, Japan. circ. 8,500. Indexed:
Chem.Abstr., INIS Atomind., JCT.
—BLDSC (6180.706000); CASDDS.
Description: Information on nuclear reactors,
nuclear fuel cycle, environment safety problems,
location problems, nuclear energy policy, utilization
of radioisotope.

NUCLEAR ENGINEERING AND DESIGN; an international
journal devoted to the thermal, mechanical,
materials, and structural aspects of nuclear fission
energy. see *ENGINEERING — Engineering
Mechanics And Materials*

539 620   **UK**   ISSN 0029-5507
TK9001   CODEN: NEINBF
NUCLEAR ENGINEERING INTERNATIONAL. (Text in
English; summaries in French, German) 1956. m.
£120($236) Reed Business Publishing Group
(Subsidiary of: Reed Elsevier group), Quadrant
House, The Quadrant, Sutton, Surrey SM2 5AS,
England. TEL 081-652-3356. FAX 081-652-3998.
(Subscr. to: Stuart House, 35 Perrymount Rd.,
Haywards Heath, W. Sussex RH19 3BN, England.
TEL 0444-445566) Ed. James Varley. adv.; bk.rev.;
charts; illus.; tr.lit.; index. circ. 5,014. (also avail. in
microform from UMI; back issues avail.; reprint
service avail. from UMI) Indexed: A.S.& T.Ind.,
Appl.Mech.Rev., Br.Tech.Ind., CAD CAM Abstr. (until
1992), Cadscan, Chem.Abstr., Curr.Cont., Energy
Info.Abstr., Energy Rev., Eng.Ind., Environ.Abstr.,
Environ.Per.Bibl., Excerp.Med., Fluidex,
Foul.Prev.Res.Dig., Fuel & Energy Abstr., Geo.Abstr.,
Key to Econ.Sci., Lead Abstr., Met.Abstr., PROMT,
Risk Abstr., Robomat. (until 1992), Sci.Abstr., World
Alum.Abstr., Zincscan. **Document type:** trade
publication.
—BLDSC (6180.717000); CIS; EI; UnCover; SWETS;
CASDDS. **CCC.**
Incorporates: Nuclear Engineering; Nuclear Power.
Description: News, comment and feature articles
on technical and commercial developments in the
exploitation of nuclear energy.

333.792   **SZ**
NUCLEAR EUROPE WORLDSCAN. (Text in English)
1981. bi-m. 160 SFr. (foreign 230 SFr.). European
Nuclear Society, c/o ATAG Ernst & Young, Postfach
5032, CH-3001 Bern, Switzerland.
FAX 031-3824466. TELEX 912110-ATAG-CH. Ed.
Dr. Peter Holt. adv.; bk.rev. circ. 22,500. Indexed:
Chem.Abstr. **Document type:** academic/scholarly
publication, trade publication.
Formerly: Nuclear Europe.

539.7 621.48   **UK**
NUCLEAR FORUM.* 1963. m. free. British Nuclear
Industry Forum, 22 Buckingham Gate, London SW1E
6LB, England. TEL 071-828-0116.
FAX 071-828-0110. Ed. N.M.G. Middlemiss. bk.rev.;
circ. 7,000. (controlled). **Document type:** bulletin.
Former title: British Nuclear Forum. Bulletin.
Description: Identifies, studies, and seeks solutions
to problems affecting the nuclear industry and
represents the industry in meeting government
requirements; also attempts to bring about a better
public understanding.

621.48   **US**   ISSN 0735-2506
TK9360   CODEN: NFCYD
NUCLEAR FUEL CYCLE. 1982. m. $155. U.S.
Department of Energy, Office of Scientific and
Technical Information, Box 62, Oak Ridge, TN
37831. TEL 615-574-0733. (Subscr. to: National
Technical Information Service, 5285 Port Royal Rd.,
Springfield, VA 22161. TEL 703-487-4630. FAX
703-324-8547) Ed. James D. Bales. **Document type:**
government publication.
Description: Presents worldwide information on all
aspects of the nuclear fuel cycle, except in-reactor
properties and performance of fuels and the
management of radioactive wastes.

NUCLEAR GEOPHYSICS; a journal of nuclear techniques
in the earth and environmental sciences, mineral
exploration, mining and process control. see *EARTH
SCIENCES — Geophysics*

NUCLEAR INDEX. see *ENERGY — Abstracting,
Bibliographies, Statistics*

621.48   **II**   ISSN 0029-5523
TK9103
NUCLEAR INDIA. (Text in English) 1962. m. free.
Department of Atomic Energy, Publications Officer,
Chhatrapati Shivaji Maharaj Marg, Bombay 400039,
India. charts; illus.; circ. 5,000 (controlled).

539 621.48   **JA**
NUCLEAR INDUSTRIAL NEWSPAPER. 1955. w.
8500 Yen. Japan Atomic Industrial Forum - Nihon
Genshiryoku Sangyo Kaigi, Toshin Bldg., 1-1-13
Shinbashi, Minato-ku, Tokyo 105, Japan.
TEL 03-3508-2411. FAX 03-3508-2094. TELEX
2226623-JAIFRM-J. **Document type:** newspaper.
Formerly: Atomic Industry News.

333.792 340   **FR**   ISSN 0304-341X
LAW
NUCLEAR LAW BULLETIN. French edition: Droit
Nucleaire (ISSN 1016-4995) (Includes supplement)
(Text in English) 1968. s-a. 170 F.($36)
Organization for Economic Cooperation and
Development, Nuclear Energy Agency, 12 bd. des
Iles, 92130 Issy-les-Moulineaux, France.
TEL 45-24-10-15. (U.S. orders to: O.E.C.D.
Publications and Information Center, 2001 L St.,
N.W., Ste. 700, Washington, DC 20036-4910. TEL
202-785-6323) index, cum.index every 5 yrs. circ.
2,400. (also avail. in microfiche from OEC) Indexed:
C.L.I., Energy Info.Abstr., Environ.Abstr., Leg.Per.
—BLDSC (6180.900000); Faxon; UnCover.
Description: Covers legislative and regulatory
developments, agreements and case law in the
nuclear field throughout the world, and reports on
regulatory initiatives of international organizations
with jurisdiction in nuclear affairs.

333.792 614.8   **US**
NUCLEAR LEMONS; an assessment of America's worst
commercial nuclear reactors. 1979. irreg., 4th ed.,
1993. $40 ($60 with Data supplement). Public
Citizen's Critical Mass Energy Project, 215
Pennsylvania Ave., S.E., Washington, DC 20003.
TEL 202-546-4996. FAX 202-547-7392. (Orders
to: Public Citizen Publications, 2000 P St., N.W.,
Washington, DC 20036. TEL 202-833-3000) (back
issues avail.)
Formerly: Nuclear Power Safety Report.
Description: Reviews accidents, management
lapses, fines, emergency plant shutdowns and other
mishaps at US commercial nuclear power plants.

ENERGY — NUCLEAR ENERGY

333.792 US ISSN 0889-3411
HD9698.A1
NUCLEAR MONITOR. 1985. fortn. $250. Nuclear Information & Resource Service, 1424 16th St., N.W., Ste. 601, Washington, DC 20036. TEL 202-328-0002. FAX 202-462-2183. Ed. Michael Mariotte. circ. 1,200. (back issues avail.) **Indexed:** Energy Rev. **Document type:** newsletter.
   Description: Covers nuclear power, radioactive waste and sustainable energy news for investment bankers, state and local officials, media and environmental activists.

333.792 US ISSN 0029-5574
QC770 CODEN: NUNWAB
NUCLEAR NEWS. 1959. m. (plus 3 special issues). $200 includes Nuclear News Buyers Guide. American Nuclear Society, 555 N. Kensington Ave., La Grange Park, IL 60525. TEL 708-352-6611. Ed. Nancy Zacha. adv.; bk.rev.; charts; illus.; tr.lit. circ. 15,000. (reprint service avail.) **Indexed:** AESIS, Chem.Abstr., Sci.Abstr., World Alum.Abstr.
●Also available online. Vendor(s): Mead Data Central, Inc.
—BLDSC (6180.950000); Faxon; UnCover; SWETS. **CCC.**
   Description: Contains organization news.

333.792 US ISSN 0029-5574
NUCLEAR NEWS BUYERS GUIDE. 1969. a. $65 or with subscr. to: Nuclear News. American Nuclear Society, 555 N. Kensington Ave., La Grange Park, IL 60525. TEL 708-352-6611. Ed. Nancy Zacha. adv. circ. 15,000.

539.7 614.8 US ISSN 0892-2055
TK1078
NUCLEAR PLANT JOURNAL. 1983. bi-m. $102. (International Nuclear Power Industry) E Q E S, Inc., Bldg. 6, Ste. 208, 799 Roosevelt Rd., Glen Ellyn, IL 60137. TEL 708-858-6161. FAX 708-858-8787. Ed. Newal K. Agnihotri. adv. contact: Kimberly R. Graba. bk.rev.; charts; illus.; stat.; tr.lit. circ. 22,000. (back issues avail.) **Document type:** trade publication.
—BLDSC (6182.430000); EI; Faxon. **CCC.**
   Formerly (until 1987): Nuclear Plant Safety (ISSN 0742-4868)
   Description: Includes technical papers, articles and departments aimed at developing better methods, systems, products, and services in the nuclear power industry.

539.7 620 US ISSN 1054-9447
NUCLEAR PLANT MAINTENANCE NEWSLETTER. 1981. m. $220 (foreign $252) (effective 1994). (Equipment Engineering & Sales, Inc.) E Q E S, Inc., Bldg. 6, Ste. 208, 799 Roosevelt Rd., Glen Ellyn, IL 60137. TEL 708-858-6161. FAX 708-858-8787. Ed. Newal K. Agnihotri. circ. 70. (back issues avail.) **Document type:** newsletter.
—**CCC.**
   Formerly: Equipment Maintenance and Qualification Newsletter (ISSN 0892-6948)
   Description: Serves the international nuclear power industry with news briefs from utilities, manufacturers, research organizations, and service vendors. Also announces meetings and training workshops.

539.7 US
NUCLEAR PLANT O & M COST DATA. (Operating & Maintenance) a. $750. Utility Data Institute (Subsidiary of: McGraw-Hill), 1200 G St., N.W., Ste. 250, Washington, DC 20005. TEL 202-924-8788; 800-486-3660. FAX 202-924-8789. (diskette format) **Document type:** trade publication.
   Description: Provides nuclear plant expense information for all U.S. nuclear plants, as reported to the Federal Energy Regulatory Commission.

621.48 JA
NUCLEAR POWER ENGINEERING CENTER. NEWSLETTER. (Text in Japanese) 1989. m. Nuclear Power Engineering Center - Genshiryoku Kogaku Shiken Senta, 3-13, Toranomon 4-chome, Minato-ku, Tokyo 105, Japan. **Document type:** newsletter.

621.48 JA ISSN 0289-9817
NUCLEAR POWER PLANTS IN THE WORLD/GENSHIRYOKU HATSUDENSHO. (Text in English) 1962. a. 3600 Yen. Japan Atomic Industrial Forum - Nihon Genshiryoku Sangyo Kaigi, Toshin Bldg., 1-1-13 Shinbashi, Minato-ku, Tokyo 105, Japan. TEL 03-3508-2411. FAX 03-3508-2094. TELEX 2226623-JAIFRM-J.

621.48 US ISSN 0735-2492
NUCLEAR REACTOR SAFETY. 1982. m. $150. U.S. Department of Energy, Office of Scientific and Technical Information, Box 62, Oak Ridge, TN 37831. TEL 615-574-0733. (Subscr. to: National Technical Information Service, 5285 Port Royal Rd., Springfield, VA 22161. TEL 703-487-4630. FAX 703-321-8547) Ed. James D. Bales. **Document type:** government publication.
   Description: Presents worldwide technical information on safety-related aspects of reactors including accident analysis, safety systems, radiation protection, decommissioning and dismantling, and security measures.

NUCLEAR REGULATION REPORTS. see LAW

539 621.48 US ISSN 0029-5604
TK9152 CODEN: NUSAAZ
NUCLEAR SAFETY; a quarterly technical progress review. (Catalog ID: NS) 1959. bi-a. $22 (foreign $27.50). U.S. Department of Energy, Office of Scientific and Technical Information, Box 62, Oak Ridge, TN 37831. TEL 615-574-0733. (Subscr. to: Superintendent of Documents, U.S. Government Printing Office, Box 371954, Pittsburgh, PA 15250-7954. TEL 202-783-3238. FAX 202-512-2233) Ed. E.G. Silver. bk.rev.; charts; illus.; index. (also avail. in microform from UMI; reprint service avail. from UMI) **Indexed:** Biol.Abstr., CAD CAM Abstr. (through 1993), Cadscan, Chem.Abstr., Curr.Cont., Energy Info.Abstr. (through 1994), Energy Rev., Eng.Ind., Environ.Abstr., Environ.Per.Bibl., Fluidex, Ind.Sci.Rev., Ind.U.S.Gov.Per., Lead Abstr., Pollut.Abstr., Risk Abstr., Sci.Abstr., Zincscan. **Document type:** government publication.
—BLDSC (6182.900000); CIS; EI; Faxon; UnCover; SWETS; UMI; CASDDS.
   Description: Evaluates scientific and technological developments relating to nuclear safety as they emerge from atomic research and development programs.

539 621.48 US ISSN 0029-5639
QC770 CODEN: NSENAO
NUCLEAR SCIENCE AND ENGINEERING; research and development related to peaceful utilization of nuclear energy. 1956. m. (3 vols./yr.). $405. American Nuclear Society, 555 N. Kensington Ave., La Grange Park, IL 60525. TEL 708-352-6611. Ed. Dan G. Cacuci. bk.rev.; abstr.; charts; illus.; index, cum.index: 1956-1973, vols.1-52. circ. 1,500. (back issues avail.; reprint service avail.) **Indexed:** Appl.Mech.Rev., Biol.Abstr., CAD CAM Abstr., Cadscan, Chem.Abstr., Comput.Abstr., Curr.Cont., Energy Ind., Energy Info.Abstr., Eng.Ind., Environ.Abstr., Excerp.Med., Ind.Sci.Rev., Lead Abstr., Met.Abstr., Risk Abstr., Sci.Abstr., Zincscan. **Document type:** academic/scholarly publication.
—BLDSC (6183.100000); EI; Faxon; UnCover; SWETS; CASDDS. **CCC.**
   Refereed Serial

621.48 US ISSN 0029-5655
NUCLEAR STANDARDS NEWS. 1970. m. $275. American Nuclear Society, 555 N. Kensington Ave., La Grange Park, IL 60525. TEL 708-352-6611. Ed. Marilyn D. Weber. charts; illus. circ. 400. (looseleaf format; reprint service avail.) **Document type:** newspaper.

333.792 UK
NUCLEAR TIMES. 1991. m. Nuclear Electric plc, Barnett Way, Barnwood, Gloucester GL4 7RS, England. TEL 0452-653700. FAX 0452-652674. Ed. Colin Bennett. circ. 26,000. **Document type:** trade publication.

333.792 US
NUCLEAR UNIT OUTAGE DATA BASE. 1981. base vol. and a. updates. $1250 for base vol.; updates $495. Utility Data Institute (Subsidiary of: McGraw-Hill), 1200 G St., N.W., Ste. 250, Washington, DC 20005. TEL 202-942-8788; 800-486-3660. FAX 202-942-8789. (diskette format) **Document type:** trade publication.
   Description: Compiles statistics on nuclear power plant outages lasting more than 24 hours.

621.48 US
NUCLEAR UNIT PERFORMANCE DATA. a. $495 includes U S Nuclear Plant Statistics. Utility Data Institute (Subsidiary of: McGraw-Hill), 1200 G St., N.W., Ste. 250, Washington, DC 20005. TEL 202-942-8788; 800-486-3650. FAX 202-942-8789. stat. (diskette format) **Document type:** trade publication.
   Description: Provides technical and performance statistics for every operating U.S. nuclear reactor.

NUCLEAR WASTE NEWS; generation, packaging, transportation, processing, disposal. see ENVIRONMENTAL STUDIES — Waste Management

333.792 US ISSN 0149-3574
TK9360
NUCLEARFUEL. 1976. fortn. $1360 (foreign $1455). McGraw-Hill, Inc., 1221 Ave. of the Americas, New York, NY 10020. Ed. Michael Knapike. charts; stat. (looseleaf format; back issues avail.; reprint service avail. from UMI)
●Also available online. Vendor(s): DIALOG Information Services, Inc. (File no.624/McGRAW-HILL PUBLICATIONS ONLINE), Dow Jones News Retrieval (NUF), Mead Data Central, Inc. (NJFUEL).
—BLDSC (6180.750000).

NUCLEONICS WEEK. see ENERGY

539 CL ISSN 0716-0054
TK9001 CODEN: NUCLEQ
NUCLEOTECNICA. (Text and summaries in English, Spanish) 1981. s-a. $6. Comision Chilena de Energia Nuclear Amunategui 95, Casilla 188-D, Santiago, Chile. TEL 56-2-699-0070. FAX 56-2-699-1818. Ed. Rosamel Munoz Quintana. adv.; cum.index: 1981-1988, 1989-1991. circ. 2,000. (back issues avail.) **Indexed:** Chem.Abstr. **Document type:** academic/scholarly publication.
●Also available online.
—BLDSC (6184 095000); CASDDS.

621.48 PK ISSN 0029-5698
TK9001.P3 CODEN: NCLEAM
NUCLEUS. (Text in English; summaries in English, French, German) 1964. q. Rs.25($8) Pakistan Atomic Energy Commission, P.O. Box 3112, Karachi-29, Pakistan. Ed. Akhtar Mahmud Faruqui. adv.; bk.rev.; abstr.; illus.; index every 2 yrs. circ. 2,000. **Indexed:** Appl.Mech.Rev., Biol.Abstr., Chem.Abstr., GeoRef., Hort.Abstr., Nucl.Sci.Abstr., Plant Grow.Reg.Abstr., Rev.Med.& Vet.Mycol., Sci.Abstr., Triticale Abstr., Virol.Abstr.
—BLDSC (6184.203000); CASDDS.

333.792 PH
NUCLEUS. (Text in English) 1960. a. P.20($20) Radioisotope Society of the Philippines, c/o Philippine Atomic Energy Commission, Don Mariano Marcos Avenue, Diliman, Quezon City, Philippines. Ed. Aida D. Davila Eugenio. circ. 500.

621.48 CU
NUCLEUS; energia nuclear. 2/yr. $24 in S. America; N. America $26; elsewhere $30. Ediciones Cubanas, Obispo No. 527, Apdo. 605, Havana, Cuba.

621.48 YU ISSN 0351-689X
NUKLEARNA TEHNOLOGIJA. 1981. q. $40. Institut za Nuklearne Nauke "Boris Kidric," Vinca - Boris Kidric Institute of Nuclear Sciences, Vinca, P.O. Box 522, Belgrade, Serbia, Yugoslavia. Ed. Naim Afgan. adv.; bk.rev.; abstr.; charts; illus. circ. 1,000. **Indexed:** Chem.Abstr.
   Supersedes: Nuklearna Energija (ISSN 0029-5914)

621.48 PL ISSN 0029-5922
TK9001 CODEN: NUKLAS
NUKLEONIKA. (Text in various languages; summaries in English, Polish, Russian) 1956. m. Polska Akademia Nauk, Instytut Chemii i Techniki Jadrowej, Ul. Dorodna 16, 03-195 Warsaw, Poland. (Dist. by: Ars Polona-Ruch, Krakowskie Przedmiescie 7, Warsaw, Poland) (Co-sponsor Urzad Energii Atomowej) Ed. Z. Szymanski. charts; illus.; index. circ. 1,400. **Indexed:** Biwk.Pap.Rad.Chem.& Photochem., C.I.S. Abstr., Chem.Abstr., Curr.Cont., GeoRef., Ind.Sci.Rev., Met.Abstr., Nucl.Sci.Abstr., Phys.Abstr., Phys.Ber., Sci.Abstr.
—BLDSC (6184.600000); CASDDS.

ENERGY — NUCLEAR ENERGY

539.7 621.042   FR   ISSN 1017-9402
O E C D NUCLEAR ENERGY AGENCY. NUCLEAR ENERGY DATA. (Text in English, French) 1983. a. price varies. Organization for Economic Cooperation and Development, Nuclear Energy Agency, 12 bd. des Iles, 92130 Issy-les-Moulineaux, France. TEL 45-24-10-15. (U.S. orders to: O.E.C.D. Publications and Information Office, 2001 L St., N.W., Ste. 700, Washington, DC 20036-4910. TEL 202-785-6323) (also avail. in microfiche from OEC,CIS) **Indexed:** IIS.
Former titles (until 1989): O E C D Nuclear Energy Agency. Electricity, Nuclear Power and Fuel Cycle in O E C D Countries. Main Data; Organization for Economic Cooperation and Development. Nuclear Energy Agency. Summary of Nuclear Power and Fuel Cycle Data in O E C D Member Countries.

539 621.042   FR
O E C D NUCLEAR ENERGY AGENCY ACTIVITIES IN (YEAR). Short title: N E A Activities in (Year). French edition: A E N Activites en (Year). (Editions in English, French) 1958. a. free. Organization for Economic Cooperation and Development, Nuclear Energy Agency, 12 bd. des Iles, 92130 Issy-les-Moulineaux, France. TEL 45-24-10-15. (U.S. orders to: O.E.C.D. Publications and Information Center, 2001 L St., N.W., Ste. 700, Washington, DC 20036-4910. TEL 202-785-6323) charts; illus.; stat. circ. 4,000. (also avail. in microfiche)
Formerly: O E C D. Nuclear Energy Agency. Activity Report (ISSN 0078-625X)
Description: Discusses agency activities in the preceding year, covering trends in nuclear power, technological developments, radiation safety and protection, waste management, research programs, and legal affairs.

621.48   DK   ISSN 0105-4899
O O A - SAERTRYK. (Organisationen til Oplysning om Atomkraft) 1974. irreg., no.25, 1985. Energibevaegelsen O O A, Ryesgade 19, DK-2200 Copenhagen, Denmark. TEL 45-1-35-55-07.

333.7   JA
OKAYAMA DAIGAKU R I KYODO RIYO TSUSHIMA SHISETSUHO/OKAYAMA UNIVERSITY. RADIOISOTOPE LABORATORY. ANNUAL REPORT. (Text in Japanese) 1991. a. Okayama Daigaku, R I Kyodo Riyo Tsushima Shisetsu, 1-1, Tsushima Naka 3-chome, Okayama-shi, Okayama-ken 700, Japan.

ONAGAWA GENSHIRYOKU HATSUDENJO KANKYO HOSHANO OYOBI ONHAISUI CHOSA KEKKA/MONITORING REPORT OF ENVIRONMENTAL RADIOACTIVITY AND WARM WASTE WATER AROUND ONAGAWA NUCLEAR POWER STATION. see ENVIRONMENTAL STUDIES — Waste Management

621.48   JA   ISSN 0912-5108
OSAKA DAIGAKU SANGYO KAGAKU KENKYUJO FUZOKU HOSHASEN JIKKENJO NENPO/OSAKA UNIVERSITY. INSTITUTE OF SCIENTIFIC AND INDUSTRIAL RESEARCH. RADIATION LABORATORY. ANNUAL REPORT. (Text in Japanese) a. Osaka Daigaku, Sangyo Kagaku Kenkyujo, Fuzoku Hoshasen Jikkenjo, 8-1, Mihogaoka, Ibaraki-shi, Osaka 567, Japan.

621.48   JA
OSAKA UNIVERSITY. INSTITUTE OF LASER ENGINEERING. RESEARCH REPORT. (Text in English) irreg. Osaka University, Institute of Laser Engineering, 2-6, Yamadaoka, Suita-shi, Osaka 565, Japan.

539.7 660   JA
P N C TECHNICAL REVIEW/DONEN GIHO. (Text in English) a. Power Reactor and Nuclear Fuel Development Corporation, Technology Management Division - Doryokuru Kaku Nenryo Kaihatsu Jigyodan Gijutsu Kyoryokubu, 9-13, Akasaka 1-chome, Minato-ku, Tokyo 107, Japan. **Indexed:** INIS Atomind.

621.48   SZ
P S I JAHRESBERICHT. (Supplements avail.: Annexes I to V) (Text in German; supplements in English) a. Paul Scherrer Institut, Wuerenlingen und Villigen, CH-5232 Villigen PSI, Switzerland. TEL 056-992111. FAX 056-982327. TELEX 827417-PSI-CH.
Formerly (until 1988): Schweizerisches Institut fuer Nuklearforschung. Jahresbericht.

PEACE MAGAZINE. see POLITICAL SCIENCE — International Relations

621.48   JA
PEOPLES IN ATOMS. (Text in Japanese) 1977. a. 7800 Yen. Japan Atomic Industrial Forum, Inc. - Nihon Genshiryoku Sangyo Kaigi, Toshin Bldg., 1-1-13 Shinbashi, Minato-ku, Tokyo 105, Japan. TEL 03-3508-2411. FAX 03-3508-2094. TELEX 2226623-JAIFRM-J.

621.48   PH
PHILIPPINE NUCLEAR RESEARCH INSTITUTE. ANNUAL REPORT. a. free. Philippine Nuclear Research Institute, Commonwealth Ave., Diliman, Quezon City, Philippines. TEL 976011. FAX 951646. TELEX 66804 PNRI PN. illus. circ. 500. **Indexed:** Biol.Abstr.
Formerly: Philippine Atomic Energy Commission. Annual Report (ISSN 0553-9978)

333.792   PL   ISSN 0551-6846
POSTEPY TECHNIKI JADROWEJ. 1957. 4/yr. Augustowka 5, 02-981 Warsaw, Poland. TEL 48-22-642-7666. Ed. Janusz Kelbasinski.
Description: Covers nuclear technics and radiology.

621.48   US
POWER PLANT DYNAMICS, CONTROL AND TESTING SYMPOSIUM. (NO.) PROCEEDINGS. irreg? $50. University of Tennessee at Knoxville, Department of Nuclear Engineering, Knoxville, TN 37996. TEL 615-974-5048. FAX 615-974-0668. Ed. B.R. Upadhyaya. **Document type:** proceedings.

333.792   UK   ISSN 0149-1970
TK9001   CODEN: PNENDE
PROGRESS IN NUCLEAR ENERGY; international review journal covering all aspects of nuclear energy. 1977. 4/yr. £255($395) (effective 1994). Elsevier Science Ltd., Pergamon, P.O. Box 800, Kidlington, Oxford OX5 1DX, England. TEL 44-865-843000. FAX 44-865-843010. (Subscr. in U.S. and Canada to: Elsevier Science, 660 White Plains Rd., Tarrytown, NY 10591-5153. TEL 914-524-9200. FAX 914-333-2444) Eds. T.D. Beynon, Bal Raj Sehgal. (also avail. in microfilm from UMI) **Indexed:** CAD CAM Abstr., Chem.Abstr., Curr.Cont., Energy Info.Abstr., Energy Rev., Environ.Per.Bibl., Excerp.Med., Geo.Abstr., Ind.Sci.Rev., Risk Abstr., Sci.Abstr. **Document type:** academic/scholarly publication.
—BLDSC (6870.542000); Faxon; UnCover; UMI; CASDDS. **CCC.**
Supersedes (in 1977): Progress in Nuclear Energy. Series 3 - Process Chemistry (ISSN 0079-6514); Progress in Nuclear Energy. Series 9 - Analytical Chemistry (ISSN 0079-6530)
Description: Covers developments in nuclear physics and engineering, as well as related issues including safety, siting, environmental problems, economics and fuel management.
Refereed Serial

PROLIFERATION WATCH. see MILITARY

539.7   CC   ISSN 1001-4322
QIANGJIGUANG YU LIZISHU/HIGH POWER LASER AND PARTICLE BEAMS. (Text in Chinese) 1989. q. $100 (effective till 1997). (Nuclear Society of China) Qiang Jiguang yu Lizishu Journal Agency, P.O. Box 511-1, Chengdu, Sichuan 610003, People's Republic of China. TEL 0816-25839. TELEX 600088 CAEP CN. Ed. Wu Yanbin. adv.; bk.rev. circ. 1,500. **Document type:** academic/scholarly publication.
—CCC.
Description: Covers the research and development in the field of high power laser and particle beams in China, including plasma physics and ICF, laser and accelerator technology.
Refereed Serial

621.48   JA
R A N D E C NEWS. (Text in Japanese) 1989. 4/yr. Research Association for Nuclear Facility Decommissioning - Genshiryoku Shisetsu Dekomisshoningu Kenkyu Kyokai, 821-100, Funaishikawa, Tokaimura, Naka-gun, Ibaraki-ken 319-11, Japan.

621.48   US
R S I C NEWSLETTER. 1965. m. free. (Oak Ridge National Laboratory) Radiation Shielding Information Center, Box 2008, Oak Ridge, TN 37831-6362. TEL 615-574-6176. Ed. Alice F. Rice. bk.rev.; abstr.; bibl. circ. 2,350. (processed) **Document type:** newsletter.

RADIATION EVENTS MONITOR. see ENVIRONMENTAL STUDIES

RADIATION RESEARCH; an international journal. see PHYSICS — Nuclear Physics

RADIOACTIVE WASTE MANAGEMENT AND ENVIRONMENTAL RESTORATION. see ENVIRONMENTAL STUDIES — Waste Management

RADIOACTIVE WASTE MANAGEMENT HANDBOOK. see ENVIRONMENTAL STUDIES — Waste Management

RADIOACTIVE WASTE MANAGEMENT SERIES. see ENVIRONMENTAL STUDIES — Waste Management

539.7 614.7   UK   ISSN 0308-4272
RADIOLOGICAL PROTECTION BULLETIN. 1972. m. £24 (foreign £30). National Radiological Protection Board, Chilton, Didcot, Oxon OX11 0RQ, England. TEL 0235-831600. FAX 0235-833891. TELEX 837124-RADPRO-G. bk.rev. circ. 1,200. **Indexed:** AESIS, C.I.S. Abstr., Curr.Adv.Ecol.Sci., INIS Atomind, Sci.Abstr. **Document type:** academic/scholarly publication.
—BLDSC (7237.970000).

621.48   FR   ISSN 0033-8451
RA569   CODEN: RAPRBA
RADIOPROTECTION. (Text and summaries in English and French) 1966. q. 950 F. (foreign 950 F.). (Societe Francaise de Radioprotection) Editions de Physique, Z.I. de Courtaboeuf, B.P. 112, 91944 Les Ulis Cedex A, France. TEL 69-07-36-88. FAX 69-28-84-91. TELEX 602 321 F. Ed. A. Teste du Bailler. adv.; charts; illus. circ. 1,000. (also avail. in microfilm from UMI) **Indexed:** Biol.Abstr., C.I.S.Abstr., Chem.Abstr., Curr.Cont., Excerp.Med., Pollut.Abstr.
—BLDSC (7240.040000); SWETS; CASDDS. **CCC.**
Description: Deals with the existing means of protection with regard to radioactivity-related problems.

RE-ACTIONS. see EDUCATION — Teaching Methods And Curriculum

621.48   JA
RESEARCH ASSOCIATION FOR NUCLEAR FACILITY DECOMMISSIONING. JOURNAL/DECOMMISSIONING GIHOU. (Text in Japanese) m. Research Association for Nuclear Facility Decommissioning - Genshiryoku Shisetsu Dekomisshoningu Kenkyu Kyokai, 821-100, Funaishikawa, Tokaimura, Naka-gun, Ibaraki-ken 319-11, Japan. TEL 0292-83-3010. FAX 0292-87-0022.

621.48   JA   ISSN 0387-6144
CODEN: BRLTD9
RESEARCH LABORATORY FOR NUCLEAR REACTORS. BULLETIN. (Text in English) 1976. a. Tokyo Institute of Technology, Research Laboratory for Nuclear Reactors - Tokyo Kogyo Daigaku Genshiro Kogaku Kenkyujo, 12-1, Ookayama 2-chome, Meguro-ku, Tokyo 152, Japan. **Indexed:** Chem.Abstr., INIS Atomind. **Document type:** bulletin.
—BLDSC (2696.502000); CASDDS.

RESPIRATORY PROTECTION NEWSLETTER. see OCCUPATIONAL HEALTH AND SAFETY

539.7 621.48   FR
REVUE GENERALE NUCLEAIRE. (Text in French; summaries in English, French) 1975. 6/yr. 680 F. (Societe Francaise d'Energie Nucleaire) Revue Generale de l'Electricite, S.A., 48 rue de la Procession, 75724 Paris Cedex 15, France. TEL 44-49-60-00. FAX 44-49-60-35. TELEX SEE 200565F. Ed. F. Sorin. adv.; bk.rev.; charts; index. circ. 6,500. **Indexed:** Excerp.Med.
Description: Offers synthesis and analyses on all aspects of nuclear development around the world: research, techniques, industrial achievements, economies, energy policy, health, environment, public opinion, international relations and cooperation.

539.7 621.48   FR   ISSN 0298-7783
REVUE GENERALE NUCLEAIRE: INTERNATIONAL EDITION. (Text in English) 1985. 2/yr. 290 F. (Societe Francaise de l'Energie Nucleaire) Revue Generale de l'Electricite S.A., 48, rue de la Procession, 75724 Paris Cedex 15, France. TEL 44-49-60-00. FAX 44-49-60-35. TELEX SEE 200565 F. Ed. M. Francis Sorin.
—BLDSC (7913.701000). **CCC.**
Description: Covers nuclear energy field. Translates some of the articles published in Revue Generale Nucleaire.

621.48 JA
RIKKYO DAIGAKU GENSHIRYOKU KENKYUJO GENSHIRO RIYO JISSEKI HOKOKU/RIKKYO UNIVERSITY. INSTITUTE FOR ATOMIC ENERGY. ANNUAL REPORT OF REACTOR UTILIZATION. (Text in Japanese) 1963. a. Rikkyo Daigaku, Genshiryoku Kenkyujo, 5-1, Nagasaka 2-chome, Yokosuka-shi, Kanagawa-ken 240-01, Japan.

621.48 JA
RIKKYO DAIGAKU GENSHIRYOKU KENKYUJO KOENKAI RONBUNSHU/RIKKYO UNIVERSITY. INSTITUTE FOR ATOMIC ENERGY. SEMINAR PROCEEDINGS. (Text in Japanese; summaries in English, Japanese) 1984. a. Rikkyo Daigaku, Genshiryoku Kenkyujo, 5-1, Nagasaka 2-chome, Yokosuka-shi, Kanagawa-ken 240-01, Japan. Document type: proceedings.

539 621.48 JA
RIKKYO UNIVERSITY. INSTITUTE FOR ATOMIC ENERGY. REPORT. (Text in English, Japanese) 1966. irreg. exchange basis. Rikkyo Daigaku, Genshiryoku Kenkyujo - Rikkyo University, Institute for Atomic Energy, 5-1, Nagasaka 2-chome, Yokosuka-shi, Kanagawa-ken 240-01, Japan. circ. 100.

RUSSIAN ACADEMY OF SCIENCE. LEBEDEV PHYSICS INSTITUTE. PROCEEDINGS. see *PHYSICS — Optics*

S C R A M SAFE ENERGY JOURNAL. (Scottish Campaign to Resist the Atomic Menace) see *ENERGY*

539 621.48 SZ ISSN 0036-777X
QC770
SCHWEIZERISCHE VEREINIGUNG FUER ATOMENERGIE. BULLETIN. French edition: Association Suisse pour l'Energie Atomique. Bulletin. 1959. s-m. 310 SFr. membership (Switzerland); Europe 370 SFr.; elsewhere 420 SFr. Schweizerische Vereinigung fuer Atomenergie - Swiss Association for Atomic Energy, Postfach 5032, CH-3001 Bern, Switzerland. TEL 031-3115882. FAX 031-3206831. Ed. Dr. Peter Zuehlke. adv.; bk.rev.; bibl.; charts; index, cum.index. circ. 1,800. Document type: academic/scholarly publication, bulletin.

621.48 JA ISSN 0915-0692
SEKAI NO GENSHIRYOKU HATSUDEN KAIHATSU NO DOKO/TRENDS OF NUCLEAR POWER GENERATION IN THE WORLD. (Text in Japanese) 1967. a. Nihon Genshiryoku Sangyo Kaigi - Japan Atomic Industrial Forum, 1-13, Shinbashi 1-chome, Minato-ku, Tokyo 105, Japan.

621.48 JA ISSN 0288-7703
SEVEN STARS OF I L E. (Text in Japanese) 1983. m. Osaka University, Institute of Laser Engineering - Osaka Daigaku Rexa Kaku Yugo Kenkyu Senta, 2-6, Yamadaoka, Suita-shi, Osaka 565, Japan.

621.48 JA
SHIMANE GENSHIRYOKU KOHO/SHIMANE ATOMIC INFORMATION. (Text in Japanese) 1988. irreg. Shimaneken Kikakubu - Shimane Prefectural Government, Planning Division, 1, Tonomachi, Matsue-shi, Shimane-ken 690, Japan. Document type: government publication.

SHIN GIJUTSU HAPPYO GAIYO/ABSTRACTS OF MEETING ON THERMAL AND NUCLEAR POWER ENGINEERING. see *ENERGY — Abstracting, Bibliographies, Statistics*

621.48 628 JA ISSN 0912-1838
SHIZUOKA GENSHIRYOKU DAYORI. (Text in Japanese) q. Shizuokaken Genshiryoku Hatsudenjo Kankyo Anzen Kyogikai - Nuclear Power Plant Environmental Association of Shizuoka Prefecture, Shizuokaken Seikatsu Kankyobu, 9-6, Ote-machi, Shizuoka-shi, Shizuoka-ken 420, Japan.

621.48 JA ISSN 0289-9833
SHOGAIKOKU NI OKERU GENSHIRYOKU HATSUDEN KAIHATSU NO DOKO/TRENDS OF NUCLEAR POWER GENERATION IN FOREIGN COUNTRIES. (Text in Japanese) m. Nihon Genshiryoku Sangyo Kaigi - Japan Atomic Industrial Forum, 1-13, Shinbashi 1-chome, Minato-ku, Tokyo 105, Japan.

621.48 SP ISSN 0214-1159
CODEN: RSESEJ
SOCIEDAD NUCLEAR ESPANOLA. REVISTA. 1982. 11/yr. $173 in Europe; America $215 (effective 1993). Sociedad Nuclear Espanola, Isla de Saipan 47, 28035 Madrid, Spain. TEL 1-37-34-750. FAX 1-316-91-77. Ed. Matilde Pelegri Torres. adv. circ. 3,000.
—BLDSC (7833.150000); CASDDS.

SOCIETA ITALIANA DI FISICA. NUOVO CIMENTO A; nuclei, particles and fields. see *PHYSICS*

SOLID STATE PHENOMENA. see *METALLURGY*

621.48 US
SPENT FUEL MANAGEMENT SEMINAR PROCEEDINGS. 1984. a. $200. Institute of Nuclear Materials Management, Inc., 60 Revere Dr., Ste. 500, Northbrook, IL 60062. TEL 708-480-9573. Ed. Barbara Scott. circ. 150. (looseleaf format; back issues avail.) Document type: proceedings.
Formerly: Spent Fuel Storage Seminar (Proceedings).
Description: Developments in dry storage technology, consolidation, transportation, instructional issues, and technical issues.

621.48 GW
STRAHLENKOMMISSION. VEROEFFENTLICHUNGEN. irreg. (Bundesminister fuer Umwelt, Naturschutz und Reaktorsicherheit) Gustav Fischer Verlag, Wollgrasweg 49, 70599 Stuttgart, Germany. TEL 0711-4580030. FAX 0711-4580334. TELEX 7111488-FIBUCH. (Subscr. to: Postfach 720143, 70577 Stuttgart, Germany) Document type: corporate report.

621.48 SW
SWEDISH NUCLEAR NEWS. (Text in English) 1975. m. free. (Swedish Atomic Forum) O K G Aktiebolag, Simpevarp, S-570 93 Figeholm, Sweden. FAX 0491-86920. Ed. Jan Petrini. adv.; bk.rev. circ. 1,200.

539.7 621.48 US
SYMPOSIUM ON FUSION ENGINEERING. PROCEEDINGS. 1965. biennial. price varies. Institute of Electrical and Electronics Engineers, Inc., 345 E. 47th St., New York, NY 10017-2394. TEL 212-705-7900. FAX 212-705-7682. (Subscr. to: Box 1331, 445 Hoes Lane, Piscataway, NJ 08855-1331) Indexed: Chem.Abstr. Document type: proceedings.
Formerly (until 1983): Symposium on Engineering Problems of Fusion Research. Proceedings (ISSN 0145-5958)
Refereed Serial

621.48 628 JA
TAKAHAMA GENSHIRYOKU HATSUDENJO KANKYO HOSHANO KANSHI KEKKA HOKOKUSHO/TAKAHAMA ATOMIC POWER PLANT. ENVIRONMENT MONITORING REPORT. (Text in Japanese) q. Kyoto Prefectural Government, Yabunouchi-cho, Shimodachuri Dori Shinmachi Nishi Iru, Kamigyo-ku, Kyoto-shi, Kyoto 602, Japan. Document type: government publication.

621.48 JA
TECHNICAL PUBLICATIONS BY J A E R I STAFF. (Text in English) a. Japan Atomic Energy Research Institute, Tokai Research Establishment - Nihon Genshiryoku Kenkyo Tokai Kenkyujo Gijutsu Johobu, Tokaimura, Naka-gun, Ibaraki-ken 319-11, Japan.

TEHNIKA. see *ENGINEERING*

TEXAS PUBLIC UTILITY NEWS. see *ENERGY*

621.48 AT ISSN 1030-5467
THIRD OPINION. 1977. q. Aus.$15($12) to individuals; institutions Aus.$25. Movement Against Uranium Mining (N.S.W.), P.O. Box K133, Haymarket, N.S.W. 2000, Australia. TEL 61-02-2814538. FAX 61-02-2815216. Ed.Bd. circ. 600. (back issues avail.)
Description: Reports on the nuclear fuel cycle, strong emphasis on environment, health, safety, economics, alternative energy, energy efficiency and conservation.

621.48 JA ISSN 0916-3328
TOKYO DAIGAKU AISOTOPU SOGO SENTA NYUSU/UNIVERSITY OF TOKYO. RADIOISOTOPE CENTER. NEWS. (Text in Japanese) 1970. q. Tokyo Daigaku, Aisotopu Sogo Senta, 11-16, Yayoi 2-chome, Bunkyo-ku, Tokyo 113, Japan.

621.48 JA ISSN 0916-152X
TOKYO DAIGAKU GENSHIRYOKU KENKYU SOGO SENTA NYUSU/UNIVERSITY OF TOKYO. RESEARCH CENTER FOR NUCLEAR SCIENCE AND TECHNOLOGY. NEWS. (Text in Japanese) 1973. 3/yr. Tokyo Daigaku, Genshiryoku Kenkyu Sogo Senta, 11-16, Yayoi 2-chome, Bunkyo-ku, Tokyo 113, Japan.

621.48 JA ISSN 0563-8488
TOKYO TORITSU AISOTOPU SOGO KENKYUJO NENPO/TOKYO METROPOLITAN ISOTOPE RESEARCH CENTER. ANNUAL REPORT. (Text in Japanese) 1962. a. Tokyo Toritsu Aisotopu Sogo Kenkyujo, 11-1, Fukazawa 2-chome, Setagaya-ku, Tokyo 158, Japan. Indexed: INIS Atomind.

621.48 JA ISSN 0289-9906
CODEN: TRCRDK
TRACER. (Text in Japanese) 1978. a. Nagoya University, Radioisotope Center - Nagoya Daigaku Aisotopu Sogo Senta, Furo-cho, Chikusa-ku, Nagoya-shi, Aichi-ken 464, Japan. Indexed: Chem.Abstr.
—CASDDS.

621.48 TU ISSN 0254-5446
CODEN: TJNSDM
TURKISH JOURNAL OF NUCLEAR SCIENCES. (Text in English, summaries in English, Turkish) 1974. s-a. $10. Turkiye Atom Enerjise Kurumu - T E A K - Turkish Atomic Energy Authority, Alacam Sokak. No. 9, 06690 Cankaya, Ankara, Turkey. TEL 4270139. FAX 4272834. TELEX ATOMTR 46459. Eds. Yalcin Sanalan, Resat Ozkan. abstr. Indexed: Energy Info.Abstr. Document type: academic/scholarly publication.
—CASDDS.
Formerly (until 1981): Turkish Atomic Energy Authority. Technical Journal.
Description: Publishes original research conducted at Turkish Atomic Energy Authority laboratories, and relevant contributions from scientists in other countries.
Refereed Serial

333.792 US
U D I MONTHLY OPERATING REPORT FOR NUCLEAR POWER PLANTS. 1991. m. $120. Utility Data Institute (Subsidiary of: McGraw Hill), 1200 G St., N.W., Ste. 250, Washington, DC 20005. TEL 202-942-8788; 800-486-3660. FAX 202-942-8789. Document type: trade publication.
Description: Includes monthly, year-to-date, and lifetime information for nuclear power plant hours of criticality, hours online, gross and net generation, availablity, capacity factor, and forced outage derived from N.R.C. data.

333.79 US
U S NUCLEAR PLANT STATISTICS. 1985. a. $225. Utility Data Institute (Subsidiary of: McGraw-Hill), 1200 G St., N.W., Ste. 250, Washington, DC 20005. TEL 202-942-8788; 800-486-3660. FAX 202-942-8789. Document type: trade publication.
Description: Provides a variety of data for U.S. nuclear plants currently operating, under construction, or cancelled.

539 621.48 UK ISSN 0082-7940
UNITED KINGDOM ATOMIC ENERGY AUTHORITY. ANNUAL REPORT. 1954. a. price varies. H.M.S.O., P.O.B. 276, London SW8 5DT, England. (reprint service avail. from UMI) Document type: government publication.

UNITED NATIONS DISARMAMENT YEARBOOK. see *MILITARY*

UNITED NATIONS ECONOMIC AND SOCIAL COUNCIL. DISARMAMENT STUDY SERIES. see *MILITARY*

621.48 US
U.S. NUCLEAR ENERGY INSTITUTE. NUCLEAR ENERGY INFO. 1975. m. membership. Nuclear Energy Institute, 1776 Eye St., N.W., Ste. 400, Washington, DC 20006-3708. TEL 202-739-8000. Ed. Leslie Lamkin. Document type: trade publication.
Description: Promotes constructive nuclear energy usage.

ENERGY — SOLAR ENERGY

539.7 621.48   US
U.S. NUCLEAR REGULATORY COMMISSION. CONSTRUCTION STATUS REPORT OF NUCLEAR POWER PLANTS. (Also called the Yellow Book) m. $100. U.S. Nuclear Regulatory Commission, 1717 H St., N.W., Washington, DC 20555. TEL 202-492-7000. (Dist. by: National Technical Information Service, Springfield, VA 22161)

333.792   US
U.S. NUCLEAR REGULATORY COMMISSION. INFORMATION REPORT ON STATE LEGISLATION. m. $25. U.S. Nuclear Regulatory Commission, Office of Public Affairs, Washington, DC 20555. TEL 202-492-7000. (Dist. by: Supt. of Documents, Washington, DC 20402)

539.7 621.48   US   ISSN 0278-3487
TK1343
U.S. NUCLEAR REGULATORY COMMISSION. LICENSED OPERATING REACTORS, STATUS SUMMARY REPORT. (Also called the Gray Book) m. $100. U.S. Nuclear Regulatory Commission, 1717 H St., N.W., Washington, DC 20555. TEL 202-492-7000. (Dist. by: NTIS, 5285 Port Royal Rd., Springfield, VA 22161) stat. (also avail. in microfiche from CIS; reprint service avail. from CIS) **Indexed:** Amer.Stat.Ind. (1975-).
Formerly (until 1981): U.S. Nuclear Regulatory Commission. Operating Units Status Report: Licensed Operating Reactors (ISSN 0193-7219)

621.48   US
U.S. NUCLEAR REGULATORY COMMISSION. POWER REACTOR EVENTS. bi-m. $9.50. U.S. Nuclear Regulatory Commission, Office of Public Affairs, 1717 H St., N.W., Washington, DC 20555. TEL 202-492-7000. (Dist. by: Supt. of Documents, Washington, DC 20402)

621.48   US
U.S. NUCLEAR REGULATORY COMMISSION. PROGRAM SUMMARY REPORT. vol.2, 1978. m. $100. U.S. Nuclear Regulatory Commission, 1717 H St., N.W., Washington, DC 20555. TEL 202-492-7000. (Dist. by: NTIS, Springfield, VA 22161)

621.48   US
U.S. NUCLEAR REGULATORY COMMISSION. PUBLICATIONS. 1978. m. U.S. Nuclear Regulatory Commission, Washington, DC 20555. TEL 202-492-7000. **Indexed:** Pollut.Abstr.

621.48   US
U.S. NUCLEAR REGULATORY COMMISSION. REPORT TO CONGRESS ON ABNORMAL OCCURRENCES. q. $11. U.S. Nuclear Regulatory Commission, 1717 H St., N.W., Washington, DC 20555. TEL 202-492-7000. (Dist. by: Supt. of Documents, Washington, DC 20402) **Indexed:** Geo.Abstr.

U.S. NUCLEAR REGULATORY COMMISSION. TITLE LIST OF DOCUMENTS MADE PUBLICLY AVAILABLE. see ENERGY — Abstracting, Bibliographies, Statistics

621.48   US
U.S. NUCLEAR REGULATORY COMMISSION. WATER REACTOR SAFETY RESEARCH INFORMATION MEETING. PROCEEDINGS. irreg., vol.4, 1984. U.S. Nuclear Regulatory Commission, Office of Nuclear Regulatory Research, Washington, DC 20555. TEL 301-492-7000. circ. 3,000. **Document type:** government publication, proceedings.

621.48   US
U.S. NUCLEAR REGULATORY COMMISSION. WEEKLY INFORMATION REPORT. w. $100. U.S. Nuclear Regulatory Commission, 1717 H St., N.W., Washington, DC 20555. TEL 202-492-7000. (Dist. by: Supt. of Documents, Washington, DC 20402) **Document type:** government publication.

621.48   CN   ISSN 1193-9796
UNIVERSITY OF ALBERTA. CENTRE FOR SUBATOMIC RESEARCH. PROGRESS REPORT. 1969. biennial. free. University of Alberta, Centre for Subatomic Research, Edmonton, AB T6G 2N5, Canada. TEL 403-492-3637. FAX 403-492-3408. circ. 300. (back issues avail.)
Formerly: University of Alberta. Nuclear Research Centre. Progress Report.

URANIUM: RESOURCES, PRODUCTION AND DEMAND/URANIUM: RESSOURCES, PRODUCTION ET DEMANDE. see MINES AND MINING INDUSTRY

VITAL SIGNS (CAMBRIDGE). see PUBLIC HEALTH AND SAFETY

539.7   MY   ISSN 0127-6948
WARTA NUKLEAR MALAYSIA/NUCLEAR BULLETIN OF MALAYSIA. (Text in English, Malay) 1984. q. Ministry of Science, Technology and the Environment, Nuclear Energy Unit - Kementerian Sains, Teknologi Dan Alam Sekitar, Unit Tenaga Nuklear, Ketua Pengarah, Kompleks Puspati, Bangi, 43000 Kajang, Malaysia. TEL 03-8250510. FAX 03-8258262. TELEX ATOMAL MA 31619. Ed. Muhamat Omar. **Document type:** government publication.
—BLDSC (9261.875700).

WASTE MANAGEMENT; industrial - radioactive - hazardous. see ENVIRONMENTAL STUDIES — Waste Management

333.792   UK
WORLD ENERGY AND NUCLEAR DIRECTORY (YEAR). 1981. irreg., 2nd ed., 1993. £250. Longman Group UK Ltd., Westgate House, 6th Fl., The High, Harlow, Essex CM20 1YR, England. TEL 0279-442601. FAX 0279-444501. (Dist. in U.S. and Canada by: Gale Research Inc., 835 Penobscot Bldg., Detroit, MI 48226) **Document type:** directory.
●Also available on CD-ROM.
Formed by the merger of: World Energy Directory & World Nuclear Directory; Which was formerly: Nuclear Research Index.

621.37   US   ISSN 0891-4435
TK1078
WORLD NUCLEAR PERFORMANCE. 1985. m. $1190. McGraw-Hill, Inc., Energy & Business Newsletters, 1221 Ave. of the Americas, 36th Fl., New York, NY 10020. TEL 212-512-6410. (And: 1120 Vermont Ave. NW, Ste. 1200, Washington, DC 20005. TEL 202-462-1611) Ed. Margaret Ryan. (back issues avail.; reprint service avail. from UMI)
●Also available online.
Description: Gives plant statistics.

WORLDWIDE REPORT: NUCLEAR DEVELOPMENTS. see MILITARY

338.4   US
WORLDWIDE URANIUM PRODUCER PROFILES. 1973; N.S. 1977. a. $3500. Nuclear Assurance Corporation, 655 Engineering Dr., Ste. 200, Norcross, GA 30092-2843. TEL 404-447-1144. FAX 404-447-1797.
Formerly: Nuclear Industry Status (ISSN 0092-9751)

621.48   CC   ISSN 1000-6931
CODEN: YKJIEZ
YUANZINENG KEXUE JISHU/SCIENCE AND TECHNOLOGY OF NUCLEAR ENERGY. (Text in Chinese) bi-m. Zhongguo Yuanzineng Kexue Yanjiuyuan - Chinese Science Academy of Nuclear Energy, 43 Fucheng Lu, Beijing 100037, People's Republic of China. TEL 8417733. Ed. Sun Zuxun.
—BLDSC (1770.250000); CASDDS.

333.792 630   CC   ISSN 0253-3596
CODEN: YTNYDT
YUANZINENG NONGYE YINGYONG/APPLICATIONS OF ATOMIC ENERGY IN AGRICULTURE. (Text in Chinese) q. $1.30 per no. Yuanzineng Chubanshe - Atomic Energy Press, 43 Fucheng Rd., Haidian District, Beijing 100037, People's Republic of China. (Dist. by: China International Book Trading Corp., P.O. Box 339, Beijing, P.R. China) **Indexed:** Chem.Abstr.

ENERGY — Solar Energy

621.47   US
A S M E SOLAR ENERGY CONFERENCE. PROCEEDINGS. a., 8th ed., 1986. $85. American Society of Mechanical Engineers, 345 E. 47th St., New York, NY 10017. TEL 212-705-7703. **Document type:** proceedings.

621.47   US   ISSN 0731-8618
TJ809
ADVANCES IN SOLAR ENERGY: AN ANNUAL REVIEW OF RESEARCH AND DEVELOPMENT. 1982. a., vol.6, 1990. price varies. (American Solar Energy Society, Inc.) Plenum Publishing Corp., 233 Spring St., New York, NY 10013-1578. TEL 212-620-8000. FAX 212-463-0742. TELEX 23-421139. Eds. K.W. Boer, J. Duffie. **Indexed:** Biol.Abstr., Energy Info.Abstr., Energy Rev. **Document type:** monographic series.
—BLDSC (0711.415000); Faxon.
Refereed Serial

621.47   US
AMERICAN SOLAR ENERGY SOCIETY. PASSIVE CONFERENCE. ANNUAL MEETING. a., latest 1992, Coco Beach, Fl. American Solar Energy Society, Inc., 2400 Central Ave., No. G-1, Boulder, CO 80301-2843. TEL 303-443-3130. Eds. M. Coleman, S.M. Burley. **Indexed:** Energy Info.Abstr., Eng.Ind.
—BLDSC (6848.093300). CCC.
Former titles: Progress in Passive Solar Energy Systems (ISSN 0731-8626); Incorporates and continues numbering of: National Passive Solar Conference. Proceedings. (ISSN 0161-7443)

621.47   US   ISSN 0894-8461
AMERICAN SOLAR ENERGY SOCIETY. PROCEEDINGS OF THE ANNUAL MEETING. 1976. a., latest 1992, Coco Beach, FL. American Solar Energy Society, Inc., 2400 Central Ave., No.G-1, Boulder, CO 80301-2843. TEL 303-443-3130. Eds. M. Coleman, S.M. Burley. **Indexed:** AESIS, Energy Info.Abstr., Eng.Ind. **Document type:** proceedings.
—CCC.
Former titles (until 1984): Progress in Solar Energy (ISSN 0731-860X); (until July, 1982): International Solar Energy Society. American Section. Annual Meeting. Proceedings (ISSN 0146-4566)

621.47   US   ISSN 0003-701X
TJ810   CODEN: ASOEA6
APPLIED SOLAR ENERGY. English translation of: Geliotekhnika (UZ ISSN 0130-0997) 1965. bi-m. $865. (Uzbek Academy of Sciences, UZ) Allerton Press, Inc., 150 Fifth Ave., New York, NY 10011. TEL 212-924-3950. FAX 212-463-9684. bk.rev.; abstr.; charts; illus.; index. **Indexed:** Appl.Mech.Rev., Energy Rev., Eng.Ind., Environ.Per.Bibl., Excerp.Med., Fuel & Energy Abstr., INIS Atomind., Sci.Abstr. **Document type:** academic/scholarly publication.
—BLDSC (0404.755000); Faxon; UnCover; SWETS. CCC.
Refereed Serial

621.47 380.1   AT
AUSTRALASIAN SOLAR INDEX AND BUYERS GUIDE. 1979. a. Aus.$25. Australian Syndicators Pty Ltd., PO Box 45, South Yarra, Vic. 3141, Australia.

C A SELECTS. SOLAR ENERGY. see ENERGY — Abstracting, Bibliographies, Statistics

621.47 690   US
CONSERVATION AND RENEWABLE ENERGY TECHNOLOGIES FOR BUILDING TECHNOLOGIES. a. free to qualified personnel. (U.S. Department of Energy, Conservation and Renewable Energy Office) Solar Energy Research Institute, Technical Inquiry Service, 1617 Cole Blvd., Golden, CO 80401-3393. TEL 303-231-1000. circ. controlled.
Formerly (until 1991): Solar Buildings Program Summary.

CONSERVATION AND RENEWABLE ENERGY TECHNOLOGIES FOR UTILITY TECHNOLOGIES. see ENERGY

ENERGIE SPEKTRUM; Magazin fuer Energiemanagement. see ENERGY

621.47   SP
ERA SOLAR. 6/yr. Costa Rica 13, 4o, Apdo. 19295, 28016 Madrid, Spain. TEL 1-250-58-85.

333.792   US
HELIO. 1976. q. $15 includes membership. Rhode Island Solar Energy Association, 42 Tremont St., Cranston, RI 02920-2543. TEL 401-942-6691. Ed. Domenic Bucci. adv.; bk.rev. circ. 350. **Document type:** newsletter.
Description: Includes articles and news relating to solar energy and related environmental issues, new member listings, board activities and a calendar of upcoming events.

INTERNATIONAL JOURNAL OF AMBIENT ENERGY. see *ENERGY*

621.47 US ISSN 0142-5919
TJ810 CODEN: IJSEEL
INTERNATIONAL JOURNAL OF SOLAR ENERGY. 1982. 8/yr. (in 2 vols., 4 nos./vol.). 127 ECU per vol. (effective 1993). Harwood Academic Publishers, 820 Town Center Dr., Langhorne, PA 19047. TEL 215-750-2642. FAX 215-750-6343. (UK subscr. to: P.O. Box 90, Reading, Berkshire RG1 8JL, England. TEL 0734-560-080) Ed. Wolfgang Palz. adv.; bk.rev.; abstr.; index. (also avail. in microfilm; back issues avail.) **Indexed:** Chem.Abstr., Energy Ind., Energy Info.Abstr., Environ.Per.Bibl. (1991-), Int.Aerosp.Abstr., Int.Build.Serv.Abstr., Sci.Abstr.
—BLDSC (4542.596000); El; Faxon; UnCover; SWETS; CASDDS. **CCC.**
Description: Covers biomass, wave generators and wave power. Examines experimental, theoretical, and applied results concerning science and engineering of solar energy.
Refereed Serial

333.792 US ISSN 1045-6325
INTERNATIONAL SOLAR ENERGY INTELLIGENCE REPORT. 1975. bi-w. $390 (effective Sep. 1992). Business Publishers, Inc., 951 Pershing Dr., Silver Spring, MD 20910-4464. TEL 301-587-6300. FAX 301-585-9075. Ed. Teki Fabian. bk.rev.; bibl. (looseleaf format) **Indexed:** Energy Info.Abstr., J.of Ferroc., PROMT. **Document type:** newsletter.
●Also available online. Vendor(s): Data-Star, DIALOG Information Services, Inc., NewsNet.
—SWETS. **CCC.**
Former titles: Solar Energy Washington Letter; Solar Outlook; Practical Solar; Solar Energy Digest (ISSN 0193-5399); Solar Energy Intelligence Report (ISSN 0148-4095); Incorporates: World Solar Markets (ISSN 0144-431X).
Description: Covers developments that affect the domestic and international market for renewable energy technologies.

621.47 US ISSN 0199-6231
TJ810 CODEN: JSEEDO
JOURNAL OF SOLAR ENERGY ENGINEERING. 1980. q. $100 to non-members; members $29. American Society of Mechanical Engineers, 345 E. 47th St., New York, NY 10017. TEL 212-705-7722. Ed. Frank Kreith. (also avail. in microform from UMI; reprint service avail. from UMI) **Indexed:** A.S.& T.Ind., Appl.Mech.Rev., Chem.Abstr., Chem.Eng.Abstr., Curr.Cont., Energy Info.Abstr., Fluidex, Ind.Sci.Rev., INIS Atomind., PROMT, Sci.Abstr., T.C.E.A.
—BLDSC (8897.060000); El; Faxon; UnCover; SWETS; UMI; CASDDS. **CCC.**
Refereed Serial

621.47 IQ ISSN 0256-7911
CODEN: JSEREU
JOURNAL OF SOLAR ENERGY RESEARCH. (Text in Arabic, English) 1983. s-a. ID.5($15) to individuals; institutions $50. Scientific Research Center, Solar Energy Research Council, Jadiriyah P.O. Box 13026, Baghdad, Iraq. TELEX 213976 SRC IK. Ed. Nidhal I. Al-Hamdani. circ. 500. **Indexed:** Chem.Abstr., Eng.Ind.
—BLDSC (5065.100000); CASDDS.

621.4 JA ISSN 0387-1029
KARYOKU GENSHIRYOKU HATSUDEN/THERMAL AND NUCLEAR POWER. (Text in Japanese) 1950. m. 1240 Yen per no. Karyoku Genshiryoku Hatsuden Gijutsu Kyokai - Thermal and Nuclear Power Engineering Society of Japan, 23-11, Toranomon 1-chome, Minato-ku, Tokyo 105, Japan. TEL 03-3592-0380. FAX 03-3592-0335. **Indexed:** INIS Atomind.

621.47 US
N R E L IN-REVIEW. 1978. q. free to qualified personnel. (U.S. Department of Energy) National Renewable Energy Laboratory, 1617 Cole Blvd., Golden, CO 80401-3393. TEL 303-231-1000. Ed. Linda Brown. circ. 7,600 (controlled). **Indexed:** Energy Rev.
Former titles: S E R I Science and Technology in Review; In Review.

621.47 333.792 US ISSN 0739-4829
P V NEWS. 1981. m. $100 (foreign $120). P V Energy Systems, Box 290, Casanova, VA 22017. TEL 703-788-9626. Ed. Paul D. Maycock. **Document type:** newsletter.
Description: Covers all aspects of photovoltaic solar energy conversion.

PHOTOVALTIC ENERGY. see *ENERGY — Abstracting, Bibliographies, Statistics*

PHOTOVOLTAIC ENERGY ABSTRACTS. see *ENERGY — Abstracting, Bibliographies, Statistics*

R E R I C NEWS. (Regional Energy Resources Information Center) see *ENERGY*

RENEW NEWSLETTER. see *ENERGY*

621.47 US
RENEWABLE ENERGY MANUFACTURERS LISTS: SOLAR ENERGY. a. $6. Synerjy, Box 1854, Cathedral Sta., New York, NY 10025. index. (also avail. in diskette format)
Description: Lists manufacturers and distributors of heating and cooling systems, collectors, sunspaces, photovoltaic cells and equipment. Organized by subject and geographic area.

621.47 II ISSN 0970-2466
TJ809
S E S I JOURNAL. (Text in English) 1987. s-a. Rs.150 (foreign $24). (Solar Energy Society of India) Tata Energy Research Institute, 9 Jor Bagh, New Delhi 110 003, India. TEL 462-3983. FAX 91-11-4621770. TELEX 31-61593 TERI IN. Ed. Veena Joshi. adv. contact: Beena Yenon. circ. 700. **Document type:** academic/scholarly publication.
—El.
Description: Covers all aspects of renewable energy.

621.47 US
S.U.N.. (Solar Utilization News) 1974. q. $175. Solar Utilization Network, 121 Chestnut St., Philadelphia, PA 19106. Ed. Joseph H. Ball. (tabloid format)

SHIN GIJUTSU HAPPYO GAIYO/ABSTRACTS OF MEETING ON THERMAL AND NUCLEAR POWER ENGINEERING. see *ENERGY — Abstracting, Bibliographies, Statistics*

621.47 US
SOLAR BEAT.* 12/yr. $5. Rte. 8, Box 31, Crossville, TN 38555. Ed. Louis Gorenflo.

SOLAR BUILDINGS TECHNOLOGY. see *ENERGY — Abstracting, Bibliographies, Statistics*

621.47 US ISSN 0197-2030
SOLAR COLLECTOR MANUFACTURING ACTIVITY. a., latest 1989. $4. U.S. Department of Energy, Energy Information Administration, National Energy Information Center, El-231, Rm. 1F-048, Forrestal Bldg., 1000 Independence Ave., S.W., Washington, DC 20585. TEL 202-586-8800. **Document type:** government publication.
Formerly: Solar Collector Manufacturing Activity and Applications in the Residential Sector.

621.47 UK ISSN 0038-092X
TJ810
SOLAR ENERGY; international journal for scientists, engineers and technologists in solar energy and its application. 1957. 12/yr. £390($600) (effective 1994). (International Solar Energy Society) Elsevier Science Ltd., Pergamon, P.O. Box 800, Kidlington, Oxford OX5 1DX, England. TEL 44-865-843000. FAX 44-865-343010. (Subscr. in U.S. and Canada to: Elsevier Science, 660 White Plains Rd., Tarrytown, NY 10591-5153. TEL 914-524-9200. FAX 914-333-2444) Ed. John Duffie. adv.; bk.rev.; abstr.; bibl.; charts; illus. circ. 13,000. (also avail. in microfiche from MIM; microfilm from UMI; back issues avail.) **Indexed:** A.S.& T.Ind., Agri.Eng.Abstr., AIT Reports, Appl.Mech.Rev., ASCA, Biol.Abstr., Chem.Abstr., Curr.Adv.Ecol.Sci., Curr.Cont., Deep Sea Res.& Oceanogr.Abstr., Energy Info.Abstr., Energy Rev., Eng.Ind., Environ.Per.Bibl. (1990-), Excerp.Med., Fuel & Energy Abstr., Meteor.& Geoastrophys.Abstr., Risk Abstr., Sci.Abstr. **Document type:** academic/scholarly publication.
—BLDSC (8327.200000); El; Faxon; UnCover; SWETS; UMI; CASDDS. **CCC.**
Description: Covers all aspects of solar energy, including technical, economic, environmental, social and legal issues.
Refereed Serial

621.47 NE ISSN 0927-0248
TJ812.7 CODEN: SEMCEQ
SOLAR ENERGY MATERIALS AND SOLAR CELLS; an international journal devoted to the material science aspects of photovoltaic, photothermal, and photochemical solar energy conversion. (Text in English) 1979. 16/yr. (in 4 vols.; 4 nos./vol.). fl.1444($781) (effective 1994). Elsevier Science B.V., P.O. Box 211, 1000 AE Amsterdam, Netherlands. TEL 31-20-5803911. FAX 31-20-5803598. TELEX 18582 ESPA NL. (Subscr. in U.S. and Canada to: Elsevier Science Inc., Box 882, Madison Sq. Sta., New York, NY 10159. TEL 212-989-5800. FAX 212-633-3990) Ed. C.M. Lampert. cum.index: vols. 1-10. (also avail. in microform from UMI; back issues avail.) **Indexed:** AESIS, ASCA, Chem.Abstr., Curr.Cont., Energy Ind., Energy Info.Abstr., Energy Rev., Eng.Ind., Environ.Abstr., Environ.Per.Bibl. (1981-), Excerp.Med., Int.Aerosp.Abstr., Met.Abstr., Phys.Ber., Sci.Abstr., World Alum.Abstr. **Document type:** academic/scholarly publication.
—BLDSC (8327.201053); El; Faxon; UnCover; SWETS; CASDDS. **CCC.**
Formerly (until 1992): Solar Energy Materials (ISSN 0165-1633); Incorporates (1979-1991): Solar Cells (ISSN 0379-6787)
Refereed Serial

621.47 NE ISSN 0167-9252
SOLAR ENERGY RESEARCH AND DEVELOPMENT IN THE EUROPEAN COMMUNITY. SERIES. A. SOLAR ENERGY APPLICATIONS TO DWELLINGS. 1982. irrege. price varies. (Commission of the European Communities, Directorate-General Information Marketing and Innovation, El) Kluwer Academic Publishers, Postbus 17, 3300 AA Dordrecht, Netherlands. TEL 31-78-334911. FAX 31-78-334254. TELEX 29245 KAPG NL (Dist. by: Kluwer Academic Publishers Group P.O. Box 322, 3300 AH Dordrecht, Netherlands. TEL 31-78-524400. FAX 31-78-524474; N. America dist. addr.: Box 358, Accord Sta., Hingham, MA 02018-0358. TEL 617-871-6600. FAX 617-871-6528) **Document type:** monographic series.
Refereed Serial

621.47 NE ISSN 0924-4727
SOLAR ENERGY RESEARCH AND DEVELOPMENT IN THE EUROPEAN COMMUNITY. SERIES B: THERMO-MECHANICAL SOLAR POWER PLANTS. 1983. irreg. price varies. (Commission of the European Communities, Directorate-General Information Marketing and Innovation, El) Kluwer Academic Publishers, Postbus 17, 3300 AA Dordrecht, Netherlands. TEL 31-78-334911. FAX 31-78-334254. TELEX 29245 KAPG NL. (Dist. by: Kluwer Academic Publishers Group, P.O. Box 322, 3300 AH Dordrecht, Netherlands. TEL 31-78-524400. FAX 31-78-524474; N. America dist. addr.: Box 358, Accord Sta., Hingham, MA 02018-0358. TEL 617-871-6600. FAX 617-871-6528) **Document type:** monographic series.
Refereed Serial

ENERGY — SOLAR ENERGY

621.47 NE ISSN 0924-4735
SOLAR ENERGY RESEARCH AND DEVELOPMENT IN THE EUROPEAN COMMUNITY. SERIES C. PHOTOVOLTAIC POWER GENERATION. 1982. irreg. price varies. (Commission of the European Communities, Directorate-General Information Marketing and Innovation, EI) Kluwer Academic Publishers, Postbus 17, 3300 AA Dordrecht, Netherlands. TEL 31-78-334911. FAX 31-78-334254. TELEX 29245 KAPG NL. (Dist. by: Kluwer Academic Publishers Group, P.O. Box 322, 3300 AH Dordrecht, Netherlands. TEL 31-78-524400. FAX 31-78-524474; N. America dist. addr.: Box 358, Accord Sta., Hingham, MA 02018-0358. TEL 617-871-6600. FAX 617-871-6528) **Document type:** monographic series.
Refereed Serial

621.47 NE ISSN 0167-7950
CODEN: SRDDD6
SOLAR ENERGY RESEARCH AND DEVELOPMENT IN THE EUROPEAN COMMUNITY. SERIES D. PHOTOCHEMICAL, PHOTOELECTROCHEMICAL AND PHOTOBIOLOGICAL PROCESSES. 1982. irreg. price varies. (Commission of the European Communities, Directorate-General Information Marketing and Innovation, EI) Kluwer Academic Publishers, Postbus 17, 3300 AA Dordrecht, Netherlands. TEL 31-78-334911. FAX 31-78-334254. TELEX 29245 KAPG NL. (Dist. by: Kluwer Academic Publishers Group, P.O. Box 322, 3300 AH Dordrecht, Netherlands. TEL 31-78-524400. FAX 31-78-524474; N. America dist. addr.: Box 358, Accord Sta., Hingham, MA 02018-0358. TEL 617-871-6600. FAX 617-871-6528) **Indexed:** Chem.Abstr. **Document type:** monographic series.
—CASDDS.
Refereed Serial

621.47 NE ISSN 0167-5494
SOLAR ENERGY RESEARCH AND DEVELOPMENT IN THE EUROPEAN COMMUNITY. SERIES E. ENERGY FROM BIOMASS. 1981. irreg. price varies. (Commission of the European Communities, Directorate-General Information Marketing and Innovation, EI) Kluwer Academic Publishers, Postbus 17, 3300 AA Dordrecht, Netherlands. TEL 31-78-334911. FAX 31-78-334254. TELEX 29245 KAPG NL. (Dist. by: Kluwer Academic Publishers Group, P.O. Box 322, 3300 AH Dordrecht, Netherlands. TEL 31-78-524400. FAX 31-78-524474; N. America dist. addr.: Box 358, Accord Sta., Hingham, MA 02018-0358. TEL 617-871-6600. FAX 617-871-6528) **Document type:** monographic series.
Refereed Serial

621.47 NE
SOLAR ENERGY RESEARCH AND DEVELOPMENT IN THE EUROPEAN COMMUNITY. SERIES F. SOLAR RADIATION DATA. 1982. irreg. price varies. (Commission of the European Communities, Directorate-General Information Marketing and Innovation, EI) Kluwer Academic Publishers, Postbus 17, 3300 AA Dordrecht, Netherlands. TEL 31-78-334911. FAX 31-78-334254. TELEX 29245 KAPG NL. (Dist. by: Kluwer Academic Publishers Group, P.O. Box 322, 3300 AH Dordrecht, Netherlands. TEL 31-78-524400. FAX 31-78-524474; N. America dist. addr.: Box 358, Accord Sta., Hingham, MA 02018-0358. TEL 617-871-6600. FAX 617-871-6528) **Document type:** monographic series.
Refereed Serial

SOLAR ENERGY RESEARCH AND DEVELOPMENT IN THE EUROPEAN COMMUNITY. SERIES G. WIND ENERGY.
see *ENERGY — Wind Energy*

621.47 630 NE ISSN 0259-8590
SOLAR ENERGY RESEARCH AND DEVELOPMENT IN THE EUROPEAN COMMUNITY. SERIES H. SOLAR ENERGY IN AGRICULTURE AND INDUSTRY. 1986. irreg. price varies. (Commission of the European Communities, Directorate-General Information Marketing and Innovation, EI) Kluwer Academic Publishers, Postbus 17, 3300 AA Dordrecht, Netherlands. TEL 31-78-334911. FAX 31-78-334254. TELEX 29245 KAPG NL. (Dist. by: Kluwer Academic Publishers Group, P.O. Box 322, 3300 AH Dordrecht, Netherlands. TEL 31-78-524400. FAX 31-78-524474; N. America dist. addr.: Box 358, Accord Sta., Hingham, MA 02018-0358. TEL 617-871-6600. FAX 617-871-6528) **Document type:** monographic series.
Refereed Serial

333.792 US ISSN 1065-321X
SOLAR ENERGY TODAY. 1980. a. $7. P V Network News, 2303 Cedros Cir., Santa Fe, NM 87505. TEL 505-473-1067. Ed. Paul Wilkins. **Document type:** newsletter.

621.47 US ISSN 0734-7472
SOLAR ENGINEERING. a. American Society of Mechanical Engineers, Solar Energy Division, 345 E. 47th St., New York, NY 10017. Ed. W.D. Turner. **Document type:** proceedings.
—CCC.

621.47 US ISSN 1050-5660
HD9681.U6 CODEN: SIJOE7
SOLAR INDUSTRY JOURNAL. 1974. q. $25 (foreign $37). Solar Energy Industries Association, 777 N. Capitol St. N.E., Ste.805, Washington, DC 20002. TEL 202-408-0660. FAX 202-408-8536. Ed. Linda Ladas. adv. circ. 4,000. **Indexed:** Energy Info.Abstr. **Document type:** trade publication.
Former titles (until 1990): Solar Energy Industries Association. (Year) Industry Journal; (until 1988): Solar Energy Industries Association. (Year) Solar Source Book.

621.47 340 US
SOLAR LAW. base vol. (plus a. supplement). $95. Shepard's - McGraw-Hill, Inc., Box 35300, Colorado Springs, CO 80935-3530. TEL 800-525-2474.
Description: Offers detailed examinations of legal issues now being resolved by the courts, including: solar easements, covenants, zoning, subdivision regulations and public and private nuisance issues.

621.47 US
SOLAR LETTER; the international newsletter on all aspects of renewable energy. 1991. bi-w. $360 (foreign $384). (Allan L. Frank Associates) A L F A Publishing, 9124 Bradford Rd., Silver Spring, MD 20901-4918. TEL 301-565-2532. FAX 301-565-3298. **Document type:** newsletter.
Description: Covers new developments and regulations in the field.

621.47 639.9 AT ISSN 0729-6436
SOLAR PROGRESS; renewable energy for Australasia. 1980. 4/yr. Aus.$50($32) Australian and New Zealand Solar Energy Society, P.O. Box 124, Caulfield East, Vic. 3145, Australia. TEL 03-571-7557. FAX 03-563-5173. Ed. Trevor Lee. adv.; bk.rev. circ. 2,500. (back issues avail.) **Document type:** trade publication.
Incorporates: South Wind.
Description: Reports on developments in renewable energy sources and energy conservation technologies throughout Australasia.

621.47 US ISSN 0741-5249
CODEN: STETD
SOLAR THERMAL ENERGY TECHNOLOGY; a current awareness bulletin. bi-m. $135. U.S. Department of Energy, Office of Scientific and Technical Information, Box 62, Oak Ridge, TN 37831. TEL 615-574-0733. (Subscr. to: National Technical Information Service, 5285 Port Royal Rd., Springfield, VA 22161. TEL 703-487-4630. FAX 703-321-8547) Ed. D. Lamar Cason. **Document type:** bulletin, government publication.
Description: Provides worldwide research and development information that would expand the technology base required for the advancement of solar thermal systems.

SOLAR THERMAL ENERGY TECHNOLOGY ABSTRACTS.
see *ENERGY — Abstracting, Bibliographies, Statistics*

621.47 US
SOLAR TIMES. 12/yr. $75. Sheldon Fredericks Adv., Inc., 655 Washington Blvd., Stamford, CT 06901-3793. TEL 203-324-0051. FAX 203-324-0520. Ed. Fred Schwartz. adv.; bk.rev. circ. 18,500. (tabloid format)

621.47 US ISSN 1042-0630
TJ809
SOLAR TODAY. 1987. bi-m. $25 (foreign $40). American Solar Energy Society, 2400 Central Ave., G-1, Boulder, CO 80301. TEL 303-443-3130. Ed. Maureen McIntyre. adv.; bk.rev. circ. 3,400. (back issues avail.) **Indexed:** Energy Info.Abstr. **Document type:** bulletin.
—BLDSC (8327.227300); Faxon; UnCover. **CCC.**
Formerly: A S E S News.
Description: Provides information in areas of solar energy for engineers, scientists, architects, educators, practitioners, researchers, and users. Includes actual case histories, as well as reviews of different technologies.

621.47 SZ
SOLARIA; Journal fuer Sonnenenergie, Solararchitektur und Alternativ-Energien. 1978. bi-m. 15 SFr. Keller und Co., Stapferstr. 27, 5200 Brugg, Switzerland. Ed. Pierre Sabady. adv.; illus.

333.792 SZ
SONNENENERGIE. 6/yr. Edisonstr. 22, CH-8050 Zurich, Switzerland. TEL 01-3120909. FAX 01-3120540. Ed. Othmar Humm. circ. 12,000.

621.47 GW ISSN 0172-5912
SONNENENERGIE UND WAERMETECHNIK; erste deutsche Zeitschrift fuer alle regenerativen Energiequellen und dezentrale Energieerzeugung. bi-m. DM.60. Bielefelder Verlagsanstalt GmbH & Co. KG, Niederwall 53, 33602 Bielefeld, Germany. circ. 11,000. **Document type:** bulletin.
Formerly: Sonnenenergie und Waermepumpe (ISSN 0172-5912)

SPACE POWER; resources, manufacturing and development. see *AERONAUTICS AND SPACE FLIGHT*

621.47 US
SUFFOLK COUNTY SOLAR ENERGY COMMISSION NEWSLETTER. m. Suffolk County Solar Energy Commission, H. Lee Dennison Bldg., 12th Fl., Veterans Memorial Hwy., Hauppauge, NY 11788. TEL 516-360-5111.

621.47 CI ISSN 0351-2797
SUNCEVA ENERGIJA/SOLAR ENERGY. (Text in Croatian; summaries in English) 1979. s-a. 500 din.($5) Hrvatsko Udruzenje za Suncevu Energiju - Croatian Solar Energy, Narodnog Ustanka 58, 51000 Rijeka, Croatia. TEL 38-51-32210. FAX 38-51-515-403. Ed. Bernard Frankovic. adv.; bk.rev. circ. 1,500. (back issues avail.)
Description: Studies solar energy and other renewable energy sources.

621.47 AT ISSN 0149-1938
TJ810 CODEN: SUNWDW
SUNWORLD.* 1976. q. $30 for individuals; institutions $40. International Solar Energy Society, c/o W.R. Read, Sec.Gen., 26 Railway Ave., P.O. Box 124, Caulfield East, Vic. 3145, Australia. TEL 505-471-0691. Ed. Debra D. Carroll. adv.; bk.rev.; charts; illus.; index. circ. 6,500. (also avail. in microform from UMI; back issues avail.) **Indexed:** Copper Abstr., Curr.Cont., Energy Ind., Energy Info.Abstr., Energy Rev., Eng.Ind., Environ.Per.Bibl.
—BLDSC (8533.830000); Faxon; UnCover; SWETS. **CCC.**

SYNERJY; a directory of renewable energy. see *ENERGY*

621.47 FR ISSN 0295-5873
SYSTEMES SOLAIRES. 1985. 11/yr. 405 F. (outside EC 540 F.). 45 rue de Richelieu, 75001 Paris, France. TEL 42-96-24-77. FAX 42-96-26-43. Ed. Y.-B. Civel. circ. 3,000.
Description: Covers scientific and industrial progress as well as applications of renewable energy

T I D E. (Teri Information Digest on Energy) see *ENERGY*

621.47 CC ISSN 0254-0096
TJ809 CODEN: TYNPDG
TAIYANG NENG XUEBAO/ACTA ENERGIAE SOLARIS SINICA. (Text in Chinese) q. $6.30 per no. (Taiyang Neng Xuehui - Solar Energy Society) Guoji Shudian, Qikan Bu, P.O. Box 399, Beijing 100044, People's Republic of China. **Indexed:** Chem.Abstr.
—CASDDS.

ENERGY — Wind Energy

621.4 US ISSN 0747-5500
A W E A WIND ENERGY WEEKLY. 1982. 50/yr. $450 (foreign $480). American Wind Energy Association, 122 C St., N.W., Ste. 400, Washington, DC 20001. TEL 202-408-8988. FAX 202-408-8536. TELEX 6502955124 MCI UW. Ed. Thomas O. Gray. adv.; index. circ. 400. (back issues avail.) Indexed: Energy Info.Abstr. **Document type:** newsletter.
Formerly: A W E A Update.

INTERNATIONAL JOURNAL OF AMBIENT ENERGY. see *ENERGY*

MOLENS/MILLS. see *CONSERVATION*

R E R I C NEWS. (Regional Energy Resources Information Center) see *ENERGY*

RENEW NEWSLETTER. see *ENERGY*

621.4 US
RENEWABLE ENERGY MANUFACTURERS LISTS: WIND AND HYDRO POWER. 1974. a. $5. Synerjy, Box 1854, Cathedral Sta., New York, NY 10025. index. (also avail. in diskette format)
Description: Covers wind and hydro power. Includes batteries, fuel cells and controls. Organized by subject and geographic area.

621.47 NE ISSN 0921-0938
SOLAR ENERGY RESEARCH AND DEVELOPMENT IN THE EUROPEAN COMMUNITY. SERIES G. WIND ENERGY. 1983. irreg. price varies. (Commission of the European Communities, Directorate-General Information Marketing and Innovation, EI) Kluwer Academic Publishers, Postbus 17, 3300 AA Dordrecht, Netherlands. TEL 31-78-334911. FAX 31-78-334254. TELEX 29245 KAPG NL. (Dist. by: Kluwer Academic Publishers Group, P.O. Box 322, 3300 AH Dordrecht, Netherlands. TEL 31-78-524400. FAX 31-78-524474; N. America dist. addr.: Box 358, Accord Station, Hingham, MA 02018-0358. TEL 617-871-6600. FAX 617-871-6528) **Document type:** monographic series.
Refereed Serial

STUDIES IN WIND ENGINEERING AND INDUSTRIAL ENGINEERING. see *ENGINEERING — Industrial Engineering*

SYNERJY; a directory of renewable energy. see *ENERGY*

T I D E. (Teri Information Digest on Energy) see *ENERGY*

333.9 UK ISSN 0260-504X
WIND AND WATER MILLS. 1980. a. £0.75 to non-members. Midland Wind and Water Mill Group, c/o John Bedington, 188 Merivale Rd., Smethwick, W. Midlands B66 4EA, England. illus.

333.9 GW ISSN 0720-3926
WIND - ENERGIE JAHRBUCH. 1970. a. DM.28($12) Wind - Energie Sekretariat, Gielsdorfer Str. 16, 53123 Bonn, Germany. Ed. Walter Schonball. adv.; bk.rev. circ. 1,200.

WIND ENERGY ABSTRACTS; the international wind power abstracts journal. see *ENERGY — Abstracting, Bibliographies, Statistics*

333.94 US ISSN 0886-2818
WIND ENERGY NEWS; international newsletter of wind power. 1987. m. $96. WindBooks, Inc., Box 4008, St. Johnsbury, VT 05819-4008. TEL 802-748-5148. FAX 802-748-3286. Ed. Farrell Smith Seiler. adv.; bk.rev. circ. 2,000. (looseleaf format) **Document type:** newsletter.
—CCC.
Description: Focuses on business, marketing and international policies of the windmill industry.

WIND ENERGY TECHNOLOGY. see *ENERGY — Abstracting, Bibliographies, Statistics*

621.4 UK ISSN 0309-524X
TA654.5 CODEN: WIENDM
WIND ENGINEERING. 1977. 6/yr. £132 (foreign £145). Multi-Science Publishing Co. Ltd., 107 High St., Brentwood, Essex CM14 4RX, England. TEL 0277-224632. FAX 0277-224632. (U.S. subscr. to: Box 176, Avenel, NJ 07001) Ed. E. Mowforth. abstr. Indexed: Energy Info.Abstr., Fluidex, Geo.Abstr., Int.Aerosp.Abstr., Meteor.& Geoastrophys.Abstr., Sci.Abstr. **Document type:** academic/scholarly publication.
—BLDSC (9319.177000); EI; Faxon; UnCover; SWETS. CCC.
Description: Covers all aspects of wind energy systems, including measurement methods and related economic and environmental topics.
Refereed Serial

WIND ENGINEERING ABSTRACTS. see *ENERGY — Abstracting, Bibliographies, Statistics*

333.9 US ISSN 0891-6403
WIND FARM PROJECT REPORT. 1986. a. $75. (California Energy Commission) WindBooks, Inc., Box 4008, St. Johnsbury, VT 05819. TEL 802-748-5148. FAX 802-748-3286. Ed. Farrell Smith Seiler. charts; illus.; stat. (looseleaf format; back issues avail.)
Description: Narrative and statistical data for more than 17,000 wind energy systems installed and operating in the U.S. and Canada.

333.9 GW
WINDKRAFT JOURNAL. 1980. q. DM.50. Verlag Natuerliche Energie GmbH, 24811 Brekendorf, Germany. TEL 04353-551. FAX 04353-796. Ed. Luise Junge. adv.; bk.rev. circ. 2,500. **Document type:** bulletin.

333.9 US ISSN 0736-7287
WINDMILLER'S GAZETTE; a journal for the preservation of America's wind power history & heritage. 1982. q. $12 (effective Jan. 1993). T. Linsday Baker, Ed. & Pub., Box 507, Rio Vista, TX 76093. adv.; bk.rev.; cum.index: 1982-1991. circ. 1,000. (back issues avail.) **Document type:** academic/scholarly publication, bibliography.
Description: Designed to inform about wind power history and wind powered water pumping for mechanical users as well as museum curators, historians and individuals restoring and preserving historic wind machines.

333.9 DK ISSN 0109-7318
CODEN: WIMOEW
WINDPOWER MONTHLY; news magazine. Danish edition: Naturlig Energi (ISSN 0106-1127) (Text in English) 1985. m. DKK 410($65) Torgny Moeller, Vrinners Hoved, DK-8420 Knebel, Denmark. TEL 86-36-59-00. FAX 86-36-56-26. TELEX 64728 NEWIND DK. (U.S. addr.: P.O. Box 496007, Ste. 217, Redding, CA 96099-6007) Eds. Lyn Harrison, Ros Davidson. adv. contact: William Canter. bk.rev.; illus. circ. 3,000. Indexed: Environ.Per.Bibl (1990-).
—BLDSC (9319.333000); UnCover.
Description: Covers international wind energy news and views on environmental impact, technological advances, market trends and industry status of wind power turbines. Includes public opinions, world news, statistics and events calendars.

ENGINEERING

see also Engineering–Chemical Engineering; Engineering–Civil Engineering; Engineering–Computer Applications; Engineering–Electrical Engineering; Engineering–Engineering Mechanics and Materials; Engineering–Hydraulic Engineering; Engineering–Industrial Engineering; Engineering–Mechanical Engineering

650 657 US
HD47 CODEN: AACTAZ
A A C E INTERNATIONAL. TRANSACTIONS OF THE ANNUAL MEETING. (American Association of Cost Engineers) 1967. a. price varies. A A C E International, Box 1557, Morgantown, WV 26507-1557. TEL 304-296-8444. FAX 304-291-5728. TELEX 887612 AACE MORG UD. Eds. Gregory A. Carte, Cathleen Falvey. circ. 1,500. (also avail. in microform from UMI; reprint service avail. from UMI) Indexed: Intl.Civil Eng.Abstr., Soft.Abstr.Eng. **Document type:** proceedings.
—BLDSC (1087.415200); EI; SWETS; UMI. CCC.
Formerly: American Association of Cost Engineers. Transactions of the Annual Meeting (ISSN 0065-7158)

620 690 US
A E M S SEMINAR (PAPERS).* 1970. a. $20. American Engineering Model Society, 1 Walnut St., Boston, MA 02108-3616. TEL 803-649-6710. circ. 750. (reprint service avail. from ISI)

A G E CURRENT AWARENESS SERVICE. (Asian Geotechnical Engineering Information Center) see *EARTH SCIENCES*

658.5 US ISSN 1054-7541
TS184 CODEN: AIFAEJ
A I P E FACILITIES. 1974. bi-m. $34 to non-members; members $19. American Institute of Plant Engineers, 8180 Corporate Park Dr., Ste. 305, Cincinnati, OH 45242-3309. TEL 513-489-2473. FAX 513-247-7422. Ed. David Macaulay. adv. circ. 9,000. **Document type:** trade publication.
—BLDSC (0773.462800); EI.
Former titles: A P E Facilities Management, Operations and Engineering (ISSN 0747-1289); (until 1984): American Institute of Plant Engineers. Journal.
Description: Covers management and engineering issues of facilities design, maintenance, energy, security, and environment.

620 531.64 690 US ISSN 8750-2046
A I P E NEWSLINE. vol.12, 1986. 6/yr. $14 (members $7). American Institute of Plant Engineers, 8180 Corporate Park Dr. Ste. 305, Cincinnati, OH 45242-3309. TEL 513-489-2473. FAX 513-247-7422. Ed. Linda Niesz. circ. 8,000. (back issues avail.) **Document type:** newsletter.
Formerly: A I P E Newsletter (ISSN 0745-5712)
Description: Covers the national, regional and local chapter activities of the American Institute of Plant Engineers.

620 TH ISSN 0125-6505
A I T REVIEW. 1962. 3/yr. free. Asian Institute of Technology, Media and Information Services Office, P.O. Box 2754, Bangkok, Thailand. FAX 662-516-2126. TELEX 84276 TH. Ed. Teresita M. Padilla. illus.; stat. circ. 9,500. **Document type:** newsletter.
Former titles: Asian Institute of Technology. Newsletter (ISSN 0004-4598); S E A T O Graduate School of Engineering. Newsletter.
Description: News about the Institute's activities, staff notes, meetings.

620 SZ
A M I V BLITZ. fortn. free. Eidgenoessische Technische Hochschule Zuerich, Universitaetsstr. 19, CH-8092 Zurich, Switzerland. TEL 01-2622072. FAX 01-6324942. Ed. Gregor Aschwanden. adv. contact: Reto Doswald. circ. 1,500. **Document type:** bulletin.

A P P A NEWSLETTER. (Association of Physical Plant Administrators) see *EDUCATION — School Organization And Administration*

ENGINEERING

620   US   ISSN 1054-0210
A S A E MONOGRAPH SERIES. 1971. irreg. price varies. American Society of Agricultural Engineers, 2950 Niles Rd., St. Joseph, MI 49085-9659. TEL 616-429-0300. FAX 616-429-3852. Ed. Pamela DeVore-Hansen. **Document type:** monographic series.
—BLDSC (1738.698000).

A S A E TRANSACTIONS. POWER & MACHINERY. (American Society of Agricultural Engineers) see *AGRICULTURE — Agricultural Equipment*

620 370   US   ISSN 1056-8077
T61   CODEN: ENEDAU
A S E E PRISM. 1910. 10/yr. $75 to non-members; libraries $125 (foreign $135). American Society for Engineering Education, 1818 N St., N.W., Ste. 600, Washington, DC 20036. TEL 202-331-3500. FAX 202-265-8504. (Subscr. to: Dept. 294, Washington, DC) Ed. P.W. Samaras. adv.; B&W page $2000; trim 7 x 9 1/2. bk.rev.; abstr.; charts; illus.; stat.; index. circ. 12,000. (also avail. in microform from UMI; microfiche from CIS; reprint service avail. from UMI) **Indexed:** Abstr.Bull.Inst.Pap.Chem., Appl.Mech.Rev., C.I.J.E., Chem.Abstr., Cont.Pg.Educ., Curr.Cont., Educ.Ind., Eng.Ind., High.Educ.Curr.Aware.Bull., Intl.Civil Eng.Abstr., Met.Abstr., Phys.Abstr., Psychol.Abstr., SRI. **Document type:** academic/scholarly publication.
—EI; Faxon; UnCover; UMI. **CCC.**
   Incorporates (in 1992): Engineering Education News; **Former titles (until 1992):** Engineering Education (ISSN 0022-0809); Journal of Engineering Education (Washington) (ISSN 0096-0640)
   Description: Presents scholarship, research and teaching methods in all disciplines of engineering education.

620   AT   ISSN 0045-0103
A S E JOURNAL.* bi-m. Australasian Society of Engineers, Victorian Branch, 15 Drummond St., North Carlton, Vic. 3054, Australia.

620   UK   ISSN 0001-110X
A U E W E S JOURNAL. (Amalgamated Union of Engineering Workers, Engineering Section) 1897. m. £5 to non-members. Amalgamated Union of Engineering Workers, Engineering Section, 110 Peckham Rd., London SE15 5EL, England. Ed. Gavin H. Laird. adv.; bk.rev.; abstr.; charts; illus.; stat.; tr.lit. circ. 145,000.
   Formerly: A E U Journal.

620   DK
AARET RUNDT. a. Teknisk Forlag A-S, Skelbaekgade 4, DK-1780 Copenhagen V, Denmark. TEL 45-31-21-68-01. FAX 45-31-21004-01. adv. circ. 72,000.

671.7   US   ISSN 0734-9629
TJ1280
ABRASIVE ENGINEERING SOCIETY. CONFERENCE PROCEEDINGS. Variant title: Annual International Technical Conference and Exhibit. 1962. a. price varies. Abrasive Engineering Society, Meadowlark Technical Services, 108 Elliot Dr., Butler, PA 16001. TEL 412-282-6210. FAX 412-282-6210. **Document type:** proceedings.
—BLDSC (0549.788000).
   Former titles: Abrasive Engineering Society. Annual International Technical Conference and Exhibit. Proceedings (ISSN 0363-8065) & Abrasive Society for Abrasive Methods. Technical Conference. Proceedings (ISSN 0066-006X)

620   US   ISSN 1050-5784
TK6592.06
ACQUISITION, TRACKING, AND POINTING. 1987. irreg. International Society for Optical Engineering (SPIE), Box 10, 1000 20th St., Bellingham, WA 98227-0010.

ACTA ACADEMIAE ABOENSIS, SERIES B: MATHEMATICA ET PHYSICA. see *MATHEMATICS*

ADDIS ABABA UNIVERSITY. COLLEGE OF TECHNOLOGY. LIBRARY BULLETIN. see *LIBRARY AND INFORMATION SCIENCES*

620   US   ISSN 0895-0407
TA418.9.C6
ADVANCED COMPOSITES. 1986. 7/yr. $35. Advanstar Communications, Inc., 7500 Old Oak Blvd., Cleveland, OH 44130. TEL 216-826-2839. FAX 216-891-2726. (Subscr. to: 131 W. First St., Duluth, MN 55802. TEL 800-346-0085) Ed. Suzanne Witzler. index. circ. 24,858. (also avail. in microfilm) **Document type:** trade publication.
—BLDSC (0696.838200); Faxon.
   Description: Focuses on practical hands-on data relating to the design, manufacturing and performance of products made or able to be made of advanced composites.

620 551.46   SI
ADVANCED SERIES ON OCEAN ENGINEERING. (Text in English) 1989. irreg., no.5, 1993. price varies. World Scientific Publishing Co. Pte. Ltd., Farrer Rd., P.O. Box 128, Singapore 9128, Singapore. TEL 3825663. FAX 3825919. TELEX RS 28561 WSPC. (UK addr.: 73 Lynton Mead, Totteridge, London N20 8DH, England. TEL 44-81-4462461; US addr.: 1060 Main St., River Edge, NJ 07661. TEL 800-227-7562) Ed. Philip L.F. Liu. **Document type:** monographic series.

ADVANCES IN BIOENGINEERING. see *BIOLOGY — Bioengineering*

ADVANCES IN CRYOGENIC ENGINEERING. see *PHYSICS — Heat*

620   US   ISSN 1053-184X
ADVANCES IN INFORMATION STORAGE SYSTEMS. 1991. q. A S M E Press, 22 Law Dr., Box 2300, Fairfield, NJ 07007-2300.
—UnCover. **CCC.**

ADVANCES IN NUCLEAR SCIENCE AND TECHNOLOGY. see *PHYSICS — Nuclear Physics*

ADVANCES IN WATER RESOURCES. see *WATER RESOURCES*

AGENCY OF INDUSTRIAL SCIENCE AND TECHNOLOGY. ELECTROTECHNICAL LABORATORY. SUMMARIES OF REPORTS. see *ENGINEERING — Electrical Engineering*

AGRICULTURAL ENGINEERING INDEX (YEARS). see *AGRICULTURE*

AKADEMIA ROLNICZA IM. HUGONA KOLLATAJA W KRAKOWIE. ZESZYTY NAUKOWE. SERIA: INZYNIERIA SRODOWISKA. see *ENVIRONMENTAL STUDIES*

620   TS
ALAM AL-HANDASAH/WORLD OF ENGINEERING. (Text in Arabic) 1981. q. membership. Jam'iat al-Muhandisin - Engineers Society, P.O. Box 4484, Dubai, United Arab Emirates. TEL 245232. FAX 245051. TELEX 46021 TRISIR. Ed. Wisam al-Dibagh. bk.rev. circ. 2,000.
   Description: Covers engineering news and research.

ALAMBRE; revista tecnica international para la industria del alambre y del cable y para todos los sectores de la elaboracion de alambres metalicos. see *ENGINEERING — Electrical Engineering*

620   LY
AL-FATEH UNIVERSITY. FACULTY OF ENGINEERING. BULLETIN. a. Al-Fateh University, Faculty of Engineering, P.O. Box 13040, Tripoli, Libya. TEL 36010. TELEX 20629.

620   UK   ISSN 0268-5280
ALUMINIUM INDUSTRY. 1982. bi-m. £55 (foreign £59). M C B University Press Ltd., 62 Toller Ln., Bradford, W. Yorks BD8 9BY, England. TEL 0274-499821. FAX 0274-547143. TELEX 51317 MCBUNI G. Ed. Roy Woodward. adv.; bk.rev. circ. 5,300. **Indexed:** Met.Abstr., World Alum.Abstr. **Document type:** trade publication.
—CCC.

620   US   ISSN 0071-0393
TA157
AMERICAN ASSOCIATION OF ENGINEERING SOCIETIES. ENGINEERING MANPOWER COMMISSION. ENGINEERING AND TECHNOLOGY DEGREES. (In 1 vol. including Part 1: By School; Part 2: Minorities; Part 3: By Curriculum) a. $230 (diskette $795) to non-members; members $140 (diskette $595). American Association of Engineering Societies, Engineering Manpower Commission, 1111 19th St. N.W., Ste. 608, Washington, DC 20036-3603. TEL 202-296-2237. FAX 202-296-1151. (also avail. in diskette format)
   Description: Analyses the degrees granted by America's engineering and technological institutions, both accredited and non-accredited.

331.7 620   US   ISSN 0071-0407
TA157
AMERICAN ASSOCIATION OF ENGINEERING SOCIETIES. ENGINEERING MANPOWER COMMISSION. ENGINEERING AND TECHNOLOGY ENROLLMENTS (YEAR). Variant title: Engineering Enrollment Data. (In 1 vol. including Part 1: Engineering Enrollments (Year); Part 2: Technology Enrollments (Year)) a. $195 (diskette $795) to non-members; members $120 (diskette $595). American Association of Engineering Societies, Engineering Manpower Commission, 1111 19th St. N.W., Ste. 608, Washington, DC 20036-3603. TEL 202-296-2237. FAX 202-296-1151. (also avail. in diskette format)
   Description: Covers today's engineering and engineering technology students from all collegiate levels, including technical schools.

331.7 620   US   ISSN 0071-0415
TA157
AMERICAN ASSOCIATION OF ENGINEERING SOCIETIES. ENGINEERING MANPOWER COMMISSION. ENGINEERS' SALARIES: SPECIAL INDUSTRY REPORT (YEAR). a. $287.50 to non-members; members $169. American Association of Engineering Societies, Engineering Manpower Commission, 1111 19th St., N.W., Ste. 608, Washington, DC 20036-3603. TEL 202-296-2237. FAX 202-296-1151.
   Description: Details breakdown of engineering salaries according to type of industry and geographic location, company size, employee years of experience, highest degree held, and supervisory status, based on salaries of over 100,000 engineers.

331.7 620   US   ISSN 0071-0423
TA157
AMERICAN ASSOCIATION OF ENGINEERING SOCIETIES. ENGINEERING MANPOWER COMMISSION. PROFESSIONAL INCOME OF ENGINEERS (YEAR). 1953. a. $115 to non-members; members $70. American Association of Engineering Societies, Engineering Manpower Commission, 1111 19th St., N.W., Ste. 608, Washington, DC 20036-3606. TEL 202-296-2237. FAX 202-296-1151.
   Description: Contains salary breakdowns for broad industry groups, excerpted from the Special Industry Report.

620   US
AMERICAN ASSOCIATION OF ENGINEERING SOCIETIES. ENGINEERING MANPOWER COMMISSION. SALARIES OF ENGINEERS IN EDUCATION (YEAR). 1972. biennial. $115 to non-members; members $70. American Association of Engineering Societies, Engineering Manpower Commission, 1111 19th St., N.W., Ste. 200, Washington, DC 20036-3606. TEL 202-296-2237. FAX 202-296-1151. Ed. Richard Ellis.
   Description: Details median, quartile, decile, and mean salaries of engineers in education institutions, quantified by academic rank, length of contract, and years experience.

620   US   ISSN 1050-2203
TA216
AMERICAN CONSULTING ENGINEER. 1990. q. $20. American Consulting Engineers Council, 1015 15th St., N.W., Washington, DC 20005. TEL 202-347-7474. FAX 202-898-0068. adv. circ. 25,417.
—UnCover.
   Description: For engineers in private practice who design and build public works and private industry projects.

ENGINEERING

620 US
AMERICAN ENGINEERING MODEL SOCIETY. NEWSLETTER.* 1968. bi-m. free. American Engineering Model Society, 1 Walnut St., Boston, MA 02108-3616. TEL 803-649-6710. Ed. Walter A. Clothier, Sr. circ. 1,500. **Document type:** newsletter.

AMERICAN INTERNATIONAL JOURNAL OF ARTS, SCIENCES, ENGINEERING AND MEDICINE. see *ART*

AMERICAN NUCLEAR SOCIETY TRANSACTIONS. see *ENERGY — Nuclear Energy*

620 US ISSN 0190-1052
T61 CODEN: ACOPDW
AMERICAN SOCIETY FOR ENGINEERING EDUCATION. ANNUAL CONFERENCE PROCEEDINGS. a. $70 to non-members; members $55. American Society for Engineering Education, 1818 N St., N.W., Ste. 600, Washington, DC 20036. TEL 202-331-3500. FAX 202-265-8504. **Document type:** proceedings.

AMERICAN SOCIETY FOR PHOTOGRAMMETRY AND REMOTE SENSING. TECHNICAL PAPERS FROM THE ANNUAL MEETING. see *GEOGRAPHY*

AMERICAN SOCIETY OF AGRICULTURAL ENGINEERS. COMPREHENSIVE INDEX OF PUBLICATIONS. see *AGRICULTURE*

620.86 US
AMERICAN SOCIETY OF SAFETY ENGINEERS. PROCEEDINGS. PROFESSIONAL DEVELOPMENT CONFERENCE. a. $41.50 to non-members; members $33.50. American Society of Safety Engineers, 1800 E. Oakton St., Des Plaines, IL 60018-2187. TEL 708-692-4121. FAX 708-296-3769. **Document type:** proceedings.
Formerly: American Society of Safety Engineers. Proceedings. Professional Conference.
Description: Covers speeches written at conference and submitted for publication in formal proceedings.

620 310 US
▼**AMERICAN STATISTICAL ASSOCIATION. PHYSICAL AND ENGINEERING SCIENCES. PROCEEDINGS.** 1993. a. $38 to non-members; members $25. American Statistical Association, 1429 Duke St., Alexandria, VA 22314-3402. TEL 703-684-1221. FAX 703-684-2037. **Document type:** proceedings.

620 CC ISSN 1000-2189
ANHUI GONGXUEYUAN XUEBAO/ANHUI INSTITUTE OF TECHNOLOGY. JOURNAL. (Text in Chinese) 1981. q. Guojia Ji-Dian Bu, Anhui Gongxueyuan - Anhui Institute of Technology, 111 Liu An Lu, Hefei, Anhui 230069, People's Republic of China. (Dist. overseas by: China Publications Foreign Trade Corp., P.O. Box 782, Beijing, P.R.C.) Eds. Shu Delin, Huang Bing.
Description: Explores theoretical and applied problems in science and technology. Covers mechanical manufacturing technology, electrical engineering, force mechanics, materials science, automotive and management engineering. Includes research papers, reports, reviews, and news of academic activities.

ANNUAL BOOK OF A S T M STANDARDS. VOLUME 12.01. NUCLEAR ENERGY (1). see *ENGINEERING — Engineering Mechanics And Materials*

ANNUAL CONFERENCE ON ACTIVATED SLUDGE PROCESS CONTROL. PROCEEDINGS. see *PUBLIC HEALTH AND SAFETY*

ANNUAL REVIEW OF BIOPHYSICS AND BIOMOLECULAR STRUCTURE. see *BIOLOGY — Biophysics*

APPLICATIONS OF DIGITAL IMAGE PROCESSING. see *PHYSICS — Optics*

APPLIED ENGINEERING IN AGRICULTURE. see *AGRICULTURE*

620.8 UK ISSN 0003-6870
TA166 CODEN: AERGBW
APPLIED ERGONOMICS; human factors in technology and society. 1969. bi-m. £180 in UK & Europe; elsewhere £190. Butterworth - Heinemann (Subsidiary of: Reed International PLC), Linacre House, Jordan Hill, Oxford OX2 8DP, England. TEL 0865-310366. FAX 0865-310898. TELEX 83111 BHPOXF G. (Subscr. to: Turpin Transactions Ltd., Distribution Centre, Blackhorse Rd., Letchworth, Herts SG6 1HN, England. TEL 0462-672555) Ed. E.N. Corlett. adv.; bk.rev.; abstr.; illus.; index. (also avail. in microform from UMI; back issues avail.) **Indexed:** Abstr.Hum.Comp.Inter., Agri.Eng.Abstr., BMT, Br.Tech.Ind., C.I.S. Abstr., Curr.Cont., Cyb.Abstr., Dok.Arbeitsmed., Eng.Ind., Ergon.Abstr., Excerp.Med., HRIS, ISMEC, Noise Pollut.Publ.Abstr., Psychol.Abstr., Psycscan, Sci.Abstr., SSCI, Trop.Dis.Bull. **Document type:** academic/scholarly publication.
—BLDSC (1572.500000); Faxon; UnCover; SWETS; UMI. **CCC.**
Description: Covers applications of ergonomics in the office, industry, consumer products, information technology and military design.
Refereed Serial

APPLIED OCEAN RESEARCH. see *EARTH SCIENCES — Oceanography*

APPLIED PHYSICS. A: SOLIDS AND SURFACES. see *PHYSICS*

APPLIED PHYSICS. B: PHOTOPHYSICS AND LASER CHEMISTRY. see *PHYSICS*

APPLIED PHYSICS AND ENGINEERING. see *PHYSICS*

APPLIED PHYSICS LETTERS. see *PHYSICS*

APPLIED SCIENTIFIC RESEARCH; an international journal on the applications of fluid dynamics. see *SCIENCES: COMPREHENSIVE WORKS*

620 CL ISSN 0716-0348
TA4
APUNTES DE INGENIERIA. (Text in Spanish; abstracts and summaries in English) 1972-1974; resumed 1981. q. $25. Pontificia Universidad Catolica de Chile, Escuela de Ingenieria, Facultad de Ingenieria, Casilla 306, Correo 22, Santiago, Chile. FAX 56-2-552-4054. TELEX 240395 PUCVACL. Ed. Ernesto Cruz. adv.; bk.rev. circ. 1,000. **Indexed:** Abstr.J.Earthq.Eng.
Description: Each issue covers a different area of engineering. Includes research that is carried out at the Catholic University of Santiago as well as by other researchers in Chile.

620 UK ISSN 0144-8609
SH1 CODEN: AQEND6
AQUACULTURAL ENGINEERING. 1982. 4/yr. £211($325) (effective 1994). Elsevier Science Ltd., Oxford Fulfilment Centre, P.O. Box 800, Kidlington, Oxford OX5 1DX, England. TEL 44-865-843000. FAX 44-865-843010. (Subscr. in U.S. and Canada to: Elsevier Science, 660 White Plains Rd., Tarrytown, NY 10591-5153. TEL 914-524-9200. FAX 914-333-2444) Eds. K.R. Murray, J. Colt. adv.; bk.rev.; charts; illus. (also avail. in microform from UMI; back issues avail.) **Indexed:** Agri.Eng.Abstr., Aqua.Sci.& Fish.Abstr., Biol.Abstr., Curr.Adv.Ecol.Sci., Curr.Cont., Curr.Ref.Fish Res., Energy Info.Abstr., Eng.Ind., Excerp.Med., Sci.Cit.Ind., Sel.Water Res.Abstr. **Document type:** academic/scholarly publication.
—BLDSC (1581.865900); EI; UnCover; SWETS. **CCC.**
Description: Covers engineering and design of aquaculture facilities; engineering-based research studies; construction experience and techniques; in-service experience, commissioning, operation; materials selection and their uses; quantification of biological data and constraints.
Refereed Serial

620 500 SU ISSN 0377-9211
Q80.S2 CODEN: AJSEDY
ARABIAN JOURNAL FOR SCIENCE AND ENGINEERING. (Text in English; summaries in Arabic, English) 1975. q. $30 King Fahd University of Petroleum and Minerals, P.O. Box 5033, Dhahran 31231, Saudi Arabia. FAX 966-3-860-5458. TELEX 801060 KFUPM SJ. E-mail: ADMAJSE@SAUPM00.BITNET. Ed. Abdullah S. Zakri. bk.rev.; abstr.; charts; illus. (also avail. in microform from UMI; reprint service avail. from ISI,UMI) **Indexed:** Appl.Mech.Rev., Chem.Abstr., Curr.Cont., GeoRef., Math.R., Petrol.Abstr., Sci.Abstr. **Document type:** academic/scholarly publication.
—BLDSC (1583.326000); UnCover; UMI; CASDDS. **CCC.**
Description: Publishes original articles in the areas of mathematics, engineering and the physical sciences, and the academic teaching of these subjects.
Refereed Serial

ARCHAEOMETRY. see *ARCHAEOLOGY*

620 GW ISSN 0939-1533
TA349 CODEN: AAMEEA
ARCHIVE OF APPLIED MECHANICS. (Text in English and German; summaries in English) 1929. 8/yr. DM.754($471) (Gesellschaft fuer Angewandte Mathematik und Mechanik) Springer-Verlag, Heidelberger Platz 3, 14197 Berlin, Germany. TEL 030-8207-1. FAX 030-8214091. (Subscr. in N. America to: Springer-Verlag New York, Inc., 44 Hartz Way, Secaucus, NJ 07096-2491. TEL 201-348-4033. FAX 201-348-4505) Ed. H. Lippmann. (also avail. in microform from UMI,PMC; back issues avail ; reprint service avail. from ISI) **Indexed:** Appl.Mech.Rev., Cadscan, Chem.Abstr., Curr.Cont., Eng.Ir.d., Fluidex, Geotech.Abstr., Ind.Sci.Rev., INIS Atomind., Int.Aerosp.Abstr., Lead Abstr., Sci.Abstr., Sci.Cit.Ind., Sh.& Vib.Dig., Zincscan. **Document type:** academic/scholarly publication.
—BLDSC (1631.315000); EI; UnCover; SWETS; UMI. **CCC.**
Formerly: Ingenieur-Archiv (ISSN 0020-1154)
Description: Encompasses the fundamentals of engineering, particularly of general mechanics. Includes hydrodynamics, strength of materials, rheology, continuum mechanics, and thermodynamics.

630 660 PL ISSN 0208-4198
CODEN: ACOMEO
ARCHIWUM COMBUSTIONIS. (Text in English) 1970. q. $52. (Polska Akademia Nauk, Komitet Termodynamiki i Spalania) Wydawnictwo Naukowe P W N, Miodowa 10, 00-251 Warsaw, Poland. TEL 48-22-312738. FAX 48-22-267163. TELEX 813763 PWN PL. Ed.Bd. bk.rev.; abstr.; illus. circ. 400. (tabloid format) **Indexed:** Chem.Abstr.
—BLDSC (1659.120000); CASDDS.
Formerly (until 1981): Archiwum Procesow Spalania - Archives of Combustion Processes (ISSN 0044-8761)

620 PL ISSN 0066-684X
TK95.P7 CODEN: AREGBO
ARCHIWUM ENERGETYKI. (Text in Polish; summaries in English and Russian) 1971. q. $36. (Polska Akademia Nauk, Komitet Problemow Energetyki) Wydawnictwo Naukowe P W N, Ul. Miodowa 10, 00-251 Warsaw, Poland. TEL 48-22-312738. FAX 48-22-267163. TELEX 813763 PWN PL. Ed. J. Marecki. bibl.; charts; illus. circ. 460. **Indexed:** Chem.Abstr., INIS Atomind.
—CASDDS.

620 614.7 US
ARGONNE NATIONAL LABORATORY. RESEARCH HIGHLIGHTS. a. free. Argonne National Laboratory, Office of Public Affairs, 9700 S. Cass Ave., Bldg. 201, Argonne, IL 60439. TEL 708-972-5575. FAX 708-252-5274.

ARHIV ZA POLJOPRIVREDNE NAUKE. see *AGRICULTURE*

620 US
ARKANSAS ENGINEER. 1922. a. University of Arkansas, College of Engineering, c/o Mary-Ann Bloss, 3158 Bell Engineering Center, Fayetteville, AR 72701. TEL 501-575-6015. adv.; bk.rev.; illus. circ. 1,700.

ENGINEERING

620   FR   ISSN 0004-3982
ARTS ET INDUSTRIES. vol.36, 1970. q. 20 F. Societe des Anciens Eleves de l'Ecole Nationale Superieure des Arts et Industries de Strasbourg, 56 bd. d'Anvers, 67000 Strasbourg, France. Ed. Alain Richard. adv.; charts; illus. circ. 3,000.

620   HK
ASIA ENGINEER. 1972. m. $78. Hong Kong Institution of Engineers, 1205 Arts Centre, 2 Harbour Rd., Hong Kong. TEL 852-824-0781. FAX 852-824-1925. Ed. K. Gopinath; Pub. Jay Henderson. adv.; bk.rev. circ. 11,600. **Indexed:** Br.Rail.Bd., Fluidex, HRIS, Intl.Civil Eng.Abstr., ISMEC, Pollut.Abstr., Sci.Abstr., Soft.Abstr.Eng.
    Former titles (until Dec. 1993): Hong Kong Engineer; Engineering Society of Hong Kong. Journal.

620   MX   ISSN 0004-4814
ASOCIACION FRANCO-MEXICANA DE INGENIEROS Y TECNICOS. BOLETIN. (Text in French and Spanish) 1955. bi-m. P.300($3.20) Asociacion Franco-Mexicana de Ingenieros y Tecnicos, Liverpool 67, Mexico 6, D.F., Mexico. Ed. Lilia R. Machuca. film rev.; bibl.; charts; illus.; index.

621.7   US   ISSN 1050-8171
TJ1320   CODEN: ASMYEQ
ASSEMBLY (CAROL STREAM); design & manufacturing technology for better assembled products. 1958. m. $60. Hitchcock Publishing (Subsidiary of: Capital Cities - A B C, Inc.), 191 S. Gary Ave., Carol Stream, IL 60188. TEL 708-665-1000. FAX 708-462-2225. Ed. Walter Maczka. adv.; bk.rev.; charts; illus.; tr.lit.; index. circ. 76,091. (also avail. in microform from UMI; reprint service avail. from UMI) **Indexed:** A.I.Abstr. (until 1992), CAD CAM Abstr. (until 1992), PROMT, Robomat. (until 1992), Tel.Abstr.
  —BLDSC (1746.569000); SWETS; UMI. **CCC.**
    Formerly (until 1990): Assembly Engineering (ISSN 0004-5063)
    Description: Provides comprehensive coverage of the methods, processes and equipment involved in assembly technology. Each issue contains articles on design and manufacturing management, the latest electronics assembly and test equipment, mechanical fastening tips and assembly systems.

621.9   US
ASSEMBLY TECHNOLOGY BUYER'S GUIDE. 1962. a. Hitchcock Publishing (Subsidiary of: Capital Cities - A B C, Inc.), 191 S. Gary Ave., Carol Stream, IL 60188. TEL 708-665-1000. FAX 708-462-2225. TELEX 72-0404. Ed. Walter Maczka. adv. circ. 40,000. (reprint service avail. from UMI)
    Former titles: Assembly Engineering Master Catalog (ISSN 0066-8702); Assembly Directory and Handbook (ISSN 0066-8699)
    Description: Provides information on products and suppliers of equipment for the assembly technology industry.

620   UA   ISSN 0254-1343
     CODEN: BFAUD9
ASSIUT UNIVERSITY. FACULTY OF ENGINEERING. BULLETIN. (Text in English) 1973. 2/yr. $20 per no. Assiut University, Faculty of Engineering, Assiut, Egypt. FAX 088322564. TELEX 92863 ASUNV UN. circ. 1,500.
  —CASDDS.

620   SZ
ASSOCIATION DES ANCIENS ELEVES DE L'ECOLE D'INGENIEURS DE GENEVE. BULLETIN TECHNIQUE. Variant title: Bulletin Technique de l'A.T.G. 1915. m. (10/yr.). 80 Fr. Association des Anciens Eleves de l'Ecole d'Ingenieurs de Geneve, Case Postale 1120, 1211 Geneva 1, Switzerland. Ed. Lakatos Laszlo. adv.; bk.rev.; bibl.; illus. circ. 2,000.
    Formerly: Association des Anciens Eleves des Ecoles Techniques Superieures de Geneve. Bulletin Technique (ISSN 0004-5349)

620   CN
ASSOCIATION OF CONSULTING ENGINEERS OF CANADA. DIRECTORY OF MEMBER FIRMS AND THEIR SERVICES. (Text in English, French) 1958. a. $100. Association of Consulting Engineers of Canada, 130 Albert St., Ste. 616, Ottawa, ON K1P 5G4, Canada. TEL 613-236-0569. FAX 613-236-6193. circ. 2,500. **Document type:** directory.
    Former titles: Consulting Engineers - Canada - Ingenieurs Conseils (ISSN 0317-6525); Association of Consulting Engineers of Canada. Specialization Typical Projects (ISSN 0084-6899)
    Description: Guide to consulting engineering firms in Canada.

620   II   ISSN 0044-9598
ASSOCIATION OF ENGINEERS, INDIA. JOURNAL. (Text in Bengali or English) 1926. q. Rs.40($16) Association of Engineers, India, 24 Netaji Subhas Rd., Calcutta 700001, India. Ed. M. Bhattacharyya. adv.; bk.rev.; bibl.; charts; illus. circ. 500. (also avail. in microfilm from UMI; reprint service avail. from ISI; UMI)

620   II
ASSOCIATION OF ENGINEERS, KERALA P.W.D. NEWS LETTER. (Text in English) 1954. m. free to members. Association of Engineers, Kerala P.W.D., c/o N. Manilal, Secretary, Vikas Bhavan, Trivandrum 695 033, India. Ed. Abraham Koshy. adv.; bk.rev.; charts; illus. circ. 600.
    Formerly: Association of Engineers, Kerala State. Journal (ISSN 0004-5713)

620   TR   ISSN 1010-7924
ASSOCIATION OF PROFESSIONAL ENGINEERS OF TRINIDAD AND TOBAGO. JOURNAL. 1961. s-a. T.T.$25($8.50) Association of Professional Engineers of Trinidad and Tobago, P.O. Box 935, Port of Spain, Trinidad & Tobago, W.I. TEL 809-627-6697. Ed. George K. Sammy. adv.; bk.rev. circ. 700. **Document type:** academic/scholarly publication.

ATOMIC ENERGY. see *ENERGY — Nuclear Energy*

620   JA   ISSN 0387-0154
ATSURYOKU GIJUTSU/JOURNAL OF HIGH PRESSURE INSTITUTE OF JAPAN. (Text in Japanese; summaries in English) 1963. bi-m. 6000 Yen. High Pressure Institute of Japan - Nippon Koatsuryoku Gijutsu Kyokai, Sakuma Bldg., 1-11 Kanda, Sakuma-cho, Chiyoda-ku, Tokyo, Japan. TEL 03-3255-3486. FAX 03-3255-3488. adv.; bk.rev. **Indexed:** INIS Atomind.

AUSTRALIA. NUCLEAR SCIENCE AND TECHNOLOGY ORGANISATION. A N S T O - E. see *ENERGY — Nuclear Energy*

620   AT   ISSN 0159-2955
AUSTRALIAN ENGINEERING DIRECTORY. a. Aus.$95. Technical Indexes Pty. Ltd., 4 Kembla St., East Cheltenham, Vic. 3192, Australia. FAX 03-584-6871. TELEX 34007. (Subscr. to: Technical Indexes Pty. Ltd., P.O. Box 98, Cheltenham, Vic. 3192, Australia) Ed. Ross Mackay. circ. 5,000.

AUSTRALIAN NUCLEAR SCIENCE AND TECHNOLOGY ORGANISATION. ANNUAL REPORT. see *ENERGY — Nuclear Energy*

AUSTRALIAN NUCLEAR SCIENCE AND TECHNOLOGY ORGANISATION - M. see *ENERGY — Nuclear Energy*

620 001.6   DK   ISSN 0105-0168
AUTOMATIK; industrial automation. 1976. m. DKK 155. Fagbladsforlaget Teknik & Viden Aps., Algade 10, P.O. 80, DK-4500 Nykoebing Sj, Denmark. FAX 45-59-93-02-10. Ed. Anker Knudsen. adv. circ. 35,315. (tabloid format) **Document type:** trade publication.

AUTOMATION NEWS. see *COMPUTERS — Automation*

B A B A TRADE ASSOCIATION FOR THE BRITISH BIOMASS INDUSTRIES. THE DIGEST. see *ENERGY*

620   CN   ISSN 0005-2906
B.C. PROFESSIONAL ENGINEER. 1950. 10/yr. Can.$25. Association of Professional Engineers and Geoscientists of British Columbia, 210 - 6400 Roberts St., Burnaby, BC V5G 4C9, Canada. TEL 604-299-7100. FAX 604-299-8006. Ed. Wayne Gibson. adv.; bk.rev.; charts; illus.; index. circ. 15,800. **Indexed:** Chem.Abstr.

620   UK   ISSN 0005-304X
B E M A BULLETIN. 1945. m. free to members. Bristol and Western Engineering Manufacturers Association Ltd., BEMA House, 4 Broad Plain, Bristol BS2 0NG, England. TEL 0272-265930. FAX 0272-230036. Ed. A.R. Angerson. adv.; illus. circ. 1,000. **Document type:** bulletin.

620   UK   ISSN 0067-5709
B E M A ENGINEERING DIRECTORY. 1937. a. £50 to non-members. Bristol and Western Engineering Manufacturers Association Ltd., BEMA House, 4 Broad Plain, Bristol BS2 0NG, England. TEL 0272-265930. FAX 0272-230036. Ed. A.R. Angerson. adv. circ. 3,000. **Document type:** directory.

B M E S BULLETIN. (Biomedical Engineering Society) see *MEDICAL SCIENCES*

620   US   ISSN 0005-4496
BALTIMORE ENGINEER. 1926. m. $12. Engineering Society of Baltimore, Inc., 11 W. Mount Vernon Place, Baltimore, MD 21201. TEL 301-539-6914. FAX 301-783-9372. Ed. John W. Duvall. adv. circ. 4,000.

BAMAARACHOT. see *LABOR UNIONS*

620   BG   ISSN 0070-8186
BANGLADESH UNIVERSITY OF ENGINEERING AND TECHNOLOGY, DHAKA. TECHNICAL JOURNAL.* (Text in English) 1962. a. Bangladesh University of Engineering and Technology, Ramna, Dhaka 2, Bangladesh.
    Supersedes: University of Dacca's Ahsanullah Engineering College. Technical Journal.

620   UK   ISSN 0951-6859
BENCHMARK. 1987. q. £30($60) National Agency for Finite Element Methods and Standards (N A F E M S), E. Kilbride, Glasgow G75 0QU, Scotland. TEL 03552-25688. FAX 03552-72749. Ed. Elliot Robertson. adv.; bk.rev. circ. 6,500. **Document type:** academic/scholarly publication.
  —BLDSC (1891.229000).
    Description: For those involved in finite analysis: analysts, researchers, code developers, and educationalists.

BENT OF TAU BETA PI. see *COLLEGE AND ALUMNI*

BERUFSPLANUNG FUER INGENIEURE. see *OCCUPATIONS AND CAREERS*

620   GW   ISSN 0409-2791
BETRIEBSTECHNIK; Monatsmagazin fuer Betriebsleiter. 1960. m. DM.89. (Bundesverband der Energieabnehmer e.V.) Resch Media Mail Verlag GmbH, Geigerstr. 13, 82166 Graefelfing, Germany. TEL 089-858070. FAX 089-85807-62. Ed.Bd. circ. 33,000. **Indexed:** C.I.S.Abstr., Excerp.Med., INIS Atomind. **Document type:** trade publication.
  —CCC.
    Description: Covers the latest research and information concerning industrial technology. Features management, marketing, energy, surface science, quality control, storing and transportation. Includes new products and association news.

BIO-MEDICAL MATERIALS AND ENGINEERING; an international journal. see *BIOLOGY — Bioengineering*

BIOMEDICAL ENGINEERING AND INSTRUMENTATION SERIES. see *BIOLOGY — Bioengineering*

BIOPROCESS ENGINEERING; bioreactors, upstream and downstream processes, measurement and control. see *BIOLOGY — Biotechnology*

BIOTECH BUYER'S GUIDE. see *BIOLOGY — Biotechnology*

620 917.306   US
BLACK PROFESSIONAL; for engineering, business, technology, and health professionals. 1989. q. $15. Career Communications Group, Inc., 729 Pratt St., Ste. 504, Baltimore, MD 21202. TEL 410-244-7101. FAX 410-752-1837. Ed. Tyrone Taborn. adv.; illus.
    Formerly: Professional.

BLECH-ROHRE-PROFILE; internationale Fachzeitschrift fuer die Herstellung und Verarbeitung von Band, Blech, Rohren und Profilen. see *METALLURGY*

620 355 JA ISSN 0385-7301
TA4 CODEN: BDRHD7
BOEI DAIGAKKO RIKOGAKU KENKYU HOKOKU/NATIONAL DEFENSE ACADEMY. SCIENTIFIC AND ENGINEERING REPORTS. (Text in Japanese; summaries in English) 1963. q. Boei Daigakko - National Defense Academy, 10-20 Hashirimizu, 1-chome, Yokosuka-shi, Kanagawa-ken 239, Japan.
—CASDDS.

BOEI GIJUTSU/DEFENSE TECHNOLOGY JOURNAL. see *MILITARY*

620 CL
BOLETIN INGENIERIA COMERCIAL.* 1975. irrege. free. Universidad Catolica de Valparaiso, Escuela de Ingenieria Comercial, Avda. Brasil 2147, Casilla 4059, Valparaiso, Chile. adv. circ. 300.

620 US
BOLTON LANDING CONFERENCE. PROCEEDINGS. 3rd, 1970. irreg., 4th, 1975. $32. Claitor's Law Book & Publishing Division, Inc., 3165 S. Arcadian at Interstate 10, Box 3333, Baton Rouge, LA 70821. TEL 504-344-0476. FAX 504-344-0480. Ed.Bd. illus. **Document type:** proceedings.

BOSCH TECHNISCHE BERICHTE. see *ENGINEERING — Electrical Engineering*

658.5 745.2 UK
BRITISH STANDARDS MICROFILE. 1970. m. Technical Indexes Ltd., Willoughby Rd., Bracknell, Berkshire RG12 8DW, England. TEL 0344-426311. FAX 0344-424971. **Document type:** abstracting/indexing.
●Also available on CD-ROM.

620 US
BUCKNELL ENGINEER. 1949. s-a. $6. Bucknell University, College of Engineering, Box 315, Marts Hall, Lewisburg, PA 17837. TEL 717-523-1271. Ed. Karen Stano. adv.; charts; illus.; pat.; stat. circ. 1,250.

620 UK ISSN 0142-310X
CODEN: BSENDV
BUILDING SERVICES & ENVIRONMENTAL ENGINEER. 1978. m. £34 (overseas £56). Batiste Publications Ltd., Pembroke House, Campsbourne Rd., Hornsey, London N8 7PE, England. TEL 44-81-340-3291. FAX 44-81-341-4840. TELEX 267727 BATGRP. Ed. Ken Sharpe. adv. **Indexed:** BMT, Int.Build.Serv.Abstr., Pollut.Abstr.
—BLDSC (2365.630000).

BUSINESS RATIO REPORT. PROCESS PLANT; an industry sector analysis. see *HEATING, PLUMBING AND REFRIGERATION*

551.46 620 CN ISSN 0381-6486
C - C O R E NEWS. 1976. 3/yr. free. Centre for Cold Ocean Resources Engineering, Memorial University, St. John's, NF A1B 3X5, Canada. TEL 709-737-8354. FAX 709-737-4706. Ed. E.A. Nesbitt. circ. 2,000. **Document type:** newsletter, academic/scholarly publication.
Description: Presents research in ice engineering, remote sensing, seabed physics, geotechnical engineering and centrifuge modelling.

THE C E R CULAR; information exchange bulletin. (U.S. Coastal Engineering Research Center) see *EARTH SCIENCES — Oceanography*

C I R A S NEWS. (Center for Industrial Research and Service) see *TECHNOLOGY: COMPREHENSIVE WORKS*

C L S U SCIENTIFIC JOURNAL. (Central Luzon State University) see *AGRICULTURE*

C S P DIRECTORY. (Board of Certified Safety Professionals) see *OCCUPATIONAL HEALTH AND SAFETY*

C T I JOURNAL. (Cooling Tower Institute) see *PETROLEUM AND GAS*

C T I NEWS. (Cooling Tower Institute) see *PETROLEUM AND GAS*

620 US
CALIFORNIA CONSULTING ENGINEER. 1988. q. $20. Consulting Engineers and Land Surveyors of California, 1303 J St., Ste. 370, Sacramento, CA 95814-2936. TEL 916-441-7991. FAX 916-441-6312. adv.: B&W page $1339.50; trim 8 1/2 x 11. circ. 3,100.
Description: Contains news about member firms.

620 370 US ISSN 0008-1027
CALIFORNIA ENGINEER. 1922. 4/yr. $5. (University of California, Berkeley, Student Engineers' Joint Council) California Engineer Publishing Co., Inc., 221 Bechtel Center, Berkeley, CA 94720. TEL 510-642-8679. Ed. David Chen. adv. contact: Florence Meza. bk.rev. circ. 10,000. **Indexed:** Cal.Per.Ind. (1980-). **Document type:** academic/scholarly publication.
—UnCover.
Description: Collegiate engineering journal serving the student, faculty, and staff of the University of California Engineering Colleges.

620 CN ISSN 0008-3267
CANADIAN CONSULTING ENGINEER; a magazine for professional engineers in private practice. 1959. bi-m. Can.$36.38($40) (foreign $61). Southam Magazine Group, 1450 Don Mills Rd., Don Mills, ON M3B 2X7, Canada. TEL 416-445-6641. FAX 416-442-2261. Ed. Sophie Peacock. adv.; bk.rev.; charts; illus.; tr.lit.; index. circ. 8,000. (also avail. in microfiche from UMI) **Indexed:** Geotech.Abstr.
—CCC.
Description: For registered professional engineers in consulting engineering and architectural practices.

620 621.9 CN ISSN 0068-8665
CANADIAN ENGINEERING & INDUSTRIAL YEAR BOOK. 1945. a. Can.$45($60) Lloyd Publications of Canada, 66 Falby Ct., Ste. 1603, Ajax, Ont. L1S 3L2, Canada. TEL 416-619-0421. Ed. J. Lloyd. adv.; index. circ. 9,500.
Formerly: Canadian Engineering and Machinery Year Book.
Description: Listing of Canadian manufacturers, distributors and wholesalers of engineering, heavy construction and utilities equipment and services. Contains three sections arranged alphabetically by name, product and trade name.

CANADIAN STEAM. see *TRANSPORTATION*

CAREERS AND THE ENGINEER. see *OCCUPATIONS AND CAREERS*

620 US ISSN 0746-6641
CERTIFIED ENGINEERING TECHNICIAN. 1967. bi-m. $12 to educational institutions; others $20. American Society of Certified Engineering Technicians, c/o Kurt H. Schuler, General Mgr., Box 371474, El Paso, TX 79937. TEL 915-591-5115. adv. contact: Kurt H. Schuler. bk.rev. circ. 3,000. **Document type:** trade publication.
Formerly (until 1973): Engineering Technician in the News (ISSN 0013-8126)
Description: Collects and disseminates information that will increase the technical knowledge of members, and provides information about engineering technology careers to the students.

620 690 XR ISSN 0001-7043
TA4.C34 CODEN: ATCVA4
CESKOSLOVENSKA AKADEMIE VED. ACTA TECHNICA. (Text and summaries in English) 1956. bi-m. DM.357. (Czechoslovak Academy of Sciences) Academia, Publishing House of the Czechoslovak Academy of Sciences, Vodickova 40, 112 29 Prague 1, Czech Republic. (Dist. in Western countries by: Kubon & Sagner, P.O. Box 34 01 08, 8000 Munich 34, Germany) Ed. Bedrich Heller. bk.rev.; charts; illus.; index. circ. 800. **Indexed:** Chem.Abstr., Eng.Ind., Met.Abstr., Sci.Abstr.
—BLDSC (0664.200000); UnCover; CASDDS.
Description: Covers the mechanics of solids, hydrodynamics, thermodynamics, theory of materials, theory of structures (such as bridges, buildings), and electrical engineering and electronics.

620 JA ISSN 0577-6848
T4 CODEN: CDKKAN
CHIBA DAIGAKU KOGAKUBU KENKYU HOKOKU/CHIBA UNIVERSITY. FACULTY OF ENGINEERING. JOURNAL. (Text in Japanese; summaries in English) 1950. s-a. free to public institutions. Chiba Daigaku Kogakubu - Chiba University, Faculty of Engineering, 1-33 Yayoicho, Chiba 280, Japan. TEL 0472-51-1111. FAX 0472-51-7337. circ. 550. **Indexed:** Chem.Abstr., INIS Atomind., JTA, Math.R., Sci.Abstr.
—CASDDS.

620 US
CHIEF ENGINEER. 1935. m. $25. Chief Engineers Association of Chicagoland, 11340 159th St., Orland Park, IL 60462-4415. TEL 708-403-2444. FAX 708-349-4507. Ed. Ernest K. Wulff. adv.: B&W page $805, color page $865; 8 1/2 x 11. bk.rev.; illus.; stat. circ. 2,000. **Document type:** trade publication.

683.83 658.5 US
CHILTON'S PRODUCT DESIGN AND DEVELOPMENT. 1946. m. $50. Chilton Co., Chilton Way, Radnor, PA 19089. TEL 215-964-4351. Ed. Robert Bierwirth. adv.; bk.rev.; illus.; tr.lit. circ. 162,079. (tabloid format; also avail. in microfilm from UMI; microfiche from BLH,UMI; reprint service avail. from UMI)
Formerly: Product Design and Development (ISSN 0032-9738)
Description: Features appliances and equipment.

551.46 620 CC ISSN 0890-5487
TC1501
CHINA OCEAN ENGINEERING. (Editions in Chinese, English) 1987. 4/yr. £220 (effective 1993). (Chinese Ocean Engineering Society) China Ocena Press, International Cooperation Department, Haimao Dalou, 1 Fuxingmenwai St., Beijing 100860, People's Republic of China. TEL 8032211. FAX 8033515. TELEX 22536 NBO CN. Ed. Qingzhi Qi; Pub. Qing Yang. adv.; index. (also avail. in microfilm from UMI; back issues avail.) **Indexed:** E&P Hlth. (1993-), Gas Process.& Ppl. (1993-), Off.Tech. (1993-), Petrol.Abstr. (1988-). **Document type:** academic/scholarly publication.
—BLDSC (3180.214500); EI; UMI.
Description: Concerned with all engineering aspects involved in the exploration and utilization of ocean resources, such as offshore engineering, dive and salvage, utilization of marine energy resources and underwater technology.
Refereed Serial

620 CH ISSN 0253-3839
TA4 CODEN: CKCKDZ
CHINESE INSTITUTE OF ENGINEERS. JOURNAL. Key Title: Zhongguo Gongcheng Xuekan. 1978. bi-m. NT.$1200($50) to individuals; institutions NT.$2200($100). Chinese Institute of Engineers, 4-F, No. 1, Jen-Ai Rd. Sec. 2, Taipei, Taiwan, Republic of China. TEL 886-2-3925128. FAX 886-2-3973003. (Subscr. to: c/o National Taiwan Institute of Technology, 43 Keelung Rd. Sec. 4, Taipei, Taiwan, Republic of China. TEL 886-2-7376104. FAX 886-2-7373196) Ed. Dr. Ching-Tien Liou. cum.index. circ. 1,800. (also avail. in microfiche; back issues avail.) **Indexed:** Eng.Ind. **Document type:** academic/scholarly publication.
—BLDSC (4729.315000); EI; UnCover.

CHOCS. see *ENERGY — Nuclear Energy*

CHUANBO GONGCHENG/SHIP ENGINEERING. see *TRANSPORTATION — Ships And Shipping*

620 JA ISSN 0910-8629
TA4 CODEN: CDKKER
CHUBU UNIVERSITY. COLLEGE OF ENGINEERING. MEMOIRS/CHUBU DAIGAKU KOGAKUBU KIYO. (Text in English or Japanese; summaries in English, French, German) 1965. irreg. (1-2/yr.). exchange basis. Chubu University, College of Engineering - Chubu Daigaku Kogakubu, Kasugai-shi, Aichi-ken 487, Japan. Ed.Bd. bibl.; charts; illus. circ. 1,000. **Indexed:** Appl.Mech.Rev., Chem.Abstr., Jap.Per.Ind., Nucl.Sci.Abstr., Sci.Abstr.
—BLDSC (5581.490000); CASDDS.
Former titles (until vol.20, 1984): Chubu Institute of Technology. Memoirs. Series A (ISSN 0009-6202); Chubu Institute of Technology. Bulletin.

ENGINEERING

628   PL
CIEPŁOWNICTWO, OGRZEWNICTWO, WENTYLACJA. 1969. m. $51. (Polskie Zrzeszenie Inzynierow i Technikow Sanitarnych) Wydawnictwo Czasopism i Ksiazek Technicznych SIGMA - NOT, Ul. Ratuszowa 11, P.O. Box 1004, 00-950 Warsaw, Poland. TEL 48-22-180918. FAX 48-22-192187. TELEX 814550 SIGMA PL. (Dist. by: Zaklad Kolportazu SIGMA-NOT, Bartycka 20, P.O. Box 1004, 00-950 Warsaw, Poland) Ed. Witold Wasilewski. adv.: Page $1260. circ. 2,000. **Indexed:** INIS Atomind.
   Description: Covers central heating, ventilation, air-conditioner, pneumatic transport, refrigeration engineering.

620   US   ISSN 0009-8809
CLEVELAND ENGINEERING. 1917. m. $24 to non-members; members $12. Cleveland Engineering Society, 3100 Chester Ave., Cleveland, OH 44114. TEL 216-361-3100. FAX 216-361-1660. Ed. Elaine Rybak. adv.; bk.rev.; abstr.; charts; illus.; index. circ. 2,500. **Document type:** newsletter.
   Description: Multidisciplinary engineering publication serving the Cleveland area.

620   BL
CLUBE DE ENGENHARIA/ENGINEERING CLUB. 1887. bi-m. Av. Passos 115, S-914, CEP 20000, Rio de Janiero, Brazil. Ed. Renato Santal Pereira. circ. 22,000.

620   US   ISSN 0013-8177
VM1
COAST GUARD ENGINEER'S DIGEST. 1933. q. free. U.S. Coast Guard, Office of Engineering, 2100 Second St., S.W., Washington, DC 20593. TEL 202-267-1134. index. circ. 3,000. **Indexed:** Ind.U.S.Gov.Per.
   Formerly: Engineer's Digest (Washington).
   Description: Aimed at sharing lessons learned and advancing engineering in the Coast Guard.

COGENERATION; the magazine for cogeneration management. see *ENERGY*

COGENERATION AND COMPETITIVE POWER JOURNAL. see *ENERGY*

620   SP
COLECCION INGENIERIA. 1982. irreg., no.2, 1987. price varies. (Universidad de Navarra, Escuela Tecnica Superior de Ingenieros Industriales) Ediciones Universidad de Navarra, S.A., Plaza de los Sauces 1 y 2, Baranain, Pamplona, Spain. TEL 94 825 6850.

610   VE   ISSN 0010-0625
COLEGIO DE INGENIEROS DE VENEZUELA. BOLETIN INFORMATIVO.* 1960. m. Colegio de Ingenieros de Venezuela, Apdo. 2006, Bosque Los Acobos, Caracas 101, Venezuela. adv.; bk.rev.; bibl.; charts; illus. circ. 5,500.

620   VE
COLEGIO DE INGENIEROS DE VENEZUELA. DIRECTORIO.* a. Colegio de Ingenieros de Venezuela, Apdo 2006, Bosque Los Caobos, Caracas 101, Venezuela. adv.

620   VE
COLEGIO DE INGENIEROS DE VENEZUELA. NOTICERO.* m. Colegio de Ingenieros de Venezuela, Apdo 2006, Bosque Los Caobos, Caracas 101, Venezuela. adv.

620   VE
COLEGIO DE INGENIEROS DE VENEZUELA. REVISTA.* 1923. q. Colegio de Ingenieros de Venezuela, Apdo 2006, Bosque Los Caobos, Caracas 101, Venezuela. Ed. Rojas Anex Asociados. adv.

620   II
COLLEGE OF ENGINEERING, TRIVANDRUM. MAGAZINE. (Text in English or Malayalam) 1942. a. Rs.10. College of Engineering, Trivandrum 16, Kerala, India. adv.; illus.

620   US   ISSN 0010-1583
COLORADO ENGINEER. 1906. 4/yr. $8 to non-engineering students. University of Colorado, College of Engineering, Engineering Center ST 3-5, Campus Box 422, Boulder, CO 80309-0421. TEL 303-492-8635. Ed. Jeffrey G. Jacot. adv.; bk.rev.; charts; illus.; stat.; tr.lit. circ. 3,000. **Indexed:** GeoRef. **Document type:** academic/scholarly publication.
   —UnCover.

621.4   US   ISSN 0010-2180
QD516   CODEN: CBFMAO
COMBUSTION AND FLAME. 1963. 16/yr. (in 4 vols.). $725 to institutions (foreign $801) (effective 1994). (Combustion Institute) Elsevier Science Inc., 655 Ave. of the Americas, New York, NY 10010. TEL 212-989-5800. FAX 212-633-3990. TELEX 420643 AEP Ul. Eds. D. Bradley, R.A. Strehlow. adv.; bk.rev.; illus.; index. (also avail. in microform from UMI) **Indexed:** API Abstr., API Catal., API Hlth.& Environ., API Oil., API Pet.Ref., API Pet.Subst., API Transport., Appl.Mech.Rev., Biol.Abstr., Br.Ceram.Abstr., Br.Tech.Ind., C.I.S.Abstr., Chem.Abstr., Chem.Eng.Abstr., Curr.Cont., Energy Abstr., Energy Info.Abstr., Eng.Ind., Environ.Per.Bibl., Excerp.Med., Fuel & Energy Abstr., Gas Abstr., Ind.Sci.Rev., INIS Atomind., Int.Aerosp.Abstr., Mass Spectr.Bull., Nucl.Sci.Abstr., Ocean Abstr., Pollut.Abstr., Sci.Abstr., Sci.Cit.Ind., T.C.E.A. **Document type:** academic/scholarly publication.
—BLDSC (3329.200000); EI; Faxon; UnCover; SWETS; CASDDS. **CCC.**
   Description: Covers experimental and theoretical investigations of combustion phenomena and closely allied matters.
   Refereed Serial

620   US
COMMUNICATIONS AND CONTROL ENGINEERING SERIES. 1982. irreg. price varies. Springer-Verlag, 175 Fifth Ave., New York, NY 10010. TEL 212-460-1500. FAX 212-473-6272. (Also: Berlin, Heidelberg, Tokyo and Vienna) Ed.Bd. **Document type:** monographic series.

COMPENSATION AND BENEFITS IN ENGINEERING FIRMS IN THE GEOTECHNICAL FIELD. see *BUSINESS AND ECONOMICS — Labor And Industrial Relations*

620   UK   ISSN 0961-9526
TA418.9.C6   CODEN: CMENEZ
COMPOSITES ENGINEERING; an international journal. 1991. 12/yr. £540($830) (effective 1994). Elsevier Science Ltd., Pergamon, P.O. Box 800, Kidlington, Oxford OX5 1DX, England. TEL 44-865-843000. FAX 44-865-843010. (Subscr. in U.S. and Canada to: Elsevier Science, 660 White Plains Rd., Tarrytown, NY 10591-5153. TEL 914-524-9200. FAX 914-333-2444) Ed. David Hui. index. (also avail. in microfilm from UMI; back issues avail.) **Document type:** academic/scholarly publication.
—BLDSC (3365.550000); UnCover; UMI; CASDDS. **CCC.**
   Description: Publishes theoretical and experimental investigations of composite structures and materials in all application areas, with particular emphasis on new vehicle related environments.
   Refereed Serial

620   US
COMPOSITES QUARTERLY. q. $45 to individuals; institutions $60. Society of Manufacturing Engineers, One SME Dr., Box 930, Dearborn, MI 48121-0930. TEL 313-271-1500. FAX 313-271-2861. TELEX 297742 SME UR (VIA RCA).

COMPUTING & CONTROL ENGINEERING JOURNAL. see *ENGINEERING — Computer Applications*

620 629.8   UK   ISSN 0268-8050
CONDITION MONITOR. 1986. 12/yr. £215($330) (effective 1994). Elsevier Science Ltd., Oxford Fulfilment Centre, P.O. Box 800, Kidlington, Oxford OX5 1DX, England. TEL 44-865-843000. FAX 44-865-843010. (Subscr. in U.S. and Canada to: Elsevier Science, 660 White Plains Rd., Tarrytown, NY 10591-5153. TEL 914-524-9200. FAX 914-333-2444) Ed. S. Barrett. adv. **Document type:** newsletter.
—Faxon. **CCC.**
   Incorporates: Condition Monitoring Journal (ISSN 0950-9178)
   Description: Covers all aspects of predictive maintenance, equipment and machinery monitoring, including techniques, applications, legislation, and operational safety.

CONFEDERATION OF INDIAN INDUSTRY. HANDBOOK OF STATISTICS. see *ENGINEERING — Abstracting, Bibliographies, Statistics*

CONFERENCE ON REMOTE SYSTEMS TECHNOLOGY. PROCEEDINGS. see *COMPUTERS — Robotics*

620   US
CONNECTICUT ENGINEER. m. Connecticut Society of Professional Engineers, 2600 Dixwell Ave., Hamden, CT 06514-1833. TEL 203-281-4322. FAX 203-248-8932. Ed: Paul Brady. adv. **Document type:** newsletter.

CONSTRUCTION ALBERTA NEWS. see *BUILDING AND CONSTRUCTION*

692.8   US   ISSN 0010-6968
CONSTRUCTIONEER; news-photo coverage of construction in New York, Pennsylvania, New Jersey, Delaware. 1945. fortn. $50. H E S, Inc., 26 Long Hill Rd., Box 362, Guilford, CT 06437. FAX 203-453-4390. Ed. Cynthia J. Pallman. adv.; charts; illus.; tr.lit. circ. 15,000. **Indexed:** Concr.Abstr.

620   CN   ISSN 1193-9990
CONSULTING ENGINEERS OF BRITISH COLUMBIA. COMMENTARY. 1978. bi-m. free. Consulting Engineers of British Columbia, 409 Granville St., Vancouver, BC V6C 1T2, Canada. TEL 604-687-2811. FAX 604-688-7110. circ. 2,000 (controlled). **Document type:** newsletter.
   Description: Offers industry profile, selection procedures, awards for engineering excellence, export activity.

620   US   ISSN 0892-5046
TA1
CONSULTING - SPECIFYING ENGINEER. 1987. 15/yr. $74.95 (Canada $112.95; Mexico $104.95; elsewhere $134.95). Cahners Publishing Company (Des Plaines), Division of Reed Elsevier Inc., 1350 E. Touhy Ave., Box 5080, Des Plaines, IL 60017-5080. TEL 708-635-8800. FAX 708-299-8622. (Subscr. to: 44 Cook St., Denver, CO 80206. TEL 800-662-7776) Ed. Paul E. Beck. adv.; bk.rev.; charts; illus.; stat.; tr.lit.; cum.index. circ. 47,550. (also avail. in microform from UMI) **Indexed:** A.S.& T.Ind., ABI Inform., ASCA, Excerp.Med., Fuel & Energy Abstr., Geotech.Abstr., INIS Atomind., Int.Build.Serv.Abstr. **Document type:** trade publication.
—BLDSC (3424.012000); Faxon; UnCover; SWETS; UMI. **CCC.**
   Formed by the 1986 merger of: Consulting Engineer (ISSN 0010-7107); Specifying Engineer (ISSN 0164-5242); Which was formerly (1958-1972): Actual Specifying Engineer (ISSN 0001-7647)
   Description: An applied technology journal serving the technical and business information needs of those engineers personally engaged in the design, specification and product selection of integrated mechanical, electrical and related systems and products for commercial, industrial and institutional buildings and plants.

CONTROL; theory and advanced technology. see *MATHEMATICS*

658.5   US   ISSN 1061-0235
TJ212   CODEN: PCTSES
CONTROLS AND SYSTEMS; the magazine of systems solutions for industry. 1954. m. $50 (free to qualified personnel). Penton Publishing (Subsidiary of: Pittway Company), 1100 Superior Ave., Cleveland, OH 44114-2543. TEL 216-696-7000. FAX 216-696-8765. (Subscr. to: Box 95759, Cleveland, OH 44101) Ed. Leslie Jasany. adv.; bk.rev.; abstr.; charts; illus.; tr.lit.; index; circ. 91,000 (controlled). (also avail. in microform from UMI; reprint service avail. from UMI) **Indexed:** A.I.Abstr. (until 1992), A.S.& T.Ind., ABI Inform., Appl.Mech.Rev., Bus.Ind., C.I.S.Abstr., CAD CAM Abstr. (until 1992), Chem.Abstr., Comput.Lit.Ind., Eng.Ind., Excerp.Med., Fluidex, ISMEC, Met.Abstr., PROMT, Robomat. (until 1992), Sci.Abstr., Tr.& Indus.Ind., World Alum.Abstr.
●Also available online. Vendor(s): DIALOG Information Services, Inc.
—Faxon; UnCover. **CCC.**
   Former titles (until 1991): Automation (ISSN 0896-6052); Production Engineering (ISSN 0146-1737); (until 1977): Automation (ISSN 0005-1160)
   Description: Technology of new processes, machines and metals.

COOLING TOWER INSTITUTE. BIBLIOGRAPHY OF TECHNICAL PAPERS. see *PETROLEUM AND GAS*

ENGINEERING 2243

620 US ISSN 0010-8790
TA1 CODEN: CNLEA
CORNELL ENGINEER.* 1885. 4/yr. $8 (foreign $12). Cornell Engineer, Inc., Cornell University, 217 Carpenter Hall, Ithaca, NY 14853. TEL 607-255-3312. FAX 607-255-9606. Ed. Beth Enslow. adv.; bk.rev.; charts; illus. circ. 5,000. (also avail. in microform from UMI) **Indexed:** GeoRef.
●Also available online.
Description: Features, interviews, editorials, and articles on current areas of interest in both the technical and nontechnical aspects of modern engineering. Written by undergraduate and graduate students of the college and university.

620 US ISSN 1067-9642
TA1
CORNELL ENGINEERING QUARTERLY. 1966. q. $6 (foreign $9). Cornell University, College of Engineering, Carpenter Hall, Campus Rd., Ithaca, NY 14853. TEL 607-255-9606. Ed. David Price. bibl.; charts; illus. circ. 7,000. (also avail. in microform from UMI; reprint service avail. from UMI) **Indexed:** GeoRef., INIS Atomind., Sel.Water Res.Abstr. **Document type:** academic/scholarly publication.
—EI; UnCover; UMI.
Formerly (until vol.26): Engineering: Cornell Quarterly (ISSN 0013-7871)
Description: Articles on scientific and technical issues and topics, particularly concerning research at the College of Engineering, with a registry of events and announcements and a list of publications by faculty.

523.01 US ISSN 0010-9525
QC801 CODEN: CSCRA7
COSMIC RESEARCH. English translation of: Kosmicheskie Issledovaniya (RU ISSN 0023-4206) 1963. bi-m. $1195 (foreign $1395) (effective 1994). (Russian Academy of Sciences, RU) Plenum Publishing Corp., Consultants Bureau, 233 Spring St., New York, NY 10013-1578. TEL 212-620-8468. FAX 212-463-0742. TELEX 23-421139. Ed. L.I. Sedov. (also avail. in microfilm from JSC; back issues avail.) **Indexed:** Appl.Mech.Rev., Energy Res.Abstr., Eng.Ind., INIS Atomind., Sci.Abstr. **Document type:** academic/scholarly publication.
—BLDSC (0411.075000); UnCover; UMI. **CCC.**
Refereed Serial

620 657 US ISSN 0274-9696
TA183
COST ENGINEERING (MORGANTOWN, 1980). 1958. m. $48 (foreign $64). A A C E International, Box 1557, Morgantown, WV 26507-1557. TEL 304-296-8444. FAX 304-291-5728. TELEX 887612 AACE MORG UD. Ed. Cathie Falvey. adv.; bk.rev.; bibl.; charts; illus.; pat.; stat.; index. circ. 6,000. (also avail. in microform from UMI; reprint service avail. from UMI) **Indexed:** Abstr.Bull.Inst.Pap.Chem., Eng.Ind., P.A.I.S., Sci.Abstr. **Document type:** trade publication.
—BLDSC (3477.239000); EI; Faxon; UnCover; SWETS; UMI. **CCC.**
Former titles: Cost Engineering Magazine (ISSN 0276-721X); Cost Engineering (1978) (ISSN 0161-6315); A A C E Bulletin (ISSN 0001-0049)
Description: For engineers specializing in cost estimating, cost control, project management, business planning and management sciences.

620 657 US
COST ENGINEERS' NOTEBOOK. 1956. irreg. $175 to non-members; members $85. A A C E International, Box 1557, Morgantown, WV 26507-1557. TEL 304-296-8444. FAX 304-291-5728. TELEX 887612 AACE MORG UD. Ed. Cathleen Falvey. circ. 6,000. (back issues avail.)

CRITICAL ISSUES IN FACILITIES MANAGEMENT. see EDUCATION — School Organization And Administration

620 II ISSN 0045-9291
CURRENT ENGINEERING PRACTICE. (Text in English) 1958. q. Rs.50. Best Books Private Ltd., Komal, First Floor, Plot 86, Road No. 2, P.B. 7205, Chembur P.O., Bombay 400071, India. Ed. K. Janakiraman. adv.; bk.rev.; bibl.; charts; illus. **Indexed:** Corros.Abstr., INIS Atomind.

CUSTOM BUILDER; the business magazine for builders of premier homes. see BUILDING AND CONSTRUCTION

620 PH ISSN 0116-7103
D L S U ENGINEERING JOURNAL. (Text in English) 1985. s-a. P.60($4.40) (De La Salle University, College of Engineering) De La Salle University Press, 2401 Taft Ave., Manila, Philippines. TEL 2-59-48-32. FAX 632-521-9094. adv.; bk.rev. circ. 300. **Document type:** academic/scholarly publication.
Description: Publishes scholarly articles reflecting significant quantitative or qualitative research.

629.8 DK ISSN 0011-6076
DANFOSS JOURNAL; automatic controls design and practice. French edition: Revue Danfoss (ISSN 0373-4862); Italian edition: Rivista Danfoss (ISSN 0106-7656); German edition: Danfoss Journal (ISSN 0106-7621); Swedish edition: Danfoss Journalen (ISSN 0106-763X); Spanish edition: Revista Danfoss (ISSN 0106-7648) (Danish edition: Danfoss Journalen (ISSN 0106-7605); Dutch edition: Danfoss Journaal (ISSN 0106-7613)) (Text in English) 1943. q. free to qualified personnel. Danfoss A-S, DK-6430 Nordborg, Denmark. FAX 74-88-490949. TELEX 50599-DANFSS-DK. Ed. T. Fich. charts; illus.; index. circ. 81,325. **Indexed:** BMT, Int.Build.Serv.Abstr., Sci.Abstr., W.R.C.Inf.
—BLDSC (3518.500000).

DENMARK. FORSKNINGSCENTER RISOE. RISOE-R. see ENERGY — Nuclear Energy

700 604.24 US
DESIGN & DRAFTING NEWS. m. membership. American Design Drafting Association, Box 799, Rockville, MD 20848-0799. TEL 301-460-6875. FAX 301-460-8591. Ed. R. Howard. adv.; bk.rev. circ. 2,500. **Document type:** newsletter.

620 CN ISSN 0011-9342
CODEN: DEENAK
DESIGN ENGINEERING. 1955. 10/yr. Can.$34. Maclean-Hunter Ltd., Business Publication Division, Maclean-Hunter Bldg., 777 Bay St., Toronto, ON M5W 1A7, Canada. TEL 416-596-6016. FAX 416-596-5881. Ed. Steve Purwitsky. adv.; illus.; tr.lit. circ. 183,363. (also avail. in microform from UMI; reprint service avail. from UMI) **Indexed:** Can.B.P.I., Eng.Ind., Fluidex, PROMT.
—Faxon; UnCover. **CCC.**

620 UK ISSN 0011-9350
DESIGN ENGINEERING. 1964. m. Morgan-Grampian (Publishers) Ltd. (Subsidiary of: Morgan-Grampian plc), Morgan-Grampian House, 30 Calderwood St., London SE18 6QH, England. TEL 081-855-7777. FAX 081-854-7476. Ed. David Wilson. adv.; bk.rev.; illus.; pat. circ. 28,811. (also avail. in microform from UMI; reprint service avail. from UMI) **Indexed:** BMT, C.I.S. Abstr., Copper Abstr., Eng.Ind., Excerp.Med., Fluidex, HRIS, ISMEC, Met.Abstr., PROMT, Sci.Abstr., World Text.Abstr. **Document type:** trade publication.

620 CN ISSN 0319-8413
DESIGN PRODUCT NEWS. 1973. 6/yr. Can.$35. Action Communications Inc., 135 Spy Court, Markham, ON L3R 5H6, Canada. TEL 905-477-3222. FAX 905-477-4320. Eds. J.C. Young, P. Eng. adv.; circ. 19,020 (controlled).

620 600 UK
DESIGN PRODUCTS AND APPLICATION. 1979. m. £50 (Europe £70). Industrial Media Ltd., Blair House, High St., Tonbridge, Kent TN9 1BE, England. TEL 0732-359990. FAX 0732-770049. TELEX 957329. Ed. Robert Brooks. adv. **Indexed:** Br.Ceram.Abstr. **Document type:** consumer publication.

620 II
DESIGNER. 1954. q. Indian Society of Engineers, 5 Lindsay St., Calcutta 7000016, India. Ed. M.K. Diwam. adv. circ. 7,651.

620 US
DESIGNFAX MAGAZINE. 1979. m. $54 (Canada $85; elsewhere $125). Huebcore Communications, Inc., 29100 Aurora Rd., Ste. 200, Solon, OH 44139. TEL 216-248-1125. FAX 612-686-0214. (Subscr. to: Box 21640, Eagan, MN 55121-0640. TEL 612-686-0303) adv. circ. 110,000.
Formerly: Designfax.
Description: Digest of changing technology and new products for design engineers and engineering managers.

620 GW
DEUTSCHES INGENIEURBLATT; Organ der deutschen Ingenieurkammern. 1970. 10/yr. DM.200($162) (Bundesingenieurkammer) Vogel Verlag und Druck KG, Max-Planck-Str. 7-9, 97082 Wuerzburg, Germany. TEL 0931-4182145. FAX 0931-4182640. (Subscr. to: Vogel Verlag, 97064 Wuerzburg, Germany; Dist. in U.S. by: Vogel Europublishing, Inc., 20092 Gibbs Dr., Sonora, CA 95370. TEL 209-533-3555. FAX 209-533-9555) Ed. Rene Peruche. adv.: B&W page DM.7298, color page DM.10238; trim 270 x 190. bk.rev.; charts; illus.; stat. circ. 10,000. (also avail. in microform from UMI) **Indexed:** Excerp.Med. **Document type:** trade publication.
—BLDSC (1892.900000). **CCC.**
Formerly (until 1994): Beratende Ingenieure (ISSN 0005-8866)
Description: Focuses on future developments and technological innovation in the building and construction industry.

DIAL. METALS, METALWORKING, MECHANICAL ENGINEERING, SHIPBUILDING, AEROSPACE, MARINE AND VEHICLE INDUSTRIES. see METALLURGY

DIGITAL TECHNICAL JOURNAL. see COMPUTERS — Computer Engineering

620 TS
DIRASAT HANDASIYYAH/ENGINEERING STUDIES. (Text in Arabic, English) 1988. a. United Arab Emirates University, Faculty of Engineering, P.O. Box 15551, Al-Ain, United Arab Emirates. TEL 637833. TELEX 33521 JAMEAH EM. Ed. Awad Salim al-Hakim. circ. 1,000.
Description: Publishes research from all fields of engineering and related technology, including environmental studies, with a focus on the Gulf region and the U.A.E.

620 US
DIRECTORY OF CONSULTING ENGINEERING SERVICES IN NORTH CAROLINA. biennial. $15. North Carolina State University, School of Engineering, Industrial Extension Service, Box 7902, Raleigh, NC 27695-7902. TEL 919-515-2358. Ed. Paul Cowgill.

620 US
DIRECTORY OF ENGINEERING - ARCHITECTURAL MINORITY AND WOMEN OWNED FIRMS. irreg. $15. American Consulting Engineers Council, 1015 15th St., N.W., Ste. 802, Washington, DC 20005-2670. TEL 202-347-7474.

620 US ISSN 0420-2155
DIRECTORY OF ENGINEERS AND LAND SURVEYORS REGISTERED IN SOUTH CAROLINA. (Continues the Board's Roster of Registered Professional Engineers and Land Surveyors) 1923. a. $15. Board of Registration for Professional Engineers and Land Surveyors, Box 50408, 2221 Devine St., Ste. 404, Columbia, SC 29250. **Document type:** directory, government publication.

DIRECTORY OF INDIAN ENGINEERING EXPORTERS. see BUSINESS AND ECONOMICS — Trade And Industrial Directories

DIRECTORY OF PERSECUTED SCIENTISTS, ENGINEERS AND HEALTH PROFESSIONALS. see POLITICAL SCIENCE — Civil Rights

DIRECTORY OF THE FRENCH NUCLEAR INDUSTRY. see ENERGY — Nuclear Energy

DIRECTORY OF THE SCIENTISTS, TECHNOLOGISTS, AND ENGINEERS OF THE P C S I R. see SCIENCES: COMPREHENSIVE WORKS

DISEGNO. see INTERIOR DESIGN AND DECORATION

DISTRIBUTED SYSTEMS ENGINEERING. see PHYSICS

DIZHEN GONGCHENG YU GONGCHENG ZHENDONG/EARTHQUAKE ENGINEERING AND ENGINEERING VIBRATION. see EARTH SCIENCES — Geophysics

DONGNAN DAXUE XUEBAO/SOUTHEAST UNIVERSITY. JOURNAL. see SCIENCES: COMPREHENSIVE WORKS

ENGINEERING

620 NE ISSN 0012-5482
DOORKIJK. 1965. 6/yr. fl.12 free. Katholiek Vrouwengilde Nederland, Bisonspoor 1204, 3605 KZ Maarssen, Netherlands. TEL 03465-73670. adv.; bk.rev.; charts; illus.; circ. 500 (controlled).

620 JA ISSN 0036-8172
CODEN: DDRKAZ
DOSHISHA DAIGAKU RIKOGAKU KENKYU HOKOKU/DOSHISHA UNIVERSITY. SCIENCE AND ENGINEERING REVIEW. (Text in English and Japanese; summaries in English) 1960. q. 1200 Yen($8) (effective 1993). Doshisha University, Science and Engineering Research Institute - Doshisha Daigaku Rikogaku Kenkyujo, Tanabe-cho, Tsuzukictun, Kyoto 610-03, Japan. FAX 75-251-3085. Ed. Y. Ishihara. indie. circ. 4,340. **Indexed:** Chem.Abstr., Dairy Sci.Abstr., Fluidex, INIS Atomind., JCT, JTA, Met.Abstr., World Alum.Abstr. **Document type:** academic/scholarly publication, bulletin.
—BLDSC (8133.100000); UnCover; CASDDS.

DRAHT; internationale Fachzeitschrift fuer die Draht- und Kabelindustrie und alle Bereiche der Drahtverarbeitung. see METALLURGY

620 SW ISSN 0345-2484
DRIFTTEKNIK. Variant title: Tidskriften Driftteknik. 1960. bi-m. SEK 75 (effective 1990). Drift- & Arbetsledarefoerbundet, c/o B. Rudhag, Irisg. 96, 703 53 Lidingoe, Sweden. (Subscr. to: Sveav. 98, 113 51 Stockholm, Sweden) adv. circ. 6,214.
Formerly (until vol.2, 1973): S L A M.

620 US ISSN 0046-0818
DUKENGINEER. 1936. s-a. Duke University, School of Engineering, Durham, NC 27706. TEL 919-684-2214. adv.; bk.rev.; illus.; stat. circ. 6,000.
Refereed Serial

620 CK ISSN 0012-7353
TN4 CODEN: DYNABV
DYNA. 1933. s-a. Col.12000($15) for 4 issues (effective 1994-95) (or exchange basis). Universidad Nacional de Colombia, Facultad Nacional de Minas, Apdo. Aereo 1027, Medellin, Colombia. TEL 2344503. FAX 2341002. Ed. Jaime Aguirre Cardona. adv.; bk.rev.; charts; illus.; bibl.; cum.index: 1933-1986; circ. 1,500 (controlled). **Indexed:** Chem.Abstr., GeoRef., Sci.Abstr., World Alum.Abstr. **Document type:** academic/scholarly publication.
—BLDSC (3637.020000); CASDDS.

620 SP ISSN 0012-7361
CODEN: DYNAAU
DYNA. 1926. m. (11/yr.). 3700 ptas.($47) Asociacion Nacional de Ingenieros Industriales de Espana - Federation of Industrial Engineering Associations, Alameda de Mazarredo, 69, Apdo. 646, 48009 Bilbao, Spain. TEL 4-423-7566. FAX 4-4234461. Dir. Jose Miguel Maranon. adv.; bk.rev.; abstr.; bibl.; charts; illus.; pat.; stat.; index. circ. 6,000. **Indexed:** Chem.Abstr., Ind.SST, Met.Abstr., Sci.Abstr.
—UMI; CASDDS. **CCC.**

510 US ISSN 1056-2176
▼**DYNAMIC SYSTEMS AND APPLICATIONS.** 1992. q. $75 to individuals (foreign $91); institutions $150 (foreign $166). Dynamic Publishers, Inc., Box 48654, Atlanta, GA 30362. TEL 404-451-3616. Ed. M. Sambandham. **Document type:** academic/scholarly publication.
—BLDSC (3637.142500). **CCC.**
Description: Provides an international forum for the information in the theory and practice of dynamic systems and applications.

E E R I NEWSLETTER. (Earthquake Engineering Research Institute) see EARTH SCIENCES

620 US ISSN 0098-6305
TA12
E N R DIRECTORY OF DESIGN FIRMS. 1974. biennial. $85 per no. McGraw-Hill, Inc., 1221 Ave. of the Americas, New York, NY 10020. TEL 212-512-2000. Ed. Paul Herrnmansfeldt. illus. circ. 12,000.

E P E. see ENGINEERING — Electrical Engineering

620 US
E-QUAD NEWS. 1988. 3/yr. free. Princeton University, School of Engineering & Applied Sciences, Publications Office, C218 Engineering Quadrangle, Princeton, NJ 08544-5263. TEL 609-258-3617. FAX 609-258-6744. Ed. Richard L. Golden. bk.rev.; circ. 12,300 (controlled).
Description: Features news and information pertaining to the School of Engineering and Applied Science, various research projects and programs, faculty, students, and alumni.

E R A TECHNOLOGY NEWS. (Electrical Research Association) see BUSINESS AND ECONOMICS — Marketing And Purchasing

620 US ISSN 8750-7811
TA1
E S D TECHNOLOGY. 1936. m. $22 (foreign $30). (Engineering Society of Detroit) Engineering Technology Publishing, 27421 Harper Ave., St. Clair Shores, MI 48081. TEL 313-774-3530. FAX 313-774-3892. Ed. Karen Shellie. adv.; illus. circ. 10,000. **Indexed:** Mich.Mag.Ind. **Document type:** trade publication.
Former titles: D E Technology; Detroit Engineer (ISSN 0011-9628)

620 US
E W DESIGN ENGINEERS' HANDBOOK AND MANUFACTURERS DIRECTORY. (Electronic Warfare) 1987. a. $35. Horizon House Publications, Inc., 685 Canton St., Norwood, MA 02062. TEL 617-769-9750. FAX 617-769-9884. Ed. Sheldon Herskovitz. adv.; index. (back issues avail.) **Document type:** directory.
Formerly: E W Design Engineers' Handbook (ISSN 0895-7541)
Description: Covers systems, analog, digital, security and MIL design.

620 BE
ECHOS-FLASH. 1963. m. 750 Fr.($15) Institut Catholique des Hautes Etudes Commerciales, Association des Licencies et Ingenieurs, Bd. Brand Whitlock 2, 1150 Brussels, Belgium. circ. 2,000.
Formerly: Echos.

ECOLOGICAL ENGINEERING; the journal of ecotechnology. see ENVIRONMENTAL STUDIES

620 RU ISSN 0203-8889
EKSPRESS-INFORMATSIYA. INFORMATIKA. 1979. w. 26.40 Rub. Vsesoyuznyi Institut Nauchno-Tekhnicheskoi Informatsii (VINITI), Baltiiskaya ul. 14, Moscow A-219, Russia.

ELECTRICITE DE FRANCE. DIRECTION DES ETUDES ET RECHERCHES. COLLECTION DE NOTES INTERNES. PRODUCTION D'ENERGIE (HYDRAULIQUE, THERMIQUE ET NUCLEAIRE). see ENGINEERING — Mechanical Engineering

621.3 KR ISSN 0453-7998
T4 CODEN: VEPIBL
ELEKTROENERGETIKA I AVTOMATIZATSIYA ENERGOUSTANOVOK. (Subseries of: Kharkivskyi Politekhnichnyi Instytut. Vestnik) 1971. irreg. price varies. Kharkivskyi Politekhnichyi Instytut, Ul. Frunze, 21, Kharkov 310002, Ukraine. illus.
—CASDDS.

ELEKTROTECHNICKY CASOPIS/ELECTROTECHNICAL JOURNAL. see ENGINEERING — Electrical Engineering

620 GW
ELSNERS HANDBUCH FUER STAEDTISCHES INGENIEURWESEN. 1973. a. DM.28.40. Otto Elsner Verlagsgesellschaft, Schoefferstr. 15, 64295 Darmstadt, Germany. Ed. Otto Sill. circ. 3,500.
Formerly: Elsners Handbuch fuer Staedtischen Ingenieurbau.

ENERGIETECHNIEK. see ENGINEERING — Electrical Engineering

ENERGY AND ENGINEERING SCIENCE. see ENERGY

ENERGY SYSTEMS AND POLICY; an international interdisciplinary journal. see ENERGY

658.5 BL
ENGENHARIA INDUSTRIAL. 1977. m. Novo Grupo Editora Tecnica Ltda., Rua Pirapitingui 186, Liverdade, CEP 01580 Sao Paulo, Brazil. TEL 011-270-7380. TELEX 1133150 NGET BR. Ed. Luiza Misao Okamoto. circ. 25,000.

620 CN
ENGINEER. 1959? bi-m. membership. Association of Professional Engineers of Nova Scotia, 1355 Barrington St., Box 129, Halifax, N.S. B3J 2M4, Canada. TEL 902-429-2250. FAX 902-423-9769. Ed.Bd. adv.; charts; illus.; maps. circ. 4,500.
Incorporates: Professional Engineer (ISSN 0225-851X); Formerly: Professional Engineer in Nova Scotia (ISSN 0033-0086)

620 UK ISSN 0013-7758
CODEN: ENGIAL
THE ENGINEER. 1856. w. Morgan-Grampian (Publishers) Ltd. (Subsidiary of: Morgan-Grampian plc), Morgan-Grampian House, 30 Calderwood St., London SE18 6QH, England. TEL 081-855-7777. FAX 081-854-7476. Ed. Chris Barrie. adv.; bk.rev.; charts; illus.; pat.; stat.; tr.lit.; index. circ. 40,592. (also avail. in microform from MIM,UMI,PMC; reprint service avail. from UMI) **Indexed:** A.S.& T.Ind., Appl.Mech.Rev., BMT, Br.Tech.Ind., Chem.Abstr., Chem.Eng.Abstr., Eng.Ind., Excerp.Med., Fluidex, Geotech.Abstr., Ind.Sci.Rev., INIS Atomind., Key to Econ.Sci., Met.Abstr., PROMT, Sci.Abstr., T.C.E.A. **Document type:** trade publication.
—BLDSC (3749.000000); SWETS. **CCC.**

620 CE
ENGINEER. (Text in English) 1973. q. Rs.40($1) per no. Institution of Engineers, Sri Lanka, 120-15 Wijerama Mawatha, Colombo 7, Sri Lanka. TEL 698426. FAX 699202. Ed.Bd. adv.; illus. circ. 3,750. **Indexed:** Fluidex, Sri Lanka Sci.Ind.

620 US ISSN 0046-1989
UG1
ENGINEER (FORT LEONARD WOOD); professional bulletin. 1971-1973; resumed 1982. q. $8.50 (foreign $10.65). U.S. Army Engineer School, Attn.: ATSE-T-PD-EB, Ft. Leonard Wood, MO 65473-6650. TEL 314-563-4104. FAX 314-563-4089. (Subscr. to: Supt. of Documents, Washington, DC 20402) **Indexed:** Ind.U.S.Gov.Per., PROMT. **Document type:** government publication.
—UnCover; UMI.

620 UK ISSN 0071-0288
THE ENGINEER BUYER'S GUIDE. 1897. a. £59 (overseas £69). Benn Business Information Services Ltd. (Subsidiary of: Morgan-Grampian plc), Riverbank House, Angel Ln., Tonbridge, Kent TN9 1SE, England. TEL 0732-362666. FAX 0732-767301. TELEX 957829 BENTON G. Ed. Maria Atkin. adv. circ. 5,000. **Document type:** directory.
Description: A buyer's guide for management within the engineering industries.

620 US ISSN 0277-1233
ENGINEER OF CALIFORNIA. 1947. m. $12. Engineers' Secretarial Service, Box 991, Alhambra, CA 91802. TEL 213-283-1986. FAX 818-281-5646. Ed. Annette Schilling. adv.; charts; illus. circ. 6,000. **Document type:** trade publication.
Formerly: Engineer of Southern California (ISSN 0013-7766)
Description: Provides engineering highlights, engineers & consultants directory, meeting notices, ads and employment opportunities.

620 UK ISSN 0013-7782
TA1 CODEN: ENGNA2
ENGINEERING. 1866. m. (except July). $100. Design Council, 28 Haymarket, London SW1Y 4SU, England. TEL 071-839-8000. Ed. A. Pye. adv.; bk.rev.; abstr.; charts; illus.; tr.lit.; s-a. index. circ. 21,336. (also avail. in microfilm from UMI,PMC; reprint service avail. from UMI) **Indexed:** A.S.& T.Ind., Appl.Mech.Rev., B.C.I.R.A., BMT, Br.Tech.Ind., C.I.S.Abstr., Cadscan, Chem.Abstr., Chem.Eng.Abstr., Copper Abstr., Eng.Ind., Excerp.Med., Fluidex, Geotech.Abstr., High.Educ.Curr.Aware.Bull., HRIS, INIS Atomind., Intl.Civil Eng.Abstr., ISMEC, Lead Abstr., Met.Abstr., Ocean.Abstr., Pollut.Abstr., RICS, Sci.Abstr., Soft.Abstr.Eng., SSCI, W.R.C.Inf., World Text.Abstr., Zincscan. **Document type:** trade publication.
—BLDSC (3752.000000); Faxon; UnCover; SWETS; UMI.
Description: Editorials covering the spectrum of the manufacturing industry.

ENGINEERING

ENGINEERING & MINING JOURNAL. see *MINES AND MINING INDUSTRY*

ENGINEERING & PRODUCT NEWS. see *MINES AND MINING INDUSTRY*

620 US ISSN 0013-7812
T171
ENGINEERING & SCIENCE. 1937. 4/yr. $8 (foreign $20) (effective 1993). California Institute of Technology, 1-71 Caltech, Pasadena, CA 91125. TEL 818-356-3630. Ed. Jane Dietrich. adv.; bk.rev.; illus. circ. 16,000.
—BLDSC (3755.290000); Faxon.

620 US
ENGINEERING AND SCIENCE REVIEW. 2/yr. Case Western Reserve University, 11111 Euclid Ave., Cleveland, OH 44106-1715. TEL 216-368-2316. FAX 216-368-4835. circ. 3,000.

ENGINEERING APPLICATIONS OF ARTIFICIAL INTELLIGENCE. see *COMPUTERS — Artificial Intelligence*

620 UK ISSN 0306-0179
ENGINEERING CAPACITY. 1959. m. International Thomson Business Publishing, 100 Avenue Road, London NW3 3TP, England. TEL 01-935-6611. adv.; circ. 10,136 (controlled).
Formerly: Engineering Capacity Register (ISSN 0013-7855)

ENGINEERING COMMITTEE ON OCEANIC RESOURCES. PROCEEDINGS OF THE GENERAL ASSEMBLY. see *WATER RESOURCES*

620 US
ENGINEERING CONTACTS.* m. Meusey Communications, 1107 Hazeltine Blvd., Ste., 478, Chaska, MN 55318-1008. TEL 612-448-5907. Ed. Jim Meusey. circ. 3,000.

620 US ISSN 1056-1773
ENGINEERING DEPARTMENT MANAGEMENT & ADMINISTRATION REPORT. m. $245. Institute of Management and Administration, 29 W. 35th St., 5th Fl., NY 10001-2299. TEL 212-244-0360. FAX 212-564-0465. Ed. Joe Mazel. index. (back issues avail.)
—CCC.

620 II
ENGINEERING DESIGN. (Text in English) 1970. q. Rs.10. Institution of Engineers (India), National Design and Research Forum, Post Office Road, Bangalore 550 001, India. TEL 0812-27361. Ed. K. N. Majumdar. adv.; illus. circ. 1,000.

620 UK ISSN 0013-7898
CODEN: ENDSA2
ENGINEERING DESIGNER.* 1950. m. £6. Courtleigh, Westbury Leigh, Westbury, Wiltshire BA13 3TA, England. Ed. P. J. Booker. adv.; bk.rev.; abstr.; charts; illus.; cum.index. circ. 10,500. Indexed: Br.Tech.Ind, Fluidex, ISMEC.
—BLDSC (3759.000000).

620 CN ISSN 0227-5147
ENGINEERING DIMENSIONS. 1980. bi-m. Can.$25. Association of Professional Engineers of Ontario, 1155 Yonge St., Toronto, ON M4T 2Y5, Canada. FAX 416-961-1499. Ed. Connie Mucklestone. adv. contact: Susan Browne. bk.rev.; abstr.; charts; illus.; pat.; stat.; tr.lit.; index. circ. 61,155. (back issues avail.) Indexed: Can.Per.Ind.
●Also available online.
Description: Business journal for professional engineers.

620 UK ISSN 0260-4922
ENGINEERING DISTRIBUTOR. 1977. 12/yr. £27 (foreign £39). Bouverie Publishing Company Ltd., 131-135 Temple Chambers, Temple Ave., London EC4Y 0DT, England. TEL 071-583-3030. FAX 071-583-6481. Ed. Paul/Newbon. adv. Document type: trade publication.
Formerly (until vol.4, no.8, 1980): Engineering Distributors Journal.

338.4 620 US ISSN 0013-791X
HD28 CODEN: ENECAR
ENGINEERING ECONOMIST. 1955. q. $24 to individuals (foreign $34); institutions $55 (foreign $78). Institute of Industrial Engineers, 25 Technology Park-Atlanta, Norcross, GA 30092. TEL 404-449-0460. FAX 404-263-8532. (Co-sponsor: American Society for Engineering Education) Ed. Jack R. Lohmann. adv.; bk.rev.; charts; illus.; index. circ. 1,300. (also avail. in microfilm from UMI; reprint service avail. from UMI) Indexed: ABI Inform., Account.Ind. (1974-), B.P.I., BMT, BPIA, Bus.Ind., Cont.Pg.Manage., Fuel & Energy Abstr., Gas Abstr., INIS Atomind., Int.Abstr.Oper.Res., Manage.Cont., Sci.Abstr., SCIMP, Tr.& Indus.Ind.
—BLDSC (3759.550000); EI; Faxon; UnCover; SWETS; UMI. CCC.
Description: Devoted to the problems of capital investment.

620 UK ISSN 0141-7592
TA157
ENGINEERING EMPLOYERS' FEDERATION DIRECTORY. a. £100. (Engineering Employers' Federation) Guardian Communications Ltd., Albany House, Hurst St., Birmingham B5 4BD, England. TEL 021-622 4011. FAX 021-625-3564. TELEX 948669-TOPJNL-G.
Description: Provides a "shop window" for British engineering at home and abroad.

ENGINEERING EVIDENCE, 2-E. see *LAW*

ENGINEERING FAILURE ANALYSIS. see *ENGINEERING — Engineering Mechanics And Materials*

620 PK ISSN 0013-7936
ENGINEERING FORUM. (Text in English) 1959. m. Rs.16.($3.30) Mohammad Yusef Kureshy, Ed. & Pub., 14 Japan Mansion, Preedy St., Saddar, Karachi 3, Pakistan. TEL 722458. adv.; bk.rev.; abstr.; charts; illus.; stat.; tr.lit. circ. 6,500. (tabloid format)

620 US
ENGINEERING FOUNDATION ANNUAL REPORT. 1914. a. free. Engineering Foundation, United Engineering Center, 345 E. 47th St., New York, NY 10017. TEL 212-705-7835. FAX 212-705-7441. circ. 300.

620 UK
ENGINEERING GAZETTE. 1940. bi-m. free to members. (Engineering Industries Association) Northern Advertising Agency Ltd., P.O. Box 19, King Cross St., Halifax HX1 2SF, England. FAX 0422-330021. Ed. Eric Ford. adv.; bk.rev.; illus.; stat. circ. 3,000. Document type: trade publication.
Former titles: Engineering Industries Gazette; Engineering Industries Journal (ISSN 0013-7995)

620.7 370.58 US
ENGINEERING GRADUATE STUDIES AND RESEARCH. DIRECTORY. (Supplement to: A S E E Prism) 1967. a. $69.95 to non-members. American Society for Engineering Education, 1818 N St., N.W., Ste. 600, Washington, DC 20036. TEL 202-331-3500. FAX 202-265-8504. Ed. Patricia W. Samaras. adv.; index. circ. 12,500. (also avail. in microfiche; microfilm; reprint service avail. from UMI) Indexed: Curr.Cont., Eng.Ind. Document type: directory.
Former titles: Engineering College Research and Graduate Study; Directory of Engineering College Research and Graduate Study (ISSN 0070-5462)

620 II ISSN 0013-7987
ENGINEERING INDUSTRIES & TRADE JOURNAL. (Text in English) m. $30. Praveen Corp., Sayajiganj, Baroda 390005, India.

620 UK ISSN 0071-0342
ENGINEERING INDUSTRIES ASSOCIATION. CLASSIFIED DIRECTORY AND BUYERS GUIDE. 1949. biennial. Northern Advertising Agency Ltd., P.O. Box 19, King Cross St., Halifax HX1 2SF, England. FAX 0422-330021. Ed. Eric Ford. adv. circ. 45,000. Document type: trade publication.

620 UK
ENGINEERING INDUSTRIES ASSOCIATION. DIARY. a. Northern Advertising Agency Ltd., P.O. Box 19, King Cross St., Halifax HX1 2SF, England. FAX 0422-330021. Document type: trade publication.

ENGINEERING MANAGEMENT & EQUIPMENT DIGEST. see *BUSINESS AND ECONOMICS — Management*

620 US ISSN 1042-9247
CODEN: EMJOEH
ENGINEERING MANAGEMENT JOURNAL. 1989. q. $40. American Society for Engineering Management, 1005 Pine St., Box 820, Rolla, MO 65401. TEL 314-341-2101. FAX 314-341-5522. Ed. Ted Eschenbach. adv.; bk.rev. circ. 2,300. Document type: academic/scholarly publication.
—BLDSC (3764.781600); UnCover; UMI.

620 658 UK ISSN 0960-7919
CODEN: EMAJEP
ENGINEERING MANAGEMENT JOURNAL. 1991. bi-m. £72 in E.C. nations; elsewhere £80. I.E.E, Michael Faraday House, Six Hills Way, Stevenage, Herts. SG1 2AY, England. TEL 0438-313311. FAX 0438-742792. TELEX 825578-IEESTV-G. (Subscr. to: Publication Sales Dept., P.O. Box 96, Stevenage, Herts. SG1 2SD, England; U.S. addr.: INSPEC/IEEE, Box 1331, 445 Hoes Ln., Piscataway, NJ 08855-1331. TEL 908-562-5549) Ed. John Cooper. Document type: academic/scholarly publication.
—BLDSC (3764.781530). CCC.
Description: Aims to assist engineers in improving their management skills through articles on recruitment, employment law, company finance, and take-overs. Also examines the strategic issues of engineering management on an international level within the context of global competition and includes case studies.

620 UK ISSN 0967-7003
▼**ENGINEERING MATERIALS**; a current awareness bulletin. 1993. m. £99 (foreign £105). (Institution of Mechanical Engineers) Mechanical Engineering Publications Ltd., Northgate Ave., Bury St. Edmunds, Suffolk IP32 6BW, England. TEL 0284-763277. FAX 0284-704006. TELEX 817376. Document type: abstracting/indexing, bulletin.
Description: Focuses on new engineering materials and alternative applications of engineering materials.

620 BG
ENGINEERING NEWS.* (Text in English) 1956. m. membership. Institution of Engineers, Ramna, Dhaka 2, Bangladesh. circ. 3,369.

620 SA ISSN 0257-8646
ENGINEERING NEWS. 1981. 48/yr. R.432 (effective 1993). Martin Creamer Publications, P.O. Box 75316, Garden View 2047, South Africa. FAX 27-11-622-3744. Ed. Martin Creamer. adv.; bk.rev.; abstr.; bibl.; charts; illus. circ. 19,104. (tabloid format; back issues avail.) Indexed: INIS Atomind.

620 US
ENGINEERING NOW. 1976. a. Virginia Polytechnic Institute and State University, College of Engineering, 333 Norris Hall, Blacksburg, VA 24061. TEL 703-961-6641. FAX 703-231-7248. Ed. Lynn A. Nystrom. circ. 15,000.

620 US ISSN 0305-215X
TA174 CODEN: EGOPAX
ENGINEERING OPTIMIZATION. 1974. 8/yr. (in 2 vols., 4 nos./vol.). 215 ECU per vol. (effective 1993). Gordon & Breach Science Publishers, 820 Town Center Dr., Langhorne, PA 19047. TEL 215-750-2642. FAX 215-750-6343. (UK subscr. to: P.O. Box 90, Reading, Berkshire RG1 8JL, England. TEL 0734-560-080) Ed. Andrew B. Templeman. adv.; bk.rev.; illus.; index. (also avail. in microform) Indexec: Appl.Mech.Rev., BMT, Curr.Cont., Int.Abstr.Oper.Res., Sci.Abstr. Document type: academic/scholarly publication.
—BLDSC (3766.145000); Faxon; UnCover; SWETS. CCC.
Refereed Serial

620 US
ENGINEERING OUTLOOK. 1960. q. free. University of Illinois at Urbana-Champaign, Engineering Publications Office, 112 Engineering Hall, 1308 W. Green St., Urbana, IL 61801. TEL 217-333-1510. FAX 217-244-7704. Ed. Maureen Tan. circ. 24,000. Indexed: Fluidex, J.of Ferroc. Document type: newsletter.
Formerly: Engineering Outlook at the University of Illinois at Urbana-Champaign (ISSN 0013-8088)

ENGINEERING

658   UK
ENGINEERING RESEARCH CENTRES. 1984. irreg., 3rd ed., 1993. £250. Longman Group UK Ltd., Westgate House, 6th Fl., The High, Harlow, Essex CM20 1YR, England. TEL 0279-442601. FAX 0279-444501. (Dist. in U.S. and Canada by: Gale Research Inc., 835 Penobscot Bldg., Detroit, MI 48277-0748) Ed.Bd. **Document type:** directory.
    Description: Provides 4,000 entries describing official laboratories, industrial research centers, and educational establishments with R&D activity in a wide range of engineering fields.

620   MY
ENGINEERING SCIENCE AND TECHNOLOGY. 1958-1988 (vol.24); resumed 1993. a. $4 (includes seamail postage). University of Malaya, Faculty of Engineering, Lembah Pantai, 59100 Kuala Lumpur, Malaysia. FAX 603-755-3466. TELEX UNIMAL MA 39845. Ed. Wan Abu Bakar Wan Abas. adv.; illus. **Indexed:** Geotech.Abstr.
    Former titles (until 1988): University of Malaya. Faculty of Engineering. Journal; University of Malaya. Department of Engineering. Journal.
    Description: Covers the latest engineering discoveries and innovations.
    Refereed Serial

620   II   ISSN 0013-8134
ENGINEERING TIMES. (Text in English) 1955. w. Rs.37. Engineering Times Publications Pvt. Ltd., Wachel Molla Mansion, 8 Lenin Sarani, Calcutta 700 072, India. Ed. E.H. Tippoo. adv.; bk.rev. circ. 19,000. **Document type:** newspaper.

620   US   ISSN 0195-6876
TA1
ENGINEERING TIMES. 1979. m. $30 (foreign $48). National Society of Professional Engineers, 1420 King St., Alexandria, VA 22314. TEL 703-684-2875. FAX 703-836-4875. Ed. Stefan Jaeger. adv.; bk.rev.; stat. circ. 75,000. (tabloid format; also avail. in microfilm; microfiche) **Indexed:** Met.Abstr., World Alum.Abstr. **Document type:** trade publication.
    Description: Contains news and feature articles on issues and events of interest to engineers. Covers legislative and governmental affairs, quality of engineering, continuing competence, ethics, employment practices, industry policies, engineering society programs and cooperative activities, employment opportunities and salary data.

620   II
ENGINEERING TIMES ANNUAL DIRECTORY. (Text in English) 14th edt., 1974. a. Engineering Times Publications Pvt. Ltd., Wachel Molla Mansion, 8 Lenin Sarani, Calcutta 700013, India.
    Formerly: Indian Engineering and Industries Register.

620   PL   ISSN 0867-888X
                                       CODEN: RZINAZ
ENGINEERING TRANSACTIONS. (Text in English) 1952. q. (Polska Akademia Nauk, Instytut Podstawowych Problemow Techniki) Wydawnictwo Naukowe P W N, Ul. Miodowa 10, 00-251 Warsaw, Poland. Ed. Marek Sokolowski. charts; illus.; index. circ. 590. **Indexed:** Appl.Mech.Rev., Eng.Ind., Geotech.Abstr., Int.Aerosp.Abstr.
—BLDSC (8036.000000).
    Formerly (until 1991): Rozprawy Inzynierskie (ISSN 0035-9408)

620   SA   ISSN 0257-196X
ENGINEERING WEEK. (Text in English) 1979. fortn. R.67. Systems Publishers (Pty) Ltd., Box 41345, Craighall 2024, Transvaal, South Africa. TEL 27-11-789-1808. FAX 27-11-789-4725. TELEX 4-24952. Ed. Janice Busse. adv.; bk.rev.; illus. circ. 13,082. (tabloid format) **Indexed:** INIS Atomind. **Document type:** newspaper.

620   US   ISSN 1072-9070
ENGINEERING WORKFORCE BULLETIN. 1965. 8/yr. $117 to non-members; members $69. American Association of Engineering Societies, 1111 19th St., N.W., Ste. 608, Washington, DC 20036-3606. TEL 202-296-2237. FAX 202-296-1151. Ed. R.A. Ellis. charts; stat. circ. 500. (back issues avail.)
    Formerly (until 1993): Engineering Manpower Bulletin (ISSN 0013-8037)
    Description: Disusses the current trends of a given subject, seen in recent historic context. Covers salaries of engineers, engineering degree statistics and trends, engineering enrollments, women in engineering, and minorities in engineering.

620   UK
ENGINEERING WORLD. 1854. q. £12 to non-members. Society of Engineers, Guinea Wiggs, Nayland, Colchester, Essex CO6 4NF, England. TEL 0206-263332. FAX 0206-262624. Ed. P. Wilson. adv.; bk.rev.; charts; illus.; index, cum.index: 1910-1978. circ. 8,000. **Indexed:** Eng.Ind., GeoRef., RICS. **Document type:** academic/scholarly publication.
    Formerly (until Mar. 1989): Society of Engineers. Journal and Transactions (ISSN 0037-9867)

620   II
ENGINEERING WORLD. (Text in English) 1971. m. Rs.35. 505 Arun Chambers, Tardeo Rd., Bombay 00 023, India. Ed. K. Multani. adv.; bibl.; charts; tr.lit.

620   AT   ISSN 1036-1677
ENGINEERING WORLD. 1991. m. Aus.$5 per no. (Institution of Engineers, Australia) Engineers Australia Pty Ltd., 2 Ernest St., P.O. Box 588, Crows Nest, N.S.W. 2065, Australia. TEL 02-438-1533. FAX 02-438-5934. Ed. Ben Bremner. adv. contact: Maria Mamone.
—BLDSC (3770.190000).

620   AT   ISSN 1032-1195
TA1   CODEN: ENAUDU
ENGINEERS AUSTRALIA. (In two editions: Civil Edition; General Edition) 1929. m. Aus.$45 (overseas Aus.$72) for each ed. (Institution of Engineers, Australia) Engineers Australia Pty. Ltd., Crows News Centre, 2 Ernest St., Crows Nest, N.S.W. 2065, Australia. TEL 02-438-1533. FAX 02-438-5934. TELEX AA62758. Ed. D. Georg. adv.; bk.rev.; bibl.; illus.; index. circ. 43,034. **Indexed:** Appl.Mech.Rev., Aus.Rd.Ind., C.I.S. Abstr., CAD CAM Abstr., Chem.Abstr., Energy Info.Abstr., Eng.Ind., Environ.Abstr., Fluidex, INIS Atomind., Intl.Civil Eng.Abstr., Met.Abstr., Sci.Abstr., Soft.Abstr.Eng., World Alum.Abstr. **Document type:** trade publication.
—El; UnCover; UMI.
    Incorporates: Engineering Associate (ISSN 0311-1008); Which was formerly: Institution of Engineers, Australia. Journal (ISSN 0020-3319)
    Description: Articles on all disciplines of engineering.

620   UK   ISSN 0013-8169
TA1   CODEN: ENDGAY
ENGINEERS' DIGEST. 1940. 10/yr. £32($100) E M A P Business Publishing, 33-39 Bowling Green Ln., London EC1R 0DA, England. TEL 071-837-1212. Ed. Ian Bowman. adv.; bk.rev.; abstr.; charts; illus.; tr.lit.; index. circ. 27,400. **Indexed:** BMT, Br.Tech.Ind., C.I.S.Abstr., Cadscan, Eng.Ind., Excerp.Med., ISMEC, Lead Abstr., Met.Abstr., Sci.Abstr., W.R.C.Inf., World Alum.Abstr., Zincscan. **Document type:** trade publication.

658.5   US   ISSN 0192-1290
ENGINEER'S DIGEST (SOLON). 1973. m. free to qualified personnel. Huebcore Communications, Inc., 29100 Aurora Rd., Ste. 200, Solon, OH 44139. TEL 216-248-1125. FAX 216-248-0187. Ed. Larry K. Beck. adv.; bk.rev.; charts; stat.; circ. 123,000 (controlled). (tabloid format; also avail. in microfilm; back issues avail.) **Indexed:** Fluidex. **Document type:** trade publication.
—CCC.
    Former titles: Plant and Industrial Engineer's Digest; Plant Engineer's Digest.

620   IE   ISSN 0332-1711
ENGINEERS JOURNAL. 1940. m. I£25. (Institution of Engineers of Ireland) Iri, 22 Clyde Rd., Ballsbridge, Dublin 4, Ireland. TEL 01-6684341. FAX 01-6685508. Ed. H.A. Kane. adv. contact: Philip Magaley. bk.rev.; charts; illus.; index. circ. 9,100. **Indexed:** Intl.Civil Eng.Abstr., Soft.Abstr.Eng. **Document type:** trade publication.
    Formerly: Irish Engineers (ISSN 0021-115X)

620   FR
ENGRENAGE. 1950. bi-m. 50 F. Association des Eleves de l'Ecole Centrale de Lyon, 36 Route de Dardilly, 69130 Ecully, France. Ed. Francois Mireville. adv. circ. 500.

620 658   JA   ISSN 0013-8444
ENJINIASU/ENGINEERS. (Text in Japanese) 1946. m. 10600 Yen. Union of Japanese Scientists and Engineers - Nihon Kagaku Gijutsu Renmei, 5-10-11 Sendagaya, Shibuya-ku, Tokyo 151, Japan. TEL 03-5379-1227. FAX 03-3225-1813. TELEX 02322485 JUSE J. Ed. Kohei Suzue. charts; circ. 11,000 (controlled). **Indexed:** JCT, JTA. **Document type:** bulletin.

620 614.7   GW
ENTSORGA-MAGAZIN - ENTSORGUNGSWIRTSCHAFT. 1982. 10/yr. DM.115 (foreign DM.135). Deutscher Fachverlag GmbH, Mainzer Landstr. 251, 60326 Frankfurt a.M., Germany. TEL 069-759501. FAX 069-75952999. (Subscr. to: Postfach 100606, 60006 Frankfurt a.M., Germany) Ed. Bernd Wassmann. circ. 16,002. **Document type:** trade publication.

ENVIRONMENTAL ENGINEER. see *ENVIRONMENTAL STUDIES*

620.8   UK   ISSN 0954-5824
TH6014   CODEN: ENENEU
ENVIRONMENTAL ENGINEERING. 1972. q. £43 (foreign £46). (Society of Environmental Engineers) Mechanical Engineering Publications Ltd., Northgate Ave., Bury St. Edmunds, Suffolk IP32 6BW, England. TEL 0284-763277. FAX 0284-704006. Ed. Sam Black. adv.; bk.rev.; index. circ. 2,000. (also avail. in microform from UMI; back issues avail.; reprint service avail. from UMI) **Indexed:** Biol.Abstr., BMT, Br.Tech.Ind., Energy Rev., Environ.Per.Bibl., Excerp.Med., HRIS, Int.Aerosp.Abstr., Int.Build.Serv.Abstr., Int.Packag.Abstr., Met.Abstr., Ocean.Abstr., Pollut.Abstr., Sci.Abstr., Sel.Water Res.Abstr., World Alum.Abstr. **Document type:** trade publication.
—BLDSC (3791.455700); EI; UnCover; SWETS; UMI. **CCC.**
    Former titles: Society of Environmental Engineers. Journal (ISSN 0374-356X); Environmental Engineering (ISSN 0013-9262)

ENVIRONMENTAL ENGINEERING SELECTION GUIDE. see *ENVIRONMENTAL STUDIES*

620.8 158.7   IT
▼**ERGONOMIA**; prodotti, lavoro, ricerca. 1993. q. L.40000($40) (Societa Italiana de Ergonomia) Moretti e Vitali Editori, Viale Vittorio Emanuele 67, 24121 Bergamo, Italy. TEL 035-239104. FAX 035-240834. Ed. Enrico Moretti.

620.8   UK   ISSN 0014-0139
TA166   CODEN: ERGOAX
ERGONOMICS; an international journal of research and practice in human factors and ergonomics. 1957. m. £378($635) (Ergonomics Society) Taylor & Francis Ltd., Rankine Rd., Basingstoke, Hants RG24 8PR, England. TEL 0256-840366. FAX 0256-479438. TELEX 858540. Ed. R. Goldsmith. adv.; bk.rev.; abstr.; bibl.; illus.; index. cum.index: 1968-1979. circ. 3,000. (also avail. in microform from KTO,MIM; back issues avail.) **Indexed:** Abstr.Anthropol., Abstr.Hum.Comp.Inter., Appl.Mech.Rev., Biol.Abstr., BMT, Br.Rail.Bd., Br.Tech.Ind., C.I.S.Abstr., Chem.Abstr., CINAHL, Curr.Cont., Cyb.Abstr., Dent.Ind., Eng.Ind., Ergon.Abstr., Excerp.Med., HRIS, Ind.Med., Ind.Sci.Rev., Int.Aerosp.Abstr., Mgmt.& Market.Abstr., Noise Pollut.Publ.Abstr., Nutr.Abstr., Psychol.Abstr., Psyscan, Risk Abstr., Sci.Cit.Ind., SSCI, Trop.Dis.Bull. **Document type:** academic/scholarly publication.
—BLDSC (3808.500000); EI; Faxon; UnCover; SWETS. **CCC.**
    Description: Concerned with the diverse interactions of humans with their working environment and equipment. Explores the psychological, physiological and engineering-design aspects of human factors as they relate to work performance and efficiency.
    Refereed Serial

620 616.89   US   ISSN 1064-8046
TA166
▼**ERGONOMICS IN DESIGN;** the magazine of human factors applications. 1993. q. $28 to non-members. Human Factors and Ergonomics Society, Box 1369, Santa Monica, CA 90406-1369. TEL 310-394-1811. FAX 310-394-2410. Ed. D.J. Gardner-Bonneau. adv. contact: L. Smith. bk.rev. circ. 6,200. (also avail. in microform from UMI)
—CCC.

ESCUELA TECNICA SUPERIOR DE INGENIEROS DE MONTES. BIBLIOTECA. BOLETIN BIBLIOGRAFICO Y DOCUMENTAL. INFORMACION FORESTAL. SERIE A: MONOGRAFIAS. see *FORESTS AND FORESTRY — Abstracting, Bibliographies, Statistics*

ESCUELA TECNICA SUPERIOR DE INGENIEROS DE MONTES. BIBLIOTECA. BOLETIN BIBLIOGRAFICO Y DOCUMENTAL. INFORMACION FORESTAL. SERIE B: PUBLICACIONES PERIODICAS. see *FORESTS AND FORESTRY — Abstracting, Bibliographies, Statistics*

ESTUDOS TECNOLOGICOS. see *SCIENCES: COMPREHENSIVE WORKS*

668.4 621   UK   ISSN 0261-2097
EUREKA; innovative engineering design. 1980. m. £60 (foreign £95). Findlay Publications Ltd., Franks Hall, Franks Ln., Horton Kirby, Kent DA4 9LL, England. TEL 0322-222222. FAX 0322-289577. Ed. Roger Bishop. adv.; bk.rev. circ. 26,704. (back issues avail.) **Indexed:** Br.Tech.Ind., Copper Abstr., Met.Abstr. **Document type:** trade publication.
—BLDSC (3828.800000); UnCover; SWETS. **CCC.**
    Incorporates (in 1990): Engineering Materials and Design (ISSN 0308-6917); Which was formerly (until 1972): E M D - Engineering Materials and Design (ISSN 0367-102X); (until 1965): Engineering Materials and Design (ISSN 0013-8045)

620   IT
EURO POWER TRANSMISSION. 2/yr. Tecniche Nuove S.p.A., Via Ciro Menotti 14, 20129 Milan, Italy. TEL 2-75701. FAX 2-76-10-351. Ed. E. Guaglione.

620 551.22   IT   ISSN 0394-5103
                                            CODEN: EEENEZ
EUROPEAN EARTHQUAKE ENGINEERING; international journal of earthquake engineering and engineering seismology. (Text in English) 1987. q. L.156000. Patron Editore, Via Badini, 12, 40050 Quarto Inferiore (Bologna), Italy. TEL 051-767003. Ed. Duilio Benedetti.
—BLDSC (3829.693500).
    Description: Dedicated to engineers, researchers and educators. Includes earthquake engineers' research about events and projects currently in progress.

620 370   UK   ISSN 0304-3797
T61   CODEN: EJEED8
EUROPEAN JOURNAL OF ENGINEERING EDUCATION. (Text in English; summaries in English, French, German) 1975. q. $144 to individuals; institutions $398 (effective 1994). (European Society for Engineering Education) Carfax Publishing Co., P.O. Box 25, Abingdon, Oxon OX14 3UE, England. TEL 44-235-555335. FAX 44-235-553559. (U.S. subscr. to: Carfax Publishing Co., Box 2025, Dunnellon, FL 34430-2025) Ed. Jean Michel. bk.rev.; index. (also avail. in microfiche) **Indexed:** Cont.Pg.Educ., Educ.Tech.Abstr., Intl.Civil Eng.Abstr., Res.High.Educ.Abstr., Sci.Abstr., Soft.Abstr.Eng., Stud.Wom.Abstr. **Document type:** academic/scholarly publication.
—BLDSC (3829.728800); SWETS. **CCC.**
Refereed Serial

EUROPEAN ORGANIZATION FOR QUALITY. CONFERENCE PROCEEDINGS. see *TECHNOLOGY: COMPREHENSIVE WORKS*

EUROPEAN QUALITY. see *TECHNOLOGY: COMPREHENSIVE WORKS*

620   CN   ISSN 1180-3711
EVANS REPORT. irreg. (6 nos./vol.). Can.$695. Evans Research Corporation, 2005 Shepard Ave., E., 4th Fl., Willowdale, ON M2J 5B1, Canada. TEL 416-497-9562. FAX 416-497-7427. Ed. Charles Whaley. (looseleaf format)
    Description: Each issue features a detailed "snapshot" of a market segment, giving an analysis of market forces, constraints and applications.

620   UK   ISSN 0968-2201
EXECUTIVE ENGINEER. 1977. q. £12 (foreign £21.50). (Institution of Incorporated Executive Engineers) Multiprint Lithographics Ltd., Unit 7, Valmar Trading Estate, Valmar Rd., London SE5 9NW, England. TEL 071-733-9977. FAX 071-274-6245. Ed. A.W. Englefield. adv. contact: Richard Languish. bk.rev.; circ. 6,000 (controlled). **Document type:** newsletter.
    Former titles (until 1993): I I E X E Newsletter; (until 1989): I E X E Newsletter.
Refereed Serial

620   US   ISSN 0894-1777
TJ260   CODEN: ETFSEO
EXPERIMENTAL THERMAL AND FLUID SCIENCE; international journal of experimental heat transfer, thermodynamics, and fluid mechanics. 1988. 8/yr. (in 2 vols; 4 nos./vol.). $484 to institutions (foreign $524) (effective 1994). Elsevier Science Inc., 655 Ave. of the Americas, New York, NY 10010. TEL 212-989-5800. FAX 212-633-3990. TELEX 420643 AEP UI. Eds. R. Shah, E.N. Ganic. **Indexed:** Appl.Mech.Rev., Chem.Eng.Abstr., Curr.Cont., Eng.Ind., Int.Aerosp.Abstr., Ref.Zh. **Document type:** academic/scholarly publication.
—BLDSC (3840.220000); EI; Faxon; UnCover; SWETS; CASDDS. **CCC.**
    Description: Provides a forum for original, previously unpublished research emphasizing experimental work that enhances understanding of heat transfer, thermodynamics, and fluid mechanics and their applications.
Refereed Serial

F I D I C INTERNATIONAL DIRECTORY OF CONSULTING ENGINEERS. (Federation Internationale des Ingenieurs Conseils) see *BUSINESS AND ECONOMICS — Trade And Industrial Directories*

620 621 389.6 535   GW   ISSN 0944-1018
Q184
F UND M, FEINWERKTECHNIK MIKROTECHNIK MESSTECHNIK; Zeitschrift fuer Elektronik, Optik, Feinmechanik und Mikrotechnik in Geraetebau und Messtechnik. (Text in German; summaries in English) 1893. 10/yr. DM.163.20. (VDI - VDE Gesellschaft Feinwerktechnik) Carl Hanser Verlag, Kolbergerstr. 22, 81679 Munich, Germany. TEL 089-998300. FAX 089-984809. (Subscr. to: Postfach 860420, 81631 Munich, Germany) Ed. Ch. Weil. adv.; bk.rev.; abstr.; charts; illus.; index. circ. 6,000. **Indexed:** Cadscan, Chem.Abstr., Curr.Cont., Excerp.Med., Fluidex, INIS Atomind., Lead Abstr., Risk Abstr., Sci.Abstr., Sh.& Vib.Dig., Zincscan. **Document type:** trade publication.
—EI. **CCC.**
    Formerly: F und M, Feinwerktechnik und Messtechnik (ISSN 0340-1952); Incorporates: Messtechnik; Which was formerly: Feinwerktechnik und Micronic; Feinwerktechnik (ISSN 0014-9713)

FAB GUIDE; guide to the UK welding & welding fabrication industry. see *METALLURGY — Welding*

658.5   US
FACILITIES FORUM. 1956. 6/yr. $25. American Institute of Plant Engineers, 8180 Corporate Park Dr., Ste. 305, Cincinnati, OH 45242-3309. TEL 513-489-2473. FAX 513-247-7422. Ed. Dave Macauly. circ. 6,000. **Document type:** newsletter.
    Formerly: A I P E Newsletter.
    Description: Covers the key business news, views and ideas essential to facilities managers.

FAST FERRY INTERNATIONAL. see *TRANSPORTATION — Ships And Shipping*

683.83   UK   ISSN 8756-758X
TA418.38   CODEN: FFESEY
FATIGUE & FRACTURE OF ENGINEERING MATERIALS AND STRUCTURES. 1979. m. £520. (European Structural Integrity Society) Structural Integrity Research Institute, University of Sheffield, Sheffield S1 3JD, England. TEL 0742-825239. FAX 0742-753671. Ed. K.J. Miller. adv.; index. circ. 2,000. (also avail. in microfilm from UMI) **Indexed:** Appl.Mech.Rev., B.C.I.R.A., Chem.Abstr., Curr.Cont., HRIS, INIS Atomind., Int.Aerosp.Abstr., ISMEC, Met.Abstr., Sci.Abstr. **Document type:** academic/scholarly publication.
—BLDSC (3897.385000); EI; Faxon; UnCover; SWETS; UMI; CASDDS. **CCC.**
    Formerly: Fatigue of Engineering Materials and Structures (ISSN 0160-4112)
    Description: Papers on science, technology and engineering relevant to the understanding of fatigue and fracture of materials, especially metals, polymers, composites and ceramics.
Refereed Serial

620 350   US
FEDERAL RESEARCH IN PROGRESS DATABASE. Short title: F E D R I P Database. (Supplement avail.: Search Guide) m. price varies. U.S. National Technical Information Service, 5285 Port Royal Rd., Springfield, VA 22161. TEL 703-487-4630.
●Available only online. Vendor(s): DIALOG Information Services, Inc. (File nos.265,266).
    Description: Covers U.S. government research and development as well as engineering projects.

IL FILO METALLICO; rivista tecnica internazionale per l'industria del filo metallico e del cavo e per tutti i settori della lavorazione del filo metallico. see *ENGINEERING — Electrical Engineering*

FINANCIAL SURVEY COMPANY DATA FOR SUCCESS. BOAT BUILDERS & MARINE ENGINEERS. see *SPORTS AND GAMES — Boats And Boating*

620   UK
FINANCIAL SURVEY COMPANY DATA FOR SUCCESS. DIE & MOULD MANUFACTURERS & DISTRIBUTORS. a. I C C Financial Surveys Ltd., Field House, 72 Oldfield Rd., Hampton, Middlesex TW12 2HQ, England. TEL 081-783-0977. FAX 081-783-1940.
    Formerly (until 1990): Financial Survey Company Directory. Die and Mould Manufacturers and Distributors (ISSN 0952-780X)

FLEXIBLE AUTOMATION. see *COMPUTERS — Automation*

620   US   ISSN 0015-4032
FLORIDA ENGINEERING SOCIETY. JOURNAL. 1917. m. $50. Florida Engineering Society, 125 S. Gadsden St., Tallahassee FL 32301. TEL 904-224-7121. FAX 904-222-4349. (Subscr. to: Box 750, Tallahassee, FL 32302) adv. contact: Nancy Taylor. bk.rev.; illus. circ. 4,500.

620   US   ISSN 0740-1973
FLORIDA SPECIFIER; Florida's environmental business & industry newspaper. 1979. m. $24.95. National Technical Communications Co., Inc., Box 2027, Winter Park, FL 32790. TEL 407-740-7950. FAX 407-740-7957. adv.; bk.rev.; charts; illus.; pat. circ. 15,500. (tabloid format; also avail. in diskette format) **Document type:** trade publication.

FOCUS ON BRITISH ENGINEERING AND COMPUTER SCIENCES RESEARCH. see *BIBLIOGRAPHIES*

620   GW   ISSN 0015-7899
TA1   CODEN: FIGWA5
FORSCHUNG IM INGENIEURWESEN. 1934. m. DM.1039($210) (Verein Deutscher Ingenieure) V D I Verlag Gmbh, Heinrichstr. 24, 40239 Duesseldorf, Germany. TEL 0211-6188-0. FAX 0211-6188-112. TELEX 8587743 (Subscr. to: Postfach 101054, 40001 Duesseldorf, Germany) Ed. E. Zimmermann. bk.rev.; charts; illus.; index. circ. 1,000. **Indexed:** Appl.Mech.Rev., Cadscan, Chem.Abstr., Curr.Cont., Eng.Ind., INIS Atomind., ISMEC, Lead Abstr., Met.Abstr., Sh.& Vib.Dig., World Alum.Abstr., Zincscan. **Document type:** trade publication.
—BLDSC (4009.100000); EI; SWETS; CASDDS. **CCC.**

620   US   ISSN 1040-3094
TA409
FRACTURE MECHANICS. (Subseries of: ASTM Special Technical Publication (ISSN 0066-0558)) a. American Society for Testing and Materials, Committee E-24 on Fracture Testing, 1916 Race St., Philadelphia, PA 19103.
    Formerly (until 1979): National Symposium on Fracture Mechanics (ISSN 1043-044X)

FRANCE. COMMISSAR AT A L'ENERGIE ATOMIQUE. ANNUAL REPORT. see *ENERGY — Nuclear Energy*

FRANCE. COMMISSARIAT A L'ENERGIE ATOMIQUE. NOTES D'INFORMATION. see *ENERGY — Nuclear Energy*

620   FR
FRANCE. COMMISSION INDUSTRIE-ADMINISTRATION POUR LA MESURE. RECUEIL DES COMMUNICATIONS. (Text in English, French) 1980. biennial, latest 1986. (Commission Industrie-Administration pour la Mesure.) Edition Kirk, B.P. 112, 94703 Maisons-Alfort Cedex, France. TEL 261-50-10.

ENGINEERING

FRANCE. SERVICE D'ETUDE DES STRATEGIES ET DES STATISTIQUES INDUSTRIELLES. SOCIETES D'ETUDES ET DE CONSEILS, INGENIEURS-CONSEILS. see *BUSINESS AND ECONOMICS*

FRONTIERS OF MEDICAL AND BIOLOGICAL ENGINEERING. see *BIOLOGY — Bioengineering*

620 US ISSN 0884-3759
TP343 CODEN: FSCTEG
FUEL SCIENCE AND TECHNOLOGY INTERNATIONAL. 1983. 12/yr. $487.50 to individuals; institutions $975 (effective 1994). Marcel Dekker, Inc., 270 Madison Ave., New York, NY 10016. TEL 212-696-9000. FAX 212-685-4540. TELEX 421419. (Subscr. to: Box 5017, Monticello, New York 12701.) Ed. James G. Speight. bk.rev.; abstr.; charts. (also avail. in microform from RPI) **Indexed:** API Abstr., API Catal., API Hlth.& Environ., API Oil., API Pet.Ref., API Pet.Subst., API Transport., Chem.Abstr., Chem.Eng.Abstr., Energy Info.Abstr., Energy Rev., Environ.Abstr., Environ.Per.Bibl. (1986-), Petrol.Abstr., T.C.E.A.
—BLDSC (4053.680000); EI; Faxon; UnCover; SWETS; CASDDS. **CCC.**
Formerly: Liquid Fuels Technology (ISSN 0737-7266)
Description: Offers articles relating to the fundamental scientific and technological aspects of fuel sources such as heavy oils, tar sands, residue, coal, oil shale and biomass.
Refereed Serial

620 SA ISSN 0071-979X
FULCRUM. 1965. a. free. University of the Witwatersrand, Johannesburg, Student Engineers Council, CM 1124-1125, P.O. Box WITS, Johannesburg 2050, South Africa. FAX 27-11-716-5467. Ed. S.D. Smith. adv.; circ. 3,000 (controlled).

620 NE
FUNDAMENTAL STUDIES IN ENGINEERING. 1978. irreg., vol.15, 1992. price varies. Elsevier Science B.V., Books Division, P.O. Box 211, 1000 AE Amsterdam, Netherlands. TEL 31-20-5803911. FAX 31-20-5803705. TELEX 18582 ESPA NL. (Subscr. in U.S. and Canada to: Elsevier Science Inc., Box 882, Madison Sq. Sta., New York, NY 10159. TEL 212-989-5800) **Document type:** monographic series.
Refereed Serial

FUNE NO KAGAKU. see *TRANSPORTATION — Ships And Shipping*

G P S A ENGINEERING DATA BOOK. (Gas Processors Suppliers Association) see *PETROLEUM AND GAS*

620 IT ISSN 1120-5377
G T. IL GIORNALE DEL TERMOIDRAULICO. 1986. m. L.40000 (foreign L.120000) (effective 1994). Tecniche Nuove s.p.a., Via Menotti 14, 20129 Milan, Italy. TEL 02-75701. FAX 02-7610351. adv.: B&W page L.4230000; trim 267 x 375. circ. 24,560.
Formerly (until 1988): Giornale del Termoidraulico (ISSN 0393-8344)

620 600 US
GATEWAY ENGINEER. 1916. m. $24. (Engineers' Club of St. Louis) Association Publishers (Subsidiary of: Association Management Professionals, Inc.), Box 13066, St. Louis, MO 63119. TEL 314-533-9333. Ed. Robert James Cimasi. adv.; bk.rev.; circ. controlled.
Formerly (until 1984): Engineers' Club of St. Louis. Journal (ISSN 0013-8150)

620 FR
GENIE INDUSTRIEL: REVUE; engineering actualites. 1969. 10/yr. 980 F. Genie Industriel Multimedia, 9 rue Denis Poisson, 75017 Paris, France. TEL 40-68-12-12. FAX 40-68-12-29. circ. 8,000. (also avail. in microform)
Formerly: Engineering-Actualites.

GEOLOGICAL SURVEY OF NAMIBIA. REPORTS ON OPEN FILE. ENGINEERING GEOLOGY. see *EARTH SCIENCES — Geology*

620 US ISSN 0016-8351
TA1
GEORGIA PROFESSIONAL ENGINEER. 1948. bi-m. membership. Georgia Society of Professional Engineers, Martin PR, Box 49482, Atlanta, GA 30359. TEL 404-355-0177. Ed. Arlene Lee. adv. circ. 300.
Description: Contains organization news.

GEOTECHNICAL ENGINEERING BULLETIN. see *EARTH SCIENCES*

620 GW ISSN 0172-6145
TA710.A1
GEOTECHNIK. 1978. q. DM.40($14) Deutsche Gesellschaft fuer Erd- und Grundbau e.V. - German National Society for Soil Mechanics and Foundation Engineering, Hohenzollernstr. 52, 45128 Essen, Germany. TEL 0201-782723. FAX 0201-782743. **Indexed:** Dok.Str., Geotech.Abstr.
—BLDSC (4158.975000).
Description: Covers research in soil mechanics, rock mechanics, foundation building, and engineering geology. Includes reports, association news, patents and a calendar of events.

620 745.2 UK
GERMAN STANDARDS (DIN) ENGLISH LANGUAGE. m. Technical Indexes Ltd., Willoughby Rd., Bracknell, Berkshire RG12 8DW, England. TEL 0344-426311. FAX 0344-424971. **Document type:** abstracting/indexing.
Description: Focuses on industrial design.

621.48 GW
GESELLSCHAFT FUER ANLAGEN- UND REAKTORSICHERHEIT. JAHRESBERICHT. 1977. a. Gesellschaft fuer Anlagen- und Reaktorsicherheit mbH, Schwertnergasse 1, 50667 Cologne, Germany. TEL 0221-2068-0. FAX 0221-2068442. TELEX 2214123-GRS-D. Ed. Regina Knoll. illus. circ. 1,000. **Document type:** trade publication.
Former titles: Gesellschaft fuer Reaktorsicherheit. Jahresbericht; Institut fuer Reaktorsicherheit der Technischen Ueberwachungs-Vereine. Taetigkeitsbericht.

620 US
GLOBAL REVIEW OF UNDERGROUND SPACE. (In 3 editions: North American, Pacific Basin, Spanish-language) a. Green Global Publications, Inc., 15 Old Mill Rd., Westport, CT 06880. TEL 203-227-6500. adv.: B&W page $2590, color page $3490; trim 8 x 10 3/4.

526.9 CE
GOVERNMENT SURVEYORS' ASSOCIATION OF SRI LANKA. NEWS SHEET. 3/yr. Government Surveyors' Association of Sri Lanka, 10 Bambalapitiya Dr., Colombo 4, Sri Lanka.

620 US ISSN 0193-2276
TA157
GRADUATING ENGINEER. 1979. 4/yr. plus 4 special issues. $16. Peterson's - C O G Publishing, 16030 Ventura Blvd., Ste. 560, Encino, CA 91436. TEL 818-789-5293. Ed. Charlotte Thomas. adv. circ. 90,000. (also avail. in microform from UMI; reprint service avail. from UMI) **Indexed:** CAD CAM Abstr.
—BLDSC (4207.514000); Faxon; UnCover; UMI.

620 BL
GRANDES VULTOS DA ENGENHARIA BRASILEIRA. 1975. a. $12. Clube de Engenharia, Av. Rio Branco 124, Rio de Janeiro, Gb, Brazil.

GREEN ENGINEERING; a current awareness bulletin. see *ENVIRONMENTAL STUDIES*

GROUND ENGINEERING YEARBOOK. see *BUSINESS AND ECONOMICS — Trade And Industrial Directories*

620 CC
GUANGDONG GONGXUEYUAN XUEBAO/GUANGDONG INSTITUTE OF ENGINEERING. JOURNAL. (Text in Chinese) q. Guangdong Gongxueyuan, No. 729, Dongfeng Donglu, Guangzhou, Guangdong 510090, People's Republic of China. TEL 766069. Ed. Liang Shi.

620 CC ISSN 1004-6062
GUANLI GONGCHENG XUEBAO/JOURNAL OF INDUSTRIAL ENGINEERING AND ENGINEERING MANAGEMENT. (Text in Chinese; abstracts in English) 1988. q. $56. Zhejiang Daxue - Zhejiang University, Yu Quan (Jade Spring), Hangzhou, Zhejiang 310027, People's Republic of China. TEL 0571-5172242. FAX 0571-571797. TELEX 35040 ZUFAO CN. Ed. Xu Qingrui. **Document type:** academic/scholarly publication.

620 FR
GUIDE DE L'INGENIERIE. 1960. a. 580 F. Genie Industriel Multimedia, 9 rue Denis Poisson, 75017 Paris, France. TEL 40-63-12-12. FAX 40-68-12-29. circ. controlled.
Formerly: Genie Industriel - Catalogue de l'Ingenierie (ISSN 0072-0844)

GUIDELINES FOR IMPROVING PRACTICE. ARCHITECTS AND ENGINEERS PROFESSIONAL LIABILITY. see *ARCHITECTURE*

GYOSEN KIKAN/FISHING BOAT ENGINEERING. see *TRANSPORTATION — Ships And Shipping*

HACETTEPE BULLETIN OF NATURAL SCIENCES AND ENGINEERING. see *SCIENCES: COMPREHENSIVE WORKS*

HACETTEPE FEN VE MUHENDISLIK BILIMLERI DERGISI. see *SCIENCES: COMPREHENSIVE WORKS*

HAKKU; Pioneerien lehti. see *MILITARY*

620 690 LE ISSN 0987-8467
AL-HANDASAH; a monthly construction, industrial & technological magazine for the Arab world. (Supplement avail.: Dalil al-Mihan al-Handasiyyah fi Lubnan - Directory of Engineering Professions in Lebanon) (Text in Arabic; summaries in English) 1985. m. $100. Al-Handasah Magazine, P.O. Box 298, Hamzieh, Lebanon. TEL 961-1-429898. FAX 961-1-429099. TELEX 44125 HANDSA LE. Ed. Joseph Asmar. adv.; illus. circ. 16,000. (back issues avail.)
Description: Trade journal for the engineering, construction and building technology industries in the Arab world.

HANDBOOK OF ENGINEERING EDUCATION. see *EDUCATION — Guides To Schools And Colleges*

HANDBOOK OF SOIL MECHANICS. see *EARTH SCIENCES*

620 387 CC ISSN 1000-1875
CODEN: HCGXEQ
HARBIN CHUANBO GONGCHENG XUEYUAN XUEBAO/HARBIN INSTITUTE OF SHIPPING ENGINEERING. JOURNAL. (Text in Chinese) 1980. q. Y8. Harbin Chuanbo Gongcheng Xueyuan, Xuebao Bianjibu, 31 Lou, Wenmiao Jie, Nangang-qu, Harbin, Heilongjiang 150001, People's Republic of China. TEL 3642571. Ed. Lu Zhonglu. **Document type:** academic/scholarly publication.
Description: Covers naval architecture and ocean engineering, electronic engineering, chemical engineering, and mechanical engineering.

HARBOR BRANCH NEWS. see *EARTH SCIENCES — Oceanography*

HARVESTER; agricultural engineering journal. see *AGRICULTURE*

620 US
HAWKEYE ENGINEER. 4/yr. $5. University of Iowa, 4101 Engineering Bldg., Iowa City, IA 52242. TEL 319-353-1538. Ed. Angela De Palma. adv.; charts; illus.; stat. circ. 1,600.
Formerly (until 1974): Iowa Transit (ISSN 0021-0706)

HAZARDOUS WASTE CONSULTANT. see *ENVIRONMENTAL STUDIES — Waste Management*

621.402 US ISSN 0017-9329
TH7121
HEAT ENGINEERING. 1927. 4/yr. free to qualified personnel. Foster Wheeler Corp., Perryville Corporate Park, Clinton, NJ 08809-4000. TEL 908-730-4000. FAX 908-730-5315. Ed. Harry Levy. abstr.; charts; illus.; cum.index. circ. 15,000. **Indexed:** ISMEC.

ENGINEERING

620 **US**
HEAT EXCHANGER DESIGN UPDATE. (Supplement to: Heat Exchanger Design Handbook) (Text in English) 1994. q. $198. (Imperial College of Scientific Technology, UK) Begell House Inc., 79 Madison Ave., New York, NY 10016-7892. TEL 212-725-1999. FAX 212-213-8368. Ed. Geoffrey F. Hewitt. **Document type:** academic/scholarly publication.
Description: Publishes a collection of information on heat exchangers and on the related subjects of heat transfer, fluid flow, physical properties and mechanical design.

620 **CC**
HEBEI GONGXUEYUAN XUEBAO/HEBEI ENGINEERING INSTITUTE. JOURNAL. (Text in Chinese) q. Hebei Gongxueyuan - Hebei Engineering Institute, Hongqiao-qu, Tianjin 300130, People's Republic of China. TEL 570233. Ed. Xia Jumin.

620 **IS**
HEHANDESIM V'ADRICHALIM. (Text in Hebrew; summaries in English) 1923. m. $50. Association of Engineers and Architects in Israel, P.O. Box 3082, Tel Aviv, Israel. TEL 972-3-5240274. FAX 972-3-5235993. Ed. Eli Tavor. adv.; bk.rev. circ. 19,000. **Indexed:** INIS Atomind.
Former titles: Handasah; Handasah ve-Adrikhalut (ISSN 0017-7164)

HEIKI TO GIJUTSU/ORDNANCE AND TECHNOLOGY. see MILITARY

HIGH TEMPERATURES - HIGH PRESSURES. see PHYSICS — Heat

620 **JA** **ISSN 0018-2060**
 CODEN: HIDKAA
HIROSHIMA UNIVERSITY. FACULTY OF ENGINEERING. BULLETIN/HIROSHIMA DAIGAKU KOGAKUBU KENKYU HOKOKU. (Text in Japanese; summaries in English) 1952. s-a. Hiroshima University, Faculty of Engineering - Hiroshima Daigaku Kogakubu, Kagamiyama, Higashi-Hiroshima 724, Japan. circ. 700. **Indexed:** Chem.Abstr., INIS Atomind., JCT, JTA, Sci.Abstr. **Document type:** bulletin.
—BLDSC (2507.950000); CASDDS.

620 **JA** **ISSN 0073-2311**
 CODEN: MFEHA6
HIROSHIMA UNIVERSITY. FACULTY OF ENGINEERING. MEMOIRS. (Text in English, French, German) 1957. a. Hiroshima University, Faculty of Engineering - Hiroshima Daigaku Kogakubu, Kagamiyama, Higashi-Hiroshima 724, Japan. Ed. Akiharu Kanamaru. circ. 750. **Indexed:** Chem.Abstr., INIS Atomind., JTA, Math.R., Sci.Abstr.
—BLDSC (5593.450000).

620 331.1 **US** **ISSN 1058-269X**
TA1
HISPANIC ENGINEER. 1984. 5/yr. Career Communications Group, Inc., 729 E. Pratt St., Ste. 504, Baltimore, MD 21202. TEL 410-244-7101. FAX 410-752-1837. adv. circ. 22,500. **Indexed:** Chic.Per.Ind.
—UnCover.

620 **JA** **ISSN 0018-2788**
 CODEN: HZOGA2
HITACHI ZOSEN TECHNICAL REVIEW/HITACHI ZOSEN GIHO. (Text in Japanese; summaries in English, Japanese) 1937. q. free. Hitachi Zosen Corporation, Technical Research Institute, 3-22, Sakurajima 1-chome, Konohana-ku, Osaka-shi, Osaka 554, Japan. FAX 06-465-4040. TELEX 63846 HZ SEK J. Ed. Satoshi Suzuki. bibl.; circ. 2,800 (controlled). **Indexed:** Chem.Abstr., Eng.Ind., Fluidex, INIS Atomind., JTA, Met.Abstr., Sci.Abstr., World Alum.Abstr.
—BLDSC (4318.830000); CASDDS.

620 378 **GW**
HOCHSCHULFUHRER. 1983. a. DM.3. Fachhochschule Muenster, Rectorate, Postfach 3020, 48016 Muenster, Germany. TEL 0251-83-1. FAX 0251-839739. adv. circ. 2,500. **Document type:** bulletin.
Description: Information about the organization, departments, and studies of the Fachhochschule Muenster; announcements for students.

HOKKAIDO KYOIKU DAIGAKU KIYO. DAI-2-BU, A. SUGAKU, BUTSURI, KAGAKU, KOGAKU-HEN/HOKKAIDO UNIVERSITY OF EDUCATION. JOURNAL. SECTION 2 A. MATHEMATICS, PHYSICS, CHEMISTRY, ENGINEERING. see MATHEMATICS

620 **JA** **ISSN 0368-9379**
 CODEN: MEHUAJ
HOKKAIDO UNIVERSITY. FACULTY OF ENGINEERING. MEMOIRS. (Text in European languages) 1927. a. exchange basis. Hokkaido University, Faculty of Engineering, Nishi 8-chome, Kita 13-jo, Kita-ku, Kita-ku, Sapporo 060, Japan. FAX 011-717-4745. TELEX 932302 HOKUEN J. Ed. T. Tsuchiya. circ. 750. (also avail. in microform) **Indexed:** Agri.Eng.Abstr., Chem.Abstr., INIS Atomind., JTA, Met.Abstr., Rev.Appl.Entomol., Sci.Abstr., World Alum.Abstr.
—BLDSC (5593.500000); CASDDS.

620 **NE**
HOOGOVENS GROEP BULLETIN. (Editions in Dutch and English) 1983. q. free. Hoogovens Groep B.V., P.O. Box 10000, 1970 CA Ijmuiden, Netherlands. TEL 31-2514-99111. FAX 31-2514-70057. TELEX 35211 HOVS NL. Ed. R. Dortmundt. circ. 7,000. (back issues avail.) **Document type:** bulletin.
Description: News from all subsidiaries of Hoogovens Groep, covering steel, steel processing, aluminium, subcontracting, engineering and trading.

HOVERFOIL NEWS. see TRANSPORTATION — Ships And Shipping

620 **CC** **ISSN 1001-5159**
HUADONG GONGXUEYUAN XUEBAO/EAST CHINA INSTITUTE OF ENGINEERING. JOURNAL. (Text in Chinese) 1977. bi-m. $30 (effective till 1995). Huadong Gongxueyuan - East China Institute of Engineering, 200 Xiaolingwei, Nanjing, Jiangsu 210014, People's Republic of China. TEL 025-431116. FAX 025-431622. TELEX 34128 EEINJ CN. Ed. Liu Yaoxing. circ. 3,000. **Document type:** academic/scholarly publication.
Description: Contains articles on the new developments of scientific research, with emphasis on fundamental theory, applied science, technical engineering, and science activities.

158.7 620.8 **US** **ISSN 0018-7208**
T58.A2 **CODEN: HUFAA6**
HUMAN FACTORS. q. $115 to non-members. Human Factors and Ergonomics Society, Box 1369, Santa Monica, CA 90406-1369. TEL 310-394-1811. FAX 310-394-2410. Ed. W.C. Howell. (also avail. in microform from UMI; reprint service avail. from UMI) **Indexed:** A.S.& T.Ind., Abstr.Anthropol., Abstr.Hum.Comp.Inter., Agri.Eng.Abstr., Biol.Abstr., BMT, C.I.S.Abstr., Commun.Abstr., Dok.Arbeitsmed., Ergon.Abstr., HRIS, Ind.Med., Ind.Sci.Rev., INIS Atomind., Mgmt.& Market.Abstr., Psychol.Abstr., Psycscan, Risk Abstr., Sci.Abstr., Sci.Cit.Ind., SSCI. **Document type:** academic/scholarly publication.
—BLDSC (4336.075000); El; Faxon; UnCover; SWETS; UMI. **CCC.**

HUMAN FACTORS AND ERGONOMICS SOCIETY ANNUAL MEETING. PROCEEDINGS. see PSYCHOLOGY

620.8 158.7 **US**
Q300
HUMAN FACTORS AND ERGONOMICS SOCIETY BULLETIN. 1958. m. $36 to non-members. Human Factors and Ergonomics Society, Box 1369, Santa Monica, CA 90406-1369. TEL 310-394-1811. FAX 310-394-2410. Ed. Richard J. Carter. adv. circ. 5,800. pp./issue: 8. (tabloid format; back issues avail.) **Indexed:** Abstr.Hum.Comp.Inter., Ergon.Abstr., Psychol.Abstr. **Document type:** newsletter.
—**CCC.**
Formerly: Human Factors Society Bulletin (ISSN 0438-1629)
Description: Contains news and information relevant to members.

HYDROLOGICAL SCIENCE AND TECHNOLOGY. see WATER RESOURCES

I A E A BULLETIN. (International Atomic Energy Agency) see ENERGY — Nuclear Energy

I A E A NEWSBRIEFS. (International Atomic Energy Agency) see ENERGY — Nuclear Energy

I A T U L QUARTERLY. (International Association of Technological Universities Libraries) see LIBRARY AND INFORMATION SCIENCES

620 **FR** **ISSN 0066-8982**
I C A M ANNUAIRE. (Institut Catholique d'Arts et Metiers de Lille) 1970. a. 750 F. Association des Ingenieurs I C A M, 15 rue de Madrid, 75008 Paris, France. TEL 45-22-74-81. adv.

620 **FR** **ISSN 0536-1362**
I D. (Ingenieurs Diplomes) 1961. 5/yr. 100 F. Conseil National des Ingenieurs et des Scientifiques de France, 7, rue Lamennais, 75008 Paris, France. TEL 45-63-89-58. FAX 42-89-82-50. Ed. P. Alba. bk.rev. circ. 5,000. **Document type:** government publication, monographic series, newsletter.
—BLDSC (4362.220000).

620 658 **US** **ISSN 0360-8581**
 CODEN: IEMRAP
I E E E ENGINEERING MANAGEMENT REVIEW. 1973. q. $108 to non-members. (I E E E, Engineering Management Society) Institute of Electrical and Electronics Engineers, Inc., 345 E. 47th St., New York, NY 10017-2394. FAX 908-981-9667. (Subscr. to: Box 1331, 445 Hoes Lane, Piscataway, NJ 08855-1331. TEL 908-981-0060) Ed. David Scott Lewis. bibl.; illus. (also avail. in microform from MIM,UMI,EEE) **Indexed:** Eng.Ind.
—BLDSC (4362.927000); El; Faxon; SWETS; UMI. **CCC.**

I E E E JOURNAL OF OCEANIC ENGINEERING. see ENGINEERING — Electrical Engineering

I E T E TECHNICAL REVIEW. (Institution of Electronics and Telecommunication Engineers) see COMMUNICATIONS

I F A W P C A NEWSLETTER. (International Federation of Asian and Western Pacific Contractors' Associations) see BUILDING AND CONSTRUCTION

I F P T E OUTLOOK. (International Federation of Professional and Technical Engineers) see BUSINESS AND ECONOMICS — Labor And Industrial Relations

620 **NE**
I-KWADRAAT - WERKTUIGBOUWKUNDE. 1985. m. fl.160 membership. (Nederlandse Ingenieurs Vereniging (NIRIA)) Ingenieurspers B.V., P.O. Box 90162, 1006 BD Amsterdam, Netherlands. TEL 020-5102922. FAX 020-5102439. Ed. C. van der Sluys. circ. 10,750. (back issues avail.)
Description: Discusses technical and managerial topics on a university level.

620 **US**
I P A - FORSCHUNG UND PRAXIS. (Text in German) vol.38, 1980. irreg. price varies. (Fraunhofer-Institute fuer Produktionstechnik und Automatisierung, GW) Springer-Verlag, 175 Fifth Ave., New York, NY 10010. TEL 212-460-1500. FAX 212-473-6272. (Also: Berlin, Heidelberg, Tokyo and Vienna) Ed. H.J. Warnecke. **Document type:** monographic series.

620 **NZ**
I P E N Z PROCEEDINGS ANNUAL CONFERENCE (YEAR). 1987. a. Institution of Professional Engineers, New Zealand, P.O. Box 12241, Wellington, New Zealand. TEL 64-4-473-9444 FAX 64-4-473-2324. (back issues avail.) **Document type:** proceedings.

620 **NE** **ISSN 0019-0578**
TA165 **CODEN: ISATAZ**
I S A TRANSACTIONS. 1961. 4/yr. fl.291($157) (effective 1994). (Instrument Society of America) Elsevier Science B.V., P.O. Box 211, 100 AE Amsterdam, Netherlands. TEL 31-20-5803911. FAX 31-20-5803598 TELEX 18582 ESPA NL. (Subscr. in U.S. and Canada to: Elsevier Science Inc., Box 882, Madison Sq. Sta., New York, NY 10159-0882. TEL 212-989-5800. FAX 212-633-3990) bibl.; charts; illus. (also avail. in microfilm from UMI; back issues avail.; reprint service avail. from ISI,UMI) **Indexed:** A.S.& T.Ind., Biol.Abstr., Chem.Abstr., Comput.Abstr., Comput.Cont., Curr.Cont., Eng.Ind., Excerp.Med., Fluidex, INIS Atomind., Int.Aerosp.Abstr., Met.Abstr., Sci.Abstr., Sci.Cit.Ind., Sh.& Vib.Dig., World Alum.Abstr. **Document type:** academic/scholarly publication.
—BLDSC (4582.700000); El; Faxon; UnCover; SWETS; CASDDS. **CCC.**
Description: Focuses on topics of importance in industrial measurement control and automation in each issue.
Refereed Serial

620 **YU** **ISSN 0019-0837**
I T NOVINE. 1963. fortn. $30. Savez Inzenjera i Tehnicara Jugoslavije, Kneza Milosa 9, Box 187, 11000 Belgrade, Yugoslavia. Ed. Djordje Adanja. adv.; bk.rev. circ. 10,000.

ENGINEERING

620   RM   ISSN 1013-5278
IASI POLYTECHNIC MAGAZINE; book and soft reviews. (Subsection of: Polytechnic Institute of Jassy. Bulletin) (Text in English, French, German and Russian) 1989. q. free. (Institutul Politehnic din Iasi - Polytechnic Institute of Jassy) International Center for Engineering Education, Mihai Eminescu Boulevard, Calea "23 August," Nr. 11-22, 6600 Iasi, Rumania. FAX 40-81-47923. Ed. Adrian Adascalitei. adv.; bk.rev. circ. 600.
Description: Focuses on engineering education and training. Includes thesis abstracts, conferences and symposia proceedings.

620   US   ISSN 0019-2015
TA1
ILLINOIS ENGINEER. 1925. bi-m. $4 to non-members. Illinois Society of Professional Engineers, 1304 S. Lowell, Springfield, IL 62704. TEL 217-544-7424. Ed. Chuck Stockus. adv.; illus. circ. 5,000. **Indexed:** Chem.Abstr.
Description: Contains organization news.

620   US
ILLINOIS TECHNOGRAPH. 1884. 6/yr. $12.95. Illini Media Co., 57 E. Green St., Champaign, IL 61820. TEL 217-333-3733. FAX 217-244-6616. Ed. George J. Thiruvathukal. adv. contact: Matthew J. Kaleba. circ. 4,500. **Document type:** academic/scholarly publication.
Description: For undergraduate and graduate students, faculty and alumni of the University.

614.7   US   ISSN 0146-2520
TN278.3   CODEN: ISOMDJ
IN SITU; a journal of earth resource utilization. 1977. 4/yr. $247.50 to individuals; institutions $495. Marcel Dekker Journals, 270 Madison Ave., New York, NY 10016. TEL 212-696-9000. FAX 212-685-4540. TELEX 421419. (Subscr. to: Box 5017, Monticello, NY 12701) Ed. K. Sepehrnoori. (also avail. in microform from RPI) **Indexed:** Avery Ind.Archit.Per., Chem.Abstr., Curr.Cont., E&P Hlth. (1993-), Energy Info.Abstr., Energy Rev., Environ.Abstr., Environ.Per.Bibl. (1977-), Gas Process.& Ppl. (1993-), Ind.Sci.Rev., INIS Atomind., Off.Tech. (1993-), Petrol.Abstr. (1979-), Sci.Cit.Ind. **Document type:** academic/scholarly publication.
—BLDSC (4372.460000); CIS; EI; Faxon; UnCover; CASDDS. CCC.
Description: Devoted to the exchange of common technology in the fields of minerals and fossil fuels.
Refereed Serial

620   UK
INDEPENDENT CONSULTING ENGINEER. 1979. q. (Federation Internationale des Ingenieurs Conseils) Rhys Jones Marketing, Halley House, 49 Burney St., Greenwich, London SE10 8EX, England. TEL 081-305-2277. FAX 081-853-3281. Ed. Sandi Rhys Jones. adv.; bk.rev. circ. 13,000. **Document type:** trade publication.
Formerly: Interview - International Consulting Engineer.
Description: Professional, legal and management issues for consulting engineers.

INDEX AND DIRECTORY OF INDUSTRY STANDARDS. see *METROLOGY AND STANDARDIZATION*

620   II   ISSN 0019-4719
INDIAN ENGINEERING EXPORTER. (Text in English) 1957. s-a. Rs.25($1) Engineering Export Promotion Council, World Trade Centre, 3rd Fl., 14-1B Ezra St., Calcutta 700001, India. TEL 91-33-250442. FAX 91-33-258968. Ed. M.K. Dutt. adv.; bk.rev.; index. circ. 2,500.

INDIAN INSTITUTE OF SCIENCE. JOURNAL. see *SCIENCES: COMPREHENSIVE WORKS*

INDIAN JOURNAL OF ENGINEERING MATHEMATICS. see *MATHEMATICS*

620   II   ISSN 0376-9852
TA103
INDIAN JOURNAL OF ENGINEERS. (Text in English) 1960. q. (plus a. supplement). Rs.300($55) (effective Jan. 1993). 7 Satyen Dutta Rd., Calcutta 700 029, India. TEL 46-1431. Ed. Mihir Sen. adv.: B&W page $300, color page $600. bibl.; charts. circ. 7,000.
Description: Covers civil, electrical and mechanical engineering, electronics & telecommunication, metallurgy, chemical engineering, glass and ceramics, and computer science.

620   II   ISSN 0073-6554
INDIAN JOURNAL OF ENGINEERS. ANNUAL FOUNDRY NUMBER. (Text in English) 1960. a. Rs.25 (foreign Rs.40). Technical and General Press, Engineers' Bureau, c/o Jyotsnmay Guha Thakurta, 21B Lansdowne Terrace, Calcutta 26, India. Ed. A.K. Bose.

INDIAN MINING & ENGINEERING JOURNAL. see *MINES AND MINING INDUSTRY*

620   II   CODEN: IEAEAS
INDIAN STEEL ANNUAL, INDIAN AUTOMOTIVE ANNUAL, CONSTRUCTION INDIA ANNUAL. (Text in English) 1858. a. Rs.70. Indian and Eastern Engineer Co. Ltd., Piramal Mansion, 235 Dr. D. Naoroji Rd., Bombay 400 001, India. TEL 2626032. FAX 22-2024548. TELEX 01183599-MUBY-IN. Ed. S.K. Ghaswala. adv.; bk.rev.; charts; illus.; tr.lit.; index. circ. 7,012. **Indexed:** Chem.Abstr., INIS Atomind., Sci.Abstr.
Formerly (until 1992): Indian and Eastern Engineer (ISSN 0019-4352); Which incorporated (1909-1944): Indian and Eastern Motors (ISSN 0367-7591)

620   US   ISSN 0748-6057
INDIANA PROFESSIONAL ENGINEER. bi-m. Indiana Society of Professional Engineers, Inc., 1810 Broad Ripple Ave., No. 14, Indianapolis, IN 46220-2357. TEL 317-255-2267. Ed. J.B. Wilson. circ. 2,500.

620   CN   ISSN 0828-7198
INDICATOR. French edition: Indicateur (ISSN 0828-7201) 1974. q. Can.$60. Canadian Council of Professional Engineers, 116 Albert St., Ste. 401, Ottawa, Ont. K1P 5G3, Canada. TEL 613-232-2474. FAX 613-230-5759. Ed. Alison Baignee. adv.; bk.rev. circ. 1,200.
Formerly (until no.49, 1984): Engineering Manpower News - Main d'Oeuvre en Genie Bulletin.
Description: Reports latest trends in the engineering labor market. Includes latest engineering manpower survey results, features timely articles on a wide range of engineering manpower issues.

INDUSTRIAL DIAMOND REVIEW. see *TECHNOLOGY: COMPREHENSIVE WORKS*

INDUSTRIAL FASTENERS. see *ENGINEERING — Engineering Mechanics And Materials*

INDUSTRIAL MAINTENANCE; for factory managers and maintenance professionals. see *OCCUPATIONAL HEALTH AND SAFETY*

620   UK   ISSN 0967-5787
INDUSTRIAL TECHNOLOGY. 1988. m. £60($130) New Wave Publishing Ltd., P.O. Box 454, Cambridge CB1 4RQ, England. TEL 061-969-7506. FAX 061-976-5349. (Subscr. to: Circulation Dept., P.O. Box 85, Sale, Cheshire M33 2BB, England) Ed. Andy Pye; Pub. Roy Bell. adv. circ. 24,000. **Document type:** trade publication.
Formerly: Advanced Industrial Technology.
Description: Provides information for mechanical and electrical design engineers with an emphasis on simultaneous engineering and designing for manufacture.

620   SZ
INDUSTRIE & TECHNIQUE - REVUE TECHNIQUE SUISSE. 24/yr. Editions de la Tour SA, Route de Cugy, CH-1052 Le Mont-sur-Lausanne, Switzerland. TEL 021-6529941. FAX 021-6527323. Ed. Walmar Isler. adv.: B&W page 2375 SFr.; trim 270 x 184. circ. 11,500. **Document type:** trade publication.

620   GW
ING.DIGEST; das Ingenieur Magazin. 1990. m. DM.48. Ingenieur Digest Verlagsgesellschaft mbH, Regattastr. 189, 12527 Berlin, Germany. TEL 030-6764516. Ed. Thomas Bencard. adv.; bk.rev. circ. 110,000. **Document type:** trade publication.
Formerly: Ing (ISSN 0863-4831)

620   IT   ISSN 0020-0905
INGEGNERE; * rivista tecnica mensile. 1926. m. L.25000. Associazione Nazionale Ingegneri e Architetti Italiani, Piazza Sallusto 24, 00187 Rome, Italy. Eds. Massimo Battaglini, Arrigo Care. adv.; bk.rev.; abstr.; bibl.; charts; illus.; mkt.; pat.; stat.; tr.mk.; index. circ. 20,000. **Indexed:** Appl.Mech.Rev., C.I.S.Abstr., Chem.Abstr., Eng.Ind., Geotech.Abstr., INIS Atomind., Intl.Civil Eng.Abstr., Sci.Abstr., Soft.Abstr.Eng.
—BLDSC (4500.000000).

620 551.22   IT   ISSN 0393-1420
INGEGNERIA SISMICA. 1984. 3/yr. Via Badini 12, 40127 Quarto Inferiore (BO), Italy. TEL 51-76-70-03. FAX 51-76-82-52.

620   CR
INGENIERIA. (Text in Spanish; abstracts in English, Spanish) 1991. s-a. Col.750($20) Editorial de la Universidad de Costa Rica, Apdo. 75-2060, Ciudad Universitaria Rodrigo Facio, 2050 San Pedro de Montes de Oca, San Jose, Costa Rica. TEL 506-25-3133. FAX 506-24-9367. TELEX UNICORI 2544. Dir. Rodolfo Herrera J. bibl.; charts; illus.

658.5   AG   ISSN 0020-1030
        CODEN: INIDDT
INGENIERIA E INDUSTRIA. 1926. m. Indupress s.r.l., Piedras 930, 1 Piso, Buenos Aires 1070, Argentina. Ed. Julio Cesar Di Pietro Paulo. adv.; charts; illus.; pat.; tr.lit. circ. 12,600.
—CASDDS.

620   CK   ISSN 0120-5609
INGENIERIA E INVESTIGACION. 1962. 4/yr. Col.$1500. Universidad Nacional de Colombia, Facultad de Ingenieria, Apdo. Aereo 5344, Bogota, Colombia. Ed. Julio Mario Rodriquez Devis. circ. 1,000.
Former titles: Ingenieria. Boletin Informativo. (ISSN 0073-7992); Universidad de Colombia, Bogota. Facultad de Ingenieria. Boletin Informativo.

658.5   CU   ISSN 0258-5960
INGENIERIA INDUSTRIAL. 1977. 3/yr. $24 in N. America; S. America $25; Europe $26. (Ministerio de Educacion Superior, Instituto Superior Politecnico) Ediciones Cubanas, Obispo No. 527, Apdo. 605, Havana, Cuba.

620   FR   ISSN 1167-1793
INGENIERIE INTERNATIONAL. s-m. (22/yr.) 5200 F. I C Publications, 10 rue Vineuse, 75116 Paris Cedex 16, France. TEL 44-30-81-00. FAX 44-30-81-11.
Former titles: Tiers Monde Ingenierie; Tiers-Monde Engineering (ISSN 0220-6102)

620   CK
INGENIERO LATINOAMERICANO. 1980. q. Transversal 6a, no. 51A43, Bogota, Colombia. TEL 240-2053. Ed. Alfonso Martinez T. circ. 8,500.

620   CL   ISSN 0716-4610
INGENIEROS. 1969. bi-m. $25. Colegios de Ingenieros de Chile, A.G., Avda. Libertador B. O'Higgins, 1170, piso 9, Santiago, Chile. TEL 2-779530. FAX 2-778467. Ed. Pedro Moral. adv. circ. 10,000.

620   NE   ISSN 0020-1146
        CODEN: INGRAO
DE INGENIEUR. (Text in Dutch) 1886. m. fl.175 (foreign fl.268). (Royal Institute of Engineers) Wegener Tijl Tijdschriften Groep B.V., P.O. Box 9943, 1006 AP Amsterdam, Netherlands. TEL 31-20-5182828. FAX 31-20-5182843. Ed. J.T. Buma. adv.; bk.rev. circ. 22,400. (back issues avail.) **Indexed:** BMT, Excerp.Med., Geotech.Abstr., Key to Econ.Sci., Sci.Abstr. **Document type:** trade publication.
Former titles (until Jan. 1990): Ingenieurs Nieuws (ISSN 0922-3339); (until 1983): Technische Weekblad voor Ingenieurs (ISSN 0922-3320); (until 1982): Beta (ISSN 0165-635X)
Description: Covers new engineering projects and technological developments in industry. Includes news, features, interviews, list of events, new publications and available positions.

620   AU
DER INGENIEUR. 1946. q. S.180. Verband Oesterreichische Ingenieure, Eschenbachgasse 9, A-1010 Vienna, Austria. adv.; bk.rev. circ. 3,200.

ENGINEERING

624 690   FR   ISSN 0046-9513
INGENIEUR - CONSTRUCTEUR. 1902. m. 290 F. Societe des Ingenieurs Diplomes E.T.P, 6 rue Vital, 75116 Paris, France. TEL 45-04-51-31. FAX 40-72-86-62. Ed. D. Babinet. bibl. circ. 6,500. **Indexed:** Geotech.Abstr.

620   GW   ISSN 0020-1170
DER INGENIEUR DER DEUTSCHEN BUNDESPOST. 1962. bi-m. DM.36. (Verband Deutscher Postingenieure) Bielefelder Verlagsanstalt GmbH & Co. KG, Niederwall 53, 33602 Bielefeld, Germany. TEL 0521-595520. Ed. Johannes Frerichs. adv.; bk.rev.; abstr.; charts; stat.; index. circ. 14,000. **Document type:** trade publication.
—CCC.

620   BE   ISSN 0775-2962
INGENIEUR ET INDUSTRIE. (Text in English, Flemish, French) 1979. 10/yr. 1200 BEF (foreign 1400 BEF). Association pour la Promotion des Publications Scientifiques (APPS), 26 av. de l'Amarante, B-1020 Brussels, Belgium. TEL 32-2-268-29-33. FAX 32-2-268-25-14. Ed. Marianne Allard. adv.; bk.rev.; circ. 20,000 (controlled).
Formerly: Revue de l'Ingenieur Industriel (ISSN 0251-0944)

620   SZ   ISSN 0251-0979
INGENIEURS ET ARCHITECTES SUISSES. (Text in French) 1875. fortn. 152 SFr. (Societe des Editions des Associations Techniques Universitaires) Ingenieurs et Architectes Suisses, Rue de Bassenges 4, CH-1024 Ecublens, Switzerland. TEL 21-6932098. FAX 21-6932084. Ed. J. P. Weibel. adv.; bk.rev.; abstr.; bibl.; charts. circ. 3,796. **Indexed:** Appl.Mech.Rev., C.I.S. Abstr., Chem.Abstr., Eng.Ind., Excerp.Med., GeoRef. **Document type:** trade publication.
Formerly: Bulletin Technique de la Suisse Romande (ISSN 0007-5744)

621 382   FR   ISSN 0989-8379
INGENIEURS SANS FRONTIERES. 3/yr. 1 pce. Valhubert, 75013 Paris, France. TEL 45-86-16-04. FAX 44-24-26-94. Ed. Michel Salem. circ. 5,000. **Document type:** newsletter.

620   NE   ISSN 0923-1919
DE INGENIEURSKRANT; vakblad voor techniek en management in industrie, technologie en zakelijke dienstverlening. 1985. bi-w. fl.160 (foreign fl.195) (effective 1993). V N U Business Publications B.V., P.O. Box 90162, 1006 BD Amsterdam, Netherlands. TEL 31-20-5102922. FAX 31-20-6174121. TELEX 14407. Ed. L. van Velzen. adv.; B&W page fl.10495, color page fl.13690; trim 290 x 420; adv. contact: Elma Klein. circ. 44,408 (paid); 24,241 (controlled). (tabloid format; back issues avail.) **Document type:** trade publication.
—SWETS.
Formerly (until 1989): Ingenieurs Informatie (ISSN 0169-4006)
Description: Managerial and technical topics of interest to engineers.

DAS INGENIEURSTUDIUM. see OCCUPATIONS AND CAREERS

620   US   ISSN 0173-0274
INGENIEURWISSENSCHAFTLICHE BIBLIOTHEK/ENGINEERING SCIENCE LIBRARY. (Text in German) 1964. irreg. price varies. Springer-Verlag, 175 Fifth Ave., New York, NY 10010. TEL 212-460-1500. FAX 212-473-6272. (Also: Berlin, Heidelberg, Tokyo and Vienna) (reprint service avail. from ISI) **Document type:** bibliography.

620   DK
INGENIOER - HVORFOR, HVORDAN. a. free. Tekniske Hoejskole, Studiekontoret, Bygn 101A, DK-2800 Lyngby, Denmark. Ed. Lise Damkjaer.
Formerly (until 1989): Ingenioer (ISSN 0109-9639)

658.5   NO   ISSN 0332-611X
INGENIOER - NYTT/ENGINEERING NEWS. 1965. 49/yr. NOK 435. Teknisk Presse A.S, Hovfaret 17, P.O. Box 235 Skoeyen, N-0212 Oslo 2, Norway. TEL 47-2-52-10-40. FAX 47-2-50-66-48. Ed. Trygve Baera. adv. circ. 71,600. (tabloid format) **Indexed:** INIS Atomind.
—CCC.
Description: Covers technical and industrial news; includes interviews, articles on product and process development, and financial surveys. Features articles on specific technical and engineering subjects.

620   DK   ISSN 0105-6220
INGENIOEREN/DANISH ENGINEER'S WEEKLY. 1892. w. DKK 463. Dansk Ingenioerforening, Ingenioer-Sammenslutningen, P.O. Box 373, DK-1503 Copenhagen V, Denmark. TEL 45-31-21-68-10. FAX 45-31217273. Ed. Torkil Morsing. adv.; bk.rev.; charts; illus. circ. 73,000. **Indexed:** Geotech.Abstr.
Formed by the merger of: Ingenioerens Ugeblad (ISSN 0020-126X) & Ingenioer- og Bygningsvaesen (ISSN 0020-1243)
Description: Presents wide ranging information about technical developments in Denmark and abroad. Examines the relationship between technology and society. Features products and investments in industry and the public sector.

620.1   SW   ISSN 1101-8704
INGENJOEREN. 1950. 8/yr. SEK 100 (effective 1991). Ingenjoersfoerbundet, Kungsgatan 29, S-111 56 Stockholm, Sweden. Ed. Tomas Pira. adv.; pat.; tr.lit. circ. 5,000. (tabloid format)
Former titles (until 1990): T L I - Ingenjoeren; (until 1972): Gymnasieingenjoeren (ISSN 0017-5919); (until 1965): T L I - Tidskrift - Gymnasieingenjoeren; (until vol.5, 1963): T L I - Tidskrift.

620   IT
INNOVAZIONE: IMPIANTI E PRODUZIONE. 1968. m. L.130000 (foreign L.155000) (effective 1993). Franco Angeli Editore, Viale Monza 106, 20127 Milan, Italy. TEL 02-28-27-651. **Indexed:** Chem.Abstr.
Formerly: Impianti.

620   II   ISSN 0020-2800
INSTITUTE OF CONSULTING ENGINEERS. JOURNAL. (Text in English) 1958. q. Rs.100($40) Institute of Consulting Engineers, 9 Hastings St., Calcutta 1, India. TEL 28-5066. Ed. U.P. Mullick. adv.; bk.rev.; abstr.; charts; illus.; pat.; stat.; tr.lit.; tr.mk. circ. 500. (reprint service avail.)

621.38   JA   ISSN 0913-5707
TK5101.A1   CODEN: DJTAER
INSTITUTE OF ELECTRONICS, INFORMATION AND COMMUNICATION ENGINEERS. TRANSACTIONS (SECTION A)/DENSHI JOHO TSUSHIN GAKKAI RONBUNSHI (A). English translation (in part): Electronics and Communications in Japan - Part 3: Fundamental Electronic Science (US ISSN 1042-0967) (Text in Japanese) 1968. m. 1030 Yen. Institute of Electronics, Information and Communication Engineers - Denshi Joho Tsushin Gakkai, c/o Kikai Shinko Kaikan, 5-8 Shiba Koen, 3-chome, Minato-ku, Tokyo 105, Japan. Ed. Michiyuki Uenohara. **Indexed:** CAD CAM Abstr., Cyb.Abstr., Int.Abstr.Oper.Res., JCT, Sci.Abstr., Tel.Abstr.
—BLDSC (8939.440500).
Formerly (until 1987): Institute of Electronics and Communication Engineers of Japan. Transactions. Section J - A (ISSN 0373-6091); Which supersedes in part (in 1968): Institute of Electronics and Communication Engineers of Japan. Journal (ISSN 0914-529X)

INSTITUTE OF ENVIRONMENTAL SCIENCES. ANNUAL MEETING. PROCEEDINGS. see ENVIRONMENTAL STUDIES

INSTITUTE OF ENVIRONMENTAL SCIENCES. JOURNAL. see ENVIRONMENTAL STUDIES

INSTITUTE OF ENVIRONMENTAL SCIENCES. TUTORIAL SERIES. see ENVIRONMENTAL STUDIES

INSTITUTE OF NUCLEAR MATERIALS MANAGEMENT. PROCEEDINGS OF ANNUAL MEETING. see ENERGY — Nuclear Energy

INSTITUTION OF ELECTRONICS AND TELECOMMUNICATION ENGINEERS. JOURNAL. see COMMUNICATIONS

INSTITUTION OF ELECTRONICS AND TELECOMMUNICATION ENGINEERS. STUDENTS' JOURNAL. see COMMUNICATIONS

620   UK   ISSN 0261-7641
INSTITUTION OF ENGINEERING DESIGNERS OFFICIAL REFERENCE BOOK AND BUYERS GUIDE.* a. £27.50. Institution of Engineering Designers, Courtleigh, Westbury Leigh, Westbury, Wiltshire BA13, England. adv.

620   II
INSTITUTION OF ENGINEERS (INDIA). HINDI SECTION. JOURNAL. (Text in Hindi) 3/yr. Rs.60($8) Institution of Engineers (India), Hindi Section, 8 Gokhale Rd., Calcutta 700 020, India. TEL 033-288334. FAX 033-288345. TELEX 0217885 IEIC IN. Ed. K.N. Majumdar. circ. 20,000. **Indexed:** INIS Atomind.

620   II   ISSN 0970-9843
TA1   CODEN: JIEEDM
INSTITUTION OF ENGINEERS (INDIA). INTERDISCIPLINARY PANELS JOURNAL. (Text in English) 1920. 3/yr. Rs.60($8) Institution of Engineers (India), 8 Gokhale Rd., Calcutta 700 020, India. TEL 033-288334. FAX 033-288345. TELEX 0217885 IEIC IN. Ed. K.N. Majumdar. circ. 10,000. **Indexed:** Sci.Abstr. **Document type:** academic/scholarly publication.
Former titles: Institution of Engineers (India). Interdisciplinary Panels and General Engineering. Journal; Institution of Engineers (India). Interdisciplinary and General Engineering Journal (ISSN 0251-1118); Institution of Engineers (India). Industrial Development and General Engineering. Journal.

620   II   ISSN 0257-6708
TA1
INSTITUTION OF ENGINEERS (INDIA). PRODUCTION ENGINEERING DIVISION. JOURNAL. (Text in English) 1984. 3/yr. Rs.60($8) Institution of Engineers (India), Production Engineering Division, 8 Gokhale Rd., Calcutta 700 020, India. TEL 033-288334. FAX 033-288345. TELEX 0217885 IEIC IN. Ed. K.N. Majumdar. adv.; charts; illus.; index. circ. 3,000.
—BLDSC (4794.090000).

620   II
INSTITUTION OF ENGINEERS (INDIA). TECHNICIANS' JOURNAL. (Text in English) q. Rs.80($10) Institution of Engineers (India), 8 Gokhale Rd., Calcutta 700 020, India. TEL 033-288334. FAX 033-288345. TELEX 0217885 IEIC IN. Ed. K.N. Majumdar. circ. 200,000.
Formerly: Institution of Engineers (India). Students' Journal.

620   II
▼**INSTITUTION OF ENGINEERS (INDIA). TECHNORAMA.** (Text in English) 1992. m. Rs.240($30) Institution of Engineers (India), 8 Gokhale Rd., Calcutta 700 020, India. TEL 033-288334. FAX 033-288345. TELEX 021-7885 EIC IN. Ed. K.N. Majumdar. adv.; bk.rev.; charts; illus. circ. 70,000.
Formerly: Institution of Engineers (India). Panorama.

620   BG   ISSN 0073-9200
INSTITUTION OF ENGINEERS. TECHNICAL JOURNAL. (Text in English) q. Tk.20. Institution of Engineers, Ramna, Dhaka 2, Bangladesh.

620   BG   ISSN 0073-9219
INSTITUTION OF ENGINEERS. YEAR BOOK.* (Text in English) a. Institution of Engineers, Ramna, Dhaka 2, Bangladesh.

620   AT
INSTITUTION OF ENGINEERS, AUSTRALIA. NATIONAL CONFERENCE PUBLICATIONS. 19/yr. (Institution of Engineers, Australia) Engineers Australia Pty. Ltd., Crows Nest Centre, 2 Ernest St., Crows Nest, N.S.W. 2065. TEL 02-438-1533. FAX 02-438-5934. charts; stat. **Document type:** trade publication.
Description: Conference publication covering all engineering disciplines.

ENGINEERING

620 AT
INSTITUTION OF ENGINEERS, AUSTRALIA. QUEENSLAND DIVISION. TECHNICAL PAPERS. 1960. m. Aus.$15. Institution of Engineers, Australia, Queensland Division, 11 National Circuit, Barton, A.C.T. 2600, Australia. TEL 062-706555. FAX 062-731488. TELEX AA62758. Ed. Gordon R. Graham. index. circ. 1,875.
Formerly: Institution of Engineers, Australia. Brisbane Division. Technical Papers (ISSN 0046-9866)

620 AT ISSN 0812-3314
INSTITUTION OF ENGINEERS, AUSTRALIA. TRANSACTIONS. MULTI-DISCIPLINARY ENGINEERING. 1983. 2/yr. Aus.$35 (overseas Aus.$50). Engineers Australia Pty. Ltd., Crows Nest Centre, 2 Ernest St., Crows Nest, N.S.W. 2065, Australia. TEL 02-438-1533. FAX 02-438-5934. Ed. W. Rourke. illus.; index. circ. 2,000. **Indexed:** Agri.Eng.Abstr., Energy Info.Abstr., Excerp.Med., INIS Atomind., Sci.Abstr.
—BLDSC (8965.000000).
Formerly: Institution of Engineers, Australia. General Engineering Transactions.
Description: Covers general engineering themes of management, environment, professional issues and engineering heritage.

620 BG ISSN 0379-4318
TA1 CODEN: JIEBAA
INSTITUTION OF ENGINEERS, BANGLADESH. JOURNAL. (Text in English) 1960. m. Rs.25($6) Institution of Engineers, Ramna, Dhaka 2, Bangladesh. Ed. Dr. Mohammad R. Bary. adv. circ. 7,000. **Indexed:** Chem.Abstr.
—CASDDS.
Formerly: Pakistan Engineer (ISSN 0030-9753)

620 JM ISSN 0046-9882
INSTITUTION OF ENGINEERS, JAMAICA. JOURNAL. 1968. s-a. free. Institution of Engineers, Jamaica, P.O. Box 122, Kingston 10, Jamaica, W.I. Ed. K.B. Martin. adv.; charts. circ. 500.

620 MY ISSN 0126-6659
INSTITUTION OF ENGINEERS, MALAYSIA. BULLETIN. 1969. m. $30. Institution of Engineers, Malaysia, P.O. Box 223, 46720 Jalan Sultan, Petaling Jaya, Selangor Darul Ehsan, Malaysia. illus. **Indexed:** Intl.Civil Eng.Abstr., Soft.Abstr.Eng. **Document type:** bulletin.

620 MY ISSN 0538-0057
INSTITUTION OF ENGINEERS, MALAYSIA. JOURNAL. s-a. $5 per no. Institution of Engineers, Malaysia, Box 223, 46720 Jalan Sultan, Petaling Jaya, Selangor Darul Ehsan, Malaysia. adv.; illus.

620 IE
INSTITUTION OF ENGINEERS OF IRELAND. REGISTER OF CHARTERED ENGINEERS AND MEMBERS. 1960. a. £6. Irish Engineering Publications Ltd., 22 Clyde Road, Ballsbridge, Dublin, 4, Ireland. adv. circ. 6,000. **Document type:** directory.
Formerly: Directory of Engineers (ISSN 0070-5489)

620 IE ISSN 0073-9790
INSTITUTION OF ENGINEERS OF IRELAND. TRANSACTIONS. 1835. a. £3. Irish Engineering Publications Ltd., 22 Clyde Road, Ballsbridge, Dublin, 4, Ireland. circ. 6,000.

620 CE
INSTITUTION OF ENGINEERS, SRI LANKA. MEMBERS DIRECTORY. 1973. irreg. $2. Institution of Engineers, Sri Lanka, 120-15 Wijerama Mawatha, Colombo 7, Sri Lanka. TEL 698426. FAX 699202. **Document type:** directory.
Formerly: Institution of Engineers, Sri Lanka. Year Book.

620 CE
INSTITUTION OF ENGINEERS, SRI LANKA. NEWSLETTER. 1982. m. Institution of Engineers, Sri Lanka, 120-15 Wijerama Mawatha, Colombo 7, Sri Lanka. TEL 698426. FAX 699202. Ed.Bd. adv.; illus. circ. 4,200. **Document type:** newsletter.

620 CE
INSTITUTION OF ENGINEERS, SRI LANKA. TRANSACTIONS. 1906. s-a. $1 per no. Institution of Engineers, Sri Lanka, 120-15 Wijerama Mawatha, Colombo 7, Sri Lanka. TEL 698426. FAX 699202. adv.; illus. circ. 4,200.

620 SP
INSTITUTO DE LA INGENIERIA DE ESPANA. HOJA INFORMATIVA. 1973. 4/yr. 300 ptas.($5) Instituto de la Ingenieria de Espana, General Arrando 38, 28010 Madrid, Spain. TEL 319-74-17. Ed. Fernendo Hevia Cangas. adv. circ. 20,000.
Formerly: Instituto Ingenieros Civiles de Espana. Boletim Informativo (ISSN 0020-4048)

620 RM
INSTITUTUL POLITEHNIC "TRAIAN-VUIA". BULETINUL STIINTIFIC SI TEHNIC. (Published in 4 series: Seria Chimia (ISSN 0374-4841); Seria Constructii; Seria Electrotehnica (ISSN 0366-3701); Seria Mecanica Teoretica si Aplicata) (Text in English, French, German, Rumanian, Russian) 1920. a. 25 lei. Institutul Politehnic "Traian Vuia", Str. 30 Decembrie Nr. 2, 1900 Timisoara, Rumania. (Subscr. to: I L E X I M , Serv. Export - Import Presa, Press Department, Str. 30 Decembrie Nr. 3-5, P.O. Box 136-137, Bucharest, Rumania) (Co-sponsor: Ministerul Educatiei si Invatamintului Bucuresti) bk.rev. circ. 500. **Indexed:** Chem.Abstr., GeoRef., Math.R., Sci.Abstr.

625 PL ISSN 0137-1991
INSTYTUT BADAWCZY DROG I MOSTOW. PRACE. (Text in Polish; summaries in English, French, German, Russian) 1974. q. 50000 Zl. per no. Instytut Badawczy Drog i Mostow, Ul. Jagiellonska 80, 03-301 Warsaw, Poland. FAX 11-17-92. illus.
Formerly (until 1974): Centralny Osrodek Badan i Rozwoju Techniki Drogowej. Prace (ISSN 0373-8108)

INTERNATIONAL ATOMIC ENERGY AGENCY. ANNUAL REPORT. see *ENERGY — Nuclear Energy*

INTERNATIONAL ATOMIC ENERGY AGENCY. NUCLEAR POWER REACTORS IN THE WORLD. see *ENERGY — Nuclear Energy*

INTERNATIONAL ATOMIC ENERGY AGENCY. PANEL PROCEEDINGS SERIES. see *ENERGY — Nuclear Energy*

INTERNATIONAL ATOMIC ENERGY AGENCY. PROCEEDINGS SERIES. see *ENERGY — Nuclear Energy*

INTERNATIONAL ATOMIC ENERGY AGENCY. TECHNICAL DIRECTORIES. see *ENERGY — Nuclear Energy*

INTERNATIONAL ATOMIC ENERGY AGENCY. TECHNICAL REPORT SERIES. see *ENERGY — Nuclear Energy*

620 NO
INTERNATIONAL CONFERENCE ON PORT AND OCEAN ENGINEERING UNDER ARCTIC CONDITIONS. PROCEEDINGS. Cover title: P O A C (Year). (In 2 vols.) (Text in English) 1971. irreg., 11th, 1991, St. John's, Canada. price varies. International Conference on Port and Ocean Engineering under Arctic Conditions, P O A C Secretariat, Norwegian Hydrotechnical Laboratory, Klaebuveien 153, N-7034 Trondheim, Norway. abstr. **Document type:** proceedings.

620 US
INTERNATIONAL CONFERENCE ON THE PROTECTION OF PIPES. PROCEEDINGS. 1975. irreg., 8th, 1989. price varies. Gulf Publishing Co., Box 2608, Houston, TX 77252-2608. TEL 713-529-4301. FAX 713-520-4433. **Document type:** proceedings.

620 600 US ISSN 1045-585X
T6
INTERNATIONAL CONGRESS ON TECHNOLOGY AND TECHNOLOGY EXCHANGE. PROCEEDINGS. 1984. a. $50. International Technology Institute, 7125 Saltsburg Road, Pittsburgh, PA 15235-2297. TEL 412-795-5300. FAX 412-795-5302. Ed. I.S. Tuba. (back issues avail.) **Document type:** proceedings.

620 US ISSN 1067-9014
TA1
INTERNATIONAL DIRECTORY OF ENGINEERING SOCIETIES AND RELATED ORGANIZATIONS. 1956. triennial. $185 to non-members; members $115. American Association of Engineering Societies, 1111 19th St., N.W., Ste. 608, Washington, DC 20036-3603. TEL 202-296-2237. FAX 202-296-1151. Ed. Gordon Davis. index.
Formerly (until 1993): Directory of Engineering Societies and Related Organizations (ISSN 0070-5470)
Description: Compilation of 950 U.S. and foreign technical and engineering non-profit organizations, with detailed profile information for each.

620 US ISSN 0074-5774
TA12
INTERNATIONAL ENGINEERING DIRECTORY. 1965. biennial. $50. American Consulting Engineers Council, 1015 15th St., N.W., Washington, DC 20005-2670. TEL 202-347-7474. circ. 5,000.
Document type: directory.

620 510 UK ISSN 0029-5981
TA335 CODEN: IJNMBH
INTERNATIONAL JOURNAL FOR NUMERICAL METHODS IN ENGINEERING. 1964. 24/yr. $1795 (effective 1994). John Wiley & Sons Ltd., Journals, Baffins Ln., Chichester, Sussex PO19 1UD, England. TEL 0243-779777. FAX 0243-775878. TELEX 86290-WIBOOK-G. Ed.Bd. bk.rev.; index. (reprint service avail. from ISI,SWZ,UMI) **Indexed:** Abstr.J.Earthq.Eng., Appl.Mech.Rev., BMT, Compumath, Curr.Cont., Eng.Ind., Fluidex, Ind.Sci.Rev., Int.Aerosp.Abstr., J.of Ferroc., Math.R., Sci.Abstr., Sci.Cit.Ind., Sh.& Vib.,Dig., W.R.C.Inf. **Document type:** academic/scholarly publication.
—BLDSC (4542.404000); El; Faxon; UnCover; SWETS; UMI. **CCC.**
Description: Provides a common platform for the presentation of papers and exchange of views on numerical methods used to solve a variety of engineering problems in such areas as heat transfer, structural analysis, fluid mechanics, network theory, electronics and optimal system design.

620 SI ISSN 0218-1274
Q172.5.C45 CODEN: IJBEE4
INTERNATIONAL JOURNAL OF BIFURCATIONS AND CHAOS IN APPLIED SCIENCES AND ENGINEERING. 1991. bi-m. $280 to individuals & institutions of developing countries; institutions of developed countries $560. World Scientific Publishing Co. Pte. Ltd., Farrer Rd., P.O. Box 128, Singapore 9128, Singapore. TEL 3825663. FAX 3825919. TELEX RS-28561-WSPC. (UK addr.: 73 Lynton Mead, Totteridge, London N20 8DH, England. TEL 44-81-4462461; US addr.: 1060 Main St., Ste. 1B, River Edge, NJ 07661. TEL 800-227-7562) Ed. L.O. Chua. **Document type:** academic/scholarly publication.
—BLDSC (4542.129500); Faxon; UnCover; SWETS.
Description: Covers experimental, computational, as well as theoretical aspects of bifurcations, chaos and complexity of biological economic, engineering, neural, physical, social and other dynamical systems.

620 SZ ISSN 0957-4344
T61 CODEN: ICEEE4
INTERNATIONAL JOURNAL OF CONTINUING ENGINEERING EDUCATION. (Text in English) 1990. q. $155 in N. America; elsewhere £100. (International Association for Continuing Engineering Education) Inderscience Enterprises Ltd., World Trade Centre Bldg., 110 Ave. Louis Casai, Case Postale 306, CH-1215 Geneva-Aeroport, Switzerland. FAX 22-7910885. TELEX 289950. (Co-sponsor: Unesco) (back issues avail.)
—BLDSC (4542.176700).
Description: Includes engineering and technology management and education as well as career development and training.

ENGINEERING

629.8   **UK**   **ISSN 0020-7179**
TJ212   **CODEN: IJCOAZ**
INTERNATIONAL JOURNAL OF CONTROL. 1965. m. £780($1310) Taylor & Francis Ltd., Rankine Rd., Basingstoke, Hants RG24 8PR, England. TEL 0256-840366. FAX 0256-479438. TELEX 858540. Ed. J. O'Reilly. adv.; bk.rev. (also avail. in microform) **Indexed:** Agri.Eng.Abstr., Appl.Mech.Rev., Chem.Abstr., Compumath, Curr.Cont., Cyb.Abstr., Eng.Ind., Ind.Sci.Rev., Math.R., Sci.Abstr., Sci.Cit.Ind., Sh.& Vib.Dig. **Document type:** trade publication.
—BLDSC (4542.177000); Faxon; UnCover; SWETS. **CCC.**
   Description: Addresses major problems of modern control theory and applications relating to a broad range of generalized systems.
   Refereed Serial

378   **GW**
INTERNATIONAL JOURNAL OF ENGINEERING EDUCATION. 1985. bi-m. Tempus Publications, Berliner Tor 21, 20099 Hamburg, Germany. TEL 040-24883014. FAX 040-24882847. Ed. Michael S. Wald. adv.; bk.rev. (also avail. in microfilm from MIM,UMI) **Indexed:** Cont.Pg.Educ., Curr.Cont., Educ.Tech.Abstr., Stud.Wom.Abstr. **Document type:** academic/scholarly publication.
—Faxon; UnCover; SWETS; UMI. **CCC.**
   Formerly (until 1992): International Journal of Applied Engineering Education (ISSN 0742-0269)

620   **UK**   **ISSN 0020-7225**
TA1   **CODEN: IJESAN**
INTERNATIONAL JOURNAL OF ENGINEERING SCIENCE. (Text in English, French and German) 1963. 12/yr. £908($1400) (effective 1994). Elsevier Science Ltd., Pergamon, P.O. Box 800, Kidlington, Oxford OX5 1DX, England. TEL 44-865-843000. FAX 44-865-843010. (Subscr. in U.S. and Canada to: Elsevier Science, 660 White Plains Rd., Tarrytown, NY 10591-5153. TEL 914-524-9200. FAX 914-333-2444) Ed. A.C. Eringen. adv.; bk.rev.; bibl.; charts; illus.; index. circ. 1,400. (also avail. in microfilm from UMI; reprint service avail. from UMI) **Indexed:** Abstr.J.Earthq.Eng., Appl.Mech.Rev., Cadscan, Chem.Abstr., Chem.Eng.Abstr., Curr.Cont., Eng.Ind., Fluidex, Geotech.Abstr., Ind.Sci.Rev., Int.Aerosp.Abstr., ISMEC, J.of Ferroc., Lead Abstr., Math.R., Met.Abstr., Sci.Abstr., Sci.Cit.Ind., Sh.& Vib.Dig., T.C.E.A., World Alum.Abstr., Zincscan. **Document type:** academic/scholarly publication.
—BLDSC (4542.240000); EI; Faxon; UnCover; SWETS; UMI; CASDDS. **CCC.**
   Incorporates (in 1978): Letters in Applied and Engineering Sciences (ISSN 0090-6913)
   Description: Original research pertaining to the application of the physical, chemical and mathematical sciences to engineering.
   Refereed Serial

620   **UK**   **ISSN 0734-743X**
TA354   **CODEN: IJIED4**
INTERNATIONAL JOURNAL OF IMPACT ENGINEERING. 1983. 6/yr. £265($410) (effective 1994). Elsevier Science Ltd., Pergamon, P.O. Box 800, Kidlington, Oxford OX5 1DX, England. TEL 44-865-843000. FAX 44-865-843010. (Subscr. in U.S. and Canada to: Elsevier Science, 660 White Plains Rd., Tarrytown, NY 10591-5153. TEL 914-524-9200. FAX 914-333-2444) Ed. Norman Jones. (also avail. in microform from UMI; back issues avail.) **Indexed:** Appl.Mech.Rev., Environ.Abstr., Int.Aerosp.Abstr., Met.Abstr., Sh.& Vib.Dig., World Alum.Abstr. **Document type:** academic/scholarly publication.
—BLDSC (4542.302500); EI; Faxon; SWETS; UMI. **CCC.**
   Description: Covers the elastic and plastic response of structures and bodies to impact and blast loading, terminal ballistics, vehicle crashworthiness, and explosive welding.
   Refereed Serial

620   **NE**   **ISSN 0169-8141**
INTERNATIONAL JOURNAL OF INDUSTRIAL ERGONOMICS. 1986. 8/yr. (in 2 vols.; 4 nos./vol.). fl.718($388) (effective 1994). (International Ergonomics Association) Elsevier Science B.V., P.O. Box 211, 1000 AE Amsterdam, Netherlands. TEL 31-20-5803911. FAX 31-20-5803598. TELEX 18582 ESPA NL. (Subscr. in U.S. and Canada to: Elsevier Science Inc., Box 882, Madison Sq. Sta., New York, NY 10159-0882. TEL 212-989-5800. FAX 212-633-3990) (Co-sponsor: International Foundation for Industrial Ergonomics and Safety Research) Ed. A. Mital. abstr. (back issues avail.) **Indexed:** Abstr.Hum.Comp.Inter., CAD CAM Abstr. (until 1992), Eng.Ind., Ergon.Abstr., ISMEC, Robomat. (until 1992). **Document type:** academic/scholarly publication.
—BLDSC (4542.303000); EI; Faxon; SWETS. **CCC.**
   Formerly: International Journal of Ergonomics.
   Description: Covers all aspects of industrial and occupational ergonomics, including human productivity, work-station design, methods engineering, musculoskeletal injuries, design of tools, machines, controls, and displays, safety, stress and fatigue, modelling of the human body and human response behavior.
   Refereed Serial

620   **UK**   **ISSN 0306-4190**
TJ1
INTERNATIONAL JOURNAL OF MECHANICAL ENGINEERING EDUCATION. 1972. q. £38.50. (University of Manchester, Institute of Science & Technology) Ellis Horwood Ltd., Market Cross House, Cooper St., Chichester, West Sussex PO19 1EB, England. Ed.Bd. adv.; bk.rev. circ. 375. (also avail. in microform; back issues avail.) **Indexed:** Biol.Abstr., Br.Tech.Ind., Cont.Pg.Educ., Educ.Tech.Abstr., Res.High.Educ.Abstr.
—BLDSC (4542.341000); Faxon; UnCover; SWETS; UMI. **CCC.**

620 658   **NE**   **ISSN 0925-5273**
TP155.6   **CODEN: IJPCEY**
INTERNATIONAL JOURNAL OF PRODUCTION ECONOMICS; an international journal for industry. (Text in English) 1976. 15/yr. (in 5 vols.; 3 nos./vol.). fl.1605($868) (effective 1994). Elsevier Science B.V., P.O. Box 211, 1000 AE Amsterdam, Netherlands. TEL 31-20-5803911. FAX 31-20-5803598. TELEX 18582 ESPA NL. (Subscr. in U.S. and Canada to: Elsevier Science Inc., Box 882, Madison Sq. Sta., New York, NY 10159. TEL 212-989-5800. FAX 212-633-3990) Ed. R.W. Grubbstroem. adv.; bk.rev.; bibl.; index. (also avail. in microform from UMI) **Indexed:** ABI Inform., BPIA, Bus.Ind., C.R.E.J., Curr.Cont., Eng.Ind., Excerp.Med., INSPEC, J.Cont.Quant.Meth., Manage.Cont., Robomat., Sci.Abstr. **Document type:** academic/scholarly publication.
—BLDSC (4542.485000); EI; Faxon; UnCover; SWETS; UMI. **CCC.**
   Former titles: Engineering Costs and Production Economics (ISSN 0167-188X); Engineering and Process Economics (ISSN 0377-841X); Incorporates (1988-1992): Journal of Manufacturing and Operations Management (ISSN 0890-2577); (1981-1987): Material Flow (ISSN 0167-1936); (1978-1986): Maintenance Management International; Which was formerly: Terotechnica (ISSN 0378-5947).
   Description: Focuses on topics treating the interface between engineering and managerial problem areas. Considers product life cycle - research, design, development, test, launch, disposal; and material flow cycle - supply, production, distribution.
   Refereed Serial

INTERNATIONAL JOURNAL OF PRODUCTION RESEARCH. see *BUSINESS AND ECONOMICS — Production Of Goods And Services*

INTERNATIONAL JOURNAL OF SCIENCE & ENGINEERING. see *SCIENCES: COMPREHENSIVE WORKS*

620   **UK**   **ISSN 0020-7721**
QA402   **CODEN: IJSYA9**
INTERNATIONAL JOURNAL OF SYSTEMS SCIENCE. 1970. m. £671($1128) Taylor & Francis Ltd., Rankine Rd., Easingstoke, Hants RG24 8PR, England. TEL 0256-840366. FAX 0256-479438. TELEX 858540. Ed. B. Porter. adv.; bk.rev. (also avail. in microform) **Indexed:** A.I.Abstr., Appl.Mech.Rev, Biol.Abstr., Biostat., CAD CAM Abstr. (until 1992), Chem.Abstr., Compumath, Comput.Abstr., Curr.Cont., Cyb.Abstr., Eng.Ind., Excerp.Med., Ird.Sci.Rev., Math.R., Oper.Res.Manage.Sci., Qual.Contr.Appl.Stat., Risk Abstr., Robomat. (until 1992), Sci.Abstr., Sci.Cit.Ind. **Document type:** academic/scholarly publication.
—BLDSC (4542.693000); Faxon; UnCover; SWETS. **CCC.**
   Description: Original contributions are published on the theory and practice of mathematical modelling, simulation, optimization and control in relation to biological, economic, environmental, industrial and transportation systems.
   Refereed Serial

INTERNATIONAL NAVIGATION ASSOCIATION NEWSLETTER. see *TRANSPORTATION — Air Transport*

620.11 620   **TU**   **ISSN 0259-8418**
INTERNATIONAL QUARTERLY OF MATERIALS SCIENCE. (Text in English) 1987. q. $215. Tahsin Yazicioglu, P. Kutusu 1318, Sirkeci, Istambul 34438, Turkey. Ed.Bd. adv.; bk.rev. **Indexed:** Chem.Abstr., Curr.Cont., Phys.Abstr., Ref.Zh., Sci.Cit.Ind.

621   **PL**
INTERNATIONAL SYMPOSIUM ON SWITCHING ARC PHENOMENA. PROCEEDINGS. (Text in English, German, Russian; summaries in English) irreg., 2nd, 1973. price varies. Wydawnictwo Politechniki Lodzkiej, Wolczanska 219, 93-085 Lodz, Poland. (Co-sponsor: Stowarzyszenie Elektrykow Polskich) illus. **Document type:** academic/scholarly publication.

620   **US**
INTERNATIONAL UNION OF THEORETICAL AND APPLIED MECHANICS. SYMPOSIA. 1956. irreg. price varies. Springer-Verlag, 175 Fifth Ave., New York, NY 10010. TEL 212-460-1500. FAX 212-473-6272. (Also: Berlin, Heideberg, Tokyo and Vienna) (reprint service avail. from SI) **Document type:** proceedings.

INTERNATIONAL WELDING ENGINEERING. see *METALLURGY — Welding*

620 608.7   **PL**   **ISSN 0208-6247**
INZYNIERIA MATERIALOWA. 1979. 6/yr. Wydawnictwo Czasopism i Ksiazek Technicznych SIGMA - NOT, Ul. Ratuszowa 11, P.O. Box 1004, 00-950 Warsaw, Poland. TEL 48-22-180918. FAX 48-22-192187. (Editorial addr.: ul. Graniczna 6, 40-017 Katowice, Poland. TEL 48-32-155-33225) Ed. Adolf Maciejny. circ. 500.

620   **US**   **ISSN 0021-0501**
IOWA ENGINEER. 1901. q. $8. Iowa Engineer, Inc., c/o Advertising Director, 16G Hamilton Hall, Iowa State University, Ames, IA 50011-0001. TEL 515-294-9390. Ed. David Shipley. adv.; charts; illus.; stat.; tr.lit.; circ. 4,000 (controlled).

620   **US**   **ISSN 0075-0433**
   CODEN: IERRAG
IOWA STATE UNIVERSITY. ENGINEERING RESEARCH INSTITUTE. ENGINEERING RESEARCH REPORT. 1949. irreg. price varies. Iowa State University, Engineering Research Institute, Ames, IA 50011. TEL 515-294-2336. FAX 515-294-9273. **Indexed:** Geotech.Abstr. **Document type:** bulletin.
   Refereed Serial

620   **RU**
ISSLEDOVANIE, KONSTRUIROVANIE I RASCHET REZBOVYKH SOEDINENII. 1973. irreg. 0.50 Rub. per no. (Ulyanovskii Politekhnicheskii Institut) Privolzhskoe Knizhnoe Izdatel'stvo, Ul. Goncharova, 52, Ulyanovsk, Russia.

ISTITUTO STORICO E DI CULTURA DELL'ARMA DEL GENIO. BOLLETTINO. see *MILITARY*

ENGINEERING

620   JA   ISSN 0085-2325
CODEN: TIWUAT
IWATE UNIVERSITY. FACULTY OF ENGINEERING. TECHNOLOGY REPORTS/IWATE DAIGAKU KOGAKUBU KENKYU HOKOKU. (Text in English) 1965-1991 (vol.25). irreg. free. Iwate University, Faculty of Engineering - Iwate Daigaku Kogakubu, 4-3-5 Ueda, Morioka 020, Iwate-ken, Japan. FAX 0196-25-7222. Ed. Kazuo Tanno. **Indexed:** Appl.Mech.Rev., GeoRef., INIS Atomind., JTA, Sci.Abstr. **Document type:** academic/scholarly publication.
—UnCover.

620   KR   ISSN 0021-3489
TS940   CODEN: IVULAU
IZVESTIYA VYSSHIKH UCHEBNYKH ZAVEDENII. SERIYA TEKHNOLOGIYA LEGKOI PROMYSHLENNOSTI. 1958. bi-m. 26.70 Rub. Tekhnologicheskii Institut Legkoy Promyshlennosti, Kiev, Ukraine. index. circ. 3,500. **Indexed:** Chem.Abstr., Nutr.Abstr., RAPRA, Sci.Abstr., World Text.Abstr.
—CASDDS.

620 375   US
J E T S REPORT; promoting interest in engineering, technology, mathematics and science in high school. 1980. s-a. free to qualified personnel. (Junior Engineering Technical Society) J E T S, Inc., 1420 King St., Ste. 405, Alexandria, VA 22314-2794. TEL 703-548-5387. FAX 703-836-4875. Ed. Cathy McGowan. circ. 35,000. **Document type:** newsletter.

J O T. (Journal fuer Oberflaechentechnik) see MACHINERY

JAPAN. MINISTRY OF AGRICULTURE, FORESTRY AND FISHERIES. NATIONAL RESEARCH INSTITUTE OF AGRICULTURAL ENGINEERING. ABSTRACTS FROM RESEARCH REPORTS. see AGRICULTURE — Agricultural Equipment

JAPAN. MINISTRY OF AGRICULTURE, FORESTRY AND FISHERIES. NATIONAL RESEARCH INSTITUTE OF AGRICULTURAL ENGINEERING. BULLETIN. see AGRICULTURE — Agricultural Equipment

JAPAN. MINISTRY OF AGRICULTURE, FORESTRY AND FISHERIES. NATIONAL RESEARCH INSTITUTE OF AGRICULTURAL ENGINEERING. TECHNICAL REPORT. see AGRICULTURE — Agricultural Equipment

620 620.11   JA   ISSN 0285-3833
CODEN: NDZKDI
JAPAN ELECTRONIC MATERIALS SOCIETY. BULLETIN/NIHON DENSHI ZAIRYO GIJUTSU KYOKAI KAIHO. (Text in Japanese) 1968. a. Japan Electronic Materials Society - Nihon Denshi Zaiyo Gijutsu Kyokai, 2-8, Toranomon 1-chome, Minato-ku, Tokyo 105, Japan.
—BLDSC (2593.579500); CASDDS.

JAPAN SOCIETY FOR COMPOSITE MATERIALS. TRANSACTIONS. see ENGINEERING — Engineering Mechanics And Materials

620 681   JA   ISSN 0916-782X
JAPAN SOCIETY FOR PRECISION ENGINEERING. INTERNATIONAL JOURNAL. (Text in European languages) 1963. q. $48. Japan Society for Precision Engineering - Seimitsu Kogakkai, Ceramics Bldg., 22-17 Hyakunincho 2-chome, Shinjuku-ku, Tokyo 169, Japan. FAX 81-3-3362-1979. Ed. Nobuyuki Akiyama. **Indexed:** Chem.Abstr., Curr.Cont., Fluidex, ISMEC, JCT, JTA, Met.Abstr., Sci.Abstr., Sci.Cit.Ind.
—BLDSC (4541.467000); SWETS.
Formerly: Japan Society of Precision Engineering. Bulletin (ISSN 0582-4206)

JAPANESE JOURNAL OF APPLIED PHYSICS. see PHYSICS

JAPANESE SOCIETY FOR STRENGTH AND FRACTURE OF MATERIALS. JOURNAL. see ENGINEERING — Engineering Mechanics And Materials

620   US   ISSN 1058-7322
JAPANESE TECHNOLOGY REVIEWS: MANUFACTURING ENGINEERING (SECTION D). 1989. 2/yr. (in 1 vol.). 60 ECU (effective 1993). Gordon and Breach Science Publishers, 820 Town Center Dr., Langhorne, PA 19047. TEL 215-750-2642. FAX 215-750-6343. (UK subscr. to: P.O. Box 90, Reading, Berkshire, RG1 8JL, England. TEL 0734-560-080) Ed. Toshiaki Ikoma. (also avail. in microform)
—BLDSC (4662.120440). CCC.
Supersedes in part: Japanese Technology Review (ISSN 0898-5693)
Refereed Serial

JOHNS HOPKINS A P L TECHNICAL DIGEST. (Applied Physics Laboratory) see PHYSICS

JOURNAL DE PHYSIQUE III. see PHYSICS

JOURNAL OF ADVANCED MATERIALS. see ENGINEERING — Engineering Mechanics And Materials

JOURNAL OF ADVANCED TRANSPORTATION. see TRANSPORTATION

JOURNAL OF AGRICULTURAL ENGINEERING. see AGRICULTURE

JOURNAL OF APPLIED PHYSICS. see PHYSICS

JOURNAL OF BIOMECHANICAL ENGINEERING. see BIOLOGY — Bioengineering

620 621.381   SI   ISSN 0218-1266
TK7800   CODEN: JCSME7
JOURNAL OF CIRCUITS, SYSTEMS AND COMPUTERS. 1991. q. $192 to institutions of developed countries; individuals & developing countries $90. World Scientific Publishing Co. Pte. Ltd., Farrer Rd., P.O. Box 128, Singapore 9128, Singapore. TEL 3825663. FAX 3825919. TELEX RS-28561-WSPC. (UK addr.: 73 Lynton Mead, Totteridge, London N20 8DH, England. TEL 44-81-4462461; US addr.: 1060 Main St., Ste. 1B, River Edge, NJ 07661. TEL 800-227-7562) Ed. W-K Chen. **Document type:** academic/scholarly publication.
—BLDSC (4958.368500).
Description: Covers a wide scope, ranging from mathematical foundations to practical engineering design in the general areas of circuits, systems and computers.

JOURNAL OF ENGINEERING AND TECHNOLOGY MANAGEMENT. see BUSINESS AND ECONOMICS — Management

620   UK   ISSN 0954-4828
TA174   CODEN: JEDSEW
JOURNAL OF ENGINEERING DESIGN. 1990. q. $118 to individuals; institutions $316 (effective 1994). Carfax Publishing Co., P.O. Box 25, Abingdon, Oxon. OX14 3UE, England. TEL 44-235-555335. FAX 44-235-553559. (U.S. subscr. to: Carfax Publishing Co., Box 2025, Dunnellon, FL 34430-2025) Ed. Derek Sheldon. **Document type:** academic/scholarly publication.
—BLDSC (4978.750000). CCC.
Description: Focuses on industrial and engineering design research activities across the major disciplines of engineering.
Refereed Serial

620   IR   ISSN 1022-3118
JOURNAL OF ENGINEERING, ISLAMIC REPUBLIC OF IRAN/MAJALLAH-I MUHANDISI, JUMHURI ISLAMI IRAN. (Text in English, summaries in English, Persian) 1988. q. $31 to individuals (Japan & USA $46); institutions $46 (Japan & USA $62). National Center for Scientific Research, 1188 Enghelab Ave., P.O. Box 13145-554, Tehran 13158, Iran. TEL 98-21-6462707. FAX 98-21-6462254. TELEX 214554 NCSR IR. Ed. K. Sadrnezhaad. bibl.; charts; illus. **Document type:** academic/scholarly publication.
Description: Provides a medium for communication of original engineering research and information among Iranian scientists and engineers and the world scientific community.

510 620   NE   ISSN 0022-0833
TA329   CODEN: JLEMAU
JOURNAL OF ENGINEERING MATHEMATICS. (Text in English) 1966. 6/yr. fl.566($295) (effective 1994). Kluwer Academic Publishers, Postbus 17, 3300 AA Dordrecht, Netherlands. TEL 31-78-334911. FAX 31-78-334254. TELEX 29245 KAPG NL. (Dist. by: Kluwer Academic Publishers Group, P.O. Box 322, 3300 AH Dordrecht, Netherlands. TEL 31-78-524400. FAX 31-78-524474; N. America dist. addr.: Box 358, Accord Sta., Hingham, MA 02018-0358. TEL 617-871-6600. FAX 617-871-6528) Ed. H.K. Kuiken. adv.; bk.rev.; charts; illus.; index. (also avail. in microform from UMI; back issues avail.; reprint service avail. from SWZ) **Indexed:** Appl.Mech.Rev., ASCA, Compumath, Curr.Cont., Eng.Ind., Fluidex, Ind.Sci.Rev., Int.Aerosp.Abstr., Intl.Civil Eng.Abstr., Math.R., Sci.Abstr., Sci.Cit.Ind., Sh.& Vib.Dig., Soft.Abstr.Eng., Zent.Math. **Document type:** academic/scholarly publication.
—BLDSC (4979.150000); EI; Faxon; UnCover; SWETS; UMI. CCC.
Refereed Serial

620 530   US   ISSN 1062-0125
TA4   CODEN: JEPTER
JOURNAL OF ENGINEERING PHYSICS AND THERMOPHYSICS. English translation of: Inzhenerno-Fizicheskii Zhurnal (BW ISSN 0021-0285) 1965. m. (2 vols./yr.). $1250 (foreign $1465) (effective 1994). (Akademiya Navuk Belarusi, BW) Plenum Publishing Corp., Consultants Bureau, 233 Spring St., New York, NY 10013-1578. TEL 212-620-8468. FAX 212-463-0742. TELEX 23-421139. Ed. O.G. Martynenko. (also avail. in microfilm from JSC; back issues avail.) **Indexed:** Appl.Mech.Rev., Chem.Titles, Elec.& Electron.Abstr., Eng.Ind., INIS Atomind., INSPEC, ISMEC. **Document type:** academic/scholarly publication.
—BLDSC (0414.420000); Faxon; UnCover; SWETS; UMI. CCC.
Formerly (until 1992): Journal of Engineering Physics (ISSN 0022-0841)

620   US   ISSN 0747-9964
TA1
JOURNAL OF ENGINEERING TECHNOLOGY. 1984. s-a. $20 (foreign $35). American Society for Engineering Education, Engineering Technology Division, c/o Carole Goodson, Ed., University of Houston, Houston, TX 77204-4083. TEL 713-743-4046. FAX 713-743-4032. (Subscr. to: c/o Thomas Bingham, Jr., St. Louis Community College at Florrisant Valley, Dept. of Engineering, 3400 Pershall Rd., Ferguson, MO 63135. TEL 314-595-4314) adv. contact: Richard M. Moore. circ. 2,000. **Indexed:** Eng.Ind. **Document type:** academic/scholarly publication.
—BLDSC (4979.235000); Faxon.
Description: Publishes papers on current subjects in engineering technology.
Refereed Serial

574.1   UK   ISSN 0889-9746
TA357
JOURNAL OF FLUIDS AND STRUCTURES. 1987. 8/yr. £195 (effective 1994). Academic Press Ltd. (Subsidiary of: Harcourt Brace & Company Ltd.), 24-28 Oval Rd., London NW1 7DX, England. TEL 44-71-267-4466. FAX 44-71-482-2293. TELEX 25775-ACPRES-G. (Subscr. to: Harcourt Brace & Company Ltd., Foots Cray High St., Sidcup, Kent DA14 5HP, England. TEL 44-81-300-3322. FAX 44-81-309-0807; Alt. addr.: Dept. of Mechanical Engineering, McGill University, Montreal, PQ H3A 2K6, Canada. TEL 514-398-6294) Ed. M.P. Paidoussis. adv.; index. (back issues avail.) **Document type:** academic/scholarly publication.
—BLDSC (4984.510000); Faxon; UnCover; SWETS. CCC.
Description: Describes original full-length papers and brief communications on any aspect of fluid-structure interaction and on the dynamics of systems related to such interactions: on the fundamental mechanisms, as well as on specific applications, analytical, experimental, or computational.

620 US ISSN 1068-3666
TA418.72 CODEN: JFWEEO
JOURNAL OF FRICTION AND WEAR. English translation of: Trenie i Iznos (BW ISSN 0202-4977) 1980. bi-m. $790. (Belarus Academy of Sciences, BW) Allerton Press, Inc., 150 Fifth Ave., New York, NY 10011. TEL 212-924-3950. FAX 212-463-9684. Ed. A.I. Sviridenok. **Indexed:** Met.Abstr., World Alum.Abstr. **Document type:** academic/scholarly publication.
—BLDSC (0414.700000). **CCC.**
 Formerly (until 1992): Soviet Journal of Friction and Wear (ISSN 0733-1924)

JOURNAL OF IMAGING SCIENCE AND TECHNOLOGY. see *PHOTOGRAPHY*

JOURNAL OF INTELLIGENT AND FUZZY SYSTEMS. see *MATHEMATICS*

620 IQ ISSN 1012-3490
JOURNAL OF IRAQI DISSERTATION ABSTRACTS. PART B: SCIENCE AND ENGINEERING. (Editions in Arabic, English) 1986. irreg. free. Scientific Research Council, Jadiriyah P.O. Box 2441, Baghdad, Iraq. TELEX 213876 SR IK. Ed. Radhwan K. Abdul-Halim. circ. 500. **Document type:** abstracting/indexing.

620 US ISSN 0742-597X
CODEN: JMENEA
JOURNAL OF MANAGEMENT IN ENGINEERING. 1985. bi-m. $112 to non-members (foreign $125); members $28 (foreign $41). American Society of Civil Engineers, Engineering Management Division, 345 E. 47th St., New York, NY 10017-2398. TEL 212-705-7288. FAX 212-980-4681. Ed. Gary Bates. illus.; index. circ. 4,900. **Indexed:** A.I.Abstr., CAD CAM Abstr., Environ.Abstr., Tel.Abstr. **Document type:** academic/scholarly publication.
—BLDSC (5011.310000); EI; Faxon; UnCover; SWETS; UMI. **CCC.**
 Description: Examines a broad spectrum of organizations: private and public; design, research, operations and maintenance; large and small.

JOURNAL OF MANUFACTURING; issues, option and strategies. see *COMPUTERS — Computer Systems*

JOURNAL OF MANUFACTURING SYSTEMS. see *COMPUTERS — Computer Systems*

620 US ISSN 0738-7989
CODEN: JMEDDD
JOURNAL OF MATERIALS EDUCATION; an international journal with a new concept in journal publication. 1979. bi-m. $245. Materials Education Council, 110 Materials Research Lab, Pennsylvania State University, University Park, PA 16802. TEL 814-865-1643. FAX 814-863-7040. Ed. Robert Berrettini. bk.rev.; charts; illus.; tr.lit.; index. circ. 300. (back issues avail.) **Indexed:** Chem.Abstr. **Document type:** academic/scholarly publication.
—BLDSC (5012.220000); Faxon; UnCover; CASDDS.
 Formerly: Journal of Educational Modules for Materials Science and Engineering.
 Description: International journal of peer-review teaching units for materials science and engineering.

JOURNAL OF NUCLEAR MATERIALS; materials aspects of fission and fusion. see *PHYSICS — Nuclear Physics*

JOURNAL OF NUCLEAR SCIENCE AND TECHNOLOGY/NIHON GENSHIRYOKU GAKKAI OBUN RONBUNSHI. see *PHYSICS — Nuclear Physics*

JOURNAL OF PETROLEUM SCIENCE AND ENGINEERING. see *PETROLEUM AND GAS*

JOURNAL OF PHYSICS D: APPLIED PHYSICS. see *PHYSICS*

JOURNAL OF PHYSICS ENGINEERING/FIZIK MUHENDISLIGI DERGISI. see *PHYSICS*

JOURNAL OF PRODUCTS AND TOXICS LIABILITY. see *LAW*

JOURNAL OF REHABILITATION RESEARCH AND DEVELOPMENT. see *MEDICAL SCIENCES — Orthopedics And Traumatology*

620 US
TA1501
JOURNAL OF RUSSIAN LASER RESEARCH. 1980. bi-m. $565 (foreign $660) (effective 1994). Plenum Publishing Corp., Consultants Bureau, 233 Spring St., New York, NY 10013-1578. TEL 212-620-8468. FAX 212-463-0742. TELEX 23-421139. Ed. N.G. Basov. index. (also avail. in microfilm from JSC; back issues avail.) **Indexed:** Appl.Mech.Rev., Biol.Abstr., Curr.Cont., Eng.Ind., INIS Atomind., INSPEC. **Document type:** academic/scholarly publication.
—BLDSC (0415.355000); Faxon; UnCover; UMI. **CCC.**
 Formerly (until 1994): Journal of Soviet Laser Research (ISSN 0270-2010)
 Refereed Serial

JOURNAL OF TECHNICAL WRITING AND COMMUNICATION. see *EDUCATION*

620 II ISSN 0047-2824
CODEN: JTBEAD
JOURNAL OF TECHNOLOGY. 1956. 2/yr. Rs.10($2.50) Bengal Engineering College, Howrah 711103, West Bengal, India. Ed. Dr. S.C. Dasgupta. bk.rev. circ. 250. (also avail. in microform from UMI; reprint service avail. from UMI) **Indexed:** Appl.Mech.Rev., Chem.Abstr., Math.R., Sci.Abstr.

614 696 US ISSN 1065-2744
TH1715.A1 CODEN: JTIEEI
JOURNAL OF THERMAL INSULATION AND BUILDING ENVELOPES. 1977. q. $205. Technomic Publishing Co., Inc., 851 New Holland Ave., Box 3535, Lancaster, PA 17604. TEL 717-291-5609. FAX 717-295-4538. TELEX 230 753565 (TECHNOMIC UD). Ed. Mark T. Bomberg. bk.rev.; charts; illus.; stat.; index. circ. 290. (back issues avail.) **Indexed:** Chem.Abstr., Excerp.Med., INIS Atomind., Met.Abstr., World Alum.Abstr. **Document type:** academic/scholarly publication.
—BLDSC (5069.098300); EI; Faxon; UnCover; SWETS; UMI; CASDDS. **CCC.**
 Formerly: Journal of Thermal Insulation (ISSN 0148-8287)
 Description: Fosters knowledge of thermal performance of materials and systems, particularly those used in building envelopes; reports advances in laboratory and field measuring techniques; and provides a forum for discussion among researchers, engineers, and consultants involved in the control of thermal energy.
 Refereed Serial

JOURNAL OF X-RAY SCIENCE AND TECHNOLOGY. see *PHYSICS*

620 GW ISSN 0174-7312
K E M - EUROPEAN DESIGN ENGINEERING; special issues of K E M. (Text in English, German) 4/yr. Konradin Verlag Robert Kohlhammer GmbH, Ernst-Mey-Str. 8, 70771 Leinfelden-Echterdingen, Germany. TEL 0711-7594-0. FAX 0711-7594-390. Ed. Herbert Neumann. adv.: B&W page DM.8340, color page DM.10380; trim 190 x 270; adv. contact: Walter Schwager. bk.rev.; charts; illus.; stat.; circ. 30,036 (controlled). (back issues avail.) **Document type:** trade publication.

KAGAKU TO KOGYO (OSAKA)/SCIENCE AND INDUSTRY. see *TECHNOLOGY: COMPREHENSIVE WORKS*

620 US ISSN 0022-8559
KANSAS ENGINEER. 1914. 3/yr. $10. University of Kansas, School of Engineering, 4010 Learned Hall, Lawrence, KS 66045. TEL 913-864-3881. Ed. Alex Mitchell. adv.; charts; illus. circ. 2,500.
 Description: Magazine published by and for the engineering students at the University of Kansas.

620 US ISSN 0047-3189
KANSAS STATE ENGINEER. 1915. q. $6. Kansas State University, College of Engineering, Durland Hall, Manhattan, KS 66506. TEL 913-532-6026. FAX 913-532-6952. Ed. Ann Ridge. adv.: B&W page $200; adv. contact: Mike Dorcey. bk.rev.; charts; illus.; stat. circ. 2,800. **Document type:** academic/scholarly publication.

621 RU
KAZANSKII UNIVERSITET. SBORNIK ASPIRANTSKIKH RABOT: TEORIYA PLASTIN I OBOLOCHEK. 1971. irreg. 0.67 Rub. Kazanskii Universitet, Ul. Lenina, 4-5, Kazan, Russia. illus. **Indexed:** Math.R.

KEMISK TIDSKRIFT. see *CHEMISTRY*

620 UK ISSN 0075-5400
TA151.A1
KEMPE'S ENGINEERS YEAR-BOOK. (In two volumes) 1894. a. £99 (foreign £109). Benn Business Information Services Ltd. (Subsidiary of: Morgan-Grampian plc), Benn House, Sovereign Way, Tonbridge, Kent TN9 1RW, England. TEL 0732-362666. FAX 0732-770483. TELEX 95162 BENTON G. Ed. Carill Sharpe. adv.; bibl.; illus.; index. circ. 5,000.

620 US ISSN 0746-2255
KENTUCKY ENGINEER. 1934. m. $15. (Kentucky Society of Professional Engineers) Broughman & Associates, 3161 Custer Dr., Lexington, KY 40502. TEL 606-271-1778. Ed. Joe Doughenty. adv.; charts; illus.; pat.; stat.; index. circ. 4,500.
 Description: Covers professional practice and current registration law matters.

620 KE
KENYA ENGINEER. 1978. bi-m. EAs.30. Institution of Engineers of Kenya, P.O. Box 41346, Nairobi, Kenya. (Subscr. to: Intercontinental Publishers Ltd., P.O. Box 45754, Nairobi, Kenya) adv.; bk.rev. circ. 3,000.
 Description: Contains news of development projects in East Africa, technical features, and information on engineers and activities.

KERNFORSCHUNGSZENTRUM KARLSRUHE. ERGEBNISBERICHT UEBER FORSCHUNG UND ENTWICKLUNG. see *ENERGY — Nuclear Energy*

KHIMIYA I TEKHNOLOGIYA TOPLIV I MASEL. see *PETROLEUM AND GAS*

620 SU ISSN 1018-3639
TA1 CODEN: JSUSEB
KING SAUD UNIVERSITY. JOURNAL. ENGINEERING SCIENCES. Key Title: Majallat Jami'at al-Malik Sa'ud, al-'Ulum al-Handasiyyah. (Other sections avail.: Administrative Sciences, Agricultural Sciences, Architecture and Planning, Arts, Computer and Information Sciences, Educational Sciences and Islamic Studies, Sciences) (Text in Arabic, English) 1975. s-a. $10. King Saud University, University Libraries, P.O. Box 22480, Riyadh 11495, Saudi Arabia. TEL 966-1-4676148. FAX 966-1-4676162. TELEX 401019 KSU SJ. Ed. Mohammed A. Alhaider. charts; illus. circ. 2,000. **Indexed:** Build.Manage.Abstr., Chem.Abstr., Curr.Cont., Met.Abstr., Sci.Abstr., World Alum.Abstr. **Document type:** academic/scholarly publication.
—BLDSC (4810.890000); CASDDS.
 Formerly (until 1939): Journal of Engineering Sciences (ISSN 0377-9254)
 Refereed Serial

620 JA ISSN 0288-738X
CODEN: KDKREY
KINKI DAIGAKU KYUSHU KOGAKUBU KENKYU HOKOKU. RIKOGAKU HEN/KINKI UNIVERSITY. FACULTY OF ENGINEERING (KYUSHU). REPORTS. SCIENCE AND TECHNOLOGY SECTION. (Text in English and Japanese; summaries in English) 1972. a. Kinki Daigaku, Kyushu Kogakubu - Kinki University, Faculty of Engineering (Kyushu Campus), 11-6 Kayanomori, Iizuka-shi, Fukuoka-ken 820, Japan.
—CASDDS.

620 537 JA
KOATSU TORONKAI KOEN YOSHISHU/HIGH PRESSURE CONFERENCE OF JAPAN. PROGRAMME AND ABSTRACTS OF PAPERS. (Text in English, Japanese) a. Nihon Koatsuryoku Gakkai - Japan Society of High Pressure Science and Technology, Seisan Kaihatsu Kagaku Kenkyujo, 15, Shimogamo Morimotocho, Sakyo-ku, Kyoto 606, Japan.

620 JA ISSN 0368-9638
CODEN: MFEKAF
KOBE UNIVERSITY. FACULTY OF ENGINEERING. MEMOIRS. (Text in Japanese) 1950. a. Kobe Daigaku, Kogakubu - Kobe University. Faculty of Engineering, Rokko, Nada-ku, Kobe-shi, Hyogo-ken, Japan. **Indexed:** Energy Info.Abstr. **Document type:** academic/scholarly publication.
—BLDSC (5593.630000); CASDDS.

KOBE UNIVERSITY OF MERCANTILE MARINE. REVIEW. PART 2. MARITIME STUDIES, AND SCIENCE AND ENGINEERING. see *SCIENCES: COMPREHENSIVE WORKS*

ENGINEERING

KOCHI UNIVERSITY. FACULTY OF AGRICULTURE. MEMOIRS. see *AGRICULTURE*

628   GW   ISSN 0450-7169
HD4659   CODEN: KMLWAB
KOMMUNALWIRTSCHAFT. 1912. m. DM.100. (Verein fuer Kommunalwirtschaft) Deutscher Kommunal Verlag GmbH, Roseggerstr. 5a, 40476 Duesseldorf, Germany. TEL 0211-624417. FAX 0211-622998. Ed. H.-J. Schumacher. adv.; charts; illus. circ. 3,900. **Indexed:** Chem.Abstr., Excerp.Med., INIS Atomind.
—CASDDS.

620   CC   ISSN 1000-8152
KONGZHI LILUN YU YINGYONG/CONTROL THEORY & APPLICATIONS. (Text in Chinese) 1984. bi-m. Zhongguo Kexueyuan, Xitong Kexue Yanjiusuo - Chinese Academy of Sciences, Institute of System Science, Huanan Ligong Daxue, Guangzhou, Guangdong 510641, People's Republic of China. TEL 20-7111464. Ed. Li Botian. **Document type:** academic/scholarly publication.
—EI.

620   CC   ISSN 1001-0920
KONGZHI YU JUECE. (Text in Chinese) bi-m. Dongbei Gongxueyuan - Northeast Institute of Engineering, No.1, Wenhua Lu 1 Duan, Heping-qu, Shenyang, Liaoning 110006, People's Republic of China. TEL 39300.

658.5   GW   ISSN 0342-7102
KONSTRUKTION ELEKTRONIK MASCHINENBAU. Abbreviated title: K E M. m. Konradin Verlag Robert Kohlhammer GmbH, Ernst-Mey-Str. 8, 70771 Leinfelden-Echterdingen, Germany. TEL 0711-7594-0. FAX 0711-7594-390. Ed. Herbert Neumann. adv.: B&W page DM.7380, color page DM.9360; trim 190 x 270; adv. contact: Walter Schwager. circ. 25,042. (back issues avail.) **Indexed:** Fluidex, INIS Atomind., Sh.& Vib.Dig. **Document type:** trade publication.
Description: Technical reports on design techniques, elements, parts, processes and practice, as well as facts on new, developed and improved products.

620   GW   ISSN 0724-1070
KONTROLLE; Analytik und Prueftechnik. 1982. 10/yr. Konradin Verlag Robert Kohlhammer GmbH, Ernst-May-Str. 8, 70771 Leinfelden-Echterdingen, Germany. TEL 0711-7594-0. FAX 0711-7594-390. Ed. Guenter Eckhardt. adv.: B&W page DM.6490; trim 190 x 270. bk.rev.; charts; illus.; stat.; circ. 20,525 (controlled).
Description: Covers the whole range of instrumentation, control and analytic engineering in industrial production.

DIE KUESTE; Archiv fuer Forschung und Technik an der Nord- und Ostsee. see *EARTH SCIENCES — Oceanography*

620   JA   ISSN 0023-5334
CODEN: MEKMAA
KUMAMOTO UNIVERSITY. FACULTY OF ENGINEERING. MEMOIRS/KUMAMOTO DAIGAKU KOGAKUBU KIYO. (Text in English) 1954. irreg. free. Kumamoto Daigaku, Kogakubu - Kumamoto University, Faculty of Engineering, 39-1, Kurokami 2-chome, Kumamoto-shi, Kumamoto-ken 860, Japan. bibl.; charts; illus. **Indexed:** Energy Info.Abstr., INIS Atomind., JCT, JTA, Met.Abstr., Sci.Abstr., World Alum.Abstr.
—BLDSC (5593.700000).

620   JA   ISSN 0023-5296
KUMAMOTO UNIVERSITY. FACULTY OF ENGINEERING. TECHNICAL REPORTS/KUMAMOTO DAIGAKU KOGAKUBU KENKYU HOKOKU. 1952. irreg. free. Kumamoto Daigaku, Kogakubu - Kumamoto University, Faculty of Engineering, 39-1, Kurokami 2-chome, Kumamoto-shi, Kumamoto-ken 860, Japan. **Indexed:** Chem.Abstr., INIS Atomind., JCT, JTA, Sci.Abstr. **Document type:** academic/scholarly publication.
—BLDSC (8716.600000).

620   JA   ISSN 0023-6063
CODEN: MEKYAC
KYOTO UNIVERSITY. FACULTY OF ENGINEERING. MEMOIRS/KYOTO DAIGAKU KOGAKUBU KIYO. (Text in European languages) 1914. q. free. Kyoto University, Faculty of Engineering - Kyoto Daigaku Kogakubu, Yoshida Hon-machi, Sakyo-ku, Kyoto 606, Japan. Ed.Bd. abstr.; charts; illus.; stat.; index; circ. controlled. **Indexed:** Appl.Mech.Rev., Chem.Abstr., Eng.Ind., Fluidex, GeoRef., INIS Atomind., Int.Aerosp.Abstr., JCT, Math.R., Met.Abstr., Sci.Abstr., World Alum.Abstr.
—BLDSC (5594.000000); EI; Faxon; UnCover; CASDDS.

620 681   JA   ISSN 0285-2969
KYOWA ENGINEERING NEWS/KYOWA GIHO. (Text in Japanese) 1958. m. 100 Yen per no. Kyowa Electronic Instruments Co., Ltd. - Kyowa Dengyo, 5-1, Chofugaoka 3-chome, Chofu-shi, Tokyo 182, Japan. Ed. Hisashi Soeda. circ. 10,000. (back issues avail.)

620   JA   ISSN 0388-1717
TA4   CODEN: SRKHEK
KYUSHU DAIGAKU DAIGAKUIN SOGO RIKOGAKU KENKYUKA HOKOKU/KYUSHU UNIVERSITY. ENGINEERING SCIENCES REPORTS. (Text in English and Japanese; summaries in English) 1974. s-a. Kyushu University, Graduate School of Engineering Sciences - Kyushu Daigaku Daigakuin Sogo Rikogaku Kenkyuka, 6-1 Kasuga Koen, Kasuga-shi, Fukuoka-ken 816, Japan. abstr. **Indexed:** INIS Atomind., Sci.Abstr.
—BLDSC (3769.980000); CASDDS.

620   JA   ISSN 0369-0512
CODEN: MKIEBJ
KYUSHU INSTITUTE OF TECHNOLOGY. MEMOIRS: ENGINEERING. (Text in English) 1971. a. exchange basis. Kyushu Institute of Technology - Kyushu Kogyo Daigaku, 1-1 Sensui-cho, Tobata, Kitakyushu 804, Japan. **Indexed:** Chem.Abstr., JCT, JTA, Sci.Abstr.
—BLDSC (5623.300000); UnCover.

620   JA   ISSN 0023-6160
CODEN: MEKSAS
KYUSHU UNIVERSITY. FACULTY OF ENGINEERING. MEMOIRS/KYUSHU DAIGAKU KOGAKUBU KIYO. (Text in English) 1913. q. exchange basis. Kyushu University, Faculty of Engineering - Kyushu Daigaku Kogakubu, 6-10-1 Hakozaki, Higashi-ku, Fukuoka 812, Japan. TEL 092-641-1101. charts; illus.; index. circ. 1,000. **Indexed:** Appl.Mech.Rev., Chem.Abstr., INIS Atomind., Int.Aerosp.Abstr., Math.R., Met.Abstr., Sci.Abstr., World Alum.Abstr.
—BLDSC (5595.000000); EI; UnCover; CASDDS.

620   JA   ISSN 0023-2718
CODEN: KDKSAX
KYUSHU UNIVERSITY. FACULTY OF ENGINEERING. TECHNOLOGY REPORTS/KYUSHU DAIGAKU KOGAKU SHUHO. (Text in Japanese) 1926. bi-m. exchange basis. Kyushu University, Faculty of Engineering - Kyushu Daigaku Kogakubu, 6-10-1 Hakozaki, Higashi-ku, Fukuoka 812, Japan. TEL 092-641-1101. circ. 800. **Indexed:** JCT, JTA, Sci.Abstr.
—BLDSC (8759.700000); CASDDS.

L S U ENGINEERING NEWS. (Louisiana State University) see *COLLEGE AND ALUMNI*

526.9   CE
LANKIAN SURVEYOR.* suspended 1982-1985, expected to resume 1986. s-a. Lankian Society of Licensed Surveyors, 81-2 Greenlands Rd., Colombo 5, Sri Lanka. Ed. M.J. Setunga. adv.; bk.rev. circ. 5,000.

620   US
LAST WORD. 1956. w. membership. American Consulting Engineers Council, 1015 15th St. N.W., Washington, DC 20005-2670. TEL 202-347-7474. Ed. Rich West. illus. circ. 9,400.
Former titles: A C E C Newsletter; C E C Newsletter (ISSN 0007-8123)

LAURENCE SCOTT ENGINEERING BULLETIN. see *ENGINEERING — Electrical Engineering*

620   US   ISSN 0176-5035
CODEN: LNENE5
LECTURE NOTES IN ENGINEERING. 1983. irreg. price varies. Springer-Verlag, 175 Fifth Ave., New York, NY 10010. TEL 212-460-1500. FAX 212-473-6272. (Also: Berlin, Heidelberg, Tokyo and Vienna) Eds. C.A. Brebbia, S.A. Orszag. **Document type:** monographic series.
—BLDSC (5180.196000).

LIGHT & ENGINEERING. see *PHYSICS — Optics*

320   FR
LIQUIDES MAGAZINE. 6/yr. Somia, 15 rue du Puits-de-l'Ermite, 75005 Paris, France. TEL 43-36-08-88. FAX 45-87-22-08. Ed. Jacques Ramond. circ. 4,000.

620 665.5   UK   ISSN 0268-9219
LIQUIDS HANDLING. 1985. 6/yr. £60($100) D M G Trinity, Times House, Station Approach, Ruislip, Middx. HA4 8NB, England. TEL 0895-677677. FAX 0895-676027. Ed. Steve Ducker. adv.; bk.rev. circ. 8,043. (back issues avail.) **Document type:** trade publication.
Description: Covers every aspect of fluids handling technology from storage to finished product.

620 614.7   US
LOGOS (ARGONNE). 3/yr. free. Argonne National Laboratory, Office of Public Affairs, 9700 S. Cass Ave., Bldg. 200, Argonne, IL 60439. TEL 708-972-5575. FAX 708-252-5274. Ed. Evelyn Brown. bk.rev.; bibl.; illus. **Indexed:** Energy Info.Abstr., Environ.Abstr.
Description: Reports on selected research programs conducted at Argonne National Laboratory, focusing on engineering research, biomedical and environmental science and technology.

620   US   ISSN 0024-6794
LOUISIANA ENGINEER. 1915. bi-m. $3. Louisiana Engineering Society, Box 2683, Baton Rouge, LA 70821. TEL 504-344-4318. Ed. Leta Bueto. adv. circ. 20,000.

620   GW
M A N FORSCHEN, PLANEN, BAUEN. English edition: M A N Research, Engineering, Manufacturing. (Editions also in French, German and Spanish) 1970. a. free. M A N Aktiengesellschaft, Ungererstr. 69, 80805 Munich, Germany. TEL 0821-322-3740. FAX 0821-322-3291. TELEX 53796-0. (Subcr. to: MAN AG, Stadtbachstr. 1, 8900 Augsburg, Germany) Ed.Bd. illus. circ. 40,000(comb.). **Indexed:** INIS Atomind., Sci.Abstr.
Description: Covers the latest research and developments in the technology in all fields of engineering and manufacturing.

M S F JOURNAL. (Manufacturing, Science and Finance Uinion) see *LABOR UNIONS*

MACHINE VIBRATION. see *MACHINERY*

MACHINE VISION & APPLICATIONS. see *COMPUTERS — Cybernetics*

620   UA
MAGALLAT AL-MOHANDESEEN/ENGINEER'S MAGAZINE. (Text in Arabic, English) 1945. 10/yr. Engineer's Syndicate, 28 av. Ramses, Cairo, Egypt. Ed. Mahmoud Sami Abdel-Kawi. adv. circ. 80,000.

620   US   ISSN 0025-2093
MANHATTAN COLLEGE ENGINEER. 1940. 3/yr. $5. Manhattan College, School of Engineering, Manhattan College Pkwy., Bronx, NY 10471. TEL 212-920-0281. FAX 212-796-8912. Ed. Tony Canale. adv.; abstr.; charts; illus. circ. 2,500.

658.5   CU
MANUAL DEL INSTRUMENTISTA. q. $34 in S. America; N. America $36; elsewhere $42. (Ministerio de la Industria Basica, Centro Nacional de Informacion Cientifico-Tecnica) Ediciones Cubanas, Obispo No. 527, Apdo. 605, Havana, Cuba.

MANUFACTURING AUTOMATION. see *BUSINESS AND ECONOMICS — Marketing And Purchasing*

658.5 UK ISSN 0956-9944
T58.A2 CODEN: MFENES
MANUFACTURING ENGINEER. 1921. bi-m. £72 in E.C. nations; elsewhere £80. I.E.E., Michael Faraday House, Six Hills Way, Stevenage, Herts. SG1 2AY, England. TEL 0438-313311. FAX 0438-742792. TELEX 825578-INSPEC-G. (Subscr. to: Publication Sales Dept., P.O. Box 96, Stevenage, Herts. SG1 2SD, England; U.S. addr.: INSPEC/IEEE, Box 1331, 445 Hoes Ln., Piscataway, NJ 08855-1331. TEL 908-562-5549) Ed. J. Cooper. adv.; bk.rev.; charts; illus.; index. circ. 16,000. (also avail. in microform from UMI; reprint service avail. from UMI) **Indexed:** Account.& Data Proc.Abstr., BMT, BPIA, Br.Tech.Ind., Chem.Abstr., Eng.Ind., Ergon.Abstr., Excerp.Med., High.Educ.Curr.Aware.Bull., Intl.Mgmt.Info, ISMEC, Met.Abstr., World Alum.Abstr. **Document type:** trade publication.
—BLDSC (5367.079000); UnCover; SWETS.
  Incorporates (in May 1989): Production Engineer (ISSN 0032-9851)
  Description: Contains independent reporting to assist I.E.E. members in their professional capacities. Covers industry manufacturing methods, quality, and processes. Also covers computerized manufacturing, manufacturing information systems, machine tools, health and safety, and industrial relations.

658.5 US ISSN 0361-0853
TJ1180.A1 CODEN: MAENDQ
MANUFACTURING ENGINEERING. 1932. m. $60. Society of Manufacturing Engineers, One SME Dr., Box 930, Dearborn, MI 48121-0930. TEL 313-271-1500. FAX 313-271-2861. TELEX 97742 SME UR (VIA RCA). Ed. John Coleman. adv.; bk.rev.; charts; illus.; tr.lit. circ. 128,000. (also avail. in microform from UMI; reprint service avail. from UMI) **Indexed:** A.I.Abstr. (until 1992), A.S.& T.Ind., ABI Inform., Appl.Mech.Rev., CAD CAM Abstr. (until 1992), Cadscan, Comput.Lit.Ind., Curr.Cont., Eng.Ind., ISMEC, Lead Abstr., Met.Abstr., Oper.Res.Manage.Sci., Q.Abstr., Qual.Contr.Appl.Stat., Robomat. (until 1992), Sci.Cit.Ind., World Alum.Abstr., Zincscan.
—BLDSC (5367.090000); El; Faxon; UnCover; SWETS; UMI. **CCC.**
  Former titles: Manufacturing Engineering and Management (ISSN 0040-9219); Tool and Manufacturing Engineer.

620 621 JA ISSN 0388-0079
MARINE ENGINEERING SOCIETY IN JAPAN. BULLETIN. (Text in English) 1973. s-a. $105. Marine Engineering Society in Japan - Nihon Hakuyo Kikan Gakkai, 3-8, Mejiro 1-chome, Tosima-ku, Tokyo 171, Japan. TEL 03-5396-0461. FAX 03-5396-0462. (Dist. by Intercontinental Marketing Corp., I.P.O. Box 5056, Tokyo 100-30, Japan. TEL 81-3-3661-7458. FAX 81-3-3667-9646) circ. 1,100. (back issues avail.)
—BLDSC (2609.760000).

620 621 JA ISSN 0388-3051
  CODEN: NHGADN
MARINE ENGINEERING SOCIETY IN JAPAN. JOURNAL. (Text in Japanese; summaries in English) 1966. m. 23700 Yen. Marine Engineering Society in Japan - Nihon Hakuyo Kikan Gakkai, 3-8, Mejiro 1-chome, Tosima-ku, Tokyo 171, Japan. TEL 03-5396-0461. FAX 03-5396-0462. **Indexed:** JTA.
—CASDDS.

MARINE GEORESOURCES AND GEOTECHNOLOGY. see EARTH SCIENCES — Oceanography

620 US ISSN 1071-1333
▼**MARINE TECHNOLOGY NEWS.** 1993. bi-w. $495 (foreign $530) (effective 1994). Phillips Business Information, Inc., 1201 Seven Locks Rd., Potomac, MD 20854. TEL 301-424-3338. FAX 301-309-3847. (back issues avail.) **Document type:** newsletter.
—CCC.

MARINE TECHNOLOGY SOCIETY JOURNAL. see EARTH SCIENCES — Oceanography

620 PL ISSN 0860-3324
MASZYNY PRZEPLYWOWE. 1988. irreg. price varies. (Polska Akademia Nauk, Oddzial w Gdansku, Instytut Maszyn Przeplywowych - Polish Academy of Sciences, Gdansk Section, Institute of Fluid-Flow Machines) Ossolineum, Publishing House of the Polish Academy of Sciences, Rynek 9, 50-106 Wroclaw, Poland. TEL 48-71-386-25. FAX 48-71-448-103. TELEX 0712771 OSS PL. Ed. Eustachy S. Burka. **Document type:** monographic series.
  Description: A series devoted to original monographic studies based on Polish and world research achievements in theory and experimental research on mechanics and thermodynamics in turbines and other fluid-flow machines.

MATERIALS RESEARCH AND ENGINEERING/REINE UND ANGEWANDTE METALLKUNDE. see METALLURGY

MATERIALS RESEARCH SOCIETY SYMPOSIUM PROCEEDINGS. see PHYSICS

620.11 NE ISSN 0166-6010
  CODEN: MSMODP
MATERIALS SCIENCE MONOGRAPHS. (Text in English) 1978. irreg., vol.77, 1992. price varies. Elsevier Science B.V., Books Division, P.O. Box 211, 1000 AE Amsterdam, Netherlands. TEL 31-20-5803911. FAX 31-20-5803705. TELEX 18582 ESPA NL. (Subscr. in U.S. and Canada to: Elsevier Science Inc., Box 882, Madison Sq. Sta., New York, NY 10159. TEL 212-989-5800) Ed. C. Laird. adv. **Indexed:** Chem.Abstr. **Document type:** monographic series.
—BLDSC (5396.436000); CASDDS. **CCC.**
  Refereed Serial

MATHEMATICS IN SCIENCE AND ENGINEERING; series of monographs and textbooks. see MATHEMATICS

620 US ISSN 0748-7002
TK435
MEANS ELECTRICAL COST DATA (YEAR). 1977. a. $79.95. R.S. Means Company, Inc., 100 Construction Plaza, Box 800, Kingston, MA 02364-0800. TEL 800-334-3509. FAX 617-585-7466. Ed. Philip R. Waier. bk.rev. circ. 10,000. (back issues avail.)
  Supersedes in part: Means Mechanical and Electrical Cost Data.

MEASUREMENTS AND CONTROL. see INSTRUMENTS

MEASUREMENTS & CONTROL NEWS. see INSTRUMENTS

620 AU
MECHANIK UND ELEKTRONIK. m. Gumpendorferstr. 130, A-1060 Vienna, Austria. TEL 01-5970222. FAX 01-597022217. Ed. Kurt Pint. circ. 2,500.

620 IS
MEHANDESIM. 10/yr. Engineering Confederation of the Histadrut, Engineer House, 200 Dizengoff St., Tel Aviv 61 030, Israel. TEL 03-431842. adv.

620 530 JA ISSN 0388-130X
  CODEN: MDKRDL
MEISEI DAIGAKU KENKYU KIYO. RIKOGAKUBU/MEISEI UNIVERSITY. RESEARCH BULLETIN. PHYSICAL SCIENCES AND ENGINEERING. (Text and summaries in English and Japanese) 1965. a. Meisei Daigaku - Meisei University, 337 Hodokubo, Hino-shi, Tokyo 191, Japan. **Indexed:** Chem.Abstr., Jap.Per.Ind. **Document type:** bulletin.
—BLDSC (7727.700000); CASDDS.

METAAL & KUNSTSTOF. see MACHINERY

METALLURGICAL TRANSACTIONS A - PHYSICAL METALLURGY AND MATERIALS SCIENCE. see METALLURGY

MICHIGAN CONTRACTOR & BUILDER; engineering and construction. see BUILDING AND CONSTRUCTION

629.8 NE
MICROPROCESSOR - BASED AND INTELLIGENT SYSTEMS ENGINEERING. 1983. irreg., vol.9, 1992. price varies. Kluwer Academic Publishers, Postbus 17, 3300 AA Dordrecht, Netherlands. TEL 31-78-334911. FAX 31-78-334254. TELEX 29245 KAPG NL. (Dist. by: Kluwer Academic Publishers Group, P.O. Box 322, 3300 AH Dordrecht, Netherlands. TEL 31-78-524400; N. America dist. addr.: Box 358, Accord Sta., Hingham, MA 02018-0358. TEL 617-871-6600) Ed. S.G. Tzafestas. **Document type:** monographic series, proceedings.
  Formerly (until vol.9, 1992): Microprocessor - Based Systems Engineering.
  Description: Publishes monographs and congress proceedings or topics pertaining to the theory and application of microprocessor-based engineering, including intelligent systems engineering.
  Refereed Serial

620 US ISSN 1050-0324
MIDNIGHT ENGINEERING. 1990. bi-m. $20 (Canada and Mexico $32; elsewhere $50). 1700 Washington Ave., Rocky Ford, CO 81067. TEL 719-254-4558. FAX 719-254-4517. Ed. William Gates. adv.; bk.rev. circ. 35,000. **Document type:** consumer publication.
  Description: Provides resources and insight for the entrepreneurial engineer.

620 US ISSN 0026-3370
TA1
MIDWEST ENGINEER; serving the engineering profession. 1948. m. (Sep.-May). $15 in the US and Canada; overseas $20 (effective Sep. 1993). Western Society of Engineers, 176 W. Adams St., Chicago, IL 60603. TEL 312-372-3760. FAX 312-372-3761. Ed. James A. Kepler. adv.; bk.rev.; charts; illus.; stat. circ. 1,000. (also avail. in microform from UMI) **Indexed:** Chem.Abstr., Eng.Ind. **Document type:** trade publication.
—UnCover; UMI.

623 US ISSN 0026-3982
TA1
MILITARY ENGINEER. 1920. bi-m. $12 to non-members; members $36 (foreign $42). Society of American Military Engineers, 607 Prince St., Alexandria, VA 22314-3117. TEL 703-549-3800. FAX 703-684-0231. Ed. Gordon Bratz. adv.; bk.rev.; bibl.; charts; illus.; index. circ. 30,000. (also avail. in microform from PMC) **Indexed:** Abstr.Mil.Bibl., Air Un.Lib.Ind., Bibl.Cart., Chem.Abstr., Concr.Abstr., Eng.Ind, Excerp.Med., GeoRef, HRIS, ISMEC, Ocean.Abstr., Pollut.Abstr., PROMT.
—BLDSC (5768.000000); El; Faxon; UnCover.

620 US
MILWAUKEE ENGINEERING. 1921. 9/yr. $8.50. Engineers and Scientists of Milwaukee Inc., Box 644, Milwaukee, WI 53201-0644. TEL 414-277-7149. Ed. John H. Farrow. adv.; stat. circ. 450. **Document type:** newsletter.

MIND: THE MEETINGS INDEX. see TECHNOLOGY: COMPREHENSIVE WORKS

MINING AND ENGINEERING & ELECTRONICS INDUSTRIES (YEAR). see MINES AND MINING INDUSTRY

620 US ISSN 0026-5691
T1
MINNESOTA TECHNOLOG. 1920. 6/yr. $12. University of Minnesota, Institute of Technology, Lind Hall, 207 Church St., S.E., Rm.5, Minneapolis, MN 55455. TEL 612-624-9816. Ed. Corinna Nelson. adv.; bk.rev.; illus. circ. 400.

620 917.306 US ISSN 0884-1829
TA157
MINORITY ENGINEER. 1980. 3/yr. $17. Equal Opportunity Publications, Inc., 150 Motor Pkwy. No. 420, Hauppauge, NY 11788-5108. TEL 516-261-8899. FAX 516-261-8935. Ed. James Schneider. adv.; bk.rev.; illus. circ. 16,000.
—UnCover.
  Description: Entry-level and professional career magazine for black engineers.

MISSISSIPPI ACADEMY OF SCIENCE. JOURNAL. see SCIENCES: COMPREHENSIVE WORKS

ENGINEERING

620   US   ISSN 0026-6558
MISSOURI ENGINEER. 1937. 11/yr. $12 to non-members; members $1. Missouri Society of Professional Engineers, 330 E. High St., Jefferson City, MO 65101. TEL 314-636-4861. Ed. Cherie L. Bishop. adv.; bk.rev.; illus. circ. 4,000.

620   JA   ISSN 0540-4924
TA1   CODEN: MYFMAN
MIYAZAKI UNIVERSITY. FACULTY OF ENGINEERING. MEMOIRS/MIYAZAKI DAIGAKU KOGAKUBU KIYO. (Text in English) 1956. irreg. exchange basis. Miyazaki Daigaku - Miyazaki University, Faculty of Engineering, 1-1 Gakuen Kibanadai Nishi, Miyazaki 889-21, Japan. TEL 0985-58-2811. FAX 0985-58-2876. Ed. Kou Kurosawa. circ. 450. **Indexed:** Math.R. **Document type:** academic/scholarly publication.
—BLDSC (5595.500000).

620   US   ISSN 1066-0763
TA654.15   CODEN: MNALEO
MODAL ANALYSIS; the international journal of analytical and experimental modal analysis. 1986. q. $75 (foreign $100) (effective 1994). Society for Experimental Mechanics, Inc., 7 School St., Bethel, CT 06801. TEL 203-790-6373. FAX 203-790-4472. Ed. Patricia K. Brothers. abstr.; index, cum.index: 1986-1990. circ. 700. (also avail. in microform; back issues avail.) **Indexed:** Appl.Mech.Rev., BMT, Eng.Ind., Int.Aerosp.Abstr., Sh.& Vib.Dig. **Document type:** academic/scholarly publication.
—BLDSC (5879.969500); EI; UnCover; UMI. **CCC.**
Formerly (until 1993): International Journal of Analytical and Experimental Modal Analysis (ISSN 0886-9367)
Description: Archival journal of original papers documenting the latest developments in dynamics and vibrations research. Covers all aspects of modal analysis from theory to application.
Refereed Serial

MODERN APPLICATIONS NEWS; the metalworking idea magazine. see METALLURGY

620   HK
MOJU GONGYE/MOULD & DIE INDUSTRY. (Text in Chinese) q. B & I Publication Co., Ltd., 18-F, First Pacific Bank Centre, 51-57 Gloucester Rd., Wanchai, Hong Kong. TEL 852-865-2633. FAX 852-866-1770.
Description: Covers the technology, machinery and market news of the mould and die industry.

620   FR
MONDE DE LA TECHNOLOGIE. 6/yr. 106 av. Felix Faure, 75015 Paris, France. TEL 45-54-54-54. Ed. A. Lemoine. circ. 5,000.
Description: For engineers and technicians.

620 530   US
MONOGRAPHS IN PHYSICAL MEASUREMENT. 1978. irreg., vol.2, 1983. Academic Press, Inc., 525 B St., Ste. 1900, San Diego, CA 92101-4495. TEL 619-231-0926. FAX 619-699-6715. (Subscr. to: Order Dept., 6277 Sea Harbor Dr., 4th Fl., Orlando, FL 32887. TEL 800-321-5068) Ed. A.H. Cook. (reprint service avail. from ISI) **Document type:** monographic series.
Refereed Serial

600   US
MONOGRAPHS ON CRYOGENICS. irreg. price varies. Oxford University Press, 200 Madison Ave., New York, NY 10016. TEL 212-679-7300. Ed. R.G. Scurlock. **Document type:** monographic series.
Refereed Serial

620   SY
AL-MUHANDIS AL-ARABI. 1961. 6/yr. $50. Order of Syrian Engineers & Architects (OSEA) - Niqabat al-Muhandisin al-Souriyyin, P.O. Box 2336, Damascus, Syria. TEL 214916. TELEX 411962 ENFUND SY. Ed. Ghassan Tayara. adv. circ. 25,000.

620   JA
MOULD ENGINEERING. (Text in Japanese) m. Nikkan Kogyo Shinbun, Ltd., 8-10, Kudan-kita, 1-chome, Chiyoda-ku, Tokyo 102, Japan. TEL 03-263-2311. FAX 03-262-4603. TELEX NIKKANKO-J29687. Ed. Kiyoshi Ido. circ. 30,000.
Description: Covers all aspects of die and mold technology.

620   IQ
MUHANDIS. 4/yr. National House for Publication, Distribution & Research, Khullani Sq., P.O. Box 5665, Baghdad, Iraq. adv.

620   BA
AL-MUHANDIS/ENGINEER. (Text in Arabic) 1975. q. $20. Bahrain Society of Engineers, P.O. Box 835, Manama, Bahrain. TEL 727100. FAX 729819. TELEX 7592. Ed. Nayef Al-Kalali. adv.

620   TS
AL-MUHANDIS. (Text in Arabic) 1983. a. exchange basis. United Arab Emirates University, Faculty of Engineering, P.O. Box 15551, Al-Ain, United Arab Emirates. TEL 637833. TELEX 33521 JAMEAH EM. Ed. Awad Salim al-Hakim. circ. 2,000.

620   US   ISSN 0276-1459
TP156.E65   CODEN: MSTEDU
MULTIPHASE SCIENCE AND TECHNOLOGY; an international series of books. 1982. irreg., no.5, 1989. price varies. C R C Press, Inc., 2000 Corporate Blvd., N.W., Boca Raton, FL 33431. TEL 407-994-0555. FAX 407-998-9784. TELEX 568689-CRC PRESS. Ed.Bd. bibl.; charts; illus.; index. (back issues avail.; reprint service avail. from UMI)
—BLDSC (5983.166000); Faxon; CASDDS. **CCC.**
Refereed Serial

MUR; arkitektur og byggeteknikk. see BUILDING AND CONSTRUCTION

625.72   US
N C E E S REGISTRATION BULLETIN. (Former name of issuing body: National Council of Engineering Examiners) 1939. q. free. National Council of Examiners for Engineering and Surveying, Box 1686, Clemson, SC 29633. TEL 803-654-6824. FAX 803-654-6033. Ed. Laura Griffis. illus. circ. 6,000. **Document type:** bulletin, newsletter.
Formerly: N C E E Registration Bulletin (ISSN 0199-8994)

620 910.03 371.42   US   ISSN 1060-3115
N S B E BRIDGE. 1990. q. National Society of Black Engineers, 344 Commerce St., Alexandria, VA 22314. TEL 703-549-2207. Ed. Carole Ragins; Pub. Norris Hite, Jr. adv.: B&W page $3000, color page $4000; trim 8 1/4 x 11; adv. contact: Guy Mitchell. circ. 100,000. **Document type:** academic/scholarly publication.
Description: For high school students with an interest in technical studies.

620   US   ISSN 1060-3123
N S B E MAGAZINE. 1985. 5/yr. $10. National Society of Black Engineers, 1454 Duke St., Alexandria, VA 22314. TEL 703-549-2207. FAX 703-683-5312. Ed. Carole Ragins; Pub. Norris Hite, Jr. adv. contact: Guy Mitchell. bk.rev. circ. 24,000. (also avail. in microform from UMI; back issues avail.)
Formerly (until 1989): N S B E Journal (ISSN 0888-0573)

620   JA   ISSN 0911-4920
N S K TECHNICAL JOURNAL. (Text in Japanese) 1954. irreg. Nippon Seiko K.K., 6-3, Osaki 1-chome, Shinagawa-ku, Tokyo 141, Japan.

620   JA   ISSN 0915-0528
N T N TECHNICAL REVIEW. (Text in Japanese; summaries in English) 1950. s-a. N T N K.K., 3-17, Kyomachibori 1-chome, Nishi-ku, Osaka-shi, Osaka 550, Japan.
Formerly (until 1988): Bearingu Enjinia (ISSN 0522-5493)

500 600   JA
    CODEN: NKSKBU
NAGAOKA COLLEGE OF TECHNOLOGY. RESEARCH REPORTS/NAGAOKA KOGYO KOTO SENMON GAKKO KENKYU KIYO. (Text in English, French, Japanese) 1962. q. free. Nagaoka College of Technology, Research Reports Committee - Nagaoka Kogyo Koto Senmon Gakko, 888 Nishi-katakai-machi, Nagaoka-shi, Niigata-ken 940, Japan. TEL 0258-36-6183. FAX 0258-36-6183. Ed.Bd. abstr.; charts; illus.; index. circ. 540. **Indexed:** Chem.Abstr., JCT, JTA, Math.R., Sci.Abstr. **Document type:** academic/scholarly publication, bulletin.
—BLDSC (7762.689000); CASDDS.
Formerly: Nagaoka Technical College. Research Reports (ISSN 0027-7568)
Description: Contains research papers on natural sciences, technological engineering, humanity sciences and literature.

620   JA   ISSN 0027-7657
TA4   CODEN: MENAAN
NAGOYA UNIVERSITY. FACULTY OF ENGINEERING. MEMOIRS/NAGOYA DAIGAKU KOGAKUBU KIYO. (Text in European languages) 1948. s-a. exchange basis. Nagoya Daigaku, Kogakubu - Nagoya University, Faculty of Engineering, Furo-cho, Chikusa-ku, Nagoya 464-01, Japan. Eds. Minoru Matsuo, Katsumi Yamaguchi. charts; illus. circ. 1,550. **Indexed:** Appl.Mech.Rev., Chem.Abstr., Fluidex, INIS Atomind., Int.Aerosp.Abstr., Sci.Abstr.
—BLDSC (5634.180000); UnCover.

625.72   US
NATIONAL COUNCIL OF EXAMINERS FOR ENGINEERING AND SURVEYING. PROCEEDINGS. a. National Council of Examiners for Engineering and Surveying, Box 1686, Clemson, SC 29633. TEL 803-654-6824. FAX 803-654-6033. **Document type:** proceedings.
Formerly: National Council of Engineering Examiners. Proceedings (ISSN 0077-4081)

620   US   ISSN 0361-7904
NATIONAL DIRECTORY OF SAFETY CONSULTANTS. 1974. biennial. $75 to non-members; members $35. American Society of Safety Engineers, 1800 E. Oakton St., Des Plaines, IL 60018-2187. TEL 708-692-4121. FAX 708-296-3769. Eds. Susan Eget, Jenell Connors. circ. 1,000. **Document type:** directory.
Description: Covers credentials and expertise areas of nearly 1000 safety and health consultants, cross-referenced by geography and expertise.

NATIONAL INDUSTRIAL RESEARCH INSTITUTE. REPORT. see TECHNOLOGY: COMPREHENSIVE WORKS

NATIONAL RESEARCH COUNCIL. NEWS REPORT. see SCIENCES: COMPREHENSIVE WORKS

620   CN   ISSN 0077-5428
    CODEN: NAGTAS
NATIONAL RESEARCH COUNCIL, CANADA. ASSOCIATE COMMITTEE ON GEOTECHNICAL RESEARCH. TECHNICAL MEMORANDUM. 1945. irreg. price varies. National Research Council of Canada, Associate Committee on Geotechnical Research, Ottawa, Ont. K1A OS2, Canada. TEL 613-993-9546. circ. 500. (back issues avail.) **Indexed:** Arct.Bibl., Eng.Ind.
●Also available online.

620   US
NATIONAL SCIENCE FOUNDATION. DIRECTORATE FOR ENGINEERING. DIRECTORY OF AWARDS. 1982. a. free. National Science Foundation, Directorate for Engineering, 1800 G St., N.W., Washington, DC 20550. TEL 202-357-9571. index. circ. 4,000. **Document type:** directory.
●Available only online.
Formerly: Recent Awards in Engineering.

620   JA   ISSN 0387-8511
    CODEN: BNSED5
NATIONAL SCIENCE MUSEUM. BULLETIN. SERIES E: PHYSICAL SCIENCES AND ENGINEERING/KOKURITSU KAGAKU HAKUBUTSUKAN KENKYU HOKOKU. E RUI, RIKOGAKU. (Text in English and Japanese; summaries in English) 1978. a. Monbu-sho, Kokuritsu Kagaku Hakubutsukan - Ministry of Education, National Science Museum, 7-20 Ueno Koen, Taito-ku, Tokyo 110, Japan.
—BLDSC (2644.060000); CASDDS.

623.8		US	ISSN 0028-1425
VM1			CODEN: NVEJAX

NAVAL ENGINEERS JOURNAL. 1889. bi-m. $65. American Society of Naval Engineers, Inc., 1452 Duke St., Alexandria, VA 22314. TEL 703-836-6727. FAX 703-836-7491. Ed. James E. Grabb. adv.; bk.rev.; charts; index. circ. 9,000. (also avail. in microform from UMI; reprint service avail. from UMI) **Indexed:** A.S.& T.Ind., Abstr.Mil.Bibl., Appl.Mech.Rev., BMT, Chem.Abstr., Curr.Cont., DM & T, Eng.Ind., Excerp.Med., ISMEC, Met.Abstr., Ocean.Abstr., Pollut.Abstr., PROMT, Sh.& Vib.Dig., World Alum.Abstr. **Document type:** academic/scholarly publication.
—BLDSC (6064.200000); Faxon; UnCover; SWETS; UMI.

620	II	ISSN 0028-162X

NAVNIRMAN. (Text in English and Gujarati) 1960. s-a. Rs.30. (Government of Gujarat, Irrigation and R & B Department) Gujarat Engineering Research Institute, Race Course, Vadodara 390 007, Gujarat, India. Ed. C. D. Thatte. abstr.; charts; illus.; maps; index, cum.index. circ. 800.

620	US

NEBRASKA BLUE PRINT. 1902. q. $5. University of Nebraska, Lincoln, College of Engineering and Technology, W. 181 Nebr. Hall, Lincoln, NE 68588-0501. TEL 402-472-9420. FAX 402-412-7792. Ed. Marc Schulte. adv.; charts; illus. circ. 2,500.

620	US

NEW ENGLAND ENGINEERING JOURNAL. vol.6, 1978. m. $5. (Engineering Societies of New England) J.C. Marketing Associates, Inc., Box 289, Wakefield, MA 01880. Ed. George Franklin. adv.; bk.rev. circ. 9,100.
Supersedes: Engineering Societies of New England. Journal (ISSN 0013-8118); Incorporates: Massachusetts Professional Engineer (ISSN 0025-486X)
Description: Contains organization news.

NEW EQUIPMENT NEWS. see *TECHNOLOGY: COMPREHENSIVE WORKS*

620	US

NEW YORK PROFESSIONAL ENGINEER. 10/yr. New York State Society of Professional Engineers, Inc., 150 State St., Albany, NY 12207-1626. TEL 518-465-7386. Ed. Christine M. Sikora.

620	NZ	ISSN 0028-808X
TA1		CODEN: NZENA5

NEW ZEALAND ENGINEERING. 1946. m. except Jan. NZ.$60. Institution of Professional Engineers, New Zealand, P.O. 12-241, Wellington, New Zealand. TEL 64-4-473-9444. FAX 64-4-473-2324. adv.; bk.rev.; charts; illus.; index. circ. 6,200. (also avail. in microfilm from UMI; reprint service avail. from UMI) **Indexed:** Chem.Abstr., Eng.Ind., Geotech.Abstr., Met.Abstr., Sci.Abstr., World Alum.Abstr.
—BLDSC (6091.000000); EI; UMI. **CCC.**

620 600	UK	ISSN 0372-0187
T1		

NEWCOMEN SOCIETY FOR THE STUDY OF THE HISTORY OF ENGINEERING AND TECHNOLOGY. TRANSACTIONS. 1922. a. £30 membership. Newcomen Society for the Study of the History of Engineering and Technology, Science Museum, South Kensington, London SW7 2DD, England. TEL 071-589-1793. Ed. L.R. Day. bibl.; charts; illus. (also avail. in microfilm) **Indexed:** Br.Hum.Ind. **Document type:** academic/scholarly publication.
—BLDSC (8989.000000).
Description: Publishes original research papers on topics relating to the history of industrialization and technological change, with particular emphasis on individuals, companies, processes and events in Britain.

620	US	ISSN 0028-9205
		CODEN: NEEOAV

NEWS IN ENGINEERING. 1929. 2/yr. Ohio State University, Engineering Experiment Station, Hitchcock Hall, Rm. 025, 2070 Neil Ave., Columbus, OH 43210. TEL 614-292-4159. Ed. Richard B. DeLong. bk.rev.; charts; illus. circ. 14,000.
—UnCover.

620	NR	ISSN 0331-5967
TA1		

NIGERIAN ENGINEER. 1962. 4/yr. £N25. Nigerian Society of Engineers, Editorial Committee, National Engineering Centre, 1 Engineering Close, P.O. Box 72667, Victoria Island Lands, Nigeria. Ed. C.O. Orangun. adv.; bk.rev. circ. 2,500.

620 537	JA

NIHON KOATSURYOKU GAKKAI GAKUJUTSU KOENKAI KOEN YOSHI/JAPAN SOCIETY OF HIGH PRESSURE SCIENCE AND TECHNOLOGY. TEXT OF SYMPOSIUM. (Text in Japanese) 1990. a. Nihon Koatsuyoku Gakkai - Japan Society of High Pressure Science and Technology, Seisan Kaihatsu Kagaku Kenkyujo, 15, Shimogamo Morimotocho, Sakyo-ku, Kyoto 606, Japan.

NIHON OYO CHISHITSU GAKKAI KENKYU HAPPYOKAI KOEN RONBUNSHU/JAPAN SOCIETY OF ENGINEERING GEOLOGY. PROCEEDINGS OF MEETING. see *EARTH SCIENCES — Geology*

NIHON OYO CHISHITSU GAKKAI KYUSHU SHIBU KAIHO/JAPAN SOCIETY OF ENGINEERING GEOLOGY. KYUSHU BRANCH REPORT. see *EARTH SCIENCES — Geology*

NIHON SEIKISHO GAKKAI ZASSHI/JAPANESE JOURNAL OF BIOMETEOROLOGY. see *METEOROLOGY*

NIHON UNIVERSITY. ATOMIC ENERGY RESEARCH INSTITUTE. ANNUAL REPORT. see *ENERGY — Nuclear Energy*

620	JA	ISSN 0913-3526

NIHON YUKI KOGAKKAISHI/JOURNAL OF SNOW ENGINEERING. (Text in Japanese; summaries in English) 1986. q. Nihon Yuki Kogakkai - Japan Society for Snow Engineering, Nihon Gakkai Jimu Senta, 16-9, Honkomagome 5-chome, Bunkyo-ku, Tokyo 113, Japan.

620	JA	ISSN 0374-4345
		CODEN: NDKHAX

NIIGATA DAIGAKU KOGAKUBU KENKYU HOKOKU/NIIGATA UNIVERSITY. FACULTY OF ENGINEERING. RESEARCH REPORT. (Text in English, Japanese; summaries in English) 1952. a. free. Niigata Daigaku, Kogakubu - Niigata University, Faculty of Engineering, 8050, Igarashi Nino-cho, Niigata-shi, Niigata-ken 950-21, Japan. TEL 025-262-6703. Ed.Bd. circ. 500.
—BLDSC (7761.710000); CASDDS.

NIIHAMA KOGYO KOTO SENMON GAKKO KIYO. RIKOGAKU HEN/NIIHAMA NATIONAL COLLEGE OF TECHNOLOGY. MEMOIRS. SCIENCE AND ENGINEERING. see *TECHNOLOGY: COMPREHENSIVE WORKS*

620	JA

NIKKEI MATERIALS & TECHNOLOGY. (Text in Japanese) 1985. m. 16800 Yen. Nikkei Business Publications, Inc. (Subsidiary of: Nihon Keizai Shimbun, Inc.), 2-7-6 Hirakawa-cho, Chiyoda-ku, Tokyo 102, Japan. TEL 03-5210-8502. FAX 03-5210-8119. Ed. Makoto Hasegawa. adv. contact: Zenta Kishi. circ. 17,687. (back issues avail.) **Document type:** trade publication.
Formerly: Nikkei New Materials (ISSN 0911-1018)
Description: Contains information on new trends, technologies and materials, as well as development processes and applications.

ENGINEERING 2259

620	UK	ISSN 0362-546X
QA299.6		CODEN: NOANDD

NONLINEAR ANALYSIS; theory, methods and applications. 1977. 24/yr. (in 2 vols., 12 nos./vol.). £945($1455) (efffective 1994). Elsevier Science Ltd., Pergamon, P.O. Box 800, Kidlington, Oxford OX5 1DX, England. TEL 44-865-843000. FAX 44-865-843010. (Subscr. in U.S. and Canada to: Elsevier Science, 660 White Plains Rd., Tarrytown, NY 10591-5153. TEL 914-524-9200. FAX 914-333-2444) Ed. V. Lakshmikantham. adv. circ. 1,000. (also avail. in microfilm from UMI; reprint service avail. from UMI) **Indexed:** Appl.Mech.Rev., Compumath, Curr.Cont., Math.R., Sci.Abstr. **Document type:** academic/scholarly publication.
—BLDSC (6117.316500); EI; Faxon; UnCover; SWETS; UMI. **CCC.**
Description: Publishes research and expository papers devoted to solving nonlinear problems in all areas of theory methods, and applications of nonlinear analysis.
Refereed Serial

NONLINEAR DYNAMICS; an international journal of nonlinear dynamics and chaos in engineering systems. see *ENGINEERING — Mechanical Engineering*

620.1 389	PL	ISSN 0029-179X

NORMALIZACJA. (Text in Polish; summaries in various languages) 1926. m. $90. (Polski Komitet Normalizacji, Miar i Jakosci - Polish Committee of Standardization, Measures and Quality Control) Wydawnictwa Normalizacyjne "Alfa", Nowogrodzka 22, Warsaw, Poland. (Dist. by: Ars Polona-Ruch, Krakowskie Przecmiescie 7, Warsaw, Poland) Ed. Bogdan Sadlik. adv.; bk.rev. circ. 5,000.

621.184	NO	ISSN 0800-7896

NORSK ENERGI. 1923. q. NOK 250($40) Kjelforeningen - Norsk Energi - Norwegian Association of Energy Users and Suppliers, P.O. Box 27 Skoeyen, N-0212 Oslo, Norway. TEL 47-2-50-61-CO. FAX 47-2-50-66-55. Ed. Hans Borchsenius. adv.; cum.index. circ. 2,500.
Formerly (until no.3, 1984): Norsk Dampkjelforening. Meddelelser (ISSN 0048-0576)
Description: Focuses on energy and industrial equipment, such as: boilers, burners, heat-exchangers, pumps, fans, pipes, valves and automation-equipment.

NORTHEAST BIOENGINEERING CONFERENCE. PROCEEDINGS. see *BIOLOGY — Bioengineering*

620	US	ISSN 0029-3083
TA1		CODEN: NOENDX

NORTHERN ENGINEER. 1968. q. $15 (foreign $20). University of Alaska at Fairbanks, Institute of Northern Engineering, Fairbanks, AK 99775-0660. TEL 907-474-6113 FAX 907-474-6087. bk.rev.; charts; illus. circ. 800. **Indexed:** GeoRef., HRIS, Pollut.Abstr.
—Faxon; UnCover.
Description: Publishes practical and theoretical cold regions related engineering articles.

620	CN	ISSN 0380-0881

NORTHPOINT. 1964. q. Can.$20 to non-members. Ontario Association of Certified Engineering Technicians and Technologists, Survey Discipline, 10 Four Seasons Pl., Ste. 404, Etobicoke, ON M9B 6H7, Canada. TEL 416-620-1885. FAX 416-621-8694. Ed. Robert Fowler. adv.: B&W page Can.$235; trim 8 1/2 x 11. circ. 1,300.

620	CK

NOTI S A I. 1960. 10/yr. $8. Sociedad Antioquena de Ingenieros y Arquitectos, Calle 71, No. 65-100, Apdo. Aereo 4754, Medellin, Colombia. TEL 257-3900. FAX 255-4584. Ed.Bd. adv.; stat.; illus.; circ. 2,500 (controlled)
Former titles (until 1987): Sociedad Antioquena de Ingenieros. Informador; (until 1975): Sociedad Antioquena de Ingenieros. Boletin (ISSN 0037-8372)

620	AG

NOTICIAS DE INGENIERIA. m. Centro de Ingenieros Provincia de Buenos Aires, Avenida 53, No. 412-1-2, La Plata, Buenos Aires, Argentina.

620 US ISSN 0029-4543
NOTRE DAME TECHNICAL REVIEW. 1949. q. $15. University of Notre Dame, Engineering Department, 218 Cushing Mall, Notre Dame, IN 46556. TEL 219-283-3524. FAX 219-239-8007. Ed. Mike Fenocketti. adv.; bk.rev.; charts; illus.; stat. circ. 1,700. **Document type:** academic/scholarly publication.
Refereed Serial

658.5 SP ISSN 0211-2124
NOVATICA. (Text in Spanish; summaries in English, French, Spanish) 1970-1977; resumed. bi-m. 8000 ptas.($100) (effective 1993). Associacio de Tecnics d'Informatica - Asociacion de Tecnicos de Informatica, Gran Via 657, ent. 1o, 08010 Barcelona, Spain. TEL 34-3-2655660. FAX 34-3-2655779. adv.; bk.rev.; illus.; tr.lit. circ. 5,000. **Indexed:** Ind.SST.
Formerly (until 1975): Novatecnia.

NOWATOR; pismo poswiecone tworczosci technicznej. see *BUSINESS AND ECONOMICS — Production Of Goods And Services*

621.48 UK ISSN 0262-5091
TK9001 CODEN: NUEND7
NUCLEAR ENGINEER. 1959. bi-m. £77. Institution of Nuclear Engineers, 1 Penerley Rd., London SE6 2LQ, England. TEL 081-698-1500. FAX 081-695-6409. Ed. S. Blackburn. adv.; bk.rev.; illus.; tr.lit. circ. 2,000. (also avail. in microform from UMI; reprint service avail. from UMI) **Indexed:** Br.Tech.Ind., Chem.Abstr., Eng.Ind., Excerp.Med., Geo.Abstr., Sci.Abstr.
—BLDSC (6180.690000); EI; Faxon; SWETS; UMI; CASDDS. **CCC**.
Former titles (until vol.21, no.3, May-June 1980): Institution of Nuclear Engineers. Journal (ISSN 0368-2595); Nuclear Energy (ISSN 0029-5485)
Description: Covers all aspects of nuclear power generation, research, marine propulsion, health and environmental topics as well as general industrial uses and applications.

NUCLEAR ENGINEERING INTERNATIONAL. see *ENERGY — Nuclear Energy*

NUCLEAR FORUM. see *ENERGY — Nuclear Energy*

NUCLEAR INDUSTRIAL NEWSPAPER. see *ENERGY — Nuclear Energy*

NUCLEAR PLANT MAINTENANCE NEWSLETTER. see *ENERGY — Nuclear Energy*

NUCLEAR SAFETY; a quarterly technical progress review. see *ENERGY — Nuclear Energy*

NUCLEAR SCIENCE AND ENGINEERING; research and development related to peaceful utilization of nuclear energy. see *ENERGY — Nuclear Energy*

NUCLEAR TECHNOLOGY; applications for nuclear science, nuclear engineering and related arts. see *PHYSICS — Nuclear Physics*

620 SW ISSN 0550-8754
NY TEKNIK. Variant title: Ny Teknik Med Teknisk Tidskrift. 1967. w. SEK 520. Ingenjoersfoerlaget AB, Box 27315, 102 54 Stockholm, Sweden. TEL 08-665-1700. TELEX 17191-TECNEWS-S. Ed. Lars Rundkvist. adv.: B&W page SEK 48200, color page SEK 59900; trim 255 x 350; adv. contact: Rolf Lindblom. bk.rev.; charts; illus.; index; circ. 126,489 (controlled). (also avail. in microfiche) **Indexed:** Appl.Mech.Rev., C.I.S.Abstr., Chem.Abstr., Eng.Ind., Met.Abstr., Sci.Abstr.
Incorporates (in 1978): Teknisk Tidskrift (ISSN 0040-2346)
Description: Technical news journal specializing in industrial news and modern technology.

O E C D NUCLEAR ENERGY AGENCY. NUCLEAR ENERGY DATA. see *ENERGY — Nuclear Energy*

O E C D NUCLEAR ENERGY AGENCY ACTIVITIES IN (YEAR). see *ENERGY — Nuclear Energy*

620 UK ISSN 0306-0381
TA174 CODEN: OEMDAF
O E M DESIGN. 1971. m. £30($99) (foreign £50). Wilmington Publishing, Wilmington House, Church Hill, Dartford, Kent UA2 7EF, England. TEL 0322-277788. FAX 0322-276476. (Subscr. to: Ferrari House, 258 Field End Rd., Ruislip, Middx HA4 9UX. TEL 081-868-4499) Ed. Doug Fears. adv.; bk.rev.; charts; illus.; pat.; tr.lit.; circ. 30,500 (controlled). **Indexed:** BMT, Br.Tech.Ind., Cadscan, Copper Abstr., Fluidex, ISMEC, Lead Abstr., Sci.Abstr., Zincscan.
—BLDSC (6235.480000). **CCC**.
Incorporates: Fastening; Materials.

O E REPORTS. (Optical Engineering) see *PHYSICS — Optics*

OCEAN ENGINEERING; an international journal of research and development. see *EARTH SCIENCES — Oceanography*

620.41 US ISSN 0197-7385
CODEN: OCNSDK
OCEANS. CONFERENCE RECORD. a. (I E E E, Oceanic Engineering Society) Institute of Electrical and Electronics Engineers, Inc., 345 E. 47th St., New York, NY 10017-2394. TEL 212-705-7900. FAX 212-705-7682. (Subscr. to: Box 1331, 445 Hoes Lane, Piscataway, NJ 08855-1331)
—BLDSC (6234.330000); UMI. **CCC**.
Former titles: I E E E International Conference on Engineering in the Ocean Environment. Record; International Conference on Engineering in the Ocean Environment. Digest (ISSN 0074-3062)
Refereed Serial

620.1 PL ISSN 0473-7733
TA418.74 CODEN: OPZKA8
OCHRONA PRZED KOROZJA. 1957. m. $71.50. (Stowarzyszenie Inzynierow i Technikow Przemyslu Chemicznego) Wydawnictwo Czasopism i Ksiazek Technicznych SIGMA - NOT, Ul. Ratuszowa 11, P.O. Box 1004, 00-950 Warsaw, Poland. TEL 48-22-180918. FAX 48-22-192187. TELEX 814550 SIGMA PL. (Dist. by: SIGMA - NOT Ltd., Ul. Bartycka 20, 00-716 Warsaw, Poland) (Co-sponsor: Polski Komitet Ochrony przed Korozja NOT) Ed. Edward Smieszek. circ. 1,950. **Indexed:** Chem.Abstr., Corros.Abstr., Met.Abstr., World Alum.Abstr., World Surf.Coat.
—CASDDS.

OFFSHORE ENGINEER. see *PETROLEUM AND GAS*

620 US ISSN 0194-9276
OHIO ENGINEER. 1943. bi-m. $15. Ohio Society of Professional Engineers, 445 King Ave., Columbus, OH 43201. TEL 614-424-6640. FAX 614-421-1257. adv.: B&W page $520; trim 8 1/2 x 11. charts; illus.; stat.; index; circ. 4,000 (controlled). (also avail. in microform; back issues avail.) **Document type:** trade publication.
Former titles: Ohio-En Engineering News; Ohio Engineering.

620 US
OHIO STATE ENGINEER. 1918. 3/yr. $5. Ohio State University, College of Engineering, 2070 Neil Ave., Columbus, OH 43210. TEL 614-292-4159. adv. circ. 10,000.

620 JA
TA1 CODEN: MFEUEF
OKAYAMA UNIVERSITY. FACULTY OF ENGINEERING. MEMOIRS. (Text in European languages) 1966. s-a. exchange basis. Okayama University, Fakulty of Engineering, Tsushima, Okayama 700, Japan. **Indexed:** Chem.Abstr., Sci.Abstr.
—BLDSC (5596.040000).
Formerly (until 1988): Okayama University. School of Engineering. Memoirs (ISSN 0475-0071)

620 US
OKLAHOMA PROFESSIONAL ENGINEER. m. Oklahoma Society of Professional Engineers, 201 N.E. 27 St., Rm. 125, Oklahoma City, OK 73105-2789. TEL 405-528-1435. FAX 405-557-1820. Ed. Ira T. Oliver. circ. 2,000.

620 US
OLE MISS ENGINEER. 1962. s-a. $1. University of Mississippi, Department of Engineering, University, MS 38677. TEL 601-232-7407. FAX 601-232-7219. Ed. J.G. Vaughan. adv.; charts; illus. circ. 2,900. **Document type:** newsletter.

620 US ISSN 0149-8029
OPFLOW. 1975. m. $10.50 to non-members (foreign $16). American Water Works Association, 6666 W. Quincy Ave., Denver, CO 80235. TEL 303-794-7711. Ed. Monica Baruth. circ. 50,000. (back issues avail.) **Document type:** newsletter, trade publication.
—BLDSC (6270.400000). **CCC**.
Description: Aims to improve practice and knowledge within the field of water supply.

OPTICAL ENGINEERING. see *PHYSICS — Optics*

OPTICAL PHYSICS AND ENGINEERING. see *PHYSICS — Optics*

OPTICS AND LASER TECHNOLOGY. see *PHYSICS — Optics*

OPTICS AND LASERS IN ENGINEERING. see *PHYSICS — Optics*

620 IT ISSN 0030-4905
ORGANI DI TRASMISSIONE. 1970. m. L.85000 (foreign L.210000) (effective 1994). (A S S I O T) Tecniche Nuove s.p.a., Via C. Menotti 14, 20129 Milan, Italy. TEL 02-75701. FAX 02-7610351. Ed. G. Nardella. adv.: B&W page L.2210000, color page L.2990000; trim 185 x 266. bk.rev.; charts; illus.; pat.; tr.lit. circ. 6,882.
Description: Covers the activities of the association of manufacturers of mechanical transmissions.

620 JA ISSN 0078-6659
TA7 CODEN: MFEOAR
OSAKA CITY UNIVERSITY. FACULTY OF ENGINEERING. MEMOIRS/OSAKA-SHIRITSU DAIGAKU KOGAKUBU OBUN KIYO. (Text and summaries in English) 1959. a. free. Osaka City University, Faculty of Engineering - Osaka-shiritsu Daigaku Kogakubu, 3-138 Sugimoto 3-chome, Sumiyoshi-ku, Osaka 558, Japan. Ed.Bd. circ. 2,000. **Indexed:** Chem.Abstr., INIS Atomind., JCT, JTA, Met.Abstr., Sci.Abstr., World Alum.Abstr. **Document type:** academic/scholarly publication.
—BLDSC (5596.050000); UnCover; CASDDS.

620 CN ISSN 0380-6251
CODEN: ODREE6
OTTAWA R & D REPORT. 1971. m. Can.$110. Intratech (Subsidiary of: E L LittleJohn and Associates), Minto Place Postal Outlet, Box 56067, Ottawa, Ont. K1R 7Z1, Canada. TEL 613-235-9183. FAX 613-594-3857. Ed. E.L. LittleJohn. circ. 300. (back issues avail.)

OYO CHISHITSU/JAPAN SOCIETY OF ENGINEERING GEOLOGY. JOURNAL. see *EARTH SCIENCES — Geology*

621.9 UK ISSN 0030-7904
P E D. (Production & Industrial Equipment Digest) 1954. m. £30($99) (foreign £50). Wilmington Publishing, Wilmington House, Church Rd., Dartford, Kent UA2 7EF, England. TEL 0322-277788. FAX 0322-276476. (Subscr. to: Ferrari House, 258 Field End Rd., Ruislip, Middx HA4 9UX. TEL 081-868-4499) Ed. Silvus Eliades. adv.; illus.; tr.lit. circ. 56,300.
—CCC.

620 551 CN ISSN 0823-1745
P E G G. (Professional Engineer, Geologist, Geophysicist) 1972. 10/yr. Can.$25 to non-members. Association of Professional Engineers, Geologists & Geophysicists of Alberta, 15 Fl., Scotia Place, Tower Canada, 10060 Jasper Ave., Edmonton, AB T5J 4A2, Canada. TEL 403-426-3990. FAX 403-426-1877. Ed. Nordahl Flakstad. adv. contact: Cathy Betker. illus. circ. 33,150. (tabloid format)
Formerly (until 1982): Mini-Pegg (ISSN 0380-4674)

620 US
P I QUALITY. (Process Industry) 1991. q. Hitchcock Publishing (Subsidiary of: Capital Cities - A B C, Inc.), 191 S. Gray Ave., Carol Stream, IL 60188. TEL 708-665-1000. FAX 708-462-2225. TELEX 72-0404. Ed. Chester Placek. circ. 42,000.
Description: Reports, analyzes and documents changes in quality practices in the process industries.

P T B - MITTEILUNGEN FORSCHEN UND PRUEFEN. (Physikalisch-Technische Bundesanstalt) see *METROLOGY AND STANDARDIZATION*

620	NE	ISSN 0032-4094
		CODEN: PTPTBP

P T - PROCESTECHNIEK. (PolyTechnisch Tijdschrift); vakblad voor de ingenieur. 1945. 10/yr. fl.197.50 (foreign fl.365) (effective 1994). Ten Hagen & Stam b.v., Postbus 235, 2280 AE Rijswijk, Netherlands. TEL 31-70-3988100. FAX 31-70-3988276. adv.: B&W page fl.2680, color page fl.4905; trim 297 x 210; adv. contact: Herman Voois. circ. 4,076. **Indexed:** Excerp.Med., Sci.Abstr., Sugar Ind.Abstr. **Document type:** trade publication.
 Description: Covers all aspects of applied and theoretical process engineering, including automation, materials, biotechnology, and more.

620	AG	ISSN 0078-8791

PAN AMERICAN FEDERATION OF ENGINEERING SOCIETIES. BULLETIN.* Running title: U P A D I Bulletin. (Text in English, Portuguese and Spanish) 1951. a. Pan American Federation of Engineering Societies, c/o Maria L. Pinero, Secr., Daig Norte 777, 8 piso, Oficina 826, 1364 Buenos Aires, Argentina.

PATTERN RECOGNITION. see *COMPUTERS — Computer Graphics*

620	UK	ISSN 0079-0869

PERGAMON UNIFIED ENGINEERING SERIES. vol.22, 1980. irreg., latest 1993. price varies. Elsevier Science Ltd., Books Division, P.O. Box 800, Kidlington, Oxford OX3 0BW, England. TEL 44-865-843000. FAX 44-865-843010. (Subscr. in U.S. and Canada to: Elsevier Science, 660 White Plains Rd., Tarrytown, NY 10591-5153. TEL 914-524-9200. FAX 914-333-2444) **Document type:** monographic series.
 Refereed Serial

620	US	

PERSPECTIVES IN ENGINEERING. 1939. q. membership only. New Jersey Society of Professional Engineers, 150 W. State St., Trenton, NJ 08608. TEL 609-393-0099. FAX 609-396-5361. Ed. John Patterson. adv. contact: John Patterson. charts; illus.; stat. circ. 3,000. **Document type:** newsletter.
 Supersedes in part (in 1989): New Jersey Professional Engineer (ISSN 0028-5900); Which was formerly: Who's Who of Engineering in New Jersey.
 Description: Newsletter of the society.

PETERSON'S GUIDE TO GRADUATE PROGRAMS IN ENGINEERING AND APPLIED SCIENCES (YEAR) (BOOK 5). see *EDUCATION — Guides To Schools And Colleges*

PETERSON'S JOB OPPORTUNITIES FOR ENGINEERING, SCIENCE, AND COMPUTER GRADUATES (YEAR). see *OCCUPATIONS AND CAREERS*

620 621	US	ISSN 0273-8139

PHARMACEUTICAL ENGINEERING. 1980. bi-m. $48. International Society for Pharmaceutical Engineering, Inc., 3816 W. Linebaugh Ave., Ste. 412, Tampa, FL 33624-4702. TEL 813-960-2105. FAX 813-264-2816. Ed. Gloria Esoda. adv.; bk.rev.; tr.lit. circ. 15,000. (back issues avail.)
 —BLDSC (6443.670000); SWETS.
 Description: For professionals in the pharmaceutical, biotechnology, medical device and diagnostic manufacturing industries.

620	UK	ISSN 0165-5817
Q1		CODEN: PHJRD9

PHILIPS JOURNAL OF RESEARCH. vol.33, 1978. 4/yr. £95($145) (effective 1994). (Philips Corporate Research Laboratories, NE) Elsevier Science Ltd., Oxford Fulfilment Centre, P.O. Box 800, Kidlington, Oxford OX5 1DX, England. TEL 44-865-843000. FAX 44-865-843010. (Subscr. in U.S. and Canada to: Elsevier Science, 660 White Plains Rd., Tarrytown, NY 10591-5153. TEL 914-524-9200. FAX 914-333-2444) Ed. M. Vincken. circ. 2,200. (also avail. in microform from PMC) **Indexed:** Br.Ceram.Abstr., CAD CAM Abstr., Cadscan, Chem.Abstr., Curr.Cont., Energy Info.Abstr., Eng.Ind., Excerp.Med., Lead Abstr., Mass Spectr.Bull., Math.R., Met.Abstr., Phys.Abstr., Sci.Abstr., Sci.Cit.Ind., World Alum.Abstr., Zincscan. **Document type:** trade publication.
 —BLDSC (6458.700000); EI; Faxon; UnCover; SWETS; CASDDS. **CCC.**
 Formerly: Philips Research Reports.
 Description: Findings of industrial researchers in many fields including mathematics, physics, chemistry and information technology.
 Refereed Serial

620	US	ISSN 1062-8630

PITTSBURGH ENGINEER. 1967. bi-m. $18. (Engineers' Society of Western Pennsylvania (ESWP)) T S G Publishing, 3090 W. Liberty Ave., Pittsburgh, PA 15216-2456. TEL 412-344-3360. FAX 412-344-3364. Ed. Peter Pennline. adv. contact: Gary Winterhalter. circ. 11,505. **Document type:** trade publication.

620	CN	ISSN 0032-0536

PLAN. (Text in English, French) 1943. m. Ordre des Ingenieurs du Quebec, 2020 University St., 14th floor, Montreal, Que. H3A 2A5, Canada. TEL 514-845-6141. FAX 514-845-1833. Ed. Jean-Marc Papineau. adv.; charts; illus.; index. circ. 38,000.

PLANT - CANADA'S INDUSTRIAL NEWSPAPER. see *BUSINESS AND ECONOMICS — Management*

658.5	UK	ISSN 0032-0838
TJ164		CODEN: PLEGAA

PLANT ENGINEER. 1946. 6/yr. £22 (overseas £30). Institution of Plant Engineers, 77 Great Peter St., London SW1P 2EZ, England. TEL 071-233-2855. FAX 071-233-2604. Ed. Peter Tye. adv.; bk.rev.; charts; pat.; tr.lit. circ. 6,500. **Indexed:** Br.Tech.Ind., Eng.Ind., ISMEC, Met.Abstr., Sci.Abstr., World Alum.Abstr. **Document type:** trade publication.
 —BLDSC (6515.900000).
 Description: Aimed at those who manage and maintain industrial, commercial or construction plant equipment and works services.

658.2	US	ISSN 0032-082X
TS155.A1		CODEN: PLENAV

PLANT ENGINEERING. 1947. 19/yr. $69.95 (Canada $103.95; Mexico $96.95; elsewhere $198.95) includes Plant Engineering Product Supplier Guide. Cahners Publishing Company (Des Plaines), Division of Reed Elsevier Inc., 1350 E. Touhy Ave., Box 5080, IL 60017-5080. TEL 708-635-8800. FAX 708-390-2636. (Subscr. to: 44 Cook St., Denver, CO 80206. TEL 800-662-7776) Ed. Richard Dunn. adv.; bk.rev.; illus.; tr.lit. circ. 128,600. (also avail. in microform; reprint service avail.) **Indexed:** A.S.& T.Ind., ABI Inform., Bus.Ind., C.I.S.Abstr., Chem.Abstr., Chem.Eng.Abstr., Eng.Ind., Excerp.Med., Geotech.Abstr., Int.Build.Serv.Abstr., PROMT, Sh.& Vib.Dig., T.C.E.A., Text.Tech.Dig., Tr.& Indus.Ind. **Document type:** trade publication.
 •Also available online. Vendor(s): DIALOG Information Services, Inc.
 —BLDSC (6516.000000); Faxon; UnCover; SWETS; UMI. **CCC.**
 Description: Serves plant engineers who are responsible for the repairs, operating and maintenance of the industrial plant. Features include job-oriented, problem-solving data on equipment and services in various manufacturing industries.

658.5	US	

PLANT ENGINEERING PRODUCT SUPPLIER GUIDE. 1965. a. (included in Plant Engineering). $25. Cahners Publishing Company (Des Plaines), Division of Reed Elsevier Inc., 1350 E. Touhy Ave., Box 5080, Des Plaines, IL 60017-5080. TEL 708-635-8800. FAX 708-390-2636. (Subscr. to: 44 Cook St., Denver, CO 80206. TEL 800-662-7776; Foreign subscr. to: J.B. Tratsart Ltd., 154-A Greenford Rd., Harrow, Middlesex HA1 3QT, England) Ed. Richard Dunn. adv.; charts; illus.; circ. controlled. **Document type:** directory.
 Former titles (until 1992): Plant Engineering Directory and Yearbook; Plant Engineering Directory; Plant Engineering Directory and Specifications Catalog (ISSN 0554-2693)

PLASTICS - COMPOSITES MOLDING DIGEST. see *PLASTICS*

620 382	PL	ISSN 0209-0260

POLISH ENGINEERING. German edition: Polnisches Engineering (ISSN 0209-0279); French edition: Engineering Polonais (ISSN 0209-0287); Russian quarterly edition: Polsky Injiniring (ISSN 0209-0295) 1970. bi-m. 19.80 Zl.($10) AGPOL - Polexportpress, Ul. Marszalkowska 124, P.O. Box 726, 00-950 Warsaw, Poland. (Dist. by: Ars-Polona, Krakowskie Przedmiescie 7-9, 00-068 Warsaw, Poland; U.S. subscr. to: European Publishers Representatives, 11-03 46th Ave., Long Island City, NY 11101) Ed. Eugenia Dmowska. adv.; tr.lit. circ. 16,500. **Indexed:** Met.Abstr., World Alum.Abstr. **Document type:** trade publication.
 Formerly: Polish Machine Industry Offers.

620	PL	ISSN 0032-3012
T26.P5		CODEN: PTRWA9

POLISH TECHNICAL REVIEW/PRZEGLAD POLSKIEJ TECHNIKI. (Text in English) 1964. bi-m. $15. Wydawnictwo Czasopism i Ksiazek Technicznych SIGMA - NOT, Ul. Ratuszowa 11, P.O. Box 1004, 00-950 Warsaw, Poland. TEL 48-22-180918. FAX 48-22-192187. TELEX 814550 SIGMA PL. (Dist. by: SIGMA NOT Ltd., Ul. Bartycka 20, 00-716 Warsaw, Poland) adv.; bk.rev.; abstr.; illus.; stat. circ. 1,700. **Indexed:** Agri.Eng.Abstr., Chem.Abstr., Curr.Adv.Ecol.Sci., Excerp.Med., ISMEC, Met.Abstr., Pollut.Abstr., Sci.Abstr., World Alum.Abstr.
 —BLDSC (6543.820000); UnCover; CASDDS.

628	PL	ISSN 0324-9719

POLITECHNIKA WROCLAWSKA. INSTYTUT INZYNIERII OCHRONY SRODOWISKA. PRACE NAUKOWE. KONFERENCJE. Name of institute before 1973: Instytut Inzynierii Sanitarnej i Wodnej. 1972. irreg., no.11, 1991. price varies. Wydawnictwo Politechniki Wroclawskiej, Wybrzeze Wyspianskiego 27, 50-370 Wroclaw, Poland. FAX 22-36-64. TELEX 712559 PWRPL. (Dist. by: Ars Polona-Ruch, Krakowskie Przedmiescie 7, Warsaw, Poland)

628	PL	ISSN 0084-2877

POLITECHNIKA WROCLAWSKA. INSTYTUT INZYNIERII OCHRONY SRODOWISKA. PRACE NAUKOWE. STUDIA I MATERIALY. Name of institute before 1973: Instytut Inzynierii Sanitarnej i Wodnej. (Text in Polish; summaries in English, French, German and Russian) 1969. irreg., no. 21, 1986. price varies. Wydawnictwo Politechniki Wroclawskiej, Wybrzeze Wyspianskiego 27, 50-370 Wroclaw, Poland. FAX 22-36-64. TELEX 712559 PWRPL. (Dist. by: Ars Polona-Ruch, Krakowskie Przedmiescie 7, Warsaw, Poland) **Indexed:** Chem.Abstr.

620	PL	ISSN 0239-3433

POLITECHNIKA WROCLAWSKA. INSTYTUT STEROWANIA I TECHNIKI SYSTEMOW. PRACE NAUKOWE. KONFERENCJE. 1983. irreg., no.3, 1989. price varies. Wydawnictwo Politechniki Wroclawskiej, Wybrzeze Wyspianskiego 27, 50-370 Wroclaw, Poland. FAX 22-36-64. TELEX 712559 PWRPL.

620	PL	ISSN 0209-2573
TJ213		CODEN: PSTMEK

POLITECHNIKA WROCLAWSKA. INSTYTUT STEROWANIA I TECHNIKI SYSTEMOW. PRACE NAUKOWE. MONOGRAFIE. 1983. irreg., no.7, 1992. price varies. Wydawnictwo Politechniki Wroclawskiej, Wybrzeze Wyspianskiego 27, 50-370 Wroclaw, Poland. FAX 22-36-64. TELEX 712559 PWRPL.

ENGINEERING

620   EC   ISSN 0032-3055
T4   CODEN: POTQAY
POLITECNICA; revista de informacion tecnico-cientifica. (Text in Spanish; summaries in English) 1967. irreg. (3-4/yr.). $60 or exchange basis. Escuela Politecnica Nacional, Isabel la Catolica y Veintimilla, Apdo. 17 01 2759, Quito, Ecuador. TEL 5932-507126. FAX 5932-567848. TELEX 2650 ESPONA. Ed. Nelson Subia. bibl.; charts; illus. **Indexed:** Biol.Abstr., Chem.Abstr., GeoRef. **Document type:** academic/scholarly publication.
—UnCover; CASDDS.

POLSKA AKADEMIA NAUK. INSTYTUT PODSTAW INZYNIERII SRODOWISKA. PRACE I STUDIA. see *ENVIRONMENTAL STUDIES*

PORT ENGINEERING MANAGEMENT. see *TRANSPORTATION — Ships And Shipping*

658.5   US   ISSN 0897-6627
                     CODEN: PBENEX
POWDER AND BULK ENGINEERING. 1987. m. $60 (free to qualified personnel). C S C Publishing, Inc., 1300 E. 66th St., Minneapolis, MN 55423. TEL 612-866-2242. FAX 612-866-1939. Ed. Sherri Weiss. adv. circ. 35,541. **Document type:** trade publication.
—BLDSC (6571.730000); EI; SWETS; CASDDS.
Description: For engineers and managers in the North American powder and bulk solids market. Covers evaluation, selection, and design of systems for handling, processing, storing, and transporting materials in powder and bulk solid form.

671.73   US   ISSN 1055-0259
TP1175.M4
POWDER COATING. 1990. bi-m. C S C Publishing, 1300 E. 66th St., Minneapolis, MN 55423. TEL 612-866-2242. FAX 612-866-1939. Ed. Peggy Koop. circ. 18,000.
Description: For management personnel responsible for powder coating of products. Covers application, pre-treatment and materials and includes case histories.

620   US   ISSN 0885-7156
                     CODEN: PODIE2
POWDER DIFFRACTION;* an international journal of materials characterization. 1986. 4/yr. $55 for individuals (foreign $75); institutions $95. Joint Committee on Powder Diffraction Standards, International Centre for Diffraction Data, Newton Sq. Corp. Camp, 12, Newton Square, PA 19073. TEL 215-328-9403. FAX 215-328-2503. TELEX 847170. Ed. Ron Jenkins. adv. circ. 1,200. **Indexed:** Soils & Fert.
—BLDSC (6571.820000); Faxon; UnCover; SWETS; CASDDS. **CCC.**
Description: Covers all applications of X-ray analysis using power diffraction; instrument design, calibration; computer programming relating to X-ray diffraction. Interest level: general to advanced.

658.5   JA   ISSN 0910-111X
POWER DESIGN. 1963. m. 930 Yen per no. Nikkan Kogyo Shinbun, Ltd., 8-10, Kudan-kita, 1-chome, Chiyoda-ku, Tokyo 102, Japan. TEL 03-263-2311. FAX 03-262-4603. TELEX NIKKANKO-J29687. Ed. Kenro Mitsuhashi. circ. 24,000.
Description: Introduces oil- and air-pressure techniques contributing to the automation and labor conservation of production equipment.

POWER ENGINEERING (TULSA). see *ENGINEERING — Electrical Engineering*

620   SW
POWER SYSTEMS COMPUTATION CONFERENCE. P S C C PROCEEDINGS. 1968. triennial. $35. Kungliga Tekniska Hoegskolan, Power Systems Research Group - Royal Institute of Technology, 100 44 Stockholm 70, Sweden. Ed. J.A. Bubenko. **Document type:** proceedings.

621.8   US   ISSN 0141-6359
TS500   CODEN: PREGDL
PRECISION ENGINEERING. 1979. q. $340 to institutions (foreign $380). (American Society for Precision Engineering) Butterworth - Heinemann, Part of the Reed Elsevier group, 313 Washington St., Newton, MA 02158. TEL 617-928-2500; 800-366-2665. FAX 617-928-1610. TELEX 880052. Ed. Tyler Estler. adv.; bk.rev.; bibl.; charts; illus.; stat.; index. (also avail. in microform from UMI; back issues avail.) **Indexed:** Curr.Cont., Fluidex, ISMEC, Met.Abstr., World Alum.Abstr. **Document type:** academic/scholarly publication.
—BLDSC (6603.996000); EI; Faxon; UnCover; SWETS; UMI; CASDDS. **CCC.**
Refereed Serial

620 720   IT
PRESENZA TECNICA. 1973. bi-m. L.40000. Edizioni P E I s.r.l., Viale Mentana 92, 43100 Parma, Italy. TEL 0039-521285949. FAX 0039-521289669. Ed. Cagozzi Carlo. adv.; bk.rev. circ. 10,000. (back issues avail.)

620   US   ISSN 1069-6113
▼**PRO-E: THE MAGAZINE.** 1993. bi-m. $60 (foreign $120). ConnectPress, Ltd., 1580 Center Dr., Santa Fe, NM 87507-7701. TEL 505-438-0360. FAX 505-438-7171. Ed. Debora Bluestone; Pub. Kate Hayward. adv.

620 600   RM
PROBLEME DE AUTOMATIZARE. 1960. s-a. Editura Academiei Romane, Calea Victoriei 125, 79717 Bucharest, Rumania. (Subscr. to: Artexim, Str. Piata Presei Libere 1, P.O. Box 33-16, 70055 Bucharest, Rumania) Eds. Gh. Cartianu, E. Nicolau. **Indexed:** Math.R.

621 001.6   UK   ISSN 0261-7412
PROCESS EQUIPMENT NEWS; new products for busy managers. 1980. 11/yr. £30($99) (foreign £50). Wilmington Publishing, Wilmington House, Church Rd., Dartford, Kent UA2 7EF, England. TEL 0322-277788. FAX 0322-276476. (Subscr. to: Ferrari House, 258 Field End Rd., Ruislip, Middx HA4 9UX. TEL 081-868-4499) Ed. Henry Skidmore. illus. circ. 22,619. **Indexed:** Br.Ceram.Abstr.
—CCC.

658.5   UK
PROCESS INDUSTRY SELECTOR. 1978. q. A.G.B. Hulton Ltd., Warwick House, Azalea Dr., Swanley, Kent BR8 8JF, England. circ. 22,619.

PROCESS PLANT LAYOUT AND PIPING DESIGN. see *HEATING, PLUMBING AND REFRIGERATION*

620   US
▼**PRODUCT DESIGN AND DEVELOPMENT EUROPE.** 1993. q. Chilton Co., Chilton Way, Radnor, PA 19089. TEL 215-964-4353. FAX 215-964-4947. adv.; B&W page $5740; trim 10 7/8 x 15 1/4. circ. 50,000.

PRODUCTION MACHINERY. see *MACHINERY*

620   CN   ISSN 0841-6427
PROFESSIONAL EDGE. 1951. 5/yr. Can.$12 to non-members. Association of Professional Engineers of Saskatchewan, 2255 13th Ave., Regina, SK S4P 0V6, Canada. TEL 306-525-9547. FAX 306-525-0851. Ed.Bd. adv.; bk.rev.; index; circ. 4,000 (controlled). **Document type:** newsletter.
Formerly: Saskatchewan Professional Engineer (ISSN 0080-6579)

620   AT
PROFESSIONAL ENGINEER. 1946. 11/yr. Aus.$60. Association of Professional Engineers, Australia, G.P.O. Box 1272L, Melbourne, Vic. 3001, Australia. FAX 03-329-1028. Ed. J.D. Vines. adv.; bk.rev. circ. 22,000.
● Also available online. Vendor(s): DIALOG Information Services, Inc., Orbit Search Service.
Former titles: P E News (ISSN 0158-3158); Professional Engineer (ISSN 0048-5438)

620   II   ISSN 0033-0078
PROFESSIONAL ENGINEER. 1963. q. Rs.100($25) (Engineers Club, India) India-International News Service, 12 India Exchange Place, Calcutta 700 001, India. Ed. H. Kothari. adv.; bk.rev.; abstr.; bibl.; charts; illus.; stat.

620   US
THE PROFESSIONAL ENGINEER (RALEIGH); the magazine of North Carolina engineering. 1968. 5/yr. $25 (effective 1993). Professional Engineers of North Carolina, Eastgate Office Center, Ste. 108, 4000 Wake Forest Rd., Raleigh, NC 27609. FAX 919-872-0683. Ed. Janet Morris Yearwood. adv. circ. 7,800. **Indexed:** W.R.C.Inf.
Description: Covers matters of interest to the engineering profession.

620   CN
PROJECT MAGAZINE;* the national magazine for engineering students - la revue nationale des etudiants en genie. (Text in English, French) 1984. s-a. Can.$6.50. Congress Federation of Engineering Students - Congres des Etudiants en Genie du Canada, 8 St. Margaret's Bay Rd., Halifax, NS B3N 1J1, Canada. TEL 416-525-9140. FAX 416-577-9099. Ed. Darryl Clarke. adv. circ. 20,000. (back issues avail.)
Description: National magazine for engineering students.

PROYECTO 2000; ingenieria del diseno y desarrollo de los productos. see *ENGINEERING — Engineering Mechanics And Materials*

620   XR   ISSN 0139-858X
PRUMYSLOVY DESIGN. (Text in Czech; summaries in English, Russian) 1968. 10/yr. 10 Kcs.($43.80) per no. (Institut Prumysloveho Designu) Nakladatelstvi Technicke Literatury, Spalena 51, 113 02 Prague 1, Czech Republic. (Dist. by: Artia, Ve Smeckach 30, 111 27 Prague 1, Czech Republic) Ed. Jitka Kikova. adv.; bk.rev. circ. 2,500.
Supersedes (in 1976): Design v Teorii a Praxi (ISSN 0323-1828)

620   SA   ISSN 0555-6945
PULSE. vol. 22, 1975. a. membership. University of Natal, Students Engineering Society, King George IV Ave., Durban 4001, South Africa. Ed. V.N. Hatley.

620   US
QUALITY AND RELIABILITY. 1985. irreg., vol.42, 1993. price varies. Marcel Dekker, Inc., 270 Madison Ave., New York, NY 10016. TEL 212-696-9000. FAX 212-685-4540. TELEX 421419. Ed. Edward G. Schilling. **Document type:** monographic series.

620   US   ISSN 0898-2112
TS156.A1   CODEN: QUENE7
QUALITY ENGINEERING. 1988. 4/yr. $35 to individuals; institutions $200. (American Society for Quality Control) Marcel Dekker Journals, 270 Madison Ave., New York, NY 10016. TEL 212-696-9000. FAX 212-685-4540. TELEX 421419 MARDEEK. (Subscr. to: Box 5017, Monticello, NY 12701) Ed. Frank Caplan. (also avail. in microform from RPI) **Indexed:** Oper.Res.Manage.Sci., Qual.Contr.Appl.Stat. **Document type:** academic/scholarly publication.
—BLDSC (7168.152050); Faxon; SWETS. **CCC.**
Refereed Serial

QUALITY NEW ZEALAND. see *BUSINESS AND ECONOMICS — Management*

620.1 389   US   ISSN 0033-524X
TS156.A1   CODEN: QUPRB3
QUALITY PROGRESS. 1944. m. $50. American Society for Quality Control, 611 E. Wisconsin Ave., Box 3005, Milwaukee, WI 53201-3005. TEL 414-272-8575. FAX 414-272-1734. Ed. Brad Stratton. adv. contact: Robert D. Brezenski. bk.rev.; bibl.; charts; illus.; index. circ. 110,000. (also avail. in microform from UMI; reprint service avail. from UMI) **Indexed:** A.S.& T.Ind., ABI Inform., BPIA, Curr.Cont., Eng.Ind., Excerp.Med., Graph.Arts Lit.Abstr., Oper.Res.Manage.Sci., Q.Abstr., Qual.Contr.Appl.Stat., Sci.Abstr. **Document type:** trade publication.
—BLDSC (7168.153000); EI; Faxon; UnCover; SWETS; UMI. **CCC.**
Supersedes in part (in 1968): Industrial Quality Control.
Description: Covers quality control management issues.
Refereed Serial

ENGINEERING

620   US
R A C JOURNAL. q. free. I I T Research Institute, Reliability Analysis Center, 201 Mill St., Rome, NY 13440. TEL 315-337-0900. FAX 315-337-9932. Ed. Anthony Coppola. adv. contact: Charles Cox. circ. 20,000 (controlled). **Document type:** trade publication.
    Formed by the 1993 merger of: R A C Newsletter & R A C Quarterly.
    Description: Current awareness topics in reliability engineering, maintainability engineering and quality engineering for the assurance science professional.

R A P R A NEWS. see *PLASTICS*

R & D CONTRACTS MONTHLY; a continuously up-dated sales and R & D tool for all research organizations and manufacturers. (Research & Development) see *SCIENCES: COMPREHENSIVE WORKS*

620   IT   ISSN 0392-6087
R C I. (Riscaldamento Climatizzazione Idronica) 1974. m. L.85000 (foreign L.210000) (effective 1994). Tecniche Nuove s.p.a., Via C. Menotti 14, 20129 Milan, Italy. TEL 02-75701. FAX 02-7610351. adv.: B&W page L.2230000, color page L.3568000; trim 185 x 266. circ. 8,749.
    Description: Technical publication on hydrothermosanitary installations.

R S I C NEWSLETTER. (Radiation Shielding Information Center) see *ENERGY — Nuclear Energy*

620   US
RECOMMENDED LATERAL FORCE REQUIREMENTS. 1959. irreg. $45. Structural Engineers Association of California, 1050 Fulton Ave., Ste. 150, Sacramento, CA 95825-4207. TEL 916-427-3647. FAX 916-974-8673. circ. 3,260. (looseleaf format) **Document type:** trade publication.

RECYCLING - RECLAMATION DIGEST. see *ENVIRONMENTAL STUDIES — Waste Management*

620 600   UK   ISSN 0951-8320
    CODEN: RESSEP
RELIABILITY ENGINEERING AND SYSTEM SAFETY. 1980. 12/yr. (in 4 vols.; 3 nos./vol.) £910($1400) (effective 1994). (European Safety and Reliability Association) Elsevier Science Ltd., Oxford Fulfilment Centre, P.O. Box 800, Kidlington, Oxford OX5 1DX, England. TEL 44-865-843000. FAX 44-865-843010. (Subscr. in U.S. and Canada to: Elsevier Science, 660 White Plains Rd., Tarrytown, NY 10591-5153. TEL 914-524-9200. FAX 914-333-2444) Ed. G.E. Apostolakis. adv.; bk.rev.; charts. (also avail. in microform from UMI; back issues avail.) **Indexed:** Appl.Mech.Rev., CAD CAM Abstr., Chem.Abstr., Curr.Cont., Energy Info.Abstr., Eng.Ind., Int.Aerosp.Abstr., Met.Abstr., Oper.Res.Manage.Sci., Phys.Ber., Qual.Contr.Appl.Stat., Risk Abstr., Robomat, Sci.Abstr., Sci.Cit.Ind., World Alum.Abstr. **Document type:** academic/scholarly publication.
    —BLDSC (7356.422700); El; Faxon; UnCover; SWETS. **CCC**.
    Incorporates (in 1990): Res Mechanica (ISSN 0143-0084); **Formerly:** Reliability Engineering (ISSN 0143-8174)
    Description: Contains information on the application of reliability and probabilistic techniques in design of plants and systems.
    Refereed Serial

620   US   ISSN 0275-7257
G70.4   CODEN: RSRVEP
REMOTE SENSING REVIEWS. q. 127 ECU (effective 1993). Harwood Academic Publishers, 820 Town Center Dr., Langhorne, PA 19047. TEL 215-750-2642. FAX 215-750-6343. (UK subscr. to: P.O. Box 90, Reading, Berkshire RG1 8JL, England. TEL 0734-560-080) Ed. N. Goel. (also avail. in microform) **Indexed:** Int.Aerosp.Abstr., Sci.Abstr.
    —BLDSC (7356.826200); El; Faxon. **CCC**.
    Refereed Serial

RENSSELAER ENGINEER. see *TECHNOLOGY: COMPREHENSIVE WORKS*

620 530   CH   ISSN 0255-6588
QH301   CODEN: PNAEE2
REPUBLIC OF CHINA. NATIONAL SCIENCE COUNCIL. PROCEEDINGS. PART A: PHYSICAL SCIENCE AND ENGINEERING. (Text in English) 1968. bi-m. NT.$360($24) National Science Council, 106 Ho-ping E. Rd. Sec. 2, Taipei, Taiwan 106, Republic of China. Ed. Chi-Fu Den. (also avail. in microfiche) **Indexed:** Biol.Abstr., Excerp.Med., GeoRef., Soils & Fert. **Document type:** academic/scholarly publication.
    —BLDSC (6769.884100); El; CASDDS.

RESALE WEEKLY. see *BUILDING AND CONSTRUCTION*

RESEARCH & DEVELOPMENT. see *EARTH SCIENCES*

620   GW
RESEARCH ENGINEERING MANUFACTURING. (Text in English, French, German, Spanish) 1970. a. M A N Aktiengesellschaft, Stabsabteilung Information und Marktbeobachtung, Ungererstr. 69, 80805 Munich, Germany. TEL 089-3223740. FAX 089-36098382. circ. 35,000.

620   US   ISSN 1060-6696
RESEARCH HORIZONS. 1973. q. free. Georgia Institute of Technology, Research Communications Office, 223 Centennial Research Bldg., Atlanta, GA 30332. TEL 404-894-6987. FAX 404-894-6983. E-mail: gopher.gatech.edn port 70. Ed. Mark Hodges. **Document type:** academic/scholarly publication.
    Former titles (until 1983): E E S Report; Georgia Institute of Technology. Engineering Experiment Station. Quarterly Report.
    Description: Discusses current research projects, trends in high technology manufacturing and applications of new technologies, as well as recent news affecting the institute.

620   UK   ISSN 0934-9839
RESEARCH IN ENGINEERING DESIGN. 1989. 4/yr. £80($122) Springer-Verlag, Springer House, 8 Alexandra Rd., London SW19 7JZ, England. TEL 081-944-2942. FAX 081-947-4651. (Subscr. in N. America to: Springer-Verlag New York, Inc., 44 Hartz Way, Secaucus, NJ 07096-2491. TEL 201-348-4033. FAX 201-348-4505) **Document type:** trade publication.
    —BLDSC (7739.100000); SWETS; UMI. **CCC**.

620   US   ISSN 0934-9847
TA417.2   CODEN: RNEVER
RESEARCH IN NONDESTRUCTIVE EVALUATION. 1989. 4/yr. $129 (effective 1995). (American Society for Nondestructive Testing) Springer-Verlag, Journals, 175 Fifth Ave., New York, NY 10010. TEL 212-460-1500. FAX 212-473-6272. (N. American subscr. to: Journal Fulfillment Services, Box 2485, Secaucus, NJ 07096-2491. TEL 800-777-4643. FAX 201-348-4505; Elsewhere: Heidelberger Platz 3, 1000 Berlin 33, Germany. TEL 030-8207-0. FAX 030-821-4091) Ed. H. Thomas Yolken. (also avail. in microform from UMI; back issues avail.) **Indexed:** Comput.& Contr.Abstr. (1989-), Elec.& Electron.Abstr. (1989-), Phys.Abstr. (1989-). **Document type:** academic/scholarly publication.
    —BLDSC (7743.891800); El; Faxon; UnCover. **CCC**.
    Description: Publishes experimental and theoretical investigations into the scientific and engineering bases of nondestructive evaluation, with discussions of measurement methodologies and applications.
    Refereed Serial

RESOURCE DIRECTORY OF SCIENTISTS AND ENGINEERS WITH DISABILITIES. see *BIOGRAPHY*

620   FR
RESPONSABLES. 1906. m. 50 F. Mouvement des Cadres Ingenieurs et Dirigeants Chretiens, 18 rue de Varenne, 75007 Paris, France. Ed. Philippe Rain. adv.; bk.rev. circ. 28,880.

620   BL   ISSN 0034-8112
REVISTA DE ENGENHARIA MACKENZIE. 1970. s-a. free. Universidade MacKenzie, Centro Academic Horacio Lane, 149 Rua Itambe, C.P. 8792, Sao Paulo, Brazil. adv.; bk.rev.; illus. circ. 10,000. **Indexed:** Chem.Abstr.

620   BL
REVISTA DE ENSINO DE ENGENHARIA. 1980. 2/yr. $10. Associacao Brasileira de Ensino de Engenharia, c/o Prof. Eduardo Cleto Pires, Ed., Escola de Engenharia de Sao Carlos, USP, C.P. 539, 13560 Sao Carlos, SP, Brazil. TEL 0162-726222. TELEX 162411 USPO BR. circ. 1,000.

620   AG   ISSN 0482-5772
REVISTA DE INGENIERIA. q. Centro de Ingenieros Provincia de Buenos Aires, Avenida 53, no. 412-1-2, La Plata, Buenos Aires, Argentina. Ed.Bd.

620   UY
REVISTA DE INGENIERIA/ENGINEERING REVIEW. 1907. q. c/o Joaquin Coenen, Rio Negro 1308, Esc. 101-Montevideo, Uruguay. adv. circ. 3,000.

620 721   CK   ISSN 0120-5862
REVISTA S A I. 1977. q. Col.$1500($11) per issue. Sociedad Antioquena de Ingenieros y Arquitectos, Calle 71, 65-100, Apdo. Aereo 4754, Medellin, Colombia. TEL 257-39-00. FAX 255-45-84. Ed.Bd. adv.; charts; illus. circ. 2,000.

620 600   FR
REVUE DES INGENIEURS ET TECHNICIENS EUROPEENS. q. 5 rue de la Grange Bateliere, 75009 Paris, France. TEL 45-23-21-50. Ed. Noel Ganem. adv. circ. 10,000.

620   FR   ISSN 0755-7868
REVUE GENERALE DU FROID. 1908. m. 525 F. (foreign 750 F.). (Association Francaise du Froid) Arts Graphiques de Perche Edition, 1 rue du Coq-Heron, 75001 Paris, France. TEL 40-26-57-08. FAX 40-26-34-40. Ed. Jacques Lucas. adv.; bk.rev. circ. 4,000. Indexed: Food Sci.& Tech.Abstr.
    —BLDSC (7910.000000).

REVUE GENERALE NUCLEAIRE. see *ENERGY — Nuclear Energy*

REVUE GENERALE NUCLEAIRE: INTERNATIONAL EDITION. see *ENERGY — Nuclear Energy*

LA REVUE POLYTECHNIQUE. see *TECHNOLOGY: COMPREHENSIVE WORKS*

REVUE ROUMAINE DES SCIENCES TECHNIQUES. SERIE ELECTROTECHNIQUE ET ENERGETIQUE. see *ENGINEERING — Electrical Engineering*

620   JA
REZA NETSU KAKO KENKYUKAI RONBUNSHU/JAPAN LASER PROCESSING SOCIETY. PROCEEDINGS. (Text in Japanese) 1988. 2/yr. Reza Netsu Kako Kenkyukai - Japan Laser Processing Society, Osaka Daigaku Kogakubu, Seisan Kako Kogaku Kyoshitsu, 2-1, Yamadaoka, Suita-shi, Osaka 565, Japan. **Document type:** proceedings

621   JA
REZA NETSU KAKO KENKYUKAI SHIRYO. (Text in English, Japanese) a. Reza Netsu Kako Kenkyukai - Japan Laser Processing Society, Osaka Daigaku Kogakubu, Seisan Kako Kogaku Kyoshitsu, 2-1, Yamadaoka, Suita-shi, Osaka 565, Japan.

620   JA
RIHA KOGAKU KANFARENSU KOEN RONBUNSHU/REHABILITATION ENGINEERING SOCIETY OF JAPAN. PROCEEDINGS OF THE CONFERENCE. (Text in Japanese) 1986. a. Nihon Rihabiriteshon Kogaku Kyokai - Rehabilitation Engineering Society of Japan, Hyogoken Rihabiiteshon Senta, 1070, Akebono-cho, Nishi-ku, Kobe-shi, Hyogo-ken 673, Japan.

RIKKYO UNIVERSITY. INSTITUTE FOR ATOMIC ENERGY. REPORT. see *ENERGY — Nuclear Energy*

620   JA   ISSN 0370-4254
    CODEN: RDRKAJ
RITSUMEIKAN DAIGAKU RIKOGAKU KENKYUJO KIYO/RITSUMEIKAN UNIVERSITY. RESEARCH INSTITUTE OF SCIENCE AND ENGINEERING. MEMOIRS. (Text in English and Japanese; summaries in English) 1956. a. Ritsumeikan Daigaku, Rikogaku Kenkyujo - Ritsumeikan University, Research Institute of Science and Engineering, Kita-machi, Tojiin, Kita-ku, Kyoto-shi, Kyoto-fu 603, Japan. abstr. **Indexed:** Chem.Abstr., INIS Atomind., Jap.Per.Ind., Sci.Abstr.
    —BLDSC (5632.400000).

620   SZ
RIVISTA TECNICA. (Text in Italian) m. Casella Postale 219, CH-6903 Lugano, Switzerland. TEL 091-561161. FAX 091-561447. circ. 3,300.

ENGINEERING

620 US ISSN 0035-7405
ROCHESTER ENGINEER. 1922. m. $13. Rochester Engineering Society, Inc., 1806 Lyell Ave., Rochester, NY 14606. TEL 716-254-2350. Ed. Joseph W. Campbell. adv.; bk.rev.; index. circ. 5,700. **Document type:** bulletin.

620 UK
ROLLS-ROYCE WORLDWIDE. 1982. bi-m. free. Rolls-Royce plc., 65 Buckingham Gate, London SW1E 6AT, England. Ed. Martin Nield. illus. circ. 6,000. **Document type:** bulletin.
Formerly (until 1990): N E I Update.

620 RM ISSN 0035-8061
ROMANIAN ENGINEERING. (Text in English, French, German and Spanish) 1966. q. $22. Chamber of Commerce and Industry of the Socialist Republic of Rumania, Bd. N. Balcescu Nr. 22, Bucharest, Rumania. (Subscr. to: ROMPRESFILATELIA, P.O. Box 12-201, Calea Grivitei 64-66, Bucharest, Rumania) adv.; bk.rev.; abstr.; bibl.; charts; illus.; pat.; tr.mk. circ. 3,500.

620 PK
ROSHAN PAKISTAN. 1961. w. Rs.12. Mohammad Yusef Kureshy, Ed. & Pub., 14 Japan Mansion, Preedy St., Saddar, Karachi 3, Pakistan. adv.: B&W and color; 375 x 525. bk.rev.; abstr.; illus. (tabloid format)
Supersedes: Engineering News (ISSN 0013-8061)

620 RU
ROSSIISKAYA AKADEMIYA NAUK. IZVESTIYA. MEKHANIKA TVERDOGO TELA. English translation: Mechanics of Solids (US ISSN 0025-6544) 1961. m. 37.20 Rub. (Otdelenie Mekhaniki i Protsessov Upravleniya) Izdatel'stvo Nauka, 90 Profsoyuznaya ul., 117864 Moscow, Russia. **Indexed:** Ceram.Abstr., Chem.Abstr., Chem.Eng.Abstr., Eng.Ind., Fluidex, Geotech.Abstr., INIS Atomind., Int.Aerosp.Abstr., ISMEC, Math.R., Met.Abstr., Sci.Abstr., World Alum.Abstr.
Former titles: Akademiya Nauk S.S.S.R. Izvestiya. Mekhanika Tverdogo Tela (ISSN 0572-3299); (until 1969): Inzhenernyi Zhurnal. Mekhanika Tverdogo Tela (ISSN 0541-4180); (until 1966): Inzhenernyi Zhurnal (ISSN 0021-0293)

ROYAL ENGINEERS JOURNAL. see *MILITARY*

ROYAL SOCIETY OF LONDON. PHILOSOPHICAL TRANSACTIONS. SERIES A. PHYSICAL SCIENCES AND ENGINEERING. see *PHYSICS*

ROZPRAWY HYDROTECHNICZNE/HYDROTECHNICAL TRANSACTIONS. see *WATER RESOURCES*

RUSSIAN ULTRASONICS. see *PHYSICS — Sound*

620 US
T171.R9
RUTGERS UNIVERSITY. BUREAU OF ENGINEERING RESEARCH. BIENNIAL REPORT. 1927. biennial. free. Rutgers University, College of Engineering, Bureau of Engineering Research, Piscataway, NJ 08855-0909. TEL 908-932-2224. FAX 908-932-5313. Ed. Alvin J. Salkind. index. circ. 500. **Document type:** corporate report.
Formerly: Rutgers University. Bureau of Engineering Research. Annual Report (ISSN 0557-5486)

620 JA ISSN 0389-102X
CODEN: BFERDK
RYUKYU DAIGAKU KOGAKUBU KIYO/UNIVERSITY OF THE RYUKYUS. FACULTY OF ENGINEERING. BULLETIN. (Text in English, Japanese) 1968. s-a. Ryukyu Daigaku, Kogakubu, 1, Senbaru, Nishihara-cho, Nakagami-gun, Okinawa-ken 903-01, Japan. **Indexed:** Jap.Per.Ind. **Document type:** academic/scholarly publication.
—BLDSC (2508.185000); CASDDS.

S F S CATALOGUE; catalogue of Finnish national standards. (Suomen Standardisoimisliitto) see *METROLOGY AND STANDARDIZATION*

S H E. (Subject Headings for Engineering) see *LIBRARY AND INFORMATION SCIENCES*

620 US
S H P E NATIONAL NEWSLETTER. bi-m. $45. Society of Hispanic Professional Engineers, 5400 E. Olympic Blvd., Ste. 306, Los Angeles, CA 90022. TEL 213-725-3970. Ed. Fred Sanchezz. adv. circ. 6,000. (back issues avail.) **Document type:** newsletter.
Description: Informs SHPE members of current events around the nation.

621.38 600 US ISSN 0097-966X
TK7882.I6 CODEN: DTPSDS
S I D INTERNATIONAL SYMPOSIUM. DIGEST OF TECHNICAL PAPERS. Key Title: Digest of Technical Papers. 1970. a. $70 to non-members (foreign $75). (Society for Information Display) Palisades Institute for Research Services, Attn: Jay Morreale, 201 Varick St., 11th Fl., New York, NY 10014. circ. 2,000.
—BLDSC (8271.680000). **CCC.**
Formerly: Symposium on Information Display. Digest of Technical Papers (ISSN 0082-0830)
Refereed Serial

S P S E ANNUAL CONFERENCE. PAPER SUMMARIES (YEAR). (Society for Imaging Science and Technology) see *PHOTOGRAPHY*

620 510 530 JA ISSN 0385-6186
Q4 CODEN: RFSSDV
SAGA DAIGAKU RIKOGAKUBU SHUHO/SAGA UNIVERSITY. FACULTY OF SCIENCE AND ENGINEERING. REPORTS. (Text in English, Japanese; summaries in English) 1973. s-a. free. Saga Daigaku, Rigaku Kogakubu - Saga University, Faculty of Science and Engineering, 1 Honjo-machi, Saga-shi, Saga-ken 840, Japan. TEL 0952-24-5191. FAX 0952-24-4253. Ed. Tatsuo Ishikawa. circ. 400. (back issues avail.) **Indexed:** Chem.Abstr., Jap.Per.Ind., JCT, JTA. **Document type:** academic/scholarly publication, proceedings.
—CASDDS.

SANGYO ANZEN KENKYUJO GIJUTSU SHISHIN/RESEARCH INSTITUTE OF INDUSTRIAL SAFETY. TECHNICAL RECOMMENDATION. see *OCCUPATIONAL HEALTH AND SAFETY*

658.5 745.2 UK
SAUDI-ARABIAN SASO STANDARDS MICROFILE. 1981. 3/yr. Technical Indexes Ltd., Willoughby Rd., Bracknell, Berkshire RG12 8DW, England. TEL 0344-426311. FAX 0344-424971. **Document type:** abstracting/indexing.

SCHWEIZER INGENIEUR UND ARCHITEKT/INGENIEURS ET ARCHITECTES SUISSES/INGEGNERI E ARCHITETTI SVIZZERI; Schweizerische bauzeitung - bulletin technique de la Suisse romande. see *ARCHITECTURE*

620 SZ ISSN 0040-151X
T3 CODEN: STZTA5
SCHWEIZERISCHE TECHNISCHE ZEITSCHRIFT; revue technique suisse. (Text in French and German) 1903. w. 85 Fr. Schweizerischer Technischer Verband, Weinbergstr. 41, CH-8006 Zurich, Switzerland. Ed. H.A. Hafner. adv.; bk.rev. circ. 12,100. **Indexed:** C.I.S. Abstr., Chem.Abstr., Excerp.Med., Sci.Abstr.
—BLDSC (8120.000000).

SCHWEIZERISCHE VEREINIGUNG FUER ATOMENERGIE. BULLETIN. see *ENERGY — Nuclear Energy*

620 510 530 JA
SCIEN TECH/SAGA DAIGAKU RIKOGAKUBU KOHO. (Text in Japanese) 1986. a. Saga Daigaku, Rigaku Kogakubu - Saga University, Faculty of Science and Engineering, 1 Honjo-machi, Saga-shi, Saga-ken 840, Japan.

620 II ISSN 0036-8164
T1
SCIENCE AND ENGINEERING. (Text in English) 1935. m. Rs.36($10) India Society of Engineers, 12B Netaji Subhas Rd., Calcutta 700001, India. Ed. Anupam Haldar. adv.; bk.rev.; illus. circ. 1,000. **Indexed:** Chem.Abstr., J.of Ferroc., Met.Abstr., World Alum.Abstr.

623 US ISSN 0093-3651
V210.A1 CODEN: SEATAD
SEA TECHNOLOGY; for design engineering and application of equipment and services for the marine environment. 1960. m. $25 (foreign $30). Compass Publications, Inc. (Arlington), Ste. 1000, 1117 N. 19th St., Arlington, VA 22209. TEL 703-524-3136. FAX 703-841-0852. Ed. David M. Graham. adv.; charts; illus.; tr.lit.; index, cum.index every 5 yrs. circ. 24,000. (also avail. in microform from UMI; reprint service avail. from UMI) **Indexed:** A.S.& T.Ind., Abstr.Mil.Bibl., AESIS, Appl.Mech.Rev., ASCA, Biol.Abstr., BMT, Curr.Cont., Curr.Tit.Ocean, Deep Sea Res.& Oceanogr.Abstr., Eng.Ind., Environ.Per.Bibl. (1988-), Excerp.Med., Fluidex, GeoRef., Ocean.Abstr., Petrol.Abstr., Pollut.Abstr., Sci.Abstr. **Document type:** trade publication.
—BLDSC (8213.670000); EI; Faxon; UnCover; SWETS; UMI. **CCC.**
Formerly: Undersea Technology (ISSN 0041-6533)
Description: For professionals working in the ocean - marine - offshore field; presents trends and news in columns, departments and editorials.
Refereed Serial

623 US
SEA TECHNOLOGY BUYERS GUIDE - DIRECTORY. 1967. a. $23.50. Compass Publications, Inc. (Arlington), 1117 N. 19th St., Ste. 1000, Arlington, VA 22209. TEL 703-524-3136. FAX 703-841-0852. Ed. David M. Graham. adv. circ. 10,000. (reprint service avail. from UMI) **Document type:** directory, trade publication.
Formerly: Sea Technology Handbook and Directory.
Description: Serves the ocean - marine - offshore community. Updated technical articles and industry reports, listing of manufacturers, cross index of products and services available, ocean research vessels, geophysical survey vessels and educational institutions.

658.5 333.79 VE
SECTOR ENERGIA E INDUSTRIA.* 1957. q. Colegio de Ingenieros de Venezuela, Apdo 2006, Bosque Los Caobos, Caracas 101, Venezuela. circ. 7,000.

620 681 JA
SEIMITSU KOGAKKAI TAIKAI GAKUJUTSU KOENKAI KOEN RONBUNSHU/JAPAN SOCIETY OF PRECISION ENGINEERING. PROCEEDINGS OF THE MEETING. (Text in Japanese) a. 7000 Yen. Seimitsu Kogakkai - Japan Society of Precision Engineering, Ceramics Bldg., 22-17, Hyakunincho 2-chome, Shinjuku-ku, Tokyo 169, Japan. TEL 81-3-3362-1979. **Document type:** proceedings.

620 681 JA ISSN 0912-0289
CODEN: SKKAEI
SEIMITSU KOGAKKAISHI/JAPAN SOCIETY FOR PRECISION ENGINEERING. JOURNAL. (Text in Japanese; summaries in English) 1933. m. 2060 Yen per no. Seimitsu Kogakkai - Japan Society for Precision Engineering, Ceramics Bldg., 22-17, Hyakunincho 2-chome, Shinjuku-ku, Tokyo 169, Japan. TEL 03-3362-1979. **Indexed:** INIS Atomind., Jap.Per.Ind., Sci.Abstr.
—BLDSC (4808.120000); EI; CASDDS.

620 SZ
SEKTIONS NACHRICHTEN S T V. 9/yr. Stuessistr. 33, CH-8006 Zurich, Switzerland. TEL 01-3625296. Ed. Werner Jost. circ. 3,300.

SENDAI DENPA KOGYO KOTO SENMON GAKKO KENKYU KIYO/SENDAI NATIONAL COLLEGE OF TECHNOLOGY. RESEARCH REPORT. see *SOCIAL SCIENCES: COMPREHENSIVE WORKS*

620 SZ
SERIES ON BULK MATERIALS HANDLING. 1975. irreg. price varies. Trans Tech Publications, Hardstr. 13, P.O. Box 100, CH-4714 Aedermannsdorf, Switzerland. FAX 062-741058. Ed. R.H. Wohlbier. adv. circ. 6,500. **Document type:** monographic series.
Formerly: Series on Bulk Materials Engineering.

SERIES ON SOFTWARE ENGINEERING & KNOWLEDGE ENGINEERING. see *COMPUTERS — Software*

SHENZHEN DAXUE XUEBAO (LIGONG BAN)/SHENZHEN UNIVERSITY. JOURNAL (SCIENCE, ENGINEERING EDITION). see *SCIENCES: COMPREHENSIVE WORKS*

620 JA ISSN 0037-3818
CODEN: SDKKBU
SHINSHU UNIVERSITY. FACULTY OF ENGINEERING. JOURNAL/SHINSHU DAIGAKU KOGAKUBU KIYO. (Text in Japanese; summaries in English) 1951. s-a. exchange basis. Shinshu University, Faculty of Engineering - Shinshu Daigaku Kogakubu, Wakasoto, Nagano 500, Japan. bibl.; charts; illus.; index, cum.index. circ. 500. **Indexed:** Chem.Abstr., Jap.Per.Ind., JCT, JTA, Math.R., Sci.Abstr.
—BLDSC (4744.200000); CASDDS.

621.4 JA ISSN 0387-1819
TJ163.3 CODEN: SHOEDS
SHO ENERUGI/ENERGY CONSERVATION. (Text in Japanese) 1978. m. 8400 Yen. Energy Conservation Center - Shou Enerugi Senta, 3-39, 2-chome, Nishi-Shinbashi, Minato-ku, Tokyo, Japan. Ed. Takeo Sawada. adv.; abstr.; bibl.; charts. circ. 15,000. (processed) **Indexed:** JCT, JTA.
—CASDDS.
Former titles (until vol.30, 1978): Netsu Kanri to Kogai - Heat Management and Pollution Control (ISSN 0302-1289); Netsu Kanri (ISSN 0028-3029)

SHOGEKI KOGAKU SHINPOJUMU. see AERONAUTICS AND SPACE FLIGHT

SIDOR HOY INTERNACIONAL. see METALLURGY

328.94 338.7 AT
SNOWY MOUNTAINS ENGINEERING CORPORATION. ANNUAL REPORT. a. price varies. Australian Government Publishing Service, G.P.O. Box 84, Canberra, A.C.T. 2601, Australia.
TEL 61-6-295-4612. FAX 61-6-295-4500. illus.

620 PE
SOCIEDAD DE INGENIEROS. INFORMACIONES Y MEMORIAS. 1975. irreg. Sociedad de Ingenieros, Avda. Nicolas de Pierola 788, Lima, Peru.

620 JA ISSN 0918-5542
SOCIETAS QUALITATIS. (Text in English) bi-m. 4500 Yen. Union of Japanese Scientists and Engineers, 5-10-11, Sendagaya, Shibuya-ku, Toyko 151, Japan. TEL 03-5379-1227.
FAX 03-3225-1813. TELEX 02322485 JUSE J.
Document type: newsletter.

SOCIETE D'ERGONOMIE DE LANGUE FRANCAISE. ACTES DU CONGRES. see PSYCHOLOGY

620.43 JA ISSN 0386-6157
CODEN: FKKADA
SOCIETY OF POWDER TECHNOLOGY, JAPAN. JOURNAL. (Text in Japanese; summaries in English, Japanese) 1964. m. 10000 Yen($60) Society of Powder Technology, Japan - Funtai Kogaku Kai, Shibunkaku-Kaikan, 2-7, Tanakasekiden-cho, Sakyo-ku, Kyoto 606, Japan. TEL 075-751-0195. FAX 075-751-2851. Ed. Yasuo Kousaka. adv.; bk.rev. circ. 2,000. **Document type:** academic/scholarly publication.
—BLDSC (4895.450000).
Supersedes: Research Association of Powder Technology, Japan. Journal (ISSN 0034-5156)

620 551 BL ISSN 0103-7021
SOLOS E ROCHAS/SOILS AND ROCKS; revista brasileira de geotecnia - Brazilian geotechnical journal. (Text in English, French, Portuguese; summaries in English) 1978. 3/yr. $12 (effective Jan. 1993). Associacao Brasileira de Mecanica dos Solos, I P T, Predio Geotecnica, Cidade Universitaria, Caixa Postal 7141, 01064-970 Sao Paulo, Brazil. TEL 011-268-7325. TELEX 83144 INPT BR. (Co-sponsor: Associacao Brasileira de Geologia de Engenharia) Ed. Mauricio Abramento. adv.; charts. circ. 1,500.
Description: Covers geotechnical engineering and engineering geology. Includes papers on practical applications and theoretical and experimental advances.
Refereed Serial

620 SA
SOUTH AFRICAN JOURNAL OF PHOTOGRAMMETRY, REMOTE SENSING AND CARTOGRAPHY. (Text in Afrikaans and English) 1959. s-a. R.20 to non-members. South African Society for Photogrammetry, Remote Sensing and Cartography, P.O. Box 69, Newlands 7725, South Africa. Ed. C.G. Martin. adv.; bk.rev. circ. 500. **Indexed:** Bibl.Cart., Geo.Abstr., GeoRef., Ind.S.A.Per.
Formerly (until 1980): South African Journal of Photogrammetry (ISSN 0085-6398)

SOUTH AFRICAN MINING, COAL, GOLD AND BASE MINERALS. see MINES AND MINING INDUSTRY

620 US ISSN 0038-4054
SOUTHERN ENGINEER. 1936. 3/yr. $5. North Carolina State University, School of Engineering, Box 7901, Raleigh, NC 27695. TEL 919-515-2310. Ed. Steven Freedman. adv.; bk.rev. circ. 3,000.

620 US ISSN 0275-911X
G70.4 CODEN: SJSEDS
SOVIET JOURNAL OF REMOTE SENSING. English translation of: Issledovanie Zemli iz Kosmosa. 1982. 6/yr. (in 1 vol., 6 nos./vol.). 400 ECU (effective 1993). Harwood Academic Publishers, 820 Town Center Dr., Langhorne, PA 19047.
TEL 215-750-2642. FAX 215-750-6343. (UK subscr. to: P.O. Box 90, Reading, Berkshire RG1 8JL, England. TEL 0734-560-080) Ed. G.T. Marchuk. adv. (also avail. in microform) **Indexed:** ASCA.
—BLDSC (0423.660000); EI. **CCC.**
Refereed Serial

620 DK ISSN 0038-8947
STADS OG HAVNEINGENIOEREN/MUNICIPAL ENGINEER. 1909. m. DKK 255. Kommunalteknisk Chefforening - Joint Council of Danish Municipal Engineers, Vagtelvej 26, DK-3460 Birkeroed, Denmark.
TEL 42-81-61-25. FAX 42-81-65-23. Ed. Kurt Ojgaard. adv.; B&W page DKK 5900, color page DKK 10925. bk.rev. circ. 3,500.

620 CE
STATE ENGINEERS. q. Frewin and Company, Baillie St., Colombo 1, Sri Lanka. adv. circ. 900.

620 UK ISSN 0264-4061
STATIONARY ENGINE. 1974. m. £16.75. Kelsey Publishing Ltd., Kelsey House, 77 High St., Beckenham, Kent BR3 1AN, England.
TEL 01-658-3531. FAX 01-650-8035. Ed. Gordon Wright. adv. circ. 5,800. (back issues avail.)
Document type: consumer publication.

STEVENS INDICATOR. see COLLEGE AND ALUMNI

620 US
STRUCTURAL ENGINEERS ASSOCIATION OF CALIFORNIA. PROCEEDINGS. a. $40. Structural Engineers Association of California, 1050 Fulton Ave., Ste. 150, Sacramento, CA 95825-4207.
TEL 916-427-8673. FAX 916-974-8673. (back issues avail.) **Document type:** proceedings.

STRUCTURAL SURVEY. see BUILDING AND CONSTRUCTION

620 CN ISSN 1188-407X
STRUCTURES NEWS. (Editions in English, French) q. free. National Research Council of Canada, Institute for Research in Construction, Ottawa, ON K1A 0R6, Canada. TEL 613-993-2463.
Description: Covers structural engineering: rehabilitation of buildings, infrastructure renewal, vibrations, seismic evaluations.

620 PL ISSN 0137-6365
TA710.A1 CODEN: SGMEDB
STUDIA GEOTECHNICA ET MECHANICA. (Text in English, French or Russian; summaries in English, French, Polish and Russian) 1970. s-a. price varies. Wydawnictwo Politechniki Wroclawskiej, Wybrzeze Wyspianskiego 27, 50-370 Wroclaw, Poland.
FAX 22-36-64. TELEX 712559 PWRPL. (Dist. by: Ars Polona-Ruch, Krakowskie Przedmiescie 7, Warsaw, Poland) Ed. Ryszard J. Izbicki. circ. 450. **Indexed:** GeoRef., Geotech.Abstr., Math.R.
—BLDSC (8482.813000).
Formerly: Studia Geotechnica.
Description: Examines theoretical and experimental problems of the engineering sciences in dealing with soils and rocks.

620 SJ ISSN 0049-2469
SUDAN ENGINEERING SOCIETY. JOURNAL. 1955. s-a. $6. Sudan Engineering Society, P.O. Box 759, Khartoum, Sudan. Ed. Abdelshakour Awadelkarim. adv.; bk.rev. circ. 600.

SUISAN KOGAKU/FISHERIES ENGINEERING. see FISH AND FISHERIES

SUISAN KOGAKU KENKYUJO GIHO. SUISAN DOBOKU/NATIONAL RESEARCH INSTITUTE OF FISHERIES ENGINEERING. TECHNICAL REPORT. AQUACULTURE AND FISHING PORT ENGINEERING. see FISH AND FISHERIES

SUISAN KOGAKJ KENKYUJO KENKYU HOKOKU/NATIONAL RESEARCH INSTITUTE OF FISHERIES ENGINEERING. BULLETIN. see FISH AND FISHERIES

620 SZ ISSN 0039-4912
TJ1 CODEN: SZTRAB
SULZER TECHNICAL REVIEW. (Editions in English, French, German, Spanish) 1919. 4/yr. 60 SFr. (Sulzer Ltd.) Sulzer Management AG, Sulzer Technical Review 0013, Postfach 414, CH-8401 Winterthur, Switzerland. TEL 052-2624097.
FAX 052-2620025. TELEX 896060-SZ-CH. Ed. Andre Schaeppi. charts; illus.; index. circ. 18,000 (for all editions). (back issues avail.) **Indexed:** Appl.Mech.Rev., B.C.I.R.A., BMT, Chem.Abstr., Chem.Eng.Abstr., Copper Abstr., Energy Info.Abstr., Eng.Ind., Environ.Abstr., Excerp.Med., Fluidex, Int.Build.Serv.Abstr., Met.Abstr., Paper & Bd.Abstr., Sci.Abstr., T.C.E.A., World Alum.Abstr., World Text.Abstr. **Document type:** trade publication.
—BLDSC (8517.000000); EI; SWETS; CASDDS.

SUPERCONDUCTOR SCIENCE & TECHNOLOGY. see PHYSICS

620 UK
SURFACE MOUNTING PRODUCTS AND REGULATIONS MICROFILE (PRISM). 1988. bi-m. Technical Indexes Ltd., Willoughby Rd., Bracknell, Berks RG12 8DW, England. TEL 0344-426311. FAX 0344-424971.
Document type: abstracting/indexing.

SURVEY (LA JOLLA). see COMPUTERS — Personal Computers

SYMPOSIUM ON WIND ENGINEERING. PROCEEDINGS. see METEOROLOGY

SYSTEMS ENGINEERING OF EDUCATION SERIES. see EDUCATION

620 NE ISSN 0731-7239
Q295 CODEN: SYREER
SYSTEMS RESEARCH. 1984. q. International Federation for Systems Research, c/o Prof. Gerrit Broekstra, Erasmus Universiteit, Postbus 1738, 3000 DR Rotterdam, Netherlands. FAX 31-222-630652. Ed. John Warfield. adv.; bk.rev.; charts; illus. (also avail. in microform from JMI) **Indexed:** Comput.Abstr., Comput.Cont., Curr.Cont., Excerp.Med., Int.Abstr.Oper.Res., Sci.Abstr., SSCI.
—BLDSC (8589.424500); Faxon; UnCover; SWETS. **CCC.**
Formerly: International Journal of Systems Research.
Description: Contains articles on the technical and philosophical aspects of systems research.

620.7 PL ISSN 0137-1223
Q295 CODEN: SYSCDP
SYSTEMS SCIENCE. (Text in English; summaries in Polish) 1975. q. $64. (Politechnika Wroclawska) Wydawnictwo Politechniki Wroclawskiej, Wybrzeze Wyspianskiego 27, 50-370 Wroclaw, Poland.
FAX 22-36-64. TELEX 712559 PWRPL. (Dist. by: Wissenschaftliche Verbandbuchhandlung Harry Munchberg, Postfach, 3394 Langelscheim 2, Germany) Ed. Zdzislaw Bubnicki. circ. 450. **Indexed:** Comput.Cont., GeoRef., Math.R., Sci.Abstr.
—BLDSC (8589.430000); EI.
Description: Devoted to general systems theories and their mathematical models.

620 JA
T E C ADVANCED ENGINEERING INFORMATION. q. Toyo Engineering Corporation, Public Relations Department, 3-2-5 Kasumigaseki, Kasumigaseki Bldg., Chiyoda-ku, Tokyo 100, Japan.
TEL 03-3592-7411. FAX 03-3593-0749.

T SQUARED NEWSLETTER. see TECHNOLOGY: COMPREHENSIVE WORKS

ENGINEERING

620   CC   ISSN 1000-1611
CODEN: TGDXEZ
TAIYUAN GONGYE DAXUE XUEBAO/TAIYUAN INDUSTRIAL UNIVERSITY. JOURNAL. (Text in Chinese) q. Taiyuan Gongye Daxue - Taiyuan Industrial University, 11 Yingze Dajie, Taiyuan, Shanxi 030024, People's Republic of China. TEL 665528. Ed. Lu Wenxiong.
—CASDDS.

620   US
TECH MINNESOTA.* 6/yr. Stolee Communications, Box 640, Duluth, MN 55801-0640. TEL 612-922-9453. FAX 612-927-9328. Ed. Margie Mac Lachian. circ. 20,000.

TECHLINK: TRANSPORTATION SAFETY. see *TRANSPORTATION*

620   NR
TECHNICAL AND COMMERCIAL MESSAGE. (Text in English) 1980. q. Alpha Publications, 6 Oyebode St., P.O. Box 1163, Aguda, Surulere, Nigeria. Ed. Charles Dodoo. adv.; bk.rev.; charts; illus. circ. 12,000.

620 666   UK
TECHNICAL CERAMICS INTERNATIONAL. 1985. bi-m. £90($170) (foreign £95). World Business Publications Ltd., Britannia House, 4th Fl., 960 High Rd., London N12 9RY, England. TEL 081-446-5141. FAX 081-446-3659. Ed. Nick C. Dellow. adv.; bk.rev. (back issues avail.) **Document type:** trade publication.
Formerly: Technical Ceramics Bulletin (ISSN 0268-8123)
Description: Provides current information on new advanced ceramics materials, from raw materials to finished products. Also examines the markets for these products.

620   XO   ISSN 0040-1056
TECHNICKA PRACA/ENGINEERING. (Text in Czech or Slovak; summaries in English and Russian) 1947. m. 42 Kcs.($18) (Slovenska Vedeckotechnicka Spolocnost - Slovak Scientific and Technical Society) Obzor, Ceskoslovenskej Armady 35, 815 85 Bratislava, Slovakia. (Subscr. to: Skulteyho 1, 815 94 Bratislava, Slovakia) Ed B. Vlasaty. adv.; bk.rev.; abstr.; bibl.; charts; illus.; index, cum.index. circ. 16,000.

620   GW
T3   CODEN: WZTKAY
TECHNISCHE UNIVERSITAET CHEMNITZ - ZWICKAU. WISSENSCHAFTLICHE ZEITSCHRIFT. 1958. bi-m. DM.25. Technische Universitaet Chemnitz - Zwickau, Postfach 964, 09111 Chemnitz, Germany. TEL 071-668536. FAX 071-668646. Eds. Christine Haeckel, Irene Roesler. charts; index. **Indexed:** Chem.Abstr., Math.R., Met.Abstr., World Text.Abstr. **Document type:** academic/scholarly publication.
Former titles: Technische Hochschule Karl-Marx-Stadt. Wissenschaftliche Zeitschrift (ISSN 0372-7610); Hochschule fuer Maschinenbau Karl-Marx-Stadt. Wissenschaftliche Zeitschrift.

620   AU   ISSN 0259-0697
TECHNISCHE UNIVERSITAET WIEN. DISSERTATIONEN. 1968. irreg., no.53, 1992. price varies. Verband der Wissenschaftlichen Gesellschaften Oesterreichs, Lindengasse 37, A-1070 Vienna, Austria. TEL 932166. (Co-sponsor: Technische Universitaet Wien)
Formerly: Technische Hochschule Wien. Dissertationen.

620   NE   ISSN 0929-0567
TECHNISCHE UNIVERSITEIT TE DELFT. BIBLIOTHEEK. LIJST VAN LOPENDE SERIELE PUBLIKATIES. Cover title: Lijst van Lopende Seriele Publikaties - List of Current Serial Publications. 1967. a. fl.35 (effective 1993). Technische Universiteit te Delft, Bibliotheek, P.O. Box 98, 2600 MG Delft, Netherlands. TEL 31-15-782854. FAX 31-15-158759. TELEX 38070 NL. index. circ. 1,000. **Document type:** bibliography.
Former titles (until 1993): Technische Universiteit te Delft. Bibliotheek. Lijst van Lopende Tijdschriftabonnementen (ISSN 0923-8689); Technische Hogeschool te Delft. Bibliotheek. Lijst van Lopende Tijdschriftabonnementen.
Description: Lists current serial and periodical subscriptions of the library.

TECHNOLOGY FOR ALASKAN TRANSPORTATION. see *TRANSPORTATION*

620   US   ISSN 0040-1706
QA276   CODEN: TCMTA2
TECHNOMETRICS; a journal of statistics for the physical, chemical and engineering sciences. 1959. q. $30 to non-members. American Statistical Association, 1429 Duke St., Alexandria, VA 22314-3402. TEL 703-684-1221. FAX 703-684-2037. (Co-sponsor: American Society for Quality Control) bk.rev.; charts; illus.; stat.; index, cum.index: vols.8-20 in vol. 20. circ. 5,200. (also avail. in microform from UMI; reprint service avail. from UMI) **Indexed:** A.S.& T.Ind., Abstr.Bull.Inst.Pap.Chem., ASCA, Biol.Abstr., Biostat., Compumath, Curr.Cont., Eng.Ind., J.Cont.Quant.Meth., Math.R., Oper.Res.Manage.Sci., Psychol.Abstr., Qual.Contr.Appl.Stat., Risk Abstr., SSCI, World Text.Abstr.
—BLDSC (8761.050000); EI; Faxon; UnCover; SWETS; UMI. **CCC.**
Refereed Serial

620   PO   ISSN 0040-1714
TECNICA; revista de engenharia. (Text in English, Portuguese) 1925. q. Esc.1400($14) Instituto Superior Tecnico, Associacao dos Estudantes, Avda. Rovisco Pais, 1000 Lisbon, Portugal. TEL 351-1-8417410. FAX 351-1-899242. TELEX 63423 ISTUTL P. Ed. Gerardo Lisboa. adv.; bk.rev.; charts; illus. circ. 5,000. **Indexed:** Chem.Abstr., Eng.Ind., Geotech.Abstr., Sci.Abstr. **Document type:** academic/scholarly publication.

TECNICA E INDUSTRIA. see *TECHNOLOGY: COMPREHENSIVE WORKS*

TEHNICKA FIZIKA/JOURNAL OF ENGINEERING PHYSICS. see *PHYSICS*

620   YU   ISSN 0350-2597
CODEN: TEHBA5
TEHNIKA. (Includes Saobracaj (ISSN 0558-6208)) (Text in Serbo-Croatian; summaries in English, Russian) 1946. m. $50. Savez Inzenjera i Tehnicara Jugoslavije, Kneza Milosa 9, Box 187, 11000 Belgrad, Yugoslavia. Ed. Borivoje Miskovic. adv.; bk.rev.; abstr.; bibl.; charts; illus.; index. circ. 1,000. **Indexed:** Chem.Abstr., Geotech.Abstr., Met.Abstr., Ref.Zh., Sci.Abstr.
—BLDSC (8763.790000); CASDDS.
Formerly: Tehnika (ISSN 0040-2176)

TEION KOGAKU/CRYOGENIC ENGINEERING. see *PHYSICS — Heat*

TEION KOGAKU CHODENDO GAKKAI KOEN GAIYOSHU/MEETING ON CRYOGENICS AND SUPERCONDUCTIVITY. see *PHYSICS — Heat*

620   BU   ISSN 0040-2168
CODEN: TKMSBM
TEKHNICESKA MISAL. (Contents page and summaries in English, German and Russian) 1964. 6/yr. 1.40 lv. per no. (Bulgarska Akademiia na Naukite) Publishing House of the Bulgarian Academy of Sciences, Acad. G. Bonchev St., Bldg. 6, 1113 Sofia, Bulgaria. (Dist. by: Hemus, 6, Rouski Blvd., 1000 Sofia, Bulgaria) Ed. Angel Balevski. bk.rev.; charts; illus.; index. circ. 2,480. (reprint service avail. from IRC) **Indexed:** BSL Geo., BSL Math., Chem.Abstr., Cyb.Abstr., Met.Abstr., Sci.Abstr., World Alum.Abstr.
—BLDSC (0180.350000); CASDDS.

620   DK   ISSN 0040-232X
TEKNISK NYT. 1963. 18/yr. free. Teknisk Forlag A-S, Skelbaekgade 4, DK-1780 Copenhagen V, Denmark. TEL 45-31-21-68-01. FAX 45-31-21-04-01. Ed. Erik Buhl. bk.rev.; charts; illus.; circ. 18,522 (controlled).
Description: Provides information to engineers and technicians in the design phase about new products in engineering, electrical and chemical technology, plastics and process automation.

620   DK
TEKNISK NYTS LEVERANDOERREGISTER. a. Teknisk Forlag A - S, Skelbaekgade 4, DK-1717 Copenhagen V, Denmark. TEL 01-21680180-55. FAX 01-212396. TELEX 16368 TEKFO DK. adv. circ. 18,522.

620   NO   ISSN 0040-2354
CODEN: TUGEAJ
TEKNISK UKEBLAD; technology review weekly. Short title: T U. (Supplement avail.: Oekonomisk Teknisk Utsyn (ISSN 0332-8759)) 1854. w. NOK 750($45) (Norske Sivilingenioerers Forening - Norwegian Society of Chartered Engineers) Ingenioerforlaget AS, P.O. Box 2476, N-Solli, 0202 Oslo, Norway. TEL 47-22-94-76-00. FAX 47-22-94-76-01. (Co-sponsors: Polytekniske Forening - Polytechnical Society; Norges Ingenioerorganisajon - Association of Norwegian Engineers) Ed. Erik B. Olimb. adv.; bk.rev.; charts; illus.; tr.lit.; index. circ. 70,000. (back issues avail.) **Indexed:** C.I.S.Abstr, Chem.Abstr., Met.Abstr., Sci.Abstr., SCIMP.
—CASDDS.
Incorporates (1930-1967): Teknikk (ISSN 0371-6341)

683.83   FR
TELEX MECANIQUE CHAUDRONNERIE. m. Groupe Alain Thirion, 6 rue Jean Viriot, 88000 Epinal, France. TEL 29-82-26-01. FAX 29-35-07-97. TELEX 960 432 F. Ed. M. Thirion. bk.rev. circ. 15,000.
Description: Reviews engineering and boilermaking.

620   US
TENNESSEE PROFESSIONAL ENGINEER. 1981. bi-m. $25. (Tennessee Society of Professional Engineers) Stewart Thomas, 3575 Earhart Rd., Mt. Juliet, TN 37122-3731. (Co-sponsor: Consulting Engineers of Tennessee)

TEORETICHESKIE OSNOVY KHIMICHESKOI TEKHNOLOGII. see *CHEMISTRY*

TEST ENGINEERING & MANAGEMENT. see *AERONAUTICS AND SPACE FLIGHT*

620   US   ISSN 0893-7877
TA1
TEXAS INSTRUMENTS TECHNICAL JOURNAL. 1984. bi-m. Texas Instruments, Box 650311, Mail Sta. 3940, Dallas, TX 75265. TEL 214-917-3906. FAX 214-917-3850. Ed. Sue Hood. circ. 14,800 (controlled).
Formerly (until 1986): Texas Instruments Engineering Journal (ISSN 0882-2557)

620   US   ISSN 0040-4632
TEXAS PROFESSIONAL ENGINEER. 1942. bi-m. $10 to non-members. Texas Society of Professional Engineers, Box 2145, Austin, TX 78768. TEL 512-472-9286. Ed. Ed O'Donnell. adv.; bk.rev.; illus. circ. 8,500.

TEXTURES AND MICROSTRUCTURES. see *EARTH SCIENCES — Geology*

THIN SOLID FILMS; an international journal on the science and technology of condensed matter films. see *PHYSICS*

620   SA   ISSN 0040-6589
THROB. 1963. 5/yr. membership. University of Natal, Students Engineering Society, King George IV Ave., Durban 4001, South Africa. Ed. James Knox. adv. circ. 1,000.

TOBA SHOSEN KOTO SENMON GAKKO KIYO/TOBA NATIONAL COLLEGE OF MARITIME TECHNOLOGY BULLETIN. see *TRANSPORTATION — Ships And Shipping*

620   JA   ISSN 0285-3817
TA4   CODEN: TKDRDA
TOHOKU KOGYO DAIGAKU KIYO, 1. RIKOGAKU HEN/TOHOKU INSTITUTE OF TECHNOLOGY. MEMOIRS. SERIES 1. SCIENCE AND ENGINEERING. (Text in English and Japanese; summaries in English) 1981. a. exchange basis only. Tohoku Kogyo Daigaku - Tohoku Institute of Technology, 35-1 Kasumi-cho, Yagiyama, Taihaku-ku, Sendai-shi, Miyagi-ken 982, Japan. Ed. Tadashi Kuroda. circ. 730. (back issues avail.) **Indexed:** Chem.Abstr., INIS Atomind., Jap.Per.Ind.
—BLDSC (5636.870000); CASDDS.
Supersedes (in 1981): Tohoku Institute of Technology. Bulletin. Section B. Sciences and Technology.

620   CN   ISSN 0049-4038
TOIKE OIKE. 1911. irreg. (5-7/yr.). Can.$2. University of Toronto Engineering Society, Sandford Fleming Bldg, Rm. SF B67, 10 King's College Rd., Toronto, Ont. M5S 1A4, Canada. Ed. Jeremy Bateson. adv. circ. 20,000. (tabloid format)

TOKYO DAIGAKU TEOIN SENTA DAYORI/UNIVERSITY OF TOKYO. CRYOGENIC CENTER. REPORT. see PHYSICS — Heat

620 621   JA   ISSN 0288-5530
TOKYO DENKI UNIVERSITY. FACULTY OF ENGINEERING. GENERAL EDUCATION. RESEARCH REPORTS. (Text in Japanese; summaries in English and Japanese) 1982. a. members only. Tokyo Denki Daigaku, Kogakubu - Tokyo Denki University, Faculty of Engineering, 2-2 Kanda Nishiki-cho, Chiyoda-ku, Tokyo 101, Japan. (back issues avail.)

620 621   JA   ISSN 0389-617X
CODEN: RPFUD8
TOKYO DENKI UNIVERSITY. FACULTY OF ENGINEERING. RESEARCH REPORTS/TOKYO DENKI DAIGAKU KOGAKUBU KENKYU HOKOKU. (Text in English, Japanese) 1951. a. members only. Tokyo Denki University, Faculty of Engineering - Tokyo Denki Daigaku Kogakubu, 2-2 Kanda Nishiki-cho, Chiyoda-ku, Tokyo 101, Japan. (back issues avail.) Indexed: INIS Atomind., JCT, JTA, Sci.Abstr. —BLDSC (7761.719000); CASDDS.

621.3   JA   ISSN 0388-1989
TOKYO DENKI UNIVERSITY. FACULTY OF SCIENCE AND ENGINEERING. RESEARCH ACTIVITIES/TOKYO DENKI DAIGAKU RIKOGAKUBU KIYO. (Text in English and Japanese; summaries in English) 1979. a. free. Tokyo Denki Daigaku, Rikogakubu - Tokyo Denki University, Faculty of Science and Engineering, Ishisaka, Hatoyama-cho, Hiki-gun, Saitama-ken 350-03, Japan. TEL 0492-96-2911. FAX 0492-96-0501. abstr. circ. 900. (also avail. in microfiche) Document type: academic/scholarly publication.
—BLDSC (7714.344000).
Description: Reports current research activities by the staff members of the Faculty of Science and Engineering.

TOOL AND ALLOY STEELS. see METALLURGY

TOPICS IN APPLIED PHYSICS. see PHYSICS

620   US
TOPICS IN BOUNDARY ELEMENTS RESEARCH. 1984. irreg. price varies. Springer-Verlag, 175 Fifth Ave., New York, NY 10010. TEL 212-460-1500. FAX 212-473-6272. (Also: Berlin, Heidelberg, Tokyo, Vienna) (reprint service avail. from ISI) Document type: monographic series.

620   JA
TOYO ENGINEERING CORPORATION. ANNUAL REPORT. a. Toyo Engineering Corporation, Public Relations Department, 3-2-5 Kasumigaseki, Kasumigaseki Bldg., Chiyoda-ku, Tokyo 100, Japan. TEL 03-3592-7411. FAX 03-3593-0749. Document type: corporate report.

620   JA   ISSN 0285-175X
TOYOOKI GIHO/TOYOOKI ENGINEERING REVIEW. (Text in Japanese) 1970. a. Toyooki Kogyo K.K., Seigyo Gijutsubu, 45, Kaizan, Hachi-cho, Okazaki-shi, Aichi-ken 444-35, Japan.

621.3   BE   ISSN 0774-3998
TRACTEBEL. ANNUAL REPORT. (Editions in Dutch, English, French) 1896. a. free. Tractebel s.a., Service Secretariat, 1 place du Trone, B-1000 Brussels, Belgium. Ed. A. Pirard. charts; illus.; stat. circ. 25,000. Document type: corporate report.
Formerly (until 1986): Tractionel. Annual Report (ISSN 0770-9595)
Description: Features information on the activities of all divisions of the Tractebel group.

658.5 670   US
TRANSACTIONS OF THE NORTH AMERICAN MANUFACTURING RESEARCH CONFERENCE. PROCEEDINGS. 1972. a. $75. Society of Manufacturing Engineers, One SME Dr., Box 930, Dearborn, MI 48121. TEL 313-271-1500. FAX 313-271-2861. TELEX 297742 SME UR (VIA RCA). circ. 600. Document type: proceedings.
Former titles: North American Manufacturing Research Conference. Proceedings; North American Manufacturing Research Conference (Publication); Manufacturing Engineering. Engineering Transactions (ISSN 0363-700X); S M E Transactions; North American Metalworking Research Conference. Proceedings (ISSN 0146-132X)

TRANSLATION SERIES IN MATHEMATICS AND ENGINEERING. see MATHEMATICS

TRANSMISSION AND DISTRIBUTION. see ENGINEERING — Electrical Engineering

TRANSMISSION & DISTRIBUTION INTERNATIONAL. see ENGINEERING — Electrical Engineering

LE TREFILE; revue technique internationale pour l'industrie du fil et du cable et tous les domaines de la transformation du fil metallique. see ENGINEERING — Electrical Engineering

620   US   ISSN 1064-4156
▼TRENCHLESS TECHNOLOGY. 1992. m. $59 (effective 1994). Trenchless Technology, Inc., 6138 Riverview Rd., Peninsula, OH 44264. TEL 216-467-7588. FAX 216-468-2289. Ed. Paul J. Miller. adv.: B&W page $2470, color page $3365; trim 8 1/8 x 10 7/8; adv. contact: Bernard P. Krzys. bk.rev. circ. 20,000. Document type: trade publication.
Description: Covers the various underground construction methods which eliminate or minimize surface disruption.

620   US   ISSN 0041-2317
TREND IN ENGINEERING. 1948. s-a. free to qualified personnel. University of Washington, College of Engineering, Office of the Dean of Engineering, Seattle, WA 98195. TEL 206-543-2520. FAX 206-685-0666. bk.rev.; bibl.; illus.; index, cum.index every 2 yrs. circ. 25,000. (tabloid format; also avail. in microform from UMI; back issues avail.; reprint service avail. from UMI) Indexed: Appl.Mech.Rev., Chem.Abstr., Eng.Ind. Document type: newsletter.

TRUCK & OFF-HIGHWAY INDUSTRIES. see TRANSPORTATION — Trucks And Trucking

620   UK   ISSN 0886-7798
TA800
TUNNELLING AND UNDERGROUND SPACE TECHNOLOGY. 1986. 4/yr. £255($395) (effective 1994). (International Tunnelling Association) Elsevier Science Ltd., Pergamon, P.O. Box 800, Kidlington, Oxford OX5 1DX, England. TEL 44-865-843000. FAX 44-865-843010. (Subscr. in U.S. and Canada to: Elsevier Science, 660 White Plains Rd., Tarrytown, NY 10591-5153. TEL 914-524-9200. FAX 914-333-2444) Eds. Einar Broch, Charles Fairhurst. (also avail. in microfilm from UMI; back issues avail.) Indexed: Environ.Per.Bibl., Geotech.Abstr., Intl.Civil Eng.Abstr., Soft.Abstr.Eng. Document type: academic/scholarly publication.
—BLDSC (9071.405000); EI; Faxon; UnCover; SWETS; UMI. CCC.
Formed by the merger of (1981-1986): Advances in Tunnelling Technology and Subsurface Use (ISSN 0275-5416); (1977-1986): Underground Space (ISSN 0362-0565); Which was formerly: Underground Space as an Urban Resource.
Refereed Serial

TUNNELLING DIRECTORY; an international yearbook of consultants and companies in sub-surface construction. see ENGINEERING — Civil Engineering

620 614   TU
CODEN: DMCBEY
TURKISH JOURNAL OF ENGINEERING AND ENVIRONMENTAL SCIENCES/TURK MUHENDISLIK VE CEVRE BILIMLERI DERGISI. (Text in English, Turkish) 1976. bi-m. $50. Scientific and Technical Research Council of Turkey - TUBITAK - Turkiye Bilimsel ve Teknik Arastirma Kurumu, Ataturk Bulvari, No. 221, Kavaklidere, 06100 Ankara, Turkey. TEL 90-312-4685300. FAX 90-312-4271336. TELEX 43186 BTAK TR. Ed. Cahit Ozgur. Indexed: Agri.Eng.Abstr., Biol.Abstr., I D A, INIS Atomind. Document type: academic/scholarly publication. —BLDSC (3614.642470); CASDDS.
Former titles (until 1984): Doga Turkish Journal of Engineering and Environmental Science - Doga Turk Muhendislik ve Cevre Bilimleri Dergisi (ISSN 1010-7606); Doga Bilim Dergisi. Series B: Engineering - Environmental Science.
Refereed Serial

620 910.03   US   ISSN 1058-2428
U S BLACK ENGINEER. 1980. bi-m. $15. Career Communications Group, Inc., 729 E. Pratt St., Ste. 504, Baltimore, MD 21202. TEL 410-244-7101. FAX 410-528-1837. adv. circ. 15,250.
Formerly: Umoja Sasa News Journal.

620   US
U S C ENGINEER. s-a. University of Southern California, Olin Hall - Engineering, Ste. 106, Los Angeles, CA 90089-1455. TEL 213-740-4530. FAX 213-740-8690. Ed. Nancie Mack. circ. 5,000.

620   US   ISSN 0272-7838
TA1
U S WOMAN ENGINEER. 1954. 6/yr. $20 to non-members. Society of Women Engineers, 120 Wall St., New York, NY 10005-3902. TEL 212-705-7355. FAX 212-319-0947. Ed. Anne M. Perusek. adv.; bk.rev.; charts; illus. circ. 16,500. —BLDSC (9124.780500).
Formerly: Society of Women Engineers. Newsletter (ISSN 0038-0067)

620   TZ   ISSN 0856-3152
UHANDISI. (Text in English) vol.2, 1975. s-a. Sh.1000($5) University of Dar es Salaam, Faculty of Engineering, Box 35131, Dar es Salaam, Tanzania. TELEX 41854 UNENG TZ. Ed. Bashira Majaja. adv.; bk.rev. circ. 200.

ULTRAHIGH SPEED AND HIGH SPEED PHOTOGRAPHY, PHOTONICS, AND VIDEOGRAPHY. see PHOTOGRAPHY

ULTRASONICS SYMPOSIUM. PROCEEDINGS. see PHYSICS — Sound

620 690   US
UNDERNEATH IT ALL. 1990. q. $3 per no. Associated Utility Contractors of Maryland, 2913 Crabapple Lane, Ellicott City, MD 21042. TEL 410-750-2554. FAX 410-750-7668. adv.: B&W page $1000; trim 7 3/8 x 10. circ. 3,000 (controlled).

UNITED KINGDOM ATOMIC ENERGY AUTHORITY. ANNUAL REPORT. see ENERGY — Nuclear Energy

620   US
U.S. ARMY. CORPS OF ENGINEERS. INFORMATION EXCHANGE BULLETIN. DREDGING RESEARCH. q. Department of the Army, Waterways Experiment Sta., Corps of Engineers, 3909 Halls Ferry Rd., Vicksburg, MS 39180-6199. TEL 601-634-2070. charts; illus.; stat. Document type: bulletin.
Description: Provides a forum whereby information on dredging research can be rapidly disseminated to Corps officers, US Government agencies, and the dredging community in general.

620   US   ISSN 0083-0313
U.S. ARMY. CORPS OF ENGINEERS. TECHNICAL REPORTS SERIES. irreg. U.S. Army, Waterways Experiment Sta., Corps of Engineers, 3909 Halls Ferry Rd., Vicksburg, MS 39180-6199. TEL 202-272-6001. (Orders from: National Technical Information Service, 5285 Port Royal Rd., Springfield, VA 22151)

ENGINEERING

623 **US**
GC1
U.S. NATIONAL OCEANIC AND ATMOSPHERIC ADMINISTRATION. NATIONAL UNDERSEA RESEARCH PROGRAM SUMMARY. 1971. irreg., latest 1993. $1. U.S. National Oceanic and Atmospheric Administration, National Undersea Research Program, Code R-OR2, SSMC-1, Rm. 5225, Silver Spring, MD 20910. TEL 301-713-2427. FAX 301-713-0799. (Orders to: NTIS, 5285 Port Royal Rd., Springfield, VA 22161) Ed. Kurt Stehling. illus. circ. 1,000. (also avail. in microfiche) **Document type:** government publication.
  Former titles (until 1984): U.S. National Oceanic and Atmospheric Administration. Undersea Research Program. Annual Report; (until 1978): Manned Undersea Science and Technology Program Report (ISSN 0092-8917)

U.S. NUCLEAR REGULATORY COMMISSION. CONSTRUCTION STATUS REPORT OF NUCLEAR POWER PLANTS. see *ENERGY — Nuclear Energy*

U.S. NUCLEAR REGULATORY COMMISSION. LICENSED OPERATING REACTORS, STATUS SUMMARY REPORT. see *ENERGY — Nuclear Energy*

620 **VE** **ISSN 0798-4065**
UNIVERSIDAD CENTRAL DE VENEZUELA. FACULTAD DE INGENIERIA. REVISTA. 1968. s-a. Universidad Central de Venezuela, Facultad de Ingenieria, Caracas, Venezuela. TEL 58-2-6626181. FAX 58-2-6627327.

526.9 **UY** **ISSN 0366-0109**
UNIVERSIDAD DE LA REPUBLICA. FACULTAD DE INGENIERIA. BOLETIN. (Text in Spanish; summaries in English and Spanish) 1935. irreg. exchange basis. Universidad de la Republica, Facultad de Ingeniera, Casilla de Correo 30, Montevideo, Uruguay. FAX 598-2-715446. TELEX 23859 FACUING UY. bk.rev.; charts; illus.; index. circ. 400. **Indexed:** Chem.Abstr., Eng.Ind., GeoRef., Sci.Abstr. **Document type:** academic/scholarly publication.
  Formerly: Universidad de la Republica. Facultad de Ingenieria y Agrimensura. Boletin (ISSN 0027-013X)

620 **SP**
UNIVERSIDAD DE SEVILLA. SERIE: INGENIERIA. irreg., latest no.7. price varies. Universidad de Sevilla, Servicio de Publicaciones, Valparaiso 5, 41013 Seville, Spain. TEL 954-231958. FAX 954-232245.
  Formerly (until 1967): Universidad Hispalense. Anales. Serie: Ingenieria.

620 **VE** **ISSN 0254-0770**
CODEN: RTFZDH
UNIVERSIDAD DE ZULIA. FACULTAD DE INGENIERIA. REVISTA TECNICA. (Text in English, Spanish) 1978. 3/yr. Bs.3000($120) Universidad de Zulia, Facultad de Ingenieria, Apdo. 10-482, Correo Bella Vista, Maracaibo, Venezuela. TEL 58-61-525730. FAX 58-61-525732. TELEX 64287. E-mail: retecin@dino.conicit.ve. Ed.Bd. adv.; bk.rev. circ. 1,000. (back issues avail.) **Indexed:** Chem.Abstr., Math.R. **Document type:** academic/scholarly publication.
  ●Also available online.
  —BLDSC (7870.930000); EI; CASDDS.
  Description: Research on all engineering fields and applied basic sciences by graduate students, faculty and other research workers.

620 610 001.3 **CK** **ISSN 0120-0852**
T4 **CODEN: RUIVAO**
UNIVERSIDAD INDUSTRIAL DE SANTANDER. REVISTA - INVESTIGACIONES. (Text in Spanish; summaries in English, French, German and Spanish) 1959. s-a. Col.$6000($8) for 2 yrs. or exchange basis. Universidad Industrial de Santander, Apdo. Aereo 678, Bucaramanga, Santander, Colombia. FAX 5776-351946. adv.; bk.rev.; bibl.; charts; illus.; stat.; cum.index every 5 yrs. circ. 1,200. **Indexed:** Met.Abstr. **Document type:** academic/scholarly publication.
  Supersedes in part (in 1969): Universidad Industrial de Santander. Revista (ISSN 0041-8587)

UNIVERSITEXTS. see *MATHEMATICS*

620 **US** **ISSN 0073-5280**
T178
UNIVERSITY OF ILLINOIS AT URBANA-CHAMPAIGN. ENGINEERING EXPERIMENT STATION. SUMMARY OF ENGINEERING RESEARCH. 1958. a. free. University of Illinois at Urbana-Champaign, College of Engineering, 112 Engineering Hall, 1308 W. Green St., Urbana, IL 61801. TEL 217-333-1510. Ed. Ann R. Sapoznik. (back issues avail.) **Document type:** academic/scholarly publication.
Refereed Serial

620 **AT** **ISSN 0811-7586**
UNIVERSITY OF NEW SOUTH WALES. FACULTY HANDBOOKS: APPLIED SCIENCE. a. Aus.$5. University of New South Wales, Kensington, N.S.W. 2052, Australia. TEL 02-697-2840. FAX 02-662-2163.

620 **AT** **ISSN 0811-7624**
UNIVERSITY OF NEW SOUTH WALES. FACULTY HANDBOOKS: ENGINEERING. a. Aus.$5. University of New South Wales, Kensington, N.S.W. 2052, Australia. TEL 02-697-2840. FAX 02-662-2163.

500 620 **JA** **ISSN 0474-7844**
TA1 **CODEN: BSKAAJ**
UNIVERSITY OF OSAKA PREFECTURE. BULLETIN. SERIES A: ENGINEERING AND NATURAL SCIENCES/OSAKA-FURITSU DAIGAKU KIYO, A. KOGAKU, SHIZEN KAGAKU. (Text in European languages) 1952. s-a. exchange basis. University of Osaka Prefecture - Osaka-furitsu Daigaku, 1-1 Gakuen-cho, Sakai-shi, Osaka 593, Japan. **Indexed:** Chem.Abstr., INIS Atomind., JTA, Math.R., Sci.Abstr. **Document type:** academic/scholarly publication.
  —BLDSC (2795.500000); EI; CASDDS.

620 375 **AT** **ISSN 1036-0670**
UNIVERSITY OF TECHNOLOGY, SYDNEY. FACULTY OF ENGINEERING HANDBOOK. 1991. a. Aus.$5 (foreign Aus.$10). University of Technology, Sydney, P.O. Box 123, City Campus, Broadway, N.S.W. 2007, Australia. TEL 02-330-1990. FAX 02-330-1551. circ. 3,000.

620 **JA** **ISSN 0040-8883**
UNIVERSITY OF TOKUSHIMA. FACULTY OF ENGINEERING. BULLETIN. (Text in English, Japanese) 1964. a. free. Tokushima Daigaku, Kogakubu - University of Tokushima, Faculty of Engineering, 2-1 Minamijosanjima-cho, Tokushima 770, Japan. TEL 0886-23-2311. FAX 0886-54-9632. Ed. Michio Hashino. charts. circ. 600. **Indexed:** JTA, Sci.Abstr. **Document type:** bulletin.
  Incorporates (in 1993): University of Tokushima. Faculty of Engineering. Scientific Papers.

620 **JA** **ISSN 0563-7937**
CODEN: JETBAN
UNIVERSITY OF TOKYO. FACULTY OF ENGINEERING. JOURNAL: SERIES B/TOKYO DAIGAKU KOGAKUBU KIYO B. (Text in European languages; summaries in English) 1898. s-a. exchange basis. University of Tokyo, Faculty of Engineering - Tokyo Daigaku Kogakubu, 7-3-1 Hongo, Bunkyo-ku, Tokyo 113, Japan. TEL 03-3812-2111. FAX 03-3818-0643. Ed. Hajime Okamura. circ. 1,250. (reprint service avail. from UMI) **Indexed:** CAD CAM Abstr., Chem.Abstr., Energy Info.Abstr., Eng.Ind., Environ.Abstr., GeoRef., INIS Atomind., JCT, JTA, Math.R., Met.Abstr., Sci.Abstr., Soft.Abstr.Eng. **Document type:** academic/scholarly publication.
  —BLDSC (4744.502000); UnCover; CASDDS.
  Description: Covers housing and urban planning, machinery, electricity and electrical engineering, architecture, chemistry, physics, transportation, atomics, metallurgy, mines, and mine engineering.

620 **US** **ISSN 0193-9637**
TA1
UNIVERSITY OF WISCONSIN, MADISON. COLLEGE OF ENGINEERING. ANNUAL REPORT. 1976. a. free. University of Wisconsin - Madison, 215 N. Randall Ave., Madison, WI 53706-1688. TEL 608-263-5988. FAX 608-263-9259. Ed. Karen Walsh. charts; illus.; circ. 6,500 (controlled). **Document type:** corporate report.
  Formerly: University of Wisconsin, Madison. Engineering Experiment Station. Annual Report (ISSN 0193-9629)

620 **US**
UNIVERSITY SERIES IN MODERN ENGINEERING. 1983. irreg. price varies. (Optimization Software Inc., New York) Springer-Verlag, 175 Fifth Ave., New York, NY 10010. TEL 212-460-1500. FAX 212-473-6272. (Also: Berlin, Heidelberg, Tokyo and Vienna) (reprint service avail. from ISI) **Document type:** monographic series.
Refereed Serial

620 **PL** **ISSN 0208-5402**
UNIWERSYTET SLASKI W KATOWICACH. PRACE NAUKOWE. PRACE WYDZIALU TECHNIKI. (Text in Polish; summaries in English and Russian) 1969. irreg. price varies. Wydawnictwo Uniwersytetu Slaskiego, Ul. Bankowa 12B, 40-007 Katowice, Poland. TEL 48-22-596-915. FAX 48-32-599-605. TELEX 48-32-315584 USKPL. (Dist. by: CHZ Ars Polona, P.O. Box 1001, 00-950 Warsaw, Poland) Ed. Barbara Woznica. **Document type:** academic/scholarly publication.
  Description: Covers engineering, scientific-technical information, electronics.

USINE. see *BUSINESS AND ECONOMICS — Management*

620 **GW** **ISSN 0083-5560**
TA3 **CODEN: VDIBAP**
V D I - BERICHTE. 1954. irreg. (20-30/yr.). price varies. (Verein Deutscher Ingenieure) V D I Verlag GmbH, Heinrichstr. 24, 40239 Duesseldorf, Germany. TEL 0211-6188-0. FAX 0211-6188-112. (Subscr. to: Postfach 101054, 40001 Duesseldorf, Germany) circ. 500. (also avail. in microform from PMC) **Indexed:** Chem.Abstr., Cyb.Abstr., Eng.Ind., Int.Aerosp.Abstr., Sh.& Vib.Dig., W.R.C.Inf. **Document type:** trade publication.
  —BLDSC (9150.240000); SWETS; CASDDS. **CCC.**

620 **GW** **ISSN 0042-1758**
CODEN: VDNAAD
V D I - NACHRICHTEN. (Verein Deutscher Ingenieure); Wochenzeitung fuer Technik und Wirtschaft, Wissenschaft und Gesellschaft. 1947. w. (Fri.). DM.199($85) V D I Verlag GmbH, Heinrichstr. 24, 40239 Duesseldorf, Germany. TEL 0211-6188-0. FAX 0211-6188-112. TELEX 8587743-VDI-D. (Subscr. to: Postfach 101054, 40001 Duesseldorf, Germany) Ed. Rudolf Schulze. adv. contact: Christel Koenigsbuescher. bk.rev.; bibl.; charts; illus.; mkt.; pat.; tr.lit.; index. circ. 155,433. (tabloid format) **Indexed:** Fluidex, Met.Abstr., Packag.Sci.Tech., World Alum.Abstr. **Document type:** newspaper.
  —CCC.

620 **GW** **ISSN 0042-1766**
TA3 **CODEN: VZGTAJ**
V D I - Z. (Verein Deutscher Ingenieure); Zeitschrift des Vereins Deutscher Ingenieure fuer Maschinenbau und Metallbearbeitung. (Includes 6 special editions) (Text in German; summaries in English) 1858. 12/yr. DM.365($141.50) V D I Verlag GmbH, Heinrichstr. 24, 40239 Duesseldorf, Germany. TEL 0211-6188-0. FAX 0211-6188-112. TELEX 8587-743. (Subscr. to: Postfach 101054, 40001 Duesseldorf, Germany) Ed. H.D. Jorissen. adv.; bk.rev.; charts; illus.; index. circ. 12,000. **Indexed:** Appl.Mech.Rev., BMT, Chem.Abstr., Eng.Ind., Excerp.Med., Fluidex, Fuel & Energy Abstr., Int.Aerosp.Abstr., Intl.Civil Eng.Abstr., Met.Abstr., Sci.Abstr., Sh.& Vib.Dig., Soft.Abstr.Eng. **Document type:** newspaper.
  —BLDSC (9150.290800); EI; SWETS; CASDDS. **CCC.**
  Incorporates (in 1993): Ingenieur Werkstoffe (ISSN 0935-5715); **Formerly:** V D I - Zeitschrift.

620 **SZ**
V S A M ANGESTELLTEN REVUE. 1919. 11/yr. membership. Rigiplatz 1, CH-8006 Zurich, Switzerland. TEL 01-3635154. FAX 01-3637978. Ed. W. Rindlisbacher. circ. 22,000. **Document type:** bulletin.

VAKUUM IN DER PRAXIS. see *PHYSICS*

VALUE ENGINEERING AND MANAGEMENT DIGEST - DEFENSE CONTRACT GUIDE. see *BUSINESS AND ECONOMICS — Management*

VENDOR CATALOG SERVICES INDEX. see *BUSINESS AND ECONOMICS — Trade And Industrial Directories*

VENTURI. see *COLLEGE AND ALUMNI*

ENGINEERING

620   GW   ISSN 0175-5315
VERFAHRENSTECHNIK. 10/yr. DM.120 (foreign DM.130). Vereinigte Fachverlage GmbH, Lise-Meitner-Str. 2, 55129 Mainz, Germany. TEL 06131-992-01. FAX 06131-992-100. TELEX 04187752. (Subscr. to: Postfach 2760, 55017 Mainz, Germany)
—SWETS.

LE VIDE, LES COUCHES MINCES. see *PHYSICS*

620   UK   ISSN 0042-5958
VIGILANCE. 1967. 2/yr. free. National Vulcan Engineering Insurance Group Ltd., St. Mary's Parsonage, Manchester M60 9AP, England. FAX 061-834-2394. TELEX 667955-BOILER-G. Ed. M. Cashman. illus.; index, cum.index every 3 yrs. circ. 22,000. **Indexed:** C.I.S. Abstr., ISMEC.
Supersedes: Vulcan.

620   US
VILLANOVA ENGINEER. 4/yr. Villanova University, School of Engineers, Box 214, Villanova, PA 19085-0214. TEL 215-645-4447. Ed. Chris Cheeseman. circ. 1,400.

620   US   ISSN 0504-4251
VIRGINIA ENGINEER. 1951. m. $15. Richard Carden, Ed. & Pub., Rte. 2, Box 58, Cumberland, VA 23040. TEL 804-492-4578. FAX 804-492-9423. adv.; bk.rev. circ. 3,700. (back issues avail.) **Document type:** trade publication.

620   II   ISSN 0042-6881
VISHWAKARMA. (Text in English) 1960. m. Rs.150. O. N. Pandeya, 105-C Block F, New Alipore, Calcutta 700053, India. Ed. L.K. Pandeya.

620   US   ISSN 0042-7136
VISTI UKRAYINS'KYKH INZHENERIV/UKRAINIAN ENGINEERING NEWS. (Contents page and summaries in English) 1950. q. $12. (Tovarystvo Ukrayins'kykh Inzheneriv Ameryki) Ukrainian Engineers' Society of America, 2 E. 79th St., New York, NY 10021. TEL 212-535-7676. (Co-sponsor: Ukrayins'ke Tekhnichne Toyarystvo V Kanadi) Ed. George Honczarenko. adv.; bk.rev.; charts; illus.; index. circ. 1,000. **Indexed:** Amer.Bibl.Slavic & E.Eur.Stud.

VOCI DEL NOSTRO TEMPO. see *LITERATURE*

624 552   RU
VOPROSY TEORII RAZRABOTKI MESTOROZHDENII POLEZNYKH ISKOPAEMYKH. a. 0.85 Rub. (Akademiya Nauk S.S.S.R., Institut Fiziki Zemli) Izdatel'stvo Nauka, 90 Profsoyuznaya ul., 117864 Moscow, Russia. TEL 234-05-84.

621   XR   ISSN 0862-2477
VYSOKA SKOLA BANSKA V OSTRAVE. SBORNIK VEDECKYCH PRACI: RADA STROJNI A ELEKTROTECHNICKA. (Text in Czech; summaries in Czech, English, German, Russian) 1967. irreg. 25 Kcs.($1) per no. Statni Pedagogicke Nakladatelstvi, Ostrovni 30, 113 01 Prague 1, Czech Republic. Ed. L. Kuchar. charts; illus.; index. circ. 600. **Indexed:** Met.Abstr., Nutr.Abstr.
Former titles (until 1982): Vysoka Skola Banska v Ostrave. Sbornik Vedeckych Praci: Rada Strojni (ISSN 0322-9335); (until 1973): Vysoka Skola Banska v Ostrave. Sbornik Vedeckych Praci: Rada Strojnicka (ISSN 0862-2485)

620   US
W B K FORSCHUNGSBERICHTE. (Text in German) 1980. irreg. price varies. (Universitaet Karlsruhe, Institut fuer Werkzeugmaschinen und Betriebstechnik, GW) Springer-Verlag, 175 Fifth Ave., New York, NY 10010. TEL 212-460-1500. FAX 212-473-6272. (Also: Berlin, Heidelberg, Tokyo and Vienna) Ed. H. Victor. (reprint service avail. from ISI) **Document type:** monographic series.
Formerly: W B K.

620   US
W F T - WERKSTOFF-FORSCHUNG UND -TECHNIK. 1984. irreg. price varies. Springer-Verlag, 175 Fifth Ave., New York, NY 10010. TEL 212-460-1500. FAX 212-473-6272. (Also: Berlin, Heidelberg, Tokyo and Vienna) (reprint service avail. from ISI) **Document type:** monographic series.

620   US   ISSN 0148-6128
TA1
W P I JOURNAL. 1897. q. free. Worcester Polytechnic Institute, Worcester, MA 01609. TEL 508-831-5609. FAX 508-831-5604. Ed. Michael W. Dorsey. bk.rev.; illus. circ. 24,000.
Formerly: Worcester Polytechnic Institute. Journal (ISSN 0043-7913)
Description: Covers science, technology, management and education for alumni and friends of the institute.

WASEDA DAIGAKU RIKOGAKU KENKYUJO HOKOKU/WASEDA UNIVERSITY. SCIENCE AND ENGINEERING RESEARCH LABORATORY. BULLETIN. see *SCIENCES: COMPREHENSIVE WORKS*

WASEDA UNIVERSITY. SCIENCE AND ENGINEERING RESEARCH LABORATORY. REPORT. see *SCIENCES: COMPREHENSIVE WORKS*

620   US   ISSN 0049-7037
WAYNE ENGINEER. 1934. bi-m. $2.50. Wayne State University, College of Engineering, Detroit, MI 48202. TEL 313-577-2424. Ed. Herman Yee. adv.; bk.rev. circ. 2,700.

658.5 389.6 681.2   UK
WEIGHING & MEASURING DIRECTORY; buyers guide. 1985. a. £15($20) Lincoln Publications, 28 Centre Point House, St. Giles High St., London WC2 8LW, England. TEL 071-240-5562. FAX 071-497-2811. Ed. James Hardwick. circ. 2,500. (back issues avail.) **Document type:** directory.
Description: Examines all aspects of industrial equipment, load sensors and transducers and computerized systems.

620   UK
WEIR BULLETIN. 1920. q. free. Weir Group PLC, 149 Newlands Rd., Cathcart, Glasgow G44 4EX, Scotland. TEL 041-637-7111. FAX 041-637-2221. Ed. Emrys Inker. circ. 19,000. (tabloid format) **Document type:** bulletin.

WERKSTATT UND BETRIEB; Zeitschrift fuer Maschinenbau, Konstruktion und Fertigung. see *MACHINERY*

620   US
WHAT EVERY ENGINEER SHOULD KNOW ABOUT SERIES. 1979. irreg., vol.31, 1993. price varies. Marcel Dekker, Inc., 270 Madison Ave., New York, NY 10016. TEL 212-696-9000. FAX 212-685-4540. TELEX 421419. **Document type:** monographic series.

620   UK
WHAT'S NEW IN DESIGN. m. Morgan-Grampian (Publishers) Ltd. (Subsidiary of: Morgan-Grampian plc), Morgan-Grampian House, 30 Calderwood St., London SE18 6QH, England. TEL 081-855-7777. FAX 081-854-7476. Ed. Nick Smith. adv. contact: Paul Connolly. circ. 32,000. **Document type:** trade publication.

620   AT   ISSN 0819-5447
WHAT'S NEW IN PROCESS ENGINEERING. 1987. m. Aus.$48. Westwick-Farrow Pty. Ltd., Cnr. Fox Valley Rd. and Kiogle St., Wahroonga, N.S.W. 2076, Australia. TEL 02-487-2700. FAX 02-489-1265. Ed. Suneel Prasad. adv.; circ. 9,200 (controlled). (back issues avail.)
Description: New product items of interest to the manufacturing and mining industries.

WHO'S WHO IN ENGINEERING. see *BIOGRAPHY*

WHO'S WHO IN ENVIRONMENTAL ENGINEERING. see *ENVIRONMENTAL STUDIES*

WHO'S WHO IN SCIENCE AND ENGINEERING. see *BIOGRAPHY*

620   AU
WIRTSCHAFTSINGENIEUR. q. Raiffeisenstr. 118-120, A-8041 Graz - Liebenau, Austria. TEL 0316-465519. FAX 0316-46551917. circ. 2,500.

620   US   ISSN 0043-6453
TA1   CODEN: WISEAS
WISCONSIN ENGINEER. 1896. 4/yr. $10. Wisconsin Engineering Journal Association, Mechanical Engineering Bldg., Univ. of Wisconsin, Madison, WI 53706. adv.; bk.rev.; charts; illus.; tr.lit.; index. circ. 3,000. **Indexed:** Chem.Abstr.
—BLDSC (9325.670000).

620   US   ISSN 0043-6615
WISCONSIN PROFESSIONAL ENGINEER. 1960. m. (Sep.-Jun.). $28 to non-members. Wisconsin Society of Professional Engineers, 6425 Odana Rd., Ste. D, Madison, WI 53719-1199. TEL 608-274-8555. Ed. Karen R. Brey. adv.; bk.rev.; illus. circ. 1,726.
Description: Geared towards the engineering professional in the state of Wisconsin.

620   UK   ISSN 0043-7298
THE WOMAN ENGINEER. 1919. 4/yr. £18 (foreign £20). Women's Engineering Society, Imperial College of Science and Technology, Dept. of Civil Engineering, mperial College Rd., London SW7 2BU. TEL 071-58C-5111. Ed. Rowena Palser. adv.: B&W page £250; trim 270 x 190. bk.rev.; charts; illus. circ. 1,250. **Indexed:** Stud.Wom.Abstr. **Document type:** trade publication.
—BLDSC (9343.000000).

620 331.4   US   ISSN 0887-2120
TA157
WOMAN ENGINEER. 1980. 3/yr. $17. Equal Opportunity Publications, Inc., 150 Motor Pkwy. No. 420, Hauppauge, NY 11788-5108. TEL 516-261-3899. FAX 516-261-8935. Ed. Anne Kelly. adv.; bk.rev.; illus. circ. 16,000.
—UnCover.
Description: Entry-level and professional career magazine for women engineers.

620 500   US
WOMEN AND MINORITIES IN SCIENCE AND ENGINEERING. 1982. q. $40 to individuals; institutions $75. (Virginia Polytechnic Institute) Begell House Inc., 79 Madison Ave., New York, NY 10016-7892. TEL 212-213-8368. FAX 212-725-1999. **Document type:** academic/scholarly publication.
Description: Publishes original papers that report innovative ideas and programs, scientific studies and formulation of concepts related to the education, recruitment, and retention of underrepresented groups in science and engineering.
Refereed Serial

WORLDWIDE PIPELINES AND CONTRACTORS DIRECTORY. see *PETROLEUM AND GAS*

620   US   ISSN 0192-5512
TA1
WORLDWIDE PROJECTS. 1967-1987; N.S. 1993. 4/yr. $38 (foreign $48). (American Society of Civil Engineers) Intercontinental Media, 25 Sylvan Rd. S., Ste. R, Westport, CT 06880. TEL 203-226-7463. (Subscr. to: ASCE, 345 E. 47th St., New York, NY 10017-2398. TEL 800-548-ASCE. FAX 212-705-7179) Ed. Virginia Fairweather. adv. circ. 16,000. **Document type:** trade publication.
Formerly: Worldwide Projects and Installation Planning (ISSN 0091-4800)
Description: Market news for international design engineers and construction companies.

620   PL   ISSN 0510-9884
WYCHOWANIE TECHNICZNE W SZKOLE. 1961. 6/yr. $24. (Ministerstwo Edukacji Narodowej) Wydawnictwa Szkolne i Pedagogiczne, Ul. Pankiewicza 3, 00-596 Warsaw, Poland. TEL 48-22-265451. (Dist. by: Ars Polona-Ruch, Krakowskie Przedmiescie 7, Warsaw, Poland) Ed. Barbara Zarzecka. circ. 4,800.
Description: For technical education teachers.

620   PL   ISSN 0324-8992
WYZSZA SZKOLA PEDAGOGICZNA, OPOLE. ZESZYTY NAUKOWE. SERIA A. NAUKI TECHNICZNE. (Text in Polish; summaries in English and Russian) 1975. irreg., vol.18, 1993. price varies or exchange basis. Wyzsza Szkola Pedagogiczna, Opole, Oleska 48, 45-951 Opole, Poland. TEL 48-77-383-87. (Dist. by: Ars Polona-Ruch, Krakowskie Przedmiescie 7, Warsaw, Poland) Ed. Maksymilian Gajek. **Document type:** academic/scholarly publication.
—BLDSC (9512.478988).

620   CH   ISSN 1017-4397
         CODEN: XGXUEY
XINGDA GONGCHENG XUEBAO/NATIONAL CHUNG HSING UNIVERSITY. JOURNAL OF ENGINEERING. (Text in Chinese; summaries in English) 1964. a. National Chung Hsing University, College of Engineering, Taipei, Taiwan, Republic of China. **Document type:** academic/scholarly publication.
—BLDSC (4978.390000); CASDDS.
Formerly (until 1990): Li-gong Xuebao (ISSN 0459-1887)

2270 ENGINEERING — ABSTRACTING, BIBLIOGRAPHIES, STATISTICS

620   CC   ISSN 1000-5781
XITONG GONGCHENG XUEBAO/JOURNAL OF SYSTEMS ENGINEERING. (Text in Chinese, abstracts in Chinese, English) 1986. s-a. (effective 1994). Tianjin Daxue, Xitong Gongcheng Yanjiusuo - Tianjin University, Systems Engineering Institute, Tianjin 300072, People's Republic of China. TEL 022-358116. FAX 022-358329. Ed. Liu Bao. **Document type:** academic/scholarly publication.

620 550   JA   ISSN 0914-9481
YAMAGUCHI GANBAN KENKYU/YAMAGUCHI ROCK ENGINEERING SOCIETY. SELECTED RESEARCH. (Text in English, Japanese) 1986. irreg. Yamaguchi Ganban Kogaku Kenkyukai, Yamaguchi Daigaku Kogakubu, Tokiwadai, Ube-shi, Yamaguchi-ken 755, Japan. **Document type:** academic/scholarly publication.

620   JA   ISSN 0513-2592
TA4   CODEN: BFEYA4
YOKOHAMA NATIONAL UNIVERSITY. FACULTY OF ENGINEERING. BULLETIN/YOKOHAMA KOKURITSU DAIGAKU KOGAKUBU KIYO. (Text in English and European languages) 1951. a. exchange basis. Yokohama Kokuritsu Daigaku, Kogakubu - Yokohama National University, Faculty of Engineering, 156 Tokiwadai, Hodogaya-ku, Yokohama-shi, Kanagawa-ken 240, Japan. circ. 800. **Indexed:** Chem.Abstr., JTA, Met.Abstr., Sci.Abstr., World Alum.Abstr.
—BLDSC (2508.200000); CASDDS.

620   JA
YUKI. (Text in Japanese) 1990. q. Yuki Senta - Snow Control Research Center, 5-12, Motoakasaka 1-chome, Minato-ku, Tokyo 107, Japan.

620   JA   ISSN 0913-2295
YUKI KOGAKU SHINPOJUMU RONBUN HOKOKUSHU/PROCEEDINGS OF SYMPOSIUM ON SNOW ENGINEERING. (Text in Japanese) 1985. a. Nihon Yuki Kogakkai - Japan Society for Snow Engineering, Nihon Gakkai Jimu Senta, 16-9, Honkogagome 5-chome, Bunkyo-ku, Tokyo 113, Japan. **Document type:** proceedings.

YUNYI TEKHNIK. see *CHILDREN AND YOUTH — For*

Z W F - C I M. (Zeitschrift fuer Wirtschaftliche Fertigung und Automatisierung) see *MACHINERY*

620   ZA
ZAMBIAN ENGINEER. (Text in English) q. Engineering Institution of Zambia, P.O. Box 837, Ndola, Zambia. **Formerly:** Engineering Institution of Zambia. Journal (ISSN 0374-4906)

620   CC   ISSN 1000-209X
CODEN: ZGXUEM
ZHEJIANG GONGXUEYUAN XUEBAO/ZHEJIANG INSTITUTE OF ENGINEERING. JOURNAL. (Text in Chinese) q. Zhejiang Gongxueyuan - Zhejiang Institute of Engineering, 6 District, Zhaohui Xinchun, Hangzhou, Zhejiang 310014, People's Republic of China. TEL 0571-5131816. FAX 0571-8074940. Ed. Zhang Kangda. **Document type:** academic/scholarly publication.
—BLDSC (4918.150030); CASDDS.

620   CC   ISSN 1000-517X
T4
ZHENGZHOU GONGXUEYUAN XUEBAO/ZHENGZHOU INSTITUTE OF ENGINEERING. JOURNAL. (Text in Chinese) 1980. q. Y12 (effective 1994). Zhengzhou Gongxueyuan, Xuebao Bianjibu, Wenhua Lu, Zhengzhou, Henan 450002, People's Republic of China. TEL 332113. Ed. Zheng Zuoding. circ. 30 (paid); 350 (controlled). **Document type:** academic/scholarly publication.

620   CC
ZHONGGUO GONGCHENGSHI/CHINESE ENGINEERS. (Text in Chinese) bi-m. Zhongguo Gongchengshi Zazhishe, No.1, Wenhua Lu 1 Duan, Heping-qu, Shenyang, Liaoning 110006, People's Republic of China. TEL 393000. Ed. Lin Sheng.

ZHONGNAN KUANGYE XUEYUAN XUEBAO/CENTRAL-SOUTH INSTITUTE OF MINING AND METALLURGY. JOURNAL. see *MINES AND MINING INDUSTRY*

622 338.2   RH   ISSN 1019-6404
ZIMBABWE ENGINEER. 1935. bi-m. Z.$31.20 (foreign Z.$38.05). (Zimbabwe Institution of Engineers) Thomson Publications Zimbabwe (Pvt) Ltd., Thomson House, P.O. Box 1683, Harare, Zimbabwe. TEL 736835. FAX 752390. TELEX 24705 ZW. Ed. M. Zhuwakivyu. **Indexed:** GeoRef., Ind.S.A.Per., P.L.E.S.A. **Document type:** trade publication.
—BLDSC (9513.230000).
Former titles (until 1992): Mining and Engineering (ISSN 0254-0304); Incorporates (in 1989): Zimbabwe Engineer (ISSN 0251-1037); Which was formerly (until 1980): Rhodesian Engineer (ISSN 0556-9532)

620   RH
ZIMBABWE INSTITUTION OF ENGINEERS. YEAR BOOK. Short title: Z I E Year Book. a. Thomson Publications Zimbabwe (Pvt) Ltd., Thomson House, P.O. Box 1683, Harare, Zimbabwe. TEL 736835. FAX 752390. TELEX 24705 ZW.

ENGINEERING — Abstracting, Bibliographies, Statistics

A G E REFDEX. (Asian Geotechnical Engineering Information Center) see *EARTH SCIENCES — Abstracting, Bibliographies, Statistics*

620   US
A M ENGINEERING DATA BASE. m. $360 per no. in U.S., Canada, Mexico; elsewhere $720. (Federal Communications Commission) U.S. National Technical Information Service, 5825 Port Royal Rd., Springfield, VA 22161. TEL 703-487-4630. Ed. Weisman. (avail. on tape only)

620   US
A M ENGINEERING DATA BASE IN ORDER BY FREQUENCY. m. $25 per issue in U.S., Canada, Mexico; elsewhere $50. (Federal Communications Commission) U.S. National Technical Information Service, 5825 Port Royal Rd., Springfield, VA 22161. TEL 703-487-4630. (microfiche)
Description: Includes information from A M Engineering Data Base and relates to Part 73 of the commission's rules.

620   US
A M ENGINEERING DATA BASE IN ORDER BY STATE. m. $25 per no. in U.S., Canada, Mexico; elsewhere $50. (Federal Communications Commission) U.S. National Technical Information Service, 5825 Port Royal Rd., Springfield, VA 22161. TEL 703-486-4630. (microfiche)
Description: Includes order by city. Relates to Part 73 of the commission's rules.

620   US
A M ENGINEERING DATABASE IN ORDER BY COUNTRY AND STATE. w. $52 per issue in US, Canada, Mexico: elsewhere $83. (Federal Communications Commission) U.S. National Technical Information Service, 5285 Port Royal Rd., Springfield, VA 22161. TEL 703-487-4630. (also avail. in microfiche)
Description: Includes information from A M Engineering Data Base and relates to Part 73 of the commission's rules.

624   US   ISSN 0742-1753
TA145
A S C E ANNUAL COMBINED INDEX. a. $48 (effective 1993). American Society of Civil Engineers, 345 E. 47th St., New York, NY 10017-2398. TEL 212-705-7520. FAX 212-980-4681. Ed. Carol Reese. cum.index. circ. 4,000. (also avail. in microfilm; microfiche; magnetic tape; back issues avail.) **Document type:** abstracting/indexing.
—BLDSC (1739.095000).

624 016   US   ISSN 0734-1962
Z5851   CODEN: ASPIDQ
A S C E PUBLICATIONS INFORMATION. 1966. bi-m. $160 to non-members. American Society of Civil Engineers, 345 E. 47th St., New York, NY 10017-2398. TEL 212-705-7288. FAX 212-980-4681. index, cum.index. circ. 1,152. (reprint service avail. from UMI) **Indexed:** GeoRef. **Document type:** academic/scholarly publication.
—SWETS. **CCC**.
Formerly (until 1982): A S C E Publications Abstracts (ISSN 0001-2432)

624.173 016   US   ISSN 0363-5732
TA658.44   CODEN: AJEEDW
ABSTRACT JOURNAL IN EARTHQUAKE ENGINEERING. 1972. a. $80 (foreign $100). University of California at Berkeley, Earthquake Engineering Research Center, 1301 S. 46th St., Richmond, CA 94804-4698. TEL 510-231-9413. FAX 510-231-9461. Ed. Ruth C. Wrentmore. index. circ. 500. (back issues avail.) **Indexed:** GeoRef. **Document type:** abstracting/indexing.
Description: Provides comprehensive, international, multidisciplinary coverage of the broad range of subjects which comprise the field of earthquake engineering and earthquake hazards mitigation.

AGRICULTURAL ENGINEERING ABSTRACTS. see *AGRICULTURE — Abstracting, Bibliographies, Statistics*

669.141   US
AMERICAN IRON AND STEEL INSTITUTE. ANNUAL STATISTICAL REPORT. a. price varies. American Iron and Steel Institute, 1101 17th St., N.W., Ste. 1300, Washington, DC 20036-4700. TEL 202-463-6573. FAX 202-463-6573. (also avail. in microfiche from CIS) **Indexed:** SRI.

624   US   ISSN 0066-0604
TA1   CODEN: TACEAT
AMERICAN SOCIETY OF CIVIL ENGINEERS. TRANSACTIONS. 1867. a. $140. American Society of Civil Engineers, 345 E. 47th St., New York, NY 10017-2398. TEL 212-705-7288. FAX 212-980-4681. Ed. Carol Reese. circ. 3,000. (also avail. in microform; reprint service avail. from UMI) **Indexed:** GeoRef., W.R.C.Inf. **Document type:** academic/scholarly publication.
—SWETS; UMI. **CCC**.

621 016   US   ISSN 0003-6900
TA1   CODEN: AMREAD
APPLIED MECHANICS REVIEWS; an assessment of world literature in engineering sciences. 1948. m. $360 to non-members; members $42. American Society of Mechanical Engineers, 345 E. 47th St., New York, NY 10017. TEL 212-705-7703. FAX 212-980-4681. Ed. A.W. Kenneth Metzner. bk.rev.; abstr.; index. circ. 5,000. (also avail. in microform from UMI; individual articles avail. on microfilm) **Indexed:** Abstr.Bull.Inst.Pap.Chem., Abstr.J.Earthq.Eng., Biol.Abstr., BMT, Chem.Abstr., Comput.Rev., Deep Sea Res.& Oceanogr.Abstr., Eng.Ind., Fluidex, GeoRef., Geotech.Abstr., Intl.Civil Eng.Abstr., Math.R., Met.Abstr., Petrol.Abstr., Soft.Abstr.Eng.
—BLDSC (1575.000000); El; UnCover; SWETS; UMI. **CCC**.
Refereed Serial

600 016 500   US   ISSN 0003-6986
Z7913
APPLIED SCIENCE & TECHNOLOGY INDEX; a cumulative subject index to English language periodicals in the fields of aeronautics and space science, computer technology and applications, chemistry, construction industry, energy resources and research, engineering, etc. 1958. m. (except Jul.), plus q. and a. cumulations. service basis. H.W. Wilson Co., 950 University Ave., Bronx, NY 10452. TEL 800-367-6770. FAX 718-590-1617. Ed. Joyce Howard. circ. 3,916. **Indexed:** Abstr.Bull.Inst.Pap.Chem. **Document type:** abstracting/indexing.
●Also available online. Vendor(s): BRS Online Products (ASTW), Wilsonline (File AST).
Also available on CD-ROM. Producer(s): H.W. Wilson.
—BLDSC (1576.600000).
Description: Cumulative index to English language periodicals consisting of subject entries to periodical articles arranged in one alphabet, with a separate listing of citations to book reviews.

624 388 015   AT   ISSN 0705-9213
AUSTRALIAN ROAD RESEARCH IN PROGRESS. (Hardcopy edition ceased with vol.7, 1986) 1980. a. Australian Road Research Board, 500 Burwood Hwy., Vermont S., Vic. 3133, Australia. TEL 03-881-1555. FAX 03-887-8104. TELEX AA33113. **Indexed:** AESIS.
●Available only online.

BIBLIOGRAFIA GOSPODARKI I INZYNIERII WODNEJ/BIBLIOGRAPHY OF WATER MANAGEMENT AND ENGINEERING. see *WATER RESOURCES — Abstracting, Bibliographies, Statistics*

ENGINEERING — ABSTRACTING, BIBLIOGRAPHIES, STATISTICS

621.2 016   IT   ISSN 0006-1042
BIBLIOGRAFIA ITALIANA DI IDRAULICA. (Text in Italian; titles in English) 1950. q. L.40000. Universita degli Studi di Padova, Istituto di Idraulica, Centro di Documentazione Idraulica, Padua, Italy. FAX 049-831463. Ed. Raffaele Cola. bk.rev.; bibl.; index, cum.index every 5 yrs. circ. 600. **Indexed:** Intl.Civil Eng.Abstr., Soft.Abstr.Eng. **Document type:** bibliography.

624 016   PO
BIBLIOGRAFIA PORTUGUESA DE ENGENHARIA CIVIL. (Text in English and Portuguese) 1963. a. Laboratorio Nacional de Engenharia Civil, Avenida do Brasil, 101, 1799 Lisbon Codex, Portugal. bk.rev. circ. 750. **Document type:** bibliography.
    Formerly: Bibliografia Portuguesa de Construcao Civil (ISSN 0067-6756)

620.1   JA
BIBLIOGRAPHY OF MATERIALS FATIGUE/ZAIRYO NO HIRO NI KANSURU KENKYU NO SUSEI. (Text in Japanese) 1983. a. 13000 Yen. Society of Materials Science, Japan - Nihon Zairyo Gakkai, 1-101, Yoshida Izumidonocho, Sakyo-ku, Kyoto 606, Japan. **Document type:** bibliography.

624 551.4 551   US   ISSN 0149-3825
BIBLIOGRAPHY ON COLD REGIONS SCIENCE & TECHNOLOGY. 1951. a. $30.50. U.S. Army, Cold Regions Research and Engineering Laboratory, 72 Lyme Rd., Hanover, NH 03755-1290. TEL 603-646-4221. FAX 603-646-4712. bibl.; index, cum.index. (also avail. in microfiche; back issues avail.) **Document type:** government publication, bibliography.
    ●Also available online. **Vendor(s):** Orbit Search Service (COLD).
    Also available on CD-ROM. **Producer(s):** NISC (Arctic & Antarctic Regions).

624 720 016   YU   ISSN 0352-1028
BILTEN DOKUMENTACIJE. GRADJEVINARSTVO - VISOKOGRADNJA I ZAVRSNI RADOVI U GRADJEVINARSTVU/BULLETIN OF DOCUMENTATION. CIVIL ENGINEERING - SUPERSTRUCTURES AND FINAL WORK. 1950. bi-m. $198. Jugoslovenski Centar za Tehnicku i Naucnu Dokumentaciju - Yugoslav Center for Technical and Scientific Documentation (YCTSD), Sl. Penezica-Krcuna 29-31, Box 724, 11000 Belgrade, Yugoslavia. Ed. Ljiljana Kojic-Bogdanovic.
    Supersedes in part: Bilten Dokumentacije. Gradjevinarstvo i Arhitektura (ISSN 0006-260X)

574.28 016   US   ISSN 1068-5693
R856.A1
BIOENGINEERING ABSTRACTS. 1974. m. $535 (foreign $595). Cambridge Scientific Abstracts, 7200 Wisconsin Ave., 6th Fl., Bethesda, MD 20814. TEL 301-961-6700. FAX 301-961-6720. (Co-publisher: Engineering Information, Inc.) (back issues avail.; reprint service avail.) **Document type:** abstracting/indexing.
    —CCC.
    Former titles (until 1992): Bioengineering and Biotechnology Abstracts (ISSN 1041-2913); Bioengineering Abstracts (ISSN 0736-6213)
    Description: Covers the world's technological literature in the area of bioengineering and biomedical engineering.

621 011   UK
BOUNDARY ELEMENTS COMMUNICATIONS. 1990. bi-m. £149($225) (International Society for Boundary Elements) Computational Mechanics Publications, Ashurst Lodge, Ashurst, Southampton SO4 2AA, England. TEL 0703-293223. FAX 0703-292853. TELEX 47388 COMPMECH. (U.S. addr.: Computational Mechanics, 25 Bridge St., Billerica, MA 01821. TEL 508-667-5841. FAX 508-667-7582) Ed.Bd. bk.rev.; abstr. **Document type:** academic/scholarly publication.
    Formerly (until 1993): Boundary Elements Abstracts and Newsletter (ISSN 0957-2902)
    Description: Publishes abstracts of journals, conference papers, theses, and reports worldwide.

C A SELECTS. CHEMICAL PROCESSING APPARATUS. see ENGINEERING — Chemical Engineering

C A SELECTS. MEMORY & RECORDING DEVICES & MATERIALS. see CHEMISTRY — Abstracting, Bibliographies, Statistics

625.7 016   II   ISSN 0045-6055
C R R I ROAD ABSTRACTS. 1961. a. free. Central Road Research Institute, P.O. Central Road Research Institute, New Delhi 110020, India. TEL 6832274. TELEX 31-75369-CRRI-IN. (Affiliate: Council of Scientific and Industrial Research) abstr.; circ. controlled. **Indexed:** Chem.Abstr., Eng.Ind. **Document type:** abstracting/indexing.

624 625   CN   ISSN 0835-1058
HD9717.5.R63
CANADA. STATISTICS CANADA. HIGHWAY, ROAD, STREET AND BRIDGE CONTRACTORS. (Catalogue 64-206) (Text in English and French) 1970. a. Can.$22($26) (foreign $31). Statistics Canada, Communications Division, 3rd Fl., R.H. Coats Bldg., Ottawa, Ont. K1A 0T6, Canada. TEL 613-951-7277. FAX 613-951-1584. (Subscr. to: Publications Sales and Services, Ottawa, Ont. K1A 0T6, Canada) (also avail. in microform from MML)
    Formerly: Canada. Statistics Canada. Highway, Road, Street and Bridge Contracting Industry (ISSN 0706-2451)
    Description: Shows aggregate activity of general contractors primarily engaged in highway, road, street and bridge construction.

690   CN   ISSN 0835-1031
HD9715.C3
CANADA. STATISTICS CANADA. MECHANICAL TRADE CONTRACTORS. (Catalogue 64-204) (Text in English and French) 1967. a. Can.$22($26) (foreign $31). Statistics Canada, Publications Sales and Services, Ottawa, Ont. K1A 0T6, Canada. TEL 613-951-7277. FAX 613-951-1584. (also avail. in microform from MML)
    Formerly: Canada. Statistics Canada. Mechanical Contracting Industry (ISSN 0576-0097)
    Description: Covers the aggregate activity of mechanical trade contractors.

CHEMICAL INDUSTRY NOTES. see CHEMISTRY — Abstracting, Bibliographies, Statistics

624   US   ISSN 1063-7338
▼**CIVIL & STRUCTURAL ENGINEERING ABSTRACTS.** 1993. m. $385 (foreign $435). Cambridge Scientific Abstracts, 7200 Wisconsin Ave., 6th Fl., Bethesda, MD 20814. TEL 301-961-6750. FAX 301-961-6720. (Co-publisher: Engineering Information, Inc.) (also avail. in magnetic tape) **Document type:** abstracting/indexing.
    Description: Gathers together the worldwide literature concerning this discipline; covers structural design, construction materials, soil mechanics, and other areas essential to planning, testing, and building of structures.

621.3   US   ISSN 1043-7258
TK1
COMBINED INDEX FOR I E E E TRANSACTIONS ON POWER DELIVERY, I E E E TRANSACTIONS ON POWER SYSTEMS, I E E E TRANSACTIONS ON ENERGY CONVERSION. 1986. a. (I E E E) Institute of Electrical and Electronics Engineers, Inc., 345 E. 47th St., New York, NY 10017-2394. TEL 908-981-1393. FAX 908-981-9667. (Subscr. to: 344 Hoes Lane, Box 1331, Piscataway, NJ 08855-1331)

624.176 016   AT   ISSN 0310-1894
Z5853.E43   CODEN: AAGACY
COMMONWEALTH SCIENTIFIC AND INDUSTRIAL RESEARCH ORGANIZATION. DIVISION OF GEOMECHANICS. ABSTRACTS OF PUBLISHED PAPERS. 1972. 2/yr. free. C.S.I.R.O., Division of Geomechanics, Box 54, Mount Waverley, Vic. 3149, Australia. **Indexed:** AESIS. **Document type:** abstracting/indexing.
    Description: Contains abstracts of papers published by divisional staff.

621.8 310   US   ISSN 0360-2877
TP885.P5
CONCRETE PIPE INDUSTRY STATISTICS. 1974. biennial. $325 to non-members; members $162.50. American Concrete Pipe Association, 8300 Boone Blvd., Ste. 400, Vienna, VA 22182-2689. TEL 703-821-1990. FAX 703-821-3054. illus.
    Description: Reports industry production nationally and for ACPA regions. Products are reported by pipe size and end use and includes figures on all concrete pipe products produced by industry.

620.2   II
CONFEDERATION OF INDIAN INDUSTRY. HANDBOOK OF STATISTICS. (Text in English) 1963. a. price varies. Confederation of Indian Industry, Secretary, 23-26 Institutional Area, Lodi Road, New Delhi 110 003, India. FAX 694298. TELEX 031-66655/65401 AIEI. Ed. Tarun Das. adv.; bk.rev. circ. 2,600.
    Former titles (until 1991): Confederation of Engineering Industry. Handbook of Statistics (ISSN 0971-1384) & Association of Indian Engineering Industry. Handbook of Statistics; Indian Engineering Association. Handbook of Statistics (ISSN 0073-6333)
    Description: Provides comprehensive data on investment, production, imports & exports, licences and collaborations.

620 615   UK
CONTAMINATION CONTROL ABSTRACTS. 1986. q. £85($140) Particle Science and Technology Information Service, Dept. of Chemical Engineering, University of Technology, Loughborough, Leics. LE11 3TU, England. TEL 0509-222528. Ed. R.W. Newbold. **Document type:** abstracting/indexing.
    Description: Annotated bibliography of journal articles, conference papers, reports, patents, theses, and books pertaining to contamination control and clean room technology.

621 016   US   ISSN 0010-9339
TA462   CODEN: CRNAA
CORROSION ABSTRACTS; abstracts of the world's literature on corrosion and corrosion mitigation. 1962. bi-m. $195 (foreign $230). National Association of Corrosion Engineers (NACE), Box 218340, Houston, TX 77218. TEL 713-492-0535. FAX 713-492-8254. TELEX 792310. Ed. R.I. Lindberg. abstr.; index. circ. 650. (reprint service avail. from UMI) **Indexed:** Art & Archaeol.Tech.Abstr. **Document type:** abstracting/indexing.
    ●Also available on CD-ROM.
    —UMI. **CCC.**
    Refereed Serial

620.43 016   UK   ISSN 0376-4842
CURRENT AWARENESS IN PARTICLE TECHNOLOGY. 1967. m. £175. Particle Science and Technology Information Service, Dept. of Chemical Engineering, University of Technology, Loughborough, Leics. LE11 3TU, England. TEL 0509-222528. Ed. R. W. Newbold. index. circ. 300. **Indexed:** Anal.Abstr. **Document type:** academic/scholarly publication.
    —BLDSC (3494.380000); SWETS.
    Continues: Particulate Information; Particle Science and Technology Information Service.
    Description: Research papers, news items, lists of products and services, bibliography of journal articles and reports, and announcements of conferences and seminars in technical advancements pertaining to particle characteristics, particle systems, gas systems, liquid systems, particle production, and particle applications.

CURRENT BIBLIOGRAPHIES ON SCIENCE & TECHNOLOGY: ELECTRICAL ENGINEERING AND ELECTRONICS. see ELECTRONICS

CURRENT BIBLIOGRAPHY ON SCIENCE AND TECHNOLOGY: CHEMISTRY AND CHEMICAL ENGINEERING (FOREIGN)/KAGAKU GIJUTSU BUNKEN SOKUHO. KAGAKU, KAGAKU KOGYO-HEN (GAIKOKU-HEN). see CHEMISTRY — Abstracting, Bibliographies, Statistics

CURRENT BIBLIOGRAPHY ON SCIENCE AND TECHNOLOGY: CHEMISTRY AND CHEMICAL ENGINEERING (JAPANESE)/KAGAKU GIJUTSU BUNKEN SOKUHO KAGAKU. KAGAKU KOGYO-HEN (KOKUNAI-HEN). see CHEMISTRY — Abstracting, Bibliographies, Statistics

624 720 016   JA   ISSN 0022-7641
CURRENT BIBLIOGRAPHY ON SCIENCE AND TECHNOLOGY: CIVIL ENGINEERING AND ARCHITECTURE/KAGAKU GIJUTSU BUNKEN SOKUHO. DOBOKU, KENCHIKU KOGAKU HEN. (Text in Japanese) 1958. s-m $1970. Japan Information Center of Science and Technology - Nihon Kagaku Gijutsu Joho Senta, 5-2 Nagata-cho, 2-chome, Chiyoda-ku, Tokyo 100, Japan. TEL 03-3581-6411. FAX 03-3581-6446. index. circ. 400. **Indexed:** Met.Abstr. **Document type:** bibliography.
    ●Also available online. **Vendor(s):** JICST.

ENGINEERING — ABSTRACTING, BIBLIOGRAPHIES, STATISTICS

621.3 016   JA   ISSN 0011-3298
CURRENT BIBLIOGRAPHY ON SCIENCE AND TECHNOLOGY: ELECTRONICS AND ELECTRICAL ENGINEERING/KAGAKU GIJUTSU BUNKEN SOKUHO. DENKI KOGAKU HEN. (Text in Japanese) 1958. s-m. $2100. Japan Information Center of Science and Technology - Nihon Kagaku Gijutsu Joho Senta, 5-2 Nagata-cho, 2-chome, Chiyoda-ku, Tokyo 100, Japan. TEL 03-3581-6411. FAX 03-3581-6446. index. circ. 800. **Document type:** bibliography.
●Also available online. Vendor(s): JICST.

621 016   JA   ISSN 0011-331X
CURRENT BIBLIOGRAPHY ON SCIENCE AND TECHNOLOGY: MECHANICAL ENGINEERING/KAGAKU GIJUTSU BUNKEN SOKUHO. KIKAI KOGAKU-HEN. (Text in Japanese) 1958. s-m. $2600. Japan Information Center of Science and Technology - Nihon Kagaku Gijutsu Joho Senta, 5-2 Nagata-cho, 2-chome, Chiyoda-ku, Tokyo 100, Japan. TEL 03-3581-6411. FAX 03-3581-6446. index. circ. 800. **Document type:** bibliography.
●Also available online. Vendor(s): JICST.

621.48 016   JA   ISSN 0011-3263
CURRENT BIBLIOGRAPHY ON SCIENCE AND TECHNOLOGY: NUCLEAR ENGINEERING/KAGAKU GIJUTSU BUNKEN SOKUHO. GENSHIRYOKU KOGAKU-HEN. (Isotopes and Radiation Chemistry Series) 1961. m. $1520. Japan Information Center of Science and Technology - Nihon Kagaku Gijutsu Joho Senta, 5-2 Nagata-cho, 2-chome, Chiyoda-ku, Tokyo 100, Japan. TEL 03-3581-6411. FAX 03-3581-6446. index. circ. 300. **Document type:** bibliography.
●Also available online. Vendor(s): JICST.

600 620 016   US   ISSN 0095-7917
Z7913   CODEN: CCESDD
CURRENT CONTENTS: ENGINEERING, TECHNOLOGY & APPLIED SCIENCES. Short title: C C: E T & A S. (Includes Author Index and Address Directory, Current Book Contents and Title Word Index) 1970. w. $442. Institute for Scientific Information, 3501 Market St., Philadelphia, PA 19104. TEL 215-386-0100. FAX 215-386-2991. (And: Brunel Science Park, Brunel University, Uxbridge UB8 3PQ, England) (also avail. in magnetic tape; diskette format) **Indexed:** Abstr.Bull.Inst.Pap.Chem., Br.Ceram.Abstr., Compumath, Ind.Sci.Rev., J.of Ferroc., Sci.Cit.Ind. **Document type:** academic/scholarly publication.
●Also available online. Vendor(s): BRS Online Products (CTOC,CBIB,ENGI), DIALOG Information Services, Inc. (File no.440).
—BLDSC (3496.167500); CASDDS.
Formerly: Current Contents: Engineering and Technology (ISSN 0011-3395)
Description: Tables of contents of the world's leading publications covering engineering, technology and applied sciences.

621.3   UK   ISSN 0011-3778
Z5832
CURRENT PAPERS IN ELECTRICAL & ELECTRONICS ENGINEERING. 1969. m. £200($345) I.E.E., Michael Faraday House, Six Hills Way, Stevenage, Herts. SG1 2AY, England. TEL 0438-313311. FAX 0438-742840. TELEX 825578-IEESTV-G. (Subscr. to: Publication Sales Dept., P.O. Box 96, Stevenage, Herts. SG1 2SD, England; US addr.: INSPEC/IEEE, Box 1331, 445 Hoes Ln., Piscataway, NJ 08855-1331. TEL 908-562-5549) bk.rev.; index. **Indexed:** Agri.Eng.Abstr., Graph.Arts Lit.Abstr. **Document type:** academic/scholarly publication.
—CCC.

660   US   ISSN 1049-1279
C2C ABSTRACTS: JAPAN - CHEMICAL ENGINEERING.* 1990. m. $200. Scan C2C, 1001 Pennsylvania Ave., N.W., No.1300, Washington, DC 20024-2505. TEL 800-525-3865. FAX 202-863-3855. **Document type:** abstracting/indexing.
●Also available online. Vendor(s): Data-Star (JPTC), DIALOG Information Services, Inc. (File no.582), European Space Agency (File no.241), Orbit Search Service (JTEC).
Also available on CD-ROM. Producer(s): DIALOG Information Services, Inc..
Description: Contains abstracts of articles from Japanese scientific, business, and technical journals. Each entry lists title, author, author affiliation, journal title, volume and number, date, abstract, number of bibliographic references, and language (if not Japanese).

620   US   ISSN 1049-1317
C2C ABSTRACTS: JAPAN - MATERIALS SCIENCE.* 1990. m. $200. Scan C2C, 1001 Pennsylvania Ave., N.W., No.1300, Washington, DC 20024-2505. TEL 800-525-3865. FAX 202-863-3855. **Document type:** abstracting/indexing.
●Also available online. Vendor(s): Data-Star (JPTC), DIALOG Information Services, Inc. (File no.582), European Space Agency (File no.241), Orbit Search Service (JTEC).
Also available on CD-ROM. Producer(s): DIALOG Information Services, Inc..
Description: Contains abstracts of articles from Japanese scientific, business, and technical journals. Covers aggregates, coatings, composites, fibers and whiskers, powder technology, processing, refractories, and wood products.

C2C ABSTRACTS: JAPAN - METALS. see
METALLURGY — Abstracting, Bibliographies, Statistics

C2C ABSTRACTS: JAPAN - SURFACE CHEMISTRY. see
CHEMISTRY — Abstracting, Bibliographies, Statistics

620   US   ISSN 1049-121X
Q1
C2C CURRENTS: JAPAN - MATERIALS.* 1989. m. $100. Scan C2C, 1001 Pennsylvania Ave., N.W., No. 1300, Washington, DC 20024-2025. TEL 800-525-3865. FAX 202-863-3855. **Document type:** abstracting/indexing.
●Also available online. Vendor(s): Data-Star (JPTC), DIALOG Information Services, Inc. (File no.582), European Space Agency (File no.241), Orbit Search Service (JTEC).
Also available on CD-ROM. Producer(s): DIALOG Information Services, Inc..
Description: Provides a summary of the contents of leading scientific and business journals in Japan. Contains tables of contents for selected journals in certain subject areas. Lists title, author, date of publication, number of pages, and source journal.

620   JA   ISSN 0288-8750
DAIGAKUIN KENKYU NENPO. 3: RIKOGAKU KENKYUKA HEN/BULLETIN OF GRADUATE STUDIES. SCIENCE AND ENGINEERING RESEARCH EDITION. (Text in English and Japanese) 1971. a. free. Chuo Daigaku - Chuo University, 742-1, Higashi-Nakano, Hachioji-shi, Tokyo 192-03, Japan. FAX 81-3-3817-1792.

621.3   JA   ISSN 0415-4096
DENRYOKU CHOSA TOKEI GEPPO/MONTHLY REPORT ON ELECTRIC POWER STATISTICS. (Text in Japanese) 1951. m. 460 Yen per no. Nihon Denki Kyokai - Japan Electric Association, 7-1, Yuraku-cho 1-chome, Chiyoda-ku, Tokyo 100, Japan. (Co-sponsor: Shigen Enerugicho Koeki Jigyobu - Agency of Natural Resources and Energy, Public Utilities Department)

621.3   FR   ISSN 1142-3153
DIFFUSION EXPRESS. Short title: D X. 1947. w. 3600 F. Electricite de France, Direction des Etudes et Recherches, Departement Systemes d'Information et de Documentation, 1, av. du General de Gaulle, 92141 Clamart, France. TEL 47-65-41-58. FAX 47-65-31-24. TELEX 204347 F EDFNORM. abstr. circ. 2,000. **Document type:** bulletin.
●Also available online. Vendor(s): European Space Agency (File no.27), Telesystemes - Questel (Base EDF.DOC).
Former titles (until 1990): Electricite de France. Bulletin de Documentation (ISSN 0249-5872); Electricite de France. Documentation Technique (ISSN 0012-4702)

625.7 016   GW   ISSN 0012-5148
DOKUMENTATION STRASSE: Kurzauszuege aus dem Schrifttum ueber das Strassenwesen. 1961. m. DM.138. Forschungsgesellschaft fuer Strassen- und Verkehrswesen, Postfach 501362, 50973 Cologne, Germany. TEL 0221-397035. FAX 0221-393747. Ed. Herbert Kuehn. bk.rev.; abstr.; cum.index. circ. 600. **Document type:** trade publication.
Description: Discusses roads and transportation science.

621   CC   ISSN 1001-6937
DONGLI JIXUE WENZHAI/POWER MACHINERY ABSTRACTS. (Text in Chinese) bi-m. Harbin Dianzhan Shebei Chengtao Sheji Yanjiusuo, Qingbao Shi, 9, Xusheng Jie, Dongli-qu, Harbin, Heilongjiang 53921, People's Republic of China. TEL 150046. Ed. Fu Qinhui. **Document type:** abstracting/indexing.

621.31   US   ISSN 0012-7612
E E I STATISTICAL RELEASES. ELECTRIC OUTPUT. 1933. w. $65. Edison Electric Institute, 701 Pennsylvania Ave., N.W., Washington, DC 20004-2696. TEL 202-508-5425. Ed. Betsy Oilman. stat. circ. 1,100.

624.173 016   US
EARTHQUAKE ENGINEERING ABSTRACTS DATABASE. 1985. irreg. University of California at Berkeley, Earthquake Engineering Research Center, 1301 S. 46th St., Richmond, CA 94804-4698. TEL 510-231-9401. FAX 510-231-9461. Ed. Ruth C. Wrentmore. **Document type:** abstracting/indexing.
●Available only online.
Description: Provides comprehensive international multidisciplinary coverage of the broad range of topics in earthquake engineering and earthquake hazards mitigation.

620 016   RU   ISSN 0131-0275
EKSPRESS-INFORMATSIYA. NADEZHNOST' I KONTROL' KACHESTVA. 1970. 48/yr. 52.80 Rub. Vsesoyuznyi Institut Nauchno-Tekhnicheskoi Informatsii (VINITI), Baltiiskaya ul., 14, Moscow A-219, Russia. (Subscr. to: Mezhdunarodnaya Kniga, Dimitrova ul. 39, 113095 Moscow, Russia)

621.4 016   RU   ISSN 0131-0356
EKSPRESS-INFORMATSIYA. PORSHNEVYE I GAZOTURBINNYE DVIGATELI. 1956. 48/yr. 38 Rub. Vsesoyuznyi Institut Nauchno-Tekhnicheskoi Informatsii (VINITI), Baltiiskaya ul., 14, Moscow A-219, Russia. (Subscr. to: Mezhdunarodnaya Kniga, Dimitrova 39, 113095 Moscow, Russia)

660.2 016   RU   ISSN 0207-5024
EKSPRESS-INFORMATSIYA. PROTSESSY I APPARATY KHIMICHESKIKH PROIZVODSTV I KHIMICHESKAYA KIBERNETIKA. 1979. 48/yr. 52.80 Rub. Vsesoyuznyi Institut Nauchno-Tekhnicheskoi Informatsii (VINITI), Baltiiskaya ul., 14, Moscow A-219, Russia. (Subscr. to: Mezhdunarodnaya Kniga, Dimitrova ul. 39, 113095 Moscow, Russia)
Formerly: Ekspress-Informatsiya. Protsessy i Apparaty Khimicheskikh Proizvodstv (ISSN 0013-368X)

621.3 016   UK   ISSN 0036-8105
Z5833
ELECTRICAL & ELECTRONICS ABSTRACTS. Alternative title: INSPEC. Section B. Represents: Science Abstracts. Section B. 1898. m. £1300($2195) I.E.E., Michael Faraday House, Six Hill Way, Stevenage, Herts. SG1 2AY, England. TEL 0438-313311. FAX 0438-742840. TELEX 825578-IEESTV-G. (Subscr. to: Publication Sales Dept., P.O. Box 96, Stevenage, Herts. SG1 2SD, England; U.S. addr.: INSPEC/IEEE, Box 1331, 445 Hoes Ln., Piscataway, NJ 08855-1331. TEL 908-562-5549) abstr.; bibl.; index, cum.index every 4 yrs. **Indexed:** Chem.Abstr., Ergon.Abstr. **Document type:** abstracting/indexing.
●Also available online. Vendor(s): BRS Online Products (INSZ), CEDOCAR, Data-Star (INZZ), DIALOG Information Services, Inc. (File nos.2,3 & 4/INSPEC), European Space Agency (File no.8/INSPEC), Orbit Search Service (INSM), Reuters, Ltd. (INZZ), STN International (INSPEC).
Also available on CD-ROM.
—BLDSC (3673.092300). CCC.
Description: Brings together summarized information of recent technical developments worldwide in all areas of electronics, radio, telecommunications, optoelectronics, and electrical power.

338 537 011   FR   ISSN 0070-9751
ELECTRICITE DE FRANCE. STATISTIQUES DE LA PRODUCTION ET DE LA CONSOMMATION. 1950. a. Electricite de France, Direction de la Production et du Transport, Departement Statistiques, 6 rue de Messine, 75008 Paris, France. circ. controlled. **Document type:** corporate report.

ENGINEERING — ABSTRACTING, BIBLIOGRAPHIES, STATISTICS

621.38 016   HU   ISSN 0231-0783
ELEKTROTECHNIKAI SZAKIRODALMI TAJEKOZTATO/ELECTRICAL ENGINEERING ABSTRACTS. 1949. m. 9200 Ft. Orszagos Muszaki Informacios Kozpont es Konyvtar (O.M.I.K.K.) - National Technical Information Centre and Library, Muzeum u. 17, PO Box 12, 1428 Budapest, Hungary. (Subscr. to: Kultura, PO Box 149, 1389 Budapest, Hungary) Ed. Ottmar Klavida. abstr.; index. circ. 520.
   Supersedes (in 1982): Muszaki Lapszemle. Elektrotechnika - Technical Abstracts. Electrical Engineering (ISSN 0133-0373); Formerly: Muszaki Lapszemle. Elektrotechnika, Hiradastechnika (ISSN 0027-4968)

ENERGY ABSTRACTS. see ENERGY — *Abstracting, Bibliographies, Statistics*

011 620   US   ISSN 0951-9998
TA401
ENGINEERED MATERIALS ABSTRACTS. 1986. m. $1275 (foreign $1450); with subscr. to Metals Abstracts $1085 (foreign $1200). A S M International, Materials Information, Materials Park, OH 44073. TEL 216-338-5151. FAX 216-338-4634. TELEX 980-619. (UK addr.: Institute of Materials, Materials Information, 1 Carlton House Terr., London SW1Y 5DB, England. TEL 071-839-4071) (Co-sponsor: Institute of Metals) **Document type:** abstracting/indexing.
  ●Also available online. Vendor(s): DIALOG Information Services, Inc. (File no.293), European Space Agency (File no.134), Orbit Search Service (EMAB), STN International (EMA).
Also available on CD-ROM. Producer(s): DIALOG Information Services, Inc.
—BLDSC (3751.950000). **CCC.**
  Description: Coverage of published literature on technical developments in polymer, ceramic and composite materials as they are applied in an engineering environment.

620   US   ISSN 0360-8557
Z5851   CODEN: EIANE9
ENGINEERING INDEX ANNUAL. 1884. a. $1820 in N. America; elsewhere $1980. Engineering Information, Inc., Castle Point on the Hudson, Hoboken, NJ 07030. TEL 201-216-8500. FAX 201-216-8532. (U.K. and Western Europe subscr. to: Thompson, Henry Ltd., London Rd., Sunningdale, Berks. SL5 OEP, England) (also avail. in microfilm from PMC; magnetic tape; reprint service avail.) **Document type:** abstracting/indexing.
  ●Also available online. Vendor(s): BRS Online Products (COMP), CEDOCAR, Data-Star, DIALOG Information Services, Inc. (File no.8), European Space Agency, Orbit Search Service, STN International.
Also available on CD-ROM. Producer(s): DIALOG Information Services, Inc. (COMPENDEX PLUS CD-ROM).
—CASDDS. **CCC.**
  Description: Presents index and abstracts of the world's engineering and technical literature.

621 011   US
ENGINEERING INDEX CUMULATIVE INDEX. 1979. irreg., no.4, 1987. $995. Engineering Information, Inc., Castle Point on the Hudson, Hoboken, NJ 07030. TEL 201-216-8500. FAX 201-216-8532. (U.K. and Western Europe subscr. to: Thompson, Henry Ltd., London Rd., Sunningdale, Berks. SL5 OEP, England) (also avail. in microfilm from PMC; back issues avail.; reprint service avail.) **Document type:** abstracting/indexing.
  Description: Subject, author and author affiliation indexes to the Engineering Index.

620 016   US   ISSN 0742-1974
                               CODEN: EIMOE4
ENGINEERING INDEX MONTHLY; abstracting and indexing services covering sources of the world's engineering literature. m. $2300 in N. America; elsewhere $2490. Engineering Information, Inc., Castle Point on the Hudson, Hoboken, NJ 07030. TEL 201-216-8500. FAX 201-216-8532. (U.K. and Western Europe subscr. to: Thompson, Henry Ltd., London Rd., Sunningdale, Berks. SL5 OEP, England) (also avail. in microfilm from PMC; back issues avail.) **Document type:** abstracting/indexing.
  ●Also available online. Vendor(s): BRS Online Products (COMP), CEDOCAR, CISTI, Data-Star, DIALOG Information Services, Inc. (File no.8), European Space Agency, Orbit Search Service, STN International (COMPENDEX).
Also available on CD-ROM. Producer(s): DIALOG Information Services, Inc. (COMPENDEX PLUS CD-ROM).
—BLDSC (3762.050000); CASDDS. **CCC.**
  Former titles: Engineering Index Monthly and Author Index (ISSN 0162-3036); Engineering Index (ISSN 0013-7960)
  Description: Covers such areas as chemical engineering, computers and electrical engineering, civil engineering, metals and mining, industrial management, mechanical engineering.

620 016   UK   ISSN 0046-2446
TA166
ERGONOMICS ABSTRACTS. 1968. bi-m. £427($718) (Ergonomics Information Analysis Centre) Taylor & Francis Ltd., Rankine Rd., Basingstoke, Hants RG24 8PR, England. TEL 0256-840366. FAX 0256-479438. TELEX 858540. Ed. C. Stapleton. adv.; bk.rev. (also avail. in microform) Indexed: Agri.Eng.Abstr., Sportsearch, World Text.Abstr. **Document type:** abstracting/indexing.
—BLDSC (3808.550000).
  Description: Provides an abstracting service for all areas of ergonomics and human factors. Invaluable source of information for everyone who needs up-to-date information in human-computer interaction, psychology, physiology, biomechanics and work design.
Refereed Serial

620   GW
FACHBUCHVERZEICHNIS PRODUKTIONSTECHNIK (YEAR). 1900. a. DM.7. Fr. Weidemanns Buchhandlung (H.Witt), Postfach 6406, 30064 Hannover, Germany. TEL 0511-16382-0. FAX 0511-1638266. Ed. Renate Boehm. circ. 20,000. **Document type:** trade publication.

625   FI   ISSN 0355-2411
FINLAND. TILASTOKESKUS. INDEKSITIEDOTUS TR. TIENRAKENNUSKUSTANNUSINDEKSI/FINLAND. STATISTIKCENTRALEN. INDEXRAPPORT TR. VAEGBYGGNADSKOSTNADSINDEX. (Subseries of: Finland. Tilastokeskus. Indeksitiedotus) (Text in Finnish, Swedish) m. FIM 60 per vol. Tilastokeskus, Annankatu 44, SF-00100 Helsinki 10, Finland.

620 016   UK   ISSN 0962-7170
FLUID ABSTRACTS: CIVIL ENGINEERING. 1991. m. (plus a. cumulation). £420($645) (effective 1994). Elsevier Science Ltd., Oxford Fulfilment Centre, P.O. Box 800, Kidlington, Oxford OX5 1DX, England. TEL 44-865-843000. FAX 44-865-843010. (Subscr. in U.S. and Canada to: Elsevier Science, 660 White Plains Rd., Tarrytown, NY 10591-5153. TEL 914-524-9200. FAX 914-333-2444) Eds. D. Hemsley, A. Hall. bk.rev.; cum.index. **Document type:** abstracting/indexing.
  ●Also available online. Vendor(s): DIALOG Information Services, Inc. (File no.96/FLUIDEX), European Space Agency (File no.48/FLUIDEX).
—**CCC.**
  Formed by the merger of (1967-1991): Civil Engineering Hydraulics Abstracts (ISSN 0305-9456); (1969-1991): Industrial Aerodynamics Abstracts (ISSN 0019-7823); (1985-1991): Offshore Engineering Abstracts (ISSN 0268-1374); (1976-1991): World Ports and Harbours Abstracts (ISSN 0264-0775); Which incorporates (in 1982): International Dredging Abstracts (ISSN 0308-1400)
  Description: Covers civil engineering applications of fluid mechanics, hydraulics of closed and open systems, flow metering and measuring, offshore engineering, environmental hydraulics, and related aspects of wind energy, the atmosphere and aerodynamics.

620.106 C16   UK   ISSN 0962-7162
TA357
FLUID ABSTRACTS: PROCESS ENGINEERING. 1991. m. (plus a. cumulation). £420($645) (effective 1994). Elsevier Science Ltd., Oxford Fulfilment Centre, P.O. Box 800, Kidlington, Oxford OX5 1DX, England. TEL 44-865-843000. FAX 44-865-843010. (Subscr. in U.S. and Canada to: Elsevier Science, 660 White Plains Rd., Tarrytown, NY 10591-5153. TEL 914-524-9200. FAX 914-333-2444) Eds. D. Hemsley, A. Hall. adv.; bk.rev.; pat.; cum.index. **Document type:** abstracting/indexing.
  ●Also available online. Vendor(s): DIALOG Information Services, Inc. (File no.96/FLUIDEX), European Space Agency (File no.48/FLUIDEX).
—**CCC.**
  Formed by the merger of (1964-1991): Fluid Power Abstracts (ISSN 0015-4644); (1965-1991): Fluid Sealing Abstracts (ISSN 0015-4660); (1969-1991): Solid-Liquid Flow Abstracts (ISSN 0038-1063); (1971-1991): Pumps and Other Fluids Machinery Abstracts (ISSN 0302-2870); (1974-1991): Fluid Flow Measurement Abstracts (ISSN 0305-9235); (1983-1991): Pipelines Abstracts (ISSN 0265-3990); (1989-1991): Computer-Aided Process Control Abstracts (ISSN 0955-4319); Mixing and Separation Technology Abstracts (ISSN 0955-7059).
  Description: Covers all aspects of hydraulics of interest to process engineers.

FUEL AND ENERGY ABSTRACTS; a summary of world literature on all scientific, technical, commercial and environmental aspects of fuel and energy. see PETROLEUM AND GAS — *Abstracting, Bibliographies, Statistics*

GALVANO-REFERATE. see METALLURGY — *Abstracting, Bibliographies, Statistics*

620 500   IQ   ISSN 1012-3393
GENERAL INDEX TO IRAQI PERIODICAL LITERATURE. PART A: SCIENCES AND ENGINEERING. (Text in Arabic, English) 1984. irreg. free. Scientific Research Council, Jadiriyah P.O. Box 2441, Baghdad, Iraq. TELEX 213976 SR IK. Ed. Radhwan K. Abdul-Halim. circ. 500. **Document type:** abstracting/indexing.

624 016   US   ISSN 0046-5658
GEODEX RETRIEVAL SYSTEM FOR GEOTECHNICAL ABSTRACTS. Issued with Geotechnical Abstracts as: Geodex System-GRS. 1970. 3/yr. $645 includes Geotechnical Abstracts. (International Society for Soil Mechanics & Foundation Engineering) Geodex Retrieval Systems, 669 Broadway, Box 279, Sonoma, CA 95476. TEL 707-939-8476. FAX 707-996-8734. Ed. Willy Norup. abstr.; cum.index. (back issues avail.) **Document type:** abstracting/indexing.

624 016   US
GEODEX SYSTEM(S) - STRUCTURAL INFORMATION SERVICE. 1956. 3/yr. $535. Geodex Retrieval Systems, 669 Broadway, Box 279, Sonoma, CA 95476. TEL 707-939-8476. FAX 707-996-8734. Ed. Willy Norup. abstr.; cum.index. (back issues avail.) **Document type:** abstracting/indexing.
  Formerly: Geodex Structural Information Service.

624.15 016   US   ISSN 0016-8491
GEOTECHNICAL ABSTRACTS. 1970. 3/yr. $280. Geodex Retrieval Systems, 669 Broadway, Box 279, Sonoma, CA 95476. TEL 707-939-8476. FAX 707-996-8734. (Co-sponsor: International Society for Soil Mechanics and Foundation Engineering) Ed. Willy Norup. index. **Document type:** abstracting/indexing.
  Description: Abstracts covering more than 500 international periodicals, serials and conference proceedings in soil mechanics, foundation engineering, rock mechanics and engineering geology.

621.9   HU   ISSN 0231-0686
GEPESZETI SZAKIRODALMI TAJEKOZTATO/MACHINERY ABSTRACTS. 1983. m. 9900 Ft. Orszagos Muszaki Informacios Kozpont es Konyvtar (O.M.I.K.K.) - National Technical Information Centre and Library, Muzeum u. 17, P.O. Box 12, 1428 Budapest, Hungary. (Subscr. to: Kultura, P.O. Box 149, 1389 Budapest, Hungary) Ed. Imre Kuruc. circ. 370. **Document type:** abstracting/indexing.
  Supersedes in part (in 1982): Muszaki Lapszemle. Gepeszet-Gepgyartastechnologia; Which was formed by the merger of: Muszaki Lapszemle. Gepeszet (ISSN 0027-5018); Muszaki Lapszemle. Gepgyartas-Technologia.

ENGINEERING — ABSTRACTING, BIBLIOGRAPHIES, STATISTICS

621.9 016   HU   ISSN 0231-0694
GEPGYARTASTECHNOLOGIAI ES SZERSZAMGEPIPARI SZAKIRODALMI TAJEKOZTATO/MECHANICAL ENGINEERING & MACHINE TOOL ABSTRACTS. 1949. m. 9900 Ft. Orszagos Muszaki Informacios Kozpont es Konyvtar (O.M.I.K.K.) - National Technical Information Centre and Library, Muzeum u. 17, Box 12, 1428 Budapest, Hungary. (Subscr. to: Kultura, Box 149, 1389 Budapest, Hungary) Ed. Denes Bernad. abstr.; index. circ. 660. **Document type:** abstracting/indexing.
  Supersedes in part (in 1982): Muszaki Lapszemle. Gepeszet-Gepgyartastechnologia (ISSN 0209-5033); Formed by the merger of: Muszaki Lapszemle. Gepeszet (ISSN 0027-5018); Muszaki Lapszemle. Gepgyartas-Technologia.

620 350   US
GOVERNMENT REPORTS ANNOUNCEMENTS AND INDEX ANNUAL INDEX. Short title: G R A & I Annual Index. 1968. a. $630 in U.S., Canada, Mexico; elsewhere $785. U.S. National Technical Information Service, 5285 Port Royal Rd., Springfield, VA 22161. TEL 703-487-4630. FAX 703-321-8547. cum.index 1968-1987. (also avail. in microfilm from PMC; back issues avail.) **Document type:** abstracting/indexing, government publication.
  Description: Focuses on research and engineering results. Lists author, sponsor, contract or grant, as well as grant and NTIS access numbers.

HIGHWAY RESEARCH ABSTRACTS. see TRANSPORTATION — Abstracting, Bibliographies, Statistics

621.3 016   US   ISSN 0046-8371
CODEN: IPBUDP
I E E E PUBLICATIONS BULLETIN. (Includes: Supplement) 1970. q. free. Institute of Electrical and Electronics Engineers, Inc., 345 W. 47th, New York, NY 10017-2394. TEL 212-705-7900. FAX 212-705-7682. (Subscr. to: Box 1331, 445 Hoes Lane, Piscataway, NJ 08855-1331) Ed. Darla Wagner. (also avail. in microform from UMI) —CASDDS. CCC.
  Description: Provides in-depth coverage of IEEE's conference proceedings, standards and special journal and transaction issues as well as magazines and other publications.

INDIAN LITERATURE IN ENVIRONMENTAL ENGINEERING; a bibliographic review. see ENVIRONMENTAL STUDIES — Abstracting, Bibliographies, Statistics

530 016   GW   ISSN 0344-7758
INFORMATIONSDIENST LAERM. 1966. m. DM.520. (Fachinformations Zentrum Technik) V D I Verlag GmbH, Heinrichstr. 24, 40239 Duesseldorf, Germany. TEL 0211-6188-0. FAX 0211-6188-112. TELEX 8587743. (Subscr. to: Postfach 101054, 40001 Duesseldorf, Germany) **Indexed:** Dok.Str. **Document type:** abstracting/indexing.
  —CCC.
  Formerly (until 1977): Schrifttumsuebersicht Laermminderung (ISSN 0036-701X)

620 016   PL
INSTYTUT OBROBKI SKRAWANIEM. PRACE. PRZEGLAD DOKUMENTACYJNY. 1957. s-m. Instytut Obrobki Skrawaniem - Institute of Metal Cutting, Ul. Wroclawska 37A, 30-011 Krakow, Poland. TEL 48-12-339333. FAX 48-12-339490. TELEX 032478 IOS PL. bibl.; pat.; index. circ. 340. **Document type:** abstracting/indexing.
  Formerly: Instytut Obrobki Skrawaniem. Informacja Ekspresowa (ISSN 0019-9834)
  Description: Abstracting publication in Polish on machine tools, tooling, jigs and holders, abrasion machining, erosion techniques and metal cutting, metrology and technical control.

624   IE   ISSN 0790-5777
INTERNATIONAL BIBLIOGRAPHY OF STRUCTURAL ENGINEERING. 1986. irreg. I£45($86) C I T I S Ltd., 2 Rosemount Terrace, Blackrock, Dublin, Ireland. TEL 353-1-886227. FAX 353-1-885971. Ed. Donald P. Murphy. bk.rev.; index. **Document type:** bibliography.
  Description: Listings of titles from "International Civil Engineering Abstracts".

624 016   IE   ISSN 0332-4095
INTERNATIONAL CIVIL ENGINEERING ABSTRACTS. C D - R O M edition: C I T I S C D - R O M - I C E A. 1974. m. (except Jan. & Aug.) I£360($660) (CD-ROM $1700). C I T I S Ltd., 2 Rosemount Terrace, Blackrock, Dublin, Ireland. TEL 353-1-2886227. FAX 353-1-885-971. Ed. Donal P. Murphy. adv.; bk.rev.; index. (back issues avail.) **Document type:** abstracting/indexing.
  ●Also available on CD-ROM.
  —BLDSC (4538.663000).
  Former titles (until 1982): I C E Abstracts (ISSN 0305-2176); (until 1975): European Civil Engineering Abstracts (ISSN 0046-273X)
  Description: Information on all aspects of civil engineering.

662 011   UK
INTERNATIONAL POWDER & BULK SOLIDS ABSTRACTS. 1984. 3/yr. (in 1 vol.). £80($168) Childwall University Press Ltd., Box 78, London NW11 0PG, England.

662 011   UK   ISSN 0266-2930
INTERNATIONAL PROCESS TECHNOLOGY ABSTRACTS. 1984. 3/yr. (in 1 vol.). £80($168) Childwall University Press Ltd., Box 78, London NW11 0PG, England. TEL 01-455-0011. **Document type:** abstracting/indexing.

620 600   HU   ISSN 0231-195X
IPARI FORMATERVEZESI SZAKIRODALMI TAJEKOZTATO/INDUSTRIAL DESIGN ABSTRACTS. 1983. q. 2300 Ft. Orszagos Muszaki Informacios Kozpont es Konyvtar (O.M.I.K.K.) - National Technical Information Centre and Library, Muzeum u. 17, P.O. Box 12, 1428 Budapest, Hungary. (Subscr. to: Kultura, P.O. Box 149, 1389 Budapest, Hungary) Ed. Eva Szentpali. circ. 150. **Document type:** abstracting/indexing.

620.1 011   US   ISSN 1066-2375
▼**J M R ABSTRACTS.** (Journal of Materials Research) (Supplement to: Journal of Materials Research (ISSN 0884-2914)) 1992. m. $60 (foreign $70) (effective 1994). Materials Research Society, 9800 McKnight Rd., Pittsburgh, PA 15237. TEL 412-367-3003. FAX 412-367-4373. Ed. Walter Brown. **Document type:** abstracting/indexing.
  Description: Contains advance information on upcoming issues of Journal of Materials Research; includes current reports on numerous materials developments.

KEY ABSTRACTS - ARTIFICIAL INTELLIGENCE. see COMPUTERS — Abstracting, Bibliographies, Statistics

621.31 016   UK   ISSN 0950-4834
TK1005
KEY ABSTRACTS - POWER SYSTEMS & APPLICATIONS. 1975. m. £90($160) INSPEC, I.E.E., Michael Faraday House, Six Hills Way, Stevenage, Herts. SG1 2AY, England. TEL 0438-313311. FAX 0438-742840. TELEX 825578-IEESTV-G. (Subscr. to: Publication Sales Dept., P.O. Box 96, Stevenage, Herts. SG1 2SD, England; U.S. addr.: INSPEC/IEEE, Box 1331, 445 Hoes Ln., Piscataway, NJ 08855-1331. TEL 908-562-5549) index. **Document type:** abstracting/indexing.
  Formerly (until 1987): Key Abstracts - Power Transmission and Distribution (ISSN 0306-5561)
  Description: Covers power networks and systems, power apparatus, electric machines, power utilization, and industrial applications of power.

KEY ABSTRACTS - ROBOTICS & CONTROL. see COMPUTERS — Abstracting, Bibliographies, Statistics

551 011   JA   ISSN 0919-4673
KYUSHU UNIVERSITY. RESEARCH INSTITUTE FOR APPLIED MECHANICS. ABSTRACTS OF PAPERS. (Text in English and Japanese) 1974. a. exchange basis. Kyushu University, Research Institute for Applied Mechanics - Kyushu Daigaku Oyorikigaku Kenkyusho, Library, 6-1, Kasuga Koen, Kasuga-shi, Fukuoka-ken 816, Japan. FAX 81-92-582-4201. Ed.Bd. circ. 600. **Indexed:** Int.Aerosp.Abstr.

620   US
▼**MANUFACTURING & PROCESS ENGINEERING ABSTRACTS.** 1993. m. $385 (foreign $435). Cambridge Scientific Abstracts, 7200 Wisconsin Ave., 6th Fl., Bethesda, MD 20814. TEL 301-961-6750. FAX 301-961-6720. (Co-publisher: Engineering Information, Inc.) (also avail. in magnetic tape) **Document type:** abstracting/indexing.
  Description: Summarizes new developments affecting all aspects of the production process for today's manufacturing industry.

628.5   UK
MANUFACTURING SYSTEMS. 8/yr. Franks Hall, Horton Kirby, Kent DA4 9LL, England. TEL 0322-222222. FAX 0322-289577. TELEX 8954447. Ed. Ian Bowman. circ. 15,111.

620   US
MATERIALS INFORMATION ENGINEERED MATERIALS SEARCH-IN-PRINT SERIES. (129 topics avail.) 1987. a. $95 per topic to non-members; members $85. A S M International, Materials Information, Materials Park, OH 44073. TEL 216-338-5151. FAX 216-338-4634. TELEX 980-619. (UK addr.: Institute of Materials, Materials Information, 1 Carlton House Terrace, London SW1Y 5DB, England. TEL 071-839-4071) **Document type:** abstracting/indexing, bibliography.
  Former titles: Materials Information Engineered Materials Published Search Series; Materials Information Engineered Materials Bibliography Series.

620   US   ISSN 1063-732X
▼**MATERIALS SCIENCE & ENGINEERING ABSTRACTS.** 1993. m. $385 (foreign $435). Cambridge Scientific Abstracts, 7200 Wisconsin Ave., 6th Fl., Bethesda, MD 20814. TEL 301-961-6750. FAX 301-961-6720. (Co-publisher: Engineering Information, Inc.) (also avail. in magnetic tape) **Document type:** abstracting/indexing.
  Description: Provides information on mechanical and physical properties of materials and commercial or industrial applications for materials.

620   US
MATERIALS SCIENCE CITATION INDEX. bi-m. $975. Institute for Scientific Information, 3501 Market St., Philadelphia, PA 19104. TEL 215-386-0100. FAX 215-386-0100. (U.K. addr.: Brunel Science Park, Brunel University, Uxbridge UB6 3PQ, England) (also avail. in magnetic tape) **Document type:** abstracting/indexing.
  ●Also available on CD-ROM.
  Description: Provides bibliographic data, cited references, related records and English-language author abstracts from international scholarly research journals and conference proceedings.

621 016   US   ISSN 1063-7311
Z5853.M2
MECHANICAL ENGINEERING ABSTRACTS. 1967. m. $895 (foreign $995). Cambridge Scientific Abstracts, 7200 Wisconsin Ave., 6th Fl., Bethesda, MD 20814. TEL 301-961-6700. FAX 301-961-6720. (Co-publisher: Engineering Information, Inc.) bibl.; cum.index. (also avail. in magnetic tape; back issues avail.) **Indexed:** Cal.Tiss.Abstr., Chemorec.Abstr., Oncol.Abstr. **Document type:** abstracting/indexing.
  ●Also available online. Vendor(s): DIALOG Information Services, Inc. (File no.14), European Space Agency (File no.10/ISMEC), STN International.
  Former titles: I S M E C - Mechanical Engineering Abstracts (ISSN 0896-7113); I S M E C Bulletin (ISSN 0306-0039)
  Description: Covers world literature on mechanical engineering, engineering management, and production engineering.

624 016   HU   ISSN 0231-0732
MELYEPITESI ES VIZEPITESI SZAKIRODALMI TAJEKOZTATO/CIVIL ENGINEERING & HYDRAULIC ENGINEERING ABSTRACTS. 1961. m. 9800 Ft. Orszagos Muszaki Informacios Kozpont es Konyvtar (O.M.I.K.K.) - National Technical Information Centre and Library, Muzeum u. 17, Box 12, 1428 Budapest, Hungary. (Subscr. to: Kultura, Box 149, 1389 Budapest, Hungary) Ed. Janos Winter. index. circ. 320. **Document type:** abstracting/indexing.
  Supersedes (in 1983): Muszaki Lapszemle. Melyepites, Vizepites - Technical Abstracts. Civil and Hydraulic Engineering (ISSN 0027-5050)

MUSZAKI-GAZDASAGI MAGAZIN/TECHNICAL ECONOMIC DIGEST. see *BUSINESS AND ECONOMICS — Abstracting, Bibliographies, Statistics*

624 016 US
N T I S ALERTS: CIVIL ENGINEERING. w. $135 (foreign $195). U.S. National Technical Information Service, 5285 Port Royal Rd., Springfield, VA 22161. TEL 703-487-4630. FAX 703-321-8547. TELEX 64617. abstr.; index. (back issues avail.)
Former titles: Abstract Newsletter: Civil Engineering (ISSN 0163-1454); Weekly Abstract Newsletter: Civil Engineering; Weekly Government Abstracts. Civil Engineering; Weekly Government Abstracts. Civil and Structural Engineering (ISSN 0145-0344)

620.1 016 US
N T I S ALERTS: MATERIALS SCIENCES. w. $145 (foreign $205). U.S. National Technical Information Service, 5285 Port Royal Rd., Springfield, VA 22161. TEL 703-487-4630. FAX 703-321-8547. TELEX 64617. index. (back issues avail.) **Indexed:** Met.Abstr.
Former titles: Abstract Newsletter: Materials Sciences; Weekly Abstract Newsletter: Materials Sciences; Weekly Government Abstracts. Materials Sciences (ISSN 0364-4928)

N T I S ALERTS: OCEAN TECHNOLOGY & ENGINEERING. see *EARTH SCIENCES — Abstracting, Bibliographies, Statistics*

620 016 US
NOTES & COMMENT. 1974. 4/yr. free. Engineering Information, Inc., Castle Point on the Hudson, Hoboken, NJ 07030. TEL 800-221-1044. FAX 201-216-8532. Ed. Michael D. Scott. (reprint service avail.)
Former titles: Engineering Information. Notes and Comment; Engineering Index. Notes and Comment (ISSN 0145-207X)
Description: Details online search strategies and hints for using the EI databases.

625.72 JA
OSAKA-FU IKKYU SUIJUN SOKURYO SEIKAHYO. (Text in Japanese) 1964. a. Osaka-fu Dobokubu - Osaka Prefectural Government, Department of Public Works, 2, Otemae, Chuoh-ku, Osaka-shi, Osaka-fu, Japan. FAX 06-949-3129. charts; stat. circ. 550.
Description: Presents land survey results of the first benchmark from Osaka Prefecture.

624 FR ISSN 1146-5093
P A S C A L. T 295: BATIMENT. TRAVAUX PUBLICS. (Text in English, French) 1984. 10/yr. 1030 F. (outside EC 1085 F.). Centre National de la Recherche Scientifique, Institut de l'Information Scientifique et Technique, 2 allee du Parc de Brabois, 54514 Vandoeuvre-les-Nancy Cedex, France. TEL 83-50-46-00. FAX 83-50-46-50. adv. contact: Veronique Guinvarc'h. index, cum.index. (also avail. in microfiche) **Document type:** bibliography.
●Also available online. Vendor(s): DIALOG Information Services, Inc. (File no.144), European Space Agency (File no.14), Telesystemes - Questel. Also available on CD-ROM.
Formerly: P A S C A L Thema. T 295: Batiment. Travaux Publics (ISSN 0761-1722); Which supersedes in part: Bulletin Signaletique. Part 892: Batiment. Travaux Publics. Transports (ISSN 0223-4254); Which supersedes in part (in 1980): Bulletin Signaletique. Part 890: Industries Mecaniques - Batiment Travaux Publics - Transports.

016 620 US ISSN 0085-4581
Z7913 CODEN: PIEGAN
P I E. (Publications Indexed for Engineering) a. $45 in N. America; elsewhere $55. Engineering Information Inc., Castle Point on the Hudson, Hoboken, NJ 07030. TEL 201-216-8540; 800-221-1044. FAX 201-216-8526. TELEX 4990438. (U.K. and Western Europe subscr. to: Thompson Henry Ltd., London Rd., Sunningdale, Berks. SL5 OEP, England. TEL (0990) 24615. FAX (0990) 26120) (reprint service avail.)
—CASDDS.
Description: Lists all source publications reviewed and indexed by EI during the year.

620 UK
PARTICLE CHARACTERIZATION ABSTRACTS. 1991. bi-m. £135. Particle Science and Technology Information Service, Department of Chemical Engineering, University of Technology, Loughborough, Leics. LE11 3TU, England. TEL 0509-222528. **Document type:** abstracting/indexing.

620.11 016.5 UK ISSN 0883-153X
CODEN: PRPCEV
POLYMER CONTENTS; international current awareness publication for polymer science and engineering. 1984. 12/yr. £199($305) (effective 1994). Elsevier Science Ltd., Oxford Fulfilment Centre, P.O. Box 800, Kidlington, Oxford OX5 1DX, England. TEL 44-865-843000. FAX 44-865-843010. (Subscr. in U.S. and Canada to: Elsevier Science, 660 White Plains Rd., Tarrytown, NY 10591-5153. TEL 914-524-9200. FAX 914-333-2444) Ed. J.R. Fried. adv. **Document type:** abstracting/indexing.
—CCC.
Description: Contains the tables of contents of the leading international polymer journals, preprints, proceedings, newsletters, and selected serial book titles.
Refereed Serial

540 016 US ISSN 0161-8032
HD9650.1
PREDICASTS OVERVIEW OF MARKETS AND TECHNOLOGY. Key Title: P R O M T. Predicasts Overview of Markets and Technologies. Short title: PROMT. 1977. m. with q. and a. cumulations. $1000 (foreign $1100). Information Access Company, 362 Lakeside Dr., Foster City, CA 94404. TEL 415-378-5200; 800-227-8431. FAX 415-358-4759. (Or: Predicasts Europe, 8-10 Denman St., London W1V 7RF, England. TEL 071-494-3817) charts; stat.; cum.index. **Document type:** abstracting/indexing.
●Also available online. Vendor(s): BRS Online Products (PTSP), Data-Star, DIALOG Information Services, Inc..
—BLDSC (6604.435000); UnCover. **CCC.**
Formed by the merger of: Chemical Market Abstracts (ISSN 0009-2606); Equipment Market Abstracts (ISSN 0098-4779); Which was formerly titled: Electronics Market Abstracts; Electronics and Equipment Market Abstracts (ISSN 0095-7275)
Description: Provides abstracts and full text coverage of industries, companies, products, and markets reported in business and trade publications, including new products and technologies, market share, financial trends, mergers and acquisitions, regulations, and other business related topics.

621 UK ISSN 0094-9477
QC319.8
PREVIEWS OF HEAT AND MASS TRANSFER. 1974. 6/yr. £170($265) (effective 1994). (International Centre for Heat and Mass Transfer, YU) Elsevier Science Ltd., Pergamon, P.O. Box 800, Kidlington, Oxford OX5 1DX, England. TEL 44-865-843000. FAX 44-865-843010. (Subscr. in U.S. and Canada to: Elsevier Science, 660 White Plains Rd., Tarrytown, NY 10591-5153. TEL 914-524-9200. FAX 914-333-2444) (Co-publisher: Rumford Publishing Co., Inc., US) Ed. T.F. Irvine. adv.; bk.rev.; abstr.; bibl. circ. 300. (also avail. in microfilm from UMI; back issues avail.; reprint service avail. from UMI) **Indexed:** Curr.Cont. **Document type:** academic/scholarly publication, abstracting/indexing.
—EI; UnCover; SWETS; UMI. **CCC.**
Description: Provides abstracts of recently published papers in heat and mass transfer from more than 100 journals worldwide.
Refereed Serial

620 001.539 UK ISSN 0269-9648
TA340
PROBABILITY IN THE ENGINEERING AND INFORMATIONAL SCIENCES. 1987. q. £54($69) to individuals (overseas 68.50); institutions £160 (overseas £174.50 ($231)). Cambridge University Press, Edinburgh Bldg., Shaftesbury Rd., Cambridge CB2 2RU, England. TEL 0223-312393. FAX 0223-315052. TELEX 851817256. (N. American addr.: Cambridge University Press, Journals Dept., 40 W. 20th St., New York, NY 10011. TEL 212-924-3900. FAX 212-691-3239) Ed. Sheldon M. Ross. adv. (back issues avail.) **Indexed:** Biostat., Comput.Abstr., Oper.Res.Manage.Sci., Qual.Contr.Appl.Stat. **Document type:** academic/scholarly publication.
—BLDSC (66_7.223200); Faxon; UnCover; SWETS; UMI. **CCC.**
Description: Researches the application of probability to a variety of fields, in the physical, engineering, biological, behavioral, economic and management sciences. Primary focus is on stochastic modeling.

660 540 016 UK ISSN 0960-5045
CODEN: CEASD7
PROCESS AND CHEMICAL ENGINEERING. 1982. m. £320($610) (Canada £336). Royal Society of Chemistry, Thomas Graham House, Science Park, Milton Rd., Cambridge CB4 4WF, England. TEL 0223-420066. FAX 0223-423623. TELEX 818293. (Subscr. to: Turpin Distribution Services Ltd., Blackhorse Rd., Letchworth, Herts. SE6 1HN, England. TEL 0462-672555. FAX 0462-480947) Ed. Gill Wood. **Document type:** abstracting/indexing, bulletin.
●Also available online. Vendor(s): Data-Star (CEAB), DIALOG Information Services, Inc. (File no.315), European Space Agency (File no.85/CHEMICAL ENGINEERING ABSTRACTS), Orbit Search Service (CEBA).
—BLDSC (6849.983280); SWETS; CASDDS.
Formerly: Chemical Engineering Abstracts (ISSN 0262-6438)
Description: Provides full coverage of the published information needed by practicing chemical engineers, production and process chemists, plant managers and industrial engineering libraries.

660 UK
PROCESS ENGINEERING INDEX. 1965. s-a. Technical Indexes Ltd., Willoughby Rd., Bracknell, Berks. RG12 8DW, England. TEL 0344-426311. FAX 0344-424971. Ed. N. Saksena. charts. circ. 3,982. **Document type:** abstracting/indexing.
Former titles: Chemical Engineering Index (ISSN 0308-8391); Chemical Product Data.

621.3 US ISSN 0033-4537
PURDUE UNIVERSITY. SCHOOL OF ELECTRICAL ENGINEERING. ANNUAL RESEARCH SUMMARY. 1964. a. free to qualified personnel. Purdue University, School of Electrical Engineering, 1285 Electrical Engineering Bldg., IN 47907-1285. TEL 317-494-3441. FAX 317-494-6400. Ed. Mary A. Moyars-Johnson. abstr. circ. 1,000. (processed) **Document type:** academic/scholarly publication.
Description: Provides abstracts of current research projects undertaken within the school, summarizes faculty publications and activities, and describes facilities and services available.

526.9 016 UK
R I C S LIBRARY INFORMATION SERVICE ABSTRACTS AND REVIEWS. 1965. m. £200 to non-members. Royal Institution of Chartered Surveyors, 12 Great George St., Parliament Square, London SW1P 3AD, England. TEL 071-222-7000. FAX 071-222-9430. Ed. Pauline Lane-Gilbert. stat.; index, cum.index: 1965-1969, 1970-1974. circ. 1,300. (reprint service avail. from UMI) **Document type:** abstracting/indexing.
Formerly: R I C S Abstracts and Reviews (ISSN 0033-6939)

ENGINEERING — ABSTRACTING, BIBLIOGRAPHIES, STATISTICS

011   GW
REFERATE: MESSEN MECHANISCHER GROESSEN/BULLETIN OF ABSTRACTS: MEASUREMENT OF MECHANICAL QUANTITIES. (Text in English and German) 1973. 12/yr. DM.200. (Bundesanstalt fuer Materialforschung und -pruefung) F I Z Technik e.V., Ostbahnhofstr. 13, 60314 Frankfurt a.M., Germany. (Co-sponsors: VDI - VDE Gesellschaft Mess- und Automatisierungstechnik) Ed. Wilfried Schulze-Eggeringhaus. cum.index. circ. 350. (back issues avail.)
●Also available online.
Formerly (until 1993): Referateorgan: Messen Mechanischer Groessen (ISSN 0722-0057)

620.11 012   GW   ISSN 0341-0544
REFERATEORGAN: ZERSTOERUNGSFREIE PRUEFUNG/ABSTRACT JOURNAL: NON-DESTRUCTIVE TESTING. 1976. 12/yr. DM.283.50. Bundesanstalt fuer Materialforschung und -pruefung, Unter den Eichen 87, 12203 Berlin, Germany. TEL 030-8104-4628. FAX 030-8112029. (Co-sponsors: Deutsche Gesellschaft fuer Zerstoerungsfreie Pruefung; Fachinformationszentrum Technik e.V.) cum.index. (back issues avail.) **Document type:** government publication.
●Also available online.
Description: Features developments in non-destructive testing for flaws and materials properties.

629.8 016 001.6   RU
REFERATIVNYI ZHURNAL. AVTOMATIKA I VYCHISLITEL'NAYA TEKHNIKA. 1955. m. 314.40 Rub. (351.80 Rub. including index). Vsesoyuznyi Institut Nauchno-Tekhnicheskoi Informatsii (VINITI), Baltiiskaya ul., 14, Moscow A-219, Russia. (Subscr. to: Mezhdunarodnaya Kniga, Dimitrova ul. 39, 113095 Moscow, Russia) **Document type:** abstracting/indexing.
Formerly: Referativnyi Zhurnal. Avtomatika, Telemekhanika i Vychislitel'naya Tekhnika (ISSN 0202-4098)

621.1 016   RU   ISSN 0034-2424
REFERATIVNYI ZHURNAL. KOTLOSTROENIE. 1963. m. 16.80 Rub. (19 Rub. including index). Vsesoyuznyi Institut Nauchno-Tekhnicheskoi Informatsii (VINITI), Baltiiskaya ul., 14, Moscow A-219, Russia. (Subscr. to: Mezhdunarodnaya Kniga, Dimitrova ul. 39, 113095 Moscow, Russia) **Document type:** abstracting/indexing.

621 016   RU   ISSN 0034-2459
REFERATIVNYI ZHURNAL. MASHINOSTROITEL'NYE MATERIALY, KONSTRUKTSII I RASCHET DETALI MASHIN. GIDROPRIVOD. 1964. m. 76.40 Rub. (80.40 Rub. including index). Vsesoyuznyi Institut Nauchno-Tekhnicheskoi Informatsii (VINITI), Baltiiskaya ul., 14, Moscow A-219, Russia. (Subscr. to: Mezhdunarodnaya Kniga, Dimitrova ul. 39, 113095 Moscow, Russia) **Document type:** academic/scholarly publication.

621 016   RU   ISSN 0034-2483
QC1   CODEN: RZMKAC
REFERATIVNYI ZHURNAL. MEKHANIKA. 1953. m. 233 Rub. (334 Rub. including index). Vsesoyuznyi Institut Nauchno-Tekhnicheskoi Informatsii (VINITI), Baltiiskaya ul., 14, Moscow A-219, Russia. (Dist. by: Mezhdunarodnaya Kniga, Dimitrova ul. 39, 113095 Moscow, Russia) (also avail. in microfiche from BHP) **Indexed:** Appl.Mech.Rev., Chem.Abstr. **Document type:** abstracting/indexing.

621.6 016 621.5   RU
REFERATIVNYI ZHURNAL. NASOSOSTROENIE I KOMPRESSOROSTROENIE. KHOLODIL'NOE MASHINOSTROENIE. 1964. m. 36.20 Rub. (37.80 Rub. including index). Vsesoyuznyi Institut Nauchno-Tekhnicheskoi Informatsii (VINITI), Baltiiskaya ul., 14, Moscow A-219, Russia. (Subscr. to: Mezhdunarodnaya Kniga, Dimitrova ul. 39, 113095 Moscow, Russia) **Indexed:** Chem.Abstr.
Formerly: Referativnyi Zhurnal. Nasosostroenie i Kompressorostroenie (ISSN 0034-2513)

625 016   RU   ISSN 0484-2480
REFERATIVNYI ZHURNAL. STROITEL'NYE I DOROZHNYE MASHINY. 1956. m. 37.60 Rub. (42 Rub. including index). Vsesoyuznyi Institut Nauchno-Tekhnicheskoi Informatsii (VINITI), Baltiiskaya ul., 14, Moscow A-219, Russia, U.S.S.R. (Subscr. to: Mezhdunarodnaya Kniga, Dimitrova ul. 39, 113095 Moscow, Russia) **Document type:** abstracting/indexing.

621.8 016 388.5   RU   ISSN 0034-2610
REFERATIVNYI ZHURNAL. TRUBOPROVODNYI TRANSPORT. 1961. m. 30.60 Rub. (32 Rub. including index). Vsesoyuznyi Institut Nauchno-Tekhnicheskoi Informatsii (VINITI), Baltiiskaya ul., 14, Moscow A-219, Russia. (Subscr. to: Mezhdunarodnaya Kniga, Moscow, Dimitrova ul. 39, 113095 Russia) **Document type:** abstracting/indexing.

621 016   RU   ISSN 0034-2629
REFERATIVNYI ZHURNAL. TURBOSTROENIE. 1956. m. 25 Rub. (28.80 Rub. including index). Vsesoyuznyi Institut Nauchno-Tekhnicheskoi Informatsii (VINITI), Baltiiskaya ul., 14, Moscow A-219, Russia. (Subscr. to: Mezhdunarodnaya Kniga, Dimitrova ul. 39, 113095 Moscow, Russia) **Document type:** abstracting/indexing.

621 016   RU   ISSN 0034-2637
REFERATIVNYI ZHURNAL. VOPROSY TEKHNICHESKOGO PROGRESSA I ORGANIZATSII PROIZVODSTVA V MASHINOSTROENII. 1956. m. 33.60 Rub. (37.80 Rub. including index). Vsesoyuznyi Institut Nauchno-Tekhnicheskoi Informatsii (VINITI), Baltiiskaya ul., 14, Moscow A-219, Russia. (Subscr. to: Mezhdunarodnaya Kniga, Dimitrova ul. 39, 113095 Moscow, Russia) **Document type:** abstracting/indexing.

SERVICIO REFERATIVO DE LA CONSTRUCCION. see *BUILDING AND CONSTRUCTION — Abstracting, Bibliographies, Statistics*

620   HU   ISSN 0231-3316
SZAMITOGEPES MUSZAKI TERVEZES/COMPUTER-AIDED DESIGN. 1983. q. 2400 Ft. Orszagos Muszaki Informacios Kozpont es Konyvtar (O.M.I.K.K.) - National Technical Information Centre and Library, Muzeum u. 17, P.O. Box 12, 1428 Budapest, Hungary. Ed. Imre Horvath. abstr. circ. 250.

TECHNICAL EDUCATION & TRAINING ABSTRACTS. see *EDUCATION — Abstracting, Bibliographies, Statistics*

TEMPLATE; the magazine of engineering systems and solutions. see *COMPUTERS — Computer Graphics*

660.2 016   UK   ISSN 0960-5053
TP1   CODEN: TCEAA7
THEORETICAL CHEMICAL ENGINEERING. 1964. m. £124($236) (Canada £130). Royal Society of Chemistry, Thomas Graham House, Science Park, Milton Rd., Cambridge CB4 4WF, England. TEL 0223-420066. FAX 0223-423623. (Dist. by: Turpin Distribution Services Ltd., Blackhorse Rd., Letchworth, Herts SG6 1HN, England. TEL 0462-672555. FAX 0462-480947) Ed. John Taylor. bk.rev.; abstr. **Indexed:** Fluidex. **Document type:** abstracting/indexing.
●Also available online. Vendor(s): Data-Star, DIALOG Information Services, Inc., European Space Agency, Orbit Search Service.
—UnCover; SWETS. **CCC.**
Formerly: Theoretical Chemical Engineering Abstracts (ISSN 0040-5787)
Description: Provides timely worldwide coverage of theoretical chemical engineering, including theory and laboratory experimentation.

624 011   TU
TURKISH CHAMBER OF CIVIL ENGINEERS. DIGEST (YEAR); extended summaries from Teknik Dergi/Technical Journal. (Text in English) 1990. a. $20 (includes q. Teknik Dergi). Turkish Chamber of Civil Engineers - Insaat Muhandislari Odasi, Selanik Caddesi 19-1, Kizilay 06650 Ankara, Turkey. TEL 90-312-4337626. FAX 90-312-4170632. Ed. A. Tugrul Tankut. charts; stat. **Document type:** abstracting/indexing, academic/scholarly publication.
Description: Presents extended summaries of original research results and case studies from Turkish civil engineering practice.
Refereed Serial

629.8 016   GW
V D I. INFORMATIONSDIENST REGELUNGSTECHNIK. (Text in English and German) 1964. m. DM.1330($526) (Fachinformations Zentrum Technik e.V.) V D I Verlag GmbH, Heinrichstr. 24, 40239 Duesseldorf, Germany. TEL 0211-6188-0. FAX 0211-6188-112. TELEX 8587743. (Subscr. to: Postfach 101054, 40001 Duesseldorf, Germany) abstr.; index. circ. 150. **Document type:** trade publication.
—**CCC.**
Former titles: Dokumentation Regelungstechnik (ISSN 0340-3955); V D I - V D E Dokumentation Regelungstechnik (ISSN 0179-0811)

621 621.9   GW   ISSN 0720-4612
V D I INFORMATIONSDIENST. DRAHTHERSTELLUNG UND DRAHTERZEUGNISSE. 1981. bi-m. DM.315. (Verein Deutscher Ingenieure) V D I Verlag GmbH, Heinrichstr. 24, 40239 Duesseldorf, Germany. TEL 0211-6188-0. FAX 0211-6188-112. TELEX 8587743. (Subscr. to: Postfach 101054, 40001 Duesseldorf, Germany) Ed. G. Gentzsch. abstr.; bibl.; charts; illus. (back issues avail.) **Document type:** trade publication.
—**CCC.**

620 016   UK
VALIDATED ENGINEERING DATA INDEX. 1966. a. E S D U International plc, 27 Corsham St., London N1 6UA, England. TEL 071-490-5151. FAX 071-490-2701. Ed. J.A. Shaw. cum.index: 1943-1992. circ. 3,000. **Indexed:** Chem.Abstr. **Document type:** abstracting/indexing.
Former titles: Engineering Sciences Data Unit Index; Engineering Sciences Data Index (ISSN 0071-0377)
Description: Contains references to data for aeronautical, chemical, mechanical and structural engineering analysis, and design use.

011 621.9   GW   ISSN 0724-1976
VEREIN DEUTSCHER INGENIEURE. INFORMATIONSDIENST. INSTANDHALTUNG.* 1983. bi-m. DM.255. Fachinformationszentrum Technik e.V., Postfach 605047, 60335 Frankfurt a.M., Germany. Ed. C. Hortin. bk.rev.; abstr.; charts; illus. (back issues avail.)
—**CCC.**

660.2 016   GW   ISSN 0042-3890
CODEN: VEBEA6
VERFAHRENSTECHNISCHE BERICHTE/CHEMICAL AND PROCESS ENGINEERING ABSTRACTS. 1954. w. DM.3715($2940) (Bayer AG) Verlag Hoppenstedt und Co., Havelstr. 9, 64295 Darmstadt, Germany. TEL 06151-380-0. FAX 06151-380360. Eds. W. Springe, E.O. Schmidt. bk.rev.; charts; index, cum.index. circ. 400. (also avail. in microfiche; magnetic tape; reprint service avail. from ISI) **Document type:** abstracting/indexing.
—**CCC.**

620 600 500   JA   ISSN 0507-9683
WASEDA DAIGAKU DAIGAKUIN RIKOGAKU KENKYU IHO/WASEDA UNIVERSITY. GRADUATE SCHOOL OF SCIENCE AND ENGINEERING. SYNOPSES OF SCIENCE AND ENGINEERING PAPERS. (Text in Japanese) 1952. a. Waseda Daigaku, Daigakuin Rikogaku Kenkyuka - Waseda University, Graduate School of Science and Engineering, 4-1, Okubo 3-chome, Shinjuku-ku, Tokyo 160, Japan. abstr.

660   JA
ZEORAITO KENKYU HAPPYOKAI KOEN YOKOSHU/JAPAN ASSOCIATION OF ZEOLITE. ABSTRACTS OF ANNUAL MEETING. (Text in Japanese) 1985. a. Zeoraito Kenkyukai - Japan Association of Zeolite, Tokyo Kogyo Daigaku Kogakubu, Kagaku Kogakka Ono Kenkyushitsu, 12-1, Ookayama 2-chome, Meguro-ku, Tokyo 152, Japan. **Document type:** abstracting/indexing.

ENGINEERING — Chemical Engineering

see also Plastics

660.2 542   US   ISSN 0569-5473
A I CH E EQUIPMENT TESTING PROCEDURES. 1952. a. $60. American Institute of Chemical Engineers, Equipment Testing Procedures Committee, 345 E. 47th St., New York, NY 10017. TEL 212-705-7657; 800-242-4363. FAX 212-705-8400. Ed.Bd. (also avail. in microform from ISI; back issues avail.) **Indexed:** Eng.Ind. **Document type:** trade publication.
—EI. **CCC**.
    Description: Prepared for the engineer involved in installed equipment and testing practices evaluation.
Refereed Serial

660   US   ISSN 0001-1541
TP1   **CODEN: AICEAC**
A I CH E JOURNAL. 1955. m. $395 to non-members (foreign $455); members $60. American Institute of Chemical Engineers, 345 E. 47th St., New York, NY 10017. TEL 212-705-7663. FAX 212-752-3294. Ed. M. Tirrell. adv.; bk.rev.; abstr.; bibl.; charts; illus.; index. circ. 4,061. (also avail. in microform from UMI; reprint service avail.) **Indexed:** A.S.& T.Ind., Abstr.Bull.Inst.Pap.Chem., AESIS, API Abstr., API Catal., API Hlth.& Environ., API Oil., API Pet.Ref., API Transport., Appl.Mech.Rev., CAD CAM Abstr., Ceram.Abstr., Chem.Abstr., Chem.Eng.Abstr., Curr.Cont., E&P Hlth. (1993-), Energy Info.Abstr., EnergyInd., Eng.Ind., Environ.Abstr., Excerp.Med., Fluidex, Gas Abstr., Gas Process.& Ppl. (1993-), INIS Atomind., ISMEC, Math.R., Off.Tech. (1993-), Oper.Res.Manage.Sci., Petrol.Abstr. (1961-), Sci.Abstr., Sci.Cit.Ind., Sel.Water Res.Abstr., Soils & Fert., T.C.E.A. **Document type:** trade publication.
—BLDSC (0773.071200); CIS; Faxon; UnCover; SWETS; UMI; CASDDS. **CCC**.
    Description: Devoted to fundamental research and development having immediate or potential impact on chemical engineering and such allied fields as biotechnology, materials and environmental engineering.
Refereed Serial

660   US   ISSN 0270-6229
TP155.75
A I CH E M I MODULAR INSTRUCTION. SERIES A: PROCESS CONTROL. 1980. irreg. $44 to non-members; members $35. American Institute of Chemical Engineers, 345 E. 47th St., New York, NY 10017. TEL 212-705-7657. FAX 212-705-8400. Ed. T.F. Edgar. bibl.; charts. (back issues avail.) **Indexed:** Eng.Ind. **Document type:** trade publication.
—**CCC**.
    Description: Teaches various aspects of chemical technology.
Refereed Serial

660   US   ISSN 0270-7624
TP156.M3
A I CH E M I MODULAR INSTRUCTION. SERIES B: STAGEWISE AND MASS TRANSFER OPERATIONS. 1980. irreg. $44 to non-members; members $35. American Institute of Chemical Engineers, 345 E. 47th St., New York, NY 10017. TEL 212-705-7657. FAX 212-752-3294. bibl.; charts. (back issues avail.) **Indexed:** Eng.Ind. **Document type:** trade publication.
    Description: Teaches various aspects of chemical technology.

660   US   ISSN 0270-7632
TP156.T7
A I CH E M I MODULAR INSTRUCTION. SERIES C: TRANSPORT. 1980. irreg. (approx. 1/yr.). $44 to non-members; members $35. American Institute of Chemical Engineers, 345 E. 47th St., New York, NY 10017. TEL 212-705-7657. FAX 212-752-3294. bibl.; charts. (back issues avail.) **Indexed:** Eng.Ind. **Document type:** trade publication.
    Description: Designed to be used in independent study, continuing education courses and traditional classes.
Refereed Serial

660   US   ISSN 0270-7640
QD504
A I CH E M I MODULAR INSTRUCTION. SERIES D: THERMODYNAMICS. 1980. irreg. $44 to non-members; members $35. American Institute of Chemical Engineers, 345 E. 47th St., New York, NY 10017. TEL 212-705-7657. FAX 212-752-3294. bibl.; charts. (back issues avail.) **Indexed:** Eng.Ind. **Document type:** trade publication.
—BLDSC (0773.072180).
    Description: Teaches various aspects of chemical technology.
Refereed Serial

660   US   ISSN 0270-7659
QD502
A I CH E M I MODULAR INSTRUCTION. SERIES E: KINETICS. 1980. irreg. $44 to non-members; members $35. American Institute of Chemical Engineers, 345 E. 47th St., New York, NY 10017. TEL 212-705-7657. FAX 212-752-3294. bibl.; charts. (back issues avail.) **Indexed:** Eng.Ind. **Document type:** trade publication.
    Description: Teaches various aspects of chemical technology.
Refereed Serial

660   US   ISSN 0270-7667
A I CH E M I MODULAR INSTRUCTION. SERIES F: MATERIAL AND ENERGY BALANCES. 1980. irreg. $44 to non-members; members $35. American Institute of Chemical Engineers, 345 E. 47th St., New York, NY 10017. TEL 212-705-7657. FAX 212-752-3294. bibl.; charts. (back issues avail.) **Indexed:** Eng.Ind. **Document type:** trade publication.
    Description: Teaches various aspects of chemical technology.
Refereed Serial

660   US   ISSN 0890-0582
A I CH E M I MODULAR INSTRUCTION. SERIES G: DESIGN OF EQUIPMENT. 1985. irreg. (approx. 1/yr.). $44 to non-members; members $35. American Institute of Chemical Engineers, 345 E. 47th St., New York, NY 10017. TEL 212-705-7657. FAX 212-752-3294. bibl.; charts. (back issues avail.) **Indexed:** Eng.Ind. **Document type:** trade publication.
    Description: Designed to be used in independent study, continuing education courses and traditional classes.
Refereed Serial

660   US   ISSN 0065-8804
    CODEN: ACEMB5
A I CH E MONOGRAPH SERIES. 1951. irreg., vol.84, 1988. price varies. American Institute of Chemical Engineers, 345 E. 47th St., New York, NY 10017. TEL 212-705-7657. FAX 212-752-3294. **Indexed:** Chem.Eng.Abstr., Eng.Ind., T.C.E.A. **Document type:** monographic series.
—**CCC**.
    Description: Contains the Institute's lecture on chemical engineering.

660.2 542   US
A I CH E PARTICLE SIZE CLASSIFIER TEST PROCEDURE. irreg., 2nd ed., 1992. $60 to non-members; members $48. American Institute of Chemical Engineers, 345 E. 47th St., New York, NY 10017. TEL 212-705-7657. FAX 212-752-3294. **Document type:** monographic series.

660   US   ISSN 0065-8812
    CODEN: ACSSCQ
A I CH E SYMPOSIUM SERIES. 1951. a., latest S-298, 1993. price varies. American Institute of Chemical Engineers, 345 E. 47th St., New York, NY 10017. TEL 212-705-7657. FAX 212-752-3294. (back issues avail.) **Indexed:** AESIS, API Abstr., API Catal., API Hlth.& Environ., API Oil., API Pet.Ref., API Pet.Subst., API Transport., Biol.Abstr., Chem.Abstr., Chem.Eng.Abstr., Dairy Sci.Abstr., Energy Ind., Energy Info.Abstr., Eng.Ind., Food Sci.& Tech.Abstr., Food Sci.& Tech.Abstr., Forest.Abstr., GeoRef., INIS Atomind., Sel.Water Res.Abstr., T.C.E.A. **Document type:** proceedings.
—BLDSC (0773.071900); Faxon; SWETS; CASDDS. **CCC**.
    Supersedes: Chemical Engineering Progress Symposium Series (ISSN 0069-2948)
    Description: Presents concentrated subjects in areas relevant to chemical engineering.
Refereed Serial

ACCELERATOR NEWSLETTER. see *CHEMISTRY*

661   US   ISSN 0001-821X
TP967   **CODEN: ADHAAO**
ADHESIVES AGE. 1957. m. (plus a. Directory). $52 (foreign $112). Argus Inc., 6151 Powers Ferry Rd., N.W., Atlanta, GA 30339-2941. TEL 404-955-2500. FAX 404-955-0400. Ed. Larry Anderson. adv.; bk.rev.; charts; illus.; pat.; tr.lit.; index. circ. 26,345. (also avail. in microform from UMI; reprint service avail. from UMI) **Indexed:** A.S.& T.Ind., Abstr.Bull.Inst.Pap.Chem., Art & Archaeol.Tec.Abstr., CAD CAM Abstr. (until 1992), Chem.Abstr., Curr.Cont., Curr.Leather Lit., Curr.Pack.Abstr., Eng.Ind., Environ.Abstr., Excerp.Med., Fluidex, Int.Aerosp.Abstr., Int.Sci.Rev., ISMEC, Print.Abstr., PROMT, Robomat. (until 1992), Sci.Cit.Ind., Text.Tech.Dig., World Surf.Coat. **Document type:** trade publication.
● Also available online.
—BLDSC (0680.950000); Faxon; UnCover; SWETS; UMI; CASDDS. **CCC**.
    Description: Covers the manufacture, application, technology, research and marketing of adhesives, sealants and related products.

668   US   ISSN 0001-821X
ADHESIVES AGE DIRECTORY. 1968. a. $51.95. Argus Inc., 6151 Powers Ferry Rd., N.W., Atlanta, GA 30339-2941 TEL 404-955-2500. FAX 404-955-0400. Ed. Barbara Katinsky. adv. circ. 26,345. **Document type:** directory.
    Formerly: Adhesives Red Book (ISSN 0065-1931)

661   US   ISSN 0890-0884
ADHESIVES & SEALANTS NEWSLETTER. 1977. m. $165 (foreign $185). Adhesive Information Services, Inc., Box 1123, Mishawaka, IN 46546-1123. TEL 219-255-6794. Ed. W.F. (Bill) Harrington. bk.rev. (looseleaf format; back issues avail.) **Document type:** newsletter.
    Description: News digest of adhesive and sealant information.

ADHESIVES DIRECTORY. see *BUSINESS AND ECONOMICS — Trade And Industrial Directories*

660   UK   ISSN 0263-6174
QD547   **CODEN: ASTEEZ**
ADSORPTION SCIENCE AND TECHNOLOGY. 1984. q. £99 (foreign £117). Multi-Science Publishing Co. Ltd., 107 High St., Brentwood, Essex CM14 4RX, England. TEL 0277-224632. (U.S. subscr. to: Box 176, Avenel, NJ 07001) Ed. P.A. Sermon. adv.; abstr.; bibl.; illus.; index. **Indexed:** Chem.Eng.Abstr., T.C.E.A. **Document type:** academic/scholarly publication.
—BLDSC (0696.627000); EI; UnCover; SWETS; CASDDS. **CCC**.

660 620   US   ISSN 1065-7355
    CODEN: ACATE9
▼**ADVANCED CEMENT BASED MATERIALS**. 1993. 6/yr. $215 (foreign $241) (effective 1994). (American Concrete Institute) Elsevier Science Inc., 655 Ave. of the Americas, New York, NY 10010. TEL 212-989-5800. FAX 212-633-3680. TELEX 420643 AEPUI. Eds. S.P. Shah, J.F. Young. **Document type:** academic/scholarly publication.
—**CCC**.
    Description: Publishes original multidisciplinary research on the preparation, characterization, processing and uses of advanced cements and concretes.
Refereed Serial

ADVANCED CERAMICS REPORT; an international newsletter. see *CERAMICS, GLASS AND POTTERY*

660   NE   ISSN 0921-8831
    CODEN: APTEEE
ADVANCED POWDER TECHNOLOGY. (Text in English) 1990. q. DM.400 (effective 1994). V S P, P.O. Box 346, 3700 AH Zeist, Netherlands. TEL 31-3404-25790. FAX 31-3404-32081. TELEX 40217 VSP NL. Ed. K. Gotoh. **Document type:** academic/scholarly publication.
—BLDSC (0696.919700); SWETS; CASDDS.
    Description: Covers all aspects of powder engineering and technology.
Refereed Serial

ENGINEERING — CHEMICAL ENGINEERING

660.2   US   ISSN 0065-2377
TP145   CODEN: ACHEAT
ADVANCES IN CHEMICAL ENGINEERING. 1956. irreg., vol.18, 1992. Academic Press, Inc., 525 B St., Ste. 1900, San Diego, CA 92101-4495. TEL 619-231-0923. FAX 619-699-6715. (Subscr. to: Order Dept., 6277 Sea Harbor Dr., 4th Fl., Orlando, FL 32887. TEL 800-321-5068) Ed.Bd. index. (reprint service avail. from ISI) **Indexed:** Chem.Eng.Abstr., T.C.E.A.
—BLDSC (0703.500000); Faxon; SWETS; CASDDS. **CCC.**
   Refereed Serial

660 541.37   GW   ISSN 0938-5193
QD552   CODEN: AESEEY
ADVANCES IN ELECTROCHEMICAL SCIENCE AND ENGINEERING. (Text in English) 1990. irreg. V C H Verlagsgesellschaft mbH, Postfach 101161, 69451 Weinheim, Germany. TEL 06201-606-0. FAX 06201-606328. TELEX 465516-VCHWH-D. (U.S. addr.: VCH Publishers Inc., 220 E. 23rd St., New York, NY 10010-4606. TEL 212-683-8333) Eds. Heinz Gerischer, Charles Tobias. **Document type:** monographic series.
—BLDSC (0704.693000); Faxon; CASDDS.

ADVANCES IN POLYMER SCIENCE/FORTSCHRITTE DER HOCHPOLYMEREN-FORSCHUNG. see *CHEMISTRY — Organic Chemistry*

661   NE   ISSN 0271-2334
QC319.8   CODEN: ATRPDU
ADVANCES IN TRANSPORT PROCESSES. (Text in English) 1980. irreg., vol.9, 1993. price varies. Elsevier Science B.V., P.O. Box 211, 1000 AE Amsterdam, Netherlands. TEL 31-20-5803911. FAX 31-20-5803705. TELEX 18582 ESPA NL. (Subscr. in U.S. and Canada to: Elsevier Science Inc., Box 882, Madison Sq. Sta., New York, NY 10159. TEL 212-989-5800) Ed. Arun S. Mujumdar. **Indexed:** Chem.Abstr. **Document type:** monographic series.
—BLDSC (0711.635000); CASDDS.
   Refereed Serial

ADVANCES IN URETHANE SCIENCE AND TECHNOLOGY. see *CHEMISTRY — Organic Chemistry*

AFINIDAD; revista de quimica teorica y aplicada. see *CHEMISTRY*

660   NE
AKZO ANNUAL REPORT (YEAR). (Editions in Dutch, English) a. free. Akzo N.V., Velperweg 76, P.O. Box 9300, 6800 SB Arnhem, Netherlands. TEL 085-664850. FAX 085-663250. TELEX 45438.

AMERICAN ASSOCIATION FOR CRYSTAL GROWTH NEWSLETTER. see *CHEMISTRY — Crystallography*

660   US
AMERICAN CARBON SOCIETY. BIENNIAL CONFERENCE ON CARBON - EXTENDED ABSTRACTS AND PROGRAM. 1953. biennial. $50. American Carbon Society, 215 Stackpole St., St. Marys, PA 15857. TEL 814-781-8410. circ. 300. (back issues avail.)

662   US   ISSN 8755-3163
AMERICAN FIREWORKS NEWS. 1982. m. $19.95. Star Rte., Box 30, Dingmans Ferry, PA 18328. TEL 717-828-8417. FAX 717-828-8695. Ed. John M. Drewes. adv.; bk.rev. circ. 2,000. **Document type:** newsletter.
   Description: Newsletter for fireworks enthusiasts.

AMERICAN OIL CHEMISTS' SOCIETY. JOURNAL. see *CHEMISTRY — Organic Chemistry*

661   US   ISSN 0360-7011
TP149   CODEN: ASAFB8
AMMONIA PLANT SAFETY AND RELATED FACILITIES; a C E P technical manual. 1959. a. price varies. American Institute of Chemical Engineers, 345 E. 47th St., New York, NY 10017. TEL 212-705-7657. FAX 212-752-3294. (back issues avail.) **Indexed:** Chem.Abstr., Chem.Eng.Abstr., Eng.Ind. **Document type:** trade publication.
—El; Faxon; UnCover; SWETS; CASDDS. **CCC.**
   Formerly (until 1969): Chemical Engineering Progress. Safety in Air and Ammonia Plants (ISSN 0069-293X)

ANGEWANDTE MAKROMOLEKULARE CHEMIE; an international journal of applied macromolecular chemistry and physics. see *CHEMISTRY — Organic Chemistry*

660   FR   ISSN 0292-627X
                     CODEN: ANNCEW
ANNALES DES COMPOSITES. (Text in French; summaries in English) 1982. s-a. 350 F. per no. to non-members. (Association pour les Materiaux Composites, Centre des Materiaux) A M A C, 60 bd. St. Michel, 75272 Paris Cedex 06, France. TEL 60-76-30-14. FAX 60-88-47-57. TELEX 600 700 CORAV. Ed.Bd. circ. 400. (back issues avail.) **Indexed:** Eng.Mat.Abstr. **Document type:** proceedings.
—CASDDS.
   Description: Covers all subjects concerned with composite science and technology.

ANNUAL BOOK OF A S T M STANDARDS. VOLUME 06.03. PAINT - FATTY OILS AND ACIDS, SOLVENTS, MISCELLANEOUS; AROMATIC HYDROCARBONS. see *ENGINEERING — Engineering Mechanics And Materials*

ANNUAL BOOK OF A S T M STANDARDS. VOLUME 15.05. ENGINE COOLANTS; HALOGENATED ORGANIC SOLVENTS; INDUSTRIAL CHEMICALS. see *ENGINEERING — Engineering Mechanics And Materials*

541.3   NE   ISSN 0926-860X
QD505   CODEN: ACAGE4
APPLIED CATALYSIS A: GENERAL; an international journal devoted to catalytic science and its applications. (Text in English) 1981. 28/yr. (in 14 vols.; 2 nos./vol.) fl.5404($2921) (with section B fl.6096($3295)) (effective 1994). Elsevier Science B.V., P.O. Box 211, 1000 AE Amsterdam, Netherlands. TEL 31-20-5803911. FAX 31-20-5803598. TELEX 18582 ESPA NL. (Subscr. in U.S. and Canada to: Elsevier Science Inc., Box 882, Madison Sq. Sta., New York, NY 10159-0882. TEL 212-989-5800. FAX 212-633-3990) Ed. B. Delmon. adv.; bk.rev.; pat. (also avail. in microform from UMI; back issues avail.) **Indexed:** Abstr.Bull.Inst.Pap.Chem., API Abstr., API Catal., API Hlth.& Environ., API Oil., API Pet.Ref., API Pet.Subst., API Transport., Biol.Abstr., Cadscan, Chem.Abstr., Chem.Eng.Abstr., Chem.Infd., Curr.Cont., Eng.Ind., Excerp.Med., Gas Abstr., Ind.Sci.Rev., Lead Abstr., Met.Abstr., Sci.Cit.Ind., T.C.E.A., World Alum.Abstr., Zincscan. **Document type:** academic/scholarly publication.
●Also available online. Vendor(s): STN International.
—BLDSC (1571.921600); Faxon; UnCover; SWETS; CASDDS. **CCC.**
   Supersedes in part (in 1992): Applied Catalysis (ISSN 0166-9834)
   Description: Covers research in catalytic phenomena occurring in industrial and related processes.
   Refereed Serial

541.3   NE   ISSN 0926-3373
QD505   CODEN: ACBEE3
APPLIED CATALYSIS B: ENVIRONMENTAL; an international journal devoted to catalytic science and its applications. (Text in English) 1981. 8/yr. (in 2 vols.; 4 nos./vol.) fl.872($471) (effective 1994). Elsevier Science B.V., P.O. Box 211, 1000 AE Amsterdam, Netherlands. TEL 31-20-5803911. FAX 31-20-5803598. TELEX 18582 ESPA NL. (Subscr. in U.S. and Canada to: Elsevier Science Inc., Box 882, Madison Sq. Sta., New York, NY 10159-0882. TEL 212-989-5800. FAX 212-633-3990) Ed. B. Delmon. cum.index. (also avail. in microform from UMI; back issues avail.) **Indexed:** Environ.Per.Bibl. **Document type:** academic/scholarly publication.
—BLDSC (1571.921700); El; Faxon; UnCover; SWETS; CASDDS. **CCC.**
   Supersedes in part (in 1992): Applied Catalysis (ISSN 0166-9834)
   Description: Forum for the exchange of results and opinions on all aspects of environmental catalysis, including processes, sensors, and elimination of environmental hazards.
   Refereed Serial

620   US   ISSN 1044-5110
TP156.S6   CODEN: ATSPE2
ATOMIZATION AND SPRAYS. 1991. bi-m. $60 to individuals; institutions $200. (International Institutes for Liquid Atomization and Spray Systems) Begell House Inc., 79 Madison Ave., New York, NY 10016-7892. TEL 212-725-1999. FAX 212-213-8368. TELEX 9102509520. Ed. Norman Chigier. **Document type:** academic/scholarly publication.
—BLDSC (1772.390000); UnCover; SWETS; CASDDS. **CCC.**
   Description: Reports on experimental and theoretical investigations of physical phenomena occurring in the breakup of liquids and the development of sprays.
   Refereed Serial

662   GW   ISSN 0005-3333
B S R. (Bohren, Sprengen, Raeumen); im Bergbau, Steinbruch, Bauwesen, in der Erdolgewinnung und Landeskultur. 1952. m. DM.42.($10.50) Erwin Barth Verlag KG, Kiesstr. 11, 31535 Neustadt, Germany. adv.; bk.rev.; bibl.; charts; illus.; pat.; stat. circ. 3,600. **Indexed:** Chem.Abstr.

662   CC   ISSN 1001-487X
BAO PO/BLASTING. (Text in Chinese; table of contents in English) 1984. q. Y10. Wuhan Gongye Daxue, Bao Po Bianjibu, 14 Luoshi Lu, Wuchang, Wuhan, Hubei 430070, People's Republic of China. Ed. Liu Qingrong. **Document type:** academic/scholarly publication.
—BLDSC (2109.032000).
   Refereed Serial

660   CC   ISSN 1000-5668
                     CODEN: BHXKE7
BEIJING HUAGONG XUEYUAN XUEBAO (ZIRAN KEXUE BAN)/BEIJING INSTITUTE OF CHEMICAL TECHNOLOGY. JOURNAL (NATURAL SCIENCE). (Text in Chinese) 1974. q. Beijing Huagong Xueyuan - Beijing Institute of Chemical Technology, Xuebao Bianjibu, 15 Beisanhuan Donglu, Beijing 100029, People's Republic of China. Ed. Fu Jufu. **Document type:** academic/scholarly publication.
—BLDSC (4707.888500); CASDDS.

BRITAIN'S TOP 500 CHEMICAL COMPANIES. see *BUSINESS AND ECONOMICS — Trade And Industrial Directories*

660   SZ   ISSN 0173-9980
BULK SOLIDS HANDLING; the international journal of powder-bulk & processing. (Text in English) 1981. q. 238 SFr. Trans Tech Publications, Hardstr. 13, P.O. Box 100, CH-4714 Aedermannsdorf, Switzerland. FAX 062-741058. Ed. Reinhard H. Woehlbier. adv.; bk.rev.; index. circ. 10,000. (back issues avail.) **Indexed:** AESIS, C.R.I. Abstr., Excerp.Med., Fluidex, INIS Atomind., Met.Abstr., World Alum.Abstr.
—BLDSC (2366.719500); EI; SWETS.
   Description: Technical publication concerned with the solution to practical problems of shipping and storing bulk materials, as well as equipment design and engineering.

660   US   ISSN 0195-4946
                     CODEN: CACAD3
C A SELECTS. CHEMICAL PROCESSING APPARATUS. s-w. $210 (effective Jan. 1994). Chemical Abstracts Service (Subsidiary of: American Chemical Society), 2540 Olentangy River Rd., Box 3012, Columbus, OH 43210-0012. TEL 614-447-3600. FAX 614-447-3713. TELEX 6842086. **Document type:** abstracting/indexing.
   Description: Covers apparatus for absorption, crystallization, distillation, extraction, filtration, purification, separation, chemical processing; and their construction, modification, and application.

660   US   ISSN 1057-1981
TP149
C C P S - A I C H E DIRECTORY OF CHEMICAL PROCESS SAFETY SERVICES. 1991. triennial. American Institute of Chemical Engineers, Center for Chemical Process Safety, 345 E. 47th St., New York, NY 10017. TEL 212-705-7319. FAX 212-752-3294. adv. **Document type:** directory.
   Description: Comprehensive listing of more than 350 organizations offering consulting services, emergency services, testing services or training courses from offices in the United States and Canada.

ENGINEERING — CHEMICAL ENGINEERING

661   **US**   ISSN 0276-8429
TP157
C E C - CHEMICAL ENGINEERING CATALOG. 1915. a. $40. Penton Publishing (Stamford) (Subsidiary of: Pittway Company), 600 Summer St., Box 1361, Stamford, CT 06904. TEL 203-348-7531. FAX 203-348-4023. adv.; tr.lit.; index. circ. 35,000. (also avail. in microfilm; reprint service avail. from UMI)
—UMI. **CCC.**
Description: Reference source used in the chemical process industries.

CANADIAN CHEMICAL NEWS/ACTUALITE CHIMIQUE CANADIENNE. see *CHEMISTRY*

660.2   **CN**   ISSN 0008-4034
TP1   CODEN: CJCEA7
CANADIAN JOURNAL OF CHEMICAL ENGINEERING. 6/yr. Can.$170($88) to non-members (foreign $225); members Can.$50 (foreign $50). Canadian Society for Chemical Engineering, 130 Slater St., Ste. 550, Ottawa, ON K1P 6E2, Canada. TEL 613-232-6252. FAX 613-232-5862. Ed. C. Robinson. illus.; index. circ. 1,300. (also avail. in microform from MIM,UMI,PMC; reprint service avail. from UMI) **Indexed:** A.I.Abstr., A.S.& T.Ind., Abstr.Bull.Inst.Pap.Chem., Acid Rain Abstr., Acid Rain Ind., API Abstr., API Catal., API Hlth.& Environ., API Oil., API Pet.Ref., API Pet.Subst., Biol.Abstr., Biotech.Abstr., C.R.I.Abstr., CAD CAM Abstr., Cadscan, Chem.Abstr., Chem.Eng.Abstr., Comput.Abstr., Corros.Abstr., Curr.Cont., E&P Hlth. (1993-), Energy Info.Abstr., Eng.Ind., Environ.Abstr., Excerp.Med., Fluidex, Foul.Prev.Res.Dig., Gas Abstr., Gas Process.& Ppl. (1993-), Ind.Sci.Rev., INIS Atomind., Lead Abstr., Met.Abstr., Off.Tech. (1993-), Petrol.Abstr. (1963-), RAPRA, Risk Abstr., Sci.Abstr., Sci.Cit.Ind., Soils & Fert., T.C.E.A., W.R.C.Inf., World Alum.Abstr., Zincscan.
—BLDSC (3030.900000); CIS; EI; Faxon; UnCover; SWETS; UMI; CASDDS. **CCC.**
Description: Publishes original papers dealing with the theory and practice of chemical engineering and applied chemistry.

CATALYSIS REVIEWS: SCIENCE AND ENGINEERING. see *CHEMISTRY — Physical Chemistry*

541.3   **NE**   ISSN 0920-5861
          CODEN: CATTEA
CATALYSIS TODAY; a serial publication dealing with topical themes in catalysis and related subjects. (Text in English) 1987. 12/yr. (in 4 vols.; 3 nos./vol.). fl.2604($1408) (effective 1994). Elsevier Science B.V., P.O. Box 211, 1000 AH Amsterdam, Netherlands. TEL 31-20-5803911. FAX 31-20-5803598. TELEX 18582 ESPA NL. (Subscr. in U.S. and Canada to: Elsevier Science Inc., Box 882, Madison Sq. Sta., New York, NY 10159-0882. TEL 212-989-5800. FAX 212-633-3990) Ed. J.R.H. Ross. adv. (also avail. in microfilm; back issues avail.) **Indexed:** Chem.Abstr., Chem.Eng.Abstr., T.C.E.A. **Document type:** academic/scholarly publication.
—BLDSC (3090.944000); EI; UnCover; SWETS; CASDDS. **CCC.**
Description: For all those in universities and in industry working in catalysis and process chemistry.
Refereed Serial

660   **GW**
▼**CHEMANAGER;** Zeitung fuer Fuehrungskraefte in der Chemie. 1992. m. DM.60 (students DM.30). G I T Verlag GmbH, Roesslerstr. 90, 64293 Darmstadt, Germany. TEL 06151-8090-0. FAX 06151-809045. Ed.Bd. adv.: B&W page DM.8400, color page DM.9900; trim 185 x 260; adv. contact: Marita Eckardt. circ. 40,000. **Document type:** trade publication.

660 665.5   **AT**
CHEMECA - AUSTRALASIAN CONFERENCE ON CHEMICAL ENGINEERING. PROCEEDINGS. 1973. a. price varies. Institution of Chemical Engineers in Australia, P.O. Box 542, Collaroy, N.S.W. 2097, Australia. TEL 02-982-7245. FAX 02-982-1065. circ. 4,000. (back issues avail.) **Document type:** proceedings.
Formerly: Australian Conference on Chemical Engineering. Proceedings.
Description: Papers on innovation: industrial, commercial and academic.

CHEMEXCIL EXPORT BULLETIN. see *BUSINESS AND ECONOMICS — International Commerce*

CHEMICAL AND BIOCHEMICAL ENGINEERING QUARTERLY. see *BIOLOGY — Bioengineering*

660   **US**   ISSN 0009-2347
TP1   CODEN: CENEAR
CHEMICAL AND ENGINEERING NEWS. (International ed. avail.) 1923. w. $115 to non-members (foreign $179). American Chemical Society, 1155 16th St., N.W., Washington, DC 20036. TEL 800-333-9511. FAX 614-447-3671. (Subscr. to: Membership and Subscription Services, Box 3337, Columbus, OH 43210. TEL 614-447-3776) Ed. Michael Heylin. adv.; bk.rev.; charts; mkt.; tr.lit.; index. circ. 135,000. (also avail. in microform from PMC; microfiche from CIS; back issues avail.) **Indexed:** A.S.& T.Ind., Abstr.Bull.Inst.Pap.Chem., Acid Pre.Dig., Acid Rain Abstr., Acid Rain Ind., Anal.Abstr., API Abstr., API Catal., API Hlth.& Environ., API Oil., API Pet.Ref., API Pet.Subst., API Transport., Art & Archaeol.Tech.Abstr., B.P.I., Biol.Abstr., Bus.Ind., C.I.J.E., C.I.S.Abstr., CAD CAM Abstr., Chem.Abstr., Chem.Eng.Abstr., Curr.Biotech.Abstr., Curr.Chem.React., Curr.Pack.Abstr., Energy.Info.Abstr., Eng.Ind., Environ.Abstr., Excerp.Med., Fluidex, Food Sci.& Tech.Abstr., Fuel & Energy Abstr., Gas Abstr., Geo.Abstr., Hlth.Ind., Ind.Chem., Ind.Hyg.Dig., Ind.Sci.Rev., Int.Lab.Doc., Key to Econ.Sci., Lab.Haz.Bull., Met.Abstr., Nutr.Abstr., Ocean.Abstr., Petrol.Abstr., Pollut.Abstr., PROMT, RAPRA, Sci.Abstr., Sci.Cit.Ind., Sel.Water Res.Abstr., Soils & Fert., SRI, T.C.E.A., Telegen, Tr.& Indus.Ind., W.R.C.Inf., World Alum.Abstr., World Text.Abstr. **Document type:** academic/scholarly publication.
—BLDSC (3138.000000); EI; Faxon; UnCover; SWETS; UMI; CASDDS. **CCC.**
Description: Keeps readers informed of all the news of the chemical world generally as it interrelates with the world at large, and of policies and activities of the ACS.

662   **US**   ISSN 0009-2355
          CODEN: CPTEAW
CHEMICAL AND PETROLEUM ENGINEERING. English translation of: Khimicheskoe i Neftyanoe Mashinostroenie (UR ISSN 0023-1126) 1965. m. $1175 (foreign $1375)(effective 1992). Plenum Publishing Corp, Consultants Bureau, 233 Spring St., New York, NY 10013-1578. TEL 212-620-8468. FAX 212-463-0742. TELEX 23-421139. Ed. A.M. Vasil'ev. (also avail. in microfilm from JSC; back issues avail.) **Indexed:** Chem.Eng.Abstr., Chem.Titles, Curr.Cont., Eng.Ind., Excerp.Med., INIS Atomind., ISMEC, T.C.E.A.
—BLDSC (0410.300000); UnCover; SWETS; UMI. **CCC.**
Formerly: Soviet Journal of Chemical Engineering.
Refereed Serial

660.2   **II**
          CODEN: CIDADU
CHEMICAL BUSINESS. Variant title: Chemical Business of India. (Text in English) 1967. m. Rs.300($120) Colour Publications Pvt. Ltd., 126-A Dhurwadi, Off Dr. Nariman Rd., Prabhadevi, Bombay 400 025, India. TEL 430-9318. TELEX 71242 CEPE IN. Ed. R.V. Raghavan. adv.; bk.rev.; abstr.; charts; illus.; mkt.; pat.; stat.; index. circ. 22,000. (processed) **Indexed:** Chem.Abstr., Curr.Cont., Excerp.Med.
Incorporates: Chemical Times; Former titles (until 1987): Chemical Industry Developments (ISSN 0302-7678); Chemical Processing and Engineering (ISSN 0009-2649)
Description: Examines developments in the various sectors of the Indian chemical industry as well as covers relevant legislative events, computer applications and performance and market analyses.

CHEMICAL EDUCATION. see *CHEMISTRY*

660.2   **UK**   ISSN 0302-0797
          CODEN: CMERA9
CHEMICAL ENGINEER; the chemical & process industries journal. 1923. fortn. £99($176) (Institution of Chemical Engineers) Taylor & Francis Ltd., Rankine Rd., Basingstoke, Hants RG24 8PR, England. TEL 0256-840366. FAX 0256-479438. TELEX 858540. (In U.S.: 1900 Frost Rd., Ste. 101, Bristol, PA 19007-1598. TEL 215-785-5800) Ed. Gerry Woolf. adv.; bk.rev.; abstr.; bibl.; charts; illus.; stat.; index, cum.index. circ. 25,695. (back issues avail.; reprint service avail. from ISI,MIM,UMI) **Indexed:** A.S.& T.Ind., AESIS, API Abstr., API Catal., API Hlth.& Environ., API Oil., API Pet.Ref., API Pet.Subst., API Transport., Biotech.Abstr., Br.Ceram.Abstr., Br.Tech.Ind., Chem.Abstr., Chem.Eng.Abstr., Curr.Biotech.Abstr., Eng.Ind., Fluidex, Fuel & Energy Abstr., High.Educ.Curr.Aware.Bull., INIS Atomind., Met.Abstr., Res.High.Educ.Abstr., Risk Abstr., Sci.Abstr., Sel.Water Res.Abstr., T.C.E.A., W.R.C.Inf., World Alum.Abstr. **Document type:** trade publication.
—BLDSC (3139.780000); EI; Faxon; UnCover; SWETS; CASDDS. **CCC.**
Formerly: Chemical Engineer and Transactions of the Institution of Chemical Engineers (ISSN 0009-2452); Supersedes in part: Institution of Chemical Engineers. Transactions (ISSN 0046-9858); Incorporates (1983-1990): Chemical Engineer Diary and Institution News (ISSN 0265-1920); Which was formerly (1922-1982): Institution of Chemical Engineers. Diary (ISSN 0020-3246)
Description: Professional journal for chemical and process engineers in the UK and worldwide.
Refereed Serial

660.2   **US**   ISSN 0009-2460
TN1   CODEN: CHEEA3
CHEMICAL ENGINEERING. 1902. m. Can.$46($35.50) in U.S.; Mexico $88; Europe and Japan $187; elsewhere $152. McGraw-Hill, Inc., 1221 Ave. of the Americas, New York, NY 10020. TEL 212-512-2000. (Subscr. to: Box 507, Hightstown, NJ 08520) Ed. Richard J. Zanetti. adv.; bk.rev.; charts; illus.; mkt.; stat.; tr.lit.; index. circ. 70,205. (also avail. in microfilm from UMI,PMC; microfiche from CIS) **Indexed:** A.I.Abstr., A.S.& T.Ind., ABI Inform., Abstr.Bull.Inst.Pap.Chem., Acid Pre.Dig., Acid Rain Abstr., Acid Rain Ind., AESIS, API Abstr., API Catal., API Hlth.& Environ., API Oil., API Pet.Ref., API Pet.Subst., API Transport., Appl.Mech.Rev., Biotech.Abstr., C.R.I. Abstr., Chem.Abstr., Chem.Eng.Abstr., Curr.Cont., Curr.Pack.Abstr., Energy Info.Abstr., Eng.Ind., Environ.Abstr., Excerp.Med., Fluidex, Foul.Prev.Res.Dig., Fuel & Energy Abstr., IN S Atomind., Key to Econ.Sci., Met.Abstr., Ocean.Abstr., Paper & Bd.Abstr., Petrol.Abstr., Pollut.Abstr., Print.Abstr., Risk Abstr., Robomat. (until 1992), Sci.Abstr., Sci.Cit.Ind., SRI, Telegen, Text.Tech.Dig., W.R.C.Inf., World Alum.Abstr.
●Also available online. Vendor(s): DIALOG Information Services, Inc. (File no.624/McGRAW-HILL PUBLICATIONS ONLINE), Dow Jones News Retrieval (CE), Mead Data Central, Inc. (CHEMEN), NewsNet (CH19).
—BLDSC (3140.000000); CIS; EI; Faxon; UnCover; SWETS; UMI; CASDDS. **CCC.**
Description: For operations and engineering managers in the chemical process industries.
Refereed Serial

660   **SZ**   ISSN 0255-2701
TP1   CODEN: CENPEU
CHEMICAL ENGINEERING AND PROCESSING. (Text in English; summaries in French, German) 1967. 6/yr. 715 SFr.($486) (effective 1994). Elsevier Science S.A., P.O. Box 564, CH-1001 Lausanne 1, Switzerland. TEL 41-21-3207381. FAX 41-21-3235444. TELEX 450620-ELSA-CH. (Subscr. in U.S. and Canada to: Elsevier Science Inc., Box 882, Madison Sq. Sta., New York, NY 10159. TEL 212-989-5800. FAX 212-633-3990) Eds. E. Schluender, V. Gnielinski. adv.; bk.rev.; abstr.; illus.; index. **Indexed:** Chem.Abstr., Chem.Eng.Abstr., Curr.Biotech.Abstr., Curr.Cont., Excerp.Med., Fluidex, ISMEC, Met.Abstr., Packag.Sci.Tech., Sci.Abstr., T.C.E.A., W.R.C.Inf., World Alum.Abstr. **Document type:** academic/scholarly publication.
—BLDSC (3142.030000); SWETS; CASDDS. **CCC.**
Formerly (until 1984): Verfahrenstechnik (ISSN 0049-5948)
Description: For practising engineers active in the chemical, process, power and manufacturing industries as well as in engineering and contracting companies.
Refereed Serial

ENGINEERING — CHEMICAL ENGINEERING

660   GW   ISSN 0930-7516
TP1   CODEN: CETEER
CHEMICAL ENGINEERING AND TECHNOLOGY. 1978. 6/yr. DM.770($510) (Gesellschaft Deutscher Chemiker) V C H Verlagsgesellschaft mbH, Postfach 101161, 69451 Weinheim, Germany. TEL 06201-606-0. FAX 06201-606328. TELEX 465516-VCHWH-D. (U.S. addr.: V C H Publishers Inc., 220 E. 23rd St., New York, NY 10010-4606) (Co-sponsor: German Society of Chemical Equipment; Society for Process Technology and Chemical Engineering) Ed. R. Pfefferkorn. adv.; index. circ. 675. (reprint service avail. from ISI) **Indexed:** Biotech.Abstr., C.R.I.Abstr., Chem.Eng.Abstr., Fluidex, INIS Atomind. **Document type:** academic/scholarly publication.
—BLDSC (3142.040000); EI; Faxon; UnCover; SWETS; CASDDS. **CCC.**
Formerly: German Chemical Engineering (ISSN 0343-5539)

660   US   ISSN 0272-4057
TP158
CHEMICAL ENGINEERING BUYER'S GUIDE. a. McGraw-Hill, Inc., 1221 Ave. of the Americas, New York, NY 10020. TEL 212-512-2197. Ed. Richard Zanetti.
Formerly: Chemical Engineering. Equipment Buyer's Guide Issue (ISSN 0094-9841)

660   US   ISSN 0098-6445
TP1   CODEN: CEGCAK
CHEMICAL ENGINEERING COMMUNICATIONS. 1973. 72/yr. (in 12 monthly vols., 6 nos./vol.). 142 ECU per vol. (effective 1993). Gordon and Breach Science Publishers, 820 Town Center Dr., Langhorne, PA 19047. TEL 215-750-2642. FAX 215-750-6343. (UK subscr. to: P.O. Box 90, Reading, Berkshire RG1 8JL, England. TEL 0734-560-080) Ed. William N. Gill. adv.; index. (also avail. in microform) **Indexed:** Abstr.Bull.Inst.Pap.Chem., Biotech.Abstr., Chem.Abstr., Chem.Eng.Abstr., Curr.Biotech.Abstr., Curr.Cont., Dairy Sci.Abstr., Excerp.Med., Fluidex, Foul.Prev.Res.Dig., Ind.Sci.Rev., Petrol.Abstr., Sci.Cit.Ind., Soils & Fert., Sugar Ind.Abstr., T.C.E.A.
—BLDSC (3143.030000); Faxon; UnCover; SWETS; CASDDS. **CCC.**

660   UK   ISSN 0734-1644
CHEMICAL ENGINEERING: CONCEPTS AND REVIEWS. 1985. irreg., vol.3, 1987. Gordon & Breach Science Publishers, P.O. Box 90, Reading, Berks. RG1 8JL, England. TEL 0734-560080. FAX 0734-568211. TELEX 849870 SCIPUB G. (U.S. addr.: 820 Town Center Dr., Langhorne, PA 19047. TEL 215-750-2642. FAX 215-750-6343) Ed. J. Ulbrecht. (also avail. in microfilm; microfiche) **Document type:** monographic series.
—BLDSC (3139.999000).
Refereed Serial

660.2 370   US   ISSN 0009-2479
TP165   CODEN: CHEDAY
CHEMICAL ENGINEERING EDUCATION. 1965. q. $20 to non-members (foreign $23.50); members $15 (foreign $18.50). American Society for Engineering Education, Chemical Engineering Division, Dept. of Chemical Engineering, University of Florida, Gainesville, FL 32611. TEL 904-392-0857. FAX 904-392-0861. Ed. Ray W. Fahien. adv.; bk.rev.; index. circ. 2,850. (also avail. in microform from UMI; reprint service avail. from UMI) **Indexed:** C.I.J.E., Chem.Abstr., Cont.Pg.Educ., Curr.Biotech.Abstr., Eng.Ind., Excerp.Med. **Document type:** academic/scholarly publication.
—BLDSC (3143.300000); EI; Faxon; UnCover; SWETS; UMI; CASDDS.
Description: Course and research articles by and for educators of chemical engineering.
Refereed Serial

660.2 378   US
CHEMICAL ENGINEERING FACULTIES. a. $60 to non-members; members $48. American Institute of Chemical Engineers, Chemical Engineering Education Projects Committee, 345 E. 47th St., New York, NY 10017. TEL 212-705-7657. FAX 212-752-3294. Ed. J.B. Rawlings. (reprint service avail. from UMI) **Document type:** trade publication.
Formerly: Chemical Engineering Faculties of Canada and the United States.
Description: International in scope; contains names, addresses, telephone numbers, degrees and accreditation status.

660.2   AT   ISSN 0157-9762
TJ1   CODEN: CCEADR
CHEMICAL ENGINEERING IN AUSTRALIA. 1976. q. Aus.$22.80 (overseas Aus.$31.20). (Institution of Engineers, Australia) Engineers Australia Pty. Ltd., Crows Nest Centre, 2 Ernest St., Crows Nest, N.S.W. 2065, Australia. TEL 02-438-1533. FAX 02-438-5934. (Co-sponsor: Institution of Chemical Engineers) Ed. Victor Rudolph. **Indexed:** AESIS, Energy Info.Abstr., Environ.Abstr., Fluidex, INIS Atomind., ISMEC, Met.Abstr., W.R.C.Inf., World Alum.Abstr.
—BLDSC (3142.175000); UnCover; CASDDS.
Formerly: Institution of Engineers, Australia. Chemical Engineering Transactions; Supersedes in part: Institution of Engineers, Australia. Mechanical and Chemical Engineering Transactions (ISSN 0020-3327)
Description: News and technical papers in general field of chemical engineering.

660.2 574.28   SZ   ISSN 0923-0467
TP1   CODEN: CMEJAJ
CHEMICAL ENGINEERING JOURNAL AND BIOCHEMICAL ENGINEERING JOURNAL; an international journal of research and development. (Text in English, French, German) 1970. 9/yr. (in 3 vols.; 3 nos./vol.). 1230 SFr.($837) (effective 1994). Elsevier Science S.A., P.O. Box 564, CH-1001 Lausanne 1, Switzerland. TEL 41-21-3207381. FAX 41-21-3235444. TELEX 450620-ELSA-CH. (Subscr. in U.S. and Canada to: Elsevier Science Inc., Box 882, Madison Sq. Sta., New York, NY 10159. TEL 212-989-5800. FAX 212-633-3990) Eds. B.A. Buffham, B. Atkinson. adv.; bk.rev.; illus.; index. (also avail. in microform from UMI) **Indexed:** Biodet.Abstr., Biotech.Abstr., Chem.Abstr., Chem.Eng.Abstr., Curr.Biotech.Abstr., Curr.Cont., Energy Ind., Energy Info.Abstr., Excerp.Med., Fluidex, Fuel & Energy Abstr., Gas Abstr., GeoRef., Ind.Sci.Rev., Math.R., Phys.Ber., Sci.Abstr., Soils & Fert., T.C.E.A. **Document type:** academic/scholarly publication.
—BLDSC (3143.700000); Faxon; UnCover; SWETS; CASDDS. **CCC.**
Formerly: Chemical Engineering Journal (ISSN 0300-9467)
Description: Provides an international forum for the presentation of original work, interpretative reviews and the discussion of the latest developments in chemical engineering.
Refereed Serial

660   NE   ISSN 0167-4188
                 CODEN: CENMDK
CHEMICAL ENGINEERING MONOGRAPHS. 1975. irreg., vol.25, 1989. price varies. Elsevier Science B.V., Books Division, P.O. Box 211, 1000 AE Amsterdam, Netherlands. TEL 31-20-5803911. FAX 31-20-5803705. TELEX 18582 ESPA NL. (Subscr. in U.S. and Canada to: Elsevier Science Inc., Box 882, Madison Sq. Sta., New York, NY 10159. TEL 212-989-5800) Ed. S.W. Churchill. **Indexed:** Chem.Abstr. **Document type:** monographic series.
—CASDDS. **CCC.**
Refereed Serial

660.2   US   ISSN 0360-7275
TP1   CODEN: CEPRA8
CHEMICAL ENGINEERING PROGRESS. 1947. m. $75 to non-members (foreign $125). American Institute of Chemical Engineers, 345 E. 47th St., New York, NY 10017. TEL 212-705-7663. FAX 212-752-3294. Ed. Mark Rosenzweig. adv.; abstr.; charts; illus.; tr.lit.; index. circ. 48,000. (also avail. in microform from UMI,PMC; reprint service avail. from UMI) **Indexed:** A.I.Abstr., A.S.& T.Ind., Abstr.Bull.Inst.Pap.Chem., Acid Rain Abstr., Acid Rain Ind., AESIS, API Abstr., API Catal., API Hlth.& Environ., API Oil., API Pet.Ref., API Pet.Subst., API Transport., Biol.Abstr., C.I.S.Abstr., Chem.Abstr., Chem.Eng.Abstr., Chem.Infd., Curr.Biotech.Abstr., Curr.Cont., E&P Hlth. (1993-), Energy Info.Abstr., Eng.Ind., Environ.Abstr., Excerp.Med., Fluidex, Foul.Prev.Res.Dig., Fuel & Energy Abstr., Gas Abstr., Gas Process.& Ppl. (1993-), Ind.Sci.Rev., INIS Atomind., Met.Abstr., Ocean.Abstr., Off.Tech. (1993-), Petrol.Abstr. (1961-1973, 1976-), Pollut.Abstr., PROMT, Risk Abstr., Sci.Abstr., Sci.Cit.Ind., Sel.Water Res.Abstr., Soils & Fert., Telegen, Text.Tech.Dig., W.R.C.Inf., World Alum.Abstr. **Document type:** trade publication.
—BLDSC (3144.000000); CIS; EI; Faxon; SWETS; UMI; CASDDS. **CCC.**
Supersedes (1908-1946): American Institute of Chemical Engineers. Transactions (ISSN 0096-7408)
Description: Covers current advances and trends in the chemical process and related industries as well as providing information on new products and materials, regulatory issues and conferences.
Refereed Serial

660.2   UK   ISSN 0263-8762
TP1   CODEN: CERDEE
CHEMICAL ENGINEERING RESEARCH & DESIGN. 1923. bi-m. £174($293) (Institution of Chemical Engineers) Taylor & Francis Ltd., Rankine Rd., Basingstoke, Hants RG24 8PR, England. TEL 0256-840366. FAX 0256-479438. TELEX 858540. (In U.S.: 1900 Frost Rd., Bristol, PA 19007-1598. TEL 215-785-5800) Ed. G.F. Hewitt. adv.; bk.rev.; film rev.; abstr.; bibl.; charts; illus.; tr.lit.; index. circ. 2,500. (also avail. in microform from UMI,PMC; reprint service avail. from UMI,ISI) **Indexed:** API Abstr., API Catal., API Hlth.& Environ., API Oil., API Pet.Ref., API Pet.Subst., API Transport., Appl.Mech.Rev., Br.Ceram.Abstr., Br.Tech.Ind., Chem.Eng.Abstr., Comput.Abstr., Curr.Biotech.Abstr., E&P Hlth. (1993-), Excerp.Med., Fluidex, Gas Process.& Ppl. (1993-), Ind.Sci.Rev., Met.Abstr., Off.Tech. (1993-), Petrol.Abstr. (1984-), Risk Abstr., Sci.Abstr., T.C.E.A., W.R.C.Inf., World Alum.Abstr. **Document type:** academic/scholarly publication.
—BLDSC (3145.350000); EI; Faxon; UnCover; SWETS; CASDDS. **CCC.**
Supersedes in part: Institution of Chemical Engineers. Transactions (ISSN 0046-9858)
Refereed Serial

660   UK   ISSN 0009-2509
TP1   CODEN: CESCAC
CHEMICAL ENGINEERING SCIENCE. (Text in English, French, German) 1951. 24/yr. £1233($1900) (effective 1994). Elsevier Science Ltd., Pergamon, P.O. Box 800, Kidlington, Oxford OX5 1DX, England. TEL 44-865-843000. FAX 44-865-843010. (Subscr. in U.S. and Canada to: Elsevier Science, 660 White Plains Rd., Tarrytown, NY 10591-513. TEL 914-524-9200. FAX 914-333-2444) Ed. J. Bridgwater. adv.; bk.rev.; charts; illus.; index. circ. 2,000. (also avail. in microform from UMI; back issues avail.) **Indexed:** Abstr.Bull.Inst.Pap.Chem., Acid Rain Abstr., API Abstr., API Catal., API Hlth.& Environ., API Oil., API Pet.Ref., API Pet.Subst., API Transport., Appl.Mech.Rev., Biotech.Abstr., Br.Tech.Ind., C.R.I. Abstr., Chem.Abstr., Chem.Eng.Abstr., Chem.Infd., Comput.Abstr., Curr.Biotech.Abstr., Curr.Cont., E&P Hlth. (1993-), Eng.Ind., Excerp.Med., Fluidex, Foul.Prev.Res.Dig., Fuel & Energy Abstr., Gas Abstr., Gas Process.& Ppl. (1993-), Ind.Sci.Rev., INIS Atomind., Off.Tech. (1993-), Petrol.Abstr. (1961-), Sci.Abstr., Sci.Cit.Ind., Sel.Water Res.Abstr., Sugar Ind.Abstr., T.C.E.A., W.R.C.Inf. **Document type:** academic/scholarly publication.
—BLDSC (3146.000000); EI; Faxon; UnCover; SWETS; UMI; CASDDS. **CCC.**
Description: Publishes papers on the fundamentals of chemical engineering, including applications of the basic sciences and mathematics.
Refereed Serial

ENGINEERING — CHEMICAL ENGINEERING

660.2   II   ISSN 0009-2517
TP1   CODEN: CEWOAY
CHEMICAL ENGINEERING WORLD; India's foremost technical journal. (Text and summaries in English) 1966. m. Rs.300($50) Industrial Publications, Taj Bldg., 3rd Fl., 210 Dr. D. N. Rd., Bombay 400001, India. TEL 91-22-2042044. FAX 91-22-2850170. Ed. Jasu Shah. adv.: B&W page $400, color page $500. bk.rev.; illus.; tr.lit.; cum.index: 1966-1974. circ. 15,000. (tabloid format; also avail. in microform from UMI) **Indexed:** C.R.I. Abstr., Chem.Abstr., Excerp.Med., Fluidex, Indian Sci.Ind., INIS Atomind., Rice Abstr., Seed Abstr., Soils & Fert., Sugar Ind.Abstr. **Document type:** trade publication.
—BLDSC (3146.100000); EI; SWETS; UMI; CASDDS.

660   US   ISSN 0009-2525
CHEMICAL EQUIPMENT. 1962. m. (includes end-of-year Chemical Equipment Literature Review). $30. Gordon Publications, Inc., Part of Cahners Publishing Company, Division of Reed Elsevier Inc., 301 Gibraltar Dr., Box 650, Morris Plains, NJ 07950-0650. TEL 201-292-5100. FAX 201-898-9281. Ed. Geoffrey Bridgman. adv.; tr.lit. circ. 100,000. (tabloid format; also avail. in microform from UMI)
—UMI. **CCC.**
Description: Serves chief engineers, design engineers, process and chemical engineers, R and D engineers, and executives in general-plant management who work in chemical process plants that are engaged in the production of chemicals, refined petroleum, food, paper and other allied products.

338.4   II   ISSN 0304-1166
TP1
CHEMICAL INDIA ANNUAL. (Text in English) a. Rs.5. c/o S.K. Bhanot, 640 Double Storey, New Rajinder Nagar, New Delhi, India. illus.

660   US
CHEMICAL INDUSTRIES SERIES. 1979. irreg., vol.51, 1993. price varies. Marcel Dekker, Inc., 270 Madison Ave., New York, NY 10016. TEL 212-969-9000. FAX 212-685-4540. TELEX 421419.

660   UK
TP1
CHEMICAL INDUSTRY EUROPE. 1923. a. £75 (foreign £85). Benn Business Information Services Ltd. (Subsidiary of: Morgan-Grampian plc), Riverbank House, Angel Ln., Tonbridge, Kent TN9 1SE, England. TEL 0732-362666. FAX 0732-767301. TELEX 957829 BENTON G. Ed. Maria Atkin. adv.; index. circ. 3,500. **Document type:** directory.
Formerly: Chemical Industry Directory (ISSN 0069-2980)
Description: Guide to European chemical manufacturers and suppliers, and process plant manufacturing industries.

660   II   ISSN 0009-2576
CHEMICAL INDUSTRY NEWS. (Text in English) 1956. m. Rs.50. Indian Chemical Manufacturers Association, Bombay Regional Office, Sir Vithaldas Chambers, 16 Bombay Samachar Marg, Bombay 400023, India. Ed.Bd. adv.; bk.rev.; abstr.; charts; illus.; pat.; stat. circ. 3,000.
—UMI.

660   US
CHEMICAL MANUFACTURERS ASSOCIATION. FEDERAL LEGISLATION. irreg. Chemical Manufacturers Association, 2501 M St., N.W., Washington, DC 20037. TEL 202-887-1100.

CHEMICAL NEWSLETTER. see *OCCUPATIONAL HEALTH AND SAFETY*

660   US   ISSN 0009-2630
TP1
CHEMICAL PROCESSING. 1938. 12/yr. $45 (foreign $70)(free to qualified personnel). Putman Publishing Co., 301 E. Erie St., Chicago, IL 60611. TEL 312-644-2020. Ed. Robert Strack. adv.; bk.rev.; charts; illus.; tr.lit.; circ. 80,042. (controlled). (also avail. in microform from UMI) **Indexed:** Acid Rain Abstr., Acid Rain Ind., Chem.Abstr., Chem.Eng.Abstr., Corros.Abstr., Environ.Abstr., Gas Abstr., INIS Atomind., Ocean.Abstr., Pollut.Abstr., PROMT, T.C.E.A.
—BLDSC (3148.990000); Faxon; SWETS; UMI. **CCC.**
Incorporates (in 1987): Chemical Product News (ISSN 0747-0398); Former titles (until 1984): Chemical Industry Products News (ISSN 0161-259X); (1961-1977): What's New in Chemical Processing Equipment (ISSN 0511-8654)

660   US
CHEMICAL PROCESSING AD-LITS. q. Putman Publishing Co., 301 E. Erie St., Chicago, IL 60611. TEL 312-644-2020. FAX 312-644-1131. Ed. John McCallion. adv. circ. 80,037.
Description: Introduces new products in the chemical process industries.

660   US
CHEMICAL PROCESSING TECHNOLOGY FOR TOMORROW. 1987. q. Putman Publishing Co., 301 E. Erie St., Chicago, IL 60611. TEL 312-644-2020. FAX 312-644-1131. Ed. John McCallion. adv.: B&W page $5540; trim 8 x 10 3/4. circ. 65,000.
Description: Covers emerging technologies that are important to the chemical process industries.

660   US   ISSN 0009-272X
TP1   CODEN: CHWKA9
CHEMICAL WEEK. 1914. w. (49/yr.). $99 includes annual Buyers' Guide (Canada $129). Chemical Week Associates, 888 Seventh Ave., New York, NY 10106. TEL 212-621-4900. FAX 212-621-4949. (Subscr. to: Box 7721, Riverton, NJ 08077-9021. TEL 609-786-0401) Ed. David Hunter. adv.; charts; illus.; index. circ. 46,440. (also avail. in microform from UMI) **Indexed:** A.I.Abstr., ABC, ABI Inform., Abstr.Bull.Inst.Pap.Chem., Acid Rain Abstr., Acid Rain Ind., AESIS, API Abstr., API Catal., API Hlth.& Environ., API Oil., API Pet.Ref., API Pet.Subst., API Transport., Art & Archaeol.Tech.Abstr., B.P.I., Biotech.Abstr., Bus.Ind., Chem.Abstr., Chem.Eng.Abstr., Chem.Infd., Curr.Biotech.Abstr., Curr.Pack.Abstr., Energy Info.Abstr., Environ.Abstr., Excerp.Med., Gas Abstr., Key To Econ.Sci., Lab.Haz.Bull., Met.Abstr., Ocean.Abstr., Oper.Res.Manage.Sci., Pollut.Abstr., PROMT, Risk Abstr., Sel.Water Res.Abstr., T.C.E.A., Telegen, Text.Tech.Dig., Tr.& Indus.Ind., World Alum.Abstr., World Surf.Coat.
●Also available online. Vendor(s): Mead Data Central, Inc.
—Faxon; UnCover; SWETS; UMI; CASDDS. **CCC.**
Former titles (until 1952): Chemical Industries Week (ISSN 0095-8409); (until 1951): Chemical Industries (ISSN 0095-8883); (until 1933): Chemical Markets (ISSN 0095-8344)
Description: News and analysis of the chemical process industries.

660   SA   ISSN 1015-230X
CHEMICALS, ADHESIVES AND PHARMACEUTICALS (YEAR). a. (South African Foreign Trade Organisation) SAFTO, Publishing Division, P.O. Box 782706, Sandton 2146, South Africa. TEL 27-11-883-3737. FAX 27-11-883-6569. TELEX 4-24111 SA. circ. controlled. **Document type:** directory.
Description: Provides information on South African producers and exporters of chemical and pharmaceutical products.

CHEMICALS IN AGRICULTURE. see *AGRICULTURE — Crop Production And Soil*

660   US
CHEMICALS TODAY.* Cover title: International Chemicals Today. 1976. m. $250. Rode Publishing Company, 189 Parsonage Hill Rd., Short Hills, NJ 07078-1523. TEL 201-273-1088. Ed. J.A.M. le Duc. bk.rev.; stat. **Document type:** academic/scholarly publication.

CHEMICKY PRUMYSL/CHEMICAL INDUSTRY. see *CHEMISTRY*

660.2   GW   ISSN 0009-2800
TP1   CODEN: CHAVBZ
CHEMIE-ANLAGEN UND VERFAHREN. 1968. 14/yr. Konradin-Verlag Robert Kohlhammer GmbH, Ernst-Mey-Str. 8, 70771 Leinfelden-Echterdingen, Germany. TEL 0711-7594-0. FAX 0711-7594390. Ed. Guenter Eckhardt. adv.: B&W page DM.7380, color page DM.9369; trim 190 x 270; adv. contact: Klaus Walker. bk.rev.; circ. 25,659 (controlled). (back issues avail.) **Indexed:** Chem.Abstr., Chem.Eng.Abstr., Excerp.Med., INIS Atomind. **Document type:** trade publication.
—BLDSC (3157.650000); CASDDS. **CCC.**
Incorporates: Chemical Plants and Processing (ISSN 0721-4553)
Description: Introduces process engineering, environmental technology, laboratory testing techniques and materials.

660.2   GW   ISSN 0009-286X
               CODEN: CITEAH
CHEMIE-INGENIEUR-TECHNIK; Zeitschrift fuer technische Chemie, Verfahrenstechnik, Apparatewesen und Biotechnologie. (Text in German; summaries in English and German) 1928. m. DM.696($470) (Gesellschaft Deutscher Chemiker) V C H Verlagsgesellschaft mbH, Postfach 101161, 69451 Weinheim, Germany. TEL 06201-606-0. FAX 06201-606328. TELEX 465516-VCHWH-D. (US addr.: V C H Publishers Inc., 220 E. 23rd St., New York, NY 10010-4606. TEL 212-683-8333) (Co-sponsors: Deutsche Gesellschaft fuer Chemisches Apparatewesen, Chemische Technik und Biotechnologie; Gesellschaft Verfahrenstechnik und Chemieingenieurwesen) Ed. R. Pfefferkorn. adv.; bk.rev.; charts; illus.; mkt.; tr.lit.; index. circ. 7,670. (also avail. in microfilm from VCI; microfiche; reprint service avail. from ISI) **Indexed:** API Abstr., API Catal., API Hlth.& Environ., API Oil., API Pet.Ref., API Pet.Subst., Appl.Mech.Rev., Biotech.Abstr., Chem.Abstr., Chem.Infd., Dok.Arbeitsmed., Eng.Ind., Excerp.Med., Fluidex, Forest Prod.Abstr., Foul.Prev.Res.Dig, Ind.Sci.Rev., INIS Atomind., Met.Abstr., Petro.Abstr., PROMT, Risk Abstr., Sci.Abstr., Sel.Water Res.Abstr., Sugar Ind.Abstr., W.R.C.Inf., World Alum.Abstr. **Document type:** academic/scholarly publication.
—BLDSC (3157.000000); EI; UnCover; SWETS; CASDDS. **CCC.**

540 660   GW
               CODEN: CHPRDW
CHEMIE PRODUKTION. 1972. 6/yr. DM.124 (foreign DM.127). Verlag Moderne Industrie, Justus-von-Liebig-Str. 1, 86899 Landsberg, Germany. TEL 08191-125-0. FAX 08191-125483. Ed. Karl-Heinz Mueller. adv.: B&W page DM.5800; trim 257 x 178; adv. contact: Helmut Kluger. bk.rev.; charts; illus.; tr.lit. circ. 7,370. **Indexed:** Chem.Abstr., Chem.Eng.Abstr., INIS Atomind., Sci.Abstr. **Document type:** trade publication.
—BLDSC (3161.600000); CASDDS. **CCC.**
Formerly: Chemische Produktion (ISSN 0170-0456)

660   GW   ISSN 0340-9961
TP1   CODEN: CMTKAT
CHEMIETECHNIK. 1971. m. DM.237 (foreign DM.259). Huethig GmbH, Postfach 102869, 69018 Heidelberg, Germany. TEL 06221-489281. FAX 06221-489205. TELEX 461727-HUEHDD. Ed. S. Neufeldt. adv.: B&W page DM.7210; trim 210 x 297; adv. contact: Friedrich Limperg. illus. circ. 23,100. **Indexed:** Biotech.Abstr., Chem.Abstr., Chem.Eng.Abstr., Curr.Biotech.Abstr., Excerp.Med., INIS Atomind., Lab.Haz.Bull., T.C.E.A. **Document type:** trade publication.
—BLDSC (3157.450000); SWETS; CASDDS.
Supersedes (in 1974): C Z-Chemie-Technik (ISSN 0366-8509)
Description: Information on machine and equipment construction, process engineering, measurement and control engineering, process regulation, environmental engineering, materials of construction, biotechnology, and laboratory and analytical equipment.

ENGINEERING — CHEMICAL ENGINEERING

660   GW   ISSN 0009-2959
TP1   CODEN: CHIUA3
CHEMISCHE INDUSTRIE. 1949. m. DM.396. (Verband der Chemischen Industrie) Verlagsgruppe Handelsblatt GmbH, Kasernenstr. 67, 40213 Duesseldorf, Germany. TEL 0211-8870. (Subscr. to: Postfach 102717, 40018 Duesseldorf, Germany) Ed. Rolf Froboese. adv.; bk.rev.; abstr.; bibl.; charts; illus.; stat.; index. circ. 4,000. (reprint service avail. from UMI) **Indexed:** BPIA, Chem.Abstr., Chem.Infd., Excerp.Med., Key to Econ.Sci., PROMT, World Surf.Coat. **Document type:** trade publication.
●Also available online.
—BLDSC (3161.000000); SWETS; CASDDS. **CCC.**

660   GW
DIE CHEMISCHE INDUSTRIE UND IHRE HELFER/CHEMICAL INDUSTRY AND ITS SUPPLIERS. 1952. a. $40. Industrie-Verlagsgesellschaft mbH, Berliner Allee 8, 64295 Darmstadt, Germany. TEL 06151-38920. FAX 06151-33164. (U.S. subscr. to: Western Hemisphere Publishing Co., Box 847, Hillsboro, OR 97123-0847. TEL 503-640-3736. FAX 503-640-2748) Ed. Margit Selka. circ. 7,000. **Document type:** directory.
●Also available online.
Also available on CD-ROM.

CHEMISTRY AND INDUSTRY. see *CHEMISTRY*

CHEMISTRY INTERNATIONAL; the news magazine of IUPAC. see *CHEMISTRY*

660   US   ISSN 0897-4756
QD1   CODEN: CMATEX
CHEMISTRY OF MATERIALS. 1988. m. $375 to non-members (foreign $415); members $49 (foreign $89). American Chemical Society, 1155 16th St., N.W., Washington, DC 20036. TEL 800-333-9511. FAX 614-447-3671. (Subscr. to: Membership and Subscription Services, Box 3337, Columbus, OH 43210. TEL 614-447-3776) Ed. Leonard V. Interrante. **Document type:** academic/scholarly publication.
—BLDSC (3172.028000); Faxon; UnCover; SWETS; CASDDS. **CCC.**
Description: Provides a molecular-level perspective at the interface of chemistry, chemical engineering, and material science.

660.2   NE   ISSN 0009-3173
CHEMPRESS; onafhankelijk financieel-economisch en technisch nieuwsblad voor de chemie in de Benelux. 1967. fortn. fl.279. C. Misset B.V., Hanzestraat 7006, 7006 RH Doetinchem, Netherlands. TEL 31-8340-49911. FAX 31-8340-43839. TELEX 45481. Ed. H. Kramer. adv.: trim 313 x 472; adv. contact: Cor van Nek. bk.rev.; bibl.; charts; illus.; stat. circ. 3,210. (tabloid format) **Document type:** trade publication, newspaper.
Description: For the chemical industry with financial, economical, technical and trade information.

660.2   SA
CHEMSA. (Text in Afrikaans, English) 1974. m. R.96. (South African Institution of Chemical Engineers) Keeble Publishing Co. Pty. Ltd., P.O. Box 3080, Johannesburg 2000, South Africa. FAX 011-402-6420. (Co-sponsors: South African Chemical Institute; South African Chemical Manufacturers Association) Ed. L. Mc Duling. adv.; bk.rev.; illus. circ. 5,000. **Indexed:** Chem.Abstr., Curr.Cont., Eng.Ind., Ind.S.A.Per., INIS Atomind., Sel.Water Res.Abstr., Sugar Ind.Abstr., W.R.C.Inf.
Formerly: Analytika.

660   US   CODEN: CHTEDD
CHEMTECH. 1970. m. $79 to non-members (foreign $100); institutions $370 (foreign $391); members $39 (foreign $60). American Chemical Society, 1155 16th St. N.W., Washington, DC 20036. TEL 800-333-9511. FAX 614-447-3671. (Subscr. to: Membership and Subscription Services, Box 3337, Columbus, OH 43210. TEL 614-447-3776) Ed. Abraham P. Gelbein. adv.; bk.rev.; abstr.; charts; illus.; pat.; stat.; tr.lit. rate. circ. 9,000. (also avail. in microform) **Indexed:** A.S.& T.Ind., Abstr.Bull.Inst.Pap.Chem., Acid Pre.Dig., Acid Rain Abstr., Acid Rain Ind., AESIS, Art & Archaeol.Tech.Abstr., Biol.Abstr., Cadscan, Chem.Abstr., Chem.Eng.Abstr., Chem.Infd., Curr.Biotech.Abstr., Curr.Cont., Deep Sea Res.& Oceanogr.Abstr., Energy Info.Abstr., Eng.Ind., Environ.Abstr., Excerp.Med., Fluidex, Fuel & Energy Abstr., Gen.Sci.Ind., GeoRef., Ind.Sci.Rev., INIS Atomind., Lead Abstr., Mass Spectr.Bull., Petrol.Abstr., PROMT, Risk Abstr., Sci.Abstr., Sci.Cit.Ind., Soils & Fert., T.C.E.A., Telegen, World Surf.Coat., World Text.Abstr., Zincscan. **Document type:** academic/scholarly publication.
—BLDSC (3172.320000); Faxon; UnCover; SWETS; CASDDS. **CCC.**
Formerly: Chemical Technology (ISSN 0009-2703)
Description: Covers all phases of innovation in chemistry and in chemically related industries.

660   IT   ISSN 0009-4315
                            CODEN: CINMAB
CHIMICA E L'INDUSTRIA; giornale di chimica industriale ed applicata. (Supplement avail: Quaderni dell'Ingegnere Chimico Italiano) 1919. m. L.80000 (foreign L.300000). Societa Chimica Italiana, Viale Abruzzi 5, 20131 Milan, Italy. TEL 2-29-40-84-96. FAX 2-20-14-38. Ed. Domenico Giusto. adv.; bk.rev.; charts; illus.; index. circ. 7,000. **Indexed:** API Abstr., Biol.Abstr., C.I.S.Abstr., Cadscan, Chem.Abstr., Chem.Eng.Abstr., Chem.Infd., Curr.Cont., Ind.Chem., Ind.Sci.Rev., INIS Atomind., Lead Abstr., Met.Abstr., Risk Abstr., Sci.Cit.Ind, T.C.E.A., World Alum.Abstr., World Surf.Coat., Zincscan.
—BLDSC (3174.600000); SWETS; UMI; CASDDS.

662   IT
CHIMICA E PETROLCHIMICA. 1971. m. (11/yr.). L.25000 (free to qualified personnel). Edizioni Periodici Tecnici, Corso Sempione 77, 20149 Milan, Italy. Ed. Antonio Casieri. adv. circ. 5,000.

660   FR   ISSN 0009-4323
TP1   CODEN: CHIABC
CHIMIE ACTUALITES; lettre hebdomadaire des industries chimiques. 1898. 43/yr. 2300 F. (foreign 2670 F.). Societe de Publications Specialisees, 142 rue Montmartre, 75002 Paris, France. TEL 40-26-83-21. FAX 40-39-97-52. TELEX 220 528 F. Ed. Charley Sifaoui. adv.; bk.rev.; bibl.; illus.; stat.; index. circ. 1,500. **Indexed:** Chem.Abstr., Met.Abstr., PROMT.
—BLDSC (3175.900000); CASDDS. **CCC.**
Incorporates: Filtration et Techniques Separatives; **Formerly:** Revue des Produits Chimiques.

660   FR   ISSN 0245-940X
CHIMIE MAGAZINE. 1981. m. 430 F. (foreign 630 F.). Societe de Publications Specialisees, 142 rue Montmartre, 75002 Paris, France. TEL 40-26-83-21. FAX 40-39-97-52. TELEX 220 528 F. Ed. Chantal Houzelle. circ. 7,000.
—**CCC.**

660   CH   ISSN 0368-1653
                           CODEN: JCICAP
CHINESE INSTITUTE OF CHEMICAL ENGINEERS. JOURNAL. Key Title: Zhongguo Huaxue Gongcheng Xuehui Huizhi. (Text in English; summaries in Chinese, English) 1970. s-a. NT.$600($44) individuals; institutions NT.$1200($68). Chinese Institute of Chemical Engineers, c/o Dept. of Chemical Engineering, National Taiwan University, Taipei, Taiwan 107, Republic of China. FAX 02-362-3040. Ed. Hsiao-Ping Huang. bk.rev.; abstr.; charts; illus. circ. 500. (back issues avail.) **Indexed:** Chem.Abstr., Chem.Eng.Abstr., Eng.Ind, T.C.E.A.
—BLDSC (4729.310000); EI; CASDDS.

660   CC   ISSN 1004-9541
TP1   CODEN: HUKHAI
CHINESE JOURNAL OF CHEMICAL ENGINEERING. English Edition (ISSN 0892-0370) 1982. s-a. $80. (Chemical Industry and Engineering Society of China) Chemical Industry Press, P.O. Box 1423, Beijing, People's Republic of China. TEL 861-4213641. FAX 861-4216682. Ed. Wang Jiading. bibl.; charts; index. circ. 500. (back issues avail.) **Indexed:** Chem.Abstr., Eng.Ind., T.C.E.A. **Document type:** academic/scholarly publication.
—BLDSC (3180.299100). **CCC.**
Formerly (until 1993): Journal of Chemical Industry and Engineering (ISSN 1000-9027).
Description: Focuses on theoretical research and practical applications in the chemical process industry.

CHINESE JOURNAL OF MATERIALS SCIENCE. see *METALLURGY*

CHINESE JOURNAL OF POLYMER SCIENCE. see *CHEMISTRY — Organic Chemistry*

660 669   CC   ISSN 1004-7646
▼**CHINESE JOURNAL OF REACTIVE POLYMERS.** (Text in English) 1992. 2/yr. Nankai University, Institute of Polymer Chemistry, Tianjin 300071, People's Republic of China. Ed. He Binglin. **Document type:** academic/scholarly publication.
—BLDSC (3180.673000).

660   UK   ISSN 0958-1960
CHROMATOGRAPHY AND ANALYSIS. 1988. bi-m. £37 (Europe £68; elsewhere £97). Rolston Gordon Communications, 1 Gable Cottages, Post House Ln., Bookham, Surrey KT23 3EA, England. TEL 0372-454891. FAX 0372-459957. Ed. Rob Macrae. adv. circ. 8,000. **Document type:** academic/scholarly publication.
—BLDSC (3182.908000).

662   US   ISSN 1068-364X
TP1
COKE AND CHEMISTRY. English translation of: Koks i Khimiya (RU ISSN 0023-2815) 1959. m. $835. (Ministry of Ferrous Metallurgy, RU) Allerton Press, Inc., 150 Fifth Ave., New York, NY 10011. TEL 212-924-3950. FAX 212-463-9684. (Co-sponsor: Central Board of the Scientific-Technical Society of Ferrous Metallurgy) Ed. N.V. Braun. bk.rev.; bibl.; charts; illus.; stat.; index. circ. 250. **Indexed:** Chem.Eng.Abstr., Eng.Ind., Excerp.Med., Fuel & Energy Abstr., INIS Atomind., T.C.E.A. **Document type:** academic/scholarly publication.
—Faxon. **CCC.**
Formerly: Coke and Chemistry U S S R (ISSN 0010-0501)
Description: For engineers, chemists and technical personnel involved with the preparation and processing of coal and chemical products. Covers mechanization and automation, environmental issues, industrial waste utilization and technological developments.

660 770   US   ISSN 0361-2317
QC494   CODEN: CREADU
COLOR RESEARCH AND APPLICATION. 1975. bi-m. $240 (foreign $322.50). John Wiley & Sons, Inc., Journals, 605 Third Ave., New York, NY 10158-0012. TEL 212-692-6000. FAX 212-850-6088. TELEX 12-7063. (Co-sponsors: Inter-Society Color Council; The Colour Group; Canadian Society for Color) Ed. Ellen Carter. bk.rev. circ. 1,300. (also avail. in microform from UMI; back issues avail.) **Indexed:** Art & Archaeol.Tech.Abstr., Br.Ceram.Abstr., Curr.Cont., Ergon.Abstr., Graph.Arts Lit.Abstr., Ind.Sci.Rev., Print.Abstr., Sci.Abstr., Sci.Cit.Ind., Text.Tech.Dig., World Surf.Coat.
—BLDSC (3320.677000); Faxon; UnCover; SWETS; UMI. **CCC.**
Description: Reports on the science, technology, and application of color in business, art, design, education, and industry.
Refereed Serial

ENGINEERING — CHEMICAL ENGINEERING

662 US ISSN 0010-5082
QD516 CODEN: CESWA4
COMBUSTION, EXPLOSION, AND SHOCK WAVES. English translation of: Fizika Goreniya i Vzryva (RU ISSN 0430-6228) 1965. bi-m. $1075 (foreign $1260) (effective 1994). (Russian Academy of Sciences, Siberian Division, RU) Plenum Publishing Corp., Consultants Bureau, 233 Spring St., New York, NY 10013-1578. TEL 212-620-8468. FAX 212-463-0742. TELEX 23-421139. Ed. V.M. Titov. (also avail. in microfilm from JSC; back issues avail.) Indexed: Appl.Mech.Rev., Chem.Abstr., Curr.Cont., Elec.& Electron.Abstr., Eng.Ind., Excerp.Med., Ind.Sci.Rev., INIS Atomind., INSPEC, ISMEC, Saf.Sci.Abstr., Sci.Abstr. Document type: academic/scholarly publication.
—BLDSC (0411.040000); Faxon; UnCover; SWETS; UMI. **CCC.**
 Description: Covers the latest in explosive materials.
 Refereed Serial

660.2 541.3 US ISSN 0010-2199
CODEN: WSCPAH
COMBUSTION INSTITUTE. WESTERN STATES SECTION. PAPERS.* 1958. s-a. price varies. Combustion Institute, Western States Section, c/o Lawrence J. Muzio, Sec., KVB, Inc., 9342 Jeronimo, Ste. 101, Irvine, CA 92718. charts. circ. 150. Indexed: Chem.Abstr., Eng.Ind., Int.Aerosp.Abstr., Nucl.Sci.Abstr.
—CASDDS.

COMPOUNDINGS. see *PETROLEUM AND GAS*

COMPRESSOR NEWS AND PATENTS. see *MACHINERY*

COMPUTER-AIDED CHEMICAL ENGINEERING. see *ENGINEERING — Computer Applications*

COMPUTERS & CHEMICAL ENGINEERING; an international journal of computer applications in chemical engineering. see *CHEMISTRY — Computer Applications*

CONGRESS F A T I P E C. see *PAINTS AND PROTECTIVE COATINGS*

CONSULTING SERVICES. see *CHEMISTRY*

660 US
COST ENGINEERING SERIES. 1978. irreg., vol.19, 1992. price varies. Marcel Dekker, Inc., 270 Madison Ave., New York, NY 10016. TEL 212-696-9000. FAX 212-685-4540. TELEX 421419.

CRYOGAS INTERNATIONAL; the source of timely and relevant information for the industrial gas and cryogenics industries. see *ENGINEERING — Mechanical Engineering*

660 GW
DEGUSSA REPORT. 1974. 6/yr. Degussa AG, 60287 Frankfurt a.M., Germany. TEL 069-21801. FAX 069-2183849. Ed. E.M. Geiblinger. circ. 21,500. Document type: newsletter.
 Incorporates (in 1992): Degussa International.

660 GW ISSN 0937-5813
DER DESINFEKTOR. 1981. m. DM.50.40. (Fachverband fuer Desinfektoren) Verlag Eduard F. Beckmann KG, Postfach 1120, 31251 Lehrte, Germany. TEL 05132-53016. FAX 05132-53100. Ed. Angelika Rasch. Document type: trade publication.

660.28 CN ISSN 0070-525X
DIRECTORY OF CHEMICAL ENGINEERING RESEARCH IN CANADA. (Text in English, French) 1961. biennial. Can.$25 to non-members. Canadian Society for Chemical Engineering, 130 Slater St., Ste.550, Ottawa, ON K1P 6E2, Canada. TEL 613-232-6252. FAX 613-232-5862. circ. 1,800. Document type: directory.
 Formerly: Directory of Chemical Engineering Research in Canadian Universities.

660 US ISSN 0012-4990
CODEN: DCHTA5
DOKLADY CHEMICAL TECHNOLOGY. English translation of: Rossiiskaya Akademiya Nauk. Doklady. 1956. s-a. $400 (foreign $470) (effective 1994). (Russian Academy of Sciences, Chemical Technology Section, RU) Plenum Publishing Corp., Consultants Bureau, 233 Spring St., New York, NY 10013-1578. TEL 212-620-8468. FAX 212-463-0742. TELEX 23-421139. Ed. V.A. Kabanov. (also avail. in microfilm from JSC; back issues avail.) Indexed: Chem.Eng.Abstr., Chem.Titles, Energy Res.Abstr., Eng.Ind., INIS Atomind., Mass Spectr.Bull., T.C.E.A. Document type: academic/scholarly publication.
—BLDSC (0411.310000); UnCover; UMI. **CCC.**
 Refereed Serial

660 540 UK ISSN 0952-8377
E C N CHEMSCOPE. (Supplement to: European Chemical News (ISSN 0014-2875)) irreg. Reed Business Publishing Group, Quadrant House, The Quadrant, Sutton, Surrey SM2 5AS, England. TEL 081-652-3153. FAX 081-652-8918. (Subscr. to: Stuart House, 35 Perrymount Rd., Haywards Heath, W. Sussex RH16 3BN, England. TEL 0444-445566) adv.; illus. Document type: trade publication.
—SWETS.

628.96 US
E P A PESTICIDE LABEL FILE. q. price varies. (Environmental Protection Agency) U.S. National Technical Information Service, 5825 Port Royal Rd., Springfield, VA 22161. TEL 703-487-4630. (microfiche)
 Description: Contains a collection of information on registered pesticide labels. Includes active ingredients and percentages of same, common name of active chemicals, sites and pests for usage, dosage, and safety information.

EASTMAN FINE CHEMICALS NEWS. see *CHEMISTRY — Organic Chemistry*

ELECTROCHEMISTRY AND INDUSTRIAL PHYSICAL CHEMISTRY/DENKI KAGAKU OYOBI KOGYO BUTSURI KAGAKU. see *CHEMISTRY — Electrochemistry*

ENBI TO PORIMA/VINYLS AND POLYMERS. see *CHEMISTRY — Organic Chemistry*

ENVIRONMENTAL PROGRESS (NEW YORK). see *ENVIRONMENTAL STUDIES*

ERDOEL UND KOHLE, ERDGAS, PETROCHEMIE; hydrocarbon technology. see *PETROLEUM AND GAS*

660 GW ISSN 0014-2484
CODEN: EUCHAD
EUROPA CHEMIE; Aktueller Nachrichtendienst der Zeitschrift Chemische Industrie. (Supplement avail.: E C Letter) 1952. w. DM.261. Verlagsgruppe Handelsblatt GmbH, Kasernenstr. 67, 40213 Duesseldorf, Germany. TEL 0211-8870. (Subcr. to: Postfach 102717, 40018 Duesseldorf, Germany) Ed. Rolf Froboese. adv.; bk.rev.; charts; illus.; stat. circ. 4,500. (reprint service avail. from UMI) Indexed: Chem.Abstr., Key to Econ.Sci., PROMT, World Surf.Coat. Document type: trade publication.
●Also available online.
—BLDSC (3829.295000); CASDDS. **CCC.**

660 UK ISSN 0014-2875
HD9650.1 CODEN: ECHNAW
EUROPEAN CHEMICAL NEWS. Key Title: E C N. European Chemical News. (Supplement avail.: E C N Chemscope (ISSN 0952-8377)) 1962. w. £255($460) Reed Business Publishing Group (Subsidiary of: Reed Elsevier group), Quadrant House, The Quadrant, Sutton, Surrey SM2 5AS, England. TEL 081-652-3153. FAX 081-652-8918. (Subscr. to: Stuart House, 35 Perrymount Rd., Haywards Heath, W. Sussex RH16 3BN, England. TEL 0444-445566) Ed. John Baker. adv.; bk.rev.; abstr.; stat.; index. circ. 10,000. (also avail. in microfilm from UMI; back issues avail.) Indexed: ABC, API Abstr., API Catal., API Hlth.& Environ., API Oil., API Pet.Ref., API Pet.Subst., API Transport., Bus.Ind., Chem.Abstr., Chem.Eng.Abstr., Curr.Biotech.Abstr., Energy Info.Abstr., Environ.Abstr., Fuel & Energy Abstr., Hlth.Ind., Key to Econ.Sci., Lab.Haz.Bull., PROMT, T.C.E.A., Tr.& Indus.Ind., World Surf.Coat. Document type: trade publication.
●Also available online.
—BLDSC (3829.600000); SWETS; CASDDS. **CCC.**
 Description: Includes analysis forecasts and market intelligence weekly contract and spot prices for bulk chemicals.

660 338 US
EXECUTIVE REPORTS. Cover title: Pest Control Executive Reports. 1991. m. $67. Pinto & Associates, Inc. 155 Oak Rd., Mechanicsville, MD 20659. TEL 301-884-3020. FAX 301-884-4068. Ed. Sandra Kraft. bk.rev.; charts; illus.; stat.; tr.lit.; circ. 350 (paid). (looseleaf format; back issues avail.) Document type: newsletter.
 Description: Provides management information relating to pest control, for owners, managers and supervisors of pest control businesses.

662 US ISSN 0014-505X
EXPLOSIVES & PYROTECHNICS. 1968. m. $42. Franklin Applied Physics, Inc., Box 313, 98 Highland Ave., Oaks, PA 19456. TEL 215-666-6645. FAX 215-666-0173. Ed. R.H. Thompson. adv.; bk.rev.; bibl.; charts; illus.; stat.; tr.lit. circ. 600. Document type: newsletter.
—BLDSC (3842.330000).
 Description: Covers events and meetings, books and reports and developments.

662 GW ISSN 0014-5068
TP270.A1
EXPLOSIVSTOFFE. (Text in English, French or German; summaries in English and German) 1906; N.S. 1952. m. DM.163. Erwin Barth Verlag KG, Kiesstr. 11, Postfach 271, 6730 Neustadt, Germany. adv.; bk.rev.; abstr.; bibl.; illus.; pat.; stat.; index. circ. 3,200. Indexed: Chem.Abstr., Eng.Ind.

628.96 US
F D A SURVEILLANCE INDEX FOR PESTICIDES. (Supplement to: Basic Manual) 3/yr. $50 per no. in U.S., Canada, Mexico; elsewhere $100. (Department of Health and Human Services, Food and Drug Administration) U.S. National Technical Information Service, 5825 Port Royal Rd., Springfield, VA 22161. TEL 703-487-4630.
 Description: Details potential health risks of individual pesticides from a dietary standpoint. Provides an evaluation of each pesticide which includes pertinent FDA monitoring results, chemical, biological, and toxicological data, usage estimates as well as other relevant data.

660 II ISSN 0250-4782
CODEN: JFTSDG
FACT TECHNICAL SOCIETY. JOURNAL. (Text in English) 1968. s-a. Rs.100($40) Fact Technical Society, Udyogamandal 683 501, Kerala, India. Ed. T.P. Jacob. adv.; bk.rev.; illus. circ. 300. Indexed: Chem.Abstr., Soils & Fert.
—CASDDS.
 Former titles: Plant Maintenance and Import Substitutions; (until 1972): Plant Maintenance.
 Description: Includes research in the chemical and fertilizer industries.

THE FERTILIZER & AG-CHEMICAL DIGEST. see *AGRICULTURE — Crop Production And Soil*

ENGINEERING — CHEMICAL ENGINEERING

664　　　　　　　　GW　ISSN 0931-5985
TP1　　　　　　　　　　CODEN: FWTEEG
FETT - WISSENSCHAFT TECHNOLOGIE/FAT - SCIENCE TECHNOLOGY. (Summaries in English, French, German and Russian) 1898. m. DM.495.60 (foreign DM.506.80). (Deutsche Gesellschaft fuer Fettwissenschaft e.V.) Konradin Verlag Robert Kohlhammer GmbH, 70771 Leinfelden-Echterdingen, Germany. TEL 0711-7594-0. FAX 0711-7594390. Ed. Dr. Heinrich Bruening. adv.; bk.rev.; abstr.; bibl.; charts; illus.; pat.; tr.lit.; index. circ. 3,069. (also avail. in microfilm from UMI; reprint service avail. from UMI) **Indexed:** Anal.Abstr., Art & Archaeol.Tech.Abstr., Biodet.Abstr., Biol.Abstr., Biotech.Abstr., C.I.S. Abstr., Cadscan, Chem.Abstr., Curr.Adv.Ecol.Sci., Curr.Cont., Curr.Pack.Abstr., Dairy Sci.Abstr., Excerp.Med., Field Crop Abstr., Food Sci.& Tech.Abstr., Herb.Abstr., Hort.Abstr., Ind.Sci.Rev., Ind.Vet., INIS Atomind., Lead Abstr., Maize Abstr., Nutr.Abstr., Packag.Sci.Tech., Pig News & Info., PROMT, Sci.Cit.Ind., Seed Abstr., Soyabean Abstr., Trop.Oil Seeds Abstr., World Surf.Coat., Zincscan. **Document type:** trade publication.
—BLDSC (3897.334000); Faxon; SWETS; UMI; CASDDS. **CCC.**
Formerly: Fette-Seifen-Anstrichmittel (ISSN 0015-038X); Which incorporated: Farben-Chemiker (ISSN 0014-7710)
Description: Includes chemistry, edible fats, fats in technical products, processing technique, packaging, transport, environmental protection, and reports of events.

660.284　　　　　　　UK　ISSN 0015-1882
　　　　　　　　　　　　CODEN: FSEPAA
FILTRATION & SEPARATION. 1964. 8/yr. £75($115) (effective 1994). (Filtration Society) Elsevier Science Ltd., Oxford Fulfilment Centre, P.O. Box 800, Kidlington, Oxford OX5 1DX, England. TEL 44-865-843000. FAX 44-865-843010. (Subscr. in U.S. and Canada to: Elsevier Science, 660 White Plains Rd., Tarrytown, NY 10591-5153. TEL 914-524-9200. FAX 914-333-2444) Ed. S. Atkinson. adv.; bk.rev.; abstr.; charts; illus.; pat.; tr.lit.; tr.mk.; index. circ. 4,060. **Indexed:** Abstr.Bull.Inst.Pap.Chem., Agri.Eng.Abstr., B.C.I.R.A., BMT, Br.Ceram.Abstr., C.I.S.Abstr., Chem.Abstr., Chem.Eng.Abstr., Eng.Ind., Excerp.Med., Fluidex, Fuel & Energy Abstr., Int.Build.Serv.Abstr., PROMT, T.C.E.A., Text.Tech.Dig., W.R.C.Inf., World Surf.Coat., World Text.Abstr. **Document type:** academic/scholarly publication.
—BLDSC (3926.770000); El; Faxon; UnCover; SWETS; CASDDS. **CCC.**
Description: Publishes international research results and general articles covering industry news, new products and developments.
Refereed Serial

FINANCIAL TIMES INDUSTRIAL COMPANIES: CHEMICALS.
see *BUSINESS AND ECONOMICS — Trade And Industrial Directories*

FLORIDA MOSQUITO CONTROL ASSOCIATION. JOURNAL.
see *BIOLOGY — Entomology*

662　　　　　　　　SW　ISSN 0348-6613
TP270.A1　　　　　　　CODEN: FOPYDX
FOEREDRAG VID PYROTEKNIKDAGEN. (Text in English, Swedish) 1955. triennial. price varies. Svenska Nationalkommitten foer Mekanik, Sektionen foer Detonik och Foerbraenning, Oskarsvaagen 32, S-172-37 Sundbyberg, Sweden. TEL 46-8-29-75-29. Ed. J. Hansson. illus. **Indexed:** Chem.Abstr., IIS. **Document type:** proceedings.
—CASDDS.

660　　　　　　　　　　US
FUNDAMENTAL AND APPLIED CATALYSIS. irreg., latest 1993. price varies. Plenum Publishing Corp., 233 Spring St., New York, NY 10013-1578. TEL 212-620-8000. FAX 212-463-0742. TELEX 23-421139. Eds. Martyn V. Twigg, Michael S. Spencer. (back issues avail.) **Document type:** monographic series.

GAOFENZI TONGXUN/BULLETIN OF HIGH POLYMERS.
see *CHEMISTRY — Physical Chemistry*

GAOFENZI XUEBAO/ACTA POLYMERICA SINICA. see *CHEMISTRY — Physical Chemistry*

660　　　　　　　　CC　ISSN 1003-9015
　　　　　　　　　　　　CODEN: GAAKDX
GAOXIAO HUAXUE GONGCHENG XUEBAO/JOURNAL OF CHEMICAL ENGINEERING OF CHINESE UNIVERSITIES. (Text in Chinese; abstracts in English) 1986. q. $32. Zhejiang Daxue, Dept. of Chemical Engineering, Hangzhou, Zhejiang 310027, People's Republic of China. TEL 0571-572242. FAX 0571-571797. TELEX 35040 ZUFAO CN. Ed. Chen Weiniu. **Document type:** academic/scholarly publication.
—BLDSC (4956.420000).

662.6　　　　　　　　GW　ISSN 0340-6067
　　　　　　　　　　　　CODEN: GAAKDX
GAS AKTUELL; Berichte aus Forschung und Technik. 1971. a. Messer Griesheim GmbH, Fuetingsweg 34, 47805 Krefeld, Germany. TEL 02151-379434. FAX 02151-379710. Ed. Wolfgang Stoll. circ. 7,000. (back issues avail.) **Document type:** trade publication.
—BLDSC (4076.200000); CASDDS.

662　　　　　　　　UK　ISSN 0950-4214
　　　　　　　　　　　　CODEN: GSEPEP
GAS SEPARATION AND PURIFICATION. 1987. q. £172 in UK and Europe; elsewhere £185. Butterworth - Heinemann (Subsidiary of: Reed International PLC), Linacre House, Jordan Hill, Oxford OX2 8DP, England. TEL 0865-310366. FAX 0865-310898. TELEX 83111 BHPOXF G. (Subscr. to: Turpin Transactions Ltd., Distribution Centre, Blackhorse Rd., Latchworth, Herts SG6 1HN, England. TEL 0462-672555) Ed.Bd. adv.; bk.rev.; index. (also avail. in microform from UMI; back issues avail.) **Indexed:** Energy Info.Abstr., Environ.Abstr. **Document type:** academic/scholarly publication.
—BLDSC (4080.996000); CIS; Faxon; UMI; CASDDS. **CCC.**
Description: Covers all aspects of gas separation and purification, with emphasis on the use of physical or chemical methods in large and small scale processing.
Refereed Serial

GLASNIK HEMICARA I TEHNOLOGA BOSNE I HERCEGOVINE. see *CHEMISTRY*

661　　　　　　　　　　MX
GUIA DE LA INDUSTRIA QUIMICA/CHEMICAL INDUSTRY GUIDE; productos quimicos. (Text in English, Spanish) 1990. a. Mex.$190($150) Informatica Cosmos, S.A. de C.V., Fernando Arrieta 5-101, Col. Los Cipreses, 04830 Mexico D.F., Mexico. TEL 525-677-48-68. FAX 525-679-35-75. Ed. Raul Macazaga. adv.; B&W page $1000; trim 211 x 274. **Document type:** directory.
Formerly: Petro Quimica.
Description: Lists over 2300 chemical suppliers in the country. Lists 7500 chemical products, minerals, specialties and raw materials.

660　　　　　　　　　　BL
GUIA DO LABORATORIO. a. Editora Quimica e Derivados Ltda., Rua Dr. Gabriel dos Santos, 55, Santa Cecilla, CEP 01231-900 Sao Paulo, SP, Brazil. TEL 011-826-6899. FAX 011-825-8192. TELEX 11-21801. Ed. Emanoel Fairbanks.

661　　　　　　　　　　BL
GUIA GERAL DE PRODUTOS QUIMICOS. a. Editora Quimica e Derivados Ltda., Rua Dr. Gabriel dos Santos, 55, Santa Cecilla, CEP 01231-900 Sao Paulo, SP, Brazil. TEL 011-826-6899. FAX 011-825-8192. TELEX 11-21801. Ed. Emanoel Fairbanks.

660　　　　　　　　　　II
GUIDE TO INDIAN CHEMICAL PLANTS AND EQUIPMENT. Bound with: Indian Chemical Directory (ISSN 0073-6295) (Text in English) 1966. triennial. $110 for Indian Chemical Directory. Technical Press Publications, 5-1 Convent St., Colaba, Bombay 400039, India. TEL 2021446. TELEX 011-83479 CHEM IN. Ed. J.P. de Sousa Jr. adv. circ. 12,000. **Document type:** directory.
Formerly: Catalogue of Indian Chemical Plants (ISSN 0069-1151)

GULF COAST PETROPROCESS DIRECTORY. see *PETROLEUM AND GAS*

660　　　　　　　　UK　ISSN 0952-2654
H T F S DIGEST. Variant title: Heat Transfer and Fluid Flow Service Digest. 1968. q. £140 (foreign £155). (Heat Transfer and Fluid Flow Service) Harwell Laboratory, B.392.7, Didcot, Oxon. OX11 ORA, England. FAX 0235-831981. Ed. Pascale Hicklin. circ. 400. (back issues avail). **Indexed:** Fluidex. **Document type:** abstracting/indexing.
●Also available online. Vendor(s): European Space Agency (File no.138/HEATFLO).
—CCC.
Incorporates (1979-1992): Fouling Prevention Research Digest (ISSN 0143-3598); Former titles (until 1986): Heat Transfer and Fluid Flow Digest (ISSN 0309-1953); And (until 1976): H T F S Digest.
Description: Examines articles on the design, performance, and operation of heat exchangers and other equipment, and the process concerning such equipment for designers and researchers.

621.402　　　　　　　　US　ISSN 0145-7632
TJ260　　　　　　　　　　CODEN: HTEND2
HEAT TRANSFER ENGINEERING. 1979. q. $176. Taylor & Francis, 1900 Frost Rd., Ste. 101, Bristol, PA 19007-1598. TEL 800-821-8312. FAX 215-785-5515. Ed. Kenneth J. Bell. adv.; bk.rev.; abstr.; bibl.; charts; illus.; index. circ. 1,000. (also avail. in microform from UMI; back issues avail.; reprint service avail. from UMI) **Indexed:** Abstr.Bull.Inst.Pap.Chem., Appl.Mech.Rev., Chem.Abstr., Chem.Eng.Abstr., Excerp.Med., Fluidex, Foul.Prev.Res.Dig., INIS Atomind., ISMEC, Met.Abstr., T.C.E.A., World Alum.Abstr. **Document type:** academic/scholarly publication.
—BLDSC (4276.093800); El; Faxon; UnCover; SWETS; CASDDS. **CCC.**
Description: Covers news on notables and developments in equipment and practices.
Refereed Serial

660　　　　　　　　YU　ISSN 0367-598X
　　　　　　　　　　　　CODEN: HMIDA8
HEMIJSKA INDUSTRIJA/CHEMICAL INDUSTRY. (Supplements avail.: Industrija Secera (ISSN 0350-249X); Plastika i Guma) (Text in Serbo-Croatian; summaries in English) 1946. m. $100. Savez Hemicara i Tehnologa Jugoslavije, Kneza Milosa 9, Box 187, 11001 Belgrade, Yugoslavia. Ed. Milesav Dragojevic. adv.; bk.rev. circ. 3,000. **Indexed:** Chem.Abstr., Chem.Eng.Abstr., Ref.Zh., T.C.E.A.
—BLDSC (4294.600000); CASDDS.

HOUSEHOLD & PERSONAL PRODUCTS INDUSTRY; the magazine for the detergent, soap, cosmetic and toiletry, wax, polish and aerosol industries. see *BUSINESS AND ECONOMICS — Marketing And Purchasing*

660　　　　　　　　　　CC
　　　　　　　　　　　　CODEN: HHKPDM
HUADONG KEXUE JISHU DAXUE XUEBAO/EAST CHINA UNIVERSITY OF SCIENCE AND TECHNOLOGY. JOURNAL. (Text in Chinese; abstracts in English) 1957. bi-m. $30. Huadong Kexue Jishu Daxue, Xuebao Bianjibu - East China Institute of Chemical Technology, 130 Meilong Lu, Shanghai 200237, People's Republic of China. TEL 4394280. FAX 4700834. TELEX 33428. Ed. Chen Minheng. adv. contact: Tao Shidi. **Document type:** academic/scholarly publication.
●Also available online. Vendor(s): DIALOG Information Services, Inc.
—CASDDS.
Formerly: Huadong Huagong Xueyuan Xuebao - East China Institute of Chemical Technology. Journal (ISSN 0253-9683)
Description: Covers the latest developments in the fields of chemical engineering, biochemical technology, polymer materials, process equipment, automatic control and electronic engineering, etc.

ENGINEERING — CHEMICAL ENGINEERING

660	CC	ISSN 0254-6094
TP155		CODEN: HUJIDJ

HUAGONG JIXIE/CHEMICAL ENGINEERING AND MACHINERY. (Text in Chinese; summaries in English) 1974. bi-m. Y6($36) Ministry of Chemical Industry, Institute of Chemical Engineering Machinery - Huaxue Gongye Bu, Huagong Jixie Yanjiusuo, 3 North Heshui Rd., Xigu, Lanzhou, Gansu Province, People's Republic of China. TEL 0931-557401. FAX 0931-558554. Ed. Zhu Yue. adv.: page Y3600; trim 165 x 245; adv. contact: Zhang Laimeng. index. circ. 10,000. **Indexed:** Corros.Abstr., T.C.E.A. **Document type:** academic/scholarly publication.
—BLDSC (3141.700000); CASDDS.
  Description: News for researchers and teachers about chemical engineering, materials and corrosion.

660 669	CC	ISSN 1001-2052
		CODEN: HUYEEF

HUAGONG YEJIN/JOURNAL OF ENGINEERING CHEMISTRY AND METALLURGY. (Text in Chinese) 1980. q. $45.60. (Chinese Academy of Sciences, Institute of Engineering Chemistry and Metallurgy) Science Press, Marketing and Sales Department, 16 Donghuangchenggen Beijie, Beijing 100707, People's Republic of China. TEL 4010642. FAX 4012180. TELEX 210247-SPBJ-CN. Ed. Mao Minghua.
—CASDDS.

660	CC

HUAXUE GONGCHENGSHI/CHEMICAL ENGINEERS. (Text in Chinese) bi-m. Heilongjiang Sheng Huagong Yanjiusuo - Heilongjiang Institute of Chemical Engineering, 334, Xinyang Lu, Daoli-qu, Harbin, Heilongjiang 150076, People's Republic of China. TEL 404133. Ed. Liu Guoliang.

665	CC	ISSN 1001-0017
		CODEN: HYZHEN

HUAXUE YU NIANHE/CHEMISTRY AND ADHESION. (Text in Chinese) 1964. q. $1.50 per no. (effective through 1995). Heilongjiang Sheng Kexueyuan, Shiyou Huaxue Yanjiusuo - Heilongjiang Academy of Sciences, Institute of Petrochemistry, 160, Zhongshan Lu, Harbin, Heilongjiang 150040, People's Republic of China. TEL 0451-223691. Ed. Ye Zhaojian. adv.; bk.rev.
—CASDDS.
  Description: Contains papers on petrochemistry, molecular materials, special synthetic polymer adhesive, and adhesive bonding technology.

HUNGARIAN JOURNAL OF INDUSTRIAL CHEMISTRY. see *CHEMISTRY*

HYDROCARBON PROCESSING. see *PETROLEUM AND GAS*

HYOMEN GIJUTSU. see *CHEMISTRY — Electrochemistry*

660	IT	ISSN 0390-2358
		CODEN: ICPDDL

I C P; rivista dell'industria chimica. (Text in Italian; summaries in English) 1972. m. L.65000. E R I S S.p.A., Via Tellini, 14, 20155 Milan, Italy. TEL 2-33-10-33-05. FAX 2-33-10-42-45. TELEX 323314 ERIS I. Ed. Stefano Meinardi. adv.: B&W page L.1800000, color page L. 2400000; trim 175 x 262. bk.rev./ pat.; index. circ. 6,860. **Indexed:** Chem.Abstr.
—BLDSC (4362.064800); CASDDS.

IMPACT PUMP NEWS AND PATENTS. see *MACHINERY*

IMPACT VALVES NEWS AND PATENTS. see *MACHINERY*

660 540	II	ISSN 0073-6295

INDIAN CHEMICAL DIRECTORY. (Bound with: Guide to Indian Chemical Plants and Equipment) (Text in English) 1955. triennial. $110. Technical Press Publications, 5-1 Convent St., Colaba, Bombay 400 039, India. TEL 2021446. TELEX 011-83479 CHEM IN. Ed. J.P. de Sousa. adv. circ. 12,000. **Document type:** directory.

660.2	II	ISSN 0019-4506
		CODEN: ICHEAF

INDIAN CHEMICAL ENGINEER. (In 2 sections; Section A: Journal of the Indian Institute of Chemical Engineers; Section B: Industry and News) 1959. q. Rs.150($40) Indian Institute of Chemical Engineers, P.O. Box 17001, Raja S C Mullick Rd., Calcutta 700 032, India. TEL 9133-473-4670. Ed. B.K. Dutta. adv.: page Rs.2000; trim 220 x 170. bk.rev.; abstr.; charts; illus. circ. 5,000. **Indexed:** Chem.Abstr., Chem.Eng.Abstr., T.C.E.A. **Document type:** academic/scholarly publication.
—BLDSC (4393.700000); CASDDS.
  Refereed Serial

661	SP	ISSN 0583-3469

INDUSTRIA QUIMICA. a. 2,000 ptas. Ministerio de Industria, Paseo de la Castellana, 160, Madrid 28046, Spain.

INDUSTRIA QUIMICA EN CIFRAS. see *CHEMISTRY — Abstracting, Bibliographies, Statistics*

660	MX	ISSN 0187-4888
HD9655.M4		

INDUSTRIA QUIMICA EN MEXICO. 1981. irreg., latest 1990. Mex.$1500($21) Instituto Nacional de Estadistica, Geografia e Informatica, Secretaria de Programacion y Presupuesto, Prol. Heroe de Nacozari, 2301, Sur, Puerta 11, Acceso, 20270 Aguascalientes, Ags., Mexico. TEL 49-18-19-48. FAX 491-80739. circ. 1,000.

660	US	ISSN 0888-5885
TP1		CODEN: IECRED

INDUSTRIAL & ENGINEERING CHEMISTRY RESEARCH. 1962. m. $567 to non-members (foreign $623); members $64 (foreign $120). American Chemical Society, 1155 16th St. N.W., Washington, DC 20036. TEL 800-333-9511. FAX 614-447-3671. (Subscr. to: Membership and Subscription Services, Box 3337, Columbus, OH 43210. TEL 614-447-3776) Ed. Donald R. Paul. bibl.; charts; illus.; index. circ. 4,437. (also avail. in microform; back issues avail.) **Indexed:** A.S.& T.Ind., Abstr.Bull.Inst.Pap.Chem., Agri.Eng.Abstr., API Catal., API Hlth.& Environ., API Oil., API Pet.Ref., API Pet.Subst., API Transport., Br.Ceram.Abstr., C.I.S.Abstr., Cadscan, Ceram.Abstr., Chem.Abstr., Chem.Eng.Abstr., Chem.Infd., Curr.Cont., Dairy Sci.Abstr., Deep Sea Res.& Oceanogr.Abstr., E&P Hlth. (1993-), Eng.Ind., Excerp.Med., Fluidex, Food Sci.& Tech.Abstr., Fuel & Energy Abstr., Gas Abstr., Gas Process.& Ppl. (1993-), Ind.Sci.Rev., INIS Atomind., Lead Abstr., Off.Tech. (1993-), Petrol.Abstr. (1963-), RAPRA, Sci.Abstr., Sci.Cit.Ind., Soils & Fert., Text.Tech.Dig., W.R.C.Inf., World Surf.Coat., World Text.Abstr., Zincscan. **Document type:** academic/scholarly publication.
●Also available online. Vendor(s): STN International (CJACS).
—BLDSC (4445.212000); EI; Faxon; UnCover; SWETS; CASDDS. **CCC.**
  Formed by the 1987 merger of: Industrial and Engineering Chemistry Product Research and Development (ISSN 0196-4321); Industrial and Engineering Chemistry Process Design and Development (ISSN 0196-4305); Industrial and Engineering Chemistry Fundamentals (ISSN 0196-4313)
  Description: Focuses on fundamental and theoretical aspects of chemical engineering, recent work on design methods and their application to processes and process equipment. Includes new technology applicable to products involving chemical engineering.

INDUSTRIAL BIOPROCESSING; a monthly intelligence service. see *CHEMISTRY — Organic Chemistry*

660	US

INFOCHEM. Spanish edition: Infoquim. (Supplement to: World Industrial Reporter) 6/yr. Keller International Publishing Corporation, 150 Great Neck Rd., Great Neck, NY 11021. TEL 516-829-9210. TELEX 221574 KELLE. circ. 51,548 (26,149 Engl. ed.; 25,399 Span. ed.). **Document type:** trade publication.

660	GW

INFORMATIONSBRIEF FUER FUEHRUNGSKRAEFTE IN DER CHEMISCHEN INDUSTRIE. 1963. m. DM.12. Dr. Curt Haefner Verlag, Bachstr. 14, 69121 Heidelberg, Germany. TEL 06221-49064. (Subscr. to: Postfach 106060, 69050 Heidelberg, Germany) Eds. Burkhard Jahn, Gerhard Wahl. abstr. circ. 37,000. (looseleaf format) **Document type:** trade publication.

660	SP	ISSN 0210-2064
		CODEN: INQUDI

INGENIERIA QUIMICA; diseno, ingenieria, construccion, operacion y mantenimiento de plantas industriales. 1969. m. 12360 ptas.($220) (effective 1993). Ingenieria Quimica, S.A., Triana 53, 28016 Madrid, Spain. TEL 341-3456400. FAX 341-3453945. Ed. Pedro de la Pezuela. adv.; bk.rev.; bibl.; charts; illus.; index. circ. 7,000. (back issues avail.) **Indexed:** Chem.Eng.Abstr., Ind.SST, T.C.E.A.
—BLDSC (4503.220000); SWETS; CASDDS. **CCC.**

660	AG

INGENIERIA QUIMICA. 1978. m. Edigar S.A., 15 de Noviembre 2547, 1261 Buenos Aires, Argentina. TEL 941-2344. TELEX 24788. Ed. Luis Mori. circ. 12,000.

INORGANIC MATERIALS. see *CHEMISTRY — Inorganic Chemistry*

628.96	UN	ISSN 1011-274X

INSECT AND PEST CONTROL NEWSLETTER. (Text in English) 1963. irreg. free. International Atomic Energy Agency, Wagramerstr. 5, P.O. Box 100, A-1400 Vienna Austria. (Co-sponsor: Food and Agriculture Organization) circ. 600. **Indexed:** Rev.Appl.Entomol.
  Formerly: Information Circular on Radiation Techniques and Their Applications to Insect Pests.

628.96	US

INSECT CONTROL GUIDE. 1982. a. $39. Meister Publishing Co., 37733 Euclid Ave., Willoughby, OH 44094. TEL 800-572-7740. FAX 216-942-0662. Ed. Stella Naegely. adv. circ. 7,151. **Document type:** trade publication.
  Formerly (until 1989): Insecticide Product Guide (ISSN 0891-1878)

628.96 633	CN

INSECT CONTROL IN FIELD CROPS. 1973. a. free. Saskatchewan Agriculture and Food, 3085 Albert St., Regina, SK S4S 0B1, Canada. TEL 306-787-6933. FAX 306-787-0216. charts. circ. 5,000. (also avail. in microfiche) **Document type:** government publication.

660.2	II	ISSN 0020-3351
TP1		CODEN: JECEAF

INSTITUTION OF ENGINEERS (INDIA). CHEMICAL ENGINEERING DIVISION. JOURNAL. (Text in English) 1920. 3/yr. Rs.60($8) Institution of Engineers (India), Chemical Engineering Division, 8 Gokhale Rd., Calcutta 700 020, India. TEL 033-288334. FAX 033-288345. TELEX 0217885 IEIC IN. Ed. K.N. Majumdar. acv.; charts;illus.; index. circ. 4,000. **Indexed:** Chem.Abstr., Eng.Ind., INIS Atomind., Met.Abstr., Sci.Abstr.
—BLDSC (4794.015000); EI; UnCover; CASDDS.

INSTITUTION OF PROFESSIONAL ENGINEERS. TRANSACTIONS. ELECTRICAL, MECHANICAL AND CHEMICAL ENGINEERING SECTION. see *ENGINEERING — Electrical Engineering*

INSTITUTUL POLITEHNIC DIN IASI. BULETINUL. SECTIA II: CHIMIE. see *CHEMISTRY*

INSTRUMENTATION IN THE CHEMICAL AND PETROLEUM INDUSTRIES. see *INSTRUMENTS*

660.2	US	ISSN 0020-6318
TP1		CODEN: INCEAX

INTERNATIONAL CHEMICAL ENGINEERING; a quarterly journal of translations from Russia, Eastern Europe, Asia, Japan, etc. 1961. q. $349 to non-members (foreign $374); members $45. American Institute of Chemical Engineers, 345 E. 47th St., New York, NY 10017. TEL 212-705-7663. FAX 212-752-3294. Ed. Renate U. Churchill. abstr.; bibl.; charts; illus.; index. circ. 1,300. (also avail. in microform from UMI; reprint service avail. from UMI) **Indexed:** API Abstr., API Catal., AP Hlth.& Environ., API Oil., API Pet.Ref., API Pet.Subst., API Transport., Chem.Abstr., Chem.Eng.Abstr., Comput.Abstr., Curr.Biotech.Abstr., E&P Hlth. (1993-), Eng.Ind., Excerp.Med., Fluidex, Foul.Prev.Res.Dig., Fuel & Energy Abstr., Gas Abstr., Gas Process.& Ppl. (1993-), INIS Atomind., Met.Abstr., Off.Tech. (1993-), Petrol.Abstr. (1963-), Soils & Fert., T.C.E.A. **Document type:** trade publication.
—BLDSC (4538.500000); Faxon; UnCover; SWETS; UMI. **CCC.**
  Description: Devoted to English-language translations of papers which have appeared in foreign-language journals.

ENGINEERING — CHEMICAL ENGINEERING

INTERNATIONAL JOURNAL OF ADHESION AND ADHESIVES. see *PLASTICS*

662   UK   ISSN 0265-5918
INTERNATIONAL JOURNAL OF BULK SOLIDS STORAGE IN SILOS. 1984. s-a. £40($84) Childwall University Press Ltd., Box 78, London NW11 0PG, England. TEL 01-455-0011. FAX 01-458-2278. TELEX 895424-POWDER-G. Ed. A.S. Goldberg.

INTERNATIONAL JOURNAL OF ENGINEERING FLUID MECHANICS. see *CHEMISTRY — Physical Chemistry*

660.284   US   ISSN 0091-4037
TA455.P58   CODEN: IJPMCS
INTERNATIONAL JOURNAL OF POLYMERIC MATERIALS. 1971. 16/yr. (in 4 vols., 4 nos./vol.). 248 ECU per vol. (effective 1993). Gordon and Breach Science Publishers, 820 Town Center Dr., Langhorne, PA 19047. TEL 215-750-2642. FAX 215-750-6343. (UK subscr. to: P.O. Box 90, Reading, Berkshire RG1 8JL, England. TEL 0734-560-080) Ed. Dusan Prevorsek. adv.; illus.; index. (also avail. in microform) **Indexed:** Cadscan, Chem.Abstr., Curr.Cont., Lead Abstr., Sci.Abstr., Zincscan.
—BLDSC (4542.475000); Faxon; UnCover; SWETS; CASDDS. **CCC.**
Refereed Serial

INTERNATIONAL POWDER & BULK SOLIDS ABSTRACTS. see *ENGINEERING — Abstracting, Bibliographies, Statistics*

660.2   II   ISSN 0047-0910
INTERNATIONAL PRESS CUTTING SERVICE: CHEMICAL PROCESS ENGINEERING. DRUGS - PHARMACEUTICALS. 1967. w. $65. International Press Cutting Service, Box 63, Allahabad 211001, India. Ed. N. Khanna. bk.rev. circ. 1,200. (processed)

INTERNATIONAL PRESS CUTTING SERVICE: DYESTUFF INDUSTRY AND CHEMICALS. see *CLEANING AND DYEING*

INTERNATIONAL PROCESS TECHNOLOGY ABSTRACTS. see *ENGINEERING — Abstracting, Bibliographies, Statistics*

662 622   US
INTERNATIONAL SOCIETY OF EXPLOSIVES ENGINEERS. ANNUAL MEMBERSHIP DIRECTORY AND DESK REFERENCE. 1975. a. $62 to non-members; members $40. International Society of Explosives Engineers, 29100 Aurora Rd., Solon, OH 44139. TEL 216-349-4004. FAX 216-349-3788. Ed. Larry Trask. adv. circ. 3,000. **Document type:** directory.
Formerly: Society of Explosives Engineers. Membership Directory and Desk Reference.

662 622   US
INTERNATIONAL SOCIETY OF EXPLOSIVES ENGINEERS. CONFERENCES ON EXPLOSIVES AND BLAST TECHNIQUE. PROCEEDINGS. 1975. a. $38 to non-members; members $26. International Society of Explosives Engineers, 29100 Aurora Rd., Solon, OH 44139. TEL 216-349-4004. FAX 216-349-3788. circ. 3,000. **Document type:** proceedings.
Formerly: Society of Explosives Engineers. Conference on Explosives and Blasting Technique. Proceedings.

660.2   US   ISSN 0071-3112
INTERNATIONAL SYMPOSIUM ON CHEMICAL REACTION ENGINEERING. PROCEEDINGS. (Each issue has a different publisher;) 1986 Pergamon Press, Headington Hill Hall, Oxford OX3 DBW, England) 1972. biennial, 11th, 1990. Inquire: Prof. Bischoff, Dept. of Chem. Eng., Univ. of Delaware, Newark, DE 19716. **Indexed:** Chem.Abstr. **Document type:** proceedings.
—**CCC.**
Supersedes: European Symposium on Chemical Reaction Engineering. Proceedings.

660.2   PL
CODEN: ICPRDT
INZYNIERIA CHEMICZNA I PROCESOWA. (Text in Polish; summaries in English, French, German, Russian) 1957. q. $40. (Politechnika Wroclawska, Instytut Inzynierii Chemicznej) Wydawnictwo Politechniki Wroclawskiej, Ul. Wybrzeze Wyspianskiego 27, 50-370 Wroclaw, Poland. (Dist. by: Ars Polona, Krakowskie Przedmiescie 7, 00-068 Warsaw, Poland) (Co-sponsor: Polska Akademia Nauk, Komitet Inzynierii Chemicznej) Ed. Roman Koch. bibl. circ. 400. **Indexed:** Chem.Abstr., Chem.Eng.Abstr., INIS Atomind., T.C.E.A.
—BLDSC (4563.610000); EI; SWETS; CASDDS.
Former titles: Inzynieria Chemiczna (ISSN 0208-6425); Chemia Stosowana. Seria B. Zagadnienia Inzynierii i Apartury Chemicznej (ISSN 0009-224X)

660   PL   ISSN 0368-0827
CODEN: IZACAX
INZYNIERIA I APARATURA CHEMICZNA. (Text in Polish; summaries in English) 1970. bi-m. $81. (Stowarzyszenie Inzynierow i Technikow Mechanikow Polskich) Oficyna Wydawnicza SIMP Press, Ltd., Ul. Swietokrzyska 14A, 00-950 Warwaw, Poland. (Dist. by: Ars Polona-Ruch, Krakowskie Przedmiescie 7, Warsaw, Poland; Editorial addr: Ul. Plebiscytowa 25, 44-101 Gliwice, Poland. TEL 48-32-319231) (Co-sponsor: Stowarzyszenie Inzynierow i Technikow Przemyslu Chemicznego) Ed. Karol Machej. adv.: B&W page $1000. circ. 1,300. **Indexed:** Chem.Eng.Abstr., T.C.E.A.
—CASDDS.

IRANIAN JOURNAL OF CHEMISTRY AND CHEMICAL ENGINEERING (INTERNATIONAL ENGLISH EDITION). see *CHEMISTRY*

660   RU   ISSN 0202-8069
CODEN: IKTVAC
ITOGI NAUKI I TEKHNIKI: KHIMIYA I TEKHNOLOGIYA VYSOKOMOLEKULYARNYKH SOEDINENII. 1969. irreg., vols.24-25, 1988. 7.80 Rub. Vsesoyuznyi Institut Nauchno-Tekhnicheskoi Informatsii (VINITI), Baltiiskaya ul. 14, Moscow A-219, Russia. (Subscr. to: Mezhdunarodnaya Kniga, Dimitrova ul. 39, 113095 Moscow, Russia) **Indexed:** Chem.Abstr.
—BLDSC (0393.847000); CASDDS.

660   RU   ISSN 0202-8018
TP155.7   CODEN: ITPTDI
ITOGI NAUKI I TEKHNIKI: PROTSESSY I APPARATY KHIMICHESKOI TEKHNOLOGII. 1973. irreg., vol.16, 1988. 6.60 Rub. Vsesoyuznyi Institut Nauchno-Tekhnicheskoi Informatsii (VINITI), Baltiiskaya ul. 14, Moscow A-219, Russia. (Subscr. to: Mezhdunarodnaya Kniga, Dimitrova ul. 39, 113095 Moscow, Russia) **Indexed:** Chem.Abstr.
—BLDSC (0134.575000); CASDDS.

660   JA   ISSN 0075-319X
JAPAN CHEMICAL ANNUAL. (Text in English) a. 11330 Yen($90) Chemical Daily Co., Ltd., International Affairs, 3-16-8, Nihonbashi Hama-cho, Chuo-ku, Tokyo 103, Japan. TEL 03-3663-7932. FAX 03-3663-2530. TELEX 2422362 NIPP J. (Dist. in U.S. by: DJK Corporation of America, Inc., 301 North Hursbourne Lane, Ste. 285, Louisville, KY 40222. TEL 502-429-6660) Ed. Tadashi Fujimoto.
—BLDSC (4648.180000).
Description: Covers the trends and results of the chemical and its related industries in Japan.

660   JA   ISSN 0075-3203
TP12
JAPAN CHEMICAL DIRECTORY (TOKYO, 1963). (Text in English) 1963. a. 27000 Yen($225) Chemical Daily Co., Ltd., International Affairs, 3-16-8 Nihonbashi Hamacho, Cho-ku, Tokyo 103, Japan. TEL 03-3663-7932. FAX 03-3663-2530. TELEX 2422362 NIPPO J. **Document type:** directory.
Description: Lists about 1,420 Japanese enterprises in the chemical and allied fields.

661   JA
JAPAN CHEMICAL INDUSTRY ASSOCIATION. ANNUAL REPORT. a. Japan Chemical Industry Association - Nihon Kagaku Kogyo Kyokai, Tokyo Club Bldg., 3-2-6 Kasumigaseki, Chiyoda-ku, Tokyo 100. TEL 03-5800751. TELEX J23557.

660   JA   ISSN 0047-1755
HD9657.J3   CODEN: JCHWAC
JAPAN CHEMICAL WEEK. (Text in English) 1960. w. $446 for North and Central America; Europe $452. Chemical Daily Co., Ltd., International Affairs, 3-16-8 Nihonbashi Hamacho, Chuo-ku, Tokyo 103, Japan. TEL 03-3663-7932. FAX 03-3663-2530. TELEX 2422362 NIPPO J. **Indexed:** Chem.Abstr., PROMT.
—BLDSC (4648.210000); SWETS; CASDDS.
Description: Provides important news and statistical data on the Japanese chemical market.

JOURNAL OF ADHESION SCIENCE AND TECHNOLOGY. see *PLASTICS*

JOURNAL OF AEROSOL SCIENCE. see *PACKAGING*

JOURNAL OF APPLIED ELECTROCHEMISTRY. see *CHEMISTRY — Electrochemistry*

660.284   US   ISSN 0021-8995
TP156.P6   CODEN: JAPNAB
JOURNAL OF APPLIED POLYMER SCIENCE. 1956. 48/yr. $3,530 (foreign $4,190) (subscr. includes Symposia). John Wiley & Sons, Inc., Journals, 605 Third Ave., New York, NY 10158-0012. TEL 212-692-6000. Ed. Eric Baer. adv.; bk.rev.; abstr.; bibl.; charts; illus.; index. circ. 2,000. (also avail. in microform from UMI; back issues avail.) **Indexed:** Appl.Mech.Rev., Biwk.Pap.Rad.Chem.& Photochem., Chem.Abstr., Chem.Eng.Abstr., Chem.Titles, Cott.& Trop.Fibr.Abstr., Curr.Cont., Dairy Sci.Abstr., Deep Sea Res.& Oceanogr.Abstr., Eng.Ind., Excerp.Med., RAPRA, Sci.Cit.Ind., T.C.E.A., World Surf.Coat.
●Also available online. Vendor(s): STN International (CJWILEY).
—BLDSC (4946.600000); Faxon; UnCover; SWETS; UMI; CASDDS. **CCC.**
Description: Provides scientists and engineers with thorough coverage of progress and significant results in the systematic practical application of polymer science.

668.4   US   ISSN 0570-4898
CODEN: APPSBX
JOURNAL OF APPLIED POLYMER SCIENCE. SYMPOSIA. 1965. irreg., no.51, 1992. price varies. John Wiley & Sons, Inc., 605 Third Ave., New York, NY 10158-0012. TEL 212-692-6000. FAX 212-850-6088. **Indexed:** Abstr.Bull.Inst.Pap.Chem., Art & Archaeol.Tech.Abstr., ASCA, Chem.Abstr., Ind.Sci.Rev., INIS Atomind., World Surf.Coat., World Text.Abstr.
—BLDSC (1576.540000); SWETS. **CCC.**
Refereed Serial

JOURNAL OF BIOMATERIALS SCIENCE. POLYMER EDITION. see *BIOLOGY — Biotechnology*

JOURNAL OF CHEMICAL AND ENGINEERING DATA. see *CHEMISTRY*

660.2   JA   ISSN 0021-9592
TP1   CODEN: JCEJAQ
JOURNAL OF CHEMICAL ENGINEERING OF JAPAN. (Text in English) 1968. bi-m. $85. Society of Chemical Engineers, Japan, Kyoritsu Bldg., 4-6-19 Kohinata, Bunkyo-ku, Tokyo 112, Japan. (Dist. by: Maruzen Co., Ltd., Export Department, Box 5050, Tokyo International, Tokyo 100-31, Japan) Ed. Takeshi Fujie. abstr. **Indexed:** API Abstr., API Catal., API Hlth.& Environ., API Oil., API Pet.Ref., API Pet.Subst., API Transport., Biotech.Abstr., Cadscan, Chem.Abstr., Chem.Eng.Abstr., Curr.Cont., Excerp.Med., Fluidex, Foul.Prev.Res.Dig., Ind.Sci.Rev., INIS Atomind., Lead Abstr., Sci.Cit.Ind., Sel.Water Res.Abstr., Sugar Ind.Abstr., T.C.E.A., Zincscan.
—BLDSC (4956.700000); Faxon; UnCover; SWETS; CASDDS. **CCC.**

JOURNAL OF CHEMICAL TECHNOLOGY AND BIOTECHNOLOGY. see *BIOLOGY — Biotechnology*

JOURNAL OF ENVIRONMENTAL POLYMER DEGRADATION. see *BIOLOGY — Biological Chemistry*

662 622   US
JOURNAL OF EXPLOSIVES ENGINEERING. bi-m. $30 (foreign $40). International Society of Explosives Engineers, 29100 Aurora Rd., Cleveland, OH 44139-1800. TEL 216-349-4004. FAX 216-349-3788.

ENGINEERING — CHEMICAL ENGINEERING

JOURNAL OF HAZARDOUS MATERIALS; management - handling - disposal - risk - assessment. see *ENVIRONMENTAL STUDIES — Waste Management*

660 UK ISSN 0950-4230
TP149
JOURNAL OF LOSS PREVENTION IN THE PROCESS INDUSTRIES. 1988. 5/yr. £225 in UK and Europe; elsewhere £245. Butterworth - Heinemann (Subsidiary of: Reed International PLC), Linacre House, Jordan Hill, Oxford OX2 8DP, England. TEL 0865-310366. FAX 0865-310898. TELEX 83111 BHPOXF G. (Subscr. to: Turpin Transactions Ltd., Distribution Centre, Blackhorse Rd., Letchworth, Herts SG6 1HN, England. TEL 0462-672555) Ed. P.F. Nolan. adv. circ. in microform from UMI; back issues avail.) **Document type:** academic/scholarly publication.
—BLDSC (5010.562000); SWETS; UMI. **CCC.**
Description: Covers all areas of process plant safety, including plant design and layout, and choice of safe materials.
Refereed Serial

660 628 JA ISSN 0916-9962
CODEN: JPESEC
▼**JOURNAL OF PESTICIDE SCIENCE (INTERNATIONAL EDITION).** Japanese edition: Nippon Noyaku Gakkaishi (ISSN 0385-1559) (Text in English) 1992. 4/yr. fl.391($211) (effective 1994). Pesticide Science Society of Japan - Nippon Noyaku Gakkai, 43-11 Komagome, 1-chome, Toshima-ku, Tokyo, 170, Japan. TEL 0427-28-3208. FAX 0427-28-3216. (Dist. outside Japan by: Elsevier Science Publishers B.V., P.O. Box 211, 1000 AE Amsterdam, Netherlands. TEL 31-20-5803911. FAX 31-20-5803598; Subscr. in U.S. and Canada to: Elsevier Science Publishing Co., Inc., Box 882, Madison Sq. Sta., New York, NY 10159-0882. TEL 212-989-5800. FAX 212-633-3990) Ed. Ko Wakabayshi. index. (back issues avail.) **Indexed:** Chem.Abstr., Crop Physiol.Abstr., Field Crop Abstr., Hort.Abstr., Maize Abstr., Plant.Grow.Reg.Abstr., Rice Abstr., Seed.Abstr., Sel.Water Res.Abstr., Soils & Fert., Weed.Abstr. **Document type:** academic/scholarly publication.
—SWETS; CASDDS.
Description: Publishes research results in pesticide science, agrochemistry and the chemistry of biologically active natural products.
Refereed Serial

660 IS ISSN 0334-6447
CODEN: JPOEEK
JOURNAL OF POLYMER ENGINEERING. 1980. q. $180. Freund Publishing House Ltd., Box 35010, 61 Nachmani St., Tel Aviv 61350, Israel. TEL 972-3-615335. FAX 972-3-5605335. (And: Chesham House, Ste. 500, 150 Regent St., London W1R 5FA, England) Ed.Bd. **Indexed:** Chem.Abstr. **Document type:** academic/scholarly publication.
—BLDSC (5040.970000); Faxon; SWETS; CASDDS.
Former titles: Polymer Engineering. Journal (ISSN 0250-8079); Polymer Engineering Reviews.

660.284 UK ISSN 0147-698X
TA418.78 CODEN: JPBTDX
JOURNAL OF POWDER & BULK SOLIDS TECHNOLOGY. 1977. q. £50($105) International Powder Institute, Box 78, London NW11 OPG, England. Ed.Bd. adv.; bk.rev. **Indexed:** C.R.I. Abstr., Chem.Abstr., Chem.Eng.Abstr., Gas Abstr., T.C.E.A.
—CASDDS.

660 UK ISSN 0260-6275
CODEN: JSPTDM
JOURNAL OF SEPARATION PROCESS TECHNOLOGY. 1979. a. £50($105) Childwall University Press Ltd., Box 78, London NW11 OPG, England. TEL 01-455-0011. FAX 01-458-2278. TELEX 8954242-POWDER-G. Ed. David Reay. **Indexed:** Chem.Abstr., Chem.Eng.Abstr., Excerp.Med., T.C.E.A.
—CASDDS.

660 JA ISSN 0914-3106
CODEN: TKHOEM
JOURNAL OF TOSOH RESEARCH/TOSOH KENKYU HOKOKU. (Text in English, Japanese) 1957. s-a. Tosoh Corporation, Research and Development Division - Tosoh Kenkyu Hokoku, 4560 Tonda, Shinnanyo-shi, Yamaguchi-ken 746, Japan. Ed. Kinji Ishibashi. charts; stat.; circ. 750 (controlled).
—BLDSC (5069.600000); CASDDS.
Formerly: Toyo Soda Manufacturing Company. Scientific Report (ISSN 0041-0144)

660 624 621 MY
JURUTERA. (Text in English, Malay) m. M.$3. Institusi Jurutera Malaysia, Lot 60 & 62, Jalan 52-4, P.O. Box 223, 46720 Petaling Jaya, Malaysia. FAX 03-7577678. TELEX MA-37299-IEM. Ed. Haron Ismail. adv. circ. 9,000. (back issues avail.)
Formerly: Institusi Jurutera Malaysia. Bulletin.

660 JA
KAGAKU GIJUTSU NYUSU/NEWS OF CHEMICAL INDUSTRY AND ENGINEERING. (Text in Japanese) s-m. 40000 Yen. Daiya Risachi - Dia Research Institute, 1-30, Shiba 2-chome, Minato-ku, Tokyo 105, Japan.

660.2 JA ISSN 0022-7676
KAGAKU KOGAKU/CHEMICAL ENGINEERING. (Text in Japanese; summaries in English) 1953. m. 22000 Yen. Society of Chemical Engineers, Japan, Kyoritsu Bldg., 4-6-19 Kohinata, Bunkyo-ku, Tokyo 112, Japan. (Orders from: Maruzen Co. Ltd., Export Department: Box 5050, Tokyo International, Tokyo 100-31, Japan) Ed. Takeshi Fujie. adv.; bk.rev.; bibl.; charts; illus.; index. (processed) **Indexed:** Biotech.Abstr., Chem.Abstr., Chem.Eng.Abstr., Ind.Sci.Rev., INIS Atomind., JCT, JTA, Risk Abstr.
—CCC.

660.2 JA ISSN 0386-216X
CODEN: KKRBAW
KAGAKU KOGAKU RONBUNSHU. (Text in Japanese: summaries and tables in English) 1975. bi-m. $40 to individuals; libraries $70. Society of Chemical Engineers, Kyoritsu Bldg., 4-6-19 Kohinata, Bunkyo-ku, Tokyo 112, Japan. TEL 03-3943-2529. FAX 03-3943-3530. (Dist. by: Maruzen Co., Ltd., Export Department, Box 5050, Tokyo International, Tokyo 100-31, Japan) Ed. Takeshi Suzuki. **Indexed:** Chem.Abstr., Curr.Cont., Foul.Prev.Res.Dig., Ind.Sci.Rev., INIS Atomind., JCT, JTA. **Document type:** academic/scholarly publication.
—BLDSC (5080.507000); CASDDS.

KAGAKU KOGYO NIPPO/CHEMICAL DAILY. see *CHEMISTRY*

KAGAKU TO KOGYO (TOKYO)/CHEMISTRY AND CHEMICAL INDUSTRY. see *CHEMISTRY*

KAOKU GAICHU/HOUSE AND HOUSEHOLD INSECT PESTS. see *BIOLOGY — Entomology*

660 FI ISSN 0355-1628
TP1 CODEN: KMKMAA
KEMIA - KEMI/FINNISH CHEMISTRY. (Text in Finnish and Swedish, summaries in English) 1974. m. FIM 490. (Suomen Kemian Seura - Association of Finnish Chemical Societies) Kemian Kustannus Oy, Hietaniemenkatu 2, 5. krs, FIN-00100 Helsinki, Finland. TEL 358-0-490-0553. FAX 358-0-407-091. (Co-sponsor: Chemical Industry Federation of Finland) Ed. Marjatta Kivimaki-Majanen. adv.; bk.rev.; abstr.; charts; illus.; mkt.; pat.; stat.; tr.lit.; tr.mk.; index. circ. 5,600. (reprint service avail. from UMI,ISI) **Indexed:** Chem.Abstr., Chem.Eng.Abstr., Curr.Biotech.Abstr., Dairy Sci.Abstr., Food Sci.& Tech.Abstr., INIS Atomind., Soils & Fert., T.C.E.A.
—BLDSC (5089.263500); EI; CASDDS.
Formed by the merger of: Kemian Teollisuus (ISSN 0022-9822) & Suomen Kemistilehti A (ISSN 0371-4098) & Finska Kemistsamfundet. Meddelanden (ISSN 0015-2498)

660.2 RU ISSN 0023-110X
CODEN: KPRMAW
KHIMICHESKAYA PROMYSHLENNOST. English translation: Russian Chemical Industry (US ISSN 1068-3704) 1924. m. 42.60 Rub. (Ministerstvo Khimicheskoi Promyshlennosti) Izdatel'stvo Khimiya, Novaya pl., 10, Moscow K-12, Russia. adv.; bk.rev.; bibl.; charts; illus.; index. circ. 5,500. **Indexed:** Abstr.Bull.Inst.Pap.Chem., Biol.Abstr., Cadscan, Chem.Abstr., Chem.Infd., Curr.Cont., Eng.Ind., INIS Atomind., Lead Abstr., Pollut.Abstr., World Surf.Coat.; Zincscan.
—BLDSC (0393.000000); CASDDS. **CCC.**

660 KR ISSN 0368-556X
CODEN: KHMTA6
KHIMICHESKAYA TEKHNOLOGIYA; nauchno-teoreticheskii zhurnal. (Text in Russian) 1960. bi-m. 7.80 Rub. (Akademiya Nauk Ukrainy, Vsesoyuznoe Khimicheskoe Obshchestvo im. D.I. Mendeleeva, Otdelenie Khimii i Khimicheskoi Tekhnologii) Izdatel'stvo Naukova Dumka, c/o Yu.A. Khramov, Dir, Ul. Repina, 3, Kiev 252 601, Ukraine. TEL 446-94-89. (Subscr. to: Mezhdunarodnaya Kniga, Moscow, G-200, Russia) Ed. K.E. Makhorun. **Indexed:** Abstr.Bull.Inst.Pap.Chem., Chem.Abstr.

662 RU ISSN 0023-1126
TP1 CODEN: KHNMAO
KHIMICHESKOE I NEFTYANOE MASHINOSTROENIE/CHEMICAL AND OIL INDUSTRY. English translation: Chemical and Petroleum Engineering (US ISSN 0009-2355) 1932. m. $99. (Gosudarstvennyi Komitet Khimicheskogo i Neftyanogo Mashinostroeniya pri Gosplane) Izdatel'stvo Mashinostroenie, 4, Stromynsky per., 107076 Moscow, Russia. TEL 095-269-7141. FAX 095-269-4897. Ed. A. Vasiliev. adv.: page DM.4000. bk.rev.; bibl.; charts; illus. **Indexed:** Chem.Abstr., INIS Atomind., ISMEC, Met.Abstr., Sugar Ind.Abstr. World Alum.Abstr. **Document type:** academic/scholarly publication.
—BLDSC (0393.450000); CASDDS.

662.6 RU ISSN 0023-1177
TP315 CODEN: KTVTBY
KHIMIYA TVERDOGO TOPLIVA. English translation: Solid Fuel Chemistry (US ISSN 0361-5219) 1967. bi-m. 33.30 Rub. (Rossiiskaya Akademiya Nauk) Izdatel'stvo Nauka, 90 Profsoyuznaya ul., 117864 Moscow, Russia. **Indexed:** Chem.Abstr., INIS Atomind.
—BLDSC (0394.585000); CASDDS.

660.2 TU ISSN 0023-1428
KIMYA MUHENDISLIGI. 1962. bi-m. $60. Turkish Chamber of Chemical Engineers, Karanfil Sok. 19-6, Kizilay 06650, Ankara, Turkey. FAX 90-4-1174824. TELEX 42396 GISE TR. Ed. Ugur Gurel. adv.; bk.rev.; abstr.; index. circ. 10,000. **Indexed:** Chem.Abstr.

KOBUNSHI/POLYMERS. see *CHEMISTRY — Organic Chemistry*

KOBUNSHI RONBUNSHU. see *CHEMISTRY — Organic Chemistry*

660.2 HU ISSN 0023-2939
TP890 CODEN: KOERA9
KOLORISZTIKAI ERTES TO/COLORISTICAL REVIEW.* (Text in English, German and Hungarian; contents page in English, German, Hungarian and Russian) 1959. bi-m. $33.50. (Anilinfestek es Vegyianyagforghimi Vallalat) Nepszava Lapkiado Vallalat, Rakoczi ut 54, 1533 Budapest, Hungary. TEL 222-408. (Subscr. to: Kultura, Box 149, 1389 Budapest, Hungary) Ed. Sandor Vass. adv.; bk.rev.; charts; illus. **Indexed** Art & Archaeol.Tech.Abstr., Chem.Abstr., Text.Tech.Dig., World Text.Abstr.

KOREAN CHEMICAL SOCIETY. BULLETIN. see *CHEMISTRY*

KOREAN CHEMICAL SOCIETY. JOURNAL/DAEHAN HWAHAK HOE JEE. see *CHEMISTRY*

620.16 XR ISSN 0452-599X
TA462 CODEN: KOCMAI
KOROZE A OCHRANA MATERIALU. (Text in Czech; summaries in English, German, Russian) 1957. 5/yr. 100 Kcs. (foreign $17). A K I - Association of Corrosion Engineers, U Mestanskeho Pivovaru 4, 170 04 Prague 7, Czech Republic. TEL 42-2-801017. FAX 42-2-809809. adv.: Page 8000 Kc. bk.rev.; charts; illus.; stat.; index. circ. 1,300. **Indexed:** Chem Abstr, Corros.Abstr., Met.Abstr., World Alum.Abstr.
—BLDSC (5113.751000); CASDDS.

KORROZIOS FIGYELO. see *PAINTS AND PROTECTIVE COATINGS*

KWAHAKGWA KWAHAKGONEOP. see *CHEMISTRY*

ENGINEERING — CHEMICAL ENGINEERING

660   NZ   CODEN: CMNZAA
LABORATORY NEWS. 1936. bi-m. NZ.$30. T.P.L. Media (Trade Publications), 308 Great South Rd., 1st Fl., Greenlane, Auckland, New Zealand. TEL 0064-9-5293000. FAX 0064-9-5293001. adv.; bk.rev.; illus. circ. 2,674. **Indexed:** Chem.Abstr., INIS Atomind.
—CASDDS. **CCC.**
Former titles: Chemistry in Industry; (until 1988): Chemistry and Industry and Laboratory Management (ISSN 0111-7734); (until 1981): Chemistry in New Zealand (ISSN 0009-3076); (until 1967): New Zealand Institute of Chemistry. Journal (ISSN 0028-8227).

LATIN AMERICAN APPLIED RESEARCH. see *CHEMISTRY*

660   UK   ISSN 0262-4230
TP1   CODEN: MCHMDI
MANUFACTURING CHEMIST. Key Title: Manufacturing Chemist (London, 1981). (Supplement avail.: Aerosol Review) 1929. m. $145. Morgan-Grampian (Process Press) Ltd. (Subsidiary of: Morgan-Grampian plc), Morgan-Grampian House, 30 Calderwood St., London SE18 6QH, England. TEL 081-855-7777. FAX 081-854-7476. Ed. Gerry Duggin. adv. contact: Clive Grant. bk.rev.; abstr.; charts; illus.; mkt.; pat.; stat.; tr.lit. circ. 5,106. (also avail. in microform from UMI,PMC; back issues avail.) **Indexed:** Anal.Abstr., Art & Archaeol.Tech.Abstr., Biotech.Abstr., Br.Tech.Ind., CAD CAM Abstr., Cadscan, Chem.Abstr., Chem.Eng.Abstr., Curr.Biotech.Abstr., Energy Ind., Energy Info.Abstr., Eng.Ind., Excerp.Med., Int.Packag.Abstr., Lab.Haz.Bull., Lead Abstr., Met.Abstr., RAPRA, Risk Abstr., Sci.Abstr., T.C.E.A., World Surf.Coat., Zincscan. **Document type:** trade publication.
—BLDSC (5366.000000); Faxon; UnCover; SWETS; CASDDS. **CCC.**
Formed by the merger of (1964-1981): Manufacturing Chemist and Aerosol News (ISSN 0025-2557); (1974-1981): Chemical Age (ISSN 0302-2900)
Description: Technical coverage of international chemical, pharmaceutical, specialty chemical, cosmetic and toiletries industries.

MATERIALS CHEMISTRY AND PHYSICS; the international journal which unites the chemical and physical fields of research in materials science. see *ENGINEERING — Engineering Mechanics And Materials*

660.284   US   ISSN 0191-5665
TA455.P58   CODEN: MCMAD7
MECHANICS OF COMPOSITE MATERIALS. English translation of: Mekhanika Kompozitaykh Materialov (LV ISSN 0135-7492) 1965. bi-m. $970 (foreign $1135) (effective 1994). (Latvian Academy of Sciences, LV) Plenum Publishing Corp., Consultants Bureau, 233 Spring St., New York, NY 10013. TEL 212-620-8468. FAX 212-463-0742. TELEX 23-421139. Ed. A.K. Malmeister. (also avail. in microfilm from JSC; back issues avail.) **Indexed:** Appl.Mech.Rev., Chem.Titles, INIS Atomind., ISMEC. **Document type:** academic/scholarly publication.
—BLDSC (0415.849000); Faxon; UnCover; SWETS; UMI. **CCC.**
Formerly: Polymer Mechanics - Mekhanika Polimerov (ISSN 0032-390X)
Refereed Serial

METALURGIJA. see *METALLURGY*

660   CC   ISSN 0253-4320
CODEN: HTKUDJ
MODERN CHEMICAL INDUSTRY. (Text in Chinese, summaries in English) 1980. m. $80 (effective through 1995). China Chemical Information Center, 53, Andingmenwai Xiaoguanjie, Beijing 100029, People's Republic of China. TEL 4266622. FAX 01-4214052. Ed. Zhang Ming. adv. circ. 20,000. (back issues avail.) **Document type:** trade publication.
—BLDSC (5885.800000); CASDDS.
Description: Covers development policies of China's chemical industry and general reviews on the progress of modern science and technology in the worldwide chemical industry.

660   NE   ISSN 0925-5125
CODEN: MOLEEV
MOLECULAR ENGINEERING; an international journal devoted to the design, characterization and application of molecules and molecular materials endowed with specific biological, chemical and physical properties. (Text in English) 1991. 4/yr. fl.382($199.50) (effective 1994). Kluwer Academic Publishers, Postbus 17, 3300 AA Dordrecht, Netherlands. TEL 31-78-334911. FAX 31-78-334254. TELEX 29245 KAPG NL. (Dist. by: Kluwer Academic Publishers Group, P.O. Box 322, 3300 AH Dordrecht, Netherlands. TEL 31-78-524400. FAX 31-78-524474; N. America dist. addr.: Box 358, Accord Sta., Hingham, MA 02018-0358. TEL 617-871-6600. FAX 617-871-6528) Eds. J. Maruani, J. Zyss. (also avail. in microform from UMI; back issues avail.) **Indexed:** Chem.Abstr. **Document type:** academic/scholarly publication.
—BLDSC (5900.817440); UMI. **CCC.**
Description: Original articles, reviews, notes and letters on the latest developments in molecular engineering.
Refereed Serial

NACHRICHTEN AUS CHEMIE, TECHNIK UND LABORATORIUM. see *CHEMISTRY*

660   CC   ISSN 1000-5994
CODEN: NAXUEI
NANJING HUAGONG XUEYUAN XUEBAO/NANJING INSTITUTE OF CHEMICAL TECHNOLOGY. JOURNAL. (Text in Chinese) 1979. q. $10. Nanjing Huagong Xueyuan - Nanjing Institute of Chemical Engineering, 5 Xinmofan Malu, Nanjing, Jiangsu 210009, People's Republic of China. TEL 316755. FAX 307716. Ed. Zhang Youheng. circ. 1,500.
●Also available online. Vendor(s): DIALOG Information Services, Inc..
—CASDDS.

NATIONAL COTTONSEED PRODUCTS ASSOCIATION. TRADING RULES. see *AGRICULTURE — Feed, Flour And Grain*

660 620.11   YU   ISSN 0350-0667
CODEN: NPGLA7
NAUCNO-TEHNICKI PREGLED. (Text in Serbian; abstracts in English and French) 1959. 10/yr. 1000 din. Vojnotehnicki Institut, Kataniceva 15, Belgrade, Yugoslavia. TEL 11672. FAX 451198. Ed. Janko Vilicic. circ. 600. **Indexed:** Chem.Abstr., Ref.Zh.
—BLDSC (6055.500000); CASDDS.

NEFT', GAZ I NEFTEKHIMIYA ZA RUBEZHOM/OIL, GAS AND PETROCHEMISTRY ABROAD. see *PETROLEUM AND GAS*

660 547   NE   ISSN 0928-1584
NEW CONCEPTS IN POLYMER SCIENCE. (Text in English) 1987. irreg., latest 1994. price varies. V S P, P.O. Box 346, 3700 AH Zeist, Netherlands. TEL 31-3404-25790. FAX 31-3404-32081. (Dist. in U.S. and Canada by: Books International Inc., Box 605, Herndon, VA 22070. TEL 703-435-7064. FAX 703-689-0660) (back issues avail.) **Document type:** monographic series.

NEW POLYMERIC MATERIALS. see *CHEMISTRY — Organic Chemistry*

546 551.46   US
NEWSLETTER GOLD, SILVER AND URANIUM FROM SEAS AND OCEANS PROGRESS UPDATE. 1989. 2/yr. $5. Ardor Publishing, 7804 Vicksburg Ave., Los Angeles, CA 90045. TEL 213-645-7571. Ed. Maksymilian Burk. bk.rev. (back issues avail.) **Indexed:** Energy Info.Abstr., Environ.Abstr.
Description: Covers extraction methods of valuable elements from seawater.

NIHON KAOKU GAICHU GAKKAI TAIKAI KENKYU HAPPYO YOSHISHU/HOUSE AND HOUSEHOLD INSECT PESTS SOCIETY OF JAPAN. ABSTRACTS OF MEETING. see *BIOLOGY — Abstracting, Bibliographies, Statistics*

660   JA   ISSN 0029-0483
CODEN: NIGEB6
NIKKAKYO GEPPO/JAPAN CHEMICAL INDUSTRY ASSOCIATION MONTHLY. (Text in Japanese) 1948. m. 9,600 Yen($70) Nihon Kagaku Kogyo Kyokai - Japan Chemical Industry Association, 3-2-6 Kasumigaseki, Chiyoda-ku, Tokyo 100, Japan. TEL 03-580-0751. FAX 03-580-0764. Ed. Masami Yamanaka. adv.; bk.rev.; abstr.; stat.; index. circ. 1,500. **Indexed:** Chem.Abstr.
—BLDSC (4648.202000); CASDDS.

NIPPON KAGAKU KAISHI/CHEMICAL SOCIETY OF JAPAN. CHEMISTRY AND INDUSTRIAL CHEMISTRY. JOURNAL. see *CHEMISTRY*

662   GW   ISSN 0029-0858
NOBEL HEFTE; Sprengmittel in Forschung und Praxis. (Text in German; summaries in English and French) 1926. 4/yr. free. Sprengtechnischer Dienst der Dynamit Nobel AG und der Wasagchemie Sythen GmbH, Maerkische Str. 56-58, 44141 Dortmund, Germany. FAX 0231-579997. Ed. J. Prinz. index; circ. controlled. (processed) **Indexed:** C.I.S.Abstr.
—BLDSC (6114.000000).

NOVYE ISSLEDOVANIYA V KHIMII, METALLURGII I OBOGASHCHENII. see *METALLURGY*

OIL CHEMICAL RUBBER WORKERS TRADE UNION OF TURKEY. YEARBOOK. see *LABOR UNIONS*

665   US   ISSN 0030-1442
CODEN: OMGAAW
OIL MILL GAZETTER. 1895. m. $13. (Oil Mill Superintendents Association) Paula Kolmar, Ed. & Pub., Box 590483, Houston, TX 77259. TEL 713-480-7889. (Co-sponsor: Tri-State Oil Mill Superintendents Association) adv.; charts; stat. circ. 1,000. **Indexed:** Chem.Abstr., Food Sci.& Tech.Abstr., Nutr.Abstr., Trop.Oil Seeds Abstr. **Document type:** trade publication.
—BLDSC (6252.110000).
Description: Contains information on oilseed processing.

OVERFLATE TEKNIKK. see *CHEMISTRY — Electrochemistry*

OZONE NEWS. see *ENVIRONMENTAL STUDIES — Pollution*

660 628.44   US   ISSN 0191-9512
QD181.O1   CODEN: OZSEDS
OZONE: SCIENCE AND ENGINEERING. 1979. 6/yr. $243 (foreign $250.95). (International Ozone Association, Inc.) Lewis Publishers, Inc., Journals Department, 2000 Corporate Blvd., N.W., Boca Raton, FL 33431. TEL 407-994-0555. FAX 407-997-0949. TELEX 568689-CRC PRESS. (Subscr. to: Lewis Publishers, Box 750, Pearl River, NY 10965-0750) Ed. Dr. Rip G. Rice. adv.; bk.rev.; illus. circ. 1,450. **Indexed:** Amer.Hist.& Life, Chem.Abstr., Curr.Cont., Energy Rev., Eng.Ind., Environ.Abstr., Environ.Per.Bibl., Geo.Abstr., Hist.Abstr., Sel.Water Res.Abstr.
—BLDSC (6321.950000); CIS; El; Faxon; SWETS; CASDDS. **CCC.**
Description: Dedicated to ozone: theory and applications to science, engineering and medicine.
Refereed Serial

P N C TECHNICAL REVIEW/DONEN GIHO. (Power Reactor and Nuclear Fuel Development Corporation) see *ENERGY — Nuclear Energy*

PACKUNG UND TRANSPORT; Fachmagazin fuer Verpackung, Materialfluss und Logistik. see *PACKAGING*

540   US   ISSN 0272-6351
TP156.P3   CODEN: PTCHDS
PARTICULATE SCIENCE AND TECHNOLOGY; an international journal. (Includes Proceedings of the Fine Particle Society) 1983. q. $166. (Fine Particle Society) Taylor & Francis, 1900 Frost Rd., Ste. 101, Bristol, PA 19007-1598. TEL 800-821-8312. FAX 215-785-5515. adv.; bk.rev.; bibl.; charts; illus.; index. circ. 600. (back issues avail.; reprint service avail. from UMI) **Indexed:** Chem.Abstr., Chem.Eng.Abstr., Met.Abstr., T.C.E.A., World Alum.Abstr.
—BLDSC (6407.557000); El; Faxon; UnCover; SWETS; CASDDS. **CCC.**
Description: Disseminates theoretical and applied aspects of particle sizing, separation, health hazards.
Refereed Serial

ENGINEERING — CHEMICAL ENGINEERING

660.2   HU   ISSN 0324-5853
CODEN: PDPTAE.
PERIODICA POLYTECHNICA. CHEMICAL ENGINEERING. (Text in English, German) 1957. q. $16. Budapesti Muszaki Egyetem - Technical University of Budapest, Periodica Polytechnica, 1521 Budapest, Hungary. FAX 1-166-6808. TELEX 22-5931 MUEGY H. (Dist. by: Kultura, P.O. Box 149, 1389 Budapest, Hungary) Ed. K. Kiss. bk.rev.; charts; illus.; pat.; tr.mk.; index. circ. 600. **Indexed:** Anal.Abstr., Appl.Mech.Rev., Ceram.Abstr., Chem.Abstr., Chem.Eng.Abstr., Chem.Infd., Curr.Cont., Eng.Ind., Met.Abstr., T.C.E.A., World Surf.Coat. **Document type:** academic/scholarly publication.
—BLDSC (6425.300000); EI; UnCover; CASDDS.

628.96   US   ISSN 0730-7608
SB950.A1
PEST CONTROL TECHNOLOGY. 1972. m. $30 (foreign $82) (effective Jan. 1994). (Group Interest Enterprises) G.I.E., Inc. Publishers, 4012 Bridge Ave., Cleveland, OH 44113. TEL 216-961-4130. FAX 216-961-0364. Ed. Dan Moreland. adv.; bk.rev. circ. 16,400. **Document type:** trade publication.
—BLDSC (6428.307000); UnCover.

623.96   US
PEST MANAGEMENT FOR PUBLIC HEALTH. a. price varies. Cornell University, Media Services, 7-8 Business and Technology Park, Ithaca, NY 14850. TEL 607-255-2080. FAX 607-255-2090.

PESTICIDE ANALYTICAL MANUAL. see *PUBLIC HEALTH AND SAFETY*

628.96   UK
PESTICIDE INDEX. 1984. irreg., latest 2nd ed., 1991. £25. Royal Society of Chemistry, Thomas Graham House, Science Park, Milton Rd., Cambridge CB4 4WF, England. TEL 0223-420066. FAX 0223-423623. TELEX 818293. (Dist. by Turpin Distribution Services Ltd., Blackhorse Rd., Letchworth, Herts. SG6 1HN, England. TEL 0462-672555. FAX 0462-480947) Eds. H. Kidd, D.R. James. **Document type:** trade publication.
Description: Lists the generic and trade names of pesticides in use worldwide.

PESTICIDES AND YOU. see *AGRICULTURE — Crop Production And Soil*

628.96   UK   ISSN 0967-6597
PESTICIDES NEWS. q. £32 to individuals; institutions £65. Pesticides Trust, 23 Beehive Place, London SW9 7QR, England. TEL 071-274-8895. FAX 071-274-9084. Ed. David Buffin. **Document type:** newsletter.

628.96   JA   ISSN 0915-1672
PESUTOROJI KENKYUKAISHI/PEST CONTROL RESEARCH. (Text in Japanese) 1986. a. Nihon Pesutoroji Kenkyukai - Japanese Society of Pestology, 7-18 Hamamatsucho 2-chome, Minato-ku, Tokyo 105, Japan.

660   CC   ISSN 1000-7466
TP690.3   CODEN: SHUSEX
PETROCHEMICAL EQUIPMENT. (Text in Chinese) 1972. bi-m. Y6 (effective 1991). China Petroleum Equipment Association, Lanzhou Petroleum Machinery Research Institute, 87 Dunhuang Rd., Qilihe, Lanzhou, Gansu, People's Republic of China. TEL 33794-335. TELEX 72010 LPM RICH. (Subscr. to: P.O. Box 782, Beijing, People's Republic of China) circ. 5,000.
—CASDDS.
Description: Information about heat exchangers, pressure vessels, distillation towers, heaters, compressors, pumps and special mechanics.

665   US   ISSN 0031-6342
PETROCHEMICAL NEWS; a weekly news service in English devoted to the worldwide petrochemical industry. 1963. w. $597. William F. Bland, Co., Box 16666, Chapel Hill, NC 27516-6666. TEL 919-490-0700. FAX 919-490-3002. TELEX 965952-BLAND. Ed. Susan D. Kensil.
—CCC.
Description: Covers worldwide petrochemical business-- new ventures, corporate mergers and acquisitions, market outlooks, new products, government actions as well as new plants and expansions.

660 655   US   ISSN 0090-3507
TP157   CODEN: PCIRAY
PETROLEUM AND CHEMICAL INDUSTRY CONFERENCE. RECORD OF CONFERENCE PAPERS. a. (I E E E, Industry Applications Society) Institute of Electrical and Electronics Engineers, Inc., 345 E. 47th St., New York, NY 10017-2394. TEL 212-705-7900. FAX 212-705-7682. (Subscr. to: Box 1331, 445 Hoes Lane, Piscataway, NJ 08855-1331)
—BLDSC (1089.680000). CCC.
Former titles: Petroleum Industry Conference. Record; Petroleum and Chemical Industry Technical Conference. Record (ISSN 0079-1288)

PETROLEUM CHEMISTRY. see *PETROLEUM AND GAS*

661   UK   ISSN 0031-8426
TP245.P5   CODEN: POPOA8
PHOSPHORUS AND POTASSIUM; covers all aspects of world phosphate and potash fertilizer industry. 1963. bi-m. £310. British Sulphur Publishing (Subsidiary of: C R U Publishing Ltd.), 31 Mount Pleasant, London WC1X 0AD, England. TEL 071-837-5600. FAX 071-837-0292. TELEX 918918-SULFEX-G. Ed. R. Manser. adv.; bk.rev.; charts; illus.; mkt.; stat.; index. circ. 599. (also avail. in microform from UMI; reprint service avail. from UMI) **Indexed:** Chem.Abstr., Fert.Abstr., PROMT, Ref.Zh., Soils & Fert. **Document type:** trade publication.
—BLDSC (6465.300000); SWETS; UMI; CASDDS.

660   US   ISSN 0272-4324
QD581   CODEN: PCPPDW
PLASMA CHEMISTRY & PLASMA PROCESSING. 1981. q. $295 (foreign $345) (effective 1994). Plenum Publishing Corp., 233 Spring St., New York, NY 10013-1578. TEL 212-620-8000. FAX 212-463-0742. TELEX 23-421139. Eds. Emil Pfender, Stan Veprek. adv. (also avail. in microfilm from JSC; back issues avail.) **Indexed:** Chem.Abstr., Curr.Cont., Eng.Ind. **Document type:** academic/scholarly publication.
—BLDSC (6528.300000); EI; Faxon; UnCover; SWETS; UMI; CASDDS. **CCC.**
Refereed Serial

668.4   SI
PLASTICHEM. 1969. a. free to qualified personnel. Singapore Polytechnic Polymer Society, Dover Rd., Singapore 5, Singapore. Ed. Tang Sook Mui. adv.; circ. 1,000 (controlled). **Indexed:** Chem.Abstr.
Formerly: Polymer Journal.

PLATT'S POLYMERSCAN. see *PETROLEUM AND GAS*

660.2   PL   ISSN 0137-2602
POLITECHNIKA LODZKA. ZESZYTY NAUKOWE. INZYNIERIA CHEMICZNA. (Text in Polish; summaries in English and Russian) 1973. irreg. price varies. Wydawnictwo Politechniki Lodzkiej, Ul. Wolczanska 219, 93-085 Lodz, Poland. (Dist. by: Ars Polona-Ruch, Krakowskie Przedmiescie 7, Warsaw, Poland) Ed. Piotr Wodzinski. circ. 166. **Document type:** academic/scholarly publication.
Description: Articles on non-Newtonian fluid mechanics, chemical apparatus, mass transfer, simultaneous heat and mass transfer.

POLITECHNIKA SLASKA. ZESZYTY NAUKOWE. CHEMIA. see *CHEMISTRY*

665   PL   ISSN 0324-9867
POLITECHNIKA WROCLAWSKA. INSTYTUT CHEMII I TECHNOLOGII NAFTY I WEGLA. PRACE NAUKOWE. KONFERENCJE. (Text in Polish and English) 1975. irreg., no.6, 1990. price varies. Wydawnictwo Politechniki Wroclawskiej, Wybrzeze Wyspianskiego 27, 50-370 Wroclaw, Poland. FAX 22-36-64. TELEX 712254 PWRPL. (Dist. by: Ars Polona-Ruch, Krakowskie Przedmiescie 7, Warsaw, Poland) circ. 375.

665   PL   ISSN 0324-9859
TP690.A1   CODEN: PCWMEP
POLITECHNIKA WROCLAWSKA. INSTYTUT CHEMII I TECHNOLOGII NAFTY I WEGLA. PRACE NAUKOWE. MONOGRAFIE. (Text in Polish; summaries in English, French and Russian) 1972. irreg., no.25, 1991. price varies. Wydawnictwo Politechniki Wroclawskiej, Wybrzeze Wyspianskiego 27, 50-370 Wroclaw, Poland. FAX 22-36-64. TELEX 712254 PWRPL. (Dist. by: Ars Polona-Ruch, Krakowskie Przedmiescie 7, Warsaw, Poland) **Indexed:** Chem.Abstr. **Document type:** monographic series.

665   PL   ISSN 0084-2818
TP690.A1   CODEN: PNTNAI
POLITECHNIKA WROCLAWSKA. INSTYTUT CHEMII I TECHNOLOGII NAFTY I WEGLA. PRACE NAUKOWE. STUDIA I MATERIALY. (Text in Polish; summaries in English, Russian) 1969. irreg., no.20, 1981. price varies. Wydawnictwo Politechniki Wroclawskiej, Wybrzeze Wyspianskiego 27, 50-370 Wroclaw, Poland. FAX 22-36-64. TELEX 712559 PWRPL. (Dist. by: Ars Polona-Ruch, Krakowskie Przedmiescie 7, Warsaw, Poland)
—CASDDS.

660 697   PL   ISSN 0324-9743
POLITECHNIKA WROCLAWSKA. INSTYTUT INZYNIERII CHEMICZNEJ I URZADZEN CIEPLNYCH. PRACE NAUKOWE. KONFERENCJE. (Text in Polish; summaries in English, French and Russian) 1972. irreg., no.12, 1990. price varies. Wydawnictwo Politechniki Wroclawskiej, Wybrzeze Wyspianskiego 27, 50-370 Wroclaw, Poland. FAX 22-36-64. TELEX 71-2559 PWRPL. (Dist. by: Ars Polona-Ruch, Krakowskie Przedmiescie 7, Warsaw, Poland)

660 697   PL   ISSN 0084-2850
TP145   CODEN: PNUCAO
POLITECHNIKA WROCLAWSKA. INSTYTUT INZYNIERII CHEMICZNEJ I URZADZEN CIEPLNYCH. PRACE NAUKOWE. MONOGRAFIE. (Text in Polish; summaries in English, French and Russian) 1970. irreg., no.40, 1992. price varies. Wydawnictwo Politechniki Wroclawskiej, Wybrzeze Wyspianskiego 27, 50-370 Wroclaw, Poland. FAX 22-36-64. TELEX 712559 PWRPL. (Dist. by: Ars Polona-Ruch, Krakowskie Przedmiescie 7, Warsaw, Poland) **Document type:** monographic series.
—CASDDS.

660 697   PL   ISSN 0324-9751
POLITECHNIKA WROCLAWSKA. INSTYTUT INZYNIERII CHEMICZNEJ I URZADZEN CIEPLNYCH. PRACE NAUKOWE. STUDIA I MATERIALY. (Text in Polish; summaries in English and Russian) 1970. irreg., no.13, 1976. price varies. Wydawnictwo Politechniki Wroclawskiej, Wybrzeze Wyspianskiego 27, 50-370 Wroclaw, Poland. FAX 22-36-64. TELEX 712559 PWRPL. (Dist. by: Ars Polona-Ruch, Krakowskie Przedmiescie 7, Warsaw Poland) **Indexed:** Chem.Abstr.

660   PL   ISSN 0084-2893
TP1   CODEN: PNPWAP
POLITECHNIKA WROCLAWSKA. INSTYTUT TECHNOLOGII NIEORGANICZNEJ I NAWOZOW MINERALNYCH. PRACE NAUKOWE. KONFERENCJE. 1972. irreg., no.19, 1989. price varies. Wydawnictwo Politechniki Wroclawskiej, Wybrzeze Wyspianskiego 27, 50-370 Wroclaw, Poland. FAX 22-36-64. TELEX 712559 PWRPL. (Dist. by: Ars Polona-Ruch, Krakowskie Przedmiescie 7, Warsaw, Poland)
—CASDDS.

660   PL   ISSN 0084-2907
POLITECHNIKA WROCLAWSKA. INSTYTUT TECHNOLOGII NIEORGANICZNEJ I NAWOZOW MINERALNYCH. PRACE NAUKOWE. MONOGRAFIE. (Text in Polish; summaries in English, Russian) 1971. irreg., no.13, 1991. price varies. Wydawnictwo Politechniki Wroclawskiej, Wybrzeze Wyspianskiego 27, 50-370 Wroclaw, Poland. FAX 22-36-64. TELEX 712559 PWRPL. **Document type:** monographic series.

660   PL   ISSN 0084-2915
POLITECHNIKA WROCLAWSKA. INSTYTUT TECHNOLOGII NIEORGANICZNEJ I NAWOZOW MINERALNYCH. PRACE NAUKOWE. STUDIA I MATERIALY. (Text in Polish; summaries in English and Russian) 1970. irreg., no.5, 1978. price varies. Wydawnictwo Politechniki Wroclawskiej, Wybrzeze Wyspianskiego 27, 50-370 Wroclaw, Poland. FAX 22-36-64. TELEX 712559 PWRPL. (Dist. by: Ars Polona-Ruch, Krakowskie Przedmiescie 7, Warsaw, Poland) **Indexed:** Chem.Abstr.

668.4   PL   ISSN 0137-1398
TP1
POLITECHNIKA WROCLAWSKA. INSTYTUT TECHNOLOGII ORGANICZNEJ I TWORZYW SZTUCZNYCH. PRACE NAUKOWE. KONFERENCJE. (Text in Polish; summaries in English and Russian) 1972. irreg., no.18, 1989. price varies. Wydawnictwo Politechniki Wroclawskiej, Wybrzeze Wyspianskiego 27, 50-370 Wroclaw, Poland. FAX 22-36-64. TELEX 712254 PWRPL. (Dist. by: Ars Polona-Ruch, Krakowskie Przedmiescie 7, Warsaw, Poland)
—BLDSC (6590.750000).

ENGINEERING — CHEMICAL ENGINEERING

668.4 PL ISSN 0239-5495
POLITECHNIKA WROCLAWSKA. INSTYTUT TECHNOLOGII ORGANICZNEJ I TWORZYW SZTUCZNYCH. PRACE NAUKOWE. MONOGRAFIE. (Text in Polish; summaries in English and Russian) 1971. irreg., no.9, 1986. price varies. Wydawnictwo Politechniki Wroclawskiej, Wybrzeze Wyspianskiego 27, 50-370 Wroclaw, Poland. FAX 22-36-64. TELEX 712559 PWRPL. (Dist. by: Ars Polona-Ruch, Krakowskie Przedmiescie 7, Warsaw, Poland) **Document type:** monographic series.

660.284 JA ISSN 0023-2564
CODEN: KOKABN
POLYMER APPLICATION/KOBUNSHI KAKO. (Text in Japanese) 1951. m. 6800 Yen. High Polymer Publishing Association - Kobunshi Kankokai, Chiekoin-Sagura, Marutamachi, Kamikyoku, Kyoto 602, Japan. Ed. Hitoshi Okuda. adv.; charts; illus.; stat. **Indexed:** Chem.Abstr., JTA.
—BLDSC (6547.702000); CASDDS.

POLYMER COMMUNICATIONS; the science and technology of polymers. see *CHEMISTRY — Organic Chemistry*

660.284 547 US ISSN 0032-3888
TP986.A1 CODEN: PYESAZ
POLYMER ENGINEERING AND SCIENCE. (Includes 6 special issues) 1961. 24/yr. $190 (foreign $220). Society of Plastics Engineers, Inc., 14 Fairfield Dr., Brookfield, CT 06804-0403. TEL 203-775-0471. FAX 203-775-8490. TELEX 643-712. Ed. Roger S. Porter. charts; illus.; index. circ. 1,800. (also avail. in microfilm from UMI; reprint service avail. from UMI) **Indexed:** A.S.& T.Ind., Chem.Abstr., Chem.Eng.Abstr., Curr.Cont., Curr.Pack.Abstr., Eng.Ind., Int.Aerosp.Abstr., RAPRA, Sci.Abstr., T.C.E.A., W.R.C.Inf. **Document type:** academic/scholarly publication.
—BLDSC (6547.705000); EI; Faxon; UnCover; SWETS; UMI; CASDDS. **CCC.**
Refereed Serial

660 547 UK ISSN 0966-7822
QD549.2.P64 CODEN: PGNEEI
▼**POLYMER GELS AND NETWORKS.** 1992. 4/yr. £151($235) (effective 1994). Elsevier Science Ltd., Oxford Fulfilment Centre, Headington Hill Hall, Kidlington, Oxford OX5 1DX, England. TEL 44-865-843000. FAX 44-865-843010. (Subscr. in U.S. and Canada to: Elsevier Science, 660 White Plains Rd., Tarrytown, NY 10591-5153. TEL 914-524-9200. FAX 914-333-2444) Ed. T. Tanaka. (also avail. in microfilm from UMI; back issues avail.) **Document type:** academic/scholarly publication.
—BLDSC (6547.706500); EI; SWETS; CASDDS. **CCC.**
Description: Provides a forum for research in the structure and properties of polymer gels and networks, including design and synthesis, characterization of physical, chemical and biological properties, and applications in biotechnology and biomedicine.
Refereed Serial

POLYMER JOURNAL. see *CHEMISTRY — Organic Chemistry*

POLYMER NEWS. see *CHEMISTRY — Organic Chemistry*

POLYMER-PLASTICS TECHNOLOGY AND ENGINEERING. see *CHEMISTRY — Organic Chemistry*

660 US ISSN 1054-3414
TP1080 CODEN: PREEEG
▼**POLYMER REACTION ENGINEERING.** 1992. 4/yr. $225. Marcel Dekker, Inc., 270 Madison Ave., New York, NY 10016. TEL 212-696-9000. FAX 212-685-4540. TELEX 421419. (Subscr. to: Box 5017, Monticello, NY 12701) Eds. A. Penlidis, K. O'Driscoll. adv.; bibl.; charts; illus. (also avail. in microfilm from RPI) **Document type:** academic/scholarly publication.
—BLDSC (6547.719500); CASDDS. **CCC.**
Refereed Serial

660 547 NE ISSN 0927-5916
▼**POLYMER RECOVERY;** an international scientific journal covering all aspects of recycling and (energy) recovery of polymeric materials. (Text in English) 1993. 4/yr. fl.379($220) (effective 1994). Kluwer Academic Publishers, Postbus 17, 3300 AA Dordrecht, Netherlands. TEL 31-78-334911. FAX 31-78-334254. TELEX 29245 KAPG NL. (Dist. by: Kluwer Academic Publishers Group, P.O. Box 322, 3300 AH Dordrecht, Netherlands. TEL 31-78-524400. FAX 31-78-524474; N. America dist. addr.: Box 358, Accord Sta., Hingham, MA 02018-0358. TEL 617-871-6600. FAX 617-871-6528) Ed. Eric J. Beckman. **Document type:** academic/scholarly publication.
Description: Provides a forum for original research from academic and industrial laboratories in the field of polymer recovery, including topics such as waste avoidance, manufacturing processing which facilitate recovery, chemical recycling technology, compostable polymeric materials, and novel energy-recovery methods.
Refereed Serial

660 US ISSN 8750-6653
POWDER BULK SOLIDS; the magazine for the processing, handling, packaging and storing of dry particulates. 1983. 12/yr. (includes end-of-year Power Bulk Solids Literature Review). $35 (free to qualified personnel). Gordon Publications, Inc., Part of Cahners Publishing Company, Division of Reed Elsevier Inc., 301 Gibraltar Dr., Box 650, Morris Plains, NJ 07950-0650. TEL 201-292-5100. FAX 201-898-9281. Ed. Kevin Cronin. adv.; tr.lit. circ. 48,000.

671 SZ ISSN 0032-5910
TP156.P3 CODEN: POTEBX
POWDER TECHNOLOGY; an international journal on the science and technology of wet and dry particulate systems. (Text in English, French, German) 1967. 12/yr. (in 4 vols.; 3 nos./vol.). 1600 SFr.($1088) (effective 1994). Elsevier Science S.A., P.O. Box 564, CH-1001 Lausanne 1, Switzerland. TEL 41-21-3207381. FAX 41-21-3235444. TELEX 450620-ELSA-CH. (Subscr. in U.S. and Canada to: Elsevier Science Inc., Box 882, Madison Sq. Sta., New York, NY 10159. TEL 212-989-5800. FAX 212-633-3990) Ed. R. Clift. adv.; bk.rev.; bibl.; illus.; index. (also avail. in microfilm from UMI) **Indexed:** Anal.Abstr., Br.Ceram.Abstr., C.R.I.Abstr., Ceram.Abstr., Chem.Abstr., Chem.Eng.Abstr., Curr.Cont., Excerp.Med., Fluidex, Fuel & Energy Abstr., Gas Abstr., GeoRef., Met.Abstr., Phys.Ber., Sci.Abstr., Sci.Cit.Ind., T.C.E.A., World Alum.Abstr., World Surf.Coat. **Document type:** academic/scholarly publication.
—BLDSC (6572.500000); Faxon; UnCover; SWETS; CASDDS. **CCC.**
Description: Publishes papers concerned with all aspects of the formation of particles and their characterization and on the study of systems containing particulate solids.
Refereed Serial

PREVIEWS OF HEAT AND MASS TRANSFER. see *ENGINEERING — Abstracting, Bibliographies, Statistics*

660.2 AT ISSN 0816-8148
PROCESS & CONTROL ENGINEERING. 1953. m. Aus.$72. Thomson Business Publishing, 47 Chippen St., Chippendale, N.S.W. 2008, Australia. TEL 02-699-2411. FAX 02-698-3920. Ed. Nicola Thompson. adv.; bk.rev.; charts; illus.; pat.; tr.mk. circ. 7,666. **Indexed:** Chem.Abstr., Petrol.Abstr., Sugar Ind.Abstr.
—BLDSC (6849.983320).
Former titles (until 1985): Thomson's P A C E (ISSN 0728-3636); Australian Chemical Processing and Engineering (ISSN 0004-8836)

662 UK ISSN 0370-1859
TP1 CODEN: PSEGAP
PROCESS ENGINEERING. 1972. m. $130. Morgan-Grampian (Process Press) Ltd. (Subsidiary of: Morgan-Grampian plc), Morgan-Grampian House, 30 Calderwood St., London SE18 6QH, England. TEL 081-855-7777. FAX 081-854-7476. Ed. Mike Spear. adv. contact: Mike Ingram. bk.rev.; index. circ. 19,168. (also avail. in microform from UMI,VCI) **Indexed:** A.S.& T.Ind., AESIS, API Abstr., API Catal., API Hlth.& Environ., API Oil., API Pet.Ref., API Pet.Subst., API Transport., Br.Ceram.Abstr., Br.Tech.Ind., C.I.S. Abstr., Cadscan, Ceram.Abstr., Chem.Abstr., Chem.Eng.Abstr., Energy Ind., Energy Info.Abstr., Eng.Ind., Excerp.Med., Fluidex, Fuel & Energy Abstr., Gas Abstr., Lead Abstr., PROMT, Sci.Abstr., T.C.E.A., World Surf.Coat., Zincscan. **Document type:** trade publication.
—BLDSC (6849.985240); Faxon; UnCover; SWETS. **CCC.**
Formed by the merger of: Chemical and Process Engineering (ISSN 0009-2371) & Process Engineering, Plant and Control (ISSN 0032-9606)
Description: Technical review of chemical processes, plants and equipment.

660 AT
PROCESS ENGINEERING. 1972. m. Aus.$60 (free to qualified personnel). Business Press International Pty. Ltd., 162 Goulburn St., Darlinghurst, N.S.W. 2010, Australia. TEL 266-9711. FAX 267-1223. Ed. Andrew Nicholls. adv.; charts; illus.; tr.lit. circ. 7,500. **Indexed:** A.S.& T.Ind., AESIS, Ceram.Abstr., Fluidex, PROMT, Sci.Abstr.
Former titles: Process Engineering News (ISSN 0159-3935); Australian Process Engineering (ISSN 0310-933X)

662 380.1 UK ISSN 0143-1455
PROCESS ENGINEERING DIRECTORY. 1978. a. £75 (overseas £90). Benn Business Information Services Ltd. (Subsidiary of: Morgan-Grampian plc), Riverbank House, Angel Ln., Tonbridge, Kent TN9 1SE, England. TEL 0732-362666. FAX 0732-767301. TELEX 957829 BENTON G. Ed. Peter Bealing. adv. circ. 1,000. **Document type:** directory.

660 US
PROCESS EQUIPMENT SERIES. 1979. irreg. Technomic Publishing Co., Inc., 851 New Holland Ave., Box 3535, Lancaster, PA 17604. TEL 717-291-5609. FAX 717-295-4538. TELEX 203 753565 (TECHNOMIC UD). Eds. Paul N. Cheremisinoff, Mahesh V. Bhatia. charts. **Document type:** monographic series.
Refereed Serial

540 660 CN
PROCESS INDUSTRIES CANADA. 1917. bi-m. Can.$51.36($74) Zanny Publications Ltd., 11966 Woodbine Ave., Gormley, ON L0H 1G0, Canada. TEL 905-887-4813. FAX 905-479-4839. Ed. Mary Ellen Jamieson. adv. contact: Ingrid Eilbracht. bk.rev.; charts; illus.; mkt.; stat.; tr.lit.; index; circ. 24,000 (controlled). (also avail. in microfiche from UMI) **Indexed:** A.S.& T.Ind., API Abstr., API Hlth.& Environ., API Oil., API Pet.Ref., API Pet.Subst., API Transport., Can.B.P.I., Chem.Abstr., Eng.Ind., Excerp.Med., Fuel & Energy Abstr., Gas Abstr., Petrol.Abstr., PROMT, Sci.Cit.Ind., Sel.Water Res.Abstr., Soils & Fert.
—**CCC.**
Formerly: Canadian Chemical Processing (ISSN 0008-3186)

660 UK
PROCESS INDUSTRY JOURNAL. 1986. m. 32 Vauxhall Bridge Rd., London SW1V 2SS, England. TEL 071-973-6404. FAX 071-233-5080. Ed. Les Hunt. adv. contact: William Butler. circ. 18,500. **Document type:** trade publication.

ENGINEERING — CHEMICAL ENGINEERING

660   US   ISSN 1066-8527
TP155.6   CODEN: PSAPE2
PROCESS SAFETY PROGRESS. 1982. q. $150 to non-members (foreign $175); members $36. American Institute of Chemical Engineers, 345 E. 47 St., New York, NY 10017. TEL 212-705-7663. FAX 212-752-3294. Ed. T.A. Ventrone. adv.; bk.rev.; charts; illus.; stat.; tr.lit. circ. 2,700. (also avail. in microform from UMI; back issues avail.; reprint service avail. from UMI) **Indexed:** API Abstr., API Catal., API Hlth.& Environ., API Oil., API Pet.Ref., API Pet.Subst., API Transport., C.I.S.Abstr., Chem.Abstr., Chem.Eng.Abstr., Eng.Ind., Soils & Fert., T.C.E.A. **Document type:** trade publication.
—BLDSC (6849.990570); Faxon; UnCover; SWETS; UMI; CASDDS. **CCC.**
    Formerly (until 1993): Plant - Operations Progress (ISSN 0278-4513)
    Description: Presents materials on design, operation and maintenance of safe installations including loss prevention, ammonia plant safety and efficient operation.

628   UK   ISSN 0305-439X
TP1   CODEN: PCSNA4
PROCESSING. 1954. m. £55 in the UK; Europe £75; elsewhere £100. I M L Group plc, Blair House, High St., Tonbridge, Kent TN9 1BQ, England. TEL 0732-359990. FAX 0732-770049. Ed. Brian Matkins. adv.; bk.rev.; charts; illus.; tr.lit.; index. circ. 17,902. (reprint service avail. from UMI) **Indexed:** Abstr.Bull.Inst.Pap.Chem., API Abstr., API Catal., API Hlth.& Environ., API Oil., API Pet.Ref., API Pet.Subst., API Transport., Appl.Mech.Rev., Br.Tech.Ind., C.I.S. Abstr., Chem.Eng.Abstr., Excerp.Med., Fluidex, Fuel & Energy Abstr., Met.Abstr., PROMT, T.C.E.A., World Alum.Abstr., World Surf.Coat., World Text.Abstr. **Document type:** academic/scholarly publication.
—BLDSC (6849.993300); Faxon; UnCover; SWETS; UMI; CASDDS.
    Formerly: Chemical Processing (ISSN 0009-2622)

660   US
PROCESSING. 1989. m. $30. Putman Publishing Co., 301 E. Erie St., Chicago, IL 60611. TEL 312-644-2020. FAX 312-644-1131. Ed. Sandra Herzog. adv.; illus.; circ. 110,000 (controlled). (tabloid format) **Document type:** trade publication.

660   US
PROCESSING AD - LITS. 1987. q. Putman Publishing Co., 301 E. Erie St., Chicago, IL 60611. TEL 312-644-2020. FAX 312-644-1131. Ed. Sandra Herzog. adv. circ. 220,083.
    Description: Introduces new products to the process industries.

660   US
PROCESSING SNAPSHOTS. s-a. Putman Publishing Co., 301 E. Erie St., Chicago, IL 60611. TEL 312-644-2020. FAX 312-644-1131. Ed. Sandra Herzog. adv. circ. 110,040.
    Description: Focuses on new products and decision making in purchasing.

660   MX
PRODUCCION QUIMICA MEXICANA. 1963. a. Mex.$100($120) Informatica Cosmos, S.A. de C.V., Fernando Arrieta 5-101, Col. Los Cipreses, 04830 Mexico D.F., Mexico. TEL 525-677-48-68. FAX 525-679-35-75. Ed. Raul Macazaga. adv.: B&W page $1000; trim 211 x 274. index, cum.index. circ. 5,000. **Document type:** directory.
    Description: Lists over 1200 chemical manufacturers. Provides descriptions of 1200 products manufactured in Mexico.

PROGRESS IN CHEMISTRY AND CHEMICAL INDUSTRY. see CHEMISTRY

660.2   UK   ISSN 0360-1285
TJ163.9   CODEN: PECSDO
PROGRESS IN ENERGY AND COMBUSTION SCIENCE; an international review journal. 1975. 6/yr. £362($555) (effective 1994). Elsevier Science Ltd., Pergamon, P.O. Box 800, Kidlington, Oxford OX5 1DX, England. TEL 44-865-843000. FAX 44-865-843010. (Subscr. in U.S. and Canada to: Elsevier Science, 660 White Plains Rd., Tarrytown, NY 10591-5153. TEL 914-524-9200. FAX 914-333-2444) Ed. Norman A. Chigier. adv.; bk.rev.; illus.; stat.; index. (also avail. in microfilm from UMI) **Indexed:** AESIS, API Abstr., API Catal., API Hlth.& Environ., API Oil., API Pet.Ref., API Pet.Subst., API Transport., Appl.Mech.Rev., Chem.Abstr., Chem.Eng.Abstr., Energy Info.Abstr., Environ.Per.Bibl. (1980-), Excerp.Med., Foul.Prev.Res.Dig., Gas Abstr., Ind.Sci.Rev., Int.Aerosp.Abstr., Pollut.Abstr. **Document type:** academic/scholarly publication.
—BLDSC (6868.330000); EI; Faxon; UnCover; SWETS; UMI; CASDDS. **CCC.**
    Description: Review articles addressing specific new developments in energy and combustion.
Refereed Serial

PROGRESS IN POLYMER SCIENCE; an international review journal. see CHEMISTRY — Organic Chemistry

662   GW   ISSN 0721-3115
TP270.A1   CODEN: PEPYD5
PROPELLANTS, EXPLOSIVES, PYROTECHNICS. (Text in English; summaries in English, French, German) 1976. 6/yr. DM.660($435) (International Pyrotechnics Society) V C H Verlagsgesellschaft mbH, Postfach 101161, 69451 Weinheim, Germany. TEL 06201-606-0. FAX 06201-606328. TELEX 465516-VCHWH-D. (U.S. addr.: V C H Publishers Inc., 220 E. 23rd St., New York, NY 10010-4606) Eds. H. Schubert, E. Kistner. circ. 800. (also avail. in microfilm from VCl; reprint service avail. from ISI) **Indexed:** Chem.Abstr., Curr.Cont., DM& T, Int.Aerosp.Abstr., PROMT. **Document type:** academic/scholarly publication.
—BLDSC (6927.270000); EI; Faxon; SWETS; CASDDS. **CCC.**
    Formerly: Propellants and Explosives (ISSN 0340-7462)

662   SA   ISSN 0033-1481
PROSPECT. (Text in English) 1962. q. free. A E C I Ltd., Box 1122, Johannesburg 2000, South Africa. TEL 011-223-9111. FAX 011-223-1929. TELEX 4-87048 SA. Ed. F.M. Putero. circ. 10,000 (controlled). **Indexed:** Aus.P.A.I.S.
    Description: Promotes interest in use of products. Brings out research and development projects, activities of various companies which are a part of the AECI group. Publicizes environmental, safety and quality of life policies of AECI.

PURE AND APPLIED CHEMISTRY. see CHEMISTRY

662.1   US   ISSN 0272-6521
TP300   CODEN: PYROEO
PYROTECHNICA; occasional papers in pyrotechnics. 1977. a. $30 to individuals; institutions $32; foreign $36. Pyrotechnica Publications, 2302 Tower Dr., Austin, TX 78703. TEL 512-476-4062. FAX 512-453-1353. Ed. Robert G. Cardwell. adv.; bk.rev.; abstr.; charts; illus. circ. 1,500. (back issues avail.) **Indexed:** Chem.Abstr. **Document type:** academic/scholarly publication.
—BLDSC (7163.515000); CASDDS.
    Description: Covers fireworks, high-temperature pyrochemistry and pyro-technology.

661 660   BL
QUEM E QUEM NA INDUSTRIA QUIMICA BRASILEIRA. a. Editora Quimica e Derivados Ltda., Rua Dr. Gabriel dos Santos, 55, Santa Cecilia, CEP 01231-900 Sao Paulo, SP, Brazil. TEL 011-826-6899. FAX 011-825-8192. TELEX 11-21801. Ed. Emanoel Fairbanks. **Document type:** directory.

660   SP   ISSN 0033-6521
                            CODEN: QUIBAL
QUIMICA E INDUSTRIA. 1954. 11/yr. 4500 ptas.($30) Asociacion Nacional de Quimicos de Espana, Lagasca, 87, 1o, 28006 Madrid, Spain. TEL 576-74-43. FAX 1-435-36-55. Ed. Silverio Legorburu Ovies. adv.; bk.rev.; bibl.; charts; index. circ. 11,000. **Indexed:** Art & Archaeol.Tech.Abstr., Chem.Abstr., Ind.SST.
—CASDDS. **CCC.**

R T E C S REGULATORY SUBFILE. REGULATIONS, RECOMMENDATIONS AND ASSESSMENTS. (Registry of Toxic Effects of Chemical Substances) see PUBLIC HEALTH AND SAFETY

660   US   ISSN 1056-0793
RADTECH REPORT. 1988. bi-m. $60. RadTech International North America, 60 Revere Dr., Ste. 500, Northbrook, IL 60062. TEL 708-480-9576. FAX 708-480-9282. Ed. James Rayball. adv. circ. 1,038.
—BLDSC (7242.275000).
    Description: Covers research, development, marketing and end use of radiation cured inks, coatings and adhesives.

660   UK   ISSN 0456-4804
RAMSAY SOCIETY OF CHEMICAL ENGINEERS. JOURNAL. 1934. a. £10 to non-members. Ramsay Society of Chemical Engineers, Dept. of Chemical and Biochemical Engineering, University College London, Torrington Place, London WC1E 7JE, England. TEL 071-387-7050. FAX 071-383-2348. TELEX 296273-UCLENG-G. Ed. A.R. Burgess. adv.; illus. circ. 1,000.
    Description: Covers all aspects of chemical and biochemical engineering; features current research in the Department

662   CC   ISSN 0253-2409
TP315   CODEN: RHXUD8
RANLIAO HUAXUE XUEBAO/JOURNAL OF FUEL CHEMISTRY AND TECHNOLOGY. (Text in Chinese; summaries in English) 1956. q. $70. (Chinese Academy of Sciences, Shanxi Institute of Coal Chemistry) Science Press, Marketing and Sales Department, 16 Donghuangchenggen Beijie, Beijing 100707, People's Republic of China. TEL 4010642. FAX 4012180. TELEX 210247-SPBJ-CN. adv. circ. 2,000. **Document type:** academic/scholarly publication.
—CASDDS.
    Description: Deals with chemistry and technology of fuels, including coal, petroleum, shale, and natural gas.
Refereed Serial

661   CC   ISSN 1001-3709
RANLIAO YU HUAGONG. (Text in Chinese) bi-m. Anshan Jiaohua Naihuo Cailiao Sheji Yanjiuyuan, Qingbao Shi, 27, Shengli Lu, Anshan, Liaoning 114002, People's Republic of China. TEL 29459. Ed. Zeng Yonglian.

660 669   NE   ISSN 0923-1137
                            CODEN: REPLEN
REACTIVE POLYMERS. (Text in English) 1982. 9/yr. (in 3 vols.; 3 nos./vol.) fl.1218($658) (effective 1994). Elsevier Science B.V., P.O. Box 211, 1000 AE Amsterdam, Netherlands. TEL 31-20-5803911. FAX 31-20-5803598. TELEX 18582 ESPA NL. (Subscr. in U.S. and Canada to: Elsevier Science Inc., Box 882, Madison Sq. Sta., New York, NY 10159-0882. TEL 212-989-5800. FAX 212-633-3990) Ed. F.G. Helfferich. bk.rev. **Indexed:** Abstr.Bull.Inst.Pap.Chem., Chem.Abstr., Chem.Eng.Abstr., Curr.Cont., Eng.Ind., Eng.Mat.Abstr., Met.Abstr., T.C.E.A. **Document type:** academic/scholarly publication.
—BLDSC (7300.282600); EI; Faxon; UnCover; SWETS; CASDDS. **CCC.**
    Formerly (until vol.14, 1991): Reactive Polymers, Ion Exchangers, Sorbents (ISSN 0167-6989)
    Description: Covers inorganic and organic functional polymers, both solid and liquid, acting as reagents, catalysts, carriers or protecting groups, templates, ion exchangers, selective sorbents, chelating agents, supports for enzymes and cells, and the like.
Refereed Serial

RECENT ADVANCES IN CROSSLINKING & CURING. see PLASTICS

RECUEIL DES TRAVAUX CHIMIQUES DES PAYS-BAS. see CHEMISTRY

660   US
REFRACTORY NEWS. 1980. m. $24 to non-members. Refractories Institute, 500 Wood St., Ste. 326, Pittsburgh, PA 15222. TEL 412-281-6781. FAX 412-281-6881. Eds. C.G. Marvin, F.R. Story. circ. 800. **Document type:** newsletter.
    Description: News of the refractories industry, covering suppliers of raw materials, manufacturers and consumers.

ENGINEERING — CHEMICAL ENGINEERING

660   US   ISSN 0034-5571
CODEN: RESRBJ
RESIN REVIEW. 1951. q. free. Rohm and Haas Co., Independence Mall West, Philadelphia, PA 19105. TEL 215-592-3000. Ed. T. Hansen. charts; illus. circ. 17,000. **Indexed:** RAPRA, Text.Tech.Dig., World Surf.Coat.
—BLDSC (7777.500000); CASDDS.

660 540   IS   ISSN 0167-8299
REVIEWS IN CHEMICAL ENGINEERING. 1983. q. $180. Freund Publishing House Ltd., P.O. Box 35010, Tel Aviv 61350, Israel. TEL 972-3-5662925. FAX 972-3-5605335. (And: Chesham House, Ste. 500, 150 Regent St., London W1R 5FA, England) Eds. Neal R. Amundson, Dan Luss. adv. (back issues avail.) **Indexed:** Chem.Abstr., Chem.Eng.Abstr., Curr.Cont., Sci.Cit.Ind., T.C.E.A. **Document type:** academic/scholarly publication.
—BLDSC (7788.945000); UnCover; SWETS. **CCC**.

660   CK   ISSN 0120-100X
CODEN: REIODU
REVISTA ION. (Text in Spanish; summaries in English) 1953. a. Col.$2000($2) or exchange basis (effective 1994). Universidad Industrial de Santander, Centro de Estudios de Ingenieria Quimica, Apdo. Aereo 678, Bucaramanga, Colombia. TEL 57-976-59654. FAX 57-976-352554. adv.: page $100; adv. contact: Clemente Retamoso. bk.rev.; bibl.; charts; illus. circ. 600. **Document type:** academic/scholarly publication.
—CASDDS.
Description: Publishes research results and academic papers of chemical engineers.

660   US   ISSN 0035-7847
HD9651.9.R6
ROHM AND HAAS REPORTER. (Editions in English and Spanish) 1943. q. free. Rohm and Haas Co., Independence Mall West, Philadelphia, PA 19105. TEL 215-592-3000. Ed. H.J. Gambino. illus. circ. 100,000. **Indexed:** Chem.Abstr., World Surf.Coat., World Text.Abstr.

540 660   RM   ISSN 0048-8577
RUMANIAN JOURNAL OF CHEMISTRY; a quarterly on trade and industry. (Editions in English, French, German and Russian) 1971. q. $30. Chamber of Commerce and Industry of the Socialist Republic of Rumania, Bd. N. Balcescu Nr. 22, Bucharest, Rumania. (Dist. by: Rompresfilatelia, P.O. Box 12-201, Calea Grivitei 64-66, Bucharest, Rumania) Ed.Bd. adv.; bk.rev.; bibl.; illus.; pat.; tr.lit. circ. 6,000. **Indexed:** Chem.Abstr., Fuel & Energy Abstr., PROMT.

RUSSIAN CHEMICAL INDUSTRY. see *CHEMISTRY*

660   US
QD71
RUSSIAN JOURNAL OF APPLIED CHEMISTRY. English translation of: Zhurnal Prikladnoi Khimii (RU ISSN 0044-4618) vol.23, 1950. s-m. $1295 (foreign $1515) (effective 1993). (Russian Academy of Sciences, RU) Plenum Publishing Corp., Consultants Bureau, 233 Spring St., New York, NY 10013-1578. TEL 212-620-8468. FAX 212-463-0742. TELEX 23-421139. Ed. V.S. Shpak. (also avail. in microfilm from JSC; back issues avail.) **Indexed:** Cadscan, Chem.Eng.Abstr., Chem.Titles, Curr.Cont., Energy Res.Abstr., Eng.Ind., Excerp.Med., Ind.Sci.Rev., INIS Atomind., Lead Abstr., Pollut.Abstr., Soils & Fert., T.C.E.A., Zincscan. **Document type:** academic/scholarly publication.
—Faxon; UnCover; UMI. **CCC**.
Former titles (until 1994): Journal of Applied Chemistry; (until 1992): Journal of Applied Chemistry of the U S S R (ISSN 0021-888X)
Refereed Serial

S E R I ETHANOL ANNUAL REPORT. (Solar Energy Research Institute) see *ENERGY*

660   UK
S P S BULLETIN. 1974. q. membership. Separation Processes Service, Bldg. 404, Harwell Laboratory, Oxon OX11 0RA, England. FAX 0235-432313. Ed. P.N. Hicklin. **Document type:** bulletin.
Description: Provides information on a selection of recently published items relevant to industrial separation processes.

665.538   US
S T L E TRIBOLOGY TRANSACTIONS. (Former name of issuing body: American Society of Lubrication Engineers) 4/yr. $144 (foreign $168) (effective 1994). Society of Tribologists and Lubrication Engineers, 840 Busse Hwy., Park Ridge, IL 60068. TEL 708-825-5536. FAX 708-825-1456. Ed. Robert Bruce. (also avail. in microform from UMI) **Indexed:** A.S.& T.Ind., API Abstr., API Catal., API Hlth.& Environ., API Oil., API Pet.Ref., API Pet.Subst., API Transport., Appl.Mech.Rev., Bibl.Ind., Chem.Abstr., Curr.Cont., Fluidex, INIS Atomind., ISMEC, Met.Abstr., Sci.Abstr., Sci.Cit.Ind., Sh.& Vib.Dig., World Alum.Abstr. **Document type:** academic/scholarly publication.
—BLDSC (9050.217820); EI; UnCover; SWETS. **CCC**.
Formerly: A S L E Transactions (ISSN 0569-8197)

SEALING TECHNOLOGY. see *PAINTS AND PROTECTIVE COATINGS*

665   JA
SENJO NI KANSURU SHINPOJUMU/SYMPOSIUM OF CLEANING. (Text in Japanese) 1969. a. membership. Nihon Yukagaku Kyokai - Japan Oil Chemists' Society, Yushi Kogyo Kaikan, 13-11, Nihonbashi 3-chome, Chuo-ku, Tokyo 103, Japan.

660 643   US   ISSN 0956-9618
TP156.S45   CODEN: SETEEX
SEPARATIONS TECHNOLOGY. 1990. q. $60 to individuals (foriegn $70); institutions $225 (foreign $265). Butterworth - Heinemann, Part of the Reed Elsevier group, 313 Washington St., Newton, MA 02158. TEL 617-928-2500; 800-366-2665. FAX 617-928-2610. TELEX 880052. Ed. Chi Tien. (back issues avail.) **Document type:** academic/scholarly publication.
—BLDSC (8242.258800); EI; UnCover; UMI; CASDDS. **CCC**.
Description: Emphasizes separations technology from a systems and engineering point of view; focuses on original research and novel application. *Refereed Serial*

SHIROARI/TERMITE. see *BIOLOGY — Entomology*

660   GW
SICHERE CHEMIEARBEIT. 1948. m. membership. Berufsgenossenschaft der Chemischen Industrie, Kurfuersten-Anlage 62, 69115 Heidelberg, Germany. TEL 06221-5230. FAX 06221-523323. TELEX 461808. Ed. Hanswerner Lauer. illus. circ. 110,000. **Indexed:** C.I.S. Abstr. **Document type:** trade publication.
Description: Covers safety, accident prevention, and health problems in the chemistry industry, as well as regulations, compensations and court decisions. Includes events.

662 622
SOCIETY OF EXPLOSIVES ENGINEERS. SYMPOSIUM ON EXPLOSIVES AND BLASTING RESEARCH. PROCEEDINGS. 1975. a. $33 to non-members; members $22. Society of Explosives Engineers, 29100 Aurora Rd., Solon, OH 44139. TEL 216-349-4004. FAX 216-349-3788. index. circ. 3,000. (also avail. in video cassette; back issues avail.) **Document type:** proceedings.

662   US   ISSN 0361-5219
TP315   CODEN: SFCHDV
SOLID FUEL CHEMISTRY. English translation of: Khimiya Tverdogo Topliva (RU ISSN 0023-1177) 1974. bi-m. $850. (Russian Academy of Sciences, RU) Allerton Press, Inc., 150 Fifth Ave., New York, NY 10011. TEL 212-924-3950. FAX 212-463-9684. Ed. Kh. Minachev. **Indexed:** Excerp.Med., GeoRef. **Document type:** academic/scholarly publication.
—BLDSC (0420.827000); Faxon; UnCover. **CCC**.
Refereed Serial

660   UK
SPECIALITY CHEMICALS; production, marketing and applications. 1981. bi-m. £108.50($184.50) (foreign £118.30). F M J International Publications Ltd., Queensway House, 2 Queensway, Redhill, Surrey RH1 1QS, England. TEL 0737-768611. FAX 0737-761685. TELEX 948669-TOPJNL-G. Ed. Tom Mulligan. **Indexed:** Anal.Abstr., World Surf.Coat. **Document type:** trade publication.
Description: Covers all aspects of the organic, intermediate, and fine chemical markers and monitors the performance of the industry.

SULPHUR; covers all aspects of world sulphur and sulphuric acid industry. see *MINES AND MINING INDUSTRY*

SURFACE TREATMENT PLANT AND PROCESSES; bi-monthly international market service and product guide. see *METALLURGY*

SVENSK FAERGHANDEL; tapet - parfym. see *PAINTS AND PROTECTIVE COATINGS*

660   US   ISSN 0082-1144
HD9999.D9
SYNTHETIC ORGANIC CHEMICALS, UNITED STATES PRODUCTION AND SALES. 1918. a. price varies. U.S. International Trade Commission, Attn: Sharon Greenfield, 500 "E" St., S.W., Rm. 513B, Washington, DC 20436. TEL 202-252-1000. FAX 202-252-1798. (Orders to: Supt. of Documents, Washington, DC 20402)
Description: Provides a producers list for thousands of chemicals; includes production and sales data.

693   GW
T I Z INTERNATIONAL. (Tonindustrie-Zeitung); Powder & Bulk Magazin. 1876. m. DM.455. Sprechsaal Publishing Group, Mauer 2, 96450 Coburg, Germany. TEL 09561-76773. FAX 09561-90009. TELEX 663226-SPRECH-D. Ed. Christoph Mueller. adv.: B&W page DM.4998; trim 270 x 185; adv. contact: Hans-Dieter Kuehn. bk.rev.; abstr.; bibl.; charts; illus.; pat.; index. circ. 8,469. **Indexed:** Br.Ceram.Abstr., C.R.I. Abstr., Chem.Abstr., Excerp.Med., Soils & Fert. **Document type:** trade publication.
Former titles: T I Z Fachberichte; Tonindustrie-Zeitung und Keramische Rundschau (ISSN 0040-9200)

TANPAKUSHITSU KOGAKU KISO KENKYU SENTA DAYORI/RESEARCH CENTER FOR PROTEIN ENGINEERING. NEWS. see *BIOLOGY — Biological Chemistry*

660 338   US   ISSN 0883-8828
TECHLETTER; for pest control technicians. 1985. bi-w. $43. Pinto & Associates, Inc., 155 Oak Rd., Mechanicsville, MD 20659. TEL 301-884-3020. FAX 301-884-4068. Ed. Sandra Kraft. bk.rev.; illus.; tr.lit.; index; circ. 1,000 (paid). (looseleaf format) **Document type:** newsletter.
Description: Training information for exterminators.

660   IT   ISSN 0392-3452
CODEN: TECCDK
TECNOLOGIE CHIMICHE. 1981. m. L.85000($139) (foreign L.170000). Stammer S.p.A., via della Liberazione 1, 20068 Peschiera Borromeo (MI), Italy. TEL 02-55302606. FAX 02-55302700. Ed. Girolamo Bellina. adv.: B&W page L.1480000, color page L.2100000; trim 185 x 267. circ. 8,000.
—BLDSC (8762.890000); CASDDS.

660.2   US   ISSN 0040-5795
TP1   CODEN: TFCEAU
THEORETICAL FOUNDATION OF CHEMICAL ENGINEERING. English translation of: Teoreticheskie Osnovy Khimicheskoi Tekhnologii (RU ISSN 0040-3571) 1967. bi-m. $1070 (foreign $1250) (effective 1994). (Russian Academy of Sciences, RU) Plenum Publishing Corp., Consultants Bureau, 233 Spring St., New York, NY 10013-1578. TEL 212-620-8468. FAX 212-463-0742. TELEX 23-421139. Ed. V.V. Kafarov. (also avail. in microfilm from JSC; back issues avail.) **Indexed:** Chem.Eng.Abstr., Eng.Ind., Pollut.Abstr., T.C.E.A. **Document type:** academic/scholarly publication.
—BLDSC (0426.600000); UnCover; SWETS; UMI. **CCC**.
Refereed Serial

THERMODYNAMICS AT TEXAS A & M. see *CHEMISTRY — Physical Chemistry*

660   UK   ISSN 0277-5883
TOPICS IN CHEMICAL ENGINEERING. 1983. irreg., vol.7, 1993. Gordon & Breach Science Publishers, P.O. Box 90, Reading, Berks. RG1 8JL, England. TEL 0734-560080. FAX 0734-568211. TELEX 849870 SCIPUB G. (U.S. addr.: 820 Town Center Dr., Langhorne, PA 19047. TEL 215-750-2642. FAX 218-750-6343) Ed. R. Hughes. bibl.; index. (also avail. in microform) **Document type:** monographic series.
—BLDSC (8867.432300).
Refereed Serial

ENGINEERING — CIVIL ENGINEERING

660   UK   ISSN 0966-4793
CODEN: TPSCE8
▼**TRENDS IN POLYMER SCIENCE**. Library compendium: Trends in Polymer Science (Reference Edition) (ISSN 0968-0047) 1993. 12/yr. £65 to individuals; institutions £318($490) includes library compendium (effective 1994). Elsevier Science Ltd., Oxford Fulfilment Centre, P.O. Box 800, Kidlington, Oxford OX5 1DX, England. TEL 44-865-843000. FAX 44-865-843010. (Subscr. in U.S. and Canada to: Elsevier Science, 660 White Plains Rd., Tarrytown, NY 10591-5153. TEL 914-524-9200. FAX 914-333-2444) Ed. W. Hawthorne. adv.; bk.rev.; bibl.; index. (also avail. in microform from UMI; back issues avail.) **Document type:** academic/scholarly publication, trade publication.
—BLDSC (9049.675500); ADONIS; CASDDS. **CCC.**
    Description: Current awareness journal for polymer scientists, covering leading edge developments in all fields related to polymers and their applications in the adhesives, chemical, plastics, electronics, rubber, textiles and other industries.
    Refereed Serial

660.284   UK   ISSN 0968-0047
▼**TRENDS IN POLYMER SCIENCE (REFERENCE EDITION)**. 1993. a. £318($490) includes Trends in Polymer Science (effective 1994). Elsevier Science Ltd., Oxford Fulfilment Centre, P.O. Box 800, Kidlington, Oxford OX5 1DX, England. TEL 44-865-843000. FAX 44-865-843010. (Subscr. in U.S. and Canada to: Elsevier Science, 660 White Plains Rd., Tarrytown, NY 10591-5153. TEL 914-524-9200. FAX 914-333-2444) Ed. Will Hawthorne. (back issues avail.) **Document type:** academic/scholarly publication.
—CCC.
    Description: Compendium of archival material from Trends in Polymer Science.
    Refereed Serial

665   GW   ISSN 0724-3472
CODEN: TRSCEM
TRIBOLOGIE UND SCHMIERUNGSTECHNIK. 1954. bi-m. DM.180 (foreign DM.204). (Gesellschaft fuer Tribologie) Vincentz Verlag, Schiffgraben 41-43, 30175 Hannover, Germany. TEL 0511-9909847. FAX 0511-9909819. (Subscr. to: Postfach 6247, 30062 Hannover, Germany) Ed. L. Vincentz. adv.; bk.rev.; abstr.; charts; illus.; pat.; stat.; index. circ. 1,350. (tabloid format; also avail. in microform from UMI; reprint service avail. from UMI) **Indexed:** API Abstr., API Catal., API Hlth.& Environ., API Oil., API Pet.Ref., API Pet.Subst., API Transport., Chem.Abstr., Eng.Ind., Fluidex. **Document type:** trade publication.
—BLDSC (9050.216500); SWETS; UMI; CASDDS. **CCC.**
    Formerly: Schmiertechnik (ISSN 0036-6218)

661 668.4   BU
TSELULOZA I KHARTIIA.* (Text in Bulgarian; summaries in Russian, German, English) 1970. bi-m. 10 lv.($10) Ministerstvo na Khimicheska Promishlenost, Sofia, Bulgaria. (Dist. by: Hemus, 6, Rouski Blvd., 1000 Sofia, Bulgaria) (Co-sponsor: Nauchno-Tekhnicheski Suiuz po Khimicheska Promishlenost) Ed. I. Genev. circ. 1,200. **Indexed:** Abstr.Bull.Inst.Pap.Chem., Chem.Abstr.

TURKIYE PETROL KIMYA, LASTIK ISCILEERI SENDIKASI. MAGAZINE. see *RUBBER*

URETHANE PLASTICS AND PRODUCTS. see *PLASTICS*

368.11   GW   ISSN 0042-1804
V F D B: ZEITSCHRIFT FUER FORSCHUNG UND TECHNIK IM BRANDSCHUTZ. (Text in German; summaries in English and French) q. DM.130. (Vereinigung zur Foerderung des Deutschen Brandschutzes e.V.) W. Kohlhammer GmbH, Hessbruehlstr. 69, 70565 Stuttgart, Germany. TEL 0711-7863-1. adv.; charts; illus.; index. circ. 1,000. **Indexed:** C.I.S. Abstr., Chem.Abstr. **Document type:** trade publication.
—SWETS. **CCC.**
    Formerly: V F D B Zeitschrift.

VEGYIPARI SZAKIRODALMI TAJEKOZTATO/CHEMICAL ENGINEERING ABSTRACTS. see *CHEMISTRY — Abstracting, Bibliographies, Statistics*

WASTE MINIMIZATION & RECYCLING REPORT; hazardous & solid waste. see *ENVIRONMENTAL STUDIES — Waste Management*

660   UK   ISSN 0268-523X
WHAT'S NEW IN PROCESSING. 1985. m. $130. Morgan-Grampian (Process Press) Ltd. (Subsidiary of: Morgan-Grampian plc), Morgan-Grampian House, 30 Calderwood St., London SE18 6QH, England. TEL 081-855-7777. FAX 081-854-7476. Ed. Mike Spear. adv. contact: Nick Collins. circ. 24,576. (back issues avail.) **Indexed:** T.C.E.A. **Document type:** trade publication.
—BLDSC (9310.337000).

628.96   UK
WORLD DIRECTORY OF PESTICIDE CONTROL ORGANISATIONS. irreg, 2nd ed., 1994. £40. Royal Society of Chemistry, Thomas Graham House, Science Park, Milton Rd., Cambridge CB4 4WF, England. TEL 0223-420066. FAX 0223-423623. TELEX 818293. (Dist. by: Turpin Distribution Services, Ltd., Blackhorse Rd., Letchworth, Herts. SG6 1HN, England. TEL 0462-672555. FAX 0462-480947) Ed. George Ekstroem. **Document type:** directory.
    Description: Lists groups and government agencies worldwide involved in the control of pesticides.

YOUR CONSULTANT. see *CHEMISTRY*

661 540   JA
YUKAGAKU. m. 21500 Yen. Nihon Yukagaku Kyokai - Japan Oil Chemists' Society.., 13-11, Yushi Kogyo Kaikan 3-chome, Nihonbashi, Chuo-ku, Tokyo 103, Japan. TEL 03-3271-7463. FAX 03-3271-7464. adv.; bk.rev. **Indexed:** Seed Abstr.

665   JA
YUKAGAKU SANKA SEMINA/SEMINAR ON OXIDATION. (Text in Japanese) 1985. a. Nihon Yukagaku Kyokai - Japan Oil Chemists' Society, Yushi Kogyo Kaikan, 13-11, Nihonbashi 3-chome, Chuo-ku, Tokyo 103, Japan.

Z K G: AUSGABE B/CEMENT - LIME - GYPSUM. EDITION B. (Zement - Kalk - Gips International) see *ENGINEERING — Civil Engineering*

660   JA
ZEORAITO/JAPAN ASSOCIATION OF ZEOLITE. BULLETIN. (Text in English, Japanese; summaries in Japanese) 1984. q. Zeoraito Kenkyukai - Japan Association of Zeolite, Tokyo Kogyo Daigaku Kogakubu, Kogaku Kogakka Ono Kenkyushitsu, 12-1, Ookayama 2-chome, Meguro-ku, Tokyo 152, Japan.

ZEORAITO KENKYU HAPPYOKAI KOEN YOKOSHU/JAPAN ASSOCIATION OF ZEOLITE. ABSTRACTS OF ANNUAL MEETING. see *ENGINEERING — Abstracting, Bibliographies, Statistics*

660   RU   ISSN 0044-4618
TP1   CODEN: ZPKHAB
ZHURNAL PRIKLADNOI KHIMII. English translation: Russian Journal of Applied Chemistry. 1928. m. 83.40 Rub. (Rossiiskaya Akademiya Nauk, Leningradskoe Otdelenie) Izdatel'stvo Nauka, 90 Profsoyuznaya ul., 117864 Moscow, Russia. (Dist. by: Mezhdunarodnaya Kniga, ul. Dimitrova D.39, 113095 Moscow, Russia) Ed. P.G. Romankov. bk.rev.; bibl.; charts; illus.; index. circ. 2,700. **Indexed:** Abstr.Bull.Inst.Pap.Chem., Anal.Abstr., Biol.Abstr., Chem.Abstr., Chem.Infd., Eng.Ind., GeoRef., Met.Abstr., RAPRA.
—BLDSC (0065.000000); CASDDS. **CCC.**

ZUMAQUE. see *PETROLEUM AND GAS*

ENGINEERING — Civil Engineering

see also Building and Construction; Transportation–Roads and Traffic

625.7   AT   ISSN 0727-0003
A.A.P.A. ASPHALT REVIEW. 1981. q. free. Australian Asphalt Pavement Association, 21 Burwood Rd., 1st Fl., Hawthorn, Vic. 3122, Australia.
TEL 03-819-4999. FAX 03-819-5278. bk.rev.
    Formerly: A.A.P.A. Technitopics (ISSN 0155-3089)
    Description: Focuses on road construction and repavement in the country.

625.7   AT   ISSN 0155-3070
A.A.P.A. NEWSLETTER. 1970. q. free. Australian Asphalt Pavement Association, 21 Burwood Rd., 1st Fl., Hawthorn, Vic. 3122, Australia. bk.rev. **Indexed:** Apic.Abstr., Aus.Rd.Ind.
    Description: Focuses on paving innovations. Includes membership news.

A A S H T O JOURNAL; weekly transportation report. (American Association of State Highway and Transportation Officials) see *TRANSPORTATION — Roads And Traffic*

625.7   US   ISSN 0147-4820
TE1
A A S H T O QUARTERLY. 1922. q. $10 (foreign $11.25). American Association of State Highway and Transportation Officials, 444 N. Capitol St., N.W., Ste. 249, Washington, DC 20001. TEL 202-624-5800. FAX 202-624-5806. Ed. Mariann Humphreys. illus.; stat. circ. 7,000. **Indexed:** Dok.Str., Eng.Ind., HRIS. **Document type:** bulletin.
—BLDSC (0537.679500); SWETS.
    Former titles (until 1976, vol.55, no.2): American Highways and Transportation; American Highways (ISSN 0002-8746)

624   CN   ISSN 0703-4288
A L S NEWS. 1970. q. free. Alberta Land Surveyor Association, 14403-115 Ave., Edmonton, AB T5M 3B8, Canada. TEL 403-452-7662. FAX 403-453-1824. Ed. Sharon Stecyk. adv.; bk.rev. circ. 700. **Document type:** newsletter.

627.8   AT   ISSN 0045-0731
A N C O L D BULLETIN. 1961. 3/yr. Aus.$30. Australian National Committee on Large Dams, c/o Water Authority of Western Australia, P.O. Box 100, Leederville, W.A. 6007, Australia. Ed. R.N. Lilly. circ. 400. **Indexed:** AESIS.
—BLDSC (0900 326800).
    Description: Papers and news items on Australian involvement in dam design, construction, operation and maintenance.

A R T B A TRANSPORTATION OFFICIALS AND ENGINEERS DIRECTORY, STATE AND FEDERAL TRANSPORTATION AGENCY PERSONNEL. (American Road and Transportation Builders Association) see *TRANSPORTATION — Roads And Traffic*

613.1   US
A S A E TRANSACTIONS. STRUCTURES & ENVIRONMENT. 1970. a. $42.50 to non-members; members $26. American Society of Agricultural Engineers, 2950 Niles Rd., St. Joseph, MI 49085-9659. TEL 616-429-0300. FAX 616-429-3852. Ed. Pamela DeVore-Hansen. circ. 100.
    Description: Addresses livestock waste, farm structures, home energy, greenhouse heating ventilation.
    Refereed Serial

624   US   ISSN 0197-4076
A S C E NEWS. 1976. m. $36. American Society of Civil Engineers, 345 E. 47th St., New York, NY 10017-2398. TEL 212-705-7512. FAX 212-705-7712. adv.: B&W page $5515; trim 11 1/2 x 16 7/8. circ. 97,268. **Document type:** newspaper.
—CCC.

624 331.1   US   ISSN 1060-121X
TA157
A S C E SALARY SURVEY. biennial. American Society of Civil Engineers, 345 E. 47th St., New York, NY 10017-2398. TEL 212-705-7288. FAX 212-980-4681. **Document type:** academic/scholarly publication.

A U A NEWS. (American Underground-Space Association) see *ARCHITECTURE*

AAKERI & TRANSPORT. see *TRANSPORTATION — Trucks And Trucking*

625.7   US   ISSN 1051-4848
ABERDEEN'S PAVEMENT MAINTENANCE. 1990. 10/yr. $15 (foreign $22). Aberdeen Group, 426 S. Westgate St., Addison, IL 60101. TEL 708-543-0870. FAX 708-543-3112. Ed. Allan Heydorn. circ. 23,000. **Document type:** trade publication.
    Formerly: Parking Area Maintenance and International Sweeper.

ENGINEERING — CIVIL ENGINEERING

624   XR   ISSN 1210-2709
ACTA POLYTECHNICA; prace CVUT v Praze. 1967. q. 32 Kcs.($6) Ceske Vysoke Uceni Technicke, Zikova 4, 166 35 Prague 6, Czech Republic. TEL 42-2-332-1111. FAX 42-2-311-7493. Ed. Lubomir Kalivoda. charts; illus. circ. 600.
—BLDSC (0661.210000).
Formed by the 1992 merger of: Acta Polytechnica. Rada 1. Stavebni (ISSN 0322-7510) & Acta Polytechnica. Rada 2. Strojni (ISSN 0554-9183) & Acta Polytechnica. Rada 3. Elektrotechnicka (ISSN 0374-2474) & Acta Polytechnica. Rada 4. Technicko-Teoreticka (ISSN 0554-9205) & Acta Polytechnica. Rada 5. Spolecensko-Vedni (ISSN 0322-7715); Acta Polytechnica. Rada 6. Vseobecna (ISSN 0139-6234).

690   FI   ISSN 0355-2705
                   CODEN: APCBAI
ACTA POLYTECHNICA SCANDINAVICA. CIVIL ENGINEERING AND BUILDING CONSTRUCTION SERIES. (Text in English) irreg., 2-3/yr. FIM 350. Teknillisten Tieteiden Akatemia - Finnish Academy of Technology, Kansakoulukatu 10 A, SF-00100 Helsinki 10, Finland. Ed. Jussi Hyyppa. index, cum.index: 1958-1991. circ. 500. (also avail. in microfilm from UMI; back issues avail.; reprint service avail. from UMI) **Indexed:** ASCA, Cadscan, Curr.Cont., GeoRef., INIS Atomind., Lead Abstr., Sci.Cit.Ind., Zincscan. **Document type:** monographic series.
—BLDSC (0661.257000); UnCover; UMI.
Description: Presents research results in civil engineering.

ADVANCED CEMENT BASED MATERIALS. see *ENGINEERING — Chemical Engineering*

624 629.13   US   ISSN 0362-188X
UG633.A1
AIR FORCE ENGINEERING & SERVICES QUARTERLY. 1960. q. $12. U.S. Air Force, Engineering and Services Center, Headquarters, Tyndall A F B, FL 32403. TEL 202-545-5700. (Dist. by: Supt. of Documents, Government Printing Office, Washington DC 20402) Ed. H. Perry Sullivan, Jr. bk.rev.; charts; illus.; tr.lit. circ. 8,000. (also avail. in microform from MIM,UMI; reprint service avail. from UMI) **Indexed:** Air Un.Lib.Ind., Eng.Ind., Geotech.Abstr., Ind.U.S.Gov.Per.
Formerly: Air Force Civil Engineer (ISSN 0002-2357)

627.1 551.44   CN
ALBERTA RESEARCH COUNCIL. RIVER ENGINEERING AND SURFACE HYDROLOGY REPORTS. irreg. price varies. Alberta Research Council, Publications Dept., P.O. Box 8330, Sta. F, Edmonton, Alta. T6H 5X2, Canada. TEL 403-450-5390. FAX 403-461-2651. TELEX 037-2147.
Formerly: Alberta Research. Highways and River Engineering Reports (ISSN 0080-1550)
Description: Reports on river engineering and surface hydrology by the Alberta Research Council.

625.72   GW   ISSN 0002-5968
TA501   CODEN: ALVNAJ
ALLGEMEINE VERMESSUNGS-NACHRICHTEN; Zeitschrift fuer alle Zweige des Vermessungs,- Karten-und Liegenschaftswesens sowie fuer Landesplanung und die Ermittlung von Grundstueckswerten. Abbreviated title: A V N. 1889. 10/yr. DM.143 (foreign DM.169). Herbert Wichmann Verlag GmbH, Amalienstr. 29, 76133 Karlsruhe, Germany. TEL 0721-91220-0. FAX 0721-9122020. TELEX 07825909. Ed. Dr. Heinz Draheim. adv.; bk.rev.; charts; illus.; tr.lit.; index. circ. 2,300. **Indexed:** Bibl.Cart., Excerp.Med., Geo.Abstr., GeoRef.
Document type: trade publication.
—CCC.

625.7   US
AMERICAN CONCRETE PAVING ASSOCIATION. NEWSLETTER. m. American Concrete Paving Association, 3800 N. Wilke, Ste. 490, Arlington Heights, IL 60004. TEL 708-394-5577. **Document type:** newsletter.

627   US
AMERICAN SOCIETY OF CIVIL ENGINEERS. OFFICIAL REGISTER. a. American Society of Civil Engineers, 345 E. 47th St., New York, NY 10017-2398. TEL 212-705-7288. FAX 212-980-4681. Ed. Nina Kramer. **Document type:** academic/scholarly publication.

624   US   ISSN 0003-1119
A1
AMERICAN SOCIETY OF CIVIL ENGINEERS. PROCEEDINGS. (Consists of the Journals of the various Divisions of the Society) 1873. m. $2289. American Society of Civil Engineers, 345 E. 47th St., New York, NY 10017-2398. TEL 212-705-7288. FAX 212-980-4681. abstr.; bibl.; charts; illus.; stat.; index. circ. 70,000 (total 20 journals). (also avail. in microform from UMI; reprint service avail. from UMI) **Indexed:** A.S.& T.Ind., Appl.Mech.Rev., Chem.Abstr., Eng.Ind., Geo.Abstr., Sh.& Vib.Dig. **Document type:** academic/scholarly publication, proceedings.
—CCC.

624.2   FR   ISSN 0152-9668
                   CODEN: APCSAZ
ANNALES DES PONTS ET CHAUSSEES. (Suspended 1971-1976) 1831; N.S. 1976. q. $135 (typically set in Jan.). Masson - Periodiques, Villa Laromiguiere, 75005 Paris, France. TEL 1-40-46-62-00. FAX 1-40-46-62-01. Ed. Jean-Yves Chauviere. adv. **Indexed:** Dok.Str., Excerp.Med., GeoRef., Intl.Civil Eng.Abstr., Soft.Abstr.Eng. **Document type:** academic/scholarly publication.

624   BE
ANNALES DES TRAVAUX PUBLICS DE BELGIQUE. Dutch edition: Tijdschrift der Openbare Werken van Belgie. (Text in Dutch, French) 1841 (French ed.); 1937 (Dutch ed.). bi-m. 1700 Fr. Ministere des Travaux Public - Ministerie van Openbaren Werken, Bd. Simon Bolivar 50, 1210 Brussels, Belgium. adv.; bk.rev.; illus. circ. 3,000. **Indexed:** GeoRef.
Description: Covers all architectural and construction undertakings for Belgium.

627   US
ANNUAL U S C O L D LECTURE. 1981. a. $40 to non-members (1993 edition). U S Committee on Large Dams, 1616 17th St., Ste. 483, Denver, CO 80202. TEL 303-628-5430. FAX 303-628-5431.

APPLIED CLAY SCIENCE; an international journal on the application and technology of clays and clay minerals. see *EARTH SCIENCES — Geology*

624   NE   ISSN 0169-4421
ARCHITECTUUR - BOUWEN/ARCHITECTURE - BUILDING. 1945. m. fl.197.50 (foreign fl.365) (effective 1994). Ten Hagen & Stam b.v., Postbus 235, 2280 AE Rijswijk, Netherlands. TEL 31-70-3988100. FAX 31-70-3988276. adv.; B&W page fl.2845, color page fl.5595; trim 297 x 210; adv. contact: Herman Voois. circ. 5,934. **Indexed:** Excerp.Med., Geotech.Abstr., HRIS. **Document type:** trade publication.
—SWETS.
Former titles (until 1984): Polytechnisch Tijdschrift: Bouwtechniek (ISSN 0169-4472); Polytechnisch Tijdschrift: Bouwkunde Wegen- en Waterbouw (ISSN 0032-4078)
Description: Documents Dutch building and design projects, and covers topics in urban development, construction engineering, interior design, and finishing techniques.

690   PL   ISSN 1230-2945
TA4
ARCHIVES OF CIVIL ENGINEERING. (Text in English) 1955. q. $44. (Polska Akademia Nauk, Komitet Inzynierii Ladowej i Wodnej) Wydawnictwo Naukowe P W N, Miodowa 10, 00-251 Warsaw, Poland. TEL 48-22-312738. FAX 48-22-267163. TELEX 813763 PWN PL. Ed. A.M. Brandt. abstr.; bibl. circ. 530. **Indexed:** Appl.Mech.Rev., Chem.Abstr., Concr.Abstr., Eng.Ind., Geotech.Abstr., Intl.Civil Eng.Abstr., Soft.Abstr.Eng.
—BLDSC (1634.070000).
Formerly (until 1992): Archiwum Inzynierii Ladowej (ISSN 0004-0797)

624   JA   ISSN 0915-6054
ASANUMAGUMI GIJUTSU KENKYUJOHO/ASANUMA TECHNICAL RESEARCH REPORT. (Text in Japanese; summaries in English, Japanese) 1989. a. Asanumagumi Gijutsu Kenkyujo - Asanuma Corp., Technical Research Institute, 24-1, Otsuka-cho 3-chome, Takatsuki-shi, Osaka 569, Japan.

624   JA   ISSN 0917-2041
ASANUMAGUMI GIJUTSU REPOTO/ASANUMA CORP. TECHNICAL REPORT. (Text in Japanese) 1977. a. Asanuma Corp., 12-6, Higashikozu-cho, Tennoji-ku, Osaka-shi, Osaka 543, Japan.

625.7   DK   ISSN 0004-4318
ASFALT. (Text in Danish; summaries in English) 1960. 4/yr. $30. Asfaltindustriens - Association of Danish Asphalt Industries, Stamholmen 91, 2650 Hvidovre, Denmark. TEL 45-31-78-08-22. FAX 45-36-77-12-08. Ed. Uno Helk. charts; illus. circ. 4,500. **Indexed:** Dok.Str., Excerp.Med. **Document type:** trade publication.
Description: Covers road and street paving techniques.

625.85   GW   ISSN 0722-821X
DIE ASPHALTSTRASSE; das stationaere Mischwerk. 1967. 8/yr. DM.135. Stein-Verlag GmbH, Josef-Herrmann-Str. 1-3, 76473 Iffezheim, Germany. TEL 07229-6060. FAX 07229-60610. Ed. Wilhelm G. Joesch. adv.; bibl.; illus. circ. 7,400. **Indexed:** Dok.Str., Excerp.Med.
Description: Information on the production of asphalt and bituminous roads in Europe.

625.8   US   ISSN 0066-9466
ASSOCIATION OF ASPHALT PAVING TECHNOLOGISTS. PROCEEDINGS.* Variant title: Asphalt Paving Technology. 1928. a. $60. Association of Asphalt Paving Technologists, 1983 Sloan Pl., No. 10, Maplewood, MN 55117. TEL 612-776-7703. Ed. E.L. Skok, Jr. cum.index: vol.1-59. (also avail. in microform from UMI; reprint service avail. from UMI) **Indexed:** API Abstr., API Catal., API Hlth.& Environ., API Oil., API Pet.Ref., API Pet.Subst., API Transport., Chem.Abstr. **Document type:** proceedings.
—BLDSC (1746.110000).

625.72   CN   ISSN 0700-5989
ASSOCIATION OF ONTARIO LAND SURVEYORS. ANNUAL REPORT. a. Can.$20. Association of Ontario Land Surveyors, 1043 McNicoll Ave, Scarborough, Ont. M1W 3W6, Canada. TEL 416-491-9020.

624   JA
ASU E NO J C C A/JAPAN CONSTRUCTION CONSULTANTS ASSOCIATION. NEWS. (Text in Japanese) q. Kensetsu Konsarutantsu Kyokai, 2-4, Kudan Minami 2-chome, Chiyoda-ku, Tokyo 102, Japan.

624 669.142   JA
ASU O KIZUKU/CONSTRUCTION TOMORROW. (Text in Japanese) 1972. 3/yr. Kokanko Kyokai - Japanese Association for Steel Pipe Piles, 2-10, Nihonbashi Kayaba-cho 3-chome, Chuo-ku, Tokyo 103, Japan.

624   JA
ATARASHII ZAIRYO KOHO KIKAI KOSHUKAI KOEN GAIYO/LECTURES ON NEW MATERIALS, METHODS AND MACHINERY IN CONSTRUCTION. SUMMARIES. (Text in Japanese) 1984. irreg. 2000 Yen. Doboku Gakkai, Doboku Seko Kenkyu Iinkai - Japan Society of Civil Engineers, Committee on Construction Technology, Yotsuya 1-chome, Shinjuku-ku, Tokyo 160, Japan. **Document type:** academic/scholarly publication.

624 551   AT
AUSTRALIA - NEW ZEALAND CONFERENCE ON GEOMECHANICS PROCEEDINGS. 1971. 4/yr. price varies. Institution of Engineers, Australia, 11 National Circuit, Barton, A.C.T. 2600, Australia. TEL 062-706555. FAX 062-731488. TELEX AA62758. (also avail. in microfiche) **Indexed:** Eng.Ind., GeoRef, Geotech.Abstr. **Document type:** proceedings.
Supersedes: Australia New Zealand Conference on Soil Mechanics and Foundation Engineering Proceedings.
Description: Proceedings of conference jointly run by Australia and New Zealand geomechanics societies.

624   AT   ISSN 0310-1258
AUSTRALIAN PIPELINER. 1972. q. free. (Australian Pipeline Industry Association) Business & Trade Publications, 23 Beatty Ave., Armadale, Vic. 3143, Australia. Ed. George Tredinnick. adv. circ. 750. (back issues avail.) **Indexed:** AESIS.

AUSTRALIAN ROAD RESEARCH BOARD. PROCEEDINGS. see *TRANSPORTATION — Roads And Traffic*

ENGINEERING — CIVIL ENGINEERING

625.72   AT   ISSN 0005-0326
TA529.A1   CODEN: AUSUAK
AUSTRALIAN SURVEYOR. 1928. q. Aus.$50 (effective Jan. 1992). Institution of Surveyors, Australia Inc., 27-29 Napier Close, Deakin, A.C.T. 2600, Australia. TEL 02-2822866. FAX 06-2822576. Eds. R.J. Wenholz, N.O. Wardz. adv.; bk.rev.; charts; illus.; stat.; index. circ. 3,800. **Indexed:** Aus.Rd.Ind., Bibl.Cart., Geo.Abstr. **Document type:** academic/scholarly publication.
—BLDSC (1822.200000).

625.7   IT   ISSN 0005-1756
AUTOSTRADE; rivista di tecnica e di informazioni autostradali. 1959. q. L.60000 (foreign L.75000). Autostrade Concessioni e Costruzioni Autostrade S.p.A., Via Bergamini 50, 00159 Rome, Italy. TEL 06-43631. FAX 06-43634887. TELEX 612235. Ed. Giuseppe Fedi. adv.; bk.rev.; charts; illus.; index. circ. 5,000. (back issues avail.) **Indexed:** Dok.Str., HRIS.

625.7   RU   ISSN 0005-2353
CODEN: AVNDAJ
AVTOMOBIL'NYE DOROGI. 1938. m. 27 Rub. Izdatel'stvo Nauka, 90 Profsoyuznaya ul., 117864 Moscow, Russia. (Dist. by: Mezhdunarodnaya Knigga, ul.Dimitrova D.39, 113095 Moscow, Russia) charts; illus.; index. **Indexed:** Chem.Abstr., Geo.Abstr., Geotech.Abstr.
—BLDSC (0004.000000); CASDDS.

624   US
B I C C GROUP WORLD. 1990. q. free. British International Cables & Construction, 1 Tanner St., London SE1 5FH, England. TEL 071-378-0002. FAX 071-378-0643. Ed. Charles Wheeldon. circ. 41,000. (tabloid format; back issues avail.)

B M T. (Baumaschine und Bautechnik) see *BUILDING AND CONSTRUCTION*

B S HANDBOOK 3. SUMMARIES OF BRITISH STANDARDS FOR BUILDING. see *BUILDING AND CONSTRUCTION*

624   BF
BAHAMAS. MINISTRY OF WORKS AND UTILITIES. ANNUAL REPORT. 1965. a. $2. Ministry of Works and Utilities, P.O. Box N8156, Nassau, Bahamas. (Orders to: Government Publications Office, Bank Lane, Nassau, Bahamas) charts; illus.; stat. circ. 100.
Formerly: Bahamas. Ministry of Works. Annual Report (ISSN 0376-5490)

BAUEN IN STAHL/CONSTRUIRE EN ACIER/COSTRUIRE IN ACCIAIO. see *ARCHITECTURE*

625.7   GW   ISSN 0005-6634
BAUGEWERBE. 1947. s-m. DM.215 (foreign DM.237). (Zentralverband des Deutschen Baugewerbes e.V.) Verlagsgesellschaft Rudolf Mueller GmbH, Stolberger Str. 86, 50933 Cologne, Germany. TEL 0221-5497-0. FAX 0221-5497326. (Subscr. to: Postfach 410949, 50869 Cologne, Germany) Ed. Rudolf Bleser. adv.: B&W page DM.6140, color page DM.9890; trim 188 x 267. bk.rev.; charts; illus.; pat.; index. circ. 23,000. **Indexed:** Dok.Str., Excerp.Med., PROMT. **Document type:** trade publication.
—BLDSC (1866.878000).
Formerly: Strassenbau-Technik (ISSN 0039-2200)

BAUINGENIEUR; Zeitschrift fuer das gesamte Bauwesen. see *BUILDING AND CONSTRUCTION*

624   GW   ISSN 0041-2368
BAUMA-TRENDS. (Text in English, French and German) 1961. s-a. DM.16. (International Construction Machinery Fair, Munich (BAUMA)) Otto Elsner Verlagsgesellschaft, Schoefferstr. 15, 64295 Darmstadt, Germany. Ed. Walter Gottstein. adv.; bk.rev.; illus. circ. 7,500.

BEIKOKU TOKKYO SHOROKU. YU'YU KIKAI, KENSETSU, DOBOKU HEN/U.S. PATENT ABSTRACTS. TRANSPORTING MACHINE, CONSTRUCTION, CIVIL ENGINEERING. see *PATENTS, TRADEMARKS AND COPYRIGHTS — Abstracting, Bibliographies, Statistics*

BEOGRAD. see *ENGINEERING — Engineering Mechanics And Materials*

624.183   GW   ISSN 0067-6365
BETON- UND FERTIGTEIL-JAHRBUCH. 1951. a. DM.48. Bauverlag GmbH, Postfach 1460, 65004 Wiesbaden, Germany. TEL 06123-700-0. FAX 06123-700-122. **Document type:** trade publication.
Formerly: Betonstein-Jahrbuch.

625.7   US   ISSN 0006-0208
CODEN: BEROAW
BETTER ROADS. 1931. m. free to qualified personnel; others $20. William O. Dannhausen, Pub., Box 558, Park Ridge, IL 60068. TEL 312-693-7710. FAX 312-696-3445. Ed. Ruth Stidger. adv.; bk.rev.; illus.; tr.lit.; circ. controlled. **Indexed:** Concr.Abstr., Eng.Ind., Environ.Abstr., HRIS. **Document type:** trade publication.
—BLDSC (1947.100000); CIS; EI; UMI.
Description: For governmental decision makers, both engineers and elected officials who are responsible for the nation's roads, streets, bridges and traffic safety.

624   JA
BIRU SHINBUN/BUILDING NEWSPAPER. (Text in Japanese) w. 400 Yen per no. Biru Shinbunsha - Building Newspaper Co., 25-4-103, Tachimachi, Aoba-ku, Sendai-shi, Miyagi-ken 980, Japan. **Document type:** newspaper.

625.7   GW   ISSN 0006-3916
CODEN: BITUAK
BITUMEN. 1931. q. free. Arbeitsgemeinschaft der Bitumen-Industrie e.V., Steindamm 71, 20099 Hamburg, Germany. TEL 040-2802939. FAX 040-2802125. Ed. R.G. Urban. bk.rev.; bibl.; charts; stat.; index, cum.index: 1931-1970, 1971-1980. circ. 9,000. (tabloid format) **Indexed:** Chem.Abstr., Dok.Str., Eng.Ind., Excerp.Med., Geotech.Abstr. **Document type:** trade publication.
—BLDSC (2097.000000); EI; CASDDS.

624   FR   ISSN 0006-4890
BLOC. 1942. bi-m. free. Association des Eleves de l'Ecole Speciale des Travaux Publics, 57 bd. St. Germain, 75005 Paris, France. TEL 43 26 26 16. adv.; charts; illus.; tr.lit. circ. 2,000.

624   JA   ISSN 0289-3894
BOSUI JANARU/BOSUI JOURNAL. (Text in Japanese) 1970. m. 1150 Yen per no. Shinjusha Inc., 15-4, Ginza 8-chome, Chuo-ku, Tokyo 104, Japan. stat.

627.8   UK   ISSN 0525-4205
BRITISH NATIONAL COMMITTEE ON LARGE DAMS. NEWS AND VIEWS. s-a. £5. (Institution of Civil Engineers) Thomas Telford Ltd., 1 Heron Quay, London E14 4JD, England. TEL 071-987-6999.
FAX 071-538-4101. adv.; bk.rev.; charts; illus.; index.

BUILDING AND ENVIRONMENT. see *BUILDING AND CONSTRUCTION*

BUILDING ENGINEER. see *ARCHITECTURE*

BUILDINGS ENERGY TECHNOLOGY ABSTRACTS. see *ENERGY — Abstracting, Bibliographies, Statistics*

BYGGFORSKNING. see *BUILDING AND CONSTRUCTION*

624   JA
C & S. (Text in Japanese) 1985. s-a. Yokogawa Gijutsu Joho - Yokogawa Techno-Information Service Inc., 3-4, Shibaura 4-chome, Minato-ku, Tokyo 108, Japan.

C I E - NEWS. (Commission Internationale de l'Eclairage) see *ENGINEERING — Electrical Engineering*

624   US
C I M CONSTRUCTION JOURNAL. 1921. w. membership. Construction Industries of Massachusetts, Inc., 1500 Providence Highway, Ste. 14, Box 667, Norwood, MA 02062. Ed. Patricia A. Mikes. adv. circ. 1,000.
Formerly: N E R B A (ISSN 0027-6464)

624 690   UK   ISSN 0305-4047
C I R I A ANNUAL REPORT. 1964. a. free. Construction Industry Research and Information Association, 6 Storey's Gate, Westminster, London SW1P 3AU, England. TEL 44-71-222-8891.
FAX 44-71-222-1708. (microfiche) **Indexed:** Concr.Abstr. **Document type:** corporate report.
Formerly: C I R I A. Bulletin (ISSN 0069-9209)

624   UK   ISSN 0306-3267
C I R I A GUIDES. 1976. a. price varies. Construction Industry Research and Information Association, 6 Storey's Gate, Westminster, London SW1P 3AU, England. TEL 44-71-222-8891.
FAX 44-71-222-1708. **Document type:** monographic series.

624 690   UK   ISSN 0141-2817
C I R I A NEWS. 1977. q. free. Construction Industry Research and Information Association, 6 Storey's Gate, Westminster, London SW1P 3AU, England. TEL 44-71-222-8891. FAX 44-71-222-1708. circ. 6,000. (microfiche) **Document type:** newsletter.
Description: Gives news about all aspects of CIRIA's work; new projects, staff changes, and new members.

624 690   UK   ISSN 0305-408X
C I R I A REPORT. 1965. irreg., (approx. 6/yr.). price varies per no. Construction Industry Research and Information Association, 6 Storey's Gate, Westminster, London SW1P 3AU, England. TEL 44-71-222-8891. FAX 44-71-222-1708. circ. 500 (controllec). (also avail. in microfiche) **Indexed:** GeoRef, Geotech.Abstr., HRIS.
—BLDSC (7412.112000).

624   UK   ISSN 0268-229X
C I R I A SPECIAL PUBLICATIONS. 1982. irreg. price varies. Construction Industry Research and Information Association, 6 Storey's Gate, Westminster, London SW1P 3AU, England. TEL 44-71-222-8891. FAX 44-71-222-1708. **Document type:** monographic series.

624 690   UK   ISSN 0305-1781
C I R I A TECHNICAL NOTE. 1968. irreg., approx. 6/yr. price varies. Construction Industry Research and Information Association, 6 Storey's Gate, Westminster, London SW1P 3AU, England. TEL 44-71-222-8891. FAX 44-71-222-1708. (also avail. in microfiche)
—BLDSC (8673.780000).

624   DR   ISSN 0045-7310
C O D I A. 1967. bi-m. Colegio Dominicano de Ingenieros, Arquitectos y Agrimensores, Calle Fantino Falco Esq. Jose Ortega y Gasset, Apdo. Postal 1514, Santo Domingo, Dominican Republic. Ed.Bd. adv.; charts; illus. **Indexed:** Br.Tech.Ind.

624   AT   ISSN 1034-9596
C S R CONSTRUCTION NEWS. 1923. bi-m. free. C S R Humes Pty. Ltd., P.O. Box 31, World Trade Centre, Vic. 3005, Australia. TEL 03-611-3311. FAX 03-614-6397. Ed. Syd Gregory. index. circ. 6,400. **Indexed:** Aus.Rd.Ind.
Formerly: Hume News (ISSN 0159-9399)
Description: Details information on various concrete products.

CANADIAN GEOTECHNICAL JOURNAL/REVUE CANADIENNE DE GEOTECHNIQUE. see *EARTH SCIENCES*

624   CN   ISSN 0315-1468
TA1   CODEN: CJCEB8
CANADIAN JOURNAL OF CIVIL ENGINEERING/REVUE CANADIENNE DE GENIE CIVIL. (Text mainly in English, occasionally in French) 1974. bi-m. Can.$77($79) to individuals; institutions Can.$238. National Research Council of Canada, Research Journals, Ottawa, Ont. K1A 0R6, Canada. TEL 613-993-9084. FAX 613-952-7656. (Co-sponsor: Canadian Society for Civil Engineering) Ed. B.G. Hutchinson. adv.: B&W page Can.$550; trim 8 1/2 x 11; adv. contact: Hoda Jabbour. bk.rev.; illus.; index. circ. 3,600. (also avail. in microform from UMI; back issues avail.; reprint service avail. from UMI) **Indexed:** Abstr.J.Earthq.Eng., Agri.Eng.Abstr., C.R.I. Abstr., Cadscan, Concr.Abstr., Curr.Cont., Energy Ind., Energy Info.Abstr., Eng.Ind., Excerp.Med., Fluidex, Geo.Abstr., GeoRef., Geotech.Abstr., Ind.Sc..Rev., INIS Atomind., Intl.Civil Eng.Abstr., J.of Ferroc., Lead Abstr., Risk Abstr., Sage Urb.Stud.Abstr., Sci.Cit.Ind., Sel.Water Res.Abstr., Sh.& Vib.Dig., Soft.Abstr.Eng., W.R.C.Inf., Zincscan. **Document type:** academic/scholarly publication.
—BLDSC (3031.030000); EI; Faxon; UnCover; SWETS; UMI. **CCC.**
Refereed Serial

ENGINEERING — CIVIL ENGINEERING

624   SP   ISSN 0008-6908
CARRETERAS. 1951. bi-m. 4500 ptas. (Europe $55; America $58). Asociacion Espanola de la Carretera, Juan Ramon Jimenez 28, 8o C, 28036 Madrid, Spain. TEL 1-350-02-75. FAX 1-345-81-08. Ed. A. Zaragoza Ramirez. adv.; abstr.; illus. circ. 5,000. **Indexed:** Ind.SST.
—BLDSC (3055.460000).

628   BL
CATALOGO BRASILEIRO DE ENGENHARIA SANITARIA E AMBIENTAL. 1965. a. $20. A B E S, Av. Beira-Mar, 216-13 andar, 20021 Rio de Janeiro, RJ, Brazil. FAX 021-262-6838. TELEX 021-31902. Ed. Antonio Romani. adv. circ. 14,000.

624   SP   ISSN 0212-761X
CAUCE 2000. 6/yr. Colegio de Ingenieros de Caminos, Canales y Puertos, Almagro 42, 28010 Madrid, Spain. TEL 1-308-19-88. FAX 1-308-39-32. Ed. Esther Diaz. circ. 15,000.

624   US   ISSN 0149-6123
TA434   CODEN: CCAGDP
CEMENT, CONCRETE, AND AGGREGATES. 1979. s-a. $48 to non-members; members $43. American Society for Testing and Materials, 1916 Race St., Philadelphia, PA 19103. TEL 215-299-5400. FAX 215-977-9679. (reprint service avail.) **Indexed:** C.R.I. Abstr., Chem.Abstr., Concr.Abstr. **Document type:** trade publication.
—BLDSC (3099.500000); EI; Faxon; UnCover; SWETS; UMI; CASDDS. **CCC.**

CENTER FOR DREDGING STUDIES NEWSLETTER. see *WATER RESOURCES*

624   JA
CENTRAL RESEARCH INSTITUTE FOR CONSTRUCTION TECHNOLOGY. NEWSLETTER. (Text in Japanese) 1988. 3/yr. free. Central Research Institute for Construction Technology - Nikon Kensetsugyo Keiei Kyokai Chuo Gijutsu Kenkyujo, 6-34, Konan 1-chome, Minato-ku, Tokyo 108, Japan. (Co-sponsor: Japan Association of Representative General Contractors) **Document type:** newsletter.

624 387.7   CI   ISSN 0411-6380
CSMVB2
CESTE I MOSTOVI/ROADS AND BRIDGES. (Text in Serbo-Croatian; summaries in English) 1953. m. $160 (typically set in Jan.). Savez Drustava za Ceste Hrvatske, Voncinina 3, 41000 Zagreb, Croatia. TEL 041-445-422. FAX 445-215. TELEX 21823 ZACEHA YU. adv.; bk.rev.; index. circ. 25,000. (back issues avail.)
—BLDSC (3123.800000).
Description: Focuses on scientific research and professional papers on the construction of roads and bridges.

624 711   CC   ISSN 1000-3363
HT169.C6   CODEN: CGHUET
CHENGSHI GUIHUA HUIKAN. (Text in Chinese) bi-m. (Tongji Daxue, Jianzhu Chengshi Guihua Xueyuan - Tongji University, Institute of Architecture and Urban Design) Tongji University Press, 1239 Siping Lu, Shanghai 200092, People's Republic of China. TEL 5455080. TELEX 33488 TJIDC CN. Ed. Dong Jianhong.

624.176 628.168   JA
CHIBAKEN NO JIBAN CHINKA TO JISHIN/RESEARCHES ON LANDSUBSIDENCE AND EARTHQUAKE IN CHIBA PREFECTURE. (Text in Japanese) a. Chibaken Suishitsu Hozen Kenkyujo - Chiba Prefectural Laboratory of Water Pollution, 5-1, Inagekaigan 3-chome, Mihama-ku, Chiba-shi, Chiba-ken 261, Japan. stat. **Document type:** academic/scholarly publication.

CHIKA KUKAN RIYO SHINPOJUMU/SYMPOSIUM ON UTILITY OF UNDERGROUND SPACE. see *EARTH SCIENCES — Geology*

624   JA
CHIZAKI KOGYO. GIHO/CHIZAKI KOGYO. TECHNICAL REPORT. (Text in Japanese) 1983. 4/yr. Chizaki Kogyo Co., Ltd., 23-1, Nishishinbashi 2-chome, Minato-ku, Tokyo 105, Japan. **Document type:** academic/scholarly publication.

624   SP   ISSN 0210-0479
CIMBRA; revista de la ingeniera tecnica de obras publicas. vol.11, 1974. 10/yr. 2500 ptas. Colegio de Ingenieros Tecnicos de Obras Publicas, Javier Ferrero 18, 28002 Madrid, Spain. TEL 1-413-49-14. FAX 1-519-38-92. Ed. Jose M. Pastor. adv.; bk.rev.; charts; illus. circ. 4,300. **Indexed:** Ind.SST.

624   NE   ISSN 0925-7128
CIVIELE TECHNIEK; vakblad voor weg- en waterbouwers. q. fl.93.50 (foreign fl.125) (effective 1994). Ten Hagen & Stam b.v., Postbus 235, 2280 AE Rijswijk, Netherlands. TEL 31-70-3988100. FAX 31-70-3988276. TELEX 33702 STAM NL. adv.: B&W page fl.2290, color page fl.4380; trim 297 x 210; adv. contact: Herman Voois. circ. 1,899 (paid). **Document type:** trade publication.
—SWETS.
Former titles: P T - Civiele Techniek (ISSN 0169-2542)
Description: Covers topics of interest to hydraulic and public works engineers, including current developments, new product reviews, soil mechanics, environmental technology, construction materials, machinery and more.

CIVIL & STRUCTURAL ENGINEERING ABSTRACTS. see *ENGINEERING — Abstracting, Bibliographies, Statistics*

624   II
CIVIL ENGINEER. 1957. q. Indian Society of Engineers, 5 Lindsay St., Calcutta 70000016, India. Ed. M.K. Diwan. adv. circ. 8,270.

624   SA   ISSN 1021-2000
TA4
CIVIL ENGINEERING/SIVIELE INGENIEURSWESE. (Text in Afrikaans and English) 1903. m. R.138. South African Institution of Civil Engineers, P.O. Box 93495, Yeoville 2143, South Africa. TEL 27-11-648-1184. FAX 27-11-648-7427. Ed. R.C. Boers. adv.; bk.rev.; charts; illus.; index. circ. 7,400. **Indexed:** Appl.Mech.Rev., Eng.Ind., Excerp.Med., Geotech.Abstr., Ind.S.A.Per., INIS Atomind., Intl.Civil Eng.Abstr., ISMEC, J.of Ferroc., Soft.Abstr.Eng.
—BLDSC (3270.006000); EI; UnCover; UMI.
Former titles: South African Institution of Civil Engineers. Journal (ISSN 1021-2019); (until 1992): Civil Engineer in South Africa - Siviele Ingenieur in Suid-Afrika (ISSN 0009-7845)

624   US   ISSN 0360-0556
             CODEN: CEASE8
CIVIL ENGINEERING A S C E; engineered design and construction. 1930. m. $85. American Society of Civil Engineers, 345 E. 47th St., New York, NY 10017-2398. TEL 212-705-7288. FAX 212-980-4681. Ed. Virginia Fairweather. adv.; bk.rev.; abstr.; bibl.; charts; illus.; stat.; tr.lit.; index. circ. 112,660. (also avail. in microform from UMI) **Indexed:** A.S.& T.Ind., ABI Inform., Appl.Mech.Rev., Biodet.Abstr., Br.Rail.Bd., Build.Manage.Abstr., CAD CAM Abstr., Chem.Abstr., Concr.Abstr., Curr.Cont., Dok.Str., Eng.Ind., Environ.Abstr., Fluidex, Geo.Abstr., GeoRef., Geotech.Abstr., HRIS, INIS Atomind., Met.Abstr., Ocean.Abstr., Pollut.Abstr., Sel.Water Res.Abstr., Sh.& Vib.Dig., W.R.C.Inf. **Document type:** academic/scholarly publication.
—BLDSC (3270.000000); CIS. **CCC.**
Formerly: Civil Engineering (New York) (ISSN 0009-7853)
Refereed Serial

624   SA
CIVIL ENGINEERING ADVISORY COUNCIL. ANNUAL REPORT/SIVIELE INGENIEURSWESE-ADVIESRAAD. JAARVERSLAG. (Text in Afrikaans, English) 1983. a. free. Department of Transport, Civil Engineering Advisory Council, P.B. X193, Pretoria 0001, South Africa. FAX 012-325-8004. circ. 1,000.

692.8   SA   ISSN 0009-7888
CIVIL ENGINEERING CONTRACTOR. (Text in English) 1966. m. (11/yr.). R.88 (Africa R.110; elsewhere R.230) (effective Apr. 1994). (Federation of Civil Engineering Contractors) Brooke Pattrick (Pty) Ltd., P.O. Box 422, Bedfordview 2008, South Africa. TEL 27-11-6224666. FAX 27-11-6167196. Ed. Errol Symons. adv.; charts; illus.; stat.; circ. 4,500 (controlled). **Indexed:** Ind.S.A.Per., INIS Atomind. **Document type:** trade publication.
Description: Information of interest to the civil engineering contractor on equipment, machinery, and instruments used in the field. Contains articles on a variety of topics related to the industry as well as current projects worldwide.

624   JA   ISSN 0578-3747
TA105   CODEN: CVEJAE
CIVIL ENGINEERING IN JAPAN. (Text in English) 1961. a. 5500 Yen. Doboku Gakkai - Japan Society of Civil Engineers, Mubanchi, Yotsuya 1-Chome, Shinjuku-ku, Tokyo 160, Japan. TEL 03-272-7211. (Subscr. to: Mazuren Co., Ltd., P.O. Box 5050, Tokyo International 100-31, Japan) adv. circ. 1,300. (back issues avail.) **Indexed:** Dok.Str., Intl.Civil Eng.Abstr., JTA, Soft.Abstr.Eng.
—BLDSC (3273.100000); EI; UnCover.

624   US   ISSN 1051-9629
CIVIL ENGINEERING NEWS.* 1988. m. $29. Civil Engineering News, Inc., 1255 Roberts Blvd., Ste. 230, Kennesaw, GA 30144-3694. TEL 404-499-1857. FAX 404-428-6418. adv.; bk.rev. circ. 30,000. **Document type:** trade publication.
Description: For civil, structural, environmental, and geotechnical engineers involved in the design, construction and maintenance of engineered projects and public works.

624   US
CIVIL ENGINEERING SERIES. 1979. irreg., vol.9, 1992. price varies. Marcel Dekker, Inc., 270 Madison Ave., New York, NY 10016. TEL 212-696-9000. FAX 212-685-4540. TELEX 421419. **Document type:** monographic series.

624   UK   ISSN 0266-139X
CIVIL ENGINEERING SURVEYOR. 1973. 10/yr. £29 (Europe £34; elsewhere £39). Institution of Civil Engineering Surveyors, 101 Bancroft, Hitchin, Herts. SG5 1NB, England. TEL 0462-440506. FAX 0462-440507. (Subscr. addr.: 26 Market St., Altringham, Ches. WA14 1PF, England. TEL 061-928-8074. FAX 061-941-6134) Ed. Stephen J. Booth. adv. contact: Stephen J. Booth. bk.rev. circ. 3,000. (back issues avail.) **Indexed:** Build.Manage.Abstr., RICS. **Document type:** trade publication.
—BLDSC (3273.325000).
Description: Aimed at quantity and land surveyors working as civil engineers.

624   US   ISSN 0263-0257
             CODEN: CESYEE
CIVIL ENGINEERING SYSTEMS; decision making & problem solving. 1983. q. 85 ECU (effective 1993). Gordon & Breach Science Publishers, 820 Town Center Dr., Langhorne, PA 19047. TEL 215-750-2642. FAX 215-750-6343. (UK subscr. to: P.O. Box 90, Reading, Berkshire RG 1 8JL, England. TEL 0734-560-080) Eds. Colin B. Brown, Paul W. Jowitt. adv.; bk.rev.; abstr.; bibl.; charts; illus.; stat.; index. (back issues avail.) **Indexed:** J.of Ferroc., Sel.Water Res.Abstr.
—BLDSC (3273.330000); UnCover; SWETS. **CCC.**
Description: Devoted to the discussion, dissemination, and development of systems techniques throughout the spectrum of civil engineering activity.

624   AT   ISSN 0156-2126
CIVIL ENGINEERING WORKING PAPERS. 1978. irreg. price varies. Monash University, Department of Civil Engineering, Wellington Rd., Clayton, Vic. 3168, Australia. TEL 03-565-4973. FAX 613-565-4944. (back issues avail.)
—BLDSC (3273.420000).
Description: Results of recent research in the Department of Civil Engineering.

ENGINEERING — CIVIL ENGINEERING

624   SW   ISSN 0348-6087
CIVILINGENJOEREN. 1954. m. (10/yr.). SEK 125 (effective 1990). Sveriges Civilingenjoersfoerbund, P.O. Box 1419, S-111 84 Stockholm, Sweden. Ed. Maarten af Ekenstam. bk.rev. circ. 40,000. (also avail. in audio cassette)
    Formerly: Civilingenjoersfoerbundets Tidskrift (ISSN 0009-8132)

627   JA   ISSN 0914-1065
COASTAL DEVELOPMENT. (Text in Japanese) 1984. s-a. Coastal Development Institute of Technology - Engan Kaihatsu Gijutsu Kenkyu, 3-16, Hayabusa-cho, Chiyoda-ku, Tokyo 102, Japan.

627   NE   ISSN 0378-3839
TC203   CODEN: COENDE
COASTAL ENGINEERING; an international journal for coastal, harbour, and offshore engineers. 1977. 12/yr. (in 3 vols., 4 nos./vol.) fl.1188($642) (effective 1994). Elsevier Science B.V., P.O. Box 211, 1000 AE Amsterdam, Netherlands. TEL 31-20-5803911. FAX 31-20-5803598. TELEX 18582 ESPA NL. (Subscr. in U.S. and Canada to: Elsevier Science Inc., Box 882, Madison Sq. Sta., New York, NY 10159. TEL 212-989-5800. FAX 212-633-3990) Ed. E.W. Bijker. (also avail. in microform from UMI; reprint service avail. from SWZ) Indexed: Appl.Mech.Rev., Br.Geol.Lit., Curr.Cont., Curr.Tit.Ocean., Deep Sea Res.& Oceanogr.Abstr., Environ.Abstr., Fluidex, Geo.Abstr., GeoRef., Geotech.Abstr., Ind.Sci.Rev., Ocean.Abstr., Petrol.Abstr., Risk Abstr., Sci.Cit.Ind., Sel.Water Res.Abstr. **Document type:** academic/scholarly publication.
  —BLDSC (3292.403000); EI; Faxon; UnCover; SWETS. **CCC.**
    Description: For engineers working in the field of marine and coastal technology.
    Refereed Serial

627   JA   ISSN 0578-5634
TC330   CODEN: CENJA8
COASTAL ENGINEERING IN JAPAN. (Text in English) 1958. s-a. 11000 Yen. Japan Society of Civil Engineers, Committee on Coastal Engineering - Doboku Gakkai Kaigan Kogaku Iinkai, Yotsuya 1-chome, Shinjuku-ku, Tokyo 160, Japan. TEL 03-373-7211. (Subscr. to: Maruzen Co., Ltd., Deport Dept., P.O. Box 5050, Tokyo International, 100-31 Tokyo, Japan) Indexed: Deep Sea Res.& Oceanogr.Abstr., Eng.Ind., Fluidex, Intl.Civil Eng.Abstr., JTA, Ocean.Abstr., Pollut.Abstr., Soft.Abstr.Eng.
  —BLDSC (3292.410000).

620   US
COASTAL ENGINEERING RESEARCH COUNCIL. PROCEEDINGS. 1954. biennial. price varies. American Society of Civil Engineers, 345 E. 47th St., New York, NY 10017-2398. TEL 212-705-7288. FAX 212-980-4681. Ed. Billy L. Edge. circ. 1,000. (back issues avail.; reprint service avail. from UMI) **Indexed:** GeoRef. **Document type:** academic/scholarly publication, proceedings.

624   SP
COLECCION DE RECOMENDACIONES Y MANUALES TECNICOS. irreg. (approx. 4/yr.). Colegio de Ingenieros de Caminos, Canales y Puertos, Almagro 42, 28010 Madrid, Spain. TEL 1-308-19-88. FAX 1-308-39-32.

624   SP
COLECCION SEINOR. irreg. (approx. 4/yr.). Colegio de Ingenieros de Caminos, Canales y Puertos, Almagro, 42, 28010 Madrid, Spain. TEL 1-308-19-88. FAX 1-308-39-32.

624   PR   ISSN 0010-0609
COLEGIO DE INGENIEROS ARQUITECTOS Y AGRIMENSORES DE PUERTO RICO. REVISTA.* (Text in English and Spanish) 1939? 4/yr. Insular Publishers Corp, Box GA, Caparra Heights, Puerto Rico, PR 00936. adv.; circ. 5,500 (controlled).

624   SP   ISSN 0010-0617
COLEGIO DE INGENIEROS DE CAMINOS, CANALES Y PUERTOS. BOLETIN DE INFORMACION. 1960. 11/yr. free. Colegio de Ingenieros de Caminos, Canales y Puertos, Almagro, 42, 28010 Madrid, Spain. TEL 1-308-19-88. FAX 1-308-39-32. bk.rev.; abstr. circ. 7,500.

624   SP
COLEGIO DE INGENIEROS DE CAMINOS, CANALES Y PUERTOS. COLECCION MONOGRAFIAS. irreg. (approx. 4/yr.). Colegio de Ingenieros de Caminos, Canales y Puertos, Almagro, 42, 28010 Madrid, Spain. TEL 1-308-19-88. FAX 1-308-39-32. **Document type:** monographic series.

COMMONWEALTH SCIENTIFIC AND INDUSTRIAL RESEARCH ORGANIZATION. DIVISION OF GEOMECHANICS. TECHNICAL REPORT. see *MINES AND MINING INDUSTRY*

COMMUNICATIONS IN APPLIED NUMERICAL METHODS. see *MATHEMATICS*

624 621   UK   ISSN 0263-8223
     CODEN: COMSE2
COMPOSITE STRUCTURES. 1983. 12/yr. (in 3 vols., 4 nos./vol.). £855($1315) (effective 1994). Elsevier Science Ltd., Oxford Fulfilment Centre, P.O. Box 800, Kidlington, Oxford OX5 1DX, England. TEL 44-865-843000. FAX 44-865-843010. (Subscr. in U.S. and Canada to: Elsevier Science, 660 White Plains Rd., Tarrytown, NY 10591-5153. TEL 914-524-9200. FAX 914-333-2444) Ed. Dr. I.H. Marshall. adv.; bk.rev.; charts; illus. (also avail. in microform from UMI; back issues avail.) Indexed: Appl.Mech.Rev., ASCA, Curr.Cont., Eng.Ind., Ind.Sci.Rev., Int.Aerosp.Abstr., Met.Abstr., Sci.Cit.Ind. **Document type:** academic/scholarly publication.
  —BLDSC (3364.970000); EI; Faxon; UnCover; SWETS. **CCC.**
    Description: Papers deal with design, research and development studies, experimental investigations, theoretical analysis and fabrication techniques relevant to the application of composites in load-bearing components for assemblies, ranging from individual components such as plates and shells to complete composite structures.
    Refereed Serial

526.9 625.72   SA
CONFERENCE OF SOUTH AFRICAN SURVEYORS. PROCEEDINGS/KONFERENSIE VAN SUID-AFRIKAANSE OPMETERS. VERRIGTINGE. quadrennial, 10th, Sun City, 1993. R.50. South African Council for Professional Land Surveyors and Technical Surveyors - Suid-Afrikaanse Raad vir Professionele Landmeters en Tegniese Opmeters, Registrar, P.O. Box 62041, Marshalltown 2107, South Africa. TEL 27-11-834-6431. FAX 27-11-836-8657. adv.; circ. 1,500 (paid). **Document type:** proceedings.
    Formerly: National Conference of South African Surveyors. Proceedings.

CONSTRUCAO REGIAO SUL. see *BUILDING AND CONSTRUCTION*

CONSTRUCAO RIO DE JANEIRO. see *BUILDING AND CONSTRUCTION*

CONSTRUCTION AND BUILDING MATERIALS. see *BUILDING AND CONSTRUCTION*

CONSTRUCTION AND CONTRACT NEWS. see *BUILDING AND CONSTRUCTION*

CONSTRUCTION AND ENGINEERING ZIMBABWE. see *BUILDING AND CONSTRUCTION*

CONSTRUCTION EQUIPMENT. see *BUILDING AND CONSTRUCTION*

CONSTRUCTION EQUIPMENT SPECIFICATIONS GUIDE. see *BUILDING AND CONSTRUCTION*

625.7   US
TE1   CODEN: HHCODD
CONSTRUCTION PRODUCTS. 1892. 6/yr. $40 (Canada $59; Mexico $55; elsewhere $60). Gordon Publications, Inc., Part of Cahners Publishing Company, Division of Reed Elsevier Inc., 301 Gibraltar Dr., Box 650, Morris Plains, NJ 07950. TEL 201-252-5100. FAX 201-539-3476. Ed. Dolly Gorbstein. adv.; bibl.; illus.; tr.lit. circ. 51,000. (tabloid format; also avail. in microform from UMI; reprint service avail. from UMI) Indexed: A.S.& T.Ind., Bus.Ind., Chem.Abstr., Dok.Str., Eng.Ind., Ind.Sci.Rev., Intl.Civil Eng.Abstr., Soft.Abstr.Eng., Tr.& Indus.Ind. **Document type:** trade publication.
  ●Also available online. Vendor(s): DIALOG Information Services, Inc.
  —BLDSC (3421.763500); EI; UnCover. **CCC.**
    Former titles (until 1992): Highway and Heavy Construction Products (ISSN 1062-5194); (until Jan.-Feb. 1991): Highway and Heavy Construction (ISSN 0362-0506); Roads and Streets (ISSN 0035-7340)
    Description: Covers the entire range of products for America's infrastructure, including machinery, material and management tools for contractors.

692.8   CN   ISSN 1182-0217
CONSTRUCTION RECORD. 1889. m. Can.$40.66($48) (foreign $75). Maclean-Hunter Ltd., 777 Bay St., Toronto, ON M5W 1A7, Canada. TEL 416-596-5839. Ed. Tim Tolton. adv.; bk.rev.; charts; illus.; mkt.; tr.lit.; index. circ. 24,269. Indexed: C.I.S. Abstr., Can.B.P.I., Chem.Abstr., Eng.Ind., Geotech.Abstr.
    Formerly: Engineering and Contract Record (ISSN 0013-7804); Incorporates: Canadian Pit and Quarry.

624   UK   ISSN 0141-5999
CONSTRUCTION TODAY. 1978. m. £59. (Institution of Civil Engineers) Thomas Telford Ltd., Thomas Telford House, 1 Heron Quay, London E14 4JD, England. TEL 071-987 6999. FAX 071-538-4656. TELEX 298105-CIVILS-G. Ed. Adrian Greeman. illus. Indexed: Cadscan, J.of Ferroc., Lead Abstr., Zincscan.
    Supersedes (as from 1985): New Civil Engineer International.
    Description: Contains news on international civil engineering and large scale building, projects, finance and planning, equipment.

624   UK   ISSN 0956-9189
TA1
CONSTRUCTION WEEKLY. 1906. w. £58($140) elsewhere $220. Morgan-Grampian (Construction Press) Ltd. (Subsidiary of: Morgan-Grampian plc), Morgan-Grampian House, 30 Calderwood St., London SE18 6QH, England. TEL 081-855-7777. FAX 081-854-7476 Ed. Richard Northcote. adv. contact: Mike Bernie. bk.rev.; abstr.; charts; illus.; mkt.; stat.; tr.lit.; index. circ. 30,463. (also avail. in microform from UMI) Indexed: A.S.& T.Ind., AESIS, Br.Ceram.Abstr., Br.Tech.Ind., C.R.I. Abstr., Cadscan, Concr.Abstr., Eng.Ind., Excerp.Med., Fluidex, Fuel & Energy Abstr., GeoRef, Geotech.Abstr., HRIS, Intl.Civil Eng.Abstr., J.of Ferroc., Lead Abstr., RICS, Risk Abstr., Soft.Abstr.Eng., W.R.C.Inf., Zincscan. **Document type:** trade publication.
  —BLDSC (3421.889500); EI; UnCover; SWETS. **CCC.**
    Incorporates: Construction Plant and Equipment; Which incorporated: Civil Engineering (ISSN 0305-6473); Which incorporated: Consulting Engineer (ISSN 0010-7093); Which was formerly: Civil Engineering and Public Works Review (ISSN 0262-5873); Which incorporated: Public Works Review.
    Description: Covers all matters related to British civil engineering.

CONSTRUCTOR. see *BUILDING AND CONSTRUCTION*

652.72 526.3   CN
CORPORATION OF BRITISH COLUMBIA LAND SURVEYORS. REPORT OF PROCEEDINGS. 1914. a. membership. Corporation of British Columbia Land Surveyors, 895 Fort St., Ste. 306, Victoria, BC V8W 1H7, Canada. TEL 604-382-4323. FAX 604-382-5092. circ. 500 (controlled). (back issues avail.) **Document type:** proceedings, academic/scholarly publication.

ENGINEERING — CIVIL ENGINEERING

624   IT   ISSN 0010-9665
COSTRUZIONI; tecnica ed organizzazione dei cantieri. 1952. m. L.120000 (foreign L.150000). Casa Editrice la Fiaccola (Milan), Via Ravizza 62, 20149 Milan, Italy. TEL 02-4814355. FAX 02-4814834. TELEX 335512 COSTRU I. Ed. G. Saronni. adv.; charts; illus.; stat. circ. 8,000. **Indexed:** C.I.S. Abstr.

624   IT   ISSN 0010-9673
COSTRUZIONI METALLICHE; rivista dei tecnici dell'acciaio. (Text in English and Italian) 1949. bi-m. L.74000($75) (effective Jan. 1994). Associazione fra i Costruttori in Acciaio Italiani, Viale Abruzzi, 66, 20131 Milan, Italy. TEL 02-29513413. FAX 02-29529824. Ed. Giuseppe Coppadoro. adv.; bk.rev.; abstr.; bibl.; charts; illus.; index. circ. 3,300. **Indexed:** Intl.Civil Eng.Abstr., Met.Abstr., Soft.Abstr.Eng., World Alum.Abstr.
 Description: Covers construction science and technique, connections, materials, wleding, fireproofing, and regulations.

COUNTRY ROADS AND CITY STREETS. see TRANSPORTATION — Roads And Traffic

CURRENT TOPICS IN TRANSPORT. see TRANSPORTATION — Roads And Traffic

624   GW   ISSN 0173-6280
TA501
D V W HESSEN MITTEILUNGEN. (Text in German; summaries in English and German) 1949. s-a. DM.5. Deutscher Verein fuer Vermessungswesen e.V., Postfach 2240, 65012 Wiesbaden, Germany. TEL 0611-535241. FAX 0611-535309. bk.rev. circ. 1,350. **Document type:** bulletin.
 Description: Covers all aspects of surveying.

624   JA   ISSN 0915-7093
DAINIPPON DOBOKU GIJUTSU KENKYUJOHO/DAI NIPPON CONSTRUCTION. TECHNICAL REPORT. (Text in Japanese; summaries in English, Japanese) 1989. a. Dainippon Doboku K.K. Gijutsu Kenkyujo - Dai Nippon Construction Co., Ltd., Research and Development Center, 56-2, Minamimachi 3-chome, Higashiyamato-shi, Tokyo 189, Japan. **Document type:** academic/scholarly publication.

624   JA   ISSN 0289-9639
DAMU GIJUTSU/ENGINEERING FOR DAMS. (Text in Japanese) 1983. m. 1000 Yen per no. Damu Gijutsu Senta - Japan Dam Engineering Center, 4-5, Azabudai 2-chome, Minato-ku, Tokyo 106, Japan.

624   JA   ISSN 0917-3145
DAMU KOGAKU/DAM ENGINEERING. (Text in Japanese; summaries in English) 1991. q. Damu Kogaku Kenkyukai - Japan Society of Dam Engineers, Damu Gijutsu Senta, 4-5, Azabudai 2-chome, Minato-ku, Tokyo 106, Japan. **Document type:** academic/scholarly publication.

624   JA
DAMU NENKAN/YEARBOOK OF DAMS. a. 20600 Yen. Nihon Damu Kyokai - Japan Dam Foundation, 14-2, Ginza 2-chome, Chuo-ku, Tokyo 104, Japan. TEL 03-3545-8361. FAX 03-3545-5055.

624   JA   ISSN 0011-5967
DAMU NIPPON/DAM DIGEST. (Text in Japanese) 1950. m. 1030 Yen per no. Nihon Damu Kyokai - Japan Dam Foundation, 14-2, Ginza 2-chome, Chuo-ku, Tokyo 104, Japan. TEL 03-3545-8361. FAX 03-3545-5055.

625.7 526.9   DK   ISSN 0011-6548
DANSK VEJTIDSSKRIFT.* 1923. m. DKK 174.35. Dansk Vejtidsskrift, Lingby, Denmark. Ed. A.O. Haugaard. adv. circ. 1,803. **Indexed:** Dok.Str., Geotech.Abstr.

624   US
DEEP FOUNDATIONS NEWS. 1977. q. membership. Deep Foundations Institute, 49 Woodport Rd., Sparta, NJ 07871. TEL 201-729-9679. FAX 201-729-0732. Ed. G. Robert Compton Jr. bk.rev.; circ. 1,000 (controlled). **Document type:** newsletter.

624 621.381   JA
DENSANKI RIYO NI KANSURU SHINPOJUMU KOENGAIYO/SYMPOSIUM OF COMPUTER RESEARCH. PROCEEDINGS. (Text in Japanese; summaries in English) 1976. a. price varies. Doboku Gakkai, Doboku Joho Shisutemu linkai - Japan Society of Civil Engineers, Mubanchi, Yotsuya 1-chome, Shinjuku-ku, Tokyo 160, Japan. (Subscr. to: JSCE or Mazuren Co., Ltd., P.O. Box 5050, Tokyo International 100-31, Japan) circ. 350. (back issues avail.) **Document type:** proceedings.

DESARROLLO NACIONAL. see PUBLIC ADMINISTRATION

624   NE
DEVELOPMENTS IN CIVIL ENGINEERING. 1979. irreg., vol.43, 1994. price varies. Elsevier Science B.V., Books Division, P.O. Box 211, 1000 AE Amsterdam, Netherlands. TEL 31-20-5803911. FAX 31-20-5803705. TELEX 18582 ESPA NL. (Subscr. in U.S. and Canada to: Elsevier Science Inc., Box 882, Madison Sq. Sta., New York, NY 10159. TEL 212-989-5800) (back issues avail.) **Document type:** monographic series.
 Refereed Serial

624.151   NE   ISSN 0165-1250
DEVELOPMENTS IN GEOTECHNICAL ENGINEERING. (Text in English) 1972. irreg., vol.75, 1994. price varies. Elsevier Science B.V., Books Division, P.O. Box 211, 1000 AE Amsterdam, Netherlands. TEL 31-20-5803911. FAX 31-20-5803705. TELEX 18582 ESPA NL. (Subscr. in U.S. and Canada to: Elsevier Science Inc., Box 882, Madison Sq. Sta., New York, NY 10159. TEL 212-989-5800) (back issues avail.) **Indexed:** Geotech.Abstr. **Document type:** monographic series.
 —BLDSC (3579.073000). **CCC**.
 Refereed Serial

624   UK   ISSN 0953-0916
DIAL BUILDING. a. Dial Industry Publications (Subsidiary of: Reed Information Services), Windsor Court, East Grinstead House, E. Grinstead, W. Sussex RH19 1XA, England. TEL 0342-326972. FAX 0342-335612. TELEX 95127-INFSER-G. **Document type:** trade publication.
 Formerly: Dial Industry. Building (ISSN 0265-9913)

624   JA   ISSN 0913-4921
DOBOKU GAKKAI HOKKAIDO SHIBU RONBUN HOKOKUSHU/JAPAN SOCIETY OF CIVIL ENGINEERS. HOKKAIDO BRANCH. RESEARCH REPORTS AT THE ANNUAL MEETING. (Text in English, Japanese) 1950. a. 4000 Yen. Doboku Gakkai Hokkaido Shibu, Nishi 2-chome, Minami 1-jo, Chuo-ku, Sapporo-shi, Hokkaido 060, Japan. **Document type:** academic/scholarly publication.

624   JA   ISSN 0285-7324
DOBOKU GAKKAI KANSAI SHIBU NENJI GAKUJUTSU KOENK AI KOEN GAIYO/JAPAN SOCIETY OF CIVIL ENGINEERS. KANSAI BRANCH. PROCEEDINGS OF ANNUAL CONFERENCE ON CIVIL ENGINEERS. (Text in Japanese) 1959. a. Doboku Gakkai Kansai Shibu, 1-4-409 Senba Chuo 2-chome, Chuo-ku, Osaka-shi, Osaka 541, Japan. **Document type:** proceedings.

624   JA
DOBOKU GAKKAI NENJI KOENKAI KOEN GAIYOSHU/JAPAN SOCIETY OF CIVIL ENGINEERS. PROCEEDINGS OF THE ANNUAL CONFERENCE. 1937. a. Doboku Gakkai - Japan Society of Civil Engineers, Mubanchi, Yotsua 1-chome, Shinjuku-ku, Tokyo 160, Japan. TEL 03-355-2441. circ. 4,850. **Document type:** proceedings.

624   JA   ISSN 0289-7806
DOBOKU GAKKAI RONBUNSHU/JAPAN SOCIETY OF CIVIL ENGINEERS. PROCEEDINGS. (Text in English and Japanese; summaries in English) 1944. m. Doboku Gakkai - Japan Society of Civil Engineers, Mubanchi, Yotsuya 1-Chome, Shinjuku-ku, Tokyo 160, Japan. TEL 03-272-7211. (Dist. by: Maruzen Co., Ltd., P.O. Box 5050, Tokyo International 100-31, Japan) circ. 28,300. **Indexed:** Concr.Abstr., Eng.Ind., INIS Atomind., INIS Atomind. **Document type:** proceedings.
 —BLDSC (6742.300000).

624   JA   ISSN 0021-468X
DOBOKU GAKKAISHI/JAPAN SOCIETY OF CIVIL ENGINEERS. JOURNAL. (Text in Japanese; contents page in English) 1914. m. 1500 Yen per no. Japan Society of Civil Engineers - Doboku Gakkai, Yotsuya 1-chome, Shinjuku-ku, Tokyo 160, Japan. Ed. Junichi Yagi. adv.; bk.rev.; bibl.; illus.; mkt.; circ. controlled. **Indexed:** Concr.Abstr., Eng.Ind., Geotech.Abstr., INIS Atomind., J.of Ferroc., JTA, Met.Abstr., W.R.C.Inf.
 —BLDSC (4807.000000); EI.

624   JA   ISSN 0285-5046
DOBOKU GIJUTSU/CIVIL ENGINEERING. (Text in Japanese) 1922. m. 850 Yen per no. Doboku Gijutsusha, 8-19, Fujimi 1-chome, Chiyoda-ku, Tokyo 102, Japan. **Indexed:** INIS Atomind.

624   JA   ISSN 0386-5886
DOBOKU GIJUTSU SHIRYO/CIVIL ENGINEERING JOURNAL. (Text in Japanese) 1959. m. 1000 Yen per no. Dobboku Gijutsu Center, 7-2, Taito 1-chome, Taito-ku, Tokyo 110, Japan. Ed. Takashi Iijima. adv. contact: Tutomu Yanagida. **Indexed:** INIS Atomind. **Document type:** proceedings.

624   JA   ISSN 0915-5333
DOBOKU JOHO SHISUTEMU SHINPOJUMU KOENSHU/SYMPOSIUM ON ENGINEERING PROCESSING SYSTEM. PROCEEDINGS. (Text in English, Japanese; summaries in English) 1976. a. Doboku Gakkai, Doboku Joho Shisutemu - Japan Society of Civil Engineers, Committee of System for Civil Engineering Information, Yotsuya 1-chome, Shinjuku-ku, Tokyo 160, Japan. **Document type:** proceedings.

624   JA   ISSN 0913-4026
DOBOKU KEIKAKUGAKU KENKYU KOENSHU/PROCEEDINGS OF INFRASTRUCTURE PLANNING. (Text in English, Japanese; summaries in English) 1979. a. 8000 Yen. Doboku Gakkai - Japan Society of Civil Engineers, Yotsuya 1-chome, Shinjuku-ku, Tokyo 160, Japan. **Document type:** proceedings.
 Supersedes in part (in 1984): Doboku Keikakugaku Kenkyu Happyokai Koenshu (ISSN 0913-4166)

624   JA   ISSN 0913-4034
DOBOKU KEIKAKUGAKU KENYU RONBUNSHU/INFRASTRUCTURE PLANNING REVIEW. (Text in Japanese; summaries in English) 1979. a. 8000 Yen. Doboku Gakkai - Japan Society of Civil Engineers, Yotsuya 1-chome, Shinjuku-ku, Tokyo 160, Japan. **Document type:** academic/scholarly publication.
 Supersedes in part (in 1984): Doboku Keikakugaku Kenkyu Happyokai Koenshu (ISSN 0913-4166)

624   JA   ISSN 0913-4050
DOBOKU KEIKAKUGAKU SHINPOJUMU/SYMPOSIUM ON CIVIL ENGINEERING PLANNING. PROCEEDINGS. 1967. a. price varies. Doboku Gakkai - Japan Society of Civil Engineers, Yotsuya 1-chome, Shinjuku-ku, Tokyo 160, Japan. TEL 03-272-7211. (Subscr. to: Maruzen Co., Ltd., P.O. Box 5050, Tokyo International 100-31, Japan) (back issues avail.) **Document type:** proceedings.

624   JA
DOBOKU KENCHIKU GYOSEI NO GAIYO/PUBLIC WORKS AND CONSTRUCTIONS IN OITA PREFECTURE. OUTLINE. (Text in Japanese) a. Oitaken Doboku Kenchikubu - Oita Prefectural Government, Civil Engineering and Building Division, 1-1, Ote-machi 3-chome, Oita-shi, Oita-ken 870, Japan.

624   JA   ISSN 0386-4995
DOBOKU KENKYUJO HOKOKU/PUBLIC WORKS RESEARCH INSTITUTE. REPORT. (Text in Japanese; summaries in Japanese, English) 1925. irreg. Kensetsusho Doboku Kenkyujo - Ministry of Construction, Public Works Research Institute, 1, Asahi, Tsukuba-shi, Ibaraki-ken 305, Japan. **Document type:** academic/scholarly publication.
 —BLDSC (7585.260000).

624   JA   ISSN 0386-586X
DOBOKU KENKYUJO IHO/PUBLIC WORKS RESEARCH INSTITUTE. TECHNICAL NOTE. (Text in Japanese; summaries in English, Japanese) 1937. irreg. Kensetsusho Doboku Kenkyujo - Ministry of Construction, Public Works Research Institute, 1, Asahi, Tsukuba-shi, Ibaraki-ken 305, Japan.
 —BLDSC (8678.068000).

ENGINEERING — CIVIL ENGINEERING

624   JA
DOBOKU KENKYUJO KENKYU HAPPYOKAI RONBUNSHU/PUBLIC WORKS RESEARCH INSTITUTE. PROCEEDINGS OF MEETING. (Text in Japanese) a. Kensetsusho Doboku Kenkyujo - Ministry of Construction, Public Works Research Institute, 1, Asahi, Tsukuba-shi, Ibaraki-ken 305, Japan. **Document type:** proceedings.

624   JA
DOBOKU KENKYUJO KOENKAI KOENSHU/PUBLIC WORKS RESEARCH INSTITUTE. PROCEEDINGS. (Text in Japanese) Kensetsusho Doboku Kenkyujo - Ministry of Construction, Public Works Research Institute, 1, Asahi, Tsukuba-shi, Ibaraki-ken 305, Japan. **Document type:** government publication, proceedings.

624   JA   ISSN 0419-4926
DOBOKU KENKYUJO NENPO/PUBLIC WORKS RESEARCH INSTITUTE. ANNUAL REPORT. (Text in Japanese) 1940. a. Ministry of Construction, Public Works Research Institute, 1, Asahi, Tsukuba-shi, Ibaraki-ken 305, Japan. abstr. **Indexed:** INIS Atomind. **Document type:** government publication.

624   JA   ISSN 0386-5878
DOBOKU KENKYUJO SHIRYO/PUBLIC WORKS RESEARCH INSTITUTE. TECHNICAL MEMORANDUM. (Text in English, Japanese; summaries in Japanese) 1964. irreg. Kensetsusho Doboku Kenkyujo - Ministry of Construction, Public Works Research Institute, 1, Asahi, Tsukuba-shi, Ibaraki-ken 305, Japan. **Document type:** government publication.

624   ISSN 0387-0790
DOBOKU SEKO/CIVIL ENGINEERING JOURNAL. (Text in Japanese) 1960. m. 910 Yen per no. Sankaido, 5-18, Hongo 5-chome, Bunkyo-ku, Tokyo 113, Japan. **Indexed:** INIS Atomind.

624   JA
DOBOKUBU GAIYO/JAPAN. SHIZUOKA PREFECTURAL GOVERNMENT. CIVIL ENGINEERING DIVISION. ANNUAL REPORT. (Text in Japanese) a. Shizuoka Prefectural Government, Civil Engineering Division, 9-6, Ote-machi, Shizuoka-shi, Shizuoka-ken 420, Japan. stat. **Document type:** government publication.

624   JA   ISSN 0916-7293
DOBOKUSHI KENKYU/HISTORICAL STUDIES IN CIVIL ENGINEERING. (Text in Japanese; summaries in English, Japanese) 4000 Yen. Doboku Gakkai - Japan Society of Civil Engineers, Yotsuya 1-chome, Shinjuku-ku, Tokyo 160, Japan. **Document type:** academic/scholarly publication.

624 388.31   JA
DOROKYO NENPO/ANNUAL REPORT OF ROAD BRIDGES. (Text in Japanese) a. 6180 Yen. Nihon Doro Kyokai - Japan Road Association, 3-1, Kasumigaseki 3-chome, Chiyoda-ku, Tokyo 100, Japan.

624   JA
DOSHITSU KISO KOGAKU RAIBURARI/SOIL MECHANICS AND FOUNDATION ENGINEERING LIBRARY. (Text in Japanese) a. 5100 Yen. Doshitsu Kogakkai - Japanese Society of Soil Mechanics and Foundation Engineering, 2-23, Kanda Awaji-cho 2-chome, Chiyoda-ku, Tokyo 101, Japan.

624   JA
DOSHITSU KISO NI KANSURU SHOMONDAI TO KAIKETSUSAKU KOSHUKAI KOEN SHIRYO/SEMINAR ON MISCELLANEOUS PROBLEMS AND BREAKTHROUGHS OF SOIL MECHANICS AND FOUNDATION ENGINEERING. PROCEEDINGS. (Text in Japanese) a. 2600 Yen. Doshitsu Kogakkai - Japanese Society of Soil Mechanics and Foundation Engineering, 2-23, Kanda Awaji-cho 2-chome, Chiyoda-ku, Tokyo 101, Japan.

624   JA
DOSHITSU KOGAKKAI. HOKKAIDO SHIBU. GIJUTSU HOKOKUSHU/JAPANESE SOCIETY OF SOIL MECHANICS AND FOUNDATION ENGINEERING. HOKKAIDO BRANCH. RESEARCH REPORT. (Text in Japanese) a. 2000 Yen. Doshitsu Kogakkai, Hokkaido Shibu, Nishi 2-chome, Minami 1-jo, Chuo-ku, Sapporo-shi, Hokkaido 060, Japan. **Document type:** academic/scholarly publication.

624.176   JA   ISSN 0385-1621
TA710.A1
DOSHITSU KOGAKKAI RONBUN HOKOKUSHU/JAPANESE SOCIETY OF SOIL MECHANICS AND FOUNDATION ENGINEERING. JOURNAL. (Text in Japanese, English; summaries in English) 1860. q. 3400 Yen. Doshitsu Kogakkai - Japanese Society of Soil Mechanics and Foundation Engineering, 2-23, Kanda Awaji-cho 2-chome, Chiyoda-ku, Tokyo 101, Japan. Ed.Bd. adv.; charts; illus.; cum.index. circ. 1,600. —BLDSC (8327.030000).

624   ISSN 0285-7340
DOSHITSU KOGAKU KENKYU HAPPYOKAI HAPPYO KOENSHU/JAPAN NATIONAL CONFERENCE ON SOIL MECHANICS AND FOUNDATION ENGINEERING. PROCEEDINGS. (Text in English, Japanese) 1966. a. 10000 Yen. Doshitsu Kogakkai - Japanese Society of Soil Mechanics and Foundation Engineering, 2-23, Kanda Awaji-cho 2-chome, Chiyoda-ku, Tokyo 101, Japan. **Document type:** academic/scholarly publication.

624   JA
DOSHITSU KOGAKU SHINPOJUMU HAPPYO RONBUNSHU/SYMPOSIUM ON SOIL MECHANICS AND FOUNDATION ENGINEERING. PROCEEDINGS. (Text in English, Japanese) 1955. a. 3300 Yen. Doshitsu Kogakkai - Japanese Society of Soil Mechanics and Foundation Engineering, 2-23, Kanda Awaji-cho 2-chome, Chiyoda-ku, Tokyo 101, Japan. **Document type:** proceedings.

DREDGING CONTRACT NEWS. see *ENGINEERING — Hydraulic Engineering*

DREDGING SEMINAR. PROCEEDINGS. see *WATER RESOURCES*

624 614   US   ISSN 8755-3457
DRINKING WATER & BACKFLOW PREVENTION. 1984. m. $32.50 (Canada and Mexico $46.50; elsewhere $50). Asay & Associates, Box 33209, Northglenn, CO 80233. TEL 303-451-0978. FAX 303-452-9776. Ed. Kristi M. James. adv.; bk.rev.; circ. 2,800 (paid). (back issues avail.) **Document type:** trade publication.
Formerly: Backflow Prevention.
Description: Dedicated to water system safety everywhere.

625.7 624.2   PL   ISSN 0012-6357
DROGOWNICTWO. 1946. m. $18. Stowarzyszenie Inzynierow i Technikow Komunikacji (SITK), Ul. Czackiego 3-5, 00-043 Warsaw, Poland. TEL 48-22-262887. (Dist. by: Ars Polona- Ruch, Krakowskie Przedmiescie 7, Warsaw, Poland) Ed. Czeslaw Krzywosz. bk.rev.; bibl.; charts; illus.; index. circ. 1,380. **Indexed:** Chem.Abstr., Geotech.Abstr.

E C A MAGAZINE. (Engineering Contractors' Association) see *BUILDING AND CONSTRUCTION*

624   US
E C A PUBLICATION. 1965. m. $10 to non-members; includes Annual Directory & Buyer's Guide. Engineering Contractors' Association, 8310 Florence Ave., Downey, CA 90240. TEL 213-861-0929. FAX 213-923-6179. Ed. John Simpson. adv. circ. 3,000.
Formerly: U E C A Publication (ISSN 0049-5166)

624   US   ISSN 0739-7704
E E R C NEWS. 1977. q. free. University of California at Berkeley, Earthquake Engineering Research Center, 1301 S. 46th St., Richmond, CA 94804-4698. TEL 510-231-9554. FAX 510-231-9461. Ed. Ruth C. Wrentmore. circ. 5,000. (back issues avail.) **Document type:** newsletter.
Description: Publishes news and new developments in the field of earthquake engineering.

624   US   ISSN 0271-0323
E E R C REPORTS. a. $325 (foreign $325-$575). University of California at Berkeley, Earthquake Engineering Research Center, 1301 S. 46th St., Richmond, CA 94804-4698. TEL 510-231-9468. FAX 510-231-9471. Ed. Carol Cameron. **Document type:** monographic series.

624   US   ISSN 0891-9526
TA1   CODEN: ENRRE5
E N R. 1874. w. $65 (Europe $128; elsewhere $144). McGraw-Hill, Inc., 1221 Ave. of the Americas, New York, NY 10020. TEL 212-512-2000. (Subscr. to: Box 516, Hightstown, NJ 08520) Ed. Howard B. Stussman. adv.; bk.rev.; charts; illus.; mkt.; stat.; tr.lit.; s-a. index. circ. 95,134. (also avail. in microfilm from UMI; microfiche from CIS; reprint service avail. from UMI) **Indexed:** A.S.& T.Ind., ABI Inform., Alt.Press Ind., B.P.I., BPIA, Bus.Ind., Chem.Abstr., Concr.Abstr., Eng.Ind., Excerp.Med., Geotech.Abstr., HRIS, Ind.Sci.Rev., INIS Atomind., Intl.Civil Eng.Abstr., J.of Ferroc., Key to Econ.Sci., Met.Abstr., Ocean.Abstr., Petrol.Abstr., Pollut.Abstr., PROMT, RICS, Search (1988-), Sel.Water Res.Abstr., Soft.Abstr.Eng., SRI, Tr.& Indus.Ind., World Alum.Abstr.
●Also available online. Vendor(s): DIALOG Information Services, Inc. (File no.624/McGRAW-HILL PUBLICATIONS ONLINE), Dow Jones News Retrieval (ENR), Mead Data Central, Inc. (ENR), NewsNet (BC06).
—BLDSC (3775.930000); EI; UnCover; SWETS; UMI. **CCC.**
Formerly: Engineering News-Record (ISSN 0013-807X)
Description: Reports on all categories of construction from around the world.

624 690   AT   ISSN 0314-4224
EARTHMOVER AND CIVIL CONTRACTOR. 1963. m. $60 (effective 1994). (Australian Earthmovers and Road Contractors Federation, Inc.) E P S Press Pty. Ltd., P.O. Box 65, Newtown, N.S.W. 2042, Australia. TEL 61-2-565-1666. FAX 61-2-565-1697. Ed. Mark Cherrington. adv.; B&W page Aus.$1455, color page $Aus.2620; adv. contact: Phil Arane. bk.rev. circ. 7,090. **Indexed:** Aus.Rd.Ind. **Document type:** trade publication.
Formerly: Earthmovers.
Description: Covers the civil construction industry. For earthmoving contractors, local government and state construction agencies throughout Australia.

624.151   UK   ISSN 0098-8847
TA654.6   CODEN: IJEEBG
EARTHQUAKE ENGINEERING AND STRUCTURAL DYNAMICS. 1972. 12/yr. $995 (effective 1994). (International Association for Earthquake Engineering) John Wiley & Sons Ltd., Journals, Baffins Ln., Chichester, Sussex PO19 1UD, England. TEL 0243-779777. FAX 0243-775878. TELEX 86290-WIBOOK-G. Ed.Bd. bk.rev.; charts; illus.; index. (reprint service avail. from ISI,SWZ,UMI) **Indexed:** A.S.& T.Ind., Abstr.J.Earthq.Eng., Appl.Mech.Rev., C.R.I. Abstr., Cadscan, Curr.Cont., Eng.Ind., Environ.Abstr., Fluidex, Geo.Abstr., GeoRef., Ind.Sci.Rev., INIS Atomind., Intl.Civil Eng.Abstr., J.of Ferroc., Lead Abstr., Ref.Zh., Risk Abstr., Sci.Abstr., Sci.Cit.Ind., Sel.Water Res.Abstr., Sh.& Vib.Dig., Soft.Abstr.Eng., Zincscan. **Document type:** academic/scholarly publication.
—BLDSC (3643.575000); Faxon; UnCover; SWETS; UMI. **CCC.**
Description: Provides a forum for the publication of papers on all aspects of engineering related to earthquakes and other types of dynamic loading.

624 690   JA   ISSN 0289-5617
EHIMEKEN KENSETSU KENKYUJO KENKYUJOHO/EHIMEKEN CONSTRUCTION LABORATORY. REPORT. (Text in Japanese) 1957. a. Ehimeken Kensetsu Kenkyujo - Ehimeken Construction Laboratory, 440, Higashiishii-machi, Mtsuyama-shi, Ehime-ken 790, Japan. **Document type:** academic/scholarly publication.

624   XO   ISSN 0013-3108
EKONOMIKA STAVEBNICTVA/ECONOMICS OF CIVIL ENGINEERING. (Text in Czech or Slovak; summaries in English, German) 1951. m. 108 Kcs.($30) Ustav Ekonomiky a Organizacie Stavebnictva - Institute of Economics and Organization of Building Industry, Ruzova Dolina 27, 024 69 Bratislava, Slovakia. (Dist. by: Slovart, nam. Slobody 6, 817 64 Bratislava, Slovakia) adv.; charts; illus.; pat. circ. 3,200.

625.7   GW
ELSNERS HANDBUCH FUER STRASSENWESEN. 1937. a. DM.28.40. Otto Elsner Verlagsgesellschaft, Schoefferstr. 15, 64295 Darmstadt, Germany. Ed. E.W. Goerner. adv. circ. 12,500.
Formerly: Elsner: Handbuch fuer Strassenbau und Strassenverkehrstechnik (ISSN 0071-0067)

ENGINEERING — CIVIL ENGINEERING

ENERGIA ELETTRICA. see *ENGINEERING — Electrical Engineering*

624   BL
ENGENHARIA CIVIL. 1917. m. $65. SM2 - Empresa Journalistica Ltda., Rua Capitao Prudente, 160, 05422 Sao Paulo, Brazil. Ed. M.R. Carrill. adv.; bk.rev.; illus. circ. 15,000.
    Supersedes in part: Engenharia (ISSN 0013-7707); Which was formerly (until 1941): Instituto de Engenharia. Boletim (ISSN 0100-9885).

628   BL
ENGENHARIA SANITARIA. 1962. q. A B E S, Av. Beira-Mar, 216-13 andar, 20021 Rio de Janeiro, RJ, Brazil. FAX 021-262-6838. TELEX 021-31902. Ed. Antonio Romani. adv. circ. 12,000.

624.151   NE   ISSN 0013-7952
TA705   CODEN: EGGOAO
ENGINEERING GEOLOGY; an international journal. (Text in English, French, German) 1965. 12/yr. (in 3 vols.; 4 nos./vol.) fl.1203($650) (effective 1994). Elsevier Science B.V., P.O. Box 211, 1000 AE Amsterdam, Netherlands. TEL 31-20-5803911. FAX 31-20-5803598. TELEX 18582 ESPA NL. (Subscr. in U.S. and Canada to: Elsevier Science Inc., Box 882, Madison Sq. Sta., New York, NY 10159-0882. TEL 212-989-5800. FAX 212-633-3990) Eds. W.R. Judd, E.L. Krinitzsky. adv.; bk.rev.; bibl.; charts; illus.; index. (also avail. in microform from UMI; back issues avail.) **Indexed:** Abstr.J.Earthq.Eng., AESIS, Appl.Mech.Rev., Br.Geol.Lit., Bull.Signal., Chem.Abstr., Curr.Cont., Deep Sea Res.& Oceanogr.Abstr., Eng.Ind., Excerp.Med., Geo.Abstr., GeoRef., Geotech.Abstr., HRIS, Ind.Sci.Rev., INIS Atomind., Petrol.Abstr., Pollut.Abstr., Saf.Sci.Abstr., Sci.Cit.Ind., Sel.Water Res.Abstr. **Document type:** academic/scholarly publication.
—BLDSC (3761.450000); EI; Faxon; UnCover; SWETS; CASDDS. **CCC.**
    Incorporates (in 1992): Mining Science and Technology (ISSN 0167-9031)
    Description: Publishes original studies, case histories, and comprehensive reviews in the field of engineering geology.
Refereed Serial

624.151 550   US
CODEN: EGSSBT
ENGINEERING GEOLOGY & GEOTECHNICAL ENGINEERING SYMPOSIUM. PROCEEDINGS. 1963. a. price varies. Engineering Geology & Geotechnical Engineering Symposium, Box 8371, Pocatello, ID 83201. TEL 208-236-3273. FAX 208-236-4538. circ. 325. **Indexed:** HRIS. **Document type:** proceedings.
—CASDDS.
    Former titles: Engineering Geology and Soils Engineering Symposium. Proceedings (ISSN 0071-0318); Engineering Geology Symposium. Proceedings.

624   US   ISSN 0013-8029
TA684   CODEN: EJASAR
ENGINEERING JOURNAL. 1964. q. $15 (foreign $18). American Institute of Steel Construction, Inc., One E. Wacker Dr., Ste. 3100, Chicago, IL 60601-2001. TEL 312-670-2400. FAX 312-670-5403. TELEX 910-350-6816. (Subscr. to: Box 806276, Chicago, IL 60680-4124) charts; illus.; index, cum.index. circ. 10,500. (also avail. in microform from UMI; back issues avail.; reprint service avail. from UMI) **Indexed:** A.S.& T.Ind., Abstr.J.Earthq.Eng., Appl.Mech.Rev., Eng.Ind., Fuel & Energy Abstr., HRIS, INIS Atomind., J.of Ferroc., Sci.Abstr.
—BLDSC (3764.005000); EI; Faxon; UnCover; UMI.

624   UK   ISSN 0141-0296
TA630   CODEN: ENSTDF
ENGINEERING STRUCTURES; the journal of earthquake, wind and ocean engineering. 1979. bi-m. £235 in UK and Europe; elsewhere £250. Butterworth - Heinemann (Subsidiary of: Reed International PLC), Linacre House, Jordan Hill, Oxford OX2 8DP, England. TEL 0865-310366. FAX 0865-310898. TELEX 83111 BHPOXF G. (Subscr. to: Turpin Transactions Ltd., Distribution Centre, Blackhorse Rd., Letchworth, Herts SG6 1HN, England. TEL 0462-672555) Eds. P.L. Gould, A.E. Long. adv.; bk.rev.; abstr.; bibl.; charts; illus.; stat.; index. (also avail. in microform from UMI; back issues avail.) **Indexed:** Abstr.J.Earthq.Eng., Appl.Mech.Rev., BMT, C.R.I. Abstr., Concr.Abstr., Curr.Cont., Deep Sea Res.& Oceanogr.Abstr., Fluidex, Ind.Sci.Rev., J.of Ferroc., Met.Abstr., Risk Abstr., Sci.Cit.Ind., Sh.& Vib.Dig., World Alum.Abstr. **Document type:** academic/scholarly publication.
—BLDSC (3770.032000); EI; Faxon; UnCover; SWETS; UMI. **CCC.**
    Description: Features theoretical and applied coverage of the dynamic effects of wind, earthquakes and waves, and of analytical methods of computing structural responses to these loadings.
Refereed Serial

ENGINEERS NEWS. see *LABOR UNIONS*

624   US
ENGINEERS NEWS REPORT. 1956. m. membership. International Union of Operating Engineers, Local 428, 1426 N. First St., Phoenix, AZ 85004. TEL 602-254-5266. FAX 602-257-8674. Ed. William Rucker. circ. 3,500 (controlled). **Document type:** newspaper.

ENTORNO. see *BUILDING AND CONSTRUCTION*

ENTREPRISE EUROPEENNE. see *BUILDING AND CONSTRUCTION*

EXCAVATING CONTRACTOR. see *BUILDING AND CONSTRUCTION*

388.4   GW   ISSN 0341-356X
FLIESEN UND PLATTEN. 1950. m. DM.205 (foreign DM.217). (Fachverband des Deutschen Fliesengewerbes) Verlagsgesellschaft Rudolf Mueller GmbH, Stolberger Str. 84, 50933 Cologne, Germany. TEL 0221-5497-221. FAX 0221-5497326. (Subscr. to: Postfach 410949, 50869 Cologne, Germany) Ed. Sabine Borgard. adv.; B&W page DM.4800, color page DM.8850; trim 188 x 267. illus. circ. 12,752. **Indexed:** Br.Ceram.Abstr. **Document type:** trade publication.

625.7 016   GW   ISSN 0340-3998
FORSCHUNG IM STRASSENWESEN. 1972. irreg. DM.50. Forschungsgesellschaft fuer Strassen- und Verkehrswesen, Postfach 501362, 50973 Cologne, Germany. TEL 0221-397035. FAX 0221-393747. Ed. Herbert Kuehn. bibl. circ. 3,000. **Document type:** trade publication.

624   GW   ISSN 0341-5872
FORSCHUNGSARBEITEN AUS DEM STRASSENWESEN. SCHRIFTENREIHE. 1952. irreg. price varies. (Forschungsgesellschaft fuer Strassen und Verkehrswesen) Kirschbaum Verlag GmbH, Siegriedstr. 28, 53179 Bonn, Germany. TEL 0228-95453-0. FAX 0228-9545327. (Subscr. to: Postfach 210209, 53157 Bonn, Germany) **Indexed:** Dok.Str. **Document type:** monographic series.

625.8   GW
FORSCHUNGSGESELLSCHAFT FUER STRASSEN- UND VERKEHRSWESEN. ARBEITSGRUPPE ASPHALT- UND TEERSTRASSEN. SCHRIFTENREIHE. 1948. irreg. price varies. (Forschungsgesellschaft fuer Strassen-und Verkehrswesen) Kirschbaum Verlag GmbH, Siegriedstr. 28, 53179 Bonn, Germany. TEL 0228-95453-0. FAX 0228-9545327. (Subscr. to: Postfach 210209, 53157 Bonn, Germany) **Document type:** monographic series.
    Formerly: Forschungsgesellschaft fuer das Strassenwesen. Arbeitsgruppe Asphalt- und Teerstrassen. Schriftenreihe (ISSN 0426-9918)

625.8   GW
FORSCHUNGSGESELLSCHAFT FUER STRASSEN- UND VERKEHRSWESEN. ARBEITSGRUPPE BETONSTRASSEN. SCHRIFTENREIHE. 1950. irreg. price varies. (Forschungsgesellschaft fuer Strassen-und Verkehrswesen) Kirschbaum Verlag GmbH, Siegriedstr. 28, 53179 Bonn, Germany. TEL 0228-95453-0. FAX 0228-9545327. (Subscr. to: Postfach 210209, 53157 Bonn, Germany) **Document type:** monographic series.
    Formerly: Forschungsgesellschaft fuer das Strassenwesen. Arbeitsgruppe Betonstrassen. Schriftenreihe (ISSN 0429-1816)

624   UK   ISSN 0015-8933
CODEN: FDFTAO
FOUNDATION FACTS.* 1965. irreg. free. International Society for Soil Mechanics and Foundation Engineering, c/o Dr. R.H.G. Perry, University Engineering Dept., Trumpington St., Cambridge CB2 1PZ, England. charts; illus. circ. 18,000. **Indexed:** Eng.Ind., Geo.Tech.Abstr.

624   FR   ISSN 0337-1573
FRANCE. LABORATOIRE CENTRAL DES PONTS ET CHAUSSEES. RAPPORT GENERAL D'ACTIVITE. 1965. a. free. Laboratoire Central des Ponts et Chaussees, 58 Blvd. Lefebvre, 75732 Paris Cedex 15, France. TEL 40-43-52-26. FAX 40-43-54-98. (back issues avail.)
—BLDSC (7288.036600).

624   FR   ISSN 0458-5860
CODEN: LBLLAE
FRANCE. LABORATOIRES DES PONTS ET CHAUSSEES. BULLETIN DE LIAISON. (Supplements avail.) (Text in French; summaries in English, French, German, Russian, Spanish) 1963. bi-m. 990 F. Laboratoire Central des Ponts et Chaussees, 58 bd. Lefebvre, 75732 Paris Cedex 15, France. TEL 40-43-52-26. index. circ. 6,250. (back issues avail.) **Indexed:** Excerp.Med., GeoRef., INIS Atomind., Pollut.Abstr.
—BLDSC (2865.759000); EI; CASDDS.

625.7   US   ISSN 0016-1705
FROM THE STATE CAPITALS. HIGHWAY FINANCING AND CONSTRUCTION. Variant title: Highway Financing and Construction from the State Capitals. 1946-1981; resumed 198? w. $295 (foreign $315). Wakeman-Walworth, Inc., 300 N. Washington St., Alexandria, VA 22314. TEL 703-549-8606. FAX 703-549-1372.
—CCC.
    Description: Provides information on allocation of funds for highway, street and bridge construction, extension, repair, renovation and replacement.

FUJIAN JIANZHU/FUJIAN ARCHITECTURE. see *ARCHITECTURE*

624   JA   ISSN 0389-5068
FUJITA KOGYO GIJUTSU KENKYUJOHO. English ed: Fujita Technical Research Institute. Journal. (Text in Japanese; summaries in English, Japanese) a. Fujita Kogyo K.K. Gijutsu Kenkyujo - Fujita Corporation, Technical Research Institute, 74, Otana-cho, Kohoku-ku, Yokohama-shi, Kanagawa-ken 223, Japan. **Document type:** academic/scholarly publication.

624   JA
FUJITA TECHNICAL RESEARCH INSTITUTE. JOURNAL. Japanese edition: Fujita Kogyo Gijutsu Kenkyujoho. (Text in English) 1990. a. Fujita Kogyo K.K. Gijutsu Kenkyujo - Fujita Corporation, Technical Research Institute, 74, Otana-cho, Kohoku-ku, Yokoha-mashi, Kanagawa-ken 223, Japan.

624   JA
FUKKEN GIHO/FUKKEN TECHNICAL REPORT. (Text in Japanese) 1987. a. Fukken Chosa Sekkei K.K. - Fukken Co., Ltd., 10-11, Hikari-cho 2-chome, Higashi-ku, Hiroshima-shi, Hiroshima-ken 732, Japan. **Document type:** academic/scholarly publication.

624 690   JA
FUKUSHIMAKEN KENSETSU GIJUTSU. FUKUKEN/FUKUSHIMA ASSOCIATION OF CONSTRUCTION. NEWS. (Text in Japanese) m. 250 Yen per no. Fukushimaken Kensetsu Gijutsu, 4-25, Satsuki-cho, Fukushima-shi, Fukushima-ken 960, Japan.

ENGINEERING — CIVIL ENGINEERING

624   JA   ISSN 0910-5646
FUKUSHIMAKEN KENSETSU GIJUTSU KENKYUJO SHOHO/FUKUSHIMA PREFECTURE CONSTRUCTIVE ENGINEERING INSTITUTE. REPORT. (Text in Japanese) 1967. a. Fukushimaken Kensetsu Gijutsu Kenkyujo, 13-1, Noborito, Timita-machi, Kooriyama-shi, Fukushima-ken 963, Japan.

624 551   JA
GANBAN RIKIGAKU NI KANSURU SHINPOJUMU RONBUNSHU/SYMPOSIUM ON ROCK MECHANICS. PROCEEDINGS. (Text in Japanese; summaries in English) 1962. a. price varies. Doboku Gakkai, Ganban Rikigaku Iinkai - Japan Society of Civil Engineers, Committee on Rock Mechanics, Yotsuya 1-chome, Shinjuku-ku, Tokyo 160, Japan. TEL 03-272-7211. (Subscr. to: Mazuren Co., Ltd., P.O. Box 5050, Tokyo International 100-31, Japan) circ. 500. (back issues avail.) **Document type:** academic/scholarly publication.

624   NE   ISSN 0046-5577
GEMEENTEWERKEN. 1933. m. fl.76.75. (Nederlands Instituut van Directeuren en Ingenieurs van Gemeentewerken) Samsom Uitgeverij B.V. (Subsidiary of: Wolters Kluwer N.V.), Postbus 4, 2400 MA Alphen aan den Rijn, Netherlands. TEL 31-1720-66822. FAX 31-1720-66639. (Co-sponsor: Hinderwet- en Bouwtoezichtvereniging) adv.; illus. circ. 3,890. **Indexed:** Avery.Ind.Archit.Per., Excerp.Med.
—BLDSC (4096.345000).
Formerly: Publieke Werken (ISSN 0033-3948)

GEODETICKY A KARTOGRAFICKY OBZOR. see *GEOGRAPHY*

624   UK   ISSN 0268-0165
TA703
GEODRILLING. 1976. bi-m. £20($35) Mining Journal Ltd., 60 Worship St., London EC2A 2HD, England. TEL 071-377-2020. FAX 071-247-4100. Ed. Alan Kennedy. adv.; bk.rev. circ. 3,048. (back issues avail.) **Document type:** trade publication.

GEOLOGIA APPLICATA E IDROGEOLOGIA. see *EARTH SCIENCES — Geology*

625.72   IT   ISSN 0016-7959
IL GEOMETRA. 1946. bi-m. L.50000. Collegio dei Geometri di Torino e Provincia, Corso Re Umberto 57, Turin, Italy. TEL 011-591348. FAX 011-5807989. Ed. Giuseppe Oberto. adv.; bk.rev.; charts. **Document type:** trade publication.

624   BE
GEOMETRAE 2000. (Text in Dutch, English, French, German) 1967. q. 140 ECU. Federation Royale des Geometres - Experts Independents - Koninklijke Federatie der Zelfstandige Landsmeters - Experten, Brusselsesteenweg 65-1, B-1500 Halle, Belgium. TEL 32-2-3568107. FAX 32-2-3611034. Ed. Johan Vanvolsem. adv.; bk.rev.; illus. circ. 500. **Document type:** bulletin, corporate report.

625.72   FR   ISSN 0016-7967
TA501   CODEN: GRGTA2
GEOMETRE. 1815. m. (11/yr.). 490 F. (foreign 740 F.). (Ordre des Geometres Experts) Publi-Topex, 13 rue Leon Cogniet, 75017 Paris, France. TEL 33-1-42-27-30-78. FAX 33-1-47-63-71-16. Ed. Helene Alvares-Correa. adv.; bk.rev.; illus. circ. 5,500. **Indexed:** Bibl.Cart.
Description: Covers surveyor's work, techniques and equipment and trade developments.

624 551   TH   ISSN 0046-5828
TA710.A1   CODEN: GTEGB2
GEOTECHNICAL ENGINEERING. (Text in English) 1970. s-a. $20 to individuals; institutions $30. Southeast Asian Geotechnical Society, c/o Asian Institute of Technology, P.O. Box 2754, Bangkok 10501, Thailand. FAX 66-2-516-2126. TELEX 84276 TH. Ed. Clive Franks. adv.; bk.rev.; charts; index. circ. 1,120. (also avail. in microfilm; microfiche; back issues avail.) **Indexed:** GeoRef., Geotech.Abstr., HRIS.
—BLDSC (4158.930000); UnCover.
Formerly: Southeast Asian Society of Soil Engineering. Journal.

GEOTECHNICAL SPECIAL PUBLICATIONS. see *EARTH SCIENCES — Geology*

624   US   ISSN 0149-6115
TA710.5   CODEN: GTJODJ
GEOTECHNICAL TESTING JOURNAL. Key Title: A S T M Geotechnical Testing Journal. 1978. q. $95 to non-members; members $86. American Society for Testing and Materials, 1916 Race St., Philadelphia, PA 19103. TEL 215-299-5400. FAX 215-977-9679. (also avail. in microform from UMI; reprint service avail. from UMI) **Indexed:** Chem.Abstr., Concr.Abstr., GeoRef., HRIS, Sel.Water Res.Abstr., W.R.C.Inf. **Document type:** trade publication.
—BLDSC (4158.960000); El; Faxon; UnCover; SWETS; UMI; CASDDS. **CCC.**
Refereed Serial

624.176   UK   ISSN 0016-8505
TA710.A1   CODEN: GTNQA8
GEOTECHNIQUE; international journal of soil mechanics. 1948. q. £129 (foreign £153). (Institution of Civil Engineers) Thomas Telford Services Ltd., Thomas Telford House, 1 Heron Quay, London E14 4JD, England. TEL 071-987-6999. FAX 071-538-4101. adv.; bk.rev.; abstr.; bibl.; charts; illus.; index. circ. 3,500. (back issues avail.) **Indexed:** Abstr.J.Earthq.Eng., AESIS, Agri.Eng.Abstr., Appl.Mech.Rev., Br.Ceram.Abstr., Br.Geol.Lit., Br.Tech.Ind., C.R.I. Abstr., Chem.Abstr., Curr.Cont., Deep Sea Res.& Oceanogr.Abstr., E&P Hlth. (1993-), Eng.Ind., Gas Process.& Ppl. (1993-), Geo.Abstr., Geotech.Abstr., HRIS, Ind.Sci.Rev., Intl.Civil Eng.Abstr., Irr.& Drain.Abstr., Off.Tech. (1993-), Petrol.Abstr. (1961-), Sci.Cit.Ind., Soft.Abstr.Eng., Soils & Fert. **Document type:** trade publication.
—BLDSC (4160.000000); El; Faxon; UnCover; SWETS. **CCC.**
Description: Studies work in theoretical and practical geotechnical engineering.

GEOTEXTILES AND GEOMEMBRANES. see *BIOLOGY — Biophysics*

625.7   GW
GERMANY (FEDERAL REPUBLIC, 1949-). BUNDESANSTALT FUER STRASSENWESEN, ERFAHRUNGSAUSTAUSCH UEBER ERDARBEITEN IM STRASSENBAU. 1972. a. free. Bundesanstalt fuer Strassenwesen, Bruederstr. 53, 51427 Bergisch-Gladbach, Germany. TEL 02204-430. FAX 02204-43833. circ. 800. **Document type:** government publication.

624 690   JA   ISSN 0911-713X
GIJUTSU KENKYUJO SHOHO/INSTITUTE OF TECHNOLOGY AND DEVELOPMENT. TECHNICAL REPORTS. (Text in Japanese; summaries in English, Japanese) 1974. a. Sumitomo Kensetsu K.K., Gijutsu Kenkyujo - Sumitomo Construction Co., Ltd., Institute of Technology and Development, 1726, Niragawa, Minami Kawachi-machi, Kawachi-gun, Tochigi-ken 329-04, Japan. TEL 0285-48-2611. FAX 0285-48-2655. Ed. Shinsuke Mori.

624 690   JA   ISSN 0388-6999
GIJUTSU KENKYUJOHO/TECHNICAL RESEARCH INSTITUTE. TECHNICAL REPORTS. (Text in Japanese; summaries in English, Japanese) 1959. a. Maeda Kensetsu Kogyo K.K., Gijutsu Kenkyujo - Maeda Construction Co., Ltd., Technical Research Institute, 10-26, Fujimi 2-chome, Chiyoda-ku, Tokyo 102, Japan.

624   IT   ISSN 0017-016X
TA4   CODEN: GIGCAO
GIORNALE DEL GENIO CIVILE. (Text in Italian; summaries in English, French, German) 1873. q. L.153000 (effective 1993). Istituto Poligrafico e Zecca dello Stato, Via Nomentana 2, 00161 Rome, Italy. FAX 039-6-8559648. Dir. Pietro Baratono. adv.; bk.rev.; bibl.; charts; illus.; index. **Indexed:** Abstr.J.Earthq.Eng., Appl.Mech.Rev., Chem.Abstr., Eng.Ind., Geotech.Abstr., Intl.Civil Eng.Abstr., Soft.Abstr.Eng. **Document type:** government publication.
—El.
Description: Covers civil engineering and especially structural and hydraulic engineering.

624   JA
GOSEI KOZO NO KATSUYO NI KANSURU SHINPOJUMU KOEN RONBUNSHU/SYMPOSIUM ON RESEARCH AND APPLICATION OF COMPOSITE CONSTRUCTIONS. PROCEEDINGS. (Text in Japanese; summaries in English) 1986. irreg. Doboku Gakkai, Kozo Kogaku Iinkai - Japan Society of Civil Engineers, Committee on Structure Engineering, Yotsuya 1-chome, Shinjuku-ku, Tokyo 160, Japan. **Document type:** proceedings.

GOVERNMENT GREEN GUIDE. see *PUBLIC ADMINISTRATION*

629   JA   ISSN 0288-5654
GOYO KENSETSU GIJUTSU KENKYUJO NENPO/PENTA-OCEAN CONSTRUCTION. ENGINEERING RESEARCH INSTITUTE. ANNUAL REPORT. (Text in Japanese) a. Goyo Kensetsu Gijutsu Kenkyujo, 11-25, Higashioi 1-chome, Shinagawa-ku, Tokyo 140, Japan. **Document type:** corporate report.

GRADBENI VESTNIK. see *BUILDING AND CONSTRUCTION*

624   UK
GREAT BRITAIN. COMMONWEALTH ASSOCIATION OF SURVEYING AND LAND ECONOMY. SURVEY REVIEW. 1931. q. £39 for Europe; US $95; elsewhere £47. 15 Greycoat Pl., London SW1P 1SB, England. TEL 071-222-8961. FAX 071-976-8304. (Dist. by: Turpin Distribution Services Ltd., Blackhorse Rd., Letchworth, Herts SG6 1HN, England. TEL 0462-672555) Ed. W.M. Barnes. adv.; bk.rev.; charts; illus.; index every 2 yrs. circ. 600. (also avail. in microform from UMI; reprint service avail. from UMI) **Document type:** government publication.
—SWETS; UMI.
Former titles: Great Britain. Directorate of Overseas Surveys. Survey Review (ISSN 0039-6265); (until 1963): Empire Survey Review.

624   UK   ISSN 0017-4653
TA715   CODEN: GRENDB
GROUND ENGINEERING. 1968. 10/yr. $70. Thomas Telford Ltd., Thomas Telford House, 1 Heron Quay, London E14 4JD, England. TEL 071-987-6999. FAX 071-538-4101. TELEX 298105 CIVILS G. Ed. Judith Cruickshank. adv.; bk.rev.; illus.; charts. circ. 5,000. **Indexed:** AESIS, Br.Ceram.Abstr., Br.Geol.Lit., Geotech.Abstr., HRIS, Intl.Civil Eng.Abstr., Soft.Abstr.Eng., W.R.C.Inf.
—BLDSC (4219.200000); Faxon; SWETS. **CCC.**

624   FR
GUIDE PRATIQUE DE L ENTREPRENEUR DU BATIMENT ET DES TRAVAUX PUBLICS. 1975. 6/yr. Editions S E R I P, 40 rue Guy-Moquet, 94500 Champigny-sur-Marne, France. Ed. Yves de Kerautem. adv. circ. 57,230.

624   UK   ISSN 0261-5207
GUIDE TO IN-CAREER TRAINING COURSES FOR CIVIL ENGINEERS. 1981. 3/yr. £12. (Institution of Civil Engineers) Thomas Telford Ltd., 1 Heron Quay, London E14 4JD, England. TEL 071-987-6999. FAX 071-538-4101.

GULF CONSTRUCTION & SAUDI ARABIA REVIEW. see *BUILDING AND CONSTRUCTION*

624   JA
GYOKO KENSETSU GIJUTSU KENKYU HAPPYOKAI KOENSHU/PROCEEDINGS OF FISHING PORT ENGINEERING. 1956. a. 3800 Yen($30) All Japan Fishing Port Association, Maru-Biru 550, Marunouchi 2-4-1, Chiyoda-Ku, Tokyo 100, Japan. TEL (03) 214.2924. Ed.Bd. circ. 1,000. **Document type:** proceedings.

624   US   ISSN 0340-4838
TC203
HAFENBAUTECHNISCHE GESELLSCHAFT. JAHRBUCH. vol.39, 1983. irreg. price varies. Springer-Verlag, 175 Fifth Ave., New York, NY 10010. TEL 212-460-1500. FAX 212-473-6272. (Also: Berlin, Heidelberg, Tokyo and Vienna) (reprint service avail. from ISI) **Document type:** academic/scholarly publication.

ENGINEERING — CIVIL ENGINEERING

621.762   NE   ISSN 0167-3785
CODEN: HPOTE9
HANDBOOK OF POWDER TECHNOLOGY. (Text in English) 1980. irreg., vol.8, 1990. price varies. Elsevier Science B.V., Books Division, P.O. Box 211, 1000 AE Amsterdam, Netherlands. TEL 31-20-5803911. FAX 31-20-5803705. TELEX 18582 ESPA NL. (Subscr. in U.S. and Canada to: Elsevier Science Inc., Box 882, Madison Sq. Sta., New York, NY 10159. TEL 212-989-5800) Eds. J.C. Williams, T. Allen. (back issues avail.) **Document type:** monographic series.
—BLDSC (4250.966000); CASDDS. **CCC.**
Refereed Serial

624   JA   ISSN 0916-1783
HASEKO GIHO/HASEKO TECHNICAL RESEARCH REPORT. (Text in Japanese; summaries in English, Japanese) 1984. a. free. Haseko Corp., Technical Research Institute, 1063 Kaneda, Atugi-shi, Kanagawa-ken 243, Japan. TEL 0462-23-5808. FAX 0462-23-2102. circ. 1,500. **Document type:** bulletin.

624   JA
HASHI/BRIDGES IN JAPAN. (Text in English, Japanese) 1967. a. 9500 Yen. Doboku Gakkai - Japan Society of Civil Engineers, Yotsuya 1-chome, Shinjuku-Ku, Tokyo 160, Japan. TEL 03-272-7211. (Subscr. to: Maruzen Co., Ltd., P.O. Box 5050, Tokyo International 100-31, Japan) circ. 800. (back issues avail.)

624   JA
HAZAMA-GUMI TOKUTEI KENKYU HOKOKU/HAZAMA CORPORATION. REPORT OF SPECIAL RESEARCH. (Text and summaries in English, Japanese) 1977. irreg. Hazama-gumi Gijyutsu Kenkyujo - Hazama Corporation, Technical Institute, 17-23, Honmachi 4-chome, Yono-shi, Saitama-ken 338, Japan.

624   JA   ISSN 0919-2174
HAZAMA KENKYU NENPO/HAZAMA TECHNICAL RESEARCH REPORT. (Text and summaries in English, Japanese) 1969. a. Hazama-gumi Gijyutsu Kenkyujo - Hazama Corporation, Technical Institute, 17-23, Honmachi 4-chome, Yono-shi, Saitama-ken 338, Japan.
Formerly (until 1992): Hazama-gumi Kenkyu Nenpo (ISSN 0385-7123)

624   GW   ISSN 0017-9442
HEBEZEUGE UND FOERDERMITTEL; Foerdertechnische Fachzeitschrift fuer Forschung, Entwicklung und Konstruktion, fuer Geraeteeinsatz und Technologie. 1961. m. DM.130. Verlag Technik GmbH, Am Friedrichshain 22, 10407 Berlin, Germany. TEL 030-4287-0. FAX 030-4261249. Ed. Norbert Hamke. adv.: B&W page DM.4500; trim 185 x 268; adv. contact: Gabriele Groschopp. bk.rev.; bibl.; charts; illus.; tr.lit.; index. circ. 9,650. **Indexed:** C.I.S. Abstr., ISMEC, Sh.& Vib.Dig. **Document type:** trade publication.
Description: Deals with design, production and organization in all fields of materials handling as well as planning and organization of international transport.

624   NE   ISSN 0046-7316
CODEN: HERNDU
HERON. vol.17, 1970. q. free to qualified personnel. Technische Universititet Delft, Faculty of Civil Engineering, Stevin-Laboratory, c/o J.G.M van Mier, P.O. Box 5048, 2600 GA Delft, Netherlands. TEL 31-15-784568. FAX 31-15-611465. TELEX 38151-BUTUD. (Co-sponsor: T.N.O. Building and Construction Research) Ed. A.C.W.M. Vrouwenvelder. bibl.; charts; circ. 2,000 (controlled). **Indexed:** Abstr.J.Earthq.Eng., Appl.Mech.Rev., Concr.Abstr., Eng.Ind. **Document type:** government publication, academic/scholarly publication, monographic series.
—BLDSC (4300.200000); EI.
Description: Contains contributions on strength of materials, structures and materials science based on research work performed in the laboratories of the Delft University of Technology and the TNO-Institute.

625.7 690   US   ISSN 0018-1692
HIGHWAY BUILDER. 1921. q. $10. (Associated Pennsylvania Constructors) Naylor Publications, Inc., 11350 McCormick Rd., Executive Plaza Three, Hunt Valley, MD 21031. TEL 410-785-2445. Ed. Ron L. Geist. adv.; illus. circ. 4,500. **Document type:** trade publication.
Description: For contractors, suppliers, engineering firms, government officials and individuals who have an interest in the Pennsylvania highway industry.

625.7   AT   ISSN 0046-7391
HIGHWAY ENGINEERING IN AUSTRALIA. 1969. bi-m. Aus.$34 (foreign Aus.$57). Editorial & Publishing Consultants Pty. Ltd., 29 First Ave., Klemzig, S.A. 5087, Australia. TEL 08-261-5837. FAX 08-261-2697. Ed. Frank H. Schmidt. adv.: B&W page Aus.$884, color page Aus.$1196. bk.rev. circ. 2,100. (also avail. in microfilm from UMI; reprint service avail. from UMI) **Indexed:** Aus.Rd.Ind., HRIS. —UMI.

625.7   II   ISSN 0970-2598
HIGHWAY RESEARCH RECORD; general report on road research work done in India during (year). (Text in English) 1974. a. $1. Indian Roads Congress, Jamnagar House, Shahjahan Rd., New Delhi 110 011, India. TEL 381649. circ. 6,600.

625.7   UK
HIGHWAYS. 1934. m. £22.50 (foreign £47). Faversham House Group Ltd., Faversham House, 111 St. James's Rd., Croydon, Surrey CR9 2TH, England. TEL 01-684-9659. Ed. Michael Gannon. adv.; bk.rev.; film rev.; abstr.; illus.; stat. circ. 7,500. (also avail. in microform from UMI; back issues avail.; reprint service avail. from UMI) **Indexed:** Br.Tech.Ind., Eng.Ind., Excerp.Med.
—BLDSC (4310.920000); EI.
Former titles (until Mar. 1985): Highways and Public Works (ISSN 0142-6168); (until Jan. 1978): Highways and Road Construction International (ISSN 0308-9533); Highways and Road Construction; Highways (ISSN 0018-1773)
Description: Covers the highway industry in Great Britain, including construction and maintenance, traffic control and street planning and management.

624 388.312   UK   ISSN 0265-6868
HIGHWAYS AND TRANSPORTATION. 1930. m. £40 (foreign £42); newsstand price: £4. Institution of Highways and Transportation, 3 Lygon Pl., Ebury St., London SW1 0JS, England. TEL 071-730-5245. FAX 071-730-1628. (Co-sponsor: Institute of Highway Incorporated Engineers) Ed. W.I. Smith. adv.; bk.rev. circ. 12,919. (back issues avail.) **Indexed:** Br.Tech.Ind., Dok.Str. **Document type:** trade publication.
—EI; UnCover; SWETS; UMI.
Description: Presents information on roads and traffic for highway and transportation engineers.

624 621   UK
HOBSON'S ENGINEERING CASEBOOK. 1979. a. £7.99. (Careers Research and Advisory Centre) Hobsons Publishing plc., Bateman St., Cambridge, England. TEL 0223-354551. FAX 0223-323154. TELEX 81746-HOBCAM-G. adv. contact: Tania West. circ. 20,000.
Description: Recent graduates discuss their jobs in the industry.

624   JA   ISSN 0912-6953
HONSHI GIHO/HONSHI TECHNICAL REPORT. (Text in Japanese) 1977. q. 2200 Yen. Kaiyo Kakyo Chosakai - Bridge and Offshore Engineering Association, 14-4, Shintomi 2-chome, Chuo-ku, Tokyo 100, Japan.

624   US   ISSN 0018-8220
TC1   CODEN: HYCOAR
HYDROTECHNICAL CONSTRUCTION. English translation of: Gidrotekhnicheskoe Stroietl'stvo (RU ISSN 0016-9714) 1967. m. $895 (foreign $1045) (effective 1994). (Ministerstvo Energetiki i Elektrifikatsii, Nauchno-Tekhnicheskoe Obshchestvo Energetike i Elektrotekhnicheskoi Promyshlennosti, RU) Plenum Publishing Corp., Consultants Bureau, 233 Spring St., New York, NY 10013-1578. TEL 212-620-8000. FAX 212-463-0742. TELEX 23-421139. Ed. N.A. Lopatin. abstr.; charts; illus. (also avail. in microform from UMI; microfilm from JSC; back issues avail.) **Indexed:** Appl.Mech.Rev., Eng.Ind., Excerp.Med., Geotech.Abstr., INIS Atomind., INSPEC, Intl.Civil Eng.Abstr., Sel.Water Res.Abstr., Soft.Abstr.Eng., W.R.C.Inf. **Document type:** academic/scholarly publication.
—BLDSC (0412.088700); Faxon; UMI. **CCC.**
Refereed Serial

624   SZ
I A B S E CONGRESS REPORT. (Text and summaries in English, French or German) 1932. quadrennial, 14th, 1992, New Delhi, India. 150 SFr. to non-members; members 100 SFr. International Association for Bridge and Structural Engineering, ETH-Hoenggerberg, CH-8093 Zurich, Switzerland. TEL 01-3772647. FAX 01-3712131. **Document type:** proceedings.
Formerly: International Association for Bridge and Structural Engineering. Final Report (of Congress) (ISSN 0074-1418)

624   SZ
I A B S E REPORT. (Text in English, French and German) 1964. irreg., no.70, 1993. 147 SFr. to non-members; members 98 SFr. International Association for Bridge and Structural Engineering, ETH-Hoenggerberg, CH-8093 Zurich, Switzerland. TEL 01-3772647. FAX 01-3712131. **Document type:** corporate report.
Formerly: International Association for Bridge and Structural Engineering. Reports of the Working Commissions (ISSN 0074-1442)

624   UK
I C E LIST OF MEMBERS. biennial. £120. (Institution of Civil Engineers) Thomas Telford Services Ltd., Thomas Telford House, 1 Heron Quay, London E14 4JD, England. TEL 071-987-6999. FAX 071-538-4101. (Dist. in U.S. by: American Society of Civil Engineers, 345 E. 47th St., New York, NY 10017) adv. **Document type:** directory.
Formerly: I C E Yearbook (ISSN 0308-4159)

624   VE   ISSN 0376-723X
I M M E BOLETIN. Variant title: I M M E Boletin Tecnico. (Text in Spanish; summaries in English) 1963. s-a. $70 or exchange basis (effective 1994). Universidad Central de Venezuela, Facultad de Ingenieria, Instituto de Materiales y Modelos Estructurales, Apdo. 50361, Caracas 1050A, Venezuela. TEL 693-14-77. FAX 662-4441. Ed. Marianela Lafuente. bk.rev.; software rev.; charts; illus.; cum.index. circ. 1,000. (back issues avail.) **Indexed:** J.of Ferroc. **Document type:** bulletin.
Description: Publishes developments in civil, structural, mechanical, materials and earthquake engineering.

624   SP   ISSN 0213-795X
I MU. (Ingenieria Municipal) 1986. m. $135 in Europe; elsewhere $160. Oilgas S.A., P. de la Habana, 48, 28036 Madrid, Spain. TEL 563-58-00. FAX 563-52-34. Ed. Carlos Martin. adv. circ. 7,500.

IDAHO TRANSPORTATION DEPARTMENT. HIGHWAY INFORMATION. see TRANSPORTATION — *Roads And Traffic*

691 624   II   ISSN 0019-4565
TA680   CODEN: ICJOAL
INDIAN CONCRETE JOURNAL. 1927. m. Rs.275 (foreign $60) (effective 1993). (Research and Consultancy Directorate) Associated Cement Companies, Ltd., C R S Complex, L.B. Shastri Marg., Thane 400 604, India. TEL 5323631. FAX 91-22-5320962. TELEX 11-72190 CRS IN. Ed. B.V.B. Pai. adv.: B&W page $250, color page $312.50. bk.rev.; charts; illus.; index. circ. 2,500. (also avail. in microfiche) **Indexed:** C.R.I.Abstr., Chem.Abstr., Concr.Abstr., Eng.Ind., Geotech.Abstr., Intl.Civil Eng.Abstr., J.of Ferroc., Soft.Abstr.Eng., W.R.C.Inf. **Document type:** trade publication.
●Also available online.
—BLDSC (4395.000000); UnCover; SWETS; UMI; CASDDS.

625.7   II   ISSN 0376-7256
INDIAN HIGHWAYS. (Includes Annual and some special numbers) (Text in English) 1973. m. Rs.100($18) Indian Roads Congress, Jamnagar House, Shahjahan Rd., New Delhi 110 011, India. TEL 381649. adv.; abstr.; bibl.; illus.; index. circ. 6,500. **Indexed:** C.R.I. Abstr., Geotech.Abstr., HRIS.
—BLDSC (4409.440000).
Formerly (until July 1973): Transport-Communications Monthly Review (ISSN 0041-1418)

ENGINEERING — CIVIL ENGINEERING

624.176 II ISSN 0019-6371
INDIAN SOCIETY OF EARTHQUAKE TECHNOLOGY. BULLETIN; journal of international earthquake engineering. (Text in English) 1964. q. Rs.80($24) Indian Society of Earthquake Technology, Roorkee, Uttar Pradesh 247667, India. Ed. R.C. Agrawal. adv.; bk.rev.; abstr.; charts; illus. circ. 700. (back issues avail.) **Indexed:** Abstr.J.Earthq.Eng., Appl.Mech.Rev., Eng.Ind., INIS Atomind.

624 II ISSN 0970-3470
INDIAN SURVEYOR. (Text in English) 1952. s-a. Rs.40. Institution of Surveyors, 15-7 Instidoual Area, New Mehrauli Rd., New Delhi 110 016, India. TEL 6863069. TELEX 031-72362 DSA-IN. Ed. S.S. Sundaram. adv.: page Rs. 1000. circ. 1,000. **Indexed:** Bibl.Cart.
Formerly: Institution of Surveyors. Journal (ISSN 0538-009X)
Description: Contains papers on the science of survey presented at the instituion's annual technical sessions, seminars and conferences.

L'INDUSTRIA DELLE COSTRUZIONI. see *BUILDING AND CONSTRUCTION*

624 720 690 IT ISSN 0391-6537
INGEGNERI ARCHITETTI COSTRUTTORI. 1949. m. L.20000. Associazione Ingegneri della Provincia di Bologna, Strada Maggiore 13, Bologna, Italy. Ed. Roberto Carassia. adv.; abstr.; charts; stat.
Formerly: Ingegneri e Costruttori.

624 720 PN
INGENIERA Y ARQUITECTURA. 6/yr. Society of Architects and Engineers of Panama, Box 6-4991, Panama 6A - Darado, Panama. TEL 696444. TELEX 2302 IALAKAS. circ. 2,831.

624 CU ISSN 0020-1022
TA4 CODEN: INCVAG
INGENIERIA CIVIL. (Text in Spanish; summaries in English and French) 1950. s-a. $24 in S. America; N. America $26; elsewhere $30. (Comite Estatal de la Construccion, Centro Tecnico Superior de la Construccion) Ediciones Cubanas, Obispo No. 527, Aptdo. 605, Havana, Cuba. Dir. Jesus Alvarez Taladrid. charts; index. circ. 2,500. **Indexed:** Chem.Abstr., Intl.Civil Eng.Abstr., Soft.Abstr.Eng.

624 MX
INGENIERIA CIVIL/CIVIL ENGINEERING. 1949. bi-m. Camino de Santa Teresa No. 187, Mexico 22, DF, Mexico. Ed. Guillermo Montemayor Gomez. adv. circ. 6,500. **Indexed:** Intl.Civil Eng.Abstr., Soft.Abstr.Eng.

624 US ISSN 0172-8008
INGENIEURBAUTEN. (Text in German) 1971. irreg. price varies. Springer-Verlag, 175 Fifth Ave., New York, NY 10010. TEL 212-460-1500. FAX 212-473-6272. (Also: Berlin, Heidelberg, Tokyo and Vienna) Eds. K. Sattler, P. Stein. (reprint service avail. from ISI) **Document type:** academic/scholarly publication.

INGENIEURS ET ARCHITECTES SUISSES. see *ENGINEERING*

624 UK ISSN 0965-089X
TA1 CODEN: PCCIEF
INSTITUTION OF CIVIL ENGINEERS. PROCEEDINGS. CIVIL ENGINEERING. 1991. q. £50. Thomas Telford Services Ltd., Thomas Telford House, 1 Heron Quay, London E14 4JD, England. TEL 071-987-6999. FAX 071-538-4101. Ed. Linda Schabedly. adv.; abstr.; bibl.; charts; illus.; stat.; cum.index. circ. 16,000. (back issues avail.) **Indexed:** Appl.Mech.Rev., Br.Geol.Lit., Br.Rail.Bd., Br.Tech.Ind., C.I.S.Abstr., C.R.I.Abstr., Cadscan, Chem.Abstr., Curr.Cont., Dok.Str., Eng.Ind., Excerp.Med., Fluidex, Geo.Abstr., High.Educ.Curr.Aware.Bull., HRIS, J.of Ferroc., Lead Abstr., Met.Abstr., RICS, Sci.Abstr., Zincscan. **Document type:** proceedings.
—BLDSC (6722.030000); EI; Faxon; UnCover; SWETS. **CCC.**
Formed by the merger of (1972-1991): Institution of Civil Engineers. Proceedings. Part 1: Design and Construction (ISSN 0307-8353); (1972-1991): Institution of Civil Engineers. Proceedings. Part 2: Research and Theory (ISSN 0307-8361); Formerly (1957-1972): Institution of Civil Engineers. Proceedings (ISSN 0020-3262); Which was formed by the merger of: Institution of Civil Engineers. Part 1: General (ISSN 0534-2759); Institution of Civil Engineers. Part 2: Engineering Divisions. Airport, Maritime, Railway, Road (ISSN 0634-2767); Institution of Civil Engineers. Part 3: Engineering Divisions. Public Health, Structural, Works Construction, Hydraulis (ISSN 0534-2775).
Description: Technical papers, notes and discussion on aspects of civil engineering research and theory.

624 UK
INSTITUTION OF CIVIL ENGINEERS. PROCEEDINGS. GEOTECHNICAL ENGINEERING. 4/yr. £48 (foreign £57). Thomas Telford Services Ltd., Thomas Telford House, 1 Heron Quay, London E14 4JD, England. TEL 071-987-6999. FAX 071-538-4101. Ed. C.R. Clayton. **Document type:** proceedings.

628 UK ISSN 0965-0903
TD159.A1
INSTITUTION OF CIVIL ENGINEERS. PROCEEDINGS. MUNICIPAL ENGINEER. 1873. bi-m. £48 (foreign £57). (Institution of Civil Engineers) Thomas Telford Services Ltd., Thomas Telford House, 1 Heron Quay, London E14 4JD, England. TEL 071-987-6999. FAX 071-538-4101. Ed. Simon Fullalove. adv.; bk.rev.; illus.; index, cum.index. circ. 3,100. (back issues avail.) **Indexed:** Br.Ceram.Abstr., Br.Tech.Ind., Chem.Abstr., Eng.Ind., Excerp.Med., Fuel & Energy Abstr., HRIS, Intl.Civil Eng.Abstr., RICS, Soft.Abstr.Eng., W.R.C.Inf. **Document type:** proceedings.
—BLDSC (6722.070000); EI; Faxon; UnCover; SWETS. **CCC.**
Former titles (until 1991): Municipal Engineer (ISSN 0263-788X); (until Apr. 1982): Chartered Municipal Engineer; Institution of Municipal Engineers. Journal (ISSN 0020-3505)
Description: Discusses management, planning, design, construction and maintenance of projects.

624 UK ISSN 0965-0911
INSTITUTION OF CIVIL ENGINEERS. PROCEEDINGS. STRUCTURES AND BUILDINGS. 4/yr. £98 (foreign £115). Thomas Telford Services Ltd., Thomas Telford House, 1 Heron Quay, London E14 4JD, England. TEL 071-987-6999. FAX 071-538-4101. Ed. J.E. Harding. **Document type:** proceedings.
—BLDSC (6722.215000); EI; Faxon; UnCover; SWETS.

624 380.5 UK ISSN 0965-092X
INSTITUTION OF CIVIL ENGINEERS. PROCEEDINGS. TRANSPORT. 4/yr. £60 (foreign £70). Thomas Telford Services Ltd., Thomas Telford House, 1 Heron Quay, London E14 4JD, England. TEL 071-987-6999. FAX 071-538-4101. Ed. J. Porter. **Document type:** proceedings.
—BLDSC (6722.217000); EI; Faxon; UnCover; SWETS.

624 UK ISSN 0965-0946
INSTITUTION OF CIVIL ENGINEERS. PROCEEDINGS. WATER, MARITIME AND ENERGY. 4/yr. £70 (foreign £81). Thomas Telford Services Ltd., Thomas Telford House, 1 Heron Quay, London E14 4JD, England. TEL 071-987-6999. FAX 071-538-4101. Ed. R.H.J. Sellin. **Document type:** proceedings.
—BLDSC (6722.220000); EI; Faxon; UnCover; SWETS.

624 II ISSN 0257-344X
TH1
INSTITUTION OF ENGINEERS (INDIA). ARCHITECTURAL ENGINEERING. (Text in English) 1984. s-a. Rs.40($5) Institution of Engineers (India), 8 Gokhale Road, Calcutta 700 020, India. TEL 033-288334. FAX 033-288345. TELEX 0217885 IEIC IN. Ed. K.N. Majumdar. adv.; charts; illus. circ. 3,500.
—BLDSC (4794.014000); EI.

624 II ISSN 0373-1995
TA1
INSTITUTION OF ENGINEERS (INDIA). CIVIL ENGINEERING DIVISION. JOURNAL. (Text in English) 1920. bi-m. Rs.120($15) Institution of Engineers (India), Civil Engineering Division, 8 Gokhale Rd., Calcutta 700 020, India. TEL 033-288334. FAX 033-288345. TELEX 0217885 IEIC IN. Ed. K.N. Majumdar. adv.; charts; illus.; index. circ. 26,000. **Indexed:** Appl.Mech.Rev., Eng.Ind., INIS Atomind., Met.Abstr., Sci.Abstr.
—EI; UnCover.

624 AT ISSN 0159-2068
TA1 CODEN: TEACDA
INSTITUTION OF ENGINEERS, AUSTRALIA. TRANSACTIONS. CIVIL ENGINEERING. 1959. q. Aus.$55 (overseas Aus.$70) (effective 1994). Engineers Australia Pty. Ltd., Crows Nest Centre, 2 Ernest St., Crows Nest, N.S.W 2065, Australia. TEL 02-438-1533. FAX 02-438-5934. adv.; illus.; index. circ. 7,500. **Indexed:** AESIS, Appl.Mech.Rev., CAD CAM Abstr., Eng.Ind., Environ.Abstr., Fluidex, Geotech.Abstr., HRIS, INIS Atomind., Met.Abstr., Sci.Abstr., World Alum.Abstr.
—BLDSC (8964.700000); UnCover.
Formerly: Institutions of Engineers, Australia. Civil Engineering Transactions (ISSN 0020-3297)
Description: Reference papers in the field of civil engineering.

624 NZ ISSN 0111-9508
 CODEN: TPCSD9
INSTITUTION OF PROFESSIONAL ENGINEERS. TRANSACTIONS. CIVIL ENGINEERING SECTION. a. NZ.$20 per no. Institution of Professional Engineers, New Zealand, P.O. Box 12241, Wellington, New Zealand. TEL 64-4-473-9444. FAX 64-4-473-2324. Ed. Peter King. circ. 3,250.
—BLDSC (8970.300000). **CCC.**
Description: Scientific papers on different aspects of civil engineering.

624 UK
TA680
INSTITUTION OF STRUCTURAL ENGINEERS. SESSIONAL YEARBOOK AND DIRECTORY OF MEMBERS. 1910. a. £100. Structural Engineers Trading Organization Ltd., 11 Upper Belgrave St., London SW1X 8BH, England. TEL 071-235-4535. FAX 071-235-4294. adv. circ. 2,000. **Document type:** directory.
Formerly: Institution of Structural Engineers. Yearbook (ISSN 0073-9847)

INSTITUTUL POLITEHNIC DIN IASI. BULETINUL. SECTIA VI: CONSTRUCTII. see *BUILDING AND CONSTRUCTION*

INSTYTUT METEOROLOGII I GOSPODARKI WODNEJ. MATERIALY BADAWCZE. SERIA: INZYNIERIA WODNA/INSTITUTE OF METEOROLOGY AND WATER MANAGEMENT. RESEARCH PAPERS SERIES: WATER ENGINEERING. see *ENGINEERING — Hydraulic Engineering*

624 SP ISSN 0304-3622
TH2416.A1 CODEN: BSSSCD
INTERNATIONAL ASSOCIATION FOR SHELL AND SPATIAL STRUCTURES. BULLETIN. 1960. 3/yr. 110 SFr. membership. International Association for Shell and Spatial Structures (I.A.S.S.), Alfonso XII 3, 28014 Madrid, Spain. FAX 3357422. Ed. L.M. Ortega. bk.rev. circ. 1,000. **Indexed:** Appl.Mech.Rev., C.R.I. Abstr., Concr.Abstr., Intl.Civil Eng.Abstr., Soft.Abstr.Eng.
—BLDSC (2587.110000); EI; UnCover.
Formerly: International Association for Shell Structures. Bulletin (ISSN 0538-4400)

INTERNATIONAL ASSOCIATION OF ENGINEERING GEOLOGY. BULLETIN. see *EARTH SCIENCES — Geology*

ENGINEERING — CIVIL ENGINEERING

624.2   US
INTERNATIONAL BRIDGE CONFERENCE. PROCEEDINGS. 1984. a. $55 (foreign $65). Engineers' Society of Western Pennsylvania, International Bridge Conference, 337 Fourth Ave., PA 15222-2097. TEL 412-261-0710. FAX 412-261-1606. adv. circ. 1,500. Document type: proceedings.
 Description: Encourages and promotes interchange of information, procedures and techniques in the bridge industry through both its technical program and exhibition.

627.8   FR   ISSN 0534-8293
INTERNATIONAL COMMISSION ON LARGE DAMS. BULLETIN. no.15, 1960. irreg. price varies. International Commission on Large Dams, 151 bd. Haussmann, 75008 Paris, France. (Dist. in the U.S. by: US Committee on Large Dams, 1616 17th St., Ste. 483, Denver, CO 80202)
 —BLDSC (2587.370000).

627.8   FR   ISSN 0074-4115
INTERNATIONAL COMMISSION ON LARGE DAMS. TRANSACTIONS. triennial since 1961; 1991, 17th, Vienna. International Commission on Large Dams, 151 Bd. Hausmann, 75008 Paris, France. (Dist. in the U.S. by: US Committee on Large Dams, 1616 17th St., Ste. 483, Denver, CO 80202)

624   UK   ISSN 0020-6415
TA1   CODEN: INCOBU
INTERNATIONAL CONSTRUCTION. (Text in English; summaries in French, German, Italian, Spanish) 1962. m. £80. Maclean Hunter Ltd., Maclean Hunter House, Chalk Lane, Cockfosters Rd., Barnet, Herts EN4 0BU, England. TEL 081-242-3193. FAX 081-242-3186. TELEX 299072-MACHUN-G. Ed. Alan Peterson. adv.; bk.rev.; charts; illus.; stat.; tr.lit.; index. circ. 42,609. (also avail. in microform from UMI; back issues avail.; reprint service avail. from UMI) Indexed: Eng.Ind., Geotech.Abstr., Intl.Civil Eng.Abstr., J.of Ferroc., Soft.Abstr.Eng., W.R.C.Inf. Document type: trade publication.
 —BLDSC (4539.401000); SWETS; UMI. CCC.
 Incorporating (1919-1987): World Construction (ISSN 0043-8375); Which superseded: Ingeneria Internacional Construccion (ISSN 0020-1065); And which incorporated (1966-1975): Engineering Construction World (ISSN 0013-7790); Which was formerly titled (1965-1966): Engineering and Construction World.
 Description: Serves construction management worldwide covering major construction projects- roads, quarrying, bridges, tunnelling, water, building, construction equipment.

INTERNATIONAL DREDGING REVIEW. see ENGINEERING — Hydraulic Engineering

624   UK   ISSN 0074-6045
 CODEN: FIPCAO
INTERNATIONAL FEDERATION OF PRESTRESSING. CONGRESS PROCEEDINGS. 1952. quadrennial, 11th, 1990, Hamburg. price varies. International Federation of Prestressing - Federation Internationale de la Precontrainte, 11 Upper Belgrave St., London SW1X 8BH, England. TEL 071-235-4535. FAX 071-235-4294. circ. 2,000. Document type: proceedings.
 —CASDDS.

INTERNATIONAL INSTITUTE OF SEISMOLOGY AND EARTHQUAKE ENGINEERING. BULLETIN. see EARTH SCIENCES — Geophysics

INTERNATIONAL INSTITUTE OF SEISMOLOGY AND EARTHQUAKE ENGINEERING. INDIVIDUAL STUDIES BY PARTICIPANTS AT I I S E E. see EARTH SCIENCES — Geophysics

INTERNATIONAL INSTITUTE OF SEISMOLOGY AND EARTHQUAKE ENGINEERING. YEAR BOOK. see EARTH SCIENCES — Geophysics

624 350   UK   ISSN 0363-9061
TA710.A1   CODEN: IJNGDZ
INTERNATIONAL JOURNAL FOR NUMERICAL AND ANALYTICAL METHODS IN GEOMECHANICS. 1977. m. $925 (effective 1994). John Wiley & Sons Ltd., Journals, Baffins Ln., Chichester, Sussex PO19 1UD, England. TEL 0243-779777. FAX 0243-775878. TELEX 86290-WIBOOK-G. Ed. C.S. Desai. adv.; bk.rev. (reprint service avail. from ISI,SWZ,UMI) Indexed: Abstr.J.Earthq.Eng., Appl.Mech.Rev., Curr.Cont., Geo.Abstr., Geotech.Abstr., HRIS, Ind.Sci.Rev., Sci.Abstr., Sci.Cit.Ind., Sh.& Vib.Dig. Document type: academic/scholarly publication.
 —BLDSC (4542.403000); EI; Faxon; UnCover; SWETS; UMI. CCC.

624   UK   ISSN 0961-5539
 CODEN: INMFEM
INTERNATIONAL JOURNAL OF NUMERICAL METHODS FOR HEAT AND FLUID FLOW. 1991. bi-m. $451. John Wiley & Sons Ltd., Baffins Ln., Chichester, Sussex PO19 1UD, England. TEL 0243-779777. FAX 0243-775878. TELEX 86290-WIBOOK-G. Eds. Roland Lewis, Cedric Taylor.
 —BLDSC (4542.406100); EI; CASDDS.
 Description: Presents information relating to the development, refinement, and application of computer-based numerical techniques for solving problems in heat and fluid flow.

624   II   ISSN 0253-4754
 CODEN: IJOSD8
INTERNATIONAL JOURNAL OF STRUCTURES. (Text in English) 1981. s-a. Rs.450($55) Nem Chand & Bros., Civil Lines, Roorkee 247667, India. TEL 01332-72258. Ed. Ashok K. Jain. adv. contact: T.K. Jain. bk.rev. circ. 1,850. Indexed: Appl.Mech.Rev., C.R.I.Abstr., Eng.Ind., Intl.Civil Eng.Abstr. Document type: academic/scholarly publication.
 —EI.
 Description: Disseminates the analysis, design, and construction of engineering structures. Topics include: concrete and steel structures, finite element and non-linear analysis, random vibrations, numerical methods, and structural reliability.
 Refereed Serial

INTERNATIONAL ROAD CONGRESSES. PROCEEDINGS. see TRANSPORTATION — Roads And Traffic

624.151   PO   ISSN 0074-848X
INTERNATIONAL SOCIETY FOR ROCK MECHANICS. CONGRESS. PROCEEDINGS. (Proceedings published in host country) (Text in English, French and German) 1966. quadrennial. price varies. International Society for Rock Mechanics, c/o Laboratorio Nacional do Brasil, 1799 Lisbon Codex, Portugal. FAX 8497660. TELEX 16760 LNEC P. Ed. Jennifer Bartholomew. Indexed: GeoRef. Document type: proceedings.

624.151   PO
TA705
INTERNATIONAL SOCIETY FOR ROCK MECHANICS. NEWS JOURNAL. 1994. q. membership. International Society for Rock Mechanics, c/o Laboratorio Nacional de Engenharia Civil, 101 Avenida do Brasil, 1799 Lisbon Codex, Portugal. FAX 8497660. TELEX 16760 LNEC P. adv. circ. 7,500.
 Formerly: International Society for Rock Mechanics. News (ISSN 0539-0281)

624   MX   ISSN 0074-3313
INTERNATIONAL SOCIETY FOR SOIL MECHANICS AND FOUNDATION ENGINEERING. PROCEEDINGS. (Text in English or French) 1936. quadrennial. $50. Sociedad Mexicana de Mecanica de Suelos - Mexican Society for Soil Mechanics, Valle de Bravo No. 19, Col. Vergel de Coyoacan, Tlalpan, 14340 Mexico, D.F., Mexico. Document type: proceedings.

625.732   US   ISSN 0074-8498
INTERNATIONAL SOCIETY FOR TERRAIN-VEHICLE SYSTEMS. PROCEEDINGS OF INTERNATIONAL CONFERENCE. 1961. irreg., latest 1992, Sacramento. International Society for Terrain-Vehicle Systems, c/o Dr. Ronald A. Liston, USACRREL, 72 Lyme Rd., Hanover, NH 03755-1290. TEL 603-646-4362. bk.rev. circ. 500. Indexed: Eng.Ind. Document type: proceedings.

625.7   BE
INTERNATIONAL SYMPOSIUM ON CONCRETE ROADS. REPORTS. 1969. quadrennial, 6th, 1990, Madrid. $290. Cimeurope, Rue d'Arlon 55, B-1040 Brussels, Belgium. TEL 32-2-2341011. FAX 32-2-2304720. TELEX 27203 CEMBUR B. circ. 1,140. Document type: proceedings.
 Formerly: European Symposium on Concrete Pavements. Reports.
 Description: Discusses various aspects of the construction of roads and streets.

624 380.5   UK   ISSN 0263-4317
INTERNATIONAL SYMPOSIUM ON THE AERODYNAMICS AND VENTILATION OF VEHICLE TUNNELS. PROCEEDINGS. irreg., 7th, 1991. price varies. Elsevier Science Ltd., Books Division, P.O. Box 800, Kidlington, Oxford OX5 1DX, England. TEL 44-865-843000. FAX 44-865-843010. (Subscr. in U.S. and Canada to: Elsevier Science, 660 White Plains Rd., Tarrytown, NY 10591-5153. TEL 914-524-9200) Document type: proceedings.
 —CCC.

INTERNATIONAL WATER POWER AND DAM CONSTRUCTION. see WATER RESOURCES

624   XO   ISSN 0021-0277
TA4   CODEN: IZYSAV
INZINIERSKE STAVBY/CIVIL ENGINEERING. (Text and summaries in Czech, English, German, Slovak) 1952. m. 240 Kcs.($40) (Ministerstvo Stavebnictva Slovenskej Republiky - Ministry of Building Industry of the Slovak Republic) Alfa, Hurbanovo nam. 3, 815 89 Bratislava, Slovakia. TEL 33-14-41. FAX 42-7-594-43. (Dist. by: Slovart, nam. Slobody 6, 817 64 Bratislava, Slovakia) adv.; bk.rev.; bibl.; illus.; index. circ. 10,000. Indexed: C.I.S. Abstr., Eng.Ind., INIS Atomind. Document type: trade publication.
 —CASDDS.

624   PL   ISSN 0021-0315
INZYNIERIA I BUDOWNICTWO. (Text in Polish; summaries in English, Polish) 1938. m. $60 (effective 1994). Polski Zwiazek Inzynierow i Technikow Budownictwa, Ul. T. Czackiego 3-5, 00-950 Warsaw, Poland. TEL 48-22-296986. FAX 48-22-268634. Ed. Stefan Pyrak. adv.: B&W page $200. bk.rev.; software rev.; bibl.; illus.; index, cum.index. Indexed: Appl.Mech.Rev., Intl.Civil Eng.Abstr., Soft.Abstr.Eng.
 Description: Covers general problems of building and civil engineering, theory of stuctures, maintenance of builidng and engineering objects, geotechnics.

625.7 388.314   RU   ISSN 0202-7844
TL4
ITOGI NAUKI I TEKHNIKI: AVTOMOBIL'NYI I GORODSKOI TRANSPORT. irreg., vol.12-13, 1988. 6.60 Rub. Vsesoyuznyi Institut Nauchno-Tekhnicheskoi Informatsii (VINITI), Baltiiskaya ul. 14, Moscow A-219, Russia. (Subscr. to: Mezhdunarodnaya Kniga, Dimitrova ul. 39, 113095 Moscow, Russia)
 —BLDSC (0004.700000).

624   YU   ISSN 0350-5421
IZGRADNJA/CONSTRUCTION. (Text in Serbo-Croatian; summaries in English) 1946. m. $240. Savez Gradjevinskih Inzenjera i Tehnicara SR Srbije, Kneza Milosa 7a, 11000 Belgrade, Yugoslavia. TEL 011-343-563. FAX 330-065. (Co-sponsors: Savez Drustava Arhitekata Srbije; Savez Urbanista Srbije) Ed. Aleksandar Flasar. adv.; bk.rev.; bibl.; charts; illus. Indexed: Geotech.Abstr.
 Description: Publishes scientific and professional papers on building, architecture, heavy construction, materials and building technology.

624   CC   ISSN 1002-8528
JIANZHU KEXUE/BUILDING SCIENCE. (Text in Chinese) 1985. q. $23.38 (effective 1994). Zhongguo Jianzhu Kexue Yanjiuyuan - China Academy of Building Research, Xiaohuangzhuang, Andingmenwai, Beijing 100013, People's Republic of China. TEL 861-4211133. FAX 861-4221369. TELEX 210332 CABR CN. (Dist. overseas by: Guoji Shudian - China International Book Trading Corp., P.O. Box 399, Beijing, P.R.C.) Ed. Zhang Weiyue. Document type: academic/scholarly publication.
 Description: Covers the scientific research achievements in design, construction, as well as codes and standards for engineering construction.

ENGINEERING — CIVIL ENGINEERING

624 **JA** ISSN 0289-9418
JIBAN TO KENSETSU/GROUND ENGINEERING. 1983. a. 1500 Yen. Doshitsu Kogakkai Chugoku Shibu - Japanese Society of Soil Mechanics and Foundation Engineering, Chuoku Branch, Hiroshima Daigaku Kogakubu Daiyonrui Doshitsu Kenkyusitsu, Shitami, Saijo-cho, Higashihiroshi-mashi, Hiroshima-ken 724, Japan.

624 **CC** ISSN 1005-0159
JIEGOU GONGCHENGSHI/STRUCTURAL ENGINEERS. (Text in Chinese) 1985. q. $10. (Tongji Daxue - Tongji University) Tongji Chubanshe, 1239 Siping Rd., Shanghai 200092, People's Republic of China. TEL 5455080. FAX 5458965. (Subscr. to: Huadong Jianzhu Shejiyuan, 151 Hankou Rd., Shanghai 200002, P.R. China. TEL 3217420) (Co-sponsor: Huadong Jianzhu Shejiyuan - East China Architectural Design Institute) Ed. Jiang Dahua. adv.: page $200. circ. 2,000 (controlled).
Description: Contains structural analysis for building and bridges, and design studies for concrete, masonry and steel structures.

JISHIN KOGAKU BUNKEN MOKUROKU/BIBLIOGRAPHY OF EARTHQUAKE ENGINEERING. see EARTH SCIENCES — Abstracting, Bibliographies, Statistics

JISHIN KOGAKU KENKYU HAPPOYOKAI KOEN GAIYO/JAPAN SOCIETY OF CIVIL ENGINEERS. EARTHQUAKE ENGINEERING SYMPOSIUM. PROCEEDIGS. see EARTH SCIENCES — Geophysics

JISHIN KOGAKU SHINKOKAI NYUSU/JAPAN SOCIETY FOR EARTHQUAKE ENGINEERING PROMOTION NEWS. see EARTH SCIENCES — Geophysics

624 **FR** ISSN 0751-5936
JOURNAL DU BATIMENT ET DES TRAVAUX PUBLICS.* 1900. w. 230 F. Hebdo Editions, B.P. 1511, 69204 Lyon Cedex, France. TEL 78-28-68-18. FAX 78-27-99-23. Dir. Jacques Matagrin. adv.; bk.rev. circ. 10,000.

624 **US** ISSN 0893-1321
CODEN: JAEEEZ
JOURNAL OF AEROSPACE ENGINEERING. 1988. q. $116 to non-members (foreign $124); members $29 (foreign $37). American Society of Civil Engineers, Aerospace Division, 345 E. 47th St., New York, NY 10017-2398. TEL 212-705-7288. FAX 212-980-4681. Ed. Manohar P. Kamat. circ. 1,300. (also avail. in microform from UMI) **Indexed:** CAD CAM Abstr., Environ.Abstr., Tel.Abstr. **Document type:** academic/scholarly publication.
—BLDSC (4919.100000); EI; Faxon; UnCover; SWETS; UMI. **CCC.**
Description: Defines the role of the civil engineer in space. Emphasis is given to practical application of civil engineering in space and on earth.
Refereed Serial

624 **IQ** ISSN 1012-3423
JOURNAL OF BUILDING RESEARCH. (Text in Arabic, English) 1982. s-a. ID.5($15) to individuals; institutions $50. Scientific Research Council, Building Research Center, Jadiriyah P.O. Box 2441, Baghdad, Iraq. TELEX 213976 SR IK. Ed. Mohammed A. Elizzi. circ. 500. **Indexed:** Ceram.Abstr., Eng.Ind., Geo.Abstr. —BLDSC (4954.610500).

624 **CH** ISSN 0253-3804
TA4 **CODEN: TMSLDD**
JOURNAL OF CIVIL AND HYDRAULIC ENGINEERING. Key Title: Tumu Shuili. (Text in Chinese; summaries in Chinese, English) 1958. q. NT.$50 per no. Chinese Institute of Civil and Hydraulic Engineering, P.O. Box No. 499, Taipei, Taiwan, Republic of China. (Dist. by: Kiji Publishing Co., 185 Po-Ai Rd., 2nd Fl., Taipei 100, Taiwan) Ed. Tsin-siang Chia. bk.rev. circ. 6,000. **Indexed:** Abstr.J.Earthq.Eng., Geo.Abstr., Geotech.Abstr.
—CASDDS.
Formerly: Journal of Civil Engineering.

624 **US** ISSN 0887-381X
CODEN: JCRGEI
JOURNAL OF COLD REGIONS ENGINEERING. 1987. q. $72 to non-members (foreign $79); members $18 (foreign $25). American Society of Civil Engineers, Technical Council on Cold Regions Engineering, 345 E. 47th St., New York, NY 10017-2398. TEL 212-705-7288. FAX 212-980-4681. Ed. Eugene L. Marvin. index. circ. 1,400. **Indexed:** Energy Info.Abstr., Environ.Abstr. **Document type:** academic/scholarly publication.
—BLDSC (4958.799400); CIS; EI; Faxon; UnCover; SWETS; UMI. **CCC.**
Description: Publishes practice- and research-oriented articles from any area of civil engineering that is substantially related to cold regions.
Refereed Serial

JOURNAL OF COMPUTING IN CIVIL ENGINEERING. see ENGINEERING — Computer Applications

624 **US** ISSN 0733-9364
TA1 **CODEN: JCEMD4**
JOURNAL OF CONSTRUCTION ENGINEERING AND MANAGEMENT. Short title: Construction. 1956. q. $112 to non-members (foreign $124); members $28 (foreign $40). American Society of Civil Engineers, Construction Division, 345 E. 47th St., New York, NY 10017-2398. TEL 212-705-7288. FAX 212-980-4681. Ed. Robert B. Harris. circ. 5,000. (also avail. in microform from UMI; reprint service avail. from UMI) **Indexed:** A.I.Abstr., A.S.& T.Ind., Br.Rail.Bd., Build.Manage.Abstr., C.R.I.Abstr., CAD CAM Abstr., Curr.Cont., Energy Info.Abstr., Eng.Ind., Excerp.Med., Fluidex, HRIS, INIS Atomind., J.of Ferroc., Sel.Water Res.Abstr. **Document type:** academic/scholarly publication.
—BLDSC (4965.185000); CIS; EI; Faxon; UnCover; SWETS; UMI. **CCC.**
Formerly (until 1982): American Society of Civil Engineers. Construction Division. Journal (ISSN 0569-7948)
Description: Aims to advance the science of construction engineering, to harmonize construction practices with design theories, and to further education and research in construction engineering and management.

624 **UK** ISSN 0143-974X
CODEN: JCSRDL
JOURNAL OF CONSTRUCTIONAL STEEL RESEARCH. 1981. 12/yr. (in 4 vols., 3 nos./vol.). £483($745) (effective 1994). Elsevier Science Ltd., Oxford Fulfilment Centre, P.O. Box 800, Kidlington, Oxford OX5 1DX, England. TEL 44-865-843000. FAX 44-865-843010. (Subscr. in U.S. and Canada to: Elsevier Science, 660 White Plains Rd., Tarrytown, NY 10591-5153. TEL 914-524-9200. FAX 914-333-2444) Eds. P.J. Dowling, J.E. Harding. adv.; bk.rev.; abstr.; charts; illus. (also avail. in microform from UMI; back issues avail.) **Indexed:** Appl.Mech.Rev., BMT, Curr.Cont., Eng.Ind., Intl.Civil Eng.Abstr., Met.Abstr., World Alum.Abstr. **Document type:** academic/scholarly publication.
—BLDSC (4965.193000); EI; Faxon; UnCover; SWETS. **CCC.**
Description: Covers developments in structural research and application.
Refereed Serial

JOURNAL OF ELASTICITY. see ENGINEERING — Engineering Mechanics And Materials

624 **US** ISSN 0733-9402
TJ1 **CODEN: JLEED9**
JOURNAL OF ENERGY ENGINEERING. Short title: Energy. 1956. irreg. (2-3/yr.). $84 to non-members (foreign $90); members $21 (foreign $27). American Society of Civil Engineers, Energy Division, 345 E. 47th St., New York, NY 10017-2398. TEL 212-705-7288. FAX 212-980-4681. Ed. Gordon L. Dugan. circ. 2,500. (also avail. in microform from UMI; reprint service avail. from UMI) **Indexed:** A.S.& T.Ind., Acid Rain Abstr., Acid Rain Ind., Chem.Abstr., Curr.Cont., Deep Sea Res.& Oceanogr.Abstr., Energy Info.Abstr., Environ.Abstr., Excerp.Med., Fluidex, GeoRef., Geotech.Abstr., Ind.Sci.Rev., INIS Atomind., Int.Abstr.Oper.Res., Sci.Cit.Ind., Sel Water Res.Abstr. **Document type:** academic/scholarly publication.
—BLDSC (4978.310000); CIS; EI; Faxon; UnCover; SWETS; UMI; CASDDS. **CCC.**
Former titles (until 1983): American Society of Civil Engineers. Energy Division. Journal (ISSN 0190-8294); (until 1979): American Society of Civil Engineers. Power Division. Journal (ISSN 0569-8030)
Description: Reports on the development of scientific and engineering knowledge in the planning, management, and generation of electrical power.

624 **US** ISSN 0733-9399
TA1 **CODEN: JENMDT**
JOURNAL OF ENGINEERING MECHANICS. 1956. m. $284 to non-members (foreign $319); members $71 (foreign $106). American Society of Civil Engineers, Engineering Mechanics Division, 345 E. 47th St., New York, NY 10017-2398. TEL 212-705-7288. FAX 212-980-4681. Ed. Zdenek P. Bazant. circ. 3,000. (also avail. in microform from UMI; reprint service avail. from UMI) **Indexed:** A.S.& T.Ind., Abstr.Bull.Inst.Pap.Chem., Appl.Mech.Rev., BMT, CAD CAM Abstr., Curr.Cont., Deep Sea Res.& Oceanogr.Abstr., E&P Hlth. (1993-), Energy Info.Abstr., Eng.Ind., Fluidex, Gas Process.& Ppl. (1993-), GeoRef., Geotech.Abstr., HRIS, Ind.Sci.Rev., Int.Aerosp.Abstr., Intl.Civil Eng.Abstr., J.of Ferroc., Off.Tech. (1993-), Petrol.Abstr. (1964-), Sci.Cit.Ind., Sel.Water Res.Abstr., Sh.& Vib.Dig., Soft.Abstr.Eng. **Document type:** academic/scholarly publication.
—BLDSC (4979.160000); EI; Faxon; UnCover; SWETS; UMI. **CCC.**
Formerly (1973-1982): American Society of Civil Engineers. Engineering Mechanics Division. Journal (ISSN 0044-7951)
Description: Covers activities and development in the field of applied mechanics as it relates to civil engineering.
Refereed Serial

JOURNAL OF ENVIRONMENTAL ENGINEERING. see ENVIRONMENTAL STUDIES

624.176 551 **US** ISSN 0733-9410
TA705 **CODEN: JGENDZ**
JOURNAL OF GEOTECHNICAL ENGINEERING. 1956. m. $212 to non-members (foreign $240); members $53 (foreign $81). American Society of Civil Engineers, Geotechnical Engineering Division, 345 E. 47th St., New York, NY 10017-2398. TEL 212-705-7288. FAX 212-980-4681. Ed. David Daniels. circ. 9,000. (also avail. in microform from UMI; reprint service avail. from UMI) **Indexed:** A.S.& T.Ind., Appl.Mech.Rev., Br.Rail.Bd., CAD CAM Abstr., Curr.Cont., Deep Sea Res.& Oceanogr.Abstr., E&P Hlth. (1993-), Energy Info.Abstr., Eng.Ind., Environ.Abstr., Environ.Per.Bibl., Excerp.Med., Fluidex, Gas Process.& Ppl. (1993-), Geo.Abstr., GeoRef., Geotech.Abstr., HRIS, Ind.Sci.Rev., INIS Atomind., Intl.Civil Eng.Abstr., Off.Tech. (1993-), Petrol.Abstr. (1980-), Sci.Cit.Ind., Sel.Water Res.Abstr., Soft.Abstr.Eng., Soils & Fert., W.R.C.Inf. **Document type:** academic/scholarly publication.
—BLDSC (4995.065000); CIS; EI; Faxon; UnCover; SWETS; UMI. **CCC.**
Former titles (until 1982): American Society of Civil Engineers. Geotechnical Engineering Division. Journal (ISSN 0093-6405); (until 1974): American Society of Civil Engineers. Soil Mechanics and Foundation Division. Journal (ISSN 0044-7994)
Description: Covers the field of soil mechanics and foundations, with emphasis on the relationship between the geologic environment and man-made works.
Refereed Serial

ENGINEERING — CIVIL ENGINEERING

624 627   US   ISSN 0733-9429
TC1   CODEN: JHEND8
JOURNAL OF HYDRAULIC ENGINEERING (NEW YORK).
1956. m. $200 to non-members (foreign $224); members $50 (foreign $74). American Society of Civil Engineers, Hydraulics Division, 345 E. 47th St., New York, NY 10017-2398. TEL 212-705-7288. FAX 212-980-4681. Ed. A. Jacob Odgaard. circ. 4,500. (also avail. in microform from UMI; reprint service avail. from UMI) **Indexed:** A.S.& T.Ind., Appl.Mech.Rev., Curr.Cont., Deep Sea Res.& Oceanogr.Abstr., Energy Info.Abstr., Environ.Abstr., Excerp.Med., Fluidex, GeoRef., Geotech.Abstr., HRIS, Ind.Sci.Rev., INIS Atomind., Int.Abstr.Oper.Res., Ocean.Abstr., Pollut.Abstr., Sci.Cit.Ind., Sel.Water Res.Abstr., Soils & Fert., W.R.C.Inf. **Document type:** academic/scholarly publication.
—BLDSC (5003.495000); CIS; EI; Faxon; UnCover; SWETS; UMI. **CCC**.
Formerly (until 1982): American Society of Civil Engineers. Hydraulics Division. Journal (ISSN 0044-796X)
Description: Describes the analysis and solutions of problems in hydraulic engineering, hydrology, and water resources.
Refereed Serial

624 630   US   ISSN 0733-9437
TC801   CODEN: JIDEDH
JOURNAL OF IRRIGATION AND DRAINAGE. 1956. bi-m. $136 to non-members (foreign $149); members $34 (foreign $47). American Society of Civil Engineers, Irrigation and Drainage Division, 345 E. 47th St, New York, NY 10017-2398. TEL 212-705-7288. FAX 212-980-4681. Ed. A. Ramachandra Rao. circ. 3,500. (also avail. in microform from UMI; reprint service avail. from UMI) **Indexed:** A.S.& T.Ind., Acid Pre.Dig., Curr.Cont., Eng.Ind., Environ.Abstr., GeoRef., Geotech.Abstr., Hort.Abstr., I D A, Ind.Sci.Rev., Int.Abstr.Oper.Res., Intl.Civil Eng.Abstr., Irr.& Drain.Abstr., Rice Abstr., Sci.Cit.Ind., Sel.Water Res.Abstr., Soft.Abstr.Eng., Soils & Fert., World Agri.Econ.& Rural Sociol.Abstr. **Document type:** academic/scholarly publication.
—BLDSC (5008.430000); CIS; EI; Faxon; UnCover; SWETS; UMI. **CCC**.
Formerly (until 1983): American Society of Civil Engineers. Irrigation and Drainage Division. Journal (ISSN 0044-7978)
Description: Covers all phases of irrigation, drainage, and related water management subjects, such as watershed management, weather modification, water quality, groundwater, and surface water.
Refereed Serial

JOURNAL OF IRRIGATION ENGINEERING AND RURAL PLANNING. see *AGRICULTURE*

624   US   ISSN 0899-1561
TA401   CODEN: JMCEE7
JOURNAL OF MATERIALS IN CIVIL ENGINEERING: PROPERTIES, APPLICATIONS, DURABILITY. 1989. q. $128 to non-members (foreign $136); members $32 (foreign $40). American Society of Civil Engineers, Materials Engineering Division, 345 E. 47th St., New York, NY 10017-2398. TEL 212-705-7288. FAX 212-980-4681. Eds. F.V. Lawrence, Jr., J.S. Ramachandsan. circ. 2,000. **Indexed:** J.of Ferroc. **Document type:** academic/scholarly publication.
—BLDSC (5012.210000); CIS; EI; Faxon; UnCover; SWETS; UMI; CASDDS. **CCC**.
Description: Covers the development, processing, evaluation, applications, and performance of construction materials in civil engineering.
Refereed Serial

624   US   ISSN 0887-3828
                           CODEN: JPCFEV
JOURNAL OF PERFORMANCE OF CONSTRUCTED FACILITIES. 1987. q. $80 to non-members (foreign $87); members $20 (foreign $27). American Society of Civil Engineers, Technical Council on Forensic Engineering, 345 E. 47th St., New York, NY 10017-2398. TEL 212-705-7288. FAX 212-980-4681. Ed. Kenneth L. Carper. circ. 2,300. **Indexed:** J.of Ferroc. **Document type:** academic/scholarly publication.
—BLDSC (5030.540000); CIS; EI; Faxon; UnCover; SWETS; UMI. **CCC**.
Description: Attempts to improve the quality of the constructed product through interdisciplinary communication. Papers examine the cause and cost of failures and other performance problems. Both catastrophic failures as well as serviceability problems are examined.

624   US   ISSN 1052-3928
TA1   CODEN: JPEPE3
JOURNAL OF PROFESSIONAL ISSUES IN ENGINEERING AND PRACTICE. 1956. q. $80 to non-members (foreign $88); members $20 (foreign $28). American Society of Civil Engineers, Professional Activities, 345 E. 47th St., New York, NY 10017-2398. TEL 212-705-7288. FAX 212-980-4681. Ed. Archie N. Carter. circ. 3,000. (also avail. in microform from UMI; reprint service avail. from UMI) **Indexed:** A.S.& T.Ind., CAD CAM Abstr., Deep Sea Res.& Oceanogr.Abstr., Energy Info.Abstr., Eng.Ind., Environ.Abstr., Fluidex, HRIS, I D A, Ind.Sci.Rev., Tel.Abstr. **Document type:** academic/scholarly publication.
—BLDSC (5042.692000); CIS; EI; Faxon; UnCover; SWETS; UMI. **CCC**.
Former titles (until 1991): Journal of Professional Issues in Engineering (ISSN 0733-9380); (until 1982): Issues in Engineering; (1973-1979): Engineering Issues (ISSN 0093-8343)
Description: Presents issues of interest and diverse views of engineering management as well as professional activities and technical problems. Papers examine the relationship between civil engineering and other disciplines and professions, with emphasis on the engineer's obligations and responsibilities.
Refereed Serial

624   US   ISSN 0733-9445
TA1   CODEN: JSENDH
JOURNAL OF STRUCTURAL ENGINEERING. 1956. m. $300 to non-members (foreign $350); members $75 (foreign $125). American Society of Civil Engineers, Structural Division, 345 E. 47th St., New York, NY 10017-2398. TEL 212-705-7288. FAX 212-980-4681. Ed. Vernon B. Watwood, Jr. circ. 7,000. (also avail. in microform from UMI; reprint service avail. from UMI) **Indexed:** A.S.& T.Ind., Appl.Mech.Rev., BMT, C.R.I.Abstr., Concr.Abstr., Curr.Cont., Deep Sea Res.& Oceanogr.Abstr., E&P Hlth. (1993-), Eng.Ind., Environ.Abstr., Forest.Abstr., Forest Prod.Abstr., Gas Process.& Ppl. (1993-), Geo.Abstr., GeoRef, Geotech.Abstr., HRIS, Ind.Sci.Rev., J.of Ferroc., Off.Tech. (1993-), Petrol.Abstr. (1964-), Risk Abstr., Sh.& Vib.Dig. **Document type:** academic/scholarly publication.
—BLDSC (5066.877200); EI; Faxon; UnCover; SWETS; UMI. **CCC**.
Formerly (1973-1982): American Society of Civil Engineers. Structural Division. Journal (ISSN 0044-8001)
Description: Reports on the science of structural design. Discusses the physical properties of engineering materials, such as steel, concrete, and wood; develops methods of analysis; and studies the relative merits of various types of structures.

624 621   II   ISSN 0970-0137
TA630   CODEN: JSENEI
JOURNAL OF STRUCTURAL ENGINEERING. (Text in English) 1973. q. Rs.250($60) Structural Engineering Research Centre, CSIR Campus, Taramani, Madras 600 113, India. TEL 044-2352175. FAX 044-2350508. TELEX 041 8906. Ed.Bd. adv.; bk.rev. circ. 400. **Indexed:** A.S.& T.Ind., Abstr.Bull.Inst.Pap.Chem., Appl.Mech.Rev., Concr.Abstr., Fluidex, HRIS, J.of Ferroc., Risk Abstr. **Document type:** academic/scholarly publication.
Description: Provides a forum for structural engineers to document, discuss, and debate current trends in analysis, design, research, and development relating to all areas of structural engineering.

625.72   US   ISSN 0733-9453
TA501   CODEN: JSUED2
JOURNAL OF SURVEYING ENGINEERING. 1956. q. $76 to non-members (foreign $82); members $19 (foreign $25). American Society of Civil Engineers, Surveying Engineering Division, 345 E. 47th St., New York, NY 10017-2398. TEL 212-705-7288. FAX 212-980-4681. Ed. Earl F. Burkholder. circ. 2,500. (also avail. in microform from UMI; reprint service avail. from UMI) **Indexed:** A.S.& T.Ind., Curr.Cont., Deep Sea Res.& Oceanogr.Abstr., Eng.Ind., Environ.Abstr., Fluidex, HRIS, Ind.Sci.Rev., Intl.Civil Eng.Abstr., Soft.Abstr.Eng. **Document type:** academic/scholarly publication.
—BLDSC (5067.700000); EI; Faxon; UnCover; SWETS; UMI. **CCC**.
Former titles: Journal of Surveying and Mapping; (until 1982): American Society of Civil Engineers. Surveying and Mapping Division. Journal (ISSN 0569-8073)
Description: Covers civil engineering developments in surveying and mapping, as well as such related fields as cartographic and interplanetry surveying.
Refereed Serial

JOURNAL OF TRANSPORTATION ENGINEERING. see *TRANSPORTATION*

JOURNAL OF URBAN PLANNING AND DEVELOPMENT. see *HOUSING AND URBAN PLANNING*

JOURNAL OF WATER CHEMISTRY AND TECHNOLOGY. see *WATER RESOURCES*

624   US   ISSN 0733-9496
TC401   CODEN: JWRMD5
JOURNAL OF WATER RESOURCES PLANNING AND MANAGEMENT. bi-m. $112 to non-members (foreign $123); members $28 (foreign $39). American Society of Civil Engineers, Water Resources Planning and Management Division, 345 E. 47th St., New York, NY 10017-2398. TEL 212-705-7288. FAX 212-980-4681. Ed. Richard Palmer. circ. 3,500. (reprint service avail. from UMI) **Indexed:** A.I.Abstr., A.S.& T.Ind., CAD CAM Abstr., Curr.Adv.Ecol.Sci., Deep Sea Res.& Oceanogr.Abstr., Energy Info.Abstr., Eng.Ind., Environ.Abstr., Environ.Ind., Fluidex, GeoRef., Ind.Sci.Rev., Int.Abstr.Oper.Res., Sel.J.Water, Sel.Water Res.Abstr. **Document type:** academic/scholarly publication.
—BLDSC (5072.539400); CIS; EI; Faxon; UnCover; SWETS; UMI. **CCC**.
Formerly (until 1982): American Society of Civil Engineers. Water Resources Planning and Management Division. Journal (ISSN 0145-0743)
Description: Reports on all phases of planning and management of water resources. Examines social, economic, environmental, and administrative concerns relating to the use and conservation of water.
Refereed Serial

627 551.46   US   ISSN 0733-950X
TC1   CODEN: JWPED5
JOURNAL OF WATERWAY, PORT, COASTAL, AND OCEAN ENGINEERING. 1956. bi-m. $100 to non-members (foreign $111); members $25 (foreign $36). American Society of Civil Engineers, Waterway, Port, Coastal, and Ocean Division, 345 E. 47th St., New York, NY 10017-2398. TEL 212-705-7288. FAX 212-980-4681. Ed. Nobuhisa Kobayashi. circ. 3,000. (also avail. in microform from UMI; reprint service avail. from UMI) **Indexed:** A.S.& T.Ind., BMT, Curr.Cont., E&P Hlth. (1993-), Energy Info.Abstr., Eng.Ind., Environ.Abstr., Fluidex, Gas Process.& Ppl. (1993-), GeoRef., Ind.Sci.Rev., Ocean.Abstr., Off.Tech. (1993-), Petrol.Abstr. (1964-), Sel.Water Res.Abstr., W.R.C.Inf. **Document type:** academic/scholarly publication.
—BLDSC (5072.545000); CIS; EI; Faxon; UnCover; SWETS; UMI. **CCC**.
Former titles (until 1982): American Society of Civil Engineers. Waterway, Port, Coastal and Ocean Division. Journal (ISSN 0148-9895); (1973-1977): American Society of Civil Engineers. Waterways, Harbors, and Coastal Engineering Division. Journal (ISSN 0044-8028); And: American Society of Civil Engineers. Waterways and Harbors Division. Journal.
Description: Presents studies of the engineering aspects of dredging, floods, ice, pollution, sediment transport, and tidal wave action that affects shorelines, waterways, and harbors.

JURUTERA. see *ENGINEERING — Chemical Engineering*

ENGINEERING — CIVIL ENGINEERING

K B S - RAPPORTER. see *HOUSING AND URBAN PLANNING*

K B S TEKNISKA FOERESKRIFTER/K B S TECHNICAL REGULATIONS; krav och raad/requirements and recommendations. see *HOUSING AND URBAN PLANNING*

624   JA   ISSN 0451-2219
KAIGAN/SEA COAST. (Text in Japanese) 1962. a. 2500 Yen. Zenkoku Kaigan Kyokai - National Association of Sea Coast, 5-11, Akasaka 2-chome, Minato-ku, Tokyo 107, Japan.

624   JA
KAIGAN JITSUMU KOGISHU/PRACTICAL LECTURE NOTES ON SEA COAST. (Text in Japanese) a. 1750 Yen. Zenkoku Kaigan Kyokai - National Association of Sea Coast, 5-11, Akasaka 2-chome, Minato-ku, Tokyo 107, Japan.

624   JA
KAIGAN KOGAKU RONBUNSHU/PROCEEDINGS OF COASTAL ENGINEERING, JSCE. (Text in Japanese) 1954. a. price varies. Doboku Gakkai - Japan Society of Civil Engineering, Yotsuya 1-chome, Shinjuku-ku, Tokyo 160, Japan. TEL 03-272-7211. (Dist. by: Mazuren Co., Ltd., P.O. Box 5050, Tokyo International 100-31, Japan) adv. circ. 1,000. (back issues avail.) **Document type:** proceedings.
   Former titles (until 1989): Kaigan Kogaku Koenkai Ronbunshu - Japanese Conference on Coastal Engineering. Proceedings (ISSN 0285-7308); (until 1970): Kaigan Kogaku Koenkai Koenshu (ISSN 0419-4918)

624   JA   ISSN 0914-8159
KAIHATSU DOBOKU KENKYUJO GEPPO/CIVIL ENGINEERING RESEARCH INSTITUTE. MONTHLY REPORT. (Text in Japanese; summaries in English, Japanese) 1949. m. Hokkaido Kaihatsucho Hokkaido Kaihatsukyoku, Kaihatsu Doboku Kenkyujo - Hokkaido Development Agency, Hokkaido Development Bureau, Civil Engineering Research Institute, 3-chome, Hiragishi 1-jo, Toyohira-ku, Sapporo-shi, Hokkaido 062, Japan. Dir. Ajio Seizaki. **Indexed:** INIS Atomind. **Document type:** academic/scholarly publication, government publication.

624   JA   ISSN 0914-8167
KAIHATSU DOBOKU KENKYUJO HOKOKU/CIVIL ENGINEERING RESEARCH INSTITUTE. REPORT. (Text in English, Japanese; summaries in English) 1940. irreg. Hokkaido Kaihatsucho Hokkaido Kaihatsukyoko, Kaihatsu Doboku Kenkyujo Hokoku - Hokkaido Development Agency, Hokkaido Development Bureau, Civil Engineering Research Institute, 3-chome, Hiragishi 1-jo, Toyohira-ku, Sapporo-shi, Hokkai 062, Japan.

624   JA   ISSN 0914-8183
KAIHATSU DOBOKU KENKYUJO KOENKAI TOKUSHUGO/CIVIL ENGINEERING RESEARCH INSTITUTE. SPECIAL REPORT FOR THE LECTURE MEETING. (Text in Japanese) 1987. a. Hokkaido Kaihatsucho Hokkaido Kaihatsukyoku, Kaihatsu Doboku Kenkyujo - Hokkaido Development Agency, Hoddaido Development Bureau, Civil Engineering Research Institute, 3-chome, Hiragishi 1-jo, Toyohira-ku, Sapporo-shi, Hokkaido 062, Japan. Dir. Akio Seizaki. **Document type:** academic/scholarly publication, government publication.

624   JA   ISSN 0914-8175
KAIHATSU DOBOKU KENKYUJO NENPO/CIVIL ENGINEERING RESEARCH INSTITUTE. ANNUAL REPORT. (Text in Japanese) 1951. a. Hokkaido Kaihatsucho Hokkaido Kaihatsukyoku, Kaihatsu Doboku Kenkyujo - Hokkaido Development Agency, Hokkaido Development Bureau, Civil Engineering Research Institute, 3-chome, Hiragishi 1-jo, Toyohira-ku, Sapporo-shi, Hokkaido 062, Japan. Dir. Akio Seizaki. **Document type:** government publication.

624   JA   ISSN 0912-7348
KAIYO KAIHATSU RONBUNSHU/OCEAN DEVELOPMENT SYMPOSIUM. PROCEEDINGS. (Text in Japanese) 1970. a. price varies. Dobuku Gakkai - Japan Society of Civil Engineers, Committee on Ocean Development, Yotsuya 1-chome, Shinjuku-ku, Tokyo 160, Japan. TEL 03-272-7211. (Subscr. to: JSCE or Maruzen Co., Ltd., P.O. Box 5050, Tokyo International 100-31, Japan) circ. 250. (back issues avail.) **Document type:** proceedings.

624   JA   ISSN 0387-0960
KAJIMA GIJUTSU KENKYUJO NENPO/KAJIMA TECHNICAL RESEARCH INSTITUTE. ANNUAL REPORT. (Text and summaries in English, Japanese) 1949. a. Kajima Gijutsu Kenkyujo - Kajima Tecchnical Research Institute, 19-1, Tobitakyu 2-chome, Chofu-shi, Tokyo 182, Japan.
—BLDSC (1315.190000).

624 614.7   JA   ISSN 0913-4093
KANKYO MONDAI SHINPOJUMU KOEN RONBUNSHU/SYMPOSIUM ON ENVIRONMENTAL PROBLEMS. PROCEEDINGS. (Text in Japanese; summaries in English) 1973. a. price varies. Doboku Gakkai - Japan Society of Civil Engineers, Committee on Environmental Problems, Mubanchi, Yotsuya 1-Chome, Shinjuku-Ku, Tokyo, 160, Japan. TEL 03-272-7211. (Subscr. to: Mazuren Co., Ltd., P.O. Box 5050, Tokyo International 100-31, Japan) circ. 350. (back issues avail.) **Document type:** proceedings.

625.7   TU   ISSN 0022-9024
KARAYOLLARI TEKNIK BULTENI. (Text in English, French, German, Turkish) 1960. q. General Directorate of Highways, Ankara, Turkey. Eds. Muhittin Ozdirim, Gungor Goktug. adv.; bibl.; charts; illus.; stat.; circ. 3,000 (controlled). (cards)

KASEN DENTO KOHO/STUDY ON THE TRADITIONAL RIVER WORKS. see *WATER RESOURCES*

624   JA
KATRI REPORT. (Text in English) 1972. irreg. Kajima Technical Research Institute - Kajima Gijutsu Kenkyujo, 19-1, Tobitakyu 2-chome, Chofu-shi, Tokyo 182, Japan.

KEEPER'S LOG. see *HISTORY*

624   JA
KENSETSU GIJUTSU SHINBUN/CONSTRUCTION ENGINEERING NEWS. (Text in Japanese) bi-w. 22000 Yen. Kensetsu Kogyo Kaihatsu Senta - Construction Industry Development Center, 1-14, Kanda Nishiki-cho, Chiyoda-ku, Tokyo 101, Japan.

624   JA   ISSN 0386-2054
KENSETSU GYOKAI/CIVIL ENGINEERING CONSTRUCTION. (Text in Japanese) 1952. m. 400 Yen per no. Nihon Doboku Kogyo Kyokai - Japan Civil Engineering Contractors' Association, Inc., 5-1, Hatchobori 2-chome, Chuo-ku, Tokyo 104, Japan.

KENSETSU KIKAI/CONSTRUCTION MACHNIERY AND EQUIPMENT. see *MACHINERY*

624 690   JA   ISSN 0288-9994
                       CODEN: KKNMDE
KENSETSU KOGAKU KENKYU SHINKOKAI NENPO/SOCIETY FOR THE PROMOTION OF CONSTRUCTION ENGINEERING. ANNUAL REPORT. (Text in Japanese) 1965. a. Kensetsu Kogaku Kenkyu Shinkokai, 4-6, Kitami-cho, Aoba-ku, Sendai-shi, Miyagi-ken 980, Japan.
—CASDDS.

624   JA   ISSN 0022-9997
KENSETSU KOGYO BUKKA CHINGIN GEPPO/MONTHLY REPORT OF PRICE AND WAGE IN CONSTRUCTION ENGINEERING. (Text in Japanese) 1916. m. free. Shimizu Corporation, 16-1 Kyobashi 2-chome, Chuo-ku, Tokyo 104, Japan. charts; mkt.; stat. circ. 2,300. (looseleaf format)
   Description: For Japanese construction industry management.

624   JA
KENSETSU KONSARUTANTSU KYOKAI KINKI SHIBU GYOMU KENKYU HAPPYOKAI RONSHU/JAPAN CIVIL ENGINEERING CONSULTANTS ASSOCIATION. KINKI BRANCH. REPORTS OF THE ANNUAL RESEARCH CONFERENCE. (Text in Japanese) 1968. a. Kensetsu Konsarutantsu Kyokai, Kinki Shibu, A-12, Uemachi, Chuo-ku, Osaka-shi, Osaka 540, Japan.

624   US   ISSN 1062-0745
TH435
KERR'S COST DATA FOR LANDSCAPE CONSTRUCTION. 1980. a. $35. Kerr Associates, 1207 Iowa Ave., Ames, IA 50010. TEL 515-292-5377. Ed. Norman L. Dietrich. circ. 3,500.
   Formerly (until 1990): Cost Data for Landscape Construction (ISSN 0271-2067)
   Description: Covers landscape construction costs, landscape architects, contractors, developers, appraisers and grounds managers.

624   JA   ISSN 0285-5356
KISOKO/FOUNDATION ENGINEERING AND EQUIPMENT. (Text in Japanese) 1973. m. 1600 Yen per no. Sogo Doboku Kenkyujo, 6-12 B-1310, Yushima 4-chome, Bunkyo-ku, Tokyo 113, Japan.

KOKUSAI JISHIN OYOBI JISHIN KOGAKU KENSHU NENPO/INTERNATIONAL STUDY REPORT ON THE EARTHQUAKE AND EARTHQUAKE ENGINEERING. see *EARTH SCIENCES*

624 690   JA   ISSN 0912-3938
KOKYO. (Text in Japanese) s-a. Nihon Kyoryo Kensetsu Kyokai - Japanese Association of Steel Bridge Construction, 2-18, Ginza 2-chome, Chuo-ku, Tokyo 104, Japan.

624 690   JA   ISSN 0911-7873
KOKYO TOSO. (Text in Japanese) 1973. q. Nihon Kokyo Toso Semonkai - Japan Association of Steel Bridge Painting Constructors, 19-22, Sendagaya 4-chome, Shibuya-ku, Tokyo 150, Japan.

KOMPASS PROFESSIONNEL. BATIMENT ET GENIE CIVIL, MANUTENTION - LEVAGE, BOIS - MEUBLES. see *BUSINESS AND ECONOMICS — Trade And Industrial Directories*

624 690   JA
KONKURITO KOGAKU RONBUNSHU/CONCRETE RESEARCH AND TECHNOLOGY. (Text in Japanese; summaries in English, Japanese) 1990. s-a. 5500 Yen($50) Nihon Konkurito Kogaku Kyokai - Japan Concrete Institute, No. 708 TBR Bldg., 5-7, Kohjimachi, Chiyoda-ku, Tokyo 102, Japan. TEL 81-3-3263-1571. FAX 81-3-3263-2115. Ed. Itsuo Honda.

624   JA   ISSN 0286-9179
KOTSUZAI SHIGEN/JAPAN INSTITUTE OF AGGREGATE TECHNOLOGY. JOURNAL. (Text in Japanese) 1969. q. Kotsuzai Shigen Kogakkai - Japan Institute of Aggregate Technology, Waseda Daigaku Rikogakubu Shigen Kogakka, 4-1, Okubo 3-chome, Shinjuku-ku, Tokyo 169, Japan.

624   JA   ISSN 0287-4733
KOWAN/PORT AND HARBOUR. (Text in Japanese) 1923. m. 800 Yen per no. Nihon Kowan Kyokai - Japan Port and Harbour Association, 2-8, Toranomon 1-chome, Minato-ku, Tokyo 105, Japan.

KOWAN GIJUTSU KENKYUJO. GAIDO/PORT AND HARBOUR RESEARCH INSTITUTE. GUIDE. see *TRANSPORTATION — Ships And Shipping*

624   JA   ISSN 0454-4641
KOWAN GIJUTSU KENKYUJO HOKOKU/PORT AND HARBOUR RESEARCH INSTITUTE. REPORT. (Text in English, Japanese) 1963. q. Un'yusho, Kowan Gijutsu Kenkyujo - Ministry of Transport, Port and Harbour Research Institute, 1-1, Nagase 3-chome, Yokosuka-shi, Kanagawa-ken 239, Japan. **Indexed:** INIS Atomind.

624   JA
KOWAN GIJUTSU KENKYUJO NENPO/PORT AND HARBOUR RESEARCH INSTITUTE. ANNUAL REPORT. (Text in Japanese) 1963. a. Un'yusho, Kowan Gijutsu Kenkyujo - Ministry of Transport, Port and Habour Research Institute, 1-1, Nagase 3-chome, Yokosuka-shi, Kanagawa-ken 239, Japan. **Document type:** government publication.

624   JA
KOWAN GIJUTSU SHINKOKAI. KOENKAI KOEN GAIYO/ASSOCIATION FOR THE PORT AND HARBOUR ENGINEERING PROMOTION. PROCEEDINGS OF THE MEETING. (Text in Japanese) 1977. a. Kowan Gijutsu Shinkokai, Ur'yusho Kowan Gijutsu Kenkyujo, 1-1, Nagase 3-chome, Yokosuka-shi, Kanagawa-ken 239, Japan. **Document type:** proceedings.

ENGINEERING — CIVIL ENGINEERING

624   JA
KOWAN GIJUTSU SHINKOKAI SHIRYO/MATERIALS FOR PORT AND HARBOUR ENGINEERING PROMOTION. (Text in Japanese) 1991. irreg. Kowan Gijutsu Shinkokai - Association for the Port and Harbour Engineering Promotion, Un'Yusho Kowan Gijutsu Kenkyujo, 1-1, Nagase 3-chome, Yokosuka-shi, Kanagawa-ken 239, Japan.

624   JA   ISSN 0454-4668
KOWAN GIKEN SHIRYO/PORT AND HARBOUR RESEARCH INSTITUTE. TECHNICAL NOTE. (Text in Japanese; summaries in English, Japanese) 1963. irreg. Un'Yusho, Kowan Gijutsu Kenkyujo - Ministry of Transport, Port and Harbour Research Institute, 1-1 Nagase 3-chome, Yokosuka-shi, Kanagawa-ken 239, Japan.

624   JA
KOWAN KOENKAI KOENSHU/SYMPOSIUM ON PORT SCIENCE. PROCEEDINGS. (Text in Japanese) 1967. a. Nihon Kowan Kyokai - Japan Port and Harbour Association, 2-8, Toranomon 1-chome, Minato, Tokyo 105, Japan. **Document type:** proceedings.

624   JA   ISSN 0910-8009
KOZO KOGAKU RONBUNSHU A/JOURNAL OF STRUCTURAL ENGINEERING A. (Text in Japanese; summaries in English) a. 6000 Yen. Doboku Gakkai - Japan Society of Civil Engineers, Yotsuya 1-chome, Shinjuku-ku, Tokyo 160, Japan. **Document type:** academic/scholarly publication.

624   JA
KOZO KOGAKU SHIRIZU/STRUCTURAL ENGINEERING SERIES. (Text in Japanese) irreg. Doboku Gakkai - Japan Society of Civil Engineers, Yotsuya 1-chome, Shinjuku-ku, Tokyo 160, Japan.

624   JA
KUMAGAI GUMI GIJYUTSUKENKYU HOKOKU/KUMAGAI TECHNICAL RESEARCH REPORT. (Text in Japanese; summaries in English, Japanese) 1967. s-a. free. Kumagai Gijutsu Kenkyujo - Kumagai Technical Research Institute, Editorial Committee, 1043 Onigakubo, Tsukua-shi, Ibaraki 300-22, Japan. TEL 81-298-47-7501. FAX 81-298-47-7480. Ed. Takeyasu Suzuki. circ. 5,000. **Document type:** academic/scholarly publication.
Formerly (until Oct. 1992): Kumagai Giho (ISSN 0388-421X)
Description: Introduces new technology and construction methods developed in Kumagai Gumi Co., Ltd.

KUNNALLISTEKNIIKKA/KOMMUNALTEKNIK. see *HOUSING AND URBAN PLANNING*

624   JA   ISSN 0287-0991
KYORYO/BRIDGE ENGINEERING. (Text in Japanese) 1965. m. 650 Yen per no. Kyoryo Hensankai, 3-1, Kanda Jinbo-cho, Chiyoda-ku, Tokyo 101, Japan.

624 690   JA
KYORYO NENKAN/STEEL BRIDGE YEARBOOK. (Text in Japanese) 1979. a. Nihon Kyoryo Kensetsu Kyokai - Japanese Association of Steel Bridge Construction, 2-18, Ginza 2-chome, Chuo-ku, Tokyo 104, Japan.

624   JA
KYORYO SHINBUN/BRIDGE NEWS. (Text in Japanese) 1973. 3/m. 88000 Yen. Tekunopakku Co., Inc., 6-6, Iriya 1-chome, Taito-ku, Tokyo 110, Japan.

624   JA   ISSN 0287-170X
KYORYO TO KISO/BRIDGE AND FOUNDATION ENGINEERING. (Text in Japanese) 1967. m. 930 Yen per no. Kensetsu Tosho, 2-17, Sotokanda 2-chome, Chiyoda-ku, Tokyo 101, Japan.
—BLDSC (2283.926400).

624   JA   ISSN 0075-7365
KYOTO UNIVERSITY. RESEARCH ACTIVITIES IN CIVIL ENGINEERING AND RELATED FIELDS. (Text in English) 1963. triennial. free. Kyoto University, School of Civil Engineering, Yoshida Honmachi, Sakyo-ku, Kyoto-shi, Kyoto 606, Japan.

624   PO   ISSN 0870-9149
LABORATORIO NACIONAL DE ENGENHARIA CIVIL. BOLETIM DE INFORMACAO TECNICA. 1949. 3/yr. Esc.500 per no. Laboratorio Nacional de Engenharia Civil, Avenida do Brasil, 101, 1799 Lisbon Codex, Portugal. abstr.; illus.; pat.; index. circ. 1,500. **Document type:** proceedings.
Formerly: Laboratorio Nacional de Engenharia Civil. Boletim Mensal de Informacao (ISSN 0032-5090)

354   LB
LIBERIA. MINISTRY OF LANDS, MINES AND ENERGY. ANNUAL REPORT.* 1961. a. Ministry of Lands, Mines and Energy, Monrovia, Liberia. circ. 600.
Formerly: Liberia. Ministry of Lands and Mines. Annual Report (ISSN 0304-7296)

LIGHTING JOURNAL. see *ENGINEERING — Electrical Engineering*

526 910   CN   ISSN 0827-6978
LINK (RICHMOND). 1977. q. Can.$20 to non-members. Corporation of British Columbia Land Surveyors, 895 Fort St., Ste. 306, Victoria, BC V8W 1H7, Canada. TEL 604-382-4323. FAX 604-382-5092. Ed. J.M. Magwood. adv. **Document type:** trade publication.

LOCAL 138 NEWS. see *LABOR UNIONS*

624   FI   ISSN 0047-5319
QB296.F5
MAANMITTAUS/SURVEYING. (Text in Finnish) 1925. s-a. Fmk.150. Finnish Society of Surveying Sciences - Maanmittaustieteiden Seura r.y., P.O. Box 84, 00521 Helsinki, Finland. TEL 358-0-4513911. Ed. Jaakko Santala. adv.; bk.rev. circ. 1,050. (tabloid format) **Indexed:** Bibl.Cart.

624   FI   ISSN 0047-5327
MAANSIIRTO/EARTHMOVING; maa- ja vesirakennusteknillinen aikakauslehti. (Text in Finnish; summaries in English and Swedish) 1960. 8/yr. FIM 220 in Finland; elsewhere FIM 320. Suomen Maarakentajien Keskusliitto ry - Central Association of Earth Moving Contractors in Finland, Asemapaallikoenkatu 12 B, SF-00520 Helsinki, Finland. TEL 358-90-144-188. FAX 358-90-147-841. Ed. Osmo Mettanen. adv.: B&W page FIM 7700, color page FIM 11900; trim 184 x 270. bk.rev.; illus.; stat. circ. 5,800.
Description: Focuses on earth moving and tunnelling techniques as well as news of the Association.

MCMAHON HEAVY CONSTRUCTION COST GUIDE. see *BUILDING AND CONSTRUCTION*

MADISON WASTE CONFERENCE. ANNUAL PROCEEDINGS; municipal and industrial waste. see *ENVIRONMENTAL STUDIES — Waste Management*

624   US   ISSN 0047-5548
MAINE TRAILS. 1941. bi-m. $20. Maine Better Transportation Association, 146 State St., Augusta, ME 04330. TEL 207-622-0526. FAX 207-623-2928. Ed. Maria R. Fuentes. adv.; illus.; circ. 1,200 (controlled).

624   JA   ISSN 0914-2495
MARIN BOISU 21/MARINE VOICE 21. (Text in Japanese) q. Nihon Umetate Shunsetsu Kyokai - Japan Dredging Reclamation Engineering Association, 2-8, Toranomon 1-chome, Minato-ku, Tokyo 105, Japan.

624 690   JA
MARIN RODO/MARINE ROAD. (Text in Japanese) 1987. s-a. Tokyowan Odan Doro K.K. - Trans-Tokyo Bay Highway Corp., 15-5, Ichiban-cho, Chiyoda-ku, Tokyo 102, Japan.

MASONRY SOCIETY JOURNAL. see *BUILDING AND CONSTRUCTION*

624   GW   ISSN 0340-983X
MATERIALIENSAMMLUNG STAEDTEBAU. 1972. irreg. price varies. Ferd. Duemmlers Verlag, Kaiserstr. 31-37, 53113 Bonn, Germany. (Subscr. to: Postfach 1480, 53004 Bonn, Germany)

624 621.9   RU   ISSN 0025-8903
MEKHANIZATSIYA STROITEL'STVA. 1939. m. 22.20 Rub. (Gosstroi) Izdatel'stvo Stroiizdat, Kalyaevskaya ul., 23a, Moscow 101442, Russia. Ed. A.G. Boiko. adv.; bk.rev.; bibl.; charts; illus.; tr.lit.; index. circ. 16,540.
—BLDSC (0113.000000).

MELYEPITESI ES VIZEPITESI SZAKIRODALMI TAJEKOZTATO/CIVIL ENGINEERING & HYDRAULIC ENGINEERING ABSTRACTS. see *ENGINEERING — Abstracting, Bibliographies, Statistics*

620 388   HU   ISSN 0025-9039
MELYEPITESTUDOMANYI SZEMLE. (Text in Hungarian; summaries in English, French, German, Russian) 1951. m. $39.50. (Kozlekedestudomanyi Egyesulet) Lapkiado Vallalat, Lenin korut 9-11, 1073 Budapest 7, Hungary. TEL 222-408. (Subscr. to: Kultura, Box 149, H-1389 Budapest, Hungary) Ed. Miklos Szucs. charts; illus. **Indexed:** Appl.Mech.Rev., Chem.Abstr., Geotech.Abstr., Hung.Build.Bull., Intl.Civil Eng.Abstr., Soft.Abstr.Eng.

MESTNYI PROIZVODSTVENNYI OPYT V STROITEL'STVE/LOCAL LEVEL EXPERIENCE IN THE CONSTRUCTION INDUSTRY; nauchno-tekhnicheskii referativnyi sbornik. see *BUILDING AND CONSTRUCTION*

624   MX   ISSN 0185-402X
TA710.4.M6
MEXICAN SOCIETY FOR SOIL MECHANICS MEETING. PROCEEDINGS. (Text in Spanish) 1970. biennial, 12th, 1984. price varies. Sociedad Mexicana de Mecanica de Suelos - Mexican Society for Soil Mechanics, Valle de Bravo 19, Col. Vergel de Coyoacan, Tlalpan, 14340 Mexico, D.F., Mexico. **Document type:** proceedings.

624   US
MICHIGAN ROADS AND CONSTRUCTION. 1905. w. $20. Baker Publishing Co., Box 25007, Lansing, MI 48909. TEL 517-332-7600. Ed. Bud Baker. adv. circ. 2,000. **Indexed:** Mich.Mag.Ind.

MICROSTATION MANAGER; the monthly independent publication for the Intergraph professional. see *ARCHITECTURE — Computer Applications*

557   US   ISSN 0076-9606
CODEN: MGEGBB
MISSOURI. DIVISION OF GEOLOGICAL SURVEY AND WATER RESOURCES. ENGINEERING GEOLOGY SERIES. 1968. irreg., no.7, 1983. price varies. Department of Natural Resources, Division of Geology and Land Survey, Box 250, Rolla, MO 65401. TEL 314-368-2125.
Refereed Serial

624   JA
MITSUI ZOSEN TEKKO KOJI GIHO/M S C TECHNICAL REVIEW. (Text in Japanese) 1987. a. Mitsui Zosen Tekko Koji K.K., 1-57, Shibatani 1-chome, Suminoe-ku, Osaka-shi, Osaka 559, Japan.

MODULO. see *BUILDING AND CONSTRUCTION*

624   AT   ISSN 0155-6282
MONASH UNIVERSITY. DEPARTMENT OF CIVIL ENGINEERING. CIVIL ENGINEERING RESEARCH REPORT. 1970. 5/yr. free. Monash University, Department of Civil Engineering, Clayton, Vic. 3168, Australia. TEL 03-565-4973. FAX 603-565-4944. circ. 100.
Description: Presents results of recent research projects in the Department of Civil Engineering.

624   FR   ISSN 0026-9700
MONITEUR DES TRAVAUX PUBLICS ET DU BATIMENT. 1903. w. 1450 F. (foreign 2170 F.). Publications du Moniteur, 17 rue d'Uzes, 75002 Paris Cedex, France. TEL 1-40-13-30-30. FAX 1-40-41-94-95. TELEX UPRESSE 680876F. Ed. Nathalie Seyer. adv.; bk.rev.; charts; illus.; mkt.; stat.; circ. 76,054 (controlled). **Indexed:** C.I.S. Abstr.

624   JA   ISSN 0288-5581
MONKEN. (Text in Japanese) a. Tokyo Kensetsu Gijutsu Kyokai - Tokyo Construction Engineers Association, Tokyo Suidokyoku Kyusuibu Rosui Boshika, 8-1, Nishishinjuku 2-chome, Shinjuku-ku, Tokyo 163-01, Japan.

ENGINEERING — CIVIL ENGINEERING

625.7 388.3　　　　GW　ISSN 0027-1470
MOT - BAU; Fachzeitschrift fuer Tiefbau, Strassenbau, Recycling, Entsorgung. 1964. m. DM.106. Stueniens Verlagsgesellschaft mbH, Luisenstr. 100-104, 47799 Krefeld, Germany. TEL 02151-853-0. FAX 02151-853103. adv.; bk.rev. circ. 8,000.
Document type: trade publication.
Description: Explores excavations, site preparation, underground workings and road building.

624　　　　　SA　ISSN 0047-8369
MUNICIPAL ENGINEER. (Text in English) 1969. m. (11/yr.). R.88 (Southern Africa R.110; elsewhere R.230) (effective Apr. 1994). Brooke Pattrick (Pty) Ltd., P.O. Box 422, Bedfordview 2008, South Africa. TEL 27-11-6224666. FAX 27-11-6167196. Ed. Helen Gow. adv.; illus.; circ. 4,357 (controlled). **Indexed**: Ind.S.A.Per. **Document type**: trade publication.
Incorporates: ReSource.
Description: Engineering journal covering all disciplines in the municipal and local government sector.

624　　　　　AT　ISSN 0311-354X
MUNICIPAL ENGINEERING IN AUSTRALIA. 1973. bi-m. Aus.$34 (foreign Aus.$57). Editorial & Publishing Consultants Pty. Ltd., 29 First Ave., Klemzig, S.A. 5087, Australia. TEL 08-261-5837. FAX 08-261-2697. Ed.Bd. adv.: B&W page Aus.$884, color page Aus.$1196. circ. 2,000. **Indexed**: Aus.Rd.Ind.

628　　　　　US　ISSN 0027-3465
TD1　　　　　　　　CODEN: MUEJAF
MUNICIPAL ENGINEERS JOURNAL. 1903. q. $8. Municipal Engineers of the City of New York, 51 Chambers St., New York, NY 10007. TEL 212-349-5795. Ed. George Ziegler. adv.; charts; illus.; index. circ. 1,000. **Indexed**: Eng.Ind., Geotech.Abstr.
Description: Contains organization news.

N C E E S REGISTRATION BULLETIN. (National Council of Examiners for Engineering and Surveying) see *ENGINEERING*

N T I S ALERTS: REGIONAL & URBAN PLANNING & TECHNOLOGY. see *HOUSING AND URBAN PLANNING*

624 631　　　　MX　ISSN 0185-4011
NABOR CARRILLO LECTURE SERIES. PROCEEDINGS. (Text in English and Spanish) 1972. biennial, 7th 1984. price varies. Sociedad Mexicana de Mecanica de Suelos - Mexican Society for Soil Mechanics, Valle de Bravo 19, Col. Vergel de Coyoacan, 14340 Mexico. **Indexed**: GeoRef. **Document type**: proceedings.

NATIONAL COOPERATIVE HIGHWAY RESEARCH PROGRAM REPORTS. see *TRANSPORTATION — Roads And Traffic*

NATIONAL COOPERATIVE HIGHWAY RESEARCH PROGRAM RESEARCH RESULTS DIGEST. see *TRANSPORTATION — Roads And Traffic*

NATIONAL COOPERATIVE HIGHWAY RESEARCH PROGRAM SYNTHESIS OF HIGHWAY PRACTICE. see *TRANSPORTATION — Roads And Traffic*

NATIONAL COUNCIL OF EXAMINERS FOR ENGINEERING AND SURVEYING. PROCEEDINGS. see *ENGINEERING*

NATIONAL DEVELOPMENT. see *PUBLIC ADMINISTRATION*

624　　　　　US　ISSN 0192-0359
NATIONAL UTILITY CONTRACTOR. 1977. m. $15 (foreign $18). National Utility Contractors Association, 4301 Fairfax Dr., No. 360, Arlington, VA 22203-1627. TEL 703-358-9300. FAX 703-358-9307. Ed. Anne Luzier. adv.; bk.rev.; charts; illus.; stat.; index. circ. 12,023. (back issues avail.)
Description: Information on the construction of water, sewer and underground utility systems.

NAVY CIVIL ENGINEER. see *MILITARY*

NEBRASKA HIGHWAY PROGRAM. see *TRANSPORTATION — Roads And Traffic*

NETHERLANDS. COMMISSIE VOOR GEODESIE. PUBLICATIONS ON GEODESY. NEW SERIES. see *GEOGRAPHY*

624　　　　　UK　ISSN 0307-7683
NEW CIVIL ENGINEER. 1972. w. £75. (Institution of Civil Engineers) Thomas Telford Ltd., Thomas Telford House, 1 Heron Quay, London E14 4JD, England. TEL 071-987-6999. FAX 081-538-4656. TELEX 298105-CIVILS-G. Ed. Ty Byrd. adv.; bk.rev.; charts; illus. circ. 62,000. (back issues avail.) **Indexed**: Br.Geol.Lit., Br.Tech.Ind., Build.Manage.Abstr., Cadscan, Fluidex, Fuel & Energy Abstr., Geotech.Abstr., High.Educ.Curr.Aware.Bull., HRIS, Intl.Civil Eng.Abstr., J.of Ferroc., Lead Abstr., RICS, Soft.Abstr.Eng., W.R.C.Inf., Zincscan.
—BLDSC (6082.690000); SWETS.
Description: Covers recent events and technological developments in structural and civil engineering worldwide.

NEW HAMPSHIRE STATUTES RELATING TO SURVEYING AND BOUNDARIES. see *LAW — Judicial Systems*

624.176　　　　NZ　ISSN 0110-0718
TH1095　　　　　　　　CODEN: NZEBA3
NEW ZEALAND NATIONAL SOCIETY FOR EARTHQUAKE ENGINEERING. BULLETIN. 1968. q. NZ.$160. New Zealand National Society for Earthquake Engineering, P.O. Box 17268 Karori, Wellington, New Zealand. TEL 04-476-6866. Ed. P. Moss. bk.rev.; illus.; cum.index every 3 yrs. circ. 900. **Indexed**: Abstr.J. Earthq.Eng., C.R.I. Abstr., Concr.Abstr., GeoRef. **Document type**: bulletin, academic/scholarly publication.
—BLDSC (2655.276000); EI. **CCC**.
Formerly (until 1974): New Zealand Society for Earthquake Engineering. Bulletin (ISSN 0550-6743)

625.72　　　　NZ　ISSN 0048-0150
NEW ZEALAND SURVEYOR. 1889. s-a. NZ.$30 (foreign NZ.$48). New Zealand Institute of Surveyors, P.O. Box 831, Wellington, New Zealand. TEL 04-471-1774. FAX 04-471-1907. Ed. N.T. Kerr. adv.; bk.rev.; stat.; index, cum.index every 3 yrs. circ. 1,340. **Indexed**: So.Pac.Per.Ind.
—BLDSC (6099.450000). **CCC**.

624　　　　　JA
NICHIBEI KYORYO WAKUSHOPPU RONBUNSHU/JAPAN - U.S. BRIDGE ENGINEERING WORKSHOP. PROCEEDINGS. (Text in English) 1983. 2/yr. Kensetsusho Doboku Kenkyujo - Ministry of Construction, Public Works Research Institute, 1, Asahi, Tsukuba-shi, Ibraki-ken 305, Japan. **Document type**: proceedings.

NIHON JISHIN KOGAKU SHINPOJUMU KOENSHU/JAPAN EARTHQUAKE ENGINEERING SYMPOSIUM. PROCEEDINGS. see *EARTH SCIENCES — Geophysics*

624　　　　　JA　ISSN 0914-7306
NIHON KYORYO GIHO/JAPAN BRIDGE TECHNICAL REPORT. (Text in Japanese) 1983. a. Nihon Kyoryo K.K. - Japan Bridge Co., Ltd., 1-30, Fukuaki, Minato-ku, Osakasi-shi, Osaka 552, Japan.

NIHON NETSU RYUTAI KOGAKKAI RONBUNSHU/JAPAN SOCIETY OF HEAT AND FLUID ENGINEERING. TRANSACTIONS. see *PHYSICS — Heat*

NIHON SHUTEI KOGYOKAIHO/JAPAN BOATING INDUSTRY ASSOCIATION. NEWS. see *SPORTS AND GAMES — Boats And Boating*

624　　　　　JA　ISSN 0289-9116
NIKKAN TONNERU KENKYU. (Text in Japanese) 1984. s-a. 2000 Yen per no. Kokusai Haiwei Purojekuto, Nikkan Tonneru Kenkyukai - International Highway Project, Japan Korean Tunnel Research Institute, 37-13, Udagawa-cho, Shibuya-ku, Tokyo 150, Japan.
—BLDSC (4833.520000).

624　　　　　JA　ISSN 0915-3470
NIKKEI CONSTRUCTION. (Text in Japanese) 1989. s-m. 15900 Yen. Nikkei Business Publications, Inc. (Subsidiary of: Nihon Keizai Shimbun, Inc.), 2-7-6 Hirakawa-cho, Chiyoda-ku, Tokyo 102, Japan. TEL 03-5210-8502. FAX 03-5210-8119. Ed. Shoji Tanabe. adv. contact: Mitsuharu Hanagami. circ. 24,652. **Document type**: trade publication.
Description: Contains information on sites, ventures, security, and environmental issues for managers, engineers, researchers, and others involved in civil engineering and construction projects.

624 551　　　　JA　ISSN 0917-2580
NISHINIHON GANBAN KOGAKU SHINPOJUMU RONBUNSHU/PROCEEDINGS OF WEST JAPAN SYMPOSIUM ON ROCK ENGINEERING. (Text in English, Japanese; summaries in English) 1985. a. Nishinihon Ganban Kogaku Kenkyukai - Committee of West Japan Symposium on Rock Engineering, c/o Mr. Tetsuro Ezaki, Kyushu Daigaku Kogakubu Kankyo Shisutemu Kogaku Kenkyu Senta, 10-1, Hakozaki 6-chome, Higashi-ku, Fukuokashi, Fukuoka-ken 812, Japan.

624 690　　　　JA
NISSAN KENSETSU K.K. GIJUTSU HONBU GIJUTSU REPOTO/NISSAN CONSTRUCTION CO., LTD. TECHNICAL DEPARTMENT. TECHNICAL REPORT. (Text in Japanese) 1969. a. Nissan Kensetsu K.K., Gijutsu Honbu, 2-6, Minamiaoyama 1-chome, Minato-ku, Tokyo 107, Japan.

NORTHWATER; notes on water resources research in Alaska. see *WATER RESOURCES*

526.9 625.72　　　　CN　ISSN 0380-9242
NOVA SCOTIAN SURVEYOR. 1952. q. Can.$12. Association of Nova Scotia Land Surveyors, 159 Portland St., Ste. 301, Dartmouth, N.S. B2Y 1H9, Canada. TEL 902-469-7962. FAX 902-466-2052. Ed. Michael Grant. adv.; bk.rev.; charts. circ. 400.
Formerly: Association of Nova Scotia Land Surveyors (ISSN 0004-5748)

624　　　　　JA　ISSN 0385-9657
　　　　　　　　　　　CODEN: OBGKAJ
OBAYASHIGUMI GIJUTSU KENKYUJOHO/OBAYASHI CORPORATION. TECHNICAL RESEARCH INSTITUTE. REPORT. (Text in Japanese; summaries in English, Japanese) 1967. s-a. Obayashigumi Gijutsu Kenkyujo, 2-3, Kanda Tsukasa-cho, Chiyoda-ku, Tokyo 101, Japan. **Indexed**: Chem.Abstr., INIS Atomind.
—BLDSC (7573.550000); CASDDS.

624 665.5　　　　UK
OFFSHORE ENGINEERING. 1979. biennial. (Federal University of Rio de Janeiro, BL - Universidade Federal do Rio de Janeiro) Pentech Press, 3 Graham Lodge, Graham Rd., London NW4 3DG, England. TEL 081-202-5373. FAX 081-203-0096. Ed. F.L.L.B. Carneiro. **Document type**: trade publication.
Description: Covers oil production systems, materials in the sea, marine geotechnics, analysis of offshore structure, hydrodynamics.

OKINAWA DOSHITSU KOGAKU KENKYU HAPPYOKAI KOEN GAIYOSHU/OKINAWA GEOTECHNICAL SOCIETY. PAPERS OF ANNUAL MEETING. see *EARTH SCIENCES — Geology*

624　　　　　IT
ONDAVERDE. 6/yr. Associazione Italiana Ingegneri del Traffico, Viale Regina Margherita 290, 00198 Rome, Italy. TEL 6-440-20-61. FAX 6-88-40-926. Ed. Pasquale Balsamo.

625.72　　　　CN　ISSN 0316-2001
ONTARIO LAND SURVEYOR. vol.20, 1977. q. Can.$40. Association of Ontario Land Surveyors, 1043 McNicoll Ave., Scarborough, Ont. M1W 3W6, Canada. TEL 416-491-9020. FAX 416-491-2576. Ed. E. Peter Jacobs Cae. adv. contact: E. Peter Jacobs Cae. circ. 1,500.

624　　　　　JA　ISSN 0914-3904
ORIENTARU KONSARUTANTSU GIJUTSUHO/ORIENTAL CONSULTANTS CO., LTD. TECHNICAL REPORT. (Text in Japanese) 1972. 3/yr. Orientaru Konsarutantsu - Oriental Consultants Co., Ltd., 16-14, Shibuya 1-chome, Shibbuya-ku, Tokyo 150, Japan.

624　　　　　RU　ISSN 0030-6223
OSNOVANIYA, FUNDAMENTY I MEKHANIKA GRUNTOV. English translation: Soil Mechanics and Foundation Engineering (US ISSN 0038-0741) 1959. bi-m. 17.10 Rub. (Gosstroi) Stroiizdat, Shchousseva, rm. 60, Moscow, Russia. Ed. T.R. Aleksandrovich. adv.; bk.rev.; bibl.; charts; illus.; index. circ. 9,000. **Indexed**: Chem.Abstr., Geotech.Abstr.

625 388　　　　FR
P C M - LE PONT. m. Association of Road and Bridge Engineers, 28 rue des Saints-Peres, 75007 Paris, France. TEL 42-60-25-33. FAX 45-23-33-58. Ed. Jean-Pierre Grezaud. circ. 5,000.

ENGINEERING — CIVIL ENGINEERING

625.7   US   ISSN 0739-3865
TA501
P O B - POINT OF BEGINNING. 1975. bi-m. $26 (free to qualified personnel). P O B Publishing Co., 5820 Lilley Rd., No.5, Canton, MI 48187. TEL 313-981-4600. FAX 313-981-0048. Ed. Edwin W. Miller; Pub. Edwin W. Miller. adv.; bk.rev.; circ. 55,000 (controlled). (back issues avail.) **Document type:** trade publication.
   Description: Provides business, technical, and professional information for members of the surveying and mapping community.

624   JA   ISSN 0389-4150
P W R I NEWSLETTER. (Text in English) 1980. q. Ministry of Construction, Public Works Research Institute, 1, Asahi, Tsukuba-shi, Ibaraki-ken 305, Japan. **Document type:** newsletter.

624   PN
PANAMA. MINISTERIO DE OBRAS PUBLICAS. MEMORIA. a. Ministerio de Obras Publicas, Panama 1, Panama. TEL 32-5572. FAX 32-5776.

625.8   US
PAVING AND TRANSPORTATION CONFERENCE. PROCEEDINGS. 1962. a. $15. University of New Mexico, Department of Civil Engineering, Albuquerque, NM 87131. TEL 505-277-2722. FAX 505-277-1986. Ed. James D. Brogan. circ. 200. (back issues avail.) **Document type:** proceedings.
   —BLDSC (6848.731500).
   Formerly: Paving Conference. Proceedings (ISSN 0079-0273)

624   HU   ISSN 0553-6626
                     CODEN: PPCBAD
PERIODICA POLYTECHNICA. CIVIL ENGINEERING. (Text in English) 1955. q. $16. Budapesti Muszaki Egyetem - Technical University of Budapest, Periodica Polytechnica, 1521 Budapest, Hungary. FAX 1-201-3207. TELEX 22-5931 MUEGY H. (Dist. by: Kultura, P.O. Box 149, 1389 Budapest, Hungary) Ed. Gy. Szilagyi. bk.rev.; charts; illus.; index. circ. 400. **Indexed:** Appl.Mech.Rev., Chem.Abstr., Eng.Ind., Fluidex, GeoRef., Geotech.Abstr., J.of Ferroc. **Document type:** academic/scholarly publication.
   —BLDSC (6425.320000); EI; CASDDS.
   Supersedes in part (in 1967): Epitoipari es Kozlekedesi Muszaki Egyetem Tudomanyos Kozlemenyei (ISSN 0524-854X); Which was formerly (until 1956): Epitoipari Muszaki Egyetem Tudomanyos Kozlemenyei (ISSN 0324-5209).

624   UK
PLANT AND CIVIL ENGINEER. 1991. m. £15. 69 Glen Rd., Comber, Newtownards, Co. Down BT23 5QS, N. Ireland. TEL 0247-872656. Ed. Michael McRitchie. adv.; bk.rev. circ. 4,000. **Document type:** trade publication.

624 690   PL   ISSN 0373-8671
POLITECHNIKA GDANSKA. ZESZYTY NAUKOWE. BUDOWNICTWO LADOWE. (Text in English, Polish; summaries in Russian and one West-European language) 1956. irreg. price varies. Politechnika Gdanska, Ul. G. Narutowicza 11-12, 80-952 Gdansk 6, Poland. (Dist. by: Osrodek Rozpowszechniania Wydawnictw Naukowych PAN, Palac Kultury i Nauki, 00-901 Warsaw, Poland) bibl.; charts; illus. **Document type:** academic/scholarly publication.
   Description: Research dealing with civil engineering, structural mechanics, steel structures, concrete buildings and bridges.

624   PL
POLITECHNIKA KRAKOWSKA. MONOGRAFIE. SERIA: INZYNIERIA LADOWA. (Subseries of: Politechnika Krakowska. Monografie (ISSN 0860-097X)) (Text in Polish; summaries in English, French, German, Russian) 1985. irreg. price varies. Politechnika Krakowska, Ul. Warszawska 24, 31-155 Krakow, Poland. TEL 48-12-374289. FAX 48-12-335773. TELEX 322468 PK PL. bibl.; charts; illus. circ. 200. **Document type:** academic/scholarly publication, monographic series.

624   PL   ISSN 0867-1788
POLITECHNIKA KRAKOWSKA. ZESZYTY NAUKOWE. INZYNIERIA LADOWA. (Text in Polish; summaries in English, French, German, Russian) 1957. irreg. price varies. Politechnika Krakowska, Ul. Warszawska 24, 31-155 Krakow, Poland. TEL 48-12-374289. FAX 48-12-335773. TELEX 322468 PK PL. bibl.; charts; illus. circ. 200. **Document type:** academic/scholarly publication.
   Formerly: Politechnika Krakowska. Zeszyty Naukowe. Budownictwo Ladowe (ISSN 0454-4862)

624   PL   ISSN 0076-0323
TA4
POLITECHNIKA LODZKA. ZESZYTY NAUKOWE. BUDOWNICTWO. (Text in Polish; summaries in English and Russian) 1967. irreg. price varies. Wydawnictwo Politechniki Lodzkiej, Ul. Wolczanska 219, 93-085 Lodz, Poland. (Dist. by: Ars Polona-Ruch, Krakowskie Przedmiescie 7, Warsaw, Poland) Ed. Marian Lukowiak. circ. 187. **Document type:** academic/scholarly publication.
   —BLDSC (9512.310000).
   Description: Articles on reinforced and pre-stressed concrete structures, geodesy, theories of building structures and applied mechanics.

624   PL   ISSN 0079-449X
POLITECHNIKA POZNANSKA. ZESZYTY NAUKOWE. BUDOWNICTWO LADOWE. (Text in Polish; summaries in English) 1956. irreg. price varies. Politechnika Poznanska, Pl. Curie Sklodowskiej 5, Poznan, Poland. Ed. Andrzej Gawecki. circ. 150. **Document type:** academic/scholarly publication.
   —BLDSC (9512.321800).
   Formerly (until 1963): Politechnika Poznanska. Zeszyty Naukowe. Budownictwo.
   Description: Investigations into engineering applications of new materials, structural optimization, numerical methods in engineering and materials and buildings technology.

624   PL   ISSN 0434-0779
TA4
POLITECHNIKA SLASKA. ZESZYTY NAUKOWE. BUDOWNICTWO. (Text in Polish; summaries in English, German, Russian) 1956. irreg. price varies. Politechnika Slaska, Katowicka 7, 44-100 Gliwice, Poland. FAX 371655. TELEX 036304. (Dist. by: Ars Polona, Krakowskie Przedmiescie 7, 00-068 Warsaw, Poland) Ed. Zdzislaw Trojan. circ. 205.

624   PL   ISSN 0324-9735
POLITECHNIKA WROCLAWSKA. INSTYTUT INZYNIERII LADOWEJ. PRACE NAUKOWE. KONFERENCJE. (Text in Polish; summaries in English) 1973. irreg., no.15, 1989. price varies. Wydawnictwo Politechniki Wroclawskiej, Wybrzeze Wyspianskiego 27, 50-370 Wroclaw, Poland. FAX 22-36-64. TELEX 712559 PWRPL. (Dist. by: Ars Polona-Ruch, Krakowskie Przedmiescie 7, Warsaw, Poland) illus.

624   PL   ISSN 0324-9727
POLITECHNIKA WROCLAWSKA. INSTYTUT INZYNIERII LADOWEJ. PRACE NAUKOWE. MONOGRAFIE. (Text in Polish; summaries in English and Russian) 1972. irreg., no.14, 1988. price varies. Wydawnictwo Politechniki Wroclawskiej, Wybrzeze Wyspianskiego 27, 50-370 Wroclaw, Poland. FAX 22-36-64. TELEX 712559 PWRPL. (Dist. by: Ars Polona-Ruch, Krakowskie Przedmiescie 7, Warsaw, Poland) **Document type:** monographic series.

624   PL   ISSN 0370-0844
POLITECHNIKA WROCLAWSKA. INSTYTUT INZYNIERII LADOWEJ. PRACE NAUKOWE. STUDIA I MATERIALY. (Text in Polish; summaries in English and Russian) 1970. irreg., no.10, 1973. price varies. Wydawnictwo Politechniki Wroclawskiej, Wybrzeze Wyspianskiego 27, 50-370 Wroclaw, Poland. FAX 22-36-64. TELEX 712559 PWRPL. (Dist. by: Ars Polona-Ruch, Krakowskie Przedmiescie 7, Warsaw, Poland)
   —EI.

PORTS AND DREDGING. see ENGINEERING — Hydraulic Engineering

624   JA   ISSN 0554-7555
PORTS AND HARBORS. (Text in English) 1956. 10/yr. 6500 Yen($43) International Association of Ports and Harbors - Kokusai Kowan Kyokai, Kotohira-Kaikan Building, 2-8, Toranomon 1-chome, Minato-ku, Tokyo 105, Japan. TEL 03-3591-4261. FAX 03-3580-0364. TELEX 2222516 IAPH J. Ed. Hiroshi Kusaka. adv.: B&W page 100000 Yen, color page 140000 Yen; trim 296 X 210; adv. contact: Izumi Hayashi. bk.rev. circ. 5,000. **Indexed:** Fluidex. **Document type:** trade publication.
   —BLDSC (6555.910000).
   Description: Committed to the exchange of ideas and technical knowledge on issues of concern to people working in ports and related industries.

624 690   PL
                    CODEN: PITBDI
PRACE INSTYTUTU TECHNIKI BUDOWLANEJ. KWARTALNIK. 1972. q. 270000 Zl. (effective 1993). Instytut Techniki Budowlanej - Building Research Institute, Ul. Filtrowa 1, 00-950 Warsaw, Poland. TEL 48-22-43-35-19. FAX 48-22-251303. TELEX 813022. bibl.; illus. circ. 400. **Document type:** bulletin.
   —CASDDS.
   Formerly: Instytut Techniki Budowlanej. Prace (ISSN 0138-0796)
   Description: Presents the reports on research projects, communiques on current and terminated study and experimental projects, information on technological implementations, courses of instruction, patents and standard acts, ITB's publications announcements.

PREVISIONS GLISSANTES DETAILLEES EN PERSPECTIVES SECTORIELLES (VOL.29): TRAVAUX PUBLICS. see BUSINESS AND ECONOMICS — Economic Situation And Conditions

PROBLEMY BOL'SHIKH GORODOV/PROBLEMS OF LARGE METROPOLITAN AREAS; obzornaya informatsiya. see ENVIRONMENTAL STUDIES

PROFESSIONAL SURVEYOR. see GEOGRAPHY

PROGRESS IN GEOTECHNICAL ENGINEERING. see EARTH SCIENCES — Geology

625.7   US   ISSN 0033-3735
TE23   CODEN: PUROAQ
PUBLIC ROADS; a journal of highway research and development. 1918. q. $12. U.S. Federal Highway Administration, 400 Seventh St., N.W., Washington, DC 20590. TEL 703-285-2104. (Subscr. to: Superintendent of Documents, U.S. Government Printing Office, Box 371954, Pittsburgh, PA 15250-7954. TEL 202-783-3238. FAX 202-512-2233) Ed.Bd. bibl.; charts; illus.; index. circ. 5,500. (also avail. in microform from UMI; microfiche from CIS; back issues avail.; reprint service avail. from CIS,UMI) **Indexed:** A.S.& T.Ind., Amer.Stat.Ind. (1974-), Chem.Abstr., Dok.Str., Eng.Ind., Excerp.Med., Geo.Abstr., GeoRef., Geotech.Abstr., HRIS, Ind.U.S.Gov.Per., Intl.Civil Eng.Abstr., P.A.I.S., PROMT, Soft.Abstr.Eng. **Document type:** government publication, academic/scholarly publication.
   —BLDSC (6969.000000); EI; Faxon; UnCover; SWETS; UMI.

624 690   JA   ISSN 0416-1351
PUBLIC WORKS RESEARCH INSTITUTE. JOURNAL OF RESEARCH. (Text in English; summaries in English, Japanese) 1954. irreg. Ministry of Construction, Public Works Research Institute, 1, Asahi, Tsukuba-shi, Ibaraki-ken 305, Japan.
   —BLDSC (5051.000000).

PURESUTORESUTO KONKURITO/JOURNAL OF PRESTRESSED CONCRETE. see BUILDING AND CONSTRUCTION

ENGINEERING — CIVIL ENGINEERING

624.151   UK   ISSN 0481-2085
TA705   CODEN: QJEGA7
QUARTERLY JOURNAL OF ENGINEERING GEOLOGY. 1967. q. £118($245) (foreign £142). (Geological Society of London) Geological Society Publishing House, Unit 7, Brassmill Enterprise Centre, Brassmill Ln., Bath BA1 3JN, England. TEL 0225-445046. FAX 0225-442836. Ed. G. West. adv.; bk.rev.; illus.; index. circ. 3,100. (back issues avail.) **Indexed:** AESIS, ASCA, Br.Geol.Lit., Chem.Abstr., Curr.Cont., Excerp.Med., Fuel & Energy Abstr., Geo.Abstr., GeoRef., HRIS, Sci.Cit.Ind., Sel.Water Res.Abstr., W.R.C.Inf. **Document type:** academic/scholarly publication.
—BLDSC (7188.600000); Faxon; UnCover; SWETS; UMI. **CCC.**

526.9 625.72 020   UK
R I C S LIBRARY INFORMATION SERVICE. WEEKLY BRIEFING; a digest of news selected from the press. 1965. w. £200 to non-members. Royal Institution of Chartered Surveyors, 12 Great George St., Parliament Square, London SW1P 3AD, England. TEL 071-222-7000. FAX 071-222-9430. TELEX 915443-RICS-G. Ed. Pauline Lane-Gilbert. circ. 1,300. (processed; reprint service avail. from UMI) **Document type:** abstracting/indexing.
Formerly: R I C S Technical Information Service. Weekly Briefing (ISSN 0033-6947)

624   UK
R I C S RESEARCH PAPER SERIES. irreg. Royal Institution of Chartered Surveyors, 12 Great George St., Parliament Sq., London SW1P 3AD, England. TEL 071-222-7000. FAX 071-222-9430. Ed. Stephen Brown. **Document type:** monographic series.

RAKENNUSEXTRA. see BUILDING AND CONSTRUCTION

RAKENNUSLEHTI. see BUILDING AND CONSTRUCTION

RAKENNUSPLUSSA. see BUILDING AND CONSTRUCTION

624   FI   ISSN 0033-913X
TH4
RAKENNUSTEKNIIKKA; Finnish civil engineering journal. (Text mainly in Finnish; occasionally in Swedish; summaries in English) 1945. 8/yr. Fmk.90($15.91) (Suomen Rakennusinsinoorien Liitto - Association of Finnish Civil Engineers) Kustannus Oy Rakennustekniikka, Merittulinkatu 16 A 5, 00170 Helsinki 17, Finland. Ed. Seppo Mustonen. adv.; bk.rev.; charts; illus.; pat.; tr.lit.; index. circ. 4,000. **Indexed:** Geotech.Abstr.

RAKENNUSTEOLLISUUS/BUILDING INDUSTRY. see BUILDING AND CONSTRUCTION

624 720   IT
RASSEGNA TECNICA DEL FRIULI VENEZIA GIULIA. 6/yr. Via Divisione Julia 30, Udine, Italy. TEL 432-50-53-05. FAX 432-501940. Ed. Gaetano Cola. circ. 5,500.

624   SP
RELACION DE INGENIEROS DE CAMINOS, CANALES Y PUERTOS. irreg., latest 1991. price varies. Colegio de Ingenieros de Caminos, Canales y Puertos, Almagro, 42, 28010 Madrid, Spain. TEL 1-308-19-88. FAX 1-308-39-32. illus.

624.151   US   ISSN 0080-2018
TA705   CODEN: GAEGA4
REVIEWS IN ENGINEERING GEOLOGY. 1961. irreg., vol.9, 1990. price varies. Geological Society of America, 3300 Penrose Pl., Box 9140, Boulder, CO 80301. TEL 303-447-2020. FAX 303-447-1133. index. (reprint service avail. from UMI) **Indexed:** GeoRef.
—BLDSC (7790.505000).
Description: Brings out details on application of geology to engineering practice.
Refereed Serial

624 690   SP
REVISTA A T E M C O P. 1968. m. $40. Asociacion Espanola de Tecnicos de Maquinaria para la Construccion, Obras Publicas y Mineria - Spanish Association for Machinery Technicians in Construction, Public Works and Mining, c/o Cruz del Sur, No. 3 bajo, 28007 Madrid, Spain. TEL 1-574-98-18. FAX 1-573-18-00. adv.; bk.rev.; circ. 5,000 (controlled).

REVISTA ACODAL. see ENGINEERING — Hydraulic Engineering

REVISTA DA CONSTRUCAO CIVIL. see BUILDING AND CONSTRUCTION

624   SP   ISSN 0034-8619
HD4242   CODEN: RVOPA9
REVISTA DE OBRAS PUBLICAS. 1853. m. (11/yr.). 7200 ptas. (foreign 10500 ptas.) (effective 1993). (Ingenieros de Caminos, Canales y Puertos) Colegio de Ingenieros de Caminos, Canales y Puertos, Almagro 42, 28010 Madrid, Spain. TEL 3081988. FAX 3191531. Ed. Juan Antonio Becerril Bustamante. adv.: B&W page 75000 ptas., color page 120000 ptas. bk.rev.; bibl.; charts; illus.; index. circ. 4,500. **Indexed:** Dok.Str., Eng.Ind., Geotech.Abstr., HRIS, Ind.SST, Intl.Civil Eng.Abstr., Sci.Abstr., Soft.Abstr.Eng.
Description: Explains civil and hydraulic engineering, public works and roads, mechanics and materials, as well as investments.

625.7   VE   ISSN 0376-7299
REVISTA LATINOAMERICANA DE GEOTECNIA. 1972. q. Sociedad Venezolana de Mecanica de Suelos e Ingenieria de Fundaciones - Soil Mechanics and Foundation Engineering Society, Edf. Fleury, PB Prolongacion Los Manolos, Av. Andres Bellos, Caracas 105, Venezuela. circ. 5,000.

REVUE FRANCAISE DU BATIMENT ET DES TRAVAUX PUBLICS. see BUILDING AND CONSTRUCTION

624 627   TI
REVUE TUNISIENNE DE L'EQUIPEMENT. 1972. q. free. Ministere de l'Equipement et de l'Habitat, Direction des Etudes, des Statistiques et Services Documentation, Cite Jardins, Tunis 1002, Tunisia. TEL 861.977. stat. circ. 2,750.
Formerly: Tunisia. Ministere des Travaux Publics et de l'Habitat. Travaux Publics et Habitat (ISSN 0330-8553)

625.7   AT   ISSN 1037-5783
TE121   CODEN: RTRREK
ROAD AND TRANSPORT RESEARCH. 1962. q. Aus.$90. ‡ Australian Road Research Board, 500 Burwood Hwy., Vermont S., Vic. 3133, Australia. TEL 03-881-1555. FAX 03-887-8104. TELEX AA33113. charts; illus. circ. 1,500. **Indexed:** Aus.Rd.Ind., Chem.Abstr., Dok.Str., Eng.Ind., Ergon.Abstr., HRIS.
—BLDSC (7994.251000); EI; SWETS.
Formerly (until 1992): Australian Road Research (ISSN 0005-0164)

625.7   US   ISSN 0080-3278
    CODEN: ABCPDX
ROAD BUILDER'S CLINIC. PROCEEDINGS. 1950. a. avail. to clinic attendees only. Washington State University, Conferences and Institutes, Van Doren 208, Pullman, WA 99164-5222. TEL 509-335-3530. FAX 509-335-0945. (Co-sponsor: University of Idaho, College of Engineering)

624   UK   ISSN 0267-050X
ROAD ENGINEERING INTELLIGENCE AND RESEARCH. 1984; suspended Sep. 1991 - Dec. 1993. bi-m. £16 (rest of Europe £20; elsewhere £25). Civil Engineering and Transport Publications, 16 Trundle View Close, Barnham, Bognor Regis, W. Sussex PO22 0JZ, England. TEL 0243-551014. FAX 0243-821511. Ed. Ian S. Menzies. bk.rev. circ. 1,000. (back issues avail.) **Document type:** newsletter.
—BLDSC (7994.580000).
Description: Covers the design, research, planning, construction and maintenance of roads, bridges, and tunnels.

625.7   US   ISSN 8750-9229
TE1
ROADS & BRIDGES. 1892. m. $20. Scranton Gillette Communications, Inc., 380 E. Northwest Hwy., Des Plaines, IL 60016. TEL 708-298-6622. FAX 708-390-0408. Ed. Tom Kuennen. adv.; bk.rev.; abstr.; charts; illus.; stat. circ. 65,000. (also avail. in microform from UMI; reprint service avail. from UMI) **Indexed:** Excerp.Med. **Document type:** trade publication.
—BLDSC (7997.490000); UnCover; UMI. **CCC.**
Former titles (until 1984): Roads (ISSN 0746-3111); (until 1983): R U R: Rural and Urban Roads (ISSN 0273-9097); Rural and Urban Roads (ISSN 0035-9998)
Description: Examines technological and industrial applications in the construction, rebuilding and the maintenance of the nation's transportation infrastructure. Includes an advertising index, lists of sales staff, product and equipment market as well as legislative updates.

ROCK MECHANICS AND ROCK ENGINEERING. see EARTH SCIENCES — Geology

624.2   US
ROMANTIC SHELTERS. 1989. irreg., latest 1989. $6 (with World Guide to Covered Bridges $12). National Society for the Preservation of Covered Bridges, Inc., c/o Mrs. Christine Ellsworth, Corr.Sec., 44 Cleveland Ave., Worcester, MA 01603. TEL 508-756-4516. Ed. Arthur Hammer. **Document type:** directory.
Description: Lists "inauthentic" covered bridges, such as small, new covered bridges on golf courses or in someone's backyard. This information was formerly included in the World Guide to Covered Bridges.

624   FR   ISSN 1011-1891
ROUTES - ROADS. (Text in English, French) 1911. 3/yr. 210 F. Permanent International Association of Road Congresses, 27 rue Guenegaud, 75006 Paris, France. TEL 46-33-71-90. FAX 46-33-84-60. Ed. Patrice Retour. adv. contact: P. Retour. illus. circ. 4,000. (back issues avail.) **Indexed:** Dok.Str., Geotech.Abstr.
—BLDSC (7997.451000).
Formerly: Association Internationale Permanente des Congres de la Route. Bulletin (ISSN 0004-556X)

RUTAS. see TRANSPORTATION — Roads And Traffic

624   SA
S A F C E C BULLETIN. w. South African Federation of Civil Engineering Contractors, P.O. Box 644, Bedfordview 2008, South Africa. TEL 611-536925. TELEX 420117.

624   JA   ISSN 0288-2124
SABO TO CHISUI/EROSION CONTROL AND RIVER WORK. (Text in Japanese) 1968. bi-m. 930 Yen per no. Zenkoku Chisui Sabo Kyokai - Japan Sabo Association, 7-5, Hirakawa-cho 2-chome, Chiyoda-ku, Tokyo 102, Japan.

SAINT-LAMBERT, L'ANNUAIRE BATIMENT ET TRAVAUX PUBLICS. see BUILDING AND CONSTRUCTION

624 690   JA   ISSN 0387-9364
SAITAMA DAIGAKU KOGAKUBU KENSETSUKEI KENKYU HOKOKU/SAITAMA UNIVERSITY. FACULTY OF ENGINEERING. DEPARTMENT OF CONSTRUCTION. RESEARCH REPORT. (Text in English, Japanese) 1970. a. Saitama Daigaku, Kogakubu, Kensetsu Kiso Kogakka - Saitama University, Faculty of Engineering, 255, Shimookubo, Urawa-shi, Saitama-ken 338, Japan.
—UnCover.

628   AG   ISSN 0371-1447
    CODEN: SNMOAJ
SANEAMIENTO.* 1937. m. $36. Obras Sanitarias de la Nacion, Rio Bamba 935, Buenos Aires, Argentina. Dir. Antonio A.J. Rotondaro. adv.; charts; illus. **Indexed:** Biol.Abstr., Chem.Abstr., Eng.Ind.
Former titles (until 1961): Revista de Obras Sanitarias de la Nacion (ISSN 0034-8627); (until 1947): Administracion Nacional del Agua. Revista (ISSN 0370-3428); (until 1944): Boletin de Obras Sanitarias de la Nacion (ISSN 0366-211X)

SCHIFF UND HAFEN. see TRANSPORTATION — Ships And Shipping

SCOTTISH BUILDING & CIVIL ENGINEERING YEAR BOOK. see BUILDING AND CONSTRUCTION

ENGINEERING — CIVIL ENGINEERING

SERIES ON ROCK AND SOIL MECHANICS. see *EARTH SCIENCES*

624   CC   ISSN 1005-684X
SHIDAI JIANZHU/MODERN ARCHITECTURE. (Text in Chinese) 1985. q. Y2.50. Tongji Daxue, Jianzhu Chengshi Guihua Xueyuan - Tongji University, Urban Architecture and Planning Institute, 1239 Siping Lu, Shanghai 200092, People's Republic of China. TEL 021-5455080. Eds. Lu Xiaowei, Wang Shaozhou. circ. 30,000. **Document type:** academic/scholarly publication.

624   JA   ISSN 0286-8385
SHIN SABO. (Text in Japanese) 1948. bi-m. 5000 Yen. Sabo Gakkai - Japan Society of Erosion Control Engineering, Sabo Kaikan, 7-5, Hirakawa-cho 2-chome, Chiyoda-ku, Tokyo 102, Japan. Ed. Takaaki Amada; Pub. Yoshinori Tsukamoto. adv.; bk.rev.

627.58   US   ISSN 0037-4237
TC330.A1   CODEN: SHBEAS
SHORE AND BEACH. 1933. q. $40 (foreign $52); includes subscr. to the Newsletter. American Shore and Beach Preservation Association, 412 O'Brien Hall, University of California, Berkeley, CA 94720. TEL 510-462-7340. FAX 510-642-9143. (Subscr. to: Business Office, 3000 Citrus Circle, Ste. 230, Walnut Creek, CA 94598) Ed. Robert L. Wiegel. adv.; bk.rev.; cum.index: 1933-1965. circ. 1,000. **Indexed:** Deep Sea Res.& Oceanogr.Abstr., Eng.Ind., Environ.Abstr., Environ.Per.Bibl. (1981-), Fluidex, Geo.Abstr., GeoRef., Ocean.Abstr. **Document type:** academic/scholarly publication.
—BLDSC (8268.440000).

624   JA   ISSN 0911-8241
SHUSUI TO SEISUI/WATER CONTROL WORKS. (Text in Japanese) 1984. 3/yr. free to members. Damu Seki Shisetsu Gijutsu Kyokai - Japan Association of Dam and Weir Equipment Engineering, 3-20, Toranomon 5-chome, Minato-ku, Tokyo 105, Japan. TEL 03-3459-8691. FAX 03-3459-0294. **Document type:** bulletin.
Description: Covers engineering reports on hydraulic gates and valves and other controlling equipment.

SICHUAN JIANZHU/SICHUAN ARCHITECTURE. see *ARCHITECTURE*

624   PO
SIMPOSIUM DA CONSTRUCAO CIVIL. 4/yr. Antonio Pereira Carrilho 38-2o, Lisbon, Portugal.

624   MX   ISSN 0185-4003
SOCIEDAD MEXICANA DE MECANICA DE SUELOS. BOLETIN. 1969. bi-m. membership. Sociedad Mexicana de Mecanica de Suelos, Valle de Bravo 19, Col. Vergel de Coyoacan, Tlalpan, 14340 Mexico, D.F., Mexico.

624 720   IT   ISSN 0004-7287
SOCIETA DEGLI INGEGNERI E DEGLI ARCHITETTI IN TORINO. ATTI E RASSEGNA TECNICA. 1867. q. L.60000 (foreign L.100000) (effective 1994). Societa degli Ingegneri e degli Architetti in Torino, Corso M. D'Azeglio 42, 10125 Turin, Italy. TEL 011-65-08-511. FAX 011-65-08-168. Ed. Marco Filippi. adv.; bk.rev.; abstr.; charts; illus.; cum.index. circ. 1,500.

624   FR
SOCIETE DES INGENIEURS-CONSEILS DE FRANCE, EN GENIE CIVIL. BULLETIN D'INFORMATION. 1963. q. free. Chambre des Ingenieurs Conseils de France, 3 rue Leon Bonnat, 75016 Paris, France. abstr.; stat.

SOIL DYNAMICS AND EARTHQUAKE ENGINEERING. see *EARTH SCIENCES — Geophysics*

624.176   JA   ISSN 0041-3798
SOIL MECHANICS AND FOUNDATION ENGINEERING/TSUCHI TO KISO. (Text in Japanese; summaries in English) 1953. m. 1500 Yen per no. Japanese Society of Soil Mechanics & Foundation Engineering - Doshitsu Kogakkai, 2-23, Kanda Awaji-cho 2-chome, Chiyoda-ku, Tokyo 101, Japan. Ed.Bd. index. circ. 15,000. (also avail. in microfilm from JSC) **Indexed:** GeoRef., W.R.C.Inf. **Document type:** academic/scholarly publication.
—BLDSC (9067.770000). **CCC.**

624.176   US   ISSN 0038-0741
TA710.A1   CODEN: SMFEAF
SOIL MECHANICS AND FOUNDATION ENGINEERING. English translation of: Osnovaniya Fundamenty i Mekhanika Gruntov (RU ISSN 0030-6223) 1964. bi-m. $1075 (foreign $1260) (effective 1994). (Gosudarstvennyi Komitet po Delam Stroitel'stva, RU) Plenum Publishing Corp., Consultants Bureau, 233 Spring St., New York, NY 10013-1578. TEL 212-620-8468. FAX 212-463-0742. TELEX 23-421139. Ed. A.Kh. Slavorosov. (back issues avail.) **Indexed:** Appl.Mech.Rev., Eng.Ind., Environ.Per.Bibl., Intl.Civil Eng.Abstr., Saf.Sci.Abstr., Soft.Abstr.Eng. **Document type:** academic/scholarly publication.
—BLDSC (0420.820000); UnCover; SWETS; UMI. **CCC.**
Refereed Serial

624.176   JA   ISSN 0038-0806
    CODEN: SOIFBE
SOILS & FOUNDATIONS. (Text in English) 1960. q. $148.50. Japanese Society of Soil Mechanics & Foundation Engineering - Doshitsu Kogakkai, 4F, Sugayama Bldg., Kanda Awaji-cho 2-23, Chiyoda-ku, Tokyo 101, Japan. (Dist. by: Intercontinental Marketing Corp., I.P.O. Box 5056, Tokyo 100-30, Japan. TEL 81-3-3661-7458. FAX 81-3-3667-9646) Ed.Bd. adv.; charts; illus.; cum.index. circ. 600. (back issues avail.) **Indexed:** Abstr.J.Earthq.Eng., Appl.Mech.Rev., GeoRef., Geotech.Abstr., HRIS.
—EI; Faxon; UnCover; SWETS. **CCC.**
Formerly: Soil and Foundation.

625.72   SA
SOUTH AFRICA. DEPARTMENT OF REGIONAL AND LAND AFFAIRS. DIRECTORATE OF SURVEYS AND LAND INFORMATION. ANNUAL REPORT OF THE CHIEF SURVEYOR-GENERAL. 1973. a. free. Department of Regional and Land Affairs, Directorate of Surveys and Land Information, Rhodes Ave., Mowbray 7705, South Africa. TEL 27-21-685-4070. FAX 27-21-6891351. TELEX 5-21418 SA. circ. 400 (controlled). **Document type:** government publication.
Former titles: South Africa. Department of Public Work and Land Affairs. Directorate of Surveys and Mapping. Annual Report of the Chief Director; (until 1984): South Africa. Department of Community Development. Division of Surveys and Mapping. Annual Report of the Chief Director; South Africa. Division of Surveys. Report of the Director-General of Surveys.

SOUTH AFRICAN CONSTRUCTION WORLD. see *BUILDING AND CONSTRUCTION*

624.72   SA
SOUTH AFRICAN JOURNAL OF SURVEYING AND MAPPING/SUID-AFRIKAANSE TYDSKRIF VIR LANDMEETKUNDE EN KARTERING. (Text and summaries in Afrikaans, English) 1924. 3/yr. $20 per no. (effective 1994). South African Council for Professional Land Surveyors and Technical Surveyors - Suid-Afrikaanse Raad vir Professionele Landmeters en Tegniese Opmeters, P.O. Box 62041, Marshalltown 2107, South Africa. TEL 27-11-8346431. FAX 27-11-836-8657. Ed. H.G. van Gysen. adv.; bk.rev.; charts; index; circ. 2,000 (controlled). **Indexed:** Bibl.Cart., Ind.S.A.Per. **Document type:** academic/scholarly publication.
Formerly (until Apr. 1989): South African Survey Journal - Suid-Afrikaanse Opmetings Tydskrif (ISSN 0038-2736).

SOUTHERN BUILDING CODE CONGRESS. STANDARD BUILDING CODE. see *BUILDING AND CONSTRUCTION*

624   UK   ISSN 0957-171X
SPON'S CIVIL ENGINEERING AND HIGHWAY WORKS PRICE BOOK. 1984. a. £60. E. & F.N. Spon, 2-6 Boundary Row, London SE1 8HN, England. TEL 071-865-0066. FAX 071-522-9623. **Document type:** directory.
—BLDSC (8419.054500).
Formerly: Spon's Civil Engineering Price Book (ISSN 0265-1025)

624   SW   ISSN 0038-8963
STADSBYGGNAD. 1935. bi-m. SEK 240 (effective 1991). Svenska Kommunal-Tekniska Foereningen - Swedish Association of Municipal Technicians, Maester Samuelsgatan 49, S-111 57 Stockholm, Sweden. Ed. Aake Lundell. adv.; illus.; mkt.; index. circ. 4,000.
—BLDSC (8426.200000).
Formerly (until 1958): Kommunalteknisk Tidskrift.

624   GW   ISSN 0038-9145
TA634   CODEN: STAHAE
STAHLBAU. (Supplement to Die Bautechnik. Ausgabe B) 1930. m. DM.385 (foreign DM.405). Wilhelm Ernst und Sohn, Muehlenstr. 33-34, 13187 Berlin, Germany. TEL 030-47889200. Ed. G. Sedlacek. adv.; bk.rev.; abstr.; charts; illus.; index. circ. 4,100. (back issues avail.) **Indexed:** Appl.Mech.Rev., Chem.Abstr., Eng.Ind., Excerp.Med., Met.Abstr., World Alum.Abstr. **Document type:** trade publication.
—ELDSC (8428.000000); EI; SWETS; UMI; CASDDS. **CCC.**

711.7 624   US
STANDARD SPECIFICATIONS FOR HIGHWAY BRIDGES. 1983. irreg. $62.25. American Association of State Highway and Transportation Officials, 444 N. Capitol St., N.W., Ste. 249, Washington, DC 20001. TEL 202-624-5800. FAX 202-624-5806. **Document type:** bulletin.

STAVEBNICKY CASOPIS. see *BUILDING AND CONSTRUCTION*

625.7   IT   ISSN 0373-2916
LE STRADE; rassegna di studi, progetti, lavori, cantieri, impianti. 1898. m. L.100000 (foreign L.120000). Casa Editrice la Fiaccola (Milan), Via Ravizza 62, 20149 Milan, Italy. TEL 02-4814355. FAX 02-4814834. TELEX 335512 COSTRU I. Dir. Felice Santagata. adv.; abstr.; charts; illus.; stat.; index. circ. 8,000. (back issues avail.) **Indexed:** Dok.Str., Geotech.Abstr.

625.7   GW   ISSN 0039-2162
TE3
STRASSE UND AUTOBAHN. (Text in German; summaries in English, French, German) 1949. m. DM.156. (Forschungsgesellschaft fuer Strassen- und Verkehrswesen) Kirschbaum Verlag GmbH, Siegfriedstr. 28, 53179 Bonn, Germany. TEL 0228-95453-0. FAX 0228-9545327. (Subscr. to: Postfach 210209, 53157 Bonn, Germany) adv.; bk.rev.; charts; illus.; tr.lit.; index. circ. 6,000. **Indexed:** Dok.Str., Eng.Ind., Excerp.Med., Geotech.Abstr. **Document type:** trade publication.
—SWETS. **CCC.**

625.7   SZ   ISSN 0039-2189
STRASSE UND VERKEHR. (Text in French, German) 1914. m. 110 SFr. (foreign 142 SFr.). Vereinigung Schweizerischer Strassenfachleute - Union des Professionnels Suisses de la Route, Seefeldstr. 9, CH-8008 Zurich, Switzerland. TEL 01-2516914. FAX 01-2523130. Ed. Didier Claivaz. adv.; bk.rev.; bibl.; charts; illus.; tr.lit.; index. circ. 4,000. **Indexed:** Chem.Abstr., Dok.Str., GeoRef., Geotech.Abstr.
—SWETS.

624   GW
STRASSEN- UND TIEFBAU VEREINIGT MIT STRASSE-BRUECKE-TUNNEL, BITUMEN-TEERE-ASPHALTS-PECHE. 1947. m. DM.128 (foreign DM.136). Giesel Verlag fuer Publizitaet GmbH, Auf der Heide 20, 30916 Isernhagen, Germany. TEL 0511-7304-0. FAX 0511-7304157. Ed. Angela Stroppe. adv.; bk.rev.; bibl.; charts; illus.; pat.; stat.; index. circ. 4,000. **Indexed:** Chem.Abstr., Dok.Str., Excerp.Med., Geotech.Abstr., INIS Atomind., Intl.Civil Eng.Abstr., Soft.Abstr.Eng. **Document type:** trade publication.
—SWETS.
Formed by the merger of: Bitumen, Teere, Asphalte, Peche (ISSN 0006-3924) & Strassen- und Tiefbau (ISSN 0039-2197).
Description: For the bitumen and asphalt industry. Features technical research in asphalt paving for roads and bridges. Includes reports of events and industry news.

ENGINEERING — CIVIL ENGINEERING

624　　　　　　　US　　ISSN 1062-8002
TH1611　　　　　　CODEN: SDTBEH
▼**STRUCTURAL DESIGN OF TALL BUILDINGS.** 1992. q. $175. John Wiley & Sons, Inc., Journals, 605 Third Ave., New York, NY 10158-0012. TEL 212-850-6000. FAX 212-850-6088. TELEX 12-7068. Ed. G.C. Hart.
—BLDSC (8476.935000); EI; UnCover; UMI.
Description: Focuses on the structural design and construction of tall buildings - at least six stories or 160 feet (49 meters) high.

624　　　　　　　UK
STRUCTURAL ENGINEER. 1922. 24/yr. £132. Structural Engineers Trading Organization Ltd., 11 Upper Belgrave St., London SW1X 8BH, England. TEL 071-235-4535. FAX 071-235-4294. Ed. B. Scanes. adv.; bk.rev.; abstr.; illus.; index. circ. 22,500. **Indexed:** Abstr.J.Earthq.Eng., Appl.Mech.Rev., ASCA, BMT, Br.Ceram.Abstr., Br.Rail.Bd., Br.Tech.Ind., Build.Manage.Abstr., C.I.S. Abstr., Curr.Cont., Eng.Ind., Excerp.Med., Fluidex, Forest.Abstr., Forest Prod.Abstr., Geotech.Abstr., High.Educ.Curr.Aware.Bull., HRIS, J.of Ferroc., Met.Abstr., RICS, Sh.& Vib.Dig., W.R.C.Inf., World Alum.Abstr. **Document type:** trade publication.
—BLDSC (8477.000000); EI; Faxon; SWETS.
Formed by the merger of: Structural Engineer. Part A; Structural Engineer. Part B; **Superseded:** Structural Engineer (ISSN 0039-2553).
Description: Theory and practice of building design and construction.
Refereed Serial

625　　　　　　　SZ
STRUCTURAL ENGINEERING DOCUMENTS. (Text in English) 1982. irreg., no.4, 1993. 63 SFr. to non-members; members 42 SFr. International Association for Bridge and Structural Engineering, ETH-Hoenggerberg, CH-8093 Zurich, Switzerland. TEL 01-3772647. FAX 01-3712131. **Document type:** academic/scholarly publication, monographic series.

624　　　　　　　JA　　ISSN 0289-8063
STRUCTURAL ENGINEERING - EARTHQUAKE ENGINEERING. (Text and summaries in English) 1984. s-a. 2500 Yen per no. (Japan Society of Civil Engineers - Doboku Gakkai) Maruzen Co., Ltd., 3-10, Nihonbashi 2-chome, Chuo-ku, Tokyo 103, Japan. **Indexed:** Eng.Ind. **Document type:** trade publication.
—BLDSC (8477.080000); EI; UnCover.

624　　　　　　　SZ　　ISSN 0377-7243
STRUCTURAL ENGINEERING INTERNATIONAL. Abbreviated title: S E I. (Text in English, French, German) q. 120 SFr. International Association for Bridge and Structural Engineering - Association Internationale des Ponts et Charpentes (Internationale Vereinigung fuer Brueckenbau und Hochbau), ETH-Hoenggerberg, CH-8093 Zurich, Switzerland. TEL 01-3772647. FAX 01-3712131. **Indexed:** Concr.Abstr., HRIS, Intl.Civil Eng.Abstr., J.of Ferroc., Soft.Abstr.Eng. **Document type:** academic/scholarly publication.
Incorporates (1977-1991): I A B S E Periodica - Surveys (ISSN 0377-7251); **(1977-1991):** I A B S E Periodica - Journal (ISSN 0377-726X); **(1977-1991):** I A B S E Periodica - Proceedings (ISSN 0377-7278); **(1977-1991):** I A B S E Periodica - Structures (ISSN 0377-7286); **(1977-1991):** I A B S E Periodica - Bulletin (ISSN 0377-7294).
Description: Information for structural engineers and those involved in the construction management industry.

624 690　　　　　　UK　　ISSN 0952-5807
TA630　　　　　　CODEN: SENRE8
STRUCTURAL ENGINEERING REVIEW. 1988. 4/yr. £122($190) (effective 1994). Elsevier Science Ltd., Pergamon, P.O. Box 800, Kidlington, Oxford OX5 1DX, England. TEL 44-865-843000. FAX 44-865-843010. (Subscr. in U.S. and Canada to: Elsevier Science, 660 White Plains Rd., Tarrytown, NY 10591-5153. TEL 914-524-9200. FAX 914-333-2444) Eds. B.H.V. Topping, R.L. Sack. adv.; bk.rev. (also avail. in microfilm from UMI; reprint service avail. from UMI) **Document type:** academic/scholarly publication.
—BLDSC (8477.202500); Faxon; SWETS; UMI. CCC.
Description: Examines structural analysis, design, methodology, design codes, construction materials, integration of computer aided design, construction and erection procedures, and the repair and maintenance of structures.
Refereed Serial

624　　　　　　　NE　　ISSN 0167-4730
STRUCTURAL SAFETY; journal on integrated risk assessment for constructed facilities. (Text in English) 1982. 6/yr. (in 2 vols.; 3 nos./vol.). fl.648($350) (effective 1994). Elsevier Science B.V., P.O. Box 211, 1000 AE Amsterdam, Netherlands. TEL 31-20-5803911. FAX 31-20-5803598. TELEX 18582 ESPA NL. (Subscr. in U.S. and Canada to: Elsevier Science Inc., Box 882, Madison Sq. Sta., New York, NY 10159. TEL 212-989-5800. FAX 212-633-3990) Ed. E.H. Vanmarcke. (also avail. in microform from UMI) **Indexed:** ASCA, Br.Tech.Ind., Risk Abstr. **Document type:** academic/scholarly publication.
—BLDSC (8478.550000); EI; UnCover; SWETS. CCC.
Description: Devoted to integrated risk assessment for a wide range of constructed facilities such as buildings, bridges, earth structures, offshore facilities, dams, lifelines and nuclear structural systems.
Refereed Serial

624　　　　　　　IT
STRUTTURE. 1968. irreg., no.9, 1990. Liguori Editore s.r.l., Via Mezzocannone, 19, 80134 Naples, Italy. TEL 081-5227139. Ed. Michele Pagano.

620　　　　　　　PL　　ISSN 0137-5393
STUDIA Z ZAKRESU INZYNIERII. (Text in Polish; summaries in English, Russian) 1958. irreg., vol.22, 1983. price varies. (Polska Akademia Nauk, Komitet Inzynierii Ladowej i Wodnej) Wydawnictwo Naukowe P W N, Miodowa 10, 00-251 Warsaw, Poland. TEL 48-22-312738. TELEX 4822-267163. bibl. **Document type:** academic/scholarly publication.
Formerly: Studia z Zakresu Budownictwa (ISSN 0081-7139)

SUIRIHO. see *AGRICULTURE*

SURVEYING AND LAND INFORMATION SYSTEMS; devoted to the advancement of the sciences of surveying and mapping. see *GEOGRAPHY*

624 622　　　　　　AT　　ISSN 0157-1672
SURVEYING AUSTRALIA. 1976. q. Aus.$38 (effective 1994). Institution of Engineering and Mining Surveyors (I.E.M.S.), 725 South Rd., Moorabin, Vic. 3189, Australia. TEL 613-555-2869. FAX 061-03-5552869. (Subscr. to: P.O. Box 2451V, Melbourne, Vic. 3001, Australia) Ed. L.D. Culliver. adv. contact: Elizabeth Curley. bk.rev. circ. 1,800. (back issues avail.) **Document type:** academic/scholarly publication.
Description: Field and office applications of civil engineering, mining and conservation survey.

624 620　　　　　　FI　　ISSN 0780-8399
SURVEYING SCIENCE IN FINLAND. (Text in English and German) 1983. s-a. FIM 150. Finnish Society of Surveying Sciences, P.O. Box 84, SF-00521 Helsinki, Finland. Ed. Jaakko Santala. adv.; bk.rev. circ. 300.
—BLDSC (8552.560000).

624　　　　　　　UK
SURVEYOR. 1892. w. £57.50. Hemming Group Ltd., 32 Vauxhall Bridge Rd., London SW1V 2SS, England. Ed. Maureen Rose. adv.; bk.rev.; charts; illus.; s-a. index. circ. 10,000. (also avail. in microfilm from UMI; reprint service avail. from UMI) **Indexed:** Biol.Abstr., Br.Geol.Lit., Br.Tech.Ind., Chem.Abstr., Eng.Ind., Excerp.Med., Geo.Abstr., W.R.C.Inf. **Document type:** trade publication.
—BLDSC (8552.750000); UnCover. CCC.
Former titles: Surveyor - Public Authority Technology; Surveyor - Local Government Technology (ISSN 0039-6303); Surveyor and Municipal Engineer.
Description: Sole publication for local government technical services in the United Kingdom.

625.7　　　　　　SW　　ISSN 1100-9438
SVENSK VAEGTIDNING. 1914. bi-m. SEK 250 (effective 1994). Svenska Vaegfoereningens Foerlags AB - Swedish Road Federation, Wallingatan 33, S-111 24 Stockholm, Sweden. TEL 46-8-23-17-35. FAX 46-8-7918158. Ed. Leif Gravenius. adv.; bk.rev.; abstr.; charts; illus.; stat.; index; circ. 3,000 (controlled). **Indexed:** Chem.Abstr., Dok.Str.
Former titles (until vol.5, 1989): Svenska Vaegfoereningens Tidskrift (ISSN 0039-6923); (until 1925): Svenska Vaegfoereningens Handlingar.

SWEDEN. STATENS RAAD FOER BYGGNADSFORSKNING. DOCUMENT. see *BUILDING AND CONSTRUCTION*

SWEDEN. STATENS RAAD FOER BYGGNADSFORSKNING. RAPPORT. see *BUILDING AND CONSTRUCTION*

624　　　　　　　US
SWEET'S CATALOG FILE FOR THE CIVIL ENGINEERING & RETROFIT MARKET. 1976. a. free to qualified personnel. Sweet's Catalog Files (Subsidiary of: McGraw-Hill, Inc.), 1221 Ave. of the Americas, New York, NY 10020. TEL 212-512-4753. FAX 212-512-2348. charts; illus.; tr.lit.; index. circ. 15,000.
Formerly: Sweet's Civil Engineering and Retrofit File.

624　　　　　　　US
TECHNICAL ENGINEERING AND DESIGN GUIDES. irreg. American Society of Civil Engineers, 345 E. 47th St., New York, NY 10017-2398. TEL 212-705-7520. FAX 212-980-4681. (Co-sponsor: U.S. Army Corps of Engineers) **Document type:** academic/scholarly publication, monographic series.

TECHNISCHE MITTEILUNGEN FUER SAPPEURE, PONTONIERE UND MINEURE. see *MILITARY*

620　　　　　　　TU
　　　　　　　　　CODEN: TDEREZ
TEKNIK DERGI/TECHNICAL JOURNAL. (Includes English supplement: Digest (Year)) (Text in Turkish; summaries in English) 1990. q. $20 (includes Digest). Turkish Chamber of Civil Engineers - Insaat Muhendisleri Odasi, Selanik Caddesi 19-1, Kizilay 06650 Ankara, Turkey. TEL 90-312-4337626. FAX 90-312-4170632. Ed. A. Tugrul Tankut. abstr.; charts. **Indexed:** Concr.Abstr., Eng.Ind., Intl.Civil Eng.Abstr. **Document type:** academic/scholarly publication.
Description: Reports original research results and case studies from the Turkish civil engineering practice.
Refereed Serial

TERRA ET AQUA. see *TRANSPORTATION — Ships And Shipping*

624　　　　　　　JA
TETTO/STEEL TOWER. (Text in Japanese) 1954. 3/yr. membership. Nihon Tetto Kyokai - Japan Steel Tower Association, 13-5, Toranomon 1-chome, Minato-ku, Tokyo 105, Japan.

624　　　　　　　US
TEXAS CIVIL ENGINEER. 1931. 6/yr. $30. American Society of Civil Engineers, Texas Section, 3501 Manor Rd., Austin, TX 78723. TEL 512-472-8905. FAX 512-472-2934. Ed. Diane Tod South. adv.; circ. 6,250 (controlled). **Document type:** trade publication.
Description: Covers educational and technical articles; includes news and notes of interest to members.

THOM'S DUBLIN & COUNTY STREET DIRECTORY. see *GEOGRAPHY*

ENGINEERING — CIVIL ENGINEERING

624 SW ISSN 0040-6937
UG1
TIDSKRIFT I FORTIFIKATION; foer fortifikationsofficerare och officerare ingenjoerer, vaeg- och vattenbyggradskaaren. Short title: T I F. 1878. 4/yr. SEK 100. Fortifikationsklubben, c/o B. Fredholm, Tvaervaegen 2, S-171 30 Solna, Sweden. TELEX 19633-MSB-SBC. (Co-sponsors: Ingenjoerstrupperna; Vaag- och Vattenbyggnadskaaren) Ed. Boerje Fredholm. adv.; bk.rev.; charts; illus. circ. 800. **Document type:** newspaper, trade publication.

624 FI ISSN 0355-7855
TIE JA LIIKENNE. (Text in Finnish; summaries in English) 1974. m. (except Jan. & July). FIM 170 (foreign FIM 250). (Finnish Road Association) Suomen Tieyhdistys r.y., Malminkaari 5, 00700 Helsinki 70, Finland. TEL 358-0-7001-0881. FAX 358-0-351-1181. Ed. Jarmo Nupponen. adv.: B&W page FIM 5800, color page FIM 9400. bk.rev.; illus.; tr.lit. circ. 5,450. **Indexed:** Dok.Str., Geotech.Abstr., HRIS. **Document type:** trade publication.
Supersedes (1931-1974): Tielehti (ISSN 0040-7267)
Description: Focuses on road and traffic engineering.

624 GW ISSN 0340-5079
TA3 CODEN: TFBABE
TIEFBAU, INGENIEURBAU, STRASSENBAU; Zeitschrift fuer Verfahrenstechnik und Bauausfuehrung. 1959. m. DM.171. Bertelsmann Fachzeitschriften GmbH, Postfach 120, 33111 Guetersloh, Germany. TEL 05241-802332. FAX 05241-73055. Ed. A. Langer. adv.: B&W page DM.4800, color page DM.7450; trim 270 x 186. bk.rev.; charts; illus.; tr.lit.; index. circ. 9,924. **Indexed:** Dok.Str., Eng.Ind., Excerp.Med., Geotech.Abstr., HRIS, Intl.Civil Eng.Abstr., Soft.Abstr.Eng. **Document type:** trade publication.
—SWETS.
Description: Trade news about process technology and execution of contruction work.

624 JA ISSN 0386-8796
TOBISHIMA GIHO, DOBOKU/TOBISHIMA ENGINEERING REPORT, CIVIL ENGINEERING. (Text in Japanese) 1973. irreg. Tobishima Kensetsu K.K., 2, Sanban-cho, Chiyoda-ku, Tokyo 102, Japan.

624 720 JA ISSN 0387-5113
TOBISHIMA GIHO, KENCHIKU/TOBISHIMA ENGINEERING REPORT, ARCHITECTURE. (Text in Japanese) 1978. s-a. Tobishima Kensetsu K.K., 2, Sanban-cho, Chiyoda-ku, Tokyo 102, Japan.

624 JA ISSN 0288-6502
TA715
TOCHI ZOSEI KOGAKU KENKYU SHISETSU HOKOKU/RECLAMATION ENGINEERING RESEARCH INSTITUTE. REPORT. (Text in English, Japanese) 1983. a. Kobe Daigaku Kogakubu, Tochi Zosei Kogaku Kenkyu Shisetsu - Kobe University, Faculty of Engineering, Reclamation Engineering Research Institute, 1-20, Hanawada 1-chome, Utsunomiya-shi, Tochigi-ken 320, Japan. **Document type:** academic/scholarly publication.

624 JA
TOHOKU GIJUTSU/TOHOKU ENGINEERING. (Text in Japanese) s-a. Kensetsusho, Tohoku Chiho Kensetsukyoku, Tohoku Gijutsu Jimusho - Ministry of Construction, Tohoku Regional Construction Bureau, Tohoku Engineering Office, 6-1, Sakuragi 3-chome, Tagajo-shi, Miyagi-ken 985, Japan. **Document type:** trade publication.

624 JA
TOHOKU GIJUTSU JIMUSHO GIJUTSU SHIRYO/TOHOKU ENGINEERING OFFICE. TECHNICAL MATERIALS. (Text in Japanese) irreg. Kensetsusho Tohoku Chiho Kensetsukyoku, Tohoku Gijutsu Jimusho - Ministry of Construction, Tohoku Regional Construction Bureau, Tohoku Engineering Office, 6-1, Sakuragi 3-chome, Tagajo-shi, Miyagi-ken 985, Japan. **Document type:** trade publication.

624 JA
TOKYO DAIGAKU. KOGAKUBU. DOBOKU KOGAKKA. RONBUN SHUROKU/UNIVERSITY OF TOKYO. FACULTY OF ENGINEERING. DEPARTMENT OF CIVIL ENGINEERING. TRANSACTIONS. (Text in Japanese; summaries in English, Japanese) 1964. a. Tokyo Daigaku, Kogakubu, Doboku Kogakka, 3-1, Hongo 7-chome, Bunkyo-ku, Tokyo 113, Japan.

624 JA ISSN 0289-1743
TOKYO KOGYO DAIGAKU. DOBOKU KOGAKKA. KENKYU HOKOKU/TOKYO INSTITUTE OF TECHNOLOGY. DEPARTMENT OF CIVIL ENGINEERING. TECHNICAL REPORT. (Text in English, Japanese) 1966. a. Tokyo Kogyo Daigaku, Kogakubu Doboku Kogakkai, 12-1, Ookayama 2-chome, Meguro-ku, Tokyo 152, Japan. **Document type:** academic/scholarly publication.

624 JA ISSN 0911-825X
TOKYO TEKKOTSU KYORYO SEISAKUSYO GIJUTSUHO/TOKYO STEEL RIB AND BRIDGE CONSTRUCTION CO., LTD. TECHNICAL REPORT. (Text in Japanese) 1976. s-a. Tokyo Tekkotsu Kyoryo Seisakusyo, 18-32, Shibaura 4-chome, Minato-ku, Tokyo 108, Japan. Ed. Koji Yuge. **Document type:** academic/scholarly publication.

624 JA ISSN 0285-631X
TONNERU TO CHIKA/TUNNELS AND UNDERGROUND. (Text in Japanese; summaries in English) 1970. m. 1030 Yen per no. Doboku Kogakusha, Meija Kagurazaka, 16, Iwato-cho, Shinjuku-ku, Tokyo 162, Japan.

624 690 UK
TRAFALGAR HOUSE TODAY. 1969. s-a. Trafalgar House Public Ltd. Co., 1 Berkeley St., London W1A 1BY, England. TEL 071-499-9020. FAX 071-499-5359. Ed. Iain Kimberley. circ. 38,000. (back issues avail.) **Document type:** newsletter.
Former titles (until 1993): Trafalgar House News (ISSN 0956-4462); (until 1991): Group News; Forum (London 1969) (ISSN 0954-1004); (until 1988): Trafalgar Forum (ISSN 0950-9534)

TRANSPORT RESEARCH LABORATORY. RESEARCH REPORTS. see *TRANSPORTATION — Roads And Traffic*

TRANSPORTATION BUILDER. see *TRANSPORTATION — Roads And Traffic*

TRANSPORTATION RESEARCH BOARD SPECIAL REPORT. see *TRANSPORTATION — Roads And Traffic*

TRANSPORTATION RESEARCH RECORD. see *TRANSPORTATION — Roads And Traffic*

624 FR ISSN 0041-1906
TA2 CODEN: TRAVAJ
TRAVAUX. 1933. m. 1100 F. (effective Oct. 1993). (Federation Nationale des Travaux Publics) Science et Industrie, 79 av. Denfert-Rochereau, 75014 Paris, France. TEL 43-26-84-94. FAX 1-43-25-36-96. Ed. Dominique Milleron. adv.; bk.rev.; abstr.; index. circ. 5,000. **Indexed:** Br.Rail.Bd., Dok.Str., Eng.Ind., Excerp.Med., Geotech.Abstr., HRIS, I D A, Intl.Civil Eng.Abstr., Soft.Abstr.Eng. **Document type:** newspaper, abstracting/indexing.
—BLDSC (9028.000000); Faxon; SWETS. **CCC.**

624 FR ISSN 0751-5944
TRAVAUX PUBLICS ET BATIMENT DU MIDI. 1961. w. 90 F. EDITEM (Marseille), 1 bd. Garibaldi, B.P. 2249, 13211 Marseille Cedex 1, France. TEL 91-48-39-45. FAX 91-47-65-16. Ed. Michel Courartou; Pub. Alain Capagorry. adv.; bk.rev. circ. 15,742. **Document type:** corporate report.

624 AT ISSN 0726-125X
TRAVERSE. 1964. q. Aus.$40. Institution of Surveyors, Victoria, 191 Royal Pde., Rm. 201, Parkville, Vic. 3052, Australia. FAX 03-347-3268. Ed. N.F. Edwards. adv.; bk.rev. circ. 700. (back issues avail.)

624 AT
TRUCK AUSTRALIA. m. Aus.$53. Thomson Business Publishing, 47 Chippen St., Chippendale, N.S.W. 2008, Australia. TEL 02-699-2411. FAX 02-698-3920. Ed. Barry Hatfield. adv. circ. 12,087. **Indexed:** Aus.Rd.Ind.
Formerly: C A R T (ISSN 0727-5447)

624 363.3 ISSN 0916-7099
TSUNAMI KOGAKU KENKYU HOKOKU/TSUNAMI ENGINEERING TECHNICAL REPORT. (Text in Japanese) 1984. a. Tohoku Daigaku, Kogakubu, Saigai Seigyo Kenkyu - Tohoku University, Faculty of Engineering, Disaster Control Research Center, Aoba, Aramaki, Aoba-ku, Sendai-shi, Miyagi-ken 980, Japan.

624 CC
TU-MU GONGCHENG XUEBAO/CHINA CIVIL ENGINEERING JOURNAL. (Text in Chinese) q. $1.80 per no. (China Civil Engineering Society) Guoji Shudian, Qikan Bu - China International Book Trading Corp., P.O. Box 399, Beijing 100044, People's Republic of China. **Indexed:** Concr.Abstr.

624 GW ISSN 0722-6241
TUNNEL; international journal for subsurface use. (Text in English, German) 1981. 6/yr. DM.93. Bertelsmann Fachzeitschriften GmbH, Postfach 120, 33111 Guetersloh, Germany. TEL 05241-802332. FAX 05241-73055. Ed. Aribert Langer. adv.: B&W page DM.3600, color page DM.6100; trim 297 x 210. circ. 3,652. **Document type:** trade publication.
—BLDSC (9071.300000).
Description: Trade news about subsurface construction, including supply and disposal of materials.

624 690 JA
TUNNELLING ACTIVITIES IN JAPAN. (Text in English) biennial. Nihon Tonneru Gijutsu Kyokai - Japan Tunnelling Association, 14-7, Shintomi 2-chome, Chuo-ku, Tokyo 104, Japan.

624 UK
TUNNELLING DIRECTORY; an international yearbook of consultants and companies in sub-surface construction. 1980. a. £43($110) Morgan-Grampian (Construction Press) Ltd. (Subsidiary of: Morgan-Grampian plc), Morgan-Grampian House, 30 Calderwood St., London SE18 6QH, England. TEL 081-855-7777. FAX 081-316-3159. Ed. P. Darling. (reprint service avail. from UMI) **Document type:** directory.

624.19 UK ISSN 0041-414X
TA800 CODEN: TUTUBV
TUNNELS & TUNNELLING. 1969. m. £45($115) Morgan-Grampian (Construction Press) Ltd. (Subsidiary of: Morgan-Grampian plc), Morgan-Grampian House, 30 Calderwood St., London SE18 6QH, England. TEL 081-855-7777. FAX 081-316-3169. Ed. Peter Darling. adv. contact: Trevor Southerden. bk.rev.; charts; illus.; tr.lit.; index. circ. 3,528. (also avail. in microform from UMI; reprint service avail.) **Indexed:** Br.Rail.Bd., Br.Tech.Ind., Eng.Ind., Excerp.Med., Fluidex, Fuel & Energy Abstr., GeoRef., Geotech.Abstr., HRIS, Intl.Civil Eng.Abstr., Soft.Abstr.Eng., W.R.C.Inf. **Document type:** trade publication.
—BLDSC (9071.500000); EI; UnCover; SWETS.

624 FR ISSN 0399-0834
TUNNELS ET OUVRAGES SOUTERRAINS. 1974. bi-m. 320 F. (Europe 485 F., elsewhere 540 F.). Specifique J L P, 1 rue e Mailly, 69300 Caluire, France. TEL 78-39-17-17. FAX 72-00-96-73. TELEX 305 348. Ed. Jean Luc Reith. adv.; bk.rev. circ. 2,000. **Indexed:** Geotech.Abstr., HRIS, Intl.Civil Eng.Abstr., Soft.Abstr.Eng. **Document type:** newspaper.
—BLDSC (9071.540000).

TURKISH CHAMBER OF CIVIL ENGINEERS. DIGEST (YEAR); extended summaries from Teknik Dergi/Technical Journal. see *ENGINEERING — Abstracting, Bibliographies, Statistics*

620 690 TU
TURKISH CONSTRUCTION CATALOG. (Text in English, Turkish) 1980. biennial. $100. Turkish Chamber of Civil Engineers - Insaat Muhendisleri Odasi, Selanik Caddesi 19-1, Kizilay 06650 Ankara, Turkey. TEL 90-4-4337626. FAX 90-4-4170632. **Document type:** catalog.
Description: Comprehensive guide to activity, companies, products and services from all fields of the construction and civil engineering sector in Turkey.

620 TU ISSN 0049-4852
TURKIYE MUHENDISLIK HABERLERI. 1954. m. $25. Turkish Chamber of Civil Engineers - Insaat Muhendisleri Odasi, Selanik Caddesi 19-1, Kizilay 06650 Ankara, Turkey. TEL 90-4-4337626. FAX 90-4-4170632. Ed. Mustafa Atmaca. adv.; index. circ. 15,000. **Document type:** bulletin.

L'UFFICIO TECNICO; rivista mensile di tecnica edilizia e urbanistica per amministrazioni pubbliche, professionisti e costruttori. see *PUBLIC ADMINISTRATION*

ENGINEERING — CIVIL ENGINEERING

624   UK   ISSN 0269-4670
UNDERGROUND; magazine for trenchless construction and microtunnelling. 1986. q. £25($45) Thomas Telford Ltd., Thomas Telford House, 1 Heron Quay, London E14 4JD, England. TEL 071-987-6999. FAX 071-538-4101. TELEX 298105-CIVILS-G. circ. 5,000.

625.7   US   ISSN 0073-2184
U.S. FEDERAL HIGHWAY ADMINISTRATION. HIGHWAY PLANNING TECHNICAL REPORTS. 1963. irreg. free. U.S. Federal Highway Administration, Department of Transportation, 400 Seventh St., S.W., Washington, DC 20590. TEL 202-426-0632. (Dist. by: Supt. of Documents, Government Printing Office, Washington, DC 20402)

U.S. OFFICE OF TECHNOLOGY ASSESSMENT. REPORTS. EXPLORATORY GROUP. see *CIVIL DEFENSE*

UNITED STATES LIGHTHOUSE SOCIETY. BULLETIN. see *HISTORY*

624.176   CN   ISSN 0068-1709
UNIVERSITY OF BRITISH COLUMBIA. DEPARTMENT OF CIVIL ENGINEERING. SOIL MECHANICS SERIES. 1966. irreg., latest no.153. price varies. University of British Columbia, Department of Civil Engineering, 2324 Main Mall, Vancouver, BC V6T 1Z4, Canada. TEL 604-822-2637. FAX 604-822-6901. **Document type:** academic/scholarly publication.
—BLDSC (8322.620000).

624   CN
UNIVERSITY OF CALGARY. DEPARTMENT OF CIVIL ENGINEERING RESEARCH REPORT. 1971. irreg. (approx. 25/yr.) free. University of Calgary, Department of Civil Engineering, Calgary, AB T2N 1N4, Canada. TEL 403-220-5821. FAX 403-282-7026.

624   PK
UNIVERSITY OF ENGINEERING AND TECHNOLOGY. RESEARCH BULLETIN. (Text in English) vol.6, 1977. q. University of Engineering and Technology, Directorate of Research, Extension and Advisory Services, Lahore 31, Pakistan. Ed.Bd. charts; illus.

624   AT   ISSN 0077-8796
UNIVERSITY OF NEW SOUTH WALES. SCHOOL OF CIVIL ENGINEERING. U N I C I V REPORTS. SERIES I. 1963. irreg. Aus.$50. University of New South Wales, Kensington, N.S.W. 2052, Australia. TEL 02-697-2840. FAX 02-662-2163. circ. 220.

624   AT   ISSN 0077-880X
UNIVERSITY OF NEW SOUTH WALES. SCHOOL OF CIVIL ENGINEERING. U N I C I V REPORTS. SERIES R. 1963. irreg. Aus.$40 (foreign Aus.$60; free to qualified libraries). University of New South Wales, School of Civil Engineering, P.O. Box 1, Kensington, N.S.W. 2033, Australia. Ed.Bd. circ. 220.
—BLDSC (9090.550000).

624   JA   ISSN 0495-7806
UNIVERSITY OF TOKYO. FACULTY OF ENGINEERING. DEPARTMENT OF CIVIL ENGINEERING. COLLECTED PAPERS. (Text in English) 1963. a. Tokyo Daigaku, Kogakubu, Doboku Kogakka, 3-1, Hongo 7-chome, Bunkyo-ku, Tokyo 113, Japan. **Document type:** academic/scholarly publication.

625   NO   ISSN 0376-7272
VAARE VEGER. 1974. 10/yr. NOK 310($40) (Norske Sivilingenioerers Forening - Norwegian Society of Chartered Engineers) Ingenioerforlaget AS, Ingenioerenes Hus, P.O. Box 2845, Solli, N-0202 Oslo, Norway. TEL 47-22-94-76-00. FAX 47-22-94-76-01. (Co-sponsor: Association of Norwegian Road Engineers) Ed. Jarle Skoglund. adv. circ. 11,051. (back issues avail.) **Indexed:** Dok.Str.

624   SW   ISSN 0347-3503
                                                CODEN: VVTBAZ
VAEG- OCH VATTENBYGGAREN. UPPLAGA B. Variant title: V - Byggaren. 1955. 20/yr. SEK 211. Svenska Vaeg- och Vattenbyggares Riksfoerbund, Box 1334, S-111 83 Stockholm, Sweden. Ed. Jan Jerstrom. adv.; bk.rev.; charts; illus.; index. circ. 6,800. **Indexed:** Eng.Ind., Geotech.Abstr.
Formerly: Vaeg- och Vattenbyggaren (ISSN 0042-2177)

624   GW
VERBAND BAUGEWERBLICHER UNTERNEHMER HESSEN. MITTEILUNGSBLATT. 1949. m. Verband Baugewerblicher Unternehmer Hessen e.V., Postfach 500251, 60392 Frankfurt a.M., Germany. TEL 069-95809-0. FAX 069-95809233. circ. 2,800. (tabloid format; back issues avail.) **Document type:** newsletter.

624   NO   ISSN 0801-714X
VERITAS FORUM. 1955. 6/yr. free. Veritas Corporate Communications, Det novske Veritas, N-1322 Hovik, Norway. Ed. R. Evans. adv.; bk.rev.; cum.index: 1983-1988; circ. 15,000 (controlled). **Indexed:** BMT, Petrol.Abstr.
—CCC.
Formerly (until 1986): Veritas (ISSN 0042-3963)
Description: Covers marine and offshore industries worldwide with particular reference to advanced technologies.

526.9 625.72   GW   ISSN 0042-4099
DER VERMESSUNGSINGENIEUR. 1950. bi-m. DM.89. (Verband Deutscher Vermessungsingenieure e.V.) Verlag Chmielorz GmbH und Co., Wilhelmstr. 42, 65185 Wiesbaden, Germany. Ed. Josef Heyink. adv.; bk.rev.; abstr.; bibl.; charts; illus.; index. circ. 4,300. **Indexed:** Bibl.Cart.
—CCC.
Formerly: Fluchtstab.

526.9   GW   ISSN 0042-4102
TA501
VERMESSUNGSTECHNIK; Zeitschrift fuer Geodaesie. Photogrammetrie und Kartographie der DDR. (Text in German; summaries in English, German, Russian) 1953. m. DM.182.40. Wichmann Verlag, Amalienstr. 29, 76133 Karlsruhe, Germany. TEL 0721-20909. Ed. Wolfgang Arndt. adv.; bk.rev.; charts; illus. **Indexed:** Bibl.Cart., Geo.Abstr.

526.9 625.72   GW   ISSN 0340-5141
TA501
VERMESSUNGSWESEN UND RAUMORDNUNG (VR). 1924. 8/yr. DM.98. Ferd. Duemmlers Verlag, Kaiserstr. 31-37, 53113 Bonn, Germany. TEL 0228-223031. FAX 0228-213040. (Subscr. to: Postfach 1480, 53004 Bonn, Germany) Ed. Dr. Hanns J. Meckenstock. adv.; bk.rev.; charts; illus. circ. 1,500. **Indexed:** Bibl.Cart., Excerp.Med., Geo.Abstr. **Document type:** academic/scholarly publication.
—BLDSC (9172.100000); SWETS. **CCC**.
Formerly: Vermessungstechnische Rundschau (VR) (ISSN 0042-4110)

624 918   US
WATER & WASTE TREATMENT: LATIN AMERICAN INDUSTRIAL REPORT. 1985. a. $235 per country report. Aquino Productions, Box 15760, Stamford, CT 06901. TEL 203-325-3138. Ed. Andres C. Aquino.

WATER QUALITY INTERNATIONAL. see *ENVIRONMENTAL STUDIES — Pollution*

624   NE   ISSN 0043-2067
TE4
WEGEN; maandblad voor verkeer, grond-, water- en wegenbouw. 1925. 10/yr. fl.75 (effective 1994). C.R.O.W., Postbus 37, 6710 BA Ede, Netherlands. TEL 31-8380-20410. FAX 31-8380-21112. (Co-sponsors: Permanente Internationale Vereniging voor Wegencongressen, Nederlandse Vereniging voor Wegenbouwers, Vereniging Het Nederlandse Wegencongres) Ed. J.G.L.M. Matser. bk.rev.; abstr.; bibl.; charts; illus.; pat.; stat.; tr.mkt.; index. circ. 3,000. **Indexed:** Dok.Str., Excerp.Med., Geotech.Abstr., HRIS, Key to Econ.Sci.
—SWETS.

625.7   US   ISSN 0083-8918
WESTERN HIGHWAY INSTITUTE. RESEARCH COMMITTEE. REPORT. 1969. irreg. price varies. Western Highway Institute, Research Committee, 1200 Bay Hill Dr., Ste. 112, San Bruno, CA 94066. TEL 415-952-4900.

623.8   US   ISSN 1045-0343
                                    CODEN: WDMCAP
WORLD DREDGING - MINING & CONSTRUCTION. 1965. m. $28. Wodcon Association (Subsidiary of: Placer Management Corp.), Box 17479, Irvine, CA 92713. TEL 714-553-0836. FAX 714-863-9261. Ed. Ron Bowman. adv.; bk.rev.; illus. circ. 3,400. **Indexed:** BMT, Eng.Ind., Excerp.Med., Fluidex, Ocean.Abstr., Pollut.Abstr. **Document type:** trade publication.
—BLDSC (9354.252500); UnCover; SWETS.
Formerly: World Dredging and Marine Construction (ISSN 0043-8405)

624   UK   ISSN 0956-8700
WORLD TUNNELLING; subsurface excavation. 1988. 10/yr. £40($75) (effective Jan. 1994). Mining Journal Ltd., 60 Worship St., London EC2A 2HD, England. TEL 071-377-2020. FAX 071-247-4100. TELEX 8952809-MINING-G. (Subscr. to: Box 10, Edenbridge, Kent, TN8 5NE, England) Ed. Michael Smith. adv.; bk.rev.; illus. circ. 6,062. (also avail. in microfilm; back issues avail.; reprint service avail.) **Document type:** trade publication.
—EI.
Description: Addresses civil and mining tunneling and underground excavations for senior technical management worldwide.

624   CC   ISSN 1000-4548
YANTU GONGCHENG XUEBAO. (Text in Chinese) 1979. bi-m. Y30. Zhongguo Tumu Gongcheng Xuehui - Chinese Society of Civil Engineering, 34 Hujuguan, Nanjing, Jiangsu 210024, People's Republic of China. TEL 025-6633662. FAX 025-3310321. (Co-sponsors: Zhongguo Lixue Xuehui, Zhongguo Jianzhu Xuehui) Ed. Shen Zhujiang. bk.rev. circ. 3,000. **Document type:** academic/scholarly publication.

624   JA   ISSN 0916-9660
YOKOGAWA BURIJJI GIHO/YOKOGAWA BRIDGE GROUP TECHNICAL REPORT. (Text in Japanese; summaries in English) 1972. a. Yokogawa Burijji, 4-44, Shibaura 4-chome, Minato-ku, Tokyo 108, Japan.

Z I INTERNATIONAL journal for the brick and tile, structural ceramics, refractory and clay pipe industries. (Ziegelindustrie) see *CERAMICS, GLASS AND POTTERY*

455.50   GW   ISSN 0722-4400
                                    CODEN: ZIEBEK
Z K G: AUSGABE B/CEMENT - LIME - GYPSUM. EDITION B. (Zement - Kalk - Gips International) (Text in German with English translations of all leading articles; summaries in French and Spanish) 1911. m. DM.600 (foreign DM.626). (German Associations of the Cement, Lime and Gypsum Industries) Bauverlag GmbH, Postfach 1460, 65004 Wiesbaden, Germany. TEL 06123-700-0. FAX 06123-700122. Ed.Bd. adv.; bk.rev.; abstr.; bibl.; charts; illus.; pat.; index. circ. 3,700. **Indexed:** Appl.Mech.Rev., Ceram.Abstr., Chem.Abstr., Eng.Ind. **Document type:** trade publication.
—BLDSC (9500.000000); EI; SWETS; CASDDS.
Supersedes in part (in 1976): Zement - Kalk - Gips (ISSN 0044-3905)
Description: For the cement, lime and gypsum industries. Covers technical information on the latest developments.

624 691   BN   ISSN 0353-4146
ZBORNIK ISTRAZIVACKIH RADOVA IZ OBLASTI MATERIJALA I KONSTRUKCIJA U GRADJEVINARSTVU. (Text in Serbo-Croatian) 1972. a. $40 (typically set in Jan.). Univerzitet u Sarajevu, Gradjevinski Fakultet, Institut za Materijale i Konstrukcije, Stjepana Tomica 5, 71000 Sarajevo, Bosnia Hercegovina. TEL 071-215-255. FAX 38-71-218-697. Ed. Stevan Kebeljic. adv. circ. 500.
Formerly (until 1987): Gradjevinski Fakultet. Institut za Materijale i Konstrukcije. Zbornik Istrazivackih Radova (ISSN 0350-1701)

ENGINEERING — Computer Applications

627.54   **GW**   ISSN 0934-666X
S605   CODEN: ZKLAEW
ZEITSCHRIFT FUER KULTURTECHNIK UND LANDENTWICKLUNG/JOURNAL OF RURAL ENGINEERING AND DEVELOPMENT. (Text in German; summaries in English and German) 1960. bi-m. DM.298($199) Verlag Paul Parey (Berlin), Seelbuschring 9-17, 12105 Berlin, Germany. TEL 030-70784-0. FAX 030-70784199. Ed.Bd. adv.; bk.rev.; abstr.; bibl.; illus.; index. (back issues avail.) **Indexed:** Agri.Eng.Abstr., Agroforest.Abstr., Biol.Abstr., Chem.Abstr., Curr.Adv.Ecol.Sci., Curr.Cont., Excerp.Med., Field Crop Abstr., Forest.Abstr., Geo.Abstr., Rural Recreat.Tour.Abstr., Soils & Fert., World Agri.Econ.& Rural Sociol.Abstr. **Document type:** academic/scholarly publication.
—BLDSC (9468.310000). **CCC.**
Formerly: Zeitschrift fuer Kulturtechnik und Flurbereinigung (ISSN 0044-2984)

526.9 625.72   **GW**   ISSN 0340-4560
TA501   CODEN: ZTVRAM
ZEITSCHRIFT FUER VERMESSUNGSWESEN. (Text in German; summaries in English) 1872. m. DM.116. (Deutscher Verein fuer Vermessungswesen) Verlag Konrad Wittwer GmbH, Nordbahnhofstr. 16, 70178 Stuttgart, Germany. TEL 0711-2507-0. FAX 0711-2507350. TELEX 723751-KAWEB-D. Eds. H. Magel, W. Torge. adv.; bk.rev.; charts; illus.; index, cum.index every 25 yrs. circ. 8,500. **Indexed:** Bibl.Cart., Excerp.Med., Geo.Abstr. **Document type:** trade publication.
—BLDSC (9489.000000); Faxon. **CCC.**
Description: Discusses the latest research and technology in the field of surveying and geodetic science. Includes list and reports of events and exhibitions, trade school information, and association reports.

624   **GW**   ISSN 0514-2938
TA680   CODEN: ZETAAQ
ZEMENT - TASCHENBUCH. 1950. biennial. DM.28. (Verein Deutscher Zementwerke e.V.) Bauverlag GmbH, Postfach 1460, 65004 Wiesbaden, Germany. TEL 06123-700-0. FAX 06123-700-122. adv.; index. **Document type:** trade publication.
—CASDDS.

624   **JA**   ISSN 0388-3345
ZENITAKAGUMI GIHO/ZENITAKA TECHNICAL RESEARCH REPORT. (Text in English, Japanese) 1975. a. Zenitakagumi, 31, Ichiban-cho, Chiyoda-ku, Tokyo 102, Japan.

625.7   **CC**   ISSN 1000-4602
TD204
ZHONGGUO GESHUI PAISHUI/CHINA WATER & WASTEWATER. (Text in Chinese) bi-m. $50. Zhongguo Shizheng Gongcheng Huabei Shijiyuan, Qixiangtai Lu, Hexi-qu, Tianjin 300074, People's Republic of China. TEL 022-3342167. Ed. Yu Zhongmin. circ. 62,000. **Document type:** academic/scholarly publication.
—BLDSC (3180.238800).

624   **GW**   ISSN 0084-5485
ZIEGELEITECHNISCHES JAHRBUCH. 1950. a. DM.54. Bauverlag GmbH, Postfach 1460, 65004 Wiesbaden, Germany. TEL 06123-700-0. FAX 06123-700-122. **Document type:** trade publication.

624   **GW**   ISSN 0340-3386
                              CODEN: RRRIDC
3 R - INTERNATIONAL. (Text in German; summaries in English, French) 1951. m. (10/yr.). DM.285. Vulkan-Verlag GmbH, Postfach 103962, 45039 Essen, Germany. TEL 0201-82002-0. FAX 0201-82002-40. Ed.Bd. adv. **Document type:** trade publication.
—BLDSC (9539.000000); SWETS; CASDDS. **CCC.**
Formerly: Rohre - Rohrleitungsbau - Rohrleitungstransport (ISSN 0035-7855)
Description: Covers the entire field of pipe manufacture, pipe fabrication, the laying of pipelines, and the design installation of pipe networks.

ENGINEERING — Computer Applications

620   **US**
A A C C NEWSLETTER. s-a. American Automatic Control Council, c/o EECS, Northwestern University, Evanston, IL 60208-3118. TEL 708-491-3641. FAX 708-491-4455. (Co-sponsors: American Institute of Aeronautics and Astronautics (AIAA); American Institute of Chemical Engineers (AIChE); American Society of Mechanical Engineers (ASME); Association of Iron and Steel Engineers (AISE); Institute of Electrical and Electronic Engineers (IEEE); Instrument Society of America (ISA); Society for Computer Simulation (SCS)) Ed. Bonnie Heck. **Document type:** newsletter.

651.8 621.3   **SW**   ISSN 0284-7590
A D B - NYTT; nyheter och information fraan Telia Data. 1984. 3/yr. free. Telia Data, P.O. Box 164, S-136 23 Haninge, Sweden. TEL 46-8-707-17-74. FAX 46-8-707-10-07. Ed. Francine Skoglund. circ. 5,500. **Document type:** trade publication.
Former titles (until 1988): A D B - Service Information; (until 1986): A D B - Service Informerar; (until vol.2, 1984): Information fraan Televerkets A D B - Avdeling.

620   **US**   ISSN 0277-1659
A - E - C AUTOMATION NEWSLETTER. (Architecture, Engineering, Construction) 1977. m. $189 (foreign $240). Technology Publications, Inc., 5920 Roswell Rd., B-107336, Atlanta, GA 30328-4922. TEL 404-565-3282. FAX 404-565-3286. Ed. Carlton R. Howk. bk.rev.; tr.lit.; circ. 4,300 (paid). (tabloid format; back issues avail.) **Document type:** newsletter.
Description: Features articles on automation in the architecture, engineering and construction fields as well as GIS mapping, written by a practicing engineer and computer-automation expert.

620 005.3   **UK**   ISSN 0965-9978
TA345
ADVANCES IN ENGINEERING SOFTWARE. 1979. 9/yr. (in 3 vols., 3 nos/vol.). £397($610) (effective 1994). Elsevier Science Ltd., Oxford Fulfilment Centre, P.O. Box 800, Kidlington, Oxford OX5 1DX, England. TEL 44-865-843000. FAX 44-865-843010. (Subscr. in the Americas to: Elsevier Science, 660 White Plains Rd., Tarrytown, NY 10591-5153. TEL 914-524-9200. FAX 914-333-2444) Ed. R.A. Adey. adv.; bk.rev. (back issues avail.) **Indexed:** Abstr.J.Earthq.Eng., Appl.Mech.Rev., Compumath, Comput.Abstr., Comput.Cont., Comput.Lit.Ind., Cyb.Abstr., Fluidex, Intl.Civil Eng.Abstr., Sci.Abstr., Soft.Abstr.Eng. **Document type:** academic/scholarly publication.
—BLDSC (0705.450000); EI; Faxon; UnCover; SWETS; UMI. **CCC.**
Incorporates (1986-1993): Microcomputers in Civil Engineering (ISSN 0885-9507); *Former titles (until 1992):* Advances in Engineering Software and Workstations (ISSN 0961-3552); (until 1991): Advances in Engineering Software (ISSN 0141-1195); *Incorporates (in 1991):* Software for Engineering Workstations (ISSN 0952-8768); Which was formerly: Microsoftware for Engineers (ISSN 0266-9463)
Description: Provides a forum for the presentation and discussion of recent advances in engineering software and a link between the originators of software and the engineering community.
Refereed Serial

ARTIFICIAL INTELLIGENCE IN ENGINEERING. see COMPUTERS — Artificial Intelligence

620   **AT**   ISSN 0084-7496
AUSTRALIAN NATIONAL UNIVERSITY, CANBERRA. DEPARTMENT OF ENGINEERING PHYSICS. PUBLICATION EP-RR. 1959. irreg. Australian National University, Research School of Physical Sciences and Engineering, Department of Engineering Physics, Energy Research Centre, Canberra, A.C.T. 0200, Australia. Ed. Prof. S. Kaneff.

C A D - C A M ABSTRACTS. (Computer Aided Design - Computer Aided Manufacturing) see COMPUTERS — Computer Engineering

620   **US**   ISSN 1045-1986
C A S E STRATEGIES. (Computer-Aided Systems Engineering); the monthly newsletter on computer-aided software engineering. 1989. m. $355 (foreign $415). Cutter Information Corp., 37 Broadway, Arlington, MA 02174. TEL 617-648-8700. FAX 617-648-8707. TELEX 650 100 9891 MCI UW. Ed. Mickey Williamson. charts; illus. (back issues avail.) **Document type:** newsletter.
●Also available online. Vendor(s): NewsNet (EC26).
—**CCC.**
Description: Covers new products, new technologies, and new methodologies for controlling and automating the analysis, design, and development of computer software. Includes independent product reviews, and industry trends.

C A TECHNIEK; tijdschrift voor industriele automatisering. see COMPUTERS — Automation

620   **US**   ISSN 1044-8179
                           CODEN: CERVEY
C E COMPUTING REVIEW. (Civil Engineers) 1989. m. American Society of Civil Engineers, 345 E. 47th St., New York, NY 10017-2398. TEL 212-705-7276. FAX 212-980-4681. **Document type:** academic/scholarly publication, newsletter.
Description: Provides software reviews, systems information and practical advice on many aspects of computing.

CHEMICAL BUSINESS. see ENGINEERING — Chemical Engineering

COMPEL; the international journal for computation and mathematics in electrical and electronic engineering. see MATHEMATICS — Computer Applications

COMPUTATIONAL MECHANICS ADVANCES. see MATHEMATICS — Computer Applications

620 510   **US**
▼**COMPUTATIONAL MECHANICS AND PHYSICS OF FRACTURE.** 1993. irreg. price varies. Nova Science Publishers, Inc., 6080 Jericho Tpke., Ste. 207, Commack, NY 11725-2808. TEL 516-499-3103. **Document type:** academic/scholarly publication.

620 660   **NE**
COMPUTER-AIDED CHEMICAL ENGINEERING. 1985. irreg., vol.5A&B, 1992. price varies. Elsevier Science B.V., Books Division, P.O. Box 211, 1000 AE Amsterdam, Netherlands. TEL 31-20-5803911. FAX 31-20-5803705. TELEX 18582 ESPA NL. (Subscr. in U.S. and Canada to: Elsevier Science Inc., Box 882, Madison Sq. Sta., New York, NY 10159. TEL 212-989-5800) **Document type:** monographic series.
—**CCC.**
Refereed Serial

521.381   **NE**
COMPUTER-AIDED DESIGN OF ELECTRONIC CIRCUITS. 1978. irreg., vol.2, 1980. price varies. Elsevier Science B.V., Books Division, P.O. Box 211, 1000 AE Amsterdam, Netherlands. TEL 31-20-5803911. FAX 31-20-5803705. TELEX 18582 ESPA NL. (Subscr. in U.S. and Canada to: Elsevier Science Inc., Box 882, Madison Sq. Sta., New York, NY 10159. TEL 212-989-5800) Ed. R. Spence. **Document type:** monographic series.
Refereed Serial

001.642 620   **US**   ISSN 0733-3536
TA345   CODEN: CCAEDJ
COMPUTER-AIDED ENGINEERING (CLEVELAND). 1982. m. $50 (free to qualified personnel). Penton Publishing (Subsidiary of: Pittway Company), 1100 Superior Ave., Cleveland, OH 44114-2543. TEL 216-696-7000. FAX 216-696-8765. Ed. John Krouse. adv.; circ. 60,000 (controlled). (reprint service avail. from UMI) **Indexed:** A.I.Abstr., Br.Tech.Ind., CAD CAM Abstr., Comput.Cont., Comput.Dtbs., Intl.Civil Eng.Abstr., Met.Abstr., Resour.Ctr.Ind., Soft.Abstr.Eng., World Alum.Abstr.
●Also available online. Vendor(s): DIALOG Information Services, Inc.
—BLDSC (3393.541200); EI; SWETS; UMI. **CCC.**
Description: All aspects of data base applications in design and manufacturing.

ENGINEERING — COMPUTER APPLICATIONS

621   US   ISSN 1061-3773
T61   CODEN: CAPEED
▼**COMPUTER APPLICATIONS IN ENGINEERING EDUCATION.** 1992. bi-m. $195. John Wiley & Sons, Inc., Wiley - Interscience, 605 Third Ave., New York, NY 10158-0012. TEL 212-850-6000. FAX 212-850-6088. TELEX 12-7068. Ed. Magdy F. Iskander.
—BLDSC (3393.646000); EI.
Description: Focuses and distributes current efforts made in computer-assisted engineering education, including new software, educational technologies, computer use in laboratories, and visualization techniques.

620   UK   ISSN 0951-5240
TS155.6   CODEN: CMASEU
COMPUTER-INTEGRATED MANUFACTURING SYSTEMS. 1988. q. £135 in UK and Europe; elsewhere £145. Butterworth - Heinemann (Subsidiary of: Reed International PLC), Linacre House, Jordan Hill, Oxford OX2 8DP, England. TEL 0865-310366. FAX 0865-310898. TELEX 83111 BHPOXF G. (Subscr. to: Turpin Transactions Ltd., Distribution Centre, Blackhorse Rd., Letchworth, Herts SG6 1HN, England. TEL 0462-672555) Ed. Ray Wild. adv.; bk.rev.; bibl.; charts; illus.; index. (also avail. in microform from UMI) **Indexed:** A.I.Abstr. (until 1992), Abstr.Hum.Comp.Inter., Robomat. (until 1992). **Document type:** academic/scholarly publication.
—BLDSC (3394.048000); EI; Faxon; UnCover; SWETS; UMI. **CCC.**
Incorporates (1988-1991): Advanced Manufacturing Engineering (ISSN 0951-5232)
Description: Devoted to the design, implementation, and management of effective CIM systems. Aims to promote collaboration and communication between academics and practitioners.
Refereed Serial

651.8 620   SZ   ISSN 0045-7825
TA345   CODEN: CMMECC
COMPUTER METHODS IN APPLIED MECHANICS AND ENGINEERING. (Text in English) 1970. 40/yr. (in 10 vols.; 4 nos./vol.). 4450 SFr.($3027) (effective 1994). Elsevier Science S.A., P.O. Box 564, CH-1001 Lausanne 1, Switzerland. TEL 41-21-3207381. FAX 41-21-3235444. TELEX 450620-ELSA-CH. (Subscr. in U.S. and Canada to: Elsevier Science Inc., Box 882, Madison Sq. Sta., New York, NY 10159. TEL 212-989-5800. FAX 212-633-3990) Ed. J.H. Argyris. adv.; bk.rev.; illus.; charts; stat.; index, cum.index. (also avail. in microform from UMI) **Indexed:** A.S.& T.Ind., Abstr.J.Earthq.Eng., Appl.Mech.Rev., Compumath, Comput.Abstr., Comput.Rev., Curr.Cont., Fluidex, GeoRef., Ind.Sci.Rev., INSPEC, Int.Aerosp.Abstr., Math.R., Phys.Ber., Sci.Abstr., Sci.Cit.Ind. **Document type:** academic/scholarly publication.
—BLDSC (3394.100000); EI; Faxon; UnCover; SWETS. **CCC.**
Description: Publishes scholarly papers on topics pertaining to applications of digital and hybrid computers in solving problems of applied mechanics and engineering.
Refereed Serial

620 001.642   US   ISSN 0888-2088
COMPUTER SOFTWARE ENGINEERING SERIES. 1978. irreg. Computer Science Press, Inc., 41 Madison Ave., 37th Fl., New York, NY 10010-3436. TEL 212-576-9400. Ed. Arthur D. Friedman. (back issues avail.)

COMPUTERS & CHEMICAL ENGINEERING; an international journal of computer applications in chemical engineering. see CHEMISTRY — Computer Applications

651.8 621.3   UK   ISSN 0045-7906
TK7885.A1   CODEN: CPEEBQ
COMPUTERS & ELECTRICAL ENGINEERING. 1973. 6/yr. £370($573) (effective 1994). Elsevier Science Ltd., Pergamon, P.O. Box 800, Kidlington, Oxford OX5 1DX, England. TEL 44-865-843000. FAX 44-865-843010. (Subscr. in U.S. and Canada to: Elsevier Science, 660 White Plains Rd., Tarrytown, NY 10591-5153. TEL 914-524-9200. FAX 914-333-2444) Ed. Mo Jamshidi. adv.; bk.rev.; film rev.; illus.; stat.; tr.lit.; index. circ. 1,200. (also avail. in microform from UMI; back issues avail.) **Indexed:** Compumath, Comput.Abstr., Comput.Cont., Curr.Cont., Math.R., Sci.Abstr. **Document type:** academic/scholarly publication.
—BLDSC (3394.680000); EI; Faxon; UnCover; SWETS; UMI. **CCC.**
Description: Provides research papers on the relationship which exists between computer technology and electrical engineering.
Refereed Serial

629.8   UK   ISSN 0045-7930
TA357   CODEN: CPFLBI
COMPUTERS & FLUIDS. 1973. 8/yr. £640($985) (effective 1994). Elsevier Science Ltd., Pergamon, P.O. Box 800, Kidlington, Oxford OX5 1DX, England. TEL 44-865-843000. FAX 44-865-843010. (Subscr. in U.S. and Canada to: Elsevier Science, 660 White Plains Rd., Tarrytown, NY 10591-5153. TEL 914-524-9200. FAX 914-333-2444) Ed. Stanley G. Rubin. adv.; software rev. circ. 1,075. (also avail. in microform from UMI; back issues avail.) **Indexed:** Appl.Mech.Rev., Biol.Abstr., CAD CAM Abstr., Chem.Abstr., Chem.Eng.Abstr., Compumath, Comput.Abstr., Comput.Cont., Curr.Cont., Fluidex, Ind.Sci.Rev., Int.Aerosp.Abstr., Int.Civil Eng.Abstr., ISMEC, Math.R., Phys.Ber., Sci.Abstr., Sci.Cit.Ind., Soft.Abstr.Eng., T.C.E.A. **Document type:** academic/scholarly publication.
—BLDSC (3394.690000); EI; Faxon; UnCover; SWETS; UMI; CASDDS. **CCC.**
Description: Multidisciplinary coverage of applications of computer techniques in studies of hydrodynamics, high-speed gas dynamics, turbulence, multiphase flow, rheology, kinetic theory, radiation, and electromagnetics.
Refereed Serial

620   UK   ISSN 0266-352X
CODEN: CGEOEU
COMPUTERS AND GEOTECHNICS. 1985. 4/yr. £199($305) (effective 1994). Elsevier Science Ltd., Oxford Fulfilment Centre, P.O. Box 800, Kidlington, Oxford OX5 1DX, England. TEL 44-865-843000. FAX 44-865-843010. (Subscr. in U.S. and Canada to: Elsevier Science, 660 White Plains Rd., Tarrytown, NY 10591-5153. TEL 914-524-9200. FAX 914-333-2444) Eds. G.N. Pande, S. Pietruszczak. adv.; bk.rev. (back issues avail.) **Indexed:** Appl.Mech.Rev., Eng.Ind., Geo.Abstr., Geotech.Abstr. **Document type:** academic/scholarly publication.
—BLDSC (3394.696000); EI; Faxon; UnCover; SWETS. **CCC.**
Description: Provides an up-to-date reference for those engaged in computer aided analysis, design and research in geotechnical engineering.
Refereed Serial

621.389 003   UK   ISSN 0360-8352
T57.5   CODEN: CINDDL
COMPUTERS & INDUSTRIAL ENGINEERING; an international journal. 1977. 8/yr (in 2 vols., 4 nos./vol.). £505($780) (effective 1994). Elsevier Science Ltd., Pergamon, P.O. Box 800, Kidlington, Oxford OX5 1DX, England. TEL 44-865-843000. FAX 44-865-843010. (Subscr. in U.S. and Canada to: Elsevier Science, 660 White Plains Rd., Tarrytown, NY 10591-5153. TEL 914-524-9200. FAX 914-333-2444) Ed. Hamed Kamel Eldin. adv.; bk.rev.; charts; illus.; index. circ. 1,000. (also avail. in microform from UMI) **Indexed:** A.I.Abstr., ABI Inform., BMT, CAD CAM Abstr., Compumath, Comput.Abstr., Comput.Cont., Curr.Cont., Eng.Ind., Intl.Civil Eng.Abstr., Oper.Res.Manage.Sci., Qual.Contr.Appl.Stat., Robomat., Sci.Abstr., Soft.Abstr.Eng. **Document type:** academic/scholarly publication.
—BLDSC (3394.713000); EI; Faxon; UnCover; SWETS; UMI. **CCC.**
Description: Provides coverage of computerized industrial engineering applications, methodology for developing computer solutions to industrial engineering problems, and the implementation of techniques in computers.
Refereed Serial

004 624   UK   ISSN 0045-7949
TA641   CODEN: CMSTCJ
COMPUTERS & STRUCTURES. (Text mainly in English) 1971. 24/yr. £1591($2450) (effective 1994). Elsevier Science Ltd., Pergamon, P.O. Box 800, Kidlington, Oxford OX5 1DX, England. TEL 44-865-843000. FAX 44-865-843010. (Subscr. in U.S. and Canada to: Elsevier Science, 660 White Plains Rd., Tarrytown, NY 10591-5153. TEL 914-524-9200. FAX 914-333-2444) Ed. Harold Liebowitz. adv.; bk.rev.; charts; illus.; index. circ. 1,500. (also avail. in microform from UMI; back issues avail.) **Indexed:** Abstr.J.Earthq.Eng., Appl.Mech.Rev., C.R.I. Abstr., CAD CAM Abstr. (until 1992), Chem.Abstr., Compumath, Comput.Abstr., Comput.Cont., Comput.Rev., Curr.Cont., Eng.Ind., HRIS, INIS Atcmind., Int.Aerosp.Abstr., Intl.Civil Eng.Abstr., ISMEC, J.of Ferroc., Math.R., Robomat. (until 1992), Sci.Abstr., Sh.& Vib.Dig., Soft.Abstr.Eng. **Document type:** academic/scholarly publication.
—BLDSC (3394.790000); EI; Faxon; UnCover; SWETS; UMI. **CCC.**
Description: Communicates information concerning applications of computers (digital, analog and hybrid) and computer programs to the solution of scientific and structural engineering problems relating to hydrospace, aerospace, and terrestrial structures.
Refereed Serial

620 330   UK   ISSN 0956-3385
TA345   CODEN: CCEJEL
COMPUTING & CONTROL ENGINEERING JOURNAL. bi-m. £105 in EC nations; elsewhere £117. I.E.E., Michael Faraday House, Six Hills Way, Stevenage, Herts. SG1 2AY, England. TEL 0438-313311. FAX 0438-313465. TELEX 825578-IEESTV-G. (Subscr. to: Publication Sales Dept., P.O. Box 96, Stevenage, Herts. SG1 2SD, England; U.S. subscr. to: INSPEC/IEEE, Box 1331, 445 Hoes Ln., Piscataway, NJ 08855-1331. TEL 908-562-5549) Ed.Bd. bk.rev. **Document type:** academic/scholarly publication.
—BLDSC (3395 016000); EI; Faxon; UnCover; SWETS. **CCC.**
Incorporates: Computer-Aided Engineering Journal (ISSN 0263-9327)
Description: Directed to engineers with information about the methods, techniques, and processes currently used in industrial, commercial, and business applications. Covers performance of languages, hardware-software boundaries. Provides user evaluations of techniques and processes, company profiles, entrepreneurial examples.

620   UK   ISSN 0956-0521
TA345   CODEN: COSEEO
COMPUTING SYSTEMS IN ENGINEERING. 1990. 6/yr. £270($415) (effective 1994). Elsevier Science Ltd., Pergamon, P.O. Box 800, Kidlington, Oxford OX5 1DX, England. TEL 44-865-843000. FAX 44-865-843010. (Subscr. in U.S. and Canada to: Elsevier Science, 660 White Plains Rd., Tarrytown, NY 10591-5153. TEL 914-524-9200. FAX 914-333-2444) Eds. A.K. Noor, B.H.V. Topping. (also avail. in microform from UMI; back issues avail.) **Document type:** academic/scholarly publication.
—BLDSC (3395.131400); Faxon; UMI. **CCC.**
Description: Communicates recent and projected advances in computational technology in the engineering disciplines.
Refereed Serial

CONFERENCE ON ARTIFICIAL INTELLIGENCE APPLICATIONS. PROCEEDINGS. see COMPUTERS — Artificial Intelligence

620   UK   ISSN 0264-6854
CODEN: CNSCEB
CONSTRUCTION COMPUTING. 1983. q. £25 (foreign £30). Englemere Services Ltd., Englemere, Kings Ride, Ascot, Berks. SL5 8BJ, England. TEL 0344-23355. FAX 0344-23467. Ed. Pauline Sargent. **Document type:** trade publication.
—BLDSC (3421.025500).
Description: Designed to provide a focal point for builders who use computers or are interested in learning about them. Includes hardware hints, perspective on the use of microcomputers in building, software advice, and case studies.

2318 ENGINEERING — COMPUTER APPLICATIONS

629.8 UK ISSN 0967-0661
TJ212 CODEN: COEPEL
▼**CONTROL ENGINEERING PRACTICE.** 1993. 6/yr. £268($415) (effective 1994). Elsevier Science Ltd., Pergamon, P.O. Box 800, Kidlington, Oxford OX5 1DX, England. TEL 44-865-843000. FAX 44-865-843010. (Subscr. in U.S. and Canada to: Elsevier Science, 660 White Plains Rd., Tarrytown, NY 10591-5153. TEL 914-524-9200. FAX 914-333-2444) Ed. M.G. Rodd. (also avail. in microfilm from UMI) **Document type:** academic/scholarly publication.
—BLDSC (3462.020000); EI; SWETS; UMI. **CCC.**
Description: Publishes papers illustrating direct applications of control theory and its supporting tools in all areas of automation.
Refereed Serial

620 US ISSN 0888-2118
DIGITAL SYSTEM DESIGN SERIES. 1975. irreg. price varies. Computer Science Press, Inc., 41 Madison Ave., 37th Fl., New York, NY 10010-3546. TEL 212-576-9400. Ed. Arthur D. Friedman. (back issues avail.)

620 380.3 US
ELECTRICAL ENGINEERING, TELECOMMUNICATIONS AND SIGNAL PROCESSING. 1981. irreg. Computer Science Press, Inc., 41 Madison Ave., 37th Fl., New York, NY 10010-3546. TEL 212-576-9400. Ed. Raymond L. Pickholtz. (back issues avail.)
Formerly: Electrical Engineering Communications and Signal Processing (ISSN 0888-2134)

620 US
ELECTRO MANUFACTURING. 1988. m. $150 (effective Jan. 1992). Worldwide Videotex, Box 3273, Boynton Beach, FL 33424-3273. TEL 407-738-2276. Ed. Mark Wright. bk.rev. (back issues avail.) **Document type:** trade publication.
●Also available online. Vendor(s): NewsNet.
Description: Provides news and information on new computer and electronic technologies being developed and applied to all areas of manufacturing to increase efficiency and productivity. Reports on the companies developing these automation technologies and those using them.

ENGINEERING APPLICATIONS OF ARTIFICIAL INTELLIGENCE. see *COMPUTERS — Artificial Intelligence*

ENGINEERING DOCUMENT MANAGEMENT SYSTEM COMPARISON REPORT. see *COMPUTERS — Data Base Management*

ENGINEERING INTELLIGENT SYSTEMS FOR ELECTRICAL ENGINEERING AND COMMUNICATIONS. see *COMPUTERS — Artificial Intelligence*

620 UK ISSN 0177-0667
TA174 CODEN: ENGCE7
ENGINEERING WITH COMPUTERS; an international journal for computer-aided mechanical and structural engineering. 1985. 4/yr. £80. Springer-Verlag, Springer House, 8 Alexandra Rd., Wimbledon, London SW19 7JZ, England. TEL 081-944-2942. FAX 081-947-4651. (Subscr. in N. America to: Springer-Verlag New York, Inc., Box 2485, Secaucus, NJ 07096-2491. TEL 201-348-4033) Eds. Ted Belytschko, Steven J. Fenves. (also avail. in microform from UMI; back issues avail.; reprint service avail. from ISI) **Indexed:** Compumath, Comput.Abstr., Curr.Cont., Eng.Ind. **Document type:** trade publication.
—BLDSC (3758.586000); EI; Faxon; UnCover; SWETS. **CCC.**
Description: Presents papers integrating analytical methods and numerical models with techniques of software engineering, including databases, geometric modeling, and computer graphics.

ENVIRONMENTAL SOFTWARE. see *ENVIRONMENTAL STUDIES — Computer Applications*

620 UK ISSN 0309-6688
FINITE ELEMENT NEWS. 1976. bi-m. £38 (foreign £43). Robinson & Associates, Great Bidlake Manor, Bridestowe, Okehampton, Devon EX20 4NT, England. TEL 083-786220. FAX 083-786638. Ed. John Robinson. adv.: B&W page £550, color page £1150; trim 180 x 260. (back issues avail.) **Document type:** trade publication.
—BLDSC (3928.322000); SWETS.
Description: Finite element news and associated topics.

620 338 NE ISSN 0168-874X
FINITE ELEMENTS IN ANALYSIS AND DESIGN; the international journal of applied finite elements and computer-aided engineering. (Text and summaries in English) 1985. 12/yr. (in 3 vols.; 4 nos./vol.). fl.1218($658) (effective 1994). North-Holland (Subsidiary of: Elsevier Science B.V.), P.O. Box 211, 1000 AE Amsterdam, Netherlands. TEL 31-20-5803911. FAX 31-20-5803598. TELEX 18582 ESPA NL. (Subscr. in U.S. and Canada to: Elsevier Science Inc., Box 882, Madison Sq. Sta., New York, NY 10159. TEL 212-989-5800. FAX 212-633-3990) Ed. Walter D. Pilkey. adv.; bk.rev.; abstr.; bibl.; illus. circ. 500. (back issues avail.) **Indexed:** Appl.Mech.Rev., CAD CAM Abstr., Comput.Abstr., J.of Ferroc. **Document type:** academic/scholarly publication.
—BLDSC (3928.322500); EI; Faxon; UnCover; SWETS. **CCC.**
Description: Aims to provide ideas and information involving the use of the finite element method, including CAD/CAM, in professional practice. Emphasizes structural, fluid, and mechanical technologies.
Refereed Serial

620 PL ISSN 0867-6356
CODEN: FCENDV
FOUNDATION OF COMPUTING AND DECISION SCIENCES. (Text and summaries in English) 1975. 4/yr. Politechnika Poznanska, Pl. Curie Sklodowskiej 5, Poznan, Poland. Ed.Bd. **Document type:** academic/scholarly publication.
Formerly (until 1990): Foundations of Control Engineering (ISSN 0324-8747)
Description: Control and optimization theory, decision theory, operations research, performance evaluation of computer systems and networks, and real-time control systems.

GEOMATICA. see *GEOGRAPHY*

620 011 FR
GUIDE DES BANQUES DE DONNEES FACTUELLES FRANCAISES SUR LES MATERIAUX. 1989. irreg. 225 F. (CODATA France) Editions F L A Consultants, 27 rue de la Vistule, 75013 Paris, France. TEL 1-45-82-75-75. FAX 1-45-82-46-04. Ed. Francois Libmann. **Document type:** directory.
Description: Provides a description of French factual materials databanks.

621.3 001.6 UK
I E E COMPUTING SERIES. 1981. irreg., vol.20, 1993. Institution of Electrical Engineers, Michael Faraday House, Six Hills Way, Stevenage, Herts SG1 2AY, England. TEL 0438-313311. FAX 0438-313465. TELEX 825578-IEESTV-G. Eds. D. Jacobs, B. Carre. **Indexed:** Sci.Abstr. **Document type:** monographic series.
Formerly: I E E Digital and Electronics and Computing Series.

621.31 US ISSN 0895-0156
TK3091 CODEN: ICAPEH
I E E E COMPUTER APPLICATIONS IN POWER. 1988. q. $75 to non-members. (I E E E, Power Engineering Society) Institute of Electrical and Electronics Engineers, Inc., 345 E. 47th St., New York, NY 10017-2394. FAX 908-981-9667. (Subscr. to: 445 Hoes Ln., Box 1331, Piscataway, NJ 08855-1331. TEL 908-981-0060) Ed. W.R. Brownlee. (also avail. in microform) **Indexed:** Sci.Abstr.
—BLDSC (4362.814200); EI; Faxon; UnCover; SWETS; UMI. **CCC.**
Description: Devoted to computer applications of the design, operation, and control of power systems.

INDUSTRIAL COMPUTING; plus programmable controls. see *COMPUTERS — Automation*

INDUSTRIAL ENGINEERING. see *ENGINEERING — Industrial Engineering*

620 GW
INDUSTRIETHEMEN; PR-Magazin fuer die Investitionsgueterindustrie. 1984. q. free. Industriethemen Verlag, Postfach 650073, 8000 Munich 65, Germany. TEL 089-8117414. FAX 089-8119931. Ed. W.G. Trapp. circ. 12,000.

620 006 GW ISSN 0170-6012
QA75.5
INFORMATIK-SPEKTRUM; archive of applied mechanics. (Text mainly in German) 1978. 6/yr. DM.318($199) (Gesellschaft fuer Informatik e.V.) Springer-Verlag, Heidelberger Platz 3, 14197 Berlin, Germany. TEL 030-8207-1. FAX 030-8214091. (Subscr. in N. America to: Springer-Verlag New York, Inc., 44 Hartz Way, Secaucus, NJ 07096-2491. TEL 201-348-4033. FAX 201-348-4505) Ed. Dr. W. Brauer. adv. (also avail. in microform from UMI; reprint service avail. from ISI) **Indexed:** INIS Atomind., Sci.Abstr. **Document type:** academic/scholarly publication.
—BLDSC (4481.367000); SWETS; UMI. **CCC.**

620 II
INSTITUTION OF ENGINEERS (INDIA). COMPUTER ENGINEERING DIVISION. JOURNAL. (Text in English) 1984. s-a. Rs.40($5) Institution of Engineers (India), Computer Engineering Division, 8 Gokhale Rd., Calcutta 700 020, India. TEL 033-288334. FAX 033-288345. TELEX 0217885 IEIC-IN. Ed. K.N. Majumdar. adv.; charts; illus.; index. circ. 2,500.

INTERNATIONAL JOURNAL FOR NUMERICAL METHODS IN FLUIDS. see *ENGINEERING — Hydraulic Engineering*

INTERNATIONAL JOURNAL OF INDUSTRIAL ERGONOMICS. see *ENGINEERING*

620 001.644 US ISSN 1050-1827
TK7876 CODEN: IMMEEC
INTERNATIONAL JOURNAL OF MICROWAVE AND MILLIMETER-WAVE COMPUTER AIDED ENGINEERING. 1991. q. $220 (foreign $275). John Wiley & Sons, Inc., Journals, 605 Third Ave., New York, NY 10158-0012. TEL 212-692-6000. FAX 212-850-6088. TELEX 12-7063. Ed. K.C. Gupta.
—BLDSC (4542.357000); EI; UnCover; UMI.
Description: Disseminates research and development results in the areas of computer-aided design and engineering of microwave and millimeter-wave components, circuits, subsystems, and antennas.

620 UK ISSN 0894-3370
TK3226 CODEN: IJNFEX
INTERNATIONAL JOURNAL OF NUMERICAL MODELLING: ELECTRONIC NETWORKS, DEVICES AND FIELDS. 1988. bi-m. $395 (effective 1994). John Wiley & Sons Ltd., Journals, Baffins Ln., Chichester, Sussex PO19 1UK, England. TEL 0243-779777. FAX 0243-775878. TELEX 86290 WIBOOK G. Ed. W.J.R. Hoefer. circ. 204. **Indexed:** CAD CAM Abstr. **Document type:** academic/scholarly publication.
—BLDSC (4542.406200); EI; Faxon; UnCover; SWETS; UMI. **CCC.**
Description: Covers numerical modelling methods and data preparation methods of electrical and electronic circuits and fields. Emphasis is on numerical modelling rather than abstract numerical mathematics.

INTERNATIONAL JOURNAL OF PRODUCTION ECONOMICS; an international journal for industry. see *ENGINEERING*

INTERNATIONAL JOURNAL OF ROBOTICS RESEARCH. see *COMPUTERS — Robotics*

INTERNATIONAL SIMULATORS CONFERENCE. PROCEEDINGS. see *COMPUTERS — Computer Simulation*

INVERSE PROBLEMS; inverse problems, inverse methods and computerized inversion of data. see *MATHEMATICS — Computer Applications*

JAPAN SOCIETY FOR SIMULATION TECHNOLOGY. JOURNAL. see *COMPUTERS — Computer Simulation*

JOURNAL OF COMPUTER & SYSTEMS SCIENCES INTERNATIONAL. see *COMPUTERS — Cybernetics*

620	US	ISSN 0887-3801
		CODEN: JCCEE5

JOURNAL OF COMPUTING IN CIVIL ENGINEERING. 1987. q. $96 to non-members (foreign $104); members $24 (foreign $32). American Society of Civil Engineers, Technical Council on Computer Practices, 345 E. 47th St., New York, NY 10017-2398. TEL 212-705-7288. FAX 212-980-4681. Ed. William J. Rasdorf. circ. 4,000. **Indexed:** A.I.Abstr., CAD CAM Abstr., Comput.Abstr., Environ.Abstr. **Document type:** academic/scholarly publication.
—BLDSC (4963.900000); EI; Faxon; UnCover; SWETS; UMI. **CCC.**
Description: Focuses on the advances and new methodology and tools emerging in computing for the civil engineer. Covers fundamental issues in computing education, research, and professional practice.

JOURNAL OF GLOBAL OPTIMIZATION. see *SCIENCES: COMPREHENSIVE WORKS — Computer Applications*

JOURNAL OF MATERIALS PROCESSING TECHNOLOGY. see *ENGINEERING — Mechanical Engineering*

KEY ABSTRACTS - COMPUTING IN ELECTRONICS & POWER. see *COMPUTERS — Abstracting, Bibliographies, Statistics*

LETTRE DE LA SURETE DE FONCTIONNEMENT. see *COMPUTERS*

MACHINE VISION & APPLICATIONS. see *COMPUTERS — Cybernetics*

620 387   UK
MARCOM; a business guide to the application of advanced electronics, information systems and computers in shipping. m. £35($110) Marcom Publications Ltd., West House, West St., Faversham, Kent ME13 7JB, England. Ed. Ken Cottrill.

MATRIX (WASHINGTON); semi-monthly industry news report for the integrated building system control and automation profession. see *BUILDING AND CONSTRUCTION*

MESURES. see *COMPUTERS — Automation*

MICRO CONTROL JOURNAL. see *MATHEMATICS — Computer Applications*

MICROSTATION MANAGER; the monthly independent publication for the Intergraph professional. see *ARCHITECTURE — Computer Applications*

N T I S BIBLIOGRAPHIC DATA BASE. (U.S. National Technical Information Service) see *PUBLISHING AND BOOK TRADE — Computer Applications*

NANOSTRUCTURED MATERIALS. see *ENGINEERING — Engineering Mechanics And Materials*

NEURAL, PARALLEL & SCIENTIFIC COMPUTATIONS. see *COMPUTERS*

624 001.642   US   ISSN 0739-697X
NEWSLETTER OF ENGINEERING ANALYSIS SOFTWARE. 1978. m. $205 (foreign $215). Frank Maga and Associates, 15452 Cabrito Rd., Ste. 220, Van Nuys, CA 91406. TEL 818-994-5179. FAX 818-994-6385. (Subscr. to: Box 2639, Sepulveda, CA 91393) Ed. Frank B. Maga. bk.rev. circ. 2,000. (looseleaf format; back issues avail.) **Document type:** newsletter.
Description: Software information source for the professional community involved in structural mechanics; includes information on conferences.

NONLINEAR DYNAMICS; an international journal of nonlinear dynamics and chaos in engineering systems. see *ENGINEERING — Mechanical Engineering*

620   NE   ISSN 0885-5110
NORTH-HOLLAND SERIES IN SYSTEM SCIENCE AND ENGINEERING. 1978. irreg., vol.13, 1987. price varies. Elsevier Science B.V., Books Division, P.O. Box 211, 1000 AE Amsterdam, Netherlands. TEL 31-20-5803911. FAX 31-20-5803705. TELEX 18582 ESPA NL. (Subscr. in U.S. and Canada to: Elsevier Science Inc., Box 882, Madison Sq. Sta., New York, NY 10159. TEL 212-989-5800). **Document type:** monographic series.
Refereed Serial

NUMERICAL HEAT TRANSFER PART A: APPLICATIONS; an international journal of computation and methodology. see *ENGINEERING — Mechanical Engineering*

NUMERICAL HEAT TRANSFER PART B: FUNDAMENTALS; an international journal of computation and methodology. see *ENGINEERING — Mechanical Engineering*

620   AU   ISSN 0254-4326
O E G A I JOURNAL. (Text in English, German; summaries in English) 1982. q. S.200($20) Oesterreichische Gesellschaft fuer Artificial Intelligence - Austrian Society for Artificial Intelligence, Postfach 177, A-1014 Vienna, Austria. TEL 01-53532810. FAX 01-630652. Ed. Paolo Petta. adv.; bk.rev. circ. 300. **Indexed:** LISA, Sci.Abstr. **Document type:** newsletter.
—EI.
Description: Information about the field of artificial intelligence.

620 510   US   ISSN 0888-2096
PRINCIPLES OF COMPUTER SCIENCE SERIES. 1981. irreg. Computer Science Press, Inc., 41 Madison Ave., 37th Fl., New York, NY 10010-3546. TEL 212-576-9400. Eds. Alfred V. Aho, Jeffrey D. Ullman. (back issues avail.) **Document type:** academic/scholarly publication.

620   UK   ISSN 0953-7287
TS155.A1   CODEN: PPCOEM
PRODUCTION PLANNING & CONTROL. 1990. bi-m. £142($238) Taylor & Francis Ltd., Rankine Rd., Basingstoke, Hants RG24 8PR, England. TEL 0256-840366. FAX 0256-479438. TELEX 858540. Ed. Asbjorn Rolstadas. bk.rev. **Document type:** academic/scholarly publication.
—BLDSC (6853.183500); EI. **CCC.**
Description: Publishes research papers on all aspects of production planning and control, with a focus on industrial applications of research, techniques, and new developments.
Refereed Serial

620 621.3   SZ   ISSN 0257-0130
    CODEN: QUSYE8
QUEUEING SYSTEMS; theory and applications. (Text in English) 1986. 3 vols./yr. 1099.50 SFr. J.C. Baltzer AG, Science Publishers, Wettsteinplatz 10, CH-4058 Basel, Switzerland. TEL 061-6918925. FAX 061-6924262. (U.S. subscr. to: J.C. Baltzer AG, Box 8577, Red Bank, NJ 07701-8577) Ed. N.U. Prabhu. index. **Indexed:** Biostat., Oper.Res.Manage.Sci., Qual.Contr.Appl.Stat. **Document type:** academic/scholarly publication.
—BLDSC (7216.384350); Faxon; UnCover; SWETS.
Description: Covers research activity on queuing systems in areas such as probability, operations research, electrical engineering and computer science.

REPORTS IN APPLIED MEASUREMENT; journal for the electrical measurement of mechanical quantities. see *ENGINEERING — Mechanical Engineering*

621.38   GW   ISSN 0341-6461
REVISTA SIEMENS. English edition: Siemens Review (ISSN 0302-2528) German edition: Siemens Zeitschrift (ISSN 0302-251X); Portuguese edition: Revista Siemens (ISSN 0937-9649) (Text in Spanish) 1941. 4/yr. DM.72. Siemens Verlag AG, Postfach 3240, 91050 Erlangen, Germany. bk.rev.; charts; illus.; index. **Indexed:** Eng.Ind., Sci.Abstr. **Document type:** bulletin.

REVUE EUROPEENNE DIAGNOSTIC ET SURETE DE FONCTIONNEMENT. see *COMPUTERS*

ROBOTER; Zeitschrift fuer Automation. see *COMPUTERS — Automation*

SCIENTIFIC PROGRAMMING: TOOLS & TECHNIQUES. see *COMPUTERS — Software*

SEMICONDUCTOR INDUSTRY PLANT SITE DATABASE DIRECTORY. see *ELECTRONICS*

621.38   GW
SIEMENS REVIEW. German edition: Siemens Zeitschrift (ISSN 0302-251X); Portuguese edition: Revista Siemens (ISSN 0937-9649); Spanish edition: Revista Siemens (ISSN 0341-6461) (Text in English) 1929. bi-m. DM.106. Siemens Verlag AG, Postfach 3240, 91050 Erlangen, Germany. TEL 09131-723004. FAX 09131-725022. bk.rev.; charts; illus.; index. **Indexed:** ASCA, Biol.Abstr., CAD CAM Abstr., Chem.Abstr., Curr.Cont., Energy Info.Abstr., Eng.Ind., Excerp.Med., Met.Abstr., Risk Abstr., Sci.Abstr., Tel.Abstr., World Alum.Abstr. **Document type:** bulletin.

621.38   GW   ISSN 0302-251X
TK3   CODEN: SIEZAB
SIEMENS ZEITSCHRIFT. English edition: Siemens Review (ISSN 0302-2528); Portuguese edition: Revista Siemens (ISSN 0937-9649); Spanish edition: Revista Siemens (ISSN 0341-6461) 1921. 6/yr. DM.106. Siemens Verlag AG, Postfach 3240, 91050 Erlangen, Germany. bk.rev.; charts; illus.; index. (also avail. in microform from PMC) **Indexed:** C.I.S. Abstr., Chem.Abstr., Eng.Ind., Fuel & Energy Abstr., Sci.Abstr. **Document type:** bulletin.
—BLDSC (8274.000000); SWETS; CASDDS.

SOFTWARE ABSTRACTS FOR ENGINEERS. see *COMPUTERS — Abstracting, Bibliographies, Statistics*

620   GW   ISSN 0934-4373
TA658.8   CODEN: SOPTEQ
STRUCTURAL OPTIMIZATION; computer-aided optimal design of stressed systems and components. 1989. 8/yr. (in 2 vols. 4 nos./vol.). DM.734($459) Springer-Verlag, Heidelberger Platz 3, 14197 Berlin, Germany. TEL 030-8207-1. FAX 030-8214091. (Subscr. in N. America to: Springer-Verlag New York, Inc., 44 Hartz Way, Secaucus, NJ 07096-2491. TEL 201-348-4033 FAX 201-348-4505) Ed. G. Rozvany. (back issues avail.) **Indexed:** Curr.Cont. **Document type:** academic/scholarly publication.
—BLDSC (8477 800000); Faxon; SWETS; UMI. **CCC.**
Description: Research papers dealing with the optimal design of systems consisting of solids subject to stresses and deformations, including mathematical foundations, software development and applications in engineering.

SURVEYING SCIENCE IN FINLAND. see *ENGINEERING — Civil Engineering*

SZAMITOGEPES MUSZAKI TERVEZES/COMPUTER-AIDED DESIGN. see *ENGINEERING — Abstracting, Bibliographies, Statistics*

620 001.644   US
V M A ENGINEERING NEWSLETTER. 1985. irreg. (approx. s-a.). free. Vanderplaats, Miura & Associates, Inc., 225 E. Cheyenne Mt. Blvd., Ste. 200B, Colorado Springs, CO 80906. TEL 719-527-2691. FAX 719-527-2692. Ed. Garret Vanderplaats. circ. 2,000. **Document type:** newsletter.
Formerly: Engineering Design Optimization. Newsletter.

620 621.3   GW
Z V E I ELEKTRO UND ELEKTRONIK - EINKAUFSFUEHRER. English edition: Z V E I Electro Electronics Buyers' Guide. French edition: Z V E I Guide de l'Equipement Electrique et Electronique. Spanish edition: Z V E I Guia de Equipos Electricos et Electronicos. (Text in English, German, French and Spanish) 1950. a. DM.59 per no. Verlag W. Sachon, Schloss Mindelburg 87714 Mindelheim, Germany. TEL 08261-999-0. FAX 08261-999-132. TELEX 539624. circ. 15,000. **Document type:** directory.
●Also available online. Vendor(s): Data-Star, FIZ Technik.
Also available on CD-ROM.
Formerly: Z V E I Elektro-Einkaufsfuehrer.

ZBORNIK OBJAVLJENIH RADOVA SARADNIKA INSTITUTA. see *ENGINEERING — Electrical Engineering*

ZEICHNEN FACHZEITSCHRIFT FUER KONSTRUIEREN UND GESTALTEN. see *ARCHITECTURE*

ENGINEERING — Electrical Engineering

621.3   SZ   ISSN 1013-3119
CODEN: ABBREZ
A B B REVIEW. French edition: Revue A B B (ISSN 1013-3127); German edition: A B B Technik (ISSN 1013-3143); Russian edition: Obsor A B B (ISSN 1017-1215); Spanish edition: Revista A B B (ISSN 1013-3135); Swedish edition: A B B Tidning (ISSN 1013-316X) (Text in English) 1988. 10/yr. 110 SFr. A B B Corporate Communications Ltd., Ruetistr. 6, CH-5401 Baden, Switzerland. TEL 056-754836. FAX 056-212274. (U.S. addr.: Asea Brown Boveri Inc., 900 Long Ridge Rd., Box 9308, Stamford, CT 06904) Ed. Werner Honisch. charts; illus.; index. circ. 50,000. (reprint service avail. from UMI, ISI) **Indexed:** A.I.Abstr., Appl.Mech.Rev., CAD CAM Abstr. (until 1992), Chem.Abstr., Energy Info.Abstr., Eng.Ind., Environ.Abstr., Excerp.Med., INIS Atomind., Met.Abstr., RAPRA, Risk Abstr., Robomat. (until 1992), Sci.Abstr., Sh.& Vib.Dig., World Alum.Abstr. **Document type:** trade publication.
●Also available online. Vendor(s): Data-Star, DIALOG Information Services, Inc..
—BLDSC (0537.724485); CIS; EI; UnCover; SWETS.
Supersedes (1924-1987): A S E A Journal (ISSN 0001-2459); (in 1987): Brown Boveri Technik; Which was formerly (1914-1984): B B C Nachrichten (ISSN 0005-2825)
Description: Covers production and transmission of electrical energy, robotics and factory automation, environmental technologies, communication.

A B M METALURGIA E MATERIAIS. (Associacao Brasileira de Metalurgia e Materiais) see *METALLURGY*

621.3   BE   ISSN 0001-0669
CODEN: ACECA8
A C E C REVIEW. (Editions in Dutch, English, French and German) 1904. q. 300 Fr.($6) Ateliers de Constructions Electriques de Charleroi, B. P. 4, 6000 Charleroi, Belgium. charts; illus. circ. 9,000. **Indexed:** Fuel & Energy Abstr., INIS Atomind., Met.Abstr., Sci.Abstr., World Alum.Abstr.

A C E INTERNATIONAL. (A C E Publishing Ltd.) see *COMMUNICATIONS — Television And Cable*

A D B - NYTT; nyheter och information fraan Telia Data. see *ENGINEERING — Computer Applications*

683.8   NE   ISSN 0001-1053
A E G - SCHAKELS. 1967. bi-m. free. A E G-Telefunken Nederland N.V., Box 1816, 1000 BV Amsterdam, Netherlands. circ. 9,000.

A.P.A.V.E. REVUE TECHNIQUE; revue technique du groupement des associations de proprietaires d'appareils a vapeur et electriques. see *HEATING, PLUMBING AND REFRIGERATION*

621.3   US
A S A E TRANSACTIONS. INFORMATION AND ELECTRICAL TECHNOLOGIES - EMERGING TECHNOLOGIES. 1970. a. $42.50 to non-members; members $26. American Society of Agricultural Engineers, 2950 Niles Rd., St. Joseph, MI 49084-9659. TEL 616-429-0300. FAX 616-429-3852. Ed. Pamela DeVore-Hansen. circ. 100. **Document type:** academic/scholarly publication.
Formerly: A S A E Transactions. Electrical and Electronic Systems - Emerging Technologies.
Description: Addresses aquaculture, bioengineering, forest engineering, knowledge systems, energy systems, electrical controls and more.
Refereed Serial

A S S P WORKSHOP ON SPECTRUM ESTIMATION AND MODELING. (Acoustics, Speech and Signal Processing Society) see *PHYSICS — Sound*

A S U I NEWSLETTER. (American Society of Utility Investors) see *BUSINESS AND ECONOMICS — Investments*

A T R JOURNAL. (Advanced Telecommunications Research Institute International) see *COMMUNICATIONS*

621.38   DK   ISSN 0106-0791
AALBORG UNIVERSITETSCENTER. INSTITUT FOR ELEKTRONISKE SYSTEMER. RAPPORT. 1977. irreg. free. Aalborg Universitetscenter, Institut for Elektroniske Systemer, Aalborg, Denmark. TELEX 69790AUB DK. Ed. Martin Raussen. illus. **Document type:** academic/scholarly publication.
—BLDSC (7254.870000).

621.3   FI   ISSN 0001-6845
TK4   CODEN: APSEA5
ACTA POLYTECHNICA SCANDINAVICA. ELECTRICAL ENGINEERING SERIES. (Text and summaries in English) irreg. (2-3/yr.). FIM 350. Teknillisten Tieteiden Akatemia - Finnish Academy of Technology, Kansakoulukatu 10 A, SF-00100 Helsinki 10, Finland. Ed. Seppo Halme. index, cum.index: 1958-1991. circ. 500. (also avail. in microfilm from UMI; back issues avail.; reprint service avail. from UMI) **Indexed:** ASCA, Cadscan, Chem.Abstr., Curr.Cont., Eng.Ind., Excerp.Med., INIS Atomind., Int.Aerosp.Abstr., Lead Abstr., Math.R., Sci.Abstr, Zincscan. **Document type:** monographic series.
—BLDSC (0661.260000); EI; UnCover; UMI.
Description: Presents research results in electrical engineering.

537.5   US   ISSN 0882-7516
QC176.8.T5
ACTIVE AND PASSIVE ELECTRONIC COMPONENTS. 12/yr. (in 3 vols.; 4 nos./vol.). 669 ECU (effective 1993). Gordon & Breach Science Publishers, 820 Town Center Dr., Langhorne, PA 19047. TEL 215-750-2642. FAX 215-750-6343. (UK subscr. to: P.O. Box 90, Reading, Berkshire RG1 8JL, England. TEL 0734-560-080) Eds. D.S. Campbell, Robert Castellano. (also avail. in microfilm; microfiche)
—BLDSC (0676.020000); UnCover; SWETS. **CCC**.
Refereed Serial

621.38   SP   ISSN 0210-6302
ACTUALIDAD ELECTRONICA. 1977. 18/yr. 7000 ptas.($80.50) (effective 1994). Cetisa - Boixareu S.A., Concepcion Arenal 5, 08027 Barcelona, Spain. TEL 93-3527061. FAX 93-3492350. Ed. Eugenio Rey. adv.; bk.rev. circ. 4,000. (back issues avail.)
—**CCC**.

621.3   JA   ISSN 0911-3428
ADDRESSER. 1984. s-a. Matsushita Denki Sangyo K.K., Shisutemu Eigyo Honbu - Matsushita Electric Industrial Co., Ltd., Sales Department, 1-2 Shiba Koen 1-chome, Minato-ku, Tokyo 105, Japan.

621.3   US   ISSN 0001-8627
ADVANCED BATTERY TECHNOLOGY. 1965. m. $120. Robert Morey Associates, Box 30, Cooperstown, NY 13326-0030. TEL 607-547-5314. FAX 607-547-5314. Ed. Robert Morey. bk.rev. **Indexed:** Cadscan, Lead Abstr., Zincscan. **Document type:** newsletter.
—BLDSC (0696.820000).

621.38 001.6   IE   ISSN 0790-8482
CODEN: AMTEER
ADVANCED MANUFACTURING TECHNOLOGY. (Text in English) 10/yr. I£15($50) Electronics Report Ltd., Computer House, 66 Patrick St., Dun Laoghaire, Co. Dublin, Ireland. TEL 353-1-2800424. FAX 353-1-2808468. Ed. J. McDonald. adv.; bk.rev. circ. 4,500.
—Faxon.
Formerly (until 1987): Electronics Report.

621.3   SI   ISSN 0218-0197
ADVANCED SERIES IN ELECTRICAL AND COMPUTER ENGINEERING. (Text in English) 1988. irreg., vol. 7, 1991. price varies. World Scientific Publishing Co. Pte. Ltd., Farrer Rd., P.O. Box 128, Singapore 9128, Singapore. TEL 3825663. FAX 3825919. TELEX RS 28561 WSPC. (UK addr.: 73 Lynton Mead, Totteridge, London N20 8DH, England. TEL 44-81-4462461; US addr.: 1060 Main St., River Edge, NJ 07661. TEL 800-227-7562) Ed. Wai-Kai Chen. **Document type:** monographic series.

537.5 621.38   US   ISSN 0065-2539
TK7800   CODEN: AEEPAR
ADVANCES IN ELECTRONICS AND ELECTRON PHYSICS. 1948. irreg., vol.87, 1993. Academic Press, Inc., 525 B St., Ste. 1900, San Diego, CA 92101-4495. TEL 619-231-0926. FAX 619-699-6715. (Subscr. to: Order Dept., 6277 Sea Harbor Dr., 4th Fl., Orlando, FL 32887. TEL 800-321-5068) Eds. Peter W. Hawkes, Benjamin Kazan. (reprint service avail. from ISI) **Indexed:** Chem.Abstr., Deep Sea Res.& Oceanogr.Abstr., Ind.Sci.Rev., INIS Atomind., Mass Spectr.Bull., Sci.Cit.Ind. **Document type:** academic/scholarly publication.
—BLDSC (0705.000000); Faxon; UnCover; SWETS; CASDDS. **CCC**.
Refereed Serial

ADVANCES IN MAGNETIC AND OPTICAL RESONANCE. see *PHYSICS*

ADVANCES IN MAGNETIC RESONANCE IMAGING. see *COMPUTERS — Computer Graphics*

537.5   US   ISSN 0065-2946
TK7876
ADVANCES IN MICROWAVES. (Vols. 1-7 out of print) 1966. irreg., vol.8, 1974. Academic Press, Inc., 525 B St., Ste. 1900, San Diego, CA 92101-4495. TEL 619-231-0926. FAX 619-699-6715. (Subscr. to: Order Dept., 6277 Sea Harbor Dr., 4th Fl., Orlando, FL 32887. TEL 800-321-5068) Ed. Leo Young. index. (reprint service avail. form ISI)
Refereed Serial

621.3 620   JA   ISSN 0388-080X
AGENCY OF INDUSTRIAL SCIENCE AND TECHNOLOGY. ELECTROTECHNICAL LABORATORY. SUMMARIES OF REPORTS. (Text in English) 1950. a. Agency of Industrial Science and Technology, Electrotechnical Laboratory - Kogyo Gijutsuin Denshi Gijutsu Sogo Kenkyujo, 1-4, Umezono 1-chome, Tsukuba-shi, Ibaraki-ken 305, Japan. TEL 0298-54-5007. circ. 1,000. **Document type:** abstracting/indexing.
—BLDSC (8521.000000).

621.3   JA   ISSN 0911-7881
AICHI DENKI GIHO/AICHI ELECTRIC TECHNICAL REPORT. (Text in Japanese; summaries in English) 1985. irreg. Aichi Denki K.K. - Aichi Electric Co., Ltd., 1, Aichi-cho, Kasugai-shi, Aichi-ken 486, Japan.

621.3   PL   ISSN 0454-4773
AKADEMIA GORNICZO-HUTNICZA IM. STANISLAWA STASZICA. ZESZYTY NAUKOWE. AUTOMATYKA. (Text and summaries in English, Polish) 1966. s-a. price varies. Wydawnictwo A G H, Al. Mickiewicza 30, 30-059 Krakow, Poland. TEL 48-12-338100. FAX 48-12-331014. TELEX 32203 AGH PL. (Dist. by: Ars Polona, Krakowskie Przedmiescie 7, 00-068 Warsaw, Polnd) Ed. Z. Kleczek. illus. circ. 150. **Document type:** academic/scholarly publication.
—BLDSC (9512.150030).

621.3   PL   ISSN 0239-5312
AKADEMIA GORNICZO-HUTNICZA IM. STANISLAWA STASZICA. ZESZYTY NAUKOWE. ELEKTROTECHNIKA/STANISLAW STASZIC UNIVERSITY OF MINING AND METALLURGY. SCIENTIFIC BULLETINS. ELECTROTECHNICS. (Text and summaries in English, Polish) 1954. irreg., no.23, 1993. price varies. Wydawnictwo A G H, Al. Mickiewicza 30, 30-059 Krakow, Poland. TEL 48-12-338100. FAX 48-12-331014. TELEX 322203 AGH PL. (Dist. by: Ars Polona, Krakowskie Przedmiescie 7, 00-068 Warsaw. Poland) Ed. Z. Kleczek. illus. circ. 300. **Document type:** academic/scholarly publication.
Supersedes in part (in 1982): Elektryfikacja i Mechanizacja Gornictwa i Hutnictwa (ISSN 0070-9964)

621.3   PL   ISSN 0239-5274
AKADEMIA GORNICZO-HUTNICZA IM. STANISLAWA STASZICA. ZESZYTY NAUKOWE. ELEKTROTECHNIKA. KWARTALNIK. (Text in English and Polish; summaries in English, Polish, Russian) 1982. q. 40000 Zl. per issue (effective 1993). Wydawnictwo A G H, Al. Mickiewicza 30, 30-059 Krakow, Poland. TEL 48-12-331800. FAX 48-12-331014. TELEX 322203 AGH PL. (Dist. by: Ars Polona, Krakowskie Przedmiescie 7, 00-068 Warsaw, Poland) Ed. Z. Kleczek. illus. circ. 300. **Document type:** academic/scholarly publication.

ENGINEERING — ELECTRICAL ENGINEERING

537.5   DK   ISSN 0105-2373
AKTUEL ELEKTRONIK. 17/yr. DKK 325. Teknisk Forlag A-S, Skelbaekgade 4, DK-1780 Copenhagen V, Denmark. TEL 45-31-21-68-01. FAX 45-31-21-04-01. Ed. Jesper Kofoed. adv.: B&W page DKK 18600, color page DKK 21450; trim 360 x 253. circ. 19,820 (controlled). **Document type:** consumer publication.
   Description: Provides the Danish electronics market with concentrated and topical trade information about current matters, including presentations of components, instruments and production equipmment.

671.84 621 669   GW   ISSN 0002-4406
                          CODEN: ALAMBE
ALAMBRE; revista tecnica international para la industria del alambre y del cable y para todos los sectores de la elaboracion de alambres metalicos. English edition: Wire (ISSN 0043-5996); French edition: Trefile (ISSN 0374-2261); German edition: Draht (ISSN 0012-5911); Italian edition: Filo Metallico (ISSN 0430-4578) (Text in Spanish) 1951. 4/yr. DM.77. Meisenbach GmbH, Hainstr. 18, 96047 Bamberg, Germany. TEL 0951-861-135. FAX 0951-861-158. (Subscr. to: Postfach 2069, 96011 Bamberg, Germany) Ed. Arnt Hannewald. adv.: B&W page DM.2776, color page DM.4471; trim 260 x 184; adv. contact: Oskar Ohler. bk.rev.; abstr.; charts; illus. circ. 4,000. **Document type:** trade publication.
—CCC.

621.3   US   ISSN 0743-1562
AMERICAN CONTROL CONFERENCE. CONFERENCE PROCEEDINGS. 1961. a. price varies. American Automatic Control Council, c/o EECS, Northwestern University, Evanston, IL 60208-3118. TEL 708-491-3641. FAX 708-491-4455. (Subscr. to: I E E E Service Center, 445 Hoes Lane, Piscataway, NJ 08854) (Co-sponsors: Instrument Society of America; American Society of Mechanical Engineers; American Institute of Chemical Engineers; Institute of Electrical and Electronics Engineers; American Institute of Aeronautics and Astronautics; Association of Iron and Steel Engineers; Society for Computer Simulation) circ. 1,500. (also avail. in microform; reprint service avail. from UMI,ISI) **Document type:** proceedings.
—BLDSC (8585.837580); EI; UMI.
   Former titles: American Control Conference. Conference Records; Joint Automatic Control Conference. Record (ISSN 0075-3939)
   Description: Provides contributed and invited papers submitted for the conference. Offers a broad range of subjects - from systems control to control technology for the disabled and robotics and industrial automation.

621.38   US
AMERICAN ELECTRONICS ASSOCIATION DIRECTORY. 1949. a. $145 to non-members; members $65; non-profit organizations $72.50. American Electronics Association, 5201 Great America Parkway, Santa Clara, CA 95054. Ed. Rick Wood. adv. circ. 12,000. **Document type:** directory.
   Formerly (until 1977): W E M A Directory (ISSN 0509-5190)

ANALES DE MECANICA Y ELECTRICIDAD. see ENGINEERING — Mechanical Engineering

ANALOG INTEGRATED CIRCUITS AND SIGNAL PROCESSING; an international journal. see COMPUTERS — Hardware

621.32   FR   ISSN 0066-264X
ANNUAIRE DE L'ECLAIRAGE. 1987. s-a. 300 F. Association Francaise de l'Eclairage, 52 Bd. Malesherbes, 75008 Paris, France. FAX 43-87-16-38. TELEX LUX 290392 F. adv.; bk.rev. circ. 4,000.
   Description: Directory of research organizations involved in the technical, scientific and artistic research of light.

621.3   US   ISSN 0732-6181
                       CODEN: PCCCDU
ANNUAL ALLERTON CONFERENCE ON COMMUNICATION, CONTROL AND COMPUTING. 1963. a. $55. University of Illinois at Urbana-Champaign, Coordinated Science Laboratory, Department of Electrical and Computer Engineering, Urbana, IL 61801. TEL 217-244-2520. FAX 217-244-1764. circ. 300. **Document type:** proceedings.
—BLDSC (6840.176000).
   Formerly: Annual Allerton Conference on Circuit and System Theory.

ANNUAL BOOK OF A S T M STANDARDS. VOLUME 02.03. ELECTRICAL CONDUCTORS. see ENGINEERING — Engineering Mechanics And Materials

ANNUAL BOOK OF A S T M STANDARDS. VOLUME 10.01. ELECTRICAL INSULATION, COMPOSITES, AND COATINGS - SOLIDS. see ENGINEERING — Engineering Mechanics And Materials

ANNUAL BOOK OF A S T M STANDARDS. VOLUME 10.03. ELECTRICAL INSULATING LIQUIDS AND GASES; ELECTRICAL PROTECTIVE EQUIPMENT. see ENGINEERING — Engineering Mechanics And Materials

ANNUAL BOOK OF A S T M STANDARDS. VOLUME 10.04. ELECTRONICS (1). see ENGINEERING — Engineering Mechanics And Materials

ANNUAL BOOK OF A S T M STANDARDS. VOLUME 10.05. ELECTRONICS (2). see ENGINEERING — Engineering Mechanics And Materials

ANNUAL FORUM REPORTS. see COMMUNICATIONS

ANNUAL REVIEW OF COMMUNICATIONS. see COMMUNICATIONS

621.3   JA   ISSN 0003-5211
ANRITSU TECHNICAL BULLETIN/ANRITSU TEKUNIKARU. (Text in Japanese; summaries in English and Japanese) 1957. s-a. free. Anritsu Corporation, 10-27, Minamiazabu 5-chome, Minato-ku, Tokyo 106, Japan. Ed.Bd. charts; illus.; stat.; circ. 5,000 (controlled). **Indexed:** JCT, JTA, Sci.Abstr. **Document type:** bulletin.
—BLDSC (1541.830000).

621.3   JA   ISSN 0914-7195
ANRITSU TECHNICAL REVIEW. (Text in English) 1982. s-a. Anritsu Corporation, 10-27, Minamiazabu 5-chome, Minato-ku, Tokyo 106, Japan.

683.83   IT   ISSN 0003-6668
APPARECCHI ELETTRODOMESTICI NELLA CASA MODERNA; export-import. 1953. m. L.130000 (effective 1993). Edizioni B.F.B. s.n.c., Via Morozzo della Rocca, No.8, 20123 Milan, Italy. TEL 02-48193936. FAX 02-48193920. Ed. Paolo Thorausch. adv.; bk.rev.; abstr.; bibl.; charts; illus.; mkt.; pat.; tr.mkt.; stat.; index, cum.index. circ. 10,500.
   Incorporates: Radiotecnica TV - Elettronik' Consumo (ISSN 0392-517X); Which was formerly: Radiotecnica TV, Hi-Fi, Elettronica Professionale.
   Description: Demonstrates many different types of Italian appliances for the home or office. Explores the various international trade fairs held in Italy and other countries.

621.3 683.8   US   ISSN 0003-6781
TP812.A1
APPLIANCE. 1944. m. $60 (foreign $70). Dana Chase Publications, Inc., 1110 Jorie Blvd., CS-9019, Oak Brook, IL 60522-9019. TEL 708-990-3484. FAX 708-990-0078. Ed. Scot M. Stevens. adv.; charts; illus.; stat.; tr.lit. circ. 29,100. (also avail. in microfiche from UMI,CIS; reprint service from UMI) **Indexed:** Fuel & Energy Abstr., PROMT, SRI. **Document type:** directory, trade publication.
●Also available online.
Also available on CD-ROM.
—BLDSC (1570.330000); SWETS; UMI. CCC.
   Incorporates: Appliance Engineer (ISSN 0003-6773)

683.83   US   ISSN 0003-679X
HD9697.U4
APPLIANCE MANUFACTURER. 1953. m. $55 (foreign $70). Business News Publishing Company, 5900 Harper Rd., No. 105, Solon, OH 44139. TEL 216-349-3060. FAX 216-498-9121. (Subscr. to: Box 2600, Troy, MI 48007) Ed. Norman C. Remich. adv.; illus.; tr.lit. circ. 34,400. **Indexed:** B.P.I., Bus.Ind., Fuel & Energy Abstr., Gas Abstr., PROMT, Tr.& Indus.Ind. **Document type:** trade publication.
●Also available online. Vendor(s): DIALOG Information Services, Inc..
—UMI. **CCC**.
   Description: Serves design engineers, production engineers and management worldwide in the manufacture of consumer, commercial or business appliances and equipment.

643.6   US   ISSN 0003-6803
TK1
APPLIANCE SERVICE NEWS. 1950. m. $13.50. Gamit Enterprises, Inc., 110 W. St. Charles Rd., Box 789, Lombard, IL 60148. TEL 708-932-9550. FAX 708-932-9552. Ed. William Wingstedt. adv.; bk.rev. circ. 51,000. **Document type:** trade publication.

APPLIED COMPUTATIONAL ELECTROMAGNETICS SOCIETY JOURNAL. see PHYSICS — Electricity

APPLIED COMPUTATIONAL ELECTROMAGNETICS SOCIETY NEWSLETTER. see PHYSICS — Electricity

621.38   US   ISSN 0066-5533
TK7871.85   CODEN: APSOB2
APPLIED SOLID STATE SCIENCE; advances in materials and device research. 1969. irreg., vol.6, 1977. Academic Press, Inc., 525 B St., Ste. 1900, San Diego, CA 92101-4495. TEL 619-231-0926. FAX 619-669-6715. (Subscr. to: Order Dept., 6277 Sea Harbor Dr., 4th Fl., Orlando, FL 32887. TEL 800-321-5068) Ed. R. Wolfe. (reprint service avail. from ISI)
   Description: Explores innovations in the electronics field.
   Refereed Serial

621.3   UK   ISSN 0964-1807
TK7872.S8   CODEN: ASUEE6
▼**APPLIED SUPERCONDUCTIVITY.** (Section of: Solid-State Electronics (ISSN 0038-1101)) 1993. 12/yr. £393($605) (effective 1994). Elsevier Science Ltd., Pergamon, P.O. Box 800, Kidlington, Oxford OX5 1DX, England. TEL 44-865-843000. FAX 44-865-843010. (Subscr. in U.S. and Canada to: Elsevier Science, 660 White Plains Rd., Tarrytown, NY 10591-5153. TEL 914-524-9200. FAX 914-333-2444) Ed. Roger B. Poeppel. index. (also avail. in microfilm from UMI) **Document type:** academic/scholarly publication.
—BLDSC (1580.073000); EI; UMI. **CCC**.
   Description: Publishes research on large and small scale applications of superconductivity, including descriptions of actual systems and processes implementing superconductors.
   Refereed Serial

621.3   GW   ISSN 0003-9039
TK3   CODEN: AELTA6
ARCHIV FUER ELEKTROTECHNIK/ARCHIVE OF ELECTRICAL ENGINEERING. (Text and summaries in English and German) 1912. 6/yr. DM.698($436) (Verband Deutscher Elektrotechniker e.V.) Springer-Verlag, Heidelberger Platz 3, 14197 Berlin, Germany. TEL 030-8207-1. FAX 030-8214091. (Subscr. in N. America to: Springer-Verlag New York, Inc., 44 Hartz Way, Secaucus, NJ 07096-2491. TEL 201-348-4033. FAX 201-348-4505) Ed. M. Stiebler. adv.; bibl.; charts; illus.; index, cum.index: 1912-1952. (also avail. in microform from UMI,PMC; back issues avail.; reprint service avail. from ISI) **Indexed:** Cadscan, Chem.Abstr., Curr.Cont., Eng.Ind., INIS Atomind., Lead Abstr., Math.R., Met.Abstr., Sci.Abstr., Sci.Cit.Ind., Zincscan. **Document type:** academic/scholarly publication.
—BLDSC (1606.000000); EI; UnCover; SWETS; UMI. **CCC**.
   Description: Covers entire range of electrical and electronic engineering, including related fields in mathematics and physics, with emphasis on the theory of electromagnetic fields, network theory, and electric machine theory.

ENGINEERING — ELECTRICAL ENGINEERING

621.3   PL   ISSN 0004-0746
CODEN: ARELA4
ARCHIWUM ELEKTROTECHNIKI/ARCHIVES OF ELECTRICAL ENGINEERING. (Text in Polish; contents in English) 1951. q. $19. (Polska Akademia Nauk, Komitet Elektrotechniki) Wydawnictwo Naukowe P W N - Polish Scientific Publishers P W N Ltd., Ul. Miodowa 10, 00-251 Warsaw, Poland. TEL 48-22-260207. FAX 48-22-267163. (Dist. by: Ars Polona, Krakowskie Przedmiescie 7, 00-251 Warsaw, Poland) Ed. Jan Maksymiuk. **Document type:** academic/scholarly publication.
—BLDSC (1660.000000); CASDDS.
Description: Publishes original papers in engineering, construction of machines and electrical systems, radioengineering, and electronics.

621.3   AG
ARGENTINA. DIRECCION GENERAL DE EVALUACION ENERGETICA. ANUARIO DE COMBUSTIBLES.. 1961. a. free. Direccion General de Evaluacion Energetica, Departamento de Informacion e Investigacion Aplicada, Av. Julio A. Roca 651, Piso 7, Sector 22, C.P. 1322 Buenos Aires, Argentina. circ. 500.
Former titles: Argentina. Direccion General de Coordinacion e Informacion Energetica. Anuario de Combustibles & Argentina. Direccion General de Planificacion y Control Energetico. Anuario Estadistico. Combustibles; Argentina. Direccion Nacional de Energia y Combustibles. Departamento de Estadistica. Anuario Estadistico Combustibles; Argentina. Oficina Sectorial de Desarrollo de Energia. Anuarios Estadisticos: Combustible. (ISSN 0066-7277)

621.3   AG
ARGENTINA. DIRECCION GENERAL DE EVALUACION ENERGETICA. ANUARIO ENERGIA ELECTRICA.. 1961. a. free. Direccion General de Evaluacion Energetica, Departamento do Informacion e Investigacion A, Av. Julio A. Roca 651, Piso 7, Sector 22, C.P. 1322 Buenos Aires, Argentina.
Former titles: Argentina. Direccion General de Coordinacion e Informacion Energetica. Anuario Energia Electrica & Argentina. Oficina Sectorial de Desarrollo de Energia. Anuarios Estadisticos. Energia Electrica (ISSN 0066-7285)

621.3   UK   ISSN 0264-3340
ASIAN ELECTRICITY. 1983. 11/yr. $215.30. Reed Business Publishing Group (Subsidiary of: Reed Elsevier group), Quadrant House, The Quadrant, Sutton, Surrey SM2 5AS, England. TEL 081-652-8773. FAX 081-652-8986. (Subscr. to: c/o Computer Action Ltd., 27 Park St., Croydon, Surrey CR0 1YD, England. TEL 081-649-7272) adv.; circ. 6,567 (controlled). **Indexed:** Energy Info.Abstr. **Document type:** trade publication.
—BLDSC (1742.417150).

621.38   HK   ISSN 1010-8327
ASIAN ELECTRONICS ENGINEER. (Text in Chinese, English, Korean) 1987. m. $39 in HK; $95 in Taiwan; elsewhere $99. Trade Magazine Productions Ltd., 20F, Vita Tower, 29 Wong Chuk Hang Rd., Hong Kong. TEL 852-555-4777. FAX 852-870-0816. TELEX 65157 TMLAS HX. (Subscr. to: P.O. Box 11112, Hong Kong; Dist. in US by: Wordright Enterprises Inc., 1020 Church St., Evanston, IL 60201. TEL 708-475-1900) Ed. Chris Everett. adv.: color page $4870; adv. contact: Jonathan Bigelow. circ. 27,500. (back issues avail.)
Description: Keeps senior electronic engineers, engineering managers and designers informed of current technology trends, new products and services.

683.83   HK   ISSN 0254-1114
ASIAN SOURCES ELECTRONICS. 1974. m. $70. Asiamag Ltd., G.P.O. Box 12367, 13-F, Amber Commercial Bldg., 70 Morrison Hill Rd., Hong Kong. (Subscr. in U.S. to: Wordright Enterprises Inc., Box 3062, Evanston, IL 60204-3062. TEL 708-475-1900) Ed. Chris Hanrahan. adv. circ. 20,100. **Document type:** consumer publication.
—BLDSC (1742.746300).
Description: Covers finished products for manufacturers and volume buyers worldwide.

621.38   HK   ISSN 0254-1122
ASIAN SOURCES ELECTRONICS COMPONENTS. 1979. m. $50. Asiamag Ltd., G.P.O. Box 12367, 13-F, Amber Commercial Bldg., 70 Morrison Hill Rd., Hong Kong. (Subscr. in U.S. to: Wordright Enterprises Inc., Box 3062, Evanston, IL 60204-3062. TEL 708-475-1900) adv. circ. 335,700.

621.3   SA
ASSOCIATION OF MUNICIPAL ELECTRICITY UNDERTAKINGS OF SOUTH AFRICA. PROCEEDINGS OF CONVENTION. (Text in Afrikaans, English) a. Association of Municipal Electricity Undertakings of South Africa, 200 Volkskas Bldg., 76 Market St., Johannesburg 2001, South Africa. TEL 011-838-7711. FAX 011-838-7713. Ed. Bennie van der Walt. adv.

621.3   SZ   ISSN 0004-587X
CODEN: BUSEAH
ASSOCIATION SUISSE DES ELECTRICIENS. BULLETIN. (Text in French and German) 1909. s-m. (14/yr.). 140 Fr. FABAG und Druckerei Winterthur AG, Ruedigerstr. 12, Postfach 229, 8021 Zurich, Switzerland. (Co-sponsor: Union des Centrales Suisses d'Electricite) Ed.Bd. adv.; bk.rev.; abstr.; bibl.; charts; illus.; stat.; index. circ. 6,350. **Indexed:** Chem.Abstr., Eng.Ind., INIS Atomind., Met.Abstr., Sci.Abstr.
—BLDSC (2404.000000); SWETS.

537 621.3   IT   ISSN 0066-9822
ASSOCIAZIONE ELETTROTECNICA ED ELETTRONICA ITALIANA. RENDICONTI DELLA RIUNIONE ANNUALE. 1928. a. price varies. Associazione Elettrotecnica ed Elettronica Italiana, Viale Monza, 259, 20126 Milan, Italy. TEL 02-257791. FAX 02-2570512. circ. 600. **Indexed:** Chem.Abstr. **Document type:** proceedings.

ATOMO PETROLIO ELETTRICITA. see *ENERGY*

621.389   IT
AUDIONEWS. 1981. 20/yr. L.28000($25) Edizioni Publitrade News, Corso Vittorio Emanuele II 187, 00186 Rome, Italy. TEL 6-686-49-51. FAX 6-68-93-274. Ed. Gardenia Zanoni. adv. circ. 7,000.

621.3   AT
TK1.A1
AUSTRALIAN, ASIAN & PACIFIC ELECTRICAL WORLD. 1936. 11/yr. Aus.$50. Reed Business Publishing Pty. Ltd (Subsidiary of: Reed International PLC), 1-5-Railway St., Chatswood, N.S.W. 2067, Australia. TEL 02-372-5222. FAX 02-419-7399. Ed. Peter Tyldsley. adv.; illus. circ. 6,653. **Indexed:** Bus.Ind., Mag.Ind., Sci.Abstr., Tr.& Indus.Ind.
—BLDSC (1797.378930).
Former titles (until Feb. 1988): Australian Electrical World (ISSN 0726-7827); Electrical World; Australian Electrical World (ISSN 0004-9034)

621.3   AT   ISSN 0812-3594
AUSTRALIAN ELECTRICAL CONTRACTOR. 1983. 11/yr. Aus.$75. National Electrical Contractors Association, 153 Wellington Parade S., Gnd. Fl., Jolimont, Vic. 3002, Australia. TEL 03-650-5120. FAX 03-654-3585. Ed. John Leah. adv.; bk.rev. circ. 6,050. **Document type:** trade publication.
—BLDSC (1798.790000).
Formerly (until 1983): Victorian Electrical Contractor.

AUTO SOUND & SECURITY. see *TRANSPORTATION — Automobiles*

AUTO-VOLT; Electrauto. see *TRANSPORTATION — Automobiles*

621.3   US   ISSN 0734-7510
TJ213   CODEN: AUPRDX
AUTOTESTCON. (Automatic Testing Conference) 1965. a. price varies. (I E E E, Aerospace and Electronic Systems Society) Institute of Electrical and Electronics Engineers, Inc., 345 E. 47th St., New York, NY 10017-2394. TEL 212-705-7900. FAX 212-705-7682. (Subscr. to: IEEE Service Center, Box 1331, 445 Hoes Ln., Piscataway, NJ 08855-1331)
—BLDSC (1835.425000); EI. **CCC**.
Formerly: Automatic Support Systems Symposium for Advanced Maintainability. Proceedings (ISSN 0067-2491)
Description: Topics covered include automatic test systems, control and support software, integrated logistics, systems design and development, cost considerations, testing philosophies, equipment reliability, optical testing, artificial intelligence, programming techniques and military testing.

AVIONICS. see *AERONAUTICS AND SPACE FLIGHT*

AVIONICS NEWS MAGAZINE. see *AERONAUTICS AND SPACE FLIGHT*

621.3 531.64   II   ISSN 0970-1540
B H E L JOURNAL. (Text in English) 1981. q. Bharat Heavy Electricals Ltd., Bhopal 462 022, India. TEL 0755-546472. FAX 0755-540425. TELEX 0705-264. Ed. Vijay Digambar Garde. circ. 2,000. (back issues avail.) **Indexed:** INSPEC, Sci.Abstr.
—BLDSC (1947.628000).

B W K; Zeitschrift des Vereins Deutscher Ingenieure fuer Energietechnik und Energiewirtschaft. (Brennstoff-Waerme-Kraft) see *ENERGY*

BAKKEN LIBRARY AND MUSEUM. see *LIBRARY AND INFORMATION SCIENCES*

683.83   UK   ISSN 0957-9249
BATTERIES INTERNATIONAL. 1989. q. £40 in Europe; elsewhere £50. Battery Publishing Ltd., Aberdeen House, Headley Rd., Grayshott, Hindhead, Surrey GU26 6LA, England. TEL 0428-605536. FAX 0428-606339. Ed. Don Gribble. adv.; pat, stat, tr.lit. circ. 6,000. (back issues avail.)
—SWETS.
Incorporates: Electric Truck and Vehicle World.
Description: Examines the manufacture and use of batteries for industrial and consumer products.

621.3 629   US   ISSN 0271-7093
BATTERY & E V TECHNOLOGY NEWS. 1977. m. $350. Business Communications Co., Inc. (Norwalk), 25 Van Zant St., Ste. 13, Norwalk, CT 06855. TEL 203-853-4266. FAX 203-853-0348. TELEX 6502934929 WUI. Ed. Donald Saxman. **Indexed:** Cadscan, Lead Abstr., Zincscan.
●Also available online. Vendor(s): Data-Star, DIALOG Information Services, Inc., NewsNet (RD30).
Formerly (until 1981): Electric Vehicle - Battery Technology (ISSN 0160-1059)
Description: Highlights technical and econimic studies of electric vehicles and battery technology.

BATTERY MAN; international journal for starting, lighting, ignition & generating systems. see *TRANSPORTATION — Automobiles*

621.35   US
BATTERY REPLACEMENT DATA BOOK. 1972. a. $5.25. Battery Council International, 401 N. Michigan Ave., Chicago, IL 60611. TEL 312-644-6610. illus. circ. 350,000. **Document type:** directory.
Description: Contains group-size numbers for replacement batteries.

BEGRIFFSBESTIMMUNGEN FUER DIE BUNDESSTATISTIKEN DER OESTERREICHISCHE ELEKTRIZITAETSWIRTSCHAFT. see *PUBLIC ADMINISTRATION*

BELGICATOM; atomic space age & electronics. see *ENERGY — Nuclear Energy*

621.32   BE
BELGIUM. ADMINISTRATION DE L'ENERGIE. BULLETIN MENSUEL DE L'ENERGIE ELECTRIQUE. 1950. m. Ministere des Affaires Economiques, Administration de l'Energie, 30 rue De Mot, 1040 Brussels, Belgium. circ. 400.

BERGER BUILDING & DESIGN COST FILE. UNIT PRICES. VOL. 2: MECHANICAL AND ELECTRICAL TRADES. see *BUILDING AND CONSTRUCTION*

621.3   CC   ISSN 1001-8425
BIANYAQI/TRANSFORMER. (Text in Chinese) 1961. m. $10.68. Shenyang Bianyaqi Yanjiusuo - Shengyang Transformer Institute, 18 Bei'er Zhonglu, Tiexi-qu, Shenyang, Liaoning 110025, People's Republic of China. TEL 86-24-565177. FAX 86-24-562293. TELEX 80366 STW CN. Ed. Zheng Shiyi. adv.: page $700. circ. 15,000. **Document type:** academic/scholarly publication.

ENGINEERING — ELECTRICAL ENGINEERING

621.3 YU
BILTEN DOKUMENTACIJE. ELEKTROTEHNIKA I ELEKTRONIKA. PROIZVODNJA ELEKTRICNIH MASINA I APARATA. PTT USLUGE/BULLETIN OF DOCUMENTATION. ELECTROTECHNICS AND ELECTRONICS. MANUFACTURE OF ELECTRICAL MACHINERY AND APPARATUS. POSTAL SERVICES. 1950. bi-m. $264. Jugoslovenski Centar za Tehnicku i Naucnu Dokumentaciju - Yugoslav Center for Technical and Scientific Documentation (YCTSD), Sl. Penezica-Krcuna 29-31, P.O. Box 724, 11000 Belgrade, Yugoslavia. Ed. Ljiljana Kojic-Bogdanovic.
Formerly: Bilten Dokumentacije. Elektrotehnika i Elektronika (ISSN 0351-2398); Supersedes in part (in 1980): Bilten Dokumentacije. Elektrotehnika (ISSN 0006-2588)

BISMUTH INSTITUTE. BULLETIN. see METALLURGY

621.3 MX ISSN 0185-0059
CODEN: BOIID8
BOLETIN I I E. 1977. bi-m. free. Instituto de Investigaciones Electricas, Division de Informacion Tecnologica y Desarrollo Profesional, Liebnitz 14, 3 piso, Col. Anzures, Del. M. Hidalgo, 11590 Mexico, D.F., Mexico. FAX 73-189-854. TELEX 173380 INIEME. Ed. Gabriel Nagore Cazares. bibl.; charts; illus.; index; circ. 5,500 (controlled). **Indexed:** Chem.Abstr.
—CASDDS.
Description: Original research papers on electrical engineering in Mexico.

621.38 FR ISSN 1169-3630
BORNES INTERACTIVES. 18/yr. 2200 F. A Jour, 11 rue du Marche St. Honore, 75001 Paris, France. TEL 42-96-67-22. FAX 40-20-07-75. TELEX 615887 AJOUR. Ed. Patricia Dreidemy.
Formerly: Tele-Achat.

621.3 GW ISSN 0006-789X
T3 CODEN: BTBCBM
BOSCH TECHNISCHE BERICHTE. (Summaries in English, French and German) 1964. irreg. free. Robert Bosch GmbH, Abteilung FSD, Postfach 106050, 70049 Stuttgart, Germany. Ed. G. Leuze. circ. controlled. **Indexed:** Sci.Abstr. **Document type:** trade publication.
—BLDSC (2251.785000).

621.3 CN
BOTTIN BLEU; repertoire de l'industrie de l'electricite. 1987. a. Can.$29($32) Groupe Constructo, 1500 boul. Jules-Poitras, St. Laurent, PQ H4N 1X7, Canada. TEL 514-745-5720. FAX 514-339-2267. Ed. Ray Gauvreau. adv.; circ. 8,200 (controlled). (back issues avail.) **Document type:** directory.
Description: Contains list of electrical distributors, suppliers, manufacturers' agents, and products.

621.3 US ISSN 0006-9809
BRIDGE OF ETA KAPPA NU.* 1904. q. $2.50. University of Missouri - Rolla, Box H K N, Rolla, MO 65401. TEL 314-341-6400. Ed. J. Robert Betten. adv.; bk.rev.; charts; illus. circ. 19,733.

BRITISH GAS. MONITOR. see PETROLEUM AND GAS

621.38 US
BROWN BOVERI SYMPOSIA. PROCEEDINGS. 1969. irreg., latest 1992. Plenum Publishing Corp., 233 Spring St., New York, NY 10013-1578. TEL 212-620-8000. FAX 212-463-0742. TELEX 23-421139. **Document type:** proceedings.
Refereed Serial

621.3 537.5 SZ
BULLETIN S E V - V S E. 1909. s-m. 165 SFr. Schweizerischer Elektrotechnischer Verein - Swiss Electrotechnical Association, Seefeldstr. 301, Postfach, CH-8034 Zurich, Switzerland. FAX 01-3849430. (Co-sponsor: Verband Schweizerischer Elektrizitaetswerke) Ed.Bd. adv.; bk.rev.; bibl.; illus. circ. 8,700. **Indexed:** C.I.S. Abstr., Excerp.Med., Sci.Abstr.
Formerly: S E V Bulletin (ISSN 0036-1321)
Description: Technical and scientific coverage of electrical engineering, information technology and electro-economics.

BUREAUX D'ETUDES. see MACHINERY

621.3 AG
C A I INFORMA. (Centro Argentino de Ingenieros) Editorial la Ingenieria, Cerrito 1250, 1010 Buenos Aires, Argentina. Dir. Carlos Federico Aragon.

621.32 US ISSN 0007-7941
C B M NEWS. 1959. q. free. Certified Ballast Manufacturers, 1422 Euclid Ave., Ste. 402, Cleveland, OH 44115. FAX 216-241-0713. Ed. M.C. Davies. stat. circ. 10,000.

621.3 CN ISSN 1188-5939
C E D A CURRENT ANNUAL. (Canadian Electrical Distributors Association) a. Can.$22.47. Kerrwil Publications Ltd., 395 Matheson Blvd. E., Mississauga, ON L4Z 2H2, Canada. TEL 905-890-1846. FAX 905-890-5769. Ed. Janet Small. adv. **Document type:** trade publication.

621.38 US ISSN 1045-2710
TK1
C E E NEWS. 1949. m. free to qualified personnel. Intertec Publishing Corp., 9800 Metcalf, Overland Park, KS 66282-2901. TEL 913-341-1300. FAX 913-967-1898. Ed. Stuart Lewis. adv.; bk.rev.; charts; illus.; stat.; tr.lit. circ. 105,700. (tabloid format) **Document type:** trade publication.
—UMI. CCC.
Former titles (until 1990): Electrical Construction Technology (ISSN 1041-4061); (until 1989): C E E (ISSN 0192-1274); Contractors' Electrical Equipment (ISSN 0010-7913)

621.32 AU
C I E - NEWS. q. Commission Internationale de l'Eclairage, Kegelgasse 27, A-1030 Vienna, Austria. TEL 0222-7143187-0. FAX 0222-713083818. bk.rev. circ. 2,700. **Document type:** trade publication.

621.38 SP ISSN 0212-4696
C Q RADIO AMATEUR. 1971. m. 13490 ptas.($43) (effective 1994). Cetisa - Boixareu S.A., Concepcion Arenal 5, 08027 Barcelona, Spain. TEL 93-3527061. FAX 93-3492350. Ed. Miquel Pluvinet. adv.; bk.rev.; abstr.; charts; illus.; stat.; index; circ. 11,500 (controlled). (back issues avail.) **Indexed:** Sci.Abstr.
—CCC.

C S E L T INFOTEL; periodico d'informazione bibliografica nelle telecomunicazioni e scienze connesse. see COMMUNICATIONS — Abstracting, Bibliographies, Statistics

621.3 CN
C W C CONNECTIONS.* q. Communications Electronic, Electrical, Technical and Salaried Workers of Canada, 350 Sparks St., Ottawa, Ont. K1R 7S8, Canada.

621.3 UK ISSN 0045-3714
CABLE. vol.6, 1971. m. free. Eastern Electricity plc, Wherstead, Ipswich, Suffolk IP9 2AQ, England. FAX 0473-554466. Ed. Peter Maginnis. bk.rev.; charts; illus. circ. 13,500. **Document type:** newspaper.

621.3 UK
CABLE TALK. q. Electrical Contractors Association of Scotland, Bush Estate, Midlothian EH26 OSB, Scotland. TEL 031-445-5577. FAX 031-445-5548. Ed. M.D. Goodwin. circ. 2,500.

621.3 CN ISSN 0576-5161
CODEN: CEAEAU
CANADIAN ELECTRICAL ASSOCIATION. ENGINEERING AND OPERATING DIVISION. TRANSACTIONS. 1962. a. Can.$150 to non-members; members Can.$100. Canadian Electrical Association, Engineering and Operating Division - Association Canadienne de l'Electricite, 1 Westmount Sq., Ste. 1600, Montreal, Que. H3Z 2P9, Canada. TEL 514-937-6181.
—BLDSC (8931.400000).

621.38 CN ISSN 1187-6026
CANADIAN ELECTRONICS. 1956-1990. 6/yr. Can.$35. Action Communications Inc., 135 Spy Ct., Markham, ON L3R 5H6, Canada. TEL 905-477-3222. FAX 905-477-4320. Ed. Peter Thorne. adv.; bk.rev.; charts; illus.; stat.; tr.lit.; index; circ. 21,000 (controlled). (also avail. in microform from UMI; reprint service avail. from UMI) **Indexed:** Can.B.P.I., Excerp.Med., INIS Atomind., PROMT, Sci.Abstr.
—BLDSC (3021.550000); UMI. CCC.
Formed by the 1990 merger of: Canadian Electronics Engineering (ISSN 0008-3461) & Electronics Times (ISSN 0832-1515)

621.38 CN
CANADIAN ELECTRONICS ENGINEERING ANNUAL BUYER'S GUIDE. 1957. a. Can.$15. Action Communications Inc., 135 Spy Ct., Markham, ON L3R 5H6, Canada. TEL 905-477-3222. FAX 905-477-4320. Ed. Peter Thorne. **Document type:** consumer publication.
Former titles: Canadian Electronics Engineering Components and Equipment Directory; Canadian Electronics Engineering Annual Buyers' Guide and Catalog Directory (ISSN 0317-0292); Key to Electronics Engineering Purchasing in Canada.

CANADIAN HARDWARE, ELECTRICAL & BUILDING SUPPLY DIRECTORY. see BUSINESS AND ECONOMICS — Trade And Industrial Directories

621.3 CN ISSN 0840-8688
TK1 CODEN: CJEEEL
CANADIAN JOURNAL OF ELECTRICAL AND COMPUTER ENGINEERING. (Text and summaries in English, French) 1965. q. Can.$20 to individuals; institutions Can.$90 (effective Jan. 1993). Canadian Society for Electrical and Computer Engineering, Engineering Institute of Canada Bldg., Ste. 700, 2050 Mansfield St., Montreal, Que. H3A 1Z2, Canada. TEL 418-656-2984. FAX 418-656-3159. Ed. M. Lecours. adv.; bk.rev. circ. 1,200. (back issues avail.) **Indexed:** Curr.Cont., Cyb.Abstr., Eng.Ind., INIS Atomind., Int.Aerosp.Abstr., Sci.Abstr., Sci.Cit.Ind. **Document type:** academic/scholarly publication.
—BLDSC (3031.320000); EI; Faxon.
Formerly: Canadian Electrical Engineering Journal (ISSN 0700-9216)

CANADIAN NATIONAL ENERGY FORUM PROCEEDINGS. see ENERGY

CANADIAN STANDARDS ASSOCIATION E - CODE, ELECTRICAL SAFETY STANDARDS. see METROLOGY AND STANDARDIZATION

CAR AUDIO & ELECTRONICS. see SOUND RECORDING AND REPRODUCTION

621.38 388.3 IT
CAR AUDIO ANNUARIO; la guida mercato del car stereo. 1987. a. L.15000. Editore Progest s.r.l., Via Rovereto, 6, 00198 Rome, Italy. TEL 06-8551972. FAX 06-8558885. Ed. Gianni Caserta.

621.38 384.54 US ISSN 0894-3443
CAR STEREO REVIEW. 1987. q. $9.98 per no. Hachette Magazines, Inc., 1633 Broadway, New York, NY 10019. TEL 212-767-6000. (Subscr. to: Box 55627, Boulder, CO 80322-5627) Ed. William Wolfe. circ. 100,000.
Description: Articles and test reports on car stereo equipment.

621.3 US
CENTER FOR THE HISTORY OF ELECTRICAL ENGINEERING NEWSLETTER. 1982. 3/yr. free. Center for the History of Electrical Engineering, Rutgers University, 39 Union St., New Brunswick, NJ 08903. TEL 908-932-1066. FAX 908-932-1193. Ed. William Aspray. bk.rev.; bibl.; illus. circ. 5,000. (back issues avail.) **Document type:** newsletter.

338.4 RH ISSN 0069-147X
HD9865.R45
CENTRAL AFRICAN POWER CORPORATION. ANNUAL REPORT AND ACCOUNTS. 1956. a. Central African Power Corporation, Box 630, Club Chambers, Baker Ave., Salisbury, Zimbabwe. index.

621.3 JA ISSN 0912-1307
CENTRAL RESEARCH INSTITUTE OF ELECTRIC POWER INDUSTRY. QUARTERLY ABSTRACTS. (Text in English) 1977. q. Central Research Institute of Electric Power Industry - Denryoku Chuo Kenkyujo, 6-1, Ote-machi 1-chome, Chiyoda-ku, Tokyo 100, Japan.
—BLDSC (7169.829500).

CERTIFICATED ENGINEER/GEDIPLOMEERDE INGENIEUR. see ENGINEERING — Mechanical Engineering

CESKOSLOVENSKA AKADEMIE VED. ACTA TECHNICA. see ENGINEERING

CHALEUR ET CLIMATS. see HEATING, PLUMBING AND REFRIGERATION

ENGINEERING — ELECTRICAL ENGINEERING

621.38 629.286 FR
CHAMBRE SYNDICALE NATIONALE DES ELECTRICIENS ET SPECIALISTES DE L'AUTOMOBILE. ANNUAIRE. 1948. a. 400 F. Electricite Automobile, 59 rue du Faubourg Poissonniere, 75009 Paris, France. TEL 48-24-66-88. FAX 48-24-19-40. Ed. Jany Chabrand. circ. 10,000.

621.3 JA
CHIIKI KAIHATSU NYUSU/REGIONAL DEVELOPMENT NEWS. (Text in Japanese) bi-m. Tokyo Denryoku K.K. - Tokyo Electric Power Co., Inc., 1-3, Uchisaiwa-cho 1-chome, Chiyoda-ku, Tokyo 100, Japan.

621.35 JA ISSN 0009-3866
CHIKUDENCHI/STORAGE BATTERY. 1962. m. 1800 Yen. Japan Storage Battery Association - Nihon Chikudenchi Kogyokai, Kikai Shinko Bldg., 5-8, Shiba Koen 3-chome, Minato-ku, Tokyo 105, Japan. FAX 03-3434-2691. Ed. Masahiko Sakatani. adv. circ. 5,000. (tabloid format)

621.38 CH ISSN 1015-0730
CHINA, REPUBLIC. TELECOMMUNICATION LABORATORIES. T L TECHNICAL JOURNAL. (Text in Chinese and English) 1971. q. $35 to Hong Kong and Macao; elsewhere $40. Telecommunication Laboratories, Ministry of Communications, PO Box 71, Chungli, Taiwan, Republic of China. TELEX 32194 TELELAB. Ed.Bd. abstr. circ. 800.
Former titles (until 1988): China, Republic. Telecommunication Laboratories. Technical Reports; China, Republic. Telecommunication Laboratories. Quarterly Report.

621.3 JA ISSN 0387-0057
CHUBU DENRYOKU K.K. KENKYU SHIRYO/CHUBU ELECTRIC POWER COMPANY. MEMOIRS. (Text in Japanese) 1952. s-a. Chubu Denryoku K.K., Gijutsu Kaihatsu Honbu - Chubu Electric Power Co., Inc., Research and Development Bureau, 20-1, Kitasekiyama, Odaka-cho, Midori-ku, Nagoya-shi, Aichi-ken 459, Japan. **Indexed:** INIS Atomind.

621.3 JA
CHUBU DENRYOKU SHINBUN/CHUBU ELECTRIC POWER NEWS. (Text in Japanese) 1952. s-m. Chubu Denryoku K.K. - Chubu Electric Power Co., Ltd., 1, Higashishin-cho, Higashi-ku, Nagoya-shi, Aichi-ken 461-91, Japan.

621.3 JA ISSN 0009-6237
CHUGOKU ELECTRIC POWER CO. TECHNICAL LABORATORY. REPORT/CHUGOKU DENRYOKU K.K. GIKEN JIHO. (Text in Japanese) 1948. s-a. Chugoku Electric Power Co., Inc., Technical Research Center - Chugoku Denryoku K.K. Gijutsu Kenkyujo, 4-32, Ozu 4-chome, Hiroshima-shi, Hiroshima-ken 730, Japan. circ. controlled.

621.3 US ISSN 0278-081X
CIRCUITS, SYSTEMS, AND SIGNAL PROCESSING. 1982. q. $184 (foreign $220). Birkhaeuser, 675 Massachusetts Ave., Cambridge, MA 02139-3309. FAX 201-348-4505. (Dist. by: Springer-Verlag New York, Inc., Journal Fulfillment Services, Box 2485, Secaucus, NJ 07096-2491. TEL 201-348-4033) Eds. Sydney R. Parker, Armen H. Zemanian. **Document type:** academic/scholarly publication.
—BLDSC (3198.844000); EI; Faxon; UnCover; SWETS; UMI. **CCC.**

CITY OF CHICAGO BUILDING CODE. see *BUILDING AND CONSTRUCTION*

COGENERATION AND COMPETITIVE POWER JOURNAL. see *ENERGY*

621.3 UK
COIL WINDING INTERNATIONAL. 1976. 3/yr. £11($21) P.O. Box 936, Parkstone, Poole, Dorset BH12 2YD, England. TEL 0202-743906. FAX 0202-736018. Ed. Timothy House. adv.; bk.rev. circ. 28,000. (back issues avail.) **Document type:** trade publication.
Description: For electric motor, transformer, coil winding, and electrical insulation manufacturing and repair company personnel.

621.3 SA
COLIMPEX ELECTRICAL EXECUPAD. (Text in Afrikaans and English) a. free to qualified personnel. Colimpex Africa (Pty) Ltd., P.O. Box 5838, Johannesburg 2000, South Africa. adv.

COLLAGE (NEW CUMBERLAND). see *BUSINESS AND ECONOMICS — Investments*

537 665.5 BE
COMITE DE CONTROLE DE L'ELECTRICITE ET DU GAZ. RAPPORT ANNUEL. 1956. a. free. Comite de Controle de l'Electricite et du Gaz - Controle Komite voor de Elektriciteit en het Gas, Boulevard deWaterloo 34, B-1000 Brussels, Belgium. FAX 32-2-510-76-12. Ed.Bd. charts; illus. circ. 5,500. **Document type:** corporate report.
Description: Covers activities of the committee as well as economic analyses in both the electrical and gas industries.

COMITE INTERNATIONAL DES POIDS ET MESURES. COMITE CONSULTATIF D'ELECTRICITE. (RAPPORT ET ANNEXES). see *METROLOGY AND STANDARDIZATION*

537 IT ISSN 0392-3479
COMMERCIO ELETTRICO. 1974. m. (11/yr.) L.75000($113) (foreign L.140000). Stammer S.p.A., Via della Liberazione 1, 20068 Peschiera Borromeo (MI), Italy. TEL 02-55302606. FAX 02-55302700. adv.: B&W page L.1680000, color page L.2300000; trim 185 x 267. circ. 6,500.

621.3 US
COMMUNICATOR (FORT WORTH). 1936. m. Texas-New Mexico Power Co., 820 Hulen Towers 11, Box 2943, Ft. Worth, TX 76113. TEL 817-731-0099. Ed. Larry Fitzgerald. bk.rev.; charts; illus.; stat.; index. circ. 1,500.

537 BL
COMPANHIA PAULISTA DE FORCA E LUZ. MERCADO DE ENERGIA ELETRICA. RELATORIO ESTADISTICO ANUAL. 1970. a. free. Companhia Paulista de Forca e Luz, Divisao de Estudos de Mercado, Rodovia Campinas Mogi-Mirim, km 2.5, Campinas, SP, CEP 13.085, Brazil. FAX 0192-527794. TELEX 191179 FLUX BR. charts; illus.; stat. circ. 100.
Former titles: Companhia Paulista de Forca e Luz. Assessoria de Planejamento e Controle. Boletim Estatistico; Companhia Paulista de Forca e Luz. Acompanhamento de Mercado.

621.3 658.478 US
COMPASS: COMPUTER ASSURANCE (CONFERENCE). 1986. a. price varies. (I E E E, Washington Section) Institute of Electrical and Electronics Engineers, Inc., 345 E. 47th St., New York, NY 10017-2394. TEL 212-750-7900. FAX 212-750-7682. (Subscr. to: 455 Hoes Ln., Box 1331, Piscataway, NJ 08855-1331) **Indexed:** Sci.Abstr.
Description: Covers computer system safety and process security problems and remedies.

COMPUTER BUSINESS. see *COMPUTERS*

COMPUTERS & ELECTRICAL ENGINEERING. see *ENGINEERING — Computer Applications*

621.3 US ISSN 1056-7046
QC173.4.C65 CODEN: CMAWE8
CONDENSED MATTER NEWS. bi-m. 350 ECU (effective 1993). Gordon & Breach Science Publishers, 820 Town Center Dr., Langhorne, PA 19047. TEL 215-750-2642. FAX 215-750-6343. (UK subscr. to: P.O. Box 90, Reading, Berkshire RG1 8JL, England. TEL 0734-560-080) (also avail. in microform)
—BLDSC (3405.705000); SWETS; CASDDS. **CCC.**
Incorporates (in 1991): Ferroelectrics Bulletin (ISSN 0887-6622); (in 1991): Molecular Crystals and Liquid Crystals Bulletin (ISSN 0884-8408); Which incorporates: Non-Linear Optics Bulletin.
Description: Focuses on research in the fields of ferroelectrics, molecular crystals and liquid crystals, and phase transitions.
Refereed Serial

621.319 621 US ISSN 0084-9162
TK3421.A1 CODEN: CEIPAZ
CONFERENCE ON ELECTRICAL INSULATION AND DIELECTRIC PHENOMENA. ANNUAL REPORT. (Former issuing body: U.S. National Research Council) 1928? a. price varies. (I E E E, Electrical Insulation Society) Institute of Electrical and Electronics Engineers, Inc., 345 E. 47th St., New York, NY 10017. TEL 212-705-7900. FAX 212-705-7682. (Subscr. to: Box 1331, 445 Hoes Lane, Piscataway, NJ 08855-1331) **Indexed:** Chem.Abstr.
—BLDSC (1509.250000); EI; UMI; CASDDS. **CCC.**
Formerly (until 1966): Conference on Electrical Insulation. Annual Report (ISSN 0737-2426)

537 US ISSN 0589-1485
CODEN: CDIGD4
CONFERENCE ON PRECISION ELECTROMAGNETIC MEASUREMENTS. DIGEST. Short title: C P E M Digest (Earlier abstracts and papers 1958-1962 published in IRE Transactions on Instrumentation, and in IEEE Transactions on Instrumentation and Measurement) 1966. biennial. (I E E E, Group on Instrumentation and Measurement) Institute of Electrical and Electronics Engineers, Inc., 345 E. 47th St., New York, NY 10017. TEL 212-705-7900. FAX 212-705-7682. (Subscr. to: Bcx 1331, 445 Hoes Ln., Piscataway, NJ 08855-1331) (Co-sponsors: U.S. National Bureau of Standards; International Scientific Radio Union)
—BLDSC (3409.748500); UMI; CASDDS.
Former titles (until 1964): International Conference on Precision Electromagnetic Measurements; (until 1960): Conference on Standards and Electronic Measurements (Proceedings); (until 1958): Conference on Electronic Standards and Measurement (Proceedings).

621.3 IT ISSN 1120-2351
CONSTATTO ELETTRICO. 1988. 9/yr. L.9000. Alberto Greco Editore, Via del Fusaro 8, 20146 Milan, Italy. TEL 02-4819096. FAX 02-4819091. Ed. Paola Pianzola. circ. 76,000.
Description: Covers information and products from the world of electric technologies.

621.32 BL
CONSUMO INDUSTRIAL DE ENERGIA ELECTRICA DO ESTADO DA BAHIA. 1975. a. free. Secretaria das Minas e Energia, Coordenacao de Energia, Av. Centro Administrativo da Bahia, Av. Luiz Viana Filho, Salvador - Bahia, Brazil. stat.

621.3 UK
CONTACT (HAYES). q. Hayes Court, W. Common Rd., Hayes, Kent BR2 7AU, England. TEL 081-462-7755. FAX 081-462-4959. Ed. John Lloyd. circ. 360,000.

621.3 UK
CONTRACT LIGHTING. 6/yr. Alpha House, Laser Quay, Culpepper Close, Medway City, Rochester, Kent ME2 4HU, England. TEL 0634-720202. FAX 0634-720188. Ed. Leon Hopkins. circ. 9,500.

621.3 US
CONVENTION OF ELECTRICAL AND ELECTRONICS ENGINEERS IN ISRAEL. PROCEEDINGS. 5th, 1965. biennial. Institute of Electrical and Electronics Engineers, Inc., 345 E. 47th St., New York, NY 10017. TEL 212-705-7900. FAX 212-705-7682. (Subscr. to: Box 1331, 445 Hoes Lane, Piscataway, NJ 08855-1331) (also avail. in microfiche)
Formerly: National Convention of Electrical and Electronics Engineers in Israel. Proceedings.

CONVERGENCE: INTERNATIONAL CONGRESS ON TRANSPORTATION ELECTRONICS. PROCEEDINGS. see *TRANSPORTATION — Automobiles*

621.3 US ISSN 0070-0002
CORNELL BIENNIAL ELECTRICAL ENGINEERING CONFERENCE. 1967. biennial. price varies. (Institute of Electrical and Electronics Engineers, Inc.) Cornell University, School of Electrical Engineering, Phillips Hall, Ithaca, NY 14853. Ed. Michael G. Adlerstein. **Indexed:** GeoRef.
Refereed Serial

COUNTRY LIVING (COLUMBUS). see *BUSINESS AND ECONOMICS — Cooperatives*

659.2 IT
CRONACHE; per il personale de Gruppo Philips. 1959. bi-m. Philips S.p.A., Piazza IV Novembre 3, 20124 Milan, Italy. Ed. Giorgio Santocanale. bk.rev. circ. 20,000.
Formerly: Philips Cronache (ISSN 0031-7896)

CRONACHE DAL GRUPPO STET. see *COMMUNICATIONS — Telephone And Telegraph*

621.31 NZ ISSN 1170-6244
CURRENT. 1991. 6/yr. NZ.$18.90 (foreign NZ$32). Electricity Supply Association of New Zealand, P.O. Box 1017, Wellington, New Zealand. TEL 385-9632. FAX 64-04-384-2519. circ. 1,500. **Document type:** consumer publication.
Description: Provides mainly articles of interest to commercial, industrial and other large users on trends and developments in electricity production, supply and use in New Zealand.

CURRENT BIBLIOGRAPHIES ON SCIENCE & TECHNOLOGY: ELECTRICAL ENGINEERING AND ELECTRONICS. see *ELECTRONICS*

CURRENT BIBLIOGRAPHY ON SCIENCE AND TECHNOLOGY: ELECTRONICS AND ELECTRICAL ENGINEERING/KAGAKU GIJUTSU BUNKEN SOKUHO. DENKI KOGAKU HEN. see *ENGINEERING — Abstracting, Bibliographies, Statistics*

CURRENT PAPERS IN ELECTRICAL & ELECTRONICS ENGINEERING. see *ENGINEERING — Abstracting, Bibliographies, Statistics*

621.3 388.3   IT
D A C. (Digital Audio Club) 1988. m. L.50000 (foreign L.123000). Gruppo Editoriale Suono s.r.l., Via Capo Peloro, 30, 00141 Rome, Italy. TEL 06-897257. FAX 06-896981. TELEX 621348 EDSUON I. Ed. Marco Iafrate. adv.: B&W page L.3900000, color page L.6900000; 185 x 245. circ. 55,000.

621.38   GW
D E - DER ELEKTROMEISTER UND DEUTSCHES ELEKTROHANDWERK. 1925. s-m. DM.172.80 (foreign DM.186.60). (Zentralverband der Deutschen Elektrohandwerke) Huethig und Pflaum Verlag, Lazarettstr. 4, 80636 Munich, Germany. TEL 089-12607-240. FAX 089-12607200. (Subscr. to: Im Weiher 10, 6900 Heidelberg 1, Germany) Ed.Bd. adv.; bk.rev.; charts; illus.; mkt.; pat.; tr.lit.; index. circ. 36,000. Indexed: C.I.S. Abstr., Sci.Abstr. Document type: trade publication.
—BLDSC (3715.783000); SWETS. CCC.
Former titles: Deutsches Elektrohandwerk (ISSN 0012-1258); Elektromeister.
Description: Trade publication for the electrotechnical industry. Covers energy supply, electrical power and installation, communication technology, controlling and regulating, and trade. Includes reports and lists of events, positions available.

621.3   DK   ISSN 0107-4466
D E K HAANDBOG. 1955. a. free. Dansk Elektroteknisk Komite, Strandgade 36, DK-1401 Copenhagen K, Denmark. FAX 45-31-57-63-50. circ. 350.

621.319   US
THE D S M LETTER; covering electric and gas utility demand-side management and marketing programs. 1973. bi-w. $195. c/o Synergic Resources Corporation, 111 Presidential Blvd., Ste. 127, Bala Cynwyd, PA 19004. TEL 215-667-2160. FAX 215-667-5593. Ed. Richard Smithers. charts; stat. circ. 400. (processed) Document type: newsletter.
Formerly: Electric Letter.
Description: Covers D S M activities via short articles; upcoming events, highlights and available publications.

621.3   DK   ISSN 0106-4711
DANSK ELFORSYNING. (Text in Danish; summaries in English) 1956. a. DKK 70. Danske Elvaerkers Forening - Association of Danish Electric Utilities, Rosenoerns Allee 9, DK-1970 Frederiksberg C, Denmark. TEL 31-39-01-11. FAX 31-39-59-58. illus. circ. 3,500.
Formerly (until 1977): Dansk Elvaerksstatistik (ISSN 0070-2803)

DANTEC INFORMATION. see *METROLOGY AND STANDARDIZATION*

DEALERSCOPE MERCHANDISING FIRST OF THE MONTH. see *BUSINESS AND ECONOMICS — Marketing And Purchasing*

621.3   JA
DENCHI GIJUTSU/BATTERY TECHNOLOGY. (Text and summaries in English, Japanese) a. Denki Kagaku Kyokai, Denchi Gijutsu Iinkai - Electrochemical Society of Japan, Committee of Battery Technology, Kyoto Daigaku Kogakubu Kogyo Kagaku Kyoshitsu, Yoshida Honmachi, Sakyo-ku, Kyoto-shi, Kyoto 606, Japan.

621.3   JA   ISSN 0287-2846
DENCHI KIGU/BATTERY AND APPLIANCE. (Text in Japanese) 1948. m. 100 Yen per no. Nihon Kandenchi Kogyokai - Japan Battery and Appliance Industries Association, 2-2, Atogo 1-chome, Minato-ku, Tokyo 105, Japan.

621.3   JA
DENCHI TORONKAI KOEN YOSHISHU/BATTERY SYMPOSIUM IN JAPAN. (Text in Japanese; summaries in English) 1960. a. Denki Kagaku Kyokai - Electrochemical Society of Japan, 12-1, Yuraku-cho 1-chome, Chiyoda-ku, Tokyo 100, Japan.

621.3   JA   ISSN 0914-7896
DENCHUKEN REVIEW. (Text in Japanese) 1967. irreg. Denryoku Chuo Kenkyujo - Central Research Institute of Electric Power Industry, 6-1, Otemachi 1-chome, Chiyoda-ku, Tokyo 100, Japan. Indexed: INIS Atomind.
Former titles (until 1987): Denken Review (ISSN 0285-7804); (until 1981): Denkenho (ISSN 0285-662X)

621.3   JA   ISSN 0418-6257
DENGEN/POWER RESOURCES. (Text in Japanese) m. Dengen Kaihatsu K.K. - Electric Power Development Co., Ltd., 15-1, Ginza 6-chome, Chuo-ku, Tokyo 104, Japan.

621.3 531.64   JA   ISSN 0385-7042
DENGEN KAIHATSU K.K. CHOSA SHIRYO/ELECTRIC POWER DEVELOPMENT CO., LTD. STUDY REPORT.* (Text in Japanese; summaries in English, Japanese) 1954. s-a. Dengen Kaihatsu K.K. - Electric Power Development Co., Ltd., 15-1, Ginza 6-chome, Chuo-ku, Tokyo 104, Japan. circ. 650.

621.3   JA
DENGEN KAIHATSU K.K. SOGO GIJUTSU SHIKENJOHO/ELECTRIC POWER DEVELOPMENT CO. ENGINEERING RESEARCH INSTITUTE. ANNUAL REPORT. (Text in Japanese) a. Dengen Kaihatsu K.K., Sogo Gijutsu Shikenjo - Electric Power Development Co., Ltd., Engineering Research Institute, 9-88, Chigasaki 1-chome, Chigasaki-shi, Kanagawa-ken 253, Japan.

621.3   JA
DENGEN KAIHATSU NO GAIYO/OUTLINE OF ELECTRIC POWER DEVELOPMENT. (Text in Japanese) a. 2500 Yen. (Shigen Enerugicho - Agency of Natural Resources and Energy) Okumura Insatsu K.K. - Okumura Printing Co., Ltd., 2-44, Kanda Jinbo-cho, Chiyoda-ku, Tokyo 101, Japan.

621.3   JA
DENGEN NYUSU/DENGEN NEWS. (Text in Japanese) 1959. irreg. Dengensha Seisakujo - Dengensha Manufacturing Co., Ltd., 23-1, Masugata 1-chome, Tama-ku, Kawasaki-shi, Kanagawa-ken 214, Japan.

621.3   JA   ISSN 0916-2275
DENJI KANKYO KOGAKU JOHO E M C/ELECTRO MAGNETIC COMPATIBILITY. (Text in Japanese) 1963. m. 38400 Yen. Mimatsu Deta Shisutemu - Mimatsu Data System, 1-1, Sugamo 3-chome, Toshima-ku, Tokyo 170, Japan.
TEL 03-3576-8571. FAX 03-3940-1880. Pub. Kouyu Matsuzuka. adv. Document type: academic/scholarly publication, newsletter.
Description: Covers EMC programs and technologies.

621.3   JA
DENJI OYO/ELECTROMAGNETIC APPLICATION TECHNIQUES. (Text in Japanese) 1982. irreg. Denji Oyo Kenkyujo - Institute of Electromagnetic Research, 1-10-808, Minamiaoyama 5-chome, Minato-ku, Tokyo 107, Japan.

621.3   JA   ISSN 0917-5555
DENJI TOKUSEI KENKYUBUKAI KOKAI KENKYU RONBUNSHU/RESEARCH GROUP ON ELECTROMAGNETIC BEHAVIORS. PROCEEDINGS OF THE MEETING. (Text in Japanese) 1991. 3/yr. Purinto Kairo Gakkai, Denji Tokusei Kenkyu Bukai - Japan Institute of Printed Circuit, Research Group on Electromagnetic Behaviors, c/o Mr. Koji Koshiji, Tokyo Rika Daigaku Rikogakubu Denki Gokakka, 2641, Yamazaki, Noda-shi, Chiba-ken 278, Japan. Document type: proceedings.

621.3   JA
DENJI TOKUSEI O KORYOSHITA PURINTO KIBAN SEKKEI KENKYU BUKAI YOKOSHU/SPECIAL INTEREST GROUP ON ELECTROMAGNETIC ANALYSIS AND DESIGN FOR PRINTED CIRCUITS. TECHNICAL REPORT. (Text in Japanese) 1988. bi-m. Purinto Kairo Gakkai, Denji Tokusei o Koryoshita Purinto Kiban Sekkei Kenkyu Bukai - Japan Institute of Printed Circuit, Special Interest Group on Electromagnetic Analysis and Design for Printed Circuits, c/o Mr. Noboru Shibuya, Takushoku Daigaku Kogakubu Joho Kogakka, 815-1, Tate-machi, Hachioji-shi, Tokyo 193, Japan.

621.3   JA
DENJIKAI SUCHI KAISEKI NI KANSURU SEMINA KOEN RONBUNSHU/PROCEEDINGS OF THE SEMINAR ON NUMERICAL ANALYSIS OF ELECTROMAGNETIC FIELD. (Text in Japanese) 1989. irreg. Denki Gakkai, Seishiki Gijutsu Iinkai - Institute of Electrical Engineers of Japan, Technical Committee on Static Apparatus, 12-1, Yuraku-cho 1-chome, Chiyoda-ku, Tokyo 100, Japan. Document type: proceedings.

621.3   JA
DENKA SHINBUN/ELECTRICAL NEWS. (Text in Japanese) 1946. w. 9600 Yen. Denka Shinbunsha, 2-5, Nihonbashi 2-chome, Chuo-ku, Tokyo 103, Japan.

621.3   JA   ISSN 0286-5629
DENKAI CHIKUDENKI HYORON/ELECTROLYTIC CONDENSER REVIEW. (Text in Japanese) irreg. Denkai Chikudenki Kenkyukai - Electrolytic Condenser Investigation Society, Nihon Denshi Kikai Kogyokai, 2-2, Marunouchi 3-chome, Chiyoda-ku, Tokyo 100, Japan.

621.3   JA   ISSN 0285-5151
DENKI/ELECTRIC MACHINE. (Text in Japanese) 1948. m. 515 Yen per no. Nihon Denki Kogyokai - Japan Electrical Manufacturers' Association, 4-15, Nagata-cho 2-chome, Chiyoda-ku, Tokyo 100, Japan.

621.3   JA
DENKI GAKKAI DENRYOKU ENERUGI BUMON TAIKAI RONBUNSHU/PROCEEDINGS OF THE POWER AND ENERGY CONFERENCE. (Text in English, Japanese; summaries in English) 1990. a. Denki Gakkai, Denryoku Energi Bumon Tokubetsu Iinkai - Institute of Electrical Engineers of Japan, Power and Energy Society, 12-1, Yuraku-cho 1-chome, Chiyoda-ku, Tokyo 100, Japan

621.3   JA
DENKI GAKKAI DENSHI JOHO SHISUTEMU BUMON ZENKOKU TAIKAI KOEN RONBUNSHU/PROCEEDINGS OF THE ELECTRONICS, INFORMATION AND SYSTEMS CONFERENCE. (Text in Japanese) 1991. a. Denkai Gakkai - Institute of Electrical Engineers of Japan, 7-1, Yuraku-cho 1-chome, Chiyoda-ku, Tokyo 100, Japan.

621.3   JA   ISSN 0415-3227
DENKI GAKKAI GIJUTSU HOKOKU, I BU/INSTITUTE OF ELECTRICAL ENGINEERS OF JAPAN. TECHNICAL REPORT. PART 1. (Text in Japanese) 1955. irreg. Denki Gakkai - Institute of Electrical Engineers of Japan, 7-1, Yuraku-cho 1-chome, Chiyoda-ku, Tokyo 100, Japan.

621.3   JA
DENKI GAKKAI GIJUTSU HOKOKU, II BU/INSTITUTE OF ELECTRICAL ENGINEERS OF JAPAN. TECHNICAL REPORT. PART 2. (Text in Japanese) 1966. irreg. Denki Gakkai - Institute of Electrical Engineers of Japan, 7-1, Yuraku-cho 1-chome, Chiyoda-ku, Tokyo 100, Japan.

621.3   JA   ISSN 0385-4205
DENKI GAKKAI RONBUNSHI. A, KISO ZAIRYO KYOTSU BUMONSHI/INSTITUTE OF ELECTRICAL ENGINEERS OF JAPAN. TRANSACTIONS. A; FUNDAMENTALS AND MATERIALS SOCIETY PUBLICATION. (Text in English, Japanese; summaries in English) 1972. m. 720 Yen per no. Denki Gakkai - Institute of Electrical Engineers of Japan, 7-1, Yuraku-cho 1-chome, Chiyoda-ku, Tokyo 100, Japan. Indexed: INIS Atomind.
—BLDSC (8939.410000).

ENGINEERING — ELECTRICAL ENGINEERING

621.3 JA ISSN 0385-4213
DENKI GAKKAI RONBUNSHI. B, DENRYOKU ENERUGI BUMONSHI/INSTITUTE OF ELECTRICAL ENGINEERS OF JAPAN. TRANSACTIONS. B; POWER AND ENERGY SOCIETY PUBLICATION. (Text in English, Japanese; summaries in English) 1972. m. 720 Yen per no. Denki Gakkai - Institute of Electrical Engineers of Japan, 7-1, Yuraku-cho 1-chome, Chiyoda-ku, Tokyo 100, Japan. **Indexed:** INIS Atomind.
—BLDSC (8939.415000).

621.3 JA ISSN 0385-4221
DENKI GAKKAI RONBUNSHI. C, DENSHI JOHO SHISUTEMU BUMONSHI/INSTITUTE OF ELECTRICAL ENGINEERS OF JAPAN. TRANSACTIONS. C; ELECTRONICS, INFORMATION AND SYSTEMS SOCIETY PUBLICATION. (Text in Japanese) 1972. m. 720 Yen per no. Denki Gakkai - Institute of Electrical Engineers of Japan, 7-1, Yuraku-cho 1-chome, Chiyoda-ku, Tokyo 100, Japan. **Indexed:** INIS Atomind.
—BLDSC (8939.420000).

621.3 JA ISSN 0913-6339
DENKI GAKKAI RONBUNSHI. D, SANGYO OYO BUMONSHI/INSTITUTE OF ELECTRICAL ENGINEERS OF JAPAN. TRANSACTIONS. D; INDUSTRY APPLICATIONS SOCIETY PUBLICATION. (Text in English, Japanese; summaries in English) 1987. m. 700 Yen per no. Denki Gakkai - Institute of Electrical Engineers of Japan, 7-1, Yuraku-cho 1-chome, Chiyoda-ku, Tokyo 100, Japan. **Indexed:** INIS Atomind.
—BLDSC (8939.421000).

621.3 JA ISSN 0020-2878
DENKI GAKKAI ZASSHI/INSTITUTE OF ELECTRICAL ENGINEERS OF JAPAN. JOURNAL. (Text in Japanese) 1888. m. 1545 Yen per no. Denki Gakkai - Institute of Electrical Engineers of Japan, 7-1, Yuraku-cho 1-chome, Chiyoda-ku, Tokyo 100, Japan. **Indexed:** INIS Atomind.
—BLDSC (4775.000000). **CCC.**

DENKI GIJUTSUSHA/ELECTRONIC ENGINEERS. see *ELECTRONICS*

621.3 JA ISSN 0285-5860
DENKI HYORON/ELECTRICAL REVIEW. (Text in Japanese) 1913. m. 720 Yen per no. Denki Hyoronsha, 14, Yosida Kawara-cho, Sakyo-ku, Kyoto-shi, Kyoto 606, Japan.
—BLDSC (3688.900000).

621.3 JA
DENKI JIGYO NO GENJO/ANNUAL REPORT OF ELECTRICAL INDUSTRY. (Text in Japanese) 1951. a. 3900 Yen. Nihon Denki Kyokai - Japan Electric Association, 7-1, Yuraku-cho 1-chome, Chiyoda-ku, Tokyo 100.

621.3 JA
DENKI JIKI ZAIRYO KENKYUJO KENKYU HOKOKU/RESEARCH INSTITUTE FOR ELECTRIC AND MAGNETIC MATERIALS. SCIENCE REPORT. (English edition avail.) (Text in Japanese; summaries in English) 1962. irreg. Denki Jiki Zairyo Kenkyujo, 1-1, Yagiyama Minami 2-chome, Taihaku-ku, Sendai-shi, Miyagi-ken 982, Japan.

621.3 JA ISSN 0285-8061
DENKI JOHO/ELECTRICAL INFORMATION. (Text in Japanese) 1957. m. 620 Yen per no. Denki Johosha, 7-9, Iidabashi 1-chome, Chiyoda-ku, Tokyo 102, Japan.

621.3 JA ISSN 0387-754X
DENKI KAKO GAKKAISHI/JAPAN SOCIETY OF ELECTRICAL - MACHINING ENGINEERS. JOURNAL. (Text in Japanese; summaries in English) 1968. 3/yr. 2000 Yen per no. Denki Kako Gakkai, Nihon Gakkai Jimu Senta, 16-9, Honkomagome 5-chome, Bunkyo-ku, Tokyo 113, Japan.

621.3 JA ISSN 0389-1550
DENKI KAKO GIJUTSU/JOURNAL OF ELECTRICAL - MACHINING TECHNOLOGY. (Text in Japanese) 3/yr. 5000 Yen. Denki Kako Gakkai - Japan Society of Electrical - Machining Engineers, Nihon Gakkai Jimu Senta, 16-9, Honkomagome 5-chome, Bunkyo-ku, Tokyo 113, Japan.

621.3 JA
DENKI KANRI GIJUTSU/ELECTRIC CONTROL ENGINEERING. (Text in Japanese) 1980. m. 350 Yen per no. Tokyo Denki Kanri Gijutsusha Kyokai - Tokyo Association of Electric Control Engineers, 3-7, Iidabashi 3-chome, Chiyoda-ku, Tokyo 102, Japan.

621.3 JA ISSN 0385-7050
DENKI KEISAN/ELECTRICAL CALCULATION. (Text in Japanese) 1933. m. 1190 Yen per no. Denki Shoin, 2-17, Tomigaya 2-chome, Shibuya-ku, Tokyo 151, Japan. **Indexed:** INIS Atomind.

621.3 JA ISSN 0385-3047
DENKI KENTEIJO GIHO/JAPAN ELECTRIC METERS INSPECTION CORPORATION. TECHNICAL REPORT. (Text in Japanese; summaries in English) 1966. q. 880 Yen per no. (Nihon Denki Keiki Kenteijo) Ohm-sha, 3-1, Kanda Nishiki-cho, Chiyoda-ku, Tokyo 101, Japan.
—BLDSC (4663.495000).

621.3 JA
DENKI KIKAKU CHOSAKAI JIGYO HOKOKU/JAPANESE ELECTRO TECHNICAL COMMITTEE. ANNUAL REPORT. (Text in Japanese) a. Denki Gakkai - Institute of Electrical Engineers of Japan, 7-1, Yuraku-cho 1-chome, Chiyoda-ku, Tokyo 100, Japan.

621.3 JA ISSN 0285-5526
DENKI KOJI NO TOMO/ELECTRICAL WORK JOURNAL. (Text in Japanese) 1948. m. 470 Yen per no. Kanto Denki Kyokai - Kanto Electric Association, 7-1, Yuraku-cho 1-chome, Chiyoda-ku, Tokyo 100, Japan.

621.3 JA ISSN 0285-8908
DENKI KOJIGYO/ELECTRICAL CONSTRUCTION INDUSTRY. (Text in Japanese) 1969. m. 450 Yen per no. Tokyoto Denki Koji Kogyo Kumiai - Tokyo Metropolitan Union on Electrical Constructing Industry, 4-13, Tsukiji 3-chome, Chuo-ku, Tokyo 104, Japan.

621.3 JA ISSN 0285-8894
DENKI KOJISHI/ELECTRICAL CONSTRUCTION ENGINEER. (Text in Japanese) 1957. m. 360 Yen per no. Nihon Denki Kojishi Kyokai - Nihon Electrical Construction Engineer's Association, 7-8, Motoakasaka 1-chome, Minato-ku, Tokyo 107, Japan.

621.3 JA ISSN 0285-5208
DENKI KYODO KENKYU/ELECTRICAL COOPERATIVE RESEARCH. (Text in Japanese) 1944. irreg. Denki Kyodo Kenkyukai - Society of Electrical Coorperative Research, 11-35, Nagata-cho 1-chome, Chiyoda-ku, Tokyo 100, Japan.

621.3 JA ISSN 0387-0758
DENKI KYOKAI ZASSHI/JAPAN ELECTRIC ASSOCIATION. JOURNAL. (Text in Japanese) 1921. m. $93.50. Nihon Denki Kyokai - Japan Electric Association, 7-1, Yuraku-cho 1-chome, Chiyoda-ku, Tokyo 100, Japan. (Dist. by: Intercontinental Marketing Corp., I.P.O. Box 5056, Tokyo 100-30. TEL 81-3-3661-7458. FAX 81-3-3667-9646)
—BLDSC (4804.890000).

621.3 JA
DENKI NIPPO/ELECTRICAL DAILY NEWS. (Text in Japanese) 1910. d. 8500 Yen. Denki Nipposha, 8-9, Shinbashi 5-chome, Chiyoda-ku, Tokyo 100, Japan. **Document type:** newspaper.

621.3 JA
DENKI SANGYO SHINBUN/ELECTRICAL INDUSTRY NEWS. (Text in Japanese) 1948. w. 8000 Yen. Denki Sangyo Shinbunsha, 5-11, Shiba Daimon 2-chome, Minato-ku, Tokyo 105, Japan.

621.3 JA
DENKI SETSUBI GAKKAI KENKYU HAPPYOKAI KOEN RONBUNSHU/INSTITUTE OF ELECTRICAL INSTALLATION ENGINEERS OF JAPAN. PROCEEDINGS OF ANNUAL MEETING. (Text in Japanese) 1983. a. 3000 Yen. Denki Setsubi Gakkai, 9-3, Nishishinjuku 6-chome, Shinjuku-ku, Tokyo 160, Japan. **Document type:** proceedings.

621.3 JA ISSN 0910-0350
DENKI SETSUBI GAKKAISHI/INSTITUTE OF ELECTRICAL INSTALLATION ENGINEERS OF JAPAN. JOURNAL. (Text in Japanese; summaries in English) 1981. m. 1000 Yen per no. Denki Setsubi Gakkai, 9-3, Nishishinjuku 6-chome, Shinjuku-ku, Tokyo 160, Japan.

621.3 JA
DENKI SHINBUN/ELECTRICAL NEWS (DAILY). (Text in Japanese) 1907. d. 3800 Yen per mo. Nihon Denki Kyokai - Japan Electric Association, 7-1, Yuraku-cho 1-chome, Chiyoda-ku, Tokyo 100, Japan. **Document type:** newspaper.

621.3 JA
DENKI SHOKO SHINBUN/ELECTRICAL BUSINESS NEWS. (Text in Japanese) 1946. w. 1200 Yen per mo. Denki Shoko Shinbunsha, 4-19, Minamimori-machi 1-chome, Kita-ku, Osaka-shi, Osaka 530, Japan.

621.3 JA
DENKI TAIMUSU/ELECTRICAL TIMES. (Text in Japanese) 1957. w. 12000 Yen. Denki Taimusu, 2-7, Shinbashi 2-chome, Minato-ku, Tokyo 105, Japan.

621.3 JA ISSN 0386-5479
DENKI TO KOJI/ELECTRICITY AND CONSTRUCTION. (Text in Japanese) 1960. m. Ohm-sha, 3-1, Kanda Nishiki-cho, Chiyoda-ku, Tokyo 101, Japan. TEL 81-3-3233-0641. circ. 63,000.

621.3 JA ISSN 0914-6733
DENNETSU/ELECTRIC HEAT. (Text in Japanese) bi-m. 1200 Yen per no. Nihon Dennetsu Kyokai - Japanese Electro - Heat Association, 9-8, Iwamoto-cho 1-chome, Chiyoda-ku, Tokyo 101, Japan.

DENRYOKU CHOSA TOKEI GEPPO/MONTHLY REPORT ON ELECTRIC POWER STATISTICS. see *ENGINEERING — Abstracting, Bibliographies, Statistics*

621.3 JA
DENRYOKU CHUO KENKYUJO NYUSU/CENTRAL RESEARCH INSTITUTE OF ELECTRIC POWER INDUSTRY. NEWS. (Text in Japanese) 1981. m. Denryoku Chuo Kenkyujo - Central Research Institute of Electric Power Industry, 6-1, Otemachi 1-chome, Chiyoda-ku, Tokyo 100, Japan.

621.3 JA
DENRYOKU JOHO. (Text in Japanese) m. Denki Joho-Sha, Yamakyo Daini Bekkan Bldg., 1-7-9 Iidabashi, Chiyoda-ku, Tokyo 102, Japan. TEL 81-3-3211-1551. circ. 10,000.

621.3 JA
DENRYOKU JUKYU NO GAIYO/SUPPLY AND DEMAND OF ELECTRIC POWER IN JAPAN. (Text in Japanese) a. 2500 Yen. (Shigen Enerugicho, Koeki Jigyobu - Agency of Natural Resources and Energy, Public Utilities Department) Chuwa Insatsu K.K., 2-14, Irifune 2-chome, Chuo-ku, Tokyo 104, Japan.

621.3 JA ISSN 0285-5534
DENRYOKU MANSURI/ELECTRIC POWER MONTHLY. (Text in Japanese) 1956. m. 150 Yen per no. Kanto Denki Kyokai - Kanto Electric Association, 7-1, Yuraku-cho 1-chome, Chiyoda-ku, Tokyo 100, Japan.

621.3 JA
DENRYOKU TO GIJUTSU. (Text in Japanese) q. Nikkan Denki Tsushinsha, 1-10, Shinbashi 3-chome, Minato-ku, Tokyo 105, Japan. TEL 81-3-3591-5919. circ. 5,000.

621.3 JA ISSN 0011-8451
DENSEI TECHNICAL JOURNAL/DENSEI.* (Text in Japanese) 1959. q. free. Nippon Electric Industry Co., Ltd. - Nihon Denki Seiki K.K., 10-12, Ueno 1-chome, Taito-ku, Tokyo 131, Japan. charts; illus.

621.3 JA
DENSEN JIHO/ELECTRIC WIRE AND CABLE TIMES. (Text in Japanese) 1948. m. 720 Yen per no. Nihon Densen Kogyokai - Japanese Electric Wire and Cable Maker's Association, 12-22, Tsukiji 1-chome, Chuo-ku, Tokyo 104, Japan.

621.3 JA
DENSEN TOKEI NENPO/ELECTRIC WIRE AND CABLE ANNUAL REVIEW. (Text in Japanese) 1950. a. 3000 Yen. Nihon Densen Kogyokai - Japanese Electric Wire and Cable Maker's Association, 12-22, Tsukiji 1-chome, Chuo-ku, Tokyo 104, Japan.

621.3 JA ISSN 0374-3128
DENSETSU KOGYO/ELECTRICAL CONSTRUCTION ENGINEERING. (Text in Japanese) 1955. m. 1200 Yen per no. (Nihon Densetsu Kogyo Kyokai - Japan Electrical Construction Association) Ohm-sha, 3-1, Kanda Nishiki-cho, Chiyoda-ku, Tokyo 101, Japan. circ. 35,000.

ENGINEERING — ELECTRICAL ENGINEERING

621.3   JA
DENSETSU SHIZAI/ELECTRICAL CONSTRUCTION DESIGN AND MATERIAL ESTIMATE AND COST DATA. (Text in Japanese) 1972. m. 1030 Yen per no. Densetsu Shuppan, Yamakyo Bldg., 1-3, Kojimachi, Chiyoda-ku, Tokyo 102, Japan.
TEL 81-3-3265-9761. circ. 40,000.

621.3   JA   ISSN 0366-9084
CODEN: DGSCA3
DENSHI GIJUTSU SOGO KENKYUJO CHOSA HOKOKU/ELECTROTECHNICAL LABORATORY. CIRCULARS. (Text in Japanese, summaries in English) 1921. irreg. Kogyo Gijutsuin Denshi Gijutsu Sogo Kenkyujo - Agency of Industrial Science and Technology, Electrotechnical Laboratory, 1-4, Umezono 1-chome, Tsukuba-shi, Ibaraki-ken 305, Japan. **Indexed:** Eng.Ind., INIS Atomind.
—BLDSC (3218.000000); CASDDS.

621.3   JA   ISSN 0366-9106
CODEN: DGSKBS
DENSHI GIJUTSU SOGO KENKYUJO KENKYU HOKOKU/ELECTROTECHNICAL LABORATORY. RESEARCHES. (Text in English, Japanese; summaries in English) 1907. irreg. Kogyo Gijutsuin Denshi Gijutsu Sogo Kenkyujo - Agency of Industrial Science and Technology, Electrotechnical Laboratory, 1-4, Umezono 1-chome, Tsukuba-shi, Ibaraki-ken 305, Japan. **Indexed:** Chem.Abstr., Eng.Ind., INIS Atomind.
—BLDSC (7775.000000); CASDDS.

621.3   JA
DENSHI GIJUTSU SOGO KENKYUJO NENPO/ELECTROTECHNICAL LABORATORY. ANNUAL REPORT. (Text in Japanese) 1910. a. Kogyo Gijutsuin Denshi Gijutsu Sogo Kenkyujo - Agency of Industrial Science and Technology, Electrotechnical Laboratory, 1-4, Umezono 1-chome, Tsukuba-shi, Ibaraki-ken 305, Japan.

621.3   JA   ISSN 0913-5685
DENSHI JOHO TSUSHIN GAKKAI GIJUTSU KENKYU HOKOKU/INSTITUTE OF ELECTRONICS, INFORMATION AND COMMUNICATION ENGINEERS. TECHNICAL REPORT. (Text in English, Japanese) 1975. irreg. Denshi Joho Tsushin Gakkai - Institute of Electronics, Information and Communication Engineers, Kikai Shinko Kaikan, 5-8, Shiba Koen 3-chome, Minato-ku, Tokyo 105, Japan.
—BLDSC (3553.218100).

DENSHI TOKYO/I E E E TOKYO SECTION. BULLETIN. see *ELECTRONICS*

621.3   JA
DENSOKEN NYUSU/ELECTROTECHNICAL LABORATORY NEWS. (Text in Japanese) 1950. m. Kogyo Gijutsuin Denshi Gijutsu Sogo Kenkyujo - Agency of Industrial Science and Technology, Electrotechnical Laboratory, 1-4, Umezono 1-chome, Tsukuba-shi, Ibaraki-ken 305, Japan.

DESIGN, CODES AND CRYPTOGRAPHY. see *MATHEMATICS*

DEVELOPMENTS IN NANOTECHNOLOGY. see *PHYSICS*

621.3   GW
DIALOG; V D E Mitgliederinformation. 1987. bi-m. Verband Deutscher Elektrotechniker e.V., Stresemannallee 15, 60596 Frankfurt a.M., Germany. Ed. Walter Boermann. circ. 36,000. **Document type:** corporate report.

621.31   CC   ISSN 1000-1344
DIAN SHIJIE/ELECTRICAL WORLD. (Text in Chinese) 1946. m. Y1.40 per no. Shanghai Jidian Gongye Guanli-ju, 27 Huqiu Lu, Shanghai 200002, People's Republic of China. TEL 3217280.
FAX 021-3213672. Ed. Feng Weitai. adv.: color page $2200; trim 15 x 22; adv. contact: Zhu Zhongqing. circ. 100,000.

621.38 614.7   CC   ISSN 1000-4742
CODEN: DYHUEU
DIANDU YU HUANBAO/ELECTROPLATING AND POLLUTION CONTROL. (Text in Chinese) 1981. bi-m. $22. Shanghai Qinggongye-ju, Keji Qingbaosuo - Light Industry Bureau, Institute of Science and Technology Information, Rm. 506, No. 19 Lane 607, Yuyao Rd., Shanghai 200042, People's Republic of China. TEL 021-2150691.
FAX 021-4031633. (Co-sponsor: Zhongguo Qinggongye Xiehui Huanjing Baohu Kexue Xuehui) Ed. Yao Xilu. adv.; bk.rev. circ. 12,000. **Document type:** academic/scholarly publication.
—BLDSC (3707.060000); CASDDS.
Description: Deals with surface treatment technologies, such as electroplating, electroless plating, anodic coatings, chemical conversion coatings and organic coatings.

621.3   CC   ISSN 1000-6753
DIANGONG JISHU XUEBAO/CHINESE ELECTROTECHNICAL SOCIETY. TRANSACTIONS. (Text in Chinese; summaries in Chinese, English) 1984. q. $32. (Chinese Electrotechnical Society) China Machine Press, 1 Nanli, Baiwanzhuang, Beijing 100037, People's Republic of China. TEL 8326677.
FAX 861-8326337. TELEX 222557 STIP CN. Ed. Yang Yingqiu. index; circ. 3,000 (controlled). (back issues avail.) **Document type:** academic/scholarly publication.
Description: Provides modern and latest technology in electric engineering to people in this field.

621.3   CC   ISSN 1000-145X
TK1001
DIANLI JISHU/ELECTRIC POWER. (Text in Chinese) m. $2 per no. Nengyuanbu, Shuilibu, Shuili Dianli Qingbao Yanjiusuo - Ministry of Energy, Bureau of Water Conservancy, Institute of Hydraulics Information, Liu Pu Kang, Dewai, Beijing 100011, People's Republic of China. TEL 4013167. Ed. Fu Congde.

621.31 629.8   CC
DIANLI XITONG ZIDONGHUA/AUTOMATION OF ELECTRIC POWER SYSTEMS. (Text in Chinese) bi-m. $3 per no. Nanjing Zidonghua Yanjiusuo, P.O. Box 323, Nanjing, Jiangsu 210003, People's Republic of China. TEL 636374. (Dist. outside China by: Guoji Shudian - China International Book Trading Corp., P.O. Box 399, Beijing, P.R.C.) Ed. Ma Jingguo. **Indexed:** Sci.Abstr.

621.31   CC   ISSN 1001-2095
DIANQI CHUANDONG/ELECTRIC DRIVE. (Text in Chinese) 1971. bi-m. Y18. Tianjin Dianqi Chuandong Sheji Yanjiusuo, Erhao Qiao (No.2 Bridge), Jin-Tang Gonglu, Tianjin 300180, People's Republic of China. TEL 490721. adv.; bk.rev. circ. 10,000.
—BLDSC (3671.532500).
Description: Publishes research papers on AC drive, DC drive, computer applications, and automatic control.

621.31   CC   ISSN 1000-3673
DIANWANG JISHU/POWER SYSTEM TECHNOLOGY. (Text in Chinese) 1977. bi-m. Y15. Nengyuan Bu, Dianli Kexue Yanjiuyuan - Ministry of Energy, Electric Power Research Institute, Qinghe, Beijing 100085, People's Republic of China. TEL 861-291-3125.
FAX 861-291-3126. Ed. Zhou Xiaoxin. adv.; bk.rev. **Document type:** trade publication.
—BLDSC (6576.915000).

621.31   CC   ISSN 1002-087X
DIANYUAN JISHU/CHINESE JOURNAL OF POWER SOURCES. (Text in Chinese) 1977. bi-m. $90. Tianjin Dianyuan Yanjiusuo - Tianjin Institute of Power Sources, P.O. Box 277, Tianjin 300381, People's Republic of China. TEL 382851. TELEX 23174 TJPIB CN-015. (Dist. outside China by: China National Publications Import & Export Company, P.O. Box 88, Beijing 100704, P.R.C.) Ed. Wang Jijiang. adv.: B&W page $500, color page $1000; trim 16 x 21; adv. contact: Jinqi Li. circ. 10,000. **Document type:** academic/scholarly publication.
Formerly: Journal of Power Sources Technology.
Description: Covers the field of electrochemistry and physical power sources, such as batteries and solar cells.

DIANZI JISHU/ELECTRONIC TECHNOLOGY. see *ELECTRONICS*

DIANZI JISHU YINGYONG/APPLICATIONS OF ELECTRONIC TECHNIQUE. see *ELECTRONICS*

DIANZI JISHU ZAZHI/JOURNAL OF ELECTRONICS TECHNOLOGY. see *ELECTRONICS*

DIANZI KEXUE JISHU/ELECTRONIC SCIENCE AND TECHNOLOGY. see *ELECTRONICS*

DIANZI KEXUE XUEKAN. see *ELECTRONICS*

DIANZI SHIJIE/ELECTRONIC WORLD. see *ELECTRONICS*

DIANZI XUEBAO/ACTA ELECTRONICA SINICA. see *ELECTRONICS*

DIFFUSION EXPRESS. see *ENGINEERING — Abstracting, Bibliographies, Statistics*

DIGITAL SIGNAL PROCESSING; a review journal. see *ELECTRONICS*

621.3   NE
DIGITALE ANALOGE TECHNOLOGIE; vakblad voor de technische professional. Cover title: D A Technologie. 11/yr. fl.142.50 (foreign fl.192.50) (effective 1993). (Nederlandse Ingenieurs Vereniging (NIRIA)) V N U Business Publications B.V., Postbus 90162, 1006 BD Amsterdam, Netherlands.
TEL 31-20-5102911. FAX 31-20-6174121.
(Co-sponsor: Koninklijk Instituut van Ingenieurs) Ed. Ruud Plaizier. adv.: B&W page fl.2860, color page fl.4855; trim 205 x 285; adv. contact: Erna Oonk. circ. 10,789. **Document type:** trade publication.

DIODE D.A.T.A. DIGEST. see *ELECTRONICS*

621.31 665.5   US
HD9685.U4
DIRECTORY OF ELECTRIC UTILITY INDUSTRY.* 1965. a. $50. Midwest Register, Inc., 1120 4th St., Tulsa, OK 74120. TEL 918-582-2000. FAX 918-587-9349. Ed. Will L. Hammack. **Document type:** directory.
Former titles (until 1992): Directory of Electric Generating and Distributing Companies; (until 1989): Directory of Electric Light and Power Companies (ISSN 0092-4970)
Description: Supplies addresses, phone numbers, fax numbers, information as to whether producer or distributor, total customers and total kilowatt hours sold and purchased.

DISCONTINUED DISCRETE SEMICONDUCTORS D.A.T.A. DIGEST. see *ELECTRONICS*

DISCONTINUED I CS D.A.T.A. DIGEST. see *ELECTRONICS*

621.3   US
DISPATCHER (COLUMBUS). 1961. m. free to qualified personnel. Nebraska Public Power District, Box 499, Columbus, NE 68602-0499. TEL 402-563-5811. FAX 402-563-5166. Ed. Sharon Soltero. circ. 3,500 (controlled). (back issues avail.)
Description: For utility employees and retirees

683.83   CC   ISSN 1001-5531
DIYA DIANQI/LOW VOLTAGE APPARTUS. (Text in Chinese, English) 1959. bi-m. Y2.50 (effective 1994). Shanghai Dianqi Kexue Yanjiusuo - Shanghai Electrical Apparatus Research Institute, 505 Wuning Rd., Shanghai 200063, People's Republic of China. TEL 2574990. Ed. Chen Lanfang. adv. **Document type:** academic/scholarly publication.
Description: Publishes research papers on design, calculation, application, test, maintenance, technology, and equipments of low voltage switch gear.

621.32 747   IT
DOSSIER COMPONENTI; international lighting technology and lighting accessories magazine. (Text in English, French, German, Italian, Spanish) 1986. q. L.80000 (typically set in Sep.). Gemini S.A.S., Via M.M. de Taddei, 3, 20146 Milan, Italy. TEL 48-14-800. FAX 48-19-3013. adv. circ. 12,500.

DRAHT; internationale Fachzeitschrift fuer die Draht- und Kabelindustrie und alle Bereiche der Drahtverarbeitung. see *METALLURGY*

DRIVES AND CONTROLS. see *ENGINEERING — Hydraulic Engineering*

ENGINEERING — ELECTRICAL ENGINEERING

338.4 US ISSN 0093-3236
TK455
E C & M'S ELECTRICAL PRODUCTS YEARBOOK.
(Electrical Construction and Maintenance) Key Title: Electrical Products Yearbook. a. $10 (free to qualified personnel). Intertec Publishing Corp., 9800 Metcalf, Overland Park, KS 66212-2215. TEL 913-341-1300. FAX 913-967-1898. Ed. John Debad. adv.; illus. circ. 102,100. **Document type:** directory.
Description: Reference issue on new electrical products.

621.3 US
E D I. (Electrical Design and Installation) 1991. m. $24. McPartland Publishing Company, Inc., 452 Hudson Terr., Englewood Cliffs, NJ 07632. TEL 201-568-2930. FAX 201-568-2988. Ed. Brian McPartland. adv. circ. 101,404. **Document type:** trade publication.
Description: Directed to electrical contractor personnel, plant and facilities electrical personnel, and inspection personnel.

621.38 338.4 UK
E E A. ASSOCIATION OF THE ELECTRONICS, TELECOMMUNICATIONS & BUSINESS EQUIPMENT INDUSTRIES. ANNUAL REPORT. bi-a. £25. Electronic Engineering Association, Leicester House, 8 Leicester St., London WC2H 7BN, England. TEL 071-437-0678. FAX 071-434-3477. TELEX 263536. circ. 25,000. **Document type:** corporate report.
Formerly: Electronic Engineering Association. Annual Report (ISSN 0070-9859)

621.3 001.6 US
E E C S - E R L NEWS. 1974. s-a. free. Electrical Engineering & Computer Sciences, Electronics Research Laboratory, c/o Industrial Liaison Program, University of California, Berkeley, 203 Cory Hall, Berkeley, CA 94720. TEL 510-643-6691. FAX 510-643-6694. Ed. Janie Ellison. circ. 1,500. **Document type:** newsletter.
Formerly (until 1988): U C Electronics News.

621.3 US
E E I ENVIRONMENTAL DIRECTORY OF U.S. POWER PLANTS. a. $225 to non-EEI members; EEI members $180. (Edison Electric Institute) Utility Data Institute (Subsidiary of: McGraw-Hill), 1200 G St., N.W., Ste. 250, Washington, DC 20005. TEL 202-942-8788; 800-486-3660. FAX 202-942-8789. **Document type:** directory.
●Also available online.
Former titles (until 1990): E E I Power Directory; Power Directory.
Description: Provides information on more than 2,500 generating units at 950 power plants in the U.S.

E E I STATISTICAL RELEASES. ELECTRIC OUTPUT. (Edison Electric Institute) see ENGINEERING — Abstracting, Bibliographies, Statistics

620 352 US ISSN 0737-349X
E E I WASHINGTON LETTER. 1945? w. $125 to non-members. Edison Electric Institute, 701 Pennsylvania Ave., N.W., Washington, DC 20004-2696. TEL 202-508-5425. FAX 202-508-5030. Ed. N. Burkey Musselman. circ. 1,200. **Document type:** newsletter.
Formerly: N A E C Weekly Newsletter.

621.3 GW ISSN 0013-5445
E M A - ELEKTRISCHE MASCHINEN. 1921. m. DM.143 (foreign DM.159.70). (Zentralverband der Deutschen Elektrohandwerke, Bundesfachgruppe Elektromaschinenbau) Huethig und Pflaum Verlag, Lazarettstr. 4, 80686 Munich, Germany. TEL 089-12607-240. FAX 089-12607200. (Subscr. to: Im Weiher 10, 6900 Heidelberg 1, Germany) Ed. Wolfgang Seher. adv.; bk.rev.; abstr.; bibl.; charts; illus.; stat.; index. circ. 2,050. **Indexed:** Sci.Abstr. **Document type:** trade publication.
—BLDSC (3711.125000). **CCC.**
Formerly: Elektrische Maschinen, Elektromaschinenbauer.
Description: Trade publication for the electric machine industry, featuring research in manufacturing, utilization and repairing. Includes trade news, reports of events, list of articles from other magazines.

621.38 US
E M C TEST AND DESIGN. (Electromagnetic Compatability) 1989. bi-m. $39 (Canada and Mexico $59; elsewhere $99). Argus Inc., 6151 Powers Ferry Rd., N.W., Atlanta, GA 30339-2491. TEL 404-955-2500. FAX 404-955-0400. Ed. Gary Breed. adv. circ. 30,980.
Description: Provides engineers with practical information on EMC design techniques and test methods.

E M F HEALTH & SAFETY DIGEST. (Electric and Magnetic Field) see OCCUPATIONAL HEALTH AND SAFETY

621.31 620 UK
E P E. 1919. m. £33 to non-members (overseas £40) (effective 1994). Engineers' and Managers' Association, Flaxman House, Gogmore Ln., Chertsey, Surrey KT16 9JS, England. FAX 0932-567707. Ed. Patricia Battams. adv.; illus.; mkt. circ. 36,000. (also avail. in microform from UMI; reprint service avail. from UMI) **Indexed:** Br.Tech.Ind. **Document type:** trade publication.
—SWETS.
Formerly: Electrical Power Engineer (ISSN 0013-4376)
Description: Contains news of technical and industrial relations developments in electricity supply industry, shipbuilding, aerospace and general engineering.

621.3 US
E P R I GUIDE. (Published in several sections: Technical Reports; Licensable Inventions; Computer Programs and Databases; Communications Resources.) 1979. a. Electric Power Research Institute, 3412 Hillview Ave., Box 10412, Palo Alto, CA 94303. TEL 415-855-2568. Ed. June Swan.
●Available only online. Vendor(s): DIALOG Information Services, Inc. (File no. 241).

E Q. see SOUND RECORDING AND REPRODUCTION

621.3 SW ISSN 0013-9939
E R A; elektricitetens rationella anvaending. 1928. m. SEK 460. Svenska Elverksfoereningen - Association of Swedish Electric Utilities, P.O. Box 3192, S-103 63 Stockholm, Sweden. TEL 08-791 69 00. Ed. Bengt Magnusson. adv.; bk.rev.; bibl.; charts; illus.; stat.; index. circ. 13,600. **Indexed:** Sci.Abstr.

621.3 GW ISSN 0939-3072
TK3 CODEN: ETEEEB
E T E P. (European Transactions on Electrical Power Engineering) (Text in English) 1979. bi-m. DM.405 (foreign DM.414). V D E-Verlag GmbH, Bismarckstr. 33, 10625 Berlin, Germany. TEL 030-348001-0. FAX 030-3417093. TELEX 181683. Ed. Ursula Sandner. adv.; bk.rev. circ. 1,300. (back issues avail.) **Indexed:** INIS Atomind., PROMT. **Document type:** trade publication.
—BLDSC (3830.314000); EI; UnCover; SWETS. **CCC.**
Formerly (until 1990): E T Z Archiv (ISSN 0170-1703)

621.3 US
E T S NEWS. (Electric Thermal Storage) 1989. q. free. Electric Power Research Institute, Inc., 236 Crim St., Bowling Green, OH 43402. TEL 419-354-7677. FAX 419-354-7756. Ed. Ben W. Strange. circ. 2,800 (controlled). **Document type:** newsletter.

621.3 GW
CODEN: EELZD3
E T Z; Fachmagazin fuer Elektrotechnik und Automation. 1880. s-m. DM.222 (foreign DM.264). (Verband Deutscher Elektrotechniker e.V.) V D E-Verlag GmbH, Bismarckstr. 33, 10625 Berlin, Germany. TEL 030-348001-0. FAX 030-3417093. TELEX 181683. Ed. Ursula Sandner. adv.; bk.rev. circ. 17,000. (back issues avail.) **Indexed:** C.I.S. Abstr., Chem.Abstr., Cyb.Abstr., Eng.Ind., Excerp.Med., Fuel & Energy Abstr., INIS Atomind., Sci.Abstr. **Document type:** trade publication.
—BLDSC (3823.400000); EI; SWETS; CASDDS. **CCC.**
Former titles: Electrotechnische Zeitschrift E T Z (ISSN 0341-1362); Electrotechnische Zeitschrift (ISSN 0170-1711); Which was formed by the Jan. 1979 merger of: Electrotechnische Zeitschrift. Ausgabe A; Elektrontechnische Zeitschrift. Ausgabe B (ISSN 0012-8031)

621.3 AU ISSN 0932-383X
TK3
E UND I. (Elektrotechnik und Informationstechnik) 1884. m. DM.280($175) (Oesterreichischer Verband fuer Elektrotechnik) Springer-Verlag, Sachsenplatz 4-6, Postfach 89, A-1201 Vienna, Austria. TEL 0222-3302415. FAX 0222-3302426. (Subscr. in N. America to: Springer-Verlag New York, Inc., 44 Hartz Way, Secaucus, NJ 07096-2491. TEL 201-348-4033. FAX 201-348-4505) Ed.Bd. adv.; bk.rev.; charts; illus.; index. (reprint service avail. from ISI) **Indexed:** C.I.S.Abstr., Chem.Abstr., Eng.Ind., Excerp.Med., Sci.Abstr. **Document type:** academic/scholarly publication.
—BLDSC (3719.700000); SWETS. **CCC.**
Formerly (until 1988): E und M (Elektrotechnik und Maschinenbau) (ISSN 0012-8058)

621.3 AU
E UND W. (Elektro und Wirtschaft) 1982. m. S.750 (foreign S.1600). Elektro und Wirtschaft Verlagsgesellschaft mbH, Wilhelminenstr. 91-IIC, A-1160 Vienna, Austria. TEL 0222-453149-0. FAX 0222-469032-30. Ed. Helmut J. Rockenbauer. **Document type:** trade publication.

537 GW
E V U PRAXIS; Zeitschrift fuer die Elektrofachkraefte in der Energieversorgung. 1961. m. DM.74. Verlags- und Wirtschaftsgesellschaft der Elektrizitaetswerke mbH, Stresemannallee 30, 60596 Frankfurt a.M., Germany. TEL 069-6304-328. FAX 069-6304359. TELEX 411284-VDEW. Ed. Guenter Fenchel. adv. circ. 7.400. **Document type:** trade publication.
Formerly (until 1992): Elektriker (ISSN 0936-3602)

621.3 CN
ECLAIRAGE PLUS MAGAZINE. 1989. q. Can.$28($33) Groupe Constructo, 1500 boul. Jules-Poitras, St. Laurent, PQ H4N 1X7, Canada. TEL 514-745-5720. FAX 514-339-2267. Ed. Robert Bastin. adv. contact: Leo Beaudoin. circ. 5,702. (back issues avail.) **Document type:** trade publication.

621.31 338.4 US
EDISON ELECTRIC INSTITUTE. STATISTICAL YEARBOOK OF THE ELECTRIC UTILITY INDUSTRY.. 1928. a. Edison Electric Institute, Statistical Committee, 701 Pennsylvania Ave., N.W., Washington, DC 20004-2696. TEL 202-508-5425. FAX 202-508-5030. Ed. Betsy DeCampo. charts; stat. circ. 3,200. **Indexed:** Fuel & Energy Abstr.

EDITTECH INTERNATIONAL; reporting worldwide on high technology. see COMMUNICATIONS — Computer Applications

621.3 NE ISSN 0167-9708
CODEN: TEUEDE
EINDHOVEN UNIVERSITY OF TECHNOLOGY. RESEARCH REPORTS. Variant title: E U T Reports. (Text in Dutch and English) 1968. irreg. exchange. Eindhoven University of Technology, Central Library, Bibliographical Department, P.O. Box 90159, 5600 RM Eindhoven, Netherlands. FAX 31-40-472531. TELEX 51163 NL. Ed.Bd. circ. 200. **Indexed:** INSPEC.
—BLDSC (3830.507150); EI.
Description: Each volume devoted to a single topic in electrical engineering.

621.31 SW ISSN 0013-399X
EL; kommer fraan din ellleverantoer. 1945. 3/yr. Svenska Elverksfoereningen - Association of Swedish Electric Utilities, P.O. Box 3192, S-103 63 Stockholm, Sweden. TEL 08-791 69 00. Ed. Inger Abrahamson. bk.rev.; charts; illus.; mkt. circ. 3,000,000. **Indexed:** Sci.Abstr.

621.3 DK ISSN 0107-3931
EL & ENERGI. 1904. bi-m. DKK 260. Danske Elvaerkers Forening, Rosenoerns Allee 9, DK-1970 Frederiksberg C, Denmark. Ed. Leif B. Christiansen. adv.; bk.rev.; charts; illus.; tr.lit.; index. circ. 4,680. **Indexed:** Chem.Abstr., Sci.Abstr.

621.3 SW ISSN 0013-4007
ELBRANSCHEN; oberoende elteknisk tidskrift. 1929. bi-m. SEK 175 (effective 1991). Elbranschen, P.O. Box 6040, S-200 11 Malmoe, Sweden. FAX 40-79737. Ed. Joergen Dahlkvist. adv.; charts; illus.; index. circ. 3,500.
Former titles (until 1965): Elbranschen med Elektriska Installatoertidningen; (until 1961): Elektriska Installatoertidningen.

ENGINEERING — ELECTRICAL ENGINEERING

621.31   FR   ISSN 0424-7701
ELECTRA. (Text in English, French) 1967. bi-m. membership. International Conference on Large High Voltage Electric Systems (CIGRE), 3-5 rue de Metz, 75010 Paris, France. TEL 33-1-42-46-50-85. FAX 33-1-42-46-58-27. Ed. C. Chabaud. adv. contact: Nathalie Raymond. bk.rev. circ. 5,500. **Indexed:** Sci.Abstr. **Document type:** academic/scholarly publication.
—BLDSC (3670.995000).

621.3   DK
ELECTRA. 1929. 11/yr. DKK 225. Elektroinstallatoerernes Landsforening, Paul Bergsoes Vej 6, 2600 Glostrup, Denmark. TEL 43-436000. FAX 43-432103. Eds. Niels Joergen Hansen, Kristina Oeby Pedersen. adv. circ. 4,150.

621.313
ELECTRIC LIGHT AND POWER. 1922. m. $42. PennWell Publishing Co., 1421 S. Sheridan Rd., Box 1260, Tulsa, OK 74101. TEL 918-835-3161. FAX 918-831-9497. Ed. Robert Smock. adv.: B&W page $5510, color page $6640; trim 10 7/8 x 14 3/4. bk.rev.; charts; illus.; stat.; tr.lit.; index. circ. 43,600. (also avail. in microform from UMI; reprint service avail. from UMI) **Indexed:** Acid Rain Abstr., Acid Rain Ind., Bus.Ind., C.I.S.Abstr., CAD CAM Abstr., Energy Info.Abstr., Fuel & Energy Abstr., SRI, Tr.& Indus.Ind.
Formed by the merger of: Electric Light and Power: Energy - Generation; Electric Light and Power: Transmission - Distribution.
Description: Serves the US electric utility industry. Covers power generation, transmission, and distribution operations in investor-owned and municipal electric utilities, rural electric and other cooperatives, federal power projects and publicly owned power companies.

621.3   US   ISSN 0731-356X
TK2000   CODEN: EMPSDO
ELECTRIC MACHINES AND POWER SYSTEMS. 1976. m. $355. Taylor & Francis, 1900 Frost Rd., Ste. 101, Bristol, PA 19007-1598. TEL 800-821-8312. FAX 215-785-5515. Ed. S.A. Nasar. adv.; bk.rev.; abstr.; bibl.; charts; illus.; index. circ. 475. (also avail. in microform from UMI; back issues avail.; reprint service avail. from UMI) **Indexed:** Cadscan, Curr.Cont., Lead Abstr., Sci.Abstr., Zincscan. **Document type:** academic/scholarly publication.
—BLDSC (3672.140000); EI; Faxon; UnCover; SWETS. **CCC.**
Formerly (1976-1982): Electric Machines and Electromechanics (ISSN 0361-6967)
Description: Theoretical and applied papers covering the field of electric machines and power systems.
Refereed Serial

621.3   US   ISSN 0364-474X
HD9685.U4
ELECTRIC PERSPECTIVES. 1976. bi-m. $35. Edison Electric Institute, 701 Pennsylvania Ave., N.W., Washington, DC 20004-2696. TEL 202-508-5000. FAX 202-508-5030. Ed. Jane Nunnelee. adv.: B&W page $3320, color page $4770. illus. circ. 24,000. (also avail. in microform from UMI,PMC; microfiche from CIS; reprint service avail.) **Indexed:** Acid Rain Abstr., Acid Rain Ind., B.P.I., Bus.Ind., Energy Info.Abstr., Environ.Abstr., INIS Atomind., PROMT, SRI.
—BLDSC (3672.165000); CIS; Faxon; UMI. **CCC.**
Supersedes: E E I Bulletin (ISSN 0012-7604)

621.3   US
HD9685.U5E44
ELECTRIC POWER ALERT. 1991. bi-w. $445 (foreign $495). Inside Washington Publishers, Box 7167, Benjamin Franklin Sta., Washington, DC 20044. TEL 703-892-8500. FAX 703-685-2606. Ed. Rick Weber. (looseleaf format; back issues avail.) **Document type:** newsletter.

621.3   US
ELECTRIC POWER EQUIPMENT REPORT. 1949. a. $20. Edison Electric Institute, Statistics Department, 701 Pennsylvania Ave., N.W., Washington, DC 20004-2696. TEL 202-508-5325. FAX 202-508-5030. Ed. Carl Tobie. charts; illus.; stat. circ. 1,000. (also avail. in microfiche from CIS) **Indexed:** SRI.
Formerly (until 1990): Electric Power Annual Report; **Incorporates (in 1982):** Year-End Summary of the Electric Power Situation in the United States (ISSN 0424-480X); **Former titles:** Annual Electric Power Survey (ISSN 0190-5600); Electric Power Survey (ISSN 0190-5589); Semi-Annual Electric Power Survey (ISSN 0190-5589).
Description: Presents data concerning the expansion of electric generating facilities, and the manufacture of heavy electric power equipment in the U.S. as of the end of the year.

621.3   UN   ISSN 0252-4406
ELECTRIC POWER IN ASIA AND THE PACIFIC. 1971. biennial, latest 1983-84. price varies. United Nations Economic and Social Commission for Asia and the Pacific (ESCAP), United Nations Bldg., Rajadamnern Ave., Bangkok 10200, Thailand. (Dist. by: United Nations Publications, Rm. DC2-0853, New York, NY 10017, USA; or Distribution and Sales Section, Palais des Nations, D-CH-1211 Geneva 10, Switzerland)

621.31 363.62   JA   ISSN 0420-9397
HD9685.J3
ELECTRIC POWER INDUSTRY IN JAPAN/NIHON NO DENKI JIGYO.* (Text in English) 1959. a. Japan Electric Power Information Center - Kaigai Denryoku Chosakai, 15-33, Shibaura 4-chome, Minato-ku, Tokyo 108, Japan.

621.3   US   ISSN 1061-2432
TK1001   CODEN: ELPIEM
ELECTRIC POWER INTERNATIONAL. 1991. q. $50. McGraw-Hill, Inc., 11 W. 19th St., New York, NY 10011. TEL 212-627-3811. FAX 212-243-3241. (Subscr. to: Box 523, Hightstown, NJ 08520-0523) Ed. Jason Makansi. adv. circ. 20,000.
Description: Directed to mechanical, electrical, chemical, civil and nuclear engineers in the electrical utilities, process and manufacturing industries.

621.31   SZ   ISSN 0378-7796
TK1   CODEN: EPSRDN
ELECTRIC POWER SYSTEMS RESEARCH; an international journal devoted to research and new applications in generation, transmission, distribution and utilization of electric power. (Text in English) 1977. 9/yr. (in 3 vols.; 3 nos./vol.). 1245 SFr.($847) (effective 1994). Elsevier Science S.A., P.O. Box 564, CH-1001 Lausanne 1, Switzerland. TEL 41-21-3207381. FAX 41-21-3235444. TELEX 450620-ELSA-CH. (Subscr. in U.S. and Canada to: Elsevier Science Inc., Box 882, Madison Sq. Sta., New York, NY 10159. TEL 212-989-5800. FAX 212-633-3990) Ed. M.E. Council. adv.; bk.rev.; illus.; index. (also avail. in microform from UMI) **Indexed:** A.I.Abstr., CAD CAM Abstr., Cadscan, Chem.Abstr., Curr.Cont., Energy Info.Abstr., Energy Rev., Environ.Abstr., INIS Atomind., Lead Abstr., Sci.Abstr., Sci.Cit.Ind., Zincscan. **Document type:** academic/scholarly publication.
—BLDSC (3672.265000); SWETS. **CCC.**
Description: Publishes original papers concerned with the generation, transmission, distribution, and utilization of electrical energy.
Refereed Serial

621.3   US
ELECTRIC UTILITY POWER PLANT CONSTRUCTION COST. 1980. a. $225 ($495 with data diskette). Utility Data Institute (Subsidiary of: McGraw-Hill), 1200 G St., N.W., Ste. 250, Washington, DC 20005. TEL 202-942-8788; 800-486-3660. FAX 202-942-8789. stat.; index. (also avail. in diskette format) **Document type:** trade publication.
Incorporates (in 1993): Construction Costs: U S Steam Electric Plants; Projected Capital Costs: U S Electric Utility Plants.
Description: Combines historical construction costs of electric generating plants online since 1966 and projected construction costs for utility-owned plants scheduled to enter service during the next 20 years.

621.3   US   ISSN 0736-413X
ELECTRIC UTILITY WEEK; the electric utility industry newsletter. 1970. w. $1225 (U.S. and Canada; elsewhere $1245). McGraw-Hill, Inc., 1221 Ave. of the Americas, New York, NY 10020. TEL 212-512-6410. Ed. Daniel Tanz. charts. (looseleaf format; reprint service avail. from UMI) **Indexed:** Energy Info.Abstr.
●Also available online. Vendor(s): DIALOG Information Services, Inc. (File no.624/McGRAW-HILL PUBLICATIONS ONLINE), Dow Jones News Retrieval (EUW), Mead Data Central, Inc. (ELUTL), NewsNet (EY65).
Formerly: Electrical Week (ISSN 0046-1695)

ELECTRIC VEHICLES. see *TRANSPORTATION*

ELECTRICAL ADVERTISER. see *ENERGY — Electrical Energy*

ELECTRICAL & ELECTRONICS ABSTRACTS. see *ENGINEERING — Abstracting, Bibliographies, Statistics*

621.3   UK   ISSN 0070-9646
ELECTRICAL AND ELECTRONICS TRADES DIRECTORY. 1883. a. Institution of Electrical Engineers, Michael Faraday House, Six Hills Way, Stevenage, Herts SG1 2AY, England. TEL 0438-313311. FAX 0438-742840. adv. **Document type:** directory.
Formerly: Electrical Trades Directory.

683.88   US   ISSN 0190-1370
TK1
ELECTRICAL APPARATUS; magazine of electromechanical operation and maintenance. 1949. m. $35 (includes Electromechanical Bench Reference). Barks Publications, Inc., 400 N. Michigan Ave., Chicago, IL 60611-4198. TEL 312-321-9440. FAX 312-321-1288. Ed. Horace B. Barks. adv.; bk.rev.; film rev.; charts; illus.; stat.; tr.lit. circ. 17,000. **Indexed:** Fuel & Energy Abstr. **Document type:** trade publication.
—BLDSC (3673.390000); SWETS. **CCC.**
Former titles: Electrical Apparatus with Electric Heat; Electric Heat and Air Conditioning (ISSN 0013-4112); Electrical Apparatus Service - Volt-Age (ISSN 0013-4236)

621.3   CN   ISSN 1187-6271
ELECTRICAL BLUEBOOK. 1979. a. Can.$59.95. Kerrwil Publications Ltd., 395 Matheson Blvd. E., Mississauga, ON L4Z 2H2, Canada. TEL 905-890-1845. FAX 905-890-5769. circ. 18,000. **Document type:** trade publication.

621.3   CN   ISSN 0013-4244
ELECTRICAL BUSINESS. 1964. m. Can.$63.13($127.33) Kerrwil Publications Ltd., 395 Matheson Blvd E., Mississauga, ON L4Z 2H2, Canada. TEL 905-890-1846. FAX 905-890-5769. Ed. Hugh McBride. adv. contact: Janet E. Small. illus. circ. 18,000. (tabloid format) **Document type:** trade publication.
Incorporates: Electrical Systems Engineer (ISSN 1182-2872)

621.3   US
ELECTRICAL CONSTRUCTION & MAINTENANCE. Short title: E C & M. 1901. m. $30 (free to qualified personnel). Intertec Publishing Corp., 9800 Metcalf, Overland Park, KS 66212-2215. TEL 913-341-1300. FAX 913-967-1898. Ed. John DeDad. adv.; bk.rev.; charts; illus.; stat. circ. 102,100. **Indexed:** A.S.& T.Ind., Bus.Ind., Eng.Ind., Sci.Abstr., Tr.& Indus.Ind. **Document type:** trade publication.
—BLDSC (3676.000000); EI; Faxon; UnCover; SWETS; UMI. **CCC.**
Description: Design, installation and maintenance of electrical systems.

621.3   US
ELECTRICAL CONTACTS: I E E E HOLM CONFERENCE ON ELECTRICAL CONTACTS (PROCEEDINGS). 1953. a. price varies. (I E E E Components, Hybrids and Manufacturing Technology Society) Institute of Electrical and Electronics Engineers, Inc., 345 E. 47th St., New York, NY 10017-2394. TEL 212-705-7900. FAX 212-705-7682. (Subscr. to: IEEE Service Center, 445 Hoes Lane, Piscataway, NJ 08854) **Document type:** proceedings.
Formerly: Holm Conference on Electrical Contacts (Proceedings).

ENGINEERING — ELECTRICAL ENGINEERING

621.3   UK
ELECTRICAL CONTRACTING NEWS. 1983. m. £30 (overseas £44). Batiste Publications Ltd., Pembroke House, Campsbourne Rd., Hornsey, London N8 7PE, England. TEL 44-81-340 3291. FAX 44-81-341-4840. TELEX 267727 BATGRP. Ed. Ann Windley. (back issues avail.) **Document type:** trade publication.

621.3   US   ISSN 0033-5118
HD9695.U5
ELECTRICAL CONTRACTOR. 1939. m. membership only. National Electrical Contractors Association, 3 Bethesda Metro Center, Ste. 1100, Bethesda, MD 20814. TEL 301-657-3110. FAX 301-961-6495. Ed. Thomas Naber. adv. contact: Joe Salimando. charts; illus.; stat.; tr.lit.; index. circ. 68,000. **Indexed:** PROMT. **Document type:** trade publication.
Formerly: Qualified Contractor.

621.3   UK   ISSN 0308-7174
ELECTRICAL CONTRACTOR (LONDON). 1903. 10/yr. £34 (overseas £43) (effective 1994). E C A Publications (Subsidiary of: Builder Group plc), Builder House 1, Millharbour, London E14 9RA, England. FAX 071-537-2019. (Subscr. to: The Builder Group, Freepost, CN 2792, Bromley BR2 9BR, England. TEL 081-402-8486) Ed. Mark Faithfull. adv. contact: Robbie Christie. bk.rev.; charts; illus.; tr.lit. circ. 10,800. **Indexed:** Br.Tech.Ind., C.I.S. Abstr., Int.Build.Serv.Abstr., Sci.Abstr. **Document type:** trade publication.
—BLDSC (3676.840000); SWETS.
Supersedes (in 1973): Electrical Contractor and Retailer (ISSN 0013-4295)

621.3   UK
ELECTRICAL DESIGN; building electrical services & lighting. 1985. q. £43 (overseas £65) (effective 1994). Builder Group plc, Builder House, 1 Millharbour, London E14 9RA, England. TEL 071-537-2222. FAX 071-537-2007. (Subscr. to: The Builder Group, Freepost, CN 2792, Bromley BR2 9BR, England. TEL 081-402-8486) Ed. Jonathan David. index. circ. 15,204. **Document type:** trade publication.

621.3 338   US   ISSN 1065-7436
ELECTRICAL DESIGN & MANUFACTURING. bi-m. $45 (Canada $60, elsewhere $110). I H S Publishing Group, Inc., 17730 W. Peterson Rd., Box 159, Libertyville, IL 60048-0159. TEL 708-362-8711. FAX 708-362-3484. Ed. Thomas A. Williams. circ. 31,000. (also avail. in microform from UMC)
—BLDSC (3678.240000); EI; UMI. **CCC.**
Former titles: Electrical Manufacturing (ISSN 0895-3716); Electri-Onics - Electrical Manufacturing Edition.
Description: Covers the design, manufacturing, and testing of electrical, electro-mechanical products and all others which are electrically operated, powered, or controlled.

621.3   US   ISSN 0422-8707
TK1
THE ELECTRICAL DISTRIBUTOR. Variant title: T E D. 1964. m. $12. National Association of Electrical Distributors, 45 Danbury Rd., Wilton, CT 06897. TEL 203-834-1908. FAX 203-834-1555. Ed. John J. Foster. adv.; bk.rev.; index; circ. 22,800 (controlled). **Document type:** trade publication.
Description: Trade journal targeted to electrical wholesaler-distributors.

621.38   US
ELECTRICAL - ELECTRONICS INSULATION CONFERENCE. PROCEEDINGS. Short title: E I C. 1958. biennial. price varies. (I E E E, Electrical Insulation Society) Institute of Electrical and Electronics Engineers, Inc., 345 E. 47th St., New York, NY 10017-2394. TEL 212-705-7900. FAX 212-705-7682. (Subscr. to: Box 1331, 445 Hoes Lane, Piscataway, NJ 08855-1331) (Co-sponsor: National Electrical Manufacturers Association) **Document type:** proceedings.
Former titles (1965-1973): Electrical Insulation Conference. Proceedings; (1962-1963): Electrical Insulation Conference: Materials and Applications. Technical Papers; (1958-1960): National Conference on the Application of Electrical Insulation. Technical Papers.
Description: Focuses on products and processes used in the field.

ELECTRICAL - ELECTRONICS INSULATION CONFERENCE. RECORD. see *ELECTRONICS*

621.31   AT   ISSN 0013-4309
ELECTRICAL ENGINEER; power generation, electricity transmission and utilization. 1924. m. Aus.$73. Thomson Business Publishing, 47 Chippen St., Chippendale N.S.W. 2008, Australia. TEL 02-699-2411. FAX 02-698-3920. Ed. Elizabeth Ban. adv.; bk.rev.; illus.; tr.lit.; index. circ. 7,388. (also avail. in microform from UMI; reprint service avail. from UMI) **Indexed:** Aus.Rd.Ind., Chem.Abstr., Eng.Ind., INIS Atomind., Met.Abstr., Sci.Abstr.
—EI; Faxon; UnCover; UMI.

621.3   PH
ELECTRICAL ENGINEER MAGAZINE. 1979. 6/yr. P.150($6) (effective 1992). Institute of Integrated Electrical Engineers of the Philippines, Inc., IIEE Bldg., 41 Monte de Piedad St., Cubao, Quezon City, Philippines 1111. TEL 7227383. FAX 632-7216442. Ed. Victoriano J. Santos. adv.; bk.rev. circ. 6,500.

621.3   US
ELECTRICAL ENGINEERING AND ELECTRONICS SERIES. 1977. irreg., vol.84, 1993. price varies. Marcel Dekker, Inc. 270 Madison Ave., New York, NY 10016. TEL 212-696-9000. FAX 212-685-4540. TELEX 421419 MARDEEK.

621.3   US   ISSN 0424-7760
TK4   CODEN: EENJAU
ELECTRICAL ENGINEERING IN JAPAN. 1963. 7/yr. $1196 (Canada and Mexico $1276; elsewhere $1306). (Institute of Electrical Engineers of Japan, JA) Scripta Technica, Inc. (Subsidiary of: John Wiley & Sons, Inc.), 7961 Eastern Ave., Silver Spring, MD 20910. TEL 301-588-0484. FAX 301-588-5278. (Dist. by: John Wiley & Sons, Inc., Periodicals Division, 650 Third Ave., New York, NY 10158. TEL 212-692-6000) Ed. Yasuji Sekine. adv.; charts; illus.; pat.; index. circ. 400. (also avail. in microform from UMI) **Indexed:** Eng.Ind., INSPEC. **Document type:** academic/scholarly publication.
—BLDSC (3681.105000); EI; Faxon; UnCover; SWETS; UMI. **CCC.**
Description: Covers power generation, transmission and conversion, and electrical machinery.

621.31   UK   ISSN 0013-4317
ELECTRICAL EQUIPMENT. 1961. 10/yr. £30($99) (foreign £50). Wilmington Publishing, Wilmington House, Church Hill, Dartford, Kent UA2 7EF, England. TEL 0322-277788. FAX 0322-276476. (Subscr. to: Ferrari House, 258 Field End Rd., Ruislip, Middx HA4 9UX. TEL 081-868-4499) Ed. Mark Healey. adv.; bk.rev.; charts; illus.; pat.; tr.lit.; index. circ. 30,000. (also avail. in microform from UMI) **Indexed:** BMT, Sci.Abstr.
—BLDSC (3681.170000). **CCC.**
Incorporates: Electrical Equipment Selector (ISSN 0046-1679)

621.3   US   ISSN 0070-9689
ELECTRICAL EQUIPMENT REPRESENTATIVES ASSOCIATION. DIRECTORY. 1951. a. free. Electrical Equipment Representatives Association, c/o John S. McDermott, Ed., 406 W. 34th St., Kansas City, MO 64111-2736. TEL 816-753-0210. FAX 816-753-1954. index; circ. 1,000 (controlled). **Document type:** directory.
Description: Membership directory of electrical manufacturers and members of the association.

(YEAR) ELECTRICAL ESTIMATOR. see *BUILDING AND CONSTRUCTION*

621.3   II   ISSN 0013-435X
  CODEN: EIDAAF
ELECTRICAL INDIA. (Text in English) 1961. fortn. Rs.150. (Indian Electrical Manufacturers' Association) Chary Publications, 14 Sidh Prasad, Ghatkopar Mahul Rd., Tilak Nagar, Bombay 400089, India. Ed. S.T. Chary. adv.; charts; illus. circ. 5,000. **Indexed:** INIS Atomind., Sci.Abstr.
—BLDSC (3681.700000).

621.3   NZ   ISSN 0027-7185
ELECTRICAL INDUSTRY. (Includes Yearbook issue and supplement: Electronic Industry) 1963. m. (11/yr.). NZ.$38.25. Ward Publishing (1988) Ltd., 568 Anglesea St., P.O. Box 9323, Hamilton North, New Zealand. TEL 07-839-1294. FAX 07-834-0390. Ed. Morgan B. Jenkins. Pub. Morgan B. Jenkins. adv.: B&W page NZ.$1384, color page NZ.$1856. bk.rev. circ. 5,000. **Document type:** trade publication.
—CCC.
Description: Covers business management, production development, electrical and electronic technology, new product information, energy efficiency and alternative energy sources.

621.3 918   US
ELECTRICAL MACHINERY: LATIN AMERICAN INDUSTRIAL REPORT. 1985. a. $235 per country report. Aquino Productions, Box 15760, Stamford, CT 06901. TEL 203-325-3138. Ed. Andres C. Aquino.

ELECTRICAL MARKETING NEWSLETTER. see *BUSINESS AND ECONOMICS — Marketing And Purchasing*

621.3   US
ELECTRICAL NEWS. (Editions in Pacific Southwest, Pacific Northwest and Rocky Mountain.) m. $18. Box 3807, Arcadia, CA 91006. TEL 818-446-8652. adv. circ. 21,100.
Description: For wholesale distributors, contractors, and plant engineers.

ELECTRICAL PRODUCT NEWS. see *BUSINESS AND ECONOMICS — Marketing And Purchasing*

621.3   UK   ISSN 0260-1656
ELECTRICAL PRODUCTS. 1978. m. £55 in the UK; Europe £75; elsewhere £100. I M L Group plc, Blair House, High St., Tonbridge, Kent TN9 1BQ, England. TEL 0732-359990. FAX 0732-770049. Ed. James Hunt. adv. circ. 30,390.
—BLDSC (3688.400000).
Incorporates (1962-1992): Electrical Wholesaling (ISSN 0953-9158)

621.3   UK   ISSN 0013-4384
TK1   CODEN: ELREAG
ELECTRICAL REVIEW. 1872. 24/yr. £104.25($271.25) Reed Business Publishing Group (Subsidiary of: Reed Elsevier group), Quadrant House, The Quadrant, Sutton, Surrey SM2 5AS, England. TEL 081-652-3495. FAX 081-652-8951. (Subscr. to: c/o Computer Action, Central House, Park St., Croydon CR0 14D, England. TEL 081-681-8416) Ed. Tim Tunbridge. adv.; bk.rev.; charts; illus.; mkt.; pat.; tr.lit.; index. circ. 15,241. (also avail. in microform from UMI,PMC; reprint service avail. from UMI) **Indexed:** Acid Rain Abstr., Acid Rain Ind., Br.Tech.Ind., C.I.S. Abstr., CAD CAM Abstr. (until 1992), Cadscan, Chem.Abstr., Energy Info.Abstr., Fuel & Energy Abstr., INIS Atomind., Int.Build.Serv.Abstr., Key to Econ.Sci., Lead Abstr., Met.Abstr., PROMT, Robomat. (until 1992), Sci.Abstr., Tel.Abstr., World Alum.Abstr., Zincscan. **Document type:** trade publication.
—BLDSC (3689.000000); EI; Faxon; UnCover; SWETS. **CCC.**
Description: Management magazine for the electrical manufacturing and elecricity uses industries and utilities.

621.3   CN
ELECTRICAL SAFETY BULLETIN. m. Can.$12. Ministry of Municipal Affairs, Recreation and Housing, Victoria, B.C., Canada. (Subscr. to: Crown Publications, 546 Yates St., Victoria, B.C. V8W 1K8, Canada. TEL 604-386-4636)

ELECTRICAL SALES BUILDERS. see *BUSINESS AND ECONOMICS — Marketing And Purchasing*

ENGINEERING — ELECTRICAL ENGINEERING

621.3   UK   ISSN 0965-5433
TK4   CODEN: ELTYEM
ELECTRICAL TECHNOLOGY. English translation of: Elektrichestvo (RU ISSN 0013-5380) 1958. 4/yr. £540($830) (effective 1994). Elsevier Science Ltd., Pergamon, P.O. Box 800, Kidlington, Oxford OX5 1DX, England. TEL 44-865-843000. FAX 44-865-843010. (Subscr. in U.S. and Canada to: Elsevier Science, 660 White Plains Rd., Tarrytown, NY 10591-5153. TEL 914-524-9200. FAX 914-333-2444) Ed. F.B. Hinderwell. adv.; bk.rev.; abstr.; charts; illus. circ. 500. (also avail. in microfilm from UMI; back issues avail.; reprint service avail. from UMI) **Indexed:** Cadscan, Curr.Cont., Eng.Ind., Lead Abstr., Sci.Abstr., Zincscan. **Document type:** academic/scholarly publication.
—SWETS; UMI. **CCC.**
Formerly (until 1992): Electric Technology U.S.S.R. (ISSN 0013-4155)
Description: Covers heavy and light current engineering and energetics. Includes computing techniques and applications of automation to process control.
Refereed Serial

621.3   UK   ISSN 0013-4414
TK1   CODEN: ELTIA4
ELECTRICAL TIMES. 1891. m. £38.25. Reed Business Publishing Group (Subsidiary of: Reed Elsevier group), Quadrant House, The Quadrant, Sutton, Surrey SM2 5AS, England. TEL 081-652-8735. FAX 081-652-8972. TELEX 892084-REEDBP-G. (Subscr. to: c/o Computer Action, Central House, Park St., Croydon CR0 14D, England. TEL 081-681-8416) Ed. Bill Evett. adv.; bk.rev.; charts; illus.; mkt.; tr.lit.; tr.mk.; s-a. index. circ. 15,000. (tabloid format; also avail. in microfilm from UMI; reprint service avail. from UMI) **Indexed:** Br.Tech.Ind., C.I.S. Abstr., Cadscan, Energy Info.Abstr., Geo.Abstr., Int.Build.Serv.Abstr., Lead Abstr., Met.Abstr., PROMT, Sci.Abstr., World Alum.Abstr., Zincscan. **Document type:** trade publication.
—BLDSC (3691.000000); CIS. **CCC.**
Description: Technical, commercial and governmental data of value to contractors in the UK.

ELECTRICAL UNION WORLD. see *LABOR UNIONS*

621.3   UK   ISSN 0013-4422
ELECTRICAL WHOLESALER. 1962. m. £25.50 (overseas £35). Batiste Publications Ltd., Pembroke House, Campsbourne Rd., Hornsey, London N8 7PE, England. TEL 44-81-340-3291. FAX 44-81-341-4840. TELEX 267727 BATGRP. Ed. S. Vassie. adv. circ. 4,500. **Document type:** trade publication.

ELECTRICAL WHOLESALING. see *BUSINESS AND ECONOMICS — Marketing And Purchasing*

621.3   US   ISSN 0013-4457
TK1   CODEN: ELWOA3
ELECTRICAL WORLD. 1874. m. $55 in U.S.; Canada $60; elsewhere $110. McGraw-Hill, Inc., 1221 Ave. of the Americas, New York, NY 10020. TEL 212-512-3288. (Subscr. to: Box 513, Hightstown, NJ 08520) Ed. Robert Schwieger. adv.; charts; illus.; mkt.; tr.lit.; s-a. index. circ. 45,398. (also avail. in microform from UMI, PMC; microfiche from CIS; reprint service avail. from UMI) **Indexed:** A.S.& T.Ind., ABI Inform., Acad.Ind., Acid Rain Abstr., Acid Rain Ind., B.P.I., C.I.S. Abstr., CAD CAM Abstr., Chem.Abstr., Energy Info.Abstr., Eng.Ind., Excerp.Med., Fuel & Energy Abstr., Ind.Sci.Rev., INIS Atomind., Mag.Ind., Met.Abstr., PROMT, Sci.Abstr., SRI, Tr.& Indus.Ind.
—BLDSC (3692.000000); CIS; EI; Faxon; UnCover; SWETS; UMI. **CCC.**
Description: For management and engineers in the electrical power industry.

621.3   US
ELECTRICAL WORLD DIRECTORY OF ELECTRIC UTILITIES. 1892? a. $365. McGraw-Hill, Inc., 1221 Ave. of the Americas, New York, NY 10020. Ed. Ann Hayes. stat.; circ. controlled.

621.3   KO
ELECTRICAL YEARBOOK/JUNKI YONKAM. 1965. a. 35000 Won. Korean Electrical Association, 11-4 Supyo-dong, Chung-ku, Seoul 100, S. Korea. FAX 02-277-5174. Ed. Ryu In-yonge. adv.; bk.rev. circ. 4,000.

621.3   PO   ISSN 0870-5364
ELECTRICIDADE. 1957. m. $100 (effective Jan. 1993). Empresa Editorial Electrotecnica Edel, Ltda., Rua de Dona Estefania 48, 3 Esq, 1000 Lisbon, Portugal. TEL 351-1-528608. FAX 351-1-3561640. Ed. Herminio Duarte-Ramos. adv.; bk.rev.; charts; illus.; stat. circ. 4,000. **Indexed:** Sci.Abstr. **Document type:** trade publication.
Former titles: Electricidade, Energia, Electronica (ISSN 0253-3367); Electricidade (ISSN 0013-4465)

621.3   PO
ELECTRICISTA. 12/yr. Rua Alves da Costa, Lote 6, Loja Esq. Bons Dias, 2675 Odivelas, Portugal. TEL 1-932-7492. Ed. Nunes Ribeiro. circ. 10,000.

621.3   BE   ISSN 0013-4481
                           CODEN: LCTRDE
ELECTRICITE/ELEKTRICITEIT. (Text in Flemish, French) 1930. s-a. free. Union des Exploitations Electriques et Gazieres en Belgique, Galerie Ravenstein 4, Bte. 6, B-1000 Brussels, Belgium. TEL 02-511-19-70. FAX 02-511-29-38. TELEX 62409 UEBRE B. Ed. Robert Mathieu. adv.; charts; illus.; stat. circ. 8,200. **Indexed:** Fuel & Energy Abstr., INIS Atomind., Met.Abstr., Sci.Abstr.
—BLDSC (3694.995000); CASDDS.

621.3 629.286   FR   ISSN 0291-8234
ELECTRICITE AUTOMOBILE. 1946. bi-m. 420 F. Electricite Automobile, 59 rue du Faubourg Poissonniere, 75009 Paris, France. TEL 48-24-66-88. FAX 48-24-19-40. Ed. Jany Chabrand. adv.; illus. **Indexed:** Sci.Abstr.

621.3   FR   ISSN 1161-0581
ELECTRICITE DE FRANCE. DIRECTION DES ÉTUDES ET RECHERCHES. COLLECTION DE NOTES INTERNES. MATERIEL ELECTRIQUE TRANSPORT ET DISTRIBUTION D'ENERGIE. (Text in French; summaries in English, French) 1966. irreg. 4000 F. Electricite de France (EDF), Direction des Etudes et Recherches, 1 av. du General de Gaulle, 92141 Clamart Cedex, France. TEL 1-47-65-43-21. FAX 1-47-65-31-24. TELEX 204 347 F. charts; illus. circ. 1,500. **Indexed:** Eng.Ind., INIS Atomind., Sci.Abstr.
—EI.
Supersedes (in 1992): Electricite de France. Direction des Etudes et Recherches. Bulletin. Serie B: Reseaux Electriques, Materiels Electriques (ISSN 0013-4503)

621.3   FR
▼**ELECTRICITE DE FRANCE. DIRECTION DES ETUDES ET RECHERCHES. COLLECTION DE NOTES INTERNES. UTILISATIONS DE L'ELECTRICITE.** 1992. irreg. 1500 F. Electricite de France (EDF), Direction des Etudes et Recherches, 1 av. du General de Gaulle, 92140 Clamart, France. TEL 1-47-65-43-21. FAX 1-47-65-31-24. TELEX 204 347 F.

338 537   FR   ISSN 0070-9735
ELECTRICITE DE FRANCE. RAPPORT D'ACTIVITE. 1950. a. Electricite de France, Service de l'Information et des Relations Publiques, 2 rue Louis Murat, 75384 Paris Cedex 08, France.

ELECTRICITE DE FRANCE. STATISTIQUES DE LA PRODUCTION ET DE LA CONSOMMATION. see *ENGINEERING — Abstracting, Bibliographies, Statistics*

ELECTRICITY AND ELECTRONICS. see *ELECTRONICS*

621.3   II   ISSN 0970-2318
ELECTRICITY CONSERVATION QUARTERLY. 1980. q. Rs.150 (foreign $30). Devki R & D Engineers, Offtel Towers, R.C. Dutt Rd., Baroda 390 005, India. TEL 0265-330066. FAX 0265-325686. TELEX 0175-6423 OFTL IN. Ed.Bd. adv.; bk.rev.; abstr.; charts; illus.; pat.; stat.; tr.lit. circ. 1,000. **Indexed:** Eng.Ind. **Document type:** academic/scholarly publication.
—BLDSC (3697.100000); EI.
Description: Covers energy conservation and other environmental issues.

621.3   UK   ISSN 0261-2127
ELECTRICITY CONSUMERS COUNCIL. ANNUAL REPORT.* 1979. a. Electricity Association, 30 Millbank, London SW1P 4RD, England.

621.3   US   ISSN 0955-5439
ELECTRICITY INTERNATIONAL. 1988. m. £55($100) I C O M, ICOM House, 17A Woodcote Rd., Wallington, Surrey SM6 0LH, England. Ed. Richard Hopper. adv. circ. 11,125. (back issues avail.)
—BLDSC (3598.105200).

621.3   CN   ISSN 0843-7343
                           CODEN: ELTDER
ELECTRICITY TODAY. 1989. 10/yr. Can.$27($33) Canadian Electricity Forum, 345 Kingston Rd., Ste. 101, Pickering, ON L1V 1A1, Canada. TEL 905-509-4448. FAX 905-509-4451. adv. circ. 12,000. **Document type:** trade publication.
Description: Dedicated to addressing the major policy and technical issues common to both Canada's electricity producers and Canada's major electricity consumers.

621.38   UK   ISSN 0960-3794
ELECTRICITY U K. 1968. q. free. Electricity Association, Public and Employment Affairs Division, 30 Millbank, London SW1P 4RD, England. TEL 071-344-5878. FAX 071-344-5967. Ed. B. Phillips. adv.; bk.rev.; illus. circ. 9,000. **Document type:** trade publication.
Formerly (until 1990): Circuit News (ISSN 0009-7292)

621.3   SP   ISSN 0212-6818
ELECTRO-OCIO. 1983. m. 1800 ptas.($30) Ediciones Ingelek, S.A., Apdo. de Correos 61294, Madrid, Spain. Ed. Antonio Ma. Ferrer. adv.; bk.rev. circ. 16,000.

621.3   SZ   ISSN 0374-3101
ELECTRO-REVUE. (Text in French and German) 1908. w. 100 SFr. Verband Schweizerischer Elektroinstallationsfirmen, Postfach 3357, CH-8031 Zurich, Switzerland. FAX 01-2714847. Ed. H. Lindauer. adv.; bk.rev. circ. 4,700. **Indexed:** INIS Atomind., Sci.Abstr. **Document type:** trade publication.
Description: Trade publication for electrical contractors focusing on energy, energy politics, energy conservation, computerization. Includes seminar reports and positions available.

686.83   BE
ELECTRO-REVUE. (Text in Dutch, French) 1935. m. A.N.P.E.B., Rue du Serpoiet 2, Bte. 1, B-1080 Brussels, Belgium. TEL 32-2-4109592. FAX 32-2-4111350. Ed. P. Carette. adv. circ. 2,000.

621.38   II   ISSN 0013-4643
                           CODEN: ELTEAQ
ELECTRO-TECHNOLOGY. (Text in English) 1957. q. membership (Rs.500 in India; elsewhere $50). Society of Electronic Engineers, Box 9324, LRDE, DRDO Complex, CV Raman Nagar, Bangalore 560 093, India. TEL 091-0812-580908. FAX 091-0812-582916. Ed. Kuldip Singh. adv.; bk.rev.; abstr.; bibl.; charts; illus.; cum.index every 5 yrs. circ. 2,000. **Indexed:** Chem.Abstr., Excerp.Med., Sci.Abstr.
—BLDSC (3709.540000).

621.3   US   ISSN 0275-7230
                           CODEN: ESMOD5
ELECTROCOMPONENT SCIENCE MONOGRAPHS. 1981. irreg., vol.7, 1986. Gordon & Breach Science Publishers, 820 Town Center Dr., Langhorne, PA 19047. TEL 215-750-2642. FAX 215-750-6343. (UK subscr. to: P.O. Box 90, Reading, Berkshire RG1 8JL, England. TEL 0734-560-080) Ed. D. Campbell. **Document type:** monographic series.
Refereed Serial

621.3   US   ISSN 0270-4935
ELECTROMAGNETIC NEWS REPORT. 1972. a. $59 in N. America; elsewhere $75 (typically set in July). Seven Mountains Scientific, Inc., Box 650, Boalsburg, PA 16827. TEL 814-466-6559. FAX 814-466-6559. Ed. Josephine Chesworth. adv.; bk.rev. circ. 1,000. **Document type:** trade publication.
Description: Presents technical articles and summaries of news about electromagnetic compatibility.

ENGINEERING — ELECTRICAL ENGINEERING

537 US ISSN 0272-6343
QC759.6 CODEN: ETRMDV
ELECTROMAGNETICS. 1981. q. $165. Taylor & Francis, 1900 Frost Rd., Ste. 101, Bristol, PA 19007-1598. TEL 800-821-8312. FAX 215-758-5515. Ed. Nicolaos G. Alexopolous. adv.; bibl.; charts; illus.; index. circ. 375. (back issues avail.; reprint service avail. from UMI) **Indexed:** Curr.Cont., Int.Aerosp.Abstr., Sci.Abstr. **Document type:** academic/scholarly publication.
—BLDSC (3699.570000); EI; Faxon; UnCover; SWETS. **CCC.**
  Description: Presents a broad range pf papers about electromagnetics.
  Refereed Serial

621.3 US
ELECTROMECHANICAL BENCH REFERENCE. 1974. a. $15 included in Electrical Apparatus. Barks Publications, Inc., 400 N. Michigan Ave., Chicago, IL 60611-4198. TEL 312-321-9440. FAX 312-321-1288. Ed. Jackie Tithof. adv.; bk.rev. circ. 17,000. **Document type:** trade publication.
  Refereed Serial

621.3 US ISSN 0965-2035
TK5105 CODEN: ELDOEE
▼**ELECTRONIC DOCUMENTS.** (Supplement avail.: Electronic Documents News Bulletin) 1992. m. $179 in U.S.; Canada and Mexico $189 (effective Oct. 1992). Learned Information, Inc., 143 Old Marlton Pike, Medford, NJ 08055-8750. TEL 609-654-6266. FAX 609-654-4309. Ed. Peter Hyams. illus.
—BLDSC (3700.865000); Faxon; SWETS.
  Description: Reviews a particular technology used to store and disseminate information electronically, from image filing to hypertext to fax on demand.

ELECTRONIC ENGINEERING. see *ELECTRONICS*

ELECTRONIC ENGINEERING INDEX. see *ELECTRONICS*

621.38 UK ISSN 0263-1474
  CODEN: EPDEDB
ELECTRONIC PRODUCT DESIGN. 1980. m. £55 in the UK; Europe £70; elsewhere £100. I M L Group plc, Blair House, High St., Tonbridge, Kent TN9 1BQ, England. TEL 0732-359990. FAX 0732-77049. TELEX 892759 TECPCO G. Ed. Graham Prophet. adv. contact: Colin Martin. bk.rev./ circ. 23,830 (controlled). **Indexed:** Fluidex, Sci.Abstr.
—BLDSC (3702.686500); EI; Faxon.

ELECTRONICS AND ELECTRICAL ENGINEERING. see *ELECTRONICS*

ELECTRONICS MANUFACTURERS DIRECTORY. see *BUSINESS AND ECONOMICS — Trade And Industrial Directories*

ELECTRONOTES. see *MUSIC*

ELECTROTECHNICAL LABORATORY. BULLETIN/DENSHI GIJUTSU SOGO KENKYUJO IHO. see *COMPUTERS*

621.38 SP ISSN 0013-5313
ELECTROTECNIA POPULAR.* m. 128 ptas. Escuela Radio Maymo, Pelayo 18, Barcelona-1, Spain. circ. 15,000. (processed)

621.38 SP
ELEKTOR. 1980. m. (11/yr.). 2750 ptas.($36) Ediciones Ingelek, S.A., Plaza Republica del Ecuador 2, 1o B, 28016 Madrid, Spain. TEL 457-69-23. FAX 1-458-18-76. Ed. Antonio M. Ferrer Abello. adv.; bk.rev. circ. 17,139. **Indexed:** Ind.SST.

621.3 RU ISSN 0013-5372
  CODEN: EKSTAP
ELEKTRICHESKIE STANTSII. (English translation: Advances in Soviet Power Systems. Part 1: Thermal and Mechanical (ISSN 0888-4536), and Part 2: Electrical Generation and Distribution (ISSN 0888-4544)) 1929. m. 42.60 Rub. Izdatel'stvo Energiya, Slyuzovaya nab., 10, Moscow 2-114, Russia. (Co-sponsor: Ministerstvo Energetiki i Elektrifikatsii) Ed. D.G. Kotilevskii. adv.; bk.rev.; bibl.; charts; illus.; stat.; index. circ. 9,000. **Indexed:** Chem.Abstr., INIS Atomind., Sci.Abstr.
—**CCC.**

621.3 RU ISSN 0013-5380
TK4 CODEN: ELEKA3
ELEKTRICHESTVO. English translation: Electric Technology (US ISSN 0965-5433) (Text in Russian; contents page in English) 1880. m. 42.60 Rub. (Rossiiskaya Akademiya Nauk) Izdatel'stvo Nauka, 90 Profsoyuznaya ul., 117864 Moscow, Russia. Ed. D.V. Razevig. adv.; bk.rev.; bibl.; charts; illus.; index. circ. 10,920. **Indexed:** Chem.Abstr., Eng.Ind., INIS Atomind., Sci.Abstr.
—BLDSC (0398.690000); CASDDS. **CCC.**

621.3 GW ISSN 0013-5399
TK3 CODEN: EKTRAO
ELEKTRIE; wissenschaftlich-technische Zeitschrift der Elektrotechnik. (Includes section Aktuelle Information) (Text in German) 1947. m. DM.160 (foreign DM.173.20). Dr. Heide und Partner GmbH, Enckevortweg 7, 10319 Berlin, Germany. TEL 030-5122236. Ed. Klaus Heide. adv.; bk.rev.; abstr.; charts; illus.; index. circ. 3,300. **Indexed:** C.I.S. Abstr., Chem.Abstr., INIS Atomind., Met.Abstr., Sci.Abstr., World Alum.Abstr. **Document type:** academic/scholarly publication.
—BLDSC (3710.710000); SWETS; CASDDS.
  Description: Technical journal of electrical engineering.

621.3 TU ISSN 0013-5402
ELEKTRIK MUHENDISLIGI. (Text in Turkish; summaries in English) 1956. m. TL.10000($25) Institute of Electrical Engineers - Elektrik Muhendisleri Odasi, Ihlamur Sokak 10-1, Yenisehir, Ankara, Turkey. Ed. Aybars Ungan. adv.; bk.rev.; charts; illus.; index. circ. 15,000. **Indexed:** Elec.& Electron.Abstr.

621.3 NO ISSN 0013-5410
ELEKTRIKEREN. vol.49, 1970. 11/yr. NOK 15. Norsk Elektriker- og Kraftstasjonforbund, Youngsgate 11, N-0181 Oslo, Norway. FAX 47-22-20-20-75. Ed. Nils Waag. adv.; illus. circ. 28,000. **Document type:** trade publication.
—**CCC.**

537 DK ISSN 0900-8268
ELEKTRIKEREN. 1908. m. Dansk El Forbund, Vodroffsvej 26, DK-1900 Copenhagen V, Denmark. TEL 45-31-21-14-00. FAX 45-31-21-84-00. adv. circ. 30,000. **Document type:** trade publication.
  Description: For electricians. Carries articles on education and training, employment, new technology and other relevant professional questions.

621.3 SW ISSN 0345-2816
ELEKTRIKERN. 1907. m. SEK 300 (effective 1990). Svenska Elektrikerfoerbundet, P.O. Box 1123, S-111 81 Stockholm, Sweden. **Document type:** trade publication.

ELEKTRISCHE BAHNEN; Zeitschrift fuer Elektrotechnik im Verkehrswesen. see *TRANSPORTATION — Railroads*

537 GW ISSN 0170-2033
ELEKTRISCHE ENERGIE TECHNIK. 1955. 6/yr. DM.112 (foreign DM.123). Huethig GmbH, Postfach 102869, 69018 Heidelberg, Germany. TEL 06221-489-0. FAX 06221-489482. TELEX 461727-HUEHD-D. Ed. W. Leidig. adv.; B&W page DM.5400; trim 210 x 297; adv. contact: Horst Schuerer. circ. 10,901. **Indexed:** C.I.S. Abstr., INIS Atomind. **Document type:** trade publication.
—BLDSC (3711.080000). **CCC.**
  Description: Trade journal for energy management and operational engineering.

621.3 380.3 GW ISSN 1242-0557
ELEKTRISCHES NACHRICHTENWESEN; technisch-wissenschaftliche Zeitschrift. 1962. q. Alcatel S E L AG, Abt. ZOE-EN, Lorenzstr. 10, 70435 Stuttgart, Germany. TEL 0711-821-4690. FAX 0711-821-6055. Ed. Andreas Ortelt. circ. 7,200. **Document type:** academic/scholarly publication.
  Formerly: Elektrische Nachrichten.

621.3 GW ISSN 0013-5496
TK3 CODEN: EKZWAZ
ELEKTRIZITAETSWIRTSCHAFT. 1901. s-m. DM.424. (Vereinigung Deutscher Elektrizitaetswerke e.V.) Verlags- und Wirtschaftsgesellschaft der Elektrizitaetswerke mbH, Stresemannallee 30, 60596 Frankfurt a.M., Germany. TEL 069-6304-311. FAX 069-6304359. TELEX 411284-VDEW. Ed. G. Andreas. adv.; bk.rev.; charts; illus.; stat.; index, cum.index: 1949-1960. **Indexed:** Chem.Abstr., Eng.Ind., Excerp.Med., Fuel & Energy Abstr., INIS Atomind., Sci.Abstr. **Document type:** trade publication.
—EI; SWETS. **CCC.**

621.3 NO ISSN 0013-550X
TK4 CODEN: EEROAV
ELEKTRO. 1886. 10/yr. NOK 330. (Norsk Elektroteknisk Forening - Norwegian Electrotechnical Society; Association of Norwegian Supply Undertakers) Ingenioerforlaget AS, P.O. Box 2476, P.O. Box 2476, Solli, N-0202 Oslo, Norway. TEL 47-22-94-76-00. FAX 47-22-94-76-01. (Co-sponsor: Norske Elektrisitetsverkers Forening) Ed. Finn Halvorsen. adv.; bk.rev.; charts; illus.; pat.; tr.lit.; index. circ. 15,300. (back issues avail.) **Indexed:** Eng.Ind., Fuel & Energy Abstr., INIS Atomind., Sci.Abstr. **Document type:** academic/scholarly publication.
—BLDSC (3715.200000). **CCC.**
  Formerly (until 1948): Elektroteknisk Tidsskrift (ISSN 0374-2946)

621.38 GW
ELEKTRO AUTOMATION. 1947. m. DM.93 (foreign DM.103.80). Konradin-Verlag Robert Kohlhammer GmbH, Ernst-Mey-Str. 8, 70771 Leinfelden-Echterdingen, Germany. TEL 0711-7594-0. FAX 0711-7594-390. Eds. Ronald Heinze, Helmut Klewe. adv.; B&W page DM.7200, color page DM.9250; trim 190 x 270; adv. contact: Klaus Paletta. bk.rev.; charts; illus.; stat. circ. 21,100. **Indexed:** INIS Atomind., Sci.Abstr. **Document type:** trade publication.
—**CCC.**
  Formerly: Elektro-Anzeiger (ISSN 0013-5518)
  Description: Provides information on companies, developments, and new and improved products in the electrical engineering and electronics industries.

683.83 GW ISSN 0343-3463
ELEKTRO BOERSE; Fach-Zeitschrift fuer Handel und Handwerk. 1948. m. DM.55. Media-Mail Verlagsgesellschaft, Postfach 2453, 96413 Coburg, Germany. TEL 0511-345358. TELEX 663241. Ed. Fred Friedrich. circ. 12,000. **Document type:** trade publication.

621.38 AU
ELEKTRO JOURNAL. m. S.628. (Bundesinnung der Elektro-, Radio- und Fernsehtechniker) Oesterreichischer Wirtschaftsverlag, Nikolsdorfer Gasse 7-11, A-1051 Vienna, Austria. TEL 0222-555585. TELEX 1-11669. Ed. Willy Duschka. adv.; illus. circ. 8,600. **Indexed:** C.I.S. Abstr.
  Former titles: Elektro and Radio (ISSN 0029-9855); Oesterreichisches Elektro- und Radio-Gewerbe.

537 NO
ELEKTRO MED ELEKTRONIK. 1888. 22/yr. Ingeniorforlaget AS, Kronprinsengate 17, P.O. Box 2476 Solli, Oslo 2, Norway. Ed. Truls Fallet. adv. circ. 13,800.

621.3 GW ISSN 0424-8562
DAS ELEKTROFACH; die Fachzeitschrift fuer Beleuchtung, Geraete und Installation. 1958. m. DM.81.60. (Bundesverband des Beleuchtungs- und Elektroeinzelhandels e.V.) Futura-Verlag, Graf-Adolf Str. 81, 40210 Dusseldorf, Germany. FAX 0211-38703-23. TELEX 8586486. adv.; bk.rev. circ. 15,300. **Document type:** trade publication.

621.3 GW ISSN 0420-9885
DER ELEKTROFACHMANN; Fachorgan der Elekto-Innung Berlin. 1953. m. membership. (Elektro-Innung, Berlin) Huethig und Pflaum Verlag, Lazarettstr. 4, 80636 Munich, Germany. TEL 089-12607240. FAX 089-12607200. (Subscr. to: Im Weiher 10, 6900 Heidelberg, Germany. TEL 06221-489281) Ed. Manfred Ladendorf. adv.; bk.rev.; charts; illus.; tr.lit.; index. circ. 1,960. **Document type:** trade publication.
—**CCC.**

ENGINEERING — ELECTRICAL ENGINEERING

621.3   SA
ELEKTRON. (Text in Afrikaans and English) 1984. m. R.90. South African Institute of Electrical Engineers, P.O. Box 93541, Yeoville 2143, South Africa. TEL 27-11-487-3003. FAX 27-11-487-3002. Ed.Bd. adv.; bk.rev.; illus. circ. 4,400. (back issues avail.) **Indexed:** Ind.S.A.Per., INIS Atomind. **Document type:** trade publication.
Description: Devoted to improving the quality of electrical and electronic engineering in South Africa.

ELEKTRONIKVAERLDEN; hi-fi, video, datorer, praktisk elektronik. see *COMMUNICATIONS*

621.38   GW   ISSN 0013-5569
ELEKTROPRAKTIKER; Fachzeitschrift fuer den Praktiker der Starkstromtechnik in Industrie und Handwerk. 1947. m. DM.54. Verlag Technik GmbH, Am Friedrichshain 22, 10407 Berlin, Germany. TEL 030-4287-0. FAX 030-4261249. Ed. Wolfgang Roenspiess. adv.: B&W page DM.6200; trim 185 x 266; adv. contact: Guenter Fitzner. bk.rev.; charts; illus.; tr.lit.; index. circ. 31,266. **Indexed:** C.I.S. Abstr., Dok.Arbeitsmed. **Document type:** trade publication.
Description: For those in industrial power engineering and allied fields.

621.38   YU
ELEKTROPRIVREDA JUGOSLAVIJE. (Text in Serbocroatian; summaries in English, French, German, Macedonian, Russian and Slovenian) 1949. bi-m. 240 din.($18) Zajednica Jugoslovenske Elektroprivrede, Balkanska 13-15, Belgrade, Serbia, Yugoslavia. Ed. Dusan Cuckovic. adv.; bk.rev.; bibl.; stat.; index. circ. 1,300. **Indexed:** INIS Atomind., Sci.Abstr.
—BLDSC (3718.300000).
Formerly: Elektroprivreda (ISSN 0013-5755)

ELEKTROSVYAZ'. see *COMMUNICATIONS*

621.38   XO   ISSN 0013-578X
CODEN: ELKCA9
ELEKTROTECHNICKY CASOPIS/ELECTROTECHNICAL JOURNAL. (Text in Slovak) 1949. m. 216 Kcs.($40) (Slovenska Akademia Vied) Veda, Publishing House of the Slovak Academy of Sciences, Klemensova 19, 814 30 Bratislava, Slovakia. (Subscr. to: Slovart, Nam. Slobody 6, 17 64 Bratislava, Slovakia) Ed. Oldrich Benda. bk.rev.; charts; illus.; index. circ. 1,200. **Indexed:** Chem.Abstr., INIS Atomind., Sci.Abstr.
—BLDSC (3718.900000); CASDDS.
Description: Deals with the problems of all electrotechnical branches, especially with those of heavy current, light-current and high frequency as well as with questions of theoretical high frequency, theoretical physics.

621.38   XR   ISSN 0013-5798
TK4   CODEN: EKOBAJ
ELEKTROTECHNICKY OBZOR/ELEKTROTECHNICAL REVIEW. (Text in Czech; contents page and summaries also in English, French, German and Russian) 1910. m. $58.40. Nakladatelstvi Technicke Literatury, Spalena 51, 113 02 Prague 1, Czech Republic. (Dist. by: Artia, Ve Smeckach 30, 111 27 Prague 1, Czech Republic) Ed. Josef Herman. adv.; bk.rev.; charts; illus.; pat.; tr.lit.; index. circ. 3,200. **Indexed:** C.I.S. Abstr., Chem.Abstr., Eng.Ind., INIS Atomind., Met.Abstr., Sci.Abstr.
—CASDDS.

621.3   GW   ISSN 0013-581X
CODEN: EKTCBE
ELEKTROTECHNIK. 1919. 10/yr. DM.115. Vogel Verlag und Druck KG, Max-Planck-Str. 7-9, 97082 Wuerzburg, Germany. TEL 0931-4182145. FAX 0931-4182640. (Subscr. to: Vogel Verlag, 97064 Wuerzburg, Germany; Dist. in U.S. by: Vogel Europublishing, Inc., 20092 Gibbs Dr., Sonora, CA 95370. TEL 209-533-3555. FAX 209-533-9555) Ed. Ernst Pohl. adv.: B&W page DM.6680, color page DM.8765; trim 270 x 190. bk.rev.; charts; illus.; pat.; stat.; index; circ. 16,000 (controlled). **Indexed:** C.I.S. Abstr., Cyb.Abstr., Excerp.Med., INIS Atomind., Key to Econ.Sci., Sci.Abstr. **Document type:** trade publication.
—BLDSC (3719.100000). **CCC.**

621.3   SZ
ELEKTROTECHNIK. 1950. 11/yr. 75 SFr. Verlag Aargauer Tagblatt AG, Bahnhofstrasse 39-43, CH-5001 Aarau, Switzerland. Ed. Hans Rudolf Ris. adv.; bk.rev.; abstr.; illus.; pat.; tr.lit.; index. circ. 7,950. **Indexed:** Sci.Abstr.
—BLDSC (3718.990000).
Supersedes (from vol.27, no.9, 1976):
Elektromonteur (ISSN 0046-1784)

621.38   XR
ELEKTROTECHNIK/ELECTROTECHNICIAN. (Text in Czech; summaries in German and Russian) 1946. m. $40. Nakladatelstvi Technicke Literatury, Spalena 51, 113 02 Prague 1, Czech Republic. (Dist. by: Artia, Ve Smeckach 30, 111 27 Prague 1, Czech Republic) Ed. Emil Sirucek. illus. circ. 22,000. **Indexed:** Sci.Abstr. **Document type:** trade publication.

621.38   HU   ISSN 0367-0708
TK4   CODEN: EKTTAU
ELEKTROTECHNIKA/ELECTRICAL ENGINEERING. (Text in Hungarian; summaries in English, German and Russian) 1908. m. $40.50. (Magyar Elektrotechnikai Egyesulet - Electrotechnical Association) Lapkiado Vallalat, Lenin Korut 9-11, 1073 Budapest 7, Hungary. TEL 222-408. (Subscr. to: Kultura, Box 149, H-1389 Budapest, Hungary) Ed. Tibor Kelemen. circ. 3,000. **Indexed:** INIS Atomind., Met.Abstr., Sci.Abstr., World Alum.Abstr.
—BLDSC (3721.000000).

ELEKTROTECHNIKAI SZAKIRODALMI TAJEKOZTATO/ELECTRICAL ENGINEERING ABSTRACTS. see *ENGINEERING — Abstracting, Bibliographies, Statistics*

621.38   CI   ISSN 0013-5844
CODEN: ELTHB2
ELEKTROTEHNIKA. (Issued also as part of Tehnika) (Text in Serbo-Croatian; summaries in English, Russian) 1958. m. 35000 din.($50) Savez Inzenjera i Tehnicara Jugoslavije, Berislaviceva 6, 41000 Zagreb, Croatia. Ed. Predrag Anastasijevic. adv.; bk.rev.; index. circ. 2,000. **Indexed:** INIS Atomind.
—BLDSC (3722.900000); CASDDS.

621.3   XV   ISSN 0013-5852
CODEN: ELVEA2
ELEKTROTEHNISKI VESTNIK/ELEKTROTECHNICAL REVIEW; revija za elektrotehniko. (Text in English or Slovenian; summaries in English) 1931. 5/yr. $40. Elektrotehniska Zveza Slovenije, Trzaska 25, Box 92-II, 61001 Ljubljana, Slovenia. TELEX 31573 ELEFAK YU. Ed. Baldomir Zajc. adv.; bk.rev.; charts; illus.; index. circ. 4,300. **Indexed:** Bull.Signal., Eng.Ind., Ref.Zh., Sci.Abstr.
—EI.

621.3   RU   ISSN 0013-5860
CODEN: ELKTAQ
ELEKTROTEKHNIKA. English translation: Russian Electrical Engineering (US ISSN 1068-3712) 1928. m. 37.80 Rub. Ministerstvo Elektricheskoi Promyshlennosti, Moscow, Russia. Ed. G.N. Petrov. adv.; bk.rev.; charts; illus. circ. 6,500. **Indexed:** Chem.Abstr., Eng.Ind., INIS Atomind., Sci.Abstr.
—BLDSC (0399.060000); CASDDS. **CCC.**

621.3   GW   ISSN 0340-3521
TK4601   CODEN: EIEBDQ
ELEKTROWAERME INTERNATIONAL. PART B: INDUSTRIELLE ELEKTROWAERME. (Text in German; summaries in English and German) 1931. 4/yr. DM.125 (combined subscr. Parts A & B DM.230). Vulkan-Verlag GmbH, Postfach 103962, 45039 Essen, Germany. TEL 0201-82002-0. FAX 0201-82002-40. Ed.Bd. adv.; bk.rev.; abstr.; bibl.; charts; illus.; pat.; tr.lit.; index. circ. 4,000. **Indexed:** Chem.Abstr., Eng.Ind., Excerp.Med., INIS Atomind., Met.Abstr., Sci.Abstr. **Document type:** trade publication.
—BLDSC (3725.974000); SWETS; CASDDS. **CCC.**
Supersedes in part: Elektrowaerme International (ISSN 0020-9147); Which was formerly: International Zeitschrift fuer Elektrowaerme.
Description: Covers the entire field of electro-heat in industry and the design and construction of electric furnaces and industrial electric heating equipment.

621.3   GW   ISSN 0013-5887
ELEKTROWIRTSCHAFT. 1946. s-m. DM.90. (Bundesverband des Elektro-Grosshandels (VEG) e.V.) Fachverlag Dr. Helmut Arnold GmbH, Siegburgstr. 5-7, 44359 Dortmund-Mengede, Germany. Ed. H. Arnold. adv.; bk.rev.; illus. circ. 4,750.

621.31   NO   ISSN 0802-3212
ELENTREPENOEREN. 1950. m. (10/yr.). NOK 350 (typically set in May-June). Norges Elektroentreprenoerforbund (NELFO) - Norwegian Electrical Contractors Association, St. Olavs gt. 21B, P. O. Box 6794, St. Olavs Plass, N-0130 Oslo, Norway. TEL 47-22-20-27-53. FAX 47-22-36-09-47. Ed. Truls Hauger. adv.: B&W page NOK 6500, color page NOK 11900; trim185 x 260; adv. contact: Kari Bue. circ. 6,500. **Document type:** trade publication.
●Also available on CD-ROM.
—CCC.
Incorporates (1974-1991): Elektro-Handel (ISSN 0046-1776); **Former titles (until 1988):** El Installasjon og Handel (ISSN 0332-8821); (until 1969): Elektro - Elektroinstallatoerens Landsforbund (ISSN 0332-916X); (until 1968): Elektro - Installatoeren (ISSN 0332-9178)

621.3   BL
ELETRICIDADE MODERNA. 1972. m. $80. Aranda Editora Ltda., Rua D. Elisa No. 167, Perdizes, 01155-900 Sao Paulo, SP, Brazil. TEL 011-826-4511. FAX 011-66-9585. Ed. Jose Roberto Gonzalves. adv.; bk.rev.; charts; illus.; tr.lit. circ. 12,000.

621.3   BL
ELETRON: REVISTA DE ENGENHARIA/ELECTRON - ENGINEERING REVIEW. 1963. bi-m. E T E G I L - Editora Tecnico-Grafica Industrial Ltda., Rua Santa Ifigenia 176, Sao Paulo, SP, Brazil. Ed. Adalberto Walter Mihe. adv.

621.38   BL
ELETRONICA PARA TODOS. 1972. m. $300. Editora Signo Ltda, Caixa Postal 2483, 20001 Rio de Janiero, Brazil. Ed. A. Fanzeres. bk.rev. circ. 50,000.

621.3   IT   ISSN 0013-6093
CODEN: ELTZAL
ELETTRIFICAZIONE. 1950. m. L.80000 (foreign L.150000). Editoriale Delfino, Via Simone d'Orsenigo 27, 20135 Milan, Italy. TEL 02-55-184932. FAX 02-55-184971. Ed. Luigi Rusconi. adv. contact: Andrea Ferriani. charts; illus.; index. circ. 7,500. **Indexed:** C.I.S. Abstr., Sci.Abstr.
—BLDSC (3729.620000).

683.83   IT   ISSN 0013-6107
ELETTRODOMESTICA; il bianco, il bruno, il piccolo e la casa del futuro. Variant title: Elettrodomestici - Gas - Casalinghi - la Tecnica nella Casa Moderna. 1977. m. L.96000 (foreign L.140000) (effective 1993). Franco Angeli Editore, Viale Monza 106, 20127 Milan, Italy. TEL 02-28-27-651. FAX 02-28-91-515. circ. 20,000.

621.310   DK   ISSN 0901-3369
ELFORSYNINGENS TIAARSOVERSIGT. (Text in Danish, English) 1986. a. DKK 85. Danske Elvaerkers Forening - Association of Danish Electric Utilities, Rosenoerns Alle 9, DK-1970 Frederiksberg C, Denmark. TEL 31-39-01-11. FAX 31-39-59-58. illus. circ. 1,100. **Document type:** corporate report.
Description: Gives Danish total energy consumption, electricity and CHP production, fuel consumption, technica systems, prices and investments in figures and tables covering the past ten years.

621.3   SW   ISSN 0013-6190
ELINSTALLATOEREN. 1934. m. SEK 330. Elektriska Installatoersorganisationen - Swedish Electrical Contractors Association, Rosenlundsgatan 40, P.O. Box 17537, S-118 91 Stockholm, Sweden. FAX 46-08-6684014. Ed. Anders Runwall. adv.; illus. circ. 8,650. **Document type:** trade publication.
—BLDSC (3730.700000).
Formerly (until 1943): Svenska Elektriska Installatoerfoereningens Facktidning.

621.3   DK   ISSN 0107-962X
ELNYT. 1953. 3/yr. free. Association of Danish Electric Utilities, Rosenoerns Alle 9, DK-1970 Frederiksberg C, Denmark. Ed. Alvin B.C. Dahlgren. adv. circ. 100,739.

ENGINEERING — ELECTRICAL ENGINEERING

537.5 GW ISSN 0170-1827
ELRAD; Magazin fuer Elektronik und technische Rechneranwendung. 1977. m. DM.79.20 (foreign DM.86.40). Verlag Heinz Heise GmbH und Co. KG, Helstorferstr. 7, 30625 Hannover, Germany. TEL 0511-5352-0. FAX 0511-5352-129. TELEX 923173-HEISE-D. Ed. Harmut Rogge. adv.; bk.rev. circ. 52,232. **Document type:** consumer publication.

621.3 537 NE ISSN 0927-4995
QC579.6.I57
▼**ELSEVIER STUDIES IN APPLIED ELECTROMAGNETICS IN MATERIALS.** (Text in English) 1992. irreg., vol.5, 1994. price varies. Elsevier Science B.V., Books Division, P.O. Box 211, 1000 AE Amsterdam, Netherlands. TEL 31-20-5803911. FAX 31-20-5803705. TELEX 18582 ESPA NL. (Subscr. in U.S. and Canada to: Elsevier Science Inc., Box 882, Madison Sq. Sta., New York, NY 10159. TEL 212-989-5800) (back issues avail.) **Document type:** monographic series, proceedings.
Refereed Serial

621.38 DK ISSN 0109-2359
ELTEKNIK. 1963. 11/yr. DKK 405. Teknisk Forlag A-S, Skelbaekgade 4, DK-1780 Copenhagen V, Denmark. TEL 31-216801. FAX 31-212396. Eds. F.C. Olesen, Jesper Koefoed. adv.: B&W page DKK 11520, color page DKK 16500; trim 265 x 185. bk.rev.; charts; illus.; tr.lit.; index; circ. 5,159 (controlled). **Indexed:** Sci.Abstr.
—BLDSC (3732.485000).
Formerly: Elektronik (ISSN 0013-5631)
Description: Presents articles of technical nature about heavy and low current on a comprehensive and serious level for technicians within this field.

621.31 NO
ELVERKET. m. (10/yr.). Norske Elverksjefers Forening, P.O. Box 74, Blindern, N-0314 Oslo, Norway. Ed. Robert Wright. adv. circ. 750. **Document type:** trade publication.

537 CL
EMPRESA NACIONAL DE ELECTRICIDAD. MEMORIA. 1944. a. free. Empresa Nacional de Electricidad, S.A., Santa Rosa 76, Casilla 1392, Santiago, Chile. circ. 3,000.

ENERGETIK. see *ENERGY*

ENERGETYKA. see *ENERGY*

ENERGIA; revista de ingenieria energetica. see *ENERGY*

621.3 IT ISSN 0013-7308
TK4 CODEN: ENELAK
ENERGIA ELETTRICA. (Text and summaries in English, French, Italian) 1923. m. L.110000($90) Associazione Elettrotecnica ed Elettronica Italiana, Viale Monza 259, 20126 Milan, Italy. TEL 02-257791. FAX 02-2570512. Ed. Luigi Paris. adv.; bk.rev.; abstr.; illus.; stat.; index. circ. 3,000. (back issues avail.) **Indexed:** Appl.Mech.Rev., C.I.S. Abstr., Chem.Abstr., Eng.Ind., Fluidex, Fuel & Energy Abstr., Geotech.Abstr., INIS Atomind., Sci.Abstr.
—BLDSC (3744.450000); Faxon. **CCC**.
Description: Contains original scientific articles in electrotechnics and subjects concerning electrical energy generation hydraulics, thermotechnics, structural engineering as well as descriptive articles on the relevant main plants.

ENERGIE TECHNOLOGIE; vakblad voor de technische professional. see *ENERGY*

621.3 NE ISSN 0927-6629
ENERGIETECHNIEK. (Text in Dutch, English, French and German) 1923. m. fl.125 (effective 1994). Stichting Energietechniek, P.O. Box 9035, 6800 ET Arnhem, Netherlands. TEL 31-85-563009. FAX 31-85-429093. TELEX 45016 KEMA NL. Ed. H.F.M. Zewald. adv.: B&W page fl.2780; trim 210 x 297. bk.rev.; abstr.; charts; illus.; stat.; tr.lit.; index, cum.index. circ. 6,200. **Indexed:** C.I.S. Abstr., Chem.Abstr., Excerp.Med., HRIS, PROMT, Sci.Abstr. **Document type:** academic/scholarly publication.
—SWETS.
Formerly (until 1992): Elektrotechniek (ISSN 0013-4627)
Description: Covers issues in electrical and nuclear engineering and energy technology.

ENERGIEWIRTSCHAFTLICHE TAGESFRAGEN; Zeitschrift fuer Energie-Wirtschaft, Recht und Technik, und Umwelt. see *ENERGY*

ENERGIJA; casopis hrvatske elektroprivrede. see *ENERGY*

ENERGY CONVERSION AND MANAGEMENT. see *ENERGY*

ENERGY FORUM. see *ENERGY*

ENERGY IN JAPAN. see *ENERGY*

ENERGY SOURCES; an international interdisciplinary journal of science and technology. see *ENERGY*

ENERGY STORAGE SYSTEMS ABSTRACTS. see *ENERGY — Abstracting, Bibliographies, Statistics*

ENERGY TRENDS. see *ENERGY*

621.3 JA ISSN 0916-3409
ENERUGI RIYO TO CHOKUSETSU HATSUDEN SHINPOJUMU/SYMPOSIUM ON EFFICIENT USE OF ENERGY AND DIRECT ELECTRICAL POWER GENERATION. (Text in Japanese) 1979. a. Hokkaido Daigaku, Kogakubu, Fuzoku Sentan Denji Ryutai Jikken Shisetsu - Hokkaido University, Faculty of Engineering, Advanced Magnetohydrodynamics Research Institute, Nishi 8-chome, Kita 13-jo, Kita-ku, Sapporo-shi, Hokkaido 060, Japan.
—BLDSC (4322.275400).

ENGINEERING INTELLIGENT SYSTEMS FOR ELECTRICAL ENGINEERING AND COMMUNICATIONS. see *COMPUTERS — Artificial Intelligence*

621.3 UK
ENGINEERING LASERS. 1989. q. £48 (overseas £64). International Business & Technical Magazines Ltd., Queensway House, 2 Queensway, Redhill, Surrey RH1 1QS, England. TEL 0737-768611. FAX 0737-760425. Ed. A. Sandiford. **Document type:** trade publication.
Description: Covers the practical and industrial applications of lasers for material processing.

621.3 UK ISSN 0963-7346
T107 CODEN: ESEJEJ
▼**ENGINEERING SCIENCE AND EDUCATION JOURNAL.** 1992. bi-m. £72 in E.C. nations; elsewhere £80. I.E.E., Michael Faraday House, Six Hills Way, Stevenage, Herts. SG1 2AY, England. TEL 0438-313311. FAX 0438-742792. TELEX 825578-IEESTV-G. (Subscr. to: Publication Sales Dept., P.O. Box 96, Stevenage, Herts. SG1 2SD, England; U.S. addr.: INSPEC/IEEE, Box 1331, 445 Hoes Ln., Piscataway, NJ 08855-1331. TEL 908-562-5549) Ed. J. Cooper. adv.; bk.rev.; index. circ. 12,000. **Document type:** academic/scholarly publication.
●Also available on CD-ROM. Producer(s): University Microfilms International.
—BLDSC (3769.806000); EI.
Description: Deals comprehensively with science, environmental and energy issues facing industry, business, commerce, government, and academia. Covers new concepts in the generation, distribution, and use of electrical energy; materials science and technology; electron physics, discharges, and applications; fundamental aspects of measurement; education and training; nondestructive testing; history of technology; electromagnetics; biomedical engineering; and health and safety.

621.3 GW ISSN 0939-205X
ENGINEERING UND AUTOMATION. English edition: Engineering & Automation (ISSN 0939-2068) bi-m. DM.138. Siemens Verlag AG, Postfach 3240, 91050 Erlangen, Germany. TEL 09131-723004. FAX 09131-725022. **Indexed:** Sci.Abstr. **Document type:** trade publication.
—SWETS.
Former titles: Siemens Energie und Automation; Siemens Energietechnik (ISSN 0170-9496)

621.3 IT
ERCOLE MARELLI. (Text in Italian; summaries in English, Italian) vol.44, 1972. q. exchange basis. Ercole Marelli & C.S.p.A., Via Borgonuovo 24, 50121 Milan, Italy. Ed. G. Voltolin. **Indexed:** Sci.Abstr.
Formerly: Marelli (ISSN 0047-5904)

621.3 331.8 FR
ESSOR DE L'ELECTRICITE ET DE L'ELECTRONIQUE. a. 590 Fr. Union Francaise d'Annuaires Professionnels, 13 av. Hennequin, B.P. 36, 78192 Trappes Cedex, France. TEL 1-30-50-61-48. FAX 1-30-50-48-27.
Formerly (until 1992): Syndicat General de la Construction Electrique. Annuaire.

621.3 US
EUROCON: EUROPEAN CONFERENCE ON ELECTROTECHNICS. (1980 & 1982 published and copyrighted by North-Holland. 1984 published by Peter Peregrinus Ltd., London, UK and copyrighted by IEEE and EUREL. 1986 published in France and copyrighted by Comite EUROCON 86.) 1971. biennial. price varies. (I E E E, Region 8) Institute of Electrical and Electronics Engineers, Inc., 345 E. 47th St., New York, NY 10017-2394. TEL 212-705-7900. FAX 212-705-7682. (Subscr. to: 445 Hoes Ln., Box 1331, Piscataway, NJ 08844-1331): **Indexed:** Sci.Abstr. **Document type:** proceedings.

621.3 GW
EUROPEAN ELECTRICAL & ELECTRONIC ENGINEERING. (Text in Chinese) a. Deutscher Fachverlag GmbH, Mainzer Landstr. 251, 60326 Frankfurt a.M., Germany. (Subscr. to: Postfach 100606, 60006 Frankfurt a.M., Germany)

621.3 UK
EUROPEAN GENERATING SET DIRECTORY. a. £47.25($73.24) F M J International Publications Ltd., Queensway House, 2 Queensway, Redhill, Surrey RH1 1QS, England. TEL 0737-768611. FAX 0737-761685. TELEX 948669-TOPJNL-G. Ed. Derek Downing. **Document type:** directory.
Incorporates: Uninterruptable Power Supply Systems Directory.
Description: Contains material of interest to specifiers, consultants, contractors, and users of generating sets. Also provides information on products, contractors, manufacturers, and suppliers.

621.3 UK
EUROPEAN MICROWAVE CONFERENCE PROCEEDINGS. 1974. a. price varies. Microwave Exhibitions & Publishers Ltd., 90 Calverley Rd., Tunbridge Wells, Kent TN1 2UN, England. TEL 0892-544027. FAX 0892-541023. TELEX 95604-MEPNCL-G. bk.rev. circ. 1,500. **Document type:** proceedings.

EUROPEAN ORGANISATION FOR CIVIL AVIATION EQUIPMENT. GENERAL ASSEMBLY. ANNUAL REPORT. see *AERONAUTICS AND SPACE FLIGHT*

621.3 UK ISSN 0261-8214
EUROPEAN POWER NEWS. 1974. 8/yr. £29.95($50.50) (foreign £31.20). F M J International Publications Ltd., Queensway House, 2 Queensway, Redhill, Surrey RH1 1QS, England. TEL 0737-768611. FAX 0737-761685. TELEX 948669-TOPJNL-G. Ed. Derek Downing. adv.; bk.rev.; illus.; tr.lit. circ. 5,103. (tabloid format; back issues avail., reprint service avail. from UMI) **Document type:** trade publication.
Formerly: Power Generation Industrial (ISSN 0308-0897)
Description: Provides up-to-date news, opinion, application studies, and information on new products and all types of generating plant and ancillary equipment.

EXTRAKTE: ELEKTRO UND UNTERHALTUNGS-ELEKTRONIK. see *ELECTRONICS*

621.3 JA
F E P C BRIEFING NOTE. (Text in Japanese) 1988. m. Federation of Electric Power Companies - Denki Jigyo Rengokai, 9-4, Ote-machi 1-chome, Chiyoda-ku, Tokyo 100, Japan.

621.3 628.53 US
F G D DESIGN & COST DATA FILE. (Flue-Gas Desulfurization) a. $100. Utility Data Institute (Subsidiary of: McGraw-Hill), 1200 G St., N.W., Ste. 250, Washington, DC 20005. TEL 202-942-8788; 800-486-3660. FAX 202-942-8789. (diskette format) **Document type:** trade publication.
Description: Provides statistics on flue-gas desulfurization equipment installed at U.S.-owned utility plants.

621.3 FR ISSN 1145-2668
F I E E INFOS. 1972. m. 300 F. Federation des Industries Electriques et Electroniques, 11-17 rue Hamelin, 75783 Paris Cedex 16, France. TEL 45-05-70-10. FAX 45-53-03-93. TELEX 611 045 F. Ed. Laurence Villeneuve. adv.; bk.rev.; charts; illus.; mkt.; stat. circ. 5,200.

ENGINEERING — ELECTRICAL ENGINEERING

621.3 380   BE   ISSN 0779-3596
F I T C E JOURNAL. 1962. q. Federation des Ingenieurs de Telecommunications de la Communaute Europeenne - Federation of Telecommunications Engineers in the European Community, 42 Rue des Palais, B-1210 Brussels, Belgium.
TEL 32-2-2174742. FAX 32-2-2172350.

355   US
F X O REPORT. 1969. w. $695. Arco Corporation, 1800 Old Meadow Rd., McLean, VA 22102. TEL 703-821-8777. FAX 703-734-3893. Ed. Arnold Rosenberg. abstr.; charts; illus.; stat. circ. 300.
   Description: Contains information on selected future Department of Defense procurements, including price history, bid abstracts, sub-contract opportunities and defense industry news.

FACHBUCHVERZEICHNIS ELEKTROTECHNIK - ELEKTRONIK (YEAR). see *ELECTRONICS*

FAIREY IN FOCUS. see *ENGINEERING — Mechanical Engineering*

338.4 621.31   BE   ISSN 0778-6336
FEDERATION PROFESSIONNELLE DES PRODUCTEURS ET DISTRIBUTEURS D'ELECTRICITE DE BELGIQUE. DISTRIBUTION DE L'ENERGIE. Dutch edition (ISSN 0778-6328) (Text in French) 1959. a. 400 BEF. Federation Professionnelle des Producteurs et Distributeurs d'Electricite de Belgique, Avenue de Tervueren 34, Boite Postale 38, B-1040 Brussels, Belgium. TEL 32-2-733-96-07. FAX 32-2-733-95-65. circ. 800.
   Formerly: Federation Professionnelle des Producteurs et Distributeurs d'Electricite de Belgique. Secteurs de Distribution (ISSN 0071-4488)

621.3   BE   ISSN 0778-631X
FEDERATION PROFESSIONNELLE DES PRODUCTEURS ET DISTRIBUTEURS D'ELECTRICITE DE BELGIQUE. REPERTOIRE DES CENTRALES ELECTRIQUES. Dutch edition (ISSN 0778-6301) (Text in French) 1959. a. 400 BEF. Federation Professionnelle des Producteurs et Distributeurs d'Electricite de Belgique, Avenue de Tervueren 34, Boite Postale 38, B-1040 Brussels, Belgium. TEL 32-2-733-96-07. FAX 32-2-733-95-65. Ed. M.C. Oz. circ. 1,000.
   Formerly: Federation Professionnelle des Producteurs et Distributeurs d'Electricite de Belgique. Repertoire des Enterprises de Production d'Electricite (ISSN 0071-4461)
   Description: Statistics on power plants and their production of electricity.

537.244   US   ISSN 0275-9608
FERROELECTRICITY AND RELATED PHENOMENA. 1988. irreg., vol.8, 1989. price varies. Gordon & Breach Science Publishers, 820 Town Center Dr., Langhorne, PA 19047. TEL 215-750-2642. FAX 215-750-6343. (UK subscr. to: P.O. Box 90, Reading, Berkshire RG1 8JL, England. TEL 0734-560-080) Eds. G.W. Taylor, L. Shuvalov. **Document type:** monographic series.
—BLDSC (3908.360000).
Refereed Serial

FERROELECTRICS. see *PHYSICS*

621.3   US   ISSN 0883-8283
FERROELECTRICS AND POLAR MATERIALS. 1988. irreg. Gordon & Breach Science Publishers, 820 Town Center Dr., Langhorne, PA 19047. TEL 215-750-2642. FAX 215-750-6343. (UK subscr. to: P.O. Box 90, Reading, Berkshire RG1 8JL, England. TEL 0734-560-080) Ed.Bd.

621.3   US   ISSN 0731-5171
QC596   CODEN: FELEDJ
FERROELECTRICS LETTERS. 12/yr. (in 2 vols., 6 nos./vol.). 116 ECU per vol. (effective 1993). Gordon & Breach Science Publishers, 820 Town Center Dr., Langhorne, PA 19047. TEL 215-750-2642. FAX 215-750-6343. (UK subscr. to: P.O. Box 90, Reading, Berkshire RG1 8JL, England. TEL 0734-560-080) Ed. George W. Taylor. adv. (also avail. in microform) **Indexed:** Cadscan, Chem.Abstr., Ind.Sci.Rev., Lead Abstr., Met.Abstr., World Alum.Abstr., Zincscan.
—BLDSC (3908.440000); SWETS; CASDDS. **CCC.**
Refereed Serial

671.84   GW   ISSN 0430-4578
CODEN: FIMEBG
IL FILO METALLICO; rivista tecnica internazionale per l'industria del filo metallico e del cavo e per tutti i settori della lavorazione del filo metallico. English edition: Wire (ISSN 0043-5996); French edition: Trefile (ISSN 0374-2261); German edition: Draht (ISSN 0012-5911); Spanish edition: Alambre (ISSN 0002-4406) 1952. 4/yr. DM.77. Meisenbach GmbH, Hainstr. 18, 96047 Bamberg, Germany. TEL 0951-861-135. FAX 0951-861-158. (Subscr. to: Postfach 2069, 96011 Bamberg, Germany) Ed. Arnt Hannewald. adv.: B&W page DM.2776, color page DM.4471; trim 260 x 184; adv. contact: Oskar Ohler. bk.rev.; charts; illus. circ. 4,100. **Document type:** trade publication.

621.3   UK
FINANCIAL SURVEY COMPANY DATA FOR SUCCESS. ELECTRONIC MANUFACTURERS & DISTRIBUTORS. a. I C C Financial Surveys Ltd., Field House, 72 Oldfield Rd., Hampton, Middlesex TW12 2HQ, England. TEL 081-783-0977. FAX 081-783-1940.
   Formerly (until 1990): Financial Company Directory. Electronic Manufacturers and Distributors (ISSN 0952-5025)

621.3   RU   ISSN 0015-3222
CODEN: FTPPA4
FIZIKA I TEKHNIKA POLUPROVODNIKOV. English translation: Semiconductors (US ISSN 1063-7826) 1967. m. 70.80 Rub. (Rossiiskaya Akademiya Nauk, S.-Peterburgskoe Otdelenie) Izdatel'stvo Nauka, Mezhdunarodnyi Otdel, Profsoyuznaya, 90, 117864 Moscow, Russia. Ed. Zh.I. Alferov. bk.rev. **Indexed:** Chem.Abstr., INIS Atomind., Met.Abstr., Sci.Abstr., World Alum.Abstr. **Document type:** academic/scholarly publication.
—BLDSC (0389.750000); CASDDS. **CCC.**

621.393   US
FLORIDA RURAL ELECTRIC NEWS. 1964. m. $1.50 to non-members. Florida Rural Electric Cooperatives Association, Box 590, Tallahassee, FL 32302. FAX 904-656-5485. adv.: B&W page $1120; adv. contact: Laura G. Harrod. charts; illus.; stat.; circ. 9,000 (controlled). **Document type:** trade publication, consumer publication.
   Former titles: Florida Electric Cooperative News; F R E N (ISSN 0014-6110)

FORMAL METHODS IN SYSTEM DESIGN; an international journal. see *COMPUTERS — Computer Systems*

537   IT
FORMALUCE; rivista di illuminazione e industrial design. (Text in Italian; contents page and summaries in English) 1967. bi-m. L.15000. Editrice Media Servici s.r.l., Via Alessandria 16, 15033 Casale Monferrato (AL), Italy. TEL 0142-338231. FAX 142-48-30-35. Ed. Giovanni Numico. adv. circ. 8,000.
   Description: Articles on latest trends in lighting and industrial design.

621.3   US
K16
FORTNIGHTLY; the North American utilities business magazine. 1929. 22/yr. $99 (foreign $137). Public Utilities Reports, Inc., 2111 Wilson Blvd., Ste. 200, Arlington, VA 22201. TEL 703-243-7000. FAX 703-527-5829. Ed. David C. Wagman. adv.: B&W page $3345, color page $5015. circ. 7,577. (also avail. in microform from UMI) **Indexed:** ABI Inform., Account.Ind. (1974-), Acid Pre.Dig., Acid Rain Abstr., Acid Rain Ind., B.P.I., BPIA, C.L.I., CAD CAM Abstr., Energy Info.Abstr., Environ.Abstr., Fuel & Energy Abstr., Gas Abstr., L.R.I., P.A.I.S., Tel.Abstr., Tr.& Indus.Ind.
●Also available online. Vendor(s): Information Access Co., Mead Data Central, Inc., West Services, Inc..
—Faxon; UnCover; SWETS. **CCC.**
   Formerly (until Oct. 1993): Public Utilities Fortnightly (ISSN 0033-3808)

621.3   FR
FRANCE. ELECTRICITE DE FRANCE INTERNATIONAL. a. Electricite de France International, Direction des Affaires Internationales, 30 rue Jacques Ibert, 75858 Paris Cedex 17, France. TEL 40-42-22-22. FAX 40-42-62-00. TELEX EDF AE 616 146 F. illus. circ. 10,000.
   Former titles: France. Activities Internationales. Rapport Annuel d'Activite-Electricite de France; France. Direction des Affaires Exterieures et de la Cooperation. Rapport d'Activite-Electricite de France.
   Description: Covers all fields of electricity generation transmission and distribution including staff training and management.

621.3   GW   ISSN 0016-1136
CODEN: FONZA3
FREQUENZ; Zeitschrift fuer Schwingungs- und Schwachstromtechnik. 1947. 6/yr. DM.588. Fachverlag Schiele und Schoen GmbH, Markgrafenstr. 11, 10969 Berlin, Germany. TEL 030-2516029. FAX 030-2517248. Ed. Rudolf Kersten. adv.; bk.rev.; charts; illus.; pat. circ. 2,500. **Indexed:** Curr.Cont., Eng.Ind., Int.Aerosp.Abstr., Sci.Abstr. **Document type:** trade publication.
—BLDSC (4036.000000); EI; Faxon. **CCC.**

621.3   US   ISSN 0190-5848
T62   CODEN: PFECDR
FRONTIERS IN EDUCATION CONFERENCE. PROCEEDINGS. Variant title: Conference Record. 1971. a. price varies. (I E E E , Education Society) Institute of Electrical and Electronics Engineers, Inc., 345 E. 47th St., New York, NY 10017. TEL 212-705-7900. FAX 212-705-7682. (Subscr. to: 445 Hoes Ln., Piscataway, NJ 08854)
—BLDSC (4042.010000); EI; UMI. **CCC.**
   Formerly: Conference on Frontiers in Education. Digest (ISSN 0069-8547)

621.3   JA   ISSN 0367-3332
FUJI ELECTRIC JOURNAL/FUJI JIHO. (Text in Japanese; summaries in English, Japanese) 1923. m. $135. (Fuji Electric Co., Ltd.) Intercontinental Marketing Corp., P.O. Box 5056, Tokyo 100-31, Japan. TEL 81-3-3661-7458. FAX 81-3-3667-9646. **Indexed:** INIS Atomind.

621.3   JA   ISSN 0429-8284
CODEN: FUERBV
FUJI ELECTRIC REVIEW. (Text in English) 1955. q. exchange basis. Fuji Electric Co., Ltd. - Fuji Denki Seizo K.K., 12-1, Yuraku-cho 1-chome, Chiyoda-ku, Tokyo 100, Japan. **Indexed:** INIS Atomind., JCT, JTA, Met.Abstr., Sci.Abstr., World Alum.Abstr.
—BLDSC (4054.845000).

621.3   JA   ISSN 0912-2761
FUJIKURA GIHO/FUJIKURA TECHNICAL REPORT. (Text in Japanese; summaries in English) 1950. s-a. Fujikura Ltd., 5-1, Kiba 1-chome, Koto-ku, Tokyo 135, Japan. **Indexed:** Chem.Abstr., INIS Atomind.
—BLDSC (4054.890400).
   Formerly (until 1985): Fujikura Densen Giho - Fujikura Cable Works. Technical Review (ISSN 0429-8357)

537   JA   ISSN 0388-225X
CODEN: FKDGAO
FUJIKURA TECHNICAL REVIEW. (Text in English) 1969. a. free. Fujikura Ltd., 5-1, Kiba 1-chome, Koto-ku, Tokyo 135, Japan. charts; illus. **Indexed:** Chem.Abstr., INIS Atomind., JTA, Sci.Abstr.
—BLDSC (4054.891000).

621.3   JA   ISSN 0016-2515
FUJITSU/FUJITSU SYSTEM SCIENCE REVIEW. (Text in Japanese; summaries in English, Japanese) 1950. bi-m. 800 Yen per no. Fujitsu Limited, 1015 Kamikodanaka, Nakahara-ku, Kawasaki-shi, Kanagawa-ken 211, Japan. Ed. Mikio Ohtsuki. illus.; index. circ. 16,000. **Indexed:** Cyb.Abstr., JCT, JTA, Sci.Abstr.
—BLDSC (4054.893000).

621.3   JA   ISSN 0915-2342
FUJITSU DENSO TECHNICAL REPORT. (Text in Japanese) 1989. s-a. Fujitsu Denso Ltd., Shin'yokohama Development Center - Fujitsu Denso K.K. Shin'yokohama Kaihatsu Senta, 2-3, Shin'yokohama 2-chome, Kohoku-ku, Yokohama-shi, Kanagawa-ken 222, Japan.

ENGINEERING — ELECTRICAL ENGINEERING

621.3   JA   ISSN 0912-2524
                                   CODEN: FUGEE5
FUJITSU GENERAL. (Text in Japanese) 1986. a. Fujitsu General, 1116, Suenaga, Takatsu-ku, Kawasaki-shi, Kanagawa-ken 213, Japan. **Indexed:** Chem. Abstr., Curr.Cont., Eng.Ind., INIS Atomind.
—CASDDS.

621.3   JA   ISSN 0016-2523
TK1   CODEN: FUSTA4
FUJITSU SCIENTIFIC & TECHNICAL JOURNAL. (Text in English) 1965. s-a. $7 per no.; or exchange basis. Fujitsu Limited, 1015 Kamikodanaka, Nakahara-ku, Kawasaki-shi, Kanagawa-ken 211, Japan. (Co-sponsor: Fujitsu Laboratories Ltd.) Ed. Shigeru Sato. bk.rev.; illus.; index. circ. 2,200. **Indexed:** Cadscan, Chem.Abstr., Curr.Cont., Cyb.Abstr., Eng.Ind., JCT, JTA, Lead Abstr., Met.Abstr., Robomat. (until 1992), Sci.Abstr., World Alum.Abstr., Zincscan. **Document type:** corporate report.
—BLDSC (4054.895000); El; UnCover; CASDDS.

621.3   JA   ISSN 0289-3789
FUJITSU TEN GIHO/FUJITSU TEN TECHNICAL REPORT. (Text in Japanese; summaries in English, Japanese) 1983. s-a. Fujitsu Ten Ltd., 2-28, Gosho Dori 1-chome, Hyogo-ku, Kobe-shi, Hyogo-ken 652, Japan.

621.3   JA   ISSN 0914-6458
FUJITSU TEN TECHICAL JOURNAL. (Text in English) 1988. a. Fujitsu Ten Ltd., 2-28, Gosho Dori 1-chome, Hyogo-ku, Kobe-shi, Hyoggo-ken 652, Japan.

621.3   JA   ISSN 0429-9159
                                   CODEN: FKDJAX
FURUKAWA DENKO JIHO. (Text in English, Japanese) 1947. s-a. free. Furukawa Denki Kogyo K.K. - Furukawa Electric Co., Ltd., 6-1, Marunouchi 2-chome, Chiyoda-ku, Tokyo 100, Japan. Ed. Katsuhisa Nakajima. circ. 3,500. (back issues avail.) **Indexed:** Chem.Abstr., Eng.Ind., INIS Atomind., Sci.Abstr.
—BLDSC (4059.540000).

621.3   JA   ISSN 0911-9280
                                   CODEN: FUREDP
FURUKAWA REVIEW. (Text in English) 1980. a. Furukawa Electric Co., Ltd. - Furukawa Denki Kogyo K.K., 6-1, Marunouchi 2-chome, Chiyoda-ku, Tokyo 100, Japan. **Indexed:** Chem.Abstr., Eng.Ind., INIS Atomind.
—BLDSC (4059.550000); CASDDS.

621.3 658   AT
G E C CONTACT. (General Electric Co.) vol.2, 1980. 4/yr. free. (G E C Electrical Wholesale (Australia)) Grahame Bunyan Publicity Pty. Ltd., P.O. Box 9, Auburn, N.S.W. 2144, Australia. TEL 02-901-3400. FAX 02-901-3332. Eds. G. Bunyan, L. Stewart. adv.; illus. circ. 28,000. (tabloid format) **Document type:** newsletter.

621.38   UK   ISSN 0264-9187
TK7800   CODEN: GJREES
G E C JOURNAL OF RESEARCH. 1928; N.S. 1983. 3/yr. General Electric Co., PLC, Marconi Research Centre, W. Hanningfield Rd., Great Baddow, Chelmsford, Essex CM2 8HN, England. Ed. A.J. Walkden. bibl.; charts; illus.; index, cum.index. circ. 10,000. (also avail. in microfilm from UMI) **Indexed:** AESIS, Br.Tech.Ind., CAD CAM Abstr., Cadscan, Chem.Abstr., Comput.Abstr., Curr.Cont., Eng.Ind., Ergon.Abstr., Excerp.Med., Lead Abstr., Met.Abstr., Sci.Abstr., Tel.Abstr., Zincscan. **Document type:** trade publication.
—BLDSC (4095.704700); El; UnCover; UMI.
    Incorporates: Marconi Review (ISSN 0025-2883); G E C Journal of Science and Technology (ISSN 0302-2587); Which was formerly: Journal of Science and Technology (ISSN 0022-4421)

621.3   UK   ISSN 0267-9337
                                 CODEN: GECREP
G E C REVIEW. 1983. 3/yr. General Electric Co., PLC, Marconi Research Centre, W. Hanningfield Rd., Great Baddow, Chelmsford, Essex CM2 8HN, England. Ed. A.J. Walkden. bibl.; charts; illus.; index, cum.index. circ. 12,000. (also avail. in microfilm from UMI,PMC) **Indexed:** AESIS, Br.Tech.Ind., Met.Abstr. **Document type:** trade publication.
—BLDSC (4095.709000); El; UnCover; UMI.
    Incorporates: G E C Engineering (ISSN 0264-0295); G E C Journal for Industry (ISSN 0262-8236)

621.3   JA   ISSN 0385-7204
                                   CODEN: GSNTAA
G S NEWS TECHNICAL REPORT. (Text in English, Japanese; summaries in English) 1927. s-a. 500 Yen per no. Japan Storage Battery Co., Ltd. - Nippon Denchi K.K., 1 Inobaba-cho, Kisshoin Nishinosho, Minami-ku, Kyoto-shi, Kyoto 601, Japan.
—CASDDS.

GEKKAN SEMICONDUCTOR WORLD. see ELECTRONICS

GIDROTEKHNICHESKOE STROITEL'STVO. see WATER RESOURCES

621.3   JA
GIJUTSU KAIHATSU NYUSU/RESEARCH AND DEVELOPMENT NEWS. (Text in Japanese; summaries in English, Japanese) 1979. q. Chubu Denryoku K.K., Gijutsu Kaihatsu Honbu - Chubu Electric Power Co., Research and Development Bureau, 20-1, Kitasekiyama, Odaka-cho, Midori-ku, Nagoya-shi, Aichi-ken 459, Japan.

621.3   JA   ISSN 0914-9589
GIJUTSU KENKYUJO DAYORI/TECHNICAL RESEARCH INSTITUTE NEWS. (Text in Japanese) 1988. s-a. Tohoku Denryoku K.K., Denryoku Gijutsu Kenkyujo - Tohoku Electric Power Co., Inc., Electricity Technology Research and Development Center, 2-1, Nakayama 7-chome, Aoba-ku, Sendai-shi, Miyagi-ken 981, Japan.

621.3 378   JA   ISSN 0918-1083
▼**GIJUTSU KYOIKU KENKYU RONBUNSHI/JOURNAL OF TECHNOLOGY AND EDUCATION.** (Text in Japanese; summaries in English, Japanese) 1992. s-a. 3000 Yen per no. Denki Kagaku Kyokai, Gijutsu Kyoiku Kenkyu Kondankai - Electrochemical Society of Japan, Technology and Education Division, c/o Mr. Nishimiya, Tokyo Kogyo Koto Senmon Gakko Kogyo Kagakka, 1220-2, Kunugida-cho, Hachioji-shi, Tokyo 193, Japan.

621.3   IT   ISSN 0392-3630
GIORNALE DELL'INSTALLATORE ELETTRICO. 1979. 18/yr. L.65000($96) (foreign L.130000). Stammer S.p.A., Via della Liberazione 1, 20068 Peschiera Borromeo (MI), Italy. TEL 02-55302606. FAX 02-55302700. Ed. Girolamo Bellina. adv. circ. 17,500.

621.3   US   ISSN 0017-3592
GRAYBAR OUTLOOK. 1936. q. Graybar Electric Co., Box 7231, St. Louis, MO 63177. TEL 314-727-3900. Ed. Daniel E. Hayes. circ. controlled.
    Description: Company magazine published for Graybar employees and retirees.

621.38   GW
GRUNDIG REPORT. 1952. bi-m. Grundig AG, Kurgartenstr. 37, 90762 Fuerth, Germany. TEL 0911-703-1. FAX 0911-709687. (back issues avail.) **Document type:** corporate report.
    Description: Provides information for and about employees of the Grundig Corporation.

621.38   CC
GUANGXIAN YU DIANLAN/OPTICAL FIBRE AND CABLE. (Text in Chinese) bi-m. Jixie Dianzi Gongye Bu, Di 23 Yanjiusuo - Ministry of Engineering and Electronic Industry, No. 23 Institute, 25 Yixian Lu, Shanghai 200433, People's Republic of China. TEL 5421305. Ed. Zhou Yihai.

GUTI DIANZIXUE YANJIU YU JINZHAN/RESEARCH & PROGRESS OF SOLID STATE ELECTRONICS. see ELECTRONICS

H D T V REPORT. (High Definition Television) see COMMUNICATIONS — Television And Cable

621.3   GW
H E A G JOURNAL; Kundenzeitschrift der Hessischen Elektrizitaets AG. 1969. q. (Hessische Elektrizitaets AG) Energie-Verlag GmbH, Haeusserstr. 36, 69115 Heidelberg, Germany. TEL 06221-90130. FAX 06221-901341. Eds. Frank Methlow, Michael Santak. circ. 277,000. **Document type:** consumer publication.

621.3   JA   ISSN 0917-3439
H V C NEWS. (Text in Japanese) 1989. bi-m. Hi-Vision Promotion Center - Haibijon Fukyu Shien Senta, 66-2, Horikawa-cho, Saiwai-ku, Kawasaki-shi, Kanagawa-ken 210, Japan.

621.3   JA   ISSN 0914-5559
H V E M REPORTS/HYAKUMAN BORUTO DENSHI KENBIKYOSHITSU KENKYU HOKOKU. (Text in English, Japanese) 1978. biennial. Tohoku University, High Voltage Electron Microscope Laboratory - Tohoku Daigaku Hyakuman Boruto Denshi Kenbikyoshitsu, 1-1, Katahira 2-chome, Aoba-ku, Sendai-shi, Miyagi-ken 980, Japan.

621.3   JA
HAKUMAKU DENSHI DEBAISU NENKAN/THIN FILM DEVICE. (Text in Japanese) a. 36000 Yen. Press Journal Inc., 2-6, Kudan Kita 1-chome, Chiyoda-ku, Tokyo 102, Japan.

HANDOTAI SANGYO SHINBUN/SEMICONDUCTOR INDUSTRY NEWS. see ELECTRONICS

HANDOTAI SHUSEKI KAIRO GIJUTSU SHINPOJUMU KOEN RONBUNSHU/PROCEEDINGS OF THE SYMPOSIUM ON SEMICONDUCTORS AND INTEGRATED CIRCUITS TECHNOLOGY. see ELECTRONICS

621.3   II   ISSN 0046-6913
HARYANA ELECTRICITY. (Text in English and Hindi) vol.3, 1970. q. Haryana State Electricity Board, Office Sector 17-D, Chandigarh, India. Ed. K.K. Sharma. adv.; charts; illus.

HEALTH & SAFETY NEWSLINE; for the engineering industry (UK). see PUBLIC HEALTH AND SAFETY

HI-FI & ELEKTRONIK. see SOUND RECORDING AND REPRODUCTION

621.3   US   ISSN 0018-1242
HI-TENSION NEWS. 1931. q. free. Ohio Brass Co., (Subsidiary of: Hubbell, Inc.), 8711 Wadsworth Rd., Wadsworth, OH 44281. TEL 216-335-2361. FAX 216-336-9252. Ed. Cheri Long. adv.; charts; illus. circ. 20,000. **Document type:** trade publication.

HIGH RELIABILITY ELECTRONIC COMPONENTS. see MILITARY

HIRADASTECHNIKA. see COMMUNICATIONS

621.3   JA   ISSN 0914-899X
HITACHI CABLE REVOEW. (Text in English) 1982. a. Hitachi Cable Co., Ltd. - Hitachi Densen K.K., 1-2, Marunouchi 2-chome, Chiyoda-ku, Tokyo 100, Japan.

621.3   JA   ISSN 0910-2817
HITACHI DENSEN. (Text in Japanese) 1981. a. Hitachi Cable Co., Ltd., 1-2, Marunouch 2-chome, Chiyoda-ku, Tokyo 100, Japan.

HITACHI DENSHI ENJINIARINGU GIHO/HITACHI ELECTRONICS ENGINEERING CO. TECHNICAL REPORT. see ELECTRONICS

537.5   GW
HOBBY MAGAZINE DER TECHNIK. 1953. m. DM.70. Top Special Verlag, Valentinskamp 24, 20354 Hamburg, Germany. FAX 040-3474927. Ed. Wolfgang Will. adv.; bk.rev. circ. 155,119.

HOBSON'S ENGINEERING CASEBOOK. see ENGINEERING — Civil Engineering

621.3   JA   ISSN 0286-3189
TK4   CODEN: ODKHEE
HOKKAIDO DAIGAKU OYO DENKI KENKYUJO GIJUTSU HOKOKU/HOKKAIDO UNIVERSITY. RESEARCH INSTITUTE OF APPLIED ELECTRICITY. TECHNICAL BULLETIN. (Text in Japanese; summaries in English, Japanese) 1949. irreg. exchange basis. Hokkaido Daigaku, Oyo Denki Kenkyujo, Nishi 6-chome, Kita 12-jo, Kita-ku, Sapporo-shi, Hokkaido 060, Japan. TEL 631-1271.
—BLDSC (6321.087500).
    Formerly (until 1982): Hokkaido Daigaku Oyo Denki Kenkyujo Hokoku (ISSN 0030-7726)

621.3   JA   ISSN 0915-2938
HOKKAIDO DENRYOKU K.K. SOGO KENKYUJO KENKYU NENPO/HOKKAIDO ELECTRIC POWER CO. GENERAL RESEARCH CENTER. ANNUAL REPORT. (Text in Japanese) 1988. a. Hokkaido Denryoku K.K., Sogo Kenkyujo - Hokkaido Electric Power Co., Ltd., Department of Research and Development, 461-6, Satozuka, Toyohira-ku, Sapporo-shi, Hokkaido 004, Japan.

ENGINEERING — ELECTRICAL ENGINEERING

621.3   JA   ISSN 0389-4983
HOKUDEN GIJUTSU KAIHATSU NYUSU/HOKURIKU ELECTRIC POWER CO. TECHNICAL DEVELOPMENT NEWS. (Text in Japanese) 1980. s-a. Hokuriku Denryoku K.K., Gijutsu Kenkyujo - Hokuriku Electric Power Co., Technical Research Institute, 2-54, Hisakata-cho, Toyama-shi, Toyama-ken 930, Japan.

621.3   JA
HOKUDEN SOKEN NYUSU/HOKKAIDO ELECTRIC POWER CO. DEPARTMENT OF RESEARCH AND DEVELOPMENT. NEWS. (Includes irreg. Special Issue) (Text in Japanese) 1987. q. Hokkaido Denryoku K.K., Sogo Kenkyujo - Hokkaido Electric Power Co., Department of Research and Development, 461-6, Satozuka, Toyohira-ku, Sapporo-shi, Hokkaido 004, Japan.

621.3   JA
HOKURIKU DENKI TO KOGYO/ELECTRICITY AND INDUSTRY IN HOKURIKU DISTRICT. (Text in Japanese) 1964. m. Tsusho Sangyosho, Chubu Tsusho Sangyokyoku, Koeki Jigyo Honkuriku Shikyoku - Ministry of International Trade and Industry, Chubu Bureau, Hokuriku Public Utilities Branch Office, 13-15, Ushijima-machi, Toyama-shi, Toyama-ken 930, Japan. (Co-sponsor: Hokuriku Denki Kyokai - Hokuriku Electric Association)

621.3   JA   ISSN 0389-6390
HOKURIKU DENRYOKU K.K. GIJUTSU KENKYUJO GIJUTSU KENKYU HOKOKU/HOKURIKU ELECTRIC POWER CO. TECHNICAL RESEARCH INSTITUTE. REPORT. (Text in Japanese) 1959. a. Hokuriku Denryoku K.K., Gijutsu Kenkyujo, 2-54, Hisakata-cho, Toyama-shi, Toyama-ken 930, Japan.

621.3   JA
HOKURIKU DENRYOKU SHAHO/HOKURIKU ELECTRIC POWER CO. NEWS. (Text in Japanese) m. Hokuriku Denryoku K.K. - Hokuriku Electric Power Co., Inc., 15-1, Ushiji-macho, Toyama-shi, Toyama-ken 930, Japan.

621.3   JA   ISSN 0286-0201
                        CODEN: HDIHDS
HOSEI DAIGAKU ION BIMU KOGAKU KENKYUJO HOKOKU/HOSEI UNIVERSITY. RESEARCH CENTER OF ION BEAM TECHNOLOGY. REPORT. (Supplement avail.: Hosei Daigaku Ion Bimu Kogaku Kenkyujo Hokoku. Bessatsu (ISSN 0914-2908)) (Text in English, Japanese) 1980. a. Hosei Daigaku, Ion Bimu Kogaku Kenkyujo, 7-2, Kajino-cho 3-chome, Koganei-shi, Tokyo 184, Japan.
—BLDSC (7589.841990); CASDDS.

683.83   DK   ISSN 0018-8107
HVIDVARE-NYT. 1967. 10/yr. DKK 400 (typically set in Jan.). Foreningen af Fabrikanter og Importoerer af Elektriske Husholdningsapparater (F E H A) - Association of Manufacturers and Importers of Domestic Electric Appliances, Naverland 34, P.O. Box 1336, DK-2600 Glostrup, Denmark. TEL 45-43-43-46-46. FAX 45-43-43-52-72. Ed. Per Grau. adv. contact: S. Bjaaland. bk.rev. circ. 4,333. **Document type:** trade publication.

363.6 621.31   CN
HYDRO-PRESSE. (Text in French) 1916. s-m. free. Hydro-Quebec, Equipe Journaux d'Entreprise, 680 Sherbrooke O., 9e etage, Montreal, Que. H3A 2M7, Canada. TEL 514-289-2293. FAX 514-289-4973. Ed. Francine Charest. charts; illus. circ. 40,000. (tabloid format) **Document type:** newspaper.
    Formerly: Entre - Nous (ISSN 0013-8991)
    Description: Covers all aspects of the energy and electricity industry, including efficiency, improvements in quality and future plans. Also covers how electricity impacts advancements in other industries.

621.3   JA
HYUMAN FAKUTA KENKYU SENTA KENKYU HOKOKU/HUMAN FACTOR RESEARCH CENTER. RESEARCH REPORT. (Text in Japanese; summaries in English, Japanese) 3/yr. Denryoku Chuo Kenkyujo, Hyuman Fakuta Kenkyu Senta - Central Research Institute of Electric Power Industry, Human Factor Research Center, 6-1, Ote-machi 1-chome, Chiyoda-ku, Tokyo 100, Japan.

621.3   US   ISSN 0020-5974
I A E I NEWS. 1929. bi-m. $30. International Association of Electrical Inspectors, 901 Waterfall Way, Ste. 602, Richardson, TX 75080. TEL 214-235-1455. FAX 214-235-3855. Ed. J. Philip Simmons. adv.: B&W page $1155, color page $2035; trim 8 1/4 x 10 7/8. bk.rev.; illus. circ. 23,000. (also avail. in record) **Indexed:** C.I.S.Abstr. **Document type:** trade publication.
    Formerly: International Association of Electrical Inspectors. News-Bulletin.
    Description: Reports on the complicated sections in the National Electrical Code and other electrical codes, hazards of code violations, electrical safety, electrical accidents, testing laboratories' reports, new products, industry news and association reports.

I B E W - A F L - C I O. LOCAL 1470 JOURNAL. (International Brotherhood of Electrical Workers, A F L - C I O) see *LABOR UNIONS*

I B E W JOURNAL. (International Brotherhood of Electrical Workers, A F L - C I O) see *LABOR UNIONS*

621.38   SZ   ISSN 0018-9138
TK1.A1   CODEN: IEBUAD
I E C BULLETIN. (Text in English, French) 1967. bi-m. free. International Electrotechnical Commission, 3 rue de Varembe, CH-1211 Geneva 20, Switzerland. TEL 022-9190266. FAX 022-9190300. (Dist. in the U.S. by: American National Standards Institute, 1430 Broadway, New York, NY 10018) Ed. Charles Gilson. bk.rev.; charts; illus.; stat. **Indexed:** BMT, Sci.Abstr. **Document type:** newsletter.

621.3   UK
I E E CIRCUITS AND SYSTEMS SERIES. irreg., vol.5, 1993. Institution of Electrical Engineers, Michael Faraday House, Six Hills Way, Stevenage, Herts SG1 2AY, England. TEL 0438-313311. FAX 0438-313465. TELEX 825578-IEESTV-G. Eds. D.J. Haigh, R.S. Soin. **Document type:** monographic series.

621.3   UK   ISSN 0537-9989
TK6573   CODEN: IECPB4
I E E CONFERENCE PUBLICATION SERIES. (Institution of Electrical Engineers) 1962. irreg. I.E.E., Michael Faraday House, Six Hills Way, Stevenage, Herts. SG1 2AY, England. TEL 0438-313311. FAX 0438-742840. TELEX 825578-IEESTV-G. (Subscr. to: Publication Sales Dept., P.O. Box 96, Stevenage, Herts. SG1 2SD, England; U.S. addr.: INSPEC/IEEE, Box 1331, 445 Hoes Ln., Piscataway, NJ 08855-1331. TEL 908-562-5549) **Indexed:** Chem.Abstr, Math.R. **Document type:** proceedings.
—BLDSC (4362.706500); UnCover; SWETS; CASDDS. **CCC**.

621.3   UK
I E E CONTROL ENGINEERING SERIES. 1976. irreg., vol.49, 1993. Institution of Electrical Engineers, Michael Faraday House, Six Hills Way, Stevenage, Herts SG1 2AY, England. TEL 0438-313311. FAX 0438-313465. TELEX 825578-IEESTV-G. Ed.Bd. **Indexed:** Math.R. **Document type:** monographic series.

621.3   US
I E E E. ORLANDO SECTION MONTHLY. 196. m. $12 to non-members. (Institute of Electrical and Electronics Engineers) Medina Software, Inc., 385 Commerce Way, No. 101, Longwood, FL 32750-7637. TEL 407-260-1676. FAX 407-260-1636. Ed. Jorge Medina. adv. contact: Carmen Medina. bk.rev. circ. 1,600. (back issues avail.) **Document type:** newsletter.

620.7 629.1   US
I E E E - A E S C O N. AEROSPACE AND ELECTRONICS SYSTEM CONFERENCE. RECORD. a. price varies. (I E E E, Aerospace and Electronics Systems Society) Institute of Electrical and Electronics Engineers, Inc., 345 E. 47th St., New York, NY 10017. TEL 212-705-7366. FAX 212-705-7682. (Subscr. to: 445 Hoes Lane, Box 1331, Piscataway, NJ 08855-1331. TEL 908-562-3948) illus. **Document type:** proceedings.
—**CCC**.
    Former titles: E A S C O N. Electronics and Aerospace System Conference and Exposition. (Record); (until 1982): E A S C O N. Annual Electronics and Aerospace Systems Conference. (Record); (until 1981): E A S C O N. Electronics and Aerospace Systems Convention. Record (ISSN 0531-6863); Until 1974: E A S C O N. Electronics and Aerospace Systems Convention. Record; (until 1967): Aerospace and Electronic Systems Convention. Record; (until 1966): Aerospace Systems Convention. Record.

621.3   US   ISSN 0018-9154
I E E E ALMANACK. 1956. m. (Sep.-May). $2 to non-members. Institute of Electrical & Electronics Engineers, Inc., Philadelphia Section, Univ. of Pennsylvania, Moore School of Electrical Engineering, Philadelphia, PA 19104. TEL 215-898-8106. Eds. W.R. Rowland, T. Lehner. adv.; illus. circ. 6,000. (also avail. in microform from UMI)

621.3   US   ISSN 1045-9243
TK7871.6   CODEN: IAPMEZ
I E E E ANTENNAS AND PROPAGATION MAGAZINE. Represents: I E E E Antennas and Propagation Society. International Symposium Digest. bi-m. $85 to non-members. (I E E E, Antennas and Propagation Society) Institute of Electrical and Electronics Engineers, Inc., 345 E. 47th St., New York, NY 10017-2394. TEL 908-981-0060. FAX 908-981-9667. (Subscr. to: 445 Hoes Lane, Box 1331, Piscataway, NJ 08855-1331) Ed. W. Ross Stone. charts. illus.; stat. (also avail. in microfiche from UMI; microfilm from EEE)
—BLDSC (4362.805600); EI; Faxon; UnCover; SWETS; UMI. **CCC**.
    Description: Covers all areas relating to antenna theory, design, and practice.

683.83   US
I E E E - C H M T INTERNATIONAL ELECTRONIC MANUFACTURING TECHNOLOGY SYMPOSIUM. Short title: I E M T. (Held twice in 1988) 1984. a. price varies. (I E E E, Components, Hybrids and Manufacturing Technology Society) Institute of Electrical and Electronics Engineers, Inc., 345 E. 47th St., New York, NY 10017-2394. TEL 212-705-7900. FAX 212-705-7682. (Subscr. to: Box 1331, 445 Hoes Lane, Piscataway, NJ 08855-1331)
    Formerly: I E E E International Electronic Manufacturing Technology Symposium.
    Description: Details new developments in and applications of automated equipment and systems.

621.3   US
I E E E CAREERS CONFERENCE. CONFERENCE RECORD. 1979. biennial. price varies. (I E E E, United States Activities Board Career Maintenance and Development Committee) Institute of Electrical and Electronics Engineers, Inc., 345 E. 47th St., New York, NY 10017-2394. TEL 212-705-7900. FAX 212-705-7682. (Subscr. to: 445 Hoes Ln., Box 1331, Piscataway, NJ 08855-1331) **Indexed:** Sci.Abstr. **Document type:** proceedings.
    Former titles (until 1983): Enhancing Engineering Careers by Fulfilling Individual and Organizational Goals. Conference Record; (until 1981): What's Working to Enrich Engineering Careers. Conference Record; (until 1979): Joint I E E E - Industry Conference on Building a Professional Work Climate. Record.
    Description: Discusses career issues for engineers.

ENGINEERING — ELECTRICAL ENGINEERING

621.3 US ISSN 0163-6804
TK5101.A1 CODEN: ICOMD9
I E E E COMMUNICATIONS MAGAZINE. 1953. m. $135 to non-members. (I E E E, Communications Society) Institute of Electrical and Electronics Engineers, Inc., 345 E. 47th St., New York, NY 10017-2349. FAX 908-981-9667. (Subscr. to: Box 1331, Hoes Lane, Piscataway, NJ 08855-1331. TEL 908-981-0060) Ed. Tom Plevyak. **Indexed:** A.S.& T.Ind., CAD CAM Abstr., Comput.Abstr., Comput.Bus., Comput.Cont., Cyb.Abstr., Ind.Sci.Rev., INIS Atomind., Int.Aerosp.Abstr., Int'l.Civil Eng.Abstr., PROMT, Sci.Abstr, Soft.Abstr.Eng., Tel.Abstr.
—BLDSC (4362.812900); EI; Faxon; UnCover; SWETS; UMI. **CCC.**
Formerly: I E E E Communications Society Magazine (ISSN 0148-9615)
Description: Provides details on conferences, short courses, standards, governmental regulations and legislation, the society's administration and elections.

621.3 US ISSN 0888-0611
TJ212 CODEN: ISMAD7
I E E E CONTROL SYSTEMS MAGAZINE. 1981. 7/yr. $136 to non-members. (I E E E, Control Systems Society) Institute of Electrical and Electronics Engineers, Inc., 345 E. 47th St., New York, NY 10017. FAX 908-981-9667. (Subscr. to: 445 Hoes Lane, Box 1331, Piscataway, NJ 08855-1331. TEL 908-981-1393) Ed. Stephen Yurkovich. adv.; bk.rev.; charts; illus.; index. (also avail. in microfiche from UMI; microfilm from EEE; back issues avail.) **Indexed:** A.I.Abstr., Abstr.Hum.Comp.Inter., CAD CAM Abstr., Comput.Cont., Comput.Dtbs., Cyb.Abstr., Eng.Ind., Int.Aerosp.Abstr., Robomat., Sci.Abstr.
—BLDSC (4362.917000); EI; Faxon; UnCover; SWETS; UMI. **CCC.**
Former titles (until 1985): Control Systems Magazine (ISSN 0272-1708); (until 1981): I E E E Control Systems Society Newsletter.
Description: Covers design tools, conference programs, educational items, and the society's activities, with emphasis on system applications.

621.38 US
I E E E CUSTOM INTEGRATED CIRCUITS CONFERENCE. PROCEEDINGS. 1979. a. (I E E E, Electron Devices Society) Institute of Electrical and Electronics Engineers, Inc., 345 E. 47th St., New York, NY 10017. TEL 212-705-7900. FAX 908-981-9667. (Subscr. to: Box 1331, 445 Hoes Lane, Piscataway, NJ 08855-1331) (Co-sponsor: I E E E Rochester Section) **Document type:** proceedings.
Formerly (until 1984): Custom Integrated Circuits Conference. Proceedings.

621.3 US ISSN 0883-7554
TK3421 CODEN: IIMAE6
I E E E ELECTRICAL INSULATION MAGAZINE. 1985. bi-m. $115 to non-members. (I E E E, Dielectrics and Electrical Insulation Society) Institute of Electrical and Electronics Engineers, Inc., 345 E. 47th St., New York, NY 10017. FAX 908-981-9667. (Subscr. to: Box 1331, 445 Hoes Lane, Piscataway, NJ 08855-1331. TEL 908-981-0060) Ed. J.A. Tanaka. (also avail. in microform)
—BLDSC (4362.917800); EI; Faxon; UnCover; SWETS; UMI. **CCC.**
Description: Data on insulation and dielectrics. Includes information on conference activities.

I E E E ENGINEERING MANAGEMENT REVIEW. see *ENGINEERING*

621.3 US
I E E E GRID. 1953. m. (except July, Aug.). $10. (Institute of Electrical and Electronic Engineers, San Francisco Bay Area Council) East - West Communications, Box 7057, San Mateo, CA 94403. TEL 415-571-0119. FAX 415-571-5585. Ed. Doug Davolt. adv. circ. 24,500.
Description: Contains news of local activities, engineering and professional news and editorials on topics of concern to the engineering community.

621 US ISSN 1049-2690
I E E E GUIDES AND STANDARDS FOR PROTECTIVE RELAYING SYSTEMS. 1988. irreg. Institute of Electrical and Electronics Engineers, Inc., 345 E. 47th St., New York, NY 10017-2394.

621.3 US
I E E E INTERNATIONAL CONFERENCE ON ACOUSTICS, SPEECH AND SIGNAL PROCESSING. PROCEEDINGS. 1976. a. price varies. (I E E E, Acoustics, Speech, and Signal Processing Society) Institute of Electrical and Electronics Engineers, Inc., 345 E. 47th St., New York, NY 10017-2394. TEL 212-705-7900. FAX 212-705-7682. (Subscr. to: Box 1331, 445 Hoes Lane, Piscataway, NJ 08855-1331) **Document type:** proceedings.
Formerly: I E E E International Conference on Acoustics, Speech and Signal Processing. Record.

621.3 US ISSN 0730-9244
TA2005
I E E E INTERNATIONAL CONFERENCE ON PLASMA SCIENCE. I E E E CONFERENCE RECORD-ABSTRACTS. Variant title, 1974-1976: International Conference on Plasma Science. Conference Record Abstracts. 1974. a. price varies. (I E E E, Nuclear and Plasma Sciences Society) Institute of Electrical and Electronics Engineers, Inc., 345 E. 47th St., New York, NY 10017-2394. TEL 212-705-7900. FAX 212-705-7682. (Subscr. to: Box 1331, 445 Hoes Lane, Piscataway, NJ 08855-1331) **Document type:** abstracting/indexing.
—UMI. **CCC.**

621.3 US
I E E E INTERNATIONAL SYMPOSIUM ON ELECTRICAL INSULATION. I E E E CONFERENCE RECORD. biennial. (I E E E, Dielectrics and Electrical Insulation Society) Institute of Electrical and Electronics Engineers, Inc., 345 E. 47th St., New York, NY 10017-2394. TEL 212-705-7900. FAX 212-705-7682. (Subscr. to: Box 1331, 445 Hoes Lane, Piscataway, NJ 08855-1331) charts. **Indexed:** Chem.Abstr. **Document type:** proceedings.

621.38 US ISSN 0190-1494
TK6553 CODEN: IISPDC
I E E E INTERNATIONAL SYMPOSIUM ON ELECTROMAGNETIC COMPATIBILITY.. a. price varies. (I E E E, Electromagnetic Compatibility Society) Institute of Electrical and Electronics Engineers, Inc., 345 E. 47th St., New York, NY 10017-2394. TEL 212-705-7900. FAX 212-705-7682. (Subscr. to: 445 Hoes Lane, Box 1331, Piscataway, NJ 08855-1331)
—BLDSC (4362.968000); EI; CASDDS. **CCC.**
Formerly (until 1977): I E E E International Symposium on Electromagnetic Compatibility Symposium Record. (ISSN 0730-1707); (until 1976): I E E E Electromagnetic Compatibility Symposium Record (ISSN 0730-1715); (until 1974): I E E E International Electromagnetic Compatibility Symposium. Record (ISSN 0074-8811); Until 1970: I E E E Electromagnetic Compatibility Symposium. Record (ISSN 0531-6847); (until 1966): National Symposium on Electromagnetic Compatibility. Symposium Record (ISSN 0730-1723); (until 1965): National Symposium on Electromagnetic Compatability. Record (ISSN 0730-1758); (until 1963): National Symposium on Radio Frequency Interference. Symposium Digest (ISSN 0730-1731).

621.38 US ISSN 1057-7157
TK7874 CODEN: JMIYET
▼**I E E E JOURNAL OF MICROELECTROMECHANICAL SYSTEMS.** 1992. q. $115 to non-members. Institute of Electrical and Electronics Engineers, Inc., 345 E. 47th St., New York, NY 10017. FAX 908-981-9667. (Subscr. to: Box 1331, 445 Hoes La., Piscataway, NJ 08855-1331. TEL 908-981-0060) Ed. William S. Trimmer. (also avail. in microform)
—BLDSC (5019.525000); EI; UnCover; SWETS; UMI; CASDDS. **CCC.**
Description: Covers all aspects of the science, engineering, design and applications in the MEMS area.

629 US ISSN 0364-9059
TC1501 CODEN: IJOEDY
I E E E JOURNAL OF OCEANIC ENGINEERING. 1976. q. $115 to non-members. (I E E E, Oceanic Engineering Society) Institute of Electrical and Electronics Engineers, Inc., 345 E. 47th St., New York, NY 10017-2394. FAX 908-981-9667. (Subscr. to: Box 1331, 445 Hoes Lane, Piscataway, NJ 08855-1331. TEL 908-981-0060) Ed. William Carey. (also avail. in microform) **Indexed:** A.S.& T.Ind., Comput.Abstr., Curr.Cont., Deep Sea Res.& Oceanogr.Abstr., Energy Ind., Energy Info.Abstr., Ind.Sci.Rev., Int.Aerosp.Abstr., Meteor.& Geoastrophys.Abstr., Ocean.Abstr., Petrol.Abstr., Sci.Abstr., Sci.Cit.Ind.
—BLDSC (4362.976500); EI; Faxon; UnCover; SWETS; UMI. **CCC.**
Description: Uses electrical and electronics engineering to advance the understanding of different facets of the ocean environment as represented by theoretical and experimental papers describing significant developments.

621.38 US ISSN 0018-9200
TK7871.85 CODEN: IJSCBC
I E E E JOURNAL OF SOLID STATE CIRCUITS. 1966. bi-m. $275 to non-members. (I E E E, Solid-State Circuits Society) Institute of Electrical and Electronics Engineers, Inc., 345 E. 47th St., New York, NY 10017-2394. FAX 908-981-9667. (Subscr. to: Box 1331, 445 Hoes Lane, Piscataway, NJ 08855-1331. TEL 908-981-0060) Ed. Asad Abidi. charts; illus.; index. (also avail. in microform from MIM,UMI,EEE) **Indexed:** A.S.& T.Ind., CAD CAM Abstr., Cadscan, Chem.Abstr., Curr.Cont., Cyb.Abstr., Eng.Ind., Ind.Sci.Rev., INIS Atomind., Int.Aerosp.Abstr., Lead Abstr., Sci.Abstr., Sci.Cit.Ind., Tel.Abstr., Zincscan.
—BLDSC (4362.985500); EI; Faxon; UnCover; SWETS; UMI; CASDDS. **CCC.**

I E E E JOURNAL ON SELECTED AREAS IN COMMUNICATIONS. see *COMMUNICATIONS*

621.38 US ISSN 0149-645X
TK7876 CODEN: IMIDDM
I E E E - M T T - S INTERNATIONAL MICROWAVE SYMPOSIUM. DIGEST. a. price varies. (I E E E, Microwave Theory and Techniques Society) Institute of Electrical and Electronics Engineers, Inc., 345 E. 47th St., New York, NY 10017-2394. FAX 908-981-9667. (Subscr. to: 445 Hoes Lane, Box 1331, Piscataway, NJ 08855-1331. TEL 908-981-0060)
—BLDSC (4362.999800); EI; UMI; CASDDS. **CCC.**
Former titles: I E E E - M T T - S International Microwave Symposium. Digest of Technical Papers; International Microwave Symposium Digest (ISSN 0074-7009)

530 621.3 US ISSN 1051-8207
TK7876 CODEN: IMGLE3
I E E E MICROWAVE AND GUIDED WAVE LETTERS. 1991. m. $150 to non-members. Institute of Electrical and Electronics Engineers, Inc., 345 E. 47th St., New York, NY 10017-2394. FAX 908-981-9667. (Subscr. to: 445 Hoes Lane, Box 1331, Piscataway, NJ 08855-1331. TEL 908-981-0060) Ed. Tatsuo Itoh. (also avail. in microform)
—BLDSC (4362.999750); EI; UnCover; SWETS; UMI. **CCC.**
Description: Research and engineering contributions in the electromagnetic spectrum from microwaves to infrared, including millimeter waves and submillimeter waves, and guided wave structures.

621.3 US
I E E E MICROWAVE AND MILLIMETER-WAVE MONOLITHIC CIRCUITS SYMPOSIUM. DIGEST OF PAPERS. 1982. a. (I E E E, Microwave Theory and Techniques Society) Institute of Electrical and Electronics Engineers, Inc., 345 E. 47th St., New York, NY 10017-2394. FAX 908-981-9667. (Subscr. to: Box 1331, 445 Hoes Lane, Piscataway, NJ 08855-1331) (Co-sponsor: I E E E Electron Devices Society)

ENGINEERING — ELECTRICAL ENGINEERING

621.3   US
I E E E MILITARY COMMUNICATIONS CONFERENCE. CONFERENCE RECORD. Short title: M I L C O M. Variant title, 1983: I E E E Military Communications Conference. Proceedings. 1982. a? (I E E E, Communications Society) Institute of Electrical and Electronics Engineers, Inc., 345 E. 47th St., New York, NY 10017-2394. TEL 212-705-7900. FAX 212-705-7682. (Subscr. to: Box 1331, 445 Hoes Lane, Piscataway, NJ 08855-1331)

621.38   US
I E E E NATIONAL RADAR CONFERENCE. PROCEEDINGS. 1984. biennial. price varies. (I E E E, Aerospace and Electronic Systems Society) Institute of Electrical and Electronics Engineers, Inc., 345 E. 47th St., New York, NY 10017-2394. TEL 212-705-7900. FAX 212-705-7682. (Subscr. to: Box 1331, 445 Hoes Lane, Piscataway, NJ 08855-1331) **Document type:** proceedings.

I E E E PARALLEL AND DISTRIBUTED TECHNOLOGY MAGAZINE. see *COMPUTERS — Computer Networks*

621.3   US   ISSN 1063-3936
QC787.P3
I E E E PARTICLE ACCELERATOR CONFERENCE. PROCEEDINGS. (Proceedings published as a special issue of the IEEE Transactions on Nuclear Science from 1965-1985) 1965. biennial. price varies. (I E E E, Nuclear and Plasma Science Society) Institute of Electrical and Electronics Engineers, Inc., 345 E. 47th St., New York, NY 10017-2394. FAX 908-981-9667. (Subscr. to: 445 Hoes Ln., Box 1331, Piscataway, NJ 08855-1331) **Indexed:** Sci.Abstr. **Document type:** proceedings.
Formerly (until 1985): Particle Accelerator Conference.
Description: Disseminates information on accelerator work serving high energy physics, nuclear physics, and a large number of applications.

I E E E PHOTONICS TECHNOLOGY LETTERS. see *PHYSICS — Optics*

621.3   US   ISSN 0160-8371
TK2960   CODEN: CRCNDP
I E E E PHOTOVOLTAIC SPECIALISTS CONFERENCE. CONFERENCE RECORD. a. price varies. (I E E E, Electron Devices Society) Institute of Electrical and Electronics Engineers, Inc., 345 E. 47th St., New York, NY 10017-2394. TEL 908-981-1393. FAX 908-981-9667. (Subscr. to: Box 1331, 445 Hoes Lane, Piscataway, NJ 08855-1331) **Indexed:** Chem.Abstr., INIS Atomind.
—BLDSC (3409.833500); El; CASDDS. **CCC.**
Description: Discusses the technical progress in solar cell technologies.

621.3 621.38   US
I E E E POSITION LOCATION AND NAVIGATION SYMPOSIUM. RECORD. Short title: P L A N S. 1976. biennial. price varies. (I E E E, Aerospace and Electronic Systems Society) Institute of Electrical and Electronics Engineers, Inc., 345 E. 47th St., New York, NY 10017-2394. TEL 908-981-1393. FAX 908-981-9667. (Subscr. to: Box 1331, 445 Hoes Lane, Piscataway, NJ 08855-1331)

621.3 378   US   ISSN 0278-6648
   CODEN: IEPTDF
I E E E POTENTIALS; the magazine for engineering students. 1982. q. $40 to non-members. Institute of Electrical and Electronics Engineers, Inc., 345 E. 47th St., New York, NY 10017-2394. TEL 908-981-0060. FAX 908-981-9667. (Subscr. to: Box 1331, 445 Hoes Lane, Piscataway, NJ 08855-1331) Ed. Edmund Miller. (also avail. in microform) **Indexed:** Sci.Abstr.
—BLDSC (4363.014000); UnCover; SWETS; UMI. **CCC.**
Description: Presents articles on management, technological and academic topics. Subjects include robotics engineering, governmental activities, outstanding advisors and counselors, competition in the electrical engineering field, investment programs and automation.

621.3   US   ISSN 0272-1724
TK1001   CODEN: IPERDV
I E E E POWER ENGINEERING REVIEW. 1981. m. $115 to non-members. (I E E E, Power Engineering Society) Institute of Electrical and Electronics Engineers, Inc., 345 E. 47th St., New York, NY 10017-2394. TEL 908-981-0060. FAX 908-981-9667. (Subscr. to: Box 1331, 445 Hoes Lane, Piscataway, NJ 08855-1331) Ed. C.J. Essel. (also avail. in microform from UMI,EEE) **Indexed:** Sci.Abstr.
—BLDSC (4363.015700); El; UnCover; SWETS; UMI. **CCC.**

621.3   US
I E E E POWER ENGINEERING SOCIETY. SUMMER MEETING. PREPRINTS. a. $6.50 to non-members. (I E E E, Power Engineering Society) Institute of Electrical and Electronics Engineers, Inc., 345 E. 47th St., New York, NY 10017-2394. TEL 908-981-1393. FAX 908-981-9667. (Subscr. to: Box 1331, 445 Hoes Lane, Piscataway, NJ 08855-1331)

621.3   US   ISSN 0073-9154
I E E E POWER ENGINEERING SOCIETY. WINTER MEETING. PREPRINTS. a. $6.50 to non-members. (I E E E, Power Engineering Society) Institute of Electrical and Electronics Engineers, Inc., 345 E. 47th St., New York, NY 10017-2394. TEL 212-705-7900. FAX 212-705-7682. (Subscr. to: Box 1331, 445 Hoes Lane, Piscataway, NJ 08855-1331)

I E E E PUBLICATIONS BULLETIN. see *ENGINEERING — Abstracting, Bibliographies, Statistics*

621.3   US   ISSN 0073-9197
I E E E REGION 5 CONFERENCE. RECORD. a. price varies. Institute of Electrical and Electronics Engineers, Inc., 345 E. 47th St., New York, NY 10017-2394. TEL 212-705-7366. FAX 212-705-7682. (Subscr. to: Box 1331, 445 Hoes Lane, Piscataway, NJ 08855-1331. TEL 908-562-3948)
—BLDSC (4363.048550).
Former titles: S W I E E C O Record of Technical Papers; Institute of Electrical and Electronics Engineers. Southwestern I E E E Conference and Exhibition. Record.

621.3 536   US   ISSN 1065-2639
KFC1030.A333
I E E E SEMICONDUCTOR THERMAL AND TEMPERATURE MEASUREMENT SYMPOSIUM. PROCEEDINGS. Short title: Semi-Therm. 1984. a. price varies. (I E E E, Components, Hybrids, and Manufacturing Technology Society) Institute of Electrical and Electronics Engineers, Inc., 345 E. 47th St., New York, NY 10017-2394. TEL 212-705-7366. FAX 212-705-7682. (Subscr. to: 445 Hoes Ln., Box 1331, Piscataway, NJ 08855-1331. TEL 908-562-3948) **Indexed:** Sci.Abstr. **Document type:** proceedings.
Description: Covers new developments and applications related to the generation and removal of heat within semiconductor devices. Examines measurement of junction temperatures under various applications and environmental conditions.

621.3   US   ISSN 1070-9908
TK5102.9   CODEN: IESPEJ
▼**I E E E SIGNAL PROCESSING LETTERS.** 1994. m. $90 to non-members. Institute of Electrical and Electronics Engineers, Inc., 345 E. 47th St., New York, NY 10017. TEL 908-981-0060. FAX 908-981-9667. (Subscr. to: Box 1331, 445 Hoes La., Piscataway, NJ 08855-1331) Ed. Ahmed Tewfik. adv. (microform)
—UnCover.
Description: Recording, reproduction and measurement of speech, signals by digital, electronic, electrical, acoustic, mechanical and optical means.

621.3   US
I E E E SOLID-STATE SENSOR AND ACTUATOR WORKSHOP. TECHNICAL DIGEST. 1984. biennial. price varies. (I E E E, Electron Devices Society) Institute of Electrical and Electronics Engineers, Inc., 345 E. 47th St., New York, NY 10017-2394. TEL 212-705-7900. FAX 212-705-7682. (Subscr. to: 445 Hoes Ln., Box 1331, Piscataway, NJ 08855-1331) **Indexed:** Sci.Abstr.
Formerly (until 1986): I E E E Solid-State Sensor Workshop.
Description: Reports on research and development in solid-state sensor materials, processes, and technologies.

621.3   US
I E E E SOUTHEASTCON (REGION 3 CONFERENCE) RECORD. Variant titles--Southeastcon. Record. Conference and Exhibition; Southeastcon. Proceedings. Conference and Exhibition. a. price varies. Institute of Electrical and Electronics Engineers, Inc., 345 E. 47th St., New York, NY 10017-2394. TEL 908-981-1393. FAX 908-981-9667. (Subscr. to: Box 1331, 445 Hoes Lane, Piscataway, NJ 08855-1331)
Supersedes: I E E E Region 3 Technical Convention. Record (ISSN 0073-9170)

621.3   US   ISSN 0018-9235
TK1   CODEN: IEESAM
I E E E SPECTRUM. (Supplement avail.: The Institute (New York)) 1964. m. $157 to non-members. Institute of Electrical and Electronics Engineers, Inc., 345 E. 47th St., New York, NY 10017-2394. TEL 908-981-0060. FAX 908-981-9667. (Subscr. to: Box 1331, 445 Hoes Lane, Piscataway, NJ 08855-1331) Ed. Murray Slovick. bk.rev.; abstr.; bibl.; charts; index. (also avail. in microform) **Indexed:** A.I.Abstr. (until 1992), A.S.& T.Ind., ABI Inform., Abstr.Hum.Comp.Inter., Appl.Mech.Rev., BMT, C.I.S.Abstr., CAD CAM Abstr. (until 1992), Chem.Abstr., Comput.Cont., Comput.Dtbs., Comput.Lit.Ind., Comput.Rev., Curr.Cont., Cyb.Abstr., Deep Sea Res.& Oceanogr.Abstr., Eng.Ind., Ergon.Abstr., Excerp.Med., Fuel & Energy Abstr., Fut.Surv., Geo.Abstr., High.Educ.Curr.Aware.Bull., Ind.Sci.Rev., INIS Atomind., Int.Aerosp.Abstr., Met.Abstr., Oper.Res.Manage.Sci., PROMT, Qual.Contr.Appl.Stat., Res.High.Educ.Abstr., Risk Abstr., Robomat. (until 1992), Sci.Abstr., Sci.Cit.Ind., Tel.Abstr., World Alum.Abstr.
—BLDSC (4363.071000); El; Faxon; UnCover; SWETS; UMI. **CCC.**
Formerly: Electrical Engineering (ISSN 0095-9197)
Description: Offers information on all aspects of electrical and electronic engineering and their applications.

621.3   US   ISSN 0362-4536
TK7800
I E E E STUDENT PAPERS. 1975. a. avail. on request only. Institute of Electrical and Electronics Engineers, Inc., IEEE Service Center, 345 E. 47th St., New York, NY 10017-2394. TEL 212-705-7900. FAX 212-705-7682. (Subscr. to: Box 1331, 445 Hoes Lane, Piscataway, NJ 08855-1331) illus.

621.3   US   ISSN 0278-520X
I E E E TECHNICAL ACTIVITIES GUIDE. Short title: T A G. q. $25. (I E E E, Technical Activities Department) Institute of Electrical and Electronics Engineers, Inc., 345 E. 47th St., New York, NY 10017-2394. TEL 908-981-0060. FAX 908-981-9667. (Subscr. to: Box 1331, 445 Hoes Lane, Piscataway, NJ 08855-1331. TEL 908-562-3948) (also avail. in microfilm from EEE)
—BLDSC (4363.089500); UnCover. **CCC.**
Description: Features a five-year advance schedule of over 150 conferences that are sponsored by IEEE societies and councils.

I E E E TECHNOLOGY AND SOCIETY MAGAZINE. see *TECHNOLOGY: COMPREHENSIVE WORKS*

ENGINEERING — ELECTRICAL ENGINEERING

621.3 US ISSN 1070-9894
CODEN: ITTEDR
I E E E TRANSACTION ON COMPONENTS, PACKAGING AND MANUFACTURING TECHNOLOGY, PART B: COMPONENTS, PACKAGING AND ADVANCED PACKAGING. 1978. q. $145 to non-members. (I E E E, Components, Hybrids, and Manufacturing Technology Society) Institute of Electrical and Electronics Engineers, Inc., 345 E 47th St., New York, NY 10017. TEL 908-981-0060. FAX 908-981-9667. (Subscr. to: Box 1331, 445 Hoes La., Piscataway, NJ 08855-1331) Ed. Che Yeu Li. adv. (microform)
—BLDSC (4363.174000); EI; Faxon; UnCover; SWETS; UMI; CASDDS. **CCC.**
Supersedes in part (in 1994): I E E E Transactions on Components, Hybrids and Manufacturing Technology (ISSN 0148-6411); Which was formed by the 1978 merger of: I E E E Transactions on Manufacturing Technology (ISSN 0046-838X); I E E Transactions on Parts, Hybrids, and Packaging; Which was formerly: I E E E Transactions on Parts, Materials and Packaging (ISSN 0018-9502)

621.38 629.13 US ISSN 0018-9251
TL3000.A1 CODEN: IEARAX
I E E E TRANSACTIONS ON AEROSPACE AND ELECTRONIC SYSTEMS. 1965. q. $140 to non-members. (I E E E, Aerospace and Electronics Systems Society) Institute of Electrical and Electronics Engineers, Inc., 345 E. 47th St, New York, NY 10017-2394. TEL 908-981-0060. FAX 908-981-9667. (Subscr. to: 445 Hoes Lane, Box 1331, Piscataway, NJ 08855-1331) Ed. Jack R. Harris. bk.rev.; abstr.; illus.; index. (also avail. in microform) **Indexed:** A.I.Abstr., A.S.& T.Ind., Appl.Mech.Rev., CAD CAM Abstr., Cadscan, Chem.Abstr., Curr.Cont., Deep Sea Res.& Oceanogr.Abstr., Eng.Ind., Excerp.Med., Ind.Sci.Rev., Int.Aerosp.Abstr., Lead Abstr., Math.R., Sci.Abstr., Sci.Cit.Ind., Tel.Abstr., Zincscan.
—BLDSC (4363.116100); EI; Faxon; UnCover; SWETS; UMI. **CCC.**
Formerly: I E E E Transaction. Aerospace.
Description: Details equipment, procedures and techniques applicable to the organization, installation and operation of functional systems designed to meet high performance requirements of earth and space systems.

621.38 US ISSN 0018-926X
TK7800 CODEN: IETPAK
I E E E TRANSACTIONS ON ANTENNAS AND PROPAGATION. 1952. m. $212 to non-members. (I E E E, Antennas and Propagation Society) Institute of Electrical and Electronics Engineers, Inc., 345 E. 47th St., New York, NY 10017-2394. TEL 908-981-0060. FAX 908-981-9667. (Subscr. to: Box 1331, 445 Hoes Lane, Piscataway, NJ 08855-1331) Ed. Ronald J. Marhefka. bk.rev.; abstr.; illus.; index. (also avail. in microform) **Indexed:** A.S.& T.Ind., Chem.Abstr., Comput.Abstr., Curr.Cont., Eng.Ind., Ind.Sci.Rev., INIS Atomind., Int.Aerosp.Abstr., Math.R., Sci.Abstr., Sci.Cit.Ind.
—BLDSC (4363.125100); EI; Faxon; UnCover; SWETS; UMI. **CCC.**
Former titles (until 1962): I R E Transactions on Antennas and Propagation; (until 1954): I R E Professional Group on Antennas. Transactions.
Description: Covers experimental and theoretical advances in electromagnetic theory. Discusses radiation, propagation and scattering and diffraction of electromagnetic waves.

621.3 US ISSN 0018-9286
TJ212 CODEN: IETAA9
I E E E TRANSACTIONS ON AUTOMATIC CONTROL. 1956. m. $390 to non-members. (I E E E, Control Systems Society) Institute of Electrical and Electronics Engineers, Inc., 345 E. 47th St., New York, NY 10017. TEL 908-981-0060. FAX 908-981-9667. (Subscr. to: Box 1331, 445 Hoes Lane, Piscataway, NJ 08855-1331) Ed. John Baillieul. bk.rev.; abstr.; illus.; index. (also avail. in microform) **Indexed:** A.I.Abstr. (until 1992), A.S.& T.Ind., Abstr.Bull.Inst.Pap.Chem., Appl.Mech.Rev., CAD CAM Abstr. (until 1992), Chem.Abstr., Compumath, Comput.Abstr., Comput.Dtbs., Curr.Cont., Cyb.Abstr., Eng.Ind., Ind.Sci.Rev., Int.Aerosp.Abstr., Math.R., Robomat. (until 1992), Sci.Abstr., Sci.Cit.Ind., Tel.Abstr.
—BLDSC (4363.143000); EI; Faxon; UnCover; SWETS; UMI. **CCC.**
Description: Explores real-time, optimal, adaptive and stochastic control, estimation and identification, linear systems, and system modeling. Includes applications to physical, economic and social systems.

I E E E TRANSACTIONS ON CIRCUITS AND SYSTEMS PART 1: FUNDAMENTAL THEORY AND APPLICATIONS. see *ELECTRONICS*

I E E E TRANSACTIONS ON CIRCUITS AND SYSTEMS PART 2: ANALOG AND DIGITAL SIGNAL PROCESSING. see *ELECTRONICS*

621.38 US ISSN 1070-9886
TK7869 CODEN: ITTEDR
I E E E TRANSACTIONS ON COMPONENTS, PACKAGING AND MANUFACTURING TECHNOLOGY, PART A: MANUFACTURING TECHNOLOGY. 1978. q. $185 to non-members. (I E E E, Components, Hybrids, and Manufacturing Technology Society) Institute of Electrical and Electronics Engineers, Inc., 345 E. 47th St., New York, NY 10017-2394. TEL 908-981-0060. FAX 908-981-9667. (Subscr. to: 445 Hoes Lane, Box 1331, Piscataway, NJ 08855-1331) Ed. Paul G. Slade. adv.; bk.rev.; index. (also avail. in microform) **Indexed:** A.I.Abstr., A.S.& T.Ind., CAD CAM Abstr., Cadscan, Ceram.Abstr., Chem.Abstr., Curr.Cont., Ind.Sci.Rev., Int.Aerosp.Abstr., Lead Abstr., Math.R., Sci.Abstr., Sci.Cit.Ind., Zincscan.
—BLDSC (4363.174000); EI; Faxon; UnCover; SWETS; UMI; CASDDS. **CCC.**
Supersedes in part (in 1994): I E E E Transactions on Components, Hybrids and Manufacturing Technology (ISSN 0148-6411); Which was formed by the 1978 merger of: I E E E Transactions on Manufacturing Technology (ISSN 0046-838X); I E E Transactions on Parts, Hybrids, and Packaging; Which was formerly: I E E E Transactions on Parts, Materials and Packaging (ISSN 0018-9502)

621.3 US ISSN 1063-6536
TJ212 CODEN: IETTE2
▼**I E E E TRANSACTIONS ON CONTROL SYSTEMS TECHNOLOGY.** 1993. q. $75. Institute of Electrical and Electronics Engineers, Inc., 345 E. 47th St., New York, NY 10017. TEL 908-981-0060. FAX 908-981-9667. (Subscr. to: Box 1331, 445 Hoes Lane, Piscataway, NJ 08855-1331) Ed. Bruce Krogh.
—BLDSC (4363.176600); EI; UnCover; SWETS; UMI.
Description: Covers the exploratory developments and practical applications of the technologies needed to implement control systems from analysis and design through simulation and hardware.

621.38 US
CODEN: DLDIAF
I E E E TRANSACTIONS ON DIELECTRICS AND ELECTRICAL INSULATION. 1965. bi-m. $195 to non-members. (I E E E, Dielectrics and Electrical Insulation Society) Institute of Electrical and Electronics Engineers, Inc., 345 E. 47th St., New York, NY 10017-2394. TEL 908-981-0060. FAX 908-981-9667. (Subscr. to: 445 Hoes Lane, Box 1331, Piscataway, NJ 08855-1331) Ed. Arend van Roggen. bk.rev.; abstr.; illus.; index. (also avail. in microform) **Indexed:** A.S.& T.Ind., Cadscan, Chem.Abstr., Curr.Cont., Eng.Ind., Ind.Sci.Rev., Int.Aerosp.Abstr., Lead Abstr., Math.R., Sci.Abstr., Sci.Cit.Ind., Zincscan.
—BLDSC (4363.179500); EI; Faxon; UnCover; UMI; CASDDS. **CCC.**
Formerly: I E E E Transactions on Electrical Insulation (ISSN 0018-9367); Incorporates (in 1979): Digest of Literature on Dielectrics (ISSN 0070-4865)

621.38 370 US ISSN 0018-9359
T61 CODEN: IEEDAB
I E E E TRANSACTIONS ON EDUCATION. 1958. q. $98 to non-members. (I E E E, Education Society) Institute of Electrical and Electronics Engineers, Inc., 345 E. 47th St., New York, NY 10017-2394. TEL 908-981-0060. FAX 908-981-9667. (Subscr. to: Box 1331, 445 Hoes Lane, Piscataway, NJ 08855-1331) Ed. Frank Barnes. bk.rev.; abstr.; illus.; index. (also avail. in microform) **Indexed:** A.S.& T.Ind., Chem.Abstr., Comput.Abstr., Cont.Pg.Educ., Curr.Cont., Cyb.Abstr., Educ.Tech.Abstr., Eng.Ind., High.Educ.Curr.Aware.Bull., Ind.Sci.Rev., Math.R., Res.High.Educ.Abstr., Sci.Abstr., Sci.Cit.Ind., SSCI, Stud.Wom.Abstr.
—BLDSC (4363.178000); EI; Faxon; UnCover; SWETS; UMI. **CCC.**
Description: Features educational methods, technology, materials and development programs. Explores the impact of research on education.

I E E E TRANSACTIONS ON ENERGY CONVERSION. see *ENERGY — Electrical Energy*

621.3 US ISSN 0018-9391
T56 CODEN: IEEMA4
I E E E TRANSACTIONS ON ENGINEERING MANAGEMENT. 1954. q. $135 to non-members. (I E E E, Engineering Management Society) Institute of Electrical and Electronics Engineers, Inc., 345 E. 47th St., New York, NY 10017-2394. TEL 908-981-0060. FAX 908-981-9667. (Subscr. to: 445 Hoes Lane, Box 1331, Piscataway, NJ 08855-1331) Ed. Dundar F. Kocaoglu. abstr.; illus.; index. (also avail. in microform) **Indexed:** A.S.& T.Ind., ABI Inform, B.P.I., BMT, BPIA, Chem.Abstr., CLOSS, Comput.Abstr., Cont.Pg.Manage., Curr.Cont., Eng.Ind., Ergon.Abstr., Ind.Sci.Rev., Int.Aerosp.Abstr., ISMEC, Math.R., Oper.Res.Manage.Sci., Qual.Contr.Appl.Stat., Risk Abstr., Sci.Abstr., Sci.Cit.Ind., SSCI, Tr.& Indus.Ind.
—BLDSC (4363.185500); EI; Faxon; UnCover; SWETS; UMI. **CCC.**
Description: For organizations engaged in or overseeing research, development, design evaluation, production or operation of electrical or electronic equipment-systems and allied activities.

621.38 US ISSN 0196-2892
QC801 CODEN: IGRSD2
I E E E TRANSACTIONS ON GEOSCIENCE AND REMOTE SENSING. 1963. bi-m. $188 to non-members. (I E E E, Geoscience and Remote Sensing Society) Institute of Electrical and Electronics Engineers, Inc., 345 E. 47th St., New York, NY 10017. TEL 908-981-0060. FAX 908-981-9667. (Subscr. to: 445 Hoes Lane, Box 1331, Piscataway, NY 08855-1331) Ed. James A. Smith. bk.rev.; charts; illus.; index. (also avail. in microform; back issues avail.) **Indexed:** A.S.& T.Ind., AESIS, Agri.Eng.Abstr., Appl.Mech.Rev., CAD CAM Abstr., Chem.Abstr., Curr.Cont., E&P Hlth. (1993-), Eng.Ind., Excerp.Med., Gas Process.& Ppl. (1993-), Geo.Abstr., Ind.Sci.Rev., INIS Atomind., Int.Aerosp.Abstr., Maize Abstr., Math.R., Meteor.& Geoastrophys.Abstr., Ocean.Abstr., Off.Tech. (1993-), Petrol.Abstr. (1965-), Pollut.Abstr., Sci.Abstr., Sci.Cit.Ind., Sel.Water Res.Abstr.
—BLDSC (4363.188400); EI; Faxon; UnCover; SWETS; UMI. **CCC.**
Formerly (until 1980): I E E E Transactions on Geoscience Electronics (ISSN 0018-9413)
Description: Examines the theory, concepts and techniques of science and engineering used in the sensing of the earth, oceans, atmosphere and space.

ENGINEERING — ELECTRICAL ENGINEERING

621.3 US ISSN 0093-9994
TK1 CODEN: ITIACR
I E E E TRANSACTIONS ON INDUSTRY APPLICATIONS. 1965. bi-m. $240 to non-members. (I E E E, Industry Applications Society) Institute of Electrical and Electronics Engineers, Inc., 345 E. 47th St., New York, NY 10017-2394. TEL 908-981-0060. FAX 908-981-9667. (Subscr. to: 445 Hoes Lane, Box 1331, Piscataway, NJ 08854-1331) Ed. Edward Rich. bk.rev.; abstr.; illus.; index. (also avail. in microform) **Indexed:** A.S.& T.Ind., C.I.S. Abstr., CAD CAM Abstr. (until 1992), Cadscan, Chem.Abstr., Comput.Abstr., Energy Info.Abstr., Eng.Ind., Environ.Abstr., Ergon.Abstr., Excerp.Med., Fuel & Energy Abstr., Ind.Sci.Rev., Int.Aerosp.Abstr., Lead Abstr., Math.R., Robomat. (until 1992), Sci.Abstr., Sci.Cit.Ind., Sh.& Vib.Dig., Zincscan.
—BLDSC (4363.196100); EI; Faxon; UnCover; SWETS; UMI; CASDDS. **CCC.**
Formerly: I E E E Transactions on Industry and General Applications (ISSN 0018-943X)
Description: Focuses on the development and application of electrical systems.

621.3 US ISSN 1041-4347
QA76.76.E95 CODEN: ITKEEH
I E E E TRANSACTIONS ON KNOWLEDGE & DATA ENGINEERING. 1989. bi-m. $310 to non-members. (I E E E) Institute of Electrical and Electronics Engineers, Inc., 345 E. 47th St., New York, NY 10017-2394. TEL 908-981-0060. FAX 908-981-9667. (Or: 10662 Los Vaqueros Circle, Box 3014, Los Alamitos, CA 90720-1264. TEL 415-821-8380) Ed. Benjamin Wah. circ. 6,000. (also avail. in microform) **Indexed:** Comput.Abstr.
—BLDSC (4363.199500); EI; Faxon; UnCover; SWETS; UMI. **CCC.**
Description: International and interdisciplinary forum on the published results of research in the design and development of data engineering methodologies, strategies and systems.

621.38 US ISSN 0018-9464
TK454.4.M3 CODEN: IEMGAQ
I E E E TRANSACTIONS ON MAGNETICS. 1965. bi-m. $263 to non-members. (I E E E, Magnetics Society) Institute of Electrical and Electronics Engineers, Inc., 345 E. 47th St., New York, NY 10017-2394. TEL 908-981-0060. FAX 908-981-9667. (Subscr. to: Box 1331, 445 Hoes Lane, Piscataway, NJ 08855-1331) Ed. William Lord. (also avail. in microform from MIM,UMI,EEE) **Indexed:** Chem.Abstr., Comput.Abstr., Curr.Cont., Energy Info.Abstr., Ind.Sci.Rev., Int.Aerosp.Abstr., Phys.Ber., Sci.Abstr., Sci.Cit.Ind.
—BLDSC (4363.200500); EI; Faxon; UnCover; SWETS; UMI; CASDDS. **CCC.**
Description: Details magnetic phenomena, materials and devices as applied to electrical engineering.

621.38 US ISSN 0018-9480
TK7800 CODEN: IETMAB
I E E E TRANSACTIONS ON MICROWAVE THEORY AND TECHNIQUES. 1953. m. $285 to non-members. (I E E E, Microwave Theory and Techniques Society) Institute of Electrical and Electronics Engineers, Inc., 345 E. 47th St., New York, NY 10017-2394. TEL 908-981-0060. FAX 908-981-9667. (Subscr. to: Box 1331, 445 Hoes Lane, Piscataway, NJ 08855-1331) Ed. Daniel Masse. bk.rev.; abstr.; illus.; index. (also avail. in microform) **Indexed:** A.I.Abstr., A.S.& T.Ind., CAD CAM Abstr., Curr.Cont., Eng.Ind., Excerp.Med., Ind.Sci.Rev., INIS Atomind., Int.Aerosp.Abstr., Math.R., Sci.Abstr., Sci.Cit.Ind., Tel.Abstr.
—BLDSC (4363.205100); EI; Faxon; UnCover; SWETS; UMI; CASDDS. **CCC.**

I E E E TRANSACTIONS ON NEURAL NETWORKS. see COMPUTERS — Artificial Intelligence

621.3 537 US ISSN 0018-9499
TK9001 CODEN: IETNAE
I E E E TRANSACTIONS ON NUCLEAR SCIENCE. 1954. bi-m. $170 to non-members. (I E E E, Nuclear and Plasma Sciences Society) Institute of Electrical and Electronics Engineers, Inc., 345 E. 47th St., New York, NY 10017-2394. TEL 908-981-0060. FAX 908-981-9667. (Subscr. to: Box 1331, 445 Hoes Lane, Piscataway, NJ 08855-1331) Ed. Paul V. Dressendorfer. bk.rev.; abstr.; illus.; index. (also avail. in microform) **Indexed:** A.S.& T.Ind., CAD CAM Abstr., Chem.Abstr., Curr.Cont., Energy Info.Abstr., Eng.Ind., Ergon.Abstr., Excerp.Med., Fuel & Energy Abstr., Ind.Sci.Rev., INIS Atomind., Int.Aerosp.Abstr., Math.R., Phys.Ber., Risk Abstr., Sci.Abstr., Sci.Cit.Ind.
—BLDSC (4363.208000); CIS; EI; Faxon; UnCover; SWETS; UMI; CASDDS. **CCC.**

I E E E TRANSACTIONS ON PARALLEL AND DISTRIBUTED SYSTEMS. see COMPUTERS — Computer Networks

621.3 US ISSN 0885-8977
TK1 CODEN: ITPDE5
I E E E TRANSACTIONS ON POWER DELIVERY. 1986. q. $170 to non-members. (I E E E, Power Engineering Society) Institute of Electrical and Electronics Engineers, Inc., 345 E. 47th St., New York, NY 10017-2394. TEL 908-981-0060. FAX 908-981-9667. (Subscr. to: Box 1331, 445 Hoes Lane, Piscataway, NJ 08855-1331) Ed. Harold Gold. (also avail. in microform) **Indexed:** A.S.& T.Ind., Comput.Abstr., INIS Atomind.
—BLDSC (4363.213500); EI; UnCover; SWETS; UMI; CASDDS. **CCC.**
Supersedes in part: I E E E Transactions on Power Apparatus and Systems (ISSN 0018-9510)
Description: Research, development, design, application, construction, installation and operation of apparatus, equipment, structures, materials and systems for safe, reliable, economic delivery and control of electrical energy.

621.3 US ISSN 0361-1434
T10.5 CODEN: IEPCBU
I E E E TRANSACTIONS ON PROFESSIONAL COMMUNICATION. 1958. q. $85 to non-members. (I E E E, Professional Communication Society) Institute of Electrical and Electronics Engineers, Inc., 345 E. 47th St., New York, NY 10017-2394. TEL 908-981-0060. FAX 908-981-9667. (Subscr. to: Box 1331, 445 Hoes Lane, Piscataway, NJ 08855-1331) Ed. Michael Markel. bk.rev.; abstr.; illus.; index. (also avail. in microform) **Indexed:** A.S.& T.Ind., ABI Inform., BPIA, Chem.Abstr., Comput.Abstr., Curr.Cont., Eng.Ind., Ergon.Abstr., Math.R., Oper.Res.Manage.Sci., Qual.Contr.Appl.Stat., Sci.Abstr., SSCI.
—BLDSC (4363.216000); Faxon; UnCover; SWETS; UMI; CASDDS. **CCC.**
Formerly: I E E E Transactions on Engineering Writing and Speech (ISSN 0018-9405)
Description: Explores the study, development, improvement and promotion of techniques used in preparing, organizing, processing, editing, collecting, conserving and disseminating data in the electrical and electronics fields.

621.38 US ISSN 0018-9529
TK7800 CODEN: IEERAJ
I E E E TRANSACTIONS ON RELIABILITY. 1952. 5/yr. $130 to non-members. (I E E E, Reliability Society) Institute of Electrical and Electronics Engineers, Inc., 345 E. 47th St., New York, NY 10017-2394. TEL 908-981-0060. FAX 908-981-9667. (Subscr. to: Box 1331, 445 Hoes Lane, Piscataway, NJ 08855-1331) Ed. Michael G. Pecht. bk.rev.; abstr.; illus.; index. (also avail. in microform) **Indexed:** A.S.& T.Ind., Chem.Abstr., Compumath, Comput.Abstr., Curr.Cont., Cyb.Abstr., Eng.Ind., Ergon.Abstr., Ind.Sci.Rev., Int.Aerosp.Abstr., Math.R., Oper.Res.Manage.Sci., Qual.Contr.Appl.Stat., Risk Abstr., Sci.Abstr., Sci.Cit.Ind.
—BLDSC (4363.219000); EI; Faxon; UnCover; SWETS; UMI. **CCC.**
Description: Principles and practices on reliability, maintainability and product liability pertaining to electrical and electronic equipment.

621.3 US ISSN 0894-6507
TK7836 CODEN: ITSMED
I E E E TRANSACTIONS ON SEMICONDUCTOR MANUFACTURING. 1988. q. $100 to non-members. (I E E E, Components, Hybrids, and Manufacturing Technology Society) Institute of Electrical and Electronics Engineers, Inc., 345 E. 47th St., New York, NY 10017-2394. TEL 908-981-0060. FAX 908-981-9667. (Subscr. to: 443 Hoes Ln., Box 1331, Piscataway, NJ 08855-1331) (Co-sponsors: Electron Devices Society; Reliability Society; Solid-State Circuits Council) Ed. Costas Spanos. (also avail. in microform) **Indexed:** CAD CAM Abstr., Oper.Res.Manage.Sci., Qual.Contr.Appl.Stat., Sci.Abstr.
—BLDSC (4363.219800); EI; Faxon; UnCover; SWETS; UMI. **CCC.**
Description: Addresses the problems of manufacturing complex microelectronic components, including VLSI circuits.

621.38 US ISSN 1053-587X
TK5981 CODEN: ITPRED
I E E E TRANSACTIONS ON SIGNAL PROCESSING. 1951. m. $400 to non-members. (I E E E, Acoustics, Speech, and Signal Processing Society) Institute of Electrical and Electronics Engineers, Inc., 345 E. 47th St., New York, NY 10017-2394. TEL 908-981-0060. FAX 908-981-9667. (Subscr. to: Box 1331, 445 Hoes Lane, Piscataway, NJ 08855-1331) Ed. Pierce Wheeler. abstr.; illus. (also avail. in microform) **Indexed:** A.S.& T.Ind., CAD CAM Abstr., Chem.Abstr., Comput.Abstr., Curr.Cont., Cyb.Abstr., Deep Sea Res.& Oceanogr.Abstr., Eng.Ind., Ergon.Abstr., Excerp.Med., Ind.Sci.Rev., Int.Aerosp.Abstr., Math.R., Sci.Abstr., Sci.Cit.Ind., Tel.Abstr.
—BLDSC (4363.219900); EI; UnCover; SWETS; UMI. **CCC.**
Former titles: I E E E Transactions on Acoustics, Speech and Signal Processing (ISSN 0096-3518); (until 1973): I E E E Transactions on Audio and Electroacoustics (ISSN 0018-9278); (until 1965): I E E E Transactions on Audio; (until 1962): I R E Transactions on Audio; (until 1955): I R E Professional Group on Audio. Transactions.
Description: Focuses on transmission, recording, processing and measurement of speech and other signals by digital, electronic, electrical, acoustic, mechanical and optical means.

621.38 US ISSN 0018-9545
TK7882.M6 CODEN: ITUTAB
I E E E TRANSACTIONS ON VEHICULAR TECHNOLOGY. 1952. q. $145 to non-members. (I E E E, Vehicular Technology Society) Institute of Electrical and Electronics Engineers, Inc., 345 E. 47th St., New York, NY 10017-2394. TEL 908-981-0060. FAX 908-981-9667. (Subscr. to: 445 Hoes Lane, Box 1331, Piscataway, NJ 08855-1331) Ed. Sang Rhee. abstr.; illus. (also avail. in microform) **Indexed:** CAD CAM Abstr., Cadscan, Chem.Abstr., Curr.Cont., Eng.Ind., Ergon.Abstr., Excerp.Med., HRIS, Ind.Sci.Rev., INIS Atomind., Int.Aerosp.Abstr., Lead Abstr., Math.R., Nucl.Sci.Abstr., Sci.Abstr., Sci.Cit.Ind., Sh.& Vib.Dig., Zincscan.
—BLDSC (4363.231000); EI; Faxon; UnCover; SWETS; UMI. **CCC.**
Formerly: I E E E Transactions on Vehicular Communications.
Description: Explores land, airborne and maritime mobile services and citizen's communications services. Includes vehicular electrotechnology, equipment and systems.

621.3 US ISSN 0882-4959
TK454.4.M3 CODEN: ITJJER
I E E E TRANSLATION JOURNAL ON MAGNETICS IN JAPAN. 1985. m. $575 to non-members. (I E E E, Magnetics Society) Institute of Electrical and Electronics Engineers, Inc., 345 E. 47th St., New York, NY 10017-2394 TEL 908-981-0060. FAX 908-981-9667. (Subscr. to: 445 Hoes Lane, Box 1331, Piscataway, NJ 08855-1331) Ed. Takao Suzuki. (also avail. in microform) **Indexed:** INIS Atomind.
—BLDSC (4363.231500); Faxon; SWETS. **CCC.**

I E E E WORKING CONFERENCE ON CURRENT MEASUREMENT. PROCEEDINGS. see EARTH SCIENCES — Oceanography

ENGINEERING — ELECTRICAL ENGINEERING

621.3   UK
I E E ELECTRICAL & ELECTRONICS MATERIALS & DEVICES SERIES. 1981. irreg., vol.10, 1992. Institution of Electrical Engineers, Michael Faraday House, Six Hills Way, Stevenage, Herts SG1 2AY, England. TEL 0438-313311. FAX 0438-313465. TELEX 825578-IEESTV-G. Ed. D.V. Morgan. **Document type:** monographic series.

621.3   UK
I E E ELECTRICAL MEASUREMENTS SERIES. irreg., vol.9, 1992. Institution of Electrical Engineers, Michael Faraday House, Six Hills Way, Stevenage, Herts SG1 2AY, England. TEL 0438-313311. FAX 0438-313465. TELEX 825578-IEESTV-G. Ed.Bd. **Document type:** monographic series.

620   UK
I E E ELECTROMAGNETIC WAVES SERIES. 1976. irreg., vol.36, 1993. Institution of Electrical Engineers, Michael Faraday House, Six Hills Way, Stevenage, Herts SG1 2AY, England. TEL 0438-313311. FAX 0438-313465. TELEX 825578-IEESTV-G. Eds. P.J.B. Clarricoats, J.R. Wait. **Document type:** monographic series.

621.3   GW   ISSN 0722-6179
I E E - INDUSTRIE, ELEKTRIK UND ELEKTRONIK; Datentechnik und Automatisierung. 1955. m. DM.224 (foreign DM.240). Huethig GmbH, Postfach 102869, 69018 Heidelberg, Germany. TEL 06221-489-0. FAX 06221-489482. TELEX 461727-HUEHDD. Ed. Wolfgang Leidig. adv.: B&W page DM.6300; trim 210 x 297; adv. contact: Walter Holzapfel. bk.rev.; abstr.; charts; illus.; stat.; tr.lit.; index; circ. 17,000. **Indexed:** INIS Atomind. **Document type:** trade publication.
—CCC.
Formerly: Industrie Elektrik und Elektronik.
Description: Trade journal for electrical/electronic automation and computer engineering.

621.3   UK
I E E POWER ENGINEERING SERIES. 1981. irreg., vol.18, 1994. Institution of Electrical Engineers, Michael Faraday House, Six Hills Way, Stevenage, Herts SG1 2AY, England. TEL 0438-313311. FAX 0438-313465. TELEX 825578-IEESTV-G. Eds. A.T. Johns, J. Platts. **Document type:** monographic series.

621.3   UK   ISSN 1350-2409
TK7867   CODEN: ICDSE7
I E E PROCEEDINGS - CIRCUITS, DEVICES AND SYSTEMS. (Institution of Electrical Engineers) 1980. bi-m. I.E.E., Michael Faraday House, Six Hills Way, Stevenage, Herts. SG1 2AY, England. TEL 0438-313311. FAX 0438-742840. TELEX 825578-IEESTV-G. (Subscr. to: Publication Sales Dept., P.O. Box 96, Stevenage, Herts. SG1 2SD, England; U.S. addr.: INSPEC/IEEE, Box 1331, 445 Hoes Ln., Piscataway, NJ 08855-1331. TEL 908-562-5549) Ed. Gill Wheeler. adv.; bk.rev.; index. circ. 3,000. **Indexed:** A.S.& T.Ind., Cadscan, Excerp.Med., Int.Aerosp.Abstr., Lead Abstr., Math.R., Sci.Abstr., Zincscan. **Document type:** proceedings.
●Also available on CD-ROM. Producer(s): University Microfilms International.
—BLDSC (4362.751857); EI; Faxon; UnCover; SWETS; UMI. **CCC.**
Formerly: I E E Proceedings G (Circuits, Devices and Systems) (ISSN 0956-3768)
Description: Covers the theory, design, and analysis of electronic circuits and systems.

621.3   UK   ISSN 1350-2425
TK1   CODEN: IPCOED
I E E PROCEEDINGS - COMMUNICATIONS. (Institution of Electrical Engineers) 1980. bi-m. I.E.E., Michael Faraday House, Six Hills Way, Stevenage, Herts. SG1 2AY, England. TEL 0438-313311. FAX 0438-742840. TELEX 825578-IEESTV-G. (Subscr. to: Publication Sales Dept., P.O. Box 96, Stevenage, Herts. SG1 2SD, England; U.S. addr.: INSPEC/IEEE, Box 1331, 445 Hoes Ln., Piscataway, NJ 08855-1331. TEL 908-562-5549) Ed. Gill Wheeler. adv.; bk.rev.; index. circ. 2,500. **Indexed:** A.S.& T.Ind., Br.Tech.Ind., Cadscan, Chem.Abstr., Excerp.Med., Int.Aerosp.Abstr., Lead Abstr., Math.R., Sci.Abstr., Sci.Cit.Ind., Zincscan. **Document type:** proceedings.
●Also available on CD-ROM. Producer(s): University Microfilms International.
—BLDSC (4362.751859); EI; Faxon; UnCover; SWETS; UMI. **CCC.**
Formerly: I E E Proceedings I (Communications, Speech and Vision) (ISSN 0956-3776)
Description: Covers adaptive equalization and echo cancellation techniques; cryptography; error detection and correction; speech analysis, image coding; and line, fixed, and mobile radio, satellite, and optical communication systems.

621.3   UK   ISSN 1350-2379
TK1   CODEN: ICTAEX
I E E PROCEEDINGS - CONTROL THEORY AND APPLICATIONS. (Institution of Electrical Engineers) 1980. bi-m. I.E.E., Michael Faraday House, Six Hills Way, Stevenage, Herts. SG1 2AY, England. TEL 0438-313311. FAX 0438-742840. TELEX 825575-IEESTV-G. (Subscr. to: Publication Sales Dept., P.O. Box 96, Stevenage, Herts. SG1 2SD, England; U.S. addr.: INSPEC/IEEE, Box 1331, 445 Hoes Ln., Piscataway 08855-1331. TEL 908-562-5549) Ed. Gill Wheeler. adv.; bk.rev.; index. circ. 3,000. **Indexed:** A.S.& T.Ind., Appl.Mech.Rev., BMT, Br.Tech.Ind., Cadscan, Chem.Eng.Abstr., Comput.Cont., Excerp.Med., Int.Aerosp.Abstr., Lead Abstr., Math.R., Sci.Abstr., Sci.Cit.Ind., Zincscan. **Document type:** proceedings.
●Also available on CD-ROM. Producer(s): University Microfilms International.
—BLDSC (4362.751863); EI; Faxon; UnCover; SWETS; UMI; CASDDS. **CCC.**
Formerly: I E E Proceedings D (Control Theory and Applications) (ISSN 0143-7054)
Description: Covers control systems, system modeling, design and implementation, identification, simulation, technological, economic, physiological systems, man-machine interfaces, robotics, and process control.

621.3   UK
TK4001   CODEN: IPPADZ
I E E PROCEEDINGS - ELECTRIC POWER APPLICATIONS. (Institution of Electrical Engineers) 1980. bi-m. I.E.E., Michael Faraday House, Six Hills Way, Stevenage, Herts. SG1 2AY, England. TEL 0438-313311. FAX 0438-742840. TELEX 825578-IEESTV-G. (Subscr. to: Publication Sales Dept., P.O. Box 96, Stevenage, Herts. SG1 2SD, England; U.S. addr.: INSPEC/IEEE, Box 1331, 445 Hoes Ln., Piscataway, NJ 08855-1331. TEL 908-562-5549) Ed. Gill Wheeler. adv.; bk.rev.; index. circ. 4,500. **Indexed:** A.S.& T.Ind., Br.Tech.Ind., Cadscan, Excerp.Med., INIS Atomind., Lead Abstr., Math.R., Sci.Abstr., Sci.Cit.Ind., Zincscan. **Document type:** proceedings.
●Also available on CD-ROM. Producer(s): University Microfilms International.
—EI; Faxon; UnCover; UMI. **CCC.**
Formerly: I E E Proceedings B (Electric Power Applications) (ISSN 0143-7038)
Description: Examines electrical equipment design, application, and development. Covers rotating electrical machines, electrically powered motors and vehicles, railway traction, and signaling, power electronics, and industrial and other applications of power.

621.3   UK   ISSN 1350-2360
TK1   CODEN: IGTDE2
I E E PROCEEDINGS - GENERATION, TRANSMISSION AND DISTRIBUTION. (Institution of Electrical Engineers) 1980. bi-m. I.E.E., Michael Faraday House, Six Hills Way, Stevenage, Herts. SG1 2AY, England. TEL 0438-313311. FAX 0438-742840. TELEX 825578-IEESTV-G. (U.S. addr.: INSPEC/IEEE, Box 1331, 445 Hoes Ln., Piscataway, NJ 08855-1331. TEL 908-562-5549) Ed. Gill Wheeler. adv.; bk.rev.; index. circ. 3,500. (also avail. in microfiche; back issues avail.) **Indexed:** A.S.& T.Ind., Br.Tech.Ind., Cadscan, Excerp.Med., Lead Abstr., Math.R., Sci.Abstr., Sci.Cit.Ind., Zincscan. **Document type:** proceedings.
—BLDSC (4362.751880); EI; Faxon; UnCover; SWETS; UMI. **CCC.**
Formerly: I E E Proceedings C (Generation, Transmission and Distribution) (ISSN 0143-7046)
Description: Covers power generation and energy storage, generators, generator operation and control, power systems, plant condition monitoring, and measurement and protection.

621.3   UK
TK1   CODEN: IMIPEP
I E E PROCEEDINGS - MICROWAVES, ANTENNAS & PROPAGATION. (Institution of Electrical Engineers) 1980. bi-m. I.E.E., Michael Faraday House, Six Hills Way, Stevenage, Herts. SG1 2AY, England. TEL 0438-313311. FAX 0438-742840. TELEX 825578-IEESTV-G. (Subscr. to: Publication Sales Dept., P.O. Box 96, Stevenage, Herts. SG1 2SD, England; U.S. addr. INSPEC/IEEE, Box 1331, 445 Hoes Ln., Piscataway, NJ 08855-1331. TEL 908-562-5549) Ed. Gill Wheeler. adv.; bk.rev.; index. circ. 2,600. **Indexed:** A.S.& T.Ind., Br.Tech.Ind., Excerp.Med., Int.Aerosp.Abstr., Math.R., Sci.Abstr., Sci.Cit.Ind. **Document type:** proceedings.
●Also available on CD-ROM. Producer(s): University Microfilms International.
—EI; Faxon; UnCover; UMI. **CCC.**
Formerly: I E E Proceedings H (Microwaves, Antennas and Propagation) (ISSN 0950-107X)
Description: Covers microwave techniques, components source and instrumentation, antennas and arrays, dipoles, monopoles, wire antennas, microwave network theory and signal-processing devices, millimeter and submillimeter techniques, radiowave propagation at all frequencies, traveling-wave antennas, waveguides, and transmission lines.

I E E PROCEEDINGS - OPTOELECTRONICS. see PHYSICS — Optics

621.3   UK   ISSN 1350-2395
TK1   CODEN: IRSNE2
I E E PROCEEDINGS - RADAR, SONAR AND NAVIGATION. (Institution of Electrical Engineers) 1980. bi-m. I.E.E., Michael Faraday House, Six Hills Way, Stevenage, Herts. SG1 2AY, England. TEL 0438-313311. FAX 0438-742840. TELEX 825578-IEESTV-G. (Subscr. to: Publication Sales Dept., P.O. Box 96, Stevenage, Herts. SG1 2SD, England; U.S. addr.: INSPEC/IEEE, Box 1331, 445 Hoes Ln., Piscataway, NJ 08855-1331. TEL 908-562-5549) Ed. Gill Wheeler. adv.; bk.rev. circ. 3,300. **Indexed:** A.S.& T.Ind., BMT, Br.Tech.Ind., Comput.Cont., Ergon.Abstr., Excerp.Med., Int.Aerosp.Abstr., Math.R., Sci.Abstr., Sci.Cit.Ind. **Document type:** proceedings.
●Also available on CD-ROM. Producer(s): University Microfilms International.
—BLDSC (4362.755550); EI; Faxon; UnCover; SWETS; UMI. **CCC.**
Formerly: I E E Proceedings F (Radar and Signal Processing) (ISSN 0956-375X)
Description: Covers acoustic image processing, adaptive filters, avionics, bearing estimation, electronic warfare, navigation systems, radar, signal processing, sonar, spectral analysis, system modeling, and identification techniques.

ENGINEERING — ELECTRICAL ENGINEERING

621.3   UK   ISSN 1350-2344
TK1   CODEN: ISMTEV
I E E PROCEEDINGS - SCIENCE, MEASUREMENT AND TECHNOLOGY. (Institution of Electrical Engineers) 1980. bi-m. I.E.E, Michael Faraday House, Six Hills Way, Stevenage, Herts. SG1 2AY, England. TEL 0438-313311. FAX 0438-742840. TELEX 825578-IEESTV-G. (Subscr. to: Publication Sales Dept., P.O. Box 96, Stevenage, Herts. SG1 2SD, England; INSPEC/IEEE, Box 1331, 445 Hoes Ln., Piscataway, NJ 08855-1331. TEL 908-562-5549) Ed. Gill Wheeler. adv.; abstr.; charts; illus.; stat.; index. circ. 3,600. **Indexed:** A.S.& T.Ind., Account.& Data Proc.Abstr., BMT, Br.Ceram.Abstr., Br.Tech.Ind., C.I.S.Abstr., Cadscan, Chem.Abstr., Curr.Cont., Educ.Tech.Abstr., Eng.Ind., Excerp.Med., High.Educ.Curr.Aware.Bull., INIS Atomind., Lead Abstr., Math.R., Met.Abstr., Meteor.& Geostrophys.Abstr., Res.High.Educ.Abstr., Sci.Abstr., Sci.Cit.Ind., World Alum.Abstr. **Document type:** proceedings.
●Also available on CD-ROM. Producer(s): University Microfilms International.
—BLDSC (4362.755580); SWETS; UMI; CASDDS.
Formerly: I E E Proceedings A (Science, Measurement and Technology) (ISSN 0960-7641)
Description: Covers alternative energy, biological aspects, including medical practice, cryogenics and superconductivity, EM theory and computer simulations, fundamentals of electrical engineering management, electric metrology, fundamental materials and properties, nondestructive testing, physics of arcs and discharges, and teaching.

621.3   UK   ISSN 1350-245X
CODEN: IVIPEK
▼**I E E PROCEEDINGS - VISION, IMAGE & SIGNAL PROCESSING.** (Institution of Electrical Engineers) 1994. bi-m. I.E.E., Michael Faraday House, Six Hills Way, Stevenage, Herts. SG1 2AY, England. TEL 0438-313311. FAX 0438-742840. TELEX 525578-IEESTV-G. (Subscr. to: Publication Sales Dept., P.O. Box 96, Stevenage, Herts. SG1 2SD, England; U.S. addr.: INSPEC/IEEE, Box 1331, 445 Hoes Ln., Piscataway, NJ 08855-1331. TEL 908-562-5549) Ed. Gill Wheeler. adv.; bk.rev.; index. circ. 2,500. **Document type:** proceedings.
●Also available on CD-ROM. Producer(s): University Microfilms International.
—BLDSC (4362.755600); SWETS; UMI.
Description: Covers signal processing, image-processing techniques, machine vision, computer imaging and computer graphics, source-coding techniques, speech analysis coding recognition and synthesis, digital filters and multirate filterbanks, signal-transformation techniques, spectral analysis, system modeling, and adaptive identification techniques.

621.3   UK
I E E RADAR, SONAR, NAVIGATION AND AVIONICS SERIES. irreg., vol.4, 1993. Institution of Electrical Engineers, Michael Faraday House, Six Hills Way, Stevenage, Herts SG1 2AY, England. TEL 0438-313311. FAX 0438-313465. TELEX 825578-IEESTV-G. Eds. E.D.R. Shearman, P. Bradsell. **Document type:** monographic series.

621.38   UK
CODEN: IEREEF
I E E REVIEW. (Institution of Electrical Engineers) N.S. 1955. bi-m. £60 in EC nations; elsewhere £66. I.E.E., Michael Faraday House, Six Hills Way, Stevenage, Herts. SG1 2AY, England. TEL 0438-313311. FAX 0438-742840. TELEX 825578-IEESTV-G. (Subscr. to: Publication Sales Dept., P.O. Box 96, Stevenage, Herts. SG1 2SD, England; U.S. addr.: INSPEC/IEEE, Box 1331, 445 Hoes Ln., Piscataway, NJ 08855-1331. TEL 908-562-5549) Ed. Tony Prins. adv.; bk.rev.; abstr.; charts; illus.; index. circ. 133,000. **Indexed:** A.S.& T.Ind., Acid Rain Abstr., Acid Rain Ind., Agri.Eng.Abstr., BMT, Br.Rail.Bd., Br.Tech.Ind., CAD CAM Abstr. (until 1992), Cadscan, Chem.Abstr., Chem.Eng.Abstr., Curr.Cont., Cyb.Abstr., Energy Info.Abstr. (through 1993), Eng.Ind., Environ.Abstr., Excerp.Med., Fluidex, Geo.Abstr., Ind.Sci.Rev., INIS Atomind., Lead Abstr., Robomat. (until 1992), Sci.Abstr., Sci.Cit.Ind., Tel.Abstr., Zincscan. **Document type:** trade publication.
●Also available on CD-ROM. Producer(s): University Microfilms International.
—UnCover; SWETS. CCC.
Incorporating: Electronics and Power (ISSN 0013-5127); I E E News (ISSN 0018-9553); Students Quarterly Journal (ISSN 0039-2871)
Description: Provides insight into the rapidly advancing world of electronics and electrical engineering, including news about the industry and the profession. Provides state-of-the-art coverage about new developments, letters, and parliamentary reports.

621.32   US   ISSN 0073-5469
I E S LIGHTING HANDBOOK. 1949. irreg., latest 1993. $389. Illuminating Engineering Society, 120 Wall St., New York, NY 10005. TEL 212-248-5000. FAX 212-248-5017. Ed. Mark Rae. circ. 10,000. **Document type:** trade publication.
—CCC.

621.3   NE
I-KWADRAAT - ELEKTROTECHNIEK - ELECTRONICA. 1985. m. fl.160 membership. (Nederlandse Ingenieurs Vereniging (NIRIA)) Ingenieurspers B.V., P.O. Box 90162, 1006 BD Amsterdam, Netherlands. TEL 020-5102922. FAX 020-5102439. Ed. C. van der Sluys. circ. 9,700. (back issues avail.)
Description: Discusses technical and managerial topics on a university level.

621.366   JA   ISSN 0289-1549
I L E QUARTERLY PROGRESS REPORT. (Text in English) 1982. q. Osaka University, Institute of Laser Engineering - Osaka Daigaku Reza Kaku Yugo Kenkyu Senta, 2-6, Yamadaoka, Suita-shi, Osaka 565, Japan.
—BLDSC (4364.144800).

621.3   US   ISSN 0190-0943
TK6553
I T E M. (Interference Technology Engineers Master); the international journal of EMC. 1971. a. $80 (effective 1993). R & B Enterprises (West Conshohocken) (Subsidiary of: Robar Industries, Inc.), 20 Clipper Rd., West Conshohocken, PA 19428. TEL 215-825-1960. FAX 215-825-1684. TELEX 510-660-8120. Ed. Michele D. Elkes. adv.; B&W page $3050; color page $3975; adv. contact: Leonard Levin. bibl.; charts; illus.; tr.lit.; index; circ. 24,325 (controlled). (record; back issues avail.)
—BLDSC (4533.473000).
Description: Design guide for the measurement and control of electromagnetic interference (EMI). Includes technical articles and an index of products, supplies and services directed towards interference control.

I W - REPORT; Informationen fuer die technisch-industrielle Werbung und Verkaufsfoerderung. see *MACHINERY*

621.393   US
ILLINOIS RURAL ELECTRIC NEWS. Cover title: R E N Illinois Rural Electric News. 1943. m. $5 to non-members; members $3.60. Association of Illinois Electric Cooperatives, Box 3787, Springfield, IL 62708. TEL 217-529-5561. FAX 217-529-5810. Ed. Larry F. Elledge. adv.; illus. circ. 142,000. **Document type:** consumer publication.

621.32   JA   ISSN 0019-2341
ILLUMINATING ENGINEERING INSTITUTE OF JAPAN. JOURNAL/SHOMEI GAKKAI SHI. (Text in Japanese; summaries in English) 1917. m. 8400 Yen. Illuminating Engineering Institute of Japan - Shomei Gakkai, 1-7-1 Yuraku-cho, Chiyoda-ku, Tokyo 100, Japan. Ed. Naohiro Ishizuka. **Indexed:** JCT, JTA, Sci.Abstr.
—BLDSC (4759.530000). CCC.

621.32   US   ISSN 0099-4480
TH7700   CODEN: JIESBS
ILLUMINATING ENGINEERING SOCIETY. JOURNAL. Key Title: Journal of the Illuminating Engineering Society. 1971. s-w. $195. Illuminating Engineering Society, 120 Wall St., New York, NY 10005. TEL 212-248-5000. FAX 212-248-5017. Ed. Kevin Heslin. bk.rev. index. circ. 10,000. (also avail. in microform from UMI,PMC) **Indexed:** A.S.& T.Ind., C.I.S.Abstr., Chem.Abstr., Curr.Cont., Ergon.Abstr., Graph.Arts Lit.Abstr., HRIS, Int.Build.Serv.Abstr., Sci.Abstr. **Document type:** bulletin.
—BLDSC (4759.560000); EI; Faxon; UnCover; SWETS; UMI; CASDDS. CCC.
Supersedes in part (in 1971): Illuminating Engineering (ISSN 0019-2333)

621.32 747   IT   ISSN 0019-2384
ILLUMINOTECNICA international lighting magazine. (Text in English, French, German, Italian, Spanish) 1960. bi-m. L.200000 (typically set in Sep.). Editrice Habitat s.r.l., Via M.M. de Taddei 3, 20146 Milan, Italy. TEL 48-14-800. FAX 48-19-3013. Ed. Manfredo Traini. adv.; charts. circ. 9,000.
Description: For exporters, importers, wholesalers, buyers, architects, interior designers and lighting engineers.

621.3   IT   ISSN 0394-5634
L'IMPIANTO ELETTRICO. 1987. m. L.95000 (foreign L.180000). Etas s.r.l., Via Mecenate 91, 20138 Milan, Italy. TEL 02-580841. FAX 02-58012592. Ed. Carlo Vitti. adv.: B&W page L.2330000, color page L.3170000; trim 182 x 257. circ. 11,670. (back issues avail.)

INDIAN JOURNAL OF POWER AND RIVER VALLEY DEVELOPMENT. see *WATER RESOURCES*

621.3   US
INDUSTRIAL AND COMMERCIAL POWER SYSTEMS TECHNICAL CONFERENCE. 1964. a. (I E E E, Industry Applications Society) Institute of Electrical and Electronics Engineers, Inc., 345 E. 47th St., New York, NY 10017-2394. TEL 212-705-7900. FAX 212-705-7682. (Subscr. to: Box 1331, 445 Hoes Lane, Piscataway, NJ 08855-1331)
Formerly (until 1972): Industrial and Commercial Power Systems and Electrical Space Heating and Air Conditioning Joint Technical Conference. Record (ISSN 0073-733X)
Description: Focuses on the engineering, operations, maintenance, and regulation of systems.

001.3   US   ISSN 0197-2618
TK5   CODEN: CIAID5
INDUSTRY APPLICATIONS SOCIETY. I E E E - I A S ANNUAL MEETING. CONFERENCE RECORD. Key Title: Conference Record, Industry Applications Society, I E E E - I A S Annual Meeting. a. (I E E E, Industry Applications Society) Institute of Electrical and Electronics Engineers, Inc., 345 E. 47th St., New York, NY 10017-2394. TEL 212-705-7366. FAX 212-705-7682. (Subscr. to: 445 Hoes Lane, Box 1331, Piscataway, NJ 08855-0331. TEL 908-562-3948)
—BLDSC (3409.821700); EI; CASDDS. CCC.
Formerly (until 1980): I A S Annual Meeting. Conference Record (ISSN 0160-8592)

537   KR
INFORMATSIONNO-IZMERITEL'NAYA TEKHNIKA. (Subseries of: Kharkivskyi Politekhnichnyi Instytut. Vestnik) (Text in Russian) 1973. irreg. Kharkivskyi Politekhnichnyi Instytut, Ul. Frunze, 21, Kharkov 310002, Ukraine. illus.
Formerly (until 1977): Elektrovymiriuvalna Tekhnika.

537 380   CR   ISSN 0074-0047
INFORME DE OPERACION DE LAS PRINCIPALES EMPRESAS PRODUCTORAS Y DISTRIBUIDORAS DE ENERGIA ELECTRICA DE COSTA RICA. 1958. 2/yr. (in 2 vols., 1 no./vol.). free. Instituto Costarricense de Electricidad (ICE), Direccion de Planificacion Electrica, P.O. Box 10032 San Jose, Costa Rica. charts; stat.; index; circ. controlled.

2344 ENGINEERING — ELECTRICAL ENGINEERING

INGENIERIA ENERGETICA. see *ENERGY*

INGENIERIA MECANICA Y ELECTRICA. see *ENGINEERING — Mechanical Engineering*

DER INGENIEUR. see *ENGINEERING*

621.3   FR   ISSN 0980-8434
INGENIEURS E S M E. 1953. 4/yr. A I E S M E, 19 rue Mayet, 75006 Paris, France. TEL 45-67-86-78. FAX 47-34-59-21. Ed. Frederic Delaitre. circ. 2,400.
Description: Provides technical and professional information for electrical, electronic and computer engineers.

621.3   FR
INGENIEURS I.N.P.G.* 1969. 4/yr. 120 F. Association des Ingenieurs Anciens Eleves de l'Institut National Polytechnique de Grenoble (Houille Blanche), 12 rue Bixio, 75007 Paris, France. TEL 45-51-77-15. Ed. Louis Consolini. adv. circ. 6,000.

INSIDE DEFENSE ELECTRONICS. see *MILITARY*

INSPEC MATTERS. see *SCIENCES: COMPREHENSIVE WORKS — Computer Applications*

INSPEC THESAURUS. see *SCIENCES: COMPREHENSIVE WORKS — Computer Applications*

621.3   NE   ISSN 0168-1109
INSTALLATIE JOURNAAL; vakblad voor de elektrotechnische installateur. 1983. m. fl.142 (effective 1994). Wegener Tijl Tijdschriften Groep B.V., Postbus 9943, 1006 AP Amsterdam, Netherlands. TEL 31-20-5182828. FAX 31-20-5182843. Ed. R. van Domburg. adv.; bk.rev. circ. 9,089. **Document type:** trade publication.
—SWETS.
Incorporates (in 1987): Electra (ISSN 0013-4104); **Formerly:** E R M Installatiejournaal.

INSTALLATION NEWS. see *COMMUNICATIONS*

537   DK   ISSN 0105-9629
INSTALLATIONS NYT. 1978. 11/yr. free to qualified personnel. Teknisk Forlag A - S, Skelbaekgade 4, DK-1780 Copenhagen V, Denmark. TEL 45-31-21-68-01. FAX 45-31-21-04-01. TELEX 16368 TEKFO DK. Ed. Peter Friis. adv.: B&W page DKK 9960; color page DKK 15360; trim 257 x 175. bk.rev.; charts; illus.; tr.lit.; circ. 8,838 (controlled).
Description: Provides information to electricians and project developers in the electrical installation field through articles about new products in installation equipment, measuring equipment, tools and machinery.

621.3   DK
INSTALLATIONS NYT. LEVERANDOERREGISTER. Variant title: Installations Nyts Leverandoerregister. 1978. a. Teknisk Forlag A-S, Skelbaekgade 4, DK-1780 Copenhagen V, Denmark. TEL 45-35-37-80-55. adv. circ. 7,873.

621.3   US   ISSN 1050-1797
THE INSTITUTE (NEW YORK). (News supplement to: I E E E Spectrum (ISSN 0018-9235)) 1977. m. $25 (only avail. to subscribers in the US). (I E E E) Institute of Electrical and Electronics Engineers, Inc., 345 E. 47th St., New York, NY 10017-2394. TEL 908-981-0060. FAX 908-981-9667. (Subscr. to: 344 Hoes Lane, Box 1331, Piscataway, NJ 08855-1331) (also avail. in microform) **Indexed:** Tel.Abstr.
Description: Provides coverage of activities, both in and outside IEEE, that impact on the electrical engineer's career and profession.

621.3   US   ISSN 0018-9219
TK5700   CODEN: IEEPAD
INSTITUTE OF ELECTRICAL AND ELECTRONICS ENGINEERS. PROCEEDINGS. 1913. m. $275 to non-members. Institute of Electrical and Electronics Engineers, Inc., 345 E. 47th St., New York, NY 10017-2394. TEL 908-981-0060. FAX 908-981-9667. (Subscr. to: Box 1331, 445 Hoes Lane, Piscataway, NJ 08855-1331) Ed. Richard Fair. adv.; bk.rev.; abstr.; bibl.; charts; illus.; tr.lit.; index. (also avail. in microform) **Indexed:** A.I.Abstr. (until 1992), A.S.& T.Ind., BMT, CAD CAM Abstr. (until 1992), Chem.Abstr., Comput.Cont., Curr.Cont., Eng.Ind., Ergon.Abstr., Excerp.Med., Fuel & Energy Abstr., Math.R., Meteor. & Geoastrophys.Abstr., Petrol.Abstr., Robomat. (until 1992), Sci.Abstr., Sh.& Vib.Dig., Tel.Abstr.
—BLDSC (6708.700000); EI; Faxon; UnCover; SWETS; UMI; CASDDS. **CCC.**
Description: Publishes invited and submitted papers on all aspects of electrical engineering and its applications.

621.3   AT   ISSN 0046-9807
INSTITUTE OF ELECTRICAL INSPECTORS. I.E.I. JOURNAL. 1947. bi-m. Aus.$36. Institute of Electrical Inspectors, P.O. Q10, Sydney, N.S.W. 2000, Australia. TEL 02-893-7531. Ed. J.J. Holtmann. adv.; bk.rev. circ. 7,000. **Document type:** trade publication.

INSTITUTE OF ELECTRONICS, INFORMATION AND COMMUNICATION ENGINEERS. TRANSACTIONS (SECTION D-I)/DENSHI JOHO TSUSHIN GAKKAI RONBUNSHI (D-I). see *COMPUTERS — Computer Systems*

INSTITUTE OF ELECTRONICS, INFORMATION AND COMMUNICATION ENGINEERS. TRANSACTIONS (SECTION D-II)/DENSHI JOHO TSUSHIN GAKKAI RONBUNSHI (D-II). see *COMPUTERS — Information Science And Information Theory*

621.38   II   ISSN 0020-3386
TK1   CODEN: JEELAC
INSTITUTION OF ENGINEERS (INDIA). ELECTRICAL ENGINEERING DIVISION. JOURNAL. (Text in English) 1920. bi-m. Rs.120($15) Institution of Engineers (India), Electrical Engineering Division, 8 Gokhale Rd., Calcutta 700 020, India. TEL 033-288334. FAX 033-288345. TELEX 0217885 IEIC IN. Ed. K.N. Majumdar. adv.; charts; illus.; index. circ. 16,000. **Indexed:** Appl.Mech.Rev., Eng.Ind., Excerp.Med., INIS Atomind., Met.Abstr., Sci.Abstr.
—BLDSC (4794.020000); EI.

621.3 660   NZ   ISSN 0111-946X
TA1   CODEN: TPESDJ
INSTITUTION OF PROFESSIONAL ENGINEERS. TRANSACTIONS. ELECTRICAL, MECHANICAL AND CHEMICAL ENGINEERING SECTION. a. NZ.$2- per no. Institution of Professional Engineers, New Zealand, P.O. Box 12241, Wellington, New Zealand. TEL 64-4-473-9444. FAX 64-4-473-2324. Ed. Peter King. circ. 2,500.
—BLDSC (8970.500000). **CCC.**
Description: Scientific papers on different aspects of electrical, mechanical and chemical engineering.

INSTITUTION OF RADIO AND ELECTRONICS ENGINEERS. MONITOR. see *COMMUNICATIONS — Television And Cable*

621.3   MX
INSTITUTO DE INVESTIGACIONES ELECTRICAS. INFORME ANUAL. (Editions in English, Spanish) 1978. a. free. Instituto de Investigaciones Electricas, Interior Internado Palmira - Institute of Electrical Research, Apdo. Postal 475, 6200 Cuernavaca, Morelos, Mexico. TEL 182527. Ed. Gabriel Nagose Cazares. charts; illus.; stat. circ. 3,000. **Document type:** corporate report.
Description: Covers research and experimental development in the electric industry.

INSTITUTO NACIONAL DE ASTROFISICA, OPTICA Y ELECTRONICA. BOLETIN. see *ASTRONOMY*

INSTITUTUL DE STUDII SI PROIECTARI ENERGETICE. BULETINUL. see *ENERGY*

621.3 629.8   RM
INSTITUTUL POLITEHNIC DIN IASI. BULETINUL. SECTIA III: ELECTROTEHNICA, ENERGETICA, ELECTRONICA. (Text in English, French, German, Italian, Russian, Spanish) 1946. s-a. exchange basis. Institutul Politehnic din Iasi, Bd. Copou 11, 6600 Jassy, Rumania. TEL 46577. FAX 40-81-78923. Eds. Alfred Braier, Hugo Rosman. adv.; bk.rev.; bibl. circ. 450. **Indexed:** Appl.Mech.Rev., Chem.Abstr., Math.R., Met.Abstr., Ref.Zh., Sci.Abstr.
Former titles: Institutul Politehnic din Iasi. Buletinul. Sectia III: Electrotehnica, Energetica, Electronica, Automatizari (ISSN 0258-9109); Institutul Politehnic Iasi. Buletinul. Sectia III: Electrotehnica, Electronica, Automatizari.

621.3   PL   ISSN 0084-2788
INSTYTUT AUTOMATYKI SYSTEMOW ENERGETYCZNYCH. PRACE. 1964. irreg., no.42, 1989. 1000 Zl. Instytut Automatyki Systemow Energetycznych, Wystawowa 1, 51-618 Wroclaw, Poland. FAX 48-21-83. TELEX 0712773-PL. Ed.Bd. circ. 220.
Description: For electrical engineers and computer specialists. Contains papers on electrical power plant automatic control and protection, electric energy transmission and distribution control and protection, electric power system operation dispatching and management.

621.3   PL   ISSN 0032-6216
CODEN: PIELA4
INSTYTUT ELEKTROTECHNIKI. PRACE. (Text in Polish; summaries in English) 1951. bi-m. $24. Instytut Elektrotechniki - Electrotechnical Research Institute, Ul. Pozaryskiego 28, 04-703 Warsaw, Poland. TEL 48-22-122471. TELEX 813279. Ed. Wieslaw Seruga. circ. 245. **Indexed:** Chem.Abstr., Sci.Abstr. **Document type:** proceedings.
—BLDSC (6580.500000).

INSTYTUT TELE- I RADIOTECHNICZNY. PRACE. see *COMMUNICATIONS — Television And Cable*

621.3   US   ISSN 1058-4587
TK7872.F44   CODEN: IFEREU
▼**INTEGRATED FERROELECTRICS.** 1992. 4/yr. 43 ECU (effective 1993). Gordon and Breach Science Publishers, 820 Town Center Dr., Langhorne, PA 19047. TEL 215-750-2642. FAX 215-750-6343. (UK subscr. to: P.O. Box 90, Reading, Berkshire RG1 8JL, England. TEL 0734-560-080) (also avail. in microform)
—BLDSC (4531.815700); CASDDS. **CCC.**
Refereed Serial

INTEGRATION; the VLSI journal. see *COMPUTERS — Hardware*

621.3   US
INTERNATIONAL CONFERENCE ON CONDUCTION AND BREAKDOWN IN DIELECTRIC LIQUIDS. CONFERENCE RECORD. Abbreviated title: I C D L. 3rd, 1968. triennial. price varies. (I E E E, Dielectrics and Electrical Insulation Society) Institute of Electrical and Electronics Engineers, Inc., 345 E. 47th St., New York, NY 10017-2394. TEL 212-705-7366. FAX 212-705-7682. (Subscr. to: Box 1331, 445 Hoes Lane, Piscataway, NJ 08855-1331. TEL 908-562-3948)

621.3   US
INTERNATIONAL CONFERENCE ON CONDUCTION AND BREAKDOWN IN SOLID DIELECTRICS. PROCEEDINGS. Abbreiviated title: I C S D. 1983. triennial. price varies. (I E E E, Dielectrics and Electrical Insulation Society) Institute of Electrical and Electronics Engineers, Inc., 345 E. 47th St., New York, NY 10017-2394. TEL 212-705-7366. FAX 212-705-7682. (Subscr. to: Box 1331, 445 Hoes Lane, Piscataway, NJ 08855-1331. TEL 908-562-3948) **Document type:** proceedings.

INTERNATIONAL CONFERENCE ON INFRARED AND MILLIMETER WAVES. CONFERENCE DIGEST. see *PHYSICS — Optics*

ENGINEERING — ELECTRICAL ENGINEERING

621.31   FR   ISSN 0074-3151
INTERNATIONAL CONFERENCE ON LARGE HIGH VOLTAGE ELECTRIC SYSTEMS. PROCEEDINGS. (Text in English, French) 1921. biennial. 3250 F. to non-members; members 2500 F. International Conference on Large High Voltage Electric Systems (CIGRE), 3-5 rue de Metz, 75010 Paris, France. TEL 33-1-42-46-50-85. FAX 33-1-42-46-58-27. Ed. C. Chabaud. (back issues avail.) **Document type:** proceedings, academic/scholarly publication.
    Formerly: International Conference on Large High Tension Electric Systems. Proceedings.

621.3   US
INTERNATIONAL DISPLAY RESEARCH CONFERENCE. CONFERENCE RECORD. (Publication rotates among Europe, U.S., and Japan; and title alternates with rotation: Eurodisplay. Japan Display.) 1970. a. (I E E E, Electron Devices Society) Institute of Electrical and Electronics Engineers, Inc., 345 E. 47th St., New York, NY 10017-2394. TEL 212-705-7900. FAX 212-705-7682. (Subscr. to: 445 Hoes Lane, Box 1331, Piscataway, NJ 08855-1331)
    Former titles (until 1981): International Display Research Conference. Proceedings; (until 1977): Biennial Display Research Conference. Conference Record; I E E E Conference on Display Devices. Conference Record.
    Description: Includes data on liquid crystal, plasma and active-matrix-addressed displays.

621.3   UK
INTERNATIONAL ELECTRICAL AND MECHANICAL CATALOGUE. 1984. a. Data Distribution Publications, Wilmington House, Church Hill, Wilmington, Dartford, Kent DA2 7EH, England. TEL 0322-277788. FAX 0322-288030. circ. 12,000. **Document type:** catalog.
    Former titles: International Electricity Catalogue; Asian Electricity Catalogue.

621.3   SZ   ISSN 0074-4697
INTERNATIONAL ELECTROTECHNICAL COMMISSION. YEARBOOK - ANNUAIRE. (Text in English and French) 1961. a. 50 SFr. International Electrotechnical Commission, 3 rue de Varembe, CH-1211 Geneva 20, Switzerland. TEL 022-9190266. FAX 022-9190300. (Dist. in the U.S. by: American National Standards Institute, 1430 Broadway, New York, NY 10018) **Document type:** corporate report.
    Formerly: International Electrotechnical Commission. Central Office Report (ISSN 0534-9907)

621.3   US
INTERNATIONAL I E E E V L S I MUTILEVEL INTERCONNECTION CONFERENCE. PROCEEDINGS. Short title: V - M I C Conference. 1984. a. price varies. (I E E E, Electron Devices Society) Institute of Electrical and Electronics Engineers, Inc., 345 E. 47th St., New York, NY 10017-2394. TEL 212-705-7900. FAX 212-705-7682. (Subscr. to: Box 1331, 445 Hoes Lane, Piscataway, NJ 08855-1331) (Co-sponsor: I E E E Components, Hybrids, and Manufacturing Technology Society) **Document type:** proceedings.

621.38   US
           CODEN: ACPRD9
INTERNATIONAL INSTITUTE OF CONNECTOR AND INTERCONNECTION TECHNOLOGY. ANNUAL CONNECTOR SYMPOSIUM. PROCEEDINGS. 1968. a. $75. International Institute of Connector and Interconnection Technology, Inc., Box 880, Westfield, NJ 07091-0880. TEL 908-233-7278. charts; illus. circ. 1,500. (also avail. in microfilm) **Document type:** proceedings.
    Formerly: Electronic Connector Study Group. Annual Connector Symposium. Proceedings (ISSN 0145-0085).

621.3   UK   ISSN 0890-6327
TJ217   CODEN: IACPED
INTERNATIONAL JOURNAL OF ADAPTIVE CONTROL AND SIGNAL PROCESSING. 1987. bi-m. $395 (effective 1994). John Wiley & Sons Ltd., Journals, Baffins Ln., Chichester, Sussex PO19 1UI, England. TEL 0243-779777. FAX 0243-775878. TELEX 86290 WIBOOK G. Ed. Mike J. Grimble. bk.rev. circ. 350. Indexed: Tel.Abstr. **Document type:** academic/scholarly publication.
    —BLDSC (4541.540000); EI; UnCover; SWETS; UMI. **CCC.**
    Description: Designed to draw together the different research communities in control signal processing. Presents papers on all aspects of adaptive systems.

621.316   NE   ISSN 0925-2096
           CODEN: IAMTE7
INTERNATIONAL JOURNAL OF APPLIED ELECTROMAGNETICS IN MATERIALS. (Text and summaries in English) 1990. 4/yr. fl.376($203) (effective 1994). Elsevier Science B.V., P.O. Box 211, 1000 AE Amsterdam, Netherlands. TEL 31-20-5803911. FAX 31-20-5803598. TELEX 18582 ESPA NL. (Subscr. in U.S. and Canada to: Elsevier Science Inc. Box 882, Madison Sq. Sta., New York, NY 10159-0882. TEL 212-989-5800. FAX 212-633-3990) Eds. R.K.T. Hsieh, K. Miya. adv.; bk.rev. circ. 900. (also avail. in microform from UMI; back issues avail.) **Indexed:** Curr.Cont., Eng.Ind., INSPEC. **Document type:** academic/scholarly publication.
    —BLDSC (4542.086000); EI; Faxon. **CCC.**
    Description: Aims to contribute to the generation of a new conceptual framework in applied electromagnetics, and to the development of technology in the industry. Covers physics and mechanics of electromagnetic materials and devices, computational electromagnetics in materials, and applications of electromagnetic fields and forces.
    Refereed Serial

621.38   UK   ISSN 0098-9886
TK454   CODEN: ICTACV
INTERNATIONAL JOURNAL OF CIRCUIT THEORY & APPLICATIONS. 1973. bi-m. $1095 (effective 1994). John Wiley & Sons Ltd., Journals, Baffins Ln., Chichester, Sussex PO19 1UD, England. TEL 0243-779777. FAX 0243-775878. TELEX 86290-WIBOOK-G. Ed. Prof. J.O. Scanlan. bk.rev.; index. (reprint service avail. from UMI, ISI) **Indexed:** Curr.Cont., Cyb.Abstr., Eng.Ind., Math.R., Ref.Zh., Sci.Abstr. **Document type:** academic/scholarly publication.
    —BLDSC (4542.167000); EI; Faxon; UnCover; SWETS; UMI. **CCC.**
    Description: Charts advances in the theory and design of analog and digital circuits together with the application of circuit theory to a wide variety of problems.

621.3 371.3   UK   ISSN 0020-7209
           CODEN: IJEEAF
INTERNATIONAL JOURNAL OF ELECTRICAL ENGINEERING EDUCATION. (Text in English; summaries in English, French, German, Spanish) vol.7, 1970. q. £45($80) to individuals; institutions £120($220). Manchester University Press, Oxford Rd., Manchester M13 9PL, England. TEL 061-273-5539. FAX 061-274-3346. TELEX 666517-UNIMAN. Eds. Michael G. Hartley, Anne Buckley. adv.; bk.rev.; abstr.; bibl.; charts; illus. circ. 500. (back issues avail.) **Indexed:** Br.Tech.Ind., Cadscan, Cont.Pg.Educ., Curr.Cont., Educ.Tech.Abstr., Eng.Ind., High.Educ.Curr.Aware.Bull., Lead Abstr., Res.High.Educ.Abstr., Sci.Abstr., Zincscan. **Document type:** academic/scholarly publication.
    —BLDSC (4542.210000); EI; Faxon; UnCover; SWETS; UMI.
    Description: Technical articles on electrical engineering, and discussions on trends in curriculum development worldwide.

621.042   UK   ISSN 0142-0615
TK1   CODEN: IEPSDC
INTERNATIONAL JOURNAL OF ELECTRICAL POWER AND ENERGY SYSTEMS. 1979. 6/yr. £250 in UK and Europe; elsewhere £270. Butterworth - Heinemann (Subsidiary of: Reed International PLC), Linacre House, Jordan Hill, Oxford OX2 8DP, England. TEL 0865-310366. FAX 0865-310898. TELEX 83111 BHPOXF G. (Subscr. to: Turpin Transactions Ltd., Distribution Centre, Blackhorse Rd., Letchworth, Herts SG6 1HN, England. TEL 0462-672555) Ed. Manja Vukorojac. adv.; bk.rev.; abstr.; charts; index. (also avail. in microform from UMI; back issues avail.) **Indexed:** A.I.Abstr., Energy Info.Abstr., Energy Rev., Sci.Abstr. **Document type:** academic/scholarly publication.
    —BLDSC (3687.900000); CIS; Faxon; UnCover; SWETS; UMI. **CCC.**
    Description: Presents papers focusing on theoretical and applied developments in power and systems, such as network planning, modelling, operations, protection, energy economics and man-machine interfaces.
    Refereed Serial

INTERNATIONAL JOURNAL OF NETWORK MANAGEMENT. see *COMMUNICATIONS*

621.3   UK   ISSN 1049-8923
TJ212   CODEN: IJRCEA
INTERNATIONAL JOURNAL OF ROBUST AND NONLINEAR CONTROL. 1991. bi-m. $395 (effective 1994). John Wiley & Sons Ltd., Journals, Baffins Ln., Chichester, Sussex PO19 1UD, England. TEL 0243-77977. FAX 0243-775878. TELEX 86290 WIBOOK G. Ed. Mike J. Grimble. circ. 165. **Document type:** academic/scholarly publication.
    —BLDSC (4542.538900); EI; SWETS; UMI.
    Description: Encourages the development of analysis and design techniques for uncertain systems.

INTERNATIONAL LIGHTING REVIEW. see *BUILDING AND CONSTRUCTION*

621.3   UK   ISSN 0141-1918
           CODEN: IPGED2
INTERNATIONAL POWER GENERATION. 1977. 6/yr. £94($184) in the UK; overseas £100 (effective 1994). International Trade Publications Ltd., Queensway House, 2 Queensway, Redhill, Surrey RH1 1QS, England. TEL 0737-768611. FAX 0737-761989. TELEX 948669-TOPJNL-G. Ed. Anthony Farrar. circ. 22,015. (reprint service avail. from UMI) **Indexed:** Excerp.Med., INIS Atomind., Sci.Abstr. **Document type:** trade publication.
    —BLDSC (4567.290500); SWETS.

INTERNATIONAL RADAR CONFERENCE. RECORD. see *COMMUNICATIONS*

621.319   US
INTERNATIONAL SYMPOSIUM ON DISCHARGES AND ELECTRICAL INSULATION IN VACUUM. PROCEEDINGS. Short title: Discharges and Electrical Insulation in Vacuum. (Published by host organization when held outside U.S.) 1954. biennial. price varies. (I E E E, Dielectrics and Electrical Insulation Society) Institute of Electrical and Electronics Engineers, Inc., 345 E. 47th St., New York, NY 10017-2394. TEL 212-705-7900. FAX 212-705-7682. (Subscr. to: Box 1331, 445 Hoes Lane, Piscataway, NJ 08855-1331)
    Former titles: International Symposium on Discharges and Electrical Insulation (Proceedings); International Symposium on Insulation of High Voltages in Vacuum (Proceedings).
    Description: Covers all areas related to vacuum insulation and conduction phenomena.

621.3   US
INTERNATIONAL SYMPOSIUM ON SUBSCRIBER LOOP AND SERVICES. PROCEEDINGS. Abbreviated title: I S S L S. (Published by host organization when held outside U.S.) biennial. Institute of Electrical and Electronics Engineers, Inc., 345 E. 47th St., New York, NY 10017-2394. TEL 212-705-7900. FAX 212-705-7682. (Subscr. to: 445 Hoes Lane, Box 1331, Piscataway, NJ 08855-1331) **Document type:** proceedings.
    Description: Covers the design and operation of telecommunications distribution networks.

338.39 621.31   FR   ISSN 0074-9486
INTERNATIONAL UNION OF PRODUCERS AND DISTRIBUTORS OF ELECTRICAL ENERGY. (CONGRESS PROCEEDINGS). 1926. triennial. Copenhagen, 1991. International Union of Producers and Distributors of Electrical Energy - UNIPEDE - Union Internationale des producteurs et Distributeurs d'Energie Electrique, c/o Georges Lucenet, Sec.-Gen., 28 rue Jacques-Ibert, 75858 Paris CEDEX 17, France. TEL 33-1-40423708. FAX 33-1-40426052. TELEX UNIPEDE 644471 F. charts; stat.
    —BLDSC (3415.690000).

621.3   JA
ION CHUNYU HYOSO SHORI SHINPOJUMU YOKOSHU/SYMPOSIUM ON SURFACE LAYER MODIFICATION BY ION IMPLANTATION. PROCEEDINGS. (Text in English, Japanese; summaries in English) 1985. a. 14000 Yen. Ion Chunyu Hyoso Shori Kenkyukai - Japanese Society of Surface Layer Modification by Ion Implantation, 3-4, Koishikawa 2-chome, Bunkyo-ku, Tokyo 112, Japan. (Co-sponsor: Aionikusu K.K. - Ionics Co., Ltd.) **Document type:** proceedings.

621.3   JA   ISSN 0388-659X
IONICS/AIONIKUSU. (Text in Japanese; summaries in English) 1975. m. 800 Yen per no. Ionics Co., Ltd. - Aionikusu K.K., 3-4, Koishikawa 2-chome, Bunkyo-ku, Tokyo 112, Japan.

2346 ENGINEERING — ELECTRICAL ENGINEERING

621.3 630   US   ISSN 0162-2412
IOWA R E C NEWS. (Rural Electric Cooperative) 1946. m. $5 (members $3.50). Iowa Association of Electric Cooperatives, 8525 Douglas Ave., Ste. 48, Urbandale, IA 50322. TEL 515-276-5350. Ed. Jody Garlock. adv.: B&W page $1152. illus.; tr.lit. circ. 116,500. (avail. on records)
   Formerly: Iowa A E C News (ISSN 0021-0641)
   Description: Provides data about the rural electrification program, co-op principles, and human interest stories.

IRRIGATION AND POWER. see *WATER RESOURCES*

621.32 747   IT
ITALIAN LIGHTING. 6/yr. L.120000. Staff Editoriale s.n.c., Via Rossetti 9, 20145 Milan, Italy. TEL 2-480-07-449. FAX 2-480-07-493. Ed. Renato Pisaniello. adv.: B&W page L.900000, color page L.1400000; 240 x 316.

683.83   RU   ISSN 0202-8301
ITOGI NAUKI I TEKHNIKI: ELEKTRICHESKIE APPARATY. irreg., vol.4, 1986. price varies. Vsesoyuznyi Institut Nauchno-Tekhnicheskoi Informatsii (VINITI), Baltiiskaya ul. 14, Moscow A-219, Russia. (Subscr. to: Mezhdunarodnaya Kniga, Dimitrova ul. 39, 113095 Moscow, Russia)
   —BLDSC (0398.633000).

683.88   RU   ISSN 0202-831X
TK2000
ITOGI NAUKI I TEKHNIKI: ELEKTRICHESKIE MASHINY I TRANSFORMATORY. irreg., vol.8, 1990. price varies. Vsesoyuznyi Institut Nauchno-Tekhnicheskoi Informatsii (VINITI), Ul. Usievicha 20-A, 125219 Moscow A-219, Russia. (Subscr. to: Mezhdunarodnaya Kniga, Moscow 121200, Russia)

621.31   RU
ITOGI NAUKI I TEKHNIKI: ELEKTRICHESKIE STANTSII I SETI. irreg., vol.14, 1989. price varies. Vsesoyuznyi Institut Nauchno-Tekhnicheskoi Informatsii (VINITI), Baltiiskaya ul. 14, Moscow A-219, Russia. (Subscr. to: Mezhdunarodnaya Kniga, Dimitrova ul. 39, 113095 Moscow, Russia)
   —BLDSC (0398.665000).
   Formerly: Itogi Nauki i Tekhniki: Elektricheskie Stantsii, Seti i Sistemy (ISSN 0202-8328)

621.3   JA   ISSN 0386-1511
IWATSU GIHO/IWATSU TECHNICAL REPORT. (Text in Japanese; summaries in English, Japanese) 1957. s-a. Iwatsu Tsushinki K.K. - Iwatsu Electric Co., Ltd., 7-41, Kugayama 1-chome, Suginami-ku, Tokyo 168, Japan.

IZVESTIYA VYSSHIKH UCHEBNYKH ZAVEDENII. SERIYA RADIOFIZIKA. see *PHYSICS*

621.3   JA
J E M I C INSTRUMENTATION CIRCLE. NEWS/J E M I C KEISOKU SAKURU NYUSU. (Text in Japanese) q. Japan Electric Meters Inspection Corporation - Nihon Denki Keiki Kenteijo, 15-7, Shibaura 4-chome, Minato-ku, Tokyo 108, Japan.

621.3   JA   ISSN 0910-9692
J P C A NYUSU/J P C S NEWS. (Text in Japanese) m. 300 Yen per no. Japan Printed Circuit Association - Nihon Purinto Kairo Kogyokai, 3-10, Toranomon 4-chome, Minato-ku, Tokyo 105, Japan.

621.3   GW   ISSN 0722-0340
JAHRBUCH ELEKTROTECHNIK. 1982. a. DM.45. V D E-Verlag GmbH, Bismarckstr. 33, 10625 Berlin, Germany. TEL 030-348001-0. FAX 030-3417093. Ed. A. Gruetz. **Document type:** trade publication.

621.3   GW
JAHRBUCH FUER ELEKTROMASCHINENBAU UND ELEKTRONIK (YEAR). 1960. a. DM.21.80. Huethig und Pflaum Verlag, Lazarettstr. 4, 80636 Munich, Germany. TEL 089-12607240. FAX 089-12607200. (Subscr. addr.: Im Weiher 10, 6900 Heidelberg 1, Germany) Ed. W. Seher. circ. 6,000.

JANE'S RADAR AND ELECTRONIC WARFARE SYSTEMS. see *MILITARY*

JAPAN ELECTRONICS BUYERS' GUIDE. see *BUSINESS AND ECONOMICS — Trade And Industrial Directories*

621.3   FR   ISSN 0021-7816
TK2   CODEN: JEEEAP
JOURNAL DE L'EQUIPEMENT ELECTRIQUE ET ELECTRONIQUE. At head of title: 3E. (In 3 editions: 3E Actualite; Techniques de l'Industrie; Techniques de l'Installation) 1949. fortn. (with bi-m. supplements). 260 F. (for all 3 editions; 180F for 3E Actualite and 1 supplement). Groupe Tests, 41 rue de la Grange aux Belles, 75483 Paris Cedex 10, France. (Subscr. to: Service Abonnement, 71 Bd. Richard Lenoir, 75011 Paris, France) Ed. Eugene Lecanon. adv.; bk.rev.; illus.; stat. circ. 8,500.
   Indexed: C.I.S.Abstr., Sci.Abstr., World Alum.Abstr.
   Incorporates: Electricien Industriel.

537   FR   ISSN 0337-8500
JOURNAL DES ELECTRICIENS. 1922. m. 210 F. Editions Presselec, 5 rue Hamelin, 75116 Paris, France. TEL 47-27-97-49. FAX 47-55-00-47. TELEX 640 118. Ed. Denis Hannotin. adv.; bk.rev.; charts; illus. circ. 4,800. **Indexed:** C.I.S.Abstr.
   —BLDSC (4974.000000).

621.3   AT   ISSN 0725-2986
TK1   CODEN: JEEADG
JOURNAL OF ELECTRICAL AND ELECTRONICS ENGINEERING, AUSTRALIA. 1937. q. Aus.$55 (overseas Aus.$70). (Institution of Engineers, Australia) Engineers Australia Pty. Ltd., Crows Nest Centre, 2 Ernest St., Crows Nest, N.S.W. 2065, Australia. TEL 02-438-1533. FAX 02-438-5934. Ed. A.V. Watt. adv.; bk.rev.; charts; illus.; index. circ. 3,000. (also avail. in microfiche from NTI) **Indexed:** CAD CAM Abstr., Chem.Abstr., Eng.Ind., INIS Atomind., Sci.Abstr., Tel.Abstr.
   —BLDSC (4973.299500); Faxon; SWETS; CASDDS.
   Former titles (until Dec. 1980): Monitor (ISSN 0314-4321); Institution of Radio and Electronics Engineers Australia. Proceedings (ISSN 0020-3521)
   Description: Scientific and research papers on electrical engineering topics relevant to Australia.

JOURNAL OF ELECTROMAGNETIC WAVES AND APPLICATIONS. see *PHYSICS*

621.38   JA   ISSN 0385-4507
TK7800   CODEN: JEENDL
JOURNAL OF ELECTRONIC ENGINEERING. Abbreviated title: J E E. (Supplement avail.: Display Devices) (Text in English) 1964. m. $105 in Asia & Oceania; the Americas $115 (elsewhere $120). Dempa Publications Inc., 1-11-15, Higashi Gotanda, Shinagawa-ku, Tokyo 141, Japan. TEL 03-3445-6111. (U.S. addr.: 275 Madison Ave., New York, NY 10016. TEL 212-682-4755) Ed. Hideo Hirayama. adv.; tr.lit. circ. 51,000. **Indexed:** Chem.Abstr., Comput.Cont., Intl.Civil Eng.Abstr., JCT, JTA, Sci.Abstr., Soft.Abstr.Eng.
   —BLDSC (4974.930000); EI; Faxon; UnCover; SWETS; CASDDS.
   Formerly: J E E: Japan Electronic Engineering (ISSN 0021-3608)
   Description: Review of advances in electrical products, processes, components, materials and research.

621.3   US   ISSN 0923-8174
   CODEN: JTTAER
JOURNAL OF ELECTRONIC TESTING; theory and applications. 1990. 4/yr. fl.434($226.50) (effective 1994). Kluwer Academic Publishers Boston, Box 358, Accord Sta., Hingham, MA 02018-0358. TEL 617-871-6600. FAX 617-871-6528. TELEX 200190. (Dist. outside N. America by: Kluwer Academic Publishers Group, P.O. Box 322, 3300 AH Dordrecht, Netherlands. TEL 31-78-524400) Ed. Vishwani Agrawal. (also avail. in microform from UMI; reprint service avail. from SWZ,UMI) **Indexed:** CAD CAM Abstr., Comput.Rev., Eng.Ind., Inform.Sci.Abstr., INSPEC. **Document type:** academic/scholarly publication.
   —BLDSC (4974.970000); EI; UnCover; UMI. **CCC.**
   Description: International forum for papers on research and applications in the area of electronic testing, including fault tolerance, fault simulation, and self-testing equipment and theory.
   Refereed Serial

537.2   NE   ISSN 0304-3886
QC570   CODEN: JOELDH
JOURNAL OF ELECTROSTATICS. 1975. 6/yr. (in 2 vol.; 3 nos./vol.). fl.762($412) (effective 1994). Elsevier Science B.V., P.O. Box 211, 1000 AE Amsterdam, Netherlands. TEL 31-20-5803911. FAX 31-20-5803598. TELEX 18582 ESPA NL. (Subscr. in U.S. and Canada to: Elsevier Science Inc., Box 882, Madison Sq. Sta., New York, NY 10159. TEL 212-989-5800. FAX 212-633-3990) Ed. D.K. Davies. adv.; bk.rev.; index. (also avail. in microform from UMI) **Indexed:** C.I.S.Abstr., Chem.Abstr., Curr.Cont., Elec.& Electron.Abstr., Eng.Ind., INIS Atom.ind., Phys.Ber., Risk Abstr., Sci.Abstr., World Text.Abstr. **Document type:** academic/scholarly publication.
   —BLDSC (4976.300000); EI; Faxon; UnCover; SWETS; CASDDS. **CCC.**
   Description: Disseminates knowledge of static electricity in its fundamental aspects, in its useful applications, and in its hazardous nature.
   Refereed Serial

JOURNAL OF LIGHT & VISUAL ENVIRONMENT. see *PHYSICS — Optics*

621.3   US
▼**JOURNAL OF MICROELECTRONIC SYSTEMS INTEGRATION.** 1993. q. $145 (foreign $170) (effective 1994). Plenum Publishing Corp., 233 Spring St., New York, NY 10013-1578. TEL 212-620-8000. FAX 212-463-0742. TELEX 23-421139. Ed. S.K. Tewkesbury. (also avail. in microfilm from JSC) **Document type:** academic/scholarly publication.
   Description: Discusses issues and research at the intersection between systems science and microelectronics.
   Refereed Serial

621.38   US   ISSN 0832-7823
TK7876   CODEN: JMPEE4
JOURNAL OF MICROWAVE POWER AND ELECTROMAGNETIC ENERGY. 1966. q. $125 (foreign $140). International Microwave Power Institute, 10210 Leatherleaf Ct., Manassas, VA 22111-4245. TEL 703-257-1415. Ed. R. LaGasse. adv.; bk.rev.; abstr.; charts; illus.; index; circ. 1,000 (controlled). **Indexed:** Biol.Abstr., CAD CAM Abstr., Chem.Abstr., Curr.Cont., Dairy Sci.Abstr., Eng.Ind., Excerp.Med., Food Sci.& Tech.Abstr., Ind.Med., INIS Atomind., Sci.Abstr.
   —BLDSC (5019.820000); EI; Faxon; UnCover; SWETS.
   Formerly (until 1984): Journal of Microwave Power (ISSN 0022-2739)
   Description: Presents a forum for advances in the field of electromagnetic energy.
   Refereed Serial

621.31   SZ   ISSN 0378-7753
TJ163.2   CODEN: JPSODZ
JOURNAL OF POWER SOURCES; the international journal on the science and technology of electrochemical energy systems. (Text in English, French, German) 1976. 15/yr. (in 5 vols., 3 nos./vol.) 2000 SFr.($1361) (effective 1994). Elsevier Science S.A., P.O. Box 564, CH-1001 Lausanne 1, Switzerland. TEL 41-21-3207381. FAX 41-21-3235444. TELEX 450620-ELSA-CH. (Subscr. in U.S. and Canada to: Elsevier Science Inc., Box 882, Madison Sq. Sta., New York, NY 10159. TEL 212-989-5800. FAX 212-633-3990) Ed.Bd. bk.rev.; bibl.; tr.lit. (also avail. in microform from UMI) **Indexed:** Cadscan, Chem.Abstr., Curr.Cont., Curr.Tit.Electrochem., Energy Info.Abstr., Environ.Abstr., Ind.Sci.Rev., INIS Atomind., Int.Aerosp.Abstr., Lead Abstr., Met.Abstr., Sci.Abstr., Sci.Cit.Ind., Zincscan. **Document type:** academic/scholarly publication.
   —BLDSC (5041.400000); Faxon; SWETS; CASDDS. **CCC.**
   Description: Provides an interdisciplinary forum on all aspects of the science, technology and commercialization of primary-secondary batteries and fuel cells, as well as on their application in important and emerging markets.
   Refereed Serial

DER JUNGE ELEKTRO-TECHNIKER. see *EDUCATION — Teaching Methods And Curriculum*

JUNIOR ELECTRONICS/SHOHO NO RAJIO. see *CHILDREN AND YOUTH — For*

ENGINEERING — ELECTRICAL ENGINEERING

621.31   KO
K E P C O ANNUAL REVIEW. (Text in English, Korean) a. Korea Electric Power Corporation, 167 Samsong-dong, Kangnam-gu, Seoul 135-791, P.O. Box 40 Yongdong Seoul, S. Korea. TEL 550-3114. TELEX KELECCO K23717. stat.
Description: Covers labor productivity, status of profit and loss, computerization, environmental preservation, technology development and corporation activities.

363.6   US
K M U NEWS REPORT. 1969. s-m. $175. Kansas Municipal Utilities, Inc., Box 1225, McPherson, KS 67460. TEL 316-241-1423. Ed. Louis Stroup, Jr. adv. circ. 705.
Formerly: K M U Monthly Newsletter (ISSN 0022-7390)

621.3   DK   ISSN 0900-7989
KABEL- OG LINIEMESTEREN. 1947. m. DKK 60. Kabel- og Liniemester Foreningen, Egealle 198, DK-8600 Silkeborg, Denmark. Ed. N. Vagn Noerskov. adv. circ. 575.

621.3   JA   ISSN 0388-4015
KAIGAI DENRYOKU/JAPAN ELECTRIC POWER INFORMATION CENTER. JOURNAL. (Text in Japanese) 1959. m. Kaigai Denryoku Chosakai - Japan Electric Power Information Center, 15-33, Shibaura 4-chome, Minato-ku, Tokyo 108, Japan.

621.3   JA   ISSN 0285-6697
                      CODEN: KDHKDV
KANSAI DENRYOKU K.K. SOKEN HOKOKU/KANSAI ELECTRIC POWER CO. TECHNICAL RESEARCH CENTER. REPORT. (Text in Japanese) 1968. s-a. Kansai Denryoku K.K., Sogo Gijutsu Kenkyujo - Kansai Electric Power Co., Ltd., Technical Research Center, 11-20, Nakoji 3-chome, Amagasaki-shi, Hyogo-ken 661, Japan. **Indexed:** Sci.Abstr.
—CASDDS.

621.3   JA
KEISAN DENKI DENSHI KOGAKU SHINPOJUMU RONBUNSHU/J S S T SYMPOSIUM ON CALCULATIONS IN ELECTRICAL AND ELECTRONICS ENGINEERING. PROCEEDINGS. (Text in English, Japanese; summaries in English) 1979. a. Nihon Shimyureshon Gakkai - Japan Society for Simulation Technology, Nihon Kagaku Gijutsu Renmei, 10-11, Sendagaya 5-chome, Shibuya-ku, Tokyo 151, Japan. **Document type:** proceedings.

KEY ABSTRACTS - POWER SYSTEMS & APPLICATIONS. see *ENGINEERING — Abstracting, Bibliographies, Statistics*

621.3   KR
KHAR'KOVSKII GOSUDARSTVENNYI UNIVERSITET. RADIOFIZIKA I ELEKTRONIKA. (Subseries of: Khar'kovskii Gosudarstvennyi Universitet. Vestnik) 1971. a. 1.10 Rub. (Khar'kovskii Gosudarstvennyi Universitet) Izdatel'stvo Vysshaya Shkola, Khar'kovskoe Otdelenie, Ul. Universitetskaya 16, 310003 Kharkov, Ukraine. Ed. L. Hizhnyak. illus. circ. 500.
Description: Presents articles on the problems of generation, propagation and scattering of electro-magnetic waves. Several articles deal with plasma physics and theory of diffraction.

621.3   JA   ISSN 0910-0792
KOKUSAI DENKI GIHO/KOKUSAI ELECTRIC TECHNICAL REPORT. (Text in Japanese; summaries in English, Japanese) irreg. Kokusai Denki K.K., Hamura Kojo Gijutsu Kanribu, Kenkyu Kanri Gurupu - Kokusai Electric Co., Ltd., Hamura Works, Corporate Engineering Administration Department, R & D Administration Group, 1-1, Shinmeidai 2-chome, Hamura-machi, Nishitama-gun, Tokyo 190-11, Japan.

683.83   CI   ISSN 0350-7696
KOMISIJA ZA ISPITIVANJE S-UREDJAJA. BILTEN. Short title: S-Bilten. (Text in Croatian; summaries in English and Russian) 1972. s-a. 360 din.($50) Komisija za Ispitivanje S-Uredjaja, Bastijanova bb, Box 304, 41001 Zagreb, Croatia. TEL 041-317-924. FAX 041-330-313. Ed. Nenad Marinovic. adv.; charts; illus. circ. 650. (also avail. in microform)
Description: Covers electrical apparatus and materials used in explosive atmospheres.

621.38   CI   ISSN 0350-5537
KONCAR STRUCNE INFORMACIJE. (Text in Croatian; summaries in English, French and Russian) 1954. irreg. free. S O U R Rade Koncar, O O U R Elektrotehnicki Institut, Bastijanova ul. bb, 41001 Zagreb, Croatia. TEL 041-312222. FAX 041-334170. TELEX 21104. Ed. Nenad Marinovic. bk.rev.; bibl.; charts; illus.; circ. 2,500 (controlled). **Indexed:** Sci.Abstr.
—BLDSC (5105.909000).
Formerly (until 1977): Informacije Rade Koncar (ISSN 0033-7536)

621.3   JA   ISSN 0289-3886
KUMANOTO DENPA KOGYO KOTO SENMON GAKKO. KENKYU KIYO/KUMAMOTO NATIONAL COLLEGE OF TECHNOLOGY. RESEARCH REPORTS. (Text in English, Japanese; summaries in English) 1974. a. Kumanoto Denpa Kogyo Koto Senmon Gakko, 2959-2, Higashiokubo, Suya, Nishigoshi-machi, Kikuchi-gun, Kumamoto-ken 861-11, Japan.

621.3   JA
KURASHI NO DENKA/ELECTRIFIED LIFE. (Text in Japanese) 1966. m. 200 Yen per no. Nikkan Denka Keizai Tsushinsha, 38-11, Chuo 5-chome, Nakano-ku, Tokyo 164, Japan.

621.38   KR   ISSN 0368-7155
QC685   CODEN: KVELA6
KVANTOVAYA ELEKTRONIKA; respublikanskii mezhvedomstvennyi sbornik nauchnykh trudov. English translation: Quantum Electronics (US ISSN 1063-7818) (Text in Russian) 1966. m. (Akademiya Nauk Ukrainy, Institut Poluprovodnikov) Vidavnitstvo Naukova Dumka, Vul. Tereshchenkivska 3, 252601 Kiev, Ukraine. TEL 044-224-4068. FAX 04-224-7060. (Dist. by: Mezhdunarodnaya Kniga, B. Yakimanka 39, 117049 Moscow, Russia) Ed. M.P. Lisitsa. **Indexed:** Chem.Abstr., Ind.Sci.Rev., INIS Atomind., Math.R., Phys.Ber., Sci.Abstr.
Document type: academic/scholarly publication.
—BLDSC (0088.570000); CASDDS. CCC.

621.3   JA   ISSN 0289-5676
KYOSAN SAKYURA/KYOSAN CIRCULAR. (Text in Japanese) 1950. bi-m. Kyosan Seisakujo Gijutsu Kanrishitsu - Kyosan Electric Manufacturing Co., Ltd., 29-1, Heiancho 2-chome, Tsurumi-ku, Yokohama-shi, Kanagawa-ken 230, Japan.

621.3   JA   ISSN 0287-9263
KYUSHU DENRYOKU K.K. SOGO KENKYUJO KENKYU KIHO/KYUSHU ELECTRIC POWER CO. RESEARCH DEPARTMENT. REPORT. (Text in Japanese) 1953. a. Kyushu Denryoku K.K., Sogo Kenkyujo, 1-47, Shiobaru 2-chome, Minami-ku, Fukuoka-shi, Fukuoka-ken 815, Japan. **Indexed:** INIS Atomind., Sci.Abstr.
—BLDSC (5135.918000).

621.3   FR   ISSN 0220-9535
L C I E INFORMATIONS. 1943. a. free. Laboratoire Central des Industries Electriques, 33 av. du General Leclerc, B.P. 8, F-92266 Fontenay aux Roses Cedex, France. TEL 40-95-60-60. FAX 40-95-60-03. TELEX 634 147 F. Ed. Brigitte Fallou. charts; illus. circ. 5,000. **Indexed:** Bull.Signal. **Document type:** bulletin.
Formerly (until 1978): Laboratoire Central des Industries Electriques. Bulletin d'Information (ISSN 0023-6675)

621.32   US   ISSN 0360-6325
TK1   CODEN: LGDAAA
L D & A. (Lighting Design & Application) 1906. m. $39. Illuminating Engineering Society, 120 Wall St., New York, NY 10005. TEL 212-248-5000. FAX 212-248-5017. adv.; bk.rev.; abstr.; bibl.; charts; illus.; tr.lit.; index. circ. 15,000. (also avail. in microfilm from UMI) **Indexed:** A.S.& T.Ind., C.I.S.Abstr., Energy Ind., Energy Info.Abstr., Eng.Ind., Graph.Arts Lit.Abstr., Ind.Sci.Rev., Sci.Abstr. **Document type:** trade publication.
—BLDSC (5214.280000); EI; Faxon; UnCover; SWETS; UMI. CCC.
Supersedes in part (as of 1971): Illuminating Engineering (ISSN 0019-2333)

LASER BULLETIN; technical advances, business news. see *PHYSICS — Optics*

LASERS & OPTRONICS. see *PHYSICS — Optics*

621.3   UK   ISSN 0023-6381
LAURENCE SCOTT ENGINEERING BULLETIN. (Summaries in English, French and German) 1949. irreg. (2-3/yr.) free. Laurence, Scott & Electromotors Ltd., Norwich NR1 1JD, England. FAX 0603-660767. TELEX 97323. Ed. P.J. Tavner. charts; illus.; cum.index: vols.1-13 (1949-1976). circ. 8,500. **Indexed:** Sci.Abstr.

LETTRE AFRIQUE ENERGIES. see *PETROLEUM AND GAS*

621.32   GW
LICHT. 1949. 10/yr. DM.156 (Europe DM.180). (Lichttechnische Gesellschaft e.V.) Richard Pflaum Verlag GmbH und Co. KG, Lazarettstr. 4, 80636 Munich, Germany. TEL 089-12607-0. FAX 089-12607-200. (Subscr. to: Postfach 190737, 80607 Munich, Germany) Ed. Regina Welk. adv.: B&W page DM.4300; trim 270 x 192; adv. contact: Annemarie Knoebel. bk.rev.; abstr.; illus.; mkt.; pat. index. circ. 12,000. **Indexed:** C.I.S.Abstr., Eng.Ind., Excerp.Med., Sci.Abstr. **Document type:** trade publication.
—SWETS. CCC.
Formerly: Lichttechnik (ISSN 0024-2861)

621.32   NE
LICHT; vakblad voor beslissers over verlichting. 1987. 7/yr. fl.98 (effective 1994). Wegener Tijl Tijdschriften Groep B.V., Postbus 9943, 1006 AP Amsterdam, Netherlands. TEL 31-20-5182828. FAX 31-20-5182843. Ed. I. de Beer. circ. 7,500. **Document type:** trade publication.
Former titles: Licht Journaal (ISSN 0926-6054); Lichtvisie.
Description: For architects, contractors, building-designers, and electrotechnical engineers: lighting techniques and professional lighting.

LIGHTING ANSWERS. see *BUILDING AND CONSTRUCTION*

621.32 747   IT
LIGHTING DESIGN. 6/yr. Stammer S.p.A., Via della Liberazione 1, 20068 Peschiera - Borromeo (MI), Italy. TEL 02-55302606. FAX 02-55302700. Ed. Manuela Battaglino. circ. 20,000.

LIGHTING EQUIPMENT NEWS. see *INTERIOR DESIGN AND DECORATION — Furniture And House Furnishings*

621.32   AT   ISSN 0728-5639
                      CODEN: LIAUD4
LIGHTING IN AUSTRALIA. 1981. bi-m. Aus.$25. (Illuminating Engineering Society of Australia) Rala Information Service Pty. Ltd., 203-205 Darling St., Balmain, N.S.W. 2041, Australia. (Subscr. to: P.O. Box 495, Kogarah, N.S.W. 2217, Australia) Ed. Warren Julian. **Indexed:** Aus.Rd.Ind., Ergon.Abstr., Sci.Abstr.

621.3   UK   ISSN 0950-4559
LIGHTING JOURNAL. 1936. q. £32. Institution of Lighting Engineers, Lennox House, 9 Lawford Rd., Rugby CV21 2DV, England. TEL 0788-576492. FAX 0788-540145. Ed. D. Barnes. adv.; bk.rev.; charts; illus.; index. circ. 2,000. (back issues avail.) **Indexed:** Br.Tech.Ind., Int.Build.Serv.Abstr.
—BLDSC (5214.451000); SWETS.
Former titles: I P L E Lighting Journal; Public Lighting (ISSN 0033-3603)
Description: Covers all forms of lighting for exterior and interior commercial use.

LIGHTING MAGAZINE. see *INTERIOR DESIGN AND DECORATION — Furniture And House Furnishings*

621.32   UK   ISSN 0024-3426
TH7700.I4   CODEN: LRTEA9
LIGHTING RESEARCH AND TECHNOLOGY. 1969. q. £40 to non-members. Chartered Institution of Building Services Engineers, Delta House, 222 Balham High Rd., London SW12 9BS, England. TEL 01-675 5211. Ed. Barry Copping. bk.rev.; abstr.; charts; illus.; index. circ. 1,000. (also avail. in microfilm from UMI) **Indexed:** Br.Tech.Ind., C.I.S.Abstr., Eng.Ind., Ergon.Abstr., HRIS, Int.Build.Serv.Abstr., Psychol.Abstr., Sci.Abstr.
—BLDSC (5214.5000CO); EI; Faxon; UMI.
Formerly: Illuminating Engineering Society. Transactions.

621.38   US
LINES AVAILABLE BULLETIN. m. Electronic Representatives Association, 20 E. Huron, Chicago, IL 60611. TEL 312-649-1333.

ENGINEERING — ELECTRICAL ENGINEERING

621.31   NZ   ISSN 0024-5143
LIVE LINES. 1956. m. (except Jan.). NZ.$22.50 (foreign NZ$31). Electricity Supply Association of New Zealand, P.O. Box 1017, Wellington, New Zealand. TEL 385-9632. FAX 64-04-384-2519. Ed. H. Duckworth. adv.; bk.rev. circ. 5,700. (tabloid format) **Document type:** newspaper.
—CCC.
   Description: Provides coverage of current events plus articles of general interest to supply authorities' personnel.

621.32   SW   ISSN 0024-5429
LJUSKULTUR. 1928. bi-m. SEK 160 (effective 1990). Svlenska Foereningen foer Ljuskultur, Skepparg 27, P.O. Box 5512, 114 85 Stockholm, Sweden. FAX 46-8-6673491. (Co-sponsors: Svenska Belysningssaellskapet; Sydsvenska Belysningssaellskapet; Vaestsvenska Belysningssaellskapet; Selskapet for Lyskultur i Norge) Ed. Magnus Frantzell. adv.; bk.rev.; illus. circ. 3,000. **Indexed:** Chem.Abstr., Int.Build.Serv.Abstr., Sci.Abstr.
   Former titles (until 1957): Tidskrift foer Ljuskultur; (until 1934): Ljuskulturens Maanadsblad.

LOCOMOTIVE. see MACHINERY

LOLA SAOPSTENJA/LOLA PROCEEDINGS. see ENGINEERING — Mechanical Engineering

621.3   US
LOUISIANA COUNTRY. m. Association of Louisiana Electric Cooperatives, Inc., 10725 Airline Highway, Baton Rouge, LA 40816-4231. TEL 504-293-3450. Ed. Whitney L. Belanger. bk.rev. circ. 175,000.

621.32   IT   ISSN 0024-7189
LUCE (MILAN). 1962. bi-m. L.35000 (foreign L.85000) (effective 1994). (Associazione Italiana di Illuminazione (A.I.D.I.)) Tecniche Nuove s.p.a., Via C. Menotti, 14, 20129 Milan, Italy. TEL 02-75701. FAX 02-7610351. Ed. Enzo Guaglione. adv.: B&W page L.1380000, color page L.2070000; trim 185 x 266. bk.rev.; abstr.; bibl.; charts; illus.; index. circ. 5,555.

LUMINAIRES ET ECLAIRAGE. see INTERIOR DESIGN AND DECORATION — Furniture And House Furnishings

621.32   FR   ISSN 0024-7669
LUX; la revue de l'eclairage. 1928; N.S. 1959. 5/yr. 350 F. (foreign 440 F.). (Association Francaise de l'Eclairage) Editions Lux, 52 bd. Malesherbes, 75008 Paris, France. TEL 43-87-21-21. FAX 43-87-16-98. TELEX 290392F. Ed. Jacques Valin. adv.; bk.rev.; abstr.; charts; illus. circ. 3,800. **Indexed:** Int.Build.Serv.Abstr.
—SWETS.
   Description: Includes studies, newest techniques, applications in architecture, history and interviews with prominent figures in the area light and luminosity.

621.32   DK   ISSN 0904-7824
LYS; miljoe-design-teknik. 1954. 4/yr. DKK 160. Lysteknisk Selskab, P.O. Box 28, Byvej 12, DK-3660 Stenloese, Denmark. TEL 45-42-17-18-00. FAX 45-42-17-08-32. (Co-sponsor: Light & Optics) Eds. Lis Johansen, Joergen Klausen. bk.rev. circ. 2,200.
   Formerly (until 1989): Lampetten (ISSN 0023-7442)

MAGNETIC AND ELECTRICAL SEPARATION. see PHYSICS

621.31   US   ISSN 0024-998X
QC717.6   CODEN: MGHDAG
MAGNETOHYDRODYNAMICS. English translation of: Magnitnaya Gidrodinamika (LV ISSN 0025-0015) 1965. q. $895 (foreign $1045) (effective 1994). (Latvian Academy of Sciences, LV) Plenum Publishing Corp., Consultants Bureau, 233 Spring St., New York, NY 10013-1578. TEL 212-620-8468. FAX 212-463-0742. TELEX 23-421139. Ed. J. Lielpeteris. (also avail. in microfilm from JSC; back issues avail.) **Indexed:** Appl.Mech.Rev., Elec.& Electron.Abstr., Eng.Ind., INSPEC, Math.R., Sci.Res.Abstr., Zent.Math. **Document type:** academic/scholarly publication.
—BLDSC (0415.810000); Faxon; UnCover; UMI. CCC.
   Refereed Serial

537   US   ISSN 0887-5707
TK454.4.E5
MAGNETS IN YOUR FUTURE. 1986. m. $150 (foreign $200). (A Z Industries, Inc.) L H Publishing Agency, Box 250, Ash Flat, AR 72513. TEL 501-856-3877. FAX 501-856-3590. Ed. Les Adam. adv.; index. circ. 3,000. (back issues avail.) **Document type:** trade publication.
   Refereed Serial

621.3   KR
MAGNITNOIMPUL'SNAYA OBRABOTKA METALLOV. (Subseries of: Kharkivskyi Politeknichnyi Instytut. Vestnik) (Text in Russian) 1971. irreg. price varies. Kharkivskyi Politeknichnyi Instytut, Ul. Frunze, 21, Kharkov 31002, Ukraine. illus.

021.38   RU
MAGNITO-POLUPROVODNIKOVYE I ELEKTROMASHINNYE ELEMENTY AVTOMATIKI. 1974. irreg. 0.52 Rub. Ryazanskii Radiotekhnicheskii Institut, Ul. Gagarina 59-1, 390024 Ryazan, Russia.

621.3   CN   ISSN 0025-0988
LE MAITRE ELECTRICIEN. 1954. m. Can.$26. Corporation des Maitres Electriciens du Quebec, 5925, boul. Decarie, No. 100, Montreal, PQ H3W 3C9, Canada. TEL 514-738-2184. FAX 514-738-2192. Ed. Helene Rioux. adv.: B&W page Can.$1790, color page Can.$2585; trim 8 1/8 x 10 7/8. charts; illus.; stat.; tr.lit. circ. 10,500. **Indexed:** Pt.de Rep. (1983-).

MANAGEMENT QUARTERLY; a guide to better management. see BUSINESS AND ECONOMICS — Management

MARCONI INSTRUMENTS MEASURE TEST; international newsletter. see INSTRUMENTS

621.38   US
MARINE ELECTRONICS.* 1973. bi-m. $15. National Marine Electronics Association, c/o Seibold-Hann Publishers, Box 1697, Vineyard Haven, MA 02568-1697. TEL 508-990-8808. Ed. Charles S. Carney. adv.; bk.rev.; index. circ. 7,254.
   Formerly: N.M.E.A. News (ISSN 0739-0815)

621.3   GW   ISSN 0344-8843
MARKT & TECHNIK. w. DM.218.40 (foreign DM.317.20). Markt und Technik Verlag AG, Hans-Pinsel-Str. 2, 85540 Haar, Germany. TEL 089-4613-0. FAX 089-4613-774. **Document type:** trade publication.
—CCC.
   Description: For professionals in the electronics industry.

537.5   US   ISSN 0163-9218
TK7800
MASSACHUSETTS INSTITUTE OF TECHNOLOGY. RESEARCH LABORATORY OF ELECTRONICS. R L E PROGRESS REPORT. 1946. a. free. Massachusetts Institute of Technology, Research Laboratory of Electronics, Cambridge, MA 02139. TEL 617-253-2566. FAX 617-258-7864. Ed. Barbara Passero. circ. 1,800.
   Formerly: Massachusetts Institute of Technology. Research Laboratory of Electronics. Quarterly Progress Report (ISSN 0025-4827)
   Description: Covers research programs at RLE for a calendar year; contains both a statement of research objectives and a summary of research efforts for each of the research groups. Includes funding sources, staff listing, and a bibliography.
   Refereed Serial

537.5   NZ   ISSN 1171-5154
MATRIX DIRECTORY OF TECHNOLOGY. 1973. a. NZ.$15.50. Matrix Publishing Ltd., P.O. Box 99-731, Auckland, New Zealand. TEL 09-357-6006. FAX 09-358-0606. **Document type:** trade publication, directory.
   Former titles (until 1992): New Zealand Directory of Technology (ISSN 0112-9058); (until 1986): Directory of Technology (ISSN 0112-0468); Which was formerly (until 1983): Directory of Electronics and Instrumentation (ISSN 0110-3792); (until 1977): Directory of N.Z. Electronics.
   Description: Index of supplies, products and services to the electronics, computing, and instrumentation industries.

621.3   JA   ISSN 0285-5054
                     CODEN: MDGID8
MATSUSHITA DENKO GIHO/A & I TECHNICAL REPORT. (Text in Japanese; summaries in English, Japanese) 1970. biennial. Matsushita Denko K.K., Kenkyu Kanribu Gijutsu Joho Senta, 1048, Kadoma, Kadoma-shi, Osaka 571, Japan. **Indexed:** Sci.Abstr.
—BLDSC (8717.107500); CASDDS.

354   MF
MAURITIUS. CENTRAL ELECTRICITY BOARD. ANNUAL REPORT. a. Central Electricity Board, Curepipe, Mauritius. illus.

MEANS MECHANICAL COST DATA (YEAR). see BUILDING AND CONSTRUCTION

MECHATRONICS; mechanics - electronics - control. see ENGINEERING — Mechanical Engineering

MECTRONIC BUYERS DIRECTORY. see BUSINESS AND ECONOMICS — Trade And Industrial Directories

621.3   US
MEDITERRANEAN ELECTROTECHNICAL CONFERENCE. Short title: M E L E C O N. 1981. biennial. Institute of Electrical and Electronics Engineers, Inc., 345 E. 47th St., New York, NY 10017-2394. TEL 212-705-7366. FAX 212-705-7682. (Subscr. to: Box 1331, 445 Hoes Ln., Piscataway, NJ 08855-1331. TEL 908-562-3948)

621.3   AG
MEGAVATIOS. 1977. m. Edigar, S.A., 15 de Noviembre 2547, 1261 Buenos Aires, Argentina. TEL 941-2344. TELEX 24788. circ. 15,000.

621.3   JA   ISSN 0386-1570
MEIDEN JIHO/MEIDEN REPORT. (Text in Japanese) 1925. bi-m. 310 Yen per no. Meidensha Electric Manufacturing Co., Ltd., 2-1, Ote-machi 2-chome, Chiyoda-ku, Tokyo 100, Japan. TEL 81-3-5487-0435. FAX 81-3-5487-0714. adv. **Indexed:** INIS Atomind. **Document type:** academic/scholarly publication.
   Former titles (until 1974): Meidensha Jiho (ISSN 0386-1562); (until 1951): Meidensha Janaru.

621.3   JA   ISSN 0387-5385
MEIDEN REVIEW. (Text in English) 1961. 3/yr. free. Meidensha Corporation, New Ohtemachi Bldg., 2-1, Ote-machi 2-chome, Chiyoda-ku, Tokyo 100, Japan. TEL 03-246-7310. FAX 03-3245-1378. TELEX 02466036-MEIDEN-J. Ed. Toru Nakamura. charts; illus.; stat. circ. 1,000. **Indexed:** JTA, Sci.Abstr.
—BLDSC (5536.325000).
   Formerly (until 1974): Meidensha Review (ISSN 0025-8741)

621.31   CC   ISSN 1000-4416
MEIQI YU RELI/GAS AND HEAT. (Text in Chinese) bi-m. Zhongguo Shizheng Gongcheng Huabei Shejiyuan - North China Municipal Engineering Design Institute, Qixiangtai Lu, Hexi Qu, Tianjin 300074, People's Republic of China. TEL 022-342167. Ed. Xiang Youqian. **Document type:** academic/scholarly publication.

MEKATORONIKUSU/MECHATRONICS DESIGN NEWS. see ENGINEERING — Mechanical Engineering

MESSTECHNISCHE BRIEFE; Zeitschrift fuer das Elektrische Messen Mechanischer Groessen. see ENGINEERING — Mechanical Engineering

METALEKTRO PROFIEL; informatie over de metaal- en elektrotechnische industrie. see MACHINERY

METALURGIA Y ELECTRICIDAD. see METALLURGY

621.38   US   ISSN 0192-6225
TK7800   CODEN: MJIEEF
MICROWAVE JOURNAL (INTERNATIONAL EDITION). 1958. m. $67 (foreign $120; free to qualified personnel). Horizon - House - Publications, Inc., 685 Canton St., Norwood, MA 02062. TEL 617-769-9750. FAX 617-762-9230. TELEX 951 659. Ed. Harlan Howe. adv.; bk.rev.; abstr.; charts; illus.; tr.lit.; index. circ. 54,833. (also avail. in microform from UMI; reprint service avail.) **Indexed:** A.S.& T.Ind., CAD CAM Abstr., Curr.Cont., Eng.Ind., Ind.Sci.Rev., Int.Aerosp.Abstr., PROMT, Sci.Abstr., Tel.Abstr.
—SWETS. CCC.
   Formerly (until 1968): Microwave Journal (ISSN 0026-2897)
   Refereed Serial

ENGINEERING — ELECTRICAL ENGINEERING

621.38   US
MICROWAVE POWER SYMPOSIUM. PROCEEDINGS. no.8, 1973. a. International Microwave Power Institute, 10210 Leatherleaf Ct., Manassas, VA 22111-4245. TEL 703-257-1415. (back issues avail.) **Document type:** proceedings.

683.83   US
MICROWAVE PRODUCT DIGEST. 1989. bi-m. Octagon Communications Corporation, 167 S. Broadway, Hastings on Hudson, NY 10706. TEL 914-478-4482. Ed. Ian Marcinko. adv.
   Description: For microwave design, research, development and application engineers, as well as engineering managers. Includes information on new products.

621.38   US   ISSN 0745-2993
TK7800   CODEN: MIRFDL
MICROWAVES & R F. 1962. m. $60. Penton Publishing (Hasbrouck Heights) (Subsidiary of: Pittway Company), 611 Rt. 46 W., Hasbrouck Heights, NJ 07604. TEL 201-393-6060. FAX 201-393-6297. (Subscr. to: Circulation Department, 1100 Superior Ave., Cleveland, OH 44114) Ed. Jack Browne. adv.; bk.rev.; charts; illus.; stat.; tr.lit. circ. 60,750. (also avail. in microform from UMI) Indexed: A.S.& T.Ind., Curr.Cont., Ind.Sci.Rev., Int.Aerosp.Abstr., Sci.Abstr.
—BLDSC (5761.254000); EI; Faxon; UnCover; SWETS; UMI. **CCC**.
   Formerly (until 1982): Microwaves (ISSN 0026-2919)
   Description: Serves engineers and engineering managers involved with RF, microwave, and optical devices. Editorial addresses a broad range of applications within the high frequency segment of the electronics original equipment market.

621.38   US
MICROWAVES & R F PRODUCT DATA DIRECTORY. 1973. a. $50. Penton Publishing (Hasbrouck Heights) (Subsidiary of: Pittway Company), 611 Rt. 46 W., Hasbrouck Heights, NJ 07604. TEL 201-393-6060. Ed. Jack Browne. adv.; illus. circ. 60,750.
   Formerly: Microwaves Product Data Directory.
   Description: Worldwide buyer's guide in the high frequency field.

537   US
MICROWAVES & R F PRODUCT EXTRA. m. free to qualified personnel. Penton Publishing (Hasbrouck Heights) (Subsidiary of: Pittway Company), 611 Rt. 46 W., Hasbrouck Heights, NJ 07604. TEL 201-393-6060. circ. 40,000 (controlled).
   Description: Provides US engineers and engineering managers working at the higher frequency bands with an overview of the new products available to help them achieve their OEM design goals.

621.3   UK   ISSN 0309-4707
MIDDLE EAST ELECTRICITY. 1976. 6/yr. £40.25($104.70) Reed Business Publishing Group (Subsidiary of: Reed Elsevier group), Quadrant House, The Quadrant, Sutton, Surrey SM2 5AS, England. TEL 081-652-8742. FAX 081-652-8972. (Subscr. to: c/o Computer Action, Central House, Park St., Croydon CR0 14D, England. TEL 081-681-8416) Ed. Pat Kimber. adv. circ. 6,000. Indexed: Energy Info.Abstr., Int.Build.Serv.Abstr. **Document type:** trade publication.
—BLDSC (5761.373700); SWETS.

621.3 355   GW   ISSN 0722-9488
MIKROWELLEN AND H F - MAGAZIN; Telecommunications. 1974. 6/yr. DM.545. Sprechsaal Publishing Group, Mauer 2, 96450 Coburg, Germany. TEL 09561-76773. FAX 09561-90009. TELEX 663226-SPRECH-D. Ed. Christoph Mueller. adv.: B&W page DM.4966; trim 270 x 185. bk.rev. circ. 14,000. Indexed: Sci.Abstr. **Document type:** trade publication.
   Formerly: Mikrowellen and Military Electronics (ISSN 0722-8244)

MILITARY & AEROSPACE ELECTRONICS. see
AERONAUTICS AND SPACE FLIGHT

MILITARY MICROWAVES (YEAR). PROCEEDINGS OF CONFERENCE. see MILITARY

621.3   JA   ISSN 0369-2302
MITSUBISHI DENKI GIHO/MITSUBISHI DENKI TECHNICAL REVIEW. (Text in Japanese; summaries in English, Japanese) 1925. m. 720 Yen per no. Mitsubishi Denki Gihosha, Mitsubishi Denki Enjiniaringu, 6-2, Ote-machi 2-chome, Chiyoda-ku, Tokyo 100, Japan. Indexed: Chem.Abstr., INIS Atomind., Sci.Abstr.
—BLDSC (5829.802000).

621.3   JA   ISSN 0913-0101
MITSUBISHI DENSEN KOGYO JIHO/MITSUBISHI CABLE INDUSTRIES REVIEW. (Text in Japanese; summaries in English) 1951. s.a. free. Mitsubishi Cable Industries, Ltd., Patent & Technology Administration Department, 15-26, Fukushima 7-chome, Fukushima-ku, Osaka-shi, Osaka 553, Japan. FAX 06-343-1285. Ed.Bd. charts; illus.; cum.index. circ. 6,500. Indexed: Chem.Abstr., Eng.Ind., INIS Atomind., JCT, JTA, Met.Abstr., Sci.Abstr., World Alum.Abstr.
—BLDSC (5829.789500).
   Formerly (until 1986): Dainichi-Nippon Densen Jiho - Dainichi-Nippon Cables Review (ISSN 0011-5541); Which was formed by the 1964 merger of: Dainichi Densen Jiho; Nippon Densen Giho.

537 600   JA   ISSN 0386-5096
MITSUBISHI ELECTRIC ADVANCE; a quarterly survey of new products, systems and technology. (Text in English) 1977. q. 6000 Yen. Mitsubishi Electric Corporation, Mitsubishi Denki Bldg., 2-3, Marunouchi 2-chome, Chiyoda-ku, Tokyo 100, Japan. TELEX J24532. Ed. Tsuneo Taoka. charts; illus. circ. 2,000. Indexed: Eng.Ind., JCT, JTA, Sci.Abstr. **Document type:** trade publication.
—BLDSC (5829.804300); EI; Faxon.

DIE MODERNE KUECHE. see INTERIOR DESIGN AND DECORATION — Furniture And House Furnishings

621.3   CN   ISSN 0026-9379
MONDE DE L'ELECTRICITE. 1965. 10/yr. Can.$32.50($59) Publications Industrielles (Subsidiary of: Kerwil Publications Ltd.), 705 Hodge St., Ste. 204, St. Laurent, PQ H4N 3A1, Canada. Ed. Robert Bastin. adv.; tr.lit. circ. 8,000. (tabloid format) **Document type:** trade publication.

621.3   UK
MONOGRAPHS IN ELECTRICAL AND ELECTRONIC ENGINEERING. irreg. price varies. Oxford University Press, Oxford Journals, Walton St., Oxford OX2 6DP, England. TEL 0865-56767. FAX 0865-56646. TELEX 837330-OXPRES-G. (U.S. subscr. to: Oxford University Press Inc., 2001 Evans Rd., Cary, NC 27513. TEL 919-677-0977) Eds. P. Hammond, D. Walsh. **Document type:** monographic series.

621.3   SZ
MONTEUR ELECTRICIEN. 10/yr. Case Postale 121, CH-1470 Estavayer-le-Lac, Switzerland. TEL 037-631213. Ed. A. Arm. circ. 2,000.

MOZAMBIQUE. INSTITUTO NACIONAL DE GEOLOGIA. BOLETIM GEOMAGNETICO PRELIMINAR. see EARTH SCIENCES — Geophysics

621.3   US   ISSN 0027-2965
MUELLER CLIPPER. 1929. q. free. Mueller Electric Co, 1583 E. 31st St, Cleveland, OH 44114. TEL 216-771-5225. Ed. Scott Mueller. circ. 8,000.

MULTIDIMENSIONAL SYSTEMS AND SIGNAL PROCESSING; an international journal. see COMPUTERS — Computer Systems

621.3   BL   ISSN 0027-3295
MUNDO ELETRICO. 1959. m. $85. Editora Gruenwald Ltda., Rua Consorcio 59, 04535 Sao Paulo, Brazil. TEL 11-280-9411. FAX 011-833-2831. TELEX 1130410. adv.; bk.rev.; charts; illus.; tr.lit.; index. circ. 33,000.

621.3   CN
N.B. POWER NEWS. 1953. irreg. (8-10/yr.). free. New Brunswick Electric Power Commission, 515 King St., Fredericton, N.B. E3B 4X1, Canada. TEL 506-458-3099. Ed. Jerome Peterson. charts; illus. circ. 3,500.
   Formerly: Current Events (Fredericton) (ISSN 0011-3468)
   Description: Contains organization news.

621.3   JA   ISSN 0547-051X
   CODEN: NECRAU
N E C RESEARCH AND DEVELOPMENT. (Text in English) 1960. q. 750 Yen per no. (N E C Corporation) N E C Creative Ltd., 29-11, Shiba 5-chome, Minato-ku, Tokyo 108, Japan. abstr.; bibl.; charts; illus.; circ. 5,000 (controlled). Indexed: CAD CAM Abstr., Chem.Abstr., Curr.Cont., Cyb.Abstr., Eng.Ind., INIS Atomind., JCT, JTA, Sci.Abstr.
—BLDSC (6068.500000); EI; Faxon; UnCover; SWETS; CASCDS.

621.3   JA   ISSN 0285-4139
N E C TECHNICAL JOURNAL/N E C GIHO. (Text in Japanese; summaries in English, Japanese) 1948. m. 500 Yen per no. (N E C Corporation) N E C Creative Ltd., 29-11, Shiba 5-chome, Minato-ku, Tokyo 108. Indexed: INIS Atomind., Sci.Abstr.
—BLDSC (6068.580000).

621.3   JA   ISSN 0910-0237
N E C UPDATE. (Text in English) 1984. s-a. Nippon Electric Company - Nippon Denki K.K., 7-1, Shiba 5-chome, Minato-ku, Tokyo 108-01, Japan.

N E I S S DATA HIGHLIGHTS. (National Electronic Injury Surveillance System) see PUBLIC HEALTH AND SAFETY

621.3   US   ISSN 0092-5187
N E M A BULLETIN. m. National Electrical Manufacturers Association, 2101 L St. N.W., Washington, DC 20037. TEL 202-457-8400. bibl. **Document type:** bulletin.
   Formerly: N E M A Report.

790.1   US   ISSN 1066-2464
N E M A NEWS. 1935. 7/yr. $95. National Electrical Manufacturers Association, 2101 L St. N.W., Washington, DC 20037. TEL 202-459-8455. Ed. Martha J. Lockwood. circ. 2,600.

621.3   US
N E T A TECHNICAL PAPERS. 1983. a. $25. InterNational Electrical Testing Association, 106 Stone St., Box 687, Morrison, CO 80465. TEL 303-697-8441. FAX 303-697-8431. Ed. Mark Lautenschlager. circ. 500. (back issues avail.) **Document type:** proceedings.

621.3   US
N E T A WORLD. 1980. q. $8.50 per no. or membership. InterNational Electrical Testing Association, 106 Stone St., Box 687, Morrison, CO 80465. TEL 303-697-8441. FAX 303-697-8431. Ed. Rod Hageman. adv. contact: Jayne Hudson. circ. 6,500. **Document type:** trade publication.
   Formerly: N E T A News.
   Description: Technical publication covering the electrical testing industry.

621.3   US
N T I S ALERT: NAVIGATION, GUIDANCE & CONTROL. w. $140 (outside N. America $195). U.S. National Technical Information Service, 5285 Port Royal Rd., Springfield, VA 22161. TEL 703-487-4650. FAX 703-321-8547. TELEX 64617. bibl. **Document type:** newsletter, government publication.

621.3   US
N T I S ALERTS: DETECTION & COUNTERMEASURES. w. $140 (outside N. America $195). U.S. National Technical Information Service, 5285 Port Royal Rd., Springfield, VA 22161. TEL 703-487-4650. FAX 703-321-8547. TELEX 64617. bibl. **Document type:** abstracting/indexing, government publication.

621.3   GW
N W AKTUELL. 1973. q. free. Neckarwerke Elektrizitaetsversorgungs AG, Kueferstr. 2, 73728 Esslingen, Germany. TEL 0711-3190-2402. FAX 0711-3190-2413. Ed. Peter Szeremeta. circ. 485,000. (back issues avail.)

621.3   NZ   ISSN 0114-8540
N Z ELECTRICAL FOCUS. 1948. bi-m. NZ.$24.95 plus postage. Associated Group Media Ltd., Private Bag 99-915, Newmarket, Auckland, New Zealand. TEL 09-379-5393. FAX 09-308-9523. Ed. Robert Stockdill. adv.; bk.rev.; stat. circ. 7,500. **Document type:** trade publication.
—CCC.
   Formerly (until Aug. 1989): New Zealand Electrician (ISSN 0028-8071)

NANOTECHNOLOGY. see PHYSICS

2350 ENGINEERING — ELECTRICAL ENGINEERING

621.3   CN
THE NATIONAL (OTTAWA).* m. Communications, Electronic, Electrical, Technical and Salaried Workers of Canada, 350 Sparks St., Ottawa, Ont. K1R 7S8, Canada.

621.3   UK
TK5101.A1   CODEN: IJDSEM
NATIONAL JOURNAL OF COMMUNICATION SYSTEMS. q. $335. John Wiley & Sons Ltd., Journals, Baffins Ln., Chichester, W. Sussex PO19 1UD, England. TEL 0243-778777. FAX 0243-775878. TELEX 0894-3982. Ed. J. Fox. circ. 222. **Indexed:** Tel.Abstr. **Document type:** trade publication.
—BLDSC (4542.185410); EI; Faxon; SWETS; UMI. CCC.
Former titles: International Journal of Digital and Analog Communication Systems (ISSN 1047-9627); International Journal of Digital and Analog Cabled Systems (ISSN 0894-3222)
Description: Provides a forum for research and development in the fast growing area of communication networks.
Refereed Serial

621.3   UK
NATIONAL POWER. ANNUAL REVIEW. a. £2 per no. National Power plc, Windmill Hill Business Park, Whitehill Way, Swindon, Wilts. SN4 6PB, England. TEL 0793-877777. FAX 0793-892781. TELEX 444574. Ed.Bd. **Document type:** corporate report.
Description: Reviews the year's activities, including environmental and regulatory issues, both within the organization and in the community at large.

621.3   UK
NATIONAL POWER. REPORT AND ACCOUNTS. a. National Power plc, Windmill Hill Business Park, Whitehill Way, Swindon, Wilts. SN5 6PB, England. TEL 0793-877777. FAX 0793-892781. TELEX 444574. Ed.Bd. **Document type:** corporate report.
Description: Reviews the past year's company finances and market trends affecting them.

621.38   US   ISSN 0077-5401
TK2851   CODEN: PRECD9
NATIONAL RELAY CONFERENCE. PROCEEDINGS; Relay Conference papers. 1952. a. $50. National Association of Relay Manufacturers, 9459 N. Broadmoor Rd., Milwaukee, WI 53217-1310. Ed. D.E. Dangott. circ. 700. (also avail. in microfilm; back issues avail.) **Document type:** proceedings.
—BLDSC (6848.946000).

621.3   US   ISSN 0077-5657
NATIONAL RURAL ELECTRIC COOPERATIVE ASSOCIATION. GOVERNMENT RELATIONS DEPARTMENT. RESEARCH DIVISION. RESEARCH PAPERS AND CIRCULARS.. 1964. q. free. National Rural Electric Cooperative Association, Government Relations Department, Research Division, 1800 Massachusetts Ave., N.W., Washington, DC 20036. TEL 202-857-9500. Ed. M.L. DuMars. circ. 200.
Former titles: National Rural Electric Cooperative Association. Legislative Research Staff. Research Paper; National Rural Electric Cooperative Association. Legislation and Communications Department. Research Division. Research Papers and Circulars.

621.3   JA   ISSN 0028-0291
CODEN: NTROAV
NATIONAL TECHNICAL REPORT. (Text in Japanese; summaries in English, Japanese) 1955. bi-m. 5400 Yen. Matsushita Electric Industrial Co., Ltd., 3-1-1 Yakumonaka-machi, Moriguchi-shi, Osaka 570, Japan. FAX 06-906-0177. TELEX 529-5733-MEIED-J. Ed. Toshiyuki Honda. charts; illus.; tr.lit.; index. circ. 4,000. (reprint service avail.) **Indexed:** Chem.Abstr., Eng.Ind., INIS Atomind., JCT, JTA, Sci.Abstr. **Document type:** corporate report.
—BLDSC (6033.120000); CASDDS.

NEON NEWS. see ART

NEUROELECTRIC NEWS. see MEDICAL SCIENCES — Psychiatry And Neurology

621.3   JA   ISSN 0286-5122
NEW ELECTRONIC PRODUCTS JAPAN. Short title: N E P. (Text in Japanese) 1982. m. 2000 Yen per no. Incom Co., Ltd., 23-6, Sekiguchi 1-chome, Bunkyo-ku, Tokyo 112, Japan. **Document type:** trade publication.

621.3   JA   ISSN 0288-8866
NIHON DENKI KYOKAI TSUJO SOKAI KENKYU HAPPYOKAI RONBUNSHU/JAPAN ELECTRIC ASSOCIATION. PROCEEDINGS OF THE MEETING. (Text in Japanese) 1958. biennial. 1000 Yen per no. Nihon Denki Kyokai - Japan Electric Association, 7-1, Yurakucho 1-chome, Chiyoda-ku, Tokyo 100, Japan. **Document type:** proceedings.

NIHON KAISUI GAKKAISHI/SOCIETY OF SEA WATER SCIENCE, JAPAN. BULLETIN. see EARTH SCIENCES — Oceanography

621.3   JA
NIKKAN DENKI TSUSHIN/DAILY ELECTRICITY NEWS. (Text in Japanese) 1952. d. 78000 Yen. Nikkan Denki Tsushinsha, 1-10, Shinbashi 3-chome, Minato-ku, Tokyo 107, Japan. **Document type:** newspaper.

621.3   JA
NIKKAN DENSEN JOHO/ELECTRIC WIRE AND CABLE INFORMATION. (Text in Japanese) 1954. s-w. 76000 Yen. Sangyo Nipposha, 9-8, Higashiueno 5-chome, Taito-ku, Tokyo 110, Japan.

NIKKEI CHODENDO/NIKKEI SUPERCONDUCTORS. see PHYSICS

621.38 380.1   JA
NIKKEI HIGH TECH REPORT. 1985. fortn. Nihon Keizai Shimbun, Inc., Nikkei Research Institute of Industry and Markets, 1-9-5 Ote-machi, Chiyoda-ku, Tokyo 100-66, Japan. TEL 03-3270-0251. **Document type:** newsletter.
—CCC.
Incorporates: Japan Electronics Today News (ISSN 0261-3506)
Description: Covers a wide range of high-tech topics, such as electronics, biotechnology and new materials.

NIPPONDENSO TECHNICAL DISCLOSURE. JOURNAL/NIPPON DENSO KOKAI GIHO. see ENGINEERING — Mechanical Engineering

621.3   JA
NISHISHIBA DENKI/NISHISHIBA REVIEW. (Text in Japanese) 1972. s-a. Nishishiba Denki K.K. - Nishishiba Electric Co., Ltd., 1000, Hamada, Aboshi-ku, Himeji-shi, Hyogo-ken 671-12, Japan.

621.3   JA   ISSN 0549-5377
NISSHIN DENKI GIHO/NISSHIN ELECTRIC REVIEW. (Text in Japanese; summaries in English) 1956. q. Nisshin Denki K.K. - Nisshin Electric Co., Ltd., 47, Umezu Takase-cho, Ukyo-ku, Kyoto-shi, Kyoto 615, Japan.

621.3   JA   ISSN 0285-2462
NITTO GIHO/NITTO TECHNICAL REPORT. (Text in English, Japanese) 1959. s-a. Nitto Denki Kogyo K.K., Gijutsu Kenkyujo - Nitto Electric Industrial Co., Ltd., Technical Laboratory, 1-2, Shimohozumi 1-chome, Ibaraki-shi, Osaka 567, Japan.

621.3   JA   ISSN 0388-5712
NITTSUKO GIHO/NITSUKO TECHNICAL REPORT. (Text in Japanese; summaries in English, Japanese) 1970. irreg. Nittsuko K.K. - Nitsuko Corp., 260, Kitamigata, Takatsuku, Kawasaki-shi, Kanagawa-ken 213, Japan.

NOVA SCOTIA POWER INC. ANNUAL REPORT. see ENERGY

537   IT
NUOVA ELETTRAUTO. 1955. m. L.63000 (foreign L.120000). Editore Morales S.r.l., Via Spreafico 10, 20052 Monza, Italy. TEL 039-2302363. FAX 039-2302364. Ed. Maria Luisa Corno; Pub. Sergio Morales. adv. circ. 14,000. **Document type:** academic/scholarly publication.
Formerly: Elettrauto.
Description: Deals with automotive electricity and electronics, technical updating for car repair shops, car hi-fi, traffic management, new technologies applied to cars, and repair equipment.

621.3   AU
OESTERREICHISCHES STATISTISCHES ZENTRALAMT. WIRTSCHAFTSSTATISTIK DER ELEKTRIZITATSVERSORGUNGSUNTERNEHMEN. 1976. a. S.80. Oesterreichisches Statistisches Zentralamt, Hintere Zollamtsstr. 2b, A-1033 Vienna, Austria. TEL 0222-71128-0. FAX 0222-7156828. Ed.Bd. circ. 310. **Document type:** government publication.
Description: Covers structure, production, and consumption of electricity companies.

OFF-SHORE TECHNOLOGY CONFERENCE. RECORD. see PETROLEUM AND GAS

621.3   JA   ISSN 0914-6741
OHKURA DENKI GIHO/OHKURA ELECTRIC ENGINEERING NEWS. (Text in Japanese) 1985. s-a. Ohkura Denki K.K., Wako Gijutsu Senta - Ohkura Electric Co., Ltd., Wako Technical Center, 9-20, Shirako 2-chome, Wako-shi, Saitama-ken 351-01, Japan.

621.3   JA   ISSN 0386-5576
OHM. Variant title: Denki Zasshi Ohm. (Text in Japanese) 1914. m. 1100 Yen per no. Ohm-sha, 3-1, Kanda Nishiki-cho, Chiyoda-ku, Tokyo 101, Japan. **Indexed:** INIS Atomind.

621.3   JA   ISSN 0286-892X
OKI DENKI KENKYU KAIHATSU/OKI REVIEW. (Text in Japanese) 1934. q. Oki Denki Kogyo K.K. - Oki Electric Industry Co., Ltd., 17-1, Toranomon 1-chome, Minato-ku, Tokyo 105, Japan. **Indexed:** Sci.Abstr.

621.3   JA   ISSN 0912-5566
OKI TECHNICAL REVIEW. (Text in English) q. Oki Electric Industry Co., Ltd. - Oki Denki Kogyo K.K., 17-1, Toranomon 1-chome, Minato-ku, Tokyo 105, Japan.
—BLDSC (6252.851000).

621.3   US
OKLAHOMA ELECTRIC CO-OP NEWS. m. Oklahoma Electric Cooperative, 242 N.W. 24th Ave., P.O. Box 1208, Norman, OK 73072. TEL 405-321-2024. FAX 405-366-0661. Ed. John Lowrey. circ. 21,000.

537.5   UK
OMNI U K. 1978. q. £25. Infonet Ltd., 5 River Park Ind. Area, Billet Lane, Berkhamsted, Herst HP4 1HL, England. TEL 04417 76661.

621.3   JA   ISSN 0474-1315
OMRON TECHNICS. (Text in Japanese; summaries in English, Japanese) 1961. q. 930 Yen per no. Omron Corporation, Research & Technology Assessment Division - Omuron K.K. Gijutsu Honbu, 20, Igadera, Shinmokaiiji, Nagaokakyo-shi, Kyoto 617, Japan.

621.3   NE   ISSN 0030-3135
ONTLADINGEN. Variant title: A E G - Telefunken Ontladingen. 1936. bi-m. free. A E G - Telefunken Nederland N.V., Box 1816, 1000 BV Amsterdam, Netherlands. circ. 11,000. **Indexed:** Excerp.Med.

OPTICAL WAVE SCIENCES AND TECHNOLOGY. see PHYSICS — Optics

OPUTORONIKUSU/OPTRONICS. see PHYSICS — Optics

621.3   JA   ISSN 0474-6767
CODEN: ORGNB5
ORIGIN TECHNICAL JOURNAL/ORIJIN GIHO. (Text in Japanese; summaries in English) 1950. a. $10. Origin Electric Co., Ltd. - Orijin Denki K.K., 18-1, Takada 1-chome, Toshima-ku, Tokyo 171, Japan. FAX 03-983-7111. **Indexed:** Chem.Abstr., JCT.
—BLDSC (6291.237300); CASDDS.

OSAKA DENKI TSUSHIN DAIGAKU KENKYU RONSHU. SHIZEN KAGAKU HEN/OSAKA ELECTRO-COMMUNICATION UNIVERSITY. MEMOIRS. NATURAL SCIENCE. see COMMUNICATIONS

621.3   US
P C P C I MEMBERSHIP DIRECTORY AND PRODUCT LISTING. a. membership. Power Conversion Products Council International, 4 Hollis St., Box 378, Sherborn, MA 01770. TEL 508-655-4409. FAX 508-651-3920.
Description: Alphabetical listing of members showing each member's principal products and the individual's name who is the company representative to PCPCI.

ENGINEERING — ELECTRICAL ENGINEERING

621.3 US
P C P C I NEWSLETTER. q. membership. Power Conversion Products Council International, 4 Hollis St., Box 378, Sherborn, MA 01770. TEL 508-655-4409. FAX 508-651-3920. **Document type:** newsletter.

621.3 UK
PANEL BUILDING. 1991. bi-m. £35 in the UK; Europe £40; elsewhere £55. I M L Group plc, Blair House, High St., Tonbridge, Kent TN9 1BQ, England. TEL 0732-359990. FAX 0732-770049. Ed. James Hunt. adv.; bk.rev. circ. 6,000. **Document type:** trade publication.

621.3 HU ISSN 0324-6000
TK4 CODEN: PPYTA7
PERIODICA POLYTECHNICA. ELECTRICAL ENGINEERING. (Text in English) 1957. q. $16. Budapesti Muszaki Egyetem - Technical University of Budapest, 151 Budapest, Hungary. FAX 1-166-6808. TELEX 22-5931 MUEGY H. (Dist. by: Kultura, P.O. Box 149, 1389 Budapest, Hungary) Ed. I. Novak. bk.rev.; charts; illus.; pat.; tr.mk.; index. circ. 530. **Indexed:** Agri.Eng.Abstr., Appl.Mech.Rev., Comput.& Contr.Abstr., Curr.Cont., Eng.Ind., Met.Abstr., Sci.Abstr.
—BLDSC (6425.340000).

PHYSICA B - PHYSICS OF CONDENSED MATTER. see *PHYSICS*

PHYSICA C - SUPERCONDUCTIVITY. see *PHYSICS*

PHYSICA D - NONLINEAR PHENOMENA. see *PHYSICS*

PLASMA TECHNOLOGY. see *PHYSICS*

POLITECHNIKA GDANSKA. ZESZYTY NAUKOWE. ELEKTRONIKA. see *COMPUTERS — Cybernetics*

621 PL ISSN 0373-8647
POLITECHNIKA GDANSKA. ZESZYTY NAUKOWE. ELEKTRYKA. (Text in English, Polish; summaries in Russian and one West-European language) 1955. irreg. price varies. Politechnika Gdanska, Ul. G. Narutowicza 11-12, 80-952 Gdansk 6, Poland. (Dist. by: Osrodek Rozpowszechniania Wydawnictw Naukowych Pan, Palac Kultury i Nauki, 00-901 Warsaw, Poland) bibl.; charts; illus. **Document type:** academic/scholarly publication.
Description: Deals with marine electrical engineering; power engines, electrical measurement, machine drive, apparatus, traction and industrial automation.

621.3 PL
POLITECHNIKA KRAKOWSKA. MONOGRAFIE. SERIA: INZYNIERIA ELEKTRYCZNA. (Subseries of: Politechnika Krakowska. Monografie (ISSN 0860-097X)) (Text in Polish; summaries in English, French, German, Russian) 1985. irreg. price varies. Politechnika Krakowska, Ul. Warszawska 24, 31-155 Krakow, Poland. TEL 48-12-374289. FAX 48-12-335773. TELEX 322468 PK PL. bibl.; charts; illus. circ. 200. **Document type:** academic/scholarly publication, monographic series.

621.3 PL
POLITECHNIKA KRAKOWSKA. ZESZYTY NAUKOWE. INZYNIERIA ELEKTRYCZNA. (Text in Polish; summaries in English, French, German, Russian) 1977. irreg. price varies. Politechnika Krakowska, Ul. Warszawska 24, 31-155 Krakow, Poland. TEL 48-12-374289. FAX 48-12-335773. TELEX 322468 PK PL. bibl.; charts; illus. circ. 200. **Document type:** academic/scholarly publication.
Former titles: Politechnika Krakowska. Zeszyty Naukowe. Inzynieria Transportowa i Elektryczna; Politechnika Krakowska. Zeszyty Naukowe. Transport (ISSN 0860-0783)

621.3 PL ISSN 0459-682X
CODEN: ZNPEAD
POLITECHNIKA LODZKA. ZESZYTY NAUKOWE. ELEKTRYKA. (Text in Polish; summaries in English and Russian) 1955. irreg. price varies. Wydawnictwo Politechniki Lodzkiej, Ul. Wolczanska 219, 93-085 Lodz, Poland. (Dist. by: Ars Polona-Ruch, Krakowskie Przedmiescie 7, Warsaw, Poland) Ed. Franciszek Mosinski. circ. 246. **Indexed:** Chem.Abstr., Comput.& Contr.Abstr., Elec.& Electron.Abstr., Phys.Abstr., Sci.Abstr. **Document type:** academic/scholarly publication.
—CASDDS.
Description: Articles on electrical apparatus, electric machines and transformers, electronics, electroenergetics and light engineering.

621.3 PL ISSN 0079-4503
POLITECHNIKA POZNANSKA. ZESZYTY NAUKOWE. ELEKTRYKA. (Text in Polish; summaries in English) 1959. irreg. price varies. Politechnika Poznanska, Pl. Curie-Sklodowskiej 5, Poznan, Poland. Ed. Zdzislaw Zalucki. circ. 150. **Document type:** academic/scholarly publication.
Description: Articles on electric power apparatus and systems.

537 621.3 PL ISSN 0072-4688
POLITECHNIKA SLASKA. ZESZYTY NAUKOWE. ELEKTRYKA. (Text in Polish; summaries in English, German, Russian) 1954. irreg. price varies. Politechnika Slaska, Katowicka 7, 44-100 Gliwice, Poland. FAX 371655. TELEX 036304. (Dist. by: Ars Polona, Krakowskie Przedmiescie 7, 00-068 Warsaw, Poland) Ed. Zofia Cichowska. circ. 205.

621.3 PL ISSN 0324-9778
CODEN: PNPKER
POLITECHNIKA WROCLAWSKA. INSTYTUT ENERGOELEKTRYKI. PRACE NAUKOWE. KONFERENCJE. (Text in Polish and English) 1973. irreg., no.31, 1991. price varies. Wydawnictwo Politechniki Wroclawskiej, Wybrzeze Wyspianskiego 27, 50-370 Wroclaw, Poland. FAX 223664. TELEX 712559 PWRPL. (Dist. by: Ars Polona-Ruch, Krakowskie Przedmiescie 7, Warsaw, Poland) circ. 480.

621.3 PL ISSN 0324-976X
POLITECHNIKA WROCLAWSKA. INSTYTUT ENERGOELEKTRYKI. PRACE NAUKOWE. MONOGRAFIE. (Text in Polish; summaries in English, French and Russian) 1972. irreg., no.27, 1992. price varies. Wydawnictwo Politechniki Wroclawskiej, Wybrzeze Wyspianskiego 27, 50-370 Wroclaw, Poland. FAX 22-36-64. TELEX 712559 PWRPL. (Dist. by: Ars Polona-Ruch, Krakowskie Przedmiescie 7, Warsaw, Poland) **Document type:** monographic series.

621.3 PL ISSN 0084-2826
POLITECHNIKA WROCLAWSKA. INSTYTUT ENERGOELEKTRYKI. PRACE NAUKOWE. STUDIA I MATERIALY. (Text in Polish; summaries in English, French, German, Russian) 1969. irreg., no.30, 1979. Wydawnictwo Politechniki Wroclawskiej, Ul. Wybrzeze Wyspianskiego 27, 50-370 Wroclaw, Poland. FAX 22-36-64. TELEX 712559 PWRPL. (Dist. by: Ars Polona-Ruch, Krakowskie Przedmiescie 7, Warsaw, Poland)

621.3 389 PL ISSN 0324-9557
TK275
POLITECHNIKA WROCLAWSKA. INSTYTUT METROLOGII ELEKTRYCZNEJ. PRACE NAUKOWE. KONFERENCJE. (Text in Polish and English) 1973. irreg., no.17, 1991. price varies. Wydawnictwo Politechniki Wroclawskiej, Wybrzeze Wyspianskiego 27, 50-370 Wroclaw, Poland. FAX 22-36-64. TELEX 712559 PWRPL. (Dist. by : Ars Polona-Ruch, Krakowskie Przedmiescie 7, Warsaw, Poland) circ. 480. **Indexed:** Sci.Abstr.

621.3 389 PL ISSN 0324-9549
TK275 CODEN: PIMWDC
POLITECHNIKA WROCLAWSKA. INSTYTUT METROLOGII ELEKTRYCZNEJ. PRACE NAUKOWE. MONOGRAFIE. (Text in Polish; summaries in English and Russian) 1974. irreg., no.10, 1991. price varies. Wydawnictwo Politechniki Wroclawskiej, Wybrzeze Wyspianskiego 27, 50-370 Wroclaw, Poland. FAX 22-36-64. TELEX 712559 PWRPL. (Dist. by: Ars Polona-Ruch, Krakowskie Przedmiescie 7, Warsaw, Poland) circ. 375.
—CASDDS.

621.3 389 PL ISSN 0084-2958
POLITECHNIKA WROCLAWSKA. INSTYTUT METROLOGII ELEKTRYCZNEJ. PRACE NAUKOWE. STUDIA I MATERIALY. (Text in Polish; summaries in English, Russian) 1970. irreg., no.8, 1982. price varies. Wydawnictwo Politechniki Wroclawskiej, Wybrzeze Wyspianskiego 27, 50-370 Wroclaw, Poland. FAX 22-36-64. TELEX 712559 PWRPL. (Dist. by: Ars Polona-Ruch, Krakowskie Przedmiescie 7, Warsaw, Poland) **Indexed:** Chem.Abstr.

621 PL ISSN 0324-9441
POLITECHNIKA WROCLAWSKA. INSTYTUT PODSTAW ELEKTROTECHNIKI I ELEKTROTECHNOLOGII. PRACE NAUKOWE. KONFERENCJE. (Text in Polish; summaries in English and Russian) 1975. irreg., no.6, 1988. price varies. Wydawnictwo Politechniki Wroclawskiej, Wybrzeze Wyspianskiego 27, 50-370 Wroclaw, Poland. FAX 22-36-64. TELEX 712559 PWRPL. (Dist. by: Ars Polona-Ruch, Krakowskie Przedmiescie 7, Warsaw, Poland)

621 PL ISSN 0324-945X
POLITECHNIKA WROCLAWSKA. INSTYTUT PODSTAW ELEKTROTECHNIKI I ELEKTROTECHNOLOGII. PRACE NAUKOWE. MONOGRAFIE. (Text in Polish; summaries in English and Russian) 1972. irreg., no.10, 1989. price varies. Wydawnictwo Politechniki Wroclawskiej, Wybrzeze Wyspianskiego 27, 50-370 Wroclaw, Poland. FAX 22-36-64. TELEX 712559 PWRPL. (Dist. by: Ars Polona-Ruch, Krakowskie Przedmiescie 7, Warsaw, Poland) circ. 250.

621.3 PL ISSN 0370-0852
TK4 CODEN: PNIPA3
POLITECHNIKA WROCLAWSKA. INSTYTUT PODSTAW ELEKTROTECHNIKI I ELEKTROTECHNOLOGII. PRACE NAUKOWE. STUDIA I MATERIALY. (Text in Polish; summaries in English and Russian) 1970. irreg., no.8, 1980. price varies. Wydawnictwo Politechniki Wroclawskiej, Wybrzeze Wyspianskiego 27, 50-370 Wroclaw, Poland. FAX 22-36-64. TELEX 712559 PWRPL. (Dist. by: Ars Polona-Ruch, Krakowskie Przedmiescie 7, Warsaw, Poland) circ. 250. **Indexed:** Chem.Abstr.
—CASDDS.

621.3 PL ISSN 0137-6276
POLITECHNIKA WROCLAWSKA. INSTYTUT ELEKTROTECHNIKI I ELEKTROTECHNOLOGII. PRACE NAUKOWE. WSPOLPRACA. (Text in Polish; summaries in English and Russian) 1977. irreg., no.2, 1986. price varies. Wydawnictwo Politechniki Wroclawskiej, Wybrzeze Wyspianskiego 27, 50-370 Wroclaw, Poland. FAX 22-36-64. TELEX 712559 PWRPL. circ. 250.

621.38 PL ISSN 0370-0887
TK7800 CODEN: PNITBG
POLITECHNIKA WROCLAWSKA. INSTYTUT TECHNOLOGII ELEKTRONOWEJ. PRACE NAUKOWE. KONFERENCJE. (Text in Polish; summaries in English, French and Russian) 1973. irreg., no.10, 1989. price varies. Wydawnictwo Politechniki Wroclawskiej, Wybrzeze Wyspianskiego 27, 50-370 Wroclaw, Poland. FAX 22-36-64. TELEX 712559 PWRPL. (Dist. by: Ars Polona-Ruch, Krakowskie Przedmiescie 7, Warsaw, Poland)
—CASDDS.

621.38 PL ISSN 0084-280X
TK7800
POLITECHNIKA WROCLAWSKA. INSTYTUT TECHNOLOGII ELEKTRONOWEJ. PRACE NAUKOWE. MONOGRAFIE. (Text in Polish; summaries in English, Russian) 1970. irreg., no.15, 1991. price varies. Wydawnictwo Politechni ki Wroclawskiej, Wybrzeze Wyspianskiego 27, 50-370 Wroclaw, Poland. FAX 22-36-64. TELEX 712559 PWRPL. (Dist. by: Ars Polona-Ruch, Krakowskie Przedmiescie 7, Warsaw, Poland) **Indexed:** Sci.Abstr. **Document type:** monographic series.

621.3 530 PL ISSN 0084-2885
TK7800 CODEN: PNITBG
POLITECHNIKA WROCLAWSKA. INSTYTUT TECHNOLOGII ELEKTRONOWEJ. PRACE NAUKOWE. STUDIA I MATERIALY. (Text in Polish; summaries in English, Russian) 1970. irreg., no.14, 1984. price varies. Wydawnictwo Politechniki Wroclawskiej, Wybrzeze Wyspianskiego 27, 50-370 Wroclaw, Poland. FAX 22-36-64. TELEX 712559 PWRPL. (Dist. by: Ars Polona-Ruch, Krakowskie Przedmiescie 7, Warsaw, Poland) **Indexed:** Chem.Abstr.

ENGINEERING — ELECTRICAL ENGINEERING

POLITECHNIKA WROCLAWSKA. INSTYTUT TELEKOMUNIKACJI I AKUSTYKI. PRACE NAUKOWE. KONFERENCJE. see *COMMUNICATIONS — Telephone And Telegraph*

POLITECHNIKA WROCLAWSKA. INSTYTUT TELEKOMUNIKACJI I AKUSTYKI. PRACE NAUKOWE. MONOGRAFIE. see *COMMUNICATIONS — Telephone And Telegraph*

POLITECHNIKA WROCLAWSKA. INSTYTUT TELEKOMUNIKACJI I AKUSTYKI. PRACE NAUKOWE. STUDIA I MATERIALY. see *COMMUNICATIONS — Telephone And Telegraph*

621.3   PL   ISSN 0324-931X
TK4   CODEN: PIUWDI
POLITECHNIKA WROCLAWSKA. INSTYTUT UKLADOW ELEKTROMASZYNOWYCH. PRACE NAUKOWE. KONFERENCJE. (Text in Polish; summaries in English and Russian) 1973. irreg., no.10, 1987. price varies. Wydawnictwo Politechniki Wroclawskiej, Wybrzeze Wyspianskiego 27, 50-370 Wroclaw, Poland. FAX 22-36-64. TELEX 712559 PWRPL. (Dist. by: Ars Polona-Ruch, Krakowskie Przedmiescie 7, Warsaw, Poland)

621.3   PL   ISSN 0137-6284
TK4   CODEN: PNUMEO
POLITECHNIKA WROCLAWSKA. INSTYTUT UKLADOW ELEKTROMASZYNOWYCH. PRACE NAUKOWE. MONOGRAFIE. (Text in Polish; summaries in English and Russian) 1969. irreg., no.10, 1992. price varies. Wydawnictwo Politechniki Wroclawskiej, Ul. Wybrzeze Wyspianskiego 27, 50-370 Wroclaw, Poland. FAX 22-36-64. TELEX 712559 PWRPL. (Dist. by: Ars Polona-Ruch, Krakowskie Przedmiescie 7, Warsaw, Poland) **Indexed:** Sci.Abstr.

621.3   PL   ISSN 0084-294X
                                  CODEN: PIUWDI
POLITECHNIKA WROCLAWSKA. INSTYTUT UKLADOW ELEKTROMASZYNOWYCH. PRACE NAUKOWE. STUDIA I MATERIALY. (Text in Polish; summaries in English and Russian) 1969. irreg., no.17, 1990. price varies. Wydawnictwo Politechniki Wroclawskiej, Ul. Wybrzeze Wyspianskiego 27, 50-370 Wroclaw, Poland. FAX 22-36-64. TELEX 712559 PWRPL. (Dist. by: Ars Polona-Ruch, Krakowskie Przedmiescie 7, Warsaw, Poland)
—CASDDS.

621.3   NE   ISSN 0925-5672
                                  CODEN: PEELEE
POLYTECHNISCH TIJDSCHRIFT - ELEKTROTECHNIEK - ELEKTRONICA; vakblad voor de ingenieur. 1945. 10/yr. fl.197.50 (foreign fl.365) (effective 1994). Ten Hagen & Stam b.v., Postbus 235, 2280 AE Rijswijk, Netherlands. TEL 31-70-3988100. FAX 31-70-3988276. adv.: B&W page fl.2680, color page fl.4905; trim 297 x 210; adv. contact: Herman Voois. circ. 5,925. **Indexed:** C.I.S. Abstr., Comput.& Contr.Abstr., Elec.& Electron.Abstr., Phys.Abstr., Sci.Abstr. **Document type:** trade publication.
—BLDSC (6549.018000).
 Former titles (until 1990): P T Elektrotechniek (ISSN 0925-5664); (until 1989): P T Elektrotechniek - Elektronica (ISSN 0032-4086).
 Description: Covers all aspects of electrical and computer engineering, including electronics, power electronics, telecommunication and data communication, measuring and control techniques.

537.5   DK
POLYTEKNISKE LAEREANSTALT, DANMARKS TEKNISKE HOEJSKOLE. ELECTRONICS INSTITUTE. ANNUAL REPORT. 1970. a. free. Polytekniske Laereanstalt, Danmarks Tekniske Hoejskole, Laboratoriet for Elektronik - Technical University of Denmark, Electronics Institute, Bygning 349, DK-2800 Lyngby, Denmark. FAX 42-88-01-17. Ed. Erik Bruun. circ. 400.
 Formerly: Polytekniske Laereanstalt, Danmarks Tekniske Hoejskole. Laboratoriet for Elektronik. Beretning.

537   PL   ISSN 0079-4260
POSTEPY NAPEDU ELEKTRYCZNEGO. 1960. irreg. price varies. (Polska Akademia Nauk, Komitet Elektrotechniki) Wydawnictwo Naukowe P W N, Ul. Miodowa 10, 00-251 Warsaw, Poland. TEL 48-22-312738. FAX 48-22-267163. TELEX 813763 PWN PL.

621.3   BE
POUR VOUS/VOOR U. (Text in Flemish and French) 1957. q. free. Union des Exploitations Electriques en Belgique, Galerie Ravenstein 4, Bte. 6, 1000 Brussels, Belgium. Ed. Robert Mathieu. adv.; illus. circ. 3,100,000.
 Formerly: Electricite pour Vous (ISSN 0013-452X)

POWER. see *BUSINESS AND ECONOMICS — Labor And Industrial Relations*

621.3   US
▼**POWER DELIVERY PRODUCT NEWS.** 1992. bi-m. $21 (N. America $36.75; elsewhere $60). PennWell Publishing Co. (Barrington), 1250 S. Grove Ave., Barrington, IL 60010. TEL 708-382-2450. FAX 708-382-2977. Ed. Wayne Beatty. adv.: B&W page $4600; trim 11 1/8 x 16. circ. 60,000 (controlled). **Document type:** trade publication.
 Description: Covers the electric power delivery market, including engineering, operations, marketing and purchasing.

621.3   US   ISSN 0032-5961
TJ1   CODEN: POENAI
POWER ENGINEERING (TULSA). 1896. m. $38 to individuals; libraries $28; foreign $66. PennWell Publishing Co., 1421 Sheridan Rd., Tulsa, OK 74101. TEL 918-835-3161. (Subscr. to: Box 1440, Tulsa, OK 74101) Ed. Robert Smock. bk.rev.; abstr.; bibl.; charts; illus.; stat.; index. circ. 50,714. (also avail. in microfilm from UMI; back issues avail.; reprint service avail.) **Indexed:** A.S.& T.Ind., ABI Inform., Acid Rain Abstr., Acid Rain Ind., Appl.Mech.Rev., CAD CAM Abstr., Chem.Abstr., Curr.Cont., Energy Info.Abstr., Eng.Ind., Excerp.Med., Fuel & Energy Abstr., INSPEC, ISMEC, Ocean.Abstr., Pollut.Abstr., Risk Abstr., Sci.Abstr., W.R.C.Inf.
—BLDSC (6575.000000); EI; Faxon; UnCover; SWETS; UMI; CASDDS. **CCC.**

621.3   UK   ISSN 0950-3366
TK1   CODEN: PEJOEE
POWER ENGINEERING JOURNAL. 1987. bi-m. £77 in EC nations; elsewhere £85. I.E.E., Michael Faraday House, Six Hills Way, Stevenage, Herts. SG1 2AG, England. TEL 0438-313311. FAX 0438-742840. TELEX 825578-IEESTV-G. (Subscr. to: Publication Sales Dept., P.O. Box 96, Stevenage, Herts. SG1 2SD, England; U.S. addr.: INSPEC/IEEE, Box 1331, 445 Hoes Ln., Piscataway, NJ 08855-1331. TEL 908-562-5549) Ed. J. Cooper. adv.; bk.rev.; index. circ. 21,000. **Indexed:** CAD CAM Abstr., Energy Info.Abstr., Sci.Abstr.
●Also available on CD-ROM. Producer(s): University Microfilms International.
—BLDSC (6575.150000); EI; Faxon; UnCover; SWETS. **CCC.**
 Description: For professional power engineers employed in the field of electrical power generation, control, distribution, and utilization. Reports on specific projects, equipment, and techniques relating to current operations worldwide.

621.3   UK
POWER IN ASIA. fortn. £544($906) (overseas £566) (effective 1993). Financial Times Business Information Ltd., 126 Jermyn St., London SW1Y 4UJ, England. TEL 071-411-4414. FAX 071-411-4415. **Document type:** newsletter.
●Also available online. Vendor(s): Data-Star, Mead Data Central, Inc..
 Description: Provides incisive news and analysis of power business opportunities in the electricity markets of Asia.

621.3   UK   ISSN 0955-6079
POWER IN EUROPE. fortn. £619($995) (overseas £622) (effective 1993). Financial Times Business Information Ltd., 126 Jermyn St., London SW1Y 4UJ, England. TEL 071-411-4414. FAX 071-411-4415. **Document type:** newsletter.
●Also available online. Vendor(s): Data-Star, Mead Data Central, Inc..
 Formerly: Power Europe (ISSN 0953-279X)
 Description: Covers all aspects on the electricity market from fuel purchasing to end use. Particular emphasis given to utility strategies, power station planning, and demand trends.

POWER LINE. see *ENERGY*

621.3   US
POWER MODULATOR SYMPOSIUM. I E E E CONFERENCE RECORD. biennial. price varies. (I E E E, Electron Devices Society) Institute of Electrical and Electronics Engineers, Inc., 345 E. 47th St., New York, NY 10017-2394. TEL 212-705-7900. FAX 212-705-7682. (Subscr. to: 445 Hoes Lane, Box 1331, Piscataway, NJ 08855-1331)
 Former titles: Power Modulator Conference. I E E E Conference Record; (until 1980): Pulse Power Modulator Symposium. I E E E Conference Record; (until 1976): Modulator Symposium. (Record).
 Description: Focuses on the latest technology, devices and systems applications associated with rep-rated power.

621.3   US   ISSN 1068-4085
POWER QUALITY ASSURANCE. Short title: P Q A Magazine. 1990. 6/yr. free to qualified personnel. Intertec International Inc., 2472 Eastman Ave., Bldg. 33, Ventura, CA 93003-5792. TEL 805-650-7052. FAX 805-650-7054. (Subscr. to: DirectLink Inc., 200 Kingston Dr., W. Lafayette, IN 47906-2045. TEL 800-841-7881. FAX 317-743-3545) Ed. John Mungenast. **Document type:** trade publication.
 Description: Provides information for those who must keep electronic systems operational despite AC power line problems.

POWER SOURCES SYMPOSIUM. PROCEEDINGS. see *ENERGY*

621.31   UK   ISSN 0951-9653
TK1001   CODEN: PTEIE8
POWER TECHNOLOGY INTERNATIONAL; international review of electrical power transmission and distribution. a. Sterling Publications Ltd., 86-88 Edgware Rd., London W2 2YW, England. TEL 01-2580066. Ed. Richard Knox.
—BLDSC (6576.965000).

POWERCONVERSION & INTELLIGENT MOTION. see *ELECTRONICS*

621.3   US
POWERLINE. bi-m. free. Electrical Generating Systems Association, 10251 West Sample Rd., Coral Springs, FL 33065. TEL 305-755-2677. FAX 305-755-2679. adv. circ. 2,000.
 Description: Focuses on the on-site power generation and related industries.

PRACTICAL WIRELESS. see *COMMUNICATIONS — Television And Cable*

745.5   AU   ISSN 0032-6755
PRAKTIKER;* die internationale Zeitschrift fuer Technik und Praxis, Industrie- und Konsumelektronik, Funk, Elektroakustik, Foto, Optik, Modellbau. 1945. s-m. S.890. Sonnenhofgasse 8, A-1051 Vienna, Austria. Ed. F. Czerny. adv.; bk.rev.; abstr.; charts; illus.; pat.; stat.; tr.lit.; tr.mk.; index. circ. 26,000. **Indexed:** Met.Abstr.
—BLDSC (6599.500000).

621.3   JA
PRESENTATION. (Text in Japanese) 1973. 2/yr. Oki Electric Industry Co., Ltd. - Oki Denki Kogyo K.K., 17-1, Toranomon 1-chome, Minato-ku, Tokyo 105, Japan.

PREVISIONS GLISSANTES DETAILLEES EN PERSPECTIVES SECTORIELLES (VOL.10): CONSTRUCTION ELECTRIQUE ET ELECTRONIQUE GRAND-PUBLIC. see *BUSINESS AND ECONOMICS — Economic Situation And Conditions*

PREVISIONS GLISSANTES DETAILLEES EN PERSPECTIVES SECTORIELLES (VOL.11): CONSTRUCTION ELECTRIQUE PROFESSIONNELLE. see *BUSINESS AND ECONOMICS — Economic Situation And Conditions*

PREVISIONS GLISSANTES DETAILLEES EN PERSPECTIVES SECTORIELLES (VOL.12): CONSTRUCTION ELECTRONIQUE PROFESSIONNELLE. see *BUSINESS AND ECONOMICS — Economic Situation And Conditions*

621.3   JA
PROCEEDINGS OF SYMPOSIUM ON DRY PROCESS/DORAI PUROSESU SHINPOJUMU. (Text in English) 1979. a. Institute of Electrical Engineers of Japan - Denki Gakkai, 7-1, Yuraku-cho 1-chome, Chiyoda-ku, Tokyo 100, Japan. **Document type:** proceedings.

ENGINEERING — ELECTRICAL ENGINEERING

621.3   JA
PROCEEDINGS OF THE SYMPOSIUM ON ACCELERATOR SCIENCE AND TECHNOLOGY. (Text in English) 1974. biennial. Ionics Co., Ltd. - Aionikusu K.K., 3-4, Koishikawa 2-chome, Bunkyo-ku, Tokyo 112, Japan. **Document type:** proceedings.

PROCEEDINGS OF THE SYMPOSIUM ON ELECTRICAL INSULATING MATERIALS/DENKI ZETSUEN ZAIRYO SHIMPOJUMU YOKOSHU. see *ENGINEERING — Engineering Mechanics And Materials*

621.3   JA   ISSN 0915-9096
PROCEEDINGS OF THE SYMPOSIUM ON ION SOURCES AND ION-ASSISTED TECHNOLOGY/ION KOGAKU SHINPOJUMU IONGEN TO ION O KISO TO SHITA OYO GIJUTSU. (Text in English, Japanese) 1977. a. Ion Engineering Society of Japan - Ion Kogakkai, 3-4, Koishikawa 2-chome, Bunkyo-ku, Tokyo 112, Japan. **Document type:** proceedings.

621.3   NE   ISSN 0922-615X
PRODUKTWIJZER - ELEKTRES. 1982. a. fl.78.75. Kluwer Technische Tijdschriften BV, Postbus 23, 7400 GA Deventer, Netherlands. FAX 05700-13080.

621.3 001.6   IT
PRODUTTRONICA. bi-m. L.50600. Gruppo Editoriale Jackson S.p.A., Via Pola 9, 20124 Milan, Italy. TEL 6948-229. FAX 6948-238. adv.: B&W page $2174, color page $3308; trim 210 x 280. circ. 6,000.
Description: Deals with CAD-CAE, assembly, printed circuits, passive components, re-working and subcontracting.

621.3   UK
PROFESSIONAL ELECTRICIAN AND INSTALLER. 1985. 11/yr. £27.50 (foreign $37.50). Hamerville Magazines Ltd., Regal House, Regal Way, Watford, Herts. WD2 4YJ, England. TEL 0923-237799. Ed. Richard Mumford. circ. 73,518. (back issues avail.)
Description: Discusses areas of contracting: circuit protection, lighting. Includes business features and new products.

629   US
PROFESSIONAL ELECTRONICS. 1975. bi-m. $12. National Electronics Service Dealers Association, 2708 W. Berry St., Fort Worth, TX 76109. TEL 817-921-9061. Ed. Wallace Harrison. adv.; bk.rev. circ. 11,000. **Document type:** trade publication.
Incorporates (in 1986): N A T E S A Scope (ISSN 0027-6030); Formerly: Service Shop.

621.389   US   ISSN 1044-4793
TK7881.4
PROFESSIONAL SOUND. 1989. a. Orion Research Corp., 14555 N. Scottsdale Rd., Ste. 330, Scottsdale, AZ 85254-3457.

PROMYSHLENNAYA ENERGETIKA. see *ENERGY*

621.3   GW   ISSN 0935-2988
PRONIC. 1989. 6/yr. DM.110. Vogel Verlag und Druck KG, Max-Planck-Str. 7-9, 97082 Wuerzburg, Germany. TEL 0931-4182145. FAX 0931-4182640. (Subscr. to: Vogel Verlag, 97064 Wuerzburg, Germany; Dist. in U.S. by: Vogel Europublishing, Inc., 20092 Gibbs Dr., Sonora, CA 95370. TEL 209-533-3555. FAX 209-533-9555) Ed. Ernst Pohl. adv.: B&W page DM.6360, color page DM.8335; trim 270 x 190. circ. 16,000. **Document type:** trade publication.

621.3 016   PL   ISSN 0033-2062
PRZEGLAD DOKUMENTACYJNY ELEKTROTECHNIKI. 1962. m. $12. Instytut Elektrotechniki, Ul. Pozaryskiego 28, 04-703 Warsaw, Poland. TEL 48-22-122062. TELEX 813279. circ. 85. (cards) **Document type:** abstracting/indexing.

621.3   PL   ISSN 0033-2097
TK4   CODEN: PZELAL
PRZEGLAD ELEKTROTECHNICZNY. (Text in Polish; summaries in English and Russian) 1919. m. $51. (Stowarzyszenie Elektrykow Polskich) Wydawnictwo Czasopism i Ksiazek Technicznych SIGMA - NOT, Ul. Ratuszowa 11, P.O. 1004, 00-950 Warsaw, Poland. TEL 48-22-180918. FAX 48-22-192187. TELEX 814550 SIGMA PL. (Dist. by: SIGMA NOT Ltd., Ul. Bartycka 20, 00-716 Warsaw, Poland) Ed. Zdobyslaw Flisowski. adv.: B&W $1260. bk.rev.; abstr.; bibl.; charts; illus.; index. circ. 3,350. **Indexed:** Chem.Abstr., Eng.Ind., Fuel & Energy Abstr., Sci.Abstr.
—BLDSC (6940.000000).

621.38   SA
PULSE BUYERS GUIDE. (Text in English) a. R.171. Pulse Publications (Pty) Ltd., P.O. Box 1884, Johannesburg 2000, South Africa. TEL 27-11-835-2221. FAX 27-11-835-1943. adv.: B&W page R.2730; trim 180 x 260. (also avail. in diskette format) **Document type:** directory.
Incorporates: Vector Buyers Guide.

621.3   JA   ISSN 0916-0043
PURINTO KAIRO GAKKAI GAKUJUTSU KOEN TAIKAI KOEN RONBUNSHU/JAPAN INSTITUTE OF PRINTED CIRCUIT. NATIONAL CONVENTION RECORD. (Text in Japanese) 1987. a. Purinto Kairo Gakkai - Japan Institute of Printed Circuit, 11-3, Azabudai 1-chome, Minato-ku, Tokyo 106, Japan.

621.3   JA
PURINTO KAIRO GAKKAI SEMINA/JAPAN INSTITUTE OF PRINTED CIRCUIT. SEMINAR. (Text in Japanese) s-a. Purinto Kairo Gakkai, Denji Tokusei o Koryo Shita Purinto Kiban Sekkei Kenkyu Bukai - Japan Institute of Printed Circuit, Special Interest Group on Electromagnetic Analysis and Design for Printed Circuits, c/o Mr. Noboru Shibuya, Takushoku Daigaku Kogakubu Joho Kogakka, 815-1, Tate-machi, Hachioji-shi, Tokyo 193, Japan.

621.3   UK   ISSN 0748-8017
TA169   CODEN: QREIE5
QUALITY AND RELIABILITY ENGINEERING INTERNATIONAL. 1985. bi-m. $495 (effective 1994). John Wiley & Sons Ltd., Journals, Baffins Ln., Chichester, Sussex PO19 1UD, England. TEL 0243-779777. FAX 0243-775878. TELEX 86290 WIBOOK G. Ed.Bd. circ. 446. (reprint service avail. from SWZ) **Indexed:** Oper.Res.Manage.Sci., Qual.Contr.Appl.Stat. **Document type:** academic/scholarly publication.
—BLDSC (7168.137300); EI; Faxon; SWETS; UMI. CCC.
Description: Concerned with case studies, tutorial type reviews and with applications of new or established theories to the solution of quality and reliability problems in engineering.

621.38   US   ISSN 1063-7818
TK8300   CODEN: QUELEZ
QUANTUM ELECTRONICS. English translation of: Kvantovaya Elektronika (KR ISSN 0368-7155) 1971. m. $1685 (foreign $1700-$1730). (Ukrainian Academy of Sciences, Institut Poluprovodnikov, KR) American Institute of Physics, 335 E. 45th St., New York, NY 10017. TEL 212-661-9404. Ed. Albin Tybulewicz. charts; illus.; stat.; index. (also avail. in microform from AIP; back issues avail.) **Indexed:** C.P.I., Eng.Ind., Gen.Phys.Adv.Abstr., INSPEC, Int.Aerosp.Abstr., Nucl.Sci.Abstr., Phys.Abstr., Phys.Ber., Sci.Abstr. **Document type:** academic/scholarly publication.
—BLDSC (0420.528000); EI; Faxon; UnCover; SWETS. CCC.
Formerly: Soviet Journal of Quantum Electronics (ISSN 0049-1748).

621.3   CN   ISSN 0075-6091
QUEEN'S UNIVERSITY AT KINGSTON. DEPARTMENT OF ELECTRICAL ENGINEERING. RESEARCH REPORT. 1962. irreg. free. Queen's University, Department of Electrical Engineering, Kingston, ON K7L 3N6, Canada. TEL 613-545-2927. FAX 613-545-6615. Ed. P.H. Wittke. circ. 50. (back issues avail.) **Document type:** academic/scholarly publication.

621.3   AT   ISSN 0033-6114
QUEENSLAND ELECTRICAL CONTRACTOR. 1957. m. Aus.$10. Electrical Contractors' Association of Queensland, 45 Berwick St., Fortitude Valley, Brisbane, Queensland 4006, Australia. Ed. R.L. Cox. adv.; bk.rev. circ. 1,000.

QUEUEING SYSTEMS; theory and applications. see *ENGINEERING — Computer Applications*

621.3   JA   ISSN 0913-4352
R & D NEWS KANSAI. (Text in Japanese) 1967. m. Kansai Electric Power Co., Ltd., Technical Research Center - Kansai Denryoku K.K. Sogo Gijutsu Kenkyujo, 11-20, Nakoji 3-chome, Amagasaki-shi, Hyogo-ken 661, Japan.

R D E - RECHT DER ENERGIEWIRTSCHAFT. see *ENERGY*

621.393   US
R E MAGAZINE. (Rural Electrification) 1946. m. $18. National Rural Electric Cooperative Association, 1800 Massachusetts Ave., N.W., Washington, DC 20036. TEL 202-857-9500. Ed. Frank Gallant. adv.; charts; illus.; tr.lit.; index. circ. 34,000.
Formerly (until 1976): Rural Electrification.

R.S.I. BLADID; felagsblad rafidnadarmanna. (Rafidnadarsamband Islands) see *LABOR UNIONS*

621.3 340   IT
RASSEGNA GIURIDICA DELL'ENERGIA ELETTRICA. 1984. q. L.85000 (foreign L.128000). Casa Editrice Dott. A. Giuffre, Via Eusto Arsizio 40, 20151 Milan, Italy. TEL 02-38000905. FAX 02-38009582.

683.88   UK
REGULATIONS FOR ELECTRICAL INSTALLATIONS. 1966. irreg., 16th ed., 1993. £34 paperback; cloth £45. INSPEC, I.E.E., Michael Faraday House, Six Hills Way, Stevenage, Herts. SG1 2AY, England. (Subscr. to: Publication Sales Dept., P.O. Box 96, Stevenage, Herts. SG1 2SD, England; U.S. addr.: INSPEC/IEEE, Box 1331, 445 Hoes Ln., Piscataway, NJ 08855-1331. TEL 908-562-5549) **Document type:** trade publication
Formerly: Regulations for the Electrical Equipment of Buildings.

621.3   US   ISSN 0149-144X
TS173
RELIABILITY AND MAINTAINABILITY SYMPOSIUM. PROCEEDINGS. 1954. a. price varies. (I E E E, Reliability Society, Institute of Electrical and Electronics Engineers, Inc., 345 E. 47th St., New York, NY 10017-2394. TEL 212-705-7900. FAX 212-705-7682. (Subscr. to: 445 Hoes Lane, Box 1331, Piscataway, NJ 08855-1331) (Co-Sponsor: American Society for Quality Control)
—BLDSC (6842.200500); UMI. **CCC.**
Former titles: Reliability and Maintainability Conference. Record; Symposium on Reliability. Proceedings (ISSN 0082-092X)
Description: Includes contributions addressing the issues facing the assurance technologies.

RESONANCE (SUMTERVILLE). see *BIOLOGY — Biophysics*

621   CL
REVISTA CONTACTOR. 1978. q. $6. Universidad Catolica de Valparaiso, Escuela de Electricidad, Casilla 4059, Valparaiso, Chile. Ed. Fernando Dona G. abstr. circ. 500.

620.1 627   BL
REVISTA DE PRECOS PARA INSTALACOES ELETRICAS E HIDRAULICAS. 1968. m. $300. Editora Revista de Precos Ltda., Av. N. Sa de Copacabana, 749 gr. 801, Rio de Janeiro, RJ, Brazil. Ed. Tatiana Salme Lowjagin. adv. circ. 16,000.

621.38   AG   ISSN 0370-7857
REVISTA ELECTROTECNICA. 1913. bi-m. $45. Asociacion Electrotecnia Argentina, Posadas 1659, C.P. 1112 Buenos Aires, Argentina. TEL 804-3454-1532. (Co-sponsor: Comite Electrotecnico Argentino) Ed. Eduardo L. Castiglioni. adv.; bk.rev.; bibl.; incex; circ. 1,600 (controlled). (back issues avail.) **Indexed:** Eng.Ind., Sci.Abstr.
—BLDSC (7853.000000).
Description: Original papers in electrical engineering.

REVISTA SIEMENS. see *ENGINEERING — Computer Applications*

621.3   CU
REVISTA TECNOLOGIA: ELECTROENERGETICA. s-a. $12. (Ministerio de la Industria Basica) Ediciones Cubanas, Obispo No. 461, Apdo. 605, Havana, Cuba. TEL 32-5556-60.

ENGINEERING — ELECTRICAL ENGINEERING

621.3   BE   ISSN 0777-2181
REVUE E/E TIJDSCHRIFT. (Text in Dutch, English and French) 1884. q. 1430 BEF membership. Societe Royale Belge des Electriciens - Koninklijke Belgische Vereniging der Electrotechnici, Pleinlaan 2, B-1050 Brussels, Belgium. TEL 32-2-6412819. FAX 32-2-6413620. (Co-sponsors: Comite Electrotechnique Belge; Laboratoire Central d'Electricite; Comite National Belge de l'Eclairage) Ed. Brigitte Sneyers. adv. contact: Brigitte Sneyers. bk.rev.; abstr.; bibl.; charts; illus.; tr.lit.; index. circ 7,000. **Indexed:** Eng.Ind., Excerp.Med., Met.Abstr., Sci.Abstr.
—BLDSC (7898.560000).
Former titles (until 1989): E S.R.B.E (ISSN 0770-0024); (until 1980): Bulletin S R B E (ISSN 0770-2833); (until 1962): Societe Royale Belge des Electriciens. Bulletin (ISSN 0037-9530)

621.3   FR   ISSN 0035-3116
CODEN: RGELAC
REVUE GENERALE DE L'ELECTRICITE. (Summaries in English, French) 1917. 11/yr. 950 F. (Societe de Electriciens et Electroniciens) Revue Generale de l'Electricite S.A., 48 rue de la Procession, 75724 Paris Cedex 15, France. TEL 44-49-60-00. FAX 44-49-60-35. TELEX SEE 200565F. Ed. M. Jacques Toulemonde. adv.; bk.rev.; charts; illus.; mkt.; index. circ. 5,500. (also avail. in microform from PMC) **Indexed:** C.I.S.Abstr., Chem.Abstr., Eng.Ind., Excerp.Med., Fuel & Energy Abstr., Met.Abstr., Phys.Abstr., PROMT, Sci.Abstr., World Alum.Abstr.
—BLDSC (7909.000000); Faxon; SWETS; CASDDS. CCC.
Incorporates: Societe Francaise des Selectriciens. Bulletin.
Description: Covers generation, distribution and transmission of electricity, industrial applications, materials, automation and operating systems.

621   RM   ISSN 0035-4066
CODEN: RTEEAE
REVUE ROUMAINE DES SCIENCES TECHNIQUES. SERIE ELECTROTECHNIQUE ET ENERGETIQUE. (Text in English, French, German and Russian) 1956. 4/yr. 220 lei($62) (Academia Romana) Editura Academiei Romane, Calea Victoriei 125, 79717 Bucharest, Rumania. (Dist. by: Rompresfilatelia, Calea Grivitei 64-66, P.O. Box 12-201, 78104 Bucharest, Rumania) Ed. Alexandru Timotin. bk.rev.; abstr.; charts; illus.; index. circ. 2,000. **Indexed:** Appl.Mech.Rev., Chem.Abstr., Math.R., Sci.Abstr.
—BLDSC (7946.680000); CASDDS.

REVUE TECHNIQUE THOMSON - C S F. see *COMPUTERS*

621.38   FR   ISSN 0040-6341
REVUE TECHNIQUE THOMSON - C S F. ELECTRONIQUE. (Text in English, French) 1969. 4/yr. 1050 F. (effective Jan. 1994). Thomson C S F, 91404 Orsay Cedex, France. TEL 60-19-70-00. (Dist. by: Centrale des Revues, 11 rue Gossin, 92543 Montrouge Cedex, France. TEL 1-46-56-52-66) Ed. Mme Warnecke. (reprint service avail. from ISI)

ROSSIISKAYA AKADEMIYA NAUK. IZVESTIYA. ENERGETIKA. see *ENGINEERING — Mechanical Engineering*

621.31   US
TK4018   CODEN: PEPCD7
RURAL ELECTRIC POWER CONFERENCE. PAPERS PRESENTED. 1977. a. (I E E E, Industry Applications Society, Rural Electric Power Committee) Institute of Electrical and Electronics Engineers, Inc., 345 E. 47th St., New York, NY 10017-2394. TEL 212-705-7900. FAX 212-705-7682. (Subscr. to: Box 1331, 445 Hoes Lane, Piscataway, NJ 08855-1331)

RURAL LIVING (GLEN ALLEN). see *GENERAL INTEREST PERIODICALS — United States*

RURAL MISSOURI. see *BUSINESS AND ECONOMICS — Cooperatives*

621.3   US   ISSN 1068-3712
TK4   CODEN: RELEEG
RUSSIAN ELECTRICAL ENGINEERING. English translation of: Elektrotekhnika (RU ISSN 0013-5860) vol.37, 1966. m. $870. (Ministerstvo Elektricheskoi Promyshlennosti, RU) Allerton Press, Inc., 150 Fifth Ave., New York, NY 10011. TEL 212-924-3950. FAX 212-463-9684. Ed. V.D. Kochetkov. bk.rev.; abstr.; charts; illus.; index. **Indexed:** Ornam.Hort., Sci.Abstr. **Document type:** academic/scholarly publication.
—Faxon; SWETS. CCC.
Formerly: Soviet Electrical Engineering (ISSN 0038-5379)
Description: Presents problems in the power industry. Covers transformers, reactors, electromagnetics, industrial automation devices and technical processes in foundry production.

621.3   AU   ISSN 0036-0708
S A F E - NACHRICHTEN. 1952. s-m. free. Salzburger Aktiengesellschaft fuer Energiewirtschaft, Schwarzstr. 44, A-5020 Salzburg, Austria. TEL 0662-8884-0. FAX 0662-8884111. Ed. Reinhard Mayrhofer. illus. circ. 100,000.

621.3   JA
S E I NEWS. 12/yr. Sumitomo Electric Industries Ltd., Public Relations Section, 4-5-33 Kitahama, Chuo-ku, Osaka 541, Japan. TEL 06-2204119. FAX 06-2223380.
Description: Features corporate and product information.

621.3   GW
S M T. (Surface Mount Technology) 1988. 9/yr. V P Verlagsgesellschaft mbH, Plapphalde 5, 71083 Herrenberg, Germany. TEL 07032-6061. FAX 07032-26940. adv.: B&W page DM.4870, color page DM.6820; trim 182 x 262. circ. 13,100. **Document type:** academic/scholarly publication.
Description: Covers all aspects of electronic manufacturing and testing.

537   IT
S P COMPUTER MAGAZINE. 1967. m. L.55000 (foreign L.84000). Gruppo Editoriale J C E, Via Ferri 6, 20092 Cinisello B. (Milan), Italy. FAX 02-7127620. TELEX 3523766 JCEMIL I. Ed. Paolo Romani. adv.; bk.rev. circ. 80,000.
Formerly (until 1988): Sperimentare.

621.3   AU
S T E W E A G RUNDSCHAU.* 1961. bi-m. free. Steirische Wasserkraft- und Elektrizitaets-AG, Leonhardguertel 10, A-8011 Graz, Austria. Ed. Gerhard Vuckovic. bk.rev.; charts; illus.; stat. circ. 2,600.
Former titles: Neues Bei Uns (ISSN 0028-3606); STEWEAG-Bote.

621.3   UK
S W E B NEWS. 1960. m. free to qualified personnel. South Western Electricity, 800 Park Ave., Aztec West, Bristol BS12 4SE, England. TEL 0454-201101. FAX 0454-616369. Ed. Janet Lawrence. adv.; bk.rev. circ. 11,500. (tabloid format)

621.3 621.381   UK   ISSN 0965-7843
SAFETY AND E M C. bi-m. £95 to non-members. E R A Technology Ltd., Cleeve Rd., Leatherhead, Surrey KT22 7SA, England. TEL 0372-374151. FAX 0372-374496. TELEX 264045. Ed. Natalie Wood. **Document type:** newsletter.
Description: Covers meetings, regulations, standards, and other issues of interest to designers and suppliers of electrical and electronic products.

621.3   FI   ISSN 0789-676X
SAKHO JA TELE. (Text in English, Finnish, Swedish) 1928. m. FIM 515. Elektroingenjoersfoerbundet - Association of Electrical Engineers in Finland, Merikasarmink. 7 J 53, SF-00160 Helsinki, Finland. TEL 358-0-1771-050. FAX 358-0-657-562. Ed. Heikki Silvan. adv.: B&W page FIM 7900, color page FIM 14800; trim 210 x 297. bk.rev.; abstr.; bibl.; charts; stat.; circ. 4,500 (controlled). **Indexed:** Sci.Abstr.
—BLDSC (8069.450000).
Former titles (until Jun. 1990): Sahko-Electricity and Electronics; (until 1981): Sahko-Elektriciten i Finland - Sahko-Elektricity in Finland (ISSN 0036-2670)
Description: Publishes technical and scientific information in the fields of electrotecnics and electronics.

621.3   FI   ISSN 0789-5437
SAHKOALA. 1958. m. FIM 410. (Finnish Electrical Association) Training and Publishing Ltd., P.O. Box 55, Harakantie 18, SF-02601 Espoo, Finland. TEL 358-0-513622. FAX 358-0-5122283. (Co-sponsor: Finnish Association of Electrical and Telecommunication Employers) Ed. Pekka Sallinen. adv.: B&W page FIM 9500, color page FIM 16500; trim 210 x 280; adv. contact: Jari Muhonen. bk.rev. circ. 4,100. **Document type:** trade publication.
Formerly (until 1991): Sahkourakoitsija (ISSN 0048-8984)
Description: Gives information about technological, economic and labour market issues. Updates readers and informs authorities and the construction industry of electrical matters of current interest.

621.3   JA   ISSN 0914-8299
SAKITTO TEKUNOROJI/CIRCUIT TECHNOLOGY. (Text in Japanese; summaries in English, Japanese) 1986. bi-m. 1500 Yen per no. Purinto Kairo Gakkai - Japan Institute of Printed Circuit, 11-3, Azabudai 1-chome, Minato-ku, Tokyo 106, Japan.

SANGYO ANZEN KENKYUJO GIJUTSU SHISHIN/RESEARCH INSTITUTE OF INDUSTRIAL SAFETY. TECHNICAL RECOMMENDATION. see *OCCUPATIONAL HEALTH AND SAFETY*

621.3   JA   ISSN 0387-2319
SANGYO TO DENKI/INDUSTRY AND ELECTRICITY. (Text in Japanese) 1952. m. 400 Yen per no. Kansai Denki Kyokai - Kansai Electric Association, 1-25, Dojimahama 2-chome, Kita-ku, Osaka-shi, Osaka 530, Japan.

621.3   JA   ISSN 0285-9815
CODEN: STEQDU
SANKEN GIHO/SANKEN TECHNICAL REPORT. (Text in Japanese; summaries in English, Japanese) 1966. a. Sanken Denki K.K. - Sanken Electric Co., Ltd., 6-3, Kitano 3-chome, Niiza-shi, Saitama-ken 352, Japan. **Indexed:** Chem.Abstr., Sci.Abstr.
—BLDSC (8074.700000); CASDDS.

621.3   JA   ISSN 0285-516X
SAN'YO DENKI GIHO/SANYO TECHNICAL REVIEW. (Text in Japanese; summaries in English, Japanese) 1969. 3/yr. 720 Yen per no. San'yo Denki K.k., Kenkyu Kaihatsu Honbu - Sanyo Electric Co., Ltd., Research & Development Department, 18-13, Hashiridani 1-chome, Hirakata-shi, Osaka 573, Japan.
—BLDSC (8075.377000).

621.31   MY   ISSN 0127-144X
SARAWAK ELECTRICITY SUPPLY CORPORATION. ANNUAL REPORT. (Text in English) 1957. a. free to qualified personnel. Sarawak Electricity Supply Corporation - Perbadanan Pembekalan Letrik Sarawak, P.O. Box 149, 93700 Kuching, Sarawak, Malaysia. TEL 082-441188. FAX 082-444082. TELEX MA-70100. stat.; circ. 2,000 (controlled).

621.3   CN
SCANNER. 10/yr. membership. Electrical and Electronic Manufacturers Association of Canada, 10 Carlson Court, Ste. 500, Rexdale, Ont. M9W 6L2, Canada. TEL 416-674-7410. FAX 416-674-7412. Ed. Ernie Welling. adv. circ. 1,951.
Former titles (until 1986): E E M A C Report; E E M A C Ottawa Report; E E M A C Newsletter; C E M A Newsletter (ISSN 0045-4702)
Description: Covers latest news in the industry especially those centered around EEMAC. Also features members news, affiliate news and calendar of events.

SCHWEIZER MASCHINENMARKT; die fuehrende polytechnische Fachzeitschrift. see *MACHINERY*

SDELOVACI TECHNIKA/TELECOMMUNICATIONS ENGINEERING. see *COMMUNICATIONS — Telephone And Telegraph*

SECTOR ENERGIA E INDUSTRIA. see *ENGINEERING*

621.3   JA   ISSN 0285-6204
SEISAN TO DENKI/PRODUCTION AND ELECTRICITY. (Text in Japanese) 1949. m. 390 Yen per no. Nihon Denki Kyokai - Japan Electric Association, 7-1, Yuraku-cho 1-chome, Chiyoda-ku, Tokyo 100, Japan.

SELENIUM - TELLURIUM DEVELOPMENT ASSOCIATION. BULLETIN. see *METALLURGY*

ENGINEERING — ELECTRICAL ENGINEERING

537.5   IT
SELEZIONE DI TECNICHE ELETTRONICHE. 1957. m. Gruppo Editoriale J C E, Via dei Lavoratori 124, 20092 Cinisello Balsamo, Italy. Ed. Ruben Castelfranchi. circ. 75,000.

621.3   JA
SHIKOKU DENKI JIGYO GAIYO/SHIKOKU ELECTRIC WORKS BULLETIN. (Text in Japanese) 1948. a. Shikoku Chiku Denryoku Juyosha Kyokai - Association for Consumers of Electric Power, Shikoku District, 7-9, Kamei-cho, Takamatsu-shi, Kagawa-ken 760, Japan.

621.3   JA
SHIKOKU ELECTRIC POWER CO. ANNUAL REPORT. a. Shikoku Electric Power Co., Inc., 2-5 Marunouchi, Takamatsu, Kagawa 760, Japan.
   Description: Features review of performance, current business operation for future growth and financial statements.

621.3   JA   ISSN 0285-6794
SHIKOKU SOGO KENKYUJO KENKYU KIHO/SHIKOKU RESEARCH INSTITUTE. SEMI-ANNUAL TECHNICAL REPORT. (Text in Japanese; summaries in English, Japanese) 1959. s-a. Shikoku Sogo Kenkyujo - Shikoku Research Institute, 2109-8, Yashima Nishimachi, Takamatsu-shi, Kagawa-ken 761-01, Japan.

621.3   JA
SHIN DENCHI KOSO BUKAI TORONKAI/ELECTROCHEMICAL SOCIETY OF JAPAN. NEW BATTERY CONCEPTIVE DIVISION. PROCEEDINGS OF DISCUSSION MEETING. (Text in English, Japanese) 1985. s-a. Denki Kagaku Kyokai, Denchi Gijutsu Iinkai, Shin Denchi Koso Bukai - Electrochemical Society of Japan, Committee of Battery Technology, New Battery Conceptive Division, Doshisha Daigaku Kogakubu, Kogyo Kagaku Kyoshitsu, Karasuma Higashi Iru, Imagegawa Dori, Kamigyo-ku, Kyoto-shi, Kyoto 602, Japan. **Document type:** proceedings.

621.3   JA   ISSN 0386-5487
SHIN DENKI/NEW ELECTRICITY. (Text in Japanese) 1947. m. 830 Yen per no. Ohm-sha, 3-1, Kanda Nishiki-cho, Chiyoda-ku, Tokyo 101, Japan.

621.3   JA   ISSN 0914-0727
SHINKO DENKI GIHO/SHINKO ELECTRIC JOURNAL. (Text in Japanese; summaries in English, Japanese) 1956. q. 290 Yen per no. Shinko Denki - Shinko Electric Co., Ltd., 12-2, Nihonbashi 3-chome, Chuo-ku, Tokyo 103, Japan. **Indexed:** Sci.Abstr.
—BLDSC (8256.803500).

621.3   JA   ISSN 0916-6718
SHOWA DENSEN REBYU/SHOWA ELECTRIC WIRE AND CABLE REVIEW. (Text in Japanese; summaries in English, Japanese) 1951. 3/yr. Showa Densen Denran K.K. - Showa Electric Wire & Cable Co., Ltd., 1-18, Toranomon 1-chome, Minato-ku, Tokyo 105, Japan. **Indexed:** INIS Atomind., Sci.Abstr.
—BLDSC (8270.100000).

SIEMENS REVIEW. see *ENGINEERING — Computer Applications*

SIEMENS ZEITSCHRIFT. see *ENGINEERING — Computer Applications*

SIGNAL (FAIRFAX). see *COMMUNICATIONS*

SLABOPROUDY OBZOR/ELECTRONICS AND TELECOMMUNICATIONS REVIEW. see *COMMUNICATIONS*

621.3   US
SLIG BUYERS' GUIDE. 1969. biennial. $19.95. Independent Battery Manufacturers Association, Inc., 100 Larchwood Dr., Largo, FL 34640. TEL 813-586-1408. FAX 813-586-1400. Ed. Celwyn E. Hopkins. adv. circ. 5,000. **Document type:** trade publication.

SMITH - KETTLEWELL TECHNICAL FILE; a biannual technical journal for the blind and visually impaired. see *HANDICAPPED — Visually Impaired*

621.3   SA   ISSN 0038-2221
TK1   CODEN: TSAEA9
SOUTH AFRICAN INSTITUTE OF ELECTRICAL ENGINEERS. TRANSACTIONS. 1909. q. R.50. South African Institute of Electrical Engineers, P.O. Box 93541, Yeoville 2143, South Africa. TEL 27-11-487-3003. FAX 27-11-487-3002. Ed. J.P. Reynders. adv.; bk.rev.; illus.; index. circ. 4,150. **Indexed:** Chem.Abstr., Eng.Ind., Excerp.Med., Ind.S.A.Per., Sci.Abstr.
—BLDSC (9009.000000).

621.3   AT   ISSN 0038-2892
SOUTH AUSTRALIAN ELECTRICAL CONTRACTOR. 1956. bi-m. Electrical Contractors Association of S.A. Inc., Box 47, Eastwood, S.A. 5063, Australia. (Co-sponsor: Electrical Contractors' Association of Tasmania) Ed. R.J. Downs. adv.; bk.rev.; illus. circ. 1,100.

621.38   US   ISSN 1059-3772
SPECIALTY REFERENCES. APPLICATION NOTES. (Subseries of D.A.T.A. Digest Electronic Information Series) 1972. a. $95. D.A.T.A. Business Publishing (Subsidiary of: Information Handling Services), 15 Inverness Way E., Box 6510, Englewood, CO 80155-6510. TEL 800-447-4666. FAX 303-799-4082. TELEX 4322083 IHS UI. adv. contact: Peggy Anderson.
—SWETS.
   Former titles (until 1989): Application Notes. Discrete Semiconductors, Integrated Circuits (ISSN 1048-2776); (until 1987): Application Notes Reference (ISSN 0732-4227); (until 1981): Semiconductor Application Notes D.A.T.A. Book (ISSN 0090-3655)
   Description: References guide covering over 10,890 application notes on discrete semiconductors from more than 300 manufacturers.

SPECIFIER REPORTS. see *BUILDING AND CONSTRUCTION*

SPON'S MECHANICAL & ELECTRICAL SERVICES PRICE BOOK. see *BUILDING AND CONSTRUCTION*

621.3   US
SPRINGER TEXTS IN ELECTRICAL ENGINEERING. 1982. irreg. price varies. Springer-Verlag, 175 Fifth Ave., New York, NY 10010. TEL 212-460-1500. FAX 212-473-6272. (Also: Berlin, Heidelberg, Tokyo and Vienna) **Indexed:** Math.R. **Document type:** monographic series.

STAND BY. see *LABOR UNIONS*

629   JA   ISSN 0387-5857
STANDARD FREQUENCY AND TIME SERVICE BULLETIN. (Includes annual number) (Text in English) 1965. m. free or exchange basis. Ministry of Posts and Telecommunications, Communications Research Laboratory - Yuseisho Tsushinsogo Kenkyujo, 2-1, Nukui Kita-machi 4-chome, Koganei-shi, Tokyo 184, Japan. TEL 0423-21-1211. TELEX 2832611-DEMPA-J. stat. **Document type:** government publication, bulletin.

621.3   JA
STANLEY PRODUCT GUIDE. (Text in French; summaries in English, Japanese) 1961. 15/yr. Stanley Electric Co., Ltd. - Sutanre Denki K.K., 9-13, Nakameguro 2-chome, Meguro-ku, Tokyo 153, Japan.

621.3   GW   ISSN 0172-0686
STEUERN IN DER ELEKTRIZITAETSWIRTSCHAFT. 1949. m. DM.139. (Vereinigung Deutscher Elektrizitaetswerke) Verlags- und Wirtschaftsgesellschaft der Elektrizitaetswerke mbH, Stresemannallee 30, 60596 Frankfurt a.M., Germany. TEL 069-6304-311. FAX 069-6304359. TELEX 411284-VDEW. **Document type:** trade publication.
—CCC.

621.3   SZ
STROM. French edition: Electricite. Italian edition: Elettricita. 1922. q. 5 Fr. Informationsstelle fuer Elektrizaetsanwendung (INFEL), Lagerstr. 1, CH-8021 Zurich, Switzerland. TEL 01-291-01-02. FAX 01-291-09-03. Ed. Norbert Kuster. adv.; abstr.; charts; illus. circ. 1,200,000.
   Former titles: Elektrizitaet (ISSN 0013-5461) & Electricite pour Tous.

621.3   GW
ZEITSCHRIFT FUER UNSERE STROMKUNDEN. 1949. 6/yr. Energie-Verlag GmbH, Haeusserstr. 36, 69115 Heidelberg, Germany. TEL 06221-90130. FAX 06221-S01341. Ed. Michael Santak. circ. 2,000,000. **Document type:** consumer publication.

621.3   GW   ISSN 0340-7519
STROMPRAXIS; Fachzeitschrift fuer Elektrohandel, -Handwerk, und -Beratung. 1950. bi-m. DM.42. (Hauptberatungsstelle fuer Elektrizitaetsanwendung e.V) Verlags- und Wirtschaftsgesellschaft der Elektrizitaetswerke mbH, Stresemannallee 30, 60596 Frankfurt a.M., Germany. TEL 069-6304-328. FAX 069-6304359. TELEX 411284-VDEW. Ed. W. Bartsch. adv. **Indexed:** Sci.Abstr. **Document type:** trade publication.
—CCC.
   Supersedes: Elektrizitaet (ISSN 0013-547X)

STRUCNI CASOPIS DURO DAKOVIC. see *ENGINEERING — Mechanical Engineering*

621.3   NE   ISSN 0167-403X
                  CODEN: SEEEDP
STUDIES IN ELECTRICAL AND ELECTRONIC ENGINEERING. 1978. irreg., vol.46, 1994. price varies. Elsevier Science B.V., Books Division, P.O. Box 211, 1000 AE Amsterdam, Netherlands. TEL 31-20-5803911. FAX 31-20-5803705. TELEX 18582 ESPA NL. (Subscr. in U.S. and Canada to: Elsevier Science Inc., Box 882, Madison Sq. Sta., New York, NY 10159. TEL 212-989-5800) **Indexed:** Chem.Abstr. **Document type:** monographic series.
—BLDSC (8490.478000); CASDDS.
Refereed Serial

621.3   US   ISSN 1058-8566
TK7871.85
SUGGESTED REPLACEMENTS D.A.T.A. DIGEST. Variant title: Discreate Semiconductors. Suggested Replacements. (Subseries of: D.A.T.A. Book Electronic Information Series) 1986. s-a. $135. D.A.T.A. Business Publishing (Subsidiary of: Information Handling Services), 15 Inverness Way E., Box 6510, Englewood, CO 80155-6510. TEL 800-447-4666. FAX 303-799-4082. Ed. Paul Magin. adv. contact: Peggy Anderson.
   Formerly (until 1991): Discrete Semiconductors. Suggested Replacement Alternate Sources (ISSN 1040-0915); Which supersedes in part (in 1988): Suggested Replacement - Alternate Source Guide for Discrete Semiconductors D.A.T.A. Book (ISSN 0887-0047)
   Description: Reference guide to suggested replacements for discrete semiconductors. Covers over 283,000 devices from more than 138 manufacturers.

621.3   JA
SUMAI TO DENKA/SAFETY CLEAN & AMENITY LIFE. (Text in Japanese) 1989. m. 1100 Yen per no. Nihon Kogyo Shuppan K.K. - Japan Industrial Publishing Co., Ltd., 3-26, Honkomagome 6-chome, Bunkyo-ku, Tokyo 113, Japan.

621.3   JA   ISSN 0562-5815
SUMITOMO DENKI. English edition: Sumitomo Electric Technical Review (ISSN 0376-1207) (Text in Japanese; summaries in English) 1933. s-a. Sumitomo Electric Industries Ltd. - Sumitomo Denki Kogyo K.K., 5-33, Kitahama 4-chome, Chuo-ku, Osaka-shi, Osaka 541, Japan.

621.3   JA   ISSN 0376-1207
SUMITOMO ELECTRIC TECHNICAL REVIEW, ENGLISH EDITION. Japanese edition: Sumitomo Denki (ISSN 0562-5815) (Text in English; summaries in English, French, German) 1962. a. Sumitomo Electric Industries Ltd. - Sumitomo Denki Kogyo K.K., 5-33, Kitahama 4-chome, Chuo-ku, Osaka, Osaka 541, Japan. Ed.Bd. circ. 1,000. **Indexed:** INIS Atomind., JCT, Sci.Abstr., W.R.C.Inf.
—BLDSC (8517.95500C); EI.

SUPERCONDUCTIVITY DIRECTORY. see *BUSINESS AND ECONOMICS — Trade And Industrial Directories*

ENGINEERING — ELECTRICAL ENGINEERING

621.3   US   ISSN 1042-4105
SUPERCONDUCTOR INDUSTRY. 1988. q. $17. Rodman Publishing Corp., 17 S. Franklin Tpk., Box 555, Ramsey, NJ 07446. TEL 201-825-2552. FAX 201-825-0553. Ed. Chris Gillespie; Pub. Rodman J. Zilenziger. adv.: B&W page $1230, color page $2160; trim 8 1/4 x 10 7/8; adv. contact: Linda Smith. circ. 7,000 (controlled). **Indexed:** Energy Info.Abstr. **Document type:** trade publication.
—CCC.
Description: Covers news and developments in superconductors, including international research, manufacturing and marketing of superconductor products and supplies.

621.3   US   ISSN 1051-7715
TK7871.85
SURFACE-MOUNTED DISCRETES D.A.T.A. DIGEST. 1990. a. $155. D.A.T.A. Business Publishing, 15 Inverness Way East, Box 6510, Englewood, CO 80155-6510. TEL 800-447-4666. FAX 303-799-4082. TELEX 4322083 IHS UI. Ed. Paul Magin. adv. contact: Peggy Anderson.
●Also available on CD-ROM.
Description: Reference guide covering up to 20 technical parameters on over 32,470 surface-mounted discrete semiconductors from more than 170 manufacturers.

621.3   US   ISSN 1051-7707
SURFACE-MOUNTED INTEGRATED CIRCUITS D.A.T.A. DIGEST. 1990. s. $180. D.A.T.A. Business Publishing (Subsidiary of: Information Handling Services), 15 Inverness Way East, Box 6510, Englewood, CO 80155-6510. TEL 800-447-4666. FAX 303-799-4082. TELEX 4322083 IHS UI. Ed. Paul Magin. adv. contact: Peggy Anderson.
●Also available on CD-ROM.
Description: Reference guide covering up to 20 technical parameters on over 77,620 surface-mounted integrated circuits from more than 450 manufacturers.

621.32   RU   ISSN 0039-7067
CODEN: SVETAG
SVETOTEKHNIKA. English translation: Light & Engineering (US ISSN 1068-9761) 1955. m. 16.20 Rub. Izdatel'stvo Kniga, 50, Gorky St., 125047 Moscow, Russia. index. **Indexed:** Biol.Abstr., C.I.S.Abstr., Chem.Abstr., Sci.Abstr.
—CASDDS. **CCC.**

621.3   US   ISSN 1056-5426
TK455
SWEET'S CATALOG FILE FOR THE ELECTRICAL ENGINEERING AND RETROFIT MARKET. 1976. a. free to qualified personnel. Sweet's Catalog Files (Subsidiary of: McGraw-Hill, Inc.), 1221 Ave. of the Americas, New York, NY 10020. TEL 212-512-4750. FAX 212-512-2348. charts; illus.; tr.lit. circ. 15,000.
Formerly: Sweet's Electrical Engineering and Retrofit File.

SYMPOSIUM ON FOUNDATIONS OF COMPUTER SCIENCE. PROCEEDINGS. see COMPUTERS — Computer Engineering

SYMPOSIUM ON FUSION ENGINEERING. PROCEEDINGS. see ENERGY — Nuclear Energy

SYSTEMS AND COMPUTERS IN JAPAN. see COMPUTERS — Computer Systems

621.3   US
T V P P A NEWS. 1948. bi-m. membership. Tennessee Valley Public Power Association, 1201 Chestnut St., Chattanooga, TN 37402-5021. TEL 615-756-6511. FAX 615-267-2280. Ed. R. Kent Lopez. adv. circ. 3,000.

621.3   JA   ISSN 0911-5439
TAIYO YUDEN GIHO/NEEDS & SEEDS. (Text in Japanese; summaries in English, Japanese) 1985. a. 1000 Yen per no. Taiyo Yuden Co., Ltd., 16-2-, Ueno 6-chome, Taito-ku, Tokyo 110, Japan.

621.3   JA   ISSN 0385-9630
TAKAOKA REBYU/TAKAOKA REVIEW. (Text in Japanese; summaries in English, Japanese) 1952. q. Takaoka Seisakujo - Takaoka Electric Manufacturing Co., Ltd., 2-1, Ote-machi 2-chome, Chiyoda-ku, Tokyo 100, Japan. **Indexed:** Sci.Abstr.
—BLDSC (8601.071700).

621.3   JA   ISSN 0388-2926
TAKUMA DENPA KOGYO KOTO SENMON GAKKO. KENKYU KIYO/TAKUMA NATIONAL COLLEGE OF TECHNOLOGY. BULLETIN. (Text in English, Japanese; summaries in English) 1973. a. Takuma Denpa Kogyo Koto Senmon Gakko, 551, Koda, Takuma-cho, Mitoyo-gun, Kagawa-ken 769-11, Japan.

537.5   GR
TECHNIKI EKLOGI/TECHNICAL CHOICE. 1965. m. $45. Nikos Mavrommatis Co., Mayer 11, 104 38 Athens, Greece. FAX 30-1-5243345. Ed. P. Heliotis. adv. contact: Tony Koutsos. bk.rev. circ. 20,000. **Document type:** consumer publication.

537   GW   ISSN 0863-0755
TECHNISCHE UNIVERSITAET CHEMNITZ. WISSENSCHAFTLICHE SCHRIFTENREIHE. 1977. irreg. Technische Universitaet Chemnitz, Postfach 964, 9010 Chemnitz, Germany. TEL 0371-668283. FAX 0371-668569. Ed.Bd. **Indexed:** Chem.Abstr. **Document type:** academic/scholarly publication.
Formerly: Technische Hochschule Karl-Marx-Stadt. Wissenschaftliche Schriftenreihe.

537.5   JA
TECHNOPOLIS. a. Tokuma Shoku, 4-10-1, Shinbashi, Minato-ku, Tokyo 105, Japan. circ. 180,000.

621.3   IT   ISSN 0390-6698
TECNOLOGIE ELETTRICHE; sistemi per l'automazione. 1974. m. L.85000($139) (foreign L.160000). Stammer S.p.A., Via della Liberazione 1, 20068 Peschiera Borromeo (MI), Italy. TEL 02-55302606. FAX 02-55302700. Ed. Girolamo Bellina. adv.: B&W page L.1680000, color page L.2300000; trim 185 x 267. circ. 8,000.
—BLDSC (8762.930000).
Formerly (until 1974): Industria Italiana Elettrotecnica ed Elettronica (ISSN 0019-7645)

621.3   IT
TECNORAMA ELETROMECCANICA E ELETTRONICA. 12/yr. Pubblicita Edizioni Associati s.r.l., Via Simone d'Orsenigo 22, 20135 Milan, Italy. TEL 2-551-18-42. FAX 2-551-85-263. Ed. Ugo Carutti. circ. 47,530.

621.3   KR   ISSN 0204-3599
TK4   CODEN: TEKEDW
TEKHNICHESKAYA ELEKTRODINAMIKA; nauchno-prikladnoi zhurnal. (Text in Russian) 1979. bi-m. 7.80 Rub. (Akademiya Nauk Ukrainy, Otdelenie Fiziko-Tekhnicheskikh Problem Energetiki) Vidavnitstvo Naukova Dumka, Vul. Tereshchenkivska 3, 252601 Kiev, Ukraine. TEL 044-224-4068. FAX 044-224-7060. (Dist. by: Mezhdunarodnaya Kniga, B. Yakimanka 39, 117049 Moscow, Russia; Dist. in U.S. by: Victor Kamkin Inc., 4956 Boiling Brook Pkwy., Rockville, MD 20852. TEL 301-881-5973. FAX 301-881-1637) Ed. A.K. Shidlouskiy. **Indexed:** Int.Aerosp.Abstr., Sci.Abstr.
—BLDSC (0180.359000). **CCC.**

621.3   GW
CODEN: FEPXAP
TELEKOM PRAXIS. 1947. m. DM.226.80. Fachverlag Schiele und Schoen GmbH, Markgrafenstr. 11, 10969 Berlin, Germany. TEL 030-2516029. FAX 030-2517248. adv.; bk.rev.; charts; illus.; index. circ. 2,750. **Indexed:** Sci.Abstr. **Document type:** trade publication.
—SWETS. **CCC.**
Formerly: Fernmelde Praxis (ISSN 0015-0118)

TEPLOENERGETIKA. see ENGINEERING — Mechanical Engineering

621.39   US   ISSN 0744-1657
TK7869   CODEN: TMWOD8
TEST & MEASUREMENT WORLD. 1981. 13/yr. $65 (Canada $96; Mexico $90; elsewhere $120) (free to qualified personnel). Cahners Publishing Company (Newton), Part of the Reed Elsevier group, 275 Washington St., Newton, MA 02158-1630. TEL 617-964-3030. FAX 617-558-4470. (Subscr. to: 44 Cook St., Denver, CO 80206-5800. TEL 800-662-7776) Ed. John Titus; Pub. Roy Forsberg. adv.; bk.rev. circ. 75,000. (also avail. in microfilm; back issues avail.) **Indexed:** Comput.Cont., Sci.Abstr. **Document type:** trade publication.
—BLDSC (8796.327700); EI; Faxon; SWETS; UMI. **CCC.**
Incorporates (in Aug. 1990): Electronics Test (ISSN 0164-9620)
Description: For electronics industry engineers and managers worldwide, responsible for selecting test, measurement and inspection of products and services.

001.6 621.3 681.2
389.6   US   ISSN 0744-1657
TEST & MEASUREMENT WORLD BUYER'S GUIDE. 1981. a. free to qualified personnel. Cahners Publishing Company (Newton), Part of the Reed Elsevier group, 275 Washington St., Newton, MA 02158-1630. TEL 617-964-3030. FAX 617-558-4470. (Subscr. to: 44 Cook St., Denver, CO 80206. TEL 800-662-7776) Ed. John Titus; Pub. Roy Forsberg. index. circ. 75,000. (also avail. in microfilm; back issues avail.) **Document type:** directory, trade publication.

THERMOPHYSICS AND ELECTRONICS NEWSLETTER. see PHYSICS — Heat

621.38   US   ISSN 1040-0222
TK7871.99.T5
THYRISTOR D.A.T.A. DIGEST. 1973. s-a. $205. D.A.T.A. Business Publishing (Subsidiary of: Information Handling Services), 15 Inverness Way E., Box 6510, Englewood, CO 80155-6510. TEL 800-447-4666. FAX 303-799-4082. TELEX 4322083 IHS UI. Ed. Paul Magin. adv. contact: Peggy Anderson.
●Also available on CD-ROM.
Formerly: Thyristor D.A.T.A. Book (ISSN 0732-6092)
Description: Reference guide covering up to 20 technical parameters on over 76,800 devices from more than 125 manufacturers.

683.83   CC   ISSN 1001-456X
TIANJIN QING GONGYE XUEYUAN XUEBAO/TIANJIN INSTITUTE OF LIGHT INDUSTRY. JOURNAL. (Text in Chinese) 1986. s-a. $14 (effective 1993). Tianjin Qing Gongye Xueyuan - Tianjin Institute of Light Industry, 1038 Dagu Nanlu, Tianjin 300222, People's Republic of China. TEL 840965.

621.3   US   ISSN 1052-2433
TODAY IN MISSISSIPPI. 1949. m. (except Jun. & Dec.) $2.50. Electric Power Associations of Mississippi, Inc., Box 7897, 2805 Greenway Dr., Jackson, MS 39284-7897. TEL 601-922-2341. FAX 601-922-9869. Ed. Hobson Waits. adv.: B&W page $1724. circ. 320,191. (tabloid format) **Document type:** consumer publication.
Formerly (until Aug. 1990): Mississippi E P A News (ISSN 0026-6175)
Description: Focuses on electrical living, homemaking, youth and senior citizens, health, the outdoors, industry and agriculture.

621.3   JA   ISSN 0285-6247
TODEN/TOKYO ELECTRIC POWER COMPANY. JOURNAL. (Text in Japanese) 1951. m. Tokyo Denryoku K.K. - Tokyo Electric Power Co., Inc., 1-3, Uchisaiwai-cho 1-chome, Chiyoda-ku, Tokyo 100, Japan.
Formerly (until 1971): Tokyo Denryoku Kabushiki Gaisha Shaho (ISSN 0285-6239)

621.3   JA
TODEN REPOTO/TOKYO ELECTRIC POWER COMPANY. REPORT. (Text in Japanese) 1980. q. Tokyo Denryoku K.K. - Tokyo Electric Power Co., Inc., 1-3, Uchisaiwai-cho 1-chome, Chiyoda-ku, Tokyo 100, Japan.

ENGINEERING — ELECTRICAL ENGINEERING

621.3　　　　　JA　　ISSN 0385-7719
TOHOKU DAIGAKU DENTSU DANWAKAI KIROKU/TOHOKU UNIVERSITY. RECORD OF ELECTRICAL AND COMMUNICATION ENGINEERING CONVERSAZIONE. (Text in English, Japanese; summaries in English) 1952. 3/yr. Tohoku Daigaku, Denki Tsushin Kenkyujo - Tohoku University, Research Institute of Electrical Communication, 1-1, Katahira 2-chome, Aoba-ku, Sendai-shi, Miyagi-ken 980, Japan.
—BLDSC (7325.700000).

621.3　　　　　JA　　ISSN 0285-5496
TOHOKU DENRYOKU K.K. KENKYU KIHO/TOHOKU ELECTRIC POWER CO. RESEARCH LABORATORY. REPORT. (Text in Japanese) s-a. Tohoku Denryoku K.K., Denryoku Gijutsu Kenkyujo - Tohoku Electric Power Co., Inc., Electricity Technology Research and Development Center, 2-1, Nakayama 7-chome, Aoba-ku, Sendai-shi, Miyagi-ken 981, Japan.

621.3　　　　　JA
TOHOKU ELECTRIC POWER CO., INC. ANNUAL REPORT (YEAR). a. free. Tohoku Electric Power Co., Inc., 7-1, Ichiban-cho 3-chome, Aoba-ku, Sendai, Miyagi-ken 980, Japan. charts; stat.; illus.; maps. **Document type:** corporate report.
Description: Features financial and operating highlights, research and development, financial statements, and objectives and visions of the company.

TOKYO DAIGAKU CHOKOATSU DENSHI KENBIKYOSHITSU NENPO/UNIVERSITY OF TOKYO. ANNUAL REPORT OF HIGH VOLTAGE ELECTRON MICROSCOPE. see *PHYSICS — Electricity*

621.3 621.38　　JA　　ISSN 0563-7929
TOKYO DAIGAKU KOGAKUBU. DENKI KOGAKU DENSHI KOGAKU IHO/UNIVERSITY OF TOKYO. ELECTRICAL AND ELECTRONIC ENGINEERING DEPARTMENTS. BULLETIN. (Text in English, Japanese) 1952. a. Tokyo Daigaku, Kogakubu, Denki Kogakka - Tokyo University, Faculty of Engineering, Department of Electrical Engineering, 3-1, Hongo 7-chome, Bunkyo-ku, Tokyo 113, Japan. Ed. K. Kikuchi. circ. 1,000.
Formerly: Tokyo Daigaku Kogakubu. Denki Kogaku Iho (ISSN 0289-9957)

621.3　　　　　JA
TOKYO DENKI DAIGAKU SOGO KENKYUJO NENPO/TOKYO DENKI UNIVERSITY. RESEARCH INSTITUTE FOR TECHNOLOGY. ANNUAL REPORT. (Text in English, Japanese; summaries in English) a. Tokyo Denki Daigaku, Sogo Kenkyujo, 2-2, Kanda Nishiki-cho, Chiyoda-ku, Tokyo 101, Japan.

TOKYO DENKI UNIVERSITY. FACULTY OF ENGINEERING. GENERAL EDUCATION. RESEARCH REPORTS. see *ENGINEERING*

TOKYO DENKI UNIVERSITY. FACULTY OF ENGINEERING. RESEARCH REPORTS/TOKYO DENKI DAIGAKU KOGAKUBU KENKYU HOKOKU. see *ENGINEERING*

621.3　　　　　JA
TOSHIBA RAITEKKU KABU DENZAI DAYORI/TOSHIBA LIGHTING AND TECHNOLOGY CORP. ELECTRICAL EQUIPMENT NEWS. (Text in Japanese) q. Toshiba Raitekku K.K. - Toshiba Lighting and Technology Corp., 4-28, Mita 1-chome, Minato-ku, Tokyo 108, Japan.

621.3　　　　　JA　　ISSN 0285-1814
TOYO DENKI GIHO. (Text in Japanese; summaries in English) 3/yr. Toyo Denki Seizo K.K., 7-2, Yaesu 2-chome, Chuo-ku, Tokyo 104, Japan.

TRACTEBEL. ANNUAL REPORT. see *ENGINEERING*

TRADE WINNERS; the international trade weekly from Asia to the world. see *COMPUTERS*

621.38　　　　US　　ISSN 1040-0230
TK7871.9
TRANSISTOR D.A.T.A. DIGEST. 1956. s-a. $205. D.A.T.A. Business Publishing (Subsidiary of: Information Handling Services), 15 Inverness Way E., Box 6510, Englewood, CO 80155-6510. TEL 800-447-4666. FAX 303-799-4082. TELEX 4322083 IHS UI. Ed. Paul Magin. adv. contact: Peggy Anderson.
●Also available on CD-ROM.
Formerly: Transistor D.A.T.A. Book (ISSN 0732-6203)
Description: Reference guide covering up to 20 technical parameters on over 147,000 devices from more than 180 manufacturers.

620　　　　　US　　ISSN 0041-1280
TJ1　　　　　CODEN: TRDIAT
TRANSMISSION AND DISTRIBUTION. 1949. m. $32 (free to qualified personnel). Intertec Publishing Corp., 9800 Metcalf, Overland Park, KS 66212-2215. TEL 913-341-1300. FAX 913-967-1904. adv.: B&W page $5135; 8 x 10 3/4. charts; illus.; tr.lit.; index; circ. 36,400 (controlled). (also avail. in microform from UMI; reprint service avail. from UMI) **Indexed:** ABI Inform., Sci.Abstr.
—BLDSC (9024.920000); Faxon; SWETS; UMI. CCC.
Description: Serves the field of electric power transmission and distribution, metering, outdoor lighting and communications in electric utilities, industrial plants, electrified railroads and government installations.

620　　　　　US　　ISSN 1050-8686
TK3001　　　　CODEN: TDINE9
TRANSMISSION & DISTRIBUTION INTERNATIONAL. 1990. q. $21. Intertec Publishing Corp., 9800 Metcalf Ave., Overland Park, KS 66212-2215. TEL 913-341-1300. FAX 913-967-1898. (Subscr. to: Box 12901, Overland Park, KS 66282-2901) Pub. Barry H. LeCerf. adv.; tr.lit.; circ. 17,000 (controlled). **Document type:** trade publication.
—BLDSC (9024.921000); UMI.
Description: Covers the international power delivery field of the electric utility industry. Covers all phases of planning, design, construction, operations and maintenance.

621.3　　　　　US　　ISSN 0041-1280
TRANSMISSION AND DISTRIBUTION SPECIFIERS & BUYERS GUIDE. 1965. a. free to qualified personnel. Intertec Publishing Corp., 9800 Metcalf, Overland Park, KS 66212-2215. TEL 913-967-1904. FAX 215-359-9379. adv. circ. 36,400. (also avail. in microfilm from UMI; reprint service avail. from UMI)

671　　　　　GW　　ISSN 0374-2261
　　　　　　　　CODEN: TREFDS
LE TREFILE; revue technique internationale pour l'industrie du fil et du cable et tous les domaines de la transformation du fil metallique. English edition: Wire (ISSN 0043-5996); German edition: Draht (ISSN 0012-5911); Italian edition: Filo Metallico (ISSN 0430-4578); Spanish edition: Alambre (ISSN 0002-4406) 1951. 4/yr. DM.77. Meisenbach GmbH, Hainstr. 18, 96047 Bamberg, Germany. TEL 0951-861-135. FAX 0951-861-158. (Subscr. to: Postfach 2069, 96011 Bamberg, Germany) Ed. Arnt Hannewald. adv.: B&W page DM.2776, color page DM.4471; trim 260 x 184; adv. contact: Oskar Ohler. bk.rev.; charts; illus. circ. 4,100. **Document type:** trade publication.

621.32　　　　HU　　ISSN 0041-4107
　　　　　　　　CODEN: TTMTAJ
TUNGSRAM TECHNISCHE MITTEILUNGEN/TUNGSRAM TECHNICAL REVIEW.* (Text in English and German) 1959. s-a. free. Tungsram Co. Ltd., Technical Information Centre, Vaci ut 77, 1340 Budapest, Hungary. bibl.; charts; illus. circ. 1,500. **Indexed:** Chem.Abstr.
—CASDDS.

354　　　　　TU
TURKISH ELECTRICITY AUTHORITY. ANNUAL REPORT. (Text in English) a. Turkish Electricity Authority - Turkiye Elektrik Kurumu, Necatibey Caddesi No. 36, Ankara, Turkey. charts; illus.; stat.

TURKISH JOURNAL OF ELECTRICAL ENGINEERING AND COMPUTER SCIENCES. see *COMPUTERS*

U E NEWS MAGAZINE. (United Electrical Radio and Machine Workers of Canada) see *LABOR UNIONS*

621.3　　　　　GW
UE Z H - REPORT. 1975. 3/yr. (Ueberland-Zentrale Helmstedt AG) Energie-Verlag GmbH, Haeusserstr. 36, 69115 Heidelberg, Germany. TEL 06221-90130. FAX 06221-901341. Ed. Ulrich Lempart, Michael Santak. circ. 110,000. **Document type:** trade publication.

UND-ODER-NOR UND STEUERUNGSTECHNIK. see *ENGINEERING — Mechanical Engineering*

621.393　　　　US　　ISSN 0083-3177
HD9688.U4
U.S. RURAL ELECTRIFICATION ADMINISTRATION. ANNUAL STATISTICAL REPORT. RURAL ELECTRIFICATION BORROWERS. a. $12. U.S. Rural Electrification Administration, U.S. Dept. of Agriculture, Washington, DC 20250. TEL 202-382-8674. FAX 202-382-1915. (Orders to: Supt. of Documents, Government Printing Office, Washington, DC 20402-9325)

621.393　　　　US　　ISSN 0083-3193
U.S. RURAL ELECTRIFICATION ADMINISTRATION. REPORT OF THE ADMINISTRATOR OF THE RURAL ELECTRIFICATION ADMINISTRATION. 1936. a. free. U.S. Rural Electrification Administration, Department of Agriculture, Washington, DC 20250. TEL 202-382-8674. FAX 202-382-1915.

621.3　　　　　AG　　ISSN 0082-6693
TK4
UNIVERSIDAD NACIONAL DE TUCUMAN. INSTITUTO DE INGENIERIA ELECTRICA. REVISTA. 1963. irreg. $1.50. Universidad Nacional de Tucuman, Instituto de Ingenieria Electrica, Avda. Independencia 1700, San Miguel de Tucuman, Argentina. Ed. Herberto Carlos Buhler. bk.rev.; index. circ. 1,500.

621.3　　　　　AT　　ISSN 0085-3259
　　　　　　　　CODEN: RUMEDU
UNIVERSITY OF MELBOURNE. DEPARTMENT OF ELECTRICAL ENGINEERING. RESEARCH REPORT. 1966. irreg. free. University of Melbourne, Department of Electrical and Electronic Engineering, Parkville, Vic. 3052, Australia. FAX 613-344-6678. Ed. R.S. Tucker. circ. 2,000.

621.3 621.381　　AT
UNIVERSITY OF NEWCASTLE. DEPARTMENT OF ELECTRICAL AND COMPUTER ENGINEERING. TECHNICAL REPORT EE. 1967. irreg. free. University of Newcastle, Department of Electrical and Computer Engineering, Calalghan, N.S.W. 2308, Australia. TEL 61-49-216026. FAX 61-49-601712. circ. 800 (controlled).
Formerly: University of Newcastle. Department of Electrical Engineering. Technical Report EE (ISSN 0085-4158)

UNIVERSITY OF TECHNOLOGY, SYDNEY. FACULTY OF LAW & LEGAL PRACTICE HANDBOOK. see *LAW*

URJA. see *ENERGY*

621.3　　　　　UK　　ISSN 0957-1787
HD2766.A3　　　CODEN: UPOLEQ
UTILITIES POLICY; strategy, performance, regulation. 1990. q. £130 in UK and Europe; elsewhere £138. Butterworth - Heinemann (Subsidiary of: Reed International PLC), Linacre House, Jordan Hill, Oxford OX2 8DP, England. TEL 0865-310366. FAX 0865-310898. TELEX 83111 BHPOXF G. (Subscr. to: Turpin Transaction Ltd., Distribution Centre, Blackhorse Rd., Letchworth, Herts. SG6 1HN, England. TEL 0462-672555) Ed. Nicky France. bk.rev. (also avail. in microform from UMI; back issues avail.) **Indexed:** Energy Info.Abstr., Energy Rev. **Document type:** academic/scholarly publication.
—BLDSC (9135.377400). CCC.
Description: Analysis, interpretation and discussion of developments and challenges facing public-sector utilities.

621.3　　　　　US　　ISSN 1053-9379
UTILITY ENVIRONMENT REPORT. bi-w. $795 (foreign $845). McGraw-Hill, Inc., Energy & Business Newsletters, 1221 Ave. of the Americas, 36th Fl., New York, NY 10020. TEL 212-512-6410. Ed. Rob Ingraham. (reprint service avail. from UMI)
●Also available online. Vendor(s): NewsNet (EV42).

UTILITY FLEET MANAGEMENT. see *TRANSPORTATION — Trucks And Trucking*

ENGINEERING — ELECTRICAL ENGINEERING

UTILITY WEEKLY. see *ENERGY*

621.3   GW   ISSN 0505-2904
V D E W DIE OEFFENTLICHE ELEKTRIZITAETSVERSORGUNG. 1953. a. DM.15.50. Vereinigung Deutscher Elektrizitaetswerke e.V., Stresemannallee 23, 60596 Frankfurt a.M., Germany. FAX 069-6304339. TELEX 412909. charts; stat.; index; circ. controlled.
Formerly: V D E W Arbeitsbericht.

V D I INFORMATIONSDIENST. ELEKTRISCH ABTRAGENDE FERTIGUNGSVERFAHREN. see *METALLURGY*

621.31   GW   ISSN 0372-5715
CODEN: VGBKB5
V G B KRAFTWERKSTECHNIK. 1920. m. DM.372. Technische Vereinigung der Grosskraftwerksbetreiber e.V., Klinkestr. 29, 45136 Essen, Germany. FAX 0201-4862688. Ed. H. Blessmann. adv.; bk.rev.; abstr.; bibl.; charts; illus. circ. 3,600. Indexed: C.I.S.Abstr., Chem.Abstr, Eng.Ind., Excerp.Med., Fuel & Energy Abstr., Met.Abstr., Sci.Abstr., W.R.C.Inf., World Alum.Abstr. —BLDSC (9231.570000); EI; SWETS; CASDDS.
Formerly: V G B Mitteilungen (ISSN 0042-3785)

V W D - ELEKTRO. see *BUSINESS AND ECONOMICS — Investments*

VASAMA. see *LABOR UNIONS*

621.3   SA   ISSN 0256-7008
VECTOR. (Text in Afrikaans, English) 1975. m. Pulse Publications (Pty) Ltd., P.O. Box 1884, Johannesburg 2000, South Africa. TEL 27-11-835-2221. FAX 27-11-835-1943. Ed. Johann Barnard. adv.: B&W page R.2730; trim 180 x 260. circ. 4,056. Indexed: Ind.S.A.Per. Document type: trade publication.
—BLDSC (9150.294570).

621.38   GW   ISSN 0935-4441
VERBINDUNGSTECHNIK IN DER ELEKTRONIK. 1989. q. DM.73 (foreign DM.77). Deutscher Verlag fuer Schweisstechnik GmbH, Aachenerstr. 172, 40223 Duesseldorf, Germany. TEL 0211-1591-0. FAX 0211-1591200. adv. circ. 7,000. (back issues avail.) Document type: trade publication.
—BLDSC (9155.760500); SWETS.

363.6   GW   ISSN 0042-4382
VERSORGUNGSWIRTSCHAFT. 1948. m. DM.287. Verlag Versorgungswirtschaft GmbH, Fraunhoferstr. 17, 80496 Munich, Germany. TEL 089-268397. FAX 089-2023055. Ed. Karl F. Markmiller. adv.; bk.rev.; index. circ. 1,200. (tabloid format) Document type: trade publication.

621.38   HU   ISSN 0042-6210
TK4   CODEN: VLMSAG
VILLAMOSSAG. (Text in several languages) 1952. m. $33.50. (Magyar Elektrotechnikai Egyesulet - Electrotechnical Association) Lapkiado Vallalat, Lenin korut 9-11, 1073 Budapest 7, Hungary. TEL 222-408. (Subscr. to: Kultura, Box 149, H-1389 Budapest, Hungary) Ed. Ferenc Kovacs. adv.; bk.rev.; abstr.; bibl.; charts; illus.; index. circ. 3,000. Indexed: Chem.Abstr., Sci.Abstr.

537   RU
VOPROSY ELEKTRONIKI TVERDOGO TELA. vol.7, 1978. irreg. 1.80 Rub. per no. Sankt-Peterburgskii Universitet, Universitetskaya Nab. 7-9, St. Petersburg V-164, Russia. abstr.; bibl. circ. 1,500.

621.38   GW
VORWERK NACHRICHTEN. 1951. bi-m. Vorwerk und Co., Muehlenweg 17-37, 42270 Wuppertal, Germany. TEL 0202-5641314. FAX 0202-5641301. TELEX 8591650-VCO-D. illus. circ. 7,500. (back issues avail.) Document type: newsletter.

621.3   US
VXIBUS NEWSLETTER. 1989. 10/yr. $195. Bode Enterprises, 8380 Hercules Dr., Ste. P3, La Mesa, CA 91942. TEL 619-697-8790. FAX 619-697-5955. Ed. Fred R. Bode. circ. 300. (looseleaf format; back issues avail.) Document type: newsletter.
Description: Covers technical and marketing developments relating to VXI modular instrumentation standards.

621.3   IT
WATT. fortn. (20/yr.). L.16800 (foreign L.33600). Gruppo Editoriale Jackson S.p.A., Via M. Gorki 69, 20092 Cinisello B. (MI), Italy. TEL 39-2-6607228. FAX 39-2-66034290. Ed. Pierantonio Palerma. adv.: B&W page L.2100000, color page L.2900000; trim 290 x 425. circ. 15,853 (controlled).
Description: Focuses on electricity and electro-mechanics.

621.38   UK   ISSN 0262-2254
WHAT'S NEW IN ELECTRONICS. 1980. m. $155. Morgan-Grampian Technical Press Ltd. (Subsidiary of: Morgan-Grampian plc), Morgan-Grampian House, 30 Calderwood St., London SE18 6QH, England. TEL 081-855-7777. FAX 081-316-3174. Ed. Paul Whytock. adv. contact: Ian Atkinson. illus. circ. 27,876. Indexed: Br.Ceram.Abstr. Document type: trade publication.

WHO'S WHO ELECTRONICS BUYERS GUIDE - MIDWESTERN EDITION. see *BUSINESS AND ECONOMICS — Trade And Industrial Directories*

WHO'S WHO ELECTRONICS BUYERS GUIDE - NORTHEASTERN EDITION. see *BUSINESS AND ECONOMICS — Trade And Industrial Directories*

WHO'S WHO ELECTRONICS BUYERS GUIDE - SOUTHEASTERN EDITION. see *BUSINESS AND ECONOMICS — Trade And Industrial Directories*

WHO'S WHO ELECTRONICS BUYERS GUIDE - SOUTHWESTERN EDITION. see *BUSINESS AND ECONOMICS — Trade And Industrial Directories*

WHO'S WHO ELECTRONICS BUYERS GUIDE - WESTERN EDITION. see *BUSINESS AND ECONOMICS — Trade And Industrial Directories*

621.3   NE   ISSN 0922-4718
WIE LEVERT (YEAR). 1937. a. fl.89.95. Kluwer Technische Tijdschriften BV, Postbus 23, 7400 GA Deventer, Netherlands. FAX 05700-13080. adv. circ. 2,750.
Formerly: Wie Levert Elektro.

WINTER SIMULATION CONFERENCE. PROCEEDINGS. see *COMPUTERS — Computer Simulation*

683.83   US   ISSN 0277-4275
TS270.A1   CODEN: WJINDF
WIRE JOURNAL INTERNATIONAL. 1968. m. $60. (Wire Association International) Wire Journal, Inc., 1570 Boston Post Rd., Box H, Guilford, CT 06437. TEL 203-453-2777. FAX 203-453-8384. Ed. Victor Bonini. adv.; bk.rev.; abstr.; charts; illus.; mkt.; stat.; tr.lit.; index. circ. 12,000. (also avail. in microform from UMI; reprint service avail. from UMI) Indexed: A.S.& T.Ind., Chem.Abstr., Copper Abstr., Eng.Ind., Excerp.Med., Met.Abstr., Sci.Abstr., World Alum.Abstr.
—BLDSC (9322.850000); EI; Faxon; UnCover; SWETS; UMI; CASDDS. CCC.
Formerly (until 1981): Wire Journal (ISSN 0043-602X)

683.83 338   US   ISSN 0277-4275
WIRE JOURNAL INTERNATIONAL REFERENCE GUIDE. 1969. a. $75 to non-members. (Wire Association International) Wire Journal, Inc., 1570 Boston Post Rd., P.O. Box H, Guilford, CT 06437. TEL 203-453-2777. FAX 203-453-8384. Ed. Janice Swindells. adv.; abstr.; tr.lit.; index. circ. 6,000.
—CCC.
Former titles: Wire Journal International Directory Catalog; Wire Journal Directory Catalog (ISSN 0512-5405)

WIRE TECHNOLOGY INTERNATIONAL. see *COMMUNICATIONS*

621.3   US   ISSN 1056-5078
▼**WIRELESS DESIGN AND DEVELOPMENT.** 1993. 12/yr. $55. Gordon Publications, Inc., Part of Cahners Publishing Company, Division of Reed Elsevier Inc., 301 Gibraltar Dr., Box 650, Morris Plains, NJ 07950-0650. TEL 201-292-5100. FAX 201-292-9281. Ed. Richard Cunningham. adv.: B&W page $3950, color page $4800; trim 11 x 15 3/4. circ. 50,000.
Description: Provides information on commercial wireless technology for engineers and technical buyers in electronics telecommunications and instrumentation.

WISCONSIN R E C NEWS. see *GENERAL INTEREST PERIODICALS — United States*

WORLD COGENERATION; a power source for partnering in the '90's. see *ENERGY*

621.38   CC   ISSN 1004-2474
YADIAN YU SHENGGUANG/PIEZOELECTRICITY AND ACOUSTO-OPTICS. (Text in Chinese; abstracts in Chinese, English) 1979. bi-m. $15. Dianzi Gongye Bu, Sichuan Yadian Yu Shengguang Jishu Yanjiusuo - Ministry of Electronic Industry, Sichuan Institute of Piezoelectric and Acousto-optic Technology, c/o Xu Hongwen, Senior Ed., Chongqing Nanping, Sichuan 630060, People's Republic of China. FAX 0811-205284. Ed. Cai Qishan.

621.3   JA   ISSN 0287-0266
YASUKAWA DENKI/YASUKAWA REVIEW. (Text in Japanese) 1935. q. $96.80. Yasukawa Denki Seisakujo - Yasukawa Electric Manufacturing Co., Ltd., 2346, Fujita, Yahata Nishi-ku, Kitakyushu-shi, Fukuoka-ken 806, Japan. (Dist. by: Intercontinental Marketing Corp., I.P.O. Box 5056, Tokyo 100-30, Japan. TEL 81-3-3661-7458. FAX 81-3-3667-9646)

621.3   JA   ISSN 0911-8977
YOKOGAWA TECHNICAL REPORT. ENGLISH EDITION. 1984. s-a. Yokogawa Electric Corp. - Yokogawa Denki K.K., 9-32, Naka-machi 2-chome, Musashino-shi, Tokyo 180, Japan.
—BLDSC (9418.850500).

621.3   JA   ISSN 0513-5532
CODEN: YOGHA7
YOKOGAWA TECHNICAL REPORT. JAPANESE EDITION/YOKOGAWA GIHO. (Text in Japanese; summaries in English, Japanese) 1957. q. Yokogawa Electric Corp. - Yokogawa Denki K.K., 9-32, Naka-machi 2-chome, Musashino-shi, Tokyo 180, Japan. Indexed: INIS Atomind., Sci.Abstr.
—BLDSC (9418.850000); CASDDS.

621.3   JA   ISSN 0513-6342
CODEN: YUJIAX
YUASA JIHO/YUASA TECHNICAL REVIEW. (Text in Japanese; summaries in English) 1928. s-a. Yuasa Denchi K.K., Chuo Kenkyujo - Yuasa Battery Co., Ltd., Central Laboratory, 6-6, Josai-cho, Takatsuki-shi, Osaka 569, Japan.
—BLDSC (9421.655000); CASDDS.

Z V E I ELEKTRO UND ELEKTRONIK - EINKAUFSFUEHRER. see *ENGINEERING — Computer Applications*

354   ZA
ZAMBIA ELECTRICITY SUPPLY CORPORATION. ANNUAL REPORT. a., latest 1973. free. Zambia Electricity Supply Corporation, PO Box 3304, Lusaka, Zambia. stat.

621.38 620   YU   ISSN 0351-4595
ZBORNIK OBJAVLJENIH RADOVA SARADNIKA INSTITUTA. (Text in English, Serbo-Croatian) 1968. a. $24. Institut Mihajlo Pupin, Volgina 15, Box 15, 11060 Belgrade, Yugoslavia. TEL 771-398. FAX 775-870. TELEX 11-584 YU IMP BG. Ed. Radivoj Petrovic. circ. 250.

ZERB. see *COMMUNICATIONS — Television And Cable*

621.3   CC   ISSN 1002-0322
ZHENKONG/VACUUM. (Text in Chinese) bi-m. Jixie Gongye Bu, Shenyang Zhenkong Jishu Yanjiusuo - Ministry of Machine Building Industry, Shenyang Vacuum Research Institute, 1 Lianhua Beili, Dadong-qu, Shenyang, Liaoning 110042, People's Republic of China. TEL 024-4809925. FAX 024-4805081. (Dist. overseas by: China International Book Trading Corp., P.O. Box 399, Beijing, P.R. China) Ed. Lu Guozhu. adv.: Donghui/Zuo.

ENGINEERING — Engineering Mechanics And Materials

620.1 US ISSN 1058-9031
A C M MONTHLY. (Supplement avail.: GraFiber News (ISSN 1058-9023)) 1971. m. (plus 6-8 supplements). Composite Market Reports, Inc., 7670 Opportunity Rd., Ste. 250, San Diego, CA 92111-2222. TEL 619-560-1085. FAX 619-560-0234. **Document type:** newsletter, trade publication.
—CCC.
Description: Non-aerospace application of advanced composites.

A S T M STANDARDIZATION NEWS. (American Society for Testing and Materials) see *METROLOGY AND STANDARDIZATION*

620.1 US ISSN 1041-2050
TP968
ADHESIVES D.A.T.A. DIGEST. ed. 4, 1986. biennial. $180. D.A.T.A. Business Publishing (Subsidiary of: Information Handling Services), 15 Inverness Way E., Box 6510, Englewood, CO 80155-6510. TEL 800-447-4666. FAX 303-799-4082. TELEX 4322083 IHS UI. adv. contact: Kori Stephens.
Formerly: Adhesives D.A.T.A. Book.
Description: Covers up to 23 technical parameters on over 7,800 adhesives, sealants and primers from more than 230 manufacturers

ADVANCED CEMENT BASED MATERIALS. see *ENGINEERING — Chemical Engineering*

620.1 389 NE ISSN 0924-3046
CODEN: ACOAEM
ADVANCED COMPOSITE MATERIALS. (Text in English) 1991. q. DM.400 (effective 1994). (Japan Society for Composite Materials, JA) V S P, P.O. Box 346, 3700 AH Zeist, Netherlands. TEL 31-3404-25790. FAX 31-3404-32081. TELEX 40217 VSP NL. Ed. H. Miyairi. **Document type:** academic/scholarly publication.
—BLDSC (0696.837500); CASDDS.
Description: Provides an international forum for research, design and manufacture in the field of composite materials and their structures.
Refereed Serial

620.1 US ISSN 1058-899X
ADVANCED COMPOSITES MONTHLY. (Supplement avail.: GraFiber (ISSN 1058-9023)) 1972. m. $2535 includes q. calendars and indexes. Composite Market Reports, Inc., 7670 Opportunity Rd., Ste. 250, San Diego, CA 92111-2222. TEL 619-560-1085. FAX 619-560-0234. Ed. Steve Loud. **Document type:** newsletter, trade publication.
—BLDSC (0696.840000).
Description: Prepared for engineering, program, and manufacturing management at primes and their subcontractors where aerospace components made of high-performance composite materials are designed, fabricated or assembled.

620.11 US ISSN 0734-7146
ADVANCED MATERIALS; the newsletter of high performance. 1979. s-m. $238 (foreign $260). Advanced Publications, Inc., Box 6249, Hilton Head, SC 29938. TEL 803-842-4940. FAX 803-842-4940. Ed. Philip West. bk.rev. circ. 5,000. **Document type:** newsletter.
—BLDSC (0696.898000).

620.11 GW ISSN 0935-9648
TA401 CODEN: ADVMEW
ADVANCED MATERIALS. (Text in English) 1989. m. DM.498($375) V C H Verlagsgesellschaft mbH, Postfach 101161, 69451 Weinheim, Germany. TEL 06201-606-0. FAX 06201-606-328. TELEX 465516-VCHWH-D. (U.S. addr.: V C H Publishers Inc., 220 E. 23rd St., New York, NY 10010-4606. TEL 212-683-8333) Ed. P. Gregory. adv.; bk.rev. circ. 3,100. **Document type:** academic/scholarly publication.
—BLDSC (0696.897800); Faxon; UnCover; SWETS; CASDDS. CCC.
Description: Covers all aspects of materials science from an interdisciplinary perspective, with emphasis on new materials and methods for their preparation, modification and investigation.

620 US ISSN 0882-7958
TA401 CODEN: AMAPEX
ADVANCED MATERIALS & PROCESSES. 1985. m. $120 (foreign $145). A S M International, Materials Park, OH 44073-0002. TEL 216-338-5151. FAX 216-338-4634. TELEX 980-619 ASMINT. Ed. William W. Scott, Jr. adv.: B&W page $3860, color page $4945. circ. 53,000. (reprint service avail. from UMI) **Indexed:** A.S.& T.Ind., AESIS, Cadscan, Copper Abstr., INIS Atomind., Lead Abstr., Zincscan. **Document type:** academic/scholarly publication.
—BLDSC (0696.898300); EI; Faxon; UnCover; SWETS; UMI; CASDDS. CCC.
Incorporates (1930-1989): Metal Progress (ISSN 0026-0665)
Description: Technical information and reports on new developments in the technology of engineered materials and manufacturing processes.

620.1 NE ISSN 0929-1881
▼**ADVANCED PERFORMANCE MATERIALS;** technological developments in materials engineering. (Text in English) 1994. 3/yr. fl.310($167) (effective 1994). Kluwer Academic Publishers, Postbus 17, 3300 AA Dordrecht, Netherlands. TEL 31-78-334911. FAX 31-78-334254. TELEX 29245 KAPG NL. (Dist. by: Kluwer Academic Publishers Group, P.O. Box 322, 3300 AH Dordrecht, Netherlands. TEL 31-78-524400. FAX 31-78-524474; N. America dist. addr.: Box 358, Accord Sta., Hingham, MA 02018-0358. TEL 617-871-6600. FAX 617-871-6528) Ed. F.H. Froes. abstr.; bibl. **Document type:** academic/scholarly publication.
Description: Publishes original research papers and comprehensive review articles dealing with new progress and developments in advanced materials, including synthesis and processing, microstructure, physical and mechanical properties and applications.
Refereed Serial

620.1 SI
ADVANCED SERIES IN FLUID MECHANICS. (Text in English) 1991. irreg. price varies. World Scientific Publishing Co. Pte. Ltd., Farrer Rd., P.O. Box 128, Singapore 9128, Singapore. TEL 3825663. FAX 3826919. TELEX RS 28561 WSPC. (UK addr.: 73 Lynton Mead, Totteridge, London N20 8DH, England. TEL 44-81-4462461; US addr.: 1060 Main St., River Ridge, NJ 07661. TEL 800-227-7562) **Document type:** monographic series.

ADVANCES IN APPLIED MATHEMATICS AND MECHANICS IN CHINA. see *MATHEMATICS*

ADVANCES IN APPLIED MECHANICS. see *PHYSICS — Mechanics*

ADVANCES IN X-RAY ANALYSIS. see *METALLURGY*

620.1 690 US ISSN 0066-0523
AMERICAN SOCIETY FOR TESTING AND MATERIALS. COMPILATION OF A S T M STANDARDS IN BUILDING CODES. (In 4 vols.) 1952. a. $410 to non-members; members $369. American Society for Testing and Materials, 1916 Race St., Philadelphia, PA 19103. TEL 215-299-5400. FAX 215-977-9679. Ed. R. Storer. circ. 2,000. (reprint service avail. from UMI) **Indexed:** GeoRef. **Document type:** trade publication.

620.1 US ISSN 0066-0531
TA401 CODEN: ATDSAY
AMERICAN SOCIETY FOR TESTING AND MATERIALS. DATA SERIES PUBLICATIONS. 1964. irreg., no.63, 1985. $12 to non-members; members $9.60. American Society for Testing and Materials, 1916 Race St., Philadelphia, PA 19103. TEL 215-299-5400. FAX 215-977-9679. (reprint service avail. from UMI) **Document type:** monographic series.
Refereed Serial

620.1 US ISSN 0066-054X
AMERICAN SOCIETY FOR TESTING AND MATERIALS. FIVE-YEAR INDEX TO A S T M TECHNICAL PAPERS AND REPORTS. (Supplements the A S T M 50-Year Index) 1950. quinquennial. $20 to non-members. American Society for Testing and Materials, 1916 Race St., Philadelphia, PA 19103. TEL 215-299-5400. FAX 215-977-9679. circ. 2,000. (reprint service avail. from UMI) **Document type:** abstracting/indexing.
Refereed Serial

620.1 US ISSN 0066-0558
CODEN: ASTTA8
AMERICAN SOCIETY FOR TESTING AND MATERIALS. SPECIAL TECHNICAL PUBLICATIONS. 1911. a. American Society for Testing and Materials, 1916 Race St., Philadelphia, PA 19103. TEL 215-299-5400. FAX 215-977-9679. (reprint service avail. from UMI) **Indexed:** Biol.Abstr., Geotech.Abstr., HRIS, INIS Atomind., Pollut.Abstr. **Document type:** trade publication.
—BLDSC (1747.090000); EI; CASDDS. CCC.
Refereed Serial

620.1 US ISSN 0066-0493
ANNUAL BOOK OF A S T M STANDARDS. VOLUME 00.01. INDEX; subject and alphanumeric. a. $54 to non-members; members $48.60. American Society for Testing and Materials, 1916 Race St., Philadelphia, PA 19103. TEL 215-299-5400. FAX 215-977-9679. (reprint service avail. from UMI) **Document type:** abstracting/indexing.
Formerly (until 1986): Annual Book of A S T M Standards. Part 48. Index.

620.1 US ISSN 0066-0183
ANNUAL BOOK OF A S T M STANDARDS. VOLUME 01.01. STEEL-PIPING, TUBING, FITTINGS. 1898. a. $89 to non-members; members $80.10. American Society for Testing and Materials, 1916 Race St., Philadelphia, PA 19103. TEL 215-299-5400. FAX 215-977-9679. Ed. R. Storer. (also avail. in microfiche; reprint service avail. from UMI) **Indexed:** Art & Archaeol.Tech.Abstr. **Document type:** trade publication.
Formerly (until 1986): Annual Book of A S T M Standards. Part 1.
Description: Contains 40 specifications for steel pipe, including seamless, welded, centrifugally cast, and electric-fusion-welded. They specify pipe requirements for high-temperature service, ordinary use, and special applications such as fire protection use.

620.1 669 US
ANNUAL BOOK OF A S T M STANDARDS. VOLUME 01.02. FERROUS CASTINGS, FERRO ALLOYS. a. $78 to non-members; members $70.20. American Society for Testing and Materials, 1916 Race St., Philadelphia, PA 19103. TEL 215-299-5400. FAX 215-977-9679. (also avail. in microfiche; reprint service avail. from UMI) **Document type:** trade publication.
Former titles: Annual Book of A S T M Standards. Volume 01.02. Ferrous Castings, Ferro Alloys; Shipbuilding; (until 1986): Annual Book of A S T M Standards. Part 2. Ferrous Castings, Ferro Alloys (ISSN 0066-0191)

620.1 US
ANNUAL BOOK OF A S T M STANDARDS. VOLUME 01.03. STEEL PLATE, SHEET, STRIP WIRE. a. $70 to non-members; members $63. American Society for Testing and Materials, 1916 Race St., Philadelphia, PA 19103. TEL 215-299-5400. FAX 215-977-9679. (also avail. in microfiche; reprint service avail. from UMI) **Document type:** trade publication.
Supersedes in part (in 1986): Annual Book of A S T M Standards. Part 3. Steel Plate, Sheet, Strip and Wire; Metallic Coated Products; Fences; Which was formerly (until 1982): Annual Book of A S T M Standards. Part 3. Steel Plate, Sheet, Strip and Wire; Metallic Coated Products; Annual Book of A S T M Standards. Part 3. Steel Strip, Bar, Rod, Wire, Chain, and Spring; Wrought Iron; Metallic Coated Products; Ferrous Surgical Implants (ISSN 0066-0205)

620.1 US
ANNUAL BOOK OF A S T M STANDARDS. VOLUME 01.04. STEEL-STRUCTURAL, REINFORCING, PRESSURE VESSEL; RAILWAY. a. $78 to non-members; members $70.20. American Society for Testing and Materials, 1916 Race St., Philadelphia, PA 19103. TEL 215-299-5400. FAX 215-977-9679. (reprint service avail. from UMI) **Document type:** trade publication.
Supersedes in part (in 1986): Annual Book of A S T M Standards. Part 4. Structural Steel; Concrete Reinforcing Steel; Pressure Vessel Plate and Forgings; Steel Rails, Wheels, and Tires; Steel Fasteners; Which was formerly: Annual Book of A S T M Standards. Part 4. Structural Steel; Concrete Reinforcing Steel; Pressure Vessel Plate; Steel Rails, Wheels, and Tires; Bearing Steel; Steel Forgings (ISSN 0066-0213)

ENGINEERING — ENGINEERING MECHANICS AND MATERIALS

620.1 US
ANNUAL BOOK OF A S T M STANDARDS. VOLUME 01.05. STEEL-BARS, BEARINGS, FORGINGS, CHAIN, SPRINGS. a. $78 to non-members; members $70.20. American Society for Testing and Materials, 1916 Race St., Philadelphia, PA 19103. TEL 215-299-5400. FAX 215-977-9679. (also avail. in microfiche; reprint service avail. from UMI) **Document type:** trade publication.
Formerly (until 1986): Annual Book of A S T M Standards. Part 5. Steel Bars, Chain, and Springs; Bearing Steel; Steel Forgings.

620 669.1 US
ANNUAL BOOK OF A S T M STANDARDS. VOLUME 01.06. COATED STEEL PRODUCTS. a. $63 to non-members; members $56.70. American Society for Testing and Materials, 1916 Race St., Philadelphia, PA 19103. TEL 215-299-5400. FAX 215-977-9679. (also avail. in microfiche; reprint service avail. from UMI) **Document type:** trade publication.
Supersedes in part (in 1986): Annual Book of A S T M Standards. Part 3. Steel Plate, Sheet, Strip and Wire; Metallic Coated Products; Fences; Which was formerly (until 1982): Annual Book of A S T M Standards. Part 3. Steel Plate, Sheet, Strip and Wire; Metallic Coated Products; Annual Book of A S T M Standards. Part 3. Steel Strip, Bar, Rod, Wire, Chain, and Spring; Wrought Iron; Metallic Coated Products; Ferrous Surgical Implants (ISSN 0066-0205).

620.11 669 US
ANNUAL BOOK OF A S T M STANDARDS. VOLUME 01.07. SHIPBUILDING. 1990. a. $93 to non-members; members $83.70. American Society for Testing and Materials, 1916 Race St., Philadelphia, PA 19103. TEL 215-299-5400. FAX 215-977-9679. (microfiche; reprint service avail. from UMI) **Document type:** trade publication.
Description: Contains 80 specifications and practices used in ship building such as the standard requirements for cast steel mooring bits, steel mess tables, vertical steel ladders, valve label plates, and mechanical piping symbols.

620.1 US
ANNUAL BOOK OF A S T M STANDARDS. VOLUME 02.01. COPPER AND COPPER ALLOYS. a. $99 to non-members; members $89.10. American Society for Testing and Materials, 1916 Race St., Philadelphia, PA 19103. TEL 215-299-5400. FAX 215-977-9679. (also avail. in microfiche; reprint service avail. from UMI) **Document type:** trade publication.
Supersedes in part (in 1986): Annual Book of A S T M Standards. Part 6. Copper and Copper Alloys (Including Electrical Conductors) (ISSN 0066-0221).

620.1 US
ANNUAL BOOK OF A S T M STANDARDS. VOLUME 02.02. DIE-CAST METALS; ALUMINUM AND MAGNESIUM ALLOYS. a. $90 to non-members; members $81. American Society for Testing and Materials, 1916 Race St., Philadelphia, PA 19103. TEL 215-299-5400. FAX 215-977-9679. (also avail. in microfiche; reprint service avail. from UMI) **Document type:** trade publication.
Formerly: Annual Book of A S T M Standards. Volume 02.02. Die-Cast; Light Metals and Alloys; Supersedes in part (in 1986): Annual Book of A S T M Standards. Part 7. Die-Cast Metals; Light Metals and Alloys (Including Electrical Conductors) (ISSN 0066-023X).

620 621.3 US
ANNUAL BOOK OF A S T M STANDARDS. VOLUME 02.03. ELECTRICAL CONDUCTORS. a. $66 to non-members; members $59.40. American Society for Testing and Materials, 1916 Race St., Philadelphia, PA 19103. TEL 215-299-5400. FAX 215-977-9679. (also avail. in microfiche; reprint service avail. from UMI) **Document type:** trade publication.
Supersedes in part (in 1986): Annual Book of A S T M Standards. Part 6. Copper and Copper Alloys (Including Electrical Conductors) (ISSN 0066-0221); (in 1986): Annual Book of A S T M Standards. Part 7. Die-Cast Metals; Light Metals and Alloys (Including Electrical Conductors) (ISSN 0066-023X)

620.1 US
ANNUAL BOOK OF A S T M STANDARDS. VOLUME 02.04. NONFERROUS METALS-NICKEL, LEAD, TIN ALLOYS, PRECIOUS, PRIMARY, REACTIVE METALS. a. $83 to non-members; members $74.70. American Society for Testing and Materials, 1916 Race St., Philadelphia, PA 19103. TEL 215-299-5400. FAX 215-977-9679. (also avail. in microfiche; reprint service avail. from UMI) **Document type:** trade publication.
Former titles: Annual Book of A S T M Standards. Volume 02.04. Nonferrous Metals - Nickel, Lead, and Tin Alloys, Precious Metals, Primary Metals; Reactive Metals; (until 1986): Annual Book of A S T M Standards. Part 8. Nonferrous Metals and Alloys (Including Corrosion Tests); Electrodeposited Metallic Coatings; Metal Powders; Surgical Implants. (ISSN 0066-0248)

620.1 US
ANNUAL BOOK OF A S T M STANDARDS. VOLUME 02.05. METALLIC AND INORGANIC COATINGS; METAL POWDERS, SINTERED P-M STRUCTURAL PARTS. a. $82 to non-members; members $73.80. American Society for Testing and Materials, 1916 Race St., Philadelphia, PA 19103. TEL 215-299-5400. FAX 215-977-9679. (also avail. in microfiche; reprint service avail. from UMI)
Formerly (until 1986): Annual Book of A S T M Standards. Part 9. Electrodeposited Metallic Coatings; Metal Powders, Sintered P-M Structural Parts.

620.1 669 US
ANNUAL BOOK OF A S T M STANDARDS. VOLUME 03.01. METALS - MECHANICAL TESTING; ELEVATED AND LOW-TEMPERATURE TESTS METALLOGRAPHY. a. $104 to non-members; members $93.60. American Society for Testing and Materials, 1916 Race St., Philadelphia, PA 19103. TEL 215-299-5400. FAX 215-977-9679. (also avail. in microfiche; reprint service avail. from UMI) **Document type:** trade publication.
Former titles: Annual Book of A S T M Standards. Volume 03.01. Mechanical Testing; Elevated and Low-Temperature Tests; Supersedes in part (in 1986): Annual Book of A S T M Standards. Part 10. Metals--Mechanical, Fracture, and Corrosion Testing; Fatigue; Erosion; Effect of Temperature; Which was formerly; Annual Book of A S T M Standards. Part 31. Metals--Physical, Mechanical, Nondestructive, and Corrosion Tests, Metallography, Fatigue, Effect of Temperature (ISSN 0066-0477)

620 669 US
ANNUAL BOOK OF A S T M STANDARDS. VOLUME 03.02. WEAR AND EROSION; METAL CORROSION. a. $63 to non-members; members $56.70. American Society for Testing and Materials, 1916 Race St., Philadelphia, PA 19103. TEL 215-299-5400. FAX 215-977-9679. (also avail. in microfiche; reprint service avail. from UMI) **Document type:** trade publication.
Supersedes in part (in 1986): Annual Book of A S T M Standards. Part 10. Metals--Mechanical, Fracture, and Corrosion Testing; Fatigue; Erosion; Effect of Temperature; Which was formerly: Annual Book of A S T M Standards. Part 31. Metals--Physical, Mechanical, Nondestructive, and Corrosion Tests, Metallography, Fatigue, Effect of Temperature (ISSN 0066-0477).

620.1 US
ANNUAL BOOK OF A S T M STANDARDS. VOLUME 03.03. NONDESTRUCTIVE TESTS. a. $75 to non-members; members $67.50. American Society for Testing and Materials, 1916 Race St., Philadelphia, PA 19103. TEL 215-299-5400. FAX 215-977-9679. (also avail. in microfiche; reprint service avail. from UMI) **Document type:** trade publication.
Formerly: Annual Book of A S T M Standards. Volume 03.03. Metallography; Nondestructive Testing; And (until 1986): Annual Book of A S T M Standards. Part 11.

620.1 US
ANNUAL BOOK OF A S T M STANDARDS. VOLUME 03.04. MAGNETIC PROPERTIES; METALLIC MATERIALS FOR THERMOSTATS, ELECTRICAL RESISTANCE, HEATING CONTACTS. a. $63 to non-members; members $56.70. American Society for Testing and Materials, 1916 Race St., Philadelphia, PA 19103. TEL 215-299-5400. FAX 215-977-9679. (also avail. in microfiche; reprint service avail. from UMI) **Document type:** trade publication.
Former titles: Annual Book of A S T M Standards. Volume 03.04. Magnetic Properties; Magnetic Materials; Metallic Materials for Thermostats, Electrical Resistance, Heating, and Contacts; (until 1986): Annual Book of A S T M Standards. Part 44. Magnetic Properties and Magnetic Materials; Metallic Materials for Thermostats and for Electrical Resistance, Heating, and Contacts; Temperature Measurement; Illuminating Standards; Annual Book of A S T M Standards. Part 8. Magnetic Properties; Metallic Materials for Thermostats and Contacts; Materials for Electron Devices and Microelectronics (ISSN 0066-0507)

620.1 542 US ISSN 0066-0485
ANNUAL BOOK OF A S T M STANDARDS. VOLUME 03.05. CHEMICAL ANALYSIS OF METALS; METAL BEARING ORES. a. $79 to non-members; members $71.10. American Society for Testing and Materials, 1916 Race St., Philadelphia, PA 19103. TEL 215-299-5400. FAX 215-977-9679. (also avail. in microfiche; reprint service avail from UMI) **Document type:** trade publication.
Formerly: Annual Book of A S T M Standards. Volume 03.05. Chemical Analysis of Metals; Sampling and Analysis of Metal Bearing Ores; And (until 1986): Annual Book of A S T M Standards. Part 12.

620 US
ANNUAL BOOK OF A S T M STANDARDS. VOLUME 03.06. ANALYTICAL ATOMIC SPECTROSCOPY; SURFACE ANALYSIS. a. $70 to non-members; members $63. American Society for Testing and Materials, 1916 Race St., Philadelphia, PA 19103. TEL 215-299-5400. FAX 215-977-9679. (also avail. in microfiche; reprint service avail. from UMI) **Document type:** trade publication.
Formerly: Annual Book of A S T M Standards. Volume 03.06. Emission Spectroscopy; Surface Analysis; Supersedes in part (in 1986): Annual Book of A S T M Standards. Part 42. Emission, Molecular, and Mass Spectroscopy; Chromatography; Resinography; Microscopy; Computerized Systems; Which was formerly: Annual Book of A S T M Standards. Part 42. Emission, Molecular, and Mass Spectroscopy; Chromotography; Resinography; Microscopy.

620.1 690 US
ANNUAL BOOK OF A S T M STANDARDS. VOLUME 04.01. CEMENT; LIME; GYPSUM. a. $69 to non-members; members $62.10. American Society for Testing and Materials, 1916 Race St., Philadelphia, PA 19103. TEL 215-299-5400. FAX 215-977-9679. (also avail. in microfiche; reprint service avail. from UMI) **Document type:** trade publication.
Former titles: Annual Book of A S T M Standards. Volume 04.01. Cement; Lime; Gypsum (Including Manual of Cement Testing); (until 1986): Annual Book of A S T M Standards. Part 13. Cement; Lime; Ceilings and Walls (Including Manual of Cement Testing); Annual Book of A S T M Standards. Part 9. Cement; Lime; Gypsum (ISSN 0066-0256)

620.1 690 US
ANNUAL BOOK OF A S T M STANDARDS. VOLUME 04.02. CONCRETE AND AGGREGATES (INCLUDING MANUAL OF AGGREGATE AND CONCRETE TESTING). a. $83 to non-members; members $74.70. American Society for Testing and Materials, 1916 Race St., Philadelphia, PA 19103. TEL 215-299-5400. FAX 215-977-9679. (also avail. in microfiche; reprint service avail. from UMI) **Indexed:** Copper Abstr. **Document type:** trade publication.
Former titles: Annual Book of A S T M Standards. Volume 04.02. Concrete and Mineral Aggregates (Including Manual of Aggregate and Concrete Testing); (until 1986): Annual Book of A S T M Standards. Part 14. Concrete and Mineral Aggregates (Including Manual of Concrete Testing) (ISSN 0066-0264)

ENGINEERING — ENGINEERING MECHANICS AND MATERIALS

620.1 US
ANNUAL BOOK OF A S T M STANDARDS. VOLUME 04.03. ROAD AND PAVING MATERIALS; PAVEMENT MANAGEMENT TECHNOLOGIES. a. $83 to non-members; members $74.70. American Society for Testing and Materials, 1916 Race St., Philadelphia, PA 19103. TEL 215-299-5400. FAX 215-977-9679. (also avail. in microfiche; reprint service avail. from UMI) **Document type:** trade publication.
Former titles: Annual Book of A S T M Standards. Volume 04.03. Road and Paving Materials; Traveled Surface Characteristics; Supersedes in part (in 1986): Annual Book of A S T M Standards. Part 15. Road and Paving Materials; Bituminous Materials for Highway Construction, Waterproofing and Roofing, and Pipe; Traveled Surface Characteristics; Which was formerly: Annual Book of A S T M Standards. Part 15. Road and Paving Materials; Bituminous Materials for Highway Construction, Waterproofing and Roofing, and Pipe; Skid Resistance; Annual Book of A S T M Standards. Part 11. Bituminous Materials for Highway Construction, Waterproofing and Roofing: Soil and Rock; Skid Resistance (ISSN 0066-0272).

620 US
ANNUAL BOOK OF A S T M STANDARDS. VOLUME 04.04. ROOFING, WATERPROOFING, AND BITUMINOUS MATERIALS. a. $56 to non-members; members $50.40. American Society for Testing and Materials, 1916 Race St., Philadelphia, PA 19103. TEL 215-299-5400. FAX 215-977-9679. (also avail. in microfiche; reprint service avail. from UMI) **Document type:** trade publication.
Supersedes in part (in 1986): Annual Book of A S T M Standards. Part 15. Road and Paving Materials; Bituminous Materials for Highway Construction, Waterproofing and Roofing, and Pipe; Traveled Surface Characteristics; Which was formerly: Annual Book of A S T M Standards. Part 15. Road and Paving Materials; Bituminous Materials for Highway Construction, Waterproofing and Roofing, and Pipe; Skid Resistance; Annual Book of A S T M Standards. Part 11. Bituminous Materials for Highway Construction, Waterproofing and Roofing; Soil and Rock; Skid Resistance (ISSN 0066-0272).

620.1 691 US
ANNUAL BOOK OF A S T M STANDARDS. VOLUME 04.05. CHEMICAL-RESISTANT MATERIALS; VITRIFIED CLAY, CONCRETE; FIBER-CEMENT PRODUCTS; MASONRY; MORTARS. a. $85 to non-members; members $76.50. American Society for Testing and Materials, 1916 Race St., Philadelphia, PA 19103. TEL 215-299-5400. FAX 215-977-9679. (also avail. in microfiche; reprint service avail. from UMI) **Document type:** trade publication.
Former titles: Annual Book of A S T M Standards. Volume 04.05. Chemical-Resistant Nonmetallic Materials; Vitrified Clay, Concrete Pipe and Tile; Masonary Mortars and Units; Fiber-Cement Products, Precast Concrete Products; (until 1986): Annual Book of A S T M Standards. Part 16. Chemical Resistant Nonmetallic Materials; Vitrified Clay, and Concrete Pipe and Tile; Masonary Mortars and Units; Fiber-Cement Products; Annual Book of A S T M Standards. Part 16. Chemical-Resistant Nonmetallic Materials. Vitrified Clay and Concrete Pipe and Tile; Masonry Mortars and Units; Asbestos-Cement Products; Annual Book of A S T M Standards. Part 12. Chemical-Resistant Nonmetallic Materials; Clay and Concrete Pipe and Tile; Masonry Mortars and Units; Asbestos-Cement Products; Natural Building Stones (ISSN 0066-0280).

620.1 US
ANNUAL BOOK OF A S T M STANDARDS. VOLUME 04.06. THERMAL INSULATION; ENVIRONMENTAL ACOUSTICS. a. $99 to non-members; members $89.10. American Society for Testing and Materials, 1916 Race St., Philadelphia, PA 19103. TEL 215-299-5400. FAX 215-977-9679. (also avail. in microfiche; reprint service avail. from UMI) **Document type:** trade publication.
Supersedes in part (in 1986): Annual Book of A S T M Standards. Part 18. Thermal Insulation; Building Seals and Sealants; Fire Tests; Building Construction; Environmental Acoustics; Which was formerly: Annual Book of A S T M Standards. Part 18. Thermal and Cryogenic Insulating Materials; Building Seals and Sealants; Fire Tests; Building Constructions; Environmental Acoustics (ISSN 0066-0302).

620 US
ANNUAL BOOK OF A S T M STANDARDS. VOLUME 04.07. BUILDING SEALS AND SEALANTS; FIRE STANDARDS; BUILDING CONSTRUCTIONS. a. $115 to non-members; members $103.50. American Society for Testing and Materials, 1916 Race St., Philadelphia, PA 19103. TEL 215-299-5400. FAX 215-977-9679. (also avail. in microfiche; reprint service avail. from UMI) **Document type:** trade publication.
Supersedes in part (in 1986): Annual Book of A S T M Standards. Part 18. Thermal Insulation; Building Seals and Sealants; Fire Tests; Building Constructions; Environmental Acoustics; Which was formerly: Annual Book of A S T M Standards. Part 18. Thermal and Cryogenic Insulating Materials; Building Seals and Sealants; Fire Tests; Building Constructions; Environmental Acoustics (ISSN 0066-0302).

620.1 US
ANNUAL BOOK OF A S T M STANDARDS. VOLUME 04.08. SOIL AND ROCK; DIMENSION STONE; GEOSYNTHETICS. a. $129 to non-members; members $116.10. American Society for Testing and Materials, 1916 Race St., Philadelphia, PA 19103. TEL 215-299-5400. FAX 215-977-9679. (also avail. in microfiche; reprint service avail. from UMI) **Document type:** trade publication.
Former titles: Annual Book of A S T M Standards. Volume 04.08. Soil and Rock; Building Stones; (until 1986): Annual Book of A S T M Standards. Part 19. Natural Building Stones; Soil and Rock; Annual Book of A S T M Standards. Part 19. Natural Building Stones; Soil and Rock; Peats, Mosses and Humus.

620.1 US
ANNUAL BOOK OF A S T M STANDARDS. VOLUME 04.09. WOOD. a. $72 to non-members; members $64.80. American Society for Testing and Materials, 1916 Race St., Philadelphia, PA 19103. TEL 215-299-5400. FAX 215-977-9679. (also avail. in microfiche; reprint service avail. from UMI) **Document type:** trade publication.
Supersedes in part (in 1986): Annual Book of A S T M Standards. Part 22. Wood; Adhesives (ISSN 0066-0329); Which was formerly: Annual Book of A S T M Standards. Part 16. Structural Sandwich Constructions; Wood; Adhesives.

620.1 665.5 US
ANNUAL BOOK OF A S T M STANDARDS. VOLUME 05.01. PETROLEUM PRODUCTS AND LUBRICANTS (1). a. $119 to non-members; members $107.10. American Society for Testing and Materials, 1916 Race St., Philadelphia, PA 19103. TEL 215-299-5400. FAX 215-977-9679. Ed. Roberta Storer. (also avail. in microfiche; reprint service avail. from UMI) **Document type:** trade publication.
Former titles: Annual Book of A S T M Standards. Volume 05.01. Petroleum Products and Lubricants (1); D 56 to D 1947; (until 1986): Annual Book of A S T M Standards. Part 23. Petroleum Products and Lubricants (1): D 56 to D 1660; Annual Book of A S T M Standards. Part 17. Petroleum Products - Fuels, Solvents, Burner Fuel Oils, Lubricating Greases, Hydraulic Fluids (ISSN 0066-0337)

620.1 665.5 US
ANNUAL BOOK OF A S T M STANDARDS. VOLUME 05.02. PETROLEUM PRODUCTS AND LUBRICANTS (2). a. $119 to non-members; members $107.10. American Society for Testing and Materials, 1916 Race St., Philadelphia, PA 19103. TEL 215-299-5400. FAX 215-977-9679. (also avail. in microfiche; reprint service avail. from UMI) **Document type:** trade publication.
Former titles: Annual Book of A S T M Standards. Volume 05.02. Petroleum Products and Lubricants (2); D 1949 to D 3601; (until 1986): Annual Book of A S T M Standards. Part 24. Petroleum Products and Lubricants (2); D 1661 to D 2896; Annual Book of A S T M Standards. Part 18. Petroleum Products - Measurement and Sampling; Liquefied Petroleum Gases; Light Hydrocarbons; Plant Spray Oils; Aerospace Materials; Sulfonates; Crude Petroleum; Petroleum; Wax; Graphite (ISSN 0066-0345).

620.1 665 5 629.3 US
ANNUAL BOOK OF A S T M STANDARDS. VOLUME 05.03. PETROLEUM PRODUCTS AND LUBRICANTS (3); CATALYSTS. a. $108 to non-members; members $97.20. American Society for Testing and Materials, 1916 Race St., Philadelphia, PA 19103. TEL 215-299-5400. FAX 215-977-9679. (also avail. in microfiche; reprint service avail. from UMI) **Document type:** trade publication.
Former titles: Annual Book of A S T M Standards. Volume 05.C3. Petroleum Products and Lubricants (3); D 3602 to Latest; Catalysts; (until 1986): Annual Book of A S T M Standards. Part 25. Petroleum Products and Lubricants (3); Aerospace Materials; Catalysts; Annual Book of A S T M Standards. Part 25. Petroleum Products and Lubricants (3); Aerospace Materials.

620.1 US
ANNUAL BOOK OF A S T M STANDARDS. VOLUME 05.04. TEST METHODS FOR RATING MOTOR, DIESEL, AND AVIATION FUELS. a. $62 to non-members; members $55.80. American Society for Testing and Materials, 1916 Race St., Philadelphia, PA 19103. TEL 215-299-5400. FAX 215-977-9679. (also avail. in microfiche; reprint service avail. from UMI) **Document type:** trade publication.
Formerly (until 1986): Annual Book of A S T M Standards. Part 47.

620.1 US
ANNUAL BOOK OF A S T M STANDARDS. VOLUME 05.05. GASEOUS FUELS; COAL AND COKE. a. $61 to non-members; members $54.90. American Society for Testing and Materials, 1916 Race St., Philadelphia, PA 19103. TEL 215-299-5400. FAX 215-977-9679. (also avail. in microfiche; reprint service avail. from UMI) **Document type:** trade publication.
Supersedes in part (in 1986): Annual Book of A S T M Standards. Part 26. Gaseous Fuels; Coal and Coke; Atmospheric Analysis; Which was formerly: Annual Book of A S T M Standards. Part 26. Gaseous Fuels; Coal and Coke (ISSN 0066-0353).

620.1 667.4 US ISSN 0066-037X
ANNUAL BOOK OF A S T M STANDARDS. VOLUME 06.01. PAINT - TESTS FOR FORMULATED PRODUCTS AND APPLIED COATINGS. a. $104 to non-members; members $93.60. American Society for Testing and Materials, 1916 Race St., Philadelphia, PA 19103. TEL 215-299-5400. FAX 215-977-9679. (also avail. in microfiche; reprint service avail. from UMI) **Document type:** trade publication.
Formerly (until 1986): Annual Book of A S T M Standards. Part 27.

620.1 667.4 US
ANNUAL BOOK OF A S T M STANDARDS. VOLUME 06.02. PAINT - PIGMENTS, RESINS AND POLYMERS. a. $77 to non-members; members $69.30. American Society for Testing and Materials, 1916 Race St., Philadelphia, PA 19103. TEL 215-299-5400. FAX 215-977-9679. (also avail. in microfiche; reprint service avail. from UMI) **Document type:** trade publication.
Formerly (until 1986): Annual Book of A S T M Standards. Part 28

620.1 US
ANNUAL BOOK OF A S T M STANDARDS. VOLUME 06.03. PAINT - FATTY OILS AND ACIDS, SOLVENTS, MISCELLANEOUS; AROMATIC HYDROCARBONS. a. $70 to non-members; members $63. American Society for Testing and Materials, 1916 Race St., Philadelphia, PA 19_03. TEL 215-299-5400. FAX 215-977-9679. (reprint service avail. from UMI) **Document type:** trade publication.
Former titles: Annual Book of A S T M Standards. Volume 06.03. Paint - Fatty Oils and Acids, Solvents, Miscellaneous; Aromatic Hydrocarbons (Includes Naval Stores); And (until 1986): Annual Book of A S T M Standards. Part 29; Annual Book of A S T M Standards. Part 20. Paint, Varnish, Lacquer, and Related Products - Materials Specifications and Tests; Naval Stores; Industrial Aromatic Hydrocarbons and Related Chemicals (ISSN 0066-0361).

ENGINEERING — ENGINEERING MECHANICS AND MATERIALS

620.1 677   US   ISSN 0066-040X
ANNUAL BOOK OF A S T M STANDARDS. VOLUME 07.01. TEXTILES - YARN, FABRICS, AND GENERAL TEST METHODS. a. $99 to non-members; members $89.10. American Society for Testing and Materials, 1916 Race St., Philadelphia, PA 19103. TEL 215-299-5400. FAX 215-977-9679. (also avail. in microfiche; reprint service avail. from UMI) **Document type:** trade publication.

620.1 677   US
ANNUAL BOOK OF A S T M STANDARDS. VOLUME 07.02. TEXTILES - FIBERS, ZIPPERS. a. $94 to non-members; members $84.60. American Society for Testing and Materials, 1916 Race St., Philadelphia, PA 19103. TEL 215-299-5400. FAX 215-977-9679. (also avail. in microfiche; reprint service avail. from UMI) **Document type:** trade publication.
   Formerly (until 1986): Annual Book of A S T M Standards. Part 33. Textiles - Fibers, Zippers; High Modulus Fibers (ISSN 0066-0418)

620.1 668.4   US
ANNUAL BOOK OF A S T M STANDARDS. VOLUME 08.01. PLASTICS (1): C 177 TO D 1600. a. $85 to non-members; members $76.50. American Society for Testing and Materials, 1916 Race St., Philadelphia, PA 19103. TEL 215-299-5400. FAX 215-977-9679. (reprint service avail. from UMI) **Document type:** trade publication.
   Supersedes in part (in 1986): Annual Book of A S T M Standards. Part 35. Plastics - General Test Methods; Nomenclature (ISSN 0066-0434)

620.1 668.4   US
ANNUAL BOOK OF A S T M STANDARDS. VOLUME 08.02. PLASTICS (2): D 1601 TO D 3099. a. $85 to non-members; members $76.50. American Society for Testing and Materials, 1916 Race St., Philadelphia, PA 19103. TEL 215-299-5400. FAX 215-977-9679. (reprint service avail. from UMI) **Document type:** trade publication.
   Supersedes in part: Annual Book of A S T M Standards. Part 36. Plastics - Materials, Film, Reinforced and Cellular Plastics; High Modulus Fibers and Their Composites; Formerly: Annual Book of A S T M Standards. Part 26. Plastics - Specifications; Methods of Testing Pipe, Film, Reinforced and Cellular Plastics (ISSN 0066-0426)

620   US
ANNUAL BOOK OF A S T M STANDARDS. VOLUME 08.03. PLASTICS (3): D 3100 TO LATEST. 1986. a. $70 to non-members; members $63. American Society for Testing and Materials, 1916 Race St., Philadelphia, PA 19103. TEL 215-299-5400. FAX 215-977-9679. (also avail. in microfiche; reprint service avail. from UMI) **Document type:** trade publication.

620.1 668.4 690   US
ANNUAL BOOK OF A S T M STANDARDS. VOLUME 08.04. PLASTIC PIPE AND BUILDING PRODUCTS. a. $112 to non-members; members $100.80. American Society for Testing and Materials, 1916 Race St., Philadelphia, PA 19103. TEL 215-299-5400. FAX 215-977-9679. (also avail. in microfiche; reprint service avail.) **Document type:** trade publication.
   Formerly (until 1986): Annual Book of A S T M Standards. Part 34. Plastic Pipe.

620.1 678.2   US
ANNUAL BOOK OF A S T M STANDARDS. VOLUME 09.01. RUBBER, NATURAL AND SYNTHETIC - GENERAL TEST METHODS; CARBON BLACK. a. $89 to non-members; members $80.10. American Society for Testing and Materials, 1916 Race St., Philadelphia, PA 19103. TEL 215-299-5400. FAX 215-977-9679. (also avail. in microfiche; reprint service avail. from UMI) **Document type:** trade publication.
   Formerly (until 1980): Annual Book of A S T M Standards. Part 37.

620.1 678.2   US
ANNUAL BOOK OF A S T M STANDARDS. VOLUME 09.02. RUBBER PRODUCTS, INDUSTRIAL - SPECIFICATIONS AND RELATED TEST METHODS; GASKETS; TIRES. a. $78 to non-members; members $70.20. American Society for Testing and Materials, 1916 Race St., Philadelphia, PA 19103. TEL 215-299-5400. FAX 615-977-9679. (also avail. in microfiche; reprint service avail. from UMI) **Document type:** trade publication.
   Formerly (until 1986): Annual Book of A S T M Standards. Part 28. Rubber; Carbon Black; Gaskets (ISSN 0066-0442)

620.1   US
ANNUAL BOOK OF A S T M STANDARDS. VOLUME 10.01. ELECTRICAL INSULATION, COMPOSITES, AND COATINGS - SOLIDS. a. $68 to non-members; members $61.20. American Society for Testing and Materials, 1916 Race St., Philadelphia, PA 19103. TEL 215-299-5400. FAX 215-977-9679. (also avail. in microfiche; reprint service avail. from UMI) **Document type:** trade publication.
   Formerly: Annual Book of A S T M Standards. Volume 10.01. Electrical Insulation - Soils (1); Supersedes in part (in 1986): Annual Book of A S T M Standards. Part 39. Electrical Insulation - Test Methods; Solids and Solidifying Fluids; Which was formerly: Annual Book of A S T M Standards. Part 39. Electrical Insulating Materials - Test Methods (ISSN 0066-0450)

620   US
ANNUAL BOOK OF A S T M STANDARDS. VOLUME 10.02. ELECTRICAL INSULATION; WIRE AND CABLE, HEATING AND ELECTRICAL TESTS - SOLIDS (2). a. $63 to non-members; members $56.70. American Society for Testing and Materials, 1916 Race St., Philadelphia, PA 19103. TEL 215-299-5400. FAX 215-977-9679. (also avail. in microfiche; reprint service avail. from UMI) **Document type:** trade publication.
   Formerly: Annual Book of A S T M Standards. Volume 10.02. Electrical Insulation - Solids (2); Supersedes in part (in 1986): Annual Book of A S T M Standards. Part 39. Electrical Insulation - Test Methods; Solids and Solidifying Fluids; Which was formerly: Annual Book of A S T M Standards. Part 39. Electrical Insulating Materials - Test Methods (ISSN 0066-0450).

620.1   US
ANNUAL BOOK OF A S T M STANDARDS. VOLUME 10.03. ELECTRICAL INSULATING LIQUIDS AND GASES; ELECTRICAL PROTECTIVE EQUIPMENT. a. $63 to non-members; members $56.70. American Society for Testing and Materials, 1916 Race St., Philadelphia, PA 19103. TEL 215-299-5400. FAX 215-977-9679. (also avail. in microfiche; reprint service avail.) **Document type:** trade publication.
   Former titles (until 1986): Annual Book of A S T M Standards. Part 40. Electrical Insulation - Specifications: Solids, Liquids, and Gases; Test Methods: Liquids and Gases; Protective Equipment; Annual Book of A S T M Standards. Part 40. Electrical Insulation - Specifications: Solids, Liquids, and Gases; Test Methods: Liquids and Gases.

620.1 621.38   US
ANNUAL BOOK OF A S T M STANDARDS. VOLUME 10.04. ELECTRONICS (1). a. $79 to non-members; members $71.10. American Society for Testing and Materials, 1916 Race St., Philadelphia, PA 19103. TEL 215-299-5400. FAX 215-977-9679. (also avail. in microfiche; reprint service avail. from UMI) **Document type:** trade publication.
   Formerly (until 1986): Annual Book of A S T M Standards. Part 43.

620   US
ANNUAL BOOK OF A S T M STANDARDS. VOLUME 10.05. ELECTRONICS (2). 1986. a. $90 to non-members; members $81. American Society for Testing and Materials, 1916 Race St., Philadelphia, PA 19103. TEL 215-299-5400. FAX 215-977-9679. (also avail. in microfiche; reprint service avail. from UMI) **Document type:** trade publication.
   Supersedes in part: Annual Book of A S T M Standards. Part 43. Electronics.

620.1   US
ANNUAL BOOK OF A S T M STANDARDS. VOLUME 11.01. WATER (1). a. $72 to non-members; members $64.80. American Society for Testing and Materials, 1916 Race St., Philadelphia, PA 19103. TEL 215-299-5400. FAX 215-977-9679. (also avail. in microfiche; reprint service avail. from UMI) **Document type:** trade publication.
   Supersedes in part (in 1986): Annual Book of A S T M Standards. Part 31. Water; Which was formerly: Annual Book of A S T M Standards. Part 23. Water; Atmospheric Analysis (ISSN 0066-0396)

620   US
ANNUAL BOOK OF A S T M STANDARDS. VOLUME 11.02. WATER (2). a. $110 to non-members; members $99. American Society for Testing and Materials, 1916 Race St., Philadelphia, PA 19103. TEL 215-299-5400. FAX 215-977-9679. (also avail. in microfiche; reprint service avail. from UMI) **Document type:** trade publication.
   Supersedes in part (in 1986): Annual Book of A S T M Standards. Part 31. Water; Which was formerly: Annual Book of A S T M Standards. Part 23. Water; Atmospheric Analysis (ISSN 0066-0396).

620   US
ANNUAL BOOK OF A S T M STANDARDS. VOLUME 11.03. ATMOSPHERIC ANALYSIS; OCCUPATIONAL HEALTH AND SAFETY. a. $85 to non-members; members $76.50. American Society for Testing and Materials, 1900 Race St., Philadelphia, PA 19103. TEL 215-299-5400. FAX 215-977-9679. (also avail. in microfiche; reprint service avail. from UMI) **Document type:** trade publication.
   Supersedes in part (in 1986): Annual Book of A S T M Standards. Part 26. Gaseous Fuels; Coal and Coke; Atmospheric Analysis; Which was formerly: Annual Book of A S T M Standards. Part 26. Gaseous Fuels; Coal and Coke (ISSN 0066-0353).

620   US
ANNUAL BOOK OF A S T M STANDARDS. VOLUME 11.04. PESTICIDES; RESOURCE RECOVERY; HAZARDOUS SUBSTANCES AND OIL SPILL RESPONSE; WASTE DISPOSAL; BIOLOGICAL EFFECTS. 1986. a. $132 to non-members; members $118.80. American Society for Testing and Materials, 1916 Race St., Philadelphia, PA 19103. TEL 215-299-5400. FAX 215-977-9679. (reprint service avail.) **Document type:** trade publication.

620.1 621.48   US
ANNUAL BOOK OF A S T M STANDARDS. VOLUME 12.01. NUCLEAR ENERGY (1). a. $96 to non-members; members $86.40. American Society for Testing and Materials, 1916 Race St., Philadelphia, PA 19103. TEL 215-299-5400. FAX 215-977-9679. (reprint service avail. from UMI) **Document type:** trade publication.
   Supersedes in part (in 1986): Annual Book of A S T M Standards. Part 45. Nuclear Standards.

620 531.6   US
ANNUAL BOOK OF A S T M STANDARDS. VOLUME 12.02. NUCLEAR ENERGY (2), SOLAR, AND GEOTHERMAL ENERGY. a. $97 to non-members; members $87.30. American Society for Testing and Materials, 1916 Race St., Philadelphia, PA 19103. TEL 215-299-5400. FAX 215-977-9679. (also avail. in microfiche; reprint service avail. from UMI) **Document type:** trade publication.
   Supersedes in part (in 1986): Annual Book of A S T M Standards. Part 45. Nuclear Standards.

620 610   US
ANNUAL BOOK OF A S T M STANDARDS. VOLUME 13.01. MEDICAL DEVICES. 1986. a. $89 to non-members; members $80.10. American Society for Testing and Materials, 1916 Race St., Philadelphia, PA 19103. TEL 215-299-5400. FAX 215-977-9679. (also avail. in microfiche; reprint service avail. from UMI) **Document type:** trade publication.

ENGINEERING — ENGINEERING MECHANICS AND MATERIALS

620.1 542   US
ANNUAL BOOK OF A S T M STANDARDS. VOLUME 14.01. ANALYTICAL METHODS - SPECTROSCOPY; CHROMATOGRAPHY; TEMPERATURE MEASUREMENT; COMPUTERIZED SYSTEMS. a. $81 to non-members; members $72.90. American Society for Testing and Materials, 1916 Race St., Philadelphia, PA 19103. TEL 215-299-5400. FAX 215-977-9679. (also avail. in microfiche; reprint service avail. from UMI) **Document type:** trade publication.
   Former titles: Annual Book of A S T M Standards. Volume 14.01. Molecular Mass Spectroscopy; Chromatography; Resinography; Temperature Measurement; Microscopy; Computerized Systems; Supersedes in part (in 1986): Annual Book of A S T M Standards. Part 42. Emission, Molecular, and Mass Spectroscopy; Chromatography; Resinography; Microscopy; Computerized Systems; Which was formerly: Annual Book of A S T M Standards. Part 42. Emission, Molecular, and Mass Spectroscopy; Chromatography; Resinography; Microscopy.

620.1   US
ANNUAL BOOK OF A S T M STANDARDS. VOLUME 14.02. GENERAL TEST METHODS, NONMETAL; LABORATORY APPARATUS; STATISTICAL METHODS; APPEARANCE OF MATERIALS; DURABILITY OF NONMETALLIC MATERIALS. a. $112 to non-members; members $100.80. American Society for Testing and Materials, 1916 Race St., Philadelphia, PA 19103. TEL 215-299-5400. FAX 215-977-9679. (also avail. in microfiche; reprint service avail. from UMI) **Document type:** trade publication.
   Supersedes in part (in 1986): Annual Book of A S T M Standards. Part 41. General Test Methods, Nonmetal; Statistical Methods; Space Simulation; Particle Size Measurement; Laboratory Apparatus; Durability of Nonmetallic Materials; Metric Practice; Solar Energy Conversion; Which was formerly: Annual Book of A S T M Standards. Part 41. General Test Methods, Nonmetal; Statistical Methods; Space Simulation; Particle Size Measurement; General Laboratory Apparatus; Durability of Nonmetallic Materials; Metric Practice; Annual Book of A S T M Standards. Part 41. General Test Methods (Nonmetal); Statistical Methods; Space Simulation; Particle Size Measurement; Deterioration of Nonmetallic Materials (ISSN 0066-0469).

620.11   US
ANNUAL BOOK OF A S T M STANDARDS. VOLUME 14.03. TEMPERATURE MEASUREMENT. a. $54 to non-members; members $48.60. American Society for Testing and Materials, 1916 Race St., Philadelphia, PA 19103. TEL 215-299-5400. FAX 215-977-9679. (also avail. in microfiche; reprint service avail. from UMI) **Indexed:** Cott.& Trop.Fibr.Abstr. **Document type:** trade publication.
   Description: Includes specifications for hydrometers, thermometers, and thermocouples and fifteen accompanying test methods.

620.1   US
ANNUAL BOOK OF A S T M STANDARDS. VOLUME 15.01. REFRACTORIES, MANUFACTURED CARBON AND GRAPHITE PRODUCTS; ACTIVATED CARBON. a. $61 to non-members; members $54.90. American Society for Testing and Materials, 1916 Race St., Philadelphia, PA 19103. TEL 215-299-5400. FAX 215-977-9679. (also avail. in microfiche; reprint service avail. from UMI) **Document type:** trade publication.
   Supersedes in part (in 1986): Annual Book of A S T M Standards. Part 17. Refractories, Glass and Other Ceramic Materials; Manufactured Carbon and Graphite Products (ISSN 0066-0299).

620   US
ANNUAL BOOK OF A S T M STANDARDS. VOLUME 15.02. GLASS; CERAMIC WHITEWARES. a. $56 to non-members; members $50.40. American Society for Testing and Materials, 1916 Race St., Philadelphia, PA 19103. TEL 215-299-5400. FAX 215-977-9679. (also avail. in microfiche; reprint service avail. from UMI) **Document type:** trade publication.
   Supersedes in part (in 1986): Annual Book of A S T M Standards. Part 17. Refractories, Glass and Other Ceramic Materials; Manufactured Carbon and Graphite Products (ISSN 0066-0299).

620   US
ANNUAL BOOK OF A S T M STANDARDS. VOLUME 15.03. SPACE SIMULATION; AEROSPACE MATERIALS; HIGH MODULUS FIBERS AND THEIR COMPOSITES. 1986. a. $73 to non-members; members $65.70. American Society for Testing and Materials, 1916 Race St., Philadelphia, PA 19103. TEL 215-299-5400. FAX 215-977-9679. (also avail. in microfiche; reprint service avail. from UMI) **Document type:** trade publication.
   Supersedes in part (in 1986): Annual Book of A S T M Standards. Part 41. General Test Methods, Nonmetal; Statistical Methods; Space Simulation; Particle Size Measurement; Laboratory Apparatus; Durability of Nonmetallic Materials; Metric Practice; Solar Energy Conversion; Which was formerly: Annual Book of A S T M Standards. Part 41. General Test Methods, Nonmetal; Statistical Methods; Space Simulation; Particle Size Measurement; General Laboratory Apparatus; Durability of Nonmetallic Materials; Metric Practice; Annual Book of A S T M Standards. Part 41. General Test Methods (Nonmetal); Statistical Methods; Space Simulation; Particle Size Measurement; Deterioration of Nonmetallic Materials (ISSN 0066-0469).

620.1   US
ANNUAL BOOK OF A S T M STANDARDS. VOLUME 15.04. SOAPS; POLISHES; CELLULOSE; LEATHER; RESILIENT FLOOR COVERING. a. $70 to non-members; members $63. American Society for Testing and Materials, 1916 Race St., Philadelphia, PA 19103. TEL 215-299-5400. FAX 215-977-9679. (also avail. in microfiche; reprint service avail. from UMI) **Document type:** trade publication.
   Supersedes (in 1986): Annual Book of A S T M Standards. Part 21. Cellulose; Leather; Flexible Barrier Materials; Supersedes in part (in 1986): Annual Book of A S T M Standards. Part 30. Soap; Engine Coolants; Polishes; Halogenated Organic Solvents; Activated Carbon (ISSN 0066-0388).

620.1   US
ANNUAL BOOK OF A S T M STANDARDS. VOLUME 15.05. ENGINE COOLANTS; HALOGENATED ORGANIC SOLVENTS; INDUSTRIAL CHEMICALS. a. $66 to non-members; members $59.40. American Society for Testing and Materials, 1916 Race St., Philadelphia, PA 19103. TEL 215-299-5400. FAX 215-977-9679. (also avail. in microfiche; reprint service avail. from UMI) **Document type:** trade publication.
   Supersedes in part (in 1986): Annual Book of A S T M Standards. Part 30. Soap; Engine Coolants; Polishes; Halogenated Organic Solvents; Activated Carbon (ISSN 0066-0388).

620   US
ANNUAL BOOK OF A S T M STANDARDS. VOLUME 15.06. ADHESIVES. a. $55 to non-members; members $49.50. American Society for Testing and Materials, 1916 Race St., Philadelphia, PA 19103. TEL 215-299-5400. FAX 215-977-9679. (also avail. in microfiche; reprint service avail. from UMI) **Document type:** trade publication.
   Supersedes in part (in 1986): Annual Book of A S T M Standards. Part 22. Wood; Adhesives (ISSN 0066-0329); Which was formerly: Annual Book of A S T M Standards. Part 16. Structural Sandwich Constructions; Wood; Adhesives.

620.1   US
ANNUAL BOOK OF A S T M STANDARDS. VOLUME 15.07. END USE PRODUCTS. a. $109 to non-members; members $98.10. American Society for Testing and Materials, 1916 Race St., Philadelphia, PA 19103. TEL 215-299-5400. FAX 215-977-9679. (also avail. in microfiche; reprint service avail. from UMI) **Document type:** trade publication.
   Formerly (until 1986): Annual Book of A S T M Standards. Part 46. End Use and Consumer Products.

620   US
ANNUAL BOOK OF A S T M STANDARDS. VOLUME 15.08. FASTENERS 1986. a. $62 to non-members; members $55.80. American Society for Testing and Materials, 1916 Race St., Philadelphia, PA 19103. TEL 215-299-5400. FAX 215-977-9679. (also avail. in microfiche; reprint service avail. from UMI) **Document type:** trade publication.
   Supersedes in part (in 1986): Annual Book of A S T M Standards. Part 4. Structural Steel; Concrete Reinforcing Steel; Pressure Vessel Plate and Forgings; Steel Rails, Wheels and Tires; Steel Fasteners; Which was formerly: Annual Book of A S T M Standards. Part 4. Structural Steel; Concrete Reinforcing Steel; Pressure Vessel Plate; Steel Rails, Wheels, and Tires; Bearing Steel; Steel Forgings (ISSN 0066-0213).

620.1   US
ANNUAL BOOK OF A S T M STANDARDS. VOLUME 15.09. PAPER; PACKAGING; FLEXIBLE BARRIER MATERIALS; BUSINESS COPY PRODUCTS. a. $130 to non-members; members $117. American Society for Testing and Materials, 1916 Race St., Philadelphia, PA 19103. TEL 215-299-5400. FAX 215-977-9679. (also avail. in microfiche; reprint service avail. from UMI) **Document type:** trade publication.
   Former titles (until 1986): Annual Book of A S T M Standards. Part 20. Paper; Packaging; Business Copy Products; Annual Book of A S T M Standards. Part 15. Paper; Packaging; Cellulose; Casein; Flexible Barrier Materials; Carbon Paper; Leather (ISSN 0066-0310).

620.11   UN   ISSN 0255-9293
ANNUAL REVIEW OF ENGINEERING INDUSTRIES AND AUTOMATION. French edition: Revue Annuelle des Industries Mecariques et Electriques et de l'Automatisation (ISSN 0256-0895) (Editions in English, French and Russian) 1979. a. price varies. (Economic Commission for Europe (ECE), Working Party on Engineering Industries and Automation) United Nations Publications, Room DC2-0853, New York, NY 10017. TEL 212-963-8300. FAX 212-963-3489. (Or: Distribution and Sales Section, Palais des Nations, 1211 Geneva 10, Switzerland) charts; stat. circ. 300. (also avail. in microfiche from CIS; back issues avail.) **Indexed:** IIS.
   Description: Provides information on international developments in trade, microelectronics, automation, engineering and the manufacturing of machinery and equipment.

620.1   US   ISSN 0084-6600
TA401   CODEN: ARMSCX
ANNUAL REVIEW OF MATERIALS SCIENCE. 1971. a. $75 (foreign $80) (effective Jan. 1994). Annual Reviews Inc., 4139 El Camino Way, Box 10139, Palo Alto, CA 94303-0139. TEL 415-493-4400; 800-523-8635. FAX 415-855-9815. Ed. Elton N. Kaufmann. adv. contact: Elizabeth Kao. bibl.; index, cum.index. (also avail. in microfilm from UMI; back issues avail.; reprint service avail.) **Indexed:** Cadscan, Chem.Abstr., Curr.Cont., Deep Sea Res.& Oceanogr.Abstr., Energy Info.Abstr., Environ.Abstr., Ind.Sci.Rev., Int.Aerosp.Abstr., Lead Abstr., M.M.R.I., Nucl.Sci.Abstr., Phys.Ber., Sci.Abstr., Zincscan. **Document type:** academic/scholarly publication.
   —BLDSC (1522.600000); EI; Faxon; UnCover; SWETS; UMI; CASDDS. CCC.
   Description: Original reviews of critical literature and current developments in materials science.

620.1   NE   ISSN 0929-189X
▼**APPLIED COMPOSITE MATERIALS.** (Text in English) 1994. 6/yr. fl.370($193) (effective 1994). Kluwer Academic Publishers Group, Postbus 17, 3300 AA Dordrecht, Netherlands. TEL 31-78-334911. FAX 31-78-334254. TELEX 29245 KAPG NL. (Dist. by: Kluwer Academic Publishers Group, P.O. Box 322, 3300 AH Dordrecht, Netherlands. TEL 31-78-524400. FAX 31-78-524474; N. America dist. addr.: Box 358, Accord Sta., Hingham, MA 02018-0358. TEL 617-871-6600. FAX 617-871-6528) **Document type:** academic/scholarly publication.
   Refereed Serial

ENGINEERING — ENGINEERING MECHANICS AND MATERIALS

620.11 669   PL   ISSN 0138-032X
TA401   CODEN: ANAMDU
ARCHIWUM NAUKI O MATERIALACH.* (Text in English, Polish, Russian; summaries in English, Polish) 1980. q. 75 Zl. Polska Akademia Nauk, Komitet Nauki o Materialach, Ul. Bankowa 12, 40-007 Katowice, Poland. Ed. Zbigniew Bojarski. circ. 350. (back issues avail.) **Indexed:** INSPEC, Ref.Zh., Sci.Abstr.
—BLDSC (1661.434000); CASDDS.

620.1   BE   ISSN 0066-8796
ASSOCIATION BELGE POUR L'ETUDE, L'ESSAI ET L'EMPLOI DES MATERIAUX. PUBLICATION A.B.E.M. (Text in Dutch, English, French; summaries in Dutch, French) 1927. irreg. price varies. Association Belge pour l'Etude, l'Essai et l'Emploi des Materiaux - Belgische Vereniging voor de Studie van Materialen, 2 De Croylaan, 3001 Heverlee, Belgium.

620.1   BE   ISSN 0066-8818
ASSOCIATION BELGE POUR L'ETUDE, L'ESSAI ET L'EMPLOI DES MATERIAUX. PROCES VERBAL DE L'ASSEMBLEE GENERALE ORDINAIRE. (Subseries of: Publication A.B.E.M.) (Text in Dutch, French) 1931. a. price varies. Association Belge pour l'Etude, l'Essai et l'Emploi des Materiaux - Belgische Vereniging voor de Studie van Materialen, 2 De Croylaan, 3001 Heverlee, Belgium.

AUSTRALIAN GEOMECHANICS NEWS. see *MINES AND MINING INDUSTRY*

620.11   GW   ISSN 0178-1510
BAUSTOFF, RECYCLING UND DEPONIETECHNIK. Short title: B R. 1985. 6/yr. DM.135. Stein-Verlag GmbH, Josef-Herrmann-Str. 1-3, 76473 Iffezheim, Germany. TEL 07229-6060. FAX 07229-60610. Ed.Bd. circ. 6,000. (back issues avail.)
Description: International magazine for recycling of building material and land-fill technology.

624   YU
BEOGRAD. 1962. m. Radne Organizacije Industrije Metalnih Konstrukcija, Francuska 52, Belgrade, Yugoslavia. Ed. Dmitrije R. Jovanovic.

620.1   PL   ISSN 0067-7701
BIBLIOTEKA MECHANIKI STOSOWANEJ. (Text in Polish; summaries in English) 1956. irreg. price varies. (Polska Akademia Nauk, Instytut Podstawowych Problemow Techniki) Wydawnictwo Naukowe P W N, Ul. Miodowa 10, 00-251 Warsaw, Poland. TEL 48-22-312738. FAX 48-22-267163. TELEX 813763 PWN PL. Ed. H. Zorski. **Indexed:** Math.R.

BIOMATERIALS. see *MEDICAL SCIENCES*

620.11   II   ISSN 0250-6327
BULLETIN OF MATERIALS SCIENCE. (Text in English) 1979. 6/yr. Rs.75($100) Indian Academy of Sciences, C.V. Raman Avenue, P.B. No. 8005, Bangalore 560 080, India. TEL 342546. FAX 91-812-346094. TELEX 0845-2178-ACAD-IN. Ed. P. Rama Rao. illus.; index. circ. 1,200. (back issues avail.) **Indexed:** Cadscan, Chem.Abstr., Curr.Cont., INIS Atomind., Lead Abstr., Met.Abstr., Sci.Abstr., World Alum.Abstr., Zincscan.

620.1   CC   ISSN 1004-793X
CAILIAO KEXUE YU GONGCHENG/MATERIAL SCIENCE AND ENGINEERING. (Text in Chinese; abstracts in English) 1982. q. $32. Zhejiang Daxue, c/o Dept. of Material Science and Engineering, Hangzhou, Zhejiang 310027, People's Republic of China. TEL 0571-572242. FAX 0571-571797. TELEX 35040 ZUFAO CN. Ed. Wu Jingbo. **Document type:** academic/scholarly publication.

622   CK
CARTA METALURGICA. 1958. q. $30. Fedemetal, Calle 35 N. 4-81, Apto. Aereo 10262 Bogota, Colombia. FAX 2857086. TELEX 45608. Ed. Amparo Segura. adv.; bk.rev. circ. 3,000.
Formerly: Metal.
Description: Articles on all major industries in Latin America, with emphasis on Colombia.

CHINESE JOURNAL OF MATERIALS SCIENCE. see *METALLURGY*

CLINICAL ENGINEERING SECTION NEWSLETTER. see *INSTRUMENTS*

620.11   US   ISSN 0739-036X
CLOSED LOOP; the magazine of testing and simulation technology. 1966. a. free. M T S Systems Corporation, 14000 Tehnology Dr., Eden Prairie, MN 55344. TEL 612-937-4554. FAX 612-937-4515. Ed. John Becker. circ. 15,000. (back issues avail.)
—BLDSC (3286.697000).
Description: Examines new developments in mechanical testing and simulation technology.

COHESION AND STRUCTURE. see *PHYSICS*

COMMUNICATIONS IN APPLIED NUMERICAL METHODS. see *MATHEMATICS*

620.1   NE   ISSN 0927-0108
COMPOSITE MATERIALS SERIES. (Text in English) 1986. irreg., vol.10, 1994. price varies. Elsevier Science B.V., Books Division, P.O. Box 211, 1000 AE Amsterdam, Netherlands. TEL 31-20-5803911. FAX 31-20-5803705. TELEX 18582 ESPA NL. (Subscr. in U.S. and Canada to: Elsevier Science Inc., Box 882, Madison Sq. Sta., New York, NY 10159. TEL 212-989-5800) Ed. Byron Pipes. (back issues avail.) **Document type:** monographic series.
—BLDSC (3364.963000).
Refereed Serial

620.1 389   UK   ISSN 0010-4361
TA418.9.C6   CODEN: CPSOAN
COMPOSITES; the international journal of the science and technology of reinforced materials. 1969. 8/yr. £275 in UK and Europe; elsewhere £290. Butterworth - Heinemann (Subsidiary of: Reed International PLC), Linacre House, Jordan Hill, Oxford OX2 8DP, England. TEL 0865-310366. FAX 0865-310898. TELEX 83111 BHPOXF G. (Subscr. to: Turpin Transactions Ltd., Distribution Centre, Blackhorse Rd., Letchworth, Herts SG6 1HN, England. TEL 0462-672555) Ed. Diane Cogan. adv.; bk.rev.; bibl.; stat.; index. (also avail. in microform from UMI; back issues avail.) **Indexed:** Appl.Mech.Rev., Br.Rail.Bd., Br.Tech.Ind., C.R.I. Abstr., Chem.Abstr., Curr.Cont., Eng.Ind., INIS Atomind., Int.Aerosp.Abstr., Met.Abstr., PROMT, RAPRA, Sci.Abstr., W.R.C.Inf., World Alum.Abstr., World Text.Abstr. **Document type:** academic/scholarly publication.
—BLDSC (3365.500000); Faxon; UnCover; SWETS; UMI; CASDDS. **CCC.**
Description: Bridges the gap between theoretical materials behavior and their actual design, testing and fabrication. Covers organic and reinforced polymer-, cement-, metal-, and ceramic-matrix composites.
Refereed Serial

COMPOSITES ENGINEERING; an international journal. see *ENGINEERING*

620.1   US
COMPOSITES IN MANUFACTURING. 1985. q. $60. Society of Manufacturing Engineers, Composites Group, One S M E Dr., Box 930, Dearborn, MI 48121. TEL 313-271-1500. FAX 313-271-2861. Ed. John R. Coleman. adv.; bk.rev. circ. 3,200.
Description: Covers all aspects of composites and advanced composite materials from development through application.

620.1   US   ISSN 1058-904X
COMPOSITES INDUSTRY MONTHLY. (Supplement to: A C M Monthly (ISSN 1058-9031)) m. $1395 includes q. calendars, meetings and other periodic supplements, and indexes. Composite Market Reports, Inc., 7670 Opportunity Rd., Ste. 250, San Diego, CA 92111-2222. TEL 619-560-1085. FAX 619-560-0234. Ed. Steve Loud. **Document type:** newsletter, trade publication.
●Also available online. Vendor(s): DIALOG Information Services, Inc., Dow Jones News Retrieval, NewsNet.
—**CCC.**
Description: Focuses on news of interest to OEMs, fabricators, users of advanced composites, and other organizations interested in tracking the latest materials, programs, and products in various commercial market sectors.

620.1 510   NE   ISSN 0927-0256
TA401   CODEN: CMMSEM
▼**COMPUTATIONAL MATERIALS SCIENCE.** (Supplement avail. on video cassette) (Text in English) 1992. 4/yr. fl.391($211) (effective 1994). Elsevier Science B.V., P.O. Box 211, 1000 AE Amsterdam, Netherlands. TEL 31-20-5803911. FAX 31-20-5803598. TELEX 18582 ESPA NL. (Subscr. in U.S. and Canada to: Elsevier Science Inc., Box 882, Madison Sq. Sta., New York, NY 10159-0882. TEL 212-989-5800. FAX 212-633-3990) Eds. Uzi Landman, Risto Nieminen. (back issues avail.) **Document type:** academic/scholarly publication.
—BLDSC (3390.610000); EI; CASDDS. **CCC.**
Description: Publishes current results and applications from experimental materials research and computational work on both existing and new advanced materials, including semiconductors, biomaterials, polymers, ceramics and composites.
Refereed Serial

COMPUTERIZATION AND NETWORKING OF MATERIALS DATABASES. see *COMPUTERS — Data Base Management*

CONCRETE PIPE INDUSTRY STATISTICS. see *ENGINEERING — Abstracting, Bibliographies, Statistics*

620.1   DK   ISSN 0108-0768
DANMARKS TEKNISKE HOEJSKOLE. AFDELINGEN FOR BAERENDE KONSTRUKTIONER. SERIE R. (Text in Danish and English) 1967. irreg. (8-10/yr.). DKK 130. Danmarks Tekniske Hoejskole, Afdelingen for Baerende Konstruktioner - Technical University of Denmark, Structural Research Laboratory, Bygning 118, DK-2800 Lyngby, Denmark. TEL 45-42-88-35-11. FAX 45-42-88-32-82. TELEX 37529. Ed. Hugo Moellman. charts; illus. circ. 300. **Indexed:** Appl.Mech.Rev., Eng.Ind.
—BLDSC (8732.357000); EI.
Description: Theoretical and experimental research in structural engineering, concrete, steel and wood.

620.11   GW
DEUTSCHE PUMPEN - KOMPRESSOREN - VAKUUMPUMPEN. (Text in English, French, German) 1981. a. DM.12. Dr. Harnisch Verlags GmbH, Blumenstr. 15, 90402 Nuernberg, Germany. TEL 0911-203658. FAX 0911-204579. Ed. Josef G. Schick. adv.: B&W page DM.10450; trim 190 x 270. circ. 20,800. (back issues avail.) **Document type:** trade publication.
Formerly: Pompes, Pompes a Vide, Compresseurs.

620.11   UK   ISSN 0955-4335
DIAL ENGINEERING. 1980. a. £110 (free to qualified personnel). (Engineering Industries Association) Dial Industry Publications (Subsidiary of: Reed Information Service), Windsor Court, East Grinstead House, E. Grinstead, W. Sussex RH19 1XA, England. TEL 0342-326972. FAX 0342-335612. TELEX 95127-INFSER-G. Ed. Les Kelly. circ. 18,000 (controlled). **Document type:** trade publication.
●Also available online. Vendor(s): Reed Information Services Ltd..
Description: For buyers and specifiers on engineering, machining, plastics, rubber, metals, industrial supplies; lists 23,000 companies.

DIAMOND AND RELATED MATERIALS. see *CHEMISTRY — Crystallography*

671.25   US   ISSN 0012-253X
TS239   CODEN: DICEAB
DIE CASTING ENGINEER. 1957. bi-m. $48 to non-members. North American Die Casting Association, 9701 W. Higgins Rd. No. 880, Rosemont, IL 60018-4721. TEL 708-292-3600. FAX 708-292-3620. Ed. Paul M. Bralower. adv.; bk.rev.; charts; illus.; stat.; tr.lit. circ. 4,000. (also avail. in microfilm from UMI; reprint service avail. from UMI) **Indexed:** Cadscan, Chem.Abstr., Curr.Cont., Eng.Ind., Lead Abstr., Met.Abstr., Risk Abstr., Robomat. (until 1992), World Alum.Abstr., Zincscan. **Document type:** trade publication.
—BLDSC (3580.475000); EI; SWETS; UMI; CASDDS.

ENGINEERING — ENGINEERING MECHANICS AND MATERIALS

620.11   FR
DYMAT JOURNAL. (Text in English, French.) q. (European Dymat Association) Editions de Physique, B.P. 112, Z.I. de Courteboeuf, 7 av. du Hoggar, 91944 Les Ulis Cedex, France. TEL 69-07-36-88. FAX 69-28-84-91. TELEX 602 321 F.
   Description: Concerned with durations of the application of stress ranging from the order of microseconds to milliseconds.
   Refereed Serial

620.11   SZ
EIDGENOESSISCHE TECHNISCHE HOCHSCHULE ZUERICH. INSTITUT FUER BAUSTATIK UND KONSTRUKTION. ALLGEMEINE BERICHTE. (Text in English and German; summaries in English, French, and German) irreg., vol.173, 1990. price varies. Birkhaeuser Verlag, P.O. Box 133, CH-4010 Basel, Switzerland. TEL 061-2717400. FAX 061-2717666. TELEX 963475-BIRKH-CH. bibl. **Document type:** academic/scholarly publication.

620.111   SZ
EIDGENOESSISCHE TECHNISCHE HOCHSCHULE ZUERICH. INSTITUT FUER BAUSTATIK UND KONSTRUKTION. VERSUCHSBERICHTE. (Text in English and German; summaries in English, French and German) irreg. price varies. Birkhaeuser Verlag, P.O. Box 133, CH-4010 Basel, Switzerland. TEL 061-2717400. FAX 061-2717666. TELEX 963475-BIRKH-CH. **Document type:** monographic series.

620   UK   ISSN 1350-6307
▼**ENGINEERING FAILURE ANALYSIS.** 1994. 4/yr. £120($185) (effective 1994). Elsevier Science Ltd., Pergamon, P.O. Box 800, Kidlington, Oxford OX5 1DX, England. TEL 44-865-843000. FAX 44-865-843010. (Subscr. in U.S. and Canada to: Elsevier Science, 660 White Plains Rd., Tarrytown, NY 10591-5153. TEL 914-524-9200. FAX 914-333-2444) **Document type:** academic/scholarly publication.
   —CCC.
   Refereed Serial

620.1   UK   ISSN 0013-7944
TA409   CODEN: EFMEAH
ENGINEERING FRACTURE MECHANICS. (Text in English; summaries in French, German) 1968. 18/yr. £1263($1945) (effective 1994). Elsevier Science Ltd., Pergamon, P.O. Box 800, Kidlington, Oxford OX5 1DX, England. TEL 44-865-843000. FAX 44-865-843010. (Subscr. in U.S. and Canada to: Elsevier Science, 660 White Plains Rd., Tarrytown, NY 10591-5153. TEL 914-524-9200. FAX 914-333-2444) Ed. Harold Liebowitz. adv.; bk.rev.; charts; illus.; stat.; index. circ. 1,600. (also avail. in microfilm from UMI; back issues avail.) **Indexed:** Appl.Mech.Rev., Chem.Abstr., Curr.Cont., Eng.Ind., Ind.Sci.Rev., INIS Atomind., Int.Aerosp.Abstr., ISMEC, Met.Abstr., Risk Abstr., Sci.Abstr., Sci.Cit.Ind., World Alum.Abstr. **Document type:** academic/scholarly publication.
   —BLDSC (3761.350000); EI; Faxon; SWETS; UMI; CASDDS. CCC.
   Description: Publishes technical papers on research and advanced applications of fracture mechanics, including contributions in the areas of mechanics and materials science as related to fracture mechanics.
   Refereed Serial

EUROPEAN JOURNAL OF MECHANICAL ENGINEERING. see ENGINEERING — Mechanical Engineering

620.1 660   NE   ISSN 0927-5010
    CODEN: EMRMEH
EUROPEAN MATERIALS RESEARCH SOCIETY. MONOGRAPHS. (Text in English) 1991. irreg., vol.7, 1993. price varies. Elsevier Science B.V., Books Division, P.O. Box 211, 1000 AE Amsterdam, Netherlands. TEL 31-20-5803911. FAX 31-20-5803705. TELEX 18582 ESPA NL. (Subscr. in U.S. and Canada to: Elsevier Science Inc., Box 882, Madison Sq. Sta., New York, NY 10159. TEL 212-989-5800) (back issues avail.) **Document type:** monographic series.
   —CASDDS.
   Refereed Serial

620.1 660   NE
EUROPEAN MATERIALS RESEARCH SOCIETY. SYMPOSIA PROCEEDINGS. (Text in English) 1989. irreg., vol.45, 1993. price varies. Elsevier Science B.V., Books Division, P.O. Box 211, 1000 AE Amsterdam, Netherlands. TEL 31-20-5803911. FAX 31-20-5803705. TELEX 18582 ESPA NL. (Subscr. in U.S. and Canada to: Elsevier Science Inc., Box 882, Madison Sq. Sta., New York, NY 10159. TEL 212-989-5800) (back issues avail.) **Document type:** proceedings.
   Refereed Serial

620.1   UK   ISSN 0967-9650
EUROPEAN SURFACE TREATMENT. q. £41 (foreign £48). Turret Group Plc., Turret House, 171 High St., Rickmansworth, Herts WD3 1SN, England. TEL 0923-777000. FAX 0923-771297. **Document type:** trade publication.
   —BLDSC (3830.234800).

620.1   US   ISSN 0014-4851
TA401   CODEN: EXMCAZ
EXPERIMENTAL MECHANICS. (Issued with Experimental Techniques) 1960. q. $167. Society for Experimental Mechanics, 7 School St., Bethel, CT 06801. TEL 203-790-6373. FAX 203-790-4472. adv.; bk.rev.; bibl.; charts; illus.; index. circ. 4,500. (also avail. in microform from UMI; reprint service avail. from UMI) **Indexed:** A.S.& T.Ind., Abstr.Bull.Inst.Pap.Chem., Appl.Mech.Rev., Br.Ceram.Abstr., Chem.Abstr., Curr.Cont., Eng.Ind., Geotech.Abstr., Ind.Sci.Rev., Int.Aerosp.Abstr., ISMEC, Met.Abstr., Sci.Abstr., Sci.Cit.Ind., Sh.& Vib.Dig., World Alum.Abstr.
   —BLDSC (3839.650000); EI; UnCover; SWETS; UMI. CCC.
   Refereed Serial

531   US   ISSN 0732-8818
TA410   CODEN: EXPTD2
EXPERIMENTAL TECHNIQUES. 1980. bi-m. $88 (subscr. includes Experimental Mechanics). Society for Experimental Mechanics, 7 School St., Bethel, CT 06801. TEL 203-790-6373. FAX 203-790-4472. Ed.Bd. adv.; bk.rev. (also avail. in microform from UMI) **Indexed:** A.S.& T.Ind., Abstr.Bull.Inst.Pap.Chem., Appl.Mech.Rev., INIS Atomind., Int.Aerosp.Abstr., Met.Abstr., Sci.Abstr., Sh.& Vib.Dig., World Alum.Abstr.
   —BLDSC (3840.190000); EI; Faxon; UnCover; SWETS; UMI. CCC.
   Incorporates: Experimentally Speaking.
   Refereed Serial

F A M - FIRE AND MATERIALS. see CHEMISTRY — Physical Chemistry

620.1   US   ISSN 0071-4046
FASTENER STANDARDS. 1941. irreg., 6th ed., 1988. $89.50 (outside N. America $135). Industrial Fasteners Institute, 1505 E. Ohio Bldg., 1717 E. Ninth St., Cleveland, OH 44114. TEL 216-241-1482. FAX 216-241-5901. Ed. Charles Wilson. index. circ. 20,000.

FINITE ELEMENT NEWS. see ENGINEERING — Computer Applications

FIZIKO-KHIMICHESKAYA MEKHANIKA MATERIALOV; nauchno-tekhnicheskii zhurnal. see CHEMISTRY — Physical Chemistry

620.1   US   ISSN 0428-7738
TJ950
FLUID POWER HANDBOOK & DIRECTORY. 1956. biennial. $60 (free to qualified personnel). Penton Publishing (Subsidiary of: Pittway Company), 1100 Superior Ave., Cleveland, OH 44114-2543. TEL 216-696-7000. FAX 216-696-8765. (Subscr. to: Box 95759, Cleveland, OH 44101) Ed. Dick Schneider. adv.; charts; illus.; stat.; tr.lit.; circ. 36,000 (controlled). (also avail. in microform; reprint service avail. from UMI) **Document type:** directory.
   —UMI.

FUSION ENGINEERING AND DESIGN; an international journal devoted to the thermal, mechanical, materials, structural and design aspects of fusion energy. see ENGINEERING — Mechanical Engineering

620.1   GW   ISSN 0934-9456
GERMANY (FEDERAL REPUBLIC, 1949-). BUNDESANSTALT FUER MATERIALFORSCHUNG UND -PRUEFUNG. JAHRESBERICHT. 1957. a. Bundesanstalt fuer Materialforschung und -pruefung, Unter den Eichen 87, 12203 Berlin, Germany. TEL 030-8104-0. FAX 030-8112029. TELEX 183261-BAMB-D. illus.; index. circ. 1,500. **Document type:** government publication.
   Formerly: Bundesanstalt fuer Materialpruefung. Jahresbericht (ISSN 0341-0528)

620.1   CC   ISSN 1001-6988
GONGYE LU/JOURNAL OF INDUSTRY FURNACE. (Text in Chinese) q. Jixie Dianzi Gongye Bu, Diwu Sheji Yanjiuyuan - Ministry of Engineering and Electronic Industry, No. 5 Design Institute, 208 Hongqi Lu, Tianjin 300190, People's Republic of China. TEL 319366. Ed. Liu Jingui.

620.1   US   ISSN 1058-9023
GRAFIBER NEWS. (Supplement to: Advanced Composites Monthly (ISSN 1058-899X), and to: A C M Monthly (ISSN 1058-9031)) 1971. m. $2535. Composite Market Reports, Inc., 7670 Opportunity Rd., Ste.250, San Diego, CA 92111-2222. TEL 619-560-1085. FAX 619-560-0234. Ed. Steve Loud. **Document type:** newsletter, trade publication.
   —CCC.
   Description: For marketing, manufacturing, and technical management personnel at US and overseas suppliers of advanced composite fibers, resins, fabrics, and related materials, plus process equipment manufacturers.

HANDBOOK ON THE PHYSICS AND CHEMISTRY OF RARE EARTHS. see PHYSICS

540   UK   ISSN 0334-6455
    CODEN: HTMPEF
HIGH TEMPERATURE MATERIALS AND PROCESSES. (Text in English) 1983. q. $200. Freund Publishing House Ltd., Ste. 500, Chesham House, 150 Regent St., London W1R 5FA, England. (Alt. addr.: P.O. Box 35010, Tel Aviv, Israel. TEL 972-3-615335) Ed. A. Rosen. adv.; bk.rev. circ. 1,000. (back issues avail.) **Document type:** academic/scholarly publication.
   —BLDSC (4307.367800); Faxon; UnCover; CASDDS.
   Formerly (until 1985): Reviews on High Temperature Materials (ISSN 0370-5331)

I E E E - C H M T INTERNATIONAL ELECTRONIC MANUFACTURING TECHNOLOGY SYMPOSIUM. see ENGINEERING — Electrical Engineering

620.1   US   ISSN 0019-0063
I M S BULLETIN. 1966. s-a. free. University of Connecticut, Institute of Materials Science, Storrs, CT 06269-3136. TEL 203-486-4623. FAX 203-486-4617. Ed. T.R. Saxton. abstr. circ. 3,500. **Document type:** newsletter.

I S I J INTERNATIONAL. (Iron and Steel Institute of Japan) see METALLURGY

620.11 669   UK   ISSN 0265-0584
INDUSTRIAL CORROSION. 1982. bi-m. £38 (foreign £50) (effective 1994). (Institute of Corrosion) Impact Company Publications, Media House, 55 Old Rd., Leighton Buzzard, Beds. LU7 7RB, England. TEL 44-535-370013. FAX 44-535-382487. Ed. Janet Brennan. adv.; bk.rev. circ. 1,800. **Indexed:** Corros.Abstr. **Document type:** trade publication.
   —BLDSC (4448.336000); Faxon.
   Description: Reference and information service to industry on all corrosion-related matters; includes R&D and new products and services, especially in the U.K. and Europe.

620   UK
INDUSTRIAL FASTENERS 1987. every 18 mos. £155 per no. Key Note Publications Ltd., Field House, Old Field Rd., Hampton TW12 2HQ, England. TEL 01 783-0755.
   Description: Overview of the industrial fasteners industry in the U.K. Includes industry structure, market size and trends, company profiles, developments and prospects.

620.11   FR   ISSN 0293-9304
INFOVRAC. 1982. 6/yr. Somia, 15 rue du Puits-de-l'Ermite, 75005 Paris, France. TEL 43-26-08-88. FAX 45-87-22-08. Ed. Jacques Ramond. circ. 5,309.

ENGINEERING — ENGINEERING MECHANICS AND MATERIALS

621   **RM**
INSTITUL POLITEHNIC DIN IASI. BULETINUL. SECTIA V: CONSTRUCTII DE MASINI. (Text in English, French, German, Italian, Russian, Spanish) 1946. s-a. exchange basis. Instutul Politehnic din Iasi, Bd. Copou 11, 6600 Jassy, Rumania. TEL 46577. FAX 40-81-47923. Eds. Alfreed Braier, Hugo Rosman. adv.; bk.rev.; bibl. circ. 450. **Indexed:** Appl.Mech.Rev., Chem.Abstr., Math.R., Met.Abstr., Ref.Zh., Sci.Abstr.
   Former titles: Institutul Politehnic Iasi. Buletinul. Sectia IV: Constructii de Masini (ISSN 1011-2855); Institutul Politehnic Iasi. Buletinul. Sectia IV: Mecanica Tehnica.

671.5 621.9   **PL**
INSTYTUT OBROBKI SKRAWANIEM. PRACE. MATERIALY INSTRUKTAZOWE. irreg. price varies. Instytut Obrobki Skrawaniem, Ul. Wroclawska 37a, 30-011 Krakow, Poland. TEL 48-22-339333. FAX 48-12-339490. TELEX 032478 IOS PL.
   Description: Provides instructions and recommendations for workshop use.

671.5 621.9   **PL**
INSTYTUT OBROBKI SKRAWANIEM. PRACE. OPRACOWANIA ANALITYCZNO-SYNTETYCZNE. irreg. price varies. Instytut Obrobki Skrawaniem, Ul. Wroclawska 37a, 30-011 Krakow, Poland. TEL 48-12-339333. FAX 48-12-339490. TELEX 032478 IOS PL. **Document type:** monographic series.
   Description: Covers metal cutting, machine tools and tolling, abrasion machining, erosion techniques, metrology and technical control.

671.5 621.9   **PL**
INSTYTUT OBROBKI SKRAWANIEM. PRACE. REFERATY. irreg. price varies. Instytut Obrobki Skrawaniem, Ul. Wroclawska 37a, 30-011 Krakow, Poland. TEL 48-12-339333. FAX 48-12-339490. TELEX 032478 IOS PL. **Document type:** corporate report.
   Description: Covers metal cutting, machine tools and tooling, abrasion machining, erosion techniques, metrology and technical control.

671.5 621.9   **PL**   **ISSN 0020-4528**
INSTYTUT OBROBKI SKRAWANIEM. PRACE. ZESZYTY NAUKOWE. (Text in Polish; summaries in English, French, German, Russian) 1959. irreg. Instytut Obrobki Skrawaniem - Institute of Metal Cutting, Ul. Wroclawska 37a, 30-011 Krakow, Poland. TEL 48-12-339333. FAX 48-12-339490. TELEX 032478 IOS PL. bibl.; charts; illus. circ. 260. **Indexed:** Ref.Zh. **Document type:** proceedings.
   Description: Scientific articles on metal cutting, machine tools and tooling, abrasion machining, erosion techniques and technical control.

620.11   **FR**   **ISSN 0762-3275**
INTERFACES LOGISTIQUES. 1976. 6/yr. Somia, 15 rue du Puits-de-l'Ermite, 75005 Paris, France. TEL 43-36-08-88. FAX 45-87-22-08. Ed. Jacques Ramond. circ. 4,476.

INTERMETALLICS. see *METALLURGY*

620.1 389   **US**   **ISSN 0140-072X**
TA417.2   **CODEN: IANTDB**
INTERNATIONAL ADVANCES IN NONDESTRUCTIVE TESTING. 1969. irreg., vol.16, 1991. Gordon & Breach Science Publishers, 820 Town Center Dr., Langhorne, PA 19047. TEL 215-750-2642. FAX 215-750-6343. (UK subscr. to: P.O. Box 90, Reading, Berkshire RG1 8JL, England. TEL 0734-560-080) Ed. Warren J. McGonnagle. adv.; charts; illus. (also avail. in microform) **Indexed:** Appl.Mech.Rev., Chem.Abstr., Curr.Cont., Eng.Ind., INIS Atomind., Sci.Abstr. **Document type:** monographic series.
   —BLDSC (4535.601000); Faxon; CASDDS. **CCC.**
   Formerly (until vol.5, 1977): International Journal of Nondestructive Testing (ISSN 0020-7470)
Refereed Serial

620.1 531   **US**   **ISSN 1063-7095**
TA349   **CODEN: IAMEEU**
INTERNATIONAL APPLIED MECHANICS. English translation of: Prikladnaya Mekhanika (KR ISSN 0032-8243) 1966. m. $1215 (foreign $1425) (effective 1994). (Ukrainian Academy of Sciences, KR) Plenum Publishing Corp., Consultants Bureau, 233 Spring St., New York, NY 10013-1578. TEL 212-620-8468. FAX 212-463-0742. TELEX 23-421139. Ed. A.N. Guz' (also avail. in microfilm from JSC; back issues avail.) **Indexed:** Appl.Mech.Rev., Eng.Ind., Math.R. **Document type:** academic/scholarly publication.
   —BLDSC (0412.732500); Faxon; UnCover; SWETS; UMI. **CCC.**
   Formerly (until 1992): Soviet Applied Mechanics (ISSN 0038-5298)
Refereed Serial

620   **GW**   **ISSN 0074-3437**
INTERNATIONAL CONGRESS FOR STEREOLOGY. PROCEEDINGS. 1963. quadriennial. price varies. International Society for Stereology, c/o Dr. Torsten Mattfeldt, Sec.-Treas., Institute of Pathology, Am Neuenheimer Feld 220-221, 69120 Heidelberg, Germany. circ. 480. **Document type:** proceedings.

INTERNATIONAL GAS TURBINE INSTITUTE TECHNOLOGY REPORT. LAND, SEA & AIR. see *MACHINERY*

INTERNATIONAL INSTRUMENTATION SYMPOSIUM. see *AERONAUTICS AND SPACE FLIGHT*

620.11   **UK**   **ISSN 0142-1123**
TA418.38   **CODEN: IJFADB**
INTERNATIONAL JOURNAL OF FATIGUE; materials, structures, components. 1979. bi-m. £220 in UK and Europe; elsewhere £235. Butterworth - Heinemann (Subsidiary of: Reed International PLC), Linacre House, Jordan Hill, Oxford OX2 8DP, England. TEL 0865-310366. FAX 0865-310898. TELEX 83111 BHPOXF G. (Subscr. to: Turpin Transactions Ltd., Distribution Centre, Blackhorse Rd., Letchworth, Herts SG6 1HN, England. TEL 0462-672555) Ed. Dr. L. Pook. adv.; bk.rev.; abstr.; bibl.; charts; illus.; stat.; index. (also avail. in microform from UMI; back issues avail.; reprint service avail.) **Indexed:** Agri.Eng.Abstr., Appl.Mech.Rev., B.C.I.R.A., Cadscan, Chem.Abstr., Curr.Cont., INIS Atomind., Int.Aerosp.Abstr., ISMEC, Lead Abstr., Met.Abstr., Sci.Abstr., Sh.& Vib.Dig., World Alum.Abstr., Zincscan. **Document type:** academic/scholarly publication.
   —BLDSC (4542.246000); Faxon; UnCover; SWETS; UMI; CASDDS. **CCC.**
   Description: Covers fatigue of the whole spectrum of materials in use for researchers, design engineers and maintenance engineers.
Refereed Serial

620.11 621   **US**   **ISSN 0920-6299**
TS155.6   **CODEN: IFMSE5**
INTERNATIONAL JOURNAL OF FLEXIBLE MANUFACTURING SYSTEMS; design, analysis and operation of manufacturing and assembly systems. 1988. q. fl.329($172) (effective 1994). Kluwer Academic Publishers Boston, Box 358, Accord Sta., Hingham, MA 02018-0358. TEL 617-871-6600. FAX 617-871-6528. TELEX 200190. (Dist. outside N. America by: Kluwer Academic Publishers Group, P.O. Box 322, 3300 AH Dordrecht, Netherlands. TEL 31-78-524400. FAX 31-78-524474) Ed. Kathryn E. Stecke. cum.index. (also avail. in microform from UMI; back issues avail.; reprint service avail. from SWZ,UMI) **Indexed:** CAD CAM Abstr. (until 1992), Robomat. (until 1992). **Document type:** academic/scholarly publication.
   —BLDSC (4542.252000); SWETS; UMI. **CCC.**
   Description: Provides a forum for the publication of original articles on all topics related to flexible manufacturing and flexible assembly systems.
Refereed Serial

620.1   **NE**   **ISSN 0376-9429**
TA409   **CODEN: IJFRAP**
INTERNATIONAL JOURNAL OF FRACTURE. (Text in English, French or German) 1965. 24/yr. fl.3012($1572) (effective 1994). Kluwer Academic Publishers, Postbus 17, 3300 AA Dordrecht, Netherlands. TEL 31-78-334911. FAX 31-78-334254. TELEX 29245 KAPG NL. (Dist. by: Kluwer Academic Publishers Group, P.O. Box 322, 3300 AH Dordrecht, Netherlands. TEL 31-78-524400. FAX 31-78-524474; N. America dist. addr.: Box 358, Accord Sta., Hingham, MA 02018-0358. TEL 617-871-6600. FAX 617-871-6528) Ed. M. L. Williams. adv.; bk.rev.; charts; illus. (also avail. in microform from UMI; back issues avail.; reprint service avail. from SWZ) **Indexed:** Appl.Mech.Rev., Chem.Abstr., Curr.Cont., Eng.Ind., Ind.Sci.Rev., Int.Aerosp.Abstr., ISMEC, Math.R., Met.Abstr., Phys.Ber., Sci.Abstr., Sci.Cit.Ind., W.R.C.Inf., World Alum.Abstr. **Document type:** academic/scholarly publication.
   —BLDSC (4542.259000); Faxon; UnCover; SWETS; UMI; CASDDS. **CCC.**
   Formerly: International Journal of Fracture Mechanics (ISSN 0020-7268)
   Description: Publishes original theoretical contributions of fracture mechanics at the micro and macro level.
Refereed Serial

620.1   **UK**   **ISSN 0020-7403**
TJ1   **CODEN: IMSCAW**
INTERNATIONAL JOURNAL OF MECHANICAL SCIENCES. 1960. 12/yr. £536($825) (effective 1994). Elsevier Science Ltd., Pergamon, P.O. Box 800, Kidlington, Oxford OX5 1DX, England. TEL 44-865-843000. FAX 44-865-843010. (Subscr. in U.S. and Canada to: Elsevier Science, 660 White Plains Rd. Tarrytown, NY 10591-5153. TEL 914-524-9200. FAX 914-333-2444) Ed. Stephen R. Reid. adv.; charts; illus.; index. circ. 1,400. (also avail. in microfilm from UMI; reprint service avail. from UMI) **Indexed:** Abstr.J.Earthq.Eng., Appl.Mech.Rev., Br.Tech.Ind., Chem.Abstr., Curr.Cont., Eng.Ind., Fluidex, Int.Aerosp.Abstr., Intl.Civil Eng.Abstr., ISMEC, J.of Ferroc., Math.R., Met.Abstr., Phys.Ber., Sci.Abstr., Sci.Cit.Ind., Sh.& Vib.Dig., Soft.Abstr.Eng., World Alum.Abstr. **Document type:** academic/scholarly publication.
   —BLDSC (4542.344000); EI; Faxon; UnCover; SWETS; UMI. **CCC.**
   Description: Publishes papers on structural mechanics, materials processing and failure, and civil engineering sciences.
Refereed Serial

620   **CN**   **ISSN 0228-6203**
TA342   **CODEN: IMSIEK**
INTERNATIONAL JOURNAL OF MODELLING & SIMULATION. 1981. 4/yr. $197. International Association of Science and Technology for Development, 4500 16th Ave., N.W., Ste. 80, Calgary, AB T3B 0M6, Canada. TEL 403-288-1195. FAX 403-247-6851. (And: P.O. Box 354, CH-8053 Zurich, Switzerland; Box 2481, Anaheim, CA 92814, USA) Ed. Nader M. Namazi. adv.; bk.rev. circ. 350. (back issues avail.) **Indexed:** A.I.Abstr., Comput.Abstr., Cyb.Abstr., Environ.Abstr., Int.Aerosp.Abstr.
   —BLDSC (4542.365000); Faxon; UnCover.
   Description: Covers modelling, simulation, languages, software, hardware, methodology, numerical and graphical methods, statistical techniques, tutorials, surveys, and applications.

620.1 531   **UK**   **ISSN 0020-7462**
QA427   **CODEN: IJNMAG**
INTERNATIONAL JOURNAL OF NON-LINEAR MECHANICS. 1966. 6/yr. £444($685) (effective 1994). Elsevier Science Ltd., Pergamon, P.O. Box 800, Kidlington, Oxford OX5 1DX, England. TEL 44-865-843000. FAX 44-865-843010. (Subscr. in U.S. and Canada to: Elsevier Science, 660 White Plains Rd., Tarrytown, NY 10591-5153. TEL 914-524-9200. FAX 914-333-2444) Ed. William A. Nash. adv.; bk.rev. circ. 1,200. (also avail. in microfilm from UMI; reprint service avail. from UMI) **Indexed:** Abstr.J.Earthq.Eng., Appl.Mech.Rev., Cadscan, Curr.Cont., Eng.Ind., Int.Aerosp.Abstr., ISMEC, Lead Abstr., Phys.Ber., Sci.Abstr., Sh.& Vib.Dig., Zincscan. **Document type:** academic/scholarly publication.
   —BLDSC (4542.392000); EI; Faxon; UnCover; SWETS; UMI. **CCC.**
   Description: Covers theoretical and applied mechanics of solids and fluids.
Refereed Serial

ENGINEERING — ENGINEERING MECHANICS AND MATERIALS

620   UK   ISSN 0749-6419
TA418.14   CODEN: IJPLER
INTERNATIONAL JOURNAL OF PLASTICITY. 1985. 8/yr. £418($645) (effective 1994). Elsevier Science Ltd., Pergamon, P.O. Box 800, Kidlington, Oxford OX5 1DX, England. TEL 44-865-843000. FAX 44-865-843010. (Subscr. in U.S. and Canada to: Elsevier Science, 660 White Plains Rd., Tarrytown, NY 10591-5153. TEL 914-524-9200. FAX 914-333-2444) Ed. A.S. Khan. (also avail. in microfilm from UMI; back issues avail.) **Indexed:** Eng.Ind., Sci.Abstr., Sci.Cit.Ind. **Document type:** academic/scholarly publication.
—BLDSC (4542.470000); EI; Faxon; UnCover; SWETS; UMI; CASDDS. **CCC.**
  Description: Publishes original research on all aspects of plastic deformation of isotropic and anisotropic solids.
  Refereed Serial

INTERNATIONAL JOURNAL OF SELF-PROPAGATING HIGH-TEMPERATURE SYNTHESIS. see *PHYSICS — Heat*

338.025   US   ISSN 1058-8914
INTERNATIONAL KEY PERSONNEL LIST. 1987. a. Composite Market Reports, Inc., 7670 Opportunity Rd., Ste. 250, San Diego, CA 92111-2222. TEL 619-560-1085. FAX 619-560-0234. **Document type:** directory.
—**CCC.**
  Description: List over 4500 key individuals in 44 countries; divided geographically into Europe and Israel; Far East; Australia, New Zealand, and Latin America.

INTERNATIONAL QUARTERLY OF MATERIALS SCIENCE. see *ENGINEERING*

620.1   US
INTERNATIONAL S A M P E TECHNICAL CONFERENCE SERIES. I S T C PREPRINT SERIES. (Fall conferences) 1969. a. $80. Society for the Advancement of Material and Process Engineering, Box 2459, Covina, CA 91722. TEL 818-331-0616. FAX 818-332-8929. **Indexed:** Chem.Abstr.
—**CCC.**
  Former titles: National S A M P E Technical Conference Series. N S T C Preprint Series (ISSN 0081-1556); Society of Aerospace Material and Process Engineers. National S A M P E Technical Conference. N S T C Preprint Series.

J M R ABSTRACTS. (Journal of Materials Research) see *ENGINEERING — Abstracting, Bibliographies, Statistics*

620.1   JA   ISSN 0368-3141
TA401.3   CODEN: JMRPA9
JAPAN CONGRESS ON MATERIALS RESEARCH. PROCEEDINGS/ZAIRYO KENKYU RENGO KOENKAI RONBUNSHU. (Text in English) 1957. a. price varies. Society of Materials Science, Japan - Nihon Zairyo Gakkai, 1-101 Yoshida Izumidono-cho, Sakyo-ku, Kyoto 606, Japan. TEL 075-761-5321. FAX 075-761-5325. (Co-sponsor: Science Council of Japan) adv. **Indexed:** Chem.Abstr. **Document type:** proceedings.
—BLDSC (6847.118000); CASDDS.

JAPAN ELECTRONIC MATERIALS SOCIETY. BULLETIN/NIHON DENSHI ZAIRYO GIJUTSU KYOKAI KAIHO. see *ENGINEERING*

620 620.11   JA   ISSN 0385-2571
                         CODEN: TJSMDT
JAPAN SOCIETY FOR COMPOSITE MATERIALS. TRANSACTIONS. s-a. $45. Japan Society for Composite Materials, c/o Business Center for Academic Societies Japan, 5-16-9 Honkomagome, Tokyo 113, Japan. TEL 03-5814-5811. FAX 03-5814-5822. **Indexed:** JTA.

620.11 669   US   ISSN 1050-1819
TA417.2
JAPANESE SOCIETY FOR NON-DESTRUCTIVE INSPECTION. TRANSACTIONS. Abbreviated title: Transactions of the J S N D I. 1988. irreg. Gordon and Breach Science Publishers, 820 Town Center Dr., Langhorne, PA 19042. TEL 215-750-2642. FAX 215-750-6343. (UK subscr. to: Box 90, Reading, Berkshire RG1 8JL, England. TEL 0734-560-080) Ed. H. Kato. **Document type:** monographic series.

620 620.11   JA   ISSN 0286-4010
                         CODEN: NZKGDH
JAPANESE SOCIETY FOR STRENGTH AND FRACTURE OF MATERIALS. JOURNAL. q. 8000 Yen. Japanese Society for Strength and Fracture of Materials, c/o Business Center for Academic Societies Japan, 5-16-9 Honkomagome, Bunkyo-ku, Tokyo 113, Japan. TEL 03-5814-5811. FAX 03-5814-5822. **Indexed:** JTA.
—CASDDS.

620.11 621   CC   ISSN 0254-6051
TN672   CODEN: JRECDB
JINSHU RECHULI/HEAT TREATMENT OF METALS. (Text in Chinese; summaries in Chinese, English) 1958. m. Y36 (foreign $60). Beijing Jidian Yanjiusuo - Beijing Research Institute of Mechanical & Electrical Technology, 18 Xueqing Lu, P.O. Box 907, Beijing 100083, People's Republic of China. TEL 2017761. FAX 2017108. TELEX 222573 RIMET CN. (Subscr. to: Guoji Shudian - China International Book Trading Corp., P.O. Box 399, Beijing 100044, P.R.C.) (Co-sponsor: China Heat Treatment Association) Ed. Cao Minda. adv.: B&W page $900, color page $1300; adv. contact: Min-Da Cao. index. circ. 20,000. (microform) **Document type:** trade publication.
—CASDDS.
  Description: Covers the field of mechanical engineering and heat treating of metals for all machine-building industries.

620.1   US
TL950   CODEN: SAMQA2
JOURNAL OF ADVANCED MATERIALS. 1969. q. $31 to non-members; members $18. Society for the Advancement of Material and Process Engineering, Box 2459, Covina, CA 91722. TEL 818-331-0616. FAX 818-332-8929. Ed. William Long. bk.rev.; abstr.; bibl.; charts; illus. circ. 2,100. **Indexed:** ASCA, Chem.Abstr., Curr.Cont., Eng.Ind., Int.Aerosp.Abstr., Met.Abstr., RAPRA, Text.Tech.Dig., World Alum.Abstr. **Document type:** trade publication.
—Faxon; UnCover; CASDDS. **CCC.**
  Former titles: S A M P E Quarterly (ISSN 0036-0821); Materials Journal.
  Description: Contains articles on subjects such as measurement apparatus, bonding, micromechanics, mechanical properties, automation applications, equipment design, adhesives and fibers.

510 620.1   UK   ISSN 0021-8928
QA801   CODEN: JAMMAR
JOURNAL OF APPLIED MATHEMATICS AND MECHANICS. At head of title: P M M. English translation of: Prikladnaya Matematika i Mekhanika (RU ISSN 0032-8235) 1958. 12/yr. (in 2 vols., 6 nos./vol.). £1160($1785) (effective 1994). (Russian Academy of Sciences) Elsevier Science Ltd., Pergamon, P.O. Box 800, Kidlington, Oxford OX5 1DX, England. TEL 44-865-843000. FAX 44-865-843010. (Subscr. in U.S. and Canada to: Elsevier Science, 660 White Plains Rd., Tarrytown, NY 10591-5153. TEL 914-524-9200. FAX 914-333-2444) Eds. G. Herrmann, R.C. Glass. adv.; charts; illus. circ. 1,200. (also avail. in microfilm from UMI; reprint service avail. from KTO,UMI) **Indexed:** A.S.& T.Ind., Appl.Mech.Rev., Compumath, Curr.Cont., Eng.Ind., Geotech.Abstr., Math.R., Met.Abstr. **Document type:** academic/scholarly publication.
—Faxon; UnCover; SWETS; UMI. **CCC.**
  Description: Covers high-level mathematical investigations of modern physical and mechanical problems, and reports current progress in this field.
  Refereed Serial

620.1   US   ISSN 0021-8944
QC1   CODEN: JMPYAQ
JOURNAL OF APPLIED MECHANICS AND TECHNICAL PHYSICS. English translation of: P M T F - Prikladnaya Mekhanika i Tekhnicheskaya Fizika (RU ISSN 0869-5032) 1965. bi-m. $1195 (foreign $1395) (effective 1994). (Russian Academy of Sciences, Siberian Division, RU) Plenum Publishing Corp., Consultants Bureau, 233 Spring St., New York, NY 10013-1578. TEL 212-620-8468. FAX 212-463-0742. TELEX 23-421139. Ed. B.A. Lugovtsov. (also avail. in microfilm from JSC; back issues avail.) **Indexed:** Appl.Mech.Rev., INIS Atomind., Math.R., Solid St.Abstr. **Document type:** academic/scholarly publication.
—BLDSC (0414.150000); Faxon; UnCover; SWETS; UMI. **CCC.**
  Refereed Serial

620.1 389   US   ISSN 0021-9983
TA418.9.C5   CODEN: JCOMBI
JOURNAL OF COMPOSITE MATERIALS. 1967. 18/yr. $795. Technomic Publishing Co., Inc., 851 New Holland Ave., Box 3535, Lancaster, PA 17604. TEL 717-291-5609. FAX 717-295-4538. TELEX 230 752565 (TECHNOMIC UD). Ed. H. Thomas Hahn. index. circ. 1,200. (also avail. in microform from UMI; reprint service avail. from UMI) **Indexed:** Abstr.Bull.Inst.Pap.Chem., Appl.Mech.Rev., Art Ind., Br.Rail.Bd., Ceram.Abstr., Chem.Abstr., Curr.Cont., Eng.Ind., Ind.Sci.Rev., INIS Atomind., Int.Aerosp.Abstr., J.of Ferroc., Met.Abstr., Phys.Ber., Risk Abstr., Sci.Abstr., Sci.Cit.Ind., Text.Tech.Dig., World Alum.Abstr. **Document type:** academic/scholarly publication.
—BLDSC (4963.400000); EI; Faxon; UnCover; SWETS; UMI; CASDDS. **CCC.**
  Refereed Serial

620.1 389   US   ISSN 0022-0434
TJ212   CODEN: JDSMAA
JOURNAL OF DYNAMIC SYSTEMS, MEASUREMENT AND CONTROL. 1971. q. $100 to non-members; members $29. American Society of Mechanical Engineers, 345 E. 47th St., New York, NY 10017. TEL 212-705-7703. Ed. D.M. Auslander. adv.; bk.rev.; bibl. circ. 2,500. (also avail. in microform from UMI; reprint service avail. from UMI) **Indexed:** A.S.& T.Ind., Abstr.Bull.Inst.Pap.Chem., Abstr.J.Earthq.Eng., Appl.Mech.Rev., Br.Rail.Bd., CAD CAM Abstr. (until 1992), Chem.Eng.Abstr., Comput.Cont., Curr.Cont., Eng.Ind., Excerp.Med., Fluidex, Ind.Sci.Rev., ISMEC, Risk Abstr., Robomat. (until 1992), Sci.Abstr., Sci.Cit.Ind., Sh.& Vib.Dig., T.C.E.A., W.R.C.Inf.
—BLDSC (8896.740000); EI; Faxon; UnCover; SWETS; UMI. **CCC.**
  Refereed Serial

620.11 624 621   NE   ISSN 0374-3535
QA931   CODEN: JELSAY
JOURNAL OF ELASTICITY. (Text in English) 1971. 12/yr. fl.1596($834) (effective 1994). Kluwer Academic Publishers, Postbus 17, 3300 AA Dordrecht, Netherlands. TEL 31-78-334911. FAX 31-78-334254. TELEX 29245 KAPG NL. (Dist. by: Kluwer Academic Publishers Group, P.O. Box 322, 3300 AH Dordrecht, Netherlands. TEL 31-78-524400. FAX 31-78-524474; N. America dist. addr.: Box 358, Accord Sta., Hingham, MA 02018-0358. TEL 617-871-6600. FAX 617-871-6528) Ed. D.E. Carlson. adv. (also avail. in microform from UMI; back issues avail.; reprint service avail. from SWZ) **Indexed:** Appl.Mech.Rev., ASCA, Curr.Cont., Eng.Ind., Ind.Sci.Rev., Int.Aerosp.Abstr., ISMEC, Math.R., Phys.Ber., Sci.Abstr., Sci.Cit.Ind., Zent.Math. **Document type:** academic/scholarly publication.
—BLDSC (4973.285000); EI; Faxon; UnCover; SWETS; UMI. **CCC.**
  Description: Reports original and significant discoveries in elasticity.
  Refereed Serial

JOURNAL OF ELECTRONIC MATERIALS. see *ELECTRONICS*

620.11   US   ISSN 0094-4289
TA1   CODEN: JEMTA8
JOURNAL OF ENGINEERING MATERIALS AND TECHNOLOGY. 1973. q. $100 to non-members; members $29. American Society of Mechanical Engineers, 345 E. 47th St., New York, NY 10017. TEL 212-705-7703. Ed. E. Krempl. adv.; bk.rev.; illus.; index. circ. 4,000. (also avail. in microform from UMI,PMC; reprint service avail. from UMI) **Indexed:** A.S.& T.Ind., Abstr.Bull.Inst.Pap.Chem., Appl.Mech.Rev., Br.Rail.Bd., CAD CAM Abstr., Chem.Abstr., Curr.Cont., Eng.Ind., Fluidex, Fuel & Energy Abstr., Ind.Sci.Rev., INIS Atomind., ISMEC, Met.Abstr., Sci.Abstr., Sci.Cit.Ind., World Alum.Abstr.
—BLDSC (8896.840000); EI; Faxon; UnCover; SWETS; UMI; CASDDS. **CCC.**
  Supersedes in part: Journal of Basic Engineering (ISSN 0021-9223)
  Refereed Serial

ENGINEERING — ENGINEERING MECHANICS AND MATERIALS

530 UK ISSN 0954-027X
TA418.45 CODEN: JOHME2
JOURNAL OF HARD MATERIALS. 1990. q. £142($292) (effective 1994). (Institute of Physics) I O P Publishing, Techno House, Redcliffe Way, Bristol BS1 6NX, England. TEL 0272-297481. FAX 0272-294318. TELEX 449149-INSTP-G. (Subscr. to: I O P Circulation Centre, Readerlink, Audit House, 260 Field End Rd., Eastcote, Ruislip, Mddx. HA4 9LT, England. TEL 081-868-4499. FAX 081-428-3117; U.S. addr.: American Institute of Physics, Member and Subscriber Services, 500 Sunnyside Blvd., Woodbury, NY 11797-2999. TEL 516-576-2200) Ed. C.A. Brookes. adv.; bk.rev. circ. 57. (also avail. in microfiche) **Document type:** academic/scholarly publication.
—BLDSC (4996.624200); CASDDS. **CCC.**
Description: Presents original research on advances in the understanding of properties of hard materials in bulk form and as coatings.

620.1 US ISSN 0884-2914
TA404.2 CODEN: JMREEE
JOURNAL OF MATERIALS RESEARCH. Variant title: J M R. (Supplement avail.: J M R Abstracts (ISSN 1066-2375)) 1986. m. $440 (foreign $470). Materials Research Society, 9800 McKnight Rd., Pittsburgh, PA 15237. TEL 412-367-3003. FAX 412-367-4373. Ed. Walter Brown. adv.: B&W page $1105, color page $1895; trim 8 1/8 x 10 7/8; adv. contact: Mary E. Kaufold. cum.index: 1986-1990. (also avail. in microfilm from AIP; reprint service avail. from UMI) **Indexed:** Appl.Mech.Rev., Ceram.Abstr., Chem.Abstr., Corros.Abstr., INIS Atomind., INSPEC, Met.Abstr., Sci.Cit.Ind., Solid St.Abstr.
—BLDSC (5012.240000); EI; Faxon; UnCover; SWETS; UMI; CASDDS. **CCC.**
Description: Provides an international forum that encompasses physical, chemical, and engineering insights on advanced materials and processing techniques.

620.1 UK ISSN 0022-2461
TA401 CODEN: JMTSAS
JOURNAL OF MATERIALS SCIENCE. 1966. 58/yr. £1865 to institutions in EC nations (North America $3170; elsewhere £2000) (subscr. includes Journal of Materials Science Letters; Journals of Materials Science: Materials in Medicine; Journal of Materials Science: Materials in Electronics). Chapman & Hall, 2-6 Boundary Row, London SE1 8HN, England. TEL 071-865-0066. FAX 071-522-9623. TELEX 290164-CHAPMAG. (Dist. by: International Thomson Publishing Services, Ltd., N. Way, Andover, Hants., SP10 5BE, England. TEL 0264-342919; US addr.: Chapman & Hall, Journals Promotion Department, One Penn Plaza, 41st Fl., New York, NY 10019. TEL 212-564-1060. FAX 212-564-1505) Ed. W. Bonfield. adv.; illus.; index, cum.index. (reprint service avail. from ISI, UMI) **Indexed:** Appl.Mech.Rev., Art & Archaeol.Tech.Abstr., ASCA, Br.Ceram.Abstr., Br.Tech.Ind., CAD CAM Abstr. (until 1992), Cadscan, Ceram.Abstr., Chem.Abstr., Curr.Cont., Eng.Ind., Excerp.Med, Ind.Sci.Rev., INIS Atomind., Int.Aerosp.Abstr., Lead Abstr., Met.Abstr., Phys.Ber., Sci.Abstr., Sci.Cit.Ind., World Alum.Abstr., World Surf.Coat., Zincscan. **Document type:** academic/scholarly publication.
—BLDSC (5012.250000); EI; Faxon; UnCover; SWETS; UMI; CASDDS. **CCC.**
Description: Contains reviews and full-length papers on the structure and properties of all engineering materials.

620.1 UK ISSN 0261-8028
TA401 CODEN: JMSLD5
JOURNAL OF MATERIALS SCIENCE LETTERS. (Companion journal to: Journal of Materials Science (ISSN 0022-2461)) 1982. 24/yr. (avail. only with subscr. to Journal of Materials Science). Chapman & Hall, 2-6 Boundary Row, London SE1 8HN, England. TEL 071-865-0066. FAX 071-522-9623. TELEX 290164-CHAPMAG. (Dist. by: International Thomson Publishing Services, Ltd., N. Way, Andover, Hants. SP10 5BE, England. TEL 0264-342919; US addr.: Chapman & Hall, Journals Promotion Department, One Penn Plaza, 41st Fl., New York, NY 10019. TEL 212-564-1060. FAX 212-564-1505) Ed. W. Bonfield. (reprint service avail. from UMI) **Indexed:** Appl.Mech.Rev., Art & Archaeol.Tech.Abstr., ASCA, Br.Ceram.Abstr., Br.Tech.Ind., Cadscan, Ceram.Abstr., Chem.Abstr., Curr.Cont., Eng.Ind., Excerp.Med., Ind.Sci.Rev., INIS Atomind., Int.Aerosp.Abstr., Lead Abstr., Met.Abstr., Phys.Ber., Sci.Abstr., Sci.Cit.Ind., Soils & Fert., W.R.C.Inf., World Alum.Abstr., World Surf.Coat., Zincscan. **Document type:** academic/scholarly publication.
—BLDSC (5012.255000); EI; Faxon; UnCover; SWETS; UMI; CASDDS. **CCC.**
Description: Provides information for scientists investigating the structure and properties of all engineering materials; restricted to short communications to ensure rapid publication.

620.11 UK ISSN 0957-4522
TK7871 CODEN: JSMEEV
JOURNAL OF MATERIALS SCIENCE: MATERIALS IN ELECTRONICS. bi-m. £150 to institutions in EC nations (North America $255; elsewhere £160). Chapman & Hall, 2-6 Boundary Row, London SE1 8HN, England. TEL 071-865-0066. FAX 071-522-9623. TELEX 290164-CHAPMAG. (Dist. by: International Thomson Publishing Services, N. Way, Andover, Hants. SP10 5BE, England. TEL 0264-342919; US addr.: Chapman & Hall, Journals Promotion Department, One Penn Plaza, 41st Fl., New York, NY 10019. TEL 212-564-1060. FAX 212-564-1505) Ed. A. Willoughby. **Indexed:** Br.Tech.Ind. **Document type:** academic/scholarly publication.
—BLDSC (5012.257000); EI; Faxon; UnCover; SWETS; CASDDS. **CCC.**
Description: Covers applied research and development in the material science of electronics, including the growth and preparation of new materials.
Refereed Serial

620.1 610 UK ISSN 0957-4530
R857.M3 CODEN: JSMMEL
JOURNAL OF MATERIALS SCIENCE: MATERIALS IN MEDICINE. 6/yr. £250 to institutions in EC nations (North America $425; elsewhere £260). (European Society for Biomaterials) Chapman & Hall, 2-6 Boundary Row, London SE1 8HN, England. TEL 071-865-0066. FAX 071-522-9623. TELEX 290164-CHAPMAG. (Dist. by: International Thomson Publishing Services, N. Way, Andover, Hants. SP10 5BE, England. TEL 0264-342919; US addr.: Chapman & Hall, Journals Promotion Department, One Penn Plaza, 41st Fl., New York, NY 10019. TEL 212-564-1060. FAX 212-564-1505) Eds. W. Bonfield, D.F. Williams. illus. (reprint service avail. from ISI,UMI) **Indexed:** Br.Tech.Ind., Excerp.Med. (1993-). **Document type:** academic/scholarly publication.
—BLDSC (5012.258000); EI; Faxon; SWETS; CASDDS. **CCC.**
Description: Publishes papers on the science and technology of biomaterials and their applications as medical or dental implants, prostheses and devices, and biological materials.
Refereed Serial

620.1 US ISSN 1064-7562
CODEN: JMSPEI
▼**JOURNAL OF MATERIALS SYNTHESIS AND PROCESSING.** 1993. 6/yr. $195 (outside N. America $230) (effective 1994). Plenum Publishing Corp., 233 Spring St., New York, NY 10013-1578. TEL 212-620-8000. FAX 212-463-0172. TELEX 23-421139. Eds. Z.A. Munir, J.B. Holt. (also avail. in microfilm from JSC) **Document type:** academic/scholarly publication.
—BLDSC (5012.265000); EI; Faxon; UnCover; CASDDS.
Description: International forum for original research and review articles on all aspects of high-temperature synthesis and processing of materials, including ceramic, intermetallic and composite materials.
Refereed Serial

620.11 US ISSN 0195-9298
TA417.2 CODEN: JNOED5
JOURNAL OF NONDESTRUCTIVE EVALUATION. 1980. q. $230 (foreign $270) (effective 1994). Plenum Publishing Corp., 233 Spring St., New York, NY 10013-1578. TEL 212-620-8000. FAX 212-463-0742. TELEX 23-421139. Ed. R. Bruce Thompson. adv.; illus. (also avail. in microfilm from JSC; back issues avail.) **Indexed:** Appl.Mech.Rev., Art & Archaeol.Tech.Abstr., Curr.Cont., Electron.& Communic.Abstr.J., INIS Atomind., Int.Aerosp.Abstr., Met.Abstr., Ref.Zh., Saf.Sci.Abstr., Sci.Abstr., Solid St.Abstr. **Document type:** academic/scholarly publication.
—BLDSC (5022.833000); EI; Faxon; UnCover; SWETS; UMI. **CCC.**
Refereed Serial

620.1 389 US ISSN 0022-4065
TS156.Q3 CODEN: JQUTAU
JOURNAL OF QUALITY TECHNOLOGY. 1944. q. $30. American Society for Quality Control, 611 E. Wisconsin Ave., Box 3005, Milwaukee, WI 53201-3005. TEL 414-272-8575. Ed. Peter Nelson. bk.rev.; stat.; index. circ. 22,000. (also avail. in microform from UMI; reprint service avail. from KTO,UMI) **Indexed:** A.S.& T.Ind., ABI Inform., Biostat., Curr.Cont., Eng.Ind., Ind.Sci.Rev., Int.Aerosp.Abstr., J.Cont.Quant.Meth., Met.Abstr., Oper.Res.Manage.Sci., Qual.Contr.Appl.Stat., Sci.Abstr., World Alum.Abstr. **Document type:** academic/scholarly publication.
—BLDSC (5043.690000); EI; Faxon; UnCover; SWETS; UMI. **CCC.**
Supersedes in part (in 1968): Industrial Quality Control.
Description: Covers statistical aspects of quality control.

620.11 668.4 US ISSN 0731-6844
TA455.P55 CODEN: JRPCDW
JOURNAL OF REINFORCED PLASTICS & COMPOSITES. 1982. m. $670. Technomic Publishing Co., Inc., 851 New Holland Ave., Box 3535, Lancaster, PA 17604. TEL 717-291-5609. FAX 717-295-4538. TELEX 230 753565 (TECHNOMIC UD). Ed. George S. Springer. index. circ. 450. (also avail. in microform from UMI) **Indexed:** Appl.Mech.Rev., Chem.Abstr., Eng.Ind., INIS Atomind., Met.Abstr., Sci.Abstr., World Alum.Abstr.
—BLDSC (5049.100000); EI; Faxon; UnCover; SWETS; UMI; CASDDS. **CCC.**
Refereed Serial

620.1 530 NE ISSN 0928-0707
▼**JOURNAL OF SOL-GEL SCIENCE AND TECHNOLOGY.** (Text in English) 1993. 6/yr. fl.640($335) (effective 1994). Kluwer Academic Publishers, Postbus 17, 3300 AA Dordrecht, Netherlands. TEL 31-78-334911. FAX 31-78-334254. TELEX 29245 KAPG NL. (Dist. by: Kluwer Academic Publishers Group, P.O. Box 322, 3300 AH Dordrecht, Netherlands. TEL 31-78-524400. FAX 31-78-524474; N. America dist. addr.: Box 358, Accord Sta., Hingham, MA 02018-0358. TEL 617-871-6600. FAX 617-871-6528) Ed. Sumio Sakka. (back issues avail.) **Indexed:** Eng.Mat.Abstr., Met.Abstr. **Document type:** academic/scholarly publication.
—BLDSC (5065.240000).
Description: Publishes original research papers on scientific and technical issues in the emergent field of sol-gel materials, including chemistry, characterization, properties and application of these materials.
Refereed Serial

ENGINEERING — ENGINEERING MECHANICS AND MATERIALS

620.1   UK   ISSN 0309-3247
TA404.8   CODEN: JSADDZ
JOURNAL OF STRAIN ANALYSIS FOR ENGINEERING DESIGN. 1965. q. £119 (foreign £127). (Joint British Committee for Stress Analysis) Mechanical Engineering Publications Ltd., Northgate Ave., Bury St, Edmunds, Suffolk IP32 6BW, England. TEL 0284-763277. FAX 0284-704006. TELEX 817376. Ed.Bd. charts; illus.; stat.; index, cum.index. circ. 900. (also avail. in microform from UMI; reprint service avail. from UMI) **Indexed:** Appl.Mech.Rev., BMT, Br.Tech.Ind., Chem.Abstr., Curr.Cont., Eng.Ind., Fluidex, Ind.Sci.Rev., Int.Aerosp.Abstr., Intl.Civil Eng.Abstr., ISMEC, Met.Abstr., Sci.Abstr., Soft.Abstr.Eng., World Alum.Abstr. **Document type:** academic/scholarly publication.
—BLDSC (5066.872100); El; Faxon; UnCover; SWETS; UMI; CASDDS. **CCC.**
    Formerly: Journal of Strain Analysis (ISSN 0022-4758)
    Description: Scholarly research articles on experimental, theoretical, and practical applications in the analysis of structural strength and joint pressure.

620.11   US   ISSN 0090-3973
TA401   CODEN: JTEVAB
JOURNAL OF TESTING AND EVALUATION. Variant title: A S T M Journal of Testing and Evaluation. 1966. bi-m. $103 to non-members; members $93. American Society for Testing and Materials, 1916 Race St., Philadelphia, PA 19103. TEL 215-299-5400. FAX 215-977-9679. bk.rev.; abstr.; charts; illus.; index. circ. 1,600. (also avail. in microform from UMI,PMC; reprint service avail. from UMI,ISI) **Indexed:** A.S.& T.Ind., Abstr.Bull.Inst.Pap.Chem., Abstr.J.Earthq.Eng., Br.Ceram.Abstr., Cadscan, Ceram.Abstr., Chem.Abstr., Energy Ind., Energy Info.Abstr., Eng.Ind., Excerp.Med., Fluidex, Ind.Sci.Rev., INIS Atomind., Int.Aerosp.Abstr., Int.Packag.Abstr., Intl.Civil Eng.Abstr., ISMEC, J.of Ferroc., Lead Abstr., Met.Abstr., Sci.Abstr., Soft.Abstr.Eng., World Alum.Abstr., Zincscan. **Document type:** trade publication.
—BLDSC (5069.040000); El; Faxon; UnCover; SWETS; UMI; CASDDS. **CCC.**
    Supersedes: Journal of Materials. (J M L S A).
    Refereed Serial

620.11 550 614.7   JA   ISSN 0453-5146
KENSETSU KOGAKU KENKYUJO HOKOKU/CONSTRUCTION ENGINEERING RESEARCH INSTITUTE FOUNDATION REPORT. (Text in Japanese; content page in English) 1960. a. exchange basis. Kensetsu Kogaku Kenkyujo - Construction Engineering Research Institute Foundation, 3-10 Tsurukabuto 1-chome, Nada-ku, Kobe-shi 657, Japan. TEL 078-851-1850. FAX 078-851-5454. charts. circ. 500. **Indexed:** INIS Atomind. **Document type:** academic/scholarly publication.
    Description: Addresses all issues concerning construction engineering research conducted by the foundation.

620.1   JA   ISSN 0452-2834
TA401   CODEN: KZAIA5
KOGYO ZAIRYO/ENGINEERING MATERIALS. (Text in Japanese) 1953. q. Industrial Daily News Ltd. - Nikkan Kogyo Shinbun Ltd., 1-8-10 Kudan Kita, Chiyoda-ku, Tokyo 102, Japan. circ. 28,000. **Indexed:** Chem.Abstr., JCT, JTA.
—BLDSC (3764.840000); CASDDS.
    Description: Focuses on the special characteristics of engineering materials, methods of processing these materials and the situation of practical application of these materials.

620.11   GW   ISSN 0937-4167
KONSTRUKTIONSPRAXIS. 1989. m. DM.220. Vogel Verlag und Druck KG, Max-Planck-Str. 7-9, 97082 Wuerzburg, Germany. TEL 0931-4182145. FAX 0931-4182640. (Subscr. to: Vogel Verlag, 97064 Wuerzburg, Germany; Dist. in U.S. by: Vogel Europublishing, Inc., 20092 Gibbs Dr., Sonora, CA 95370. TEL 209-533-3555. FAX 209-533-9555) Ed. Ulrich Hoeltkemeier. adv.: B&W page DM.7060, color page DM.9460; trim 270 x 190. circ. 30,000 (controlled). **Document type:** trade publication.

KYUSHU UNIVERSITY. RESEARCH INSTITUTE FOR APPLIED MECHANICS. ABSTRACTS OF PAPERS. see ENGINEERING — *Abstracting, Bibliographies, Statistics*

621 539.7   JA   ISSN 0030-7734
TA349
KYUSHU UNIVERSITY. RESEARCH INSTITUTE FOR APPLIED MECHANICS. BULLETIN/KYUSHU DAIGAKU OYORIKIGAKU KENKYUSHO SHOHO. (Text in Japanese) 1952. s-a. exchange basis. Kyushu University, Research Institute for Applied Mechanics - Kyushu Daigaku Oyorikigaku Kenkyusho, Libary, 6-1, Kasuga-Koen, Kasuga, Fukuoka 816, Japan. FAX 81-92-582-4201. abstr.; bibl.; charts; illus.; stat. circ. 500. **Indexed:** INIS Atomind., Jap.Per.Ind.
—BLDSC (2694.810000).

620.1   JA   ISSN 0023-6195
TA350   CODEN: RMKUA9
KYUSHU UNIVERSITY. RESEARCH INSTITUTE FOR APPLIED MECHANICS. REPORTS/OYORIKIGAKU KENKYUSHO OBUN HOKOKU. (Text and summaries in English) 1952. s-a. exchange basis. Kyushu University, Research Institute for Applied Mechanics - Kyushu Daigaku Oyorikigaku Kenkyusho, Library, 6-1, Kasuga-Koen, Kasuga, Fukuoka 816, Japan. FAX 81-92-582-4201. abstr.; bibl.; charts; illus.; index. circ. 800. **Indexed:** Appl.Mech.Rev., BMT, Chem.Abstr., Fluidex.
—BLDSC (7591.000000); CASDDS.

620.1   US
LAWRENCE BERKELEY LABORATORY. MATERIALS AND CHEMICAL SCIENCES DIVISION. ANNUAL REPORT. a. University of California, Berkeley, Materials and Chemical Sciences Division, Berkeley, CA 94720. TEL 415-422-1100. (Dist. by: National Technical Information Service, 5285 Port Royal Rd., Springfield, VA 22151) illus.
    Former titles: Lawrence Berkeley Laboratory. Materials and Molecular Research Division. Annual Report; Lawrence Berkeley Laboratory. Inorganic Materials Research Division. Annual Report (ISSN 0092-6248)
    Refereed Serial

621.86   FR   ISSN 0295-4192
LOGISTIQUES MAGAZINE. 1952. 10/yr. 415 F. (foreign 506 F.) (effective Jan. 1994). Groupe Information et Professions, 1 cite Bergere, 75009 Paris, France. TEL 44-69-55-50. FAX 40-22-02-70. TELEX 650702. Ed. Rene Lebailly. adv.; bk.rev.; bibl.; charts; illus.; pat.; stat.; tr.lit. circ. 8,000. **Indexed:** C.I.S. Abstr.
—BLDSC (5292.354000).
    Former titles: Manutention (ISSN 0397-3816); M T D; Manutention-Stockage (ISSN 0025-2654)

LUBRICATION SCIENCE; physics and chemistry of lubricants in tribological systems. see PETROLEUM AND GAS

669   NE
M B PRODUKTIETECHNIEK. (Text in Dutch; summaries in English) 1934. m. fl.365. (Society of Mechanical Engineers) Technische Uitgeverij de Vey Mestdagh BV, Markt 51, 4331 LK Middelburg, Netherlands. TEL 31-1180-81240. FAX 31-1180-81215. Ed. D.J. de Korte. adv.; bk.rev.; charts; illus.; tr.lit.; index. circ. 3,700. (also avail. in microform from UMI) **Indexed:** C.I.S. Abstr., Chem.Abstr., Excerp.Med., Key to Econ.Sci. **Document type:** trade publication.
    Formerly: Metaalbewerking (ISSN 0026-0487)

M - MODERNE METALLTECHNIK; das Magazin fuer Ausbildung und Beruf. see METALLURGY

620.1   US   ISSN 0883-7694
TA401   CODEN: MRSBEA
M R S BULLETIN. 1976. m. $112 (foreign $165). Materials Research Society, 9800 McKnight Rd., Pittsburgh, PA 15237. TEL 412-367-3003. FAX 412-367-4373. Eds. Elizabeth Fleischer, Elton Kaufmann. adv.: B&W page $1245, color page $2210; trim 8 1/8 x 10 7/8; adv. contact: Mary E. Kaufold. bk.rev.; charts; illus.; tr.lit. circ. 11,000. (reprint service avail. from UMI)
—BLDSC (5980.805700); El; UnCover; SWETS; UMI; CASDDS. **CCC.**
    Description: Serves as a forum for analysis and discussion of technical developments on a broad range of issues touching the materials community. Includes technical review articles, professional opportunities, and news on national and international materials policy and directions.

620.1   CN   ISSN 0076-2059
MCMASTER UNIVERSITY, HAMILTON, ONTARIO. INSTITUTE FOR MATERIALS RESEARCH. ANNUAL REPORT. 1967. a. free. McMaster University, Institute for Materials Research, 1280 Main St., W., Hamilton, Ont. L8S 4M1, Canada. TEL 416-525-9140. FAX 416-521-2773. circ. 750.

620.11 621.8   US
MATERIALLY SPEAKING. 1985. q. $30 (effective 1991). Southern Illinois University, Carbondale, Materials Technology Center, Carbondale, IL 62901-4303. TEL 618-536-7525. FAX 618-453-8216. Ed. Maurice A. Wright. index. circ. 5,500. (tabloid format; back issues avail.) **Document type:** newsletter.
    Description: Discusses composites and other materials, as well as the activities of the Materials Technology Center.

620   BU   ISSN 0204-7535
TA401   CODEN: MTEKDE
MATERIALOZNANIE I TEKHNOLOGIIA. 1975. irreg. 1.20 lv. per no. (Bulgarska Akademiia na Naukite) Publishing House of the Bulgarian Academy of Sciences, Acad. G. Bonchev St., Bldg. 6, 1113 Sofia, Bulgaria. circ. 470. (reprint service avail. from IRC) **Indexed:** Chem.Abstr., Met.Abstr., World Alum.Abstr.
—BLDSC (0101.077000); CASDDS.

620   UK   ISSN 0264-1275
TA401   CODEN: MADSD2
MATERIALS & DESIGN. 1978. 6/yr. £160 in UK and Europe; elsewhere £170. Butterworth - Heinemann (Subsidiary of: Reed International PLC), Linacre House, Jordan Hill, Oxford OX2 8DP, England. TEL 0865-310366. FAX 0865-310898. TELEX 83111 BHPOXF G. (Subscr. to: Turpin Transactions Ltd., Distribution Centre, Blackhorse Rd., Letchworth, Herts SG6 1HN, England. TEL 0462-672555. FAX 0462-480947) Ed. L. Bovey. bk.rev. (back issues avail.) **Indexed:** Abstr.Bull.Inst.Pap.Chem., B.C.I.R.A., BMT, Br.Ceram.Abstr., Ceram.Abstr., Chem.Abstr., INIS Atomind., Int.Aerosp.Abstr., Met.Abstr., World Alum.Abstr. **Document type:** academic/scholarly publication.
—BLDSC (5393.974000); El; Faxon; UnCover; SWETS; UMI; CASDDS. **CCC.**
    Former titles (until June 1982): Materials in Engineering (ISSN 0261-3069); (until 1980): International Journal of Materials in Engineering Applications (ISSN 0141-5530)
    Description: Promotes a greater understanding of the attributes and capabilities of all types of modern engineering materials.

620.11 669   UK   ISSN 0960-3409
TA418.26   CODEN: MHTEEM
MATERIALS AT HIGH TEMPERATURES; materials generation applications. 1982. q. £225 in UK and Europe; elsewhere £240. Butterworth - Heinemann (Subsidiary of: Reed International PLC), Linacre House, Jordan Hill, Oxford OX2 8DP, England. TEL 0865-310366. FAX 0865-310898. TELEX 83111 BHPOXF G. (Subscr. to: Turpin Transactions Ltd., Distribution Centre, Blackhorse Rd., Letchworth, Herts SG6 1HN, England. TEL 0462-672555) Ed. Diane Cogan. adv.; bk.rev.; abstr.; bibl.; charts; illus.; stat.; index. (also avail. in microform from UMI; back issues avail.) **Indexed:** Br.Ceram.Abstr., Energy Info.Abstr., INIS Atomind., Met.Abstr., Sci.Abstr., World Alum.Abstr. **Document type:** academic/scholarly publication.
—BLDSC (5395.029000); CIS; SWETS. **CCC.**
    Formerly (until 1990): High Temperature Technology (ISSN 0261-9180)
    Description: For scientists and engineers concerned with the behavior of materials at high temperature.

ENGINEERING — ENGINEERING MECHANICS AND MATERIALS

620.11 540   SZ   ISSN 0254-0584
CODEN: MCHPDR
MATERIALS CHEMISTRY AND PHYSICS; the international journal which unites the chemical and physical fields of research in materials science. (Text in English, French or German) 1976. 12/yr. (in 3 vols.; 4 nos./vol.) 1110 SFr.($755) (effective 1994). (Chinese Society for Materials Science) Elsevier Science S.A., P.O. Box 564, CH-1001 Lausanne 1, Switzerland. TEL 41-21-3207381. FAX 41-21-3235444. TELEX 450620-ELSA-CH. (Subscr. in U.S. and Canada to: Elsevier Science Inc., Box 882, Madison Sq. Sta., New York, NY 10159. TEL 212-989-5800. FAX 212-633-3990) Eds. L.-J. Chen, K.-N. Tu. bk.rev.; abstr.; bibl.; illus.; index. (also avail. in microform from UMI) **Indexed:** ASCA, Br.Ceram.Abstr., Cadscan, Chem.Abstr., Curr.Cont., Curr.Tit.Electrochem., Eng.Ind., Ind.Sci.Rev., Lead Abstr., Met.Abstr., Met.Finish.Abstr., Phys.Abstr., Sci.Abstr., Sci.Cit.Ind., Soils & Fert., World Alum.Abstr., World Surf.Coat., Zincscan. **Document type:** academic/scholarly publication.
—BLDSC (5394.107100); EI; Faxon; UnCover; SWETS; CASDDS. **CCC.**
Formerly (until 1982): Materials Chemistry (ISSN 0390-6035)
Description: For scientists and researchers working in the field of materials science and engineering.
Refereed Serial

620.1   US   ISSN 0025-5319
TN1
CODEN: MAENBO
MATERIALS ENGINEERING. 1929. m. $50 (free to qualified personnel). Penton Publishing (Subsidiary of: Pittway Company), 1100 Superior Ave., Cleveland, OH 44114-2543. TEL 216-696-7000. FAX 216-696-8765. TELEX 4218245. (Subscr. to: Box 95759, Cleveland, OH 44101) Ed. Maragaret Hunt. adv.; bk.rev.; abstr.; charts; illus.; tr.lit.; index; circ. 56,000 (controlled). (also avail. in microform from UMI; reprint service avail. from UMI) **Indexed:** A.S.& T.Ind., Cadscan, Chem.Abstr., Chem.Eng.Abstr., Copper Abstr., Corros.Abstr., Curr.Cont., Deep Sea Res.& Oceanogr.Abstr., Eng.Ind., Excerp.Med., INIS Atomind., Int.Packag.Abstr., ISMEC, Key to Econ.Sci., Lead Abstr., Met.Abstr., PROMT, World Alum.Abstr., Zincscan.
—Faxon; UnCover. **CCC.**
Formerly: Materials in Design Engineering.
Description: Covers the application of all types of materials, their forms, properties, and processing characteristics.

620.1   IT
MATERIALS ENGINEERING; an international journal on preparation, processing, application and evaluation of engineering materials. 1990. 3/yr. L.200000 (foreign L.220000). Mucchi Editore s.r.l., Via Emilia Est. 1527, 41100 Modena, Italy. Ed.Bd.

620.1 389   US   ISSN 0025-5327
CODEN: MAEVAD
MATERIALS EVALUATION. 1942. m. $85. American Society for Nondestructive Testing, 1711 Arlingate Lane, Box 28518, Columbus, OH 43228-0158. TEL 614-274-6003. FAX 614-274-6899. Ed. Charles Lopez. adv.; bk.rev.; abstr.; charts; illus.; pat.; tr.lit.; index, cum.index. circ. 11,000. (also avail. in microform from UMI; reprint service avail. from UMI) **Indexed:** A.S.& T.Ind., Appl.Mech.Rev., Cadscan, Ceram.Abstr., Chem.Abstr., Curr.Cont., E&P Hlth. (1993-), Eng.Ind., Gas Process.& Ppl. (1993-), HRIS, Ind.Sci.Rev., INIS Atomind., Int.Aerosp.Abstr., Lead Abstr., Met.Abstr., Off.Tech. (1993-), Petrol.Abstr. (1965-), Sci.Abstr., Sci.Cit.Ind., World Alum.Abstr., Zincscan. **Document type:** trade publication.
—BLDSC (5394.300000); EI; Faxon; UnCover; SWETS; UMI; CASDDS. **CCC.**
Formerly: Nondestructive Testing (Chicago) (ISSN 0096-7955)
Description: Technical papers featuring industrial inspection methods such as infrared, X-ray, and ultrasound.
Refereed Serial

620.1 389   US   ISSN 0094-1492
TA462
CODEN: MTPFBI
MATERIALS PERFORMANCE; articles on corrosion science and engineering solutions for corrosion problems. 1962. m. $65 (foreign $80). National Association of Corrosion Engineers (NACE), Box 218340, Houston, TX 77218. TEL 713-492-0535. FAX 713-492-8254. TELEX 792310. Ed. Theresa Baer. adv.; bk.rev.; charts; illus.; index. circ. 17,000. (also avail. in microform from UMI; reprint service avail. from UMI) **Indexed:** A.S.& T.Ind., Abstr.Bull.Inst.Pap.Chem., API Abstr., API Catal., API Hlth.& Environ., API Oil., API Pet.Ref., API Pet.Subst., API Transport., Art & Archaeol.Tech.Abstr., Biol.Abstr., BMT, Cadscan, Ceram.Abstr., Chem.Abstr., Copper Abstr., Corros.Abstr., Curr.Cont., Deep Sea Res.& Oceanogr.Abstr., Eng.Ind, Excerp.Med., Fluidex, Foul.Prev.Res.Dig., Fuel & Energy Abstr., HRIS, INIS Atomind., Lead Abstr., Met.Abstr., Petrol.Abstr., Sci.Abstr., Soils & Fert., World Alum.Abstr., World Surf.Coat., Zincscan.
—BLDSC (5396.050000); EI; Faxon; UnCover; SWETS; UMI; CASDDS. **CCC.**
Former titles: Materials Protection and Performance; Materials Protection (ISSN 0025-5378)

MATERIALS RESEARCH BULLETIN. see *CHEMISTRY — Crystallography*

620.1   UK
MATERIALS RESEARCH CENTRES; a world directory of organizations and programmes in materials science. 1983. irreg., 5th ed., 1993. £275($425) Longman Group UK Ltd., Longman House, Burnt Mill, Harlow, Essex CM20 2JE, England. TEL 0279-442601. FAX 0279-444501. (Dist. in U.S. & Canada by: Gale Research Inc., 835 Penobscot Bldg., Detroit, MI 48226) **Document type:** directory.

620.1   SZ   ISSN 0921-5093
TA401
CODEN: MSAPE3
MATERIALS SCIENCE AND ENGINEERING A: STRUCTURAL MATERIALS: PROPERTIES, MICROSTRUCTURES AND PROCESSING. (Text and summaries in English, French, German) 1967. 30/yr. (in 15 vols.; 2 nos./vol.) 4950 SFr.($3367) (combined subscr. to parts A, B, C & R 7500 SFr.($5102)) (effective 1994). Elsevier Science S.A., P.O. Box 564, CH-1001 Lausanne 1, Switzerland. TEL 41-21-3207381. FAX 41-21-3235444. TELEX 450620-ELSA-CH. (Subscr. in U.S. and Canada to: Elsevier Science Inc., Box 882, Madison Sq. Sta., New York, NY 10159. TEL 212-989-5800. FAX 212-633-3990) Ed. H. Herman. adv.; bk.rev.; bibl.; illus.; index. (also avail. in microform from UMI) **Indexed:** Appl.Mech.Rev., Cadscan, Ceram.Abstr., Chem.Abstr., Copper Abstr., Curr.Cont., Eng.Ind., Fuel & Energy Abstr., GeoRef., Ind.Sci.Rev., INSPEC, Int.Aerosp.Abstr., Lead Abstr., Met.Abstr., Phys.Ber., Sci.Abstr., Sci.Cit.Ind., World Alum.Abstr., Zincscan. **Document type:** academic/scholarly publication.
—BLDSC (5396.430100); EI; Faxon; UnCover; SWETS; CASDDS. **CCC.**
Supersedes in part (in 1988): Material Sciences and Engineering (ISSN 0025-5416)
Description: Discusses experimental and theoretical studies pertaining to relationships among microstructure, properties, and processing of structural materials in their varied forms. Focuses on mechanical, thermal and chemical properties.
Refereed Serial

620.11   SZ   ISSN 0921-5107
TA401
CODEN: MSBTEK
MATERIALS SCIENCE & ENGINEERING B: SOLID-STATE MATERIALS FOR ADVANCED TECHNOLOGY. (Text in English) 1988. 21/yr. (in 7 vols.; 3 nos./vol.) 2310 SFr.($1571) (combined subscr. to Parts A, B, C & R 7500 SFr.($5102)) (effective 1994). Elsevier Science S.A., P.O. Box 564, CH-1001 Lausanne 1, Switzerland. TEL 41-21-3207381. FAX 41-21-3235444. TELEX 450620-ELSA-CH. (Subscr. in U.S. and Canada to: Elsevier Science Inc., Box 882, Madison Sq. Sta., New York, NY 10159. TEL 212-989-5800. FAX 212-633-3990) Ed.Bd. **Document type:** academic/scholarly publication.
—BLDSC (5396.430200); EI; Faxon; UnCover; SWETS; CASDDS. **CCC.**
Supersedes in part (in 1988): Material Sciences and Engineering (ISSN 0025-5416)
Description: Addresses the interface between the disciplines of materials science and engineering, solid-state physics, solid-state chemistry, and solid-state electronics.
Refereed Serial

620.1 660   SZ   ISSN 0928-4931
CODEN: MSCEEE
▼**MATERIALS SCIENCE AND ENGINEERING C: BIOMIMETIC MATERIALS, SENSORS AND SYSTEMS.** (Text in English) 1993. 4/yr. 330 SFr.($224) (effective 1994). Elsevier Science S.A., P.O. Box 564, CH-1001 Lausanne 1, Switzerland. TEL 41-21-3207381. FAX 41-21-3235444. TELEX 450620-ELSA-CH. (Subscr. in U.S. and Canada to: Elsevier Science Inc., Box 882, Madison Sq. Sta., New York, NY 10159. TEL 212-989-5800. FAX 212-633-3990) Ed.Bd. **Document type:** academic/scholarly publication.
—BLDSC (5396.428000); EI; Faxon; SWETS; CASDDS. **CCC.**

620.1 530   SZ   ISSN 0927-796X
TA401
MATERIALS SCIENCE AND ENGINEERING R: REPORTS. (Text in English) 1986. 16/yr. (in 2 vols.; 8 nos./vol.). 660 SFr.($449) (combined subscr. to Parts A, B, C & R 7500 SFr.($5102)) (effective 1994). Elsevier Science S.A., P.O. Box 564, CH-1001 Lausanne 1, Switzerland. TEL 41-21-3207381. FAX 41-21-3235444. TELEX 450620-ELSA-CH. (Subscr. in U.S. and Canada to: Elsevier Science Inc., Box 882, Madison Sq. Sta., New York, NY 10159. TEL 212-989-5800. FAX 212-633-3990) Eds. S.S. Lau, F.W. Saris. (back issues avail.) **Document type:** academic/scholarly publication.
—BLDSC (5396.430300); EI; Faxon; UnCover; SWETS. **CCC.**
Formerly (until 1993): Materials Science Reports (ISSN 0920-2307)
Description: Provides a general background of materials science and presents specialized reviews on current and significant developments in the field.
Refereed Serial

620.1   US   ISSN 0076-5201
CODEN: MTSRAY
MATERIALS SCIENCE RESEARCH. 1963. irreg., vol.21, 1987. price varies. Plenum Publishing Corp., 233 Spring St., New York, NY 10013-1578. TEL 212-620-8000. FAX 212-463-0742. TELEX 23-421139. Ed.Bd. **Document type:** monographic series.
—BLDSC (5396.440000); CASDDS. **CCC.**
Refereed Serial

620.1   US
TA401
MATERIALS SCIENCES. English translation of: Fiziko-Khimicheskaya Mekhanika Materialov (KR ISSN 0430-6252) 1965. bi-m. $1075 (foreign $1260) (effective 1994). (Ukrainian Academy of Sciences, KR) Plenum Publishing Corp., Consultants Bureau, 233 Spring St., New York, NY 10013-1578. TEL 212-620-8468. FAX 212-463-0742. TELEX 23-421139. Ed. V.V. Panasyuk. (also avail. in microfilm from JSC; back issues avail.) **Indexed:** Appl.Mech.Rev., Chem.Titles, Curr.Cont., Eng.Ind., INSPEC, ISMEC, Solid St.Abstr. **Document type:** academic/scholarly publication.
—Faxon. **CCC.**
Formerly (until 1994): Soviet Materials Sciences (ISSN 0038-5565)
Refereed Serial

MATERIALS WORLD. see *METALLURGY*

658.2 658.5   FR   ISSN 0032-6895
TA401
CODEN: MATCBW
MATERIAUX ET TECHNIQUES. 1913. m. 1100 F. S.I.R.P.E., 76 rue de Rivoli, 75004 Paris, France. TEL 33-1-42-78-52-20. FAX 33-1-42-74-40-48. Ed. Roger Drouhin. adv.: B&W page 7950 F., color page 11550 F. bk.rev.; charts; illus.; index. circ. 5,000. (also avail. in microfilm from UMI) **Indexed:** Chem.Abstr., Eng.Ind., Excerp.Med., INIS Atomind., Int.Aerosp.Abstr., Met.Abstr., World Alum.Abstr.
—BLDSC (5398.660000); EI; SWETS; CASDDS. **CCC.**
Formerly: Pratique des Industries Mecaniques.
Description: Publishes selected studies, recent discoveries and developments in materials research, use and technology; metals, plastics, composite materials and ceramics.

MECCANICA. see *PHYSICS — Mechanics*

MECHANICS. see *PHYSICS — Mechanics*

ENGINEERING — ENGINEERING MECHANICS AND MATERIALS

620   NE   ISSN 0167-6636
TA405   CODEN: MSMSD3
MECHANICS OF MATERIALS; an international journal. 1982. 8/yr. (in 2 vols.; 4 nos./vol.) fl.852($461) (effective 1994). North-Holland (Subsidiary of: Elsevier Science B.V.), P.O. Box 211, 1000 AE Amsterdam, Netherlands. TEL 31-20-5803911. FAX 31-20-5803598. TELEX 18582 ESPA NL. (Subscr. in U.S. and Canada to: Elsevier Science Inc., Box 882, Madison Sq. Sta., New York, NY 10159. TEL 212-989-5800. FAX 212-633-3990) Eds. S. Nemat-Nasser, Johannes Weertman. (back issues avail.) **Indexed:** Appl.Mech.Rev., Geotech.Abstr., Int.Aerosp.Abstr., Met.Abstr., Phys.Ber., Sci.Abstr., World Alum.Abstr. **Document type:** academic/scholarly publication.
—BLDSC (5424.105000); EI; Faxon; UnCover; SWETS; CASDDS. **CCC.**
    Description: Provides a forum for original scientific research on the flow, fracture, and general constitutive behavior of geophysical, geotechnical, and technological materials, with balanced coverage of theoretical, experimental, and field investigations.
Refereed Serial

620   UK   ISSN 0093-6413
TA349   CODEN: MRCOD2
MECHANICS RESEARCH COMMUNICATIONS. 1974. 6/yr. £325($500) (effective 1994). (International Centre for Mechanical Sciences) Elsevier Science Ltd., Pergamon, P.O. Box 800, Kidlington, Oxford OX5 1DX, England. TEL 44-865-843000. FAX 44-865-843010. (Subscr. in U.S. and Canada to: Elsevier Science, 660 White Plains Rd., Tarrytown, NY 10591-5153. TEL 914-524-9200. FAX 914-333-2444) Ed. Bruno A. Boley. adv.; bk.rev.; charts; illus.; index. circ. 1,100. (also avail. in microform from UMI) **Indexed:** Appl.Mech.Rev., Curr.Cont., Ind.Sci.Rev., Math.R., Sci.Abstr., Sh.& Vib.Dig. **Document type:** academic/scholarly publication.
—BLDSC (5424.120000); EI; Faxon; UnCover; SWETS; UMI. **CCC.**
    Description: Research on the behavior of fluids, solids, particles, continua, rigid bodies, mechanisms and systems.
Refereed Serial

620.1 531   PL   ISSN 0079-3701
QA801   CODEN: MTYSAX
MECHANIKA TEORETYCZNA I STOSOWANA; journal of theoretical and applied mechanics. (Text in English; summaries in English, Polish) 1963. q. $80. Polskie Towarzystwo Mechaniki Teoretycznej i Stosowanej - Polish Society of Theoretical and Allied Mechanics, Palac Kultury, p.309, 00-901 Warsaw, Poland. (Dist. by: Ars Polona, Krakowskie Przedmiescie 7, 00-068 Warsaw, Poland) (Co-sponsor: State Committee for Scientific Research) Ed. Wojciech Nowakli. bk.rev.; index; circ. 400 (controlled). **Indexed:** Geotech.Abstr., INIS Atomind., Int.Aerosp.Abstr., Math.R., Sci.Abstr. **Document type:** academic/scholarly publication.
Refereed Serial

620.11 669 671.52   UK   ISSN 0264-7303
METALLIC MATERIALS. English translation of: Kovove Materialy (CS ISSN 0023-432X) 1982. bi-m. £105($175) Riecansky Science Publishing Co., 7 Meadow Walk, Great Abington, Cambridge CB1 6AZ, England. TEL 0223-893295. FAX 0223-893295. Ed. V.E. Riecansky. (back issues avail.) **Indexed:** Eng.Ind., Met.Abstr., Phys.Abstr.
—BLDSC (5692.476000); Faxon; UnCover.

METALS MATERIALS AND PROCESSES. see *METALLURGY*

620.11 658   JA
METALWORKING: ENGINEERING AND MARKETING. (Text in English) 1979. bi-m. $25. News Digest Publishing Co. Ltd., 5-3, 3-chome, Uchiyama, Chikusa-ku, Nagoya 464, Japan. circ. 48,000. **Indexed:** CAD CAM Abstr. (until 1992), Robomat. (until 1992).

620.1   US
METRIC FASTENER STANDARDS. 1976. irreg., 2nd ed., 1983. $60 (outside N. America $95). Industrial Fasteners Institute, 1105 E. Ohio Bldg., 1717 E. Ninth St., Cleveland, OH 44114. TEL 216-241-1482. FAX 216-241-5901.

MICROPOROUS MATERIALS; an international journal devoted to their applications and science. see *CHEMISTRY — Physical Chemistry*

621.9 669   US
N A D C A INTERNATIONAL DIE CASTING CONGRESS. TRANSACTIONS. (Former name of issuing body: Society of Die Casting Engineers, Inc.) 1960. biennial. $165 to non-members; members $100. North American Die Casting Association, 9701 W. Higgins Rd. 880, Rosemont, IL 60018-4721. TEL 708-292-3600. FAX 708-292-3620. cum.index: 1960-1989. circ. 500. (also avail. in microfilm from UMI; reprint service avail. from UMI) **Document type:** proceedings.
    Former titles: S D C E International Die Casting Congress. Transactions (ISSN 0074-4557); S D C E International Die Casting Congress. Transactions; National Die Casting Congress. Transactions.

620.1   AT   ISSN 0311-8185
N.A.T.A. ANNUAL DIRECTORY. 1968. a. Aus.$140. National Association of Testing Authorities, 7 Leeds St., Rhodes, N.S.W. 2138, Australia. TEL 02-736-8222. Ed. P.H. Davies. circ. 1,000. **Document type:** directory.
    Incorporates: N A T A Register of Laboratories. Quarterly Amendment Sheets; Which was formerly: N.A.T.A. Directory; Supersedes: N.A.T.A. Index.

620.1 389 016   UK   ISSN 0963-8695
TA417.2   CODEN: NDTIEH
N D T & E INTERNATIONAL; the independent journal of non-destructive testing. 1967. bi-m. £145 in UK and Europe; elsewhere £155. Butterworth - Heinemann (Subsidiary of: Reed International PLC), Linacre House, Jordan Hill, Oxford OX2 8DP, England. TEL 0865-310366. FAX 0865-310898. TELEX 83111 BHPOXF G. (Subscr. to: Turpin Transactions Ltd., Distribution Centre, Blackhorse Rd., Letchworth, Herts SG6 1HN, England. TEL 0462-672555) Ed. Lynne Clayton. adv.; bk.rev.; abstr.; bibl.; charts; stat.; index. (also avail. in microform from UMI; back issues avail.) **Indexed:** Abstr.Bull.Inst.Pap.Chem., Appl.Mech.Rev., B.C.I.R.A., BMT, Br.Tech.Ind., C.R.I. Abstr., Chem.Abstr., Curr.Cont., Eng.Ind., Int.Aerosp.Abstr., Met.Abstr., Sci.Abstr., Sh.& Vib.Dig., W.R.C.Inf., World Alum.Abstr. **Document type:** academic/scholarly publication.
—Faxon; UnCover; SWETS; UMI. **CCC.**
    Former titles: N D T International (ISSN 0308-9126); Non-Destructive Testing (ISSN 0029-1021)
Refereed Serial

620.1   UK   ISSN 0965-9773
T174.7   CODEN: NMAEE7
▼**NANOSTRUCTURED MATERIALS**. 1992. 8/yr. £275($420) (effective 1994). (Acta Metallurgica, Inc.) Elsevier Science Ltd., Pergamon, P.O. Box 800, Kidlington, Oxford OX5 1DX, England. TEL 44-865-843000. FAX 44-865-843010. (Subscr. in U.S. and Canada to: Elsevier Science, 660 White Plains Rd., Tarrytown, NY 10591-5153. TEL 914-524-9200. FAX 914-333-2444) Ed.Bd. (also avail. in microform from UMI; back issues avail.) **Document type:** academic/scholarly publication.
—BLDSC (6015.335535); EI; SWETS; UMI. **CCC.**
    Description: Covers the synthesis, processing, theory, computational modeling, structure, properties, performance and applications of nanostructured materials of all types.
Refereed Serial

NAUCNO-TEHNICKI PREGLED. see *ENGINEERING — Chemical Engineering*

620.11 621.9   CC   ISSN 1000-0925
NEIRANJI GONGCHENG/CHINESE INTERNAL COMBUSTION ENGINE ENGINEERING. (Text in Chinese) q. $1.50 per no. Guoji Shudian - China International Book Trading Corp., P.O. Box 399, Beijing 100044, People's Republic of China.

620.1   AT   ISSN 0157-6461
TA417.2   CODEN: NTAUDZ
NON-DESTRUCTIVE TESTING - AUSTRALIA; a journal of measurement control & testing. 1964. m. Aus.$72. (Australian Institute for Non-Destructive Testing) Research Publications Pty. Ltd., 27A Boronia Rd., Vermont, Vic. 3133, Australia. TEL 03-873-1450. Ed. G.G. Martin. adv.; bk.rev.; bibl.; charts; illus. circ. 750. **Indexed:** AESIS, Aus.Rd.Ind., Met.Abstr.
—BLDSC (6117.012000).
    Former titles: Non-Destructive Testing; Testing, Instruments, and Controls (ISSN 0040-3997).

620.11   US   ISSN 1058-9759
TA417.2   CODEN: NTEVEP
NONDESTRUCTIVE TESTING AND EVALUATION. 1982. 6/yr. 80 ECU (effective 1993). Gordon and Breach Science Publishers, 820 Town Center Dr., Langhorne, PA 19047. TEL 215-750-2642. FAX 215-750-6343. (UK subscr. to: P.O. Box 90, Reading, Berkshire RG1 8JL, England. TEL 0734-560-080) Ed. Stuart Palmer. (also avail. in microform) **Indexed:** Int.Aerosp.Abstr., Met.Abstr., World Alum.Abstr.
—BLDSC (6117.044700). **CCC.**
    Formerly (until 1988): Nondestructive Testing Communications (ISSN 0278-0895)
Refereed Serial

620.11   US   ISSN 0730-7152
NONDESTRUCTIVE TESTING MONOGRAMS AND TRACTS. 1983. irreg., vol.6, 1988. Gordon & Breach Science Publishers, 820 Town Center Dr., Langhorne, PA 19047. TEL 215-750-2642. FAX 215-750-6343. (UK subscr. to: P.O. Box 90, Reading, Berkshire RG1 8JL, England. TEL 0734-560-080) Ed. W. McGonnagle.
—BLDSC (6117.047000).
Refereed Serial

620   US
NORTHWESTERN UNIVERSITY. MATERIALS RESEARCH CENTER. ANNUAL TECHNICAL REPORT. 1961. a. free. (National Science Foundation) Northwestern University, Materials Research Center, 2145 Sheridan Rd., Evanston, IL 60208-3116. TEL 708-491-3606. FAX 312-491-4181. circ. controlled. (processed) **Document type:** academic/scholarly publication.

620.11 620   SZ   ISSN 0029-5493
TK9001   CODEN: NEDEAU
NUCLEAR ENGINEERING AND DESIGN; an international journal devoted to the thermal, mechanical, materials, and structural aspects of nuclear fission energy. (Text in English) 1965. 24/yr. (in 8 vols.; 3 nos./vol.). 4040 SFr.($2748) (combined with Fusion Engineering and Design 4774 SFr.($3480)) (effective 1994). Elsevier Science S.A., P.O. Box 546, CH-1001 Lausanne 1, Switzerland. TEL 41-21-3207381. FAX 41-21-3235444. TELEX 450620-ELSA-CH. (Subscr. in U.S. and Canada to: Elsevier Science Inc., Box 882, Madison Sq. Sta., New York, NY 10159. TEL 212-989-5800. FAX 212-633-3990) Ed. K. Kussmaul. adv.; bk.rev.; charts; index. (also avail. in microform from UMI; back issues avail.) **Indexed:** Abstr.J.Earthq.Eng., Appl.Mech.Rev., CAD CAM Abstr., Cadscan, Chem.Abstr., Curr.Cont., Energy Ind., Energy Info.Abstr., Eng.Ind., Fluidex, Foul.Prev.Res.Dig., Geotech.Abstr., Ind.Sci.Rev., Lead Abstr., Met.Abstr., Pollut.Abstr., Risk Abstr., Sci.Abstr., Sh.& Vib.Dig., World Alum.Abstr., Zincscan. **Document type:** academic/scholarly publication.
—BLDSC (6180.713000); Faxon; UnCover; SWETS; CASDDS. **CCC.**
    Formerly: Nuclear Structural Engineering (ISSN 0369-5816)
    Description: For civil, mechanical and chemical engineers. Focuses on problems with nuclear fission and fusion energy.
Refereed Serial

PHALANX; bulletin of military operations research and related sciences. see *MILITARY*

620.11 540 530   UK   ISSN 0264-729X
PHYSICS AND CHEMISTRY OF MATERIALS TREATMENT. English translation of: Fizika i Khimiya Obrabotki Materialov (UR ISSN 0015-3214) 1983. bi-m. £220($350) (Rossiiskaya Akademiya Nauk, RU) Riecansky Science Publishing Co., 7 Meadow Walk, Great Abington, Cambridge CB1 6AZ, England. TEL 0223-893295. FAX 0223-893295. Ed. V.E. Riecansky. (back issues avail.) **Indexed:** Eng.Ind., Met.Abstr., Phys.Abstr.
—BLDSC (0416.825000); Faxon; SWETS.

ENGINEERING — ENGINEERING MECHANICS AND MATERIALS

531 KR ISSN 0556-171X
CODEN: PPCNBG
PROBLEMY PROCHNOSTI; vsesoyuznyi nauchno-tekhnicheskii zhurnal. English translation: Strength of Materials (US ISSN 0039-2316) (Text in Russian; summaries in English and Russian) 1969. m. $239. (Akademiya Nauk Ukrainy, Institut Problem Prochnosti) Vidavnitstvo Naukova Dumka, Vul. Tereshchenkivska 3, 252601 Kiev, Ukraine. TEL 296-56-57. (Dist. in U.S. by: 4956 Boiling Brook Pkwy., Rockville, MD 20852. TEL 301-881-5973. FAX 301-881-1637) Ed. G.S. Pisarenko. bk.rev.; bibl.; index. circ. 2,150. **Indexed:** Chem.Abstr., Int.Aerosp.Abstr., ISMEC, Met.Abstr., Sci.Abstr., World Alum.Abstr.
—BLDSC (0133.595000); CASDDS. **CCC.**

620.1 621.3 JA
PROCEEDINGS OF THE SYMPOSIUM ON ELECTRICAL INSULATING MATERIALS/DENKI ZETSUEN ZAIRYO SHIMPOJUMU YOKOSHU. (Text in English, Japanese) 1968. a. Institute of Electrical Engineers of Japan, Committee on Dielectrics and Electrical Insulation - Denki Gakkai Yudo Zetsuen Zairyo Gijutsu linkai, 12-1, Yuraku-cho 1-chome, Chiyoda-ku, Tokyo 100, Japan. **Indexed:** Eng.Ind. **Document type:** proceedings.

666 UK ISSN 0960-3158
CODEN: PADMEI
PROCESSING OF ADVANCED MATERIALS. 1991. q. £120 to institutions in EC nations (North America $210; elsewhere £130). Chapman & Hall, 2-6 Boundary Row, London SE1 8HN, England. TEL 071-865-0066. FAX 071-522-9623. TELEX 290164-CHAPMAG. (Dist. by: International Thomson Publishing Services, N. Way, Andover, Hants. SP10 5BE, England. TEL 0264-342919; US addr.: Chapman & Hall, Journals Promotion Department, One Penn Plaza, 41st Fl., New York, NY 10019. TEL 212-564-1060. FAX 212-564-1505) Eds. J.A. McGeough, M. Datta. **Document type:** academic/scholarly publication.
—BLDSC (6849.993400); CASDDS.
Description: Publishes original papers on the theoretical, experimental, and industrial research and development work in advanced materials.
Refereed Serial

620.11 FR ISSN 0999-4297
PRODUITS EQUIPEMENTS INDUSTRIELS. Abbreviated title: P E I. 1989. 10/yr. 500 F. 128 rue d'Aguesseau, 92100 Boulogne-Billancourt, France. TEL 46-03-44-99. FAX 48-25-14-00. Ed. Robert Fraisse. adv. circ. 50,010.

620.1 UK ISSN 0079-6425
QC1 CODEN: PRMSAQ
PROGRESS IN MATERIALS SCIENCE; an international review journal. 1949. 5/yr. £316($485) (effective 1994). Elsevier Science Ltd., Pergamon, P.O. Box 800, Kidlington, Oxford OX5 1DX, England. TEL 44-865-843000. FAX 44-865-843010. (Subscr. in U.S. and Canada to: Elsevier Science, 660 White Plains Rd., Tarrytown, NY 10591-5153. TEL 914-524-9200. FAX 914-333-2444) Ed.Bd. index. (also avail. in microfilm from UMI) **Indexed:** Appl.Mech.Rev., Chem.Abstr., Curr.Cont., Eng.Ind., GeoRef., Ind.Sci.Rev., Int.Aerosp.Abstr., Met.Abstr., Phys.Ber., Sci.Abstr., World Alum.Abstr. **Document type:** academic/scholarly publication.
—BLDSC (6868.900000); El; Faxon; UnCover; SWETS; UMI; CASDDS. **CCC.**
Description: Reviews of recent advances in the science of materials, with emphasis on the fundamentals of the subject.
Refereed Serial

620 700 SP ISSN 0213-6171
PROYECTO 2000; ingenieria del diseno y desarrollo de los productos. 1984. bi-m. 6300 ptas.($79) (effective 1993). Pulsar, S.A., Gran Via Corts Catalanes, 322-324, 08004 Barcelona, Spain. TEL 3-425-45-44. FAX 3-425-03-68. Ed. Daniel Crespo. adv.; bk.rev.; bibl.; charts; illus. circ. 5,000.

QUARTERLY JOURNAL OF MECHANICS AND APPLIED MATHEMATICS. see *MATHEMATICS*

RANDOM MATERIALS AND PROCESSES. see *PHYSICS*

620 CL
REVISTA DE INGENIERIA MECANICA. 1976. s-a. free. Universidad Catolica de Valparaiso, Escuela de Mecanica, Casilla 4059, Valparaiso, Chile. Ed. Ramon Aldunate B. abstr.; illus. circ. 350.

620.1 540 FR ISSN 1169-7954
REVUE DES COMPOSITES ET DES MATERIAUX AVANCES. 1991. 2/yr. 480 F. (foreign 580 F.). Editions Hermes, 14 rue Lantiez, 75017 Paris, France. TEL 42-29-44-66. FAX 42-29-15-56. Ed. Daniel Gay.
Formerly (until 1992): Revue des Composites et des Nouveaux Materiaux (ISSN 1169-7946)

620.1 540 FR
▼**REVUE EUROPEENNE DES ELEMENTS FINIS.** 1992. 4/yr. 750 F. (foreign 850 F.). (Ministere de la Recherche et de l'Espace) Editions Hermes, 14 rue Lantiez, 75017 Paris, France. TEL 42-29-44-66. FAX 42-29-15-56. Ed. Chantal Menasce. adv. contact: Jean Philippe.

620.11 FR
REVUE FRANCAISE DE LOGISTIQUE. 10/yr. Sepaic, 42 rue du Louvre, B.P. 551, 75027 Paris Cedex 01, France. TEL 42-21-84-00. FAX 42-21-85-97. TELEX 212 646 F. Ed. Catherine Fournier. circ. 10,000.

620.1 JA ISSN 0917-0928
RYUSHISEN NO SENTANTEKI OYO GIJUTSU NI KANSURU WAKUSHOPPU/PROCEEDINGS OF THE WORKSHOP ON BEAM ENGINEERING OF ADVANCED MATERIAL SYNTHESES. (Text in English, Japanese; summaries in English) 1990. a. (Ryushisen Gijutsu Wakushoppu Jikko linkai - Beam Engineering Workshop Committee) Ionics Co., Ltd., 3-4, Koishikawa 2-chome, Bunkyo-ku, Tokyo 112, Japan. **Document type:** proceedings.

620.11 US ISSN 0091-1062
TL950 CODEN: SAJUAX
S A M P E JOURNAL. 1965. bi-m. $65 (foreign $105). Society for the Advancement of Material and Process Engineering, S A M P E Journal, Covina, CA 91724. TEL 818-331-0610. FAX 818-332-8929. 1161 Parkview Dr. adv.; bk.rev.; abstr.; tr.lit. circ. 8,000. (back issues avail.; reprint service avail.) **Indexed:** Abstr.Bull.Inst.Pap.Chem., ASCA, Chem.Abstr., Corros.Abstr., Curr.Cont., Met.Abstr., World Alum.Abstr.
—BLDSC (8072.480000); El; Faxon; UnCover; SWETS; CASDDS. **CCC.**
Description: Provides coverage of all aspects of advanced materials and processes technology. Contains reports on materials applications, materials and processes in dentistry, composite bonding, lubrication, polymers, surface coating, automation and fiber optics.

620.1 389 US ISSN 1046-6789
S E M PROCEEDINGS. (Former issuing body: Society for Experimental Stress Analysis) 1943. a. $100. Society for Experimental Mechanics, 7 School St., Bethel, CT 06801. TEL 203-790-6373. illus.; index, cum.index: vols.1-50. **Indexed:** Chem.Abstr., Eng.Ind., Met.Abstr.
—Faxon. **CCC.**
Formerly: S E S A Proceedings (ISSN 0036-1313)

620.1 US ISSN 0080-7559
SCIENCE OF ADVANCED MATERIAL AND PROCESS ENGINEERING SERIES. (Spring Symposia) 1959. a. $85. Society for the Advancement of Material and Process Engineering, Box 2459, Covina, CA 91722. TEL 818-331-0610. FAX 818-332-8929. **Indexed:** Chem.Abstr. **Document type:** monographic series.
—CCC.
Refereed Serial

SEISANZAI/INDUSTRIAL MARKETING. see *BUSINESS AND ECONOMICS — Marketing And Purchasing*

620.112 JA ISSN 0914-9902
SHIN BUSSHITSU KENKYU KONDANKAI KENKYU HAPPYOKAI YOKOSHU/NEW MATERIALS RESEARCH SYMPOSIUM. PREPRINTS. (Text in English, Japanese; summaries in English) 1987. 2/yr. 3000 Yen. (Shin Busshitsu Kenkyu Kondankai - Organizing Committee of New Materials Research Symposium) Aionikusu K.K. - Ionics Co., Ltd., 3-4, Koishikawa 2-chome, Bunkyo-ku, Tokyo 112, Japan.

620.11 US ISSN 0583-1024
Z5853.V6 CODEN: SHVDAN
THE SHOCK AND VIBRATION DIGEST. 1969. bi-m. $250 (Canada $275; elsewhere $300). Vibration Institute, 6262 S. Kingery Hwy., Ste. 212, Willowbrook, IL 60514. TEL 708-654-2254. FAX 708-654-2271. Ed. Vicki M. Pate. bk.rev.; abstr.; index. circ. 1,000. (also avail. in microform from UMI; reprint service avail. from UMI) **Indexed:** BMT, Deep Sea Res.& Oceanogr.Abstr., Excerp.Med., Fluidex, Fuel & Energy Abstr., Int.Packag.Abstr., Sh.& Vib.Dig. **Document type:** academic/scholarly publication.
●Also available online.
—BLDSC (8267.470000); Faxon; UnCover; SWETS; UMI.

621.9 US ISSN 0081-1653
SOCIETY OF MANUFACTURING ENGINEERS. TECHNICAL PAPERS. (Published in sets on various topics) q. $845 (microfiche $795). Society of Manufacturing Engineers, One SME Dr., Box 930, Dearborn, MI 48121-0930. TEL 313-271-1500. FAX 313-271-2861. TELEX 297742 SME UR (VIA RCA). (also avail. in microfiche)
—CCC.

620.11 621.8 US
SOUTHERN ILLINOIS UNIVERSITY, CARBONDALE. MATERIALS TECHNOLOGY CENTER. CONFERENCE PROCEEDINGS. 1985. irreg., 1992. price varies. Southern Illinois University, Carbondale, Materials Technology Center, Carbondale, IL 62901. TEL 618-536-7525. FAX 618-453-8216. (back issues avail.) **Document type:** proceedings.
Description: Covers carbon-composite and other materials technologies.

620.11 621.8 US
SOUTHERN ILLINOIS UNIVERSITY, CARBONDALE. MATERIALS TECHNOLOGY CENTER. DISTINGUISHED LECTURES SERIES. 1985. irreg., latest 1990. $25 per no. Southern Illinois University, Carbondale, Materials Technology Center, Carbondale, IL 62901. TEL 618-536-7525. FAX 618-453-8216. (back issues avail.) **Document type:** monographic series.
Description: Includes papers on carbon and carbon composite materials.

STANDARD SPECIFICATIONS FOR TRANSPORTATION MATERIALS AND METHODS OF SAMPLING AND TESTING. see *METROLOGY AND STANDARDIZATION*

620.1 UK
STRATA. q. Europa Way, Unit 7, Boley Park Industrial Estate, Lichfield, Staffs WS14 9TZ, England. TEL 0543-268977. Ed. Dick Bird. circ. 8,000.

620.1 US ISSN 0039-2316
TA405 CODEN: SMTLB5
STRENGTH OF MATERIALS. English translation of: Problemy Prochnosti (KR ISSN 0556-171X) 1969. m. $1345 (foreign $1575) (effective 1994). (Ukrainian Academy of Sciences, KR) Plenum Publishing Corp., Consultants Bureau, 233 Spring St., New York, NY 10013-1578. TEL 212-620-8468. FAX 212-463-0742. TELEX 23-421139. Ed. V.T. Troshchenko. (also avail. in microfilm from JSC; back issues avail.) **Indexed:** Appl.Mech.Rev., Energy Res.Abstr., INSPEC, ISMEC, Solid St.Abstr. **Document type:** academic/scholarly publication.
—BLDSC (0425.890300); Faxon; UnCover; UMI. **CCC.**
Refereed Serial

620.11 690 RU ISSN 0039-2383
STROITEL'NAYA MEKHANIKA I RASCHET SOORUZHENII. English translation: Soviet Journal on Structural Mechanics and Design of Structures. 1959. bi-m. 24 Rub. (Gosstroi) Stroiizdat, Shchousseva, rm. 60, Moscow, Russia. Ed. A. Smirnof. bk.rev.; charts; illus.; index.
—BLDSC (0170.700000).

SURFACE ENGINEERING. see *METALLURGY*

SURFACE MODIFICATION TECHNOLOGY NEWS. see *PHYSICS*

620 US ISSN 0886-618X
SURFACE MOUNT TECHNOLOGY TODAY.* Short title: S M T T. 1985. m. $395. Micro Process Technology, 6 Sea Shell Cir., Half Moon Bay, CA 94019-2319. TEL 408-298-4264. Ed. David H. Francis. (looseleaf format; back issues avail.)

620.1 SZ ISSN 0379-6779
TN693.T7 CODEN: SYMEDZ
SYNTHETIC METALS; an international journal integrating research and applications on intercalation compounds of graphite, transition metal compounds, and quasi-one-dimensional conductors. (Text in English) 1979. 24/yr. (in 8 vols.; 3 nos./vol.). 2960 SFr.($2014) (effective 1994). Elsevier Science S.A., P.O. Box 564, CH-1001 Lausanne 1, Switzerland. TEL 41-21-3207381. FAX 41-21-3235444. TELEX 450620-ELSA-CH. (Subscr. in U.S. and Canada to: Elsevier Science Inc., Box 882, Madison Sq. Sta., New York, NY 10159. TEL 212-989-5800. FAX 212-633-3990) Ed. A.J. Heeger. bk.rev.; pat. (also avail. in microform from UMI) **Indexed:** ASCA, Chem.Abstr., Chem.Infd., Curr.Cont., Met.Abstr., Phys.Ber., Sci.Abstr., World Alum.Abstr. **Document type:** academic/scholarly publication.
—BLDSC (8586.889000); EI; Faxon; UnCover; SWETS; CASDDS. **CCC**.
 Description: Publishes original research papers, short communications and subject reviews dealing with research on and applications of synthetic metals.
 Refereed Serial

620.1 530 US ISSN 0073-5264
CODEN: ITAMCN
T & A M REPORT. 1946. irreg., no.437, 1979. University of Illinois at Urbana-Champaign, Department of Theoretical and Applied Mechanics, 216 Talbot Laboratory, Urbana, IL 61801. TEL 217-333-1000. circ. 120 (controlled).

TECHNICAL AID TO THE DISABLED JOURNAL. see *HANDICAPPED*

620.1 JA ISSN 0563-6590
CODEN: TDSKBD
TOHOKU UNIVERSITY. RESEARCH INSTITUTE FOR STRENGTH AND FRACTURE OF MATERIALS. REPORTS/TOHOKU DAIGAKU KOGAKUBU ZAIRYO KYODO KENKYU SHISETSU HOKOKU. (Text in English) 1965. s-a. exchange basis. Tohoku Daigaku, Kogakubu Zairyo Kyodo Kenkyu Shisetsu - Tohoku University, Research Institute for Strength and Fracture of Materials, Aoba, Aramaki, Sendai-shi, Miyagi-ken 980, Japan. **Indexed:** Met.Abstr., Sci.Abstr., World Alum.Abstr.

620.1 US
TREATISE ON MATERIALS SCIENCE & TECHNOLOGY. 1972. irreg., vol.33, 1991. Academic Press, Inc., 525 B St., Ste. 1900, San Diego, CA 92101-4495. TEL 619-231-0926. FAX 619-699-6715. (Subscr. to: Order Dept., 6277 Sea Harbor Dr., 4th Fl., Orlando, FL 32887. TEL 800-321-5068) Ed. H. Herman. (reprint service avail. from ISI) **Indexed:** Chem.Abstr.
 Refereed Serial

338.025 US ISSN 1058-9015
U S KEY PERSONNEL LIST. 1971. a. Composite Market Reports, Inc., 7670 Opportunity Rd., Ste. 250, San Diego, CA 92111-2222. TEL 619-560-1085. FAX 619-560-0234. **Document type:** directory.
—**CCC**.
 Description: Lists over 6100 names of individuals, and over 1000 organizations for aerospace and non-aerospace firms, US and Canadian Government agencies, material suppliers, machinery manufacturers, consultants and reps, industry associations, universities, and research institutes.

U.S. OFFICE OF TECHNOLOGY ASSESSMENT. REPORTS. ENERGY AND MATERIALS PROGRAM. see *ENERGY*

669 GW
UNIVERSITAET HANNOVER. INSTITUT FUER STAHLBAU. SCHRIFTENREIHE. 1960. irreg. price varies. Universitaet Hannover, Institut fuer Stahlbau, Callinstr. 32, 30167 Hannover, Germany.
 Formerly: Technische Universitaet Hannover. Lehrstuhl fuer Stahlbau. Schriftenreihe (ISSN 0073-0289)

624.17 GW
UNIVERSITAET HANNOVER. INSTITUT FUER STATIK. MITTEILUNGEN. 1959. irreg., no.40, 1991. price varies. Universitaet Hannover, Institut fuer Statik, Appelstr. 9A, 30167 Hannover, Germany. TEL 0511-762-2510. FAX 0511-762-4209. Ed. H. Rothert. circ. 150. **Document type:** monographic series.
—BLDSC (5855.400000).
 Formerly: Technische Universitaet Hannover. Institut fuer Statik. Mitteilungen (ISSN 0073-0300)

620.1 CN ISSN 0317-7130
UNIVERSITY OF WATERLOO. SOLID MECHANICS DIVISION. PAPERS. 1969. irreg. free. University of Waterloo, Solid Mechanics Division, Waterloo, Ont. N2L 3G1, Canada. TEL 519-885-1211.

620.1 CN ISSN 0317-7114
UNIVERSITY OF WATERLOO. SOLID MECHANICS DIVISION. REPORTS. 1969. irreg. free. University of Waterloo, Solid Mechanics Division, Waterloo, Ont. N2L 3G1, Canada. TEL 519-885-1211.
 Formerly: University of Waterloo. Solid Mechanics Division. Technical Notes.

620.1 CN ISSN 0318-3122
UNIVERSITY OF WATERLOO. SOLID MECHANICS DIVISION. STUDIES SERIES. 1969. irreg. price varies. University of Waterloo, Solid Mechanics Division, Waterloo, Ont. N2L 3G1, Canada. TEL 519-885-1211.
—BLDSC (8309.944000).

V D I INFORMATIONSDIENST. KALTMASSIVUMFORMUNG. see *METALLURGY*

621 RU ISSN 0042-4633
CODEN: VMASAV
VESTNIK MASHINOSTROENIYA. 1921. m. 129.60 Rub. (Gosudarstvennyi Komitet Soveta Ministrov po Nauke i Tekhnike) Izdatel'stvo Mashinostroenie, 4, Stromynsky per., 107076 Moscow, Russia. TEL 095-269-7141. FAX 095-269-4897. Ed. D.I. Polyakov. adv.: page DM.4000. bk.rev.; abstr.; bibl.; charts; illus.; index. circ. 8,000. **Indexed:** Appl.Mech.Rev., BMT, C.I.S. Abstr., Chem.Abstr., Eng.Ind., ISMEC, Met.Abstr., Sci.Abstr., World Alum.Abstr. **Document type:** academic/scholarly publication.
—BLDSC (0033.300000); CASDDS. **CCC**.
 Description: Covers the aspects of the development of the machine building industry as a whole, development and introduction of high technology, new types of materials, including composite materials, plastics, ceramics, technical renovation of enterprises, improvements in the organization of production, environmental protection.

620.11 US
VIBRATION INSTITUTE. ANNUAL MEETING PROCEEDINGS. 1978. a. Vibration Institute, 6262 S. Kingery Hwy., Ste. 212, Willowbrook, IL 60514. TEL 708-654-2254. FAX 708-654-2271. **Document type:** proceedings.
 Description: Introduces vibration, shock and acoustics research presented at meeting.

W R I JOURNAL. (Welding Research Institute) see *METALLURGY — Welding*

620.1 536 JA ISSN 0288-562X
ZEISEI/OSAKA UNIVERSITY. MECHANICAL TESTING FACILITIES OF THE LAW TEMPERATURE CENTER. ANNUAL REPORTS. Variant title: Osaka Daigaku Teion Senta Zeisei Shikenkishitsu Seika Hokokusho. (Text in Japanese) 1983. a. Osaka Daigaku, Teion Senta Zeisei Shikenkishitsu - Osaka University, Low Temperature Center, Mechanical Testing Facilities, 2-1, Yamadaoka, Suita-shi, Osaka 565, Japan.

ENGINEERING — Hydraulic Engineering

627 VE ISSN 0044-6890
AGUA; revista hidraulica. 1971. q. free. Sociedad Venezolana de Ingenieria Hidraulica, Colegio de Ingenieros de Venezuela, Apdo. 2006, Los Caobos, Caracas, Venezuela. (Co-sponsors: Venezuela. Ministerio del Ambiente y Recursos Naturales Renovables; Instituto Nacional de Obras Sanitarias; Laboratorio Nacional de Hidraulica) Ed.Bd. adv.; bk.rev.; bibl.; charts; illus.; stat.; index, cum.index. circ. 2,000.
 Formed by the 1976 merger of: Ingenieria Hidraulica; Instituto Nacional de Obras Sanitarias. Division de Hidrologia. Anuario Climatologico.
 Description: Original research papers in water resources.

627 NZ ISSN 0571-9291
AUSTRALASIAN CONFERENCE ON HYDRAULICS AND FLUID MECHANICS. PROCEEDINGS. 1962. triennial; 9th Auckland. N.Z., 1986. price varies. University of Auckland, Faculty of Engineering, Auckland, New Zealand. TEL 737-999. FAX 366-0702. circ. 300. **Indexed:** GeoRef. **Document type:** proceedings.

AUTOMATION. see *COMPUTERS — Automation*

627 CN ISSN 0005-2892
B C POWER ENGINEER.* 1959. q. Can.$2. Institute of Power Engineers, c/o S.W.T. Gilbert, Ed., 2555 W. 15th Ave., Vancouver, B.C. 9, Canada. illus.

BEITRAEGE ZUR HYDROLOGIE. see *EARTH SCIENCES — Hydrology*

627 JA
BRIDGESTONE MARINE AND INDUSTRY NEWS. (Text in English) 1974. a. free. Bridgestone Corp., International Incustrial Rubber Products Sales Department - Burijisuton K.K. Kogyo Yohin Kaigaibu, 10-1, Kyobashi 1-chome, Chuo-ku, Tokyo 104, Japan.

627 CC ISSN 1001-5485
CHANGJIANG KEXUEYUAN YUANBAO/YANGTZE RIVER SCIENTIFIC RESEARCH JOURNAL. (Text in Chinese; summaries in English) 1984. q. Y89.44($18.94) Changjiang Kexueyuan, Jiu Wan Fang, Zhao Jia Tiao, Wuhan, Hubei 430010, People's Republic of China. TEL 027-229904. TELEX 40139-HBYVO-CH. (Dist. overseas by: China International Book Trading Corp., P.O. Box 399, Beijing, P.R.C.) Ed. Gong Zhaoxiong. **Document type:** proceedings.
—BLDSC (4917.509000).
 Description: Reports mainly scientific research results of large hydroelectric projects. Includes engineering hydraulics, river and sediment engineering, rock and soil mechanics, hydrostructures, engineering materials, seismicity and vibration, and new blasting techniques.

627 JA ISSN 0386-7471
CHOSETSU KOHO NIIGATA/NIIGATA INVESTIGATION AND DESIGN OFFICE. NEWS. (Text in Japanese) 1978. a. Un'yusho Daiichi Kowan Kensetsukyoku, Niigata Chosa Sekkei Jimusho - Ministry of Transport, First District Port Construction Bureau, Niigata Investigation and Design Office, 332, Hakusan'ura 1-chome, Niigata-shi, Niigata-ken 951, Japan. **Document type:** government publication.

627 SZ
CONTROL REVUE. q. 112 SFr. for 2 yrs. Agifa Verlag AG, Bruggacherstr. 26, CH-8117 Faellenden, Switzerland. TEL 01-8256464. FAX 01-8256465. Ed. Rudolph Weber. circ. 7,000. **Document type:** academic/scholarly publication.

D N O C S - FINS E ATIV DADES. (Departamento Nacional de Obras Contra as Secas) see *AGRICULTURE — Crop Production And Soil*

627 DK ISSN 0109-5110
DANISH HYDRAULICS. 1981. a. free. Danish Hydraulic Institute, Agern Alle 5, 2970 Hoersholm, Denmark. TEL 45-45-76-95-55. FAX 45-45-76-25-67. TELEX 37402-DHICPH-DK. Ed. Bo Mogensen. bk.rev.; illus. circ. 7,500. **Document type:** newsletter.

ENGINEERING — HYDRAULIC ENGINEERING

627 624   US
DREDGING CONTRACT NEWS. 1983. fortn. $120. International Dredging Review, Box 1487, Ft. Collins, CO 80522-1487. TEL 303-484-9562. FAX 303-484-5778. Ed. Judith Powers. circ. 65. (looseleaf format; back issues avail.)

627   UK   ISSN 0950-5490
DRIVES AND CONTROLS. 1983. 10/yr. £60 (foreign £65). Kamtech Publishing Ltd., Northdowns House, 2 Stanley Rd., Carshalton, Surrey SM5 4LF, England. TEL 081-669-5227. FAX 081-669-6593. Ed. Bob Dobson. adv.; bk.rev.; index. circ. 18,000. (back issues avail.) **Document type:** trade publication.
    Description: Directed to engineers and managers in the UK who have professional interests in drives, motors, or control systems.

EIDGENOESSISCHE TECHNISCHE HOCHSCHULE ZUERICH. VERSUCHSANSTALT FUER WASSERBAU, HYDROLOGIE UND GLAZIOLOGIE. JAHRESBERICHT. see *EARTH SCIENCES — Hydrology*

EIDGENOESSISCHE TECHNISCHE HOCHSCHULE ZUERICH. VERSUCHSANSTALT FUER WASSERBAU, HYDROLOGIE UND GLAZIOLOGIE. MITTEILUNGEN. see *EARTH SCIENCES — Hydrology*

627   UK
▼**ELSEVIER HANDLING AND PROCESSING OF SOLIDS SERIES.** 1992. irregr. price varies. Elsevier Science Ltd., Books Division, P.O. Box 800, Kidlington, Oxford OX5 1DX, England. TEL 44-865-843000. FAX 44-865-843010. (Subscr. in U.S. and Canada to: Elsevier Science, 660 White Plains Rd., Tarrytown, NY 10591-5153. TEL 914-524-9200) Ed.Bd. bibl. **Document type:** monographic series.
    Description: Scholarly monographs on topics in hydraulics and structural engineering, flow and transfer processes, and environmental engineering aspects of the handling of solids.
    Refereed Serial

ENERGIA ELETTRICA. see *ENGINEERING — Electrical Engineering*

FAIREY IN FOCUS. see *ENGINEERING — Mechanical Engineering*

FLOOD REPORT. see *EARTH SCIENCES — Hydrology*

627 621.5   GW
FLUID; Zeitschrift fuer Hydraulik, Pneumatik, Elektronik. 1967. m. DM.158 (foreign DM.170). Verlag Moderne Industrie, Justus-von-Liebig-Str. 1, 86899 Landsberg, Germany. TEL 08191-125-0. FAX 08191-125-483. Ed. Eugen Muehlberger. adv.: B&W page DM.6070; trim 257 x 178; adv. contact: Ulrich Monschke. bk.rev.; film rev.; charts; illus.; mkt.; pat.; stat.; tr.lit.; index. circ. 11,513. **Indexed:** Fluidex, INIS Atomind. **Document type:** trade publication.
    Former titles: Fluidtechnik; Fluid (ISSN 0015-461X)

621.2 621.5   IT   ISSN 0374-3225
FLUID: APPARECCHIATURE IDRAULICHE E PNEUMATICHE; olio e aria sotto pressione lubrificazione. 1961. m. L.86000 (foreign L.162000). Etas s.r.l., Via Mecenate, 91, 20138 Milan, Italy. TEL 02-580841. FAX 02-58012592. Ed. Rosario Fiansaca. adv.: B&W page L.2400000, color page L.3250000; trim 181 x 270. circ. 5,091. **Indexed:** Fluidex, Sci.Abstr.
    Formerly: Apparecchiature Idrauliche e Pneumatiche (ISSN 0003-6676)
    Description: Industrial application of hydraulics, pneumatics, lubrification techniques, vacuum systems, fluidics and conveyance of "difficult" fluids.

627 621   NE   ISSN 0169-5983
    CODEN: FDRSEH
FLUID DYNAMICS RESEARCH; an international journal. (Text in English) 1986. 12/yr. (in 2 vols.; 3 nos./vol.) fl.848($458) (effective 1994). (Japan Society of Fluid Mechanics, JA) North-Holland (Subsidiary of: Elsevier Science B.V.), P.O. Box 211, 1000 AE Amsterdam, Netherlands. TEL 31-20-5803911. FAX 31-20-5803598. TELEX 18582 ESPA NL. (Subscr. in U.S. and Canada to: Elsevier Science Inc., Box 882, Madison Sq. Sta., New York, NY 10159. TEL 212-989-5800. FAX 212-633-3990) Ed. H. Hasimoto. (reprint service avail. from ISI) **Document type:** academic/scholarly publication.
    —BLDSC (3961.650000); EI; Faxon; UnCover; SWETS. **CCC.**
    Description: Covers all aspects of fluid dynamics.
    Refereed Serial

627   UK   ISSN 0269-6541
FLUID POWER. 1969. irregr., 9th, 1990. Elsevier Science Ltd., Books Division, P.O. Box 800, Kidlington, Oxford OX5 1DX, England. TEL 44-865-843000. FAX 44-865-843010. (Subscr. in U.S. and Canada to: Elsevier Science, 660 White Plains Rd., Tarrytown, NY 10591-5153. TEL 914-524-9200. FAX 914-333-2444) **Document type:** proceedings.
    —BLDSC (3962.200200).
    Supersedes (in 1988): Fluid Power Symposium. Proceedings (ISSN 0140-2099)

620   US
FLUID POWER AND CONTROL SERIES. 1983. irregr. vol.10, 1990. Marcel Dekker, Inc., 270 Madison Ave., New York, NY 10016. TEL 212-696-9000. FAX 212-685-4540; TELEX 421419. Eds. Z.L. Lansky, F. Yeaple.

627   UK
FLUID POWER MAGAZINE. q. P.O. Box 282, Watford, Herts WD1 4EE, England. TEL 0923-226210. FAX 0923-819761. Ed. Robbie Robinson. circ. 15,000.

627   SP   ISSN 0211-1136
FLUIDOS; oleohidraulica, neumatica, automacion. 1972. 10/yr. 7400 ptas.($84) (effective 1992). Publica, S.A., Ecuador, 75, entlo., 08029 Barcelona, Spain. TEL 93-321-50-46. FAX 93-322-19-72. Ed. Juan Balague Castella. circ. 3,000. **Indexed:** Ind.SST.
    —BLDSC (3962.258300).

627   GW
TC1
FRANZIUS - INSTITUT FUER WASSERBAU UND KUESTENINGENIERURWESEN. MITTEILUNGEN. (Text mainly in German; partially in English) 1952. s-a. DM.35. Franzius-Institut fuer Wasserbau und Kuesteningenieurwesen, Universitaet Hannover, Nienburger Str. 4, 30167 Hannover, Germany. TEL 0511-7622572. FAX 0511-762-3456. TELEX 923868-UNIHND. circ. 800. **Indexed:** Deep Sea Res.& Oceanogr.Abstr.
    —BLDSC (5843.730000).
    Formerly: Technische Universitaet Hannover. Franzius - Institut fuer Wasserbau und Kuesteningenieurwesen. Mitteilungen (ISSN 0340-0077)

G T. IL GIORNALE DEL TERMOIDRAULICO. see *ENGINEERING*

627   PL   ISSN 0016-5352
    CODEN: GWTSAV
GAZ, WODA I TECHNIKA SANITARNA. 1921. m. $61. (Polskie Zrzeszenie Inzynierow i Technikow Sanitarnych) Wydawnictwo Czasopism i Ksiazek Technicznych SIGMA - NOT, Ul. Ratuszowa 11, P.O. Box 1004, 00-950 Warsaw, Poland. TEL 48-22-180918. FAX 48-22-192187. TELEX 814550 SIGMA PL. (Dist. by: SIGMA NOT Ltd., Ul. Bartycka 20, 00-716 Warsaw, Poland) Ed. Marek Roman. adv.; bk.rev.; abstr.; bibl.; charts; illus.; index. circ. 3,450. **Indexed:** Biol.Abstr., C.I.S. Abstr., Chem.Abstr., Excerp.Med., INIS Atomind.
    —CASDDS.

627   US
GREAT LAKES AND CONNECTING CHANNELS: WATER LEVELS AND DEPTHS. bi-w. free. U.S. Army, Corps of Engineers, Detroit District, Box 1027, Detroit, MI 48231. TEL 313-226-6443. (also avail. in microfiche from CIS; reprint service avail. from CIS) **Indexed:** Amer.Stat.Ind. (1977-).

600 627 621.8   GW   ISSN 0440-7059
HERION - INFORMATIONEN. 1962. a. free. Herion-Werke KG, Stuttgarter Str. 120, 70736 Fellbach, Germany. TEL (0711)5209-435. FAX 0711-5209-614. Ed. Erich Herion.

HOKKAIDO NO CHUSHO KASEN/MEDIUM AND SMALL SCALE RIVER IN HOKKAIDO. see *WATER RESOURCES*

621.2 621.5   US   ISSN 0018-814X
TC1   CODEN: HYDPAZ
HYDRAULICS & PNEUMATICS; the magazine of fluid power and motion control systems. 1947. m. $45 (free to qualified personnel). Penton Publishing (Subsidiary of: Pittway Company), 1100 Superior Ave., Cleveland, OH 44114-2543. TEL 216-696-7000. FAX 216-696-8765. (Subscr. to: Box 95759, Cleveland, OH 44101) Ed. Dick Schneider. adv.; charts; illus.; pat.; tr.lit.; index; circ. 52,000 (controlled). (also avail. in microform from UMI; reprint service avail. from UMI) **Indexed:** A.S.& T.Ind., Agri.Eng.Abstr., Appl.Mech.Rev., Eng.Ind., Excerp.Med., Fluidex, Ind.Sci.Rev., INIS Atomind., ISMEC, Sci.Abstr., Sh.& Vib.Dig., Tr.& Indus.Ind.
    ●Also available online. **Vendor(s):** DIALOG Information Services, Inc..
    —BLDSC (4342.150000); EI; Faxon; UnCover; SWETS; UMI. **CCC.**
    Former titles (until 1960): Applied Hydraulics and Pneumatics (ISSN 0361-0136); (until 1958): Applied Hydraulics (ISSN 0096-3933)
    Description: Details innovative design ideas, practical applications of components and systems, and continuing constructive updating.

612.8   JA   ISSN 0385-3780
HYDRAULICS AND PNEUMATICS. (Text in Japanese) 1963. m. 1000 Yen per no. Industrial Daily News Ltd. - Nikkan Kogyo Shinbun Ltd., 1-8-10 Kudan Kita, Chiyoda-ku, Tokyo 102, Japan. circ. 24,000. **Indexed:** JTA.

627   FR
HYDRO-PLUS. 6/yr. Hydro-Plus - C M C I, 2 rue Henri Barbusse, 13241 Marseille Cedex 01, France. TEL 91-08-61-14. FAX 91-56-27-82. TELEX 441 247 COMERIN. Ed. Christian Apotheloz. circ. 12,000.

HYDROPNEUMA. see *ENGINEERING — Industrial Engineering*

627   UK   ISSN 0263-4171
TJ898   CODEN: HYTRDM
HYDROTRANSPORT. irregr., 11th, 1988. price varies. Elsevier Science Ltd., Books Division, P.O. Box 800, Kidlington, Oxford OX5 1DX, England. TEL 44-865-843000. FAX 44-865-843010. (Subscr. in U.S. and Canada to: Elsevier Science, 660 White Plains Rd., Tarrytown, NY 10591-5153. TEL 914-524-9200) **Document type:** proceedings.
    —CASDDS. **CCC.**
    Formerly (until 1980): British Hydromechanics Research Association. Proceedings of Hydrotransport (ISSN 0306-6916)

627   GW   ISSN 0073-7755
TD896   CODEN: IABWAP
INDUSTRIEABWAESSER. 1958. a. DM.15. Deutscher Kommunal Verlag GmbH, Roseggerstr. 5a, 40470 Duesseldorf, Germany. TEL 0211-624417. FAX 0211-622998. **Indexed:** Chem.Abstr.
    —CASDDS.

627   CU   ISSN 0253-0678
INGENIERIA HIDRAULICA. 3/yr. $24 in N. America; S. America $25; Europe $26. (Ministerio de Educacion Superior, Instituto Superior Politecnico) Ediciones Cubanas, Obispo No. 527, Apdo. 605, Havana, Cuba.

627   RU
INSTITUT VODNOGO TRANSPORTA, LENINGRAD. GIDROTEKHNICHESKAYA LABORATORIYA. MATERIALY.* (Subseries of: Institut Vodnogo Transporta, Leningrad. Trudy) irregr. 0.85 Rub. Izdatel'stvo Transport, Basmanny tupik 6A, 107174 Moscow, Russia. TEL 095-262-6773. illus.

ENGINEERING — HYDRAULIC ENGINEERING

627   II
INSTITUTION OF ENGINEERS (INDIA). MARINE ENGINEERING DIVISION. JOURNAL. (Text in English) 1978. s-a. Rs.40($5) Institution of Engineers, Marine Engineering Division, 8 Gokhale Rd., Calcutta 700 020, India. TEL 033-288334. FAX 033-288345. TELEX 0217885 IEIC IN. Ed. K.N. Majumdar. adv.; charts; illus.; index. circ. 2,000.

INSTITUTUL POLITEHNIC DIN IASI. BULETINUL. SECTIA VI: CONSTRUCTII. see *BUILDING AND CONSTRUCTION*

INSTITUTUL POLITEHNIC DIN IASI. BULETINUL. SECTIA VII: HIDROTEHNICA. see *EARTH SCIENCES — Hydrology*

627   PL   ISSN 0239-6254
INSTYTUT METEOROLOGII I GOSPODARKI WODNEJ. MATERIALY BADAWCZE. SERIA: INZYNIERIA WODNA/INSTITUTE OF METEOROLOGY AND WATER MANAGEMENT. RESEARCH PAPERS SERIES: WATER ENGINEERING. (Text in Polish; summaries in English and Russian) 1979. irreg. $15. Instytut Meteorologii i Gospodarki Wodnej - Institute of Meteorology and Water Management, 61 Podlesna St., 01-673 Warsaw, Poland. FAX 48-22-345466. TELEX 814331. circ. 200.
  Description: Articles on water engineering, dams, river regulation, measurements and research works.

627   NE   ISSN 0074-1477
INTERNATIONAL ASSOCIATION FOR HYDRAULIC RESEARCH. CONGRESS PROCEEDINGS. 1935. biennial, 24th, 1991, Madrid. fl.330 for 24th Congress. International Association for Hydraulic Research - Association Internationale de Recherches Hydrauliques, Rotterdamseweg 185, P.O. Box 177, 2600 MH Delft, Netherlands. TEL 31-15-569353. FAX 31-15-619674. TELEX 38176. (also avail. in microform) **Indexed:** Intl.Civil Eng.Abstr., Soft.Abstr.Eng. **Document type:** proceedings.
  —BLDSC (3415.450000).
  Description: Proceedings published in host countries.

627.52   II   ISSN 0074-2732
INTERNATIONAL COMMISSION ON IRRIGATION AND DRAINAGE. CONGRESS REPORTS. 1951. triennial since 1951, 14th Rio de Janeiro, Brazil. price varies. International Commission on Irrigation and Drainage - Commission Internationale des Irrigations et du Drainage, 48 Nyaya Marg, Chanakyapuri, New Delhi 1100021, India.

627 624   US   ISSN 0737-8181
INTERNATIONAL DREDGING REVIEW. 1981. 6/yr. $35. Box 1487, Fort Collins, CO 80522-1487. TEL 303-484-9562. FAX 303-484-5778. Ed. Judith Powers. adv. contact: Annie Mullins. bk.rev.; illus.; tr.lit.; index. circ. 2,200. (back issues avail.) **Indexed:** Fluidex. **Document type:** trade publication.
  —CCC.
  Description: Covers engineering, economic and environmental aspects of dredging activities around the world, including new developments in equipment, legislation and insurance.

620.106 621.381   UK   ISSN 0271-2091
QA901   CODEN: IJNFDW
INTERNATIONAL JOURNAL FOR NUMERICAL METHODS IN FLUIDS. 1980. 24/yr. $1225 (effective 1994). John Wiley & Sons Ltd., Journals, Baffins Ln., Chichester, Sussex PO19 1UD, England. TEL 0243-779777. FAX 0243-775878. TELEX 86290-WIBOOK-G. Eds. Cedric Taylor, Philip M. Gresho. (reprint service avail. from ISI,SWZ,UMI) **Indexed:** Abstr.Bull.Inst.Pap.Chem., Appl.Mech.Rev., BMT, Compumath, Curr.Cont., Fluidex, Geo.Abstr., INIS Atomind., Int.Aerosp.Abstr., Math.R., Phys.Ber., Sci.Abstr. **Document type:** academic/scholarly publication.
  —BLDSC (4542.406000); El; Faxon; SWETS; UMI; CASDDS. **CCC.**
  Description: Provides information relating to the development, refinement and application of computer-based numerical techniques for solving problems in fluids.

627   CN   ISSN 1180-0402
INTERNATIONAL JOURNAL OF WATER JET TECHNOLOGY. 1991. irreg. Can.$70 to individuals; institutions Can.$210. International Society of Water Jet Technology, Box 46039, 2339 Ogilvie Rd., Glouchester, ON K1J 9M7, Canada. TEL 613-993-2731. FAX 613-952-1395. Ed. M.M. Vijay.
  —Faxon; UnCover.
  Refereed Serial

INTERNATIONAL WATER CONFERENCE. PROCEEDINGS. see *WATER RESOURCES*

JET CUTTING TECHNOLOGY. see *ENGINEERING — Mechanical Engineering*

627   JA   ISSN 0385-308X
       CODEN: SDKND7
JIBAN SUIRI JIKKEN SHISETSU NENPO/HYDROSCIENCE AND GEOTECHNOLOGY LABORATORY. ANNUAL REPORT. (Text in English, Japanese; summaries in English) 1975. a. Saitama Daigaku, Kogakubu Fuzoku, Jiban Suiri Jikken Shisetsu - Saitama University, Faculty of Engineering, Hydroscience and Geotechnology Laboratory, 255, Shimookubo, Urawa-shi, Saitama-ken 338, Japan.
  —CASDDS.

532   UK   ISSN 0022-1120
QA901   CODEN: JFLSA7
JOURNAL OF FLUID MECHANICS. 1956. 24/yr. £339($595) to individuals (overseas $504); institutions £649 (overseas £814 ($1197)). Cambridge University Press, Edinburgh Bldg., Shaftesbury Rd., Cambridge CB2 2RU, England. TEL 0223-312393. FAX 0223-315052. TELEX 851817256. (N. American addr.: Cambridge University Press, Journals Dept., 40 W. 20th St., New York, NY 10011. TEL 212-924-3900. FAX 212-691-3239) Ed. G.K. Batchelor. adv.; bk.rev.; charts; illus.; index, cum.index: vols.1-20, 21-40. (also avail. in microform from UMI,PMC; back issues avail.; reprint service avail. SWZ) **Indexed:** Abstr.Bull.Inst.Pap.Chem., Appl.Mech.Rev., Biol.Abstr., BMT, Br.Tech.Ind, Chem.Abstr., Chem.Eng.Abstr., Curr.Cont., Deep Sea Res.& Oceanogr.Abstr., E&P Hlth. (1993-), Eng.Ind., Excerp.Med., Fluidex, Foul.Prev.Res.Dig., Fuel & Energy Abstr., Gas Process.& Ppl. (1993-), Geo.Abstr., GeoRef., Ind.Sci.Rev., INIS Atomind., Intl.Civil Eng.Abstr., ISMEC, Math.R., Meteor.& Geoastrophys.Abstr., Off.Tech. (1993-), Petrol.Abstr. (1961-), Phys.Ber., Sci.Abstr., Sel.Water Res.Abstr., Soft.Abstr.Eng., W.R.C.Inf. **Document type:** academic/scholarly publication.
  —BLDSC (4984.500000); Faxon; UnCover; SWETS; UMI; CASDDS.
  Description: Explores fundamental fluid mechanics and its applications to aeronautics, astrophysics, chemical and mechanical engineering, colloid science, combustion, hydraulics and meteorology.

627   US   ISSN 0098-2202
TA357   CODEN: JFEGA4
JOURNAL OF FLUIDS ENGINEERING. 1919. q. $100 to non-members; members $29. American Society of Mechanical Engineers, 345 E. 47th St., New York, NY 10017. TEL 212-705-7703. Ed. F.M. White. adv.; bk.rev. circ. 4,000. (also avail. in microform from UMI,PMC; reprint service avail. from UMI) **Indexed:** A.S.& T.Ind., Abstr.Bull.Inst.Pap.Chem., API Abstr., API Catal., API Hlth.& Environ., API Oil., API Pet.Ref., API Pet.Subst., API Transport., Appl.Mech.Rev., Br.Rail.Bd., Chem.Abstr., Chem.Eng.Abstr., Curr.Cont., E&P Hlth. (1993-), Eng.Ind., Excerp.Med., Fluidex, Gas Process.& Ppl. (1993-), Ind.Sci.Rev., INIS Atomind., Int.Build.Serv.Abstr., ISMEC, Off.Tech. (1993-), Petrol.Abstr. (1974-), Sci.Abstr., Sci.Cit.Ind., T.C.E.A.
  —BLDSC (8896.920000); El; Faxon; SWETS; UMI; CASDDS. **CCC.**
  Supersedes in part: Journal of Basic Engineering (ISSN 0021-9223)
  Refereed Serial

627   US   ISSN 1051-2705
TC1
▼**JOURNAL OF HYDRAULIC ENGINEERING (BRISTOL).** 1992. q. £147($250) Taylor & Francis, 1900 Frost Rd., Ste. 101, Bristol, PA 19007-1598. TEL 215-785-5800. FAX 215-785-5515.
  Description: Provides current information on various aspects of hydraulic engineering research, particularly in China.
  Refereed Serial

JOURNAL OF HYDRAULIC ENGINEERING (NEW YORK). see *ENGINEERING — Civil Engineering*

627   NE   ISSN 0022-1686
       CODEN: JHYRAF
JOURNAL OF HYDRAULIC RESEARCH. (Text in English; summaries in English, French) 1963. 6/yr. fl.550 (effective 1994). International Association for Hydraulic Research - Association Internationale de Recherches Hydrauliques, Rotterdamsweg 185, P.O. Box 177, 2600 MH Delft, Netherlands. TEL 31-15-569353. FAX 31-51-619674. TELEX 38176. acv.; bk.rev.; index. circ. 3,500. (also avail. in microfilm) **Indexed:** Appl.Mech.Rev., Curr.Cont., Deep Sea Res.& Oceanogr.Abstr., Fluidex, GeoRef., Ind.Sci.Rev., Irr.& Drain.Abstr., Sci.Cit.Ind., Sel.Water Res.Abstr., Soils & Fert., W.R.C.Inf. **Document type:** academic/scholarly publication.
  —BLDSC (5003.600000); El; Faxon; UnCover.

627   JA   ISSN 0912-2508
JOURNAL OF HYDROSCIENCE AND HYDRAULIC ENGINEERING. (Text in English) 1983. s-a. 3000 Yen per no. Japan Society on Civil Engineers, Committee on Hydraulic Engineering - Doboku Gakkai Suiri Iinkai, Yotsuya 1-chome, Shinjuku-ku, Tokyo 160, Japan.
  —BLDSC (5003.900000); Faxon.

KOMPASS PROFESSIONNEL. TECHNIQUES HYDRAULIQUES ET PNEUMATIQUES, CLIMATISATION. see *BUSINESS AND ECONOMICS — Trade And Industrial Directories*

MELYEPITESI ES VIZEPITESI SZAKIRODALMI TAJEKOZTATO, CIVIL ENGINEERING & HYDRAULIC ENGINEERING ABSTRACTS. see *ENGINEERING — Abstracting, Bibliographies, Statistics*

386   US
MONTHLY BULLETIN OF LAKE LEVELS FOR THE GREAT LAKES. m. free. U.S. Army, Corps of Engineers, Detroit District, Box 1027, Detroit, MI 48231. TEL 313-226-6443. charts; stat. (also avail. in microfiche from CIS; reprint service avail. from CIS) **Indexed:** Amer.Stat.Ind. (1977-). **Document type:** government publication, bulletin.

627 621 531   JA   ISSN 0286-3154
       CODEN: NAGAE9
NAGARE/JAPAN SOCIETY OF FLUID MECHANICS. JOURNAL. (Text in Japanese; summaries in English, Japanese) 1982 q. Nihon Ryutai Rikigakkai - Japan Society of Fluid Mechanics, 16-5, Haramachi 1-chome, Meguro-ku, Tokyo 152, Japan. **Indexed:** INIS Atomind.
  —CASDDS.

627 011   US   ISSN 0160-8428
TC5   CODEN: PCFPAD
NATIONAL CONFERENCE ON FLUID POWER. PROCEEDINGS. 1947. a. $60 per vol. National Fluid Power Association, 3333 N. Mayfair Rd., Milwaukee, WI 53222-3219. TEL 414-778-3363. FAX 414-778-3361. Ed.Bd. circ. 600. **Document type:** proceedings.
  —BLDSC (6847.850000).
  Formerly: National Conference on Industrial Hydraulics.
  Description: Articles and presentations on research in the field of fluid power by representatives from the industry, government, and academia.

NAUCNO-TEHNICKI PREGLED. see *ENGINEERING — Chemical Engineering*

627   NO
NORWEGIAN HYDROTECHNICAL LABORATORY. BULLETIN. (Text in English) 1959. a. free. Norwegian Hydrotechnical Laboratory, Klaebuveien 153, N-7034 Trondheim-NTH, Norway. circ. 1,200.
  Formerly: Universitet i Trondheim. Norges Tekniske Hoegskole. Vassdrags- og Havnelaboratoriet. Meddlelelse (ISSN 0082-6618)

627.8   US   ISSN 0078-4508
OKLAHOMA. GRAND RIVER DAM AUTHORITY. ANNUAL REPORT. 1967. a. free. Grand River Dam Authority, Box 409, Vinita, OK 74301. TEL 918-256-5545.

2376 ENGINEERING — HYDRAULIC ENGINEERING

621.3   PK   ISSN 0083-8349
PAKISTAN. WATER AND POWER DEVELOPMENT AUTHORITY. REPORT. (Text in English) 1958. a. Rs.250. Water and Power Development Authority, WAPDA House, Shara-e-Quaid-e-Azam, Lahore, Pakistan. TEL 212900. TELEX 44869 WAPDA PK. circ. 1,000.
Description: Report of the total activities of the Water and Power Development Authority in the fields of development of water and power resources and financial status at the end of every financial year.

627   LV   ISSN 0130-8246
                      CODEN: PMVKDF
POLIMERY V MELIORATSII I VODNOM KHOZYAISTVE. 1974. irreg. 0.44 Rub. Latvijas Hidrotehnikas un Melioracijas Zinatniski Petnieciskais Instituts - Latviiskii Naucho-Issledovatel'skii Institut Gidrotekhniki i Melioratsii, Ul. Revoliutsiias, 43, Elgava, Latvia. illus.
—CASDDS.

627   PL   ISSN 0373-8663
TC1
POLITECHNIKA GDANSKA. ZESZYTY NAUKOWE. BUDOWNICTWO WODNE. (Text in English, Polish; summaries in Russian and one West-European language) 1956. irreg. price varies. Politechnika Gdanska, Ul. G. Narutowicza 11-12, 80-952 Gdansk 6, Poland. (Dist. by: Osrodek Rozpowszechniania Wydawnictw Naukowych PAN, Palac Kultury i Nauki, 00-901 Warsaw, Poland) bibl.; charts; illus. **Document type:** academic/scholarly publication.
Description: Focuses on all aspects of hydraulic engineering: constructions, ground mechanics and foundations, hydromechanics and geodesy.

POLITECHNIKA KRAKOWSKA. MONOGRAFIE. SERIA: INZYNIERIA SANITARNA I WODNA. see *WATER RESOURCES*

POLITECHNIKA KRAKOWSKA. ZESZYTY NAUKOWE. INZYNIERIA SANITARNA I WODNA. see *WATER RESOURCES*

627.2   NE   ISSN 0166-5766
TC203   CODEN: PORDBK
PORTS AND DREDGING. (Text in English) 1946. q. free. I H C Holland, P.O. Box 204, 3360 AE Sliedrecht, Netherlands. FAX 31-1840-11884. TELEX 26734. illus. circ. 7,000. **Indexed:** BMT, Fluidex.
—BLDSC (6555.900000).
Supersedes: Ports and Dredging and Oil Report (ISSN 0477-6801); Which was formed by the merger of: Ports and Dredging; Oil Report (Papendrecht).

POWER INTERNATIONAL. see *ENGINEERING — Mechanical Engineering*

627   US
PROFESSIONAL REPORT. 1957. 6/yr. membership. Fluid Power Society, 2433 N. Mayfair Rd., Ste. 111, Milwaukee, WI 53226-1406. TEL 414-257-0910. FAX 414-257-4092. Ed. Jim Morgan. adv. circ. 2,500. **Document type:** newsletter.
Formerly: F P S Newsletter.

620.11   FR
PROMOFLUID. 9/yr. 367 F. (foreign 503 F.). Promotion-Presse International, 7 ter, Cour des Petites-Ecuries, 75010 Paris, France. Ed. H. Thiron. adv. circ. 8,049. **Indexed:** Fluidex.

627   UK
PUMP TALK. 3/yr. Grundfos Pumps, Grovebury Rd., Leighton Buzzard, Beds LU7 8TL, England. TEL 0525-850000. FAX 0525-850011. Ed. Jane Farrar. circ. 30,000.

627 621 531   JA
RANRYU SHINPOJUMU KOEN RONBUNSHU/PROCEEDINGS OF SYMPOSIUM ON TURBULENCE. (Text in English, Japanese) 1984. a. Nihon Ryutai Rikigakkai - Japan Society of Fluid Mechanics, 16-5, Haramachi 1-chome, Meguro-ku, Tokyo 152, Japan. **Document type:** proceedings.

RENMIN HUANG HE/PEOPLE'S YELLOW RIVER. see *GEOGRAPHY*

624   CK   ISSN 0120-0798
REVISTA ACODAL. 1957. bi-m. Col.400($10) Asociacion Colombiana de Ingenieria Sanitaria y Ambiental, Calle 26 no. 2-44, Planta San Diego, Apdo. Aereo 5820, Bogota, Colombia. TEL 572-430617. FAX 572-86030. Dir. Jose David Moreno R. adv. circ. 1,000.

627   SP
REVISTA DE BOMBAS Y COMPRESORES. Short title: R B C. 12/yr. Baeza, 6 1o, puerta 11, 28002 Madrid, Spain. TEL 415-90-72. Ed. J. Luis Dorado.

REVISTA DE PRECOS PARA INSTALACOES ELETRICAS E HIDRAULICAS. see *ENGINEERING — Electrical Engineering*

REVUE TUNISIENNE DE L'EQUIPEMENT. see *ENGINEERING — Civil Engineering*

532   JA
RYUTAI RIKIGAKU KOENKAI KOENSHU/PROCEEDINGS OF THE SYMPOSIUM ON FLUID MECHANICS. (Text in English, Japanese) 1969. a. 3500 Yen. Nihon Koku Uchu Gakkai - Japan Society for Aeronautical and Space Sciences, 18-2, Shinbashi 1-chome, Minato-ku, Tokyo 105, Japan. **Document type:** proceedings.

SAFETY NEWS (DENVER). see *WATER RESOURCES*

627 697   LI   ISSN 0208-2438
SANTECHNIKA IR HIDRAULIKA/SANITARY ENGINEERING AND HYDRAULICS. (Text in Lithuanian, Russian) 1971. a. price varies. Vilnius Technical University, Souletekio aleja 11, 2054 Vilnius, Lithuania. (Co-sponsor: Lithuanian Ministry of Culture and Education) Ed. M. Gedgaudas. charts; illus. circ. 400. **Document type:** academic/scholarly publication.
Description: Covers sanitation of water supply systems, heating and ventilation systems.

627   CC   ISSN 1000-0860
SHUILI SHUIDIAN JISHU/WATER RESOURCES AND HYDROPOWER ENGINEERING. (Text in Chinese) 1959. m. $22.20. (Shuili Shuidian Qingbao Yanjiusuo - Information Research Institute of Water Resources & Electric Power) Shuili Dianli Chubanshe - Water Resources and Electric Power Press, No.6, Sanlihe Lu, Beijing 100044, People's Republic of China. TEL 8413063. FAX 8412023. Ed. He Guxin. adv.: B&W page $1200, color page $2000; trim 260 x 184; adv. contact: Shuquan Zhang. circ. 30,000. **Document type:** bulletin.
Description: Covers water resources, water economics, and river basin planning. Contains papers on exploration, design, construction, operation and management.

627   CC
SHUILI XUEBAO/JOURNAL OF HYDRAULIC ENGINEERING. (Text in Chinese) m. $3 per no. Guoji Shudian, Qikan Bu - China International Book Trading Corp., P.O. Box 399, Beijing 100044, People's Republic of China. **Indexed:** Appl.Mech.Rev., Irr.& Drain.Abstr.

627   PL   ISSN 0208-516X
STEROWANIE I NAPED HYDRAULICZNY. Short title: S I N H. 1980. 6/yr. (Stowarzyszenie Inzynierow i Technikow Mechanikow Polskich) Oficyna Wydawnicza SIMP Press, Ltd., Swietokrzyska 14A, 00-950 Warsaw, Poland. TEL 48-22-271637. Ed. Jacek Koral. circ. 1,100.
Description: Presents research papers on hydraulic systems and machines.

627   GW   ISSN 0931-1955
STOCHASTIC HYDROLOGY AND HYDRAULICS. (Text in English) 1987. 4/yr. DM.348($218) Springer-Verlag, Heidelberger Platz 3, 14197 Berlin, Germany. TEL 030-8207-1. FAX 030-8214091. (Subscr. in N. America to: Springer-Verlag New York, Inc., 44 Hartz Way, Secaucus, NJ 07096-2491. TEL 201-348-4033. FAX 201-348-4505) Ed. J.H. Cushman. (also avail. in microform from UMI; back issues avail.) **Indexed:** Compumath, Sel.Water Res.Abstr. **Document type:** academic/scholarly publication.
—BLDSC (8465.270000); Faxon; UnCover; SWETS; UMI. **CCC.**
Description: Encompasses stochastic differential equations in hydrology and hydraulics, parameter estimation and identification techniques, random hydrodynamic fields, multivariate analysis, real-time hydrologic forecasting, and geostatistics.

627   JA
SUIKOGAKU NI KANSURU KAKI KENSHUKAI KOGISHU/SUMMER SEMINAR ON HYDRAULIC ENGINEERING. LECTURE NOTES. (Text in Japanese) 1965. a. 3800 Yen. Doboku Gakkai, Suiri Iinkai - Japan Society of Civil Engineering, Committee on Hydraulic Engineering, Yotsuya 1-chome, Shinjuku-ku, Tokyo 160, Japan.

627   JA
SUIKOGAKU RONBUNSHU/PROCEEDINGS OF HYDRAULICS ENGINEERING. (Text in English, Japanese; summaries in English) 1956. a. Doboku Gakkai - Japan Society of Civil Engineers, Yotsuya 1-chome, Shinjuku-ku, Tokyo 160, Japan. **Document type:** proceedings.

627   JA   ISSN 0562-5548
SUIMON TEKKAN/HYDRAULIC GATE AND PENSTOCK. (Text in Japanese) 1957. 4/yr. Suimon Tekkan Kyokai - Hydraulic Gate and Penstock Association, Toranomon Jitsugyo Kaikan, 1-20, Toranomon 1-chome, Minato-ku, Tokyo 105, Japan.

627   JA
SUIRI KENKYUSHITSU RONBUNSHU/HYDRAULIC REPORTS. (Text in Japanese) 1987. biennial. Toa Kensetsu Kogyo K.K., Gijutsu Kenkyujo - Toa Corp., Technical Research Institute, 1-3, Anzen-cho, Tsurumi-ku, Yokohama-shi, Kanagawa-ken 230, Japan.

627   US
U.S. BUREAU OF RECLAMATION. ENGINEERING MONOGRAPH. no.6, 1950. irreg., no.41, 1980. U.S. Bureau of Reclamation, Denver Office, Box 25007, Denver Federal Center, Denver, CO 80225. TEL 303-236-6741. **Indexed:** Geotech.Abstr.
Formerly: U.S. Water and Power Resources Service. Engineering Monograph.

UNIVERSITATEA POLITEHNICA BUCURESTI. BULETIN STIINTIFIC. INGINERIE MECANICA/POLYTECHNICAL UNIVERSITY OF BUCHAREST. SCIENTIFIC BULLETIN. MECHANICAL ENGINEERING. see *ENGINEERING — Mechanical Engineering*

VESITALOUS; Finnish journal of water economy, hydraulic and agricultural engineering. see *WATER RESOURCES*

627 333.91 338   XR   ISSN 0862-5549
                       CODEN: VOHSEG
VODNI HOSPODARSTVI/WATER MANAGEMENT. (Text in Czech; summaries in English and Russian) 1950. m. 60 Kcs.($39.60) (Ministerstvo Lesniho a Vodniho Hospodarstvi Ceske Republiky) Statni Zemedelske Nakladatelstvi, Vaclavske nam. 47, 113 11 Prague 1, Czech Republic. TEL 26 59 51. (Subscr. to: Artia, Ve Smeckach 30, 111 27 Prague 1, Czech Republic) Ed. Josef Benes. adv.; illus. circ. 4,000. **Indexed:** Biol.Abstr., Geotech.Abstr., W.R.C.Inf.
—CASDDS.
Formed by the 1990 merger of: Vodni Hospodarstvi. Rada A (ISSN 0322-8282) & Vodni Hospodarstvi. Rada B (ISSN 0322-8231)

VODNI PROBLEMI. see *WATER RESOURCES*

627 333.91   CU   ISSN 0505-9461
TC433.C8   CODEN: VOHIAG
VOLUNTAD HIDRAULICA. 1963. s-a. $18 in S. America; N. America $20; elsewhere $22. (Desarrollo Agropecuario del Pais, Grupo Hidraulico) Ediciones Cubanas, Obispo No. 527, Apdo. 605, Havana, Cuba. Ed. P.L. Dorticus. bk.rev.; abstr.; bibl.; illus. **Indexed:** GeoRef.

VON KARMAN INSTITUTE FOR FLUID DYNAMICS. LECTURE SERIES. see *AERONAUTICS AND SPACE FLIGHT*

627   UK   ISSN 0140-1742
WATER SERVICES YEAR BOOK. 1929. a. £65($150) in the UK; overseas £75 (effective 1994). International Trade Publications Ltd., Queensway House, 2 Queensway, Redhill, Surrey RH1 1QS, England. TEL 0737-768611. FAX 0737-761989. TELEX 948669-TOPJNL-G. Ed. Stephen Wadey. adv. **Document type:** trade publication.
—BLDSC (9275.470000).
Former titles: Water Services Handbook (ISSN 0307-1782); Water Engineer's Handbook (ISSN 0083-7644)

627 PL ISSN 0510-4262
WIADOMOSCI MELIORACYJNE I LAKARSKIE. 1958. q. $33. Stowarzyszenie Inzynierow i Technikow Wodnych i Melioracyjnych, Ul. Czackiego 3-5, 00-043 Warsaw, Poland. TEL 48-22-273878. (Dist. by: Ars Polona-Ruch, Krakowskie Przedmiescie 7, Warsaw, Poland) Ed. Tytus Bartoszek. adv.: B&W page $1010. circ. 1,000. **Indexed:** Field Crop Abstr., Geo.Abstr., Herb.Abstr.

627 621 JA ISSN 0286-6900
YUATSU TO KUKIATSU/JAPAN HYDRAULICS AND PNEUMATICS SOCIETY. JOURNAL. (Text in Japanese; summaries in English) 1970. 7/yr. 1000 Yen per no. Nihon Yukuatsu Gakkai - Japan Hydraulics and Pneumatics Society, c/o Kikai Shinko Kaikan, 5-8, Shiba Koen 3-chome, Minato-ku, Tokyo 105, Japan. **Indexed:** INIS Atomind.
—BLDSC (4805.130000).

627 621 JA ISSN 0913-9486
YUKUATSU/FLUID POWER. (Text in Japanese) 1987. q. Nihon Yukuatsu Kogyokai - Japan Hydraulics and Pneumatics Association, c/o Mr. Hiroshi Setoguchi, Gen. Mgr., 5-8, Shiba Koen 3-chome, Minato-ku, Tokyo 105, Japan.

627 621 JA ISSN 0913-2058
YUKUATSU GEPPO/FLUID PNEUMATICS. (Text in Japanese) 1956. m. Nihon Yukuatsu Kogyokai - Japan Hydraulics and Pneumatics Association, c/o Mr. Hiroshi Setoguchi, Gen. Mgr., 5-8, Shiba Koen 3-chome, Minato-ku, Tokyo 105, Japan.

627 621 JA ISSN 0914-6253
YUKUATSU GIJUTSU/HYDRAULICS AND PNEUMATICS. (Text in Japanese) 1962. m. 1200 Yen per no. Nihon Kogyo Shuppan K.K. - Japan Industrial Publishing Co., Ltd., 3-26, Honkomagome 6-chome, Bunkyo-ku, Tokyo 113, Japan. **Indexed:** INIS Atomind. **Document type:** trade publication.

627 621 JA
YUKUATSU KOENKAI KOEN RONBUNSHU/JAPAN HYDRAULICS AND PNEUMATICS SOCIETY. PROCEEDINGS OF MEETING. (Text in English, Japanese) s-a. Nihon Yukuatsu Gakkai - Japan Hydraulics and Pneumatics Society, c/o Kikai Shinko Kaikan, 5-8, Shiba Koen 3-chome, Minato-ku, Tokyo 105, Japan. **Document type:** proceedings.

ZBORNIK OBJAVLJENIH RADOVA SARADNIKA INSTITUTA. see ENGINEERING — Electrical Engineering

627 RH
ZIMBABWE. MINISTRY OF ENERGY AND WATER RESOURCES AND DEVELOPMENT. HYDROLOGICAL SUMMARIES. 1965. biennial, latest 1980. $30. Ministry of Energy and Water Resources and Development, c/o Chief Hydrological Engineer, P.O. Box 8132, Causeway, Harare, Zimbabwe.
Former titles: Zimbabwe. Ministry of Water Resources and Development. Hydrological Summaries (ISSN 0080-2832); Zimbabwe. Division of Water Development. Hydrological Summaries.

ENGINEERING — Industrial Engineering

628.5 US ISSN 1052-3693
HC426
ADVANCES IN CHINESE INDUSTRIAL STUDIES. 1990. a. J A I Press Inc., 55 Old Post Rd., No. 2, Greenwich, CT 06836-1678. Ed. N. Campbell. **Document type:** monographic series.
—BLDSC (0703.830000).

628.5 NE ISSN 0923-814X
ADVANCES IN INDUSTRIAL ENGINEERING. 1985. irreg., vol.19, 1993. price varies. Elsevier Science B.V., Books Division, P.O. Box 211, 1000 AE Amsterdam, Netherlands. TEL 31-20-5803911. FAX 31-20-5803705. TELEX 18582 ESPA NL. (Subscr. in U.S. and Canada to: Elsevier Science Inc., Box 882, Madison Sq. Sta., New York, NY 10159. TEL 212-989-5800) (back issues avail.) **Document type:** monographic series.
Refereed Serial

628.5 UK ISSN 0941-0635
▼**THE INTERNATIONAL JOURNAL OF DIGITAL AND ANALOGUE SIGNAL PROCESSING.** 1994. 4/yr. £120($200) Springer-Verlag, Springer House, 8 Alexandra Rd., London SW19 7JZ, England. TEL 081-944-2942. FAX 081-947-4651. (Subscr. to: Heidelberger Platz 3, 1000 Berlin 33, Germany. TEL 030-8207-0. FAX 030-821-4091; N. American subscr. to: Journal Fulfillment Services, Box 2485, Secaucus, NJ 07096. TEL 800-777-4643. FAX 201-348-4505) (also avail. in microform from UMI) **Document type:** academic/scholarly publication.

628.5 GW
BALL AND ROLLER BEARING ENGINEERING - INDUSTRIAL ENGINEERING. German edition: Waelzlagertechnik - Industrietechnik (ISSN 0934-8875); French edition: Technique du Roulement - Technique Industrielle (ISSN 0934-926X); Spanish edition: Tecnica de los Rodamientos - Tecnica Industrial (ISSN 0934-9278); Italian edition: Cuscinetti Volventi - Techniche Industriali (ISSN 0170-3048) (Text in English) 1962. s-a. free. F A G Kugelfischer Georg Schaefer KGaA, Postfach 1260, 97402 Schweinfurt, Germany. **Indexed:** Eng.Ind., Fluidex, ISMEC. **Document type:** trade publication.
—BLDSC (1860.800000).
Formerly: Ball and Roller Bearing Engineering (ISSN 0522-0629)

628.5 621 JA ISSN 0385-6933
BEARINGU/BEARING. (Text in Japanese) 1958. m. Nihon Bearingu Kogyokai - Japan Bearing Industrial Association, 5-8, Shiba Koen 3-chome, Minato-ku, Tokyo 105, Japan.

628.5 NE ISSN 0927-0299
BEDRIJFSKUNDING VAKBLAD B & I D. Key Title: B & I D. 1989. 8/yr. fl.108 (foreign fl.140) (effective 1993). (Nederlandse Ingenieurs Vereniging (NIRIA)) V N U Business Publications B.V., Postbus 9194, 1006 CC Amsterdam, Netherlands. TEL 31-20-5102911. FAX 31-20-6174121. (Co-sponsor Koninklijk Instituut van Ingenieurs) Ed. Ruud Plaizier. adv.: B&W page fl.2850, color page fl.4150; adv. contact: Erna Oonk. circ. 7,238. **Document type:** trade publication.
—SWETS.

628.5 US
CLEANROOMS. 1988. m. Witter Publishing Company, 84 Park Ave., Flemington, NJ 08822-1171. TEL 908-788-0343. FAX 908-788-3782. Ed. Thomas M. Brotzman; Pub. Andrew Witter. adv.; circ. 42,000 (controlled). **Document type:** trade publication.
Description: Discusses engineering, management and quality control issues relating to controlled environment manufacturing.

628.5 SP
COLEGIO OFICIAL DE INGENIEROS INDUSTRIALES. BOLETIN DE INFORMACION. 6/yr. Colegio Oficial de Ingenieros Industriales - Madrid College of Industrial Engineers and Craftsmen, Carrera de San Jeronimo 5, 28014 Madrid, Spain. TEL 521-65-56. circ. 6,000.

COMPUTERS & INDUSTRIAL ENGINEERING; an international journal. see ENGINEERING — Computer Applications

CONTROL ENGINEERING PRACTICE. see ENGINEERING — Computer Applications

628.5 UK ISSN 0010-9606
THE COST ENGINEER. 1962. bi-m. £35 (foreign £42). Association of Cost Engineers, Lea House, 5 Middlewich Rd., Sandbach, Cheshire CW11 9XL, England. TEL 44-270-764798. FAX 44-270-766180. Ed. V. Thompson. adv.; bk.rev.; abstr.; bibl.; stat. circ. 2,250. (tabloid format) **Indexed:** BMT, Chem.Abstr.
—BLDSC (3477.238000).
Description: Covers cost management of industrial engineering construction.

628.5 GW
DESIGN AUSWAHL (YEAR)/DESIGN SELECTION (YEAR). (Text in English, German) a. Design Center Stuttgart, Willi-Bleicher-Str. 19, 70174 Stuttgart, Germany. TEL 0711-1232536. Eds. Helga Baumann, Wolfgang Berger. **Document type:** trade publication.

628.5 US
DESIGN PERSPECTIVES. 1981. 10/yr. $30. Industrial Designers Society of America, 1142 E. Walker Rd., Great Falls, VA 22066. TEL 703-759-0100. FAX 703-759-7679. Ed. Karen Van Buren. adv.; bk.rev. circ. 2,600. **Document type:** newsletter.

628.5 US ISSN 1051-8843
CODEN: MRSPDH
FLY ASH AND COAL CONVERSION BY-PRODUCTS CHARACTERIZATION, UTILIZATION AND DISPOSAL. 1985. a. Materials Research Society, 9800 McKnight Rd., Ste. 327, Pittsburgh, PA 15237.

FOOD PLANT STRATEGIES. see FOOD AND FOOD INDUSTRIES

628.5 US
▼**FORMING AND FABRICATING.** 1994. 9/yr. $70. Society of Manufacturing Engineers, Fabricating Technologies Association, One SME Dr., Box 930, Dearborn, MI 48121. TEL 313-271-1500. FAX 313-271-2861. Ed. John Coleman. adv.: B&W page $3700. circ. 68,000. **Document type:** trade publication.

FORTSCHRITTLICHE BETRIEBSFUEHRUNG UND INDUSTRIAL ENGINEERING. see BUSINESS AND ECONOMICS — Management

628.5 BA
GULF INDUSTRY & SAUDI ARABIA REVIEW. (Text in English) bi-m. Al Hilal Publishing & Marketing Group, P.O. Box 224, Manama, Bahrain. TEL 973-293131. FAX 973-293400. TELEX 8981 HILAL BN. (In U.K: Hilal International (UK) Ltd., Crescent Ct., 102 Victor Rd., Teddington, Middx TW11 8SS, England. TEL 081-943-3630) adv.: B&W page $2625, color page $3290. circ. 7,167. **Document type:** trade publication.
Description: For individuals with an involvement or interest in the industrial development of the Gulf region.

628.5 GW ISSN 0343-8759
HANDLING; das Fachjournal fuer Automation, Montagesysteme, Logistik und Verpackungstechnik. 1972. 7/yr. free. Verlag Hoppenstedt GmbH, Havelstr. 9, 64295 Darmstadt, Germany. TEL 06151-380-0. FAX 06151-380-360. Ed. Dieter Capelle. circ. 28,000. **Document type:** trade publication.

628.5 BE ISSN 0773-3186
HYDROPNEUMA. (Text in Dutch, French) 1978. q. 600 BEF($18) F M O P - C C I B, 50 Louisalaan, 1050 Brussels, Belgium. TEL 32-2-6407735. FAX 32-2-6408480. circ. 10,000 (controlled). (back issues avail.)
Description: Covers products and systems and other matters of interest to fluid power engineers.

628.5 BE
I E N - EUROPE. (Industrial Engineering News) 1975. 9/yr. $95 (free to qualified personnel). I E N Europe N.V. (Subsidiary of: Reed Elsevier plc), Rue Verte 216, B-1210 Brussels, Belgium. TEL 32-2-2402611. FAX 32-2-2427111. TELEX 25828. Ed. E. De Schutter. adv.; bk.rev.; circ. 50,000 (controlled). **Indexed:** Br.Ceram.Abstr.
Description: Reports on new industrial products and equipment emphasizing on high-tech sector and other advanced technology products.

ENGINEERING — INDUSTRIAL ENGINEERING

628.5 US
I I E TRANSACTIONS; industrial engineering research and development. 1969. q. $95 to non-members (foreign $105); members $35; institutions $121 (foreign $130). Institute of Industrial Engineers, 25 Technology Park-Atlanta, Norcross, GA 30092. TEL 404-449-0460. FAX 404-263-8532. bibl.; charts; index. (also avail. in microfilm from UMI; reprint service avail. from UMI) **Indexed:** ABI Inform., BMT, BPIA, Bus.Ind., Comput.Cont., Curr.Cont., Data Process.Dig., Eng.Ind., Ergon.Abstr., Int.Abstr.Oper.Res., J.Cont.Quant.Meth., Oper.Res.Manage.Sci., Qual.Contr.Appl.Stat., Sci.Abstr., Sci.Cit.Ind.
—**CCC.**
Formerly (until 1982): A I I E Transactions (ISSN 0569-5554)
Description: Presents new ideas in industrial engineering research and development. Articles focus on theoretical advances in industrial engineering and the application of these advances for solving industrial, social and information problems.
Refereed Serial

INDUSTRIAL CHEMISTRY LIBRARY. see *CHEMISTRY*

INDUSTRIAL ENERGY TECHNOLOGY ABSTRACTS. see *ENERGY — Abstracting, Bibliographies, Statistics*

628.5 AT
INDUSTRIAL ENGINEER. 1958. q. Aus.$40 (effective Mar. 1992). Institute of Industrial Engineers, Science Centre, Private Bag No. 1, Darlingurst, N.S.W. 2010, Australia. FAX 02-331-7296. Ed. Brian M. Alexander. adv.; bk.rev. circ. 1,300. **Indexed:** Biol.Dig., Curr.Cont.
Formerly: Human Environment.
Description: Articles on latest technology and techniques in the manufacturing and commercial fields.

628.5 US ISSN 0019-8234
T55.4 CODEN: IDLEB9
INDUSTRIAL ENGINEERING. 1969. m. $49 to non-members (foreign $61). Institute of Industrial Engineers, 25 Technology Park-Atlanta, Norcross, GA 30092. TEL 404-449-0460. Ed. Eric E. Torrey. adv.; bk.rev.; abstr.; charts; illus.; index. circ. 35,000. (also avail. in microfilm from UMI; reprint service avail. from KTO,UMI) **Indexed:** A.S.& T.Ind., ABI Inform., Account.& Data Proc.Abstr., Anbar, Appl.Mech.Rev., ASEAN Manage.Abstr., Biol.Abstr., BMT, BPIA, C.I.S. Abstr., CAD CAM Abstr. (until 1992), Cadscan, Comput.Cont., Comput.Dtbs., Comput.Lit.Ind., Cont.Pg.Manage., Data Process.Dig., Eng.Ind., Ergon.Abstr., Excerp.Med., Int.Abstr.Oper.Res., Intl.Mgmt.Info., ISMEC, Lead Abstr., Manage.Cont., Math.R., Oper.Res.Manage.Sci., Q.Abstr., Qual.Contr.Appl.Stat., Robomat. (until 1992), Sci.Abstr., Soft.Abstr.Eng., Tr.& Indus.Ind., Work Rel.Abstr., Zincscan.
●Also available online. Vendor(s): DIALOG Information Services, Inc.
—BLDSC (4450.356000); EI; Faxon; UnCover; SWETS; UMI. **CCC.**
Supersedes: Journal of Industrial Engineering (ISSN 0022-183X)
Description: Provides comprehensive coverage of industrial engineering applications in various industries. Subjects contained are robotics, mini-microcomputers, manufacturing systems, automated manufacturing, conveyors and office systems.

628.5 US
INDUSTRIAL ENGINEERING: A SERIES OF REFERENCE BOOKS & TEXTBOOKS. 1978. irreg., vol.17, 1990. price varies. Marcel Dekker, Inc., 270 Madison Ave., New York, NY 10016. TEL 212-696-9000. FAX 212-685-4540. TELEX 421419.

628.5 658.5 II ISSN 0019-8242
INDUSTRIAL ENGINEERING AND MANAGEMENT. (Text in English) 1966. q. Rs.20. (Indian Institution of Industrial Engineering) Chary Publications, 14 Sidh Prasad, Ghatkopar Mahul Rd., Tilak Nagar, Bombay 400089, India. Ed. S. T. Chary. adv.; charts; stat. circ. 6,000.

628.5 UK
INDUSTRIAL ENGINEERING NEWS. 9/yr. 6 Gload Crescent, Orpington, Kent BR5 4PR, England. TEL 0689-833300. Ed. Keith Pegg. circ. 50,000.

628.5 669 US ISSN 0019-8374
TH7201 CODEN: INHTAZ
INDUSTRIAL HEATING. 1934. m. $39 (foreign $75). Business News Publishing Company, 755 W. Big Beaver Rd., Ste. 1000, Troy, MI 48084. TEL 313-362-3700. FAX 313-362-0317. (Subscr. to: Box 2600, Troy, MI 48007) Ed. Stanley B. Lasday. adv.; bk.rev.; illus.; pat.; tr.lit.; circ. 22,516 (controlled). **Indexed:** B.C.I.R.A., Br.Ceram.Abstr., Cadscan, Chem.Abstr., Eng.Ind., Excerp.Med., Fuel & Energy Abstr., Gas Abstr., Ind.Hyg.Dig., INIS Atomind., ISMEC, Lead Abstr., Met.Abstr., World Alum.Abstr., Zincscan. **Document type:** trade publication.
—BLDSC (4455.000000); EI; Faxon; UnCover; SWETS; UMI.
Description: Covers manufacturing and production systems involved in primary metals producing, metals and ceramics, heat treating, brazing, forging, casting, cleaning and finishing, as well as analysis of thermal process control and heat containment.

INDUSTRIAL SAFETY SERIES. see *OCCUPATIONAL HEALTH AND SAFETY*

628.5 GW ISSN 0943-934X
▼**INDUSTRIEARMATUREN;** Zeitschrift fuer die Praxis der Armaturentechnologie. 1993. q. DM.120. Vulkan-Verlag GmbH, Postfach 103962, 45039 Essen, Germany. TEL 0201-82002-0. FAX 0201-8200240. Ed. W. Moenning. adv.: B&W page DM.2780, color page DM.4730; trim 250 x 171; adv. contact: H. Pelzer. circ. 5,000. **Document type:** trade publication.
—BLDSC (4464.805000); SWETS.
Description: Covers the entire field of industrial valve and fitting technology.

628.5 US ISSN 0731-2334
INNOVATION. 1982. q. $45. Industrial Designers Society of America, 1142 E. Walker Rd., Great Falls, VA 22066. TEL 703-759-0100. FAX 703-759-7679. Ed. Kristina Goodrich. adv.; bk.rev. circ. 2,600. **Indexed:** Environ.Abstr. **Document type:** trade publication.
—BLDSC (4515.480100).

628.5 US ISSN 0895-2280
T55.45
INSTITUTE OF INDUSTRIAL ENGINEERS. INTEGRATED SYSTEMS CONFERENCE. PROCEEDINGS. 1978. s-a. price varies. Institute of Industrial Engineers, 25 Technology Park-Atlanta, Norcross, GA 30092. TEL 404-449-0460. (reprint service avail. from UMI) **Indexed:** BPIA, Comput.Cont. **Document type:** proceedings.
—**CCC.**
Formerly (until 1987): Institute of Industrial Engineers. Fall Industrial Engineering Conference. Proceedings (ISSN 0163-1810); Which superseded: American Institute of Industrial Engineers. Systems Engineering Conference. Proceedings.

628.5 UK ISSN 0890-6955
TJ1180.A1 CODEN: IMTME3
INTERNATIONAL JOURNAL OF MACHINE TOOLS & MANUFACTURE; design, research & application. 1961. 8/yr. £460($710) (effective 1994). Elsevier Science Ltd., Pergamon, P.O. Box 800, Kidlington, Oxford OX5 1DX, England. TEL 44-865-843000. FAX 44-865-843010. (Subscr. in U.S. and Canada to: Elsevier Science, 660 White Plains Rd., Tarrytown, NY 10591-5153. TEL 914-524-9200. FAX 914-333-2444) Ed. R. Davies, T.A. Dean. adv.; bk.rev.; charts; illus.; index. circ. 1,000. (also avail. in microfilm from UMI; reprint service avail. from UMI) **Indexed:** Appl.Mech.Rev., Br.Tech.Ind., Curr.Cont., Eng.Ind., ISMEC, Sh.& Vib.Dig. **Document type:** academic/scholarly publication.
—BLDSC (4542.323000); EI; Faxon; UnCover; SWETS; UMI. **CCC.**
Formerly: International Journal of Machine Tool Design and Research (ISSN 0020-7357); Which supersedes: Advances in Machine Tool Design and Research (ISSN 0065-2857)
Refereed Serial

628.5 II
JOURNAL OF INDUSTRIAL ENGINEERING. (Text in English) 1956. q. $10 (by air mail only). T.S.N. Rao, Ed. & Pub., West View, 309 Ghodbunder Rd., 4th Fl., Santacruz West, Bombay 54, India. adv.; bk.rev.; illus. circ. 7,500. (reprint service avail. from KTO) **Indexed:** A.S.& T.Ind., Sci.Cit.Ind.

628.5 UK ISSN 0938-7706
JOURNAL OF SYSTEMS ENGINEERING. 1991. q. £136. Springer-Verlag, Springer House, 8 Alexandra Rd., London SW19 7JZ, England. TEL 081-944-2942. FAX 081-947-4651. (U.S. subscr. to: Springer-Verlag New York, Inc., Box 2485, Secaucus, NJ 07096-2491. TEL 201-348-4033) Ed. D.T. Pham. **Document type:** trade publication.
—BLDSC (5068.073000).
Description: Publishes fundamental and applied work in the field of systems engineering.
Refereed Serial

628.5 GW ISSN 0942-8186
K E M DIGEST. (Konstruktion Elektronik Maschinenbau) a. Konradin Verlag Robert Kohlhammer GmbH, Ernst-Mey-Str. 8, 70771 Leinfelden-Echtderdingen, Germany. TEL 0711-7594-0. FAX 0711-7594390. Ed. Herbert Neumann. adv.: B&W page DM.8340, color page DM.10380; trim 190 x 270. circ. 30,065. **Document type:** trade publication.
Description: Contains product information from important industrial sectors.

628.5 JA ISSN 0289-8705
KAWADA GIHO/KAWADA TECHNICAL REPORT. (Text in English, Japanese) 1978. a. Kawada Kogyo K.K. - Kawada Industries, Inc., 45-4, Nishigahara 3-chome, Kita-ku, Tokyo 114, Japan.

658.5 UK
MANUFACTURING MANAGEMENT. 1977. m. £48($100) Industrial Trade Journals Ltd., Stakes House, Quebec Sq., Westerham, Kent TN16 1TD, England. TEL 0959-564212. FAX 0959-562325. Ed. Paddy Baker. illus.; tr.lit. circ. 20,000. (back issues avail.) **Indexed:** BMT, Fluidex, Int.Build.Serv.Abstr., World Surf.Coat., World Text.Abstr. **Document type:** trade publication.
Former titles (until 1993): Plant Engineering and Manufacturing Management; (until 1992): Plant Engineering & Maintenance.
Description: Maintenance and management of industrial and commercial plant.

623.8 387 SA
MARITIME HANDBOOK OF SOUTHERN AFRICA. (Text in English) 1990. biennial, 2nd ed., 1992. George Warman Publications (Pty.) Ltd., P.O. Box 704, Cape Town 8000, South Africa. TEL 27-21-245320. FAX 27-21-261332. Ed. Paddy Attwell. adv. contact: Abdul Rawoot. **Document type:** directory.
Description: Covers all areas of the maritime industry of Southern Africa.

628.5 US
▼**MARKET UPDATE FROM DESIGN NEWS.** 1992. m. Cahners Publishing Company (Newton), A Division of Reed Elsevier Inc., 275 Washington St., Newton, MA 02158. TEL 617-964-3030. FAX 617-558-4402. Ed. Nicole M. Borden. **Document type:** newsletter.

628.5 JA ISSN 0915-3594
CODEN: MARAEJ
MATERIALS LIFE/MATERIARU RAIFU. (Text in English, Japanese) 1989. q. 2000 Yen per no. Materials Life Society, Japan - Materiaru Raifu Gakkai, Nihon Gakkai Jimu Senta, 1609, Honkomagome 5-chome, Bunkyo-ku, Tokyo 113, Japan. TEL 03-3817-5801. FAX 03-3817-5800.
—BLDSC (5396.003000); CASDDS.

MATHEMATICAL ENGINEERING IN INDUSTRY. see *MATHEMATICS*

628.5 510 UK ISSN 0932-4194
MATHEMATICS OF CONTROL, SIGNALS AND SYSTEMS. 1988. 4/yr. £120. Springer-Verlag, Springer House, 8 Alexandra Rd., London SW19 7JZ, England. TEL 081-944-2942. FAX 081-947-4651. **Document type:** trade publication.
—BLDSC (5405.810000); EI; Faxon; UnCover; SWETS; UMI. **CCC.**

658.5 GW
▼**MESSTEC SPEZIAL.** 1993. q. DM.60 (students DM.30). G I T Verlag GmbH, Roesslerstr. 90, 64293 Darmstadt, Germany. TEL 06151-8090-0. FAX 06151-809045. Ed. Albert Sachs. adv.: B&W page DM.5510, color page DM.8030; trim 185 x 260; adv. contact: Ute Weber. circ. 15,000. **Document type:** trade publication.

MISSET BULK; magazine voor stortgoedtechnologie. see *TRANSPORTATION*

ENGINEERING — MECHANICAL ENGINEERING

628.5   UK   ISSN 0262-0227
PLANT & WORKS ENGINEERING. 1981. m. £45. Industrial Trade Journals Ltd., Stakes House, Quebec Sq., Westerham, Kent TN16 1TD, England. TEL 0959-564212. FAX 0959-562325. Ed. Arthur Potter. adv.; illus. circ. 20,500. **Indexed:** BMT.

POLYTECHNISCH TIJDSCHRIFT: WERKTUIGBOUW; vakblad voor de ingenieur. see *ENGINEERING — Mechanical Engineering*

628.5   NE   ISSN 0924-7343
             CODEN: PRTEEN
PROCES TECHNOLOGIE; vakblad voor de technische professional. 1985. 11/yr. fl.142.50 (foreign fl.192.50) (effective 1993). (Nederlandse Ingenieurs Vereniging (NIRIA)) V N U Business Publications B.V., Postbus 90162, 1006 BD Amsterdam, Netherlands. TEL 31-20-5102911. FAX 31-20-6174121. (Co-sponsor: Koninklijk Instituut van Ingenieurs) Ed. Ruud Plaizier. adv.: B&W page fl.2860, color page fl.4855; trim 205 x 285; adv. contact: Erna Oonk. circ. 8,756. **Document type:** trade publication.
— BLDSC (6849.982645); SWETS; CASDDS.
Formerly (until 1991): I 2 - Procestechnologie (ISSN 0169-4200)

628.5   SZ
▼**PROCESS ENGINEERING FOR THE CHEMICAL, METALS AND MINERALS INDUSTRIES SERIES.** 1993. irreg. Gordon and Breach Science Publishers SA, Chemin de la Sallaz, CH-1400 Yverdon, Switzerland. TEL 024-239670. FAX 024-239671. (U.S. subscr. to: Box 786, Cooper Sta., New York, NY 10276. TEL 212-206-8900. FAX 212-645-2459) Ed.Bd. **Document type:** monographic series.

628.5 530   NE   ISSN 0921-8610
             CODEN: PTPREM
PROCESS TECHNOLOGY PROCEEDINGS. 1984. irreg., vol.11, 1994. price varies. Elsevier Science B.V., Books Division, P.O. Box 211, 1000 AE Amsterdam, Netherlands. TEL 31-20-5803911. FAX 31-20-5803705. TELEX 18582 ESPA NL. (Subscr. in U.S. and Canada to: Elsevier Science Inc., Box 882, Madison Sq. Sta., New York, NY 10159. TEL 212-989-5800) (back issues avail.) **Indexed:** Sugar Ind.Abstr. **Document type:** monographic series, proceedings.
— BLDSC (6849.990850); CASDDS.
Refereed Serial

628.5   IT
RIVISTA DELL'ASSITAL. 12/yr. Viale Monza 106, 20127 Milan, Italy. TEL 2-282-76-51. FAX 2-28-91-515. Ed. Franco Signoracci. circ. 8,000.

S A E GROUND VEHICLE LIGHTING MANUAL. (Society of Automotive Engineers) see *TRANSPORTATION — Automobiles*

STRUCTURAL OPTIMIZATION; computer-aided optimal design of stressed systems and components. see *ENGINEERING — Computer Applications*

621.4   NE
STUDIES IN WIND ENGINEERING AND INDUSTRIAL ENGINEERING. 1983. irreg., vol.4, 1985. price varies. Elsevier Science B.V., Books Division, P.O. Box 211, 1000 AE Amsterdam, Netherlands. TEL 31-20-5803911. FAX 31-20-5803705. TELEX 18582 ESPA NL. (Subscr. in U.S. and Canada to: Elsevier Science Inc., Box 882, Madison Sq. Sta., New York, NY 10159. TEL 212-989-5800) (back issues avail.) **Document type:** monographic series.
Refereed Serial

628.5   GW   ISSN 0934-926X
TECHNIQUE DU ROULEMENT - TECHNIQUE INDUSTRIELLE. English edition: Ball and Roller Bearing Engineering - Industrial Engineering (ISSN 0934-9251); German edition: Waelzlagertechnik - Industrietechnik (ISSN 0934-8875); Italian edition: Cuscinetti Volventi - Techniche Industriali (ISSN 0170-3048); Spanish edition: Tecnica de los Rodamientos - Tecnica Industrial (ISSN 0934-9278) (Text in French) 1962. irreg. (1-3/yr.). F A G Kugelfischer Georg Schaefer KGaA, Postfach 1260, 97402 Schweinfurt, Germany. **Document type:** trade publication.
Formerly: Technique du Roulemont (ISSN 0170-303X)

628.5   GW   ISSN 0934-9278
TECNICA DE LOS RODAMIENTOS - TECNICA INDUSTRIAL. English edition: Ball and Roller Bearing Engineering - Industrial Engineering (ISSN 0934-9251); French edition: Technique du Roulement - Technique Industrielle (ISSN 0934-926X); German edition: Waelzlagertechnik - Industrietechnik (ISSN 0934-8875); Italian edition: Cuscinetti Volventi - Techniche Industriali (ISSN 0170-3048) (Text in Spanish) 1962. irreg. (1-3/yr.). F A G Kugelfischer Georg Schaefer KGaA, Postfach 1260, 97402 Schweinfurt, Germany. **Document type:** trade publication.
Formerly: Tecnica de los Rodamientos (ISSN 0170-3056)

628.5   GW   ISSN 0934-8875
WAELZLAGERTECHNIK - INDUSTRIETECHNIK. English edition: Ball and Roller Bearing Engineering - Industrial Engineering (ISSN 0934-9251); French edition: Technique du Roulement - Technique Industrielle (ISSN 0934-926X); Italian edition: Cuscinetti Volventi - Techniche Industriali (ISSN 0170-3048); Spanish edition: Tecnica de los Rodamientos - Tecnica Industrial (ISSN 0934-9278) 1962. irreg. (1-2/yr.). free. F A G Kugelfischer Georg Schaefer KGaA, Postfach 1260, 8720 Schweinfurt 1, Germany. circ. 90,000. **Document type:** trade publication.
Formerly: Waelzlagertechnik (ISSN 0511-0653)
Description: Technical publication describing the use of ball and roller bearings in automobiles and in machinery in different industrial processes.

ENGINEERING — Mechanical Engineering

see also Machinery

A B B REVIEW. see *ENGINEERING — Electrical Engineering*

621   JA
A B T E C KOEN RONBUNSHU/A B T E C PROCEEDINGS. (Text in English, Japanese; summaries in English) a. Toryu Kako Gakkai - Japan Society of Grinding Engineers, 22-17, Hyakunin-cho 2-chome, Shinjuku-ku, Tokyo 169, Japan.

621 530   US
A I A A - A S M E JOINT FLUID MECHANICS, PLASMA DYNAMICS, AND LASER CONFERENCE. PROCEEDINGS. irreg., 4th, 1986, Atlanta, Georgia. price varies. (American Institute of Aeronautics and Astronautics) American Society of Mechanical Engineers, 345 E. 47th St., New York, NY 10017. TEL 212-705-7703.

621 697   US   ISSN 0884-0490
TH7201
A S H R A E TECHNICAL DATA BULLETIN. 1985. irreg. American Society of Heating, Refrigerating and Air-Conditioning Engineers, Inc., 1791 Tullie Circle, N.E., Atlanta, GA 30329. TEL 404-636-8400. FAX 404-321-5478.
— CCC.
Description: For graduate engineers and above. Covers technology of ventilating, air-conditioning, heating, and refrigeration systems in a variety of specific situations.

621   US   ISSN 0279-9316
A S M E NEWS. m. (except Aug.-Sep.). American Society of Mechanical Engineers, 345 E. 47th St., New York, NY 10017. TEL 212-705-7782. Ed. Charles W. Beardsley. **Indexed:** BMT, GeoRef.
— CCC.
Description: Provides information for members on topics such as mechanical engineering, robotics, CAD-CAM, machinery and nuclear engineering. Features include letters to the editor, news briefs, people in the news and announcements of upcoming conferences and courses.

621   NE   ISSN 0165-5108
AANDRIJFTECHNIEK; elektrisch, mechanisch, hydraulisch, pneumatisch. 1978. m. fl.191. C. Misset B.V., Hanzestr. 1, 7006 RH Doetinchem, Netherlands. TEL 31-8340-49911. FAX 31-8340-63638. (Subscr. to: Postbus 4, 7000 BA Doetinchem, Netherlands) Ed. W. Wijnands. adv.: B&W page fl.2520; 187 x 257; adv. contact: Cor van Nek. bk.rev.; illus.; index. circ. 5,000. (back issues avail.) **Indexed:** Excerp.Med. **Document type:** trade publication.
— SWETS.
Description: Technical magazine dealing with mechanical, pneumatic, electric and hydraulic driving and control

ABRASIVE ENGINEERING SOCIETY MAGAZINE. see *MACHINERY*

621   AU
ABSOLVENTEN ZEITUNG OESTERREICH. m. Hohe Mark 12, A-2398 Harrislee, Austria. TEL 2252-80572. Ed. K. Kluettermann.

620.1 690   PL   ISSN 0860-2956
ACTA ACADEMIAE AGRICULTURAE AC TECHNICAE OLSTENENSIS. AEDIFICATIO ET MECHANICA/AGRICULTURAL AND TECHNICAL ACADEMY IN OLSZTYN. MECHANICS AND BUILDING ENGINEERING. (Supplement avail.: Aedificatio et Mechanica) (Text in Polish; summaries in English and Russian) 1974. irreg. price varies. (Akademia Rolniczo-Techniczna im. M. Oczapowskiego) Wydawnictwo A R T Olsztyn, Blok 21, 10-957 Olsztyn-Kortowo, Poland. TEL 48-89-273310. TELEX 0526419. (Dist. by: Ars Polona-Ruch, Krakowskie Przedmiescie 7, 00-901 Warsaw, Poland) bibl.; charts; illus.; circ. 140 (controlled). **Indexed:** Agri.Eng.Abstr., Herb.Abstr., Ref.Zh. **Document type:** academic/scholarly publication.
Formerly (until 1986): Akademia Rolniczo-Techniczna w Olsztynie. Zeszyty Naukowe. Mechanika i Budownictwo Ladowe (ISSN 0324-9182)

621 531   AU   ISSN 0001-5970
TA349   CODEN: AMHCAP
ACTA MECHANICA. 1965. 24/yr. (in 6 vols., 4 nos./vol.). DM.2436($1523) Springer-Verlag, Sachsenplatz 4-6, Postfach 89, A-1201 Vienna, Austria. TEL 0222-3302415. FAX 0222-3302426. (Subscr. in N. America to: Springer-Verlag New York, Inc., 44 Hartz Way, Secaucus, NJ 07096-2491. TEL 201-348-4033. FAX 201-348-4505) Ed.Bd. adv.; charts; illus. (also avail. in microform from UMI; reprint service avail. from ISI) **Indexed:** Appl.Mech.Rev., ASCA, Chem.Abstr., Curr.Cont., Eng.Ind., INIS Atomind., Int.Aerosp.Abstr., Int.Sci.Rev., Math.R., Phys.Ber., Sci.Abstr., Sci.Cit.Ind., Sh.& Vib.Dig. **Document type:** academic/scholarly publication.
— BLDSC (0632.300000); Faxon; UnCover; SWETS; UMI. **CCC.**

621 531   AU   ISSN 0939-7906
ACTA MECHANICA. SUPPLEMENTUM. irreg., no. 2, 1991. Springer-Verlag, Sachsenplatz 4-6, A-1201 Vienna, Austria. TEL 0222-3302415. FAX 0222-3302426. Eds. O.E. Barndorff-Nielsen, B.B. Willetts. **Document type:** academic/scholarly publication.
— BLDSC (0632.610600).

621   FI   ISSN 0001-687X
TJ7   CODEN: APMNA2
ACTA POLYTECHNICA SCANDINAVICA. MECHANICAL ENGINEERING SERIES. (Text and summaries in English) irreg. (2-3/yr.). FIM 350. Teknillisten Tieteiden Akatemia - Finnish Academy of Technology, Kansakoulukatu 10 A, SF-00100 Helsinki 10, Finland. Ed. Matti Ranta. index, cum.index: 1958-1991. circ. 500. (also avail. in microfilm from UMI; back issues avail.; reprint service avail. from UMI) **Indexed:** Appl.Mech.Rev., ASCA, Cadscan, Curr.Cont., INIS Atomind., Int.Aerosp.Abstr., ISMEC, Lead Abstr., Sci.Abstr., Zincscan. **Document type:** monographic series.
— BLDSC (0661.267000); EI; UnCover; UMI.
Description: Presents research results in mechanical engineering.

ENGINEERING — MECHANICAL ENGINEERING

621 669   US   ISSN 1065-5824
TN695   CODEN: APMME3
ADVANCES IN POWDER METALLURGY & PARTICULATE MATERIALS. 1989. a. price varies. Metal Powder Industries Federation, 105 College Rd. E., Princeton, NJ 08540. TEL 609-452-7700. FAX 609-987-8523. Document type: proceedings. —BLDSC (0710.635000); EI; CASDDS.
Formerly (until 1992): Advances in Powder Metallurgy (ISSN 1042-8860)

621.5   FR   ISSN 0002-225X
AIR COMPRIME. 1955. q. free. Atlas Copco France S.A., 326 rue du General-Leclerc, 95130 Franconville, France. Ed. J.C. Corvisier. charts; illus. circ. 1,500.

621   PL   ISSN 0239-5320
TA349
AKADEMIA GORNICZO-HUTNICZA IM. STANISLAWA STASZICA. ZESZYTY NAUKOWE. MECHANIKA/STANISLAW STASZIC UNIVERSITY OF MINING AND METALLURGY. SCIENTIFIC BULLETINS. MECHANICS. (Text in English or Polish; summaries in English, Polish) 1954. irreg., no.28, 1993. price varies. Wydawnictwo A G H, Al. Mickiewicza 30, paw. A-1, 30-059 Krakow, Poland. (Dist. by: Ars Polona, Krakowskie Przedmiescie 7, 00-068 Warsaw, Poland) Ed. Z. Kleczek. illus. circ. 200. Document type: academic/scholarly publication.
Supersedes in part (in 1982): Elektryfikacja i Mechanizacja Gornictwa i Hutnictwa (ISSN 0070-9964)

621   PL   ISSN 0239-5282
TA349
AKADEMIA GORNICZO-HUTNICZA IM. STANISLAWA STASZICA. ZESZYTY NAUKOWE. MECHANIKA. KWARTALNIK. (Text in English or Polish; summaries in English, Polish, Russian) 1982. q. 40000 Zl. per issue (effective 1993). Wydawnictwo A G H, Al. Mickiewicza 30, 30-059 Krakow, Poland. TEL 48-12-338100. FAX 48-12-331014. TELEX 322203 AGH PL. (Dist. by: Ars Polona, Krakowskie Przedmiescie 7, 00-068 Warsaw, Poland) Ed. Z. Kleczek. illus. circ. 300. Document type: academic/scholarly publication.

621   PL   ISSN 0137-1800
AKADEMIA ROLNICZA, POZNAN. ROCZNIKI. MECHANICZNA TECHNOLOGIA DREWNA. (Text in Polish; summaries in English and Russian) 1974. irreg. price varies. Akademia Rolnicza, Poznan, Ul. Wojska Polskiego 28, 60-637 Poznan, Poland. FAX 48-61-411022. TELEX 0413322 ARPL. Indexed: Bibl.Agri. Document type: academic/scholarly publication.
Description: Wood science, technology of wood-base materials, furniture trade, hydro-thermal processing and modification of wood, wood gluing, economics of wood trade, wooden constructions, processing and wood machine tools.

AKADEMIA ROLNICZA WE WROCLAWIU. ZESZYTY NAUKOWE. MECHANIZACJA ROLNICTWA. see AGRICULTURE — Agricultural Equipment

621 531   AI
AKADEMIYA NAUK ARMENII. IZVESTIYA. SERIYA MEKHANIKA. (Text in Russian; summaries in Armenian) 1965. bi-m. 13.20 Rub. Akademiya Nauk Armenii, Pr. Marshala Bagramayana, 24, 375019 Erevan, Armenia. TEL 885-523480. TELEX 243344. charts; illus.; index. Indexed: Math.R., Met.Abstr., World Alum.Abstr.
Formerly: Akademiya Nauk Armyanskoi S.S.R. Izvestiya. Seriya Mekhanika (ISSN 0002-3051)

620.118   US   ISSN 1064-3834
AMERICAN FASTENER JOURNAL. 1984. bi-m. $30 (foreign $48). 293 Hopewell Dr., Powell, OH 43065-9350. TEL 614-848-3232. FAX 614-848-5045. Ed. Carol McGuire. adv. circ. 8,600. (back issues avail.) Document type: trade publication. —UMI.
Description: Directed toward fasteners distributors and manufacturers; informs and educates readers on the technical aspects of fasteners and fastener applications.

AMERICAN SOCIETY FOR HOSPITAL ENGINEERING TECHNICAL DOCUMENT SERIES. see HOSPITALS

621 621.3   SP   ISSN 0003-2506
  CODEN: AMEMA6
ANALES DE MECANICA Y ELECTRICIDAD. 1922. bi-m. 650 ptas. Asociacion de Ingenieros del I.C.A.I., Reina 31, 28004 Madrid, Spain. TEL 5226772. FAX 5226281. Ed Luis G-C. Basagoiti. adv.; bk.rev.; abstr.; bibl.; charts; illus.; index. circ. 5,000. Indexed: Ind.SST, Met.Abstr., Sci.Abstr., World Alum.Abstr. —BLDSC (0890.000000).

520   FR   ISSN 0294-1228
  CODEN: AFMCE5
ANNALES FRANCAISES DE MICROTECHNIQUES ET DE CHRONOMETRIE. 1931. q. 320 F.($50) Societe Francaise de Microtechnique et de Chronometrie, 41 bis av. de l'Observatoire, 25044 Besancon Cedex, France. bk.rev. circ. 1,000. Indexed: Astron.& Astrophys.Abstr., Sci.Abstr.
Former titles: Annales Francaises de Chronometrie et de Microtechniques (ISSN 0221-0665); Annales Francaises de Chronometrie et de Micromecanique (ISSN 0066-2143)

621   US   ISSN 1068-7181
TJ4
APPLIED ENERGY RESEARCH: RUSSIAN JOURNAL OF FUEL, POWER, AND HEAT SYSTEMS ENGINEERING. English translation of: Rossiiskaya Akademiya Nauk. Izvestiya. Energetika. 1974. bi-m. $865. (Rossiiskaya Akademiya Nauk, RU) Allerton Press, Inc., 150 Fifth Ave., New York, NY 10011. TEL 212-924-3950. FAX 212-463-9684. K.S. Demirchyan. Indexed: Sel.Water Res.Abstr. Document type: academic/scholarly publication. —BLDSC (0404.690000); Faxon. CCC.
Formerly: Power Engineering (U S S R Academy of Sciences) (ISSN 0160-5216)

ARCHIVES OF MECHANICS. see PHYSICS — Mechanics

745   FR   ISSN 0004-4008
ARTS ET METIERS. 1858. 10/yr. 315 F. Societe des Anciens Eleves de l'Ecole Nationale Superieure d'Arts & Metiers, 9 bis, Av. d'Iena, 75783 Paris Cedex 16, France. FAX 47-20-58-48. Ed. Jacqueline Delatte. adv.; bk.rev.; bibl.; illus.
Description: Discusses industrial and mechanical sciences.

ASSEMBLY AUTOMATION. see COMPUTERS — Automation

621   JA
▼**AUDIO VISUAL SYMPOSIUM ON DYNAMICS.** (Text in Japanese; summaries in English) 1992. irreg. 8000 Yen per no. Nihon Kikai Gakkai - Japan Society of Mechanical Engineers, 4-9, Yoyogi 2-chome, Shibuya-ku, Tokyo 151, Japan.

THE AUSTRALIAN GAS INDUSTRY DIRECTORY (YEAR). see PETROLEUM AND GAS

AUTOMATICA E INSTRUMENTACION; automatizacion, medida, control, instrumentacion, sistemas, tratamiento de informacion. see COMPUTERS — Automation

621   HU   ISSN 0133-1620
TJ212
AUTOMATIZALAS/AUTOMATION. (Text in Hungarian; summaries in English, German, Russian) 1968. m. 960 Ft. Prodinform Muszaki Tanacsodo Vallalat - Prodinform Technical Consulting Company, Munkacsy Mihaly u. 16, P.O. Box 453, H-1372 Budapest, Hungary. TEL 361-317-569. TELEX 227750-PROD-H. (Subscr. to: Kultura, P.O. Box 149, H-1389 Budapest, Hungary) (Co-sponsor: Hungexpo - Hungarian Foreign Trade Office) adv.; bk.rev. circ. 1,500. Indexed: INIS Atomind.

621.824   JA   ISSN 0914-4994
BANE/SPRING. (Text in Japanese) 1975. bi-m. Nihon Bane Kogyokai - Japan Spring Manufacturers Association, 9-9, Kaji-cho 1-chome, Chiyoda-ku, Tokyo 101, Japan.

621.824   JA   ISSN 0385-6917
BANE RONBUNSHU/RESEARCH PAPERS ON SPRING. (Text in Japanese; summaries in English, Japanese) 1952. a. Nihon Bane Kogyokai - Japan Spring Manufacturers Association, 9-9, Kaji-cho 1-chome, Chiyoda-ku, Tokyo 101, Japan.

621   GW
BAYERN METALL. 1948. m. DM.30. Fachverband Metall Bayern, Erhardtstr. 6, 80469 Munich, Germany. TEL 089-2014936. FAX 089-2010023. Ed. Egon Bluemel. adv.; bk.rev.; illus.; stat.; index. circ. 6,000. Document type: trade publication.

BEAM MODIFICATION OF MATERIALS. see PHYSICS — Optics

BEARINGU/BEARING. see ENGINEERING — Industrial Engineering

745   US   ISSN 0765-0639
BIBLIOTHEQUE DU C N A M. 1985. irreg. (Conservatoire National des Arts et Metiers) Gordon and Breach Science Publishers, 820 Town Center Dr., Langhorne, PA 19047. TEL 215-750-2642. FAX 215-750-6343. (UK subscr. to: Box 90, Reading, Berkshire RG1 8JL, England. TEL 0734-560-080)

621   YU   ISSN 0351-8906
BILTEN DOKUMENTACIJE. METALOPRERADJIVACKA DELATNOST. PROIZVODNJA RAZNOVRSNIH PROIZVODA/BULLETIN OF DOCUMENTATION. MANUFACTURE OF FABRICATED METAL PRODUCTS. MANUFACTURE OF MISCELLANEOUS PRODUCTS. 1951. bi-m. $264. Jugoslovenski Centar za Tehnicku i Naucnu Dokumentaciju - Yugoslav Center for Technical and Scientific Documentation (YCTSD), Sl. Penezica-Krcuna 29-31, Box 724, 1100 Belgrade, Yugoslavia. Ed. Ljiljana Kojic-Bogdanovic.
Formed by the merger of: Bilten Dokumentacije. Masinska Tehnologija i Radne Masine (ISSN 0006-2634); Bilten Dokumentacije. Pogonske Masine i Masinski Delovi (ISSN 0006-2650)

536.7 621.4   IT   ISSN 0006-6885
BOLLETTINO TERMOMECCANICA.* (Text in Italian; summaries in English and French) 1953. m. free. Termomeccanica Italiana S.p.A., Via del Molo, 19100 La Spezia, Italy. Ed. Vittorio Bertiati. circ. 7,000.

621.8   UK
BULK HANDLING. 1974. bi-m. £74. Turret Group Plc., Turret House, 171 High St., Rickmansworth, Herts WD3 1SN, England. TEL 0923-777000. FAX 0923-771297. Ed. Alan Davies. illus. circ. 9,500. Indexed: Agri.Eng.Abstr. Document type: trade publication.
Former titles: Bulk Handling: Storage, Movement, Control; Bulk: Storage, Movement, Control (ISSN 0305-3709)

BULK SOLIDS HANDLING; the international journal of powder-bulk & processing. see ENGINEERING — Chemical Engineering

621   JA
C F D WAKUSHOPPU SEIKA HOKOKUSHU. (Text in Japanese) 1990. irreg. 4000 Yen per no. Nihon Kikai Gakkai - Japan Society of Mechanical Engineers, 4-9, Yoyogi 2-chome, Shibuya-ku, Tokyo 151, Japan.

621   SZ   ISSN 0007-8506
T175   CODEN: CIRAAT
C.I.R.P. ANNALS. (Text in English, French or German) q. 325 SFr. (foreign 361 SFr.). (International Institution for Production Engineering Research - College International pour l'Etude Scientifique des Techniques de Production Mecanique) Hallwag AG, Nordring 4, CH-3001 Bern, Switzerland. TEL 031-3323131. FAX 031-3314133. TELEX 912661-CH. Ed.Bd. charts; illus.; tr.lit. Indexed: Chem.Abstr., Excerp.Med., ISMEC, Met.Abstr., Sci.Abstr., World Alum.Abstr. Document type: academic/scholarly publication. —BLDSC (1022.250000); EI; SWETS; CASDDS. CCC.
Formerly: C.I.R.P. (ISSN 0373-7284)

ENGINEERING — MECHANICAL ENGINEERING

621   CN   ISSN 0315-8977
TJ1   CODEN: TCMEAP
CANADIAN SOCIETY FOR MECHANICAL ENGINEERING. TRANSACTIONS. (Text in English or French) 1972. q. Can.$30 to non-members; members Can.$15; institutions Can.$75. Canadian Society for Mechanical Engineering - Societe Canadienne de Genie Mecanique, Dept. of Mechanical Engineering, University of Alberta, Rm. 4-9 Mec.E. Bldg., Edmonton, AB T6G 2G8, Canada.
TEL 403-492-0416. FAX 403-492-2200. Ed. Tom W. Forest. bk.rev.; circ. 350 (controlled). (back issues avail.; reprint service avail. from UMI) **Indexed:** A.S.& T.Ind., Appl.Mech.Rev., Eng.Ind., Fluidex. **Document type:** academic/scholarly publication, proceedings.
—BLDSC (8910.400000); EI; UnCover; UMI.
Description: Publishes reference or archival papers. *Refereed Serial*

CENTRE D'INFORMATION ET DE DOCUMENTATION SUR LE BRUIT. BULLETIN TECHNIQUE. see *ENVIRONMENTAL STUDIES — Pollution*

621   SA   ISSN 0009-0409
CODEN: CEENA9
CERTIFICATED ENGINEER/GEDIPLOMEERDE INGENIEUR. 1928. bi-m. R.60. (Institution of Certificated Mechanical and Electrical Engineers) Keeble Publishing Co. Pty. Ltd., P.O. Box 3080, Johannesburg 2000, South Africa.
FAX 011-402-6420. Ed. Gerry Bester. adv.; bk.rev.; abstr.; charts; illus.; index. circ. 5,000. **Indexed:** Eng.Ind., Ind.S.A.Per., INIS Atomind., Intl.Mgmt.Info., Sci.Abstr.
—BLDSC (3120.180000).
Incorporates: Engineering Now.
Description: Contains technical data for mechanical and electrical engineers employed in South African mines, utilities, and general industry, especially power generation. Includes industrial and commercial news and professional data.

621   CC   ISSN 1001-4357
CHAIYOU JI/DIESEL ENGINE. (Text in Chinese) bi-m. Shanghai Chuanyong Chaiyouji Yanjiusuo - Shanghai Marine Diesel Engine Research Institute, 105 Qinghai Lu, Shanghai 200041, People's Republic of China. TEL 2530009. Ed. Yao Jingzhe.

621   CC   ISSN 1000-9345
TJ1   CODEN: CJMEER
CHINESE JOURNAL OF MECHANICAL ENGINEERING. Chinese edition: Jixie Gongcheng Xuebao (ISSN 0577-6686) (Text in English) 1988. q. Y98 to individuals (foreign $118); institutions $156 (foreign $176). (Chinese Mechanical Engineering Society) China Machine Press, 1 Nanjie, Baiwanzhuang, Beijing 100037, People's Republic of China. TEL 8317766. FAX 01-3211613. TELEX 222557 STIP CN. (Overseas dist. by: Science Press New York, Ltd., 63-117 Alderton St., Rego Park, NY 11374. TEL 718-459-4638) Ed. Mei Zhongqin. (also avail. in microform; back issues avail.)
—BLDSC (3180.410000); UMI. **CCC.**
Description: Contains original contributions in addition to the translations of some articles in the Chinese edition.
Refereed Serial

CHINO IDO ROBOTTO SHINPOJUMU SHIRYO/INTELLIGENT ROBOT SYMPOSIUM. PROCEEDINGS. see *COMPUTERS — Robotics*

CLOSED LOOP; the magazine of testing and simulation technology. see *ENGINEERING — Engineering Mechanics And Materials*

621   CN
COLLOQUIUM. 1989. s-a. free. University of Alberta, c/o Dean of Engineering, 5-1 Mechanical Engineering Bldg., Edmonton, AB T6G 2G8, Canada. TEL 403-492-4514. FAX 403-492-0500. Ed. M.M. Thompson. bk.rev.; circ. 11,600 (controlled). **Document type:** newsletter.

COMPOSITE STRUCTURES. see *ENGINEERING — Civil Engineering*

621   UK   ISSN 0956-7143
CODEN: CMAUE2
COMPOSITES MANUFACTURING. (Text in English; Summaries in English, French, German) 1990. q. £130 in UK and Europe; elsewhere £140. Butterworth - Heinemann (Subsidiary of: Reed International PLC), Linacre House, Jordan Hill, Oxford OX2 8DP, England. TEL 0865-310366. FAX 0865-310898. TELEX 83111 BHPOXF G. (Subscr. to: Turpin Transactions Ltd., Distribution Centre, Blackhorse Rd., Letchworth, Herts SG6 1HN, England. TEL 0462-672555) Ed. Janet Miles. adv.; bk.rev.; abstr.; illus.; pat.; index. (also avail. in microform from UMI; back issues avail.) **Document type:** academic/scholarly publication.
—BLDSC (3365.580000); EI; Faxon; SWETS; UMI; CASDDS. **CCC.**
Refereed Serial

621.5   US   ISSN 0010-4426
TJ981   CODEN: COAIBB
COMPRESSED AIR; a magazine of applied technology and industrial management. 1896. 8/yr. $15. Compressed Air Magazine Co., (Subsidiary of: Ingersoll-Rand Co.), 253 E. Washington Ave., Washington, NJ 07882. TEL 908-850-7818. FAX 908-689-5576. Ed. S.M. Parkhill. bk.rev.; tr.lit.; circ. 150,000 (controlled). (also avail. in microform from UMI; reprint service avail. from UMI) **Indexed:** Abstr.Bull.Inst.Pap.Chem., Acid Rain Abstr., Acid Rain Ind., BMT, CAD CAM Abstr., Chem.Abstr., Energy Info.Abstr., Energy Rev., Eng.Ind., Environ.Abstr., Environ.Per.Bibl., Excerp.Med., Fuel & Energy Abstr., Gas Abstr., INIS Atomind., ISMEC, Met.Abstr., Ocean.Abstr., Pollut.Abstr., PROMT, Sci.Cit.Ind., World Alum.Abstr. **Document type:** trade publication.
—BLDSC (3366.400000); CIS; EI; Faxon; UnCover; SWETS; UMI.
Former titles (until 1965): Compressed Air Magazine (ISSN 0097-1952); (until 1908): Compressed Air (ISSN 0898-445X)
Description: Informational briefs, articles, and technical notes on the management of technology in the fields of transportation, construction, industry, and petrochemicals.

COMPUTATIONAL MECHANICS; solids, fluids, fracture, transport phenomena, multi-body dynamics and variational methods. see *MATHEMATICS — Computer Applications*

621   RM
CONSTRUCTIA DE MASINI. (Text in Rumanian; summaries in English, French, German) 1949. m. 150 lei($30) Ministerul Industriei Constructiilor de Masini, Cod 71102, Calea Victoriei, 133, CP 22-125 Bucharest, Rumania. (Dist. by: Rompresfilatelia, Soc. Export-Import presa, P.O. Box 12-201, Calea Grivitei nr.64-66, Bucharest, Rumania) Ed. Marin Nedelcu. adv.; bk.rev.; bibl.; pat.; index. circ. 2,500. **Indexed:** C.I.S. Abstr., Chem.Abstr., Ref.Zh.

COPPER TOPICS. see *METALLURGY*

621   US   ISSN 0010-9312
TA462   CODEN: CORRAK
CORROSION; journal of science and engineering. 1945. m. $100 (foreign $120). National Association of Corrosion Engineers (NACE), Box 218340, Houston, TX 77218. TEL 713-492-0535.
FAX 713-492-8254. Ed. Jesse B. Lumsden. adv.; charts; illus.; index. circ. 7,000. (reprint service avail. from UMI) **Indexed:** A.S.& T.Ind., Abstr.Bull.Inst.Pap.Chem., AESIS, API Abstr., API Catal., API Hlth.& Environ., API Oil., API Pet.Ref., API Transport., Art & Archaeol.Tech.Abstr., BMT, Cadscan, Chem.Abstr., Chem.Eng.Abstr., Copper Abstr., Corros.Abstr., Deep Sea Res.& Oceanogr.Abstr., E&P Hlth. (1993-), Energy Rev., Environ.Per.Bibl., Excerp.Med., Fluidex, Foul.Prev.Res.Dig., Fuel & Energy Abstr., Gas Process.& Ppl. (1993-), Ind.Sci.Rev., INIS Atomind., Int.Aerosp.Abstr., Int.Packag.Abstr., ISMEC, Lead Abstr., Mass Spectr.Bull., Met.Abstr., Off.Tech. (1993-), Petrol.Abstr. (1961-), Sci.Abstr., Sci.Cit.Ind., Soils & Fert., T.C.E.A., World Alum.Abstr., World Surf.Coat., Zincscan.
—BLDSC (3473.000000); EI; Faxon; UnCover; SWETS; UMI; CASDDS. **CCC.**
Description: Contains scientific and engineering articles on corrosion theory and research applications.
Refereed Serial

621   US   ISSN 1052-0139
CRYOGAS INTERNATIONAL; the source of timely and relevant information for the industrial gas and cryogenics industries. 1963. m. (11/yr.). $150 (foreign $180). J.R. Campbell & Associates, Inc., 5 Militia Dr., Lexington, MA 02173.
TEL 617-862-0624. FAX 617-863-9411. Ed. Kay Deans. adv. B&W page $750. bk.rev.; abstr.; pat.; index. circ. 480. **Document type:** newsletter.
—UnCover.
Formerly (until Nov. 1990): Cryogenic Information Report (ISSN 0011-2259)
Description: Reports developments in technology, market development, and new products for the industrial gases and cryogenic equipment industries, including non-cryogenic gas production processes and specailty and medical gases.

621   GW   ISSN 0011-815X
DEMAG KURIER. 1958. irreg. (5-6/yr.) free. Mannesmann Demag AG, Wolfgang-Reuter-Platz, 47053 Duisburg, Germany. Ed. E. Schmacke. charts; illus.; stat. circ. 35,000. (tabloid format) **Indexed:** C.I.S. Abstr.

621   JA   ISSN 0910-3902
DENGYOSHA KIKAI/DENGYOSHA TECHNICAL REVIEW. (Text in Japanese; summaries in English) 1977. s-a. Dengyosha Kikai Seisakujo - Dengyosha Machine Works, Ltd., 5-1, Omori Kita 1-chome, Ota-ku, Tokyo 143, Japan.

621 551.46   NE   ISSN 0928-2009
DEVELOPMENTS IN MARINE TECHNOLOGY. (Text in English) 1984. irreg., vol.10, 1992. Elsevier Science B.V., Books Division, P.O. Box 211, 1000 AE Amsterdam, Netherlands. TEL 31-20-5803911. FAX 31-20-5803705. TELEX 18582 ESPA NL. (Subscr. in U.S. and Canada to: Elsevier Science Inc., Box 882, Madison Sq. Sta., New York, NY 10159. TEL 212-989-5800) **Document type:** monographic series.
—BLDSC (3579.084550).
Refereed Serial

621 657 613.62   UK   ISSN 0269-0225
DIAGNOSTIC ENGINEERING. 1984. bi-m. £48($60) Institution of Diagnostic Engineers, 3 Wycliffe St., Leicester LE1 5LR, England. TEL 053-3759-2552. FAX 053-3759-2444. Ed. R.A. Collacott. adv.; bk.rev. circ. 9,000. **Document type:** newsletter.
—BLDSC (3579.657200).
Description: Contains theoretical, analytical, and informational articles on the technical aspects of managing and monitoring engineering systems.

DIAL ENGINEERING. see *ENGINEERING — Engineering Mechanics And Materials*

621 530   JA   ISSN 0917-4540
CODEN: DFTEEB
DIAMOND FILMS AND TECHNOLOGY. (Text in English) 1991. q. $200. M Y U, Scientific Publishing Division, 2-32-3 Sendagi, Bunkyo-ku, Tokyo 113, Japan. TEL 81-3-3821-2930.
FAX 81-3-3827-8547. Ed. Masanori Yoshikawa. **Document type:** academic/scholarly publication.
—BLDSC (3579.837300).
Description: Covers diamond cutting tools, protective coatings, heat management, active electronics, windows, lenses, domes and sensors for researchers and manufacturers of diamond.

621 380.5   IT
DIESEL; mensile di cultura, attualita, tecnica che tratta di tutte le motorizzazioni diesel per usi industriali, agricoli, nautici. 1986. m. L.42000 (foreign L.120000). Vado e Torno Edizioni S.r.l., Via Lattanzio 77, 20137 Milan, Italy.
TEL 02-55193629. FAX 02-55193660. Ed. Maurizio Cervetto. circ. 10,000. (back issues avail.)

ENGINEERING — MECHANICAL ENGINEERING

621   US   ISSN 0278-5994
TJ795.A1
DIESEL & GAS TURBINE WORLDWIDE; the international engine power systems magazine. 1969. 10/yr. $55. Diesel & Gas Turbine Publications, 13555 Bishop's Ct., Brookfield, WI 53005-6286. TEL 414-784-9177. FAX 414-784-8133. TELEX 275398. Ed. Joseph M. Kane. adv.: B&W page $3350, color page $3725; trim 7 x 10. circ. 21,000 (controlled). **Indexed:** BMT, Gas Abstr., Met.Abstr.
—BLDSC (3580.614000); EI; SWETS.
Formerly: Diesel and Gas Turbine Progress Worldwide (ISSN 0149-4465)
Description: Covers the design, application and operation of large diesel, gas and gas turbine engine systems in the power generation, oil and gas, marine and railroad industries.

621   US   ISSN 1070-4884
DIESEL AND GAS TURBINE WORLDWIDE CATALOG. 1935. a. $75. Diesel & Gas Turbine Publications, 13555 Bishop's Court, Brookfield, WI 53005. TEL 414-784-9177. FAX 414-784-8133. TELEX 275398. adv. circ. 14,501. **Document type:** catalog.
Former titles (until 1992): Diesel and Gas Turbine Catalog (ISSN 1064-2366); (until 1989): Diesel and Gas Turbine World Wide Catalog (ISSN 0070-4822)

DIESEL EQUIPMENT SUPERINTENDENT; the information source for truck fleet equipment managers. see TRANSPORTATION — Trucks And Trucking

621.436   FI   ISSN 0012-2629
DIESEL - LEHTI. 1952. 8/yr. $90. Suomen Dieselliitto r.y. - Diesel Association of Finland, P.O. Box 176, 00171 Helsinki 17, Finland.
FAX 358-90-1355028. Dir. Olof Enbom. adv.; bk.rev.; charts; illus.; mkt. circ. 5,500.

621.43   US   ISSN 1040-8878
TJ795   CODEN: DPNAD4
DIESEL PROGRESS ENGINES & DRIVES; for engine, drive and hydraulic system engineering and equipment management. 1935. m. $60. Diesel & Gas Turbine Publications, 13555 Bishop's Court, Brookfield, WI 53005-6286. TEL 414-784-9177.
FAX 414-784-8133. TELEX 275398. Ed. Michael J. Osenga. adv.; charts; illus.; stat.; tr.lit. circ. 28,400. (also avail. in microfilm from UMI; reprint service avail. from UMI) **Indexed:** Fuel & Energy Abstr., ISMEC, Met.Abstr., Petrol.Abstr., PROMT, Sh.& Vib.Dig., Tr.& Indus.Ind., World Alum.Abstr. **Document type:** trade publication.
—BLDSC (3581.400000); EI; Faxon; UnCover; SWETS; UMI.
Former titles: Diesel Progress North American (ISSN 0744-0073); (until 1980): Diesel and Gas Turbine Progress (ISSN 0012-2602); Diesel and Gas Engine Progress.

DINAMIKA I PROCHNOST' MASHIN. see PHYSICS — Mechanics

621   CC   ISSN 1000-6761
DONGLI GONGCHENG/POWER ENGINEERING. (Text in Chinese) bi-m. Dongli Gongcheng Xuehui - Chinese Society of Power Engineering, 1115 Minhang Jianchuan Lu, Shanghai 200240, People's Republic of China. TEL 021-4358722. (Co-sponsor: Shanghai Fadian Shebei Chengtao Sheji Yanjiusuo) Ed. Shu Zongxun.
—BLDSC (6575.002000).

DONGLI JIXUE WENZHAI/POWER MACHINERY ABSTRACTS. see ENGINEERING — Abstracting, Bibliographies, Statistics

DRIVES AND CONTROLS. see ENGINEERING — Hydraulic Engineering

621.5   GW
DRUCKLUFTTECHNIK. 1969. 6/yr. DM.120 (foreign DM.130). Vereinigte Fachverlage GmbH, Lise-Meitner-Str. 2, 55129 Mainz, Germany. TEL 06131-992-01. FAX 06131-992-100. TELEX 04187752. (Subscr. to: Postfach 2760, 55017 Mainz, Germany) Ed. Michael Pfister. adv.; bk.rev.; charts; illus.; pat.; stat.; index. circ. 18,000. **Indexed:** Fluidex.
Former titles: Druckluft-Praxis; Pneumatik Digest und Druckluftpraxis (ISSN 0048-4504)

DVIGATELI VNUTRENNEGO SGORANIYA. see PHYSICS — Mechanics

621   JA
DYNAMICS AND DESIGN CONFERENCE. (Text in English, Japanese) a. Japan Society of Mechanical Engineers - Nihon Kikai Gakkai, 4-9, Yoyogi 2-chome, Shibuya-ku, Tokyo 151, Japan.

621 668.4   GW   ISSN 0940-2470
TS176   CODEN: EPOEEX
E P E. (European Production Engineering) (Text in English) 1976. 2/yr. DM.44.80. Carl Hanser Verlag, Kolbergerstr. 22, 81679 Munich, Germany. TEL 089-998300. FAX 089-984809. (Subscr. to: Postfach 860420, 81631 Munich, Germany) adv.; bk.rev.; bibl.; charts; illus.; pat.; stat.; tr.lit.; index. circ. 25,000. **Indexed:** ISMEC, Met.Abstr., World Surf.Coat. **Document type:** trade publication.
—BLDSC (3829.799700); EI; SWETS. CCC.
Formerly (until 1991): I P E - Industrial and Production Engineering (ISSN 0343-334X)
Description: Covers production engineering, metalworking and surface treatment from a technical perspective worldwide.

621   JA   ISSN 0385-3004
                      CODEN: EHJIAS
EBARA JIHO/EBARA ENGINEERING REVIEW. (Text in Japanese; summaries in English) 1952. q. Ebara Seisakujo - Ebara Corp., 11-1, Haneda Asahi-cho, Ota-ku, Tokyo 144, Japan. **Indexed:** INIS Atomind.
—BLDSC (3647.120000); CASDDS.

621 621.3 621.48   FR
ELECTRICITE DE FRANCE. DIRECTION DES ETUDES ET RECHERCHES. COLLECTION DE NOTES INTERNES. PRODUCTION D'ENERGIE (HYDRAULIQUE, THERMIQUE ET NUCLEAIRE). (Supplements avail.) (Text in French; summaries in English) 1962. irreg. 4000 F. Electricite de France (EDF), Direction des Etudes et Recherches, 1 av. du General de Gaulle, 92141 Clamart Cedex, France. TEL 1-47-65-43-21.
FAX 1-47-65-31-24. TELEX 204 347 F. charts; illus.; cum.index. circ. 1,500. **Indexed:** Eng.Ind., INIS Atomind., Sci.Abstr.
Supersedes (in 1992): Electricite de France. Direction des Etudes et Recherches. Bulletin. Serie A: Nucleaire, Hydraulique, Thermique (ISSN 0013-449X); Bulletin du Centre Recherches et d'Essais de Chatou.

621   AU   ISSN 1019-410X
ELEKTRONIK REPORT; die Kennziffer-Fachzeitschrift fuer die Industrielle Elektronik. 1976. m. S.630. Verlag Technik - Report GmbH, Markgraf-Ruediger-Str. 8, A-1150 Vienna, Austria. TEL 01-98170-0.
FAX 01-9817033. TELEX 135041. Ed. Karl Pichler. adv. circ. 14,650. **Document type:** trade publication.
Description: Specializes in industrial electronics.

621   TU
ENDUSTRI MUHENDISLIGI. 1989. bi-m. Chamber of Mechanical Engineers, Sumer Sokak, 36-1-A Demirtepe, 06440 Ankara, Turkey.
TEL 4-2313164. FAX 4-2313165. Ed. Yusuf Unler. adv.; circ. 5,000 (controlled).
Description: Publishes original technical papers of interest to industrial engineers and technical managers.

ENERGETICHESKOE MASHINOSTROENIE. see PHYSICS — Mechanics

620   II
ENGINEER - I.M.E. NEWS. (Text in English) 1920. m. Rs.150($30) Institution of Mechanical Engineers (India), Janmabhoomi Chambers, 3rd Fl., 29 W. Hirachand Marg, Ballard Estate, Bombay 400 038, India. TEL 22-2612207. (And: Post Bag No. 10146, Bombay 400 001, India) Ed. H.M. Desai. adv.; bk.rev.; illus. circ. 22,000. **Document type:** newsletter.
Formerly: Engineer and M.E.A. News.
Description: Covers scientific engineering and technological development in India and the world.

ENGINEERED SYSTEMS; serving the heating, ventilating, air conditioning and refrigerating engineering community. see HEATING, PLUMBING AND REFRIGERATION

621   UK   ISSN 0955-7997
TA347.B69   CODEN: EABAEL
ENGINEERING ANALYSIS WITH BOUNDARY ELEMENTS. 1984. 8/yr. (in 2 vols., 4 nos./vol.). £416($640) (effective 1994). Elsevier Science Ltd., Oxford Fulfilment Centre, P.O. Box 800, Kidlington, Oxford OX5 1DX, England. TEL 44-865-843000.
FAX 44-865-843010. (Subscr. in U.S. and Canada to: Elsevier Science, 660 White Plains Rd., Tarrytown, NY 10591-5153. TEL 914-524-9200. FAX 914-333-2444) Eds. C.A. Brebbia, M. Tanaka. adv. **Indexed:** A.I.Abstr., Appl.Mech.Rev., CAD CAM Abstr., Comput.& Info.Sys., Eng.Ind., Met.Abstr., Sci.Abstr. **Document type:** academic/scholarly publication.
—BLDSC (3753.350000); EI; Faxon; UnCover; SWETS. CCC.
Formerly (until 1991): Engineering Analysis (ISSN 0264-682X)
Description: International coverage of innovations in boundary elements, finite elements and computational techniques.
Refereed Serial

621   UK
ENGINEERING DESIGN AND MANUFACTURING INDEX. 1967. s-a. Technical Indexes Ltd., Willoughby Rd., Bracknell, Berks. RG12 8DW, England. TEL 0344-426311. FAX 0344-424971. Ed. R. Miller. circ. 9,009. **Document type:** abstracting/indexing.
Engineering Components and Materials Index (ISSN 0308-8383)

621   JA   ISSN 0385-9274
ENGINEERING INDUSTRIES IN JAPAN. (Text in English) 1969. a. Kikai Shinko Kyokai, Keizai Kenkyujo - Japan Society for the Promotion of Machine Industry, Economic Research Institute, 5-8, Shiba Koen 3-chome, Minato-ku, Tokyo 105, Japan.
—BLDSC (3762.097000).

621.8   FR
ENTRAINEMENTS; et systemes des transmissions mecaniques, hydrauliques, pneumatiques, commandes et assertissements. 1967. 8/yr. 320 F. (foreign 398 F.). S O P R O G E, S.A., 7 ter, Cour des Petites-Ecuries, 75010 Paris, France. Ed. H. Thiron. adv.; bibl.; charts; illus.; pat.; index. circ. 5,000.
Former titles: Revue Generale des Transmissions Mecaniques, Hydrauliques, Pneumatiques, Commandes et Assertissements; Revue Generale des Transmissions (ISSN 0048-8100)

ENTROPIE; revue internationale d'energetique, genie chimique, genie biologique. see ENERGY

EUREKA; innovative engineering design. see ENGINEERING

621   GW   ISSN 0937-8243
EUROPEAN JOURNAL FOR FLUID POWER. (Text in English) 1990. s-a. DM.20. Vereinigte Fachverlage GmbH, Lise-Meitner-Str. 2, 55129 Mainz, Germany. TEL 06131-992-01. FAX 06131-992-100. (Subscr. to: Postfach 2760, 55017 Mainz, Germany) Ed. Wilfried Bork. adv. contact: Annemarie Benthin.
—BLDSC (3829.729000).

621 539.7   BE   ISSN 0777-2734
EUROPEAN JOURNAL OF MECHANICAL ENGINEERING. (Text and summaries in Dutch, English, French) 1954. q. 3500 BEF (foreign 4250 BEF) (effective 1994). Societe Belge des Mecaniciens - Belgian Society of Mechanical Engineers, 21 rue des Drapiers, B-1050 Brussels, Belgium.
TEL 32-2-5118286. Ed. R. Jacques. adv. contact: F. Crepain. bk.rev.; abstr.; bibl.; tr.lit.; index. circ. 1,900. (back issues avail.) **Document type:** academic/scholarly publication.
—BLDSC (3829.731270); EI; Faxon. CCC.
Formerly (until June 1989): Revue "M" Mecanique (ISSN 0035-3612)
Description: Publishes original papers on general and theoretical mechanics, mechanics of fluids and gases, metrology and manufacturing control, thermodynamics, and tribology. Also includes information on technical novelties on the market, calls for papers, survey of journals.
Refereed Serial

ENGINEERING — MECHANICAL ENGINEERING

621　　　　　GW　ISSN 0723-4864
　　　　　　　　　　CODEN: EXFLDU
EXPERIMENTS IN FLUIDS; experimental methods and their applications to fluid flow. 1983. 12/yr. (in 2 vols., 6 nos./vol.). DM.1078($674) Springer-Verlag, Heidelberger Platz 3, 14197 Berlin, Germany. TEL 030-8207-1. FAX 030-8214091. (Subscr. in N. America to: Springer-Verlag New York, Inc., 44 Hartz Way, Secaucus, NJ 07096-2491. TEL 201-348-4033. FAX 201-348-4505) Ed.Bd. adv. (also avail. in microfiche from UMI; reprint service avail. from ISI) **Indexed:** Appl.Mech.Rev., Chem.Abstr., Curr.Cont., Fluidex, INIS Atomind., Int.Aerosp.Abstr. **Document type:** academic/scholarly publication.
—BLDSC (3841.760000); Faxon; UnCover; SWETS; UMI; CASDDS. **CCC.**
　Description: Reports on the development of new measuring techniques or the extension and improvement of existing methods for the measurement of fluid flow properties for their better understanding and application in science and engineering.

021　　　　　US
F P D A NEWS. 1974. bi-m. free to members. Fluid Power Distributors Association, 201 Barclay Pavilion West, Cherry Hill, NJ 08034. TEL 609-795-6113. FAX 609-795-6362. Ed. Mary Connor. adv. circ. 1,200. **Document type:** newsletter.
　Formerly: F D P A Power Planner.
　Description: Contains news of interest to fluid power distributors.

F UND M, FEINWERKTECHNIK MIKROTECHNIK MESSTECHNIK; Zeitschrift fuer Elektronik, Optik, Feinmechanik und Mikrotechnik in Geraetebau und Messtechnik. see *ENGINEERING*

FACTORY EQUIPMENT NEWS. see *TECHNOLOGY: COMPREHENSIVE WORKS*

621 627　　　　UK
FAIREY IN FOCUS. 1978. q. free. Fairey Group PLC, Cranford Lane, Heston, Middlesex TW5 9NQ, England. TEL 01759 4811. FAX 081-7599461. Ed. Derek Thurgood. circ. 5,000.

621　　　　　JA　ISSN 0914-5478
FAKUTORI OTOMESHON. (Text in Japanese) 1983. m. 1300 Yen per no. Nihon Kogyo Shuppan K.K., 3-26, Honkomagome 6-chome, Bunkyo-ku, Tokyo 113, Japan.

620.1　　　　RU　ISSN 0015-3214
TA401　　　　　　　CODEN: FKOMAT
FIZIKA I KHIMIYA OBRABOTKI MATERIALOV. English translation: Physics and Chemistry of Materials Treatment (UK ISSN 0264-729X) 1965. bi-m. $120. (Rossiiskaya Akademiya Nauk) Izdatel'stvo Nauka, 90 Profsoyuznaya ul., 117864 Moscow, Russia. (Dist. in U.S. by: Victor Kamkin Inc., 4956 Boiling Brook Pkwy., Rockville, MD 20852. TEL 301-881-5973. FAX 301-881-1637) **Indexed:** Chem.Abstr., INIS Atomind., Met.Abstr., Sci.Abstr., World Alum.Abstr.
—BLDSC (0389.780000); CASDDS. **CCC.**

621　　　　　KR　ISSN 0203-4654
　　　　　　　　　　CODEN: FTVDDZ
FIZIKA I TEKHNIKA VYSOKIKH DAVLENII; respublikanskii mezhvedomstvennyi sbornik nauchnykh trudov. (Text in Russian; summaries in English and Russian) 1980. 3/yr. (Akademiya Nauk Ukrainy, Donetskii Fiziko-Tekhnicheskii Institut) Vidavnitstvo Naukova Dumka, Vul. Tereshchenkivska 3, 252601 Kiev, Ukraine. TEL 044-224-4068. FAX 044-224-7060. (Dist. by: Mezhdunarodnaya Kniga, B. Yakimanka 39, 117049 Moscow, Russia) Ed. E.A. Zavadskii. **Indexed:** Chem.Abstr., Met.Abstr., World Alum.Abstr.
—CASDDS.

FLUID; Zeitschrift fuer Hydraulik, Pneumatik, Elektronik. see *ENGINEERING — Hydraulic Engineering*

FLUID: APPARECCHIATURE IDRAULICHE E PNEUMATICHE; olio e aria sotto pressione lubrificazione. see *ENGINEERING — Hydraulic Engineering*

FLUID DYNAMICS RESEARCH; an international journal. see *ENGINEERING — Hydraulic Engineering*

621　　　　　US　ISSN 1052-0228
TA357.5.M43
FLUID MEASUREMENTS AND INSTRUMENTATION FORUM. 1986. a. American Society of Mechanical Engineers, 345 E. 47th St., New York, NY 10017.

621　　　　　US　ISSN 1064-2277
QC145.2
FLUID MECHANICS RESEARCH. 1972. bi-m. $896 (Canada & Mexico $956; elsewhere $978.50) (effective 1993). Scripta Technica, Inc. (Subsidiary of: John Wiley & Sons, Inc.), 7961 Eastern Ave., Silver Spring, MD 20910. TEL 301-588-0484. FAX 301-588-5278. (Dist. by: John Wiley & Sons, Inc., Periodicals Division, 650 Third Ave., New York, NY 10158. TEL 212-852-6000; Subscr. outside the Americas to: John Wiley & Sons, Ltd., Baffins Ln., Chichester, Sussex PO19 1UD, England. TEL 44-243-779777) Ed. Novak Zuber. adv.; bk.rev.; abstr.; bibl.; illus. circ. 400. (also avail. in microform from UMI) **Indexed:** Appl.Mech.Rev., INIS Atomind., INSPEC. **Document type:** academic/scholarly publication.
—BLDSC (3962.130000); EI; Faxon; UnCover; SWETS; UMI. **CCC.**
　Formerly (until 1993): Fluid Mechanics - Soviet Research (ISSN 0096-0764)
　Description: Publishes translations of theoretical and research papers from Russian and Ukrainian journals relating to compressible and incompressible fluids, two-phase flow, turbulence, boundary layers, wakes, channel and nozzle flow, aerodynamics and rheology.

621　　　　　US
FLUID POWER STANDARDS. irreg. National Fluid Power Association, 3333 N. Mayfair Rd., Milwaukee, WI 53222. TEL 414-778-3363. FAX 414-778-3361. (also avail. in microfilm; back issues avail.) **Indexed:** PROMT.

FLUIDOS; oleohidraulica, neumatica, automacion. see *ENGINEERING — Hydraulic Engineering*

621　　　　　GW　ISSN 0178-9562
FORTSCHRITT-BERICHTE V D I. REIHE 13: FOERDERTECHNIK. irreg. V D I Verlag GmbH, Heinrichstr. 24, 40239 Duesseldorf, Germany. TEL 0211-6188-0. FAX 0211-6188112. (Subscr. to: Postfach 101054, 40001 Duesseldorf, Germany) **Document type:** trade publication.
—BLDSC (4018.591000).

621　　　　　US　ISSN 1044-5951
TA357
FORUM ON UNSTEADY FLOW. 1989. a. American Society of Mechanical Engineers, United Engineering Center, 345 E. 47th St., New York, NY 10017.

621　　　　　JA　ISSN 0429-8349
FUJIKOSHI GIHO/FUJIKOSHI ENGINEERING REVIEW. (Text in Japanese; summaries in English, Japanese) 1955. irreg. Fujikoshi Eigyo Suishinbu, 4-1, Hamamatsu-cho 2-chome, Minato-ku, Tokyo 105, Japan.

621.483　　　　SZ　ISSN 0920-3796
　　　　　　　　　　CODEN: FEDEEE
FUSION ENGINEERING AND DESIGN; an international journal devoted to the thermal, mechanical, materials, structural and design aspects of fusion energy. (Text in English) 1984. 12/yr. (in 3 vols.; 4 nos./vol.). 1530 SFr.($1041) (combined subscr. with Nuclear Engineering and Design 5115 SFr.($3480)) (effective 1994). Elsevier Science S.A., P.O. Box 564, CH-1001 Lausanne 1, Switzerland. TEL 41-21-3207381. FAX 41-21-3235444. TELEX 450620 ELSA-CH. (Subscr. in U.S. and Canada to: Elsevier Science Inc., Box 882, Madison Sq. Sta., New York, NY 10159. TEL 212-989-5800. FAX 212-633-3990) Ed. Robert W. Conn. (back issues avail.) **Document type:** academic/scholarly publication.
—BLDSC (4059.671000); Faxon; UnCover; SWETS; CASDDS. **CCC.**
　Formerly (until 1986): Nuclear Engineering and Design, Fusion (ISSN 0167-899X)
　Description: Provides civil and mechanical engineers as well as reactor designers with the latest information on fusion technology, especially engineering aspects of systems and component design.
　Refereed Serial

G E C JOURNAL OF RESEARCH. see *ENGINEERING — Electrical Engineering*

G E C REVIEW. (General Electric Co., PLC) see *ENGINEERING — Electrical Engineering*

621 790　　　　US
GAS ENGINE MAGAZINE. m. $27. Stemgas Publishing Co., 41 N. Charlotte St., Lancaster, PA 17603. TEL 717-392-0733. FAX 717-392-1341. Ed. Linda Sharron. adv. contact: Judy Whiteside. cum.index: 1966-1977, 1978-1982, 1983-1987. circ. 23,000. (back issues avail.) **Document type:** consumer publication.
　Description: Contains useful information for collectors of antique gas engines and tractors including restoration ideas, related associations, and show news.

621　　　　　JA
GAS TURBINE SOCIETY OF JAPAN. BULLETIN. (Text in English) q. Gas Turbine Society of Japan - Nihon Gasu Tabin Gakkai, 5-3, Nishishinju-ku 7-chome, Shinjuku-ku, Tokyo 160, Japan.

621　　　　　JA
GASU TABIN SEMINA SHIRYOSHU/GAS TURBINE SOCIETY OF JAPAN. SEMINAR REPORT. (Text in Japanese) 1974. a. Nihon Gasu Tabin Gakkai - Gas Turbine Society of Japan, 5-13, Nishishinju-ku 7-chome, Shinjuku-ku, Tokyo 169, Japan.

621　　　　　US　ISSN 0743-6858
TJ184　　　　　　　CODEN: GEATEL
GEAR TECHNOLOGY; the journal of gear manufacturing. 1984. bi-m. $40. Randall Publishing, Inc., 1425 Lunt Ave., Elk Grove Village, IL 60007. TEL 708-437-6604. FAX 708-437-6618. (Subscr. to: Box 1426, Elk Grove Village, IL 60009) Ed. Michael Goldstein. circ. 6,500. (back issues avail.) **Document type:** trade publication.
—BLDSC (4095.470000); EI; SWETS.
　Description: Covers all aspects of gear design, research and manufacture for professional engineers, gear designers and researchers.

621.89　　　　JA　ISSN 0914-6121
GEKKAN TORAIBOROJI/TRIBOLOGY. (Text in Japanese) 1987. m. 720 Yen per no. Shinjusha Inc., 15-4, Ginza 8-chome, Chuo-ku, Tokyo 104, Japan.

GIDRAVLICHESKIE MASHINY. see *PHYSICS — Mechanics*

621　　　　　JA
GURAINDINGU AKADEMI TEKISUTO/TEXTBOOK FOR GRINDING ACADEMY. (Text in Japanese) a. Toryu Kako Gakkai - Japan Society of Grinding Engineers, 22-17, Hyakunin-cho 2-chome, Shinjuku-ku, Tokyo 169, Japan.

621　　　　　US
H P A C TECHLIT SELECTOR. (Heating Piping Air Conditioning) 1929. s-a. free to qualified personnel. Penton Publishing (Subsidiary of: Pittway Company), 1100 Superior Ave., Cleveland, OH 44114-2543. TEL 216-696-7000. FAX 216-696-8765. (Subscr. to: Box 95759, Cleveland, OH 44101) adv.; circ. 52,000 (controlled).

621　　　　　JA　ISSN 0438-3664
HAGURUMA/GEAR. (Text in Japanese) 1953. a. Osaka Kogyo Daigaku, Kikai Kogaku Kenkyubu - Osaka Institute of Technology, Mechanical Engineering Circle, 16-1, Omiya 5-chome, Asahi-ku, Osaka-shi, Osaka 535, Japan.

621　　　　　JA　ISSN 0385-9894
　　　　　　　　　　CODEN: HAGIBW
HAIKAN GIJUTSU/PIPING ENGINEERING. (Text in Japanese) 1959. m. 1300 Yen per no. Nihon Kogyo Shuppan K.K. - Japan Industrial Publishing Co., Ltd., 3-26, Honkomagome 6-chome, Bunkyo-ku, Tokyo 113, Japan.
—CASDDS.

621　　　　　JA　ISSN 0288-2302
HAIKAN TO SOCHI/PIPING AND PROCESS EQUIPMENT. (Text in Japanese) 1951. m. 720 Yen per no. Sanko Kikaku - Sanko Advertising Inc., 11-5, Uchikanda 2-chome, Chiyoda-ku, Tokyo 101, Japan.

621 546　　　　US
HANDBOOK OF BINARY PHASE DIAGRAMS. base vol. plus updates 3/yr. $109 (foreign $126). Genium Publishing Corp., 1 Genium Plaza, Schenectady, NY 12304-4690. TEL 518-377-8854; 800-243-6486. FAX 518-377-1891. Ed. Robert A. Roy. (looseleaf format)

HANDLING EQUIPMENT DIRECTORY (YEAR); unit loads, fluids, loose materials. see *MACHINERY*

ENGINEERING — MECHANICAL ENGINEERING

621   JA
HANSHIN GIJUTSU NYUSU/HANSHIN TECHNICAL NEWS. (Text in Japanese) a. Hanshin Nainenki Kogyo K.K. - Hanshin Diesel Works, Ltd., 8, Kaigan Dori, Chuo-ku, Kobe-shi, Hyogo-ken 650, Japan.

HEALTH & SAFETY NEWSLINE; for the engineering industry (UK). see *PUBLIC HEALTH AND SAFETY*

621   US
HEAT PUMP TECHNOLOGY CONFERENCE PROCEEDINGS. 1975. irreg. $25. Oklahoma State University, College of Engineering, Engineering Extension, 512 Engineering North, Stillwater, OK 74078. TEL 405-624-5033. **Document type:** proceedings.

HEAT TRANSFER ENGINEERING. see *ENGINEERING — Chemical Engineering*

621 690   US
HEAT TRANSFER - FLUID FLOW DATA BOOKS. base vols. plus updates 3/yr. $125 (foreign $183). Genium Publishing Corp., 1 Genium Plaza, Schenectady, NY 12304-4690. TEL 518-377-8854; 800-243-6486. FAX 518-377-1891. Ed. Robert A. Roy. (looseleaf format)

536   US   ISSN 0096-0802
QC320   CODEN: HTJPAU
HEAT TRANSFER - JAPANESE RESEARCH. 1972. 8/yr. $850 (Canada & Mexico $930; elsewhere $960). Scripta Technica, Inc. (Subsidiary of: John Wiley & Sons, Inc.), 7961 Eastern Ave., Silver Spring, MD 20910. TEL 301-588-0484. FAX 301-588-5278. (Dist. by: John Wiley & Sons, Inc., Periodicals Division, 650 Third Ave., New York, NY 10158. TEL 212-692-6000) Eds. Thomas F. Irving, Jr., K. Suzuki. adv.; bibl.; charts; index. circ. 400. (also avail. in microform from UMI) **Indexed:** Appl.Mech.Rev., Chem.Eng.Abstr., INIS Atomind., INSPEC, T.C.E.A. **Document type:** academic/scholarly publication.
—BLDSC (4276.094000); EI; Faxon; UnCover; SWETS; UMI. **CCC.**
Description: Covers the entire field of heat transfer and pertinent areas of fluid dynamics.

536   US   ISSN 1064-2285
QC320   CODEN: HTREE7
HEAT TRANSFER RESEARCH. 1969. 8/yr. $1196 (Canada & Mexico $1276; elsewhere $1306). (American Society of Mechanical Engineers) Scripta Technica, Inc. (Subsidiary of: John Wiley & Sons, Inc.), 7961 Eastern Ave., Silver Spring, MD 20910. TEL 301-588-0484. FAX 301-588-5278. (Dist. by: John Wiley & Sons, Inc., Periodicals Division, 650 Third Ave., New York, NY 10158. TEL 212-692-6000) Ed. James P. Hartnett. adv. circ. 500. (also avail. in microform from UMI) **Indexed:** Appl.Mech.Rev., Chem.Eng.Abstr., Excerp.Med., INIS Atomind., INSPEC, T.C.E.A. **Document type:** academic/scholarly publication.
—BLDSC (4276.094700); EI; Faxon; UnCover; SWETS; UMI. **CCC.**
Formerly (until 1992): Heat Transfer - Soviet Research (ISSN 0440-5749)
Description: Covers the entire field of heat transfer, including conduction, convection and radiation, boiling, heat exchanger design and testing, nuclear reactors, mass transfer, geothermal heat recovery and thermophysical properties of materials.

621   US   ISSN 1041-5416
TJ795.A1
HIGH-SPEED DIESELS AND DRIVES; the international engine drive and hydraulic systems magazine for engineering and equipment management. 1982. 9/yr. $50. Diesel & Gas Turbine Publications, 13555 Bishop's Court, Brookfield, WI 53005. TEL 414-784-9177. FAX 414-784-8133. TELEX 275398. Ed. Rob Wilson. adv.; B&W page $2550, color page $3300; trim 8 1/4 x 11 1/4. circ. 14,676. (also avail. in microfilm; back issues avail.)
—BLDSC (4307.358370); SWETS.
Formerly: High Speed Diesel Report (ISSN 0730-5303)
Description: Covers diesel and gas turbine engines in the U.S. and Canada.

621   JA
HITACHI CHIHO KOENKAI KOEN RONBUNSHU/HITACHI DISTRICT CONFERENCE. PROCEEDINGS. (Text in Japanese; summaries in English) a. 3000 Yen. Nihon Kikai Gakkai - Japan Society of Mechanical Engineers, 4-9, Yoyogi 2-chome, Shibuya-ku, Tokyo 151, Japan.

HITACHI MAIKON GIHO/HITACHI MAIKON TECHNICAL JOURNAL. see *ELECTRONICS*

621   JA   ISSN 0918-1423
HITO PAIPU GIJUTSU/JAPANESE ASSOCIATION FOR HEAT PIPES. JOURNAL. (Text in Japanese; summaries in English) 1987. q. Nihon Hito Paipu Kyokai - Japanese Association for Heat Pipes, Seikei Daigaku Kogakubu, Kikai Kogakka Netsu Kikan Kenkyushitsu, 3-1, Kichijoji Kitamachi 3-chome, Musashino-shi, Tokyo 180, Japan.

HOBSON'S ENGINEERING CASEBOOK. see *ENGINEERING — Civil Engineering*

621   US   ISSN 1046-6282
QC276
HOSTILE ENVIRONMENTS AND HIGH TEMPERATURE MEASUREMENTS. irreg. Society for Experimental Mechanics, 7 School St., Bethel, CT 06801.
—**CCC.**
Formerly (until 1989): Hostile Environments and High Temperature Measurements Conference Proceedings (ISSN 1046-6746)

HYDRAULICS & PNEUMATICS; the magazine of fluid power and motion control systems. see *ENGINEERING — Hydraulic Engineering*

IMPACT VALVES NEWS AND PATENTS. see *MACHINERY*

INDIANA UNIVERSITY MATHEMATICS JOURNAL. see *MATHEMATICS*

621   IT   ISSN 0393-1331
INDUSTRIA MECCANICA. 1948. m. (11/yr.) L.100000 (foreign L.170000). Federazione delle Associazione Nazionali dell'Industria Meccanica Varia ed Affine, Vie Battistotti Sassi, 11, 20133 Milan, Italy. TEL 2-72-13-11. FAX 2-861-306. adv. circ. 8,000.

621   IT   ISSN 0393-599X
INDUSTRIA MERCATO; rivista dell'industria meccanica. (Text in Italian; summaries in English) 1973. 19/yr. L.58000. E R I S S.p.A., Via E. Tellini 14, 20155 Milan, Italy. TEL 2-33-103-305. FAX 2-33-10-42-45. Ed. Graziella Rotta. adv.; B&W page L.3200000; trim 271 x 363. bk.rev.; pat.; index. circ. 52,285. **Indexed:** Chem.Abstr.
Former titles: Industria Meccanica; I M U (ISSN 0391-7363); Incorporates: T I M (ISSN 0391-3953)

621.89   UK   ISSN 0036-8792
TJ1075.A2   CODEN: ILTRA7
INDUSTRIAL LUBRICATION & TRIBOLOGY; technical journal devoted exclusively to the science and practice of lubrication and tribology. 1948. bi-m. $649.95. M C B University Press Ltd., 60-62 Toller Ln., Bradford, W. Yorks BD8 9BY, England. TEL 0274-499821. FAX 0274-547143. TELEX 51317-MCBUNI-G. Ed. Bill Wilson. adv.; bk.rev.; charts; illus.; pat.; tr.lit.; index. (reprint service avail. from SWZ) **Indexed:** API Abstr., API Catal., API Hlth.& Environ., API Oil., API Pet.Ref., API Pet.Subst., API Transport., BMT, Br.Tech.Ind., Chem.Abstr., Eng.Ind., Fluidex, Met.Abstr., Sh.& Vib.Dig., World Alum.Abstr. **Document type:** academic/scholarly publication.
—BLDSC (4457.610000); EI; UnCover; SWETS; UMI.
Formerly: Scientific Lubrication
Description: Covers all aspects of tribology: lubricants, lubrications, friction and wear. Specific emphasis is given to the development of alternatives to finite hydrocarbons.

621   CU   ISSN 0258-5952
INGENIERIA ESTRUCTURAL. 1977. 3/yr. $24 in N. America; S. America $24; Europe $26. (Ministerio de Educacion Superior, Instituto Superior Politecnico) Ediciones Cubanas, Obispo No. 527, Apdo. 605, Havana, Cuba.

621 621.3   MX   ISSN 0374-339X
INGENIERIA MECANICA Y ELECTRICA. 1946. m. Asociacion Mexicana de Ingenieros Mecanicos y Electricistas, Culiacan 115, Mexico 11 D.F., Mexico. adv. circ. 7,000. **Indexed:** Sci.Abstr.
—BLDSC (4503.180000).

621   UK
INSTITUTE OF ENGINEERS & TECHNICIANS JOURNAL. 1948. q. $35 to non-members. (Institute of Engineers and Technicians) Deeson Editorial Services Ltd., Ewell House, Graveney Rd., Faversham, Kent ME13 8UP, England. FAX 01-795-535469. Ed. Dominic Deeson. adv.; bk.rev.; charts; illus.; circ. 6,500 (controlled). **Document type:** academic/scholarly publication.

621   UK
INSTITUTION OF DIESEL AND GAS TURBINE ENGINEERS. TRANSACTIONS. 6/yr. £71 (foreign £76). Mechanical Engineering Publications Ltd., Northgate Ave., Bury St. Edmunds, Suffolk IP32 6BW, England. TEL 0284-763277. FAX 0284-704006. TELEX 817376. **Indexed:** BMT. **Document type:** trade publication.
—BLDSC (7085.350000); EI; SWETS. **CCC.**
Formerly: Diesel Engineers and Users Association. Transactions (ISSN 0261-0345)
Description: Research articles, schematics, and photography on diverse technical subjects of interest to the field.

621   II   ISSN 0020-3408
TJ1   CODEN: JEMDAS
INSTITUTION OF ENGINEERS (INDIA). MECHANICAL ENGINEERING DIVISION. JOURNAL. (Text in English) 1920. bi-m. Rs.120($15) Institution of Engineers, Mechanical Engineering Division, 8 Gokhale Rd., Calcutta 700 020, India. TEL 033-288334. FAX 033-288345. TELEX 0217885 IEIC IN. Ed. K.N. Majumdar. adv.; charts; illus.; index. circ. 20,000. **Indexed:** Appl.Mech.Rev., Eng.Ind., Fluidex, Geotech.Abstr., Int.Aerosp.Abstr., ISMEC, Met.Abstr., Sci.Abstr.
—BLDSC (4794.029500); EI.

621 660.2   AT   ISSN 0727-7369
TJ1   CODEN: TEAMD6
INSTITUTION OF ENGINEERS, AUSTRALIA. TRANSACTIONS. MECHANICAL ENGINEERING. 1979. q. Aus.$55 (overseas Aus.$70). Engineers Australia Pty. Ltd., Crows Nest Centre, 2 Ernest St., Crows Nest, N.S.W. 2065. TEL 02-438-1533. FAX 02-438-5934. illus.; index. circ. 4,000. **Indexed:** Appl.Mech.Rev., CAD CAM Abstr. (until 1992), Energy.Info.Abstr., Eng.Ind., Fluidex, INIS Atomind., ISMEC, Robomat. (until 1992), Sci.Abstr.
—BLDSC (8964.900000).
Formerly: Institutions of Engineers, Australia. Mechanical Engineering Transactions (ISSN 0313-5519); Supersedes in part: Institution of Engineers, Australia. Mechanical and Chemical Engineering Transactions (ISSN 0020-3327)
Description: Papers in the field of mechanical engineering.

621   UK   ISSN 0957-6509
TJ1   CODEN: PMAEET
INSTITUTION OF MECHANICAL ENGINEERS. PROCEEDINGS. PART A: JOURNAL OF POWER AND ENERGY. 1983. q. £135($269) for part A; £844($1999) for parts A-J. Mechanical Engineering Publications Ltd., Northgate Ave., Bury St. Edmunds, Suffolk IP32 6BW, England. TEL 0284-763277. FAX 0284-704006. TELEX 817376. Ed. A.J. Reynolds. bibl.; illus.; index, cum.index. circ. 1,426. (also avail. in microform from UMI,PMC; reprint service avail. from UMI) **Indexed:** A.S.& T.Ind., API Abstr., API Catal., API Oil., API Pet.Ref., API Transport., Appl.Mech.Rev., B.C.I.R.A., BMT, Br.Ceram.Abstr., Br.Rail.Bd., Br.Tech.Ind., Chem.Abstr., Curr.Cont., Eng.Ind., Math.R., Met.Abstr., Sci.Abstr., World Alum.Abstr. **Document type:** academic/scholarly publication, proceedings.
—BLDSC (6724.900140); EI; Faxon; UnCover; SWETS; UMI. **CCC.**
Former titles (until 1990): Institution of Mechanical Engineers. Proceedings. Part A: Journal of Power Engineering (ISSN 0954-4046); Institution of Mechanical Engineers. Proceedings. Part A: Power and Process Engineering (ISSN 0263-7138); Supersedes in part: Institution of Mechanical Engineers. Proceedings (ISSN 0020-3483)
Description: Focuses on power and process engineering.

ENGINEERING — MECHANICAL ENGINEERING

621   UK   ISSN 0954-4054
TJ1   CODEN: PIBMEU
INSTITUTION OF MECHANICAL ENGINEERS. PROCEEDINGS. PART B: JOURNAL OF ENGINEERING MANUFACTURE. 1983. q. £135($269) for Part B; £844($1999) for parts A-J. Mechanical Engineering Publications Ltd., Northgate Ave., Bury St. Edmunds, Suffolk IP32 6BW, England. TEL 0284-763277. FAX 0284-704006. TELEX 817376. Ed. A.N. Bramley. bibl.; illus.; index, cum.index. circ. 1,201. (also avail. in microform from UMI,PMC) **Indexed:** A.S.& T.Ind., Appl.Mech.Rev., BMT, Br.Rail.Bd., Br.Tech.Ind., Chem.Abstr., Curr.Cont., Eng.Ind., Fluidex, Math.R., Met.Abstr., Sci.Abstr., World Alum.Abstr. **Document type:** academic/scholarly publication, proceedings.
—BLDSC (6724.900350); EI; UnCover; SWETS; UMI. **CCC.**
   Formerly: Institution of Mechanical Engineers. Proceedings. Part B: Management and Engineering Manufacture (ISSN 0263-7146); Which supersedes in part: Institution of Mechanical Engineers. Proceedings (ISSN 0020-3483)
   Description: Scholarly research articles on power and process engineering, management and engineering manufacturing, mechanical engineering science, and transport engineering.

621   UK   ISSN 0954-4062
TJ5   CODEN: MESCEO
INSTITUTION OF MECHANICAL ENGINEERS. PROCEEDINGS. PART C: JOURNAL OF MECHANICAL ENGINEERING SCIENCE. 1983. 6/yr. £178($359) for Part C; £189($1999) for Parts A-J. Mechanical Engineering Publications Ltd., Northgate Ave., Bury St. Edmunds, Suffolk IP32 6BW, England. TEL 0284-763277. FAX 0284-704006. TELEX 817376. Ed. R.C. Baker. bibl.; charts; illus. circ. 1,397. (also avail. in microform from UMI) **Indexed:** A.S.& T.Ind., Abstr.J.Earthq.Eng., Appl.Mech.Rev., B.C.I.R.A., BMT, Br.Rail.Bd., Br.Tech.Ind., Curr.Cont., Eng.Ind., Fluidex, Fuel & Energy Abstr., Ind.Sci.Rev., Int.Aerosp.Abstr., ISMEC, Met.Abstr., Sci.Abstr. **Document type:** academic/scholarly publication, proceedings.
—BLDSC (6724.900500); EI; SWETS; UMI. **CCC.**
   Formerly: Institution of Mechanical Engineers. Proceedings. Part C: Mechanical Engineering Science (ISSN 0263-7154); Which supersedes: Journal of Mechanical Engineering Science (ISSN 0022-2542)
   Description: Focuses on mechanical engineering.

INSTITUTION OF MECHANICAL ENGINEERS. PROCEEDINGS. PART D: JOURNAL OF AUTOMOBILE ENGINEERING. see *TRANSPORTATION — Automobiles*

621   UK   ISSN 0954-4089
TS176   CODEN: PMEEEF
INSTITUTION OF MECHANICAL ENGINEERS. PROCEEDINGS. PART E: JOURNAL OF PROCESS MECHANICAL ENGINEERING. 2/yr. £78($159) for Part E; £84($1999) for Parts A-J. Mechanical Engineering Publications Ltd., Northgate Ave., Bury St. Edmunds, Suffolk IP32 6BW, England. TEL 0284-763277. FAX 0284-704006. TELEX 817376. Ed. G. Thompson. circ. 1,400. **Indexed:** Br.Tech.Ind. **Document type:** academic/scholarly publication, proceedings.
—BLDSC (6724.900830); EI; SWETS; UMI. **CCC.**

INSTITUTION OF MECHANICAL ENGINEERS. PROCEEDINGS. PART F: JOURNAL OF RAIL AND RAPID TRANSIT. see *TRANSPORTATION — Railroads*

INSTITUTION OF MECHANICAL ENGINEERS. PROCEEDINGS. PART G: JOURNAL OF AEROSPACE ENGINEERING. see *AERONAUTICS AND SPACE FLIGHT*

INSTITUTION OF MECHANICAL ENGINEERS. PROCEEDINGS. PART H: JOURNAL OF ENGINEERING IN MEDICINE. see *BIOLOGY — Bioengineering*

621   UK   ISSN 0959-6518
TJ5   CODEN: PMJEE6
INSTITUTION OF MECHANICAL ENGINEERS. PROCEEDINGS. PART I: JOURNAL OF SYSTEMS AND CONTROL ENGINEERING. q. £135($269) for part I; £144($1999) for parts A-J. Mechanical Engineering Publications Ltd., Northgate Ave., Bury St. Edmunds, Suffolk IP32 6BW, England. TEL 0284-763277. FAX 0284-704006. TELEX 817376. Eds. C.R. Burrows, R. Whalley. (reprint service avail. from WDS) **Document type:** academic/scholarly publication, proceedings.
—BLDSC (6724.900903); SWETS; UMI.
   Description: Covers experimental, application and industrial studies as well as new theoretical developments likely to provide the foundation for future applications.

621   UK   ISSN 1350-6501
TJ1075.A2
▼**INSTITUTION OF MECHANICAL ENGINEERS. PROCEEDINGS. PART J: JOURNAL OF ENGINEERING TRIBOLOGY.** 1994. q. £135($269) for part J; £144($1999) for parts A-J. Mechanical Engineering Publications Ltd., Northgate Ave., Bury St. Edmunds, Suffolk IP32 6BW, England. TEL 0284-763277. FAX 0284-704006. TELEX 817376. Ed. C.M. Taylor. **Document type:** academic/scholarly publication.
—BLDSC (6724.900905); SWETS.
   Description: Presents papers devoted to the engineering science and technological application of tribology associated with lubricated machine elements.

INSTITUTION OF PROFESSIONAL ENGINEERS. TRANSACTIONS. ELECTRICAL, MECHANICAL AND CHEMICAL ENGINEERING SECTION. see *ENGINEERING — Electrical Engineering*

INSTITUTUL POLITEHNIC DIN IASI. BULETINUL. SECTIA V: CONSTRUCTII DE MASINI. see *ENGINEERING — Engineering Mechanics And Materials*

621   US
INTEGRATED MANUFACTURING TECHNOLOGY. 1988. q. American Society of Mechanical Engineers, 345 E. 47th St., New York, NY 10017. TEL 212-705-7722. adv. circ. 2,500.

621   US
INTERNATIONAL CENTRE FOR MECHANICAL SCIENCES. COURSES AND LECTURES. (Text mainly in English) 1969. irreg. price varies. Springer-Verlag, 175 Fifth Ave., New York, NY 10010. TEL 212-460-1500. FAX 212-473-6272. (Also: Berlin, Heidelberg, Tokyo and Vienna) (reprint service avail. from ISI) **Document type:** catalog, academic/scholarly publication.

621   UK   ISSN 0735-1933
QC319.8   CODEN: IHMTDL
INTERNATIONAL COMMUNICATIONS IN HEAT AND MASS TRANSFER. (Text in English, French, German) 1974. 6/yr. £280($430) (combined subscr. with International Journal of Heat and Mass Transfer £1344($2070)) (effective 1994). (International Centre for Heat and Mass Transfer) Elsevier Science Ltd., Pergamon, P.O. Box 800, Kidlington, Oxford OX5 1DX, England. TEL 44-865-843000. FAX 44-865-843010. (Subscr. in U.S. and Canada to: Elsevier Science, 660 White Plains Rd., Tarrytown, NY 10591-5153. TEL 914-524-9200. FAX 914-333-2444) Eds. J.P. Hartnett, W.J. Minkowycz. adv.: B&W page $550, color page $1350. bk.rev.; abstr.; index. circ. 1,050. (also avail. in microfilm from UMI; back issues avail.) **Indexed:** Abstr.Bull.Inst.Pap.Chem., Appl.Mech.Rev., Chem.Abstr., Chem.Eng.Abstr., Curr.Cont., Fluidex, Foul.Prev.Res.Dig., INIS Atomind., Int.Aerosp.Abstr., Sci.Abstr., T.C.E.A. **Document type:** academic/scholarly publication.
—BLDSC (4538.722800); EI; Faxon; UnCover; SWETS; UMI; CASDDS. **CCC.**
   Formerly: Letters in Heat and Mass Transfer (ISSN 0094-4548)
   Description: Rapid publication journal for new ideas, techniques and findings in heat and mass transfer.
Refereed Serial

621   UK   ISSN 0269-655X
INTERNATIONAL CONFERENCE ON PRESSURE SURGES. PROCEEDINGS. 1973. irreg., 6th, 1990. price varies. Elsevier Science Ltd., Books Division, P.O. Box 800, Kidlington, Oxford OX5 1DX, England. TEL 44-865-843000. FAX 44-865-843010. (Subscr. in U.S. and Canada to: Elsevier Science, 660 White Plains Rd., Tarrytown, NY 10591-5153. TEL 914-524-9200) **Document type:** proceedings.
—CCC.
   Former titles (until 1986): Papers Presented at the International Conference on Pressure Surges (ISSN 0263-4147); (until 1983): International Conference on Pressure Surges. Proceedings (ISSN 0140-2080)

621.4   UK   ISSN 0074-4077
INTERNATIONAL CONGRESS ON COMBUSTION ENGINES. PROCEEDINGS. 1951. biennial; 20th UK, 1993. price varies. International Council on Combustion Engines - Conseil International des Machines a Combustion (CIMAC), 1 Birdcage Walk, London SW1H 9JJ, England. TEL 071-973-1275. FAX 071-973-0180. TELEX 914944 IMELDN. circ. 1,000. **Document type:** proceedings, monographic series.

621.8   UK   ISSN 0141-9501
INTERNATIONAL DISTRIBUTION & HANDLING REVIEW. 1971. bi-m. £88 (overseas £110). National Materials Handling Centre, Cranfield University, Cranfield, Beds. MK43 0AL, England. TEL 0234-750323. FAX 0234-750875. TELEX 825072-CITECH-G. Ed. H.P. Keeble. bk.rev.; index. **Document type:** trade publication.
   Description: Offers information and abstracts relating to storage, handling, distribution and logistics.

621 621.9   UK   ISSN 0268-3768
TS176   CODEN: IJATEA
INTERNATIONAL JOURNAL OF ADVANCED MANUFACTURING TECHNOLOGY. 1985. 6/yr. £156. Springer-Verlag, Springer House, 8 Alexandra Rd., London SW19 7JZ, England. TEL 081-944-2942. FAX 081-947-4651. Eds. B.J. Davies, U. Rembold. circ. 400. (back issues avail.) **Document type:** academic/scholarly publication.
—BLDSC (4541.572000); Faxon; SWETS; UMI. **CCC.**
   Incorporates: Robotersysteme (ISSN 0178-0026)
   Description: Aims to bridge the gap between pure research journals and more practical publications on factory automation systems.
Refereed Serial

INTERNATIONAL JOURNAL OF APPLIED ELECTROMAGNETICS IN MATERIALS. see *ENGINEERING — Electrical Engineering*

621.5 533   UK
TJ950
INTERNATIONAL JOURNAL OF APPLIED PNEUMATICS. 1952. 2/yr. free. Norgren Martonair Ltd., Campden Rd., Shipston-on-Stour, Warwickshire CV36 4PX, England. TEL 0608-661676. FAX 0608-663688. TELEX 83208-NORMAR-G. Ed. Roger Tidball. adv.; charts; illus. circ. 30,000. **Indexed:** Fluidex, Sci.Abstr., World Text.Abstr. **Document type:** consumer publication.
   Formerly: Journal of Applied Pneumatics (ISSN 0003-6978)

621   US   ISSN 1056-7895
TA409   CODEN: IDMEEH
▼**INTERNATIONAL JOURNAL OF DAMAGE MECHANICS.** 1992. q. $215. Technomic Publishing Co., Inc., 851 New Holland Ave., Box 3535, Lancaster, PA 17604. TEL 717-291-5609. FAX 717-295-4538. TELEX 230-753565 (TECHNOMIC UD). Ed. C.L. Chow. circ. 115. **Document type:** academic/scholarly publication.
—BLDSC (4542.183000); EI; SWETS; UMI; CASDDS. **CCC.**
   Description: Presents original research studies on the mechanics of fracture and damage in engineering materials and structure with emphasis on continuum damage mechanics.
Refereed Serial

INTERNATIONAL JOURNAL OF ENGINEERING FLUID MECHANICS. see *CHEMISTRY — Physical Chemistry*

ENGINEERING — MECHANICAL ENGINEERING

INTERNATIONAL JOURNAL OF FLEXIBLE MANUFACTURING SYSTEMS; design, analysis and operation of manufacturing and assembly systems. see ENGINEERING — Engineering Mechanics And Materials

INTERNATIONAL JOURNAL OF HEAT AND FLUID FLOW. see PHYSICS — Heat

536   UK   ISSN 0017-9310
QC320   CODEN: IJHMAK
INTERNATIONAL JOURNAL OF HEAT AND MASS TRANSFER. 1960. 18/yr. £1135($1750) (combined subscr. with International Communications in Heat and Mass Transfer £1344($2070)) (effective 1994). (International Centre for Heat and Mass Transfer) Elsevier Science Ltd., Pergamon, P.O. Box 800, Kidlington, Oxford OX5 1DX, England. TEL 44-865-843000. FAX 44-865-843010. (Subscr. in U.S. and Canada to: Elsevier Science, 660 White Plains Rd., Tarrytown, NY 10591-5153. TEL 914-524-9200. FAX 914-333-2444) Eds. J.P. Harnett, W.J. Minkowycz. adv.: B&W page $550, color page $1350. bk.rev.; bibl.; charts; illus.; index. circ. 2,500. (also avail. in microfiche from MIM; microfilm from UMI; reprint service avail. from UMI) **Indexed:** API Abstr., API Catal., API Hlth.& Environ., API Oil., API Pet.Ref., API Pet.Subst., API Transport., Appl.Mech.Rev., Chem.Abstr., Chem.Eng.Abstr., Curr.Cont., Deep Sea Res.& Oceanogr.Abstr., E&P Hlth. (1993-), Energy Info.Abstr., Eng.Ind., Excerp.Med., Fluidex, Foul.Prev.Res.Dig., Gas Abstr., Gas Process.& Ppl. (1993-), Ind.Sci.Rev., INIS Atomind., Int.Aerosp.Abstr., ISMEC, Off.Tech. (1993-), Petrol.Abstr. (1963-), Phys.Ber., Sci.Abstr., Sci.Cit.Ind., T.C.E.A. **Document type:** academic/scholarly publication.
—BLDSC (4542.280000); EI; Faxon; UnCover; SWETS; UMI; CASDDS. **CCC.**
Description: Publishes papers on all aspects of heat and mass transfer, including new methods of measuring or correlating transport-property data, energy engineering, and environmental applications of heat and mass transfer.
Refereed Serial

621   UK   ISSN 0301-9322
TA357   CODEN: IJMFBP
INTERNATIONAL JOURNAL OF MULTIPHASE FLOW. (Text in English; summaries in French, German, Russian) 1974. 7/yr. £585($900) (effective 1994). Elsevier Science Ltd., Pergamon, P.O. Box 800, Kidlington, Oxford OX5 1DX, England. TEL 44-865-843000. FAX 44-865-843010. (Subscr. in U.S. and Canada to: Elsevier Science, 660 White Plains Rd., Tarrytown, NY 10591-5153. TEL 914-524-9200. FAX 914-333-2444) Ed. G. Hetsroni. adv.; bk.rev.; charts; illus.; index. circ. 1,000. (also avail. in microfilm from UMI; reprint service avail. from UMI) **Indexed:** Abstr.Bull.Inst.Pap.Chem., API Abstr., API Catal., API Hlth.& Environ., API Oil., API Pet.Ref., API Pet.Subst., API Transport., Appl.Mech.Rev., Chem.Abstr., Chem.Eng.Abstr., Curr.Cont., E&P Hlth. (1993-), Fluidex, Foul.Prev.Res.Dig., Fuel & Energy Abstr., Gas Abstr., Gas Process.& Ppl. (1993-), Ind.Sci.Rev., Off.Tech. (1993-), Petrol.Abstr. (1978-), Phys.Ber., Sci.Abstr., T.C.E.A. **Document type:** academic/scholarly publication.
—BLDSC (4542.366000); EI; Faxon; UnCover; SWETS; UMI; CASDDS. **CCC.**
Incorporates (in 1990): Physicochemical Hydrodynamics (ISSN 0191-9059)
Description: Publishes theoretical and experimental investigations of multiphase flow.
Refereed Serial

621 665.5 551.46   US   ISSN 1053-5381
TC1665   CODEN: IOPEE7
INTERNATIONAL JOURNAL OF OFFSHORE AND POLAR ENGINEERING. 1991. q. $120 (effective 1994). International Society of Offshore and Polar Engineers, Box 1107, Golden, CO 80402-1107. TEL 303-273-3673. FAX 303-420-3760. Ed. Jin S. Chung. adv.: bk.rev.; index. circ. 950. (back issues avail.) **Indexed:** E&P Hlth. (1993-), Gas Process.& Ppl. (1993-), Off.Tech. (1993-), Petrol.Abstr. (1992-). **Document type:** academic/scholarly publication.
—BLDSC (4542.424200); EI; UnCover.
Description: Covers mechanics, materials, energy and resources related to the ocean, and offshore and polar engineering and environments.
Refereed Serial

621   UK   ISSN 0308-0161
CODEN: PRVPAS
INTERNATIONAL JOURNAL OF PRESSURE VESSELS AND PIPING. 1972. 12/yr. (in 4 vols., 3 nos/vol.). £976($1505) (effective 1994). Elsevier Science Ltd., Oxford Fulfilment Centre, P.O. Box 800, Kidlington, Oxford OX5 1DX, England. TEL 44-865-843000. FAX 44-865-843010. (Subscr. in U.S. and Canada to: Elsevier Science, 660 White Plains Rd., Tarrytown, NY 10591-5153. TEL 914-524-9200. FAX 914-333-2444) Ed. Dr. R.W. Nichols. adv.; bk.rev.; illus.; index. (also avail. in microform from UMI; back issues avail.) **Indexed:** Abstr.J.Earthq.Eng., Appl.Mech.Rev., Chem.Abstr., Chem.Eng.Abstr., Curr.Cont., E&P Hlth. (1993-), Eng.Ind., Fluidex, Fuel & Energy Abstr., Gas Process.& Ppl. (1993-), INIS Atomind., Met.Abstr., Off.Tech. (1993-), Petrol.Abstr. (1982-), Risk Abstr., Sci.Cit.Ind., T.C.E.A., World Alum.Abstr. **Document type:** academic/scholarly publication.
—BLDSC (4542.483000); EI; Faxon; SWETS; CASDDS. **CCC.**
Formerly: Pressure Vessels and Piping.
Description: Covers design, materials, manufacture, inspection, operation and maintenance of pressure vessels, piping and other pressurized components.
Refereed Serial

INTERNATIONAL JOURNAL OF RAPID SOLIDIFICATION. see METALLURGY

INTERNATIONAL JOURNAL OF VEHICLE DESIGN; journal of vehicle engineering, automotive technology and components. see TRANSPORTATION

621   RU   ISSN 0202-7542
TJ782
ITOGI NAUKI I TEKHNIKI: DVIGATELI VNUTRENNEGO SGORANIYA. 1974. irreg., latest vol.4, 1985. price varies. Vsesoyuznyi Institut Nauchno-Tekhnicheskoi Informatsii (VINITI), Baltiiskaya ul. 14, Moscow A-219, Russia. (Subscr. to: Mezhdunarodnaya Kniga, Dimitrova ul. 39, 113095 Moscow, Russia)
Description: Information on internal combustion engines.

621   RU   ISSN 0202-781X
QC138   CODEN: ITSGDS
ITOGI NAUKI I TEKHNIKI: MEKHANIKA ZHIDKOSTI I GAZA. vol.21, 1987. irreg., vol.23, 1989. 8 Rub. Vsesoyuznyi Institut Nauchno-Tekhnicheskoi Informatsii (VINITI), Baltiiskaya ul. 14, Moscow A-219, Russia. (Subscr. to: Mezhdunarodnaya Kniga, Dimitrova ul. 39, 113095 Moscow, Russia) **Indexed:** Chem.Abstr.
—BLDSC (0114.220000).

621   RU   ISSN 0202-7917
ITOGI NAUKI I TEKHNIKI: TRUBOPROVODNYI TRANSPORT. (Text in Russian) 1966. irreg., 12th ed., 1988. 3.30 Rub. Vsesoyuznyi Institut Nauchno-Tekhnicheskoi Informatsii (VINITI), Baltiiskaya ul. 14, Moscow A-219, Russia. (Subscr. to: Mezhdunarodnaya Kniga, Dimitrova ul. 39, 113095 Moscow, Russia)
—BLDSC (0182.900000).

IZVESTIYA VYSSHIKH UCHEBNYKH ZAVEDENII. SERIYA MATEMATIKA. see MATHEMATICS

621   JA   ISSN 0914-8809
TJ1   CODEN: JSSMEH
J S M E INTERNATIONAL JOURNAL. SERIES 1: SOLID MECHANICS, STRENGTH OF MATERIALS. (Text in English) 1958. m. 30000 Yen($375) to non-members; members 20000 Yen ($200). Japan Society of Mechanical Engineers - Nihon Kikai Gakkai, Sanshin Hokusei Bldg., 4-9, Yoyogi 2-chome, Shibuya-ku, Tokyo 151; Japan. TEL 03-3278-9224. (Subscr. in U.S. to: American Society of Mechanical Engineers, 22 Law Dr., Box 2300, Fairfield, NJ 07007-2300. TEL 800-843-2763) Ed. Masahiro Suyana. adv.; abstr.; charts; mkt.; index, cum.index. circ. 1,300. **Indexed:** Appl.Mech.Rev., BMT, Chem.Abstr., Chem.Eng.Abstr., Curr.Cont., Eng.Ind., Excerp.Med., Fluidex, Int.Aerosp.Abstr., ISMEC, JCT, Math.R., Met.Abstr., Sci.Abstr., Sci.Cit.Ind., Sh.& Vib.Dig., T.C.E.A., World Alum.Abstr.
—BLDSC (5073.769200); EI; Faxon; UnCover; SWETS. **CCC.**
Supersedes in part (in 1988): J S M E International Journal (ISSN 0913-185X); Which was formerly (until 1986): J S M E Bulletin (ISSN 0021-3764)

621   JA   ISSN 0914-8817
TJ1   CODEN: JSFPET
J S M E INTERNATIONAL JOURNAL. SERIES 2: FLUIDS ENGINEERING, HEAT TRANSFER, POWER, COMBUSTION, THERMOPHYSICAL PROPERTIES. (Text in English) 1958. q. 2500 Yen per no. Japan Society of Mechanical Engineers - Nihon Kikai Gakkai, Sanshin Hokusei Bldg., 4-9, Yoyogi 2-chome, Shibuya-ku, Tokyo 151, Japan. (Subscr. in U.S. to: American Society of Mechanical Engineers, 22 Law Dr., Box 2300, Fairfield, NJ 07007-2300. TEL 800-843-2763) **Indexed:** Chem.Abstr., Curr.Cont., Eng.Ind., INIS Atomind., Math.R.
—BLDSC (5073.769400); EI; Faxon; UnCover; SWETS. **CCC.**
Supersedes in part (in 1988): J S M E International Journal (ISSN 0913-185X); Which was formerly (until 1986): J S M E Bulletin (ISSN 0021-3764)

621   JA   ISSN 0914-8825
TJ1
J S M E INTERNATIONAL JOURNAL. SERIES 3: VIBRATION, CONTROL ENGINEERING, ENGINEERING FOR INDUSTRY. (Text in English) 1958. q. 2500 Yen per no. Japan Society of Mechanical Engineers - Nihon Kikai Gakkai, Sanshin Hokusei Bldg., 4-9, Yoyogi 2-chome, Shibuya-ku, Tokyo 151, Japan. (Subscr. in U.S. to: American Society of Mechanical Engineers, 22 Law Dr., Box 2300, Fairfield, NJ 07007-2300. TEL 800-843-2763) **Indexed:** Curr.Cont., Eng.Ind., INIS Atomind., Math.R.
—BLDSC (5073.769600); EI; Faxon; UnCover; SWETS. **CCC.**
Supersedes in part (in 1988): J S M E International Journal (ISSN 0913-185X); Which was formerly (until 1986): J S M E Bulletin (ISSN 0021-3764)

621   JA   ISSN 0021-4728
  CODEN: NKGKA3
J S M E JOURNAL. (Text in Japanese) 1897. m. Japan Society of Mechanical Engineers - Nihon Kikai Gakkai, Sanshin Hokusei Bldg., 4-9 Yoyogi, 2-chome, Shibuya-ku, Tokyo 151, Japan. TEL 81-3-3379-6781. **Indexed:** ISMEC, JTA.
—BLDSC (4808.000000); CASDDS.

621   JA
J S M E NEWS. (Text in English) 1990. s-a. Japan Society of Mechanical Engineers - Nihon Kikai Gakkai, Sanshin Hokusei Bldg., 4-9, Yoyogi 2-chome, Shibuya-ku, Tokyo 151, Japan.

621   GW
JAHRBUCH SCHLEIFEN, HONEN, LAEPPEN UND POLIEREN, VERFAHREN UND MASCHINEN. 1932. a. DM.84. Vulkan-Verlag GmbH, Postfach 103962, 45039 Essen, Germany. TEL 0201-82002-0. FAX 0201-82002-40. Ed.Bd. adv. circ. 2,500. **Document type:** trade publication.
Former titles: Jahrbuch der Schleif-, Hon-, Laepp- und Poliertechnik (ISSN 0075-2398); Jahrbuch der Schleif- und Poliertechnik und der Oberflaechenbehandlung.

JAPAN SOCIETY FOR TECHNOLOGY OF PLASTICITY. JOURNAL/SOSEI TO KAKO. see TECHNOLOGY: COMPREHENSIVE WORKS

621   US   ISSN 1045-7828
TJ1075.A2
JAPANESE JOURNAL OF TRIBOLOGY. English translation of: Tribologist (JA ISSN 0915-1168) 1989. m. $545. (Japanese Society of Tribologists, JA) Allerton Press, Inc., 150 Fifth Ave., New York, NY 10011. TEL 212-924-3950. FAX 212-463-9684. Ed. Kyosuke Ono. **Document type:** academic/scholarly publication.
—BLDSC (4658.930000); SWETS. **CCC.**
Description: Covers tribological research and development in Japan, including tribological surfaces, contact problems, fluid lubrication, and wear.

621   HU   ISSN 0021-5511
TJ1
JARMUVEK, MEZOGAZDASAGI GEPEK; motorok, vasuti jarmuvek, kozuti jarmuvek, hajok, mezogazdasagi gepek, epitoipari gepek, repulogepek. (Text in Hungarian; summaries in English, German, Russian) 1954. m. $33. (Gepipari Tudomanyos Egyesulet) Lapkiado Vallalat, Lenin korut 9-11, 1073 Budapest 7, Hungary. TEL 222-408. (Subscr. to: Kultura, Box 149, H-1389 Budapest, Hungary) adv.; bk.rev. **Indexed:** Agri.Eng.Abstr., Appl.Mech.Rev., Chem.Abstr., Hort.Abstr., Hung.Build.Bull., Nutr.Abstr.

ENGINEERING — MECHANICAL ENGINEERING

JERN- OG MASKININDUSTRIEN. see *METALLURGY*

621   UK   ISSN 0269-6533
JET CUTTING TECHNOLOGY. 1972. irreg., 10th, 1991. price varies. Elsevier Science Ltd., Books Division, P.O. Box 800, Kidlington, Oxford OX5 1DX, England. TEL 44-865-843000. FAX 44-865-843010. (Subscr. in U.S. and Canada to: Elsevier Science, 660 White Plains Rd., Tarrytown, NY 10591-5153. TEL 914-524-9200) **Document type:** proceedings.
Formerly (until 1986): International Symposium on Jet Cutting Technology. Proceedings (ISSN 0306-2732)

JIDOSHA KOGAKU/AUTOMOBILE ENGINEERING. see *TRANSPORTATION — Automobiles*

JINSHU RECHULI/HEAT TREATMENT OF METALS. see *ENGINEERING — Engineering Mechanics And Materials*

621   CC   ISSN 1000-3401
TA645   CODEN: JJLYEN
JISUAN JIEGOU LIXUE JIQI YINGYONG/JOURNAL OF COMPUTATIONAL STRUCTURAL MECHANICS AND APPLICATIONS. (Text in Chinese; English) 1984. q. Y8.50 per no. Dalian Ligong Daxue - Dalian University of Science and Engineering, P.O. Box 320, Dalian, Liaoning 116023, People's Republic of China. TEL 0411-471511. FAX 0411-471009. TELEX 86231 DUT CN. (Dist. overseas by: China International Book Trading Corp., P.O. Box 399, Beijing, P.R. China) Eds. Qian Lingxi, Deng Keshun. **Document type:** academic/scholarly publication.
—BLDSC (3390.625150).
Description: Covers the latest development of computational structural mechanics and its applications in engineering. Also covers structural analysis, artificial intelligence, and software.
Refereed Serial

621.9   CC   ISSN 1000-3738
TA401
JIXIE GONGCHENG CAILIAO/MATERIALS FOR MECHANICAL ENGINEERING. (Text in Chinese) 1977. bi-m. $15. Shanghai Cailiao Yanjiusuo - Shanghai Material Research Institute, 99 Handan Lu, Shanghai 200433, People's Republic of China. TEL 5420775. Ed. Feng Guoguang. adv. circ. 12,000. **Document type:** academic/scholarly publication.
Description: Covers machine design, tool and die design.

621   CC   ISSN 0577-6686
     CODEN: CHHKA2
JIXIE GONGCHENG XUEBAO. English edition: Chinese Journal of Mechanical Engineering (ISSN 1000-9345) (Text in Chinese; summaries in Chinese, English) 1953. bi-m. Y60. (Chinese Mechanical Engineering Society) China Machine Press, 1 Nanjie, Baiwanzhuang, Beijing 100037, People's Republic of China. TEL 8317766. FAX 01-8326337. TELEX 222557 STIP CN. (Dist. outside China by: China International Book Trading Corp., P.O. Box 399, Beijing, P.R. China) Ed. Mei Zhongqin. index. circ. 4,500. **Indexed:** Chem.Abstr., Met.Abstr., Sci.Abstr., World Alum.Abstr. **Document type:** academic/scholarly publication.
—BLDSC (3180.400000); CASDDS.
Description: Covers the science and technology of the machinery industry.

620.1   US   ISSN 0021-8936
TA1   CODEN: JAMCAV
JOURNAL OF APPLIED MECHANICS. (Series E of the Transactions of the ASME) 1935. q. $120 (members $29). American Society of Mechanical Engineers, 345 E. 47th St., New York, NY 10017. TEL 212-705-7722. Ed. L.B. Freund. adv.; bk.rev.; bibl.; charts. circ. 5,000. (also avail. in microform from UMI,PMC; reprint service avail. from UMI) **Indexed:** A.S.& T.Ind., Abstr.Bull.Inst.Pap.Chem., Abstr.J.Earthq.Eng., Appl.Mech.Rev., Br.Ceram.Abstr., Br.Rail.Bd., CAD CAM Abstr., Chem.Abstr., Curr.Cont., Eng.Ind., Fluidex, Fuel & Energy Abstr., GeoRef., Geotech.Abstr., INIS Atomind., ISMEC, J.of Ferroc., Met.Abstr., Sci.Abstr., Sci.Cit.Ind., Sh.& Vib.Dig., World Alum.Abstr.
—BLDSC (8896.680000); EI; Faxon; UnCover; SWETS; UMI; CASDDS. **CCC**.

621   US   ISSN 0884-6804
     CODEN: JCTRER
JOURNAL OF COMPOSITES TECHNOLOGY AND RESEARCH. 1979. q. $95 to non-members; members $86. American Society for Testing and Materials, 1916 Race St., Philadelphia, PA 19103. TEL 215-299-5400. FAX 215-977-9679. bk.rev.; abstr.; index. (back issues avail.; reprint service avail. from UMI) **Indexed:** Appl.Mech.Rev., Chem.Abstr., Int.Aerosp.Abstr., ISMEC, Met.Abstr., Text.Tech.Dig., World Alum.Abstr. **Document type:** trade publication.
—BLDSC (4963.420000); EI; Faxon; UnCover; SWETS; UMI; CASDDS. **CCC**.
Formerly (until 1985): Composites Technology Review (ISSN 0733-9011)
Refereed Serial

621   UK   ISSN 0962-4694
     CODEN: JDMAEG
JOURNAL OF DESIGN & MANUFACTURING; the research journal of concurrent engineering. 1991. q. £110 to institutions in EC nations (North America $190; elsewhere £120). Chapman & Hall, 2-6 Boundary Row, London SE1 8HN, England.
TEL 071-865-0066. FAX 071-522-9623. TELEX 290164-CHAPMAG. (Dist. by: International Thomson Publishing Services, Ltd., N. Way, Andover, Hants. SP10 5BE, England. TEL 0264-342919; US addr.: Chapman & Hall, Journals Promotion Department, One Penn Plaza, 41st Fl., New York, NY 10019. TEL 212-244-3336. FAX 212-564-1505) Ed. Bartholomew O. Nnaji. bk.rev. **Document type:** academic/scholarly publication.
—BLDSC (4968.795000).
Description: Covers the broad area of contemporary design and manufacturing methodologies; reports on the activities that spur the development of design principles.
Refereed Serial

JOURNAL OF DYNAMIC SYSTEMS, MEASUREMENT AND CONTROL. see *ENGINEERING — Engineering Mechanics And Materials*

JOURNAL OF ELASTICITY. see *ENGINEERING — Engineering Mechanics And Materials*

JOURNAL OF ENERGY RESOURCES TECHNOLOGY. see *ENERGY*

621.8   US   ISSN 0742-4795
TJ1   CODEN: JETPEZ
JOURNAL OF ENGINEERING FOR GAS TURBINES AND POWER. 1878? q. American Society of Mechanical Engineers, 345 E. 47th St., New York, NY 10017. TEL 212-705-7722. **Indexed:** Energy Info.Abstr., Environ.Abstr.
—BLDSC (8896.795000); CIS; EI; Faxon; UnCover; SWETS; UMI; CASDDS. **CCC**.

621   US   ISSN 0022-0817
TA1   CODEN: JEFIA8
JOURNAL OF ENGINEERING FOR INDUSTRY. (Series B of the Transactions of the ASME) vol.92, 1970. q. $100 to non-members; members $29. American Society of Mechanical Engineers, 345 E. 47th St., New York, NY 10017. TEL 212-705-7703. Ed. C. Monahan. adv.; bk.rev.; bibl.; charts. circ. 3,200. (also avail. in microform from UMI,PMC; reprint service avail. from UMI) **Indexed:** A.S.& T.Ind., API Abstr., API Catal., API Hlth.& Environ., API Oil., API Pet.Ref., API Pet.Subst., API Transport., Appl.Mech.Rev., Br.Rail.Bd., CAD CAM Abstr., Chem.Abstr., Curr.Cont., Eng.Ind., Excerpt.Med., Fluidex, Fuel & Energy Abstr., INIS Atomind., Met.Abstr., Petrol.Abstr., Sci.Abstr., Sci.Cit.Ind., Sh.& Vib.Dig., Text.Tech.Dig., World Alum.Abstr.
—BLDSC (8896.800000); EI; Faxon; UnCover; SWETS; UMI; CASDDS. **CCC**.

JOURNAL OF ENGINEERING MATERIALS AND TECHNOLOGY. see *ENGINEERING — Engineering Mechanics And Materials*

621 536   US   ISSN 1065-3090
     CODEN: JFVPEI
▼**JOURNAL OF FLOW VISUALIZATION AND IMAGE PROCESSING.** 1993. q. $45 to individuals; institutions $145. Begell House Inc., 79 Madison Ave., New York, NY 10016-7892.
TEL 212-725-1999. FAX 212-213-8368. TELEX 9102509520. Eds. Wen-Jei Yang, R. Reznicek. index. **Document type:** academic/scholarly publication.
—CCC.
Description: Publishes original papers to disseminate and exchange the knowledge and information obtained through research on the principles and applications of flow visualization techniques including flow image processing.
Refereed Serial

627 621.2   US   ISSN 8755-8564
TJ840
JOURNAL OF FLUID CONTROL; applications and research on fluid control, hydraulics and pneumatics, instrumentation, and fluidics. 1967. q. $145 per vol. Delbridge Publishing Co., Box 160817, Cupertino, CA 95016. TEL 408-446-3131. FAX 408-446-3131. Ed. David H. Tarumoto. bk.rev.; abstr.; bibl.; charts; illus.; index. circ. 800. (back issues avail.) **Indexed:** Appl.Mech.Rev., Eng.Ind., Fluidex, Int.Aerosp.Abstr., ISMEC, Phys.Ber., Sci.Abstr.
—EI; Faxon; SWETS. **CCC**.
Incorporates: Fluidics Quarterly (ISSN 0015-4687)
Description: Technical papers on applied and basic research and engineering on fluid control, hydraulics and pneumatics, instrumentation and fluidics.
Refereed Serial

536   US   ISSN 0022-1481
TA1   CODEN: JHTRAO
JOURNAL OF HEAT TRANSFER. vol.92, 1970. q. $155 to non-members; members $29. American Society of Mechanical Engineers, 345 E. 47th St., New York, NY 10017. TEL 212-705-7722. Ed. K.T. Yang. adv.; bk.rev.; bibl.; charts. circ. 2,900. (also avail. in microform from UMI,PMC; reprint service avail. from UMI) **Indexed:** A.S.& T.Ind., API Abstr., API Catal., API Hlth.& Environ., API Oil., API Pet.Ref., API Pet.Subst., API Transport., Appl.Mech.Rev., Chem.Abstr., Chem.Eng.Abstr., Curr.Cont., E&P Hlth. (1993-), Energy Info.Abstr., Eng.Ind., Environ.Abstr., Fluidex, Foul.Prev.Res.Dig., Fuel & Energy Abstr., Gas Process.& Ppl. (1993-), INIS Atomind., Int.Build.Serv.Abstr., ISMEC, Off.Tech. (1993-), Petrol.Abstr. (1961, 1963-), Phys.Ber., Sci.Abstr., Sci.Cit.Ind., T.C.E.A.
—BLDSC (8896.940000); EI; Faxon; UnCover; SWETS; UMI; CASDDS. **CCC**.
Refereed Serial

JOURNAL OF MACHINERY MANUFACTURE AND RELIABILITY. see *COMPUTERS — Automation*

620   NE   ISSN 0924-0136
TS200   CODEN: JMPTEF
JOURNAL OF MATERIALS PROCESSING TECHNOLOGY. 1977. 28/yr. (in 7 vols.; 4 nos./vol.). fl.2737($1479) (effective 1994). Elsevier Science B.V., P.O. Box 211, 1000 AE Amsterdam, Netherlands. TEL 31-20-5803911.
FAX 31-20-5803598 TELEX 18582 ESPA NL. (Subscr. in U.S. and Canada to: Elsevier Science Inc., Box 882, Madison Sq. Sta., New York, NY 10159. TEL 212-989-5800. FAX 212-633-3990) Ed. F.W. Travis. adv.; bk.rev.; index. (also avail. in microform from UMI) **Indexed:** Appl.Mech.Rev., CAD CAM Abstr., Chem.Abstr., Curr.Cont., Eng.Ind., Fluidex, Met.Abstr., Sci.Cit.Ind., World Alum.Abstr. **Document type:** academic/scholarly publication.
—BLDSC (5012.235000); EI; Faxon; SWETS. **CCC**.
Formerly (until 1989) Journal of Mechanical Working Technology (ISSN 0378-3804)
Description: Contains full research papers and short communications of industrial relevance. Includes papers on the use of the computer in simulation of metal flow and the modelling of processes, papers on computer-aided metal forming systems and on computer-aided design of metal working tooling.
Refereed Serial

ENGINEERING — MECHANICAL ENGINEERING

621   US   ISSN 1050-0472
CODEN: JMDEEC
JOURNAL OF MECHANICAL DESIGN. 1978. q. $100 to non-members; members $29. American Society of Mechanical Engineers, 22 Law Dr., Box 2300, Fairfield, NJ 07007-2300. TEL 800-321-2633. Ed. S. Dubowsky. **Indexed:** A.I.Abstr. (until 1992), Appl.Mech.Rev., CAD CAM Abstr. (until 1992), Energy Info.Abstr., Fluidex, Ind.Sci.Rev., Met.Abstr., Risk Abstr., Robomat. (until 1992), Sci.Cit.Ind.
—BLDSC (8896.980000); EI; Faxon; UnCover; SWETS; UMI. **CCC.**
    Formerly (until 1990): Journal of Mechanisms, Transmissions and Automation in Design (ISSN 0738-0666); Supersedes in part (in 1978): Journal of Mechanical Design (ISSN 0161-8458)
Refereed Serial

621   UK   ISSN 0960-1317
QC176.8.M5   CODEN: JMMIEZ
JOURNAL OF MICROMECHANICS AND MICROENGINEERING. 1991. q. £152($326) (Institute of Physics) I O P Publishing, Techno House, Redcliffe Way, Bristol, Avon BS1 6NX, England. TEL 0272-297481. FAX 0272-294318. Eds. W.N. Carr, H. Guckel. adv.; abstr.; index; circ. 400 (paid). (also avail. in microfiche; back issues avail.) **Indexed:** Bull.Signal., INSPEC. **Document type:** academic/scholarly publication.
—BLDSC (5019.640000); EI; UnCover; SWETS; CASDDS. **CCC.**
    Description: Covers the emerging fields of microelectromechanics, micromechanics, and vacuum microelectronics, and related structures, devices, and systems.

625   US   ISSN 0892-7219
TC1665
JOURNAL OF OFFSHORE MECHANICS AND ARCTIC ENGINEERING. (Series A of the Transactions of the A S M E) 1987. q. $100 to non-members; members $29. American Society of Mechanical Engineers, 345 E. 47th St., New York, NY 10017. TEL 212-705-7722. **Indexed:** E&P Hlth. (1993-), Gas Process.& Ppl. (1993-), Off.Tech. (1993-), Petrol.Abstr. (1988-).
—BLDSC (8897.000000); EI; Faxon; UnCover; SWETS; UMI. **CCC.**
Refereed Serial

621   US   ISSN 0094-9930
TS283   CODEN: JPVTAS
JOURNAL OF PRESSURE VESSEL TECHNOLOGY. 1974. q. $100 to non-members; members $29. American Society of Mechanical Engineers, 345 E. 47th St., New York, NY 10017. TEL 212-705-7722. Ed. G.E.O. Widera. adv.; bk.rev.; illus.; index. circ. 1,900. (also avail. in microform from UMI; reprint service avail.) **Indexed:** A.S.& T.Ind., Abstr.J.Earthq.Eng., Appl.Mech.Rev., Br.Rail.Bd., Chem.Abstr., Curr.Cont., E&P Hlth. (1993-), Eng.Ind., Fluidex, Fuel & Energy Abstr., Gas Process.& Ppl. (1993-), GeoRef, Ind.Sci.Rev., INIS Atomind., Met.Abstr., Off.Tech. (1993-), Petrol.Abstr. (1976-), Sci.Abstr., Sh.& Vib.Dig., World Alum.Abstr.
—BLDSC (8897.020000); EI; Faxon; UnCover; SWETS; UMI; CASDDS. **CCC.**

JOURNAL OF STRUCTURAL ENGINEERING. see *ENGINEERING — Civil Engineering*

620   US   ISSN 0149-5739
TA418.58   CODEN: JTSTDA
JOURNAL OF THERMAL STRESSES; an international quarterly. 1978. q. $325. Taylor & Francis, 1900 Frost Rd., Ste. 101, Bristol, PA 19007-1598. TEL 800-821-8312. FAX 215-785-5515. Ed. Richard B. Hetnarski. adv.; bk.rev.; abstr.; bibl.; charts; illus.; stat.; index. circ. 325. (also avail. in microform from UMI; back issues avail.; reprint service avail. from UMI) **Indexed:** Appl.Mech.Rev., Curr.Cont., Int.Aerosp.Abstr., Math.R., Met.Abstr., Sci.Abstr., World Alum.Abstr. **Document type:** academic/scholarly publication.
—BLDSC (5069.099000); EI; Faxon; UnCover; SWETS. **CCC.**
    Description: International journal devoted exclusively to thermal stress; theory and industrial applications of thermal stresses.
Refereed Serial

JOURNAL OF TRIBOLOGY. see *PETROLEUM AND GAS*

621.8   US   ISSN 0889-504X
TJ267   CODEN: JOTUEI
JOURNAL OF TURBOMACHINERY. (Series A of the Transactions of the ASME) 1878? q. $100 to non-members; members $29. American Society of Mechanical Engineers, 345 E. 47th St., New York, NY 10017. TEL 212-705-7722. Ed. J.J. Jaklitsch, Jr. adv.; bk.rev.; bibl.; charts. circ. 3,000. (also avail. in microform from UMI,PMC; reprint service avail. from UMI) **Indexed:** A.S.& T.Ind., API Abstr., API Catal., API Hlth.& Environ., API Oil., API Pet.Ref., API Pet.Subst., API Transport., Appl.Mech.Rev., Br.Rail.Bd., CAD CAM Abstr. (until 1992), Ceram.Abstr., Chem.Abstr., Energy Info.Abstr., Eng.Ind., Excerp.Med., Fluidex, Foul.Prev.Res.Dig., Fuel & Energy Abstr., Ind.Sci.Rev., INIS Atomind., Met.Abstr., PROMT, Robomat. (until 1992), Sci.Abstr., Sci.Cit.Ind., Sh.& Vib.Dig., World Alum.Abstr.
—BLDSC (8897.072000); EI; Faxon; UnCover; SWETS; UMI. **CCC.**
    Former titles (until 1986): Journal of Gas Turbines; (until 1984): Journal of Engineering for Power (ISSN 0022-0825)
Refereed Serial

621   US   ISSN 1048-9002
TA174
JOURNAL OF VIBRATION AND ACOUSTICS. 1978. q. $100 to non-members; members $29. American Society of Mechanical Engineers, 22 Law Dr., Box 2300, Fairfield, NJ 07007-2300. TEL 800-321-2633. Ed. F.F. Ehrich. (also avail. in microform from UMI; reprint service avail from UMI) **Indexed:** Appl.Mech.Rev., Br.Rail.Bd., CAD CAM Abstr., Curr.Cont., Energy Info.Abstr., Eng.Ind., Environ.Abstr., Excerp.Med., Fluidex, Met.Abstr., Sh.& Vib.Dig., Tel.Abstr., World Alum.Abstr.
—BLDSC (8897.085000); EI; Faxon; UnCover; SWETS; UMI. **CCC.**
    Formerly (until 1990): Journal of Vibration, Acoustics, Stress and Reliability in Design (ISSN 0739-3717); Which supersedes in part (in 1983): Journal of Mechanical Design (ISSN 0161-8458)
Refereed Serial

621   NE   ISSN 0167-6105
TA654.5   CODEN: JWEAD6
JOURNAL OF WIND ENGINEERING AND INDUSTRIAL AERODYNAMICS. 1975. 15/yr. (in 5 vols.; 3 nos./vol.) fl.2055($1111) (effective 1994). (International Association for Wind Engineering) Elsevier Science B.V., P.O. Box 211, 1000 AE Amsterdam, Netherlands. TEL 31-20-5803911. FAX 31-20-5803598. TELEX 18582 ESPA NL. (Subscr. in U.S. and Canada to: Elsevier Science Inc., Box 882, Madison Sq. Sta., New York, NY 10159. TEL 212-989-5800. FAX 212-633-3990) Ed. R.I. Harris. (also avail. in microform from UMI) **Indexed:** A.I.Abstr., Agri.Eng.Abstr., Appl.Mech.Rev., Curr.Cont., Energy Info.Abstr., Eng.Ind., Environ.Abstr., Fluidex, Geo.Abstr., Ind.Sci.Rev., INSPEC, Int.Build.Serv.Abstr., Sci.Abstr., Sci.Cit.Ind. **Document type:** academic/scholarly publication.
—BLDSC (5072.632000); EI; UnCover; SWETS. **CCC.**
    Formerly: Journal of Industrial Aerodynamics (ISSN 0304-3908)
    Description: Provides papers describing full-scale measurements, wing-tunnel simulation studies or theoretical methods, as well as papers dealing with the development of techniques and apparatus for wind engineering experiments.
Refereed Serial

621   JA   ISSN 0285-2217
JUKI MAGAZINE. (Text in Japanese) 1960. q. free. Juki Corporation, 2-1, Kokuryo-cho 8-chome, Chofu-shi, Tokyo 182, Japan. TEL 03-3480-5905. FAX 03-3480-7666. Ed. Akira Yamada. circ. 13,000.
    Description: Introduces new machinery to Japanese garment factories and provides such information as how to manage apparel production and educate employees.

621   JA   ISSN 0916-6890
JUNKATSU KEIZAI/JOURNAL OF ECONOMIC MAINTENANCE TRIBOLOGY. (Text in Japanese) 1960. bi-m. 1200 Yen per no. Junkatsu Tsushinsha K.K. - Lubrication Technology Inc., 3-3, Iwamoto-cho 3-chome, Chiyoda-ku, Tokyo 101, Japan.

JURUTERA. see *ENGINEERING — Chemical Engineering*

621   JA
KENKYU JISSHI GAIKYO HOKOKUSHO/SUMMARY REPORT OF FLUID POWER TECHNOLOGY. (Text in Japanese) 1986. irreg. Yukuatsu Kiki Gijutsu Shinko Zaidan - Fluid Power Technology Promotion Foundation, 1-1, Kitaeguchi 1-chome, Higashiyodogawa-ku, Osaka-shi, Osaka 533, Japan.

621   JA   ISSN 0451-9396
CODEN: KIGIAI
KIKAI GIJUTSU/MECHANICAL ENGINEERING. (Text in Japanese) 1953. m. 1030 Yen per no. Industrial Daily News Ltd. - Nikkan Kogyo Shinbun Ltd., 1-8-10 Kudan Kita, Chiyoda-ku, Tokyo 102, Japan. circ. 36,000. **Indexed:** Chem.Abstr., JCT, JTA.
—CASDDS.
    Description: General magazine of international mechanical technology.

621   JA
KIKAI GIJUTSU KENKYUHO NENPO/MECHANICAL ENGINEERING LABORATORY. ANNUAL REPORT. (Text in Japanese) 1950. a. Kogyo Gijutsuin, Kikai Gijutsu Kenkyujo - Agency of Industrial Science and Technology, Mechanical Engineering Laboratory, 1-2, Namiki, Tsukuba-shi, Ibaraki-ken 305, Japan.

621   JA
KIKAI GIJUTSU KENKYUJO. KENKYU KOENKAI SHIRYO/MECHANICAL ENGINEERING LABORATORY. PROCEEDINGS OF THE STUDY MEETING. (Text in Japanese) s-a. 2500 Yen per no. Kogyo Gijutsuin, Kikai Gijutsu Kenkyujo - Agency of Industrial Science and Technology, Mechanical Engineering Laboratory, 1-2, Namiki, Tsukuba-shi, Ibaraki-ken 305, Japan. (Co-sponsor: Nihon Sangyo Gijutsu Shinko Kyokai - Japan Industrial Technology Association)

621   JA   ISSN 0286-2255
KIKAI GIJUTSU KENKYUJO HOKOKU/MECHANICAL ENGINEERING LABORATORY. REPORT. (Text in Japanese; summaries in English) 1950. irreg. Kogyo Gijutsuin, Kikai Gijutsu Kenkyujo - Agency of Industrial Science and Technology, Mechanical Engineering Laboratory, 1-2, Namiki, Tsukuba-shi, Ibaraki-ken 305, Japan.
—BLDSC (7537.980000).

621   JA   ISSN 0286-2263
KIKAI GIJUTSU KENKYUJO SHIRYO/MECHANICAL ENGINEERING LABORATORY. TECHNICAL NOTE. (Text in Japanese) 1955. irreg. Kogyo Gijutsuin, Kikai Gijutsu Kenkyujo - Agency of Industrial Science and Technology, Mechanical Engineering Laboratory, 1-2, Namiki, Tsukuba-shi, Ibaraki-ken 305, Japan. **Indexed:** INIS Atomind.

621   JA   ISSN 0388-4252
CODEN: KGKSBL
KIKAI GIJUTSU KENKYUJO SHOHO/MECHANICAL ENGINEERING LABORATORY. JOURNAL. (Text in Japanese; summaries in English) 1943. bi-m. 500 Yen per no. Kogyo Gijutsuin, Kikai Gijutsu Kenkyujo - Agency of Industrial Science and Technology, Mechanical Engineering Laboratory, 1-2, Namiki, Tsukuba-shi, Ibaraki-ken 305, Japan. **Indexed:** Chem.Abstr., Eng.Ind., INIS Atomind.
—BLDSC (4822.300000); EI; CASDDS.

621   JA   ISSN 0912-9626
KIKAI GIJUTSU KYOKAI NYUSU/ASSOCIATION OF MECHANICAL TECHNOLOGY. NEWS. (Text in Japanese) 1986. s-a. Kikai Gijutsu Kyokai, 5-8, Shibakoen 3-chome, Minato-ku, Tokyo 105, Japan.

621   JA   ISSN 0387-1053
CODEN: KITKAL
KIKAI TO KOGU/TOOL ENGINEER. (Text in Japanese) 1957. m. 960 Yen per no. Kogyo Chosakai Publishing Co., Ltd., 14-7, Hongo 2-chome, Bunkyo-ku, Tokyo 113, Japan.
—CASDDS.

621   JA   ISSN 0286-2271
KIKAIKEN NYUSU. (Text in Japanese) 1952. m. Kogyo Gijutsuin, Kikai Gijutsu Kenkyujo - Agency of Industrial Science and Technology, Mechanical Engineering Laboratory, 1-2, Namiki, Tsukuba-shi, Ibaraki-ken 305, Japan.

KLOECKNER WERKE HEUTE; Stahl, Maschinenbau, Kunststoff. (Kloeckner-Werke AG) see *METALLURGY*

ENGINEERING — MECHANICAL ENGINEERING

621   JA
KOKUSAI KOSAKU KIKAI GIJUTSUSHA KAIGI TEKISUTO/INTERNATIONAL MACHINE TOOL ENGINEERS CONFERENCE. PROCEEDINGS. (Text in Japanese; summaries in English, Japanese) 1984. biennial. Nihon Kosaku Kikai Kogyokai - Japan Machine Tool Builder's Association, 5-8, Shiba Koen 3-chome, Minato-ku, Tokyo 105, Japan. **Document type:** proceedings.

621   ISSN 0916-796X
KOMATSU TECHNICAL REPORT. (Text in Japanese; summaries in English, Japanese) 1954. s-a. Komatsu Technical Division, Planning and Administration Department - Komatsu Gijutsu Honbu Gyomubu, 3-6, Akasaka 2-chome, Minato-ku, Tokyo 107, Japan. **Indexed:** INIS Atomind.

KOMPASS PROFESSIONNEL. MACHINES - OUTILS, ROBOTIQUE, MECANIQUE GENERALE.. see *BUSINESS AND ECONOMICS — Trade And Industrial Directories*

621   530   JA   ISSN 0914-2843
KONSORYU/JAPANESE JOURNAL OF MULTIPHASE FLOW. (Text in English, Japanese; summaries in English) 1987. q. 2500 Yen per no. Nihon Konsoryu Gakkai - Japan Society of Multiphase Flow, Gakujutsu Shuppan Insatsu K.K., 7-202, Kinmitsucho 9-chome, Ashiya-shi, Hyogo-ken 659, Japan. **Indexed:** INIS Atomind.
—BLDSC (4656.550000).

621   530   JA
KONSORYU SHINPOJUMU KOEN RONBUNSHU/SYMPOSIUM ON MULTIPHASE FLOW. PROCEEDINGS. (Text in English, Japanese; summaries in English) a. Nihon Konsoryu Gakkai - Japan Society of Multiphase Flow, Gakujitsu Shuppan Insatsu K.K., 7-202, Kinmitsucho 9-chome, Ashiya-shi, Hyogo-ken 659, Japan. **Document type:** proceedings.

KOROZE A OCHRANA MATERIALU. see *ENGINEERING — Chemical Engineering*

621   JA   ISSN 0911-145X
KOYO ENGINEERING JOURNAL. (Text in Japanese; summaries in English) 1955. irreg. Koyo Seiki Co., Ltd., 5-8, Minami Senba 3-chome, Chuo-ku, Osaka-shi, Osaka 542, Japan.

621.822   SW   ISSN 0347-1748
KULLAGERTIDNINGEN. English edition: Ball Bearing Journal (ISSN 0308-1664); French edition: Revue des Roulements (ISSN 0373-3955); German edition: Kugellager-Zeitschrift (ISSN 0340-5575); Spanish edition: Revista de Rodamientos (ISSN 0347-495X); Italian edition: Rivista dei Cuscinetti (ISSN 0391-1675) 1926. q. free. S K F, Hornsgatan 1, S-415 50 Gothenburg, Sweden. Ed. Lars Berntsson. illus.; cum.index. circ. 55,000. **Indexed:** Br.Tech.Ind, Fluidex. **Document type:** trade publication.

621   JA   ISSN 0285-3892
KUREN/CRANE. (Text in Japanese) 1963. m. 400 Yen per no. Nihon Kuren Kyokai - Japan Crane Association, 13-12, Higashigotanda 1-chome, Shinagawa-ku, Tokyo 141, Japan.

621   JA
KUREN NENKAN/YEARBOOK OF CRANE AND SIMILAR EQUIPMENT. (Text in Japanese) 1971. a. 2500 Yen. Nihon Kuren Kyokai - Japan Crane Association, 13-12, Higashigotanda 1-chome, Shinagawa-ku, Tokyo 141, Japan.

621   531   CC   ISSN 1000-0879
TA349
LIXUE YU SHIJIAN/MECHANICS AND PRACTICE. (Text in Chinese) 1978. bi-m. $76.80. Science Press, Marketing and Sales Department, 16 Donghuangchenggen Beijie, Beijing 100707, People's Republic of China. TEL 4010642. FAX 4012180. TELEX 210247-SPBJ-CN. Ed. Ben Lan-Gui. adv. circ. 16,000.
  Formerly: Mechanics and Experiment.
  Description: Contains mainly articles on the practical role of mechanics in engineering techniques, new experiments and methods of calculation in mechanics and its branches. Also introduces ancient and contemporary scholars and their achievements in this field.
Refereed Serial

621   621.3   YU   ISSN 0352-8456
LOLA SAOPSTENJA/LOLA PROCEEDINGS. (Text in Serbo-Croatian) 1966. irreg. (2-3/yr.). exchange basis. Ivo Lola Rabar, H.C., Lola Institute, Kneza Viseslava 70a, 11030 Belgrade, Yugoslavia. TEL 11-541-423. TELEX 11-543-194. Ed. Vladimir B. Solaja. circ. 1,000. (back issues avail.)
—BLDSC (5292.825000).
  Formerly (until 1985): Saopstenja I A M A (Institute za Alatne Masine i Alate).

665.538   US   ISSN 0024-7154
TJ1075.A2   CODEN: LUENAG
LUBRICATION ENGINEERING. 1945. m. $61 (foreign $90) (effective 1994). Society of Tribologists and Lubrication Engineers, 840 Busse Hwy., Park Ridge, IL 60068-2376. TEL 708-825-5536. FAX 708-825-1456. Ed. J.S. McCoy. adv.; bk.rev.; abstr.; charts; illus.; pat.; tr.lit.; index. circ. 5,800. (also avail. in microfilm from UMI,PMC) **Indexed:** A.S.& T.Ind., API Abstr., API Catal., API Hlth.& Environ., API Oil., API Pet.Ref., API Pet.Subst., API Transport., Appl.Mech.Rev., Br.Rail.Bd., Chem.Abstr., Curr.Cont., Eng.Ind., Excerp.Med., Fluidex, Fuel & Energy Abstr., Ind.Sci.Rev., Int.Aerosp.Abstr., ISMEC, Met.Abstr., Sh.& Vib.Dig., World Alum.Abstr. **Document type:** academic/scholarly publication.
—BLDSC (5302.000000); EI; Faxon; UnCover; SWETS; UMI; CASDDS. **CCC**.

621   NE
M B - EXTRA. 1987. s-m. fl.50.88. Technische Uitgeverij de Vey Mestdagh BV, Markt 51, 4331 LK Middelburg, Netherlands. TEL 31-1180-81240. FAX 31-1180-81215. Ed. H. Koopmans. circ. 23,000. **Document type:** trade publication.
  Description: Covers the whole field of mechanical engineering and manufacturing, for small and medium sized businesses.

M B PRODUKTIETECHNIEK. see *ENGINEERING — Engineering Mechanics And Materials*

621   669   US
M I T E. (Manufacturing Ideas for Today's Engineers) 1987. m. Hitchcock Publishing (Subsidiary of: Capital Cities - A B C, Inc.), 191 S. Gary Ave., Carol Stream, IL 60188. TEL 708-665-1000. FAX 708-462-2225. TELEX 72-0404. Ed. John R. Coleman. circ. 110,408.

621   CN   ISSN 0076-1966
MCGILL UNIVERSITY, MONTREAL. MECHANICAL ENGINEERING RESEARCH LABORATORIES. REPORT. 1962. irreg. McGill University, Mechanical Engineering Department, 817 Sherbrooke St. W., Montreal, Que. H3A 2K6, Canada. TEL 514-392-4311.

621   CN   ISSN 0076-1974
MCGILL UNIVERSITY, MONTREAL. MECHANICAL ENGINEERING RESEARCH LABORATORIES. TECHNICAL NOTE. 1962. irreg. free when avail. McGill University, Mechanical Engineering Department, 817 Sherbrooke St. W., Montreal, Que. H3A 2K6, Canada. TEL 514-392-4311.

621.9   US   ISSN 0024-9114
TJ1   CODEN: MADEAP
MACHINE DESIGN; magazine of applied technology for design engineering. (Includes: Machine Design Reference Issues and Penton Executive Network) 1929. 28/yr. $180 (free to qualified personnel). Penton Publishing (Subsidiary of: Pittway Company), 1100 Superior Ave., Cleveland, OH 44114-2543. TEL 216-696-7000. FAX 216-696-0177. (Subscr. to: Box 95759, Cleveland, OH 44101) Ed. Ronald Khol. adv.; bk.rev.; charts; illus.; pat.; tr.lit.; index; circ. 180,000 (controlled). (also avail. in microfilm from UMI; reprint service avail. from UMI) **Indexed:** A.I.Abstr., A.S.& T.Ind., ABI Inform, Abstr.Bull.Inst.Pap.Chem., Agri.Eng.Abstr., Art & Archaeol.Tech.Abstr., C.I.S. Abstr., C.R.I. Abstr., CAD CAM Abstr. (until 1992), Chem.Abstr., Energy Info.Abstr., Eng.Ind., Environ.Abstr., Excerp.Med., Fluidex, Fuel & Energy Abstr., HRIS, Ind.Sci.Rev., ISMEC, Met.Abstr., Petrol.Abstr., Robomat. (until 1992), Sci.Abstr., Sh.& Vib.Dig., Tr.& Indus.Ind., W.R.C.Inf., World Alum.Abstr.
● Also available online. Vendor(s): DIALOG Information Services, Inc.
—BLDSC (5323.000000); EI; UnCover; SWETS; UMI. **CCC**.
  Description: Solutions to design problems, new technological developments and information about the engineering profession.

621   JA   ISSN 0387-1045
MACHINE DESIGN/KIKAI SEKKEI. (Text in Japanese) 1957. m. 1030 Yen per no. Industrial Daily News Ltd. - Nikkan Kogyo Shinbun Ltd., 1-8-10 Kudan Kita, Chiyoda-ku, Tokyo 102, Japan. circ. 36,500. **Indexed:** CAD CAM Abstr., INIS Atomind.
  Description: Furnishes readers with information and concrete data for designing machinery and equipment.

621   UK   ISSN 0140-9360
MACHINE TOOL ENTERPRISE; newspaper of the British machine tool trade. 1977. 2/yr. free. Machine Tool Technologies Association, 62 Bayswater Rd., London W2 3PS, England. TEL 071-402-6671. FAX 071-724-7250. TELEX 9312134349 MTG. Ed. Paul Harbinson. bk.rev. circ. 20,000. **Document type:** newspaper.

MACHINERY & EQUIPMENT M R O. see *MACHINERY*

MACHINERY WORLD. see *MACHINERY*

621   NE
MACHINIST. 1946. s-m. fl.30 membership. Vakvereniging Het Zwarte Corps, Postbus 2060, 3430 Nieuwegein, Netherlands. TEL 03402-65754. FAX 03402-67044. Ed. V. Verkruisen. adv. circ. 9,500.
  Description: News for engineering and workshop personnel.

532.5   LV   ISSN 0025-0015
QC718   CODEN: MAGIAI
MAGNITNAYA GIDRODINAMIKA. English translation: Magnetohydrodynamics (US ISSN 0024-998X) 1965. q. ls.1.60 per no. (Latijas Zinatnu Akademijas, Institut Phiziki) Izdevejs Zinatne, Turgeneva iela, 19, Riga LV-1530, Latvia. TEL 371-2-212797. Ed. T. Lielpeteros. bk.rev.; index. circ. 70,568. (tabloid format) **Indexed:** Chem.Abstr., INIS Atomind., Int.Aerosp.Abstr., Sci.Abstr.
—BLDSC (0098.430000); CASDDS. **CCC**.

621   TU   ISSN 0025-1135
MAKINA MUEHENDISLERI ODASI HAFTALIK HABERLER GAZETESI.* 1968. w. TL.60. Makina Muhendisleri Odasi, Sumer Sokak 36-1, Demirtepe-Ankara, Turkey. Ed. Muzaffer Gurel. adv.; bk.rev.; abstr.; bibl.; illus. (tabloid format)

MANUTENCION Y ALMACENAJE. see *MACHINERY*

MARINE ENGINEERING SOCIETY IN JAPAN. BULLETIN. see *ENGINEERING*

MARINE ENGINEERING SOCIETY IN JAPAN. JOURNAL. see *ENGINEERING*

620.4162   UK   ISSN 0951-8339
MARINE STRUCTURES; design, construction and safety. 1988. 6/yr. £259($400) (effective 1994). (International Ship and Offshore Structures Congress) Elsevier Science Ltd., Oxford Fulfilment Centre, P.O. Box 800, Kidlington, Oxford OX5 1DX, England. TEL 44-865-843000. FAX 44-865-843010. (Subscr. in U.S. and Canada to: Elsevier Science, 650 White Plains Rd., Tarrytown, NY 10591-5153. TEL 914-524-9200. FAX 914-333-2444) Ed.Bd. adv.; bk.rev.; charts; illus.; index. circ. 250. (back issues avail.) **Indexed:** Appl.Mech.Rev., Corros.Abstr., Intl.Civil. Eng.Abstr., Ocean.Abstr., Sel.Water Res.Abstr. **Document type:** academic/scholarly publication.
—BLDSC (5378.167000); EI; Faxon; SWETS. **CCC**.
  Description: Presents and discusses latest developments in research design, fabrication and in-service experience relating to marine structures.
Refereed Serial

621   US
MATERIAL ENGINEERING SERIES. 1985. irreg., vol.4, 1993. price varies. Marcel Dekker, Inc., 270 Madison Ave., New York, NY 10016. TEL 212-696-9000. FAX 212-685-4540. TELEX 421419 MARDEEK.

MATERIALLY SPEAKING. see *ENGINEERING — Engineering Mechanics And Materials*

ENGINEERING — MECHANICAL ENGINEERING

621 668.4 UK
MATERIALS AND MANUFACTURE. 1984. m. £85($200) Publication Service, 33 Foxley Lane, High Salvington, Worthing, W. Sussex BN13 3AD, England. TEL 0903-265405. Ed. Roy D. Cullum. bk.rev.; charts; illus.; tr.lit. (back issues avail.) **Document type:** trade publication.
Description: For engineering designers and manufacturing managers.

621 US ISSN 1042-6914
TS183 CODEN: MMAPET
MATERIALS & MANUFACTURING PROCESSES. 1986. 6/yr. $35 to individuals; institutions $545. Marcel Dekker Journals, 270 Madison Ave., New York, NY 10016. TEL 212-696-9000. FAX 212-685-4540. TELEX 421419. (Subscr. to: Box 5017, Monticello, NY 12701) Eds. T.S. Sudarshan, T.S. Srivatsan. (also avail. in microform from RPI) **Indexed:** Corros.Abstr. **Document type:** academic/scholarly publication.
—BLDSC (5393.993000); EI; Faxon; SWETS; CASDDS. **CCC.**
Formerly (until 1989): Advanced Materials and Manufacturing Processes (ISSN 0884-2558)
Description: Provides an international forum for current developments and future direction in the area of materials manufacturing processes.
Refereed Serial

621 PL ISSN 0137-1339
TA403 CODEN: MSCJDS
MATERIALS SCIENCE. (Text in English) 1975. q. price varies. (Politechnika Wroclawska) Wydawnictwo Politechniki Wroclawskiej, Wybrzeze Wyspianskiego 27, 50-370 Wroclaw, Poland. FAX 22-36-64. TELEX 712559 PWRPL. (Dist. by: Ars Polona-Ruch, Krakowskie Przedmiescie 7, Warsaw, Poland) Eds. Boguslaw Kedzia, Walter Wojciechowski. circ. 350. **Indexed:** Cadscan, Chem.Abstr., INIS Atomind., Lead Abstr., Sci.Abstr., W.R.C.Inf., Zincscan.
—BLDSC (5396.426000); EI; CASDDS.
Description: Articles on electronics and molecular structure of chemical compounds.

MEASUREMENT. see *METROLOGY AND STANDARDIZATION*

621.3 FR ISSN 1244-9091
TJ2
MECANIQUE INDUSTRIELLE ET MATERIAUX. 1916. 5/yr. 640 F. (foreign 690 F.). (Groupement pour l'Avancement de la Mecanique Industrielle (G.A.M.I.)) V B Promotion, 15 rue du 19 Janvier, 92380 Garches, France. TEL 47-01-44-74. FAX 47-01-44-74. TELEX VB PROMO 631 191. Ed. Daniel Pfrimmer. adv. contact: Patricia Hernandez. charts; illus.; index. circ. 4,500. **Indexed:** Chem.Abstr., Excerp.Med., Fluidex, INIS Atomind., Met.Abstr., World Alum.Abstr.
Former titles (until 1993): Mecanique Materiaux Electricite (ISSN 0025-6439); Mecanique Electricite (ISSN 0369-1616)

621 IT
MECCANICA ITALIANA. 1955. m. (11/yr.). $25. Associazione Nazionale di Meccanica, Piazzale Rodolfo Morandi 2, 20121 Milan, Italy. TEL 2-784-991. FAX 2-78-42-36. TELEX 323831 FEDAS I. Ed. Alberto Quaranta. adv.; bk.rev. circ. 8,000. **Indexed:** Met.Abstr., World Alum.Abstr.

621 IT ISSN 0393-5558
MECCANICA MODERNA. 1981. 10/yr. L.65000 (foreign L.175000) (effective 1994). Tecniche Nuove S.p.A., Via C. Menotti 14, 20129 Milan, Italy. TEL 02-75701. FAX 02-7610351. Ed. G. Nardella. adv.: B&W page L.2030000, color page L.2780000; trim 185 x 266. circ. 8,500.
—BLDSC (6407.979000).
Formerly (until 1985): Meccanica Pratica (ISSN 0392-4815)
Description: Practical information for the workshop technician.

MECHANICAL CONTRACTOR LITERATURE SHOWCASE. see *BUILDING AND CONSTRUCTION*

621 US ISSN 0025-6501
TJ1 CODEN: MEENAH
MECHANICAL ENGINEERING. 1906. m. $45 to non-members; members $17. American Society of Mechanical Engineers, 345 E. 47th St., New York, NY 10017. TEL 212-705-7722. Ed. C.W. Beardsley. adv.; bk.rev.; abstr.; illus.; tr.lit.; index. circ. 80,000. (also avail. in microform from UMI,PMC) **Indexed:** A.I.Abstr. (until 1992), A.S.& T.Ind., ABI Inform, Abstr.Bull.Inst.Pap.Chem., Acid Rain Abstr., Acid Rain Ind., API Abstr., API Catal., API Hlth.& Environ., API Oil., API Pet.Ref., API Pet.Subst., API Transport., Appl.Mech.Rev., BMT, Br.Rail.Bd., C.I.S. Abstr., CAD CAM Abstr. (until 1992), Chem.Abstr., Eng.Ind., Excerp.Med., Fluidex, Fuel & Energy Abstr., HRIS, INIS Atomind., Int.Aerosp.Abstr., Intl.Mgmt.Info., ISMEC, Met.Abstr., Petrol.Abstr., Robomat. (until 1992), Sci.Abstr., Sel.Water Res.Abstr., Sh.& Vib.Dig., World Alum.Abstr. **Document type:** trade publication.
●Also available online. Vendor(s): Mead Data Central, Inc..
—BLDSC (5418.000000); EI; Faxon; UnCover; SWETS; UMI; CASDDS. **CCC**
Refereed Serial

621 II ISSN 0379-5527
TJ1 CODEN: MEGBBQ
MECHANICAL ENGINEERING BULLETIN. (Text in English) 1970. s-a. Rs.15($4.50) (students Rs.12). Central Mechanical Engineering Research Institute, Duragapur 9, West Bengal, India. (Affiliate: Council of Scientific and Industrial Research) Ed. B.K. Sinha. adv.; bk.rev.; abstr.; pat. circ. 500. (also avail. in microform from UMI; reprint service avail.) **Indexed:** Anal.Abstr., Appl.Mech.Rev., Br.Tech.Ind., Chem.Abstr., Eng.Ind., Fluidex, Sci.Abstr. **Document type:** bulletin.
—CASDDS.

621 JA ISSN 0374-2725
MECHANICAL ENGINEERING LABORATORY. BULLETIN. (Text in English) 1971. irreg. Agency of Industrial Science and Technology, Mechanical Engineering Laboratory - Kogyo Gijutsuin, Kikai Gijutsu Kenkyujo, 1-2, Namiki, Tsukuba-shi, Ibaraki-ken 305, Japan. **Indexed:** Eng.Ind., INIS Atomind. **Document type:** bulletin.
—BLDSC (2612.070000).

621 US
MECHANICAL ENGINEERING SERIES. 1978. irreg., vol.86, 1993. Marcel Dekker, Inc., 270 Madison Ave., New York, NY 10016. TEL 212-696-9000. FAX 212-658-4540. TELEX 421419. **Document type:** monographic series.
Refereed Serial

621 UK ISSN 0954-6529
TA1
MECHANICAL INCORPORATED ENGINEER. 1981. 6/yr. £25($80) to non-members. Institution of Mechanical Incorporated Engineers, 3 Birdcage Walk, Westminster, London SW1H 9JN, England. TEL 071-799-1808. FAX 071-799-2243. Ed. Rebecca Booth. adv.; bk.rev.; illus. circ. 8,000. **Indexed:** Br.Tech.Ind., Sci.Abstr. **Document type:** academic/scholarly publication, trade publication.
—BLDSC (5419.250000); EI.
Formerly: Mechanical Engineering Technology (ISSN 0261-7188); Incorporates: General Engineer (ISSN 0308-650X); Which was formerly: Institution of General Technician Engineers Journal (ISSN 0022-6610); Junior Institution of Engineers Journal.

621 UK ISSN 0888-3270
TA654
MECHANICAL SYSTEMS & SIGNAL PROCESSING. 1987. bi-m. £165 (effective 1994). Academic Press Ltd. (Subsidiary of: Harcourt Brace & Company Ltd.), 24-28 Oval Rd., London NW1 7DX, England. TEL 44-71-267-4466. FAX 44-71-482-2293. TELEX 25775-ACPRES-G. (Subscr. to: Harcourt Brace & Company Ltd., Foots Cray High St., Sidcup, Kent DA14 5HP, England. TEL 44-81-300-3322. FAX 44-81-309-0807) Ed. S.G. Braun. index. (back issues avail.) **Document type:** academic/scholarly publication.
—BLDSC (5419.760000); Faxon; UnCover; SWETS. **CCC.**
Description: Provides a forum for the discussion of research findings in dynamics in its broadest sense; applications are stressed with a balance between fundamental and experimental establishments.

621 530.13 NE ISSN 0926-9282
MECHANICS AND PHYSICS OF DISCRETE SYSTEMS. (Text in English) 1988. irreg., vol.3, 1994. price varies. Elsevier Science B.V., Books Division, P.O. Box 211, 1000 AE Amsterdam, Netherlands. TEL 31-20-5803911. FAX 31-20-5803705. TELEX 18582 ESPA NL. (Subscr. in U.S. and Canada to: Elsevier Science Inc., Box 882, Madison Sq. Sta., New York, NY 10159. TEL 212-989-5800) (back issues avail.) **Document type:** monographic series.
—BLDSC (5424.038000).
Refereed Serial

621 US ISSN 0890-5452
TA645 CODEN: MSMAEI
MECHANICS OF STRUCTURES AND MACHINES; an international journal. 1972. 4/yr. $297.50 to individuals; institutions $595. Marcel Dekker Journals, 270 Madison Ave., New York, NY 10016. TEL 212-696-9000. FAX 212-685-4540. TELEX 421419 MARDEEK. (Subscr. to: Box 5017, Monticello, NY 12701) Ed. E. Haug. adv.; abstr.; charts. (also avail. in microform from RPI) **Indexed:** Abstr.J.Earthq.Eng., Appl.Mech.Rev., Curr.Cont., Geotech.Abstr., Ind.Sci.Rev., Int.Aerosp.Abstr., J.of Ferroc., Math.R., Sci.Abstr., Sh.& Vib.Dig. **Document type:** academic/scholarly publication.
—BLDSC (5424.159000); Faxon; UnCover; SWETS; UMI. **CCC.**
Former titles: Journal of Structural Mechanics (ISSN 0360-1218); Structural Mechanics (ISSN 0039-2561)
Refereed Serial

621 PL ISSN 0025-6552
CODEN: MCNKA5
MECHANIK; miesiecznik naukowo-techniczny. 1909. m. $54. (Stowarzyszenie Inzynierow i Technikow Mechanikow Polskich) Oficyna Wydawnicza SIMP Press, Ltd., Ul. Swietokrzyska 14A, 00-950 Warsaw, Poland. (Dist. by: Ars Polona-Ruch, Krakowskie Przedmiescie 7, Warsaw, Poland) Ed. Kazimierz Oczos. adv.: B&W page $1260. bk.rev.; bibl.; charts; illus.; pat.; stat.; index. circ. 15,300. **Indexed:** C.I.S. Abstr., Eng.Ind.
—CASDDS.

621 NE
MECHANISCHE TECHNOLOGIE; vakblad voor de technische professioneel. 11/yr. fl.142.50 (foreign fl.192.50) (effective 1993). (Nederlands Ingenieurs Vereniging (NIRIA)) V N U Business Publishers B.V., Postbus 90162, 1006 BD Amsterdam, Netherlands. TEL 31-20-5102911. FAX 31-20-6174121. (Co-sponsor: Koninklijk Instituut van Ingenieurs) Ed. Ruud Plaizier. adv.: B&W page fl.2860, color page fl.4855; trim 205 x 285; adv. contact: Corine Vijn. circ. 11,478. **Document type:** trade publication.

531 UK ISSN 0094-114X
TJ1 CODEN: MHMTAS
MECHANISM AND MACHINE THEORY. 1966. 8/yr. £585($900) (effective 1994). (International Federation for the Theory of Machines and Mechanisms) Elsevier Science Ltd., Pergamon, P.O. Box 800, Kidlington, Oxford OX5 1DX, England. TEL 44-865-843000. FAX 44-865-843010. (Subscr. in U.S. and Canada to: Elsevier Science, 660 White Plains Rd., Tarrytown, NY 10591-5153. TEL 914-524-9200. FAX 914-333-2444) Ed. Terry E. Shoup. adv.; bk.rev.; illus. circ. 1,000. (also avail. in microfilm from UMI) **Indexed:** Appl.Mech.Rev., CAD CAM Abstr., Comput.Cont., Curr.Cont., Eng.Ind., Ind.Sci.Rev., ISMEC, Sci.Abstr., Sh.& Vib.Dig. **Document type:** academic/scholarly publication.
—BLDSC (5424.570800); EI; Faxon; UnCover; SWETS; UMI. **CCC.**
Formerly: Journal of Mechanisms (ISSN 0022-2569)
Description: Provides coverage of all aspects of mechanisms and machine theory.
Refereed Serial

MECHANIZACJA I AUTOMATYZACJA GORNICTWA; czasopismo naukowo-techniczne. see *MINES AND MINING INDUSTRY*

ENGINEERING — MECHANICAL ENGINEERING

621 UK ISSN 0957-4158
TS155.6
MECHATRONICS; mechanics - electronics - control. 1990. 8/yr. £250($385) (effective 1994). Elsevier Science Ltd., Pergamon, P.O. Box 800, Kidlington, Oxford OX5 1DX, England. TEL 44-865-843000. FAX 44-865-843010. (Subscr. in U.S. and Canada to: Elsevier Science, 660 White Plains Rd., Tarrytown, NY 10591-5153. TEL 914-524-9200. FAX 914-333-2444) Eds. R.W. Daniel, J.R. Hewit. index. (also avail. in microfilm from UMI; back issues avail.) **Document type:** academic/scholarly publication.
—BLDSC (5424.620220); Faxon; UnCover; SWETS; UMI. **CCC.**
 Description: Reports on research progress in mechanical and electrical engineering disciplines relating to system and device design, with emphasis on applications to computer integration, instrumentation, and manufacturing methods rather than theoretical topics.
Refereed Serial

621 JA ISSN 0285-4287
MEKATORONIKUSU/MECHATRONICS DESIGN NEWS. (Text in Japanese) 1976. m. 7200 Yen. Gijutsu Chosakai, 8-1, Kudan Kita 1-chome, Chiyoda-ku, Tokyo 102, Japan.

547 LV ISSN 0135-7492
TA455.P58 CODEN: MKMIDJ
MEKHANIKA KOMPOZITNYKH MATERIALOV. English translation: Mechanics of Composite Materials (US ISSN 0191-5665) (Text in Russian; summaries in English) 1965. bi-m. 39.90 Rub. (Latvijas Zinatnu Akadeija) Izdevejs Zinatne, Turgeneva iela 19, Riga LV-1530, Latvia. TEL 371-313797. Ed. V. Tamuzs. bk.rev.; index. circ. 70,569. **Indexed:** Chem.Abstr., Int.Aerosp.Abstr., ISMEC, Sci.Abstr.
—CASDDS.
 Formerly: Mekhanika Polimerov (ISSN 0025-8865)

MEMBRANE TECHNOLOGY; an international newsletter. see *CHEMISTRY*

621.3 GW ISSN 0930-8644
MESSTECHNISCHE BRIEFE; Zeitschrift fuer das Elektrische Messen Mechanischer Groessen. Short title: M T B. 1965. 2/yr. free. Hottinger Baldwin Messtechnik GmbH, Im Tiefen See 45, 64293 Darmstadt, Germany. TEL 06151-803-300. FAX 06151-803417. Ed. Stefan Keil. bk.rev. circ. 20,000. **Indexed:** C.I.S. Abstr. **Document type:** trade publication.
—BLDSC (5682.830000).
 Formerly: Messtechnische Briefe fuer Elektrisches Messen Mechanischer Groessen (ISSN 0026-0428)
 Description: Covers research and new developments in measuring technology in all fields such as civil engineering, ship building, transport, geology and machine optimization.

621 531.64 RU ISSN 0202-6309
TS1
MESTNYI PROIZVODSTVENNYI OPYT V PROMYSHLENNOSTI/LOCAL LEVEL EXPERIENCE IN THE MANUFACTURING INDUSTRY; nauchno-tekhnicheskii referativnyi sbornik. 1948. m. 14.40 Rub. Moskovskii Gorodskoi Territorial'nyi Tsentr Nauchno-Tekhnicheskoi Informatsii i Propagandy, Pr. Serova 5, 101958 Moscow, Russia. TEL 921-67-05. (Co-sponsor: State Planning Committee of R.S.F.S.R.) Ed. Arnold P. Kudryashov. circ. 5,540. (back issues avail.)
—BLDSC (0108.060000).

METALWORKING PRODUCTION. see *METALLURGY*

MONOGRAPHS IN P - M SERIES. see *METALLURGY*

621 RU ISSN 0236-3941
MOSKOVSKII GOSUDARSTVENNYI TEKHNICHESKII UNIVERSITET. VESTNIK. MEKHANICHESKOE MASHINOSTROENIE/MOSCOW STATE TECHNICAL UNIVERSITY. PROCEEDINGS. MECHNICAL ENGINEERING. (Text in Russian; summaries in English, Russian) 1990. q. $200. Moskovskii Gosudarstvennyi Tekhnicheskii Universitet - Moscow State Technical University, 2-ya Baumanskaya, 5 MGTU, 107005 Moscow, Russia. TEL 263-6045. FAX 95-267-9893. Ed. Igor Borisovich Feodorov. adv. circ. 1,000. **Document type:** proceedings.
 Description: Discusses fundamental problems of mechanical engineering, process simulation, design and manufacturing engineering.

621 TU ISSN 0027-304X
MUHENDIS VE MAKINA. 1957. m. TL.90000($40) Chamber of Mechanical Engineers, Sumer Sokak, 36-1-A Demirtepe, 06440 Ankara, Turkey. TEL 4-2313164. FAX 4-2313165. Ed. Tulay Akarson. adv.; illus.; index, cum.index; circ. 30,000 (controlled).

621 BL ISSN 0102-0145
MUNDO MECANICO. 1976. m. $85. Editora Gruenwald Ltda, Rua Consorcio 59, 04535 Sao Paulo, Brazil. FAX 011-829-0042. TELEX 1130410. adv.; bk.rev.; charts; illus.; tr.lit.; index. circ. 29,000.

621 PO
MUNDO MOTORIZADO. 12/yr. Esc.3500. S E P, Rua do Alecrim 53 r-c F, 1200 Lisbon, Portugal. TEL 3423225. FAX 346-58-58. Ed. Joao Vieira. circ. 17,500. **Document type:** consumer publication.

621 JA
N A B U K O GIHO/N A B C O ENGINEERING REPORT. (Text in Japanese) 1962. s-a. Nippon Eya Bureki K.K., 1-46, Wakinohama Kaigan Dori, Chuo-ku, Kobe-shi, Hyogo-ken 651, Japan.

621 387 JA ISSN 0388-600X
N K K NEWS; steelmaking, engineering, construction & shipbuilding, advanced materials, electronics, urban development, biotechnology. (Text in English) 1961. m. free. N K K Corporation - Nippon Kokan K.K., 1-1-2 Marunouchi, Chiyoda-ku, Tokyo 100, Japan. FAX 03-3214-8435. Ed. Motoo Ono. circ. 7,500. **Indexed:** Met.Abstr., World Alum.Abstr. **Document type:** newsletter.
 Formerly: Japan Steel News.
 Description: Company newsletter for overseas customers and other general circles.

621 US
N T I S ALERTS: COMBUSTION, ENGINES & PROPELLANTS. w. $160 (outside N. America $225). U.S. National Technical Information Service, 5285 Port Royal Rd., Springfield, VA 22161. TEL 703-487-4650. FAX 703-321-8547. TELEX 64617. bibl. **Document type:** newsletter, government publication.

621 669 IT
N T TECNICA E TECNOLOGIA. 6/yr. Via Vincenzo Vela 17, 10128 Turin, Italy. TEL 11-57-181. FAX 11-571-83-79. TELEX 221641 UNIND I. Ed. Pier Luigi Bassignana. circ. 2,500.

NAGARE/JAPAN SOCIETY OF FLUID MECHANICS. JOURNAL. see *ENGINEERING* — *Hydraulic Engineering*

621 JA ISSN 0387-1142
NAINEN KIKAN/INTERNAL COMBUSTION ENGINE. (Text in English, Japanese; summaries in English) 1937. m. 1240 Yen per no. Sankaido, 5-18, Hongo 5-chome, Bunkyo-ku, Tokyo 113, Japan.

621 JA
NAINEN KIKAN GODO SHINPOJUMU KOEN RONBUNSHU/INTERNAL COMBUSTION ENGINE SYMPOSIUM. PROCEEDINGS. (Text in Japanese; summaries in English) 1979. irreg. 14000 Yen per no. Nihon Kikai Gakkai - Japan Society of Mechanical Engineers, 4-9, Yoyogi 2-chome, Shibuya-ku, Tokyo 151, Japan. **Document type:** proceedings.

NATIONAL CONFERENCE ON FLUID POWER. PROCEEDINGS. see *ENGINEERING* — *Hydraulic Engineering*

621.3 US ISSN 0027-9218
TJ1 CODEN: NAENAY
NATIONAL ENGINEER. 1897. m. $23.40 ($32.50 to Canada & Mexico; elsewhere $65). National Association of Power Engineers, Inc., 5-7 Springfield St., Chicopee, MA 01013-2624. TEL 413-592-6273. FAX 413-592-1998. Ed. W.F. Judd. adv.; bk.rev.; abstr.; charts; illus.; tr.lit.; index. circ. 7,000. (reprint service avail.) **Indexed:** Chem.Abstr., Eng.Ind., Excerp.Med. **Document type:** trade publication.
—BLDSC (6022.000000); CASDDS.
 Description: Focuses on power plant operations.

621 US
NATIONAL FLUID POWER ASSOCIATION. DIRECTORY AND MEMBER GUIDE (YEAR). 1955. a. $150. National Fluid Power Association, 3333 N. Mayfair Rd., Milwaukee, WI 53222. TEL 414-778-3347. FAX 414-778-3361. circ. 2,000. **Document type:** directory.
 Former titles: N F P A Directory and Member Guide; N F P A Directory.

621 US ISSN 0272-782X
NATIONAL FLUID POWER ASSOCIATION. REPORTER. Cover title: N F P A Reporter. 1953. bi-m. $50 (foreign $75). National Fluid Power Association, 3333 N. Mayfair Rd., Milwaukee, WI 53222. TEL 414-778-3347. FAX 414-778-3361. Ed. Carrie Tatman Schwartz. circ. 2,000. **Document type:** newsletter.
 Description: Covers developments in fluid power technology.

621 CC ISSN 1000-0909
NEIRANJI XUEBAO/CHINESE SOCIETY FOR INTERNAL COMBUSTION ENGINES. TRANSACTIONS. (Text in Chinese; summaries in English) 1983. q. $23.86 (effective 1992). Chinese Society for Internal Combustion Engines, 92 Weijin Lu, Tianjin, People's Republic of China. TEL 841-3063. (Dist. by: China International Book Trading Corp. - Guoji Shudian, P.O. Box 399, Beijing 100044, P.R.C.) Ed. Shi Lianyou. adv.; abstr. circ. 6,000. (back issues avail.) **Document type:** academic/scholarly publication.
—BLDSC (8929 220000); EI.
 Description: Introduces new results in IC Engine research, production, and up-to-date engine developing levels.

621 JA
NEJI/FASTENERS. (Text in Japanese) 1957. m. 500 Yen per no. Nihon Neji Kogyo Kyokai - Fasteners Institute of Japan, 5-8, Shiba Koen 3-chome, Minato-ku, Tokyo 105, Japan.

621 JA
NETSU KOGAKU SUKURINGU & WAKUSHOPPU SHIRYO/SCHOOLING & WORKSHOP. (Text in Japanese; summaries in English) irreg. 4500 Yen per no. Nihon Kikai Gakkai - Japan Society of Mechanical Engineers, 4-9, Yoyogi 2-chome, Shibuya-ku, Tokyo 151, Japan.

NEW PERSPECTIVES IN POWDER METALLURGY. see *METALLURGY*

621 JA
NEWS AKASAKA. (Text in Japanese; summaries in English) 1956. s-a. Akasaka Diesels Ltd., Kasumigaseki Biru 26-26, 2-5, Kasumigaseki 3-chome, Chiyoda-ku, Tokyo 100, Japan.

621 JA ISSN 0287-122X
NICHINAIREN JOHO/JAPAN INTERNAL COMBUSTION ENGINE FEDERATION. INFORMATION. (Text in Japanese) 1977. irreg. Nihon Nainen Kikan Rengokai - Japan Internal Combustion Engine Federation, 11-5, Shinbashi 1-chome, Minato-ku, Tokyo 105, Japan.

621 JA
NICHIYU NYUSU/NIPPON YUSOKI COMPANY. NEWS. (Text in Japanese) 1975. 2/yr. Nippon Yusoki Co., Ltd., 1-1, Higashikotari 2-chome, Nagaokakyo-shi, Kyoto 617, Japan.

621 JA ISSN 0387-4168
NIHON GASU TABIN GAKKAISHI/GAS TURBINE SOCIETY OF JAPAN. JOURNAL. (Text in English, Japanese; summaries in English) 1973. q. Nihon Gasu Tabin Gakkai, 5-13, Nishishinjuku 7-chome, Shinjuku-ku, Tokyo 160, Japan.
—BLDSC (4755.565000)

621 JA
NIHON KIKAI GAKKAI. KOENKAI KOEN RONBUNSHU/JAPAN SOCIETY OF MECHANICAL ENGINEERS. PREPRINTS OF THE MEETING. (Text in Japanese) 1978. irreg. Nihon Kikai Gakkai - Japan Society of Mechanical Engineers, 4-9, Yoyogi 2-chome, Shibuya-ku, Tokyo 105, Japan.

ENGINEERING — MECHANICAL ENGINEERING

621   JA   ISSN 0387-5008
CODEN: NKGADA
NIHON KIKAI GAKKAI RONBUNSHU. A HEN/JAPAN SOCIETY OF MECHANICAL ENGINEERS. TRANSACTIONS. SERIES A. (Text in Japanese; summaries in English) 1935. m. 3650 Yen per no. Nihon Kikai Gakkai - Japan Society of Mechanical Engineers, 4-9, Yoyogi 2-chome, Shibuya-ku, Tokyo 151, Japan. (US subscr. to: American Society of Mechanical Engineers, 22 Law Dr., Box 2300, Fairfield, NJ 07007-2300) **Indexed:** Chem.Abstr., Eng.Ind., Fluidex, INIS Atomind., ISMEC, JCT, JTA.
—BLDSC (8975.010000); EI; CASDDS. **CCC.**
   Supersedes in part (in 1978): Nihon Kikai Gakkai Ronbunshu (ISSN 0029-0270)

621   JA   ISSN 0387-5016
CODEN: NKGBDD
NIHON KIKAI GAKKAI RONBUNSHU. B HEN/JAPAN SOCIETY OF MECHANICAL ENGINEERS. TRANSACTIONS. SERIES B. (Text in Japanese; summaries in English) 1935. m. 5150 Yen per no. Nihon Kikai Gakkai, 4-9, Yoyogi 2-chome, Shibuya-ku, Tokyo 151, Japan. **Indexed:** Chem.Abstr., Eng.Ind., INIS Atomind.
—BLDSC (8975.020000); EI; CASDDS. **CCC.**
   Supersedes in part (in 1978): Nihon Kikai Gakkai Ronbunshu (ISSN 0029-0270)

621   JA   ISSN 0387-5024
CODEN: NKCHDB
NIHON KIKAI GAKKAI RONBUNSHU. C HEN/JAPAN SOCIETY OF MECHANICAL ENGINEERS. TRANSACTIONS. SERIES C. (Text in Japanese; summaries in English) 1935. m. 4000 Yen per no. Nihon Kikai Gakkai, 4-9, Yoyogi 2-chome, Shibuya-ku, Tokyo 151, Japan. **Indexed:** Chem.Abstr., Eng.Ind., INIS Atomind.
—BLDSC (8975.030000); EI; CASDDS. **CCC.**
   Supersedes in part (in 1978): Nihon Kikai Gakkai Ronbunshu (ISSN 0029-0270)

621   JA   ISSN 0287-8313
NIHON NEJI KENKYU KYOKAISHI/JAPAN RESEARCH INSTITUTE FOR SCREW THREADS AND FASTENERS. JOURNAL. (Text in Japanese) 1970. m. Nihon Niji Kenkyu Kyokai, 5-8, Shiba Koen 3-chome, Minato-ku, Tokyo 105, Japan.

621   JA   ISSN 0285-6867
CODEN: NRKRDS
NIHON REITO KYOKAI GAKUJUTSU KOENKAI KOEN RONBUNSHU/JAPANESE ASSOCIATION OF REFRIGERATION. PROCEEDINGS OF ANNUAL CONFERENCE. (Text in Japanese) a. 3000 Yen. Nihon Reito Kyokai - Japanese Association of Refrigeration, 8, San'ei-cho, Shinjuku-ku, Tokyo 160, Japan. **Document type:** proceedings.
—CASDDS.

621   JA   ISSN 0385-2911
NIHON SUPINDORU GIHO/NIHON SPINDLE TECHNICAL REPORT. (Text in Japanese) 1950. irreg. 1000 Yen (foreign 1500 Yen) free to qualified personnel. Nihon Supindoru Seizo K.K. - Nihon Spindle Manufacturing Co., Ltd., 2-30, Shioe 4-chome, Amagasaki-shi, Hyogo-ken 661, Japan. TEL 81-06-499-4304. FAX 81-06-499-5631. Ed. Mitsuaki Sakaue. adv. contact: Yutaka Fujii. circ. 1,000 (controlled). **Document type:** bulletin.
   Description: Contains technical reviews and introduction of new products and patents.

621   JA
NIKKEI MECHANICAL. (Text in Japanese) 1979. fortn. 18000 Yen. Nikkei Business Publications, Inc. (Subsidiary of: Nihon Keizai Shimbun, Inc.), 2-7-6 Hirakawa-cho, Chiyoda-ku, Tokyo 102, Japan. TEL 03-5210-8502. FAX 03-5210-8119. Ed. Minoru Tsuboi. adv. contact: Kazuhisa Hagiwara. circ. 40,004. **Indexed:** JCT, JTA. **Document type:** trade publication.
   Description: Provides close-ups of advanced technologies and developments in design, measurement, control, and production systems used in or related to mechanical engineering.

621 621.3   JA   ISSN 0285-0303
TL159
NIPPONDENSO TECHNICAL DISCLOSURE. JOURNAL/NIPPON DENSO KOKAI GIHO. (Text in Japanese) 1976. bi-m. free. Nippondenso Co., Ltd., 1-1, Showa-cho, Kariya-shi, Aichi-ken 448, Japan. FAX 566-25-4554. Ed. Hiroshi Hattori; Pub. Hiroshi Hattori. circ. 140. **Document type:** bulletin.
   Description: Discloses minor inventions made at Nippondenso and not applied for patents.

620.23 614   US   ISSN 0736-2501
TD891   CODEN: NCEJD5
NOISE CONTROL ENGINEERING JOURNAL. 1973. bi-m. $60. Institute of Noise Control Engineering, Department of Mechanical Engineering, Auburn University, Auburn, AL 36849-5341. TEL 205-844-3306. FAX 205-844-3307. TELEX 593404 WAREAGLE1 AUBN. (Subscr. to: Box 3206, Arlington Branch, Poughkeepsie, NY 12603) (Co-sponsor: Acoustical Society of America) Ed. Malcolm J. Crocker. adv. contact: Lee Wilkins. bk.rev. circ. 2,500. (also avail. in microform from UMI) **Indexed:** A.S.& T.Ind., Appl.Mech.Rev., Biol.Abstr., BMT, C.I.S.Abstr., Curr.Cont., Environ.Abstr., Environ.Ind., Environ.Per.Bibl., Excerp.Med., Geo.Abstr., Int.Aerosp.Abstr., ISMEC, Noise Pollut.Publ.Abstr., Ocean.Abstr., Pollut.Abstr., Sci.Abstr., Sh.& Vib.Dig. **Document type:** academic/scholarly publication.
—BLDSC (6116.052000); EI; Faxon; UnCover; SWETS; UMI. **CCC.**
   Formerly: Noise Control Engineering (ISSN 0093-9978)
   Description: Contains technical articles for professionals concerned with noise reduction in industry, buildings, transportation, products and communities. Includes issues such as hearing protection and legislation, machinery diagnostics, building vibrations, and the effects of noise and vibration on people.
Refereed Serial

621   NE   ISSN 0924-090X
CODEN: NODYES
NONLINEAR DYNAMICS; an international journal of nonlinear dynamics and chaos in engineering systems. (Text in English) 1990. 8/yr. fl.932($459) (effective 1994). Kluwer Academic Publishers, Postbus 17, 3300 AA Dordrecht, Netherlands. TEL 31-78-334911. FAX 31-78-334254. TELEX 29245 KAPG NL. (Dist. by: Kluwer Academic Publishers Group, P.O. Box 322, 3300 AH Dordrecht, Netherlands. TEL 31-78-524400. FAX 31-78-524474; N. America dist. addr.: Box 358, Accord Sta., Hingham, MA 02018-0358. TEL 617-871-6600. FAX 617-871-6528) Ed. A.H. Nayfeh. (also avail. in microform from UMI; back issues avail.; reprint service avail. from SWZ) **Indexed:** Appl.Mech.Rev., SH.& Vib.Dig. **Document type:** academic/scholarly publication.
—BLDSC (6117.316700); SWETS; UMI. **CCC.**
   Description: Encompasses all nonlinear dynamic phenomena associated with mechanical, structural, civil, aeronautical, ocean, electrical, and control systems.
Refereed Serial

621   US
NOZZLE CHATTER. bi-m. (free to members). Association of Diesel Specialists, 9140 Ward Pkwy., Kansas City, MO 64114. FAX 816-444-0330. Ed. Robert Guy Stewart. adv. **Document type:** newsletter.

621   US   ISSN 1040-7782
QC319.8   CODEN: NHAAES
NUMERICAL HEAT TRANSFER PART A: APPLICATIONS; an international journal of computation and methodology. 1978. 8/yr. $530. Taylor & Francis, 1900 Frost Rd., Ste. 101, Bristol, PA 19007-1598. TEL 800-821-8312. FAX 215-785-5515. Ed. W.J. Minkowycz. adv.; bk.rev.; abstr.; bibl.; charts; illus.; stat.; index. circ. 550. (back issues avail.; reprint service avail. from UMI) **Indexed:** Appl.Mech.Rev., ASCA, Chem.Eng.Abstr., Eng.Ind., Fluidex, Ind.Sci.Rev., Int.Aerosp.Abstr., Met.Abstr., Sci.Abstr., T.C.E.A., World Alum.Abstr. **Document type:** academic/scholarly publication.
—BLDSC (6184.692600); EI; Faxon; UnCover; SWETS; CASDDS. **CCC.**
   Supersedes in part: Numerical Heat Transfer (ISSN 0149-5720)
   Description: Methodology and results of numerical solutions of problems in heat and mass transfer and in related fluid flows.
Refereed Serial

621   US   ISSN 1040-7790
QC319.8.N833   CODEN: NHBFEE
NUMERICAL HEAT TRANSFER PART B: FUNDAMENTALS; an international journal of computation and methodology. 1978. 8/yr. $330. Taylor & Francis, 1900 Frost Rd., Ste. 101, Bristol, PA 19007-1598. TEL 800-821-8312. FAX 215-785-5515. Ed. W.J. Minkowycz. adv. contact: Elizabeth D'Costa. **Indexed:** Curr.Cont., Sci.Cit.Ind.
—BLDSC (6184.692700); EI; Faxon; UnCover; SWETS; CASDDS. **CCC.**
   Supersedes in part: Numerical Heat Transfer (ISSN 0149-5720)
   Description: Addresses all aspects of the methodology for the numerical solution of heat problems in heat and mass transfer as well as fluid flow.
Refereed Serial

621.2 621.5   GW   ISSN 0029-8697
TJ843   CODEN: OEPNAQ
OELHYDRAULIK UND PNEUMATIK; Zeitschrift fuer Fluidtechnik. (Text in German; index in English and German) 1957. m. DM.236 (foreign DM.254). Vereinigte Fachverlage GmbH, Lise-Meitner-Str. 2, 55129 Mainz, Germany. TEL 06131-992-01. FAX 06131-992-100. TELEX 04187752. (Subscr. to: Postfach 2760, 55017 Mainz, Germany) Ed. Wolfgang Backe. adv.; bk.rev.; abstr.; charts; illus.; index. circ. 10,000. **Indexed:** Fluidex, Sci.Abstr.
—BLDSC (6255.155000).

OFFSHORE BUSINESS; engineering and project management. see *PETROLEUM AND GAS*

621 551.46   US
OFFSHORE MECHANICS AND ARCTIC ENGINEERING SYMPOSIUM. PROCEEDINGS. irreg.; last meeting 1986, Tokyo, Japan. $150 (members $120). American Society of Mechanical Engineers, 345 E. 47th St., New York, NY 10017. TEL 212-705-7722. **Document type:** proceedings.

621.2 621.5   IT   ISSN 0391-8645
OLEODINAMICA - PNEUMATICA - LUBRIFICAZIONE. 1960. m. L.85000 (foreign L.210000) (effective 1994). Tecniche Nuove s.p.a., Via C. Menotti 14, 20129 Milan, Italy. TEL 02-75701. FAX 02-7610351. Ed. G. Nardella. adv.: B&W page L.2210000, color page L.2990000; trim 185 x 266. bk.rev.; abstr.; charts; illus.; pat.; tr.lit. circ. 6,900. **Indexed:** Fluidex.
—BLDSC (6255.020000).
   Former titles: Oleodinamica - Pneumatica (ISSN 0030-2104); Lubrificazione Industriale e per Autoveicoli (ISSN 0024-7162)
   Description: Contributions to the diffusion and development of oleodynamic and pneumatic automation.

621   AT   ISSN 0030-2392
ON WATCH.* 1957. m. Aus.$28. Australian Institute of Marine and Power Engineers, 52 Buckingham St., Surry Hills, N.S.W. 2010, Australia. Ed. B. Dailey. adv.; bk.rev.; charts; illus. circ. 4,000.

OYO KIKAI KOGAKU/MECHANICAL ENGINEERING APPLICATIONS. see *MACHINERY*

621   RU   ISSN 0869-5032
QC1   CODEN: ZPMFAF
P M T F. (Prikladnaya Mekhanika i Tekhnicheskaya Fizika) English translation: Journal of Applied Mechanics and Technical Physics (US ISSN 0021-8944) 1960. bi-m. 44.10 Rub. Rossiiskaya Akademiya Nauk, Sibirskoe Otdelenie, Pr. Akademika Lavrenteva 17, 630090 Novisibirsk, Russia. Ed. B.A. Lugovtsov. index. (tabloid format) **Indexed:** Chem.Abstr., Math.R., Met.Abstr., Phys.Ber., Sci.Abstr., World Alum.Abstr. **Document type:** academic/scholarly publication.
—CASDDS.
   Formerly: Zhurnal Prikladnoi Mekhaniki i Tekhnicheskoi Fiziki (ISSN 0044-4626)

ENGINEERING — MECHANICAL ENGINEERING

621 330   US   ISSN 1045-3962
CODEN: PTDIE3
P T DISTRIBUTOR. (Power Transmission); helping power transmission distribution add value to products and services. 1987. q. $20 (free to qualified personnel). Penton Publishing (Subsidiary of: Pittway Company), 1100 Superior Ave., Cleveland, OH 44114-2543. TEL 216-696-7000. FAX 216-696-8765. (Subscr. to: Box 95759, Cleveland, OH 44101) Ed. Carolyn Rohan. circ. 10,000 (controlled). (reprint service avail. from UMI)
—UMI. **CCC**.
   Description: Helps power transmission distributors reach customers and suppliers.

PARTICULATE SCIENCE AND TECHNOLOGY; an international journal. see *ENGINEERING — Chemical Engineering*

621 629.286   US
PEOPLE 'N PRIDE. 1985. m. free. General Motors Corp. - U.A.W., G-3248 Van Slyke, Flint, MI 48552. TEL 313-236-7622. FAX 313-236-2802. Ed. Dennis S. Wisniewski. cum.index: 1985-1992. circ. 5,000. (back issues avail.)
   Description: Contains automotive news and views for employees and suppliers.

621   HU   ISSN 0324-6051
TA4   CODEN: PPMMBT
PERIODICA POLYTECHNICA. MECHANICAL ENGINEERING. (Text in English, German) 1957. q. $16. Budapesti Muszaki Egyetem - Technical University of Budapest, Periodica Polytechnica, 1521 Budapest, Hungary. FAX 1-166-6808. TELEX 22-5931 MUEGY H. (Dist. by: Kultura, P.O. Box 149, 1389 Budapest, Hungary) Ed. L. Radonyi. bk.rev.; charts; illus.; index. circ. 520. **Indexed:** Agri.Eng.Abstr., Appl.Mech.Rev., Curr.Cont., Eng.Ind., Fluidex, Int.Aerosp.Abstr., Met.Abstr. **Document type:** academic/scholarly publication.
—BLDSC (6425.500000); EI. **CCC**.
   Formerly (until 1968): Periodica Polytechnica. Engineering, Maschinen- und Bauwesen (ISSN 0031-5338)

621 540 530   US   ISSN 0734-1520
QC173.4.S94   CODEN: PCMSER
PHYSICS, CHEMISTRY AND MECHANICS OF SURFACES. 24/yr. (in 2 vols.; 12 nos./vol.). 521 ECU per vol. (effective 1993). Gordon & Breach Science Publishers, 820 Town Center Dr., Langhorne, PA 19047. TEL 215-750-2642. FAX 215-750-6343. (UK subscr. to: P.O. Box 90, Reading, Berkshire RG1 8JL, England. TEL 0734-560-080) Ed. Yu.A. Ossipian. index. (also avail. in microform; back issues avail.)
—BLDSC (0416.827000). **CCC**.
   Refereed Serial

621   UK
PLANT AND CONSTRUCTION ENGINEERING. q. 41 Bond St., Brighton, E. Sussex BN1 1RD, England. TEL 0273-820888. FAX 0273-746768. Ed. Piers Bravery. circ. 5,000.

621   JA
PLANT ENGINEER. (Text in Japanese) 1968. m. (Japan Institute of Plant Engineers) Nippon Naritsu Kyokai, 3-1-22 Shiba Koen, Minato-ku, Tokyo, Japan. adv. **Indexed:** C.I.S. Abstr., JTA.

621 621.9   US   ISSN 0199-8013
TS184
PLANT SERVICES. 1980. m. $35. Putman Publishing Co., 301 E. Erie St., Chicago, IL 60611. Ed. Charles Boyles. circ. 98,000. (also avail. in microfilm)
—SWETS; UMI. **CCC**.

621 658   US
PLANT SERVICES' HANDBOOK OF COMPUTERIZED MANAGEMENT AND PREDICTIVE MAINTENANCE. a. Putman Publishing Co., 301 E. Erie St., Chicago, IL 60611. TEL 312-644-2020. FAX 312-644-6709. Ed. Charles Boyles. adv.: B&W page $5490; trim 8 1/8 x 10 7/8. circ. 106,015.

621 658   US
PLANT SERVICES' LITERATURE UPDATE. m. Putman Publishing Co., 301 E. Erie St., Chicago, IL 60611. TEL 312-644-2020. FAX 312-644-6709. Ed. Charles Boyles. adv.: B&W page $5490; trim 8 1/8 x 10 7/8. circ. 106,015. **Document type:** catalog.

621   AT
PLANTLINE. 1981. m. Aus.$80 (free to qualified personnel). Reed Business Publishing Pty. Ltd. (Subsidiary of: Reed International PLC), 1-5- Railway St., Chatswood, N.S.W. 2067, Australia. TEL 02-372-5222. FAX 02-419-7399. Ed. Bruce McEwan. circ. 14,973. (tabloid format)

621   SZ
PLANUNG UND PRODUKTION. 11/yr. Postfach 350, CH-8401 Winterthur, Switzerland. TEL 052-236858. FAX 079-913939. Ed. Christian Schlumpf. circ. 7,500.

621   PL   ISSN 0072-0380
POLITECHNIKA GDANSKA. ZESZYTY NAUKOWE. MECHANIKA. (Text in English, Polish; summaries in Russian and one West-European language) 1956. irreg. price varies. Politechnika Gdanska, Ul. G. Narutowicza 11-12, 80-952 Gdansk 6, Poland. (Dist. by: Osrodek Rozpowszechniania Wydawnictw Naukowych PAN, Palac Kultury i Nauki, 00-901 Warsaw, Poland) bibl.; charts; illus. **Document type:** academic/scholarly publication.
—BLDSC (9512.300000).
   Description: Deals with hydraulic turbines and pumps, handling equipment, piston steam engines, refrigeration technology, materials strength and machine measurement.

621   PL
POLITECHNIKA KRAKOWSKA. MONOGRAFIE. SERIA: MECHANIKA. (Subseries of: Politechnika Krakowska. Monografie (ISSN 0860-097X)) (Text in Polish; summaries in English, French, German, Russian) 1985. irreg. price varies. Politechnika Krakowska, Ul. Warszawska 24, 31-155 Krakow, Poland. TEL 48-12-374289. FAX 48-12-335773. TELEX 322468 PK PL. bibl.; charts; illus. circ. 200. **Document type:** academic/scholarly publication, monographic series.

621.8   PL   ISSN 0137-2661
POLITECHNIKA LODZKA. ZESZYTY NAUKOWE. CIEPLNE MASZYNY PRZEPLYWOWE. (Text in various languages; summaries in English and Russian) irreg. price varies. Wydawnictwo Politechniki Lodzkiej, Ul. Wolczanska 219, 93-085 Lodz, Poland. (Dist. by: Ars Polona-Ruch, Krakowskie Przedmiescie 7, Warsaw, Poland) Ed. Ryszard Przybylski. circ. 146. **Document type:** academic/scholarly publication.
   Description: Articles on thermal flow machines, pumps and hydraulic turbines.

621   PL   ISSN 0458-1563
TJ4   CODEN: ZPLMAV
POLITECHNIKA LODZKA. ZESZYTY NAUKOWE. MECHANIKA. (Text in Polish; summaries in English and Russian) 1954. irreg. price varies. Wydawnictwo Politechniki Lodzkiej, Ul. Wolczanska 219, 93-085 Lodz, Poland. TEL 84-07-93. (Dist. by: Ars Polona-Ruch, Krakowskie Przedmiescie 7, Warsaw, Poland) Ed. Andrzej Jopkiewicz. circ. 216. **Indexed:** Chem.Abstr., Met.Abstr. **Document type:** academic/scholarly publication.
—BLDSC (9512.320300); CASDDS.
   Description: Articles on materials technology, strength of materials, car engines, metallurgy and automobile construction.

621 631   PL   ISSN 0137-6918
POLITECHNIKA POZNANSKA. ZESZYTY NAUKOWE. MASZYNY ROBOCZE I POJAZDY. (Text in Polish; summaries in English) 1956. irreg. price varies. Politechnika Poznanska, Pl. Curie-Sklodowskiej 5, Poznan, Poland. Ed. Henryk Kozlowiecki. **Document type:** academic/scholarly publication.
—BLDSC (9512.323000).
   Formerly (until 1970): Politechnika Poznanska. Zeszyty Naukowe. Mechanizacja i Elektryfikacja Rolnictwa (ISSN 0076-5805)
   Description: Articles on rail and automotive vehicles, agricultural and food industry machines, thermal engineering, machine elements construction and testing.

POLITECHNIKA POZNANSKA. ZESZYTY NAUKOWE. MECHANIKA. see *PHYSICS — Mechanics*

620   PL   ISSN 0434-0817
CODEN: PSMEBQ
POLITECHNIKA SLASKA. ZESZYTY NAUKOWE. MECHANIKA. (Text in Polish; summaries in English, German, Russian) 1955. irreg. price varies. Politechnika Slaska, Katowicka 7, 44-100 Gliwice, Poland. FAX 371655. TELEX 036304. (Dist. by: Ars Polona, Krakowskie Przedmiescie 7, 00-068 Warsaw, Poland) Ed. Jerzy Dziubinski. circ. 205.
—CASDDS.

621   PL   ISSN 0324-9573
POLITECHNIKA WROCLAWSKA. INSTYTUT MATERIALOZNAWSTWA I MECHANIKI TECHNICZNEJ. PRACE NAUKOWE. KONFERENCJE. (Text in Polish; summaries in English and Russian) 1974. irreg., no.3, 1989. Wydawnictwo Politechniki Wroclawskiej, Wybrzeze Wyspianskiego 27, 50-370 Wroclaw, Poland. FAX 22-36-64. TELEX 712559 PWRPL. (Dist. by: Ars Polona-Ruch, Krakowskie Przedmiescie 7, Warsaw, Poland) illus.

621   PL   ISSN 0867-7778
POLITECHNIKA WROCLAWSKA. INSTYTUT TECHNOLOGII MASZYN I AUTOMATYZACJI. PRACE NAUKOWE. KONFERENCJE. (Text in Polish; summaries in English and Russian) 1975. irreg., no.18, 1991. price varies. Wydawnictwo Politechniki Wroclawskiej, Wybrzeze Wyspianskiego 27, 50-370 Wroclaw, Poland. FAX 22-36-64. TELEX 712559 PWRPL. (Dist. by: Ars Polona-Ruch, Krakowskie Przedmiescie 7, Warsaw, Poland)
—BLDSC (6590.730000).
   Formerly: Politechnika Wroclawska. Instytut Technologii Budowy Maszyn. Prace Naukowe. Konferencje (ISSN 0324-9379)

621   PL   ISSN 0867-5325
T4
POLITECHNIKA WROCLAWSKA. INSTYTUT TECHNOLOGII MASZYN I AUTOMATYZACJI. PRACE NAUKOWE. MONOGRAFIE. (Text in Polish; summaries in English and Russian) 1972. irreg., no.13, 1991, price varies. Wydawnictwo Politechniki Wroclawskiej, Wybrzeze Wyspianskiego 27, 50-370 Wroclaw, Poland. FAX 22-36-64. TELEX 712559 PWRPL. (Dist. by: Ars Polona-Ruch, Krakowskie Przedmiescie 7, Warsaw, Poland) **Document type:** monographic series.
   Formerly: Politechnika Wroclawska. Instytut Technologii Budowy Maszyn. Prace Naukowe. Monografie (ISSN 0324-9352)

621   PL
POLITECHNIKA WROCLAWSKA. INSTYTUT TECHNOLOGII MASZYN I AUTOMATYZACJI. PRACE NAUKOWE. STUDIA I MATERIALY. (Text in Polish; summaries in English and Russian) 1970. irreg., no.17, 1988. price varies. Wydawnictwo Politechniki Wroclawskiej, Wybrzeze Wyspianskiego 27, 50-370 Wroclaw, Poland. FAX 22-36-64. TELEX 712559 PWRPL. (Dist. by: Ars Polona-Ruch, Krakowskie Przedmiescie 7, Warsaw, Poland) **Indexed:** Chem.Abstr.
   Formerly: Politechnika Wroclawska. Instytut Technologii Budowy Maszyn. Prace Naukowe. Studia i Materialy (ISSN 0324-9360)

621   PL   ISSN 0079-3205
TJ4   CODEN: PIMZAI
POLSKA AKADEMIA NAUK. INSTYTUT MASZYN PRZEPLYWOWYCH. PRACE/POLISH ACADEMY OF SCIENCES. INSTITUTE OF FLUID-FLOW MACHINERY. TRANSACTIONS. (Text in Polish; summaries in English and Russian) 1960. irreg., vol.93, 1992. price varies. Wydawnictwo Naukowe P W N, Ul. Miodowa 10, 00-257 Warsaw, Poland. TEL 48-22-312738. FAX 48-22-267163. TELEX 813763 PWN PL. Ed. Kazimierz Steller. bibl, charts, illus.
—CASDDS.

621   NE   ISSN 0032-4108
CODEN: PTWTAP
POLYTECHNISCH TIJDSCHRIFT: WERKTUIGBOUW; vakblad voor de ingenieur. 1945. m. fl.197 (foreign fl.365) (effective 1994). Ten Hagen & Stam b.v., Postbus 235, 2280 AE Rijswijk, Netherlands. TEL 31-70-3988100. FAX 31-70-3988276. adv.: B&W page fl.2680, color page fl.4905; trim 297 x 210; adv. contact: Herman Voois. circ. 6,885. **Indexed:** C.I.S. Abstr., Excerp.Med., Sci.Abstr. **Document type:** trade publication.
—SWETS.
   Description: For design, construction, production and management engineers in the mechanical engineering and industrial automation fields.

ENGINEERING — MECHANICAL ENGINEERING

621   PL   ISSN 0137-4478
CODEN: PTMUDF
POSTEPY TECHNOLOGII MASZYN I URZADZEN. (Text in Polish; summaries in English, Russian) 1977. 4/yr. Wydawnictwo Gebethner i S-ka, Ul. Swietokrzyska 21, p.533, 00-049 Warsaw, Poland. TEL 48-22-269806. FAX 48-22-269805. Ed. Jan Kaczmarek.
—CASDDS.

621.3   US   ISSN 0032-5929
TJ1   CODEN: POWEAD
POWER (NEW YORK). 1882. m. free to qualified personnel in U.S.; Canada $60; elsewhere $150. McGraw-Hill, Inc., 1221 Ave. of the Americas, New York, NY 10020. TEL 212-512-2000. (Subscr. to: Box 521, Hightstown, NJ 08520) Ed. Robert G. Schwieger. adv.; bk.rev.; abstr.; charts; illus.; stat.; tr.lit.; index. circ. 61,349. (also avail. in microform from UMI; reprint service avail. from UMI) **Indexed:** A.S.& T.Ind., Abstr.Bull.Inst.Pap.Chem., API Abstr., Appl.Mech.Rev., Chem.Abstr., Eng.Ind., Environ.Abstr., Excerp.Med., Fluidex, Petrol.Abstr., Sci.Abstr., Sel.Water Res.Abstr., Sh.& Vib.Dig., Tr.& Indus.Ind.
—BLDSC (6573.000000); CIS; Faxon; UnCover; SWETS; UMI; CASDDS. **CCC.**
Description: For management engineers in the total power market, including utilities and energy-intensive process and manufacturing industries.
Refereed Serial

621 629.286   US
POWER BUILDERS. 1982. s-w. free. General Motors Corp. - U.A.W., G-3248 Van Slyke, Flint, MI 48552. TEL 313-236-8980. cum.index: 1982-1992. circ. 2,000. (looseleaf format; back issues avail.)
Description: Employee and automotive news.

621.2 621.5   UK   ISSN 0950-1487
TJ840   CODEN: PIHEE2
POWER INTERNATIONAL. 1955. 12/yr.(in 4 vols.). £150 (foreign £165). Lincoln Publications Ltd., 28 Centre Point House, St. Giles High St., London WC2 8LW, England. TEL 071-2405562. FAX 071-4972811. Ed. Richard Jorro. adv.; bk.rev.; bibl.; charts; illus.; tr.lit.; index; circ. 5,900 (controlled). **Indexed:** BMT, Br.Tech.Ind., Bus.Ind., C.I.S. Abstr., Eng.Ind., Excerp.Med., Fluidex, ISMEC, Sci.Abstr. **Document type:** trade publication.
—BLDSC (6576.220000); SWETS. **CCC.**
Former titles (until 1985): Hydraulic Pneumatic Mechanical Power (ISSN 0306-4069); Hydraulic Pneumatic Power (ISSN 0018-8131)
Description: Devoted to oil-hydraulic, pneumatic, mechanical, and electronic power transmission and control.
Refereed Serial

POWER LETTER. see *ENERGY*

621.8   US   ISSN 0032-6070
TJ1045   CODEN: PWTDAH
POWER TRANSMISSION DESIGN; the motion and control magazine. 1959. m. $50 (free to qualified personnel). Penton Publishing (Subsidiary of: Pittway Company), 1100 Superior Ave., Cleveland, OH 44114-2543. TEL 216-696-7000. FAX 216-696-8765. (Subscr. to: Box 95759, Cleveland, OH 44101) Ed. Phil Kingsley. adv.; bk.rev.; film rev.; charts; illus.; pat.; tr.lit.; tr.mkt.; index; circ. 52,000 (controlled). (also avail. in microform from UMI; reprint service avail. from UMI) **Indexed:** Eng.Ind., Sci.Abstr., Sh.& Vib.Dig.
—BLDSC (6577.050000); UMI. **CCC.**
Description: Selection, application, maintenance and replacement of bearings, motors and drives, controls and power transmission accessories.

621.31   US
POWER TRANSMISSION DESIGN HANDBOOK. 1961. a. $30 (free to qualified personnel). Penton Publishing (Subsidiary of: Pittway Company), 1100 Superior Ave., Cleveland, OH 44114-2543. TEL 216-696-7000. FAX 216-696-8765. (Subscr. to: Box 95759, Cleveland, OH 44101) Ed. Phil Kingsley. adv.; circ. 52,000 (controlled). (reprint service avail. from UMI)
Formerly: Power Transmission and Bearing Handbook (ISSN 0554-890X)

621   JA   ISSN 0916-8311
TS500   CODEN: BLPTDL
PRECISION AND INTELLIGENCE. (Text in English) 1956. s-a. exchange basis. Tokyo Institute of Technology, Research Laboratory of Precision Machinery and Electronics - Tokyo Kogyo Daigaku, 4259 Nagatsuta, Midori-ku, Yokohama 227, Japan. Ed.Bd. circ. 450. **Indexed:** Appl.Mech.Rev., Fluidex, JCT, Math.R., Met.Abstr., Sci.Abstr., World Alum.Abstr. **Document type:** bulletin.
—BLDSC (2884.140000).
Former titles: Research Laboratory of Precision Machinery and Electronics. Bulletin (ISSN 0385-7832); Research Laboratory of Precision Machinery and Electronics. Report.

621   KR   ISSN 0032-8243
TA349   CODEN: PKMKAL
PRIKLADNAYA MEKHANIKA; vsesoyuznyi nauchno-tekhnicheskii zhurnal. English translation: International Applied Mechanics (US ISSN 1063-7095) 1955. m. 16.80 Rub.($38.40) (Akademiya Nauk Ukrainy, Institut Mekhaniki) Izdatel'stvo Naukova Dumka, c/o Yu.A. Khramov, Dir, Ul. Repina, 3, Kiev 252 601, Ukraine. TEL 446-62-92. Ed. A.N. Guz' bk.rev.; abstr.; bibl.; charts; illus.; index. circ. 1,950. **Indexed:** Appl.Mech.Rev., Chem.Abstr., Eng.Ind., Geotech.Abstr., Int.Aerosp.Abstr., ISMEC, Math.R., Sci.Abstr.
—CASDDS. **CCC.**

621   UK   ISSN 0266-8920
TA340   CODEN: PEMEEX
PROBABILISTIC ENGINEERING MECHANICS. 1986. 4/yr. £192($295) (effective 1994). Elsevier Science Ltd., Oxford Fulfilment Centre, P.O. Box 800, Kidlington, Oxford OX5 1DX, England. TEL 44-865-843000. FAX 44-865-843010. (Subscr. in U.S. and Canada to: Elsevier Science, 660 White Plains Rd., Tarrytown, NY 10591-5153. TEL 914-524-9200. FAX 914-333-2444) Eds. M. Shinozuka, P.D. Spanos. adv. (back issues avail.) **Indexed:** Appl.Mech.Rev., Comput.& Info.Sys., Curr.Cont., Met.Abstr., Sci.Abstr. **Document type:** academic/scholarly publication.
—BLDSC (6617.209600); EI; Faxon; UnCover; SWETS. **CCC.**
Description: Forum for scholarly research addressing probabilistic and statistical approaches to contemporary solid and fluid mechanics problems, with emphasis on aerospace, civil, mechanical, nuclear and marine engineering.
Refereed Serial

621   SP
PROCESOS. 6/yr. Ronda de la Universidad 14, 2o, 08007 Barcelona, Spain. TEL 3-412-38-00. FAX 3-318-88-52.

621   UK   ISSN 0953-6639
TJ1   CODEN: PFLEEZ
PROFESSIONAL ENGINEERING. 1954. 22/yr. £107 (foreign £114). (Institution of Mechanical Engineers) Mechanical Engineering Publications Ltd., Northgate Ave., Bury St. Edmunds, Suffolk IP32 6BW, England. TEL 0284-763277. FAX 0284-704006. TELEX 817376. Ed. K. Fenwick. adv.; bk.rev.; illus.; index. circ. 70,000. (also avail. in microform from UMI; reprint service avail. from UMI) **Indexed:** Account.& Data Proc.Abstr., Agri.Eng.Abstr., Appl.Mech.Rev., B.C.I.R.A., BMT, Br.Tech.Ind., C.I.S. Abstr., Cadscan, Chem.Abstr., Chem.Eng.Abstr., Comput.Rev., Eng.Ind., Ergon.Abstr., Excerp.Med., Fluidex, Int.Build.Serv.Abstr., Intl.Mgmt.Info., Lead Abstr., Met.Abstr., Res.High.Educ.Abstr., Sci.Abstr., Sh.& Vib.Dig., World Alum.Abstr., Zincscan. **Document type:** trade publication.
—BLDSC (6858.370000); EI; Faxon; UnCover; SWETS; UMI. **CCC.**
Incorporates (in 1993): Engineering News (ISSN 0267-5145); **Supersedes (in 1988):** Chartered Mechanical Engineer (ISSN 0306-9532)
Description: News briefs, informational items, and research articles on recent technological, design, and product development in all aspects of mechanical engineering, with service guides and lists of industry contacts.

621   IT   ISSN 0391-741X
PROGETTO (MILAN). (Text in Italian; summaries in English) 1978. m. L.25000. E R I S S.p.A., Piazza della Repubblica 26, 20124 Milan, Italy. Ed. Enrico Palumbo. adv.; bk.rev.; pat.; index.

621   KR   ISSN 0204-3602
TJ260   CODEN: PRTLD9
PROMYSHLENNAYA TEPLOTEKHNIKA; nauchno-prikladnoi zhurnal. (Text in Russian; summaries in English and Russian) 1979. bi-m. $161. (Akademiya Nauk Ukrainy, Otdelenie Fiziko-tekhnicheskikh Problem Energetiki) Vidavnitstvo Naukova Dumka, Vul. Tereshchenkivska 3, 252601 Kiev, Ukraine. TEL 446-48-67. (Dist. by: Mezhdunarodnaya Kniga, B. Yakimanke 39, 117049 Moscow, Russia; Dist. by: Victor Kamkin Inc., 4956 Boiling Brook Pkwy., Rockville, MD 20852. TEL 301-881-5973. FAX 301-881-1637) Ed. A.A. Dolinskii. **Indexed:** Chem.Abstr., Int.Aerosp.Abstr.
—BLDSC (0134.235000); CASDDS. **CCC.**
Formerly: Teplofizika i Teplotekhnika (ISSN 0564-6170)

621   PL   ISSN 0033-2259
TJ4   CODEN: PPRMDM
PRZEGLAD MECHANICZNY. 1935. fortn. $138. (Stowarzyszenie Inzynierow i Technikow Mechanikow Polskich - Polish Mechanical Engineers Association) Oficyna Wydawnicza SIMP Press, Ul. Swietokrzyska 14A, 00-940 Warsaw, Poland. (Dist. by: Ars Polona-Ruch, Krakowskie Przedmiescie 7, Warsaw, Poland) Ed. Jacek Kostmanowicz. adv.: B&W page $1300. bk.rev.; bibl.; charts; illus.; pat.; tr.lit.; index. circ. 4,000. **Indexed:** C.I.S. Abstr., Chem.Abstr., Eng.Ind., Fluidex, Met.Abstr.
—CASDDS.
Description: Covers industrial novelties (Polish and foreign), patents, modern technics of production.

621   CC   ISSN 1001-5884
QILUNJI JISHU/STEAM TURBINE TECHNOLOGY. (Text in Chinese) bi-m. Harbin Qilunji Chang - Harbin Steam Turbine Company, 1, Daqing Lu, Harbin, Heilongjiang 150040, People's Republic of China. TEL 281403.

621   CC   ISSN 1000-2073
QIZHONG YUNSHU JIXIE/MECHANICAL HANDLING EQUIPMENT. (Text in Chinese) m. $1 per no. Beijing Qizhong Yunshu Yanjiusuo - Beijing Institute of Mechanical Handling Equipment, 52 Yonghegong Dajie, Beijing 100007, People's Republic of China. TEL 5123339.

QUALITY AND RELIABILITY ENGINEERING INTERNATIONAL. see *ENGINEERING — Electrical Engineering*

621   UK   ISSN 0264-2344
QUALITY TESTING TODAY. 6/yr. £38.50. Warwick House, Azalea Dr., Swanley, Kent BR8 8HY, England. TEL 0322-660070. FAX 0322-667633. Ed. Tony Doran. adv. circ. 10,000. **Document type:** trade publication.
—BLDSC (7168.175000); SWETS.

621 629.   UK   ISSN 0432-2924
R E M E JOURNAL. 1951. a. £2.50. Royal Electrical & Mechanical Engineers, Isaac Newton Rd., Arborfield, Reading, Berks. RG2 9LN, England. TEL 0734-763502. Ed. D.J. Wright. adv.; bk.rev. circ. 3,000. **Indexed:** Sci.Abstr. **Document type:** academic/scholarly publication.
Description: Items of military interest, technical, engineering, scientific and historical matters, together with relevant features.

RANRYU SHINPOJUMU KOEN RONBUNSHU/PROCEEDINGS OF SYMPOSIUM ON TURBULENCE. see *ENGINEERING — Hydraulic Engineering*

RECURSOS HIDRICOS. see *WATER RESOURCES*

621   CC   ISSN 1001-2060
RENENG DONGLI GONGCHENG/JOURNAL OF ENGINEERING FOR THERMAL ENERGY AND POWER. (Text in Chinese) 1986. bi-m. Y15 (foreign $62). Zhongguo Chuanbo Zonggongsi, Harbin 703 Yanjiusuo - China State Shipbuilding Corporation, Harbin 703 Institute, P.O. Box 77-7, Harbin, Heilongjiang 150036, People's Republic of China. TEL 86-451-5662881. FAX 86-451-5662885. TELEX 87157 HMBTR CN. Ed. Li Shangfu. adv.: color page $2000; trim 260 x 188. circ. 5,000.
Description: Covers the latest developments and research findings in the field of power engineering design and testing techniques, focusing on gas turbines, steam turbines, boilers and gear transmission.

ENGINEERING — MECHANICAL ENGINEERING

621.3　　　　　GW　ISSN 0930-7923
REPORTS IN APPLIED MEASUREMENT; journal for the electrical measurement of mechanical quantities. (Text in English) 1985. 2/yr. free. Hottinger Baldwin Messtechnik GmbH, Im Tiefen See 45, 64293 Darmstadt, Germany. TEL 06151-803-0. FAX 06151-803417. TELEX 419341. (U.S. addr.: 19 Bartlett St., Marlboro, MA 01752. TEL 508-624-4500) Ed. Stefan Keil. circ. 13,000. **Document type:** trade publication.
—BLDSC (7638.524500).

621 669　　　　US　ISSN 1063-5750
　　　　　　　　　　　CODEN: RPRMEB
▼**REVIEWS IN PARTICULATE MATERIALS**. 1993. irreg., latest no. 1, 1993. $75 (foreign $85). Metal Powder Industries Federation, 105 College Rd. E., Princeton, NJ 08540. TEL 609-987-8523. FAX 609-987-8523. Ed.Bd. **Document type:** academic/scholarly publication.
—BLDSC (7793.846300); CASDDS.
　Description: Serves as an international forum for comprehensive reviews on all aspects of particulate materials technology, encompassing powder metallurgy, ceramics, intermetallics, and composites.
　Refereed Serial

REVISTA TECNICA AUTOMOVEL. see *TRANSPORTATION — Automobiles*

536.7 621.4　　　FR　ISSN 0035-3159
　　　　　　　　　　　CODEN: RGTHA7
REVUE GENERALE DE THERMIQUE;* combustibles, energie, equipements thermiques. (Summaries in English, French, German, Italian, Russian, Spanish) 1962. 10/yr. 1088 F. Editions Europeennes Thermique et Industrie, 3 rue Henri Heine, 75016 Paris, France. TEL 45-20-56-04. FAX 40-50-07-54. TELEX 615 867 IFENERG. Ed. Bernard Pierre. adv.; bk.rev.; abstr.; bibl.; charts; stat. circ. 1,200. **Indexed:** Appl.Mech.Rev., C.I.S. Abstr., Ceram.Abstr., Chem.Abstr., Chem.Eng.Abstr., Curr.Cont., Eng.Ind., Excerp.Med., Fluidex, Fuel & Energy Abstr., Gas Abstr., Int.Build.Serv.Abstr., Met.Abstr., World Alum.Abstr.
—BLDSC (7916.080000); UnCover; SWETS; CASDDS. **CCC.**

620.1　　　　　　RM　ISSN 0035-4074
　　　　　　　　　　　CODEN: RTMAA8
REVUE ROUMAINE DES SCIENCES TECHNIQUES. SERIE DE MECANIQUE APPLIQUEE. (Text in English, French, German, Russian) 1956. 6/yr. 330 lei($69) (Academia Romana) Editura Academiei Romane, Calea Victoriei 125, 79717 Bucharest, Rumania. (Dist. by: Rompresfilatelia, Calea Grivitei 64-66, P.O. Box 12-201, 78104 Bucharest, Rumania) Ed. Ioan Anton. bk.rev.; illus.; index. **Indexed:** Appl.Mech.Rev., Chem.Abstr., Eng.Ind., Fluidex, Int.Aerosp.Abstr., Math.R., Sh.& Vib.Dig.
—BLDSC (7946.700000); UnCover.

REZANIE I INSTRUMENT. see *PHYSICS — Mechanics*

621　　　　　　　JA　ISSN 0911-4858
RIKUYO NAINEN KIKAN/LAND ENGINE MANUFACTURERS. (Text in Japanese) 1959. q. Rikuyo Nainen Kikan Kyokai - Land Engine Manufacturers Association, 1-2, Ichigaya Sadohara-cho, Shinjuku-ku, Tokyo 162, Japan.

ROBOTIKUSU MEKATORONIKUSU KOENKAI KOEN RONBUNSHU/ANNUAL CONFERENCE ON ROBOTICS AND MECHATRONICS. PROCEEDINGS. see *COMPUTERS — Robotics*

621　　　　　　　UK　ISSN 0142-9469
ROLLS-ROYCE MAGAZINE. 1979. q. free. Rolls-Royce plc., 65 Buckingham Gate, London SW1E 6AT, England. Ed. Graham Truscott. illus. circ. 14,500. **Document type:** bulletin.
—BLDSC (8019.315800).
　Description: Articles relating to Rolls-Royce aero, industrial and marine gas turbines, power generation and transmission, and general engineering.

621　　　　　　　RU
ROSSIISKAYA AKADEMIYA NAUK. IZVESTIYA. ENERGETIKA. English translation: Applied Energy Research: Russian Journal of Fuel, Power, and Heat Systems (US ISSN 1068-7181) 1963. bi-m. 30.90 Rub. Izdatel'stvo Nauka, 90 Profsoyuznaya ul., 117864 Moscow, Russia. (Dist. by: Mezhdunarodnaya Kniga, ul. Dimitrova D.39, 113095 Moscow, Russia) Ed. V.I. Popkov. adv.; bk.rev.; abstr.; charts; illus.; index. circ. 1,600. **Indexed:** Chem.Abstr., INIS Atomind., Sci.Abstr.
—CCC.
　Formerly: Akademiya Nauk S.S.S.R. Izvestiya. Energetika i Transport (ISSN 0002-3310)

RUSSIAN CASTINGS TECHNOLOGY. see *METALLURGY*

RUSSIAN ENGINEERING RESEARCH. see *MACHINERY*

621　　　　　　　JA
RYUTAI KOGAKU BUMON KOENKAI KOEN RONBUNSHU/FLUIDS ENGINEERING CONFERENCE. (Text in Japanese; summaries in English) 1991. a. 5000 Yen. Nihon Kikai Gakkai - Japan Society of Mechanical Engineering, 4-9, Yoyogi 2-chome, Shibuya-ku, Tokyo 151, Japan.

621　　　　　　　JA
RYUTAI SEIGYO SHINPOJUMU KOEN RONBUNSHU/SYMPOSIUM ON FLUID CONTROL. PAPERS. (Text in English, Japanese; summaries in English) 1986. a. Keisoku Jido Seigyo Gakkai - Society of Instrument and Control Engineers, 35-28-303, Hongo 1-chome, Bunkyo-ku, Tokyo 113, Japan.

621　　　　　　　US　ISSN 0742-972X
S A E UPDATE. 1984. m. $2. Society of Automotive Engineers, 400 Commonwealth Dr., Warrendale, PA 15096-0001. TEL 412-776-4841. FAX 412-776-2103. Ed. Martha B. Swiss. adv. circ. 55,000.
—CCC.

S E N CONFERENCE PROCEEDINGS. (Subsea Engineering News) see *PETROLEUM AND GAS*

621　　　　　　　US　ISSN 1041-9489
SAFETY BRIEF. 1981. bi-m. free. Triodyne, 5950 W. Touhy, Niles, IL 60714. TEL 708-677-4730. (back issues avail.)

621　　　　　　　JA
SANKO GROUP. TECHNICAL REPORT. (Text in Japanese) 1988. s-a. Sanko Group, Sanko Kontororu K.K., 1727, Ogura, Saiwa-ku, Kawasaki-shi, Kanagawa-ken 211, Japan.

621　　　　　　　JA
SANWA SHINBUN/SANWA TIMES. (Text in Japanese) 1952. m. 80 Yen per no. Sanwa Shinbunsha, Sanwa Tekki K.K., 5-19, Minamishingagawa 6-chome, Shinagawa-ku, Tokyo 140, Japan.

SCHIFFSBETRIEBSTECHNIK FLENSBURG. see *TRANSPORTATION — Ships And Shipping*

621　　　　　　　JA　ISSN 0288-8785
SEIKI TECHNICAL NEWS. (Text in Japanese) 1953. a. Hitachi Seiki Co., Ltd., 1, Abiko, Abiko-shi, Chiba-ken 270-11, Japan.

621　　　　　　　JA
SEISAN GIJUTSU KODOKA NI KANSURU CHOSA KENKYU HONKIKUSHO. (Text in Japanese) a. Kikai Gijutsu Kyokai - Association of Mechanical Technology, 5-8, Shiba Koen 3-chome, Minato-ku, Tokyo 105, Japan.

621　　　　　　　JA
SEKKEI SHINPOJUMU KOEN RONBUNSHU/DESIGN SYMPOSIUM. PROCEEDINGS. (Text in Japanese) 1983. a. 4000 Yen. Nihon Kikai Gakkai - Japan Society of Mechanical Engineers, 4-9, Yoyogi 2-chome, Shibuya-ku, Tokyo 151, Japan. **Document type:** proceedings.

621　　　　　　　US　ISSN 1054-6693
TL272.5
SENSORS AND ACTUATORS. a. price varies. Society of Automotive Engineers, 400 Commonwealth Dr., Warrendale, PA 15096-0001. TEL 412-776-4841. FAX 412-776-3036. **Indexed:** Energy Info.Abstr. (until 1994), Environ.Abstr. **Document type:** academic/scholarly publication.

621　　　　　　　JA
SENTAN GIJUTSU FORAMU SHIRYO/FORUM ON ADVANCED TECHNOLOGY. PAPERS. (Text in Japanese) 1986. irreg. Kikai Gijutsu Kyokai - Association of Mechanical Technology, 5-8, Shiba Koen 3-chome, Minato-ku, Tokyo 105, Japan.

621　　　　　　　JA　ISSN 0914-8698
SENTAN KAKO GIJUTSU/ADVANCED MACHINING TECHNOLOGY. (Text in Japanese) 1982. 3/yr. Sentan Kako Kikai Gijutsu Shinko Kyokai - Advanced Machining Technology and Development Association, 2-29, Toranomon 1-chome, Minato-ku, Tokyo 105, Japan.

621　　　　　　　JA　ISSN 0371-005X
　　　　　　　　　　　CODEN: SHHYAG
SHIMAZU HYORON/SHIMADZU REVIEW. (Text in Japanese; summaries in English, Japanese) 1940. q. 830 Yen per no. Shimazu Hyoron Henshubu, Shimazu Seisakujo, 1, Nishinokyo Kuwabara-cho, Nakagyo-ku, Kyoto-shi, Kyoto 604, Japan.
—CASDDS.

621　　　　　　　JA
SHINKO PANTEKKU GIHO/SHINKO PANTEC ENGINEERING REPORTS. (Text in Japanese; summaries in English, Japanese) 1953. 3/yr. Shinko Pantekku K.K., 4-78, Wakihamacho 1-chome, Chuo-ku, Kobe-shi, Hyogo-ken 651, Japan. TEL 81-078-992-6525. FAX 81-078-992-6504. Ed. Kenji Tachi. circ. controlled. **Document type:** corporate report.

621　　　　　　　JA　ISSN 0915-5031
SHINKO TEKUNO GIHO/SHINKO TECHNO ENGINEERING REPORTS. (Text in Japanese) 1989. s-a. Shinko Tekuno K.K. - Shinko Techno Engineering Co., Ltd., 10-26, Wakihamacho 2-chome, Chuo-ku, Kobe-shi, Hyogo-ken 651, Japan. TEL 078-261-2311. FAX 078-261-2310. Ed. Yoshihiro Ichikawa.

SHOBO KENKYUJO HOKOKU/FIRE RESEARCH INSTITUTE OF JAPAN. REPORT. see *FIRE PREVENTION*

621 629.286 057.8　XV
SKOZI T A M. (Text in Slovenian) 1952. w. 9000 din. Towarne Avtomobilov in Motorjev, Ptujska 184, Maribor, Slovenia. TEL 062 411321. circ. 12,000.
　Formerly: Skozi Ziv T A M.
　Description: News about truck and bus manufacturing; aimed at workers of TAM.

621 534　　　　US　ISSN 0038-1810
TA365　　　　　　　CODEN: SOVIAJ
SOUND AND VIBRATION. Short title: S & V. 1967. m. free to qualified personnel; Canada $25; others $60. Acoustical Publications, Inc., Box 40416, Bay Village, OH 44140 TEL 216-835-0101. FAX 216-835-9303. Ed. Jack K. Mowry. adv.; bk.rev.; charts; illus.; index; circ. 22,000 (controlled). (also avail. in microform from UMI; reprint service avail. from UMI) **Indexed:** A.S.& T.Ind., Agri.Eng.Abstr., ASCA, BMT, C.I.S. Abstr., CAD CAM Abstr., Curr.Pack.Abstr., Eng.Ind., Environ.Abstr., Environ.Per.Bibl., Excerp.Med., Ind.Hyg.Dig., Int.Aerosp.Abstr., ISMEC, Key to Econ.Sci., Lang.& Lang.Behav.Abstr., Ocean.Abstr., Pollut.Abstr., Sci.Abstr., Sh.& Vib.Dig. **Document type:** trade publication.
—BLDSC (8330.393000); CIS; EI; Faxon; UnCover; SWETS; UMI. **CCC.**
　Description: Covers noise and vibration control, machinery monitoring, structural analysis, dynamic measurements and dynamic testing.

621　　　　　　　SA　ISSN 0038-2442
TJ1　　　　　　　　CODEN: SAMEAY
SOUTH AFRICAN MECHANICAL ENGINEER. (Text in English) 1951. m. (11/yr.) R.182.40 (foreign R.190) (effective 1994). (South African Institution of Mechanical Engineers) Promech Publishing, P.O. Box 85502, Emmarentia 2029, South Africa. TEL 27-11-8884047. FAX 27-11-7824476. (Co-sponsors: South African Institution of Tribology; South African Institute of Nuclear Engineers) Ed. S. Custers. adv.; B&W page R.2300, color R.3100; trim 297 x 210; adv. contact: Diana Just. bk.rev.; tr.lit.; index. circ. 4,068. (also avail. in microform from PMC) **Indexed:** Appl.Mech.Rev., Chem.Abstr., Curr.Cont., Energy Ind., Energy Info.Abstr., Eng.Ind., Fluidex, Fuel & Energy Abstr., Ind.S.A.Per., ISMEC, Met.Abstr., Sci.Abstr., World Alum.Abstr. **Document type:** trade publication.
—BLDSC (8341.500000); UnCover.

ENGINEERING — MECHANICAL ENGINEERING

SOUTHERN BUILDING CODE CONGRESS. STANDARD MECHANICAL CODE. see *BUILDING AND CONSTRUCTION*

SOUTHERN ILLINOIS UNIVERSITY, CARBONDALE. MATERIALS TECHNOLOGY CENTER. CONFERENCE PROCEEDINGS. see *ENGINEERING — Engineering Mechanics And Materials*

SOUTHERN ILLINOIS UNIVERSITY, CARBONDALE. MATERIALS TECHNOLOGY CENTER. DISTINGUISHED LECTURES SERIES. see *ENGINEERING — Engineering Mechanics And Materials*

621   US   ISSN 0584-9667
SPRINGS. 1962. s-a. free. Spring Manufacturers Institute, Inc., 2001 Midwest Rd., Ste. 106, Oak Brook, IL 60521-1335. TEL 708-495-8588. FAX 708-495-8595. Ed. Ken Boyce. adv.: B&W page $1810; color page $2170; trim 8 1/2 x 11. bk.rev. circ. 7,700. **Document type:** trade publication.
—BLDSC (8424.970000); EI; UnCover.
Description: Aimed at middle and senior managers at firms that manufacture precision springs. Topics include inspection methods, manufacturing processes, design, finishes, materials and equipment.

STAMPING QUARTERLY. see *METALLURGY*

681   RU   ISSN 0038-9811
CODEN: STINA4
STANKI I INSTRUMENTY. English translation: Russian Engineering Research (US ISSN 1068-798X) 1930. m. $82.80. Izdatel'stvo Mashinostroenie, 4, Stromynsky per., 107076 Moscow, Russia. TEL 095-269-7141. FAX 095-269-4897. Ed. O.A. Korolev. adv.: page DM.4000. bk.rev.; bibl.; charts; illus.; index. circ. 13,600. **Indexed:** Chem.Abstr., Eng.Ind., ISMEC, Met.Abstr., Sci.Abstr., World Alum.Abstr. **Document type:** academic/scholarly publication.
—BLDSC (0168.000000).
Description: Publishes articles about the development and installation of all-around automated bays, and about the design and use of industrial robots.

STAVEBNICKY CASOPIS. see *BUILDING AND CONSTRUCTION*

STEAM AUTOMOBILE. see *TRANSPORTATION — Automobiles*

621   CI   ISSN 0562-1887
CODEN: STJSAO
STROJARSTVO; casopis za teoriju i praksu u strojarstvu/journal for the theory and application in mechanical engineering. (Text in English, German or Yugoslavian languages; contents page and summaries in English, German, Russian and one of the Yugoslavian languages) 1959. 6/yr. 500 din.($72) Izdavacki Savjet Casopisa Strojarstvo, Berislaviceva 6, 41000 Zagreb, Croatia. Ed. Rudolf Buljan. adv.; bk.rev.; abstr.; bibl.; charts; illus.; pat.; index, cum.index. circ. 2,500. (back issues avail.) **Indexed:** ASCA, BMT, CAD CAM Abstr., Chem.Abstr., Corros.Abstr., Curr.Cont., Energy Info.Abstr., Eng.Ind., Environ.Abstr., Fluidex, ISMEC, Met.Abstr., World Alum.Abstr., World Text.Abstr.
—CASDDS.

531 624   XO   ISSN 0039-2472
STROJNICKY CASOPIS/MECHANICAL ENGINEERING MAGAZINE. (Text in Czech, English, French, German, Russian, Slovak; contents page in Czech or Slovak, English and Russian) 1949. bi-m. 132 Kcs.($36) (Slovenska Akademia Vied, Ustav Materialov a Mechaniky Strojov) Veda, Publishing House of the Slovak Academy of Sciences, Klemensova 19, 814 30 Bratislava, Slovakia. (Dist. by: Slovart, Nam. Slobody 6, 817 64 Bratislava, Slovakia) (Co-sponsor: Ceskoslovenska Akademie Ved) Ed. Norbert Szuttor. bk.rev.; charts; illus.; index. circ. 1,100. **Indexed:** Appl.Mech.Rev., Fluidex, Met.Abstr., Ref.Zh., Sh.& Vib.Dig., World Alum.Abstr.
—BLDSC (8474.650000).
Description: Devoted to theoretical questions and their applications in mechanical engineering (statics, cinematics and dynamics, theory of mechanism and machines, vibration and machine parts balance, motion stability, mechanization and automation, automatic regulation and control, control of production processes by means of computers, biomechanics, etc.).

531   XV   ISSN 0039-2480
STROJNISKI VESTNIK/MECHANICAL ENGINEERING JOURNAL. 1955. q. $65. Zveza Strojnih Inzenirjev in Tehnikov Slovenije - Association of Mechanical Engineers and Technicians of Slovenia, Murnikova 2, P.O. Box 197-IV, 61001 Ljubljana, Slovenia. FAX 061-218-567. TELEX 32240 FAKSTR YU. Ed. Joze Puhar. adv.; bk.rev.; charts; illus.; index, cum.index every 4-5 yrs. circ. 2,400. (also avail. in microfilm) **Indexed:** ISMEC, Met.Abstr., World Alum.Abstr.
—EI.

621 621.3   CI   ISSN 0351-627X
STRUCNI CASOPIS DURO DAKOVIC. 1965. s-a. 3000 din.($2.20) Njegoseva 1, 55000 Slavonski Brod, Croatia. TEL 055 231-011. Ed. Zdravko Valter. index. circ. 1,500. (back issues avail.)

621 370.196   US   ISSN 0899-5427
STUDENT ACTION IN ENGINEERING. 1972. q. membership. Society of Automotive Engineers, 400 Commonwealth Dr., Warrendale, PA 15096-0001. TEL 412-776-4841. FAX 412-776-2103. Ed. Alison Frederick. adv.; charts; illus.; stat.; tr.lit. circ. 11,000. (tabloid format)
Description: Contains information for college level engineering students on automotive design competitions, scholarships, careers, and clubs.

621   NE
STUDIES IN MECHANICAL ENGINEERING. 1980. irreg., vol.14, 1993. price varies. Elsevier Science B.V., Books Division, P.O. Box 211, 1000 AE Amsterdam, Netherlands. TEL 31-20-5803911. FAX 31-20-5803705. TELEX 18582 ESPA NL. (Subscr. in U.S. and Canada to: Elsevier Science Inc., Box 882, Madison Sq. Sta., New York, NY 10159. TEL 212-989-5800) **Document type:** monographic series.
Refereed Serial

SUBSEA ENGINEERING NEWS; including pipeline and floater update. see *PETROLEUM AND GAS*

SUBSEA PRODUCTION YEARBOOK. see *PETROLEUM AND GAS*

SUNWORLD. see *COMPUTERS*

621   JA   ISSN 0911-3916
SURFACE CONTROL & SENJO SEKKEI. (Text in Japanese) q. 11000 Yen. Kindai Henshusha, 23-5, Hirai 5-chome, Edogawa-ku, Tokyo 132, Japan.

621 541.37   US   ISSN 1068-3755
TK7881
SURFACE ENGINEERING AND APPLIED ELECTROCHEMISTRY. English translation of: Elektronnaya Obrabotka Materialov (MV ISSN 0013-5739) 1984. bi-m. $855. (Moldavian Academy of Sciences, Institute of Applied Physics, MV) Allerton Press, Inc., 150 Fifth Ave., New York, NY 10011. TEL 212-924-3950. FAX 212-463-9684. Ed. M.K. Bologa. **Document type:** academic/scholarly publication.
—BLDSC (0425.821500). CCC.
Formerly: Soviet Surface Engineering and Applied Electrochemistry (ISSN 8756-7008)

623.82   CI   ISSN 0350-3097
SVEUCILISTE U ZAGREBU. FAKULTET STROJARSTVA I BRODOGRADNJE. ZBORNIK RADOVA. (Text in Croatian; summaries in English or German) 1970. a. free. Sveuciliste u Zagrebu, Fakultet Strojarstva i Brodogradnje - University of Zagreb, Faculty of Mechanical Engineering and Naval Architecture, Djure Salaja 5, Zagreb, Croatia. TEL 3841-611-944. FAX 514-535. Ed. Zora Smolcic-Zerdik. illus.
Description: Presents papers and essays showing the scientific research activity of the teaching staff in the faculty.

621   US
SWEET'S MECHANICAL ENGINEERING AND RETROFIT FILE. a. free to qualified personnel. Sweet's Catalog Files (Subsidiary of: McGraw-Hill, Inc.), 1221 Ave. of the Americas, New York, NY 10020. TEL 212-512-3536. FAX 212-512-2348. circ. 15,000.

001.6 629.8   AU   ISSN 1019-4118
T G A - REPORT; die Kennziffer-Fachzeitschrift fuer technische Gebaeudeausruestung. 1989. m. S.540. Verlag Technik - Report GmbH, Markgraf-Ruediger-Str. 8, A-1150 Vienna, Austria. TEL 01-98170-0. FAX 01-9817033. TELEX 135041. Ed. Manfred Krejci. adv. circ. 17,140. **Document type:** trade publication.
Description: For building, energy and eco-specialists as well as decision makers, buyers and operators of building-automation plants.

T P Q: THE TUBE & PIPE QUARTERLY. see *METALLURGY*

621   US
T S I JOURNAL OF PARTICLE INSTRUMENTATION. (Abstracts in English, French, German) 1977. s-a. free. T S I Incorporated, 500 Cardigan Rd., Box 64394, St. Paul, MN 55164. TEL 612-490-2833. FAX 612-490-3860. TELEX 6879024. Ed. Ron Grogg. circ. 12,000 (controlled). (back issues avail.) **Document type:** academic/scholarly publication.
Supersedes in part (1986): T S I Quarterly.

621   JA   ISSN 0385-8839
TABO KIKAI/TURBOMACHINERY. (Text in Japanese) 1973. m. 1100 Yen per no. (Tabo Kikai Kyokai - Turbomachinery Society of Japan) Nihon Kogyo Shuppan K.K. - Japan Industrial Publishing Co., Ltd., 3-26, Honkomagome 6-chome, Bunkyo-ku, Tokyo 113, Japan.

621   JA
TABO KIKAI KOENKAI/TURBOMACHINERY SOCIETY OF JAPAN. PROCEEDINGS. (Text in Japanese) a. 4000 Yen. Tabo Kikai Kyokai - Turbomachinery Society of Japan, 3-26, Honkomagome 6-chome, Bunkyo-ku, Tokyo 113, Japan. **Document type:** proceedings.

621   JA   ISSN 0285-2152
TANGAROI/TUNGALOY. (Text in Japanese) 1952. irreg. Toshiba Tungaloy Co., Ltd., 1-7, Tsukagoshi, Saiwai-ku, Kawasaki-shi, Kanagawa-ken 210, Japan.

621   HU   ISSN 0237-6016
TECHNICAL UNIVERSITY FOR HEAVY INDUSTRY. SERIES C, MECHANICAL ENGINEERING. PUBLICATIONS. (Text in English, German, Russian) irreg., vol.42, no.2-4, 1988. Nehezipari Muszaki Egyetem, Miskolc, Hungary. TEL 46-65-111. FAX 46-69554. TELEX 62223-NMEMIS. Ed.Bd. bibl.; index. circ. 300.
—BLDSC (7113.413300).
Formerly (until 1984): Technical University for Heavy Industry. Series C, Machinery. Publications (ISSN 0133-297X)

621   AU   ISSN 0377-1725
TECHNIK REPORT; die Kennziffer-Fachzeitschrift fuer die Oesterreichische Industrie. 14/yr. S.750. Verlag Technik - Report GmbH, Markgraf-Ruediger Str. 8, A-1150 Vienna, Austria. TEL 01-98170-0. FAX 01-9817033. TELEX 135041. Ed. Franz Lunacek. adv. circ. 15,660. **Indexed:** Cyb.Abstr.
Description: For technical and commercial management in industry, trade and service companies.

621   GW   ISSN 0040-1439
CODEN: TEMIAH
TECHNISCHE MITTEILUNGEN. 1907. 4/yr. DM.140. (Haus der Technik e.V., Essen) Vulkan-Verlag GmbH, Postfach 103962, 45039 Essen, Germany. TEL 0201-82002-0. FAX 0201-82002-40. Ed. E. Steinmetz. adv.; bk.rev.; charts; illus.; pat.; index. circ. 7,000. (also avail. in microform from PMC) **Indexed:** Chem.Abstr., Eng.Ind., Excerp.Med., Geo.Abstr., Met.Abstr., World Alum.Abstr. **Document type:** trade publication.
—BLDSC (8750.500000); SWETS; CASDDS. CCC.
Description: Presents reviews of particular technical and scientific subject areas.

TECHNISCHE MITTEILUNGEN KRUPP. see *TECHNOLOGY: COMPREHENSIVE WORKS*

ENGINEERING — MECHANICAL ENGINEERING

621 330 001.535   BE   ISSN 0771-4025
TECHNIVISIE/TECNOPOLE; zakenblad voor de industrie. (Text in Dutch and French) 1983. s-m. 1800 Fr. Technipress, 26 Albert Temmermanstraat, B-1731 Zellik, Belgium. TEL 021-466-06-55. FAX 021-466-09-20. TELEX 62862 B. Ed. Johan Carton. adv.; bk.rev. circ. 45,000. (tabloid format; back issues avail.)
Description: Covers all aspects of industrial engineering. Occasionally devotes an entire issue to a specific topic. Includes current updates on technological developments, and new product announcements.

TECNOLOGIA DELLA DEFORMAZIONE. see *MACHINERY*

621   CU
TECNOLOGIA MECANICA. 3/yr. $20 in S. America; N. America $32; elsewhere $36. Ediciones Cubanas, Obispo No. 527, Apdo. 605, Havana, Cuba.

TECNOLOGIE MECCANICHE; sistemi per produrre. see *METALLURGY*

621   IT
TECNORAMA MECCANICA. 12/yr. Pubblicita Edizioni Associate s.r.l., Via Simone d'Orsenigo 22, 20135 Milan, Italy. TEL 2-551-18-42. Ed. Ugo Carutti. circ. 10,000.

621   TU
TEKNIK VE UYGULAMA. (Text in Turkish) 1985. bi-m. Chamber of Mechanical Engineers, Sumer Sokak, 36-1-A Demirtepe, 06440 Ankara, Turkey. TEL 4-2313164. FAX 4-2313165. Ed. Ugur Dogan. adv. circ. 3,000.
Description: Provides a forum for translation of engineering papers and product specifications of interest to practicing engineers, students and other technical personnel.

TEORIYA MEKHANIZMOV I MASHIN. see *PHYSICS — Mechanics*

536.7 621.4   RU   ISSN 0040-3636
TJ4   CODEN: TPLOA5
TEPLOENERGETIKA. 1954. m. 42.60 Rub. Izdatel'stvo Energiya, Slyuzovaya nab., 10, Moscow Z-114, Russia. Ed. K.D. Lavrenenko. bk.rev.; bibl.; illus. circ. 9,800. **Indexed**: Chem.Abstr., Eng.Ind., ISMEC, Met.Abstr., Sci.Abstr., World Alum.Abstr.
—BLDSC (0179.000000); CASDDS. **CCC**.

621 519.2   NE
TEXTS ON COMPUTATIONAL MECHANICS. (Text in English) 1991. irreg., vol.5, 1991. price varies. Elsevier Science B.V., Books Division, P.O. Box 211, 1000 AE Amsterdam, Netherlands. TEL 31-20-5803911. FAX 31-20-5803705. TELEX 18582 ESPA NL. (Subscr. in U.S. and Canada to: Elsevier Science Inc., Box 882, Madison Sq. Sta., New York, NY 10159. TEL 212-989-5800) (back issues avail.) **Document type**: monographic series.
Refereed Serial

621   US   ISSN 0040-6015
CODEN: THENAD
THERMAL ENGINEERING. English translation of: Teploenergetika. 1964. m. $875 (foreign $904) (effective 1993). Interperiodica, Box 1831, Birmingham, AL 35201. TEL 800-633-4931. FAX 205-995-1588. Ed. P.R. Clarke. adv.; bk.rev.; charts; illus.; index. circ. 400. **Indexed**: Appl.Mech.Rev, ASCA, Chem.Eng.Abstr., Curr.Cont., Eng.Ind., Excerp.Med., Fluidex, Foul.Prev.Res.Dig., Fuel & Energy Abstr., Int.Aerosp.Abstr., Int.Build.Serv.Abstr., ISMEC, Met.Abstr., Sci.Abstr., T.C.E.A., World Alum.Abstr. **Document type**: academic/scholarly publication.
—BLDSC (0427.300000); EI; Faxon; UnCover; SWETS.

621   UK   ISSN 0263-8231
CODEN: TWASDE
THIN-WALLED STRUCTURES. 1983. 12/yr. (in 3 vols., 4 nos./vol.). £463($715) (effective 1994). Elsevier Science Ltd., Oxford Fulfilment Centre, P.O. Box 800, Kidlington, Oxford OX5 1DX, England. TEL 44-865-843000. FAX 44-865-843010. (Subscr. in U.S. and Canada to: Elsevier Science, 660 White Plains Rd., Tarrytown, NY 10591-5153. TEL 914-524-9200. FAX 914-333-2444) Eds. J. Rhodes, K.P. Chong. adv.; bk.rev.; abstr.; charts; illus. (also avail. in microform from UMI; back issues avail.) **Indexed**: Appl.Mech.Rev., ASCA, Curr.Cont., Eng.Ind., Int.Aerosp.Abstr., Int'l.Civil Eng.Abstr., Met.Abstr., Sci.Cit.Ind., World Alum.Abstr. **Document type**: academic/scholarly publication.
—BLDSC (8820.121000); EI; Faxon; UnCover; SWETS. **CCC**.
Description: Covers construction and material concerned with thin-walled structures.
Refereed Serial

621   JA   ISSN 0385-8561
TOKICO REVIEW. (Text in Japanese; summaries in English, Japanese) 1958. q. membership. Tokico Ltd., 5-6, Kudan Minami 1-chome, Chiyoda-ku, Tokyo 102, Japan.

TOKYO DENKI UNIVERSITY. FACULTY OF ENGINEERING. GENERAL EDUCATION. RESEARCH REPORTS. see *ENGINEERING*

TOKYO DENKI UNIVERSITY. FACULTY OF ENGINEERING. RESEARCH REPORTS/TOKYO DENKI DAIGAKU KOGAKUBU KENKYU HOKOKU. see *ENGINEERING*

621   JA
TORAIBOROJI KAIGI YOKOSHU/JAPANESE SOCIETY OF TRIBOLOGISTS. CONFERENCE PROCEEDINGS. (Text in Japanese) s-a. Nihon Toraiboroji Gakkai - Japanese Society of Tribologists, 5-8, Shiba Koen 3-chome, Minato-ku, Tokyo 105, Japan. **Document type**: proceedings.

621   JA   ISSN 0915-1168
TJ1075.A2   CODEN: TORAEO
TORAIBOROJISUTO/JAPANESE SOCIETY OF TRIBOLOGISTS. JOURNAL. English translation: Japanese Journal of Tribology (US ISSN 1045-7828) (Text in Japanese) 1956. m. $90 (effective till Mar. 1994). Japanese Society of Tribologists, Kikaishinko Kaikan, Rm. 407-2, 5-8 Shibakoen, 3-chome, Minato-ku, Tokyo 105, Japan. TEL 03-3434-1926. FAX 03-3434-3556. adv.; charts; illus. circ. 5,000. **Indexed**: Chem.Abstr., Curr.Cont., Fluidex, INIS Atomind., JTA. **Document type**: academic/scholarly publication.
—BLDSC (4809.519500); EI; UMI; CASDDS.
Formerly (until Jan. 1989): Japan Society of Lubrication Engineers. Journal (ISSN 0449-4156)
Description: Covers tribological research and development in Japan, including tribological surfaces, contact problems, fluid lubrication, and wear.

621   JA
TORISHIMA REBYU/TORISHIMA REVIEW. (Text in English, Japanese; summaries in English) 1987. a. Torishima Seisakujo - Torishima Pump Manufacturing Co., Ltd., 1-8, Miyada-cho 1-chome, Takatsuki-shi, Osaka 569, Japan.

621   JA   ISSN 0917-172X
TOYODA KOKI KOKAI GIHO/TOYODA KOKI TECHNICAL DISCLOSURE. (Text in Japanese) 1989. q. Toyoda Koki K.K. - Toyoda Machine Works, Ltd., Chiteki Zaisanbu, 1-1, Asahi-cho, Kariya-shi, Aichi-ken 448, Japan.

621   NE   ISSN 0923-5280
CODEN: TPENE5
TRANSPORT PROCESSES IN ENGINEERING. (Text in English) 1989. irreg., vol.6, 1994. price varies. Elsevier Science B.V., Books Division, P.O. Box 211, 1000 AE Amsterdam, Netherlands. TEL 31-20-5803911. FAX 31-20-5803705. TELEX 18582 ESPA NL. (Subscr. in U.S. and Canada to: Elsevier Science Inc., Box 882, Madison Sq. Sta., new York, NY 10159. TEL 212-989-5800) (back issues avail.) **Document type**: monographic series.
—BLDSC (9025.877000); CASDDS.
Refereed Serial

TRANSPORTATION SYSTEMS. see *TRANSPORTATION*

621   IT
TRASMISSIONI DI POTENZA; guida italiana dei fornitori. 1960. a. L.40000 (foreign L.70000). Tecniche Nuove s.p.a. Via Menotti 14, 20129 Milan, Italy. TEL 02-75701. circ. 6,000.
Description: Offers a general view of the industries operating in the fields of oleohydraulic-pneumatic equipment and mechanical propeller gears.

621   YU
TRIBOLOGIJA U INDUSTRIJI. (Text in Serbo-Croatian; summaries in English and Russian) 1979. q. $34. Masinski Fakultet - Kragujevac, Sestre Janjic 6, 34000 Kragujevac, Yugoslavia. TEL 034 67-500. Ed. Branko Ivkovic. adv.; bk.rev.; abstr.; bibl.; charts; illus. circ. 500.

621.89   UK   ISSN 0301-679X
TJ1075.A2   CODEN: TRBIBK
TRIBOLOGY INTERNATIONAL; the practice & technology of lubrication, wear prevention & friction control. 1968. bi-m. £180 in UK and Europe; elsewhere $195. Butterworth - Heinemann (Subsidiary of: Reed International PLC), Linacre House, Jordan Hill, Oxford OX2 8DP, England. TEL 0865-310366. FAX 0865-310898. TELEX 83111 BHPOXF G. (Subscr. to: Turpin Transactions Ltd., Distribution Centre, Blackhorse Rd., Letchworth, Herts SG6 1HN, England. TEL 0462-672555) Ed. Marija Vukovojac. adv.; bk.rev.; abstr.; bibl.; charts; illus.; stat.; index. (also avail. in microform from UMI; back issues avail.) **Indexed**: Agri.Eng.Abstr., API Abstr., API Catal., API Hlth.& Environ., API Oil., API Pet.Ref., API Pet.Subst., API Transport., Appl.Mech.Rev., ASCA, B.C.I.R.A., BMT, Br.Rail.Bd., Br.Tech.Ind., C.I.S. Abstr., Chem.Abstr., Curr.Cont., Eng.Mat.Abstr., Excerp.Med., Fluidex, ISMEC, Met.Abstr., PROMT, Sci.Abstr., Sh.& Vib.Dig., World Alum.Abstr. **Document type**: academic/scholarly publication.
—BLDSC (9050.217300); EI; Faxon; UnCover; SWETS; UMI; CASDDS. **CCC**.
Formerly: Tribology (ISSN 0041-2678)
Refereed Serial

621.89 531.43   NE   ISSN 0167-8922
CODEN: TRISDJ
TRIBOLOGY SERIES. (Text in English) 1978. irreg., vol.26, 1993. Elsevier Science B.V., Books Division, P.O. Box 211, 1000 AE Amsterdam, Netherlands. TEL 31-20-5803911. FAX 31-20-5803705. TELEX 18582 ESPA NL. (Subscr. in U.S. and Canada to: Elsevier Science Inc., Box 882, Madison Sq. Sta., New York, NY 10159. TEL 212-989-5800) charts. (back issues avail.) **Indexed**: Chem.Abstr. **Document type**: monographic series.
—BLDSC (9050.217800); CASDDS. **CCC**.
Refereed Serial

TRUCK AND BUS BUILDER; the international newsletter of commercial vehicle manufacturing, developments. see *TRANSPORTATION — Trucks And Trucking*

621   JA
TSUBAKI TECHNICAL REVIEW. (Text in English, Japanese) 1991. a. Tsubakimoto Chain Co., 17-96, Tsurumi 4-chome, Tsurumi-ku, Osaka-shi, Osaka 538, Japan.

621.433   US   ISSN 0149-4147
TJ266   CODEN: TUINDP
TURBOMACHINERY INTERNATIONAL; covering the selection, operation, maintenance and overhaul of rotating equipment 1959. 7/yr. $49. Turbomachinery International Publications (Subsidiary of: Business Journals, Inc.), Box 5550, Norwalk, CT 06856. TEL 203-853-6015. FAX 203-852-8175. TELEX 353706 BUSJOURNORWK. Ed. Rena D. Hines. adv.; charts; illus.; stat.; tr.lit.; index. circ. 11,000. (also avail. in microform from UMI; reprint service avail. from UMI) **Indexed**: Fluidex, Gas Abstr., ISMEC, Sh.& Vib.Dig. **Document type**: trade publication.
—BLDSC (9071.832000); EI; UnCover; SWETS; UMI.
Former titles (until 1977): Sawyer's Gas Turbine International (ISSN 0163-7134); (until 1976): Gas Turbine International (ISSN 0435-1312); Gas Turbine Magazine (ISSN 0016-500X)
Description: For key management and engineering personnel in turbomachinery-using industries. Keeps readers informed of all developments in the field.
Refereed Serial

ENGINEERING — MECHANICAL ENGINEERING

621.4 US ISSN 0748-0903
TJ266
TURBOMACHINERY INTERNATIONAL HANDBOOK. 1963. a. $50. Turbomachinery International Publications (Subsidiary of: Business Journals, Inc.), Box 5550, Norwalk, CT 06856. TEL 203-853-6015. FAX 203-852-8175. Ed. Rena Hines. adv. (reprint service avail. from UMI) **Document type:** trade publication.
Former titles: Turbomachinery Catalog and Workbook; Sawyer's Gas Turbine Catalog; Gas Turbine Catalog (ISSN 0072-0267)

TYAZHELOE MASHINOSTROENIE. see *MACHINERY*

621.9 US
U S MACHINE TOOL DIRECTORY. a. free. N M T B A - Association for Manufacturing Technology, 7901 Westpark Dr., McLean, VA 22102. TEL 703-893-2900. FAX 703-827-5263. circ. 30,000. **Document type:** directory.
Formerly: Directory of Machine Tools and Related Products (ISSN 0070-5772)

621 GW ISSN 0342-8834
TJ212 CODEN: UONSDY
UND-ODER-NOR UND STEUERUNGSTECHNIK. 1970. m. DM.44 (foreign DM.52). Vereinigte Fachverlage GmbH, Lise-Meitner-Str. 2, 55129 Mainz, Germany. TEL 06131-992-01. FAX 06131-992-100. TELEX 04187752. (Subscr. to: Postfach 2760, 55017 Mainz, Germany) adv.; bk.rev.; illus. circ. 17,000. **Indexed:** Sci.Abstr.
Formed by 1974 merger of: Steuerungstechnik (ISSN 0039-131X); Und-oder-nor (ISSN 0342-8931)

UNIVERSITAET STUTTGART. INSTITUT FUER STEUERUNGSTECHNIK DER WERKZEUGMASCHINEN UND FERTIGUNGSEINRICHTUNGEN. I S W BERICHTE. see *MACHINERY*

621 627 380.5 RM ISSN 1220-3041
TA349
UNIVERSITATEA POLITEHNICA BUCURESTI. BULETIN STIINTIFIC. INGINERIE MECANICA/POLYTECHNICAL UNIVERSITY OF BUCHAREST. SCIENTIFIC BULLETIN. MECHANICAL ENGINEERING. (Text in English, French, or German) 1929. 4/yr. $195. Universitatea Politehnica Bucuresti, Splaiul Independentei 313, 77206 Bucharest 16, Rumania. FAX 401-312-01-88. TELEX IPOLB R 10252. bk.rev.; abstr.; bibl.; charts. circ. 1,300. **Indexed:** Appl.Mech.Rev., B.C.I.R.A., Chem.Abstr., Eng.Ind., INIS Atomind., Math.R., Sci.Abstr. **Document type:** academic/scholarly publication, bulletin.
—BLDSC (8177.824000); EI.
Formerly: Institutul Politehnic Bucuresti. Buletin Stiintific. Inginerie Mecanica; Formed by the 1990 merger of: Institutul Politehnic Bucuresti. Buletin. Seria Mecanica (ISSN 1012-3199) & Institutul Politehnic Bucuresti. Buletin. Seria Constructii de Masini (ISSN 1012-3237) & Institutul Politehnic Bucuresti. Buletin. Seria Transporturi - Aeronave (ISSN 1220-0301); Seria Mecanica was formerly (until 1983): Institutul Politehnic Gheorghe Gheorghiu-Dej Bucuresti. Buletin. Seria Mecanica (ISSN 1010-9463) and Seria Constructii de Masini was formerly (until 1983): Institutul Politehnic Gheorghe Gheorghiu-Dej Bucuresti. Buletin. Seria Constructii de Masini (ISSN 0256-4572) and Seria Transporturi-Aeronave was formerly: Institutul Politehnic Gheorghe Gheorghiu-Dej Bucuresti. Seria Transporturi-Aeronave (ISSN 0256-7946); All three superseded in part (in 1982): Institutul Politehnic Gheorghe Gheorghiu-Dej Bucuresti. Buletin. Seria Mecanica, Constructii de Masini, TraAeronave (ISSN 1010-9455); Which had former titles (until 1982): Institutul Politehnic Gheorghe Gheorghiu-Dej Bucuresti. Buletin. Seria Mecanica (ISSN 0378-9632); (until 1976): Institutul Politehnic Gheorghe Gheorghiu-Dej Bucuresti. Buletin (ISSN 0366-0419); (until 1965): Institutul Politehnic Bucuresti. Buletin (ISSN 0020-4242).

621.8 RM ISSN 1220-9465
UNIVERSITATEA TRANSILVANIA DIN BRASOV. BULETINUL. SERIA A. MECANICA APLICATA. ELECTROTEHNICA SI ELECTRONICA. CONSTRUCTIA DE MASINI SI TEHNOLOGIA PRELUCRARII METALELOR/TRANSYLVANIA UNIVERSITY OF BRASOV. BULLETIN. SERIES A. MECHANICAL ENGINEERING. ELECTRICAL AND ELECTRONIC ENGINEERING. (Text in English, French, German) 1956. a. price varies. Universitatea Transilvania din Brasov - Transylvania University of Brasov, Bd. Eroilot, Nr. 29, 2200 Brasov, Rumania. bibl.; illus. **Indexed:** Sci.Abstr.
Formerly: Universitatea din Brasov. Buletinul. Seria A. Mecanica Aplicata. Constructii de Masini. Electrotehnica.

621 SA
UNIVERSITY OF THE WITWATERSRAND, JOHANNESBURG. SCHOOL OF MECHANICAL ENGINEERING. RESEARCH REPORTS. 1957. irreg. free. University of the Witwatersrand, Johannesburg, School of Mechanical Engineering, Jan Smuts Ave., Johannesburg, South Africa. Eds. H.H. Jawurek, C.J. Rallis. circ. 250. (also avail. in microfiche)

621 CN ISSN 0082-5182
CODEN: TMEPAK
UNIVERSITY OF TORONTO. DEPARTMENT OF MECHANICAL ENGINEERING. TECHNICAL PUBLICATION SERIES. 1962. irreg. University of Toronto, Department of Mechanical Engineering, Toronto, Ont., Canada. TEL 613-978-7198. circ. 100.

V D I INFORMATIONSDIENST. DRAHTHERSTELLUNG UND DRAHTERZEUGNISSE. (Verein Deutscher Ingenieure) see *ENGINEERING — Abstracting, Bibliographies, Statistics*

621 GW ISSN 0720-9886
V D I INFORMATIONSDIENST. MECHANISCHE VERBINDUNGSTECHNIK. (Verein Deutscher Ingenieure) 1977. q. DM.270. (Fachinformations Zentrum Technik e.V.) V D I Verlag GmbH, Heinrichstr. 24, 40239 Duesseldorf, Germany. TEL 0211-6188-0. FAX 0211-6188-112. TELEX 8587743. (Subscr. to: Postfach 101054, 40001 Duesseldorf, Germany) Ed. G. Gentzsch. adv.; abstr.; bibl.; charts; illus. **Document type:** trade publication.

621 NE ISSN 0042-3114
TL243 CODEN: VSDYA4
VEHICLE SYSTEM DYNAMICS; international journal of vehicle mechanics and mobility. (Supplement avail.) (Text in English) 1972. 8/yr. $416 includes supplement (effective 1994). Swets & Zeitlinger bv, Heereweg 347, 2161 CA Lisse, Netherlands. TEL 31-2521-35111. FAX 31-2521-15888. TELEX 41325. (Dist. in N. America by: Swets & Zeitlinger, 440 Creamery Way, Ste. A, Exton, PA 19341. TEL 800-447-9387. FAX 610-524-5366) Eds. P. Lugner, J. Karl Hedrick. adv.; bk.rev.; bibl.; charts; illus.; index. circ. 1,000. (also avail. in microform from SWZ) **Indexed:** Agri.Eng.Abstr., Appl.Mech.Rev., Br.Rail.Bd., Curr.Cont., Fluidex, HRIS, ISMEC, Sci.Abstr., Sh.& Vib.Dig. **Document type:** academic/scholarly publication.
—BLDSC (9153.670000); EI; Faxon; UnCover; SWETS. CCC.

VEREIN DEUTSCHER INGENIEURE. INFORMATIONSDIENST. INSTANDHALTUNG. see *ENGINEERING — Abstracting, Bibliographies, Statistics*

621 SW ISSN 0283-4669
VERKO; annonsregistret. 1957. 11/yr. SEK 2800. Verko Maskinkontakt AB, Datavaegen 10, S-436 32 Askim, Sweden. FAX 031-680009. TELEX 21131. Ed. Bjoern Johansson. adv.; circ. 3,034 (paid); 4,466 (controlled). **Document type:** directory, consumer publication, trade publication.
Formerly (until 1983): Annonsregistret.

VERKSTAEDERNA. see *MACHINERY*

621.2 HU ISSN 0042-7616
GB726.H8 CODEN: VIKOA7
VIZUGYI KOZLEMENYEK. (Text in Hungarian: summaries in English, French, German, Russian) 1879. q. $36. Vizgazdalkodasi Tudomanyos Kutato Kozpont, Kvassay J.ut 1, 1095 Budapest, Hungary. (Subscr. to: Kultura, Box 149, H-1389 Budapest, Hungary) Ed. K. Stelczer. bk.rev.; charts; illus.; maps; index, cum.index: 1897-1980. circ. 2,300. **Indexed:** Appl.Mech.Rev., Chem.Abstr., Eng.Ind., Excerp.Med., Fluidex, GeoRef., Geotech.Abstr., Rice Abstr., Rural Recreat.Tour.Abstr., World Agri.Econ.& Rural Sociol.Abstr.

620.1 RU
VOPROSY INZHENERNOI GEOLOGII I GRUNTOVEDENIYA; proceedings of the seminar of the chair of the theory of elasticity under the guidance A.A. Ilushin. 1963. biennial. 4.20 Rub. Moskovskii Universitet, Kafedra Gruntovedeniya i Inzhenernoi Geologii, Ul. Gertsena 5-7, 103009 Moscow, Russia. Ed. P.U. Ogibalov. **Document type:** proceedings.

621.89 SZ ISSN 0043-1648
TA401 CODEN: WEARAH
WEAR; international journal on the science and technology of friction, lubrication and wear. (Text in English, French, German) 1958. 20/yr. (in 10 vols.; 2 nos./vol.). 3800 SFr.($2585) (effective 1994). Elsevier Science S.A., P.O. Box 564, CH-1001 Lausanne 1, Switzerland. TEL 41-21-3207381. FAX 41-21-3235444. TELEX 450620-ELSA-CH. (Subscr. in U.S. and Canada to: Elsevier Science Inc., Box 882, Madison Sq. Sta., New York, NY 10159. TEL 212-989-5800. FAX 212-633-3990) Ed. D. Dowson. adv.; bk.rev.; abstr.; illus.; index. (also avail. in microform from UMI) **Indexed:** Agri.Eng.Abstr., API Abstr., API Catal., API Hlth.& Environ., API Oil., API Pet.Ref., API Pet.Subst., API Transport., Appl.Mech.Rev., Br.Rail.Bd., Ceram.Abstr., Chem.Abstr., Copper Abstr., Curr.Cont., Eng.Ind., Excerp.Med., Fluidex, HRIS, INSPEC, Int.Aerosp.Abstr., ISMEC, Met.Abstr., Phys.Ber., RAPRA, Sci.Abstr., Sci.Cit.Ind., Sh.& Vib.Dig., World Alum.Abstr. **Document type:** academic/scholarly publication.
—BLDSC (9281.800000); EI; Faxon; UnCover; SWETS; CASDDS. **CCC.**
Description: International forum for multidisciplinary communications on topics such as: applications of fundamental wear phenomena in engineering, design and materials; wear control and prevention; lubricants and the mechanics of lubrciation; controlled wear by abrasion; and the physics and chemistry of related surface phenomena.
Refereed Serial

621 GW
WER BAUT MASCHINEN IN DEUTSCHLAND. English edition: Who Makes Machinery in Germany. French edition: Qui Construit des Machines en Allemagne. Spanish edition: Quien Construye Maquinas en Alemania. 1928. a. DM.45. (Verband Deutscher Maschinen und Anlagenbau e.V.) Verlag Hoppenstedt GmbH, Havelstr. 9, 64295 Darmstadt, Germany. TEL 06151-380-0. FAX 06151-380-360. adv. **Document type:** directory.
●Also available online. Vendor(s): Data-Star, FIZ Technik.
Former titles: Wer Baut Maschinen und Anlagen; Wer Baut Maschinen (ISSN 0083-9299)

WERKSTATT UND BETRIEB; Zeitschrift fuer Maschinenbau, Konstruktion und Fertigung. see *MACHINERY*

621.6 UK ISSN 0262-1762
TJ899 CODEN: WOPUD4
WORLD PUMPS. (Text in English, French, German) 1960. 10/yr. £98($150) (effective 1994). Elsevier Science Ltd., Oxford Fulfilment Centre, P.O. Box 800, Kidlington, Oxford OX5 1DX, England. TEL 44-865-843000. FAX 44-865-843010. (Subscr. in U.S. and Canada to: Elsevier Science, 660 White Plains Rd., Tarrytown, NY 10591-5153. TEL 914-524-9200. FAX 914-333-2444) Ed. Mark Purvis. adv.; bk.rev.; abstr.; bibl.; charts; illus.; stat.; index. circ. 5,000. **Indexed:** BMT, Br.Tech.Ind., Excerp.Med., Fluidex, Met.Abstr., W.R.C.Inf. **Document type:** trade publication.
—BLDSC (9358.500000); EI; SWETS. **CCC.**
Supersedes: Pumps - Pompes - Pumpen (ISSN 0033-426X); Pumping.
Description: Devoted to the selection, application, installation and maintenance of pumps and pumping machinery.

621   CC
XIAOXING NEIRANJI. (Text in Chinese) bi-m. Tianjin Neiranji Yanjiusuo - Tianjin Internal Combustion Institute, 92 Weijin Lu, Nankai Qu, Tianjin 300072, People's Republic of China. TEL 333707. Ed. Xu Rongda.

YANSHI LIXUE YU GONGCHENG XUEBAO/JOURNAL OF ROCK MECHANICS AND ENGINEERING. see PHYSICS — Mechanics

YRKESBIL. see TRANSPORTATION — Trucks And Trucking

YUATSU TO KUKIATSU/JAPAN HYDRAULICS AND PNEUMATICS SOCIETY. JOURNAL. see ENGINEERING — Hydraulic Engineering

YUKUATSU/FLUID POWER. see ENGINEERING — Hydraulic Engineering

YUKUATSU GEPPO/FLUID PNEUMATICS. see ENGINEERING — Hydraulic Engineering

YUKUATSU GIJUTSU/HYDRAULICS AND PNEUMATICS. see ENGINEERING — Hydraulic Engineering

YUKUATSU KOENKAI KOEN RONBUNSHU/JAPAN HYDRAULICS AND PNEUMATICS SOCIETY. PROCEEDINGS OF MEETING. see ENGINEERING — Hydraulic Engineering

Z W F - C I M. (Zeitschrift fuer Wirtschaftliche Fertigung und Automatisierung) see MACHINERY

621   PL   ISSN 0137-5474
ZAGADNIENIA EKSPLOATACJI MASZYN/EXPLOITATION PROBLEMS OF MACHINES. (Text in Polish; summaries in English, French, German, Russian) 1966. q. $30. (Polska Akademia Nauk, Komitet Budowy Maszyn) Wydawnictwo Naukowe P W N, Ul. Miodowa 10, 00-251 Warsaw, Poland. Ed. Stefan Ziemba. bibl. circ. 760. **Indexed:** Appl.Mech.Rev.

621   JA
ZAIRYO RIKIGAKU KOENKAI KOEN RONBUNSHU/CONFERENCE ON MATERIALS AND MECHANICS. PROCEEDINGS. (Text in English, Japanese; summaries in English) a. 7000 Yen. Nihon Kikai Gakkai - Japan Society of Mechanical Engineers, 4-9, Yoyogi 2-chome, Shibuya-ku, Tokyo 151, Japan. **Document type:** proceedings.

621   JA   ISSN 0916-6424
ZEKUSERU TEKKU REBYU/ZEXEL TECH REVIEW. (Text in Japanese) s-a. Zexel Corporation, 13-26, Yakyu-cho 3-chome, Higashimatsuyamashi, Saitama-ken 355, Japan.

ZHONGGUO DIANTI/CHINA ELEVATOR. see BUILDING AND CONSTRUCTION

ENTOMOLOGY

see Biology-Entomology

ENVIRONMENTAL STUDIES

see also Environmental Studies-Pollution; Environmental Studies-Toxicology and Environmental Safety; Environmental Studies-Waste Management; Biology; Conservation; Public Health and Safety; Water Resources

A A S H T O ENVIRONMENTAL BULLETIN. (American Association of State Highway and Transportation Officials) see TRANSPORTATION — Roads And Traffic

A E R O SUN TIMES. (Alternative Energy Resource Organization) see ENERGY

614.7   IT   ISSN 0391-7339
                 CODEN: AESIDB
A E S. (Ambiente e Sicurezza); rivista dell'antiquinamento. (Text in Italian; summaries in English) 1979. m. L.43000. E R I S S.p.A., Via E. Tellini 14, 20155 Milan, Italy. Ed. Stefano Meinardi. adv.; bk.rev.; pat.; index. **Indexed:** Chem.Abstr.
—CASDDS.

A F S E E E ACTIVIST; news for members, locally active in national forest issues. (Association of Forest Service Employees for Environmental Ethics) see FORESTS AND FORESTRY

A M S - RAPPORT. (Arkeologisk Museum i Stavanger) see ARCHAEOLOGY

A M S - SKRIFTER. (Arkeologisk Museum i Stavanger) see ARCHAEOLOGY

A M S - SMAATRYKK. (Arkeologisk Museum i Stavanger) see ARCHAEOLOGY

A M S - TILVEKST. see ARCHAEOLOGY

A M S - VARIA. (Arkeologisk Museum i Stavanger) see ARCHAEOLOGY

A R M OUTREACH. (Atmospheric Radiation Measurement) see METEOROLOGY

A S A E TRANSACTIONS. STRUCTURES & ENVIRONMENT. (American Society of Agricultural Engineers) see ENGINEERING — Civil Engineering

A S H E S ANNUAL CONFERENCE. PROCEEDINGS MANUAL. (American Society for Healthcare Environmental Services) see HOSPITALS

A S L O BULLETIN. (American Society of Limnology and Oceanography) see EARTH SCIENCES — Oceanography

A S P E. (Agenzia di Stampa sui Problemi dell'Emarginazione) see SOCIAL SERVICES AND WELFARE

613   US
ACCESS E P A. irreg. $24 in N. America; overseas $48. U.S. Environmental Protection Agency, Information Management and Service Division, 401 M St., S.W., Rm. 2003, 3404, Washington, DC 20460. (Subscr. to: National Technical Information Service, 5285 Port Royal Rd., Springfield, VA 22161. TEL 703-487-4650. FAX 703-321-8547) **Document type:** government publication, directory.
   Description: Aims at improving public access to EPA's environmental information, whether in printed records or online.

ACCESS TO ENERGY; pro-science, pro-technology, pro-free enterprise monthly newsletter. see ENERGY

614.7   SW   ISSN 0281-5087
ACID NEWS. (Supplement avail.) 1982. 4-5/yr. free. Swedish N G O Secretariat on Acid Rain, P.O. Box 245, S-401 24 Goteborg, Sweden. TEL 031-15-39-55. FAX 031-15-09-33. (Co-publisher: The Swedish Society for the Conservation of Nature) Ed. Christer Aagren. bk.rev. circ. 5,000. (also avail. in microfilm from HPL) **Indexed:** Energy Info.Abstr., Environ.Abstr. **Document type:** newsletter.
—BLDSC (0576.874000).
   Description: Presents information on the subjects of air pollution, acid rain and the acidification of the environment, climate change, energy and transport policies.

614.7   US   ISSN 0741-5230
                 CODEN: APREE
ACID PRECIPITATION; a current awareness bulletin. m. $145. U.S. Department of Energy, Office of Scientific and Technical Information, Box 62, Oak Ridge, TN 37831. TEL 615-574-0733. (Subscr. to: National Technical Information Service, 5285 Port Royal Rd., Springfield, VA 22161. TEL 703-487-4630. FAX 703-321-8547) Ed. T. Dennis Taylor. **Indexed:** Environ.Abstr. **Document type:** bulletin, government publication.
   Description: Presents acid-precipitation-related subjects, including wet and dry deposition, long-range transport, environmental effects, modeling, and socioeconomic effects.

614.7   US   ISSN 0894-623X
ACID RAIN RESOURCES DIRECTORY. 1982. irreg., latest 1988. $10. Acid Rain Foundation, Inc., 1410 Varsity Dr., Raleigh, NC 27606-2010. TEL 919-829-9443. **Document type:** directory.

614.7   IT   ISSN 0391-5557
                 CODEN: AQARDW
ACQUA ARIA. 1948. 10/yr. L.90000 (foreign L.215000). Editrice Arti Poligrafiche Europee, Via Casella 16, 20156 Milan, Italy. TEL 02-330221. FAX 02-39214341. adv.: B&W page L.2400000, color page L.3350000; trim 180 x 265. circ. 5,000 (controlled). **Indexed:** Art & Archaeol.Tech.Abstr., Biodet.Abstr., Chem.Abstr., Sugar Ind.Abstr.
—BLDSC (0578.708000); CASDDS.
   Supersedes (with no.6, 1977): Ecologia Acqua e Aria Suolo.

ACTA BOTANICA CROATICA. see BIOLOGY — Botany

614.7 634.96   US
ACTION ALERTS. m. $25 membership. Rainforest Action Network, 450 Sansome St., Ste. 700, San Francisco, CA 94111. TEL 415-398-4404. FAX 415-398-2732. TELEX 151276475. **Document type:** newsletter.
   Description: Focuses on environmental issues requiring immediate public action; includes addresses and advice to members.

ADBUSTERS QUARTERLY; journal of the mental environment. see COMMUNICATIONS — Television And Cable

613.1   US
▼**ADIRONDACK JOURNAL OF ENVIRONMENTAL STUDIES.** Short title: A J E S. 1994. s-a. $10. (Paul Smith's College) Chimera Press, AJES, SSHE Division, Paul Smith's College, Paul Smiths, NY 12970. TEL 518-327-6377. FAX 518-327-6369. Ed. Gary Chilson. bk.rev. (back issues avail.) **Document type:** academic/scholarly publication.
   Description: Promotes sustainable development within the region broadly defined by the Champlain-Adirondack Biosphere Reserve.

ADVANCES IN BIOCLIMATOLOGY. see METEOROLOGY

574.5   US   ISSN 0065-2504
QH540   CODEN: AELRAY
ADVANCES IN ECOLOGICAL RESEARCH. 1962. irreg., vol.25, 1993. Academic Press, Inc., 525 B St., Ste. 1900, San Diego, CA 92101-4495. TEL 619-231-0926. FAX 619-699-6715. (Subscr. to: Order Dept., 6277 Sea Harbor Dr., 4th Fl., Orlando, FL 32887. TEL 800-321-5068) Eds. A. MacFadyen, E.D. Ford. (reprint service avail. from ISI) **Indexed:** Bio-Contr.News & Inf., Biol.Abstr., Biol.& Agr.Ind., Curr.Adv.Ecol.Sci., Deep Sea Res.& Oceanogr.Abstr., Excerp.Med., Field Crop Abstr., Forest.Abstr., Forest Prod.Abstr., Herb.Abstr., Ind.Sci.Rev., Plant Breed.Abstr., Sci.Cit.Ind., Sel.Water Res.Abstr.
—BLDSC (0704.500000); Faxon; UnCover; CASDDS.
   Refereed Serial

ADVANCES IN ENVIRONMENTAL PSYCHOLOGY. see PSYCHOLOGY

600   US   ISSN 0141-8106
TD169   CODEN: AESEDX
ADVANCES IN ENVIRONMENTAL SCIENCE AND ENGINEERING. 1979. irreg., vol.5, 1986. price varies. Gordon & Breach Science Publishers, 820 Town Center Dr., Langhorne, PA 19047. TEL 215-750-2642. FAX 215-750-6343. (UK subscr. to: P.O. Box 90, Reading, Berkshire RG1 8JL, England. TEL 0734-560-080) Eds. J.R. Pfafflin, E.N. Ziegler. **Indexed:** Chem.Abstr. **Document type:** monographic series.
—BLDSC (0705.505000).
   Refereed Serial

614.7   US   ISSN 0065-2563
TD180   CODEN: AESTC9
ADVANCES IN ENVIRONMENTAL SCIENCE AND TECHNOLOGY. 1969. irreg., vol.25, 1992. price varies. Krieger Publishing Co., Box 9542, Melbourne, FL 32902. TEL 407-951-3671. Ed. Jerome O. Nriagu. **Indexed:** Biol.Abstr.
—BLDSC (0705.510000); Faxon; SWETS; CASDDS.
   Formerly: Advances in Environmental Sciences (ISSN 0095-4535)
   Refereed Serial

AEROSPACE TESTING SEMINAR. PROCEEDINGS. see AERONAUTICS AND SPACE FLIGHT

ENVIRONMENTAL STUDIES

301.31   SG   ISSN 1010-5522
QH194
AFRICAN ENVIRONMENT; environmental studies and regional planning bulletin. French edition: Environnement Africain (ISSN 0850-8518) (Text in English, French) 1975. q. $35 to individuals; to institutions $50. E N D A Publications, Box 3370, Dakar, Senegal. TEL 22-42-29. TELEX 456 ENDA TM SG. Ed. Gideon Pinsler Omolu. adv.; bk.rev. circ. 2,200. Indexed: Curr.Cont.Africa, Documentatieblad, Environ.Per.Bibl. (1989-), Geo.Abstr., Rural Recreat.Tour.Abstr., Soils & Fert., World Agri.Econ.& Rural Sociol.Abstr.
—BLDSC (0732.439000).
  Supersedes: Environment in Africa.
  Description: Addresses problems of environment and development in Africa.

301.31   SG   ISSN 0850-8526
AFRICAN ENVIRONMENT. OCCASIONAL PAPERS - ETUDES ET RECHERCHES; supplements to African Environment. (Text in English or French) 1976. 8/yr. $60 to individuals; institutions $85. E N D A Publications, Box 3370, Dakar, Senegal. TEL 22-42-29. TELEX 456 ENDA TM SG. Ed. Gideon Pinsler Omolu. circ. 15,000.
—BLDSC (0732.439500).
  Description: Case studies on environmental and development issues.

AGRICULTURAL RESEARCH DEPARTMENT. WINAND STARING CENTRE FOR INTEGRATED LAND, SOIL AND WATER RESEARCH. REPORTS. see AGRICULTURE — Crop Production And Soil

AGRICULTURE, ECOSYSTEMS AND ENVIRONMENT. see AGRICULTURE

AGRIFACK. see AGRICULTURE

614.71   US   ISSN 1047-3289
TD883   CODEN: JAWAEB
AIR & WASTE MANAGEMENT ASSOCIATION. JOURNAL. Cover title: Journal of the Air & Waste Management Association. 1951. m. $90 to nonprofit institutions; others $200 (includes the annual issue of Directory of Governmental Air Pollution Agencies). Air & Waste Management Association, Three Gateway Center, Four West, Pittsburgh, PA 15222.
TEL 412-232-3444. FAX 412-232-3450. (Subscr. to: Box 2861, Pittsburgh, PA 15230) Ed. Harold M. Englund. adv.; bk.rev.; abstr.; bibl.; charts; illus.; stat.; index. circ. 10,000. (also avail. in microform from UMI; reprint service avail. from UMI) Indexed: A.S.& T.Ind., Abstr.Bull.Inst.Pap.Chem., Acid Rain Ind., API Abstr., API Catal., API Hlth.& Environ., API Oil., API Pet.Ref., API Pet.Subst., API Transport., Biol.Abstr., C.I.S. Abstr., C.R.I. Abstr., Cadscan, Chem.Abstr., Chem.Eng.Abstr., Curr.Adv.Ecol.Sci., Curr.Cont., Deep Sea Res.& Oceanogr.Abstr., Energy Info.Abstr., Energy Rev., Eng.Ind., Environ.Abstr., Environ.Ind., Environ.Per.Bibl. (1972-), Excerpt.Med., Field Crop Abstr., Fluidex, Fuel & Energy Abstr., Gas.Abstr., Geo.Abstr., Herb.Abstr., Hort Abstr., HRIS, Ind.Hyg.Dig., Ind.Med., INIS Atomind., Intl.Civil Eng.Abstr., Lead Abstr., Noise Pollut.Publ.Abstr., Ocean.Abstr., Pollut.Abstr., Risk Abstr., Sci.Abstr., Sel.Water Res.Abstr., Soft.Abstr.Eng., Soils & Fert., T.C.E.A., Zincscan.
—CIS; EI; Faxon; UnCover; SWETS; UMI.
  Former titles: J A P C A (ISSN 0894-0630); Air Pollution Control Association. Journal (ISSN 0002-2470)
  Description: Articles on air pollution control and hazardous waste management.

628.4   US   ISSN 1052-6102
RA565.A2   CODEN: PAMEE5
AIR & WASTE MANAGEMENT ASSOCIATION. MEETING PROCEEDINGS. 1989. a. Air & Waste Management Association, Three Gateway Center, Four West, Pittsburgh, PA 15222. TEL 412-232-3444. FAX 412-232-3450. **Document type:** proceedings.
—CASDDS.

614.7   US
AIR POLLUTION MANAGEMENT. q. $975 includes monthly reports. McIlvanine Co., 2970 Maria Ave., Northbrook, IL 60062. TEL 708-272-0010. FAX 708-272-9673. Ed. Robert McIlvaine.
  Formerly: Gold Dust.
  Description: Provides market data, management advice and support for the world's air pollution control industry.

614.7   US
AIR QUALITY DATA FOR ARIZONA. 1972. a. Department of Health Services, Bureau of Air Quality Control, 1740 W. Adams St., Phoenix, AZ 85007. TEL 602-255-1142. Ed. James L. Guyton. illus.; circ. controlled.
  Former titles: Air Pollution Effects Surveillance Network Data Report (ISSN 0092-1009); Air Quality Monitoring Network Data.

614.7   US   ISSN 0002-2608
          CODEN: AWPREE
AIR - WATER POLLUTION REPORT; weekly report on environmental protection. 1963. w. $580 (effective Sep. 1992). Business Publishers, Inc., 951 Pershing Dr., Silver Spring, MD 20910-4464. TEL 301-587-6300. FAX 301-585-9075. Ed. David Goeller. bk.rev.; stat. (looseleaf format; also avail. in microform from UMI; reprint service avail. from UMI) **Document type:** newsletter.
●Also available online. Vendor(s): Data-Star, DIALOG Information Services, Inc., NewsNet (EV10).
—UMI. CCC.
  Incorporates: Air and Water News.
  Description: Reports on legislative and regulatory issues, policy trends, personalities, litigation, research and business news.

628 631   PL
▼**AKADEMIA ROLNICZA IM. HUGONA KOLLATAJA W KRAKOWIE. ZESZYTY NAUKOWE. SERIA: INZYNIERIA SRODOWISKA.** (Text in Polish; summaries in English) 1963. a. price varies. Akademia Rolnicza im. Hugona Kollataja w Krakowie, Al. 29 Listopada 46, 31-425 Krakow, Poland. TEL 48-12-119144. FAX 48-12-336245. TELEX 322469 PL. Ed. Zdzislaw Piskornik. circ. 120 (paid). **Document type:** academic/scholarly publication.
  Former titles: Akademia Rolnicza im. Hugona Kollataja w Krakowie. Zeszyty Naukowe. Seria: Melioracja (ISSN 0239-9318); (until 1979): Akademia Rolnicza w Krakowie. Zeszyty Naukowe. Melioracja (ISSN 0137-186X); (until 1973): Wyzsza Szkola Rolnicza w Krakowie. Zeszyty Naukowe. Melioracja (ISSN 0452-6686)
  Description: Covers environmental protection, agrometeorology, water amelioration, agricultural construction.

626.44   PL   ISSN 1230-4484
▼**AKADEMIA ROLNICZA WE WROCLAWIU. ZESZYTY NAUKOWE. INZYNIERIA SRODOWISKA.** (Subseries of: Akademia Rolnicza we Wroclawiu. Zeszyty Naukowe (ISSN 0867-7964)) (Text in Polish; summaries in English) 1992. irreg. Akademia Rolnicza We Wroclawiu, Ul. Norwida 25, 50-375 Wroclaw, Poland. FAX 22-96-76. (Subscr. to: Dzial Wydawnictw i Poligrafii Akademii Rolniczej, ul. Sopocka 23, 50-344 Wroclaw, Poland. TEL 21-12-77) circ. 250. **Document type:** academic/scholarly publication.

ALABAMA ENVIRONMENTAL COMPLIANCE UPDATE. see LAW

354   CN
HC117.A6
ALBERTA. DEPARTMENT OF ENVIRONMENTAL PROTECTION. ANNUAL REPORT. a. Department of Environmental Protection, 9820 106th St., Edmonton, AB T5K 2J6, Canada. TEL 403-422-2813.
  Formerly: Alberta. Department of the Environment. Annual Report (ISSN 0383-3739)
  Description: Description of programs and services of the department, account of expenditures.

333.7   CN   ISSN 0707-2783
ALBERTA. FISH AND WILDLIFE DIVISION. FISHERIES POLLUTION REPORT. 1978. irreg. Fisheries Management Branch, Fish and Wildlife Division, Main Fl., N. Tower, Petroleum Plaza 9945 108 St., Edmonton, AB T5K 2G6, Canada. bibl.; charts; illus.
  Formerly: Alberta. Fish and Wildlife Division. Pollution Report (ISSN 0707-2791)

341.762   NE   ISSN 0928-1894
▼**ALLIANCE ENVIRONMENTAL LAW NEWSLETTER.** (Text in English) 1993. 3/yr. fl.200($108) (effective 1994). Kluwer Law and Taxation Publishers (Subsidiary of: Wolters Kluwer N.V.), P.O. Box 23, 7400 GA Deventer, Netherlands.
TEL 31-5700-47261. FAX 31-5700-22244. (Dist. by: Libresso Distribution Centre, P.O. Box 23, 7400 GA Deventer, Netherlands. TEL 31-5700-33155. FAX 31-5700-33834; In N. America: Kluwer Law and Taxation Publishers, 675 Massachusetts Ave., Cambridge, MA 02139. TEL 617-354-0140. FAX 617-354-8595) Ed.Bd. **Document type:** newsletter.
  Description: Covers major recent environmental law developments in individual countries, EC environmental law, and other developments affecting industrial and corporate attorneys.

DAS ALTERNATIVE BRANCHENBUCH. see CONSERVATION

ALTERNATIVE ENERGY SOURCEBOOK. see ENERGY

ALTERNATIVE TRANSPORTATION NEWS. see TRANSPORTATION

614.7   CN   ISSN 0002-6638
HC79.E5
ALTERNATIVES; perspectives on society technology and environment. 1971. q. Can.$23.50 to individuals (foreign Can.$27.50); institutions Can.$47 (foreign Can.$55). University of Waterloo, Faculty of Environmental Studies, Waterloo, ON N2L 3G1, Canada. TEL 519-885-1211. FAX 519-746-0292. E-mail: ALTERNAT@WATERSRV1.UWATERLOO.CA. Ed. Robert Gibson. adv.: B&W page Can.$300; 9 3/4 x 7 5/16. bk.rev.; circ. 4,000 (paid). (also avail. in microfilm from MML,UMI; back issues avail.) Indexed: Abstr.Mil.Bibl., Alt.Press Ind., C.I.J.E., Can.Per.Ind., CMI, Ecol.Abstr., Energy Info.Abstr., Energy Rev., Environ.Abstr., Environ.Per.Bibl. (1981-), Fuel & Energy Abstr., Geo.Abstr., I D A, INIS Atomind., Ocean.Abstr., Pollut.Abstr. **Document type:** academic/scholarly publication.
—BLDSC (0803.680000); Faxon; UnCover; UMI.
  Description: Provides critical and informed analysis of environmental problems, related social issues and technological developments.
  Refereed Serial

620.85   IT
AMBIENTE (ROME); analisi e strumenti per il governo del territorio. 1989. m. (11/yr.) L.60000 (foreign L.80000). Ceep s.r.l. Editore, Via del Tritone, 46, 00187 Rome, Italy. TEL 06-6781713. Ed. Pietro Metalli.

614   IT   ISSN 0393-0521
AMBIENTE RISORSE SALUTE; scienza, tecnica e cultura per uno sviluppo di qualita. (Text in Italian; summaries in English) 1982. m. L.90000. Centro Studi "l'Uomo e l'Ambiente", Via delle Palme 13, 35137 Padova, Italy. TEL 049-8759622. FAX 049-8761945. Ed. Franco Spelzini. adv.: B&W page L.3100000, color page L.3700000; 210 x 297. bk.rev.; charts; stat. circ. 6,000. (back issues avail.) **Document type:** newsletter.
  Description: Environmental pollution, utilization of resources and development of new and clean technologies are considered with special reference to community medicine and law.

614.7 614.4   IT
AMBIENTE SALUTE TERRITORIO. 1986. q. L.50000($50) (effective 1993). Casa Editrice Idelson Liviana, Via A. de Gasperi 55, 80133 Naples, Italy. TEL 081-5524733. FAX 081-5518295. Ed. Eugenia Aloj.

ENVIRONMENTAL STUDIES

614.7   SW   ISSN 0044-7447
QH540   CODEN: AMBOCX
AMBIO; a journal of the human environment. (Text and summaries in English) 1972. 8/yr. SEK 350 to individuals ($61 in the Americas; elsewhere DM.95); institutions SEK 1140 ($170 in the Americas; elsewhere DM.308) (effective 1994). Royal Swedish Academy of Sciences, P.O. Box 50005, S-104 05 Stockholm. TEL 46-8-673-95-51.
FAX 46-8-166251. TELEX 17073 ROYACAD S. (Dist. in U.S. by: Allen Press, Inc., Box 1897, Lawrence, KS 66044-8897. TEL 913-843-1234) Ed. Elisabeth Kessler. bk.rev.; abstr.; bibl.; charts; illus. circ. 4,000. (also avail. in microform from MIM,UMI; back issues avail.; reprint service avail.) **Indexed:** Abstr.Hyg., Acid Pre.Dig., Acid Rain Abstr., Acid Rain Ind., AESIS, Agroforest.Abstr., ASSIA, Biodet.Abstr., Biol.Abstr., C.I.S. Abstr., Cadscan, Chem.Abstr., Curr.Cont., Deep Sea Res.& Oceanogr.Abstr., Energy Info.Abstr., Energy Rev., Eng.Ind., Environ.Abstr., Environ.Ind., Environ.Per.Bibl. (1982-), Excerp.Med. (until 1992), Food Sci.& Tech.Abstr., Forest.Abstr., Forest Prod.Abstr., Fut.Surv., Geo.Abstr., GeoRef., I D A, Ind.Sci.Rev., INIS Atomind., Irr.& Drain.Abstr., Key Word Ind.Wildl.Res., Lead Abstr., Mid.East: Abstr.& Ind., Ocean.Abstr., Pollut.Abstr., Rice Abstr., Risk Abstr., Rural Devel.Abstr., Sage Fam.Stud.Abstr., Sage Pub.Admin.Abstr., Sage Urb.Stud.Abstr., Sci.Cit.Ind., Sel.Water Res.Abstr., So.Pac.Per.Ind., Soils & Fert., Trop.Dis.Bull., VITIS, W.R.C.Inf., World Agri.Econ.& Rural Sociol.Abstr., Zincscan. **Document type:** academic/scholarly publication.
—BLDSC (0808.900000); CIS; Faxon; UnCover; SWETS; UMI; CASDDS. **CCC.**
   Description: International journal publishing original articles, reports and comments on developments and issues in environmental research, policy and related activities, including environmental management, sustainable technology and use of natural resources.
   Refereed Serial

AMENAGEMENT ET MONTAGNE. see *ARCHITECTURE*

614.7   US   ISSN 1051-2306
TD178.8.U5   CODEN: AELAEL
AMERICAN ENVIRONMENTAL LABORATORY. bi-m. International Scientific Communications, 30 Controls Dr., Shelton, CT 06484-6111. TEL 203-926-9300. FAX 203-926-9310. Ed. Brian Howard. circ. 37,054.

AMERICAN INSTITUTE OF HYDROLOGY. BULLETIN. see *WATER RESOURCES*

614.7 551.46   US   ISSN 0517-4856
AMERICAN SHORE AND BEACH PRESERVATION ASSOCIATION. NEWSLETTER. 1954. q. $40 to individuals (foreign $52); students $20 (foreign $32); institutions $200 (foreign $260) for 5 copies; includes subscr. to Shore & Beach. American Shore and Beach Preservation Association, 412 O'Brien Hall, University of California at Berkeley, Berkeley, CA 94720. TEL 510-642-6777.
FAX 510-642-9143. (Subscr. to: Business Office, 3000 Citrus Circle, Ste. 230, Walnut Creek, CA 94598) Ed. Gerald J. Giefer. circ. 1,200. **Indexed:** Environ.Abstr., Ocean.Abstr. **Document type:** newsletter.

AMERICAN UNIVERSITY STUDIES. SERIES 21. REGIONAL STUDIES. see *ETHNIC INTERESTS*

550   US   ISSN 0276-7201
S930
AMICUS JOURNAL. 1979. q. $10 to non-members; libraries $8. Natural Resources Defense Council Inc., 40 W. 20th St., New York, NY 10011.
TEL 212-727-2700. FAX 212-727-1773. Ed. Francesca Lyman. bk.rev.; illus.; index, cum.index. circ. 120,000. (also avail. in microform from UMI; back issues avail.; reprint service avail. from WSH) **Indexed:** Alt.Press Ind., C.L.I., Energy Rev., Environ.Abstr., Environ.Per.Bibl. (1986-), Leg.Per., P.A.I.S., Urb.Aff.Abstr.
—BLDSC (0858.920000); Faxon; UnCover; UMI.
   Formerly: Amicus (ISSN 0192-5776); Incorporates (in 1992): N R D C Newsline.
   Description: Contains news about the environment and NRDC activities.

AMOEBA. see *BIOLOGY*

ANNALES DES SCIENCES FORESTIERES. see *FORESTS AND FORESTRY*

ANNUAL BOOK OF A S T M STANDARDS. VOLUME 11.01. WATER (1). see *ENGINEERING — Engineering Mechanics And Materials*

614.7   US   ISSN 0272-9008
TD172
ANNUAL EDITIONS: ENVIRONMENT. 1979. a. $11.95. Dushkin Publishing Group, Inc., Sluice Dock, Guilford, CT 06437-9989. TEL 203-453-4351.
FAX 203-453-6000. Ed. John L. Allen; Pub. Lan Nielsen. illus. **Document type:** academic/scholarly publication.
   Formerly: Readings in Environment (ISSN 0196-4542)
   Refereed Serial

614   US   ISSN 1018-290X
ANNUAL REPORT ON THE ENVIRONMENT AND NATURAL RESOURCES. Spanish edition: Informe Anual sobre el Medio Ambiente y los Recursos Naturales (ISSN 1018-2918) a. Inter-American Development Bank, 1300 New York Ave., N.W., Washington, DC 20577. TEL 202-623-1000.

574.5   US   ISSN 0066-4162
QH540   CODEN: ARECBC
ANNUAL REVIEW OF ECOLOGY AND SYSTEMATICS. 1970. a. $47 (foreign $52) (effective Jan. 1994). Annual Reviews Inc., 4139 El Camino Way, Box 10139, Palo Alto, CA 94303-0139.
TEL 415-493-4400; 800-523-8635.
FAX 415-855-9815. TELEX 910-290-0275. Ed. Daphne Gail Fautin. adv. contact: Elizabeth Kao. bibl.; index, cum.index. (also avail. in microfilm from UMI; back issues avail., reprint service avail.) **Indexed:** Bio-Contr.News & Info., Biol.Abstr., Biol.& Agr.Ind., Chem.Abstr., Curr.Adv.Ecol.Sci., Curr.Cont., Deep Sea Res.& Oceanogr.Abstr., Field Crop Abstr., Forest.Abstr., Forest Prod.Abstr., Geo.Abstr., Helminthol.Abstr., Herb.Abstr., Ind.Sci.Rev., M.M.R.I., Plant Breed.Abstr., Rev.Appl.Entomol., Sel.Water Res.Abstr., So.Pac.Per.Ind., Soils & Fert. **Document type:** academic/scholarly publication.
—BLDSC (1522.400000); CIS; Faxon; UnCover; SWETS; UMI; CASDDS. **CCC.**
   Description: Original reviews of critical literature and current developments in ecology and systematics.

614.7 352.7 340   IT
ANNUARIO EUROPEO DELL'AMBIENTE. English edition: European Environmental Yearbook. 1984. biennial. L.150000 (English ed.: £60). (Istituto di Studi e Documentazione per il Territorio - Institute for Environmental Studies) Pirola Editore, Foro Bonaparte 12, 20121 Milan, Italy.
TEL 02-8693994. FAX 02-72002398. (Eng. ed. distr. by: Docter International U.K. Ltd., 5 Manfred Rd., London SW1S 2RS, England) (Co-sponsor: Commission of the European Communities (EEC)) Ed. Achille Cutrera. adv.; bk.rev.; bibl. circ. 4,500. (back issues avail.)

ANTARCTICA PROJECT. see *CONSERVATION*

ANTHROZOOS; a multidisciplinary journal on the interactions of people, animals, and nature. see *ANTHROPOLOGY*

628   SP   ISSN 1133-2875
▼**ANUARIO PROFESIONAL DEL MEDIO AMBIENTE.** 1992. a. 7500 ptas. (effective 1993). S.P.A., Pintor Rosales 36, 28008 Madrid, Spain.
TEL 34-1-541-6768. FAX 34-1-542-8309.
Document type: directory.
   Description: Lists corporations, institutions and universities in Spain.

ANZEIGER FUER SCHAEDLINGSKUNDE, PFLANZENSCHUTZ, UMWELTSCHUTZ. see *BIOLOGY — Entomology*

613.1 333.7   US
APPALACHIAN ALTERNATIVES. 1977. q. $4. Appalachia - Science in the Public Interest, Rt. 5, Box 423, Livingston, KY 40445-9506. TEL 606-453-2105.
FAX 606-453-3115. (Subscr. to: Box 298, Livingston, KY 40445) (looseleaf format; back issues avail.) **Document type:** newsletter.

APPLIED CATALYSIS B: ENVIRONMENTAL; an international journal devoted to catalytic science and its applications. see *ENGINEERING — Chemical Engineering*

APPLIED CLAY SCIENCE; an international journal on the application and technology of clays and clay minerals. see *EARTH SCIENCES — Geology*

APPLIED ENERGY. see *ENERGY*

614.7   US
AQUASPHERE. 1963. q. $2.50 to institutions only. New England Aquarium, Central Wharf, Boston, MA 02110. TEL 617-742-8830. Ed. Jean Roberts. bk.rev.; illus.; circ. 13,000 (controlled). **Indexed:** Deep Sea Res.& Oceanogr.Abstr., GeoRef.

614.7   UK   ISSN 0953-4466
QH541.5.W3
AQUATIC ENVIRONMENT PROTECTION; Analytical Methods. 1988. irreg. free. Ministry of Agriculture, Fisheries and Food, Directorate of Fisheries Research, Lowestoft, Suffolk NR33 OHT, England. TEL 0502-562244. **Document type:** government publication.
—BLDSC (1582.377000).

AQUATIC PLANT STUDIES. see *BIOLOGY — Botany*

ARCHIVES OF ENVIRONMENTAL HEALTH. see *MEDICAL SCIENCES*

614.7   PL   ISSN 0324-8461
TD169   CODEN: AOSRD6
ARCHIWUM OCHRONY SRODOWISKA. (Text in Polish; summaries in English and Russian) 1950. q. $40. Polska Akademia Nauk, Instytut Podstaw Inzynierii Srodowiska, Ul. M. Sklodowskiej-Curie 34, 41-800 Zabrze, Poland. TEL 48-32-716481.
FAX 48-32-717470. TELEX 036401. Ed. Stefan Godzik. circ. 600. **Indexed:** Biol.Abstr., Chem.Abstr. **Document type:** academic/scholarly publication.
—CASDDS.
   Description: Archives of environmental protection. Resources of the natural environment and problems of its protection.

ARGONNE NATIONAL LABORATORY. RESEARCH HIGHLIGHTS. see *ENGINEERING*

363.6   US
ARIZONA. COMMISSION ON THE ARIZONA ENVIRONMENT. ANNUAL REPORT. 1965. a. $10. Commission on the Arizona Environment, 1645 W. Jefferson, Ste. 416, Phoenix, AZ 85007.
TEL 602-542-2102. illus. circ. 1,000.
   Former titles: Arizona. Governor's Commission on Arizona Environment. Annual Report; Arizona. Governor's Commission on Arizona Environment. Biennial Report; Arizona. Governor's Commission on Arizona Environment. Annual Report (ISSN 0097-9953)

363.6   US
ARIZONA. COMMISSION ON THE ARIZONA ENVIRONMENT. PROCEEDINGS OF QUARTERLY CONFERENCES. 1972. q. Commission on the Arizona Environment, 1645 W. Jefferson, Ste. 416, Phoenix, AZ 85007. TEL 602-542-2102. **Document type:** proceedings.
   Formerly: Arizona. Governor's Commission on Arizona Environment. Proceedings of Annual Summer Conference.

ARIZONA ENVIRONMENTAL COMPLIANCE UPDATE. see *LAW*

ARIZONA RADIATION REVIEW. see *ENERGY — Nuclear Energy*

ARIZONA WILDLIFE VIEWS. see *CONSERVATION*

ENVIRONMENTAL STUDIES

614.7   US   ISSN 1068-2643
ASBESTOS & LEAD ABATEMENT REPORT; inspection, analysis, removal, maintenance, alternatives. 1987. 26/yr. $507. Business Publishers, Inc., 951 Pershing Dr., Silver Spring, MD 20910-4464. TEL 301-587-6300. FAX 301-587-1081. Ed. Liz Lohr. **Document type:** newsletter.
●Also available online. Vendor(s): Data-Star, DIALOG Information Services, Inc., Human Resources Information Network, NewsNet (EV27).
—CCC.
Former titles (until 1993): Asbestos Abatement Report (ISSN 0893-858X); (until 1991): Asbestos Control Report (ISSN 0893-4533)
Description: Covers areas of control techniques, worksite health and safety, new federal standards, medical research efforts, state and local regulations, waste disposal, insurance, documentation, financing, contract management, analysis technology, and certification rules.

ASBESTOS M D L 875 UPDATE. see *LAW*

628 333.7   PH   ISSN 0116-2993
CODEN: ASENEL
ASIAN ENVIRONMENT; journal of environmental science and technology for balanced development. (Text and summaries in English) 1978. q. $30 to libraries. Asian Environment Journals, P.O. Box 90 MCC, Makati, Philippines. TELEX 63199-ETPI-MO-PH-OUANTECH. (Co-sponsors: Pollution Control Association of Philippines; Philippine Society of Sanitary Engineers; Indonesian Society of Sanitary Engineers) Ed. E.A.R. Ouano. adv.; bk.rev.; index. circ. 2,000. (back issues avail.) **Indexed:** Ecol.Abstr., Environ.Per.Bibl. (1990-), Excerp.Med., HR Rep., I D A, Pollut.Abstr., W.R.C.Inf.
—BLDSC (1742.417180); CASDDS.

614.7 915 333.7   MY   ISSN 0127-7170
ASIAN-PACIFIC ENVIRONMENT; newsletter of the Asia Pacific people's environment network. (Text in English) 1982. q. M.16($30) Sahabat Alam Malaysia - Friends of the Earth Malaysia, 19 Kelawai Rd., 10250 Pulau Pinang, West Malaysia, Malaysia. TEL 6-04-376930. FAX 6-04-375705. Ed. Vasentha Sampasivam. bk.rev. circ. 2,500. (back issues avail.) **Indexed:** Alt.Press Ind. **Document type:** newsletter.

628.44 333.91   SI   ISSN 0218-4559
ASIAN WATER & SEWAGE; Asia's journal of environmental technology. 1984. bi-m. $140. Toucan Publications Pte Ltd., 322-C King George's Ave., Singapore 0820, Singapore. TEL 65-299-7121. FAX 65-299-7545. (Dist. in U.S. by: Rovert A. Baer Co., 62 Glasco Turnpike, Woodstock, NY 12498. TEL 914-679-5482) Ed. Kevin Chang. adv.: B&W page $1200, color page $1650; trim 210 x 297. circ. 6,842. **Indexed:** Fluidex, W.R.C.Inf. **Document type:** trade publication.
—BLDSC (1742.756920).
Description: Covers major events, issues and developments in water, sewage, waste management and environment conservation industries.

613.1   US   ISSN 1043-5972
QC912.3
THE ATMOSPHERE CRISIS. (Subseries of: S I R S Critical Issues (ISSN 0893-7605)) 1989. a. price varies; a. supplement $17. Social Issues Resources Series, Box 2348, Boca Raton, FL 33427-2348. TEL 407-994-0079; 800-232-7477. FAX 407-994-4704. (looseleaf format; also avail. in microfiche; back issues avail.)
Description: Reprints articles that examine tropical rain forest destruction and the impact of global warming and the destruction of the ozone layer.

ATMOSPHERIC ENVIRONMENT. see *ENVIRONMENTAL STUDIES — Pollution*

333.7   US   ISSN 0898-915X
AUDUBON ACTIVIST. 9/yr. membership only. National Audubon Society, 700 Broadway, New York, NY 10003. TEL 212-979-3094. FAX 212-353-0190. Ed. Fred Baumgarten. illus. circ. 20,000.
Former titles (until 1986): Audubon Action (ISSN 0738-2111); N A S News Journal.
Description: Describes society activities and environmental issues throughout the country.

614.7   PL
AURA. 1973. m. $30.50. Wydawnictwo Czasopism i Ksiazek Technicznych SIGMA - NOT, Ul. Ratuszowa 11, P.O. Box 1004, 00-950 Warsaw, Poland. TEL 48-22-180918. FAX 48-22-192187. TELEX 814550 SIGMA PL. (Dist. by: SIGMA NOT Ltd., Ul. Bartycka 20, 00-716 Warsaw, Poland) circ. 14,000.
Description: Deals with problems of the preservation of man's environment.

AUSTRALASIAN SCIENCE MAGAZINE. see *SCIENCES: COMPREHENSIVE WORKS*

153   AT   ISSN 0726-6987
AUSTRALIAN WASTE DISPOSAL CATALOGUE. 1979. a. Aus.$10. Editorial and Publishing Consultants Pty. Ltd., 29 First Ave., Klemzig, S.A. 5087, Australia. TEL 08-26158377. FAX 08-261-2697. Ed. Frank H. Schmidt. adv. circ. 2,500. **Document type:** catalog.
—BLDSC (1824.160000).
Description: Lists equipment, machinery, products and services under seven categories in solid and liquid waste management.

B A N NEWSLETTER. (Blacks Against Nukes) see *ENERGY — Nuclear Energy*

614.7   GW
B B U INFO-DIENST; Meldungen und Meinungen aus der Umwelt- und Friedensbewegung. 1987. bi-m. DM.25. Bundesverband Buergerinitiativen Umweltschutz, Prinz-Albert-Str. 43, 53113 Bonn, Germany. TEL 0228-214032. FAX 0228-214033. **Document type:** bulletin.

613.   US
▼**B N A CALIFORNIA - ENVIRONMENT REPORT REFERENCE FILE.** 1992. w. $1319. The Bureau of National Affairs, Inc., 1231 25th St., N.W., Washington, DC 20037. TEL 202-452-4200. FAX 202-822-8092. TELEX 285656 BNAI WSH. (Subscr. to: 9435 Key West Ave., Rockville, MD 20850. TEL 800-372-1033) Ed. Glenn Totten. index. (looseleaf format; back issues avail.)

614.7 340   US   ISSN 1052-813X
KFC610.A15
B N A CALIFORNIA - ENVIRONMENT REPORTER. 1990. bi-w. $522. The Bureau of National Affairs, Inc. (Sacramento), 770 L St., Ste. 1100, Sacramento, CA 95814. TEL 202-452-4200. FAX 916-552-6503. TELEX 285656 BNAI WSH. (Subscr. to: 9435 Key West Ave., Rockville, MD 20850. TEL 800-372-1033) Ed. Glenn Totten. (back issues avail.)
—CCC.
Description: Notification service covering state, local and pertinent federal legislative, regulatory, legal and enforcement developments across all environmental areas: air pollution, hazardous waste, solid waste, and water pollution.

B N A'S ENVIRONMENTAL COMPLIANCE BULLETIN. see *LAW*

B N A'S ENVIRONMENTAL DUE DILIGENCE GUIDE. see *LAW*

613.1 614   US   ISSN 1065-8084
▼**B N A'S FEDERAL ENVIRONMENT & SAFETY REGULATORY MONITORING REPORT.** 1993. bi-w. $395 395. The Bureau of National Affairs, Inc., 1231 25th St., N.W., Washington, DC 20037. TEL 202-452-4200. FAX 202-822-8092. TELEX 285656 BNAI WSH. (Subscr. to: 9435 Key West Ave., Rockville, MD 20850. TEL 800-372-1033) Ed. Susan Korn. (back issues avail.)
—CCC.
Description: Summarizes all regulatory activities from EPA and OSHA, as well as DOT hazardous materials transportation issues.

B N A'S NEW JERSEY ENVIRONMENTAL COMPLIANCE BULLETIN. see *LAW*

613.1 614   US   ISSN 1065-8076
▼**B N A'S STATE ENVIRONMENT & SAFETY REGULATORY MONITORING REPORT.** 1993. bi-w. $895. The Bureau of National Affairs, Inc., 1231 25th St., N.W., Washington, DC 20850. TEL 202-452-4200. FAX 202-822-8092. TELEX 285656 BNAI WSH. (Subscr. to: 9435 Key West Ave., Rockville, MD 20850. TEL 800-372-1033) Ed. Susan Korn. (back issues avail.)
—CCC.
Description: Covers regulatory developments for all 50 states and the District of Columbia.

B N A'S TEXAS ENVIRONMENTAL COMPLIANCE BULLETIN. see *LAW*

614.7   US
B P I NEWSLETTER.* 1974. q. $35. Business and Professional People for the Public Interest, 17 E. Monroe St., Ste. 212, Chicago, IL 60603-5609. TEL 312-641-5570. Ed.Bd. bibl.; illus. circ. 2,00.

BAD HAIRCUT. see *POLITICAL SCIENCE*

614.7   BG
BANGLADESH ENVIRONMENTAL NEWSLETTER. 1990. 4/yr. $20. Bangladesh Centre for Advanced Studies, 620 Road 10A, Dhanmondi, G.P.O. Box 3971, Dhaka 1205, Bangladesh. TEL 880-2-815829. FAX 880-2-863379. Ed. Saleemul Huq. bk.rev. **Document type:** academic/scholarly publication.
Description: Discusses all aspects of environmental issues.

BASIC LEGAL DOCUMENTS ON REGIONAL ENVIRONMENTAL COOPERATION. see *LAW — International Law*

BATIMENT - ENTRETIEN. see *OCCUPATIONAL HEALTH AND SAFETY*

BEAR NEWS. see *CONSERVATION*

613.1 333.7   US
THE BEAVER DEFENDERS; they shall never be trapped anymore. 1970. q. $10 membership. Unexpected Wildlife Refuge, Box 765, Newfield, NJ 08344. TEL 609-697-3541. Ed. Hope S. Buyukmichi. bk.rev. circ. 200. (back issues avail.) **Document type:** newsletter.
Description: Examines the natural history of beavers, the happenings at the wildlife refuge, solving beaver problems, and humane education.

363 159   GW   ISSN 0340-5443
QL750   CODEN: BESOD6
BEHAVIORAL ECOLOGY AND SOCIOBIOLOGY. 1976. 12/yr. (in 2 vols., 6 nos./vol.). DM.1624($1015) Springer-Verlag, Heidelberger Platz 3, 14197 Berlin, Germany. TEL 030-8207-1. FAX 030-8214091. (Subscr. in N. America to: Springer-Verlag New York, Inc., 44 Hartz Way, Secaucus, NJ 07096-2491. TEL 201-348-4033. FAX 201-348-4505) Ed. K. Eduard Linsenmair. (also avail. in microform from UMI; reprint service avail. from ISI) **Indexed:** Biol.Abstr., Curr.Adv.Ecol.Sci., Curr.Cont., Deep Sea Res.& Oceanogr.Abstr., Environ.Per.Bibl. (1985-), Helminthol.Abstr., Ind.Sci.Rev., Psychol.Abstr., Sci.Cit.Ind., Soils & Fert., Weed Abstr. **Document type:** academic/scholarly publication.
—BLDSC (1877.400000); Faxon; UnCover; SWETS; UMI. CCC.
Description: Deals with quantitative, empirical and theoretical studies in the field of analysis of animal behavior.

614.7   CC
BEIFANG HUANJING/NORTHERN ENVIRONMENT. (Text in Chinese) q. Heilongjiang Sheng Huanjing Baohuju, Keji Chu, 72, Dazhi Jie, Nangang-qu, Harbin, Heilongjiang 150001, People's Republic of China. TEL 249273. Ed. Liu Hongnian.

614.7   GW   ISSN 0340-9716
BEITRAEGE ZUR UMWELTGESTALTUNG. REIHE A. 1971. irreg., no.134, 1993. price varies. Erich Schmidt Verlag GmbH & Co. (Berlin), Genthiner Str. 30G, 10785 Berlin, Germany. TEL 030-2500850. FAX 030-25008521. **Document type:** monographic series.

BEN-GURION UNIVERSITY OF THE NEGEV. INSTITUTES FOR APPLIED RESEARCH. SCIENTIFIC ACTIVITIES. see *AGRICULTURE*

THE BENCH SHEET. see *CHEMISTRY — Analytical Chemistry*

BERLINER NATURSCHUTZBLAETTER; Zeitschrift fuer Berlin und Brandenburg. see *BIOLOGY*

BERMUDA. BIOLOGICAL STATION FOR RESEARCH. SPECIAL PUBLICATIONS. see *EARTH SCIENCES — Oceanography*

BEZPIECZENSTWO JADROWE I OCHRONA RADIOLOGICZNA. see *PUBLIC HEALTH AND SAFETY*

BIO-NYT/BIO-NEWS; biologi, medicin, natur, miljoe. see *BIOLOGY*

ENVIRONMENTAL STUDIES 2403

BIODIVERSITY LETTERS. see *BIOLOGY*

BIOLOGISCHE ZEITSCHRIFT. see *BIOLOGY — Entomology*

BIOMASS & BIOENERGY. see *ENERGY*

613.1 199 GR ISSN 1012-2516
BIONEWS. 1987. q. membership. Biopolitics International Organisation, c/o Dr. Agni Vlavianos-Arvanitis, 10 Tim. Vassou, 115 21 Athens, Greece. TEL 30-1-64332419. FAX 30-1-6434093. **Document type:** academic/scholarly publication.
 Description: Summarizes the organization's international effort to introduce an ethically based environmental curriculum in schools and universities worldwide.

613.1 199 GR ISSN 1012-2532
BIOPOLITICS. (Text in English) 1988. a. Biopolitics International Organisation, c/o Dr. Agni Vlavianos-Arvanitis, 10 Tim. Vassou St., 115 21 Athens, Greece. TEL 30-1-6432419. FAX 30-1-6434093. circ. 1,000. (back issues avail.) **Document type:** academic/scholarly publication.
 Formerly: Biopolitics International Organization Report.
 Description: Contains essays from the International Conference on Biopolitics promoting international cooperation for the better understanding, protection, and enhancement of life.

613.1 199 GR
BIOPOLITICS - THE BIO ENVIRONMENT. SYMPOSIUM PROCEEDINGS. (Text in English and language of host country) 1985. a. price varies. Biopolitics International Organisation, c/o Dr. Agni Vlavianos-Arvanitis, 10 Tim. Vassou, 115 21 Athens, Greece. TEL 30-1-64332419. FAX 30-1-6434093. **Document type:** proceedings.
 Description: Summarizes the international effort to introduce ethically based environmental curricula in schools and universities.

628 US ISSN 1064-2455
BIOREMEDIATION REPORT. 1991. m. $395. King Communications Group, 627 National Press Bldg., Washington, DC 20045. TEL 202-638-4260. Ed. Mick Rood. **Document type:** newsletter.

614.7 333.7 IS
HABIOSPHERA. (Text in Hebrew) 1973. m. free. Ministry of the Environment, P.O. Box 6234, Jerusalem 91061, Israel. TEL 972-2-701606. FAX 972-2-513945. Ed. Yosef Hirschberg. circ. 2,500. **Document type:** government publication.
 Description: Covers national and international environmental news, environmental research and development, and environmental legislation.

BIOTRONICS; environment control and environmental biology. see *BIOLOGY — Biotechnology*

614.7 SP
BIZIA. 1990. 10/yr. 4500 ptas. Euskal Comunicacion, S.A., Blas de Otero, 37, Trasera (Ionja), 48014 Bilbao, Spain. TEL 4-447-84-14. FAX 4-476-11-87. Ed. Javier Bustamante. adv. circ. 12,000.

BLUE JAY NEWS. see *SCIENCES: COMPREHENSIVE WORKS*

BLUEPRINT (LONDON). see *BUSINESS AND ECONOMICS*

BOGONG. see *CONSERVATION*

BOHANNON'S NEW MEXICO ENVIRONMENTAL LAW HANDBOOK; a practical guide to New Mexico laws and regulations. see *LAW*

BOLETIN DE MEDIO AMBIENTE Y URBANIZACION. see *HOUSING AND URBAN PLANNING*

614.7 SA
BONTEBOK. (Text in Afrikaans and English) 1981. irreg. free. Cape Department of Nature and Environmental Conservation, Private Bag 9086, Cape Town 8000, South Africa. circ. 1,000. (back issues avail.)

614.7 US ISSN 0190-7034
K5 CODEN: BCERDX
BOSTON COLLEGE ENVIRONMENTAL AFFAIRS LAW REVIEW. 1971. q. $22. Boston College, School of Law, 885 Centre St., Newton, MA 02159. TEL 617-552-4354. Ed.Bd. adv.; bk.rev.; bibl.; charts. circ. 800. (back issues avail.; reprint service avail. from RRI) Indexed: Acid Rain Abstr., Acid Rain Ind., Biol.Abstr., C.C.L.P., C.L.I., Chem.Abstr., Deep Sea Res.& Oceanogr.Abstr., Energy Rev., Environ.Abstr., Environ.Per.Bibl. (1973-), Fut.Surv., Geo.Abstr., GeoRef., Hwy.Res.Abstr., L.R.I., Leg.Cont., Leg.Per., Mar.Aff.Bibl., Ocean.Abstr., P.A.I.S., Pollut.Abstr., Sel.Water Res.Abstr., Soc.Sci.Ind. **Document type:** academic/scholarly publication.
●Also available online.
—BLDSC (2251.811500); CIS; Faxon; UnCover; SWETS.
 Formerly (until vol.7, 1978): Environmental Affairs (ISSN 0046-2225)
 Description: Analysis of environmental issues from legal, political and scientific experts.

BOTSWANA. DEPARTMENT OF MINES. AIR POLLUTION CONTROL. ANNUAL REPORT. see *ENVIRONMENTAL STUDIES — Pollution*

BROADSIDES. see *CONSERVATION*

BULLETIN DE DROIT DE L'ENVIRONNEMENT. see *LAW*

614.7 330.9 US ISSN 1052-7206
BUSINESS AND THE ENVIRONMENT; twice-monthly global news and analysis. 1991. s-m. $397 to individuals (foreign $497); universities $197 (foreign $237). Cutter Information Corp., 37 Broadway, Arlington, MA 02174-5539. TEL 617-648-8700. FAX 617-648-8708. TELEX 650-100-9891 MCI UW. Ed. Kathleen M. Victory. (back issues avail.) **Document type:** newsletter.
●Also available online. Vendor(s): NewsNet (EV36).
—CCC.
 Description: Covers corporate initiatives to protect the environment. Includes product development, process redesign, packaging, business strategy, response to changing regulatory environment.

613.1 330 199 GR
▼**BUSINESS STRATEGY FOR THE BIO-ENVIRONMENT.** (Text mainly in Greek; occasionally in English) 1992. a. price varies. Biopolitics International Organisation, c/o Dr. Agni Vlavianos-Arvanitis, 10 Tim. Vassou, 114 21 Athens, Greece. TEL 30-1-6432419. FAX 30-1-6434093. **Document type:** proceedings.
 Description: Publishes papers given at symposia on applying an environmental ethic in the business world.

BYGD OCH NATUR; tidskrift foer hembygdsvaard. see *CONSERVATION*

C A L M SCIENCE. (Conservation and Land Management) see *CONSERVATION*

C D I A C COMMUNICATIONS. (Carbon Dioxide Information Analysis Center) see *METEOROLOGY*

614.7 BL
C E T E S B JORNAL. 1976. m. free. Companhia de Tecnologia de Sanemento Ambiental, Av. Professor Frederico Hermann Jr. 345, CEP 05459, Alto de Pinheiros-Sao Paulo, Brazil. illus.

628 UK ISSN 0268-4918
C H E C JOURNAL. 1973. irreg. (every 18-24 m.). £5($9) (includes C H E C Points (ISSN 0142-1972)). Commonwealth Human Ecology Council, 58 Stanhope Garden, London SW7 5RF, England. TEL 071-373-6761. FAX 071-244-7470. TELEX 8951182-GECOMS-G. Ed. Zena Daysh. bk.rev. circ. 2,000.
 Former titles: C H E C News (ISSN 0307-2827); C H E C Newsletter.

628 UK ISSN 0142-1972
C H E C POINTS. 1978. irreg. (2-3/yr.). free with C H E C Journal (ISSN 0268-4918). Commonwealth Human Ecology Council, 58 Stanhope Gardens, London SW7 5RF, England. TEL 071-373-6761. FAX 071-244-7470. TELEX 8951182-GECOMS-G.

628 665.5 614 BE
▼**C O N C A W E REVIEW.** 1992. 2/yr. free. C O N C A W E, Madouplein 1, 1030 Brussels, Belgium.
 Description: Contains news about CONCAWE, descriptions of its technical reports and introductory articles on topics such as sulfur dioxide emissions controls, oil pipeline integrity and prevention of major accidents.

301.31 US ISSN 0148-0324
HC107.C23
CALIFORNIA ENVIRONMENTAL DIRECTORY; a guide to organizations and resources. 1973. irreg., 5th ed., 1993. 40. California Institute of Public Affairs, Box 189040, Sacramento, CA 95818. TEL 916-442-CIPA. FAX 916-442-2478. (Affiliate: The Claremont Graduate School) Eds. Jennifer Caughman, Thaddeus C. Trzyna. illus.; index. circ. 1,000. **Document type:** directory.
 Formerly: California Environmental Yearbook and Directory (ISSN 0092-1343)
 Description: Descriptive directory of governmental, private organizations and academic programs in California concerned with environmental protection and management of natural resources.

320.85 340 US ISSN 1059-5414
KFC610.A15
CALIFORNIA ENVIRONMENTAL LAW AND REGULATION REPORTER. 1991. m. $290. Shepard's - McGraw-Hill, Inc., Box 35300, Colorado Springs, CO 80935-3530. TEL 719-488-3000. FAX 800-525-0053. Ed. Rafael Barnardino. index. (looseleaf format) **Document type:** newsletter.

620.85 340 US ISSN 1061-365X
CALIFORNIA ENVIRONMENTAL LAW REPORTER. 1991. s-m. $335. Matthew Bender & Co., Inc., 11 Penn Plaza, New York, NY 10001. TEL 212-967-7707. Ed. Bill Ryan. (looseleaf format; back issues avail.) **Document type:** newsletter.

614.7 US
CALIFORNIA REPORT. w. $425 (foreign $475). Inside Washington Publishers, Box 7167, Benjamin Franklin Sta., Washington, DC 20044. TEL 703-892-8500. FAX 703-685-2606. Ed. Laura Catalano. **Document type:** newsletter.

617.7 333.7 US ISSN 0739-8042
CALIFORNIA TODAY. 1972. bi-m. $33. Planning and Conservation League, 926 J St., Ste. 612, Sacramento, CA 95814-2707. TEL 916-444-8726. FAX 916-448-1789. Ed. Gerald Meral. circ. 9,000. **Document type:** newsletter.
 Description: Details the activities of the league.

614.7 333.7 551.46 US ISSN 8756-6354
QH91.A1
CALYPSO LOG. 6/yr. $20 individual membership; family $28. Cousteau Society, Inc., 870 Greenbrier Cir., Ste. 402, Chesapeake, VA 23320. FAX 804-523-2747. Ed. Mary Batten. circ. 260,000. Indexed: Biol.Dig., Environ.Abstr.
—UnCover.
 Description: Presents articles for members about Cousteau Society expeditions, ecology, conservation, oceans, and marine animals.

CANADA. AGRICULTURE CANADA. ANNUAL REPORT OF PRAIRIE FARM REHABILITATION ADMINISTRATION. see *AGRICULTURE — Crop Production And Soil*

614.7 CN ISSN 0711-1320
HC120.E5
CANADA. ENVIRONMENT CANADA. ANNUAL REPORT. (Text in English, French) a. free. Environment Canada, Ottawa, ON K1A 0H3, Canada. TEL 819-997-2800. FAX 819-953-2225. index. Indexed: Environ.Abstr.
 Description: Summarizes the activities undertaken throughout the year by the various sectors of the department.

614.7 631.4 CN
CANADA. ENVIRONMENT CANADA. ENVIRONMENTAL PROTECTION SERIES REPORTS. 1984. irreg. free. Environment Canada, E P Publications, Ottawa, ON K1A 0H3, Canada. FAX 819-953-9029. circ. 2,000. Indexed: Meteor.& Geoastrophys.Abstr.
 Description: Addresses developments in the effort to preserve the environment.

ENVIRONMENTAL STUDIES

338.9   CN
CANADIAN ARCTIC RESOURCES COMMITTEE. MEMBERS' UPDATE. 4/yr. Can.$30. Canadian Arctic Resources Committee, 1 Nicholas St., Ste. 412, Ottawa, ON K1N 7B7, Canada. TEL 613-236-7379. FAX 613-232-4665. illus.; circ. 3,500 (paid).

614.7   CN   ISSN 0318-0794
KE3575.A13
CANADIAN ENVIRONMENTAL CONTROL NEWSLETTER. m. Can.$390. C C H Canadian Ltd., 6 Garamond Ct., North York, ON M3C 1Z5, Canada. TEL 416-441-2992. FAX 416-444-9011. index. **Document type:** newsletter.
Description: Publication on pollution and the environment control measures designed to fight it.

613.1   CN   ISSN 1187-1202
CANADIAN ENVIRONMENTAL DIRECTORY. 1991. a. $215. Canadian Almanac & Directory Publishing Co., 55 St. Clair Ave. W., Ste. 225, Toronto, ON M5W 2J8, Canada. TEL 416-972-6645. FAX 416-972-6648. (Dist. in US by: Gale Research Inc., 835 Penobscot Bldg., Detroit, MI 48226. TEL 313-961-2242; Dist. in UK by: Wm. Snyder Publishing, 5 Five Mile Dr., Oxford OX2 8HT, England) Ed. Peter Asselstine. bibl. **Document type:** directory.
Description: Lists individuals, agencies, firms, and associations active in environment related activities in Canada.

CANADIAN ENVIRONMENTAL LAW. see *LAW*

614.7 340   CN   ISSN 0707-7874
KE3612
CANADIAN ENVIRONMENTAL LAW REPORTS. NEW SERIES. 1972; N.S. 1987. 3 vols./yr. Can.$118 per vol. (Canadian Institute for Environmental Law & Policy) Carswell, One Corporate Plaza, 2075 Kennedy Rd., Scarborough, ON M1T 3V4, Canada. TEL 416-609-8000. FAX 416-298-5094. Ed. Marcia A. Valiante. adv. contact: M. Lalani. bk.rev.; cum.index. **Indexed:** Environ.Abstr.
—CCC.
Formerly: Canadian Environmental Law News.
Description: Features all important environmental law decisions from all Canadian jurisdictions selected by experts in the field. Includes cases dealing with pollution control, radioactive waste, environmental protection legislation and procedure before environmental law tribunals.

614.7   CN   ISSN 0831-4020
CANADIAN ENVIRONMENTAL MEDIATION NEWSLETTER. 1986. 3/yr. Can.$15($15) to individuals; institutions Can.$30($30). Conflict Management Resources, c/o Osgoode Hall Law School, York University, 4700 Keele St., North York, ON M3J 1P3, Canada. Eds. Doreen C. Henley, D. Paul Emond. bk.rev. circ. 600. **Indexed:** Environ.Abstr. **Document type:** newsletter.

614.7   CN
CANADIAN ENVIRONMENTAL PROTECTION. 1989. 9/yr. Can.$35 (U.S. Can.$45). Baum Publications Ltd., 1625 Ingleton Ave., Burnaby, BC V5C 4L8, Canada. TEL 604-291-9900. FAX 604-291-1906. Ed. Dan Kennedy. adv.; tr.lit.; circ. 23,393 (controlled). (tabloid format; back issues avail.)

614.7 551.46   CN   ISSN 0706-6473
                           CODEN: CMRSDC
CANADIAN MANUSCRIPT REPORT OF FISHERIES AND AQUATIC SCIENCES. French edition (ISSN 0706-6589) 1925. irreg. price varies. Department of Fisheries and Oceans, 1202-200 Kent St., Ottawa, ON K1A 0E6, Canada. TEL 613-998-4931. (also avail. in microfilm from MML)
—CASDDS.
Incorporates: Canada. Marine Environmental Data Service. Manuscript Report Series.

CANADIAN SOCIETY OF ENVIRONMENTAL BIOLOGISTS NEWSLETTER. see *CONSERVATION*

CARBON DIOXIDE AND CLIMATE. see *METEOROLOGY*

CARDINAL. see *BIOLOGY — Ornithology*

CARNIVORE; interfacing biology, anthropology and environmental studies. see *BIOLOGY*

333.7   US   ISSN 0194-1445
TD172
CATALYST FOR ENVIRONMENT - ENERGY. 1970. irreg. $16 for 4 nos. Catalyst for Environment, Energy, 274 Madison Ave., New York, NY 10016. TEL 212-685-8310. Ed. Laura E. Freed. adv.; bk.rev.; illus. circ. 30,000. (also avail. in microform from UMI) **Indexed:** Ocean.Abstr., Pollut.Abstr.
Formerly (until vol.6, 1979): Catalyst for Environmental Quality (ISSN 0008-7688)
Refereed Serial

614.7   US
CENTER VIEW.* 1976. 5/yr. $25. Peninsula Conservation Center, 3921 E. Bayshore Rd., Palo Alto, CA 94303-4303. TEL 415-494-9301. FAX 415-494-1946. Ed. Debbie Mytels. adv.; bk.rev.; illus. circ. 1,400. **Document type:** newsletter.
Description: Articles on local environmental issues, Peninsula Conservation Center programs and lists of volunteer projects.

614.7 322.4   AT   ISSN 0312-1372
CHAIN REACTION. 1975. q. Aus.$15. Chain Reaction Co-operative Ltd., G.P.O. Box 90, Adelaide, S.A. 5001, Australia. FAX 61-8-293-8535. Ed.Bd. adv.; bk.rev.; charts. circ. 4,000. (back issues avail.) **Indexed:** Alt.Press Ind., GdIns.
Description: Reports on environmental and social justice issue.

CHALMERS UNIVERSITY OF TECHNOLOGY. DEPARTMENT OF SANITARY ENGINEERING. PUBLICATIONS; current reports on research in water supply and sewage disposal. see *WATER RESOURCES*

613.1   NE   ISSN 0925-5478
CHANGE. 1989. q. free. (National Research Programme on Global Air Pollution and Climate Change) Kluwer Academic Publishers, Postbus 17, 3300 AA Dordrecht, Netherlands. TEL 31-78-334911. FAX 31-78-334254. (Dist. by: Kluwer Academic Publishers Group, P.O. Box 322, 3300 AH Dordrecht, Netherlands. TEL 31-78-524400. FAX 31-78-524474; N. America dist. addr.: Box 358, Accord Sta., Hingham, MA 02018-0358) Ed. Job Dronkers. **Document type:** newsletter.

CHELMER WORKING PAPERS IN ENVIRONMENTAL PLANNING. see *SOCIAL SCIENCES: COMPREHENSIVE WORKS*

628   US   ISSN 0738-7776
                           CODEN: CHMCE7
CHEMECOLOGY; covering health, safety and the environment. 1967. m. free. Chemical Manufacturers Association, 2501 M St., N.W., Washington, DC 20037. TEL 202-887-1100. FAX 202-887-1237. Ed. Rebecca Swinehart. illus. circ. 66,000. (back issues avail.) **Indexed:** Biol.Dig., Energy Ind., Energy Info.Abstr., Environ.Abstr., Environ.Per.Bibl. (1990-), Ind.Hyg.Dig., Telegen.
—BLDSC (3133.495000).
Formerly (until 1972): Currents (ISSN 0011-4006)
Description: Articles on issues and concerns in contemporary environmental health and safety affecting the American public.

CHEMICAL & ENVIRONMENTAL RESEARCH. see *CHEMISTRY*

CHEMICAL INFORMATION ALERT. see *CHEMISTRY*

THE CHEMICAL PACKAGING REVIEW; the journal of hazardous materials regulation and distribution. see *PACKAGING*

540 350   US   ISSN 0148-7973
KF3958.A15   CODEN: CRERDD
CHEMICAL REGULATION REPORTER; a weekly review of activity affecting chemical users and manufacturers. (Subseries of: Chemical Regulation Reporter) 1977. w. (plus irreg. supplements). $1583. The Bureau of National Affairs, Inc., 1231 25th St., N.W., Washington, DC 20037. TEL 202-452-4200. FAX 202-822-8092. TELEX 285656 BNAI WSH. (Subscr. to: 9435 Key West Ave., Rockville, MD 20850. TEL 800-372-1033) Ed. Bill Bank. index. (looseleaf format; back issues avail.)
●Also available online. Vendor(s): Human Resources Information Network (File DD), Mead Data Central, Inc. (BNA-CHEM), West Services, Inc..
—BLDSC (3150.410000); CASDDS. **CCC.**
Description: Notification and reference service covering federal chemical regulation.

614.7   UK   ISSN 0954-2299
TD196.C45   CODEN: CHSBEY
CHEMICAL SPECIATION AND BIOAVAILABILITY. 1989. q. $140. Science and Technology Letters, P.O. Box 81, Northwood, Middlesex HA6 3AA, England. TEL 0923-823586. FAX 0923-825066. Ed.Bd. **Document type:** academic/scholarly publication.
—BLDSC (3151.573000); CASDDS. **CCC.**
Description: Presents papers in an interdisciplinary forum that explore the chemical, physical, biological and ecological effects of chemical species in the environment.

614.7   US   ISSN 0889-0633
KF3945.A59
CHEMICAL WASTE LITIGATION REPORTER. 1980. m. $1500. Computer Law Reporter, Inc., 1519 Connecticut Ave., N.W., Ste. 200, Washington, DC 20036. TEL 202-462-5755. FAX 202-328-2430. Ed. John Clewett. (looseleaf format; back issues avail.) **Document type:** newsletter.
Formerly (until 1985): Chemical and Radiation Waste Litigation Reporter (ISSN 0731-8839)

620.58   US
CHEMICALS IN PROGRESS BULLETIN. 1980. irreg. (2-4/yr.). free. U.S. Environmental Protection Agency, Office of Pollution Prevention and Toxics, Environmental Assistance Division (7408), 401 M St., S.W., Washington, DC 20460. TEL 202-554-1404. FAX 202-554-5603. (Avail. from: Superintendent of Documents, U.S. Government Printing Office, Box 371954, Pittsburgh, PA 15250-7954. TEL 202-783-3238. FAX 202-512-2233) Ed. Jane Gurin. circ. 13,000. **Document type:** government publication, bulletin.
Description: Informs the toxics community of the activities of the organization.

CHEMISTRY AND ECOLOGY. see *CHEMISTRY*

614.7   US   ISSN 0742-5066
QH104.5.C45
CHESAPEAKE BAY FOUNDATION. ANNUAL REPORT. a. Chesapeake Bay Foundation, 162 Prince George St., Annapolis, MD 21401. TEL 410-268-8816.
Formerly: Chesapeake Bay Journal.

614.7   US
CHESAPEAKE BAY FOUNDATION NEWS. 1976. q. $25. Chesapeake Bay Foundation, 162 Prince George St., Annapolis, MD 21401. TEL 301-268-8816. Ed. Flannery Davis. circ. 85,000. (looseleaf format)
Description: Articles and editorials on legislative policy, and ecological issues of interest to the public in the area.

CHEWONKI CHRONICLE. see *CONSERVATION*

CHIBA DAIGAKU RIGAKUBU KAIYO SEITAIKEI KENKYU SENTA NENPO/CHIBA UNIVERSITY. MARINE ECOSYSTEM RESEARCH CENTER. ANNUAL REPORT. see *EARTH SCIENCES — Oceanography*

CHILDREN'S ENVIRONMENTS; theory, research, policy and applications. see *PSYCHOLOGY*

CHILDREN'S WHALEWATCH. see *CHILDREN AND YOUTH — For*

628   CC
CHINA ENVIRONMENT NEWS. (Text in English) 1989. m. $24. China Environment News, Circulation Dept., 15A Xiaoxinglong Jie, Beijing 100062, People's Republic of China. (Co-sponsor: United Nations Environment Programme) **Document type:** newspaper.
Description: Contains information about Chinese policies, technologies and research for environmental protection in industry and agriculture.

614.7   CC   ISSN 1003-1189
CHINESE ENVIRONMENTAL SCIENCE. Chinese edition: Zhongguo Huanjing Kexue (ISSN 1000-6923) (Text in English) 1990. q. $32. Chinese Society for Environmental Sciences, No.115, Xizhimennei Nanxiaojie, Beijing 100035, People's Republic of China. TEL 6066498. FAX 6020031. circ. 500. **Document type:** academic/scholarly publication.
—BLDSC (3180.142200).
Refereed Serial

CHOCONUT FOUNDATION NEWSLETTER. see *SPORTS AND GAMES — Outdoor Life*

614.7 CC ISSN 1001-2141
CHONGQING HUANJING KEXUE/CHONGQING ENVIRONMENTAL SCIENCES. (Text in Chinese) 1979. bi-m. Y9. Chongqing Huanjing Kexue Xuehui - Chongqing Society of Environmental Sciences, 212 Renmin Lu, Chongqing, Sichuan 630015, People's Republic of China. TEL 54425. (Dist. outside China by: China National Publishing Industry Trading Corp., P.O. Box 782, Beijing, P.R. China) (Co-sponsor: Chongqing Bureau of Environmental Protection) Ed. Luo Xingtao. adv.; bk.rev.; circ. 5,000 (controlled). Document type: academic/scholarly publication.

CHRONMY PRZYRODE OJCZYSTA. see CONSERVATION

614.7 US
CITIZEN ALERT NEWSLETTER. 1976. q. $15. Citizen Alert, 3680 Grant Dr., Box 5339, Reno, NV 89513. TEL 702-827-4200. FAX 702-827-4299. Ed. Fielding M. McGehee III. adv.; bk.rev. circ. 12,500. (back issues avail.) Document type: newspaper.

614.7 917.4 US
CITY SIERRAN; newsletter of the New York City Group of the Sierra Club. q. $7.50. Sierra Club, 625 Broadway, 2nd Fl., New York, NY 10012. (Subscr. to: Sierra Club, Dept. H-112, PO Box 7959 San Francisco, CA 94120-7959) Ed. Henry Pita. adv. Document type: newsletter.
Description: Contains information about preserving the environment in New York City, news items, and calendar of events.

CIVIC TRUST AWARDS. see ARCHITECTURE

614.7 333.91 US ISSN 0747-2218
CLEARWATER NAVIGATOR. 1969. bi-m. $3. Hudson River Sloop Clearwater, Inc., 112 Market St., Poughkeepsie, NY 12601. TEL 914-454-7673. FAX 914-454-7953. Ed. John Mylod. bk.rev. circ. 11,100. (back issues avail.) Document type: newsletter.
Description: Chronicles activities of this environmental education organization which is dedicated to preservation and restoration of the Hudson River.

580 590 579 AT
CLEMATIS. 1962. a. Aus.$5 (typically set in Dec.). Bairnsdale Field Naturalists' Club, P.O. Box 563, Bairnsdale, Vic. 3875, Australia. Ed. Ronald S. Yeates. circ. controlled.

CLIMATE CHANGE DIGEST. see METEOROLOGY

COASTAL MANAGEMENT; an international journal of marine environment, resources, law and society. see EARTH SCIENCES — Oceanography

COASTWATCH. see EARTH SCIENCES — Oceanography

614 FR
CODE PERMANENT ENVIRONNEMENT ET NUISANCES. m. 1140 F. base vols. (m. updates 320 F.). Editions Legislatives et Administratives, 80, ave. de la Marne, 92546 Montrouge Cedex, France. TEL 1-40-92-68-68. FAX 1-46-56-00-15. TELEX 632 855 F. (looseleaf format)
Description: Focuses on the effects on the environment of commerce and industry, water, air and noise pollution.

614.7 US ISSN 0276-0231
COLORADO. DIVISION OF WILDLIFE. DIVISION REPORT. 1974. irreg., no.16, 1992. $2 per issue. Division of Wildlife, 317 W. Prospect, Ft. Collins, CO 80526. TEL 303-484-2836. Ed. Nancy W. McEwen. bibl.; charts; illus.; stat. circ. 1,200. (back issues avail.)

COLORADO ENVIRONMENTAL COMPLIANCE UPDATE. see LAW

COLORADO JOURNAL OF INTERNATIONAL ENVIRONMENTAL LAW AND POLICY. see LAW — International Law

COLUMBIA JOURNAL OF ENVIRONMENTAL LAW. see LAW

054.1 FR ISSN 0184-7473
COMBAT NATURE. 1966. q. 200 F. Edinat S.A.R.L., B.P. 3046, 24003 Perigueux Cedex, France. TEL 53-08-29-01. FAX 53-09-52-52. Ed. Alain de Swarte. adv.; bk.rev.; index. circ. 12,000. (back issues avail.) Indexed: Acid Pre.Dig.
Former titles (until 1971): Association Ecologiques et de Defense de 'Environnement. Revue; Maisons et Paysages - Nature et Environnement; Fermettes et Residences Secondaires (ISSN 0015-007X)

628 FR ISSN 0999-6249
COMITE FRANCAIS POUR L'ENVIRONNEMENT. LETTRE. Key Title: Lettre du C F E. (Supplement avail.: Cleaner Production) 1989. q. 500 F. Comite Francais pour l'Environnement, B.P. 43, 92204 Neuilly-sur-Seine Cedex, France.

614.7 531.64 AT
COMMONWEALTH SCIENTIFIC AND INDUSTRIAL RESEARCH ORGANIZATION. DIVISION OF COAL AND ENERGY TECHNOLOGY. ANNUAL REPORT. 1982. biennial. C.S.I.R.O., Division of Coal and Energy Technology, P.O. Box 136, North Ryde, N.S.W. 2113, Australia. FAX 02-887-8909. circ. 1,200. —BLDSC (7666.782000).
Formerly (until 1991): C S I R O Division of Coal Technology and Division of Fuel Technolgy. Annual Reports (ISSN 1033-2472); Supersedes (in 1987): Commonwealth Scientific and Industrial Research Organization. Division of Fossil Fuels. Report of Research (ISSN 0728-7615)

COMMUNITY EDUCATION INTERNATIONAL. see EDUCATION — Adult Education

350 001.3 US
COMMUNITY SPIRIT MAGAZINE (CARMEL). 1981. m. $18. (Monterey Peninsula Community Wellness Center) Community Spirit Publications, Box 4628, Carmel, CA 93921. TEL 408-625-1557. FAX 408-625-3424. Ed. Jonathan C. Drake; Pub. Stewart Long. adv.; bk.rev. circ. 65,000. (back issues avail.) Document type: consumer publication.

COMPACT. see MINES AND MINING INDUSTRY

COMPENDIUM NEWSLETTER; your guide to the world's environmental crisis. see CONSERVATION

614.7 US
COMPREHENSIVE ENVIRONMENTAL RESPONSE, COMPENSATION AND LIABILITY INFORMATION. q. $2880 for 6250 bpi in U.S., Canada, Mexico; elsewhere $1600. (Environmental Protection Agency) U.S. National Technical Information Service, 5825 Port Royal Rd., Springfield, VA 22161. TEL 703-487-4630. (magnetic tape)
Description: Contains data on hazardous waste sites that have been reported to the EPA by states, municipalities, private companies, and private persons, pursuant to Section 103 of the Comprehensive Environmental Response, Compensation and Liability Act of 1980 (CERLA), as amended. May not contain all the potential hazardous sites that exist.

CONDOR CALL. see CONSERVATION

CONFERENCE ON SPACE SIMULATION. PROCEEDINGS. see AERONAUTICS AND SPACE FLIGHT

550 UN ISSN 0250-4499
CONNECT; Unesco-UNEP environmental education newsletter. French edition: Connexion (ISSN 0376-9496); Spanish edition: Contacto (ISSN 0250-4480); Russian edition: Kontakt (ISSN 0250-4510); Arabic edition: Al-Rabita (ISSN 0250-4502) (Text in English) 1976. q. free. Unesco, 7-9 Place de Fontenoy, 75700 Paris, France. Ed. Joseph Barry. bibl. Document type: newsletter.
—BLDSC (3417.612500).

363.6 US ISSN 0095-4624
TD171.3.C6
CONNECTICUT. COUNCIL ON ENVIRONMENTAL QUALITY. ANNUAL REPORT. Key Title: Annual Report - State of Connecticut, Council on Environmental Quality. 1973. a. Council on Environmental Quality, 79 Elm St., Hartford, CT 06106. TEL 203-566-3510. circ. 1,200.

CONNECTICUT ENVIRONMENTAL COMPLIANCE UPDATE. see LAW

ENVIRONMENTAL STUDIES 2405

614.7 US
CONSCIOUS CONSUMER; products and services that help the earth and society. 1990. q. $19.95 to individuals; libraries $49.95. New Consumer Institute, Inc., Box 51, Wauconda, IL 60084. TEL 708-526-0522. FAX 708-885-1878. Ed. John F. Wasik. stat.; circ. controlled. Document type: newsletter.
Description: Serves as a clearing house for socially responsible and environmentally sound product information. Covers national trends, business and product news, media and legislative issues.

CONSERVATION AERONAUTICS. see TRANSPORTATION — Air Transport

CONSERVATION NORTH QUEENSLAND. see CONSERVATION

614.7 320 333.7 US
CONSERVATION VOTER. 1981. triennial. $30 includes membership. California League of Conservation Voters (CLCV), 10951 W. Pico Blvd., Ste. 201, Los Angeles, CA 90064. TEL 310-441-4162. FAX 310-441-1685. Ed. Christine Quirk. adv.; bk.rev. circ. 50,000. (tabloid format; back issues avail.) Document type: newsletter.

CONSUMING INTEREST. see CONSUMER EDUCATION AND PROTECTION

CONTINENTAL SHELF RESEARCH. see EARTH SCIENCES — Oceanography

333.7 US ISSN 1066-7938
▼**CORPORATE ENVIRONMENTAL STRATEGY**; the journal of environmental leadership. 1993. q. $195 (foreign $245) (effective 1993). P R I Publishing, 32 B Wernik Pl., Metuchen, NJ 08840. TEL 908-548-5827. FAX 908-548-2268. (Subscr. to: Box 509, Metuchen, NJ 08840-9828) Ed. Bruce Piasecki. bk.rev.; abstr.; charts; stat.
Description: Focuses on the formulation and administration of corporate environmental policies and procedures, and documents the experience of executive management.

COUNCIL FOR A LIVABLE WORLD. NEWSLETTER. see MILITARY

614.7 333.91 VI
COVICRIER. 1977. q. free. College of the Virgin Islands, Caribbean Research Institute, St. Thomas, VI 00801. Ed. Anna Mae Brown-Comment. circ. 200.

CO2 TECHNICAL REPORT. see METEOROLOGY

CRITICAL ISSUES. see POLITICAL SCIENCE

CRUISER. see FORESTS AND FORESTRY

CURRENT TOPICS IN ENVIRONMENTAL AND TOXICOLOGICAL CHEMISTRY. see ENVIRONMENTAL STUDIES — Toxicology And Environmental Safety

CURRENTS (DES MOINES); news and views on Iowa's energy and environment. see ENERGY

CURTIN UNIVERSITY OF TECHNOLOGY. MULGA RESEARCH CENTRE JOURNAL. see BIOLOGY

747 UK
D I A YEARBOOK. 1916. a. £6. Design and Industries Association, Ste. 142 Business Design Centre, Upper St., Islington Green, London N1 0QH. TEL 071-288-6212. FAX 071-288-6219. Ed. Raymond Plummer. adv.; bk.rev. circ. 2,000.
Former titles: D I A Yearbook - Design Action (ISSN 0306-6185); Design and Industries Association. Year Book and Membership List (ISSN 0070-3834)

614.7 GW ISSN 0179-017X
D N R - KURIER. 1980. bi-m. DM.15. Deutscher Naturschutzring e.V., Am Michaelshof 8, 53117 Bonn, Germany. TEL 0228-359005. FAX 0228-359096. adv.; bk.rev. circ. 5,000. Document type: bulletin.

D R C BOOK & MONOGRAPH SERIES. (Disaster Research Center) see PUBLIC HEALTH AND SAFETY

614.7 MX
D U M A C. 1978. bi-m. membership. Ducks Unlimited de Mexico, A.C., Apdo. Fostal 776, 64000 Monterrey, Nuevo Leon, Mexico. Ed. Sergio Robles Puga. adv. circ. 11,000.

ENVIRONMENTAL STUDIES

614.7 340 US ISSN 1060-2976
KF3775.A15
▼**DAILY ENVIRONMENT REPORT.** 1992. d. $2900. The Bureau of National Affairs, Inc., 1231 25th St., N.W., Washington, DC 20037. TEL 202-452-4200. FAX 202-822-8092. TELEX 285656 BANI WSH. (Subscr. to: 9435 Key West Ave., Rockville, MD 20850. TEL 800-372-1033) Ed. Bernard S. Chabel. (back issues avail.)
—CCC.
  Description: Provides comprehensive coverage of national and international environmental news.

DAKOTA COUNSEL. see *ENERGY*

614.7 333.7 IT
DAL COMUNE-NOTIZIE. 1970. m. free. Comune di Parma, Palazzo del Comune, Parma, Italy. TEL 218327. FAX 0521-282913. TELEX 532233. Ed. Francesca Carra. adv.; charts; illus.
  Formerly: Parma Realta.

614.7 AT
DEEP ECOLOGIST; learning to see with the eyes of compassion. 1982. q. Aus.$10($15) c/o P.O. Box 519, Claxton, Vic. 3168, Australia. Eds. Jane Carter, Alex Shtargot. bk.rev. circ. 500. (back issues avail.)

DEFENDERS. see *CONSERVATION*

614.7 DK ISSN 0900-3738
DENMARK. BETAENKNING FRA MILJOESTYRELSEN. 1985. irreg. price varies. Miljoestyrelsen - Danish Environmental Protection Agency, Strandgade 29, DK-1401 Copenhagen K, Denmark.

614.7 340 DK ISSN 0900-2758
DENMARK. LOVINFORMATION FRA MILJOESTYRELSEN. 1985. irreg. price varies. Miljoestyrelsen - Danish Environmental Protection Agency, Strandgade 29, DK-1401 Copenhagen K, Denmark.

614.7 DK ISSN 0903-5907
DENMARK. MILJOE DANMARK. 1974. 6/yr. DKK 68. Miljoestyrelsen - Danish Environmental Protection Agency, Strandgade 29, DK-1401 Copenhagen K, Denmark. Ed. Niels Moeller Madsen. circ. 12,000.
  Supersedes (in 1985): Denmark. Nyt fra Miljoestyrelsen (ISSN 0105-5836)

DENMARK. MILJOEMINISTERIET. MILJOEMINISTERIETS LOVREGISTER; retsinformation, lovregister, stikordsregister. see *LAW*

614.7 DK
DENMARK. MILJOEMINISTERIET. DANMARKS MILJOEUNDERSOGELSER. AFDELING FOR MILJOEKEMI. 1971. a. Miljoministeriet, Moerkhoej Bygade 26, DK-2860 Soeborg, Denmark. TEL 45-1-697088. (back issues avail.)
  Former titles: Denmark. Miljoestyrelsen Analytisk-Kemiske Laboratorium. Aarsberetning & Denmark. Miljoestyrelsen Kemikaliekontrol. Aarsberetning (ISSN 0900-1646)

614.7 DK ISSN 0107-2722
DENMARK. ORIENTERING FRA MILJOESTYRELSEN. 1985. irreg. price varies. Miljoestyrelsen - Danish Environmental Protection Agency, Strandgade 29, DK-1401 Copenhagen K, Denmark.
  Incorporates: Denmark. Miljoestyrelsen. Oversigt over Godkendte Bekaempelsesmidler (ISSN 0107-1815)

614.7 DK ISSN 0900-6788
DENMARK. REDEGOERELSE FRA MILJOESTYRELSEN. 1985. irreg. price varies. Miljoestyrelsen - Danish Environmental Protection Agency, Strandgade 29, DK-1401 Copenhagen K, Denmark.

614.7 DK
DENMARK. VEJLEDNING FRA MILJOESTYRELSEN. 1974. irreg. price varies. Miljoestyrelsen - Danish Environmental Protection Agency, Strandgade 29, DK-1401 Copenhagen K, Denmark.

DEVELOPMENT EDUCATION. see *EDUCATION — Teaching Methods And Curriculum*

333.91 NE
DEVELOPMENTS IN ENVIRONMENTAL ECONOMICS. (Text in English) 1991. irreg., vol.3, 1993. price varies. Elsevier Science B.V., Books Division, P.O. Box 211, 1000 AE Amsterdam, Netherlands. TEL 31-20-5803911. FAX 31-20-5803705. TELEX 18582 ESPA NL. (Subscr. in U.S. and Canada to: Elsevier Science Inc., Box 882, Madison Sq. Sta., New York, NY 10159. TEL 212-989-5800) (back issues avail.) **Document type:** monographic series.
  Refereed Serial

DEVELOPMENTS IN LANDSCAPE MANAGEMENT AND URBAN PLANNING. see *HOUSING AND URBAN PLANNING*

DIANDU YU HUANBAO/ELECTROPLATING AND POLLUTION CONTROL. see *ENGINEERING — Electrical Engineering*

DICKINSON JOURNAL OF ENVIRONMENTAL LAW & POLICY. see *LAW*

DIENST LANDBOUWKUNDIG ONDERZOEK. STARING CENTRUM, INSTITUUT VOOR ONDERZOEK VAN HET LANDELIJKE GEBIED. JAARVERSLAG. see *AGRICULTURE — Crop Production And Soil*

DIENST LANDBOUWKUNDIG ONDERZOEK. STARING CENTRUM, INSTITUUT VOOR ONDERZOEK VAN HET LANDELIJK GEBIED. RAPPORT. see *AGRICULTURE — Crop Production And Soil*

DIGEST OF ENVIRONMENTAL LAW. see *LAW*

614.7 US
DIRECTORY OF ENVIRONMENTAL INFORMATION SOURCES. irreg. (approx. every 18 mos.). $74 (effective Nov. 1992). Government Institutes, Inc., 4 Research Pl., Ste. 200, Rockville, MD 20850-3226. TEL 301-921-2300. FAX 301-921-0373. Ed. Thomas F.P. Sullivan. **Document type:** directory.

DIRECTORY OF ENVIRONMENTAL ORGANIZATIONS. see *CONSERVATION*

614.7 333.7 US ISSN 1040-1555
TD171
THE DIRECTORY OF NATIONAL ENVIRONMENTAL ORGANIZATIONS. 1984. irreg., latest 1992. $59. (U S Environmental Directories, Inc.) Roger N. McGrath, Box 65156, St. Paul, MN 55165. Ed. John C. Brainard. **Document type:** directory.
  Description: Lists addresses and descriptions of non-governmental environmental and conservation organizations in alphabetical order.

DIRECTORY OF OFFICIAL ARCHITECTURE AND PLANNING. see *ARCHITECTURE*

DIRECTORY OF U S AND CANADIAN SCRAP PLASTICS PROCESSORS AND BUYERS. see *BUSINESS AND ECONOMICS — Trade And Industrial Directories*

614.7 US
DISCUSSIONS IN ENVIRONMENTAL HEALTH PLANNING. 1977? irreg., latest 1982. Cornell University, Department of City and Regional Planning, College of Architecture, Art, and Planning, 106 W. Sibley Hall, Ithaca, NY 14853-6701. (reprint service avail. from UMI)

614 CL
DOCUMENTOS TALLER MULTIDISCIPLINARIO DEL MEDIO AMBIENTE. 1978. a. free. Universidad Catolica de Valparaiso, Vicerrectoria Academica Direccion General de Investigacion, Casilla 4059, Valparaiso, Chile. Ed.Bd. abstr. circ. 1,000.

DOLPHIN LOG. see *CHILDREN AND YOUTH — For*

DROIT DE L'ENVIRONNEMENT. see *LAW*

DRUSTVO EKOLOGA BOSNE I HERCEGOVINE. BILTEN. SERIJA A - EKOLOSKE MONOGRAFIJE. see *BIOLOGY — Botany*

DRUSTVO EKOLOGA BOSNE I HERCEGOVINE. BILTEN. SERIJA B - NAUCNI SKUPOVI I SAVJETOVANJA. see *BIOLOGY — Botany*

614.7 630 FR ISSN 1143-3833
DU SOL A LA TABLE. 1964. 4/yr. 110 F. Defense de la Culture Biologique, 8 place Republique, 49320 Brissac Quince, France. TEL 41-54-21-17. FAX 41-54-21-75. TELEX 710645. Ed. Antoine Lemaire. adv. circ. 12,415.
  Formerly (until 1989): Agriculture et Vie.

E A N H S BULLETIN. (East Africa Natural History Society) see *BIOLOGY*

E & P ENVIRONMENT. (Exploration & Production) see *PETROLEUM AND GAS*

613.1 338 US
E C M NEWSLETTER. (Environmentally Conscious Manufacturing) 1989. irreg. (approx. q.). free. Sandai National Laboratories, c/o Tracy Dunham, Division 6611, Box 5800, Albuquerque, NM 87185. TEL 505-845-9776. FAX 505-844-0116. **Document type:** newsletter.
  Description: Disseminates information obtained from research and development programs and demonstration, testing, and evaluation projects at research facilities on environmentally conscious manufacturing processes.

614.7 333.8 US
E C O L NEWS. 1972. s-a. free. (Environmental Conservation Library) Minneapolis Public Library and Information Center, 300 Nicollet Mall, Minneapolis, MN 55401. TEL 612-372-6570. Ed. Wm. Johnston. bk.rev.; bibl. circ. 3,200. (back issues avail.) **Document type:** newsletter.

613.7 340 US ISSN 0163-2566
E D F LETTER. 1970. bi-m. $20 includes membership. Environmental Defense Fund, 257 Park Ave. S., New York, NY 10010. TEL 212-505-2100. FAX 212-505-2375. Ed. Norma H. Watson. circ. 200,000. **Document type:** newsletter.
  Formerly: E D F Newsletter.
  Description: Covers issues relating to the environment and public health.

E E I SUPERDIRECTORY OF POWER PLANT ENVIRONMENTAL DATA. see *ENERGY — Electrical Energy*

614.7 UN
E E R. (Environmental Events Record) 1990. m. United Nations Environment Programme, Information Service, Box 30552, Nairobi, Kenya.
  Description: Intended as a record of recent significant environmental events for reference purposes.

613 011 US
▼**E FOR ENVIRONMENT;** an annotated bibliography of children's books with environmental themes. 1992. irreg. $39.95. R.R. Bowker, A Reed Reference Publishing Company, Part of the Reed Elsevier group, 121 Chanlon Rd., New Providence, NJ 07974. TEL 908-464-6800. FAX 908-665-6688. TELEX 138 755. (Subscr. to: Order Dept., Box 31, New Providence, NJ 07974-9903. TEL 800-521-8110) Ed. Patti K. Sinclair.
  ●Also available on CD-ROM.
  Description: Features over 500 listings of books on topics from preserving endangered species and eliminating pollution to waste disposal and recycling.

ENVIRONMENTAL STUDIES

614.7 US
RA565.A1 CODEN: EVHPAZ
E H P SUPPLEMENTS. (Environmental Health Perspectives) 1972. bi-m. $39 (foreign $48.75) (effective Oct. 1993). U.S. Department of Health and Human Services, National Institute of Environmental Health Sciences, Box 12233, Research Triangle Park, NC 27709. TEL 919-541-3406. FAX 919-541-0273. (Dist. by: Supt. of Documents, U.S. Government Printing Office, Washington, DC 20402) Eds. George W. Lucier, Gary E.R. Hook. bibl.; charts; illus. circ. 2,900. (also avail. in microform from UMI,PMC; reprint service avail. from UMI) **Indexed:** Abstr.Hyg., Acid Pre.Dig., Acid Rain Abstr., Acid Rain Ind., Biol.Abstr., Biol.Dig., C.I.S.Abstr., Cadscan, Chem.Abstr., Curr.Adv.Ecol.Sci., Curr.Cont., Deep Sea Res. & Oceanogr.Abstr., Dent.Ind., Environ.Abstr., Environ.Per.Bibl. (1974-), Excerp.Med., Food Sci.& Tech.Abstr., Ind.Hyg.Dig., Ind.Med., Ind.Sci.Rev., Ind.U.S.Gov.Per., INIS Atomind., Lead Abstr., NRN, Pollut.Abstr., Poult.Abstr., Rev.Med.& Vet.Mycol., Risk Abstr., Sel.Water Res.Abstr., Vet.Bull., W.R.C.Inf., Zincscan. **Document type:** government publication, academic/scholarly publication, proceedings.
—BLDSC (3791.499000); CIS; Faxon; UnCover; UMI; CASDDS.
Formerly (until 1993): E H P (ISSN 0091-6765)
Description: Includes conference and workshop proceedings, perspective statements on selected problem areas, toxicologic information summaries, overviews of areas on environmental health, and reviews on specific environmental problems and agents.
Refereed Serial

631.1 US
E M A P MONITOR. (Environmental Monitoring and Assessment Program) (Publication PB91-191320) m. $17.50 per no. U.S. Environmental Protection Agency, Office of Research and Development, 401 M St., S.W., Washington, DC 20460. TEL 202-655-4000. (Orders to: National Technical Information Service, 5285 Port Royal Rd., Springfield, VA 22161. TEL 703-487-4650. FAX 703-321-8547) **Document type:** government publication.
Description: Informs on current findings and activities of the program, which monitors the condition of the nation's ecological resources.

E M F HEALTH & SAFETY DIGEST. (Electric and Magnetic Field) see *OCCUPATIONAL HEALTH AND SAFETY*

614.7 US ISSN 1046-8021
TD171.7
E MAGAZINE; the environmental magazine. 1990. bi-m. $20 in US; N. America $25; elsewhere $30. Earth Action Network, Box 5098, Westport, CT 06881. TEL 203-854-5559. FAX 203-866-0602. (Subscr. to: Box 6667, Syracuse, NY 13217. TEL 800-825-0061) Ed. Doug Moss. illus.: B&W page $2100, color page $3155; trim 8 1/8 x 10 7/8. bk.rev. circ. 75,000. **Indexed:** Access (1991-), Alt.Press Ind., Environ.Per.Bibl. (1989-). **Document type:** consumer publication.
—BLDSC (3637.663000); Faxon; UnCover; UMI.
Description: Provides information on current environmental issues.

614.7 UK ISSN 0966-4076
E N D S REPORT. 1978. m. £197($360) Environmental Data Services Ltd., Finsbury Business Centre, 40 Bowling Green Ln., London EC1R 0NE, England. TEL 071-278-4745. FAX 071-415-0106. Ed. Marek Mayer. adv. circ. 20,000. **Indexed:** GeoRef., Risk Abstr. **Document type:** academic/scholarly publication.
—BLDSC (3791.436000); SWETS.
Formerly: Environmental Data Services. Report (ISSN 0260-1249)
Description: Publishes environmental information for business.

614.7 TH ISSN 0125-1783
E N F O NEWSLETTER. (Text in English) q. $80 to individuals; institutions $130. Asian Institute of Technology, Environmental Systems Information Center, P.O. Box 2754, Bangkok 10501, Thailand. TEL 66-2-5245863. FAX 66-2-5245870. TELEX 84276 AIT TH. adv.: page $300; trim 19 x 25. **Document type:** newsletter.
—BLDSC (3747.906000).
Description: Provides readers with information on new technologies or recently completed projects, news and views, and notes on forthcoming events.

613.1 340 US
E P A ADMINISTRATIVE LAW REPORTER. m. $750. Computer Law Reporter, Inc., 1519 Connecticut Ave., N.W., Ste. 200, Washington, DC 20036. TEL 202-462-5755. FAX 202-328-2430. Ed. Neil J. Cohen. (back issues avail.)

614.7 340 US
E P A FASTSEARCH; Environmental Protection Agency regulations. 1992. q. (plus m. updates). $995. D M S A Corporation, FastSearch Corporation, 1000 Shelard Pkwy., Ste. 200, Minneapolis, MN 55426. TEL 612-595-0244; 800-232-4590. FAX 612-595-0229. Ed. Alan Rosenauer. circ. 1,300.

614.7 US ISSN 0145-1189
TD169 CODEN: EPAJDB
E P A JOURNAL. (Publication code S174) 1975. bi-m. $10 (foreign $12.50). U.S. Environmental Protection Agency, Office of Public Affairs, Waterside Mall, 401 M St., S.W., Washington, DC 20460. TEL 919-655-4000. (Subscr. to: New Orders, Superintendent of Documents, Box 371954, Pittsburgh, PA 15250-7954. TEL 202-783-3238. FAX 202-512-2233) Ed. John Heritage. adv. circ. 30,000. **Indexed:** Abstr.Bull.Inst.Pap.Chem., Acid Rain Abstr., Acid Rain Ind., C.I.J.E., Energy Info.Abstr., Environ.Abstr., Environ.Ind., Environ.Per.Bibl. (1991-), Excerp.Med., Gen.Sci.Ind., Ind.U.S.Gov.Per., MEDOC, P.A.I.S., Pollut.Abstr., Soc.Sci.Ind., Telegen. **Document type:** government publication, academic/scholarly publication.
—BLDSC (3793.301800); CIS; Faxon; UnCover; SWETS; UMI.
Description: Covers all major environmental topics and issues, including ozone depletion, Superfund liability, stormwater permits, and indoor air pollution.

614.7 US
E P A POLICY ALERT. (Environmental Protection Agency) bi-w. $425 (foreign $475). Inside Washington Publishers, Box 7167, Ben Franklin Sta., Washington, DC 20044. TEL 703-892-8500.

620.85 340 US ISSN 1065-920X
E P A WATCH. (Environmental Protection Agency) s-m. $135. DeWeese Company, Inc., 14140L Park Long Court, Chantilly, VA 22021. TEL 703-968-9768. FAX 703-968-9771. Ed. Bonner R. Cohen.
Description: Contains surveys of environmental regulatory activities undertaken by the EPA, OSHA, the White House, the U.S. Congress and federal, state and local agencies.

614 US ISSN 0546-4552
CODEN: NUPEAW
E S E NOTES. (Environmental Sciences and Engineering) 1964. 3/yr. free to alumni. University of North Carolina at Chapel Hill, School of Public Health, Department of Environmental Sciences and Engineering, CB 7400, Chapel Hill, NC 27599-7400. TEL 919-966-4175. FAX 919-966-2583. Ed. Frank Pore. circ. 2,200 (controlled). **Document type:** newsletter.
Description: Covers issues related to aquatic and atmospheric sciences; air, radiological, and industrial hygiene; environmental health sciences; environmental management and policy; and water resources engineering.

E S F QUARTERLY. (Environmental Science and Forestry) see *FORESTS AND FORESTRY*

E T R NEWS. (Employer Trip Reduction) see *PUBLIC ADMINISTRATION*

614.7 333.7 US
EAGLE (GALENA).* 1972. q. $7.50. Eagle Foundation, Box 1767, Madison, WI 53701-1767. Ed. James C. Clark. adv.; bk.rev. circ. 1,700.
Description: Membership magazine of the Eagle Foundation, with articles on wildlife subjects, focusing on the bald eagle.

051 US
▼**THE EAGLE (MOUNT VERNON);** strength - courage - hope - vision. 1993. m. $24 (foreign $38) (effective 1994). Partners in the Environment, Box 292, Mt. Vernon, VA 22121. TEL 703-768-4287. FAX 703-765-8426. Ed. Elmer M. Savilla. illus. (tabloid format) **Document type:** newspaper.
Description: Publishes national and international news on the environment, including social aspects of environmental degradation, and discusses self-help and remediation initiatives.

EARTH FIRST!: the radical environmental journal. see *CONSERVATION*

614.7 US ISSN 1041-0406
EARTH ISLAND JOURNAL; an international environmental news magazine. 1986. q. $25 (foreign $30) (includes membership). Earth Island Institute, 300 Broadway, Ste. 28, San Francisco, CA 94133-3312. TEL 415-788-3666. FAX 415-788-7324. TELEX 6502829302 MCI UW. Ed. Gar Smith. adv.: page $500; trim 7 1/4 x 10. index. circ. 20,000. (also avail. in microform from UMI; back issues avail.) **Indexed:** Alt.Press Ind., Environ.Abstr., Environ.Per.Bibl. (1991-).
—BLDSC (3643.155000); Faxon; UnCover; UMI.
Descriptor: Preservation of world's living resources - native cultures, rain forests, marine mammals. Critical assessments of the impacts of technology on global future.

613.1 333.7 US
▼**EARTH NEWS.** 1992. m. Mother Earth Newsletter, Box 1620, Agoura Hills, CA 91376. Ed. Adam Rogers. **Document type:** newsletter.

EARTH OBSERVER. see *AERONAUTICS AND SPACE FLIGHT*

614.7 CN ISSN 1181-7828
EARTHKEEPER. 6/yr. Can.$24. c/o Scott Black, Ed., P.O. Box 1649, Guelph, ON N1H 6R7, Canada. TEL 519-763-9357. circ. 11,000. **Document type:** consumer publication.

614 US ISSN 1041-5483
GE1
EARTHQUEST. 1987. q. free. University Corporation for Atmospheric Research, Office for Interdisciplinary Earth Studies, Box 3000, Boulder, CO 80307-3000. TEL 303-497-2692. FAX 303-497-2699. E-mail: EHRET@NCAR.UCAR.EDU. Ed. Tom M.L. Wigley. circ. 12,000. **Indexec:** Environ.Abstr. **Document type:** newsletter.
Description: Studies the earth as an interconnected system. Serves the needs of the US Global Change Program and the International Geosphere-Biosphere Programme through advocacy and other means.

614.7 US
EARTHWATCH OREGON. 1969. 4/yr. $25. Oregon Environmental Council, 027 S.W. Arthur St., Portland, OR 97201. TEL 503-222-1963. FAX 503-222-1405. Ed. Jane Haley. adv.; bk.rev. circ. 1,600. **Document type:** newsletter.
Formerly: Oregon Environmental Council Newsletter (ISSN 0048-2145)
Description: Publishes issue updates, environmental tips, and columns from council officers.

EARTHWORK. see *OCCUPATIONS AND CAREERS*

ECO. see *CONSERVATION*

ECO (MOUNT KISCO); business & environment. see *BUSINESS AND ECONOMICS*

614.7 US
ECO-PROFITEER. 1991. m. $96. Soundview Publications, Inc., 1350 Center Dr., Ste. 100, Dunwoody, GA 30338-4134. TEL 404-668-0432. FAX 404-668-0692. Ed. Franklin Sanders. circ. 3,000. **Document type:** newsletter.
Formerly: G E O Report.

614.7 333.79 CN ISSN 0833-448X
ECOALERT. vol.17, 1985. bi-m. Can.$18. Conservation Council of New Brunswick, Inc., 180 St. John St., Fredericton, N.B. E3B 4A9, Canada. TEL 506-458-8747. Ed. Merredith Brewer. adv.; bk.rev. circ. 550.
Formerly: Conservation.
Description: Covers environmental issues with particular attention to New Brunswick.

614.7 CN ISSN 1183-2355
ECODECISION. (Text in English, French) 1991. 4/yr. Can.$50. Environment and Policy Society, 276 St. Jacques St. West, Ste. 924, Montreal, PQ H2Y 1N3, Canada. TEL 514-284-3043. FAX 514-284-3045. Ed. Elizabeth Campbell. adv.; bk.rev. circ. 5,000. **Indexed:** Environ.Per.Bibl. (1991-), Per.Islam. (1991-).
—BLDSC (3648.617000).

ENVIRONMENTAL STUDIES

614.7   KE   ISSN 0250-9989
ECOFORUM. (Text in Arabic, English, French, Spanish) 1974. bi-m. $30. Environment Liaison Centre International, P.O. Box 72461, Nairobi, Kenya. TEL 562015. FAX 254-2-562175. TELEX 23240 ELC KE. Ed. William Allen. adv.; bk.rev.; illus. circ. 5,000. (back issues avail.) **Indexed:** Acid Rain Abstr., Acid Rain Ind., Energy Rev.
—BLDSC (3648.625000).
Description: Provides useful information on environmental issues. Serves as an exchange forum.

574.5 919.8   DK   ISSN 0906-7590
QH84.1   CODEN: HOECD2
ECOGRAPHY; pattern and diversity in ecology. (Text and summaries in English) 1978. q. DKK 645. (Nordic Society Oikos) Munksgaard International Publishers Ltd., 35 Noerre Soegade, P.O. Box 2148, DK-1016 Copenhagen K, Denmark. TEL 33-127030. FAX 33-129387. TELEX 19431-MUNKS-DK. (Co-sponsor: Nordic Publishing Board in Science) Ed. Sven Johansson. adv.; bk.rev.; charts; illus.; index. circ. 625. (reprint service avail. from ISI) **Indexed:** Biol.Abstr., Chem.Abstr., Curr.Adv.Ecol.Sci., Curr.Cont., Curr.Ref.Fish Res., Deep Sea Res.& Oceanogr.Abstr., Environ.Per.Bibl. (1990-), Forest.Abstr., Forest Prod.Abstr., Geo.Abstr., Ind.Sci.Rev., INIS Atomind., Rev.Plant Path., Sci.Cit.Ind., Sel.Water Res.Abstr., Soils & Fert. —BLDSC (3648.627000); Faxon; UnCover; SWETS; CASDDS. **CCC.**
Formerly (until 1992): Holarctic Ecology (ISSN 0105-9327)
Refereed Serial

614.7   US
ECOL NEWS. 1972. s-a. free. Minneapolis Public Library and Information Center, 300 Nicollet Mall, Minneapolis, MN 55401. TEL 612-372-6570. Ed. William L. Johnston. bk.rev. circ. 3,200. (looseleaf format; back issues avail.) **Document type:** newsletter.
Description: Examines deforestation and its impact on society, agricultural problems facing today's farmer, and potential alternative solutions to those problems.
Refereed Serial

ECOLOGIA AGRARIA. see *AGRICULTURE*

614.7   BL
ECOLOGIA E DESENVOLVIMENTO; revista mensal brasileira de ecologia e meio ambiente. 1991. m. Cr.$18000. Editora Terceiro Mundo, Rua da Gloria, 122, 20241 Rio de Janeiro, Brasil. TEL 021-252-7440. FAX 021-252-8455. TELEX 21-33054 CTMB BR. Ed. Neiva Moreira.

ECOLOGIA Y DESARROLLO. see *BIOLOGY*

614.7 574.5   US   ISSN 1051-0761
QH540   CODEN: ECAPE7
ECOLOGICAL APPLICATIONS. 1991. q. $60. Ecological Society of America (Ithaca), c/o Center for Environmental Studies, Arizona State University, Tempe, AZ 85287. TEL 602-965-3000. FAX 602-965-8087. Ed. Simon Levin. (also avail. in microfilm from UMI) **Indexed:** Environ.Per.Bibl. (1990-), Meteor.& Geoastrophys.Abstr. —BLDSC (3648.855000); Faxon; UnCover; SWETS.
Description: Publishes articles on the ecological basis for decision making and policy in the areas of global change, biogeochemistry, conservation biology, ecotoxicology, pollution ecology, fisheries and wildlife ecology, forestry, agroecosystems, range management, soils, hydrology and groundwater, landscape ecology, and epidemiology.
Refereed Serial

333.7   NE   ISSN 0921-8009
HC59.72.E5   CODEN: ECECEM
ECOLOGICAL ECONOMICS. 1989. 9/yr. (in 3 vols.; 3 nos./vol.) fl.870($470) (effective 1994). (International Society for Ecological Economics) Elsevier Science B.V., P.O. Box 211, 1000 AH Amsterdam, Netherlands. TEL 31-20-5803911. FAX 31-20-5803598. TELEX 18582 ESPA NL. (Subscr. in U.S. and Canada to: Elsevier Science Inc., Box 882, Madison Sq. Sta., New York, NY 10159. TEL 212-989-5800. FAX 212-633-3990) Ed. Robert Costanza. (back issues avail.) **Indexed:** Energy Info.Abstr., Environ.Abstr., Environ.Per.Bibl. (1989-). **Document type:** academic/scholarly publication. —BLDSC (3648.867000); Faxon; UnCover; SWETS. **CCC.**
Description: Includes neoclassical environmental economics and ecological impact studies as subjects, and encourages new ways of thinking about the linkages between ecological and economic systems.
Refereed Serial

620.85   NE   ISSN 0925-8574
TD1
ECOLOGICAL ENGINEERING; the journal of ecotechnology. (Text in English) 1991. 4/yr. fl.361($195) (effective 1994). Elsevier Science B.V., P.O. Box 211, 1000 AE Amsterdam, Netherlands. TEL 31-20-5803911. FAX 31-20-5803705. TELEX 18582 ESPA NL. (Subscr. in U.S. and Canada to: Elsevier Science Inc., Box 882, Madison Sq. Sta., New York, NY 10159. TEL 212-989-5800. FAX 212-633-3990) Ed. William J. Mitsch. (also avail. in microform from UMI; back issues avail.) **Document type:** academic/scholarly publication.
—BLDSC (3648.869000); UnCover. **CCC.**
Description: Publishes contributions in ecotechnology, including synthetic ecology, bioengineering, pollution control, and sustainable agriculture.
Refereed Serial

ECOLOGICAL MODELLING; international journal on ecological modelling and engineering and systems ecology. see *ENVIRONMENTAL STUDIES — Computer Applications*

614.7 574.5   US   ISSN 0012-9615
QH540   CODEN: ECMOAQ
ECOLOGICAL MONOGRAPHS. 1931. q. $45. Ecological Society of America, c/o Center for Environmental Studies, Arizona State University, Tempe, AZ 85287. TEL 602-965-3000. FAX 602-965-8087. Ed. Lee N. Miller. bibl.; charts; illus.; index, irreg. cum.index. circ. 5,800. (also avail. in microform from UMI,PMC; back issues avail.) **Indexed:** Biol.Abstr., Biol.& Agr.Ind., Chem.Abstr., Curr.Adv.Ecol.Sci., Curr.Cont., Curr.Ref.Fish Res., Deep Sea Res.& Oceanogr.Abstr., Energy Ind., Energy Info.Abstr., Energy Rev., Environ.Per.Bibl. (1989-), Excerp.Med., Field Crop Abstr., Forest Abstr., Forest.Prod.Abstr., Gen.Sci.Ind., Geo.Abstr., Helminthol.Abstr., Herb.Abstr., Ind.Sci.Rev., INIS Atomind., Key Word Ind.Wildl.Res., Meteor.& Geoastrophys.Abstr., Nutr.Abstr., Plant Breed.Abstr., Sci.Cit.Ind., Seed Abstr., Sel.Water Res.Abstr., Weed Abstr. **Document type:** monographic series.
—BLDSC (3649.000000); Faxon; UnCover; SWETS; UMI.
Refereed Serial

614.7   DK
    CODEN: ECBUDQ
ECOLOGICAL RESEARCH COMMITTEE. ECOLOGICAL BULLETINS. (Text in English) 1968. irreg. price varies. Munksgaard, Box 2148, DK 1016 Copenhagen, Denmark. TEL 46-46-148188. FAX 46-46-11-95-52. Ed. Pehr H. Enckell. circ. 500. (back issues avail.) **Indexed:** Biol.Abstr., Environ.Abstr., Geo.Abstr., GeoRef. **Document type:** academic/scholarly publication, monographic series. —BLDSC (3648.860000); Faxon; SWETS; CASDDS.
Formerly: Swedish Natural Science Research Council. Ecological Bulletins (ISSN 0346-6868)

614.7 574.5   US   ISSN 0012-9623
    CODEN: BECLAG
ECOLOGICAL SOCIETY OF AMERICA. BULLETIN. 1917. q. $25. Ecological Society of America, Center for Environmental Studies, Arizona State University, Tempe, AZ 85287. TEL 602-965-3000. FAX 602-965-8087. Ed. Calbert Cushing. bk.rev.; abstr. circ. 6,079. **Indexed:** Biol.Abstr., Deep Sea Res.& Oceanogr.Abstr., Field Crop Abstr., Herb.Abstr., Hort.Abstr. **Document type:** bulletin. —BLDSC (2498.200000); Faxon; UnCover; SWETS; UMI.
Description: Publishes brief articles about the science of ecology, including news, meeting arrangements, reviews of meetings and software, and awards of the Ecological Society of America.

614.7   UK   ISSN 0261-3131
QH540   CODEN: ECLGEZ
THE ECOLOGIST (1979). 1970. bi-m. $34 (institutions $78; students $25). Ecosystems Ltd., Agriculture House, Bath Rd., Sturminster Newton, Dorset DT10 1DU, England. TEL 0258-473476. FAX 0258-473748. (Dist. by: M I T Press, Journals, 55 Hayward St., Cambridge, MA 02142. TEL 617-253-2889) Ed. Nicholas Hildyard. adv. contact: Sarah Sexton. bk.rev.; charts; stat.; index. circ. 9,000. (also avail. in microform from UMI; reprint service avail. from UMI) **Indexed:** Abstr.Rural Dev.Trop., Acid Pre.Dig., Alt.Press Ind., Biol.Abstr., Br.Tech.Ind., Curr.Adv.Ecol.Sci., Energy Rev., Environ.Abstr., Environ.Ind., Environ.Per.Bibl. (1979-), Excerp.Med., Forest.Abstr., Gen.Sci.Ind., I D A, Ind.Sci.Rev., INIS Atomind., Key to Econ.Sci., Ocean.Abstr., Pollut.Abstr., Rural Devel.Abstr., Soils & Fert., Vet.Bull. **Document type:** academic/scholarly publication.
—BLDSC (3649.400000); Faxon; UnCover; SWETS; UMI.
Former titles (until vol.9, 1979): New Ecologist (ISSN 0141-6952); Ecologist Quarterly (ISSN 0142-0399)

614.7 574.5   US   ISSN 0012-9658
QH540   CODEN: ECOLAR
ECOLOGY. 1920. 8/yr. $130 to individuals; institutions $210. Ecological Society of America, c/o Center for Environmental Studies, Arizona State University, Tempe, AZ 85287. TEL 602-965-3000. FAX 602-965-8087. Ed. Lee N. Miller. bk.rev.; bibl.; charts; illus.; index, cum.index. circ. 7,200. (also avail. in microform from UMI; microfilm from PMC) **Indexed:** Acid Pre.Dig., Anim.Breed.Abstr., Biol.Abstr., Biol.& Agr.Ind., Bk.Rev.Ind. (1991-), Chem.Abstr., Child.Bk.Rev.Ind. (1991-), Curr.Cont., Curr.Ref.Fish Res., Deep Sea Res.& Oceanogr.Abstr., Energy Ind., Energy Info.Abstr., Energy Rev., Environ.Per.Bibl. (1973-), Excerp.Med., Field Crop Abstr., Forest.Abstr., Forest Prod.Abstr., Gen.Sci.Ind., Geo.Abstr., Helminthol.Abstr., Herb.Abstr., Hort.Abstr., Ind.Sci.Rev., INIS Atomind., Irr.& Drain.Abstr., Meteor.& Geoastrophys.Abstr., Mid.East: Abstr.& Ind., Nutr.Abstr., Plant Breed.Abstr., Pollut.Abstr., Poult.Abstr., Rev.Appl.Entomol., Risk Abstr., Sci.Cit.Ind., Sel.Water Res.Abstr., Soils & Fert., W.R.C.Inf., Weed Abstr. —BLDSC (3650.000000); Faxon; UnCover; SWETS; UMI; CASDDS.
Refereed Serial

ECOLOGY & CONSERVATION STUDIES. see *CONSERVATION*

614.7   US
ECOLOGY CENTER TERRAIN. 1970. m. $25 (Canada and Mexico $30, elsewhere $35). Ecology Center, 2530 San Pablo Ave., Berkeley, CA 94702. TEL 510-548-2220. Ed. Chris Clarke. adv.; bk.rev.; illus.; circ. 7,500 (controlled). (tabloid format; also avail. in microform from UMI; reprint service avail. from UMI)
Formerly (until 1991): Ecology Center Newsletter.

614.7   US
ECOLOGY DIGEST. 1978. q. $6.50. Box 60961, Sacramento, CA 95860. TEL 916-961-2942. Ed. Max Peters. adv.; bk.rev. circ. 2,500. (back issues avail.)

333.79 NE ISSN 0926-9754
ECOLOGY, ECONOMY & ENVIRONMENT. (Text in English) 1991. irreg., vol.3, 1993. price varies. Kluwer Academic Press, Postbus 17, 3300 AA Dordrecht, Netherlands. TEL 31-78-334911. FAX 31-78-334254. TELEX 29245 KAPG NL. (Dist. by: Kluwer Academic Publishers Group, P.O. Box 322, 3300 AH Dordrecht, Netherlands. TEL 31-78-524400. FAX 31-78-524474; N. America dist. addr.: Box 358, Accord Sta., Hingham, MA 02018-0358. TEL 617-871-6600. FAX 617-871-6528) (back issues avail.) **Document type:** monographic series.
Refereed Serial

ECOLOGY LAW QUARTERLY. see *LAW*

614.7 US
ECOLOGY REPORTS. 1970. 5/yr. $30. Ecology Center of Ann Arbor, Inc., 417 Detroit St., Ann Arbor, MI 48104. TEL 313-761-3186. Ed. Stacey Fallis. adv.; bk.rev.; illus. circ. 2,000. **Document type:** newsletter.
 Description: Focuses on local environmental issues, such as safe water, energy conservation, pest control.

614.7 US ISSN 0098-6615
QH104
ECOLOGY U S A. 1972. bi-w. $107. Business Publishers Inc., 951 Pershing Dr., Silver Spring, MD 20910-4464. TEL 301-587-6300. FAX 301-587-1081. Ed. Elaine Eiserer. illus. (looseleaf format) **Indexed:** Bio-Contr.News & Info., Field Crop Abstr., Forest.Abstr., Herb.Abstr., Maize Abstr., Seed Abstr., Soils & Fert., Triticale Abstr., Weed Abstr. **Document type:** newsletter.
—Faxon. CCC.
 Description: Comprehensive coverage of the ecosystem as a whole with its complex interrelationships.

614.7 US
ECON: THE ENVIRONMENTAL MAGAZINE FOR REAL PROPERTY TRENDS. 1986. m. $45. P T N Publishing Corp., 445 Broad Hollow Rd., Ste. 21, Melville, NY 11747-4722. TEL 516-845-2700. FAX 516-845-7109. Ed. Judith Hogan. circ. 25,050. (back issues avail.) **Document type:** trade publication.
 Formerly (until 1990): Econ: Environmental Contractor (ISSN 1041-1372)
 Description: Trade news for professionals engaged in the removal of asbestos and other hazardous waste.

614.7 US ISSN 0885-7237
ECONEWS; newsletter of the Northcoast Environmental Center. 1971. m. (11/yr.) $20 (students & retired $15; Canada, Mexico $45; elsewhere $50). Northcoast Environmental Center, Inc., 879 Ninth St., Arcata, CA 95521. TEL 707-822-6918. FAX 707-822-0827. Eds. Sidney Dominitz, Andrew Alm. adv.; bk.rev.; illus.; circ. 5,200 (paid); 3,300 (controlled). **Document type:** newsletter.
●Also available online. Vendor(s): CompuServe, Inc..
 Description: Presents articles on environmental issues including old-growth forests, public lands, pollution and energy.

614.7 UK ISSN 0955-6176
ECONEWS. 1978. 6/yr. membership. Green Party, 10 Station Parade, Balham High Rd., London SW12 9AZ, England. Ed. Dave Bradney. adv.; bk.rev. circ. 30,000.

ECONOMIA MONTANA - LINEA ECOLOGICA. see *FORESTS AND FORESTRY*

620.85 BL ISSN 0104-0030
ECORIO; revista brasileira de informacao ambiental, politica, social, cientifica e cultural. 1991. m. Tricontinental Editora Ltda., Av. Presidente Antonio Carlos 54, 20020 Centro - Rio de Janeiro RJ, Brazil. TEL 021-533-0269. **Document type:** consumer publication.

614.7 AT ISSN 0311-4546
ECOS. 1974. q. Aus.$22 (effective 1994). C.S.I.R.O., 314 Albert St., E. Melbourne, Vic. 3002, Australia. Ed. B. Bennett. circ. 8,000. (back issues avail.) **Indexed:** AESIS, Aus.Rd.Ind., Curr.Adv.Ecol.Sci., Environ.Per.Bibl. (1989-), Gdlns, Geo.Abstr., INIS Atomind.
 —BLDSC (3659.531000). CCC.

614.7 RU ISSN 0869-6357
ECOS. (Text in English, Russian) 1990. q. (International Peace Fund Association) Ecos, Zubovsky Bulvar, 4, 119021 Moscow, Russia. TEL 201-85-10. FAX 2302170. TELEX 411327. (Co-sponsors: Novosti Information Russian Agency; Social Ecological Union) Ed. V.B. Rudenko. adv. contact: E.N. Kortunova. illus. circ. 100,000. **Document type:** academic/scholarly publication.
 Description: Concerned with issues of nature conservation and the ecological situation in Russia, the New Commonwealth of Independent States and around the world.

ECOSPHERE. see *TRAVEL AND TOURISM*

628 NE
ECOSYSTEMS OF THE WORLD. 1977. irreg., vol.8B, 1993. price varies. Elsevier Science B.V., Books Division, P.O. Box 211, 1000 AE Amsterdam, Netherlands. TEL 31-20-5803911. FAX 31-20-5803705. TELEX 18582 ESPA NL. (Subscr. in U.S. and Canada to: Elsevier Science Inc., Box 882, Madison Sq. Sta., New York, NY 10159. TEL 212-989-5800) Ed. D.W. Goodall. (back issues avail.) **Indexed:** Herb.Abstr. **Document type:** monographic series.
Refereed Serial

614.7 IT
ECOTIME. 37/yr. Via Olindo Guerrini 5, 20133 Milan, Italy. TEL 2-26-63-605. FAX 2-70-60-24-99. Ed. Marco Bindi. circ. 25,000.

620.85 AG ISSN 0327-9499
▼**ECOVIDA.** 1993. s-a. $10. Universidad del Salvador, Vicerrectorado de Investigacion y Desarrollo, Rodriguez Pena 770, 2o piso, 1020 Buenos Aires, Argentina. TEL 42-1381. FAX 42-0631. bibl.
 Description: Publishes papers and brief notes related to environmental topics.

ECOVILLAGE NEWSLETTER. see *HOUSING AND URBAN PLANNING*

614.7 001.3 IT ISSN 1120-1819
EDIZIONI PER LA CONSERVAZIONE; periodico internazionale di prevenzione e conservazione. (Text in English, French, Italian) 1989. bi-m. L.75000($115) (effective 1993). Semar Editore, Via della Reginella, 29-29A, 00186 Rome, Italy. TEL 396-6876523. FAX 396-68308601. Ed. Luciano Sahlan Momo. adv.; page $800. bk.rev.; abstr.; bibl.; charts; illus.; index, cum.index. circ. 3,000. (also avail. in diskette format; back issues avail.) **Document type:** monographic series.
 Description: Covers technical, scientific, artistic, ethic, philosophical and symbolic aspects of the preservation, conservation and restoration of cultural heritage and the environment.

613.1 574.5 ER ISSN 0868-5894
QH540
EESTI TEADUSTE AKADEEMIA. TOIMETISED. OKOOLOOGIA/ESTONIAN ACADEMY OF SCIENCES. PROCEEDINGS. ECOLOGY. (Text in English; summaries in Estonian, French, Russian) 1991. q. $40 (effective 1994). Teaduste Akadeemia Kirjastus, Estonia pst.7, EE-0100 Tallinn, Estonia. TEL 7-3722-454156. (Subscr. to: Akateeminen Kirjakauppa 128 SF, 00101 Helsinki, Finland. Or: Bibliotekstjanst AB 200, S22100 Lund, Sweden) Ed. Juri Martin. circ. 650. **Document type:** proceedings.

ELECTRICITE DE FRANCE. DIRECTION DES ETUDES ET RECHERCHES. COLLECTION DE NOTES INTERNES. BIOLOGIE, SCIENCES DE LA TERRE ET ENVIRONNEMENT. see *BIOLOGY*

ELEPAIO. see *BIOLOGY — Ornithology*

628 600 UN
▼**EN T A NEWSLETTER.** (Environmental Technology Assessment) (Supplement to: Industry and Environment (ISSN 0378-9993)) 1994. 2/yr. United Nations Environment Programme, Industry and Environment Programme Activity Centre, 39-43 quai Andre Citroen, 73739 Paris Cedex 15, France. TEL 44-37-14-50. FAX 44-37-14-74. **Document type:** newsletter.

613.1 US
▼**ENCYCLOPEDIA OF ENVIRONMENTAL INFORMATION SOURCES.** 1992. biennial. $125. Gale Research Inc., 835 Penobscot Bldg., Detroit, MI 48226. TEL 313-961-2242. FAX 313-961-6083. Ed. Sarojini Balachandran. **Document type:** directory.
 Description: Lists over 20,000 sources of information in over 800 subject areas.

ENDANGERED SPECIES UPDATE. see *CONSERVATION*

ENERGIE; das Magazin fuer Wirtschaft, Forschung, Technik, Umwelt. see *ENERGY*

ENERGIE ALTERNATIVE: HABITAT, TERRITORIO, ENERGIA. see *ENERGY*

ENERGIEONDERZOEK CENTRUM NEDERLAND. JAARVERSLAG/NETHERLANDS ENERGY RESEARCH FOUNDATION. ACTIVITIES REPORT. see *ENERGY*

ENERGY; the international journal. see *ENERGY*

ENERGY & ENVIRONMENT. see *ENERGY*

ENERGY AND ENVIRONMENT ALERT; brief notes by and about N.C.E.B. and N.C.E.B. associates. see *ENERGY*

ENERGY DIGEST. see *ENERGY*

614.7 US ISSN 1059-5813
CODEN: EECCEQ
ENERGY, ECONOMICS AND CLIMATE CHANGE; update on energy policies and economic studies. 1991. m. $547 (foreign $647). Cutter Information Corp., 37 Broadway, Arlington, MA 02174. TEL 617-648-8700. FAX 617-648-8707. TELEX 650 100 9891 MCI UW. Eds. Bradford J. Hurley, Nicholas A. Sundt. charts. (back issues avail.) **Document type:** newsletter.
●Also available online. Vendor(s): NewsNet (EY81).
—CCC.
 Description: Reviews economic models used to develop energy policies for national and international regions.

ENERGY ENVIRONMENT MONITOR. see *ENERGY*

ENERGY ENVIRONMENT REPORT. see *ENERGY*

ENERGY IN JAPAN. see *ENERGY*

ENERGY MAGAZINE. see *ENERGY*

ENERGY MANAGEMENT AND FEDERAL ENERGY GUIDELINES. see *ENERGY*

THE ENERGY NEWSBRIEF. see *ENERGY*

ENERGY POLICY; international journal of the political, economic, planning and social aspects of energy. see *ENERGY*

ENERGY STUDIES REVIEW. see *ENERGY*

614.7 US ISSN 0276-9956
ENFO. Title varies--Enfo Newsletter. 1971. 4/yr. $20 to individuals; institutions $25. Florida Conservation Foundation, Environmental Information Center, 1251 Miller Ave., Ste. B, Winter Park, FL 32789-4827. Ed. Linda Lord. bk.rev. circ. 1,200. **Indexed:** W.R.C.Inf.
 Description: Covers different environmental topics of importance to Florida, such as water, land, wildlife and wastes.

ENGINEERING DIMENSIONS. see *ENGINEERING*

613.1 UK ISSN 1351-9158
ENTEC DIRECTORY OF ENVIRONMENTAL TECHNOLOGY. (Text in English, French, German) a. £125. (Entec Press) Kogan Page Ltd., 120 Pentonville Rd., London N1 9JN, England. TEL 071-278-0433. FAX 071-837-6348. TELEX 263088-KOGAN-G. **Document type:** directory.

ENTSORGA-MAGAZIN - ENTSORGUNGSWIRTSCHAFT. see *ENGINEERING*

614.7 GW ISSN 0935-7688
ENTSORGUNGS-TECHNIK; Zeitschrift fuer Abfallwirtschaft Umweltschutz Recycling. 1989. bi-m. DM.54. Ecomed Verlagsgesellschaft mbH und Co. KG, Rudolf-Diese-Str. 3, 86887 Landsberg-Lech, Germany. TEL 08191-125-0. FAX 08191-125-513. Ed. Susanne Wieland adv.; color page DM.3920; trim 190 x 270; adv contact: Petra Fischer. circ. 10,000. **Document type:** trade publication.

ENVIRONMENTAL STUDIES

614.7   GW   ISSN 0724-6870
ENTSORGUNGSPRAXIS; ein Bertelsmann Fachmagazin fuer Umwelttechnik in Industrie und Kommunalwirtschaft. 1983. m. DM.114. Bertelsmann Fachzeitschriften GmbH, Postfach 120, 33111 Guetersloh, Germany. TEL 05241-802332. FAX 05241-73055. Ed. Ulrich Knorra. adv.: B&W page DM.5760, color page DM.8610; trim 297 x 210. circ. 15,895. **Indexed:** INIS Atomind., Packag.Sci.Tech. **Document type:** trade publication.
—SWETS.
Description: Deals with environmental technology in industry and municipal economy.

628   GW
ENVIRING INTERNATIONAL. (Text in English, French) 1989. irreg. DM.30. Deutscher Fachverlag GmbH, Mainzer Landstr. 251, 60326 Frankfurt a.M., Germany. TEL 069-7595-01. FAX 069-7595-2999. adv.: B&W page DM.5400; trim 210 x 297. circ. 16,000. **Document type:** monographic series.
Description: Covers environmental issues such as: wastewater, environmental protection, garbage and industry regulations.

ENVIRO; magazine of transboundary pollution. see *ENVIRONMENTAL STUDIES — Pollution*

614.7   US
ENVIROFAX. (Avail. by fax only) w. $187. Business Publishers, Inc., 951 Pershing Dr., Silver Spring, MD 20910-4464. TEL 301-587-6300; 800-BPI-0122. FAX 301-585-9075.
Description: Covers a wide range of environmental issues: hazardous, radioactive, medical, and solid wastes; air pollution; asbestos and lead contamination; surface and groundwater contamination; hazardous materials spills and control; and environmental remediation.

614.7   TR
ENVIRON; patterns of progress in the Caribbean. 1977. a. $6.50. Key Caribbean, 1 El Socorro Extension Rd., Kirpalani's Complex, San Juan, Trinidad & Tobago, W.I. (Subscr. to: P.O. Box 21, Port-of-Spain, Trinidad & Tobago, W.I.) Ed. Roy Boyke. circ. 5,000. (back issues avail.)

614.7   US   ISSN 0883-9719
ENVIRON; a magazine for ecologic living & health. irreg. (2-4/yr.) $18 for 4 nos. (Canada $21; elsewhere $28); libraries $30 (all foreign $40). Wary Canary Press, Box 2204, Ft. Collins, CO 80522. TEL 303-224-0083. Eds. Suzanne & Ed Randegger. adv. contact: Ed Randegger. circ. 5,000 (paid); 2,000 (controlled). (back issues avail.) **Indexed:** Environ.Abstr.
Description: Informs readers about consumer alternatives for ecologically sound life-styles; alerts them to hazardous chemicals in food, water, and air. Offers sustainable solutions for businesses and governments.

614.7 574 531.64
052   AT
ENVIRONMENT; exploring the social and physical environments of W.A. 1975. q. Aus.$12. Environment Centre of W.A. Inc., 587 Wellington St., Perth 6000, WA, Australia. FAX 619-0322-3045. Ed. Jeff Bryant. adv.; bk.rev. circ. 800. **Document type:** newsletter.
Formerly: Environment W.A. (ISSN 0313-9549)

614.7   US   ISSN 0013-9157
UF767   CODEN: ENVTAR
ENVIRONMENT (WASHINGTON). 1958. m. (except Jan.-Feb., July-Aug. combined). $33 to individuals; institutions $66. (Scientists' Institute for Public Information) Heldref Publications, 1319 Eighteenth St., N.W., Washington, DC 20036-1802. TEL 202-296-6267. FAX 202-296-5149. (Co-sponsor: Helen Dwight Reid Educational Foundation) Ed. Barbara Richman. adv. contact: Raymond Rallo. bk.rev.; bibl.; charts; illus.; index, cum.index. circ. 10,400. (also avail. in microform; reprint service avail.) **Indexed:** Abstr.Hyg., Acad.Ind., Acid Pre.Dig., Acid Rain Abstr., Biol.Abstr., Biol.& Agr.Ind., Bk.Rev.Ind. (1976-), C.I.J.E., Chem.Abstr., Child.Bk.Rev.Ind. (1976-), Curr.Adv.Ecol.Sci., Curr.Cont., Dairy Sci.Abstr., Deep Sea Res.& Oceanogr.Abstr., Energy Ind., Energy Rev., Environ.Abstr., Environ.Per.Bibl. (1980-), Excerp.Med., G.Soc.Sci.& Rel.Per.Lit., Gen.Sci.Ind., Geo.Abstr., Hlth.Ind., INIS Atomind., Key to Econ.Sci., Mag.Ind., Meteor.& Geoastrophys.Abstr., Mid.East: Abstr.& Ind., Nutr.Abstr., Ocean.Abstr., Peace Res.Abstr., PMR, Pollut.Abstr., R.G., Risk Abstr., Sci.Cit.Ind., Sel.Water Res.Abstr., So.Pac.Per.Ind., Soc.Sci.Ind., SSCI, Trop.Dis.Bull., Urb.Aff.Abstr. **Document type:** academic/scholarly publication.
—BLDSC (3791.091000); Faxon; UnCover; SWETS; UMI; CASDDS. **CCC**.
Formerly: Scientist and Citizen.
Refereed Serial

614.7 352   US
▼**ENVIRONMENT & DEVELOPMENT.** 1992. m. $50 (foreign $60). American Planning Association, 1313 E. 60th St., Chicago, IL 60637. TEL 312-955-9100. FAX 512-955-8312. (And: 1776 Massachusetts Ave., N.W., Washington, DC 20036. TEL 202-872-0611)

614.7   II   ISSN 0970-0420
QH301   CODEN: ENECEV
ENVIRONMENT AND ECOLOGY. 1983. q. Rs.85($100) to individuals; institutions Rs.250 ($100) (effective 1992). (Kalyani University, Department of Zoology) M K K Publications, 91A Ananda Palit Rd., Calcutta, West Bengal 700 014, India. TELEX (03162) 220-XIO. Ed. S.K. Konar. adv.; bk.rev. circ. 20,000. (back issues avail.) **Indexed:** Bio-Contr.News & Info., Cott.& Trop.Fibr.Abstr., Crop Physiol.Abstr., Dairy Sci.Abstr., Energy Rev., Environ.Per.Bibl., Field Crop Abstr., Herb.Abstr., Hort.Abstr., Ind.Vet., Irr.& Drain.Abstr., Maize Abstr., Ornam.Hort., Plant Grow.Reg.Abstr., Rice Abstr., Sci.Abstr., Seed Abstr., Sel.Water Res.Abstr., Soils & Fert., Sorghum & Millets Abstr., Soyabean Abstr., Triticale Abstr., Trop.Oil Seeds Abstr. **Document type:** academic/scholarly publication.
●Also available on CD-ROM.
—BLDSC (3791.099500); CASDDS.

333.7   NE   ISSN 0926-9711
ENVIRONMENT & MANAGEMENT. (Text in English) 1991. irreg. price varies. Kluwer Academic Publishers, Postbus 17, 3300 AA Dordrecht, Netherlands. TEL 31-78-334911. FAX 31-78-334254. TELEX 29245 KAPG NL. (Dist. by: Kluwer Academic Publishers Group, P.O. Box 322, 3300 AH Dordrecht, Netherlands. TEL 31-78-524400. FAX 31-78-524474; N. America dist. addr.: Box 358, Accord Sta., Hingham, MA 02018-0358. TEL 617-871-6600. FAX 617-871-6528) **Document type:** monographic series.
Refereed Serial

ENVIRONMENT AND PLANNING A. see *HOUSING AND URBAN PLANNING*

614.7   UK   ISSN 0956-2478
HT243.D44   CODEN: ENUREK
ENVIRONMENT AND URBANIZATION. (Text in English; summaries in English, French, Spanish) 1989. s-a. £17($31) (effective 1993). International Institute for Environment and Development (IIED), Human Settlements Programme, 3 Endsleigh St., London WC1H 0DD, England. TEL 44-71-388-2117. FAX 44-71-388-2826. Ed. David Satterthwaite. bk.rev. circ. 2,500. (back issues avail.) **Document type:** academic/scholarly publication.
—BLDSC (3791.115000); UnCover.
Description: Presents articles on environment and development in cities, with a focus on Third World cities, and carries profiles of Third World nongovernmental organizations active in urban issues.

614.7   UK   ISSN 0959-7042
TD194   CODEN: ENVBEB
ENVIRONMENT BUSINESS. 1990. 24/yr. £237 (foreign £267) (effective Jan. 1992). Information for Industry Ltd., 521 Old York Rd., London SW18 1TG, England. TEL 081-877-9130. FAX 081-877-9938. Ed. Ian Grant.
—BLDSC (3791.133000).
Incorporates: P M Environment & Greengauge.
Description: Contains articles and reports for senior management in industry, covering pollution control, environmental protection and waste management.

628   UK
ENVIRONMENT ENCYCLOPEDIA AND DIRECTORY: A WORLD SURVEY. irreg. $325. Europa Publications Ltd., 18 Bedford Sq., London WC1B 3JN, England. TEL 071-580-8236. FAX 071-636-1664. TELEX 21540-EUROPA-G. **Document type:** directory.
Description: Defines environmental terms and lists prominent persons in various ecological fields. Also lists governmental and nongovernmental organizations and environmental periodicals.

614.7   EI
ENVIRONMENT FEATURES. (Text in English, French) 1974. 6/yr. free. Council of Europe, Centre Naturopa, 67075 Strasbourg Cedex, France. TEL 88-41-20-00. FAX 88-41-27-15. TELEX 870 943 EUR F.

614.7   UK   ISSN 0160-4120
TD169   CODEN: ENVIDV
ENVIRONMENT INTERNATIONAL; a journal of science technology, health, monitoring and policy. 1978. 6/yr. £303($465) (effective 1994). Elsevier Science Ltd., Pergamon, P.O. Box 800, Kidlington, Oxford OX5 1DX, England. TEL 44-865-843000. FAX 44-865-843010. (Subscr. in U.S. and Canada to: Elsevier Science, 660 White Plains Rd., Tarrytown, NY 10591-5153. TEL 914-524-9200. FAX 914-333-2444) Eds. Alan Moghissi, Barbara Moghissi. adv.; bk.rev.; charts; stat.; index. circ. 2,000. (also avail. in microfilm from UMI; back issues avail.; reprint service avail.) **Indexed:** Acid Pre.Dig., Acid Rain Abstr., Acid Rain Ind., Biodet.Abstr., Biol.Abstr., Chem.Abstr., Curr.Adv.Ecol.Sci., Curr.Cont., Deep Sea Res.& Oceanogr.Abstr., Energy Info.Abstr., Energy Res.Abstr., Energy Rev., Eng.Ind., Environ.Abstr., Environ.Per.Bibl. (1980-), Excerp.Med., Geo.Abstr., I D A, INIS Atomind., Meteor.& Geoastrophys.Abstr., Pollut.Abstr., Sci.Cit.Ind., Sel.Water Res.Abstr., Soils & Fert., W.R.C.Inf. **Document type:** academic/scholarly publication.
—BLDSC (3791.330000); EI; Faxon; UnCover; SWETS; UMI; CASDDS. **CCC**.
Formerly: International Journal of the Environment.
Description: Forum of original environmental literature. Includes data, causes of pollution, methods for protection and various topics of environmental protection.
Refereed Serial

ENVIRONMENT LAW BRIEF. see *LAW*

ENVIRONMENT MAGAZINE. see *TRANSPORTATION*

658   US
ENVIRONMENT NEWS. 1991. m. membership only. International Mass Retail Association, 1901 Pennsylvania Ave., N.W., Washington, DC 20006. TEL 202-861-0774. FAX 202-785-4588. Ed. Robin Lanier. circ. 270. **Document type:** newsletter.

614.7   US
ENVIRONMENT NEWS DIGEST. 1933. q. $5 (effective 1994). Foodservice & Packaging Institute, Inc., 1901 N. Moore St., Ste. 1111, Arlington, VA 22209. TEL 703-527-7505. FAX 703-527-7512. Ed. Charles W. Felix. circ. 6,000. **Document type:** consumer publication.

614.7 333.7   WS   ISSN 0257-3962
ENVIRONMENT NEWSLETTER. (Text in English or French) 1986. q. $24. South Pacific Regional Environment Programme, P.O. Box 240, Apia, Western Samoa. TEL 685-21929. FAX 685-20231. bk.rev.; circ. 1,000 (controlled). **Document type:** newsletter.
Description: Presents current news and information on national and regional environmental events and projects in the Pacific islans.

ENVIRONMENTAL STUDIES

614.7   PL   ISSN 0324-8828
TD169   CODEN: EPEND9
ENVIRONMENT PROTECTION ENGINEERING. (Text in English; summaries in Polish and Russian) 1975. q. price varies. (Politechnika Wroclawska) Wydawnictwo Politechniki Wroclawskiej, Wybrzeze Wyspianskiego 27, 50-370 Wroclaw, Poland. TEL 20-23-04. FAX 22-36-64. TELEX 712559 PWRPL. (Dist. by: Ars Polona-Ruch, Krakowskie Przedmiescie 7, Warsaw, Poland) Eds. Tomasz Winnicki, Lucjan Pawlowski. bk.rev. circ. 600. **Indexed:** Chem.Abstr., Environ.Abstr., INIS Atomind., Pollut.Abstr. —BLDSC (3791.338000); EI; SWETS; CASDDS. **CCC.**
   Description: Papers dealing with water purification, waste water treatment, solid waste disposal, neutralization and sterilization.

614.7   US   ISSN 0013-9203
ENVIRONMENT REPORT. 1970. s-m. $650. Trends Publishing Inc., National Press Bldg., Washington, DC 20045. TEL 202-393-0031. FAX 202-393-1732. Ed. A. Kranish. bk.rev.; abstr.; bibl.; pat.; stat. (looseleaf format; also avail. in microform from UMI; reprint service avail. from UMI) **Document type:** academic/scholarly publication.
—UMI.
   Description: Covers environmental pollution problems such as acid rain, water and air quality, industrial waste disposal, carcinogens, irrigation and water reclamation.

614.7   US   ISSN 0013-9211
ENVIRONMENT REPORTER. 1970. w. $2553. The Bureau of National Affairs, Inc., 1231 25th St., N.W., Washington, DC 20037. TEL 202-452-4200. FAX 202-822-8092. TELEX 285656 BNAI WSH. (Subscr. to: 9435 Key West Ave., Rockville, MD 20850. TEL 800-372-1033) Ed. Wallis E. McClain, Jr. bk.rev.; bibl.; index. (looseleaf format; back issues avail.)
●Also available online. Vendor(s): Human Resources Information Network, Mead Data Central, Inc. (ENVREP), West Services, Inc. (BNA-ER).
—CIS; Faxon. **CCC.**
   Description: Notification and reference service covering the full-spectrum of legislative, administrative, judicial, industrial, and technological developments affecting pollution control and environmental protection.

614.7   UK   ISSN 0965-3813
HD2755.5   CODEN: ENRIEC
▼**ENVIRONMENT RISK.** 1992. 10/yr. £220($385) Euromoney Publications PLC, Westor House, Playhouse Yard, London EC4V 5EX, England. TEL 071-779-8660. FAX 071-779-8667. (Subscr. to: Quadrant Subscr. Services, Oakfield House, Perrymount Rd., Haywards Heath, RH16 2DH, England. TEL 444-440421) Ed. Josephine Carr.
—UMI.
   Description: Approaches topical environmental issues from the perspective of multi-national companies.

574.5   US
ENVIRONMENT TODAY; the newsmagazine of environmental management and pollution control. 1990. 12/yr. $56 (foreign $125) (effective 1993). Enterprise Communications Inc., 1483 Chain Bridge Rd., Ste. 202, McLean, VA 22101. TEL 703-448-0336. FAX 403-448-0270. (Subscr. to: 1165 Northchase Pkwy., N.E., Ste. 350, Marietta, GA 30067. TEL 404-988-9558) Ed. Paul Harris. adv. circ. 54,600. **Document type:** trade publication.
   Description: For top executives, plant site management, environmental engineers, scientific professionals and consulting engineers serving business and government facilities engaged in controlling air, water, ground pollution and hazardous waste.

ENVIRONMENT VICTORIA. see *CONSERVATION*

614.7   CN   ISSN 0701-9637
ENVIRONMENT VIEWS. 1977. q. free. Department of Environmental Protection, Communications Branch, 9820 106th St., Edmonton, AB T5K 2J6, Canada. TEL 403-422-2813. Ed. Maryhelen Vicars. circ. 18,500. **Indexed:** Acid Pre.Dig., Acid Rain Abstr., Acid Rain Ind., ASSIA, Environ.Abstr., Environ.Per.Bibl. (1992-), Pollut.Abstr.
   Formerly: Environment News (ISSN 0319-3608)
   Description: Devoted to increasing public awareness of environmental issues.

613.1 382   US
▼**ENVIRONMENT WATCH: EAST EUROPE, RUSSIA & EURASIA;** news and analysis for business and policy professionals. 1992. m. $577 (foreign $637). Cutter Information Corp., 37 Broadway, Arlington, MA 02174-5539. TEL 800-888-8939. FAX 617-648-8707. TELEX 650-100-9891 MCIUW. Ed. Phillip Clendenning. (back issues avail.) **Document type:** newsletter.
   Description: Covers business and regulatory trends and their implications for companies doing business in the former "Soviet bloc." Features global funding sources, resource alert, and decision of developments in these regions.

613.1 327   US   ISSN 1060-1414
GE160.L29
ENVIRONMENT WATCH: LATIN AMERICA; news and analysis for business and policy professionals. 1991. m. $537 (foreign $597). Cutter Information Corp., 37 Broadway, Arlington, MA 02174-5539. TEL 800-888-8939. FAX 617-648-8707. TELEX 650-100-9891 MCIUW. Ed. James Lahive. (back issues avail.) **Document type:** newsletter.
●Also available online. Vendor(s): NewsNet (EV44).
—**CCC.**
   Description: Covers the business implications of policy developments in the environmental arena; includes corporate initiatives, regulatory trends, and research. Focuses on Brazil, Mexico, the Southern Cone, the Andean Nations, and Central America.

631.1 382   US
▼**ENVIRONMENT WATCH: WEST EUROPE.** 1992. s-m. $555 (foreign $657). Cutter Information Corp., 37 Broadway, Arlington, MA 02174-5539. TEL 800-888-8939. FAX 617-648-8707. TELEX 650 100 9891 MCI UW. Eds. Tony Carritt, Stephanie Gehlen. **Document type:** newsletter.

614.7   US   ISSN 1041-8105
TD171
ENVIRONMENT WEEK. 1988. w. $690. King Publishing Group, Inc., 627 National Press Bldg., Washington, DC 20045. TEL 202-638-4260. FAX 202-662-9744. Ed. Dennis Wamsted. bk.rev. (back issues avail.) **Document type:** newsletter.
●Also available online. Vendor(s): Data-Star, DIALOG Information Services, Inc., Mead Data Central, Inc., NewsNet (EV25).
—**CCC.**
   Description: Covers environmental policy debates in the US and abroad for senior level business executives.

614.7   US   ISSN 0013-922X
HC110.E5   CODEN: ENACDA
ENVIRONMENTAL ACTION. 1970. q. $25 to individuals; institutions $35. Environmental Action, Inc., 6930 Carroll Ave., Ste. 600, Takoma Park, MD 20912. TEL 301-891-1106. FAX 301-891-2218. Ed. Barbara Ruben. adv.; bk.rev.; film rev.; illus.; index. circ. 15,000. (also avail. in microform from UMI; back issues avail.; reprint service avail. from UMI) **Indexed:** Acid Rain Abstr., Acid Rain Ind., Alt.Press Ind., Biol.Dig., Energy Rev., Environ.Abstr., Environ.Ind., Environ.Per.Bibl. (1974-), INIS Atomind., Mid.East: Abstr.& Ind., P.A.I.S., Telegen. **Document type:** consumer publication.
●Also available on CD-ROM. Producer(s): University Microfilms International.
—BLDSC (3791.372000); CIS; Faxon; UnCover; UMI. **CCC.**
   Incorporates (as of vol.7, no.2, 1987): Resources (Washington, 1980) (ISSN 0883-993X); (1970-1978): Rodale's Environment Action Bulletin (ISSN 0048-850X); Which was formerly: Environmental Action Bulletin.
   Description: Publishes current news, analysis and resources for action on the key environmental issues facing the country.

614.7   US
ENVIRONMENTAL AND ENERGY STUDY INSTITUTE. WEEKLY BULLETIN. Short title: E E S I Weekly Bulletin. 1975. w. (while Congress is in session). $395. Environmental and Energy Study Institute, 122 C St., N.W., Ste. 700, Washington, DC 20001. TEL 202-628-1400. FAX 202-628-1825. **Document type:** newsletter.
   Former titles: U.S. Congress. Environmental and Energy Study Conference. Weekly Bulletin; U.S. Congress. Environmental Study Conference. Weekly Bulletin.
   Description: Provides analysis of pending legislation, highlights of the upcoming committee hearings and floor activity in both the House and the Senate, forecasts positions of key players, and a calendar of key congressional events.

ENVIRONMENTAL AND EXPERIMENTAL BOTANY; an international journal. see *BIOLOGY — Botany*

333.8 340   US
ENVIRONMENTAL AND LAND USE LAW. q. $20. Washington State Bar Association, 500 Westin Bldg., 2001 Sixth Ave., Seattle, WA 98121. TEL 206-727-8239. FAX 206-727-8320. (looseleaf format) **Document type:** newsletter.

ENVIRONMENTAL AND NATURAL RESOURCES PERMITS; federal approval standards and procedures. see *LAW*

ENVIRONMENTAL AND PLANNING LAW JOURNAL. see *LAW*

333.91 614.7   NE   ISSN 0924-6460
HC79.E5   CODEN: ERECEP
ENVIRONMENTAL AND RESOURCE ECONOMICS. (Text in English) 1991. 6/yr. fl.530($276) (effective 1994). (European Association of Environmental and Resource Economists) Kluwer Academic Publishers, Postbus 17, 3300 AA Dordrecht, Netherlands. TEL 31-78-334911. FAX 31-78-334254. TELEX 29245 KAPG N.. (Dist. by: Kluwer Academic Publishers Group, P.O. Box 322, 3300 AH Dordrecht, Netherlands. TEL 31-78-524400. FAX 31-78-524474; N. America dist. addr.: Box 358, Accord Sta., Hingham, MA 02018-0358. TEL 617-871-6600. FAX 617-871-6528) Ed. J.B. Opschoor. (also avail. in microform from UMI; back issues avail.) **Indexed:** Environ.Abstr., Environ.Per.Bibl. (1992-), Geo.Abstr. **Document type:** academic/scholarly publication.
—BLDSC (3791.383300); UnCover; SWETS; UMI. **CCC.**
   Description: Covers applications of economic theory and methods to environmental issues.
Refereed Serial

614.7 352.7   US   ISSN 1044-033X
HC107.F63
ENVIRONMENTAL AND URBAN ISSUES. 1973. q. free. Florida Atlantic University - Florida International University, Joint Center for Environmental and Urban Problems, 220 S.E. Second Ave., Ste. 709, Ft. Lauderdale, FL 33301. TEL 305-355-5255. FAX 305-760-5666. Ed. M.J. Matthews. bk.rev.; cum.index: 1973-1980, 1980-1987, 1987-1990, 1990-1993; circ. 3,800 (controlled). (back issues avail.) **Indexed:** Geo Abstr.
—UnCover.
   Formerly: Florida Environmental and Urban Issues (ISSN 0145-5885) Supersedes (in 1988): Florida Planning and Development (ISSN 0015-4210)
   Description: Contains articles chronicling growth management, land use planning, and environmental policies throughout the US and the world, with emphasis on Florida

614.7 340   CN
ENVIRONMENTAL APPROVALS IN CANADA; practice and procedure. 1989. s-a. Can.$140. Butterworths Canada Ltd., Part of the Reed Elsevier group, 75 Clegg Rd., Markham, ON L6G 1A1, Canada. TEL 905-479-2665. FAX 905-479-2826. Ed. Michael I. Jeffery.
   Description: Discusses the process from pre-hearing activity and public participation to the hearing itself.

ENVIRONMENTAL STUDIES

614.7 US
ENVIRONMENTAL AUDITS. 1988. irreg. (approx. every 18 mos.). $75. Government Institutes, Inc., 4 Research Pl., Ste. 200, Rockville, MD 20850-3226. TEL 301-921-2300. FAX 301-921-0373. Eds. Lawrence Cahill, Raymond W. Kane.
  Description: Contains the step-by-step guidance needed for conducting a successful environmental audit.

333.7 II ISSN 0254-8798
ENVIRONMENTAL AWARENESS. (Text in English) 1977. q. membership. International Society of Naturalists (INSONA), c/o Maharaja Fatehsingh Zoo Trust, Indumati Mahal, Jawaharlal Nehru Marg, Baroda 390 001, India. (Subscr. to: General Secretary, Oza Building, Salatwada, Baroda 390 001, India) Ed. Dr. G.M. Oza. adv.; bk.rev. circ. 1,000. **Indexed:** Biol.Abstr., Forest.Abstr., Indian Sci.Abstr.
  Description: Issues of international environmental conservation and animal conservation.

614.7 574.5 US
ENVIRONMENTAL BIOLOGY. 1972. irreg. $3 per issue. Cornell University, Department of Entomology, 6126 Comstock Hall, Ithaca, NY 14853. TEL 607-255-2212. FAX 607-255-0939. E-mail: dp18@cornell.edu. Ed. David Pimentel. (back issues avail.) **Indexed:** Biol.Abstr. **Document type:** monographic series.

333.8 340 US
ENVIRONMENTAL BRIEFING. q. free to qualified personnel. Sachnoff & Weaver, Ltd., 20 S. Wacker Dr., Ste. 2900, Chicago, IL 60606. TEL 312-207-1000. FAX 312-207-6400. Ed. J.J. Brown. circ. 1,200. (back issues avail.) **Document type:** newsletter.

ENVIRONMENTAL BUILDING NEWS; a newsletter on environmentally sustainable design and construction. see BUILDING AND CONSTRUCTION

614.7 330 US ISSN 1045-8611
HD9718.U6 CODEN: EBUJEE
ENVIRONMENTAL BUSINESS JOURNAL; strategic information for a changing industry. 1988. m. $395 (foreign $445). Environmental Business Publishing, Inc., 4452 Park Blvd., 306, San Diego, CA 92116-4039. TEL 619-295-7685. FAX 619-295-5743. (Subscr. to: Box 371769, San Diego, CA 92137-1769) Ed. Grant Ferrier. circ. 1,000. (back issues avail.)
  Description: Activities in the environmental and pollution generating industries to minimize environmental effects.

613.1 330 US ISSN 1067-8735
▼**ENVIRONMENTAL BUSINESS TRENDLETTER**; environmental news for business & agriculture. 1993. q. $65 (foreign $95). Freiberg Publishing Company, 2302 W. First St., Cedar Falls, IA 50613. TEL 319-277-3599. FAX 319-277-3783. Ed.Bd.

ENVIRONMENTAL CARCINOGENESIS & ECOTOXICOLOGY REVIEWS. see ENVIRONMENTAL STUDIES — Toxicology And Environmental Safety

614.7 US
ENVIRONMENTAL CAREERS BULLETIN. 1989. m. free to qualified personnel. 11693 San Vicente Blvd., Ste. 327, Los Angeles, CA 90049. TEL 310-399-3533. FAX 310-399-8763. Ed. David Cook. circ. 30,000 (controlled). **Document type:** bulletin.
  Description: Advertises firms recruiting degreed environmental professionals and environmentally related products and services.

620.85 371.42 US
ENVIRONMENTAL CAREERS ORGANIZATION. CONNECTIONS. 1972. irreg. (3-4/yr.). Environmental Careers Organization, Inc., 286 Congress St., 3rd Fl., Boston, MA 02210-1009. TEL 617-426-4375. FAX 617-423-0998. Ed. Greta Zettergren. illus.; circ. 5,000 (controlled). **Document type:** newsletter.
  Formerly (until 1992): C E I P Fund. Connections.
  Description: Protects and enhances the environment through the development of professionals, the promotion of careers, and the inspiration of individual action.

ENVIRONMENTAL CITIZEN SUITS. see LAW

614.7 340 US ISSN 1040-6026
K5
ENVIRONMENTAL CLAIMS JOURNAL. 1988. q. $189 (foreign $239). Executive Enterprises Publications Co., Inc., 22 W. 21st St., New York, NY 10010-6904. TEL 212-645-7880. FAX 212-645-1160. Ed. Deborah C.K. Wenger. (also avail. in microform from WSH; reprint service avail. from WSH)
  —BLDSC (3791.412500); UnCover; UMI. **CCC**.
  Description: Covers the prevention and litigation of environmental claims, including risk assessment and management, trial tactics and strategies, insurance, claims investigation and management, and technical management.

ENVIRONMENTAL COALITION ON NUCLEAR POWER NEWSLETTER. see ENERGY

614.7 US ISSN 1072-1029
ENVIRONMENTAL COMMUNICATOR. 1972. 6/yr. $35 membership. North American Association for Environmental Education, Box 400, Troy, OH 45373. TEL 513-676-2514. Ed. Andrea Shotkin. bk.rev. circ. 2,500. (processed) **Document type:** newsletter.
  Formerly: N A E E Newsletter.

614.7 340 US ISSN 1050-4605
TD194
ENVIRONMENTAL COMPLIANCE.* 1990. a. Environmental Compliance Group, 206 Elm St., Ste. 106, Lewisville, TX 75057. TEL 214-436-8797.

614.7 333.7 SZ ISSN 0376-8929
TD169 CODEN: EVCNA4
ENVIRONMENTAL CONSERVATION; international journal devoted to maintaining global vitality through exposing and countering environmental deterioration resulting from human population pressure and unwise technology. (Text in English) 1974. 4/yr. 290 SFr.($197) (effective 1994). (Foundation for Environmental Conservation) Elsevier Science S.A., P.O. Box 564, CH-1001 Lausanne 1, Switzerland. TEL 41-21-3207381. FAX 41-21-3235444. TELEX 450620-ELSA-CH. (Subscr. in U.S. and Canada to: Elsevier Science Inc., Box 882, Madison Sq. Sta., New York, NY 10159. TEL 212-989-5800. FAX 212-633-3990) Ed. Nicholas Polunin. bk.rev. (also avail. in microform from UMI) **Indexed:** Abstr.Rural Dev.Trop., Acid Pre.Dig., Agroforest.Abstr., Biol.Abstr., Biol.Dig., Chem.Abstr., Curr.Adv.Ecol.Sci., Curr.Cont., Curr.Ref.Fish Res., Deep Sea Res.& Oceanogr.Abstr., Energy Ind., Energy Info.Abstr., Energy Rev., Environ.Abstr., Environ.Ind., Environ.Per.Bibl. (1974-), Excerp.Med., Geo.Abstr., Helminthol.Abstr., I D A, Ind.Sci.Rev., Int.Lab.Doc., Key Word Ind.Wildl.Res., Meteor.& Geoastrophys.Abstr., Mid.East: Abstr.& Ind., Ocean.Abstr., Pollut.Abstr., Rev.Appl.Entomol., Risk Abstr., Rural Devel.Abstr., Rural Recreat.Tour.Abstr., Sci.Cit.Ind., Sel.Water Res.Abstr., So.Pac.Per.Ind., Soils & Fert., W.R.C.Inf., Weed Abstr., World Agri.Econ.& Rural Sociol.Abstr. **Document type:** academic/scholarly publication.
  —BLDSC (3791.415000); EI; Faxon; SWETS; CASDDS. **CCC**.
  Description: Advocates timely action for the protection and amelioration of the environment of man and nature throughout the world.
  Refereed Serial

THE ENVIRONMENTAL CONTRACT OPPORTUNITY REPORT. see PUBLIC ADMINISTRATION

333.8 340 US
ENVIRONMENTAL CONTROL LAW. 1970. q. $14 to members. Illinois State Bar Association, Section on Environmental Control Law, Illinois Bar Center, Springfield, IL 62701. TEL 217-525-1760. FAX 217-525-0172. Ed. J.J. Brown. circ. 1,100. (looseleaf format; back issues avail.) **Document type:** newsletter.

614.7 US ISSN 0013-9238
ENVIRONMENTAL CONTROL NEWS FOR SOUTHERN INDUSTRY. 1971. m. $29.95. E.F.W. Commercial Ventures Inc., Box 241813, Memphis, TN 38124-1813. TEL 901-685-2077. FAX 901-684-1852. Ed. Edward F. Williams III. adv.; bk.rev. circ. 300. (looseleaf format; also avail. in microfilm from UMI) **Document type:** newsletter.

613.1 346 US ISSN 1041-3863
KF3775.A15
ENVIRONMENTAL COUNSELOR. 1988. m. $225. Business Laws, Inc., 11630 Chillicothe Rd., Chesterland, OH 44026. TEL 216-729-7996. FAX 216-729-0645. Ed. William A. Hancock. index, cum.index. (back issues avail.) **Document type:** newsletter.
  —CCC.
  Description: Environmental issues for corporate attorneys.

301.31 US ISSN 0091-9837
HC110.E5
ENVIRONMENTAL DEFENSE FUND. ANNUAL REPORT. a. membership. Environmental Defense Fund, 257 Park Ave. S., New York, NY 10010. TEL 212-505-2100. FAX 212-505-2375.

614.7 UK
ENVIRONMENTAL DIRECTORY. 1968. irreg. £4. Civic Trust, 17 Carlton House Terr., London SW1Y 5AW, England. TEL 44-71-930-0914. FAX 44-71-321-0180. Ed. Saskia Hallam. **Document type:** directory.

614.7 US
▼**ENVIRONMENTAL DIRECTORY OF CENTRAL AND LATIN AMERICA.** 1994. $148. Business Publishers, Inc., 951 Pershing Dr., Silver Spring, MD 20910-4464. TEL 301-589-5103; 800-BPI-0122. FAX 301-585-9075. **Document type:** directory.
  Description: Includes more than 10,000 detailed listings of private- and public-sector organizations, including contact names, titles, company names, addresses and phone numbers.

628 370 UK ISSN 0309-8451
ENVIRONMENTAL EDUCATION. 1973. 3/yr. £14 (foreign £22). National Association for Environmental Education, Wolverhampton University, Walsall Campus, W. Midlands WS1 3BD, England. TEL 0922-31200. FAX 0902-323177. Ed. Philip Neal. adv. contact: Helen Warner. bk.rev. circ. 2,000. (back issues avail.) **Document type:** academic/scholarly publication.

614.7 UK ISSN 0144-9281
ENVIRONMENTAL EDUCATION AND INFORMATION. (No issues published in 1983) 1981. q. £21 (foreign £29) (effective 1993). University of Salford, Environmental Resources Unit, Newton Building, Salford M5 4WT, England. TEL 061-745-5221. FAX 061-745-5999. Ed. G. Ashworth. adv.; bk.rev. circ. 300. **Indexed:** C.I.J.E., Energy Rev., Environ.Per.Bibl. (1984-), ERIC, Geo.Abstr., Sel.Water Res.Abstr. **Document type:** academic/scholarly publication.
  —BLDSC (3791.445000).
  Description: Aims to encourage knowledge, understanding, awareness and protection of the global environment.

614.7 620 US ISSN 1068-4654
ENVIRONMENTAL ENGINEER. 1966. q. $20. American Academy of Environmental Engineers, 130 Holiday Ct., Ste. 100, Annapolis, MD 21401. TEL 410-266-3311. FAX 410-266-7653. circ. controlled. **Document type:** trade publication.
  Former titles: Diplomate (ISSN 0886-6465); American Academy of Environmental Engineers. Diplomate Newsletter.

ENVIRONMENTAL ENGINEERING. see ENGINEERING

614.7 628.44 US
ENVIRONMENTAL ENGINEERING NEWSLETTER. 1944. m. free. Purdue University, School of Civil Engineering, W. Lafayette, IN 47907. TEL 317-494-2194. FAX 317-496-1107. Ed. John M. Bell. circ. 3,000. (processed) **Document type:** newsletter.
  Description: Presents new facts on environmental issues.

614.7 620 US ISSN 0896-3827
TD169.6
ENVIRONMENTAL ENGINEERING SELECTION GUIDE. 1985. a. free. American Academy of Environmental Engineers, 130 Holiday Ct., Ste. 100, Annapolis, MD 21401. TEL 410-266-3311. FAX 410-266-7653. Ed. William C. Anderson. circ. 10,000. **Document type:** trade publication.
  Formerly: American Academy of Environmental Engineers. Consultant Directory.

ENVIRONMENTAL STUDIES

ENVIRONMENTAL ETHICS; an interdisciplinary journal dedicated to the philosophical aspects of environmental problems. see *PHILOSOPHY*

614.7 US ISSN 0731-5732
KF3775.A15
ENVIRONMENTAL FORUM; the policy journal of the Environmental Law Institute. 1981-1986; resumed 1988. bi-m. $75. Environmental Law Institute, 1616 P.St., N.W., Ste. 200, Washington, DC 20036. TEL 202-328-5150. FAX 202-328-5002. Ed. Stephen Dujack. **Indexed:** Acid Pre.Dig., Acid Rain Abstr., Acid Rain Ind., C.L.I., Environ.Per.Bibl. (1989-), P.A.I.S., Sel.Water Res.Abstr.
—BLDSC (3791.466500); Faxon; UnCover.
Formerly (until 1982): E L I Associates Newsletter.
Description: Designed for professionals in environmental law, policy and management.

614.7 622 UK ISSN 0269-4042
TD195.M5 CODEN: EGHEE3
ENVIRONMENTAL GEOCHEMISTRY AND HEALTH. 1979. q. $164. Science and Technology Letters, P.O. Box 81, Northwood, Middlesex HA6 3DN, England. TEL 09274-23586. FAX 09274-25066. Ed. Brian E. Davies. abstr.; bibl.; illus. **Indexed:** AESIS, Cadscan, Chem.Abstr., Curr.Adv.Ecol.Sci., Curr.Cont., Energy Ind., Energy Info.Abstr., Environ.Abstr., Environ.Per.Bibl., Excerp.Med., Field Crop Abstr., Geo.Abstr., GeoRef., Ind.Vet., Lead Abstr., Risk Abstr., Soils & Fert., Triticale Abstr., Zincscan. **Document type:** academic/scholarly publication.
—BLDSC (3791.466800); CIS; Faxon; UnCover; SWETS; UMI; CASDDS. **CCC.**
Incorporates: Minerals and the Environment (ISSN 0142-7245)

613.1 US ISSN 1043-5700
KF3946.A15
ENVIRONMENTAL HAZARDS. 1989. m. Prentice Hall Law & Business, 270 Sylvan Ave., Englewood Cliffs, NJ 07632-2513.

614.7 UN ISSN 0250-863X
RA1190 CODEN: EHCRDN
ENVIRONMENTAL HEALTH CRITERIA. French edition: Criteres d'Hygiene de l'Environnement (ISSN 0250-846X); Spanish edition: Criterios de Salud Ambiental (ISSN 0250-8478); Russian edition: Kriterii Sanitarno-Gigieniceskogo Sostojanija Okruzajuscej Sredy (ISSN 0250-8648) 1976. irreg. (approx. 15/yr.). 200 SFr.($160) World Health Organization, Distribution and Sales, 1211 Geneva 27, Switzerland. TEL 022-7912111. FAX 022-788-0401. TEL 022-27821-OMS. circ. 5,000. (back issues avail.) **Indexed:** Dairy Sci.Abstr., Diar.Dis.Res., Environ.Abstr., Excerp.Med., Ind.Vet., Vet.Bull. **Document type:** monographic series.
—BLDSC (3791.491000); CIS; El; SWETS.
Description: Examines the risks to human health and the environment of selected chemicals and environmental pollutants.

ENVIRONMENTAL HEALTH LETTER; policy, technology, research. see *MEDICAL SCIENCES*

614.7 US
ENVIRONMENTAL HEALTH MONTHLY. 1988. m. $35. Citizens Clearinghouse for Hazardous Wastes, Inc., Box 6806, Falls Church, VA 22040. TEL 703-237-2249. Ed. Stephen Lester. circ. 700. (back issues avail.)

614.7 US
ENVIRONMENTAL HEALTH NEWS. 1987. 3/yr. free. University of Washington, Department of Environmental Health, SC-34, 461 Health Science Bldg., Seattle, WA 98195. TEL 206-543-6959. FAX 206-543-8123. Ed. Dr. T. Burbacher. circ. 2,500. (back issues avail.)
Description: Aims to inform researchers, teachers, and workers about current news and issues in environmental health.

614.7 US
ENVIRONMENTAL HEALTH PERSPECTIVES. m. $36 (foreign $45) (effective Oct. 1993). U.S. Department of Health and Human Services, National Institute of Environmental Health Sciences, Box 12233, Research Triangle Park, NC 27709. TEL 919-541-3406. FAX 919-541-0273. (Dist. by: Supt. of Documents, U.S. Govt. Printing Office, Washington, DC 20402) Eds. George W. Lucier, Gary E.R. Hook. **Document type:** government publication, academic/scholarly publication.
Description: Includes original scientific articles concerning all aspects of environmental health and science, up-to-date news items and articles on important and controversial environmental issues.
Refereed Serial

ENVIRONMENTAL HEALTH REVIEW. see *PUBLIC HEALTH AND SAFETY*

614.7 973 US
ENVIRONMENTAL HISTORY REVIEW. 1976. q. $24 to individuals (foreign $32); institutions $30 (foreign $38); students and retired $12. American Society for Environmental History, c/o Center for Technology Studies, New Jersey Institute of Technology, Newark, NJ 07102. TEL 201-596-3270. FAX 201-565-0586. Ed. Hal K. Rothman. adv.; bk.rev.; bibl. circ. 800. (also avail. in microform from UMI; reprint service avail. from UMI) **Indexed:** Amer.Hist.& Life, Energy Rev., Environ.Abstr., Environ.Per.Bibl. (1977-), ERIC, Hist.Abstr., I D A.
—UnCover. **CCC.**
Formerly (until 1989): Environmental Review (ISSN 0147-2496); Which incorporates (in 1983): Environmental History Newsletter.
Description: International journal that seeks understanding of the human experience of the environment. Emphasis is on the perspectives of history and the liberal arts and sciences.

ENVIRONMENTAL HONG KONG (YEAR). see *PUBLIC ADMINISTRATION*

614.7 US ISSN 0195-9255
TD194.6 CODEN: EIARDK
ENVIRONMENTAL IMPACT ASSESSMENT REVIEW. Short title: E I A Review. 1980-1983; resumed 1985. 6/yr. $235 to institutions (foreign $270) (effective 1994). (Massachusetts Institute of Technology, Center for Technology, Policy, and Industrial Development) Elsevier Science Inc., 655 Ave. of the Americas, New York, NY 10010. TEL 212-989-5800. FAX 212-633-3990. TELEX 420643 AEP UI. Eds. Lawrence E. Susskind, Teresa Hill. (also avail. in microform from UMI; microfilm from JSC) **Indexed:** Curr.Cont., Deep Sea Res.& Oceanogr.Abstr., Ecol.Abstr., Energy Rev., Eng.Ind., Environ.Per.Bibl. (1986-), Excerp.Med., Geo.Abstr., Geophys.Abstr., I D A, INIS Atomind., Pollut.Abstr., Ref.Zh., Sage Pub.Admin.Abstr., Sci.Abstr., Sel.Water Res.Abstr. **Document type:** academic/scholarly publication.
—BLDSC (3791.510500); El; Faxon; UnCover; SWETS. **CCC.**
Description: Highlights advances in impact assessment, environmental decision making, and the resolution of environmental disputes.

614.7 TH
ENVIRONMENTAL INDEX. (Text in English) 1979. 3/yr. $80 to individuals; institutions $130. Asian Institute of Technology, Environmental Systems Information Center, P.O. Box 2754, Bangkok 10501, Thailand. FAX 66-2-5245870. TELEX 84276 AIT TH. adv.; bk.rev.; abstr.; bibl. circ. 400. (also avail. in microfiche; back issues avail.) **Document type:** abstracting/indexing.
●Also available online.
Formerly (until 1992): Environmental Sanitation Abstracts - Low Cost Options (ISSN 0125-2186)
Description: A holding list of new records added to the ENSIC database and documents available from member countries of ENSICNET.

ENVIRONMENTAL INDUSTRIES MARKETPLACE. see *BUSINESS AND ECONOMICS — Trade And Industrial Directories*

614.7 330 US
ENVIRONMENTAL INDUSTRY YEARBOOK. 1988. a. $75. Environmental Economics, 1026 Irving St., Philadelphia, PA 19107. TEL 215-925-7168. Ed. Michael Silverstein. **Document type:** directory.
Formerly: Directory of Environmental Investing.

ENVIRONMENTAL INSURANCE COVERAGE; state law and regulation. see *INSURANCE*

614.7 US ISSN 1042-5209
ENVIRONMENTAL LAB. 1989. bi-m. $57 (foreign $92). Leo Douglas, Inc., 9609 Gayton Rd., Ste. 100, Richmond, VA 23233. TEL 804-741-6704. FAX 804-750-2399. Ed. Mary Benke. adv. contact: Betty Jo Bass. circ. 20,000. **Indexed:** Ind.Hyg.Dig. **Document type:** trade publication.
—BLDSC (3791.512700).
Description: For environmental testing professionals Includes scientific techniques, instrumentation focus, regulatory compliance, certification and accreditation, and business management and development.

614.7 US ISSN 0046-2276
K5
ENVIRONMENTAL LAW (PORTLAND). 1970. 4/yr. $24 (foreign $32). Northwestern School of Law, Lewis and Clark College, 10015 S.W. Terwilliger Blvd., Portland, OR 97219. TEL 503-768-6700. FAX 503-768-5671. Ed. Todd Glass. adv.; bk.rev.; bibl.; charts; index. circ. 1,100. (also avail. in microform from UMI; back issues avail.; reprint service avail. from RRI,UMI) **Indexed:** C.L.I., Deep Sea Res.& Oceanogr.Abstr., Energy Info.Abstr., Energy Rev., Environ.Abstr., Environ.Per.Bibl. (1972-), Excerp.Med., L.R.I., Leg.Cont., Leg.Per., Noise Pollut.Publ.Abstr., Ocean.Abstr., Pollut.Abstr., W.R.C.Inf. **Document type:** academic/scholarly publication.
●Also available online. Vendor(s): Mead Data Central, Inc., West Services, Inc..
—BLDSC (3791.513000); CIS; Faxon; UnCover; SWETS; UMI.
Description: Forum providing information on environmental issues of importance to the legal community.

ENVIRONMENTAL LAW (WASHINGTON). see *LAW*

ENVIRONMENTAL LAW ALERT. see *LAW*

ENVIRONMENTAL LAW AND ENERGY JOURNAL. see *ENERGY*

ENVIRONMENTAL LAW AND MANAGEMENT. see *LAW*

ENVIRONMENTAL LAW ANTHOLOGY. see *LAW*

614.7 340 US
ENVIRONMENTAL LAW HANDBOOK. 1973. biennial. $68. Government Institutes, Inc., 4 Research Pl., Ste. 200, Rockville, MD 20850-3226. TEL 301-921-2300. FAX 301-921-0373. (back issues avail.)
Description: Provides practical and current information on all major areas of environmental law.

614.7 240 US ISSN 1048-0420
ENVIRONMENTAL LAW IN NEW YORK; developments in federal and state law. no.7, 1990. m. $300. Matthew Bender & Co., Inc., 11 Penn Plaza, New York, NY 10001. TEL 212-216-8198. FAX 212-594-6921. Ed. Michael B. Gerrard.

ENVIRONMENTAL LAW JOURNAL. see *LAW*

614.7 JA
ENVIRONMENTAL LAW JOURNAL. (Text and summaries in Japanese) 1974. a. 3800 Yen. Japan Center for Human Environmental Problems, 2-17 Jinbo-cho, Kanda, Chiyoda-ku, Tokyo, Japan. TEL 03-3264-1311.

ENVIRONMENTAL LAW MONTHLY. see *LAW*

333.8 340 US
ENVIRONMENTAL LAW NEWS. irreg. (2-4/yr.). membership. State Bar of Wisconsin, Environmental Law Section, 402 W. Wilson St., Madison, WI 53703. TEL 608-257-3838. FAX 608-257-5502. circ. 850. (back issues avail.) **Document type:** newsletter.

614.7 AT
ENVIRONMENTAL LAW REFORM GROUP. PUBLICATION. no.2, 1972. irreg. Environmental Law Reform Group, c/o Dr. R.J.K. Chapman, Dept. of Political Science, University of Tasmania, Box 252c, Hobart, Tas. 7001, Australia. circ. 500. **Document type:** monographic series.

ENVIRONMENTAL STUDIES

614.7 340 US ISSN 0046-2284
KF3775.A6
ENVIRONMENTAL LAW REPORTER. 1971. m. $995. Environmental Law Institute, 1616 P St., N.W., Ste. 200, Washington, DC 20036. TEL 202-328-5150. Ed. Adam Babich. index. circ. 1,000. (looseleaf format) **Indexed:** C.L.I., Energy Rev., Environ.Abstr., Environ.Ind., Environ.Per.Bibl. (1983-), L.R.I., P.A.I.S. ●Also available online. Vendor(s): Mead Data Central, Inc., West Services, Inc..
—BLDSC (3791.515200); CIS.
Description: Analyzes current legal issues, provides full text of recent court decisions, and comments on key ongoing litigation.

ENVIRONMENTAL LAW REPORTS. see *LAW*

ENVIRONMENTAL LIABILITY; law and strategy for businesses and corporations. see *LAW*

ENVIRONMENTAL LIABILITY. see *LAW*

614.7 US ISSN 0364-152X
TD169 CODEN: EMNGDC
ENVIRONMENTAL MANAGEMENT (NEW YORK); an international journal for decision-makers and scientists. 1977. 6/yr. $299 (effective 1995). Springer-Verlag, Journals, 175 Fifth Ave., New York, NY 10010. TEL 212-460-1500. FAX 212-473-6272. (N. American subscr. to: Journal Fulfillment Services, Box 2485, Secaucus, NJ 07096-2491. TEL 800-777-4643. FAX 201-348-4505; Elsewhere: Heidelberger Platz 33, 1000 Berlin 33, Germany. TEL 030-8207-1. FAX 030-8214091) Ed. David Alexander. adv.; bk.rev.; charts; illus.; index. circ. 1,000. (also avail. in microform from UMI; reprint service avail. from ISI) **Indexed:** Acid Pre.Dig., Acid Rain Abstr., Acid Rain Ind., Agroforest.Abstr., Chem.Abstr., Curr.Cont., Deep Sea Res.& Oceanogr.Abstr., Eng.Ind., Eng.Ind., Environ.Abstr., Environ.Ind., Excerp.Med., Forest.Abstr., Forest Prod.Abstr., Ind.Sci.Rev., INIS Atomind., NRN, Ocean.Abstr., Pollut.Abstr., Risk Abstr., Rural Recreat.Tour.Abstr., Sci.Cit.Ind., Sel.Water Res.Abstr., Soils & Fert., W.R.C.Inf., Weed Abstr., World Agri.Econ.& Rural Sociol.Abstr. **Document type:** academic/scholarly publication.
—BLDSC (3791.519000); CIS; Faxon; UnCover; SWETS; UMI; CASDDS. **CCC.**
Description: Publishes material pertaining to ecological modeling, resource management, energy, hazard response, environmental monitoring, and hazardous substances mangement.
Refereed Serial

610 UK ISSN 0956-6163
RA565.A1 CODEN: EMHEEB
ENVIRONMENTAL MANAGEMENT & HEALTH. 1990. 4/yr. $659.95. M C B University Press Ltd., 60-62 Toller Ln., Bradford, W. Yorks BD8 9BY, England. TEL 0274-499821. FAX 0274-547143. TELEX 51317-MCBUNI-G. (US subscr. to: Box 1943, Birmingham, AL 35201. TEL 800-633-4931) Ed. J. Rose. **Indexed:** Environ.Per.Bibl. (1990-). **Document type:** academic/scholarly publication.
—BLDSC (3791.519200); UMI.
Description: Examines environmental factors and their impact on human health.

614.7 340 658 US ISSN 1041-8172
KF3775.A15
ENVIRONMENTAL MANAGEMENT REVIEW. 1986. q. $188 (foreign $252). Government Institutes, Inc., 4 Research Pl., St. 200, Rockville, MD 20850-3226. TEL 301-921-2300. FAX 301-921-0373. Ed. Thomas F.P. Sullivan. adv.; bk.rev. circ. 300. (back issues avail.) **Indexed:** Environ.Abstr., Herb.Abstr. Formerly (until 1990): Environmental Management Report (ISSN 0889-4663)
Description: Original articles analyzing daily environmental challenges.

614.7 658 US ISSN 1043-786X
TD897.5 CODEN: ENVMEA
ENVIRONMENTAL MANAGER; environmental solutions that make good business sense. 1989. m. $162 (foreign $239). Executive Enterprises Publications Co., Inc., 22 W. 21st St., New York, NY 10010-6904. TEL 212-645-7880. FAX 212-645-1160. Ed. Jean Stephenson. **Indexed:** Environ.Abstr. **Document type:** newsletter.
—BLDSC (3791.521500); UMI. **CCC.**
Description: Features news and case studies dealing with environmental problems such as toxic waste cleanups, waste minimization, underground storage tank leaks, and clean air standards.

ENVIRONMENTAL MANAGER. see *LAW*

614.7 US ISSN 0887-9753
KF3775.A15
ENVIRONMENTAL MANAGER'S COMPLIANCE ADVISOR. 1985. bi-w. $249.50. Business & Legal Reports, Inc., 39 Academy St., Madison, CT 06443-1513. TEL 203-245-7448. FAX 203-245-2559. Ed. Alan J. Borner. circ. 3,000. (back issues avail.)
—CCC.

ENVIRONMENTAL MEDICINE. see *MEDICAL SCIENCES*

614.7 NE ISSN 0167-6369
TD169 CODEN: EMASDH
ENVIRONMENTAL MONITORING AND ASSESSMENT; an international journal. 1981. 15/yr. fl.1465($765) (effective 1994). Kluwer Academic Publishers, Postbus 17, 3300 AA Dordrecht, Netherlands. TEL 31-78-334911. FAX 31-78-334254. TELEX 29245 KAPG NL. (Dist. by: Kluwer Academic Publishers Group, P.O. Box 322, 3300 AH Dordrecht, Netherlands. TEL 31-78-524400. FAX 31-78-524474; N. America dist. addr.: Box 358, Accord Sta., Hingham, MA 02018-0358. TEL 617-871-6600. FAX 617-871-6528) Ed. G. Bruce Wiersma. adv.; bk.rev.; illus. (also avail. in microform from UMI; reprint service avail. from SWZ) **Indexed:** Acid Pre.Dig., Acid Rain Abstr., Acid Rain Ind., ASCA, Biodet.Abstr., Biol.Abstr., Chem.Abstr., Curr.Adv.Ecol.Sci., Curr.Cont., Deep Sea Res.& Oceanogr.Abstr., Energy Info.Abstr., Energy Rev., Environ.Abstr., Environ.Ind., Environ.Per.Bibl. (1982-), Excerp.Med., Field Crop Abstr., Geo.Abstr., Ind.Vet., Key to Econ.Sci., Pollut.Abstr., Sage Pub.Admin.Abstr., Sci.Abstr., Sel.Water Res.Abstr., Soils & Fert., Soyabean Abstr., Triticale Abstr., W.R.C.Inf. **Document type:** academic/scholarly publication.
—BLDSC (3791.523300); CIS; Faxon; UnCover; SWETS; UMI; CASDDS. **CCC.**
Description: Covers progress in pollution monitoring, emphasizing technical developments, monitoring systems and the use of environmental monitoring data in assessing pollution risks to mankind and the environment.
Refereed Serial

614.7 II
ENVIRONMENTAL N G O'S IN INDIA; a directory. (Text in English) irreg., 5th ed. 1992. (Ministry of Environment and Forests, Environmental Information System) World Wide Fund for Nature - India, 172-B, Lodhi Estate, New Delhi 110 003, India. **Document type:** directory.

614.7 333.7 550 MY ISSN 0127-7162
ENVIRONMENTAL NEWS DIGEST. (Text in English) 1983. 3/yr. M.$30($30) Sahabat Alam Malaysia - Friends of the Earth Malaysia, 19 Kelawai Rd., 10250 Pulau Pinang, Malaysia. TEL 6-04-376930. FAX 6-04-375705. Ed. David Heath. bk.rev.; charts; illus.; stat. circ. 500. (back issues avail.)

628 US
▼**ENVIRONMENTAL NEWS NETWORK.** 1993. s-a. $125. Box 1996, Sunvalley, ID 83353. TEL 208-726-3649. FAX 208-726-2476. **Document type:** academic/scholarly publication, trade publication.

613.1 AT ISSN 0314-8742
ENVIRONMENTAL NEWSLETTER. 1976. irreg. free. University of Newcastle, Board of Environmental Studies, Newcastle, N.S.W. 2308, Australia. **Document type:** newsletter.

614.7 US
ENVIRONMENTAL NEWSLINE. m. Kentucky Chamber of Commerce, Box 817, Frankfort, KY 40602-9971. TEL 502-695-4700. FAX 502-695-6824. Ed. Tony Sholar.

614.7 639.9 US ISSN 0736-9603
ENVIRONMENTAL OPPORTUNITIES. 1982. m. $47. Box 788, Walpole, NH 03608-0788. TEL 603-756-4553. Ed. Sanford Berry. adv. circ. 4,000. (back issues avail.)

614.7 US
ENVIRONMENTAL OUTLOOK. 10/yr. (except July & Aug.). price varies. University of Washington, Institute for Environmental Studies, 211 Engineering Annex FM-12, Seattle, WA 98195. TEL 206-543-1812. FAX 206-543-2025. Ed. Polly Dyer. circ. 2,000. **Document type:** newsletter.
Description: Provides a calendar of environmental courses, conferences, meetings, and hearings, as well as information about faculty activities. Includes short notes on environmental curricula at the University and on regional environmental topics.

614.7 352.7 IS
ENVIRONMENTAL PLANNING. (Text in English and Hebrew) 1966. 3/yr. $25. Israeli Association for Environmental Planning, 5 Gazit St., Tel Aviv 69 417, Israel. Ed. Dan Soen. bk.rev. circ. 500.

614.7 US
ENVIRONMENTAL POLICY ALERT. bi-w. $485 (foreign $535). Inside Washington Publishers, Box 7167, Benjamin Franklin Sta., Washington, DC 20044. TEL 703-892-8500. FAX 703-685-2606. **Document type:** newsletter.

344.04 NE ISSN 0378-777X
LAW
ENVIRONMENTAL POLICY AND LAW. (Text in English, French) 1975. 6/yr. fl.434($231) (effective 1994). (International Council for Environmental Law) I O S Press, Van Diemenstraat 94, 1013 CN Amsterdam, Netherlands. TEL 31-20-6382189. FAX 31-20-6203419. (In N. America: Box 10558, Burke, VA 22009-0558. TEL 703-323-5554. FAX 703-250-4705) Ed. Wolfgang E. Burhenne. adv.; bk.rev.; bibl.; charts; illus.; index. (also avail. in microform; back issues avail.) **Indexed:** Acid Rain Abstr., Curr.Cont., ELLIS, Energy Ind., Energy Info.Abstr., Energy Rev., Environ.Abstr., Environ.Per.Bibl., Excerp.Med., Geo.Abstr., GeoRef., Int.Polit.Sci.Abstr., Key to Econ.Sci., Pollut.Abstr., Sci.Cit.Ind., SSCI, W.R.C.Inf. **Document type:** academic/scholarly publication.
—BLDSC (3791.537000); CIS; EI; UnCover; SWETS. **CCC.**

614.7 IS ISSN 0792-0032
HC340.E5 CODEN: EPRFEH
ENVIRONMENTAL POLICY REVIEW: THE SOVIET UNION AND EAST EUROPE. (Text in English) 1987. 2/yr. $15 (effective 1992). Hebrew University, Marjorie Mayrock Center for Soviet and East European Research, c/o Faculty of Social Sciences, Mount Scopus, Jerusalem 91905, Israel. TEL 972-2-883180. FAX 972-2-322545. TELEX 26458. Ed. Ze'ev Wolfson. circ. 200. **Document type:** academic/scholarly publication.
—BLDSC (3791.537500); Faxon.
Description: Monitors ecological problems, policies and responses, with a focus on the aftermath of the Chernobyl nuclear disaster.

614.7 US ISSN 0191-5398
CODEN: EPROD9
ENVIRONMENTAL PROFESSIONAL. 1979. q. $95. (National Association of Environmental Professionals) Blackwell Scientific Publications, Inc., 238 Main St., Ste. 501, Cambridge, MA 02142. TEL 617-876-7000. FAX 617-876-7022. Ed. John Lemons. adv.; bk.rev. circ. 4,000. (also avail. in microform from UMI; reprint service avail. from UMI) **Indexed:** Acid Rain Abstr., Acid Rain Ind., Curr.Cont., Ecol.Abstr., Energy Ind., Energy Info.Abstr., Energy Rev., Environ.Abstr., Environ.Per.Bibl. (1986-), INIS Atomind., Mid.East: Abstr.& Ind., Pollut.Abstr., Sel.Water Res.Abstr., World Agri.Econ.& Rural Sociol.Abstr. **Document type:** academic/scholarly publication.
—BLDSC (3791.547200); CIS; Faxon; UnCover; UMI. **CCC.**
Description: Publishes interdisciplinary papers on significant environmental issues.
Refereed Serial

ENVIRONMENTAL STUDIES

614.7 660 US ISSN 0278-4491
TD1 CODEN: ENVPDI
ENVIRONMENTAL PROGRESS (NEW YORK). 1982. q. $150 to non-members (foreign $175); members $36. American Institute of Chemical Engineers, 345 E. 47th St., New York, NY 10017. TEL 212-705-7663. FAX 212-752-3294. Ed. Gary F. Bennett. circ. 5,000. (also avail. in microform from UMI; back issues avail.; reprint service avail. from UMI) **Indexed:** Acid Rain Abstr., Acid Rain Ind., API Abstr., API Catal., API Hlth.& Environ., API Oil., API Pet.Ref., API Pet.Subst., API Transport., Chem.Abstr., Chem.Eng.Abstr., Energy Info.Abstr., Environ.Abstr., Gas Abstr., INIS Atomind., Risk Abstr., Risk Abstr., Sel.Water Res.Abstr., Soils & Fert., T.C.E.A., W.R.C.Inf. **Document type:** trade publication.
—BLDSC (3791.547300); CIS; Faxon; UnCover; SWETS; UMI; CASDDS. **CCC.**
Description: Covers current technological advances with an emphasis on practical applications of chemical engineering to pollution abatement.

614.7 333.7 US
ENVIRONMENTAL PROGRESS (SPRINGFIELD). 1976. q. free. Environmental Protection Agency, Office of Public Information, 2200 Churchill Rd., Box 19276, Springfield, IL 62794-9276. TEL 217-782-5562. FAX 217-782-9039. Ed. Joan Muraro. bibl.; charts; stat. circ. 9,575. **Indexed:** Energy Info.Abstr. (until 1994), Environ.Abstr. **Document type:** government publication, newsletter.
—UnCover.
Formerly: Progress (Springfield) (ISSN 0073-5108)
Description: Covers environmental issues such as new regulations, environmental legislation, recycling and waste management. Publishes hearings, meetings and notices.

614.7 US ISSN 1057-4298
TD169 CODEN: ENPRET
ENVIRONMENTAL PROTECTION. 1990. 8/yr. $90. Stevens Publishing Corporation, 225 N. New Rd., Waco, TX 76710. TEL 817-776-9000. Ed. Carol Mouche. adv. circ. 91,000. **Indexed:** Environ.Abstr., Environ.Per.Bibl. (1990-), Ind.Hyg.Dig., Sel.Water Res.Abstr.
—BLDSC (3791.547495); UnCover. **CCC.**
Description: Presents articles in the field of environmental control written by experts in the areas of air and water pollution, waste water treatment and hazardous materials management.
Refereed Serial

363.6 US ISSN 0509-769X
RA569 CODEN: ERSSD6
ENVIRONMENTAL RADIATION SURVEILLANCE IN WASHINGTON STATE. ANNUAL REPORT. 1961. a. Department of Health, Division of Radiation Protection, Box 47827, Olympia, WA 98504-7827. TEL 206-586-3306. FAX 206-753-1496. Ed. John L. Erickson. illus. circ. 500. **Document type:** government publication.

613.1 669 US
ENVIRONMENTAL REGULATIONS MANUAL. a. $295. Metal Treating Institute, 302 Third St., Ste. 1, Neptune Beach, FL 32266. TEL 904-249-0448. FAX 904-249-0459.

613.1 US
▼**ENVIRONMENTAL REMEDIATION TECHNOLOGY.** 1993. bi-w. $390. Business Publishers, Inc., 951 Pershing Dr., Silver Spring, MD 20910-4464. TEL 301-587-6300; 800-BPI-0122. FAX 301-589-5103. **Document type:** newsletter.
Description: Provides the latest news and analysis of technological developments in the field of environmental remediation technology.

614.7 US ISSN 0013-9351
RA565 CODEN: ENVRAL
ENVIRONMENTAL RESEARCH; a journal of environmental medicine and the environmental sciences. 1967. 8/yr. $714 (foreign $810). Academic Press, Inc., Journal Division, 525 B St., Ste. 1900, San Diego, CA 92101-4495. TEL 619-230-1840. FAX 619-699-6800. (Subscr. to: Box 620000, Orlando, FL 32891-8340. TEL 800-543-9534) Ed. Philip J. Landrigan. adv.; bk.rev.; illus.; index. (back issues avail.) **Indexed:** A.S.& T.Ind., Acid Rain Abstr., Anim.Breed.Abstr., API Abstr., API Catal., API Hlth.& Environ., API Oil., API Pet.Ref., API Pet.Subst., API Transport., Biol.Abstr., C.I.S. Abstr., Cadscan, Chem.Abstr., Curr.Adv.Ecol.Sci., Dairy Sci.Abstr., Environ.Abstr., Environ.Ind., Environ.Per.Bibl., Excerp.Med., Field Crop Abstr., GeoRef, Helminthol.Abstr., Ind.Med., Ind.Vet., INIS Atomind., Lead Abstr., Meteor.& Geoastrophys.Abstr., Noise Pollut.Publ.Abstr., NRN, Nutr.Abstr., Ocean.Abstr., Pollut.Abstr., Poult.Abstr., Risk Abstr., Sci.Cit.Ind., Soc.Sci.Ind., Soils & Fert., Trop.Dis.Bull., Vet.Bull., Zincscan. **Document type:** academic/scholarly publication.
—BLDSC (3791.590000); CIS; Faxon; UnCover; SWETS; CASDDS. **CCC.**
Description: Publishes original reports describing studies of the toxic effects of environmental agents in humans and animals.
Refereed Serial

614.7 JA
ENVIRONMENTAL RESEARCH IN JAPAN. (Text in English) 1975. a. free. Environment Agency, 1-2-2 Kasumigaseki, Chiyoda-ku, Tokyo 100, Japan. TEL 03-3580-1703. FAX 03-3580-3542. index; circ. 320 (controlled). (back issues avail.) **Document type:** government publication.
Description: Provides summarized reports of environmental preservation researches and studies undertaken by national research institutes.

614.7 EI ISSN 1017-4508
ENVIRONMENTAL RESEARCH NEWSLETTER. s-a. free. Environment Institute, Joint Research Institute, 21020 Ispra, Italy. FAX 39-332-78-96-23. (Dist. by: Office for Official Publications of the European Communities, 2 rue Mercier, 2985 Luxembourg, Luxembourg. TEL 49-92-81) **Document type:** newsletter.

ENVIRONMENTAL RESPONSIBILITIES LAW (N.S.W.). see *LAW*

613.1 CN ISSN 1181-8700
GE1
▼**ENVIRONMENTAL REVIEWS.** 1993. q. Can.$55($60) to individuals; institutions Can.$160 ($160). National Research Council of Canada, Ottawa, Ont. K1A 0R6, Canada. TEL 613-993-9084. FAX 613-952-7656. adv.
—BLDSC (3791.598020); UMI.
Description: Deals with the environmental sciences with emphasis on the effects on and responses of both natural and man-made ecosystems to anthropogenic stress.

613.1 US ISSN 1062-0834
ENVIRONMENTAL RISK WATCH; current developments in environmental and human health risk assessment. 1991. bi-w. Ebasco Environmental (Subsidiary of: Ebasco Services Inc.), 2 World Trade Center, New York, NY 10048. (Subscr. to: Ebasco Environmental, 10900 N.E. 8th St., Bellevue, WA 98004-4405. TEL 206-451-4619) Ed. Elaine Dorward King.

614.7 US
ENVIRONMENTAL SAFETY DIGEST. 1990. m. $60 includes membership. Environmental Safety Council of America, Inc., Box 471, Forest Hills, NY 11375. TEL 718-997-7387. circ. 300.

614.7 CN ISSN 0835-605X
ESECEW
ENVIRONMENTAL SCIENCE & ENGINEERING. 1988. bi-m. Can.$48. Davcom Communications Inc., 10 Petch Cr., Aurora, ON L4G 5N7, Canada. TEL 416-727-4666. Ed. Tom Davey. adv. circ. 19,092. **Document type:** trade publication.

614.7 628.5 US ISSN 0194-0287
ENVIRONMENTAL SCIENCE AND TECHNOLOGY (NEW YORK). 1982. irreg., latest 1993. price varies. John Wiley & Sons, Inc., 605 Third Ave., New York, NY 10158-0012. TEL 212-850-6000. FAX 212-850-6088. TELEX 12-7063. Ed. R.L. Metcalf. **Document type:** monographic series.

614.7 628.5 US ISSN 0013-936X
TD180 CODEN: ESTHAG
ENVIRONMENTAL SCIENCE & TECHNOLOGY (WASHINGTON). 1967. m. $89 to non-members (foreign $146); institutions $444 (foreign $501); members $43 (foreign $100). American Chemical Society, 1155 16th St., N.W., Washington, DC 20036. TEL 800-333-9511. FAX 614-447-3671. (Subscr. to: Membership and Subscription Services, Box 3337, Columbus, OH 43210. TEL 614-447-3776) Ed. William H. Glaze. adv.; bk.rev.; abstr.; bibl.; charts; illus.; stat.; tr.lit.; index. circ. 12,400. (also avail. in microform; microfiche) **Indexed:** A.S.& T.Ind., Abstr.Bull.Inst.Pap. Chem., Acid Pre.Dig., Acid Rain Abstr., Acid Rain Ind., Anal.Abstr., API Abstr., API Catal., API Hlth.& Environ., API Oil., API Pet.Ref., API Pet.Subst., API Transport., Biodet.Abstr., Biol.Abstr., Biol.& Agr.Ind., Biol.Dig., Biotech.Abstr., Biwk.Pap.Rad.Chem.& Photochem., Br.Rail.Bd., C.I.S. Abstr., Cadscan, Chem.Abstr., Curr.Adv.Eco.Sci., Curr.Biotech.Abstr., Curr.Cont., Dairy Sci.Abstr., Deep Sea Res.& Oceanogr.Abstr., E&P Hlth. (1993-), Energy Info.Abstr., Energy Rev., Eng.Ind., Environ.Abstr., Environ.Ind., Environ.Per.Bibl. (1972-), Excerp.Med., Field Crop Abstr., Fuel & Energy Abstr., Gas Abstr., Gas Process.& Ppl (1993-), Gen.Sci.Ind., Geo.Abstr., GeoRef., Herb Abstr., Ind.Hyg.Dig., Ind.Sci.Rev., Int.Aerosp.Abstr., Intl.Civil Eng.Abstr., Key to Econ.Sci., Lab.Haz.Bull., Lead Abstr., Mass Spectr.Bull., Met.Abstr., Meteor.& Geoastrophys.Abstr., Mid.East: Abstr.& Ind., NRN, Ocean.Abstr., Off.Tech. (1993-), Petrol.Abstr. (1970-), Pollut.Abstr., Risk Abstr., Sci.Abstr., Sci.Cit.Ind., Sel J.Water, Sel.Water Res.Abstr., Soft.Abstr.Eng. Soils & Fert., W.R.C.Inf., Weed Abstr., World Alum.Abstr., World Surf.Coat., Zincscan. **Document type:** academic/scholarly publication.
●Also available online. Vendor(s): STN International (CJACS).
—BLDSC (3791.600000); EI; Faxon; UnCover; SWETS; CASDDS. **CCC.**
Description: Contains research articles on various aspects of environmental chemistry, interpretative articles by invited experts, and commentary on the scientific aspects of environmental management.

574 US ISSN 0090-0427
CODEN: EVSRBT
ENVIRONMENTAL SCIENCE RESEARCH. 1972. irreg., vol.45, 1993. price varies. Plenum Publishing Corp., 233 Spring St., New York, NY 10013-1578. TEL 212-620-8000. FAX 212-463-0742. TELEX 23-421139. Ed. Herbert S. Rosenkranz. (back issues avail.) **Document type:** proceedings.
—BLDSC (3791.620000); CASDDS.
Refereed Serial

613.1 620.85 JA
ENVIRONMENTAL SCIENCES. (Text in English) 1991. q. $180. M Y U, Scientific Publishing Division, 2-32-3 Sendagi, Bunkyo-ku, Tokyo 113, Japan. Eds. Humio Tsunoda, Ming-Ho Yu.

628 681 UK ISSN 1351-1386
▼**ENVIRONMENTAL SENSORS.** 1993. m. £195($320) (effective 1994). (Institute of Physics) I O P Publishing Ltd., Techno House, Redcliffe Way, Bristol BS1 6NX, England. TEL 0272-297481. FAX 0272-294318. (Subscr. to: I O P Circulation Centre, Readerlink, Audit House, 260 Field End Rd., Eastcote, Ruislip, Mddx. HA4 9LT, England. TEL 081-868-4499. FAX 081-429-3117; U.S. addr.: American Institute of Physics, Member and Subscriber Services, 500 Sunnyside Blvd., Woodbury, NY 11797-2999. TEL 516-576-2200) Ed. Dennis Moralee. **Document type:** newsletter.
Description: Covers all aspects of environmental measurement and instrumentation.

614.7 340 US ISSN 0736-573X
KF3775.A29
ENVIRONMENTAL STATUTES. 1979. a. $49 for softcover; hardcover $59 (effective Feb. 1993). Government Institutes, Inc., 4 Research Pl., Ste. 200, Rockville, MD 20850-3226. TEL 301-921-2300. FAX 301-921-0373. **Indexed:** Chem.Abstr.

ENVIRONMENTAL STUDIES

628.5   US
ENVIRONMENTAL SUCCESS INDEX (YEAR). a. $25 to non-members; members $15. Renew America, 1400 16th St., N.W., Ste. 710, Washington, DC 20036. TEL 202-232-2252. bibl.; illus.; stat. **Document type:** directory.
    Description: Lists more than 1600 successful environmental programs solving problems in the United States with overviews of environmental issues in 20 categories, descriptions of programs, names and addresses.

614.6   TH
ENVIRONMENTAL SYSTEMS INFORMATION CENTER. OCCASIONAL PUBLICATIONS. irreg. price varies. Environmental Systems Information Center, P.O. Box 2754, Bangkok 10501, Thailand. TEL 66-2-5245863. FAX 66-2-5245870. TELEX 84276 AIT TH.
    Description: Contains booklets, do-it-yourself manuals, reports and proceedings on subjects of current interest.

614.7   TH
ENVIRONMENTAL SYSTEMS REVIEWS. (Text in English) 2/yr. $80 to individuals; institutions $130. Asian Institute of Technology, Environmental Systems Information Center, P.O. Box 2754, Bangkok 10501, Thailand. FAX 66-2-5245870. TELEX 84276 AIT TH.
—BLDSC (3791.598500).
    Formerly (until 1992): Environmental Sanitation Reviews (ISSN 0125-5088)
    Description: Publishes state-of-the-art reviews on various aspects of water and environmental topics with an emphasis on pressing issues facing developing countries today.

614.7   UK   ISSN 0959-3330
TD1   CODEN: ENVTEV
ENVIRONMENTAL TECHNOLOGY. 1980. m. £210($375) Selper Ltd., 79 Rusthall Ave., Chiswick, London W4 1BN, England. FAX 081-995-4160. Eds. J.N. Lester, R.M. Harrison. adv.; bk.rev.; index. (reprint service avail. from ISI) **Indexed:** Acid Rain Abstr., Acid Rain Ind., Biodet.Abstr., Biol.Abstr., Cadscan, Chem.Abstr., Curr.Adv.Ecol.Sci., Curr.Cont., Energy Info.Abstr., Energy Rev., Environ.Abstr., Environ.Ind., Environ.Per.Bibl. (1980-), Excerp.Med., Ind.Sci.Rev., Ind.Vet., Lead Abstr., Met.Abstr., Poult.Abstr., Sci.Cit.Ind., Sel.Water Res.Abstr., Soils & Fert., Sugar Ind.Abstr., W.R.C.Inf., Weed Abstr., World Alum.Abstr., Zincscan. **Document type:** academic/scholarly publication.
—BLDSC (3791.698800); CIS; Faxon; UnCover; SWETS; CASDDS.
    Formerly (until 1990): Environmental Technology Letters (ISSN 0143-2060)

614.7   US
ENVIRONMENTAL TELEPHONE DIRECTORY. biennial. $59 (effective Nov. 1991). Government Institutes, Inc., 4 Research Pl., Ste. 200, Rockville, MD 20850-3226. TEL 301-921-2300. FAX 301-921-0373. **Document type:** directory.

614.7   US
▼**ENVIRONMENTAL TESTING AND ANALYSIS**. 1992. bi-m. $40 (free to qualified personnel). Target Group, 1907 W. Burbank Blvd., 2nd Fl., Burbank, CA 91506. TEL 818-842-4777. FAX 818-842-0578. adv.; B&W page $2800, color page $3700; trim 8 x 10 3/4. circ. 20,000. **Indexed:** Ind.Hyg.Dig.
    Description: Contains news, regulations, methods, technologies, scientific breakthroughs and management concerns.

614.7   US   ISSN 1046-5294
ENVIRONMENTAL TOPICS. irreg., latest vol.3. Gordon and Breach Science Publishers, 820 Town Center Dr., Langhorne, PA 19047. TEL 215-750-2642. FAX 215-750-6343. (UK subscr. to: P.O. Box 90, Reading, Berkshire RG1 8JL, England. TEL 0734-560-080) Ed. J. Rose. **Document type:** monographic series.
—BLDSC (3791.783000).
    Refereed Serial

613.1 300   UK   ISSN 0963-2719
▼**ENVIRONMENTAL VALUES**. 1992. 4/yr. £32($60) to individuals; institutions £64($110). White Horse Press, 10 High St., Knapwell, Cambridge CB3 8NR, England. TEL 095-267527. (Subscr. to: 1 Strond, Isle of Harris PA83 3UD, Scotland. TEL 085-982204) Ed. Alan Holland. adv. circ. 500. **Indexed:** Environ.Abstr., Environ.Per.Bibl., Sociol.Abstr. **Document type:** academic/scholarly publication.
—BLDSC (3791.788100); CIS; UnCover.
    Description: International journal concerned with the rational basis and justification of environmental policy. Aims to clarify the relationship between practical policy issues and more fundamental underlying principles or assumptions.
    Refereed Serial

613.1   US
▼**ENVIRONMENTAL VIEWPOINTS**. 1992. a. $49.95. Gale Research Inc., 835 Penobscot Bldg., Detroit, MI 48226. TEL 313-961-2242. FAX 313-961-6083. Ed. Daniel G. Marowski.
    Description: Presents over 200 articles on U.S. and global environmental topics extracted from over 100 popular and professional periodicals.

614.7   US   ISSN 1049-8877
ENVIRONMENTAL WATCH. 1988. q. $40 to non-members (foreign $45); affiliates $25. Appraisal Institute, 875 N. Michigan Ave., Ste. 2400, Chicago, IL 60611-1980. TEL 312-335-4100. FAX 312-335-4400. Ed. Joy White. circ. 15,000.
    Description: Environmental news affecting commercial, industrial, and residential properties.

614.7   UK   ISSN 0251-1088
ENVIRONMENTALIST; the international journal concerned with environmental awareness. 1980. q. $180. (Institution of Environmental Sciences) Science and Technology Letters, P.O. Box 81, Northwood, Middlesex HA6 3DN, England. TEL 09274-23586. FAX 09274-25066. Ed. John F. Potter. adv. **Indexed:** Acid Rain Abstr., Acid Rain Ind., Deep Sea Res.& Oceanogr.Abstr., Energy Info.Abstr., Energy Rev., Environ.Abstr., Environ.Per.Bibl. (1986-), Excerp.Med., Geo.Abstr., I D A, Risk Abstr., Sage Urb.Stud.Abstr., W.R.C.Inf. **Document type:** academic/scholarly publication.
—BLDSC (3791.790000); CIS; Faxon; SWETS. CCC.

614.7 352   CN   ISSN 0711-6780
    CODEN: ENVREP
ENVIRONMENTS; a journal of interdisciplinary studies. 1969. 3/yr. Can.$37.45 (foreign Can.$45). University of Waterloo, Faculty of Environmental Studies, Waterloo, ON N2L 3G1, Canada. TEL 519-885-1211. FAX 519-746-2031. Ed. Harry Coblentz. adv.; bk.rev. circ. 700. (back issues avail.) **Indexed:** Can.Per.Ind., Energy Rev., Environ.Per.Bibl. (1985-), Geo.Abstr. **Document type:** academic/scholarly publication.
—BLDSC (3791.795000); Faxon; UnCover.
    Former titles: Contact (Waterloo) (ISSN 0317-8625); Contact in Urban and Regional Affairs (ISSN 0045-8309)

613.1   UK   ISSN 1180-4009
GE45.S73   CODEN: ENVCEE
ENVIRONMETRICS. 1991. q. $275 (effective 1994). John Wiley & Sons Ltd., Journals, Baffins Ln., Chichester, Sussex PO19 1UD, England. TEL 0243-779777. FAX 0243-775878. TELEX 86290 WIBOOK G. Eds. A.H. El-Shaarawi, I.B. MacNeil. circ. 314. **Document type:** academic/scholarly publication.
—BLDSC (3791.797000); SWETS; UMI.
    Description: Concerned with the development and application of statistical methodology in the environmental sciences.

614.7   US
ENVIRONS.* 1982. q. Department of Environmental Protection, Office of Public Affairs, 59-17 Junction Blvd., 3rd Fl., Flushing, NY 11373-5107. TEL 212-669-8200. FAX 212-669-2522. Ed. Andrew McCarthy. circ. 6,000.
    Description: Focuses on the city's DEP staff, explaining how the workers do the various things the agency is responsible for.

ERETZ; hayael. see *CONSERVATION*

614.7   FR
ESPACE 90. 1969. m. 90 F. Confederation Nationale pour l'Amenagement Rural, 129 bd. Saint Germain, 75006 Paris, France. Ed. Jacques Fournol. adv.; illus.

ESTUARIES; a journal of research on any aspect of natural science and management applied to estuaries. see *BIOLOGY*

981   BL   ISSN 0014-1607
    CODEN: ESLED4
ESTUDOS LEOPOLDENSES. (Text in Portuguese; summaries in English) 1966. 4/yr. Cr.$20000($24) or exchange basis. (Universidade do Vale do Rio dos Sinos) Unisinos, Av. Unisinos, 950, 93010 Sao Leopoldo RS, Brazil. TEL 051-5926333. FAX 0512-921035. TELEX 5244076. Ed. Rev. Egidio F. Schmitz. bk.rev.; abstr.; bibl.; charts; illus.; circ. 1,400 (controlled). **Document type:** academic/scholarly publication.

614.7   IT   ISSN 0394-0276
ETA VERDE. 1974. bi-m. L.20000($8) (effective 1993). Associazione l'Eta Verde, Casella Postale 443, 00100 Rome Centre, Italy. TEL 06-70451588. FAX 06-7573680. Ed.Bd. adv.; bk.rev. (back issues avail.) **Document type:** consumer publication.

EUPOLIS; rivista critica di ecologia territoriale. see *HOUSING AND URBAN PLANNING*

614.7   BE   ISSN 1021-416X
EUROPE ENVIRONMENT. French edition: Europe Environnement (ISSN 1021-4178) (Text in English) 1975. fortn. 24950 BEF (includes q. surveys) (effective 1994). Europe Information Service, Rue de Geneve, 6, 1140 Brussels, Belgium. TEL 32-2-242-6020. FAX 32-2-242-9410. s-a. index. **Indexed:** Acid Pre.Dig., Cadscan, ELLIS, Lead Abstr., Zincscan.
●Also available online. Vendor(s): Mead Data Central, Inc..

EUROPEAN ENVIRONMENTAL LAW REVIEW. see *LAW*

614.7 640.73   EI
EUROPEAN PARLIAMENT. RESEARCH AND DOCUMENTATION PAPERS; resolutions of the European Parliament in the field of environment, public health and consumer protection. (Editions in English, French, German) irreg. European Parliament, Directorate General for Research, L-2929 Luxembourg, Luxembourg. (also avail. in microfiche from CIS) **Indexed:** IIS.

EVERGLADES REPORTER. see *CONSERVATION*

EVERYONE'S BACKYARD. see *ENVIRONMENTAL STUDIES — Waste Management*

614.7   UK   ISSN 0269-7653
    CODEN: EVECEJ
EVOLUTIONARY ECOLOGY. 1987. bi-m. £220 to institutions in EC nations (North America $375; elsewhere £230). Chapman & Hall, 2-6 Boundary Row, London SE1 8HN, England. TEL 071-865-0066. FAX 071-522-9623. TELEX 290164-CHAPMAG. (Dist. by: International Thomson Publishing Services, Ltd., N. Way, Andover, Hants. SP10 5EB, England. TEL 0264-342919; US addr.: Chapman & Hall, Journals Promotion Department, One Penn Plaza, 41st Fl., New York, NY 10019. TEL 212-564-1060. FAX 212-564-1505) Ed. M.L. Rosenzweig. adv. (back issues avail.; reprint service avail. from UMI) **Indexed:** Environ.Per.Bibl. (1991-).
—BLDSC (3834.430000); Faxon; UnCover; SWETS; UMI. CCC.
    Description: Provides a forum for the exchange of ideas in evolutionary ecology.

EXHAUST NEWS. see *TECHNOLOGY: COMPREHENSIVE WORKS*

EXPLORATION AND PRODUCTION HEALTH, SAFETY AND ENVIRONMENT. see *PETROLEUM AND GAS — Abstracting, Bibliographies, Statistics*

EXPLORER (CLEVELAND). see *SCIENCES: COMPREHENSIVE WORKS*

ENVIRONMENTAL STUDIES

614.7 581 AT ISSN 0811-9066
EYESPY; the discovery magazine for kids. 1983. bi-m. Aus.$25.50 (foreign Aus.$37). Ashton Scholastic Pty. Ltd., Railway Crescent, Lisarow, N.S.W. 2250, Australia. TEL 043-28-2205. FAX 043-23-3827. (Subscr. to: P.O. Box 579, Gosford, N.S.W. 2250, Australia. TEL 02-4164000) Ed. Carole Hunter. circ. 35,000. (back issues avail.)
—CCC.

F E M S. MICROBIOLOGY ECOLOGY. (Federation of European Microbiological Societies) see *BIOLOGY — Microbiology*

FACETS OF FRESHWATER. see *WATER RESOURCES*

FARM AND FOOD SOCIETY NEWSLETTER. see *AGRICULTURE*

FEDERAL ENVIRONMENTAL LAWS. see *LAW*

614.7 340 US
FEDERAL ENVIRONMENTAL REGULATION. 1990. 2 base vols. (plus supplements). $165. Butterworth Legal Publishers (Salem) (Subsidiary of: Reed Elsevier plc), 8 Industrial Way, Bldg. C, Salem, NH 03079. TEL 800-548-4001. FAX 603-898-9858. (looseleaf format)

614.7 US ISSN 1048-4078
K6
FEDERAL FACILITIES ENVIRONMENTAL JOURNAL. 1990. q. $175 (foreign $225). Executive Enterprises Publications Co., Inc., 22 W. 21st St., New York, NY 10010-6904. TEL 212-645-7880. FAX 212-645-1160. (also avail. in microform from WSH; reprint service avail. from WSH) **Indexed:** Environ.Abstr.
—UnCover; UMI. **CCC**.
Description: Includes case studies of agency and contractor solutions to current problems and recommendations for avoiding future problems. Analysis of latest actions by federal and state agencies.

FEDERAL PARKS & RECREATION. see *CONSERVATION*

614.772 US ISSN 0049-6987
CODEN: WPCHA
FEDERATION HIGHLIGHTS. (Former name of issuing body: Water Polution Control Federation) 1964. m. $19 (foreign $29). Water Environment Federation, 601 Wythe St., Alexandria, VA 22314-1994. TEL 703-684-2400. FAX 703-684-2492. Ed. Nancy Blatt. illus. circ. 40,000. (also avail. in microfilm) **Indexed:** Excerp.Med. **Document type:** newsletter.

614.7 UK ISSN 0428-304X
QH137 CODEN: FSTUBX
FIELD STUDIES. 1959. a. £12 to non-members. Field Studies Council, Central Services, Preston Montford, Montford Bridge, Shrewsbury SY4 1HW, England. TEL 07-43-850674. FAX 07-43-850178. Ed. J.H. Crothers. bk.rev.; bibl.; cum.index every 4 yrs. circ. 2,000. **Indexed:** Biol.Abstr., Br.Archaeol.Abstr., Br.Geol.Lit., Curr.Adv.Ecol.Sci., Forest.Abstr., Geo.Abstr., GeoRef., Herb.Abstr., Irr.& Drain.Abstr., Soils & Fert., Zoo.Rec.
—BLDSC (3920.700000).
Description: Multi-disciplinary journal covering all the field sciences.

614.7 UK
FIELD STUDIES COUNCIL. OCCASIONAL PUBLICATIONS. irreg. price varies. Field Studies Council, Preston Montford, Shrewsbury SY4 1HW, England.
Description: A vehicle for material which, because of its format, is unsuitable for the journal "Field Studies."

FILTRATION & SEPARATION. see *ENGINEERING — Chemical Engineering*

614.7 665.5 US
FILTRATION NEWS. 1982. bi-m. Eagle Publications, Inc., 42400 Nine Mile Rd., Ste. B, Novi, MI 48375. TEL 313-347-3490; 800-783-3491. FAX 313-347-3492. adv.; circ. 30,000 (controlled). **Document type:** trade publication.
Description: Published for those who are interested in liquid & air filtration inside the industrial manufacturing plant.

FINNISH METEOROLOGICAL INSTITUTE. REPORTS. see *METEOROLOGY*

333.8 340 US
FLORIDA BAR. ENVIRONMENTAL AND LAND USE LAW SECTION. REPORTER. 1977. 4/yr. $50 to non-members. Florida Bar, Environmental and Land Use Law Section, 650 Apalachee Pkwy., Tallahasee, FL 32399-2300. TEL 904-561-5623. circ. 2,090. **Document type:** newsletter.

FLORIDA ENVIRONMENTAL COMPLIANCE UPDATE. see *LAW*

FLORIDA MOSQUITO CONTROL ASSOCIATION. JOURNAL. see *BIOLOGY — Entomology*

FOCUS ON BRITISH ENVIRONMENTAL SCIENCES RESEARCH. see *BIBLIOGRAPHIES*

613.1 US ISSN 1062-3086
FOCUS ON: GLOBAL CHANGE. 1990. fortn. $395. Institute for Scientific Information, 3501 Market St., Philadelphia, PA 19104. (diskette format) **Document type:** newsletter.

FOCUS ON INTERNATIONAL JOINT COMMISSION ACTIVITIES. see *WATER RESOURCES*

FORESTRY RESEARCH WEST. see *FORESTS AND FORESTRY*

FORTH NATURALIST AND HISTORIAN. see *SCIENCES: COMPREHENSIVE WORKS*

333.79 US ISSN 0887-8218
H96
FORUM FOR APPLIED RESEARCH AND PUBLIC POLICY. 1986. q. $28 to individuals (foreign $34); institutions $36 (foreign $42) (effective 1994). University of Tennessee at Knoxville, Energy, Environment and Resources Center, Knoxville, TN 37996-0710. FAX 615-974-1838. (Subscr. to: Executive Sciences Institute, 1005 Mississippi Ave., Davenport, IA 52803. TEL 919-966-3561) (Co-sponsor: Oak Ridge National Laboratory) Ed. Daniel Schaffer. adv.; bk.rev. circ. 2,000. (back issues avail.) **Indexed:** Energy Info.Abstr. (until 1993), Energy Rev., Environ.Abstr., Environ.Per.Bibl. (1989-), Forest.Abstr., INIS Atomind., P.A.I.S., Soils & Fert., World Agri.Econ.& Rural Sociol.Abstr. **Document type:** academic/scholarly publication.
—BLDSC (4024.084400); CIS; EI; Faxon; UnCover; UMI.
Description: Presents a discussion of policy options by academic, government and corporate experts in energy, environment and economic development.
Refereed Serial

FORUM LOCCUM. see *POLITICAL SCIENCE*

614.7 GW ISSN 0342-202X
TD3 CODEN: FSHYDL
FORUM STAEDTE-HYGIENE. 1949. bi-m. DM.198.90. Patzer Verlag GmbH und Co. KG, Koenigsallee 65, 14193 Bremen, Germany. TEL 030-895903-0. FAX 030-89590317. Eds. K.H. Knoll, Bernhard Patzer. circ. 1,000. (back issues avail.) **Indexed:** Biol.Abstr., Chem.Abstr., Excerp.Med., INIS Atomind., Trop.Dis.Bull., W.R.C.Inf. **Document type:** bulletin.
—BLDSC (4024.108000); CASDDS.

FRA HAUG OG HEIDNI. see *ARCHAEOLOGY*

FRAGMENTA FLORISTICA ET GEOBOTANICA. see *GARDENING AND HORTICULTURE*

FRANC - VERT. see *CONSERVATION*

363.6 FR
FRANCE. MINISTERE DE L'ENVIRONNEMENT. BILAN D'ACTIVITE DES AGENCES FINANCIERES DE BASSIN. irreg. Ministere de l'Environnement, 45 ave. Georges Mandel, 75016 Paris, France. TEL 45-49-61-62. illus.
Formerly: France. Ministere de la Culture et de l'Environnement. Bilan d'Activite des Agences Financieres de Bassin.

614.7 SZ ISSN 1018-4619
CODEN: FENBEL
▼**FRESENIUS ENVIRONMENTAL BULLETIN**. (Text in English) 1992. m. 268 SFr.($182) Birkhaeuser Verlag, P.O. Box 133, CH-4010 Basel, Switzerland. TEL 061-2717400. FAX 061-2717666. TELEX 963475-BIRKH-CH. (Dist. in N. America by: Springer-Verlag, Mercedes Distribution Center, 160 Imlay St., Brooklyn, NY 11231, USA) Ed. F. Korte. **Document type:** bulletin.
—BLDSC (4036.370000); CASDDS.

614.7 US ISSN 1054-1829
QH540
FRIENDS OF THE EARTH. 1970. bi-m. $25. Friends of the Earth, 1025 Vermont Ave., N.W., Ste. 300, Washington, DC 20005. TEL 202-783-7400. FAX 202-783-0444. Ed. Dena Leibman. adv.; bk.rev.; illus. circ. 10,000. (tabloid format) **Indexed:** Alt.Press Ind., Curr.Adv.Ecol.Sci., Energy Rev., Environ.Abstr., Environ.Per.Bibl., New Per.Ind., Telegen.
—CIS; UnCover.
Formerly (until Sep. 1990): Not Man Apart (ISSN 0194-1062)
Description: For activists and inquisitive citizens who enjoy the mix of action news and information articles.

614.7 CC
FUJIAN HUANJING/FUJIAN ENVIRONMENT. (Text in Chinese) bi-m. Fujiansheng Huanjing Kexue Xuehui - Fujian Association of Environmental Science, Hualin Lu, Fuzhou, Fujian 350003, People's Republic of China. TEL 570146. Ed. Gan Jinggao.
Description: Focuses on the prevention of industrial pollution, and on issues in environmental management and education.

FUKUOKA-KEN E SEI KOGAI SENTA NENPO/FUKUOKA ENVIRONMENTAL RESEARCH CENTER. ANNUAL REPORT. see *PUBLIC HEALTH AND SAFETY*

FUKUSHIMAKEN GENSHIRYOKU SENTA. GYOMU NENPO/FUKUSHIMA ENVIRONMENTAL RADIOACTIVITY RESEARCH CENTER. ANNUAL REPORT. see *ENERGY — Nuclear Energy*

FUNCTIONAL ECOLOGY. see *CONSERVATION*

614.7 AG
FUNDACION BARILOCHE. GRUPO DE ANALISIS DE SISTEMAS ECOLOGICOS. PUBLICACIONES. irreg. price varies. Fundacion Bariloche, Grupo de Analisis de Sistemas Ecologicos, Casilla de Correo 138, 8400 San Carlos de Bariloche - Rio Negro, Argentina. **Indexed:** GeoRef.
Supersedes in part: Fundacion Bariloche. Departamento de Recursos Naturales y Energia. Publicaciones (ISSN 0071-9846)

614.7 600 IT
FUORISTRADA. s-a. G. Cassini Editore s.r.l., Via Cavour, 3, Biella, Italy. TEL 015-352766. FAX 015-352766.

614.7 500 GW ISSN 0175-4521
RA569
G S F MENSCH UND UMWELT. 1984. a. free. G S F - Forschungszentrum fuer Umwelt und Gesundheit, Ingolstaedter Landstr. 1, 85764 Oberschleissheim, Germany. TEL 089-3187-2711. FAX 089-3187-3324. Eds. Cordula Klemm, Heinz-Joerg Haury. circ. 20,000. (back issues avail.) **Document type:** bulletin.
Description: Scientific information for the public on environmental and health research topics.

GABBIANI NEWS. see *CHILDREN AND YOUTH — For*

613.1 US ISSN 1059-0919
GE20
▼**GALE ENVIRONMENT SOURCEBOOK**. 1992. biennial. Gale Research, Inc., 835 Penobscot Bldg., Detroit, MI 48226.

GARNER'S ENVIRONMENTAL LAW. see *LAW*

GAZETA OBSERWATORA I M G W/JOURNAL OF I M W M OBSERVER. (Instytut Meteorologii i Gospodarki Wodnej) see *METEOROLOGY*

614.7 IT ISSN 0394-8382
GEA; governo locale ed economia dell'ambiente. 1986. bi-m. L.120000 to individuals; institutions L.175000 (effective 1994). Maggioli Editore, Viale Vespucci 12-n, Casella Postale 290, 47037 Rimini, Italy. TEL 0541-626777. FAX 0541-622020. Ed. Ario Rupeni. adv.; B&W page L.2000000, color page L.3100000; trim 178 x 255.

ENVIRONMENTAL STUDIES

363.74   NE   ISSN 0925-9406
GELUID. q. (Nederlands Stichting Geluidshinder) Samsom Uitgeverij B.V. (Subsidiary of: Wolters Kluwer N.V.), Postbus 4, 2400 MA Alphen aan den Rijn, Netherlands. TEL 31-1720-66822. FAX 31-1720-66639.
—SWETS.
  Formerly (until 1991): Geluid en Omgeving (ISSN 0165-2982)
  Description: Follows latest developments in noise control.

613.1 539.7   JA
GENSHI NENRYO SAIKURU SHISETSU KANKYO HOSHASENTO JIZEN CHOSA HOKOKUSHO/REPORT OF ENVIRONMENTAL RADIOLOGY OF NUCLEAR FUEL CYCLE FACILITIES. (Text in Japanese) 1990. q. Aomoriken Kankyo Hokenbu - Aomori Prefectural Government, Environmental Health Division, 1-1, Nagashima 1-chome, Aomori-shi, Aomori-ken 030, Japan.

910   GW
GEO. 1976. m. DM.108 (Europe DM.150; elsewhere DM.252). Gruner und Jahr AG & Co., Am Baumwall 11, 20459 Hamburg, Germany. TEL 040-3703-0. FAX 040-37035604. Ed. Werner Funk. circ. 622,604. **Document type:** academic/scholarly publication.

GEOECOLOGICAL RESEARCH. see *EARTH SCIENCES*

GEOFILE. see *GEOGRAPHY*

GEOFORUM; the international multi-disciplinary journal for the rapid publication of research results and critical review articles in the physical, human and regional geosciences. see *GEOGRAPHY*

614.7 340   US   ISSN 1042-1858
GEORGETOWN INTERNATIONAL ENVIRONMENTAL LAW REVIEW. vol.4, 1991. s-a. $35. Georgetown University Law Center, 600 New Jersey Ave., N.W., Washington, DC 20001. TEL 202-662-9468. bk.rev. (back issues avail.; reprint service avail. from WSH)
●Also available online. Vendor(s): West Services, Inc..
—BLDSC (4158.269600); UnCover.
  Description: Covers environmental issues and the legal implications of legislation, actions and developments.

GEORGIA ENVIRONMENTAL LAW LETTER. see *LAW*

628.44   US
GEORGIA GEOLOGIC SURVEY. EDUCATIONAL SERIES. 1976. irreg., no.2, 1990. price varies. Department of Natural Resources, Georgia Geologic Survey, 19 Martin Luther King Jr. Dr., S.W., Rm. 400, Atlanta, GA 30334. TEL 404-656-3214. maps.
  Description: Covers a specific topic for laypeople.

GEOTECHNICAL SCIENCE LABORATORIES. PUBLICATIONS, REPORTS, AND THESES. see *EARTH SCIENCES — Abstracting, Bibliographies, Statistics*

614.7   GW
GESELLSCHAFT FUER VERANTWORTUNG IN DER WISSENSCHAFT. SCHRIFTEN. 1983. irreg. price varies. E. Schweizerbart'sche Verlagsbuchhandlung, Johannesstr. 3A, 70176 Stuttgart, Germany. TEL 0711-625001. FAX 0711-625005. TELEX 723363-SCHB-D. Ed. Hans-Joachim Elster. **Document type:** monographic series.

614.7   GW   ISSN 0367-4223
CODEN: GEPFAG
GESUNDE PFLANZEN; Pflanzenschutz, Verbraucherschutz, Umweltschutz. (Text in German; summaries in English) 1947. m. DM.148($99) Verlag Paul Parey (Berlin), Seelbuschring 9-17, 12105 Berlin, Germany. TEL 030-70784-0. FAX 030-70784199. Ed. Hansgeorg Pag. adv.; bk.rev.; index. circ. 3,500. (back issues avail.) **Indexed:** Agroforest.Abstr., Bio-Contr.News & Info., Biotech.Abstr., Excerp.Med., Field Crop Abstr., Forest.Abstr., Helminthol.Abstr., Maize Abstr., Ornam.Hort., Plant Grow.Reg.Abstr., Soils & Fert., Triticale Abstr., Weed Abstr., World Agri.Econ.& Rural Sociol.Abstr. **Document type:** bulletin.
—BLDSC (4163.850000); SWETS; CASDDS.

614.7 350 635   US
GILDEA REVIEW. 1986. s-a. $25. (Gildea Resource Center) Community Environmental Council, Inc., 930 Miramonte Dr., Santa Barbara, CA 93109. TEL 805-963-0583. FAX 805-962-9080. Ed. Michael Colin. bk.rev.; illus. circ. 700. (back issues avail.)
  Formerly (until 1985): C E C Member's Report.
  Description: Covers solid waste management, environmental, public policy, land-use policy and sustainable agriculture.

THE GIST. see *FOOD AND FOOD INDUSTRIES*

613.1   SW   ISSN 0284-5865
GLOBAL CHANGE NEWSLETTER. 1989. irreg. free. Royal Swedish Academy of Science, International Geosphere-Biosphere Programme, P.O. Box 50005, S-104 05 Stockholm, Sweden. (Co-sponsor: International Council of Scientific Unions) Ed. Suzanne Nash. **Document type:** newsletter.
—UnCover.

614.7   US   ISSN 0897-4268
QC981.8.C5
GLOBAL CLIMATE CHANGE DIGEST; a guide to current information on greenhouse gases and ozone depletion. 1988. m. $325 (foreign $370). Center for Environmental Information, 50 Main St. W., 4th fl., Rochester, NY 14614-1218. TEL 716-262-2870. Ed. Robert W. Pratt. bk.rev. circ. 300. **Document type:** abstracting/indexing, bulletin.
  Description: An interdisciplinary guide to current general and technical information related to climate change resulting from human activities, particularly global warming by greenhouse gases and stratospheric ozone depletion.

613.1   UK
GLOBAL ECOLOGY AND BIOGEOGRAPHY LETTERS. Issues with: Journal of Biogeography (ISSN 0305-0270) bi-m. Blackwell Scientific Publications Ltd., Osney Mead, Oxford OX2 OEL, England. TEL 0865-240201. FAX 0865-721205. TELEX 83355-MEDBOK-G. Ed. P. Scott. **Indexed:** Environ.Abstr., Environ.Per.Bibl. **Document type:** academic/scholarly publication.

614.7   UK   ISSN 0959-3780
HC79.E5
GLOBAL ENVIRONMENTAL CHANGE; human and policy dimensions. 1990. q. £110 in UK and Europe; elsewhere £115. Butterworth - Heinemann (Subsidiary of: Reed International PLC), Linacre House, Jordan Hill, Oxford OX2 8DP, England. TEL 0865-310366. FAX 0865-310898. TELEX 83111 BHPOXF G. (Subscr. to: Turpin Transactions Ltd., Distribution Centre, Blackhorse Rd., Letchworth, Herts SG6 1HN, England. TEL 0462-672555) Ed. Penny Street. bk.rev. (also avail. in microform from UMI; back issues avail.) **Indexed:** Environ.Per.Bibl. (1991-). **Document type:** academic/scholarly publication.
●Also available online. Vendor(s): Data-Star, DIALOG Information Services, Inc., NewsNet.
—BLDSC (4195.397000); Faxon; UnCover; SWETS; UMI. **CCC.**
  Description: International journal addressing the human, ecological and public policy dimensions of environmental issues.

614.7   US   ISSN 1049-9083
GLOBAL ENVIRONMENTAL CHANGE REPORT; policy, science, and industry news worldwide. 1990. s-m. $447 (foreign $547). Cutter Information Corp., 37 Broadway, Arlington, MA 02174. TEL 617-648-8700. FAX 617-648-8707. TELEX 650 100 9891 MCI UW. Ed. Bradford J. Hurley. (back issues avail.) **Document type:** newsletter.
●Also available online. Vendor(s): NewsNet (EV31).
—SWETS. **CCC.**
  Description: Covers developments around the world relating to climate change, including global warming, acid rain, deforestation, biodiversity, and sustainable development. Reports on scientific, governmental, and industrial developments.

614.7   GW   ISSN 0931-539X
GLOBUS - BEGLEITHEFTE. 1982. m. DM.49. Bund fuer Umwelt und Naturschutz Deutschland, Landesverband Baden-Wuerttemberg e.V., Rotebuehlstr. 86-I, 70178 Stuttgart, Germany. TEL 0711-619700. FAX 0711-6197070. Ed. Erich Kimmich. adv.: B&W page DM.3900; trim 180 x 247; adv. contact: Thomas Hitschler. bk.rev. circ. 15,000. **Document type:** academic/scholarly publication.
  Description: Studies environmental protection and conservation issues.

614.7   UK
GOOD BEACH GUIDE; indicates which beaches are likely to be polluted and which are believed to be free from sewage pollution. 1960. a. £6.99. Marine Conservation Society, 9 Gloucester Rd., Ross-on-Wye, Herefordshire HR9 5BU, England. TEL 0989-66017. Ed. Catherine Loretto. circ. 55,000. **Document type:** bulletin.
  Incorporates: Golden List of British Beaches; *Formerly:* Golden List of Beaches.
  Description: Guide to beaches in the UK, detailing information on water quality, access, and bathing safety.

614.7 375   AT   ISSN 1039-0588
GOULD LEAGUE OF VICTORIA. GREENPRINT. 1983. 6/yr. Aus.$20. Gould League of Victoria Inc., Genoa St., Moorabbin, Vic. 3189, Australia. TEL 03-510-1493. FAX 03-521-1217. Ed. Gayle Seddon. bk.rev.; bibl.; illus. circ. 2,500.
  Formerly (until 1992): Gould League of Victoria. Newsletter (ISSN 1032-9219)
  Description: News about Gould League and its activities with focus on environmental education for adults, especially teachers.

GOVERNMENT GREEN GUIDE. see *PUBLIC ADMINISTRATION*

301.31   UK
GREAT BRITAIN. DEPARTMENT OF THE ENVIRONMENT. REPORT ON RESEARCH AND DEVELOPMENT. 1973. a. price varies. (Department of the Environment) H.M.S.O. Books, Publications Centre, 51 Nine Elms Ln., London SW8 5DR, England. TEL 071-873-0011. FAX 071-873-8463. (Subscr. to: H.M.S.O. Books, P.O. Box 276, London SW8 5DT, England. TEL 071-873-9090. FAX 071-873-8200) **Document type:** government publication.

614.7 639.22   UK   ISSN 0142-2499
CODEN: AEMRD8
GREAT BRITAIN. MINISTRY OF AGRICULTURE, FISHERIES AND FOOD. DIRECTORATE OF FISHERIES RESEARCH. AQUATIC ENVIRONMENT MONITORING REPORT. 1979. s-a. free. Ministry of Agriculture, Fisheries and Food, Directorate of Fisheries Research, Lowestoft, Suffolk NR33 OHT, England. TEL 0502-562244. **Indexed:** Aqua.Sci.& Fish.Abstr., Chem.Abstr. **Document type:** government publication.
—BLDSC (1582.375000); UnCover; CASDDS. **CCC.**

GREAT BRITAIN. MINISTRY OF AGRICULTURE, FISHERIES AND FOOD. DIRECTORATE OF FISHERIES RESEARCH. FISHERIES RESEARCH TECHNICAL REPORT. see *FISH AND FISHERIES*

GREAT BRITAIN. MINISTRY OF AGRICULTURE, FISHERIES AND FOOD. RESEARCH INTO FISHERIES AND THE MARINE ENVIRONMENT. REPORT OF THE DIRECTOR OF FISHERIES RESEARCH. see *FISH AND FISHERIES*

614.7   UK
GREAT BRITAIN. NATURAL ENVIRONMENT RESEARCH COUNCIL. INSTITUTE OF TERRESTRIAL ECOLOGY. ANNUAL REPORT. 1965. a. £8. Natural Environment Research Council, Institute of Terrestrial Ecology, Merlewood Research Station, Windermere Rd., Grange-over-Sands, Cumbria LA1 6JU, England. TEL 05395-32264. FAX 05395-34705. TELEX 65102. circ. 1,000. **Document type:** government publication.

628.5   UK   ISSN 0141-3279
GREAT BRITAIN. WARREN SPRING LABORATORY. ANNUAL REVIEW. a. free. Warren Spring Laboratory, Gunnels Wood Rd., Stevenage, Herts. SG1 2BX, England. TEL 0438-741122. FAX 0438-360858.

GREAT BRITAIN. WARREN SPRING LABORATORY. U K SMOKE AND SULPHUR DIOXIDE MONITORING NETWORKS. see *ENVIRONMENTAL STUDIES — Pollution*

GREEN ALTERNATIVES. see *CONSUMER EDUCATION AND PROTECTION*

GREEN ANARCHIST; global anarchist 'zine. see *POLITICAL SCIENCE*

614.7 US ISSN 1055-6893
HD9718.U63
THE GREEN BOOK: ENVIRONMENTAL RESOURCE DIRECTORY. (In 3 regional eds.) 1991. a. $89.95. Green Book, Inc., Corporate Place, 100 Burh Rd., Andover, MA 01810. TEL 508-474-5000. FAX 508-474-5054. adv.; circ. 120,000 (controlled). **Document type:** directory.
  Description: Lists products and services in over 300 categories. Includes regional and national organizations, EPA listings, a glossary of environmental terms, engineering constants, NPL information and on-line services.

GREEN BUSINESS LETTER. see *BUSINESS AND ECONOMICS*

GREEN CONSUMER LETTER. see *CONSUMER EDUCATION AND PROTECTION*

614.7 UK ISSN 0960-8796
GREEN ENGINEERING; a current awareness bulletin. m. £114($219) (foreign £121). Mechanical Engineering Publications Ltd., Northgate Ave., Bury St. Edmunds, Suffolk IP32 6BW, England. TEL 0284-763277. FAX 0284-704006. Ed. Elizabeth Ellis. **Document type:** academic/scholarly publication, newsletter.
  Description: Focuses on environmental issues for the engineering profession.

614.7 US
GREEN GUERILLA VITISVINE; a newsletter devoted to the greening of our environment. 1978. 4/yr. $25 includes membership. Green Guerillas, Inc., 625 Broadway, New York, NY 10012. TEL 212-674-8124. Ed. Barbara Earnest. bk.rev. circ. 1,000. **Document type:** newsletter.
  Formerly: Green Guerilla Report.
  Description: News on recent activities pertaining to and technical advice on community gardening and neighborhood horticulture in New York City.

614.7 020 US ISSN 1059-0838
GE30
▼**GREEN LIBRARY JOURNAL**; environmental topics in the information world. 1992. 3/yr. $20 (foreign $25) to individuals; institutions $40 (foreign $45). (University of Idaho Library) Green Library, Inc., 2161 Shattuck Ave., Berkeley, CA 83843. TEL 208-885-6260. FAX 208-885-6817. (Subscr. to: Box 11284, Berkeley, CA 94701) Ed. Maria Anna Jankowska. adv. contact: Katie Manjotich. bk.rev.; software rev.; bibl.; illus. circ. 750. **Indexed:** Environ.Abstr. **Document type:** academic/scholarly publication.
  —BLDSC (4214.942035); UnCover.
  Description: Contains information about international sources on environmental protection, conservation, management of natural resources, and ecologically-balanced regional development.
  Refereed Serial

614.7 UK ISSN 1352-450X
GREEN LINE. 1982. m. £9 (foreign £12-£15). Catalyst Collective Ltd., P.O. Box 5, Lostwithiel PL22 0YT, Scotland. Ed. Paul Ingram. adv.; bk.rev. circ. 1,500. (back issues avail.)

614.7 UK ISSN 0957-6029
GREEN MAGAZINE. 1989. 13/yr. £48. Northern & Shell Publications, Northern & Shell Bldg., P.O. Box 381, Millharbour, London E14 9TW, England. TEL 071-987-5090. FAX 071-987-2160. Ed. Alistair Townley. adv.: color page £4200; adv. contact: Mary Anne Lambertucci. circ. 50,000. **Indexed:** Energy Rev., Environ.Per.Bibl. (1990-). **Document type:** bulletin.
  Description: Aims to increase public awareness of green issues. Highlights local, as well as national and international, areas of concern.

614.7 US ISSN 1052-1755
HF5413
GREEN MARKET ALERT; tracking corporate environmentalism and green business strategies. 1990. m. $295. Bridge Group, 345 Wood Creek Rd., Bethlehem, CT 06751-1014. TEL 203-266-7209. FAX 203-266-5049. Ed. Carl Frankel. **Document type:** newsletter.
  ●Also available online. Vendor(s): NewsNet (AD21).

614.7 CN
GREEN MARKET ALERT NEWSLETTER. m. Can.$212.93 (foreign $279). Southam Information and Technology Group, 1450 Don Mills Rd., Don Mills, ON M3B 2X7, Canada. TEL 416-445-6641. FAX 416-442-2077. Ed. Ian Rhind. **Document type:** newsletter.
  Description: Provides actionable and current information on green marketing: regulations, consumer segmentation, success stories, interest groups, contact names and numbers.

GREEN PAGES: DIRECTORY OF NON-GOVERNMENT ENVIRONMENTAL GROUPS IN AUSTRALIA. see *CONSERVATION*

GREEN PERSPECTIVES. see *POLITICAL SCIENCE*

GREEN SYNTHESIS (SAN PEDRO); a newsletter and journal for social ecology, deepecology, bioregionalism, eco feminism, and the green movement. see *LITERARY AND POLITICAL REVIEWS*

GREEN TEACHER. see *EDUCATION — Teaching Methods And Curriculum*

658.401 UK ISSN 0966-9671
▼**GREENER MANAGEMENT INTERNATIONAL**; the journal of corporate environmental strategy and practice. 1993. q. £150($250) Greenleaf Publishing, Interleaf Productions Ltd., Exchange Works, Sidney St., Sheffield S1 3QF, England. TEL 0742-739721. FAX 0742-767037. bk.rev.; video rev. **Document type:** academic/scholarly publication.
  —BLDSC (4214.942452).
  Description: Covers ways in which corporate managers can conduct business in an environmentally sustainable manner. Also lists forthcoming environmental events.

613.1 UK ISSN 0964-9107
GREENHOUSE GASES BULLETIN. 1991. s-a. £60 to members; non-members £180. I E A, Greenhouse Gas R & D Programme, Stoke Orchard, Cheltenham, Glos GL52 4RZ, England. Ed. Deborah Norman. **Document type:** abstracting/indexing.

614.7 US
GREENPEACE FUTUREFILE. bi-m. Greenpeace, National Office, 1436 U St., N.W., Washington, DC 20009. TEL 202-462-1177. FAX 202-462-4507. Ed. Andrew Davis.

614.7 GW ISSN 0939-3234
GREENPEACE MAGAZIN. 1982. q. DM.20. (Greenpeace e.V.) Greenpeace Umweltschutzverlag GmbH, Deichstr. 17, 20459 Hamburg, Germany. TEL 040-31186-0. FAX 040-31186-212. Ed. Manfred Pietschmann. bk.rev. circ. 650,000. **Document type:** bulletin.
  Formerly (until 1990): Greenpeace Nachrichten (ISSN 0178-5745)

GREENPEACE NEWSLETTER. see *POLITICAL SCIENCE*

614 LU ISSN 1019-0287
GRENGESPOUN. 1988. w. 2080 BEF. P.O.B. 684, L-2016 Luxembourg, Luxembourg. TEL 352-22-11-55. FAX 352-22-11-53. Eds. Renee Wagener, Richard Graf. adv.; bk.rev. circ. 1,600. **Document type:** newspaper.
  Description: Information on ecological, economical, social, political and cultural matters.

GROENSAKEN. see *POLITICAL SCIENCE*

GROUND WATER MONITOR; legislation, regulation, litigation, technology. see *WATER RESOURCES*

614.7 GW
GRUENSTIFT (RATTINGEN); Umweltmagazin fuer Duesseldorf. 1989. q. DM.15 (foreign DM.25). Bund-NW e.V., Graf-Adolph-Str. 9, 40878 Ratingen, Germany. adv.; bk.rev.; illus. circ. 3,000. (back issues avail.)

GULL. see *BIOLOGY — Ornithology*

H M C R I. (Hazardous Materials Control Resources Institute) see *ENVIRONMENTAL STUDIES — Waste Management*

H M C R I FOCUS. (Hazardous Materials Control Resources Institute) see *ENVIRONMENTAL STUDIES — Waste Management*

614.7 IT
HABITAT FLAG. m. Calegari Edizioni s.r.l., Via Sismondi 62, 20133 Milan, Italy. TEL 02-738-94-14. FAX 02-738-12-66.

614.7 309 UK ISSN 0197-3975
GF101
HABITAT INTERNATIONAL; journal for the study of human settlements. 1976. 4/yr. £363($560) (effective 1994). Elsevier Science Ltd., Pergamon, P.O. Box 800, Kidlington, Oxford OX5 1DX, England. TEL 44-865-843000. FAX 44-865-843010. (Subscr. in U.S. and Canada to: Elsevier Science, 660 White Plains Rd., Tarrytown, NY 10591-5153. TEL 914-524-9200. FAX 914-333-2444) Ed.Bd. adv.; bk.rev. bibl.; charts; illus.; stat.; index. circ. 350. (also avail. in microfilm from UMI) **Indexed:** Abstr.Rural Dev.Trop., AESIS, Biol.Abstr., Curr.Adv.Ecol.Sci., Curr.Cont., E.I., Energy Rev., Environ.Abstr., Environ.Per.Bibl. (1982-), Excerp.Med., I D A, J.of Ferroc., Sage Fam.Stud.Abstr., SSCI. **Document type:** academic/scholarly publication.
  —BLDSC (4237.403000); Faxon; UnCover; SWETS; UMI. **CCC.**
  Formerly (until 1977): Habitat (Oxford) (ISSN 0361-3690)
  Description: Publishes original research, review articles and case studies concerned with all aspects of human settlements, and monitors the implementation of the recommendations of the UN Habitat Conference.
  Refereed Serial

614.7 CC
HAIYANG HUANJING KEXUE. (Text in Chinese) q. Guojia Haiyang Ju, Haiyang Huanjing Baohu Yanjiusuo, P.O. Box 303, Dalian, Liaoning 116023, People's Republic of China. TEL 471429. Ed. Qian Wanying.

HANDBOOK OF ENVIRONMENTAL CHEMISTRY. see *CHEMISTRY*

HANDBOOK OF ENVIRONMENTAL ISOTOPE GEOCHEMISTRY. see *EARTH SCIENCES*

HANDBOOK OF NATURAL PRODUCTS DATA. see *CHEMISTRY*

531.64 614.7 US
HARBINGER FILE; a descriptive directory of organizations concerned with environmental issues in California. 1979. biennial. $18.50. Harbinger Communications, 250 Homestead Trail, Santa Cruz, CA 95060. TEL 408-429-8727. Ed. Bill Leland. (back issues avail.) **Document type:** directory.
  Description: Describes 1576 organizations.

HARBOR BRANCH NEWS. see *EARTH SCIENCES — Oceanography*

HAZARD TECHNOLOGY. see *CIVIL DEFENSE*

613.7 US ISSN 0893-6242
RA565.A1 CODEN: HENDEF
HEALTH & ENVIRONMENT DIGEST. 1987. m. $115 to individuals (foreign $130); government or non-profit $90 (foreign $105). Freshwater Foundation, 725 County Rd. 6, Wayzata, MN 55391. TEL 612-449-0092. FAX 612-449-0592. Ed. Tim Burkhardt. index. circ. 1,850. (looseleaf format; back issues avail.) **Indexed:** Environ.Abstr., Environ.Ind. **Document type:** newsletter.
  —BLDSC (4274.810500).

HEALTHCARE ENVIRONMENTAL SERVICES. see *HOSPITALS*

HEDESELSKABETS TIDSSKRIFT; tidsskrift for grundforbedring og skovbrug. see *FORESTS AND FORESTRY*

HEIDEMTIJDSCHRIFT. see *AGRICULTURE*

614.7 GW ISSN 0933-6346
HEIMATPFLEGE IN WESTFALEN. 1930. bi-m. free. Westfaelischer Heimatbund, Kaiser-Wilhelm-Ring 3, 48145 Muenster, Germany. FAX 0251-5914028. Ed. Edeltraud Klueting. bk.rev. circ. 14,000. **Document type:** bulletin.
  Formerly (until 1988): Westfaelischer Heimatbund. Rundschreiben.

HELICTITE; journal of Australasian cave research. see *EARTH SCIENCES — Geology*

ENVIRONMENTAL STUDIES

HERITAGE NEWS. see *ARCHITECTURE*

HIDROLOGIAI KOZLONY. see *WATER RESOURCES*

070 614.7 US ISSN 0191-5657
HIGH COUNTRY NEWS. 1970. bi-w. $28 to individuals (foreign $34); institutions $38 (foreign $44). High Country Foundation, Box 1090, Paonia, CO 81428. TEL 303-527-4898. Ed. Betsy Marston. adv.; bk.rev.; index; circ. 14,000 (paid). (tabloid format; also avail. in microfiche; back issues avail.) **Indexed:** Acid Rain Abstr., Energy Info.Abstr., Energy Rev., Environ.Abstr., Environ.Per.Bibl. (1981-). **Document type:** newspaper.
—CIS. CCC.
Description: Environmental newspaper that covers conservation and natural resource issues in the Western United States.

628 US
HIGH GROUND. bi-m. membership. Association of New Jersey Environmental Commissions Highlands Coalition, Box 157, Mendham, NJ 07945. TEL 201-539-7547. Ed. Marcianna Caplis. **Document type:** newsletter.
Description: Discusses events and legislation affecting the Highlands region of New Jersey, an area of exceptional ecological diversity.

HIGHLANDS VOICE. see *CONSERVATION*

613.1 591 II ISSN 0970-2903
QL1
HIMALAYAN JOURNAL OF ENVIRONMENT AND ZOOLOGY. (Text in English) 1987. s-a. Rs.200 (foreign $25). Indian Academy of Environmental Sciences, c/o Dept. of Zoology, Gurukula Kangri University, Hardwar 249404, India. TEL 0133-425793. Ed. B.D. Joshi. adv.: page Rs.2000. bk.rev. (back issues avail.) **Indexed:** Sel.Water Res.Abstr.
—BLDSC (4315.002000).
Description: Covers fields of zoology and environmental sciences.

333.7 JA
HOPPO KAGAKU CHOSA HOKOKU/HUMAN CULTURE AND ENVIRONMENTAL STUDIES IN NORTHERN HOKKAIDO.* (Text in Japanese) 1980. a. Tsukuba Daigaku, Suiri Jikken Senta - University of Tsukuba, Environmental Research Center, 1-1, Tennodai 1-chome, Tsukuba-shi, Ibaraki-ken 305, Japan.

614.7 CC
HUANJING DAOBAO/ENVIRONMENT HERALD. (Text in Chinese) bi-m. Jiangsu Sheng Huanbao Ju - Jiangsu Environmental Protection Bureau, 70 Beijing Xilu, Building No.81, Nanjing, Jiangsu 210013, People's Republic of China. TEL 635194. (Co-sponsor: Chinese Society of Environmental Science) Ed. Hu Rongmei.

HUANJING HUAXUE/JOURNAL OF ENVIRONMENTAL CHEMISTRY. see *CHEMISTRY*

614.7 CC ISSN 0250-3301
TD4 CODEN: HCKHDV
HUANJING KEXUE. English edition: Journal of Environmental Sciences (ISSN 1001-0742) (Text in Chinese) 1976. bi-m. $79.20. (Chinese Academy of Sciences, Environmental Science Committee) Science Press, Marketing and Sales Department, 16 Donghuangchenggen Beijie, Beijing 100707, People's Republic of China. TEL 4010642. FAX 4012180. TELEX 210247-SPBJ-CN. Ed. Wu Lin. adv. circ. 21,000. **Indexed:** Biol.Dig., Chem.Abstr., Dairy Sci.Abstr., Geo.Abstr., Int.Aerosp.Abstr., Sugar Ind.Abstr.
—BLDSC (3180.317700); CASDDS.
Description: Publishes mainly research papers, review articles, notes, and communications in environmental science and environmental protection.
Refereed Serial

620.85 CC ISSN 0253-2468
TD4 CODEN: HKXUDL
HUANJING KEXUE XUEBAO/ACTA SCIENTIAE CIRCUMSTANTIAE. (Text in Chinese; summaries in English) 1981. q. $80.40. (Chinese Academy of Sciences, Ecology and Environment Research Centre) Science Press, Marketing and Sales Department, 16 Donghuangchenggen Beijie, Beijing 100707, People's Republic of China. TEL 4010642. FAX 4012180. TELEX 210247-SPBJ-CN. adv. circ. 11,000. **Indexed:** Chem.Abstr.
—CASDDS.
Description: Contains original research papers on the theory and practice of environmental science in China. Introduces such research results as new technology, methods, and tools.
Refereed Serial

614.7 CC ISSN 1001-3865
CODEN: HWYFEW
HUANJING WURAN YU FANGZHI/ENVIRONMENTAL POLLUTION AND PREVENTION. (Text in Chinese) bi-m. Zhejiang Huanjing Baohu Kexue Yanjiusuo - Zhejiang Institute of Environmental Protection, 43 Tianmushan Lu, Hangzhou, Zhejiang 310007, People's Republic of China. TEL 882847. Ed. Wong Shizhen. **Indexed:** Biodet.Abstr., Sugar Ind.Abstr.
—BLDSC (3791.543000); CASDDS.

614.7 614 CC ISSN 1001-5914
HUANJING YU JIANKANG ZAZHI/JOURNAL OF ENVIRONMENT AND HEALTH. (Text in Chinese) 1984. bi-m. Y6. Tianjin Shi Weisheng Fangbing Zhongxin - Tianjin Municipal Center of Health and Disease Prevention, 76 Tianshanshe Dajie, Hedong-qu, Tianjin 300011, People's Republic of China. TEL 719908. Ed. Dong Shanheng. adv. **Document type:** academic/scholarly publication.

614.7 531.64 US ISSN 0888-661X
HUDSON VALLEY G R E E N TIMES. 1981. 4/yr. $15. Hudson Valley Grass Roots Energy and Environmental Network, Box 208, Red Hook, NY 12571. TEL 914-758-4484. Ed.Bd. adv.; bk.rev.; abstr.; charts; illus. circ. 10,000. (tabloid format; back issues avail.) **Document type:** newspaper.

640.73 333.7 US ISSN 8755-7878
THE HUMAN ECOLOGIST. 1979. q. $20. Human Ecology Action League, Box 49126, Atlanta, GA 30359-1126. TEL 404-248-1898. FAX 404-248-0162. Ed. Diane Thomas. adv.; bk.rev.; cum.index: 1979-1986. circ. 5,000. (back issues avail.)
Description: Explains adverse reactions of humans to chemicals found in air, water, food, drugs, pesticides, and habitat resulting in multiple chemical sensitivities.

HUMAN ECOLOGY FORUM. see *SOCIAL SCIENCES: COMPREHENSIVE WORKS*

HUMAN SURVIVAL. see *POPULATION STUDIES*

HUMBOLDT SOCIETY NEWSLETTER. see *HOMOSEXUALITY*

HYDROLOGICAL SCIENCE AND TECHNOLOGY. see *WATER RESOURCES*

613.1 US ISSN 0264-5092
HYPOTENUSE. 1980. q. Research Triangle Institute, Box 12194, Research Triangle Park, NC 27709-2194. **Indexed:** Environ.Abstr.

614.7 UK
I C C E T ANNUAL REPORT. 1978. a. free. Imperial College of Science, Technology, and Medicine, University of London, Centre for Environmental Technology, 48 Prince's Gardens, London SW7 2PE, England. FAX 071-584-7596. Ed. Angela Mawle. circ. 1,200.

I C E S COOPERATIVE RESEARCH REPORT/RAPPORT DES RECHERCHES COLLECTIVES. (International Council for the Exploration of the Sea) see *FISH AND FISHERIES*

I C E S IDENTIFICATION LEAFLETS FOR DISEASES AND PARASITES OF FISH AND SHELLFISH/FICHES D'IDENTIFICATION DES MALADIES ET PARASITES DES POISSONS, CRUSTACES ET MOLLUSQUES. see *BIOLOGY — Zoology*

I C E S MARINE SCIENCE SYMPOSIA/ACTES DU SYMPOSIUM. (International Council for the Exploration of the Sea) see *FISH AND FISHERIES*

614 581 635 US
I E S NEWSLETTER. 1984. bi-m. membership. Institute of Ecosystem Studies, Education Program, Box R, Millbrook, NY 12545. TEL 914-677-5359. FAX 914-677-6455. Ed. Jill Cadwallader. circ. 1,100. (back issues avail.) **Document type:** newsletter.
Formerly: Cary Arboretum Newsletter.
Description: For readers interested in current research and education programs at the Institute, and general features on ecology, the environment and natural history.

614.7 UK ISSN 0260-4833
I E S PROCEEDINGS. 1980. irreg. £1.50 per issue to non-members. Institution of Environmental Sciences, 14 Princes Gate, London SW7 1PU, England. FAX 0252-549682. TELEX 034999TX LINK G. Ed. John F. Potter. circ. 700. **Document type:** proceedings.

613.1 SW ISSN 0284-8015
I G B P GLOBAL CHANGE REPORT. 1986. irreg. free. Royal Swedish Academy of Sciences, International Geosphere-Biosphere Programme, P.O. Box 50005, S-104 05 Stockholm, Sweden. **Document type:** monographic series.

614.7 340 IT
I J O NEWSLETTER. (Text in English, Italian) 1988. q. $25 membership. International Juridicial Organization for Environment and Development, Via Barberini 3, 00187 Rome, Italy. TEL 6-474-21-17. FAX 6-474-57-79. Ed. Mario Guttieres. adv. contact: Guy R. Bayley. bk.rev.; bibl. circ. 450. (reprint service avail.) **Document type:** academic/scholarly publication, newsletter.
●Also available online.
Description: Includes sections on environment and sustainable development in five continents, protection of oceans, industry and environment, and human rights.

628 GW
I N E M BULLETIN. irreg. DM.50 to non-members. International Network for Environmental Management, Hellgrund 92, 22880 Wedel, Germany. **Document type:** bulletin.
Description: Looks at environmental management techniques and sustainable development in industry.

I P N - BLAETTER. (Institut fuer die Paedagogik der Naturwissenschaften) see *SCIENCES: COMPREHENSIVE WORKS*

614.7 SI ISSN 0129-3486
I S E A S ENVIRONMENT AND DEVELOPMENT SERIES. (Text in English) 1991. irreg. price varies. Institute of Southeast Asian Studies, Heng Mui Keng Terrace, Off Pasir Panjang Rd., Singapore 0511, Singapore. TEL 778-0955. FAX 778-1735. TELEX RS 37068 ISEAS. (Subscr. in U.S. to: Ashgate, Old Post Rd., Brookfield, VT 05036. TEL 802-276-3162) **Document type:** academic/scholarly publication.
Description: Covers environmental and development issues in Asia and the Pacific.

I T C JOURNAL. see *GEOGRAPHY*

628.5 SW ISSN 0019-0896
I V L - NYTT. 1966. q. free. Institutet foer Vatten- och Luftvaardsforskning - Swedish Environmental Research Institute, P.O. Box 21060, 100 31 Stockholm, Sweden. TEL 08-7291519. FAX 08-318516. TELEX 15581 IVLS. Ed. Carina Bergqvist. adv.; illus. **Document type:** newsletter.
Description: Features articles on research conducted at the Institute.

628.5 SW ISSN 0283-1511
I V L - REFERAT. (Text in English, Swedish) 1985. q. free. Institutet foer Vatten- och Luftvaardsforskning - Swedish Environmental Research Institute, P.O. Box 21060, 100 31 Stockholm, Sweden. TEL 08-7291519. FAX 08-318516. TELEX 15581 IVLS.
Description: Research reports from the institute in a summarized form.

I W L - UMWELTBRIEF; Fakten, Hintergruende und Entscheidungshilfen fuer Unternehmer. (Institut fuer Gewerbliche Wasserwirtschaft und Luftreinhaltung e.V.) see *CONSERVATION*

I W R B NEWS. (International Waterfowl and Wetlands Research Bureau) see *BIOLOGY — Zoology*

ENVIRONMENTAL STUDIES 2421

614.9 US
TD181.N93
ILLAHEE: JOURNAL OF THE NORTHWEST ENVIRONMENT. 1984. q. $25 to individuals; N. American libraries and other institutions $40 (foreign $50). University of Washington, Institute for Environmental Studies, Engineering Annex FM-12, Seattle, WA 98195. TEL 206-543-1812. FAX 206-543-2025. E-mail: EWC@U.WASHINGTON.EDU. Eds. J.R. Karr, E.W. Chu. bibl.; illus. **Indexed:** Curr.Adv.Ecol.Sci., Environ.Per.Bibl. (1985-), Geo.Abstr. **Document type:** academic/scholarly publication.
—BLDSC (6151.740000); Faxon.
Formerly (until Jan. 1994): Northwest Environmental Journal (ISSN 0749-7962)
Description: Publishes articles, columns, and opinion essays on the environmental dimensions of the natural, social, and engineering sciences in addition to environmental ethics, business, law, and education, particularly in the Northwest.
Refereed Serial

ILLINOIS ENVIRONMENTAL LAW LETTER. see *LAW*

614.7 IT
IMPRESA AMBIENTE. 6/yr. Media Economici Seme S.p.A., Via P. Lomazzo 52, 20154 Milan, Italy. TEL 2-310-31. FAX 2-310-37-18. circ. 8,000.

IN BRIEF (SAN FRANCISCO, 1983); a quarterly newsletter on environmental law. see *LAW*

IN THE ANACOSTIA WATERSHED. see *WATER RESOURCES*

INDEPENDENT ENERGY; the industry's business magazine. see *ENERGY*

634.9 320 CN
INDEPENDENT NATIONAL EDITION; a monthly journal for thoughtful Canadians. 1986. m. Can.$18($15) (effective 1994). North Waterloo Publishing Ltd., 15 King St., Elmira, ON N3B 2R1, Canada. TEL 519-669-5155. FAX 519-669-5928. Ed. Bob Verdun. adv.; bk.rev.; play rev. circ. 9,500. (also avail. in microfilm; back issues avail.)

614.7 II ISSN 0970-8480
INDIAN ASSOCIATION FOR ENVIRONMENTAL MANAGEMENT. JOURNAL. (Text in English) 1965. 3/yr. $40 membership. Indian Association for Environmental Management, NEERI, P.O., Nagpur 440 020, India. FAX 0712-522725. TELEX 0715-7233 NERI IN. Ed. A.G. Bhole. bk.rev. circ. 2,000. **Document type:** academic/scholarly publication.
—BLDSC (4761.960000).
Formerly: I A W P C Technical Annual (ISSN 0970-1621)

614.7 II ISSN 0304-5250
QH183 CODEN: IJECDC
INDIAN JOURNAL OF ECOLOGY. (Text in English) 1974. s-a. Rs.140($60) Indian Ecological Society, Punjab Agricultural University, Ludhiana 141004, Punjab, India. Ed. A.K. Srivastava. adv.; bk.rev. circ. 700. **Indexed:** Aqua.Sci.& Fish.Abstr., Bio-Contr.News & Info., Biol.Abstr., Chem.Abstr., Cott.& Trop.Fibr.Abstr., Curr.Adv.Ecol.Sci., Dairy Sci.Abstr., Ecol.Abstr., Energy Info.Abstr., Environ.Abstr., Environ.Per.Bibl., Excerp.Med., Field Crop Abstr., Forest.Abstr., Herb.Abstr., Hort.Abstr., Indian Sci.Abstr., Int.Abstr.Biol.Sci., Irr.& Drain.Abstr., Maize Abstr., Nutr.Abstr., Potato Abstr., Rice Abstr., Seed Abstr., Soils & Fert., Triticale Abstr., Trop.Oil Seeds Abstr., Weed Abstr., World Agri.Econ.& Rural Sociol.Abstr.
—CASDDS.

INDIAN JOURNAL OF ENVIRONMENTAL HEALTH. see *PUBLIC HEALTH AND SAFETY*

614.7 II ISSN 0253-7141
TD171.5.I4 CODEN: IJEPDH
INDIAN JOURNAL OF ENVIRONMENTAL PROTECTION. 1981. m. Rs.1000 (foreign $250). Kalpana Corporation, P.O. Box 5, Varanasi 221 010, India. Ed. Surendra Kumar. adv.; bk.rev.; index. circ. 1,000. (back issues avail.) **Indexed:** Acid Rain Abstr., Acid Rain Ind., Chem.Abstr., Energy Info.Abstr., Environ.Abstr., Excerp.Med., INIS Atomind.
—BLDSC (4412.120000); CIS; UnCover; CASDDS. CCC.
Description: Covers all aspects of environmental pollution and its control.

333.7 US
INDIANA. DEPARTMENT OF ENVIRONMENTAL MANAGEMENT. ANNUAL REPORT. 1973. a. free. Department of Environmental Management, 105 S. Meridian, Box 601, Indianapolis, IN 46206-6015. TEL 317-633-8404. charts; illus.
Formerly: Indiana. Environmental Management Board. Annual Report (ISSN 0094-5749)

613 320 340 US ISSN 1071-4359
INDIANA CENTER ON GLOBAL CHANGE AND WORLD PEACE. OCCASIONAL PAPER SERIES. 1990. q. price varies. Indiana Center on Global Change and World Peace, Indiana University, 1217 E. Atwater, Bloomington, IN 47405. TEL 812-855-8859. FAX 812-855-3209. Ed. Victoria J. Cuffel. (back issues avail.) **Document type:** monographic series, academic/scholarly publication.
Description: Attempts to investigate and understand the causes of conflict on local, national and international levels with the intention of suggesting possible solutions to political, social, environmental and economic problems.

INDIANA ENVIRONMENTAL LAW LETTER. see *LAW*

628 614 US ISSN 1055-1050
INDOOR AIR REVIEW. m. $72 (foreign $108). I A Q Publishers, Inc., 4520 East-West Hwy., Ste. 610, Bethesda, MD 20814. TEL 301-913-0115. FAX 301-913-0119. (back issues avail.) **Document type:** newspaper.

614.7 UN ISSN 0378-9993
TD169 CODEN: IENVDB
INDUSTRY AND ENVIRONMENT. (Includes supplements: Cleaner Production Newsletter; APELL Newsletter; EnTA Newsletter) (Text and summaries in English, French, Spanish) 1978. q. $45. United Nations Environment Programme, Industry and Environment Programme Activity Centre, 39-43, quai Andre Citroen, 73739 Paris cedex 15, France. TEL 44-37-14-50. FAX 44-37-14-74. TELEX 204997F. (Subscr. to: UN Bookshop-sales unit, Palais des Nations, CH-1211 Geneva 10, Switzerland) Ed. Jacqueline Aloisi de Larderel. bk.rev.; abstr. circ. 11,000. (back issues avail.) **Indexed:** CAD CAM Abstr., Cadscan, ELLIS, Environ.Abstr., Excerp.Med., Geo.Abstr., I D A, Lead Abstr., Zincscan. **Document type:** academic/scholarly publication.
—BLDSC (4476.256000); El; SWETS.
Description: Provides a forum for the exchange of research and experiences. Presents articles written by and for industry managers, government officials and researchers in the field of sustainable industrial development.

614.7 FR ISSN 0241-7375
INFO DECHETS. ENVIRONNEMENT ET TECHNIQUE. 1980. m. (10/yr.). 580 F. (foreign 760 F.). Societe Envrionnement et Techniques, 7 chemin de Gordes, 38100 Grenoble, France. TEL 76-43-28-64. FAX 76-56-94-09. adv.; bk.rev. circ. 8,000.
Formerly: Information Dechets.

614.7 US ISSN 0275-522X
INFORM REPORTS. 1974. q. $25. Inform, Inc., 381 Park Ave S., New York, NY 10016. TEL 212-689-4040. FAX 212-447-0689. Ed. Mimi Bluestone. circ. 3,000. **Indexed:** Environ.Abstr.
—CIS.
Formerly (until 1980): Inform News.
Description: Describes the latest developments in INFORM's research projects, the project findings, and activities in communicating the findings to business, government and environmental leaders. Areas covered include chemical hazards prevention, municipal solid wastes, air quality, and alternative vehicle fuels.

614.7 US ISSN 1050-8953
INFORM SPECIAL REPORTS. 1990. irreg. price varies. Inform, Inc., 381 Park Ave. S., New York, NY 10016. TEL 212-689-4040. FAX 212-447-0689. Ed. Mimi Bluestone.
Description: Includes individual reports that cover the full range of environmental issues: chemical hazards prevention, municipal solid wastes, air quality, and alternative vehicle fuels.

614 IT ISSN 1122-0481
INFORMAZIONE INNOVATIVA; agenzia quindicinale di documentazione internazionale servizio di informazione innovativa scientifica tecnologica legislativa per la produzione, l'ambiente, la sanita. Short title: inf-Inn. (Text in Italian; summaries in English) 1985. s-m. L.600000. Centro Studi "l'Uomo e l'Ambiente", Via delle Palme, 13, 35137 Padova, Italy. TEL 049-8759622. FAX 049-8761945. Ed. Franco Spelzini. adv.: B&W page L.3100000, color page L.3700000; 210 x 297. bk.rev. circ. 1,000. (back issues avail.) **Document type:** bulletin.
Description: Clean technologies, mechanical and electrical engineering, energy sources, industrial health and safety are treated as part of the fundamental relationship between technological developments and sound environment.

614.7 338.91 UN ISSN 0252-3213
INFOTERRA; international directory of sources. (Text and summaries in English, French, Russian and Spanish) 1977. biennial. $250. United Nations Environment Programme, Infoterra Programme Activity Centre, P.O. Box 30552, Nairobi, Kenya. FAX 254-2-226949. TELEX 22068 KE. Ed. Linda Spencer. circ. 200. (also avail. in diskette format) **Document type:** directory.

INNER VOICE; forest service employees speaking as concerned citizens. see *FORESTS AND FORESTRY*

628.168 IT ISSN 0001-4982
TD204 CODEN: IQAAAW
INQUINAMENTO; acqua, aria, suolo, rumore. 1959. m. L.120000 (foreign L.230000). Etas s.r.l., Via Mecenate 91, 20138 Milan, Italy. TEL 02-580841. FAX 02-58012592. Ed. Paolo Berbenni. adv.: B&W page L.2800000, color page L.3640000; trim 181 x 270. circ. 7,868. **Indexed:** Chem.Abstr., INIS Atomind., W.R.C.Inf.
—BLDSC (4516.050000); CASDDS.
Supersedes: Acqua Industriale.
Description: Technical publication for water, air, soil, waste, noise, recycle and clean energy treatment techniques.

614.7 US ISSN 0270-8965
INSIDE E P A WEEKLY REPORT. (Environmental Protection Agency) 1980. w. $790 (foreign $825). Inside Washington Publishers, Box 7167, Benjamin Franklin Sta., Washington, DC 20044. TEL 703-892-8500. FAX 703-685-2606. **Document type:** newsletter.
Formerly: Inside E P A.

614.7 US ISSN 1050-1436
KF3775.A15
INSIDE E P A'S ENVIRONMENTAL DOCUMENT SERVICE. m. Inside Washington Publishers, Box 7167, Ben Franklin Sta., Washington, DC 20044. TEL 703-892-8500. FAX 703-685-2606.

INSTITUT FUER STADTBAUWESEN. VEROEFFENTLICHUNGEN. see *TRANSPORTATION — Roads And Traffic*

INSTITUT ROYAL DES SCIENCES NATURELLES DE BELGIQUE. BULLETIN. SERIE BIOLOGIE. see *BIOLOGY*

INSTITUTE FOR SOCIAL ECOLOGY NEWSLETTER. see *SOCIAL SCIENCES: COMPREHENSIVE WORKS*

574.5 US ISSN 0073-9227
CODEN: IESPAF
INSTITUTE OF ENVIRONMENTAL SCIENCES. ANNUAL MEETING. PROCEEDINGS. 1960. a. price varies. Institute of Environmental Sciences, 940 E. Northwest Hwy., Mt. Prospect, IL 60056. TEL 708-255-1561. FAX 708-255-1699. (also avail. in microfilm from UMI; reprint service avail. from UMI) **Indexed:** Biol.Abstr., Chem.Abstr., Sh.& Vib.Dig. **Document type:** proceedings.
—El; CASDDS.

ENVIRONMENTAL STUDIES

614.7 US ISSN 1052-2883
TA1 CODEN: JOIEEH
INSTITUTE OF ENVIRONMENTAL SCIENCES. JOURNAL.
1959. bi-m. $35 to non-members (foreign $70). Institute of Environmental Sciences, 940 E. Northwest Hwy., Mt. Prospect, IL 60056. TEL 708-255-1561. FAX 708-255-1699. Ed. Janet A. Ehmann. adv.; bk.rev.; abstr.; illus. circ. 6,000. (also avail. in microform from UMI; reprint service avail. from UMI) **Indexed:** A.S.& T.Ind., Acid Pre.Dig., Acid Rain Abstr., Acid Rain Ind., Biol.Abstr., Biol.Dig., Chem.Abstr., Corros.Abstr., Curr.Cont., Energy Rev., Environ.Abstr., Environ.Per.Bibl., Excerp.Med., Geo.Abstr., GeoRef., Ind.Sci.Rev., INIS Atomind., Noise Pollut.Publ.Abstr., Ocean.Abstr., Oper.Res.Manage.Sci., Pollut.Abstr., Qual.Contr.Appl.Stat., Ref.Sour., Sci.Abstr., Sci.Cit.Ind., Sel.Water Res.Abstr., Sh.& Vib.Dig., W.R.C.Inf.
—BLDSC (4759.420000); CIS; EI; Faxon; UnCover; SWETS; UMI; CASDDS. **CCC.**
Formerly: Journal of Environmental Sciences (ISSN 0022-0906)
Refereed Serial

574.5 US ISSN 0073-9251
INSTITUTE OF ENVIRONMENTAL SCIENCES. TUTORIAL SERIES. irreg. price varies. Institute of Environmental Sciences, 940 E. Northwest Hwy., Mt. Prospect, IL 60056. TEL 312-255-1561. FAX 708-255-1561.

INSTITUTE OF URBAN STUDIES. see *HOUSING AND URBAN PLANNING*

INSTITUTION OF ENGINEERS (INDIA). ENVIRONMENTAL ENGINEERING DIVISION. JOURNAL. see *PUBLIC HEALTH AND SAFETY*

INSTITUTION OF WATER AND ENVIRONMENTAL MANAGEMENT. NEWSLETTER. see *WATER RESOURCES*

INSTYTUT METEOROLOGII I GOSPODARKI WODNEJ. MATERIALY BADAWCZE. SERIA: GOSPODARKA WODNA I OCHRONA WOD/INSTITUTE OF METEOROLOGY AND WATER MANAGEMENT. RESEARCH PAPERS SERIES: WATER MANAGEMENT AND WATER PROTECTION. see *WATER RESOURCES*

INSTYTUT METEOROLOGII I GOSPODARKI WODNEJ. ODDZIAL MORSKI W GDYNI. MATERIALY. WARUNKI SRODOWISKOWE POLSKIEJ STREFY POLUDNIOWEGO BALTYKU. see *EARTH SCIENCES — Oceanography*

INSTYTUT ZOOTECHNIKI. ROCZNIKI NAUKOWE ZOOTECHNIKI/ANNALS OF ANIMAL SCIENCE. see *AGRICULTURE — Poultry And Livestock*

INTEGRAL. see *CONSERVATION*

628 UK ISSN 0962-1113
▼**INTEGRATED ENVIRONMENTAL MANAGEMENT.** 1992. 10/yr. £65 to individuals; institutions £195 (effective 1994). Blackwell Scientific Publications Ltd., Osney Mead, Oxford OX2 0EL, England. TEL 0865-240201. FAX 0865-721205. TELEX 83355-MEDBOK-G. **Document type:** newsletter.
—BLDSC (4531.815500).

614.7 US
INTEGRATED RISK INFORMATION SYSTEM (FOR MICROCOMPUTERS). Short title: I R I S. q. $520 (foreign $1040). (Environmental Protection Agency) U.S. National Technical Information Service, 5825 Port Royal Rd., Springfield, VA 22161. TEL 703-487-4630. (also avail. in diskette format)
Description: Provides information regarding the effects of chemicals on human health and includes reference doses and carcinogen assessments. A primary source for EPA risk assessment on chemicals of environmental concern.

614.7 US ISSN 8756-6281
INTERACTION (WASHINGTON, 1981); global - national - local. 1981. q. $25 membership. Global Tomorrow Coalition, 1325 G St., N.W., Ste. 1010, Washington, DC 20005-3104. TEL 202-628-4016. FAX 202-628-4018. Ed. Donald R. Lesh. bk.rev.; charts; illus. circ. 17,000. (tabloid format) **Document type:** newspaper.
Description: Covers the environment, ecology, public policy. Contains commentary and a calendar of events.

INTERNATIONAL BEAR NEWS. see *BIOLOGY — Zoology*

341 NE
INTERNATIONAL ENCYCLOPAEDIA OF LAWS. ENVIRONMENTAL LAW. (Text in English) 1991. 2 base vols. (plus irreg. updates). fl.475($203) (effective 1994). Kluwer Law and Taxation Publishers (Subsidiary of: Wolters Kluwer N.V.), P.O. Box 23, 7400 GA Deventer, Netherlands. TEL 31-5700-47261. FAX 31-5700-22244. TELEX 49295 KLUDV. (Dist. by: Libresso Distribution Centre, P.O. Box 23, 7400 GA Deventer, Netherlands. TEL 31-5700-33155. FAX 31-5700-33834; In N. America: Kluwer Law and Taxation Publishers, 675 Massachusetts Ave., Cambridge, MA 02139. TEL 617-354-0140. FAX 617-354-8595) Ed. M. Boes. (looseleaf format) **Document type:** monographic series.
Description: Publishes comparative studies of national and international environmental law, including international legislation and treaties, EEC environmental legislation, and discussions of the background, principles and sources of environmental law and legislation in individual countries.

614.7 UK ISSN 0141-4836
CODEN: IESAD7
INTERNATIONAL ENVIRONMENT AND SAFETY. 1978. q. £70. International Labmate Ltd., 12 Alban Park, Hatfield Rd., St. Albans AL4 0JJ, England. Ed. M.H. Pattison. circ. 10,500. (back issues avail.) **Indexed:** C.I.S. Abstr., Chem.Abstr., Lab.Haz.Bull.

614.9 US ISSN 0149-8738
TD169
INTERNATIONAL ENVIRONMENT REPORTER. 1978. m. $1583. The Bureau of National Affairs, Inc., 1231 25th St., N.W., Washington, DC 20037. TEL 202-452-4200. FAX 202-822-8092. TELEX 285656 BNAI WSH. (Subscr. to: 9435 Key West Ave., Rockville, MD 20850. TEL 800-372-1033) Ed. Marlon B. Allen. index. (looseleaf format; back issues avail.)
●Also available online. Vendor(s): Mead Data Central, Inc.
—BLDSC (4540.016000). **CCC.**
Description: Information and reference service covering international environmental law and developing policy in the major industrial nations.

614.7 US ISSN 1041-4665
HC79.E5 CODEN: IEAFEZ
INTERNATIONAL ENVIRONMENTAL AFFAIRS; a journal for research and policy. 1989. q. $50 to individuals (foreign $70); institutions $85 (foreign $105); students $35 (foreign $55). University Press of New England, 23 S. Main St., Hanover, NH 03755-2048. TEL 603-643-7111; 800-421-1561. FAX 603-643-1540. Ed. K. von Moltke. adv. contact: Tom Johnson. bk.rev. (back issues avail.) **Indexed:** Energy Rev., Environ.Abstr., Environ.Per.Bibl. (1990-). **Document type:** academic/scholarly publication.
—BLDSC (4540.016200); Faxon; UnCover; SWETS. **CCC.**
Description: Seeks to improve knowledge of environmental policy and management at the international level.

340 628 NE
▼**INTERNATIONAL ENVIRONMENTAL LAW AND POLICY.** (Text in English) 1992. irreg., latest 1993. price varies. Kluwer Academic Publishers, Postbus 17, 3300 AA Dordrecht, Netherlands. TEL 31-78-334911. FAX 31-78-334254. TELEX 29245 KAPG NL. (Dist. by: Kluwer Academic Publishers Group, P.O. Box 322, 3300 AH Dordrecht, Netherlands. TEL 31-78-524400. FAX 31-78-524474; N. America dist. addr.: Box 358, Accord Sta., Hingham, MA 02018-0358. TEL 617-871-6600. FAX 617-871-6528) (back issues avail.) **Document type:** monographic series.
Refereed Serial

INTERNATIONAL ENVIRONMENTAL LAW AND REGULATION; a practical guide. see *LAW — International Law*

628 SP ISSN 1133-5610
▼**INTERNATIONAL ENVIRONMENTAL YEARBOOK.** (Text in English) 1993. a. 11000 ptas. (effective 1993). S.P.A., Pintor Rosales 36, 28008 Madrid, Spain. TEL 34-1-541-6768. FAX 34-1-542-8309. **Document type:** directory.
Description: Lists worldwide information sources: publications, databases, sources of financing, government institutions, associations, fairs and congresses.

614.7 II ISSN 0377-015X
QH540 CODEN: IJESDQ
INTERNATIONAL JOURNAL OF ECOLOGY AND ENVIRONMENTAL SCIENCES. (Text in English) 1974. 3/yr. $60. International Scientific Publications (Subsidiary of: Scientific and Environmental Educational Society), 50-B Pocket C, Sidhartha Extension, New Delhi 110 014, India. TEL 91-11-632169. Ed. P.S. Ramakrishnan. adv.; bk.rev. circ. 600. **Indexed:** Acid Pre.Dig., Appl.Ecol.Abstr., Biol.Abstr., Chem.Abstr., Curr.Cont., Environ.Per.Bibl., Excerp.Med., Geo.Abstr., Sel.Water Res.Abstr., W.R.C.Inf. **Document type:** academic/scholarly publication.
—Faxon; CASDDS. **CCC.**

INTERNATIONAL JOURNAL OF ENERGY - ENVIRONMENT - ECONOMICS. see *ENERGY*

INTERNATIONAL JOURNAL OF ENVIRONMENTAL AND ANALYTICAL CHEMISTRY. see *CHEMISTRY — Analytical Chemistry*

614.7 UK ISSN 0960-3123
RA566.27 CODEN: IJEREO
INTERNATIONAL JOURNAL OF ENVIRONMENTAL HEALTH RESEARCH. 1991. q. £110 to institutions in EC nations (North America $190; elsewhere £120). Chapman & Hall, 2-6 Boundary Row, London SE1 8HN, England. TEL 071-865-0066. FAX 071-522-9623. TELEX 290164-CHAPMAG. (Dist. by: International Thomson Publishing Services, Ltd., N. Way, Andover, Hants. SP10 5BE, England. TEL 0264-3342919; US addr.: Chapman & Hall, Journals Promotion Department, One Penn Plaza, 41st Fl., New York, NY 10019. TEL 212-564-1060. FAX 212-564-1505) Ed.Bd. **Indexed:** Environ.Per.Bibl., Excerp.Med. (1993-). **Document type:** academic/scholarly publication.
—BLDSC (4542.242000); ADONIS; SWETS; CASDDS.
Description: Examines the interaction between the environment and human health as it relates to the natural environment, the built environment, and communicable diseases.

INTERNATIONAL JOURNAL OF ENVIRONMENTAL ISSUES IN MINERALS & ENERGY INDUSTRY. see *MINES AND MINING INDUSTRY*

614.7 628.5 US ISSN 0020-7233
HC79.E5 CODEN: IJEVAW
INTERNATIONAL JOURNAL OF ENVIRONMENTAL STUDIES. SECTIONS A & B. 1970. 8/yr. (in 2 vols., 4 nos./vol.). 212 ECU per vol. (effective 1993). Gordon and Breach Science Publishers, 820 Town Center Dr., Langhorne, PA 19047. TEL 215-750-2642. FAX 215-750-6343. (UK subscr. to: P.O. Box 90, Reading, Berkshire RG1 8JL, England. TEL 0734-560-080) Ed. J. Rose. adv.; bk.rev.; charts; illus.; index. (also avail. in microform) **Indexed:** Abstr.Hyg., API Abstr., API Catal., API Hlth.& Environ., API Oil., API Pet.Ref., API Pet.Subst., API Transport., Appl.Mech.Rev., Biol.Abstr., Biotech.Abstr., Cadscan, Chem.Abstr., Curr.Adv.Ecol.Sci., Curr.Cont., Energy Ind., Energy Info.Abstr., Environ.Per.Bibl. (1991-), Excerp.Med., Forest.Abstr., Forest Prod.Abstr., Geo.Abstr., Helminthol.Abstr., Herb.Abstr., HRIS, I D A, Irr.& Drain.Abstr., Lead Abstr., Meteor.& Geoastrophys.Abstr., Ocean.Abstr., Pollut.Abstr., Risk Abstr., Rural Devel.Abstr., Rural Recreat.Tour.Abstr., Sci.Abstr., Sel.Water Res.Abstr., Soils & Fert., SSCI, Trop.Dis.Bull., W.R.C.Inf., Weed Abstr., World Agri.Econ.& Rural Sociol.Abstr., Zincscan.
—BLDSC (4542.243000); Faxon; UnCover; SWETS; CASDDS. **CCC.**
Refereed Serial

613.1 338 US ISSN 1062-6832
TS183
▼**INTERNATIONAL JOURNAL OF ENVIRONMENTALLY CONSCIOUS MANUFACTURING.** 1992. q. $295. Environmentally Conscious Manufacturing, Box 20959, Albuquerque, NM 87154. Eds. Mo Jamshidi, Mo Shahinpoor. **Document type:** academic/scholarly publication.
Description: Provides a forum for addressing the existing and the emerging relationships between manufacturing and environment.

INTERNATIONAL JOURNAL OF HUMANITIES AND PEACE; synergy, synthesis, transformation. see *HUMANITIES: COMPREHENSIVE WORKS*

ENVIRONMENTAL STUDIES

INTERNATIONAL LAKE ENVIRONMENT COMMITTEE FOUNDATION. NEWSLETTER. ENGLISH EDITION. see *EARTH SCIENCES — Hydrology*

INTERNATIONAL LAKE ENVIRONMENT COMMITTEE FOUNDATION. NEWSLETTER. JAPANESE EDITION. see *EARTH SCIENCES — Hydrology*

INTERNATIONAL LIGHTING REVIEW. see *BUILDING AND CONSTRUCTION*

THE INTERNATIONAL PERMACULTURE SOLUTIONS JOURNAL. see *BIOLOGY*

INTERNATIONAL PRESS CUTTING SERVICE: WEEKLY ENERGY - ECOLOGY - POLLUTION REPORT. see *ENERGY*

INTERNATIONAL SYMPOSIUM ON WASTEWATER TREATMENT. see *WATER RESOURCES*

614.7 333.7 069   US   ISSN 0890-1538
INTERP CENTRAL CLEARINGHOUSE NEWSLETTER. 1977. bi-m. $30 to individuals; institutions $50. Interp Central, Inc., 18255 Cavanaugh Lake Rd., Box 28, Chelsea, MI 48118. TEL 313-475-7070. Ed. Gabriel J. Cherem. circ. 100. (looseleaf format; back issues avail.) **Document type:** newsletter.
Description: Information transmittal forum for organizations and individuals involved with interpretive and public contact programs.

614.7   UK
INTERPRETATION JOURNAL. 1975. 3/yr. £20 to individuals; libraries £20. Society for the Interpretation of Britain's Heritage (SIBH), 201 Buryfield Rd., Solihull, West Midlands B91 2BB, England. TEL 021-704-3961. Ed. Ken Jackson. adv.; bk.rev. circ. 600. **Indexed:** Art.Hosp.& Tour.
Former titles: Heritage Interpretation (ISSN 0265-3664); Interpretation.
Description: Journal of the society, an association of professionals, whose purpose is the interpretation of the cultural and natural heritage of Britain.

301.31   US   ISSN 0095-6945
HC79.E5
INTERSECTIONS; a journal of urban and environmental studies. 1973. a. Rensselaer Polytechnic Institute, Center for Urban and Environmental Studies, Sage Bldg., Troy, NY 12181. TEL 518-276-6565. Ed. Peg Olsen. bk.rev.; illus. circ. 1,000. **Indexed:** Avery Ind.Archit.Per.

INTERSPECIES NEWSLETTER. see *COMMUNICATIONS*

628.168   US
INTERSTATE COMMISSION ON THE POTOMAC RIVER BASIN. TECHNICAL REPORTS. 1977. irreg. Interstate Commission on the Potomac River Basin, 6110 Executive Blvd., Ste. 300, Rockville, MD 20852. TEL 301-984-1908.
Supersedes: Interstate Commission on the Potomac River Basin. Technical Bulletin (ISSN 0074-9966).
Description: Land uses research reports on water quality, supply and natural resources.

614.7 340   CN   ISSN 0820-3458
INTERVENOR. 1976. bi-m. Can.$20 to individuals; students Can.$18. Canadian Environmental Law Association, 517 College St., Ste. 401, Toronto, ON M6G 4A2, Canada. TEL 416-960-2284. FAX 416-960-9392. Ed. Jill Cameron. bk.rev. circ. 1,000. **Document type:** newsletter.
Formerly (until 1985): C E L A Newsletter.
Description: Informative reporting of environmental issues and legal cases and notices of upcoming events and conferences.

IOWA SIERRAN. see *CLUBS*

628   IS
TD187.5.I75
ISRAEL. MINISTRY OF THE ENVIRONMENT. MISRAD LE-ICHUT HA-SVIVAH. DOCH SHNATI. (Text in Hebrew) 1974. a. free. Ministry of the Environment, P.O. Box 6234, Jerusalem 91061, Israel. TEL 972-2-701606. FAX 972-2-513945. TELEX 25629-ENVIR-IL. Ed. Tamar Ben-Yeshaiya. circ. 2,500. **Document type:** government publication.
Former titles: Israel. Environmental Protection Service. Ekhut ha-Svivah be-Yisrael. Luakh Shnati (ISSN 0334-3162); Israel. Environment Protection Agency. Ekhut ha-Svivah be-Yisrael. Luakh Shnati.

ISRAEL. MINISTRY OF THE INTERIOR. CITY AND REGION - IR VE EZOR. see *HOUSING AND URBAN PLANNING*

614.7   IS   ISSN 0334-3804
ISRAEL ENVIRONMENT BULLETIN. (Text in English) 1974. q. free. Ministry of the Environment, P.O. Box 6234, Jerusalem 91061, Israel. TEL 972-2-701606. FAX 972-2-513945. TELEX 25629-ENVIR-IL. Ed. Shoshana Gabbay. bk.rev. circ. 2,500. **Indexed:** Energy Info.Abstr., Environ.Abstr. **Document type:** government publication, bulletin.
Description: Survey of environmental policy, activities, legislation and news in Israel.

628   UK   ISSN 1350-7583
▼**ISSUES IN ENVIRONMENTAL SCIENCE AND TECHNOLOGY.** 1994. s-a. £25($47) in E.C. nations; Canada £28; elsewhere £27. Royal Society of Chemistry, Thomas Graham House, Cambridge DB4 4WF, England. TEL 0223-420066. FAX 0223-423429. (Subscr. to: Turpin Distribution Services Ltd., Blackhorse Rd., Letchworth, Herts. SG6 1HN, England. TEL 0462-672555. FAX 0462-480947) **Document type:** monographic series.
Description: Discusses topics in environmental science from the perspective of all disciplines

614.7 363.35 312   IT
ITALIA NOSTRA. SEZIONE DI TRENTO. BOLLETTINO. 1972. s-a. L.25000. Via Oss Mazzurana, 54, 38100 Trento, Italy. TEL 0461-37336. Ed.Bd. circ. 1,500. (back issues avail.) **Document type:** bulletin.

614.7   RU   ISSN 0202-7321
QH75
ITOGI NAUKI I TEKHNIKI: OKHRANA PRIRODY I VOSPROIZVODSTVO PRIRODNYKH RESURSOV. 1968. irreg., latest vols.23-25, 1989. 6.60 Rub. Vsesoyuznyi Institut Nauchno-Tekhnicheskoi Informatsii (VINITI), Baltiiskaya ul. 14, Moscow A-219, Russia. (Subscr. to: Mezhdunarodnaya Kniga, Dimitrova ul. 39, 113095 Moscow, Russia)
—BLDSC (0128.690000).

575.1   JA
J E M S NEWS. (Japan - Environmental Mutagen Society) (Text in Japanese) 1972. s-a. Nihon Kankyo Hen'igen Gakkai, c/o Mr. Toshio Sofuni, Kokuritsu Eisei Shikenjo, 18-1 Kamiyoga 1-chome, Setagaya-ku, Tokyo 158, Japan.

574.5   IR
JANGAL VA MARTA'. (Text in Persian) no.8, 1991. q. IRl.200 per no. Sazman-i Jangalha va Marati'i Kishvar - Organization of Jungles and Meadows, 1 Lashgark Rd., Post Code 19564, P.O. Box 19575-567, Tehran, Iran.
Description: Discusses issues relating to the ecology and preservation of jungles and pasture lands in Iran and the world.

614.7   JA
JAPAN AIR CLEANING ASSOCIATION. JOURNAL. 1964. 8/yr. $115. (Japan Air Cleaning Association) Intercontinental Marketing Corp., P.O. Box 5056, Tokyo 100-31, Japan. FAX 81-3-3667-9646.

574.5   JA   ISSN 0021-5007
QH540   CODEN: NSGSAF
JAPANESE JOURNAL OF ECOLOGY/NIPPON SEITAI GAKKAISHI. (Text in English, Japanese) 1954. 3/yr. $40. Ecological Society of Japan - Nihon Seitai Gakkai, Hokkaido Daigaku Daigakuin Kankyo Kagaku Kenkyukai, Nishi 5-chome, Kita 10-jo, Kita-ku, Sapporo-shi, Hokkaido 060, Japan. Ed.Bd. bk.rev.; charts; illus.; index. circ. 2,500. **Indexed:** Agrindex, Biol.Abstr., Chem.Abstr., Crop Physiol.Abstr., Deep Sea Res.& Oceanogr.Abstr., Field Crop Abstr., Forest.Abstr., Forest Prod.Abstr., Geo.Abstr., GeoRef., Herb.Abstr., Jap.Per.Ind., Sel.Water Res.Abstr., Soils & Fert., W.R.C.Inf., Weed Abstr.
—UnCover.

JERSEY SIERRAN. see *CONSERVATION*

614.7   CC
JIAOTONG HUANBAO (SHUIYUN BAN)/ENVIRONMENTAL PROTECTION IN TRANSPORTATION (WATER TRANSPORT EDITION). (Text in Chinese) bi-m. Jiaotongbu, Tianjin Shuiyun Gongcheng Keyan-suo - Ministry of Transportation, Tianjin Water Transport Engineering Institute, Xin Gang, Tangguqu, Tianjin 300456, People's Republic of China. TEL 975508. Ed. Wang Shuitian.

JOURNAL OF AGRICULTURAL AND ENVIRONMENTAL ETHICS. see *PHILOSOPHY*

628.1   NE   ISSN 0925-1014
QH541.5.W3   CODEN: JAQHE2
JOURNAL OF AQUATIC ECOSYSTEM HEALTH. (Text in English) 1991. 4/yr. fl.387($202) (effective 1994). (Aquatic Ecosystem Health and Management Society) Kluwer Academic Publishers, Postbus 17, 3300 AA Lordrecht, Netherlands. TEL 31-78-334911. FAX 31-78-334254. TELEX 29245 KAPG NL. (Dist. by: Kluwer Academic Publishers Group, P.O. Box 322, 3300 AH Dordrecht, Netherlands. TEL 31-78-524400. FAX 31-78-524474; N. America dist. addr.: Box 358, Accord Sta., Hingham, MA 00018-0158. TEL 617-871-6600. FAX 617-871-6528) Ed. M. Munawar. (also avail. in microform from UMI; back issues avail.) **Indexed:** Environ.Abstr. **Document type:** academic/scholarly publication.
—BLDSC (4947.158700); UnCover; UMI. **CCC.**
Description: Covers topics relating to the health of biological components of aquatic ecosystems.
Refereed Serial

JOURNAL OF ARID ENVIRONMENTS. see *GEOGRAPHY*

614.7 540   US   ISSN 0098-0331
QD1   CODEN: JCECD8
JOURNAL OF CHEMICAL ECOLOGY. 1975. m. $655 (foreign $765) (effective 1994). Plenum Publishing Corp., 233 Spring St., New York, NY 10013-1578. TEL 212-620-8000. FAX 212-463-0742. TELEX 23-421139. Eds. Robert M. Silverstein, John B. Simeone. adv. (also avail. in microfilm from JSC) **Indexed:** Abstr.Bull.Inst.Pap.Chem., Bio-Contr.News & Info., Biol.Abstr., Biotech.Abstr., Chem.Abstr., Cott.& Trop.Fibr.Abstr. Curr.Adv.Biochem., Curr.Cont., Curr.Ref.Fish Res., Deep Sea Res.& Oceanogr.Abstr., Excerp.Med., Fababean Abstr., Field Crop Abstr., Forest.Abstr., Forest Prod.Abstr., Helminthol.Abstr., Herb.Abstr., Ind.Sci.Rev., INIS Atomind., Maize Abstr., Plant Grow.Reg.Abstr., Potato Abstr., Rev.Appl.Entomol., Rice Abstr., Sci.Cit.Ind., Seed Abstr., Soils & Fert., Soyabean Abstr., Triticale Abstr., Weed Abstr. **Document type:** academic/scholarly publication.
—BLDSC (4955.965000); Faxon; UnCover; SWETS; UMI; CASDDS. **CCC.**
Refereed Serial

JOURNAL OF ENERGY, NATURAL RESOURCES AND ENVIRONMENTAL LAW. see *ENERGY*

614.7   II   ISSN 0254-8704
CODEN: JEBIDP
JOURNAL OF ENVIRONMENTAL BIOLOGY; a quarterly research journal. (Text in English) 1980. q. Rs.150 to individuals (foreign $80); institutions Rs.250 (foreign $120). (J E B Foundation) J E B Foundation, 711, Civil Lines (South), Muzaffarnagar 251 001, India. TEL 01312-25306. Ed. Kiran Dalela. adv.; bk.rev. circ. 1,000. (back issues avail.) **Indexed:** Biol.Abstr., Cadscan., Chem.Abstr., Curr.Adv.Ecol.Sci., Curr.Cont., Curr.Ref.Fish Res., Ecol.Abstr., Energy Info.Abstr., Environ.Abstr., Excerp.Med., Indian Sci.Abstr., Lead Abstr., Tox.Abstr., Zincscan.
—BLDSC (4979.359000); CIS; Faxon; CASDDS.
Description: Serves as the exclusive research journal in India concerned with environmental pollution and toxicology.

333.7   US   ISSN 0095-0696
HC79.P55   CODEN: JEEMDI
JOURNAL OF ENVIRONMENTAL ECONOMICS AND MANAGEMENT. 1975. bi-m. $222 (foreign $272). (Association of Environmental and Resource Economists) Academic Press, Inc., Journal Division, 525 B St., Ste. 190C, San Diego, CA 92101-4495. TEL 619-230-1840. FAX 619-699-6800. (Subscr. to: Box 620000, Orlando, FL 32891-8340. TEL 800-543-9534) Ed. Ronald G. Cummings. (back issues avail.) **Indexed:** ABI Inform, Acid Pre.Dig., Acid Rain Abstr., Acid Rain Ind., Biol.Abstr., BPIA, Bus.Ind., Curr.Cont., Deep Sea Res.& Oceanogr.Abstr., Excerp.Med., Geo.Abstr., GeoRef, Ind.Sci.Rev., INIS Atomind., J.of Econ.Lit, Manage.Cont., Ocean.Abstr., Pollut.Abstr., RICS, Risk Abstr., Sci.Cit.Ind., Sel.Water Res.Abstr., SSCI, Tr.& Indus.Ind., W.R.C.Inf. **Document type:** academic/scholarly publication.
—BLDSC (4979.360000); Faxon; UnCover; SWETS; UMI. **CCC.**
Description: Publishes theoretical and empirical papers concerned with the linkage between economic systems and environmental and natural resources systems.

ENVIRONMENTAL STUDIES

614.7 US ISSN 0095-8964
S946 CODEN: JEVEB9
THE JOURNAL OF ENVIRONMENTAL EDUCATION. 1969. q. $33 to individuals; institutions $63. (Helen Dwight Reid Educational Foundation) Heldref Publications, 1319 Eighteenth St., N.W., Washington, DC 20036-1802. TEL 202-296-6267. Ed. Martha Fogelman. adv. contact: Raymond Rallo. bibl.; charts; stat.; index. circ. 1,200. (also avail. in microfiche from KTO; reprint service avail.) Indexed: Acid Pre.Dig., Avery Ind.Archit.Per., Biol.Abstr., C.I.J.E., Cont.Pg.Educ., Curr.Cont., Deep Sea Res.& Oceanogr.Abstr., Educ.Ind., Energy Ind., Energy Info.Abstr., Environ.Abstr., Environ.Ind., Environ.Per.Bibl. (1974-), Excerp.Med., Geo.Abstr., Mid.East: Abstr.& Ind., Psychol.Abstr., So.Pac.Per.Ind., SSCI. **Document type:** academic/scholarly publication.
—BLDSC (4979.370000); CIS; Faxon; UnCover; SWETS; UMI. **CCC.**
Formerly: Environmental Education (ISSN 0013-9254)
Refereed Serial

624 US ISSN 0733-9372
TD1 CODEN: JOEEDU
JOURNAL OF ENVIRONMENTAL ENGINEERING. 1956. bi-m. $136 to non-members (foreign $159); members $34 (foreign $57). American Society of Civil Engineers, Environmental Engineering Division, 345 E. 47th St., New York, NY 10017-2398. TEL 212-705-7288. FAX 212-980-4681. Ed. Steve C. McCutcheon. circ. 6,100. (also avail. in microform from UMI; reprint service avail. from UMI) Indexed: A.I.Abstr., A.S.& T.Ind., Abstr.Bull.Inst.Pap.Chem., Acid Pre.Dig., Acid Rain Abstr., Acid Rain Ind., Biol.Abstr., Chem.Abstr., Curr.Adv.Ecol.Sci., Curr.Cont., Deep Sea Res.& Oceanogr.Abstr., Eng.Ind., Environ.Abstr., Environ.Per.Bibl., Excerp.Med., Fluidex, Geo.Abstr., GeoRef., HRIS, Ind.Sci.Rev., INIS Atomind., Intl.Civil Eng.Abstr., Ocean.Abstr., Pollut.Abstr., Risk Abstr., Sci.Cit.Ind., Sel.J.Water, Sel.Water Res.Abstr., Soils & Fert., W.R.C.Inf. **Document type:** academic/scholarly publication.
—BLDSC (4979.373000); CIS; EI; Faxon; UnCover; SWETS; UMI; CASDDS. **CCC.**
Former titles (1973-1982): American Society of Civil Engineers. Environmental Engineering Division. Journal (ISSN 0090-3914); American Society of Civil Engineers. Sanitary Engineering Division. Journal (ISSN 0044-7986)
Description: Reports solution of problems involving environmental sanitation and considers the social and environmental impact of those solutions. Focuses on the provision of safe, palatable, and ample public water supplies and the proper treatment and management of hazardous, solid, and liquid wastes.
Refereed Serial

614 US ISSN 0022-0892
RA565.A1 CODEN: JEVHAH
JOURNAL OF ENVIRONMENTAL HEALTH. 1938. 10/yr. $75 (foreign $100) (effective 1994). National Environmental Health Association, 720 S. Colorado Blvd., No. 970 S. Tower, Denver, CO 80222-1904. TEL 303-756-9090. FAX 303-691-9490. Ed. Simonne Gallaty. adv. contact: Scott Houston. bk.rev.; charts; illus.; index. circ. 6,000. (also avail. in microfilm from UMI; reprint service avail. from UMI) Indexed: A.S.& T.Ind., Bibl.Agri., Biol.Abstr., C.I.J.E., C.I.S. Abstr., Cadscan, Chem.Abstr., Curr.Cont., Dairy Sci.Abstr., Energy Info.Abstr., Energy Rev., Environ.Abstr., Environ.Per.Bibl. (1972-), Excerp.Med., Food Sci.& Tech.Abstr., Gen.Sci.Ind., Helminthol.Abstr., Hosp.Lit.Ind., Ind.Sci.Rev., INIS Atomind., Lead Abstr., Noise Pollut.Publ.Abstr., Nutr.Abstr., Ocean.Abstr., Pollut.Abstr., Risk Abstr., Sci.Cit.Ind., Sel.Water Res.Abstr., W.R.C.Inf., Zincscan. **Document type:** academic/scholarly publication.
—BLDSC (4979.380000); CIS; Faxon; UnCover; SWETS; UMI; CASDDS.
Description: Collection of analyses on environmental health vis-a-vis the law, new consumer products, hazardous wastes and other issues.
Refereed Serial

614.7 340 UK ISSN 0952-8873
K10 CODEN: JELAEI
JOURNAL OF ENVIRONMENTAL LAW. 1989. 2/yr. £53($101) (effective 1994). Oxford University Press, Oxford Journals, Walton St., Oxford OX2 6DP, England. TEL 0865-56767. FAX 0865-56646. TELEX 837330-OXPRES-G. (U.S. subscr. to: Oxford University Press Inc., 2001 Evans Rd., Cary, NC 27513. TEL 919-677-0977) Ed. Richard Macrory. adv. contact: Jane Parker. bk.rev. circ. 850. **Document type:** academic/scholarly publication.
—BLDSC (4979.381400); UnCover; SWETS; UMI. **CCC.**
Description: Environmental law in pollution control, waste management, habitat protection, biotechnology and regimes for common natural resources.

JOURNAL OF ENVIRONMENTAL LAW AND PRACTICE. see *LAW*

614.7 UK ISSN 0301-4797
HC79.E5 CODEN: JEVMAW
JOURNAL OF ENVIRONMENTAL MANAGEMENT. 1973. m. (2 vols./yr.). £260 (effective 1994). Academic Press Ltd. (Subsidiary of: Harcourt Brace & Company Ltd.), 24-28 Oval Rd., London NW1 7DX, England. TEL 44-71-267-4466. FAX 44-71-482-2293. TELEX 25775-ACPRES-G. (Subscr. to: Harcourt Brace & Company Ltd., Foots Cray High St., Sidcup, Kent DA14 5BR. TEL 44-81-300-3322. FAX 44-81-309-0807) Ed. J.N.R. Jeffers. Indexed: Acid Pre.Dig., Acid Rain Abstr., Acid Rain Ind., Art.Hosp.& Tour, Biol.Abstr., Curr.Cont., Energy Info.Abstr., Energy Info.Abstr., Energy Rev., Environ.Abstr., Environ.Per.Bibl., Excerp.Med., Field Crop Abstr., Forest.Abstr., Forest Prod.Abstr., Geo.Abstr., GeoRef., Herb.Abstr., I D A, Ind.Sci.Rev., INIS Atomind., Int.Abstr.Oper.Res., Int.Lab.Doc., Irr.& Drain.Abstr., Maize Abstr., Mid.East: Abstr.& Ind., Ocean.Abstr., Pollut.Abstr., Rice Abstr., Risk Abstr., Rural Devel.Abstr., Sci.Cit.Ind., Sel.Water Res.Abstr., Soils & Fert., Soyabean Abstr., SSCI, Triticale Abstr., W.R.C.Inf., Weed Abstr., World Agri.Econ.& Rural Sociol.Abstr. **Document type:** academic/scholarly publication.
—BLDSC (4979.383000); CIS; Faxon; UnCover; SWETS. **CCC.**
Description: Presents papers on all aspects of management and use of the environment, both natural and man-made.

614.7 US ISSN 1058-1367
K10
JOURNAL OF ENVIRONMENTAL PERMITTING. 1991. q. $175 (foreign $225). Executive Enterprises Publications Co., Inc., 22 W. 21st St., 10th Fl., New York, NY 10010-6904. TEL 212-645-7880. FAX 212-645-1160. Ed. Isabelle Cohen.
—BLDSC (4979.384700); UnCover; UMI. **CCC.**
Description: Discusses air operating, water, and RCRA permits. Covers basic permitting issues, including technology assessment, data collection and management, and engineering judgment precedents.

JOURNAL OF ENVIRONMENTAL PLANNING AND MANAGEMENT. see *HOUSING AND URBAN PLANNING*

614.7 630 US ISSN 0047-2425
S1 CODEN: JEVQAA
JOURNAL OF ENVIRONMENTAL QUALITY. 1972. q. $100. American Society of Agronomy, Inc., 677 S. Segoe Rd., Madison, WI 53711. TEL 608-273-8080. FAX 608-273-2021. Ed. R.J. Wagenet. adv.; bk.rev.; bibl.; charts; illus.; stat. circ. 3,000. Indexed: Acid Pre.Dig., Acid Rain Abstr., Acid Rain Ind., Biol.Abstr., Biol.& Agr.Ind., Biol.Dig., Biotech.Abstr., Cadscan, Chem.Abstr., Crop Physiol.Abstr., Curr.Cont., Dairy Sci.Abstr., Deep Sea Res.& Oceanogr.Abstr., Dok.Arbeitsmed., Energy Ind., Energy Info.Abstr., Energy Rev., Environ.Abstr., Environ.Per.Bibl. (1972-), Excerp.Med., Field Crop Abstr., Forest.Abstr., Forest Prod.Abstr., Geo.Abstr., GeoRef., Helminthol.Abstr., Herb.Abstr., Hort.Abstr., Ind.Sci.Rev., Ind.Vet., INIS Atomind., Irr.& Drain.Abstr., Lead Abstr., Maize Abstr., Noise Pollut.Publ.Abstr., Ocean.Abstr., Plant Breed.Abstr., Pollut.Abstr., Rev.Plant Path., Sci.Cit.Ind., Sel.J.Water, Sel.Water Res.Abstr., Soils & Fert., Soyabean Abstr., Triticale Abstr., Vet.Bull., W.R.C.Inf., Weed Abstr., World Agri.Econ.& Rural Sociol.Abstr., Zincscan.
—BLDSC (4979.390000); CIS; EI; Faxon; UnCover; SWETS; UMI; CASDDS.
Description: Presents reviews and technical reports concerned with protection and improvement of environmental quality in natural and agricultural systems.
Refereed Serial

614.7 574.191 UK ISSN 0265-931X
CODEN: JERAEE
JOURNAL OF ENVIRONMENTAL RADIOACTIVITY. 1984. 12/yr. (in 4 vols., 3 nos./vol.). £420($645) (effective 1994). (University of Glasgow, Department of Chemistry) Elsevier Science Ltd., Oxford Fulfilment Centre, P.O. Box 800, Kidlington, Oxford OX5 1DX, England. TEL 44-865-843000. FAX 44-865-843010. (Subscr. in U.S. and Canada to: Elsevier Science, 660 White Plains Rd., Tarrytown, NY 10591-5153. TEL 914-524-9200. FAX 914-333-2444) Ed. M.S. Baxter. adv. Indexed: Biol.Abstr., Curr.Cont., Deep Sea Res.& Oceanogr.Abstr., Energy Rev., Eng.Ind., Environ.Abstr., Environ.Per.Bibl. (1986-), Excerp.Med., Geo.Abstr., INIS Atomind., Soils & Fert. **Document type:** academic/scholarly publication.
—BLDSC (4979.392000); EI; Faxon; UnCover; SWETS; CASDDS. **CCC.**
Description: International forum for original research on any aspect of radioactivity in natural systems.
Refereed Serial

614.7 US ISSN 1055-758X
K10
JOURNAL OF ENVIRONMENTAL REGULATION. 1991. q. $175 (foreign $225). Executive Enterprises Publications Co., Inc., 22 W. 21st St., 10th Fl., New York, NY 10010-6904. TEL 212-645-7880. FAX 212-645-1160.
—BLDSC (4979.392500); UnCover; UMI. **CCC.**
Description: Provides a detailed overview of all major environmental regulations.

614.7 II
JOURNAL OF ENVIRONMENTAL SCIENCE. (Text in English) 1987. s-a. Orissa Environmental Society, c/o R.C. Das, Ed., State Prevention & Control of Pollution Board, Orissa, Bhubaneswar 751 012, India.

ENVIRONMENTAL STUDIES

614.7   US   ISSN 0360-1226
TD1   CODEN: JESEDU
JOURNAL OF ENVIRONMENTAL SCIENCE AND HEALTH. PART A: ENVIRONMENTAL SCIENCE AND ENGINEERING. 1968. 10/yr. $725 (for Parts A, B, and C $1295). Marcel Dekker Journals, 270 Madison Ave., New York, NY 10016. TEL 212-696-9000. FAX 212-685-4540. TELEX 421419. (Subscr. to: Box 5017, Monticello, NY 12701) Ed. James W. Robinson. (also avail. in microform from RPI) **Indexed:** Acid Rain Abstr., Acid Rain Ind., Anal.Abstr., Biol.Abstr., Cadscan, Chem.Abstr., Curr.Cont., Dairy Sci.Abstr., Energy Info.Abstr., Energy Rev., Environ.Abstr., Environ.Per.Bibl., Excerp.Med., Geo.Abstr., GeoRef., Herb.Abstr., Hort.Abstr., Ind.Sci.Rev., Ind.Vet., INIS Atomind., Irr.& Drain.Abstr., Lab.Haz.Bull., Lead Abstr., Ocean.Abstr., Pollut.Abstr., Rice Abstr., Sel.Water Res.Abstr., Soils & Fert., Sugar Ind.Abstr., Vet.Bull., W.R.C.Inf., Weed Abstr., Zincscan. **Document type:** academic/scholarly publication.
—BLDSC (4979.393000); CIS; EI; Faxon; UnCover; SWETS; CASDDS. **CCC.**
Supersedes in part: Environmental Letters (ISSN 0013-9300)
Refereed Serial

614.7   US   ISSN 0360-1234
QH545.A1   CODEN: JPFCD2
JOURNAL OF ENVIRONMENTAL SCIENCE AND HEALTH. PART B: PESTICIDES, FOOD CONTAMINANTS, AND AGRICULTURAL WASTES. 1975. 6/yr. $475 (for Parts A, B, and C $1295). Marcel Dekker Journals, 270 Madison Ave., New York, NY 10016. TEL 212-696-9000. FAX 212-685-4540. TELEX 421419. (Subscr. to: Box 5017, Monticello, NY 12701) Ed. S.U. Khan. (also avail. in microform from RPI) **Indexed:** Agri.Eng.Abstr., Anal.Abstr., Bio-Contr.News & Info., Biol.Abstr., Biotech.Abstr., Cadscan, Chem.Abstr., Cott.& Trop.Fibr.Abstr., Curr.Cont., Dairy Sci.Abstr., Dok.Arbeitsmed., Environ.Abstr., Environ.Per.Bibl. (1977-), Excerp.Med., Food Sci.& Tech.Abstr., Helminthol.Abstr., Hort.Abstr., Ind.Med., Ind.Sci.Rev., Ind.Vet., INIS Atomind., Lead Abstr., Maize Abstr., Ocean.Abstr., Pollut.Abstr., Poult.Abstr., Rev.Med.& Vet.Mycol., Rev.Plant Path., Rice Abstr., Sci.Cit.Ind., Sel.Water Res.Abstr., Soils & Fert., Sugar Ind.Abstr., Triticale Abstr., Vet.Bull., W.R.C.Inf., Weed Abstr., Zincscan. **Document type:** academic/scholarly publication.
—BLDSC (4979.394000); CIS; EI; Faxon; SWETS; CASDDS. **CCC.**
Supersedes in part: Environmental Letters (ISSN 0013-9300)
Refereed Serial

614.7   CC   ISSN 1001-0742
TD187.5.C6   CODEN: JENSEE
JOURNAL OF ENVIRONMENTAL SCIENCES. Chinese edition: Huanjing Kexue (ISSN 0250-3301) 1989. 4/yr. fl.384($205) (effective 1994). (Chinese Academy of Sciences, Environmental Science Committee) Journal of Environmental Sciences, P.O. Box 2871, Beijing 100085, People's Republic of China. (Dist. outside China by: I O S Press, Van Diemenstraat 94, 1013 CN Amsterdam, Netherlands. TEL 31-20-6382189. FAX 31-20-6203419; Subscr. in U.S. and Canada to: I O S Press, Inc., Box 10558, Burke, VA 22009-0558. TEL 703-323-5554. FAX 703-250-4705) Ed. Liu Tung-Sheng. **Indexed:** Environ.Abstr. **Document type:** academic/scholarly publication.
—BLDSC (4979.420000); EI; CASDDS.
Description: Publishes original research papers on environmental sciences. Includes basic and applied research on pollution control and abatement technology in atmospheric, terrestrial, and aquatic environments, conservation, health studies and toxicology, and environmental quality assessment, standards, and criteria.

614.7   US   ISSN 0047-2433
TD1   CODEN: JEVSBH
JOURNAL OF ENVIRONMENTAL SYSTEMS. 1971. q. $112. Baywood Publishing Co., Inc., 26 Austin Ave., Box 337, Amityville, NY 11701. TEL 516-691-1270. FAX 516-691-1770. Ed. Sheldon Reaven. bk.rev.; abstr.; bibl.; charts; illus.; stat. (back issues avail.) **Indexed:** Biol.Abstr., Curr.Cont., Energy Rev., Eng.Ind., Environ.Abstr., Environ.Per.Bibl. (1973-), Excerp.Med., HRIS, Key to Econ.Sci., Ocean.Abstr., Pollut.Abstr., Risk Abstr., Sel.Water Res.Abstr., SSCI. **Document type:** academic/scholarly publication.
—BLDSC (4979.450000); EI; Faxon; UnCover; SWETS.
Description: Deals with the analysis of and solution to problems which relate to the system-complexes which make up our total societal environment.
Refereed Serial

614.7 613   US   ISSN 1053-4245
RA565.A1   CODEN: JEAEE9
JOURNAL OF EXPOSURE ANALYSIS AND ENVIRONMENTAL EPIDEMIOLOGY. 1991. q. $180 (effective 1994). (International Society of Exposure Analysis) Princeton Scientific Publishing Co., Inc., Box 2155, Princeton, NJ 08543. TEL 609-683-4750. FAX 609-683-0838. Ed. Edo Pellizzari. **Indexed:** Excerp.Med. (1993-), Ind.Med. (1992-). **Document type:** academic/scholarly publication.
—BLDSC (4983.085000); CASDDS. **CCC.**
Description: Covers new and emerging areas of human exposure assessment: measurement; monitoring methods; modeling; dose-effect relationships; multimedia exposure assessment; biomarkers; and environmental and epidemiological studies involving molecular biomarkers.

JOURNAL OF FRESHWATER ECOLOGY. see *EARTH SCIENCES — Hydrology*

551.48 614.7   US   ISSN 0380-1330
GB1627.G8   CODEN: JGLRDE
JOURNAL OF GREAT LAKES RESEARCH; devoted to research on large lakes of the world. 1975. q. $35 to individuals; libraries $75. International Association for Great Lakes Research, c/o Thomas J. Murphy, Ed., Dept. of Chemistry, DePaul University, 1036 W. Belden Ave., Chicago, IL 60614. TEL 312-362-8191. FAX 312-362-5324. bk.rev.; cum.index: 1953-1982. circ. 1,000. (also avail. in microfilm from UMI; reprint service avail.) **Indexed:** Acid Pre.Dig., Acid Rain Abstr., Acid Rain Ind., Aqua.Sci. & Fish.Abstr., Biol.Abstr., Chem.Abstr., Curr.Adv.Ecol.Sci., Curr.Cont., Curr.Ref.Fish Res., Curr.Tit.Ocean., Deep Sea Res.& Oceanogr.Abstr., Ecol.Abstr., Environ.Abstr., Environ.Per.Bibl. (1989-), Excerp.Med., Geo.Abstr., Geophys.Abstr., GeoRef., Ind.Sci.Rev., INIS Atomind., Meteor.& Geoastrophys.Abstr., Mich.Mag.Ind., Pollut.Abstr., Risk Abstr., Sci.Abstr., Sci.Cit.Ind., Sel.Water Res.Abstr., W.R.C.Inf., Water.Resour.Abstr. **Document type:** academic/scholarly publication.
—BLDSC (4996.520000); CIS; EI; Faxon; UnCover; SWETS; UMI; CASDDS.
Supersedes: Conference on Great Lakes Research. Proceedings (ISSN 0045-8058)
Description: Articles which encompass all aspects of research applicable to the understanding of the world's large lakes and to the human societies surrounding them.

• 614.7 338.91   II   ISSN 0250-8346
JOURNAL OF HIMALAYAN STUDIES AND REGIONAL DEVELOPMENT. (Text in English) 1977. a. Rs.100($15) Garhwal University, Institute of Himalayan Studies and Regional Development, Box 12, Srinagar, Garhwal 246174, India. Ed. Dr. Shankar Kala. adv.; bk.rev. circ. 1,000. **Indexed:** Geo.Abstr.
Formerly: Himalaya.

614.7 572   II   ISSN 0970-9274
GF661   CODEN: JHECEA
JOURNAL OF HUMAN ECOLOGY. (Text in English) 1990. 4/yr. Rs.400($40) to individuals; institutions Rs.500 ($60); students Rs.300 ($30). Kamla-Raj Enterprises, 2273 Gali Bari Paharwali, Chawri Bazar, Delhi 110 006, India. (Editorial addr.: Dept. of Anthropology, University of Delhi, Delhi 110 007, India) Ed. M.K. Bhasin, adv. contact: Gulashan Rai. bk.rev. circ. 150. **Document type:** academic/scholarly publication
Description: Publishes articles in the fields of human ecology, biology, genetics, and culture related to environmental issues. Aims to disseminate knowledge which may solve the deteriorating man-environment relationship. Also contains technical reports and brief communications.

614.7   US   ISSN 0892-4880
JOURNAL OF LAND USE AND ENVIRONMENTAL LAW. 1985. s-a. $28. Florida State University, College of Law, Tallahassee, FL 32306. TEL 904-644-4240. FAX 904-644-5487. Ed. Rebecca Cunningham. circ. 750. (reprint service avail. from RRI) **Indexed:** Environ.Abstr., Environ.Per.Bibl. (1992-).
—CIS; Faxon

614.7 351.46   US   ISSN 1061-026X
GC1000   CODEN: JMEEEH
▼**JOURNAL OF MARINE ENVIRONMENTAL ENGINEERING.** 1993. q. 227 ECU (effective 1993). Gordon & Breach Science Publishers, 820 Town Center Dr., Langhorne, PA 19047. TEL 215-750-2642. FAX 215-750-6343. (UK subscr. to: P.O. Box 90, Reading, Berkshire RG1 8JL, England. TEL 0734-560-080) (also avail. in microform)
—CCC.
Description: Covers the issues that confront engineers and scientists seeking solutions to environmental problems in ocean and estuary waters, and inland seas.

JOURNAL OF PALEOLIMNOLOGY. see *PALEONTOLOGY*

614.7   US   ISSN 0893-357X
JOURNAL OF PESTICIDE REFORM. 1979. q. $15 to individuals; institutions $25; foreign $20. Northwest Coalition for Alternatives to Pesticides, Box 1393, Eugene, OR 97440-1393. TEL 503-344-5044. Ed. Caroline Cox. bk.rev.; circ. 1,500 (paid). (back issues avail.) **Indexed:** Environ.Per.Bibl. (1989-). **Document type:** newsletter.
—BLDSC (5030.975000).
Formerly (until vol.5, no.1, 1985): N C A P News.
Description: Comprehensive publication covering citizen reform actions, legal issues, research results, progressive pesticide legislation, alternatives to pesticide use, and documented cases of successful sustainable pest management.

JOURNAL OF PLANNING AND ENVIRONMENT LAW. see *LAW*

JOURNAL OF RADIOLOGICAL PROTECTION. see *ENERGY — Nuclear Energy*

614.7   US   ISSN 0745-6999
TD785
JOURNAL OF RESOURCE MANAGEMENT AND TECHNOLOGY. 1972. q. $60 in continental U.S; Alaska, Canada & Mexico $65; elsewhere $70 (effective 1993). National Center for Resource Recovery and Management, University of Pennsylvania, 220 S. 33rd St., Towne Bldg., Rm. 229, PA 19104-6315. TEL 215-898-2771. FAX 215-573-2065. adv.; bibl.; index. circ. 500. **Indexed:** Acid Rain Abstr., Acid Rain Ind., Energy Rev., Environ.Abstr., Environ.Per.Bibl. (1981-), PROMT. **Document type:** academic/scholarly publication.
—BLDSC (5052.038000); CIS; UnCover.
Formerly: N C R R Bulletin (ISSN 0099-1821)
Description: Publishes papers on scientific, technological, economics and management aspects of environmental and solid waste issues, material resources, minerals, fuel and other natural resources.
Refereed Serial

JOURNAL OF SUSTAINABLE TOURISM. see *TRAVEL AND TOURISM*

ENVIRONMENTAL STUDIES

614.7 UK ISSN 0266-4674
QH541.5.T7 CODEN: JTECEQ
JOURNAL OF TROPICAL ECOLOGY. q. £37($72) to individuals (overseas £53); institutions £89 (overseas £105 ($165)). (International Association for Ecology) Cambridge University Press, Edinburgh Bldg., Shaftesbury Rd., Cambridge CB2 2RU, England. TEL 0223-312393. FAX 0223-315052. TELEX 851817256. (N. American addr.: Cambridge University Press, Journals Dept., 40 W. 20th St., New York, NY 10011. TEL 212-924-3900. FAX 212-691-3239) Ed. Adrian G. Marshall. adv. (also avail. in microform from UMI; back issues avail.; reprint service avail. from SWZ) **Indexed:** Agroforest.Abstr., ASCA, Curr.Adv.Ecol.Sci., Curr.Cont., Environ.Per.Bibl., Maize Abstr., Sel.Water Res.Abstr., Soils & Fert. **Document type:** academic/scholarly publication.
—BLDSC (5070.670000); Faxon; UnCover; SWETS; UMI. **CCC.**
Description: Features papers on the ecology of tropical regions, original research and reviews.

613.1 SZ
JOURNAL ROMAND DE L'ENVIRONNEMENT. 1964. 6/yr. Postfach 114, CH-1017 Lausanne 17, Switzerland. TEL 040-200322. FAX 021-9611340. Ed. Jean-Pierre Aubert. adv. circ. 1,200. **Document type:** bulletin.
Formerly: Bulletin A R P E A Magazine.

JUGENDPRESSEDIENST DES V N J. see *CHILDREN AND YOUTH — For*

614.7 JA
JUMIN KATSUDO.* 1972. q. 250 Yen per no. Shinseikatsu Undo Kyokai, 1-3 Hibiya Koen, Chiyoda-ku, Tokyo, Japan.
Supersedes: Shinseikatsu Tokushin.

613.1 GW ISSN 0303-4003
CODEN: KKBRAY
K F K REPORTS. irreg. Kernforschungszentrum Karlsruhe GmbH, Postfach 3640, 76021 Karlsruhe, Germany. FAX 07247-825802. **Document type:** monographic series.
—BLDSC (5089.867000); CASDDS.

KAIHATSU RONSHU/JOURNAL OF DEVELOPMENT POLICY STUDIES. see *BUSINESS AND ECONOMICS — Economic Situation And Conditions*

KAN ANDERS. see *POLITICAL SCIENCE — International Relations*

613.1 551 JA ISSN 0917-7183
KANKYO CHISHITSUGAKU SHINPOJUMU KOEN RONBUNSHU/SYMPOSIUM ON GEO-ENVIRONMENTS. PROCEEDINGS. (Text in English, Japanese; summaries in English) 1991. a. Nihon Chishitsu Gakkai, Kankyo Chishitsu Kenkyu Iinkai - Geological Society of Japan, Committee of Environmental Geology, 10-4, Kajicho 1-chome, Chiyoda-ku, Tokyo 101, Japan. **Document type:** proceedings.

614.7 JA ISSN 0022-8389
KANKYO EISEI/ENVIRONMENTAL SANITATION. (Text in Japanese) 1954. m. 1800. Yen. Kankyo Eisei Kenkyukai - Environmental Sanitation Research Association, 3-3 Kanda Jinbo-cho, Chiyoda-ku, Tokyo 101, Japan. Ed. Miyoko Hayama. adv.; charts; illus.; stat.; tr.lit. circ. 10,000.

614.7 JA ISSN 0388-9459
CODEN: KAGIDX
KANKYO GIJUTSU/ENVIRONMENTAL CONSERVATION ENGINEERING. (Text in Japanese; summaries in English) 1972. m. 15000 Yen. Kankyo Gijutsu Kenkyu Kyokai - Environmental Conservation Engineering Association, Matsumo Bldg., 2-1-20 Tenma, Kita-ku, Osaka 530, Japan. FAX 06-357-7612. Ed. S. Iwai. adv.; bk.rev.; charts; illus.; tr.lit.; index. circ. 3,000. **Indexed:** Chem.Abstr. **Document type:** academic/scholarly publication.
—BLDSC (3791.416000); CASDDS. **CCC.**
Description: Covers basic technical matters pertaining to global problems including environment issues.

575.1 JA ISSN 0910-0865
CODEN: KHKEEN
KANKYO HEN'IEGN KENKYU/ENVIRONMENTAL MUTAGEN RESEARCH COMMUNICATIONS. (Text in English, Japanese) 1878. 3/yr. membership. Nihon Kankyo Hen'igen Gakkai - Environmental Mutagen Society of Japan, c/o Mr. Toshio Sofuni, Kokuritsu Eisei Shikenjo, 18-1, Kamiyoga 1-chome, Setagaya-ku, Tokyo 158, Japan. **Indexed:** Chem.Abstr.
—CASDDS.

613.1 JA ISSN 0915-0048
KANKYO KAGAKKAISHI/ENVIRONMENTAL SCIENCE. (Text in Japanese; summaries in English, Japanese) 1988. q. 10000 Yen. Kankyo Kagakkai - Society of Environmental Science, Japan, Kokuritsu Kankyo Kenkyujo, 16-2, Onogawa, Tsukuba-shi, Ibaraki-ken 305, Japan. TEL 0298-58-6120. FAX 0298-53-6709.

KANKYO KAGAKU/JOURNAL OF ENVIRONMENTAL CHEMISTRY. see *CHEMISTRY*

KANKYO MONDAI SHINPOJUMU KOEN RONBUNSHU/SYMPOSIUM ON ENVIRONMENTAL PROBLEMS. PROCEEDINGS. see *ENGINEERING — Civil Engineering*

KANSAS - IOWA ENVIRONMENTAL LAW LETTER. see *LAW*

614.7 US
KEEP TAHOE BLUE. 1965. q. membership. League to Save Lake Tahoe, 989 Tahoe Keys Blvd., Ste. 6, S. Lake Tahoe, CA 96150. TEL 916-541-5388. bk.rev. circ. 5,500. **Document type:** newsletter.
Description: Dedicated to preserving the environmental balance, scenic beauty and recreational opportunities of the Lake Tahoe Basin.

KENSETSU KOGAKU KENKYUJO HOKOKU/CONSTRUCTION ENGINEERING RESEARCH INSTITUTE FOUNDATION REPORT. see *ENGINEERING — Engineering Mechanics And Materials*

614.7 II
KERALA (INDIA). BOARD FOR PREVENTION AND CONTROL OF WATER POLLUTION. ANNUAL REPORT. (Text in English) a. Board for Prevention and Control of Water Pollution, Trivandrum 685001, India. stat.

KEVO SUBARCTIC RESEARCH INSTITUTE. REPORTS. see *BIOLOGY*

KICK IT OVER. see *POLITICAL SCIENCE*

KIND NEWS JR. see *CHILDREN AND YOUTH — For*

KIND NEWS PRIMARY. see *CHILDREN AND YOUTH — For*

KIND NEWS SR. see *CHILDREN AND YOUTH — For*

333.7 500 JA ISSN 0285-6905
QE1 CODEN: HDSKEK
KISO, KANKYO KAGAKU KENKYU/HIROSHIMA UNIVERSITY. FACULTY OF INTEGRATED ARTS AND SCIENCES. SCIENCE REPORTS. (Text and summaries in English and Japanese) 1975. a. Hiroshima Daigaku, Sogo Gakakubu - Hiroshima University, Faculty of Integrated Arts and Sciences, 1-89 Higashisenda-cho 1-chome, Naka-ku, Hiroshima-shi, Hiroshima-ken 730, Japan. **Indexed:** Jap.Per.Ind.
—CASDDS.

614.7 JA
KOGAI CHOSA HOKOKUSHO/REPORT OF ENVIRONMENTAL POLLUTION IN MEGURO WARD. 1971. a. free. Meguro Ward Office, Environmental Pollution Department, 4-5, 2-Chome, Chuo-Chyou, Meguro-ku, Tokyo 152, Japan. FAX 3716-7169.

614.7 US ISSN 1064-2498
KOKOPELLI NOTES; walking and bibycling for a greener planet. 1990. 4/yr. $16. Kokopelli Council, Inc., Box 8186, Asheville, NC 28814. TEL 704-683-4844. Ed. Patrick Clark. adv.; bk.rev. circ. 1,500. **Document type:** consumer publication.

614.7 GW ISSN 0938-5851
KOMMISSION FUER OEKOLOGIE. RUNDGESPRAECHE. 1990. irreg. price varies. (Bayerischen Akademie der Wissenschaften - Bavarian Academy of Sciences) Verlag Dr. Friedrich Pfeil, Postfach 650086, 81214 Munich, Germany. TEL 089-188058. FAX 089-8341873. circ. 1,000. **Document type:** proceedings.
Description: Results of ecological meetings of the academy.

628.44 GW ISSN 0341-1478
CODEN: KOABDC
KORRESPONDENZ ABWASSER; Wasser - Abwasser - Abfall. (Text in German; summaries in English, French, German) 1954. m. DM.190.45. Gesellschaft zur Foerderung der Abwassertechnik, Postfach 1165, 53758 Hennef, Germany. TEL 022421-8720. FAX 022421-872151. (Co-sponsor: Abwassertechnische Vereinigung e.V.) Ed. Rainer M. Kieslinger. adv.; bk.rev. circ. 14,000. **Indexed:** INIS Atomind. **Document type:** trade publication.
—SWETS; CASDDS.

DIE KUESTE; Archiv fuer Forschung und Technik an der Nord- und Ostsee. see *EARTH SCIENCES — Oceanography*

LAKE & RESERVOIR MANAGEMENT. see *WATER RESOURCES*

LAND AND ENVIRONMENT COURT LAW AND PRACTICE NEW SOUTH WALES. see *LAW*

LAND & WATER. see *CONSERVATION*

LAND ECONOMICS; a quarterly journal devoted to the study of economic and social institutions. see *AGRICULTURE — Agricultural Economics*

333.7 NE ISSN 0023-7582
TC343
LAND EN WATER; magazine vook civiele- en milieu-techniek. (Includes supplement: Land en Water Catalogus) 1957. 12/yr. fl.160 (foreign fl.220) (effective 1993). V N U Business Publications B.V., Postbus 9194, 1006 CC Amsterdam, Netherlands. TEL 31-20-5102911. FAX 31-20-6174121. Ed. Bas Keijts. adv.: B&W page fl.2975, color page fl.5125; 207 x 297; adv. contact: Sonja Francois. charts; illus.; mkt. circ. 10,922. **Document type:** trade publication.

LAND LINK. see *CONSERVATION*

340 574.5 US ISSN 0192-8309
KF3790.A2
LAND USE & ENVIRONMENT LAW REVIEW. 1970. a. $85. Clark - Boardman - Callaghan Company Ltd., 375 Hudson St., New York, NY 10014. TEL 212-929-7500; 800-221-9428. FAX 212-924-0460. Ed. Frederic Strom. index. (back issues avail. from WSH) **Indexed:** C.L.I., Environ.Per.Bibl., GeoRef., INIS Atomind., L.R.I., Leg.Per.
—Faxon; UnCover.
Formerly: Environment Law Review (ISSN 0071-0830)
Description: Contains articles on land use law, environmental law, and related topics.

LANDBOUW, MILIEU EN ECONOMIE. see *AGRICULTURE — Abstracting, Bibliographies, Statistics*

LANDSCAPE AND URBAN PLANNING; an international journal on landscape design, conservation and reclamation, planning and urban ecology. see *CONSERVATION*

ENVIRONMENTAL STUDIES

620.85　　　　　　　NE　　ISSN 0921-2973
QH75.A1　　　　　　　　CODEN: LAECEH
LANDSCAPE ECOLOGY. (Text in English) 1987. 4/yr. fl.280($165) (effective 1994). S P B Academic Publishing b.v., P.O. Box 97747, 2509 GC The Hague, Netherlands. Ed. Frank B. Golley. (back issues avail.) **Document type:** academic/scholarly publication.
—BLDSC (5153.145700); UnCover; SWETS.
　Description: Publishes papers on fundamental and applied research exploring the structure and functioning of landscapes and their mutual relations with mankind, and contributions on integrated landscape research including biological, abiotic, and anthropogenic aspects, as well as relevant papers in land-use, nature management and environmental conservation.
　Refereed Serial

614.7　　　　　　US　　ISSN 1059-4930
▼**LEAD DETECTION & ABATEMENT REPORT.** 1992. m. $325. I A Q Publications, Inc., 4520 East-West Hwy., Ste. 610, Bethesda, MD 20814. TEL 301-913-0115. FAX 301-913-0119. **Document type:** newsletter.

LEAGUE LEADER. see *CONSERVATION*

614.7 333.91　　US　　ISSN 1068-3941
LEGAL TIDES. 1986. s-a. free. University of North Carolina Sea Grant, Box 8605, Raleigh, NC 27695-8605. TEL 919-515-2454. FAX 919-515-7095. Ed. Walter F. Clark. circ. 3,000. (back issues avail.) **Document type:** newsletter.

628 340　　　　　　　　　LO
▼**LESOTHO ENVIRONMENT AND ENVIRONMENT LAW.** 1992. irreg.? $38.50. National University of Lesotho, Faculty of Law, P.O. Roma 180, Lesotho. TEL 0266-340-601. FAX 813-778-4832. (Dist. in S. and N. America by: Wm. W. Gaunt & Sons, Inc., Gaunt Bldg., 3011 Gulf Dr., Holmes Beach, FL 34217-2199. TEL 813-778-5211) Eds. Guenter Witzsch, David Ambrose.

628.44　　　　　　　　　FR
LETTRE DE L'ENVIRONNEMENT. 22/yr. 2800 F. A Jour, 11 rue du Marche St. Honore, 75001 Paris, France. TEL 42-96-67-22. FAX 40-20-07-75. TELEX 615887F AJOUR. Ed. Cecile Cliquot de Mentque. circ. 3,000.

614.7 352.7　　　　　　　FR
LIGUE URBAINE ET RURALE CAHIERS. 1963. q. 180 F. Ligue Urbaine et Rurale, 8 rue Meissonier, 75017 Paris, France. TEL 42-67-06-06. Ed.Bd. bk.rev.; charts; illus. circ. 3,500. **Document type:** academic/scholarly publication.

LIST OF HYDROBIOLOGICAL PAPERS OF BRITISH FRESH WATERS. see *ENVIRONMENTAL STUDIES — Abstracting, Bibliographies, Statistics*

614.7 351.46 333.7 US
LIVING WITH THE SHORE. 1983. irreg. price varies. Duke University Press, 6697 College Station, Durham, NC 27708. TEL 919-687-3600. FAX 919-688-4574. Eds. Orrin H. Pilkey, Jr., William J. Neal.

LOCAL GOVERNMENT AND ENVIRONMENTAL REPORTS OF AUSTRALIA. see *LAW — Judicial Systems*

LOCAL GOVERNMENT PLANNING & ENVIRONMENT SERVICE N S W. see *PUBLIC ADMINISTRATION*

LOGOS (ARGONNE). see *ENGINEERING*

LOUISIANA ENVIRONMENTAL COMPLIANCE UPDATE. see *LAW*

614.7 342　　US　　ISSN 1055-257X
LOUISIANA INDUSTRY ENVIRONMENTAL ALERT. 1987. m. $255 (effective 1992). Environmental Compliance Reporter, Inc., 3154B College Dr., Ste. 522, Baton Rouge, LA 70808. TEL 504-383-3937. FAX 504-344-4521. Ed. Karen Bye. (back issues avail.)
　Description: Covers information concerning changes in state and federal laws and regulations.

333.9　　　　　　　　　AU
LUDWIG BOLTZMANN-INSTITUT FUER UMWELTWISSENSCHAFTEN UND NATURSCHUTZ. MITTEILUNGEN. 1975. irreg. Ludwig Boltzmann-Institut fuer Umweltwissenschaften und Naturschutz, Oesterreichischen Akademie der Wissenschaften, Heinrichstr. 5, A-8010 Graz, Austria.

613.1　　　　　　　　　SZ
LUFTPOST. q. Postfach, CH-9001 St. Gallen, Switzerland. TEL 071-233151. FAX 071-231337. Ed. Heinzpeter Studer. circ. 2,500.

613　　　　　　　　　　UK
M E T REPORT. (Munters Environmental Technology) 1990. s-a. Munters Ltd., Blackstone Rd., Huntingdon, Cambridgeshire PE18 6EF, England. TEL 0480-432243. FAX 0480-413147. Ed. N. Standing. circ. 12,500 (controlled). (back issues avail.) **Document type:** newsletter.
　Formerly: Humidity Control News.
　Description: Explores Munters' innovative solutions to environmental technology, especially with regard to humidity control, water treatment and gas cleaning.

M I. (Mladi Istrazivaci Srbije) see *EDUCATION*

MACKINAC. see *CONSERVATION*

MAINE AGRICULTURAL AND FOREST EXPERIMENT STATION. ANNUAL REPORT. see *AGRICULTURE*

614.7　　　　　US　　ISSN 0161-2107
MAINE ENVIRONNEWS. 1974. bi-m. free. Department of Environmental Protection, Office of the Commissioner, State House Sta. No. 17, Augusta, ME 04333. TEL 207-287-2812. FAX 207-287-7826. (Street addr.: Ray Bldg., AMHI Complex, Augusta, ME 04333) Ed. Deborah Garrett. bk.rev.; illus. circ. 1,800. (looseleaf format) **Document type:** government publication.
　Description: Covers environmental issues in Maine including programs involving air, land and water quality, hazardous materials and solid waste issues.

614.7　　　　　US　　ISSN 0025-0783
MAINE TIMES; Maine statewide weekly of news and opinion. 1968. w. $25 (effective Apr. 1992). Maine Times, Inc., One Main St., Topsham, ME 04086. FAX 207-729-2699. Ed. Peter Cox. adv.; bk.rev.; film rev.; play rev. circ. 22,000. (tabloid format; also avail. in microform from KTO,MIM,UMI)
—UMI.

MALCRIADO. see *LABOR UNIONS*

614.7 301.3　　US　　ISSN 0025-1550
NA2543.S6
MAN - ENVIRONMENT SYSTEMS. 1969. bi-m. $25 to individuals; libraries $37.50; students $15. Association for the Study of Man-Environment Relations, Box 57, Orangeburg, NY 10962. TEL 914-634-8221. Ed. Aristide H. Esser. adv.; bk.rev.; bibl.; index. circ. 600. (looseleaf format; also avail. in microform from UMI; back issues avail.)
Indexed: Environ.Per.Bibl., Geo.Abstr., Lang.& Lang.Behav.Abstr., Psychol.Abstr., Psycscan, Sage Urb.Stud.Abstr., Sociol.Abstr.
—BLDSC (5358.016500); UMI.

354　　　　　　CN　　ISSN 0380-9803
TD171.5.C2
MANITOBA. ENVIRONMENTAL COUNCIL. ANNUAL REPORT. 1973. a. free. Environmental Council, Bldg. 2, 139 Tuxedo Ave., Winnipeg, MB R3N 0H6, Canada. TEL 204-945-7031. illus. circ. 900. (also avail. in microfiche from MML)

354　　　　　　CN　　ISSN 0380-979X
MANITOBA. ENVIRONMENTAL COUNCIL. STUDIES. 1973. irreg. free. Environmental Council, Bldg. 2, 139 Tuxedo Ave., Winnipeg, MB R3N 0H6, Canada. TEL 204-945-7031. illus. circ. 1,000. (also avail. in microform from MML)

354　　　　　　CN　　ISSN 0711-8422
MANITOBA. ENVIRONMENTAL COUNCIL. TOPICS. 1982. irreg. free. Environmental Council, Bldg. 2, 139 Tuxedo Ave., Winnipeg, Man. R3N 0H6, Canada. TEL 204-947-7031.

MARYLAND ENVIRONMENTAL LAW. see *LAW*

MASSACHUSETTS ENVIRONMENTAL COMPLIANCE UPDATE. see *LAW*

614.7 640.73　　US　　ISSN 8750-8516
MASSCITIZEN. 1980. q. $15 to members. Massachusetts Public Interest Research Group (MASSPIRG), 29 Temple Place, Boston, MA 02111. TEL 617-292-4800. FAX 617-292-8057. Ed. Kathleen Traphagen. circ. 95,795. **Document type:** newsletter.
　Description: Covers activities of largest state environmental, energy and consumer citizens group in U.S.

MEALEY'S LITIGATION REPORT: LEAD. see *LAW — Civil Law*

MEALEY'S LITIGATION REPORT: TOXIC TORTS. see *LAW — Civil Law*

MEDDELELSER OM GROENLAND, BIOSCIENCE. see *BIOLOGY*

MEDECINE - BIOLOGIE - ENVIRONNEMENT/MEDICINE - BIOLOGY - ENVIRONMENT/GENEESKUNDE - BIOLOGIE - LEEFMILIEU. see *MEDICAL SCIENCES — Oncology*

614.7　　　　　　　　　SP
MEDI NATURAL. 1990. irreg., no.2, 1992. Generalitat Valenciana, Conselleria de Medi Ambient, Centre de Proteccio i Estudi del Medi Natural, Avda. Los Pinares 106, El Saler, 46012 Valencia, Spain. Ed. Juan Antonio Gomez Lopez. circ. 1,000.

301.3　　　　　　　CL
　　　　　　　　　　CODEN: MEAMEW
MEDIO AMBIENTE. (Text in English, Spanish; summaries in English) 1975. s-a. $30. Universidad Austral de Chile, Instituto de Ecologia y Evolucion, Facultad de Ciencias, Casilla 567, Valdivia, Chile. FAX 063-221344. TELEX 71035 UNAUS. Ed. Carlos A. Moreno. bk.rev. circ. 500. (reprint service avail.) *Indexed:* Aquacult.Abstr. **Document type:** academic/scholarly publication.
●Also available online.

614.7　　　　　　　　　SP
MEDIO AMBIENTE EN ESPANA. vol.2, 1978. a. 1500 ptas. Ministerio de Obras Publicas y Urbanismo, Secretaria General Tecnica, Centro de Publicaciones, Paseo de la Castellana, 67, 28071 Madrid, Spain. TEL 2531600. TELEX MOPU 22325. (Subscr. to: Caja Postal de Ahorros de Madrid, Oficina 2088, Sucursal 9002, Madrid, Spain)

614.7　　　　　　　　　JA
MEGURO-KU NO KOGAI/ENVIRONMENTAL POLLUTION IN MEGURO WARD. (Text and summaries in Japanese) 1971. a. free. Meguro Ward Office, Environmental Pollution Department, 4-5, 2-chome, Chuo-Chiyou, Meguro-ku, Tokyo 152, Japan. FAX 03-3716-7169.

614.7 640.73　　BL　　ISSN 0103-913X
MEIO AMBIENTE. 1978. q. Cr.$40($40) Thesaurus Editora, SIG-Quadra 8-Lote 2356, 70610 Brasilia, D.F., Brazil. TEL 061-225-3011. FAX 061-3210401.

MERIGAL; a voice for the dingo. see *CONSERVATION*

MESECHABE: THE JOURNAL OF SURREGIONALISM. see *PHILOSOPHY*

614.7 333.792　　US
THE MESSENGER (HEWITT); environment, nuclear hazards and alternative energies. 1966. m. $10 to individuals; students and retirees $5. Citizens Energy Council, Advisory Committee, Box U, Hewitt, NJ 07421. TEL 201-728-7835. FAX 201-728-7664. Ed. Karin Westdyk. bk.rev. circ. 20,000. (tabloid format)
　Former titles: Energy News Digest (ISSN 0270-5540); Nuclear Opponents - International; Watch on the Atomic Energy Commission.

614.7　　　　　GW　　ISSN 0720-3934
MESSERGEBNISSE DES ZENTRALEN IMMISSIONSMESSNETZES. MONATSBERICHT. 1978. m. Landesamt fuer Umweltschutz und Gewerbeaufsicht, Rheinallee 97, Abt. 3, 55118 Mainz, Germany. TEL 06131-967306. Ed. Horst Borchert. circ. 500. **Document type:** bulletin.

MICHIGAN ENVIRONMENTAL COMPLIANCE UPDATE. see *LAW*

2428 ENVIRONMENTAL STUDIES

614.7 917.7 US ISSN 0747-735X
MICHIGAN ENVIRONMENTAL REPORT. 1984. bi-m. $25 to individuals; institutions $55. Michigan Environmental Council, 115 W. Allegan, Ste. 10-B, Lansing, MI 48933. TEL 517-487-9539. Ed. Carol Misseldine. index. circ. 500. (looseleaf format; back issues avail.) **Document type:** newsletter.
  Description: Presents in-depth coverage on vital and timely environmental issues in Michigan.

MICHIGAN SPORTSMAN. see SPORTS AND GAMES — Outdoor Life

MICROBIOLOGICAL RESEARCH. see BIOLOGY — Microbiology

614 JA
MIE-KEN KOGAI SENTA NENPO/MIE PREFECTURE. ENVIRONMENTAL SCIENCE INSTITUTE. ANNUAL REPORT. (Text in Japanese) 1973. a. Kogai Senta - Environmental Science Institute, 8-12 Shinjo 4-chome, Yokkaichi, Mie-ken, Japan.

614.7 CN ISSN 0380-2760
MILIEU. English edition (ISSN 0835-1457) 1972. s-a. Environment Canada, 3 Buade, C.P. 6060, Quebec, PQ G1R 4V7, Canada. TEL 418-648-7204. FAX 418-649-6140. bk.rev.; bibl. circ. 10,000. **Indexed:** Pt.de Rep. (1982-).

628 NE
MILIEUMARKT; vakblad voor milieuverantwoordelijke managers. 11/yr. (includes MilieuMarkt Wijzer). fl.150 (foreign fl.165) (effective 1993). V N U Business Publishers B.V., Postbus 9194, 1006 CC Amsterdam, Netherlands. TEL 31-20-5102911. FAX 31-20-6174121. Ed. Marc van der Put. adv.: B&W page fl.3290, color page fl.5470; trim 207 x 297; adv. contact: Sonja Francois. illus. circ. 11,943. **Document type:** trade publication.

614.7 SW ISSN 0345-7621
MILJOE I SVERIGE; ekonomi, teknik. 1973. 8/yr. SEK 270 (effective 1973). Miljoe i Sverige Foerlags AB, P.O. Box 1167, S-221 05 Lund, Sweden. Ed. Haakan Almstroem. adv.; bk.rev. circ. 4,965.

363.7 SW ISSN 0345-7958
MILJOE O FRAMTID. 1972. 8/yr. SEK 150 (effective 1990). Stiftelsen Miljoe o Framtid, Ullasaxv. 14, S-756 48 Uppsala, Sweden.

363.7 614 SW ISSN 0282-955X
MILJOE OCH HAELSA. 1970. q. SEK 200 membership (effective 1990). Miljoe- och Haelsoskyddstjaenstemannafoerbundet, P.O. Box 90, S-175 22 Jaerfaella, Sweden.
  Former titles (until 1985): Haelsovaardskontakt; (until 1979): Kontakt.

363.7 SW ISSN 1100-5114
MILJOE & UTVECKLING. 1989. bi-m. SEK 396 (effective 1993). Kvalitets Foerlaget, P.O. Box 5866, S-102 40 Stockholm, Sweden.

614.7 600 DK ISSN 0901-747X
MILJOE & TEKNOLOGI. bi-m. DKK 340. Forlaget John Vaboe A-S, Hartmannsvej 47-49, DK-2920 Charlottenlund, Denmark. TEL 39-40-80-00. FAX 39-40-82-80.

363.7 SW ISSN 0345-763X
MILJOEAKTUELLT. 1973. 10/yr. SEK 225 (effective 1994). Statens Naturvaardsverk - Swedish Environmental Protection Agency, S-171 85 Solna, Sweden. circ. 34,000.

363.7 SW ISSN 0345-7966
MILJOEJOURNALEN. 1966-1987; resumed 1988. irreg. (3-4/yr.). SEK 50 (effective 1991). Stadsmiljoegruppen, c/o K. Kaellmin, Solaengsv. 8, S-172 37 Sundbybert, Sweden.

363.7 SW ISSN 1101-699X
MILJOEMATRIKEL. 1990. a. SEK 440 (effective 1990). (Statens Naturvaardsverk, Forskningsraadsnaemnden) Natlikan, P.O. Box 1152, S-181 23 Lidingoe, Sweden.

MILJOEMEDICIN/ENVIRONMENTAL MEDICINE. see PUBLIC HEALTH AND SAFETY

614.7 DK
MILJOEPROJEKT. 1975. irreg., no.62, 1985. price varies. Miljoestyrelsen, Strandgade 29, DK-1401 Copenhagen K, Denmark. TEL 32-66-01-00. FAX 32-66-04-79.
  —BLDSC (5768.563000).
  Formerly: Miljoe-Projekter (ISSN 0105-3094)

363.7 SW ISSN 1101-4245
MILJOERAPPORTEN; nyhetsbrev om miljoe - i Sverige och internationellt. 1989. 11/yr. SEK 2310 (effective 1990). Tomorrow Media, Kungsg. 27, S-111 56 Stockholm, Sweden. (Subscr. to: Finansrutin, P.O. Box 19072, S-104 32 Stockholm, Sweden)

363.7 SW ISSN 0282-2113
MILJOETIDNINGEN. 1977. irreg. (approx. 8/yr.). Miljoefoerbundet, P.O. Box 7048, S-402 31 Goeteborg, Sweden.
  Incorporates (in 1988): Miljoefoerbundaren; (until 1983): Veckans Eko; (until 1982): Miljoetidningen; Supersedes in part: Miljoebulletinen.

614.7 DK ISSN 0108-8203
QH132.G73
MILJOEUNDERSOEGELSER VED IVIGTUT. (Text in Danish; summaries in English or Greenlandic) 1982. irreg. price varies. Groenlands Fiskeriundersoegelser, Tagensvej 135, DK-2200 Copenhagen K, Denmark. FAX 45-35-82-14-20. **Document type:** government publication.

614.7 DK
QH545.H42
MILJOEUNDERSOEGELSER VED MARMORILIK. (Text in Danish; summaries in English, Greenlandic) 1974. irreg. price varies. Groenlands Miljoeundersoegelser, Tagensvej 135, DK-2200 Copenhagen N, Denmark. FAX 45-35-82-14-20. **Document type:** government publication.
  Formerly: Recipientundersoegelser ved Marmorilik (ISSN 0107-7090)

MIND MATTERS REVIEW. see PSYCHOLOGY

MINING AND THE ENVIRONMENT. see MINES AND MINING INDUSTRY

MINING ENVIRONMENTAL MANAGEMENT. see MINES AND MINING INDUSTRY

MINING REVIEW. see MINES AND MINING INDUSTRY

MINNESOTA ENVIRONMENTAL COMPLIANCE UPDATE. see LAW

613.1 NE
MISSET'S MILIEU MAGAZINE. 1989. 10/yr. fl.124.50 (2450 BEF). Audet Tijdschriften B.V. (Subsidiary of: C. Misset B.V.), Postbus 9000, 6800 DA Arnhem, Netherlands. TEL 31-85-209911. FAX 31-85-233007. adv.: B&W page fl.3285, color page fl.5395; trim 215 x 285; adv. contact: Cor van Nek. illus. circ. 15,000. **Document type:** trade publication.
  Description: Covers technical and scientific developments, government regulations and business news of interest to environmental safety professionals in industry and government.

628 US
MISSISSIPPI TIMES. q. $15 donation. Sierra Club Mississippi River Basin Program, 214 N. Henry, Ste. 203, Madison, WI 53703. TEL 608-257-4994. **Document type:** newsletter.
  Description: Offers lively commentary on the ecology of the Mississippi River Basin.

MISSOURI ENVIRONMENTAL LAW LETTER. see LAW

MITTEILUNGEN DER HEIMSTAETTEN UND LANDESENTWICKLUNGSGESELLSCHAFTEN. see HOUSING AND URBAN PLANNING

614.7 AT
MONASH UNIVERSITY. DEPARTMENT OF GEOGRAPHY AND ENVIRONMENTAL SCIENCE. ENVIRONMENTAL PAPERS. 1984. irreg., no.10, 1993. price varies. Monash University, Department of Geography and Environmental Science, Clayton, Vic. 3168, Australia. FAX 03-565-2948. bibl.; illus.; index. circ. 100. **Document type:** academic/scholarly publication, monographic series.

614.7 AT
MONASH UNIVERSITY. DEPARTMENT OF GEOGRAPHY AND ENVIRONMENTAL SCIENCE. ENVIRONMENTAL REPORTS. 1977. irreg., no.32, 1989. price varies. Monash University, Department of Geography and Environmental Science, Clayton, Vic. 3168, Australia. FAX 03-565-2948. bibl.; illus.; index. circ. 100. **Document type:** academic/scholarly publication, monographic series.

MONITOR (LONDON); packaging's environmental news watch. see PACKAGING

MONO LAKE COMMITTEE NEWSLETTER. see WATER RESOURCES

MONTHLY PLANET. see POLITICAL SCIENCE — International Relations

MOONBI. see CONSERVATION

614.7 LI
MUSU GAMTA. 1964. m. Rudens 33B, Vilnius 232600, Lithuania. TEL (0122) 696-964. Ed. Rimantas Budrys.

N A C D S ENVIRONMENTAL AFFAIRS NEWSLETTER. (National Association of Chain Drug Stores) see PHARMACY AND PHARMACOLOGY

614.7 US
N A E P NEWSLETTER. 6/yr. National Association of Environmental Professionals, 5165 MacArthur Blvd., N.W., Washington, DC 20016-3315. TEL 202-966-1500. FAX 202-966-1977. Ed. Dennis Poulsen. adv.: B&W page $350. circ. 3,900. **Document type:** newsletter.

613.1 UK ISSN 0141-674X
N A F S O JOURNAL. 1971. a. £4.50 (foreign £6). National Association of Field Study Officers, Hengistbury Head Outdoor Education Centre, Broadway, Southbourne, Bournemouth, Dorset BM6 4EN, England. TEL 0202-425173. FAX 0202-430132. Ed. Peter Hawes. adv.; bk.rev. circ. 500. (back issues avail.) **Document type:** bulletin.

614.7 NE ISSN 0258-1256
CODEN: NASGEJ
N A T O ADVANCED SCIENCE INSTITUTES SERIES G: ECOLOGICAL SCIENCES. 1983. irreg., vol.12, 1986. (North Atlantic Treaty Organization, Scientific Affairs Division, BE) Kluwer Academic Publishers, Postbus 17, 3300 AA Dordrecht, Netherlands. TEL 31-78-334911. FAX 31-78-334254. TELEX 29245 KAPG NL. (Dist. by: Kluwer Academic Publishers Group, P.O. Box 322, 3300 AH Dordrecht, Netherlands. TEL 31-78-524400; N. America dist. addr.: Box 358, Accord Sta., Hingham, MA 02018-0358. TEL 617-871-6600) **Document type:** monographic series.
●Also available online. Vendor(s): European Space Agency (File no.128).
  —BLDSC (6033.648810); CASDDS.
  Formerly: N A T O Advanced Study Institute Series G: Ecological Sciences.
  Refereed Serial

500 US ISSN 0730-9600
CODEN: NCMSD4
N A T O CHALLENGES OF MODERN SOCIETY. (Includes subseries: Air Pollution Modeling and its Applications) 1981. irreg., vol.17, 1992. price varies. (North Atlantic Treaty Organization, BE) Plenum Publishing Corp., 233 Spring St., New York, NY 10013-1578. TEL 212-620-8000. FAX 212-463-0742. TELEX 23-421139. (back issues avail.) **Document type:** proceedings.
  —BLDSC (6033.649500); CASDDS.
  Refereed Serial

N B I A NEWSLETTER. (New Brunswick Institute of Agrologists) see AGRICULTURE

614.7 344.046 US
N C A M P'S TECHNICAL REPORT. 1986. m. $20 to members. National Coalition Against the Misuse of Pesticides, 701 E St., S.E., Ste. 200, Washington, DC 20003. TEL 202-543-5450. Ed. Jay Feldman. cum.index: 1986-1989. circ. 300. (back issues avail.) **Document type:** bulletin.

ENVIRONMENTAL STUDIES

614.7 UK ISSN 0951-5305
QH1
N E R C NEWS. 1970. q. free. Natural Environment Research Council, Polaris House, North Star Ave., Swindon SN2 1EU, England. TEL 0793-411500. FAX 0793-411610. TELEX 444293-ENVRE-G. Ed. Leslie Jones. adv.; bk.rev.; charts; illus. circ. 6,000. **Indexed:** Curr.Adv.Ecol.Sci., Fluidex, Fuel & Energy Abstr., Geo.Abstr., Ind.Vet., Meteor.& Geoastrophys.Abstr., Rev.Med.& Vet.Mycol. **Document type:** bulletin.
—BLDSC (6076.140000).
Formerly (until 1987): N E R C News Journal (ISSN 0305-8336)
Description: Informational items and research articles on current political, legislative, technological and scientific developments in the environmental sciences, with announcements of seminars and meetings.

614.7 US
N E T A NEWS. 1977. bi-m. $20 membership only. National Environmental Training Association, 2930 E. Camelback Rd., No. 185, Phoenix, AZ 85016-4412. TEL 602-951-1440. Ed. C.L. Richardson. circ. 1,500. **Document type:** newsletter.

320 US
N G O NETWORKER. (Non-Governmental Organization) q. free. World Resources Institute, 1709 New York Ave., N.W., Washington, DC 20006. Ed. Sarah Burns; Pub. Jonathan Lash. **Document type:** newsletter.
Description: Provides information on nongovernmental environmental activities and endeavors.

333.7 NO ISSN 0801-1699
N I B R RAPPORT. (Text in Norwegian; summaries in English) 1965. irreg. price varies. Norsk Institutt for By- og Regionforskning - Norwegian Institute for Urban and Regional Research, Gaustadalleen 21, P.O. Box 44 Blindern, N-0313 Oslo, Norway. TEL 47-22-95-88-00. FAX 47-22-60-77-74. **Document type:** academic/scholarly publication.
Formerly (until 1973): Norsk Institutt for By- og Regionforskning. Rapport (ISSN 0085-4263)

614.7 UK ISSN 0140-6787
N.S.C.A. MEMBERS HANDBOOK. 1950. a. £11.95. National Society for Clean Air and Environmental Protection, 136 North St., Brighton BN1 1RG, England. TEL 0273-26313. FAX 0273-735802. circ. 2,000. **Document type:** bulletin.

711.558 US ISSN 0895-819X
NATIONAL ASSOCIATION FOR OLMSTED PARKS. NEWSLETTER. 1981. s-a. $12. National Association for Olmsted Parks, Inc., 7315 Wisconsin Ave., Ste. 504 E., Bethesda, MD 20814-3202. TEL 202-362-9511. FAX 301-469-3841. Ed. Susan L. Klaus. bk.rev. circ. 1,100. **Document type:** newsletter.
Description: News, events and financial matters pertaining to parks throughout the US designed by Frederick Law Olmsted.

620.85 CN ISSN 1185-9660
NATIONAL CONTAMINATED SITES REMEDIATION PROGRAM. ANNUAL REPORT/PROGRAMME NATIONAL D'ASSAINISSEMENT DES LIEUX CONTAMINES. RAPPORT ANNUEL. 1990. a. Canadian Council of Ministers of the Environment, National Contaminated Sites Remediation Program - Conseil Canadien des Ministres de l'Environnement, 326 Broadway, Ste. 400, Winnipeg, MB R3C 0S5, Canada. TEL 204-948-2090. FAX 204-948-2125.
Description: Deals with properties across the country that have been polluted with hazardous materials.

614.7 US
NATIONAL ENVIRONMENTAL ENFORCEMENT JOURNAL. 1986. m. (11/yr.). $195 to individuals; institutions $95. National Association of Attorneys General, 444 N. Capitol St., N.W., Ste. 403, Washington, DC 20001. TEL 202-628-0435. Ed. Cindy H. Evans. bk.rev.; index. circ. 850. (back issues avail.) **Formerly:** Environmental Protection Report.

614.7 US ISSN 1067-2583
THE NATIONAL ENVIRONMENTAL JOURNAL. 1991. bi-m. $38 (Canada and Mexico $45; elsewhere $70). Campbell Publishing, Inc., 5636 Whitesville Rd., Ste. A-2, Columbus, GA 31904. TEL 706-324-6746. FAX 706-324-1177. (Subscr. to: Box 2567, Columbus, GA 31902-2567) Ed. Paul N. Cheremisinoff. adv. circ. 68,000. **Indexed:** Environ.Abstr., Sel.Water Res.Abstr. **Document type:** trade publication.
—BLDSC (6022.650500).
Description: For environmental - pollution control professionals who have the responsibility for designing, specifying, maintaining and purchasing equipment, services, systems and components.

614.599 617.6 US ISSN 0027-9269
NATIONAL FLUORIDATION NEWS; covering reports on research into the toxicity of fluoride, news on accidents, election outcomes and general information on the issue. 1955. q. $10. Shirley Graves, Ed. & Pub., Box 1611, San Anselmo, CA 94960. TEL 415-453-0158. bk.rev.; illus. circ. 5,000. (tabloid format) **Document type:** newspaper.

340 614.9 US ISSN 0164-0712
NATIONAL WETLANDS NEWSLETTER. 1979. bi-m. $48. Environmental Law Institute, 1616 P St., N.W., Ste. 200, Washington, DC 20036. TEL 202-328-5150. Ed. Moira McDonald. bk.rev.; film rev.; bibl. circ. 1,000. **Indexed:** Energy Rev., Environ.Abstr., Environ.Per.Bibl. (1984-), P.A.I.S. **Document type:** newsletter.
—UnCover.
Description: Federal and state coverage of wetlands science, management and policy.

614.7 333.7 DK ISSN 0107-1653
NATUR OG MILJOE. 1974. q. DKK 165 membership. Danmarks Naturfredningsforening - Danish Society for the Conservation of Nature, Noerregade 2, 1165 Copenhagen K, Denmark. TEL 45-33-32-2021. FAX 45-33-32-22-02. Ed. David Rehling. adv.; bibl.; charts; illus. circ. 300,000.

614.7 NO ISSN 0802-4618
NATUR OG MILJOE. 1989. 6/yr. NOK 340 in the Nordic countries; elsewhere NOK 395. Norges Naturvernforbund, Postboks 2113, Grunerhokka, N-0505 Oslo 5, Norway. Ed. Ragnhild Sved. circ. 45,000.
Formerly (until 1989): Miljoemagasinet (ISSN 0332-6179)
Description: Focuses on nature and the environment.

614.7 IT ISSN 0393-8875
NATURA E SOCIETA; trimestrale d'informazione ecologica. 1982. q. L.5000($5) Federazione Nazionale pro Natura, Via Delle Palme 20-1, 35137 Padova, Italy. TEL 049-664952. Ed. Edoardo Vernier. bk.rev.; bibl.; illus. circ. 5,000.
Description: Presents articles on the protection of nature, naturalistic education, current events on nature, conservative and legislative laws for nature.

614.7 IT
NATURA IN VIDEO. m. Gruppo Editoriale Ambrosiano Veneto, Via S. Calimero 3, 20122 Milan, Italy. TEL 02-55-18-00. FAX 02-5518-73-39. circ. 15,000. (video cassette)

614 333 US ISSN 0885-8608
QH76 CODEN: NAJOEW
NATURAL AREAS JOURNAL. 1981. q. $25 to individuals; libraries $50; institutions $100. Natural Areas Association, 108 Fox St., Mukwonago, WI 53149. TEL 414-363-5500. FAX 414-363-4949. Ed. Don Leopold. adv.; bk.rev.; circ. 2,100 (paid). **Indexed:** Environ.Per.Bibl. (1985-), Forest.Abstr., Gard.Lit. (1992-), Herb.Abstr., P.A.I.S., Weed Abstr. **Document type:** academic/scholarly publication.
—BLDSC (6037.106000); UnCover.
Formerly (until 1982): Natural Areas Association. Journal.
Description: Scientific journal on the preservation, management, inventory and study of natural areas, endangered species and other aspects of nature conservation.
Refereed Serial

614.7 UK ISSN 0072-7008
NATURAL ENVIRONMENT RESEARCH COUNCIL. REPORT. 1967. a. Natural Environment Research Council, Polaris House, N. Star Ave., Swindon, Wilts. SN2 1EU, England. TEL 0793-411500. FAX 0793-411501. TELEX 444293-ENVRE-G. Ed. L.T. Jones. **Indexed:** Field Crop Abstr., Herb.Abstr. **Document type:** corporate report.
—BLDSC (7522.790000).
Incorporating (in 1985): Institute of Terrestrial Ecology. Annual Report (ISSN 0308-1125)

333.7 NE
NATURAL RESOURCES MANAGEMENT AND POLICY. (Text in English) irreg., vol.3, 1993. price varies. Kluwer Academic Publishers, Postbus 17, 3300 AA Dordrecht, Netherlands. TEL 31-78-334911. FAX 31-78-334254. TELEX 29245 KAPG NL. (Dist. by: Kluwer Academic Publishers Group, P.O. Box 322, 3300 AH Dordrecht, Netherlands. TEL 31-78-524400. FAX 31-78-524474; N. America dist. addr.: Box 358, Accord Sta., Hingham, MA 02018-0358. TEL 617-871-6600. FAX 617-871-6528) **Document type:** monographic series.
Refereed Serial

614.7 340 US
NATURAL RIGHTS. 1978. q. $25 to individuals; libraries $15. (Plenty U.S.A.) Natural Rights Center, Box 90, Summertown, TN 38483. TEL 615-964-3992. TELEX 6502745871 MCI. Ed. Albert Bates. circ. 1,500. (tabloid format; back issues avail.)
Formerly: Shutdown News.
Description: Covers nuclear power, nuclear weapons, global climates, human rights, genetic engineering and toxic wastes.

614.7 340 US
NATURAL RIGHTS CENTER ANNUAL REPORT. 1983. a. free. Natural Rights Center, Box 90, Summertown, TN 38483. TEL 615-964-3992. Ed. Albert Bates. circ. 2,000. (tabloid format; back issues avail.) **Document type:** corporate report.
Description: Review of the work of the Natural Rights Center in protecting the global environment.

NATURE AND RESOURCES; international news about research on environment, resources, and conservation of nature. see *CONSERVATION*

NATURE CANADA. see *CONSERVATION*

NATURE CONSERVANCY MAGAZINE. see *CONSERVATION*

NATURE CONSERVATION NEWS. see *CONSERVATION*

614.7 FR
NATURE ET MIEUX-VIVRE. 1977. m. Sodeco, B.P. 3, 32350 Gavarret, France. Ed. Jean P. Rousseau. adv.; illus.

333.7 US ISSN 0028-0860
NATURE STUDY. 1946. q. $18. American Nature Study Society, c/o Dr. John Gustafson, 5881 Cold Brook Rd., Homer, NY 13077. Ed. Helen Ross Russell. adv.; bk.rev.; illus.; index. circ. 800. (also avail. in microform from UM; reprint service avail. from UMI) **Indexed:** C.I.J.E. **Document type:** academic/scholarly publication, newsletter.
—UnCover; UMI.
Formerly: A N S S News.
Description: Provides articles, teaching tips, and news of value to teachers, nature interpreters, and others.

NEBELHORN; Regionalmagazin fuer Politik und Kultur. see *BUSINESS AND ECONOMICS — Labor And Industrial Relations*

NEIGHBORHOOD WORKS. see *HOUSING AND URBAN PLANNING*

NETHERLANDS JOURNAL OF HOUSING AND ENVIRONMENTAL RESEARCH. see *HOUSING AND URBAN PLANNING*

614.7 SZ
NETWORK (YEAR). (Editions in English, Portuguese, Russian, Spanish) 1990. m. $30. Centre for Our Common Future, 52 rue des Paquis, CH-1201 Geneva, Switzerland. TEL 022-7327117. FAX 022-7385046. Ed. Joanne Barr. circ. 25,000. (back issues avail.) **Document type:** newsletter.

ENVIRONMENTAL STUDIES

614.7 370   CN   ISSN 0834-969X
NEW CATALYST. 1985. q. $5. Catalyst Education Society, P.O. Box 189, Gabriola, BC V0R 1X0, Canada. TEL 604-247-9737. FAX 604-247-7471. Eds. Christopher & Judith Plant. adv.; bk.rev. circ. 25,000. (tabloid format) Indexed: Alt.Press Ind.
   Description: Covers alternative culture and politics, the environment, proregionalism and major issues of the region.

614.7   US
NEW CRUCIBLE; a magazine about man and his environment. Variant title: Crucible. 1964. irreg. $24 for 12 nos. De Young Press, RR 1 Box 76, Stark, KS 66775-9802. Ed. Garry De Young. adv.; bk.rev. circ. 2,500. **Document type:** consumer publication.
   Incorporates: Naturalist (ISSN 8756-3592); Former titles: Crucible and Scientific Atheist (ISSN 8756-1247); Scientific Atheist.
   Description: Deals with the total human environment including all ecological factors impacting upon man such as political, psychological, religious, and physical.

NEW ENGLAND SIERRAN. see CONSERVATION

NEW GROUND. see POLITICAL SCIENCE

NEW GROUND; the journal of development and environment. see BUSINESS AND ECONOMICS — International Development And Assistance

353.9   US   ISSN 0092-3311
TD171.3.N48
NEW JERSEY. DEPARTMENT OF ENVIRONMENTAL PROTECTION. ANNUAL REPORT. Key Title: Annual Report - Department of Environmental Protection (Trenton). 1972. a. free. Department of Environmental Protection, Office of Communications and Public Education, 401 E. State St., CN 402, Trenton, NJ 08625. TEL 609-633-1317. illus. circ. 5,000. **Document type:** government publication.

614.7   US
NEW JERSEY. ENVIRONMENTAL NEWS. 1970. bi-m. free. Department of Environmental Protection, Office of Communications and Public Education, 401 E. State St., Trenton, NJ 08625. Ed. Edith H. Joseph. illus. circ. 16,000. **Document type:** government publication.

NEW JERSEY ENVIRONMENTAL LAW LETTER. see LAW

614.7   US   ISSN 1055-2588
NEW JERSEY INDUSTRY ENVIRONMENTAL ALERT. 1990. 22/yr. $295 (effective 1992). Environmental Compliance Reporter, Inc., 1977 N. Olden Ave., Ste. 152, Trenton, NJ 08618. TEL 609-394-0999; 800-729-1964. Ed. Natale Nogosek. (back issues avail.)

614.7 628.5   US   ISSN 0028-5889
NEW JERSEY OUTDOORS. 1968; N.S. 1974. q. $15. Department of Environmental Protection and Energy, Office of Communications and Public Education, CN 402, Trenton, NJ 08625. (Subscr. to: CN 417, Trenton, NJ 08625-0417. TEL 800-645-0038) Ed. George Klenk. bk.rev.; charts; illus. circ. 58,000. Indexed: Sportsearch.
   Former titles: New Jersey Environmental Times (ISSN 0047-9756); New Jersey Air, Water and Waste Management Times (ISSN 0028-5498)
   Description: Covers seasonal events, conservation, recreation, gardens, history and wildlife.

333.8 340   US
NEW JERSEY STATE BAR ASSOCIATION. ENVIRONMENTAL LAW SECTION. NEWSLETTER. 1982. 3/yr. membership only. New Jersey State Bar Association, Environmental Law Section, 1 Constitution Sq., New Brunswick, NJ 08901-1500. TEL 908-249-5000. FAX 908-249-2815. Ed. Brian P. Batz. bk.rev. circ. 900. (back issues avail.) **Document type:** newsletter.

614.7   US
NEW OHIO JOURNAL.* 1990. bi-m. $20. David Smigelski, Ed. & Pub., 328 W. Hubbard Ave., Columbus, OH 43215-1343. TEL 614-593-0166. FAX 614-593-4229.
   Description: Covers personal and environmental health.

NEW SOLUTIONS; a journal of environmental and occupational health policy. see OCCUPATIONAL HEALTH AND SAFETY

614.7   US
▼**NEW WORLD JOURNAL (NEW YORK)**; people, news, environment. 1993. q. $8.95. New World Journal Corp., 330 W. 56th St., Ste. 3G, New York, NY 10019-4241. TEL 212-265-7970. FAX 212-265-8052. Ed. Rick Bard. adv.; bk.rev. circ. 100,000.
   Description: Broad-based environmental magazine, with focus on people, news, environment.

614.7   US
NEW YORK CITY ENVIRONMENTAL BULLETIN. 1973. bi-m. free. Council on the Environment of New York City, 51 Chambers St., Rm. 228, New York, NY 10007. TEL 212-788-7900. Ed. Veronica Green. bk.rev.; illus. circ. 150. **Document type:** bulletin.

344   US   ISSN 8756-9280
NEW YORK STATE BAR ASSOCIATION. ENVIRONMENTAL LAW SECTION. JOURNAL. Key Title: Environmental Law Section Journal. 1981. irreg. (3-4/yr.). $35 to non-members. New York State Bar Association, Environmental Law Section, 1 Elk St., Albany, NY 12207-1096. TEL 518-463-3200. FAX 518-487-5699. Ed. Kevin A. Reilly. adv.; bk.rev.; circ. 900 (controlled). (back issues avail.) **Document type:** academic/scholarly publication, newsletter.
   Formerly: New York State Bar Association. Environmental Law Section. Newsletter (ISSN 0736-7104)

613.1 340   US   ISSN 1061-8651
K14
▼**NEW YORK UNIVERSITY ENVIRONMENTAL LAW JOURNAL.** 1992. s-a. $10 (foreign $12). New York University, Environmental Law Journal, 110 W. Third St., New York, NY 10012. TEL 212-998-6560. FAX 212-995-4032. bk.rev. **Document type:** academic/scholarly publication.
—UnCover.

614   NZ   ISSN 0110-9944
TD196.R3
NEW ZEALAND. DEPARTMENT OF HEALTH. NATIONAL RADIATION LABORATORY. ENVIRONMENTAL RADIOACTIVITY ANNUAL REPORT. 1961. a. NZ.$20 (foreign NZ.$25). Department of Health, National Radiation Laboratory, P.O. Box 25-099, Christchurch, New Zealand. TEL 3-3665059. FAX 3-3661156. Ed. K.M. Matthews. circ. 300. (back issues avail.) Indexed: Biol.Abstr., Dairy Sci.Abstr. **Document type:** government publication.
   Description: Report summarizes results of environmental radioactivity monitoring operations conducted in New Zealand and the South Pacific during the year.

614.7   NZ   ISSN 0110-6287
NEW ZEALAND ENVIRONMENT. 1971. q. NZ.$19 (foreign NZ$23). Environmental Publications Trust, 34 Norana Ave., Remuera, Auckland 1105, New Zealand. TEL 9-524-2949. Ed. Robert Mann. bk.rev.; charts; illus.; stat.; cum.index. circ. 1,000. (back issues avail.) Indexed: Biol.Abstr.
—CCC.

614.7   US
NEWS FROM E C N P. 1971. irreg. Environmental Coalition on Nuclear Power, 433 Orlando Ave., State College, PA 16803. TEL 814-237-8900.

NIHON SEIKISHO GAKKAI ZASSHI/JAPANESE JOURNAL OF BIOMETEOROLOGY. see METEOROLOGY

NIHON SEITAI GAKKAI KANTO CHIKUKAI KAIHO/ECOLOGICAL SOCIETY OF JAPAN. KANTO BRANCH. NEWS. see BIOLOGY

NIHON SEITAI GAKKAI KYUSHU CHIKUKAI KAIHO/ECOLOGICAL SOCIETY OF JAPAN. KYUSHU BRANCH. NEWS. see BIOLOGY

NIHON SEITAI GAKKAI TOHOKU CHIKUKAI KAIHO/ECOLOGICAL SOCIETY OF JAPAN. TOHOKU BRANCH. NEWS. see BIOLOGY

614.7   JA
NIIGATA-SHI NI OKERU KOGAI/ENVIRONMENTAL POLLUTION IN NIIGATA CITY. a. free. 866 Rokuban-cho, Nishibori-dori, Niigata-shi 951, Japan.

NISSE HULT. see POLITICAL SCIENCE

NONGAME NEWS. see BIOLOGY — Zoology

614.7 630   CC   ISSN 1000-0267
S589.75
NONGYE HUANJING BAOHU/AGRO-ENVIRONMENTAL PROTECTION. (Text in Chinese) 1982. bi-m. Y9. Zhongguo Nongye Shengtai Huanjing Baohu Xiehui - Chinese Society of Agro-ecological Environment Protection, 31 Kangfu Lu, Nankai Qu, Tianjin 300191, People's Republic of China. TEL 361247. Ed. Mai Yongbin. adv.
   Description: Reports new achievements, technology and experiences of agro-environmental research in China.
   Refereed Serial

NORBA: REVISTA DE GEOGRAFIA. see GEOGRAPHY

NORTH CAROLINA ENVIRONMENTAL LAW LETTER. see LAW

613.1   US
NORTHBOUND. 1984. q. $15 membership. Trees For Tomorrow, 611 Sheridan St., Box 609, Eagle River, WI 54521. TEL 715-479-6456. Ed. Angela Cannon. bk.rev. circ. 4,400.
   Formerly: Tree Tips.
   Description: Focuses on education about natural resource and environmental issues for teachers and their students in Wisconsin, northern Illinois, and the Upper Penensula of Michigan.

614.7   US
NORTHERN LINE. 1971. q. $30. Northern Alaska Environmental Center, 218 Driveway, Fairbanks, AK 99701. TEL 907-452-5021. FAX 907-452-3100. Ed. Mary Zalar. adv.; bk.rev. circ. 1,000.
   Formerly: Alaska Environmental Notes.

338.9 600   CN   ISSN 0380-5522
CODEN: NPEREJ
NORTHERN PERSPECTIVES. 1973. 4/yr. Can.$30. Canadian Arctic Resources Committee, 1 Nicholas St., Ste. 412, Ottawa, ON K1N 7B7, Canada. TEL 613-236-7379. FAX 613-232-4665. Ed. Alan Saunders. illus. circ. 3,500. (back issues avail.)

NORTHROP UNIVERSITY LAW JOURNAL OF AEROSPACE, BUSINESS AND TAXATION. see AERONAUTICS AND SPACE FLIGHT

NORTHWEST ENERGY NEWS. see ENERGY

NORTHWEST REPORT. see BUSINESS AND ECONOMICS — Economic Situation And Conditions

LE NOUVEL HUMANISME. see POLITICAL SCIENCE

354   CN   ISSN 0317-3526
HC120.E5
NOVA SCOTIA. ENVIRONMENTAL CONTROL COUNCIL. ANNUAL REPORT. 1973. a. Environmental Control Council, Box 2107, Halifax, NS B3J 3B7, Canada. TEL 902-424-6387. FAX 902-424-0503.

NUCLEAR AWARENESS NEWS. see ENERGY — Nuclear Energy

NUCLEAR GEOPHYSICS; a journal of nuclear techniques in the earth and environmental sciences, mineral exploration, mining and process control. see EARTH SCIENCES — Geophysics

NUCLEUS (CAMBRIDGE). see ENERGY

574.5 614.7   IT
NUOVA ECOLOGIA; il mensile dei verdi e dei consumatori. m. L.57000 includes bi-m. supplement (foreign L.80000). Editrice Periodici Culturali S.p.A., Via Savoia 37, 00198 Rome, Italy. TEL 06-8558990. FAX 06-8416256. Ed. Paolo Gentiloni. adv.; bk.rev.

614.7   US   ISSN 0896-9949
KF3566.A3
O S H A COMPLIANCE ADVISOR. (Occupational Safety and Health Administration) 1986. s-m. $249.50. Business & Legal Reports, Inc., 39 Academy St., Madison, CT 06443-1513. TEL 203-245-7448. FAX 203-245-2559. Ed. Eleanor McKernan. circ. 2,638. (back issues avail.)
—CCC.
   Incorporates: (in 1988): Right to Know Compliance Advisor (ISSN 0888-8582)

ENVIRONMENTAL STUDIES

628.44 614.85 US ISSN 0896-9957
O S H A TRAINING BULLETIN FOR SUPERVISORS.
(Occupational Safety and Health Administration)
1982. m. $84. Business & Legal Reports, Inc., 39 Academy St., Madison, CT 06443-1513.
TEL 203-245-7448. FAX 203-245-2559. Ed. John F. Brady. adv.; index. circ. 1,721. (back issues avail.) **Document type:** bulletin.
—CCC.
Former titles: Hazardous Materials Training Bulletin for Supervisors; Hazardous Waste Training Bulletin for Supervisors (ISSN 0744-4168)
Description: Reports on right-to-know regulations and OSHA details.

OAK RIDGE NATIONAL LABORATORY REVIEW. see *ENERGY*

OASIS; mensile di natura, ecologia, fotografia e viaggi. see *CONSERVATION*

OCCUPATIONAL HAZARDS; magazine of health & environment. see *OCCUPATIONAL HEALTH AND SAFETY*

OCEANS POLICY NEWS. see *LAW — Maritime Law*

613.1 SZ
OEKO JOURNAL. 1972. 6/yr. 40 SFr. Postfach 745, CH-8021 Zurich, Switzerland. TEL 01-4629080. Ed. Rene-Jacques Weber. adv.; bk.rev. circ. 1,600.
Document type: bulletin.

614.7 GW
OEKO-MITTEILUNGEN; Informationen aus dem Institut fuer angewandte Oekologie e.V. 1977. 4/yr. Oeko-Institut e.V., Binzengruen 34a, 79114 Freiburg, Germany. TEL 0761-473031. FAX 0761-475437. Ed. Joern Ehlers. adv.: B&W page DM.1100; trim 182 x 250; adv. contact: Joern Ehlers. circ. 7,000. **Document type:** trade publication.

OEKO-TEST MAGAZIN; oekologische Verbraucherzeitschrift. see *CONSUMER EDUCATION AND PROTECTION*

OEKOWERKMAGAZIN; Naturschutz in Berlin und Brandenburg. see *CONSERVATION*

OHIO ECOLOGICAL FOOD AND FARM ASSOCIATION NEWS. see *AGRICULTURE — Crop Production And Soil*

OHIO ENVIRONMENTAL LAW LETTER. see *LAW*

614.7 340 US ISSN 1063-9594
OHIO ENVIRONMENTAL MONTHLY. 1989. m. $170. Banks - Baldwin Law Publishing Co., University Center, Box 1974, Cleveland, OH 44106.
TEL 216-721-7373. FAX 216-721-8055. Ed. Michael L. Hardy.
Formerly (until 1991): Environmental Law Journal of Ohio (ISSN 1045-599X)
Description: Current coverage and commentary on both state and federal developments affecting Ohio environmental attorneys, engineers, officials, architects, and contractors, manufacturing legal departments, and commercial real estate lawyers. Includes hard-to-find state regulatory actions, case digests, and legislative updates.

614.7 333.7 US
OHIO ENVIRONMENTAL REPORT. 1969. m. $20. Ohio Environmental Council, Inc., 400 Dublin Ave., Ste. 120, Columbus, OH 43215-2333.
TEL 614-224-4900. FAX 614-224-4914. Ed. Richard Sahli. circ. 2,000. (tabloid format; back issues avail.)
Formerly: Environmental Hotline (Columbus).
Description: Provides timely information on environmental issues in Ohio, as well as public policy and legislative initiatives.

574.5 DK ISSN 0030-1299
QH540 CODEN: OIKSAA
OIKOS; a journal of ecology. (Text and summaries in English) 1948. 9/yr. DKK 2250. (Nordic Society Oikos) Munksgaard International Publishers Ltd., 35 Noerre Soegade, P.O. Box 2148, DK-1016 Copenhagen K, Denmark. TEL 33-127030.
FAX 33-129387. Ed. Nils Malmer. adv.; bk.rev. circ. 1,550. (reprint service avail. from ISI) **Indexed:** Bio-Contr.News & Info., Biol.Abstr., Cadscan, Chem.Abstr., Curr.Adv.Ecol.Sci., Curr.Cont., Deep Sea Res.& Oceanogr.Abstr., Environ.Per.Bibl., Field Crop Abstr., Forest.Abstr., Forest Prod.Abstr., Geo.Abstr., Helminthol.Abstr., Herb.Abstr. (1976-), Ind.Vet., Irr.& Drain.Abstr., Lead Abstr., Nutr.Abstr., Plant Breed.Abstr., Rev.Appl.Entomol., Risk Abstr., Sci.Cit.Ind., Seed Abstr., Sel.Water Res.Abstr., Weed Abstr., Zincscan.
—BLDSC (6248.000000); Faxon; UnCover; SWETS; CASDDS. **CCC.**
Refereed Serial

OIL SPILL INTELLIGENCE REPORT; an international weekly newsletter. see *PETROLEUM AND GAS*

614.7 US
OKLAHOMA NATURAL RESOURCES REPORT. fortn. Scissortail Ventures, Inc., 710 Beacon Building, Tulsa, OK 74103. TEL 918-583-2333. Ed. Gary Percefull.

OLIPHANT WASHINGTON SERVICE. ENERGY SUMMARY. see *ENERGY*

613.1 333.7 US
ON THE WILD SIDE. q. $25 includes membership. American Wildlands, 40 E. Main St., Ste. 2, Bozeman, MT 59715-4758. TEL 406-586-8175. FAX 406-586-8242. circ. 2,000. (back issues avail.) **Document type:** newsletter.

323.4 US ISSN 1018-9300
ONE COUNTRY; the earth is but one country, and mankind its citizens. French edition (ISSN 1145-4644); Chinese edition (ISSN 1018-9289) (Text in English) 1989. q. free to qualified personnel. Baha'i International Community, 866 United Nations Plaza, Ste. 120, New York, NY 10017. TEL 212-756-3500. FAX 212-756-3573. TELEX 666363 BICNY. Ed. Brad Pokorny. bk.rev. circ. 15,000.
Description: Reports on the activities of the worldwide Baha'i community as they relate to environment, development, peace, racial harmony, women's rights, and other issues of global concern.

ONTARIO ENVIRONMENTAL PROTECTION ACT ANNOTATED. see *LAW*

613.1 AU ISSN 0252-9572
OPTIONS. q. free. International Institute for Applied Systems Analysis, A-2361 Laxenburg, Austria.
Document type: newsletter.
—BLDSC (6275.270000).

ORDNANCE SURVEY PUBLICATION NEWS. see *GEOGRAPHY*

ORGANIC GROWER. see *GARDENING AND HORTICULTURE*

574 333.7 US ISSN 1058-3130
QH1
ORION (NEW YORK); people and nature. 1982. q. $18 (foreign $28). Myrin Institute, Inc., 136 E. 64th St., New York, NY 10021. TEL 212-758-6475.
FAX 212-758-6784. (Co-sponsor: Conservation International) Ed. George K. Russell. bk.rev.; illus. circ. 11,000. (back issues avail.) **Indexed:** Environ.Abstr., Environ.Per.Bibl. (1991-).
—BLDSC (6291.280500).
Formerly (until 1991): Orion Nature Quarterly (ISSN 0732-0876)
Description: Focuses on the interconnection between nature and human culture. Includes environmental study and conservation of natural resources.

613.1 US
OUR CHANGING PLANET. 1989. a. free. U.S. Geological Survey, Committee on Earth and Environmental Sciences, 104 National Center, 12201 Sunrise Valley Dr., Reston, VA 22092. **Document type:** newsletter.

614.7 333.7 UN ISSN 1013-7394
HC79.E5 CODEN: OUPLEY
OUR PLANET. French edition: Notre Planete. Spanish edition: Nuestro Planeta. 1974. q. free. United Nations Environment Programme, Information Service, P.O. 30552, Nairobi, Kenya.
TEL 254-2-230800. FAX 254-2-226831. TELEX 22068-UNEP-KE. Ed. Shane Cave. bk.rev.; charts; illus. circ. 17,000. (back issues avail.)
—BLDSC (6314.346000); Faxon; UnCover.
Supersedes: U N E P News (ISSN 0256-2456); Which was formerly: Uniterra (ISSN 0379-3192); Which superseded: U N E P News.
Description: Promotes international awareness in all aspects of the present environmental and conservation crisis.

OUTDOOR AMERICA. see *CONSERVATION*

OZONE: SCIENCE AND ENGINEERING. see *ENGINEERING — Chemical Engineering*

613.1 JA ISSN 0917-8260
OZONEWS IN JAPAN. (Text in Japanese) 1991. q. Nihon Ozon Kyokai - Japan Ozone Association, Zosu Sokushin Senta, 3-4, Akasaka 2-chome, Minato-ku, Tokyo 107, Japan.

PACE ENVIRONMENTAL LAW REVIEW. see *LAW*

614.7 US
EL PAISANO. 1955. q. membership. Desert Protective Council, Inc., Box 2312, Valley Center, CA 92082-2312. TEL 619-749-3485. Ed. Harriet Allen. circ. 500 **Document type:** newsletter.
Description: Reports on membership activities and status of current projects.

628 FR ISSN 0246-1579
PARC NATUREL REGIONAL ET DES RESERVES NATURELLES DE CORSE. TRAVAUX SCIENTIFIQUES.
1985. 5/yr. 140 F. (effective 1991). Parc Naturel Regional de Corse, B.P. 417, 20184 Ajaccio Cedex, France. TEL 95-21-56-54.

PARK WATCH. see *CONSERVATION*

614.7 UK ISSN 0960-233X
PARKS; the international magazine dedicated to the protected areas of the world. 1990. 3/yr. £30($55.50) (Commission on National Parks and Protected Areas (CNPPA)) Science and Technology Letters, P.O. Box 81, Northwood, Middlesex HA6 3DN, England. TEL 09274-23586.
FAX 09274-25066. Ed. Paul Goriup. **Document type:** consumer publication.
—BLDSC (6406.793700).

PEACE MAGAZINE. see *POLITICAL SCIENCE — International Relations*

PEAK AND PRAIRIE. see *CONSERVATION*

PEDESTRIAN RESEARCH. see *TRANSPORTATION — Roads And Traffic*

301.31 US ISSN 0092-7937
HC107.P43
PENNSYLVANIA. CITIZENS ADVISORY COUNCIL TO THE DEPARTMENT OF ENVIRONMENTAL RESOURCES. ANNUAL REPORT. Key Title: Annual Report - Citizens Advisory Council (Harrisburg). 1971. a. free. Citizens Advisory Council to the Pennsylvania Department of Environmental Resources, Box 8459, Harrisburg, PA 17105-8459. Ed. Susan M. Wilson. stat. circ. 2,500. **Document type:** government publication.

333.8 340 US
PENNSYLVANIA BAR ASSOCIATION. ENVIRONMENTAL, MINERAL & NATURAL RESOURCES LAW SECTION. NEWSLETTER. 4/yr. membership. Pennsylvania Bar Association, Environmental, Mineral & Natural Resources Law Section, 100 South St., Harrisburg, PA 17108. TEL 717-238-6715.
FAX 717-238-7182. **Document type:** newsletter.

PENNSYLVANIA ENVIRONMENTAL COMPLIANCE UPDATE. see *LAW*

PESCA IN. see *SPORTS AND GAMES — Outdoor Life*

PESTICIDES AND YOU. see *AGRICULTURE — Crop Production And Soil*

ENVIRONMENTAL STUDIES

614.7 333.7   PH
PHILIPPINES. MINISTRY OF NATURAL RESOURCES. ANNUAL REPORT. a. Department of Natural Resources, Diliman, Quezon City, Philippines.

PHILIPPINES. MINISTRY OF NATURAL RESOURCES. PLANS AND PROGRAMS. see *CONSERVATION*

628.44   SZ
PHOENIX INTERNATIONAL. (Text in English) 1983. bi-m. 60 Fr.($60) Sonneggstrasse 21, 8006 Zurich, Switzerland. TEL 01-2523444. Ed. Juerg Schnyder. circ. 19,000. Indexed: W.R.C.Inf.
Description: International trade publication on waste technology, environmental protection and recycling. Includes a news review, list of events and exhibitions, and list of suppliers.

671   US
HD9975.U5
PHOENIX: VOICE OF THE SCRAP RECYCLING INDUSTRIES. 1969. irreg. free. Institute of Scrap Recycling Industries, Inc., 1325 G St., Ste. 1000, Washington, DC 20005. TEL 202-466-4050. FAX 202-775-9109. Ed. David K. Krohne. illus.; circ. 40,000 (controlled). **Indexed:** Energy Rev., Environ.Abstr., Environ.Per.Bibl. (1972-), Met.Abstr., Pollut.Abstr., World Alum.Abstr. **Document type:** consumer publication.
Formerly: Phoenix Quarterly (ISSN 0031-837X)

614.7 574.1   JA   ISSN 0370-9612
QH188   CODEN: PEJAE6
PHYSIOLOGY AND ECOLOGY JAPAN. (Text in English) 1947. s-a. $30 to individuals; institutions $60. Physiology and Ecology Japan Editorial Office - Seiri Seitai Kankokai, Kyoto Daigaku Rigakubu Dobutsugaku Kyoshitsu, Kitashirakawa, Sakyo-ku, Kyoto 606, Japan. FAX 075-751-6149. TELEX J-5422302-SCIKYU. Ed. Hiroya Kawanabe. bk.rev. circ. 700. (back issues avail.) **Indexed:** Biol.Abstr., Curr.Adv.Ecol.Sci., Sel.Water Res.Abstr.
—BLDSC (6488.205000).
Description: Covers all fields of physiology and ecology.

620.85   IT
PIOVEGO; foglio mensile si cultura ambientalista. 1988. m. (Amissi del Piovego) Libraria Padovana Editrice, Via Marconcelli, 123 ter, 35129 Padova, Italy. TEL 049-8075286. Ed. GianPietro Tonon.

614.7   CN   ISSN 0847-9607
PITCH-IN NEWS. 1973. 2/yr. Can.$15. Pitch-In Canada, 200-1676 Martin Dr., White Rock, BC V4A 6E7, Canada. TEL 604-538-0577. FAX 604-538-3497. Ed. Allard W. Van Veen. bk.rev. circ. 10,000. (tabloid format; back issues avail.)
Formerly: Newslitter (ISSN 0383-9168)

800   US
PLANET DRUM BUNDLES. 1973. irreg. price varies. Planet Drum Foundation, Box 31251, San Francisco, CA 94131. TEL 415-285-6556. FAX 415-285-6563. circ. 3,000. (back issues avail.)
Formerly: Planet Drum.

PLANETARY ASSOCIATION FOR CLEAN ENERGY. NEWSLETTER. see *ENERGY*

614.7 340   AT
PLANNING & ENVIRONMENT LAW SERVICE - VICTORIA. 2 base vols. (plus bi-m. update). $395. Butterworths, 271-273 Lane Cove Rd., P.O. Box 345, North Ryde, N.S.W. 2113, Australia. TEL 02-335-4444. FAX 02-335-4678. (looseleaf format)

PLANT PROTECTION NEWS. see *AGRICULTURE — Crop Production And Soil*

574.5   PL   ISSN 0324-8763
QH540   CODEN: PECTDR
POLISH ECOLOGICAL STUDIES. (Text in English; summaries in Polish) 1975. q. $88 (effective 1992). Polska Akademia Nauk, Instytut Ekologii, Dziekanow Lesny k-Warszawy, 05-092 Lomianki, Poland. TEL 48-22-513-046. FAX 48-22-513-100. (Dist. by: Ars Polona, Krakowskie Przedmiescie 7, 00-068 Warsaw, Poland) Ed. J. Luczak. bibl. circ. 430. **Indexed:** Biol.Abstr., Chem.Abstr., Curr.Adv.Ecol.Sci., Excerp.Med., Geo.Abstr., GeoRef., Plant Breed.Abstr.
—BLDSC (6543.583000); CASDDS. **CCC.**
Description: Publishes original papers form the range of the experimental, descriptive and theoretical ecology and other branches of sciences closely connected with broad ecological, environmental aspects.

613.1   PL   ISSN 1230-1485
         CODEN: PJESE2
▼**POLISH JOURNAL OF ENVIRONMENTAL STUDIES.** (Text in English) 1992. q. 200000 Zl.($40) (Ministerstwo Ochrony Srodowiska, Zasobow Naturalnych i Lesnictwa - Polish Ministry of Environmental Protection, Natural Resources and Forestry) Hard, P.O. Box, 10-718 Olsztyn 5, Poland. TEL 48-89-233-615. FAX 48-89-273-908. Ed. Jerzy Radecki. adv.; bk.rev.
—CASDDS.
Description: Publishes original papers on different aspects of environmental protection; includes conference reports, scientific and technical reports.

628.44   PL   ISSN 0867-6038
POLITECHNIKA SLASKA. ZESZYTY NAUKOWE. INZYNIERIA SRODOWISKA. (Text in Polish; summaries in English, Germen, Russian) 1960. irreg. price varies. Politechnika Slaska, Katowicka 7, 44-100 Gliwice, Poland. FAX 371655. TELEX 036304. (Dist. by: Ars Polona, Krakowskie Przedmiescie 7, 00-068 Warsaw, Poland) Ed. Helena Koscielniak. circ. 205.
Formerly (until vol.25, 1985): Politechnika Slaska. Zeszyty Naukowe. Inzynieria Sanitarna (ISSN 0072-4696)

628.44 627   PL   ISSN 0084-2869
POLITECHNIKA WROCLAWSKA. INSTYTUT INZYNIERII OCHRONY SRODOWISKA. PRACE NAUKOWE. MONOGRAFIE. (Text in Polish; summaries in English, French, German, Russian) 1969. irreg., no.34, 1991. price varies. Wydawnictwo Politechniki Wroclawskiej, Wybrzeze Wyspianskiego 27, 50-370 Wroclaw, Poland. FAX 22-36-64. TELEX 712559 PWRPL. (Dist. by: Ars Polona-Ruch, Krakowskie Przedmiescie 7, Warsaw, Poland) **Document type:** monographic series.

614.7 620   PL   ISSN 0208-4112
POLSKA AKADEMIA NAUK. INSTYTUT PODSTAW INZYNIERII SRODOWISKA. PRACE I STUDIA. (Text in Polish; summaries in English and Russian) irreg., no.40, 1990. price varies. Ossolineum, Publishing House of the Polish Academy of Sciences, Rynek 9, 50-106 Wroclaw, Poland. TEL 48-71-386-25. FAX 48-71-448-103. TELEX 0712771 OSS PL. Ed. Stefan Godzik. **Indexed:** Pollut.Abstr. **Document type:** academic/scholarly publication.
Supersedes (in 1971): Polska Akademia Nauk. Centrum Badan Naukowych w Wojewodztwie Katowickim. Prace i Studia (ISSN 0079-3582)

POLYMER RECOVERY; an international scientific journal covering all aspects of recycling and (energy) recovery of polymeric materials. see *ENGINEERING — Chemical Engineering*

POPULATION (BOCA RATON). see *POPULATION STUDIES*

PORTLAND ALLIANCE. see *LABOR UNIONS*

614.7   PO
PORTUGAL. MINISTERIO DA QUALIDADE DE VIDA. COMISSAO NACIONAL DO AMBIENTE. BOLETIM. 1974. m. free. Ministerio da Qualidade de Vida, Comissao Nacional do Ambiente, Praca Duque de Saldanha 31, 1096 Lisbon Codex, Portugal. circ. 5,000.
Former titles: Portugal. Ministerio da Habitacao e Obras Publicas. Comissao Nacional do Ambiente. Relatorio de Actividades; Portugal. Ministerio do Equipamento Social e do Ambiente. Comissao Nacional do Ambiente. Relatorio de Actividades.

POTOMAC BASIN REPORTER. see *WATER RESOURCES*

333.7   US
POWDER RIVER BREAKS. 1975. bi-m. $30 membership. Powder River Basin Resource Council, Box 1178, Douglas, WY 82633. TEL 307-358-5002. Ed. Melody Kuecks. circ. 975 (controlled). **Document type:** newsletter.
Description: Promotes the preservation and enrichment of Wyoming's agricultural heritage and rural lifestyle. Discusses the conservation of its land, minerals, water and clean air consistent with responsible use of these resources to sustain the livelihood of present and future generations.

614.7   UK   ISSN 0262-4540
PRACTICAL ALTERNATIVES. 1981. irreg. £7 per 6 issues. David Stephens, Ed. & Pub., Victoria House, Bridge St., Rhayader, Mid Wales LD6 5AG, England. TEL 0597-810929. Ed. David Stephens. circ. 2,000.
Incorporates: Ecological Life Style. News Letter & Environmental Building Developments Ltd. News.
Description: Reports on building of solar village with new 'survivor' design of passive solar house as a means of reducing energy consumption drastically.

500 333.7   CN   ISSN 0317-6282
F1060.A1   CODEN: PFOREL
PRAIRIE FORUM. 1976. s-a. Can.$23 to individuals; institutions Can.$28. Canadian Plains Research Center, University of Regina, Regina, SK S4S 0A2, Canada. TEL 306-585-4795. FAX 306-585-4699. Ed. Alvin Finkel. adv.: B&W page Can.$100; trim 6 x 9. bk.rev. circ. 350. (also avail. in microform from MML; back issues avail.) **Indexed:** Amer.Bibl.Slavic & E.Eur.Stud., Amer.Hist.& Life, Can.Per.Ind., CMI, Geo.Abstr., Hist.Abstr. **Document type:** academic/scholarly publication.
—BLDSC (6598.550900).
Description: Interdisciplinary journal of research relating to the Canadian Plains region: man and nature on the prairies.
Refereed Serial

614.7 340   US   ISSN 0882-715X
KF4310.A15
PRESERVATION LAW REPORTER. 1982. q. $195. National Trust for Historic Preservation, 1785 Massachusetts Ave., N.W., Washington, DC 20036. TEL 202-673-4000. Ed. Stefan Nagel. bibl.; cum.index. circ. 450. (looseleaf format; back issues avail.)

614   FR   ISSN 0753-2989
PRESSE ENVIRONNEMENT; politique et economie de l'environnement. 45/yr. 4300 F. Innovapresse, 29 rue Faubourg-Poissioniere, 75009 Paris, France. TEL 48-24-08-97. FAX 42-47-00-76. TELEX 280 114 F. Ed. Antoine Loubiere; Pub. Jean Audouin. circ. 1,000. **Document type:** newsletter.
Description: Covers the political and economic relationships to the environment.

628   CN
PRINCE EDWARD ISLAND. DEPARTMENT OF COMMUNITY AND CULTURAL AFFAIRS. ANNUAL REPORT. 1970. a. free. Department of Community Affairs, Box 2000, Charlottetown, P.E.I. C1A 7N8, Canada. TEL 902-892-3561. FAX 902-368-5544. Ed.Bd. circ. 150.
Former titles: Prince Edward Island. Department of Community Affairs. Annual Report (ISSN 0701-6956); (until 1980): Prince Edward Island. Department of the Environment Annual Report (ISSN 0085-5138); Prince Edward Island. Water Authority. Annual Report.

614.7   IT
PRO NATURA GENOVA; periodico di informazione ai soci. 1976? q. exchange basis. Pro Natura Genova, c/o Museo di Storia Naturale, Via Brigata Liguria 9, 16121 Genova, Italy. Dir. Pierluigi Oneto. bk.rev.; illus.; stat. circ. 1,000.
Formerly (until 1982, vol.34): Ambiente Naturale e Urbano (ISSN 0390-1246)

ENVIRONMENTAL STUDIES

614.7 US ISSN 0278-4750
GB611 CODEN: PDEDDG
PROBLEMS OF DESERT DEVELOPMENT. English translation of: Problemy Osvoeniya Pustyn' (TK ISSN 0032-9428) 1980. bi-m. $750. (Akademiya Nauk Turkmenii, Institut Pustyn', TK) Allerton Press, Inc., 150 Fifth Ave., New York, NY 10011. TEL 212-924-3950. FAX 212-463-9684. Ed. A.G. Babaev. Indexed: Agroforest.Abstr., Biol.Abstr., Forest.Abstr., Hort.Abstr., Irr.& Drain.Abstr., Maize Abstr. **Document type:** academic/scholarly publication.
—BLDSC (0416.919500); UnCover. CCC.
Refereed Serial

PROBLEMY BIOSPHERY. see *CONSERVATION*

628.44 352.7 RU ISSN 0233-5816
PROBLEMY BOL'SHIKH GORODOV/PROBLEMS OF LARGE METROPOLITAN AREAS; obzornaya informatsiya. 1971. s-m. 10 Rub. Moskovskii Gorodskoi Territorial'nyi Tsentr Nauchno-Tekhnicheskoi Informatsii i Propagandy, Pr. Serova 5, 101958 Moscow, Russia. TEL 921-67-05. (Co-sponsor: State Planning Committe of the R.S.F.S.R.) Ed. Irina P. Mikhailova. circ. 800. (back issues avail.)
—BLDSC (0133.156000).
Description: Covers urban environmental protection development, urban traffic improvement, energy and water supply problems, recreation.

614.7 KR ISSN 0135-2253
CODEN: PKZZDW
PROBLEMY KONTROLYA I ZASHCHITA ATMOSFERY OT ZAGRYAZNENIYA; respublikanskii mezhvedomstvennyi sbornik nauchnykh trudov. (Text in Russian) 1974. a. (Akademiya Nauk Ukrainskoi S.S.R, Institut Tekhnicheskoi Teplofiziki) Izdatel'stvo Naukova Dumka, c/o Yu.A. Khramov, Dir, Ul. Repina, 3, Kiev 252 601, Ukraine. (Subscr. to: Mezhdunarodnaya Kniga, Moscow, G-200, Russia) Ed. A.N. Shcherban' Indexed: Chem.Abstr., Int.Aerosp.Abstr.
—BLDSC (0133.374000); CASDDS.

PROCESS SAFETY AND ENVIRONMENTAL PROTECTION; transactions: part B. see *CHEMISTRY*

PRODDER NEWSLETTER. see *BUSINESS AND ECONOMICS — International Development And Assistance*

614.7 333.91 II
PROGRESS IN ENVIRONMENTAL SCIENCE & TECHNOLOGY. 1984. a. $50. Divyajyoti Prakashan, 5 Bhagat-ki-kothi, Jodhpur 342 003, India. (Co-sponsor: Geo-Environ Academia) Eds. Alam Singh, U.S. Sharma. **Document type:** academic/scholarly publication.
—BLDSC (6868.355000).
Former titles: Current Practices in Environmental Science and Engineering (ISSN 0970-0668); Current Practices in Environmental Engineering (ISSN 0253-5114)

PROGRESS IN PHYSICAL GEOGRAPHY; an international review of geographical work in the natural and environmental sciences. see *GEOGRAPHY*

613.1 GW ISSN 0931-2749
PROJEKT EUROPAEISCHES FORSCHUNGSZENTRUM FUER MASSNAHMEN ZUR LUFTREINHALTUNG. irreg. Kernforschungszentrum Karlsruhe GmbH, Postfach 3640, 76021 Karlsruhe, Germany.
FAX 07247-825802. **Document type:** monographic series.
—BLDSC (5089.867600).

614.7 GW ISSN 0940-3000
PROJEKT UMWELT UND GESUNDHEIT. irreg. Kernforschungszentrum Karlsruhe GmbH, Postfach 3640, 76021 Karlsruhe, Germany.
FAX 07247-825802. **Document type:** monographic series.
—BLDSC (4011.554600).

614.7 IT ISSN 1120-1681
PROTEC; il progresso e l'ambiente. (Includes a directory: L'Ambiente in Italia) (Text in Italian; summaries in English, Italian) 1986. 9/yr. L.56000($106) Publi & Consult S.p.A., Via Tagliamento, 29, 00198 Rome, Italy. TEL 06-8543603. FAX 06-8440697. TELEX 622368 AVDEFE I. Ed. Paolo F. Bancale. adv.: B&W page $2430, color page $3630; trim 185 x 275; adv. contact: Sabrina Soldati.
Description: Covers the environmental and civil defense industry in Italy.

614.7 US
PROTECT. 1973. 4/yr. $50. Tennessee Environmental Council, 1700 Hayes St., Ste.101, Nashville, TN 37203-2921. TEL 615-321-5075. Ed. Jennifer Walker. bk.rev. circ. 2,020. **Document type:** newsletter.
Formerly: Tennessee Environmental Report.
Description: Calendar of events and legislative agenda affecting the constituency of the Tennessee Environmental Council.

628 659.1 US
PROTECTING THE ENVIRONMENT (YEAR). 1989. a. free. Mobil Corporation, 3225 Gallows Rd., Fairfax, VA 22037-0001. **Document type:** consumer publication.
Description: Discusses the company's efforts to protect the environment.

PUBLIC INTEREST BRIEFS. see *LAW — Legal Aid*

PUBLIC LANDS NEWS. see *CONSERVATION*

614.9 531.6
150.198 US ISSN 1041-6773
PULSE OF THE PLANET. 1989. 4/yr. $40. Orgone Biophysical Research Laboratory, Box 1395, El Cerrito, CA 94530. TEL 510-526-5978. Ed. James Demeo. bk.rev. **Document type:** academic/scholarly publication.
Description: Environmental research journal focusing on alternative energy research applications of Wilhelm Reich's work, with translations of related papers from Germany and other countries.

614.7 581 US
PYMATUNING SYMPOSIA IN ECOLOGY. 1956. irreg., no.6, 1982. price varies. University of Pittsburgh, Pymatuning Laboratory of Ecology, RR 1, Box 7, Linesville, PA 16424. TEL 814-683-5813. Ed. Richard T. Hartman. (back issues avail.) **Document type:** proceedings.

614.7 SP ISSN 0212-0054
QUERCUS; revista de estudio y defensa de la naturaleza. 1981. 12/yr. 4900 ptas. (effective 1993). La Pedriza 1, 28002 Madrid, Spain. TEL 1-413-40-75. FAX 1-519-21-94. Ed. Rafael Serra. adv.; bk.rev.
Description: Covers the study and conservation of nature.

QUINNEHTUKQUT. see *CONSERVATION*

R & D FOCUS. see *METALLURGY — Welding*

613.1 333.7 US
R F F RESEARCH DIGEST. q. free. Resources for the Future, 1616 P St., N.W., Washington, DC 20036. Ed. K. Storck. **Document type:** newsletter.

620.85 352.7 NE ISSN 1380-7153
R O M MAGAZINE; vaktijdschrift voor ruimtelijke ordening en milieubeheer. 1977. 10/yr. fl.120. Delwel Uitgeverij B.V., Postbus 19110, 2500 The Hague, Netherlands. TEL 31-70-3624800. FAX 31-70-3605606. Ed. H.J. Bakker. **Document type:** trade publication.
Former titles: R O M - Ruimtelijke Ordening en Milieubeheer (ISSN 0923-7674); Incorporates (1983-1988): R O M Bulletin (ISSN 0920-1394); (until 1988): R O M Magazine (ISSN 0169-6270); Which was formed by the 1983 merger of: P K B - Berichten over Planologische Kernbeslissingen (ISSN 0166-977X); V M (ISSN 0920-4369)

620.85 US ISSN 1065-4623
RACHEL'S HAZARDOUS WASTE NEWS; providing news and resources for environmental justice. 1986. w. $25 to incividuals; government agencies $80; businesses $400. Environmental Research Foundation, Box 5036, Annapolis, MD 21403-7036. TEL 410-263-1584. FAX 410-253-8944. Ed. Peter Montague.
Description: Covers international and U.S. hazardous waste issues, including air pollution, landfills, incineration and public health, radiation and nuclear wastes, environmental justice, pollution prevention, regulatory actions, and citizen law-reform campaigns.

614.7 539.7 US
RADIATION EVENTS MONITOR. 1986. irreg. $25 to individuals; libraries $35; institutions $50. Center for Atomic Radiation Studies, Inc. (CARS), Box 1036, Cambridge, MA 02238-1036. TEL 617-497-2277. Ed. William Boardman. circ. 2,000. **Document type:** newsletter.
Description: Covers the spectrum of issues and events involving radiation with emphasis on environmental and health hazards.

RADIATION PROTECTION DOSIMETRY. see *PHYSICS — Nuclear Physics*

RADIOLOGICAL PROTECTION BULLETIN. see *ENERGY — Nuclear Energy*

614.7 US ISSN 0739-621X
RAIN. 1974-1987 (vol.13, no.1); resumed 1991. q. $20. Rain Magazine, Box 30097, Eugene, OR 97403-1097. TELEX 154 256 491. Eds. Danielle Janes, Greg Bryant. bk.rev.; film rev.; software rev.; bibl.; illus. (back issues avail.) Indexed: Alt.Press Ind., Environ.Abstr., Environ.Per.Bibl. (1991-), Fut.Surv., Media Rev.Dig., New.Per.Ind. **Document type:** consumer publication.
Description: Explores alternative political, social and economic organizational strategies and practices to encourage the development of self-reliant, directly democratic and ecologically viable communities

051 US ISSN 0278-7016
RAISE THE STAKES; the Planet Drum review. 1979. 2/yr. $20 membership; $25 outside N. America. Planet Drum Foundation, Box 31251, San Francisco, CA 94131. TEL 415-285-6556. FAX 415-285-6563. Ed.Bd. bk.rev. circ. 3,000. Indexed: Alt.Press Ind.
Description: Present thought provoking essays on bioregional issues ranging from restoration ecology to the greening of cities.

RANGER RICK'S NATURESCOPE. see *EDUCATION — Teaching Methods And Curriculum*

RAUM UND ZEIT; Visionen der Wissenschaft fuer ein besseres Morgen. see *MEDICAL SCIENCES*

REAL ESTATE - ENVIRONMENTAL LIABILITY NEWS; the bi-weekly report on litigation, regulation, and industry practice. see *LAW*

REALITY NOW; for defense of life on Earth. see *LITERARY AND POLITICAL REVIEWS*

614 622 CN ISSN 0826-7049
RECLAMATION NEWSLETTER. (Text in English, French) 1977. 3/yr. Can.$4C to individuals; libraries Can.$10. (American Society for Surface Mining and Reclamation, US) Canadian Land Reclamation Association, Box 682, Guelph, Ont. N1H 6L3, Canada. TEL 403-427-4147. FAX 403-422-8233. Ed. Chris Powter. bk.rev.; charts; illus.; stat. circ. 950.

RECOVER; the environmental magazine. see *CONSERVATION*

614.7 US ISSN 1053-0525
RECYCLING RELATED NEWSLETTER, PUBLICATIONS, PERIODICALS; an updating reference. 1990. biennial. $7.50. Continnuus, c/o Prosperity & Profits Unlimited, Box 416, Denver, CO 80201-0416. TEL 303-575-5676. Ed. A.C. Doyle. circ. 2,000. **Document type:** newsletter.
Description: References on recycling and waste management.

ENVIRONMENTAL STUDIES

614.7   UK   ISSN 0886-9375
TC530   CODEN: RRRMEP
REGULATED RIVERS: RESEARCH AND MANAGEMENT; an international journal devoted to river research and management. 1986. q. $310 (effective 1994). John Wiley & Sons Ltd., Journals, Baffins Ln., Chichester, Sussex PO19 1UD, England. TEL 0243-779777. FAX 0243-775878. TELEX 86290 WIBOOK G. Ed. G. Petts. adv.; bk.rev.; illus.; maps. circ. 262. (reprint service avail. from SWZ) **Indexed:** Energy Info.Abstr., Environ.Abstr., Environ.Per.Bibl. (1990-), Sel.Water Res.Abstr. **Document type:** academic/scholarly publication.
—BLDSC (7345.650000); UnCover; SWETS; UMI. **CCC.**
    Description: Devoted to interdisciplinary research and covers activity from the effects of major dams, weirs, canalisation and more; includes original papers.

620.85   PO   ISSN 0871-4819
RELATORIO DO ESTADO DO AMBIENTE E ORDENAMENTO DO TERRITORIO. 1987. a. Ministerio do Planeamento e Administracao Territorio, Departamento Central de Planeamento, Gabinete de Estudos e Planeamento da Administracao do Territorio, Avda. D. Carlos I, 126, 1200 Lisbon, Portugal. circ. 1,500.

REMINERALIZE THE EARTH. see AGRICULTURE — Crop Production And Soil

REMOTE SENSING OF ENVIRONMENT. see GEOGRAPHY

614.7   US
RENE DUBOS CENTER FOR HUMAN ENVIRONMENTS. NEWSLETTER. irreg. Rene Dubos Center for Human Environment, Inc., 100 E. 85th St., New York, NY 10028. TEL 212-249-7745.

614.7   US
RENEW AMERICA REPORT. 1988. q. $25 membership. Renew America, 1400 16th St., N.W., Ste. 710, Washington, DC 20036. TEL 202-232-2252. FAX 202-232-2617. Ed. John Jester.
    Description: Provides information to state groups and elected officials to assist in establishing local agendas for environmental protection. Details environmental success stories from across the nation.

RENEWABLE ENERGY BULLETIN. see ENERGY

333.79 628.4   US   ISSN 0738-6532
                                  CODEN: RRJOEP
RENEWABLE RESOURCES JOURNAL. 1982. q. $19 to individuals; institutions $36. Renewable Natural Resources Foundation, 5430 Grosvenor Ln., Bethesda, MD 20814. TEL 301-493-9101. FAX 301-493-6148. Ed. Norah D. Davis. bk.rev.; index. circ. 2,500. (back issues avail.) **Indexed:** Energy Rev., Environ.Per.Bibl. (1986-).
—BLDSC (7364.192300); UnCover.

REPORT FROM THE HILL. see LAW

614.7 333.91   CN   ISSN 0838-519X
REPORT ON THE INDUSTRIAL DIRECT DISCHARGES IN ONTARIO. a. free. Ministry of Environment and Energy, Water Resources Branch, 135 St. Clair Ave. W., Toronto, Ont. M4V 1P5, Canada. TEL 416-323-4321. FAX 416-323-4564. **Document type:** government publication.
    Former titles (until 1986): Report on the Industrial Discharges in Ontario (ISSN 0838-5181); (until 1985): Report on the Industrial Discharges into the Great Lakes Basin, Ontario (ISSN 0838-5173)

028.5   US
REPORTS TO THE NATION ON OUR CHANGING PLANET. 1991. a. free. University Corporation for Atmospheric Research, Office for Interdisciplinary Earth Studies, Box 3000, Boulder, CO 80307. TEL 303-497-2692. FAX 303-497-2699. E-mail: EHRET@NCAR.UCAR.EDU. Ed.Bd. illus. **Document type:** monographic series.
    Description: Geared to the lay public and to students on the junior high and high school level. Presents complex phenomena through the integration of graphics and text.

614.7   JA
RESEARCH ON ENVIRONMENTAL DISRUPTION/KOGAI KENKYU; toward interdisciplinary cooperation. 1971. q. 4000 Yen. Iwanami Shoten Publishers, 2-5-5 Hitotsubashi, Chiyoda-ku, Tokyo 101-02, Japan. FAX 03-3239-9618. (Dist. overseas by: Japan Publications Trading Co., Ltd., Box 5030, Tokyo International, Tokyo 100-31, Japan; Or: 1255 Howard St., San Francisco, CA 94103) **Indexed:** Chem.Abstr.

RESEARCHES ON POPULATION ECOLOGY/KOTAIGUN SEITAIGAKU NO KENKYU. see POPULATION STUDIES

RESOURCES. see ENERGY

RESOURCES (WASHINGTON, 1959). see CONSERVATION

RESOURCES, CONSERVATION AND RECYCLING. see ENVIRONMENTAL STUDIES — Waste Management

THE RESOURCES OF INTERNATIONAL PERMACULTURE. see BIOLOGY

RESOURCES POLICY. see ENERGY

613.1 333.7   US   ISSN 1061-2971
QH541.15.R45
▼**RESTORATION ECOLOGY.** 1993. q. $70 to individuals; institutions $120. (Society for Ecological Restoration) Blackwell Scientific Publications, Inc., 238 Main St., Ste. 501, Cambridge, MA 02142-1413. TEL 617-876-7000. FAX 617-876-7022. Ed. William A. Niering. **Document type:** academic/scholarly publication.
—BLDSC (7777.835000); UMI. **CCC.**
    Description: Publishes research papers, reviews, opinions of readers, and technical reports on the process of ecological restoration, defined as the international alteration of a site to establish a defined, indigenous, historic ecosystem.

614.7 341   UK   ISSN 0962-8797
KJE6242.A13
▼**REVIEW OF EUROPEAN COMMUNITY AND INTERNATIONAL ENVIRONMENTAL LAW.** 1992. 4/yr. Basil Blackwell Ltd., 108 Cowley Rd., Oxford OX4 1JF, England. TEL 0865-791100. FAX 0865-791347. TELEX 837022-OXBOOK-G.
—BLDSC (7790.535000); UnCover; SWETS; UMI. **CCC.**

614.7   UK   ISSN 0048-7554
RA565.A1   CODEN: REVHA3
REVIEWS ON ENVIRONMENTAL HEALTH. (Text in English) 1972. q. $200. Freund Publishing House Ltd., Ste. 500, Chesham House, 150 Regent St., London W1R 5FA, England. (Alt. addr.: P.O. Box 35010, Tel Aviv, Israel. TEL 972-3-615335) Ed. S. Samueloff. adv.; bk.rev.; index. (back issues avail.) **Indexed:** Abstr.Hyg., Chem.Abstr., Curr.Adv.Ecol.Sci., Curr.Cont., Dok.Arbeitsmed., Energy Rev., Environ.Per.Bibl., Excerp.Med., I.P.A, Ind.Med. **Document type:** academic/scholarly publication.
—BLDSC (7790.525000); SWETS; CASDDS.

628   FR   ISSN 0249-7395
QH540
REVUE D'ECOLOGIE: LA TERRE ET LA VIE; revue d'ecologie appliquee a la protection de la nature. (Supplement avail.) 1854. q. 400 F. (foreign 430 F.). Societe Nationale de Protection de la Nature, 57 rue Cuvier, 75005 Paris, France. TEL 47-07-31-95. Ed. Francois Bourliere. bk.rev.; bibl.; illus. circ. 1,200. (back issues avail.) **Indexed:** Biol.Abstr., Curr.Cont., Geo.Abstr., Helminthol.Abstr., Soils & Fert.
—BLDSC (7898.718000); UnCover; SWETS.
    Formerly: Terre et Vie (ISSN 0040-3865)
    Description: Presents technical data as related to France. Discusses relationships between plant and animal life with the intention of conserving and maintaining the delicate balance of nature.

614.7   FR
REVUE JURIDIQUE DE L'ENVIRONNEMENT. q. 280 F. (Societe Francaise pour le Droit de l'Environnement) Publications Periodiques Specialisees, 11 rue d'Algerie, 69001 Lyon, France. Ed. M. Prieur. **Indexed:** ELLIS.

REVUE SUISSE DE LA SECURITE ET DE L'ENVIRONMENT. see CRIMINOLOGY AND LAW ENFORCEMENT — Security

RIVERS; studies in the science, environmental policy and law of instream flow. see WATER RESOURCES

LA RIVISTA DEI COMBUSTIBILI. see PETROLEUM AND GAS

RIVISTA DI IDROBIOLOGIA. see BIOLOGY

614.7 398   US   ISSN 1041-5955
ROBIN. 1984. irreg. (3-5/yr.). $16.50. Yankee Permaculture, Box 672, Dahlonega, GA 30533-0672. (Co-sponsors: Elfin Permaculture, Solutions Network, Forest Ecosystem Rescue Network) Ed. Dan Hemenway. bk.rev. circ. 200. (back issues avail.) **Document type:** newsletter.
    Description: Contains announcements of Elfin Permaculture workshops and courses, coordinates seed collection and dispersal for the Forest Ecosystem Rescue Network, provides a forum for discussing permaculture philosophy, and reports on the accomplishments of the group's volunteers.

ROCKY MOUNTAIN INSTITUTE NEWSLETTER. see ENERGY

RUNNING WILD; the trailrunner's magazine. see SPORTS AND GAMES — Outdoor Life

RURAL WALES - CYMRU WLEDIG. see CONSERVATION

574   US
QH540
RUSSIAN JOURNAL OF ECOLOGY. English translation of: Ekologiya (RU ISSN 0367-0597) 1970. bi-m. $875 (foreign $1025) (effective 1994). Plenum Publishing Corp., Consultants Bureau, 233 Spring St., New York, NY 10013-1578. TEL 212-620-8468. FAX 212-463-0742. TELEX 23-421139. Ed. L.F. Semerikov. charts; illus.; index. (also avail. in microfilm from JSC; back issues avail.) **Indexed:** Biol.Abstr., Curr.Adv.Ecol.Sci., Curr.Cont., Deep Sea Res.& Oceanogr.Abstr., Energy Ind., Energy Info.Abstr., Energy Res.Abstr., Environ.Per.Bibl., Helminthol.Abstr., Herb.Abstr., Ind.Med., Pollut.Abstr., Saf.Sci.Abstr., Sel.Water Res.Abstr., Soils & Fert., Weed Abstr. **Document type:** academic/scholarly publication.
—Faxon; UnCover. **CCC.**
    Former titles (until 1994): Soviet Journal of Ecology (ISSN 0096-7807); Ecology (ISSN 0531-8432)
    Refereed Serial

S A P T NEWSLETTER. (Scottish Association for Public Transport) see TRANSPORTATION

574.5   US   ISSN 1062-936X
                                 CODEN: SQERED
▼**S A R AND Q S A R IN ENVIRONMENTAL RESEARCH.** 1993. q. 58 ECU (effective 1993). Gordon & Breach Science Publishers, 820 Town Center Dr., Langhorne, PA 19047. TEL 215-750-2642. FAX 215-750-6343. (UK subscr. to: P.O. Box 90, Reading, Berkshire RG1 7JL, England. TEL 0734-560-080) (also avail. in microform) **Document type:** academic/scholarly publication.
—CASDDS. **CCC.**
    Description: Covers SAR and QSAR models in environmental sciences, agrochemistry, toxicology, pharmacology and applied chemistry.

614.7 333.79   SZ   ISSN 1016-8397
S E B E S. (Strategies Energetiques Biosphere et Societe) 1990. s-a. 40 SFr. Editions Medecine et Hygiene, Case Postale 456, CH-1211 Geneva 4, Switzerland. TEL 022-3469355. FAX 022-3475610. **Document type:** academic/scholarly publication.

614.7   UK   ISSN 0307-2614
S E E JOURNAL.* 1968. s-a. £2. Society for Environmental Education, 16 Trinity Road, Enderby, Leicester, England. Ed. R. Edwards. bk.rev. circ. 200.

614.7   CN
S E S NEWSLETTER. 1975. bi-m. Can.$20. Saskatchewan Environmental Society, Box 1372, Saskatoon, SK S7K 3N9, Canada. TEL 306-665-1915. FAX 306-665-2128. Ed. Heather Trueman. bk.rev.; illus. circ. 450. **Document type:** newsletter.
    Supersedes (as of 1981): Environment Probe (ISSN 0381-646X); Probe (ISSN 0316-0033)
    Description: News of the Society and environmental issues of concern to Saskatchewan people.

ENVIRONMENTAL STUDIES

613.1 US
S M E NEWS. 9/yr. membership. Society of Manufacturing Engineers, One SME Dr., Box 930, Dearborn, MI 48121-0930. TEL 313-271-1500.
Formerly (until 1983): S M E Newsletter and Technical Digest.

614.7 US
S O C M SENTINEL. 1972. m. $10. Save Our Cumberland Mountains, Box 479, Lake City, TN 37769. TEL 615-426-9455. circ. 1,450. **Document type:** newsletter.
Description: Looks at environmental and social justice issues.

614.7 333.7 WS
S P R E P ENVIRONMENTAL CASE STUDIES. 1986. irreg., no.5, 1989. South Pacific Regional Environment Programme, P.O. Box 240, Apia, Western Samoa.

614.7 333.7 WS
S P R E P FACT SHEET. irreg., no.6, 1989. South Pacific Regional Environment Programme, P.O. Box 240, Apia, Western Samoa.

614.7 333.7 WS
S P R E P MEETING REPORTS. (Text in English or French) 1981. irreg. South Pacific Regional Environment Programme, P.O. 240, Apia, Western Samoa.

614.7 333.7 WS
S P R E P OCCASIONAL PAPERS. 1989. irreg., no.8, 1990. $3 per no. South Pacific Regional Environment Programme, P.O. Box 240, Apia, Western Samoa. TEL 685-21929. FAX 686-20231. **Document type:** monographic series.

614.7 333.7 WS
S P R E P TOPIC REVIEW. 1983. irreg., no.34, 1988. South Pacific Regional Environment Programme, P.O. Box 240, Apia, Western Samoa.

614.7 333.7 WS
S P R E P TRAINING REPORTS. 1987. irreg., no.3, 1988. South Pacific Regional Environment Programme, P.O. Box 240, Apia, Western Samoa.

613.1 JA
SABO. (Text in Japanese) 1976. q. Sabo Jisuberi Gijutsu Senta, 3-4, Ichigaya Sadohara-cho, Shinjuku-ku, Tokyo 162, Japan.

SAFETY AND HEALTH; the international safety, health and environmental magazine. see *OCCUPATIONAL HEALTH AND SAFETY*

SAFETY RESOURCES; safety and environmental news for employers. see *OCCUPATIONAL HEALTH AND SAFETY*

614.7 UK
SAFETYMATE. 1978. q. £70. International Labmate Ltd., 12 Alban Park, Hatfield Rd., St. Albans AL4 0JJ, England. TEL 0727-55574. Ed. Mike Patisson. adv.; bk.rev. circ. 13,061. **Document type:** trade publication.

363.739 BE ISSN 0775-3691
SAMSOM MILIEU & BEDRIJF. French edition: Samsom Environnement et Gestion (ISSN 0776-8982) (Supplement avail.) (Text in Flemish) 1987. s-m. 3510 BEF. C E D Samsom (Subsidiary of: Wolters Samsom Belgie n.v.), Kouterveld 14, B-1831 Diegem, Belgium. TEL 32-2-7231111. index.
Description: Explores the latest laws, activities and studies relevant to environmental protection.

354 CN
HC117.S3
SASKATCHEWAN. DEPARTMENT OF THE ENVIRONMENT AND RESOURCE MANAGEMENT. ANNUAL REPORT. 1973. a. free. Department of the Environment and Resource Management, Education and Communication Services, 3211 Albert St., Regina, SK S4S 5W6, Canada. TEL 306-787-2700. FAX 306-787-3941. illus.; stat. circ. 400. **Document type:** government publication.
Former titles: Saskatchewan. Department of the Environment and Public Safety. Annual Report; Saskatchewan. Department of the Environment. Annual Report (ISSN 0317-4611)
Description: Compiles the department's managerial and financial accomplishments for the noted year.

SATSANG. see *AGRICULTURE*

SAVANNA; a journal of the environmental & social sciences. see *SOCIAL SCIENCES: COMPREHENSIVE WORKS*

614.7 551.48 US
SAVE THE HARBOR - SAVE THE BAY NEWSLETTER. 1986. q. membership. Save the Harbor - Save the Bay, 25 W. St., 4th Fl., Boston, MA 02111. Ed. Beth Nicholsen. circ. 1,200. (back issues avail.) **Document type:** newsletter.
Description: Covers the organization's related issues, plus Boston Harbor & Mass. Bay issues, activities, and events.

SCAN. see *AGRICULTURE — Crop Production And Soil*

SCHWEIZERISCHE ZEITSCHRIFT FUER OBST UND WEINBAU. see *BEVERAGES*

614.7 II
SCIENCE AND ENVIRONMENT. s-a. Rs.80($20) to individuals; institutions Rs.160($44). M. Abdula Munim, Ed. & Pub., Wahid Manzil, Civil Lines, Aligarh 202 001, India.

614.7 FR
SCIENCE ET CHANGEMENT PLANETAIRES, SECHERESSE. q. 340 F. to individuals; institutions 540 F.; students 245 F. John Libbey Eurotext, 6 rue Blanche, 92120 Montrouge, France. TEL 1-47-35-85-52. FAX 1-46-57-10-09. (Subscr. to: A T E I, 23-25 rue Fernand Combette, 93100 Montreuil sous Bois, France. TEL 48-59-58-11. FAX 48-59-57-99) **Document type:** academic/scholarly publication.
Description: For those who work to fight drought and its physical, human, economic and social consequences.

614.7 NE ISSN 0048-9697
RA565 CODEN: STENDL
THE SCIENCE OF THE TOTAL ENVIRONMENT; an international journal for scientific research into the environment and its relationship with man. 1972. 48/yr. (in 16 vols.; 3 nos./vol.) fl.4416($2387) (effective 1994). Elsevier Science B.V., P.O. Box 211, 1000 AE Amsterdam, Netherlands. TEL 31-20-5803911. FAX 31-20-5803598. TELEX 18582 ESPA NL. (Subscr. in U.S. and Canada to: Elsevier Science Inc., Box 882, Madison Sq. Sta., New York, NY 10159-0882. TEL 212-989-5800. FAX 212-633-3990) Eds. E.I. Hamilton, J.O. Nriagu. adv.; bk.rev.; charts; illus.; index. (also avail. in microform from UMI) **Indexed:** Acid Pre.Dig., Acid Rain Abstr., Acid Rain Ind., ASCA, Biol.Abstr., Biotech.Abstr., C.I.S. Abstr., Chem.Abstr., Curr.Adv.Biochem., Curr.Adv.Ecol.Sci., Curr.Cont., Dairy Sci.Abstr., Deep Sea Res.& Oceanogr.Abstr., Dok.Arbeitsmed., Energy Ind., Energy Info.Abstr., Energy Rev., Environ.Abstr., Environ.Per.Bibl. (1972-), Excerp.Med., Field Crop Abstr., Food Sci.& Tech.Abstr., Forest.Abstr., Geo.Abstr., GeoRef., Ind.Med., Ind.Vet., Mid.East: Abstr.& Ind., Nutr.Abstr., Ocean.Abstr., Pollut.Abstr., Potato Abstr., Rice Abstr., Risk Abstr., Sel.Water Res.Abstr., Soils & Fert., Vet.Bull., W.R.C.Inf. **Document type:** academic/scholarly publication.
—BLDSC (8165.030000); EI; Faxon; UnCover; SWETS; CASDDS. **CCC.**
Description: Publishes research into man-made changes in the environment, especially disturbances of the natural levels and distribution of chemical elements and compounds and the impact of this on the living world. Particular emphasis is given to applications of environmental chemistry to nutrition, pollution control, environmental medicine, planning and policy.
Refereed Serial

614.7 340 IT
SCIENZA, DIRITTO E ECONOMIA DELL'AMBIENTE. 6/yr. Edizioni Giuridico Scientifiche s.r.l., Via G. Donizetti 37, 20122 Milan, Italy. TEL 2-79-41-46. FAX 2-760-09-444. Ed. Ennio Alessio Mizzau. circ. 5,500.

613.1 551.46 CN ISSN 1011-1603
SEA WIND. 1987. q. $25 to individuals; institutions $50. Ocean Voice International, 2883 Otterson Dr., Ottawa, ON K1V 7B2, Canada. TEL 613-990-2207. FAX 613-521-4205. Ed. Don E. McAllister. adv.: Page Can.$1000. bk.rev.; index. circ. 150. (back issues avail.) **Document type:** bulletin.
Description: Covers diversity of marine life and its conservation, protection of marine ecosystems, environmental impacts and practical solutions and the sustainable, equitable harvesting of marine resources with local community management.

SEEVOEGEL. see *BIOLOGY — Ornithology*

613.1 GW
▼**SEIBT UMWELT TECHNIK.** 1992. a. DM.32. Seibt Verlag GmbH, Leopoldstr. 208, 80804 Munich, Germany. TEL 089-360903-0. FAX 089-364317. circ. 8,000. **Document type:** directory.
●Also available online.
Also available on CD-ROM.

SEIBUTSU KANKYO CHOSETSU/ENVIRONMENT CONTROL IN BIOLOGY. see *BIOLOGY*

628.5 614 JA ISSN 0037-1025
CODEN: STKADC
SEIKATSU TO KANKYO/LIFE AND ENVIRONMENT.* (Text in Japanese) 1956. m. Nihon Kankyo Eisei Senta - Japan Environmental Sanitation Center, 10-6 Yotsuya, Kami-cho, Kawasaki-ku, Kawasaki-shi 210, Japan. Ed. Kazumi Kuroda. adv.; charts; illus.; index. circ. 10,000. **Indexed:** Chem.Abstr.
—BLDSC (8219.713000); CASDDS.

SHANDI YANJIU/MOUNTAIN RESEARCH. see *EARTH SCIENCES — Geology*

614.7 CC ISSN 1000-3975
CODEN: SHUKE9
SHANGHAI HUANJING KEXUE/SHANGHAI ENVIRONMENTAL SCIENCES. (Text in Chinese, table of contents in English) 1982. m. Y12. (Shanghai Huanjing Baohu Ju - Shanghai Environmental Protection Bureau), Shanghai Huanjing Kexue Zazhishe, 508, Qinzhou Lu, Shanghai 200233, People's Republic of China. TEL 021-4365379. (Dist. outside China by: Guoji Shudian - China International Book Trading Corp., P.O. Box 399, P.R.C.) Ed. Chen Jiangtao. **Document type:** academic/scholarly publication.
—BLDSC (8254.589230); CASDDS.

614.7 US
SHARE THE EARTH NEWSLETTER. 1976. 4/yr. $10. Jim Morris, Ed. & Pub., Box 831, Boulder, CO 80306. TEL 303-444-6430. bk.rev. circ. 3,000.

614.7 CC ISSN 1000-0933
QH540
SHENGTAI XUEBAO/ACTA ECOLOGICA SINICA. (Text in Chinese; summaries in English) 1981. q. $63.60. (Zhongguo Shengtaixue Xuehui - Ecological Society of China) Science Press, Marketing and Sales Department, 16 Donghuangchenggen Beijie, Beijing 100707, People's Republic of China. TEL 4010642. FAX 4012180. TELEX 210247-SPBJ-CN. adv.; bk.rev. circ. 6,000. **Indexed:** Hort.Abstr., Rice Abstr.
Description: Contains original papers describing research on ecology, especially those dealing with new perspectives on ecology, or those contributing to the modernization of China.
Refereed Serial

614.7 CC ISSN 1000-4890
SHENGTAIXUE ZAZHI/JOURNAL OF ECOLOGY. (Text in Chinese) bi-m. Zhongguo Shengtaixue Xuehui - Chinese Society of Ecology, 72, Wenhua Lu, Shenyang, Liaoning 110015, People's Republic of China. TEL 483329. Ed. Gao Zhengmin.

SHEPARD'S ENVIRONMENTAL LIABILITY IN COMMERCIAL TRANSACTIONS. see *LAW*

614.7 JA
SHINOBAZU DAYORI/NEWS OF SHINOBAZU. (Text in Japanese) 1976. irreg. 1000 Yen. Shinobazu Shizen Kansatsukai - Society of Natural Observation in Shinobazu, c/o Kiyoshi Ogawa, Ed., 1-59 Ueno Koen, Taito-ku, Tokyo 110, Japan. circ. 250.

ENVIRONMENTAL STUDIES

500   JA
SHIZEN KANSATSUKAI KAIHO. (Text in Japanese) q. Shizen Kansatsukai, c/o Mr. Okubo, 2-4 Yotsuya, Shinjuku-ku, Tokyo 160, Japan.
    Description: Contains news of this association for the observation of nature.

SHIZUOKA GENSHIRYOKU DAYORI. see *ENERGY — Nuclear Energy*

SICHERHEIT IN CHEMIE UND UMWELT. see *CHEMISTRY*

614.7   CC   ISSN 1001-3644
TD171.5.C62   CODEN: SIHUEF
SICHUAN HUANJING/SICHUAN ENVIRONMENT. (Text in Chinese; abstracts in English) 1979. q. $40. (Sichuan Research Institute of Environmental Protection) Sichuan Huanjing Bianjibu, 18 Renmin Nanlu 4 Duan (Section 4), Chengdu, Sichuan 610041, People's Republic of China. TEL 580473. (Co-sponsors: Sichuan Environmental Sciences Society, Sichuan Science and Technology Information Network of Environmental Protection) Ed. Zhan Yongdong. adv.; bk.rev. circ. 2,050. **Document type:** academic/scholarly publication.
    Description: Publishes national and local policies, laws and regulations on environmental protection and introduces the development of environmental sci-tech both at home and abroad.

SIERRA. see *CONSERVATION*

SIERRA ATLANTIC. see *CONSERVATION*

SIERRA REPORT. see *CONSERVATION*

614.7   AT   ISSN 0314-3155
SIMPLY LIVING.* 1983. bi-m. Aus.$35. Front Publishers, 78 Renwick St., Redfern, N.S.W. 2016, Australia. Ed. Samantha Trenoweth. adv.; bk.rev.; film rev. circ. 35,000. (back issues avail.)

614.7   SI   ISSN 0217-5487
SINGAPORE. MINISTRY OF THE ENVIRONMENT. ANNUAL REPORT. (Text in English) 1972. a. S.$18 (effective 1991). Ministry of the Environment, Environment Bldg., 40 Scotts Rd., Singapore 0922, Singapore. FAX 065-7319866. illus.; circ. controlled. **Document type:** government publication.

SMALLHOLDER. see *AGRICULTURE*

SOCIETY & ANIMALS; social scientific studies of the human experience of other animals. see *ANIMAL WELFARE*

614.7   300   UK   ISSN 0894-1920
HC10   CODEN: SNREEI
SOCIETY AND NATURAL RESOURCES. bi-m. £100($169) Taylor & Francis Ltd., Rankine Rd., Basingstoke, Hants RG24 8PR, England. TEL 0256-840366. FAX 0256-479438. TELEX 858540. Eds. D.R. Field, R.J. Burdge. **Indexed:** Environ.Abstr., Environ.Per.Bibl. (1990-), Irr.& Drain.Abstr., Soils & Fert., Soyabean Abstr., World Agri.Econ.& Rural Sociol.Abstr. **Document type:** academic/scholarly publication.
—BLDSC (8319.192500); Faxon; UnCover. **CCC.**
    Description: Provides knowledge about natural resource management issues, on biological and physical changes resulting from acid rain, biological and genetic diversity in worldwide agriculture as well as water resource degradation.
    Refereed Serial

628   320   US   ISSN 1062-9599
▼**SOCIETY & NATURE;** the international journal of political ecology. 1992. 3/yr. $25 (effective Jan. 1993). Aigis Publications, 1449 W. Littleton Blvd., Ste. 200, Littleton, CO 80120. TEL 303-730-6232. FAX 303-798-6568. Ed. Takis Fotopoulos. adv. contact: Cassandra Medrano. bk.rev./ circ. 1,000 (paid). (back issues avail.) **Document type:** bulletin.
—CCC.
    Description: Provides a comprehensive forum for dialogue between social ecologists, eco-socialists, feminists, radical greens and activists in the land-based and indigenous movements.

SOFT DRINK RECYCLER. see *BUSINESS AND ECONOMICS*

SOFT TECHNOLOGY; technology for a sustainable future. see *CONSERVATION*

SOLAR MIND. see *TECHNOLOGY: COMPREHENSIVE WORKS*

628   US   ISSN 0038-1128
TD795
SOLID WASTE REPORT; resource recovery, recycling, collection, disposal. 1970. w. $500 (effective Sep. 1992). Business Publishers, Inc., 951 Pershing Dr., Silver Spring, MD 20910-4464. TEL 301-587-6300. FAX 301-585-9075. Ed. Ruhan Memishi. bk.rev. (looseleaf format) **Document type:** newsletter.
●Also available online. Vendor(s): NewsNet (EV20).
—CCC.
    Description: For waste managers, collectors, transporters, site operators, equipment vendors, regulators and consultants. Covers municipal, commercial, agricultural, and nonhazardous industrial refuse; generation, collection, transportation, processing, resource recovery, recycling and ultimate disposal.

SOUTH AFRICAN GEOGRAPHER/SUID-AFRIKAANSE GEOGRAAF. see *GEOGRAPHY*

614.7   AT
SOUTH AUSTRALIA. DEPARTMENT OF HOUSING AND URBAN DEVELOPMENT. ADELAIDE STATISTICAL DIVISION. LAND MONITORING REPORT. LAND SALES, PRICES, LAND DIVISION AND LAND STOCKS STATISTICS. 1980. q. Aus.$10. Department of Housing and Urban Development, Adelaide Statistical Division, G.P.O. Box 667, Adelaide, S.A. 5001, Australia. TEL 618-207-2000. FAX 618-207-2050. Ed. Ian McQueen. circ. 200. **Document type:** government publication.
    Former titles: South Australia. Department of Environment and Planning. Adelaide Statistical Division. Land Monitoring Report. Land Sales, Prices, Land Division and Land Stock Statistics (ISSN 0726-1926); South Australia. Department of Environment and Planning. Land Monitoring Report.

614.7   AT
SOUTH AUSTRALIA. DEPARTMENT OF HOUSING AND URBAN DEVELOPMENT. FORECAST PRODUCTION AND USAGE OF RESIDENTIAL ALLOTMENTS FOR PRIVATE PURPOSES. irreg. Aus.$15. Department of Housing and Urban Development, G.P.O. Box 667, Adelaide, S.A. 5001, Australia. TEL 618-207-2000. FAX 618-207-2050. **Document type:** government publication.
    Formerly: South Australia. Department of Environment and Planning. Forecast Production and Usage of Residential Allotments for Private Purposes (ISSN 1030-4320)

614.7   AT
SOUTH AUSTRALIA. DEPARTMENT OF HOUSING AND URBAN DEVELOPMENT. METROPOLITAN ADELAIDE DEVELOPMENT PROGRAM. 1984. irreg. Aus.$15. Department of Housing and Urban Development, G.P.O. Box 667, Adelaide, S.A. 5001, Australia. TEL 618-207-2000. FAX 618-207-2050. Ed. Terry Bell. circ. 500. **Document type:** government publication.
    Formerly: South Australia. Department of Environment and Planning. Metropolitan Adelaide Development Program.

SOUTH CAROLINA ENVIRONMENTAL COMPLIANCE UPDATE. see *LAW*

SOUTH CAROLINA OUT-OF-DOORS. see *CONSERVATION*

SOUTHERN SIERRAN. see *CONSERVATION*

614.7   JA
SOZO NO SEKAI/WORLD OF THE CREATION. (Text in Japanese) 1971. q. 3400 Yen. Shogakukan Inc., 3-1, 2-chome, Hitotsubashi, Chiyoda-ku, Tokyo, Japan. FAX 03-3230-0956. Ed. Shigeto Maeshiba.
    Description: Opinion magazine for well-educated Japanese with high incomes.

SPAIN. INSTITUTO NACIONAL DE INVESTIGACIONES AGRARIAS. COMUNICACIONES. SERIE: RECURSOS NATURALES. see *CONSERVATION*

614.7   SP
SPAIN. INSTITUTO NACIONAL PARA LA CONSERVACION DE LA NATURALEZA. MONOGRAFIAS. 1974. irreg. (exchange basis). Instituto Nacional para la Conservacion de la Naturaleza, Gran via San Francisco 35, Madrid 5, Spain. bibl.; charts; illus. circ. 1,000. (back issues avail.) **Indexed:** Aqua.Sci.& Fish.Abstr., Biol.Abstr., Chem.Abstr., Curr.Cont., Wild Life Rev., Zoo.Rec. **Document type:** monographic series.

614.7   JA   ISSN 0915-6690
SPEAKING OUT. (Text in English) 1989. a. Toyota Motor Corporation, International Public Affairs Division, 1-4-18, Koraku, Bunkyo-ku, Tokyo 112, Japan. FAX 03-3817-9017. circ. 13,000. **Document type:** monographic series.
    Description: Provides a public forum for discussion of international issues such as the quality of life in the 1990s and global environmental protection.

SPORTS TURF BULLETIN. see *AGRICULTURE — Crop Production And Soil*

SPORTS TURF RESEARCH INSTITUTE. JOURNAL. see *AGRICULTURE — Crop Production And Soil*

614.7   US   ISSN 0172-6161
SPRINGER SERIES ON ENVIRONMENTAL MANAGEMENT. 1979. irreg. price varies. Springer-Verlag, 175 Fifth Ave., New York, NY 10010. TEL 212-460-1500. FAX 212-473-6272. (Also: Berlin, Heidelberg, Tokyo and Vienna) Ed. Dr. Robert DeSanto. (reprint service avail. from ISI) **Document type:** monographic series.

STANFORD ENVIRONMENTAL LAW JOURNAL. see *LAW*

353.00   US   ISSN 0275-2271
HC110.E5
STATE - E P A AGREEMENTS. ANNUAL REPORT. a. U.S. Environmental Protection Agency, Program Evaluation Division, 401 M St., S.W., Washington, DC 20460. TEL 202-655-4000. (Orders to: National Technical Information Service, 5285 Port Royal Rd., Springfield, VA 22161. TEL 703-487-4650. FAX 703-321-8547) **Document type:** government publication, corporate report.

531.64 614.7   US
STATEWATCH. vol.3, 1980. 6/yr. $20. Minnesota Public Interest Research Group, 2512 Delaware St., S.E., Minneapolis, MN 55414-3432. TEL 612-376-7554. Ed. Lisa Doerr. adv.; bk.rev.; illus. circ. 40,000. (tabloid format)
    Formerly: M P I R G State Watch.

614.7   JA
STATISTICAL TABLES OF PUBLIC NUISANCE, TOKYO. 1970. biennial. 520 Yen. Tokyo Metropolitan Research Institute for Environmental Protection, 7-5, Shinsuna 1-Chome, Koto-Ku, Tokyo 136, Japan.

628.53   GW   ISSN 0039-0771
TD881   CODEN: STRHAV
STAUB, REINHALTUNG DER LUFT. (Text in English, German) 1950. m. DM.398($249) (Verein Deutscher Ingenieure, Kommission Reinhaltung der Luft) Springer-Verlag, Heidelberger Platz 3, 14197 Berlin, Germany. TEL 030-8207-1. FAX 030-8214091. (Subscr. in N. America to: Springer-Verlag New York, Inc., 44 Hartz Way, Secaucus, NJ 07096-2491. TEL 201-348-4033. FAX 201-348-4505) Eds. K. Grefen, K. Justel. adv.; bk.rev.; abstr.; charts; illus.; pat.; index. circ. 2,400. **Indexed:** Abstr.Hyg., API Abstr., API Catal., API Hlth.& Environ., API Oil., API Pet.Ref., API Pet.Subst., API Transport., Art & Archaeol.Tech.Abstr., Br.Ceram.Abstr., C.I.S. Abstr., Chem.Abstr., Chem.Eng.Abstr., Curr.Cont., Energy Ind., Energy Info.Abstr., Eng.Ind., Excerp.Med., Met.Abstr., Risk Abstr., T.C.E.A, Trop.Dis.Bull. **Document type:** academic/scholarly publication.
—BLDSC (8459.010000); EI; SWETS; UMI; CASDDS. **CCC.**
    Description: Publishes original research in air quality control and related fields.
    Refereed Serial

STEAM AND STONE. see *HISTORY — History Of North And South America*

STRAHLENKOMMISSION. VEROEFFENTLICHUNGEN. see *ENERGY — Nuclear Energy*

STRATEGIC PLANNING FOR ENERGY AND THE ENVIRONMENT. see *ENERGY*

ENVIRONMENTAL STUDIES 2437

614.7 UK ISSN 0957-6517
STREETWISE; magazine of urban studies and environmental education. 1971. q. £15.50 to individuals; institutions £22.50. National Association for Urban Studies (NAUS), Lewis Cohen Urban Studies Centre, University of Brighton, 68 Grand Parade, Brighton BN2 2JY, England. TEL 0273-673416. FAX 0273-679179. Ed. Richard Welsh. adv.: B&W page £200. bk.rev.; charts; illus. circ. 1,000. (also avail. in microfilm from UMI) **Indexed:** C.I.J.E., Cont.Pg.Educ., Geo.Abstr. **Document type:** bulletin.
—BLDSC (8474.108300).
Formerly (until 1989): B E E - Bulletin of Environmental Education (ISSN 0045-1266)
Description: News and comment about urban policy issues and curriculum development in environmental education in Britain and worldwide.

STUDIA OECOLOGICA. see *BIOLOGY*

502 NE ISSN 0166-1116
CODEN: SENSDA
STUDIES IN ENVIRONMENTAL SCIENCE. 1978. irreg., vol.58, 1994. price varies. Elsevier Science B.V., Books Division, P.O. Box 211, 1000 AE Amsterdam, Netherlands. TEL 31-20-5803911. FAX 31-20-5803705. TELEX 18582 ESPA NL. (Subscr. in U.S. and Canada to: Elsevier Science Inc., Box 882, Madison Sq. Sta., New York, NY 10159. TEL 212-989-5800) **Indexed:** Chem.Abstr., W.R.C.Inf. **Document type:** monographic series.
—BLDSC (8490.531000); CASDDS. **CCC.**
Refereed Serial

574.5 PL ISSN 0324-8666
STUDIES IN HUMAN ECOLOGY. (Text in English) 1973. a. Polska Akademia Nauk, Instytut Ekologii, Dziekanow Lesny k-Warszawy, 05-092 Lomianki, Poland. TEL 48-22-513-046. FAX 48-22-513-100. Ed. Napoleon Wolanski.
Description: Publishes reports of original research on all aspects of human ecology, theoretical papers and review articles.

STUDIES IN NATURAL PRODUCTS CHEMISTRY. see *CHEMISTRY*

SUARA SAM; Malaysia's leading environmental newspaper. see *CONSERVATION*

614.7 SJ
SUDAN ENVIRONMENT. 1981. 3/yr. University of Khartoum, Institute of Environmental Studies, Box 321, Khartoum, Sudan. Ed. M. Tag el Seed.

628.44 JA ISSN 0385-907X
SUIRI JIKKEN SENTA HOKOKU/ENVIRONMENTAL RESEARCH CENTER. BULLETIN. (Text in Japanese) 1977. a. exchange basis. Tsukuba Daigaku, Suiri Jikken Senta - University of Tsukuba, Environmental Research Center, 1-1, Tennodai 1-chome, Tsukuba-shi, Ibaraki-ken 305, Japan. TEL 81-298-53-2532. FAX 81-298-53-2530. Ed. Kazuo Kotoda. **Document type:** academic/scholarly publication, bulletin.
Description: Contains papers on all aspects of environmental studies with emphasis on meteorological, hydrological, geomorophorogical and ecological researches.

614 US
SUPERFUND WEEK. 1987. w. $470 (foreign $500). Pasha Publications Inc., 1616 N. Ft. Myer Dr., Ste. 1000, Arlington, VA 22209-3107. TEL 703-528-1244. FAX 703-528-1253. Ed. Jeff Stanfield. **Document type:** newsletter.
●Also available online. Vendor(s): Data-Star, DIALOG Information Services, Inc., NewsNet (EV22).
—**CCC.**
Formerly (until 1992): Superfund (ISSN 0892-2985)
Description: Reports on Superfund litigation cases, innovative cleanup methods and costs, cleanup standards and noncompliance penalties.

614.7 IS ISSN 0333-6697
QH540
SVIVOT/ENVIRONMENTS; semi-annual on questions in environmental education. 1981. s-a. $16. Ben Gurion College, Unit for Developing Programs in Environmental Education, Cooperative of Sdeh-Boker College, Sde-Boker 84990, Israel. TEL 972-7-565720. FAX 972-7-558352. (Co-sponsor: Israel Academy of Sciences and Humanities) Ed. Ezra Orion. circ. 400.

SYLVANIAN. see *CONSERVATION*

SYSTEMS APPROACHES FOR SUSTAINABLE AGRICULTURAL DEVELOPMENT. see *AGRICULTURE*

TAKAHAMA GENSHIRYOKU HATSUDENJO KANKYO HOSHANO KANSHI KEKKA HOKOKUSHO/TAKAHAMA ATOMIC POWER PLANT. ENVIRONMENT MONITORING REPORT. see *ENERGY — Nuclear Energy*

614.7 US
TAKING SIDES: CLASHING VIEWS ON CONTROVERSIAL ENVIRONMENTAL ISSUES. irreg., 4th ed., 1991. $12.95. Dushkin Publishing Group, Inc., Sluice Dock, Guilford, CT 06437-9989. TEL 203-453-4351. FAX 203-453-6000. Ed. Theodore D. Goldfarb; Pub. Lan Nielsen. illus. **Document type:** academic/scholarly publication.

TALKING LEAVES. see *EDUCATION — Teaching Methods And Curriculum*

628.168 AT
TASMANIA. HOBART REGIONAL WATER BOARD. ANNUAL REPORT. 1963. a. free. Hobart Regional Water Board, P.O. Box 1060, Glenorcht, Tas., Australia. TEL 002-336533. FAX 002-739205.
Formerly: Tasmania. Metropolitan Water Board. Report. (ISSN 0082-2094)

TASMANIAN CONSERVATIONIST. see *CONSERVATION*

TASMANIAN NATURALIST. see *BIOLOGY*

614.7 US ISSN 1058-0905
TD899.P3
TECHNICAL ASSOCIATION OF THE PULP AND PAPER INDUSTRY. ENVIRONMENTAL CONFERENCE PROCEEDINGS (YEAR). a. Technical Association of the Pulp and Paper Industry, Inc., Technology Park-Atlanta, Box 105113, Atlanta, GA 30348. TEL 404-446-1400. FAX 404-446-6947. **Indexed:** Corros.Abstr. **Document type:** proceedings.
Refereed Serial

614.7 540 DK ISSN 0903-2606
GC1080 CODEN: TMESEX
TECHNIQUES IN MARINE ENVIRONMENTAL SCIENCES. (Text in English) 1987. irreg., no.16, 1991. DKK 40 per issue. International Council for the Exploration of the Sea, Palaegade 2-4, DK-1261 Copenhagen K, Denmark. FAX 33-93-4215. TELEX 22498 ICES DK. Ed. J. Pawlak. circ. 500. (back issues avail.) **Document type:** monographic series.
—BLDSC (8745.216700); CASDDS.

TENNESSEE ENVIRONMENTAL LAW LETTER. see *LAW*

620.85 IT ISSN 0394-3283
TERRA; rivista di scienze ambientale e territoriali. 1987. a. L.60000. Patron Editore, Via Badini 12, Quarto Inferiore 40127 Bologna, Italy. TEL 051-767003. Ed. Augusto Cagnardi.

614.7 910 SZ ISSN 1011-5196
TERRA GRISCHUNA - GRAUBUENDEN; Zeitschrift fuer buendner Natur, Kultur und Freizeit. (Text in German; summaries in Italian, Romansch) 1942. bi-m. 59.70 SFr.($33.15) Terra Grischuna Verlag, Talholzstr. 2, CH-4103 Bottmingen, Switzerland. TEL 061-4010011. FAX 061-4015005. adv.; bk.rev. circ. 24,000. (back issues avail.) **Document type:** consumer publication.

614.7 IT
TERRE ACQUE MONTAGNE. 1990. irreg., no.2, 1991. price varies. Edizioni di Storia e Letteratura s.r.l., Via Lancellotti 18, 00186 Rome, Italy. TEL 65-40-556. FAX 06-6872567.

TEVA VA-ARETZ. see *CONSERVATION*

333.7 US
TEXAS. NATURAL RESOURCES INFORMATION SYSTEM. NEWSLETTER. 1976. q. free. Natural Resources Information System, Box 13231, Austin, TX 78711. TEL 512-463-8337. FAX 512-475-2053. Ed. Laverne Willis. circ. 500. **Document type:** government publication, newsletter.

TEXAS ENVIRONMENTAL LAW LETTER. see *LAW*

614.7 342 US ISSN 1055-2561
TEXAS INDUSTRY ENVIRONMENTAL ALERT. 1988. 22/yr. $345. Environmental Compliance Reporter, Inc., 3202 W. Anderson Lane, Ste. 208-170, Austin, TX 78757. TEL 800-766-6904. Ed. Duggan Flanakin. (back issues avail.)
Description: Provides information regarding changes in environmental law.

620.85 615.9 II
THIRD WORLD SCIENCE & ENVIRONMENT PERSPECTIVES. 1989. q. Rs.80 to individuals (foreign $20); institutions Rs.120 (foreign $25); students Rs.60 (foreign $15). Centre for Science Technology and Environmental Policy Studies, C-5, Jangpura Extension, New Delhi 110 014, India. Ed. Ashok Raj.
Description: Features research articles in various aspects of science and environment policies in the Third World countries.

TIDE. see *CONSERVATION*

614.7 333.91 US
TIDINGS (BOSTON). q. $25 membership. Friends of the Boston Harbor Islands, Inc., Box 9025, Boston, MA 02114. TEL 617-523-8386. Ed. Robert Scenna. circ. 800. **Document type:** newsletter.
Description: Contains information on upcoming events, history and anecdotes about the Boston Harbor Islands State Park.

TIERFREUND; die Jugendzeitschrift fuer Tier-, Natur- und Umweltschutz. see *CHILDREN AND YOUTH — For*

620.85 333.7 UY
TIERRA AMIGA. 1991. q. Amigos de la Tierra de America Latina y el Caribe, Avda. Millan 4113, 12900 Montevideo, Uruguay. TEL 35-62-65. FAX 38-16-40.

613.1 UK ISSN 0967-3458
▼**TIGER EYE.** 1992. q. free. Natural Environment Research Council, Institute of Terrestrial Ecology, Bush Estate, Penicuik, Midlothian EH26 OAB, Scotland. TEL 031-445-4343. FAX 031-445-3943. Eds. Graham Bell, Thomas Murray. circ. 1,200. (back issues avail.) **Document type:** government publication, newsletter.

614.7 II ISSN 0970-9703
TISGLOW. (Text in English) 1990. s-a. Rs.200 (foreign $25). Tata Energy Research Institute, 9 Jor Bagh, New Delhi 110 003, India. TEL 462-3983. FAX 91-11-4621770. TELEX 31-61593 TERI IN. Ed. B. Anil Kumar. bk.rev.; abstr.; bibl. circ. 1,000. **Indexed:** Energy Info.Abstr. **Document type:** academic/scholarly publication.
—EI.
Description: Contains reviews and articles on developments in global warming and climate change research of interest to policy makers, scientists and technologists.

614.7 AT
TODAY (WARRIEWOOD);* the environment magazine. bi-m. Australian Hi-Fi & Specialist Magazines Group Pty. Ltd., Unit 6, 5 Vuko Pl., Warriewood, N.S.W. 2102, Australia. Ed. June McGovan. circ. 40,000.

TOPICS IN ENVIRONMENTAL HEALTH. see *BIOLOGY*

614.7 028.5 NR ISSN 1115-0351
TORTOISE; the conservation magazine. 1989. q. £N10. Nigerian Conservation Foundation, Plot 5, 5, Moseley Rd., P.O. Box 74638, Victoria Island, Lagos, Nigeria. TEL 633663. FAX 6864717. Eds. A.A. Mohammed, A.S. Noibi.

614.7 US ISSN 1055-7571
TD194
TOTAL QUALITY ENVIRONMENTAL MANAGEMENT. 1991. q. $175 (foreign $225). Executive Enterprises Publications Co., Inc., 22 W. 21st St., 10th Fl., New York, NY 10010-6904. TEL 212-645-7880. FAX 212-645-1160. Ed. Jane G. Bensahel.
—BLDSC (8870.272000); UMI. **CCC.**
Description: Discusses the unique application of total quality management to the environmental issues facing business and industry today.

TOYOTA; environmental programs and activities. see *TRANSPORTATION — Automobiles*

ENVIRONMENTAL STUDIES

TRACE SUBSTANCES IN ENVIRONMENTAL HEALTH. see *ENVIRONMENTAL STUDIES — Toxicology And Environmental Safety*

TRACES (JACKSON). see *CLUBS*

TRAILHEAD. see *LEISURE AND RECREATION*

TRANSPORT RETORT. see *TRANSPORTATION*

TREELINES. see *FORESTS AND FORESTRY*

TRENDS (YEAR); a compendium of data on global change. see *METEOROLOGY*

TRENDS IN ECOLOGY AND EVOLUTION. see *BIOLOGY*

TRENDS IN ECOLOGY AND EVOLUTION (REFERENCE EDITION). see *BIOLOGY*

614.7 350 330.9   IT
TRENTINO; rivista della provincia autonoma di Trento. (Supplement avail.: Quaderni) 1963. m. (10/yr.). L.5000($3) Provincia Autonoma di Trento, Piazza Dante, 15, 38100 Trento, Italy. TEL 0461-895371. FAX 0461-8954712. TELEX 400492 PA TN I. Ed. Franco Battisti. circ. 40,000.

614.7 100   CN   ISSN 0832-6193
TRUMPETER; journal of ecosophy. 1983. q. Can.$20. (Canadian Ecophilosophy Network) Lightstar Press, Box 5853, Stn. B, Victoria, BC V8R 6S8, Canada. TEL 604-598-7004. FAX 604-598-9901. Ed. Alan R. Drengson. bk.rev.; film rev.; bibl.; illus. circ. 850. (back issues avail.) Indexed: Environ.Per.Bibl. (1992-).
   Description: Dedicated to the exploration of and contributions to a new ecological consciousness and the practice of forms of life inbued with ecosophy (ecological wisdom).

613.1 340   US   ISSN 1047-6857 K24
TULANE ENVIRONMENTAL LAW JOURNAL. 1987. 2/yr. $20. Tulane University School of Law, 6108 Freret St., Joseph Merrick Jones Hall, New Orleans, LA 70118. TEL 504-865-5309. FAX 504-865-6748. Ed.Bd. circ. 350. **Document type:** academic/scholarly publication.
   ●Also available online. Vendor(s): Mead Data Central, Inc., West Services, Inc.
   —BLDSC (9070.250000).

TURKISH JOURNAL OF ENGINEERING AND ENVIRONMENTAL SCIENCES/TURK MUHENDISLIK VE CEVRE BILIMLERI DERGISI. see *ENGINEERING*

613.1   US
TWO'S NEWS. 1982. m. $6. Technocracy, Inc., Section 2, Reg. Div. 11833, 435 E. Market St., Long Beach, CA 90805. TEL 310-428-4915. Ed. A. Adams. circ. 100. (looseleaf format; back issues avail.)
   Description: Educates members about the environment.

U C A T NEWS AND VIEWS. (University of California, Davis) see *TECHNOLOGY: COMPREHENSIVE WORKS*

614.7   UK   ISSN 0268-7402
U K CENTRE FOR ECONOMIC AND ENVIRONMENTAL DEVELOPMENT BULLETIN. 1984. bi-m. £15 (foreign £20). U K Centre for Economic and Environmental Development, 3E King's Parade, Cambridge CB2 1SJ, England. TEL 0223-67799. FAX 0223-67794. Ed. Justine Harbinson. adv.; bk.rev.; charts; illus.; cum.index 1984-1994. circ. 5,000. (back issues avail.) **Document type:** bulletin.
   Description: Economic analysis of environmental issues.

614.7   UN
U N E P INFORMATION. (Text in English) 1975. irreg., no.86, 1983. United Nations Environment Programme, Information Service, Box 30552, Nairobi, Kenya.

613.1 340   GW
U P R - UMWELT- UND PLANUNGSRECHT. m. DM.332. Verlagsgruppe Jehle - Rehm, Einsteinstr. 172, 81675 Munich, Germany. TEL 089-416006-0. FAX 089-4706998. Ed. Joachim Kormann. **Document type:** bulletin.

614.7 340   US
U S ENVIRONMENTAL LAWS. irreg., latest 1991 ed. $58. B N A Books (Subsidiary of: The Bureau of National Affairs, Inc.), 1231 25th St., N.W., Washington, DC 20037. TEL 202-833-7470; 800-372-1033. FAX 202-833-7490. (Subscr. to: BNA Books Distribution Center, 300 Raritan Canter Parkway, Box 7816, Edison, NJ 08818-7816. TEL 908-225-1900. FAX 908-417-0482) Ed. Wallis E. McClain.

UMI TO ANZEN. see *EARTH SCIENCES — Oceanography*

UMWELT; Immissionsschutz - Abfall - Gewaesserschutz. see *ENVIRONMENTAL STUDIES — Pollution*

333.7   AU
UMWELT AKTUELL. bi-m. S.120. Oswald Moebius Verlag, Amerlingstr. 19, A-1060 Vienna, Austria. Ed. Erwin H. Aglas. adv.

613.1   SZ
UMWELT INFORMATION. q. 45 SFr. Schaffhauserstr. 125, CH-8057 Zurich, Switzerland. TEL 01-3629490. FAX 01-3629413. bk.rev. circ. 2,500. **Document type:** academic/scholarly publication.

613.1   AU
UMWELT SCHRIFTENREIHE FUER OEKOLOGIE UND ETHOLOGIE. 1985. irreg., vol.20, 1993. Verein fuer Oekologie und Umweltforschung, Glasergasse 20-3, A-1090 Vienna, Austria. TEL 02214-8561. FAX 02214-3331. **Document type:** academic/scholarly publication, monographic series.

613.1   GW
UMWELT-SERVICE. q. DM.10. (Institut der Deutschen Wirtschaft) Deutscher Instituts Verlag GmbH, Postfach 510670, 50942 Cologne, Germany. TEL 0221-3708341. FAX 0221-3708191. **Document type:** bulletin.
   Formerly: Umweltreport Intern.

614.7   GW   ISSN 0941-2026 CODEN: UTAKEF
UMWELT TECHNOLOGIE AKTUELL. 1990. 6/yr. DM.104 (students DM.52). G I T Verlag GmbH, Roesslerstr. 90, 64293 Darmstadt, Germany. TEL 06151-8090-0. FAX 06151-809045. Ed. Ernst Giebeler. adv.: B&W page DM.5580, color page DM.7815; trim 185 x 260; adv. contact: Marita Eckardt. circ. 16,500. **Document type:** trade publication.
   —BLDSC (9135.158800); CASDDS.
   Formerly: Supplement Umweltanalytik - Umweltschutz.

UMWELT UND TECHNIK; Zeitschrift fuer angewandte Umweltschutz. see *BUSINESS AND ECONOMICS — Investments*

614.7   GW
UMWELTBUNDESAMT. JAHRESBERICHT. 1975. a. Umweltbundesamt, Zentrale Fachbibliothek, Postfach 330022, 14191 Berlin, Germany. TEL 030-8903-2610. FAX 030-89032285. TELEX 183756. Ed. Holger Brackemann. circ. 15,000. **Document type:** government publication.

614.   GW   ISSN 0341-1206
UMWELTMAGAZIN; Fachzeitschrift fuer Umwelttechnik in Industrie und Kommune. 1971. m. DM.156. Vogel Verlag und Druck KG, Max-Planck-Str. 7-9, 97082 Wuerzburg, Germany. TEL 0931-4182145. FAX 0931-4182640. (Subscr. to: Vogel Verlag, 97064 Wuerzburg, Germany; Dist. in U.S. by: Vogel Europublishing, Inc., 20092 Gibbs Dr., Sonora, CA 95370. TEL 209-533-3555. FAX 209-533-9555) Ed. J. Jobst. adv.: B&W page DM.5680, color page DM.7460; trim 270 x 190. circ. 18,000 (controlled). Indexed: Dok.Arbeitsmed., Key to Econ.Sci. **Document type:** consumer publication.
   —BLDSC (9083.330000); SWETS. **CCC.**
   Formerly: U - das Technische Umweltmagazin (ISSN 0173-363X)

UMWELTSCHUTZ. see *PUBLIC HEALTH AND SAFETY*

628   SZ
UMWELTTECHNIK. 1966. m. 75 Fr. (Schweizerische Vereinigung fuer Gesundheitstechnik - Association Suisse de Technique Sanitaire) Cicero Verlag Ag, Spindelstr. 2, Postfach, CH-8021 Zurich, Switzerland. TEL 01-488-8400. Ed. P. Schaetzle. index. circ. 3,100. Indexed: Chem.Abstr., Excerp.Med., W.R.C.Inf.
   Former titles: Umweltschutz Gesundheitstechnik; (until vol.11, no.1, 1977): Gesundheitstechnik (ISSN 0435-852X)

614.7   AT
UNDERWOOD PUBLICATIONS. ISSUES. 1987. q. Aus.$20.95. Underwood Publications, P.O. Box 489, Bayswater 3153, Australia. TEL 03-764-1110. Ed. Gary Underwood. cum.index: 1987-1989. circ. 1,000. (back issues avail.) Indexed: Environ.Per.Bibl.
   Description: Examines the environmental and human issues of Australia and the world. Written for secondary education students and teachers.

614   FR   ISSN 0069-2603
UNION DES INDUSTRIES ET ENTREPRISES DE L'EAU ET DE L'ENVIRONNEMENT. ANNUAIRE. 1963. a. 50 F. 10 rue Washington, 75008 Paris, France. TEL 45-63-70-40. FAX 42-25-96-41. adv.
   Formerly (until 1991): Chambre Syndicale Nationale des Entreprises et Industries de l'Hygiene Publique. Annuaire.

613.1   UN   ISSN 0956-9324 GE1
UNITED NATIONS ENVIRONMENT PROGRAMME. ENVIRONMENTAL DATA REPORT. 1987. a. £50. (United Nations Environment Programme) Basil Blackwell Ltd., 108 Cowley Rd., Oxford OX4 1JF, England. TEL 0865-791100. FAX 0865-791347. TELEX 837022-OXBOOK-G. (also avail. in microfiche from CIS) Indexed: IIS.
   —BLDSC (3791.434700).

614.7   UN
UNITED NATIONS ENVIRONMENT PROGRAMME. EVALUATION REPORT (YEAR). a. United Nations Environment Programme, P.O. Box 30552, Nairobi, Kenya.

614.7   UN
UNITED NATIONS ENVIRONMENT PROGRAMME. FEATURE. Variant title: U N E P Feature. (Text in English) 1976. irreg. United Nations Environment Programme, Information Service, P.O. Box 30552, Nairobi, Kenya. Indexed: W.R.C.Inf.

614.7   UN
UNITED NATIONS ENVIRONMENT PROGRAMME. GOVERNING COUNCIL. REPORT ON THE WORK OF ITS SESSION. (Text in English) a. United Nations Environment Programme, Governing Council, Information Service, P.O. Box 30552, Nairobi, Kenya. TEL 2-333930. FAX 2-520711.

614.7   UN
UNITED NATIONS ENVIRONMENT PROGRAMME. THE STATE OF THE ENVIRONMENT; REPORT OF THE EXECUTIVE DIRECTOR. Title varies; State of the Environment: Selected Topics; Report of the Executive Director. (Text in English) a. United Nations Environment Programme, Information Service, P.O. Box 30552, Nairobi, Kenya. (also avail. in microfiche from CIS) Indexed: IIS.

UNITED NATIONS UNIVERSITY. WORK IN PROGRESS. see *BUSINESS AND ECONOMICS — International Development And Assistance*

614.7   US
U.S. COAST GUARD. ENVIRONMENTAL PROTECTION NEWSLETTER. 1973. q. U.S. Coast Guard, Commandant G-WEP-4, 2100 Second St., S.W., Washington, DC 20593. TEL 202-267-2823. bibl.; illus.; circ. controlled. **Document type:** newsletter.

628 630   US
U.S. DEPARTMENT OF AGRICULTURE. WETLANDS RESERVE PROGRAM. REPORT TO CONGRESS. a. U.S. Department of Agriculture, Agricultural Stabilization and Conservation Service, Box 2415, Washington, DC 20013. TEL 202-720-7093. (Subscr. to: Superintendent of Documents, U.S. Government Printing Office, Box 317954, Pittsburgh, PA 15250-7954. TEL 202-783-3238. FAX 202-512-2233) **Document type:** government publication.

ENVIRONMENTAL STUDIES 2439

614.7   US
U.S. ENVIRONMENTAL PROTECTION AGENCY. OFFICE OF RESEARCH AND DEVELOPMENT. PROGRAM GUIDE. 1977? a. free. U.S. Environmental Protection Agency, Office of Research and Development, Washington, DC 20460. TEL 513-569-7562. FAX 513-569-7566. (Avail. through: Superintendent of Documents, U.S. Government Printing Office, Box 371954, Pittsburgh, PA 15250-7954. TEL 202-783-3238. FAX 202-512-2233) circ. 12,000. (also avail. in microfilm; reprint service avail.) **Document type:** government publication.

U.S. NATIONAL OCEANIC AND ATMOSPHERIC ADMINISTRATION. REPORT TO THE CONGRESS ON OCEAN POLLUTION, OVERFISHING, AND OFFSHORE DEVELOPMENT. see *ENVIRONMENTAL STUDIES — Pollution*

U.S. OFFICE OF TECHNOLOGY ASSESSMENT. REPORTS. FOOD AND RENEWABLE RESOURCES PROGRAM. see *AGRICULTURE*

628   US
U.S. OFFICE OF TECHNOLOGY ASSESSMENT. REPORTS. OCEANS AND ENVIRONMENT PROGRAM. irreg. price varies. U.S. Office of Technology Assessment, Publication Distribution, U.S. Congress, 600 Pennsylvania Ave., S.E., Washington, DC 20510-8025. TEL 202-224-8996. FAX 202-228-6009. E-mail: PUBREQUEST@OTA.GOV. (Dist. by: Superintendent of Documents, U.S. Government Printing Office, Box 371954, Pittsburgh, PA 15250-7954. TEL 202-783-3238. FAX 202-512-2250; And: National Technical Information Service, 5285 Port Royal Rd., Springfield, VA 22161. TEL 703-487-4650. FAX 703-321-8547) (also avail. in microfiche from CIS; back issues avail.; reprint service avail. from CIS) **Document type:** monographic series, government publication.
    Formerly: U.S. Office of Technology Assessment. Reports. Oceans Program.
    Description: Reports provide technical information on pollution to oceans, groundwater, and the atmosphere.

UNIVERSIDAD DE MURCIA. ANALES DE BIOLOGIA. SECCION BIOLOGIA AMBIENTAL. see *BIOLOGY*

UNIVERSITY OF CALGARY. ARCHAEOLOGICAL ASSOCIATION. ARCHAEOLOGICAL CONFERENCE. PROCEEDINGS. see *ARCHAEOLOGY*

614 301.32   TZ   ISSN 0084-960X
H62.5.T36
UNIVERSITY OF DAR ES SALAAM. BUREAU OF RESOURCE ASSESSMENT AND LAND USE PLANNING. ANNUAL REPORT. 1968. a. free. University of Dar es Salaam, Bureau of Resource Assessment and Land Use Planning, Box 35097, Dar es Salaam, Tanzania. Ed. Adolfo Mascarenhas. circ. 250.

614 301.32   TZ   ISSN 0084-9626
UNIVERSITY OF DAR ES SALAAM. BUREAU OF RESOURCE ASSESSMENT AND LAND USE PLANNING. RESEARCH PAPER. 1968. irreg., no.60, 1979. $50. University of Dar es Salaam, Bureau of Resource Assessment and Land Use Planning, Box 35097, Dar es Salaam, Tanzania. Ed. Adolfo Mascarenhas. circ. 200.

614 301.32   TZ   ISSN 0084-9634
UNIVERSITY OF DAR ES SALAAM. BUREAU OF RESOURCE ASSESSMENT AND LAND USE PLANNING. RESEARCH REPORT. 1969. irreg., no.39, 1979 (N.S.). price varies. University of Dar es Salaam, Bureau of Resource Assessment and Land Use Planning, Box 35097, Dar es Salaam, Tanzania. Ed. Adolfo Mascarenhas. circ. 200. **Indexed:** Geo.Abstr.

UNIVERSITY OF DELAWARE. DISASTER RESEARCH CENTER. DISSERTATIONS. see *PUBLIC HEALTH AND SAFETY*

UNIVERSITY OF DELAWARE. DISASTER RESEARCH CENTER. FINAL PROJECT REPORTS. see *PUBLIC HEALTH AND SAFETY*

UNIVERSITY OF DELAWARE. DISASTER RESEARCH CENTER. MISCELLANEOUS REPORTS. see *PUBLIC HEALTH AND SAFETY*

UNIVERSITY OF DELAWARE. DISASTER RESEARCH CENTER. PRELIMINARY PAPERS. see *PUBLIC HEALTH AND SAFETY*

UNIVERSITY OF DELAWARE. DISASTER RESEARCH CENTER. REPORT SERIES. see *PUBLIC HEALTH AND SAFETY*

574.5   US   ISSN 0094-9205
QH105.G4
UNIVERSITY OF GEORGIA. INSTITUTE OF ECOLOGY. ANNUAL REPORT. Key Title: Annual Report - University of Georgia, Institute of Ecology. Cover title: Ecology. 1972. a. free. University of Georgia, Institute of Ecology, Athens, GA 30602-2202. TEL 706-542-2968. FAX 706-542-6040. Ed. Janice Sand. bibl. circ. 1,200. **Document type:** corporate report.

UNIVERSITY OF MANCHESTER. DEPARTMENT OF PLANNING AND LANDSCAPE. OCCASIONAL PAPERS. see *HOUSING AND URBAN PLANNING*

613.1   AT
UNIVERSITY OF NEWCASTLE. BOARD OF ENVIRONMENTAL STUDIES. PROCEEDINGS OF SEMINARS. irreg. Aus.$25. University of Newcastle, Board of Environmental Studies, Newcastle, N.S.W. 2308, Australia. FAX 049-216905. **Document type:** proceedings.

614.7   AT
UNIVERSITY OF NEWCASTLE. BOARD OF ENVIRONMENTAL STUDIES. RESEARCH PAPERS. 1973. a. price varies. University of Newcastle, Board of Environmental Studies, Newcastle, N.S.W. 2308, Australia. FAX 049-216905. Ed.Bd. bk.rev.; bibl.; charts. circ. 200. **Document type:** academic/scholarly publication.

614.7   US
UNIVERSITY OF NORTH DAKOTA. INSTITUTE FOR ECOLOGICAL STUDIES. RESEARCH REPORT. 1971. irreg., no.30, 1981. price varies. Institute for Ecological Studies, University of North Dakota, Box 8278, University Sta., Grand Forks, ND 58202. TEL 701-777-2851. Ed. S.S. Vanderpool. circ. 200. **Indexed:** Wild Life Rev.
    Refereed Serial

614.7 530   JA   ISSN 0917-1630
                                                                                                                                                                       CODEN: ARROAA
UNIVERSITY OF OSAKA PREFECTURE. RESEARCH INSTITUTE FOR ADVANCED SCIENCE AND TECHNOLOGY. ANNUAL REPORT/OSAKA-FURITSU-DAIGAKU FUZOKUKENKYUSHO NENPO. (Text in English, Japanese) 1960. a. exchange basis. University of Osaka Prefecture, Research Institute for Advanced Science and Technology, 1-2 Gakuen-cho, Sakai, Osaka 593, Japan. TEL 81-722-36-2221. FAX 81-722-36-3876. Ed. Tatsuo Tabata. circ. 800. **Indexed:** Biol.Abstr., Chem.Abstr., INIS Atomind. **Document type:** academic/scholarly publication.
—BLDSC (1410.250000).
    Former titles (until 1991): Osaka (Prefecture). Radiation Research Institute. Annual Report (ISSN 0474-7879); Osaka (Prefecture). Radiation Center. Annual Report.

614.7   AT   ISSN 1034-1412
UNIVERSITY OF TASMANIA. CENTRE FOR ENVIRONMENTAL STUDIES. OCCASIONAL PAPER. 1976. irreg. price varies. University of Tasmania, Centre for Environmental Studies, G.P.O. Box 252C, Hobart, Tas. 7001, Australia. FAX 002-202989. Ed. John Todd. circ. 200. (back issues avail.) **Indexed:** AESIS, Biol.Abstr. **Document type:** academic/scholarly publication.
—BLDSC (3791.685000).
    Former titles (until 1989): Environmental Studies Occasional Paper (ISSN 0810-4395); (until 1981): University of Tasmania. Centre for Environmental Studies. Occasional Paper (ISSN 0810-6606)

UNIVERSITY OF TASMANIA. CENTRE FOR ENVIRONMENTAL STUDIES. WORKING PAPERS. see *CONSERVATION*

333.77   CN   ISSN 0713-8466
UNIVERSITY OF WATERLOO. SCHOOL OF URBAN AND REGIONAL PLANNING. WORKING PAPERS SERIES. 1977. irreg., no.25, 1988. price varies. University of Waterloo, School of Urban and Regional Planning, Waterloo, ON N2L 3G1, Canada. TEL 519-885-1211. FAX 519-746-2031. circ. 100.
    Formerly (until 1987): University of Waterloo. Department of Geology. Working Papers Series.

UNIVERZA V LJUBLJANI. FILOZOFSKA FAKULTETA. ODDELEK ZA GEOGRAFIJO. DELA. see *GEOGRAPHY*

UNSER NEUSTADT. see *CONSERVATION*

UPWELLINGS. see *WATER RESOURCES*

333.7   UK   ISSN 0967-4764
HT243.G7
URBAN FOCUS. 1981-19?? q. £10.50 (Europe £16; elsewhere £18). Civic Trust, 17 Carlton House Terr., London SW1 5AW, England. TEL 44-71-930-0914. FAX 44-71-321-0180. Ed. Iain Sharpe. adv.; bk.rev.; bibl.; illus.; index. circ. 10,000. **Indexed:** Art.Hosp.& Tour., Geo.Abstr.
    Formerly (until 1992): Heritage Outlook (ISSN 0261-1988); Supersedes (as of no.82, Dec. 1980): Civic Trust News (ISSN 0306-090X)
    Description: Covers urban planning, the environment, urban and rural regeneration, new legislation work of local amenity societies, architecture, and heritage.

URBAN WILDLIFE NEWS. see *BIOLOGY*

628.44   NE   ISSN 0042-1715
V A M MEDEDELINGEN. 1946. 4/yr. free. N.V. V A M, Postbus 6500, 1200 HK Hilversum, Netherlands. TEL 31-35-897300. FAX 31-35-856400. Ed. H.M. Swinkels. illus.; stat. circ. 9,000. **Document type:** corporate report
    Description: Covers the activities of the company concerning waste removal, treatment, recycling, soil pollution, and new product research.

614.7   DK   ISSN 0109-4130
VAND OG MILJOE. 1984. q. DKK 480. (Keemp & Lauritzen, Vandteknisk Afdelning) Forlaget John Vaboe A-S, Hartmannsvej 47-49, DK-2920 Charlottenlund, Denmark. TEL 39-40-80-00. FAX 39-40-82-80.

614.7 627   US   ISSN 0093-6332
VANDERBILT UNIVERSITY. DEPARTMENT OF ENVIRONMENTAL AND WATER RESOURCES ENGINEERING. TECHNICAL REPORTS. 1962. irreg., no.43, 1984. price varies. Vanderbilt University, Department of Civil & Environmental Engineering, Box 6304, Sta. B, Nashville, TN 37235. TEL 615-322-2720. Ed. Edward L. Thackston. circ. 100. **Document type:** academic/scholarly publication.
    Refereed Serial

VATTEN/WATER; tidskrift foer vattenvaard/periodical on water conservation. see *WATER RESOURCES*

VEGETATION HISTORY AND ARCHAEOBOTANY. see *BIOLOGY — Botany*

VEREIN FUER WASSER-, BODEN- UND LUFTHYGIENE. SCHRIFTENREIHE. see *CONSERVATION*

613.1   US
VERMONT ENVIRONMENTAL REPORT. bi-a. Vermont Natural Resources Council, 9 Bailey Ave., Montpelier, VT 05602. TEL 802-223-2328. FAX 802-223-0287. **Indexed:** Environ.Abstr. **Document type:** newsletter, bulletin.

620.85 352.7   US
VERMONT NATURAL RESOURCES COUNCIL. BULLETIN. s-a. $35 membership. Vermont Natural Resources Council, 9 Bailey Ave., Montpelier, VT 05602. TEL 802-223-2328. FAX 802-223-0287.
    Formerly: Vermont Growth Management News.
    Description: Covers statewide water-quality, forest-planning issues. Also covers legislative issues.

VEROEFFENTLICHUNGEN FUER NATURSCHUTZ UND LANDSCHATSPFLEGE IN BADEN-WUERTTEMBERG. see *CONSERVATION*

614.7   SP   ISSN 0210-3605
QL84.4.S7
VIDA SILVESTRE. 1971. 2/yr. 1500 ptas. (foreign 2400 ptas.)(effective 1992). Ministerio de Agricultura, Pesca y Alimentacion, Instituto Nacional para la Conservacion de la Naturaleza, Centro de Publicaciones, Paseo de la Infanta Isabel 1, 28071 Madrid, Spain. TEL 91-227-39-39. (I.N.C.N. addr.: Gran Via de San Francisco, 35-41, 28005 Madrid, Spain. TEL 91-347-61-44) Ed. Ramon Hernandez. bibl.; illus. circ. 6,000. (back issues avail.)

VIE MANCELLE; revue mensuelle de l'Association Culturelle et Touristique du Maine. see *TRAVEL AND TOURISM*

ENVIRONMENTAL STUDIES

340 US
VIEWPOINTS. 1983. q. $20. Scenic America, 21 DuPont Circle, N.W., Washington, DC 20036. TEL 202-833-4300. FAX 202-833-4304. bk.rev. circ. 5,000. (back issues avail.)
Formerly: Sign Control News.
Description: Presents summary of news, legal decisions, and other developments regarding sign control, view protection, and other aesthetic regulations.

VIRGINIA WILDLIFE FEDERATION. FEDERATION RECORD. see *CONSERVATION*

614.7 US
VISION (STAMFORD). 1967. 4/yr. free. Keep America Beautiful, Inc., Mill River Plaza, 9 W. Broad St., Stamford, CT 06902-3734. TEL 203-323-8987. Ed. John W. Kazzi. circ. 2,000. (controlled).
Former titles (until 1986): Keep America Beautiful; C C S Bulletin; K A B Reports.
Description: Covers the litter prevention and waste handling programs of the organization, its local affiliates and member companies.

628 US
▼VITAL SIGNS (YEAR). 1992. a. $10.95 (hardcover $19.95). Worldwatch Institute, 1776 Massachusetts Ave., N.W., Washington, DC 20036. TEL 202-452-1999. (also avail. in diskette format) **Document type:** monographic series.

614.7 IT
VIVEREVERDE NOTIZIE. 1977. m. L.4000. Vivereverde s.a.s., Via Gadames 128, 20151 Milan, Italy. TEL 02-301-37-77. Ed. Roberto de Mattei. adv. circ. 25,000.

VÖGELKUNDLICHE BERICHTE AUS NIEDERSACHSEN. see *BIOLOGY — Ornithology*

614.7 IO
VOICE OF NATURE. (Editions in English, Indonesian) 1987. m. Rps.5000($3) (effective 1991). Pt. Suara Alam, Jln. Palmerah Barat 31, Jakarta 10270, Indonesia. TEL 549-5358. FAX 62-21-549-5360. Ed. Linus Simanjuntak. circ. 12,000.
Description: Covers conservation, environment, peoples, culture, nature and wildlife.

613.1 333.7 II ISSN 0971-2666
W W F INDIA QUARTERLY. (Text in English) 1990. q. World Wide Fund for Nature - India, 172-B, Lodhi Estate, New Delhi 110 003, India.

W W F NEWS. (World Wide Fund For Nature) see *CONSERVATION*

WADDEN SEA NEWSLETTER. see *CONSERVATION*

613.1 UK
WARMER BULLETIN. 1984. q. free. World Resource Foundation, Bridge House, 97-101 High St., Tonbridge, Kent TN9 1DP, England. TEL 0732-368333. FAX 0732-368337. Ed. Maggie Thurgood. bk.rev.; abstr.; bibl.; charts; illus.; stat. circ. 65,000. (back issues avail.) **Indexed:** Environ.Abstr. **Document type:** bulletin.

614.7 US ISSN 0899-1405
WARY CANARY; a news network for allergics, "sensitive birds," & environmental health advocates. 1986. q. $20 (Canada $24; elsewhere $27). Wary Canary Press, Box 2204, Ft. Collins, CO 80522. TEL 303-224-0083. Eds. Suzanne & Ed Randegger. circ. 750. **Indexed:** Environ.Abstr. **Document type:** consumer publication.
Description: Covers preventive self-care and recovery from environmentally and chemically induced illness, toxic responses syndromes and allergies, including geographic relocation for health, sources and resources of nontoxic materials, dietary strategies and nontraditional medical alternatives.

WASHINGTON ENVIRONMENTAL COMPLIANCE UPDATE. see *LAW*

614.7 333 US ISSN 0014-9136
WASHINGTON ENVIRONMENTAL PROTECTION REPORT; twice-monthly letter on contracting opportunities, legislation, research & development, and rules & regulations for the nation's environmental programs. 1966. s-m. $190. Callahan Publications, Box 1173, McLean, VA 22101. TEL 703-356-1925. FAX 703-356-9614. Ed. Vincent F. Callahan, Jr. bk.rev.; charts. (processed) **Document type:** trade publication.
Formerly: Federal Program Letter.

WASHINGTON LAND USE AND ENVIRONMENTAL PRACTICE. see *LAW*

WASHINGTON STATE ENVIRONMENTAL POLICY ACT; a legal and policy analysis. see *LAW*

613.1 SZ
WASSER - BODEN - LUFT UMWELTSCHUTZ. 1963. 10/yr. 68 SFr. Verlag Laupper AG, Postfach 659, CH-4142 Muenchenstein 1, Switzerland. TEL 061-4113646. FAX 061-4119020. Ed. Barbara Hartmann. circ. 6,000.

WASSER, LUFT UND BODEN; unabhaengige Zeitschrift fuer Wasserwirtschaft, Luftreinhaltung, Abfallverwertung und Umwelttechnik. see *ENVIRONMENTAL STUDIES — Pollution*

WASTE MINIMIZATION & RECYCLING REPORT; hazardous & solid waste. see *ENVIRONMENTAL STUDIES — Waste Management*

WATER, AIR AND SOIL POLLUTION; an international journal of environmental pollution. see *ENVIRONMENTAL STUDIES — Pollution*

614.7 US ISSN 1044-9493
TD365 CODEN: WAETEJ
WATER ENVIRONMENT & TECHNOLOGY. (Supplement avail.: a. Buyer's Guide and Yearbook) 1989. 13/yr. $144 (foreign $187). Water Environment Federation, 601 Wythe St., Alexandria, VA 22314-1994. TEL 703-684-2400. FAX 703-684-2492. Ed. Elizabeth Ford Wilkins. adv.: B&W page $2770, color page $3820; trim 8 3/16 x 10 7/8. **Indexed:** Environ.Abstr., Environ.Per.Bibl (1992-), Sel.Water Res.Abstr. —BLDSC (9270.004300); El; Faxon; UnCover; SWETS; UMI. **CCC**.
Supersedes in part (in 1989): Water Pollution Control Federation. Journal (ISSN 0043-1303); Which was formerly (until 1960): Sewage and Industrial Wastes (ISSN 0096-364X); (until 1950): Sewage Works Journal (ISSN 0096-9362)

613.1 JA
WATER REPORT. (Text in English) 1991. q. $100. M Y U, Scientific Publishing Division, 2-32-3 Sendagi, Bunkyo-ku, Tokyo 113, Japan. Ed. Junko Nakanishi. **Document type:** academic/scholarly publication.

WATERFRONT WORLD SPOTLIGHT. see *HOUSING AND URBAN PLANNING*

WERK UND ZEIT. see *ARCHITECTURE*

614.7 387 GW ISSN 0043-2849
DIE WESER. 1922. 4/yr. DM.39. Weserbund e.V., Erste Schlachtpforte 1, 28195 Bremen, Germany. TEL 0421-325868. FAX 0421-323289. Ed. Ralf Heinrich. adv.; bk.rev.; bibl.; charts; illus.; index; circ. 1,200 (controlled). **Document type:** bulletin.
Description: Covers important aspects of the Weser, Werra and Fulda regions of Germany, including ecology, economy, energy, traffic, tourism and history.

614.7 CN ISSN 0715-4275
WEST COAST ENVIRONMENTAL LAW RESEARCH FOUNDATION NEWSLETTER. (Text in English) 1977. q. Can.$20. West Coast Environmental Law Research Foundation (WCELRF), 1001-207 W. Hastings, Vancouver, BC V6B 1H7, Canada. TEL 604-684-7378. FAX 604-684-1312. bk.rev. circ. 600. **Document type:** newsletter.

WESTERN AUSTRALIA. ENVIRONMENTAL PROTECTION AUTHORITY. ANNUAL REPORT. see *CONSERVATION*

WESTERN GEOGRAPHICAL SERIES. see *GEOGRAPHY*

WETLANDS. see *WATER RESOURCES*

WETLANDS ECOLOGY AND MANAGEMENT. see *WATER RESOURCES*

WHALEWATCH. see *ANIMAL WELFARE*

WHAT WORKS: AN ANNOTATED BIBLIOGRAPHY OF CASE STUDIES OF SUSTAINABLE DEVELOPMENT. see *BIOLOGY — Abstracting, Bibliographies, Statistics*

WHO IS WHO IN SERVICE TO THE EARTH; people, projects, organizations, key words. see *BIOGRAPHY*

614.7 620 US ISSN 1062-6433
TD12
WHO'S WHO IN ENVIRONMENTAL ENGINEERING. 1956. a. $75. American Academy of Environmental Engineers, 130 Holiday Ct., Ste. 100, Annapolis, MD 21401. TEL 410-266-3311. FAX 410-266-7653. bk.rev. **Document type:** directory.
Formerly: American Academy of Environmental Engineers. Roster (ISSN 0065-6860)

WILD EARTH INFORMATION. see *CONSERVATION*

WILD LANDS ADVOCATE. see *CONSERVATION*

WILDERNESS. see *CONSERVATION*

614.7 634.9 AT
WILDERNESS NEWS. 1978. bi-m. Aus.$36 (foreign Aus.$71). Wilderness Society, 130 Davey St., Hobart, Tas. 7000, Australia. TEL 002-349-799. FAX 022-235-112. Ed. Howard Stringer. adv.; bk.rev. circ. 16,000.
●Also available online.
Formerly (until 1992): Wilderness (ISSN 1035-6622)
Description: Current national and international wilderness and environmental issues.

WISCONSIN. DEPARTMENT OF NATURAL RESOURCES. ANNUAL WATER QUALITY REPORT TO CONGRESS. see *WATER RESOURCES*

WISCONSIN ENVIRONMENTAL COMPLIANCE UPDATE. see *LAW*

614.7 333.7 US
WISCONSIN ENVIRONMENTAL DECADE. 1974. 4/yr. $30. Wisconsin's Environmental Decade, Inc., 122 State St., Ste. 200, Madison, WI 53703. TEL 608-251-7020. Ed. Philip Wiseley. adv.; bk.rev. circ. 20,000. **Document type:** newsletter.
Former titles: Second Decade; Eco-Bulletin.

WOHNUNG & GESUNDHEIT; Fachzeitschrift fuer oekologisches Bauen & Leben. see *ARCHITECTURE*

WOMEN AND ENVIRONMENTS. see *WOMEN'S STUDIES*

THE WORLD BANK AND THE ENVIRONMENT. see *BUSINESS AND ECONOMICS — International Commerce*

613.1 US
▼WORLD CLIMATE REVIEW. 1992. q. free. University of Virginia, Department of Environmental Sciences, Clark Hall, Charlottesville, VA 22903. Ed. Patrick Michaels. **Document type:** bulletin.

WORLD DIRECTORY OF ENVIRONMENTAL ORGANIZATIONS; a handbook of national and international organizations and programs, governmental and non-governmental, concerned with protecting the earth's resources. see *CONSERVATION*

614.7 US
WORLD ENVIRONMENT REPORT. 1974. bi-w. $468. Business Publishers, Inc., 951 Pershing Dr., Silver Spring, MD 20910-4464. TEL 301-587-6300; 800-BPI-0122. FAX 301-585-9075. Ed. Hiram Reisner. bk.rev.; bibl. (looseleaf format; back issues avail.) **Document type:** newsletter.
●Also available online. Vendor(s): NewsNet (EV29). —BLDSC (9354.827000). **CCC**.
Former titles (until 1988): Multinational Environmental Outlook (ISSN 0899-5079); (until 1987): World Environment Report (ISSN 0098-8235)
Description: Reports on environmental policies, politics and regulations all over the world.

ENVIRONMENTAL STUDIES — ABSTRACTING, BIBLIOGRAPHIES, STATISTICS

628.5 330 UK
WORLD ENVIRONMENTAL BUSINESS HANDBOOK. 2nd ed., 1993. irreg. £95($190) Euromonitor, 87-88 Turnmill St., London EC1M 5QU, England. TEL 071-541-8024. FAX 071-608-3149. (Addr. in N. America: Euromonitor International, 111 W. Washington St., Ste. 920, Chicago, IL 60602. TEL 312-541-8024. FAX 312-541-1567) **Document type:** trade publication.
Description: Examines how environmental issues affect all areas of business.

614.7 US ISSN 0094-4742
TD12
WORLD ENVIRONMENTAL DIRECTORY. 1974. irreg., latest no.6, 1991. $108. Business Publishers, Inc., 951 Pershing Dr., Silver Spring, MD 20910-4464. TEL 301-587-6300. Ed. Beverly E. Gough. adv. circ. 2,500. **Document type:** directory.
—BLDSC (9354.830000).

551.5 614.7 UN ISSN 0302-9328
WORLD METEOROLOGICAL ORGANIZATION. SPECIAL ENVIRONMENTAL REPORTS. (Subseries of: World Meteorological Organization. W M O (Publications)) 1970. irreg., latest no.16. World Meteorological Organization, 41 Av. Giuseppe Motta, CH-1211 Geneva 2, Switzerland. TEL 730-8111. (Dist. in US by: American Meteorological Society, 45 Beacon St., Boston, MA 02108. TEL 617-227-2425) illus. **Indexed:** Biol.Abstr., Meteor.& Geoastrophys.Abstr.

614.7 634.96 US
WORLD RAINFOREST REPORT. 1985. q. $25 membership. Rainforest Action Network, 450 Sansome St., Ste. 700, San Francisco, CA 94111. TEL 415-398-4404. FAX 415-398-2732. TELEX 151276475. Ed. Jim Rendon. bk.rev. circ. 35,000. (back issues avail.) **Document type:** newsletter.
Description: Reports current threats to the world's rainforests and their indigenous people, and suggests what members can do to help.

614.7 333.7 US ISSN 1042-8011
HC10 CODEN: WRRVE5
WORLD RESOURCE REVIEW. 1989. q. $72 to individuals (foreign $96.60); institutions $143 (foreign $167.60). 7501 Lemont, Box 5275, IL 60517-0275. TEL 708-910-1551. FAX 708-910-1561. Ed. Sinyan Shen. adv.; bk.rev.; charts; illus.; index. circ. 2,100. (also avail. in microform from UMI; microfilm from UMI) **Indexed:** Curr.Cont. **Document type:** trade publication.
—UnCover.
Description: Critically reviews all phases of scientific and policy activities in environment and industrial development, with a focus on the sound management of natural resources in the context of global change.

WORLD RESOURCES (YEAR). see CONSERVATION

628 US ISSN 0896-0615
CODEN: WOWAEE
WORLD WATCH. bi-m. $15 (foreign $30). Worldwatch Institute, 1776 Massachusetts Ave., N.W., Washington, DC 20036. TEL 202-452-1999. Ed. Lester R. Brown. **Indexed:** Abstr.Rural Dev.Trop., Energy Rev., Environ.Abstr., Environ.Per.Bibl. (1989-). **Document type:** academic/scholarly publication.
—BLDSC (9360.172500); CIS; Faxon; UnCover; SWETS; UMI.
Description: Discusses important worldwide economic and social issues pertaining to environmental degradation and conservation.

300 US
WORLDWATCH PAPERS. 1975. irreg., no.113, 1993. $25 (includes State of the World) (single papers $5 per no.). Worldwatch Institute, 1776 Massachusetts Ave., N.W., Washington, DC 20036. TEL 202-452-1999. circ. 5,000. (back issues avail.) **Indexed:** Biol.Abstr., Environ.Abstr., Forest.Abstr., Forest Prod.Abstr., Geo.Abstr., I D A, Popul.Ind., Rural Recreat.Tour.Abstr., World Agri.Econ. & Rural Sociol.Abstr. **Document type:** monographic series.
Description: Presents significant global ecological, social, and economic topics relating to environmental degradation and conservation.

YAMAGUCHI-KEN EISEI KOGAI KENKYU SENTA GYOSEKI HOKOKU. see PUBLIC HEALTH AND SAFETY

614.7 CC CODEN: YSXUER
YINGYONG SHENGTAI XUEBAO/CHINESE JOURNAL OF APPLIED ECOLOGY. (Text in Chinese or English) 1990. q. $120. (Zhongguo Kexueyuan, Shenyang Yingyong Shengtai Yanjiusuo - Chinese Academy of Sciences, Shenyang Institute of Applied Ecology) Science Press, Marketing and Sales Department, 16 Donghuanchengen Beijie, Beijing 100717, People's Republic of China. TEL 4018833. FAX 4012180. TELEX 210247 SPBJ CN. Ed. Shen Shanmin. **Document type:** academic/scholarly publication.
Description: Covers forest ecology, agricultural ecology, fisheries ecology, natural resource ecology, landscape ecology, and ecological engineering.

028.5 US ISSN 0886-5299
YOUR BIG BACKYARD. 1979. m. $12. National Wildlife Federation, 1400 16th St., N.W., Washington, DC 20036. TEL 202-797-6800. FAX 703-442-7332. (Subscr. to: 8925 Leesburg Pike, Vienna, VA 22184-0001. TEL 800-822-9919. FAX 703-790-4039; Dist. in Canada by: Canadian Wildlife Federation, 2740 Queensview Dr., Ottawa, ON K2B 1A2, Canada. TEL 800-563-9453) Ed. E. Gerald Bishop. illus. circ. 470,000. **Document type:** consumer publication.
Description: General science for children ages three to five, developing awareness of the environment and conservation. Includes puzzles, an activities page, and experiments to perform under the supervision of an adult.

YUSHU KOGAI BOSHI SOCHI/SUPERIOR EQUIPMENT OF POLLUTION PREVENTION. see MACHINERY

614.7 LI
ZALIOJI LIETUVA. 1989. w. Jaksto 9-127, Vilnius 232300, Lithuania. TEL (0122) 766-737. FAX 0122-766-737. Ed. Daina Karlonaite.

614.7 340 GW ISSN 0940-5178
▼**ZEITSCHRIFT FUER OEKOLOGIE UND NATURSCHUTZ.** 1992. 4/yr. DM.104 (foreign DM.112). Gustav Fischer Verlag Jena, Villengang 2, 07745 Jena, Germany. TEL 03641-27332. FAX 03641-22638. (Subscr. to: Postfach 100537, 07705 Jena, Germany) **Document type:** academic/scholarly publication.
—BLDSC (9475.615000).

614.7 GW
HC79.E5
ZEITSCHRIFT FUER UMWELTPOLITIK UND UMWELTRECHT. q. DM.306 (foreign DM.322). (International Institute for Environment and Society) Deutscher Fachverlag GmbH, Mainzer Landstr. 251, 60326 Frankfurt a.M., Germany. TEL 069-759501. FAX 069-75952999. (Subscr. to: Postfach 100606, 60006 Frankfurt a.M., Germany) Ed.Bd. circ. 400. **Document type:** bulletin.
—BLDSC (9487.381000); SWETS.
Formerly: Zeitschrift fuer Umweltpolitik (ISSN 0343-7167)

ZHIWU SHENGTAIXUE YU DIZHIWUXUE XUEBAO/ACTA PHYTOECOLOGICA ET GEOBOTANICA SINICA. see BIOLOGY — Botany

ZHIWU ZIYUAN YU HUANJING/JOURNAL OF PLANT RESOURCES AND ENVIRONMENT. see BIOLOGY — Botany

614.7 CC ISSN 1000-6923
CODEN: ZHKEEI
ZHONGGUO HUANJING KEXUE. English edition: Chinese Environmental Science (ISSN 1003-1189) (Text in Chinese) q. Chinese Society for Environmental Sciences, No.115, Xizhimennei Nanxiaojie, Beijing 100035, People's Republic of China. TEL 6066498. FAX 6020031. **Document type:** academic/scholarly publication.
—BLDSC (3180.142000); CASDDS.
Description: Discusses the major environmental problems in China. Reflects the developing tendency and the latest achievements in Chinese environmental sciences and technology fields.
Refereed Serial

ZIRAN ZIYUAN/NATURAL RESOURCES. see CONSERVATION

614.7 XO ISSN 0044-4863
ZIVOTNE PROSTREDIE. (Text in Slovak; summaries in English, German, Russian) bi-m. fl.72($14) (Slovenska Akademia Vied) Veda, Publishing House of the Slovak Academy of Sciences, Klemensova 19, 814 30 Bratislava, Slovakia. (Dist. in Western countries by: John Benjamins B.V., Amsteldijk 44, Amsterdam (Z.), Netherlands) Ed. Ludovit Weismann. **Indexed:** C.I.S. Abstr.

ZONING NEWS. see HOUSING AND URBAN PLANNING

ZYCIE GOSPODARCZE; tygodnik spoleczno-gospodarczy. see BUSINESS AND ECONOMICS

ENVIRONMENTAL STUDIES — Abstracting, Bibliographies, Statistics

A P T FOR LIBRARIES (YEAR); alternative press titles for the general reader. see BIBLIOGRAPHIES

615.9 II
ABSTRACTS OF CURRENT LITERATURE IN TOXICOLOGY. (Text in English) q. Rs.250($25) to individuals; institutions Rs.400($40). Industrial Toxicology Research Centre, Mahatma Gandhi Marg, P.O. Box 80, Lucknow 226001, U.P., India. TEL 248227. **Document type:** abstracting/indexing.
Description: Includes selected original scientific research work published in 250 journals received in ITRC library.

ABSTRACTS OF PUBLIC ADMINISTRATION, DEVELOPMENT AND ENVIRONMENT. see PUBLIC ADMINISTRATION — Abstracting, Bibliographies, Statistics

ADVANCES IN RISK ANALYSIS. see PUBLIC HEALTH AND SAFETY — Abstracting, Bibliographies, Statistics

AGRICULTURAL & ENVIRONMENTAL BIOTECHNOLOGY ABSTRACTS. see AGRICULTURE — Abstracting, Bibliographies, Statistics

614.7 016 628.53 US ISSN 0002-2497
Z5862.2.A4
AIR POLLUTION TITLES. 1965. bi-m. $120 (foreign $130); microfiche $65 (foreign $70) (effective 1993). Pennsylvania State University, Environmental Resources Research Institute, Center for Air Environment Studies, 226 Fenske Laboratory, University Park, PA 16802. TEL 814-865-1415. FAX 814-863-1696. Ed. Elizabeth Carroll. bibl.; cum.index. circ. 70. (processed; also avail. in microfiche) **Document type:** bibliography.
Description: Bibliographic guide to current research literature on air environment, including monitoring and control of air pollution, health effects, effects on agriculture, forests, toxic air contaminants, and global atmospheric processes.

614.7 011 BL
ALERTA ECOLOGIA E CIENCIAS DO AMBIENTE. 1991. m. $20. Universidade de Sao Paulo, Escola Superior de Agricultura "Luiz de Queiroz", Caixa Postal 9, 13418-900 Piracicaba, SP, Brazil. TEL 0194-29-4311. FAX 0194-33-2014. TELEX 19-1141 EALQ. **Document type:** abstracting/indexing.
Description: Gives the contents pages from 32 journals related to ecology and environmental sciences.

613.1 US
▼**AMERICAN STATISTICAL ASSOCIATION. SECTION ON STATISTICS AND THE ENVIRONMENT. PROCEEDINGS.** 1992. a. $38 to non-members; members $25. American Statistical Association, 1429 Duke St., Alexandria, VA 22314-3402. TEL 703-684-1221. FAX 703-684-2037. **Document type:** proceedings.

AQUALERT; selective dissemination of information. see WATER RESOURCES — Abstracting, Bibliographies, Statistics

AQUALINE ABSTRACTS. see WATER RESOURCES — Abstracting, Bibliographies, Statistics

AQUATIC SCIENCES & FISHERIES ABSTRACTS. PART 3: AQUATIC POLLUTION AND ENVIRONMENTAL QUALITY. see FISH AND FISHERIES — Abstracting, Bibliographies, Statistics

ENVIRONMENTAL STUDIES — ABSTRACTING, BIBLIOGRAPHIES, STATISTICS

620.85 631   NE
ATTENDERINGSBULLETIN BIBLIOTHEEK STARING-GEBOUW: LAND, BODEM, WATER. bi-m. (Dienst Landbouwkundig Onderzoek) International Institute for Land Reclamation and Improvement, Library - Staring Building, P.O. Box 45, 6700 AC Wageningen, Netherlands. TEL 31-873074751. FAX 31-8730-24812. abstr. **Document type:** abstracting/indexing.
● Also available online.
    Description: Current awareness service on land, soil and water research.

614.7 016   BE   ISSN 0379-1815
BELGIAN ENVIRONMENTAL RESEARCH INDEX. 1969. a. 300 Fr. Centre National de Documentation Scientifique et Technique - National Center for Scientific and Technical Documentation, 4 Bd. de l'Empereur, B-1000 Brussels, Belgium. TEL 02-519-56-50. FAX 02-519-56-79. TELEX 21157. Ed. L. Dooms. **Indexed:** Pollut.Abstr.
    Description: Covers articles published in Belgium or articles published by Belgian authors in foreign periodicals. Belgian patents, books, conferences, symposia and congresses are also cited.

613.1   US   ISSN 1063-6153
Z5861
BIBLIOGRAPHIC GUIDE TO THE ENVIRONMENT.* 1991. a. $165 (foreign $185). G.K. Hall & Co., c/o MacMillan Publishing Co., 866 Third Ave., 18th fl., New York, NY 10022. TEL 212-702-6789. (Orders to: MacMillan Distribution Center, 100 Front St., Box 500, Riverside, NJ 08075-7500. TEL 800-257-5755) **Document type:** bibliography.
    Description: Covers books, reports, conference papers and miscellaneous publications in the New York Public Library and the Library of Congress. Subjects include: conservation, pollution, atmospheric trends, alternative and renewable energy, waste management, public policy issues, endangered species, environmental laws and legislation.

BIODETERIORATION ABSTRACTS. see *BIOLOGY — Abstracting, Bibliographies, Statistics*

614.7   UK   ISSN 0961-7299
BOOKS ON THE ENVIRONMENT AND RELATED TOPICS. 1991. q. £25($48) Bibliographic Press, 2 Little Paddocks, Ferring, Worthing, W. Sussex BN12 5NH, England. TEL 44-903-504019. Ed. E. N. Edwards. circ. 90. **Document type:** abstracting/indexing.
    Description: Contains bibliography and index of nonserial titles published in the Roman alphabet.

614.7 660   US   ISSN 0884-7452
                 CODEN: CBEBEO
C A S BIOTECH UPDATES. ENVIRONMENTAL BIOTECHNOLOGY. s-w. $210 (effective Jan. 1994). Chemical Abstracts Service (Subsidiary of: American Chemical Society), 2540 Olentangy River Rd., Box 3012, Columbus, OH 43210-0012. TEL 614-447-3600. FAX 614-447-3713. TELEX 6842086. **Document type:** abstracting/indexing.
    Description: Covers treatment and disposal of industrial, municipal, domestic, and laboratory wastes and sewage; biochemical implications in water treatment, air pollution, and industrial hygiene.

614.7 628.53   US   ISSN 0885-0097
                 CODEN: CSRAEZ
C A SELECTS. ACID RAIN & ACID AIR. s-w. $210 (effective Jan. 1994). Chemical Abstracts Service (Subsidiary of: American Chemical Society), 2540 Olentangy River Rd., Box 3012, Columbus, OH 43210. TEL 614-447-3600. FAX 614-447-3713. TELEX 6842086. **Document type:** abstracting/indexing.
    Description: Covers occurance, causes, and effects of acidity in the atmosphere and in precipitation, including preventive measures.

540 628.53   US   ISSN 0895-5980
                 CODEN: CSAPET
C A SELECTS. AIR POLLUTION (BOOKS & REVIEWS). 1988. s-w. $210 (effective Jan. 1994). Chemical Abstracts Service (Subsidiary of: American Chemical Society), 2540 Olentangy River Rd., Box 3012, Columbus, OH 43210. TEL 614-447-3600. FAX 614-447-3713. TELEX 6842068. **Document type:** abstracting/indexing.
    Description: Covers pollution of the atmosphere by fixed and mobile sources; effects of air pollution on animals and vegetation; pollution-abatement procedures.

614.7 628.5   US   ISSN 0160-9041
                 CODEN: CSPODW
C A SELECTS. ENVIRONMENTAL POLLUTION. s-w. $210 (effective Jan. 1994). Chemical Abstracts Service (Subsidiary of: American Chemical Society), 2540 Olentangy River Rd., Box 3012, Columbus, OH 43210-0012. TEL 614-447-3600. FAX 614-447-3713. TELEX 6842086. **Document type:** abstracting/indexing.
    Description: Covers the pollution of the environment by gaseous, liquid, solid, and radioactive wastes.

C A SELECTS. INDOOR AIR POLLUTION. see *PUBLIC HEALTH AND SAFETY — Abstracting, Bibliographies, Statistics*

614.7 628.5   US   ISSN 0160-9149
                 CODEN: CSPMDQ
C A SELECTS. POLLUTION MONITORING. s-w. $210 (effective Jan. 1994). Chemical Abstracts Service (Subsidiary of: American Chemical Society), 2540 Olentangy River Rd., Box 3012, Columbus, OH 43210-0012. TEL 614-447-3600. FAX 614-447-3713. TELEX 6842086. **Document type:** abstracting/indexing.
    Description: Covers analytical techniques and equipment related to monitoring pollution of land, water, and atmosphere by solid, liquid, and gaseous waste products.

333.7 011   UK   ISSN 0955-6648
QH540
CURRENT ADVANCES IN ECOLOGICAL AND ENVIRONMENTAL SCIENCES. Diskette edition (ISSN 1350-6528) 1975. 12/yr. £675($1040) (effective 1994). Elsevier Science Ltd., Pergamon, P.O. Box 800, Kidlington, Oxford OX5 1DX, England. TEL 44-865-843000. FAX 44-865-843010. (Subscr. in U.S. and Canada to: Elsevier Science, 660 White Plains Rd., Tarrytown, NY 10591-5153. TEL 914-524-9200. FAX 914-333-2444) adv.; bk.rev.; illus.; stat.; index. circ. 1,000. (also avail. in microfilm from UMI; diskette format; reprint service avail. from UMI) **Document type:** abstracting/indexing.
● Also available online. Vendor(s): BRS Online Products (CABS).
— BLDSC (3494.062800); UMI.
    Formerly: Current Advances in Ecological Sciences (ISSN 0306-3291)
    Description: Current awareness service for biologists, ecologists and environmental scientists. Gives listings of titles of ecological papers published throughout the world classified into 61 main areas and provides a comprehensive listing of review articles.

615   UK   ISSN 0965-0512
Z6665.A1
CURRENT ADVANCES IN TOXICOLOGY. 1984. 12/yr. £395($610) (effective 1994). Elsevier Science Ltd., Pergamon, P.O. Box 800, Kidlington, Oxford OX5 1DX, England. TEL 44-865-843000. FAX 44-865-843010. (Subscr. in U.S. and Canada to: Elsevier Science, 660 White Plains Rd., Tarrytown, NY 10591-5153. TEL 914-524-9200. FAX 914-333-2444) adv.: B&W page $550, color page $1350. circ. 1,100. (also avail. in microfilm from UMI) **Indexed:** Curr.Cont. **Document type:** abstracting/indexing.
● Also available online. Vendor(s): BRS Online Products (CABS).
— BLDSC (3494.068200); UMI.
    Formerly (until 1992): Current Advances in Pharmacology and Toxicology (ISSN 0741-1685)
    Description: Provides a current awareness service in the sphere of toxicology. Gives listings of titles of toxicological papers published throughout the world, classified into 127 main subject areas, and provides a comprehensive listing of review articles.

CURRENT AWARENESS IN BIOLOGICAL SCIENCES. see *BIOLOGY — Abstracting, Bibliographies, Statistics*

614.7 016 628.5   JA   ISSN 0385-6011
CURRENT BIBLIOGRAPHY ON SCIENCE AND TECHNOLOGY: ENVIRONMENTAL POLLUTION/KAGAKU GIJUTSU BUNKEN SOKUHO. KANKYO KOGAI-HEN. (Text in Japanese) 1975. m. $1170. Japan Information Center of Science and Technology - Nihon Kagaku Gijutsu Joho Senta, 5-2 Nagata-cho, 2-chome, Chiyoda-ku, Tokyo 100, Japan. TEL 03-3581-6411. FAX 03-3581-6446. abstr.; bibl. circ. 600. **Document type:** bibliography.
● Also available online. Vendor(s): JICST.
    Formerly (until 1975): Bibliography of Environmental Pollutions.

CURRENT CONTENTS: AGRICULTURE, BIOLOGY & ENVIRONMENTAL SCIENCES. see *AGRICULTURE — Abstracting, Bibliographies, Statistics*

CURRENT INDIAN FORESTRY, ENVIRONMENT & WILDLIFE ABSTRACTS. see *FORESTS AND FORESTRY — Abstracting, Bibliographies, Statistics*

350   CN
DATABASES FOR ENVIRONMENTAL ANALYSIS: PROVINCIAL AND TERRITORIAL GOVERNMENTS. (Catalogue 11-529) irreg. $90. Statistics Canada, Publications Division, Ottawa, ON K1A 0T6, Canada. TEL 800-267-6677. FAX 613-951-1582. (also avail. in diskette format) **Document type:** government publication.
    Description: Comprehensive guide to the availability of environmental data throughout Canada.

DIRECTORY OF PUBLISHED PROCEEDINGS. SERIES P C E: POLLUTION CONTROL & ECOLOGY. see *MEETINGS AND CONGRESSES — Abstracting, Bibliographies, Statistics*

DOKUMENTATION NATURSCHUTZ UND LANDSCHAFT. see *CONSERVATION — Abstracting, Bibliographies, Statistics*

614.7 016   US   ISSN 0364-1074
E I S; digests of environmental impact statements. 1970. bi-m. $525 (foreign $575); with a. index $745 (foreign $880). Cambridge Scientific Abstracts, 7200 Wisconsin Ave., 6th Fl., Bethesda, MD 20814. TEL 301-961-6750. FAX 301-961-6720. Ed. Stuart Stern. abstr.; index. (also avail. in microfilm; magnetic tape; back issues avail.) **Indexed:** Comput.& Info.Sys., INIS Atomind. **Document type:** abstracting/indexing.
    Description: Summarizes and indexes all environmental impact statements filed with the US federal government.

614.7   US   ISSN 0190-0250
TD194.6
E I S CUMULATIVE. (Environmental Impact Statement) 1970. a. $350 (foreign $390). Cambridge Scientific Abstracts, 7200 Wisconsin Ave., 6th Fl., Bethesda, MD 20814. TEL 301-961-6700. FAX 301-961-6720.

614.7 016   US   ISSN 0196-0091
Z5863.P7
E P A PUBLICATIONS BIBLIOGRAPHY QUARTERLY ABSTRACTS BULLETIN. (Publication PB94-904200) q. $145 (Canada and Mexico $290). U.S. Environmental Protection Agency, 401 M St., S.W., Washington, DC 20460. TEL 202-655-4000. (Subscr. to: National Technical Information Service, 5285 Port Royal Rd., Springfield, VA 22161. TEL 703-487-4650. FAX 703-321-8547) abstr.; bibl. (also avail. in microfiche from CIS; reprint service avail. from CIS) **Indexed:** Amer.Stat.Ind. (1975-), MEDOC, World Text.Abstr. **Document type:** government publication, bibliography.
    Formerly: E P A Reports Bibliography Quarterly (ISSN 0360-2265)
    Description: Contains full bibliographic records of E.P.A. reports available from N.T.I.S.

614.7 604.7   US
E P I: ENVIRONMENTAL PRODUCT INDEX. 1989. q. free. P T N Publishing Corp., 445 Broad Hollow Rd., Ste. 21, Melville, NY 11747-4722. TEL 516-845-2700. FAX 516-845-7109. Ed. Judy Hogan. adv. circ. 25,050. (tabloid format; back issues avail.) **Document type:** trade publication.
    Description: Product technology information used by professionals in hazardous waste cleanup.

ENVIRONMENTAL STUDIES — ABSTRACTING, BIBLIOGRAPHIES, STATISTICS

614.7 016 628.4   CN   ISSN 0824-7528
KE3612
ECO-LOG CANADIAN POLLUTION LEGISLATION. 1972. m. Can.$994.03 (foreign Can.$1049). Southam Information and Technology Group, 1450 Don Mills, Don Mills, ON M3B 2X7, Canada. TEL 416-445-6641. FAX 416-442-2200. Ed. Mary Mancini. (looseleaf format)
   Description: Provides references to environmental legislation, regulations, guidelines and objectives arranged by province, territory and federal jurisdiction.

614.7 016 628.4   CN   ISSN 0315-0380
ECO-LOG WEEK; a report on waste management and industrial pollution control. 1972. w. (50/yr.). Can.$593.85 (foreign Can.$655). Southam Information and Technology Group, 1450 Don Mills Rd., Don Mills, ON M3B 2X7, Canada. TEL 416-445-6641. FAX 416-442-2200. TELEX 06-966612. Ed. Mary Mancini. bk.rev.; q. index. (back issues avail.) **Document type:** newsletter.
●Also available online. Vendor(s): Southam Electronic Publishing.
   Description: Covers relevant conferences and seminars, reviews the latest environmental literature and government reports, shows regular updates of government activities on a province-by-province basis.

614.7 016   UK   ISSN 0305-196X
QH540
ECOLOGICAL ABSTRACTS. 1974. 12/yr. (plus a. cumulation). £600($925) (effective 1994). Elsevier - Geo Abstracts (Subsidiary of: Elsevier Science Ltd.), Regency House, 34 Duke St., Norwich NR3 3AP, England. TEL 44-603-626327. FAX 44-603-667934. TELEX 975247 CHACOM G. (Subscr. to: Elsevier Science Ltd., Oxford Fulfilment Centre, P.O. Box 800, Kidlington, Oxford OX5 1DX, England. TEL 44-865-843000. FAX 44-865-843010; Subscr in U.S. and Canada to: Elsevier Science, 660 White Plains Rd., Tarrytown, NY 10591-5153. TEL 914-524-9200. FAX 914-333-2444) Ed. P.J. Jarvis. index. circ. 600. (back issues avail.) **Indexed:** Field Crop Abstr., Forest.Abstr., Forest Prod.Abstr., Herb.Abstr. **Document type:** abstracting/indexing.
●Also available online. Vendor(s): DIALOG Information Services, Inc. (File no.292), Orbit Search Service (GEOB).
—BLDSC (3648.850000). **CCC.**
   Description: International abstracting service for ecologists and biologists.

016 333.91 614.7   US   ISSN 0143-3296
QH540
ECOLOGY ABSTRACTS. 1975. m. $825 (foreign $985). Cambridge Scientific Abstracts, 7200 Wisconsin Ave., 6th Fl., Bethesda, MD 20814. TEL 301-961-6750. FAX 301-961-6720. Ed. Robert Hilton. adv.; bk.rev.; index. (also avail. in magnetic tape; back issues avail.) **Indexed:** Cal.Tiss.Abstr., Chemorec.Abstr., Comput.& Info.Sys., Oncol.Abstr., Pollut.Abstr. **Document type:** abstracting/indexing.
●Also available online. Vendor(s): DIALOG Information Services, Inc. (File no.76/LIFE SCIENCES COLLECTION), STN International.
Also available on CD-ROM. Producer(s): SilverPlatter Information, Inc.
—BLDSC (3650.030000).
   Formerly: Applied Ecology Abstracts (ISSN 0305-3040)
   Description: Covers the interaction of all types of organisms with their environments.

ECONOMIA MONTANA - LINEA ECOLOGICA. see *FORESTS AND FORESTRY*

620.85   CN   ISSN 1181-9707
ECOSOURCE. (Text in English) 1990. 10/yr. Can.$399($399) EcoSource, Inc., Box 1270, Guelph, Ont. N1H 6N6, Canada. TEL 519-763-8888. FAX 519-763-6202. Ed. Tony Leighton.
   Description: Surveys and condenses press and periodical reports of ecological and environmental news and developments for business and government.

ENERGIE & MILIEUSPECTRUM. see *ENERGY*

ENERGY REVIEW (SANTA BARBARA). see *ENERGY — Abstracting, Bibliographies, Statistics*

613.85   US   ISSN 1070-1818
▼**ENVIRO - NEWS DIGEST.** 1993. m. $189 (foreign $264). Butterfield Communications, Inc., Box 1119, Parker, CO 80134-9936. TEL 303-840-2214. FAX 303-840-2398. Ed. Rucker W. Burks. (back issues avail.) **Document type:** abstracting/indexing.
   Description: Contains abstracts of vital environmental technical information such as air quality, hazardous materials, recycling, solid waste, wastewater, and regulations and laws.

614.7 574 895   US
ENVIROFICHE. m. $8985 (effective 1994). Congressional Information Service, A Reed Reference Publishing Company, Part of the Reed Elsevier group, 4520 East-West Hwy., Bethesda, MD 20814-3389. TEL 301-654-1550; 800-838-8380. FAX 301-654-4033. Ed. Anila Rao Banerjee. (microfiche; back issues avail.)
   Description: Full text of the vast majority of abstracted articles in Environment Abstracts. Items on microfiche are linked to the print and electronic services through the unique accession number. Includes a listing of conferences and events.

614.7 574 895
628.4   US   ISSN 0093-3287
GF1
ENVIRONMENT ABSTRACTS. 1970. m. $1070 (effective 1994). Congressional Information Service, A Reed Reference Publishing Company, Part of the Reed Elsevier group, 4520 East-West Hwy., Bethesda, MD 20814-3389. TEL 301-654-1550; 800-638-8380. FAX 301-654-4033. Ed. Anila Banerjee. **Document type:** abstracting/indexing.
●Also available online. Vendor(s): CISTI (ENVIRO), DIMDI (ENVIROLINE), Data-Star (NVER/Acid Rain Abstracts NVAR), DIALOG Information Services, Inc. (File no.40), European Space Agency (File no.11/ENVIROLINE and File no.109/Acid Rain Abstracts), FIZ Technik (ENVIROLINE), Orbit Search Service (ENVIROLINE).
Also available on CD-ROM. Producer(s): Bowker - Reed Reference Electronic Publishing (Enviro/Energyline Abstracts PLUS).
—CCC.
   Incorporates (1985-1991): Acid Rain Abstracts (ISSN 0882-1402); **Formerly:** Environment Information Access (ISSN 0013-9181)
   Description: Addresses the impact of humankind and technology on the environment with attention to air, water, and noise pollution; solid and toxic wastes; radiological contamination; toxicological effects; control technologies; resource management; population; endangered species; and geophysical and climatic change. Information is abstracted and indexed from scientific, technical, and business journals; conference and symposium proceedings; newsletters; and academic and government reports. Includes a listing of conferences and events.

614.7 016 628.4   US   ISSN 0000-1198
Z5322.E2
ENVIRONMENT ABSTRACTS ANNUAL; a guide to the key environmental literature of the year. 1970. a. $495. Congressional Information Service, A Reed Reference Publishing Company, Part of the Reed Elsevier group, 4520 East-West Hwy., Ste. 800, Bethesda, MD 20814-3389. TEL 301-654-1550; 800-638-8380. FAX 301-654-4033. Ed. Anila Banerjee. **Document type:** abstracting/indexing.
●Also available online. Vendor(s): DIMDI, Data-Star (NVER/Acid Rain Abstracts NVAR), DIALOG Information Services, Inc. (File no.40), European Space Agency (File no.11/ENVIROLINE and File no.109/Acid Rain Abstracts), Orbit Search Service (Enviroline).
Also available on CD-ROM. Producer(s): Bowker - Reed Reference Electronic Publishing (Enviro/Energyline Abstracts PLUS).
—BLDSC (3791.095200). **CCC.**
   Incorporates (in 1990): Acid Rain Abstracts Annual (ISSN 0000-1228); Which was formerly (until 1988): Acid Rain Annual Index; Incorporates (in 1988): Environment Index (ISSN 0090-791X)
   Description: Cumulation of all abstracts and indexes from a calendar year (volume) of Environment Abstracts; also includes articles and year-end reviews of environmental issues.

613.1   US   ISSN 1063-7346
▼**ENVIRONMENTAL ENGINEERING ABSTRACTS.** 1993. m. $385 (foreign $435). Cambridge Scientific Abstracts, 7200 Wisconsin Ave., 6th Fl., Bethesda, MD 20814. TEL 301-961-6750. FAX 301-961-6720. (Co-publisher: Engineering Information, Inc.) (also avail. in magnetic tape) **Document type:** abstracting/indexing.
   Description: Gathers together the world literature pertaining to technological and engineering aspects of air and water quality, environmental safety, and alternative energy sources.

614.7   US   ISSN 0897-862X
ENVIRONMENTAL HEALTH REPORT.* 1986. m. $39. S.D. Gregory & Associates, Box 181002, Dallas, TX 75218-8002. TEL 214-357-1636. bk.rev. circ. 1,000.
   Description: Reviews over 200 publications for current information on the complex chemical environmental issues of health.

ENVIRONMENTAL INDEX. see *ENVIRONMENTAL STUDIES*

614.7 016   US
Z5863.E57
ENVIRONMENTAL PERIODICALS BIBLIOGRAPHY; a current awareness bibliography featuring citations of scientific and popular articles in serial publications in the area of the environment. 1972. bi-m. price varies. International Academy at Santa Barbara, Environmental Studies Institute, 800 Garden St., Ste. D, Santa Barbara, CA 93101-1552. TEL 805-965-5010. FAX 805-965-6071. Ed. Miriam Flacks. index. cum.index. circ. 400. (also avail. in microfilm from PMC) **Document type:** bibliography.
●Also available online. Vendor(s): DIALOG Information Services, Inc. (File no.68).
Also available on CD-ROM. Producer(s): NISC.
—CCC.
   Former titles: Environmental Periodicals Bibliography: Indexed Article Titles (ISSN 0145-3815); Environmental Periodicals: Indexed Article Titles (ISSN 0046-2306)
   Description: Covers tables of contents of more than 500 international periodicals on the environment. Includes subject areas: human ecology, air, energy, land resources, water resources, and nutrition and health.

613.1   II   ISSN 0970-7719
ENVIRONMENTAL RESOURCES ABSTRACTS. (Text in English) 1983. q. World Wide Fund for Nature - India, 172-B, Lodhi Estate, New Delhi 110 003, India. **Document type:** abstracting/indexing.

614.7 016 628.5   NE   ISSN 0300-5194
                                                   CODEN: EHPCA6
EXCERPTA MEDICA. SECTION 46: ENVIRONMENTAL HEALTH AND POLLUTION CONTROL. 1971. 10/yr. fl.1404($759) (effective 1994). Excerpta Medica (Subsidiary of: Elsevier Science B.V.), P.O. Box 548, 1000 AM Amsterdam, Netherlands. TEL 31-20-580391. FAX 31-20-5803222. TELEX 18582 ESPA NL. (Dist. by: Elsevier Science Ireland Ltd., P.O. Box 85, Limerick, Ireland. TEL 353-61-471944. FAX 353-61-472144; Subscr. in U.S. and Canada to: Elsevier Science Inc., Box 882, Madison Sq. Sta., New York, NY 10159. TEL 212-989-5800. FAX 212-633-3990) Ed.Bd. adv.; index, cum.index. **Document type:** abstracting/indexing.
●Also available online. Vendor(s): BRS Online Products, DIMDI, Data-Star, DIALOG Information Services, Inc., JICST.
Also available on CD-ROM. Producer(s): SilverPlatter Information, Inc.
—BLDSC (3835.830320). **CCC.**
   Formerly: Excerpta Medica. Section 46: Environmental Health (ISSN 0046-2268)
   Description: Covers all aspects of air, soil and water pollution, noise hindrance and radioactivity as related to the general environment.

ENVIRONMENTAL STUDIES — ABSTRACTING, BIBLIOGRAPHIES, STATISTICS

615.9 NE ISSN 0167-8353
CODEN: TXICDD
EXCERPTA MEDICA. SECTION 52: TOXICOLOGY. 1983. 20/yr. (in 2 vols.; 10 nos./vol.). fl.1954($1056) (effective 1994). Excerpta Medica (Subsidiary of: Elsevier Science B.V.), P.O. Box 548, 1000 AM Amsterdam, Netherlands. TEL 31-20-5803911. FAX 31-20-5803222. TELEX 18582 ESPA NL. (Dist. by: Elsevier Science Ireland Ltd., P.O. Box 85, Limerick, Ireland. TEL 353-61-471944. FAX 353-61-472144; Subscr. in U.S. and Canada to: Elsevier Science Inc., Box 882, Madison Sq. Sta., New York, NY 10159. TEL 212-989-5800. FAX 212-633-3990) Ed.Bd. adv.; index, cum.index. **Document type:** abstracting/indexing.
●Also available online. Vendor(s): BRS Online Products, DIMDI, Data-Star, DIALOG Information Services, Inc., JICST.
Also available on CD-ROM. Producer(s): SilverPlatter Information, Inc.
—BLDSC (3835.881500). **CCC.**
   Description: Covers the toxic mechanisms and effects of both medicinal and non-medicinal substances.

628.44 FI
FINLAND. TILASTOKESKUS. TILASTOLLISIA TIEDONANTOJA. YMPAERISTOETILASTO/FINLAND. STATISTIKCENTRALEN. STATISTISKA MEDDELANDEN. MILJOESTATISTIK/FINLAND. CENTRAL STATISTICAL OFFICE. STATISTICAL SURVEYS. ENVIRONMENTAL STATISTICS. (Text in English, Finnish, and Swedish) 1977. irreg., latest 1986. FIM 72. Tilastokeskus, Annankatu 44, SF-00100 Helsinki 10, Finland.

614.7 016 FR ISSN 0980-949X
FRANCE. SECRETARIAT D'ETAT CHARGE DE L'ENVIRONNEMENT ET DE LA QUALITE DE LA VIE. BULLETIN DE DOCUMENTATION DE L'ENVIRONNEMENT. 5/yr. 210 F. (Europe 275 F., elsewhere 375 F.). (Secretariat d'Etat Charge de l'Environnement et de la Qualite de la Vie) Documentation Francaise, 29-31 Quai Voltaire, 75340 Paris Cedex 7, France. TEL 1-40-15-70-00. FAX 40-15-72-30. TELEX 215 666 DOCFRAN. (Subscr. to: Documentation Francaise, 124 rue Henri Barbusse, 93308 Aubervillers, France. TEL 48-39-56-00. FAX 48-39-56-01) (also avail. in microfiche from DFR) **Document type:** government publication.
   Formerly: France. Ministere de la Qualite de la Vie. Bulletin de Documentation.

FRESHWATER BIOLOGICAL ASSOCIATION CURRENT AWARENESS SERVICE. see *BIOLOGY — Abstracting, Bibliographies, Statistics*

301.31 016 UK ISSN 0141-2604
Z5861
GREAT BRITAIN. DEPARTMENT OF THE ENVIRONMENT AND DEPARTMENT OF TRANSPORT. LIBRARY SERVICES. ANNUAL LIST OF PUBLICATIONS. 1971. a. price varies. Department of the Environment and Department of Transport, Publications Sales Unit, Bldg. 1, Victoria Rd., Middlesex HA4 0NZ, England. Ed. S. Perrott. bibl. circ. 2,000.
—BLDSC (1087.307000). **CCC.**
   Formerly: Great Britain. Department of the Environment. Library Services. D.O.E. Annual List of Publications.

HABITAT INTERNATIONAL; journal for the study of human settlements. see *ENVIRONMENTAL STUDIES*

613.1 CN
HUMAN ACTIVITY AND THE ENVIRONMENT. (Catalogue 11-509) irreg. Can.$35($42) Statistics Canada, Publications Division, Ottawa, ON K1A 0T6, Canada. TEL 800-267-6677. FAX 613-951-1582. **Document type:** government publication.
   Description: Provides and overview of the interrelationships between population growth, resource availability, economic development and environmental quality.

340 333.7 016 GW
I C E L REFERENCES. (Text in various languages) 1970. 4/yr. DM.70($50) to individuals; institutions DM.105($75). International Council of Environmental Law, Adenauerallee 214, 53113 Bonn, Germany. TEL 0228-2692231. FAX 0228-2692250. Ed. Torsten Waesch. circ. 300. **Document type:** bibliography.
   Description: Provides information on the legal and policy aspects of natural resources conservation and use, environmental quality and land-use management.

614.7 016 660 II
INDIAN LITERATURE IN ENVIRONMENTAL ENGINEERING; a bibliographic review. (Text in English) 1971. a. Rs.80($5) National Environmental Engineering Research Institute, Documentation and Library Services, Nehru Marg, Nagpur 440020, India. (Affiliate: Council of Scientific and Industrial Research) Ed.Bd. author and geographical indexes. (processed)

614.7 HU ISSN 0231-0716
KORNYEZETVEDELMI SZAKIRODALMI TAJEKOZTATO/ENVIRONMENTAL CONTROL ABSTRACTS. 1983. bi-m. 5500 Ft. Orszagos Muszaki Informacios Kozpont es Konyvtar (O.M.I.K.K.) - National Technical Information Centre and Library, Muzeum u. 17, P.O. Box 12, 1428 Budapest, Hungary. (Subscr. to: Kultura, P.O. Box 149, 1389 Budapest, Hungary) Ed. Eszter Molnar. circ. 380.

614.7 551.48 UK
LIST OF HYDROBIOLOGICAL PAPERS OF BRITISH FRESH WATERS. 1976. a. £25. Freshwater Biological Association, The Ferry House, Ambleside, Cumbria LA22 0LP, England. **Document type:** bibliography.
   Description: Bibliographic references arranged by British geographical areas.

LITERATURE ABSTRACTS: HEALTH & ENVIRONMENT. see *MEDICAL SCIENCES — Abstracting, Bibliographies, Statistics*

614.7 551.46 016
628.116 UK ISSN 0264-8059
MARINE POLLUTION RESEARCH TITLES. 1974. m. £86($185) Plymouth Marine Laboratory, Citadel Hill, Plymouth PL1 2PB, England. TEL 0752-222772. FAX 0752-226865. Ed. L. Noble. adv.: bk.rev. circ. 200. (also avail. in microfiche) **Indexed:** Aqua.Sci.& Fish.Abstr., Copper Abstr. **Document type:** abstracting/indexing.
●Also available on CD-ROM. Producer(s): NISC (Oceanographic & Marine Resources - Vol.1).

614.7 016 628.5 US
N T I S ALERTS: ENVIRONMENTAL POLLUTION & CONTROL. w. $150 (foreign $205). U.S. National Technical Information Service, 5285 Port Royal Rd., Springfield, VA 22161. TEL 703-487-4630. FAX 703-321-8547. TELEX 64617. index. (back issues avail.)
   Former titles: Abstract Newsletter: Environmental Pollution and Control; Weekly Abstract Newsletter: Environmental Pollution and Control; Weekly Government Abstracts. Environmental Pollution and Control (ISSN 0364-4936)

620.85 US
NATURAL RESOURCES METABASE. a. $595. National Information Services Corporation (NISC), Ste. 6, Wyman Towers, 3100 St. Paul St., Baltimore, MD 21218. TEL 301-243-0797. FAX 301-243-0982.
●Available only on CD-ROM. Producer(s): NISC.
   Description: Provides database information on research in ecosystems, resource management, endangered species, national parks, wetland, Pacific islands, and more.

333.7 314.9 NE ISSN 0168-5236
HD9555.N4
NETHERLANDS. CENTRAAL BUREAU VOOR DE STATISTIEK. NEDERLANDSE ENERGIEHUISHOUDING. 1961. q. Centraal Bureau voor de Statistiek, Prinses Beatrixlaan 428, Voorburg, Netherlands. (Subscr. to: SDU - Publishers, Christoffel Plantijnstraat, The Hague, Netherlands) circ. 375. **Document type:** government publication.

614.7 016 620.2 UK ISSN 0029-0947
NOISE & VIBRATION BULLETIN. 1970. m. £96 (foreign £102). Multi-Science Publishing Co. Ltd., 107 High St., Brentwood, Essex CM14 4RX, England. TEL 0277-224632. FAX 0277-224632. (U.S. subscr. to: Box 176, Avenel, NJ 07001) Ed. B. Hughes. adv.; bk.rev. **Indexed:** Noise Pollut.Publ.Abstr. **Document type:** bulletin.
—BLDSC (6115.850000). SWETS. **CCC.**
   Description: Focuses on noise pollution, noise control, vibration in buildings or other structures, and instrumentation.

620.85 FR
O E C D ENVIRONMENTAL DATA COMPENDIUM. biennial. price varies. Organization for Economic Cooperation and Development, 2 rue Andre-Pascal, 75775 Paris Cedex 16, France. (U.S. orders to: O.E.C.D. Publications and Information Center, 2001 L St., N.W., Ste. 700, Washington, DC 20036-4910. TEL 202-785-6323) (also avail. in microfiche)

614.7 016 628.5 FR ISSN 1146-5433
P A S C A L E 36: POLLUTION DE L'EAU, DE L'AIR ET DU SOL - DECHETS - BRUIT. 1984. 10/yr. 1140 F. (outside EC 1210 F.). Centre National de la Recherche Scientifique, Institut de l'Information Scientifique et Technique, 2 allee du Parc de Brabois, 54514 Vandoeuvre-Les-Nancy, France. TEL 83-50-46-00. FAX 83-50-46-50. adv. contact: Veronique Guinvarc'h. abstr.; index, cum.index. (also avail. in microfiche) **Document type:** bibliography.
●Also available online. Vendor(s): DIALOG Information Services, Inc. (File no.144), European Space Agency (File no.14), Telesystemes - Questel. Also available on CD-ROM.
   Former titles: P A S C A L Explore. E 36: Pollution de l'Eau, de l'Air et du Sol, Dechets, Bruit (ISSN 0246-117X); P A S C A L Explore. Part 36: Pollution de l'Eau, de l'Air et du Sol; Which supersedes (1971-1984): Bulletin Signaletique. Part 885: Nuisances (ISSN 0301-3499); Bulletin Signaletique. Part 885: Eau et Assainissement. Pollution Atmospherique (ISSN 0007-5698)

615.9 016 FR ISSN 1146-5514
P A S C A L E 63: TOXICOLOGIE. 1961. 10/yr. 935 F. (outside EC 990 F.). Centre National de la Recherche Scientifique, Institut de l'Information Scientifique et Technique, 2 allee du Parc de Brabois, 54514 Vandoeuvre-Les-Nancy Cedex, France. TEL 83-50-46-00. FAX 83-50-46-50. adv. contact: Veronique Guinvarc'h. index, cum.index. (also avail. in microfiche) **Document type:** bibliography.
●Also available online. Vendor(s): DIALOG Information Services, Inc. (File no.144), European Space Agency (File no.14), Telesystemes - Questel. Also available on CD-ROM.
   Former titles: P A S C A L Explore. E 63: Toxicologie (ISSN 0761-215X); P A S C A L Explore. Part 63: Toxicologie; Which superseded in part (in 1984): Bulletin Signaletique. Part 330: Sciences Pharmacologiques - Toxicologie (ISSN 0007-5442)

P A S C A L F 23: GENIE CHIMIQUE. INDUSTRIES CHIMIQUE ET PARACHIMIQUE. see *CHEMISTRY — Abstracting, Bibliographies, Statistics*

632.95 016 668 US ISSN 0093-3295
RA1270.P4
PESTICIDES ABSTRACTS. m. $21. U.S. Environmental Protection Agency, Office of Pesticides and Toxic Substances, Washington, DC 20460. TEL 919-655-4000. (Subscr. to: Supt. of Documents, Washington, DC 20402) index. (also avail. in microform from UMI,MIM; reprint service avail. from UMI) **Indexed:** Rev.Appl.Entomol., Weed Abstr.
   Continues: Health Aspects of Pesticides: Abstract Bulletin.

613.1 310 PL ISSN 0867-0838
POLAND. GLOWNY URZAD STATYSTYCZNY. RAPORT OF STANIE, ZAGROZENIU I OCHRONIE SRODOWISKA (YEAR). (Subseries of: Studia i Analizy Statystyczne (ISSN 0209-3871)) a.? 1400 Zl. Zaklad Wydawnictw Statystycznych, Ul. Niepodleglosci 208, 00-925 Warsaw, Poland.

ENVIRONMENTAL STUDIES — COMPUTER APPLICATIONS

614.7 016 628.5   US   ISSN 0032-3624
TD172   CODEN: PLNAB4
POLLUTION ABSTRACTS. 1970. m. $745 (foreign $930); with index $885 (foreign $995); index only $390 (foreign $430). Cambridge Scientific Abstracts, 7200 Wisconsin Ave., 6th Fl., Bethesda, MD 20814. TEL 301-961-6750. FAX 301-961-6720. Ed. Evelyn Beck. adv.; abstr.; bibl.; index, cum.index. (tabloid format; also avail. in magnetic tape; back issues avail.) **Indexed:** Cal.Tiss.Abstr., Chemorec.Abstr., Comput.& Info.Sys., Oncol.Abstr., Pollut.Abstr. **Document type:** abstracting/indexing.
●Also available online. Vendor(s): Data-Star (POLL), DIALOG Information Services, Inc. (File no.41), European Space Agency (File no.18/POLLUTION), STN International.
Also available on CD-ROM. Producer(s): SilverPlatter Information, Inc.
—BLDSC (6544.270000).
   Description: Covers environmental quality, including air and water pollution, waste disposal, radiation and pesticides.

614.7   RU   ISSN 0234-7059
QH75.A1
REFERATIVNYI ZHURNAL. ENVIRONMENT MANAGEMENT ABSTRACTS. (Text in English) 1987. m. 29.40 Rub. Vsesoyuznyi Institut Nauchno-Tekhnicheskoi Informatsii (VINITI), Baltiiskaya ul. 14, A-219 Moscow, Russia. **Document type:** abstracting/indexing.
—BLDSC (0411.742000).

628.44 016   RU   ISSN 0206-6157
REFERATIVNYI ZHURNAL. OKHRANA I ULUCHSHENIE GORODSKOI SREDY. 1980. m. 38.40 Rub. (50.40 Rub. with index). Vsesoyuznyi Institut Nauchno-Tekhnicheskoi Informatsii (VINITI), Baltiiskaya ul. 14, Moscow A-219, Russia. (Subscr. to: Mezhdunarodnaya Kniga, Dimitrova ul. 39, 113095 Moscow, Russia) **Document type:** abstracting/indexing.

333.72 639.9 016   RU   ISSN 0202-9332
REFERATIVNYI ZHURNAL. OKHRANA PRIRODY I VOSPROIZVODSTVO PRIRODNYKH RESURSOV. 1975. m. 79.80 Rub. (97 Rub. including index). Vsesoyuznyi Institut Nauchno-Tekhnicheskoi Informatsii (VINITI), Baltiiskaya ul. 14, Moscow A-219, Russia. (Subscr. to: Mezhdunarodnaya Kniga, Dimitrova ul. 39, 113095 Moscow, Russia) **Document type:** abstracting/indexing.

614.7 016   RU   ISSN 0206-6149
REFERATIVNYI ZHURNAL. SISTEMY, PRIBORY I METODY KONTROLYA KACHESTVA OKRUZHAYUSHCHEI SREDY. 1980. m. 20.20 Rub. (27.80 Rub. including index). Vsesoyuznyi Institut Nauchno-Tekhnicheskoi Informatsii (VINITI), Baltiiskaya ul. 14, Moscow A-219, Russia. (Subscr. to: Mezhdunarodnaya Kniga, Dimitrova ul. 39, 113095 Moscow, Russia) **Document type:** abstracting/indexing.

614.7 016   RU   ISSN 0206-6130
REFERATIVNYI ZHURNAL. TEKHNOLOGICHESKIE ASPEKTY OKHRANY OKRUZHAYUSHCHEI SREDY. 1980. m. 58.80 Rub. (65.80 including index). Vsesoyuznyi Institut Nauchno-Tekhnicheskoi Informatsii (VINITI), Baltiiskaya ul. 14, Moscow A-219, Russia. (Subscr. to: Mezhdunarodnaya Kniga, Dimitrova ul. 39, 113095 Moscow, Russia) **Document type:** abstracting/indexing.

150 011 628   US   ISSN 0824-3336
HD61
RISK ABSTRACTS; a quarterly journal of abstracts, reviews and references. 1984. q. $185 (foreign $195). (University of Waterloo, Institute for Risk Research, CN) Cambridge Scientific Abstracts, 7200 Wisconsin Ave., 6th Fl., Bethesda. TEL 301-961-6700. FAX 301-961-6720. Ed. Jatin Nathwani. bk.rev.; abstr.; bibl.; index. (also avail. in magnetic tape; back issues avail.) **Indexed:** Risk Abstr. **Document type:** abstracting/indexing.
—BLDSC (7972.582000).
   Description: Covers risk from industrial, technological, environmental, medical and other sources, with emphasis on risk assessment and management.

620.85 631   NE   ISSN 0924-9370
SCOOP. (Text in Dutch, English) 1989. 3/yr. free. Dienst Landbouwkundig Onderzoek, Staring Centrum, Instituut voor Onderzoek van het Landelijk Gebied - D L O Winand Staring Centre for Integrated Land, Soil and Water Research, P.O. Box 125, 6700 AC Wageningen, Netherlands. TEL 31-8370-74200. FAX 31-8370-24812. TELEX 75230 VISI NL. Ed. E.C.W.M. Ruyten. **Document type:** abstracting/indexing.
●Also available online.
   Description: Abstract bulletin covering agricultural, ecological, hydrological and related research results from the center's publications and its library holdings.

614.7   UK
SCOTTISH ENVIRONMENT STATISTICS. 1987. biennial. £10. The Scottish Office, Central Statistics Unit, New St. Andrew's House, Edinburgh EH1 3TG, Scotland. TEL 031-244-4989. FAX 031-244-4785. circ. 600. **Document type:** bulletin.
   Description: Provides detailed information on most aspects of the Scottish environment.

614.7   US
STATISTICAL RECORD OF THE ENVIRONMENT. 1991. biennial. $105 (effective Oct. 1993). Gale Research Inc., 835 Penobscot Bldg., Detroit, MI 48266. TEL 313-961-2242; 800-877-4253. FAX 313-961-6083. Ed. Arsen J. Darnay. (also avail. in diskette format; magnetic tape)
   Description: Contains information on enviromental issues as analyzed in government and scientific literature as well as influential periodicals.

614   SW   ISSN 0282-3500
HD761.A1
SWEDEN. STATISTISKA CENTRALBYRAAN. STATISTISKA MEDDELANDEN. SERIE NA, NATURRESURSER OCH MILJOE. (Text in Swedish; summaries in English) 1985. irreg. SEK 1100 (effective 1992). Statistiska Centralbyraan, Publishing Unit, S-701 89 Oerebro, Sweden. **Document type:** abstracting/indexing.

TISGLOW. see ENVIRONMENTAL STUDIES

614.7 615.9   US
TOXIC SUBSTANCES CONTROL ACT - TEST SUBMISSION DATABASE. Short title: T S C A - T S C A T S. irreg. $1440 in U.S., Canada, Mexico; elsewhere $2880. (Environmental Protection Agency) U.S. National Technical Information Service, 5285 Port Royal Rd., Springfield, VA 22161. TEL 703-487-4630. (microfiche)

315.61   TU
TURKEY. DEVLET ISTATISTIK ENSTITUSU. GEVRE ISTATISTIKLERI - HAVA KIRLILIGI/TURKEY. STATE INSTITUTE OF STATISTICS. ENVIRONMENTAL STATISTICS - AIR POLLUTION. (Text in English, Turkish) 1991. a. $60. Devlet Istatistik Enstitusu - State Institute of Statistics, Necatibey Caddesi No. 114, 06100 Ankara, Turkey. TEL 90-312-4185027. FAX 90-312-4170432. (also avail. in diskette format) **Document type:** government publication.
   Description: Provides statistical information on air pollution parameters, including sulfur dioxide and particulate matter concentrations, data for motor vehicle fuels, lignite consumption, active thermoelectric power plants and manufacturing establishments, at regional, provincial and national levels.

614.7 011   GW   ISSN 0932-2892
UMWELTMEDIZIN. (Text in English or German) 1987. irreg. DM.10 per no. Institut fuer Dokumentation und Information, Sozialmedizin und Oeffentliches Gesundheitswesen, Westerfeldstr. 35-37, 33611 Bielefeld, Germany. TEL 0521-86033. (Subscr. to: Postfach 201012, 33548 Bielefeld, Germany) bk.rev. circ. 350.

614.7   US
U.S. ENVIRONMENTAL PROTECTION AGENCY. JOURNAL HOLDINGS REPORT. 1971. a. U.S. Environmental Protection Agency, Information Management and Services Division, 401 M St., S.W., Rm. 2003, 3404, Washington, DC 20460. TEL 703-487-4630. FAX 202-321-8547. (Subscr. to: National Technical Information Service, 5285 Port Royal Rd., Springfield, VA 22161. TEL 703-487-4650. FAX 703-321-8547) circ. 250. **Document type:** government publication.
   Description: Attempts to improve access to journals and to encourage resource sharing among the 28 libraries in the EPA Library Network.

URBAN ABSTRACTS. see PUBLIC ADMINISTRATION — Abstracting, Bibliographies, Statistics

628.16 016   SW   ISSN 0042-1995
VA-NYTT; litteratur om miljoevaard. 1966. 6/yr. SEK 700. BYGGDOK, Swedish Institute of Building Documentation, Environmental Department, Haelsingegatar 47, S-113 31 Stockholm, Sweden. TEL 46-8-34-01-70. FAX 46-8-32-48-59. TELEX 12563. Ed. Gerard Lingre. adv.; bk.rev. circ. 1,000.

614.7 016 628.4   UK   ISSN 0965-4496
Z5862
WASTE & ENVIRONMENT TODAY; news and bibliographic journal. Variant title: International Journal for the Waste and Environmental Management Professional. 1973. m. £220 (foreign £240). A E A Technology, 7-12 Harwell, Didcot, Oxon. OX11 ORA, England. TEL 0235-433484. FAX 0235-432854. Ed. Peter Doyle. **Document type:** trade publication.
—BLDSC (9266 554000).
   Description: Contains news articles and technical abstracts for people in all branches of waste and environmental management.

WASTE INFORMATION DIGESTS. see ENVIRONMENTAL STUDIES — Waste Management

011 614.7   US   ISSN 0195-4636
WORKBOOK. 1974. q. $12 to individuals; institutions $25; students $8.50. Southwest Research and Information Center, Box 4524, 105 Stanford, S.E., Albuquerque, NM 87106. TEL 505-262-1862. FAX 505-262-1864. Ed. Kathy Cone. bk.rev.; bibl.; cum.index. (back issues avail.) **Indexed:** Alt.Press Ind., Bk.Rev.Ind. (1989-), Child.Bk.Rev.Ind. (1989-), P.A.I.S.
—Faxon; UnCover.

ENVIRONMENTAL STUDIES — Computer Applications

613.1 338.1   US   ISSN 1051-8266
HC10   CODEN: AIALER
A I APPLICATIONS; natural resources, agriculture and environmental sciences. 1987. 3/yr. $37 to individuals (foreign $72). University of Idaho, Box 3066, Moscow, ID 83843. TEL 208-885-7033. FAX 208-885-6226. Ed. Molly Stock. bk.rev.; index. **Indexed:** Environ.Per.Bibl. (1989-). **Document type:** academic/scholarly publication.
—BLDSC (0772.323900); Faxon; UnCover.
   Formerly: A I Applications in Natural Resource Management.

C I S NEWS. (Chemical Information Systems, Inc.) see CHEMISTRY — Computer Applications

ENVIRONMENTAL STUDIES — POLLUTION

003 352   UK   ISSN 0198-9715
HT166   CODEN: CEUSD5
COMPUTERS, ENVIRONMENT AND URBAN SYSTEMS; an international journal. 1975. 6/yr. £332($510) (effective 1994). Elsevier Science Ltd., Pergamon, P.O. Box 800, Kidlington, Oxford OX5 1DX, England. TEL 44-865-843000. FAX 44-865-843010. (Subscr. in U.S. and Canada to: Elsevier Science, 660 White Plains Rd., Tarrytown, NY 10591-5153. TEL 914-524-9200. FAX 914-333-2444) Ed. David Prosperi. adv.: B&W page $550, color page $1350. bk.rev.; charts; illus.; index. circ. 850. (also avail. in microfilm from UMI) **Indexed**: Compumath, Comput.Abstr., Comput.Cont., Curr.Cont., Environ.Per.Bibl. (1972-), Excerp.Med., I D A, Psychol.Abstr., Sage Pub.Admin.Abstr., Sage Urb.Stud.Abstr., Sci.Abstr. **Document type**: academic/scholarly publication.
—BLDSC (3394.914000); EI; Faxon; UnCover; SWETS; UMI. **CCC**.
Former titles: Urban Systems (ISSN 0147-8001); Computers and Urban Society.
Description: Focuses on the development, enhancement, and use of computer-based methodologies for understanding and improving environmental and urban systems.
Refereed Serial

504 003   NE   ISSN 0167-8892
CODEN: DEMODW
DEVELOPMENTS IN ENVIRONMENTAL MODELLING. (Text in English) 1981. irreg., vol.19, 1994. price varies. Elsevier Science B.V., Books Division, P.O. Box 211, 1000 AE Amsterdam, Netherlands. TEL 31-20-5803911. FAX 31-20-5803705. TELEX 18582 ESPA NL. (Subscr. in U.S. and Canada to: Elsevier Science Inc., Box 882, Madison Sq. Sta., New York, NY 10159. TEL 212-989-5800) (back issues avail.) **Document type**: monographic series.
—BLDSC (3579.071440); Faxon; CASDDS.
Refereed Serial

621.39 003   NE   ISSN 0304-3800
QH541.15.M3   CODEN: ECMODT
ECOLOGICAL MODELLING; international journal on ecological modelling and engineering and systems ecology. (Text in English) 1975. 24/yr. (in 6 vols.; 4 nos./vol.). fl.1956($1057) (effective 1994). Elsevier Science B.V., P.O. Box 211, 1000 AE Amsterdam, Netherlands. TEL 31-20-5803911. FAX 31-20-5803598. TELEX 18582 ESPA NL. (Subscr. in U.S. and Canada to: Elsevier Science Inc., Box 882, Madison, Sq. Sta., New York, NY 10159. TEL 212-989-5800. FAX 212-633-3990) Ed. S.E. Joergensen. adv.; bk.rev.; bibl.; illus.; index. (also avail. in microform from UMI; reprint service avail. from SWZ) **Indexed**: A.I.Abstr., Acid Rain Abstr., Appl.Ecol.Abstr., Bio-Contr.News & Info., Biodet.Abstr., Biol.Abstr., Biostat., Chem.Abstr., Crop Physiol.Abstr., Curr.Adv.Ecol.Sci., Curr.Cont., Deep Sea Res.& Oceanogr.Abstr., Ecol.Abstr., Energy Ind., Energy Info.Abstr., Energy Rev., Environ.Abstr., Environ.Abstr., Environ.Per.Bibl. (1978-), Excerp.Med., Field Crop Abstr., Forest.Abstr., Geo.Abstr., GeoRef., Ind.Sci.Rev., Irr.& Drain.Abstr., Key Word Ind.Wildl.Res., Maize Abstr., Rev.Appl.Entomol., Sci.Cit.Ind., Sel.Water Res.Abstr., Soils & Fert., Soyabean Abstr., Triticale Abstr., W.R.C.Inf. **Document type**: academic/scholarly publication.
—BLDSC (3648.899000); Faxon; UnCover; SWETS; CASDDS. **CCC**.
Description: Combines mathematical modelling, systems analysis and computer techniques with ecology and environmental management.
Refereed Serial

005.3   UK   ISSN 0266-9838
TD169   CODEN: ENSOEZ
ENVIRONMENTAL SOFTWARE. 1986. 4/yr. £213($330) (effective 1994). Elsevier Science Ltd., Oxford Fulfilment Centre, P.O. Box 800, Kidlington, Oxford OX5 1DX, England. TEL 44-865-843000. FAX 44-865-843010. (Subscr. in U.S. and Canada to: Elsevier Science, 660 White Plains Rd., Tarrytown, NY 10591-5153. TEL 914-524-9200. FAX 914-333-2444) Ed. Paolo Zannetti. adv.; software rev. (back issues avail.) **Indexed**: A.I.Abstr., Comput.Abstr., Comput.Lit.Ind., Energy Rev., Eng.Ind., Environ.Abstr., Environ.Per.Bibl. (1986-), Excerp.Med., Pollut.Abstr., Sci.Abstr., W.R.C.Inf. **Document type**: academic/scholarly publication.
—BLDSC (3791.648000); EI; SWETS. **CCC**.
Description: Provides an indispensable link between the development of analytical and numerical techniques in environmental sciences and engineering and their computer software implementation.
Refereed Serial

613.1 005.3   US   ISSN 1043-2884
ENVIRONMENTAL SOFTWARE REPORT. 1988. 8/yr. $95 (effective Oct. 1993). Donley Technology, Box 335, Garrisonville, VA 22463. TEL 703-659-1954. Ed. Veronica Deschambault. adv. (back issues avail.) **Document type**: newsletter.
Description: Covers the latest developments in the environmental software industry. Examines commercial and government software packages, databases and on-line systems for environmental professionals.

GEO INFO SYSTEMS; applications of GIS and related spatial information technologies. see GEOGRAPHY — Computer Applications

628   JA
GIKEN GEPPO/TECHNICAL MONTHLY REPORT OF COMPUTER APPLICATIONS. (Text in Japanese) 1985. m. Computer Applications Co., Ltd., 3-1, Hitotsubashi 2-chome, Chiyoda-ku, Tokyo 101, Japan.

613.1   US   ISSN 0890-5673
NATURAL RESOURCES COMPUTER NEWSLETTER. 1986. 9/yr. $98. Michaelsen's Micro Magic, Inc., Box 7332, Fredericksburg, VA 22404. TEL 703-775-3059. Ed. Nancy Michaelsen. circ. 1,000. **Document type**: newsletter.
Description: Computer information and products for professionals in fields involving natural resources.

613.1   GW   ISSN 0940-693X
UMWELT PRODUKT INFO SERVICE. 1991. irreg., no.10, 1992. Fachinformationszentrum Karlsruhe, Gesellschaft fuer Wissenschaftlich-Technische Information mbH, 76344 Eggenstein-Leopoldshafen, Germany. TEL 07247-808333. FAX 07247-808135. TELEX 724710-FIZKA. (looseleaf format) **Document type**: bulletin.

ENVIRONMENTAL STUDIES — Pollution

628.168   US   ISSN 0890-0396
KF3786.A3   CODEN: AWPCE3
AIR & WATER POLLUTION CONTROL. (Subseries of: B N A Policy and Practice Series, and Environment, Safety and Health Series) 1986. bi-w. $301. The Bureau of National Affairs, Inc., 1231 25th St., N.W., Washington, DC 20037. TEL 202-452-4200. FAX 202-822-8092. TELEX 285656 BNAI WSH. (Subscr. to: 9435 Key West Ave., Rockville, MD 20850. TEL 800-372-1033) Ed. Randy Kubetin. (back issues avail.) **Document type**: newsletter.
—**CCC**.
Description: Review of developments in pollution laws, regulations, and trends in government and industry.

614.7   US   ISSN 0400-8510
AIR CURRENTS. 1959. m. free. Bay Area Air Quality Management District, 939 Ellis St., San Francisco, CA 94109. TEL 415-749-4900. FAX 415-928-8560. Ed. Dave Davis. bibl.; charts; illus. circ. 3,000. **Document type**: consumer publication.
Description: Designed to keep readers alert of air quality issues, new regulations, clean-air legislation and other matters affecting the Bay Area.

628.53   US   ISSN 1058-6628
TD883.2   CODEN: APOCEH
THE AIR POLLUTION CONSULTANT. 1991. bi-m. $395 (foreign $455) (effective 1994). Elsevier Science Inc., 655 Ave. of the Americas, New York, NY 10010. TEL 212-989-5800. FAX 212-633-3990. (Subscr. to: Box 889, Madison Sq. Sta., New York, NY 10159-0882) Ed. Eric Weber.
—**CCC**.
Description: Provides information on air pollution issues.

628.53   US   ISSN 0196-7150
KF3812.A15
AIR POLLUTION CONTROL (WASHINGTON). (Subseries of: B N A Policy and Practice Series; Environment, Safety, and Health Series) 1980. bi-w. $707. The Bureau of National Affairs, Inc., 1231 25th St., N.W., Washington, DC 20037. TEL 202-452-4200. FAX 202-822-8092. TELEX 285656 BNAI WSH. (Subscr. to: 9435 Key West Ave., Rockville, MD 20850. TEL 800-372-1033) Ed. Randy Kubetin. index. (looseleaf format; back issues avail.) **Indexed**: Int.Aerosp.Abstr. **Document type**: newsletter.
—**CCC**.
Description: Reference and advisory service on the control of air pollution, designed to meet the information needs of individuals responsible for complying with EPA and state air pollution control regulations.

AIR POLLUTION TITLES. see ENVIRONMENTAL STUDIES — Abstracting, Bibliographies, Statistics

614.7   US   ISSN 1066-193X
AIRTECH NEWS. 1991. m. $345 (foreign $360) (effective Jan. 1994). Haztech Publications, Inc., 14120 Huckleberry La., Silver Spring, MD 20906. TEL 301-871-3289. FAX 301-460-5859. Ed. Cathy Dombrowski.
Description: Covers air pollution control technologies.

614.7 628.53   UK
TD881   CODEN: AEBAE5
ATMOSPHERIC ENVIRONMENT. (Text in English, French, German) 1967. 22/yr. £1297($1995) (effective 1994). Elsevier Science Ltd., Pergamon, P.O. Box 800, Kidlington, Oxford OX5 1DX, England. TEL 44-865-843000. FAX 44-865-843010. (Subscr. in U.S. and Canada to: Elsevier Science, 660 White Plains Rd., Tarrytown, NY 10591-5153. TEL 914-524-9200. FAX 914-333-2444) Ed.Bd. adv.; bk.rev.; charts; illus.; index. circ. 2,600. (also avail. in microfiche from MIM; microfilm from UMI; back issues avail.; reprint service avail.) **Indexed**: A.S.& T.Ind., Acid Pre.Dig., Acid Rain Abstr., Acid Rain Ind., Agri.Eng.Abstr., Anal.Abstr., API Abstr., API Catal., API Hlth. & Environ., API Oil., API Pet.Ref., API Pet.Subst., API Transport., Appl.Mech.Rev., Biol.Abstr., Biol.& Agr.Ind., C.I.S. Abstr., CAD CAM Abstr., Cadscan, Chem.Abstr., Chem.Eng.Abstr., Curr.Cont., Deep Sea Res.& Oceanogr.Abstr., Energy Info.Abstr., Energy Rev., Eng.Ind., Environ.Abstr., Environ.Ind., Environ.Per.Bibl. (1972-), Excerp.Med., Field Crop.Abstr., Forest Abstr., Forest Prod.Abstr., Fuel & Energy Abstr., Geo.Abstr., Herb.Abstr., Hort.Abstr., Ind.Med., INIS Atomind., INSPEC, Intl.Civil Eng.Abstr., Lead Abstr., Mass Spectr.Bull., Meteor.& Geoastrophys.Abstr., Ocean.Abstr., Ornam.Hort., Pollut.Abstr., Risk Abstr., Sci.Abstr., Sci.Cit.Ind., Sel.Water Res.Abstr., Soft.Abstr.Eng., Soils & Fert., T.C.E.A., Triticale Abstr., W.R.C.Inf., Zincscan. **Document type**: academic/scholarly publication.
—EI; Faxon; UnCover; SWETS; UMI; CASDDS. **CCC**.
Formed by the **1993 merger of**: Atmospheric Environment. Part A, General Topics (ISSN 0960-1686) & Atmospheric Environment. Part B, Urban Atmosphere (ISSN 0957-1272); Which supersedes in part (in 1990): Atmospheric Environment (ISSN 0004-6981)
Description: Covers all subjects related to the atmosphere and human interactions with it.
Refereed Serial

ENVIRONMENTAL STUDIES — POLLUTION

628.53 LI
CODEN: FZATAH
ATMOSPHERIC PHYSICS. (Text and summaries in English) 1973. a. $5. Institute of Physics, A. Gostauto Str. 12, Vilnius 2600, Lithuania. TEL 61-26-10. FAX 3702-617070. **Document type:** proceedings.
—CASDDS.
Formerly: Fizika Atmosfery - Atmospheros Fizika (ISSN 0135-1419)
Description: Treats problems of the atmosphere's and hydrosphere's pollution by radioactive and chemical substances.

623.53 US
ATMOSPHERIC POLLUTION & ABATEMENT NEWS; a monthly newsletter. m. $295. Business Communications Co., Inc. (Norwalk), 25 Van Zant St., Ste. 13, Norwalk, CT 06855. TEL 203-853-4266. FAX 203-853-0348. TELEX 6502934929 WUI. **Document type:** academic/scholarly publication, newsletter.
● Also available online. Vendor(s): NewsNet.
Formerly: Atmospheric Monitoring and Abatement News.
Description: Reports on recent data concerning atmospheric testing: CFCs and ozone depletion, carbon dioxide and global warming, sulfur dioxide and acid rain, solvent emissions, automotive emissions, other toxic emissions and particulates, indoor air pollution.

AUSTRALIAN POLLUTION LAW (CONTROL). see *LAW*

AUSTRALIAN POLLUTION LAW NEW SOUTH WALES. see *LAW*

AUSTRALIAN POLLUTION LAW VICTORIA. see *LAW*

363.73 US
BAY WATCH. 1985. bi-m. free. Massachusetts Coastal Zone Management Office, 100 Cambridge St., Boston, MA 02738. TEL 617-727-9530. Ed. Mara B. Altman. circ. 3,000. **Document type:** newsletter.
Description: Reports news of pollution clean up and monitoring efforts of the Buzzards Bay Project, an Environmental Protection Agency Estuary Program participant.

628.53 BS
BOTSWANA. DEPARTMENT OF MINES. AIR POLLUTION CONTROL. ANNUAL REPORT. a. P.1. Department of Mines, Mining Commissioner, Private Bag 0049, Gaborone, Botswana. TEL 352641. FAX 352141. TELEX 2557 BD. **Document type:** government publication.
Description: Provides data on air quality in several areas within Botswana. Addresses subsequent effects of pollution upon the environment.

C A SELECTS. ACID RAIN & ACID AIR. see *ENVIRONMENTAL STUDIES — Abstracting, Bibliographies, Statistics*

C A SELECTS. AIR POLLUTION (BOOKS & REVIEWS). see *ENVIRONMENTAL STUDIES — Abstracting, Bibliographies, Statistics*

C A SELECTS. ENVIRONMENTAL POLLUTION. see *ENVIRONMENTAL STUDIES — Abstracting, Bibliographies, Statistics*

C A SELECTS. POLLUTION MONITORING. see *ENVIRONMENTAL STUDIES — Abstracting, Bibliographies, Statistics*

628.53 US ISSN 0068-5496
TD883.5.C2
CALIFORNIA. AIR RESOURCES BOARD. ANNUAL REPORT. a. free. Air Resources Board, Box 2815, Sacramento, CA 95812. TEL 916-322-2990.

628.53 US
CALIFORNIA. AIR RESOURCES BOARD. BULLETIN. 1967. m. free. Air Resources Board, Information Office, Box 2815, Sacramento, CA 95812. TEL 916-322-2990. bibl.; charts.

628.53 US
CALIFORNIA. AIR RESOURCES BOARD. FACT SHEETS. 1972. irreg. free. Air Resources Board, Information Office, Box 2815, Sacramento, CA 95812. TEL 916-322-2990.

628.53 US
CALIFORNIA AIR BASINS. 1969. irreg. free. Air Resources Board, Box 2815, Sacramento, CA 95812. TEL 916-322-2990. charts; illus.; stat. (processed)

628.53 US
CALIFORNIA AIR QUALITY DATA. (Annual edition avail.) 1968. q. free. California Air Resources Board, Technical Support Division, Box 2815, Sacramento, CA 95812. TEL 916-445-6059. charts; stat.; cum.index: 1968-1981. circ. 1,500. (also avail. in magnetic tape; back issues avail.) **Indexed:** Biol.Abstr., Cal.Per.Ind. (1990), Pollut.Abstr.

CALIFORNIA WATER POLLUTION CONTROL ASSOCIATION. BULLETIN. see *WATER RESOURCES*

628.53 CN ISSN 0381-2995
CANADA. ENVIRONMENT CANADA. CONSERVATION AND PROTECTION SERVICE. ANNUAL SUMMARY: NATIONAL AIR POLLUTION SURVEILLANCE. Key Title: National Air Pollution Surveillance. (Subseries of: Canada. Environment Canada. Surveillance Report - Environmental Protection Directorate) (Text in English, French) 1970. a. free. Environment Canada, E P Publications, Ottawa, ON K1A 0H3, Canada. FAX 819-953-9029. illus. circ. 600. (also avail. in microfiche)
Former titles: Canada. Environment Canada. Environment Protection Service. Annual Summary: National Air Pollution Surveillance; Canada. Air Pollution Control Directorate. Annual Summary: National Air Pollution Surveillance.
Description: Monitors and assesses on a continuing basis, the quality of the ambient air in the urban regions of Canada.

628.53 CN ISSN 0381-3002
CANADA. ENVIRONMENT CANADA. CONSERVATION AND PROTECTION SERVICE. MONTHLY SUMMARY: NATIONAL AIR POLLUTION SURVEILLANCE. Key Title: National Air Pollution Surveillance. Monthly Summary. m. Environment Canada, E P Publications, Ottawa, ON K1A 0H3, Canada. FAX 819-953-9029.
Formerly: Canada. Environmental Canada. Environmental Protection Service. Monthly Summary: National Air Pollution Surveillance.
Description: Provides readings by location, number of hourly samples, and monthly averages for concentration of pollutants in the air.

CARRYING CAPACITY NETWORK CLEARINGHOUSE BULLETIN. see *CONSERVATION*

620.3 FR ISSN 1145-4660
CENTRE D'INFORMATION ET DE DOCUMENTATION SUR LE BRUIT. BULLETIN TECHNIQUE. 1976. irreg. Centre d'Information et de Documentation sur le Bruit, 4 rue Beffroy, 92200 Neuilly-sur-Seine, France. bibl.
Former titles (until 1989): Centre d'Information et de Documentation sur le Bruit. Bulletin (ISSN 0240-3668); (until 1979): Centre d'Information et de Documentation sur les Problemes du Bruit. Bulletin (ISSN 0240-365X)

CHEMECOLOGY; covering health, safety and the environment. see *ENVIRONMENTAL STUDIES*

CHIBAKEN NO JIBAN CHINKA TO JISHIN/RESEARCHES ON LANDSUBSIDENCE AND EARTHQUAKE IN CHIBA PREFECTURE. see *ENGINEERING — Civil Engineering*

628.53 614.7 AT ISSN 0009-8647
CODEN: CLNABV
CLEAN AIR. 1967. q. Aus.$50 (foreign Aus.$39). Clean Air Society of Australia & New Zealand, c/o J.N. O'Heare, Ed., 12 Pall Mall, Mouth Warerley, Vic. 3149, Australia. adv.; bk.rev.; bibl.; index. circ. 400. (also avail. in microform from UMI; back issues avail.) **Indexed:** Aus.Rd.Ind., Biol.Abstr., Br.Ceram.Abstr., Br.Tech.Ind., Chem.Abstr., Curr.Cont., Energy Info.Abstr., Energy Rev., Environ.Abstr., Environ.Per.Bibl. (1972-), Sci.Abstr. **Document type:** academic/scholarly publication.
—BLDSC (3278.330000).

628.53 614.712 UK ISSN 0300-5143
CODEN: CLNABV
CLEAN AIR. 1929. q. £22. National Society for Clean Air and Environmental Protection, 136 North St., Brighton BN1 1RG, England. TEL 0273-26313. FAX 0273-735802. adv.; bk.rev.; charts; illus.; pat.; tr.mk. circ. 2,250. **Indexed:** Acid Pre.Dig., B.C.I.R.A., Biol.Abstr., Br.Tech.Ind., Chem.Abstr., Energy Rev., Environ.Per.Bibl. (1972-), Excerp.Med., Meteor.& Geoastrophys.Abstr., Ocean.Abstr., Pollut.Abstr., Trop.Dis.Bull. **Document type:** bulletin.
—BLDSC (3278.300000).
Incorporates: Smokeless Air (ISSN 0037-7368)
Description: Articles and information on air pollution and noise.

613.1 US
CLEAN AIR ACT HANDBOOK: A PRACTICAL GUIDE TO COMPLIANCE. a. $85. Clark - Boardman - Callaghan Company Ltd., 375 Hudson St., New York, NY 10014. TEL 212-929-7500; 800-221-9428. FAX 212-924-0460. Eds. Craig A. Moyer, Michael A. Francis.
Description: Offers interpretation of the Clean Air Act, including analysis of potential problem areas, deadlines, enforcement, and compliance.

628.53 UK ISSN 0301-9039
TD883.7.G7 CODEN: NSCAA9
CLEAN AIR CONFERENCE. a. £30. National Society for Clean Air and Environmental Protection, 136 North St., Brighton, Sussex BN1 1RG, England. TEL 0273-26313. FAX 0273-735802. **Document type:** proceedings.
Description: Proceedings of the annual National Society for Clean Air Conference.

628.5 US
CLEAN AIR REPORT. bi-w. $460 (foreign $510). Inside Washington Publishers, Box 7167, Benjamin Franklin Sta., Washington, DC 20044. TEL 202-892-8500. FAX 202-685-2606. **Document type:** newsletter.

628.168 US ISSN 0009-8620
CLEAN WATER REPORT; legislation, resources, pollution, technology. 1964. bi-w. $235. Business Publishers, Inc., 951 Pershing Dr., Silver Spring, MD 20910-4464. TEL 301-587-6300. FAX 301-587-1081. Ed. Elaine Eiserer. (looseleaf format) **Document type:** newsletter.
—CCC.
Incorporates: Drinking Water News.
Description: Provides current information from the offices of the EPA for wastewater treatment plant operators, equipment manufacturers, consulting engineers, or government regulators.

614.7 US
CLEARWATERS. vol.7, 1977. q. $6. New York Water Pollution Control Association, Inc., 90 Presidential Plaza, Ste. 122, Syracuse, NY 13202. TEL 315-422-7811. Ed. Laurie Harrington. adv.; bk.rev.; illus. circ. 3,000.

628.53 US
CLIMATE ALERT. 1988. 10/yr. $95. Climate Institute, 324 Fourth St., N.E., Washington, DC 20002. Ed. Nancy Wilson. **Document type:** newsletter.

CONNECTICUT WATER RESOURCES BULLETINS. see *WATER RESOURCES*

628 IE
CO-OP IRELAND. 12/yr. Poolbeg House, 1-2 Poolbeg St., Dublin 2, Ireland. TEL 719244. FAX 719263. Ed. M. Henry. circ. 2,750.

628.53 CN
CO2 - CLIMATE REPORT. 1990. s-a. free. Canadian Climate Centre, 4905 Dufferin St., Downsview, ON M3H 5T4, Canada. Ed. Pam Kertland. **Document type:** newsletter.

ENVIRONMENTAL STUDIES — POLLUTION

614.7 363.73 US ISSN 1064-3389
TD172 CODEN: CRETEK
CRITICAL REVIEWS IN ENVIRONMENTAL SCIENCE & TECHNOLOGY. 1970. q. $265 (foreign $272.95). C R C Press, Inc., 2000 Corporate Blvd., N.W., Boca Raton, FL 33431. TEL 407-994-0555. FAX 407-998-9784. TELEX 568689-CRC PRESS. Ed. Conrad P. Straub. bibl.; charts; illus. circ. 630. (back issues avail.) **Indexed:** Biodet.Abstr., Biol.Abstr., Cadscan, Chem.Abstr., Curr.Adv.Ecol.Sci., Curr.Cont., Dairy Sci.Abstr., Deep Sea Res.& Oceanogr.Abstr., Energy Info.Abstr., Environ.Abstr., Excerp.Med., Food Sci.& Tech.Abstr., Ind.Sci.Rev., INIS Atomind., Lead Abstr., Ocean.Abstr., Pollut.Abstr., Protozool.Abstr., Sci.Cit.Ind., Sel.Water Res.Abstr., Soils & Fert., W.R.C.Inf., Zincscan. **Document type:** academic/scholarly publication.
—BLDSC (3487.475100); Faxon; UnCover; SWETS; CASDDS. **CCC.**
Former titles (until vol.23, 1992): Critical Reviews in Environmental Control (ISSN 1040-838X); C R C Critical Reviews in Environmental Control (ISSN 0007-8999)
Description: Provides comprehensive review articles relevant to the area of environmental control encompassing many disciplines in the basic and applied sciences as well as in the social sciences.

CURRENT BIBLIOGRAPHY ON SCIENCE AND TECHNOLOGY: ENVIRONMENTAL POLLUTION/KAGAKU GIJUTSU BUNKEN SOKUHO. KANKYO KOGAI-HEN. see ENVIRONMENTAL STUDIES — Abstracting, Bibliographies, Statistics

ECO-LOG CANADIAN POLLUTION LEGISLATION. see ENVIRONMENTAL STUDIES — Abstracting, Bibliographies, Statistics

628.168 628.3 UK ISSN 0013-2217
TD511 CODEN: EWTJAG
EFFLUENT AND WATER TREATMENT JOURNAL. 1961. m. £72. Thunderbird Enterprises Ltd., Omega Lodge, Troutstream Way, Rick Mansworth, Herts. WD3 4JN, England. Ed. S.J. Tucker. adv.; bk.rev.; charts; illus.; tr.lit.; index. circ. 6,000. **Indexed:** Abstr.Bull.Inst.Pap.Chem., Agri.Eng.Abstr., Biol.Abstr., Br.Tech.Ind., Cadscan, Chem.Abstr., Chem.Eng.Abstr., Curr.Biotech.Abstr., Curr.Cont., Dairy Sci.Abstr., Energy Ind., Energy Info.Abstr., Energy Rev., Eng.Ind., Environ.Per.Bibl., Excerp.Med., Food Sci.& Tech.Abstr., Fuel & Energy Abstr., Geo.Abstr., Intl.Civil Eng.Abstr., Lead Abstr., Met.Abstr., Ocean.Abstr., Pollut.Abstr., Risk Abstr., Sel.Water Res.Abstr., Soft.Abstr.Eng., W.R.C.Inf., World Alum.Abstr., Zincscan.

628.5 SW ISSN 1101-7341
QH545.A17 CODEN: EVIREG
ENVIRO; magazine of transboundary pollution. Alternate title: Acid Enviro. (Text in English) 1984. s-a. free. Swedish Environmental Protection Agency, S171 85 Solna, Sweden. FAX 46-8-984513. TELEX 11131 ENVIRON S. Ed. Peter Hanneberg. adv.; illus. circ. 20,000. **Indexed:** Acid Rain Abstr., Acid Rain Ind., AESIS, Energy Info.Abstr., Environ.Abstr., Environ.Per.Bibl (1992-). **Document type:** government publication.
Formerly (until vol.9, 1990): Acid Magazine (ISSN 0282-0196)

ENVIRONMENT ABSTRACTS. see ENVIRONMENTAL STUDIES — Abstracting, Bibliographies, Statistics

ENVIRONMENT ABSTRACTS ANNUAL; a guide to the key environmental literature of the year. see ENVIRONMENTAL STUDIES — Abstracting, Bibliographies, Statistics

628 IE
ENVIRONMENT BULLETIN. irreg. Department of the Environment, Customs House, Dublin 1, Ireland. TEL 793377. Ed. Michael Davitt.

620 CN ISSN 1183-8795
ENVIRONMENT DIGEST; Canada's bi-weekly environment news review. 1990. bi-w. Can.$235. Sydenham Publishing, 344 23rd St. W., Owen Sound, ON N4K 4G7, Canada. TEL 519-371-6289. FAX 519-371-3676. Ed. Stella Coultas. adv. contact: Jeff Elie. bk.rev.; s-a. index. **Document type:** newsletter.

614.7 UK ISSN 0269-7491
TD172 CODEN: ENPOEK
ENVIRONMENTAL POLLUTION. 1970. 12/yr. (in 4 vols., 3 nos./vol.). £812($1250) (effective 1994). Elsevier Science Ltd., Oxford Fulfilment Centre, P.O. Box 800, Kidlington, Oxford OX5 1DX, England. TEL 44-865-843000. FAX 44-865-843010. (Subscr. in U.S. and Canada to: Elsevier Science, 660 White Plains Rd., Tarrytown, NY 10591-5153. TEL 914-524-9200. FAX 914-333-2444) Eds. J.P. Demster, J.W. Manning. adv.; bk.rev.; illus.; index. (also avail. in microform from UMI; back issues avail.) **Indexed:** Abstr.Hyg., Acid Pre.Dig., Acid Rain Abstr., Acid Rain Ind., Agri.Eng.Abstr., API Abstr., API Catal., API Hlth.& Environ., API Oil., API Pet.Ref., API Pet.Subst., API Transport., Bio-Contr.News & Info., Biodet.Abstr., Biol.Abstr., Biol.& Agr.Ind., Biol.Dig., Cadscan, Chem.Abstr., Cott.& Trop.Fibr.Abstr., Crop Physiol.Abstr., Curr.Adv.Ecol.Sci., Curr.Cont., Dairy Sci.Abstr., Deep Sea Res.& Oceanogr.Abstr., Energy Ind., Energy Info.Abstr., Energy Rev., Eng.Ind., Environ.Abstr., Environ.Per.Bibl. (1988-), Excerp.Med., Field Crop Abstr., Food Sci.& Tech.Abstr., Forest.Abstr., Forest Prod.Abstr., Fuel & Energy Abstr., Geo.Abstr., GeoRef., Helminthol.Abstr., Herb.Abstr., Hort.Abstr., Ind.Sci.Rev., Ind.Vet., Irr.& Drain.Abstr., Lead Abstr., Maize Abstr., Mid.East: Abstr.& Ind., Ocean.Abstr., Petrol.Abstr., Plant Grow.Reg.Abstr., Pollut.Abstr., Poult.Abstr., Rice Abstr., Risk Abstr., Sci.Cit.Ind., Seed Abstr., Sel.J.Water, Sel.Water Res.Abstr., Soils & Fert., Sorghum & Millets Abstr., Soyabean Abstr., Triticale Abstr., Trop.Dis.Bull., Vet.Bull., W.R.C.Inf., Weed Abstr., Zincscan. **Document type:** academic/scholarly publication.
—BLDSC (3791.539000); Faxon; UnCover; SWETS; CASDDS. **CCC.**
Formed by the 1987 merger of: Environmental Pollution. Series A. Ecological and Biological (ISSN 0143-1471); Environmental Pollution. Series B. Chemical and Physical (ISSN 0143-148X); Formerly (until 1980): Environmental Pollution (ISSN 0013-9327)
Description: An international journal concerned with the biological, chemical and physical aspects of environmental pollution and pollution control. Publishes research and review articles on the distribution and ecological effects of environmental pollutants and on new techniques for their study and measurement.
Refereed Serial

628.53 FR ISSN 0071-1942
ETUDES DE POLLUTION ATMOSPHERIQUE A PARIS ET DANS LES DEPARTMENTS PERIPHERIQUES. 1964. a. free. Prefecture de Police, Laboratoire Central, 39 bis rue de Dantzig, 75015 Paris, France. bk.rev. **Indexed:** Bull.Signal.

628.168 NE ISSN 0925-5060
TD255 CODEN: EWPCED
EUROPEAN WATER POLLUTION CONTROL. 1991. 6/yr. fl.296($160) (effective 1994). (European Water Pollution Control Association) Elsevier Science B.V., P.O. Box 211, 1000 AE Amsterdam, Netherlands. TEL 31-20-5803911. FAX 31-20-5803598. TELEX 18582 ESPA NL. (Subscr. in U.S. and Canada to: Elsevier Science Inc., Box 882, Madison Sq. Sta., New York, NY 10159-0882. TEL 212-989-5800. FAX 212-633-3990) Ed. J. de Jong. bk.rev. (back issues avail.) **Indexed:** Environ.Per.Bibl., Sel.Water Res.Abstr. **Document type:** academic/scholarly publication.
—BLDSC (3830.370680); El; Faxon; SWETS. **CCC.**
Description: Publishes technical papers, review articles, new product and industry information, association news and reports of interest to practitioners and researchers in the field of water pollution control.
Refereed Serial

F G D DESIGN & COST DATA FILE. (Flue-Gas Desulfurization) see ENGINEERING — Electrical Engineering

628.5 FI ISSN 1235-8843
TD883.7.F5
FINNISH METEOROLOGICAL INSTITUTE. AIR QUALITY MEASUREMENTS. (Text in English, Finnish) a. price varies. Ilmatieteen Laitos - Finnish Meteorological Institute, P.O. Box 503, SF-0101 Helsinki, Finland. FAX 1929218. (Dist. by: Oy Painatuskeskus AB, Publ. Division, P.O. Box 516, FIN-00101, Helsinki, Finland) **Document type:** government publication.

628.53 FI ISSN 0782-6095
FINNISH METEOROLOGICAL INSTITUTE. PUBLICATIONS ON AIR QUALITY/ILMATIETEEN LAITOS. ILMANSUOJELUN JULKAISUJA. irreg. Ilmatieteen Laitos - Finnish Meteorological Institute, P.O. Box 503, SF-00101 Helsinki, Finland. FAX 1929218. TELEX 124436 EFKL SF. (Dist. by: Oy Painatuskeskus AB, P.O. Box 516, SF-00101 Helsinki, Finland) **Indexed:** Meteor.& Geoastrophys.Abstr. **Document type:** government publication.

FOCUS: CARRYING CAPACITY SELECTIONS. see CONSERVATION

FOCUS ON WATER QUALITY. see WATER RESOURCES

614.7 NE ISSN 0197-4823
CODEN: FAPSEK
FUNDAMENTAL ASPECTS OF POLLUTION CONTROL AND ENVIRONMENTAL SCIENCE. (Text in English) 1977. irreg., vol.8, 1987. price varies. Elsevier Science B.V., Books Division, P.O. Box 211, 1000 AE Amsterdam, Netherlands. TEL 31-20-5803911. FAX 31-20-5803705. TELEX 18582 ESPA NL. (Subscr. in U.S. and Canada to: Elsevier Science Inc., Box 882, Madison Sq. Sta., New York, NY 10159. TEL 212-989-5800) **Indexed:** GeoRef. **Document type:** monographic series.
—CCC.
Refereed Serial

628.53 UK
GREAT BRITAIN. WARREN SPRING LABORATORY. U K SMOKE AND SULPHUR DIOXIDE MONITORING NETWORKS. a. price varies. Warren Spring Laboratory, Gunnels Wood Rd., Stevenage, Herts. SG1 2BX, England. TEL 0438-741122. FAX 0438-360858.
Formerly (until 1982): Great Britain. Warren Spring Laboratory. Investigation of Air Pollution: National Survey, Smoke and Sulphur Dioxide (ISSN 0585-2730)

628.5 JA
HOKKAIDO RESEARCH INSTITUTE FOR ENVIRONMENTAL POLLUTION. REPORT/HOKKAIDO KOGAI BOSHI KENKYUJO HO. (Text in Japanese; summaries in English or Japanese.) 1975. irreg. Hokkaido Research Institute for Environmental Pollution - Hokkaido Kogai Boshi Kenkyujo., Nishi 12-chome, Kita 19-Jo, Kita-ku, Sapporo 060, Japan. Ed. K. Nakamura. illus.

I A Q PRODUCT & SERVICE GUIDE; the directory of products and services for control of indoor air quality. see BUSINESS AND ECONOMICS — Trade And Industrial Directories

614.7 II
CODEN: TAICDM
I A W P C TECHNICAL ANNUAL. (Text in English) a. Indian Association for Water Pollution Control, Nehru Marg, Nagpur 440 020, India. **Indexed:** Sel.Water Res.Abstr.

628.168 US
IDAHO CURRENTS. m. free. Department of Water Resources, Statehouse Mail, Boise, ID 83720. **Indexed:** Environ.Abstr. **Document type:** government publication.
Description: Covers energy and water issues in the state of Idaho.

628.53 US
ILLINOIS. BUREAU OF AIR. ANNUAL AIR QUALITY REPORT. 1968. a. free. Environmental Protection Agency, Bureau of Air, Ambient Air Monitoring Section, 2200 Churchill Rd., Springfield, IL 62706. circ. 1,000.
Former titles: Illinois. Division of Air Pollution Control. Annual Air Quality Report; (until 1975): Illinois Air Quality Report (ISSN 0360-9162); Incorporates: Illinois. Division of Air Pollution Control. Semi-Annual Report; (in 1974): Illinois Air Sampling Network Report (ISSN 0092-3281)

628.53 US ISSN 1055-5242
INDOOR AIR BULLETIN; technology, research, and news for indoor environmental quality. 1991. m. $195 (foreign $235). Indoor Information Service, Inc., 2548 Empire Grade, Santa Cruz, CA 95060. FAX 408-426-6522. (Subscr. to: Box 8446, Santa Cruz, CA 95061-8446. TEL 408-426-6624) Ed. Hal Levin. bk.rev. **Document type:** newsletter.

ENVIRONMENTAL STUDIES — POLLUTION

INDOOR POLLUTION LAW REPORT. see *LAW*

628.53   US   ISSN 0896-8594
                                CODEN: IPONE2
INDOOR POLLUTION NEWS; the bi-weekly newsletter on regulation, legislation, and litigation. 1988. bi-w. $507. Business Publishers, Inc., 951 Pershing Dr., Silver Spring, MD 20910-4464. TEL 301-587-6300. FAX 301-585-9075. Ed. Richard Hagan. Document type: newsletter.
—CCC.
Description: Concerned with problems of air quality in buildings (radon, formaldehyde, solvents, asbestos, lead, especially in pipes). Includes information on technological developments.

620.3   US   ISSN 0105-175X
INTERNATIONAL CONFERENCE ON NOISE CONTROL ENGINEERING. PROCEEDINGS. Key Title: Inter-Noise - International Conference on Noise Control Engineering. Cover title: Inter-Noise (Year). (In 3 vols.) 1972. irreg., approx. a., 23nd, 1994, Yokohama. price varies. Noise Control Foundation, Box 2469, Arlington Branch, Poughkeepsie, NY 12603. TEL 914-462-4006. (back issues avail.)
Document type: academic/scholarly publication, proceedings.
—BLDSC (4557.220500).
Description: Publishes lectures, reports and research presented at the conference.

628.168   CN   ISSN 0842-3733
TD223.3
INTERNATIONAL JOINT COMMISSION FROM THE INTERNATIONAL REFERENCE GROUP ON GREAT LAKES POLLUTION FROM LAND USE ACTIVITIES. ANNUAL PROGRESS REPORT. 1975. q. International Joint Commission, Great Lakes Regional Office, 100 Ouellette Ave., Windsor, Ont. N9A 6T3, Canada.

614.7 639.9   SZ   ISSN 0957-4352
TD1   CODEN: IJVLEN
INTERNATIONAL JOURNAL OF ENVIRONMENT AND POLLUTION. (Text in English) 1991. q. $155 in North America; elsewhere £100. (European Centre for Pollution Research, UK) Inderscience Enterprises Ltd., World Trade Centre Bldg., 110 Ave. Louis Casai, Case Postale 309, CH-1215 Geneva-Aeroport, Switzerland. FAX 22-7910885. TELEX 289950. (Co-sponsor: Unesco) Indexed: Environ.Abstr., Environ.Per.Bibl. (1991-).
—BLDSC (4542.240800); CASDDS.
Description: Examines environmental policy, pollution control as well as sustainable development in these fields.

INTERNATIONAL OIL SPILL CONTROL DIRECTORY. see *PETROLEUM AND GAS*

INTERNATIONAL OIL SPILL DATABASE; international summary and review. see *PETROLEUM AND GAS — Abstracting, Bibliographies, Statistics*

628.53   JA   ISSN 0039-9000
JAPAN SOCIETY OF AIR POLLUTION. JOURNAL/TAIKI OSEN KENKYU. (Includes Taiki Osen Nyusu) (Text in Japanese; summaries in English) 1966. bi-m. 10000 Yen($70) Japan Society of Air Pollution - Taiki Osen Kenkyu Kyokai, 1-29-8 Shinjuku, Shinjuku-ku, Tokyo 160, Japan. TEL 03-3341-5632. FAX 03-3341-8224. Ed. Keiichi Furuya. adv.; bk.rev. circ. 2,000. Indexed: Biol.Abstr., C.I.S.Abstr., Chem.Abstr., Excerp.Med., Int.Aerosp.Abstr.

628.168 371.42   US
JOB BANK. bi-w. $72 (foreign $84). Water Environment Federation, 601 Wythe St., Alexandria, VA 22314-1994. TEL 703-684-2400. FAX 703-684-2492. Ed. Macarena De La Piedra.
Document type: newsletter.
Description: Keeps readers posted on the latest job openings for water quality personnel across the country.

614.7   US   ISSN 1052-1062
TD194   CODEN: JCTSEU
JOURNAL OF CLEAN TECHNOLOGY AND ENVIRONMENTAL SCIENCES. 1991. q. $120 (effective 1994). Princeton Scientific Publishing Co., Inc., Box 2155, Princeton, NJ 08543. TEL 609-683-4750. FAX 609-683-0838. Eds. M.A. Mehlman, S.P. Maltezov. Document type: academic/scholarly publication.
—BLDSC (4958.369710); CASDDS. **CCC**.
Description: Covers pollution prevention and clean technology, management issues, new environmental methods of identifying pollutants, toxicology, evaluation and assessment of hazardous chemicals, toxic metals, and environmental and occupational chemicals.

551.4 628.18   NE   ISSN 0169-7722
                             CODEN: JCOHE6
JOURNAL OF CONTAMINANT HYDROLOGY. (Text and summaries in English) 1986. 12/yr. (in 3 vols.; 4 nos./vol.). fl.1173($553) (effective 1994). Elsevier Science B.V., P.O. Box 211, 1000 AH Amsterdam, Netherlands. TEL 31-20-5803911. FAX 31-20-5803598. TELEX 18582 ESPA NL. (Subscr. in U.S. and Canada to: Elsevier Science Inc., Box 882, Madison Sq. Sta., New York, NY 10159-0882. TEL 212-989-5800. FAX 212-633-3990) Ed.Bd. adv.; bk.rev. circ. 800. (also avail. in microform from UMI; back issues avail.) Indexed: Environ.Abstr., Environ.Per.Bibl. (1989-), Excerp.Med., Sel.Water Res.Abstr., Soils & Fert.
Document type: academic/scholarly publication.
—BLDSC (4965.220500); EI; Faxon; UnCover; SWETS; CASDDS. **CCC**.
Description: Publishes scientific articles pertaining to the contamination of groundwater.
Refereed Serial

JOURNAL OF ECOTOXICOLOGY & ENVIRONMENTAL MONITORING; an international journal for scientific research on toxicology and pollution. see *ENVIRONMENTAL STUDIES — Toxicology And Environmental Safety*

620.8   II   ISSN 0970-2083
                       CODEN: JIPCE4
JOURNAL OF INDUSTRIAL POLLUTION CONTROL. (Text in English) 1985. s-a. Rs.100 to individuals (foreign $50); institutions Rs.200 (foreign $100). Enviro Media, Post Box 90, Karad 415 110, India. TEL 91-02164-44369. Ed. R.K. Trivedy. bk.rev.
Document type: academic/scholarly publication.
—BLDSC (5006.347000); Faxon; CASDDS.
Description: Publishes research papers and news on all aspects of industrial pollution and control.

614.7 631   US   ISSN 1058-8337
TD878   CODEN: JSOCEZ
▼ **JOURNAL OF SOIL CONTAMINATION.** 1992. q. $175 to individuals (foreign $182.95); institutions $350 (foreign $357.95). (Association for the Environmental Health of Soils) C R C Press, Inc., 2000 Corporate Blvd., N.W., Boca Raton, FL 33431. TEL 407-994-0555. FAX 407-998-9784. TELEX 568689-CRC PRESS. (Subscr. to: Box 750, Pearl River, NY 10965-0750. TEL 800-272-7737) Ed. James Dragun. Indexed: Environ.Abstr., Environ.Per.Bibl. (1992-).
—BLDSC (5064.965000); EI; Faxon; SWETS; CASDDS. **CCC**.
Description: Provides a direct link between the association's membership and those disciplines concerned with the technical, regulatory, and legal challenges of contaminated soil.
Refereed Serial

628.168   US   ISSN 0709-0013
LAKES LETTER. 1969. s-a. International Association for Great Lakes Research, 2200 Bonisteel Blvd., Ann Arbor, MI 48109. Indexed: Environ.Abstr.
—CIS.

628.5   GW   ISSN 0340-4900
Z6673
LITERATURBERICHTE UEBER WASSER, ABWASSER, LUFT UND FESTE ABFALLSTOFFE. irreg. DM.470 (foreign DM.476). Gustav Fischer Verlag, Wollgrasweg 49, 70599 Stuttgart, Germany. TEL 0711-458030. FAX 0711-4580334. TELEX 7111488-FIBUCH. (Subscr. to: Postfach 720143, 70577 Stuttgart, Germany; U.S. address: Gustav Fischer New York Inc., 220 E. 23rd St., Ste. 909, New York, NY 10010) Ed. F. Meinck. Document type: academic/scholarly publication.
—CCC.

363.739   NE   ISSN 0925-9953
LUCHT. 1984. q. Samsom Uitgeverij B.V. (Subsidiary of: Wolter Kluwer N.V.), Postbus 4, 2400 MA Alphen aan den Rijn Netherlands. TEL 31-1720-66822. FAX 31-1720-66639.
—SWETS.
Formerly (until 1991): Lucht en Omgeving (ISSN 0168-8138)
Description: Depicts latest developments in control of air pollution.

628.53   GW
LUFTHYGIENISCHER MONATSBERICHT. 1973. m. DM.30. Landesanstalt fuer Umwelt, Postfach 3209, 65022 Wiesbaden, Germany. TEL 0611-69390. FAX 0611-6939555. TELEX 4186278-HLFU-D. Pub. Klaus Hanewald. circ. 400. (back issues avail.) Document type: government publication.
Formerly: Bericht ueber Schwebstaubmessungen in Hessen im Messjahr (Year).

628.53   GW   ISSN 0460-2374
TD881   CODEN: LFTVAA
LUFTVERUNREINIGUNG. 1973. a. DM.15. Deutscher Kommunal Verlag GmbH, Roseggerstr. 5a, 40470 Duesseldorf, Germany. TEL 0211-624417. FAX 0211-622998. Ed. H.J. Schumacher. adv.; bk.rev.; charts; ilus.
—BLDSC (5304.171000); CASDDS.

628.5 551.46   UK   ISSN 0141-1136
QH545.W3   CODEN: MERSDW
MARINE ENVIRONMENTAL RESEARCH. 1978. 8/yr. (in 2 vols., 4 nos./vol.). £360($555) (effective 1994). Elsevier Science Ltd., Oxford Fulfilment Centre, P.O. Box 800, Kidlington, Oxford OX5 1DX, England. TEL 44-865-843000. FAX 44-865-843010. (Subscr. in U.S. and Canada to: Elsevier Science, 660 White Plains Rd., Tarrytown, NY 10591-5153. TEL 914-524-9200. FAX 914-333-2444) Eds. G. Roesijadi, R.B. Spies. adv.; bk.rev.; illus.; index. (also avail. in microform from UMI; back issues avail.) Indexed: API Abstr., API Catal., API Hlth.& Environ., API Oil., API Pet.Re^2., API Pet.Subst., API Transport., Aqua.Sci.& Fish.Abstr., Biol.Abstr., Cadscan, Chem.Abstr., Curr.Adv.Ecol.Sci., Curr.Cont., Curr.Ref.Fish Res., Deep Sea Res.& Oceanogr.Abstr., E&P Hlth. (1993-), Energy Ind., Energy Info.Abstr., Energy Rev., Eng.Ind., Environ.Abstr., Environ.Per.Bibl. (1985-), Excerp.Med., Gas Process.& Ppl. (1993-), Geo.Abstr., GeoRef., Ind.Sci.Rev., Ind.Vet., Lead Abstr., Mar.Sci.Cont.Tab., Ocean.Abstr., Off.Tech. (1993-), Petrol.Abstr. (1981-), Pollut.Abstr., Risk Abstr., Sel.Water Res.Abstr., Soils & Fert., Vet.Bull., W.R.C.Inf., Zincscan. Document type: academic/scholarly publication.
—BLDSC (5375.270000); EI; Faxon; UnCover; SWETS; CASDDS. **CCC**.
Incorporates (1982-1991): Oil and Chemical Pollution (ISSN 0269-8579); Which was formerly: Journal of Oil and Petrochemical Pollution (ISSN 0143-7127)
Description: Provides research papers on chemical, physical and biological interactions in the oceans and coastal waters. Serves as a forum for new information on biology, chemistry and toxicology.
Refereed Serial

ENVIRONMENTAL STUDIES — POLLUTION

628.5 — UK — ISSN 0025-326X
GC1080 — CODEN: MPNBAZ
MARINE POLLUTION BULLETIN; the international journal for marine environmentalists, scientists, engineers, administrators, politicians and lawyers. 1970. 24/yr. (in 2 vols.). £278($430) (effective 1994). Elsevier Science Ltd., Pergamon, P.O. Box 800, Kidlington, Oxford OX5 1DX, England. TEL 44-865-843000. FAX 44-865-843010. (Subscr. in U.S. and Canada to: Elsevier Science, 660 White Plains Rd., Tarrytown, NY 10591-5153. TEL 914-524-9200. FAX 914-333-2444) Ed. C. Sheppard. adv.; bk.rev.; illus.; stat.; index. circ 2,000. (also avail. in microfilm from UMI) **Indexed:** Acid Pre.Dig., API Abstr., API Catal., API Hlth.& Environ., API Oil., API Pet.Ref., API Pet.Subst., API Transport., Biol.Abstr., Cadscan., Chem.Abstr., Curr.Adv.Ecol.Sci., Curr.Cont., Curr.Ref.Fish Res., Curr.Tit.Ocean, Deep Sea Res.& Oceanogr.Abstr., E&P Hlth. (1993-), ELLIS, Energy Rev., Environ.Abstr., Environ.Per.Bibl. (1972-), Excerp.Med., Food Sci.& Tech.Abstr., Gas Process.& Ppl. (1993-), Geo.Abstr., GeoRef., Helminthol.Abstr., Ind.Sci.Rev., Ind.Vet., INIS Atomind., Lead Abstr., Ocean.Abstr., Off.Tech. (1993-), Petrol.Abstr. (1981-), Pollut.Abstr., Risk Abstr., Sci.Abstr., Sel.Water Res.Abstr., Vet.Bull., W.R.C.Inf., Weed Abstr., Zincscan. **Document type:** academic/scholarly publication, bulletin.
—BLDSC (5377.500000); EI; Faxon; UnCover; SWETS; UMI; CASDDS. **CCC.**
Description: Concerned with the rational use of maritime and marine resources in estuaries, seas and oceans.
Refereed Serial

MARINE POLLUTION RESEARCH TITLES. see *ENVIRONMENTAL STUDIES — Abstracting, Bibliographies, Statistics*

628.5 — US
MARYLAND AIR AND RADIATION MANAGEMENT ADMINISTRATION. DATA REPORT. Cover title: Maryland Air Quality Data Report. 1971. a. $5. Maryland Air and Radiation Management Administration, Division of Quality Assurance and Information Systems, 2500 Broening Highway, Baltimore, MD 21224. TEL 401-631-3280. illus. circ. 400. **Document type:** government publication.
Former titles: Maryland Air Management Administration. Data Report; Maryland Air Quality Programs. Data Report; Maryland Air Quality Programs; Maryland. Bureau of Air Quality and Noise Control. Data Report; Maryland. Bureau of Air Quality Control. State-Local Cooperative Air Sampling Program Yearly Data Report (ISSN 0094-4629)

628.5 — US
N E I W P C C ANNUAL REPORT. a. New England Interstate Water Pollution Control Commission, 255 Ballardvale St., Wilmington, MA 01887-1013. TEL 508-658-0500. FAX 508-658-5509. illus.

628.5 — US
N E I W P C C WATER CONNECTION. 1970. q. free. New England Interstate Water Pollution Control Commission, 255 Ballardvale Rd., Wilmington, MA 01887-1013. TEL 508-658-0500. FAX 508-658-5509. Ed. Ellen Frye. charts; illus. circ. 1,800. **Indexed:** Environ.Abstr. **Document type:** newsletter.
Formerly (until 1984): N E I W P C C Aqua News (ISSN 0550-4791)

363.73 — US
N O A C A NEWS. 1969. q. free. Northeast Ohio Areawide Coordinating Agency, Atrium Office Plaza, 668 Euclid Ave., Cleveland, OH 44115-3000. TEL 216-241-2414. FAX 216-621-3024. Eds. Steven A. Jones, Cheryl Onesky. bk.rev.; illus. circ. 2,500. **Document type:** newsletter.

628.53 — UK
N.S.C.A. POLLUTION HANDBOOK; comprehensive guide to all aspects of air pollution control, noise, waste and other environmental matters. 1978. a. £21.95. National Society for Clean Air and Environmental Protection, 136 North St., Brighton BN1 1RG, England. TEL 0273-26313. FAX 0273-735802. Ed. Lovedy Murley. adv.; index. **Document type:** bulletin.
Former titles: N.S.C.A. Reference Book (ISSN 0140-6795); N.S.C.A. Yearbook; Clean Air Year Book (ISSN 0069-4606)
Description: Information on U.K. pollution legislation.

N T I S ALERTS: ENVIRONMENTAL POLLUTION & CONTROL. see *ENVIRONMENTAL STUDIES — Abstracting, Bibliographies, Statistics*

628.53 — US — ISSN 0885-2448
NATIONAL AIR QUALITY AND EMISSIONS TRENDS REPORT. Variant title: Ambient Assessment Air Portion. 1973. a. price varies. U.S. Environmental Protection Agency, Office of Air Quality Planning and Standards, Technical Support Division (MD-14), Research Triangle Park, NC 27711. TEL 919-541-5558. (Orders to: National Technical Information Service, 5285 Port Royal Rd., Springfield, VA 22161. TEL 703-487-4650. FAX 703-512-2233) Ed. Thomas C. Curran. charts; stat. circ. 5,000. (also avail. in microfiche from NTI) **Document type:** government publication.
Formerly (until 1977): National Air Monitoring Program Air Quality and Emissions Trends. Report (ISSN 0092-9670)

628.5 — US
NATIONAL COUNCIL OF THE PAPER INDUSTRY FOR AIR AND STREAM IMPROVEMENT. TECHNICAL BULLETIN. Short title: N C A S I Technical Bulletin. 1945. irreg. (approx. 32/yr.). $1200. National Council of the Paper Industry for Air and Stream Improvement, Inc., 260 Madison Ave., New York, NY 10016. TEL 212-532-9000. FAX 212-779-2849. index. circ. 1,500. (back issues avail.) **Indexed:** Abstr.Bull.Inst.Pap.Chem., Forest Prod.Abstr. **Document type:** bulletin.
Formed by the merger of: Stream Improvement Technical Bulletin (ISSN 0360-8751); Atmospheric Quality Improvement Technical Bulletin (ISSN 0360-8778); Which was formerly: Atmospheric Pollution Technical Bulletin.
Description: Publishes results of research efforts and technical studies programs conducted by the council.

628.53 — US — ISSN 0077-8451
NEW JERSEY CLEAN AIR COUNCIL. REPORT. a. Department of Environmental Protection, New Jersey Clean Air Council, 401 E. State St., Trenton, NJ 08625. TEL 609-292-2885. FAX 609-292-6704.

NOISE & VIBRATION BULLETIN. see *ENVIRONMENTAL STUDIES — Abstracting, Bibliographies, Statistics*

620.3 — US — ISSN 0736-2935
NOISE-CON PROCEEDINGS. Represents: National Conference on Noise Control Engineering. Proceedings. 1973. irreg., approx. a., 13th, 1994, Ft. Lauderdale. $95 (effective 1994). Noise Control Foundation, Box 2469, Arlington Branch, Poughkeepsie, NY 12603. TEL 914-462-4006. (back issues avail.) **Document type:** proceedings.
—BLDSC (6115.950000).

620.3 — US — ISSN 1021-643X
NOISE - NEWS INTERNATIONAL. 1972. q. $40 (overseas $52) (effective 1994). Institute of Noise Control Engineering, Box 3206, Arlington Branch, Poughkeepsie, NY 12603. TEL 914-462-4006. Ed. G.C. Maling, Jr. bk.rev.; illus. circ. 4,300. **Document type:** academic/scholarly publication.
—BLDSC (6116.077000).
Formerly (until 1993): Noise - News (ISSN 0146-4809)
Description: Reports on activities in noise control.

628.78 — US — ISSN 1043-5565
TD891
NOISE REGULATION REPORT. 1971. bi-w. $429 (effective Sep. 1992). Business Publishers, Inc., 951 Pershing Dr., Silver Spring, MD 20910-4464. TEL 301-587-6300. FAX 301-585-9075. Ed. Bryan K. Morris. bk.rev. (looseleaf format) **Document type:** newsletter.
●Also available online. Vendor(s): NewsNet (EV19). —**CCC.**
Incorporates (1974-1988): Noise Regulation Reporter (ISSN 0148-7957); Formerly: Noise Control Report (ISSN 0146-4817)
Description: Regulations and technology in noise control, especially for industrial machinery and airplanes.

NONSMOKERS' VOICE. see *TOBACCO*

628.53 — BE — ISSN 0377-7669
TD881
NORTH ATLANTIC TREATY ORGANIZATION. EXPERT PANEL ON AIR POLLUTION MODELING. PROCEEDINGS. (Subseries of: Air Pollution) a. North Atlantic Treaty Organization, Committee on the Challenges of Modern Society, B-1110 Brussels, Belgium. TEL 32-2-7284567. **Document type:** proceedings.

628.168 — US
OBSERVER (ANCHORAGE). 1991. q. free. Regional Citizens' Advisory Council of Prince William Sound, 750 W. Second Ave., No. 100, Anchorage, AK 99501-2167. TEL 907-277-7222. FAX 907-277-4523. Ed. Patty Ginsburg. **Document type:** newsletter.
Description: Reports on environmental impacts associated with the terminal and tanker fleet.

OIL SPILL CONTINGENCY PLANNER; the compliance guide for vessels, facilities, and pipelines. see *PETROLEUM AND GAS*

628.5 — CN — ISSN 0078-5148
ONTARIO. MINISTRY OF THE ENVIRONMENT. POLLUTION CONTROL BRANCH. RESEARCH PUBLICATION. 1959. irreg. free. Ministry of the Environment, Pollution Control Branch, 135 St. Clair Ave. W., Toronto, Ont. M4V 1P5, Canada. TEL 416-965-6971. circ. 300. **Indexed:** GeoRef., Pollut.Abstr.

628.53 551.6 — UN
OZONE LAYER BULLETIN. (Text in English) 1978. s-a. United Nations Environment Programme, Information Service, Box 30552, Nairobi, Kenya.

628.53 550.5 — US — ISSN 1065-5905
OZONE NEWS. 1973. bi-m. $100. International Ozone Association, c/o Dr. Rip G. Rice, Ed., 1331 Patuxent Dr., Ashton, MD 20861. TEL 301-924-4224. FAX 301-774-4493. TELEX 1-440730-ITS-UT. adv. contact: Rip G. Rice. bk.rev. circ. 1,500. **Document type:** newsletter.
Description: Information about ozone technology, Association meetings and activities.

P A S C A L E 36: POLLUTION DE L'EAU, DE L'AIR ET DU SOL - DECHETS - BRUIT. see *ENVIRONMENTAL STUDIES — Abstracting, Bibliographies, Statistics*

628.5 — UK — ISSN 0048-4784
POLLUTION; environmental news bulletin. 1971. m. £82.50 (foreign £87.50). Springfield Information Services, P.O. Box 31, Peterborough, Cambs., PE1 1SD, England. TEL 0733-267272. Ed. John Franks. bk.rev.; abstr.; tr.lit. (back issues avail.) **Indexed:** Key to Econ.Sci. **Document type:** newsletter.
—BLDSC (6544.265000).

363.73 — US — ISSN 0273-253X
POLLUTION. (Subseries of: S I R S Social Issues (ISSN 0740-3127)) 1974. a. price varies; a. supplement $17. Social Issues Resources Series, Box 2348, Boca Raton, FL 33427-2348. TEL 407-994-0079; 800-232-7477. FAX 407-994-4704. (looseleaf format; also avail. in microfiche; back issues avail.)
Description: Reprints articles on the social implications of air, water, and noise pollution.

POLLUTION ABSTRACTS. see *ENVIRONMENTAL STUDIES — Abstracting, Bibliographies, Statistics*

628.53 — FR — ISSN 0032-3632
CODEN: POATBH
POLLUTION ATMOSPHERIQUE. (Text in French; summaries in English, French) 1959. q. 445 F. (foreign 645 F.) (effective 1994). Association pour la Prevention de la Pollution Atmospheriques, 58 rue du Rocher, 75008 Paris, France. TEL 42-93-69-30. FAX 42-93-41-99. Ed. M. Sommer. adv.; bk.rev.; bibl.; charts; illus.; stat.; circ. 2,000 (controlled). **Indexed:** Acid Pre.Dig., Biol.Abstr., C.I.S. Abstr., Chem.Abstr., Excerp.Med. (until 1993), Meteor.& Geostrophys.Abstr., Ocean.Abstr., Pollut.Abstr. —BLDSC (6544.280000); SWETS; CASDDS.

ENVIRONMENTAL STUDIES — POLLUTION

628.5 US ISSN 0032-3640
TD172 CODEN: PLENBW
POLLUTION ENGINEERING; magazine of environmental control. 1969. 13/yr. (includes a. Product - Service Locator). $70 (Canada $102; Mexico $95; elsewhere $130). Cahners Publishing Company (Des Plaines), Division of Reed Elsevier Inc., 1350 E. Touhy Ave., Box 5080, Des Plaines, IL 60017-5080. TEL 708-635-8800. FAX 708-390-2636. (Subscr. to: 44 Cook St., Denver, CO 80206. TEL 800-662-7776) Ed. Diane Pirocanac. adv.; bk.rev.; charts; illus.; tr.lit.; index; circ. 58,000 (controlled). (also avail. in microform from UMI) **Indexed**: A.S.& T.Ind., Acid Pre.Dig., Acid Rain Abstr., Acid Rain Ind., API Abstr., API Catal., API Hlth.& Environ., API Oil., API Pet.Ref., API Pet.Subst., API Transport., Biol.Abstr., Chem.Abstr., Energy Info.Abstr., Eng.Ind., Environ.Abstr., Environ.Per.Bibl., Excerp.Med., Geo.Abstr., Key to Econ.Sci., Ocean.Abstr., Pollut.Abstr., Sci.Abstr., Sel.Water Res.Abstr., Telegen., W.R.C.Inf. **Document type**: trade publication.
—BLDSC (6544.290000); CIS; EI; Faxon; UnCover; SWETS; UMI; CASDDS. **CCC**.

POLLUTION ENGINEERING PRODUCT - SERVICE LOCATOR. see *ENVIRONMENTAL STUDIES — Waste Management*

628.5 US ISSN 0032-3659
TD1
POLLUTION EQUIPMENT NEWS. 1968. 8/yr. $35 ($50 outside N. America) (free to qualified personnel). Rimbach Publishing, Inc., 8650 Babcock Blvd., Pittsburgh, PA 15237. TEL 412-364-5366. Ed. David C. Lavender. adv.; bk.rev. circ. 91,925. (tabloid format) **Indexed**: Curr.Pack.Abstr., W.R.C.Inf. **Document type**: trade publication.
—SWETS.
Description: Information on air, water, wastewater and hazardous waste pollution control.

POLLUTION LAW REPORTING SERVICE. see *LAW*

628.5 US
POLLUTION PREVENTION; the journal for the protection of the environment. 1991. 7/yr. £50($90) 3300 S. Gessner, Ste. 118, Houston, TX 77063. TEL 713-266-0610. FAX 713-266-6657.

POLLUTION PREVENTION REVIEW. see *ENVIRONMENTAL STUDIES — Waste Management*

628.5 II ISSN 0257-8050
CODEN: PORSDX
POLLUTION RESEARCH. (Text in English) 1982. q. Rs.200($50) to individuals; institutions Rs.400 ($150). (Indian Association for Pollution Chemists and Biologists) Enviro Media, Post Box 90, Karad 415 110, India. Ed. R.K. Trivedy. adv.; bk.rev. **Document type**: academic/scholarly publication.
—BLDSC (6544.296650); CASDDS.
Description: Contains research papers, and technical notes on all aspects of environmental issues.

628.5 US ISSN 0090-516X
CODEN: PTERDY
POLLUTION TECHNOLOGY REVIEW. 1973. irreg., no.214, 1994. price varies. Noyes Data Corporation, 120 Mill Rd., Park Ridge, NJ 07656. TEL 201-391-8484. FAX 201-391-6833. Pub. Roger Noyes. **Document type**: academic/scholarly publication, monographic series.
—BLDSC (6544.298000).
Formerly: Pollution Control Review (ISSN 0079-3116)
Description: In-depth studies of specific topics pertaining to technology, pollution and the environment, including municipal waste treatment, hazardous waste clean-up, remediation, containment, spill prevention, and hazardous materials handling.

628.53 540 LI ISSN 0203-7483
PROTECTION OF ATMOSPHERE AGAINST POLLUTION; determination of atmospheric background pollution in South Prebaltic. (Text and summaries in English) 1973. a. $5. Institute of Physics, A. Gostauto Str. 12, Vilnius 2600, Lithuania. TEL 641154.
Description: Methods for determining background concentration of chemical admixture in air and precipitation. Includes experimental data.

628.1 NE
REINWATER. 1980. q. fl.47.50. Stichting Reinwater, Vossiusstraat 20, 1071 AD Amsterdam, Netherlands. TEL 31-20-719322. FAX 31-20-753806. Ed. W. Verhoog. bk.rev. circ. 1,500. **Document type**: bulletin.
Description: Covers the problems and solutions of water pollution in the Netherlands by focusing on the condition of the main European rivers.

628.5 MX
REUNION NACIONAL SOBRE PROBLEMAS DE CONTAMINACION AMBIENTAL. MEMORIA. 1973. irreg. Secretaria de Salud, Av. Dr. Francisco de P. Miranda 177, Col. Merced Gomez, Deleg. Alvaro Obregon, C.P. 01600, Mexico, D.F., Mexico. illus.

628.5 CN ISSN 0823-4574
S T O P PRESS. (Text in English, French) 1970. q. Can.$35. Society to Overcome Pollution, Inc., 716 St-Ferdinand, Montreal, Que. H4C 2T2, Canada. TEL 514-932-7267. FAX 514-932-7267. Ed. D. O'Leary. adv.; bk.rev. circ. 2,500. (back issues avail.)
Formerly (until 1982): S O S Montreal (ISSN 0383-6347); Which incorporated (in 1977): S O S Press (ISSN 0705-1212); (until 1972): S T O P Newsletter (ISSN 0381-9000)

628.168 614.85 US
SAFETY AND HEALTH BULLETIN. q. $15 (foreign $20). Water Environment Federation, Safety and Occupational Health Committee, 601 Wythe St., Alexandria, VA 22314-1994. TEL 703-684-1994. FAX 703-684-2492. Ed. Jerry Wright. **Document type**: newsletter.
Description: Informs readers about on-the-job accidents, so they can learn to avoid or prevent the conditions and practices that contributed to the accident.

628.53 GW ISSN 0724-4770
SCHWEBSTAUBMESSUNGEN IN HESSEN. BERICHT IM MESSJAHR. 1977. irreg. Hessische Landesanstalt fuer Umwelt, Rheingaustr. 186, 65203 Wiesbaden, Germany. TEL 0611-69390. FAX 0611-6939555. TELEX 4186278-HLFU-D. circ. 500. (back issues avail.) **Document type**: government publication.

THE SCIENCE OF THE TOTAL ENVIRONMENT; an international journal for scientific research into the environment and its relationship with man. see *ENVIRONMENTAL STUDIES*

613.1 US
▼**SHEPARD'S CLEAN AIR ACT REPORTER**. 1992. m. $250. Shepard's - McGraw-Hill, Inc., 555 Middle Creek Pkwy., Colorado Springs, CO 80921-3630. TEL 800-525-2474. (Subscr. to: Box 35300, Colorado Springs, CO 80935-3530) Ed. Edward J. McGrath.
Description: Focuses on the industrial impact of the Clean Air Act, the federal and state regulations issued under it, and how businesses can comply with these regulations.

628.53 JA
TAIKI OSEN BUSSHITSU NO REBYU/REVIEW OF ATMOSPHERIC POLLUTANTS. (Text in Japanese) irreg. Japan Information Center of Science and Technology - Nihon Kagaku Gijutsu Joho Senta, 5-2, Nagatacho 2-chome, Chiyoda-ku, Tokyo 100, Japan.

628.168 US
▼**TECHLINK: AIR POLLUTION**. 1993. m. $200 (outside N. America $280). U.S. National Technical Information Service, 5285 Port Royal Rd., Springfield, VA 22161. TEL 703-487-4650. FAX 703-321-8547. (Co-sponsor: Engineering Information, Inc.) bibl. (annual summary avail.) **Document type**: newsletter, government publication.
Description: Draws upon technical, scientific and engineering data on air pollution contained in the Compendex Plus and NTIS Bibliographic databases.

628.168 US
▼**TECHLINK: WATER POLLUTION**. (Order no.: PB93-972200) 1993. m. $300 (outside N. America $280). U.S. National Technical Information Service, 5285 Port Royal Rd., Springfield, VA 22161. TEL 703-487-4630. FAX 703-321-8547. (Co-sponsor: Engineering Information, Inc.) bibl. (yearbook avail.) **Document type**: newsletter, government publication.
Description: Draws upon the scientific, technical and engineering data on water pollution contained in the Compendex Plus and NTIS Bibliographic databases.

628.5 US
TEXAS POLLUTION REPORT. 1964. every 10 days. $70. Box 12368, Capitol Station, Austin, TX 78711. TEL 512-478-5663. FAX 512-478-5663. Ed. Bill Kidd. bk.rev. circ. 400.

TOXIC CHEMICALS - INDOOR POLLUTION LITIGATION REPORTER; the national journal of record for litigation involving claims of personal injury and/or property damage from exposure to toxic chemicals. see *LAW*

628.53 551.5 SA ISSN 0379-4709
TYDSKRIF VIR SKOONLUG/CLEAN AIR JOURNAL. (Text in Afrikaans, English) 1971. s-a. R.25 (effective 1994). National Association for Clean Air, P.O. Box 5777, Johannesburg 2000, South Africa. TEL 27-11-6462210. FAX 27-11-6462210. Ed. G. Kornelius. adv.; circ. 480 (paid). **Indexed**: INIS Atomind. **Document type**: academic/scholarly publication.
Description: Examines remedies to air pollution.

628.5 GW ISSN 0041-6355
TD172 CODEN: UMWLDA
UMWELT; Immissionsschutz - Abfall - Gewaesserschutz. 1971. 9/yr. DM.250($87.50) includes 2 special supplements. (Verein Deutscher Ingenieure) V D I Verlag GmbH, Heinrichstr. 24, 40239 Duesseldorf, Germany. TEL 0211-6188-0. FAX 0211-6188-112. TELEX 8587743. (Subscr. to: Postfach 101054, 40001 Duesseldorf, Germany) Ed. R.B. Firnhaber. adv.; bk.rev.; abstr.; charts; illus.; pat.; stat. circ. 17,500. **Indexed**: Chem.Abstr., Key to Econ.Sci., W.R.C.Inf. **Document type**: academic/scholarly publication.
—SWETS; CASDDS. **CCC**.

628 343.01 US
U.S. ARMY. ENVIRONMENTAL COMPLIANCE ASSESSMENT SYSTEM (ECAS). ANNUAL REPORT. a. U.S. Department of the Army, Aberdeen Proving Ground, MD 21010-5401. **Document type**: government publication.
Description: Summarizes the status of the U.S. Army Environmental Compliance Assessment System.

U.S. DEPARTMENT OF THE INTERIOR. A L J DECISIONS. see *PUBLIC ADMINISTRATION*

U.S. DEPARTMENT OF THE INTERIOR. INTERIOR BOARD OF LAND APPEALS. see *PUBLIC ADMINISTRATION*

333.9 US ISSN 0098-4922
GC1085
U.S. NATIONAL OCEANIC AND ATMOSPHERIC ADMINISTRATION. REPORT TO THE CONGRESS ON OCEAN POLLUTION, OVERFISHING, AND OFFSHORE DEVELOPMENT. Key Title: Report to the Congress on Ocean Pollution, Overfishing, and Offshore Development. 1973. a. $1.45. U.S. National Oceanic and Atmospheric Administration, 6010 Executive Blvd., Rockville, MD 20852. TEL 301-655-4000. (Orders to: NTIS, 5285 Port Royal Rd., Springfield, VA 22161)
Formerly: U.S. National Oceanic and Atmospheric Administration. Report to the Congress on Ocean Dumping and Other Man-Induced Changes to Ocean Ecosystems (ISSN 0094-5196)

628.5 GW ISSN 0938-8303
CODEN: WWBOE7
WASSER, LUFT UND BODEN; unabhaengige Zeitschrift fuer Wasserwirtschaft, Luftreinhaltung, Abfallverwertung und Umwelttechnik. Short title: W L B. (Includes annual issue: W L B - Handbuch-Umwelttechnik) 1957. 9/yr. DM.198 (foreign DM.230). Vereinigte Fachverlage GmbH, Lise-Meitner-Str. 2, 55129 Mainz, Germany. TEL 06131-992-01. FAX 06131-992-100. TELEX 04187752. (Subscr. to: Postfach 2760, 55017 Mainz, Germany) Ed. Hans Joachim Schmitz. adv.; bk.rev.; abstr.; charts; illus.; index. circ. 15,000. **Indexed**: Chem.Abstr., Dok.Str., Eng.Ind., Excerp.Med., Food Sci.& Tech.Abstr., Key to Econ.Sci., Nutr.Abstr., Ocean.Abstr., Pollut.Abstr., Sel.Water Res.Abstr.
—BLDSC (9264.700000); EI; SWETS; CASDDS. **CCC**.
Formerly (until 1989): Wasser, Luft und Betrieb (ISSN 0341-2679)

WASTEWATER TECHNOLOGY CENTRE NEWSLETTER/CENTRE TECHNIQUE DES EAUX USEES. BULLETIN. see *WATER RESOURCES*

ENVIRONMENTAL STUDIES — TOXICOLOGY AND ENVIRONMENTAL SAFETY

WASTEWATER WORKS NEWS. see *WATER RESOURCES*

628.5   NE   ISSN 0049-6979
TD172   CODEN: WAPLAC
WATER, AIR AND SOIL POLLUTION; an international journal of environmental pollution. (Text in English) 1971. 28/yr. fl.2912($1519) (effective 1994). Kluwer Academic Publishers, Postbus 17, 3300 AA Dordrecht, Netherlands. TEL 31-78-334911. FAX 31-78-334254. TELEX 29245 KAPG NL. (Dist. by: Kluwer Academic Publishers Group, P.O. Box 322, 3300 AH Dordrecht, Netherlands. TEL 31-78-524400. FAX 31-78-524474; N. America dist. addr.: Box 358, Accord Sta., Hingham, MA 02018-0358. TEL 617-871-6600. FAX 617-871-6528) Ed. Billy M. McCormac. adv.; bk.rev.; illus.; index. (also avail. in microform from UMI; reprint service avail. from SWZ) **Indexed:** Acid Pre.Dig., Acid Rain Abstr., Acid Rain Ind., API Abstr., API Catal., API Hlth.& Environ., API Oil., API Pet.Ref., API Pet.Subst., API Transport., Aqua.Sci.& Fish.Abstr., ASCA, Biol.Abstr., Biotech.Abstr., Bull.Signal, Chem.Abstr., Curr.Adv.Ecol.Sci., Curr.Biotech.Abstr., Curr.Cont., Dairy Sci.Abstr., Deep Sea Res.& Oceanogr.Abstr., Energy Rev., Eng.Ind., Environ.Abstr., Environ.Ind., Environ.Per.Bibl. (1982-), Environ.Per.Bibl., Excerp.Med., F.A.C.T., Field Crop Abstr., Fluidex, Forest.Abstr., Forest Prod.Abstr., Geo.Abstr., GeoRef., Herb.Abstr., Hort.Abstr., I D A, IBR, IBZ, Ind.Vet., INIS Atomind., Int.Aerosp.Abstr., Irr.& Drain.Abstr., Maize Abstr., Ocean.Abstr., Ornam.Hort., Phys.Ber., Pollut.Abstr., Ref.Zh., Risk Abstr., Sci.Abstr., Sci.Cit.Ind., Sel.Water Res.Abstr., Soils & Fert., Vet.Bull., W.R.C.Inf., Weed Abstr. **Document type:** academic/scholarly publication.
—BLDSC (9267.550000); CIS; El; Faxon; UnCover; SWETS; UMI; CASDDS. **CCC.**
   Description: Publishes interdisciplinary work on all the physical and biological processes affecting flora, air, water and solid earth in relation to environmental pollution.

628   UK   ISSN 0969-9775
TD201   CODEN: WTSVAK
WATER AND ENVIRONMENT INTERNATIONAL. 1899. m. £100 (overseas £110($203)) (effective 1994). International Trade Publications Ltd., Queensway House, 2 Queensway, Redhill, Surrey RH1 1QS, England. TEL 0737-768611. FAX 0737-761989. TELEX 948669-TOPJNL-G. Ed. J. Manson. adv.; bk.rev.; abstr.; illus.; stat.; tr.lit.; index. circ. 8,600. (also avail. in microform from UMI) **Indexed:** Br.Geol.Lit., Br.Tech.Ind., Chem.Abstr., Curr.Cont., Eng.Ind., Excerp.Med., Fluidex, GeoRef., Intl.Civil Eng.Abstr., Soft.Abstr.Eng., W.R.C.Inf. **Document type:** trade publication.
—BLDSC (9275.450000); UnCover; SWETS; CASDDS.
   Formerly (until 1991): Water Services (ISSN 0301-7028); (until 1974): Water and Water Engineering (ISSN 0043-1168)
   Description: Covers water pollution and treatment from an environmental perspective.

WATER & POLLUTION CONTROL. see *WATER RESOURCES*

614.7   US
WATER ENVIRONMENT FEDERATION. ANNUAL CONFERENCE PROCEEDINGS. 46th, 1973. a. $1100. Water Environment Federation, 601 Wythe St., Alexandria, VA 22314-1994. TEL 703-684-2400. FAX 703-684-2492. charts; illus. **Indexed:** Biol.Abstr. **Document type:** proceedings.
   Formerly: Water Pollution Control Federation Conference. Abstracts of Technical Papers.

628.168   US
WATER ENVIRONMENT REGULATION WATCH. m. $79 (foreign $99). Water Environment Federation, 601 Wythe St., Alexandria, VA 22314-1994. TEL 703-684-2400. FAX 703-684-2492. Ed. Steve Bagwell. **Document type:** trade publication.
   Formerly: Washington Bulletin.
   Description: Covers and analyzes all the legislative and regulatory actions affecting the water quality profession.

628.168   US   ISSN 1061-4303
TD365   CODEN: WAERED
WATER ENVIRONMENT RESEARCH. 1928. m. $144 (foreign $187). Water Environment Federation, 601 Wythe St., Alexandria, VA 22314-1994. TEL 703-684-2400. FAX 703-684-2492. Ed. Peter J. Piecuch. adv.; bk.rev.; illus.; index, cum.index: vols.1-42, 1928-1970. circ. 10,000. (also avail. in microform from UMI,PMC) **Indexed:** A.S.& T.Ind., Abstr.Bull.Inst.Pap.Chem., Acid Pre.Dig., Anal.Abstr., API Abstr., Appl.Mech.Rev., Biol.Abstr., Biotech.Abstr., Cadscan., Chem.Abstr., Chem.Eng.Abstr., Curr.Adv.Ecol.Sci., Curr.Biotech.Abstr., Curr.Cont., Dairy Sci.Abstr., Energy Ind., Eng.Ind., Environ.Abstr., Environ.Ind., Environ.Per.Bibl. (1991-), Excerp.Med., Fuel & Energy Abstr., Geo.Abstr., GeoRef., Helminthol.Abstr., Ind.Med., INIS Atomind., Irr.& Drain.Abstr., Lead Abstr., Ocean.Abstr., Pollut.Abstr., Risk Abstr., Sci.Abstr., Sel.J.Water, Sel.Water Res.Abstr., Soils & Fert., T.C.E.A., W.R.C.Inf., Zincscan. **Document type:** trade publication.
—BLDSC (9270.004600); CIS; El; Faxon; UnCover; SWETS; UMI; CASDDS. **CCC.**
   Formerly (until Jan. 1992): Water Pollution Control Federation. Research Journal (ISSN 1047-7624); Which supersedes in part (in 1989): Water Pollution Control Federation. Journal (ISSN 0043-1303); Which was formerly (until 1960): Sewage and Industrial Wastes (ISSN 0096-364X); (until 1950): Sewage Works Journal (ISSN 0096-9362)
   Refereed Serial

WATER NEWSLETTER; water supply, waste disposal, conservation, pollution. see *WATER RESOURCES*

WATER POLLUTION: A SERIES OF MONOGRAPHS. see *WATER RESOURCES*

614.7   US   ISSN 0194-0147
KF3786.A3
WATER POLLUTION CONTROL; a biweekly summary of industrial practices, regulatory trends, and control techniques. (Subseries of: B N A Policy and Practice Series; Environment, Safety, and Health Series) 1979. bi-w. $612. The Bureau of National Affairs, Inc., 1231 25th St., N.W., Washington, DC 20037. TEL 202-452-4200. FAX 202-822-8092. TELEX 285656 BNAI WSH. (Subscr. to: 9435 Key West Ave., Rockville, MD 20850. TEL 800-372-1033) Ed. Randy Kubetin. index. (looseleaf format; back issues avail.) **Indexed:** Chem.Abstr., Curr.Adv.Ecol.Sci., Environ.Per.Bibl., Forest.Abstr., Pollut.Abstr., Soils & Fert., World Text.Abstr. **Document type:** newsletter.
—CCC.
   Description: Reference and advisory service on the control of water pollution. Designed to meet the information needs of individuals responsible for complying with agency, federal and state water pollution control regulations.

614.7   CN   ISSN 0197-9140
TD419.5   CODEN: WRJCD9
WATER POLLUTION RESEARCH JOURNAL OF CANADA. (Text in English, French) 1966. 4/yr. Can.$150 (outside Canada and US Can.$200). National Water Research Institute, 867 Lakeshore Re., Box 5050, Burlington, ON L7R 4L7, Canada. TEL 905-336-4884. FAX 905-336-6444. (Subscr. to: Dr. H.R. Eisenhauer, Technology Development Branch, Environment Canada, 425 St. Joseph blvd., 4th Fl., Hull, PQ K1A 0H3, Canada. TEL 819-953-9365. FAX 819-953-9029) Ed. Suzanne Pontoy. adv. circ. 437. (also avail. in microform from MIM,UMI; back issues avail.) **Indexed:** Biol.Abstr., Chem.Abstr., Energy Ind., Energy Info.Abstr., Eng.Ind., Environ.Per.Bibl. (1991-), Excerp.Med., GeoRef., Sci.Abstr. **Document type:** academic/scholarly publication.
—BLDSC (9271.217000); El; UnCover; CASDDS. **CCC.**
   Former titles: Canadian Symposium on Water Pollution Research. Water Pollution Research in Canada. Proceedings (ISSN 0576-6176); Water Pollution Research in Canada (ISSN 0705-288X)
   Description: Publishes papers on all aspects of water pollution research.
   Refereed Serial

WATER QUALITY DATA FOR ONTARIO LAKES AND STREAMS. CENTRAL REGION. see *WATER RESOURCES*

WATER QUALITY DATA FOR ONTARIO LAKES AND STREAMS. NORTHEASTERN REGION. see *WATER RESOURCES*

WATER QUALITY DATA FOR ONTARIO LAKES AND STREAMS. NORTHWESTERN REGION. see *WATER RESOURCES*

WATER QUALITY DATA FOR ONTARIO LAKES AND STREAMS. SOUTHEASTERN REGION. see *WATER RESOURCES*

WATER QUALITY DATA FOR ONTARIO LAKES AND STREAMS. SOUTHWESTERN REGION. see *WATER RESOURCES*

WATER QUALITY DATA FOR ONTARIO LAKES AND STREAMS. WEST CENTRAL REGION. see *WATER RESOURCES*

614.7 624   UK   ISSN 0892-211X
TD365   CODEN: WQINEV
WATER QUALITY INTERNATIONAL. 1987. 4/yr. £80($125) (effective 1994). (International Association on Water Quality) Elsevier Science Ltd., Pergamon, P.O. Box 800, Kidlington, Oxford OX5 1DX, England. TEL 44-865-843000. FAX 44-865-843010. (Subscr. in U.S. and Canada to: Elsevier Science, 660 White Plains Rd., Tarrytown, NY 10591-5153. TEL 914-524-9200. FAX 914-333-2444) Ed. W.A. Horobin. adv. circ. 5,500. (also avail. in microform from UMI) **Indexed:** Sel.Water Res.Abstr. **Document type:** academic/scholarly publication.
• Also available online.
—BLDSC (9273.125000); El; SWETS; UMI. **CCC.**
   Formerly (until 1986): I A W P R C Newsletter (ISSN 0256-4513)
   Description: Geared to professionals: worldwide developments in the scientific and technical aspects of water pollution control.
   Refereed Serial

WATER RESEARCH CENTRE. ANNUAL REVIEW. see *WATER RESOURCES*

WATER SCIENCE AND TECHNOLOGY. see *WATER RESOURCES*

WATER TECHNOLOGY; the magazine for the water treatment professional. see *WATER RESOURCES*

WYOMING. WATER QUALITY DIVISION. STATE - E P A AGREEMENT. see *WATER RESOURCES*

628   GW   ISSN 0173-6507
TD264.R47
ZAHLENTAFELN DER PHYSIKALISCH-CHEMISCHEN UNTERSUCHUNGEN DES RHEINWASSERS/TABLEAUX NUMERIQUES DES ANALYSES PHYSICO-CHIMIQUES DES EAUX DU RHIN. (Text in French, German) 1963. a. DM.10. International Commission for the Protection of the Rhine Against Pollution - Internationale Kommission zum Schutze des Rheins gegen Verunreinigung, Hohenzollernstr. 18, 56003 Koblenz, Germany. TEL 0261-12495. FAX 0261-36572. Ed.Bd. circ. 1,200. **Document type:** bulletin.
   Formerly (until 1978): Zahlentafeln der Physikalisch-Chemischen Untersuchungen des Rheins sowie der Mosel (ISSN 0539-1539)

ENVIRONMENTAL STUDIES — Toxicology And Environmental Safety

ABSTRACTS OF CURRENT LITERATURE IN TOXICOLOGY. see *ENVIRONMENTAL STUDIES — Abstracting, Bibliographies, Statistics*

615.9   IT   ISSN 0393-635X
    CODEN: ATTHEH
ACTA TOXICOLOGICA ET THERAPEUTICA; international journal of toxicology, pharmacology and therapy. (Text in English, French, Italian) 1980. q. L.60000 (foreign L.120000) (effective 1994). C E M Casa Editoriale Maccari, Via Trento 53, 43100 Parma, Italy. FAX 039-521-771268. Eds. A. Cerrati, M. Debernarm. index. circ. 1,700. **Indexed:** Excerp.Med.
—BLDSC (0665.600000); UMI; CASDDS.

615.9   US   ISSN 0899-7195
RA1247.C65
ADVANCES IN COMBUSTION TOXICOLOGY. 1988. a. Technomic Publishing Co., Inc., 851 New Holland Ave., Box 3535, Lancaster, PA 17604. TEL 717-291-5609. FAX 717-295-4583. TELEX 230 753565 (TECHNOMIC UD). Ed. Ed Kladky. **Document type:** academic/scholarly publication.
—BLDSC (0704.020000).

ENVIRONMENTAL STUDIES — TOXICOLOGY AND ENVIRONMENTAL SAFETY

ADVERSE DRUG REACTIONS AND TOXICOLOGICAL REVIEWS. see *PHARMACY AND PHARMACOLOGY*

AGRICULTURAL AND BIOLOGICAL RESEARCH. see *AGRICULTURE*

615.9 US ISSN 0737-402X
RA1199 CODEN: AMTOEN
ALTERNATIVE METHODS IN TOXICOLOGY SERIES. 1983. irreg. (approx. a.), no.7, 1989. price varies. Mary Ann Liebert, Inc., 1651 Third Ave., New York, NY 10128. TEL 212-289-2300. FAX 212-289-4697. Ed. Alan M. Goldberg. **Document type:** monographic series.
—BLDSC (0803.589000); SWETS; CASDDS.

ALTLASTEN - SPEKTRUM; Erfassung - Bewertung - Sanierung. see *ENVIRONMENTAL STUDIES — Waste Management*

615.9 US ISSN 0730-0913
RA1190 CODEN: JACTDZ
AMERICAN COLLEGE OF TOXICOLOGY. JOURNAL. PART A. 1982. bi-m. $187 (foreign $240); with Part B $280 (foreign $380). Mary Ann Liebert, Inc., 1651 Third Ave., New York, NY 10128. TEL 212-289-2300. FAX 212-289-4697. Ed. Robert M. Diener. adv. **Indexed:** Chem.Abstr., Curr.Adv.Ecol.Sci., Energy Info.Abstr., Environ.Abstr., Excerp.Med., NRN.
—BLDSC (4685.785000); Faxon; SWETS; CASDDS.
Description: Includes safety evaluation and risk assessment, carcinogenesis, mechanisms of toxicity, quality assurance, and general, developmental, reproductive, clinical, genetic, forensic, immuno-, and veterinary toxicology.
Refereed Serial

AMERICAN COLLEGE OF TOXICOLOGY. JOURNAL. PART B; acute toxicity data. see *PHARMACY AND PHARMACOLOGY*

ANNUAL REVIEW OF PHARMACOLOGY AND TOXICOLOGY. see *PHARMACY AND PHARMACOLOGY*

615.9 NE ISSN 0166-445X
QH545.W3 CODEN: AQTODG
AQUATIC TOXICOLOGY. (Text in English) 1981. 12/yr. (in 3 vols.; 4 nos./vol.) fl.1338($723) (effective 1994). Elsevier Science B.V., P.O. Box 211, 1000 AE Amsterdam, Netherlands. TEL 31-20-5803911. FAX 31-20-5803598. TELEX 18582 ESPA NL. (Subscr. in U.S. and Canada to: Elsevier Science Inc., Box 882, Madison Sq. Sta., New York, NY 10159-0882. TEL 212-989-5800. FAX 212-633-3990) Eds. D.C. Malins, A. Jensen. adv.; charts; illus.; stat.; index. (back issues avail.) **Indexed:** Biol.Abstr., Chem.Abstr., Curr.Adv.Ecol.Sci., Curr.Cont., Energy Ind., Energy Info.Abstr., Excerp.Med., Geo.Abstr., Mar.Sci.Cont.Tab., Sci.Cit.Ind. **Document type:** academic/scholarly publication.
—BLDSC (1582.480000); EI; Faxon; UnCover; SWETS; CASDDS. **CCC.**
Description: For environmental toxicologists, ecotoxicologists, marine biologists, biochemical toxicologists, environmental monitoring researchers, and conservationists.
Refereed Serial

615.9 US ISSN 0090-4341
QH545.P4 CODEN: AECTCV
ARCHIVES OF ENVIRONMENTAL CONTAMINATION AND TOXICOLOGY. 1972. 8/yr. $499 (effective 1995). Springer-Verlag, Journals, 175 Fifth Ave, New York, NY 10010. TEL 212-460-1500. FAX 212-473-6272. (N. American subscr. to: Journal Fulfillment Services, Box 2485, Secaucus, NJ 07096-2491. TEL 800-777-4643. FAX 201-348-4505; Subscr. outside N. America to: Heidelberger Platz 3, 1000 Berlin 33, Germany. TEL 030-8207-1) Ed. Arthur Bevenue. charts. (also avail. in microform from UMI; reprint service avail. from ISI) **Indexed:** Acid Pre.Dig., Acid Rain Abstr., Acid Rain Ind., Anal.Abstr., Biodet.Abstr., Biotech.Abstr., Cadscan, Chem.Abstr., Crop Physiol.Abstr., Curr.Adv.Ecol.Sci., Curr.Cont., Dairy Sci.Abstr., Deep Sea Res. & Oceanogr.Abstr., Dok.Arbeitsmed., Environ.Abstr., Environ.Abstr., Environ.Ind., Environ.Per.Bibl. (1991-), Excerp.Med., Field Crop Abstr., Food Sci.& Tech.Abstr., Forest.Abstr., Forest Prod.Abstr., GeoRef., Herb.Abstr., Hort.Abstr., Ind.Med., Ind.Sci.Rev., Ind.Vet., Irr.& Drain.Abstr., Lab.Haz.Bull., Lead Abstr., NRN, Ocean.Abstr., Pollut.Abstr., Rev.Appl.Entomol., Rev.Med.& Vet.Mycol., Risk Abstr., Sci.Cit.Ind., Sel.Water Res.Abstr., Soils & Fert., Triticale Abstr., Vet.Bull., W.R.C.Inf., Weed Abstr., Zincscan. **Document type:** academic/scholarly publication.
—BLDSC (1634.240000); CIS; Faxon; UnCover; SWETS; UMI; CASDDS. **CCC.**
Description: Contains detailed reports of important advances and discoveries in the fields of air, water, and soil contamination and pollution.

615.9 GW ISSN 0340-5761
CODEN: ARTODN
ARCHIVES OF TOXICOLOGY. 1930. 10/yr. DM.1528($955) (Deutsche Gesellschaft fuer Pharmakologie und Toxikologie) Springer-Verlag, Heidelberger Platz 3, 14197 Berlin, Germany. TEL 030-8207-1. FAX 030-8214091. (Subscr. in N. America to: Springer-Verlag New York, Inc., 44 Hartz Way, Secaucus, NJ 07096-2491. TEL 201-348-4033. FAX 201-348-4505) (Co-sponsor: Deutsche Gesellschaft fuer Rechtsmedizin) Ed. H.M. Bolt. adv.; bibl.; charts; illus. (also avail. in microform from UMI; back issues avail.; reprint service avail. from ISI) **Indexed:** Biol.Abstr., Biotech.Abstr., C.I.S. Abstr., Chem.Abstr., Curr.Adv.Ecol.Sci., Curr.Cont., Dairy Sci.Abstr., Dent.Ind., Dok.Arbeitsmed., Environ.Abstr., Excerp.Med., Helminthol.Abstr., Ind.Med., Ind.Sci.Rev., Ind.Vet., INIS Atomind., Lab.Haz.Bull., Nutr.Abstr., Pollut.Abstr., Protozool.Abstr., Rev.Med.& Vet.Mycol., Sci.Cit.Ind., Vet.Bull. **Document type:** academic/scholarly publication.
—BLDSC (1643.510000); ADONIS; Faxon; UnCover; SWETS; UMI; CASDDS. **CCC.**
Former titles: Archiv fuer Toxikologie (ISSN 0003-9446); Fuehner-Wieland's Sammlung von Vergiftungsfaellen.
Description: Reports on studies done on the mechanisms of effects of chemicals in man or in experimental animals.

ARCHIVES OF TOXICOLOGY. SUPPLEMENT. see *PHARMACY AND PHARMACOLOGY*

ARCHIVOS DE FARMACOLOGIA Y TOXICOLOGIA. see *PHARMACY AND PHARMACOLOGY*

613.62 615.9 CI ISSN 0004-1254
RA1211 CODEN: AHRTAN
ARHIV ZA HIGIJENU RADA I TOKSIKOLOGIJU/ARCHIVES OF INDUSTRIAL HYGIENE AND TOXICOLOGY. (Text in Croatian and English) 1950. q. $40. Sveuciliste u Zagrebu, Institut za Medicinska Istrazivanja i Medicinu Rada - University of Zagreb, Institute for Medical Research and Occupational Health, Ksaverska Cesta 2, P.O. Box 291, 41001 Zagreb, Croatia. FAX 38-41-274-572. Ed. R. Plestina. adv.; bk.rev.; bibl.; charts; illus.; stat.; index. circ. 2,000. **Indexed:** Biodet.Abstr., Biol.Abstr., C.I.S. Abstr., Curr.Abstr., Curr.Adv.Ecol.Sci., Dok.Arbeitsmed., Ergon.Abstr., Excerp.Med., Ind.Hyg.Dig., Ind.Med., INIS Atomind., Nucl.Sci.Abstr., Occup.Saf.& Health Abstr.
—BLDSC (1666.200000); CASDDS.

574 US ISSN 0892-7014
QH91.8.M3 CODEN: BFOUEC
BIOFOULING. 3/yr. (in 2 vol., 4 nos./vol.) 109 ECU per vol. (effective 1993). Harwood Academic Publishers, 820 Town Center Dr., Langhorne, PA 19047. TEL 215-750-2642. FAX 215-750-6343. (UK subscr to: P.O. Box 90, Reading, Berkshire RG1 8JL, England. TEL 0734-560-080) Ed. Len Evans. (also avail. n microform) **Indexed:** Biodet.Abstr., Environ.Per Bibl.
—BLDSC (2072.146500); CASDDS. **CCC.**
Refereed Serial

615.9 US ISSN 0007-4861
RA565.A1 CODEN: BECTA6
BULLETIN OF ENVIRONMENTAL CONTAMINATION AND TOXICOLOGY. 1966. m. $399 (effective 1995). Springer-Verlag, Journals, 175 Fifth Ave., New York, NY 10010. TEL 212-460-1500. FAX 212-473-6272. (N. American subscr. to: Journal Fulfillment Services, Box 2485, Secaucus, NJ 07096-2491. TEL 800-777-4643. FAX 201-348-4505; Elsewhere: Heidelberger Platz 3, 1000 Berlin 33, Germany. TEL 030-8207-1. FAX 030-8214091) Ed. H.N. Nigg. adv. (also avail. in microform from UMI; back issues avail.; reprint service avail. from ISI) **Indexed:** Abstr.Bull.Inst.Pap.Chem., Acid Pre.Dig., Acid Rain Abstr., Anal.Abstr., Biodet.Abstr., Biol.Abstr., Biol.& Agr.Ind., Biotech.Abstr., Cadscan, Chem.Abstr., Curr.Adv.Ecol Sci., Curr.Cont., Curr.Ref.Fish Res., Dairy Sci.Abstr., Deep Sea Res.& Oceanogr.Abstr., Dok.Arbeitsmed., E&P Hlth. (1993-), Energy Rev., Eng.Ind., Environ.Abstr., Environ.Ind., Environ.Per.Bibl., Excerp.Med., Field Crop Abstr., Food Sci.& Tech.Abstr., Forest.Abstr., Gas Process.& Ppl. (1993-), Helminthol.Abstr., Hort.Abstr., Ind.Med., Ind.Sci.Rev., Ind.Vet., INIS Atomind., Lab.Haz.Bull., Lead Abstr., Maize Abstr., Mass Spectr.Bull., Nutr.Abstr., Ocean.Abstr., Off.Tech. (1993-), Petrol.Abstr. (1981-), Pig News & Info., Pollut.Abstr., Poult.Abstr., Rev.Appl.Entomol., Rev.Med.& Vet.Mycol., Rev.Plant Path., Risk Abstr., Sci.Cit.Ind., Sel.J.Water, Sel.Water Res.Abstr., Soils & Fert., Soyabean Abstr., Vet.Bull., W.R.C.Inf., Weed Abstr., Zincscan. **Document type:** academic/scholarly publication.
—BLDSC (2853.300000); CIS; Faxon; UnCover; SWETS; UMI; CASDDS. **CCC.**
Description: Disseminates advances and discoveries in the areas of soil, air, and food contamination and pollution.
Refereed Serial

615.9 688.8 US
C O P P E QUARTERLY. vol.6, no.2, 1992. q. Council on Plastics and Packaging in the Environment, 1001 Connecticut Ave., N.W., Ste. 401, Washington, DC 20036-5504. TEL 202-331-0099.

574.8 NE ISSN 0742-2091
QH573 CODEN: CBTOE2
CELL BIOLOGY AND TOXICOLOGY; an international journal devoted to research at the cellular level. 1984. 6/yr. fl.400($208.50) (effective 1994). (Genetic Toxicology Association) Kluwer Academic Publishers, Postbus 17, 3300 AA Dordrecht, Netherlands. TEL 31-78-334911. FAX 31-78-334254. TELEX 29245 KAPG NL. (Dist. by: Kluwer Academic Publishers Group, P.O. Box 322, 3300 AH Dordrecht, Netherlands. TEL 31-78-524400. FAX 31-78-524474; N. America dist. addr.: Box 358, Accord Sta., Hingham, MA 02018-0358. TEL 617-871-6600. FAX 617-871-6528) Ed. Dr. Gary M. Williams. adv.; index. circ. 1,000. **Indexed:** Chem.Abstr., Excerp.Med., Ind.Med., Ind.Vet. **Document type:** academic/scholarly publication.
—BLDSC (3097.706000); Faxon; UnCover; SWETS; CASDDS. **CCC.**
Refereed Serial

E

ENVIRONMENTAL STUDIES — TOXICOLOGY AND ENVIRONMENTAL SAFETY

615.9   US   ISSN 0893-228X
RA1190   CODEN: CRTOEC
CHEMICAL RESEARCH IN TOXICOLOGY. 1988. bi-m. $311 to non-members (foreign $330); members $46 (foreign $65). American Chemical Society, 1155 16th St., N.W., Washington, DC 20036. TEL 800-333-9511. FAX 614-447-3671. (Subscr. to: Membership and Subscription Services, Box 3337, Columbus, OH 43210. TEL 614-447-3776) Ed. Lawrence J. Marnett. (also avail. in microform from UMI; back issues avail.) **Indexed:** Curr.Adv.Genetics & Molec.Biol., Environ.Abstr., Excerp.Med., Sel.Water Res.Abstr., Telegen. **Document type:** academic/scholarly publication.
●Also available online. Vendor(s): STN International.
—BLDSC (3150.465000); Faxon; UnCover; SWETS; CASDDS. **CCC.**
Description: Publishes full papers, rapid communications, and invited reviews on structural, mechanistic, and technological advances in research concerned with the toxicological effects of chemical agents.
Refereed Serial

615.9   UK
CHEMICAL SAFETY DATA SHEETS. 1989. irreg., latest 1992. £54.95. Royal Society of Chemistry, Thomas Graham House, Science Park, Milton Rd., Cambridge CB4 4WF, England. TEL 0223-420066. FAX 0223-423623. TELEX 818293. (Dist. by: Turpin Distribution Services Ltd., Blackhorse Rd., Letchworth, Herts. SG6 1HN, England. TEL 0762-672555. FAX 0762-480947) (back issues avail.) **Document type:** monographic series.
Description: Discusses the prevention and treatment of exposure to hazardous chemicals.

615.9 540   IE   ISSN 0009-2797
QP501   CODEN: CBINA8
CHEMICO-BIOLOGICAL INTERACTIONS; a journal of molecular and biochemical toxicology. 1969. 12/yr. (in 4 vols.; 3 nos./vol.). I£568($829) (effective 1994). Elsevier Science Ireland Ltd., P.O. Box 85, Limerick, Ireland. TEL 353-61-471944. FAX 353-61-472144. (Subscr. in U.S. and Canada to: Elsevier Science Inc., Box 882, Madison Sq. Sta., New York, NY 10159. TEL 212-989-5800. FAX 212-633-3990) Ed.Bd. bibl.; charts; illus. (also avail. in microform from UMI) **Indexed:** Biol.Abstr., Chem.Abstr., Curr.Adv.Biochem., Curr.Adv.Cancer Res., Curr.Adv.Ecol.Sci., Curr.Cont., Deep Sea Res.& Oceanogr.Abstr., Excerp.Med., Helminthol.Abstr., Ind.Med., Ind.Sci.Rev., Ind.Vet., Pig News & Info., Sci.Cit.Ind., Vet.Bull. **Document type:** academic/scholarly publication.
—BLDSC (3155.500000); ADONIS; Faxon; UnCover; SWETS; CASDDS. **CCC.**
Description: Devoted to the mechnisms by which exogenous chemicals produce changes in biological systems.
Refereed Serial

614.7   UK   ISSN 0045-6535
QH540   CODEN: CMSHAF
CHEMOSPHERE; chemistry, biology and toxicology as related to environmental problems. (Text in English, French, German) 1972. 24/yr. £970($1495) (effective 1994). Elsevier Science Ltd., Pergamon, P.O. Box 800, Kidlington, Oxford OX5 1DX, England. TEL 44-865-843000. FAX 44-865-843010. (Subscr. in U.S. and Canada to: Elsevier Science, 660 White Plains Rd., Tarrytown, NY 10591-5153. TEL 914-524-9200. FAX 914-333-2444) Eds. T. Stephen, O. Hutzinger. adv. circ. 1,000. (also avail. in microfilm from UMI) **Indexed:** Acid Pre.Dig., Biodet.Abstr., Biol.Abstr., Biotech.Abstr., C.I.S. Abstr., Cadscan, Chem.Abstr., Curr.Adv.Ecol.Sci., Curr.Cont., Curr.Ref.Fish Res., Dairy Sci.Abstr., Deep Sea Res.& Oceanogr.Abstr., Energy Ind., Energy Rev., Environ.Abstr., Environ.Per.Bibl. (1974-), Excerp.Med., Field Crop Abstr., Forest.Abstr., Forest Prod.Abstr., Helminthol.Abstr., Herb.Abstr., Ind.Sci.Rev., Ind.Vet., INIS Atomind., Irr.& Drain.Abstr., Lead Abstr., Mass Spectr.Bull., Nutr.Abstr., Ocean.Abstr., Pollut.Abstr., Potato Abstr., Protozool.Abstr., Risk Abstr., Sci.Cit.Ind., Sel.Water Res.Abstr., Soils & Fert., Triticale Abstr., W.R.C.Inf., Weed Abstr., Zincscan. **Document type:** academic/scholarly publication.
—BLDSC (3172.280000); EI; Faxon; UnCover; SWETS; UMI; CASDDS. **CCC.**
Description: Publishes original research in environmental protection from the fields of chemistry, biology, physics, toxicology and inter-related disciplines.
Refereed Serial

500   US   ISSN 0886-5140
   CODEN: COTXEI
COMMENTS ON TOXICOLOGY. 1986. 6/yr. (in 1 vol., 6 nos./vol.). 130 ECU (effective 1993). Gordon & Breach Science Publishers, 820 Town Center Dr., Langhorne, PA 19047. TEL 215-750-2642. FAX 215-750-6343. (UK subscr. to: P.O. Box 90, Reading, Berkshire RG1 8JL, England. TEL 0734-560-080) Ed. A. Wallace Hayes. (also avail. in microform) **Indexed:** Rev.Med.& Vet.Mycol., Soils & Fert.
—BLDSC (3336.042500); Faxon; CASDDS. **CCC.**

COMPARATIVE BIOCHEMISTRY AND PHYSIOLOGY. PART C: COMPARATIVE PHARMACOLOGY & TOXICOLOGY. see *BIOLOGY — Biological Chemistry*

COMPARATIVE HAEMATOLOGY INTERNATIONAL. see *MEDICAL SCIENCES — Hematology*

615.9   US   ISSN 1040-8444
RA1190   CODEN: CRTXB2
CRITICAL REVIEWS IN TOXICOLOGY. 1971. bi-m. $265 (foreign $272.95). C R C Press, Inc., 2000 Corporate Blvd., N.W., Boca Raton, FL 33431. TEL 407-994-0555. FAX 407-998-9784. TELEX 568689-CRC PRESS. Ed. Dr. Roger O. McClellan. bibl.; charts; illus. circ. 640. (back issues avail.) **Indexed:** Biol.Abstr., Chem.Abstr., Curr.Adv.Ecol.Sci., Curr.Cont., Dok.Arbeitsmed., Environ.Abstr., Environ.Per.Bibl. (1992-), Excerp.Med., Food Sci.& Tech.Abstr., Ind.Med., Ind.Sci.Rev., Ind.Vet., INIS Atomind., Lab.Haz.Bull., Nutr.Abstr., Pollut.Abstr., Sci.Cit.Ind.
—BLDSC (3487.484000); ADONIS; CIS; Faxon; UnCover; SWETS; CASDDS. **CCC.**
Formerly: C R C Critical Reviews in Toxicology (ISSN 0045-6446)
Description: Aimed at making available critical assessments of subjects that are part of the advancing frontiers of toxicology and related basic scientific disciplines.
Refereed Serial

CURRENT ADVANCES IN TOXICOLOGY. see *ENVIRONMENTAL STUDIES — Abstracting, Bibliographies, Statistics*

615.9   US
CURRENT ISSUES IN TOXICOLOGY. 1984. irreg. price varies. (International Life Science Institute) Springer-Verlag, 175 Fifth Ave., New York, NY 10010. TEL 212-460-1500. FAX 212-473-6272. (Also: Berlin, Heidelberg, Tokyo, and Vienna) (reprint service avail. from ISI) **Document type:** monographic series.

540 615.9   UK   ISSN 0275-2581
CURRENT TOPICS IN ENVIRONMENTAL AND TOXICOLOGICAL CHEMISTRY. 1976. irreg., vol.13, 1983. price varies. Gordon & Breach Science Publishers, P.O. Box 90, Reading, Berks. RG1 8JL, England. TEL 0734-560080. FAX 0734-568211. TELEX 849870 SCIPUB G. (U.S. addr.: 820 Town Center Dr., Langhorne, PA 19047. TEL 215-750-2642. FAX 215-750-6343) Eds. R.W. Frei, O. Hutzinger. (also avail. in microform; microfiche) **Document type:** monographic series.
—BLDSC (3504.882000).
Refereed Serial

CURRENT TOPICS IN PULMONARY PHARMACOLOGY AND TOXICOLOGY. see *PHARMACY AND PHARMACOLOGY*

615.9   US   ISSN 1069-4587
   CODEN: CUTOEX
▼**CURRENT TOXICOLOGY.** 1993. q. $295 (effective 1994). Nova Science Publishers, Inc., 6080 Jericho Tpke., Ste. 207, Commack, NY 11725-2808. TEL 516-499-3103. Ed. S.N. Golikov. **Document type:** academic/scholarly publication.
—CASDDS.
Description: Covers general toxicology and toxic effects; genetic toxicology, metabolism of xenobiotics; anti-poison studies, environmental toxicology, clinical approaches, and chemobiokinetics.

615.9   NE   ISSN 0165-2214
DEVELOPMENTS IN TOXICOLOGY AND ENVIRONMENTAL SCIENCE. 1977. irreg., vol.15, 1987. price varies. Elsevier Science B.V., Books Division, P.O. Box 211, 1000 AE Amsterdam, Netherlands. TEL 31-20-5803911. FAX 31-20-5803705. TELEX 18582 ESPA NL. (Subscr. in U.S. and Canada to: Elsevier Science Inc., Box 882, Madison Sq. Sta., New York, NY 10159. TEL 212-989-5800) **Indexed:** Chem.Abstr., Dok.Arbeitsmed., Ind.Med., Ind.Vet., Pig News & Info., Rev.Med.& Vet.Mycol., Weed Abstr. **Document type:** monographic series.
—SWETS.
Refereed Serial

615.9   UK
▼**DIALOG ONDISC ENVIRONMENTAL CHEMISTRY, HEALTH AND SAFETY.** 1994. base vol., with q. updates. £1495. Royal Society of Chemistry, Thomas Graham House, Science Park, Milton Rd., Cambridge CB4 4WF, England. TEL 0223-420066. FAX 0223-423623. TELEX 818293. (Subscr. to: Turpin Distribution Services Ltd., Blackhorse Rd., Letchworth, Herts. SG6 1HN, England. TEL 0462-672555. FAX 0462-480947) **Document type:** academic/scholarly publication.
●Available only on CD-ROM.
Description: Provides comprehensive scientific and technical information on environmental safety.

DRUG AND CHEMICAL TOXICOLOGY; an international journal for rapid communication. see *PHARMACY AND PHARMACOLOGY*

DRUG AND CHEMICAL TOXICOLOGY SERIES. see *PHARMACY AND PHARMACOLOGY*

615.9   UK   ISSN 0963-9292
   CODEN: ECOTEL
▼**ECOTOXICOLOGY.** 1992. q. £110 to institutions in EC nations (North America $190; elsewhere £120). Chapman & Hall, 2-6 Boundary Row, London SE1 8HN, England. TEL 071-865-0066. FAX 071-522-9623. TELEX 290164-CHAPMAG. (Dist. by: International Thomson Publishing Services, Ltd., N. Way, Andover, Hants. SP10 5BE, England. TEL 0264-332919; US addr.: Chapman & Hall, Journals Promotion Department, One Penn Plaza, 41st Fl., New York, NY 10119. TEL 212-564-1060. FAX 212-564-1505) **Document type:** academic/scholarly publication.
—BLDSC (3659.553500); ADONIS; UnCover; SWETS; CASDDS.
Description: Publishes fundamental research in ecotoxicology.

615.9   US   ISSN 0147-6513
QH545.A1   CODEN: EESADV
ECOTOXICOLOGY AND ENVIRONMENTAL SAFETY. 1977. 9/yr. $351 (foreign $434). (International Society of Ecotoxicology and Environmental Safety) Academic Press, Inc., Journal Division, 525 B St., Ste. 1900, San Diego, CA 92101-4495. TEL 619-250-1840. FAX 619-699-6800. (Subscr. to: Box 620000, Orlando, FL 32891-8340. TEL 800-543-9534) Ed. Frederick Coulston. adv.; index. (back issues avail.) **Indexed:** Acid Rain Abstr., Acid Rain Ind., Biodet.Abstr., Cadscan, Curr.Cont., Curr.Ref.Fish Res., Dairy Sci.Abstr., Environ.Abstr., Environ.Ind., Excerp.Med., Geo.Abstr., Ind.Med., Ind.Sci.Rev., Ind.Vet., INIS Atomind., Irr.& Drain.Abstr., Lead Abstr., Pollut.Abstr., Risk Abstr., Sel.Water Res.Abstr., Soils & Fert., Vet.Bull., W.R.C.Inf., Weed Abstr., Zincscan. **Document type:** academic/scholarly publication.
—BLDSC (3659.555000); CIS; Faxon; UnCover; SWETS; CASDDS. **CCC.**
Description: Examines the biologic and toxic effects of natural or synthetic chemical pollutants on animal, plant, or microbial ecosystems, and their routes into the affected organisms.
Refereed Serial

EKSPERIMENTAL'NAYA I KLINICHESKAYA FARMAKOLOGIYA/EXPERIMENTAL AND CLINICAL PHARMACOLOGY. see *PHARMACY AND PHARMACOLOGY*

ENVIRONMENTAL STUDIES — TOXICOLOGY AND ENVIRONMENTAL SAFETY

616.99 614.7 US ISSN 1059-0501
RC268.5 CODEN: JSHREB
ENVIRONMENTAL CARCINOGENESIS & ECOTOXICOLOGY REVIEWS. Variant title: Journal of Environmental Science and Health. Part C: Environmental Carcinogenesis & Ecotoxicology Reviews. 1971. 2/yr. $125 to individuals; institutions $250 (for Parts A, B, and C $1170). Marcel Dekker Journals, 270 Madison Ave., New York, NY 10016. TEL 212-696-9000. FAX 212-685-4540. TELEX 421419. (Subscr. to: Box 5017, Monticello, NY 12701) Ed. Yin-Tak Woo. (also avail. in microform from RPI) Indexed: Cadscan, Chem.Abstr., Environ.Abstr., Environ.Per.Bibl. (1983-), Excerp.Med., Ind.Sci.Rev., Lead Abstr., Pollut.Abstr., Sci.Cit.Ind., Sel.Water Res.Abstr., Zincscan. Document type: academic/scholarly publication.
—BLDSC (4979.394300); CIS; Faxon; UnCover; SWETS; CASDDS. **CCC.**
 Former titles (until 1991): Environmental Carcinogenesis Reviews (ISSN 0882-8164); (until 1984): Journal of Environmental Science and Health. Part C: Environmental Carcinogenesis Reviews (ISSN 0736-3001); Journal of Environmental Science and Health. Part C: Environmental Health Sciences (ISSN 0360-1242); Supersedes in part: Environmental Letters (ISSN 0013-9300).
 Refereed Serial

615.9 US
RC585
ENVIRONMENTAL MEDICINE. 1982. q. $40 to individuals (foreign $45); institutions $75 (foreign $80). Environmental Medicine Publications, Inc., Box 101059, Denver, CO 80250-1059. Eds. John W. Gerrard, Del Stigler. adv.; bk.rev. circ. 1,200. Indexed: Art & Archaeol.Tech.Abstr., Biol.Abstr., Rev.Med.& Vet.Mycol. Document type: academic/scholarly publication.
—BLDSC (3286.273900).
 Former titles: Clinical Ecology (ISSN 0735-9306); Archives for Clinical Ecology.

615.9 UK ISSN 0730-7268
QH545.A1 CODEN: ETOCDK
ENVIRONMENTAL TOXICOLOGY AND CHEMISTRY. 1982. 12/yr. £335($515) (effective 1994). (Society of Environmental Toxicology and Chemistry) Elsevier Science Ltd., Pergamon, P.O. Box 800, Kidlington, Oxford OX5 1DX, England. TEL 44-865-843000. FAX 44-865-843010. (Subscr. in U.S. and Canada to: Elsevier Science, 660 White Plains Rd., Tarrytown, NY 10591-5153. TEL 914-524-9200. FAX 914-333-2444) Ed. Calvin Herbert Ward. adv.; index. (also avail. in microform from UMI; back issues avail.) Indexed: ASCA, Biodet.Abstr., Biol.Abstr., Biotech.Abstr., Chem.Abstr., Crop Physiol.Abstr., Curr.Adv.Ecol.Sci., Curr.Cont., Energy Ind., Energy Info.Abstr., Environ.Abstr., Environ.Per.Bibl. (1990-), Excerp.Med., Field Crop Abstr., Hort.Abstr., Ind.Sci.Rev., Ind.Vet., INIS Atomind., Risk Abstr., Sci.Cit.Ind., Sel.Water Res.Abstr., Soils & Fert., Soyabean Abstr., Triticale Abstr., W.R.C.Inf., Weed Abstr. Document type: academic/scholarly publication.
—BLDSC (3791.785000); EI; Faxon; UnCover; SWETS; UMI; CASDDS. **CCC.**
 Description: Covers environmental chemistry, environmental toxicology and hazard assessment.
 Refereed Serial

614 US ISSN 1053-4725
QH90.57.B5 CODEN: ETWQEZ
ENVIRONMENTAL TOXICOLOGY AND WATER QUALITY; an international journal. 1986. 4/yr. $250 to institutions (foreign $235). John Wiley & Sons, Inc., Journals, 605 Third Ave., New York, NY 10158-0012. TEL 212-850-6000. FAX 212-850-6088. TELEX 12-7063. Eds. Dickson Liu, Bernard J. Dutka. (also avail. in microform from UMI) Indexed: Environ.Per.Bibl. (1991-), Excerp.Med., Sel.Water Res.Abstr.
—BLDSC (3791.786000); SWETS; UMI; CASDDS. **CCC.**
 Formerly: Toxicity Assessment (ISSN 0884-8181)
 Description: Original research papers on all aspects of environmental toxicology and water quality research, monitoring, standards and policies.
 Refereed Serial

628.5 612 NE
ETHEL BROWNING'S TOXICITY AND METABOLISM OF INDUSTRIAL SOLVENTS. (Text in English) 1987. irreg., vol.3, 1992. price varies. Elsevier Science B.V., Books Division, P.O. Box 211, 1000 AE Amsterdam, Netherlands. TEL 31-20-5803911. FAX 31-20-5803705. TELEX 18582 ESPA NL. (Subscr. in U.S. and Canada to: Elsevier Science Inc., Box 882, Madison Sq. Sta., New York, NY 10159. TEL 212-989-5800) (back issues avail.) Document type: monographic series.
 Refereed Serial

620.85 615.9 NE ISSN 0926-6917
CODEN: EPEPEG
▼**EUROPEAN JOURNAL OF PHARMACOLOGY. ENVIRONMENTAL TOXICOLOGY AND PHARMACOLOGY SECTION.** (Section of: European Journal of Pharmacology (ISSN 0014-2999)) (Text in English) 1992. 4/yr. fl.430($232) (subscr. to all sections of European Journal of Pharmacology fl.7810($4222)) (effective 1994). Elsevier Science B.V., P.O. Box 211, 1000 AE Amsterdam, Netherlands. TEL 31-20-5803911. FAX 31-20-5803598. TELEX 18582 ESPA NL. (Subscr. in U.S. and Canada to: Elsevier Science Inc., Box 882, Madison Sq. Sta., New York, NY 10159-0882. TEL 212-989-5800. FAX 212-633-3990) Eds. J.H. Koeman, F.P. Nijkamp. Indexed: Biol.Abstr., Bull.Signal., Chem.Abstr., Curr.Cont., Excerp.Med. (1993-), Ind.Med. Document type: academic/scholarly publication.
—ADONIS; Faxon; UnCover; SWETS. **CCC.**
 Description: Publishes research in mechanistic studies concerning the toxic effects in man and vertebrate animals of drugs and environmental contaminants.
 Refereed Serial

EXCERPTA MEDICA. SECTION 30: CLINICAL AND EXPERIMENTAL PHARMACOLOGY. see *PHARMACY AND PHARMACOLOGY — Abstracting, Bibliographies, Statistics*

EXPERIMENTAL AND TOXICOLOGIC PATHOLOGY. see *MEDICAL SCIENCES*

615.9 US ISSN 0899-7845
RM388
FOCUS ON PULMONARY PHARMACOLOGY AND TOXICOLOGY. 1989. a. C R C Press, 2000 Corporate Blvd., N.W., Boca Raton, FL 33431.

615.9 UK ISSN 0278-6915
RA1190 CODEN: FCTOD7
FOOD AND CHEMICAL TOXICOLOGY. (Text in English, French or German) 1963. 12/yr. £557($1170) (effective 1994). (British Industrial Biological Research Association) Elsevier Science Ltd., Pergamon, P.O. Box 800, Kidlington, Oxford OX5 1DX, England. TEL 44-865-843000. FAX 44-865-843010. (Subscr. in U.S. and Canada to: Elsevier Science, 660 White Plains Rd., Tarrytown, NY 10591-5153. TEL 914-524-9200. FAX 914-333-2444) Eds. S.D. Gangolli, Robert A. Neal. adv.; bk.rev.; charts; illus.; index. circ. 1,900. (also avail. in microfilm from UMI; back issues avail.) Indexed: Biol.Abstr., Biotech.Abstr., Chem.Abstr., Curr.Adv.Ecol.Sci., Curr.Cont., Curr.Pack.Abstr., Dairy Sci.Abstr., Dent.Ind., Dok.Arbeitsmed., Environ.Per.Bibl., Excerp.Med., Fababean Abstr., Food Sci.& Tech.Abstr., Ind.Med., Ind.Sci.Rev., Ind.Vet., Lab.Haz.Bull., Mass Spectr.Bull., NRN, Nutr.Abstr., Packag.Sci.Tech., Pig News & Info., Poult.Abstr., Rev.Med.& Vet.Mycol., Rev.Plant Path., Risk Abstr., Sci.Cit.Ind., Sel.Water Res.Abstr., Sugar Ind.Abstr., Vet.Bull., W.R.C.Inf., Weed Abstr., World Surf.Coat. Document type: academic/scholarly publication.
—BLDSC (3977.026900); ADONIS; Faxon; UnCover; SWETS; UMI; CASDDS. **CCC.**
 Formerly (until 1982): Food and Cosmetics Toxicology (ISSN 0015-6264)
 Description: Reports of research on the metabolism and toxicology of foods and food additives, as well as studies of carcinogens, mutagens, and drug-nutrient interactions.
 Refereed Serial

615.9 US ISSN 0272-0590
RA1190 CODEN: FAATDF
FUNDAMENTAL AND APPLIED TOXICOLOGY. 1980. 8/yr. $339 (foreign $388). (Society of Toxicology) Academic Press, Inc., Journal Division, 525 B St., Ste. 1900, San Diego, CA 92101-4495. TEL 619-230-1840. FAX 619-699-6800. (Subscr. to: Box 620000, Orlando, FL 32891-8340. TEL 800-543-9534) Ed. Henry Heck. index. (back issues avail.) Indexed: Curr.Adv.Ecol.Sci., Curr.Adv.Genetics & Molec.Biol., Dairy Sci.Abstr., Dok.Arbeitsmed., Excerp.Med., Ind.Hyg.Dig., Ind.Med., Ind.Vet., INIS Atomind., NRN, Pig News & Info., Rev.Med.& Vet.Mycol., Sel.Water Res.Abstr., Small Anim.Abstr., Vet.Bull. Document type: academic/scholarly publication.
—BLDSC (4056.030500); ADONIS; Faxon; UnCover; SWETS; CASDDS. **CCC.**
 Description: Presents current articles and reports relating to those broad aspects of toxicology relevant to assessing the risk of exposure of toxic agents (chemicals, including drugs and natural products or forms of energy) to humans and other animals health.
 Refereed Serial

615.9 UK
CODEN: HUTODJ
HUMAN & EXPERIMENTAL TOXICOLOGY; an international journal. 1981. m. £260 (foreign £275). (British Toxicology Society) Macmillan Press Ltd., Scientific & Medical Division, Houndmills, Basingstoke, Hampshire RG21 2XS, England. TEL 0256-29242. FAX 0256-28339. Eds. Paul Turner, Anthony Dayan. index. (also avail. in microform from UMI) Indexed: Chem.Abstr., Curr.Adv.Ecol.Sci., Curr.Adv.Genetics & Molec.Biol., Curr.Cont., Dent.Ind., Dok.Arbeitsmed., Energy Ind., Energy Info.Abstr., Excerp.Med., Ind.Med., Ind.Sci.Rev., Ind.Vet., INIS Atomind., Lab.Haz.Bull., NRN, Rev.Med.& Vet.Mycol., Sci.Cit.Ind., Small Anim.Abstr., Vet.Bull. Document type: academic/scholarly publication.
—UnCover. **CCC.**
 Formerly: Human Toxicology (ISSN 0144-5952)
 Description: Articles on all aspects of clinical toxicology.

615.9 US ISSN 0888-319X
CODEN: IVTOE4
IN VITRO TOXICOLOGY; a journal of molecular and cellular toxicology. q. $142 (foreign $182). Mary Ann Liebert, Inc., 1651 Third Ave., New York, NY 10128. TEL 212-289-2300. FAX 212-289-4697. Ed. David J. Brusick. Indexed: Environ.Per.Bibl. (1991-), Excerp.Med. (1993-). Document type: academic/scholarly publication.
—BLDSC (4372.502000); Faxon; SWETS; CASDDS.
 Description: Examines the molecular and cellular basis and expression of toxic phenomena. Covers methods, developments, and validation of tests, the impact of in vitro toxicology on product safety testing, and methods for in vitro to in vivo extrapolation.

615.9 US ISSN 0895-8378
CODEN: INHTE5
INHALATION TOXICOLOGY. 1989. q. $130. Taylor & Francis, 1900 Frost Rd., Ste. 101, Bristol, PA 19007-1598. TEL 800-821-8312. FAX 215-785-5515. Ed. Donald E. Gardner. (also avail. in microform from UMI; reprint service avail. from UMI) Indexed: Environ.Abstr. Document type: academic/scholarly publication.
—BLDSC (4513.340800); CIS; CASDDS. **CCC.**
 Description: Presents the latest advances in all aspects of inhalation toxicology.
 Refereed Serial

INTERNATIONAL JOURNAL OF CLINICAL PHARMACOLOGY, THERAPY AND TOXICOLOGY. see *PHARMACY AND PHARMACOLOGY*

615.9 613.62 II ISSN 0971-2615
CODEN: IJTHEZ
INTERNATIONAL JOURNAL OF TOXICOLOGY, OCCUPATIONAL AND ENVIRONMENTAL HEALTH. (Text in English) q. Rs.1200($120) (I T R C) Wiley Eastern Ltd., Journals Division, 4835-24 Ansari Rd., Daryaganj, New Delhi 110 002, India. TEL 3267996. FAX 91-11-3267437. TELEX 031-66507-WELIN. circ. 500.
—CASDDS.

JAPANESE JOURNAL OF FORENSIC TOXICOLOGY/HO CHUDOKU. see *MEDICAL SCIENCES — Forensic Sciences*

ENVIRONMENTAL STUDIES — TOXICOLOGY AND ENVIRONMENTAL SAFETY

613 JA ISSN 0013-273X
CODEN: JJTHEC
JAPANESE JOURNAL OF TOXICOLOGY AND ENVIRONMENTAL HEALTH. Key Title: Eisei Kagaku. (Text in English or Japanese; summaries, captions in English) 1955. bi-m. $47. Pharmaceutical Society of Japan - Nihon Yakugakkai, 12-15-201, Shibuya 2-chome, Shibuya-ku, Tokyo 150, Japan. Ed. Kiyomi Kikukawa. adv.; charts; stat.; index; circ. 1,700 (controlled). **Indexed:** Anal.Abstr., Biol.Abstr., C.I.S. Abstr., Chem.Abstr., Curr.Adv.Ecol.Sci., Dairy Sci.Abstr., Excerp.Med., Food Sci.& Tech.Abstr., Ind.Med., INIS Atomind., Mass Spectr.Bull., Sel.Water Res.Abstr., Sugar Ind.Abstr., W.R.C.Inf., Weed Abstr. **Document type:** academic/scholarly publication.
—BLDSC (4658.905000); SWETS; CASDDS.
Formerly: Journal of Hygienic Chemistry.

JOURNAL DE MEDECINE LEGALE DROIT MEDICAL; expertise medicale, deontologie, urgence medicale. see MEDICAL SCIENCES — Forensic Sciences

615.9 US ISSN 0146-4760
RA1221 CODEN: JATOD3
JOURNAL OF ANALYTICAL TOXICOLOGY. 1977. 7/yr. $220 (effective 1994). Preston Publications, Inc., 7800 Merrimac Ave., Box 48312, Niles, IL 60714. TEL 708-965-0566. FAX 708-965-7639. Ed. Randall Baselt. adv.; bk.rev.; charts; illus.; index. circ. 1,350. (also avail. in microfilm from MML; microfiche; back issues avail.) **Indexed:** Anal.Abstr., Biol.Abstr., Chem.Abstr., Dairy Sci.Abstr., Dent.Ind., Excerp.Med., HRIS, Ind.Med., Ind.Sci.Rev., Ind.Vet., INIS Atomind., Mass Spectr.Bull., Rev.Med.& Vet.Mycol., Sci.Cit.Ind., Sel.Water Res.Abstr., Small Anim.Abstr., Vet.Bull., Weed Abstr. **Document type:** academic/scholarly publication.
—BLDSC (4928.700000); Faxon; UnCover; SWETS; CASDDS. **CCC.**
Refereed Serial

615.9 UK ISSN 0260-437X
RA1190 CODEN: JJATDK
JOURNAL OF APPLIED TOXICOLOGY. 1981. bi-m. $495 (effective 1994). John Wiley & Sons Ltd., Journals, Baffins Ln., Chichester, Sussex PO19 1UD, England. TEL 0243-779777. FAX 0243-775878. TELEX 86290 WIBOOK G. (In U.S.: 200 Meachem Ave, Elmont, NY 10016-7892) Ed. H. Salem. adv.; bk.rev.; index. circ. 377. (microfiche; also avail. in microfilm; back issues avail.; reprint service avail. from SWZ) **Indexed:** ASCA, Chem.Abstr., Curr.Adv.Cancer Res., Curr.Adv.Genetics & Molec.Biol., Curr.Cont., Dok.Arbeitsmed., Energy Info.Abstr., Environ.Abstr., Environ.Per.Bibl., Excerp.Med., Ind.Hyg.Dig., Ind.Med., Ind.Sci.Rev., NRN, Petrol.Abstr., Sci.Cit.Ind., World Surf.Coat. **Document type:** academic/scholarly publication.
—BLDSC (4947.130000); ADONIS; Faxon; UnCover; SWETS; UMI; CASDDS. **CCC.**
Description: Encompasses, but is not limited to, the study of the toxic effects of chemicals and materials in the field of teratology, reproduction, mutagenesis, carcinogenesis, health, the environment, pathology, pharmacokinetics and biochemical mechanisms.

574.192 GW ISSN 0887-2082
CODEN: JBTOEB
JOURNAL OF BIOCHEMICAL TOXICOLOGY. (Text in English) 1986. 6/yr. DM.450($250) V C H Verlagsgesellschaft mbH, Postfach 101161, 69451 Weinheim, Germany. TEL 06201-606-0. FAX 06201-606328. TELEX 465516-VCHWH-D. (U.S. addr.: V C H Publishers Inc., 220 E. 23rd St., New York, NY 10010-4606. TEL 212-683-8333) Ed. E. Hodgson. (also avail. in microform from VCI) **Document type:** academic/scholarly publication.
—BLDSC (4951.800000); Faxon; UnCover; CASDDS. **CCC.**

628 574 US
▼**JOURNAL OF ECOLOGICAL SAFETY.** 1993. q. $265 (effective 1993). Nova Science Publishers, Inc., 6080 Jericho Tpke., Ste. 207, Commack, NY 11725-2808. TEL 516-499-3103. **Document type:** academic/scholarly publication.

615.9 II ISSN 0971-0965
JOURNAL OF ECOTOXICOLOGY & ENVIRONMENTAL MONITORING; an international journal for scientific research on toxicology and pollution. (Text in English) 1991. q. $150 (effective 1994). Palani Paramount Publications, 69D, Anna Nagar, Palani 624 602, India. TEL 04545-42332. FAX 04545-42199. Ed. S. Palanichamy. adv.: page $125. circ. 300. **Document type:** academic/scholarly publication.
—BLDSC (4973.095800).
Description: Reports laboratory and field researches pertaining to toxicology and environmental pollution.
Refereed Serial

615.9 US ISSN 0731-8898
RA1190 CODEN: JEPOEC
JOURNAL OF ENVIRONMENTAL PATHOLOGY, TOXICOLOGY AND ONCOLOGY. 1981. bi-m. $79.95 to individuals; institutions $195. (International Society for Environmental Toxicology and Cancer) C R C Press, Inc., 2000 Corporate Blvd., N.W., Boca Raton, FL 33431. TEL 407-994-0555. FAX 407-997-0949. TELEX 568689-CRC PRESS. Ed.Bd. adv.; bk.rev.; index. circ. 1,000. (also avail. in microfiche; back issues avail.) **Indexed:** Chem.Abstr., Curr.Adv.Cancer Res., Curr.Cont., Dok.Arbeitsmed., Environ.Per.Bibl., Excerp.Med., Ind.Med., Ind.Sci.Rev., Ind.Vet., INIS Atomind., Ocean.Abstr., Pollut.Abstr., Rev.Plant Path., Sel.Water Res.Abstr., Soils & Fert., Vet.Bull. **Document type:** academic/scholarly publication.
—BLDSC (4979.384400); Faxon; UnCover; SWETS; UMI; CASDDS. **CCC.**
Formerly: Journal of Environmental Pathology and Toxicology (ISSN 0146-4779)
Description: Provides an international forum for works that relate to toxicology and pathology.
Refereed Serial

JOURNAL OF OCCUPATIONAL MEDICINE AND TOXICOLOGY; an international journal. see OCCUPATIONAL HEALTH AND SAFETY

615.9 US ISSN 1056-8719
QP901 CODEN: JPTMEZ
JOURNAL OF PHARMACOLOGICAL AND TOXICOLOGICAL METHODS. 1978. 8/yr. (in 2 vols.; 4 nos./vol.) $458 to institutions (foreign $498) (effective 1994). Elsevier Science Inc., 655 Ave. of the Americas, New York, NY 10010. TEL 212-989-5800. FAX 212-633-3990. TELEX 420643 AEP UI. Eds. P.S. Spencer, J.H. McNeill. (also avail. in microform from UMI) **Indexed:** Biol.Abstr., Biotech.Abstr., Chem.Abstr., Curr.Adv.Ecol.Sci., Curr.Cont., Dent.Ind., Excerp.Med., I.P.A., Ind.Med., INIS Atomind. **Document type:** academic/scholarly publication.
—BLDSC (5032.650000); ADONIS; Faxon; UnCover; SWETS; CASDDS. **CCC.**
Formerly (until 1992): Journal of Pharmacological Methods (ISSN 0160-5402)
Description: Publishes original articles on current methods of investigation used in pharmacology and toxicology.
Refereed Serial

615.9 JA ISSN 0914-9198
CODEN: JTPAE7
JOURNAL OF TOXICOLOGIC PATHOLOGY. s-a. Japanese Society of Toxicologic Pathology, c/o Eisei Ishikawa, Ed., 3-25-8 Nishi-shinbashi, Minato-ku, Tokyo 105, Japan. **Document type:** academic/scholarly publication.
—BLDSC (5069.732000); CASDDS.
Description: Publishes original papers, notes, and review articles from the members of the society.

JOURNAL OF TOXICOLOGY. CUTANEOUS AND OCULAR TOXICOLOGY. see PHARMACY AND PHARMACOLOGY

JOURNAL OF TOXICOLOGY. TOXIN REVIEWS. see PHARMACY AND PHARMACOLOGY

616.863 615.9
614.7 US ISSN 0098-4108
RA1190 CODEN: JTEHD6
JOURNAL OF TOXICOLOGY AND ENVIRONMENTAL HEALTH. 1975. m. (3 vols./yr., 4 nos./vol.). $750. Talyor & Francis, 1900 Frost Rd., Ste. 101, Bristol, PA 19007-1598. TEL 800-821-8312. FAX 215-785-5515. Ed. Renate D. Kimbrough. adv.; abstr.; bibl.; charts; illus.; index. circ. 1,000. (also avail. in microform from UMI; back issues avail.; reprint service avail. from UMI) **Indexed:** Abstr.Hyg., Acid Rain Abstr., Acid Rain Ind., Biol.Abstr., Biol.Dig., Biotech.Abstr., C.I.S.Abstr., Cadscan, Chem.Abstr., Curr.Adv.Cell & Devel.Biol., Curr.Adv.Ecol.Sci., Curr.Cont., Dairy Sci.Abstr., Deep Sea Res.& Oceanogr.Abstr., Dent.Ind., Environ.Abstr., Environ.Per.Bibl. (1977-), Excerp.Med., Food Sci.& Tech.Abstr., Helminthol.Abstr., Ind.Hyg.Dig., Ind.Med., Ind.Sci.Rev., Ind.Vet., INIS Atomind., Lab.Haz.Bull., Lead Abstr., Maize Abstr., Nutr.Abstr., Poult.Abstr., Rev.Med.& Vet.Mycol., Rev.Plant Path., Risk Abstr., Sel.Water Res.Abstr., Telegen, Trop.Dis.Bull., Trop.Oil Seeds Abstr., Vet.Bull., Weed Abstr., Zincscan. **Document type:** academic/scholarly publication.
—BLDSC (5069.735000); ADONIS; CIS; Faxon; UnCover; SWETS; CASDDS. **CCC.**
Description: Contains original research in the field of environmental toxicology.
Refereed Serial

615.9 US ISSN 0731-3810
RA1190 CODEN: JTCTDW
JOURNAL OF TOXICOLOGY: CLINICAL TOXICOLOGY. 1968. 6/yr. $49.75 to individuals; institutions $795. (American Academy of Clinical Toxicology) Marcel Dekker Journals, 270 Madison Ave., New York, NY 10016. TEL 212-696-9000. FAX 212-685-4540. TELEX 421419. (Subscr. to: Box 5017, Monticello, NY 12701) (Co-sponsor: European Association of Poison Centres and Clinical Toxicologoists) Ed. Carol R. Angle. adv. (also avail. in microform from RPI) **Indexed:** Abstr.Hyg., Biol.Abstr., Biol.Dig., Biotech.Abstr., C.I.S.Abstr., Chem.Abstr., Curr.Adv.Ecol.Sci., Curr.Cont., Dairy Sci.Abstr., Dent.Ind., Energy Rev., Environ.Abstr., Environ.Per.Bibl. (1991-), Excerp.Med., I.P.A., Ind.Med., Ind.Sci.Rev., Ind.Vet., INIS Atomind., JAMA, Lab.Haz.Bull., Med.Abstr., Nutr.Abstr., Rev.Plant Path., Risk Abstr., Sci.Cit.Ind., Trop.Dis.Bull., Vet.Bull., Weed Abstr. **Document type:** academic/scholarly publication.
●Also available online.
—BLDSC (5069.736000); ADONIS; Faxon; UnCover; SWETS; CASDDS. **CCC.**
Supersedes (in 1981): Clinical Toxicology (ISSN 0009-9309)
Description: Correlates the various disciplines that deal directly with and contribute to the practical aspects of poisoning per se.
Refereed Serial

LACTIC ACID BACTERIA. see BIOLOGY — Microbiology

MODERN PHARMACOLOGY - TOXICOLOGY SERIES. see PHARMACY AND PHARMACOLOGY

MUTATION RESEARCH - ENVIRONMENTAL MUTAGENESIS AND RELATED SUBJECTS INCLUDING METHODOLOGY; international journal on mutagenesis, chromosome breakage and related subjects. see BIOLOGY — Genetics

MUTATION RESEARCH - GENETIC TOXICOLOGY TESTING. see BIOLOGY — Genetics

MUTATION RESEARCH - REVIEWS IN GENETIC TOXICOLOGY. see BIOLOGY — Genetics

NATURAL TOXINS. see CHEMISTRY — Analytical Chemistry

NAUNYN-SCHMIEDEBERG'S ARCHIVES OF PHARMACOLOGY. see PHARMACY AND PHARMACOLOGY

NEUROTOXICOLOGY AND TERATOLOGY. see MEDICAL SCIENCES — Psychiatry And Neurology

P A S C A L E 63: TOXICOLOGIE. see ENVIRONMENTAL STUDIES — Abstracting, Bibliographies, Statistics

P A S C A L F 70: PHARMACOLOGIE. TRAITEMENTS MEDICAMENTEUX. see PHARMACY AND PHARMACOLOGY — Abstracting, Bibliographies, Statistics

ENVIRONMENTAL STUDIES — TOXICOLOGY AND ENVIRONMENTAL SAFETY

PEDIATRIC PRIMARY CARE; practical pediatrics for the pediatric practitioner. see *MEDICAL SCIENCES — Abstracting, Bibliographies, Statistics*

615.9 340 US
PESTICIDE LITIGATION MANUAL. a. $85. Clark - Boardman - Callaghan Company Ltd., 375 Hudson St., New York, NY 10014. TEL 212-929-7500; 800-221-9428. FAX 212-924-0460. Eds. John M. Johnson, George W. Ware.
 Description: Contains detailed analysis of pesticide litigation issues, including theories of liability, methods of apportioning liability, issues frequently briefed in pesticide cases, and analysis of damage theories.

PESTICIDES ABSTRACTS. see *ENVIRONMENTAL STUDIES — Abstracting, Bibliographies, Statistics*

PHARMACEUTICA ACTA HELVETIAE. see *PHARMACY AND PHARMACOLOGY*

PHARMACOLOGY AND THERAPEUTICS; journal of the International Encyclopedia of Pharmacology and Therapeutics. see *PHARMACY AND PHARMACOLOGY*

PHARMACOLOGY & TOXICOLOGY. see *PHARMACY AND PHARMACOLOGY*

615.1 DK ISSN 0901-9936
 CODEN: PTSUEC
PHARMACOLOGY & TOXICOLOGY. SUPPLEMENTUM. (Text in English) 1947. irreg. free. Munksgaard International Publishers Ltd., 35 Noerre Soegade, P.O. Box 2148, DK-1016 Copenhagen K, Denmark. TEL 33-127030. FAX 33-129387. Ed. Jens Schou. (reprint service avail. from ISI) **Indexed**: Biol.Abstr., Chem.Abstr., Curr.Cont., Excerp.Med., Ind.Med., INIS Atomind., Nutr.Abstr.
 —ADONIS; SWETS. **CCC**.
 Formerly: Acta Pharmacologica et Toxicologica. Supplementum (ISSN 0065-1508)
 Refereed Serial

PHARMACOLOGY, BIOCHEMISTRY AND BEHAVIOR. see *BIOLOGY — Biological Chemistry*

PROGRESS IN PESTICIDE BIOCHEMISTRY AND TOXICOLOGY. see *AGRICULTURE — Crop Production And Soil*

THE QUAD REPORT; covering efficiency, demand-side management, and energy policy. see *CONSUMER EDUCATION AND PROTECTION*

QUAD REPORT CASE STUDIES. see *CONSUMER EDUCATION AND PROTECTION*

615.9 340.6 US ISSN 0273-2300
RA1190 CODEN: RTOPDW
REGULATORY TOXICOLOGY AND PHARMACOLOGY. 1981. bi-m. $210 (foreign $270). Academic Press, Inc., Journal Division, 525 B St., Ste. 1900, San Diego, CA 92101-4495. TEL 619-230-1840. FAX 619-699-6800. (Subscr. to: Box 620000, Orlando, FL 32891-8340. TEL 800-543-9534) Eds. Frederick Coulston, Albert C. Kolbye, Jr. adv.; index. (back issues avail.) **Indexed**: Chem.Abstr., Curr.Adv.Cancer Res., Curr.Adv.Ecol.Sci., Dok.Arbeitsmed., Energy Ind., Energy Info.Abstr., Excerp.Med., Ind.Med., Lab.Haz.Bull., Risk Abstr., Sel.Water Res.Abstr. **Document type**: academic/scholarly publication.
 —BLDSC (7350.040000); ADONIS; Faxon; UnCover; SWETS; CASDDS. **CCC**.
 Description: Reports the concepts and problems involved with the generation, evaluation, and interpretation of experimental animal and human data in the large perspective of the societal considerations of protecting human health and the environment.
 Refereed Serial

618 615.9 UK ISSN 0890-6238
 CODEN: REPTED
REPRODUCTIVE TOXICOLOGY. 1988. 6/yr. £320($495) (effective 1994). (Reproductive Toxicology Center, US) Elsevier Science Ltd., Pergamon, P.O. Box 800, Kidlington, Oxford OX5 1DX, England. TEL 44-865-843000. FAX 44-865-843010. (Subscr. in U.S. and Canada to: Elsevier Science, 660 White Plains Rd., Tarrytown, NY 10591-5153. TEL 914-524-9200. FAX 914-333-2444) Ed. Dr. Anthony R. Scialli. (also avail. in microfilm from UMI; back issues avail.) **Indexed**: Ind.Med. (1992-). **Document type**: academic/scholarly publication.
 —BLDSC (7713.706500); Faxon; UnCover; SWETS; UMI; CASDDS. **CCC**.
 Description: Publishes original research on the influence of chemical and physical agents on reproduction, focusing on the application of in vitro, animal and clinical research to the practice of clinical medicine.
 Refereed Serial

REVIEWS IN BIOCHEMICAL TOXICOLOGY. see *BIOLOGY — Biological Chemistry*

615.9 NE ISSN 0168-7255
QH545.A1 CODEN: RETXEB
REVIEWS IN ENVIRONMENTAL TOXICOLOGY. (Text in English) 1984. irreg., vol.3, 1987. price varies. Elsevier Science B.V., Books Division, P.O. Box 211, 1000 AE Amsterdam, Netherlands. TEL 31-20-5803911. FAX 31-20-5803705. TELEX 18582 ESPA NL. (Subscr. in U.S. and Canada to: Elsevier Science Inc., Box 882, Madison Sq. Sta., New York, NY 10159. TEL 212-989-5800) **Document type**: monographic series.
 —BLDSC (7790.525600); CASDDS.
 Refereed Serial

REVISTA DE TOXICOLOGIA. see *PHARMACY AND PHARMACOLOGY*

RISK ABSTRACTS; a quarterly journal of abstracts, reviews and references. see *ENVIRONMENTAL STUDIES — Abstracting, Bibliographies, Statistics*

SAFE FOOD NEWS. see *CONSUMER EDUCATION AND PROTECTION*

615.9 UK ISSN 0938-5215
SAFETY, ENVIRONMENTAL PROTECTION, AND ANALYSIS. m.? £115($220) (Canada £121). Royal Society of Chemistry, Thomas Graham House, Science Park, Milton Rd., Cambridge CB4 4WF, England. TEL 0223-420066. FAX 0223-423623. TELEX 818293. (Dist. by: Turpin Distribution Services Ltd., Blackhorse Rd., Letchworth, Herts. SG6 1HN, England. TEL 0462-672555. FAX 0462-480947) **Document type**: abstracting/indexing.
 Description: Summarizes articles for environmental safety professionals.

THE SCIENCE OF THE TOTAL ENVIRONMENT; an international journal for scientific research into the environment and its relationship with man. see *ENVIRONMENTAL STUDIES*

615.9 US
TARGET ORGAN TOXICOLOGY SERIES. irreg., latest 1992. Raven Press (Subsidiary of: Wolters Kluwer N.V.), 1185 Ave. of the Americas, New York, NY 10036. TEL 212-930-9500. FAX 212-869-3495. TELEX 640073. Ed.Bd. (reprint service avail. from UMI) **Document type**: monographic series.
 Formerly: Target Organ Toxicity.
 Refereed Serial

TERATOLOGY; the international journal of abnormal development. see *BIOLOGY*

THIRD WORLD SCIENCE & ENVIRONMENT PERSPECTIVES. see *ENVIRONMENTAL STUDIES*

TOPICS IN CHEMICAL MUTAGENESIS. see *BIOLOGY — Biological Chemistry*

TOXIC SUBSTANCES CONTROL ACT - TEST SUBMISSION DATABASE. see *ENVIRONMENTAL STUDIES — Abstracting, Bibliographies, Statistics*

TOXIC SUBSTANCES JOURNAL. see *ENVIRONMENTAL STUDIES — Waste Management*

616.07 US ISSN 0192-6233
RB1 CODEN: TOPADD
TOXICOLOGIC PATHOLOGY. 1973. bi-m. $150 to individuals (foreign $170); institutions $170 (foreign $190) (effective 1993). Society of Toxicologic Pathologists, c/o Dr. Benjamin F. Trump, Ed., Dept. of Pathology, School of Medicine, Univ. of Maryland, Baltimore, MD 21201. TEL 410-706-7070. FAX 410-706-3743. (Subscr. to: Allen Press, Inc., 1041 New Hampshire Ave., Box 1897, Lawrence, KS 66044-8897. TEL 913-843-1221) adv.; bk.rev.; charts; illus.; circ. 810 (controlled). (back issues avail.) **Indexed**: Biol.Abstr., Chem.Abstr., Curr.Cont., Excerp.Med., Ind.Med., Rev.Med.& Vet.Mycol.
 —BLDSC (8873.015000); Faxon; UnCover; SWETS; CASDDS. **CCC**.
 Formerly (until vol.6, no.2, 1978): Society of Pharmacological and Environmental Pathologists. Bulletin (ISSN 0094-1824)
 Refereed Serial

540 615.9 US ISSN 0277-2248
RA1190 CODEN: TECSDY
TOXICOLOGICAL AND ENVIRONMENTAL CHEMISTRY. 20/yr. (in 5 vols., 4 nos./vol.) 1980 ECU per vol. (effective 1993). Gordon and Breach Science Publishers, 820 Town Center Dr., Langhorne, PA 19047. TEL 215-750-2642. FAX 215-750-6343. (UK subscr. to: P.O. Box 90, Reading, Berkshire RG1 8JL, England. TEL 0734-560-080) Eds. Otto Hutzinger, Roland W. Frei. adv. (also avail. in microform) **Indexed**: ASCA, Biol.Abstr., Chem.Abstr., Curr.Adv.Ecol.Sci., Energy Ind., Energy Info.Abstr., Environ.Per.Bibl. (1991-), Excerp.Med., Sel.Water Res.Abstr., W.P.C.Inf. **Document type**: academic/scholarly publication.
 —BLDSC (8873.028000); Faxon; UnCover; SWETS; CASDDS. **CCC**.
 Formerly: Toxicological and Environmental Chemistry Reviews (ISSN 0092-9867)
 Refereed Serial

615.9 IE ISSN 0300-483X
RA1190 CODEN: TXCYAC
TOXICOLOGY; an international journal concerned with the effects of chemicals on living systems. 1973. 21/yr. (in 7 vols.; 3 nos./vol.). I£980($1431) (effective 1994). Elsevier Science Ireland Ltd., P.O. Box 85, Limerick, Ireland. TEL 353-61-471944. FAX 353-61-472144. (Subscr. in U.S. and Canada to: Elsevier Science Inc., Box 882, Madison Sq. Sta., New York, NY 10159. TEL 212-989-5800. FAX 212-633-3990) Eds. H.P. Witschi, K.J. Netter. adv.; charts; illus.; index. (also avail. in microform from UMI) **Indexed**: ASCA, Biol.Abstr., Biotech.Abstr., Chem.Abstr., Curr.Adv.Cancer Res., Curr.Adv.Ecol.Sci., Curr.Cont., Dent.Ind., Dok.Arbeitsmed., Energy Ind., Energy Info.Abstr., Environ.Per.Bibl. (1991-), Excerp.Med., Ind.Med., Ind.Vet., Lab.Haz.Bull., Pig News & Info., Pollut.Abstr., Poult.Abstr., Rev.Med.& Vet.Mycol., Small Anim.Abstr., Vet.Bull., Weed Abstr. **Document type**: academic/scholarly publication.
 —BLDSC (8873.035000); ADONIS; Faxon; UnCover; SWETS; CASDDS. **CCC**.
 Description: Publishes original scientific papers on the biological effects arising from the administration of chemical compounds, principally to animals, tissues or cells, but also to man.

TOXICOLOGY ABSTRACTS. see *PHARMACY AND PHARMACOLOGY — Abstracting, Bibliographies, Statistics*

ENVIRONMENTAL STUDIES — WASTE MANAGEMENT

615.9 US ISSN 0041-008X
RA1190 CODEN: TXAPA9
TOXICOLOGY AND APPLIED PHARMACOLOGY; for those working in the fields of toxicology, pharmacology, biochemistry, nutrition, veterinary medicine. 1959. m. $852 (foreign $1005). Academic Press, Inc., Journal Division, 525 B St., Ste. 1900, San Diego, CA 92101-4495. TEL 619-230-1840. FAX 619-699-6800. (Subscr. to: Box 620000, Orlando, FL 32891-8340. TEL 800-543-9534) Ed. Edward Beresnick. adv.; bk.rev.; bibl.; charts; cum.index every 5 yrs. (back issues avail.) **Indexed:** Abstr.Hyg., ASCA, Biol.Abstr., Biotech.Abstr., C.I.S.Abstr., Chem.Abstr., Curr.Adv.Ecol.Sci., Curr.Adv.Genetics & Molec.Biol., Curr.Cont., Dairy Sci.Abstr., Dent.Ind., Dok.Arbeitsmed., Excerp.Med., Food Sci.& Tech.Abstr., Helminthol.Abstr., I.P.A., Ind.Hyg.Dig., Ind.Med., Ind.Vet., Lab.Haz.Bull., Nutr.Abstr., Ocean.Abstr., Pollut.Abstr., Protozool.Abstr., Rev.Med.& Vet.Mycol., Rev.Plant Path., Sel.Water Res.Abstr., Sugar Ind.Abstr., Vet.Bull., W.R.C.Inf., Weed Abstr. **Document type:** academic/scholarly publication.
●Also available online.
—BLDSC (8873.040000); ADONIS; Faxon; UnCover; SWETS; CASDDS. **CCC.**
Description: Covers scientific research pertaining to action on tissue structure or function resulting from administration of chemicals, drugs, or natural products to animals and humans.
Refereed Serial

615.9 US ISSN 0748-2337
RA1199 CODEN: TIHEEC
TOXICOLOGY AND INDUSTRIAL HEALTH; an international journal. 1985. bi-m. $148 (foreign $168) (effective 1994). Princeton Scientific Publishing Co., Inc., Box 2155, Princeton, NJ 08543. TEL 609-683-4750. FAX 609-683-0838. Ed. James Withey. adv.; bk.rev.; index. (back issues avail.) **Document type:** academic/scholarly publication.
—BLDSC (8873.040500); Faxon; SWETS; CASDDS. **CCC.**
Description: Publishes basic and applied research in the fields of toxicology, biochemical toxicology, genetic and cellular toxicology, including risk assessment associated with hazardous wastes and ground water contamination.
Refereed Serial

615.9 UK ISSN 0887-2333
CODEN: TIVIEQ
TOXICOLOGY IN VITRO. 1987. 6/yr. £260($400) (effective 1994). (British Industrial Biological Research Association) Elsevier Science Ltd., Pergamon, P.O. Box 800, Kidlington, Oxford OX5 1DX, England. TEL 44-865-843000. FAX 44-865-843010. (Subscr. in U.S. and Canada to: Elsevier Science, 660 White Plains Rd., Tarrytown, NY 10591-5153. TEL 914-524-9200. FAX 914-333-2444) Eds. S.D. Gangolli, I.F.H. Purchase. (also avail. in microfilm from UMI; back issues avail.) **Indexed:** Excerp.Med. **Document type:** academic/scholarly publication.
—BLDSC (8873.043400); ADONIS; Faxon; SWETS; UMI; CASDDS. **CCC.**
Description: Research on the use of in vitro techniques for determining the toxic effects of chemicals and elucidating their mechanisms of action.
Refereed Serial

615.9 IE ISSN 0378-4274
CODEN: TOLED5
TOXICOLOGY LETTERS; an international journal for the rapid publication of short reports on biochemical mechanisms of mammalian toxicity. 1977. 15/yr. (in 5 vols.; 3 nos./vol.). I£752($1098) (effective 1994). Elsevier Science Ireland Ltd., P.O. Box 85, Limerick, Ireland. TEL 353-61-471944. FAX 353-61-472144. (Subscr. in U.S. and Canada to: Elsevier Science Inc., Box 882, Madison Sq. Sta., New York, NY 10159. TEL 212-989-5800. FAX 212-633-3990) Eds. H. Kappus, D.B. Menzel. adv. (also avail. in microform from UMI) **Indexed:** ASCA, Biol.Abstr., Biotech.Abstr., Chem.Abstr., Curr.Adv.Biochem., Curr.Adv.Ecol.Sci., Curr.Cont., Curr.Ref.Fish Res., Dairy Sci.Abstr., Dent.Ind., Dok.Arbeitsmed., Energy Ind., Energy Info.Abstr., Excerp.Med., Helminthol.Abstr., I.P.A., Ind.Med., Ind.Vet., Lab.Haz.Bull., Rev.Med.& Vet.Mycol., Sel.Water Res.Abstr., Vet.Bull., W.R.C.Inf., Weed Abstr. **Document type:** academic/scholarly publication.
●Also available online.
—BLDSC (8873.042000); ADONIS; Faxon; UnCover; SWETS; CASDDS. **CCC.**
Description: Provides a forum for original and pertinent contributions in toxicology research.
Refereed Serial

615.9 US ISSN 1051-7235
RA1221 CODEN: TOMEEB
TOXICOLOGY METHODS. 1991. q. $90 to individuals; institutions $148 (effective 1994). Raven Press (Subsidiary of Wolters Kluwer N.V.), 1185 Ave. of the Americas, New York, NY 10036. TEL 212-930-9500. FAX 212-869-3495. TELEX 640073. Ed. Shayne C. Gad. adv. contact: Phyllis Noyes. charts; illus. circ. 1,000. (reprint service avail. from UMI) **Document type:** academic/scholarly publication.
—BLDSC (8873.042100); SWETS; UMI; CASDDS. **CCC.**
Description: Covers new methods and test designs in safety assessment, new in vivo and in vitro models, modifications to existing procedures, commentaries, and new technology and equipment.
Refereed Serial

TOXICON; an international journal specialising in toxins. see PHARMACY AND PHARMACOLOGY

615.9 NE
TRACE METALS IN THE ENVIRONMENT. (Text in English) 1991. irreg., vol.3, 1993. price varies. Elsevier Science B.V., Books Division, P.O. Box 211, 1000 AE Amsterdam, Netherlands. TEL 31-20-5803911. FAX 31-20-5803705. TELEX 18582 ESPA NL. (Subscr. in U.S. and Canada to: Elsevier Science Inc., Box 882, Madison Sq. Sta., New York, NY 10159. TEL 212-989-5800) (back issues avail.) **Document type:** monographic series.
Refereed Serial

614 UK ISSN 0361-5162
RA565.A1 CODEN: PUMTAG
TRACE SUBSTANCES IN ENVIRONMENTAL HEALTH. 1967. a. $60. Science Reviews Ltd., 18 Oaklands Gate, Northwood, Middlesex HA6 3AA, England. TEL 0923-823586. FAX 0923-825066. index. circ. 2,000. **Indexed:** Biol.Abstr., Chem.Abstr., GeoRef., Nutr.Abstr., Pollut.Abstr. **Document type:** academic/scholarly publication.
—BLDSC (8876.900000); CASDDS.
Formerly: Conference on Trace Substances in Environmental Health. Proceedings (ISSN 0069-8741)
Description: Explores the biological, ecological, and health significance of the numerous inorganic and organic chemical substances which are present (normally in trace amounts) in the air, food and water.
Refereed Serial

TRENDS IN PHARMACOLOGICAL SCIENCES. see PHARMACY AND PHARMACOLOGY

TRENDS IN PHARMACOLOGICAL SCIENCES (REFERENCE EDITION). see PHARMACY AND PHARMACOLOGY

U.S. NATIONAL TOXICOLOGY PROGRAM. ANNUAL REPORT ON CARCINOGENS. see MEDICAL SCIENCES — Oncology

615.9 US
V N R HAZCHEM ALERT. 1986. bi-w. $270 (foreign $325). Van Nostrand Reinhold, 115 Fifth Ave., New York, NY 10003. TEL 212-254-3232. FAX 212-673-1239. (back issues avail.)
Description: Provides worldwide news on hazardous chemicals and potential-risk substances. Includes current news on toxicology, industrial hygiene, occupational health and safety, environmental compliance, R&D, and government research.

615.9 US ISSN 0145-6296
SF757.5 CODEN: VHTODE
VETERINARY AND HUMAN TOXICOLOGY. 1958. bi-m. $50 (Canada $60; elsewhere $70). (American Academy of Veterinary and Comparative Toxicology) Comparative Toxicology Laboratories, Publication Office, Kansas State University, Manhattan, KS 66506-5606. TEL 913-532-4334. FAX 913-532-4481. TELEX 82 1034. (Co-sponsors: American Board of Medical Toxicology; American Academy of Clinical Toxicology; American Association of Poison Control Centers; American Board of Veterinary Toxicology) Ed. Frederick W. Oehme. adv.; bk.rev.; abstr.; bibl.; charts; illus. circ. 2,000. (reprint service avail. from ISI) **Indexed:** Biol.Abstr., Biol.Dig., Chem.Abstr., Curr.Adv.Ecol.Sci., Curr.Cont., Dairy Sci.Abstr., Dent.Ind., Energy Ind., Energy Info.Abstr., Excerp.Med., Helminthol.Abstr., Herb.Abstr., Ind.Med., Ind.Vet., Maize Abstr., Med.Abstr., Rev.Med.& Vet.Mycol., Rev.Plant Path., Risk Abstr., Sci.Cit.Ind., Triticale Abstr., Vet.Bull., Weed Abstr. **Document type:** academic/scholarly publication.
—BLDSC (9226.700000); Faxon; UnCover; SWETS; UMI; CASDDS.
Former titles (until 1976): Veterinary Toxicology (ISSN 0091-5300); (1970-1973): News from the American College of Veterinary Toxicologists.
Description: Contains contributions in the broad field of toxicology. Includes manuscripts of original research, scientific reviews, field observations in man or domestic and wild animals, papers presented at meetings, news items and announcements, and information of general educational value to toxicologists and related scientists.
Refereed Serial

XENOBIOTICA; the fate of foreign compounds in biological systems. see BIOLOGY — Biological Chemistry

615 CC ISSN 1000-3002
CODEN: ZYYZEW
ZHONGGUO YAOLIXUE YU DULIXUE ZAZHI/CHINESE JOURNAL OF PHARMACOLOGY AND TOXICOLOGY. (Text in Chinese, English) 1986. q. $18.72 (foreign $55.32). Chinese Pharmacological Society, 27, Taiping Rd., Beijing 100850, People's Republic of China. TEL 812343. TELEX 861-8211656. (Overseas subscr. to: China International Book Trading Corp., P.O. Box 399, Beijing 100044, P.R. China) Ed. Rong Kangtai. adv.: page $250; adv. contact: Tao Shi. circ. 4,000. (also avail. in microfiche) **Indexed:** Excerp.Med. **Document type:** academic/scholarly publication.
—BLDSC (3180.474000); CASDDS.
Description: Reports the research achievements in the field of pharmacology and toxicology in China.

ENVIRONMENTAL STUDIES — Waste Management

628.4 GW ISSN 0932-3708
A W T. (Abwassertechnik); Abfalltechnik and Recycling. 1949. 6/yr. DM.137 (foreign DM.161). Bauverlag GmbH, Postfach 1460, 65004 Wiesbaden, Germany. TEL 06123-700-0. FAX 06123-700122. Ed. H. Wendt. adv. contact: E. Gross. bk.rev. circ. 5,000. **Indexed:** Chem.Abstr., Excerp.Med. **Document type:** trade publication.
—BLDSC (0570.400000); EI.
Former titles: Abwassertechnik mit Abfalltechnik (ISSN 0342-4022); Abwassertechnik.
Description: Trade publication for the waste water removal industry. Devoted to treatment of sewerage, recycling, and water pollution.

628.4 SZ
ABFALL SPEKTRUM. 6/yr. 69 SFr. (foreign 86 SFr.). Graf und Neuhaus AG, Moehrlistr. 69, CH-8033 Zurich, Switzerland. TEL 01-3615600. FAX 01-3617715. Ed. P. Neuhaus. circ. 5,000. **Document type:** trade publication.

ENVIRONMENTAL STUDIES — WASTE MANAGEMENT

628.4   GW   ISSN 0934-6422
ABFALLWIRTSCHAFTS JOURNAL; Fachzeitschrift fuer Vermeidung, Verwertung und Behandlung von Abfaellen. m. DM.170. E F Verlag fuer Energie- und Umwelttechnik GmbH, Im Schwarzen Grund 20, 14195 Berlin, Germany. TEL 030-8312990. Ed. Karl Thome-Kozmiensky. adv. contact: Cerstin Gammelin. **Document type:** trade publication.
—BLDSC (0539.195000); SWETS.

AIR & WASTE MANAGEMENT ASSOCIATION. MEETING PROCEEDINGS. see ENVIRONMENTAL STUDIES

604.7 628   GW   ISSN 0942-3818
▼**ALTLASTEN - SPEKTRUM**; Erfassung - Bewertung - Sanierung. 1992. q. DM.67.20. (Ingenieurtechnischer Verband Altlasten e.V.) Erich Schmidt Verlag GmbH & Co. (Berlin), Genthiner Str. 30G, 10785 Berlin, Germany. TEL 030-250085-0. FAX 030-25008521. adv. **Document type:** trade publication.
—BLDSC (0803.877300).

628.4   US   ISSN 1055-6176
KF5709.Z95
B O C A NATIONAL PRIVATE SEWAGE DISPOSAL CODE. 1990. triennial. Building Officials and Code Administrators International, 4051 W. Flossmoor Rd., Country Club Hills, IL 60478-5795.

604.7 351   US
BEYOND WASTE. 1978. m. free. Department of Environmental Quality, 811 S.W. Sixth Ave., Portland, OR 97201. TEL 503-229-6044. FAX 503-229-6124. Ed. Jo Brooks. circ. 3,000. **Document type:** government publication.
Description: Covers Oregon State hazardous and solid waste management programs, with information on state and federal requirements, procedures for legal compliance, technical information and more.

628.44   US   ISSN 0276-5055
S661   CODEN: BCYCDK
BIOCYCLE; journal of composting and recycling. 1960. m. $63 (foreign $90). J G Press, Inc., 419 State Ave., Emmaus, PA 18049. TEL 215-967-4135. Ed. Jerome Goldstein. adv.; bk.rev.; charts; illus.; index. circ. 14,500. (also avail. in microform from UMI; back issues avail.) **Indexed:** Agri.Eng.Abstr.; Biodet.Abstr., Biol.Abstr., Biotech.Abstr., Chem.Abstr., Curr.Adv.Ecol.Sci., Curr.Biotech.Abstr., Curr.Cont., Energy Info.Abstr., Energy Rev., Eng.Ind., Environ.Abstr., Environ.Per.Bibl. (1989-), Excerp.Med., Gas Abstr., Geo.Abstr., Hort.Abstr., Met.Abstr., Ocean.Abstr., Pollut.Abstr., Risk Abstr., Sel.Water Res.Abstr., Soils & Fert., W.R.C.Inf.
—BLDSC (2071.220000); CIS; EI; Faxon; UnCover; SWETS; UMI; CASDDS. **CCC**.
Former titles: Compost Science - Land Utilization (ISSN 0160-7413); Compost Science (ISSN 0010-4388)
Description: For municipal and industrial managers of solid waste and sludge, focusing on composting and recycling techniques--from collection and processing to materials and marketing.
Refereed Serial

628.4   NE   ISSN 0923-9820
QR97.X46   CODEN: BIODEG
BIODEGRADATION. (Text in English) 1990. 4/yr. fl.442($230.50) (effective 1994). Kluwer Academic Publishers, Postbus 17, 3300 AA Dordrecht, Netherlands. TEL 31-78-334911. FAX 31-78-334254. TELEX 29245 KAPG NL. (Dist. by: Kluwer Academic Publishers Group, P.O. Box 322, 3300 AH Dordrecht, Netherlands. TEL 31-78-524400. FAX 31-78-524474; N. America dist. addr.: Box 358, Accord Sta., Hingham, MA 02018-0358. TEL 617-871-6600. FAX 617-871-6528) Ed.Bd. (also avail. in microform from UMI; back issues avail.; reprint service avail. from SWZ) **Indexed:** ASCA, Biol.Abstr., Chem.Abstr., Environ.Abstr., Environ.Per.Bibl. **Document type:** academic/scholarly publication.
—BLDSC (2071.240000); CIS; UnCover; SWETS; UMI; CASDDS. **CCC**.
Description: Presents papers on all aspects of science pertaining to the detoxification, recycling, amelioration or other treatment of waste materials and pollutants by naturally-occurring or recombinant organisms.
Refereed Serial

BRIATIN'S WASTE MANAGEMENT INDUSTRY. see BUSINESS AND ECONOMICS — Trade And Industrial Directories

604.7   UN
C E P NEWS. 1987. q. free. Caribbean Environment Programme, United Nations Environment Programme, Regional Co-ordinating Unit, 14-20 Port Royal St., Kingston, Jamaica, W.I. TEL 809-922-9267. FAX 809-922-9292. TELEX 3672 UNEPCAR JA. bk.rev. circ. 5,000. **Indexed:** Environ.Abstr.

604.7   UN
C E P TECHNICAL REPORT. irreg., no.23, 1993. Caribbean Environment Programme, United Nations Environment Programme, Regional Co-ordinating Unit, 14-20 Port Royal St., Kingston, Jamaica, W.I. TEL 809-922-9267. FAX 809-922-9292. TELEX 3672 UNEPCAR JA.

CARGO TANK HAZARDOUS MATERIAL REGULATIONS. see TRANSPORTATION — Trucks And Trucking

628.4   UK
CLEANING & HYGIENE TODAY. 1989. m. £48. Market Place Publishing Ltd., Scorpio House, 79 Dartmouth Rd., London SE23 3HT, England. TEL 081-699-7995. FAX 081-291-1672. Ed. Jan Hobbs. circ. 12,462. **Document type:** trade publication.

COGENERATION; the magazine for cogeneration management. see ENERGY

604.6 631   US   ISSN 1065-657X
TD796.5
▼**COMPOST SCIENCE & UTILIZATION**. 1993. q. $125 (Canada $145; elsewhere $150). J G Press, Inc., 419 State Ave., Emmaus, PA 18049. TEL 215-967-4135. Ed. Clarence Golueke. **Indexed:** Environ.Per.Bibl. **Document type:** trade publication.
—BLDSC (3366.225200); CIS; EI.
Description: Focuses on management techniques to improve compost process control and product quality, with special emphasis on the utilization of composted materials.
Refereed Serial

613.1   CN
COMPOSTERS' JOURNAL. q. membership. Recycling Council of Ontario, 489 College St., Ste. 504, Toronto, Ont. M6G 1A5, Canada. TEL 416-960-1025. FAX 416-960-8053. **Document type:** consumer publication.
Description: Covers small-scale, on site, backyard and worm composting.

604.6 635   US   ISSN 1064-1440
▼**COMPOSTING NEWS**. 1992. m. $83 (Canada & Mexico $90; elsewhere $105). McEntee Media Corp., 13727 Holland Rd., Cleveland, OH 44142. TEL 216-362-7979. FAX 216-362-4623. Ed. Ken McEntee. adv. contact: Rick Downing. circ. 5,000. **Document type:** newsletter
Description: Features news, trends, and legislation in private, public and home composting.

346 628.4   US
CORPORATE ENVIRONMENTAL DATA CLEARINGHOUSE REPORTS. 1991. q. $250 per no. Council for Economic Priorities, 30 Irving Pl., New York, NY 10003-2386. TEL 212-420-1133. FAX 212-420-0988. Ed. Alice Tapper Marlin. **Document type:** corporate report.
Description: Comprehensive reports analyzing corporate environmental compliance records, energy efficiency, hazardous waste disposal policies, and other important environmental issues. Each report covers all aspects of a single company and compares that company's performance to industry averages.

614.7 333.7   US
CYCLE (NEW YORK, 1970). 1970. q. $20. Environmental Action Coalition, 625 Broadway, New York, NY 10012. TEL 212-677-1601. bk.rev. Incorporates (1979-198?): Waste Paper (ISSN 0738-7695)
Description: Focuses on waste management, energy conservation, recycling techniques, urban forestry, environmental education, and environmental crisis resolution.

628.4   US   ISSN 1052-0635
DEFENSE CLEANUP. 1990. w. $475 (foreign $505). Pasha Publications Inc., 1616 N. Ft. Myer Dr., Ste. 1000, Arlington, VA 22209-3107. TEL 703-528-1244. FAX 703-528-1253. Ed. Bowman Ccx. **Document type:** newsletter.
● Also available online. Vendor(s): Data-Star, DIALOG Information Services, Inc.
—**CCC**.
Description: Covers environmental cleanup issues, including new waste management laws, technology, businesses, evolving regulations and standards, and political factors influencing the cleanup industry.

604.7   CN   ISSN 1194-2355
DIRECTORY OF HAZARDOUS WASTE SERVICES. 1985. a. Can.$95. Southam Information and Technology Group, 1450 Don Mills Road, Don Mills, ON M3B 2X7, Canada. TEL 416-445-6641. FAX 416-442-2200. Ed. Mary Mancini. adv. circ. 1,200. **Document type:** directory.
Description: Covers more than 1200 Canadian hazardous waste managemet companies.

604.7   US
DIRECTORY OF RADIOACTIVE WASTE OFFICIALS. irreg., 2nd ed., 1992. $89. Business Publishers, Inc., 951 Pershing Dr., Silver Spring, MD 20910-4464. TEL 301-587-6300; 800-BPI-0122. FAX 301-589-5103. **Document type:** directory.
Description: Includes name, title, organization, address, and phone number for more than 1,250 radwaste leaders.

604.7   US   ISSN 1042-251X
HD9975.U5   CODEN: EDIGER
E I DIGEST; industrial and hazardous waste management. 1989. m. $1250 (effective 1993). Environmental Information, Ltd., 4801 W. 81st St., Ste. 119, Minneapolis, MN 55437. TEL 612-831-2473. FAX 612-831-6550. Ed. Cary Perket. index. (back issues avail.) **Document type:** trade publication
—CASDDS.
Description: Covers company profiles, state programs, facility profiles, regulatory issues, technology reviews and other industry aspects.

E M PROGRESS. see ENERGY

E P I: ENVIRONMENTAL PRODUCT INDEX. see ENVIRONMENTAL STUDIES — Abstracting, Bibliographies, Statistics

ECO-LOG WEEK; a report on waste management and industrial pollution control. see ENVIRONMENTAL STUDIES — Abstracting, Bibliographies, Statistics

ELSEVIER HANDLING AND PROCESSING OF SOLIDS SERIES. see ENGINEERING — Hydraulic Engineering

604.7 614.8   US
KF3945.A15
ENVIRONMENT ADVISOR; monthly information report on congressional and regulatory activity to control, monitor or eliminate hazards created by hazardous and toxic substances. 1980. m. $90. J.J. Keller & Associates, Inc., 3003 W. Breezewood Lane, Box 368, Neenah, WI 54957-0368. TEL 414-722-2848. FAX 414-727-7516. Ed. Linda S. Wereley. circ. 1,0CO. (looseleaf format)
Formerly: Hazardous Substance Advisor (ISSN 0196-3767)

ENVIRONMENTAL COMPLIANCE & LITIGATION STRATEGY. see LAW

628.4   UK   ISSN 1352-0342
▼**ENVIRONMENTAL MANAGEMENT BRIEFING**. 1993. m. £95. E H A S Group, The Lansbury Estate, Lower Guildford Rd., Knaphill, Woking, Surrey GU21 2EP, England. TEL 0483-797625. FAX 0483-797839. Eds. V. Quayle, D. Denton. (also avail. in diskette format) **Document type:** bulletin, abstracting/indexing.
Description: Provides summaries of U.K. and EC legislation, reports, and other official and authoritative information on the environment, pollution control, waste, and related topics.

ENVIRONMENTAL STUDIES — WASTE MANAGEMENT

604.7 340 US
▼**ENVIRONMENTAL SPILL REPORTING MANUAL.** 1992. a. Clark - Boardman - Callaghan Company Ltd., 375 Hudson St., New York, NY 10014. TEL 212-929-7500; 800-221-9428. FAX 212-924-0460. Ed.Bd.
  Description: Features detailed guidance on state and federal requirements on reporting spills of hazardous substances.

604.7 US ISSN 1049-4715
TD811.5 CODEN: EWMAEQ
ENVIRONMENTAL WASTE MANAGEMENT. 1983. bi-m. $30. International Association of Environmental Managers, 243 W. Main St., Kutztown, PA 19530. TEL 215-683-5098. FAX 215-683-3171. Ed. Laura L. Rhein. adv.; bk.rev. circ. 34,000. **Indexed:** Environ.Per.Bibl. (1992-).
  Formerly: Hazardous Waste Management (ISSN 1047-479X)

628.4 CN
▼**ENVIROTECH.** (Text in French) 1993. 6/yr. Can.$34.25. Societe Ecopolis Inc., 1124 Marie-Anne E., Ste. 31, Montreal, PQ H2J 2B7, Canada. TEL 514-526-9205. FAX 514-524-7771. Ed. Perry Niro. adv.; B&W page Can.$1600, color page Can.$2200; trim 8 1/2 x 11. circ. 8,000.

604.6 GW
EUROPAEISCHER WIRTSCHAFTSDIENST. RECYCLING-DIENST. fortn. DM.495. Casimir Katz Verlag, Bleichstr. 20-22, 76593 Gernsbach, Germany. TEL 07224-9397-0. FAX 07224-939750. **Document type:** trade publication.

604.7 US ISSN 0749-3940
EVERYONE'S BACKYARD. 1982. bi-m. $25. Citizens Clearinghouse for Hazardous Wastes, Inc., Box 6806, Falls Church, VA 22040. TEL 703-237-2249. Ed. Kim Gunther. bk.rev.; film rev.; charts; illus. circ. 6,000. (back issues avail.) **Indexed:** Environ.Per.Bibl. (1989-). **Document type:** newsletter.
  Incorporates (1983-1990): Action Bulletin (ISSN 0749-3959)

628.3 US ISSN 1061-9682
FROM THE STATE CAPITALS. ENVIRONMENTAL REGULATION. Variant title: Environmental Regulation from the State Capitals. 1946. w. $215 (foreign $235) (effective Dec. 1990). Wakeman-Walworth, Inc., 300 N. Washington St., Alexandria, VA 22314. TEL 703-549-8606. FAX 703-549-1372. (processed)
  ●Also available online. Vendor(s): West Services, Inc.
  —CCC.
  Incorporates: From the State Capitals. Water Supply (ISSN 0734-1237) & From the State Capitals. Environmental Health (ISSN 0741-3580); Former titles: From the State Capitals. Waste Disposal and Pollution Control (ISSN 0749-2758); From the State Capitals. Water and Air Pollution Abatement Developments (ISSN 1049-3115); From the State Capitals. Sewage and Waste Disposal (ISSN 0016-1926)
  Description: Information on state laws concerning air and water pollution, solid waste, resource recovery and recycling, hazardous waste, radioactive waste.

604.6 US ISSN 1044-3061
TD785 CODEN: GARBEO
GARBAGE; the practical journal for the environment. 1989. 6/yr. $21. Old-House Journal Corporation, 2 Main St., Gloucester, MA 01930-5726. TEL 508-283-3200. FAX 508-283-5715. (Subscr. to: Box 55197, Boulder, CO 80322-6519. TEL 800-234-3797) Ed. Patricia Poore. adv. circ. 120,000. **Indexed:** Environ.Abstr., Environ.Ind., Environ.Per.Bibl. (1992-), Gard.Lit. (1992-), Ind.How To Do It (1990-). **Document type:** consumer publication.
  —BLDSC (4069.825000); Faxon; UnCover; UMI.
  Description: Covers environmental items such as recycling, composting, garbage disposal and energy, for a general audience.

604.7 333.8 US
GENERATOR'S JOURNAL. 1988. q. free. U S Pollution Control, Inc., 515 W. Greens Rd., Ste. 500, Houston, TX 77067. TEL 713-775-7910. Ed. Priscilla Proctor. illus.; tr.lit. circ. 18,000. (back issues avail.)
  Description: Covers hazardous waste legislative and technological developments affecting environmental managers and hazardous waste generators.

604.7 665 US ISSN 1051-6255
GOLOB'S OIL POLLUTION BULLETIN. 1989. fortn. $335 (foreign $375). World Information Systems, Box 535, Harvard Sq. Sta., Cambridge, MA 02238. FAX 617-491-5100. TELEX 710-320-1628. Ed. Richard S. Golob. adv.; index. (back issues avail.) **Document type:** newsletter.
  ●Also available online. Vendor(s): NewsNet (EV05).
  —SWETS. **CCC.**
  Formerly: Oil Pollution Bulletin.
  Description: Provides news analysis on oil pollution prevention, control, and cleanup. Covers oil spills worldwide, regulations, legislation and rulings, court decisions, new equipment and products, contract opportunities and awards, and conference notices.

604.7 US
H M C R I. bi-m. Hazardous Materials Control Resources Institute, 1 Church St., Ste. 200, Rockville, MD 20850-4129. TEL 301-251-1900. FAX 301-738-2330. Ed. Patrick Zickler. circ. 35,811. **Indexed:** Ind.Hyg.Dig.

614.7 US
H M C R I FOCUS. vol.2, 1984. m. membership. Hazardous Materials Control Resources Institute, 1 Church St., Ste. 200, Rockville, MD 20850-4129. TEL 301-251-1900. FAX 301-738-2330. Ed. E. Martin. adv.; bk.rev. circ. 5,000. **Indexed:** Energy Info.Abstr., Environ.Abstr.
  Formerly: H M C R I Forum.
  Description: Supplies current updates and overviews of the hazardous materials control field.

604.7 JA ISSN 0917-0855
CODEN: HAGAEB
HAIKIBUTSU GAKKAISHI/WASTE MANAGEMENT RESEARCH. (Supplement avail.) (Text in Japanese; summaries in English) 1990. q. 11000 Yen (effective 1994). Japan Society of Waste Management Experts, 2F 13-11 Shiba 5-chome, Minato-ku, Tokyo 108, Japan. TEL 81-3-3769-5099. FAX 81-3-3769-1492. Ed. Masakatsu Hanashima. adv.: page 100000Yen. bk.rev. circ. 3,000. **Document type:** academic/scholarly publication.
  —BLDSC (9266.690200); CASDDS.
  Description: Dedicated to the waste management research and conservation of natural resources.
  Refereed Serial

604.7 340 US
HAZARD COMMUNICATION HANDBOOK; a right-to-know compliance guide. a. $90. Clark - Boardman - Callaghan Company Ltd., 375 Hudson St., New York, NY 10014. TEL 212-929-7500; 800-221-9428. FAX 212-924-0460. Eds. Craig A. Moyer, Michael A. Francis.
  Description: Offers guidelines for complying with federal right-to-know laws, and guidance toward establishing an effective compliance program.

HAZARDOUS COMMODITY HANDBOOK. see
TRANSPORTATION — Trucks And Trucking

628.4 US ISSN 1062-8096
HAZARDOUS EMERGENCY RESPONSE. m. $299 (Canada $335; Mexico $349; elsewhere $383) (effective 1993). Stevens Publishing, 225 N. New Rd., Waco, TX 76710. TEL 817-776-9000; 800-727-7573. FAX 817-776-9018. Ed. Adam Glenn. (looseleaf format) **Document type:** newsletter.
  Description: Discusses the legislation, enforcement, and technology of emergency response to spills of hazardous materials.

604.7 US ISSN 0895-3260
CODEN: HMCOEF
HAZARDOUS MATERIALS CONTROL. 1988. bi-m. $18. Hazardous Materials Control Resources Institute, 1 Church St., Ste. 120, Rockville, MD 20850-4129. TEL 301-251-1900. FAX 301-738-2330. Ed. Patricia Segato. adv. circ. 33,000. **Indexed:** Environ.Abstr., Environ.Ind.
  —BLDSC (4274.440500); CASDDS.
  Description: Devoted to hazardous materials and hazardous waste control. Covers information on technology, services, products and regulations.

604.7 US
HAZARDOUS MATERIALS INTELLIGENCE REPORT. 1980. w. $375 (foreign $445). World Information Systems, Box 535, Harvard Sq. Sta., Cambridge, MA 02238. TEL 617-491-5100. FAX 617-492-3312. Ed. George Stubbs. **Document type:** newsletter.
  ●Also available online. Vendor(s): NewsNet.
  Description: Provides news analysis on environmental business, hazardous materials, waste management, and pollution prevention and control. Covers regulations, legislation and court decisions, new technology, contract opportunities and awards, and conference notices.

604.7 CN ISSN 0843-9303
HAZARDOUS MATERIALS MANAGEMENT; the Canadian publication of pollution prevention and control. (Bi-monthly supplement avail.: Compliance Monitor) 1989. bi-m. Can.$39.50($49.50) C H M M Inc., 401 Richmond St. W., Ste. 139, Toronto, ON M5V 1X3, Canada. TEL 416-348-9922. FAX 416-348-9744. Ed. Guy Crittenden; Pub. Todd Latham. adv.: B&W page Can.$2450; adv. contact: Arnie Gess. bk.rev.; charts; illus.; tr.lit. circ. 18,000. **Indexed:** Environ.Abstr., Environ.Per.Bibl. (1992-). **Document type:** trade publication.
  —BLDSC (4274.448000).
  Description: Directed to large waste-generating industries in Canada. Informs readers about the latest equipment and technology for environmental protection, as well as the legal aspects of new regulations.

HAZARDOUS MATERIALS TRANSPORTATION. see
TRANSPORTATION

604.7 US
HAZARDOUS SUBSTANCES & PUBLIC HEALTH. 1990. q. free. U.S. Department of Health and Human Services, Agency for Toxic Substances and Disease Registry, 1600 Clifton Rd., N.E., Mail Stop E-33, Atlanta, GA 30333. TEL 404-639-6206. FAX 404-639-6208. Ed. Teresa Ramsey. circ. 10,000. **Indexed:** Environ.Abstr., Ind.Hyg.Dig. **Document type:** newsletter, government publication.
  Description: Examines the issue of and corrective measures for hazardous waste as it affects human health.

620 US ISSN 0882-5696
TD811.5 CODEN: HWHME2
HAZARDOUS WASTE & HAZARDOUS MATERIALS; a journal for technology, health, environment and policy. 1984. q. $152 (foreign $192). (Hazardous Materials Control Research Institute) Mary Ann Liebert, Inc., 1 Church St., Ste. 200, Rockville, MD 20850-4129. TEL 301-251-1900. FAX 301-738-2330. Ed. James Noble. adv. **Indexed:** A.I.Abstr., Curr.Adv.Ecol.Sci., Curr.Cont., Environ.Abstr., Environ.Per.Bibl., Excerp.Med., Ind.Hyg.Dig., Risk Abstr., Sel.Water Res.Abstr., W.R.C.Inf. **Document type:** academic/scholarly publication.
  —BLDSC (4274.451430); CIS; Faxon; UnCover; SWETS; CASDDS.
  Supersedes: Hazardous Waste (ISSN 0738-6168)
  Description: Provides information on technology, health and environmental effects, and public policy for hazardous materials. Designed for a professional readership, aims to bring together the contributions of several disciplines.

628.44 US
HAZARDOUS WASTE BUSINESS. bi-w. $695 (foreign $720). McGraw-Hill, Inc., Energy & Business Newsletters, 1221 Ave. of the Americas, 36th Fl., New York, NY 10020. TEL 212-521-6410. Ed. Kevin Hamilton. (reprint service avail. from UMI)
  ●Also available online. Vendor(s): NewsNet (EV41).

ENVIRONMENTAL STUDIES — WASTE MANAGEMENT

604.7   US   ISSN 0738-0232
TD811.5
HAZARDOUS WASTE CONSULTANT. 1983. bi-m. $495 to institutions (foreign $555) (effective 1994). Elsevier Science Inc., 655 Ave. of the Americas, New York, NY 10010. TEL 212-989-5800. FAX 212-633-3990. TELEX 420643 AEP UI. (Subscr. to: Box 882, Madison Sq. Sta., New York, NY 10159-0882) Ed. Paul Gallagher. bk.rev. (back issues avail.) **Indexed**: Eng.Ind. **Document type**: academic/scholarly publication.
—BLDSC (4274.451440). **CCC**.
Description: Covers hazardous waste management topics by experts. Includes in-depth articles on technology, regulations and legal issues.

604.7   CN   ISSN 0711-7140
HAZARDOUS WASTE MANAGEMENT HANDBOOK. 1982. a. Can.$189.39 (foreign $177). Southam Information and Technology Group, 1450 Don Mills Rd., Don Mills, ON M3B 2X7, Canada. TEL 416-445-6641. FAX 416-442-2200. TELEX 06-966612. Ed. Mary Mancini.
Description: Provides all relevant hazardous waste policies.

604.7   US   ISSN 0275-374X
HAZARDOUS WASTE NEWS. (Includes Nuclear Waste Bulletin) 1979. w. $540. Business Publishers, Inc., 951 Pershing Dr., Silver Spring, MD 20910-4464. TEL 301-587-6300. FAX 301-585-9075. Ed. James Byrne. (looseleaf format; back issues avail.) **Indexed**: Biol.Dig., Energy Rev. **Document type**: newsletter.
●Also available online. Vendor(s): DIALOG Information Services, Inc., NewsNet (CH10).
—**CCC**.
Incorporates (in 1988): Lab Waste and Hazards Management (ISSN 0893-6234)
Description: Covers federal and state regulations on hazardous waste, cleanup funding, new technology, business news. Includes a special liability feature.

604.7   US   ISSN 1074-1291
THE HAZARDOUS WASTE REGULATORY UPDATE SERVICE. vol.12, 1994. 12/yr. $475 (effective 1994). Elsevier Science, Inc., 655 Ave. of the Americas, New York, NY 10010. TEL 212-633-3950. FAX 212-633-3990. (Subscr. to: Box 882, Madison Sq. Sta., New York, NY 10159-0882) (looseleaf format)
Description: Provides timely updates on current EPA actions, regulations, and interpretations.

604.7   US   ISSN 1054-7142
HAZMAT NEWS; the authoritative news resource for hazardous materials control and waste management. 1990. bi-w. Stevens Publishing Corporation, 225 N. New Rd., Waco, TX 76710-6931. TEL 817-776-9000. FAX 817-776-9018. Ed. Christine Rixen.

604.7 380.5   US
HAZMAT TRANSPORT NEWS. 1980. bi-w. $390 (effective Sep. 1992). Business Publishers, Inc., 951 Pershing Dr., Silver Spring, MD 20910-4464. TEL 301-587-6300. FAX 301-585-9075. Ed. Roger Gilroy. (looseleaf format) **Document type**: newsletter.
●Also available online. Vendor(s): NewsNet (CH14).
—**CCC**.
Formerly: Toxic Materials Transport (ISSN 0275-3766)
Description: Presents federal laws relating to transport of dangerous goods, developments in hazardous materials safety and response to emergencies.

604.7   US   ISSN 1062-6026
HAZMAT TRANSPORTATION MANAGEMENT. m. $316 (Canada $353; Mexico $367; elsewhere $401) (effective 1993). Stevens Publishing, 225 New Rd., Waco, TX 76710. TEL 817-776-9000; 800-727-7573. FAX 817-776-9018. Ed. Jerome Ashton. (looseleaf format) **Document type**: newsletter.
Description: Discusses federal policy on the transport of hazardous materials.

628.44 604.7   US   ISSN 0898-5685
TD1060   CODEN: HMWOED
HAZMAT WORLD. (Hazardous Materials); the magazine for environmental management. 1988. m. $50 (Canada $60; elsewhere $90). Advanstar Communications, Inc., 7500 Old Oak Blvd., Cleveland, OH 44130. TEL 216-826-2839. FAX 216-891-2726. (Subscr. to: 1 E. First St., Duluth, MN 55082. TEL 800-346-0085) Ed. Jim Bishop. adv.; bk.rev. circ. 49,530. (back issues avail.) **Indexed**: Environ.Abstr. **Document type**: trade publication.
—BLDSC (4274.464501). **CCC**.
Description: Provides information for individuals who specify and purchase products, systems, equipment and services used for environmental management.

614   UK   ISSN 0953-5357
HAZNEWS; international hazardous waste management monthly. 1988. m. £200 in Europe and rest of world; N. America $340; academics and developing nations half price. Profitastral Ltd., Park House, 140 Battersea Park Rd., London SW11 4NB, England. TEL 071-498-2511. FAX 071-498-2343. Ed. David Coleman; Pub. David Coleman. adv.: full page £330($550); adv. contact: Katie Roy. bk.rev. (back issues avail.) **Document type**: newsletter.
●Also available online. Vendor(s): Data-Star (PTBN,PTSP), DIALOG Information Services, Inc. (File nos.636 & 16), Information Access Co.
—BLDSC (4274.464505); SWETS.
Description: International business newsletter on hazardous waste management and reduction, and contaminated site clean-up.

614.7   US   ISSN 1051-3221
   CODEN: HTNEEL
HAZTECH NEWS. 1986. bi-w. $360 (foreign $375). Haztech Publications, Inc., 14120 Huckleberry La., Silver Spring, MD 20906. TEL 301-871-3289. FAX 301-460-5859. Ed. Cathy H. Dombrowski. (looseleaf format; back issues avail.) **Indexed**: Met.Abstr. **Document type**: newsletter.
Description: Covers hazardous waste treatment and site remediation technology and business news.

604.7 628.168   US   ISSN 0073-7682
TP995.A1   CODEN: PIWCAX
INDUSTRIAL WASTE CONFERENCE, PURDUE UNIVERSITY, LAFAYETTE, INDIANA. PROCEEDINGS. 1944. a. $69.95. Purdue University, School of Civil Engineering, W. Lafayette, IN 47907. TEL 317-494-2194. FAX 317-496-1107. Eds. Ronald F. Wukasch, Cindy S. Dalton. **Indexed**: Abstr.Bull.Inst.Pap.Chem., Biol.Abstr., Chem.Abstr. **Document type**: proceedings.
—BLDSC (6844.240000); EI; SWETS; CASDDS.
Description: Contains technical papers on environmental engineering presented at the annual Waste Conference.

INDUSTRIAL WASTEWATER. see *WATER RESOURCES*

604.7   US
INFECTIOUS WASTES NEWS. fortn. National Solid Wastes Management Association, 1730 Rhode Island Ave., Ste. 1000, N.W., Washington, DC 20036-3196. TEL 202-861-0708. FAX 202-659-0925. Ed. Michael Malloy.

628.5   JA
INFORMATION ON ENVIRONMENTAL POLLUTION IN FOREIGN COUNTRIES. 1968. a. Tokyo Metropolitan Research Institute for Environmental Protection, 7-5, Shinsuna 1-Chome, Koto-Ku, Tokyo 136, Japan.

614.7   US   ISSN 1061-3943
INSIDE WASTE. 1990. m. $275. (Cupps Associates) Capitol Reports, 1090 W. El Camino Ave., Ste. 216, Sacramento, CA 95833-1945. TEL 916-441-4427. FAX 916-441-4560. Ed. John Cupps.

604.7   US
INSITES. 1988. q. free. University of Tennessee at Knoxville, Department of Waste Management Research and Education, 327 Stadium Hall, Knoxville, TN 37996-0710. TEL 615-974-4251. FAX 615-974-1838. Ed. Daniel Schaffer. circ. 3,100. **Document type**: newsletter.
Formerly: University of Tennessee at Knoxville. Waste Management Research and Education. Newsletter.
Description: Reports on interdisciplinary energy research activities.

604.7 621.042   US
INTEGRATED WASTE MANAGEMENT. fortn. $775 (foreign $800). McGraw-Hill, Inc., Energy & Business Newsletters, 1221 Ave. of the Americas, 36th Fl., New York, NY 10020. TEL 212-512-6410. Ed. Kevin Hamilton.
●Also available online. Vendor(s): DIALOG Information Services, Inc. (File no. 624/McGRAW-HILL PUBLICATIONS ONLINE), Dow Jones News Retrieval, Mead Data Central, Inc., NewsNet (EV40).
Formerly: Waste-to-Energy Report.
Description: Offers comprehensive coverage of the worldwide conversion of municipal, industrial and agricultural waste.

628.4   UK   ISSN 1352-0164
▼**INTERNATIONAL DIRECTORY OF SOLID WASTE MANAGEMENT**. 1993. a. £49.50($75) (International Solid Waste Association) James & James (Science Publishers) Ltd., 5 Castle Rd., London NW1 3PR, England. TEL 071-284-3833. FAX 071-284-3737. (Dist. in N. America by: International Books, Box 605, Herndon, VA 22070. TEL 703-435-7064. FAX 703-689-0660) Ed. Jeanne Moller. **Document type**: directory.

JOURNAL OF CLEAN TECHNOLOGY AND ENVIRONMENTAL SCIENCES. see *ENVIRONMENTAL STUDIES* — *Pollution*

604.7 628   NE   ISSN 0304-3894
T55.3.H3   CODEN: JHMAD9
JOURNAL OF HAZARDOUS MATERIALS; management - handling - disposal - risk - assessment. 1976. 12/yr. (in 4 vols.; 3 nos./vol.) fl.1664($899) (effective 1994). Elsevier Science B.V., P.O. Box 211, 1000 AE Amsterdam, Netherlands. TEL 31-20-5803911. FAX 31-20-5803598. TELEX 18582 ESPA NL. (Subscr. in U.S. and Canada to: Elsevier Science Inc., Box 882, Madison Sq. Sta., New York, NY 10159. TEL 212-989-5800. FAX 212-633-3990) Eds. G.F. Bennett, R.E. Britter. adv.; bk.rev.; index. (also avail. in microform from UMI) **Indexed**: A.S.& T.Ind., Biol.Abstr., C.I.S.Abstr., Cadscan, Chem.Abstr., Chem.Eng.Abstr., Curr.Adv.Ecol.Sci. Curr.Cont., Energy Ind., Energy Info.Abstr., Energy Rev., Eng.Ind., Environ.Abstr., Environ.Per.Bibl. (1978-), Excerpt.Med., INIS Atomind., INSPEC Lab.Haz.Bull., Lead Abstr., Ocean.Abstr., Pollut.Abstr., Risk Abstr., Sci.Cit.Ind., Sel.Water Res.Abstr., T.C.E.A., Trop.Dis.Bull., W.R.C.Inf., Zincscan. **Document type**: academic/scholarly publication.
—BLDSC (4996.630000); EI; Faxon; UnCover; SWETS; CASDDS. **CCC**.
Description: Covers all the environmental problems arising from the manufacture, use and disposal of potentially hazardous materials.
Refereed Serial

628.4   US   ISSN 1053-7899
TD788
M S W MANAGEMENT; the journal for municipal solid waste professionals. 1991. 7/yr. $60 (effective Jan. 1993). Forester Communications, Inc., 216 E. Gutierrez St., Santa Barbara, CA 93101-1705. TEL 805-899-3355. FAX 805-899-3350. Ed. Daniel Waldman. adv. contact: Dan Alpern. circ. 24,000 (controlled). (back issues avail.) **Indexed**: Environ.Per.Bibl. **Document type**: academic/scholarly publication, trade publication.
Description: Covers landfills, incineration, recycling and composting.

628.44   US
MADISON WASTE CONFERENCE. ANNUAL PROCEEDINGS; municipal and industrial waste. 1978. a. $40 (foreign $60). University of Wisconsin-Madison, Department of Engineering Professional Development, 432 N. Lake St., Madison, WI 53706. TEL 608-262-0493. FAX 608-263-3160. Ed. Philip R. O'Leary. cum.index: 1982-1984. circ. 500. **Indexed**: Chem.Abstr., Environ.Abstr., Water Resour.Abstr. **Document type**: proceedings.
Formerly: Annual Madison Conference of Applied Research and Practice on Municipal and Industrial Waste.

ENVIRONMENTAL STUDIES — WASTE MANAGEMENT

604.6   NE   ISSN 0921-9773
MAGAZINE RECYCLING BENELUX. (Text in Dutch and French) 1967. bi-m. fl.65 (1200 BEF). Audet Tijdschriften bv (Subsidiary of: C. Misset B.V.), Postbus 9000, 6800 DA Arnhem, Netherlands. TEL 31-85-209911. FAX 31-85-233007. Ed.Bd. adv.: B&W page fl.1517, color page fl.3512; trim 210 x 297; adv. contact: Cor van Nek. bk.rev.; charts; illus.; stat. circ. 2,840. **Document type:** trade publication.
—SWETS.
   Former titles (until 1988): Magazine Recycling (ISSN 0169-2526); (until 1981): Recuperatie (ISSN 0034-1916)
   Description: Information on reclamation and recycling markets and techniques.

MATERIALS RECLAMATION WEEKLY. see *METALLURGY*

614.7 628.44   US
MATERIALS RECOVERY AND RECYCLING YEARBOOK. 1990. biennial. $250 to non-profit and government agencies (foreign $290); private industry $345 (foreign $385). Governmental Advisory Associates, Inc., 177 E. 87th St., Ste. 506-A, New York, NY 10128. TEL 212-410-4165. FAX 212-410-6607. Ed. Robert Gould. (also avail. in diskette format)
   Description: Provides design, operating, and financial information on 257 planned and operating materials recycling facilities in the US.

MEALEY'S LITIGATION REPORT: SUPERFUND. see *LAW — Civil Law*

628.4   US   ISSN 1048-4493
MEDICAL WASTE NEWS. 1989. bi-w. $377. Business Publishers, Inc., 951 Pershing Dr., Silver Spring, MD 20910-4432. TEL 301-587-6300. FAX 301-585-9075. Ed. Carl Ayers. (looseleaf format; back issues avail.) **Document type:** newsletter.
● Also available online. Vendor(s): Data-Star, DIALOG Information Services, Inc., NewsNet (EV30).
—CCC.
   Description: Studies regulation and litigation in reducing problems of medical waste, including hazardous and radioactive wastes.

628.4 333.79   US
METHANE RECOVERY FROM LANDFILL YEARBOOK. 1986. biennial. $225 to non-profit and government agencies (foreign $265); private industries $275 (foreign $315). Governmental Advisory Associates, Inc., 177 E. 87th St., Ste. 506-A, New York, NY 10128. TEL 212-410-4165. FAX 212-410-6607. Ed. Robert Gould. (also avail. in diskette format)
   Description: Provides a comprehensive survey of landfill gas recovery projects in the US, including financial and operating statistics.

628.4   US
MORRIS COUNTY RESOURCE RECOVERY REPORT. q. free. Municipal Utilities Authority, Office of Solid Waste Management, Box 900, Morristown, NJ 07963-0900. TEL 201-285-8390. (Alt. addr.: 380 West Hanover Ave., Morris Township, NJ 07960) **Document type:** government publication, newsletter.
   Description: Informs county residents of what is being done and can be done to better manage solid waste.

628.44   GW   ISSN 0934-3482
MUELLMAGAZIN; Fachzeitschrift fuer oekologische Abfallwirtschaft, Abfallvermeidung und Umweltvorsorge. 1988. q. DM.60. Institut fuer Oekologisches Recycling e.V. (IfoeR), Kurfuerstenstr. 14, 10785 Berlin, Germany. TEL 030-2628021. FAX 030-2650366. Ed. Bernhard Reiser. adv.: B&W page DM.1300; trim 182 x 254; adv. contact: Anne Wispler. bk.rev. circ. 2,500. (back issues avail.) **Document type:** trade publication.
—BLDSC (5983.073000).
   Description: Provides information about concepts, policies, research and technologies of waste prevention, waste minimization and recycling.

628.4   GW
MULLMAGAZIN; Fachzeitschrift fuer Oekologische Abfallwirtschaft, Abfallvermeldung und umweltvorsorge. 1988. q. $60. Institut fur Oekologisches Recycling, Kurfuerstenstr. 14, 10785 Berlin, Germany. TEL 030-2628021. FAX 030-2650366. Ed. Bernhard Reiser. adv.: B&W page DM.1300; trim 182 x 254; adv. contact: Anne Wispler. circ. 2,500. **Document type:** trade publication.
   Description: Contains information on concepts, policies, research, and technologies of waste prevention, waste minimization and recycling.

628.44   US   ISSN 1062-8967
TD788
MUNICIPAL SOLID WASTE NEWS. 1977. m. $100 to the public sector; private sector $250. Solid Waste Association of North America, 1100 Wayne Ave., Ste. 700, Box 7219, Silver Spring, MD 20910. TEL 301-585-2898. FAX 301-589-7068. Ed. Christopher Voell. adv.; charts; illus.; stat. (back issues avail.) **Document type:** newsletter, trade publication.
   Formerly: G R C O A Newsletter.
   Description: Informs and educates members about solid waste management issues.

628.4   US   ISSN 1049-6955
HD4479.N4
NEW JERSEY WASTEWATER TREATMENT TRUST. ANNUAL REPORT. 1987. a. free. New Jersey Wastewater Treatment Trust, CN 425, Trenton, NJ 08625. TEL 609-292-1840. FAX 609-633-8165. **Document type:** government publication.

628.4   US
NEWS SWEEP.* q. membership only. National Solid Wastes Management Association, Contract Sweepers Institute, 338 S. Main St., Phillipsburg, NJ 08865-2824. TEL 908-704-9646. Ed. Denise Naidu. circ. 6,000. **Document type:** newsletter.
   Description: Covers solid wastes management issues affecting contract sweepers.

628.44   FR
NUCLEAR WASTE BULLETIN/BULLETIN SUR LES DECHETS NUCLEAIRES. 1979. irreg. free. Organization for Economic Cooperation and Development, Nuclear Energy Agency, 12 bd. des Iles, 92130 Issy-les-Moulineaux, France. TEL 45-24-10-15. (U.S. orders to: O.E.C.D. Publications and Information Center, 2001 L St., N.W., Ste. 700, Washington, DC 20036-4910. TEL 202-785-6323) circ. 1,000.
   Formerly: Newsletter on Radionuclides Migration in the Geosphere.

604.7   US   ISSN 0276-2897
NUCLEAR WASTE NEWS; generation, packaging, transportation, processing, disposal. 1981. w. $650 (effective Sep. 1992). Business Publishers, Inc., 951 Pershing Dr., Silver Spring, MD 20910-4464. TEL 301-587-6300. FAX 301-585-9075. Ed. Thecla Fabian. (looseleaf format) **Document type:** newsletter.
● Also available online. Vendor(s): NewsNet (EV03).
—CCC.
   Description: News about management of radioactive waste from energy production, weapons production and medical science.

628.168 621.48   JA   ISSN 0910-7193
ONAGAWA GENSHIRYOKU HATSUDENJO KANKYO HOSHANO OYOBI ONHAISUI CHOSA KEKKA/MONITORING REPORT OF ENVIRONMENTAL RADIOACTIVITY AND WARM WASTE WATER AROUND ONAGAWA NUCLEAR POWER STATION. (Text in Japanese) 1981. 5/yr. Miyagiken Hoken Kankyobu, 8-1, Honcho 3-chome, Aoba-ku, Sendai-shi, Miyagi-ken 980, Japan.

628.44   CN   ISSN 1188-4762
TD897   CODEN: OIWPAR
ONTARIO. MINISTRY OF THE ENVIRONMENT. WASTE MANAGEMENT CONFERENCE. PROCEEDINGS. 1954. a. free. Ministry of the Environment, Waste Management Branch, First Clair Ave., 4th Fl., Toronto, Ont. M4V 1K6, Canada. TEL 416-965-6141. Ed M.F. Cheetham. circ. controlled. **Document type:** proceedings.
   Formerly (until 1988): Ontario. Ministry of the Environment. Industrial Waste Conference. Proceedings (ISSN 0078-4893)

628.4   CN   ISSN 0823-6143
ONTARIO RECYCLING UPDATE. 1981. 8/yr. membership. Recycling Council of Ontario, 489 College St., Ste. 504, Toronto, Ont. M6G 1A5, Canada. TEL 416-960-1025. FAX 416-960-8053. Ed. Pat McFarlane. adv.: page Can.$600; trim 8 1/2 x 11. bk.rev.; cum.index: 1985-1991. circ. 1,400.
   Description: Covers waste reduction, reuse, recycling and composting.

THE PAPER STOCK REPORT. see *PAPER AND PULP*

PLASTICS RECYCLING AS A FUTURE BUSINESS OPPORTUNITY. see *PLASTICS*

604.6 628.4 668.4   US   ISSN 1052-4908
PLASTICS RECYCLING UPDATE. 1988. m. $49. Resource Recycling, Inc., Box 10540, Portland, OR 97210. TEL 503-227-1319; 800-227-1424. FAX 503-227-6135. Ed. Jerry Powell. adv.; stat.; tr.lit. circ. 2,000. (looseleaf format; back issues avail.) **Document type:** newsletter.
   Description: Provides information on all aspects of the plastics recycling process, including markets, legislation, research, collection techniques, and economic issues.

628.4 670   US
POLLUTION ENGINEERING PRODUCT - SERVICE LOCATOR. (Supplement to: Pollution Engineering) 1989. a. $24.95. Cahners Publishing Company (Des Plaines), Division of Reed Elsevier Inc., 1350 E. Touhy Ave., Box 5080, Des Plaines, IL 60017-5080. TEL 708-635-8800. FAX 708-390-2636. (Subscr. to: 44 Cook St., Denver, CO 80206. TEL 800-662-7776) adv. circ. 58,000. **Document type:** directory.
   Formerly (until 1992): Pollution Engineering Locator.
   Description: For the specifiers and buyers of environmental control equipment, products and services used in air, water, wastewater pollution control, hazardous and toxic waste disposal, energy control as well as environmental conservation.

628.4   US   ISSN 1053-4253
TD896
POLLUTION PREVENTION REVIEW. 1990. q. $175 (foreign $225). Executive Enterprises Publications Co., Inc., 22 W. 21st St., 10th Fl., New York, NY 10010-6904. TEL 800-332-8804. FAX 212-645-1160. Ed. Jean Stephenson. (back issues avail.)
—UMI. CCC.
   Description: Covers both source reduction and recycling with case studies, applications of new technologies, processes, substitute materials and recycling programs in use at companies. Includes federal developments, state developments and review of the literature.

604.7   US
POST-SOVIET NUCLEAR COMPLEX MONITOR; nuclear materials management & facility cleanup. 26/yr. $995 (foreign $1015). Exchange Publications, 2014 P St., N.W., Ste. 300, Washington, DC 20036. TEL 202-296-2814. FAX 202-296-2805. Ed. T. Scott Nadler.

PROGRESS IN PAPER RECYCLING. see *PAPER AND PULP*

628.4   IT   ISSN 0394-5391
R S RIFIUTI SOLIDI. (Text in Italian; summaries in English, Italian) 1987. 6/yr. L.90000 (foreign L.180000) (effective 1994). (Centro di Ingegneria per la Protezione dell'Ambiente) C I P A s.r.l., Via Palladio, 26, 20135 Milan, Italy. TEL 02-58301528. FAX 02-58301550. Dir. Raffaello Cossu. **Document type:** trade publication.
   Description: Covers solid waste management.

RACHEL'S HAZARDOUS WASTE NEWS; providing news and resources for environmental justice. see *ENVIRONMENTAL STUDIES*

604.7   US   ISSN 0891-3013
RADIOACTIVE EXCHANGE; to promote the exchange of views and information on radioactive waste management. 1982. 23/yr. $549 (foreign $569). Exchange Publications, 2014 P St., N.W., Ste. 300, Washington, DC 20036. TEL 202-296-2814. FAX 202-296-2805. (Subscr. to: Box 5757, Washington, DC 20016. TEL 800-776-1314) Ed. Maureen Conley.

ENVIRONMENTAL STUDIES — WASTE MANAGEMENT

604.7 US ISSN 0275-3707
CODEN: RWAMD
RADIOACTIVE WASTE MANAGEMENT (OAK RIDGE). 1981. m. $180. U.S. Department of Energy, Office of Scientific and Technical Information, Box 62, Oak Ridge, TN 37831. TEL 615-574-0733. (Subscr. to: National Technical Information Service, 5285 Port Royal Rd., Springfield, VA 22161. TEL 703-487-4630. FAX 703-321-8547) Ed. James D. Bales. **Indexed:** AESIS, Sci.Abstr. **Document type:** government publication.
  Description: Presents worldwide information on the critical topics of spent-fuel transport and storage, radioactive effluents from nuclear facilities, and techniques of processing wastes, their storage, and ultimate disposal.

604.7 US
TD812 CODEN: RWMCD4
RADIOACTIVE WASTE MANAGEMENT AND ENVIRONMENTAL RESTORATION. 1980. 8/yr. (in 2 vols., 4 nos./vol.). 134 ECU per vol. (effective 1993). Harwood Academic Publishers, 820 Town Center Dr., Langhorne, PA 19047. TEL 215-750-2642. FAX 215-750-6343. (UK subscr. to: P.O. Box 90, Reading, Berkshire RG1 8JL, England. TEL 0734-560-080) Ed. A.M. Platt. (also avail. in microfilm) **Indexed:** AESIS, Chem.Abstr., Deep Sea Res.& Oceanogr.Abstr., Energy Ind., Energy Info.Abstr., Environ.Abstr., Environ.Ind., Environ.Per.Bibl. (1991-), Excerp.Med., Geo.Abstr., GeoRef.
—BLDSC (7234.229300); CASDDS. **CCC.**
  Former titles (until vol.17): Radioactive Waste Management and the Nuclear Fuel Cycle (ISSN 0739-5876); Radioactive Waste Management (ISSN 0142-2405).
  Refereed Serial

604.7 US ISSN 0898-8161
CODEN: RMHAE6
RADIOACTIVE WASTE MANAGEMENT HANDBOOK. irreg. Harwood Academic Publishers, 820 Town Center Dr., Langhorne, PA 19047. TEL 215-750-2642. FAX 215-750-6343. (UK subscr. to: Box 90, Reading, Berkshire RG1 8JL, England. TEL 0734-560-080) Eds. D.W. Tedder, A.M. Platt. (also avail. in microform)
—CASDDS.
  Refereed Serial

604.7 US ISSN 0275-7273
CODEN: RAWMDV
RADIOACTIVE WASTE MANAGEMENT SERIES. irreg. Harwood Academic Publishers, 820 Town Center Dr., Langhorne, PA 19047. TEL 215-750-2642. FAX 215-750-6343. (UK subscr. to: Box 90, Reading, Berkshire RG1 8JL, England. TEL 0734-560-080) Ed.Bd. (also avail. in microform) **Indexed:** Energy Rev.
—CASDDS.
  Refereed Serial

621.9 GW ISSN 0174-1446
RECYCLING. vol.26, 1975. 3/yr. DM.30. (Bundesverband der Deutschen Schrottwirtschaft) Verlagsgruppe Handelsblatt GmbH, Kasernenstr. 67, 40213 Duesseldorf, Germany. TEL 0211-8870. (Subscr. to: Postfach 102717, 40018 Duesseldorf, Germany) Ed. Rolf Willeke. adv.; charts; illus.; stat.; tr.lit. circ. 1,000. (reprint service avail. from UMI) **Indexed:** C.I.S.Abstr., Key to Econ.Sci. **Document type:** bulletin.
—SWETS. **CCC.**
  Formerly: Schrottbetrieb.

604.6 CN ISSN 1183-8809
RECYCLING CANADA; a monthly insider's report on waste management for resource recovery. 1990. m. Can.$110. Sydenham Publishing, 344 23rd St. W., Owen Sound, ON N4K 4G7, Canada. TEL 519-371-6289. FAX 519-371-3676. Ed. Stella Coultas. adv. contact: Jeff Elie. bk.rev.; index. (back issues avail.) **Document type:** newsletter.
  Description: Aimed at waste specialists in government, industry and commerce.

669 604.6 US
RECYCLING MANAGER. bi-w. $125 in US, Canada and Mexico; elsewhere $190. Chilton Publications (Subsidiary of: Capital Cities - A B C Publishing Group), 825 Seventh Ave., New York, NY 10019. TEL 212-887-8528. FAX 212-887-8520. (Subscr. to: 825 7th Ave., New York, NY 10019) **Document type:** trade publication.

604.6 CN
▼**RECYCLING PRODUCT NEWS.** 1992. 6/yr. Baum Publications Ltd., 1625 Ingleton Ave., Burnaby, BC V5C 4L8, Canada. TEL 604-291-9900. FAX 604-291-1906. Ed. Dan Kennedy. adv.: B&W page Can.$3875; trim 11 x 15. circ. 15,000. (tabloid format) **Document type:** trade publication.

614.7 333.7 US ISSN 1063-3251
TD799.5
RECYCLING - RECLAMATION DIGEST. 1991. m. $155 to non-members (foreign $175); members $130 (foreign $145). A S M International, Materials Information, Materials Park, OH 44073. TEL 216-338-5151. FAX 216-338-4634. TELEX 980-619. (UK addr.: Institute of Materials, Materials Information, 1 Carlton House Terr., London SW1Y 5DB, England. TEL 071-839-4071) **Document type:** abstracting/indexing.
  Description: Selection of recycling and reclamation information published in Engineered Materials Abstracts, Metals Abstracts, and the Materials Business Information series.

604.6 US ISSN 1064-4938
TD794.5
▼**RECYCLING SOURCEBOOK.** 1993. biennial. Gale Research Inc., 835 Penobscot Bldg., Detroit, MI 48226. TEL 313-961-2242. FAX 313-961-6083. Eds. Thomas J. Cichonski, Karen Hill. **Document type:** directory.

628.44 US ISSN 1042-0614
RECYCLING TIMES. 1989. 26/yr. $95. National Solid Wastes Management Association, 1730 Rhode Island Ave., N.W., Ste. 1000, Washington, DC 20036. TEL 202-861-0708. FAX 202-659-0925. Ed. Kathleen Meade. adv. circ. 5,000. (tabloid format)
  Description: Covers commercial and municipal solid waste recycling. Geared toward public interest organizations, producers and distributors of recyclable material, buyers and sellers of recyclable wastes, and private and municipal waste professionals.

628.44 669 US
RECYCLING TODAY. 1963. m. $28 (foreign $98) (effective Jan. 1994). (Group Interest Enterprises) G.I.E. Inc., Publishers, 4012 Bridge Ave., Cleveland, OH 44113. TEL 216-961-4130. FAX 216-961-0364. Ed. John Bruening. adv.; charts; illus.; mkt.; stat. **Indexed:** Environ.Abstr., Environ.Per.Bibl. (1989-), Excerp.Med., Met.Abstr., World Alum.Abstr. **Document type:** trade publication.
—BLDSC (7331.157000).
  Formerly: Recycling Today (Scrap Market Edition) (ISSN 1051-1091); Which superseded in part (in May 1990): Recycling Today (ISSN 0887-6649); Which was formerly: Secondary Raw Materials (ISSN 0037-0584).
  Description: Covers issues pertaining to the traditional scrap recycling market.

614.7 US ISSN 0736-1890
RECYCLING UPDATE. 1983. s-a. $6. Update Publicare Co., c/o Prosperity & Profits Unlimited, Box 416, Denver, CO 80201-0416. TEL 303-575-5676. Ed. A. Doyle. adv.; bibl. circ. 2,000. (looseleaf format; also avail. in microfiche) **Document type:** newsletter.
—CCC.
  Description: Lists new products, publications and conventions.

628.44 US
RECYCLING WORLD. irreg. free. Environmental Defense Fund, 257 Park Ave. S., New York, NY 10010. TEL 212-505-2100. FAX 212-505-2375. **Document type:** newsletter.

604.6 UK
RECYCLING WORLD. 1987. fortn. £23.50 (EEC members £45; rest of world £65). Scrap Market Ltd., Hilltop, Offchurch Rd., Webheath, Redditch, Worcs B77 5PQ, England. TEL 0527-404550. FAX 0527-404644. Ed. Chris Floate. adv.; bk.rev. circ. 6,150. **Document type:** trade publication.
  Formerly: Scrap and Reclamation Market.

REGIONAL WORKSHOP ON WASTE HEAT RECOVERY TECHNOLOGY IN COCONUT PROCESSING. see AGRICULTURE — Crop Production And Soil

628.44 US ISSN 1051-5658
TD1
REMEDIATION; the journal of environmental cleanup costs, technologies & techniques. 1990. q. $175 (foreign $225). Executive Enterprises Publications Co., Inc., 22 W. 21st St., 10th Fl., New York, NY 10010-6990. TEL 212-645-7880. FAX 212-645-1160. Ed. Deborah C.K. Wenger. (also avail. in microform from WSH; back issues avail.; reprint service avail. from WSH) **Indexed:** Environ.Abstr.
—BLDSC (7356.806000); UMI. **CCC.**
  Description: Focuses on environmental remediation techniques and technologies: if and how they work, what the advantages and disadvantages are, how close they come to achieving the desired state and federal "standards" and the costs involved.

604.7 333.7 US
REMEDIATION REVIEW; a newsletter of hazardous waste remediation. 1988. 4/yr. free. Department of Environmental Conservation, Division of Hazardous Waste Remediation, Bureau of Program Management, 50 Wolf Rd., Albany, NY 12233-7010. TEL 518-457-1684. Ed. D.M. Ritter. illus. circ. 13,000. **Indexed:** Environ.Abstr. **Document type:** newsletter.
  Description: Provides information about New York State's Hazardous Waste Site Remediation Program.

RENEWABLE ENERGY BULLETIN. see ENERGY

RENEWABLE RESOURCES JOURNAL. see ENVIRONMENTAL STUDIES

613.1 CN
RENEWS. q. membership. Recycling Council of Ontario, 489 College St., Ste. 504, Toronto, ON. M6G 1A5, Canada. TEL 416-960-1025. FAX 416-960-8053. **Document type:** newsletter.
  Description: Keeps members informed on the RCO, provides a calendar of events.

604.6 US
RENEWS (BATON ROUGE); is good news. m. Department of Environmental Quality, Local Programs Division, Box 44066, Baton Rouge, LA 70804. TEL 504-765-0674. FAX 504-765-0744228. Ed. Elizabeth Tarver. circ. 8,500. **Document type:** newsletter.
  Description: Promotes recycling in the state.

628.4 US ISSN 1043-268X
REPORT ON DEFENSE PLANT WASTE. 1988. bi-w. $481. Business Publishers, Inc., 951 Pershing Dr., Silver Spring, MD 20910-4464. TEL 301-587-6300. FAX 301-585-9075. Ed. Kathleen Hart. (looseleaf format; back issues avail.) **Document type:** newsletter.
●Also available online. Vendor(s): NewsNet (EV28).
—CCC.
  Description: Business opportunities in cleaning up United States government facilities, including Department of Defense and Energy.

628.4 CN ISSN 1183-8787
REPORT ON THE DISCHARGES FROM MUNICIPAL S T PS IN ONTARIO. (Sewage Treatment Plants) 1975. a. free. Ministry of Environment and Energy, Water Resources Branch, 135 St. Clair Ave. W., Toronto, Ont. M4V 1P5, Canada. TEL 416-323-4321. FAX 416-323-4564. **Document type:** government publication.
  Formerly: Report on the Discharges from Sewage Treatment Plants in Ontario (ISSN 0840-7142)

628.4 CN ISSN 0225-5804
RESILOG; an exchange of views and information on hazardous waste management across Canada. (Text in English, French) s-a. free. Environment Canada, Office of Waste Management, Hazardous Waste Management Division, Ottawa, ON K1A 0H3, Canada. TEL 819-997-3377. FAX 819-997-3068. Ed. Paul Topping.
  Description: Features upcoming conferences and publications about waste treatment and pertinent laws.

628.4 604.6 US ISSN 0735-3081
RESOURCE RECOVERY REPORT. 1976. m. $217. 5313 38th St., N.W., Washington, DC 20015. TEL 202-362-6034. FAX 202-362-6632. Ed. Frank McManus. bk.rev.; stat.; tr.lit. circ. 950. **Indexed:** Environ.Abstr. **Document type:** newsletter.
  Description: Reports on news relating to waste management recycling, composting and resource recovery.

ENVIRONMENTAL STUDIES — WASTE MANAGEMENT

628.4 333.8   US   ISSN 0893-4673
TD794.5
RESOURCE RECOVERY YEARBOOK. 1982. biennial. $350 to non-profit and government agencies (foreign $415); private industry $495 (foreign $565). Governmental Advisory Associates, Inc., 177 E. 87th St., Ste. 506-A, New York, NY 10128. TEL 212-410-4165. FAX 212-410-6607. Ed. Robert Gould. circ. 500. (also avail. in diskette format)
—BLDSC (7777.604820).
   Description: Provides comprehensive information on more than 450 operating and planned waste-to-energy projects throughout the US.

604.6 628.4   US   ISSN 0744-4710
TD794.5   CODEN: REREEC
RESOURCE RECYCLING; North America's recycling journal. 1982. m. $42. Resource Recycling, Inc., Box 10540, Portland, OR 97210. TEL 503-227-1319; 800-227-1424. FAX 503-227-6135. Ed. Jerry Powell. adv.; bk.rev.; charts; illus.; stat.; index. circ. 16,000. (back issues avail.; reprint service avail.) **Indexed:** Energy Info.Abstr., Energy Rev., Environ.Abstr., Environ.Per.Bibl. (1982-), P.A.I.S.
—BLDSC (7777.604830); Faxon; UnCover.
   Description: Focuses on multi-material, post-consumer recycling: waste paper, scrap metals, glass, plastics, yard debris, oil and rubber.

628.4 658.788   US   ISSN 1052-4916
RESOURCE RECYCLING'S BOTTLE - CAN RECYCLING UPDATE; markets, legislation, research, data, technology, economics. 1990. m. $75. Resource Recycling, Inc., Box 10540, Portland, OR 97210. TEL 503-227-1319; 800-227-1424. FAX 503-227-6135. Ed. Jerry Powell. stat.; tr.lit. circ. 1,000. (looseleaf format; back issues avail.) Document type: newsletter.
   Description: Covers recycling of aluminum, glass, plastic, tin, and bi-metal containers, including markets, legislation, technology, and economic issues.

604.6 333.79   NE   ISSN 0921-3449
TD794.5   CODEN: RCREEW
RESOURCES, CONSERVATION AND RECYCLING. (Text in English) 1975. 12/yr. (in 3 vols., 4 nos./vol.). fl.1380($746) (effective 1994). Elsevier Science B.V., P.O. Box 211, 100 AE Amsterdam, Netherlands. TEL 31-20-5803911. FAX 31-20-5803598. TELEX 18582 ESPA NL. (Subscr. in U.S. and Canada to: Elsevier Science Inc., Box 882, Madison Sq. Sta., New York, NY 10159. TEL 212-989-5800. FAX 212-633-3990) Eds. Harvey Alter, Michael E. Henstock. adv.; bk.rev.; abstr.; illus.; stat.; index. circ. 1,035. (also avail. in microform from UMI; back issues avail.) **Indexed:** AESIS, Agri.Eng.Abstr., Biol.Abstr., Cadscan, Chem.Abstr., Curr.Adv.Ecol.Sci., Curr.Cont., Deep Sea Res.& Oceanogr.Abstr., Energy Info.Abstr., Energy Rev., Environ.Abstr., Environ.Per.Bibl. (1977-), Excerp.Med., Geo.Abstr., Int.Packag.Abstr., Lead Abstr., Met.Abstr., Paper & Bd.Abstr., Pollut.Abstr., Risk Abstr., Sel.Water Res.Abstr., Soils & Fert., Sugar Ind.Abstr., W.R.C.Inf., World Alum.Abstr., Zincscan. Document type: academic/scholarly publication.
—BLDSC (7777.606950); El; Faxon; UnCover; SWETS. **CCC.**
   Incorporates (1976-1987): Conservation and Recycling (ISSN 0361-3658); (1981-1987): Resources and Conservation (ISSN 0166-3097); Which was formerly (until 1981): Resource Recovery and Conservation (ISSN 0304-3967)
   Description: Provides comprehensive analysis and review of interdisciplinary aspects of renewable and non-renewable resource management, with an emphasis on conservation.
   Refereed Serial

604.6   US   ISSN 0048-7457
REUSE - RECYCLE. 1971. m. $185. Technomic Publishing Co. Inc., 851 New Holland Ave., Box 3535, Lancaster, PA 17604. TEL 717-291-5609. FAX 717-295-4538. TELEX 230 753565 (TECNHOMIC UD). Ed. Jack Milgrom. adv.; bk.rev.; charts; illus. circ. 200. (looseleaf format) Document type: academic/scholarly publication.
—UMI. **CCC.**
   Refereed Serial

S O N R E E L MONOGRAPH SERIES. (Section of Natural Resources, Energy, and Environmental Law) see *LAW*

628.4   CN
SANITATION CANADA. 1979. 6/yr. $20. Perks Publications Inc., 1735 Bayly St., Ste. 7A, Pickering, Ont. L1W 3G7, Canada. TEL 416-831-4711. FAX 416-831-4725. Ed. Tanja Nowotny. adv. circ. 4,033.

628.3   US   ISSN 0148-4125
TD523
SLUDGE NEWSLETTER; generation, treatment, utilization, disposal. 1978. bi-w. $325 (effective Sep. 1992). Business Publishers, Inc., 951 Pershing Dr., Silver Spring, MD 20910-4464. TEL 301-587-6300. FAX 301-585-9075. Ed. Chuck Anderson. bk.rev.; stat. (looseleaf format) Document type: newsletter.
●Also available online. Vendor(s): NewsNet (CH13).
—**CCC.**
   Description: Monitors sludge management developments in Washington and around the country.

631.4 628.44   US   ISSN 1056-0157
SOILS. 1990. 9/yr. $36 (Canada $45; elsewhere $60). Group III Communications, 10229 E. Independence Ave., Independence, MO 64053. TEL 816-254-8735. FAX 816-254-2128. adv. circ. 10,258. **Indexed:** Environ.Abstr.
   Description: Focuses on contaminated soil and cleanup.

628.4   US
SPILL BRIEFS. 1974. m. membership. 400 Renaissance Ctr., Ste. 1900, Detroit, MI 48243. (back issues avail.)
   Formerly: Spill Control Association of America. Newsletter.

604.7 340   US
SPILL REPORTING PROCEDURES GUIDE. 1989. a. $180. B N A Books (Subsidiary of: The Bureau of National Affairs, Inc.), 1231 25th St., N.W., Washington, DC 20037. TEL 202-833-7470; 800-372-1033. FAX 202-833-7490. (Subscr. to: BNA Books Distribution Center, 300 Raritan Center Pkwy., Box 7816, Edison, NJ 08818-7816. TEL 908-225-1900. FAX 908-417-0482) Eds. Robert E. Abbott, James E. Leemann.
   Description: For individuals responsible for reporting releases of hazardous substances.

340 604.7   US
STATE HAZARDOUS WASTE REGULATION. 1991. base vol. (plus a. supplement). $110. Butterworth Legal Publishers (Salem) (Subsidiary of: Reed Elsevier plc), 8 Industrial Way, Bldg. C, Salem, NH 03079. TEL 800-548-4001. FAX 603-898-9858. Ed. Mitchell L. Lathrop. (looseleaf format)
   Description: Includes a description of the agencies which administer the environmental statutes and regulations of the fifty states.

604.7   US
SUPERFUND REPORT. bi-w. $450 (foreign $540). Inside Washington Publishers, Box 7167, Benjamin Franklin Sta., Washington, DC 20044. TEL 703-892-8500. FAX 703-685-2606. Document type: newsletter.

604.7   US
▼**TECHLINK: SOLID AND HAZARDOUS WASTE.** 1993. m. $200 (outside N. America £280). U.S. National Technical Information Service, 5285 Port Royal Rd., Springfield, VA 22161. TEL 703-487-4630. FAX 703-321-8547. (Co-sponsor: Engineering Information, Inc.) bibl. (yearbook avail.) Document type: newsletter, government publication.
   Description: Draws upon scientific, technical and engineering data on solid and hazardous wastes contained in the Compendex Plus and NTIS Bibliographic databases.

TEXAS ON-SITE INSIGHTS; information on on-site wastewater treatment systems in Texas. see *WATER RESOURCES*

604.7   US   ISSN 0093-5891
TOXIC MATERIALS NEWS; weekly business newsletter published from the nation's capital. 1974. w. $540 (effective Sep. 1992). Business Publishers, Inc., 951 Pershing Dr., Silver Spring, MD 20910-4464. TEL 301-587-6300. FAX 301-585-9075. Ed. Charles Knebl. bk.rev. (looseleaf format) Document type: newsletter.
●Also available online. Vendor(s): NewsNet (CH12).
—BLDSC (8873.007970). **CCC.**
   Description: Provides current information on the myriad laws, regulations and court cases that affect toxic chemicals.

604.7   US   ISSN 0199-3178
RA1190   CODEN: TSUJDP
TOXIC SUBSTANCES JOURNAL. 1979. q. $158. Talyor & Francis, 1900 Frost Rd., Ste. 101, Bristol, PA 19007-1598. TEL 800-821-8312. FAX 215-785-5515. Ed. George S. Dominguez. circ. 600. (back issues avail.; reprint service avail. from UMI) **Indexed:** BPIA, Bus.Ind., Chem.Abstr., Environ.Abstr., Environ.Per.Bibl. (1990-), Excerp.Med. (1992-), Hlth.Ind., Pollut.Abstr., Tr.& Indus.Ind. Document type: academic/scholarly publication.
—BLDSC (8873.008400); CIS; Faxon; UnCover; CASDDS. **CCC.**
   Description: Interdisciplinary journal that examines all aspects of toxic substances and global perspectives with an emphasis on public policy considerations.
   Refereed Serial

TOXIC TORT LITIGATION. see *LAW*

604.7 340   US
TOXIC TORT LITIGATION HANDBOOK; a step-by-step guide with forms. a. $85. Clark - Boardman - Callaghan Company Ltd., 375 Hudson St., New York, NY 10014. TEL 212-929-7500; 800-221-9428. FAX 212-924-0460. Ed. Michael Dore.
   Description: Provides practical advice on litigating toxic tort claims: preparing for each step of pretrial and trial process, managing complex cases, drafting standard and specialized litigation documents, and handling risk assessments and other technical issues.

TOXIC TORTS; litigation of hazardous substance cases. see *PUBLIC HEALTH AND SAFETY*

604.7 340   US   ISSN 0887-7394
KF1246.A3   CODEN: TLREEF
TOXICS LAW REPORTER; a weekly review of toxic torts, hazardous waste, and insurance litigation. 1986. w. $1287. The Bureau of National Affairs, Inc., 1231 25th St. N.W., Washington, DC 20037. TEL 202-452-4200. FAX 202-822-8092. TELEX 285656-BNAI-WSH. (Subscr. to: 9435 Key West Ave., Rockville, MD 20850. TEL 800-372-1033) Ed. Gary A. Weinstein. (back issues avail.)
●Also available online. Vendor(s): Human Resources Information Network (CDD, HDD).
—**CCC.**
   Description: Covers legal developments concerning toxic tort and hazardous waste lawsuits and related insurance issues.

WASSERABWASSERPRAXIS. see *WATER RESOURCES*

628.4   US   ISSN 0043-1001
WASTE AGE. 1970. m. $45. National Solid Wastes Management Association, Ste. 1000, 1730 Rhode Island Ave. N.W., Washington, DC 20036. TEL 202-659-4613. FAX 202-659-0925. Ed. John T. Aquino. adv.; bk.rev. circ. 35,000. (also avail. in microfiche; reprint service avail. from UMI) **Indexed:** Energy Info.Abstr., Energy Rev., Environ.Abstr., Environ.Per.Bibl. (1992-), Excerp.Med., Key to Econ.Sci., Ocean.Abstr., Pollut.Abstr., PROMT.
—BLDSC (9266.550000); El; Faxon; UnCover; SWETS; UMI.

WASTE & ENVIRONMENT TODAY; news and bibliographic journal. see *ENVIRONMENTAL STUDIES — Abstracting, Bibliographies, Statistics*

ENVIRONMENTAL STUDIES — WASTE MANAGEMENT

614.7   CN   ISSN 1185-4731
CODEN: WBWEE3
WASTE BUSINESS WEST. 1990. bi-m. Can.$45($39) Ecolands Publishing, 85 Somerset Ave., Toronto, Ont. M6H 2R3, Canada. TEL 416-658-7519. FAX 416-658-9708. Ed. Matt Keegan. circ. 15,000. **Indexed:** Environ.Abstr.
Formerly: Waste Business International West (ISSN 1185-474X)
Description: Provides western waste generating companies with information on new pollution control technologies and environmental regulations.

628.44   AT   ISSN 0311-3558
WASTE DISPOSAL AND WATER MANAGEMENT IN AUSTRALIA. 1974. bi-m. Aus.$34 (foreign Aus.$57). Editorial & Publishing Consultants Pty. Ltd., 29 First Ave., Klemzig, S.A. 5087, Australia. TEL 02-261-5837. FAX 08-261-2697. Ed. Frank H. Schmidt. adv.; B&W page Aus.$884, color page Aus.$1196. bk.rev.; charts; tr.lit. circ. 2,200. **Indexed:** AESIS.
—BLDSC (9266.650000).

628.4   US
WASTE DYNAMICS OF NEW ENGLAND. m. Business Publications, Inc. (Manchester), 150 Dow St., Manchester, NH 03101-1227. TEL 603-624-1442. FAX 603-624-1310. Ed. Rich Williams. circ. 24,000.

628.44   US   ISSN 1050-3153
WASTE INFORMATION DIGESTS. 1990. m. $240. International Academy at Santa Barbara, Environmental Studies Institute, 800 Garden St., Ste. D, Santa Barbara, CA 93101. TEL 805-965-5010. FAX 805-965-6071. Ed. Mary Ann Short. **Document type:** abstracting/indexing.
●Also available online. Vendor(s): Data-Star, DIALOG Information Services, Inc.
—CCC.
Description: Summarizes articles, books, news releases, documents and reports relating to waste disposal and waste utilization.

628.44 604.7   UK   ISSN 0956-053X
TD811.5   CODEN: WAMAE2
WASTE MANAGEMENT; industrial - radioactive - hazardous. 1980. 8/yr. £435($670) (effective 1994). Elsevier Science Ltd., Pergamon, P.O. Box 800, Kidlington, Oxford OX5 1DX, England. TEL 44-865-843000. FAX 44-865-843010. (Subscr. in U.S. and Canada to: Elsevier Science, 660 White Plains Rd., Tarrytown, NY 10591-5153. TEL 914-524-9200. FAX 914-333-2444) Ed. W.A. Cawley. adv.; illus. circ. 1,100. (also avail. in microform from UMI; reprint service avail. from UMI) **Indexed:** A.S.& T.Ind., Chem.Abstr., Curr.Cont., Deep Sea Res.& Oceanogr.Abstr., Energy Rev., Environ.Per.Bibl. (1982-), Excerp.Med., Geo.Abstr., GeoRef., Ind.Sci.Rev. **Document type:** academic/scholarly publication.
—BLDSC (9266.674500); EI; Faxon; UnCover; SWETS; UMI; CASDDS. **CCC.**
Formerly: Nuclear and Chemical Waste Management (ISSN 0191-815X)
Description: Covers the entire field of research in industrial waste management and handling.
Refereed Serial

628.4   AT
WASTE MANAGEMENT & ENVIRONMENT. 1989. m. Aus.$152($120) Rala Information Service Pty. Ltd., 203-205 Darling St., Balmain, N.S.W. 2041, Australia. TEL 61-2-555-1944. Ed. Barbara Cail. adv. contact: David Williams. bk.rev.; bibl.; charts; illus.; tr.lit.; index; circ. 6,000 (paid). (back issues avail.) **Document type:** trade publication.
Description: Aimed at persons involved in the treatment, storage and generation of waste; provides solutions to environmental problems.

628.4   UK   ISSN 0734-242X
TD896   CODEN: WMARD8
WASTE MANAGEMENT AND RESEARCH. 1983. bi-m. £175 (effective 1994). (International Solid Wastes and Public Cleansing Association) Academic Press Ltd. (Subsidiary of: Harcourt Brace & Company Ltd.), 24-28 Oval Rd., London NW1 7DX, England. TEL 44-71-267-4466. FAX 44-71-482-2293. TELEX 25775-ACPRES-G. (Subscr. to: Harcourt Brace & Company Ltd., Foots Cray High St., Sidcup, Kent DA14 5HP, England. TEL 44-81-300-3322. FAX 44-81-309-0807) Ed. P. Rushbrook. **Indexed:** AIT Reports, Chem.Abstr., Curr.Adv.Ecol.Sci., Curr.Cont., Energy Rev., Environ.Abstr., Environ.Per.Bibl. (1992-), I D A, Risk Abstr., Sel.Water Res.Abstr., W.R.C.Inf. **Document type:** academic/scholarly publication.
—BLDSC (9266.677500); Faxon; UnCover; SWETS; CASDDS. **CCC.**
Description: Presents papers on all aspects of solid waste management, focusing on the discussion of solutions to problems that arise primarily from municipal and industrial solid wastes and sludges.

628.4   US   ISSN 1062-7529
WASTE MANAGEMENT NEWS. bi-m. $322 (Canada $360; Mexico $374; elsewhere $408) (effective 1993). Stevens Publishing, 225 N. New Rd., Waco, TX 76710. TEL 817-776-9000; 800-727-7573. FAX 817-776-9018. Ed. Adam Glenn. (looseleaf format) **Document type:** newsletter.
Description: Covers news and regulatory developments in the field of waste management.

614   UK
THE WASTE MANAGER. 10/yr. £80 (foreign £95). National Association of Waste Disposal Contractors, Mountbarrow House, 6-20 Elizabeth St., London SW1W 9RB, England. TEL 071-824-8882. FAX 071-824-8753. Ed. Julian Rose. bk.rev.; circ. 3,000 (controlled). **Document type:** trade publication.
Formerly (until 1993): N A W D C News.

604.7 628.4 614.7   US   ISSN 0890-5509
WASTE MINIMIZATION & RECYCLING REPORT; hazardous & solid waste. 1986. m. $198 (foreign $252). Government Institutes, Inc., 4 Research Pl., Ste. 200, Rockville, MD 20850-3226. TEL 301-921-2300. Ed. Charlene Ikonomou. index. (back issues avail.)
—BLDSC (4274.389000).
Description: Reports practical information and case studies concerning waste reduction program.

WASTE PAPER NEWS. see *PACKAGING*

628.4   US   ISSN 0889-0072
WASTE RECOVERY REPORT; recycling and reprocessing of resources. 1976. m. $50 (foreign $75). I C O N Information Concepts, Inc., 211 S. 45th St., Philadelphia, PA 19104. TEL 215-349-6500. FAX 215-349-6502. Ed. Alan Krigman. bk.rev. circ. 450. **Indexed:** Energy Rev. **Document type:** newsletter.
Formerly (until 1985): Recovery Engineering News.

628.44   US
WASTE TECH NEWS.* bi-w. $25 (foreign $65; free to qualified personnel). 1026 Banmock St., Denver, CO 80204-4037. TEL 303-394-2905. **Indexed:** Environ.Abstr., Environ.Ind.

628.44   US   ISSN 0885-0003
WASTE TREATMENT TECHNOLOGY NEWS. 1985. m. $350. Business Communications Co., Inc. (Norwalk), 25 Van Zant St., Norwalk, CT 06855. TEL 203-853-4266. FAX 203-853-0348. TELEX 6502934929 WUI. Ed. Donald Saxman. pat. (back issues avail.) **Indexed:** Environ.Abstr.
●Also available online. Vendor(s): NewsNet (EV26).
—CCC.

614.7 333.7   US
WASTELINE. 1987. q. free. Department of Environmental Conservation, Division of Solid Waste, 50 Wolf Rd., Albany, NY 12233-4010. TEL 518-457-2344. FAX 518-457-1283. Ed. Brian W. Swinn. charts; illus. circ. 12,000. **Document type:** government publication, newsletter.
Description: Devoted to solid waste issues in New York State, with emphasis on regulatory matters.

604.7   UK
WASTES MANAGEMENT. 1910. m. £33 (foreign £39). Institute of Wastes Management, 14 Thetford Close, Wood Bank, Bury, Lancs. BL8 1XB, England. FAX 0604-21339. Ed. D. Taylor. adv.; bk.rev.; illus.; index. circ. 3,000. **Indexed:** Br.Tech.Ind., Excerp.Med. Pollut.Abstr., W.R.C.Inf.
Former titles (until 1982): Solid Wastes (ISSN 0306-6509); Solid Wastes Management; Public Cleansing (ISSN 0033-3433)

WATER AND ENVIRONMENT INTERNATIONAL. see *ENVIRONMENTAL STUDIES — Pollution*

WATER AND WASTE TREATMENT. see *WATER RESOURCES*

604.7 628.1   US   ISSN 0043-1141
WATER AND WASTES DIGEST. 1961. 8/yr. $10 (free to qualified personnel). Scranton Gillette Communications, Inc., 380 E. Northwest Hwy., Des Plaines, IL 60016-2282. TEL 708-298-6622. FAX 708-390-0408. adv. circ. 100,000. (also avail. in microform from UMI) **Indexed:** Abstr.Bull.Inst Pap.Chem., Energy Ind., Energy Info.Abstr. **Document type:** trade publication.
—UMI. **CCC.**
Description: Product information and reviews in wastewater and water pollution technology, with an index of advertisers.

WATER ENGINEERING AND MANAGEMENT. see *WATER RESOURCES*

WATER SEWAGE AND EFFLUENT. see *WATER RESOURCES*

628.44   US
WATER TECHNOLOGY NEWS. m. $295. Business Communications Co., Inc. (Norwalk), 25 Van Zant St., Norwalk, CT 06855. TEL 203-853-4266. FAX 203-853-0348. **Document type:** newsletter.
Description: Highlights industry developments, important regulations, and novel process technology and their applications.

WATERLINES; the journal of appropriate water supply and sanitation technologies. see *WATER RESOURCES*

604.7   US
WEAPONS COMPLEX MONITOR; waste management and cleanup. 26/yr. $995 (foreign $1015). Exchange Publications, 2014 P St., N.W., Ste. 300, Washington, DC 20036. TEL 202-296-2814. FAX 202-296-2305. Ed. Brenda Flory Firod.

WESTERN CANADA WATER AND WASTE WATER ASSOCIATION. BULLETIN. see *WATER RESOURCES*

WORLD COGENERATION; a power source for partnering in the '90's. see *ENERGY*

628.445 604.7   US   ISSN 1064-8429
TD791   CODEN: WASTEL
WORLD WASTES; the independent voice of the industry. 1957. m. $48 (foreign $108). Argus Inc., 6151 Powers Ferry Rd., N.W., Atlanta, GA 30329-2941. TEL 404-955-2500. FAX 404-955-0400. Ed. William Wolpin. adv.; bk.rev.; charts; illus.; stat.; tr.lit. circ. 36,819. (also avail. in microform from UMI; reprint service avail. from UMI) **Indexed:** A.S.& T.Ind., Energy Rev., Eng.ind., Environ.Abstr., Environ.Per.Bibl. (1972-), Ind.Sci.Rev., Ocean.Abstr., Pollut.Abstr. **Document type:** trade publication.
●Also available online.
—Faxon; UnCover; UMI. **CCC.**
Formerly (until 1992): Management of World Wastes (ISSN 0745-6921); *Incorporates* (1963-1991): World Wastes Specification Catalog; *Former titles (until 1983):* Solid Wastes Management; (until 1981): Solid Wastes Management - Refuse Removal Journal and Liquid Wastes Management (ISSN 0161-035X); (until 1973): Solid wastes Management - Refuse Removal Journal (ISSN 0038-1136); Refuse Removal Journal.
Description: Business publication for professionals in the solid, liquid and hazardous wastes management industry.

ESTATE PLANNING LAW

628.445 US
▼WORLD WASTES - INTERNATIONAL EDITION. 1993. 6/yr. Argus Inc., 6151 Powers Ferry Rd., N.W., Atlanta, GA 30339-2941. TEL 404-955-2500. FAX 404-955-0400. Ed. William Wolpin. circ. 12,000. **Document type:** trade publication.
Description: For refuse contractors, government officials and consulting engineers in Europe, Asia, the Pacific Rim, Central America and the Middle East. Helps international waste professionals manage their daily operations, from collection and processing to transportation and disposal.

ZHONGGUO WUZI ZAISHENG/CHINESE NATIONAL RESOURCES RECYCLING. see METALLURGY

ESTATE PLANNING LAW

see Law–Estate Planning

ETHNIC INTERESTS

917.306 US
DJK36.U6
A A A S S DIRECTORY OF PROGRAMS IN RUSSIAN, EURASIAN & EAST EUROPEAN STUDIES. 1987. triennial. $33 to non-members (foreign $34); members $23 (foreign $24). American Association for the Advancement of Slavic Studies, Stanford University, Jordan Quad - Acacia Bldg., Stanford, CA 94305-4130. TEL 415-723-9668. circ. 1,000. (back issues avail.) **Document type:** directory.
Formerly: A A A S S Directory of Programs in Soviet and East European Studies (ISSN 0889-9487)
Description: Selected listing of American and Canadian colleges, universities, and institutions that offer courses-programs in Russian, Eurasian and East European studies.

A A C P A NEWSLETTER. (Asian American Certified Public Accountants) see BUSINESS AND ECONOMICS — Accounting

A A M O A REPORTS. (Afro-American Music Opportunities Association) see MUSIC

A & T REGISTER. (Agricultural & Technical) see COLLEGE AND ALUMNI

A B B W A JOURNAL; the trade publication of the Black book industry. (American Black Book Writers Association, Inc.) see PUBLISHING AND BOOK TRADE

A B N F JOURNAL. (Association of Black Nursing Faculty in Higher Education) see MEDICAL SCIENCES — Nurses And Nursing

296 IS ISSN 0333-7286
A.B. - THE SAMARITAN NEWS. (Text in Arabic, English, Hebrew) 1969. bi-w. $105. P.O. Box 1029, Holon 58110, Israel. TEL 03-5567229. Ed. Benyamim Tsedaka, Yefet Ben-Ratson Tsedaka. adv.; bk.rev. circ. 2,000.

910.3 US ISSN 1051-0842
DT1
A C A S BULLETIN. 1987. s-a. Association of Concerned Africa Scholars, c/o Lisa Alfred, Executive Secretary, 1806 C St., SE 4, Washington, DC 20003-2515. **Document type:** academic/scholarly publication.
Formerly: A C A S Newsletter (ISSN 0741-9600)

A D L LAW REPORT. (Anti-Defamation League) see LAW

A H A! HISPANIC ARTS NEWS. (Association of Hispanic Arts) see ART

938 369 US ISSN 0746-133X
A H E P A N. 1928. q. $10. (American Hellenic Educational Progressive Association) Order of Ahepa, 1909 Q St., N.W., Ste. 500, Washington, DC 20009. TEL 202-232-6300. FAX 202-232-2140. Ed. George Savidis. adv.; bk.rev.; charts; illus. circ. 35,000. (back issues avail.)
Description: Aimed at individuals with an interest in Greek culture.

917.306 US
A H N; the voice of the African American community in Hawaii. 1987. bi-m. $18. Rainbow Bridge Consultants, Box 1337, Pahoa, HI 96778. TEL 808-966-8511. adv.; bk.rev. (back issues avail.) **Document type:** newspaper.
Formerly: Afro-Hawaii News.
Description: Covers community activities, arts and cultural events, small business concerns of interest to the African American community.

973.950 US
A I. (Asian Insights) q. Nguyen & Associates, 255 N. Market St., Ste. 270, San Jose, CA 95110. TEL 408-288-3443. Ed. Andrew Lam.

970.1 US
A I C H COMMUNITY BULLETIN. 1969. 5/yr. donation. American Indian Community House, 404 Lafayette St., 2nd Fl., New York, NY 10003. TEL 212-598-0100. FAX 212-598-4909. Ed. Justine Smith.

A J L NEWSLETTER. (Association of Jewish Libraries) see LIBRARY AND INFORMATION SCIENCES

A J P R S REPORTER. (American Jewish Public Relations Society) see ADVERTISING AND PUBLIC RELATIONS

296 US ISSN 0364-0094
BM1
A J S REVIEW. 1975. s-a. $15. (Association for Jewish Studies) Ktav Publishing House, 900 Jefferson St., No.6249, Hoboken, NJ 07030-7205. TEL 201-963-9524. FAX 201-963-0102. Ed. Norma Stillman. bk.rev.; bibl. circ. 1,500. **Indexed:** Amer.Bibl.Slavic & E.Eur.Stud., Amer.Hist.& Life, Hist.Abstr.
Refereed Serial

917.306 US
A. MAGAZINE: THE ASIAN AMERICAN QUARTERLY. 1991. q. $12. Metro East Publications, Inc., 296 Elizabeth St., Ste. 2F, New York, NY 10012. TEL 212-505-1416; 800-446-6235. Ed. Jeff Yang; Pub. Phoebe Eng. adv. contact: Karen Wang. **Document type:** newsletter.
Description: Covers political, social and cultural issues of interest to young Asian Americans.

A R A NEWSLETTER. (American Romanian Academy of Arts and Sciences) see EDUCATION — Higher Education

915.306 CN ISSN 0700-9771
A R C ARABIC JOURNAL. (Arab Republic Community) (Text in Arabic, English and French) 1974. s-m. Can.$48 to individuals; institutions Can.$96. Allam Arabic Publishing & Advertising Co., 511 Queen St.E., Toronto, Ont. M5A 1V1, Canada. TEL 416-362-0304. Ed. Salah Allam. adv.; bk.rev. circ. 10,521.
Former titles (until 1975): A R C Journal (ISSN 0700-9763); (until 1974): A R C Magazine (ISSN 0700-9755)
Description: News for the Egyptian community in Canada.

A R S HAI SIRD. (Armenian Relief Society, Inc.) see SOCIAL SERVICES AND WELFARE

960 US ISSN 0278-2219
DT19.9.U5
A S A NEWS. 1968. 4/yr. $85 includes membership. African Studies Association, Credit Union Bldg., Emory University, Atlanta, GA 30322. TEL 404-329-6410. Ed. Edna G. Bay. bibl.; tr.lit. circ. 3,000. **Indexed:** HR Rep. **Document type:** newsletter.
—BLDSC (1738.575000).
Former titles (until vol.13): African Studies Newsletter (ISSN 0002-0214); African Studies Association. Newsletter.

960 US
A S A PAPERS. 1960. a. $6. African Studies Association, Credit Union Bldg., Emory University, Atlanta, GA 30322. TEL 404-329-6410. (also avail. in microfiche; microfilm)

960 US
A S C NEWSLETTER (EAST LANSING). s-a. free. Michigan State University, African Studies Center, 100 International Center, E. Lansing, MI 48824-1035. TEL 517-353-1700. FAX 517-535-7254. TELEX 650-277-3148 MCI. circ. 1,000. (back issues avail.) **Document type:** newsletter.
Description: Contains African-related articles on African visitors, African accomplishments by MSU scholars, literature, film, and general announcements.

A S I POSTEN. (American Swedish Institute) see MUSEUMS AND ART GALLERIES

AALAM AL-RIYADAH. see SPORTS AND GAMES

917.106 CN ISSN 0715-4135
AAWAZ. (Text in English and Urdu) 1980. fortn. Can.$15($20) Aawaz, 2 Middleport Cres., Scarborough, ON M1B 4L5, Canada. TEL 416-283-7255. Ed. Sohail Akhtar. circ. 2,000. (back issues avail)

917.106 CN ISSN 0382-9251
ABAKA. (Text in Armenian, English, French) 1975. w. Can.$55. Tekeyan Armenian Cultural Association of Montreal, 825 Rue Manoogian, St. Laurent, PQ H4N 1Z5, Canada. TEL 514-747-6680. Ed. Arsene Mamourian. adv.; bk.rev. circ. 1,200. (tabloid format)

ABORIGINAL CHILD AT SCHOOL. see EDUCATION

910.03 US ISSN 1060-3905
ABOUT...TIME. 1972. m. $11. About...Time Magazine Inc., 283 Genesee St., Rochester, NY 14611. TEL 716-235-7150. Ed. Carolyne S. Blount. adv.; bk.rev.; index. circ. 28,000. (back issues avail.) **Indexed:** Ind.Per.Blacks.
Description: Offers articles on various subjects relating to the African-American experience. Incorporates Black contributions to American history for all to share.

917.06 CN ISSN 0843-7815
ABOVE & BEYOND. 1988. q. Can.$14($17) (typically set in Jan.). Jake Ootes, Ed. & Pub., Box 2348, Yellow Knife, NT X1A 2P7, Canada. TEL 403-873-2299. FAX 403-873-2295. adv.; bk.rev.; circ. 1,800 (paid); 28,200 (controlled).

970.1 323.4 US
E59.G6
ABYA YALA NEWS; linking Indian people of the Americas. (Editions in English, Spanish) 1984. q. $15 to individuals (Canada and Mexico $20; elsewhere $25); institutions $25 (Canada and Mexico $30; elsewhere $35) (membership). South and Meso-American Indian Information Center (SAIIC), Box 28703, Oakland, CA 94604-8703. TEL 510-834-4263. FAX 510-834-4264. Ed. Constanza Castro. circ. 4,000. (also avail. in microform) **Document type:** academic/scholarly publication.
Formerly (until 1993): South and Meso-American Indian Information Center (SAIIC) Newsletter (ISSN 1056-5876)
Description: Covers the struggles for survival and self-determination of Indian people in South and Meso-America.

056.9 CN
▼ACONTECE. (Text in Portuguese) 1992. m. Can.$18 (US Can.$21, elsewhere Can.$26). Kaplan Graphics, P.O. Box 614, Sta. C, Toronto, ON M6J 3R9, Canada. TEL 416-538-9937. FAX 416-538-9937. adv.: B&W page Can.$864, color page Can.$1080. circ. 1,800. (tabloid format) **Document type:** newspaper.
Formerly: Abacaxi Times (ISSN 1194-3106)

914.9 CN ISSN 0713-8539
ACROPOLIS. (Text in English, Greek) 1956. m. Can.$25($20) 2122 W. 47th Ave., Vancouver, BC V6M 2M7, Canada. TEL 604-266-6137. FAX 604-266-3595. adv.; bk.rev. circ. 7,000. (back issues avail.)

917.306 US
ACROSS THE SEA. 1990. q. Vietnamese American Student Publications, 700 Eshleman Hall, University of California, Berkeley, CA 94710. Eds. Jeffrey Hung Nguygen, Quyen Le.

ETHNIC INTERESTS   2467

917.306   US
AD KAAN; Hamagshimim newsletter. 1968. s-m. membership. Hadassah Zionist Youth Commission, 50 W. 58th St., New York, NY 10019. TEL 212-355-7900. charts; illus. **Document type:** newsletter.
    Description: Contains articles of interest to the Jewish community.

056.1   US   ISSN 0044-6238
ADELANTE (ORLANDO); al servicio de la comunidad Latinoamericana. 1972. m. $2. Amado F. Hernandez, Ed. & Pub., Box 811, Orlando, FL 32802. TEL 305-831-0181. adv.; bk.rev.; charts; illus. circ. 5,000. (tabloid format)

ADRIFT; writings: Irish, Irish-American and ... see *LITERATURE*

915.606   IQ
AFAQ ARABIYA. 1975. bi-m. ID.10($84) Ministry of Cultural Affairs, P.O. Box 4032 (Adhamiya), Baghdad, Iraq. TEL 443-54-46. FAX 4446780. TELEX 21-4135. Ed. Muhsin al-Musawi. circ. 12,000.
    Description: Theoretical with wide interests, especially in Arabic life.

956.940 296   US   ISSN 0030-7718
AFN SHVEL. (Text in Yiddish) 1941. q. $15. League for Yiddish, Inc., 200 W. 72nd St., Ste. 40, New York, NY 10023. TEL 212-787-6675. Ed.Bd. adv.; bk.rev.; bibl.; illus.; cum.index. circ. 1,350. (back issues avail.)
    Description: Covers Yiddish and its standardization as a living, spoken language.

910.03   US   ISSN 1041-6854
AFRAM COMMUNIQUE. 6/yr. $50. Afram Associates, Inc., 2322 Third Ave., 2nd Fl., New York, NY 10035. TEL 212-289-9155. FAX 212-722-5194.

910.03   US   ISSN 1041-5076
AFRAM DRUM. 1971. 12/yr. $15. Afram Associates, Inc., 2322 Third Ave., 2nd Fl., New York, NY 10035. TEL 212-289-9155. FAX 212-722-5194. Ed.Bd. adv.; bk.rev.; illus. circ. 1,000.
    Former titles: National Afrikan Kalendar of Events and Information; National Black Calendar.
    Description: Contains calender of events and information on blacks in South Africa.

AFRAM NEWSLETTER. see *LITERATURE*

910.03   US   ISSN 0893-4290
AFRICAN-AMERICAN FAMILY HISTORY ASSOCIATION NEWSLETTER. 1977. q. $12. African-American Family History Association, Inc., Box 115268, Atlanta, GA 30310. TEL 404-344-7405. FAX 404-730-1990. Ed. Herman Mason. bk.rev. circ. 100. **Document type:** newsletter.

AFRICAN AMERICAN LITERARY REVIEW. see *LITERATURE*

917.309 800   US   ISSN 1062-4783
E185.5
AFRICAN AMERICAN REVIEW. 1967. q. $20 to individuals (foreign $27); institutions $42 (foreign $49). Indiana State University, Department of English, Terre Haute, IN 47809. TEL 812-237-2968. Ed. Joe Weixlmann. adv.; bk.rev.; bibl.; index. circ. 1,200. (also avail. in microform from UMI; reprint service avail. from ISI,UMI) **Indexed:** A.I.P.P., Abstr.Engl.Stud., Amer.Hum.Ind., Arts & Hum.Cit.Ind., Bk.Rev.Ind. (1984-), Bk.Rev.Ind., Child.Bk.Rev.Ind. (1984-), Curr.Cont., Film Lit.Ind., Hum.Ind., Ind.Amer.Per.Verse, LCR, M.L.A., Ref.Sour. **Document type:** academic/scholarly publication.
    —BLDSC (0732.312100); Faxon; UnCover; UMI.
    Former titles: Black American Literature Forum (ISSN 0148-6179); (until 1976): Negro American Literature Forum (ISSN 0028-2480)
    Description: Publishes essays on Black American literature, art, and culture; interviews; and poems.

AFRICAN-AMERICAN SITES & INSIGHTS; a guide to places to go and people to know. see *TRAVEL AND TOURISM*

910.03   US   ISSN 1069-8205
AFRICAN HERALD. 1989. m. $15 (effective 1993). Good Hope Enterprises, Inc., Box 2394, Dallas, TX 75221-2394. TEL 214-823-7666. FAX 214-823-7373. Ed. Richard O. Nwachukwu. circ. 12,500. (tabloid format) **Document type:** newspaper.
    Formerly: Good Hope News.
    Description: News on Africa and African Americans. Covers current affairs, civil rights, politics, ethnic interests and international relations.

960   CN
▼**AFRICAN IDENTITY**. 1993. m. Can.$24($20.40) Afrimedia Communications, 236 Albion Rd., Ste. 1910, Rexdale, ON M9W 6A6, Canada. TEL 416-743-1900. FAX 416-923-1599. Ed. George Marcells; Pub. Kingsley Marfo. adv.: B&W page Can.$2500, color page Can.$3375; trim 8 1/4 x 10 3/4. circ. 5,750. **Document type:** consumer publication.

296   SA   ISSN 0044-6556
AFRICAN JEWISH NEWSPAPER; Africa's only Yiddish newspaper. (Text in Yiddish) 1930. w. African Jewish Newspaper (Pty) Ltd., P.O. Box 6169, Johannesburg 2000, South Africa. TEL 27-11-6468292. Ed. Levi Shalit. adv.; bk.rev.; film rev.; play rev.; illus. circ. 6,180. **Document type:** newspaper.

960   NR   ISSN 0002-0087
AFRICAN NOTES. (Not published 1973-1979) (Text in English) 1963. s-a. $12. University of Ibadan, Institute of African Studies, Ibadan, Nigeria. Ed. Alex Iwara. adv.; bk.rev.; bibl.; charts; illus.; cum.index. circ. 2,500. **Indexed:** Amer.Hist.& Life, Anthropol.Lit., Bibl.Ling., Curr.Cont.Africa, Documentatieblad, Hist.Abstr., M.L.A. **Document type:** academic/scholarly publication.
    —UnCover.

960   UK   ISSN 0305-862X
DT19.8
AFRICAN RESEARCH AND DOCUMENTATION. 1973. 3/yr. £13($32) (foreign £20($46)). Standing Conference on Library Materials on Africa, c/o Main Library, University of Birmingham, P.O. Box 363, Birmingham B15 2TT, England. TEL 021-414-6570. FAX 021-471-4691. TELEX 338938. Ed. J. McIlwaine. adv.; bk.rev.; index. circ. 400. (processed) **Indexed:** A.I.C.P., Amer.Hist.& Life, Bibl.Ling., CERDIC, Curr.Cont.Africa, Documentatieblad, Hist.Abstr., LISA. **Document type:** academic/scholarly publication.
    —BLDSC (0732.917000).
    Supersedes: African Studies Association of the United Kingdom. Bulletin (ISSN 0002-0192); Library Materials on Africa (ISSN 0024-239X)
    Description: Covers current research and studies on African culture, politics, economics, history and sociology.

960   US
AFRICAN RURAL AND URBAN STUDIES. 3/yr. $30 to individuals (foreign $50); institutions $40 (foreign $60). (Michigan State University, African Studies Center) Michigan State University Press, Manly Miles Bldg., Ste. 25, 1405 S. Harrison Rd., East Lansing, MI 48823-5202. TEL 517-355-9543. FAX 517-336-2611. Ed. David Wiley. **Document type:** academic/scholarly publication.

960   US
AFRICAN STUDIES. 1985. irreg., latest no.34. $39.95 per no. Edwin Mellen Press, 415 Ridge St., Box 450, Lewiston, NY 14092. TEL 716-754-2788. FAX 716-754-4056. Ed. Herbert Richardson. **Document type:** monographic series.

960   US   ISSN 0002-0206
DT1
AFRICAN STUDIES REVIEW. 1958. 3/yr. membership. African Studies Association, Credit Union Bldg., Emory University, GA 30322. TEL 404-329-6410. Ed. Mark DeLancey. adv.; bk.rev. circ. 3,000. **Indexed:** A.B.C.Pol.Sci., Amer.Hist.& Life, ASSIA, Bibl.Ind., Bibl.Ling., CERDIC, Curr.Cont.Africa, Documentatieblad, Geo.Abstr., Hist.Abstr., HR Rep., Int.Lab.Doc. M.L.A., Mid.East: Abstr.& Ind., Rural Devel.Abstr., Rural Recreat.Tour.Abstr., Soc.Sci.Ind., Trop.Oil Seeds Abstr., World Agri.Econ.& Rural Sociol.Abstr. **Document type:** academic/scholarly publication.
    —BLDSC (0734.800000); Faxon; UnCover; SWETS; UMI.
    Incorporates: African Studies Bulletin.
    Description: Covers all aspects of African studies.

960   US   ISSN 0736-6760
HT148.A2
AFRICAN URBAN STUDIES. 1966; N.S. 1975. irreg. $21 in U.S.; Africa $18; elsewhere $24. Michigan State University, African Studies Center, 100 Center for International Programs, E. Lansing, MI 48824-1035. TEL 517-353-1700. FAX 517-353-7254. TELEX 650-277-3148 MCI. bibl.; charts; illus.; stat. circ. 600. **Indexed:** Amer.Hist.& Life, Anthropol.Lit., Curr.Cont.Africa, Documentatieblad, Hist.Abstr., I D A, Mid.East: Abstr.& Ind. **Document type:** academic/scholarly publication.
    Formerly (until 1978): African Urban Notes (ISSN 0044-6629)

AFRICANA MARBURGENSIA. see *HISTORY — History Of Africa*

AFRICANA RESEARCH BULLETIN. see *SOCIAL SCIENCES: COMPREHENSIVE WORKS*

960   GW
AFRIKA-POST; Magazine fuer Politik, Wirtschaft und Kultur Afrikas. 1976. m. DM.70 (foreign DM.79). (Deutsche Afrika-Stiftung e.V.) Europa Union Verlag GmbH, Bachstr. 32, Postfach 1529, 53115 Bonn, Germany. TEL 0228-7290010. FAX 0228-695734. TELEX 8-86822. circ. 3,500. (back issues avail.)

AFRO-AMERICAN CULTURE AND SOCIETY MONOGRAPH SERIES. see *SOCIAL SCIENCES: COMPREHENSIVE WORKS*

AFRO-AMERICAN HISTORICAL AND GENEALOGICAL SOCIETY. JOURNAL. see *GENEALOGY AND HERALDRY*

AFRO-AMERICAN HISTORICAL AND GENEALOGICAL SOCIETY. NEWSLETTER. see *GENEALOGY AND HERALDRY*

917.306   US   ISSN 0364-2437
F128.9.N4
AFRO-AMERICANS IN NEW YORK LIFE AND HISTORY. 1977. s-a. $8. Afro-American Historical Association of the Niagara Frontier, Box 63, Buffalo, NY 14207. Ed. Dr. Monroe Fordham. adv.; bk.rev.; illus. circ. 700. (also avail. in microfilm; back issues avail.; reprint service avail. from UMI) **Indexed:** Amer.Hist.& Life, Hist.Abstr.
    —Faxon; UMI.

960   ML
AFRO - ARAVE REVUE. q. Rue Mohamed V, B.P. 2044, Bamako, Mali. Ed. Mohamed ben Baba Ahmed. circ. 1,000.

960   US   ISSN 0278-8969
PQ7081.A1
AFRO-HISPANIC REVIEW. 1982. s-a. $10 to individuals; institutions $15. University of Missouri at Columbia, Romance Languages Department, c/o Dr. Edward Mullen, 143, Arts & Sciences, Columbia, MO 65211. Eds. Marvin A. Lewis, Edward J. Mullen. adv.; bk.rev. circ. 500. (back issues avail.) **Indexed:** Hisp.Amer.Per.Ind., M.L.A. **Document type:** academic/scholarly publication.
    —Faxon; UnCover; UMI.
    Description: Covers literary criticism, translations, creative writing, and relevant developments in Afro-Hispanic literature and culture.

ULRICH'S INTERNATIONAL PERIODICALS DIRECTORY 1994-95

ETHNIC INTERESTS

910.03 US ISSN 0894-0762
AFRO SCHOLAR NEWSLETTER. s-a. Northeastern University, African-American Studies Department, 360 Huntington Ave., Boston, MA 02115-5096. TEL 617-437-2000. **Document type:** newsletter.

960 910.03 US
AFROAMERICANIST. 1985. s-a. University of Illinois, Afro-American Studies & Research Program, 606 S. Gregory, Urbana, IL 61801. TEL 217-244-5258. Ed. Valinda Littlefield. bk.rev. circ. 2,000. (back issues avail.)

296 800 US ISSN 0740-2392
BM1
AGADA; an illustrated Jewish literary magazine. 1981. 3/yr. $14 to institutions. 2020 Essex St., Berkeley, CA 94703. TEL 415-848-0965. Ed. Reuven Goldfarb. adv.: B&W page $150. bk.rev.; illus. circ. 1,000. **Indexed:** Amer.Hum.Ind.
  Description: Includes a contemporary sensibility in poetry, fiction, midrash, essay, memoir, art and photography.

929 US ISSN 0146-020X
E184.S75
AGENDA (WASHINGTON); a journal of Hispanic issues. 1970. q. free. National Council of La Raza, 810 First St., N.E., Ste. 300, Washington, DC 20002-4272. TEL 202-289-1380. FAX 202-289-8173. Ed. Lisa Navarette. adv.; bk.rev.; bibl. circ. 5,000. **Indexed:** Abstr.Engl.Stud.; Arts & Hum.Cit.Ind., C.I.J.E., Curr.Lit.Fam.Plan., Hisp.Amer.Per.Ind., Mid.East: Abstr.& Ind. **Document type:** newsletter.
  Description: Provides information on legislative and social issues affecting Hispanic people and coverage of NCLR activities.

296 070.48 US ISSN 1048-2326
AGENDA IN BRIEF.* 1979. 6/yr. $18. New Jewish Agenda, 345 Eighth Ave., Apt. 3H, New York, NY 10001-4834. FAX 212-962-6211. Ed. Annette G. Jaffe. bk.rev. circ. 3,500. (looseleaf format)
  Formerly: Agenda (New York); **Supersedes:** Shalom Network Newsletter.

AGING IN THE JEWISH WORLD: CONTINUITY AND CHANGE. see GERONTOLOGY AND GERIATRICS

917.306 US
AGORA; an alternative journal of Romanian culture. 1987. q. $30 (foreign $35). Foreign Policy Research Institute, 3615 Chestnut St., Philadelphia, PA 19104. TEL 215-382-0685. FAX 215-382-0131. Ed. Dorin Tudoran.
  Description: Includes essays, short stories, poems by Romanians in exile, by Romanians inside the country, and other East European intellectuals and artists.

914.406 FR
AGUR. 1954. bi-m. 110 Fr. Eskual Etxea, 7 rue du Palais de l'Ombriere, 33000 Bordeaux, France.
  Description: Basque interests.

917.306 323.4 US
AIM MAGAZINE (CHICAGO). 1974. q. $10. Aim Magazine Publishing Company, 7308 S. Eberhart, Box 20554, Chicago, IL 60620. TEL 312-874-6184. Ed. Ruth Apilado. adv. contact: David Smallwood. bk.rev. circ. 10,000. (back issues avail.)
  Description: Covers the evil of racism.

947 US ISSN 0516-3145
AKADEMISKA DZIVE/ACADEMIC LIFE. (Text in Latvian; summaries in English) 1958. a. $7. Association of Latvian Academic Societies, One Vincent Ave. S., Minneapolis, MN 55405. Ed.Bd. bk.rev.; illus. circ. 900. **Indexed:** Amer.Hist.& Life, Hist.Abstr., M.L.A. **Document type:** academic/scholarly publication.

296 IS
AKI YERUSHALAYIM; revista kulturala Djudeo-espanyola. (Text in Judeo-Spanish) 1979. s-a. $25. Sefarad - Association for the Preservation and Promotion of Judeo-Spanish Culture, P.O. Box 8175, Jerusalem 91080, Israel. FAX 972-2-631906. Ed. Moshe Shaul. adv.; bk.rev.
  Description: Covers issues relating to Judeo-Spanish culture and its preservation.

910.03 US
AKRON CALL & POST. 1927. w. $35. P.W. Publishing Co., 1949 E. 105th St., Cleveland, OH 44106. TEL 216-791-7600. FAX 216-791-6568. adv. contact: John Lenear. circ. 5,000. **Document type:** newspaper.

970.1 US
AKWE KON JOURNAL. 1984. q. $18 to individuals; institutions $35. Akwe Kon Press, 300 Caldwell Hall, Cornell University, Ithaca, NY 14853. TEL 607-255-4308. FAX 607-255-0185. Ed. Jose Barreiro. adv.; bk.rev. circ. 2,200. **Indexed:** Alt.Press Ind. **Document type:** bulletin.
  Former titles (until 1992): Northeast Indian Quarterly (ISSN 0897-2354); Indian Times.
  Description: A multi-disciplinary journal dedicated to the coverage of Indian issues, such as politics, indigenous economics, Native intellectual traditions, eco-systemic thinking and systems, history and art, both from a community perspective and through the writing of nationally respected Native and non-Native authors.

970.1 US ISSN 0002-3949
E75
AKWESASNE NOTES; a journal for native and natural people. 1968. bi-m. $20. Mohawk Nation at Akwesasne, Box 196, Rooseveltown, NY 13683-0196. TEL 518-358-9531. FAX 613-575-2064. Ed. Douglas George. adv.; illus. circ. 5,000. (tabloid format; also avail. in microform from UMI,MCA,KTO; reprint service avail. from UMI) **Indexed:** A.I.C.P., Alt.Press Ind., Chic.Per.Ind., HR Rep.—UMI.

917.396 US ISSN 1053-9492
DR901
ALBANICA. (Text in Albanian, English, French, German, Italian) 1990. q. $30 to individuals; institutions $60. Albanic Inc., 134 G St., N.W., Washington, DC 20024. TEL 202-479-0633. Ed. Arshi Pipa. bk.rev.; index. circ. 1,000. **Document type:** academic/scholarly publication.
  Description: Devoted to Albanian culture on a scholarly level.

949 GW ISSN 0930-1437
ALBANISCHE HEFTE; Zeitschrift fuer Berichte, Analysen, Meinungen aus und ueber Albanien. 1972. q. DM.25. Deutsch - Albanische Freundschaftsgesellschaft e.V., Bilserstr. 9, 22297 Hamburg, Germany. TEL 040-5111320. FAX 040-5111320. Ed. Bodo Gudjons. bk.rev. circ. 1,200. (back issues avail.) **Document type:** newsletter.
  Description: News about the people of Albania.

914.5 CN
ALBERTA ITALIAN TIMES.* (Text in English, Italian) 1988. m. Webco Lynard Publisher Ltd., 504 Alder Ave., Sherwood Park, AB T8A 1S9, Canada. TEL 403-472-6397. FAX 403-478-5493. circ. 5,000. (tabloid format) **Document type:** newspaper.

296 US
ALGEMEINER JOURNAL. (Text in English, Yiddish) 1972. w. $35. Algemeiner Journal, 211 63rd St., Brooklyn, NY 11220. TEL 718-492-6420. FAX 718-492-6571. Ed. Gershon Jacobson. adv. contact: Boruch Jacobson. bk.rev.; film rev.; play rev.; illus.; circ. 212,000 (paid). (broadsheet format; also avail. in diskette format) **Document type:** newspaper.
  Description: An independent publication serving the Jewish community in the U.S. and abroad.

ALL AMERICAN AVIATION ASSOCIATION NEWS. see TRANSPORTATION — Air Transport

917.306 US
▼**ALLER SIMPLE.** (Text in French) 1992. m. $3 per no. Aller Simple, Ltd., 10510 Woodbine St., Ste. 209, Los Angeles, CA 90034. TEL 310-838-7480. FAX 310-559-7702. adv.; B&W page $500, color page $900; trim 8 1/2 x 11. circ. 3,000. **Document type:** consumer publication.

296 GW ISSN 0340-272X
ALLGEMEINE JUEDISCHE WOCHENZEITUNG. 1946. w. (Thu.). (Zentralrat der Juden in Deutschland) Juedische Presse GmbH, Ruengsdorfer Str. 6, 53173 Bonn, Germany. TEL 0228-351021. FAX 0228-355469. Ed. Daniel Dagan. adv. contact: Eveline Krauthaeuser. bk.rev.; film rev.; play rev.; charts. circ. 10,000. (tabloid format) **Document type:** newspaper.
  Formerly (until 1973): Allgemeine Unabhaengige Juedische Wochenzeitung (ISSN 0002-5941)
  Description: Covers Jewish interests.

917.106 CN
ALLIANCE AUTOCHTONE DU QUEBEC. m. Native Alliance of Quebec, 21 Brodeur, Hull, Que. J8Y 2P6, Canada. TEL 819-770-7763. FAX 819-770-6070.

057.91 CN ISSN 0441-1196
ALMANAKH GOMONU UKRAINY. 1956 (Suspended during 1974). a. Homin Ukrainy Publishing Co., 140 Bathurst St., Toronto, Ont. M5V 2R3, Canada. TEL 416-368-3443. illus.

296 FR ISSN 0240-902X
ALTA NIZZA. (Text in French and Hebrew) 1974. q. $2. Association Traditionnelle Israelite Sefarade, 1 bis Boissy d'Anglas, 06000 Nice, France. Ed. Joseph Pardo.

914.506 IT ISSN 1120-0413
JV6005
ALTREITALIE; international journal of studies on the peoples of Italian origin in the world. (Text in various languages.) 1989. s-a. L.60000 (effective 1993). Fondazione Giovanni Agnelli, Via Giacosa 38, 10125 Turin, Italy. TEL 011-658666. FAX 011-6502777. Ed. Maddalena Tirabassi. bk.rev. circ. 1,000. **Document type:** academic/scholarly publication.
  Description: Devoted to the study of Italian communities in the Americas and Australia on an interdisciplinary basis. Deals with historiography, literature, sociology, demography and ethnology.

917.306 US
AM-POL EAGLE. 1950. w. $17.50. Matthew W. Pelczynski, Ed. & Pub., 1335 E. Delavan Ave., Buffalo, NY 14215. adv.; bk.rev. circ. 25,000. (reprint service avail.)
  Description: Polish-American interests.

914.206 UK ISSN 0264-1453
AMAR DEEP; Hindi weekly London. (Text in Hindi; summaries in English and Hindi) 1971. w. £25. Joy Quest Ltd., 36 Trent Ave., London W5 4LT, England. TEL 071-840-3534. (Subscr. to: 2 Chepstow Rd., London W7 2BG, England) Ed. J.M. Kaushal. adv.; bk.rev.; film rev. circ. 30,000.

AMERASIA JOURNAL. see SOCIOLOGY

917.306 US
AMERASIAN UPDATE; an international service on behalf of the resettlement of Vietnamese Amerasians. 1988. m. $20 (foreign $25) (effective June 1993). (Inter Action) Amerasian Update, 1717 Massachusetts Ave. N.W., 8th Fl., Washington, DC 20036. TEL 202-667-8227. FAX 202-667-8236. Ed. Anita L. Menghetti. illus. **Document type:** newsletter.

918.206
▼**AMERICA MILENARIA.** 1992. bi-m. Centro de Estudios, Divulgacion y Apoyo a las Culturas Indigenas, 25 de Mayo 385, Temperley, Pcia., Buenos Aires, Argentina.

917.306 US
AMERICAN-ARAB MESSAGE. 1937. w. $25. A A Printing and Publishing Co., 17514 Woodward Ave., Detroit, MI 48203. TEL 313-868-2266. FAX 313-868-2267. Ed. Imam Hussein. circ. 8,700. (tabloid format) **Document type:** newspaper.

AMERICAN COUNCIL FOR JUDAISM. SPECIAL INTEREST REPORT; a digest of news items and articles in the area of the council's interest. see RELIGIONS AND THEOLOGY — Judaic

917.306 US
AMERICAN CROAT/AMERICKI HRVAT. vol.11, 1975. q. $6. (Croatian Information Service) Peter Radielovic, Ed. & Pub., Box 3025, Arcadia, CA 91006. bk.rev.; illus. circ. 3,000. (back issues avail.)

ETHNIC INTERESTS

917.309   US   ISSN 0739-9170
AMERICAN DANE. 1916. m. $12. Danish Brotherhood in America, 3717 Harney St., Omaha, NE 68131-3844. TEL 800-553-1937. FAX 402-341-0830. Ed. Jennifer Denning-Kock. adv.; illus. circ. 6,000. **Indexed:** Phys.Ed.Ind.
   Description: Promotes and perpetuates Danish culture and traditions, and provides fraternal benefits and family protection.

929 947   US   ISSN 0162-8283
E184.R85
AMERICAN HISTORICAL SOCIETY OF GERMANS FROM RUSSIA. JOURNAL. 1978. 4/yr. membership. American Historical Society of Germans From Russia, 631 D St., Lincoln, NE 68502. TEL 402-474-3363. FAX 402-474-7229. bk.rev. circ. 6,000. **Indexed:** Amer.Bibl.Slavic & E.Eur.Stud., Amer.Hist.& Life, Hist.Abstr.
   —UnCover.
   Supersedes (1970-1978): American Historical Society of Germans from Russia. Work Paper (ISSN 0145-6105)
   Description: Articles on the history and culture of Germans who settled throughout Czarist Russia and then immigrated to N. America. Contains articles on genealogy.

AMERICAN HUNGARIAN EDUCATOR. see *EDUCATION*

970.1 301.1 150   US   ISSN 0893-5394
RC451.5.I5
AMERICAN INDIAN AND ALASKA NATIVE MENTAL HEALTH RESEARCH. 1978. 3/yr. $35 (foreign $44). (National Center for American Indian Mental Health Research) University Press of Colorado, Box 849, Niwot, CO 80544. TEL 303-530-5337. FAX 303-530-5306. index. circ. 1,000. (back issues avail.) **Indexed:** Abstr.Health Care Manage.Stud., Anthropol.Lit., C.I.J.E., Psychol.Abstr., Soc.Work Res. & Abstr., Sociol.Abstr. **Document type:** academic/scholarly publication.
   —BLDSC (0819.638000); UnCover.
   Former titles (until 1986): White Cloud Journal of American Indian Mental Health (ISSN 0886-5027); (until 1982): White Cloud Journal of American Indian - Alaska Native Mental Health (ISSN 0190-2482)
   Description: Provides empirical research, program evaluation, case studies and unpublished dissertations.

AMERICAN INDIAN BASKETRY AND OTHER NATIVE ARTS. see *ARTS AND HANDICRAFTS*

970.1   US   ISSN 0161-6463
E75
AMERICAN INDIAN CULTURE AND RESEARCH JOURNAL. 1971. q. $20 to individuals (foreign $25); institutions $30 (foreign $35). University of California at Los Angeles, American Indian Studies Center, 3220 Campbell Hall, Los Angeles, CA 90024-1548. TEL 310-825-7315. FAX 310-206-7060. Ed. Duane Champagne. adv.: B&W page $100; adv. contact: J. St.George. bk.rev.; cum.index: 1977-1982. circ. 1,600. (also avail. in microfilm; reprint service avail. from UMI) **Indexed:** Abstr.Anthropol., Amer.Hist.& Life, Amer.Hum.Ind., Anthropol.Lit., ASCA, Bibl.Ling., C.I.J.E., Curr.Cont., Hist.Abstr., Mult.Ed.Abstr., Sociol.Abstr., Sp.Ed.Needs Abstr. **Document type:** academic/scholarly publication.
   —BLDSC (0819.650000); Faxon; UnCover; UMI.
   Formerly: American Indian Culture Center. Journal.
   Description: Takes an interdisciplinary look at the indigenous peoples of North America.
   Refereed Serial

970.1   US
AMERICAN INDIAN DEFENSE NEWS. 1984. q. $10 for 6 issues. Big Chief International, 15 N. Plum St., Ste. B, Box 3121, Hutchinson, KS 67501. TEL 316-665-3614. Ed. M.L. Webber (Chief Thunderbird Webber). adv.; bk.rev. circ. 2,000. **Document type:** newspaper.

AMERICAN INDIAN LAW REVIEW. see *LAW*

970.1   US   ISSN 0193-8207
Z711.8
AMERICAN INDIAN LIBRARIES NEWSLETTER. 1976. q. $10 to individuals; institutions $25. American Indian Library Association, School of Library and Information Studies, University of Oklahoma, 401 W. Brooks, Norman, OK 73019. TEL 405-325-3921. FAX 405-325-7648. Ed. Lotsee Patterson. bk.rev.; circ. 500 (paid). **Document type:** newsletter.
   —UMI.
   Description: Covers American Indian interests with news and information of importance to American Indian librarians.

970.1   US
AMERICAN INDIAN REPORT. vol.3, 1987. m. $79. Falmouth Institute, Inc., 3918 Prosperity Ave., Ste. 302, Fairfax, VA 22031-3333. TEL 703-641-9100. FAX 703-641-1558. circ. 7,000. **Document type:** newsletter.
   Description: Covers news, events, and Federal Register announcements affecting the Indian community.

970.1   US   ISSN 1058-563X
AMERICAN INDIAN STUDIES. irreg. Peter Lang Publishing, Inc., 62 W. 45th St., 4th Fl., New York, NY 10036. TEL 212-302-6740. FAX 212-302-7574. Ed. Rodney Simard. **Document type:** academic/scholarly publication.
   Description: Covers all aspects of American Indian history and culture, with an emphasis on contemporary ideas and issues.

914.506   US
AMERICAN ITALIAN HERITAGE ASSOCIATION NEWSLETTER. 1979. bi-m. $12 (effective 1994). American Italian Heritage Association, Box 419, Morrisville, NY 13408. TEL 315-684-9502. Ed. Philip J. Di Novo. adv. contact: Philip J. Di Novo. circ. 1,020. **Document type:** newsletter.
   Description: Covers Italian traditions and customs, history, news from Italy and the Italian American community.

917.309   US   ISSN 0569-5961
AMERICAN ITALIAN HISTORICAL ASSOCIATION. NEWSLETTER. 1967. 4/yr. $10 (effective 1992). American Italian Historical Association, 209 Flagg Place, Staten Island, NY 10304. TEL 718-667-6628. Ed. Anthony J. Taburri. adv.; bk.rev. circ. 700. (reprint service avail. from UMI) **Document type:** newsletter, proceedings.
   Description: Contains information and activities new of the association, bibliographical notes on Italian American studies, and miscellaneous news on conferences, symposia, events, and achievements of Italian Americans.

917.306   US
AMERICAN ITALIAN HISTORICAL ASSOCIATION. PROCEEDINGS. (Each vol. has distinctive title) 1968. a. $9.95 or membership. American Italian Historical Association, 209 Flagg Pl., Staten Island, NY 10304. TEL 212-667-6628. circ. 1,200. **Document type:** proceedings.

AMERICAN JEWISH ALTERNATIVES TO ZIONISM. REPORT. see *POLITICAL SCIENCE — International Relations*

296 900   US   ISSN 0002-905X
E184.J5
AMERICAN JEWISH ARCHIVES; devoted to the preservation and study of the American Jewish experience. 1948. s-a. free to qualified personnel. American Jewish Archives, 3101 Clifton Ave., Cincinnati, OH 45220. TEL 513-221-1875. FAX 513-221-7812. Eds. Jacob R. Marcus, Abraham J. Peck. bk.rev.; bibl.; illus.; index. circ. 5,000. (also avail. in microfiche) **Indexed:** Amer.Bibl.Slavic & E.Eur.Stud., Amer.Hist.& Life & Hum.Cit.Ind., Curr.Cont., Hist.Abstr., Ind.Jew.Per., Mid.East: Abstr.& Ind., Rel.Ind.One.
   —BLDSC (0820.920000); UnCover; UMI.

296   US   ISSN 0163-1365
DS101
AMERICAN JEWISH CONGRESS. CONGRESS MONTHLY; a journal of opinion and Jewish affairs. Key Title: Congress Monthly. 1933. 7/yr. $11. American Jewish Congress, 15 E. 84th St., New York, NY 10028. TEL 212-879-4500. Ed. Maier Deshell. adv.; bk.rev.; film rev.; play rev. circ. 31,000. **Indexed:** HR Rep., Ind.Jew.Per., Mid.East: Abstr.& Ind. —UnCover.
   Formerly: American Jewish Congress. Congress Bi-Weekly (ISSN 0010-5872)

973 296   US   ISSN 0164-0178
E184.J5
AMERICAN JEWISH HISTORY. 1893. q. $50 to libraries; members $50. American Jewish Historical Society, Two Thornton Rd., Waltham, MA 02154. TEL 617-891-8110. FAX 617-899-9208. Ed. Marc Raphael. adv.; bk.rev.; bibl.; charts; illus.; index. circ. 3,600. (also avail. in microfiche; microfilm from KTO; reprint service avail. from ISI,KTO) **Indexed:** Amer.Bibl.Slavic & E.Eur.Stud., Amer.Hist.& Life, Arts & Hum.Cit.Ind., Curr.Cont., Hist.Abstr., Hum.Ind., Ind.Jew.Per., Mid.East: Abstr.& Ind., SSCI. **Document type:** academic/scholarly publication.
   —BLDSC (0820.935000); Faxon; UnCover.
   Former titles: American Historical Society. Publications (ISSN 0146-5511); American Jewish Historical Quarterly (ISSN 0002-9068)

296   US   ISSN 0002-9084
AMERICAN JEWISH WORLD; voice of Minnesota Jewry. 1912. w. $19. A J W Publishing, Inc., 4509 Minnetonka Blvd., Minneapolis, MN 55416-9714. TEL 612-920-7000. FAX 612-920-6205. Ed. Marshall Hoffman. adv.; bk.rev.; charts; illus. circ. 7,000. (tabloid format; also avail. in microfilm from AJP) **Document:** newspaper.

910.03   US
AMERICAN NEWS - SAN BERNARDINO. 1969. w. $15. San Bernardino American, 1583 W. Base Line St., Box 7010, San Bernardino, CA 92411. TEL 714-889-7677. adv. contact: Sam Martin, Jr. circ. 5,000. **Document type:** newspaper.

296   US
AMERICAN O R T FEDERATION. YEARBOOK. (Organization for Rehabilitation through Training) 1952. a. free. American O R T Federation, 817 Broadway, New York, NY 10003. TEL 212-677-4400. FAX 212-979-9545. TELEX 66468. Ed. Avi Feinglass. stat.; index. circ. 22,000. (back issues avail.) **Document type:** corporate report.
   Description: Reports on the international ORT Network of schools and training centers which provide vocational and technical training for 250,000 students in 50 countries throughout the world.

296   US
AMERICAN O R T FEDERATION BULLETIN. q. American O R T Federation, 817 Broadway, New York, NY 10003. TEL 212-677-4400. FAX 212-979-9545. TELEX 66468. (back issues avail.) **Document type:** bulletin.
   Description: Covers present and future Federation activities and operations.

947   US
AMERICAN ROMANIAN ACADEMY OF ARTS AND SCIENCES. PUBLICATIONS. a., vol.14, 1992. A R A Publications, 3328 Monte Vista Ave., Davis, CA 95616. TEL 916-758-7720. **Document type:** bulletin.

296   US   ISSN 0003-102X
DS101
AMERICAN SEPHARDI. 1966. s-a. $15. Yeshiva University, Sephardic Studies Program, 500 W. 185 St., New York, NY 10033. TEL 212-960-5277. Ed. H.P. Salomon. bk.rev.; bibl.; illus. circ. 7,000. **Indexed:** M.L.A.
   Description: Contains articles of interest to the Jewish community.

917.109   US
AMERICAN SRBOBRAN/AMERICAN SERBIAN. (Text in English, Serbian) 1929. w. $40 to non-members; members $20. Serb National Federation, One Fifth Ave., 7th Fl., Pittsburgh, PA 15222. TEL 412-642-7372. FAX 412-642-1372. Ed. Robert Rade Stone. circ. 3,500. **Document type:** newspaper.

2470 ETHNIC INTERESTS

917.306 398   US   ISSN 0895-0482
AMERICAN UNIVERSITY STUDIES. SERIES 21. REGIONAL STUDIES. (Text in English and other West European languages) 1988. irreg. Peter Lang Publishing, Inc., 62 W. 45th St., 4th Fl., New York, NY 10036. TEL 212-302-6740. Ed. Michael Flamini. Document type: academic/scholarly publication.

910.03 960   US   ISSN 0884-9390
E185.5
AMERICAN VISIONS; the magazine of Afro-American culture. 1986. bi-m. $18 (foreign $30). (Visions Foundation) Dialogue Diaspora, Inc., 2101 S St., N.W., Washington, DC 20008-4011. TEL 202-462-1779. FAX 202-463-3997. (Subscr. to: Box 614, Mt. Morris, IL 61054. TEL 800-998-0864) Ed. Gary A. Phekrein. adv. contact: Mel Fallis. bk.rev.; index. circ. 125,000. (also avail. in microform from UMI; back issues avail.) Indexed: Acad.Ind., Mag.Ind. Document type: consumer publication.
—Faxon; UnCover; UMI.
   Description: Promotes an appreciation of African-American history and culture, with a focus on the arts.

AMERICAN ZIONIST. see POLITICAL SCIENCE

THE AMERICAS REVIEW (HOUSTON); a review of Hispanic literature and art of the U S A. see LITERATURE

917.306   US
AMERIKA WOCHE. (Text in English and German) 1972. m. $32.50. Courier Press U S A Inc., 4732 N. Lincoln Ave., Chicago, IL 60625. TEL 312-275-5054. Ed. Werner Baroni. adv.; bk.rev. circ. 20,000. (tabloid format) Document type: newspaper.
   Former titles: Deutschamerikaner; Deutschamerikaner National Kongres. DANK Mitteilungen.

917.306   US   ISSN 0194-7990
AMERIKAI MAGYAR SZO/HUNGARIAN WORD. (Text in Hungarian) 1952. w. $30. Hungarian Word, Inc., 130 E. 16th St., New York, NY 10003-3593. TEL 212-254-0397. Ed.Bd. adv.; bk.rev.; charts; illus. circ. 1,800. Document type: newspaper.

917.306   US   ISSN 0745-9971
AMERIKAN UUTISET. (Text in English, Finnish) 1932. w. $26. Amerikan Uutiset, Inc., 445 Lantana Rd., W., Lake Worth, FL 33462-1725. TEL 407-588-9770. FAX 407-588-3229. Ed. Aarne A. Aaltonen. adv.; bk.rev.; illus. circ. 3,100. Document type: newspaper.
   Formerly: Parta.
   Description: Covers Finnish interests.

949.7   US
AMERISKA DOMOVINA/AMERICAN HOME. (Text in English, Slovenian) 1898. w. $25. Ameriska Domovina - American Home, 6117 St. Clair Ave., Cleveland, OH 44103. TEL 216-431-0628. Ed. Rudolph M. Susel. circ. 5,000. (tabloid format) Document type: newspaper.

296   US   ISSN 0747-0258
DS150.R3
AMIT WOMAN. (Text in English) 1926. 4/yr. membership. Amit Women, 817 Broadway, New York, NY 10003. TEL 212-477-4720. FAX 212-353-2312. Ed. Micheline Ratzersdorfer. adv. contact: Gladup Neustadter. bk.rev.; illus. circ. 30,000.
   Former titles: American Mizrachi Woman; Mizrachi Woman (ISSN 0026-7007)
   Description: Contains articles of interest to the Jewish community.

296 378   US
AMUDIM. 1986. a. free. Center for Jewish Studies, University of Florida, 401 Grinter Hall, Gainesville, FL 32611. TEL 904-392-9247. FAX 904-392-5378. Ed. Warren Bargad. circ. 6,500. (back issues avail.) Document type: newsletter.
   Description: Provides information on events and lectures sponsored by the center, gifts, Judaica library, graduates, courses, and special programs in Jewish studies.

914.06   PO
ANGLO-PORTUGUESE NEWS. (Supplement avail. weekly: Money Matters) (Text in English) 1937. w. Esc.13500($100) (effective Jan. 1992). A P N Publications, Apdo. 113, 2765 Estoril, Portugal. TEL 244-3950. FAX 244-3739. TELEX 66973 APNP. Ed. Nigel Batley. film rev.; play rev. circ. 9,000. (back issues avail.)
   Description: Contains news of Portugal for foreign residents. Includes supplement on property, business, finance and investment.

ANNUAL EDITIONS: RACE & ETHNIC RELATIONS. see SOCIOLOGY

ANNUAL STATUS REPORT, MINORITIES IN HIGHER EDUCATION. see EDUCATION — Higher Education

ANTHROPOLOGIE ET SOCIETES. see ANTHROPOLOGY

ANUARIO HISPANO. see OCCUPATIONS AND CAREERS

917.306   US
AQUI (PHOENIX).* (Text in English) 1989. q. Wilcox Graphics, c/o Owens and Associates, 6530 N. 16th St., Ste. 101, Phoenix, AZ 85016-1311. TEL 602-230-2424. FAX 602-274-5130. Ed. Bill Meek. adv.; circ. 10,000. (controlled).
   Description: Focuses on current events and issues as they affect Hispanics in Arizona.

AQUI (RIVER EDGE). see MEN'S INTERESTS

956   US   ISSN 0742-9576
E184.A65
ARAB AMERICAN ALMANAC. 1974. irreg., 4th ed., 1992. $19.95. News Circle Publishing House - Dar Halqat al-Akbar lil-Nashr wal-I'lam, Box 3684, Glendale, CA 91201. TEL 818-545-0333. FAX 818-242-5039. Ed. Joseph R. Haiek. adv.; bibl.; illus. circ. 20,000. Document type: directory.
   Description: Reference book on the history and present cultural, social religious and economic activities of the Arab-American community, including biographies of notable figures, as well as information on the Arab world.

915.306   CN   ISSN 0706-7917
ARAB DIRECTORY/DALIL EL ARAB. (Text and summaries in Arabic and English) 1979. s-m. Can.$25($45) Allam Arabic Publishing & Advertising Co., 511 Queen St.E., Toronto, Ont. M5A 1V1, Canada. TEL 416-362-0304. Ed. Salah Allam. adv.; illus. circ. 4,000.
   Description: Directory of Arab-run businesses and services in Canada.

915.306   CN
ARAB GUIDE.* (Text in Arabic, English) 1979. s-m. $20 (foreign $96). Allam Arabic Publishing & Advertising Co., 511 Queen St.E., Toronto, Ont. M5A 1V1, Canada. TEL 416-362-0304. Ed. Faysal Ahmed. adv. circ. 5,000.

915.306   CN   ISSN 0839-4547
ARAB NEWS INTERNATIONAL. (Text in Arabic and English) 1978. s-m. Can.$48 to individuals; institutions Can.$96. Allam Arabic Publishing & Advertising Co., 511 Queen St.E., Toronto, Ont. M5A 1V1, Canada. TEL 416-362-0304. adv. circ. 7,000.
   Formerly: Arab News of Toronto - Akhbar al-Arab fi Toronto (ISSN 0707-3372)
   Description: National newspaper for Arabs in Canada.

917.406   US   ISSN 0271-3519
DS36
ARAB STUDIES QUARTERLY.* 1979. q. $24 to individuals; institutions $40. Association of Arab-American University Graduates, Inc., Box 408, Normal, IL 61761-0408. TEL 617-484-5483. Ed. Jamal R. Nassar. adv.; bk.rev.; bibl. circ. 2,000. (also avail. in Braille; back issues avail.) Indexed: Amer.Hist.& Life, Bibl.Ling., Hist.Abstr., HR Rep., Mid.East: Abstr.& Ind., P.A.I.S.For.Lang.Ind., P.A.I.S., Per.Islam. (1991-).
—BLDSC (1583.296000); Faxon; UnCover; SWETS; UMI.

915.6   CN   ISSN 0821-6428
ARAB VOICE.* (Text in Arabic, English) 1981. w. Box 791, Brantford, Ont. N3T 5R7, Canada. TEL 416-752-7845. adv.

953.006   FR   ISSN 0983-1509
ARABIES. 1987. m. (11/yr.). 600 F. to individuals; institutions 800 F. Societe de Conseil en Communication, 92 rue Jouffroy, 75017 Paris, France. TEL 47-66-46-00. FAX 43-80-73-62. Ed. Yasser Mawary. adv. contact: Mrs. Hawary. circ. 35,000. (back issues avail.) Document type: newspaper.
   Description: Covers the major political, economic, and financial issues of the Arab world.

915.206 665.5   US   ISSN 1044-1891
AP2
ARAMCO WORLD. 1949. bi-m. free. (Saudi Aramco - Saudi Arabian Oil Company) Aramco Services Company, Box 4534, Houston, TX 77210-4534. TEL 713-423-4426. FAX 713-432-5536. TELEX 6719442 ASC UW. Ed. Robert Arndt. illus.; cum.index. circ. 180,000. Indexed: Geo.Abstr., Ind.Free Per., Key to Econ.Sci., Mid.East: Abstr.& Ind., Numis.Lit., P.A.I.S., Per.Islam. (1991-). Document type: consumer publication.
—BLDSC (1583.700000); Faxon; UnCover.
   Former titles: (until 1987): Aramco World Magazine (ISSN 0146-4132); (until 1968): Aramco World (ISSN 0003-7567)
   Description: Covers the history, geography, culture, economy and natural history of the Arab and Muslim worlds. It is non-political and used as an educational supplement from junior high through university levels.

970.1 320   SW   ISSN 1102-1802
ARAUCO DOCUMENTOS. (Text in Spanish) 1991. q. SEK 50 membership (effective 1991). Asociacion Arauco, Koralg. 56, S-214 70 Malmoe, Sweden.

450   US   ISSN 0271-0730
PQ5902.S5
ARBA SICULA; Sicilian language, folklore and literary review. (Text in English, Sicilian) 1979. 2/yr. $20. Arba Sicula Inc., St. John's University, Jamaica, NY 11439. TEL 718-990-6161. Ed. Gaetano Gipolla. adv.; bk.rev. circ. 2,000. (back issues avail.)

971.3   AT   ISSN 0570-720X
DU122.L3
ARCHIVS. (Text and summaries in Latvian) 1960. a. $10. World Federation of Free Latvians, Karla Zarina Fonds, 3 Dickens St., Elwood 3184, Australia. Ed. Edgars Dunsdorfs. circ. 2,000. (back issues avail.) Indexed: M.L.A. Document type: abstracting/indexing.

AREV. see LITERARY AND POLITICAL REVIEWS

059.91   AG   ISSN 0004-1106
ARGENTINOS LIETUVIU BALSAS/VOZ DE LOS LITUANOS EN LA ARGENTINA. (Text in Lithuanian) 1927. s-m. A10($7) c/o Francisco Ozinskas, J.L. Suarez 5684, Buenos Aires 1439, Argentina. adv.; bk.rev.; abstr.; bibl.; illus.; stat. circ. 2,500.
   Description: Contains articles of interest to the Lithuanian community.

910.3   US
ARIZONA INFORMANT. 1958. w. $20 in state; out of state $22.50. Arizona Informant Publishing Co., Inc., 1746 E. Madison, Ste. 2, Phoenix, AZ 85034. TEL 602-257-9300. Ed. Cloues C. Campbell. adv. circ. 8,000. (tabloid format) Document type: newspaper.

296   US
ARIZONA JEWISH POST. 1946. fortn. $18. Jewish Federation of Southern Arizona, 3812 E. River Rd., Tucson, AZ 85718-6600. TEL 602-529-1500. FAX 602-577-0734. Ed. Sandra R. Heiman. adv. contact: Ann B. Goldfein. bk.rev. circ. 7,000. (tabloid format; also avail. in microfilm; back issues avail.) Document type: newspaper.
   Formerly: Arizona Post.
   Description: Presents in-depth reporting of local, national and international Jewish news.

ARKANSAS LEGIONNAIRE. see CLUBS

378   US
ARKANSAS STATE PRESS. 1941. w. $20. 221 W. 2nd St., Ste. 608, Little Rock, AR 72201-2511. TEL 501-371-9991. FAX 501-371-9128. Pub. Janetta Kearney. adv. circ. 5,000. Document type: newspaper.

ETHNIC INTERESTS

917.309   US   ISSN 0004-2323
ARMENIAN DIGEST. 1970. m. $25. Gulf Publishing Ltd., G.P.O. Box 2754, New York, NY 10116. Ed. Hagop Tankian. adv.; bk.rev.; charts; illus. circ. 25,000.

320   US   ISSN 1050-3471
DS161
ARMENIAN INTERNATIONAL MAGAZINE.* 1990. m. $45. A I M, Inc., Box 10064, Glendale, CA 91207-3064. TEL 818-546-2241. FAX 818-546-2283. (Subscr. to: Box 3296, Manhattan Beach, CA 90266) Ed. Vartan Oskanian. adv.; bk.rev. circ. 30,000. (back issues avail.; reprint service avail.)
   Description: Disseminates news and information about the Republic of Armenia, the Caucasus Region and the worldwide Armenian diaspora.

917.309   US   ISSN 0004-234X
ARMENIAN MIRROR - SPECTATOR. 1932. w. $60. Baikar Association, Inc., 755 Mt. Auburn St., Box 302, Watertown, MA 02272. TEL 617-924-4420. Ed. Ara Kalaydjian. adv.; bk.rev.; illus. circ. 3,327. **Document type:** newspaper.

917.309   US   ISSN 0044-894X
ARMENIAN OBSERVER. 1971. w. $10. Osheen Keshishian, Ed. & Pub., 6646 Hollywood Blvd., Ste. 207, Hollywood, CA 90028. TEL 213-820-6024. adv.; bk.rev.; play rev.; illus. circ. 4,500. (tabloid format) **Document type:** newspaper.

917.309   US   ISSN 0004-2374
ARMENIAN WEEKLY. 1933. w. $60. Hairenik Association, Inc., 80 Bigelow Ave., Watertown, MA 02172. TEL 617-926-3974. Ed. Vahe Habeshian. adv.; bk.rev.; illus. **Document type:** newspaper. —UMI.

942 929   UK   ISSN 0265-2269
ARMSTRONG NEWS. 1973. s-a. membership. Armstrong Clan Association, c/o R.S. Armstrong, Ed., 102 Yorkshire Dr., Pittsburgh, PA 15238. bk.rev. circ. 750. (back issues avail.)

970.1   US
ARROW (ASHLAND). 1937. m. $0.05 per issue. St. Labre Indian School, Ashland, MT 59003. TEL 406-784-2746. circ. 200. (processed)
   Description: Discusses American Indian culture.

ARTS OF AFRICA. see *ART*

ASBAREZ. see *LITERARY AND POLITICAL REVIEWS*

296   AU   ISSN 1016-4987
DS135.G3
ASCHKENAS; Zeitschrift fuer Geschichte und Kultur der Juden. 1991. s-a. S.398. Boehlau Verlag GmbH & Co.KG., Sachsenplatz 4-6, A-1201 Vienna, Austria. TEL 0222-3302427-0. FAX 0222-3302432. TELEX 114506-SPRIW-A. bk.rev. **Indexed:** Amer.Hist.& Life (1992-), Hist.Abstr. (1992-). **Document type:** academic/scholarly publication.

915.506 892.1   IR
ASHUR. (Text in Assyrian) 1969. m. W. Bet-Mansour, Ed. & Pub., Ostad Motahhari Ave., 11-21 Kuhe Nour Ave., Teheran, Iran. TEL 021-622117.

960 327   NR
ASIA - AFRICA FORUM. s-a. $35.95 to individuals (£25.95); institutions $65.95 (£46.95). Obafemi Awolowo University, Department of International Relations, University P.O. Box 1044, Ile-Ife, Osun State, Nigeria. (Subscr. to: College Press, 27 Are Ave., New Bodija, Secretariat, P.O. Box 30678, Ibadan, Nigeria. TEL 234-36-231780) Eds. Jide Owoeye, Wontak Park. bk.rev. **Document type:** academic/scholarly publication.
   Description: Devoted to the study, assessment, research dissemination, and exchange of knowledge and information on all aspects of the past, present, and future analysis of the similarities and differences between Africa and Asia.

917.306   US
THE ASIAN AMERICAN. 1990. irreg. University of California, Riverside, Asian Pacific American Student Programs, 234 Commons, Riverside, CA 92521. Eds. Mitzi Takeuchi, Paiwei Wei. adv.; illus.

917.03 323.4   US   ISSN 1062-1830
E184.06
ASIAN AMERICAN POLICY REVIEW. 1990. a. $10 to individuals; institutions $25; students $5. John F. Kennedy School of Government, Harvard University, 79 John F. Kennedy St., T269, Cambridge, MA 02138. TEL 617-495-1311. FAX 617-496-9027. Ed.Bd. adv.: Page $300. bk.rev. circ. 1,000. **Document type:** academic/scholarly publication.
   Description: Presents analyses of political, cultural and economic issues confronting Asian Pacific Americans in the United States form an academic and practitioner's perspective.

915 917   US   ISSN 1059-2458
E184.06
▼**ASIAN AMERICANS INFORMATION DIRECTORY.** 1992. biennial. $75 (effective Dec. 1993). Gale Research, Inc., 835 Penobscot Bldg., Detroit, MI 48226-4094. TEL 313-961-2242; 800-877-4253. FAX 313-961-6815. Ed. Charles B. Montney. (also avail. in diskette format; magnetic tape) **Document type:** directory.
   Description: Covers organizations, agencies, institutions, programs, publications and services concerned with Asian American nationalities and ethnic groups in the U.S.

052   UK
ASIAN TIMES. 1980. w. £42 (rest of Europe £52; elsewhere £70). Hansib Publishing Ltd., Tower House, 3rd Fl., 139-149 Fonthill Rd., London N4 3HF, England. TEL 071-281-1191. FAX 071-263-9656. (Dist. by: Magazine Marketing Company, Octagon House, White Heart Meadows, Ripley, Woking, Surrey Gu23 6HR. TEL 0483-211222. FAX 0483-211731) Ed. Arif Ali. adv.; bk.rev.; illus. circ. 25,000. (back issues avail.) **Document type:** newspaper.
   Formerly (until 1983): Asian Digest (ISSN 0144-9753)

954.005   CN   ISSN 0707-3380
ASIAN TRIBUNE. 1978. fortn. Can.$8 per no. Perdesi Panjab Publications, 853 Gladstone Ave., Toronto, Ont. M6H 3J7, Canada. Ed. G.S. Chauhan. adv.; bk.rev. circ. 4,000.
   Description: Contains articles of interest to Canadian Indians.

915.06   US   ISSN 0195-2056
ASIANWEEK; the English language journal for the Asian American community. 1979. w. $28. Pan Asia Venture Capital Corporation, 809 Sacramento St., San Francisco, CA 94108. TEL 415-397-0220. FAX 415-397-7258. Ed. Linda Sherry. adv. contact: Jacqueline N. Rondina. bk.rev. circ. 24,000. **Document type:** newspaper.
   ●Also available online. Vendor(s): Mead Data Central, Inc. (Ethnic Newswatch).
   Also available on CD-ROM.
   Description: Covers news, politics, people, the arts and more.

ASIATIC SOCIETY. ANNUAL REPORT. see *GENERAL INTEREST PERIODICALS — India*

301   AT
ASPECTS OF FRANCE. biennial. Aus.$4. Courrier Australien, 506-149 Castlereagh, Sydney, N.S.W. 2000, Australia. Ed. J.P. Sourdin. illus. circ. 15,000.
   Description: Covers a general background on France to enable children doing essays on the country.

296   US
ASSOCIATION FOR THE SOCIAL SCIENTIFIC STUDY OF JEWRY. NEWSLETTER. 2/yr. Association for the Social Scientific Study of Jewry, Research Dept., Philadelphia Geriatric Center, 5301 Old York Rd., Philadelphia, PA 19141. TEL 212-642-2180. Ed. G. Glicksman. **Document type:** newsletter.

ASSOCIATION OF ADVANCED RABBINICAL AND TALMUDIC SCHOOLS. ACCREDITATION COMMISSION. HANDBOOK. see *EDUCATION — Higher Education*

ASSOCIATION OF JEWISH SPONSORED CAMPS. CAMP DIRECTORY. see *SPORTS AND GAMES — Outdoor Life*

917.306   US   ISSN 0066-9717
DK1
ASSOCIATION OF RUSSIAN - AMERICAN SCHOLARS IN THE U S A. TRANSACTIONS/ZAPISKI. (Text in English, Russian) 1967. a. $30 (effective 1994). Association of Russian - American Scholars in the U S A, Inc., Box 180035, Richmond Hill, NY 11418-0035. TEL 518-785-6780. FAX 518-388-6462. Ed. Nadja Jernakoff. bk.rev. circ. 500. **Document type:** academic/scholarly publication.
   Description: Covers Russian culture.

059   UK   ISSN 0144-7122
ASSYRIAN OBSERVER. 1978. q. £10($15) Assyrian Observer Inc , 108 Alderney Rd., Slade Green, Kent DA8 2JD, England. TEL 0322-331711. Ed. Andrious Mama Jotyar. adv.; bk.rev.; illus. circ. 250. **Document type:** academic/scholarly publication.
   Formerly: Assyrian.
   Description: Dedicated to the promotion and preservation of the Assyrian language, heritage, and culture.

917.309   US   ISSN 0004-6051
ASSYRIAN STAR. (Text in Assyrian, English) 1951. bi-m. $20. Assyrian-American National Federation, c/o Executive Secretary, 2935 Jessie Ct., San Jose, CA 95124. TEL 408-723-1646. adv.; bk.rev.; abstr.; illus.; circ. 1,500 (controlled). (also avail. in microform)

ATLANTA BRAVES REVISTA MUNDIAL. see *SPORTS AND GAMES — Ball Games*

296   US   ISSN 0892-3345
ATLANTA JEWISH TIMES. 1925. w. $37 in state; out of state $34. 1575 Northside Dr., N.W., Bldg. 400, Ste. 470, Atlanta, GA 30318. TEL 404-352-2400. FAX 404-355-9388. Ed. Neil Rubin. adv.; bk.rev.; illus. circ. 10,000. (tabloid format; also avail. in microfiche; microfilm from AJP) **Document type:** newspaper.
   Formerly: Southern Israelite (ISSN 0038-4224)
   Description: Contains articles of interest to the Jewish community.

910.03   US
ATLANTA VOICE. 1966. w. $39. Janis Ware, Ed. & Pub., 633 Pryor St., S.W., Atlanta, GA 30312. TEL 404-524-6426. adv.; bk.rev.; film rev.; play rev.; illus. circ. 103,000. (also avail. in microform from BLH) **Document type:** newspaper.
   Description: Contains articles of interest to the black community.

917.309   US   ISSN 0004-7813
AUFBAU/RECONSTRUCTION. (Text in German) 1934. bi-w. $48.50. New World Club, Inc., 2121 Broadway, New York, NY 10023. TEL 212-873-7400. FAX 212-496-5736. Ed. Henry Marx. adv.; bk.rev.; dance rev.; film rev.; play rev.; record rev.; bibl.; charts; illus.; mkt. circ. 30,000. (tabloid format; also avail. in microfilm from AJP,KTO)

AUSTIN MINORITY BUSINESS GUIDE. see *BUSINESS AND ECONOMICS*

AUSTRALASIAN MUSLIM TIMES. see *RELIGIONS AND THEOLOGY — Islamic*

919.4 052   AT   ISSN 1036-4420
GN666
AUSTRALIA. ABORIGINAL AND TORRES STRAIT ISLANDER COMMISSION. ANNUAL REPORT. 1975. a. price varies. Australian Government Publishing Service, G.P.O. Box 84, Canberra, A.C.T. 2601, Australia. TEL 61-6-295-4612. FAX 61-6-295-4500. illus. **Document type:** government publication.
   Formed by the merger of (1975-1990): Australia. Department of Aboriginal Affairs. Report (ISSN 0313-1033); (1981-1990): Australia. Aboriginal Development Commission (ISSN 0810-252X)
   Description: Native Australian interests.

ETHNIC INTERESTS

296   AT   ISSN 0819-0615
DS135.A88
AUSTRALIAN JEWISH HISTORICAL SOCIETY. JOURNAL.
1939. s-a. Aus.$35 (effective 1992). Australian Jewish Historical Society Inc., 166 Castlereagh St., Sydney, N.S.W. 2000, Australia. TEL 261-8407. Ed. S. Rutland. bk.rev.; bibl.; charts; illus.; stat.; cum.index: vol.1-9. circ. 296. (tabloid format) **Indexed:** Amer.Hist.& Life, Aus.P.A.I.S., Hist.Abstr. **Document type:** academic/scholarly publication.
Formerly (until 1986): Australian Jewish Historical Society (ISSN 0004-9360)

296   AT   ISSN 0816-7141
DS135.A88
AUSTRALIAN JEWISH HISTORICAL SOCIETY. NEWSLETTER. 1968. q. Aus.$35 to members. Australian Jewish Historical Society Inc., 166 Castlereagh, Sydney, N.S.W. 2000, Australia. TEL 261-8407. Ed. Bruce Le Bransky. (looseleaf format; back issues avail.) **Document type:** newsletter.

296   AT
AUSTRALIAN JEWISH NEWS (DARLINGHURST). (Includes monthly children's section: Junior Times) 1894. w. Aus.$122. Australian Jewish Press Pty. Limited, c/o Susan Bures, Ed., 146 Darlinghurst Rd., Darlinghurst, N.S.W. 2010, Australia. TEL 02-360-5100. FAX 02-332-4207. adv.; bk.rev.; film rev.; circ. 15,000 (paid). (tabloid format)
Formerly: Australian Jewish Times (ISSN 0725-4385); Incorporates: Melbourne Jewish News & Sydney Jewish News (ISSN 0039-758X)
Description: International, Australian and community news of interest to the Jewish community in Australia or at large.

052   UK   ISSN 0965-3740
AUSTRALIAN NEWS. 1989. m. £12.95 (foreign £25). Outbound Newspapers, 1 Commercial Rd., Eastbourne, E. Sussex BN21 3XQ, England. TEL 0323-412001. FAX 0323-649249. Ed. Steve Hartridge. circ. 20,000. (tabloid format; back issues avail.) **Document type:** newspaper.
Formerly: Australasian News.
Description: Gives potential migrants and travelers to Australia from the United Kingdom information about real estate, employment, education, investing, and lifestyle.

994 301.4   AT   ISSN 0005-0482
AUSTRALIJAS LATVIETIS/AUSTRALIAN LATVIAN; a Latvian newspaper in Australia. (Text in Latvian) 1949. w. Aus.$80. P.O. Box 23, Kew, Vic. 3101, Australia. Ed. Emil Delins. adv.; bk.rev.; charts; illus. (tabloid format)

914.406   AT
AUSZTRALIAI MAGYAR UJSAF. HUNGARIAN WEEKLY. 1950. irreg. Aus.$0.20. c/o F. Antal, Ed., P.O. Box 66, Fitzroy, Vic. 3065, Australia.

317.306 330
AVANCE HISPANO.* (Text in Spanish) 1989. m. $10. 3247 24th St., San Francisco, CA 94110-3927. TEL 415-821-3777. adv. circ. 20,000.
Description: Includes ways to help Hispanic entrepreneurs in the San Francisco Bay area with their businesses, keeps them informed on ways to save money and how to invest it.

AVOTAYNU. see GENEALOGY AND HERALDRY

970.1   CN
AWASIS JOURNAL. irreg. Can.$25. (Indian and Native Education Council) Saskatchewan Teachers' Federation, Box 1108, Saskatoon, SK S7K 3N3, Canada. TEL 306-373-1660.

970.1   CN
AWASIS NEWSLETTER. irreg. Can.$25. (Indian and Native Education Council) Saskatchewan Teachers' Federation, Box 1108, Saskatoon, SK S7K 3N3, Canada. TEL 306-373-1660. **Document type:** newsletter.

296 327   US
AYIN LTZION. 1966. 3/yr. free. Zionist Organization of America, Masada Youth Movement, Jacob and Libby Goodman Z.O.A. House, 4 E. 34th St., New York, NY 10016. TEL 212-481-1500. Ed.Bd. adv.; bk.rev.; charts; illus.; circ. 2,500 (controlled). **Indexed:** Ind.Jew.Per.

300 700   US
AZTLAN: A JOURNAL OF CHICANO STUDIES. 1970. 2/yr. $25 to individuals; institutions $20. University of California, Los Angeles, Chicano Studies Research Center, 405 Hilgard Ave., Los Angeles, CA 90024. TEL 415-825-2642. FAX 213-206-1784. Ed.Bd. bk.rev.; bibl. circ. 800. (also avail. in microform from UMI; back issues avail.; reprint service avail. from UMI) **Indexed:** Acad.Ind., Amer.Hist.& Life, Chic.Per.Ind., Hisp.Amer.Per.Ind., Hist.Abstr., P.A.I.S., Soc.Sci.Ind., Sociol.Abstr.
—BLDSC (1841.800000); Faxon; UnCover; UMI.
Former titles: Aztlan - International Journal of Chicano Studies Research; Aztlan (ISSN 0005-2604)

B & G MAGAZINE; a different point of view. see HOMOSEXUALITY

910.03   SA
B L A C. (Text in Afrikaans and English) irreg. Black Literature and Arts Congress, 1 Long St., Mowbray, South Africa.

B-MEN. see HOMOSEXUALITY

B P A QUARTERLY. (Black Psychiatrists of America) see MEDICAL SCIENCES — Psychiatry And Neurology

910.03   US
B R I C S BRACS;* a quarterly reviewing journal of Afro-American resources. 1977. q. $15. Black Resources Information Coordinating Services, Inc., 614 Howard Ave., Talahassee, FL 32310-6222. TEL 904-576-7522. Ed. Emily A. Copeland. adv.; bk.rev.; film rev.; play rev.; abstr.; bibl.; illus.; index, cum.index.
Description: Contains articles of interest to the black community.

BA PAPYRUS. see GIFTWARE AND TOYS

057   AT
AL-BAIRAK. (Text in Arabic) 3/w. Aus.$90. Foreign Language Publications Pty. Ltd., P.O. Box 146, Broadway, Sydney, N.S.W. 2007, Australia. TEL 02-660-2033. FAX 02-692-0649. Ed. Spyra Smyrnis. adv. contact: George Antoniou. circ. 7,088. (tabloid format) **Document type:** newspaper.

910.3   US
BAKERSFIELD NEWS OBSERVER. 1977. w. $35. Observer Group Newspapers, Box 3624, Bakersfield, CA 93385. TEL 805-324-9466. FAX 805-324-9472. Ed. Joseph L. Coley. adv. contact: Ellen Cleek. bk.rev. circ. 18,000. **Document type:** newspaper.
Description: Black community newspaper.

BALCANICA; storia, cultura, politica. see LITERARY AND POLITICAL REVIEWS

917.106   CN
BALITA. (Text in Filipino) s-m. Kalayaan Media Ltd., 149 Islington Ave., Etobicoke, Ont. M8V 2B8, Canada. TEL 416-252-9954. FAX 416-252-3093. Ed. Ruben J. Cusipag. circ. 9,000.

071   US
BALTIMORE AFRO-AMERICAN. (Supplement avail.: Dawn) 1892. w. $26. Afro-American Co. of Baltimore City, 628 N. Eutaw St., Baltimore, MD 21201. TEL 410-728-8200. FAX 410-383-3213. circ. 32,000. (also avail. in microfilm from UMI; back issues avail.) **Document type:** newspaper.
Description: Contains articles of interest to the African American community.

296   US   ISSN 0005-450X
BALTIMORE JEWISH TIMES. (Supplements avail. bi-m.) 1919. w. $33.60 local; $42 out of state. 2104 N. Charles St., Baltimore, MD 21218. TEL 410-752-3504. FAX 410-852-2370. Ed. Charles A. Buerger. adv.; play rev.; illus. circ. 20,000. (tabloid format) **Document type:** newspaper.

947   GW   ISSN 0177-4859
BALTISCHES JAHRBUCH. 1984. a. DM.20. Baltischer Christlicher Studentenbund, Annabergerstr. 400, 53175 Bonn, Germany. TEL 0228-316244. Ed.Bd. circ. 500.

320 330.9   II
BANGLADESH NEWS. (Text in English) 1974. s-m. free. Ministry of Information & Broadcasting, Publications Division, Patiala House, Tilak Marg, New Delhi 110001, India. Ed. Mohammad A. Hye. illus.

BAPTIST INFORMER. see RELIGIONS AND THEOLOGY — Protestant

BAR-ILAN: ANNUAL OF BAR-ILAN UNIVERSITY. see RELIGIONS AND THEOLOGY — Judaic

296   IS
BATFUTZOT; newsletter on Jewish life in the Diaspora. (Text in Hebrew) 1974. bi-m. free. World Jewish Congress, P.O. Box 4293, Jerusalem 91042, Israel. TEL 972-2-635262. FAX 972-2-635544. Ed. Simona Kedmi. circ. 2,000. **Document type:** newsletter.

914.706   CN   ISSN 0824-4979
BATKIVSHCHYNA/OUR COUNTRY. (Text in Ukrainian) 1952. m. Can.$1 per no. Our Country Publishing Co., Ltd., Box 308, Sta. M, Toronto, Ont. M6S 4T6, Canada. Ed. M. Korolyshyn. adv.
Formerly (until 1955): Nasa Derzava (ISSN 0837-0575)
Description: Contains articles of interest to the Ukranian community.

BAY ZIKH. see LITERATURE

BAYERISCHES JAHRBUCH FUER VOLKSKUNDE. see FOLKLORE

917.306   US
BAYOU TALK; a Cajun creole community newspaper. 1987. m. $13. Jo-Val, Inc., Box 1344, West Covina, CA 91793-1344. TEL 818-856-0403. **Document type:** newspaper.

THE BEAT (LOS ANGELES); Reggae, African, Caribbean, world music. see MUSIC

BEBOP DRAWING CLUB BOOK. see ART

BELARUSKI INSTYTUT NAVUKII MASTATSTVA. ZAPISY/BELARUSAN INSTITUTE OF ARTS AND SCIENCES. ANNALS. see HISTORY — History Of Europe

929   US   ISSN 1046-0462
BELGIAN LACE. 1976. q. $12 (foreign $14). Belgian Researchers, 62073 Fruitdale Ln., La Grande, OR 97850-5312. TEL 503-963-6697. Ed. Leen J. Inghels. bk.rev. circ. 350. (back issues avail.) **Document type:** newsletter.
Description: Covers the history of the Belgian generation in the US.

917.306   US
LA BELLA FIGURA.* (Text in English, Italian) 1988. q. $8. 39 Van Zandt Dr., Sommerville, NJ 08876-4370. Ed. Rose Romano. bk.rev. circ. 100.
Description: Focuses on Italian-American interests.

910.03   US
BERKELEY TRI-CITY POST. 1970. s-w. $80. Alameda Publishing Corp., Box 1350, Oakland, CA 94604. TEL 510-763-1120. FAX 510-763-9670. Ed. Loraine Strain. adv. contact: Jeff Douvel. circ. 20,000. **Document type:** newspaper.

BEST OF HEALTH. see WOMEN'S HEALTH

BETA THETA PI. see COLLEGE AND ALUMNI

960   GW   ISSN 0179-0315
BETO; magazine Africain independent - unabhaengiges Afrikanisches Magazin. (Text in French and German) 1985. q. DM.25. Postfach 1607, D-4000 Dusseldorf, Germany. TEL 0211-673393. Ed. Franklin N'Kangou. (back issues avail.)
Description: Magazine of African culture, politics and arts.

915.4   CN
BHARAT DARSHAN.* s-m. 3127 Purnell Ct., Malton, Mississauga, Ont. L4T 2J7, Canada. TEL 416-767-2726.

ETHNIC INTERESTS

970.1 011   US   ISSN 1064-5144
Z1209.2.N67
BIBLIOGRAPHY OF NATIVE NORTH AMERICANS ON DISC.
a. $795. A B C-Clio, 130 Cremona Dr., Box 1911, Santa Barbara, CA 93116-1911. TEL 805-968-1911. FAX 805-685-9685. Ed.Bd; Pub. Heather Cameron. adv. contact: Laura Wilson. **Document type:** bibliography.
● Available only on CD-ROM.
   Description: Contains over 60,000 citations of journal articles, essays, monographs, dissertations and US government documents related to Native North American history, culture and life.

BIBLIOTHEQUE AFRICAINE. LISTE DES ACQUISITIONS. see *BIBLIOGRAPHIES*

917.309   US   ISSN 0006-209X
BIELARUS; Belarusan newspaper in the Free World. (Text in Byelorussian, English) 1950. m. $25. Belarusan American Association, Inc., c/o Zora Kipel, Ed., Box 310178, Jamaica, NY 11431-0178. adv.; bk.rev.; illus. circ. 2,000. (also avail. in microfilm) **Document type:** newspaper.

917.306   US
BIELARUSKAYA DUMKA. (Text in Byelorussian, English) 1960. s-a. $3. Byelorussian Publishing Association, Box 26, S. River, NJ 08882. Ed. Joseph Leschanka. bk.rev. circ. 1,000.
   Description: Belorussian political, civil, cultural and arts life here and abroad.

914.706   CN   ISSN 0837-0648
BIELARUSKI HOLAS/BYELORUSSIAN VOICE/VOIX BIELARUSIENNE. (Text in Belorussian) 1949. m. Can.$10. Federation of Free Byelorussian Journalists, c/o Marian Ziniak, Ed., 24 Tarlton Rd., Toronto, Ont. M5P 2M4, Canada. TEL 416-488-0048. Ed. M.S. Ziniak. adv.; bk.rev.; illus. circ. 1,000. (tabloid format)

BILINGUAL FAMILY NEWSLETTER. see *LINGUISTICS*

BILINGUAL REVIEW/REVISTA BILINGUE. see *LINGUISTICS*

BIRACIAL CHILD. see *CHILDREN AND YOUTH — About*

910.3   US
BIRMINGHAM TIMES. 1964. w. $25. Box 10503, Birmingham, AL 35202. TEL 205-251-5158. FAX 205-323-2294. Ed. Hollis Wormsby. adv.; bk.rev. circ. 10,000. **Document type:** newspaper.

BITZARON: A QUARTERLY OF HEBREW LETTERS. see *LITERARY AND POLITICAL REVIEWS*

366   AT
BIULETYN/BULLETIN OF POLONIA. (Text in Polish) 1952. m. Aus.$2 per no. Polonia-Polish Association of Queensland, P.O. Box 1808, Brisbane, Qld. 4001, Australia. TEL 07-233-6169. Ed. Janusz Rygielski. adv.; bk.rev. circ. 400.

BLAC-TRESS. see *BEAUTY CULTURE*

910.03   US   ISSN 0882-6595
BLACFAX; journal of Black history and opinion. 1982. q. $8. Blacfax Publications, Box 803, College Sta., New York, NY 10030. TEL 212-234-4115. Ed. Janet Hughes. adv.; bk.rev.; illus. circ. 400.
   Description: Presents little-known information about African-American culture and history. Provides profiles of prominent blacks, including their personal reflections and memoirs.

910.03   US
BLACK AMERICAN HISTORY RHYME; a newsletter. 1991. a. $3. Sought After Publications, c/o Prosperity & Profits Unlimited, Box 416, Denver, CO 80201-0416. TEL 303-575-5676. Ed. A. Doyle. circ. 1,500. (looseleaf format; back issues avail.) **Document type:** newsletter.

910.03   US   ISSN 1048-6992
E185.5
BLACK AMERICANS. 1990. a. $39.95 paperbound; $49.95 library edition. Numbers & Concepts, 2525 Arapaho Ave., Ste. E4-221, Boulder, CO 80302. TEL 303-444-3462. **Document type:** monographic series.
   Description: Statistical summary of information published by the U.S. government about Black Americans.

910.03   US   ISSN 1045-8050
E185.5
BLACK AMERICANS INFORMATION DIRECTORY (YEAR). 1989. irreg. $75. Gale Research Inc., 835 Penobscot Bldg., Detroit, MI 48226. TEL 800-877-4253. FAX 313-961-6083. TELEX 810-221-7086. Ed. Darren L. Smith.
   Description: Provides reference to approximately 4,700 organizations, agencies, institutions, programs, and publications relating to African American life and culture.

BLACK ARTS ANNUAL. see *ART*

BLACK ARTS NEW YORK. see *ART*

BLACK AUTHORS & PUBLISHED WRITERS DIRECTORY. see *BIOGRAPHY*

BLACK BEAUTY HANDBOOK. see *BEAUTY CULTURE*

910.03   US   ISSN 1053-3893
BLACK BOTTOMLINE; a magazine of Black progress. 1990. bi-m. $15.20. Black BottomLine, Inc., 1503 E. Kildare St., Lancaster, CA 93535-9975. TEL 805-948-6983. Ed. John M. Ward. circ. 2,000.
   Description: Promotes black self-pride and economic self-reliance.

BLACK CAMERA. see *MOTION PICTURES*

BLACK CHILD ADVOCATE. see *CHILDREN AND YOUTH — About*

BLACK COLLEGIAN; the career and self-development magazine for African-American. see *COLLEGE AND ALUMNI*

BLACK CONGRESSIONAL MONITOR; reporting on activities of the US Congress and executive departments and agencies; initiatives of particular interest and benefit to African Americans and by African American members of Congress. see *POLITICAL SCIENCE*

BLACK CONVENTION MAGAZINE. see *MEETINGS AND CONGRESSES*

BLACK DATA PROCESSING ASSOCIATES. DATA NEWS. see *COMPUTERS — Electronic Data Processing*

BLACK DATA PROCESSING ASSOCIATES. NATIONAL JOURNAL. see *COMPUTERS — Electronic Data Processing*

BLACK ELECTED OFFICIALS; a national roster. see *PUBLIC ADMINISTRATION*

910.03   US   ISSN 0885-9647
BLACK ELEGANCE. 1986. 9/yr. $16.99. Starlog Group, Inc., 475 Park Ave. S., New York, NY 10016. TEL 212-689-2830. FAX 212-889-7933. Ed. Sharyn Skeeter. **Document type:** consumer publication.
   Description: For the upscale Black woman who strives for achievement and quality in her career and life-style. Highlights the dignity and self-esteem of Black women.

331.1   US   ISSN 1053-704X
BLACK EMPLOYMENT AND EDUCATION. 1990. q. $15. Hamdani, Inc., 2625 Piedmont Rd., Ste. 56-282, Atlanta, GA 30324. TEL 404-469-5891. Ed. S. Barry Hamdani. adv.; bk.rev.; circ. 30,000 (paid); 120,000 (controlled). **Document type:** trade publication.
   Description: Addresses career opportunities here and abroad and includes people and company profiles. Specializes in careers in business and healthcare administration.

BLACK ENTERPRISE. see *BUSINESS AND ECONOMICS*

BLACK FACE. see *MOTION PICTURES*

910.03   US   ISSN 0279-0718
BLACK FAMILY. 1980. m. $30 (foreign $45). Black Family Publishing, Box 1046, Herndon, VA 22070-1046. TEL 202-628-7479. Ed. Frank C. Kent. adv.; bk.rev.; cum.index: 1980-1987. circ. 201,877. (back issues avail.)

BLACK FILM REVIEW. see *MOTION PICTURES*

910.03 613.7   US   ISSN 1042-329X
BLACK HEALTH. 1988. q. $10 to individuals; institutions $15. Black Health, Inc., Box 4095, Madison, CT 06443-4000. TEL 203-431-3454. Ed. Bonnie Maynard. adv. circ. 25,000.
   Description: Focuses on black health issues.

BLACK HISTORY NEWS & NOTES. see *HISTORY — History Of North And South America*

BLACK ISSUES IN HIGHER EDUCATION. see *EDUCATION — Higher Education*

BLACK LACE. see *HOMOSEXUALITY*

910.03 286   US
BLACK MINISTRIES. a. Episcopal Commission for Black Ministries, Executive Council, 815 Second Ave., New York, NY 10C17. TEL 212-867-8400.

BLACK MUSIC RESEARCH JOURNAL. see *MUSIC*

910.03   US
BLACK NEW YORK MAGAZINE. 1987. q. $9. Mandingo Communications, Box 7620, Corona, NY 11373. TEL 718-260-9820. Ed. C. Rapulu Okeya.

BLACK NEWS DIGEST. see *BUSINESS AND ECONOMICS — Labor And Industrial Relations*

BLACK NEWSPAPER INDEX. see *ETHNIC INTERESTS — Abstracting, Bibliographies, Statistics*

BLACK ORPHEUS; journal of African and Afro-American literature. see *LITERATURE*

BLACK PAGES. see *BUSINESS AND ECONOMICS — Trade And Industrial Directories*

910.03
BLACK PAGES PAMPHLET SERIES. 1973. irreg. $1.50 per copy. Institute of Positive Education, 7524 S. Cottage Grove Ave., Chicago, IL 60619. TEL 312-651-0700. Ed. Haki Madhubuti. bibl.; illus. circ. 5,000.

BLACK PROFESSIONAL; for engineering, business, technology, and health professionals. see *ENGINEERING*

910.03   US   ISSN 0882-0643
E185.5
BLACK RESOURCE GUIDE; a national Black directory. 1981. a. $69.95. Black Resource Guide Inc., 501 Oneida Pl., N.W., Washington, DC 20011. TEL 202-291-4373. Ed. R. Benjamin Johnson. bk.rev. circ. 10,000 **Document type:** directory.
   Description: Features over 4,500 listings in 54 major categories of Black Americans.

BLACK SACRED MUSIC; a journal of theomusicology. see *MUSIC*

960   US   ISSN 0006-4246
E185.5
BLACK SCHOLAR; journal of black studies and research. 1969. q. $30 to individuals; institutions $50. Black World Foundation, Box 2869, Oakland, CA 94609. TEL 510-547-6633. Ed. Robert Chrisman. adv.; bk.rev.; stat.; index. circ. 10,000. (also avail. in microform from UMI,MIM; reprint service avail. from UMI) **Indexed:** Abstr.Engl.Stud., Acad.Ind., Alt.Press Ind., Amer.Hist.& Life, Bk.Rev.Ind. (1977-), C.I.J.E., Child.Bk.Rev.Ind. (1977-), Cont.Pg.Educ., Curr.Cont.Africa, Curr.Cont., Hist.Abstr., Lang.& Lang.Behav.Abstr., Left Ind. (1982-), P.A.I.S., Soc.Sci.Ind., Soc.Work Res.& Abstr., SSCI, Stud.Wom.Abstr. **Document type:** academic/scholarly publication.
   —BLDSC (2107.2000C0); Faxon; UnCover; UMI.
   Description: For those interested in the theory and practice of the Black civil rights movement. Includes some of the most struggle-tempered veterans as well as younger activists and intellectuals.

910.03   US
BLACK SPOTS. 1984. q. $6 Black Spots Publishing, 1283 S. LaBrea Ave., Ste. 304, Los Angeles, CA 90019. TEL 213-938-0101. Ed. Cynthia E. Griffin. adv.; circ. 10,000 (contrclled). **Document type:** consumer publication.
   Description: Life-style magazine focusing on the African, African-American, Afro-Latin and Caribbean cultures.

ETHNIC INTERESTS

301.45   US
BLACK STUDIES SERIES. irreg., latest 1989. $16.95. Edward-Lynne Jones & Associates, Inc., 5517 17th Ave. N.E., Seattle, WA 98105. TEL 206-524-9604. Ed. E.L. Jones. (reprint service avail. from UMI) **Indexed:** M.L.A. **Document type:** monographic series, academic/scholarly publication.

910.03   US
BLACK VOICE NEWS. 1972. w. $32.33. Brown Publishing Company, Box 1581, Riverside, CA 92502. TEL 714-682-6070. FAX 714-889-0506. Ed. Billy Johnson. adv.; bk.rev.; film rev.; play rev. circ. 7,500. (also avail. in microfilm from LIB; reprint service avail.) **Document type:** newspaper.
   Description: Focuses on the African-American community.

910.03 800   US
BLACK WRITER. Variant title: Black Writer Magazine. 1970. q. $16. International Black Writers Conference, Box 1030, Chicago, IL 60690. TEL 312-924-3818. Ed. Mildred Johnson. adv. contact: Rachel McMillan. bk.rev.; abstr.; bibl.; charts; film rev.; illus.; pat.; play rev.; stat.; index. circ. 5,000. **Document type:** newsletter.
   Formerly (until 1979): Black Writers' News.
   Description: Publishes poetry, articles, short fiction, writing tips and techniques for writers.

BLACKFIRE. see *HOMOSEXUALITY*

361 353   US
BLACKS IN GOVERNMENT - NEWS.* q. (free to members). Blacks in Government, 1820 11th St., N.W., Washington, DC 20002. TEL 202-667-3280.
   Description: Geared toward employees at all levels of government concerned with the status and future of African-Americans in government.

BLACKS IN LAW ENFORCEMENT; a living tribute to Black history. see *CRIMINOLOGY AND LAW ENFORCEMENT*

296   PL   ISSN 0006-470X
DS135.P6
BLETER FAR GESZICHTE. (Text in Yiddish; summaries in English, Polish) 1948. a. $20. Zydowski Instytut Historyczny w Polsce, Ul. Tlomackie 3-5, 00-090 Warsaw, Poland. TEL 48-22-279221. FAX 48-22-278372. Ed. R. Sakowska. adv.; bk.rev.; charts; illus.; cum.index. circ. 410. **Indexed:** Amer.Hist.& Life, Hist.Abstr. **Document type:** academic/scholarly publication.
   Description: Covers Jewish interests.

BLK; the national black lesbian and gay newsmagazine. see *HOMOSEXUALITY*

BLUSHING BRIDE. see *MATRIMONY*

296   US   ISSN 0279-3415
HS2228.B4
B'NAI B'RITH INTERNATIONAL JEWISH MONTHLY. 1886. 10/yr. $12. B'nai B'rith International, 1640 Rhode Island Ave., N.W., Washington, DC 20036. TEL 202-857-6645. FAX 202-296-1092. Ed. Jeff Rubin. adv.; bk.rev.; play rev.; illus.; index. circ. 170,000. (also avail. in microform from UMI; back issues avail.) **Indexed:** Amer.Bibl.Slavic & E.Eur.Stud, Ind.Jew.Per., Mid.East: Abstr.& Ind.
   —UMI.
   Formerly: National Jewish Monthly (ISSN 0027-9552).
   Description: Explores the social, cultural, historical and political issues that affect the Jewish community in the United States and abroad.

296   US   ISSN 0006-5277
B'NAI B'RITH MESSENGER.* 1897. w. $28. B'nai B'rith Messenger, Inc., Box 35915, Los Angeles, CA 90035-0915. TEL 213-380-5000. Ed. Rabbi Yale B. Butler. adv.; bk.rev.; film rev.; play rev.; illus. circ. 67,000. (tabloid format; also avail. in microfilm from AJP,KTO)

917.206   US
▼**BOLETIN INFORMATIVO DE LA NACION TAINA.** (Text in English, Spanish) 1993. m. Box 883, New York, NY 10025. TEL 212-866-4573. (And: Res. Jaguas C5, Ciales, PR 00638).

BOLLETTINO DELL'ATLANTE LINGUISTICO ITALIANO. see *LINGUISTICS*

296   US
BORO PARK VOICE/KOL BORO PARK; serving the Boro Park & Flatbush communities. 1976. m. Council of Jewish Organizations of Boro Park, 4616 13th Ave., Brooklyn, NY 11219. TEL 718-436-1800. FAX 718-972-7254. Ed. Abraham Friedlander. adv.; bk.rev. circ. 40,000.

296   US   ISSN 8750-1961
BOSTON JEWISH TIMES. 1947. bi-w. $12. Jewish Times Publishing Company of New England, 169 Norfolk Ave., Boston, MA 02119. TEL 617-442-9680. Ed. Sten Lukin. adv. contact: Sarabeth Lukin. bk.rev.; illus. circ. 11,500. (tabloid format; also avail. in microform) **Document type:** newspaper.
   Formerly: Jewish Times (Boston) (ISSN 0021-6771)

BOULITE. see *FOLKLORE*

917.106 382   US   ISSN 0741-0298
BRASILIANS JOURNAL. (Text in English, Portuguese) 1972. m. $20. Brasilians Press & Publications, Box 985, New York, NY 10185. TEL 212-382-1630. FAX 212-719-4142. TELEX 261024 BACC-UR. Ed. Edilberto Mendes. circ. 45,000. (tabloid format; back issues avail.)

971 301.4   CN   ISSN 0006-9264
BRATSTVO/FRATERNITY; casopis za jacanje nacionalno-politickog jedinstva Srba pravoslavnih i muslimana. (Text in English and Serbian) 1954. m. Can.$35. 1 Secroft Cres., North York, ON M3N 1R5, Canada. TEL 416-769-7181. FAX 416-850-4401. Ed. William DuRovic. adv.; bk.rev.; illus. circ. 2,200.

943.006   GW
BRAUNAUER RUNDBRIEF. 1946. bi-m. DM.36. Benediktinerabtei Braunau, 93352 Rohr, Germany. TEL 08783-96000. FAX 08783-960022. Ed. P. Benedikt Gleissner. adv.; bk.rev. circ. 3,000. (back issues avail.) **Document type:** newsletter.
   Description: Newsletter for expellees from Eastern Bohemia.

BRAVO; the poet's magazine. see *LITERATURE — Poetry*

918.106   BL
BRAZIL. FUNDACAO NACIONAL DO INDIO. INFORMATIVO.* no.8, 1973. q. Fundacao Nacional do Indio, Departamento de Comunicacao Social, SEP Quadra 702 Sul, Edificio Lex, 3 andar, sala 3, CEP 70330 Brasilia, Brazil.

BRAZIL. MUSEU DO INDIO. BOLETIM. DOCUMENTACAO. see *ANTHROPOLOGY*

BRIDES TODAY. see *MATRIMONY*

917.306 398   US   ISSN 0741-1200
E184.S19
BRIDGE (SALEM). 1978. s-a. $15. Danish American Heritage Society, 1132 Newport Dr., S.E., Salem, OR 97306. TEL 503-588-1331. (Subscr. to: 132 N. 132nd St., Ste. 301, Seattle, WA 98133) Ed. Egon Bodtker. bk.rev.; cum.index. circ. 700. (back issues avail.) **Document type:** academic/scholarly publication.
   Description: Focuses on Danish immigration history, including diaries, articles, books, fiction and poetry by and about immigrants.

914.706   US   ISSN 8750-8028
BRIDGES; Lithuanian-American news journal. Key Title: Bridges (Brooklyn). vol.9, 1985. 11/yr. $7. Lithuanian-American Community, U.S.A., Inc., 2715 E. Allegheny Ave., Philadelphia, PA 19134. TEL 215-739-9353. FAX 215-739-6587. Ed. Rimantas Stirbys. circ. 1,800. **Document type:** newsletter.

BRIDGES: A JOURNAL FOR JEWISH FEMINISTS AND OUR FRIENDS. see *WOMEN'S STUDIES*

BRIEFING: WEEKLY INSIDE PERSPECTIVE ON TURKISH POLITICAL, ECONOMIC AND BUSINESS AFFAIRS. see *POLITICAL SCIENCE*

994   GW
BRIVAIS VARDS; latviesu preses biedribas bileteiu. 1971. q. E.-M.-Arndt-Str. 120, 38304 Wolfenbüttel, Germany. TEL 053-31-41207. Ed. Arthur Klimanis.

296   US
BROWARD JEWISH WORLD. 1986. w. $24. Jewish Media Group, 3550 Biscayne Blvd., Third Fl., Miami, FL 33137-3845. TEL 305-576-9500. FAX 305-573-9551. Ed. Gloria Katz. adv.; bk.rev. circ. 35,000.
   Description: Serves the Jewish community of Broward County, Florida.

910.03   US   ISSN 1065-1462
BROWARD TIMES. (Supplements avail: Caribbean Focus, Business Monthly) 1990. w. $35. Broward Times, Inc., 1001 W. Cypress Creek Rd., Ste. 111, Fort Lauderdale, FL 33309-1947. Pub. Keith A. Clayborne. bk.rev.; circ. 25,000 (controlled). **Document type:** newspaper.

296   US
BROWN UNIVERSITY. PROGRAM IN JUDAIC STUDIES. ANNUAL REPORT. 1983. a. free. Brown University, Program in Judaic Studies, 163 George St., Providence, RI 02912-1826. TEL 401-863-3900. FAX 401-863-3938. Ed. Ernest S. Frerichs. circ. 2,500. **Document type:** academic/scholarly publication.

BRUCKA; 'n brug na buite. see *GENERAL INTEREST PERIODICALS — South Africa*

917.306   US
BUCHANAN BANNER. 1976. q. membership. Clan Buchanan Society, 466 Century Vista Dr., Arnold, MD 21012. TEL 301-544-0290. Ed. Louis B. McCaslin, Jr. adv.; bk.rev. circ. 2,000. (looseleaf format)

910.03 051   US   ISSN 0045-3285
BUCKEYE REVIEW. 1937. w. $15. Williams Publishing Co., 626 Belmont Ave., Youngstown, OH 44502. TEL 216-743-2250. Ed. Crystal Ann Williams. adv.; bk.rev. circ. 20,000. (tabloid format)
   Description: Covers African-American interests.

052   HU   ISSN 1215-0959
BUDAPEST WEEK; Hungary's international weekly. (Text in English) 1991. w. 2958 Ft.($120) (effective 1994). CitiMedia Kft., Bajcsy-Zsilinszky ut 63, 1065 Budapest, Hungary. TEL 361-111-8491. FAX 361-112-6303. (Subscr. to: Central European Press Services, 4 Watchfield St., Sutton Court Rd., London SW4 4NA, England) Ed. Adam LeBor. adv.: B&W page $1750, color page $2190; adv. contact: Betty Stein. circ. 20,000. **Document type:** newspaper.
   Description: Covers news and entertainment in a western style for the English-speaking community in Hungary.

BUENA SALUD. see *PHYSICAL FITNESS AND HYGIENE*

910.03   US
BUFFALO CRITERION. 1925. w. $14.95 (outside Buffalo $19.95). Frank E. Merriweather, Ed. & Pub., 623-25 William St., Buffalo, NY 14206. TEL 716-882-9570. FAX 716-882-9570. circ. 12,000. **Document type:** newspaper.

910.03   US
BUFFALO FINE PRINT NEWS. 1971. w. free. Fine Print News, 806 Fillmore Ave., Buffalo, NY 14212. TEL 716-855-3810. FAX 716-855-3810. Ed. Carolyn C. Fleming. adv.; bk.rev. circ. 32,000. (tabloid format) **Document type:** newspaper.

296   US
BUFFALO JEWISH REVIEW. Also known as: Jewish Review. 1920. w. $20. 15 E. Mohawk St., Buffalo, NY 14203. TEL 716-854-2192. FAX 716-854-2198. Ed. Harlan Abbey. adv.; bk.rev.; film rev.; illus. circ. 4,000 (controlled). (also avail. in microfilm from AJP) **Document type:** directory.

BUILDING CONCERNS. see *BUILDING AND CONSTRUCTION*

917.306   US
BUILDINGBLOCKS. 1980. q. National Center for Urban Ethnic Affairs, Box 20 Cardinal Sta., Washington, DC 20064. TEL 202-232-3600. circ. 17,500.

910.03   US
THE BULLETIN. 1959. w. $26. 2490 Martin Luther King Jr. Way, Sarasota, FL 34230. TEL 813-953-9990. FAX 813-955-5300. Ed. Richard Wright; Pub. Fred L. Bacon. adv. contact: Ralph Pompey. illus. circ. 18,000. **Document type:** newspaper.

ETHNIC INTERESTS

BULLETIN DE L'AFRIQUE NOIRE. see *POLITICAL SCIENCE*

059.8   UK   ISSN 0267-3517
BULLETIN OF FORTHCOMING ANGLO-HELLENIC EVENTS. 1984. bi-m. £50. Kyriakos H. Metaxas, Ed. & Pub., 35 Burnham Court, Moscow Rd., London W2 4SW, England. TEL 071-727-1121. FAX 071-727-1444. TELEX 298839-GRKGZT-G. adv. circ. 12,000.
    Description: Covers all aspects of British literary events of an Anglo-Hellenic nature.

296 956.940   AU
DER BUND. 1966. 6/yr. Bund werktaetiger Juden-Poale Zion, Desider-Friedmann-Platz 1, A-1010 Vienna, Austria. Ed. Ernst M. Stern. adv.; bk.rev. circ. 5,000.

917.306   US
BYELORUSSIAN YOUTH.* 1972. q. $4. Byelorussian-American Youth Organization, Box 1123, New Brunswick, NJ 08903. Ed. Raisa Stankievic. bk.rev.; bibl.; illus. circ. 500.

917.306 323.4   US
C A A NEWSLETTER (SAN FRANCISCO). 1969. q. membership. Chinese for Affirmative Action, 17 Walter U. Lum Place, San Francisco, CA 94108. TEL 415-274-6750. FAX 415-397-8770. Ed. Mimi Kuo. bibl.; illus. circ. 3,000. *Document type:* newsletter.

C A A S SPECIAL PUBLICATION SERIES. (Center for Afro-American Studies) see *SOCIAL SCIENCES: COMPREHENSIVE WORKS*

C B M R DIGEST. (Center for Black Music Research) see *MUSIC*

C B M R MONOGRAPHS. (Center for Black Music Research) see *MUSIC*

914.5   CN
C I A O MAGAZINE. m. C I A O Publishing Co., 1081 Bas de l'Assomption Nord, Ville de l'Assomption, Que. J0K 1G0, Canada. TEL 514-589-7195. FAX 514-589-4485.

910.03   GO
C I C I B A LETTRE D'INFORMATION. 1986. bi-m. 30 Fr.CFA($6) C I C I B A, Service des Productions Culturelles, B.P. 770, Libreville, Gabon. TEL 70-09-52. Ed. Simao Souindoula. (back issues avail.)

C J F ENDOWMENT REVIEW. (Council of Jewish Federations, Inc.) see *SOCIAL SERVICES AND WELFARE*

296 301   US   ISSN 0887-1639
C M J S CENTERPIECES. 1985. a. free. Cohen Center for Modern Jewish Studies, Brandeis University, Waltham, MA 02254. TEL 617-736-2063. FAX 617-736-2070. Ed. Sylvia Barack Fishman. bk.rev.; charts; stat. circ. 8,500.

C O R E MAGAZINE. (Congress of Racial Equality) see *POLITICAL SCIENCE — Civil Rights*

917.309   US
C S A JOURNAL. (Czechoslovak Society of America) 1891. m. $12. (C S A Fraternal Life) Cicero-Berwyn Press, 2701 S. Harlem Ave., Berwyn, IL 60402. Ed. Marie V. Jensen. adv.; bk.rev.; charts; illus.; circ. 11,000 (controlled).

910.03   US
CALIFORNIA ADVOCATE NEWSPAPER. 1967. w. $15. c/o Lesly H. Kimber, Box 11826, Fresno, CA 93775. TEL 209-268-0941. Ed. Pauline Kimber. adv.; bk.rev.; illus. circ. 12,500. *Document type:* newspaper.
    Description: Black interests.

917.309   US   ISSN 0008-0950
CALIFORNIA COURIER. 1958. w. $39. Harut Sassounian, Ed. & Pub., Box 5390, Glendale, CA 91221-5390. TEL 818-409-0949. FAX 818-500-7372. adv.; bk.rev.; circ. 3,000 (paid). *Document type:* newspaper.

053.1   US   ISSN 0890-1473
CALIFORNIA STAATS-ZEITUNG. (Text in German) 1891. w. $22 in California; elsewhere $35. 1201 N. Alvarado St., Box 26308, Los Angeles, CA 90026-0308. TEL 213-413-5500. FAX 213-413-5469. Ed. Peter Teichmann. adv.; bk.rev.; play rev.; charts; illus. circ. 18,000. *Document type:* newspaper.
    Description: German interests.

917.306   US   ISSN 0882-2719
CALIFORNIA VECKOBLAD. (Text in English, Swedish) 1910. s-m. $15. 10921 Paramount Blvd., Downey, CA 90241. TEL 310-862-4880. Ed. Mary Hendricks. circ. 1,500. (also avail. in microfilm) *Document type:* newspaper.

910.03   US   ISSN 0745-7057
CALIFORNIA VOICE; the weekender. 1919. w. $10. Reporter Publishing Co. (San Francisco), 1366 Turk St., San Francisco, CA 94115. TEL 415-931-5778. FAX 415-931-0214. Ed. Ruth Love. adv. contact: Jack Kisbey. circ. 37,263. *Document type:* newspaper.
    Description: Magazine for the Black community.

917.109   US   ISSN 0744-8600
CALIFORNIAI MAGYARSAG/CALIFORNIA HUNGARIANS WEEKLY. (Text in Hungarian) 1922. w. $24. 207 S. Western Ave., Ste. 201, Los Angeles, CA 90004. TEL 213-463-3473. FAX 213-384-7642. Ed. Maria Fenyes. adv.; bk.rev.; circ. 7,500. (also avail. in microform) *Document type:* newspaper.

917.309   US   ISSN 0045-4036
CALL AND POST. 1919. w. $25. P W Publishing Co., Inc., 1949 E. 105th St., Cleveland, OH 44106. TEL 216-791-7600. Ed. Andre Bustamente. adv.; bk.rev. circ. 42,000. (also avail. in microfilm from BLH) *Document type:* newspaper.

CALLALOO; a journal of African-American and African arts and letters. see *LITERATURE*

917.306   US
CALLING ALL SCOTS. 1970. q. $25 including membership. American Scottish Foundation, Inc., Box 537, Lenox Hill Sta., New York, NY 10021. TEL 212-988-4468. Ed. Charles H. Haws. adv.; bk.rev. circ. 3,000. (back issues avail.)

970   US
CALUMET.* 1976. bi-m. United South & Eastern Tribes, Inc., 711 Stewarts Ferry Pike, Ste. 100, Nashville, TN 37214-2634. Ed. Rex Evans. circ. 3,500. (back issues avail.)
    Description: American Indian interests.

917.306   US
CAMBIO!; Hispanic bilingual magazine. (Text in English and Spanish) 1988. bi-w. $30. L.M. Ortiz & Associates, Inc., Box 33904, Phoenix, AZ 85067-3904. TEL 602-395-9111. Ed. Luis Ortiz. adv. circ. 20,000.
    Description: Provides nonpartisan analysis of problems affecting the Hispanic community.

917.309   US   ISSN 0022-8206
CAMPANA. 1917. s-m. $20. Greek-American Review, 30-96 42nd St., Astoria, NY 11103. TEL 718-278-3014. FAX 718-278-3023. Ed. Costas Athanasiades. adv.; bk.rev.; film rev.; music rev.; play rev.; rec.rev.; mkt.; stat. circ. 9,500. (tabloid format) *Document type:* newspaper.

CANADA. SPECIAL COMMITTEE ON INDIAN SELF-GOVERNMENT. PROCEEDINGS AND EVIDENCE. MINUTES. see *POLITICAL SCIENCE*

915.306   CN   ISSN 0706-7909
CANADA & ARAB WORLD. (Text in Arabic and English) 1975. bi-m. Can.$48 to individuals; institutions Can.$96. Allam Arabic Publishing & Advertising Co., 511 Queen St.E., Toronto, Ont. M5A 1V1, Canada. TEL 416-362-0304. adv.
    Description: Newspaper for Arabs in Ottawa, Ontario.

915.4   CN
CANADA DARPAN. (Text in Punjabi) w. Darpan International Publications, 11913-72A Ave., Delta, B.C. V4C 1B4, Canada. adv.

058.7   CN   ISSN 0045-4249
CANADA-SVENSKEN/SWEDISH CANADIAN. (Text in Swedish) 1960. s-m. Can.$30. Scandinavian News Co., 65 Joanna Dr., Scarborough, Ont. M1R 4J2, Canada. TEL 416-444-2983. Ed. T. Wiik. adv.; bk.rev. circ. 1,852. (tabloid format)

917.106   CN
CANADA TIMES.* (Text in Japanese) s-w. 312 Dundas St., W., Toronto, ON M5T 1G5, Canada. TEL 416-593-2777. FAX 416-593-9769. Ed. Harry Taba. circ. 4,000.

917.109   CN   ISSN 0008-2775
CANADAN UUTISET. (Text in English, Finnish) 1915. w. Can.$51 (foreign Can.$80)(typically set in Nov.); newsstand price: Can.$1.25. Finnews Ltd., 218 Wilson St., Thunder Bay, ON P7B 1M8, Canada. TEL 807-344-1611. FAX 807-344-1879. Ed. Matti Nummelin. adv.: page Can.$882; adv. contact: Helena Itkonen. bk.rev.; illus. circ. 2,100. cols./p.: 6; pp./issue: 16. (tabloid format; also avail. in microfilm; back issues avail.) *Document type:* newspaper.
    Description: Local and international news and sports, community services, reader viewpoints.

915.306   CN
CANADIAN ARAB WORLD REVIEW/REVUE DU MONDE ARABE. (Text in Arabic, English, and French) 1969. m. Can.$20. 10935 Jeanne Mance St., Montreal, Que. H3L 3C7, Canada. FAX 514-332-1607. Ed. R.R. Kneider. adv.; bk.rev. circ. 5,000.
    Description: Brings about a Canadian-Arab exchange of ideas and culture.

CANADIAN ASSOCIATION OF AFRICAN STUDIES. NEWSLETTER/ASSOCIATION CANADIENNE DES ETUDES AFRICAINES. BULLETIN. see *EDUCATION — Higher Education*

917.106   CN   ISSN 0008-3496
CANADIAN ETHNIC STUDIES. 1969. 3/yr. Can.$35 to individuals; institutions Can.$40; students $15. Canadian Ethnic Studies Association, Research Centre for Canadian Ethnic Studies, University of Calgary, 2500 University Dr., Calgary, AB T2N 1N4, Canada. TEL 403-220-7257. FAX 403-282-8606. Eds. James Frideres, A.W. Rasporich. adv.; bk.rev. circ. 1,000. (also avail. in microfilm from MMI,MML) *Indexed:* A.I.C.P., Amer.Hist.& Life, Can.Per.Ind., Can.Wom.Per.Ind., Hist.Abstr., Per.Islam. (1992-), Refug.Abstr. *Document type:* academic/scholarly publication.
—BLDSC (3022.060000); UnCover. **CCC.**
    Description: Publishes scholarly articles, research notes and bibliographic information.

917.106   CN   ISSN 0315-8705
F1035.A1
CANADIAN ETHNIC STUDIES ASSOCIATION. BULLETIN/SOCIETE CANADIENNE D'ETUDES ETHNIQUES. BULLETIN. (Text in English, French) 1974. 2/yr. Car.$45 individual membership; institutions $55; students $15. Canadian Ethnic Studies Association, Centre for Ukrainian Canadian Studies, University of Manitoba, Winnipeg, MB, Canada. bk.rev.; bibl. circ. 1,000. *Indexed:* Can.Rev.Comp.Lit., M.L.A., Mult.Ed.Abstr., Sp.Ed.Needs Abstr. *Document type:* bulletin.
—BLDSC (2434.160000).
    Description: Provides information on the Association, current developments in ethnic studies, research projects, forthcoming meetings, conferences and publications.

059.94   CN
CANADIAN FREE PRESS. Hungarian edition: Magyar Naplo. 1966. w. Can.$15. C F P Publications, Ltd., P.O. Box 771, Station "A", Toronto, ON M5W 1G3, Canada. TEL 416-921-6161. FAX 416-283-2357. Ed. V. Szabo. adv. bk.rev. circ. 85,000. (tabloid format)

296   CN   ISSN 0576-5528
F1035.J5
CANADIAN JEWISH ARCHIVES (NEW SERIES). 1955; N.S. 1974. irreg. price varies. Canadian Jewish Congress, 1590 Dr. Penfield Ave., Montreal, PQ H3G 1C5, Canada. TEL 514-931-7531. FAX 514-931-5408. Ed. David Rome. circ. 200. (back issues avail.)

ETHNIC INTERESTS

296   CN   ISSN 0824-8907
CANADIAN JEWISH CONGRESS. NATIONAL ARCHIVES NEWSLETTER. (Text in English and French) 1984. s-a. free. Canadian Jewish Congress, 1590 Dr. Penfield Ave., Montreal, PQ H3G 1C5, Canada. TEL 514-931-7531. FAX 514-931-5408. Ed. Janice Rosen. bibl. circ. 800. **Document type:** newsletter.

320.9 296   CN   ISSN 0706-280X
DS101
CANADIAN JEWISH HERALD. 1977. irreg. price varies. Dawn Publishing Co. Ltd., 17 Anselme Lavigne Blvd., Dollard des Ormeaux, Montreal, Que. H9A 1N3, Canada. TEL 514-683-3623. Ed. Dan Nimrod. adv.; bk.rev. circ. 15,000.
Description: Provides an in depth comprehensive overview on current affairs with a historical perspective.

296 971   CN   ISSN 0706-3547
F1035.J5
CANADIAN JEWISH HISTORICAL SOCIETY JOURNAL. 1977. s-a. Can.$8 to individuals; institutions Can.$20. (Canadian Jewish Congress) Sumner Press, 4600 Bathurst St., Willowdale, Ont. M2R 3V2, Canada. Eds. R. Menkis, Irving Abella. adv.; bk.rev. circ. 500. Indexed: Amer.Bibl.Slavic & E.Eur.Stud., Amer.Hist.& Life, Hist.Abstr. —BLDSC (4723.036000).
Formerly: Jewish Historical Society of Canada. Journal (ISSN 0702-9233)

296   CN   ISSN 0008-3941
CANADIAN JEWISH NEWS. 1961. 47/yr. Can.$21.40. 10 Gateway Blvd., Ste. 420, Don Mills, ON M3C 3A1, Canada. TEL 416-422-2331. Ed. Patricia Rucker. adv. contact: Vera Gillman. circ. 51,000. (tabloid format; also avail. in microfilm from AJP) Indexed: Can.Per.Ind., CMI. **Document type:** newspaper.
Supersedes: Canadian Jewish Chronicle Review (ISSN 0008-3925)
Description: Presents international, national and local news, including arts and business, of interest to the Canadian Jewish community.

CANADIAN JOURNAL OF IRISH STUDIES. see *HUMANITIES: COMPREHENSIVE WORKS*

CANADIAN JOURNAL OF NATIVE EDUCATION. see *EDUCATION*

CANADIAN MUSLIM. see *RELIGIONS AND THEOLOGY — Islamic*

CANADIAN NATIVE LAW REPORTER. see *LAW*

917.1   CN   ISSN 0703-1599
CANADIANA GERMANICA; a journal of German-Canadian Studies. q. Can.$16 (effective 1994). Historical Society of Mecklenburg Upper Canada, P.O. Box 1251, Sta. K, Toronto, ON M4P 3E5, Canada. bk.rev.

917.306 327   US   ISSN 0576-6478
CANADO-AMERICAIN. 1900. q. $10 to non-members. Association Canado-Americaine, 52 Concord St., Box 989, Manchester, NH 03105-0989. TEL 603-625-8577. FAX 603-625-1214. Ed. Julien Olivier. adv.; bk.rev.; illus. circ. 34,000. (also avail. in microform)
Description: Provides news and articles of interest to members. Includes literary and cultural items relating to the French-speaking world.

917.306   US   ISSN 1042-3281
CANALES; New York's Latin magazine. (Text in English, Spanish) 1973. m. $18. Canales Publications, Inc., 215 W. 92nd St., Ste. 8E, New York, NY 10025. TEL 212-724-8805. Ed. Fernando Campos. circ. 88,000. (back issues avail.)
Description: General interest magazine with emphasis on entertainment and Hispanic personalities.

CANBERRA LINGUIST. see *LINGUISTICS*

CAPE BRETON'S MAGAZINE; devoted to history, natural history & future of Cape Breton Island. see *HISTORY — History Of North And South America*

915.1   CN
CAPITAL CHINESE NEWS. (Text in Chinese, English) 1977. m. Can.$10 (foreign $15). 695 Somerset St. W., Ottawa, Ont. K1R 6P5, Canada. Ed. P.J. Chiu. bk.rev. circ. 4,500.
Description: Special interests for overseas Chinese.

051 910.03   US
CAPITAL OUTLOOK: TALLAHASSEE. 1975. w. $30. Syndicated Programming, Inc., 417 N. Duval, Tallahasse, FL 32301. TEL 904-681-1852. FAX 904-681-1093. Ed. Roosevelt Wilson. adv. contact: Van R. Wilson. circ. 12,000. **Document type:** newspaper.

CARAVELLE; cahiers du monde hispanique et luso-bresilien. see *HISTORY — History Of North And South America*

CAREER FOCUS. see *OCCUPATIONS AND CAREERS*

CAREER OPPORTUNITIES FOR MINORITY COLLEGE GRADUATES. see *OCCUPATIONS AND CAREERS*

917.306   US
CARIBBEAN LIFE. 1990. m. Courier-Life Publications Inc., 1733 Sheepshead Bay Rd., Brooklyn, NY 11235. TEL 718-769-4400. FAX 718-769-5048. Ed. Simone Gill. adv.
Description: Provides current news and information of the whole Caribbean region.

910.3   UK   ISSN 0951-6379
CARIBBEAN TIMES. 1981. w. £42 (rest of Europe £52; elsewhere £70). Hansib Publishing Ltd., Tower House, 3rd Fl., 139-149 Fonthill Rd., London N4 3HF, England. TEL 071-281-1191. FAX 071-263-9656. (Dist. by: Magazine Marketing Company, Octagon House, White Heart Meadows, Ripley, Woking, Surrey GU23 6HR, England. TEL 0483-211222. FAX 0483-211731) Ed. Arif Ali. abstr.; film rev.; play rev. circ. 30,000. (back issues avail.) **Document type:** newspaper.

970.1   US   ISSN 0739-1730
CAROLINA INDIAN VOICE. 1972. w. First American Publications, Inc., Box 1075, Pembroke, NC 28372. TEL 910-521-2826. Ed. Connee Brayboy. adv. **Document type:** newspaper.

910.03   US
CAROLINA PEACEMAKER. 1967. w. $18.90. 400 Summit Ave., Greensboro, NC 27405. TEL 919-274-6210. FAX 919-272-4779. Ed. Hal Sieber. adv. contact: Thomas E. Price, Jr. circ. 8,000. **Document type:** newspaper.

917.306 900 011   US   ISSN 0749-9213
E184.U5
CARPATHO-RUSYN AMERICAN. 1978. q. $12. Carpatho - Rusyn Research Center, 355 Delano Pl., Fairview, NJ 07022. TEL 412-371-3823. FAX 412-681-6830. (Subscr. to: 132 Hawthorne St., Pittsburgh, PA 15218-1416) Ed. Patricia Krafcik. bk.rev.; bibl.; illus. circ. 800. (back issues avail.) Indexed: Amer.Bibl.Slavic & E.Eur.Stud.

LA CARTA. see *FOOD AND FOOD INDUSTRIES*

917.306   US   ISSN 0198-1021
PS508.M4
CARTA ABIERTA; keeping an eye on the Chicano literary world. (Text in English, Spanish) 1975. q. $10 to individuals; institutions $20. Texas Lutheran College, Center for Mexican American Studies, Sequin, TX 78155. Ed. Juan Rodriguez. adv.; play rev.; bibl. circ. 1,000. (looseleaf format; back issues avail.)

990   CN
CELEBRASIAN. 1983. 6/yr. Can.$12($12) Gay Asians Toronto, 17 St. Joseph St., Ste. 214, Toronto, Ont. M4Y 2J4, Canada. TEL 416-963-4300. adv.; bk.rev. circ. 525.
Description: Promotes ideas, issues and concerns relating to Asians who are gay or lesbian.

296   US
CENTRAL CALIFORNIA JEWISH HERITAGE. w. $8.50. Heritage Publishing Co., 2130 S. Vermont Ave., Los Angeles, CA 90007. (Subscr. to: 333 W. Shaw, Ste. 8, Fresno, CA 93704) Ed. Dan Brin. adv. (tabloid format)

CENTRO DE ESTUDIOS INDIGENAS. ANUARIO. see *ANTHROPOLOGY*

917.306   US
CESKOSLOVENSKE NOVINY; nezavisly ceskoslovensky dvoutydenik pro Ameriku a Kanadu. (Text in Czech) bi-w. $25 in U.S.; Canada $27. C S Noviny, 1406 Ave. Z, Box 194, Brooklyn, NY 11235. TEL 718-891-8675. Ed.Bd. **Document type:** newspaper.

296   US
CHAI TODAY. 1989. bi-m. $18 (foreign $32). Chai Publications, Inc., 420 Lincoln Rd., Ste. 409, Miami Beach, FL 33139. FAX 305-673-1283. (Subscr. to: Box 403126, Miami Beach, FL 33140) Ed. Rabbi Michael Lozenik. adv.; bk.rev. circ. 150,000.
Description: Includes articles of interest to the Jewish reader.

910.03   US   ISSN 1040-8886
CHALLENGER (BUFFALO). w. $15. Alnisa Banks, Ed. & Pub., 1303 Fillmore Ave., Buffalo, NY 14211. TEL 716-897-0442. FAX 716-897-3307. bk.rev. circ. 12,000. (tabloid format) **Document type:** newspaper.
Description: Covers local and international topics of interest to the African-American of Greater Buffalo.

970.1 398   US   ISSN 0528-8592
CHAR-KOOSTA NEWS; a weekly newspaper covering the Flathead Indian Reservation and the surrounding area. 1956. w. $18 (foreign $45). (Confederated Salish and Kootenai Tribes) Char-Koosta Printing and Publishing, Highway 93 S., Box 278, Pablo, MT 59855. TEL 406-675-3000. FAX 406-675-2806. Ed. Ronald B. Bick. adv.; bk.rev. circ. 4,000. (back issues avail.) **Document type:** newspaper.
Description: Includes items of local interest, court news, legal notices, tribe histories and school issues.

915.4   CN   ISSN 0845-3772
CHARHDI KALA. 1986. w. Can.$70. Charhdi Kala Weekly Punjabi Newspaper, 7743 - 128th St., Unit 6, Surrey, BC V3W 4E6, Canada. TEL 604-590-6397. FAX 604-591-6397. Ed. Hardip Singh. adv. circ. 48,000. **Document type:** newspaper.

CHARIOTEER; an annual review of modern Greek culture. see *GENERAL INTEREST PERIODICALS — Greece*

910.03   US
CHARLESTON BLACK TIMES. 1982. w. $25. S C Black Media Group, 1310 Harden St., Columbia, SC 29204. TEL 803-799-5252. FAX 803-799-7709. Ed. Bernard Legette. adv. contact: JoannnMcInnis. illus. circ. 6,000. **Document type:** newspaper.

910.03   US
CHARLESTON CHRONICLE. 1971. w. $20 for 6 mos. (effective April 1993). J. John French, Ed. & Pub., 534 King St., Charleston, SC 29403. TEL 803-723-2785. FAX 803-577-6099. (Subscr. to: Box 20548, Charleston, SC 29413-0548) circ. 6,000. **Document type:** newspaper.

910.03   US
CHARLOTTE POST. 1878. w. $21. Charlotte Post Publishing Co., Box 30144, Charlotte, NC 28230. TEL 704-376-0496. FAX 704-342-2160. (Street addr.: 1531 Camden Rd., Charlotte, NC 28203) adv. contact: Fran Farrer. illus.; tr.lit. circ. 60,000. **Document type:** newspaper.

910.03   US
CHATHAM CITIZEN. 1965. w. $25. William Garth, Ed. & Pub., 412 E. 87th St., Chicago, IL 60619. TEL 312-487-7700. FAX 312-487-7931. adv. contact: William D. Garth, Jr. circ. 27,000. (tabloid format) **Document type:** newspaper.

917.206   GT
CHATWALIJOQ. vol.4, 1989. Asociacion de Escritores Mayances de Guatemala, 5a. Calle 14-54, Zona 3, Apdo. Postal 1568, Quetzaltenango, Guatemala.

970.1   US
CHEROKEE ADVOCATE. 1828. m. $12.50 to individuals; seniors $10. Cherokee Nation Communications, Communications Department, Box 948, Tahlequah, OK 74465. TEL 918-456-0671. FAX 918-456-6485. Ed. Lynn Howard. adv.; bk.rev.; illus. circ. 5,000. **Document type:** newspaper.
Formerly (until 1834): Cherokee Phoenix (ISSN 0009-322X)
Description: Contains items of interest to the American Indian community.

ETHNIC INTERESTS

970.1 — US
CHEROKEE BOYS CLUB NEWSLETTER. 1965. q. free. Cherokee Boys Club, Inc., Box 507, Cherokee, NC 28719. TEL 704-497-9101. FAX 704-497-3140. Ed. Joy Evans-Widenhouse. circ. 5,000. (also avail. in microfilm from MCA) **Document type:** newsletter.
Description: Contains information of interest to Native Americans, especially Cherokee descent.

970.1 — US — ISSN 0890-4448
CHEROKEE ONE FEATHER. 1966. w. $20. Eastern Band of Cherokee Indians, Tribal Council, Box 501, Cherokee, NC 28719. TEL 704-497-5513. FAX 704-497-4810. Ed. Richard Welch. adv.: B&W page $195. bk.rev.; film rev. circ. 2,700. (tabloid format)
Description: Contains items of interest to the American Indian community.

CHEROKEE VOICE. see *SOCIAL SERVICES AND WELFARE*

910.03 — US
CHICAGO CRUSADER. 1940. w. $15. 6429 S. King Dr., Chicago, IL 60637. TEL 312-752-2500. FAX 312-752-2817. Ed. D.R. Leavell. circ. 63,000. **Document type:** newspaper.

910.03 — US
CHICAGO INDEPENDENT BULLETIN. 1963. w. $15. Hurley Green, Ed. & Pub., 2037 W. 95th St., Chicago, IL 60643. TEL 312-783-1040. adv. contact: Hurley Green, III. circ. 56,000. (tabloid format) **Document type:** newspaper.

917.06 — US — ISSN 0009-370X
THE CHICAGO SHIMPO; the Chicago Japanese American news. 1945. s-w. $50. 4670 N. Manor Ave., Chicago, IL 60625. TEL 312-478-6170. FAX 312-478-9360. adv. contact: Kayoko Kawaguchi. **Document type:** newspaper.

910.03 — US
CHICAGO SHORELAND NEWS. 1974. w. $26. Chicago Shoreland News, 11740 S. Elizabeth, Chicago, IL 60643. TEL 312-568-7091. Ed. Al Johnson. adv. contact: Janis Nelson. circ. 38,000. (tabloid format) **Document type:** newspaper.

915.906 — US
CHICAGO SOUTH ASIA NEWSLETTER. 1977. 3/yr. free. South Asia Outreach Educational Project, 5848 University Ave., Rm. 416, Chicago, IL 60637. TEL 312-702-8635. FAX 312-702-9673. Ed. Sandra K. Mulholland. bk.rev.; film rev. circ. 2,500. (back issues avail.) **Document type:** newsletter.
Description: Features Chicago area and University of Chicago events related to South Asian topics of interest to teachers and students at the high school, junior college, and university levels.

910.03 — US
CHICAGO SOUTH SHORE SCENE. 1954. w. $25. Chicago South Shore Scene, Box 49007, Chicago, IL 60649. TEL 312-363-0441. Ed. Claudette McFarland. adv. contact: Janis Nelson. circ. 80,000. (tabloid format) **Document type:** newspaper.

910.03 — US
CHICAGO WEEKEND. 1977. w. $25. William Garth, Ed. & Pub., 412 E. 87th St., Chicago, IL 60619. TEL 312-487-7700. FAX 312-487-7931. adv. contact: William D. Garth, Jr. circ. 22,500. (tabloid format) **Document type:** newspaper.

917.309 — US
EL CHICANO; una ventana abierta para la comunidad. Variant title: Chicano de San Bernardino. (Text in English, Spanish) 1969. w. $35. Box 6247, San Bernardino, CA 92412-6247. TEL 909-381-9898. FAX 909-384-0406. Ed. Gloria Macias. adv.; bk.rev.; stat. circ. 10,000. (tabloid format; also avail. in microform from UMI; microfilm from LIB) **Document type:** newspaper.
—UMI.
Formerly: Chicano Community Newspaper (ISSN 0009-3777)
Description: Contains items of interest to the Mexican-American community.

917.306 011 — US
CHICANO DATABASE ON C D - R O M. (Includes: Chicano Index (ISSN 1044-3487)) 1990. base vol. (plus s-a. updates). $1350. University of California at Berkeley, Chicano Studies Library Publications Unit, c/o Lillian Castillo-Speed, 3404 Dwinelle Hall, Berkeley, CA 94720. TEL 510-642-3859. FAX 510-642-6453.
●Available only on CD-ROM.
Description: Provides a comprehensive database on all aspects of Latin American life, culture, economics, politics, and literature.

CHICANO - LATINO LAW REVIEW. see *LAW*

970.1 — US
CHICANO STUDIES LIBRARY NEWSLETTER. 1986. s-a. free. Chicano Studies Library, Publication Unit, University of California at Berkeley, 3404 Dwinelle Hall, Berkeley, CA 94702. TEL 510-642-3859. FAX 510-642-6456. circ. 300. **Document type:** newsletter.
Description: Documents Chicano Studies Library activities.

917.306 — US
CHICO NEWS & REVIEW. (Supplements avail.) 1977. w. $25. Chico Community Publishing, Inc., 353 E. Second St., Chico, CA 95928. TEL 916-894-2300. Ed. Robert Speer. adv.; bk.rev. circ. 46,000. (tabloid format) **Document type:** newspaper.

CHILD HEALTH TALK. see *CHILDREN AND YOUTH — About*

917.309 — CN — ISSN 0009-4501
CHINATOWN NEWS. (Text in English) 1953. s-m. Can.$25 (foreign Can.$27). Chinese Publicity Bureau Ltd., 459 E. Hastings St., Vancouver, B.C. V6A 1P5, Canada. TEL 604-254-2533. FAX 604-254-3033. Ed. Roy Q. Mah. adv.; bk.rev.; illus.; cum.index. circ. 24,000. (back issues avail.)
Description: Contains items of news and general interest to the Chinese community in North America.

951 — US — ISSN 1051-7642
E184.C5
CHINESE AMERICA; history and perspectives. 1987. a. $17.50 or membership. Chinese Historical Society of America, 650 Commercial St., San Francisco, CA 94111. TEL 415-391-1188. Pub. H.M. Lai. illus. **Indexed:** Amer.Hist.& Life, Hist.Abstr. **Document type:** academic/scholarly publication.
Description: Recounts history of Chinese Americans through scholarly essays, oral histories, memoirs, and translations.

917.106 — CN
CHINESE - CANADIAN MAGAZINE. (Text in Chinese) s-m. C C M I Holdings Inc., 100 Dynamic Dr., Units 18-22, Scarborough, Ont. M1V 5C4, Canada. TEL 416-299-8229. FAX 416-292-8684. Ed. Miranda Tsang. circ. 40,000.

917.306 — US
CHINESE CULTURE ASSOCIATION, MAGAZINE. (Text in Chinese) 1966. a. $10. Chinese Culture Association, Box 1272, Palo Alto, CA 94301. Ed. P.F. Tao. adv.; bk.rev. circ. 2,500. **Document type:** proceedings.

973 917.306 — US — ISSN 0577-9065
E184.C5
CHINESE HISTORICAL SOCIETY OF AMERICA. BULLETIN. 1966. 10/yr. membership; includes anniversary issue. Chinese Historical Society of America, 650 Commercial St., San Francisco, CA 94711. TEL 415-391-1188. Ed.Bd. circ. 1,000. **Indexed:** Amer.Hist.& Life, Hist.Abstr. **Document type:** bulletin.
Description: News and announcements of the activities of the Chinese Historical Society of America, and items of related interest.

917.106 — CN — ISSN 0837-3809
CHINESE TIMES. (Text in Chinese) 1915. d. (Chinese Free Masons) Canada Publishers Ltd., 1 E. Pender St., Vancouver, B.C. V6A 1S9, Canada. TEL 604-685-8575. FAX 604-685-1196. Ed. Quan Lim. circ. 5,000. (also avail. in microfilm from CML) **Document type:** newspaper.

CHOCOLATE SINGLES. see *SINGLES' INTERESTS AND LIFESTYLES*

970.1 — US
CHOCTAW COMMUNITY NEWS. (Text mainly in English; occasionally n Choctaw) 1970. m. free. Mississippi Band of Choctaw Indians, Box 6010, Philadelphia, MS 39350. TEL 601-656-1521. FAX 601-656-1992. Ed. Julie Kelsey. illus. circ. 7,000. (tabloid format; also avail. in microfilm from MCA)
Description: Contains items of interest to the American Indian community.

CHRISTIAN IRELAND TODAY. see *SOCIOLOGY*

910.03 — US
CHRONICLE (FORT PIERCE). 1957. w. $21. Lincoln Park Publishing, 1527 Ave. D, Fort Pierce, FL 34950. Ed. C.E. Bolen. circ. 5,000. **Document type:** newspaper.

296 — IS
CHRONIKA. (Text in Greek) 1984. a. Center for Research on Saloniki Jewry, Rehov Levinsky 68, Tel Aviv, Israel.

914.506 — CN — ISSN 0382-8557
CIAO; l'unica rivista italiana edita in Nord America. (Text in Italian) 1970. m. Can.$15($15) Ciao Publishing Co., 1081 Bas l'Assomption Nord, Ville de l'Assomption, Que. J0K 1G0, Canada. FAX 514-589-4485. Ed. Pascal Barrasso. adv.; bk.rev.; film rev.; circ. 40,000 (controlled). (also avail. in microform)

910.03 — US
CINCINNATI HERALD. 1956. w. $30. Marjorie Parham, c/o News Ed. Donald K. Anthony, 863 Lincoln Ave., Cincinnati, OH 45206. TEL 513-221-5440. FAX 513-221-2959. adv. contact: Jermaine Hill. circ. 25,400. (also avail. in microfilm from UMI) **Document type:** newspaper.
Description: Contains items of interest to the black community.

971 — CN — ISSN 0009-7667
CITTADINO CANADESE. (Text in English, French, Italian) 1941. w. Can.$20. Cittadino Canadese, 6020 Jean-Talon Est, Ste. 600, Montreal, PQ H1S 3B1, Canada. TEL 514-253-2332. FAX 514-253-6574. Ed. Basilio Giordano. adv.; illus. circ. 54,850. (tabloid format; also avail. in microfiche) **Document type:** newspaper.
Description: Contains items of interest to the Italian community

910.03 — US — ISSN 8750-2720
CITY SUN. 1984. w. $32. City Sun Publishing, Inc., Box 020560, Brooklyn, NY 11202-0013. TEL 718-624-5959. FAX 718-596-7429. Ed. Andrew W. Cooper (tabloid format) **Document type:** newspaper.

917.306 — US
CITY TERRACE COMET. (Text in English, Spanish) 1974. w. $62.50 (effective Oct. 1993). Eastern Group Publications, Inc., 3643 E. First St., Los Angeles, CA 90063. TEL 213-263-5743. (Subscr. to: P.O. Box 33803, Los Angeles, CA 90033) Ed. Dolores Sanchez. adv. circ. 3,000. **Document type:** newspaper.
Description: Community newspaper focusing on Hispanic topics.

914.1 929 — US — ISSN 0731-2032
CLAN ROSS NEWSLETTER.* 1981. q. membership. Clan Ross Association of the United States, Inc., 55 Land Harbor, Newland, NC 28657. TEL 912-727-2560. Ed. Betty Ross. bk.rev.; circ. 400 (controlled). (looseleaf format) **Document type:** newsletter.

941 929 — CN — ISSN 0832-5189
CLANSMAN (HALIFAX). (Text in English, Gaelic) 1987. bi-m. Can.$14.25($15.75) Clansman Publishing Ltd., P.O. Box 8805, Halifax, MS B3K 5M4, Canada. TEL 902-835-6244. FAX 902-835-0080. Ed. Alexa Thompson. adv. contact: Donna Pickren. bk.rev. circ. 18,200. (back issues avail.)
Description: Focuses on Scottish, Irish, and Gaelic languages, cultures, music and dance.

ETHNIC INTERESTS

296 US ISSN 0009-8825
CLEVELAND JEWISH NEWS. 1964. w. $27 in Ohio; other states $32. Cleveland Jewish Publication Co., 3645 Warrensville Center Rd., Ste. 230, Cleveland, OH 44122-5210. TEL 216-991-8300. FAX 216-991-9556. Ed. Cynthia Dettelbach. adv. contact: Marcia Sollisch. bk.rev.; illus. circ. 14,800. (also avail. in microfilm from AJP) **Document type:** newspaper.
  Description: Contains items of interest to the Jewish community.

CLUES (LINCOLN). see *GENEALOGY AND HERALDRY*

972 860 CR
COLECCION MIGUEL SALGUERO. irreg. no.4, 1981. Editorial Universidad Estatal a Distancia, Apdo. 474-2050, San Pedro Montes de Oca, San Jose, Costa Rica.

COLLABORATION. see *PHILOSOPHY*

296 BE ISSN 0777-785X
COLLECTION DE LA REVUE DES ETUDES JUIVES. (Supplement to: Revue des Etudes Juives) 1981. irreg. price varies. (Societe des Etudes Juives, FR) Editions Peeters s.p.r.l., Bondgenotenlaan 153, B-3000 Louvain, Belgium. TEL 32-16-235170. FAX 32-16-228500. **Document type:** monographic series.
—SWETS.

910.03 US
COLUMBIA BLACK NEWS. 1974. w. $25. S C Black Media Group, 1310 Harden St., Box 11128, Columbia, SC 29204. FAX 803-799-7709. Ed. Bernard Legette. illus. circ. 50,000. **Document type:** newspaper.

910.03 US
COLUMBUS TIMES. 1969. w. $15.60. c/o Ophelia Mitchell, Ed., 4650 Dawn Ct., Columbus, GA 31907. TEL 404-324-2404. FAX 404-324-2405. (Subscr. to: 2230 Buena Vista Rd., Box 2845, Columbus, GA 31906) adv: B&W page $1836.96. bk.rev.; film rev.; play rev. circ. 20,000. (also avail. in talking book; back issues avail.) **Document type:** newspaper.

COMMENTATOR. see *COLLEGE AND ALUMNI*

COMMUNITY (CHICAGO). see *SOCIOLOGY*

296 320.9 CN
COMPARE NOTES SERIES. irreg. price varies. Dawn Publishing Co. Ltd., 17 Anselme Lavigne Blvd., Dollard des Ormeaux, Montreal, Que. H9A 1N3, Canada. Ed. Dan Nimrod.

296 IT
COMUNITA EBRAICA DI MILANO. BOLLETTINO. 1945. m. L.50000 membership (foreign L.60000) (effective 1994). Comunita Ebraica di Milano, Via Sally Mayer 2, 20146 Milan, Italy. TEL 02-48302806. FAX 02-48304660. Ed. Annie Sacerdoti. adv.; bk.rev.; illus. circ. 4,000. **Document type:** bulletin.
  Formerly: Comunita Israelitica di Milano. Bollettino (ISSN 0010-5074)

296 US ISSN 0160-7057
DS101
CONFERENCE OF PRESIDENTS OF MAJOR AMERICAN JEWISH ORGANIZATIONS. ANNUAL REPORT. 1965. a. free. Conference of Presidents of Major American Jewish Organizations, 110 E. 59th St., New York, NY 10022. TEL 212-752-1616. Ed. Richard Cohen. illus. **Document type:** corporate report.
  Former titles: Conference of Presidents of Major American Jewish Organizations. Report; Conference of Presidents of Major American Jewish Organizations. Annual Report (ISSN 0160-7049)

CONGREGATION NEWS. see *HANDICAPPED — Hearing Impaired*

296 AG
CONGRESO JUDIO LATINOAMERICANO. BOLETIN INFORMATIVO O J I. 1970. m. free. Congreso Judio Latinoamericano - World Jewish Congress, Larrea 744, 1030 Buenos Aires, Argentina. TEL 541-962-5028. FAX 541-961-4534. Ed. Pedro J. Olschansky. bk.rev. circ. 5,000.

914.5 CN
CONGRESSO. (Text in Italian) 1982. m. Can.$20 (typically set in Nov.) Cura Enterprises Ltd., 10865 96th St., No. 11, Edmonton, Alta. T5H 2K2, Canada. TEL 403-424-3010. adv.; bk.rev.; circ. 2,500 (paid); 5,000 (controlled). (tabloid format)
  Description: Publishes local, national and international news, culture, music and sports.

CONNAISSANCE DU PAYS D'OC. see *TRAVEL AND TOURISM*

CONTEMPORARY BLACK BIOGRAPHY. see *BIOGRAPHY*

296 US ISSN 0147-1694
DS101
CONTEMPORARY JEWRY; a journal of sociological inquiry. 1974. a., latest vol.14, 1993 (for the year 1991). $18. Association for the Sociological Study of Jewry, Box 5302, Connecticut College, New London, CT 06320. TEL 203-439-2241. FAX 203-439-2700. Ed. J. Alan Winter. adv.; bk.rev. circ. 300. (also avail. in microform from UMI; reprint service avail. from UMI) Indexed: Sociol.Abstr. (1977-). **Document type:** academic/scholarly publication.
—BLDSC (3425.190100). CCC.

917.306 US
CONTRAPUNTO. (Text in Spanish) 1990. m. $18. Contrapunto, Inc., 6621 S.W. 8th St., Miami, FL 33144. TEL 305-266-0150. (Subscr. to: Box 440739, Miami, FL 33144-0739) Dir. Nicolas Rios. **Document type:** consumer publication.
  Description: Forum for serious analysis of world events, especially those of interest to the Hispanic-American population.

917 US ISSN 0196-7088
CONTRIBUTIONS IN ETHNIC STUDIES. 1980. irreg., no.30, 1992. price varies. Greenwood Press, Inc. (Subsidiary of: Greenwood Publishing Group Inc.), 88 Post Rd. W., Box 5007, Westport, CT 06881-5007. TEL 203-226-3571. FAX 203-222-1502. Ed. Leonard W. Doob.
—BLDSC (3458.415000).

CONTRIBUTIONS TO THE STUDY OF WORLD HISTORY. see *HISTORY*

910.03 US
CORDELE SOUTHEASTERN NEWS. 1965. w. $40. Drawer 489, Cordele, GA 31015. TEL 912-273-6714. FAX 912-273-6714. Ed. Eugene Ruthland. circ. 20,000. **Document type:** newspaper.

942 UK ISSN 0306-9079
CORNISH BANNER/BANER KERNEWEK. 1975. q. £7.50 (foreign £8.50) (effective 1993). (Cornish Nationalist Party) C N P Publications, Roseland, Gorran, St. Austell, Kernow-Cornwall, England. FAX 0726-843501. Ed. J. Whetter. adv.; bk.rev. circ. 500.
  Description: Discusses contemporary life, history, poetry and the arts in Cornwall.

CORNISH BIOLOGICAL RECORDS. see *BIOLOGY*

056.9 CN ISSN 0045-8643
CORREIO PORTUGUES. (Text in Portuguese) 1963. s-m. Can.$40($50) 793 Ossington Ave., Toronto, ON M6G 3T8, Canada. TEL 416-532-9894. FAX 416-532-1475. Ed. M.A. Ribeiro; Pub. Antonio Ribeiro. adv. circ. 15,100.

056.9 AT
CORREIO PORTUGUES. (Text in Portuguese) 1977. w. Aus.$40. Kizeve Pty. Ltd., 1st Fl., New Canterbury Rd., Petersham, N.S.W. 2049, Australia. TEL 560-6722. FAX 560-6044. TELEX 75930 PORNEW. Ed. Ana Ferreira. adv. circ. 3,000. (tabloid format)

917.306 US ISSN 1075-6876
▼**CORREO DEL HUDSON.** (Text in Spanish) 1992. bi-m. free. Asociacion Cultural Venezolano-Americana, Box 963, New York, NY 10116-0963. Ed. Victor Roa. adv. circ. 1,000. **Document type:** newspaper.

914.6 US
CORREO LATINOAMERICANO. (Text in Spanish) w. 2413 Dundas St. W., P.O. Box 1108, Adelaide St. Stn., Toronto, ON M5C 2K5, Canada. TEL 416-538-0588. FAX 416-531-7187. circ. 2,000. **Document type:** newspaper.

055.1 CN ISSN 0045-866X
CORRIERE CANADESE/CANADIAN COURIER. (Text in English, Italian) 1954. 3/w. Can.$154. October Press Ltd., 1100 Caledonia Rd., Ste.200, Toronto, ON M6A 2W5, Canada. TEL 416-785-4300. FAX 416-785-4329. Ed. E. Caprile. adv.; bk.rev. circ. 22,710. (also avail. in microfilm from CML)

055.1 GW ISSN 0010-924X
CORRIERE D'ITALIA; settimanale italiano. (Text in Italian) 1951. w. DM.75. Ente pro Italis, Speyererstr. 2, 60327 Frankfurt a.M., Germany. TEL 069-732011. FAX 069-7391370. Ed. Giuseppe Bassanelli. adv.; bk.rev.; charts; illus.; stat.; tr.lit. circ. 16,500. **Document type:** newspaper.

055.1 VE ISSN 0010-9231
CORRIERE DI CARACAS; settimanale italiano indipendente. (Text in Italian and Spanish) 1949. w. Bs.210($50) Corriere di Caracas, C.A., Apdo. 2560, Caracas, Venezuela. Ed. Franco Pattarino. adv.; bk.rev.; bibl.; illus.; stat. circ. 28,000. **Document type:** newspaper.

361 353 US
COUNCIL OF JEWISH ORGANIZATIONS IN CIVIL SERVICE. COUNCIL NEWS. bi-w. Council of Jewish Organizations in Civil Service, 45 E. 33rd St., Rm. 604, New York, NY 10016. TEL 212-689-2015. **Document type:** newspaper.
  Description: Aimed at Jewish civil servants at all levels of government who are concerned about job discrimination.

296 US
COUNTRY YOSSI FAMILY MAGAZINE; it's Gevaldig. 1988. 6/yr. $25 (foreign $45). 2920 Ave. R, Ste. 200, Brooklyn, NY 11229. FAX 718-338-9593. adv.; bk.rev. circ. 20,000.
  Description: Features articles of interest to Orthodox Jews.

361 350 US
COUNTY COMPASS. q. free. National Organization of Black County Officials, 440 First St., N.W., Ste. 500, Washington, DC 20001. TEL 202-347-6953. FAX 202-393-6596. Ed. Jacqueline Davison. adv. circ. 3,500. **Document type:** newsletter.

917.106 CN
COURRIER GREC. (Text in Greek) w. Can.$50. Hellenic Postman of Canada Inc., 3620 St. Lawrence Blvd., Montreal, Que. H2X 2V4, Canada. TEL 514-849-9745. FAX 514-842-5932. Ed. Christos Kolivas. circ. 17,000.

296 CN
COVENANT. 1970. 10/yr. Can.$75. B'nai Brith Canada, 15 Hove St., Downsview, Ont. M3H 4Y8, Canada. TEL 416-633-6224. FAX 416-630-2159. adv. circ. 55,000. (tabloid format)

323.4 US ISSN 0011-1422
E185.5
CRISIS (NEW YORK, 1910);* a record of the darker races. 1910. m. (bi-m. June-July; Aug.-Sep.). $15. (National Association for the Advancement of Colored People (NAACP)) Crisis Publishing Co., 4017 24th St. San Francisco, CA 94114-3715. TEL 212-481-4100. (Subscr. to: Cirsis Publishing Co., 4895 Mt. Hope Dr., Baltimore, MD 21215. TEL 410-358-8900; Alt. addr.: 319 N. Fourth St., St. Louis, MI 63102. TEL 341-241-0001) Ed. Garland Thompson. adv.; bk.rev.; film rev.; illus.; index. circ. 400,000. (also avail. in microform from UMI,KTO,BHP; reprint service avail.from UMI) Indexed: Amer.Hist.& Life (until 1988), C.I.J.E., Hist.Abstr. (until 1988), Ind.Per.Negroes, Soc.Sci.Ind. —Faxon; UnCover; UMI.
  Description: Feature articles on civil rights from an African-American perspective. Includes information on the association's programs and activities.

917.206 US
CRITICA; a journal of critical essays. 1984. a. $8 to individuals; institutions $10. University of California, San Diego, Chicano Studies, Third College, D-009, San Diego, La Jolla, CA 92093. Ed. Rosaura Sanchez. adv.; bk.rev. circ. 500.

910.03 398 US
CRITICAL STUDIES ON BLACK LIFE AND CULTURE. irreg. vol.24, 1982. price varies. Garland Publishing, Inc., 1000A Sherman Ave., Hamden, CT 06514. TEL 800-627-6273. (And: 717 Fifth Ave., New York, NY 10022. TEL 212-751-7447) Ed. Henry Louis Gates, Jr.

CROSS OF LANGUEDOC. see *RELIGIONS AND THEOLOGY — Protestant*

296   AG
CUADERNOS DE ESTUDIOS JUDIOS. 1973. irreg. Arg.$1.50. Comite Judio Americano, Oficina Sudamericana, Bartolome Mitre 1943, 1-B, Buenos Aires, Argentina. Eds. Natalio Mazar, Santiago E. Kovadloft.
    Description: Contains items of interest to the Jewish community.

LA CUENTA. see *BUSINESS AND ECONOMICS — Accounting*

917.106   CN   ISSN 0715-7045
CURRENTS; readings in race relations. 1983. q. $20 to individuals; institutions Can.$30. Urban Alliance on Race Relations, 675 King St. W., Ste. 203, Toronto, Ont. M5V 1M9, Canada. TEL 416-363-2607. Ed. Tim Rees. circ. 1,000. **Indexed:** HR Rep.

CWY YE: CHEROKEE BLOOD NEWSLETTER. see *GENEALOGY AND HERALDRY*

057.85   CN   ISSN 0045-9445
CZAS/POLISH TIMES. (Text in Polish; summaries in English) 1914. w. Can.$38.30 (foreign Can.$39.32. Polish Press Ltd., 1150 Main St., Winnipeg, MB R2W 3S6, Canada. TEL 204-582-4392. Ed. Halina Fracz. adv. circ. 3,000. (also avail. in microfilm from KTO) **Document type:** newspaper.
    Description: Contains items of interest to the Polish community.

917.306 327   US   ISSN 0896-9809
CZECHOSLOVAK HISTORY NEWSLETTER. 1976. s-a. $8. Czechoslovak History Conference, Valdosta State College, Department of Political Science, Valdosta, GA 31698. TEL 912-333-5771. FAX 912-333-7408. Ed. James W. Peterson. adv. circ. 125. **Document type:** newsletter.

D F W EMPOWERMENT REPORT. (Dallas - Fort Worth) see *BUSINESS AND ECONOMICS — Small Business*

297   UK
DAILY JANG LONDON. (Text in English, Urdu) 1971. d. £196. Jang Publications Ltd., 57 Lant St., London SE1 1QN, England. FAX 01-403-6740. TELEX 28208. Ed. Ashraf K. Kazi. adv.; bk.rev. circ. 19,427. (back issues avail.)
    Description: News from U.K. and Indo-Pakistan sub-continent.

910.03   US   ISSN 0746-7303
DALLAS POST TRIBUNE. 1947. w. $25. T.R. Lee, Jr., Ed. & Pub., 2726 S. Beckley, Dallas, TX 75224. TEL 214-946-7678. FAX 214-946-6823. adv.; bk.rev.; illus.; tr.lit. circ. 18,000. **Document type:** newspaper.

910.03   US
DALLAS WEEKLY. 1953. w. $60. 3101 Martin Luther King Blvd., Dallas, TX 75215. TEL 214-428-8958. FAX 214-428-2807. Ed. Ylonda Adams. adv.; bk.rev. circ. 21,095. (tabloid format) **Document type:** newspaper.

DANICA; hrvatski tjednik. see *RELIGIONS AND THEOLOGY — Roman Catholic*

917.106   CN   ISSN 0833-3831
DANNZHA; Yukon's native magazine. 1973. 6/yr. Can.$25 to individuals; institutions Can.$37. Ye Sa To Communications Society, 22 Nisutlin Dr., Whitehorse, Y.T. Y1A 3S5, Canada. TEL 403-667-6932. FAX 403-668-6577. Ed. Doris Bill. adv. circ. 6,000. (back issues avail.)
    Former titles: Dan Sha News (ISSN 0382-7305); (1973-1985): Yukon Indian News.

948   US   ISSN 0747-3869
DANSKE PIONEER/DANISH PIONEER. (Text in Danish and English) 1872. fortn. $22. Bertelsen Publishing Co., 1582 Glen Lake Rd., Hoffman Estates, IL 60195. TEL 708-882-2552. FAX 708-882-7082. Ed. Chris Steffensen. adv.; bk.rev.; circ. 3,400 (controlled). (tabloid format) **Document type:** newspaper.

910.03   US
DATA NEWS WEEKLY. 1966. w. $15. Data Enterprises, Box 51933, New Orleans, LA 70151. TEL 504-522-1418. FAX 504-523-7364. Ed. June Hazeur. circ. 20,000. (tabloid format) **Document type:** newspaper.

917.309   CN   ISSN 0418-4297
AP95.L4
DAUGAVAS VANAGU MENESRAKSTS. (Text in Latvian) 1965. bi-m. Can.$22($20) (Latvian Relief Society of Canada - Daugavas Vanagi) Daugavas Vanags Publishing Ltd., 125 Broadview Ave., Toronto, ON M4M 2E9, Canada. Ed. I. Purus. adv.; bk.rev.; illus. circ. 3,000.
    Description: Contains items of interest to the Latvian community.

296   AG
DAVKE; revista Israelita. (Text in Spanish and Yiddish) 1949. q. Brandsen 1634, Buenos Aires, Argentina. Ed. Salomon Suskovich. bk.rev.; bibl.

910.03   US
DAWN MAGAZINE (BALTIMORE). 1973. 9/yr. $26. Afro-American Co. of Baltimore City, 628 N. Eutaw St., Baltimore, MD 21201. TEL 410-554-8200. FAX 410-383-3213. Ed. Eve Ferguson. adv.; illus. circ. 510,500. (tabloid format; reprint service avail. from BLH)
    Description: Contains articles of interest to the African American community.

915.606   GW
DAYANISMA; Stadtteilzeitung fuer die Bremen-Vahr. (Text in German and Turkish) 1984. q. free. (Buergerzentrum Vahr) Dayanisma Kulturhaus, Postfach 410137, 28311 Bremen, Germany. TEL 0421-465599. Ed. Ali Sahin. circ. 1,200. (back issues avail.)
    Description: Provides information on the political rights and education of the Turkish minority in Bremen.

970.1   US
DAYBREAK; dedicated to land and life and the seventh generation. m. $12. Box 315, Williamsville, NY 14231-0315. **Indexed:** Alt.Press Ind.

970.1 028.5   US
DAYBREAK STAR INDIAN READER. 1974. 8/yr. $16 to teachers; libraries $24; students $5.75. United Indians of All Tribes Foundation, 1945 Yale Pl. E., Seattle, WA 98102. TEL 206-325-0070. Ed.Bd. bk.rev. circ. 4,500. (tabloid format)
    Formerly: Daybreak Star.
    Description: Children's learning resource featuring culturally-focused articles and activities of interest to students in grades 4-6. Covers American Indian interests.

296   US
DAYTON JEWISH CHRONICLE.* 1961. w. $13. Ami Publishing, Inc., 6929 N. Main St., No. B, Dayton, OH 45415-2508. TEL 513-222-0783. Ed. Leslie Cohen Zukowsky. adv.; bk.rev. circ. 1,450. (also avail. in microfilm from AJP)

910.03   US
DAYTONA TIMES. 1978. w. $25. 427 S. Martin Luther King Blvd., Daytona Beach, FL 32114. TEL 904-253-0321. FAX 094-254-7510. Ed. Charles W. Cherry. adv. contact: Cassandra Cherry. illus.; circ. 15,000 (paid). **Document type:** newspaper.

910.03   US   ISSN 0011-7498
DEFENDER (WILMINGTON). 1962. w. $25. Defender Publishing Co., Inc., 1702 Locust St., Box 828, Wilmington, DE 19801. TEL 302-656-3252. FAX 215-471-1130. Ed. A.G. Hibbert. adv.; bk.rev. circ. 9,000. **Document type:** newspaper.
    Description: Contains items of interest to the black community.

DEMB AK TEY/YESTERDAY AND TODAY; a journal of myths and legends. see *LITERATURE*

059.918   US   ISSN 0744-6586
DENNI HLASATEL/CZECHOSLOVAK DAILY - HERALD. (Text in Czech, English, Slovak) 1891. s-w. $80. Denni Hlasatel Printing and Publishing Co., 6426 W. Cermak Rd., Berwyn, IL 60402. TEL 708-749-1891. FAX 708-749-1935. Ed. Josef Kucera. adv. contact: Josef Kucera, Jr. circ. 10,000. (tabloid format; also avail. in microform; back issues avail.) **Document type:** newspaper.

910.03   US
DENVER WEEKLY NEWS;* printed for better understanding. 1971. w. $15.20. Box 38939, Denver, CO 80238-0939. Ed. F. Cosmo Harris. adv.; illus. circ. 5,000. (tabloid format) **Document type:** newspaper.
    Description: Contains items of interest to the black community.

910.03 320   US
DESTINY; the new Black American mainstream. 1990. 6/yr. $14.95. Destiny Publications, P.O. Box 19284, Lansing, MI 48901. TEL 517-484-2576. Ed. Emmanuel McLittle. adv. contact: Ted Mann. (back issues avail.)
    Description: Covers political, economic and socio-cultural issues for Black conservatives.

296   US   ISSN 0011-9644
DETROIT JEWISH NEWS. 1942. w. $33. Detroit Jewish News Partnership, Ltd., 27676 Franklin Rd., Southfield, MI 48034-8203. TEL 313-354-6060. FAX 313-354-6069. Ed. Phil Jacobs. adv. contact: Arthur Horwitz. bk.rev.; film rev.; illus.; play rev. circ. 20,300. (tabloid format; also avail. in microfilm from AJP) **Document type:** newspaper.

943.206   GW
DEUTSCH-CHINESISCHES FORUM. 1982. irreg. (3-4/yr.). DM.4 per no. Friedrich Reinecke Verlag GmbH, Hartwicusstr. 3-4, 22087 Hamburg, Germany. TEL 040-228070. FAX 040-22807260. TELEX 214733. circ. 26,000. (also avail. in microfiche) **Document type:** consumer publication.

914.3   CN
DEUTSCHE PRESSE. (Text in English, German) 1978. w. Can.$61. Austrian Publications, Ltd., 455 Spadina Ave., Ste. 303, Toronto, Ont. M5S 2G8, Canada. TEL 416-595-9714. FAX 416-595-9716. adv. circ. 35,000. (tabloid format; back issues avail.)

053.1   CN   ISSN 0046-0141
DEUTSCHE VEREINIGUNG VON WINNIPEG. MITTEILUNGEN. 1968. 10/yr. membership. German Society of Winnipeg, 121 Charles St., Winnipeg, Man. R2W 4A6, Canada. TEL 204-589-7724. Ed. G. Stein Born. adv. circ. 1,050. (looseleaf format)

DEUTSCHER VOLKSKALENDER NORDSCHLESWIG. see *POPULATION STUDIES*

DIALOGOS; Hellenic studies review. see *CLASSICAL STUDIES*

917.306   US   ISSN 0742-9428
EL DIARIO - LA PRENSA. (Text in Spanish) 1913. d. (except Sat.) $266 13. 143-155 Varick St., New York, NY 10013. TEL 212-807-4600. Ed. Fernando Moreno.

DIECIOCHO; Hispanic enlightenment, aesthetics and literary theory. see *LITERATURE*

917.306   US   ISSN 0890-4294
AC40
DIFFERENTIA; review of Italian thought. 1986. s-a. $20 to individuals (foreign $25); institutions $30 (foreign $35). Differentia, Ltd., City University of New York, Queens College, Kiely Hall 243, 65-30 Kissena Blvd., Flushing, NY 11367-0904. TEL 718-997-5660. FAX 718-358-4542. Ed. Peter Carravetta. adv.; bk.rev.
    —UnCover.
    Description: Expands and intensifies the dialogue between the Anglo-American and Italian cultures. Covers contemporary Italian thought and philosophy with emphasis on the history of ideas, social criticism, political theory and literary studies.

320   US   ISSN 0882-1240
DIMENSIONS: A JOURNAL OF HOLOCAUST STUDIES. 1985. 3/yr. $15. (Braun Center for Holocaust Studies) Anti-Defamation League, 823 United Nations Plaza, New York, NY 10017. TEL 212-490-2525. Ec.Bd. illus. **Indexed:** Avery Ind.Archit.Per., HR Rep. **Document type:** academic/scholarly publication.
    —BLDSC (3588.469700).

DIOZESE GURK. JAHRBUCH/KRSKE SKOFIJE. ZBORNIK. see *RELIGIONS AND THEOLOGY — Roman Catholic*

ETHNIC INTERESTS

917.306 440 US ISSN 0734-0591
DIPOSITIO. (Text in English and Spanish) 1976. 2/yr. $25 to institutions; students $10; faculty $15. University of Michigan, Department of Romance Languages, Ann Arbor, MI 48109-1275. TEL 313-747-2383. FAX 313-764-8163. Ed. Walter Mignolo. adv.; bk.rev.; index. circ. 500. **Indexed:** Amer.Bibl.Slavic & E.Eur.Stud, Arts & Hum.Cit.Ind., Curr.Cont., M.L.A., RILA. **Document type:** academic/scholarly publication.
—UnCover.

910.03 US
DIRECTORY OF AFRIKANAMERICAN RESEARCH CENTERS. biennial. $10. Afram Associates, Inc., 2322 Third Ave., 2nd Fl., New York, NY 10035. TEL 212-289-9155. FAX 212-722-5194. **Document type:** directory.

DIRECTORY OF DAY SCHOOLS IN THE UNITED STATES AND CANADA. see EDUCATION — Guides To Schools And Colleges

296 US
DIRECTORY OF JEWISH COMMUNITY CENTERS. a. $30 to non-members. (Jewish Welfare Board) J W B Jewish Book Center, 15 E. 26 St., New York, NY 10010. TEL 212-532-4949. FAX 212-481-4174. **Document type:** directory.

DIRECTORY OF SPECIAL PROGRAMS FOR MINORITY GROUP MEMBERS; CAREER INFORMATION SERVICES, EMPLOYMENT SKILLS, BANKS, FINANCIAL AID SOURCES. see BUSINESS AND ECONOMICS — Trade And Industrial Directories

DIRECTORY OF WORLD JEWISH PRESS AND PUBLICATIONS. see PUBLISHING AND BOOK TRADE

917.309 US
DIRVA. (Text in Lithuanian) 1915. w. $30. (American Lithuanian Press Radio Association) Viltis, Inc., 19807 Cherokee Ave., Cleveland, OH 44119-0191. TEL 216-531-8150. FAX 216-531-8428. Ed. Balys Gaidziunas. adv.; bk.rev.; illus. circ. 2,500. (tabloid format) **Document type:** newspaper.
Description: Contains items of interest to the Lithuanian community.

DOLLARS & SENSE. see BUSINESS AND ECONOMICS — Economic Situation And Conditions

947 GW ISSN 0012-5423
DER DONAUSCHWABE; Bundesorgan der Heimatvertriebenen aus Jugoslawien, Rumaenien und Ungarn. 1951. w. DM.158. (Heimatvertriebene aus Suedosteuropa) Konrad Theiss Verlag GmbH, Postfach 1680, 73406 Aalen, Germany. TEL 07316-594395. FAX 07361-594535. Ed. Wolfgang Gleich. adv.; bk.rev.; charts; illus.; stat. circ. 8,000. **Document type:** newsletter.

914.5 CN
DONNA. m. Inkerman Bldg., Ste. 100, 166 Woodbridge Ave., Woodbridge, Ont. L4L 2S7, Canada. TEL 416-856-2823. FAX 416-856-2825. Ed. Giovanna Tozzi. adv.

296 SA
DOREM AFRIKE. (Text in Yiddish) 1948. q. $12. S.A. Yiddish Cultural Federation, 253 Bree St., Box 9664, Johannesburg 2000, South Africa. Ed. Z. Levy. adv.; bk.rev. circ. 700.
Description: Contains items of interest to the Jewish community.

DOROT. see GENEALOGY AND HERALDRY

917.306 282 US
DRAUGAS. 1909. 5/w. $80. Lithuanian Catholic Press Society, 4545 W. 63rd St., Chicago, IL 60629. TEL 312-585-9500. FAX 312-585-8284. Ed. Rev. F. Garsva. adv. circ. 7,000. **Document type:** newspaper.

DREAD TIMES; news for the Nazarite. see RELIGIONS AND THEOLOGY

914.106 CN ISSN 0703-1491
DROCHAID/BRIDGE. 1976. 5/yr. Can.$8($9) (effective 1992). Clans & Scottish Societies of Canada, 695 Liverpool Rd. S., Pickering, Ont. L1W 1R6, Canada. circ. 250.
Description: Provides information on Scottish clans, societies, groups, activities and events in Canada and elsewhere.

DRUM; Africa's leading magazine beating to the pulse of the times. see GENERAL INTEREST PERIODICALS — South Africa

960 800 US
▼**DRUM VOICES;** a confluence of literary, cultural and vision arts. 1992. s-a. $10. Southern Illinois University, English Department, Box 1431, Edwardsville, IL 62026. Ed. Eugene Redmond. illus.

390 CI
DUMKI Z DUNAJU. (Text in Russian, Ruthenian, Serbo-Croatian, Ukrainian) 1989. a. 50 din.($10) (effective Mar. 1991). Sojuz Rusinoh i Ukrajincoh Horvatskej, Marsala Tiata 11-I, 56230 Vukovar, Croatia. TEL 56-44-932. Ed. Vlado Kostelnik. circ. 1,000.
Description: Publishes articles on social and political life, education, culture, history, literature and art.

914.106 US ISSN 0741-5273
DUNROBIN PIPER. 1976. m. membership. Clan Sutherland Society of North America, Inc., 2922 Primrose Circle, Nashville, TN 37212. TEL 615-297-1528. FAX 615-343-6909. Ed. Mary Nell Snoddy. bk.rev. circ. 325. (back issues avail.)
Description: Information on Society's activities.

943.8 800 PL
DYSKUSJA. 4/yr. Wojewodzki Dom Kultury w Bialymstoku, Ul. Kilinskiego 8, Bialystok, Poland. Ed. Iwona Wasowicz-Szczepanska.
Description: Socio-cultural magazine with empahsis on Byelorussians in Poland.

943.8 320 UK
DZIENNIK POLSKI I DZIENNIK ZOLNIERZA/POLISH DAILY AND THE SOLDIERS DAILY. (Text in Polish) 1941. d. £165 (foreign £195). Polish Cultural Foundation, 9 Charleville Rd., London W14 9JL, England. TEL 385 9393. Ed. Andrzej Czyzowski. adv.; bk.rev.; film rev.; play rev.; illus. circ. 20,000. (tabloid format; back issues avail.)

917.306 US ISSN 0742-6615
DZIENNIK ZWIAZKOWY/POLISH DAILY; an American daily in the Polish language. (Supplement avail.: Kalejdoskop) (Text in Polish) d. $80 (foreign $135). Alliance Printers and Publishers, Inc., 5711 N. Milwaukee Ave., Chicago, IL 60646. TEL 312-736-3343. FAX 312-763-3450. Ed. Wojciech Bialasiewicz. adv.; bk.rev. circ. 25,000. **Document type:** newspaper.

051 917.06 US
E M: EBONY MAN. 1985. w. $16. Johnson Publishing Company Co., Inc., 820 S. Michigan Ave., Chicago, IL 60605. TEL 312-322-9200. Ed. Alfred Fornay. adv.; bk.rev.; illus. circ. 200,000.

296 US ISSN 0737-9021
E M I E BULLETIN. 1981. q. $10 to individuals; institutions $15. (American Library Association, Ethnic Materials Information Exchange Round Table) David Cohen, Ed. & Pub., Queens College of the City University of New York, 65-30 Kissena Blvd., Flushing, NY 11367. TEL 718-997-3626. FAX 718-997-3753. bk.rev. circ. 800. **Document type:** newsletter.
Formerly (until 1983): E M I E Reporter.
Description: Emphasizes multicultural librarianship and the business activity of the EMIE Round Table, plus various booklists.

E R I C - C U E TRENDS AND ISSUES. (Educational Resource Information Center, Clearinghouse on Urban Education) see EDUCATION

E R I C CLEARINGHOUSE ON URBAN EDUCATION. DIGEST. see EDUCATION

970.1 974 US
EAGLE (NAUGATUCK). 1981. bi-m. $15 (foreign $30). Eagle Wing Press, Inc., Box 579-MO, Naugatuck, CT 06770. TEL 203-729-0035. Ed. Richard G. Carlson. adv.; bk.rev.; film rev.; illus.; stat. circ. 3,500. (tabloid format; back issues avail.) **Document type:** newspaper.
Formerly: Eagle Wing Press (ISSN 0740-834X)
Description: Native American news of New England.

970.1 US ISSN 0046-0915
EAGLE'S EYE. 1970. 2/yr. free. Brigham Young University, Student Leadership Development, 128 ELWC, Provo, UT 84602. TEL 801-378-7084. FAX 801-378-6366. Ed. Valerie Shewfelt. bk.rev. circ. 3,500.
Description: Contains items of interest to the American Indian and multicultural community.

296 001.3 IS
EAST AND MAGHREB. (Text mainly in Hebrew, occasionally in European languages; summaries in English) 1974. irreg., latest vol.6. $22 per vol. Bar-Ilan University Press, Ramat Gan 52900, Israel. TEL 972-3-531840. Ed. S. Schwarzfuchs. **Document type:** monographic series.
Description: Research in the history of the Jews in the Orient and North Africa.

917.309 US ISSN 0046-0966
EAST ST. LOUIS MONITOR. 1963. s-w. $25. Anne E. Jordan, Ed. & Pub., 1501 State St., Box 2137, East St. Louis, IL 62292-2137. adv.; bk.rev.; play rev. circ. 22,500. **Document type:** newspaper.
Description: Contains items of interest to the black community.

917.306 US
EAST - WEST TIES; Asian Pacific newsmagazine of U C Irvine. 1983? 3/yr. University of California, Irvine, Cross Cultural Center, Irvine, CA 92715. Ed.Bd. adv.; illus. circ. 5,000. (tabloid format)
Description: Covers topics of interest to Asian Americans.

915.4 CN
EASTERN NEWS. 1979. s-m. Box 1061, Stn. B, Mississauga, ON L4Y 2E0, Canada. TEL 905-858-7525. FAX 905-858-7951. Ed. Masood Khan. adv. contact: Shamin Ahmed.

917.306 US
EASTSIDE SUN. (Text in English, Spanish) 1945. w. $62.50 (effective Oct. 1993). Eastern Group Publications, Inc., 3643 E. First St., Los Angeles, CA 90063. TEL 213-263-5743. Ed. Dolores Sanchez. adv.; bk.rev. circ. 58,000. (back issues avail.) **Document type:** newspaper.
Supersedes: Mexican American Sun.
Description: Chicano and other Hispanic interests.

910.03 051 US ISSN 0012-9011
AP2
EBONY. 1945. m. $16 (foreign $28). Johnson Publishing Co., Inc., 820 S. Michigan Ave., Chicago, IL 60605. TEL 312-322-9200.
FAX 312-322-9375. Ed. Lerone Bennett Jr. adv.; bk.rev.; illus. circ. 1,800,000. (also avail. in microform from UMI; reprint service avail. from UMI) **Indexed:** Abr.R.G., Acad.Ind., Curr.Cont.Africa, Film Lit.Ind. (1973-), Hlth.Ind., Ind.Sel.Per., Jun.High.Mag.Abstr., Mag.Ind., Media Rev.Dig., PMR, PSI, R.G., TOM.
—Faxon; UnCover; UMI.
Description: Magazine geared to interests of black Americans. Features black Americans in politics, business and the arts.

296 US ISSN 0743-7757
ECHAD; a whole global anthology of Jewish writers. 1978. irreg., vol.5, 1990. price varies. Micah Publications, 255 Humphrey St., Marblehead, MA 01945. TEL 617-631-7601. Ed. Roberta Kalechofsky. circ. 1,000.

917.306 US
THE ECHO (PROVIDENCE); the Italian-American voice of Rhode Island. 1894. s-m. $19.95. Echo Publishing Company, 200 Dyer St., Providence, RI 02903-3902. TEL 401-621-8900.
FAX 401-273-8961. Ed. Trisha Guramma; Pub. Richard Baccari. adv. contact: Paula Cresto. bk.rev.; film rev. circ. 15,300. (tabloid format; also avail. in microfilm) **Document type:** newspaper.
Formerly: Italian Echo.
Description: Dedicated to reviving interest in Italian-American culture.

914.106 CN
ECO D'ITALIA. (Text in Italian) 1955. w. Can.$45($57) Zone Publishing Ltd., 3849 E. Hastings St., Burnaby, BC V5C 2H7, Canada. TEL 604-294-8707. FAX 604-291-1707. Ed. Anna Foschi; Pub. Daniel Iannuzzi. adv.; bk.rev. circ. 4,800. (tabloid format) **Document type:** newspaper.

ETHNIC INTERESTS

ECONOMIC IMPACT OF THE NEGRO TRAVELER. see *TRAVEL AND TOURISM*

910.03   US
ECORSE TELEGRAM. 1945. w. $25. J.C. Wall, Ed. & Pub., 4122 10th St., Ecorse, MI 48229. TEL 313-928-2955. FAX 313-928-2958. (Subscr. to: Box 4585, Detroit, MI 48204) adv. circ. 12,500. (tabloid format) **Document type:** newspaper.

917.306   US
EL EDITOR (LUBBOCK). (Text in English, Spanish) 1977. w. (Thu.) $56. El Editor Newspapers, 1502 Ave. M, Lubbock, TX 79401. TEL 806-763-3841. Pub. Bidal Aguero. adv. **Document type:** newspaper.

917.306   US
EL EDITOR PERMIAN BASIN. (Text in English, Spanish) 1981. w. (Wed.) $56. El Editor Permian Basin, 1401 Rankin Hwy., Midland, TX 79701. TEL 915-570-0405. FAX 915-687-3972. Ed. Manuel J. Orona. adv.; bk.rev. circ. 10,000. (back issues avail.) **Document type:** newspaper.

EDMONTON NATIVE NEWS. see *GENERAL INTEREST PERIODICALS — Canada*

059.94   UK
EESTI HAAL/ESTONIAN NEWS. (Text in Estonian) 1947. fortn. £15 (foreign £17) (effective Jan. 1993). Association of Estonians in Great Britain, c/o Estonian House, 18 Chepstow Villas, London W11 2RB, England. TEL 44-71-229-6700. FAX 44-71-792-0218. Ed. A. Eistrat. adv.; bk.rev. circ. 650. **Document type:** newsletter.
Description: Contains items of interest to the Estonian community in the U.K.

917.306   US
EINTRACHT. (Supplement avail.) 1921. w. $25. Walter Juengling, Ed. & Pub., 9456 N. Lawler, Skokie, IL 60077. TEL 708-677-9456. FAX 708-677-9471. adv.; bk.rev. circ. 25,000. **Document type:** newspaper.

917.306   US
EKO MAGAZINE.* (Text in Spanish) 1984. bi-w. Box 430969, Houston, TX 77243-0969. TEL 713-932-1906. adv. circ. 41,000.
Description: Contains interviews with entertainment personalities. Covers beauty, advice and family psychology, music, culture, cooking, and good family living.

296 296   UK   ISSN 0142-2049
LE'ELA; a journal of judaism today. 1975. s-a. £8 (foreign £12). (Office of the Chief Rabbi) Jews' College Publications, 44a Albert Rd., London NW4 2SJ, England. TEL 081-203-6427. FAX 081-203-6420. Ed. Philip Ginsbury. adv.; bk.rev. circ. 5,000. **Document type:** academic/scholarly publication.
Description: Contains articles about the role of Jewish people in society and perspectives on various issues of current interest, studies and reviews.

974.8   US
ES ELBEDRITSCH; All die Nei-ichkeete unn Schtofft vun Deitsche Wege. (Text in English, Pennsylvania Dutch) 3/yr. $40 membership includes all Society publications. Pennsylvania German Society, Box 397, Birdsboro, PA 19508. TEL 215-582-1441. Ed. Don Yoder. **Document type:** newsletter.
Description: Contains news of Society activities and items of interest to students of Pennsylvania Dutch folklore, culture and history.

ELDER VOICES. see *GERONTOLOGY AND GERIATRICS*

914.406   FR
ELGAR. 1932. m. 50 F. 4 rue Brochant, 75017 Paris, France. Ed. Pantxika Beraza. circ. 18,000.
Description: Contains items of interest to the Basque community.

059.8   AT
ELLINIS. (Text in Greek) 1969. w. Aus.$130. Foreign Language Publications Pty. Ltd., P.O. Box 146, Broadway, Sydney, N.S.W. 2007, Australia. TEL 02-660-2033. FAX 02-692-0649. Ed. Mrs. Patsalidou. adv. contact: George Antoniou. bk.rev. circ. 10,000. **Document type:** newspaper.
Description: Contains items of interest to the Greek community.

919.406   AT
EMEK. m. Aus.$6. Australian Turkish Cultural Association, 85 Church St., Richmond, Vic. 3121, Australia. TEL 428-8250. Ed. Kenan Ozturk. adv. circ. 3,000.

910.03 051   US   ISSN 0899-1154
E185.5
EMERGE;* our voice in today's world. 1989. 10/yr. $16.97. Emerge Communications, Inc., 1700 N. Moore St., Ste. 2200, Arlington, NY 22209-1903. (Subscr. to: Box 7127, Red Oak, IA 51591-0127) Ed. George E. Curry. adv.; bk.rev.; film rev.; music rev. circ. 150,000.
Description: General interest newsmonthly written and targeted to the upwardly-mobile African American. Covers issues, ideas and events from a black perspective.

059.91   UK   ISSN 0013-7596
ENFYS. (Text in English, Welsh) 1948. q. £10. Wales International, Muriau Gwyn, Beulah, Newcastle Emlyn, Dyfed SA38 9QE, Wales. TEL 0239-811655. Ed. Gerwyn Morgan. adv.; bk.rev.; illus. circ. 2,000. **Document type:** newsletter.
Description: Keeps people of Welsh descent in touch with Wales.

052   UK   ISSN 0013-8509
ENQUIRY.* 1970. q. 60p. Trinidad & Tobago Association, 380 Green Lanes, London, N4, England. Ed. C.J. Mungo. adv.; bk.rev.; play rev.; charts. (processed)
Description: Contains items of interest to the West Indian community.

910.03   IV   ISSN 0013-8630
ENTENTE AFRICAINE. (Text in French) 1969. q. $11. Inter Afrique Presse, 01 Box 3901, Abidjan, Ivory Coast. Ed. Justin Vieyra. adv.; bk.rev.; illus. circ. 15,000. **Indexed:** Curr.Cont.Africa, Rural Recreat.Tour.Abstr., World Agri.Econ.& Rural Sociol.Abstr.

917.306   US
ENTERESE!. (Text in Spanish) vol.15, 1993. m. $18. Sun Periodical Corp., Box 42423, Miami, FL 33152. (Subscr. to: Spanish Periodical & Book Sales, 10100 N.W. 25th St., Miami FL 33172) Dir. Julian Dominguez. adv. **Document type:** consumer publication.
Description: Covers general interest and celebrity stories.

301.45   US
EQUAL OPPORTUNITY. 1969. 3/yr. $13. Equal Opportunity Publications, Inc., 150 Motor Pkwy. No. 420, Hauppauge, NY 11788-5108. TEL 516-261-8899. FAX 516-261-8935. Ed. James Schneider. adv.; bk.rev. circ. 15,000. —Faxon; UnCover.
Formerly: Equal Opportunity: The Minority Student Magazine (ISSN 0071-1039)
Description: Entry-level career magazine for minority college graduates.

919.7   CN
EQUALITY NEWS.* w. Equality News International, 2627 Eglinton Ave., E., Ste. 3, Toronto, ON M1K 2S2, Canada. TEL 416-266-9711. FAX 416-282-6534. adv. circ. 35,000.

939   TU   ISSN 1010-867X
ERDEM. (Text and summaries in English, French, German and Turkish) 1985. 3/yr. $30. Ataturk Kultur Merkezi - Ataturk Cultural Centre, Ataturk Bulvari 225, Kavaklidere, Ankara, Turkey. TEL 90-312-4285286. FAX 90-312-4269330. Ed. Sadik Tural. circ. 5,000. **Document type:** academic/scholarly publication.

ESKIMO. see *RELIGIONS AND THEOLOGY — Roman Catholic*

ESSENCE (NEW YORK); the magazine for today's black woman. see *WOMEN'S INTERESTS*

917.306   US   ISSN 0748-3058
ESTO AMERICA.* 1983. 6/yr. $30. Esto America Publishing, 113 E. 31st St., Ste. 4C, New York, NY 10016. TEL 212-722-8581. (Subscr. to: 1742 Second Ave., Rm. 122, New York, NY 10128) Ed. Peter Ristsoo. adv.; bk.rev. circ. 1,000.
Description: Contains items of interest to the Estonian community.

296   IS
ET-MOL. 1975 bi-m. IS.15. P.O. Box 23078, Tel Aviv 61230, Israel. Ed.Bd.

ETHNIC AMERICAN VOLUNTARY ORGANIZATIONS. see *SOCIAL SERVICES AND WELFARE*

914.2 323.4   UK   ISSN 0141-9870
HT1501
ETHNIC AND RACIAL STUDIES. 1978. q. £28 (foreign £35) to individuals; institutions £70(foreign £75). Routledge, 11 New Fetter Ln., London EC4P 4EE, England. TEL 071-583-9855. FAX 071-583-0701. TELEX 263398-ROUT-G. (Subscr. to: ITPS Ltd., Cheriton House, Andover, Hants SP10 5BE, England. TEL 0264-342919. FAX 0264-342807) Ed. Martin Bulmer. adv.; bk.rev.; index. (back issues avail.) **Indexed:** A.B.C.Pol.Sci., Adol.Ment.Hlth.Abstr., Amer.Hist.& Life, Asian-Pac.Econ.Lit., ASSIA, Curr.Cont., Documentatieblad, E.I., Hist.Abstr., Lang.& Lang.Behav.Abstr., Mult.Ed.Abstr., Per.Islam. (1991-), Soc.Sci.Ind., Soc.Work Res.& Abstr., SSCI. **Document type:** academic/scholarly publication. —BLDSC (3814.834000); Faxon; UnCover; SWETS. CCC.
Description: Provides an interdisciplinary academic forum for the presentation of research and theoretical analysis, drawing on sociology, social policy, anthropology, political science, economics, international relations, history and social psychology.

914   US   ISSN 0278-9078
E184.A1
ETHNIC FORUM; journal of ethnic studies and ethnic bibliography. 1980. 2/yr. $22.50 to individuals; institutions $27.50. Kent State University, Center for the Study of Ethnic Publications, University Library, Rm. 318, Kent, OH 44242. TEL 216-672-2121. FAX 216-672-2782. Ed. Lubomyr R. Wynar. adv.; bk.rev. circ. 500. (back issues avail.) **Indexed:** Amer.Bibl.Slavic & E.Eur.Stud., Amer.Hist.& Life, C.I.J.E., Hist.Abstr. —Faxon; UnCover.

917.309   US   ISSN 0308-6860
GN495.4   CODEN: ETGREQ
ETHNIC GROUPS. 4/yr. (in 1 vol., 4 nos./vol.) 98 ECU (effective 1993). Gordon and Breach Science Publishers, 820 Town Center Dr., Langhorne, PA 19047. TEL 215-750-2642. FAX 215-750-6343. (UK subscr. to: P.C. Box 90, Reading, Berkshire RG1 8JL, England. TEL 0734-560-080) Eds. A.L. LaRuffa, Joel Savishinsky. adv.; bk.rev.; index. (also avail. in microform from MIM) **Indexed:** Amer.Bibl.Slavic & E.Eur.Stud., Amer.Hist.& Life, Anthropol.Lit., Hist.Abstr., Lang.& Lang.Behav.Abstr., Mid.East: Abstr.& Ind., Soc.Sci.Ind., SSCI. —BLDSC (3814.835300); Faxon; UnCover. CCC. **Incorporates:** Afro-American Studies (ISSN 0002-0575)
Refereed Serial

910   US   ISSN 0272-9865
ETHNIC GROUPS (BOCA RATON). (Subseries of: S I R S Social Issues (ISSN 0740-3127)) 1975. a. price varies; a. supplement $17. Social Issues Resources Series, Box 2348, Boca Raton, FL 33427-2348. TEL 407-994-0079; 800-232-7477. FAX 407-994-4704. (looseleaf format; also avail. in microfiche; back issues avail.)
Description: Reprints articles that explore what prompted various ethnic groups to settle in the U.S., how they have been treated, and their hopes for the future.

917.306   US
ETHNIC GROUPS IN CALIFORNIA; a guide to organizations and information resources. 1981. irreg. 2nd ed., 1988. $21.50. California Institute of Public Affairs, Box 189040, Sacramento, CA 95818. TEL 916-442-CIPA. FAX 916-442-2478. (Affiliate: The Claremont Graduate School) circ. 500. **Document type:** directory.
Description: Lists organizations and publications concerned with nearly 100 ethnic groups.

917.06   US
ETHNIC HISTORY OF CHICAGO. irreg. price varies. University of Illinois Press, 1325 S. Oak St., Champaign, IL 61820. TEL 217-333-0950. FAX 217-244-8082. **Document type:** academic/scholarly publication.
Refereed Serial

ETHNIC INTERESTS

917.306 US ISSN 0738-1719
E184.A1
ETHNIC INFORMATION SOURCES OF THE U S. 1976. irreg., 2nd ed., 1983. $175. Gale Research Inc., 835 Penobscot Bldg., Detroit, MI 48226. TEL 313-961-2242. FAX 313-961-6083. TELEX 810-221-7086. Eds. Paul Wasserman, Alice Kennington.
Description: Sources of information on minorities in the U.S.

920 UK
ETHNIC MINORITIES DIRECTORY; a commercial and social directory of African, Asian, and Caribbean communities in Britain. Variant title: E M Directory. 1994. irreg. £40. Hansib Publishing Ltd., Tower House, 3rd Fl., 139-149 Fonthill Rd., London N4 3HF, England. TEL 071-281-1191. FAX 071-263-9656. **Document type:** directory.
Description: Lists ethnic minority businesses and social organizations in the U.K.

917.306 US
ETHNIC REPORTER. 1976. s-a. $35 membership. National Association for Ethnic Studies, Inc., Dept. of English, Arizona State University, Tempe, AZ 85287-0302. TEL 602-965-2197. FAX 602-965-3451. Ed. Miguel A. Carranza. adv.; bk.rev.; index. circ. 325. (also avail. in microfiche; back issues avail.) **Indexed:** Amer.Hist.& Life, Hist.Abstr., M.L.A. **Document type:** newsletter. Former titles: Ethnic Newsletter; N A E S Newsletter.
Description: Reports on the activities of the Association, provides news on conferences and research opportunities of interest to members.

917.306 US
ETHNIC REVIEW. irreg. Hungarian Freedom Fighters (Guardian) World Federation, Inc., Box 441, Gracie Sta., New York, NY 10028.

915.5 CE ISSN 1010-5832
ETHNIC STUDIES REPORT. (Text in English) 1983. s-a. $18. International Centre for Ethnic Studies, 554-1 Peradeniya Rd., Kandy, Sri Lanka. TEL 08-23095. Ed. K.M. de Silva. **Document type:** academic/scholarly publication.

ETHNIC WOMAN. see WOMEN'S STUDIES

ETHNICITY & DISEASE. see MEDICAL SCIENCES

919.6 915.9 FR ISSN 0295-9151
GN380
ETHNIES; droits de l'homme et peuples autochtones. 1985. s-a. 250 F. (foreign 280 F.). Survival International (France), 45, rue du Faubourg-du-Temple, 75010 Paris, France. TEL 42-41-47-62. FAX 42-45-34-51. bk.rev.
Description: Reports on indigenous tribes throughout the world.

917.306 US
ETHNIKOS KIRIX/NATIONAL HERALD. Variant title: National Herald Greek-American Daily. (Text in Greek) 1915. d. $129. National Herald, Inc., 41-17 Crescent St., Long Island City, NY 11101. TEL 718-784-5255. FAX 718-472-0510. Ed. A. Diamataris. circ. 50,000. **Document type:** newspaper.

ETHOS - DIE ZEITSCHRIFT FUER DIE GANZE FAMILIE. see RELIGIONS AND THEOLOGY

945.206 IT
ETNIE; scienza, politica e cultura dei popoli minoritari. 1980. s-a. L.35000 (foreign L.70000). Centro Gutenberg, Via Bligny 22, 20136 Milan, Italy. TEL 02-8375525. Ed. Miro Merelli. circ. 5,000. (back issues avail.)

970.3 305.897 CN ISSN 0701-1008
E99.E7
ETUDES INUIT. Variant title: Inuit Studies. (Text in English, French) 1977. s-a. $29 to individuals; institutions $47; students $18. Inuksiutiit Katimajiit Association, Inc., c/o Pavillon Jean-Durand, Universite Laval, Quebec, PQ G1K 7P4, Canada. TEL 418-656-2353. FAX 418-656-3023. Ed. Francois Therien. adv.; bk.rev. circ. 600. (back issues avail.) **Indexed:** Abstr.Anthropol., Anthropol.Lit., ASTIS, Bibl.Ling., Bull.Signal., M.L.A., Pt.de Rep. (1983-), Sociol.Abstr.
Description: Devoted to the study of Inuit societies, either traditional or contemporary, in the perspective of the social sciences.

940 AU ISSN 0014-2492
EUROPA ETHNICA; Vierteljahresschrift fuer Nationalitaetenfragen. (Text in English, French and German) 1958. q. S.430. Wilhelm Braumueller, Universitaets-Verlagsbuchhandlung GmbH, Servitengasse 5, A-1092 Vienna, Austria. TEL 0222-3191159. FAX 0222-3102805. adv.; bk.rev.; index. circ. 1,000. **Indexed:** Amer.Hist.& Life, Hist.Abstr., Lang.& Lang.Behav.Abstr., Per.Islam. (1991-). **Document type:** academic/scholarly publication.

970.1 GW ISSN 0238-1486
EUROPEAN REVIEW OF NATIVE AMERICAN STUDIES. 1987. s-a. DM.40($25) c/o Christian Feest, Fasanenweg 4A, 63674 Altenstadt, Germany. TEL 06047-67566. adv.; bk.rev. circ. 600. **Indexed:** Anthropol.Lit., Bibl.Ling. **Document type:** academic/scholarly publication.

EVANGELICAL MAGAZINE OF WALES. see RELIGIONS AND THEOLOGY — Protestant

910.03 US
EVERY WEDNESDAY. 1984. w. Afro-American Co. of Baltimore City, 628 N. Eutaw St., Baltimore, MD 21201. TEL 410-728-8200. FAX 410-383-3213. circ. 15,000 (controlled).
Description: Contains general consumer information and some articles of interest to the African American community.

910.03 US ISSN 0164-9329
EVERYBODY'S; the Caribbean-American magazine. 1977. 10/yr. $13.95. Herman Hall Communications, Inc., 1630 Nostrand Ave., Brooklyn, NY 11226. TEL 718-941-1879. FAX 718-941-1886. Ed. Basil Wilson.

910.03 US ISSN 0893-5017
EXCEL MAGAZINE; quarterly journal for black professionals. 1984. q. $12 for 5 nos. P O C (People of Color) Enterprises, Inc., 1347 Divisadero St., Ste. 620, San Francisco, CA 94115. TEL 415-567-2000. FAX 415-267-3056. (Subscr. to: Box 12100, San Francisco, CA 94112) Ed. Herb Boyd. adv.; bk.rev.; film rev.; play rev.; illus. circ. 150,000.
Formerly: B U M P (Black Upwardly Mobile Professionals).
Description: For today's Black professionals in America.

EXECUTIVE SUITE. see BUSINESS AND ECONOMICS

296 CN
EXODUS. 1983. m. Can.$12 (foreign Can.$24). Jewish Russian Community Centre of Toronto, 18 Rockford Rd., Willowdale, Ont. M2R 3K3, Canada. TEL 416-665-9600. FAX 416-665-9644. Ed. Marsha Gershtein. adv. circ. 5,300.

917.306 US ISSN 0730-904X
E184.A1 CODEN: EETSEN
EXPLORATIONS IN ETHNIC STUDIES. (Supplement avail: Explorations in Sights and Sounds) 1978. s-a. $35 membership (includes all NAES publications). National Association for Ethnic Studies, Inc., Dept. of English, Arizona State University, Tempe, AZ 85287-0302. TEL 602-965-2197. FAX 602-965-3451. Ed. Miguel Carranza. bk.rev. circ. 350. (back issues avail.) **Indexed:** Adol.Ment.Hlth.Abstr., Amer.Bibl.Slavic & E.Eur.Stud., Amer.Hist.& Life, Hist.Abstr., M.L.A. **Document type:** academic/scholarly publication.
—BLDSC (3842.205200); UnCover; UMI.
Description: Interdisciplinary study of ethnicity, ethnic groups, intergroup relations, and the cultural life of ethnic peoples. Serves as an advocate for socially responsible research.
Refereed Serial

910.03 US ISSN 0733-3323
E184.A1
EXPLORATIONS IN SIGHTS AND SOUNDS. (Supplement to: Explorations in Ethnic Studies) 1981. a. $35 membership (includes all NAES publications). National Association for Ethnic Studies, Inc., Dept. of English, Arizona State University, Tempe, AZ 85287-0302. TEL 602-965-2197. FAX 602-965-3451. Ed. Miguel Carranza. adv.; bk.rev. circ. 350. (back issues avail.) **Document type:** academic/scholarly publication.
—BLDSC (3842.207470); UMI.
Description: Covers print and non-print media of interest to teachers, students, librarians, and scholars in ethnic studies as well as to community organizations.

056.1 US
EXTRA - SPANISH LANGUAGE NEWSPAPER. (Text in Spanish) 1987. w. $1.44 per no. 2405 S. Buckner Blvd., Box 270432, Dallas, TX 75227-0432. TEL 214-388-0506. FAX 214-388-8436. Ed. Emmy Silva. circ. 27,962. **Document type:** newspaper.
Description: Provides general news.

917.306 US
F F P BULLETIN. 1973. q. $5. Friends of the Filipino People, Box 2125, Durham, NC 27702. TEL 919-489-0002. Ed. Jim Kaufmann. circ. 1,200. **Indexed:** HR Rep. **Document type:** bulletin.

296 UK
F W Z REVIEW. 1974. s-a. membership. Federation of Women Zionists of Great Britain and Ireland, 107 Gloucester Place, London W1H 4BY, England. Ed.Bd. adv.; bk.rev.; charts; illus.; tr.lit. circ. 15,000.
Supersedes: Jewish Woman's Review.
Description: In-house forum for members of the Federation.

910.03 US ISSN 0427-8879
FACTS. Variant title: Tacoma Facts. 1962. w. $40. Alzene Publishing Co., 2765 E. Cherry St., Box 22015, Seattle, WA 98122. TEL 206-324-0552. Ed. Fitzgerald Beaver. adv.; film rev.; play rev. circ. 10,000. (also avail. in microform from UMI) **Indexed:** Art & Archaeol.Tech.Abstr., World Alum.Abstr.
Description: Contains items of interest to the black community.

914.8 DK ISSN 0107-6183
FACTSHEET DENMARK. French edition: Documentation Danoise (ISSN 0107-6205); German edition: Daenische Themen (ISSN 0107-6191) 1981. irreg. free. Udenrigsministeriet, Asiatisk Plads 2, DK-1448 Copenhagen K, Denmark. Eds. Preben Hansen, Flemming Rovsen Olsen. illus. **Document type:** government publication.

917.306 US
LA FAMILIA DE HOY. bi-m. Whittle Communications L.P., 333 Main Ave., Knoxville, TN 37902. TEL 615-595-5300. FAX 615-595-5670. Ed. Ashley Shoemaker.
Description: Provides information to Hispanics about life in the United States.

917.306 US
LA FAMILIA DE LA CIUDAD; ideas para una vila mejor. English edition: City Family. (Editions in English, Spanish) q. Box 748, Ansonia Sta., New York, NY 10023.

914.306 301.412 US
FEDERATION FEMININE FRANCO-AMERICAINE. BULLETIN. 1932. q. $2. (Federation Feminine Franco-Americaine) Layfayette Press, 140 Blaine St., Manchester, NH 03102. TEL 603-622-8142. (Subscr. to: Eleanore Perron, 120 S. Branch Pkwy., Springfield, MA 01118) Ed. Marthe Biron Peloguin. (also avail. in microfilm; back issues avail.)

918.306 CL
FELEY KAM FELELAY; revista de produccion mapuche. q. $200 to Mapuche individuals; Chileans $300; institutions and foreign $500. Casilla 33005, Estacion Central, Santiago, Chile. Ed. Fernando Kilaleo A.
Description: Covers aspects of the Mapuche indigenous culture.

917.309 US
DAS FENSTER. (Text in German) 1904. m. $15. Die Hausfrau, Inc., 1060 Gaines School Rd., Ste. B-3, Athens, GA 30605-3136. TEL 706-548-4382. FAX 706-548-4382. Eds. Roswitha Shapland, Alex Mazeika. adv.; bk.rev. circ. 20,000.
   Formerly: Hausfrau (ISSN 0017-842X)
   Description: Contains articles of interest to the German community.

FIAT LUX. see *PUBLIC ADMINISTRATION*

917.309 US ISSN 0015-0991
FILIPINO-AMERICAN HERALD.* 1969. m. $6. Emiliano A. Francisco, Ed. & Pub., 2824 S. Brandon, Seattle, WA 98108-3028. TEL 206-725-6606. adv. circ. 8,000. (tabloid format)

915.906 CN ISSN 1186-1436
FILIPINO JOURNAL. 1987. s-m. Molave Publishing Inc., 483 Bannatyne Ave., Winnipeg, MB R3A 0G2, Canada. TEL 204-943-4512. FAX 204-489-8894. Ed. Linda Cantiveros; Pub. Rod Cantiveros. adv. circ. 5,000. **Document type:** newspaper.

948 US
FINNAM NEWSLETTER. (Text mainly in English; occasionally in Finnish) 1962. q. $7.50 membership. Finnish-American Historical Society of the West, Box 5522, Portland, OR 97208. TEL 503-654-0448. Ed. Gene A. Knapp. bk.rev. circ. 500. (back issues avail.) **Document type:** newsletter.
   Description: Covers current affairs and Finnish-American history.

FINNISH AMERICAN CHAMBER OF COMMERCE NEWSLETTER. see *BUSINESS AND ECONOMICS — Chamber Of Commerce Publications*

917.306 929 US
FLEMISH AMERICAN HERITAGE. 1983. s-a. $10 membership includes 2 magazines and 2 newsletters; libraries $5. Genealogical Society of Flemish Americans, 18740-13 Mile Rd., Roseville, MI 48066. Ed. Margaret Roets. adv.; index. circ. 235. (back issues avail.)
   Description: General information and articles on Flemish culture and history. Includes specific family charts.

910.03 US
FLORENCE BLACK SUN. 1982. w. $25. S C Black Media Group, 1310 Harden St., Columbia, SC 29204. TEL 803-799-5252. FAX 803-799-7709. Ed. Issac Washington. adv. contact: Melocy Harris. illus. circ. 5,500. **Document type:** newspaper.

910.03 US
FLORIDA SENTINEL BULLETIN. 1945. s-w. $44. Box 3363, Tampa, FL 33601. TEL 813-248-1921. FAX 813-248-4507. Ed. Gwen Hayes. adv. contact: Betty Dawkins. circ. 23,000. (tabloid format) **Document type:** newspaper.

FLOWER OF THE FOREST BLACK GENEALOGICAL JOURNAL. see *GENEALOGY AND HERALDRY*

FOC NOU; revista al servei dels Cristians. see *RELIGIONS AND THEOLOGY*

FOCUS (WASHINGTON, 1970). see *POLITICAL SCIENCE — Civil Rights*

051 US ISSN 8750-5622
FOCUS MAGAZINE (HARTFORD). 1980. bi-m. $12. Inquirer Communication Group, Inc., 3281 Main St., Hartford, CT 06120. (Subscr.to: Box 538, Hartford, CT 06141) Ed. William R. Hales. adv.; bk.rev. circ. 225,000. (back issues avail.)

296 IS
FOLK UN MEDINE. (Text in Yiddish) 1973. $7. Committee for Jewish Culture, 9 Mendele St., Fl. 4, Tel Aviv, Israel. (Subscr. to: P.O. Box 1217, Tel Aviv, Israel) Ed. I. Yahosowicz. bk.rev. circ. 1,300.
   Description: Covers Jewish interests.

296 IS ISSN 0302-8186
DS101
FOLK, VELT UN MEDINE/AM, OLAM U-MEDINAH. (Text in Yiddish) m. Komitet far Yidisher Kultur in Yisroel, 228 Bnei Ephraim St., Maoz-Aviv, Tel Aviv, Israel. (Co-sponsor: World Jewish Congress)
   Formerly: Folk Un Medine - Am u-Medinah.
   Description: Covers Jewish interests.

FORD FOUNDATION ANNUAL REPORT. see *SOCIAL SCIENCES: COMPREHENSIVE WORKS*

FORD FOUNDATION REPORT. see *SOCIAL SCIENCES: COMPREHENSIVE WORKS*

970.1 US
FORT APACHE SCOUT. 1962. bi-w. $8 to reservation residents; state residents $10; elswhere in the U.S. $16. (Fort Apache Tribe) White Mountain Apache Tribe, P.O. Box 700, Whiteriver, AZ 85941-0100. (P.O. Box 898, Whiteriver, AZ 85941-0898) adv.; bk.rev. circ. 2,450. (looseleaf format)
   Description: Contains items of interest to the American Indian community.

910.03 US
FORT LAUDERDALE - WESTSIDE GAZETTE. 1971. w. $22.50. 701 N.W. 18th Ave., Fort Lauderdale, FL 33311. TEL 305-523-5115. FAX 305-522-2553. (Subscr. to: Box 5304, Ft. Lauderdale, FL 33310) Ed. Pamela Lewis. bk.rev. circ. 35,000. **Document type:** newspaper.

917.106 CN ISSN 0832-3453
FORTNIGHTLY AL-HILAL. (Text in Urdu) 1972. fortn. $20. Lateef Owaisi, Ed. & Pub., 338 Hollyberry Tr., Willowdale, ON M2H 2P6, Canada. TEL 416-493-4374. Ed. Umme Ali. adv.; bk.rev. circ. 2,000. **Document type:** newspaper.

915.4 CN ISSN 1194-0980
FORTNIGHTLY UNIVERSAL NEWS. (Text in English, Urdu) 1991. s-m. Can.$20($23) (foreign Can.$40). P.O. Box 21051, Bridgeview P.O., Windsor, ON N9R 3T4, Canada. TEL 519-253-5851. FAX 519-253-8658. Ed. Amir Khan. circ. 1,000.

296 US
FORUM (NEW YORK, 1982). 1982. 7/yr. New York University, Jewish Culture Foundation, Loeb Student Center, 566 LaGuardia Pl., New York, NY 10012-1097. TEL 212-998-4945. Ed.Bd. adv.; bk.rev.; film rev.; play rev. circ. 3,000. (tabloid format)

917.309 US ISSN 0015-8399
DK508.A2
FORUM (SCRANTON); a Ukrainian review. 1967. q. $10 (foreign $8.50). Ukrainian Fraternal Association, 440 Wyoming Ave., Scranton, PA 18503. TEL 717-342-0937. FAX 717-347-5649. Ed. Andrew Gregorovich. bk.rev.; film rev.; play rev.; bibl.; charts; illus. circ. 4,500. Indexed: M.L.A.
   Description: Contains items of interest to the Ukrainian community in the U.S.A. and Canada.

322.4 US ISSN 0015-8577
FORUMEER.* (Text in English and Spanish) vol.39, 1978. m. $10. American Gl Forum of the United States, 621 Gabaldon Rd., N.W., Albuquerque, NM 87104. TEL 505-243-7551. Ed. Louis W. Gonzalez. adv.; bk.rev.; illus. circ. 6,500. (tabloid format; also avail. in microform from UMI)

296 US ISSN 1051-340X
FORWARD (NEW YORK). 1990. w. $34.46. Forward Association, 45 E. 33rd St., New York, NY 10016. TEL 212-889-8200. FAX 212-447-6406. Ed. Seth Lipsky. circ. 40,000. **Document type:** newspaper.
   Description: Publishes items of interest to the Jewish community.

910.03 US
FORWARD TIMES. 1960. w. $25. Houston Forward Times Publishing Co., c/o Lenora Carter, 4411 Almeda Rd., Box 8346, Houston, TX 77004. TEL 713-526-4727. Ed. George "Bud" Johnson. adv. circ. 160,000.
   Description: Contains items of interest to the black community.

FOUNDER'S SOUNDER. see *MUSIC*

FOUR DIRECTIONS. see *ARCHAEOLOGY*

917.306 US ISSN 0747-2757
AP21
FRANCE - AMERIQUE. (Text and summaries in French) 1828. w. $42. Trocadero Publishing, Inc., 1560 Broadway, Ste. 511, New York, NY 10036. TEL 212-221-6700. FAX 212-221-6997. Ed. J.L. Turlin. adv.; bk.rev.; film rev.; play rev. circ. 20,000. (also avail. in microform) **Document type:** newspaper.

296 809 GW ISSN 0342-0078
FRANKFURTER JUDAISTISCHE BEITRAEGE. 1973. a. price varies. Gesellschaft zur Foerderung Judaistischer Studien e.V., Postfach 150216, 60062 Frankfurt a.M., Germany. TEL 069-7982677. bk.rev.; index. circ. 250.
   Document type: academic/scholarly publication.
   Description: Contains items of interest to the Jewish community.

DE FRANSE NEDERLANDEN/PAYS-BAS FRANCAIS. see *LITERARY AND POLITICAL REVIEWS*

FREE SONS REPORTER. see *CLUBS*

323.4 US ISSN 0016-061X
HT1581.A2
FREEDOMWAYS; a quarterly review of the Freedom Movement. 1961. q. $7.50. Freedomways Associates, Inc., 799 Broadway, Ste. 542, New York, NY 10003. TEL 212-477-3985. Eds. Esther Jackson, Jean Carey Bond. adv.; bk.rev.; bibl.; illus. circ. 7,000. (a so avail. in microform from UMI; back issues avail.; reprint service avail. from UMI,KTO) Indexed: Alt.Press Ind., Amer.Hist.& Life, C.I.J.E., Film Lit.Ind., Hist.Abstr., Ind.Per.Blacks, Media Rev.Dig., Soc.Sci.Ind.

FROM MY BOOKSHELF; books noted for you. see *LITERATURE*

052 UK
FRONTLINE. 1981. a. £9. Karnak House, 300 Westbourne Park Rd., London W11 1EH, England. FAX 01-229-3086. Ed. Amon Saba Saakana. adv.; bk.rev.; film rev.; play rev.; illus. circ. 3,000. (back issues avail.)

915.124 US
FUJIAN QIAO BAO/NEWS OF FUJIAN. (Text in Chinese) w. $41.80. China Books & Periodicals, Inc., 2929 24th St., San Francisco, CA 94110. TEL 415-282-2994. FAX 415-282-0994. **Document type:** newspaper.
   Description: For Fukienese living outside of China.

917.309 US
FURDEK.* 1960. a. First Catholic Slovak Union, 6611 Rockside Rd., Cleveland, OH 44131-2398. Ed. Joseph C. Krajsa. bibl.; index.
   Description: Contains articles of interest to the Slovakian community.

917.306 320 US ISSN 1062-3868
E184.G3
G A N P A C BRIEF. 1983. m. $50 (effective July 1993). German-American National Political Action Committee, Box 1137, Santa Monica, CA 90406. FAX 903-425-6835. Ed. Hans Schmidt. (back issues avail.) **Document type:** newsletter.
   Description: Covers politics, race, nationalism and world economy from a German viewpoint.

G B U REPORTER. (Greater Beneficial Union of Pittsburgh) see *INSURANCE*

973
AN GAEL. 1975. q. $25. An Claidheamh Soluis - Irish Arts Center, 553 W. 51st St., New York, NY 10019. TEL 212-757-3318. Ed. Sandy Boyle. adv.; bk.rev.; illus. circ. 3,500.
   Former titles: Ais-Eiri (ISSN 0360-5388) & Sword of Light.
   Description: Contains articles of interest to the Irish community.

296 IS ISSN 0334-4258
DS135.P6
GAL-ED; on the history of the Jews in Poland. (Text in Hebrew; summaries in English) 1973. irreg., vol.12, 1990. $30. Tel Aviv University, Diaspora Research Institute, c/o Publication Department, 69978 Ramat Aviv, Israel. FAX 972-3-6409648. TELEX 342171-VERSY-IL. Ed. E. Melzer. Indexed: Amer.Hist.& Life, Hist.Abstr. **Document type:** academic/scholarly publication.

915.406 UK ISSN 0961-7140
GARAVI GUJARAT. (Text in Gujarati) 1968. w. £19 (rest of Europe £40; elsewhere £55). Garavi Gujarat Publications Ltd., Garavi Gujarat House, 1-2 Silex St., London SE1 0DW, England. TEL 071-928-1234. FAX 071-261-0055. Ed. Ramniklal Solanki. adv. contact: Jayanti Solanki. bk.rev. circ. 42,000.

ETHNIC INTERESTS

916.306 282   US   ISSN 0896-3371
GARSAS. 1917. m. $5. Lithuanian Catholic Alliance, 71-73 S. Washington St., Wilkes Barre, PA 18701. TEL 717-823-8876. Eds. Florence Eckert, Rev. Cornelius Bucmys. bk.rev. circ. 2,000. **Document type:** newspaper.

910.03   US
GARY AMERICAN. 1927. w. $12. 2268 Broadway, Gary, IN 46407. TEL 219-883-4903. Ed. Fred Harris. adv. circ. 12,000. (tabloid format; back issues avail.) **Document type:** newspaper.

GASPESIE. see *HISTORY — History Of North And South America*

917.306   US
GAZETA POLSKA. (Text in Polish) w. Michal Kucheida Chemigraph Co., 5242 W. Diversey Ave., Chicago, IL 60639. TEL 312-685-1281. FAX 312-283-1675. Ed.Bd. **Document type:** newspaper.

917.106   CN
GAZZETTA.* (Text in English and Italian) 1972. w. Can.$10. La Gazzetta Publishing Co. Ltd., 909 Howard Ave., Windsor, Ont. N9A 1S3, Canada. TEL 519-253-8883. FAX 519-253-3280. Ed. Walter Temelini. adv. circ. 10,000. (tabloid format) **Indexed:** Can.Lit.Ind.
Description: Contains items of interest to the Italian community.

GEBORENER DEUTSCHER; a newsletter for German-born adoptees and their birth-adoptive families. see *GENEALOGY AND HERALDRY*

DIE GEMEINDE. see *POLITICAL SCIENCE*

GENERATION AFTER. see *HISTORY*

917.906 970.1   US
GENTE DE AZTLAN. once every 5 weeks during academic yr. 308 Westwood Pl., 112D Kerckhoff Hall, Los Angeles, CA 90024. TEL 213-825-9836. circ. 10,000.
Description: Student publications at UCLA to serve the Native American, Chicano and Latino communities.

910.03   US
GENTLEMAN OF COLOR.* 1978. m. $15. Thomas Rivers Publishing Co., 16781 Torrence Ave., No. 354, Lansing, IL 60438-6018. adv. circ. 230,000.
Description: Contains articles of interest to the Black community.

917.306   US
GERMAN AMERICAN JOURNAL. 1958. m. $15. German American National Congress, 4740 N. Western Ave., Chicago, IL 60625. TEL 312-275-1100. FAX 312-274-4010. Ed. Ernst Ott. circ. 10,000. **Document type:** newspaper.

917.1   CN   ISSN 0316-8603
GERMAN-CANADIAN YEARBOOK/DEUTSCHKANADISCHES JAHRBUCH. (Text in English and German) 1973. a. Can.$19. Historical Society of Mecklenburg Upper Canada, P.O. Box 1251, Sta. K, Toronto, ON M4P 3E5, Canada. TEL 416-635-6529. Ed. Harmut Froeschle. bk.rev.; illus. circ. 1,000. **Indexed:** Amer.Bibl.Slavic & E.Eur.Stud., M.L.A.
Description: Covers German-Canadian interests.

917.306   US   ISSN 0890-9490
GERMAN QUERIES. 1986. irreg. $5.50 per issue. Topp of the Line, W. 1304 Cliffwood Ct., Spokane, WA 99218-2917. TEL 509-467-2299. Ed. Bette Butcher Topp. bk.rev.

296   IS   ISSN 0435-8406
DS101
GESHER; semi-annual journal of Jewish affairs. (Text in Hebrew) vol.24, 1978. s-a. IS.35. World Jewish Congress, P.O. Box 4293, Jerusalem 91042, Israel. FAX 972-2-635544. Ed. Shlomo Shafir. circ. 1,100. **Indexed:** Ind.Heb.Per.

GESTOS; teoria y practica del teatro hispanico. see *THEATER*

919.406   AT   ISSN 0725-6590
GHALIB. (Text in Urdu) 1980. m. Aus.$12. Mateen & Salma Abbas, 23 Emily St., Hurstville, N.S.W. 2220, Australia. TEL 02-50-6054. Ed. Mateen Abbas. adv.; bk.rev. circ. 3,500. **Document type:** newspaper.
Description: Includes news, comments, stories, poetry, literature, community announcements, religion, and TV and radio program reviews.

GIANTS FANATICO; the San Francisco Giants' official Hispanic fan magazine. see *SPORTS AND GAMES — Ball Games*

914.506   CN
▼**GIORNALE ITALIANO DEL MANITOBA.** (Text in English, Italian) 1994. m. Ethnic Media Publishers, 520 Corydon Ave., Winnipeg, MB R3L 0P1, Canada. TEL 204-477-1221. FAX 204-453-8244. Pub. Tony Carta. adv. contact: Bruno Fisch. circ. 3,500. cols./p.: 5. (tabloid format)

914.7   CN   ISSN 0837-2071
GLASNIK HRVATSKE SELJACKE STRANKE. (Text in Serbo-Croatian) 1985. m. Can.$35. P.O. Box 82187, North Burnaby, BC V5C 5P2, Canada. TEL 604-524-2813. FAX 604-521-0030. Ed. George Durkovich. circ. 2,000. **Document type:** newspaper.

GLENBOW - ALBERTA INSTITUTE. OCCASIONAL PAPERS. see *HISTORY — History Of North And South America*

GLOBAL LINKS. see *BUSINESS AND ECONOMICS — International Development And Assistance*

910.03   US
GLOBE (FLUSHING). fortn. City University of New York, Queens College, Student Union, Rm. B-24, 65-30 Kissena Blvd., Flushing, NY 11367.

GLORY; a Baha'i youth deepening magazine. see *CHILDREN AND YOUTH — For*

917.306 332.1   US
GLOS. (Text in Polish) m. free. Polish & Slavic Center, 140 Greenpoint Ave., Brooklyn, NY 11222. (Co-sponsor: Polish & Slavic Federal Credit Union) Ed. Andrzej Dobrowolski. circ. 15,000. **Document type:** newspaper.

917.306   US   ISSN 0199-0462
GLOS POLEK/POLISH WOMENS' VOICE. (Text in English and Polish) 1910. fortn. membership. Polish Women's Alliance of America, 205 S. Northwest Hwy., Park Ridge, IL 60068. FAX 708-692-2675. Ed. Mary Mirecki-Piergies. bk.rev.; bibl. circ. 58,000.
Description: Contains articles of interest to the Polish community.

028.5 920   US   ISSN 0046-6077
GOLDEN LEGACY;* illustrated history magazine series. 1966. irreg. for each set of 16 titles. Fitzgerald Publishing Co., Inc., Box 541, Huntington Sta., NY 11746-0427. TEL 516-549-8055. Ed. Bertram A. Fitzgerald.
Description: Contains articles of interest to the black community.

910.03   US
GRAND RAPIDS TIMES. 1957. w. $16. Yergan Pulliam, Ed. & Pub., Box 7258, Grand Rapids, MI 49510. TEL 616-245-8737. FAX 616-245-1026. circ. 5,000. (tabloid format) **Document type:** newspaper.

917.106   CN   ISSN 1182-0225
GREATER VANCOUVER JAPANESE CANADIAN CITIZENS ASSOCIATION. BULLETIN; a monthly publication containing news and articles of interest to Japanese Canadians. (Text in English, Japanese) 1959. m. Can.$25. Japanese Canadian Citizens Association of Greater Vancouver, 348 Powell St., Vancouver, BC V6A 1G4, Canada. TEL 604-681-5222. FAX 604-682-5220. (Subscr. to: Box 2108, Vancouver, BC V6B 3T5, Canada) Ed. John Endo Greenaway. adv.; bk.rev.; film rev. circ. 10,000. (tabloid format; back issues avail.) **Document type:** bulletin.
Former titles (until 1989): J C C A Bulletin (ISSN 0845-2520); (until 1988): Greater Vancouver Japanese Canadian Citizens Association. Bulletin (ISSN 0827-7230); (until 1984): Greater Vancouver J C C A Bulletin (ISSN 0316-3288); (until 1972): Vancouver J C C A Bulletin (ISSN 0316-3296).

917.106   CN
GREEK CANADIAN ACTION - DRASSIS. (Text in English, French and Greek) 1971. bi-w. Can.$20. Newspaper Greek Canadian Action Inc., 4879 Faulkner St., Chomedy, Laval, Que. H7W 1H9, Canada. Ed. George S. Guzmas. adv. circ. 19,000. (tabloid format)

917.106   CN
GREEK CANADIAN REPORTAGE. (Text in English and Greek) 1974. w. Can.$50. 7438 Durocher St., Montreal, Que. H3N 2A3, Canada. TEL 514-279-2610. Ed. Anthony Bartzakos. adv. (tabloid format)
Description: Contains articles of interest to the Greek community.

059.8   AT
GREEK HERALD. (Text in English, Greek) 1926. d. Aus.$90. Foreign Language Publications Pty. Ltd., P.O. Box 146, Broadway, Sydney, N.S.W. 2007, Australia. TEL 02-660-2033. FAX 02-692-0649. Ed. Spyra Smyrnis. adv. contact: George Antoniou. circ. 27,000. (tabloid format; back issues avail.) **Document type:** newspaper.
Formerly: Hellenic Herald (ISSN 0018-0033)
Description: Contains articles of interest to the Greek community.

059.8 281.9   UK   ISSN 0265-6922
GREEK ORTHODOX CALENDAR. 1983. a. £12. Kyriakos H. Metaxas, Ed. & Pub., 35 Burnham Court, Moscow Rd., London W2 4SW, England. TEL 071-727-1121. FAX 071-727-1444. TELEX 298839-GRKGZT-G. adv. circ. 12,000.

917.306   US   ISSN 0745-9645
GREEK PRESS/ELLENIKOS TYPOS. 1911. bi-w. $20. National Greek Publishing Co., 808 W. Jackson Blvd., Chicago, IL 60607. TEL 708-766-2955. FAX 708-766-3069. (Subscr. to: Box 99, Wood Dale, IL 60191) Ed. Aris Angelopoulos. adv. contact: Helen Angelos. bk.rev. circ. 14,000. (tabloid format) **Document type:** newspaper.
Description: News of interest to the Greek-American community.

949.506   UK   ISSN 0262-8864
GREEK REVIEW INTERNATIONAL. 1982. fortn. £25 europe £28.50; rest of world £35. Linnerlake Ltd., 59 Stroud Green Rd., London N4 3EG, England. TEL 071-272-2722. FAX 071-272-7274. Ed. Joanna Jones. adv.; bk.rev.; film rev.; play rev. circ. 9,700. (back issues avail.) **Document type:** consumer publication.
Description: Contains general news from Greece and Cyprus, and information on the arts and fashion.

917.306   US
THE GREEKAMERICAN. Greek edition: Proini. w. $45. Petallides Publishing, Inc., 25-50 Crescent St., Astoria, NY 11102. TEL 718-626-7676. FAX 718-956-8076. Ed. Tina Maurikos. adv. contact: Dimy Chryssanithou. **Document type:** newspaper.
Description: Coverage of international and domestic news and issues affecting Greek-Americans.

910.03   US
GREENVILLE BLACK STAR. 1982. w. $25. S C Black Media Group, 1310 Harden St., Columbia, SC 29204. TEL 804-799-5252. (Subscr. to: Box 11128, Columbia, SC 29211) Ed. Issac Washington. adv. contact: Melody Harris. illus. circ. 6,000. **Document type:** newspaper.

GREENWOOD ENCYCLOPEDIA OF BLACK MUSIC. see *MUSIC*

910.03   US   ISSN 0737-0873
GRIOT. 1981. s-a. $25. Southern Conference on Afro-American Studies, Inc., Box 134, Berea College, Berea, KY 40404. Ed. Andrew Baskin. adv.; bk.rev. circ. 250. **Document type:** academic/scholarly publication.
—Faxon; UnCover.
Description: Contains information relative to any disciplinary perspective in the humanities which further enhances knowledge of the Africa, African-American, Caribbean experience.

GUADALUPE REVIEW. see *LITERATURE*

ETHNIC INTERESTS

910.03   US
GUIDE TO AFRO-AMERICAN RESOURCES.* 1973. biennial. $50. Black Resources Information Coordinating Services, Inc., 614 Howard Ave., Tallahassee, FL 32310-6222. TEL 904-576-7522. Ed. Emily A. Copeland.
    Formerly: Guide to Minority Resources.
    Description: Contains articles of interest to the black community.

GUIDE TO REVIEWS OF BOOKS FROM AND ABOUT HISPANIC AMERICA/GUIA A LAS RESENAS DE LIBROS DE Y SOBRE HISPANOAMERICA. see *PUBLISHING AND BOOK TRADE*

914   BE
GUIDE TOURISTIQUE EUROPEEN POUR ISRAELITES/EUROPEAN TRAVEL GUIDE FOR JEWS. (Text in English, French) 1961. a. 350 Fr. Belgisch Israelitisch Weekblad, Pelikaanstraat 106, B-2018 Antwerp, Belgium. TEL 03-233-70-94. (Co-sponsor: Belgian National Tourist Office) adv.; illus.

917.306   US   ISSN 0740-5944
GWIAZDA POLARNA/NORTH STAR. (Monthly supplement in English avail.: G P Light) (Text in Polish) 1908. w. $40. Point Publications, Inc., 2619 Post Rd., Stevens Point, WI 54481. TEL 715-345-0744. FAX 715-345-1913. Ed. Malgorzata Terentiew-Cwiklinska. adv.: B&W page $1200; adv. contact: Barbara Bublitz. bk.rev.; illus. circ. 12,500. **Document type:** newspaper.
    Description: Covers general issues of interest to the Polish community.

296   NE   ISSN 0017-6346
HABINJAN; de opbouw. 1947. m. Portugees-Israelietische Gemeente - Spanish and Portuguese Jewish Community at Amsterdam, Gerrit van der Veenstr. 141, 1077 DX Amsterdam, Netherlands. TEL 31-20-6762041. Eds. Dr. J.Z. Baruch, Rabbi B. Drukarch. bk.rev. circ. 13,000.
    Description: Contains articles of interest to the Jewish community.

296   FR   ISSN 0292-7993
HABONE; le batisseur. 15 F. Consistoire Israelite de Marseille, 119 rue Breteuil, 13006 Marseille, France. Ed. Joseph Sitruk.

956.940 296   US   ISSN 0017-6516
DS101
HADASSAH MAGAZINE. 1921. m. (10/yr.). $25. Hadassah, The Women's Zionist Organization of America, 50 W. 58th St., New York, NY 10019. TEL 212-333-5946. Ed. Alan M. Tigay. adv.; bk.rev.; film rev.; play rev.; illus. circ. 355,000. (also avail. in microform from AJP,UMI; reprint service avail. from UMI) **Indexed:** Ind.Jew.Per.
    —UnCover; UMI.
    Formerly: Hadassah Newsletter.
    Description: Contains articles of interest to the Jewish community.

DE HALVE MAEN. see *HISTORY — History Of North And South America*

296   US
HAMAGSHIMIM JOURNAL. 1968. 3/yr. membership. Hadassah Zionist Youth Commission, 50 W. 58th St., New York, NY 10019. TEL 212-355-7900. bk.rev.; illus.

296   CN
▼**HAMEKOMON.** (Text in Hebrew) 1992. bi-w. free. S & D Marketing, Box 54025, Lawrence Plaza, Toronto, Ont. M6A 3B7, Canada. TEL 416-782-3017. FAX 416-782-9981. adv.; bk.rev. circ. 10,000. (tabloid format) **Document type:** newspaper.

HAMEVASER. see *RELIGIONS AND THEOLOGY — Judaic*

HAMORE; revue trimestrielle des enseignants juifs. see *EDUCATION — Teaching Methods And Curriculum*

296   US
HAOR. (Text in English) vol.4, 1973. m. City University of New York, Queens College, Student Activities Corp., Student Union, Rm. B-43, Box 5, Flushing, NY 11367. TEL 718-591-1096. Ed. Kenneth M. Simckes. adv.; bk.rev. circ. 15,000. (reprint service avail.)

914.406   FR
HARATCH. 1925. d. 83 rue d'Hauteville, 75010 Paris, France. Ed. Ms. A. Missakian.
    Description: Contains articles of interest to the Armenian community.

917.306 320   US
HARVARD JOURNAL OF HISPANIC POLICY. a. $15 to individuals; institutions $45. Harvard Journal of Hispanic Policy, JFK School of Government, Harvard University, 79 John F. Kennedy St., Cambridge, MA 02138. TEL 617-495-1311. FAX 617-496-9027. Ed. Lisa Baltazar. circ. 1,000. **Document type:** government publication.
    —UnCover.
    Former titles: Journal of Hispanic Policy (ISSN 0892-6115); (until 1985): Journal of Hispanic Politics.
    Description: Serves as a forum for meaningful analysis, discussion, and debate of policy questions affecting the Hispanic community in the United States.

296   US
HARVARD JUDAIC MONOGRAPHS. 1975. irreg., no.5, 1985. price varies. Harvard University, Center for Jewish Studies, Cambridge, MA 02138. (Distr. by: Harvard University Press, 79 Garden St., Cambridge, MA 02138) **Document type:** academic/scholarly publication, monographic series.

HARVARD UKRAINIAN STUDIES. see *HISTORY — History Of Europe*

296   SA
HASHALOM. 1923. m. R.20 (overseas R.30). Council of Natal Jewry, P.O. Box 10797, Marine Parade 4056, South Africa. FAX 031-379600. (Co-sponsors: Natal Zionist Council; Durban Jewish Club) Ed. Ms. T. Lazarus. adv. contact: Jack B. Notelovitz. bk.rev. circ. 2,000.
    Description: Covers Jewish interests.

296   GW
HASKALA; wissenschaftliche Abhandlungen. 1991. irreg., vol.10, 1993. DM.58. (Moses Mendelssohn Zentrum fuer Europaeisch-Juedische Studien) Georg Olms Verlag, Hagentorwall 7, 31134 Hildesheim, Germany. TEL 05121-1501-0. FAX 05121-150150. (U.S. subscr. to: 111 W. 57th St., New York, NY 10019. TEL 212-757-5237) (Co-sponsor: Salomon Ludwig Steinheim Institut fuer Deutsch-Juedische Geschichte) **Document type:** monographic series.

HEART & SOUL (EMMAUS). see *PHYSICAL FITNESS AND HYGIENE*

917.106   CN
HEBREW JOURNAL. (Text in English and Hebrew) w. Can.$15. 304 Adelaide St. W., Toronto, Ont. M5V 1P6, Canada. TEL 416-593-2514. Ed. S.B. Rose. adv. (tabloid format; also avail. in microfilm from AJP)
    Description: Contains articles of interest to the Jewish community.

296 956.94   US   ISSN 0360-9049
BM11
HEBREW UNION COLLEGE ANNUAL. (Supplement avail.) (Text in English, French, German, Hebrew) 1924. a. $30. Hebrew Union College - Jewish Institute of Religion (Cincinnati), 3101 Clifton Ave., Cincinnati, OH 45220. TEL 513-221-1875. Ed. Herbert H. Paper. cum.index: 1924-1982 in 1982 vol. circ. 2,500. (also avail. in microfilm from AJP; back issues avail.) **Indexed:** Amer.Hist.& Life, Bibl.Ling., CERDIC, Hist.Abstr., New Test.Abstr., Old Test.Abstr., Rel.& Theol.Abstr. (1978-), Rel.Ind.One.
    —UMI.
    Supersedes: Journal of Jewish Lore and Philosophy (ISSN 0190-4361)

296   US   ISSN 0275-9993
HEBREW UNION COLLEGE ANNUAL SUPPLEMENTS. 1976. irreg. Hebrew Union College - Jewish Institute of Religion (Cincinnati), 3101 Clifton Ave., Cincinnati, OH 45220. TEL 513-221-1875. (Distr. by: Behrman House, Inc., 235 Watchung Ave., W. Orange, NJ 07052) Ed. Herbert H. Paper. **Indexed:** Old Test.Abstr.

362.8   GW   ISSN 0017-9612
DAS HEILIGE BAND; der Galiziendeutsche. 1947. m. DM.15. Hilfskomitee der Galiziendeutschen, Markus-Scheicher-Str. 25b, 70565 Stuttgart, Germany. Ed. Josef Lanz. bk.rev. circ. 1,200.
    Description: Covers Galician interests.

HEIMATRECHT; Informationen fuer Freiheit und Selbstbestimmung. see *FOLKLORE*

914.9   CN
HELLENIC CANADIAN CHRONICLES. w. 437 Danforth Ave., Toronto, Ont. M4K 1P1, Canada. TEL 416-465-4628. FAX 416-462-0051. adv.; bk.rev.

917.306   US
HELLENIC CHRONICLE. 1950. w. $20. A.A. Agris, Ed. & Pub., 324 Newbury St., Boston, MA 02115. TEL 617-262-4500. adv. contact: Peter Agris. bk.rev. circ. 37,993. **Document type:** newspaper.

914.9   CN
HELLENIC HAMILTON NEWS. 1980. m. 8 Morris Ave., Apt.2, Hamilton, Ont. L8L 1X7, Canada. FAX 519-549-7935. adv. circ. 2,000.

914.206   US
HELLENIC JOURNAL. (Text in English and Greek) 1975. fortn. $21.65. Western Hellenic Journal, Inc., 200 Valley Dr., Ste. 20, Brisbane, CA 94005-1206. TEL 415-467-2611. FAX 415-468-3549. Ed. Soterios D. Chalios. adv.; bk.rev.; film rev.; illus. circ. 3,000. (tabloid format; back issues avail.)
    Formerly: Western Hellenic Journal.
    Description: Contains articles of interest to the Greek community.

917.106   CN   ISSN 0821-7270
HELLENIC NEWS. (Text in English, Greek) 1982. m. Can.$15. Alpha Omega Communications, 37 Hillsmount Rd., London, ON N6K 1W1, Canada. TEL 519-472-4807. FAX 519-451-4599. Ed. Anita Drossos. adv.; bk.rev. circ. 5,000. (also avail. in microfilm; back issues avail.)

917.106   CN
HELLENIC POSTMAN. (Text in English and Greek) 1958. w. Can.$8. 3622 St. Lawrence Blvd., Montreal, Que., Canada. TEL 514-849-9745. Ed. Christos El. Kolivas. adv. (tabloid format)
    Description: Contains articles of interest to the Greek community.

917.306   US   ISSN 1059-2121
HELLENIC TIMES. 1973. bi-w. $20. Hellenic Times, Inc., 823 11th Ave., 5th Fl., New York, NY 10019-3535. TEL 212-986-6881. FAX 212-977-3662. Ed. Jimmy Kapsalis. adv.; bk.rev. circ. 15,000. (tabloid format) **Document type:** newspaper.
    Description: Contains articles of interest to the Greek community.

296   SA
HERALD TIMES. w. R.52 (foreign R.200). South African Jewish Times (Pty) Ltd., P.O. Box 31015, Braamfontein 2017, Johannesburg, South Africa. TEL 011-887-6500. FAX 011-8876551. Ed. Maurice Dorfan. adv. circ. 5,210.
    Formerly: South African Jewish News.
    Description: Contains articles of interest to the Jewish community.

917.306   US
HERALDO DE BROWARD Y PALM BEACH. (Text in Spanish) 1974. w. free. Heraldo de Broward, 1975 E. Sunrise Blvd., Ste. 100, Fort Lauderdale, FL 33304. TEL 305-527-0627. FAX 305-792-7402. Ed. Elaine Miceli; Pub. E.M. Vasquez. adv.: B&W page $450; 10 1/4 x 16. illus. circ. 12,000. (tabloid format; back issues avail.) **Document type:** newspaper.
    Formerly: Heraldo de Broward.

917.306   US
HERALDO DE CHICAGO. (Text in English, Spanish) 1975. w. $45 (effective 1992). Heraldo Neuvo Ltd., 760 N. Ogden Ave., Chicago, IL 60622. TEL 312-455-0300. FAX 312-666-6397. TELEX 495-3255. Ed. Gonzalo Sanchez. adv.; bk.rev.; film rev.; bibl.; illus.; stat. circ. 15,000. (tabloid format; also avail. in microfiche; back issues avail.) **Document type:** newspaper.
    Description: Targets the Hispanic consumer in Chicago.

ETHNIC INTERESTS

960 NR ISSN 0794-3415
HERITAGE; the African quarterly of arts and letters. (Text in English) 1970. q. $120. Heritage Books, 2-8 Calcutta Crescent, Gate 4, Box 610, Apapa, Lagos, Nigeria. TEL 234-1-871333. Ed. Naiwu Osahon. adv.; bk.rev. circ. 6,000. **Indexed:** Documentatieblad. **Document type:** academic/scholarly publication.
  Formerly (until 1984): Third World First (ISSN 0331-8508)

HERITAGE. see *ART*

051 US ISSN 0895-0792
HERITAGE (CARSON); magazine of Filipino culture, arts and letters and the Filipino American experience. 1987. q. $15 to individuals; institutions and libraries $20. Heritage Publishers, 20218 Tajauta Ave., Carson, CA 90746. (Subscr. to: Box 9160, Long Beach, CA 90810) Ed. Victor P. Gendrano. adv.; bk.rev. (back issues avail.)
  Description: Promotes Philippine cultural heritage and the Filipino-American experience.

917.306 US
HERITAGE (CHICAGO). 1977. q. free. (Illinois Ethnic Consultation) Heritage News Service, 55 E. Jackson Blvd., Ste. 1880, Chicago, IL 60604. TEL 312-663-5400. Ed. Pamela DeFiglio. bk.rev.; film rev.; play rev.; illus. (back issues avail.)
  Description: Explores social policy topics: education, immigration, business as they relate to ethnic groups.

390 US ISSN 0162-8267
F645.R85
HERITAGE REVIEW. (Text in English and German) 1971. 4/yr. $25. Germans from Russia Heritage Society, 1008 E. Central Ave., Bismarck, ND 58501-1936. TEL 701-223-6167. Ed. Armand Bauer. bk.rev.; index. circ. 2,000. (back issues avail.) **Indexed:** Amer.Bibl.Slavic & E.Eur.Stud.; Amer.Hist.& Life, Hist.Abstr.
  Incorporates (in 1981): Stammbaum.
  Description: Brochure and list of publications and maps on this ethnic group's ancestry, European migration and exodus to the United States, early days on the American plains, and current culture, with cookbooks, songbooks, recordings, and photography also available from the society's bookstore.

296 US ISSN 0018-0726
HERITAGE - SOUTHWEST JEWISH PRESS. (Separate editions: Greater Los Angeles, Central California, Orange County; San Diego County) 1914. w. $20. Heritage Publishing Co., 2130 S. Vermont Ave., Los Angeles, CA 90007. Ed. Dan Brin. adv.; bk.rev.; film rev.; illus.; play rev. circ. 44,000 (combined). (tabloid format; also avail. in microfilm from LIB)
  Description: Contains articles of interest to the Jewish community.

296 US ISSN 0744-1444
HERZL INSTITUTE BULLETIN.* 1964. bi-w. (Sep.-May). $10. (World Zionist Organization, American Section) Theodor Herzl Institute, 110 E. 59th St., New York, NY 10022. TEL 212-339-6000. Ed. Philip S. Gutride. bk.rev.; illus. circ. 2,000.
  Description: Explores Jewish interests.

398 572 GW
HESSISCHE BLAETTER FUER VOLKS- UND KULTURFORSCHUNG. 1899. s-a. DM.36. Hessische Vereinigung fuer Volkskunde, c/o Institut fuer Europaeische Ethnologie, Bahnhofstr. 3, 35057 Marburg, Germany. Ed. Andreas C. Bimmer. adv.; bk.rev. circ. 1,000. **Indexed:** M.L.A.
  Formerly: Hessische Blaetter fuer Volkskunde.

917.706 US ISSN 0161-5378
E184.S3
HIGHLANDER (BARRINGTON); the magazine of Scottish heritage. 1963. 7/yr. $16.50. Angus J. Ray Associates, Inc., Box 397, Barrington, IL 60011. TEL 708-382-1035. FAX 708-382-0322. (Subscr. to: Circulation Department, Box 44086, Chicago, IL 60644) Ed. Angus J. Ray. adv.; bk.rev.; illus.; tr.lit.; circ. 40,000 (paid). **Document type:** consumer publication.

296 US ISSN 0018-1862
HILLEL GATE. 1969. m. (during school year). free. B'nai B'rith Hillel Foundation at Brooklyn College, 2901 Campus Rd., Brooklyn, NY 11210. TEL 718-859-1151. Eds. Paul Appelbaum, Barbara Robinson. adv.; bk.rev.; film rev.; play rev.; illus. circ. 4,000. (tabloid format; also avail. in microfilm from AJP)
  Description: Contains articles of interest to the Jewish community.

917.306 US ISSN 0898-3097
E184.S75
HISPANIC; the magazine for and about Hispanics. 1988. m. (11/yr.). $24 (Canada and Mexico $27; elsewhere $29). Hispanic Publishing Corp., 111 Massachusetts Ave., N.W., Ste. 410, Washington, DC 20001. TEL 202-682-3000. FAX 202-682-4091. Ed. Alfredo Estrada. adv. contact: Dalia Almanza. bk.rev.; illus. (back issues avail.) **Indexed:** Mag.Ind.
  —Faxon; UnCover.
  Description: Focuses on upbeat success stories which present the achievements and contributions that today's Hispanics are making in American society.

917.106 031 US
▼**HISPANIC - AMERICAN ALMANAC.** 1992. quinquennial. $99.50. Gale Research Inc., 835 Penobscot Bldg., Detroit, MI 48226. TEL 313-961-2242; 800-877-4253. FAX 313-961-6083. Ed. Nicolas Kanellos. charts; illus.
  Description: Covers all major aspects of the culture and civilization of Hispanics living in the U.S.

917.306 US ISSN 1046-3933
E184.S75
HISPANIC AMERICANS INFORMATION DIRECTORY. 1990. biennial. $75. Gale Research Inc., 835 Penobscot Bldg., Detroit, MI 48226. TEL 313-961-2242. FAX 313-961-6083. TELEX 810-221-7086.
  Description: Covers organizations, agencies, institutions, programs, and publications concerned with Hispanic American life and culture.

HISPANIC BOOKS BULLETIN. see *PUBLISHING AND BOOK TRADE*

HISPANIC BUSINESS MAGAZINE. see *BUSINESS AND ECONOMICS*

917.306 US ISSN 0271-0986
PC4001
HISPANIC JOURNAL. 1979. s-a. $15 to individuals; institutions $30. Indiana University of Pennsylvania, Department of Spanish and Classical Languages, 462 Sutton Hall, Indiana, PA 15705. TEL 412-357-5598. Ed. David Foltz. bk.rev.; abstr.; bibl. circ. 450. (back issues avail.) **Indexed:** Hisp.Amer.Per.Ind.; M.L.A. **Document type:** academic/scholarly publication.
  —BLDSC (4315.772500); Faxon; UnCover.

HISPANIC JOURNAL OF BEHAVIORAL SCIENCES. see *PSYCHOLOGY*

980 US
HISPANIC LINK WEEKLY REPORT. 1983. w. $113 to individuals; institutions $128. Hispanic Link News Service, 1420 N St., N.W., Washington, DC 20005. TEL 202-234-0280. FAX 202-234-4090. Ed. Jonathan Higuera. adv.; bk.rev. circ. 1,400. **Document type:** consumer publication.
  Description: Covers issues and trends of U.S. Hispanics.

914.606 US
HISPANIC LITERATURE. irreg., latest no.22. $39.95 per no. Edwin Mellen Press, 415 Ridge St., Box 450, Lewiston, NY 14092. TEL 716-754-2788. FAX 716-754-4056. **Document type:** monographic series.

917.306 378 US ISSN 1054-2337
HISPANIC OUTLOOK IN HIGHER EDUCATION. 1990. m. $60. Hispanic Outlook in Higher Education Publishing Company, Inc., 17 Arcadian Ave., Ste. 202, Paramus, NJ 07652. TEL 201-587-8800. FAX 201-268-0433. (Subscr. to: Box 68, Paramus, NJ 07652) Ed. Marilyn Gilroy; Pub. Jose Lopez-Isa. adv. contact: Juan A. Gutierrez. illus. circ. 15,000.
  —UnCover.

917.106 US
▼**HISPANIC REPORTER.** 1992. w. free. 3121 W. Temple St., Los Angeles, CA 90026. TEL 213-487-5095. FAX 213-385-0269. Ed. Harry Tarsky. adv.; B&W page $875; trim 11 x 17. circ. 30,000. **Document type:** newspaper.
  Description: For English-speaking Hispanics and those interested in the Hispanic marketplace.

917.306 US
HISPANIC RESOURCE DIRECTORY. 1988. biennial. $47.50. Denali Press, Box 021535, Juneau, AK 99802-1535. TEL 907-586-6014. FAX 907-463-6780. Ed. Alan Edward Schorr. index. **Document type:** directory.
  Description: Covers information on 6,200 Hispanic organizations, institutions, and agencies in the United States.

HISPANIC TIMES MAGAZINE; the nation's only career and business magazine for Hispanics, American Indians and native Americans. see *OCCUPATIONS AND CAREERS*

917.306 US ISSN 8750-880X
HISPANIC U S A MAGAZINE. (Text in English, Spanish) 1984. m. $24. Hispanic U S A Corp., 230 N. Michigan Ave., Chicago, IL 60601. TEL 312-977-1975. FAX 312-977-0097. Ed. Jose Martinez. adv.; bk.rev. circ. 118,500. (back issues avail.; reprint service avail.)

HISPANISTICA; Indian journal of Spanish & Latin American Studies. see *LITERATURE*

917.306 US
EL HISPANO. 1967. w. $28. El Hispano, 928 Second St., Ste. 300, Sacramento, CA 95814. TEL 916-442-0267. FAX 209-547-1132. Ed. Pedro Chavez. circ. 20,250. **Document type:** newspaper.

917.309 US
AP62
EL HISPANO NEWS; official Spanish language newspaper of the state of New Mexico. 1966. w. $10. Hispano Inc., 900 Park S.W., Albuquerque, NM 87102. TEL 505-243-6161. FAX 505-842-5464. Ed. A.B. Collado. adv. contact: Francisco Collado. bk.rev.; film rev.; charts; illus.; tr.lit.; circ. 10,000 (paid). (tabloid format; also avail. in microfilm; back issues avail.) **Document type:** newspaper.
  Formerly: Hispano (ISSN 0018-2184)

917.306 US
HISPANOS UNIDOS. (Text in Spanish) 1987. w. $17. Hispanos Unidos, 411 W. Ninth Ave., Escondido, CA 92025-5034. TEL 619-740-9561. FAX 619-747-1626. Ed. Jaime A. Castaneda. circ. 17,000. **Document type:** newspaper.

910.03 US
HISTORIC LANDMARKS OF BLACK AMERICA. 1991. irreg. $29.95. Gale Research Inc., 835 Penobscot Bldg., Detroit, MI 48226-4094. TEL 313-961-2242. FAX 313-961-6083. TELEX 810-221-7086. Ed. George Cantor. illus.; maps.
  Description: Describes 300 sites significant to African-American history.

296 320.9 CN
HISTORIC PALESTINE SERIES. irreg. price varies. Dawn Publishing Co. Ltd., 17 Anselme Lavigne Blvd., Dollard des Ormeaux, Montreal, Que. H9A 1N3, Canada.

917.306 US
HOKUBEI MAINICHI. (Text in English, Japanese) 1947. d. (5/wk.). $99. Hokubei Mainichi, 1746 Post St., San Francisco, CA 94115. TEL 415-567-7323. FAX 415-567-3926. Ed. Atsuyo Hiramoto. adv. contact: Atsuko Saito. bk.rev. circ. 10,000. **Document type:** newspaper.

917.106 CN ISSN 0837-1342
HOLLANDSE KRANT. (Text in Dutch) 1969. m. $15. J.I. Timmer Publishing Co. Ltd., 12-20505 Fraser Highway, Langley, BC V3A 4G3, Canada. TEL 604-530-9446. FAX 604-530-9766. (U.S. addr.: Box 8110-310, Blaine, WA 98230) Ed. Gerald Bonekamp. adv.; bk.rev. circ. 7,350. (tabloid format)

910.03   US
HOLLYWOOD HAPPENINGS. 1962. w. $35. Observer Newspapers, Box 209, Sacramento, CA 95812. TEL 916-452-4781. FAX 916-452-7744. Ed. William H. Lee. adv.; bk.rev.; illus. circ. 97,500. (tabloid format) **Document type:** newspaper.

HOLOCAUST STUDIES ANNUAL. see HISTORY — History Of Europe

917.309   CN   ISSN 0018-4284
HOMIN UKRAINY/UKRAINIAN ECHO. 1948. w. Can.$35. Homin Ukrainy Publishing Co., 140 Bathurst St., Toronto, Ont. M5V 2R3, Canada. TEL 416-368-3443. Ed. O. Romanyshyn. adv.; bk.rev.; illus. circ. 11,000. (also avail. in microform from CML)
  Description: Contains articles of interest to the Ukranian community.

917.106   US   ISSN 1066-6311
HON VIET MAGAZINE. (Text in Vietnamese) 1976. m. $32. Box 609, Midway City, CA 92655. TEL 714-839-6517. FAX 714-839-2607. Ed. Kiem Them; Pub. Kiem Ngoc Nguyen. adv.; bk.rev. circ. 15,000.

HONG KONG MUSLIM HERALD. see RELIGIONS AND THEOLOGY — Islamic

HONOR THE PROMISE. see RELIGIONS AND THEOLOGY

917.106   CN   ISSN 0708-580X
HORIZON ARMENIAN WEEKLY. (Text in Armenian) 1979. w. Can.$55($75) 3401 Olivar-Asselin, Montreal, PQ H4J 1L5, Canada. TEL 514-332-3757. FAX 514-332-4870. Ed. Giro Manoyan. adv.; bk.rev. circ. 2,200. **Document type:** newspaper.

HORIZONS INTERCULTURELS. see HUMANITIES: COMPREHENSIVE WORKS

917.306   US
HORIZONTES (SAN FRANCISCO). (Text in Spanish) 1983. s-m. $50 to individuals; institutions $75. Horizontes, 2601 Mission St., Ste. 900, San Francisco, CA 94110. TEL 415-641-6051. FAX 415-282-3320. Ed. Juan Pifarre. adv.; bk.rev.; film rev.; play rev.; circ. 300 (paid); 19,700 (controlled). (tabloid format; back issues avail.) **Document type:** newspaper.
● Also available on CD-ROM.
  Description: News and features on Latin American art, politics and social issues. Coverage of Latinos in the US and California.

917.306   US   ISSN 0018-599X
HOSPODAR. (Text in Czech) 1890. m. $25 (foreign $27). Jan Vaculik, Ed. & Pub., Box 301, West, TX 76691. TEL 817-826-3838. adv.; bk.rev. circ. 1,800. (tabloid format; also avail. in microform) **Document type:** newspaper.

HRVATSKA SLOBODA. see POLITICAL SCIENCE — Civil Rights

057.82   CI
HRVATSKI ISELJENICKI ZBORNIK (YEAR). (Text in Croatian, English, Spanish) 1954. a. $20. Hrvatska Matica Iseljenika, Trnjanska bb, 41000 Zagreb, Croatia. Eds. Boris Maruna, Nenad Gol. circ. 12,000. (back issues avail.)
  Formerly: Iseljenicki Kalendar (ISSN 0543-1077)

917.306   US
HUNGARIAN INSIGHTS. 1980. q. $25. (United Hungarian Fund) Hungarian Insights, 6020 Pearl Rd., Cleveland, OH 44130. TEL 216-842-4651. Ed. Lel F. Somogyi. bk.rev. circ. 1,500. **Document type:** newspaper.

917.306   US
HUTSULIYA. (Text in Ukrainian) 1967. q. $10. Hutsuliya, P.O. Box 39149, Chicago, IL 60639. TEL 312-267-7783. Ed. N. Domashevsky. bk.rev.; film rev.; play rev.; abstr.; bibl.; illus.; stat.; tr.lit.; index, cum.index. circ. 1,000. (back issues avail.) **Indexed:** Amer.Bibl.Slavic & E.Eur.Stud.
  Description: Covers news and items of interest to Ukrainian Americans.

910.03   US
HYDE PARK CITIZEN. 1988. w. $25. William Garth, Ed. & Pub., 412 E. 87th St., Chicago, IL 60619. TEL 312-487-7700. FAX 312-487-7931. adv. contact: William D. Garth, Jr. circ. 16,000. (tabloid format) **Document type:** newspaper.

HYPE HAIR; for Black teens. see BEAUTY CULTURE

296 323.4   UK   ISSN 0257-6406
I J A. RESEARCH REPORTS. 1968. irreg. (6-10/yr.). £30($60) Institute of Jewish Affairs, 79 Wimpole St., London W1M 7DD, England. TEL 071-935-8266. FAX 071-935-3252. (Co-sponsor: World Jewish Congress) Ed. A. Lerman. abstr. circ. 1,500. (also avail. in microform from UMI) **Indexed:** HR Rep. **Document type:** academic/scholarly publication.
— BLDSC (7762.354200).
  Description: Contains background surveys and analyses of topical, social, political, legal, economic and international issues relevant to world Jewry.

322.4   US
I LAISVE./TOWARD FREEDOM; Lithuanian magazine of politics. (Text in Lithuanian) 1941. 3/yr. $7. Friends of the Lithuanian Front, 1634-49th Ave., Cicero, IL 60650. (Subscr. to: I. Laisve, 14 Thelma Dr., Bakersfield, CA 93305) Ed. Vacys Rociunas. bk.rev.; circ. controlled. **Indexed:** Amer.Bibl.Slavic & E.Eur.Stud.
  Description: Contains articles of interest to the Lithuanian community.

I W G I A DOCUMENTS; documentation of oppression of ethnic groups in various countries. (International Work Group for Indigenous Affairs) see ANTHROPOLOGY

I W G I A NEWSLETTER. (International Work Group for Indigenous Affairs) see ANTHROPOLOGY

I W G I A YEARBOOK. (International Work Group for Indigenous Affairs) see ANTHROPOLOGY

917.306   US   ISSN 1068-9117
ICELANDIC - AMERICAN SOCIETY OF NEW YORK. SOCIETY NEWS. 1991. irreg. (4-5/yr.). membership. Icelandic-American Society of New York, 370 Lexington Ave., Ste. 505, New York, NY 10017. TEL 212-796-0761. FAX 212-796-3564. Ed. Eva Becker. adv.; B&W page $90; trim 6 3/4 x 9 1/2; adv. contact: Eva Becker. bk.rev.; film rev.; play rev.; illus. circ. 500. **Document type:** newsletter.
  Description: Directed to the Icelandic community in New York and the tri-state area as well as to non-Icelandic people with interest in Iceland and Icelandic culture. Covers news and current events of interest to members. Features articles on economy, history and culture.

IDAHO. STATE SUPERINTENDENT OF PUBLIC INSTRUCTION. ANNUAL REPORT. STATE OF IDAHO JOHNSON-O'MALLEY PROGRAM. see EDUCATION

IDENTITY. see LITERATURE

296   US
IGERET; national newsletter. 8/yr. B'nai B'rith Hillel Foundations (Washington), 1640 Rhode Island Ave., N.W., Washington, DC 20036. TEL 202-857-6560. FAX 202-857-6933. Ed. Ruth Fredman Cernea, Ph.D. bk.rev. circ. 800. **Document type:** newsletter.

956.646   IS
IGUD YOTZEI SIN. BULLETIN. (Text in English, Hebrew and Russian) 1954. q. $25. Igud Yotzei Sin, P.O. Box 1601, Tel Aviv, Israel. FAX 03-51997. Ed. Boris G. Mirkin. circ. 1,000. **Document type:** bulletin.

960   NR   ISSN 0331-0205
IKENGA. 1972. s-a. £N60($30) per no. University of Nigeria, Nsukka, Institute of African Studies, Nsukka, Nigeria. FAX 234-42-770644. TELEX 51496 ULIONS NIG. Ed. A.I. Okpoko. bk.rev. circ. 3,000. (back issues avail.) **Document type:** academic/scholarly publication.

296 051   AU
ILLUSTRIERTE NEUE WELT; Unabhaengige internationale Zeitschrift. 1897. m. S.500 (foreign S.650). I N W - Pressedienst, Judengasse Ia-V-25, A-1010 Vienna, Austria. TEL 0222-5356301. FAX 0222-5355780. Ed. Joanna Nittenberg. adv.; bk.rev.; illus.
  Supersedes: Neue Welt.

ETHNIC INTERESTS 2487

980   PN
IMAGEN.* 1982. bi-m. Bl.9. Universidad de Panama, Direccion de Extension Cultural, Ciudad Universitaria, El Congrejo, Apdo. Estateta Universitaria, Panama, Panama. Ed. Ornel Urriola. adv.; bk.rev. circ. 2,000.

IMMIGRANT COMMUNITIES & ETHNIC MINORITIES IN THE UNITED STATES & CANADA. see POPULATION STUDIES

IMMIGRANTS & MINORITIES. see POPULATION STUDIES

917.106   US
IMPACTO LATIN NEWS. (Text in Spanish) 1968. w. $20. Impacto Latin News Inc., 853 Broadway, Ste. 811, New York, NY 10003. TEL 212-505-0288. FAX 212-948-9414. adv. circ. 53,500. (looseleaf format; back issues avail.)
  Description: Covers news, sports, community entertainment, food and movies.

917.306   US   ISSN 0738-9116
IMPARTIAL CITIZEN. 1980. s-m. $15. Impartial Citizen, Inc., Box 98, Syracuse, NY 13205. TEL 315-638-7868. FAX 315-638-0778. Ed. Antoine J. Polgar. adv.; bk.rev. circ. 10,000. (also avail. in microform; back issues avail.)

915.4   CN
IMROZE.* (Text in Urdu) s-m. 93 Larkin Ave., Markham, ON L3P 4R1, Canada. TEL 416-297-0110.

917.306   US
IN AMERICA; perspectives on refugee resettlement. bi-m. free. Refugee Service Center, Center for Applied Linguistics, 1118 22nd St. N.W., Washington, DC 20037. Eds. Douglas F. Gilzow, Donald A. Ranard.

IN FOCUS (LOS ANGELES). see MOTION PICTURES

910.03 355.115   US   ISSN 1053-7864 UB357
IN PERSPECTIVE OF THE BLACK AMERICAN VETERAN. 1991. q. Elramco Enterprises, Inc., 257 Osborne Rd., Albany, NY 12211.

910.03   US   ISSN 1050-2882
IN-SIDE HARLEM. 12/yr. $15 to individuals; institutions $50. Afram Associates, Inc., 2322 Third Ave., 2nd Fl., New York, NY 10035. TEL 212-289-9155. FAX 212-722-5194.
  Description: Documents the Harlem story.

IN TOUCH (CHICAGO). see LITERATURE

915   US
INDEPENDENT SCHOLARS OF ASIA NEWSLETTER. 1981. 3/yr. $12. (Association for Asian Studies, Inc.) Independent Scholars of Asia, Inc., 2321 Russell, No. 3A, Berkeley, CA 94705. TEL 510-849-3791. Ed. Ruth-Inge Heinze. adv.; bk.rev.; circ. 200 (paid). (back issues avail.) **Document type:** newsletter.
  Incorporates: Asian Folklore Studies Group Newsletter.
  Description: Discusses changing role of experts on Asia (history, culture, and literature of Asia, ethnomedicine, international relations, religious studies, social sciences, etc.); informs on grants and research in Asia, conferences, workshops, book announcements, and brief essays on Asian culture.

917.306 954   US   ISSN 0046-8932
INDIA ABROAD. 1970. w. $29. India Abroad Publications, Inc., 43 W. 24th St., 7th Fl., New York, NY 10010. TEL 212-929-1727. FAX 212-691-0873. Ec. Gopal Raju; Pub. Gopal Raja. adv.; bk.rev.; illus. circ. 40,000. (tabloid format) **Document type:** newspaper.
  Description: Provides news from India and neighboring countries, as well as Indian-American issues.

915.4   CN
INDIA CALLING. bi-m. 1693 Pengilley Place, Mississauga, Ont. L5J 4F4, Canada. TEL 416-823-2541. adv.

ETHNIC INTERESTS

917.306 051   US   ISSN 0896-095X
DS480.853
INDIA CURRENTS; California's magazine of Indian arts, entertainment & dining. 1987. m. $19.95 (typically set Apr.). India Currents, Box 21285, San Jose, CA 95151. TEL 408-274-6966. FAX 408-274-2733. Ed. Arvind Kumar. adv.; bk.rev.; film rev.; play rev.; illus. circ. 23,000 (13,500 Northern CA ed., 9,500 Southern CA ed.). (back issues avail.) **Document type:** consumer publication.
    Description: Covers Indian events, films, music, books and travel.

917.306   US   ISSN 0883-721X
INDIA - WEST. 1975. w. $28. India - West Publications Inc., 5901 Christie Ave., No. 301, Emeryville, CA 94608-1934. FAX 510-652-7968. Ed. Ms. Bina A. Murarka. adv.; bk.rev.; circ. 14,000 (paid). (tabloid format; back issues avail.) **Document type:** newspaper.
    Description: News from India and Indian - American communities in the U.S.

INDIAN AFFAIRS. see POLITICAL SCIENCE — Civil Rights

INDIAN - ARTIFACT MAGAZINE. see ARCHAEOLOGY

970.1   745.5   US
INDIAN ARTS & CRAFTS ASSOCIATION NEWSLETTER. 1974. m. membership. Indian Arts & Crafts Association, 122 La Veta Dr. N.E., Albuquerque, NM 87108-1613. TEL 505-265-9149. FAX 505-262-2312. Ed. Helen Skredergard. adv.; bk.rev. circ. 850. (looseleaf format) **Document type:** newsletter.

970.1   US
INDIAN AWARENESS CENTER NEWSLETTER. 1984. q. $5. Fulton County Historical Society, Inc., 37 E, 375 N, Rochester, IN 46975. TEL 219-223-4436. Ed. Shirley Willard. adv.; bk.rev. circ. 80. **Document type:** newsletter.

970.1   US
INDIAN BUSINESS AND MANAGEMENT. 1990. q. $4 per issue. National Center for American Indian Enterprise Development, 953 E. Juanita Ave., Mesa, AZ 85204-6622. Ed. Steven L.A. Stallings. adv.; illus.

970.1   US   ISSN 1066-5501
E78.S63
INDIAN COUNTRY TODAY. 1981. w. $48. Box 2180, Rapid City, SD 57709. Ed. Pam Stillman; Pub. Tim Giago. adv.; bk.rev.; illus. circ. 8,000. **Document type:** newspaper.
    Formerly (until 1992): Lakota Times (ISSN 0744-2238)
    Description: Contains articles of interest to the American Indian community.

970.1   US
INDIAN CRUSADER. 1954. 4/yr. $5 contribution. American Indian Liberation Crusade, Inc., 4009 Halldale Ave., Los Angeles, CA 90062. TEL 213-299-1810. Ed. Basil M. Gaynor, Jr. circ. 8,000 (controlled). **Document type:** newsletter.
    Description: Chronicles the outreach and releif programs to the reservation Indian by their non-profit organization.

INDIAN HISTORY AND CULTURE. SERIES. see HISTORY — History Of Asia

296   IS
INDIAN JEWRY. 1984. irreg. $10. Beit Eliahu V'Leah Institute for Jewish Studies, P.O. Box 781, Haifa 31007, Israel. Ed. Ben Eliahu Eliah. circ. 500. **Document type:** monographic series.

INDIAN LAW REPORTER. see LAW

INDIAN LEADER. see COLLEGE AND ALUMNI

970.1   CN   ISSN 0226-9317
INDIAN LIFE. 1967. bi-m. $7. Intertribal Christian Communications, Box 3765, Sta. B, Winnipeg, MB R2W 3R6, Canada. TEL 204-661-9333. FAX 204-661-3982. Ed. Edward Hughes. adv.; bk.rev. circ. 20,000.
    Formerly: American Indian Life.

970.1   US   ISSN 0019-6193
INDIAN PROGRESS. 1955. 3/yr. $3 to non-members. Associated Committee of Friends on Indian Affairs, Box 1661, Richmond, IN 47375. TEL 317-962-9169. Ed. Harold Smuck. bk.rev. circ. 2,600. **Document type:** newsletter.
    Description: Covers religious programming at centers operated by ACFIA.

970.1   US   ISSN 0046-9076
INDIAN TRADER, INC.. 1970. m. $18 (foreign $30). Indian Trader, Inc., Box 1421, Gallup, NM 87305. TEL 505-722-6694. Ed. Bill Donovan. adv.; bk.rev.; illus.; tr.lit. circ. 7,500. (tabloid format)
    Description: Covers American Indian interests.

INDIAN YOUTH OF AMERICA NEWSLETTER. see CHILDREN AND YOUTH — About

296   US
INDIANA JEWISH HISTORICAL SOCIETY. NEWSLETTER. 1973. q. membership. Indiana Jewish Historical Society, 310 Central Bldg., 203 W. Wayne St., Ft. Wayne, IN 46802-3610. TEL 219-422-3862. FAX 219-422-3862. Ed. Eileen Baitcher. circ. 875. **Document type:** newsletter, academic/scholarly publication.
    Description: Covers Jewish interests.

296   US
INDIANA JEWISH POST AND OPINION. 1933. w. $36. Spokesman Co., Inc., c/o Gabriel M. Cohen, Pub., 2120 N. Meridian St., Indianapolis, IN 46202. TEL 317-927-7800. Ed. Edward Stattmann. adv.; bk.rev. circ. 129,301. (reprint service avail.)
    Description: Contains articles of interest to the Jewish community.

917.106   CN   ISSN 0708-949X
INDO CANADIAN TIMES. (Text in Punjabi) 1978. w. Can.$60. 12414 82 Ave., Ste. 103, Surrey, BC V3W 3R9, Canada. TEL 604-599-5408. FAX 604-599-5415. Ed. Tara Singh Hayer. adv.; bk.rev. circ. 15,200. (tabloid format; back issues avail.) **Document type:** newspaper.

980 954   CN
INDO CARIBBEAN WORLD; keeping alive the ties that bind. 1983. s-m. Can.$30 (foreign $35). 312 Brownridge Dr., Thornhill, ON L4J 5X1, Canada. TEL 416-738-5005. FAX 416-738-3927. Ed. Harry Ramkhelawan. adv.; bk.rev. circ. 30,000. (tabloid format) **Document type:** newspaper.

954   CN   ISSN 1194-3882
INDO PAK COMMUNITY VOICE. 1983. fortn. Can.$26 (in U.S. $30; elsewhere $50). Directories International Ltd., Box 44007, 370 Main St. N., Brampton, ON L6V 4H5, Canada. TEL 905-452-8133. FAX 905-455-9839. Ed. Sabih Mansoor. adv. circ. 3,000. (tabloid format; back issues avail.) **Document type:** newspaper.

362.8 323.4   AT   ISSN 0815-6905
INFOCUS NEWS MAGAZINE. 1975. bi-m. Aus.$10. Ethnic Communities' Council of N.S.W., 221 Cope St., Waterloo, N.S.W. 2017, Australia. FAX 02-319-4229. Ed. Gosia Dybka. adv.; bk.rev. circ. 1,500. (back issues avail.) **Document type:** newsletter.
    Formerly (until 1984): Ethnic Communities' Council of N.S.W. Newsletter (ISSN 0157-3942)

296   FR   ISSN 0020-0107
INFORMATION JUIVE. 1948. m. 175 F. Consistoire Israelite de Paris, 17 rue Saint-Georges, 75009 Paris, France. TEL 48-74-29-87. FAX 48-74-41-97. Ed. Jacques Lazarus. adv.; bk.rev.; bibl. circ. 11,000. (also avail. in microform from UMI; reprint service avail. from UMI)
    Incorporates: Journal des Communautes (ISSN 0021-8022)
    Description: Studies the problems of Israel, aspects of Judaism in France and abroad, Jewish thought.

953.206   GW
INFORMATIONSBULLETIN KURDISTAN. 1987. bi-m. DM.3. Komkar, Hansaring 28, 50670 Cologne, Germany. TEL 0221-123376. FAX 0221-123485. Ed. A. Saydam. circ. 2,500. (looseleaf format; back issues avail.) **Document type:** bulletin.

918.106   BL
▼**INFORMATIVO GRUMIN**. 1993. a. Grumin - Grupo Mulher - Educacao Indigena, Rua da Quitanda 185-503, 20091-000 Rio de Janeiro RJ, Brazil. TEL 021-293-1745.

910.03   US
INFORMER AND TEXAS FREEMAN. 1983. w. $32. Marshall - Butler Newspapers, Inc., 4209 Dowling, Box 3086, Houston, TX 77253-3086. TEL 713-527-8261. Ed. George McElroy. adv. circ. 30,000. (also avail. in microfilm)

910.3   US   ISSN 1067-2567
INNER CITY NEWS. 1977. w. $25. Box 1545, Mobile, AL 36633-1545. TEL 205-452-9330. Ed. Charles W. Porter. adv. contact: Harry McGadney. bk.rev. circ. 8,000. **Document type:** newspaper.

296   US   ISSN 0199-7602
DS101
INSIDE (PHILADELPHIA); the Jewish exponent magazine. 1980. q. $6.95. (Federation of Jewish Agencies of Greater Philadelphia) Jewish Exponent, 226 S. 16th St., Philadelphia, PA 19102. TEL 215-893-5700. Ed. Jane Biberman. adv. circ. 73,000.
    Formerly: Expo (Philadelphia) (ISSN 0164-6753)

917.106   CN   ISSN 0837-1091
INSIEME. (Text in Italian) 1973. w. Can.$18. Publications Ensemble Inc., 4358 rue Charleroi, Montreal-Nord, PQ H1H 1T3, Canada. TEL 514-328-2062. FAX 514-328-6562. Ed. P. Giuseppe De Rossi. adv.; illus.; circ. 16,000 (paid); 2,000 (controlled). (tabloid format) back issues avail.)
    Description: International, national and local news to inform the Italian community.

914.106   UK
INSTITUTE OF CORNISH STUDIES. CORNISH STUDIES. vol. 1, 1973; vol. 2, 1993. irreg., no. 16 (1988). price varies. (Institute of Cornish Studies) University of Exeter Press, Trevithick Centre, Trevenson Rd., Pool Redruth, Redruth, Cornwall TR15 3PL, England. TEL 0209-712203. Philip Payton, Dir. circ. 300. **Document type:** academic/scholarly publication.
    Formerly: Institute of Cornish Studies. Special Bibliography.

947   US   ISSN 0738-7105
INSTITUTE OF MODERN RUSSIAN CULTURE NEWSLETTER. 1979. 2/yr. $25. Institute of Modern Russian Culture, Box 4353, USC, Los Angeles, CA 90089-4353. TEL 213-740-2735. FAX 213-740-9354. TELEX 674803UNIVSOCALLSA. Ed. John E. Bowlt. circ. 1,000 (controlled). **Document type:** bulletin.
    Description: Propagates literary and artistic achievements of modern Russian culture.

INSTITUTO AMERICANO DE ESTUDIOS VASCOS. BOLETIN. see HISTORY — History Of North And South America

914.467   SP   ISSN 0211-2329
DP402.G4
INSTITUTO DE ESTUDIOS GERUNDENSES. ANALES. (Text in Spanish and Catalan) 1946. a. 2000 ptas.($40) Instituto de Estudios Gerundenses, Forca 27, Gerona, Spain. bk.rev. (back issues avail.) **Indexed:** Amer.Hist.& Life, Hist.Abstr.

914.467   SP   ISSN 0211-2477
INSTITUTO DE ESTUDIOS GERUNDENSES. SERIE MONOGRAFICA. 1947. irreg. price varies. Instituto de Estudios Gerundenses, Forca 27, Gerona, Spain.

914   PO   ISSN 0871-178X
INSTITUTO DE INVESTIGACAO CIENTIFICA TROPICAL. COMUNICACOES. SERIE DE CIENCIAS ETNOLOGICAS E ETNOMUSEOLOGICAS. irreg. price varies. Instituto de Investigacao Cientifica Tropical, Rua Jua, 54, 1300 Lisbon, Portugal. TEL 364-5321. FAX 363-1460. (Subscr. to: Centro de Documentacao e Informacao, Rua Jau 47, 1300 Lisbon, Portugal) circ. 1,000. **Document type:** monographic series.

296   CN   ISSN 0835-7420
INTERCOM (MONTREAL). q. free. Canadian Jewish Congress, 1590 Docteur Penfield Ave., Montreal, PQ H3G 1C5, Canada. Ed. Mike Cohen.

INTERCULTURE; exploring the frontiers of cross-cultural understanding. see HUMANITIES: COMPREHENSIVE WORKS

ETHNIC INTERESTS

296 US ISSN 0047-0511
INTERMOUNTAIN JEWISH NEWS. 1913. w. $42.50. 1275 Sherman St., Ste. 214, Denver, CO 80203. TEL 303-861-2234. FAX 303-832-6942. Ed. Miriam H. Goldberg. adv.: B&W page $1361.60; adv. contact: Hillel J. Goldberg. bk.rev.; film rev.; charts; illus.; circ. 9,742 (paid). (tabloid format; also avail. in microfilm from AJP) **Document type:** newspaper.
  Description: Contains international, national, regional and local news of interest to its Jewish readership.

INTERNATIONAL CONNECTOR FOR JEWISH SINGLES. see *SINGLES' INTERESTS AND LIFESTYLES*

INTERNATIONAL JOURNAL OF KURDISH STUDIES. see *GENERAL INTEREST PERIODICALS — Middle East*

INTERNATIONAL LATIN MUSIC BUYER'S GUIDE. see *MUSIC*

INTERNATIONAL MIGRATION REVIEW; a quarterly studying sociological, demographic, economic, historical, and legislative aspects of human migration movements and ethnic group relations. see *POPULATION STUDIES*

INTERNATIONAL REVIEW OF AFRICAN AMERICAN ART; an international publication. see *ART*

917.306 US ISSN 1047-5370
HQ1031
INTERRACE; the source for interracial living. 1989. bi-m. $24 (effective 1994). Interrace Magazine, Box 12048, Atlanta, GA 30355-2048. TEL 404-364-9690. FAX 404-364-9965. Ed. Candy Mills. adv.: B&W page $800, color page $1180; adv. contact: Gabe Grosz. bk.rev.; circ. 25,000 (paid). (back issues avail.) **Document type:** consumer publication.
—UnCover.
  Description: For interracial couples and families, biracial and multiracial people, transracial adoption, and race relations.

INVANDRARRAPPORT; invandrarnas debatt- och kulturtidskrift. see *POPULATION STUDIES*

917.106 US
IRAN TIMES INTERNATIONAL. (Text in English, Farsi (Persian)) 1970. w. $70 to individuals; institutions $95. 2727 Wisconsin Ave., N.W., Washington, DC 20007. TEL 202-659-9868. FAX 202-337-7449. Ed. Javad Khakbaz. adv.; bk.rev. (also avail. in microfilm; back issues avail.) **Document type:** newspaper.

910.03 US
IREDALL COUNTY NEWS. 1980. w. $15. Iredall Publishing Company, 505 S. Center St., Statesville, NC 28677. TEL 704-873-1054. FAX 704-873-1054. (Subscr. to: Box 407, Statesville, NC 28677) Ed. Mason McCullough; Pub. Mason McCullough. adv. contact: Daon Bailey. circ. 2,400. **Document type:** newspaper.

IRIS: A JOURNAL ABOUT WOMEN. see *WOMEN'S INTERESTS*

301 US ISSN 0884-4240
E184.I6
IRISH AMERICA MAGAZINE.* 1984. m. $20. Irish America Inc., 432 Park Ave. So., No. 1000, New York, NY 10016-8013. Ed.Bd. film rev.; play rev.; bibl. circ. 35,000. (tabloid format; back issues avail.)

914.206 US ISSN 0192-1215
IRISH ECHO. 1928. w. $25. Irish Echo Newspaper Corporation, 309 Fifth Ave., New York, NY 10016. TEL 212-686-1266. FAX 212-686-1756. Ed. John Thornton. adv.; bk.rev.; film rev.; play rev.; illus. circ. 61,300. (tabloid format)
  Description: Contains articles of interest to the Irish community.

917.306 US
IRISH HERALD; America's first newspaper. 1962. m. $15. Irish Enterprises, 2123 Market St., San Francisco, CA 94114. Ed. John Whooley. adv.; bk.rev. circ. 7,000. (tabloid format) **Document type:** newspaper.
  Description: Covers Irish American interests.

052 UK ISSN 0260-650X
IRISH IN BRITAIN DIRECTORY. 1979. a. £5.99. Brent Irish Advisory Service, 99 Villiers Rd., London NW2 5QB, England. TEL 081-830-3232. FAX 081-451-8865. Ed. Catherine Mulvenna. adv. circ. 10,000. **Document type:** directory.

IRISH LITERARY SUPPLEMENT. see *LITERATURE*

841.306 US
IRISH PEOPLE (NEW YORK).* 1972. w. $15. Irish People, Inc., 363 7th Ave., Ste. 405, New York, NY 10001-3904. TEL 212-567-1611. Ed. Martin Galvin. adv. circ. 10,000.
  Description: Contains articles of interest to the Irish community.

IRISH STUDIES. see *HISTORY — History Of Europe*

IRISH STUDIES IN BRITAIN. see *HISTORY — History Of Europe*

301 US
IRISH VOICE. w. Irish America Inc., 432 Park Ave. South, Suite 1000, New York, NY 10016. TEL 212-684-3366. FAX 212-779-1198.

ISHA L'ISHA NEWSLETTER. see *WOMEN'S INTERESTS*

ISKRA. see *RELIGIONS AND THEOLOGY — Eastern Orthodox*

917.306 956 US
ISLAMIC AFFAIRS. (Text mainly in English; occasionally in Arabic) 1969. w. $25. (National Council on Islamic Affairs) Islamic Affairs, P.O. Box 416, New York, NY 10017. TEL 212-972-0460. FAX 212-682-1405. Ed. Dr. M. T. Mehdi. adv. contact: Ghazi Khankan. bk.rev.; charts; illus. circ. 15,000. (tabloid format) **Document type:** newspaper.
  Formerly (until 1992): Action (New York) (ISSN 0001-7388)

296 US
ISRAELI FOLK DANCE CLEARINGHOUSE CALENDAR.* 1986. bi-m. $9 (foreign $10). American Zionist Youth Foundation, Israel Folk Dance Institute, 110 E. 59th St., New York, NY 10022. TEL 212-318-6123. Ed. Honey Goldfein-Perry. bk.rev. circ. 100. (back issues avail.)
  Description: Calendar of related activities world-wide.

296 SZ ISSN 0021-2342
ISRAELITISCHES WOCHENBLATT FUER DIE SCHWEIZ/REVUE JUIVE. Abbreviated title: I W. (Text in German) 1901. w. 136 SFr. Verlag Manfred Marx AG, Florastr. 14, CH-8034 Zurich, Switzerland. TEL 01-3837094. FAX 01-3833371. adv.; bk.rev. circ. 5,500.
  Description: Covers Jewish interests.

918.106 BL
ITAICI; revista de espiritualidade inaciana. 1989. 4/yr. foreign $15. Centro de Espiritualidade Inaciana de Itaici, Caixa Postal 09, Vila Kostka, 13330-970 Indaiatuba SP, Brazil. TEL 0192-75-0055. FAX 0192-75-9966. Pub. Luis Gonzalez-Quevedo. circ. 900.
  Description: Concerned with Ignatian spirituality and spiritual exercises of St. Ignatius of Loyola.

323.1 947 IS
ITALIA; a periodical on the literature and culture of Italian Jews. (Text in English, French, Hebrew and Italian) 1976. irreg., latest vol.9. $12. (Hebrew University of Jerusalem, Institute of Languages and Literatures) Magnes Press, Hebrew University, Jerusalem, P.O. Box 7695, Jerusalem, Israel. TEL 972-2-660341. FAX 972-2-633370. Eds. R. Bonfil, G. Sermoneta. abstr. **Document type:** academic/scholarly publication.

914.506 US
ITALIAN-AMERICAN DIGEST. 1974. q. $4. Box 2392, New Orleans, LA 70176-2392. TEL 504-891-1904. FAX 504-822-1659. Ed. Joseph Maselli. adv.; bk.rev. circ. 10,000. (tabloid format; also avail. in microfilm; back issues avail.)

973 US ISSN 0096-8846
E184.I8
ITALIAN AMERICANA. 1974-1986; resumed 1990. s-a. $15 to individuals; institutions $22.50 (foreign $35). University of Rhode Island, College of Continuing Education, 199 Promenade St., Providence, RI 02908-5090. TEL 401-277-3824. FAX 401-227-6180. (Co-sponsors: American Italian Historical Association, University of Rhode Island) Ed. Carol Bonomo Albright. adv.: B&W page $150. bk.rev.; film rev.; bibl. circ. 1,000. Indexed: Amer.Hist.& Life, Hist.Abstr., M.L.A. **Document type:** academic/scholarly publication, monographic series.
—UnCover.
  Description: Historical perspective on the Italian experience in America, including fiction and poetry.

317.306 US ISSN 0740-2597
ITALIAN TRIBUNE NEWS. (Text in English) 1931. w. $20. Italian Tribune Publishing Co., 427 Bloomfield Ave., Newark, NJ 07107. TEL 201-485-6000. FAX 201-485-8967. Ed. Joan Alagna. adv. contact: David Aaron. bk.rev.; film rev.; play rev. circ. 25,000. (tabloid format) **Document type:** newspaper.
  Description: Covers news for the Italian-American community.

917.406 US
ITALIAN VOICE/VOCE ITALIANA. 1932. w. $17. Emilio Augusto Publishing Company, Box 9, Totowa, NJ 07511-0009. TEL 201-942-5028. Ed. Mrs. Cesarina Augusto Earl. adv. circ. 6,250.
  Description: Disseminates general and cultural news of interest to the Italian-American community.

914.506 US
L'ITALO AMERICANO NEWSPAPER. (Text in English and Italian) 1908. w. $20. Fathers of St. Charles, 10631 Vinedale St., Sun Valley, CA 91352. TEL 818-767-3413. FAX 818-767-1410. Ed. Fr. August Feccia. adv.; bk.rev.; film rev.; illus.; stat. circ. 35,000. (tabloid format; back issues avail.; reprint service avail.) **Document type:** newspaper.
  Description: Covers news from Los Angeles, San Francisco and San Diego and community and local events.

J A I A. see *GENERAL INTEREST PERIODICALS — Indonesia*

917.306 US
J T A COMMUNITY NEWS REPORTER. w. $65. Jewish Telegraphic Agency, 330 Seventh Ave., 11th Fl., New York, NY 10001. TEL 212-643-1890. FAX 212-643-8498. TELEX 12-6978. Ed. Mark Joffe. (processed; also avail. in microfilm from AJP)
  Description: Weekly newsletter focusing on honors, appointments and events within Jewish communities around the continent.

296 US ISSN 0021-3772
DS101
J T A DAILY NEWS BULLETIN. 1922. d. (except Sat. & Sun.). $280. Jewish Telegraphic Agency, 330 Seventh Ave, 11th Fl. New York, NY 10001. TEL 212-643-1890. FAX 212-643-8498. TELEX 126978. Ed. Mark Joffe. circ. 2,500. (also avail. in microfilm from AJP)
  Description: Daily chronicle of international events affecting Jews and Jewish communities.

296 US ISSN 0021-3799
J.W.V.A. BULLETIN. vol.12 1970. q. $1. Jewish War Veterans of the USA, Inc., National Ladies Auxiliary, 1811 R St., N.W., Washington, DC 20009. TEL 202-667-9061. Ed. Emma-Lou Rosenstein. charts; illus.
  Description: Covers Jewish interests.

910.03 US ISSN 0047-1704
JACKSON ADVOCATE. (Supplement avail.) 1938. w. $20 in state; out of state $25. 300 N. Farish St., Jackson, MS 39202. TEL 601-948-4122. FAX 601-948-4125. (Subscr. to: Box 3708, Jackson, MS 39207) Ed. Charles Tisdale. adv. contact: O.J. Daniels. circ 25,000. **Document type:** newspaper.

ETHNIC INTERESTS

910.03 323.4   US
JACKSONVILLE FREE PRESS. 1986. w. $26.50. Jacksonville Free Press, 1603-1 Edgewood Ave., W., Box 43580, Jacksonville, FL 32203-3580. TEL 904-634-1993. FAX 904-384-0235. Ed. Sylvia Carter. adv.; bk.rev. circ. 17,500. (also avail. in microfilm; back issues avail.) **Document type:** newspaper.
  Former titles: Jacksonville Advocate Free Press; Jacksonville Advocate.
  Description: Presents Black history features by local and national writers. Contains church, social and community news and current events.

320.9   FJ   ISSN 0021-3969
JAGRITI;* only Hindi tri-weekly in Pacific. (Text in Hindustani) 1950. 3/wk. $6.50. Pacific Periodicals Ltd., Box 9, Nadi, Fiji. Ed. R.N. Sharma. adv.; bk.rev.; illus.; stat. circ. 5,000.
  Description: Covers Hindi interests.

051   US
JAMAICAN TIMES. 1991. m. $18. Deanne Lucey, Ed. & Pub., 1402 J.F. Kennedy Causeway, Ste. 240, N. Bay Village, FL 33141. TEL 305-758-6122. FAX 305-866-0334. adv. contact: Jean Hudson.

051   CN
JAMAICAN WEEKLY GLEANER. 1958. w. Can.$54.57($51) Gleaner Co. Inc., 4161 Sladeview Cres., Ste. 14, Mississauga, Ont. L5L 5R3, Canada. Ed. Gail Scala. adv.: B&W page Can.$1170; adv. contact: Sheila Alexander. circ. 20,147. (tabloid format)

954.92   UK
JANOMOT BENGALI NEWSWEEKLY. (Text in Bengali) 1969. w. £20 (foreign £40). Unilink Printing & Publishing Co. Ltd., Unit 2, 20B Spelman St., London E1 5LQ, England. TEL 071-377-6032. FAX 071-247-0141. Ed. Syed Samadul Haque. adv.; bk.rev. circ. 20,000. (back issues avail.)

057.8   CI   ISSN 0021-5791
JEDNOTA. 1946. w. 150 din.($19.70) Cehoslovacki Svaz V SR Hrvatskoj, Trg Marsala Tita 7, Daruvar, Croatia. Ed. Josef Matusek. adv.

917.306 282   US
JEDNOTA/UNION. (Text in English, Slovak) 1890. w. $25 (foreign $30). First Catholic Slovak Union, 6611 Rockside Rd., Independence, OH 44131-2398. TEL 800-533-6682. (Subscr. to: Box 150, Middletown, PA 17057. TEL 717-944-0461) Ed. Joseph C. Krajsa. adv.; illus. circ. 35,000.

296   IS   ISSN 0792-7304
DS140
JERUSALEM LETTER - VIEWPOINTS. (Text in English) 1977. 20/yr. $40 to individuals; institutions $55. Jerusalem Center for Public Affairs, 13 Tel Hai St., Jerusalem 92107, Israel. TEL 972-2-619281. FAX 972-2-619112. (U.S. subscr. to: Center for Jewish Community Studies, 1616 Walnut St., No. 513, Phialdelphia, PA 19103. TEL 215-204-1459. FAX 215-204-7784)
  Formerly (until 1979): Jerusalem Letter (ISSN 0334-4096)
  Description: Information and analysis on Israeli and Jewish issues.

JET. see GENERAL INTEREST PERIODICALS — United States

296   YU   ISSN 0021-6240
JEVREJSKI PREGLED. (Text in Serbo-Croatian; summaries in English) 1950. m. $20. Savez Jevrejskih Opstina Jugoslavije - Federation of Jewish Communities in Yugoslavia, 7. Jula 71a, Belgrade, Yugoslavia. Ed. Luci Petrovic. illus. circ. 2,700.

296   SA   ISSN 0021-6313
JEWISH AFFAIRS. 1941. q. R.8.25 per no. South African Jewish Board of Deputies, P.O. Box 1180, Johannesburg, South Africa. TEL 27-12-486-1434. FAX 27-12-646-4940. Ed. Joseph Sherman. adv.; bk.rev.; illus. circ. 2,000. **Indexed:** Ind.S.A.Per. **Document type:** academic/scholarly publication.
  Description: Contains articles of interest to the Jewish community, with a specific focus on South Africa and its politics and culture.
  Refereed Serial

917.309   US   ISSN 0085-2368
JEWISH BOSTON; guide to Jewish life in the greater Boston Jewish community with a Massachusetts supplement. 1969. biennial? $2.50. Jewish Boston, Inc., 233 Bay State Rd., Boston, MA 02215. Eds. Morey Schapira, Chaim Casper. adv.; bk.rev.; illus. circ. 10,000.
  Formerly: Jewish Boston and New England Jewry.

296   US
JEWISH BULLETIN OF NORTHERN CALIFORNIA. 1946. w. $38. San Francisco Jewish Community Publications, Inc., 88 First St., Ste. 300, San Francisco, CA 94105. TEL 415-957-9340. FAX 415-957-0266. Ed. Marc S. Klein. adv.; bk.rev. circ. 30,000. (tabloid format; also avail. in microfilm from AJP) **Document type:** newspaper.
  Former titles: Northern California Jewish Bulletin; San Francisco Jewish Bulletin; Jewish Community Bulletin (ISSN 0021-6364)

296   US
JEWISH CHICAGO.* m. $20. Jewish Chicago, Inc., 2653 W. Pratt Blvd., Chicago, IL 60645-4528.

JEWISH CHRONICLE; the world's leading Jewish newspaper. see LITERARY AND POLITICAL REVIEWS

296   US
JEWISH CHRONICLE LEADER. 1926. fortn. $11. Mar-Len Publications, 131 Lincoln St., Worcester, MA 01605. TEL 508-752-2512. FAX 508-752-9057. Ed. Sondra Shapiro. adv.; bk.rev.; circ. 3,500 (paid). (tabloid format; back issues avail.) **Document type:** newsletter.

296   US   ISSN 0021-6348
JEWISH CIVIC PRESS. 1965. m. $50. 924 Valmont St., New Orleans, LA 70115. TEL 504-895-8784. Ed. Abner L. Tritt. adv.; bk.rev.; film rev.; play rev.; illus.; circ. 3,285 (controlled). (tabloid format; also avail. in microfilm from AJP) **Document type:** newspaper.

296   US   ISSN 0191-3034
JEWISH CIVILIZATION: ESSAYS AND STUDIES. 1980. a. price varies. Reconstructionist Press, Church Rd. and Greenwood Ave., Wyncote, PA 19095. TEL 215-576-0800. FAX 215-576-6143. circ. 1,000. **Indexed:** Ind.Jew.Per.

296   US
JEWISH COMMUNITY CHRONICLE. 1947. s-m. $20. Jewish Community Federation, 3801 E. Willow St., Long Beach, CA 90815-1791. TEL 310-595-5543. FAX 310-424-3915. Ed. Harriette R. Ellis. adv.; bk.rev.; film rev. circ. 5,500. (back issues avail.) **Document type:** newspaper.
  Formerly (until June, 1992): Jewish Federation News.
  Description: Contains news on politics, social issues, events, and editorials geared toward Jewish life and culture.

296   US   ISSN 0021-6380
JEWISH CURRENT EVENTS.* 1959. bi-w. $5.95. Current Publishing Co., 184 Grantham F., Deerfield Beach, FL 33442-3416. Ed. Samuel Deutsch. bk.rev.; film rev.; play rev.; illus.; stat. (tabloid format; also avail. in microfilm from AJP)
  Description: Contains items of interest to the Jewish community.

296   US   ISSN 0021-6399
DS133
JEWISH CURRENTS. 1946. m. $20. Association for Promotion of Jewish Secularism, Inc., 22 E. 17th St., Rm. 601, New York, NY 10003. TEL 212-924-5740. Ed. Morris U. Schappes. adv.; bk.rev.; film rev.; play rev.; record rev.; index. circ. 2,536. (also avail. in microform from UMI; reprint service avail. from UMI) **Document type:** consumer publication.
  —Faxon; UnCover; UMI.
  Description: Covers secular Jewish interests, pro-Israel though non-Zionist. Covers Holocaust - Resistance commemoration, Black - Jewish relations, labor struggle, and Yiddish culture.

322.4 323.1 296   US
JEWISH DEFENSE LEAGUE ITON. 1968. m. $12. Jewish Defense Organization, 134 W. 32nd St., Rm. 602, New York, NY 10001. TEL 212-239-0447. Ed. Sheldon Davis. adv.; illus. circ. 25,000.
  Formerly: Jewish Defense League Newsletter (ISSN 0021-6402)

296   CN
JEWISH DIRECTORY OF GREATER TORONTO. a. free. Jewish Directory Inc. of Greater Toronto, 281 Sandringham Dr., Ste. 100, North York, Ont. M3H 1G4, Canada. TEL 416-787-5603. FAX 416-784-1370. adv. circ. 30,000.
  Formerly: Jewish Directory.
  Description: Listings of name, address and telephone numbers of Jewish services, facilities and organizations.

296   US
JEWISH EXECUTIVE. 1976-1981; resumed 1982. m. $25 per no. Klass Publications, Inc, 338 3rd Ave., Brooklyn, NY 11215. Ed. Arthur Kass. adv.; illus. circ. 7,500.

296   US   ISSN 0021-6437
JEWISH EXPONENT. 1887. w. $30. Federation of Jewish Agencies of Greater Philadelphia, 226 S. 16th St., Philadelphia, PA 19102. TEL 215-893-5700. FAX 215-790-0087. Ed. Al Erlick. adv.; bk.rev.; illus. circ. 80,000. (tabloid format; also avail. in microfilm from AJP) **Document type:** newspaper.
  Description: Contains items of interest to the Jewish community.

296   US   ISSN 0890-9113
JEWISH FOLKLORE AND ETHNOLOGY REVIEW. 1977. s-a. (American Folklore Society, Jewish Folklore Section) Oberlin College, Department of Judaic and Near Eastern Studies, Oberlin, OH 44074. (Subscr. to: 3822 S. Troost, Tulsa, OK 74105) Ed. Guy Haskell. adv.; bk.rev.; film rev.; illus. (back issues avail.)
  Formerly (until 1986): Jewish Folklore and Ethnology Newsletter (ISSN 0737-559X)

296   US   ISSN 0021-6453
DS149
JEWISH FRONTIER.* 1934. bi-m. $15. Labor Zionist Letters, Inc., 275 7th Ave., Rm. 17R, New York, NY 10001-6776. Ed. Nahum Guttman. adv.; bk.rev.; film rev. circ. 12,500. (also avail. in microform from UMI; reprint service avail. from UMI) **Indexed:** G.Soc.Sci.& Rel.Per.Lit., Ind.Bk.Rev.Hum., Ind.Jew.Per., P.A.I.S.
  —UnCover; UMI.

296   UK   ISSN 0021-6461
JEWISH GAZETTE. (In three editions: Manchester, Leeds, Merseyside) 1928. w. £25. Jewish Gazette Ltd., 27 Bury Old Rd., Prestwich, Manchester M25 8EY, England. TEL 061-740-5171. FAX 061-688-6666. Ed. Lindy Ruth. adv. contact: Leslie Holt. bk.rev.; illus. circ. 13,000. cols./p.: 6; pp./issue: 28. (also avail. in microform from UMI; reprint service avail. from UMI) **Document type:** newspaper.
  Description: Contains articles of interest to the Jewish community.

JEWISH GUARDIAN. see RELIGIONS AND THEOLOGY — Judaic

956.940 296   SA   ISSN 0021-647X
JEWISH HERALD; national Jewish weekly. 1937. w. R.17.50. (Zionist Revisionist Organisation of South Africa) Jewish Herald (Pty) Ltd., Box 4474, Johannesburg, South Africa. Ed. Maurice Dorfan. adv.; bk.rev.; film rev.; play rev.; illus. circ. 10,000(approx.). (tabloid format)
  Description: Covers Jewish interests.

296   US   ISSN 0021-6488
JEWISH HERALD-VOICE. 1908. w. (plus 2 special issues). $32. 3403 Audley, Box 153, Houston, TX 77001. TEL 713-630-0391. FAX 713-630-0404. Ed. Jeanne F. Samuels. adv. contact: Vicki Samuels. bk.rev.; illus. circ. 6,600. (tabloid format; also avail. in microfilm from AJP; avail. on records) **Document type:** newspaper.

296   US
JEWISH HISTORICAL SOCIETY OF NEW YORK. PUBLICATIONS. 1976. irreg., no.4, 1987. Jewish Historical Society of New York, 8 W. 70th St., New York, NY 10023. TEL 212-415-5544. **Document type:** monographic series.

ETHNIC INTERESTS

296   IS   ISSN 0334-701X
DS101
JEWISH HISTORY. (Text in English and Hebrew) 1986. q. $25 to individuals; institutions $40. Haifa University Press, Mount Carmel, Haifa 31999, Israel. TEL 972-4-240601. FAX 972-4-342245. (Dist. by: University Press of New England, 23 S. Main St., Hanover NH 03755-2048. TEL 603-643-7100) Ed. Kenneth R. Stow. adv.; bk.rev. circ. 500. **Document type**: academic/scholarly publication.
—UnCover. **CCC**.

296   US
JEWISH INFORMATION AND REFERRAL SERVICE DIRECTORY. 1980. a. $50. U J A Federation of Jewish Philanthropies of N.Y., 130 E. 59th St., New York, NY 10022. TEL 212-980-1000. cum.index. (looseleaf format)

396   US
JEWISH JOURNAL OF SAN ANTONIO. 1973. m. (except July). free to qualified personnel. Jewish Federation of San Antonio, 8434 Ahern Dr, San Antonio, TX 78216. TEL 512-341-8234. FAX 512-341-2843. Ed. Marion Bernstein. adv.; bk.rev. circ. 3,800. (back issues avail.) **Document type**: newspaper.
    Description: Contains local, national, and international news and features of interest to the local Jewish community.

296 331   US
JEWISH LABOR COMMITTEE REVIEW. vol.8, 1973. 2-3/yr. free. Jewish Labor Committee, 25 E. 21st St., New York, NY 10010-6207. TEL 212-477-0707. FAX 212-477-1918. Ed. Arieh Lebowitz. illus. circ. 5,000. **Document type**: newsletter.
    Former titles: J L C Review; (until 1985): J L C News (ISSN 0447-2276)

296   US
JEWISH LEADER. 1974. fortn. $25. Jewish Federation of Eastern Connecticut, 28 Channing Street, Box 1468, New London, CT 06320. TEL 203-442-8062. Ed. Trudy Rand. adv.; bk.rev. circ. 2,200.
    Description: Contains articles of interest to the Jewish community.

296   US   ISSN 0021-6550
JEWISH LEDGER. 1926. w. $19. Expositor Ledger Newspapers, 2535 Brighton Henrietta Town-Line Rd., Rochester, NY 14623-2711. TEL 716-427-2468. FAX 716-427-8521. Ed. Barbara Morgenstern. adv.; bk.rev.; illus. circ. 8,000. **Document type**: newspaper.

917.1 296   CN
F1035.J5
JEWISH LIFE AND TIMES. 1970. a. Can.$12. Jewish Historical Society of Western Canada, 365 Hargrave St., Rm. 404, Winnipeg, MB R3B 2K3, Canada. TEL 204-942-4822. circ. 500.
    Formerly: Jewish Historical Society of Western Canada. Annual Publication (ISSN 0317-1655)

JEWISH LINGUISTIC STUDIES. see LINGUISTICS

296   US   ISSN 1070-5848
JEWISH NEWS OF GREATER PHOENIX. 1948. w. $39. Phoenix Jewish News, Inc., Box 26590, Phoenix, AZ 85068. TEL 602-870-9470. FAX 602-870-0426. Ed. Florence Eckstein. adv.; bk.rev.; play rev.; circ. 6,500 (paid). (tabloid format; also avail. in microform) **Document type**: newspaper.
    Former titles: Greater Phoenix Jewish News (ISSN 0747-444X); Phoenix Jewish News (ISSN 0031-8353)
    Description: Contains articles of interest to the Jewish community.

JEWISH POLITICAL STUDIES REVIEW. see POLITICAL SCIENCE

296   CN
JEWISH POST AND NEWS. 1925. w. Can.$36.48($70) Jewish Post Ltd., 117 Hutchings St., Winnipeg, MB R2X 2V4, Canada. TEL 204-694-3332. FAX 204-694-3916. Ed. Matt Bellan. adv.; bk.rev. circ. 3,600. (also avail. in microform from AJP)
    Formerly: Jewish Post.

296   US   ISSN 0021-6674
JEWISH PRESS (BROOKLYN). 1950. w. $30. Jewish Press, Inc., c/o Sholom Klass, Ed. & Pub., 338 Third Ave., Brooklyn, NY 11215. TEL 718-330-1100. FAX 718-935-1215. adv.; bk.rev.; film rev.; play rev.; bibl.; illus. circ. 173,000. (tabloid format; also avail. in microfilm from AJP,KTO)

296   US   ISSN 0021-6666
JEWISH PRESS (OMAHA). 1921. w. $24 (foreign $27). Jewish Federation of Omaha, 333 S. 132nd St., Omaha, NE 68154. TEL 402-334-8200. FAX 402-333-5422. Ed. Morris Maline. adv.; bk.rev.; illus. circ. 3,480. (tabloid format; also avail. in microfilm from AJP,BLH)
    Description: Contains local, national and international items of interest to the Jewish community.

296   UK   ISSN 0449-010X
JEWISH QUARTERLY. 1953. q. £17.50. Jewish Literary Trust Ltd., P.O. Box 1148, London NW5 2AZ, England. TEL 071-485-4062. Ed. Colin Schindler. adv.; bk.rev.; play rev.; bibl.; index; circ. 3,000 (controlled). (also avail. in microform from UMI; reprint service avail. from UMI) **Indexed**: Abstr.Engl.Stud. **Document type**: bulletin.
—UnCover. UMI.
    Description: Covers Jewish interests.

296   US
JEWISH RECORD.* 1939. w. $7 to New Jersey residents; non-residents $7.50. 1525 S Main St., Pleasantville, NJ 08232. TEL 609-344-5119. Ed. Martin Korik. adv.; bk.rev. circ. 3,294. (tabloid format; also avail. in microfilm from AJP)
    Description: Contains articles of interest to the Jewish community.

296   IS
JEWISH SAMIZDAT. (Sub-series of: Jews in Soviet Russia) (Text in Hebrew) irreg., latest vol.27. $10 per vol. Magnes Press, P.O. Box 7695, Jerusalem 91076, Israel. TEL 972-2-754660. FAX 972-2-633370.

JEWISH SINGLES MAGAZINE (BLOOMFIELD). see SINGLES' INTERESTS AND LIFESTYLES

JEWISH SINGLES MAGAZINE (NEWTON). see SINGLES' INTERESTS AND LIFESTYLES

JEWISH SOCIAL STUDIES; history, culture and society. see SOCIAL SCIENCES: COMPREHENSIVE WORKS

JEWISH SPECTATOR. see RELIGIONS AND THEOLOGY — Judaic

296   CN   ISSN 0021-6739
JEWISH STANDARD. 1929. s-m. Can.$20. Julius Hayman Ltd., Ste. 16, 77 Mowat Ave., Toronto, Ont. M6K 3E3, Canada. adv.; illus. circ. 10,100.
    Description: Covers activities of the Jewish community.

296   US   ISSN 0021-6747
JEWISH STANDARD; New Jersey's oldest English-Jewish newspaper. 1931. w. $25. Jewish Standard Co., 1086 Teaneck Rd., Teaneck, NJ 07666. TEL 201-837-8818. FAX 201-833-4959. Ed. Rebecca Boroson. adv.; bk.rev.; illus. circ. 20,000. (tabloid format)
    Description: Contains articles of interest to the Jewish community.

296   US
JEWISH STAR (BIRMINGHAM). 1976. m. $10. Jewish Star Media, 3608 Rockhill Rd., Birmingham, AL 35223. TEL 205-956-3929. FAX 205-967-1417. (Subscr. to: Box 130603, Birmingham, AL 35213) Ed. Margie Rudolph. adv.; bk.rev. circ. 8,000. (tabloid format; back issues avail.) **Document type**: newspaper.
    Formerly: Jewish Star - Holyland Features.

296   US
JEWISH STAR (SAN FRANCISCO); independent newspaper. 1948. bi-m. $12. Fraternal Media, 109 Minna St., Ste. 323, San Francisco, CA 94105-3701. TEL 415-421-4874. FAX 415-398-7983. Ed. Nevon Stuckey. adv.; bk.rev.; film rev.; play rev.; circ. 3,000 (controlled). (tabloid format; also avail. in microfilm from AJP)
    Description: Contains items of interest to the Jewish community.

JEWISH STORYTELLING NEWSLETTER. see LITERATURE

296   US
JEWISH STUDIES. 1986. irreg., latest no.13. $39.95 per no. Edwin Mellen Press, 415 Ridge St., Box 450, Lewiston, NY 14092. TEL 716-754-2788. FAX 716-754-4056. **Document type**: monographic series.

296   GW   ISSN 0944-5706
▼ **JEWISH STUDIES QUARTERLY**. 1993. q. DM.148. Verlag J.C.B. Mohr (Paul Siebeck), Wilhelmstr. 18, 72074 Tuebingen, Germany. TEL 07071-923-0. FAX 07071-51104. TELEX 7262872-MOHR-D. (Subscr. to: Postfach 2040, 72010 Tuebingen, Germany) Eds. Joseph Dan, Peter Schaefer. **Document type**: academic/scholarly publication.

296   UK   ISSN 0021-6755
JEWISH TELEGRAPH. (In four editions: Manchester and the North West, Liverpool and Merseyside, Leeds and Yorkshire, Scotland) 1950. w. £30 for Manchester edition (Leeds edition £20; Liverpool edition £23; Glasgow edition £28). Jewish Telegraph Ltd., Telegraph House, 11 Park Hill, Bury Old Rd., Prestwich, Manchester M25 8HH, England. TEL 061-740-9321. FAX 061-740-9325. TELEX 9312132018-JT-G. Ed. Paul Harris. adv.: page £2495 (for all editions); 260 x 400. bk.rev.; film rev.; play rev.; illus. circ. 13,000. (tabloid format) **Document type**: newspaper.
    Description: Serves the Jewish community with local, national, and international news.

296   US
JEWISH TIMES (HUNTINGDON VALLEY). 1975. w. $13.97. (Jewish Federation of Greater Philadelphia) Jewish Publishing Group, 103A Tomlinson Rd., Huntingdon Valley, PA 19006. TEL 215-938-1177. FAX 215-938-0692. (Subscr. to: 226 S. 16th St., Philadelphia, PA, 19102. TEL 215-893-5700) Ed. Matthew Schuman. adv. contact: Larry Salamon. bk.rev. circ. 32,500. (tabloid format; back issues avail.) **Document type**: newspaper.

JEWISH TRADITION. see RELIGIONS AND THEOLOGY — Judaic

296   US   ISSN 0021-678X
JEWISH TRANSCRIPT. 1924. s-m. $22.50. Jewish Federation of Greater Seattle, 2031 3rd Ave., No. 200, Seattle, WA 98121-2418. TEL 206-441-4553. FAX 206-441-2736. Ed. Craig Degginger. adv. contact: Karen Chachkes. bk.rev.; charts; illus. circ. 4,200. (tabloid format; also avail. in microfilm from AJP) **Document type**: newspaper.
    Formerly: Transcript.

296   UK
JEWISH TRIBUNE. 1962. w. £29 (Europe £38; Israel £39). Agudas Israel of Great Britain, 97 Stamford Hill, London N16X 5TR, England. TEL 01-800-6688. FAX 01-800-5000. Ed. Jacob Bentov. adv.; bk.rev.
    Description: Covers Jewish interests.

JEWISH VETERAN; the patriotic voice of American Jewry. see MILITARY

296   US   ISSN 0745-5356
DS101
JEWISH WEEK. 1970. w. $35 (foreign $52). Jewish Week Inc., 1501 Broadway, New York, NY 10036. TEL 212-921-7822. FAX 212-921-8420. Ed. Phillip Ritzenberg. adv.; bk.rev.; charts; illus. circ. 110,000. (also avail. in microfilm from AJP) **Document type**: newspaper.
    Formerly: Jewish Week and American Examiner (ISSN 0021-6852)
    Description: Covers political, social, religious and cultural events concerning the Jewish people.

296   US   ISSN 0021-6860
JEWISH WEEKLY NEWS. 1945. w. $19 to Massachusetts residents; non-residents $35. Kenneth G. White, Ed. & Pub., Box 1569, Springfield, MA 01101. TEL 413-739-4771. adv.; bk.rev.; illus. circ. 8,235. (tabloid format; also avail. in microfilm from AJP) **Document type**: newspaper.
    Description: Contains articles of interest to the Jewish community.

ETHNIC INTERESTS

296   CN   ISSN 0021-6879
JEWISH WESTERN BULLETIN. 1929. w. Can.$42.80($43) Anglo-Jewish Publishers, 3268 Heather St., Vancouver, BC V5Z 3K5, Canada. TEL 604-879-6575. FAX 604-879-6573. Ed. Samuel Kaplan. adv.; bk.rev.; illus.; circ. 2,402 (controlled). (tabloid format; also avail. in microfiche) **Document type:** bulletin.

296 070.48   US   ISSN 0199-4441
JEWISH WORLD. 1965. w. $21. Jewish World, Inc., 1104 Central Ave., Albany, NY 12205. TEL 518-459-8455. FAX 518-459-8289. Ed. Laurie J. Clevenson. adv.; bk.rev. circ. 10,150. (tabloid format; back issues avail.) **Document type:** newspaper, consumer publication.
    Description: Covers local, regional, national, and international events of concern to Jews.

296   IS   ISSN 0792-6111
JEWISH WORLD; yearbook for Jewish communities and organizations. (Text in English, Hebrew) 1970. a. $50. P.O. Box 5086, Ramat Gan 52150, Israel. TEL 972-3-6736571. FAX 972-3-6727317. Ed. Zvi Porath-Noy. adv.
    Formerly: Yearbook for Jewish Communities and Organizations (ISSN 0334-5904)

296   IS   ISSN 0334-438X
DS135.R92
JEWS AND THE JEWISH PEOPLE - JEWISH SAMIZDAT/EVREI I EVREISKII NAROD - EVREISKII SAMIZDAT. (Text in Russian) 1974. irreg., no.27, 1991. $20 per no. Hebrew University, Centre for Research and Documentation of East European Jewry, Givat Ram, Jerusalem 91904, Israel. TEL 972-2-584271. FAX 972-2-666804. Ed. Sima Ycikas. bk.rev. circ. 300.
    Description: Covers periodicals and other Jewish unofficial publications that have reached the West.

296   IS
JEWS IN SOVIET RUSSIA. (Consists of 5 sub-series: Jews and the Jewish People; Petitions, Letters and Appeals from Soviet Jews; Jewish Samizdat; Anti-Jewish Trials in the U.S.S.R; Anti-Semitism in the Soviet Union) (Text in Hebrew) irreg. $10 per vol. Magnes Press, Hebrew University, Jerusalem, P.O. Box 7695, Jerusalem 91076, Israel. TEL 972-2-660341. FAX 972-2-633370. **Document type:** monographic series.

970.1   US   ISSN 0021-695X
JICARILLA CHIEFTAIN. (Text occasionally in Apache) 1962. bi-w. $12 in county; out of county $18; foreign $24. Jicarilla Apache Tribe Dulce, Dulce, NM 87528. TEL 505-759-3242. Ed. Mary Polanco. adv. circ. 1,100. (tabloid format)
    Description: Contains articles of interest to the American Indian community.

917.306   US   ISSN 0746-5432
JINSHAN SHIBAO/CHINESE TIMES. (Text in Chinese) 1959. d. $110. Chinese Times Publishing Co., 686 Sacramento St., San Francisco, CA 94111. TEL 415-982-0135. FAX 415-982-3387. Ed. Mike Lee. circ. 200,000. **Document type:** newspaper.

296   DK   ISSN 0021-7131
JOEDISK ORIENTERING. 1929. m. DKK 400 (foreign DKK 800). Mosaisk Trossamfund i Koebenhavn - Jewish Congregation in Copenhagen, Ny Kongensgade 6, 1472 Copenhagen K, Denmark. TEL 33931912. FAX 33141332. Ed. Lui Beilin. adv.; bk.rev.; illus.; bibl. circ. 3,000.
    Formerly: Joedisk Samfund.
    Description: Covers activities of the Danish Jewish community.

JORNAL DA F U N A I. see POLITICAL SCIENCE — Civil Rights

918.106   BL
JORNAL DO GRUMIN. vol.3, 1991. bi-m.? Grumin - Grupo Mulher - Educacao Indigena, Rua da Quitanda 185, Sala 503, 20091 Rio de Janeiro RJ, Brazil. TEL 021-293-1745. **Document type:** newspaper.

JOURNAL OF AFRO-LATIN AMERICAN STUDIES AND LITERATURES. see HUMANITIES: COMPREHENSIVE WORKS

917.106   US   ISSN 0278-5927
E184.A1   CODEN: JAEHEA
JOURNAL OF AMERICAN ETHNIC HISTORY. 1981. q. $30 to individuals (foreign $64); institutions $60 (foreign $84). (Immigration History Society) Transaction Publishers, Transaction Periodicals Consortium, Department 3092, Rutgers University, New Brunswick, NJ 08903. TEL 908-932-2280. FAX 908-932-3138. Ed. Ronald H. Bayor. adv.; bk.rev. circ. 1,300. (also avail. in microform from UMI; reprint service avail. from UMI) **Indexed:** Amer.Hist.& Life, Arts & Hum.Cit.Ind., Chic.Per.Ind., Chic.Per.Ind., Curr.Cont., Hist.Abstr., SSCI. **Document type:** academic/scholarly publication.
    —BLDSC (4927.241000); Faxon; UnCover; UMI. CCC.
    Description: Addresses various aspects of American immigration and ethnic history, including background of emigration, ethnic and racial group.

970.1 370   US   ISSN 0021-8731
E97
JOURNAL OF AMERICAN INDIAN EDUCATION. 1961. 3/yr. (Oct., Jan. & May). $16 (foreign $18.50). Arizona State University, Center for Indian Education, College of Education, Box 871311, Tempe, AZ 85287-1311. TEL 602-965-6292. Ed. Karen Swisher. cum.index. circ. 1,000. (also avail. in microform from JAI,KTO,UMI; reprint service avail. from UMI) **Indexed:** C.I.J.E., Educ.Ind., Lang.& Lang.Behav.Abstr.
    —BLDSC (4927.290000); Faxon; UnCover; UMI.
    Description: Publishes papers directly related to the education of North American Indians and Alaska Natives, with an emphasis on basic and applied research.
    Refereed Serial

970.1 929   US   ISSN 0730-6148
JOURNAL OF AMERICAN INDIAN FAMILY RESEARCH. 1980. q. $25. Histree, 23011 Moulton Pkwy. D-12, Laguna Hills, CA 92653. TEL 714-859-1659. Ed. Larry S. Watson. adv.; bk.rev.; index, cum.index. circ. 600. (back issues avail.) **Document type:** monographic series.
    —UnCover.

970.1 929   US   ISSN 1040-6581
JOURNAL OF AMERICAN INDIAN FAMILY RESEARCH MONTHLY NEWSLETTER. 1988. m. $59. Histree, 23011 Moulton Pkwy. D-12, Laguna Hills, CA 92653. TEL 714-859-1659. Ed. Larry S. Watson. adv. circ. 100. (back issues avail.) **Document type:** newsletter.
    Description: Covers events and activities that are of interest to Native Americans. Includes calendar of events for the upcoming month.

JOURNAL OF BLACK PSYCHOLOGY. see PSYCHOLOGY

JOURNAL OF BLACK STUDIES. see SOCIAL SCIENCES: COMPREHENSIVE WORKS

910.03 378   US
▼**JOURNAL OF BLACKS IN HIGHER EDUCATION.** 1993. q. $24. CH II Publishers, Inc., 200 W. 57th St., New York, NY 10019. TEL 212-399-1084. Ed. Theodore Cross. adv.: B&W page $1275. **Document type:** academic/scholarly publication.

917.306   US   ISSN 0190-2008
F2155
JOURNAL OF CARIBBEAN STUDIES. (Text in English, French and Spanish) 1978. q. $50 to individuals; institutions $200. Association of Caribbean Studies, Box 22202, Lexington, KY 40522-2202. TEL 606-257-6966. FAX 606-258-1072. Ed. O.R. Dathorne. bk.rev.; bibl.; cum.index. circ. 1,000. (back issues avail.) **Indexed:** ERIC, M.L.A.
    —Faxon; UnCover. CCC.

JOURNAL OF CHEROKEE STUDIES. see HISTORY — History Of North And South America

JOURNAL OF ETHNOGERONTOLOGY. see GERONTOLOGY AND GERIATRICS

296 340   US   ISSN 0730-2614
BM520
JOURNAL OF HALACHA AND CONTEMPORARY SOCIETY. 1980. s-a. $10 (foreign $12). Rabbi Jacob Joseph School, 3495 Richmond Rd., Staten Island, NY 10306. TEL 718-979-6333. FAX 212-941-1986. Ed. Rabbi Alfred Cohen. circ. 3,250. **Document type:** academic/scholarly publication.

JOURNAL OF MODERN GREEK STUDIES. see HISTORY — History Of Europe

917.306   US   ISSN 0743-7749
DF701
JOURNAL OF MODERN HELLENISM. 1984. a. $15. (Hellenic College) Hellenic College Press, 50 Goddard Ave., Brookline, MA 02146. TEL 617-731-3500. (Co-sponsor: Queens College, CUNY) Ed.Bd.

JOURNAL OF MULTICULTURAL COUNSELING AND DEVELOPMENT. see PSYCHOLOGY

JOURNAL OF NEGRO EDUCATION. see EDUCATION

910.03   US   ISSN 0022-2992
JOURNAL OF NEGRO HISTORY. 1916-1982; resumed 1983. q. $30 (effective 1994). Association for the Study of Afro-American Life and History, Inc., c/o Alton Hornsby, Jr., Ed., Dept. of History, Morehouse College, Atlanta, GA 30314. TEL 404-215-2620. (also avail. in microform from UMI; reprint service avail. from UMI) **Indexed:** Acad.Ind., Amer.Hist. & Life, Arts & Hum.Cit.Ind., Biog.Ind., Bk.Rev.Ind. (1965-1983), C.I.J.E., Child.Bk.Rev.Ind. (1965-1983), Curr.Cont., Hist.Abstr., Hum.Ind., Ind.Sel.Per. (1950-1982), Mag.Ind., Numis.Lit., PMR, R.G., Ref.Sour., Soc.Sci.Ind. **Document type:** academic/scholarly publication.
    —BLDSC (5021.397000); Faxon; SWETS; UMI.

930   US   ISSN 0364-2976
DF701
JOURNAL OF THE HELLENIC DIASPORA; critical thoughts on Greek and world issues. 1974. q. $20 to individuals (foreign $25); institutions $30 (foreign $35) (effective 1993). Pella Publishing Company, 337 W. 36th St., New York, NY 10018. Ed.Bd. adv.; bk.rev.; illus.; index. circ. 1,000. **Indexed:** Amer.Bibl.Slavic & E.Eur.Stud., Amer.Hist.& Life, Hist.Abstr., Int.Polit.Sci.Abstr., Lang.& Lang.Behav.Abstr., M.L.A., Psychol.Abstr., Sociol.Abstr.
    —BLDSC (4996.945000).
    Formerly: Hellenic American Society. Journal (ISSN 0195-4342)
    Description: Contains items of interest to the Greek community.

JOURNAL OF TWENTIETH CENTURY AFRICAN AMERICAN ACTIVISM. see HISTORY — History Of North And South America

296   XR   ISSN 0022-5738
DS135.C95
JUDAICA BOHEMIAE. (Text in English, French, German, Russian) 1965. s-a. 40 Kcs.($31.40) (Statni Zidovske Museum) Panorama, Halkova 1, 120 72 Prague 2, Czech Republic. Ed. Osakar Petrik. bk.rev.; bibl.; stat. circ. 500. **Indexed:** Amer.Hist.& Life, Hist.Abstr.
    Description: Contains articles of interest to the Jewish community.

JUDAICA BOOK NEWS. see PUBLISHING AND BOOK TRADE

572   CL
JUDAICA IBEROAMERICANA. 1973. irreg., no.6, 1986. Universidad de Chile, Centro de Estudios de Cultura Judaica, Miguel Claro 182, Casilla 13583, Santiago, Chile. Ed. Gunter Bohm. circ. 1,000. (back issues avail.)

JUDAICA LIBRARIANSHIP. see LIBRARY AND INFORMATION SCIENCES

JUDARNA I F.D. SOVJET. see POLITICAL SCIENCE — Civil Rights

296   GW
JUEDISCHE GEMEINDEZEITUNG FRANKFURT. AMTLICHES ORGAN. 1965. 5/yr. $15. Juedische Gemeindezeitung Frankfurt, Westendstr. 43, 60325 Frankfurt a.M., Germany. TEL 069-740721. FAX 069-746874. adv.; bk.rev. circ. 4,500.
    Description: Covers Jewish issues and cultural events in Frankfurt and western Germany.

JUEDISCHE RUNDSCHAU MACCABI; la gazette Juive. see POLITICAL SCIENCE

296 GW
▼**JUEDISCHER ALMANACH.** 1992. a. (Leo-Baeck-Institut) Juedischer Verlag, Lindenstr. 29-35, 60325 Frankfurt a.M., Germany. Ed. Jakob Hessing. **Document type:** academic/scholarly publication.

943.8 UK ISSN 0022-7137
DK401
JUTRO POLSKI/POLAND OF TOMORROW.* (Text in Polish) 1942. m. £5($10) (Polish Populist Party) Jutro Polski Ltd., c/o Polish Library, 238-246 King St., London W6 ORF, England. Ed. F.J. Wilk. adv.; bk.rev.; bibl. circ. 4,000.
   Description: Contains articles of interest to the Polish community.

970.1 CN ISSN 0047-3081
KAINAI NEWS. 1968. w. Can.$20($25) Indian News Media, Box 120, Standoff, Alta., Canada. TEL 403-653-3301. FAX 403-653-3437. Ed. Mary Weasel Fat. adv.; bk.rev. circ. 3,500. (also avail. in microform from MML)
   Description: Covers Canadian Indian interests.

917.106 CN
KALEIDOSCOPE (DARTMOUTH). irreg. (10-12/yr.). Kaleidoscope Publishing, 475 Windmill Rd., Ste. 200, Dartmouth, NS B3B 1B2, Canada. TEL 902-468-2920. FAX 902-468-2858. Ed. Juan Carlos Canales. circ. 5,000. **Document type:** newspaper.
   Formerly: Atlantic Kaleidoscope.

917.106 CN ISSN 0832-5081
KALENDAR - AL'MANAKH NOVOHO SHLIAKHU/NEW PATHWAY ALMANAC. (Text in Ukrainian) 1936. a. Can.$15($15) (Ukrainian National Federation of Canada) New Pathway Publishing Co. Ltd., 297 College St., Toronto, ON M5T 1S2, Canada. TEL 416-960-3424. FAX 416-928-6706. Ed. Paul Dorozynsky. adv. circ. 2,000.

KALEVALASEURAN VUOSIKIRJA. see FOLKLORE

917.106 053.1 CN
KANADA KURIER. (Text in German) 1889. w. Can.$64. Courier Press Ltd., 955 Alexander Ave., Winnipeg, MB R3C 2X8, Canada. TEL 204-774-1883. FAX 204-783-5740. Ed. Ralf Neuendorff. adv.; bk.rev. circ. 19,500. (tabloid format; back issues avail.) **Document type:** newspaper.

917.109 CN ISSN 0022-8281
KANADAI MAGYARSAG/CANADIAN HUNGARIANS. 1950. w. Can.$40. Vorosvary Publishing Co. Ltd., 412 Bloor St. W., Toronto, ON M5S 1X5, Canada. TEL 416-924-2502. Ed. Stephen Vorosvary. adv.; bk.rev. circ. 6,000. (also avail. in microfilm from CML)
   Description: Contains articles of interest to the Hungarian community.

914.7 CN ISSN 0449-7368
KANADSKE LISTY/CANADIAN PAGES. (Text in Czech, English) 1966. m. Can.$19($22) Czechoslovak Newcomers Club, 388 Atwater Ave., Mississauga, ON L5G 2A3, Canada. TEL 416-278-4116. Ed. Mirko Janecek. adv.; bk.rev.; illus. circ. 2,500. (tabloid format) **Document type:** newspaper.

917.106 CN ISSN 0022-829X
KANADSKI SRBOBRAN/CANADIAN SERBIAN. (Text in Serbian) 1951. w. Can.$25. Serbian League of Canada, 335 Britannia Ave., Hamilton, Ont. L8H 1Y4, Canada. TEL 416-549-4079. FAX 416-549-8552. Ed.Bd. adv.; bk.rev. circ. 1,750. (tabloid format)
   Description: Contains articles of interest to the Serbian community.

057.8 CN ISSN 0047-3154
KANADSKY SLOVAK/CANADIAN SLOVAK. (Text in English and Slovak) 1942. w. Can.$40. (Canadian Slovak League) Slovak Canadian Publications Inc., 1736 Dundas St. W., Toronto, Ont. M6K 1V5, Canada. TEL 416-531-2055. FAX 416-533-6924. Ed. Marian Jankovsky. adv. circ. 2,000.

918.206 AG
▼**K'ANAMARKA;** vocero de la cultura qheswa. 1993. Av. Corrientes 932, 4o 10, 1043 Buenos Aires, Argentina. TEL 326-2208. Ed. P. Alberto Alvarez Lazarte. adv.

910.03 US
KANSAS CITY CALL. 1919. w. $20. Lucille Blueford, Ed. & Pub., 1715 E. 18th St., Kansas City, MO 64108. TEL 816-842-3804. FAX 816-842-4420. adv. contact: J. Reuben Benton. circ. 15,000. **Document type:** newspaper.

910.03 US
KANSAS CITY GLOBE. 1972. w. $32.50. Marion Jordon, Ed. & Pub., 615 E. 29th St., Kansas City, MO 64109. TEL 816-531-5253. FAX 816-531-5256. circ. 20,000. **Document type:** newspaper.

296 US ISSN 0022-8524
KANSAS CITY JEWISH CHRONICLE. 1920. w. $30. Sun Publications, Inc., 7373 W. 107th St., Overland Park, KS 66212. TEL 913-648-4620. Ed. Ruth Baum Bigus. adv.; bk.rev.; charts; illus. circ. 12,120. (tabloid format; also avail. in microfilm from AJP)
   Description: Contains articles of interest to the Jewish community.

943 GW
KARLSBADER ZEITUNG. 1950. m. DM.40 (foreign DM.46). Verlag Helmut Preussler, Rothenburger Str. 25, 90443 Nuremberg, Germany. TEL 0911-262323. index.

AL-KARMIL. see LITERATURE

943 GW ISSN 0022-9105
DIE KARPATENPOST. 1949. m. DM.34. Arbeitsgemeinschaft der Karpatendeutschen aus der Slowakei, Schlossstr. 92, 70176 Stuttgart, Germany. TEL 0711-626262. FAX 0711-625576. Ed. Oskar Marczy. adv.; bk.rev.; illus. circ. 4,100. **Document type:** newsletter.
   Description: General publication for Germans who lived in Slovakia until 1945. Includes news and religious information.

914.706 RM
KARPATENRUNDSCHAU. (Text in German) 1968. w. (Thu.) 3000 lei; newsstand price: 40 lei. Department of Culture, M. Sadoveanu 3, 2200 Brasov, Rumania. TEL 40-68143624. Ed. Dieter Drotleff. bk.rev. cols./p.: 4; pp./issue: 8. **Document type:** newspaper.
   Formerly: Volkszeitung.
   Description: Covers social issues, culture, history and folklore.

917.306 US
KARPATHOS. 1982? s-a? Federation of Karpathian Societies of America, Inc., 335 92nd St., Brooklyn, NY 11209.

917.306 US
KASHMIR REPORT. (U S Edition) vol.2, 1990. q. free. Kashmiri-American Council, 733 15th St. NW, Ste. 1100, Washington, DC 20005. TEL 202-628-6789. FAX 202-393-0062. (Co-sponsor: International Institute of Kashmir Studies, London) circ. 20,000. **Document type:** newsletter.

KASHRUS FAXLETTER. see FOOD AND FOOD INDUSTRIES

KASHRUT GUIDE. see RELIGIONS AND THEOLOGY — Judaic

KATOLIKUS MAGYAROK VASARNAPJA/CATHOLIC HUNGARIANS' SUNDAY. see RELIGIONS AND THEOLOGY — Roman Catholic

KATUAH; bioregional journal of the Southern Appalachians. see CONSERVATION

KELTIA; organe de recherche d'un Celtisme moderne. see PHILOSOPHY

917.306 US ISSN 1057-7475
KELTIC FRINGE. 1986. q. $10 to individuals; institutions $12. Kittatinny Press, Box 251, R.D. 1, Uniondale, PA 18470. TEL 717-679-2745. FAX 717-222-9103. Ed. Maureen Williams. adv.; bk.rev. circ. 400.
   Description: Covers cultural, economic, and political news of Celtic regions of the world and Celtic communities in North America.

KELTICA; the Inter-Celtic journal. see HISTORY — History Of Europe

910.03 US
KENTUCKY DIRECTORY OF BLACK ELECTED OFFICIALS. see PUBLIC ADMINISTRATION

296 US
KENTUCKY JEWISH POST AND OPINION. 1931. w. $36. Spokesman Co., Inc., c/o Gabriel M. Cohen, Pub., 2120 N. Meridian St., Indianapolis, IN 46202. TEL 317-927-7800. (Alt. addr.: 1551 Bardstown Rd., Louisville, KY 40205) (tabloid format; reprint service avail. from UMI)
   Description: Contains items of interest to the Jewish community.

917.106 CN
KERALA EXPRESS; popular Malayam newspaper of the continent. (Text in Malayalam) 1979. w. Can.$30. 18 Greenbrook Dr., Toronto, ON M6M 2J9, Canada. TEL 415-654-0431. (Subscr. to.: P.O. Box 34556, 1565 Jane St., Toronto, ON M9N 2R3, Canada) Eds. J.P. George, V.P. George. adv.; bk.rev. circ. 2,000. (tabloid format; back issues avail.) **Document type:** newspaper.

AL-KERAZEH. see RELIGIONS AND THEOLOGY — Other Denominations And Sects

960 ML
KIBARU. (Text in Eambara and 3 other languages) m. B.P. 1463, Bamako, Mali. Ed. Amadou Gagny Kante. circ. 5,000.

KISWAHILI. see LINGUISTICS

910.03 US
KITSAP COUNTY DISPATCH. 1988. d. (Mon.-Fri.). $30. Dispatch Newspapers, Box 5637, Tacoma, WA 98415. TEL 206-272-7587. FAX 206-272-4418. Ed. Virginia Taylor. adv. contact: Lou Taylor. circ. 5,000. (tabloid format) **Document type:** newspaper.

KIVA. see ARCHAEOLOGY

296 US
KOIHAP'NUAH. 4/yr. $5. Hadassah Zionist Youth Commission, 50 W. 58th St., New York, NY 10019. TEL 212-355-7900.

952 059.956 JA ISSN 0385-230X
KOKUSAI KORYU. (Text in Japanese) 1974. q. 319 Yen per no. Japan Foundation, Park Bldg., 3-6, Kioi-cho, Chiyoda-ku, Tokyo 102, Japan. TEL 03-3263-4491. FAX 03-3234-7884. Ed. Yasuda Fonio. circ. 6,000. (back issues avail.) **Document type:** academic/scholarly publication.
   —BLDSC (5101.786600).
   Description: Covers Japanese cultural interests.

296 US ISSN 0742-5031
KOL HA-T'NUAH/VOICE OF THE MOVEMENT. vol.32, 1975. m. $1.25. National Young Judaea, 50 W. 58th St., New York, NY 10019. TEL 212-247-9222. FAX 212-247-9240. Ed. David Dashefsky. illus. (tabloid format)
   Description: Covers Jewish interests.

KOL NECEI MILCHAMA. see SOCIAL SERVICES AND WELFARE

917.106 CN
KOREA TIMES TORONTO. (Text in Korean) 1975. d. Can.$173.34. Lawrence M. Kim, 146 Hallam St., Toronto, ON. M6H 1X2, Canada. TEL 416-533-1111. FAX 416-533-6763. Ed. Woon Y. Kim. adv. circ. 7,000. (back issues avail.)
   Formerly (until Jun. 1981): Canada News (ISSN 0319-2962)

917.306 US
KOREAM JOURNAL; Korean American news magazine. (Text in English, Korean) 1990. m. $30. KoreAm Journal, 17813 S. Main St., Ste. 112, Gardena, CA 90248. TEL 310-769-4913. Ed. Jung Shig Ryu. adv.; bk.rev.; illus. circ. 20,000. (tabloid format)

952 US ISSN 0270-1618
DS904
KOREAN CULTURE. 1980. c. $12. Korean Cultural Center, 5505 Wilshire Blvd., Los Angeles, CA 90036. TEL 213-936-7141. FAX 213-936-5712. Ed. Robert Buswell. bk.rev. circ. 4,000. **Document type:** academic/scholarly publication.
   —UnCover.

ETHNIC INTERESTS

917.106   CN   ISSN 0700-3226
KOREAN JOURNAL.* (Text in English and Korean) w. 649 A Bloor St. W., Toronto, Ont. M6G 1L1, Canada. TEL 416-588-4988. Ed. Young-Rin Ryu. adv. circ. 1,270.
    Description: Contains articles of interest to the Korean community.

057.85   US
KOSCIUSZKO FOUNDATION NEWSLETTER. 1946. q. membership only. Kosciuszko Foundation, 15 E. 65th St., New York, NY 10021. TEL 212-734-2130. FAX 212-628-4552. Ed. Monika Jasinska. adv.; bk.rev.; illus. circ. 5,000. (tabloid format) **Document type:** newsletter.
    Formerly: Kosciuszko Foundation Monthly Newsletter.
    Description: Information on current and future events of the Foundation and progress in cultural and scientific exchanges with Poland.

296   US
KOSHER DIRECTORY. a. $10. Union of Orthodox Jewish Congregations of America, Kashruth Division, 333 Seventh Ave., 18th fl., New York, NY 10001-5004. TEL 212-563-4000. FAX 212-564-9058. Ed. Zahava Fulda. adv. circ. 20,000.

917.106   CN
KULISY POLONII. (Text in Polish) bi-w. 10505 107th St., Edmonton, Alta. T5H 2Y5, Canada. TEL 403-425-0232. Eds. M. Carlton, J. Lenik. circ. 3,000.

917.106   CN
KULISY SPORTU. (Text in Polish) m. 150 Paisley Blvd., W., Ste. 1508, Mississauga, Ont. L5B 1E8, Canada. TEL 416-896-1064. circ. 5,000.

915.906   GW   ISSN 0938-619X
KULTUR JOURNAL; Zeitschrift fuer Afghanen und Deutsche. (Text in Dari, German and Pashto) 1986. 2/yr. DM.20 (foreign DM.30). Afghanistan Zentrum e.V., Hausdorffstr. 163, 53129 Bonn, Germany. TEL 0228-549324. FAX 0228-549172. bk.rev. circ. 1,000. (back issues avail.) **Document type:** academic/scholarly publication.

296   US   ISSN 0023-513X
KULTUR UN LEBN. (Text in Yiddish) 1967. 4/yr. $12. Workmen's Circle, Yiddish Division - Arbeter Ring, 45 E. 33rd St., New York, NY 10016. TEL 212-889-6800. FAX 212-532-7518. Ed. Joseph Mlotek. illus. circ. 40,000.
    Formed by the merger of: Friend; Culture and Education.
    Description: Covers American and East European Jewish culture.

914.706 920   ER   ISSN 0134-5605
KULTUUR JA ELU/CULTURE AND LIFE. (Text in Estonian) 1958. m. $48 (effective 1993). Kirjastus Perioodika, Parnu mnt. 8, 0090 Tallinn, Estonia. TEL 0142-441-262. FAX 0142-442-484. (Subscr. to: Narva mnt. 5, P.O. Box 51, 0090 Tallinn, Estonia) Ed. Sirje Endre. circ. 3,000. (back issues avail.)

KURDISH LIFE. see GENERAL INTEREST PERIODICALS — Middle East

914.706   LI
KURIER WILENSKI. (Text in Polish; summaries in Lithuanian, English) 1953. 5/w. $10. Parliament of the Republic of Lithuania, Laisves 60, Vilnius 2056, Lithuania. TEL 42-79-01. FAX 42-72-65. Ed. Zbigniew Balcewicz. circ. 20,000 (controlled). **Document type:** newspaper.
    Formerly (until 1990): Czerwony Sztandar.
    Description: Covers history and international relations.

914.8 914.7   SW   ISSN 0345-6706
KUSTBON; foerbindelseslaenk foer Estlands svenskar. 1918 in Estonia; 1944 in Sweden. q. SEK 220 (effective 1993). Kulturfoereningen Svenska Odlingens Vaenner, Vikingagatan 25, S-113 42 Stockholm, Sweden. Ed. Thomas Lorentz. adv.; bk.rev. circ. 1,500.

KUUMBA. see HOMOSEXUALITY

LA-MATHIL (AMERICAN EDITION); a voweled Hebrew newspaper. see LINGUISTICS

305.891   IT   ISSN 0394-2791
LACIO DROM; rivista bimestrale di studi zingari. 1965. bi-m. L.28000 (foreign L.35000) (effective 1994). Centro Studi Zingari, Via dei Barbieri 22, 00186 Rome, Italy. TEL 6833181. Ed. Mirella Karpati. bk.rev. circ. 1,000.

055.1   IT
LADINIA; sfoi cultural dai Ladins dles Dolomites. (Text in German, Italian, Ladin) 1977. a. L.28000 (foreign L.33000). Istitut Cultural Ladin "Micura de Ru", 39030 San Martin de Tor, Italy. TEL 0474-523110. FAX 0474-523455. adv.; bk.rev. (back issues avail.) **Indexed:** Bibl.Ling.

917.306   US
LAIKS/LATVIAN NEWS. (Text and summaries in Latvian) 1949. s-w. $65. 7307 Third Ave., Brooklyn, NY 11209. TEL 718-836-6382. FAX 718-748-1426. Ed. Ilgvars Spilners. adv.; bk.rev.; film rev.; play rev.; illus. circ. 11,800. (also avail. in microform) **Document type:** newspaper.
    Description: Contains articles of interest to the Latvian community.

296   US
LA'INYAN; the progressive Zionist Journal. (Text in English, Hebrew) 1982. q. Progressive Zionist Caucus, 27 W. 20th St., New York, NY 10011. TEL 212-675-1168. Ed. Stephanie Genkin. film rev.; illus. circ. 3,000. (back issues avail.)

917.306   US
LAKE CHAMPLAIN PRESS. 1965. w. C. Schongar, Ed. & Pub., Box 91, Redford, NY 12978. TEL 518-293-7941. adv. circ. 20,000. **Document type:** newspaper.

296 634.9   US
LAND AND LIFE. q. (free to qualified personnel). Jewish National Fund, 42 E. 69th St., New York, NY 10021. TEL 212-879-9300. FAX 212-517-3293. Ed. Abby Meth Kanter. adv. circ. 40,000. (also avail. in microfilm from AJP)
    Description: Publishes information about the JNF activities in Israel, project dedications in Israel and visits to JNF sites by prominent people. Includes reports on JFN activities in the United States.

971.006   CN   ISSN 0832-1922
LANG VAN; tap chi thong tin chinh tri van hoc nghe thuat. (Text in Vietnamese) 1984. m. $75. Lang Van of Canada, Inc., P.O. Box 218, Sta. U, Toronto, ON M8Z 5P1, Canada. TEL 905-670-8010. FAX 905-670-8011. Ed. Nguyen Huu Nghia. adv.; bk.rev.; illus.; tr.lit. circ. 7,000. (back issues avail.)
    Formerly: Saigon Thoi Bao.

LANGSTON HUGHES REVIEW. see LITERATURE

296   US
LAS VEGAS ISRAELITE. 1965. fortn. $24. Michael Tell, Ed. & Pub., Box 14096, Las Vegas, NV 89114. TEL 702-876-1255. FAX 702-364-1009. adv. contact: Joan Gassman. bk.rev.; illus. circ. 43,000. (also avail. in microfilm from AJP) **Document type:** newspaper.
    Description: Features fact finding editorials that are of interest to the Jewish community of Las Vegas and the nation.

LATEINAMERIKA NACHRICHTEN. see BUSINESS AND ECONOMICS — International Development And Assistance

917.306   US
LATIN AMERICA - CHICAGO. (Text in English, Spanish) 1978. m. free. University of Chicago, Center for Latin American Studies, 5848 S. University Ave., Chicago, IL 60637. TEL 312-702-8420. FAX 312-702-1755. Ed. Mary Anne A. Mohanraj. circ. 1,500 (controlled). (looseleaf format) **Document type:** newsletter.
    Description: Lists events that take place in the Chicago area that have some relevance to Latin America.

LATIN AMERICAN INDIAN LITERATURES JOURNAL; a review of American Indian texts and studies. see LITERATURE

LATIN AMERICAN JEWISH STUDIES NEWSLETTER. see HISTORY — History Of North And South America

LATIN BEAT MAGAZINE; salsa, afro-antillana, latin jazz and more ... see MUSIC

LATINO STUDIES JOURNAL. see POLITICAL SCIENCE — International Relations

320   US   ISSN 1062-9505
DK504.8
LATVIAN DIMENSIONS. 1976. q. $25. American Latvian Association in the United States, Inc., 400 Hurley Ave., Box 4578, Rockville, MD 20850. TEL 301-340-8174. FAX 301-340-8732. TELEX 6504716169 MCI UW. Ed. Martins Zvaners. adv.; B&W page $100; trim 8 1/2 x 11. bk.rev. circ. 2,000. **Document type:** newsletter.
    Formerly (until 1992): Latvian News Digest.
    Description: Reviews timely issues in Latvia and current affairs in the Latvian community in the United States.

917.309   CN   ISSN 0023-8902
LATVIJA AMERIKA; np. (Text in Latvian) 1950. w. Can.$75. Latvija Amerika Publishing Ltd., 125 Broadview Ave., Toronto, Ont. M4M 2E9, Canada. FAX 416-465-7902. Ed. Ingrid Viksna. adv. contact: A. Jakobsons. bk.rev. circ. 2,500. (tabloid format)

917.306   US   ISSN 0093-8920
DK511.L15
LATVIJA SODIEN. 1972. a. $10 per no. World Federation of Free Latvians, 400 Hurley Ave., Box 4016, Rockville, MD 20850. TEL 301-340-7646. Ed. Dr. I. Spilners. bk.rev.; illus. circ. 2,000.

LATVJU MAKSLA. see ART

LAVENDER GODZILLA. see HOMOSEXUALITY

917.306   US
LEA MAGAZINE. (Text in Spanish) 1986. m. $30. 4471 N.W. 36th St., Ste. 227, Miami Springs, FL 33166. TEL 305-888-3551. FAX 305-885-9346. Ed. Rafael Vega Jacome. adv. circ. 35,000. (reprint service avail.)
    Description: Covers political, economic, financial and community issues of interest to Colombians and other Hispanics in the U.S. Highlights tourist destinations in Colombia.

960   UK   ISSN 0024-0249
LEEDS AFRICAN STUDIES BULLETIN. 1965. s-a. free. University of Leeds, African Studies Unit, Leeds LS2 9JT, England. TEL 0532-33-5069. Ed. Kate Banham. circ. 350. (processed) **Document type:** academic/scholarly publication, bulletin.

LEGON OBSERVER. see POLITICAL SCIENCE

296 320.9   CN
LEONARD HORWIN COLLECTION. irreg. price varies. Dawn Publishing Co. Ltd., 17 Anselme Lavigne Blvd., Dollard des Ormeaux, Montreal, Que. H9A 1N3, Canada.

IL LEONE; giornale ufficiale della grande loggia di California dell'Ordine Figli d'Italia in America. see CLUBS

914.1   UK
LEOPARD; the quality magazine for North East Scotland. 1974. m. £15 (foreign £28). Ardo Publishing Co., Mill Business Centre, Udny, Aberdeenshire AB41 0RQ, Scotland. TEL 0651-842772. Ed. Susan Allan. adv. contact: Charles Allan. bk.rev.; play rev.; illus. circ. 6,000. (back issues avail.) **Document type:** consumer publication.
    Formerly: Aberdeen Leopard.
    Description: Reflects the past and present in the area for people who live there, or for those who have emigrated.

LIBRARY & ARCHIVES NEWS. see HISTORY

960   UK
LIBRARY OF PEASANT STUDIES. 1975. irreg., vol.4, 1977. price varies. Frank Cass & Co. Ltd., Gainsborough House, 11 Gainsborough Rd., London E11 1RS, England. TEL 081-530-4226. FAX 081-530-7795. (Dist. in US by: ISBS, 5804 N.E. Hassalo St., Portland, OR 97213-3644) bibl.; index. **Document type:** academic/scholarly publication.

ETHNIC INTERESTS

917.309 US ISSN 0024-2950
AP95.L5
LIETUVIU DIENOS/LITHUANIAN DAYS. (Text in English and Lithuanian) 1950. m. (except Jul. and Aug.) $20. Anthony F. Skirius, 4364 Sunset Blvd., Los Angeles, CA 90029. TEL 213-664-2919. Ed. Ruta Skirius. adv.; bk.rev.; illus. circ. 3,000. (tabloid format)
Description: Contains items of interest to the Lithuanian community.

917.406 US
LIFE & SCHOOL/ZHYTTIA I SHKOLA; independent cultural & educational periodical. (Text in Ukrainian.) 1954. bi-m. $8. Dr. W.O. Luciw, Ed. & Pub., 418 W. Nittany Ave., State College, PA 16801. TEL 814-238-5215. adv.; bk.rev.; play rev.; bibl.; illus. circ. 1,000. (also avail. in microfilm; microfiche)
Description: Contains articles of interest to the Ukranian community.

917.306 910.09 US
▼**LIFE STYLES.** 1993. a. free. National Life Styles Inc., 407 E. 25th St., Ste. 610, Chicago, IL 60616. TEL 312-808-1800. adv.: B&W page $5000, color page $8000; trim 8 x 10 3/4.
Description: Travel guide for minorities.

915.206 059.956 US
LIFESTYLE - U S A. (Text in Japanese) 1991. q. $14.97 (effective 1992). Meadow Publications, Inc., 126 Library Ln., Mamaroneck, NY 10543. TEL 914-381-4740. Ed. Susan Meadow. adv. contact: Eric Meadow. illus. circ. 50,000. **Document type:** consumer publication.
Description: Covers fashion, travel, American life-style and culture for Japanese residents in the greater New York metropolitan area.

LILITH. see WOMEN'S INTERESTS

910.03 US ISSN 0192-5083
E185.5
LINCOLN REVIEW; a quarterly journal. 1979. q. $12. Lincoln Institute for Research & Education, 1001 Connecticut Ave, N.W., Ste. 1135, Washington, DC 20036. TEL 202-223-5110. Ed. J.A. Parker. adv.; bk.rev.; film rev.; play rev.; illus. circ. 5,000. (also avail. in Braille; microfilm)
—UnCover.
Description: Contains items of interest to the black community.

915.406 CN ISSN 0380-299X
LINK (VANCOUVER). 1973. 2/w. Can.$72($150) Link Communications Ltd., 225 E. 17th Ave., Ste. 201, Vancouver, BC V5V 1A6, Canada. TEL 604-876-9300. FAX 604-876-8500. Ed. Promod Puri. adv. circ. 10,000. **Document type:** newspaper.

917.306 069 US ISSN 0889-5872
LITHUANIAN MUSEUM REVIEW. 1966. bi-m. $35. Balzekas Museum of Lithuanian Culture, 6500 S. Pulaski Rd., Chicago, IL 60629-5136. TEL 312-582-6500. FAX 312-582-5133. Ed. Loreta Visomirskte. circ. 14,000. (looseleaf format; back issues avail.) **Document type:** academic/scholarly publication.

917.309 US
LITOPYS BOYKIVSHCHYNY; ethnological journal. (Text in Ukrainian) 1969. s-a. $8. Boykivshchyna, 2222 Brandywine St., Philadelphia, PA 19130. TEL 215-567-3186. Ed. Myron Utrysko. circ. 750. (back issues avail.) Indexed: Amer.Bibl.Slavic & E.Eur.Stud.
Description: Covers Ukrainian interests.

059.91 US ISSN 0024-5089
DK511.L2
LITUANUS; Baltic states quarterly journal of arts and sciences. 1954. q. $10 to individuals; institutions $15. Lituanus Foundation, Inc., 6621 S. Troy St., Chicago, IL 60629. TEL 312-434-0706. Ed. Antanas Klimas. bk.rev.; bibl.; illus.; cum.index: vols.1-24. circ. 4,200. (also avail. in microfilm from UMI; back issues avail.; reprint service avail. from UMI) Indexed: Amer.Bibl.Slavic & E.Eur.Stud., Amer.Hist.& Life, Bibl.Ling., Hist.Abstr., M.L.A., P.A.I.S. **Document type:** academic/scholarly publication.
—Faxon; UnCover; UMI.

296 US ISSN 0199-2899
LONG ISLAND JEWISH WORLD. 1971. w. $15. Empire Publishing Corp., 115 Middle Neck Rd., Great Neck, NY 11021. TEL 516-829-4000. Ed. Naomi Lippman. adv.; bk.rev. circ. 45,000.
Description: Contains articles of interest to the Jewish community.

LOOYS. see RELIGIONS AND THEOLOGY — Other Denominations And Sects

310.03 US
LOS ANGELES BAY NEWS OBSERVER. 1977. w. $50. Observer Group Newspapers of Southern CA, 1219 20th St., Bakersfield, CA 93301. TEL 805-324-9466. FAX 805-324-9472. Ed. Ellen Coley. adv. contact: Joseph Coley. circ. 18,000. **Document type:** newspaper.

910.03 US
LOS ANGELES CENTRAL NEWS. 1963. d. $78. Central News Wave Publications, 2621 W. 54th St., Los Angeles, CA 90043. TEL 213-290-3000. FAX 213-291-0219. Ed. C.G. Wilson. circ. 4,500. **Document type:** newspaper.

910.03 US
LOS ANGELES SOUTHSIDE JOURNAL. 1963. d. $78. Central News Wave Publications, 2621 W. 54th St., Los Angeles, CA 90043. TEL 213-290-3000. FAX 213-291-0219. Ed. C.G. Wilson. circ. 18,400. **Document type:** newspaper.

917.306 US ISSN 0898-9052
LUSO - AMERICANO. (Text in Portuguese) 1928. s-w. $35. Luso-Americano Co., Inc., 88 Ferry St., Newark, NJ 07105. TEL 201-589-4600. FAX 201-589-3848. TELEX 139099 LUSO-AMERICANO. Ed. Antonio Matinho. adv.; bk.rev. circ. 34,000. (tabloid format) **Document type:** newspaper.

917.306 323.4 US
M A L D E F NEWSLETTER. 1968. 2/yr. $35 contribution. Mexican American Legal Defense and Educational Fund, 634 S. Spring St., 11th Fl., Los Angeles, CA 90014. TEL 213-629-2512. FAX 213-629-1916. Ed. Abelardo de la Pena, Jr. bibl. circ. 15,000. **Document type:** newsletter.

917.206 US
M A N A. vol.2, 1984. q. $25. Mexican American Women's National Association, 1101 17th St. N.W., No.803, Washington, DC 20036-4704. circ. 2,000.

M A R GOSPEL MINISTRIES NEWSLETTER. (Middle Atlantic Regional) see RELIGIONS AND THEOLOGY

M E L U S. (Society for the Study of the Multi-Ethnic Literature of the United States) see LITERATURE

296 US
MABUEY HANCHAL. 1983. q. 35 Lee Ave., Brooklyn, NY 11211. Ed. Rabbi Mordechai Turetz.

917.306 US
MACEDONIA. (Text in English, Greek) 1953. q. free to members. Pan-Macedonian Association Inc., 246 Eighth Ave., New York, NY 10011. TEL 212-924-1442. Eds. Alkis Papademetrion, Olga Kazixnis. adv.; bk.rev. circ. 6,000. (back issues avail.)

949.506 CN
MACEDONIAN LINK. (Text in English, Macedonian) m. P.O. Box 291, West Hill Sta., Scarborough, ON M1E 4R5, Canada. TEL 416-286-7673. adv. contact: L. Kostadinova. circ. 2,000. cols./p.: 5. (tabloid format) **Document type:** newspaper.

MACEDONIAN REVIEW; history, culture, literature, arts. see LITERATURE

MACEDONIAN TRIBUNE. see CLUBS

910.03 US
MACON COURIER. 1974. w. $12.60 local; out of town $16. Melvyn J. Williams, Ed. & Pub., 1055 Walnut, Macon, GA 31201. TEL 912-742-4508. FAX 912-742-4274. (Subscr. to: Box 52201, Macon, GA 31208. TEL 912-746-5605) circ. 17,100. (back issues avail.) **Document type:** newspaper.
Description: Contains articles of interest to the black community.

057.85 LI ISSN 0236-4719
MAGAZYN WILENSKI. (Text in Polish) 1990. s-m. $48. P.O. Box 163040, 2010 Vilnius, Lithuania. TEL 037-474-007. Ed. Michal Mackiewicz. adv.: B&W page $100. circ. 9,000.

296 VE
MAGEN-ESCUDO. 1970. q. $40. Centro de Estudios Sefardies de Caracas, Box 17216, Caracas 1015 A, Venezuela. FAX 582-5722129. adv.; bk.rev. circ. 3,000. (also avail. in microfilm)

MAGNES NEWS. see MUSEUMS AND ART GALLERIES

059.94 CN ISSN 0047-5513
MAGYAR ELET/HJNGARIAN LIFE. (Text in Hungarian) 1948. w. Can.$40. Reform-Hungaria Publishing Service Inc., 313 Sheppard Ave. E., North York, ON M2N 3B3, Canada. TEL 416-221-6195. FAX 416-221-5358. Ed. Laszlo Schnee; Pub. Agnes Somorjai. adv.; bk.rev. circ. 7,812. (also avail. in microfilm from CML) **Document type:** newspaper.
Description: Contains articles of interest to the Hungarian community.

917.306 US
MAGYAR HOLNAP/HUNGARIAN TOMORROW. (Text in Hungarian) m. $6. Hungarian Freedom Fighters (Guardian) World Federation, Inc., Box 441 Gracie Station, New York, NY 10028. adv.; illus. (tabloid format)
Description: Covers Hungarian interests.

059.94 CN
MAGYAR NAPLO (TORONTO, 1966). English edition: Canadian Free Press. 1966. w. $10. C F P Publications Ltd., P.O. Box 771, Station A, Toronto, ON M5W 1G3, Canada. TEL 416-921-6161. FAX 416-283-2357. Ed. V. Szabo. adv. circ. 85,000. (tabloid format)
Formerly: Kanadai Fuggetlen Hirlap (ISSN 0047-3146)

917.306 US
MAGYARSAG/HUNGARIAN PEOPLE. (Text in Hungarian) 1910. bi-w. $20. 315 Walsh St., South Bend, IN 46617. TEL 219-288-0373. Ed. Jeno Szebedinszky. adv.; bk.rev. circ. 1,800. (tabloid format; back issues avail.)

MAHOGANY. see ART

051 CN
MAL-I-MIC NEWS. 1973. m. Can.$12. (New Brunswick Aboriginal Peoples Council) Daily Gleaner, P.O. Box 3370, Fredericton, N.B. E3B 5A2, Canada. TEL 506-452-6671. (Subscr. to: 320 St. Mary's St., Fredericton, N.B. E3A 2S4, Canada) Ed. Jennifer Sappier. circ. 1,200.
Description: Covers aboriginal and treaty rights, land claims, education, native economic development.

915 CN
MALAYALEE. s-m. 275 Lansdowne Ave., Toronto, Ont. M6K 2W2, Canada. adv.

910.03 US ISSN 1044-9116
MALCOLM X LOVERS NETWORK. 12/yr. $15. Afram Associates, Inc., 2322 Third Ave., 2nd Fl., New York, NY 10035. TEL 212-289-9155. FAX 212-722-5194.
Description: Documents Malcolm X's legacy.

059 AT
MALTESE HERALD. (Text in English and Maltese) 1961. w. Aus.$75. Maltese News and Information Pty. Ltd., 195 Merrylands Rd., P.O. Box 330, Merrylands, N.S.W. 2160, Australia. FAX 682-1923. Ed. Lino C. Vella. adv.; bk.rev. circ. 5,250. (tabloid format) **Document type:** newspaper.
Description: Covers Maltese interests nationally and overseas.

917.306 056.1
EL MANANA DAILY; primero y unico diario Espanol - the first and only Spanish daily. (Text in Spanish) 1971. d. $180. 2700 S. Harding Ave., Chicago, IL 60623. TEL 312-521-9137. FAX 312-521-5351. Ed. Sergio Enriquez. adv.; bk.rev. circ. 60,000. (tabloid format) **Document type:** newspaper.

ETHNIC INTERESTS

301 296 US
MANASSEH/MENASHEH. q. $24 (foreign $30). Eagle Communications, 29 Brimmer St., Brewer, MN 04412.
  Description: Contains articles of interest to the Jewish community.

951.006 CC
MANZU YANJIU/MANCHU STUDIES. (Text in Chinese) q. Liaoning Minzu Yanjiusuo, 43, Heping Nandajie, Shenyang, Liaoning 110003, People's Republic of China. TEL 463523. Ed. Guan Zaihan.

296 323.4 940 US ISSN 0892-1571
MARTYRDOM AND RESISTANCE. 1974. bi-m. $10. International Society for Yad Vashem, Inc., 48 W. 37th St. 9th Fl., New York, NY 10018-7408. TEL 212-654-1865. FAX 212-268-0529. Ed. Dr. Harvey Rosenfeld. bk.rev.; illus. circ. 26,000. (tabloid format; also avail. in microfiche)
  Formerly: Martyrdom and Freedom.
  Description: Contains articles of interest to the Jewish community.

914.309 UK ISSN 0025-4584
MASHRIQ; Urdu news weekly. (Text in Urdu) 1961. w. £24. Loxton Publishers Ltd, 82 Caledonian Rd., London N.1, England. Ed. Ali Kiani. adv.; bk.rev.; film rev.; illus. circ. 30,000. (tabloid format)
  Description: For the Urdu speaking community in Great Britain.

917.306 US
MASHRIQ. (Text in Arabic) 1924. w. $15. 25639 Southwood, Southfield, MI 48075. Ed. Hanna Yatooma. adv. circ. 900.
  Description: Contains items of interest to the Arabic community.

296 IS ISSN 0542-9943
MASSUA. 1973. a. Massua - Center for Holocaust Studies, Kibbutz Tel Yitzhak, Doar Tel Yitzhak 45808, Israel. TEL 972-53-699997. FAX 972-53-697410.
  Description: Presents materials relating to the Holocaust and its continued relevance to Jewish society.

917.306 US
MATANCER LIBRE; for a better community - por una comunidad mejor. (Text in Spanish) 1966. d. $24 (free locally). 904 S.W. 23rd Ave., Miami, FL 33135. TEL 305-643-4888. FAX 305-649-2767. Ed. Demetrio Perez Jr. adv.; illus. **Document type:** newspaper.
  Description: For Hispanics in the Miami area.

377 IS ISSN 0543-1786
MA'YANOT. 1952. irreg., latest issue no.4. price varies. World Zionist Organization, P.O. Box 92, Jerusalem 91920, Israel. TEL 02-527156. FAX 02-533542.

917.309 US ISSN 0025-6218
MAZPUTNINS; Latvian children's magazine. (Text in Latvian) 1959. m. $30 (typically set in Jan.). Latvian Institute, Inc., 100 Cherry Hill Dr., Kalamazoo, MI 49006. TEL 616-343-1838. Ed. Liene Dindonis. bk.rev.; illus.; index. circ. 1,000.
  Description: Aimed at children aged 4-12.

989 301.2 PY ISSN 1017-2793
MBYA GUARANI. (Text in English, Spanish) 1990. q. $10. Centro de Estudios Humanitarios, Azara 3267, Asuncion, Paraguay. Ed. Esther Prieto. circ. 500.
  Description: Covers the rights of the Myba Guarani native community.

MEDICINA Y CULTURA. see *MEDICAL SCIENCES*

296 778.5 781.7 US
MEDIUM (NEW YORK).* 1974. 3/yr. $10 for 4 nos. Jewish Media Service, Box 2037, Teaneck, NJ 07666. Ed. Eric A. Goldman. adv.; film rev.; bibl. circ. 12,000. (back issues avail.)
  Description: Contains articles of interest to the Jewish community.

MEDIUM RARE. see *JOURNALISM*

970.1 US
MEETING GROUND. 1973. a. free. Newberry Library, D'Arcy McNickle Center for the History of the American Indian, 60 W. Walton St., Chicago, IL 60610. TEL 312-943-9090. Ed. Jay Miller. bk.rev. circ. 4,000. **Document type:** newsletter.

917.206 CN
▼**MEHFIL MAGAZINE**. 1993. 6/yr. Can.$12. V I G Communications Inc., 2050 Clark Dr., Vancouver, BC V5N 3G7, Canada. TEL 604-254-9015. FAX 604-420-0626. adv.: B&W page Can.$1080, color page Can.$1512. circ. 28,000.

059.94 CN ISSN 0047-665X
MEIE ELU/OUR LIFE. (Text in Estonian) 1950. w. Can.$81. Estonian Publishing Co. Toronto Ltd., 958 Broadview Ave., Toronto, ON M4K 2R6, Canada. TEL 416-466-0951. FAX 416-466-4339. Ed. Tonu Parming. adv.; bk.rev. circ. 2,500. (also avail. in microfilm from CML) **Document type:** newspaper.
  Description: Contains information about Estonians in Canada, the US and Sweden, with current reporting from Estonia.

917.309 US ISSN 0025-8768
MEIE TEE. (Text in Estonian) 1931. s-m. $5. World Association of Estonians, Inc., Estonian House, 243 E. 34th St., Box 123, New York, NY 10016. TEL 212-686-3356. Ed. Harald Raudsepp. adv.; illus. circ. 1,600.
  Description: Contains articles of interest to the Estonian community.

914.3 CN ISSN 0705-4041
MENNONITISCHE POST. (Text in German) 1977. s-m. Can.$21.40. Box 1120, Steinbach, MB R0A 2A0, Canada. TEL 204-326-6790. FAX 204-326-6302. Ed. Isbrand Hiebert. adv.; bk.rev. circ. 5,225. **Document type:** newspaper.

917.106 CN
MENORA. (Text in Hungarian) w. Can.$42.80. 87 Searle Ave., Downsview, ON M3H 4A6, Canada. TEL 416-783-4508. Ed. Andrew Tarjan.

296 CK ISSN 0025-939X
MENORAH. 1950. m. $40. Editorial Menorah, Calle 38, no. 73-89 Int.1, Apdo. Aereo 9081, Bogota, Colombia. TEL 2632783. Ed. Eliecer Celnik. adv.; bk.rev. circ. 10,000.

296 US
MENORAH REVIEW. 1984. q. free. Virginia Commonwealth University, Judaic Studies Program, Richmond, VA 23284-0001. Ed. Jack D. Spiro. bk.rev. circ. 5,000. (also avail. in microfilm from KTO)
  Formerly: Menorah.
  Description: Covers Jewish interests.

914.6 CN
MENSAGEIRO. fortn. 6926 Tyne St., Vancouver, B.C. V5S 3M6, Canada. circ. 3,500.

MESCALITO - SPRUNG IN DIE UNMOEGLICHKEIT; Magazin fuer Magie und Schamanismus. see *PARAPSYCHOLOGY AND OCCULTISM*

917.106 CN ISSN 0228-2828
MESSENGER. (Text in English and Urdu) 1978. s-m. Can.$20($25) Messenger, 2 Middleport Cr., Scarborough, Ont. M1B 4L5, Canada. TEL 416-283-7255. Ed. Sohail Akhtar. adv.; bk.rev. circ. 3,000. (back issues avail)

METMENYS; kuryba ir analize. see *LITERATURE*

910.03 US
METRO COURIER (AUGUSTA). 1983. w. $20 in the State of Georgia; elsewhere $25. 314 Walton Way, Augusta, GA 30901. TEL 404-724-6556. FAX 404-724-5643. Ed. Barbara Gordon. adv.; bk.rev. circ. 19,000. **Document type:** newspaper.
  Description: Addresses issues and concerns of the Black community.

910.03 US
METRO REPORTER GROUP. 1973. w. free. Reporter Publications (San Francisco), 1366 Turk St., San Francisco, CA 94115. TEL 415-931-5778. FAX 415-793-0214. Ed. Gary Raynaldo. circ. 99,915. **Document type:** newspaper.

910.03 US
METRO TIMES NEWSPAPER. 1975. w. $15. Box 1659, Goldsboro, NC 27533. TEL 919-734-0302. FAX 919-736-0483. Ed. Ken Plummer. circ. 85,000. **Document type:** newspaper.

917.206 US
MEXICAN AMERICAN STUDIES SERIES. 1975. irreg. price varies. (Center for Mexican American Studies) University of Texas Press, Austin, TX 78712. TEL 512-471-4557. FAX 512-471-9639. Ed.Bd. circ. 1,500. **Document type:** monographic series.
  Formerly: Mexican American Monograph Series.

917.306 US
MEXICAN AMERICAN SUN. (Text in English, Spanish) 1949. w. $62.50. Eastern Group Publications, Inc., 3643 E. First St., Los Angeles, CA 90063. TEL 213-263-5743. (Subscr. to: P.O. Box 33803, Los Angeles, CA 90033) Ed. Dolores Sanchez. adv.; bk.rev. circ. 10,000. (tabloid format; back issues avail.) **Document type:** newspaper.
  Description: Hispanic community newspaper.

296 US ISSN 0891-6659
MIAMI JEWISH TRIBUNE. 1986. w. $24. Jewish Media Group, 3350 Biscayne Blvd. Third Fl., Miami, FL 33137-3845. TEL 305-576-9500. FAX 305-573-9551. Ed. Maureen Berkowitz. adv.; bk.rev. circ. 22,000.
  Description: Serves the greater Miami Jewish community.

910.03 US
MIAMI TIMES. 1923. w. $35. 900 N.W. 54th St., Miami, FL 33127. TEL 305-757-1147. FAX 305-756-0771. Ed. Rachel Reeves. circ. 26,691. **Document type:** newspaper.

296 IS ISSN 0334-4150
MICHAEL; on the history of the Jews in the Diaspora. (Text in English, French, German, Hebrew and Italian) 1972. irreg., vol.12, 1990. $35 per vol. Tel-Aviv University, Diaspora Research Institute, c/o Publication Department, 69978 Ramat Aviv, Israel. FAX 972-3-6409468. TELEX 342171-VERSY-IL. Ed.Bd. **Indexed:** Amer.Hist.& Life, Hist.Abstr., Ind.Heb.Per. **Document type:** academic/scholarly publication.

910.03 US ISSN 1072-2041
MICHIGAN CITIZEN. 1979. w. $21. Newday Publishing, 12541 Second, Box 03560, Highland Park, MI 48203. TEL 313-869-0033. FAX 313-869-0430. Ed. Teresa M. Kelly. adv. contact: Charles Kelly. bk.rev.; illus.; tr.lit. circ. 48,200. **Document type:** newspaper.
  ●Also available online. Vendor(s): Mead Data Central, Inc. (ETHNIC NEWSWATCH).

970.1 CN ISSN 0026-2528
MICMAC NEWS. 1966. m. Can.$40 (foreign $40)(effective Apr. 1991). Native Communications Society of Nova Scotia, Box 344, 3 Kateri St., Sydney, N.S. B1P 6H2, Canada. TEL 902-539-0430. FAX 902-539-0045. Ed. Clifford Paul. adv.; bk.rev.; illus. circ. 1,600. (tabloid format; also avail. in microfilm)
  Description: Contains articles of interest to the Canadian Indian community.

296 US
MIDDLE EAST MEMO. 1973. 16/yr. free. Conference of Presidents of Major American Jewish Organizations, 110 E. 59th St., New York, NY 10022. TEL 212-752-1616. Ed. Richard Cohen.
  Description: Contains items of interest to the Jewish community.

917.106 CN
MIDDLE EAST REPORT. (Text in Arabic) w. Middle East Consultants, 511 Queen St., E., Ground Fl., Toronto, Ont. M5A 1V1, Canada. TEL 416-362-0304. FAX 416-861-0238. Ed. S. Soliman. circ. 6,000.

MIGRATION; a European journal of international migration and ethnic relations. see *SOCIOLOGY*

MIGRATION WORLD; a bi-monthly magazine focusing on the newest immigrant and refugee groups; policy and legislation; resources. see *POPULATION STUDIES*

955 US
MILITARY AND DIPLOMATS WORLD NEWS. (Text in English and Farsi) 1978. bi-m. $18. Box 1929, Falls Church, VA 22041. TEL 703-845-0077. Ed. Steve Sami. adv.; bk.rev. circ. 8,000. (back issues avail.)
  Formerly (until 1985): Peyvand.

ETHNIC INTERESTS

910.03   US
MILWAUKEE COMMUNITY JOURNAL. 1976. 2/wk.; d. (City Editions). $85. Milwaukee Community Journal, Inc., 3612 N. Martin Luther King Dr., Milwaukee, WI 53212. TEL 414-265-5300. FAX 414-265-1536. Ed. Michael Holt. adv. contact: Robert J. Thomas. bk.rev. circ. 62,000. (tabloid format) **Document type:** newspaper.

917.309   US   ISSN 0026-4350
MILWAUKEE COURIER. 1964. w. $12.50. 2431 W. Hopkins St., Milwaukee, WI 53206. TEL 414-449-4860. FAX 414-449-4872. Ed. Joni Alston. adv.; bk.rev.; film rev.; play rev.; illus. circ. 15,000. **Document type:** newspaper.
Description: Contains articles of interest to the black community.

914.3   US
MILWAUKEE HERALD.* (Text in German) 1855. w. $10. 2321 W. Kenboern Dr., Glendale, WI 53209. adv.; bk.rev.; film rev. circ. 14,212. (tabloid format)
Description: Covers German American interests.

910.03   US
MILWAUKEE STAR. 1961. w. $9.50. 3815 N. Teutonia, Milwaukee, WI 53206. TEL 414-449-4867. FAX 414-449-4872. Ed. Joni Alston. adv. circ. 25,000.

MIN SU/FOLK CUSTOMS. see FOLKLORE

915.1   CN
MING PAO DAILY NEWS. (Text in Chinese) d. Ming Pao Newspaper Ltd., 1355 Huntingwood Dr., Scarborough, ON M1S 3J1, Canada. TEL 416-321-0088. FAX 416-321-6339. adv. contact: Peter Li. circ. 15,000. **Document type:** newspaper.

780.406   SR
MINI WORLD.* bi-m. Albergastraat 29, Box 2440, Paramaribo, Suriname. Ed. Shinichiro Mikuni.

917.106 059.957   CN   ISSN 0225-1205
MINJOONG SHINMOON; Korean-Canadian community newspaper. (Text in Korean) 1979. w. Can.$70. 802 Bloor St., W., Toronto, Ont. M6G 1L9, Canada. TEL 416-537-3473. FAX 416-537-9624. Ed. Se-Yong Jeong. circ. 4,300.

910.03   US
MINNEAPOLIS SPOKESMAN. 1935. w. $20. 3744 Fourth Ave., S., Minneapolis, MN 55409. TEL 612-827-4021. FAX 612-827-0577. circ. 16,000. **Document type:** newspaper.

MINORITIES AND WOMEN IN BUSINESS. see BUSINESS AND ECONOMICS — Small Business

MINORITY BUSINESS ENTREPRENEUR. see BUSINESS AND ECONOMICS — Small Business

MINORITY ENGINEER. see ENGINEERING

MINORITY FUNDING REPORT. see EDUCATION — School Organization And Administration

MINORITY M B A. see OCCUPATIONS AND CAREERS

917.306   US
MINORITY ORGANIZATIONS: A NATIONAL DIRECTORY. 1978. a. $50. Garrett Park Press, Box 190F, Garrett Park, MD 20896. TEL 301-946-2553. **Document type:** directory.
Description: Lists professional minority associations, trade groups, historical and cultural organizations.

917.306   US
MINORITY TODAY. 1983. m. Eastern Illinois University, Journalism Department, Charleston, IL 61920. TEL 217-581-2812. FAX 217-581-2923. Ed. Jacenta Wilson. circ. 7,000. **Document type:** newspaper.
Description: Covers minority interest news and features for college students.

951   CC
MINZU/NATIONAL MINORITIES MONTHLY. (Editions in Chinese, Tibetan and Yi) 1984. m. Y0.75 per no. (effective 1992). (Sichuan Sheng Minzu Gongzuo Weiyuanhui - Sichuan Nationalities Affairs Commission) Minzu Zazhishe, 18 Wenshuyuan Jie, Chengdu, Sichuan 610017, People's Republic of China. TEL 028-768173. (Dist. overseas by: Jiangsu Publications Import & Export Corp., 56 Gao Yun Ling, Nanjing, Jiangsu, P.R.C.) Ed. Li Liusun. circ. 15,000.
Description: Covers ethnic politics, economy, history and culture.

915.106 572 390   CC   ISSN 0540-1224
MINZU HUABAO/NATIONALITY PICTORIAL. (Editions in Chinese, Kazakh, Korean, Mongolian, Tibetan, Uighur) 1955. m. Y36($85.50) (Guojia Minzu Shiwu Weiyuanhui) Minzu Huabao She, 14, Heping Li Beijie, Anding Menwai, Beijing 100013, People's Republic of China. TEL 421-1147. (Dist. outside China by: China International Book Trading Corp., P.O. Box 2820, Beijing, P.R.C.; Dist. in US by: China Books & Periodicals, Inc., 2929 24th St., San Francisco, CA 94110. TEL 415-282-2994) Ed. Chun Shizeng. illus. (tabloid format)

390 915.106   CC   ISSN 0544-2206
MINZU TUANJIE/UNITY OF NATIONALITIES. (Editions in Chinese, Kazakh, Korean, Mongolian and Uighur) 1957. m. Y8.40($30.50) (Guojia Minzu Shiwu Weiyuanhui) Minzu Tuanjie Zazhishe, 14 Hepingli Beijie, Beijing 100013, People's Republic of China. TEL 4211261. (Dist. outside China by: China International Book Trading Corp., P.O. Box 399, Beijing, P.R.C.; Dist. in US by: China Books & Periodicals, Inc., 2929 24th St., San Francisco, CA 94110. TEL 415-282-2994) Ed. Fan Peilian.

MINZU WENXUE/JOURNAL OF MINORITY LITERATURE. see LITERATURE

MINZU WENXUE YANJIU/RESEARCH IN NATIONAL MINORITY LITERATURE. see LITERATURE

MINZU YANJIU/STUDY IN NATIONALITIES. see ORIENTAL STUDIES

MINZU ZUOJIA. see LITERATURE

MISLI/THOUGHTS. see RELIGIONS AND THEOLOGY — Roman Catholic

910.03   US
MISSISSIPPI MEMO DIGEST. 1961. w. $10.40. 2511 Fifth St., Box 5782, Meridian, MS 39301. TEL 601-693-2372. Ed. Robert E. Williams. adv.; bk.rev. circ. 2,950. (back issues avail.) **Document type:** newspaper.
Description: Contains articles of interest to the black community.

910.3   US
MOBILE BEACON. 1943. w. $19. Box 1407, 2311 Castarides St., Mobile, AL 36633. TEL 205-479-0629. Ed. Cleretta T. Blackmon. adv. circ. 4,971. **Document type:** newspaper.

910.03   US
MOBILE NEW TIMES. 1981. fortn. $11. 156 S. Broad St., Mobile, AL 36602. TEL 205-432-0356. FAX 205-432-8320. Ed. Vivian Davis Figures. circ. 5,000. **Document type:** newspaper.

917.306   US   ISSN 0884-8432
DF701
MODERN GREEK STUDIES YEARBOOK. (Supplement avail.) 1985. a. $30. Modern Greek Studies, 325 Social Science Bldg., University of Minnesota, 267-19th Ave., S., Minneapolis, MN 55455. FAX 612-626-2242. Ed. Theofanis G. Stavrou, Joan Sommerfeld. bk.rev. circ. 500.
—UnCover.
Description: Publishes scholarly information in the field of modern Greek studies.

296   US
MODERN JEWISH MASTERS. 1985. irreg. price varies. New York University Press, 70 Washington Square S., New York, NY 10012. TEL 212-998-2575. FAX 212-995-3833. TELEX 235128 NYU UR. Ed. Steven Katz. **Document type:** monographic series.
Description: Explores the lives and works of 20th century Jewish thinkers.

MODERN JEWISH STUDIES ANNUAL. see LITERATURE

058.8   CN   ISSN 0047-7788
MODERSMAALET/MOTHER TONGUE. (Text in Danish) 1956. fortn. Can.$15. Melander Publishing Co., P.O. Box 306, Oakville, Ont. L6J 5A2, Canada. TEL 416-825-2229. Ed. Jonna Melander. adv. circ. 3,861.

296   US   ISSN 0099-0280
DS101
MOMENT. 1975. 6/yr. $29.50 (foreign $35.50). (Jewish Educational Ventures, Inc.) Moment Magazine, 3000 Connecticut Ave., N.W., Ste. 300, Washington, DC 20008. TEL 202-387-8888. FAX 202-483-3423. (Subscr. to: Box 11235, Des Moines, IA 50340) Eds. Hershel Shanks, Elizabeth Snider. adv. contact: Michael Mouheit. bk.rev.; illus. circ. 30,000. (also avail. in microform from UMI)
Indexed: Amer.Bibl.Slavic & E.Eur.Stud., Ind.Jew.Per., Mid.East: Abstr.& Ind.
—UnCover; UMI.
Description: International coverage of politics, culture and social issues affecting Jewish people.

296   FR   ISSN 0026-9425
DS101
MONDE JUIF. 1946; N.S. 1955. q. 180 F. (foreign 250 F.). Centre de Documentation Juive Contemporaine, 17 rue Geoffroy-l'Asnier, 75004 Paris, France. Dir. Georges Bensoussan. adv.; bk.rev. circ. 3,000.
Indexed: Amer.Hist.& Life, Hist.Abstr.

057   AT
IL MONDO. (Text in Italian) 2/w. Aus.$90. Foreign Language Publications Pty. Ltd., P.O. Box 146, Broadway, Sydney, N.S.W. 2007, Australia. TEL 02-660-2033. FAX 02-692-0649. Ed. Tony Palumbo. adv. contact: George Antoniou. circ. 8,230. (tabloid format) **Document type:** newspaper.
Description: Serves the Italian community in Australia.

MONITOR (WASHINGTON). see POLITICAL SCIENCE — Civil Rights

052   UK   ISSN 0262-6845
MONITOR WEEKLY. 1981. w. £25. Muslim Monitor Ltd., 70 Leathwaite Rd., London SW11, England. illus.

917.306   US
MONTEBELLO COMET. (Text in Spanish) 1974. w. $62.50. Eastern Group Publications, Inc., 3643 E. First St., Los Angeles, CA 90063. TEL 213-263-5743. Ed. Dolores Sanchez. adv.; bk.rev. circ. 6,000. (tabloid format; back issues avail.) **Document type:** newspaper.
Description: Community newspaper.

917.306   US
MONTEREY PARK COMET. (Text in English, Spanish) 1974. w. $62.50. Eastern Group Publications, Inc., 3643 E. First St., Los Angeles, CA 90063. TEL 213-263-5743. (Subscr. to: P.O. Box 33803, Los Angeles, CA 90033) Ed. Dolores Sanchez. adv. circ. 10,000. (back issues avail.) **Document type:** newspaper.
Description: Local newspaper that specially covers the Chinese and Hispanic communities.

296 929   US   ISSN 1044-6737
MORASHA/HERITAGE. 1985. q. $21. Jewish Genealogy Society of Illinois, 1492 Edgewood Lane, Winnetka, IL 60093. TEL 708-441-9369. (Subscr. to: c/o Don Kraft, 9325 Kenneth Ave., Skokie, IL 60076. TEL 708-673-0596) Ed. Dorothy D. Nesbitt. bk.rev.; abstr.; charts; stat. circ. 275. (looseleaf format)
Description: Promotes the study of Jewish genealogy, and informs members world-wide of society meetings, activities, and current news.

296   US   ISSN 1046-5596
MOSAIC (CAMBRIDGE); a review of Jewish thought and culture. 1960-1973; N.S. 1986. s-a. $15 to individuals; institutions $25. Harvard University, Mosaic, 74 Mt. Auburn St., Cambridge, MA 02138. TEL 617-495-4696. Ed. Ariela Dubler. adv.; bk.rev. circ. 1,600. (also avail. in microfiche) **Document type:** academic/scholarly publication.
Description: Publishes fiction; non-fiction, art, poetry, photographs, reviews, and translations of Jewish interest.

ETHNIC INTERESTS

296 US
▼**MOSAIC (NEW YORK).** 1992. bi-m. $42. Mirich Publishing Co., 45 W. 34th St., Rm. 600, New York, NY 10001. TEL 212-239-0855. FAX 212-967-4184. adv.: B&W page $19856, color page $22503; trim 9 x 10 7/8. circ. 400,000.

360 NO ISSN 0802-3182
MOSAIKK. 1988. bi-m. NOK 120. Norwegian Directorate of Immigration, P.O. Box 8108, 0032 Oslo 1, Norway. TEL 02-530890. FAX 02-125272. Ed. Oeivind Fjeldstad. bk.rev. circ. 6,000.
—CCC.
  Supersedes: Invandrerinformasjon (ISSN 0800-0824)
  Description: Provides a broad view of refugees and immigrants in Norway.

MULTICULTURAL EDUCATION. see *EDUCATION*

917.106 CN ISSN 0834-3713
MULTICULTURAL MAGAZINE. 1979. w. Can.$12. Merrick Enterprises, 349 Claremont Cres., Oakville, Ont. L6J 6J9, Canada. Ed. J. Merrick. adv.
  Formerly (until 1986): Oakville Multicultural Council. Newsletter (ISSN 0821-2392)

MULTICULTURAL PUBLISHERS EXCHANGE NEWSLETTER. see *PUBLISHING AND BOOK TRADE*

MULTICULTURAL REVIEW; dedicated to a better understanding of ethnic, racial and religious diversity. see *EDUCATION — Teaching Methods And Curriculum*

910.03 US
MUNCIE TIMES. 1991. bi-m. free. 1304 N. Broadway, Muncie, IN 47303. TEL 317-741-0037. FAX 317-741-0037. Ed. Beatrice Moten-Foster. circ. 8,000. (tabloid format) **Document type:** newspaper.

917.306 US
EL MUNDO. (Text in English, Spanish) 1963. w. $52. Alameda Publishing, 630 20th St., Oakland, CA 94612. TEL 510-763-1120. (Subscr. to: c/o Frances Melton, The Post Newspaper, Box 1350, Oakland, CA 94604-1350) Ed. Anna Parker. film rev.; play rev.; bibl. circ. 30,000. (back issues avail.) **Document type:** newspaper.

917.306 US ISSN 1051-4147
MUNDO HISPANICO. (Text in Spanish, English) 1979. fortn. $30. Mundo Hispanico, Inc., Box 13808, Sta. K, Atlanta, GA 30324-0808. TEL 404-881-0441. FAX 404-881-6085. (Subscr. to: 1929 Piedmont Circle, Atlanta, GA 30324) Ed. Lino H. Dominguez. adv.; bk.rev.; film rev. circ. 22,100. (tabloid format; also avail. in microfiche; back issues avail.)
●Also available on CD-ROM.
  Description: Reports Hispanic news; and publishes calendar of events.

MUNDO ISRAELITA; actualidad de la semana en Israel y en el mundo judio. see *GENERAL INTEREST PERIODICALS — Israel*

917.306 US
MUNDO - SPANISH NEWSPAPER. (Text in Spanish) 1980. w. $40. El Mundo Inc., 845 No Eastern Ave., Las Vegas, NV 89101. TEL 702-649-8553. FAX 702-649-7429. Ed. Frank Corro. adv. contact: Eddie Escobedo, Jr. circ. 12,500. (back issues avail.) **Document type:** newspaper.
  Description: Covers general Hispanic news.

970 US
MUSEUM OF AFRICAN-AMERICAN HISTORY. NEWSLETTER. 1965. q. membership. Museum of African American History, 301 Frederick Douglass, Detroit, MI 48208-4024. Ed. Stephanie Wright Griggs. adv.; bk.rev. circ. 2,500. (tabloid format)
  Former titles: Afro-American Museum of Detroit. Newsletter; International Afro-American Museum. Newsletter (ISSN 0047-0538)
  Description: News of developments at the Museum. Includes business news, exhibits and progress reports.

398 AT
MUSU PASTOGE/OUR HAVEN. (Text in Lithuanian) 1949. w. Aus.$35 (effective July 1992). Lithuanian Community Publishing Society, P.O. Box 550, Bankstown, N.S.W. 2200, Australia. TEL 03-790-3233. FAX 03-790-3233. (Subscr. to: P.O. Box 550, Bankstown, N.S.W. 2200, Australia) Ed. Bronius Zalys. adv. contact: Bronius Zalys. bk.rev. circ. 1,200. **Document type:** newspaper.

200 US
MUSU ZINIOS. (Text in Lithuanian) 1972. bi-m. $5. Tevai Jezuitai Cikagoje - Jesuit Fathers of Della Strada, Inc., 2345 West 56th St., Chicago, IL 60636. TEL 312-737-8400. Ed. Antanas Saulaitis, S.J. adv.; bk.rev.; illus. circ. 1,700. (back issues avail.) **Document type:** bulletin.

MUZEUM ARCHEOLOGICZNE I ETNOGRAFICZNE, LODZ. PRACE I MATERIALY. SERIA ETNOGRAFICZNA. see *ANTHROPOLOGY*

MWENDO. see *LITERATURE*

960 TZ ISSN 0856-0722
MWENGE/FIREBRAND. 1937. m. free. POB 1, Peramiho, Tanzania. Ed. Baltasar Chale. circ. 33,000.
  Description: Contains studies on African peoples.

N A A C P ANNUAL REPORT. (National Association for the Advancement of Colored People) see *SOCIOLOGY*

910.03 070 US
N A B J JOURNAL. 1984. 10/yr. $50. National Association of Black Journalists, 11600 Sunrise Valley Dr., Reston, VA 22091. TEL 703-648-1270. FAX 703-476-6245. Eds. Don Williamson, Michelle Johnson; Pub. Dorothy Butler Gilliam. adv.; bk.rev. circ. 2,400. **Document type:** newspaper.
  Formerly: N A B J Newsletter.

340 US ISSN 0739-862X
KF8201.A3
N A R F LEGAL REVIEW. 1972. s-a. contribution. Native American Rights Fund, 1506 Broadway, Boulder, CO 80302-6296. TEL 303-447-8760. FAX 303-443-7776. Ed. Ray Ramirez. circ. 34,000. (back issues avail.)
—UnCover.
  Formerly (until 1983): Native American Rights Fund. Announcements.

N E M L A ITALIAN STUDIES; selected proceedings of the Italian section of N E M L A. (Northeast Modern Language Association Conference) see *LITERATURE*

N I M A - NELSON DIRECTORY OF MINORITY & WOMAN-OWNED INVESTMENT MANAGERS. (National Investment Managers Association) see *BUSINESS AND ECONOMICS — Trade And Industrial Directories*

N S B E BRIDGE. (National Society of Black Engineers) see *ENGINEERING*

N S B E MAGAZINE. (National Society of Black Engineers) see *ENGINEERING*

296 GW
NACHRICHTEN FUER DEN JUEDISCHEN BUERGER FUERTHS. 1948. a. DM.10. Israelitische Kultusgemeinde Fuerth, Blumenstr. 31, 90762 Fuerth, Germany. Ed. Ruben Rosenfeld. adv.; bk.rev. circ. 5,000. **Document type:** bulletin.
  Formerly: Israelitische Kultusgemeinde Fuerth.
  Description: Historical information and articles on the Jews of Franconia, especially Fuerth.

917.306 US
EL NACIONAL DE OKLAHOMA; Oklahoma Spanish-English newspaper. (Text in English, Spanish) 1988. w. $20. El Nacional Inc., 304 S.W. 25th, Oklahoma City, OK 73109. TEL 405-632-4531. FAX 405-632-4533. Ed. Rosa Q. King; Pub. Rosa Q. King. adv. circ. 7,750. (back issues avail.) **Document type:** newspaper.

970.1 US
▼**NAKODABI;** the Assiniboine people. 1993. q. $25 membership. Friends of the Assiniboines Foundation, 623 Knapp, Wolf Point, MT 59201. TEL 406-653-1804. Ed. Bob Saindon.

917.309 US ISSN 0027-7894
NAROD POLSKI. (Text in English and Polish) 1897. s-m. membership. Polish Roman Catholic Union of America, 984 Milwaukee Ave., Chicago, IL 60622. TEL 312-278-3210. FAX 312-278-4595. Ed. Kathryn G. Rosypal. bk.rev.; circ. 30,000 (controlled). (also avail. in microfilm) **Document type:** newspaper.
  Description: Contains articles of interest to the Polish community.

NARODNA UMJETNOST. see *FOLKLORE*

917.309 US ISSN 0027-7940
NARODNE NOVINY. (Text in English, Slovak) 1910. m. $5 to non-members. National Slovak Society of U.S.A., 2325 E. Carson St., Pittsburgh, PA 15203. TEL 412-488-1890. FAX 412-488-0327. Ed. Joseph Stefka. adv.; bk.rev. circ. 11,000. (also avail. in microfilm) **Document type:** newspaper.
  Description: Contains articles of interest to the Slovakian community.

917.306 US ISSN 0164-470X
NASA NADA/OUR HOPE. 1922. bi-w. $20. Croatian Catholic Union of USA & Canada, 1 West Old Ridge Rd., Hobart, IN 46342. TEL 219-942-1191. FAX 219-942-8808. Ed. Melchior Masina. bk.rev. circ. 3,500. **Document type:** newspaper.

917.106 CN
NASHA META/OUR AIM. (Text in English and Ukrainian) w. Our Aim Publishing Co., 278 Bathurst St., Toronto, Ont. M5T 2S3, Canada. TEL 416-368-3519. Ed. Micheal Poroniuk. adv. circ. 2,500.
  Description: Contains items of interest to the Ukranian community.

914.7 US ISSN 0744-6594
NASINEC. 1914. w. $25. Nasinec, 206 E. Davilla St., Box 636, Granger, TX 76530. TEL 512-859-2238. Ed. Joe D. Vrabel; Pub. Joe O. Vrabel. circ. 750. (tabloid format; back issues avail.) **Document type:** newspaper.
  Description: Covers topics of interest to Czech Americans

NATIONAL ASSOCIATION OF BLACK ACCOUNTANTS. CHAPTER TO CHAPTER. see *BUSINESS AND ECONOMICS — Accounting*

NATIONAL ASSOCIATION OF BLACK ACCOUNTANTS. NEWS PLUS. see *BUSINESS AND ECONOMICS — Accounting*

361 353 US
NATIONAL ASSOCIATION OF BLACKS WITHIN GOVERNMENT. NEWSLETTER. s-a. National Association of Blacks Within Government, 1820 11th St., N.W., Washington, DC 20001-5015. TEL 202-667-3280.

NATIONAL BLACK LAW JOURNAL. see *LAW*

NATIONAL CONGRESS OF JEWISH DEAF. QUARTERLY. see *HANDICAPPED — Hearing Impaired*

917.306 US
NATIONAL DIRECTORY OF LATIN AMERICANISTS. 1965. irreg., latest 1992. $55.70. U.S. Library of Congress, Hispanic Division, Washington, DC 20540. TEL 202-707-5400. Ed. Jacqueline m. Nickel. **Document type:** directory.

296 US ISSN 1068-123X
NATIONAL JEWISH ADVOCATE. 1924. s-m. $25. (Southern Independent Operators, Inc.) First Coast Media Group, Inc., 8301 Cypress Plaza Dr., Ste. 124, Jacksonville, FL 32256. TEL 904-281-0888. Ed. Lester N. Garripee. adv.; bk.rev.; film rev.; play rev.; bibl.; illus.; circ. 28,500 (controlled). (tabloid format; also avail. in microform from LCP; microfilm from AJP) **Document type:** newspaper.
  Formerly (until 1993): Southern Jewish Weekly (ISSN 0038-4240)
  Description: Contains articles of interest to the Jewish community.

296 700 US
NATIONAL JEWISH ARTS NEWSLETTER. 1981. q. $18. Martin Steinberg Center for Jewish Artists, 15 E. 84th St., New York, NY 10028. TEL 212-879-4500. Ed. Chava Miller. circ. 3,000. (back issues avail.)

ETHNIC INTERESTS 2499

296 US ISSN 1043-2795
NATIONAL JEWISH NEWS. 1973. w. $22. 11071 Ventura Blvd., Studio City, CA 91604. TEL 818-786-4000. FAX 818-760-4640. Ed. Phil Blazer. adv.; bk.rev.; film rev.; play rev. circ. 106,000. (tabloid format; also avail. in microfilm from AJP; back issues avail.)
 Formerly: Israel Today.

296 US ISSN 0888-0379
NATIONAL JEWISH POST AND OPINION. 1931. w. $29. Spokesman Co., Inc., c/o Gabriel M. Cohen, Ed. & Pub., 2120 N. Meridian St., Indianapolis, IN 46202. TEL 317-927-7800. adv.; bk.rev. (also avail. in microfilm from AJP,UMI; reprint service avail. from UMI) **Document type:** newspaper.
 —UMI.
 Formerly: Jewish Post and Opinion (ISSN 0021-6658)
 Description: Contains items of interest to the Jewish Community.

910.03 500 US
NATIONAL TECHNICAL ASSOCIATION. JOURNAL. 1927. 3/yr. $30. Black Collegiate Services, Inc., 1240 S. Broad St., New Orleans, LA 70125. TEL 504-821-5694. FAX 504-821-5713. Ed. George C. Carruthers. adv. circ. 15,000. **Indexed:** INIS Atomind.

970.1 US ISSN 1063-9632
E76.2
▼**NATIVE AMERICANS INFORMATION DIRECTORY.** 1992. irreg. $75. Gale Research Inc., 835 Penobscot Bldg., Detroit, MI 48226. TEL 313-961-2242; 800-877-4253. FAX 313-961-6083. Ed. Julia C. Furtaw. (also avail. in diskette format; magnetic tape) **Document type:** directory.
 Description: Includes nearly 4500 organizations, agencies, institutions, programs, services and publications concerned with Native American life and culture.

970.1 CN ISSN 0820-4322
NATIVE ISSUES. 1979. irreg. approx. a. Can.$10. Native Peoples Support Group of Newfoundland & Labrador, Box 961, Station "C", St. John's, Nfld. A1C 5M3, Canada. circ. 200. (back issues avail.)
 Formerly (until 1983): Indian and Inuit Supporter.

970.1 US ISSN 1061-7884
NATIVE MONTHLY READER; a scholastic newspaper for young adults. 1990. 8/yr. $15. RedSun Institute, Box 122, Crestone, CO 81131. Ed. Pat Caverly. illus. circ. 5,000. **Document type:** newspaper, academic/scholarly publication.
 Description: Presents a postive image of Natives for grades 5 through 12

970.1 CN ISSN 1182-2740
NATIVE NETWORK NEWS. 1988. 12/yr. Can.$25. Alberta Native Information Network Ltd., 13140 St. Albert Tr., Edmonton, AB T5L 4R8, Canada. TEL 403-454-7076. FAX 403-452-3468. adv.; bk.rev. circ. 15,000. (also avail. in microfilm) **Document type:** newspaper.

970.1 US ISSN 0028-0534
NATIVE NEVADAN. 1963. m. $15. Reno - Sparks Indian Colony, Tribal Council, 98 Colony Rd., Reno, NV 89502. TEL 702-329-2936. FAX 702-359-9501. Ed. Andree Y. Bouty. adv.; bk.rev.; illus. circ. 5,500.
 Description: Contains articles of interest to the American Indian community.

917.306 US ISSN 0895-7606
E75
NATIVE PEOPLES; the arts and lifeways. 1987. q. $18 (foreign $25). (National Museum of the American Indian, Smithsonian Institution) Media Concepts Group, Inc., 5333 N. 7th St., Ste. C-224, Phoenix, AZ 85014. TEL 602-252-2236. FAX 602-265-3113. Ed. Gary Avey. adv. circ. 105,000. **Document type:** consumer publication.
 —UnCover.
 Description: Dedicated to the sensitive portrayal of the arts of native peoples of the Americas.

970.1 CN ISSN 0831-585X
NATIVE STUDIES REVIEW. 1985. s-a. $20 to individuals; institutions $35. University of Saskatchewan, Native Studies Department, 104 McLean Hall, Saskatoon, Sask. S7N 0W0, Canada. Eds. James B. Waldram, Frank Tough. illus.
 Refereed Serial

970.1 CN ISSN 0028-0542
NATIVE VOICE. 1946; N.S. 1970. bi-m. Can.$20. Native Brotherhood of British Columbia, 200-1755 East Hasting St., Vancouver, B.C. V5L 1T1, Canada. TEL 604-255-3137. FAX 604-251-7107. Ed. Joy Hall. adv.; bk.rev.; charts; illus. circ. 2,500. (also avail. in microfilm from MML; microform from UMI)

NATURHISTORISCHE GESELLSCHAFT NUERNBERG. ABHANDLUNGEN. see *ARCHAEOLOGY*

908 US
NAUKOVE TOVARYSTVO IMENI SHEVCHENKA. UKRAINS'KYI ARKHIV/UKRAINIAN ARCHIVES. (Text in Ukrainian; summaries in English) no.16, 1960. irreg. price varies. Shevchenko Scientific Society, 63 Fourth Ave., New York.

917.306 US
NAUKOVE TOVARYSTVO IMENI SHEVCHENKA. ZAPYSKY/SHEVCHENKO SCIENTIFIC SOCIETY. MEMOIRS/MITTEILUNGEN. (Text in Ukrainian; summaries in English) 1892. irreg. price varies. Shevchenko Scientific Society, 63 Fourth Ave., New York, NY 10003. TEL 212-254-5130. cum.index: 1892-1982. (also avail. in microfiche from IDC)

970.1 US
NAVAHO. q. $12. Maazo Publishing, Box 1245, Window Rock, AZ 86515. TEL 602-729-2233. Ed. Michael Benson. circ. 7,000.
 Description: Covers history, art, culture, events, and people relevant to the Navajo Indians.

970.1 US
NAVAJO TIMES. 1957. w. $30. Navajo Times Company, Box 310, Window Rock, AZ 86515. TEL 602-871-6641. FAX 602-871-7359. Ed. Tom Arviso, Jr. adv. contact: Eugene Tapahe. bk.rev. circ. 17,000. (also avail. in microfilm; back issues avail.) **Document type:** newspaper.
 Former titles (until 1987): Navajo Times Today (ISSN 8750-3468); (until 1984): Navajo Times (ISSN 0470-5106)
 Description: Contains articles of interest to the American Indian community and the Navajo People.

491 US
NAVASART MONTHLY.* (Text in Armenian) 1982. m. $35. Navasart Foundation, Inc., 807 E. Wilson Ave., Glendale, CA 91206-4460. TEL 818-241-5933. FAX 818-241-6515. Ed. Armen Donoyan. adv.; bk.rev. circ. 1,500.
 Description: Literary magazine promoting Armenian culture, and featuring international writers.

059.8 052 AT
NEA ELLADAS/GREEK TIMES. (Text in English, Greek) 1964. w. Aus.$80. Ethnic Publications Pty Ltd, 600 Nicholson St., N. Fitzroy, Vic. 3068, Australia. TEL 03-482-4433. FAX 03-482-2962. Ed. D. Gogos. adv. contact: Claire Gazis. bk.rev.; circ. 17,000 (paid). **Document type:** newspaper.

917.106 CN ISSN 0316-9782
NEDERLANDSE COURANT.* (Text in Dutch) 1953. bi-w. Can.$14($15) 241837 Publications Ltd., 3019 Harvester Rd., Burlington, Ont. L7N 3G4, Canada. TEL 416-264-2672. FAX 416-261-6078. Ed. Thea Schryer. adv.; bk.rev. circ. 4,200.

960 031 US
NEGRO ALMANAC: A REFERENCE WORK ON THE AFRICAN AMERICAN. irreg., latest 5th ed., 1990. $110. Gale Research Inc., 835 Penobscot Bldg., Detroit, MI 48226. TEL 800-877-4253. FAX 313-961-6083. TELEX 810-221-7086. Eds. Harry A. Ploski, James Williams. illus.
 Description: Provides information on the history and culture of blacks in America, Africa, and the Western Hemisphere.

NEGRO EDUCATIONAL REVIEW. see *EDUCATION*

910.03 US ISSN 0028-2529
E185.5
NEGRO HISTORY BULLETIN. 1937-1987; resumed vol.51, 1994. q. $16 to individuals; institutions $25 (effective 1994). Association for the Study of Afro-American Life and History, Inc., 1407 14th St., N.W., Washington, DC 20005. TEL 202-667-2822. Ed. Alton Hornsby. adv.; bk.rev.; illus.; index. circ. 22,000. (also avail. in microform from UMI,PMC; reprint service avail. from UMI) **Indexed:** Acad.Ind., Amer.Hist.& Life, Arts & Hum.Cit.Ind., Biog.Ind., Bk.Rev.Ind. (1965-1983), C.I.J.E. (1976-), Child.Bk.Rev.Ind. (1965-1983), Curr.Cont., Hist.Abstr., Hum.Ind., Ind.Sel.Per. (1950-), M.L.A., Mag.Ind. (1977-), Numis.Lit., PMR, R.G. (1952-1986), Ref.Sour., Soc.Sci.Ind. **Document type:** bulletin.
 —BLDSC (6075.170000); UnCover; UMI.

059.91 GW ISSN 0028-260X
NEMUNO KRASTAS; the country on the Njemen-River. 1964. q. (Text in English, German and Lithuanian) DM.24($12) Zimmermann-Verlag, Haus Nr. 4, Postfach 252 3430 Witzenhausen-Werra, Germany. Ed. Hans Masalskis. adv.; bk.rev. circ. 2,300. **Indexed:** Hum. nd., Soc.Sci.Ind.
 Description: Cultural and literary publication of the German-Lithuanian Society.

994 949.5 AT ISSN 0028-2693
NEOS KOSMOS. (Text in English, Greek) 1957. s-w. $150. Ethnic Publications Pty. Ltd., 600 Nicholson St., N. Fitzroy, Vic. 3068, Australia. TEL 03-482-4433. FAX 03-482-2962. Ed. Demetrios Gogos. adv. contact: Claire Gazis. bk.rev.; illus. circ. 30,000. **Document type:** newspaper.
 Description: Contains articles of interest to the Greek community.

917.109 CN ISSN 0047-9357
NEPRIKLAUSOMA LIETUVA. (Text in Lithuanian) 1940. w. Can.$25. Independent Lithuanian Publishing Co. Ltd., 7722 George St., La Salle 690, Quebec, PQ H8P 1C4, Canada. TEL 514-366-6220. Ed. Birute Nagys. adv. contact: A. Myles. bk.rev.; film rev.; play rev.; bibl.; charts; illus. circ. 1,200. **Document type:** newspaper.

943.106 GW ISSN 0172-4878
DAS NEUE CHINA. 1974. bi-m. DM.30 (foreign DM.40). (Gesellschaft fuer Deutsch-Chinesische Freundschaft e.V.) China Studien- und Verlagsgesellschaft mbH, Eschenheimer Anlage 28, 60318 Frankfurt, Germany. TEL 059-5970206. adv.; bk.rev. circ. 5,000. (back issues avail.)
 Description: General news about China, Hong Kong, Taiwan.

914.706 HU ISSN 0415-3049
NEUE ZEITUNG; ungarndeutsches Wochenblatt. (Text in German) 1957. w. 130 Ft.($26.50) Hirlapkiado Vallalat, Nagymezo u. 49, Pf. 224, 1391 Budapest, Hungary. TEL 132-6334. TELEX 22-5554. Ed. Johan Schutl. adv.; bk.rev. circ. 4,500. (back issues avail. from NRP)
 Description: For German minorities in Hungary.

296 US
NEVER AGAIN. $0.25 per no. Jewish Defense Organization, Youth Movement, 134 W. 32nd St., Rm. 602, New York, NY 10001. TEL 212-239-0447. adv.; illus.
 Description: Contains articles of interest to the Jewish community.

917.309 US ISSN 0300-5453
NEW AL-HODA; the new guidance. (Text in Arabic) 1898. m. $50. New Al-Hoda, Inc., 34 W. 28th St., New York, NY 10001. TEL 212-686-7398. FAX 212-684-1119. Ed. Fares K. Stephen. adv.; bk.rev. circ. 1,500. (also avail. in microform) **Document type:** newspaper.
 Formerly: Al-Hoda.
 Description: Contains articles of interest to the Arab community.

296 US
THE NEW ALIYON. 1971. q. $20. North American Aliyah Movement, 110 E. 59th St., New York, NY 10022. FAX 212-826-8959. Ed. Rebecca Rowe. adv.; bk.rev.; index, cum.index: 1971-1976, 1982-1986. circ. 10,000.
 Formerly: Aliyon.
 Description: Ideological and practical information relating to Zionism and life in Israel.

ETHNIC INTERESTS

910.03 US
NEW AMERICAN (NEW YORK). 1962. w. $33. Box 4233, Brooklyn, NY 11247. TEL 718-399-2271. FAX 718-857-9115. Ed. Eleanor D. Branch. adv.; bk.rev.; bibl.; charts; illus.; stat. circ. 54,355.
 Formerly (until 1990): Black American.
 Description: Includes cultural and political developments which affect African Americans.

910.03 US
NEW BAYVIEW. 1976. bi-w. $15. New Bayview Newspaper, 4401 Third St., San Francisco, CA 94124. TEL 415-695-0713. FAX 415-695-1845. Ed. Mary Ratcliff. adv.: B&W page $800; adv. contact: Mary Ratcliff. bk.rev.; illus.; circ. 10,000 (controlled). (tabloid format) **Document type:** newspaper.
 Description: Publishes articles of interest to the African American community in the Bayview Hunters Point section of San Francisco.

917.109 CN ISSN 0028-4394
NEW CANADIAN. (Text in English and Japanese) 1939. w. Can.$35. Japan Communications Inc., 524 Front St. W. 2nd Fl., Toronto, Ont. M5V 1B8, Canada. TEL 416-593-6118. FAX 416-593-1871. Ed. Shin Kawai. adv. circ. 4,600. (tabloid format; also avail. in microfilm from CML)

059.8 AT
NEW COUNTRY. (Text in Greek) w. Aus.$90. Foreign Language Publications Pty. Ltd., P.O. Box 146, Broadway, Sydny, N.S.W. 2007, Australia. TEL 02-660-2033. FAX 02-692-0649. Ed. Mr. Mystakidis. adv. contact: George Antoniou. circ. 26,435. (tabloid format; back issues avail.) **Document type:** newspaper.
 Description: Contains articles of interest to the Greek community.

917.306 US
NEW DIMENSIONS (PHILADELPHIA). 1979. 2/yr. $25. Balch Institute for Ethnic Studies, 18 S. Seventh St., Philadelphia, PA 19106. TEL 215-925-8090. Ed. M. Mark Stolarik. circ. 5,000.
 Description: Describes the exhibit, library and education activities of the institute for members.

NEW HAVEN LOCAL NEWS. see GENERAL INTEREST PERIODICALS — United States

914.7 US ISSN 0364-8184
E184.P7
NEW HORIZON - POLISH AMERICAN REVIEW. 1975. m. $15. Bicentennial Publishing Corp., 333 W. 38th St., New York, NY 10018-2914. TEL 212-354-0490. Ed. B. Wierzbianski. adv.; bk.rev.; film rev.; charts; illus. circ. 15,000. (tabloid format)
 Description: Contains items of interest to the Polish community.

320.9 CN
NEW INDIA BULLETIN. 1975. bi-m. Can.$10. Indian People's Association in North America, Box 37, Westmount Post Office, Montreal, Que., Canada. adv.; bk.rev.; illus. circ. 2,000.

910.03 US
NEW JERSEY AFRO-AMERICAN. 1940. w. $12. 9 Lincoln Park, Newark, NJ 07102-2301. Ed. Robert Queen. circ. 5,692. (tabloid format; also avail. in microfilm; back issues avail.)
 Description: Contains articles of interest to the black community.

917.306 US
NEW JERSEY FREIE ZEITUNG. 1858. w. $33. New Jersey Freie Zeitung, 500 S. 31st St., Kenilworth, NJ 07033. TEL 908-245-7995. Ed. Eberhard Schweizer. circ. 3,000. (tabloid format) **Document type:** newspaper.

917.306 US
NEW KOREA. (Text in Korean) 1905. w. $54. 545 S. Serrano Ave., Los Angeles, CA 90020. TEL 213-382-9345. FAX 213-382-1678. Ed. Woon-Ha Kim. adv. contact: Marsha Kim. bk.rev.; illus. circ. 3,000. (also avail. in microfilm) **Document type:** newspaper.
 Description: Contains articles of interest to the Korean community.

915.1 CN
NEW KOREA TIMES. (Text in Korean) w. 720 Spadina Ave., Ste. 503, Toronto, Ont. M5S 2T9, Canada. TEL 416-925-3250. circ. 2,900.

910.03 US
NEW ORLEANS LOUISIANA WEEKLY. 1925. w. $15. Box 53008, New Orleans, LA 70153. TEL 504-524-5563. FAX 504-527-5826. Ed. Lisa Burns. circ. 5,000. **Document type:** newspaper.

910.03 US
NEW ORLEANS TRIBUNE. 1985. m. $18. McKenna Publishing Co., 2335 Esplanada Ave., New Orleans, LA 70119. TEL 504-945-0772. adv. circ. 20,000.
 Description: Contains news for upscale African-Americans in the greater New Orleans area.

917.109 CN
NEW PERSPECTIVES. (Supplement to: Novy Shliakh/New Pathway/Le Nouveau Chemin) (Text in English) m. Can.$12. (Ukrainian National Federation of Canada) New Pathway Publishing Co. Ltd., 297 College St., Toronto, ON M5T 1S2, Canada. TEL 416-960-3424. illus. circ. 5,000.

910.03 US
NEW PITTSBURGH COURIER. 1969. s-w. $40. 315 E. Carson St., Pittsburgh, PA 15219. TEL 412-481-8302. Ed. John Sengstacke. circ. 31,000. **Document type:** newspaper.

NEW SENSE; the literary quarterly of African American students. see LITERARY AND POLITICAL REVIEWS

917.309 US ISSN 0028-7121
NEW YORK AMSTERDAM NEWS. 1909. w. $18. Powell-Savory Corp., 2340 Frederick Douglass Blvd., New York, NY 10027. TEL 212-932-7400. FAX 212-222-3842. adv.; illus. circ. 50,000. (also avail. in microform from UMI) **Document type:** newspaper.
—UMI.
 Description: Contains articles of interest to the black community.

910.03 US ISSN 1052-2948
NEW YORK OBSERVER. 1987. w. $22. New York Observer Co., Inc., 54 E. 64th St., New York, NY 10021. TEL 212-755-2400. FAX 212-688-4889. illus. circ. 51,000. **Document type:** newspaper.

914.906 US ISSN 0737-5379
NEW YORK SPECTATOR; quarterly of culture and tradition. 1982. q. (in 2 issues, 2 nos./issue). $100 donation. American Institute for Writing Research, Box 1364, Grand Central Station, New York, NY 10163. TEL 718-266-2897. Ed. Serban C. Andronescu. adv.; bk.rev.; bibl.; illus. circ. 2,000. (also avail. in microfilm from BHP,KTO)

917.306 US ISSN 1050-4591
NEW YORKER STAATS-ZEITUNG UND HEROLD. 1934. w. $49.50 (effective 1994). New Yorker Staats-Zeitung und Herold, 160 W. 71st St., New York, NY 10023-3944. TEL 212-875-0769. FAX 212-875-0534. Ed. Egon Stadelmann. adv. circ. 16,000. **Document type:** newspaper.

917.306 US ISSN 0895-5549
NEW YORKIN UUTISET/FINNISH NEW YORK NEWS. (Text in English and Finnish) 1906. w. $25. Finnish Newspaper Co., 4422 8th Ave., Brooklyn, NY 11220. TEL 718-435-0800. FAX 718-871-7230. Ed. Leena Isbon. adv.; bk.rev. circ. 2,000. (tabloid format; also avail. in microform) **Document type:** newspaper.
 Description: Contains articles of interest to the Finnish community.

917.306 US ISSN 0193-1814
E184.A65
NEWS CIRCLE/HALQAT AL-AKHBAR; Arab-American monthly. 1972. m. $25. News Circle Publishing House - Dar Halqat al-Akhbar lil-Nashr wal-I'lam, Box 3684, Glendale, CA 91201. TEL 818-545-0333. FAX 818-242-5039. Ed. Joseph Haiek. adv. contact: Cathy Haiek. bk.rev.; bibl.; illus.; stat. circ. 5,000. **Document type:** newspaper.
 Description: Issues and news of the Arab-American community and the Arab world.

790.1 US
NEWS FROM INDIAN COUNTRY. 1988. s-m. $24 to individuals; institutions $40. Indian Country Communications, Box 2900-A, Hayward, WI 54843. TEL 715-634-5226. FAX 715-634-3243. Ed. Paul DeMain. adv.; bk.rev.; illus. circ. 6,800. **Document type:** newspaper.
 Formerly: Lac Courte Oreilles Journal.
 Description: Provides news of national events, pow wows, culture.

970.1 979 US ISSN 1040-5437
E78.C15
NEWS FROM NATIVE CALIFORNIA. 1987. q. $17.50. Heyday Books, Box 9145, Berkeley, CA 94709. TEL 510-549-3564. FAX 510-549-1889. Ed. Jeannine Gendar. adv.; bk.rev.; index; circ. 4,500 (paid). (back issues avail.) **Indexed:** Cal.Per.Ind. (1989-). **Document type:** consumer publication.
 Description: Covers California Indian culture and concerns, past and present.

917.306 US ISSN 0199-901X
NEWS INDIA. vol.7, 1977. w. $26. Hannah Worldwide Publishing, 244 Fifth Ave., New York, NY 10001. TEL 212-481-3110. FAX 212-889-5774. Ed. John Perry. adv. contact: Vijay Anand. bk.rev. circ. 47,000. (also avail. in microfilm) **Document type:** newspaper.
 Formerly: News and Cine India.
 Description: Presents news from India and relating to Indian and South East Asia; addresses Indian issues in American news. Also caters to the second generation of Asian Indians in US.

948 US ISSN 0028-9272
D731
NEWS OF NORWAY. 1941. m. free. Royal Norwegian Embassy, 2720-34th St., N.W., Washington, DC 20008. TEL 202-333-6000. FAX 202-337-0870. bk.rev.; illus.; index. circ. 16,000. **Indexed:** PROMT. **Document type:** newsletter.
—UMI.
 Description: Covers Norwegian interests.

321 305.895 US
NEWS TIBET. 1964. 6/yr. (effective 1994). Office of Tibet, 241 E. 32nd St., New York, NY 10016. TEL 212-213-5010. FAX 212-779-9245. Ed. Thubten Samphel. adv.; bk.rev.; charts; stat. circ. 5,000. **Indexed:** HR Rep.
 Description: Provides information on the current situation in Tibet and Tibetan civilization. Includes feature articles on the various aspects of Tibetan life: Buddhism, culture, medicine, arts, history, and the activities of the Tibetans in exile.

NEWSWATCH. see POLITICAL SCIENCE — Civil Rights

917.306 US ISSN 1064-444X
NEZAVISIMAYA GAZETA. Selected version of Russian daily: Nezavisimaya Gazeta. (Selected semi-monthly English translation also avail.: Independent Newspaper from Russia (ISSN 1064-4431)) (Text in Russian) 1991. s-m. Cynthia Neu, Ed. & Pub., 7338 Dartford Dr., Ste. 9, McLean, VA 22102. TEL 703-827-0414. FAX 703-827-8923. circ. 3,000.

910.03 US
NIGERIAN TIMES. m. $6. Network Nigeria Group, 368 Broadway, Ste. 307, New York, NY 10013. TEL 212-791-0777. FAX 212-791-4074. Ed. Chika A. Onyeani. illus. (tabloid format)
 Formerly: African Enquirer.

915.4 CN
NILZLAL. 1986. m. Can.$2 per no. (typically set in Jan.). Jeeva Publishing, 1108 Bay St., Toronto, Ont. M5S 2W9, Canada. TEL 416-975-0196. FAX 416-975-0759. adv.; bk.rev. circ. 1,500.

942.306 398 US ISSN 0890-0485
NINNAU. 1975. 11/yr. $15. Ninnau Publications Inc., 11 Post Terrace, Basking Ridge, NJ 07920. TEL 908-766-6736. FAX 908-221-0744. Ed. A.L. Roberts; Pub. A.L. Roberts. adv.; bk.rev.; circ. 3,500 (paid). (tabloid format; also avail. in microfilm; back issues avail.) **Document type:** newspaper.
 Description: Provides a forum for the discussion of North American Welsh people and Wales. Attempts to educate the Welsh people in their traditions.

NOAH'S ARK; a newspaper for Jewish children. see CHILDREN AND YOUTH — For

917.306 US
NORDAMERIKANISCHE WOCHEN-POST. (Text in German) 1854. w. $44.95. Detroit Abend-Post Publishing Co., 1120 E. Long Lake Rd., Troy, NE 48098. TEL 313-528-2810. FAX 313-528-2714. Ed. Regina Bell. adv.; bk.rev.; film rev. circ. 20,137. (also avail. in microform) **Document type:** newspaper.
 Formerly: Sonntagspost.
 Description: Keeps German-speaking Americans abreast of the latest happenings in German-speaking Europe.

ETHNIC INTERESTS 2501

917.306 US
NORDEN. 1896. w. $25. Norden News, Inc., 123 W. 44th St., Ste. 12C, New York, NY 10036. TEL 212-944-0775. FAX 212-944-0763. adv. contact: Erik Hermans. bk.rev. circ. 800. (tabloid format) **Document type:** newspaper.

970.1 US
▼**NORTH AMERICAN INDIAN ALMANAC.** 1993. every 5 yrs. $95. Gale Research Inc., 835 Penobscot Bldg., Detroit, MI 48226. TEL 313-961-2242. FAX 313-961-6083. Ed. Duane Champagne. charts; illus.; maps.
Description: Covers all major aspects of the civilization and culture of the indigenous peoples of the U.S. and Canada.

917.036 381 US ISSN 8756-6451
NORTH AMERICAN POST/HOKUBEI HOCHI. (Text in Japanese) 1946. 3/w. $65. North American Post Publishing Inc., 662 1/2 S. Jackson St., Seattle, WA 98104. TEL 206-623-0100. FAX 206-625-1424. Ed. Akiko Kusunose. adv. contact: Mieko Kurihara. circ. 3,000. (tabloid format; back issues avail.) **Document type:** newspaper.
Description: Publishes international and local news for the Japanese community.

960 US
NORTHEAST AFRICAN MONOGRAPH SERIES. irreg., no.19. 1989. price varies. Michigan State University, African Studies Center, Committee on Northeast African Studies, 100 International Center, E. Lansing, MI 48824-1035. TEL 517-353-1700. FAX 517-353-7254. TELEX 650-277-3148 MCI. **Document type:** monographic series.
Formerly: Ethiopian Monograph Series.

960 US ISSN 0740-9133
DT367.A2
NORTHEAST AFRICAN STUDIES. 1979. 3/yr. $30 (foreign $50) to individuals; institutions $40 (foreign $60). (Michigan State University, African Studies Center) Michigan State University Press, Manly Miles Bldg., Ste. 25, 1405 S. Harrison Rd., East Lansing, MI 48823-5202. TEL 517-355-9543. FAX 517-336-2611. Ed. Harold G. Marcus. bk.rev. circ. 200. (back issues avail.) **Indexed:** Amer.Hist.& Life, Bibl.Ling., Documentatieblad, Hist.Abstr., Rural Devel.Abstr., World Agri.Econ.& Rural Sociol.Abstr. **Document type:** academic/scholarly publication.
—BLDSC (6150.253000).
Incorporates: Ethiopianist Notes.

917.306 US
NORTHEAST SUN (LOS ANGELES). (Text in English, Spanish) 1986. w. $62.50. Eastern Group Publications, Inc., 3643 E. First St., Los Angeles, CA 90063. TEL 213-263-5743. Ed. Dolores Sanchez. adv.; bk.rev. circ. 10,000. (tabloid format; back issues avail.) **Document type:** newspaper.
Description: Community newspaper with Hispanic focus.

917.106 CN
NORTHERN MOSAIC. 1975. q. Can.$5 to individuals; institutions Can.$7. Thunder Bay Multicultural Association, 17 N. Court St., Thunder Bay, Ont. P7A 4T4, Canada. TEL 807-345-0551. Ed. John Potestio. adv.; bk.rev. circ. 2,000. (tabloid format; back issues avail.)

NORTHIAN. see EDUCATION

910.03 US ISSN 1058-9627
NORTHWEST DISPATCH. 1982. 5/w. $60. Dispatch Newspapers, Box 5637, Tacoma, WA 98415. TEL 206-272-7587. adv. contact: Lou Taylor. bk.rev.; illus. circ. 15,000. **Document type:** newspaper.

917.306 US
NORTHWEST ETHNIC NEWS. 1984. m. $12 to individuals; institutions $30. Ethnic Heritage Council of the Pacific Northwest, 305 Harrison St., Ste. 326, Seattle, WA 98109-4645. TEL 206-328-9204. FAX 206-726-0528. Ed. Sarah Sarai. adv.; bk.rev.; film rev.; music rev.; play rev. circ. 12,000. (tabloid format; back issues avail.)

917.306 US ISSN 0891-6322
NORWAY TIMES/NORDISK TIDENDE. (Text in English, Norwegian) 1891. w. $42 (foreign $78) (effective 1994). Norse News, Inc., 481 81st St., Brooklyn, NY 11209. TEL 718-238-1100. FAX 718-921-9648. Ed. Tom Roren. adv. contact: Judith Andersen. circ. 6,000. (tabloid format; back issues avail.) **Document type:** newspaper.
Description: Covers news from Norway and other topics of interest to Norwegian-Americans and Norwegian residents of the US.

917.306 US
NOSOTROS.* (Text in Spanish) 1987. m. $1.75 per no. Chanti Publications, Inc., 853 Broadway, Ste. A11, New York, NY 10003. TEL 212-505-0288. Ed. Alberto Correa. adv.
Description: Contains information on night clubs, museums, art galleries, festivals, carnivals, and parks.

NOTABLE HISPANIC AMERICAN WOMEN. see WOMEN'S STUDIES

914 791.4 IT
NOTIZIE MESE. m. Sogeco s.a.s., Via Fiume, 13, 20059 Vimercate, Italy. Ed. Silvana Antonioli. circ. 8,000.

NOTRE VOIX. see POLITICAL SCIENCE

917.306 US
▼**NOVEDADES.** (Text in Spanish) 1992. w. free. Four Star Productions, 2585 Commerce Way, Los Angeles, CA 90040. TEL 213-725-0141. FAX 213-725-2521. Ed. Armando Gaytan. adv.: B&W page $1836; adv. contact: Robert Soto. circ. 100,000. (tabloid format; reprint service avail.) **Document type:** consumer publication, newspaper.
Description: Covers current events, food, automobiles, entertainment, celebrities, health and beauty, sports and more.

917.106 CN
NOVO MUNDO. (Text in Portuguese) w. Portuguese World News, 803 Dundas St., W., Toronto, Ont. M6J 1V2, Canada. TEL 416-868-6621. Ed. Fernando Raposo. circ. 9,000.

057 AT
NOVOSTI; independent newspaper for Serbian settlers in Australia. (Text in Slovenian) 3/w. Foreign Language Publications Pty. Ltd., P.O. Box 146, Broadway, Sydney, N.S.W. 2007, Australia. TEL 02-660-2033. FAX 02-692-0649. Ed. Mr. Siljecovic. adv. contact: George Antoniou. circ. 6,260. (tabloid format) **Document type:** newspaper.

057.1 914.706 US ISSN 0730-8949
NOVOYE RUSSKOYE SLOVO;* Russian American daily newspaper. (Text in Russian) 1910. d. $130. Novoye Russkoye Slovo Publishing Corp., 111 Fifth Ave., 5th Fl., New York, NY 10003-1005. TEL 212-564-8544. Ed. Andrei Sedych. adv.; film rev.; illus. **Document type:** newspaper.
Description: Covers local and world news of interest to Russian Americans.

057.8 CN
NOVY DOMOV/NEW HOMELAND. (Text in Czech, Slovak) 1949. fortn. Can.$26($36) (effective Jan. 1993). Masaryk Memorial Inst. Inc., 450 Scarborough Golf Club Rd., Scarborough, ON M1G 1H1, Canada. TEL 416-439-4646. FAX 416-439-4646. Ed. Vera M. Roller. adv.; bk.rev. circ. 2,700. **Document type:** newspaper.

917.109 CN ISSN 0029-5310
NOVY SHLIAKH/NEW PATHWAY/NOUVEAU CHEMIN; Ukrains'ky tyznevyk. (Supplement avail.: New Perspectives) (Text in Ukrainian) 1930. w. Can.$45 (effective Mar. 1991). (Ukrainian National Federation of Canada) New Pathway Publishing Co. Ltd., 297 College St., Toronto, ON M5T 1S2, Canada. TEL 416-960-3424. Ed. P. Dorozynsky. adv.; bk.rev.; film rev.; play rev.; bibl.; illus. circ. 5,100. (tabloid format; back issues avail.)

917.309 US ISSN 0029-5337
AP50
NOVYI ZHURNAL/NEW REVIEW. (Text in Russian) 1942. q. $40 to individuals (foreign $50); institutions $60 (foreign $73). New Review Inc., 611 Broadway, Ste. 842, New York, NY 10012-2608. TEL 212-353-1478. Ed. George Kashkarov. adv.; bk.rev.; circ. 1,300 (controlled). **Indexed:** Amer.Bibl.Slavic & E.Eur.Stud., M.L.A. **Document type:** academic/scholarly publication.
Description: Covers Russian interests.

057.91 CN ISSN 0048-1017
AP58.U5
NOWI DNI; Ukrainian universal journal. (Text in Ukrainian) 1950. m. Can.$30 (foreign $30). Nowi Dni Co. Ltd., P.O. Box 400, Sta."D", Toronto, ON M6P 3J9, Canada. TEL 416-767-8440. FAX 416-234-1213. Ed. M. Dalney. adv.; bk.rev. circ. 1,500. **Indexed:** M.L.A.
Description: Explores Ukrainian Canadian and East European interests.

917.306 US
NOWY DZIENNIK/POLISH DAILY NEWS. (Text in Polish) d. $70. Bicentennial Publishing Corp., 333 W. 38th St., New York, NY 10018-2914. TEL 212-594-2266. Ed. Boleslaw Wierzbianski. adv. contact: Peter Burlinski. circ. 25,000. **Document type:** newspaper.

NUEVA LUZ. see PHOTOGRAPHY

917.306 US
EL NUEVO PATRIA; South Florida's first Hispanic Weekly. (Text in Spanish) 1959. w. (Thu.) $24 (foreign $36) (effective 1993). El Nuevo Patria Publishing Company, Box 2, Miami, FL 33135. TEL 305-530-8787. FAX 305-577-8989. Ed. Carlos Diaz Lujan. adv. contact: Eladio Armesto III. film rev.; play rev.; circ. 7,640 (paid); 20,360. (tabloid format; back issues avail.) **Document type:** newspaper.
Description: Covers national and local economic and political news, sports, arts, theater.

919.406 AT
NUNGALINYA OCCASIONAL BULLETIN. 1978. irreg. Aus.$3 per no. P.O. Box 40371, Casuarina, N.T. 5792, Australia. TEL 089-27-1093.
Description: Papers concerning aboriginal affairs.

917.106 CN
IL NUOVO MUNDO.* (Text in Italian) 1979. s-m. Can.$18. 8720 - 137 Ave., Edmonton, AB T5E 1X4, Canada. TEL 403-472-6397. FAX 403-478-5493. Ed. Josephine Sicoli. adv.; B&W page Can.$1968.72, color page Can.$2368.72. circ. 9,000. (tabloid format) **Document type:** newspaper.

NYT FRA DANMARK. see GENERAL INTEREST PERIODICALS — Denmark

917.306 US
O C A IMAGE; a national magazine for all Chinese Americans in the United States. 1980. q. membership. Organization of Chinese Americans, 1001 Connecticut Ave., N.W., Ste. 707, Washington, DC 20036. TEL 202-223-5500. FAX 202-296-0540. Ed. Cindy Tong. adv.; bk.rev. circ. 8,000. **Document type:** newsletter.
Description: Discusses subjects of concern to Chinese Americans. Includes calendar of events.

917.306 US
O C S NEWS. (Text in Japanese) 1975. bi-w. $30. O C S America Inc., 5 E. 44th St., New York, NY 10017. TEL 212-599-4506. FAX 212-599-4528. Ed. Ms A. Iimura. adv.; B&W page $2950; trim 9 3/8 x 13 7/8. circ. 17,168. **Document type:** newspaper.
Description: For Japanese people living in the US or coming to the US.

970.1 US
O I O NEWS. 1966. q. $1. Oklahomans for Indian Opportunity, 555 Constitution, Norman, OK 73069. TEL 405-329-3737. Ed. Iola Hayden. circ. 7,000.
Former titles: O I O Journal; O I O Newsletter.
Description: Covers American Indian interests.

ULRICH'S INTERNATIONAL PERIODICALS DIRECTORY 1994-95

ETHNIC INTERESTS

296 US
O R T BULLETIN. q. free. (American Organization for Rehabilitation Through Training Federation) American O R T Federation, 817 Broadway, New York, NY 10003. TEL 212-677-4400. FAX 212-979-9545. TELEX 66468. circ. 18,000. (back issues avail.) Document type: bulletin.

OBSIDIAN II: BLACK LITERATURE IN REVIEW. see *LITERATURE*

059.91 AU ISSN 0030-6398
OESTERREICH - POLEN, AUSTRIA - POLSKA. 1953. 3/yr. S.60. Oesterreichisch-Polnische Gesellschaft, Biberstr. 4, A-1010 Vienna, Austria. TEL 01-522374. Ed. Theodor Kanitzer. adv.; bk.rev.; illus. circ. 10,000. Document type: bulletin.
 Description: Covers Austrian Polish interests.

970.1 320 US ISSN 1068-5987
E185.5
OFARI'S BI-MONTHLY. 1984. s-m. $10 to individuals; institutions $18. Middle Passage Press, 5517 Secrest Dr., Los Angeles, CA 90043. TEL 213-298-0266. Ed. Earl Ofari Hutchinson. circ. 250 (paid); 50 (controlled). (looseleaf format; back issues avail.) Document type: newsletter.
 Former titles: Black View; Impact News; Ofari's Bi-Monthly.
 Description: Black domestic news issues including annual reports, media analysis, and political criticism.

917.306 US ISSN 1042-6965
OGGI 7. (Text in Italian) w. $80. Gruppo Editoriale Oggi, 41 Bergenline Ave., Westwood, NJ 07675. TEL 201-358-6692. FAX 212-268-0379. Ed. Andrea Mantineo.

296 US
OHR HAKOLLEL. 1981. bi-m. $10. Zeirei Agudath Israel of America, 84 William St., New York, NY 10038. TEL 212-797-9000. FAX 212-269-2843. Ed. Yonah Weinrib. adv. circ. 3,000. (back issues avail.)
 Description: Articles of interest to the English-speaking Jewish population.

917.206 MX ISSN 0188-6592
OJARASCA. m. Mex.$80 (America: $60 to individuals; institutions $100). Pro Mexico Indigena A.C., Cuautla 10, Col. Condesa, 06140 Mexico DF, Mexico. TEL 286-5171.

OKIKE; an African journal of new writing. see *LITERATURE*

OLAM HADASH. see *CHILDREN AND YOUTH — For*

O'LOCHLAINNS IRISH FAMILY JOURNAL. see *GENEALOGY AND HERALDRY*

914.506 GW
OLTRECONFINE; libera voce degli italiani in Germania. (Text in Italian) 1969. bi-m. DM.25. (C T I M) Oltreconfine, Postfach 105561, 70048 Stuttgart, Germany. TEL 0711-297117. Ed. Bruno Zoratto. adv.: B&W page DM.4500; trim 262 x 180. circ. 10,000. Document type: newspaper.

917.306 US ISSN 0276-590X
LA OPINION. (Text in Spanish) 1926. d. $140 (foreign $250). Lozano Enterprises, Inc., 411 W. Fifth St., Los Angeles, CA 90013. TEL 213-896-2150. FAX 213-896-2151. Ed. Monica Lozano. adv. contact: Pamela Austin. Document type: newspaper.

914.5 CN
ORA DI OTTAWA. 1968. w. Can.$18. 203 Louisa St., Ottawa, Ont. K1R 6Y9, Canada. TEL 613-232-5689. FAX 613-563-2573. adv.

296 US
ORAH. 1960. q. membership. Canadian Hadassah-WIZO, Rm. 900, 1310 Greene Ave., Westmount, Que. H3Z 2B8, Canada. TEL 514-937-9431. FAX 514-933-6483. Ed. Esther Matlow. adv.; bk.rev. circ. 15,000.
 Description: Contains articles of interest to the Jewish community.

296 US ISSN 0030-4298
ORANGE COUNTY JEWISH HERITAGE. 1958. w. $25. 1833 E. 17th St., No. 316, Santa Ana, CA 92701-2915. TEL 714-543-0321. Ed. Dan Brin. adv.; bk.rev.; film rev.; play rev. circ. 11,300. (tabloid format)

910.03 US
ORANGEBURG BLACK VOICE. 1982. w. $25. S C Black Media Group, 1310 Harden St., Columbia, SC 29204. TEL 803-799-5252. FAX 803-799-7709. Ed. Issac Washington. adv. contact: Melody Harris. illus. circ. 5,400. Document type: newspaper.

ORGANIZATION OF BLACK AIRLINE PILOTS. CONVENTION JOURNAL. see *AERONAUTICS AND SPACE FLIGHT*

ORGANIZATION OF BLACK AIRLINE PILOTS. NEWSLETTER. see *AERONAUTICS AND SPACE FLIGHT*

ORITA; Ibadan journal of religious studies. see *RELIGIONS AND THEOLOGY*

ORTHODOX HERALD. see *RELIGIONS AND THEOLOGY — Eastern Orthodox*

OSCAR ISRAELOWITZ'S GUIDE TO JEWISH NEW YORK CITY. see *TRAVEL AND TOURISM*

970.1 US
OSHKAABEWIS NATIVE JOURNAL. 1990. q. $20 to individuals; institutions $30. American Indian Studies Center, Bemidji State University, Sanford Hall, No. 19, 1500 Birchmont Dr., N.E., Bemidji, MN 56601-2699. Ed. David Gonzales. bk.rev.

949.706 GW ISSN 0179-3071
OST-DIENST; Suedosteuropa Sonderdienst. 1950. w. DM.180($110) Ost-Dienst, Hudtwalckerstr. 26, 22299 Hamburg, Germany. TEL 040-462702. FAX 040-460-2769. Ed. Hans Peter Rullmann. circ. 1,000. Document type: bulletin.
 Description: News about Yugoslavia: politics, economics and culture.

OSTEOPATHIC MEDICAL EDUCATION: A HANDBOOK FOR MINORITY APPLICANTS. see *EDUCATION — Higher Education*

910.03 301.4157 US
OTHER BLACK WOMAN; an international magazine for women. 1981. q. $9.95. 72-15 41 Ave., Station D43, Jackson Heights, NY 11372.

OTHER COUNTRIES: BLACK GAY VOICES. see *HOMOSEXUALITY*

971.3 CN ISSN 0315-0771
F1059.5.O9
OTTAWA ETHNIC GROUPS DIRECTORY.* 1971. a. Can.$5. Ottawa-Carleton Immigrant Services Organization, 959 Wellington St., Ottawa, ON K1Y 4W1, Canada. TEL 613-725-0202. Ed. N. Tran. circ. 1,000.

296 CN
OTTAWA JEWISH BULLETIN. 1974. 19/yr. Can.$20. Jewish Community Council of Ottawa, 151 Chapel St., Ottawa, ON K1N 7Y2, Canada. TEL 613-789-7306. Ed. Myra Aronson. adv.; bk.rev. circ. 10,000. (tabloid format) Document type: bulletin.
 Formerly: Ottawa Jewish Bulletin and Review (ISSN 0319-1303); Which was formed by the 1974 merger of: Ottawa Jewish Digest and Review (ISSN 0319-1281); Ottawa Jewish Bulletin (ISSN 0319-129X)
 Description: Contains articles of interest to the Jewish community.

917.306 US ISSN 0740-0225
HQ1104
OUR LIFE. (Text in English, Ukrainian) vol.32, 1975. m. $30 (effective Jan. 1994). Ukrainian National Women's League of America, Inc., 108 Second Ave., New York, NY 10003. TEL 212-674-5508. FAX 212-254-2672. Ed. Irena Chaban. bk.rev.; illus. circ. 4,000. (also avail. in microfilm)
 Description: Covers Ukrainian culture, history and personalities, community affairs, social services and homemaking. Includes art, folklore and literature.

296 CN ISSN 0834-0242
OUTLOOK. 1963. 10/yr. Can.$25 to individuals; institutions Can.$35. Canadian Jewish Outlook Society, 6184 Ash St., Ste. 3, Vancouver, B.C. V5Z 3G9, Canada. TEL 604-324-5101. FAX 604-325-2470. Ed. Henry Rosenthal. adv.; bk.rev.; index. circ. 4,000. (also avail. in microfilm)
 Formerly: Canadian Jewish Outlook (ISSN 0045-5059)
 Description: Provides a Jewish secular humanist perspective on political and cultural issues.

947 US
OUTREACH (NEW YORK). 1977. m. free. Armenian Apostolic Church of America, 138 E. 39th St., New York, NY 10016. TEL 212-689-7810. FAX 212-689-7168. Ed. Iris Papazian. adv.; bk.rev. circ. 10,500.

OVERTURE (NEW YORK); a Black theatre annual. see *THEATER*

914.706 US
P A C NEWSLETTER. 1945. irreg. Polish American Congress Charitable Foundation, Inc., 5711 N. Milwaukee Ave., Chicago, IL 60646-6215. TEL 312-763-9944. FAX 312-763-7114. TELEX 503807 POLAMCON. Ed. Kazimierz Lukomski. circ. 15,000. (back issues avail.)

917.309 US ISSN 0739-9766
P A H A NEWSLETTER. 1944. q. $25 to individuals; institutions $35. Polish American Historical Association, c/o James S. Pula, Ed., 984 Milwaukee Ave., Chicago, IL 60622. bk.rev. circ. 800. (processed) Document type: newsletter.
 Formerly: P A H A Bulletin.
 Description: Polish immigration studies.

917.309 US ISSN 0030-8579
PACIFIC CITIZEN. 1929. w. (45/yr.). $25 (foreign $38). Japanese American Citizens League, 2 Coral Circle, Ste. 204, Monterey Park, CA 91775. TEL 213-725-0083. FAX 213-725-0064. Eds. Richard Suenaga, Gwen Muranaka. adv.: B&W page $1440, color page $1820. bk.rev.; abstr.; illus. circ. 24,000. (also avail. in microfilm) Document type: newspaper.
 Description: Covers Japanese interests.

PACIFIC STUDIES; an interdisciplinary journal devoted to the study of the Pacific--its islands and adjacent countries. see *SOCIAL SCIENCES: COMPREHENSIVE WORKS*

917.106 CN ISSN 0711-4222
PAKEEZA INTERNATIONAL. (Text in Urdu) 1979. s-m. Can.$26. Directories International Ltd., 17 Burnhope Dr., Brampton, ON L6X 3R9, Canada. TEL 905-924-7444. FAX 905-455-9839. Ed. Shahtaj Fatima. adv.; bk.rev. circ. 3,000. (tabloid format)
 Formerly: Pakeeza (ISSN 0711-4214)

LA PALABRA. see *LITERATURE*

051 US
PALM BEACH GAZETTE. 1989. w. $25. Palm Beach Gazette, Inc., P.O. Drawer 18469, W. Palm Beach, FL 33416-8469. TEL 407-844-5501. FAX 407-844-5551. Ed. Lee Ivory; Pub. Gwen Ivory. adv. circ. 3,000. Document type: newspaper.
 Description: News of Palm Beach county for African-Americans.

296 US
PALM BEACH JEWISH WORLD. 1982. w. $24. Jewish Media Group, 3550 Biscayne Blvd. Third Fl., Miami, FL 33137-3845. TEL 305-576-9500. FAX 305-573-9551. Ed. Stacy Zolotin. adv.; bk.rev. circ. 26,000.
 Description: Serves the Jewish community of Palm Beach County, Florida.

917.309 US
PAMIR MAGAZINE/PA MI ERH ZAZHI. (Text in Chinese and English) 1964. m. $6.50. Chinese - American Cultural Association, Inc., 8122 Mayfield Rd., Box 8, Chesterland, OH 44026. TEL 216-729-9937. Ed. Peter Chieh Wang. adv.; bk.rev.; illus.; tr.lit. circ. 7,500.
 Formerly: Pamir Monthly (ISSN 0031-0530)
 Description: Chinese cultural interests.

970.1 US ISSN 1068-7297
PAN-AMERICAN INDIAN ASSOCIATION NEWS. 1984. q. $8. (Pan-American Indian Association) Chief Piercing Eyes, Ed. & Pub., Box 244, Nocatee, FL 33864-0244. TEL 813-494-6930. adv.; bk.rev. circ. 5,000. Document type: newspaper.
 Formerly (until May 1985): Tribal Advisor.
 Description: For persons formerly unaware of Indian heritage or other ethnic traditions. Help with genealogy, resources, and contact.

914.406   FR
PAROLE UKRAINIENNE. (Text in Ukrainian) w. 290 F. Premiere Imprimerie Ukrainienne en France, 3 rue du Sabot, 75006 Paris, France.
   Description: Contains items of interest to the Ukrainian community.

296 808.87
PASSAGES. 1987. m. 17 rue Simone Weil, 75013 Paris, France. TEL 1-45-86-30-02. Ed. Bernard Ulmann. circ. 75,000.

THE PATRIOT REVIEW. see *POLITICAL SCIENCE*

390   FR
LE PAYS BRETON. (Text in Breton and French) vol.10, 1975. m. 90 Fr. Union des Societes Bretonnes de l'Ile de France, 19 rue du Depart, 75014 Paris, France. Ed. Jean le Lagadec. illus. (tabloid format)

053.1   CN   ISSN 0048-3095
PAZIFISCHE RUNDSCHAU/PACIFIC REVIEW. (Text in German) 1965. fortn. Can.$20 (typically set in Jan.). Ackermann Advertising and News Service, Box 88047, Richmond, BC V6X 3T6, Canada. TEL 604-270-2923. FAX 604-273-9365. (U.S. addr.: Box 1170, Blaine, WA 98231-1770) Ed. Baldwin Ackermann. adv. contact: Baldwin Ackermann. bk.rev. circ. 15,000. **Document type:** newspaper.
   Formerly: Dies und Das (ISSN 0715-5239)
   Description: Covers German interests.

PELANGI; Indonesian-English bilingual magazine. see *EDUCATION — Teaching Methods And Curriculum*

573   US
PENNSYLVANIA ETHNIC STUDIES NEWSLETTER. 1975. 3/yr. $3. University of Pittsburgh, Pennsylvania Ethnic Heritage Studies Center, 405 Belle Field Hall, Pittsburgh, PA 15260. TEL 412-624-4141. Ed. Joseph Makarewicz. bk.rev. circ. 3,500. **Indexed:** A.I.C.P.

974.8   US
PENNSYLVANIA GERMAN SOCIETY. ANNUAL VOLUME SERIES. (Each vol. has distinctive title) 1968. a. $40 includes all Society publications (institutions $50). Pennsylvania German Society, Box 397, Birdsboro, PA 19508. TEL 215-582-1441. (back issues avail.) **Document type:** monographic series.
   Description: Publishes studies of the history, culture, folklore and cuisine of the Pennsylvania Dutch community.

914.706   FR   ISSN 0757-2239
PENSEE RUSSE. Variant title: Russkaja Mysl. 1947. w. 400 F.($75) (foreign 600 F.). Presse Libre S.A., 217 rue du Faubourg, St. Honore, 75008 Paris, France. TEL 42-25-56-81. FAX 40-74-04-97. Ed. Irina Ilovaisky Alberti. adv.; bk.rev. circ. 20,000.

917.306   US
IL PENSIERO. (Text in English, Italian) 1904. s-m. $10 (Canada $15). 10001 Stonell Dr., St. Louis, MO 63123. TEL 314-638-3446. FAX 314-638-8222. Ed. A. Gandolfo; Pub. Antonino Lombardo. adv.; bk.rev.; tr.lit. circ. 7,000. (tabloid format) **Document type:** newspaper.
   Description: News of Italy and other items of interest to Italian-Americans, especially in the St. Louis area.

910.03   US
PEOPLE'S CRUSADER. 1971. w. $15. 1959 Boulevard Dr., S.E., Atlanta, GA 30317. TEL 404-373-5751. FAX 404-681-1688. Ed. Terrie L. Randolph. circ. 20,000. (tabloid format) **Document type:** newspaper.

287   US
EL PERICO. (Text in English, Spanish) 1977. m. $10 donation. United Methodist Urban Ministry, 1611 N. Mosley, Wichita, KS 67214. TEL 316-263-1041. Ed. Al Hernandez. circ. 3,500. (tabloid format) **Document type:** newspaper.
   Description: News and information of interest to the Hispanic community.

056.1   US   ISSN 0899-5176
EL PERIODICO U S A. 1986. w. $36. Brito & Associates, 4200 N. Bicentennial Dr., Box 5356, McAllen, TX 78502. TEL 210-631-5628. FAX 212-631-0832. adv. contact: Tom Wittmer. bk.rev. circ. 151,000. (looseleaf format; reprint service avail.) **Document type:** newspaper.
   Description: Features world information directed to the Hispanic market.

296   US
PERSPECTIVES (NEW YORK). m. Columbia University, 105 Earl Hall, New York, NY 10027. TEL 212-280-5111. Ed. Judy Yellin.

917.309   US   ISSN 0048-3508
PERSPECTIVES (WASHINGTON, 1971).* a Polish-American educational and cultural bi-monthly. 1971. bi-m. $6.50. Perspectives, Inc., c/o Marta Korwin Rhodes, 7300 Connecticut Ave., Bethesda, MD 20815-4930. TEL 202-554-4267. Ed. Krystyna Kusielewicz. adv.; bk.rev.; bibl.; illus. circ. 8,000. (tabloid format; also avail. in microform from UMI; reprint service avail. from UMI) **Indexed:** C.I.J.E., Ind.U.S.Gov.Per.
—UMI.
   Description: Covers Polish American interests.

919   AT
PERTHI MAGYAR HIREK/PERTH HUNGARIAN NEWS. (Text in English and Hungarian) 1969. m. Aus.$12. Australian Hungarian Associations in Western Australia, 5 Hove Court, Mollamara, W.A. 6061, Australia. Ed. John C. Veszely. adv.; bk.rev. circ. 3,800.

PEUPLES NOIRS, PEUPLES AFRICAINS. see *LITERARY AND POLITICAL REVIEWS*

910.03   US   ISSN 0746-956X
PHILADELPHIA TRIBUNE. 1884. 3/w. $38. 522 S. 16th St., Philadelphia, PA 19146. TEL 215-893-4050. FAX 215-735-3612. Ed. Paul A. Bennett. bk.rev. circ. 108,000. (also avail. in microform) **Document type:** newspaper.
   Description: For Philadelphia's African American community.

917.306   US
PHILIPPINES MAIL. 1930. m. $5. Filipino-American Media of California, 830 Central Ave., Box 1783, Salinas, CA 93901. Ed. Delfin C. Fruz. adv.; bk.rev. circ. 5,000.

970.1   CN
PHOENIX (TORONTO, 1980). 1980. 4/yr. Can.$20 (foreign $30); libraries Can.$25 (foreign Can.$35). Canadian Alliance in Solidarity with Native Peoples (CASNP), P.O. Box 574, Sta. P, Toronto, ON M5S 2T1, Canada. TEL 416-972-1573. FAX 416-972-6232. Ed. Sharon O'Sullivan. bk.rev. circ. 3,500. **Indexed:** Bibl.Ling. **Document type:** newsletter.
   Description: Covers crucial issues of importance to the Native people and all Canadians. Includes Native poetry and a guide to action.

059.89 916.206   UA
PHOS. (Text in Greek) 1896. d. 14 Sharia Zakaria Ahmad, Cairo, Egypt. Ed. S. Pateras. circ. 20,000. **Document type:** newspaper.

915.4   CN
PHULWARI. (Text in English, Punjabi) s-m. Phulwari Publications, 14199-72A Ave., Surrey, B.C. V3W 2R2, Canada. TEL 604-594-1288. FAX 604-597-7971.

PIAZZA GRANDE; mensile di annuci economici, cultura e informazione. see *GENERAL INTEREST PERIODICALS — Italy*

PILIPINAS; an interdisciplinary scholarly journal of Philippine studies. see *HISTORY — History Of Asia*

917.106 200   CN   ISSN 0846-5320
PIONEER CHRISTIAN MONTHLY. m. Council of the Reformed Church in Canada, RR 4, Cambridge, Ont. N1R 5S5, Canada. TEL 519-622-1777. FAX 519-622-1993. Ed. Jeff Kingswood. circ. 3,000.

PITTSBURGH JEWISH CHRONICLE. see *JOURNALISM*

910.03   US
PITTSBURGH RENAISSANCE NEWS. 1967. w. $15. Renaissance Publications, 1516 Fifth Ave., Pittsburgh, PA 15219. TEL 412-391-8208. FAX 412-391-8006. Ed. Connie Portis. adv.; bk.rev. circ. 30,000. (tabloid format) **Document type:** newspaper.

PLANNING AND THE BLACK COMMUNITY. see *HOUSING AND URBAN PLANNING*

051   US   ISSN 0149-466X
AP2
PLAYERS. 1973. m. $25. Players International Publications, 8060 Melrose Ave., Los Angeles, CA 90046. FAX 213-655-9452. Ed. Cecil D. Wells. adv. contact: Doug Johnson. bk.rev.; film rev.; play rev.; illus. circ. 150,000. **Indexed:** Abstr.Engl.Stud. **Document type:** consumer publication.

POGROM. see *POLITICAL SCIENCE — Civil Rights*

917.306   US   ISSN 8750-9075
POLAND TODAY.* 1978. q. $10. Polamerica Press, Box 12268, Seattle, WA 98102-0268. Ed. Czeslaw Z. Banasiewicz. adv. circ. 3,000. (back issues avail.)
   Formerly (until Spring 1984): Polamerica (ISSN 0163-1853)
   Description: Contains articles of interest to the Polish community.

296 320.9   CN
POLEMICAL DOCUMENTS SERIES. irreg. price varies. Dawn Publishing Co. Ltd., 17 Anselme Lavigne Blvd., Dollard des Ormeaux, Montreal, Que. H9A 1N3, Canada.

296   UK   ISSN 0268-1056
DS135.P6   CODEN: POLNEN
POLIN; a journal of Polish-Jewish studies. 1986. a. £55($105) (Institute for Polish-Jewish Studies) Basil Blackwell Ltd., 108 Cowley Rd., Oxford OX4 1JF, England. TEL 0865 791100. FAX 0865-791347. TELEX 837022-OXBOOK-G. Ed. Antony Polonsky. adv.; bk.rev. (also avail. in microform) **Indexed:** Zion.Lit. **Document type:** academic/scholarly publication.
—BLDSC (6543.430000); UMI.

917.309   US   ISSN 0032-2792
POLISH AMERICAN JOURNAL. At head of title: Polonia's Voice. Variant title: Pol-Am Journal. (Published in 6 editions: National; Buffalo; Cleveland; Metro NY & New Jersey; New York; Philadelphia) 1911. m. $12.50. Panagraphics Corporation, 1275 Harlem Rd., Buffalo, NY 14206-1960. TEL 716-893-5771. FAX 716-893-5783. Ed. Mark Kohan. adv. contact: Katherine Sobccinski. bk.rev.; charts; illus.; tr.lit.; circ. B&W page: $1 000 (National ed.), $600 (Regional eds.) (paid). (tabloid format; also avail. in microfilm from BLI) **Document type:** newspaper.
   ●Also available online.
   Also available on CD-ROM.
   Description: Covers news about Poles and Americans of Polish descent.

943.8   US   ISSN 0032-2806
E184.P7
POLISH AMERICAN STUDIES; a journal devoted to Polish American history and culture. 1944. s-a. $25 to individuals; institutions $35. (Polish Museum of America) Polish American Historical Association, c/o James S. Pula, Ed., 984 Milwaukee Ave., Chicago, IL 60622. bk.rev.; bibl.; cum.index in prep. circ. 1,000. (back issues avail.) **Indexed:** Amer.Hist.& Life, Cath.Ind., Hist.Abstr. **Document type:** academic/scholarly publication.
—Faxon; UnCover.

917.309   US
POLISH AMERICAN WORLD. 1959. w. $15. 3100 Grand Blvd., Baldwin, NY 11510. TEL 516-223-6514. Ed. Thomas Poskropski. adv.; bk.rev.; circ. 6,000 (controlled). (tabloid format; also avail. in microform; reprint service avail. from UMI) **Document type:** newspaper.
   Description: Serves the English speaking Polish American community.

917.106   CN   ISSN 0319-5147
POLISH CANADIAN COURIER/NOWY KURIER. (Text in English and Polish) 1972. s-m. Can.$24. J. Cabay, Ed. & Pub., P.O. Box 161, Station "P", Toronto, ON M5S 2S7, Canada. TEL 416-259-4353. adv. circ. 20,000. **Document type:** newspaper.
   Formerly: Polish Canadian Independent Courier.
   Description: Contains items of interest to the Polish Canadian community.

917.306   US   ISSN 1070-7581
POLISH DIGEST. 1991. m. $20. Artex Publishing, Inc., c/o Horyzonty, 1924 N. 7th St., Sheboygan, WI 53081-2724. TEL 715-341-6959. FAX 715-346-7516. Ed. Leszek Zeilinski. adv.; bk.rev. circ. 2,000. (reprint service avail.)
   Description: Covers history of Poland; news from Poland; culture.

ETHNIC INTERESTS

917.306 US
POLISH FEST NEWS. 1989. q. Polish Festivals, Inc., 7128 W. Rawson Ave., Franklin, WI 53132. TEL 414-529-2140. Ed. Ray Trzesniewski, Jr. adv. circ. 5,000.

914.706 US ISSN 0735-9209
E184.P7
POLISH HERITAGE. 1957. q. $10 (foreign $12). American Council for Polish Culture, 6507 107th Ter., Pinellas Park, FL 34666-2432. TEL 813-541-7875. Ed. Wallace M. West. adv.; bk.rev.; illus. circ. 4,500. **Indexed:** Amer.Bibl.Slavic & E.Eur.Stud.
    Former titles (until 1981): Quarterly Review of Polish Heritage; (until 1976): American Council of Polish Cultural Clubs. Quarterly Review (ISSN 0569-4108)

917.03 US
POLISH HERITAGE SOCIETY BIULETYN; monthly newsletter. (Text in English, Polish) 1963. m. $20. Polish Heritage Society, Box 1844, Grand Rapids, MI 49501-1844. TEL 616-456-5353. FAX 616-456-8929. Ed. Pat McBride. adv.; bk.rev.; film rev.; illus.; circ. 1,000 (paid). (tabloid format) **Document type:** newsletter.
    Description: Encourages the preservation and understanding of Polish and Polish-American culture and history.

919.309 AT ISSN 0032-2954
POLISH NEWS/WIADOMOSCI POLSKIE. (Text in Polish) 1942. w. Aus.$60. (Polish Communities in Australia and New Zealand) Ingos Pty. Ltd., King York House, 3rd Fl., 32 York St., Sydney, N.S.W. 2000, Australia. TEL 02-299-1248. Ed. Jan Dunin-Karwicki. adv.; B&W page Aus.$800. bk.rev.; film rev.; play rev.; abstr.; bibl. circ. 5,000.
    Description: Contains articles of interest to the Polish community.

947 US
POLISH STUDIES NEWSLETTER. 1979. m. $17. 3433 Gregg Rd., Brookeville, MD 20833. TEL 301-774-4560. Ed. Albin S. Wozniak. adv.; bk.rev.; film rev.; play rev.; bibl. circ. 350. (looseleaf format) **Indexed:** ERIC. **Document type:** newsletter.
    Description: Covers Polish interests.

POLISH WESTERN ASSOCIATION OF AMERICA. QUARTERLY. see *POLITICAL SCIENCE*

917.306 US
POLISH WORLD. 1904. w. $35. Polish Daily News, Inc., 11903 Jos Campau St., Hamtramck, MI 48212. TEL 313-365-1990. FAX 313-365-0850. Ed. Ewa Matuszewski. adv. contact: Stan Zych. bk.rev. circ. 15,500. (tabloid format) **Document type:** newspaper.

296 320.9 CN
POLITICAL DIGEST SERIES. irreg. price varies. Dawn Publishing Co. Ltd., 17 Anselme Lavigne Blvd., Dollard des Ormeaux, Montreal, Que. H9A 1N3, Canada.

POLKA; Polish women's quarterly magazine. see *WOMEN'S INTERESTS*

917.106 CN ISSN 1196-1899
POLONIA. (Text in English, Polish) 1990. m. Can.$15 (typically set in Jan.). Ethnographic Publications, Inc., 324 Selkirk Ave., Winnipeg, MB R2W 2M1, Canada. TEL 204-582-5733. FAX 204-582-5772. Ed. Ted Sosnowski. adv.; bk.rev. circ. 500.
    Formerly (until 1994): Polonia Voice (ISSN 1183-8000)
    Description: Reports on Poland and the Polish community throughout the world.

971.3 CN ISSN 0704-7002
F1059.7.A1
POLYPHONY. 1977. s-a. Can.$20. Multicultural History Society of Ontario, 43 Queen's Park Cres. E., Toronto, Ont. M5S 2C3, Canada. TEL 416-979-2973. FAX 416-979-7947. illus. circ. 2,000. **Indexed:** Can.Per.Ind., CMI.

914.4 929 US ISSN 0747-6558
E184.G3
DIE POMMERSCHEN LEUTE. 1982. 7/yr. $10 (effective Jan. 1992). 1260 Westhaven Dr., Oshkosh, WI 54904. TEL 414-235-7398. Ed. Myron E. Gruenwald. bk.rev.; charts; stat. circ. 800. (looseleaf format; back issues avail.)
    Description: News and information on the ancestry and immigrant genealogy of the German-Prussian duchy of Pomerania. Includes geographical and historical facts about Pomerania and adjacent areas, and analyses of the influence of Pomeranian immigrants on Wisconsin and American culture.

914.5 US
IL POPOLO ITALIANO. (Text in English, Italian) 1936. bi-m. $5. Arnold Orsatti, Ed. & Pub., 21 S. Chalfont Ave., Atlantic City, NJ 08401-7307. TEL 609-345-0663. FAX 609-822-2364. adv. circ. 5,000.

914.6 CN ISSN 0382-9308
POPULAR/SPANISH DAILY NEWS. 1970. d. 2413 Dundas St. W., Toronto, ON M6P 1X3, Canada. TEL 416-531-2495. FAX 416-531-7187. Ed. Jesus David. adv.; circ. 10,000 (paid). **Document type:** newspaper.

917 US
EL POPULAR. (Text in Spanish) 1990. w. $30. El Popular Newspaper Group of California, 1206 California Ave., Bakersfield, CA 93304. TEL 805-398-1000. FAX 805-325-1351. adv. circ. 22,000. (back issues avail.) **Document type:** newspaper.
    Description: Covers news, entertainment, sports, food, lifestyle and other subjects of interest to the Spanish-speaking communities.

PORTLAND ALLIANCE. see *LABOR UNIONS*

910.03 US
PORTLAND OBSERVER. 1970. w. $30. Cory's Publishing Co., Inc., Box 3137, Portland, OR 97208. TEL 503-283-2487. Ed. Joyce Washington. circ. 30,000. **Document type:** newspaper.

917.106 CN
PORTUGAL ILLUSTRADO. (Text in Portuguese) w. 60 Hanson Rd., Unit 138, Mississauga, ON L5B 2P6, Canada. TEL 416-279-8368. FAX 416-588-8216. Ed. Manuel Pliveira Neto. circ. 10,000.

949.006 AT
O PORTUGUES NA AUSTRALIA. (Text in Portuguese) 1971. w. Aus.$72. O & G Investment Pty. Ltd., 47 New Canterbury Rd., P.O. Box 133, Petersham, N.S.W. 2049, Australia. TEL 560-6722. FAX 560-6044. Ed. M.A. Gaspar. adv.: page Aus.$1080. circ. 8,000. (tabloid format; back issues avail.) **Document type:** newspaper.

917.306 US
PORTUGUESE - AMERICAN NEWSPAPER. (Supplement avail.: Revista) 1928. 2/w. $20. Antonio S. Matinho, Ed. & Pub., 88 Ferry St., Newark, NJ 07105. TEL 201-589-4600. FAX 201-589-3848. adv.; bk.rev. circ. 15,460. (tabloid format) **Document type:** newspaper.

917.309 US ISSN 0032-5163
PORTUGUESE JOURNAL/JORNAL PORTUGUES. (Text in English, Portuguese) 1888. w. $25. Alberto S. Lemos, Ed. & Pub., 1912 Church Lane, San Pablo, CA 94806. TEL 510-237-0888. FAX 510-237-3790. adv. contact: Maria C. Leal. bk.rev.; illus. circ. 6,200. (tabloid format; back issues avail.) **Document type:** newspaper.

917.406 320 US ISSN 0746-3928
PORTUGUESE TIMES. (Text in English and Portuguese) 1970. w. $15. Portuguese Times, Inc., 1501 Acushnet Ave., New Bedford, MA 02746-1288. FAX 508-990-1231. TELEX 9102400449. Ed. Manuel Ferreira. adv.; charts; illus. circ. 12,000. (tabloid format) **Document type:** newspaper.
    Description: Contains items of interest to the Portuguese American community.

917.309 US ISSN 0300-6786
POST EAGLE; America's leading independent American-Polish weekly. 1962. w. $22. Post Publishing Co. Inc., 800 Van Houten Ave., Clifton, NJ 07013. TEL 201-476-5414. FAX 201-473-3211. Eds. Chester and Christine Grabowski. adv.; bk.rev.; play rev.; circ. 17,000 (controlled). (tabloid format; also avail. in microfilm) **Document type:** newspaper.

917.306 US ISSN 0888-0107
POST-GAZETTE. 1896. w. $20. Pamela Donnaruma, Ed. & Pub., 5 Prince St., Boston, MA 02113. TEL 617-227-8929. circ. 15,900. **Document type:** newspaper.

970.1 US
POW WOW JOURNAL. Cover title: Shinnecock Labor Day Pow Wow. a. Shinnecock Indian Reservation, Box 560, Southampton, NY 11969.
    Description: Informs persons interested in the Shinnecock nation's annual gathering to promote understanding and goodwill.

970.1 US
POWHATAN NEWSPAPER. 1976. m. Powhatan Renape Nation, Box 225, Rancocus, NJ 08073. TEL 609-261-4747. Eds. Jack D. Forbes, Chief Roy Crazy Horse. circ. 12,000.
    Formerly: Powhatan Newsletter.

940 GW ISSN 0344-7006
PRAGER NACHRICHTEN. 1950. bi-m. DM.40. Marie Hermerle Verlag, Abt. Prager Nachrichten, Schuberstr. 8a, 85591 Vaterstetten, Germany. Ed. Rudolf Hemmerle. circ. 1,200.

943.7 XR ISSN 0139-8792
PRAGER VOLKSZEITUNG. (Text in German) 1951. w. 78 Kcs.($26.40) Svaz Nemcu, Kulturni Sdruzeni v Ceske Republice - Union of Germans, Cultural Association in the Czech Repulbic, Krymska 12, 101 00 Prague 10, Czech Republic. (Dist. by: Artia, Ve Smeckach 30, 111 27 Prague 1, Czech Republic) Ed. Uwe Muller. circ. 17,000.
    Formerly: Aufbau und Frieden.
    Description: Covers German interests.

914.6 CN
PREGONERO HISPANO. bi-m. Can.$12. 344 Bloor St. W., Ste.609, Toronto, Ont. M5S 1W9, Canada. TEL 416-962-8811. circ. 5,000.

917.306 US ISSN 0738-9183
LA PRENSA SAN DIEGO. (Text in English, Spanish) 1976. w. $36. La Prensa Munoz Inc., 1950 Fifth Ave., Stes. 1-3, San Diego, CA 92101. TEL 619-231-2873. FAX 619-231-9180. Ed. Daniel H. Munoz, Jr. adv.; bk.rev. circ. 20,000. **Document type:** newspaper.

910.03 CK
PRESENCIA NEGRA. 1977. m. $50. Centro para la Investigacion de la Cultura Negra, Carrera 20 No. 44-20, Apdo. Aereo 2363, Bogota, Colombia. Ed. Amir Smith Cordoba. adv. circ. 10,000. (also avail. in microfiche)
    Formerly: Negritud.
    Description: Covers Black interests.

970.1 CN
PRESS INDEPENDENT. 1971. w. Can.$32.10($30) (US Can.$50, elsewhere Can.$75). D M Communications Ltd., P.O. Box 1919, Yellowknife, N.W.T. X1A 2P4, Canada. TEL 403-873-2661. FAX 403-920-4205. Ed. Lee Selleck. adv.; bk.rev.; music rev.; video rev.; illus. circ. 5,600. (tabloid format; also avail. in microfilm from MML; back issues avail.)
    Formerly: Native Press (ISSN 0833-093X)
    Description: News and features from the Western Northwest Territories, especially of interest to the Indian and Metis community.

296 US
▼**PRIME TIME ADVOCATE.** 1993. m. $15. First Coast Media Group, Inc., 8301 Cypress Plaza Dr., Ste. 124, Jacksonville, FL 32256. TEL 904-281-0888. FAX 905-281-0922. Ed. Lester N. Garripee. circ. 22,000. (tabloid format) **Document type:** newspaper.

296 320.9 CN
PROFILE OF JEWISH DISSIDENTS SERIES. irreg. price varies. Dawn Publishing Co. Ltd., 17 Anselme Lavigne Blvd., Dollard des Ormeaux, Montreal, Que. H9A 1N3, Canada.

917.306 US ISSN 0749-3126
I PROINI. English edition: GreekAmerican. (Text in Greek) d. $112. Petallides Publishing, Inc., 25-50 Crescent St., Astoria, NY 11102. TEL 718-626-7676. FAX 718-267-1112. Ed. Ioannia Farmakis. adv. contact: Dimy Chrissanithou. **Document type:** newspaper.

ETHNIC INTERESTS   2505

971.3   CN
PROJECTION (MONTREAL). (Text in English and French) 1974. m. free. Employment and Immigration Canada, Public Affairs, 1441 St-Urbaine St., 8th Fl., Montreal, Que. H2X 2M6, Canada. TEL 514-283-4695. bk.rev.
 Formerly: Kaleidoscope Canada (ISSN 0707-8897)

917.309   US   ISSN 0033-1090
PROMIEN. (Text in English and Polish) 1970. q. Polish National Alliance of North America, Sports Youth Commission, 6100 N. Cicero Ave., Chicago, IL 60646-4385. Ed. Rich Piasecki. adv. contact: Bogdan Mazur. charts; illus. **Document type:** newspaper.
 Description: Covers Polish interests.

917.106 301.412   CN   ISSN 0380-2140
PROMIN. (Text in English, Ukrainian) 1960. m. Can.$17 (typically set in Jan.). Ukrainian Women's Association of Canada, 612 24th St. E., Saskatoon, Sask. S7K 0L1, Canada. TEL 306-244-1188. FAX 204-586-3618. Ed. Olena Hryn. adv. circ. 2,350.
 Description: Serves as a communication link for Ukrainian women throughout the world.

PROSPECTS; an annual of American cultural studies. see HISTORY — History Of North And South America

017.306   US
PROSVETA. (Text in English, Slovene) 1906. w. $16. Slovene National Benefit Society, 247 W. Allegheny Rd., Imperial, PA 15126-9726. TEL 412-695-1100. Ed. Jay Sedmak. circ. 21,000. **Document type:** newspaper.
 Description: Provides fraternal and cultural news to members of the organization.

970.1   US   ISSN 0048-5632
PROUD. 1970. q. $3.50. Proud, Inc., 625 N. Euclid Ave., No. 200, St. Louis, MO 63108-1605. Ed. Betty J. Lee. adv.; bk.rev. circ. 20,000. (tabloid format)
 Description: Covers Black interests.

PROVIDENT BOOK FINDER. see RELIGIONS AND THEOLOGY — Protestant

943.806   GW   ISSN 0179-2636
PRZEGLAD TYGODNIA; polski magazyn informacyjny. (Text in Polish) 1983. m. DM.30. P T Verlag GmbH, Landgraf Phillip Str. 57, 60431 Frankfurt a.M., Germany. TEL 069-562037. FAX 069-562027. TELEX 4175833-PTF-D. Ed. Wieslaw Bicz. adv.; bk.rev.; film rev.; play rev. circ. 5,000. (back issues avail.)

910.03   US
PUBLIC POST. 1981. w. $10. Roosevelt McPherson, Ed. & Pub., 122 W. Elmwood Ave., Box 1093, Raeford, NC 28376. TEL 919-875-8938. adv. **Document type:** newspaper.
 Description: Community news with a Black orientation.

956.906   CN
▼**QALAM**. (Text in English) 1992. 4/yr. Can.$10 (foreign Can.$160). Qalam International Inc., 42 Rosepac Ave., Brampton, ON L6Z 2S4, Canada. TEL 905-840-6778. FAX 905-840-6778. Ed. Khizar Hayat. adv.: B&W page Can.$1200, color page Can.$2000; trim 8 1/2 x 11. circ. 8,000.

917.306   US
QUE PASA FLORIDA GULF COAST. (Text in Spanish) 1991. m. free. Que Pasa Publishing Co., 1828 S.E. 13th Terrace., Cape Coral, FL 33990. TEL 813-574-9365. FAX 813-574-9365. Ed. Matha C. Hill; Pub. Martha C. Hill. adv.: B&W page $450; trim 8 1/2 x 11. circ. 10,000. **Document type:** consumer publication.
 Description: Covers current events in the U.S. and Latin America for a Hispanic audience. Includes interviews and educational materials of interest to all ages.

QUEBECER. see POLITICAL SCIENCE

QUINAULT NATURAL RESOURCES. see CONSERVATION

R M S NEWS. (Regional Multilanguage Services) see LIBRARY AND INFORMATION SCIENCES

RACHNA. see LITERARY AND POLITICAL REVIEWS

RAFT; a journal of Armenian poetry and criticism. see LITERATURE — Poetry

917.306   US
RAFU SHIMPO. (Annual supplement avail.) (Text in English, Japanese) 1903. d. $60. Rafu Shimpo, 259 S. Los Angeles St., Los Angeles, CA 90012. TEL 213-629-2231. FAX 213-687-0737. Ed. Naomi Hirahara. adv.; bk.rev.; circ. 24,000 (paid). **Document type:** newspaper.
 Description: For the Japanese American community.

296   SP   ISSN 0212-6753
RAICES; revista judia de cultura. 1986. q. 4800 ptas. (Europe 7200 ptas.; America 8000 ptas.; elsewhere 9600 ptas.). Sefarad Editores, Neila, 6, 28230 Las Rozas (Madrid), Spain. TEL 91-637-5365. Dir. Horacio Kohan. adv.: B&W 100000 ptas., color page 160000 ptas.; trim 180 x 262. bk.rev. circ. 4,500. **Document type:** academic/scholarly publication.
 Description: Provides opinion, analysis, and information on Jewish culture.

948   US   ISSN 1059-4779
RAIVAAJA/PIONEER. (Text in English and Finnish) 1905. w. $23. (Finnish American League for Democracy) Raivaaja Publishing Co., 147 Elm St., Box 600, Fitchburg, MA 01420. TEL 508-343-3822. FAX 508-343-1007. Ed. Marita Cautnen. adv.; bk.rev. circ. 2,100. (also avail. in microfilm; back issues avail.) **Document type:** newspaper.
 Description: Covers activities of the Finnish American community.

296 948   DK   ISSN 0907-2160
DS135.D4
RAMBAM. 1980. q. DKK 75. (Selskabet for Dansk Joedisk Historie) C.A. Reitzel AS, Noerregade 20, DK-1165 Copenhagen K, Denmark. Ed. Bent Bludnikow. bk.rev.; illus. circ. 500.
 Former titles (until 1991): Tidsskrift for Dansk Joedisk Historie (ISSN 0904-8073); (until 1988): Dansk Joedisk Historie (ISSN 0107-6418)

RAMPANT LION. see HISTORY — History Of Europe

RAVI; Asian newspaper. see LITERARY AND POLITICAL REVIEWS

970.1   US   ISSN 0300-6328
RAWHIDE PRESS. 1969? m. $10. Spokane Tribe of Indians, Spokane Tribal Business Council, Box 373, Wellpinit, WA 99040. TEL 509-258-4581. Ed. Mary L. Wynne. adv.; illus. circ. 1,400. (tabloid format; also avail. in microfilm from MCA)
 Description: Covers American Indian interests.

949.17   XV
RAZPRAVE IN GRADIVO/TREATISES AND DOCUMENTS. (Text mainly in Slovenian; summaries and abstracts in English, German, Italian) 1960. s-a. $5. Institut za Narodnostna Vprasanja - Institute for Ethnic Studies, Erjavceva 26, 61000 Ljubljana, Slovenia. TEL 061-210-879. FAX 061-210-964. Ed. Miran Komac. adv. circ. 1,000. Indexed: Amer.Hist.& Life, Hist.Abstr.
 Former titles (nos.20, 21).: Journal of Ethnic Studies - Treatises and Documents; Razprave in Gradivo - Treatises and Documents (ISSN 0034-0251)

910.03   US   ISSN 1049-1392
E185.5
RECONSTRUCTION. 1990. q. $25 to individuals; institutions $40. New Departure, 1563 Massachusetts Ave., Cambridge, MA 02138. TEL 617-495-0907. FAX 617-496-5515. Ed. Randall Kennedy. adv.; bk.rev.; illus.
 —UnCover.

LA RED - THE NET. see EDUCATION — Higher Education

LA RED - THE NET HOTLINE; the Hispanic journal of education, commentary, and reviews. see EDUCATION — Higher Education

970.1   US
REFERENCE ENCYCLOPEDIA OF THE AMERICAN INDIAN. biennial. $59.50 paper; cloth $125. Todd Publications, 18 N. Greenbush Rd., W. Nyack, NY 10994. TEL 914-358-6213. Ed. Barry Klein. circ. 5,000. **Document type:** directory.

REFORMA NEWSLETTER. see LIBRARY AND INFORMATION SCIENCES

974.8   US   ISSN 0034-3269
F160.G3
DER REGGEBOGE/RAINBOW. 1967. a. $40 to individuals; institutions $50 (includes Es Elbedritsch newsletter & Annual Volume). Pennsylvania German Society, Box 397, Birdsboro, PA 19508. TEL 215-582-1441. Eds. Dr. Don Yoder, Rev. Willard Wetzel. bk.rev.; illus. circ. 2,000.
 —Faxon.
 Description: Covers Pennsylvania Dutch history, culture and folklore.

960   US   ISSN 0360-7410
E185.5
RENAISSANCE TWO; journal of Afro-American studies. Key Title: Renaissance 2. 1972. a. $3.50. Yale University, Afro-American Cultural Center, 211 Park St., New Haven, CT 06520. TEL 203-436-8700. adv.; bk.rev.; illus. circ. 10,000.

917.106   CN   ISSN 0709-9487
RENCONTRE. English edition (ISSN 0709-9495) (Text in French) 1979. q. free. Secretariat aux Affaires Autochtones, 875 Grande Allee est, Ed. H, 2e etage, Quebec, PQ G1R 4Y8, Canada. TEL 418-643-3166. FAX 418-646-4918. Ed. Gilles Chaumel. bk.rev. circ. 43,500. (back issues avail.) **Document type:** government publication.
 Description: Provides news and comments, government information and information on available programs to Quebec's Amerindian and Inuit population.

917.106   CN   ISSN 0708-1510
HS1841
REPERTOIRE DE LA VIE FRANCAISE EN AMERIQUE. 1965. a. Can.$35($41.50) Conseil de la Vie Francaise en Amerique, 56 rue St. Pierre, 1er etage, Quebec, PQ G1K 4A1, Canada. TEL 418-692-1150. circ. 600.
 Description: Lists provincial, national and international organizations with francophone liasons.

917.106   CN   ISSN 0849-0449
F1035.A1
REPERTOIRE ETHNOCULTUREL DU CANADA. 1990. biennial. Monchanin Cross-Cultural Centre, 4917 St. Urbain St., Montreal, PQ H2T 2W1, Canada.

917.306   US
REPLICA. (Text in Spanish) 1970. m. $2 per no. Replica Publishing, Inc., 2994 N.W. Seventh St., Miami, FL 33125. TEL 305-643-5481. FAX 305-541-7410. Ed. Max Edgardo Lesnick. adv. circ. 109,026.
 Description: Promotes Hispanic culture, heritage and language. Covers Hispanic art, literature and business.

918.206   AG
REPUBLICA HRVATSKA/REPUBLICA CROATA. (Text mainly in Croatian) 1951. q. $16. Croatian Republican Party, Casilla de Correo 2959, Buenos Aires, Argentina. FAX 541-305869. TELEX 25602 KORSKY AR. Ed. Carlos Juan L. Korsky. bk.rev.; charts. circ. 2,000.

RESEARCH IN AFRICAN LITERATURES. see LITERATURE

RESEARCH IN RELIGION AND FAMILY: BLACK PERSPECTIVES. see RELIGIONS AND THEOLOGY

301.45   BL
RESENHA JUDAICA. 1970. fortn. $20. Empresa Jornalistica Resenha Judaica Ltda., Rua Cacapava 49, 13o, 01408 Sao Paulo, Brazil. TEL 55-11-64-2537. FAX 55-11-853-9179. Ed. Oscar Nimitz. adv.; bk.rev.; illus. circ. 45,000. (also avail. in microfilm from AJP).
 Description: Information about the Jewish community in Brazil. Includes items of general interest.

296   US   ISSN 1055-3703
RESPONSE (LOS ANGELES). q. Simon Wiesenthal Center, 9760 W. Pico Blvd., Los Angeles, CA 90035. TEL 310-553-9036.

ETHNIC INTERESTS

296 US ISSN 0034-5709
BM1
RESPONSE (NEW YORK, 1967); a contemporary Jewish review. 1967. q. $16. 27 W. 20th St., 9th Fl., New York, NY 10011-3707. TEL 212-675-1168. FAX 212-929-3459. Ed. Adam Margolis. adv.; bk.rev.; illus. circ. 1,500. (tabloid format; also avail. in microform from UMI; back issues avail.) **Indexed**: A.I.P.P., CERDIC, Ind.Jew.Per. —UMI.
Description: Contains articles of interest to the Jewish community.

052 930.1 UK
REVIEW OF SCOTTISH CULTURE. Cover title: R O S C. 1984. a. £10. Scotland Inheritance Fund, c/o National Museums of Scotland, York Bldgs., Queen St., Edinburgh EH2 1JD, Scotland. TEL 031-225-7534. (Co-sponsor: National Museums of Scotland) Ed. Alexander Fenton. bk.rev. circ. 1,000. (back issues avail.) **Document type**: academic/scholarly publication.
Description: Covers all aspects of Scottish ethnology at all social levels over the historical periods.

917.31 US
LA REVISTA. (Text in Spanish) no.26, Nov.1993. m. $18. Astoria Printing, 46-18 Broadway, Long Island City, NY 11103. TEL 718-626-7440. FAX 718-956-3258. Dir. Alejandro Vallejo. adv.

918.106 BL
REVISTA DE ESTUDOS IBERO-AMERICANOS. 1975. s-a. $15. Pontificia Universidade Catolica do Rio Grande do Sul, Pos-Graduacao em Historia da Cultura, c/o Nilo Berto, Editorial da PUCRS, Caixa Postal 1429, 90,000 Porto Alegre, Brazil. Dir. Braz Augusto Aquino Brancato. adv.; bk.rev. circ. 1,000. **Indexed**: Arts & Hum.Cit.Ind., Curr.Cont., M.L.A.
Formerly: Estudos Ibero-Americanos (ISSN 0101-4064)
Description: Covers Latin American studies.

REVISTA INTERNACIONAL DE ESTUDOS AFRICANOS. see *HISTORY — History Of Africa*

956 FR ISSN 0252-8290
DS119.7
REVUE D'ETUDES PALESTINIENNES. (Text in French) 1981. q. 250 F. (Institut des Etudes Palestiniennes) Editions de Minuit, 7 rue Bernard-Palissy, 75006 Paris, France. TEL 44-39-39-20. FAX 45-44-82-36. Ed. Elias Sanbar. **Indexed**: HR Rep.
Description: Provides an international forum for individuals engaged in the study of Palestinian affairs and the Arab-Israeli conflict and its peaceful resolution.

REVUE DES ETUDES JUIVES. see *RELIGIONS AND THEOLOGY — Judaic*

975.606 US ISSN 0890-9555
REVUE FRANCOPHONE DE LOUISIANE. 1986. s-a. $22 to individuals; institutions $25. University of Southwestern Louisiana, Conseil International d'Etudes Francophones, Box 43331, Lafayette, LA 70504. TEL 318-231-6811. FAX 318-231-5446. Ed. A. David Barry. bk.rev. circ. 450. (back issues avail.)
Refereed Serial

296 US
RHODE ISLAND HERALD. w. $10. Herald Way (off Webster St.), Pawtucket, RI 02861.
Description: Covers Jewish interests.

296 US ISSN 0556-8609
F90.J5
RHODE ISLAND JEWISH HISTORICAL NOTES. 1954. a. $20 (typically set in Oct.). Rhode Island Jewish Historical Association, 130 Sessions St., Providence, RI 02906. TEL 401-331-1360. Ed. Judith Weiss Cohen. bk.rev.; bibl.; charts; illus.; stat.; cum.index every 4 yrs. circ. 700. (processed) **Indexed**: Amer.Hist.& Life, Hist.Abstr.
Description: Articles on the history of Jews in Rhode Island.

051 US
RICHMOND AFRO-AMERICAN; and the Richmond Planet. 1882. w. $26. Afro-American Co. of Baltimore City, 628 N. Eutaw St., Baltimore, MD 21201. TEL 410-728-8200. FAX 804-649-8477. (Subscr. to: 214 E. Clay St., Richmond, VA 23219. TEL 804-649-8478) Ed. Lynda Sharp Anderson. adv.; bk.rev.; film rev.; illus. circ. 10,000. (also avail. in microform from UMI)
Description: Covers Black interests.

910.03 US
RICHMOND POST. 1970. 2/w. $80. Alameda Publishing Corp., Box 1350, Oakland, CA 94604. TEL 510-763-1120. FAX 510-763-9670. Ed. Tom Nash. circ. 13,654. **Document type**: newspaper.

790 US ISSN 0048-8305
RIGHT ON!. 1971. m. $20. Sterling - Macfadden Partnership, 233 Park Ave. S., New York, NY 10003. TEL 212-949-6850. FAX 212-986-5926. Ed. Cindy Horner. adv.; illus. circ. 300,000.

917.106 CN ISSN 0380-8416
RINCONTRO. (Text in Italian) 1971. m. Can.$9. 6675 Wilderton Ave., Montreal, Que. H3S 2L8, Canada. TEL 514-272-0344. Ed. Tony Vellone. adv. circ. 13,000. **Indexed**: M.L.A.
Description: Contains articles of interest to the Italian community.

051 US
ROANOKE TRIBUNE. 1939. w. $14 (effective 1993). Box 6021, Roanoke, VA 24017. TEL 703-343-0326. Ed. Claudia A. Whitworth. adv. circ. 5,000. **Document type**: newspaper.
Description: Contains items of interest to the Black community.

ROCHESTER MUSEUM AND SCIENCE CENTER. RESEARCH DIVISION. RESEARCH RECORDS. see *ARCHAEOLOGY*

910.03 US
ROCK HILLS BLACK VIEWS. 1982. w. $25. S C Black Media Group, 1310 Harden St., Columbia, SC 29204. TEL 803-799-5252. FAX 803-799-7709. Ed. Issac Washington. adv. contact: Melody Harris. illus. circ. 5,500. **Document type**: newspaper.

296 US
ROCKY MOUNTAIN JEWISH HISTORICAL NOTES. 1977. q. $30. (Rocky Mountain Jewish Historical Society) University of Denver, Department of Graphics, Center for Judaic Studies, Denver, CO 80208. TEL 303-871-2959. Ed. John Livingston. circ. 600. **Document type**: academic/scholarly publication.
Description: Covers Jewish historical interests in the Rocky Mountain area.

917.309 XV ISSN 0557-2282
AP58.S55
RODNA GRUDA; revija za Slovence po svetu. 1954. m. 15000 SLT($30) Slovenska Izseljenska Matica, Cankarjeva 1, Box 169, 61001 Ljubljana, Slovenia. FAX 38-61-210-732. Ed. Joze Preseren. adv.; bk.rev.; charts; illus. circ. 20,000.

ROLA BOZA/GOD'S FIELD. see *RELIGIONS AND THEOLOGY — Roman Catholic*

915.406 II
ROMA; journal of life, language and culture. (Supplements avail.) (Text in English) 1974. s-a. Rs.30 (US $20; Europe £10). Roma Publications, 3290, 15-D Chandigarh, Chandigarh 160 015, India. TEL 42891. Ed. W.R. Rishi. adv.; bk.rev. circ. 400. (back issues avail.)
Description: Examines the life, culture, and language of Roma, also known as the Gypsies of the world.

910.03 JM
ROOTS VIEW. q. Jam.$16($12) Xtract Art Ltd., P.O. Box 8057, C.S.O. Kingston, Jamaica, W.I. Ed. Janhoi M. Jaja.

ROUGH ROCK NEWS. see *EDUCATION*

947 GW ISSN 0557-4250
ROZHLAD. (Text in Sorbian) m. DM.36. Domowina Verlag GmbH, Tuchmacher-Str. 27, 02625 Bautzen, Germany. **Document type**: bulletin.

RUSSIA AND HER NEIGHBORS; facts and views on daily life. see *ANTHROPOLOGY*

947 US
RUSSIAN ARCHIVAL SERIES. 1982. irreg. $36 per issue. (Columbia University, Harriman Institute) Oriental Research Partners, Box 158, Newtonville, MA 02160. Ed. Leo Haimson.

057 US ISSN 0883-6639
RUSSIAN LIFE DAILY. (Text in Russian) 1921. d. (5/wk.). $90. Russian Life, Inc., 2458 Sutter St., San Francisco, CA 94115. TEL 415-921-5380. FAX 415-921-8726. Ed.Bd. adv. contact: Anna Zeltzer. bk.rev.; film rev.; play rev.; bibl. circ. 1,500. **Document type**: newspaper.
Description: Covers Russian interests.

917.306 US ISSN 0036-0406
RUSSKY GOLOS/RUSSIAN VOICE. 1917. w. $30. Russky Golos Publishing Corp., 130 E. 16th St., New York, NY 10003. TEL 212-475-7595. adv. circ. 3,000. (tabloid format) **Document type**: newspaper.

320 059.919 US ISSN 1062-9130
▼**S A L - NEWS**. 1992. q. American Latvian Association in the United States, Inc., Office of Support and Aid to Latvia, 400 Hurley Ave., Box 4578, Rockville, MD 20850. TEL 301-340-8174. FAX 301-340-8732.

914.706 US
S A Y N. (Slovak-American Youth News) 1980. m. (10/yr.). $12. Summit Impressions, Inc., Highway 36, Airport Plaza, Hazlet, NJ 07730. TEL 908-264-2324. Eds. Sue Tretina, Jan Tretina. adv.; illus.

S H P E NATIONAL NEWSLETTER. (Society of Hispanic Professional Engineers) see *ENGINEERING*

S I F C POWWOW TIMES. (Saskatchewan Indian Federated College) see *COLLEGE AND ALUMNI*

914 IT
SABATO SERA. w. L.40000. Viale Zappi, 58, Imola (BO), Italy. TEL 0542-31555. Ed. Giorgio Bettini. circ. 12,000.

917.309 US ISSN 0036-2212
SACRAMENTO OBSERVER. 1962. w. $35. William H. Lee, Ed. & Pub., 3540 Fourth Ave., Sacramento, CA 95801. TEL 916-452-4781. FAX 916-452-7744. adv.; bk.rev.; film rev.; bibl.; illus. circ. 49,600. (tabloid format; also avail. in microfilm from LIB) **Document type**: newspaper.
Description: Contains items of interest to the Black community.

SAGE: A SCHOLARLY JOURNAL ON BLACK WOMEN. see *WOMEN'S STUDIES*

910.03 US
ST. LOUIS CRUSADER. (Supplement avail. m.: Black Monitor) 1961. w. $26. 4371 Finney Ave., St. Louis, MO 63113. TEL 314-531-5860. Ed. Floyd Edmonds. adv. circ. 10,500. **Document type**: newspaper.

296 US ISSN 0036-2964
ST. LOUIS JEWISH LIGHT; the newspaper of the Jewish community of Greater St. Louis. (Text in English; occasionally in Hebrew and Yiddish) 1947. w. $36. (Jewish Federation of St. Louis) St. Louis Jewish Light, Inc., 12 Millstone Campus Dr., St. Louis, MO 63146. TEL 314-432-3353. FAX 314-432-0515. Ed. Robert A. Cohn. adv.; bk.rev. circ. 14,000. (tabloid format; also avail. in microfilm from AJP)

SALES WAYS. see *BUSINESS AND ECONOMICS — Marketing And Purchasing*

317.306 US
SALUDOS HISPANOS.* (Text in English, Spanish) 1984. q. Saludos Hispanicos, 41-550 Eclectic St.,Ste. 102, Palm Desert, CA 92260-1922. TEL 818-609-0511. FAX 818-992-7916. adv. circ. 300,000.
Description: Covers travel, news, personalities, sports, politics, social issues, community action, career options, personal finance, lifestyle and cooking.

917.306 US ISSN 0738-4467
SAMPAN; the only bilingual newspaper in New England serving the Asian community. (Text in Chinese, English) 1972. s-m. free. Chinese-American Civic Association, 90 Tyler St., Boston, MA 02111. TEL 617-426-9492. FAX 617-482-2315. Eds. Catherine Anderson, Carmen Chan. adv.; bk.rev. circ. 18,000. **Document type:** newspaper.
   Description: Covers news and issues concerning Asian-American residents of greater Boston, Massachusetts.

910.03 US
SAN ANTONIO REGISTER. 1931. w. $22. 235 St. Charles, San Antonio, TX 78296. TEL 210-222-1721. Ed. Ed Glosson. adv. contact: Cathy Little. circ. 7,800. **Document type:** newspaper.

296 US
SAN DIEGO JEWISH PRESS HERITAGE. 1914. w. $15. Heritage Publishing Co., 2130 S. Vermont Ave., Los Angeles, CA 90007. Ed. Dan Brin. adv.
   Description: Covers Jewish interests.

910.03 US
SAN FERNANDO NEWS OBSERVER. 1978. w. $35 in state; out of state $50. Observer Group Newspapers, Box 3624, Bakersfield, CA 93385. TEL 805-324-9466. FAX 805-324-9472. Ed. Joseph Coley. adv. contact: Ellen Cleek. circ. 10,500. **Document type:** newspaper.

910.03 US
SAN FRANCISCO POST. 1963. s-w. $80. Alameda Publishing Corp., 630 20th St., Oakland, CA 94612. TEL 510-763-1120. FAX 510-763-1120. Ed. Tom Berkley. adv. contact: Jeff Douvel. circ. 18,287. **Document type:** newspaper.

SAN YUE SAN. see *LITERATURE*

917.306 US ISSN 8750-2348
SANDARA/LEAGUE. 1918. m. $10. Lithuanian National League of America, Inc., 208 W. Natoma Ave., Box 241, Addison, IL 60601. TEL 708-543-8198. Ed. G.J. Lazauskas. adv.; bk.rev. circ. 1,200. (tabloid format) **Document type:** newspaper.
   Description: Covers Lithuanian interests.

917.306 US
SANGBAD BICHITRA. (Text in Bengali) 1971. 26/yr. (every 2 wks.). $15. Cultural Association of Bengal, 101 Iden Ave., Pelham Manor, NY 10803. TEL 914-738-5727. FAX 914-738-4775. Ed. Mira Das. adv.; bk.rev. circ. 1,000. **Document type:** newsletter.
   Description: News and literary articles concerning India and Bangladesh.

917.309 US
SANGER-HILSEN/SINGERS GREETINGS. (Text in English and Norwegian) 1910. bi-m. $5. Norwegian Singers Association of America, Inc., 10217 Pilgrim Ln. N., Maple Grove, MN 55369-2960. TEL 612-925-4658. Ed. Erling Stone.
   Description: Covers Norwegian interests.

917.306 US ISSN 0894-783X
SANTA ROSA NEWS. (Text in English, Spanish) 1924. w. $15 in Guadalupe County; outside Guadalupe County $20; elsewhere $35. Santa Rosa News, 108 Fifth St., P.O. Box Drawer F, Santa Rosa, NM 88435. TEL 505-472-5454. Ed. Darrel Freeman. circ. 2,200. (back issues avail.)

917.306 808.8 US ISSN 1059-5872
E184.P7
SARMATIAN REVIEW. 1981. 3/yr. $12 to individuals in the Americas (elsewhere $18); institutions $18 (elsewhere $24). Polish Institute of Arts and Science of America, Inc., Houston Circle, Box 79119, Houston, TX 77279. TEL 713-467-5836. FAX 713-467-6348. Ed. Ewa M. Thompson. adv.; bk.rev.; bibl.; illus. circ. 500. (back issues avail.) **Document type:** academic/scholarly publication.
   Formerly: Houston Sarmatian (ISSN 0892-1466)
   Description: Scholarly analysis and evaluation of Polish and Eastern European affairs and their implications for the United States.

970.1 CN ISSN 0048-9204
E75
SASKATCHEWAN INDIAN. 1970. m. Can.$12. Federation of Saskatchewan Indians, 1100 First Ave. E., Prince Albert, Sask. S6V 2A7, Canada. TEL 306-764-3411. Ed. Rod Andrews. adv.; bk.rev. circ. 11,000. (also avail. in microform from UMI)
   Description: Covers Canadian Indian interests.

970.1 CN ISSN 0828-3907
SASKATCHEWAN INDIAN FEDERATED COLLEGE JOURNAL. (Text mainly in English; occasionally in Cree, Ojibway) 1985. s-a. Can.$15($15) to individuals; institutions Can.$25($25). Saskatchewan Indian Federated College, University of Regina, 127 College West, Regina, Sask. S4S 0A2, Canada. TEL 306-779-6235. FAX 306-584-0955. Ed. Joel Demay. adv.; bk.rev. circ. 1,000. (back issues avail.)
   Description: Covers subjects of interest to professionals involved in native Indian issues.

914.706 CN
SATELLITE 1-416. (Text in Czech, English, Slovak) 1991. bi-w. Can.$22($30); newsstand price: Can.$1. P.O. Box 176, Sta. E, Toronto, ON M6H 4E2, Canada. Owner(s): ABE, 698 Ossington Ave., Toronto, ON M6G 3T7, Canada. TEL 416-530-4222. FAX 416-530-4222. Ed. Alej Brezina. adv. contact: Alej Brezina. illus. cols./p.: 4; pp./issue: 8. (tabloid format) **Document type:** newspaper.

910.03 US
SAVANNAH HERALD. 1945. w. $15.90 in state; out-of-state $18.02. Herald of Savannah, 1803 Barnard St., Savannah, GA 31401. TEL 912-232-4505. FAX 912-232-4079. Ed. Floyd Adams, Jr. adv. contact: Floyd Adams Jr. circ. 8,000. (tabloid format) **Document type:** newspaper.

917.306 US
SAVANNAH JEWISH NEWS. 1949. m. $18. Savannah Jewish Federation, 5111 Abercorn St., Box 23527, Savannah, GA 31403. TEL 912-355-8111. Ed. Midge Lasky Schildkraut. adv. circ. 1,800. (tabloid format; also avail. in microfilm from AJP; back issues avail.)
   Formerly: Savannah Jewish Law.

910.03 US
SAVANNAH TRIBUNE. 1875. w. $18 in state; out of state $20. 916 Montgomery St., Savannah, GA 31402. TEL 912-233-6128. Ed. Shirley B. James. adv.; bk.rev. circ. 8,000. **Document type:** newspaper.

370 US ISSN 0036-5467
SCAN (NEW YORK). 1952. 4/yr. membership. American-Scandinavian Foundation, 725 Park Ave., New York, NY 10021. TEL 212-879-9779. FAX 212-249-3444. TELEX 661553WUI. circ. 3,500. (reprint service avail. from UMI) **Document type:** consumer publication.
   Description: Covers foundation events, as well as general news items from Scandinavia.

917.306 US ISSN 0048-9263
SCANDINAVIAN - AMERICAN BULLETIN. 1956. bi-m. $10. Erik J. Friis, Ed.& Pub., 481 81st St., Brooklyn, NY 11209. adv.; bk.rev.; illus. circ. 1,000.
   Description: Contains articles of interest to the Scandinavian community.

914.8 CN ISSN 0836-2149
SCANDINAVIAN FORUM. 1985-1993; suspended. q. Can.$23.54 to individuals (foreign Can.$28); institutions Can.$37.45 (foreign Can.$38). E. Terp Enterprises, Inc., 54 Lesgay Cres., Willowdale, ON M2J 2J1, Canada. TEL 416-495-8591. FAX 416-495-9289. circ. 2,500. **Document type:** consumer publication.

917.306 US ISSN 0098-857X
AP2
SCANDINAVIAN REVIEW. 1913. 3/yr. $15. American-Scandinavian Foundation, 725 Park Ave., New York, NY 10021. TEL 212-879-9779. FAX 212-249-3444. TELEX 661553 WUI. adv.; bk.rev.; film rev.; illus.; index. circ. 3,500. (also avail. in microform from UMI; microfiche; reprint service avail. from UMI) Indexed: M.L.A., P.A.I.S., Soc.Sci.Ind. **Document type:** consumer publication.
   —Faxon; UncOver; UMI.
   Formerly (until 1975): American Scandinavian Review (ISSN 0003-0910)
   Description: Covers culture, business, economics, and contemporary life in all Scandinavian countries.

914.806 US
SCANDINAVIAN STUDIES (LEWISTON). irreg., latest no.2. Edwin Mellen Press, 415 Ridge St., Box 450, Lewiston, NY 14092. TEL 716-754-2788. FAX 716-754-4056. **Indexed:** Bibl.Ling. **Document type:** monographic series.

910.03 US
SCHREVEPORT SUN. 1920. w. $20.60 in state; out of state $25. Shreveport Sun, Inc., 2224 Juvella Ave., Box 38357, Shreveport, LA 71109. TEL 318-631-6222. Ed. Sonya Collins Landry. adv. contact: Ron Collins. circ. 5,900. **Document type:** newspaper.

917.306 US ISSN 0273-0693
DA750
SCOTIA; interdisciplinary journal of Scottish studies. 1977. a. $10. Old Dominion University, Department of History, Arts and Letters Building, Norfolk, VA 23529. TEL 804-683-3933. FAX 804-683-3241. Ed. William S. Rodner. adv.; bk.rev. circ. 250. **Document type:** academic/scholarly publication.
   Supersedes in 1976: Conference on Scottish Studies. Proceedings.

941.206 UK ISSN 1350-7508
▼**SCOTLANDS;** the interdisciplinary journal of Scottish culture. 1994. s-a. £20($38.50) Edinburgh University Press, 22 George Sq., Edinburgh EH8 9LF, Scotland. TEL 031-650-4218. FAX 031-662-0053. Ed. Christopher MacLachlan. adv. contact: Kathryn MacLean. circ. 500. **Document type:** academic/scholarly publication.
   Description: Publishes articles and essays celebrating the richness of Scottish culture found in literature, history, music, art, film and television.
   Refereed Serial

917.106 US
SCOTTISH BANNER. 1978. m. $18 (Canada $19) (effective 1993). Scottish Banner Publications, Inc., 755 Center St., Lewiston, NY 14092. TEL 800-729-8950. FAX 716-754-9020. Ed. Valerie Cairney. adv. circ. 81,000. (also avail. in microfilm from CML,UMI; back issues avail.) **Document type:** newspaper.
   Incorporates: Scottish American.

910.03 US
SEATTLE MEDIUM. 1970. w. $20. Tiloben Publishing Co., Box 22047, Seattle, WA 98122. TEL 206-627-1103. Ed. Christopher Bennett. adv. contact: Joan Owens. circ. 50,000. **Document type:** newspaper.

910.03 US
SEATTLE NORTHWEST FACTS. 1961. w. $52. 2765 E. Cherry, Seattle, WA 98122. TEL 206-324-1007. FAX 206-324-1007. Ed. Elizabeth Beaver. circ. 50,000. **Document type:** newspaper.

917.306 US
SEATTLE SKANNER. w. $25. I.M.M. Publications, Inc., Box 5455, 2337 N. Williams, Portland, OR 97228. TEL 503-287-3562. (And: 1326 Fifth Ave., Ste. 825, Seattle, WA 98101) Pub. Bobbie Dore Foster. **Document type:** newspaper.
   Formerly: Skanner Newspaper.

SEFARAD; revista de estudios Hebraicos, Sefardies y de Oriente Proximo. see *HISTORY — History Of The Near East*

915.106 CN
SEI PING MONTHLY. (Text in Chinese) m. Richmond Review, 507-13231 Delf Pl., Richmond, BC V6V 2A2, Canada. TEL 604-273-7744. FAX 604-273-5272. adv. contact: Ken Simms. circ. 8,000. (tabloid format) **Document type:** newspaper.

SEIPONE. see *GENERAL INTEREST PERIODICALS — South Africa*

SEMANA INTERNACIONAL DE ANTROPOLOGIA VASCA. ACTAS. see *ANTHROPOLOGY*

ETHNIC INTERESTS

296   AG   ISSN 0037-1858
SEMANARIO ISRAELITA; unabhaengiges juedisches Wochenblatt. (Text in German and Spanish) 1969. fortn. $25. Editorial Semanario Israelita, Pasteur 341, 1028 Buenos Aires, Argentina. FAX 541-325-6965. Ed. Werner M. Finkelstein. adv.; bk.rev.; film rev.; play rev.; abstr.; bibl. circ. 5,000. (tabloid format) **Document type:** newspaper.
    Formerly: Semana Israelita.
    Description: Contains items of interest to the Jewish community.

970.1   US   ISSN 0891-8252
SEMINOLE TRIBUNE. 1973. fortn. $15. (Seminole Tribal Council) Seminole Tribe of Florida, 6333 N.W. 30th St., Hollywood, FL 33024. FAX 305-983-4205. Ed. Twila Perkins. adv.; bk.rev. circ. 5,000. **Document type:** newspaper.
    Formerly: Alligator Times.

910.03   US
SENTINEL (SEASIDE). 1946. w. $58. Box 1309, Seaside, CA 93955. TEL 408-899-2305. FAX 408-394-8401. Ed. David Bennett. adv. contact: Jono Spaulding. bk.rev.; illus. circ. 10,000. **Document type:** newspaper.

970.1   US
SENTINEL: BULLETIN - N C A I NEWS.* vol.31, 1975. m. $15. National Congress of American Indians, 900 Pennsylvania Ave., Washington, DC 20003. TEL 202-546-9404. adv.; bk.rev.; bibl.; illus. circ. 4,000.
    Former titles: National Congress of American Indians. Bulletin (ISSN 0047-8784); N.C.A.I. News Bulletin (ISSN 0466-1761)
    Description: Covers American Indian interests.

892.49 956.94   US
SEPHARDIC SCHOLAR. 1973. a. $15. (American Society of Sephardic Studies) Yeshiva University, Sephardic Studies Program, 500 W. 185th St., New York, NY 10033. TEL 212-960-5277. Ed. D. Attabe. bk.rev. circ. 5,000.
    Formerly (until 197?): American Society of Sephardic Studies Series.

917.306   US   ISSN 8756-5579
DR1955
SERB WORLD U.S.A.. 1979. bi-m. $19.50. Serb World U.S.A., Inc., 415 E. Mabel, Tucson, AZ 85705. TEL 602-624-4887. Ed. Mary Nicklanovich Hart. adv.; bk.rev.; film rev.; bibl.; circ. 4,000 (paid). **Indexed:** Amer.Bibl.Slavic & E.Eur.Stud. **Document type:** consumer publication.
    Formerly: Serb World.
    Description: Covers Serbian-American cultural and historical interests.

917.606   US   ISSN 0279-1293
SERBIAN STRUGGLE/SRPSKA BORBA. (Text in Serbian) 1946. m. $30. Serbian Literary Association, Box 14, Little Neck Sta., Flushing, NY 11363. TEL 718-229-8973. FAX 718-331-1365. Ed. Budimir D. Sreckovich. adv.; bk.rev. circ. 2,500. (tabloid format) **Document type:** newspaper.
    Description: Contains items of interest to the Serbian community.

325   AT
SERBIAN STRUGGLE. (Australian Edition) 1946. w. Aus.$15. Serbian Cultural Club "St. Sava" in New South Wales, Box 183, Cabramatta, N.S.W. 2166, Australia. Ed. S. Draskovic. adv.; bk.rev. circ. 450.
    Description: Covers Serbian interests.

SERIE DE VOCABULARIOS Y DICCIONARIOS INDIGENAS "MARIANO SILVA Y ACEVES". see LINGUISTICS

917.2 810   US   ISSN 0190-3640
SEZ; a multi-racial journal of poetry & people's culture. (Text in English and Spanish) 1978. irreg. $7 to individuals; institutions $8.50. Shadow Press, U.S.A., Box 8803, Minneapolis, MN 55408. TEL 612-822-3488. Ed. Jim Dochniak. adv.; bk.rev.; bibl.; illus. circ. 1,500. (back issues avail.)

200   US   ISSN 0270-9368
SHAKER MESSENGER. 1978. q. $14. World of Shaker, Box 1645, Holland, MI 49422-1645. TEL 616-396-4588. Ed. Diana Van Kolken. adv.; bk.rev.; charts; illus.; cum.index every 10 yrs. circ. 1,000. (back issues avail.) **Document type:** academic/scholarly publication.
    Supersedes: World of Shaker.
    Description: Devoted to information about the Shakers and the Shaker life-style, past and present, and persons involved with or interested in the Shaker heritage.

296   IT   ISSN 0037-3265
SHALOM. 1967. m. L.70000 to non-members (foreign L.140000). Comunita Ebraica di Roma, Lungotevere Cenci, 00186 Rome, Italy. TEL 06-6876816. FAX 02-6876816. Ed. Lia Levi. adv.; bk.rev.; film rev.; illus. circ. 10,000. (tabloid format)
    Formerly: Voce della Comunita.

SHALOM; Jewish peace letter. see POLITICAL SCIENCE — Civil Rights

296   BL
SHALOM. (Text in Portuguese) vol.7, 1971. m. Cr.$1000. Editora Shalom Ltda., R. da Graca 201, 7 Andar, 01125 Sao Paulo, Brazil. Ed. Patricia Finzi Fingermann. adv.; bk.rev.; charts; illus. circ. 10,000.
    Description: Contains articles of interest to the Jewish community.

296 028.5   BL
SHALOM INFANTIL. 1976. Cr.$20 per no. Editora Shalom Ltda, Rua da Graca 201, 01125 Sao Paulo, 7 andar, Brazil. Ed. Eveline Alperowitch.
    Description: Covers Jewish interests.

296   CN   ISSN 0827-4916
SHALOM MAGAZINE. 1975. q. Can.$25. (Atlantic Jewish Council) Kaleidoscope Publishing, 475 Windmill Rd., Ste. 200, Dartmouth, NS B3B 1B2, Canada. TEL 902-468-2920. FAX 902-468-2858. Ed. Edwin Rubin. bk.rev. circ. 1,400. **Document type:** newsletter.
    Description: Presents local, national and international news relating to the Jewish community.

915.4   CN
SHAMA. (Text in Urdu) 1980. m. Can.$45. Urdu Promotion Board, P.O. Box 1061, Sta. B, Mississauga, Ont. L4Y 2E0, Canada. TEL 416-858-7525. FAX 416-858-7951. Ed. Alia Sultana. circ. 5,000. (tabloid format; back issues avail.)
    Description: Contains news, fiction and poetry.

SHAMAN'S DRUM; a journal of experiential Shamanism. see ANTHROPOLOGY

910.03   CN
SHARE. w. Can.$135. Arnold A. Auguste Associates Ltd., 1554 A Eglinton Ave. W., Toronto, ON M6E 2G8, Canada. TEL 416-789-0691. FAX 416-789-0696. Pub. Arnold A. Auguste. circ. 42,800.

SHEKEL. see NUMISMATICS

970.1   US
SHENANDOAH NEWSLETTER. 1973. m. $13.50 to individuals; institutions $18.50. Shenandoah, 736 W. Oklahoma St., Appleton, WI 54914. TEL 414-832-9525. Ed. Paul A. Sken Doa. bk.rev.; charts; illus.; stat. circ. 1,000. **Document type:** newsletter.
    Description: Presents information for Native American Indians to gain national or sovereign rights for all Native peoples in the land known as the Great Turtle Island (North America).

917.306   CN
SHING WAH NEWS. (Text in Chinese) 1922. m. Can.$12. Shing Wah Association, 793-795 Gerrard St. E., Toronto, Ont. M4M 1Y5, Canada. TEL 416-778-1854. Ed. Sang Yee. circ. 10,000.
    Formerly: Shing Wah Daily News.

296   US   ISSN 0049-0385
SH'MA; a journal of Jewish responsibility. 1970. 20/yr. $18. Sh'ma Inc., 99 Park Ave., Ste. S-300, New York, NY 10016. TEL 212-867-8888. FAX 212-867-8853. Ed. Nina Beth Cardin. bk.rev.; cum.index. circ. 6,784. (also avail. in microform from UMI; reprint service avail. from UMI)
    —UMI.

296   IS
SHMA YISRAEL;* a magazine of Jewish thought and culture. (Text in English) 1974. q. $1.25 per. no. Ohr Somayach Institutions, Joseph and Faye Tanenbaum College of Judaic Studies, P.O.B. 15014, 76 Shmuel Hanavi-3 Tidhar Sts., Jerusalem, Israel. Ed. Nota Schiller. adv.; bk.rev.; illus. circ. 10,000.

SHOFAR (MENVILLE). see CHILDREN AND YOUTH — For

SHOFAR (WASHINGTON); the high school Jewish newspaper. see CLUBS

960 917.306   US   ISSN 0892-1407
PS508.N3
SHOOTING STAR REVIEW; Black literary magazine. 1987. q. $12 to individuals; institutions $15. Sandra Gould Ford, Ed. & Pub., 7123 Race St., Pittsburgh, PA 15208. TEL 412-731-7464. adv.; bk.rev. circ. 1,500.
    Description: Employs the arts to build an awareness and appreciation of the Black experience.

SHUPIHUI. see RELIGIONS AND THEOLOGY

296   IS
SHVUT; Jewish problems in the USSR and Eastern Europe. (Text in Hebrew; summaries in English) 1973. irreg., vol.16, 1992. $15. Tel Aviv University, Diaspora Research Institute, c/o Publication Department, 69978 Ramat Aviv, Israel. FAX 972-3-6409648. TELEX 342171-VERSY-IL. Ed. M. Minc. bk.rev. circ. 1,500. **Indexed:** Amer.Hist.& Life, Hist.Abstr., Ind.Heb.Per. **Document type:** academic/scholarly publication.

SIDA; todo lo que usted debe saber. see MEDICAL SCIENCES — Communicable Diseases

970.1   CN
SIGNES DES AMERIQUES. irreg. price varies. Societe de Recherches Amerindiennes au Quebec, 6742 rue St-Denis, Montreal, PQ H2S 2S2, Canada. TEL 514-277-6178. **Document type:** monographic series.

915.106   CN
SING PAO DAILY NEWS. (Text in Chinese) 1968. d. Can.$17.75. Overseas Chinese Newspapers Sales (Ontario) Inc., 200 Sparks Ave., North York, ON M2H 2S4, Canada. TEL 416-490-8888. FAX 416-490-0819. Ed. Henry Liu. adv.; B&W page Can.$800, color page Can.$1800; trim 15 x 22. (broadsheet format) **Document type:** newspaper.

917.106   CN
SING TAO JIH PAO. (Text in Chinese) d. Sing Tao Newspaper (Canada), 549 Main St., Vancouver, B.C. V6A 2V1, Canada. TEL 604-669-9133. FAX 604-662-8663. Ed. Paul Tsang. circ. 15,000.

943 320 323.4   IT
SKUPNOST; glasilo slovenske skupnosti. (Text in Slovenian) 1977. m. L.10000 (effective 1994). Slovenska Skupnost - Unione Slovena, Via Machiavelli 22, 34132 Trieste, Italy. TEL 040-639126. circ. 5,000 (controlled). (tabloid format; back issues avail.)

SLAVICA HIEROSOLYMITANA; Slavic studies of the Hebrew University. see LINGUISTICS

282   US
SLOVAK CATHOLIC FALCON. 1911. w. $20. Slovak Catholic Sokol, 205 Madison St., Passaic, NJ 07055. TEL 201-777-4010. FAX 201-779-8245. Ed. Daniel F. Tanzone. bk.rev.; illus. circ. 10,000. **Document type:** newspaper.
    Formerly: Katolicky Sokol.

917.309   US   ISSN 0037-6914
SLOVAK PRESS DIGEST.* 1968. irreg. free. Slovak-American Cultural Center, 202-19 36th Ave., Bayside, NY 11361. Ed. Jozef Ihnat. bk.rev.; abstr.; bibl.; stat.; tr.lit. circ. 500. (looseleaf format)

366 325   AT
SLOVAK SHIELD. (Text in Slovak) 1950. m. Aus.$15. Association of Australian Slovaks, Box 273, Sydney, N.S.W. 2001, Australia. Ed. Ivan Hupka. adv.; bk.rev. circ. 500.

917.406   US
SLOVAK V AMERIKE/SLOVAK AMERICAN. (Text in Slovak) 1889. m. $20 (foreign $30). Slovak-American Publishing, Inc., 1414 Main Ave., Clifton, NJ 07011. FAX 201-812-0554. Ed. John A. Holy. adv.; bk.rev. circ. 1,200. (tabloid format; also avail. in microfilm)

943.7   US   ISSN 0583-5623
DB661
SLOVAKIA. 1951. a. $6 softbound; hardbound $8. Slovak League of America, 870 Rifle Camp Rd., W. Paterson, NJ 07424. Ed. Mark Stolarik. bk.rev.; bibl. circ. 1,500. (also avail. in microform from UMI; reprint service avail. from UMI) **Indexed:** Amer.Bibl.Slavic & E.Eur.Stud., Amer.Hist.& Life, Hist.Abstr., M.L.A. **Document type:** academic/scholarly publication.
—BLDSC (8309.566000); Faxon; UMI.
Description: Scholarly publication devoted to the history, literature, and culture of Slovaks worldwide.

SLOVANSKE STUDIE. see HISTORY — History Of Europe

914.506   IT
SLOVENI IN ITALIA. s-m. Via dei Montecchi, 6, Trieste 34137, Italy.
Formerly: Bollettino d'Informazione degli Sloveni in Italia.

949.7   XV   ISSN 0353-118X
SLOVENIJA. 1987. q. $20. Slovenska Izseljenska Matica - Slovene Emigrant Association, Cankarjeva 1, 61001 Ljubljana, Slovenia. Ed. Joze Preseren. adv.; illus.
Description: Serves as a means of communication for the Slovenian ethnic groups in the United States, Canada, Australia, and the English-speaking European countries.

SLOVENSKA DRZAVA; for a free Slovenia. see POLITICAL SCIENCE

301.2 398   XO   ISSN 0037-7023
SLOVENSKY NARODOPIS/SLOVAK ETHNOGRAPHY. (Text in Slovak; summaries in English, French, German) 1953. q. 104 Kcs.($22) (Slovenska Akademia Vied, Narodopisny Ustav) Veda, Publishing House of the Slovak Academy of Sciences, Klemensova 19, 814 30 Bratislava, Slovakia. (Dist. in Western countries by: John Benjamins B.V., Amsteldijk 44, Amsterdam (Z.), Netherlands) Ed. Bozena Filova. bk.rev.; bibl.; charts; illus.; index. **Indexed:** A.I.C.P., Bibl.Ling., M.L.A.
Description: Deals with the culture of Slovak people in all their elements and manifestation, including architecture, clothes, art, handicrafts, songs, stories, habits. Publishes ethnographical materials of museums and archives, works from abroad, mainly comparative works.

914.7   AG   ISSN 0326-3193
SLOVENSKY ZIVOT/SLOVAK LIFE IN ARGENTINA. 1975. q. $20. Asociacion Cultural Eslovaca, Casilla 963, 1000 Buenos Aires, Argentina. TEL 805-8888. Ed. Eva Jankovicova. adv.; bk.rev. circ. 1,000.

SNENG KHASI. see ANTHROPOLOGY

SOCIEDAD DE ESTUDIOS VASCOS. CUADERNOS DE SECCION. ANTROPOLOGIA Y ETNOGRAFIA. see ANTHROPOLOGY

917.306   US   ISSN 1042-3230
SOCIETY FARSAROTUL NEWSLETTER. 1987. s-a. $18. Society Farsarotul, 799 Silver Lane, Box 753, Trumbull, CT 06611. TEL 203-375-0600. FAX 203-375-5003. Ed. Nicholas Balamaci. bk.rev. circ. 400. (tabloid format; back issues avail.) **Document type:** newsletter.
Description: Covers the history, language and culture of the Arumanians (Vlachs).

917.106 800 700   US   ISSN 0747-9301
DS161
SOCIETY FOR ARMENIAN STUDIES. JOURNAL.* Short title: J S A S. 1984. a. $20. Society for Armenian Studies, 983 Memorial Dr., Ste. 302, Cambridge, MA 02138-5742. TEL 212-923-7800. Ed. James R. Russell. adv.; bk.rev.; charts; illus. circ. 750. **Indexed:** Bibl.Ling.
—BLDSC (4880.788000).

SOGLASIE. see LITERARY AND POLITICAL REVIEWS

SOKOL POLSKI/POLISH FALCON. see CLUBS

917.306   US
EL SOL. (Text in English, and some Spanish) m. $35. California Chicano News Media Association, University of Southern California, School of Journalism, University Park, Los Angeles, CA 90089-1695. TEL 213-743-7158. FAX 213-744-1809. Ed. Henry Mendoza. circ. 1,700. **Document type:** newsletter.
Formerly: C N M A News.
Description: Promotes Latinos in the media by providing information on jobs, internships, issues, conferences, and workshops.

056.1   US
EL SOL DE TEXAS. (Text in Spanish) 1966. w. Organizacion Editorial Hispana, Inc., 4260 Spring Valley Rd., Dallas, TX 75244. TEL 214-386-9120. FAX 214-386-7125. Ed. Rogelio Santillan. adv. contact: Barbara Lopez. bk.rev.; circ. 26,000 (controlled). **Document type:** newspaper.
Description: Spanish language community newspaper.

296   FR
SOLIDARITE; bulletin d'information des refugies victimes du nazisme. (Text in French, German) 1956. 4/yr. 20 F.($15) Societe Mutualiste, 14 rue Saint Lazare, 75009 Paris, France. Ed. Erwin Neu. adv.; bk.rev. **Document type:** bulletin.

367   US   ISSN 0038-1454
SONS OF ITALY TIMES. 1936. bi-m. $5. Order of the Sons of Italy in America, Grand Lodge of Pennsylvania, 414 Walnut St., 4th Fl., Philadelphia, PA 19106-3703. TEL 215-592-1713. FAX 215-592-9152. Ed. John B. Acchione, III. adv.; bk.rev. circ. 15,500. (tabloid format) **Document type:** newspaper.

917.309   US   ISSN 0038-1462
HS1923.S6
SONS OF NORWAY VIKING. 1903. m. $20 membership. Sons of Norway, 1455 W. Lake St., Minneapolis, MN 55408. TEL 612-827-3611. FAX 612-827-0658. Ed. Karin Miller. adv.; bk.rev.; play rev.; illus.; stat.; tr.lit. circ. 55,000.
—UnCover.
Description: Articles on Norwegian history and culture, with information on the Sons of Norway programs and activities.

SOPHISTICATE'S BLACK HAIR; styles and care guide. see BEAUTY CULTURE

SOUTH AFRICAN JOURNAL OF ETHNOLOGY/SUID-AFRIKAANSE TYDSKRIF VIR ETNOLOGIE. see ANTHROPOLOGY

296   SA
SOUTH AFRICAN ZIONIST FEDERATION. NEWS AND VIEWS. q. membership. South African Zionist Federation, 84 de Villiers St., Johannesburg, South Africa.
Description: Covers Jewish interests.

SOUTH ASIAN MINORITY AFFAIRS. see POLITICAL SCIENCE — Civil Rights

296   US   ISSN 1042-2986
SOUTH JERSEY JEWISH COMMUNITY VOICE. 1941. fortn. $10. Jewish Federation of Southern New Jersey, 2393 W. Marlton Pike, Cherry Hill, NJ 08002. TEL 609-665-6100. FAX 609-665-0074. Ed. Harriet Kessler. adv.; bk.rev. circ. 11,200. (tabloid format; also avail. in microfilm from AJP)

910.03   US
SOUTH SUBURBAN CITIZEN. 1985. w. $25. Chicago Citizen, 412 E. 87th St., Chicago, IL 60619. TEL 312-487-7700. FAX 312-487-7931. Ed. William D. Garth. adv. contact: William D. Garth. bk.rev. circ. 20,000. (tabloid format) **Document type:** newspaper.

917.306   US
SOUTHEAST ASIAN REFUGEE STUDIES NEWSLETTER. q. free. Southeast Asian Refugee Studies Project, Center for Urban and Regional Affairs, University of Minnesota, 330 Humphrey Center, 301 19th Ave. S., Minneapolis, MN 55455. TEL 612-625-5535. FAX 612-626-0273. Eds. Glenn L. Hendricks, Karen Yang. **Document type:** newsletter.
Description: Discusses the plight of refugees in Southeast Asia.

ETHNIC INTERESTS

917.306   US
SOUTHEAST ASIAN REFUGEE STUDIES PROJECT. OCCASIONAL PAPERS. 1983. irreg., no.11, 1991. price varies. Southeast Asian Refugee Studies Project, Center for Urban and Regional Affairs, University of Minnesota, 330 Humphrey Center, 301 19th Ave. S., Minneapolis, MN 55455. TEL 612-625-5535. FAX 612-626-0273. (back issues avail.) **Document type:** monographic series.
Description: Describes Southeast Asian cultures and the problems their people face.

SOUTHERN AFRICA REPORT. see POLITICAL SCIENCE — Civil Rights

910.03   US
SOUTHWEST DIGEST. 1977. w. $15. 902 E. 28th St., Lubbock, TX 79404. TEL 806-762-3612. Eds. T.J. Patterson, E. Richardson. adv. contact: Eddie P. Richardson. bk.rev. circ. 10,000. **Document type:** newspaper.

SOVIET BIOGRAPHICAL SERVICE. see BIOGRAPHY

057   AT
SPANISH HERALD. (Text in Spanish) 2/w. Aus.$90. Foreign Language Publications Pty. Ltd., P.O. Box 146, Broadway, Sydney, N.S.W. 2007. TEL 02-660-2033. FAX 02-692-0649. Ed. Santiago Pozo. adv. contact: George Antoniou. circ. 7,100. (tabloid format; back issues avail.) **Document type:** newspaper.
Description: Serves the Australian and South American Spanish communities.

SPAWNING THE MEDICINE RIVER. see LITERATURE

914.5   CN
SPECCHIO. w. 166 Woodbridge Ave., Inkerman Bldg., Ste.100, Woodbridge, Ont. L4L 2S7, Canada. TEL 416-856-2823. FAX 416-856-2825. Ed. Sergio J. Tagliavini.

SPECTRUM (GREENBELT). see BUSINESS AND ECONOMICS — Accounting

910.03   US
SPICE (NEW YORK). 1986. m. $15.99. Starlog Group, Inc., 475 Park Ave. S., New York, NY 10016. TEL 212-689-2830. FAX 212-889-7933. Ed. Chris Botta. **Document type:** consumer publication.
Formerly: Black Teen.

SPIEGEL LECTURES IN EUROPEAN JEWISH HISTORY. see HISTORY — History Of Europe

914.206   UK
SPIRIT.* 1972. bi-m. 75p. 303 Portobello Rd., London W10, England. Ed. Sebastian Clarke. bk.rev.; illus.
Description: Covers Black interests.

990.006 059.918   AT
SPREMOST CROATIAN WEEKLY. (Text in Croatian, English) 1957. w. Central Council of Croatian Associations in Australia, G.P.O. Box 5335, Sydney, N.S.W. 2001, Australia. TEL 02-50-4074. FAX 02-502-4403. Ed. Fabian Lovokovic. bk.rev.; bibl.; charts; illus.; stat. circ. 5,000. (tabloid format)
Description: Covers current affairs and general interest in Australia, Croatia and the world.

SPUTNIK JUNIOR. see CHILDREN AND YOUTH — For

917.106   CN   ISSN 0715-5921
SRBIJA/SERBIA. (Text in Serbian) m. Can.$10. Serbian Chetniks - War Vets Association, 269 Glower Rd., Stoney Creek, ON L8E 5H6, Canada. Ed. M. Devrnja. adv. circ. 4,000. **Document type:** newspaper.
Description: Contains articles of interest to the Serbian community.

296   US   ISSN 0745-8509
STAR (NEW YORK, 1945). 1945. q. $3 to non-members. B'nai B'rith, District One, 823 United Nations Plaza, New York, NY 10017. TEL 212-983-5800. FAX 212-986-7487. Ed. Sherry A. Bigelisen. adv.; bk.rev.; illus.; stat. circ. 57,500. (tabloid format)
Formerly: Metropolitan Star (ISSN 0026-1580)
Description: Contains articles of interest to the Jewish community.

ETHNIC INTERESTS

917.309 US
STARK JEWISH NEWS. 1920. 10/yr. $10. Canton Jewish Community Federation, 2631 Harvard Ave., N.W., Canton, OH 44709. TEL 216-452-6444. FAX 216-452-4487. Ed. Adele Gelb. adv.; bk.rev.; play rev.; illus. circ. 20,000. (also avail. in microfilm from AJP) **Document type:** newspaper.

917.309 US
STRAZ/GUARD. (Text in English and Polish) 1897. w. $7. Polish National Union of America, 1004 Pittston Ave., Scranton, PA 18505. TEL 717-344-1513. FAX 717-961-5961. Ed. Mitchell Grochowski. adv.; bk.rev.; circ. 10,000 (controlled). (also avail. in microfilm) **Document type:** newspaper.
Description: Covers Polish interests.

945 IT
STUDI LUNIGIANESI. 1971. biennial. Associazione Manfredo Giupiani, Via dei Mupini, 54028 Villafranca Lunigiana, Italy. bk.rev. circ. 1,500. (back issues avail.)

960 GH ISSN 0163-2965
DT1
STUDIA AFRICANA. 1977. s-a. $15 to individuals; institutions $20. African Institute for the Study of Human Values, P.O. Box 12683, Accra North, Ghana. Ed. Francis A. Botchway. bk.rev. circ. 700. (reprint service avail. from UMI)

949.7 AG ISSN 0326-7997
STUDIA CROATICA; revista trimestral de estudios politicos y culturales. 1960. q. $30. Instituto Croata Latinoamericano de Cultura, Carlos Pellegrini 743, 3-18, 1009 Buenos Aires, Argentina. TEL 322-7254. Ed. Radovan Latkovic. bk.rev.; illus.; maps. circ. 2,000.
Description: Covers Croatian history, culture and politics.

STUDIA ROSENTHALIANA; tijdschrift voor Joodse wetenschap en geschiedenis in Nederland/journal for Jewish literature and history in the Netherlands. see LITERATURE

STUDIES IN AFRICAN LINGUISTICS. see LINGUISTICS

STUDIES IN AMERICAN INDIAN LITERATURES. see LITERATURE

296 US ISSN 0081-7511
STUDIES IN AMERICAN JEWISH HISTORY. 1951. irreg., no.5, 1968. price varies. American Jewish Historical Society, 2 Thornton Rd., Waltham, MA 02154. TEL 617-891-8110. FAX 617-899-9208. index. circ. 1,000. **Document type:** monographic series.

807 296 US ISSN 0271-9274
PS153.J4
STUDIES IN AMERICAN JEWISH LITERATURE. 1975; N.S. 1981. a. $15 to individuals; institutions $25. Pennsylvania State University, Department of English, University Park, PA 16802. TEL 814-863-3753. Ed. Daniel Walden. adv.; bk.rev. circ. 250. (reprint service avail. from UMI) **Indexed:** Abstr.Engl.Stud., Amer.Bibl.Slavic & E.Eur.Stud., M.L.A. **Document type:** academic/scholarly publication.
—BLDSC (8489.077000); Faxon; UnCover; SWETS; UMI.

STUDIES IN BIBLICAL GREEK. see RELIGIONS AND THEOLOGY

STUDIES IN BLACK AMERICAN LITERATURE. see LITERATURE

296 US ISSN 0740-8625
DS125
STUDIES IN CONTEMPORARY JEWRY. 1984. a. $30. (Institute of Contemporary Jewry) Oxford University Press, 200 Madison Ave., New York, NY 10016. TEL 212-679-7300. FAX 212-282-6249. Ed.Bd. bk.rev.; bibl. circ. 2,500. (back issues avail.)
—BLDSC (8490.307140).

917.306 940 US
STUDIES IN GERMAN THOUGHT AND HISTORY. irreg., latest vol.14. $39.95 per no. Edwin Mellen Press, 415 Ridge St., Box 450, Lewiston, NY 14092. TEL 716-754-2788. FAX 716-754-4056. **Document type:** monographic series.

STUDIES IN HISPANIC AMERICAN AND LATIN AMERICAN THEATRE. see THEATER

STUDIES IN ITALIAN CULTURE: LITERATURE IN HISTORY. see LITERATURE

STUDIES IN JEWISH EDUCATION. see EDUCATION

296 US ISSN 0884-6952
STUDIES IN JUDAICA & THE HOLOCAUST. 1985. irreg., no.12, 1993. price varies. Borgo Press, Box 2845, San Bernardino, CA 92406. TEL 909-884-5813. FAX 909-888-4942. Ed. Nathan Kravetz.
Description: Monographs on all aspects of Jewish civilization, history, and culture, including the Jewish Holocaust of the 1940s.

STUDIES IN SOUTHERN ITALIAN AND ITALIAN-AMERICAN CULTURE/STUDI SULLA CULTURA DELL'ITALIA MERIDIONALE E ITALO-AMERICANA. see SOCIOLOGY

STUDIES IN ZIONISM; a journal of Israel studies. see HISTORY

296 309 US ISSN 0734-4937
HN660
STUDIES OF ISRAELI SOCIETY. 1981. a. $49.95 cloth; paper $24.95. (Israel Sociological Society) Transaction Publishers, Transaction Periodicals Consortium, Department 3092, Rutgers University, New Brunswick, NJ 08903. TEL 908-932-2280. FAX 908-932-3138. Ed. Ernest Krausz. **Document type:** academic/scholarly publication.
Description: Presents, in a single forum, social science investigations of Israeli society that were previously published in a variety of international journals.

910.03 US
SUCCESSGUIDE (YEAR); the guide to black resources. 1989. a. $249 for cloth; paper $149; CD-ROM $249 (typically set in Oct.). SuccessSource, Inc., 1949 E. 105th St., Ste. 100, Cleveland, OH 44106. TEL 216-791-9330. FAX 216-791-9436. Ed. Margaret Thoren. adv. contact: Jim Moore. circ. 180,000. (also avail. in microfiche) **Document type:** newsletter.
Description: Combines editorial features and listings of names, titles and phone numbers of local black professionals and entrepreneurs in eight major American cities: Atlanta, Chicago, Cincinnati, Dayton, Cleveland, Detroit, Los Angeles, New York City, and Washington D.C.

951 CH
SUI YUAN WEN HSIEN. (Text in Chinese) 1977. a. donation. Association of Fellow Provincials of Sui Yuan - Sui Yuan Wen Hsien Sheh, 101 4th St., Chung Yang Rd., Hsin Tien, Taipei Hsien, Taiwan 23127, Republic of China. Ed. Lee Ch'i-yuan. maps; illus. circ. 1,500. (back issues avail.)
Description: Aims to facilitate communication between former inhabitants of Suiyuan Province in northern China. Introduces famous or interesting personalities from Suiyuan, presents historical articles and accounts of return visits. Also lists names, addresses, and phone numbers of expatriate Suiyuanese, as well as obituaries.

910.03 US
SUMTER BLACK POST. 1982. w. $25. S.C. Black Media Group, 1310 Harden St., Columbia, SC 29204. TEL 803-799-5252. Ed. Isaac Washington. illus. circ. 5,600. **Document type:** newspaper.

916 US
SUN REPORTER. 1943. w. $11. Reporter Publishing Co. (San Francisco), 1366 Turk St., San Francisco, CA 94115. TEL 415-931-5778. Ed. Thomas Fleming. adv.; bk.rev.; film rev.; illus. circ. 11,216. (tabloid format) **Document type:** newspaper.
Description: Weekly news from a black perspective.

059.94 FI ISSN 0039-5625
SUOMEN SILTA/SUOMI BRIDGE. (Text in English and Finnish) 1927. bi-m. $13. Suomi-Seura r.y. - Suomi Society, Mariankatu 8, 00170 Helsinki 17, Finland. Ed. Martti Haikio. adv.; bk.rev. circ. 100,000.

325 AT
SUOMI. 1926. s-m. Aus.$40. Suomi Newspaper Pty. Ltd., Box 303, Malvern, Vic. 3144, Australia. TEL 03-572-2543. FAX 03-562-6223. Ed. Risto Soder. circ. 1,200.

914.802 FI ISSN 0782-8454
SUOMI - FINLAND U S A. 1946. bi-m. Fmk.70. Suomi-Amerikka Yhdistysten Liitto - League of Finnish-American Societies, Mechelininkatu 10A, 00100 Helsinki, Finland. FAX 0-408974. Ed. Aarne I. Valikangas. adv.; bk.rev.; circ. 40,000 (controlled).

SV. PRANCISKAUS VARPELIS/BELL OF ST. FRANCIS. see RELIGIONS AND THEOLOGY — Roman Catholic

917.306 US
SVESOS KRASTOS. (Text in Latvian) 1959. q. free. Philadelphia Society of Free Letts, 531 N. Seventh St., Philadelphia, PA 19123-3501. TEL 215-922-9798. Ed. Niklass Lazdins. bk.rev.; play rev.; bibl. circ. 850. (back issues avail.)

917.309 US ISSN 0300-6212
SVITHIOD JOURNAL. 1898. m. $1. Independent Order of Svithiod, 5518 W. Lawrence Ave., Chicago, IL 60630-3493. TEL 312-736-1191. Ed. Betty Jane Clausen. adv.; bk.rev. circ. 2,000.
Description: Contains articles submitted by some of the lodges as well as advertisements of coming events, announcements of Lodge activities, an obituary column and an officers' list.

917.306 US ISSN 0274-6964
SVOBODA/LIBERTY. (Text in Ukrainian) 1892. d. $15 to members; non-members $40. Ukrainian National Association, 30 Montgomery St., Jersey City, NJ 07302. TEL 201-434-0237. FAX 201-451-5486. Ed. Zenon Snylyk. adv.; bk.rev. **Document type:** newspaper.
Description: Serves the U.S. Ukrainian community.

917.306 US ISSN 1042-1777
SWEDEN & AMERICA. 1987. q. $7.95 (foreign $10). Swedish Council of America, 2600 Park Ave., Minneapolis, MN 55407. TEL 612-871-0593. FAX 612-871-8682. Ed. Christopher Olsson. adv.; bk.rev. circ. 29,500. **Document type:** newsletter.
Description: General information on cultural relations between Sweden and America. Features articles on food and travel as well.

917.106 CN ISSN 0839-2323
SWEDISH PRESS/NYA SVENSKA PRESSEN. (Text in English and Swedish) 1929. m. Can.$20. Swedish Press Society, 1294 W. 7th Ave., Vancouver, BC V6H 1B6, Canada. TEL 604-731-6381. FAX 604-731-6361. Ed. Anders Neumueller. adv.; bk.rev. circ. 5,000. **Document type:** consumer publication.

917.306 US ISSN 0895-7126
SWENSON CENTER NEWS. 1986. a. free. Swenson Swedish Immigration Research Center, Augustana College, 639 38th St., Rock Island, IL 61201-2273. TEL 309-794-7204. FAX 309-794-7443. Ed. Dag Blanck. adv.; bk.rev.; circ. 4,000 (controlled). **Document type:** newsletter.
Description: Publicizes the resources (archival and library), programs, activities and research of the center for the study of the complete impact of Swedish immigration to North America. Includes feature articles on various aspects of Swedish-American history.

948.06 US
SWISS AMERICAN; a publicaiton for the North American Swiss Alliance. 1883. bi-m. $5. North American Swiss Alliance, 2590 Lakeside Ave. NW, Canton, OH 44708. TEL 216-456-1983. adv. circ. 2,600. (tabloid format; back issues avail.)
Description: Explores the shared ethnic and bi-cultural interests of the Swiss American community including food, gardening, history, hobbies, and heritage values.

053.5 US
SWISS AMERICAN REVIEW. 1868. w. $30. 608 Fifth Ave., New York, NY 10020. TEL 212-247-0459. FAX 212-397-2473. Ed. karl Vonlanthen. adv.; bk.rev.; play rev.; abstr.; bibl.; charts; illus.; stat. circ. 3,500. (tabloid format) **Document type:** newspaper.

051 CN ISSN 0049-2728
SWISS CANADIAN NEWS. 1960. m. membership. Swiss Club Toronto, Box 823, Station Q, Toronto, Ont. M4T 2N7, Canada. Ed. A. Mettler. adv. circ. 800.
Description: Covers Swiss interests.

SYNAGOGUE LIGHT - KOSHER LIFE. see RELIGIONS AND THEOLOGY — Judaic

ETHNIC INTERESTS

971.004 CN ISSN 0700-5199
SZAMADAS. (Text in Hungarian) 1975. m. Can.$0.50 per no. Box 42, Station W, Toronto, Ont. M6M 4V9, Canada.
Description: Contains articles of interest to the Hungarian community.

917.306 US ISSN 0270-5508
PH3001
SZIVARVANY. 1980. 3/yr. $30 (effective Mar. 1993). (Hungarian Cultural & Educational House) Framo Publishing, 561 W. Diversey Parkway, Chicago, IL 60614. TEL 312-477-1485. FAX 312-477-2698. Ed. Mozsi Ferenc. bk.rev.; circ. 1,500 (controlled).
Document type: academic/scholarly publication.
Description: Focuses on Hungarian literature. Includes critiques of the ex-communist system and contemporary American literature.

T R A C E. (Travaux et Recherches dans les Ameriques du Centre) see *ANTHROPOLOGY*

910.03 US
TACOMA TRUE CITIZEN. 1974. w. $20. Tiloben Publishing Co., Box 22047, Seattle, WA 98122. TEL 206-627-1103. FAX 206-322-6518. Ed. Christopher Bennett. adv. contact: Prescilla Hailey. circ. 15,000. Document type: newspaper.

915.106 CC
TAI SHENG/VOICE OF TAIWAN. (Text in Chinese) 1983. m. $33.20. (Zhonghua Quanguo Taiwan Tongbao Lianyihui - All-China Federation of Taiwan Compatriots) Tai Sheng Zazhishe, No. A-15, Wanshou Lu, Beijing 100036, People's Republic of China. TEL 812277. (Dist. in US by: China Books & Periodicals, Inc., 2929 24th St., San Francisco, CA 94110. TEL 415-282-2994)
Description: Aims to serve as a means of communication between Taiwan and the Chinese mainland, and Taiwanese living abroad. Includes articles on China, and selections from discussions of unification by Taiwanese.

TALLADEGAN. see *COLLEGE AND ALUMNI*

TAMIL CIVILIZATION. see *HISTORY — History Of Asia*

296 US
TARBUT; Israeli cultural affairs in North America. 1989. 3/yr. Consulate General of Israel in New York, Department of Cultural Affairs, 800 Second Ave., New York, NY 10017. TEL 212-351-5242. FAX 212-351-5280. Ed. Eliza de Sola Mendes. bk.rev. Document type: government publication.

917.309 US ISSN 0039-9914
TATRZANSKI ORZEL/TATRA EAGLE. (Text in English and Polish) 1947. q. $3.50. Polish Tatra Mountaineers Alliance, c/o J.W. Gromada, 264 Palsa Ave., Elmwood Park, NJ 07407. Eds. Thaddeus V. Gromada, Jane Kedron. adv.; bk.rev.; illus. circ. 1,000.
Description: Contains items of interest to the Polish American community.

917.306 US
EL TECOLOTE; a totally bilingual newspaper in the Bay Area. (Text in English, Spanish) 1970. m. $35 to institutions. Accion Latina, 2017 Mission St., Ste. 200, San Francisco, CA 94110. TEL 415-252-5957. FAX 415-883-9318. (Subscr. to: Box 40037, San Francisco, CA 94140) Ed. Juan Gonzales. adv.; bk.rev.; film rev, play rev.; circ. 10,000 (controlled). (tabloid format; also avail. in microfilm from LIB) Document type: newspaper.
Description: Local community news with emphasis on social issues, popular culture, and news of Latin America.

970.1 CN ISSN 0300-3159
TEKAWENNAKE. Title varies: Tekawennake. Six Nations - New Credit Reporter. (Text in English) 1967. w. Can.$55. Ohsweken Post Office, Ohsweken, ON N0A 1M0, Canada. TEL 519-445-2238. FAX 519-445-2434. Ed. G. Scott Smith. adv.; bk.rev.; illus. circ. 2,500. Document type: newspaper.
Former titles (until 1968): New Credit - Six Nations Reporter (ISSN 0315-5129); New Credit Reporter (ISSN 0315-5137).
Description: Native news serving Southern Ontario.

056.1 US ISSN 0040-2869
TEMAS; revista ilustrada. (Text in Spanish) 1950. m. $19. Temas Magazine, Inc., 1650 Broadway, New York, NY 10019. Ed. Jose De La Vega. adv.; bk.rev.; illus. circ. 114,000.

910.03 US
TENDERLOIN TIMES. 1977. m. $11. Central City Hospitality House, 146 Leavenworth St., San Francisco, CA 94102. TEL 415-776-2102. Ed. Sara Colm. adv. circ. 20,000.

918.106 BL ISSN 0103-2437
TERRA INDIGENA. 1983. bi-m. exchange basis. Centro de Estudos Indigenas, UNESP, Fac. de Ciencias e Letras, Depto. de Antropologia, Politica e Filosofia, Caixa Postal 174, 14800 Araraquara, SP, Brazil.

917.106 CN ISSN 0040-4063
TEVISKES ZIBURIAI/LIGHTS OF HOMELAND. (Text in Lithuanian) 1949. w. Can.$35. Lithuanian Canadian R.C. Cultural Society "Ziburiai," Inc., 2185 Stavebank Rd., Mississauga, ON L5C 1T3, Canada. TEL 416-275-4672. FAX 416-275-1336. Ed. Dr. Pr. Gaida. adv.; bk.rev. circ. 5,300. (also avail. in microfilm from CML)

917.309 US ISSN 0040-4071
TEVYNE. 1910. m. $4. Lithuanian Alliance of America, 307 W. 30th St., New York, NY 10001. Ed. Genevieve Meilunas. adv.; bk.rev.; illus. circ. 3,500.

917.306 US ISSN 1055-2944
TEXAS HISPANIC MAGAZINE; the magazine of and for Hispanics. 1990. m. $18. Texas Hispanic Publishing Co., 3006 Garrow, Houston, TX 77003. TEL 713-926-0854. FAX 713-926-8035. Ed. Miguel Barrientos. adv.; bk.rev. circ. 20,000. (back issues avail.)
Description: Recognizes the achievements and contributions of Hispanics and reports on issues such as education, health, politics, business and culture.

296 US ISSN 0040-439X
TEXAS JEWISH POST; the Southwest's leading English - Jewish weekly newspaper. 1947. w. $32 in Texas; rest of U.S. $39 (foreign $70). 3120 S. Freeway, Ste.213, Fort Worth, TX 76110. TEL 817-927-2831. (And: 11133 N. Central Expy., Dallas TX 75243) Ed. J.A. Wisch. adv.; bk.rev.; film rev.; play rev.; illus. circ. 8,000. (tabloid format; also avail. in microfilm from AJP)

296 301.412 US
TEXTURES; Hadassah National Jewish studies bulletin. (Text in English, Hebrew) 1982. 2/yr. $3. Hadassah, The Women's Zionist Organization of America, 50 W. 58th St., New York, NY 10019. TEL 212-355-7900. Ed. Carol Diament. circ. 4,500.
Description: Covers Jewish art, thought, daily life in Israel; discusses Hebrew and biblical text, poetry and the role of the Jewish woman.

THAT WAS YUGOSLAVIA. see *POLITICAL SCIENCE*

THIRD FORCE. see *POLITICAL SCIENCE*

920 UK
THIRD WORLD IMPACT. irreg., 8th ed., 1994. £15.95. Hansib Publishing Ltd., Tower House, 3rd Fl., 139-149 Fonthill Rd., London N4 3HF, England. TEL 071-281-1191. FAX 071-263-9656. Ed. Arif Ali.
Description: Provides reference material on such issues as legal rights, education, immigration and nationality legislation, housing, trade unions, the arts, sports, and women's rights in developing nations.

910.03 US
THURSTON COUNTY DISPATCH. 1989. w. $25. Dispatch Newspapers, Box 5367, Tacoma, WA 98415. TEL 206-272-7587. FAX 206-272-4418. Ed. Virginia Taylor. adv. contact: Lou Taylor. circ. 5,000. (tabloid format) Document type: newspaper.

950 US ISSN 0883-7732
DS785.A1
TIBET SOCIETY BULLETIN. 1967. irreg. membership. Tibet Society, Inc., Box 1968, Bloomington, IN 47402. TEL 812-335-8222.
Formerly: Tibet Society Newsletter (ISSN 0363-311X).
Description: Articles of general interest about Tibetan culture.

914.606 US
TIEMPO LATINO. (Text in Spanish) 1976. w. free. Tiempo Latino News, 3288 21st St., Box 9, San Fransisco, CA 94110. TEL 415-512-1820. adv.; circ. 40,00 (controlled). Document type: newspaper.
Description: Covers local, national and international news with emphasis on Hispanic concerns and interests from politics to cultural arts, health and education.

296 US ISSN 0887-9982
DS101
TIKKUN MAGAZINE; a bi-monthly Jewish critique of politics, culture and society. 1986. bi-m. $31. Institute for Labor & Mental Health, 5100 Leona St., Oakland, CA 94619. TEL 510-482-0805. FAX 510-482-3379. (Subscr. to: Box 332, Mt. Morris, IL, 61054-0332) Ed. Michael Lerner. adv.; bk.rev. circ. 40,000. (back issues avail.) Indexed: Acad.Ind., Alt.Press Ind., Bk.Rev.Ind. (1989-), Child.Bk.Rev. nd. (1989-), Ind.Jew.Per., Left Ind. (1988-), Mag.Ind., Polit.Sci.Abstr., Rel.Ind.One. —Faxon; UnCover; UMI.

296 US
TIKVAH. Variant title: Ha Tikvah. q. Brooklyn College, Jewish Student Press Service, 2901 Campus Rd., Brooklyn, NY 11210. TEL 718-859-1151. Eds. Leon Zacharowicz, Barbara Blum.
Description: Covers Jewish interests.

059 051 AT
TIMES OF MALTA (Text in English and Maltese) vol.5, 1972. fortn. Aus.$10. 511 Sydney Rd., Brunswick, Vic. 3056, Australia. Ed. Alfred Ciantar. adv.; illus. circ. 2,000.
Formerly: Times of Malta and Australia.

DER TIROLER; Zeitung fuer ein einiges und freies Tirol. see *HISTORY — History Of Europe*

296 SA
TNUAT ALIYAH. m. membership. South African Zionist Federation, 84 de Villiers St., Johannesburg, South Africa.
Description: Covers Jewish interests.

TODAY'S BLACK FATHER. see *CHILDREN AND YOUTH — About*

296 US ISSN 0040-9081
TOLEDO JEWISH NEWS;* the monthly newspaper for the Jewish community of greater Toledo. 1951. m. $6. Jewish Federation of Greater Toledo, 3211 W. Lincolnshire, Toledo, OH 43606. TEL 216-531-5985. Ed. Fred Flox. adv.; bk.rev. circ. 2,900. (tabloid format; also avail. in microfilm from AJP)

910.03 US
TOLEDO JOURNAL. 1975. w. $25. 3021 Douglas Rd., Toledo, OH 43606. TEL 419-472-4521. Ed. Myron Stewart. adv. contact: Sandra Stewart. bk.rev. circ. 17,000. (tabloid format) Document type: newspaper.

296 CN ISSN 0049-4186
TORONTO JEWISH PRESS. 1969. fortn. Can.$50. Box 428, Downsview, ON M3M 3A8, Canada. TEL 416-633-0202. Ed. G. Kissin. adv.
Description: Contains articles of interest to the Jewish community

TRANSAFRICAN JOURNAL OF HISTORY. see *HISTORY*

917.309 US
TRANSCEND. 1989. q. $7.95. Transcend Publications, 4 Daniels Farm Rd., Ste. 134, Trumbull, CT 06611. Ed. Quentin J. Plair circ. 15,000 (controlled).
Formerly (until 1990): Youth Focus.
Description: Attempts to motivate and inspire black youth by providing positive role models, promoting positive thinking, and creating a link to their past.

917.306 US ISSN 0892-5747
TRANSPACIFIC. 1986. m. $38 (typically set in Mar.). Transpacific Media Inc., 23715 W. Malibu Rd., No.390, Malibu, CA 90265-5000. TEL 310-456-0790. FAX 310-456-3724. Pub. Tom Kagy. adv.; illus. circ. 47,500. Document type: consumer publication.
Formerly (until 1989): AsiAm.

TRAVELER & CONVENTIONEER. see *TRAVEL AND TOURISM*

ETHNIC INTERESTS

970.1 US
TREATY COUNCIL NEWS.* 12/yr. $10 to individuals; institutions $15. International Indian Treaty Council, Information Office, 123 Townsend St., Ste. 575, San Francisco, CA 94107-1907.
Description: Covers American Indian interests.

910.03 US
TRI STATE DEFENDER. 1951. w. $20. Sengstacks Enterprises, Box 2065, Memphis, TN 38101. TEL 901-523-1818. FAX 901-523-1820. Ed. Arelya J. Mitchell. adv. contact: Judy Seals. circ. 15,000. **Document type:** newspaper.

055.1 CN ISSN 0049-464X
TRIBUNA ITALIANA.* 1963. w. Can.$5. 257 Dante St., Montreal 327, Que., Canada. Ed. Camillo Carli.
Description: Contains items of interest to the Italian community.

TRUE LOVE AND FAMILY. see WOMEN'S INTERESTS

TRY US; national minority business directory. see BUSINESS AND ECONOMICS — Trade And Industrial Directories

053.1 GW
TUDUV-STUDIE. REIHE KULTURWISSENSCHAFTEN. 1974. irreg. price varies. Tuduv Verlagsgesellschaft mbH, Gabelsbergerstr. 15, 8000 Munich 2, Germany.

296 US
TULSA JEWISH REVIEW. 1930. m. $15. Jewish Federation of Tulsa, 2021 E. 71st St., Tulsa, OK 74136-5408. FAX 918-495-1220. Ed. Ed Ulrich. adv.; bk.rev. circ. 1,400. **Document type:** newspaper.

970.1 917.906 US ISSN 0049-4801
TUNDRA TIMES. 1962. bi-w. $20. Eskimo, Indian, Aleut Publishing Co., Box 92247, Anchorage, AK 99509-2247. TEL 907-274-2512. FAX 907-277-7217. Eds. Anna M. Pickett, Jeff Richardson. adv.; bk.rev.; stat. circ. 4,000. **Document type:** newspaper.
Description: Presents articles and commentary of particular interest to Alaska natives.

956.1 071 US ISSN 1043-0164
THE TURKISH TIMES. 1989. fortn. $25 (first class $55) (effective 1994). Assembly of Turkish American Associations, 1602 Connecticut Ave., Ste. 303, Washington, DC 20009. TEL 202-483-9090. Ed. Dr. Ugur Akimci. adv. **Indexed:** Per.Islam. (1991-). **Document type:** newspaper.
Description: Covers news relating to Turkey, including U.S., European, Turkish and international politics, minority rights issues, social and cultural issues.

970.1 US ISSN 0896-2022
TURTLE QUARTERLY MAGAZINE. 1979. q. $15 (effective 1992). Native American Center for the Living Arts, 25 Rainbow Blvd. S., Niagara Falls, NY 14303. Ed. Tim Johnson. adv.; bk.rev. circ. 5,000.
—UnCover.
Formerly: Turtle (Niagara Falls).

TWENTIETH - CENTURY AMERICAN JEWISH WRITERS. see LITERATURE

917.306 057.85 US
▼**TYGODNIK KONTAKTY.** (Text in Polish) 1994. w. newsstand price: $1.50. Polonia Publishing House, Inc., 861 Manhattan Ave., Brooklyn, NY 11222. TEL 718-349-6212. FAX 718-349-3238. Ed. Ewa Szczukajtys-Gajda. adv. contact: Dorota Mlynek. illus. (tabloid format) **Document type:** newspaper.
Description: General information of interest to Polish community.

296 US
U C S J MEMBERSHIP REPORT. a. free. Union of Councils for Soviet Jews, 1819 H St., N.W., Ste. 230, Washington, DC 20006-3603. TEL 202-775-9770. FAX 202-775-9776.
Formerly (until 1992): U C S J Quarterly Report (ISSN 0897-0572)
Description: Covers Jewish interests.

296 US
U C S J MONITOR. bi-m. membership. Union of Councils for Soviet Jews, 1819 H St., N.W., Ste. 230, Washington, DC 20006-3603. TEL 202-775-9770. FAX 202-772-9776. **Document type:** newsletter.
Description: Contains news on Jewish issues concerning the transformation to a democratic society in the former Soviet Union.

U S BLACK ENGINEER. see ENGINEERING

U S IMMIGRATION. see LAW

U S SPORTS. see SPORTS AND GAMES

323.4 DT1 US ISSN 0041-5715
UFAHAMU. 1970. 3/yr. $17 to individuals (overseas $19); institutions $23 (overseas $25). University of California at Los Angeles, James S. Coleman African Studies Center, 10244 Bunche Hall, 405 Hildegard Ave., Los Angeles, CA 90024. TEL 310-825-3686. adv.; bk.rev.; index. circ. 350. **Indexed:** Curr.Cont.Africa, Documentatieblad, M.L.A. **Document type:** academic/scholarly publication.
—Faxon; UnCover.
Description: Articles by graduate students and faculty dealing with African and Afro-American history, politics, culture, and economics. Includes poetry.

296 HU ISSN 0133-1353
UJ ELET; magyar izraelitak lapja. vol.31, 1976. fortn. $15.50. Magyar Izraelitak Orszagos Kepviselete, Sip u. 12, 1075 Budapest, Hungary. TEL 122-2829. Ed. Istvan Doman. adv.; bk.rev. circ. 7,000. (tabloid format)

947 AS36.U4 US ISSN 0503-1001
UKRAINIAN ACADEMY OF ARTS AND SCIENCES IN THE U S. ANNALS. 1951. irreg. (approx. a.). $30 per no. Ukrainian Academy of Arts and Sciences in the U.S., Inc., c/o Dr. William Omelchenko, 206 W. 100th St., New York, NY 10025. TEL 212-222-1866. bk.rev. circ. 1,000. **Indexed:** Amer.Bibl.Slavic & E.Eur.Stud., Amer.Hist.& Life, Biol.Abstr., Hist.Abstr. **Document type:** academic/scholarly publication.

917.109 CN
UKRAINIAN CANADIAN CONGRESS. BULLETIN. (Text in English and Ukrainian) 1953. q. Can.$10. Ukrainian Canadian Congress, 456 Main St., Winnipeg, MB R3B 1B6, Canada. TEL 204-942-4627. FAX 204-947-3882. Ed. Ihor Shawarsky. bk.rev.; illus. circ. 6,700. **Document type:** bulletin.
Formerly: Komitet' Ukrainstsiv Kanady. Biuleten' (ISSN 0503-1036)
Description: News of interest to Ukrainian people in Canada.

914.7 US
UKRAINIAN NATIONAL WORD/UKRAINSKE NARODNE SLOVO. (Text in English and Ukrainian) 1914. q. $8. Ukrainian National Aid Association of America, 925 N. Western Ave., Chicago, IL 60622. TEL 312-342-5102. Ed. Wolodymyr Masur. adv.; illus. circ. 4,000.
Description: Contains articles of interest to the Ukrainian American community.

917.109 CN ISSN 0041-6002
UKRAINIAN NEWS/UKRAINSKI VISTI. 1929. w. Can.$20($14) Ukrainian News Publishers Ltd., 12227 - 107 Ave., No. 1, Edmonton, AB T5M 1Y9, Canada. TEL 403-488-3860. FAX 403-488-3859. Ed. Marco Levytsky. adv. contact: Richard Sheps. bk.rev.; bibl.; illus. circ. 3,000. (tabloid format) **Document type:** newspaper.
Description: Covers Ukrainian interests.

UKRAINIAN ORTHODOX WORD. see RELIGIONS AND THEOLOGY — Eastern Orthodox

057.9 DK508.A2 UK ISSN 0041-6029
UKRAINIAN REVIEW. 1954. 4/yr. £20($40) Association of Ukrainians in Great Britain Ltd., 49 Linden Gardens, London W2 4HG, England. TEL 071-792-2499. Ed.Bd. bk.rev.; illus. **Indexed:** Amer.Hist.& Life, Hist.Abstr., M.L.A. **Document type:** academic/scholarly publication.
—UnCover.
Description: Contains articles of interest to the Ukrainian community.

057.9 UK
UKRAINIAN THOUGHT. (Text in Ukrainian) 1947. w. £40($90) Association of Ukrainians in Great Britain Ltd., 49 Linden Gardens, London W2 4HG, England. TEL 071-229-8392. FAX 071-792-2499. Ed. S.M. Fostun. adv.; bk.rev. circ. 3,000. **Document type:** academic/scholarly publication.

917.109 CN ISSN 0041-6037
UKRAINIAN VOICE/UKRAINSKY HOLOS. (Text in English, Ukrainian) 1910. w. Can.$35($44) (effective Jan. 1991). Trident Press Ltd., 842 Main St., Winnipeg, Man. R2W 3N8, Canada. TEL 204-589-5101. FAX 204-586-3618. Ed.Bd. adv.; bk.rev. circ. 4,000. **Document type:** newspaper.
Incorporating: Canadian Farmer (ISSN 0045-4745)

917.306 US ISSN 0273-9348
UKRAINIAN WEEKLY. 1933. w. $20 to non-members; members $10. Ukrainian National Association, Inc., 30 Montgomery St., Jersey City, NJ 07302. TEL 201-434-0237. FAX 201-451-5486. Ed. Roma Hadzewycz. adv.; bk.rev. circ. 10,500. (also avail. in microfilm) **Indexed:** HR Rep. **Document type:** newspaper.
Description: Serves the U.S. Ukrainian community.

917.306 US ISSN 1055-2413
UKRAINSKI VISTI. (Editions in English, Ukrainian) 1957. w. (English ed. m.). Ukrainian Daily News, Inc., 85 E. Fourth St., New York, NY 10003. **Document type:** newspaper.

914.4 840 AP20 FR ISSN 1143-3914
ULYSSES INTERNATIONAL; magazine du sud en France. 1989. s-a. 350 F. Ulys Editions, B.P. 6039, 34030 Montpellier Cedex 1, France. TEL 67-54-25-24. FAX 67-41-39-09. Eds. Alain Foubert, Gerard Ribot. adv.; bk.rev. circ. 10,000. (back issues avail.)
Description: Covers the southern region of France, French-speaking countries, literature, and travel.

960 US
UMOJA; a scholarly journal of black studies. 1974; N.S. 1977. 3/yr. $15 to individuals; institutions $18. University of Colorado, Black Studies Program, Campus Box 294, Boulder, CO 80309. TEL 303-629-2700. Ed. William M. King. adv.; bk.rev. circ. 200. **Indexed:** Amer.Hist.& Life, Hist.Abstr.

296 DS150.L3 CN ISSN 0382-0610
UNDZER VEG. (Text in English and Yiddish) 1932. q. Can.$2($2.50) Achdut Ha-Avoda-Poale Zion of Canada, 272 Codsell Ave., Downsview, Ont. M3H 3X2, Canada. Eds. J. Kligman, Y. Tyberg. adv.; bk.rev.; film rev.; play rev.; circ. 4,000 (controlled).
Description: Covers Jewish interests.

919.406 AT
UNIFICATION/EDINENIE. (Text and summaries in Russian) 1950. w. Aus.$75. Unification Printers & Publishers Pty. Ltd., 12 Vernon St., Strathfield, N.S.W. 2135, Australia. TEL 02-746-8789. FAX 02-7642058. Ed. G.C. Amosow. adv.; bk.rev.; film rev.; play rev.; circ. 4,300 (controlled). (tabloid format) **Document type:** newspaper.

914.206 US
UNION JACK. 1982. m. $28. Union Jack Publishing, Box 1823, La Mesa, CA 91944-1823. TEL 619-466-3129. Ed. Ronald Choularton. adv.; bk.rev. circ. 200,000.
Description: Brings news of Britain to the British community in the U.S.

UNIQUE HAIR TODAY. see BEAUTY CULTURE

917.306 US ISSN 0891-1436
UNITED JOURNAL. Variant title: Chinese United Journal. (Text in Chinese) 1942. d. $96. Chinese United Journal, Inc., 83-85 White St., New York, NY 10013. TEL 212-513-1440. FAX 212-693-1302. Ed. Yuk Tsun Wang. adv.; bk.rev. circ. 20,000. **Document type:** newspaper.
Description: Explains America to the ethnic reader. Covers local, national and international news.

ETHNIC INTERESTS 2513

970.1 US
UNITED LUMBEE NATION TIMES. 1979. 3/yr. $5 for 4 issues. United Lumbee Nation of N.C. & America, Box 512, Fall River Mills, CA 96028. TEL 916-336-6701. Ed. Silver Star Reed. adv.; bk.rev. circ. 1,000. (tabloid format) **Document type:** newspaper.
  Description: Covers the history and culture of the Lumbee Indians.

970.1 US
▼**UNITED NATIVE CULTURE AND LANGUAGE EXCHANGE.** 1993. q. $50 (foreign $100). Earthentics, 33 Essex St., Hackensack, NJ 07601. TEL 201-489-5057. FAX 201-489-2508. Ed. Joe Campagna. **Document type:** corporate report.
  Description: Promotes opportunities for businesses and private individuals to share in economic stimulation from American indigenous products.

U.S. DEPARTMENT OF COMMERCE. MINORITY BUSINESS DEVELOPMENT AGENCY. FRANCHISE OPPORTUNITIES HANDBOOK. see *BUSINESS AND ECONOMICS — Small Business*

917.106 CN
UNITY.* q. Association of Iroquois and Allied Indians, R.R. 2, Southwold, Ont. N0L 2G0, Canada. Ed. Shelly E. Bressette.
  Formerly (until 1985): Strength in Unity.

910.03 810
UNIVERSAL BLACK WRITER. 1979. q. $7 to individuals; institutions $12. c/o Linda Cousins, Ed., Box 5, Radio City Sta., New York, NY 10101. bk.rev. circ. 200.

UNIVERSITE DE BORDEAUX II. CAHIERS ETHNOLOGIQUES. see *ANTHROPOLOGY*

UNIVERSITY OF ABERDEEN. AFRICAN STUDIES GROUP. BULLETIN. see *HISTORY — History Of Africa*

917.306 US ISSN 1047-2932
UNIVERSITY OF NEVADA. BASQUE STUDIES PROGRAM NEWSLETTER. (Text in English; occasionally Basque) 1968. 2/yr. free. University of Nevada, Basque Studies Program, Getchell Library, Reno, NV 89557-0012. TEL 702-784-4854. FAX 702-784-6010. Ed. Linda White. circ. 8,500. (processed) **Document type:** newsletter.
  Description: Provides information an articles about the Basque Studies Program at UNR.

UNIVERSITY OF NEW MEXICO. LATIN AMERICAN INSTITUTE. RESEARCH PAPER SERIES. see *SOCIAL SCIENCES: COMPREHENSIVE WORKS*

910.03 US ISSN 1047-2592
UPSCALE. 1989. 9/yr. $9.95. Upscale Communications, Inc., 594 Fielding Lane, Atlanta, GA 30310. TEL 800-877-2253. FAX 404-752-7655. adv.: B&W page $5500, color page $8400; trim 8 1/8 x 10 7/8. circ. 237,720.

910.03 US
UPTOWN; the voice of Minisink Townhouses and Camp. 1979. m. free. Minisink Town House, 646 Lenox Ave., New York, NY 10037. TEL 212-368-8400. FAX 212-926-4431. Ed. Gregory W. Gardner. bk.rev.; film rev.; illus. circ. 1,000.
  Description: Contains articles of interest to the African American community and on human services issues.

910.03 301 323.4 US ISSN 0147-1740
E185.86
URBAN LEAGUE REVIEW. 1975. s-a. $30 to individuals (foreign $50); institutions $60 (foreign $80). (National Urban League, Research Department) Transaction Publishers, Transaction Periodicals Consortium, Department 3092, New Brunswick, NJ 08903. TEL 908-932-2280. FAX 908-932-3138. Ed. Dionne J. Jones. bk.rev.; illus. circ. 500. (also avail. in microform from UMI; reprint service avail. from UMI) **Indexed:** C.I.J.E., Curr.Cont., Soc.Work Res.& Abstr. **Document type:** academic/scholarly publication.
  —BLDSC (9123.688550); Faxon; UnCover; UMI. CCC.
  Description: Examines the social and economic conditions of blacks and other minorities in the US.

970.1 US ISSN 0300-6808
UTE BULLETIN; news from Ute country. s-m. $20 (typically set in Oct.). (Ute Indian Tribe) Uintah Basin Standard, Box 400, Fort Duchesne, UT 84026. TEL 801-722-5131. Ed. Larry Cesspooch. circ. 1,800. **Document type:** bulletin.

917.306 US ISSN 8755-5808
VABA EESTI SONA/FREE ESTONIAN WORD. 1949. w. $52. Nordic Press, Inc., 243 E. 34th St., New York, NY 10016. TEL 212-686-3356. FAX 212-686-3356. Ed. Raudsepp Roosaare; Pub. Hans Kobin. circ. 3,000. **Document type:** newspaper.

917.106 CN ISSN 0837-0672
VABA EESTLANE/FREE ESTONIA. (Text in Estonian) 1952. s-w. Can.$86 (foreign Can.$115). Free Estonian Publishers Ltd., 120A Willowdale Ave., Willowdale, ON M2N 4Y2, Canada. TEL 416-733-4551. FAX 416-733-4550. Ed. Arvi Tinits. adv.; bk.rev. circ. 2,900. (also avail. in microfilm from CML) **Document type:** newspaper.
  Description: Covers Estonian interests.

914.09 SW ISSN 0049-5808
VALISEESTI.* 1944. s-m. SEK 165. Box 2171, 103 14 Stockholm, Sweden. Ed. Prof. Per Wieselgren. adv.; charts; illus. circ. 4,000.
  Description: Covers Swedish Estonian interests.

917.306 US
VAN NGHE TIEN PHONG. 1976. s-m. $110. Tien Phong, Inc., 15 N. Highland St., Arlington, VA 22201. TEL 703-522-7151. Ed. Hoang Thanh Nguyen. circ. 13,000. (back issues avail.)

917.106 CN ISSN 1236-1275
VAPAA SANA/FREE PRESS. (Text in English and Finnish) 1932. w. Can.$51($45) Vapaa Sana Press Ltd., 50 Weybright Court no.22, Scarborough, ON M1S 5A8, Canada. TEL 416-321-0808. FAX 416-321-0811. Ed. H. Hyvarinen. adv.; bk.rev. circ. 3,000. (also avail. in microfilm from CML)

917.306 US
VECINOS DEL VALLE. (Text in Spanish) 1990. w. $29.29. Daily News, 21221 Oxnard St., Woodland Hills, CA 91367. TEL 818-713-3229. FAX 818-713-3024. (Subsr. to: P.O. Box 4200, Woodland Hills, CA 91365) Ed. Aida Ferrarone. adv.; bk.rev.; film rev.; play rev.; illus. circ. 48,000. (looseleaf format; back issues avail.) **Document type:** newspaper.
  Description: Keeps the local Hispanic community informed of their activities, educational changes, health news, Latin America political events, entertainment and sports.

945 327 320 IT
VENTO DEL SUD; periodico di lotta meridionale. 1973. bi-m. L.5000. Casella Postle 188, 89100 Reggio Calagria, Italy. circ. 3,000. (tabloid format; back issues avail.)

943 GW
VEREIN FUER NIEDERSAECHSISCHES VOLKSTUM. BREMER HEIMATBUND. MITTEILUNGEN. 1925. irreg. membership. Verein fuer Niedersaechsisches Volkstum e.V., Erlanstr. 76, 2800 Bremen 1, Germany. TEL 504216. Eds. Karl Dillschneider, Wilhelm Klooke. adv.; bk.rev. circ. 1,000. **Document type:** newsletter.
  Formerly: Verein fuer Niedersaechsisches Volkstum. Mitteilungen.

LA VETTA D'ITALIA; mensile di politica e di cultura dell'Alto Adige. see *BIOGRAPHY*

917.309 US ISSN 0049-6073
VIBRATION. 1968. q. $5. Vibration Press, Box 08152, Cleveland, OH 44108. Eds. Norma and Don Freeman. bk.rev. circ. 250,000.
  Description: Covers Black interests.

917.306 US
VIENYBE. (Text in English and Lithuanian) 1886. fortn. $7. 192 Highland Blvd., Brooklyn, NY 11207. TEL 718-277-7257. Ed. Jonas Valaitis. adv.; illus. (tabloid format)
  Description: Covers Lithuanian interests.

059.959 US ISSN 1055-4610
VIET NAM HTHMAI NGOAI. (Text in Vietnamese) 1977. bi-m. $48 (effective Jan. 1992). Box 4108, Huntington Beach, CA 92605-4108. TEL 714-771-4483. FAX 714-633-9360. Ed. Tuong Thang. adv. circ. 5,000. (back issues avail.) **Document type:** consumer publication.
  Description: Covers Vietnamese politics and news of Vietnamese communities around the world.

296 CN ISSN 0042-5818
DS101
VIEWPOINTS. (Supplement to: Canadian Jewish News) 1970. 6/yr. c/o Canadian Jewish Congress, 1590 Avenue Docteur Penfield, Montreal, Que. H3G 1C5, Canada. FAX 514-931-0548. Ed. William Abrams. bk.rev. circ. 48,000.
  Description: Highlights Canadian-Jewish writers.

296 327
VIGIL/HA-MISHMAR. 1972. bi-m. membership. Washington Committee for Soviet Jewry, c/o Ruth Newman, Ed., 1401 Blair Mill Rd., No. 101, Silver Spring, MD 20910. circ. 3,900. **Document type:** newsletter.
  Description: Informational newsletter on Soviet Jewry.

494.545 011 AT ISSN 1030-7699
VIRGATS. (Text in Estonian) 1971. m. Aus.$20. Adelaide Estonian Society Inc., 200 Jeffcott St., North Adelaide, S.A. 5006, Australia. TEL 08-267-1649. Ed. Ilmar Magraken. bk.rev.; index. circ. 300. **Document type:** newsletter.
  Formerly: Virgats-Teataja.
  Description: News of the Estonian community in Australia and information from other Estonian communities world wide, including Estonia.

917.106 CN
VISION HISPANO AMERICANA. (Text in Spanish) w. 344 Bloor St., W., Ste. 504, Toronto, Ont. M5S 1W9, Canada. TEL 416-924-5888. Ed. Alfredo Saavedra. circ. 5,000.

378 US
VISIONS (KANSAS CITY). 1985. s-a. $3. Communications Publishing Group, Inc., 250 Mark Twain Tower, 106 W. 11th St., Ste. 250, Kansas City, MO 64105-1806. TEL 816-221-4404. FAX 816-221-1112. adv. circ. 100,000.
  Description: For Native-American students who want to pursue a higher education.

917.106 CN
VITA ITALIANA. (Text in Italian) 1967. w. Can.$10. Ethnic Press Council of Canada Inc., Box 158, Station L, Toronto, Ont. M6E 4Y5, Canada. TEL 416-656-2050. Ed. Rev. Dr. Mario Caligiure Varano. adv.; bk.rev. circ. 25,000.
  Description: Contains articles of interest to the Italian community.

VITAL ISSUES; the journal of African American speeches. see *POLITICAL SCIENCE*

055.1 SA
LA VOCE; organo d'informazione della comunita italiana in Sud Africa. (Text in Italian) 1975. w. R.50 (foreign R.150). Associazione per l'Informazione agli Italiani in Sud Africa, P.O. Box 95063, Grant Park 2051, Johannesburg, South Africa. TEL 27-11-728-7568. FAX 27-11-728-4918. Ed. P.L. Porciani. adv. contact: Rosa Di Benedetto. bk.rev. circ. 4,000. **Document type:** newspaper.
  Description: News from Italy and the world for the Italian community in South Africa.

055.1 916.206 UA
VOCE D'ITALIA. (Text in Italian) fortn. 90 Sharia Farahde, Alexandria, Egypt. Ed. R. Avellino.

055.1 UK ISSN 0042-7810
LA VOCE DEGLI ITALIANI; British-Italian fortnightly. (Text in Italian) 1948. fortn. £10. Pious Society of the Missionaries of St. Charles, 20 Brixton Rd., London SW9 6BU, England. TEL 071-735-5164. FAX 071-793-0385. Ed. Gaetano Parolin. adv.: page £500; trim 270 x 330. bk.rev.; abstr.; illus.; stat. circ. 6,000. (tabloid format) **Document type:** newspaper.

ETHNIC INTERESTS

055.1   CN
VOCE DEGLI ITALO CANADESI. Variant title: Voce d'Italia in Canada. 1968. s-m. Can.$15. 6736 Monk Blvd., Montreal, Que. H4E 3J1, Canada. TEL 514-769-5711. FAX 514-769-5711. Ed. Carlo Gatti. adv.; bk.rev. circ. 11,750. (reprint service avail.)
    Description: Contains articles of interest to the Italian community.

945 360   IT   ISSN 0394-8153
VOCE DELL'EMIGRANTE. (Supplement avail.) 1974. m. L.15000 (foreign L.25000). Comitato Regionale Emigranti Abruzzesi, Vico Sportello, 10, Casella Postale 7, 67035 Pratola Peligna (AQ), Italy. TEL 864-53147. FAX 864-52785. Ed. Angelo De Bartolomeis. adv.; bk.rev.; bibl.; charts; illus.; stat.; tr.lit. circ. 12,000. (tabloid format; back issues avail.) **Document type:** newspaper.
    Description: Focuses on immigration and emigration issues.

VOCE SERAFICA DELLA SARDEGNA. see *RELIGIONS AND THEOLOGY — Roman Catholic*

323.4   US   ISSN 0042-8183
VOICE OF THE BLACK COMMUNITY. 1968. w. $24. (Black Marble Inc., N N P A) Voice Newspaper, 625 E. Wood St., Decatur, IL 62522. TEL 217-423-5043. Ed. Horace G. Livingston Jr. adv.; illus. circ. 20,000. (tabloid format) **Document type:** newspaper.

970.1 811.051   US   ISSN 0894-9123
THE VOICE OF ZEWAM.* 1984. s-a. $6. Polaris Press, 15 Main St., Dobbs Ferry, NY 10522. TEL 914-693-8366. Ed. Brendan Donegan. bk.rev.; charts; illus. circ. 750. (back issues avail.)
    Description: Covers Native American affairs, political events as well as experimental literature.

296   CN   ISSN 0704-5352
VOIX SEPHARADE. 1960. 5/yr. Can.$25 (foreign $36). Communaute Sepharade du Quebec, 4735 Chemin de la Cote Ste. Catherine, Montreal, PQ H3W 1M1, Canada. FAX 514-733-3158. Ed. Judah Castiel. adv.; bk.rev. circ. 6,000.

956.940 296   IS   ISSN 0042-8671
VOLUNTEER. 1968. s-m. World Zionist Organization, Youth and Hechalutz Department, P.O. Box 92, Jerusalem 91920, Israel. TEL 02-732312. FAX 02-732159. Ed. Richard Levy. charts; illus.

917.106 320   CN
VORWAERTS/FORWARD; democratic monthly. (Text in German) 1947. bi-m. Can.$6. Sudeten Club, 179 Durant Ave., Toronto, Ont. M4J 4W5, Canada. Ed. Henry Weisbach. bk.rev. circ. 500. (tabloid format)
    Description: Covers German interests.

296   US   ISSN 0746-7869
VORWAERTS/FORWARD. (Text in Yiddish) 1897. w. $36 (effective 1994). Forward Association, 45 E. 33rd St., New York, NY 10016. TEL 212-889-8200. FAX 212-447-6406. **Document type:** newspaper.

917.306   US
LA VOZ (SEATTLE). (Text in English, Spanish) 1978. m. (except Jan. & Aug.). $10. Concilio for the Spanish Speaking, 157 Yesler Way., Ste. 400, Seattle, WA 98104-2572. TEL 206-461-4891. FAX 206-461-4893. adv.; bk.rev.; circ. 1,000 (paid); 14,000 (controlled). (tabloid format)
    Description: Covers community events, people, business, the arts, entertainment, sports and news.

056.1   CN
▼**VOZ DE MONTREAL.** (Text in Spanish) 1992. 50/yr. Can.$21($75) (foreign $120). 6020 Jean Talon E., Ste. 600, Montreal, PQ H1S 3B1, Canada. TEL 514-253-2332. FAX 514-253-6574. Ed. Basilio Giordano; Pub. Basilio Giordano. adv. circ. 12,000. (tabloid format) **Document type:** newspaper.

917.106   CN   ISSN 0049-6790
A VOZ DE PORTUGAL. (Text in Portuguese) 1961. w. Typogal Ltee., 4181 St. Dominique, Montreal, PQ H2W 2A7, Canada. TEL 514-844-0388. FAX 514-844-6283. Ed. Valdaline Ferreira. circ. 10,000.

948.406   US   ISSN 0742-7018
W I T S: I. (Wisconsin Introductions to Scandinavia); essay series. 1982. irreg. $3 per no. University of Wisconsin, Department of Scandinavian Studies, 1306 Van Hise Hall, Madison, WI 53706. TEL 608-262-2090. Eds. Harald S. Naess, Niels Ingwersen. circ. 2,000. (back issues avail.)
    Description: Pamphlet series providing short introductions to various aspects of Scandinavian life and civilization.

948.406   US   ISSN 0742-7026
W I T S: II. (Wisconsin Introductions to Scandinavia); text series. 1982. irreg. $3 per no. University of Wisconsin, Department of Scandinavian Studies, 1306 Van Hise Hall, Madison, WI 53706. TEL 608-262-2090. Eds. Harald S. Naess, Niels Ingwersen.

970.1 810   US
WANBLI HO/EAGLE'S VOICE. (Text in English, Lakota) 1975. a. $4.50. Sinte Gleska College, Box 8, Mission, SD 57555. TEL 605-856-2321. Ed. Gloria Dyc. circ. 500.
    Description: Literature on the experiences of Native Americans and-or land and people of the high plains.

914.706   CN   ISSN 1180-2901
WANDERING VOLHYNIANS; a magazine for the descendents of Germans from Volhynia and Poland. q. Can.$12 (US $12; elsewhere Can.$14). Wandering Volhynian Group, 3492 W. 39th Ave., Vancouver, B.C. V6N 3A2, Canada. TEL 604-263-4444. FAX 604-263-4444. Ed. Ewald Wuschlie. bk.rev.; maps. circ. 600. (back issues avail.)

917.309   US   ISSN 0043-0447
WASHINGTON AFRO-AMERICAN. 1892. w. $26. Afro-American Co. of Baltimore City, 628 N. Eutaw St., Baltimore, MD 21201. TEL 410-728-8200. FAX 202-939-7461. (Subscr. to: 2002 11th St., N.W., Washington, DC 20001. TEL 202-332-0080) adv.; bk.rev.; illus. circ. 25,000. (also avail. in microfilm from UMI; reprint service avail. from UMI) **Document type:** newspaper.

WASHINGTON - JAPAN JOURNAL. see *POLITICAL SCIENCE — International Relations*

910.63   US
WASHINGTON LIVING. 1982. m. $16.80. Spears Publishing Co., 6506 McCahill Dr., Laurel, MD 20707. Ed. Sandy Spears.
    Description: Contains items of interest to the Black community.

910.03   US   ISSN 1042-4229
WASHINGTON VIEW.* 1989. bi-m. $12 (typically set in May). Viewcomm, Inc., 6856 Eastern Ave. N.W. No.309, Washington, DC 20012-2165. TEL 202-371-1313. FAX 202-842-0215. Ed. Malcolm E. Beech Sr. adv. circ. 40,000.
    Description: Targeted to upscale blacks living in the Washington area. Provides articles on lifestyle and entertainment, working women, small business and government.

915.406   UK
WATAN WEEKEND. (Text in Urdu) 1969. w. 40p. per no. Watan Publications Ltd., 261 Hoe St., London E 17, England. Ed. A. Razzaq. adv.; bk.rev. circ. 29,500.
    Formerly: Akhbar-e-Watan Urdu Newsweekly (ISSN 0308-1656)

WATANI. see *RELIGIONS AND THEOLOGY — Other Denominations And Sects*

910.03   US
WAVE NEWSPAPER GROUP. (Published in regional editions: Southwest Wave - Southwest News; Angeles Mesa - Tribune News Wave; Southwest Topics - Sun Wave; Inglewood - Hawthorne Wave; Culver City Star; Westchester Star; Compton - Carson Wave; Lynwood Press; Central News - Star - Journal Wave) 1918. w. $78; newsstand price: $0.26. Central News - Wave Publications, 2621 W. 54th St., Los Angeles, CA 90043. TEL 213-290-3000. FAX 213-291-0219. Ed. Alice Marshall; Pub. C.Z. Wilson. adv. circ. 635,000. cols./p.: 6. **Document type:** newspaper.
    Description: Covers news and events in the many ethnically diverse communities in and near Los Angeles.

917.106   CN   ISSN 0703-9387
WAWATAY NEWS. (Text in English, Oji-Cree) 1974. bi-w. Can.$26.75 to individuals; institutions Can.$32.10; US Can.$40. Wawatay Native Communications Society, 16 Fifth Ave., P.O. Box 1180, Sioux Lookout, ON P8T 1B7, Canada. TEL 807-737-2951. FAX 807-737-3224. Ed. Diane Millar. circ. 5,500. **Document type:** newspaper.
    Description: Reports on events, issues and news affecting Native people across the province.

THE WAY/SHLIAKH; Ukrainian Catholic bi-weekly. see *RELIGIONS AND THEOLOGY — Roman Catholic*

943.106   AT
WELFARER. (Text in English, German) 1971. bi-m. Aus.$5. Australian-German Welfare Society Inc., 1a Leicester Ave., Strathfield, N.S.W. 2135, Australia. TEL 02-746-6274. adv.; bk.rev. circ. 1,000. (looseleaf format; back issues avail.) **Document type:** newsletter.
    Description: Covers social services and welfare issues.

WELLSPRINGS; a quarterly journal exploring the inner dimensions of Torah and Jewish life. see *RELIGIONS AND THEOLOGY — Judaic*

917.306   US
WELSH STUDIES. irreg., latest no.10. $39.95 per no. Edwin Mellen Press, 415 Ridge St., Box 450, Lewiston, NY 14092. TEL 716-754-2788. FAX 716-754-4056. **Document type:** monographic series.

917.306   US
THE WEST NEWS. 1890. w. $18. Czechoslovak Publishing Co. Inc., Box 82, West, TX 76691. TEL 817-826-3718. FAX 817-826-3719. Ed. Larry Knapek. adv. contact: Sue Pescaia. bk.rev. circ. 3,100. **Document type:** newspaper.

910.03   US   ISSN 0043-3373
WESTCHESTER COUNTY PRESS. 1928. w. $25. Negro Publishers of Westchester, Inc., Box 1631, White Plains, NY 10602. TEL 914-684-0006. Ed. M. Paul Redd; Pub. M. Paul Redd. adv. contact: Jo Pease. bk.rev.; film rev.; play rev.; illus. circ. 7,500. (tabloid format; reprint service avail. from ISI) **Document type:** newspaper.

910.03
E185.5   US   ISSN 0197-4327
WESTERN JOURNAL OF BLACK STUDIES. 1977. q. $25 to individuals (overseas $32.50); institutions $35 (overseas $42.50) (effective 1994). (Washington State University, Comparative American Cultures Program) Washington State University Press, Pullman, WA 99164-5910. TEL 509-335-3518. FAX 509-3335-8568. Ed. Talmage Anderson. bk.rev.; film rev.; play rev. circ. 600. (back issues avail.; reprint service avail. from UMI) Indexed: Amer.Hist.& Life (1993-), Amer.Hum.Ind., C.I.J.E., ERIC, Hist.Abstr. (1993-), Psychol.Abstr., R.G. **Document type:** academic/scholarly publication. —BLDSC (9300.829000); Faxon; UnCover; UMI.

296 900   US
WESTERN STATES JEWISH HISTORY. 1968. q. $20. Western States Jewish History Association, 7106 Owensmouth Ave., Canuga Park, CA 91303. TEL 818-346-1410. FAX 818-346-4236. Ed. Dr. William M. Kramer. bk.rev.; charts; illus.; index. circ. 1,000. **Indexed:** Amer.Hist.& Life, Hist.Abstr., Ind.Jew.Per.
    Formerly (until 1983): Western States Jewish Historical Quarterly (ISSN 0043-4221)
    Description: Studies Jewish history west of the Mississippi, including Alaska, Hawaii, the Pacific Rim, and western Mexico.

917.806   US
WESTERN VIKING. (Text in Norwegian and English) 1889. w. $27.50. Western Viking Inc., 2405 N.W. Market St., Ste. 202, Seattle, WA 98107. TEL 206-784-4617. FAX 206-784-4856. Ed. Alf L. Knudsen. adv.; bk.rev.; illus.; circ. 3,000 (controlled). (tabloid format) **Document type:** newspaper.
    Description: Covers Norwegian interests.

ETHNIC INTERESTS

970.1   US   ISSN 0300-6565
E75
WHISPERING WIND; American Indian: past & present. 1967. bi-m. $16. (Written Heritage) Jack Heriard, Ed. & Pub., 8009 Wales St., New Orleans, LA 70126-1952. TEL 504-246-3742. adv.; bk.rev.; illus. circ. 14,000. (back issues avail.) **Document type:** academic/scholarly publication.
    Description: Material, culture, and history of the North American Indian.

WHO'S WHO AMONG HISPANIC AMERICANS. see *BIOGRAPHY*

WHO'S WHO IN BLACK DENTISTRY IN AMERICA. see *MEDICAL SCIENCES — Dentistry*

WHO'S WHO IN WORLD JEWRY; a biographical encyclopedia of outstanding Jews. see *BIOGRAPHY*

970.1 378   US   ISSN 0749-6427
E96
WICAZO SA REVIEW/RED PENCIL REVIEW; a journal of Native American Studies. (Text in English; occasionally in American Indian languages) 1985. s-a. $20 (effective 1993). Wicazo Sa Review, Rte.8, Box 510, Dakota Meadows, Rapid City, SD 57702. TEL 509-359-2871. (Co-sponsor: Eastern Washington University, Indian Studies Department) Ed. Elizabeth Cook-Lynn. adv.; bk.rev. circ. 680. (back issues avail.) **Document type:** academic/scholarly publication.
    —UnCover.
    Description: Focuses on scholarship in the field of Native American studies, and the devlopment of this academic discipline.

970.1   US   ISSN 0889-7867
WILDFIRE; a "plus" network magazine. 1966. q. $15 (Canada $22.50; elsewhere $32.50). Bear Tribe Medicine Society, Box 199, Devon, PA 19333. Ed. Elizabeth Robinson. adv.; bk.rev. circ. 10,000. (also avail. in microfilm from UMI; back issues avail.)
    Formerly (until 1984): Many Smokes (ISSN 0025-2670)

296   US
WILLIAM PETSCHEK NATIONAL JEWISH FAMILY CENTER. NEWSLETTER. 1980. s-a. $10 membership. American Jewish Committee, Jewish Communal Affairs Department, 165 E. 56th St., New York, NY 10022. TEL 212-751-4000. FAX 212-751-4018. Ed. Sherry Rosen. bk.rev. circ. 5,000. **Document type:** newsletter.
    Description: Covers Jewish family interests.

917.106   CN
THE WINDMILL (ONTARIO EDITION). (Text in Dutch) 1958. m. Can.$20. P.O. Bag 9033, Surrey, BC V3T 4X3, Canada. TEL 416-287-6487. adv.; bk.rev. circ. 5,100.

917.106   CN   ISSN 0837-3299
WINDMILL HERALD: CENTRAL EAST CANADA. (Text in Dutch and English) 1954. fortn. $20.40. Vanderheide Publishing Co. Ltd., P.O. Bag 9033, Surrey, BC V3T 4X3, Canada. TEL 604-597-2144. (U.S. dist. addr.: Box 313, Lynden, WA 98264-0313) Ed. Albert Van der Heide. bk.rev. (tabloid format)
    Formerly: Hollandia News.

917.106   CN   ISSN 0712-6417
WINDMILL HERALD: WESTERN EDITION. (Text in Dutch and English) 1958. fortn. $20.40. Vanderheide Publishing Co. Ltd., P.O. Bag 9033, Surrey, BC V3T 4X3, Canada. TEL 604-597-2144. (U.S. dist. addr.: Box 313, Lynden, WA 98264-0313) Ed. Albert Van der Heide.

WINDOW (RESEDA); view of the Armenian Church. see *RELIGIONS AND THEOLOGY — Other Denominations And Sects*

330 370   US   ISSN 0888-8612
WINDS OF CHANGE; American Indian education & opportunity. 1986. q. $24 (Canada $34). (American Indian Science & Engineering Society) A I S E S Publishing, 1630 30th St., Ste. 301, Boulder, CO 80301. TEL 303-444-9099. FAX 303-444-6607. Ed. James R. Weidlein. adv.; bk.rev. circ. 60,000.
    —UnCover.
    Description: Topics oriented toward career development and enhancement, plus information on tribal culture and activity.

917.106   CN   ISSN 0834-177X
WINDSPEAKER. 1983. bi-w. Can.$28($40) Aboriginal Multi-Media Society of Alberta, 15001 112th Ave., Edmonton, AB T5N 2V6, Canada. TEL 403-455-2700; 800-661-5469. FAX 403-455-7639. Ed. Linda Caldwell; Pub. Bert Crowfoot. adv. contact: Paul Macedo. circ. 12,000 (paid); 3,000 (controlled). (tabloid format; also avail. in microfiche; microfilm; back issues avail.) **Document type:** newspaper.
    Formerly (until 1986): A M M S A. Aboriginal Multi-Media Society of Alberta (ISSN 0822-6245)
    Description: Covers the news, information and issues which impact Aboriginal people throughout Canada and around the world.

910.03   US
WINSTON-SALEM CHRONICLE. (Supplement avail. m.: Black College Sports Review) 1974. w. $30.72. Chronicle Publishing Co., Inc., 617 N. Liberty St., Winston-Salem, NC 27101. TEL 919-722-8624. Ed. Deby Jo Ferguson. adv. circ. 9,251. **Document type:** newspaper.

296   US   ISSN 0043-6488
WISCONSIN JEWISH CHRONICLE. 1921. w. $30. Milwaukee Jewish Federation, Inc., 1360 N. Prospect Ave., Milwaukee, WI 53202. TEL 414-271-2992. FAX 414-271-0487. Ed. Andrew Muchin. adv.; bk.rev.; film rev.; play rev. circ. 5,300. **Document type:** newspaper.
    ●Also available online.

052   AT   ISSN 0043-7123
WOCHE IN AUSTRALIEN; an independent Australian-German newspaper. (Text in German) 1956. w. Aus.$90. Euro Media Pty. Ltd., 1-3 Seddon St., Bankstown, N.S.W 2200, Australia. TEL 02-707-4999. FAX 02-708-6025. (Dist. by: Euro Media Pty. Ltd., P.O. Box 36, Bankstown, N.S.W. 2200, Australia; Dist. in Europe by: Unipress GmbH, Rosental 3, 80331 Munich, Germany. TEL 089-2609014) Ed. John Jakobi. adv.; B&W page Aus.$1600. illus. circ. 9,600. (tabloid format) **Document type:** newspaper.

WOMEN AND MINORITIES IN SCIENCE AND ENGINEERING. see *ENGINEERING*

WOMEN'S WORLD. see *WOMEN'S INTERESTS*

WOMEN'S ZIONIST ORGANIZATION OF SOUTH AFRICA. NEWS AND VIEWS. see *POLITICAL SCIENCE*

WORD UP! (WASHINGTON). see *JOURNALISM*

296   US   ISSN 0043-8111
THE WORKMEN'S CIRCLE - ARBITER RING CALL. 1932. q. $12. Workmen's Circle - Arbeter Ring, 45 E. 33 St., New York, NY 10016. TEL 212-898-6800. FAX 212-532-7518. Ed. Diane H. Merlin. bk.rev.; circ. 30,000 (controlled). **Document type:** newsletter.
    Description: Highlights organizational activities, Jewish communal affairs.

WORLD JEWISH DIRECTORY. see *RELIGIONS AND THEOLOGY — Judaic*

915.1   CN
WORLD JOURNAL. (Text in Chinese) d. 2288 Clark Dr., Vancouver, BC V5N 3G8, Canada. TEL 604-876-1338. FAX 604-876-9191. Ed. John Hsu. adv. contact: Daniel Liu. **Document type:** newspaper.

917.306   US
WORLD JOURNAL/WORLD JOURNAL. (Text in Chinese) d. $128. T.W. Wang Inc., 141-07 20th Ave., Whitestone, NY 11357. TEL 718-746-9006. Ed. Louis Chiu. adv. contact: Eshin Nee. **Document type:** newspaper.
    Description: Contains news of interest to Chinese communities in the United States.

WORLD NEWS DIGEST. see *POLITICAL SCIENCE*

296   CN   ISSN 1186-6713
WORLD OF CHABAD. (Text in English, Hebrew, Russian) 1987. bi-m. Lubavitch British Columbia, 5750 Oak St., Vancouver, BC V6M 2V9, Canada. TEL 604-266-1313. FAX 604-263-7934. Ed. Angelina Spilberg. adv.; B&W page Can.$1125; adv. contact: Kevin Abrams. bk.rev. circ. 6,000. (tabloid format)
    Description: Jewish religious and philosophical articles, stories and announcements.

296   IS   ISSN 0333-9068
WORLD UNION OF JEWISH STUDIES. Represents: World Congress of Jewish Studies. Proceedings. quadrennia, 10th, 1989. price varies. Magnes Press, Hebrew University, Jerusalem, P.O. Box 7695, Jerusalem 91076, Israel. TEL 972-2-660341. FAX 972-2-633370. (back issues avail.) **Document type:** proceedings.

917.306   US
WOTANIN - WOWAPI. 1969. w. $30 (effective Sep. 1990). Fort Peck Assiniboine and Sioux Tribes, Box 1027, Poplar, MT 59255. TEL 406-768-5155. FAX 406-768-5478. Ed. Bonnie Red Elk. adv. contact: Marian Montclair. bk.rev.; illus. circ. 2,500. **Document type:** newspaper.
    Formerly: Wotanin.
    Description: Covers American Indian interests.

XIBEI MINZU YANJIU/NORTHWEST MINORITIES STUDIES. see *ORIENTAL STUDIES*

917.306   US
XIN SHI SHI/NEW CREATION CONNECTION. (Text in Chinese) 1991. w. free. 1967 Oak Tree Rd., Ste. 2A, Edison, NJ 08820. TEL 908-906-2028. FAX 908-906-2015. (tabloid format) **Document type:** newspaper.
    Description: Contains news of interest to Chinese communities in New Jersey.

917.306   US
XINYA SHIBAO/NEO ASIAN AMERICAN TIMES. (Text in Chinese) w. free. 35-20 156 St., Flushing, NY 11354. TEL 718-225-8686. FAX 718-463-8024. adv. **Document type:** newspaper.
    Description: Contains news of interest to Chinese communities in the United States.

Y S B. (Young Sisters & Brothers) see *CHILDREN AND YOUTH — For*

970.1   US   ISSN 0199-3046
YAKIMA NATION REVIEW. 1970. s-m. $26 (foreign $52). Yakima Indian Nation, Box 310, Toppenish, WA 98948-0310. TEL 509-865-5121. Ed. Ronn L. Washines. adv.; bk.rev.; stat. circ. 2,000. **Document type:** newspaper.
    Description: Covers American Indian interests.

YE OLDE DUTCH MILL. see *CLUBS*

296   US
YESHIVA UNIVERSITY SEPHARDIC BULLETIN. 1973. a. free. Yeshiva University, Sephardic Studies Program, 500 W. 185th St., New York, NY 10033. TEL 212-960-5277. Ed. Rabbi M. Mitchell Serels. circ. 24,000. **Document type:** bulletin.

YIDDISH. see *LITERATURE*

296   IS
YIDDISH WELT. (Text in Yiddish) 1983. m. $20. World Council for Yiddish and Jewish Culture, 9 Mendele St., Tel Aviv 63431, Israel. Ed. Yitzhak Yanosowich. adv.; bk.rev.; play rev.; bibl. circ. 3,000. (back issues avail.)

296   US   ISSN 0044-0426
AP91
YIDDISHE KULTUR. (Text in Yiddish) 1938. 10/yr. $20. Yiddisher Kultur Farband Inc., 1133 Broadway, Ste. 1019, New York, NY 10010. TEL 212-691-0708. Ed. I. Goldberg. adv.; bk.rev. circ. 3,000. **Indexed:** M.L.A.
    Description: Covers Jewish interests.

956.940 296   US   ISSN 0044-0434
YIDDISHER KEMFER.* (Text in Yiddish) 1906. bi-w. $30. (Labor Zionist Alliance) Labor Zionist Letters, Inc., 275 Seventh Ave., Rm. 17R, New York, NY 10001-6776. Ed. M. Strigler. adv.; bk.rev. circ. 3,500. (tabloid format; also avail. in microfilm from AJP; reprint service avail. from UMI)

YIVO ANNUAL. see *SOCIAL SCIENCES: COMPREHENSIVE WORKS*

YOD; revue des etudes hebraiques et juives modernes et contemporaines. see *RELIGIONS AND THEOLOGY — Judaic*

ETHNIC INTERESTS — ABSTRACTING, BIBLIOGRAPHIES, STATISTICS

296 301.4157   US
HA-YONAH/DOVE. 1982. m. Congregation Ahavat Shalom, Box 14392, San Francisco, CA 94114-0392. TEL 415-621-1020. Ed. David May. adv.; illus. circ. 350. (looseleaf format; back issues avail.)
   Description: Community interest for gay, lesbian and bisexual Jews.

YORKER PALATINE NEWSLETTER. see *POPULATION STUDIES*

YOUNG HORIZONS INDIGO. see *CHILDREN AND YOUTH — About*

296   US   ISSN 0044-0817
AP222
YOUNG JUDAEAN. 1910. 4/yr. $5. Hadassah Zionist Youth Commission, 50 W. 58th St., New York, NY 10019. TEL 212-355-7900. bk.rev.; film rev.; play rev. circ. 5,000. (back issues avail.) **Indexed:** Ind.Jew.Per.

YOUR CHILD. see *EDUCATION*

956.940 296   UK   ISSN 0044-1155
YOUTH ALIYAH REVIEW. 1956. q. free. Children and Youth Aliyah Committee for Great Britain & Eire, Britannia House, 960 High Rd., N. Finchley, London N12 9YA, England. TEL 081-446-4321. FAX 081-343-7383. Ed. Lucie Kaye. adv.; bk.rev.; illus. circ. 5,000. **Document type:** newsletter.

410 800
YUGNTRUF; Yiddish student quarterly. (Text in Yiddish) 1963. q. $18 to individuals; students $10. Yugntruf - Youth for Yiddish, Inc., 200 W. 72nd St., Ste. 40, New York, NY 10023. TEL 212-787-6675. Ed. David Braun. adv.; bk.rev.; illus. circ. 1,200. **Indexed:** M.L.A.

917.406   US
ZAJEDNICAR. (Text and summaries in English and Croatian) 1902. w. $45 includes membership. Croatian Fraternal Union of America, 100 Delaney Dr., Pittsburgh, PA 15235. TEL 412-351-3909. FAX 412-823-1594. Ed. Edward J. Verlich. bk.rev.; stat.; circ. 40,000 (controlled). (also avail. in microfilm)
   Description: Contains articles of interest to the Croatian community.

916.9   MF
ZAMANA. (Text in English, French and Hindi) 1948. s-m. $1. c/o B. Bucktowarsingh, Ed., 14 Vallonville St., Port Louis, Mauritius. bibl. circ. 1,000.

917.309   US   ISSN 0044-1848
ZARJA/DAWN. (Text in English and Slovenian) 1928. m. membership. Slovenian Women's Union of America, 431 N. Chicago St., Joliet, IL 60432. TEL 815-727-1926. Ed. Corinne Leskovar. adv. circ. 10,000.
   Description: Covers Slovenian interests.

059.9199 079.569   LE
ZARTONK. (Text in Armenian) 1937. d. Rue Nahr Ibrahim, P.O. Box 617, Beirut, Lebanon. Ed. P. Tomassian. **Document type:** newspaper.

914.3   CN
ZEIT. w. Can.$69. Team Publications, Ltd., 29 Coldwater Rd., Toronto, ON M3B 1Y8, Canada. TEL 416-391-4196. circ. 9,075.

917.302   US
ZGODA; fraternal, cultural, sports and general news. (Text in English and Polish) 1881. s-m. membership. Polish National Alliance of North America, 6100 N. Cicero Ave., Chicago, IL 60646-4385. TEL 312-286-0500. FAX 312-286-0842. Ed. Wojciech A. Wierzewski. bk.rev.; illus.; circ. 72,200 (controlled). (also avail. in microfilm)
   Description: Contains articles of interest to the Polish-American community.

ZGODOVINSKI CASOPIS; istoriceskij zurnal. see *HISTORY — History Of Europe*

ZHONGGUO CHAOXIANZU JIAOYU/KOREAN CHINESE EDUCATION. see *EDUCATION*

ZHONGGUO SHAOSHU MINZU. see *ORIENTAL STUDIES*

ZHONGGUO ZANGXUE/STUDY - TIBETAN NATIONALITIES. see *ORIENTAL STUDIES*

951.906   CC   ISSN 1000-8667
ZHONGYANG MINZU XUEYUAN XUEBAO/CENTRAL INSTITUTE OF NATIONALITIES. JOURNAL. (Text in Chinese) bi-m. Zhongyang Minzu Xueyuan, Xuebao Bianjibu, No.27, Baishiqiao, Beijing 100081, People's Republic of China. TEL 8022288. Ed. Li Yaozong.

296   IS   ISSN 0044-4758
DS101
ZION; a quarterly for research in Jewish history. (Text in Hebrew; summaries in English) 1935. q. $50 to individuals; institutions $70 (effective 1994). Historical Society of Israel, P.O. Box 4179, Jerusalem 91041, Israel. TEL 972-2-637171. FAX 972-2-662135. Ed.Bd. adv.: B&W page $400. bk.rev.; bibl. circ. 1,000. (reprint service avail. from ISI) **Indexed:** Amer.Hist.& Life, Arts & Hum.Cit.Ind., Curr.Cont., Hist.Abstr., Ind.Heb.Per., Int.Z.Bibelwiss., Rel.& Theol.Abstr. (1978-). **Document type:** academic/scholarly publication.

296   SA   ISSN 0044-4782
ZIONIST RECORD AND S.A. JEWISH CHRONICLE; the organ of South African Jewry. (Text in Afrikaans, English) 1908. w. R.15. South African Zionist Federation, 84 De Villiers St., Johannesburg, South Africa. Ed. Mervyn Lax. adv.; illus. circ. 12,000.
   Description: Covers Jewish interests.

ZSHURNALIST. see *JOURNALISM*

ZUKUNFT/FUTURE. see *LITERARY AND POLITICAL REVIEWS*

949.7 398 790.13   CI
ZUMBERACKE NOVINE. (Text in Serbo-Croatian) 1966. q. 1000 din.($15) (Kulturno Prosvjetno Drustvo "Zumberak") Vjesnik, Avenija Bratstva Jedinstva 1, Zagreb, Croatia. adv.; bk.rev. circ. 2,000. (back issues avail.)

917.106   CN
ZWIAZKOWIEC/ALLIANCER. (Text in English, Polish) 1930. w. Polish Alliance Press Ltd., 1638 Bloor St. W., Toronto, Ont. M6P 4A8, Canada. TEL 416-531-2491. Ed. Jacek Borzecki. adv. circ. 8,878. (also avail. in microfilm from CML)
   Description: Covers activities of the Polish community.

900 296   PL   ISSN 0006-4033
DS135.P6
ZYDOWSKI INSTYTUT HISTORYCZNY W POLSCE. BIULETYN. (Text in Polish; summaries in English, Yiddish) 1951. q. $25. Zydowski Instytut Historyczny w Polsce, Ul. Tlomackie 3-5, 00-090 Warsaw, Poland. Ed. Daniel Grinberg. bk.rev.; charts; illus.; cum.index. circ. 580. (tabloid format) **Indexed:** Amer.Hist.& Life, Hist.Abstr., Numis.Lit. **Document type:** academic/scholarly publication.
   —SWETS.
   Description: Covers Jewish interests.

917.306   US
20 DE MAYO SPANISH NEWSPAPER. (Text in Spanish) 1969. a. $30 (effective 1992). 20 de Mayo Spanish Newspaper, 1824 Sunset Blvd., Ste. 202, Los Angeles, CA 90026. TEL 213-483-8511. FAX 213-483-6474. Ed. Abel Perez. adv. contact: Gina Perez. bk.rev.; cum.index. circ. 25,000. (tabloid format; back issues avail.) **Document type:** newspaper.
   Description: Covers any subject of interest to the Hispanic community of Southern California in particular and the U.S. in general.

ETHNIC INTERESTS — Abstracting, Bibliographies, Statistics

970.1   US
AMERICAN INDIAN BIBLIOGRAPHIC SERIES. 1977. a. University of California, Los Angeles, American Indian Studies Center, 405 Hilgard Ave., 3220 Campbell Hall, Los Angeles, CA 90024-1548. Ed. Duane Champagne. circ. 500. (reprint service avail.) **Document type:** academic/scholarly publication, bibliography.

910.03 016   US   ISSN 0360-2710
Z1361.N39
BIBLIOGRAPHIC GUIDE TO BLACK STUDIES.* 1975. a. $160 (foreign $180). G.K. Hall & Co., c/o MacMillan Publishing Co., 866 Third Ave., 18th fl., New York, NY 10022. TEL 212-702-6789. (Orders to: MacMillan Distribution Center, 100 Front St., Box 500, Riverside, NJ 08075-7500. TEL 800-257-5755) **Document type:** bibliography, abstracting/indexing.
   —BLDSC (1964.879000).
   Description: Provides an annual survey of non-serial literature in black studies. Lists materials catalogued during the past year by the New York Public Library, Schomburg Center for Research in Black Culture.

917.306   US   ISSN 1046-7882
BIBLIOGRAPHIES AND INDEXES IN ETHNIC STUDIES. 1990. irreg. price varies. Greenwood Press, Inc. (Subsidiary of: Greenwood Publishing Group Inc.), 88 Post Rd. W., Box 5007, Westport, CT 06881-5007. TEL 203-226-3571. FAX 203-222-1502. **Document type:** bibliography, monographic series.

BIBLIOGRAPHISCHE INFORMATIONEN ZU MIGRATION UND ETHNIZITAET. see *SOCIOLOGY — Abstracting, Bibliographies, Statistics*

960   US   ISSN 0882-7044
BIO-BIBLIOGRAPHIES IN AFRO-AMERICAN AND AFRICAN STUDIES. 1985. irreg. price varies. Greenwood Press, Inc. (Subsidiary of: Greenwood Publishing Group Inc.), 88 Post Rd. W., Box 5007, Westport, CT 06881-5007. TEL 203-226-3571. FAX 203-222-1502.

910.03 011   US
BLACK NEWSPAPER INDEX. 1977. q. $860. University Microfilms International, 300 N. Zeeb Rd., Ann Arbor, MI 48106. TEL 313-761-4700; 800-521-0600. FAX 313-761-1203. **Document type:** abstracting/indexing.
   ●Also available online. Vendor(s): DIALOG Information Services, Inc.

016 910.03   US   ISSN 0093-5697
BLACK PRESS PERIODICAL DIRECTORY.* Variant title: Black Communicators. 1973. irreg., latest 1984. $65. Black Newspaper Clipping Bureau, Inc., 42 Macombs Place, Harlem, NY 10039. TEL 212-491-9031. Ed. Lawrence T. Jackson. adv.; stat. circ. 3,000. (looseleaf format)

917.306 011   US   ISSN 1044-3487
Z1361.M4
CHICANO INDEX. 1981. a. $90. University of California at Berkeley, Chicano Studies Library Publication Unit, 3404 Dwinelle Hall, Berkeley, CA 94702. TEL 510-642-3859. FAX 510-642-6456. Ed. Lillian Castillo-Speed. circ. 500. (back issues avail.) **Document type:** abstracting/indexing.
   ●Also available on CD-ROM.
   Formerly (until 1989): Chicano Periodical Index (ISSN 0891-6985)
   Description: Indexes Chicano periodicals, books and selective indexes approximately 400 mainstream periodicals; also includes new Chicano books and articles in anthologies.

305.868 917.306   US   ISSN 1056-7992
E184.S75
HISPANIC AMERICANS; a statistical sourcebook. 1991. a. $44 paperbound; library ed. $54 (effective 1992). Numbers & Concepts, 2525 Arapahoe Ave., Ste. E4-221, Boulder, CO 80302. TEL 303-444-3462. Ed. Alfred Garwood. **Document type:** monographic series.
   Description: Statistical summary of information published by the U.S. government about Hispanic Americans.

980.2   US
HISPANIC FOCUS. 1982. irreg. free. U.S. Library of Congress, Hispanic Division, Washington, DC 20540. TEL 202-707-5400. circ. 1,000.

296 016   IS   ISSN 0073-5817
INDEX OF ARTICLES ON JEWISH STUDIES/RESHIMAT MA'AMARIM BE-MADA'E HA-YAHADUT. (Text in various languages) 1969. s-a. $20. Jewish National and University Library, P.O. Box 34165, Jerusalem 91341, Israel. TEL 972-2-585039. FAX 972-2-586315. TELEX 25367. Ed. Bitya Ben-Shammai. circ. 1,200. **Document type:** abstracting/indexing.
● Also available online.
  Description: Bibliography of articles and book reviews dealing with all aspects of Jewish studies, and the land and state of Israel, in Hebrew and all European languages.

016.5   US   ISSN 0899-6253
AI3
INDEX TO BLACK PERIODICALS. 1960. a. $95 (foreign $125). G.K. Hall & Co., c/o MacMillan Publishing Co., 866 Third Ave., 18th Fl., New York, NY 10022. TEL 212-702-6789. (Orders to: MacMillan Distribution Center, 100 Front St., Box 500, Riverside, NJ 08075-7500. TEL 800-257-5755) (Co-sponsor: Schomburg Collection of Negro Literature and History) **Document type:** abstracting/indexing.
  Former titles: Index to Periodical Articles By and About Blacks (ISSN 0161-8245); Index to Periodical Articles By and About Negroes (ISSN 0073-5973); Index to Selected Periodicals.
  Description: Index to Afro-American periodicals of general and scholarly interest.

JEWISH EDUCATIONAL STATISTICS. see EDUCATION — Abstracting, Bibliographies, Statistics

016 910.03   US
MINORITY INFORMATION TRADE ANNUAL;* publishers and producers lists of Afro-American material. 1977. a? $35. Black Resources Information Coordinating Services, Inc., 614 Howard Ave., Tallahassee, FL 32310-6222. TEL 904-576-7522. Ed. Emily A. Copeland.

N A B W A CONVENTION BULLETIN. (National Association of Black Women Attorneys) see LAW

N A B W A NEWS. (National Association of Black Women Attorneys) see LAW

N B A BULLETIN. (National Bar Association) see LAW

N B A JOURNAL. (National Bar Association) see LAW

N B A MAGAZINE. (National Bar Association) see LAW

N C W B A NEWSLETTER. (National Conference of Women's Bar Associations) see LAW

NATIONAL BLACK COALITION OF FEDERAL AVIATION EMPLOYEES. UPDATE. see PUBLIC ADMINISTRATION

NATIONAL CONFERENCE OF BLACK LAWYERS. NOTES. see LAW

016.342   US
NATIONAL INDIAN LAW LIBRARY. CATALOGUE; an index to Indian legal materials and resources. 1974. every 5 yrs. $75. Native American Rights Fund, National Indian Law Library, 1522 Broadway, Boulder, CO 80302-6296. TEL 303-447-8760. bibl. circ. 1,000. **Document type:** abstracting/indexing.
  Formerly: Native American Rights Fund. Catalogue (ISSN 0092-3419)

970.1 016   US   ISSN 1040-9629
NATIVE AMERICAN BIBLIOGRAPHY SERIES. 1980. irreg., latest no.16. price varies. Scarecrow Press, Inc., Box 4167, Metuchen, NJ 08840. TEL 800-537-7107. Ed. Jack W. Marken. **Document type:** bibliography.

THE NETWORKER (WASHINGTON). see PUBLIC ADMINISTRATION

PUERTO RICAN BAR ASSOCIATION. NEWSLETTER. see LAW

917.306   US
▼**STATISTICAL RECORD OF HISPANIC AMERICANS.** 1993. biennial. $89.50 (effective June 1993). Gale Research Inc., 835 Penobscot Bldg., Detroit, MI 48226. TEL 313-961-2242. FAX 313-961-6083. Ed. Marlita A. Reddy.
  Description: Contains about 900 statistical graphs, charts, and tables.

970.1   US
▼**STATISTICAL RECORD OF NATIVE NORTH AMERICANS.** 1993. biennial. $89.50. Gale Research Inc., 835 Penobscot Bldg., Detroit, MI 48226. TEL 313-961-2242; 800-877-4253. FAX 313-961-6083. Ed. Marlita A. Reddy. charts; stat.
  Description: Offers current and historical data in the form of 900 statistical tables, graphs and charts.

WIND RIVER RENDEZVOUS. see HISTORY — History Of North And South America

EXPERIMENTAL MEDICINE, LABORATORY TECHNIQUE

see Medical Sciences–Experimental Medicine, Laboratory Technique

FAMILY AND MATRIMONIAL LAW

see Law–Family and Matrimonial Law

FASHIONS

see Clothing Trade–Fashions

FEED, FLOUR AND GRAIN

see Agriculture–Feed, Flour and Grain

FIRE PREVENTION

614.84   US   ISSN 0001-0960
A D T TRANSMITTER.* 1929. q. free. American District Telegraph Co., 300 Interpace Pkwy., Parsippany, NJ 07054-1113. Ed. B.F. Biondo. illus. circ. 50,000.

614.8   BE   ISSN 0778-7383
A N P I MAGAZINE - PROTECTION INCENDIE ET VOL. Dutch edition: N V B B Magazine - Brand- en Diefstalbeveiliging (ISSN 0778-7391) (Text in French) 1969. bi-m. 1800 BEF. Association Nationale pour la Protection contre l'Incendie et l'Intrusion - Nationale Vereiniging voor Beveiliging tegen Brand en Binnendringing, Parc Scientifique, B-1348 Louvain-la-Neuve, Belgium. TEL 32-10-47-52-91. FAX 32-10-47-52-70. Ed. L. De Vreese. adv.; bk.rev. circ. 5,000. **Indexed:** C.I.S.Abstr.
  Formerly (until 1991): Revue Belge du Feu (ISSN 0771-4033)

614.84 364.4   SZ
ALARM/ALLARME/ALARME; modern fire protection and security systems bulletin. (Editions in English, French, German and Italian) 1956. 3/yr. free. Cerberus AG, CH-8708 Maennedorf, Switzerland. TEL 1-9226111. FAX 1-9226450. TELEX 875528 CSM CH. (U.K. distr. addr.: 1 Ashville Way, Molly Millar's Lane, Wokingham, Berks RG11 2PL, England) Ed. Hubert Angst. charts; illus.; stat. circ. 29,900. **Indexed:** Sci.Abstr. **Document type:** trade publication.
  Formerly: Cerberus Alarm (ISSN 0528-5984)
  Description: Describes devices, methods, and necessity for fire protection and security. Includes list of exhibitions.

614.8   FR   ISSN 0044-7358
ALLO DIX-HUIT. 1946. m. (11/yr.). 20 F. Association pour le Developpement des Oeuvres Sociales des Sapeurs-Pompiers de Paris, 1 Place Jules Renard, B.P. 31, 75823 Paris Cedex 17, France. TEL 40-11-17-27. FAX 47-54-68-86. Ed. Lieutenant-Colonel Peronne. adv.; illus. circ. 17,000. **Indexed:** C.I.S. Abstr.

614.84   US
AMERICAN FIRE JOURNAL. 1950. m. $19.95. Fire Publications, Inc., c/o J.A. Ackerman, Pub., 9072 E. Artesia Blvd., Bellflower, CA 90706. TEL 213-866-1664. Ed. Carol Carlsen Brooks. adv.; bk.rev.; illus. circ. 6,000. **Document type:** trade publication.
  Formerly (until 1984): Western Fire Journal (ISSN 0043-3705)

614.84   US
AMERICAN FIRE SPRINKLER ASSOCIATION. MEMBERGRAM. 1986. m. membership. American Fire Sprinkler Association, 12959 Jupiter Rd., Ste. 142, Dallas, TX 75238. TEL 214-349-5965. FAX 214-343-8898. Ed. Janet Knowles. circ. 550. **Document type:** newsletter.
  Description: Informs members of legislation, codes; includes chapter news, success stories, as well as membership benefits.

614.84   IT   ISSN 0393-7089
ANTINCENDIO. 1949. m. L.205000. Edizioni di Protezione Civile s.r.l., Via dell'Acqua Traversa 187-189, 00135 Rome, Italy. TEL 6-33-13-000. FAX 6-331-32-12. TELEX 626462 EPCINF. Ed. Pier Roberto Pais. adv. contact: Roberto Barberini. bk.rev.; abstr.; bibl.; charts; illus.; tr.lit.; cum.index: 1949-1968. circ. 9,000.
  Former titles (until 1986): Antincendio, Sicurezza sul Lavoro, e Protezione Civile (ISSN 0394-4891); (until 1979): Antincendio e Protezione Civile (ISSN 0394-4905); Which was formed by the 1973 merger of: Antincendio e Protezione Industriale (ISSN 0003-5734); And: Antincendio e Protezione Civile (ISSN 0033-1813); Which superseded (in 1967): Antincendio e Protezione Civile (ISSN 1120-2653); Which was formerly (until 1959): Antincendio (ISSN 0402-6071).

ARSON REPORTER; arson cases and legislation. see LAW

614.84   CN   ISSN 0838-679X
ATLANTIC FIREFIGHTER. 1987. m. Can.$35. Hilden Publishing Ltd., Box 919, Amherst, NS B4H 4E1, Canada. TEL 902-667-5102. FAX 902-667-0419. Ed. Doug Harkness. adv.; bk.rev. circ. 9,000. (back issues avail.)
  Description: Covers fire services in the four Atlantic provinces.

344.73   US   ISSN 0897-0084
KF3975
B O C A NATIONAL FIRE PREVENTION CODE. 1966. triennial. $36. Building Officials and Code Administrators International, 4051 W. Flossmoor Rd., Country Club Hills, IL 60477-5795.
  Formerly: B O C A Basic Fire Prevention Code.

614.84   AU   ISSN 0006-9035
BRAND AUS. 1886. m. S.195. Niederoesterreichischer Landesfeuerwehrverband, Landesfeuerwehrkommando, Bankgasse 2, A-1014 Vienna, Austria. Ed. Erwin Nowak. adv.; bk.rev.; bibl.; charts; illus.; stat.; index. circ. 13,000.

614.84   NE   ISSN 0165-4675
BRAND & BRANDWEER. 1950. m. fl.45 (effective 1993). Koninklijke Vermande B.V., Platinastraat 33, Postbus 20, 8242 EA Lelystad, Netherlands. TEL 31-3200-22944. FAX 31-3200-26334. Ed. Mrs. L. Helwig-Dockheer; Pub. Mrs. L. Vroegindeweij. adv. contact: H. den Hartog. bk.rev.; illus. circ. 10,000. **Indexed:** C.I.S. Abstr. **Document type:** bulletin.
  Formerly (until 1977): Brand (ISSN 0006-9027)
  Description: Covers fire prevention, fire fighting, prevention of disasters and accidents, assistance, society news, reports and announcements of events, and positions available.

614.84   SW   ISSN 0283-1155
BRAND & RAEDDNING. 1986. m. SEK 208. Svenska Brandfoersvarsfoereningen - Swedish Fire Protection Association, S-115 87 Stockholm, Sweden. TEL 08-783-7000. FAX 08-661-2284. Ed. Marianne Sjoeborg. adv.; bk.rev.; bibl.; illus.; index. circ. 19,000.
  Formerly: Brandfoersvar (ISSN 0006-9051)

FIRE PREVENTION

614.84 GW ISSN 0006-906X
DIE BRANDHILFE. 1954. m. DM.45.50($10.71) (Landesfeuerwehrverband Baden-Wuerttemberg) Neckar Verlag GmbH, Postfach 1820, 78008 Villingen-Schwenningen, Germany. TEL 07221-8987-0. FAX 07221-898750. Ed. Werner Jauch. bk.rev.; illus. circ. 10,000. **Document type:** trade publication.
—CCC.

628.92 DK ISSN 0106-8725
BRANDMANDEN. 1922. 8/yr. DKK 128. Brandfolkenes Organisation, Frederiksundsvej 121, DK-2700 Broenshoej, Denmark. Ed. Sven Praest. adv. circ. 2,600.

614.84 900 GW ISSN 0006-9094
BRANDSCHUTZ; Deutsche Feuerwehr-Zeitung. 1946. m. DM.126. W. Kohlhammer GmbH, Hessbruehlstr. 69, 70565 Stuttgart, Germany. TEL 0711-7863-1. (back issues avail.) **Indexed:** INIS Atomind. **Document type:** trade publication.
—BLDSC (2269.600000); SWETS. CCC.

614.84 DK ISSN 0106-6072
TH9549
BRANDVAERN. (Text in Danish; summaries in English) 1970. m. DKK 480 in Europe; elsewhere DKK 630. Dansk Brandinspektoerforening, Datavej 48, DK-3460 Birkeroed, Denmark. TEL 45-82-00-99. FAX 45-82-24-99. (Co-sponsor: Dansk Brandvaerns-Komite) Eds. H.J. Salomonsen, Ole B. Kristensen. adv.; index. circ. 5,500. **Indexed:** C.I.S. Abstr.
Formed by the merger of: Dansk Brandvaern (ISSN 0011-622X) & Brandfare og Brandvaern.

614.84 AU ISSN 0029-8956
BRANDVERHUETUNG; Fachzeitschrift fuer den vorbeugenden Brandschutz. 1956. q. S.105. Landesstelle fuer Brandverhuetung in Steiermark, Roseggerkai 3-III, A-8010 Graz, Austria. FAX 0316-827471-21. Ed. Guenther Gerger. bk.rev. circ. 13,000.

614.84 GW ISSN 0006-9116
TH9211
BRANDWACHT; Fachschrift fuer Brand- und Katastrophenschutz. 1946. m. DM.25. Landesamt fuer Brand- und Katastrophenschutz, Puendterplatz 5, Postfach 400226, 80803 Munich, Germany. TEL 089-391053. FAX 089-898096. TELEX 522424-LABUK-D. adv.; bk.rev.; charts; illus. circ. 17,700. **Indexed:** C.I.S. Abstr. **Document type:** government publication.

614.84 NO ISSN 0801-6763
BRANN OG SIKKERHET. 1925. 8/yr. membership. Norsk Brannvern Forening, Boks 6703, St. Olavs Pl., Oslo 1, Norway. Ed. Jan Erik Thoresen. adv. circ. 12,500.
—CCC.
Formerly: Mot Brann (ISSN 0332-7094)

614.8 NO ISSN 0045-2696
BRANNMANNEN. 1945. bi-m. NOK 30($3) Oslo Brannkorpsforening, Arne Garborgs Plass 1, Oslo 1, Norway. Ed. Karl Ivan Ingvaldsen. adv.; bk.rev.; illus.; index. circ. 2,000.
—CCC.

614.84 UK
BRITISH FIRE SERVICES ASSOCIATION. JOURNAL. 1950. q. £1 to non-members. (British Fire Services Association) North West Publications (U.K.) Ltd., Bootle, Merseyside L20 3ES, England. Ed. D.G. Varnfield. adv.; bk.rev.; charts; illus. circ. 3,000. **Indexed:** Ref.Zh. **Document type:** trade publication.
Formerly: Journal of the British Fire Services Association and Industrial Fire Protection Association.

614.84 CN ISSN 0706-1382
C A F C DIALOGUE/A C C P DIALOGUE. q. Canadian Association of Fire Chiefs - Association Canadienne des Chefs de Pompiers, 2425 - 1 Don Reid Dr., Ottawa, ON K1H 1A4, Canada. TEL 613-736-0576. FAX 613-736-0684.

628.92 US
CALIFORNIA FIRE SERVICE. 1927. m. $45. California State Firefighters' Association, 3246 Ramos Cir., Sacramento, CA 95827-2513. TEL 916-368-2578. FAX 916-368-8191. Ed. Gary C. Giacomo. adv. contact: Colt Stewart. bk.rev.; charts; illus.; stat.; tr.lit.; index, cum.index. circ. 30,000. (back issues avail.) **Document type:** trade publication.
Formerly: California Fireman.
Description: Firefighter news in the areas of fire suppression, prevention, emergency medical services, hazardous materials and disaster response.

CANADIAN EMERGENCY NEWS. see HOSPITALS

614.84 CN ISSN 0704-6391
CANADIAN FIREFIGHTER. (Text in English, French) 1976. 6/yr. Can.$12 (foreign Can.$36). (Chiefs and Firefighters Association) The Canadian Firefighter Publishing Co. Ltd., Box 95, Sta. D, Etobicoke, ON M9A 4X1, Canada. TEL 416-233-2516. FAX 416-233-2051. Pub. Lorne Campbell. adv.: B&W and color, B&W page Can.$1185; trim 8 1/4 x 11. circ. 12,000.

COMBUSTION AND FLAME. see ENGINEERING

363.37 US
COMMISH. 1991. m. $68 (effective 1993). Quinlan Publishing Co., Inc., 23 Drydock Ave., 2nd Fl., Boston, MA 02210-2387. TEL 617-542-0048; 800-229-2084. FAX 617-345-9646. Ed. Leo D. Stapleton. index. (looseleaf format; back issues avail.) **Document type:** newsletter.
Description: For fire chiefs, firefighters and other members of the firefighting community.

614.84 US
CONTRACTOR NETWORK. 1986. m. American Fire Sprinkler Association, 12959 Jupiter Rd., Ste. 142, Dallas, TX 75238. TEL 214-349-5965. FAX 214-343-8898. Ed. Janet Knowles. circ. 500. **Document type:** newspaper.
Description: Informs contractors about current union activities, industry news.

614.84 747.5 US
DIRECTORY OF MATERIALS SUPPLIERS. 1978. a. free. Upholstered Furniture Action Council, Box 2436, High Point, NC 27261. TEL 919-885-5065. FAX 919-884-5303. Ed. E.L. Briggs. circ. 5,000. **Document type:** directory.
Description: For furniture manufacturers, retailers and suppliers; encourages more cigarette resistant upholstering methods.

628.92 US
EMERGENCY PRODUCTS UPDATE. m. Pulse Communications, Box 240, Flanders, NJ 07836-9306. TEL 201-927-9110. FAX 201-584-3047. Ed. Doug Fenichel. circ. 2,000.

363.37 629.222 US ISSN 0362-2487
TH9371
ENJINE!-ENJINE!. 1973. q. membership. Society for the Preservation & Appreciation of Antique Motor Fire Apparatus in America, Box 2005, Syracuse, NY 13220-2005. Ed. Walter M.P. McCall. adv.; bk.rev.; bibl.; charts; illus.; stat. circ. 2,000. (also avail. in microfilm; back issues avail.)

F A M - FIRE AND MATERIALS. see CHEMISTRY — Physical Chemistry

614.8 FR ISSN 0014-6269
FACE AU RISQUE. (Bi-monthly supplement avail.) (Text in French; summaries in English) 1956. m. 990 F. (foreign 1300 F.) Centre National de Prevention et de Protection, 5 rue Daunou, 75002 Paris, France. FAX 49-27-09-43. (Subscr. to: B.P. 2265, 27950 Saint-Marcel, France) Ed. Marc Bohy. adv.; bk.rev.; bibl.; index. circ. 5,000. (back issues avail.) **Indexed:** C.I.S.Abstr.

614.84 ISSN 0014-6595
TH9201
FACTORY MUTUAL RECORD; the magazine of property conservation. 1924. bi-m. $15. Factory Mutual Engineering Corp., 1151 Boston-Providence Turnpike, Norwood, MA 02062. TEL 617-762-4300. FAX 617-769-8239. Ed. Ellen K. Casaccio. illus.; index. circ. 60,000. (also avail. in microfiche)

628.92 164.84 GW ISSN 0071-4674
FEUERWEHR-JAHRBUCH; ein Jahresbericht ueber das Feuerwehrwesen in der Bundesrepublik Deutschland. 1964. a. DM.19.80. Deutscher Feuerwehrverband Medien GmbH, Koblenzerstr. 133, 53177 Bonn, Germany. adv. circ. 5,000. **Document type:** trade publication.
Formerly: Freiwilliger Feuerwehren.

614.84 GW ISSN 0178-5214
DER FEUERWEHRMANN. 1951. m. DM.42. (Landesfeuerwehrverband Nordrhein-Westfalen e.V.) Deutscher Gemeindeverlag GmbH, Postfach 400263, 50832 Cologne, Germany. TEL 02234-1060. FAX 02234-106284. circ. 7,200. (reprint service avail.) **Document type:** trade publication.
—SWETS.

628.92 UK ISSN 0015-2544
FIRE; journal of the fire protection profession. 1908. m. £44.80($102.50) (foreign £66.20). F M J International Publications Ltd., Queensway House, 2 Queensway, Redhill, Surrey RH1 1QS, England. TEL 0737-768611. FAX 0737-761685. TELEX 948669-TOPJNL-G. Ed. Val Hargreaves. **Indexed:** Br.Tech.Ind., C.I.S. Abstr. **Document type:** trade publication.
—SWETS.
Description: Covers all areas of the fire industry, from firefighting to fire protection and prevention.

628.92 678.2 UK ISSN 0952-2727
FIRE & FLAMMABILITY BULLETIN; an international newsletter. 1979. m. £253($390) (effective 1994). (Rubber and Plastics Research Association of Great Britain) Elsevier Science Ltd., Oxford Fulfilment Centre, P.O. Box 800, Kidlington, Oxford OX5 1DX, England. TEL 44-865-843000. FAX 44-865-843010. (Subscr. in U.S. and Canada to: Elsevier Science, 660 White Plains Rd., Tarrytown, NY 10591-5153. TEL 914-524-9200. FAX 914-333-2444) Ed. Steve Grayson. bk.rev.; pat. (back issues avail.) **Document type:** bulletin, newsletter.
—BLDSC (3930.170000). CCC.
Formerly: Rubber and Plastics Fire and Flammability Bulletin (ISSN 0142-9353)
Description: Provides data on comprehensive monitoring, fire safety, prevention, detection and control.

FIRE AND POLICE PERSONNEL REPORTER. see BUSINESS AND ECONOMICS — Personnel Management

614.84 AT ISSN 1032-6529
FIRE AUSTRALIA. 1966. q. membership. Australian Fire Protection Association Pty. Ltd., 633 Queensberry St., North Melbourne, Vic. 3051, Australia. TEL 03-329-5577. FAX 03-329-6838. (Co-sponsor: Institution of Fire Engineers) Ed. Margaret Hurst. adv.; bk.rev. circ. 3,000.
Formerly: Fire Journal.
Description: Provides information on latest innovation, technical developments and future progressions in fire protection and fire engineering areas.

614.84 US ISSN 0015-2552
TH9111
FIRE CHIEF; administration, training, operations. 1956. m. $52 (foreign $112). Argus Inc., 6151 Powers Ferry Rd., N.W., Atlanta, GA 30339-2941. TEL 404-955-2500. FAX 404-955-0400. (And: 35 E. Wacker Dr., Chicago, IL 60601-2198. TEL 312-726-7277) Ed. Scott Baltic. adv.; bk.rev.; charts; illus. circ. 44,000. (also avail. in microform from UMI; reprint service avail. from UMI) **Document type:** trade publication.
—UMI. CCC.
Incorporates: Volunteer Firefighter & Volunteer Fire Chief.
Description: Emphasizes helping fire administrators to solve their administrative and management problems and to meet today's challenges in five major areas of fire department responsibility: fire prevention, fire suppression, public education, emergency medical response and personal safety.

FIRE PREVENTION 2519

628.92 US ISSN 0889-5740
FIRE CONTROL DIGEST. 1975. m. $145. Washington Capital News Reports, Inc., 3918 Prosperity Ave., Ste.318, Fairfax, VA 22031-3334. TEL 703-573-1600. FAX 703-573-1604. Ed. Susan Kernus; Oub. R.J. O'Connell. circ. 300. (looseleaf format; back issues avail.) **Document type:** newsletter.
  Description: Contains information about Federal and State programs, budgets, and emergency medical service for fire prevention professionals.

628.92 UK
FIRE DIRECTORY. a. £61.90($95.95) F M J International Publications Ltd., Queensway House, 2 Queensway, Redhill, Surrey RH1 1QS, England. TEL 0737-768611. FAX 0737-761685. TELEX 948669-TOPJNL-G. **Document type:** directory.
  Description: Covers the public and industrial fire protection industry in the UK, including organizational, technical, and marketing information.

614.84 US ISSN 0015-2587
TH9111 CODEN: FIENA2
FIRE ENGINEERING; the journal of fire suppression and protection. 1877. m. $23.50 (foreign $40). PennWell Publishing Co. (Saddle Brook), Park 80 W. Plaza 2, Saddle Brook, NJ 07662-5812. TEL 201-845-0800. FAX 201-845-6275. Ed. William A. Manning. adv.; bk.rev.; charts; illus.; stat.; tr.lit.; index. circ. 43,000. (also avail. in microform from UMI; reprint service avail. from UMI) **Indexed:** A.S.& T.Ind., C.I.S. Abstr., Chem.Abstr., Eng.Ind, Excerp.Med., Ind.Sci.Rev., Sci.Cit.Ind. **Document type:** trade publication.
  —BLDSC (3932.000000); Faxon; UnCover; SWETS; UMI. **CCC.**
  Description: For municipal firefighters, fire officers, chief fire officials; fire marshals and commissioners; fire protection engineers; industrial and institutional fire department members. Covers issues relating to training in the suppression and prevention of fires.

614.84 UK ISSN 0143-5337
FIRE ENGINEERS JOURNAL.* 1924. q. £10. (Institution of Fire Engineers) Technical Journals Ltd., Tunbridge Wells, Kent, England. Ed. Norman Anderson. adv.; bk.rev.; abstr.; bibl.; charts; illus.; cum.index. circ. 9,000. (also avail. in microform from UMI; reprint service avail. from UMI) **Indexed:** C.I.S.Abstr., RICS. **Document type:** trade publication.
  —BLDSC (3932.010000); EI; Faxon.
  Formerly: Institution of Fire Engineers Quarterly (ISSN 0020-3424)

614.84 CN ISSN 0015-2595
FIRE FIGHTING IN CANADA. 1957. 9/yr. Can.$17($35) (effective Jan. 1991). N C C Publishing, 222 Argyle Ave., Delhi, Ont. N4B 2Y2, Canada. TEL 519-582-2513. FAX 519-582-4040. Ed. Don Glendinning. adv.; tr.lit. circ. 6,296. (back issues avail.)
  Description: Covers fire industry reports, new fire industry equipment and services geared toward Canadian Fire Chiefs.

614.84 UK ISSN 0015-2609
TH9111 CODEN: FINTAV
FIRE INTERNATIONAL. (Text, title and contents page in English; summaries in French & German) 1963. q. £55.60($96.25) (foreign £62.10). F M J International Publications Ltd., Queensway House, 2 Queensway, Redhill, Surrey RH1 1QS, England. TEL 0737-768611. FAX 0737-761685. Ed. Norman Anderson. adv.; bibl.; charts; illus. **Indexed:** C.I.S. Abstr. **Document type:** trade publication.
  —BLDSC (3932.100000); SWETS.
  Description: Reports on fire and firefighting worldwide. Includes features, news, and articles for persons involved in international firefighting, fire prevention, and fire protection.

FIRE LINES. see LABOR UNIONS

FIRE MARK CIRCLE OF THE AMERICAS JOURNAL. see INSURANCE

FIRE MARK CIRCLE OF THE AMERICAS NEWSLETTER. see INSURANCE

628.9 US ISSN 0090-5313
TH9502
FIRE MARSHALS ASSOCIATION OF NORTH AMERICA. DIRECTORY. a. membership. Fire Marshals Association of North America, NFPA, Baterymarch Park, Quincy, MA 02269-9101. TEL 617-770-3000. circ. 1,400 (controlled). **Document type:** directory.
  Description: Focuses on the objectives, membership requirements, and membership benefits of the association, with announcements of meetings and a directory of members.

614.84 US ISSN 0015-2625
TH9111
FIRE NEWS. 1916. 6/yr. membership. National Fire Protection Association, 1 Batterymarch Park, Quincy, MA 02269. TEL 617-770-3500. Ed. Catherine G. Cronin. illus. circ. 57,000. (tabloid format) **Indexed:** C.I.S. Abstr.
  —BLDSC (3932.300000); SWETS; UMI.

628.92 CN
FIRE NEWS. (Editions in English, French) q. free. National Research Council of Canada, Institute for Research in Construction, Ottawa, ON K1A 0R6, Canada. TEL 613-993-2463.
  Former titles: Fire Research News (ISSN 1188-4053); (until 1991): I R C Fire Research News (ISSN 0840-4968); (until 1988): Fire News (ISSN 0846-4987)
  Description: Contains information pertaining to fire and smoke research.

614.84 UK ISSN 0262-4451
FIRE NEWS (LONDON). 1981. q. £6. British Safety Council, 62 Chancellor's Rd., London W6 9RS, England. illus.

FIRE PHOTOGRAPHERS JOURNAL. see PHOTOGRAPHY

614.84 UK ISSN 0309-6866
CODEN: FPRVD7
FIRE PREVENTION. 1948. 10/yr. £100 for both corporate and private subscr. (effective Oct. 1993). Fire Protection Association, 140 Aldersgate St., London EC1A 4HX, England. TEL 071-606-3757. FAX 071-600-1487. Ed. Lynn Jackson. adv. contact: Michael Gale. bk.rev.; charts; illus.; stat. circ. 7,500. (also avail. in microform from UMI; reprint service avail. from UMI) **Indexed:** Account.& Data Proc.Abstr., BMT, C.I.S. Abstr., Chem.Abstr., Copper Abstr., Int.Build.Serv.Abstr., Lab.Haz.Bull., Text.Tech.Dig., World Surf.Coat., World Text.Abstr. **Document type:** trade publication.
  —BLDSC (3932.550000); EI; SWETS. **CCC.**
  Formerly: F.P.A. Journal (ISSN 0014-6072)
  Description: Reports on new developments in the fire protection industry, good practice, case studies and statistics.

614.84 CN
FIRE PREVENTION CANADA. INFORMATION. irreg. membership. Canadian Association of Fire Chiefs - Association Canadienne des Chefs de Pompiers, 2425 - 1 Don Reid Dr., Ottawa, ON K1H 1A4, Canada. TEL 613-736-8131. FAX 613-736-0684. (Co-sponsor: Fire Prevention Canada)
  Formerly: Fire Prevention Canada Association. Information.

614.84 CN
FIRE PREVENTION CANADA. PUBLIC REPORT/PREVENTION DES INCENDIES CANADA. RAPPORT PUBLIC. (Text in English, French) a. membership. Canadian Association of Fire Chiefs - Association Canadienne de Chefs de Pompiers, 2425 - 1 Don Reid Dr., Ottawa, ON K1H 1A4, Canada. TEL 613-736-8131. FAX 613-736-0684. (Co-sponsor: Fire Prevention Canada)
  Formerly: Fire Prevention Canada Association Public Report.

628.92 US ISSN 1043-2485
FIRE PROTECTION CONTRACTOR.* 1978. m. $65. H.B. Brumbeloe & Associates, 12972 Earhart Ave., Ste. 302, Auburn, CA 95602-9538. TEL 916-823-0706. FAX 916-823-6937. Ed. Brant Brumbeloe. adv. circ. 2,150.
  Description: Covers fixed piping fire protection systems for the fire sprinkler industry.

614.84 US ISSN 0071-5417
FIRE PROTECTION HANDBOOK. 1896. quinquennial. $125 to non-members; members $112.50. National Fire Protection Association, 1 Batterymarch Park, Quincy, MA 02269. TEL 617-770-3000. FAX 617-471-5231. Ed. Gordon P. McKinnon. (reprint service avail. from UMI)

614.4 UK ISSN 0261-1589
FIRE RESEARCH NEWS. 1981. 2/yr. free. Home Office, Fire and Emergency Department, Horseferry House, Dean Ryle St., London SW1P 2AW, England. TEL 0608-650004. FAX 0608-651281. Ed. M. Andrews. illus. circ. 4,000. **Document type:** government publication.
  —**CCC.**
  Description: Contains recent research and development work of the Home Office: fire extinguishing media studies, communications, health studies of firefighters, combustion science.

628.9 UK
FIRE SAFETY ENGINEERING. 1972. bi-m. £25. (Incorporated Association of Architects and Surveyors, Fire Surveyors Section) Paramount Publishing Ltd , 17-21 Shenley Rd., Borehamwood, Herts. WD6 1RT, England. FAX 081-207-2598. (Co-sponsor: Institute of Fire Safety) Ed. J.W. Northey. adv.; bk.rev.; illus. circ. 5,600. **Indexed:** Int.Build.Serv.Abstr., Lab.Haz.Bull. **Document type:** trade publication.
  Formerly (until 1993): Fire Surveyor (ISSN 0262-7981)

614.84 UK ISSN 0379-7112
TH9111 CODEN: FSJODZ
FIRE SAFETY JOURNAL. 1977. 8/yr. (in 2 vols., 4 nos./vol.). £330($510) (effective 1994). Elsevier Science Ltd., Oxford Fulfilment Centre, P.O. Box 800, Kidlington, Oxford OX5 1DX, England. TEL 44-865-843000. FAX 44-865-843010. (Subscr. in U.S. and Canada to: Elsevier Science, 660 White Plains Rd., Tarrytown, NY 10591-5153. TEL 914-524-9200. FAX 914-333-2444) Ed. D.D. Drysdale. adv. (also avail. in microform from UMI) **Indexed:** C.I.S. Abstr., Chem.Abstr., Curr.Cont., Eng.Ind., Excerp.Med., Met.Abstr., Risk Abstr., Sci.Cit.Ind. **Document type:** academic/scholarly publication.
  —BLDSC (3933.285000); EI; Faxon; SWETS; CASDDS. **CCC.**
  Formerly (until vol.3, no.1, 1980): Fire Research (ISSN 0378-7761)
  Description: Serves as a forum for the dissemination of ideas from the areas of research, education and practice within the fire safety engineering field.
  Refereed Serial

628.92 JA ISSN 0285-9521
TH9111 CODEN: FSCTDC
FIRE SCIENCE AND TECHNOLOGY. 1981. 2/yr. $100. Science University of Tokyo, Center for Fire Science and Technology, 1-3 Kagurazaka, Shinjuku-ku, Tokyo 162, Japan. TEL 81-3-3260-4271. FAX 81-3-3235-2214. Ed. Tadahiro Ishii. **Document type:** academic/scholarly publication; bulletin.
  —BLDSC (3933.288000); Faxon; CASDDS.

614.84 US ISSN 0015-2668
FIRE SERVICE INFORMATION. 1946. bi-m. $10. Iowa State University, Extension to Communities, Fire Service Bldg., Ames, IA 50011. TEL 515-294-6817. FAX 515-294-2156. Ed. Michelle Schlicht. bk.rev.; stat. circ. 2,000. **Document type:** newsletter.
  Description: Contains technical articles and information concerning fire services and programs.

614.84 US
FIRE SYSTEMS. 1987. 2/yr. $10. National Association of Fire Equipment Distributors, 401 N. Michigan Ave., Chicago, IL 60611-4390. TEL 312-644-6610. FAX 312-321-6869. Ed. Eva Hofmann. adv. circ. 2,500. (back issues avail.)
  Description: Engineered fire protection systems.

2520   FIRE PREVENTION

614.84 US   ISSN 0015-2684
TH9111   CODEN: FITCAA
FIRE TECHNOLOGY; an international journal of fire protection research and engineering. 1965. q. $39.50 (foreign $49.50). National Fire Protection Association, 1 Batterymarch Park, Quincy, MA 02269. TEL 617-770-3000. FAX 617-471-5231. Ed.Bd. bk.rev.; abstr.; charts; illus.; index in each issue. circ. 6,000. (also avail. in microfilm from UMI; reprint service avail. from UMI) **Indexed**: A.S.& T.Ind., C.I.S. Abstr., Chem.Abstr., Eng.Ind, Gas Abstr., Ind.Sci.Rev., Int.Aerosp.Abstr., PROMT, Sci.Cit.Ind, Text.Tech.Dig.
—BLDSC (3933.600000); Faxon; UnCover; SWETS; UMI; CASDDS.

628.92   790.13   UK   ISSN 0262-3242
FIRE WORLD. 1982. 4/yr. Ian Henry Publications Ltd., 20 Park Dr., Romford, Essex RM1 4LH, England. TEL 44-708-749119. Ed. John Creighton. adv.; bk.rev.; illus. circ. 2,000.

614.84   US   ISSN 1061-4818
FIREFIGHTER'S NEWS.* bi-m. $15. Lifesaving Communications, HC 1 Box 1111, Nassau, DE 19969-9999. TEL 302-422-2772. FAX 302-422-0552. Ed. W.H. Stevenson. adv. circ. 43,234. **Document type**: trade publication.
Description: Provides information and skills for fire service decision makers.

628.92   US   ISSN 0145-4064
TH9111
FIREHOUSE. 1976. m. $24. P T N Publishing Corp., 445 Broad Hollow Rd., Ste. 21, Melville, NY 11747-4722. TEL 516-845-2700. FAX 516-845-7109. Ed. Barbara Dunleavy. adv.; bk.rev.; illus. circ. 110,600. (back issues avail.) **Document type**: trade publication.
Description: Covers historic and dramatic fires, techniques, rescues. Anything and everything about fire fighting and firefighters.

363.37   US   ISSN 0896-8314
FIREHOUSE LAWYER MONTHLY NEWSLETTER. 1988. m. $57. Quinlan Publishing Co., Inc., 23 Drydock Ave., Boston, MA 02210-2387. TEL 617-542-0048; 800-229-2084. FAX 617-345-9646. Ed. Leo Stapleton. index. (looseleaf format; back issues avail.) **Document type**: newsletter.
—UMI. **CCC**.
Description: For firefighting personnel. Covers recent court decisions on liability, disability and workers compensation, discipline, arson, and more.

628.92   US   ISSN 0276-4881
TH9360
FIREHOUSE MAGAZINE BUYERS GUIDE. 1981. a. $24. P T N Publishing Corp., 445 Broad Hollow Rd., Ste. 21, Melville, NY 11747. TEL 516-845-2700. Ed. Barbara Dunleavy. adv.; charts; stat. circ. 29,000. (back issues avail.) **Document type**: directory.

614.84   AT   ISSN 0812-0056
FIREMAN. 1947. m. Aus.$15. (Country Fire Authority, Victoria) H.L. King Publishing P-L, P.O. Box 187, Oakleigh, Vic. 3166, Australia. TEL 03-568-2117. FAX 03-568-2117. Ed. Alan E. King. adv.; bk.rev. circ. 6,600. (tabloid format; back issues avail.)

628.92   US
FIREMAN'S JOURNAL. 1976. 3/yr. $10. Knight Communications, Inc., 4801 E. Independence Blvd., Charlotte, NC 28212. TEL 704-568-7804. FAX 704-563-4286. Ed. Lyn Morgan. adv.; B&W page $1850, color page $2450; trim 11 x 15; adv. contact: Lyn Morgan. circ. 25,000.
Description: For medium to small-sized firefighting and rescue departments.

614.84   US   ISSN 0273-6101
FIREPLUG. 1980. q. $20. Michigan State Firemen's Association, 9001 Miller Rd., Ste. 10, Swartz Creek, MI 48473. TEL 810-635-9513. FAX 810-635-2858. (Subscr. to: Box 405, Swartz Creek, MI 48473. TEL 810-635-9832) Ed. J.J. Edgerton. adv. circ. 3,600. **Document type**: trade publication.
Description: Fire service information.

614.84   US
FIREWATCH!. 1963. q. $10. National Association of Fire Equipment Distributors, 401 N. Michigan Ave., Chicago, IL 60611-4390. TEL 312-644-6610. FAX 312-321-6869. Ed. Eva Hofmann. adv. circ. 3,500. (back issues avail.)
Description: Industry news about fire prevention and fire equipment distribution.

FIREWORKS. see *CHEMISTRY*

FIREWORKS BUSINESS. see *BUSINESS AND ECONOMICS — Domestic Commerce*

614.84   UK   ISSN 0307-2118
HT9361
FITECH INTERNATIONAL; the international equipment guide for the emergency services. (Text in English, French, German, Spanish) 1971. a. £53.20($82.50) F M J International Publications Ltd., Queensway House, 2 Queensway, Redhill, Surrey RH1 1QS, England. TEL 0737-768611. FAX 0737-761685. TELEX 948669-TOPJNL-G. circ. controlled. **Document type**: directory.
Formerly: Fitech.
Description: Contains an international guide to fire protection, prevention, and fighting equipment.

FLAME RETARDANT NEWS. see *TECHNOLOGY: COMPREHENSIVE WORKS*

628.92   540   US   ISSN 0361-6320
                CODEN: FRPMBG
FLAME RETARDANCY OF POLYMERIC MATERIALS PROCEEDINGS (YEAR). 1973. a. $250. Business Communications Co., Inc. (Norwalk), 25 Van Zant St., Norwalk, CT 06855. TEL 203-853-4266. FAX 203-853-0348.
—CASDDS.

614   US   ISSN 0899-6652
TH9446.3
FLAMMABILITY AND SENSITIVITY OF MATERIALS IN OXYGEN-ENRICHED ATMOSPHERES. 1982. irreg. American Society for Testing and Materials, 1916 Race St., Philadelphia, PA 19103. TEL 215-299-5400. FAX 215-977-9679.

614.84   US   ISSN 0274-8797
FLORIDA FIREMAN. 1931. m. $15. (Florida State Firemen's Association, Inc.) Special Editions Publishing, Inc., Box 968, Avon Park, FL 33825. TEL 813-453-4817. Ed. H.M. Flowers. adv.; bk.rev.; charts; illus. circ. 7,000.

614.84   US   ISSN 1061-9704
FROM THE STATE CAPITALS: PUBLIC SAFETY AND JUSTICE POLICIES. Variant title: Public Safety and Justice Policies from the State Capitals. 1946. w. $215 (foreign $235) (effective Dec. 1990). Wakeman-Walworth, Inc., 300 N. Washington St., Alexandria, VA 22314. TEL 703-549-8606. FAX 703-549-1372. (processed)
—CCC.
Formed by the merger of: From the State Capitals. Justice Policies (ISSN 0749-2790) & From the State Capitals. Public Safety (ISSN 0749-2782); Which incorporated: From the State Capitals. Police Administration (ISSN 0734-1148); From the State Capitals. Disaster and Emergency Planning (ISSN 0734-0869); Formerly: From the State Capitals. Fire Administration (ISSN 0734-1059); Incorporates: From the State Capitals. Drug Abuse Control (ISSN 0734-0877); Which was formerly: From the State Capitals. Drug Abuse Control Report (ISSN 0097-4862); Justice Policies was formed by the merger of: From the State Capitals. Prision Administration (ISSN 0734-0885); & From the State Capitals. Judicial Administration (ISSN 0734-1091).
Description: Updates on police and fire administration, disaster and emergency planning, highway safety, gun control laws, drug abuse rulings.

614.84   US
GATED WYE; Oregon Fire Service news. 1966. m. $15. Office of State Fire Marshal, 4760 Portland Rd., N.E., Salem, OR 97305-1760. TEL 503-378-3473. FAX 503-373-1540. Ed. Colleen Olson. bk.rev. circ. 1,200. (back issues avail.)
Formerly: Fire Service Bulletin.
Description: Covers activities of State Fire Marshal's office and includes state and nationwide fire protection news, health and safety information, and state-wide fire prevention and hazardous materials response activities.

614.84   690   UK
GREAT BRITAIN. BUILDING RESEARCH ESTABLISHMENT. REPORTS. 1961. irreg. price varies. Building Research Establishment, Garston, Watford WD2 7JR, England. TEL 0923-894040. FAX 0923-664010.
Supersedes: Great Britain. Department of the Environment. Fire Research Station. Fire Notes (ISSN 0071-5379) & Great Britain. Department of the Environment. Fire Research Station. Technical Papers (ISSN 0071-545X)

614.84   FR   ISSN 0337-5781
GUIDE DU FEU. 1962. a. France-Selection, 9-13 rue de la Nouvelle France, B.P. 118, 93303 Aubervilliers Cedex, France. TEL 48-33-18-18. FAX 48-33-21-60. adv. contact: Frederique Fardeau. bk.rev.
Formerly: Guide du Feu et de la Protection Civile (ISSN 0072-8047)

HEALTH & SAFETY NEWSLINE; for the engineering industry (UK). see *PUBLIC HEALTH AND SAFETY*

352.3   US
HOUSTON FIRE FIGHTER. 1968. m. $15. Houston Professional Firefighters Association, 1907 Freeman St., Houston, TX 77009. TEL 713-223-9166. FAX 713-237-0912. Ed. L.W. Tyra. circ. 4,000 (controlled). (tabloid format) **Document type**: newspaper.

614.84   US   ISSN 0893-3936
I A F C ON SCENE. 1934. s-m. $60 (foreign $80). International Association of Fire Chiefs, 4025 Fair Ridge Dr., Fairfax, VA 22033-2868. TEL 703-273-0911. FAX 703-273-9363. Ed. Tim Elliott. adv.; bk.rev.; film rev.; abstr.; bibl.; charts; illus.; pat.; stat.; tr.lit.; cum.index: 1970-1975. circ. 10,000. (back issues avail.) **Document type**: trade publication.
Former titles: International Fire Chief; International Association of Fire Chiefs. Official Publication (ISSN 0161-2158); International Fire Chief (ISSN 0364-8958)
Description: For fire service leaders. Provides an overview of the types of things that will affect change in the fire service and gives specifics about where to obtain useful references.

628.92   US   ISSN 1066-3940
▼**INDUSTRIAL FIRE CHIEF**. 1992. bi-m. $24 (foreign $64). Argus Inc., 6151 Powers Ferry Rd., N.W., Atlanta, GA 30339-2941. TEL 404-955-2500. FAX 404-955-0400. (And: 35 E. Wacker Dr., Chicago, IL 60601-2198. TEL 312-726-7277. FAX 312-726-0241) adv.: B&W page $2460, color page $3310; trim 8 1/8 x 10 7/8. circ. 18,000. **Document type**: trade publication.
—UMI.
Description: For industrial fire service executives and emergency management personnel responsible for industrial fire and safety prevention, protection and suppression operations in industrial plants, field operations and commercial buildings.

614.84   US   ISSN 0749-890X
INDUSTRIAL FIRE WORLD. 1985. bi-m. 208 C Southwest Parkway East, College Station, TX 77840. TEL 409-693-7105. FAX 409-764-0691. Ed. Tammy Randermann. circ. 25,833.

628.92   US
INSTRUCT - O - GRAM. m. International Society of Fire Service Instructors, 30 Main St., Ashland, MA 01721. TEL 508-881-5800. FAX 508-881-6829. Ed. Edward H. McCormack, Jr. circ. 6,000. (back issues avail.)
Description: Covers technical issues about fire service like building construction and firefighting operations.

INSULATION HANDBOOK. see *BUILDING AND CONSTRUCTION*

INSULATION JOURNAL. see *BUILDING AND CONSTRUCTION*

628.92   634.9   US   ISSN 1051-4198
SD420.5
INTERNATIONAL DIRECTORY OF WILDLAND FIRE. 1990. a. $125. International Association of Wildland Fire, Box 328, Fairfield, WA 99012-0328. TEL 509-283-2397; 800-697-3443. FAX 509-283-2264. circ. 600 (paid). **Document type**: directory.
Description: Lists 27000 names and addresses of people involved with fire worldwide.

FIRE PREVENTION 2521

614.84 UK ISSN 0961-3730
INTERNATIONAL FIRE & SECURITY PRODUCT NEWS.
1975. 6/yr. free. Paramount Publishing Ltd., 17-21 Shenley Rd., Borehamwood, Herts. WD6 1RT, England. FAX 081-207-2598. **Indexed:** Br.Ceram.Abstr. **Document type:** newsletter.
Formerly: International Fire Security Safety News.

614.84 US ISSN 0020-6733
INTERNATIONAL FIRE FIGHTER. 1918. bi-m. International Association of Fire Fighters, 1750 New York Ave., N.W., Washington, DC 20006-5301. TEL 202-737-8484. FAX 202-737-8418. Ed. Alfred Whitehead. circ. 195,000 (controlled). (tabloid format) **Document type:** newspaper.

628.92 634.9 US ISSN 1049-8001
INTERNATIONAL JOURNAL OF WILDLAND FIRE. q. $60 to members; non-members $95. International Association of Wildland Fire, Box 328, Fairfield, WA 99012-0328. circ. 500 (paid). **Indexed:** Environ.Per.Bibl. **Document type:** academic/scholarly publication.
—BLDSC (4542.701250); CIS; UnCover.
Description: Contains scientific articles on forest fires.

614.84 US
IOWA SMOKE-EATER. 1955. m. $10. Smoke-Eater Publications, Box 129, Pierce, NE 68767. TEL 402-329-4665. Ed. Randee D. Falter. adv. circ. 8,887.
Description: Articles on the volunteer firemen of Iowa.

628.92 US ISSN 1044-4300
TH9112 CODEN: JFSCEW
JOURNAL OF APPLIED FIRE SCIENCE. 1990. q. $95 to institutions. Baywood Publishing Co., Inc., 26 Austin Ave., Box 337, Amityville, NY 11701. TEL 516-691-1270. FAX 516-691-1770. Ed. Prof. Paul R. DeCicco. bk.rev. (back issues avail.) **Document type:** academic/scholarly publication.
—BLDSC (4942.610000); CASDDS.
Description: Directed to bridging the formidable and widening information gap between recent advances in fire chemistry, fire physics, and theoretical fire dynamics; and the development and implementation of practical solutions to problems facing the fire protection community.

628.92 US ISSN 0734-9041
TH9446.3 CODEN: JFSCDV
JOURNAL OF FIRE SCIENCES. 1983. bi-m. $295. Technomic Publishing Co., Inc., 851 New Holland Ave., Box 3535, Lancaster, PA 17604. TEL 717-291-5609. FAX 717-295-4538. TELEX 230 753565 (TECHNOMIC UD). Ed. Gordon E. Hartzell. index. circ. 500. (also avail. in microfiche from UMI) **Indexed:** Chem.Abstr., Eng.Ind., Excerp.Med., Ind.Sci.Rev., Int.Aerosp.Abstr., Sci.Cit.Ind., World Text.Abstr. **Document type:** academic/scholarly publication.
—BLDSC (4984.279500); EI; Faxon; SWETS; UMI; CASDDS. **CCC.**
Refereed Serial

614.84 JA ISSN 0023-6020
KYOTO SHOBO/FIRE PREVENTION; Kyoto fire service. (Text in Japanese) 1948. m. 4440 Yen($3.25) Kyoto Shobo Henshu Iinkai, c/o Kyoto-shi Shobo Gakko, Fukakusa Echigo Yashiki-cho, Fushimi-ku, Kyoto 612, Japan. TEL 075-641-2376. FAX 075-644-2092. Ed. Hideo Fujino. adv.; bk.rev.; charts; illus.; stat.; index. (processed)

614.84 US ISSN 1040-3469
LINK (ASHLAND). 1979. w. $90 to non-members; members $45. International Society of Fire Service Instructors, 30 Main St., Ashland, MA 01721. TEL 508-881-5800. FAX 508-881-6829. Ed. Edward H. McCormack, Jr. circ. 900.
Formerly: Communications Link.
Description: Provides up-to-date information on relevant fire service issues at the national, state and local levels.

LOS ANGELES FIREFIGHTER. see *LABOR UNIONS*

MAPFRE SEGURIDAD. see *OCCUPATIONAL HEALTH AND SAFETY*

614.84 MF
MAURITIUS. GOVERNMENT FIRE SERVICES. ANNUAL REPORT. (Text in English) a. Government Printing Office, Elizabeth II Ave., Port Louis, Mauritius.

614.84 US
MINNESOTA SMOKE-EATER. 1949. m. $10. Smoke-Eater Publications, Box 129, Pierce, NE 68767. TEL 402-329-4665. Ed. Randee D. Falter. adv.; stat.; illus. circ. 12,028. (tabloid format)
Description: Articles on the volunteer firemen of Minnesota.

614.84 US
N A F I NEWSLETTER. 1962. q. membership. National Association of Fire Investigators, Box 957257, Hoffman Estates, IL 60195-7257. Ed. P.M. Kennedy. bk.rev.; charts; stat. circ. 3,000. **Document type:** newsletter.

352.3 UK ISSN 0141-8777
N A F O YEARBOOK. 1971. a. membership. National Association of Fire Officers, Hayes Court, W. Common Rd., Bromley, Kent BR2 7AU, England. Ed. R. Phythian. adv. circ. 8,000.

614.84 US
TH9116.5
N F P A BUYER'S GUIDE. 1975. a. National Fire Protection Association, 1 Batterymarch Park, Quincy, MA 02269. TEL 617-770-3000. FAX 617-471-5231. adv.; index. circ. 90,000. (reprint service avail. from UMI)
Formerly: Fire Protection Reference Directory (ISSN 0361-8382)

614.84 US ISSN 1054-8793
CODEN: NFJOEX
N F P A JOURNAL. 1991. bi-m. $75 membership (foreign $110). National Fire Protection Association, 1 Batterymarch Park, Quincy, MA 02269. TEL 617-770-3000. FAX 617-471-5231. Ed. Joyce Keefe. adv.; bk.rev.; charts; illus.; tr.lit.; index. circ. 57,000. (also avail. in microfilm from UMI; reprint service avail. from UMI) **Indexed:** A.S.& T.Ind., C.I.S. Abstr., Chem.Abstr., Eng.Ind, Fuel & Energy Abstr., Gas Abstr., Ind.Sci.Rev., Sci.Cit.Ind.
—BLDSC (6109.083000); SWETS; UMI.
Formed by the merger of (1907-1991): Fire Journal (ISSN 0015-2617) & Fire Command (ISSN 0746-9586); Which was formerly (until 1983): Fire Service Today (ISSN 0279-3563); (1933-1970): Fire Command (ISSN 0015-2560).
Description: Covers fire protection engineering, investigation reports, profiles, and fire suppression.

614.84 US ISSN 0077-4553
TH9503
N F P A TECHNICAL COMMITTEE. REPORT. 1917. s-a. National Fire Protection Association, 1 Batterymarch Park, Quincy, MA 02269. TEL 617-770-3000. FAX 617-471-5231. (reprint service avail. from UMI)

614.8 364 BE ISSN 0778-7391
N V B B MAGAZINE - BRAND- EN DIEFSTALBEVEILIGING. French edition: A N P I Magazine - Protection Incendie et Vol (ISSN 0778-7383) (Text in Dutch) 1969. bi-m. 1900 BEF. Nationale Vereniging voor Beveiliging tegen Brand en Binnendringing - Association Nationale pour la Protection contre l'Incendie et l'Intrusion, Parc Scientifique, B-1348 Louvain-la-Neuve, Belgium. TEL 32-10-47-52-91. FAX 32-10-47-52-70. Ed. L. De Vreese. adv.; bk.rev. circ. 5,000.
Formerly (until 1991): Belgisch Brandtijdschrift (ISSN 0771-2642)
Description: Covers fire prevention and anti-crime matters.

670 US
NATIONAL CHIMNEY SWEEP GUILD. NEWSLINK. m. $12 membership only. National Chimney Sweep Guild, 1601 Industrial Dr., Ste. 8, Gaithersburg, MD 20877. TEL 301-936-5600. **Document type:** newsletter.

614.84 617.3 US
▼ **NATIONAL DIRECTORY OF FIRE CHIEFS, RESCUE & EMERGENCY DEPARTMENTS.** 1992. a. $30. Span Publishing, Box 365, 1052 Main St., Ste. 207, Steven Point, WI 54481-0365. TEL 715-345-2772. FAX 715-345-7288. Ed. Kathleen J. Nason. (also avail. in diskette format) **Document type:** directory.

364 343 US ISSN 1064-4814
NATIONAL FIRE AND ARSON REPORT. 1982. q. $28 (Canada $36, elsewhere $55). Investigative Research International, Inc., Box 411087, Charlotte, NC 28241-1087. TEL 800-488-6327. FAX 704-588-1248. Ed. Barbara P. Goodnight. adv.; index. circ. 10,000. (back issues avail.) **Document type:** newsletter.
Description: Provides comprehensive information and training materials pertinent to professionals concerned with fire, arson and fraud investigation as well as general investigative resources.

614.84 US ISSN 0077-4545
TH9111
NATIONAL FIRE PROTECTION ASSOCIATION. NATIONAL FIRE CODES. Key Title: National Fire Codes. (In 11 vols.; supplement avail.) 1938. a. $497.50 to non-members; members $447.75. National Fire Protection Association, 1 Batterymarch Park, QUnicy, MA 02269. TEL 617-770-3000. FAX 617-471-5231. (also avail. in microform; reprint service avail. from UMI)
—BLDSC (6022.880000).
Description: All codes, standards, recommended practices, and manuals by technical committees of the NFPA.

614.84 US
NATIONAL FIRE PROTECTION ASSOCIATION. NATIONAL FIRE CODES. SUBSCRIPTION SERVICE. 1951. a. $55 to non-members; members $49.50. National Fire Protection Association, 1 Batterymarch Park, Quincy, MA 02269. TEL 617-770-3000. FAX 617-471-5231. index. circ. 22,000. (looseleaf format; also avail. in microfiche; reprint service avail. from UMI)
Formerly: National Fire Protection Association. National Fire Codes. Supplement.
Description: All codes, standards, recommended practices and guides by technical committees of the NFPA, plus automatic update materials.

614.84 US
NEBRASKA SMOKE-EATER. 1946. m. $10. Smoke-Eater Publications, Box 129, Pierce, NE 68767. TEL 402-329-4665. Ed. Randee D. Falter. adv.; stat.; illus. circ. 10,350. (tabloid format)
Description: Articles on the volunteer firemen of Nebraska.

614.84 US
NEW JERSEY. BUREAU OF FIRE SAFETY NEWSLETTER. 1984. s-m. $30 includes New Jersey State Fire Code. Bureau of Fire Safety, C.N. 809, Trenton, NJ 08625. TEL 609-633-6071. FAX 609-633-6134. Ed. Mike Matcho. circ. 13,000. **Document type:** government publication, newsletter.
Description: Trade news for fire service and related organizations.

614.84 US
NEW JERSEY STATE FIRE CODE. 1985. irreg. (plus s-a. update). $20 (with Newsletter $30). Bureau of Fire Safety, C.N. 809, Trenton, NJ 08625. TEL 609-633-6130. FAX 609-633-6134. **Document type:** government publication.

NEW YORK CITY FIRE LAW HANDBOOK. see *LAW*

614.8 NO
NORWAY. DIREKTORATET FOR BRANN OG EKSPLOSJONSVERN. AARSBERETNING. 1915. a. Direktoratet for Brann og Eksplosjonvern, Postboks 355, 3101 Toensberg, Norway. TEL 47 33 398800. FAX 47-33-310660. illus. circ. 2,500.
Document type: corporate report.
Former titles: Norway. Statens Sprengstoffinspeksjon. Aarsberetning; Norway. Sprengstoffinspeksjonen. Aarsberetning.

614.84 CN ISSN 0085-4395
TH9506
NOVA SCOTIA. FIRE MARSHAL. ANNUAL REPORT. a. Department of Labour, Research Division, Box 697, Halifax, NS B3J 2T8, Canada. TEL 902-424-4313.
Description: Summary of the year's activities of the Fire Marshal of Nova Scotia.

O H & A THE AUSTRALIAN JOURNAL OF WORKPLACE HEALTH AND SAFETY. see *PUBLIC HEALTH AND SAFETY*

FIRE PREVENTION

614.84 AU ISSN 0029-9030
DIE OESTERREICHISCHE FEUERWEHR. 1947. m. S.561. (Oesterreichischer Bundes-Feuerwehrverband) Bohmann Druck und Verlag GmbH & Co. KG, Leberstr. 122, A-1110 Vienna, Austria. TEL 0222-74095-0. FAX 0222-74095-183. TELEX 132312. adv.; charts; illus. circ. 5,000. **Document type:** trade publication.

614.84 JA
OKINAWA PREFECTURE. ANNUAL REPORT OF FIRE AND DISASTER PREVENTION. 1973. a. free. Okinawa-ken, 2-2, 1-chome, Izumizaki, Naha-shi, Okinawa-ken 900, Japan. TEL 098-866-2143. FAX 098-866-3204. circ. 500. **Document type:** government publication.

614.84 FI ISSN 0031-0476
CODEN: PALODT
PALONTORJUNTATEKNIIKA; the trade journal of structural fire safety. (Text in Finnish; summaries in English and Swedish) 1971. 4/yr. FIM 115. Palo- ja Pelastustieto, Pieni Roobertinkatu 8 B, 00130 Helsinki 13, Finland. Ed. Juhani Katajamaki. adv.; charts; illus. circ. 3,500. (also avail. in microfilm) **Indexed:** Chem.Abstr. **Document type:** trade publication.
—BLDSC (6345.567000); CASDDS.

614.84 FI ISSN 0031-0468
PELASTUSTIETO/RAEDDNING; trade journal of the fire safety field in Finland. (Text in Finnish, Swedish; summaries in English and Swedish) 1950. 10/yr. FIM 185. Palo- ja Pelastustieto, Pieni Roobertinkatu 8 B, 00130 Helsinki 13, Finland. Ed. Juhani Katajamaki. adv.; charts; illus. circ. 11,950. (also avail. in microfilm) **Document type:** trade publication.
Formerly: Palontorjunta.

352.3 628.92 BN ISSN 0351-4714
POZAR EKSPLOZIJA PREVENTIVA; naucni, strucni i informativni casopis. (Text in Serbo-Croatian) 1980. q. 2000 din. (typically set in Dec.) Institut Zastite od Pozara i Eksplozije, Romanijska 10, 71000 Sarajevo, Bosnia Hercegovina. TEL 071 538-480. FAX 071-468-108. TELEX 071-41667. Ed. Ratko Vujovic. adv.; bk.rev.; abstr.; bibl.; charts; illus.; index, cum.index. circ. 2,000. (back issues avail.)

614.84 XO ISSN 0231-617X
POZIARNIK. 1924. s-m. $47. (Zvaz Poziarnej Ochrany - Union of Fire Protection) Obzor, Ceskoslovenskej Armady 35, 815 85 Bratislava, Slovakia.

614.84 US
PROFESSIONAL FIRE FIGHTER. 1970. s-a. membership only. (Professional Fire Fighters of Georgia) Dale Corporation, 84 Executive Dr., Troy, MI 48083-4504. TEL 313-597-9040. FAX 313-597-0082. Ed. Kate Nuernberger. adv.: page $895. circ. 2,500. (controlled).
Description: Provides information for professionals in the fire service.

614.84 US
PUBLIC FIRE EDUCATION DIGEST. q. Fire Bldg., Stillwater, OK 74078. TEL 405-744-5727. Ed. Jan Thomas.

614 UK ISSN 0260-101X
RETAIL SECURITY & FIRE PREVENTION. 1980. q. Batiste Publications Ltd., Pembroke House, Campsbourne Rd., Hornsey, London N8 7PE, England. TEL 081-340-3291. FAX 081-341-4840. TELEX 267727 BATGRP.

352.3 350 JA
SAIGAI NO JITTAI TO SHOBO NO GENKYO/ANNUAL REPORT OF FIRE AND DISASTER PREVENTION. (Text and summaries in Japanese) 1967. a. free. General Affairs Department of Miyagi Prefecture, Fire and Disaster Prevention Section, 8-1, 3-chome, Honcho, Aoba-ku, Sendai-shi 980, Japan. FAX 022-211-2399. Ed. Keisuke Kudo. circ. 400.

614.84 FR ISSN 0036-469X
SAPEUR-POMPIER. 1889. 10/yr. 315 F. Federation Nationale des Sapeurs-Pompiers Francais, 27 rue de Dunkerque, 75010 Paris, France. TEL 45-26-18-18. FAX 45-96-01-10. Ed. l. de Pampelonne. adv.; B&W page 12570 F., color page 16328 F.; trim 297 x 210. bk.rev.; charts; stat.; index. circ. 70,000. **Indexed:** C.I.S.Abstr. **Document type:** newspaper.

614.84 FR
SAPEUR POMPIER DE L'ESSONNE. 2/yr. B.P. 7235, 103 rue Bechevelin, 69354 Lyon Cedex 07, France. TEL 78-72-13-08. FAX 72-72-98-37. Ed. Commandant Peres. circ. 3,000.

614 FR
SAUVER. 1971. q. 100 F. Union Regionale des Sapeurs-Pompiers Professionnels et Volontaires d'Aquitaine, B.P. 921, 33063 Bordeaux Cedex, France. FAX 56-82-47-84. adv.; illus.

614.84 GW ISSN 0343-3560
CODEN: SCHDDN
SCHADENPRISMA; Zeitschrift fuer Schadenverhuetung und Schadenforschung der oeffentlich-rechtlichen Versicherer. 1972. q. DM.16. Feuersozietaet Berlin, Am Karlsbad 4-5, 10785 Berlin, Germany. TEL (030)2633353. Ed. H.-W. Brenner. adv.; index. circ. 13,000. **Indexed:** C.I.S. Abstr., Chem.Abstr.
—BLDSC (8088.300000); SWETS; CASDDS.
Formerly: Brandverhuetung und Brandbekaempfung (ISSN 0006-9108)

628.92 GW ISSN 0937-2555
SCHUTZ AKTUELL; magazin fuer sicherheit. 1986. q. DM.30. Thome Verlag GmbH, Goethestr. 21, 80336 Munich, Germany. TEL 089-591964. FAX 089-553079. Ed. Doris Tegethoff. adv.; bk.rev. circ. 6,500. (back issues avail.) **Document type:** trade publication.
Formerly: Katastrophenschutz Aktuell (ISSN 0930-1240)

614.84 SZ
SCHWEIZERISCHE FEUERWEHR-ZEITUNG. (Text in French, German and Italian) 1874; N.S. 1965. m. 42 SFr. (foreign 52 SFr.). Schweizerischer Feuerwehrverband, Ensingerstr. 37, CH-3000 Bern 16, Switzerland. TEL 031-3528311. FAX 031-3523464. (Subscr. to: Staempfli und Cie AG, Hallerstr. 7, CH-3001 Bern, Switzerland) Ed. Christian Jaberg. adv.; bk.rev.; bibl.; index; circ. 22,000 (controlled). **Document type:** trade publication.

614.84 UK ISSN 0307-4676
SECURITY AND FIRE EQUIPMENT SELECTOR. 1975. s-a. free. Batiste Publications Ltd., Pembroke House, Campsbourne Rd., Hornsey, London N8 7PE, England. TEL 081-340-3291. FAX 081-341-4840. TELEX 267727 BATGRP. adv. circ. 10,000.

SECURITY AUSTRALIA. see *CRIMINOLOGY AND LAW ENFORCEMENT — Security*

628.92 621 JA ISSN 0426-2700
CODEN: SHKHBF
SHOBO KENKYUJO HOKOKU/FIRE RESEARCH INSTITUTE OF JAPAN. REPORT. (Text in Japanese; summaries in English) 1950. s-a. free. Fire Research Institute of Japan - Shobo Kenkyujo, 3-14-1, Nakahara, Mitaka, Tokyo 181, Japan. FAX 0422-42-7719.
—BLDSC (7471.200000); CASDDS.

614 JA
SHOBO KENSHU. (Text in Japanese) 1965. s-a. Shobo Daigakko - Fire Defense College, 14-1 Nakahara, 3-chome, Mitaka, Tokyo 181, Japan. circ. 1,600.

614.84 SW ISSN 0346-1351
SKORSTENSFEJARMAESTAREN; tidning for sotningsvaesendet. 1965. 6/yr. SEK 120. Sveriges Skorstensfejaremaestares Riksfoerbund, Styrmansgatan 19, 114 54 Stockholm, Sweden. FAX 46-8-661-31-58. Ed. Bjoern Karlsson. adv.; bk.rev.; index. circ. 1,400.

614.84 SW ISSN 0283-5452
SKYDD & SAEKERHET/SAFETY AND SECURITY. 1986. 10/yr. SEK 224. Svenska Brandfoersvarsfoereningen - Swedish Fire Protection Association, S-115 87 Stockholm, Sweden. TEL 08-783-7000. FAX 08-661-2284. (Co-sponsors: Swedish Theft Prevention Association; Swedish Emergency Services Ltd.) Ed. Georg Hahne. circ. 13,000.
Incorporates: Stoeldskydd; Supersedes in part: Brandfoersvar.

614.84 SA ISSN 0038-2159
SOUTH AFRICAN FIRE SERVICES INSTITUTE. QUARTERLY/SUID-AFRIKAANSE BRANDWEERINSTITUT KWARTAALBLAD.* (Text in Afrikaans and English) 1960. q. membership. South African Fire Services Institute, Fire Department, Nigel, South Africa. Ed. E.S.C. Barber. circ. 1,200 (controlled). (tabloid format)

SOUTHERN BUILDING CODE CONGRESS. STANDARD FIRE PREVENTION CODE. see *BUILDING AND CONSTRUCTION*

614.84 US
SPEAKING OF FIRE. 1976. q. free. (International Fire Service Training Association) Fire Protection Publications, Oklahoma State University, Stillwater, OK 74078-0118. TEL 405-744-5723. FAX 405-744-8204. Ed. Cindy Brakhage. adv.; bk.rev. circ. 122,000. (tabloid format)

628.92 US ISSN 0896-2685
SPRINKLER AGE. 1981. m. $75 (foreign $100) (free to qualified personnel). American Fire Sprinkler Association, 12959 Jupiter Rd., Ste. 142, Dallas, TX 75238. TEL 214-349-5965. FAX 214-343-8898. Ed. Janet Knowles. adv. contact: Roger K. Gragg. circ. 3,900 (controlled). **Document type:** trade publication.
Description: Devoted to the professional development of the fire sprinkler industry.

614.84 US
SUMMARIES OF B F R L FIRE RESEARCH IN-HOUSE AND GRANTS (YEAR). a. U.S. National Institute of Standards and Technology, Fire Research Information Services, Bldg. 224, Rm. A252, Gaithersburg, MD 20899. TEL 301-975-6862. Ed. Nora H. Jason. (also avail. in microfiche; back issues avail.)
Formerly: Annual Conference on Fire Research. *Refereed Serial*

614.84 US ISSN 1041-6692
SWEEPING. 1979. m. $36 membership only. National Chimney Sweep Guild, 16021 Industrial Dr., Ste. 8, Gaithersburg, MD 20877. TEL 301-963-5600. Ed. Sue Jaidman. illus.; tr.lit. circ. 1,000. **Document type:** trade publication.
Description: Contains technical information about chimneys and sweeping, product reviews, business information, and news about the heating and venting industry.

628.92 GW ISSN 0942-6566
THUERINGER FEUERWEHRZEITSCHRIFT. 6/yr. DM.45. (Thueringer Feuerwehrverband e.V.) W. Kohlhammer GmbH, Hessbruehlstr. 69, 70565 Stuttgart, Germany. TEL 0711-7863-1. **Document type:** trade publication.

628.92 US
TODAY'S FIREMAN. 1960. q. $9. Towerhigh Publications Inc., Box 875108, Los Angeles, CA 90087. TEL 213-881-3360. Ed. Donald Mack. circ. 15,500. (tabloid format) **Document type:** trade publication.
Description: Covers the fire service and fire fighting for both the public and the professional.

614.84 XO
TUZOLTO. (Text in Hungarian) m. $78. (Fire Protection Union) Obzor, Ceskoslovenskej Armady 35, 815 85 Bratislava, Slovakia.

747.5 614.84 US
U F A C (YEAR). 1985. a. free. Upholstered Furniture Action Council, Box 2436, High Point, NC 27261. TEL 919-885-5065. FAX 919-884-5303. Ed. E.L. Briggs. circ. 5,000.
Description: For furniture manufacturers, retailers and suppliers; encourages more cigarette resistant upholstering methods.

614.84 747.5 US
U F A C VOLUNTEER. 1983. q. free. Upholstered Furniture Action Council, Box 2436, High Point, NC 27261. TEL 919-885-5065. FAX 919-884-5303. Ed. E.L. Briggs. circ. 5,000. (back issues avail.)
Description: For furniture manufacturers, retailers and suppliers; encourages more cigarette resistant upholstering methods.

628.92   US   ISSN 0889-6038
U S FIRE SPRINKLER REPORTER. 1986. m. $60 (foreign $78) (effective Dec. 1990). Wakeman-Walworth, Inc., 300 N. Washington St., Alexandria, VA 22314. TEL 703-549-8606. FAX 703-549-1372. Ed. Keyes Walworth. adv.
  Description: Reports on the fire sprinkler and related industries.

628.92   GW   ISSN 0500-6260
TH9111
UNABHAENGIGE BRANDSCHUTZZEITSCHRIFT. 1951. m. DM.54. Verlag Technik GmbH, Am Friedrichshain 22, 10407 Berlin, Germany. TEL 030-4287-0. FAX 030-4261249. Ed. Udo Malik. adv.: B&W page DM.4600; trim 185 x 250; adv. contact: Ulrich Leps. bk.rev.; index. circ. 24,671. (back issues avail.) **Document type:** trade publication.

628.92 352.3   US   ISSN 1040-1121
VOICE (ASHLAND). m. $72. International Society of Fire Service Instructors, 30 Main St., Ashland, MA 01721. TEL 508-881-5800. FAX 508-881-6829. Ed. Edward H. McCormack, Jr. adv. circ. 6,000.
  Description: Covers training and education, fire prevention and public education and safety, hazardous materials, administration and management, firefighting and emergency operations.

614.84   US   ISSN 1071-1767
W F S QUARTERLY. 1986. q. $25 to individuals (foreign $30); institutions $40 (foreign $45). Women in the Fire Service, Box 5446, Madison, WI 53705. TEL 608-233-4768. FAX 608-233-4768. Ed. Terese M. Floren. circ. 250. (looseleaf format; back issues avail.) **Document type:** newsletter.
  Description: Discusses issues relating to the gender integration of the fire service.

614.84   US   ISSN 0042-9775
TH9111
W N Y F. (With New York Firefighters) 1940. q. $15 (foreign $18). N Y C Fire Department, Publications Control Unit, Fire Academy, Randalls Island, NY 10035. TEL 212-860-9243. FAX 212-860-9485. Ed. Gloria Sturzenacker. charts; illus. circ. 14,000.
  Description: Includes fire stories, technical articles, photos, and other job-related information for members of New York City Fire Department.

WHO'S WHO IN THE EMERGENCY & RESCUE SERVICES (YEAR). see PUBLIC HEALTH AND SAFETY

628.92 634.9   US   ISSN 1064-1831
SD420.5
WILDFIRE. q. $30. International Association of Wildland Fire, Box 328, Fairfield, WA 99012-0328. circ. 2,500 (paid).
  Description: Contains news and articles on forest fires.

628.92   US
WISCONSIN FIRE JOURNAL.* 1975. 6/yr. $6. Wisconsin State Firefighters Association, Box 606, Spring Greeb, WI 53588. TEL 414-241-3565. Ed. Barbara J. Eckle. adv. circ. 10,500.
  Description: For those interested in fire control and prevention.

628.92   US
WYOMING FIRE NEWS. q. Wyoming State Department of Fire Prevention, 122 W. 25th St., Cheyenne, WY 82002. TEL 307-777-7907. FAX 307-777-7119. Ed. Donna R. Depew. **Document type:** government publication, newsletter.
  Description: Provides information about fire prevention with advice, seminar schedules, public awareness tips, rulings, commentary, and a calendar of events.

614.84   JA   ISSN 0910-4208
YOBO JIHO/ACCIDENT PREVENTION JOURNAL. (Text in Japanese) 1950. q. free. Marine and Fire Insurance Association of Japan, 9, Kanda Awajicho 2-Chome, Chiyoda-Ku, Tokyo 101, Japan. Ed. Yushi Yamada. circ. 14,000. (back issues avail.)

628.92 363.35   YU   ISSN 0351-9783
ZASTITA OD POZARA/FIREFIGHTING PROTECTION. (Text in Serbo-Croatian; summaries in English) 1960. q. 100000 din.($20) Vatrogasni Savez Jugoslavije, Andricev Venac 2-4, 11000 Belgrade, Serbia, Yugoslavia. TEL 011 330-169. Ed. Mirjana Guberinic.

628.92   CC   ISSN 1000-1107
ZHONGGUO XIAOFANG/FIRE PROTECTION IN CHINA. (Text in Chinese) 1980. bi-m. Y10.80. Gong'an-bu, Xiaofang-ju - Ministry of Public Security, Fire Bureau, 14 East Chang'an St., Beijing 100741, People's Republic of China. TEL 5122831. (Dist. overseas by: China International Book Trading Corp., P.O. Box 399, Beijing, P.R. China) Ed. Wang Li. adv. contact: Dong Liming. bk.rev. circ. 40,000.
  Description: Aims to disseminate knowledge about fire prevention and protection.

9-1-1 MAGAZINE. see CRIMINOLOGY AND LAW ENFORCEMENT

628.92   GW   ISSN 0724-7443
112 - MAGAZIN DER FEUERWEHR. m. DM.95. Lothar Haus Druck und Verlag, Hainstr. 50, 63526 Erlensee, Germany. TEL 06183-3012. FAX 06183-3033. Ed. Helmut Raab. illus. **Document type:** trade publication.

FIRE PREVENTION — Abstracting, Bibliographies, Statistics

C A SELECTS. FLAMMABILITY. see CHEMISTRY — Abstracting, Bibliographies, Statistics

363.3   UK   ISSN 0968-0357
TH9537
CHARTERED INSTITUTE OF PUBLIC FINANCE AND ACCOUNTANCY. FIRE STATISTICS. ACTUALS & ESTIMATES. 1949. a. £50. Chartered Institute of Public Finance and Accountancy, 3 Robert St., London WC2N 6BH, England. TEL 071-895-8823. FAX 071-895-8825. stat. (back issues avail.)
  Formed by the merger of: Chartered Institute of Public Finance and Accountancy. Fire Service Statistics. Actuals (ISSN 0309-622X) & Chartered Institute of Public Finance and Accountancy. Fire Service Statistics. Estimates (ISSN 0307-0573)

628.92 634.9   US   ISSN 1063-049X
Z5991
CURRENT TITLES IN WILDLAND FIRE. m. $50 (diskette $60). International Association of Wildland Fire, Box 328, Fairfield, WA 99012-0328. circ. 500 (paid). **Document type:** bibliography.
  Description: Contains current international bibliographic citations on forest fire.

352.3   CN
FIRE LOSSES IN CANADA. ANNUAL REPORT/PERTES CAUSEES PAR L'INCENDIE AU CANADA. RAPPORT ANNUEL. (Text in English, French) 1921. a. free. Labour Canada, Publications Distribution, Ottawa, Ont K1A 0J2, Canada. TEL 819-994-0543. FAX 819-997-1664. circ. 700. **Document type:** government publication.
  Description: Statistics compiled on fire losses, including property classification, dollar loss, fire deaths, and fire injuries.

352.3   CN
FIRE LOSSES IN GOVERNMENT OF CANADA PROPERTIES. REPORT/PERTES DUES A L'INCENDIE DE BIENS IMMOBILIERS DE L'ADMINISTRATION FEDERALE. (Text in English, French) 1962. a. free. Labour Canada, Publications Distribution, Ottawa, Ont. K1A 0J2, Canada. TEL 819-994-0543. FAX 819-997-1664. TELEX 819-997-3453. circ. 700.
  Description: Statistics compiled on fire losses in properties owned and leased by the government of Canada, including property classification, department, over 1,000 deaths and fire injuries.

614.84   US
FIRE RESEARCH PUBLICATIONS. 1972. irreg., latest 1988. price varies. (U.S. National Bureau of Standards) U.S. National Technical Information Service, 5285 Port Royal Rd., Springfield, VA 22161. TEL 703-487-4600. Ed. Nora H. Jason. (also avail. in microfiche)

614.84   UK   ISSN 0260-3098
FIRE STATISTICS UNITED KINGDOM. 1946. a. price varies. Home Office, 50 Queen Anne's Gate, London SW1H 9AT, England. TEL 081-760-2850. circ. 900. **Document type:** government publication.
  —BLDSC (3933.390000). CCC.
  Former titles (until 1977): United Kingdom Fire Statistics; United Kingdom Fire and Loss Statistics (ISSN 0082-7959)

614.84 011   NE   ISSN 0077-6955
NETHERLANDS. CENTRAAL BUREAU VOOR DE STATISTIEK. STATISTIEK DER BRANDEN/NETHERLANDS. CENTRAL BUREAU OF STATISTICS. FIRE STATISTICS. (Text in Dutch and English) 1950. a. fl.26.75. Centraal Bureau voor de Statistiek, Prinses Beatrixlaan 428, Voorburg, Netherlands. (Dist. by: SDU - Publishers, Christoffel Plantijnstraat 2, Postbus 20014, 2500 EA The Hague, Netherlands) **Document type:** government publication.

FISH AND FISHERIES

see also Biology–Zoology

799.1   UK   ISSN 0044-8257
A.C.A. REVIEW. 1948. a. membership. Anglers' Co-operative Association, 23 Castlegate, Grantham, Lincs. NG31 5SW, England. TEL 44-476-60900. FAX 44-476-60900. Ed. Michael D. Jacobson. adv.; bk.rev. circ. 20,000. **Indexed:** Sportsearch. **Document type:** corporate report.

639.2   US
A F T M A TRADE SHOW DIRECTORY AND BUYERS' GUIDE. a. $25. American Fishing and Tackle Manufacturing Association, 1250 Grove Ave., Ste. 300, Barrington, IL 60010. TEL 312-381-9490. FAX 708-381-9518. adv.; circ. 10,000 (controlled). **Document type:** directory.

A M U NEWS. (American Malacological Union, Inc.) see BIOLOGY — Zoology

639   BE
AANVOER EN BESOMMING VAN DE BELGISCHE ZEEVISSERIJ. 1973. a. Dienst voor de Zeevisserij, Bestuur voor de Ekonomische Diensten, Administratief Centrum, Vrijhavenstr. 5, B-8400 Oostende, Belgium. TEL 32-59-508966. FAX 32-59-807693. TELEX 81075 DZVOST. **Document type:** government publication.

639   NO   ISSN 0365-8252
AARSBERETNING VEDKOMMENDE NORGES FISKERIER. 1894. a. free. Fiskeridirektoratet - Directorate of Fisheries, Box 185, N-5002 Bergen, Norway. FAX 05-238090. TELEX 42151. **Indexed:** Biol.Abstr. **Document type:** academic/scholarly publication.
  —CCC.
  Description: Includes the following subtitles: statistics on trawling, fisheries in Lofoten (cod), fishing fleets and seal catch; also contains annual reports from Directorate of Fisheries.

ACTA ACADEMIAE AGRICULTURAE AC TECHNICAE OLSTENENSIS. PROTECTIO AQUARUM ET PISCATORIA/AGRICULTURAL AND TECHNICAL ACADEMY IN OLSZTYN. WATER CONSERVATION AND INLAND FISHERIES. see WATER RESOURCES

ACTA ADRIATICA. see EARTH SCIENCES — Oceanography

597   PL   ISSN 0137-1592
                                   CODEN: AIPSCJ
ACTA ICHTHYOLOGICA ET PISCATORIA. (Text and abstract in English) 1970. s-a. price varies. Akademia Rolnicza w Szczecinie - Academy of Agriculture in Szczecin, Dzial Wydawnictw, Ul. Doctora Judyma 22, 71-460 Szczecin. TEL 48-91-71667. FAX 48-91-70877. TELEX 0425494 AR. Ed. Antoni Furowicz. bk.rev. **Indexed:** Anim.Breed.Abstr., Chem.Abstr., Curr.Ref.Fish Res., Field Crop Abstr., Inc.Vet., Nutr.Abstr., Protozool.Abstr., Vet.Bull. **Document type:** academic/scholarly publication.
  —CASDDS.

639.5 574   II
▼**ADVANCES IN FISH BIOLOGY AND FISHERIES.** (Text in English) 1993. irreg. 23. Hindustan Publishing Corp., 6-U.B. Jawahar Nagar, Delhi 110007, India. TEL 9-11-2915059. FAX 9-11-6863511. Ed. H.R. Singh.

639.2   SP
AETINAPE. 1982. q. Asociacion Espanola de Titulados Nautico-Pesqueros, Avda. General Sanjurjo, 8-1 izda., 15006 La Coruna, Spain. TEL (986)29 95 77.

FISH AND FISHERIES

574.92   UG   ISSN 0002-0036
CODEN: AJTHBC
AFRICAN JOURNAL OF TROPICAL HYDROBIOLOGY AND FISHERIES.* (Text in English and French) 1971-19??; resumed. s-a. Uganda Freshwater Fisheries Research Organisation, P.O. Box 343, Jinja, Uganda. Ed. A.W. Kudhongania. bk.rev. **Indexed:** Biol.Abstr.

639.2 630   SP
AGRICULTURA, LA PESCA Y LA ALIMENTACION ESPANOLAS. 1979. a. 2800 ptas. Ministerio de Agricultura, Pesca y Alimentacion, Centro de Publicaciones, Paseo de la Infanta Isabel 1, 28071 Madrid, Spain. TEL 3475551.
Formerly: Agricultura y la Pesca Espanolas.

AGRINDEX; international information system for the agricultural sciences and technology. see *AGRICULTURE*

639.2   SP
AGRIPESCA; revista tecnica de informacion agraria. 1985. q. free. Delegacion Provincial de Agricultura y Pesca de la Junta de Andalucia, Avda. Ana de Viya, 3-3, 11009 Cadiz, Spain. TEL (956)27 45 00-04-08. Ed. Jose Cabral Fernandez.

639.2 664   PL   ISSN 0239-9180
AKADEMIA ROLNICZA W SZCZECINIE. ZESZYTY NAUKOWE. RYBACTWO MORSKIE I TECHNOLOGIA ZYWNOSCI. 1966. a. price varies. Akademia Rolnicza w Szczecinie, Dzial Wydawnictw, Ul. Doctora Judyma 22, 71-460 Szczecin, Poland. TEL 48-91-71667. FAX 48-91-70877. TELEX 0425494 AR. Ed. Antoni Furowicz. bk.rev. **Indexed:** Chem.Abstr., Field Crop Abstr., Nutr.Abstr. **Document type:** academic/scholarly publication.

639.34   DK   ISSN 0108-2396
AKVARIEBLADET. 1969. 10/yr. DKK 155. Koebenhavns Akvarieforening, Eksp. Henning Nielsen, Taarnvej 352, DK-2610 Roedovre, Denmark. Ed. Benny B. Larsen. adv.; bk.rev.; illus. circ. 4,000.

639.34   XR   ISSN 0002-3930
AKVARIUM A TERARIUM; casopis cs. akvaristu a teraristu. 1958. 6/yr. 30 Kcs.($26.90) Panorama, Halkova 1, 120 72 Prague 2, Czech Republic. Ed. Jirina Crhova. abstr.; illus. circ. 30,000.
—BLDSC (0786.250000).

639.9   US
SH11
ALASKA. DEPARTMENT OF FISH AND GAME. TECHNICAL FISHERY REPORT. irreg. Department of Fish and Game, Division of Commercial Fisheries, Box 3-2000, Juneau, AK 99802. TEL 907-465-4210. illus.
Formerly: Alaska. Department of Fish and Game. Technical Data Report (ISSN 0095-4632)

639.2   US   ISSN 0164-8330
ALASKA FISHERMAN'S JOURNAL. 1977. m. $21. Waterfront Press Co., 1115 N.W. 46th St., Seattle, WA 98107. TEL 206-789-6506. FAX 206-789-9193. Ed. John Van Amerongen. adv.; bk.rev. circ. 15,500. (tabloid format)

639.2   US   ISSN 1052-2727
SK367
ALASKA'S WILDLIFE. 1986. bi-m. $12. Department of Fish and Game, Division of Commercial Fisheries, Box 3-2000, Juneau, AK 99802. TEL 907-465-4112. Ed. Sheila Nickerson. circ. 15,000.
Formerly: Alaska Fish and Game.
Description: Promotes appreciation of the state's living resources.

ALBERTA. FISH AND WILDLIFE DIVISION. FISHERIES POLLUTION REPORT. see *ENVIRONMENTAL STUDIES*

639.2   US   ISSN 8755-7894
ALTERNATIVE AQUACULTURE NETWORK NEWSLETTER. 1981. q. $14. Alternative Aquaculture Association, Box 109, Breinigsville, PA 18031. TEL 215-395-5854. FAX 215-683-9280. Ed. Steven van Gorder. bk.rev. circ. 500. (back issues avail.) **Document type:** newsletter.

639.2   US   ISSN 0097-0638
CODEN: AFPUA2
AMERICAN FISHERIES SOCIETY. SPECIAL PUBLICATION. 1948. irreg. no.22, 1991. price varies. American Fisheries Society, 5410 Grosvenor Ln., Ste. 110, Bethesda, MD 20814-2199. TEL 301-897-8616. FAX 301-897-8096. Ed. Robert L. Kendall. **Indexed:** Biol.Abstr., Chem.Abstr., Curr.Cont., Deep Sea Res.& Oceanogr.Abstr., Ocean.Abstr., Pollut.Abstr.
—BLDSC (8372.320000). **CCC.**

639.2   US   ISSN 0892-2284
CODEN: AFSSEF
AMERICAN FISHERIES SOCIETY. SYMPOSIUM. 1987. irreg., no.12, 1991. price varies. American Fisheries Society, 5410 Grosvenor Ln., Ste. 110, Bethesda, MD 20814-2199. TEL 301-897-8616. FAX 301-897-8096. Ed. Robert L. Kendall.
—**CCC.**

639.2   US   ISSN 0002-8487
SH1   CODEN: TAFSAI
AMERICAN FISHERIES SOCIETY. TRANSACTIONS. 1870. bi-m. $30 to individuals (foreign $35); libraries $400 (foreign $425) (includes all journals put out by the American Fisheries Society). American Fisheries Society, 5410 Grosvenor Ln., Ste. 110, Bethesda, MD 20814-2199. TEL 301-897-8616. FAX 301-897-8096. Eds. Charles C. Coutant, Thomas A. Edsall. bk.rev.; index, cum.index: 1929-1952, 1953-1976 (in 2 vols.). circ. 3,700. (also avail. in microfiche; microfilm from PMC; back issues avail.) **Indexed:** Abstr.Bull.Inst.Pap.Chem., Acid Rain Abstr., Acid Rain Ind., Agri.Eng.Abstr., Anim.Breed.Abstr., Aqua.Sci.& Fish.Abstr., Biol.Abstr., Biol.& Agr.Ind., Chem.Abstr., Curr.Adv.Ecol.Sci., Curr.Cont., Deep Sea Res.& Oceanogr.Abstr., Environ.Abstr., Environ.Per.Bibl., Excerp.Med., Geo.Abstr., Helminthol.Abstr., Ind.Vet., Nutr.Abstr., Ocean.Abstr., Pollut.Abstr., Sel.Water Res.Abstr., Vet.Bull., W.R.C.Inf.
—BLDSC (8886.800000); Faxon; UnCover; SWETS; CASDDS. **CCC.**
Description: Features the results of basic and applied research into all aspects of fish and fisheries in freshwater and marine environments.
Refereed Serial

639.2   US   ISSN 0362-1715
CODEN: MAFCDW
AMERICAN FISHERIES SOCIETY MONOGRAPH. 1976. irreg., no.6, 1992. price varies. American Fisheries Society, 5410 Grosvenor Ln., Ste. 110, Bethesda, MD 20814-2199. TEL 301-897-8616. FAX 301-897-8096. Ed. Robert L. Kendall. **Indexed:** Deep Sea Res.& Oceanogr.Abstr. **Document type:** monographic series.
—BLDSC (5914.225200); CASDDS. **CCC.**

639.3   US   ISSN 0002-967X
QL638.C96
AMERICAN KILLIFISH ASSOCIATION. JOURNAL. 1964. bi-m. $24. American Killifish Association, 556 W. Cedar Pl., Louisville, CO 80027. TEL 914-782-0977. (Subscr. to: 903 Merrifield Pl., Mishawaka, IN 46544) Ed. Roger Langton. bk.rev. circ. 1,500. **Document type:** bulletin.
Incorporates (in 1974): A K A Killie Notes.

639.2   US   ISSN 1050-0839
CODEN: ASIREJ
AMERICAN SEAFOOD INSTITUTE REPORT. 1990. m. free to qualified personnel (foreign $35). American Seafood Institute, 212 Main St., Ste. 3, Wakefield, RI 02879-3512. TEL 401-783-4200. FAX 401-789-9727. TELEX 952051-FISHDEV. Ed. Colleen Coyne-Boragine. adv. contact: Ralph Boragine. bk.rev. circ. 10,000. (back issues avail.) **Document type:** trade publication.

639   FR   ISSN 0066-2623
SH269
ANNUAIRE DE L'ARMEMENT A LA PECHE; guide de la peche professionelle francaise. 1956. a. 650 F. Editions Maritimes, 190 bd. Haussmann, 75008 Paris, France. TEL 45-63-11-55. TELEX NAVIMAR 290131F. index.
Description: Covers fishing fleet, owners, professional and state organizations in France.

639   FR   ISSN 0767-3841
SH1
ANNUAIRE DE LA MAREE ET DE L'AQUACULTURE; guide de la commercialisation des produits de la mer. 1930. a. 500 F. Editions Maritimes, 190, bd. Haussmann, Paris 75008, France. TEL 16-33-31-06-13. TELEX NAVIMAR 290131F. index.
—BLDSC (1070.760000).
Formerly (until 1986): Annuaire de la Maree (ISSN 0767-3833)
Description: Covers wholesale and retail fish trade in French markets.

639.3   US
ANNUAL REPORT ON WORLD SHRIMP FARMING. (Supplement to: World Shrimp Farming) a. $25. Aquaculture Digest, 11057 Negley Ave., San Diego, CA 92131. TEL 619-271-6354. (Subscr. to: 9434 Kearny Mesa Rd., San Diego, CA 92126) **Document type:** consumer publication, trade publication.
Description: Features country-by-country status reports. Contains background information, production statistics, maps, recommended publications, and highlights of events.

639.34   NE   ISSN 0044-8486
SH1   CODEN: AQCLAL
AQUACULTURE; an international journal devoted to fundamental aquatic food resources. (Text in English, French, German) 1972. 40/yr. (in 10 vols.; 4 nos./vol.). fl.2960($1600) (effective 1994). Elsevier Science B.V., P.O. Box 211, 1000 AE Amsterdam, Netherlands. TEL 31-20-5803911. FAX 31-20-5803598. TELEX 18582 ESPA NL. (Subscr. in U.S. and Canada to: Elsevier Science Inc., Box 882, Madison Sq. Sta., New York, NY 10159-0882. TEL 212-989-5800. FAX 212-633-3990) Ed.Bd. adv.; bk.rev.; bibl.; charts; illus.; stat.; index. circ. 650. (also avail. in microform from UMI; reprint service avail. from SWZ) **Indexed:** Agri.Eng.Abstr., Anim.Breed.Abstr., Aqua.Sci.& Fish.Abstr., Biodet.Abstr., Biol.Abstr., Chem.Abstr., Curr.Adv.Ecol.Sci., Curr.Adv.Genetics & Molec.Biol., Curr.Cont., Deep Sea Res.& Oceanogr.Abstr., Environ.Abstr., Excerp.Med., Food Sci.& Tech.Abstr., Helminthol.Abstr., Ind.Vet., Irr.& Drain.Abstr., Maize Abstr., Mar.Sci.Cont.Tab., Nutr.Abstr., Ocean.Abstr., Pollut.Abstr., Protozool.Abstr., Rev.Med.& Vet.Mycol., Rice Abstr., Sci.Cit.Ind., Sel.J.Water, Sel.Water Res.Abstr., Soils & Fert., Soyabean Abstr., Sugar Ind.Abstr., Triticale Abstr., Vet.Bull., W.R.C.Inf., Weed Abstr. **Document type:** academic/scholarly publication.
—BLDSC (1581.866000); Faxon; UnCover; SWETS; CASDDS. **CCC.**
Description: Covers diseases, parasites and predators; economics and marketing; genetics and breeding; husbandry and management; nutrition; physiology and endocrinology.
Refereed Serial

639.3   CH   ISSN 0254-6493
AQUACULTURE. Key Title: Shuichan Yangzhi. (Text in Chinese or English) 1970. irreg. exchange basis. Taiwan Fisheries Research Institute, Tungkang Marine Laboratory, Tungkang, Pingtung, Taiwan, Republic of China. Ed. I-Chiu Liao. adv.; bk.rev. **Indexed:** Deep Sea Res.& Oceanogr.Abstr.

639.2   UK   ISSN 0266-996X
SH1   CODEN: AFMAEX
AQUACULTURE AND FISHERIES MANAGEMENT. 1970. m. £330 in Europe; elsewhere £363 ($540) (effective 1994). Blackwell Scientific Publications Ltd., Osney Mead, Oxford OX2 OEI, England. TEL 0865-240201. FAX 0865-721205. TELEX 83355-MEDBOK-G. Ed.Bd. adv.; bk.rev.; abstr.; bibl.; charts; illus. circ. 1,000. (also avail. in microform from UMI; back issues avail.) **Indexed:** Acid Rain Abstr., Acid Rain Ind., Biol.Abstr., Curr.Adv.Ecol.Sci., Environ.Abstr., Environ.Per.Bibl., Excerp.Med., Geo.Abstr., Ind.Vet., Sel.Water Res.Abstr., Vet.Bull., W.R.C.Inf. **Document type:** academic/scholarly publication.
—BLDSC (1581.866030); UnCover; SWETS; UMI; CASDDS. **CCC.**
Incorporates (1994-1995): Fisheries Management and Ecology (ISSN 0969-997X); **Formerly (until 1985):** Fisheries Management (ISSN 0141-9862)
Refereed Serial

FISH AND FISHERIES

639.2 UK ISSN 0967-6120
SH1
▼AQUACULTURE INTERNATIONAL. 1993. q. £120 to institutions in EC nations (N. America $102; elsewhere £130); individuals in EC nations £50 (North America $85; elsewhere £50). (European Aquaculture Society) Chapman & Hall, 2-6 Boundary Row, London SE1 8HN, England. TEL 071-865-0066. FAX 071-865-9623. TELEX 290164-CHAPMAG. (Dist. by: International Thomson Publishing Services, Ltd., N. Way, Andover, Hants. SP10 5BE, England. TEL 0264-332919; US addr.: Chapman & Hall, Journals Promotion Department, One Penn Plaza, 41st Fl., New York, NY 10019. TEL 212-564-1060. FAX 212-564-1505) Ed. Michael G. Poxton. Document type: academic/scholarly publication.
—BLDSC (1581.866065).
Description: Publishes original research papers, short communications, technical notes, and review papers on all aspects of aquaculture.

639.2 US ISSN 0199-1388
SH1 CODEN: AQMAE8
AQUACULTURE MAGAZINE. 1969. bi-m. $15. Achill River Corp., Box 2329, Asheville, NC 28802. TEL 704-254-7334. FAX 704-253-0677. Ed. Kay Homer. adv.; bk.rev.; charts; illus.; tr.lit. circ. 7,392. Indexed: Deep Sea Res.& Oceanogr.Abstr., Environ.Abstr., Ind.Vet., Vet.Bull.
—BLDSC (1581.866080); CIS; UnCover; SWETS.
Former titles: Commercial Fish Farmer and Aquaculture News (ISSN 0099-0353); Commercial Fish Farmer; Catfish Farmer and World Aquaculture News (ISSN 0095-0491); Formed by the merger of: American Fish Farmer (ISSN 0002-8479); American Fishes and U.S. Trout News (ISSN 0002-8509); Catfish Farmer (ISSN 0008-7858); Catfish Farming Industries.

AQUAPHYTE. see BIOLOGY — Botany

639.34 639.34 NE ISSN 0003-729X
AQUARIUM; maandblad voor aquarium-, terrarium- en insektariumkunde. 1930. m. fl.48. Nederlandse Bond "Aqua-Terra", Havenstraat 83, 1211 K H Hilversum, Netherlands. Ed. N.H. de Jong. adv.; bk.rev.; charts; illus.; index. circ. 30,000. Indexed: Biol.Abstr.

639.34 GW ISSN 0341-2709
AQUARIUM. 1967. m. DM.88. Birgit Schmettkamp Verlag, Weidenbachweg 6a, 53332 Bornheim, Germany. TEL 02227-1557. FAX 02227-7662. adv.; bk.rev. circ. 13,400. (back issues avail.) Indexed: Biol.Abstr. Document type: consumer publication.
—BLDSC (1582.150000).
Description: Reports on how to keep and care for freshwater and saltwater fishes, reptiles and aquarium plants.

639.34 AT ISSN 0044-8508
AQUARIUM SOCIETY OF NEW SOUTH WALES. MONTHLY JOURNAL. 1951. m. Aus.$10. Aquarium Society of New South Wales, Box 89, Strathfield, N.S.W. 2135, Australia. Ed. Juan Alberto Rojas. adv.; bk.rev. circ. 250.

639.2 US
AQUATIC FARMING NEWSLETTER. q. California Aquaculture Association, Box 1004, Niland, CA 92257. TEL 619-359-FISH. Document type: newsletter.
Description: Covers culture techniques, industry trends, and current concerns.

639.2 FR ISSN 0990-7440
SH1 CODEN: ALREEA
AQUATIC LIVING RESOURCES; international journal devoted to aquatic resources. (Text in English, French, Spanish) 1928. q. 1070 F. Gauthier-Villars, 15 rue Gossin, 92543 Montrouge Cedex, France. TEL 33-1-40-92-65-00. FAX 33-1-40-92-65-97. (Subscr. to: Dunod, 11 rue Gossin, 92543 Montrouge Cedex, France) Ed.Bd. charts; illus.; tr.lit. circ. 950. (also avail. in microform) Indexed: Aqua.Sci.& Fish.Abstr., Biol.Abstr., Bull.Signal., Food Sci.& Tech.Abstr., Ocean.Abstr., Sel.Water Res.Abstr., Zoo.Rec.
—BLDSC (1582.388000). CCC.
Incorporates: Revue des Travaux de l'Institut des Peches Maritimes; Formerly (until 1987): Aquatic Living; I F R E M E R. Revue des Travaux (ISSN 0020-2231)
Description: Contains original research papers and review articles on living resources in the oceans, coastal waters, rivers and lakes. Includes all fields of biology as well as exploitation processes and environmental management.

639.2 GW ISSN 0944-1921
SH1 CODEN: AVFSAO
ARCHIV FUER FISCHEREI UND MEERESFORSCHUNG. 1949. 3/yr. DM.206 (foreign DM.209). (Bundesforschungsanstalt fuer Fischerei) Gustav Fischer Verlag, Wollgrasweg 49, 70599 Stuttgart, Germany. TEL 0711-458030. FAX 0711-4580334. TELEX 7111488-FIBUCH. (Subscr. to: Postfach 720143, 70577 Stuttgart, Germany) Eds. Klaus Tiews, Dietrich Sahrhage. adv.; bk.rev.; charts; illus.; maps. Indexed: Aqua.Sci.& Fish.Abstr., Biol.Abstr., Chem.Abstr., Curr.Adv.Ecol.Sci., Curr.Cont., Deep Sea Res.& Oceanogr.Abstr., Excerp.Med., Food Sci.& Tech.Abstr., Helminthol.Abstr., INIS Atomind., Sci.Cit.Ind., Sel.Water Res.Abstr., W.R.C.Inf. Document type: academic/scholarly publication.
—BLDSC (1608.000000); CASDDS.
Formerly (until 1993): Archiv fuer Fischereiwissenschaft (ISSN 0003-9063)

639.3 JA ISSN 0289-5242
ARIAKE FISHERIES EXPERIMENT STATION. ANNUAL REPORT. (Text in Japanese) 1948. a. free. Fukuoka Prefecture, Ariake Fisheries Experiment Station, 728-5 Yoshidomi-Cho, Yanagawa-Shi 832, Japan. TEL 0944-72-5338. FAX 0944-72-6170. Ed. Yoich Suzaki. circ. 200. (back issues avail.) Document type: academic/scholarly publication.

799.2 639.2 US
ARIZONA GAME AND FISH DEPARTMENT WILDLIFE BULLETIN. 1953. w. free. Game and Fish Department, 2222 W. Greenway, Phoenix, AZ 85023. TEL 602-942-3000. Ed. Mark Jecker. bk.rev. circ. 275. Document type: bulletin.
Description: Presents news stories distributed primarily to the news media.

ARIZONA WILDLIFE VIEWS. see CONSERVATION

ASIAN FISHERIES SCIENCE. see BIOLOGY — Zoology

639.2 CN
ATLANTIC FISHERMAN. 1984. m. $15 for Atlantic Canada; rest of Canada $37; U.S. $50. Graphic Advocate Co. Ltd., P.O. Box 1000, Pictou, N.S. B0K 1H0, Canada. TEL 902-485-8014. FAX 902-752-4816. (Subscr. to: 11 George St., P.O. Box 342, Pictou, N.S. B0K 1H0, Canada) Ed. Heather Richards. adv. circ. 13,376. (tabloid format)
Description: For the commercial fisherman; covers the industry, and government.

639.2 333.7 CN
ATLANTIC SALMON FEDERATION. SPECIAL PUBLICATION SERIES. 1971. irreg. (1-2/yr.). price varies. Atlantic Salmon Federation, P.O. Box 429, St. Andrews, NB E0G 2X0, Canada. TEL 506-529-4581. circ. 300. (back issues avail.) Indexed: Biol.Abstr., Deep Sea Res.& Oceanogr.Abstr., Ocean.Abstr.
Formerly: International Atlantic Salmon Foundation. Special Publication Series.

639.2 799 CN ISSN 0044-992X
CODEN: ATSJAE
ATLANTIC SALMON JOURNAL. 1952. q. membership. Atlantic Salmon Federation, P.O. Box 429, St. Andrews, NB E0G 2X0, Canada. TEL 506-529-4581. Ed. Harry Bruce. adv.; bk.rev.; illus. circ. 21,000. Indexed: Biol.Abstr.
—BLDSC (1765.930000).

639.2 GL ISSN 0107-9417
AULISARNERMIT NUTARSIAGSSAT/GROENLANDS FISKERITIDENDE. (Text in Eskimo and Danish) 1981. bi-m. DKK 25. P.O. Box 450, 3900 Nuuk, Greenland.

639.2 AT
AUSTRALIA. DEPARTMENT OF PRIMARY INDUSTRIES AND ENERGY. RECOMMENDED MARKETING NAMES FOR FISH. 1985. irreg. Department of Primary Industries and Energy, Fisheries Policy Branch, G.P.O. Box 858, Canberra, A.C.T. 2601, Australia. FAX 06-272-4215. Document type: government publication.

AUSTRALIAN CENTRE FOR MARITIME STUDIES. OCCASIONAL PAPERS IN MARITIME AFFAIRS. see TRANSPORTATION — Ships And Shipping

639.2 AT ISSN 0004-9115
SH131
AUSTRALIAN FISHERIES. 1942. m. Aus.$50. Australian Fisheries Management Authority, P.O. Box 7051, Mail Centre, Canberra, A.C.T. 2610. TEL 062-72-5187. FAX 062-72-5036. TELEX AA62505 FISHE. Ed. Margaret Macreadie. adv. contact: Angela Bird. bk.rev.; illus.; index. circ. 41,000. Indexed: Biol.Abstr., Curr.Adv.Ecol.Sci., Curr.Ref.Fish Res., Deep Sea Res.& Oceanogr.Abstr., Environ.Abstr., Food Sci.& Tech.Abstr., INIS Atomind., Nutr.Abstr., Ocean.Abstr., Pollut.Abstr., So.Pac.Per.Ind. Document type: government publication.
—BLDSC (1798.935000); UnCover. CCC.
Former titles (until 1969): Australian Fisheries Newsletter (ISSN 0818-7371); (until 1965): Fisheries Newsletter (ISSN 0818-7363)
Description: Covers latest news, issues, policies, events.

639.2 AT ISSN 0157-9630
AUSTRALIAN FISHING INDUSTRY DIRECTORY (YEAR). 1985. biennial. free. Department of Primary Industries and Energy, Fisheries Policy Branch, G.P.O. Box 858, Canberra, A.C.T. 2601, Australia. FAX 062-725036. Document type: directory.

639.2 AT ISSN 0817-7724
AUSTRALIAN OYSTER. 1981-1992 (Aug.); resumed 1994. 2/yr. Aus.$15 (foreign Aus.$25). Oyster Farmer's Association of New South Wales, P.O. Box 254, Turramurra, N.S.W. 2074, Australia. TEL 02-487-3566. adv.; bk.rev. circ. 600. (back issues avail.)
Description: All aspects of oyster husbandry in Australia and overseas.

639 CN ISSN 0827-570X
B.C. FISHING DIRECTORY & ATLAS; B.C. lakes & streams. (Freshwater and Saltwater editions avail.) 1984. a. Can.$10.95. A. Belhumeur Ent. Ltd., 1640 Western Dr., Port Coquitlam, B.C. V3C 2X3, Canada. TEL 604-942-5671. FAX 604-942-7395. Ed. A. Belhumeur. adv. circ. 20,000.
Formerly: Okay Anglers Fishing Directory & Atlas.

639.3 799.1 US ISSN 0884-4739
BASSIN'; official magazine of the weekend angler. 1974. 8/yr. $13.95 for 6 issues. NatCom, Inc., 15115 S. 76th E. Ave., Bixby, OK 74008. TEL 918-366-4441. FAX 918-366-4439. Ed. Simon McCaffery. adv.: color page $7794; adv. contact: Ellie Shimer. circ. 250,000. Document type: consumer publication.
Formerly (until 1985): Pro Bass.
Description: Guide for the weekend bass angler.

BEIKOKU TOKKYO SHOROKU. OYO YUKI KAGAKU, NOSUISAN, IJUTSU HEN/U.S. PATENT ABSTRACTS. APPLIED ORGANIC CHEMISTRY, AGRICULTURE AND FISHERY, MEDICINE. see PATENTS, TRADEMARKS AND COPYRIGHTS — Abstracting, Bibliographies, Statistics

639.3 BE ISSN 0303-9072
BELGIUM. RIJKSSTATION VOOR ZEEVISSERIJ. MEDEDELINGEN. 1969. irreg. free. Rijksstation voor Zeevisserij, Ankerstraat 1, B-8400 Oostende, Belgium. FAX 059-330629. Dir. P. Hovart. circ. 500. (back issues avail.) Indexed: Biol.& Agr.Ind. Document type: monographic series.

BERMUDA. DEPARTMENT OF AGRICULTURE, FISHERIES AND PARKS. MONTHLY BULLETIN. see AGRICULTURE

FISH AND FISHERIES

BERMUDA. DEPARTMENT OF AGRICULTURE, FISHERIES AND PARKS. REPORT FOR THE YEAR. see *AGRICULTURE*

BIOCHEMISTRY & MOLECULAR BIOLOGY OF FISHES. see *BIOLOGY — Zoology*

639 591 CL ISSN 0067-8767
BIOLOGIA PESQUERA. 1961. a. $15 or exchange basis. Universidad Catolica de la Santisima Concepcion, Casilla 297, Concepcion, Chile. TEL 056-41-246175. FAX 056-41-245908. Ed. Mario George-Nascimento F. circ. controlled. (also avail. in microform) **Indexed:** Biol.Abstr. **Document type:** academic/scholarly publication.

639 IE ISSN 0791-5950
BORD IASCAIGH MHARA. TUARASCAIL AGUS CUNTAISI/IRISH SEA FISHERIES BOARD. ANNUAL REPORT. (Text in English and Gaelic) 1953. a. free to libraries & institutions. Irish Sea Fisheries Board, P.O. Box 12, Crofton Rd., Dun Laoghaire, Co. Dublin, Ireland. TEL 01-2841544. FAX 01-2841123. Ed. Sean Freeman. circ. 3,500 (controlled).

639.54 IO ISSN 0126-1924
SH380.6
BRACKISHWATER AQUACULTURE DEVELOPMENT CENTRE. BULLETIN. (Text in English; summaries in Indonesian) 1975. s-a. exchange basis. (Directorate General of Fisheries) Brackishwater Aquaculture Development Centre, Pemandian Kartini, Box 1, Jepara, Central Java, Indonesia. Ed. Sukotojo Adisukresno. **Indexed:** Biol.Abstr. **Document type:** bulletin.
Formerly: Jepara. Shrimp Culture Research Centre. Bulletin (ISSN 0216-4000)

639 BL ISSN 0374-6658
TC841 CODEN: BTOCAI
BRAZIL. DEPARTAMENTO NACIONAL DE OBRAS CONTRA AS SECAS. BOLETIM TECNICO. (Text in Portuguese; summaries in English) 1967. bi-m. free. Departamento Nacional de Obras Contra as Secas, Divisao Documentacao, Av. Duque de Caxias 1700, 4 Andar Sala 411-a, 60000 Fortaleza, Ceara, Brazil. bibl.; charts; illus.; stat. circ. 5,000. **Indexed:** Biol.Abstr.
—CASDDS.
Formerly: Brazil. Divisao de Pesquisas Ictiologicas. Serie Circular (ISSN 0068-0796)

BURKINA FASO. DIRECTION DES EAUX ET FORETS ET DE LA CONSERVATION DES SOLS. RAPPORT ANNUEL. see *FORESTS AND FORESTRY*

639.2 II ISSN 0970-6143
C I C F R I NEWSLETTER. (Text in English) 1976. bi-m. Central Inland Capture Fisheries Research Institute, Barrackpore 743 101, W. Bengal, India. TELEX 021-8552 CIFI IN. Ed. V.V. Sugunan. **Document type:** newsletter.
Formerly: Central Inland Fisheries Research Institute Newsletter.

639.2 UN ISSN 0379-5616
C I F A TECHNICAL PAPERS. 1972. irreg., no.15, 1986. Food and Agriculture Organization of the United Nations, Committee for Inland Fisheries of Africa, Distribution and Sales Section, Via delle Terme di Caracalla, I-00100 Rome, Italy. Ed. J.J. Kambona. (also avail. in microfiche) **Indexed:** Biol.Abstr., Curr.Adv.Ecol.Sci., World Agri.Econ.& Rural Sociol.Abstr.

639 551.46 AT ISSN 1031-9956
SH317
C S I R O DIVISION OF FISHERIES. RESEARCH REPORT. 1961. biennial. free. Commonwealth Scientific and Industrial Research Organization, Division of Fisheries, G.P.O. Box 1538, Hobart, Tas. 7001, Australia. FAX 002-240-530. TELEX AA57182. circ. 1,000. **Indexed:** Biol.Abstr.
Supersedes in part (in 1984): Commonwealth Scientific and Industrial Research Organization. Marine Laboratories. Research Report (ISSN 0726-4291); *Which supersedes:* Commonwealth Scientific Industrial Research Organization. Division of Fisheries and Oceanography. Report (ISSN 0069-7397)

587 US ISSN 0575-3317
SH351.S3 CODEN: COFRAS
CALIFORNIA COOPERATIVE OCEANIC FISHERIES INVESTIGATIONS REPORTS. (Editions in English and Spanish) 1950. a. free. California Cooperative Oceanic Fisheries Investigations, Scripps Institution of Oceanography, University of California, La Jolla, CA 92093-0227. TEL 619-534-4236. FAX 619-534-6500. TELEX 188929. Ed. Julie Olfe. circ. 1,500 (controlled). (back issues avail.) **Indexed:** Aqua.Sci.& Fish.Abstr., Curr.Cont., Ocean.Abstr., Ocean Ind., Sci.Abstr. **Document type:** academic/scholarly publication.
—BLDSC (3012.100000); UnCover.
Refereed Serial

639 CN ISSN 0711-0782
SH223
CANADA. DEPARTMENT OF FISHERIES AND OCEANS. ANNUAL REPORT. 1931. a. Department of Fisheries and Oceans, Ottawa, Ont. K1A 0E6, Canada. TEL 613-993-0999. circ. 700.
Supersedes in part: Canada. Fisheries and Environment Canada. Annual Report (ISSN 0068-7375)

639.2 CN
CANADA. MINISTERE DE L'AGRICULTURE, DES PECHERIES ET DE L'ALIMENTATION. CATALOGUE DES ENGINS DE PECHE DU QUEBEC. a. Can.$13 per no. Ministere de l'Agriculture, des Pecheries et de l'Alimentation, Direction de la Recherche Scientifique et Technique, Secretariat d'Edition, 96 Montee Sandy-Beach, C.P. 1070, Gaspe, Que. G0C 1R0, Canada. TEL 418-368-2642. FAX 418-368-1275. (Subscr. to: C.P. 1693, Quebec, Que. G1K 7K8, Canada)
Description: Covers most of the available information concerning the construction of different types of fishing gear well adapted to either fishing vessels or the species of fish sought.

639 574.92 CN ISSN 0706-6503
  CODEN: CBFSDB
CANADIAN BULLETIN OF FISHERIES AND AQUATIC SCIENCES. French edition (ISSN 0706-6511) (Text in English) 1918. irreg., no.224, 1991. price varies. Department of Fisheries and Oceans, Communications Directorate, 200 Kent St., Ottawa, Ont. K1A 0E6, Canada. TEL 613-990-0229. Ed. J. Camp. circ. 10,000. (also avail. in microfiche from MML) **Indexed:** Aqua.Sci.& Fish.Abstr., Arct.Bibl., Biol.Abstr., Chem.Abstr., Curr.Adv.Ecol.Sci., Deep Sea Res.& Oceanogr.Abstr., Food Sci.& Tech.Abstr., Helminthol.Abstr., Ocean.Abstr., Sel.Water Res.Abstr.
—Faxon; CASDDS.
Formerly: Canada. Fisheries Research Board. Bulletin (ISSN 0068-7537)

639.2 CN ISSN 0835-9946
HD9464.C19
CANADIAN FISHERIES PRODUCTS AND INVENTORIES. 1987. m. National Research Council of Canada, Research Journals, Ottawa, ON K1A 0R6, Canada. TEL 613-993-9084. FAX 613-952-7656.

639.2 551.46 CN ISSN 0704-3694
SH223 CODEN: CRFSDL
CANADIAN INDUSTRY REPORT OF FISHERIES AND AQUATIC SCIENCES. French edition: Rapport Canadien a l'Industrie sur les Sciences Halieutiques et Aquatiques (ISSN 0704-3708) (Text in English, French) 1966. irreg. price varies. Department of Fisheries and Oceans, Communications Directorate, 200 Kent St., Ottawa, ON K1A 0E6, Canada. circ. 250. (also avail. in microfiche from MML) **Indexed:** Aqua.Sci.& Fish.Abstr., Biol.Abstr.
—CASDDS.

639.2 CN ISSN 0706-652X
QH1 CODEN: CJFSDX
CANADIAN JOURNAL OF FISHERIES AND AQUATIC SCIENCES. (Supplement avail.) (Text in English or French) 1901. m. Can.$135 to individuals; institutions Can.$360. National Research Council of Canada, Research Journals, Ottawa, ON K1A 0R6, Canada. TEL 613-993-9084. FAX 613-952-7656. Ed. D.G. Cook. bibl.; charts; illus.; index. circ. 3,000. (also avail. in microform from UMI; reprint service avail. from UMI) **Indexed:** Abstr.Bull.Inst.Pap.Chem., Acid Pre.Dig., Acid Rain Abstr., Acid Rain Ind., Anim.Breed.Abstr., Aqua.Sci.& Fish.Abstr., Biol.Abstr., Cadscan, Chem.Abstr., Curr.Adv.Ecol.Sci., Curr.Adv.Genetics & Molec.Biol., Curr.Cont., Curr.Ref.Fish Res., Dairy Sci.Abstr., Deep Sea Res.& Oceanogr.Abstr., Environ.Abstr., Environ.Abstr., Environ.Ind., Environ.Per.Bibl., Excerp.Med., Food Sci.& Tech.Abstr., Geo.Abstr., GeoRef., Helminthol.Abstr., Ind.Sci.Rev., Ind.Vet., INIS Atomind., Lead Abstr., Mar.Sci.Cont.Tab, Meteor.& Geoastrophys.Abstr., Ocean.Abstr., Pollut.Abstr., Risk Abstr., Sci.Cit.Ind., Sel.Water Res.Abstr., Vet.Bull., W.R.C.Inf., Weed Abstr., Zincscan.
—BLDSC (3031.490000); CIS; Faxon; SWETS; UMI; CASDDS. **CCC.**
Formerly: Canada. Fisheries Research Board. Journal (ISSN 0008-2686)
Description: Publishes original research articles, critical reviews, perspectives (essays of opinion or hypothesis), and comments.

CANADIAN SOCIETY OF ENVIRONMENTAL BIOLOGISTS NEWSLETTER. see *CONSERVATION*

639.2 CN ISSN 0706-6481
  CODEN: CSPSDA
CANADIAN SPECIAL PUBLICATION OF FISHERIES AND AQUATIC SCIENCES. French edition: Publication Speciale Canadienne des Sciences Halieutiques et Aquatiques (ISSN 0706-649X) (Text in English) 1929. irreg., no.120, 1993. price varies. National Research Council of Canada, Research Journals, Bldg. M-55, Ottawa, ON K1A 0R6, Canada. TEL 613-993-1513. FAX 613-952-7656. Ed. G. Neville. circ. 8,500. (also avail. in microfiche from MML) **Indexed:** Aqua.Sci.& Fish.Abstr., Biol.Abstr., Chem.Abstr., Deep Sea Res.& Oceanogr.Abstr.
—BLDSC (3044.744000).
Formerly: Canada. Fisheries Research Board. Miscellaneous Special Publication Series.

639 574.92 CN ISSN 0706-6457
  CODEN: CTRSDR
CANADIAN TECHNICAL REPORT OF FISHERIES AND AQUATIC SCIENCES. French edition: Rapport Technique Canadien des Sciences Halieutiques et Aquatiques (ISSN 0706-6570) (Text in English) 1967. irreg. price varies. Department of Fisheries and Oceans, 200 Kent St., Ottawa, Ont. K1A 0E6, Canada. TEL 613-993-0999. circ. 350. (also avail. in microfiche from MML) **Indexed:** Aqua.Sci.& Fish.Abstr., Biol.Abstr., Chem.Abstr., Deep Sea Res.& Oceanogr.Abstr., GeoRef.
—BLDSC (3044.947000); CASDDS. **CCC.**
Formerly: Canada. Fisheries and Marine Service. Technical Report Series (ISSN 0068-7553)

639.2 CL
▼**CATALOGO DE NAVES PESQUERAS Y REMOLCADORES DE ALTA MAR.** 1993. a. $50. Ediciones Tecnicas Ltda., Perex Valenzuela 1098, Oficina 98 - Providencia, Santiago 09, Chile. TEL 56-2-235-8100. FAX 56-2-235-8068. (Subscr. to: P.O. Box 3074, Correo Central, Santiago, Chile) Eds. Ricardo Cortes, Roly Solis. adv.: B&W page $2700, color page $3400; trim 10 7/8 x 8 1/8. bk.rev.; index. circ. 10,000. (back issues avail.) **Document type:** catalog.

639.2 II ISSN 0970-6267
CENTRAL INLAND CAPTURE FISHERIES RESEARCH INSTITUTE. ANNUAL REPORT. (Text in English) 1967. a. exchange basis. Central Inland Capture Fisheries Research Institute, Barrackpore 743 101, W. Bengal, India. TELEX 021-8552 CIFI IN. Ed. V.V. Sugunan. charts; stat. **Indexed:** Biol.Abstr.
Formerly: Central Inland Fisheries Research Institute. Annual Report.

639.2   II   ISSN 0970-616X
SH299
CENTRAL INLAND CAPTURE FISHERIES RESEARCH INSTITUTE. BULLETIN. 1963. irreg. exchange basis. Central Inland Capture Fisheries Research Institute, Barrackpore 743 101, W. Bengal, India. TELEX 021-8552 CIFI IN. Ed. V.V. Sugunan. abstr.; bibl. circ. 132. (processed) **Indexed:** Biol.Abstr., Helminthol.Abstr., Sci.Cit.Ind. **Document type:** bulletin.

597 551.46   II   ISSN 0577-084X
SH1   CODEN: BCMFAY
CENTRAL MARINE FISHERIES RESEARCH INSTITUTE. BULLETIN. (Text in English) 1968. irreg. price varies. Central Marine Fisheries Research Institute, P.B. No. 1603, Cochin 682 014, India. TEL 351867. Ed. Dr. P.S.B.R. James. (looseleaf format) **Indexed:** Biol.Abstr., Deep Sea Res.& Oceanogr.Abstr. **Document type:** bulletin.

CENTRE DE RECHERCHES OCEANOGRAPHIQUES D'ABIDJAN. DOCUMENTS SCIENTIFIQUES. see *EARTH SCIENCES* — *Oceanography*

CENTRO DE PESQUISAS DO CACAU. INFORME DE PESQUISAS. see *AGRICULTURE*

639 591   CL   ISSN 0716-0976
CHILE. SERVICIO NACIONAL DE PESCA. ANUARIO ESTADISTICO DE PESCA. 1944. a. exchange basis. Servicio Nacional de Pesca, Departamento Sistemas de Informacion y Estadisticas Pesqueras, Yungay 1731 4o piso, Valparaiso, Chile. FAX 259564. TELEX 230481 PESCA CL. stat.; circ. controlled. **Document type:** government publication.
 Former titles: Chile. Servicio Agricola y Ganadero. Division Proteccion Pesquera. Anuario Estadistico (ISSN 0069-3537); Chile. Direccion de Agricultura y Pesquera. Departamento Estadistica. Anuario Estadistico de Pesca.
 Description: Covers Chilean fishery.

CHIRIBOTAN. see *BIOLOGY* — *Zoology*

639.2   JA
                             CODEN: TSKKA9
CHUO SUISAN KENKYUJO KENKYU HOKOKU/NATIONAL RESEARCH INSTITUTE OF FISHERIES SCIENCE. REPORT. (Text and summaries in English and Japanese) 1950. q. exchange basis only. Suisan-cho Chuo Suisan Kenkyujo - National Research Institute of Fisheries Science, Attn. Director, 5-1 Kachidoki 5-chome, Chuo-ku, Tokyo 104, Japan. FAX 03-533-5693. **Indexed:** Biol.Abstr., Chem.Abstr., Curr.Adv.Ecol.Sci., Deep Sea Res.& Oceanogr.Abstr., Food Sci.& Tech.Abstr., Ocean.Abstr., Pollut.Abstr.
 Formerly: Tokai Regional Fisheries Research Laboratory (Report) (ISSN 0040-8859)

639.2   CU   ISSN 0864-3873
CIENCIA Y TECNOLOGIA PESQUERA. (Text in Spanish; abstracts in English) s-a. Ministerio de la Industeria Pesquera, Departamento de Informacion y Documentacion Cientifico-Tecnica, 5a Avenida y 248, Barlovento, Santa Fe, Havana, Cuba. TELEX 0511444 MIP. Ed. Juan Julian Martinez. circ. 250.
 Supersedes (in 1989): Pesca al Dia.
 Description: Publishes original works of processing, sensorial assessment, chemistry, microbiology and quality control of fishing products.

CLEARWATER NAVIGATOR. see *ENVIRONMENTAL STUDIES*

639.2   US   ISSN 1055-4238
COLORADO. DIVISION OF WILDLIFE. TERRESTRIAL AND AQUATIC WILDLIFE RESEARCH. RESEARCH REVIEW. 1991. m. Division of Wildlife, Terrestrial and Aquatic Wildlife Research, Research Center Library, 317 W. Prospect Rd., Fort Collins, CO 80526. Ed. Nancy Wild McEwen.

639.2   US
COMMERCIAL FISHERIES NEWS. 1973. m. $18. Compass Publications Inc., Fisheries Division, Box 37, Stonington, ME 04681. TEL 207-367-2396. FAX 207-367-2490. Ed. Robin Alden. adv. circ. 9,000. (reprint service avail.)

639.2   AT   ISSN 1030-0759
COMMERCIAL VESSEL YEARBOOK. 1979. a. free to subscribers of Professional Fisherman. Baird Publications Pty. Ltd., 10 Oxford St., S. Yarra, Vic. 3141, Australia. TEL 03-826-8741. FAX 03-827-0704. Ed. Neil Baird. adv.; bk.rev. circ. 4,000.
 Incorporates: Australasian Marine Directory; **Formerly:** Professional Fisherman's Fishing Vessel Yearbook.
 Description: For owners of small ships and fishing boats.

639 551.46   AT   ISSN 0725-4598
                             CODEN: RCMLDR
COMMONWEALTH SCIENTIFIC AND INDUSTRIAL RESEARCH ORGANIZATION. MARINE LABORATORIES. REPORT. 1956. irreg. free. C.S.I.R.O., Marine Laboratories, G.P.O. Box 1538, Hobart, Tas. 7001, Australia. FAX 002-240-530. TELEX AA57182. circ. 600. **Indexed:** Biol.Abstr., Deep Sea Res.& Oceanogr.Abstr., Ocean.Abstr. **Document type:** government publication.
 —BLDSC (7410.132000); CASDDS.
 Supersedes: Commonwealth Scientific and Industrial Research Organization. Division of Fisheries and Oceanography. Report (ISSN 0069-7370)

639.2   CL   ISSN 0717-0599
▼**COMPENDIO ACUICOLA DE CHILE.** 1993. a. $50. Ediciones Tecnicas Ltda., Perez Valenzuela 1098, Oficina 98 - Providencia, Santiago 09, Chile. TEL 562-235-8100. FAX 562-235-8068. (Subscr. to: P.O. Box 3074, Correo Central, Santiago, Chile) Eds. Ricardo Cortes, Roly Solis. adv.: B&W page $2700, color page $3400; trim 10 7/8 x 8 1/8. bk.rev.; index. circ. 10,000. (back issues avail.)

799   IT
CORRIERE DELLA PESCA E DELL'AQUACOLTURA; organo di formazione, informazione della federcoopesca. 1945. m. L.4000 to non-members. Ministero della Marina Mercantile, Federazione Nazionale Cooperativa della Pesca Pubblicato, Via Benedetto Croce n. 68-116, Palazzina ENPAIA Scala C int.2, 00142 Rome, Italy. TEL 06-541-0546. FAX 06-54-15-093. Ed. Gianfranco Bianchi. adv. circ. 18,000.
 Formerly: Corriere della Pesca.

639.2   US   ISSN 1064-1262
SH1
▼**CRITICAL REVIEWS IN FISHERIES SCIENCE.** 1992. 4/yr. $84 to individuals (foreign $91.95); institutions $210 (foreign $217.95). C R C Press, Inc., 2000 Corporate Blvd., N.W., Boca Raton, FL 33431. TEL 407-994-0555. FAX 407-998-9784. TELEX 568689-CRC PRESS.

CROPS IN INDIA. see *AGRICULTURE*

639.3   US   ISSN 0739-540X
Z7996.F5
CURRENT REFERENCES IN FISH RESEARCH. 1976. a. $18. Rt. 1, Box 84, Chippewa Falls, WI 54729. TEL 715-836-4166. FAX 715-723-0098. Ed. Victor Cvancara. adv. circ. 1,500. **Document type:** abstracting/indexing, bibliography.
 Description: Listing of current references in fisheries research. Includes author, keyword and scientific name indexes.

639.3   FR   ISSN 0399-0974
QL614   CODEN: CYBIDK
CYBIUM; revue europeenne d'ichtyologie. (Text and summaries in English, French) 1977. q. 450 F.($75) to non-members; members 320 F.($55). (Museum National d'Histoire Naturelle) Societe Francaise d'Ichtyologie, 43 rue Cuvier, 75231 Paris Cedex 05, France. TEL 40-79-37-49. FAX 33-1-40-79-37-71. TELEX MUSNAHN 202641F. Ed. J.Y. Sire. adv.; bk.rev.; illus. circ. 550. (back issues avail.) **Indexed:** Aqua.Sci.& Fish.Abstr., Biol.Abstr., Bull.Signal., Curr.Adv.Ecol.Sci., Curr.Ref.Fish Res., Curr.Tit.Ocean, Helminth.Abstr., Mar.Sci.Tech.Abstr., Ocean.Ind., Zoo.Rec. **Document type:** academic/scholarly publication.
 Description: Covers basic and applied ichthyology, freshwater, marine and fossil fishes.

354.564 333.7   CY   ISSN 0379-086X
CYPRUS. DEPARTMENT OF FISHERIES. ANNUAL REPORT ON THE DEPARTMENT OF FISHERIES AND THE CYPRUS FISHERIES. (Text in English) 1963. a. free. Department of Fisheries, Nicosia, Cyprus. TEL 2-30-3279. TELEX 4660 MINAGRI CY. Ed. A. Demetropoulos. circ. 1,000.
 Supersedes: Cyprus. Department of Fisheries. Annual Report of the Cyprus Fisheries.

639.34   GW   ISSN 0941-8393
D A T Z. AQUARIEN, TERRARIEN. (Die Aquarien- und Terrarien-Zeitschrift) 1948. m. DM.108.60. (Verband Deutscher Vereine fuer Aquarien- und Terrarienkunde) Verlag Eugen Ulmer GmbH, Wollgrasweg 41, 70599 Stuttgart, Germany. TEL 0711-4507-0. FAX 0711-4507-120. TELEX 7-23634-ULMER-D. (Subscr. to: Postfach 700561, 70574 Stuttgart, Germany) Ed. R. Stawikowski. adv.; bk.rev.; charts; illus. circ. 38,000. **Document type:** consumer publication.
 —BLDSC (3535.845000). CCC.
 Formerly (until 1990): D A T Z (ISSN 0723-4066); Incorporates (1967-1988): Aquarien Magazin (ISSN 0003-7257); (1954-1990): Aquarien Terrarien (ISSN 0323-5610); Which was formerly: Aquarien- und Terrarien-Zeitschrift (ISSN 0003-7265)

639.2   DK   ISSN 0109-4432
D F H - RAPPORT. 1984. a. Danmarks Fiskeri og Havundersoegelser, Charlottenlund Slot, Jaegersborg Alle 1, 2920 Charlottenlund, Denmark.
 Formerly: Danmarks Fiskeri og Havundersoegelser. Intern Rapport.

639   CC   ISSN 1000-9957
DALIAN SHUICHAN XUEYUAN XUEBAO/DALIAN FISHERIES COLLEGE. JOURNAL. (Text in Chinese) 1980. q. $4. Dalian Shuichan Xueyuan - Dalian Fisheries College, Heishijiao Xicun, Dalian, Liaoning 116024, People's Republic of China. TEL 4671025. Ed. Ding Dianjun. **Document type:** academic/scholarly publication.

639   DK   ISSN 0106-553X
QH90   CODEN: DANADZ
DANA; a journal of fisheries and marine research. (Text in English) 1904. N.S. 1980. irreg. price varies. Danmarks Fiskeri- og Havundersoegelser - Danish Institute for Fisheries and Marine Research, Charlottenlund Castle, 2920 Charlottenlund, Denmark. Ed. E. Hoffmann. index, cum.index: 1904-1983. **Indexed:** Aqua.Sci.& Fish.Abstr., Biol.Abstr., Curr.Adv.Ecol.Sci., Curr.Cont., Deep Sea Res.& Oceanogr.Abstr., Ref.Zh., Sci.Cit.Ind.
 —BLDSC (3517.990000).
 Formerly: Denmark. Danmarks Fiskeri- og Havundersoegelser. Meddelelser (ISSN 0070-3435)

639.2   DK   ISSN 0011-6270
DANSK FISKERITIDENDE. 1882. w. DKK 310. Dansk Fiskeriforening, Studiestraede 3, 2, 1455 Copenhagen K, Denmark. FAX 33-32-32-38. Ed. Ole Soerensen. adv.; bk.rev.; charts; illus.; stat.; index, cum.index. circ. 17,500. (tabloid format)
 Supersedes: Danmarks Havfiskeri (ISSN 0011-6130)

639.2   IS   ISSN 0011-7110
SH307.I7
DAYIG U-MIDGEH BE-YISRAEL/FISHERIES AND FISHBREEDING IN ISRAEL. (Text in Hebrew, summaries in English) 1963. q. $30 (effective 1994). (Ministry of Agriculture, Department of Fisheries) Fish Breeders Association in Israel, P.O. Box 33750, Haifa 31 337, Israel. TEL 972-4-627618. FAX 972-4-675388. Ed. R. Rosenzweig. bk.rev.; index. circ. 900. **Document type:** government publication, academic/scholarly publication.
 Supersedes: Fishermen's Bulletin.

639.2   NL   ISSN 1017-9259
DEEP SEA FISHERIES DEVELOPMENT PROJECT REPORTS. French edition: Rapport sur le Projet de Developpement de la Peche Profonde en Nouvelle-Caledonie (ISSN 1017-9267) (Text in English) 1974. irreg., latest 1992. South Pacific Commission, B.P. D5, Noumea Cedex, New Caledonia. TEL 26-2000. FAX 687-263818. TELEX 3139 NM SOPACOM. **Document type:** monographic series.

FISH AND FISHERIES

639.2 551.46   US
DELAWARE SEA GRANT REPORTER. 1982. s-a. free. University of Delaware, Sea Grant College Program, Newark, DE 19716-3530. TEL 302-831-8083. FAX 302-831-2005. Ed. Tracey Bryant. bk.rev. circ. 5,200. (back issues avail.) **Indexed:** Aqua.Sci.& Fish.Abstr., Sci.Abstr. **Document type:** newsletter.
   Description: Informs the public of marine research, issues and events that affect Delaware.

639 574.92   DK   ISSN 0070-3605
SH267
DENMARK. FISKERIMINISTERIET. FORSOEGSLABORATORIUM. AARSBERETNING. 1952. a. free. Fiskeriministeriet, Forsoegslaboratorium - Ministry of Fisheries, Technological Laboratory, Polytekniske Laereanstalt, Danmarks Tekniske Hoejskole, Building 221, 2800 Lyngby, Denmark. FAX 45-42-88-47-74. TELEX 37529 DTHDIA. circ. 2,000. **Indexed:** Aqua.Sci.& Fish.Abstr., Chem.Abstr., Food Sci.& Tech.Abstr. **Document type:** government publication.

639.2   DK
DETAIL-FISKEHANDLER-BLADET. 1917. 6/yr. DKK 175 (typically set in Jan.). (Landsorganisationen af Danmarks Detailfiskehandlere) Danmarks Fiskehandlers Sekretariat, Peblinge Dosseringen 36, DK-2200 Copenhagen N, Denmark. TEL 35-372023. FAX 35-371788. Ed. Hans Erik Hansen. adv. circ. 1,260.

DEVELOPMENTS IN AQUACULTURE AND FISHERIES SCIENCE. see BIOLOGY — Zoology

639.2   CE
DHIVARA. (Text in Sinhalese) 1978. m. Ministry of Fisheries, Galle Face, Colombo 3, Sri Lanka.

639.3   US
DIRECTORY OF SHRIMP FARMING IN THE WESTERN HEMISPHERE. (Supplement to: World Shrimp Farming) a. $25. Aquaculture Digest, 11057 Negley Ave., San Diego, CA 92131. TEL 619-271-6354. FAX 619-271-0324. (Subscr. to: 9434 Kearny Mesa Rd., San Diego, CA 92126) **Document type:** consumer publication, directory, trade publication.
   Description: Contains names, titles, addresses, specialties and communication numbers of Aquaculture Digest's contacts in the Western hemisphere, Europe, and Southeast Asia.

639.2   GW
DISKUS BRIEF; die Deutsche Diskus-Zeitschrift. (Editions in English, German, Chinese) 1986. q. DM.36. Postfach 101926, 86009 Augsburg, Germany. TEL 0821-782158. FAX 0821-781149. Ed. Horst Koehler. adv.; bk.rev.; index. circ. 4,000. **Document type:** newsletter.

ECOLOGY OF FRESHWATER FISH. see BIOLOGY

639.3   IC
ELDISFRETTIR; serrit um fiskeldis- og hafbeitarmal. 1986. q. ISK 2500($35) (Landssamband Fiskeldis- og Hafbeitarstoedva - Association of Fish Farmers in Iceland) Utgafufelag Eldisfretta, Hlidarhjalli 41 C, 200 Kopavogur, Iceland. TEL 354-1-642313. Ed. Vilhjalmur Gudmundsson. adv.: color page $850. circ. 500 (paid).
   Description: Covers research and development in aquaculture in Iceland and the marketing of salmon and trout.

639.2   FR   ISSN 0765-5320
                        CODEN: EQUIEE
EQUINOXE; the magazine on living resources of the sea. 1953. 6/yr. 130 F. Institut Francais de Recherche pour l'Exploitation de la Mer (IFREMER), Rue de l'Ile-d'Yeu, B.P. 1049, 44037 Nantes Cedex 01, France. FAX 40-37-40-40-01. TELEX 711196. bk.rev.; charts; illus. circ. 1,500. **Indexed:** Aqua.Sci.& Fish.Abstr., Biol.Abstr., Bull.Signal., Chem.Abstr., Ocean.Abstr. **Document type:** government publication.
   —BLDSC (3794.532700).
   Formerly: Science et Peche (ISSN 0036-8350)
   Description: Information on living resources of the oceans. Covers environmental issues and aquacultural concerns.

639.2   UK   ISSN 0140-8720
EUROFISH REPORT. 1977. fortn. £500 in the UK; in Europe £525; elsewhere £550. Agra Europe (London) Ltd., 25 Frant Rd., Tunbridge Wells, Kent TN2 5JT, England. TEL 44-892-533813. FAX 44-892-544895. TELEX 95114 AGRA TW G. q. and a. indexes. **Document type:** newsletter.
   Description: Review of European fishing and fisheries with coverage of EC legislation and Common Fisheries policy.

EUROPEAN AQUACULTURE SOCIETY. SPECIAL PUBLICATIONS. see EARTH SCIENCES — Oceanography

639.2   MY
EUROPEAN FISH PRICE REPORT. m. $350 includes Infofish Trade News (bi-w.), Globefish Highlights (q.), and Infofish International (bi-m.). Infofish, P.O. Box Box 10899, 50728 Kuala Lumpur, Malaysia. TEL 03-2914466. FAX 03-2916804. TELEX INFISH MA 31560.

639.2   UN   ISSN 0429-9329
SH1
F A O FISHERIES CIRCULARS. irreg., no.792, 1985. price varies. Food and Agriculture Organization of the United Nations, Sales & Distribution Section, Via delle Terme di Caracalla, 0010 Rome, Italy. (microfiche) **Indexed:** Biol.Abstr., Curr.Adv.Ecol.Sci., Deep Sea Res.& Oceanogr.Abstr., Ocean.Abstr.

639.2   UN   ISSN 0429-9337
SH331   CODEN: FOFRAR
F A O FISHERIES REPORTS. irreg., latest no.474. price varies. Food and Agriculture Organization of the United Nations, c/o UNIPUB, 4611-F Assembly Dr., Lanham, MD 20706-4391. **Indexed:** Biol.Abstr., Curr.Adv.Ecol.Sci., Deep Sea Res.& Oceanogr.Abstr., Excerp.Med., INIS Atomind., Ocean.Abstr. **Document type:** monographic series.
   —BLDSC (3865.637000); UnCover; CASDDS.
   Incorporates: Indian Ocean Fishery Commission. Report of the Session; (in 1975): C I F A Report; C O P E S C A L Reports; C E A F Reports; Indo-Pacific Fishery Commission: Working Party of Experts.

639   UN   ISSN 0259-2509
F A O FISHERIES SERIES. (Text in English, French and Spanish) irreg., no.41, 1993. price varies. Food and Agriculture Organization of the United Nations, c/o UNIPUB, 4611-F Assembly Dr., Lanham, MD 20706-4391. Ed. Chris A. Theodore. (also avail. in microfiche from BHP) **Indexed:** Nutr.Abstr. **Document type:** monographic series.
   Incorporates: Yearbook of Fishery Statistics (ISSN 0084-375X); **Formerly:** F A O Fisheries Studies (ISSN 0071-7037)

639   UN   ISSN 0014-5602
SH1
F A O FISHERIES SYNOPSIS. 1962. irreg., no.125, 1993. Food and Agriculture Organization of the United Nations, c/o UNIPUB 4611-F Assembly Dr., Lanham, MD 20706-4391. FAX 301-459-0056. **Indexed:** Curr.Adv.Ecol.Sci. **Document type:** monographic series.
   Formerly: Fisheries Biology Synopsis (ISSN 0374-7603)

639   UN   ISSN 0429-9345
SH1   CODEN: FFTPBT
F A O FISHERIES TECHNICAL PAPER. irreg., no.332, 1993. Food and Agriculture Organization of the United Nations, c/o UNIPUB, 4611-F Assembly Dr., Lanham, MD 20706-4391. **Indexed:** Biodet.Abstr., Biol.Abstr., Curr.Adv.Ecol.Sci., Deep Sea Res.& Oceanogr.Abstr., Excerp.Med., Food Sci.& Tech.Abstr., Nutr.Abstr., Ocean.Abstr., Rural Devel.Abstr. **Document type:** monographic series.
   —BLDSC (3865.641000).
   Former titles (until 1963): F A O Fisheries Papers (ISSN 0428-9269); (until 1959): Fisheries Biology Technical Paper (ISSN 0374-7611)

F R P GYOSEN/F R P FISHING BOAT. see TRANSPORTATION — Ships And Shipping

639   FI   ISSN 0301-908X
SH1   CODEN: FNFRAK
FINNISH FISHERIES RESEARCH. (Text and summaries in English) 1972. a. exchange basis. Finnish Game and Fisheries Research Institute, Fisheries Division, Aquaculture Division, P.O. Box 202, SF-00151 Helsinki, Finland. TEL 358-0-624211. FAX 358-0-631513. TELEX 19101236 VDX. Ed. Pekka Tuunainen. circ. 800. **Indexed:** Aqua.Sci.& Fish.Abstr., Biol.Abstr., Deep Sea Res.& Oceanogr.Abstr., Protozool.Abstr., Sel.Water Res.Abstr., Sport Fish.Abstr.
   —BLDSC (3929.134000).

639.2   GW   ISSN 0015-2854
DAS FISCHERBLATT; Mitteilungsblatt fuer die Kutter- und Kuesten-fischerei. 1953. m. membership. Landesfischereiverband Schleswig Holstein, Holstenstr. 108, 24103 Kiel, Germany. TEL 0431-9797311. FAX 0431-9797120. Ed. Karl Ruoff. adv.: B&W page DM.450; trim 165 x 110. bk.rev. circ. 1,500. **Document type:** newsletter.
   Description: Provides information on the international fishing industry. Includes news for seafarers, fishing regulations and a list of courses.

639.2   GW   ISSN 0930-6544
FISCHMAGAZIN. 1948. m. DM.170 (foreign DM.182). S N Verlag Michael Steinert, An der Alster 21, 20099 Hamburg, Germany. TEL 040-240852. FAX 040-2803788. Ed. J. Ruediger. adv.; bk.rev.; charts; illus.; mkt.; pat.; stat.; tr.mk. circ. 4,200. **Indexed:** Biol.Abstr., Chem.Abstr.
   Formerly (until 1986): A F Z - Fischmagazin (ISSN 0178-2797); Which was formed by the merger of: Fisch Magazin (ISSN 0723-3035); A F Z (ISSN 0001-1258)

639.2   UK
FISH. 1987. membership. Institute of Fisheries Management, 22 Rushworth Ave., W. Bridgford, Notts. NG7 7LF, England. TEL 0602-822317. FAX 0602-826150. Ed. P. Spillett. circ. 1,500 (controlled). (back issues avail.) **Document type:** academic/scholarly publication.
   Description: Covers modern fisheries management techniques, conservation, fish biology, and current affairs.

639.3   JA   ISSN 0044-0671
FISH CULTURE/YOSHOKU. (Text in Japanese) 1964. 14/yr. 13400 Yen. Midori - Shobo Co., Ltd. (Subsidiary of: Midori Group), Ikebukuro Nishiguchi Sky Bldg., 2-14-4 Ikebukuro, Toshima-ku, Tokyo 171, Japan. FAX 03-3590-4446. Ed. Maki Kimora. adv.; charts; illus.

639.3   US   ISSN 0015-2919
FISH CULTURIST. 1920. m. (except Jul. & Aug.). $10 membership; foreign $12. Pennsylvania Fish Culturists Association, 16 Wexford Rd., Gibbsboro, NJ 08026. (Subscr. to: Jare A. Sausaman, 6804 N. Tenth St., Philadelphia, PA 19126-2905) Ed. Robert W. Britton. adv.; bk.rev.; illus.; stat.; cum.index. circ. 600. **Document type:** bulletin.
   Description: Examines breeding, maintenance procedures and disease problems and cures related to fresh water tropical marine fish and plants in home aquaria.

639   US   ISSN 0071-5492
SH171
FISH DISEASE LEAFLETS. 1966. irreg., no.66, 1983. U.S. Fish and Wildlife Service, Dept. of the Interior, Washington, DC 20240. TEL 703-358-1711. (looseleaf format)

639.2   UK   ISSN 0262-9615
FISH FARMER. 1977. bi-m. £30 (Europe £40; elsewhere £45). Amber Publications, 34 Amberley Dr., Woodham, Addlestone, Surrey KT15 3SL, England. TEL 44-932-851668. FAX 44-932-859747. Ed. Stuart Banks. adv.: B&W page £596, color page £888. bk.rev. circ. 5,000. **Indexed:** Biodet.Abstr., Ind.Vet., RICS, Vet.Bull., W.R.C.Inf. **Document type:** trade publication, academic/scholarly publication.
   —BLDSC (3935.055000).
   Description: Covers all aspects of aquaculture, including freshwater and marine finfish, shellfish and crustacea. Information on developments in fish husbandry, disease control, new products, scientific research and marketing are regularly covered.

FISH AND FISHERIES

639.2 UK ISSN 0262-0820
SH1
FISH FARMING INTERNATIONAL. 1973. m. £30 (foreign £35). E M A P Heighway, Meed House, 21 John St., London WC1N 2BP, England. TEL 071-404-4513. FAX 071-831-9362. TELEX 881 3483 FISH. Ed. Peter Hjul. adv.; bk.rev.; illus.; stat. circ. 3,733. **Indexed:** Biol.Abstr., Curr.Adv.Ecol.Sci., Deep Sea Res.& Oceanogr.Abstr., Fuel & Energy Abstr., Nutr.Abstr., Ocean.Abstr., Pollut.Abstr., PROMT. **Document type:** newspaper.
—BLDSC (3935.065000). **CCC.**

639.2 GW ISSN 0930-6552
FISH INTERNATIONAL. 6/yr. DM.80 (foreign DM.90). S N Verlag Michael Steinert, An der Alster 21, 20099 Hamburg, Germany. TEL 040-240852. FAX 040-2803788.
Formerly (until 1986): A F Z International (ISSN 0177-2112)

639.2 JA
FISH MAGAZINE. m. 9080 Yen. Midori - Shobo Co., Ltd. (Subsidiary of: Midori Group), Ikebukuro Nishiguchi Sky Bldg., 1-14-4 Ikebukuro, Toshima-ku, Tokyo 171, Japan. TEL 03-3590-4441. FAX 03-3590-4446. Ed. Kiyoshi Shiina. circ. 88,000. **Document type:** trade publication.
Description: Designed for aqualists, researchers, and manufacturers. Covers freshwater tropical fishes, gold fish, koi, and more.

FISH PHYSIOLOGY & BIOCHEMISTRY. see BIOLOGY — Zoology

639.2 UK ISSN 0143-7771
FISH TRADER. 1883. 24/yr. £70.60($155) (foreign £99.20). F M J International Publications Ltd., Queensway House, 2 Queensway, Redhill, Surrey RH1 1QS, England. TEL 0737-768611. FAX 0737-761685. TELEX 948669-TOPJNL-G. Ed. Mick Whitworth. adv.; bk.rev.; charts; film rev.; illus.; mkt.; tr.lit. circ. 2,772. **Document type:** trade publication.
Formerly: Fish Trades Gazette (ISSN 0015-2943)
Description: Covers the supply chain from loading through consumption. Aimed at merchanting, processing, trading, wholesaling, retailing, and catering.

639.2 UK ISSN 0953-8860
FISH TRADER YEARBOOK. a. £33.80($52.40) (Sea Fish Industry Authority) F M J International Publications Ltd., Queensway House, 2 Queensway, Redhill, Surrey RH1 1QS, England. TEL 0737-768611. FAX 0737-761685. TELEX 948669-TOPJNL-G. Ed. Mick Whitworth. **Document type:** trade publication.
—BLDSC (3935.174000).
Formerly (until 1987): Fish Trader Handbook (ISSN 0265-6450)
Description: Covers all aspects of the commercial fishing industry in the U.K. Includes a detailed directory of seafood suppliers, equipment companies, and trade organizations.

639.2 AT ISSN 0046-3965
FISH TRADES REVIEW.* 1952. m. Aus.$2.20. 24 Henry St., Carlton, N.S.W. 2218, Australia.

639.2 US ISSN 0363-2415
SH1
FISHERIES. 1976. m. $66.50 (foreign $70.50). American Fisheries Society, 5410 Grosvenor Ln., Ste. 110, Bethesda, MD 20814-2199. TEL 301-897-8616. FAX 301-897-8096. Ed. Kristin Merriman-Clarke. adv.; bk.rev.; bibl.; charts; illus.; index. circ. 9,500. (back issues avail.) **Indexed:** Acid Pre.Dig., Acid Rain Abstr., Acid Rain Ind., Aqua.Sci.& Fish.Abstr., Biol.Abstr., Chem.Abstr., Curr.Adv.Ecol.Sci., Curr.Adv.Genetics & Molec.Biol., Curr.Cont., Curr.Ref.Fish Res., Deep Sea Res.& Oceanogr.Abstr., Energy Ind., Energy Info.Abstr., Environ.Abstr., Excerp.Med., Forest.Abstr., Geo.Abstr., Helminthol.Abstr., Ind.Sci.Rev., Ocean.Abstr., Pollut.Abstr., Risk Abstr., Sci.Cit.Ind., Sel.Water Res.Abstr., W.R.C.Inf.
—BLDSC (3935.220000); Faxon; UnCover; SWETS. **CCC.**
Supersedes (in 1976): American Fisheries Society. Newsletter (ISSN 0044-7692)
Refereed Serial

639.2 799.1 US ISSN 0891-7523
FISHERIES AND WILDLIFE RESEARCH AND DEVELOPMENT. 1958. a. U.S. Fish and Wildlife Service, Dept. of the Interior, Washington, DC 20240. TEL 202-226-9403. (Subscr. to: Supt. of Documents, Washington, DC 20402) illus.
Former titles (until 1982): Fisheries and Wildlife Research (ISSN 0193-4163); Sport Fishery and Wildlife Research (ISSN 0362-0700); U.S. Fish and Wildlife Service. Progress in Sport Fishery Research (ISSN 0079-6794)

591 236 IE ISSN 0332-4338
FISHERIES BULLETIN. 1981. irreg. free. Department of the Marine, Library, Abbotstown, Castleknock, Dublin 15, Ireland. TEL 01-8210111. FAX 01-8205078. bk.rev. circ. 350. **Indexed:** Biol.Abstr. **Document type:** government publication.
—BLDSC (3935.450000).

639.2 NL ISSN 0248-076X
FISHERIES NEWSLETTER. French edition: Lettre d'Information sur les Peches (ISSN 0248-0735) (Text in English) 1978. q. South Pacific Commission, B.P. D5, Noumea, Cedex, New Caledonia. **Document type:** newsletter.

639.2 597 UK ISSN 1054-6006
SH343.2 CODEN: FIOCEN
▼**FISHERIES OCEANOGRAPHY.** 1992. q. $55 to individuals in Europe (elsewhere £60 ($89)); institutions in Europe £95 (elsewhere £105 ($135)) (effective 1994). Blackwell Scientific Publications Ltd., Osney Mead, Oxford OX2 OEL, England. TEL 0865-240201. FAX 0865-721205. TELEX 83355-MEDBOK-G. Ed. T.R. Parsons. circ. 400. (also avail. in microform from UMI; back issues avail.) **Document type:** academic/scholarly publication.
—BLDSC (3939.467000); UMI. **CCC.**
Description: Presents articles relating to the production and dynamics of fish populations and the marine environment for fisheries biologists, biological and physical oceanographers and fishery managers.
Refereed Serial

338.3 US
FISHERIES OF THE UNITED STATES. 1942. a. U.S. National Marine Fisheries Service, National Oceanic and Atmospheric Administration, 1335 East-West Hwy., Silver Spring, MD 20910. TEL 301-713-2328. (Dist. by: Superintendent of Documents, U.S. Government Printing Office, Box 371954, Pittsburgh, PA 15250-7954. TEL 202-783-3238. FAX 202-512-2233) stat. circ. 1,700. (also avail. in microfiche from BHP) **Indexed:** C.I.S. Ind. **Document type:** government publication.
Formerly: Fishery Statistics of the United States (ISSN 0071-5603); Which supersedes: U.S. Bureau of Commercial Fisheries. United States Fisheries.

639.2 US ISSN 1047-2525
FISHERIES PRODUCT NEWS. 1986. 6/yr. free in U.S.; foreign $15. Compass Publications Inc., Fisheries Division, Box 37, Stonington, ME 04681. TEL 207-367-2396. FAX 207-367-2490. Ed. Rick Martin. adv.; bk.rev. circ. 25,000. (tabloid format)
—**CCC.**
Formerly: Commercial Fisheries Product News.
Description: Reviews gears and equipment for commercial fishing, seafood processing, and aquaculture.

639.3 NE ISSN 0165-7836
SH1 .F819 CODEN: FISRDJ
FISHERIES RESEARCH; an international journal on fishing technology, fisheries science and fisheries management. (Text in English) 1982. 12/yr. (in 3 vols.; 4 nos./vol.). fl.1023($553) (effective 1994). Elsevier Science B.V., P.O. Box 211, 1000 AE Amsterdam, Netherlands. TEL 31-20-5803911. FAX 31-20-5803598. TELEX 18582 ESPA NL. (Subscr. in U.S. and Canada to: Elsevier Science Inc., Box 882, Madison Sq. Sta., New York, NY 10159. TEL 212-989-5800. FAX 212-633-3990) Ed. A.D. McIntyre. adv.; bk.rev.; bibl.; charts; illus.; index. (also avail. in microform; back issues avail.) **Indexed:** Aqua.Sci.& Fish.Abstr., Biol.Abstr., Curr.Adv.Ecol.Sci., Curr.Cont., Deep Sea Res.& Oceanogr.Abstr., Energy Rev., Environ.Per.Bibl. (1990-), Mar.Sci.Cont.Tab, Sel.Water Res.Abstr. **Document type:** academic/scholarly publication.
—BLDSC (3939.570000); Faxon; UnCover; SWETS. **CCC.**
Description: Covers all aspects of fisheries, including economics, in salt, brackish and freshwater systems.
Refereed Serial

639.2 JA
FISHERIES RESEARCH. bi-m. 7570 Yen. Midori - Shobo Co., Ltd. (Subsidiary of: Midori Group), Ikebukuro Nishiguchi Sky Bldg., 1-14-4 Ikebukuro, Toshima-ku, Tokyo 171, Japan. TEL 03-3590-4441. FAX 03-3590-4446. Ed. Kiyoshi Siina. circ. 38,000.
Description: Covers fishery, processing industry and fish culture for researchers and manufacturers.

639.2 UK ISSN 0264-5130
SH255
FISHERIES RESEARCH DATA REPORT. 1983. irreg. free. Ministry of Agriculture, Fisheries and Food, Directorate of Fisheries Research, Lowestoft, Suffolk NR33 0HT, England. TEL 0502-562244. **Document type:** academic/scholarly publication.
—BLDSC (3939.650000); UnCover.

639 338.1 JA ISSN 0071-5581
FISHERIES STATISTICS OF JAPAN. (Text in English) 1963. a. (Ministry of Agriculture, Forestry and Fisheries, Statistics and Information Department - Otori Building) Association of Agriculture-Forestry Statistics, 11-14, Meguro 2-chome, Megro-ku, Tokyo 153, Japan. (Dist. by: Government Publications Service Center, 2-1, Kasumigaseki 1-chome, Chiyoda-ku, Tokyo 100, Japan) cum.index: 1963-89.

639.2 CN ISSN 0015-2986
FISHERMAN. 1937. m. Can.$20($30) (United Fishermen & Allied Workers Union) Fisherman Publishing Society, 111 Victoria Dr., No. 160, Vancouver, B.C. V5L 4C4, Canada. TEL 604-255-1366. FAX 604-255-3162. Ed. David Lane. adv.; bk.rev.; charts; illus.; stat. circ. 10,500 (controlled). (tabloid format)

639.2 IO
FISHERMAN UNION OF INDONESIA. CENTRAL GOVERNING BOARD. ANNUAL REPORT/HIMPUNAN NELAYAN SELURAH INDONESIA. DEWAN PIMPANAN PUSAT. LAPORAN KEGIATAN. (Text in Indonesian) 1980. a. $5. Fisherman Union of Indonesia, Central Governing Board, Jalan Juanda no. 2, Jakarta, Indonesia. Ed. E.Q. Datikusumo. adv.; bk.rev. circ. 5,000.

639.2 US ISSN 0015-2994
FISHERMEN'S NEWS. 1945. m. $15. Fishermen's News, Inc., W. Wall Bldg., Rm. 110, Fisherman's Terminal, Seattle, WA 98119. TEL 206-282-7545. FAX 206-283-5123. adv.; bk.rev.; illus. circ. 15,918. (tabloid format)
Description: Covers fishing in the Pacific Coast area.

FISH AND FISHERIES

639.2　　　　　　　US　　ISSN 0090-0656
SH11　　　　　　　　　CODEN: FSYBAY
FISHERY BULLETIN. 1881. q. $27 (foreign $33.75). U.S. National Marine Fisheries Service, Scientific Publications Office, 7600 Sandpoint Way, N.E., Bin C15700, Seattle, WA 98115. TEL 206-526-6107. FAX 206-526-6426. TELEX 910-444-2786. (Subscr. to: Superintendent of Documents, U.S. Government Printing Office, Box 371954, Pittsburgh, PA 15250-7954. TEL 202-783-3238. FAX 202-512-2233) Ed. Ronald Hardy. charts; illus.; stat. circ. 2,000. (also avail. in microform from NTI, UMI; reprint service avail. from NTIS) **Indexed:** Aqua.Sci.& Fish.Abstr., Bibl.Agri., Biol.Abstr., Chem.Abstr., Curr.Adv.Ecol.Sci., Curr.Cont., Environ.Abstr., Food Sci.& Tech.Abstr., Geo.Abstr., Helminthol.Abstr., Ind.Sci.Rev., Ind.U.S.Gov.Per., INIS Atomind., Nutr.Abstr., Ocean.Abstr., Pollut.Abstr., Sci.Cit.Ind., Sel.Water Res.Abstr., Sel.Water.Res.Abstr., So.Pac.Per.Ind. **Document type:** academic/scholarly publication, government publication.
—BLDSC (3940.900000); CIS; Faxon; UnCover; SWETS; UMI.
　Description: Publishes original research reports and technical notes on investigations in fishery science.

639.2　　　　　　　II　　ISSN 0015-3001
SH335　　　　　　　　CODEN: FITEAG
FISHERY TECHNOLOGY. (Text in English) 1964. s-a. Rs.150($40) (effective from 1990). Society of Fisheries Technologists (India), Matsyapuri P.O., Cochin 682029, India. TELEX CN-440. Ed. Jose Joseph. bk.rev.; abstr.; charts. circ. 750. **Indexed:** Aqua.Sci.& Fish.Abstr., Biol.Abstr., Chem.Abstr., Food Sci.& Tech.Abstr., Nutr.Abstr.
—BLDSC (3945.100000); UnCover; CASDDS.

639.2　　　　　　　AT　　ISSN 1033-1247
FISHING BOAT WORLD. 1989. m. £35($65) Baird Publications Pty. Ltd., 10 Oxford St., South Yarra, Vic. 3141, Australia. TEL 03-826-8741. FAX 03-827-0704. (Addr. in the U.K.: 4A Carmelite St., London EC4V 0BN, England) Ed. Neil Baird. adv.; bk.rev.; circ. 4,000 (controlled). **Document type:** trade publication.
—BLDSC (3945.209000).
　Description: International newsmagazine of commercial fishing and the commercial fishing boat industry.

639.2 623.82　　　　　FR
FISHING BUSINESS INTERNATIONAL. Short title: F B I. (Text in English, French) bi-m. 180 F.($30) Box 6359, 35063 Rennes Cedex, France. TEL 33-99-32-21-21. FAX 33-99-32-14-17. Ed. Michel le Stunff. adv.; B&W page £1300, color page £1600; trim 265 x 185; adv. contact: David Blatt. tr.lit. circ. 14,000.
　Formerly: Fishing Boat International.
　Description: Covers the spectrum of the international commercial fishing industry from politics to packaging.

639　　　　　　　　US
FISHING: LATIN AMERICAN INDUSTRIAL REPORT. (Avail. for each of 22 Latin American countries) 1985. a. $435 per country report. Aquino Productions, Box 15760, Stamford, CT 06901. TEL 203-325-3138. Ed. Andres C. Aquino.

639.2　　　　　　　UK　　ISSN 0015-3036
FISHING NEWS. 1913. w. £30 (Europe £40; elsewhere £47). E M A P Heighway, Meed House, 21 John St., London WC1N 2BP, England. TEL 071-404-5513. FAX 071-831-9362. TELEX 881 3483 FISHL. Ed. T. Oliver. adv.; bk.rev.; charts; illus.; mkt. circ. 23,000. **Document type:** newspaper.

639.2　　　　　　　UK　　ISSN 0015-3044
FISHING NEWS INTERNATIONAL. 1961. m. £30 (Europe £35; elsewhere £40). E M A P Heighway, Meed House, 21 John St., London WC1N 2BP, England. TEL 071-404-5513. FAX 071-831-9362. TELEX 881 3483 FISHL. Ed. Ian Strutt. adv.; bk.rev.; charts; illus. circ. 5,400. (also avail. in microform from UMI; reprint service avail. from UMI) **Indexed:** Biol.Abstr., Br.Tech.Ind., Chem.Abstr., Deep Sea Res.& Oceanogr.Abstr., Food Sci.& Tech.Abstr., Ocean.Abstr., Packag.Sci.Tech., Pollut.Abstr., PROMT, So.Pac.Per.Ind. **Document type:** newspaper.
—BLDSC (3945.270000); SWETS; UMI. CCC.

FISHING WORLD. see SPORTS AND GAMES — Outdoor Life

639.34　　　　　　　US
FISHLINES. 1982. q. $15 membership. National Aquarium Society, Department of Commerce Bldg., Rm. B-037, 14th St. and Constitution Ave., N.W., Washington, DC 20230. TEL 202-782-2826. FAX 202-482-4946. Ed. Jennifer Cotting. bk.rev. circ. 700. **Document type:** newsletter.
　Formerly: Tank Talk.
　Description: Geared to the general public, with information on current marine research and events.

639 574.92　　　　　DK　　ISSN 0105-9211
FISK OG HAV. 1904; N.S. 1972. irreg. price varies. Danmarks Fiskeri- og Havundersoegelser - Danish Institute for Fisheries and Marine Research, Charlottenlund Castle, DK-2920 Charlottenlund, Denmark. Ed. Erik Hoffmann. cum.index: 1904-1952.
—BLDSC (8299.690000).
　Formerly: Denmark. Danmarks Fiskeri- og Havundersoegelser. Skrifter fra.

639.2　　　　　　　NO　　ISSN 0015-3095
FISKAREN. 1923. s-w. (except Jul., w.). price varies. A-S Fiskaren, Slottsgt. 3, Box 4053, N-5015 Bergen-Dreggen, Norway. Eds. Lars J. Odland, Per Helge Pedersen. adv.; abstr.; illus. circ. 18,640.
—CCC.

639　　　　　　　　NO　　ISSN 0071-5638
SH1
FISKEN OG HAVET. (Reports published from 1960 to 1976 in Fiskets Gang.) (Text in Norwegian; occasionally in English) 1959. irreg. Fiskeridirektoratet, Havforskningsinstituttet - Directorate of Fisheries, Institute of Marine Research, P.O. Box 1870-Nordnes, N-5024 Bergen, Norway. TEL 47-55-23-85-00. FAX 47-55-23-85-31. **Indexed:** Aqua.Sci.& Fish.Abstr., Biol.Abstr., Deep Sea Res.& Oceanogr.Abstr., Ocean.Abstr., Pollut.Abstr.
—BLDSC (3945.800000). CCC.

639.2 387.5　　　　DK　　ISSN 0907-8258
FISKERI OG SKIBSFART. 1955. q. DKK 50 (effective 1993). R. Wittendorff, Ed. & Pub., Niels W. Gades Vej 1, DK-8000 Aarhus C, Denmark. TEL 86-118680. FAX 86-144452. circ. 3,500. **Document type:** trade publication.
　Former titles (until 1993): Fisker Bladet (ISSN 0902-9281); (until 1975): Fisker og Arbejder (ISSN 0906-8422)

639.2　　　　　　　DK　　ISSN 0900-9787
FISKERIAARBOGEN. 1894. a. DKK 110. Iver C. Weilbach & Co. A-S, 35 Toldbodgade, DK-1253 Copenhagen K, Denmark. TEL 45-33-13-59-27. FAX 45-33-93-59-27. TELEX 19709. adv. circ. 4,500.
　Description: Devoted to material of interest to Danish fishermen.

639.2 799　　　　　　NO
FISKERIBLADET. 1946. s-w. NOK 80. Boks 562, 9401 Harstad, Norway. Ed. Freder Frederiksen. adv. circ. 20,600.

639.2　　　　　　　FI　　ISSN 0015-3125
FISKERITIDSKRIFT FOER FINLAND. (Text in Swedish) 1892. 6/yr. FIM 170. Kalatalouden Keskusliitto - Federation of Finnish Fisheries Associations, Koydenpunojankatu 7 B 23, 00180 Helsinki 18, Finland. TEL 358-0-640126. FAX 358-0-608309. Ed. Gunnar Lundquist. adv.; B&W page FIM 3000; trim 158 x 230; adv. contact: Jouku Poutanen. bk.rev.; illus.; index; circ. 4,878 (controlled). **Document type:** monographic series.
　Description: Directed to Swedish speaking commercial fishermen in Finland.

639.2　　　　　　　DK　　ISSN 0905-5193
FISKERIUNDERSOEGELSER I GROENLAND. AARSBERETNING. Greenlandic edition: Kalaallit Nunaani Aalisakkanik Misissuinerit. Ukiumoortumik Nalunaarusiaq (ISSN 0905-5215) 1971. a. free. Groenlands Fiskeriundersoegelser, Tagensvej 135-1, DK-2200 Copenhagen N, Denmark. TEL 45-31-85-44-44. FAX 45-35-82-18-50. Ed. Finn O. Kapel. illus. circ. 500. **Document type:** corporate report.
　Former titles (until 1988): Fiskeri- og Miljoeundersoegelser i Groenland. Serie 1. Aarsberetning (ISSN 0109-3010); (until 1981): Fiskeriet ved Groenland og Groenlands Fiskeriundersoegelsers Aktivitet (ISSN 0108-8629); (Until 1980): Fiskeri og Fiskeriundersoegelser ved Groenland (ISSN 0015-9033)
　Description: Annual report on fisheries research in Greenland.

639.2　　　　　　　NO　　ISSN 0015-3133
SH279
FISKETS GANG. (Text in Norwegian; summaries in English) 1910. m. NOK 200 in the Nordic countries; elsewhere NOK 330. Fiskeridirektoratet - Directorate of Fisheries, Box 185, 5002 Bergen, Norway. Ed. Sigbjoern Lomelde. adv.; charts; stat.; index. circ. 1,600. (back issues avail.; reprint service avail.) **Indexed:** Chem.Abstr. **Document type:** academic/scholarly publication.
—BLDSC (3948.080000). CCC.
　Description: Includes information on industry, fish markets, research, registered sales of fishing boats, fishery regulations and catch statistics.

639.2　　　　　　　IC　　ISSN 1017-3536
FISKIFRETTIR; Iceland's weekly newspaper on fishing industry. (Includes Sjavarfrettir) 1983. 48/yr. ISK 10512 (effective Jan. 1994). Frodi Ltd., Armuli 18, 108 Reykjavik, Iceland. TEL 354-1-812300. FAX 354-1-812946. Ed. Gudjon Einarsson. adv. contact: Hildur Gudnadottir. circ. 6,000. **Document type:** newspaper.

639　　　　　　　　UN　　ISSN 0258-6096
FOOD AND AGRICULTURE ORGANIZATION OF THE UNITED NATIONS. EUROPEAN INLAND FISHERIES ADVISORY COMMISSION. OCCASIONAL PAPERS. (Editions in English and French) 1968. irreg. free. Food and Agriculture Organization of the United Nations, European Inland Fisheries Advisory Commission, Secretariat, Via delle Terme di Caracalla, I-00100 Rome, Italy. TEL 06-57971. FAX 5146172. TELEX 610181 FAO I. circ. 2,000. (also avail. in microfiche; back issues avail.)

639　　　　　　　　UN　　ISSN 0532-940X
　　　　　　　　　　　CODEN: EIFPA2
FOOD AND AGRICULTURE ORGANIZATION OF THE UNITED NATIONS. EUROPEAN INLAND FISHERIES ADVISORY COMMISSION. TECHNICAL PAPERS. (Editions in English and French) 1964. irreg. free. Food and Agriculture Organization of the United Nations, European Inland Fisheries Advisory Committee, Secretariat, Via delle Terme di Caracalla, I-00100 Rome, Italy. TEL 06-57971. FAX 5146172. TELEX 610181 FAO I. circ. 2,000. (also avail. in microfiche; back issues avail.)
—BLDSC (3665.130000).

639.2　　　　　　　UN
FRESHWATER AND AQUACULTURE CONTENTS TABLES. (Text in English, French, Spanish, Russian) 1978. m. free. Food and Agriculture Organization of the United Nations, Fisheries Department, Via delle Terme di Caracalla, 00100 Rome, Italy. FAX 06-5797-6500. Ed. G. Landi. circ. 2,400.

639.2　　　　　　　NZ　　ISSN 0111-3232
FRESHWATER CATCH. q. NZ.$13.50 (foreign NZ$35). (Ministry of Agriculture and Fisheries) Freshwater Fisheries Centre, P.O. Box 8324, Riccarton, Christchurch, New Zealand. Ed. Paul Sager.
—UnCover.
　Formerly (until 1979): Catch (ISSN 0110-1722)
　Description: Details all aspects of New Zealand's fishing industry.

FISH AND FISHERIES

639   UK   ISSN 0951-3752
FRESHWATER FISHERIES LABORATORY PITLOCHRY. ANNUAL REVIEW. 1977. a. free. Scottish Office of Agriculture and Fisheries Department, Freshwater Fisheries Laboratory, Faskally, Pitlochry, Perthshire PH16 5LB, Scotland. TEL 0796-472060. FAX 0796-473523. Ed. R.G.J. Shelton. circ. 1,250. **Indexed:** Aqua.Sci. & Fish.Abstr. **Document type:** academic/scholarly publication.
● Also available online. Vendor(s): DIALOG Information Services, Inc.
    Formerly (until 1985): Freshwater Fisheries Laboratory Pitlochry. Triennial Review of Research (ISSN 0140-5004)
    Description: Includes summaries of current progress in the main areas of the laboratory's research program.

639.2   CC
FUJIAN SHUICHAN/FUJIAN AQUATIC PRODUCTS. (Text in Chinese) q. Fujian Shuichan Yanjiusuo - Fujian Aquatic Product Research Institute, 7 Haishan Lu, Dongdu, Xiamen, Fujian 361012, People's Republic of China. TEL 43165. Ed. Zheng Zhen'an.

GAZETTE OFFICIELLE DE LA PECHE. see *SPORTS AND GAMES — Outdoor Life*

639.2   IT
GAZZETTINO DELLA PESCA. 1954. m. L.40000 (Europe L.60000, elsewhere L.70000) (effective 1994). Ente Autonomo Fiera di Ancona, Largo Fiera della Pesca, 11, C.P. 352, 60125 Ancona, Italy. TEL 071-58971. FAX 071-5897213. adv.: B&W page L.700000; trim 180 x 267. circ. 7,000.
    Description: Covers new technology, equipment, fish processing and conservation, the economic market and trends and government legislation.

639   UN   ISSN 0072-0755
SH1
GENERAL FISHERIES COUNCIL FOR THE MEDITERRANEAN. REPORTS OF THE SESSIONS. 1968. irreg., no.19, 1989. price varies (latest issue $20). Food and Agriculture Organization of the United Nations, c/o UNIPUB, 4611-F Assembly Dr., Lanham, MD 20706-4391. FAX 301-459-0056. **Indexed:** Aqua.Sci.& Fish.Abstr., Biol.Abstr., Ocean.Abstr. **Document type:** monographic series.

639   UN   ISSN 0374-7840
GENERAL FISHERIES COUNCIL FOR THE MEDITERRANEAN. STUDIES AND REVIEWS. Spanish edition: Consejo General de Pesquerias del Mediterraneo. Analisis y Estudios (ISSN 1014-1081); French edition: Conseil General des Peches pour la Mediterranee. Etudes et Revues (ISSN 1014-109X) 1957. irreg., no.64, 1993. price varies. Food and Agriculture Organization of the United Nations, c/o UNIPUB, 4611-F Assembly Dr., Lanham, MD 20706-4391. FAX 301-459-0056. **Indexed:** Biol.Abstr. **Document type:** monographic series.

GIDROBIOLOGICHESKII ZHURNAL; nauchnyi zhurnal. see *BIOLOGY*

639.2   JA   ISSN 0389-6927
GIFU PREFECTURAL FISHERIES EXPERIMENTAL STATION. REPORT. (Text in Japanese) 1952. a. free. Gifu Prefectural Fisheries Experimental Station, 2605, Hane, Hagiwara-cho, Mashita-gun, Gifu 509-25, Japan. Ed.Bd. circ. 300.

GREAT BRITAIN. MINISTRY OF AGRICULTURE, FISHERIES AND FOOD. DIRECTORATE OF FISHERIES RESEARCH. AQUATIC ENVIRONMENT MONITORING REPORT. see *ENVIRONMENTAL STUDIES*

639.22 614.7   UK   ISSN 0308-5589
            CODEN: FRTRDJ
GREAT BRITAIN. MINISTRY OF AGRICULTURE, FISHERIES AND FOOD. DIRECTORATE OF FISHERIES RESEARCH. FISHERIES RESEARCH TECHNICAL REPORT. 1971. irreg. free. Ministry of Agriculture, Fisheries and Food, Directorate of Fisheries Research, Lowestoft, Suffolk NR33 0HT, England. TEL 0502-562244. **Indexed:** Aqua.Sci.& Fish.Abstr., Chem.Abstr., Deep Sea Res.& Oceanogr.Abstr. **Document type:** government publication.
—BLDSC (3939.820000). CCC.

639.22   UK   ISSN 0955-2855
SH257
GREAT BRITAIN. MINISTRY OF AGRICULTURE, FISHERIES AND FOOD. DIRECTORATE OF FISHERIES RESEARCH. FISHERIES SPOTLIGHT. 1969. a. free. (Ministry of Agriculture, Fisheries and Food) Marine Laboratory, P.O. Box 101, Victoria Rd., Aberdeen AB9 8DB, Scotland. **Indexed:** Aqua.Sci.& Fish.Abstr. **Document type:** government publication.
—BLDSC (3940.130000). CCC.
    Former titles: Great Britain. Ministry of Agriculture, Fisheries and Food. Directorate of Fisheries Research. Fishing Prospects (ISSN 0308-0935); Fish Stock Record (ISSN 0264-1240)

639.22   UK   ISSN 0143-8018
GREAT BRITAIN. MINISTRY OF AGRICULTURE, FISHERIES AND FOOD. DIRECTORATE OF FISHERIES RESEARCH. LABORATORY LEAFLET. irreg. free. Ministry of Agriculture, Fisheries and Food, Directorate of Fisheries Research, Lowestoft, Suffolk NR33 0HT, England. TEL 0502-562244. **Indexed:** Biol.Abstr., Hort.Abstr., Nutr.Abstr. **Document type:** government publication.
—CCC.

639.22 614.7   UK   ISSN 0957-7025
GREAT BRITAIN. MINISTRY OF AGRICULTURE, FISHERIES AND FOOD. RESEARCH INTO FISHERIES AND THE MARINE ENVIRONMENT. REPORT OF THE DIRECTOR OF FISHERIES RESEARCH. biennial. free. Ministry of Agriculture, Fisheries and Food, Directorate of Fisheries Research, Lowestoft, Suffolk NR33 0HT, England. TEL 0502-562244. **Document type:** government publication.
—CCC.
    Formerly (until 1989): Great Britain. Ministry of Agriculture, Fisheries and Food. Directorate of Fisheries Research. Report of the Director of Fisheries Research. (ISSN 0308-5570)

639   UK
GREAT BRITAIN. SEA FISH INDUSTRY AUTHORITY. ANNUAL REPORT AND ACCOUNTS. 1952. a. free. Sea Fish Industry Authority, 18 Logie Mill, Logie Green Rd., Edinburgh EH7 4HG, Scotland. TEL 031-558-3331. FAX 031-558-1442. circ. 1,200. **Document type:** government publication.
    Former titles (until 1980): Great Britain. Herring Industry Board. Annual Report (ISSN 0072-6419); Great Britain. White Fish Authority. Annual Report and Accounts (ISSN 0072-7261)
    Description: Activities and financial report and accounts of the Sea Fish Industry Authority; statistics of UK fish industry.

639   UK   ISSN 0142-937X
GREAT BRITAIN. SEA FISH INDUSTRY AUTHORITY. EUROPEAN SUPPLIES BULLETIN. 1979. q. £85 in U.K.; Europe £95; elsewhere £105. Sea Fish Industry Authority, 18 Logie Mill, Logie Green Rd., Edinburgh EH7 4HG, Scotland. TEL 031-558-3331. FAX 031-558-1442. Ed. M. Duran. circ. 170. (back issues avail.) **Document type:** government publication.
    Description: Statistics on landings and values of international trade in fish.

639   UK   ISSN 0309-4294
GREAT BRITAIN. SEA FISH INDUSTRY AUTHORITY. FISHERIES ECONOMICS NEWSLETTER. 1974. s-a. £30($55) Sea Fish Industry Authority, 18 Logie Mill, Logie Green Rd., Edinburgh EH7 4HG, Scotland. TEL 031-558-3331. FAX 031-558-1442. Ed. G. Buck. adv.: bk.rev. circ. 300. (back issues avail.) **Document type:** government publication.
—BLDSC (3939.190000).
    Description: Papers and abstracts of papers on fisheries economics from around the world. Includes workshop announcements.

639.2   UK   ISSN 0262-3269
GREAT BRITAIN. SEA FISH INDUSTRY AUTHORITY. HOUSEHOLD FISH CONSUMPTION IN GREAT BRITAIN. 1982. q. £55. Sea Fish Industry Authority, 18 Logie Mill, Logie Green Rd., Edinburgh EH7 4HG, Scotland. TEL 031-558-3331. FAX 031-558-1442. Ed. K. Cormack. circ. 80. (back issues avail.) **Document type:** government publication.
    Description: Analysis of sales of fish by species for household consumption in Britain.

639   UK
GREAT BRITAIN. SEA FISH INDUSTRY AUTHORITY. TRADE BULLETIN. m. £35 (Europe £45; elsewhere £55). Sea Fish Industry Authority, 18 Logie Mill, Logie Green Rd., Edinburgh EH7 4HG, Scotland. TEL 031-558-3331. FAX 031-558-1442. circ. 270. **Document type:** government publication.
    Description: Information on the quantity and value of imports and exports of fish for human consumption for the U.K.

639   CN
GV198.65.G7
GREAT LAKES FISHERMAN. 1973. m. Can.$20. Nan-Sea Publications, 542 George St., Port Stanley, Ont. N5L 1H3, Canada. TEL 519-782-3412. FAX 519-782-3412. Ed. Frank Prothero. adv.; bk.rev.; illus. circ. 1,500. **Document type:** trade publication.

639.2   US
GREAT LAKES FISHERY COMMISSION. SPECIAL PUBLICATION. irreg., no.92-3, 1992. $10.50. Great Lakes Fishery Commission, 2100 Commonwealth Blvd., Ste. 209, Ann Arbor, MI 48105. TEL 313-662-3209. FAX 313-741-2010.
    Description: Reports, analysis, and data concerning biological, institutional and socioeconomic components of Great Lakes fish and fisheries.

639   US   ISSN 0072-7296
SH221   CODEN: GLFRAH
GREAT LAKES FISHERY COMMISSION (UNITED STATES AND CANADA) ANNUAL REPORT. 1956. a. free. Great Lakes Fishery Commission, 2100 Commonwealth Blvd., Ste. 209, Ann Arbor, MI 48105. TEL 313-662-3209. FAX 313-741-2010. circ. 900. **Indexed:** Biol.Abstr.

639   US   ISSN 0072-730X
SH36   CODEN: GLFTAN
GREAT LAKES FISHERY COMMISSION (UNITED STATES AND CANADA) TECHNICAL REPORT SERIES. 1961. irreg., no.59, 1993. free. Great Lakes Fishery Commission, 2100 Commonwealth Blvd. Ste. 209, Ann Arbor, MI 48105. TEL 313-662-3209. FAX 313-741-2010. circ. 900. **Indexed:** Biol.Abstr. —UnCover.
    Description: Articles on fish dynamics, habitat, socioeconomics and sea lamprey control pertaining to the Great Lakes.

639 664.94   CN   ISSN 0826-9653
GUIDE TO EATING ONTARIO SPORT FISH. 1973. biennial. free. Ministry of Environment and Energy, Environmental Monitoring and Reporting Branch, 135 St. Clair Ave. W., Toronto, ON M4V 1P5, Canada. TEL 416-314-7886. FAX 416-314-7930. (Co-sponsor: Ministry of Natural Resources) circ. controlled. **Document type:** government publication.
    Formed by the 1985 merger of: Guide to Eating Ontario Sport Fish. Northern Ontario, Lake Superior (ISSN 0713-4223); & Guide to Eating Ontario Sport Fish. Southern Ontario, Great Lakes (ISSN 0713-4215)

639   US   ISSN 0072-9019
GULF AND CARIBBEAN FISHERIES INSTITUTE. ANNUAL PROCEEDINGS. 1948. a. $30 (foreign $35). University of Miami, Gulf and Caribbean Fisheries Institute, Inc., 38 Wentworth St., Charleston, SC 29401. FAX 803-727-2080. Eds. Melvin Goodwin, Gregg Waugh. adv.; cum.index: 1948-1964. circ. 1,000. **Indexed:** Biol.Abstr., Deep Sea Res.& Oceanogr.Abstr. **Document type:** proceedings.
    Description: Technical reports on current issues and progress related to fisheries management and development in the Caribbean.

GYOGYO TO KISHO/FISHERY AND METEOROLOGY. see *METEOROLOGY*

639.2   JA   ISSN 0426-3111
GYOSEN/FISHING BOAT. (Text in Japanese) 1936. bi-m. Gyosen Kyokai - Fishing Boat Association of Japan, 15-16, Toranomon 1-chome, Minato-ku, Tokyo 105, Japan.
—BLDSC (4754.120000).

FISH AND FISHERIES

639.2 551.46   IC   ISSN 0258-381X
HAFRANNSOKNIR. (Text in Icelandic; summaries in English) 1969. irreg., vol.45, 1994. exchange basis. Hafrannsoknastofnunin - Marine Research Institute, Skulagata 4, P.O. Box 1390, 121 Reykjavik, Iceland. TEL 354-1-20240. Ed. Eirikur T. Einarsson. circ. 420 (controlled). **Document type:** academic/scholarly publication.
    Description: Contains report of the Institute and occasional research papers.

639.3   CC   ISSN 1004-2490
HAIYANG YUYE/MARINE FISHERIES. (Text in Chinese) 1979. bi-m. Y6. Zhongguo Shuichan Kexue Yuanjiuyuan, Donghai Shuichan Yanjiusuo, 300 Jungong Lu, Shanghai 200090, People's Republic of China. TEL 86-21-5434690. FAX 86-21-5432926. Ed. Qiu Yonggen. adv.; bk.rev.; circ. 5,000 (paid); 500 (controlled).

639.2   HU   ISSN 0133-1922
HALASZAT/FISHING. 1899. q. 400 Ft. (Ministry of Agriculture) Agroinform Kiado es Nyomda Kft., Kitaibel Pal u. 4, 1024 Budapest II, Hungary. TEL 135-1927. FAX 135-0344. Ed. Pinter Karoly. adv. **Document type:** newsletter.

639.3   SW   ISSN 0374-8030
HAVSFISKELABORATORIET. MEDDELANDE. (Text in English or Swedish) 1962. irreg. free. National Board of Fisheries, Institute of Marine Research, Box 4, 453 21 Lysekil, Sweden. TEL 46-523-14180. FAX 46-523-13977. Ed. Bernt I. Dybern. circ. 450. **Indexed:** Biol.Abstr. **Document type:** government publication, bulletin.

HIROSHIMA DAIGAKU SEIBUTSU SEISAN GAKUBU KIYO. see AGRICULTURE — Dairying And Dairy Products

639.3   JA
HOKKAIDO SALMON HATCHERY. TECHNICAL REPORT. (Text in English) q. Fisheries Agency of Japan, Hokkaido Salmon Hatchery, 2-2 Nakanoshima, Toyohira-ku, Sapporo 062, Japan. FAX 011-823-8979.
    Formerly (until 1991): Fish and Eggs.

639.2   JA   ISSN 0018-3458
SH301   CODEN: HOSGAD
HOKKAIDO UNIVERSITY. FACULTY OF FISHERIES. BULLETIN. (Text in English and Japanese) 1950. q. exchange basis. Hokkaido University, Faculty of Fisheries, 3-1-1 Minato-machi, Hakodate, Hokkaido 041, Japan. abstr.; illus.; stat.; index. circ. 850. **Indexed:** Anim.Breed.Abstr., Biol.Abstr., Chem.Abstr., Curr.Adv.Ecol.Sci., Deep Sea Res.& Oceanogr.Abstr., Food Sci.& Tech.Abstr., Ind.Vet., INIS Atomind., Nutr.Abstr., Ocean.Abstr., Pollut.Abstr., Sel.Water Res.Abstr., Vet.Bull.
—BLDSC (2508.350000); UnCover; CASDDS.

HOKKAIDO UNIVERSITY. FACULTY OF FISHERIES. DATA RECORD OF OCEANOGRAPHIC OBSERVATIONS AND EXPLORATORY FISHING/KAIYO CHOSA GYOGYO SHIKEN YOHO. see EARTH SCIENCES — Oceanography

639.2   JA   ISSN 0018-3466
SH1   CODEN: MFHOA8
HOKKAIDO UNIVERSITY. FACULTY OF FISHERIES. MEMOIRS. 1953. s-a. exchange basis. Hokkaido University, Faculty of Fisheries, 3-1-1 Minato-machi, Hakodate, Hokkaido 041, Japan. Ed.Bd. bibl.; charts; illus.; index. circ. 850. **Indexed:** Biol.Abstr., Chem.Abstr., Curr.Adv.Ecol.Sci., Deep Sea Res.& Oceanogr.Abstr., Ocean.Abstr., Pollut.Abstr.
—BLDSC (5596.300000).

639.2   JA
HOKKAIDO WAKKANAI FISHERIES EXPERIMENTAL STATION. ANNUAL REPORT. 1964. a. free. Hokkaido Wakkanai Fisheries Experimental Station, Horai 4-5-4, Wakkanai, Hokkaido 097, Japan. TEL 0162-23-2126. FAX 0162-23-2134. Ed.Bd. circ. 340.

639.2 574.192   JA   ISSN 0914-6830
SH302.H6   CODEN: HSSHEE
HOKKAIDORITSU SUISAN SHIKENJO KENKYU HOKOKU/HOKKAIDO FISHERIES EXPERIMENTAL STATION. SCIENTIFIC REPORTS. (Text in Japanese, English; summaries in English) 1963. 2/yr. 1120 Yen. Hokkaido Central Fisheries Experimental Station, Hamanaka-cho, Yoichi-machi, Hokkaido 046, Japan. TEL 0135-23-7451. FAX 0135-23-3141. Ed. Kazuhiro Kawamuta. circ. 900. **Indexed:** Biol.Abstr., Curr.Adv.Ecol.Sci., Deep Sea Res.& Oceanogr.Abstr., Food Sci.& Tech.Abstr., Ind.Vet., Vet.Bull. **Document type:** bulletin.
—BLDSC (8197.710000); CASDDS.
    Formerly (until 1988): Hokkaidoritsu Suisan Shikenjo Hokoku (ISSN 0441-084X)

639.2   JA   ISSN 0914-6849
HOKUSUISHI DAYORI/HOKKAIDO FISHERIES EXPERIMENTAL STATION. JOURNAL. (Text in Japanese) 1944. 4/yr. 960 Yen. Hokkaidoritsu Chuo Suisan Shikenjo - Hokkaido Central Fisheries Experimental Station, 238 Hamanaka-cho, Yoichi-machi, Yoichi-gun, Hokkaido 046, Japan. TEL 0135-23-7451. FAX 0135-23-3141. Ed. Kazuhiro Kawamura. bk.rev.; illus.; stat.; index. circ. 1,670. **Indexed:** Biol.Abstr., Chem.Abstr. **Document type:** bulletin.
    Formerly (until 1988): Hokusuishi Geppo (ISSN 0018-3504)

639.2   US
HOOK, LINE & SINKER. 1989. 4/yr. $6. Fish Wagon Inc., Rt. 3, Box 337-C, Harrisburg, AR 72432. TEL 501-578-5489. FAX 800-621-9955. Ed. Jimmy Philamlee. adv. circ. 1,500.
    Description: Provides owners of small lakes and ponds with practical information on fishing and management, and gives practical advice on how to catch more fish in cages, how to correct unbalanced ponds, and how to solve vegetation problems. Includes new innovations in the fish industry.

HYDROBIOLOGICAL JOURNAL. see BIOLOGY

639.3 333.7   DK   ISSN 1017-6195
    CODEN: CRRPC3
I C E S COOPERATIVE RESEARCH REPORT/RAPPORT DES RECHERCHES COLLECTIVES. (Text in English or French) 1972. irreg., no.194, 1993. price varies. International Council for the Exploration of the Sea, Palaegade 2-4, DK-1261 Copenhagen K, Denmark. FAX 33-934215. TELEX 22498 ICES DK. (Subscr. to: C.A. Reitzels Boghandel, Noerregade 20, DK-1165, Copenhagen K) circ. 400. (back issues avail.) **Indexed:** Biol.Abstr., Curr.Adv.Ecol.Sci. **Document type:** monographic series.
—BLDSC (3464.890000); UnCover.
    Formerly: International Council for the Exploration of the Sea. Cooperative Research Report (ISSN 0105-3213); Which was formed by the merger of (1962-1972): International Council for the Exploration of the Sea. Cooperative Research Report. Series A (ISSN 0074-431X) & (1966-1972): International Council for the Exploration of the Sea. Cooperative Research Report. Series B (ISSN 0374-8502).

I C E S IDENTIFICATION LEAFLETS FOR DISEASES AND PARASITES OF FISH AND SHELLFISH/FICHES D'IDENTIFICATION DES MALADIES ET PARASITES DES POISSONS, CRUSTACES ET MOLLUSQUES. see BIOLOGY — Zoology

I C E S IDENTIFICATION LEAFLETS FOR PLANKTON/FICHES D'IDENTIFICATION DU PLANCTON. see BIOLOGY — Zoology

I C E S JOURNAL OF MARINE SCIENCE. (International Council for the Exploration of the Sea) see EARTH SCIENCES — Oceanography

639 333.7 551.46   DK   ISSN 0906-060X
GC1   CODEN: IMSSEG
I C E S MARINE SCIENCE SYMPOSIA/ACTES DU SYMPOSIUM. (Text in English or French) 1903. irreg., no.197, 1993. price varies. International Council for the Exploration of the Sea, Palaegade 2-4, DK-1261 Copenhagen K, Denmark. FAX 33-93-4215. TELEX 22498 ICES DK. (Subscr. to: C.A. Reitzels Boghandel, Noerregade 20, DK-1165, Copenhagen K, Denmark) circ. 700. (back issues avail.) **Indexed:** Biol.Abstr., Curr.Adv.Ecol.Sci., Deep Sea Res.& Oceanogr.Abstr., Nutr.Abstr., Ocean.Abstr. **Document type:** proceedings, academic/scholarly publication.
—BLDSC (4361.495000); SWETS.
    Formerly (until 1991): Conseil International pour l'Exploration de la Mer. Rapports et Proces-Verbaux des Reunions (ISSN 0074-4336)

639.2 597   PH   ISSN 0115-4435
I C L A R M CONFERENCE PROCEEDINGS. (Text in English) 1979. irreg. price varies. International Center for Living Aquatic Resources Management, M.C.P.O. Box 2631, 0718 Makati, Metro Manila, Philippines. TEL 2-818-0466. FAX 2-816-3183. TELEX 64794-ICLARM-PN. abstr.; bibl.; illus.; index. circ. 1,200. (back issues avail.) **Indexed:** Curr.Cont. **Document type:** proceedings.

639.2   PH   ISSN 1047-9694
I C L A R M CONTRIBUTION. (Text in English) irreg. International Center for Living Aquatic Resources Management, M.C.P.O. Box 2631, 0718 Makati, Metro Manila, Philippines. TEL 63-2-817-5163. FAX 63-2-816-3183.

639.2   PH   ISSN 0116-5720
I C L A R M EDUCATION SERIES. (Text in English) irreg. International Center for Living Aquatic Resources Management, M.C.P.O. Box 2631, 0718 Makati, Metro Manila, Philippines. TEL 63-2-818-3186. FAX 63-2-826-3183. **Document type:** monographic series.

639.2   PH   ISSN 0115-4494
I C L A R M REPORT. (Text in English) 1977. a. International Center for Living Aquatic Resources Management, M.C.P.O. Box 2631, 0718 Makati, Metro Manila, Phillipines. TEL 83-2-817-5163. FAX 83-2-816-3183.

I C L A R M SOFTWARE. (International Center for Living Aquatic Resources Management) see COMPUTERS — Software

639.2   PH   ISSN 0115-4389
    CODEN: ISRVES
I C L A R M STUDIES AND REVIEWS. (Text in English) 1979. irreg. price varies. International Center for Living Aquatic Resources Management, M.C.P.O. Box 2631, 0718 Makati, Metro Manila, Philippines. TEL 2-818-0466. FAX 2-816-3183. TELEX 64794-ICLARM-PN. **Document type:** monographic series.

639.2   PH   ISSN 0115-5547
I C L A R M TECHNICAL REPORTS. (Text in English) 1981. irreg. price varies. International Center for Living Aquatic Resources Management, M.C.P.O. Box 2631, 0718 Makati, Metro Manila, Philippines. TEL 2-818-0466. FAX 2-816-3183. TELEX 64794-ICLARM-PN. **Document type:** monographic series.
—BLDSC (4362.048060).

639.2   PH   ISSN 0115-4141
I C L A R M TRANSLATIONS. (Text in English) irreg. price varies. International Center for Living Aquatic Resources Management, M.C.P.O. Box 2631, 0718 Makati, Metro Manila, Philippines. TEL 2-818-0466. FAX 2-816-3183. TELEX 64794-ICLARM-PN.

639.2   IC   ISSN 1018-5984
ICELANDIC FISHERIES LABORATORIES. REPORT. (Text in English) 1968. biennial. exchange basis. Icelandic Fisheries Laboratories, P.O. Box 1405, 121 Reykjavik, Iceland. TEL 354-1-620240. FAX 354-1-620740. E-mail: postmaster@rfisk.is. Ed. Rosa Sveinsdottir. circ. 3,000. (back issues avail.) **Indexed:** Biol.Abstr.
—BLDSC (7515.480000).
    Formerly (until 1988): Rannsoknastofnum Fiskidnadarins. Arsskyrsla (ISSN 0378-231X)

FISH AND FISHERIES

639.2   IC
▼**ICELANDIC FISHING NEWS**. 1993. w. $39 per m. Midlun hf., Fjoelmidlavaktin - Midlun Ltd., Media Monitoring, Aegisgata 7, P.O. Box 155, IS-121 Reykjavik, Iceland. TEL 354-1-622288. FAX 354-1-26994. Ed. Einar Sigvaldason. (also avail. by fax) **Document type:** newsletter.
    Description: Contains a summary of the latest developments in the Icelandic fishing industry, based on newspapers, local papers, specialized magazines, radio and TV news, and company newsletters.

IDAHO. DEPARTMENT OF FISH AND GAME. FEDERAL AID INVESTIGATION PROJECTS. PROGRESS REPORTS AND PUBLICATIONS. see *CONSERVATION*

639.2
INDIAN FISHERY HANDBOOK. irreg. $20. Marine Products Export Development Authority, MPEDA House, Panampilly Avenue Rd., P.B. No. 1663, Cochin 682 015, India. TEL 311979. TELEX 0885-6288. **Document type:** trade publication.

597   II   ISSN 0537-2003
SH1   CODEN: IJFIAW
INDIAN JOURNAL OF FISHERIES. (Text in English) 1954. q. Rs.140($28) Indian Council of Agricultural Research, Krishi Anusandhan Bhavan, Pusa, New Delhi 110012, India. Ed. V.S. Bhatt. adv.; bk.rev.; charts; illus.; index. circ. 2,000. (looseleaf format; also avail. in microfilm from UMI; reprint service avail. from UMI) **Indexed:** Biol.Abstr., Chem.Abstr., Curr.Adv.Ecol.Sci., Deep Sea Res.& Oceanogr.Abstr., Food Sci.& Tech.Abstr., Helminthol.Abstr., Nutr.Abstr., Pollut.Abstr., Sel.Water Res.Abstr.

664.94   II   ISSN 0019-6347
INDIAN SEAFOODS. (Text in English) 1963. m. free to qualified personnel. Marine Products Export Development Authority, MPEDA House, Panampilly Avenue Rd., P.B. No. 1663, Cochin 682 015, India. TEL 311979. TELEX 0885-6288. Ed. P. Jacob Daniel. charts; illus.; stat. **Document type:** trade publication.

369.2   UN
INDO-PACIFIC FISHERY COMMISSION. REPORT. 1949. biennial. free. Indo-Pacific Fishery Commission, c/o Secretary, F A O Regional Office for Asia and the Pacific, Maliwan Mansion, Phra Atit Rd., Bangkok 10200, Thailand. FAX 662-2800-445. TELEX 82815 FOODAG. circ. 1,000. (controlled) **Indexed:** Biol.Abstr. **Document type:** proceedings.
    Former titles: I P F C Report; I P F C Proceedings; (until 1976): Indo-Pacific Fisheries Council. Proceedings.

639.2   MY
INFOFISH FULLNET: GLOBEFISH HIGHLIGHT. (Text in English) q. $350 includes Trade News(fortn.) and Infofish International(bi-m). Infofish, P.O. Box 10899, 50728 Kuala Lumpur, Malaysia. TEL 03-2914466. FAX 03-2916804. TELEX INFISH-MA-31560. **Document type:** newsletter.
    Description: Commodity report covering medium and long-term trends based on Globefish databank.

639.2   MY   ISSN 0127-9114
INFOFISH FULLNET: TRADE NEWS. (Text in English) 1984. bi-w. (23/yr.). $350 includes Globefish and Infofish International. Infofish, P.O. Box 10899, 50728 Kuala Lumpur, Malaysia. TEL 03-2914466. FAX 03-2916804. TELEX INFISH-MA-31560. **Document type:** bulletin.
    Description: Features the latest news on indicative prices, holdings and short-term trends in major markets.

639.2   MY   ISSN 0127-2012
INFOFISH INTERNATIONAL. bi-m. $50 (developing countries $25). Infofish, P.O. Box 10899, 50728 Kuala Lumpur, Malaysia. TEL 03-2914466. FAX 03-2916804. TELEX INFISH-MA-31560. adv.: B&W page $1160, color page $1680; trim 181 x 247. circ. 7,000.
—BLDSC (4478.878880).
    Description: Provides marketing information and technical advisory services for fishery products in the Asia and Pacific region.

639.2   GW   ISSN 0020-0344
INFORMATIONEN FUER DIE FISCHWIRTSCHAFT. 1954. 4/yr. DM.40. Bundesforschungsanstalt fuer Fischerei, Informations- und Dokumentationsstelle, Palmaille 9, 22767 Hamburg, Germany. FAX 040-38905129. Ed. H. Bahl. adv.; bk.rev.; bibl.; charts; illus.; stat. circ. 1,300. **Indexed:** Aqua.Sci.& Fish.Abstr., Food Sci.& Tech.Abstr., Nutr.Abstr. **Document type:** government publication.
—BLDSC (4496.473000).

639.2   GW   ISSN 0020-0379
SH1
INFORMATIONEN UEBER DIE FISCHWIRTSCHAFT DES AUSLANDES. 1951. bi-m. DM.38.50. Bundesforschungsanstalt fuer Fischerei, Informations- und Dokumentationsstelle, Palmaille 9, 22767 Hamburg, Germany. TEL 040-38905141. FAX 040-38905129. Ed. W.W. Kuehnhold. bk.rev.; abstr.; stat. circ. 600. (processed) **Document type:** government publication.
    Description: Shows trends in economics and politics, aquaculture, commodities, technology and statistics.

INFORMES TECNICOS DE SCIENTIA MARINA. see *EARTH SCIENCES — Oceanography*

639.2   NL   ISSN 1018-3116
▼**INSHORE FISHERIES RESEARCH PROJECT TECHNICAL DOCUMENT**. 1992. irreg. South Pacific Commission, B.P. D.5, Noumea, Cedex, New Caledonia. **Document type:** monographic series.

639   BL   ISSN 0046-9939
SH236   CODEN: BINPED
INSTITUTO DE PESCA, SAO PAULO. BOLETIM. (Text in Portuguese; summaries in English) 1971. s-a. exchange basis. Instituto de Pesca, Av. Francisco Matarazzo, 455, 05031-900 Sao Paulo, SP, Brazil. Ed. Dr. Heloisa Maria Godinho. adv. circ. 1,000. **Indexed:** Deep Sea Res.& Oceanogr.Abstr., Food Sci.& Tech.Abstr., Nutr.Abstr.

630   BL
INSTITUTO DE PESCA, SAO PAULO. BOLETIM. SERIE DE DIVULGACAO. 1972. irreg. free or exchange basis. Instituto de Pesca, Av. Francisco Matarazzo, 455, 05031-900 Sao Paulo, SP, Brazil. Ed. Dr. Heloisa Maria Godinho. circ. 1,000. **Indexed:** Nutr.Abstr.

639.1 639.2   PE   ISSN 0378-7699
QH95.52
INSTITUTO DEL MAR DEL PERU. BOLETIN. (Text in Spanish; summaries in English) 1963. irreg. (4-5/yr.). $40. Instituto del Mar del Peru, Centro de Informacion, Apdo. 22, Callao, Peru. **Indexed:** Biol.Abstr., Curr.Adv.Ecol.Sci., Deep Sea Res.& Oceanogr.Abstr.
—BLDSC (2178.400000).

639.2 639.3   PE   ISSN 0378-7702
INSTITUTO DEL MAR DEL PERU. INFORME. (Text in Spanish; summaries in English) 1962. irreg. (4-5/yr.). $40. Instituto del Mar del Peru, Centro de Informacion, Apdo. 22, Callao, Peru. bibl.; charts; illus.; stat. **Indexed:** Biol.Abstr.

639.2   AG   ISSN 0325-6987
INSTITUTO NACIONAL DE INVESTIGACION Y DESARROLLO PESQUERO. MEMORIA. a. Instituto Nacional de Investigacion y Desarrollo Pesquero, Casilla de Correo 175, 7600 Mar del Plata, Argentina. TELEX 39975 INIDP.

639.2   AG   ISSN 0325-6375
QL614   CODEN: RIDPE3
INSTITUTO NACIONAL DE INVESTIGACION Y DESARROLLO PESQUERO. REVISTA. 1979. s-a. exchange basis. Instituto Nacional de Investigacion y Desarrollo Pesquero, Casilla de Correo 175, 7600 Mar del Plata, Argentina. TELEX 39975 INIDP. **Indexed:** Aqua.Sci.& Fish.Abstr.

639.2   AG   ISSN 0325-6790
                       CODEN: CNINES
INSTITUTO NACIONAL DE INVESTIGACION Y DESARROLLO PESQUERO. SERIE CONTRIBUCIONES. (Text in English or Spanish; summaries in English, French and Spanish) 1961. irreg. exchange basis. Instituto Nacional de Investigacion y Desarrollo Pesquero, Casilla de Correo 175, 7600 Mar del Plata, Argentina. TELEX 39975 INIDP. index. **Indexed:** Aqua.Sci.& Fish.Abstr., Curr.Adv.Ecol.Sci., Deep Sea Res.& Oceanogr.Abstr., Ocean.Abstr.
—BLDSC (3426.560000).
    Formerly: Instituto de Biologia Marina. Serie Contribuciones (ISSN 0076-4302)

639   US   ISSN 0074-1000
INTER-AMERICAN TROPICAL TUNA COMMISSION. ANNUAL REPORT/COMISION INTERAMERICANA DEL ATUN TROPICAL. INFORME ANUAL. (Text in English and Spanish) 1951. a. price varies. Inter-American Tropical Tuna Commission, c/o Scripps Institution of Oceanography, 8604 La Jolla Shores Dr., La Jolla, CA 92037-1508. TEL 619-546-7100. FAX 619-546-7133. TELEX 697115. Ed. William H. Bayliff. circ. 1,200. (also avail. in microfiche from CIS) **Indexed:** IIS.

639   US   ISSN 0074-0993
QL614
INTER-AMERICAN TROPICAL TUNA COMMISSION. BULLETIN/COMISION INTERAMERICANA DEL ATUN TROPICAL. BOLETIN. (Text in English and Spanish) 1954. irreg., vol.20, no.9, 1993. price varies. Inter-American Tropical Tuna Commission, c/o Scripps Institution of Oceanography, 8604 La Jolla Shores Dr., La Jolla, CA 92037-1508. TEL 619-546-7100. FAX 619-546-7133. TELEX 697115. Ed. William H. Bayliff. circ. 1,000. **Indexed:** Biol.Abstr., Deep Sea Res.& Oceanogr.Abstr. **Document type:** bulletin.
—BLDSC (2586.600000).

639   US   ISSN 0538-3609
INTER-AMERICAN TROPICAL TUNA COMMISSION. DATA REPORT. 1966. irreg., no.7, 1984. price varies. Inter-American Tropical Tuna Commission, c/o Scripps Institution of Oceanography, 8604 La Jolla Shores Dr., La Jolla, CA 92037-1508. TEL 619-546-7100. FAX 619-546-7133. TELEX 697115. Ed. William H. Bayliff. circ. 100. **Indexed:** Deep Sea Res.& Oceanogr.Abstr.

639.2   US   ISSN 1048-6259
SH351.T8
INTER-AMERICAN TROPICAL TUNA COMMISSION. QUARTERLY REPORT/COMISION INTERAMERICANA DEL ATUN TROPICAL. INFORME TRIMESTRAL. (Text in English and Spanish) 1951. q. free to qualified personnel. Inter-American Tropical Tuna Commission, c/o Scripps Institution of Oceanography, 8604 La Jolla Shores Dr., La Jolla, CA 92037-1508. TEL 619-546-7100. FAX 619-546-7133. TELEX 697115. Ed. William H. Bayliff. circ. 380. (also avail. in microfiche from CIS) **Indexed:** IIS.

639   US
INTER-AMERICAN TROPICAL TUNA COMMISSION. SPECIAL REPORT. 1975. irreg., no.8, 1993. price varies. Inter-American Tropical Tuna Commission, c/o Scripps Institution of Oceanography, 8604 La Jolla Shores Dr., La Jolla, CA 92037-1508. TEL 619-546-7100. FAX 619-546-7133. TELEX 697115. Ed. William H. Bayliff. circ. 500. (also avail. in microfiche from CIS) **Indexed:** Biol.Abstr., IIS.

639.2   SP
INTERNATIONAL COMMISSION FOR THE CONSERVATION OF ATLANTIC TUNAS. COLLECTIVE VOLUME OF SCIENTIFIC PAPERS. (Text in English, French and Spanish) 1973. a. 2500 ptas.($25) avail. to qualified personnel only. International Commission for the Conservation of Atlantic Tunas, Principe de Vergara 17, 28001 Madrid, Spain. Ed. P.M. Miyake. circ. controlled. (also avail. in microfiche from CIS) **Indexed:** IIS.

639.2   SP
INTERNATIONAL COMMISSION FOR THE CONSERVATION OF ATLANTIC TUNAS. DATA RECORD. (Text in English, French and Spanish) 1973. a. 2500 ptas.($25) avail. to qualified personnel only. International Commission for the Conservation of Atlantic Tunas, Principe de Vergara 17, 28001 Madrid, Spain. Ed. P.M. Miyake. circ. controlled. (also avail. in microfiche from CIS) **Indexed:** IIS.

FISH AND FISHERIES

639.2   SP
INTERNATIONAL COMMISSION FOR THE CONSERVATION OF ATLANTIC TUNAS. NEWSLETTER. (Editions in English, French and Spanish) 1971. irreg. (3-4/yr.) International Commission for the Conservation of Atlantic Tunas, Principe de Vergara 17, 28001 Madrid, Spain. Ed. P.M. Miyake. **Indexed:** IIS.

639   UK
INTERNATIONAL HATCHERY PRACTICE. 1985. 8/yr. £30. Positive Action Publications Ltd., P.O. Box 4, Driffield, N. Humberside YO25 9DJ, England. TEL 0377-241724. FAX 0377-241910. Ed. Nigel Horrox; Pub. Nigel Horrox. adv. contact: Brent Roach. bk.rev. circ. 14,500. **Indexed:** Rev.Med.& Vet.Mycol. **Document type:** trade publication.

639.2   US   ISSN 1048-9509
INTERNATIONAL INSTITUTE OF FISHERIES ECONOMICS AND TRADE NEWSLETTER. 1983. s-a. $30. International Institute of Fisheries Economics and Trade, Dept. of Agricultural and Resource Economics, Oregon State University, Corvallis, OR 97331. TEL 503-737-1420. FAX 503-737-2563. TELEX 510-596-0686 OSUCID COVS. E-mail: Shrivera@CCMAIL.ORST.EDU. Ed. Ann L. Shriver. bk.rev.; abstr.; illus. circ. 400.
Description: Contains brief news articles on the economics, publications, employment and research of fisheries. Describes conferences, short courses and other events sponsored by the IIFET and other organizations.

639   US   ISSN 0074-7238
                                                     CODEN: IPHCBX
INTERNATIONAL PACIFIC HALIBUT COMMISSION (U.S. AND CANADA). ANNUAL REPORT. 1969. a. free. International Pacific Halibut Commission, Box 95009, Seattle, WA 98145-2009. TEL 206-634-1838. FAX 206-632-2983. circ. 7,000. (also avail. in microfiche from CIS; back issues avail.) **Indexed:** Biol.Abstr., IIS, Ocean.Abstr. **Document type:** corporate report.
—BLDSC (1311.690000).

639   US   ISSN 0074-7246
INTERNATIONAL PACIFIC HALIBUT COMMISSION (U.S. AND CANADA). SCIENTIFIC REPORTS. 1930. irreg., no.77, 1991. free. International Pacific Halibut Commission, Box 95009, Seattle, WA 98145-2009. TEL 206-634-1838. FAX 206-632-2983. circ. 1,500. **Indexed:** Biol.Abstr., Ocean.Abstr. **Document type:** monographic series.
—BLDSC (8198.303000).

639   US   ISSN 0579-3920
                                                     CODEN: IHCTB3
INTERNATIONAL PACIFIC HALIBUT COMMISSION (U S AND CANADA). TECHNICAL REPORTS. 1969. irreg., no.26, 1991. free. International Pacific Halibut Commission, Box 95009, Seattle, WA 98145-2009. TEL 206-634-1838. FAX 206-632-2983. circ. 3,000. (back issues avail.) **Indexed:** Biol.Abstr., Ocean.Abstr. **Document type:** monographic series.
—BLDSC (8715.898800).
Formerly: International Pacific Halibut Commission. Report (ISSN 0096-1221)

639.28 591   UK   ISSN 0143-8700
SH381
INTERNATIONAL WHALING COMMISSION. ANNUAL REPORTS. 1950. a. price varies. International Whaling Commission, The Red House, Station Rd., Histon, Cambs. CB4 4NP, England. TEL 0223-233971. FAX 0223-232876. Ed. G.P. Donovan. illus.; stat. circ. 500. (also avail. in microfiche from CIS; back issues avail.) **Indexed:** Biol.Abstr., Ecol.Abstr., IIS, Zoo.Rec. **Document type:** academic/scholarly publication.
—BLDSC (7524.351000).
Formerly: International Whaling Commission. Report (ISSN 0074-9591)

INZYNIERIA MORSKA I GEOTECHNIKA. see *TRANSPORTATION — Ships And Shipping*

639.2 574   IE
IRISH FISHERIES INVESTIGATIONS. SERIES A: FRESHWATER. 1967. irreg. Department of the Marine, Library, Fisheries Research Centre, Abbotstown, Castleknock, Dublin 15, Ireland. TEL 01-8210111. FAX 01-8205078. circ. 390. (back issues avail.) **Indexed:** Biol.Abstr., Deep Sea Res.& Oceanogr.Abstr. **Document type:** government publication.

639.2 574.92   IE
IRISH FISHERIES INVESTIGATIONS. SERIES B: MARINE. 1967. irreg. Department of the Marine, Library, Fisheries Research Centre, Abbotstown, Castleknock, Dublin 15, Ireland. TEL 01-8210111. FAX 01-8205078. circ. 350. (back issues avail.) **Indexed:** Biol.Abstr., Deep Sea Res.& Oceanogr.Abstr. **Document type:** government publication.

639.2 623.82   IE
IRISH SKIPPER. 1964. m. I£13.80. Mac Publishing Ltd., Taney Hall, Eglinton Terrace, Dundrum, Dublin 14, Ireland. TEL 01-2960000. FAX 01-2960383. Ed. Niall Fallon. adv.: color page I£640; trim 405 x 250; adv. contact: James Small. circ. 4,600. **Document type:** trade publication.

639.3   IS   ISSN 0792-156X
SH117.I75   CODEN: IJABEO
ISRAELI JOURNAL OF AQUACULTURE - BAMIDGEH; international journal on aquaculture. (Text and summaries in English) 1952. q. $30 (effective 1992). c/o Department of Animal Sciences, Faculty of Agriculture, Hebrew University of Jerusalem, P.O. Box 12, Rehovot 76100, Israel. FAX 972-2-658-3900. TELEX 46832-ND. (Subscr. to: Israeli Journal of Aquaculture - Bamidgeh, Editorial Office, Nir-David 19150, Israel) (Co-sponsors: Ministry of Agriculture, Department of Fisheries; Fish Breeders Association in Israel) Ed. Jaap van Rijn. adv.; bk.rev.; bibl.; charts; illus.; stat.; index. circ. 1,300. (back issues avail.; reprint service avail. from ISI) **Indexed:** Aqua.Sci.& Fish.Abstr., Biol.Abstr., Chem.Abstr., Sel.Water Res.Abstr., Sport Fish.Abstr. **Document type:** academic/scholarly publication.
—BLDSC (4583.961400); Faxon; UnCover; SWETS.
Formerly: Israel. Ministry of Agriculture. Department of Fisheries. Bamidgeh (ISSN 0005-4577)
Description: Covers experimental field and laboratory work in the disciplines of temperate and tropical aquaculture.

639.3 551.46   IT   ISSN 0393-3571
ISTITUTO RICERCHE PESCA MARITTIMA. QUADERNI. (Text in English or Italian; summaries in English, French, Italian) 1970. irreg. exchange basis only. Istituto Ricerche sulla Pesca Marittima, Molo Mandracchio, 60100 Ancona, Italy. FAX 39-71-55313. Ed. C. Froglia. circ. 500.
Formerly: Laboratorio di Tecnologia della Pesca. Quaderni.

639   GW   ISSN 0075-2851
JAHRESBERICHT UEBER DIE DEUTSCHE FISCHWIRTSCHAFT. 1949. a. DM.61.50. Bundesministerium fuer Ernaehrung, Landwirtschaft und Forsten, 53107 Bonn, Germany. **Document type:** government publication.

639.2 551.46   JA
JAPAN SEA REGIONAL FISHERIES RESEARCH INSTITUTE. BULLETIN/NIHONKAIKU SUISAN KENKYUJO KENKYU HOKOKU. (Text in Japanese, or English; abstracts in English) 1951. a. exchange basis. Japan Sea National Fisheries Research Institute, 5939-22, Suido-cho 1-chome, Niigata-shi, Niigata 951, Japan. TEL 25-228-0451. FAX 25-224-0950. TELEX NSK NG J 3122-171. Ed. Minoru Fujimoto. circ. 650. **Indexed:** Aqua.Sci.& Fish.Abstr., Biol.Abstr., Curr.Adv.Ecol.Sci., Deep Sea Res.& Oceanogr.Abstr., Helminthol.Abstr., Mar.Sci.Cont.Tab., Ocean.Abstr. **Document type:** bulletin.
—BLDSC (2593.830000).
Formerly (until 1990): Japan Sea Regional Fisheries Research Laboratory. Bulletin (ISSN 0021-4620)
Description: Covers marine biology, fisheries, oceanography and aquaculture.
Refereed Serial

JAPANESE JOURNAL OF ICHTHYOLOGY/GYORUIGAKU ZASSHI. see *BIOLOGY — Zoology*

639.2   JA   ISSN 0021-5392
SH1   CODEN: NSUGAF
JAPANESE SOCIETY OF SCIENTIFIC FISHERIES. BULLETIN/NIPPON SUISAN GAKKAISHI. (Text in English or Japanese; summaries in English) 1932. m. 15000 Yen. Japanese Society of Scientific Fisheries - Nihon Suisan Gakkai, 4-5-7 Konan, Minato-ku, Tokyo 108, Japan. TEL 81-3-3371-2165. Ed. Chiaki Koizumi. adv.; index. circ. 4,300. (reprint service avail. from UMI) **Indexed:** Anim.Breed.Abstr., Biol.Abstr., Cadscan, Chem.Abstr., Curr.Adv.Ecol.Sci., Curr.Cont., Deep Sea Res.& Oceanogr.Abstr., Food Sci.& Tech.Abstr., Geo.Abstr., GeoRef., Helminthol.Abstr., Ind.Vet., Lead Abstr., Nutr.Abstr., Ocean.Abstr., Pollut.Abstr., Rev.Med.& Vet.Mycol., Sci.Cit.Ind., Sel.Water Res.Abstr., Vet.Bull., Zincscan.
—BLDSC (2594.000000); UnCover; SWETS; CASDDS. **CCC**.

639.2   US   ISSN 1045-4438
SH1   CODEN: JAAQEH
JOURNAL OF APPLIED AQUACULTURE. 1991. q. $28 to individuals; institutions $48; libraries $75. Haworth Press, Inc., Food Products Press, 10 Alice St., Binghamton, NY 13904. TEL 607-722-1695. FAX 607-722-1424. Ed. Douglas Tave. (also avail. in microform from HAW; reprint service avail. from HAW) **Indexed:** Environ.Abstr. **Document type:** academic/scholarly publication.
—BLDSC (4939.940000); UnCover.
Description: Devoted to innovative research and ideas that will advance knowledge about the production, domestication, and husbandry of aquatic animals and plants.
Refereed Serial

639.2   II   ISSN 0970-0846
JOURNAL OF AQUACULTURE IN THE TROPICS. 1986. q. fl.125($70) (effective 1993). Oxford & I.B.H. Publishing Co. Pvt. Ltd., 66 Janpath, New Delhi 110 001, India. FAX 91-11-3322639. TELEX 3161990-AM-IN. (Co-published and distributed outside India by: A.A. Balkema, P.O. Box 1675, 3000 BR Rotterdam, Netherlands. TEL 31-10-4145822. FAX 31-10-4135947) Ed. A.A. Bose. Excerp.Med., Rice Abstr. **Document type:** academic/scholarly publication.
—BLDSC (4947.155000); UnCover; SWETS. **CCC**.
Description: International coverage of topics in aquaculture including fisheries science and technology, management of freshwater, brackish water and marine environments.
Refereed Serial

639.3   US   ISSN 0899-7659
                                                     CODEN: JAAHEO
JOURNAL OF AQUATIC ANIMAL HEALTH. 1989. q. $25 to members (foreign $28); libraries $400; foreign $425 (includes all society publications). American Fisheries Society, 5410 Grosvenor Ln., Ste. 110, Bethesda, MD 20814-2199. TEL 301-897-8616. FAX 301-897-8096. Ed. Wilmer A. Rogers. charts; illus.; stat.; index. circ. 1,500. (back issues avail.) **Indexed:** Environ.Abstr.
—BLDSC (4947.156800); UnCover; SWETS. **CCC**.
Description: Carries research papers on the causes, effects, treatments and prevention of diseases, particularly of fish and shellfish.
Refereed Serial

JOURNAL OF AQUATIC FOOD PRODUCT TECHNOLOGY. see *FOOD AND FOOD INDUSTRIES*

639   UK   ISSN 0140-7775
                                                    CODEN: JFIDDI
JOURNAL OF FISH DISEASES. 1978. bi-m. £266 in Europe; elsewhere £293 ($437) (effective 1994). Blackwell Scientific Publications Ltd., Osney Mead, Oxford OX2 0EL, England. TEL 0865-240201. FAX 0865-721205. TELEX 83355-MEDBOK-G. Eds. R.J. Roberts, R. Wootten. adv.; bk.rev.; abstr.; bibl.; illus.; index. circ. 600. (also avail. in microform from UMI; back issues avail.; reprint service avail. from ISI) **Indexed:** ASCA, Biol.Abstr., Chem.Abstr., Curr.Adv.Biochem., Curr.Adv.Cancer Res., Curr.Adv.Genetics & Molec.Biol., Curr.Cont., Curr.Ref.Fish Res., Excerp.Med., Helminthol.Abstr., Ind.Sci.Rev., Ind.Vet., Ocean.Abstr., Protozool.Abstr., Rev.Med.& Vet.Mycol., Rev.Plant Path., Sci.Cit.Ind., Vet.Bull. **Document type:** academic/scholarly publication.
—BLDSC (4984.285000); Faxon; UnCover; SWETS; UMI; CASDDS. **CCC**.
Refereed Serial

FISH AND FISHERIES

639   CN   ISSN 0250-6408
SH1   CODEN: JNFSD2
JOURNAL OF NORTHWEST ATLANTIC FISHERY SCIENCE. 1964. s-a. Can.$10. Northwest Atlantic Fisheries Organization, P.O. Box 638, Dartmouth, NS B2Y 3Y9, Canada. TEL 902-469-9105. FAX 902-469-5729. TELEX 019-31475. Ed.Bd. Indexed: Biol.Abstr., Curr.Adv.Ecol.Sci., Deep Sea Res.& Oceanogr.Abstr., Geo.Abstr.
—BLDSC (5022.844800).
Formerly (until 1979): International Commission for the Northwest Atlantic Fisheries. Research Bulletin (ISSN 0074-2651)
Description: Original research papers on environmental, biological, ecological and fishery aspects of living marine resources and ecosystems in the Northwest Atlantic.

639   CH   ISSN 1018-7324
JOURNAL OF TAIWAN FISHERIES RESEARCH. (Text mainly in Chinese; occasionally in English) 1953. s-a. Taiwan Fisheries Research Institute, 199 Hou-Ih Rd., Keelung, Taiwan, Republic of China. TEL 886-2-462-8283. FAX 886-2-4629388. E-mail: GOVE554@TWNMOE10.EDU.TW. Ed. I-Chiu Liao. circ. 500.
—BLDSC (2772.070000).
Formerly (until 1992): Taiwan Fisheries Research Institute, Keelung. Bulletin. (ISSN 0253-8830)
Description: Focuses on marine fisheries, fishery biology, aquaculture, and marine food processing or technology.

639.2   DK   ISSN 0905-5215
KALAALLIT NUNAANI AALISAKKANIK MISISSUINERIT. UKIUMOORTUMIK NALUNAARUSIAQ. Danish edition: Fiskeriundersoegelser i Groenland. Aarsberetning (ISSN 0905-5193) (Text in Greenlandic) 1975. a. free. Groenlands Fiskeriundersoegelser, Tagensvej 135-1, 2200 Copenhagen N, Denmark. FAX 45-35-821850. Ed. Finn O. Kapel. **Document type:** corporate report.
Former titles (until 1988): Aalisakkanik Pinngortitamillu Avatangiisimik Kalaallit Nunanni; (until 1982): Kalaallit Nunaata Imartaant Aalisarneq Aalisarnikkullu Mississuisut; (until 1979): Aulisarneq Ama Aulisagkanik Misigssuineq Kalatdlit Nunane (ISSN 0108-8645)

639   FI   ISSN 0085-2449
KALAMIES. (Text mainly in Finnish; occasionally in Swedish) 1951. 10/yr. FIM 85. Suomen Kalamiesten Keskusliitto - Finlands Fritidsfiskares Centralfoerbund (Finnish Recreational Fishers' Central Organization), Svinhufvudsvaegen 11, 00570 Helsinki, Finland. TEL 0-6849022. FAX 0-6849904. Ed. Timo Seppaelae. adv.; bk.rev. circ. 74,000.

639.2   FI   ISSN 0357-8682
KALASTAJA. 5/yr. FIM 95. Kalatalouden Keskusliitto - Federation of Finnish Fisheries Associations, Koydenpunojankatu 7 B 23, 00180 Helsinki 18, Finland. TEL 358-0-640-126. FAX 358-0-608-309. Ed. Rauno Kostiainen. adv.; B&W page FIM 9900; trim 250 x 380; adv. contact: Jouko Poutanen. circ. 9,636 (controlled). **Document type:** monographic series.
Description: Directed to Finnish commercial fishermen.

639.2   AT   ISSN 0814-1487
CODEN: KCREEN
KAPALA CRUISE REPORT. 1971. irreg. free. New South Wales Department of Fisheries, Fisheries Research Institute, P.O. Box 21, Cronulla, N.S.W. 2230, Australia. FAX 02-527-8576. circ. 800. **Document type:** government publication.
Formerly (until 1983): F R C Kapala Cruise Report (ISSN 0727-4335)

639   TH   ISSN 0125-7978
KASETSART UNIVERSITY, BANGKOK, THAILAND. FACULTY OF FISHERIES. NOTES. (Text in English) 1965. irreg. exchange basis. Kasetsart University, Faculty of Fisheries, Bangkok 10900, Thailand. FAX 5795579. circ. 500. **Document type:** academic/scholarly publication.

639.34   JA
KEIKYU ABURATSUBO MARIN PAKU SUIZOKUKAN NENPO/KEIKYU ABURATSUBO MARINE PARK AQUARIUM. ANNUAL REPORT. (Text in English, Japanese) 1968. a. Keikyu Aburatsubo Marin Paku, 1082 Koajiro Jonouchi, Misakicho, Miura-shi, Kanagawa-ken 238-02, Japan.

639   KE
KENYA FISHERIES REPORTS. irreg. Ministry of Tourism and Wildlife, Box 30027, Nairobi, Kenya.

639.2   KO
KOREAN FISHERIES SOCIETY. BULLETIN. (Text in English, French or Korean) 1968. bi-m. 10000 Won($15) Korean Fisheries Society, c/o National Fisheries University of Busan, Namgu, Pusan 608-737, S. Korea. FAX 051-6264158. Ed. Dr. Sing Yun Hong. adv. circ. 700. (back issues avail.) Indexed: Aqua.Sci.& Fish.Abstr., Biol.Abstr., Chem.Abstr., Deep Sea Res.& Oceanogr.Abstr., Food Sci.& Tech.Abstr., INIS Atomind., Nutr.Abstr.

597 574.5   KU   ISSN 0250-362X
CODEN: KBMSDW
KUWAIT BULLETIN OF MARINE SCIENCE. (Not published 1990-1993) (Text and summaries in Arabic and English) 1979. irreg. free. Kuwait Institute for Scientific Research, Mariculture and Fisheries Department, Library, P.O. Box 1638, Salmiya, Kuwait. TEL 965-575-1984. FAX 965-571-1293. Ed. M.S. Abdulla. charts; illus.; stat.; cum.index; circ. 700 (controlled). (back issues avail.) **Indexed:** Aqua.Sci.& Fish.Abstr., Biol.Abstr., Deep Sea Res.& Oceanogr.Abstr. **Document type:** academic/scholarly publication.
—BLDSC (5131.920000).
Description: General marine science with a regional focus.

KYOTO FURITSU KAIYO SENTA JIGYO GAIYO/KYOTO INSTITUTE OF OCEANIC AND FISHERY SCIENCE. REPORT. see *EARTH SCIENCES* — *Oceanography*

KYOTO FURITSU KAIYO SENTA KENKYU HOKOKU/KYOTO INSTITUTE OF OCEANIC AND FISHERY SCIENCE. BULLETIN. see *EARTH SCIENCES* — *Oceanography*

KYOTO FURITSU KAIYO SENTA KENKYU RONBUN/KYOTO INSTITUTE OF OCEANIC AND FISHERY SCIENCE. SPECIAL REPORT. see *EARTH SCIENCES* — *Oceanography*

639.2 591   JA   ISSN 0453-0314
SH301
KYUSHU DAIGAKU NOGAKUBU SUISANGAKKA GYOSEKISHU/KYUSHU UNIVERSITY. CONTRIBUTIONS FROM THE DEPARTMENT OF FISHERIES AND THE FISHERY RESEARCH LABORATORY. (Text in English, Japanese) 1942. a. exchange basis. Kyushu University, Department of Fisheries - Kyushu Daigaku Nogakubu Suisan Gakka, 3575-1 Hakozaki, Higashi-ku, Fukuoka 812, Japan. TEL 092-641-1101. FAX 092-641-2928.

LOUISIANA COASTAL LAW; coastal zone management, marine resource law, and environmental law related to coastal and marine issues. see *LAW*

LOUISIANA STATE UNIVERSITY. SCHOOL OF FORESTRY, WILDLIFE AND FISHERIES. RESEARCH REPORTS. see *FORESTS AND FORESTRY*

639.2   MW
MALAWI. FISHERIES DEPARTMENT. FISHERIES BULLETIN. 1971. irreg. Fisheries Department, Ministry of Agriculture and Natural Resources, Capital City, Box 30134, Lilongwe 3, Malawi. illus.

639.2   MY   ISSN 0126-8856
SH307.M3
MALAYSIA. MINISTRY OF AGRICULTURE. FISHERIES DIVISION. ANNUAL FISHERIES STATISTICS/MALAYSIA. KEMENTERIAN PERTANIAN. BAHAGIAN PERIKANAN. PERANGKAAN TAHUNAN PERIKANAN. (Text in English and Malay) 1954. a. M.$10. Ministry of Agriculture, Department of Fisheries, Jln. Sultan Salahuddin, 50628 Kuala Lumpur, Malaysia. TEL 2982011. FAX 2910305. TELEX KL FISH 28157. Ed. Rabihah Mahmood. illus. circ. 500.
Description: Provides data and information on the fisheries sector of Malaysia.

MALAYSIA. MINISTRY OF AGRICULTURE. TECHNICAL AND GENERAL BULLETINS. see *AGRICULTURE*

639.2   CU   ISSN 0025-2735
SH1
MAR Y PESCA; la revista del hombre de mar. (Text in Spanish; tables of contents in English and French) 1957. m. $20 in N. America; S. America $26; Europe $29; elsewhere $41. (Instituto Nacional de la Pesca de Cuba) Ediciones Cubanas, Obispo No. 527, Aptdo. 605, Havana, Cuba. TEL 7-60-4569. Dir. Arnaldo Nunez. bibl.; charts; illus.; stat. circ. 42,000. Indexed: Biol.Abstr., Deep Sea Res.& Oceanogr.Abstr.

639   FR
MARCHES DE LA MER. 5/yr. 9 rue Labie, 75017 Paris, France. TEL 45-74-21-62. FAX 40-26-37-11. TELEX 640 279 F. Ed. Georges Golan. circ. 5,000.
Description: Covers the distribution and commercialization of sea and river products.

639.2   FR   ISSN 0025-2905
MAREE DE FRANCE. 1949. m. 150 F. Editions Max Brezol, 9 rue Labie, 75838 Paris Cedex 17, France. Ed. Francis Luzin. adv.; bk.rev.; bibl.; illus.; stat.; tr.lit. circ. 12,000. (looseleaf format)

639.2   FR
LE MARIN. 1946. w. 650 F. Le Marin, 35051 Rennes Cedex, France. TEL 99-32-62-98. FAX 99-32-64-42. Ed. M. Tarin. adv. circ. 25,000.
Description: Covers economic, technological, commercial and cultural aspects of the fishing and shipping industry.

MARINE BEHAVIOUR AND PHYSIOLOGY. SECTIONS A & B. see *BIOLOGY*

639   LY
MARINE BIOLOGY RESEARCH CENTRE. BULLETIN. 1980. a. Marine Biology Research Centre, P.O. Box 30830, Tajura, Libya. Indexed: Curr.Adv.Ecol.Sci.

MARINE BULLETIN. see *CONSERVATION*

551.46   US
MARINE FISH MANAGEMENT. 1975. m. $87.50 (foreign $92.50). Nautilus Press, Inc., 1201 National Press Bldg., Washington, DC 20045. TEL 202-347-6543. Ed. John R. Botzum. (looseleaf format; back issues avail.) **Document type:** newsletter.
Description: Reports on U.S. fisheries policies in the U.S. 200-mile zone.

639.2   US   ISSN 0090-1830
SH11   CODEN: MFSRA4
MARINE FISHERIES REVIEW. 1939. q. $7 (foreign $8.75). U.S. National Marine Fisheries Service, Scientific Publications Office, 7600 Sandpoint Way, N.E., Bin C15700, Seattle, WA 98115. TEL 206-526-6107. FAX 206-526-6426. (Subscr. to: Supt. of Documents, U.S. Government Printing Office, Washington, DC 20402. TEL 202-783-3238. FAX 202-512-2233) Ed. Willis Hobart. bk.rev.; abstr.; charts; illus.; mkt.; stat.; index. circ. 2,000. (also avail. in microfiche from NTI; microfiche from CIS; reprint service avail. from CIS) Indexed: Amer.Stat.Ind. (1975-1985), Biol.Abstr., Bus.Ind., Chem.Abstr., Curr.Adv.Ecol.Sci., Curr.Cont., Curr.Ref.Fish Res., Environ.Abstr., Food Sci.& Tech.Abstr., Geo.Abstr, Helminthol.Abstr., Ind.Sci.Rev., Ind.U.S.Gov.Per., INIS Atomind., Mid.East: Abstr.& Ind., Nutr.Abstr., Ocean.Abstr., Vet.Bull. **Document type:** academic/scholarly publication, government publication.
—BLDSC (5375.330000); Faxon; UnCover; SWETS; UMI.
Formerly: Commercial Fisheries Review (ISSN 0010-2989)
Description: Contains articles, reports, and notes on the science, engineering, and economics of commercial and recreational fisheries. Includes marine mammal studies and aquaculture and examines U.S. and foreign fisheries developments.

639.2   US   ISSN 0161-522X
SH328   CODEN: MRFIEY
MARINE RECREATIONAL FISHERIES. 1976. a. $15. Sport Fishing Institute, 1010 Massachusetts Ave., N.W., Ste. 320, Washington, DC 20001. TEL 202-898-0770. Ed. Henry Clepper. circ. 1,500. (back issues avail.)
—BLDSC (5377.900000).

FISH AND FISHERIES

639 551.46 — US
MARINE RESOURCE BULLETIN; a sea grant advisory service. 1968. q. free. Virginia Institute of Marine Science, Gloucester Point, VA 23062.
TEL 804-642-7175. circ. 6,500.
Formerly: Marine Resource Information Bulletin.

639 — IE — ISSN 0791-1548
MARINE TIMES; newspaper to the Irish fishing industry. m. I£11 (foreign I£13). St. Catherines Rd., Killybegs, Co. Donegal, Ireland. TEL 073-31239. FAX 073-31822. Ed. Aidan O'Connell. bk.rev. circ. 3,500. **Document type:** newspaper, trade publication.

MARITIME STUDIES. see TRANSPORTATION — Ships And Shipping

MARLIN; the international sportfishing magazine. see SPORTS AND GAMES — Boats And Boating

639 — NO
ME'A. 1946. m. NOK 100. Norges Fiskarlag, Postboks 519, 7001 Trondheim, Norway. Ed. Martin Dahle. adv.

639.2 — DK
MEDDELELSER FRA FERSKVANDSFISKERILABORATORIET. 1979. irreg. price varies. Institut for Ferskvandsfiskeri og Fiskepleje, Ferskvandsfiskerilaboratoriet, Lysbrogade 52, DK-8600 Silkeborg, Denmark.
TEL 68-81-47-22. FAX 96-80-35-53. circ. 300. **Indexed:** Deep Sea Res.& Oceanogr.Abstr., Geo.Abstr.
Formerly: Danmarks Fiskeri- og Havundersoegelser. Ferskvandsfiskerilaboratoriet. Meddelelser. (ISSN 0108-4844)

639 — JA
MIE UNIVERSITY. FACULTY OF FISHERIES. JOURNAL. (Text in English and Japanese; summaries in English) 1950. a. exchange basis. Mie Daigaku, Suisan Gakubu - Mie University, Faculty of Fisheries, 2-80 Edobashi, Tsu-shi, Mie-ken 514, Japan. circ. controlled. **Indexed:** Biol.Abstr., Ind.Vet., Nutr.Abstr., Protozool.Abstr., Vet.Bull.
Formerly: Mie Prefectural University. Faculty of Fisheries. Bulletin (ISSN 0539-998X)

639 — US
MINNESOTA FISHERIES INVESTIGATIONAL REPORTS.
1958. irreg. free to qualified personnel. Department of Natural Resources, Division of Fish and Wildlife, 500 Lafayette Rd., St. Paul, MN 55155-4012. TEL 612-296-3325. FAX 612-297-4916. Ed. P.J. Wingate. **Indexed:** Biol.Abstr.
Former titles: Minnesota Fisheries Investigations (ISSN 0076-9150); Minnesota Fish and Game Investigations. Fish Series.

353.9 — US — ISSN 0733-2017
QL84.22.M7
MISSISSIPPI. DEPARTMENT OF WILDLIFE CONSERVATION. ANNUAL REPORT. a. Department of Wildlife Conservation, Box 451, Jackson, MS 39205. TEL 601-961-5310.
Former titles: Mississippi. Department of Wildlife Conservation. Annual Report to the Regular Session of the Mississippi Legislature (ISSN 0731-4221); Mississippi. State Game and Fish Commission. Annual Report to the Regular Session of the Mississippi Legislature (ISSN 0098-7840)

639.2 — AT — ISSN 0026-7732
MODERN FISHING. 1969. m. Aus.$47. Federal Publishing Company, 140 Bourke Rd., Alexandria, N.S.W. 2015, Australia. Ed. Glen Booth. adv.; bk.rev.; charts; illus. circ. 19,400. (processed) **Indexed:** Pinpointer.
Description: Covers all types of fishing including bieach, rock, river and boat.

639.2 — CI — ISSN 0027-1209
MORSKO RIBARSTVO/MARINE FISHERIES; jugoslavenski strucno-popularni casopis za pitanja ribarske privrede na moru. 1949. q. 40000 din.($12) Poslovna Zajednica Morskog Ribarstva, Park Narodnog Heroja V. Vlahovica 6, Zagreb, Croatia. Ed. Franko Stipkovic. adv. circ. 1,300.

639 — CN — ISSN 0704-4798
SH1
N A F O ANNUAL REPORT. 1951. a. price varies. Northwest Atlantic Fisheries Organization, P.O. Box 638, Dartmouth, NS B2Y 3Y9, Canada. TEL 902-469-9105. FAX 902-469-5729. TELEX 019-31475. Ed. L. Chepel. **Indexed:** Biol.Abstr.
Former titles (until 1980): International Commission for the Northwest Atlantic Fisheries. Annual Report (ISSN 0303-4151); International Commission for the Northwest Atlantic Fisheries. Annual Proceedings (ISSN 0074-2627)
Description: Administrative report with summaries of meetings.

639 — CN — ISSN 0250-7811
SH344.8.B6
N A F O LIST OF FISHING VESSELS. triennial. price varies. Northwest Atlantic Fisheries Organization, P.O. Box 638, Dartmouth, N.S. B2Y 3Y9, Canada. TEL 902-469-9105. FAX 902-469-5729. TELEX 019-31475. circ. controlled. (also avail. in microfiche from CIS) **Indexed:** IIS.
Formerly (until 1980): International Commission for the Northwest Atlantic Fisheries. List of Fishing Vessels (ISSN 0074-2635)
Description: Information on fishing vessels (over 50 GRT) of various countries which fish in the Northwest Atlantic.

639 — CN — ISSN 0250-6416
SH213.5
N A F O SCIENTIFIC COUNCIL REPORTS. a. price varies. Northwest Atlantic Fisheries Organization, P.O. Box 638, Dartmouth, NS B2Y 3Y9, Canada. TEL 902-469-9105. FAX 902-469-5729. TELEX 019-31475. Ed. T. Amaratunga. **Indexed:** Biol.Abstr.
—BLDSC (8178.200000).
Formerly (until 1980): International Commission for the Northwest Atlantic Fisheries. Redbook (ISSN 0074-2643)
Description: Edited reports of the council's meetings.

639 — CN — ISSN 0250-6432
SH213.5
N A F O SCIENTIFIC COUNCIL STUDIES. 1980. irreg. price varies. Northwest Atlantic Fisheries Organization, P.O. Box 638, Dartmouth, NS B2Y 3Y9, Canada. TEL 902-469-9105. FAX 902-469-5729. TELEX 019-31475. Ed. T. Amaratunga. **Indexed:** Biol.Abstr.
—BLDSC (8178.220000).
Formerly (until 1980): International Commission for the Northwest Atlantic Fisheries. Selected Papers (ISSN 0380-4933)
Description: Fishery research papers for the scientific community.

639.2 591 — PH — ISSN 0116-290X
N A G A: I C L A R M QUARTERLY. 1978. q. $20. International Center for Living Aquatic Resources Management, M.C.P.O. Box 2631, 0718 Makati, Metro Manila, Philippines. TEL 2-818-0466. FAX 2-816-3183. TELEX 64794-ICLARM-PN. Ed. Jay L. Maclean. bk.rev.; bibl.; stat. circ. 3,500. (back issues avail.) **Indexed:** Curr.Tit.Ocean.
—BLDSC (6013.240050).
Formerly (until 1986): I C L A R M Newsletter (ISSN 0115-4575)
Description: Carries news and articles on tropical aquatic resource research.

NANSEIKAI BUROKKU KAIYO KENKYUKAI HOKOKU/SOCIETY OF NANSEI NATIONAL FISHERIES RESEARCH INSTITUTE. JOURNAL. see EARTH SCIENCES — Oceanography

639.2 — US — ISSN 1043-299X
SH11 — CODEN: FEDSEM
NATIONAL FISH HATCHERY SYSTEM. FISH AND FISH EGG DISTRIBUTION REPORT. 1872. a. free. U.S. Fish and Wildlife Service, Division of Fish Hatcheries, Dept. of the Interior, 1849 C St., Washington, DC 20240. TEL 202-653-7581. stat. circ. 1,275.
Formerly (until 1986): Propagation and Distribution of Fishes from National Fish Hatcheries for the Fiscal Year (ISSN 0197-4106)

NATIONAL FISHERIES UNIVERSITY OF PUSAN. INSTITUTE OF MARINE SCIENCES. CONTRIBUTIONS. see BIOLOGY

639.2 — US — ISSN 0027-9250
SH1
NATIONAL FISHERMAN. 1904. 12/yr. $22.95. Journal Publications (Rockland), Box 908, Rockland, ME 04841-0908. TEL 207-594-6222. FAX 207-594-8978. (Subscr. to: National Fisherman, Subscription Service Department, Box 52549, Boulder CO 80322-2549) Ed. James W. Fullilove. adv.; bk.rev.; illus.; stat. circ. 44,000. (tabloid format; also avail. in microform from UMI; back issues avail.; reprint service avail. from UMI) **Indexed:** Bus.Ind., Ocean.Abstr., Pollut.Abstr., Tr.& Indus.Ind.
—UnCover; UMI.
Combined with: Maine Coast Fisherman.
Description: Trade magazine for commercial fishermen, boatbuilders and gear suppliers.

639.3 — JA — ISSN 0389-5858
SH109 — CODEN: YKHKDU
NATIONAL RESEARCH INSTITUTE OF AQUACULTURE. BULLETIN/TANSUI-KU SUISAN KENKYUJO KENKYU HOKOKU. (Text in English or Japanese; summaries in English) 1952. s-a. exchange basis. National Research Institute of Aquaculture - Tansui-ku Suisan Kenkyujo, c/o Library, Nansei, Mie-ken 516-01, Japan. FAX 05996-6-1962. Ed.Bd. charts. circ. 1,000. **Indexed:** AGRINDEX, Anim.Breed.Abstr., Aqua.Sci.& Fish.Abstr., Biol.Abstr., Deep Sea Res.& Oceanogr.Abstr., Excerp.Med., Ind.Vet., Nutr.Abstr., Sel.Water Res.Abstr., Vet.Bull.
—BLDSC (2643.210000); CASDDS.
Formerly (until 1979): Freshwater Fisheries Research Laboratory, Tokyo. Bulletin (ISSN 0049-4054)

639.7 597 333.91 — JA
NATIONAL RESEARCH INSTITUTE OF FAR SEAS FISHERIES. BULLETIN. (Text in English, Japanese) 1969. a. Fisheries Agency, National Research Institute of Far Seas Fisheries, 5-7-1 Orido, Shimizu 424, Japan. TEL 0543-34-0715. FAX 0543-35-9642. TELEX 03965689 FARSEA J. **Indexed:** Biol.Abstr., Curr.Adv.Ecol.Sci., Deep Sea Res.& Oceanogr.Abstr., Helminthol.Abstr. **Document type:** bulletin.
—BLDSC (2643.225000).
Formerly (until 1990): Far Seas Fisheries Research Laboratory. Bulletin (ISSN 0386-7285)

639.3 597 — JA
NATIONAL RESEARCH INSTITUTE OF FAR SEAS FISHERIES. S SERIES. (Text in English, Japanese) irreg. Fisheries Agency, National Research Institute of Far Seas Fisheries, 5-7-1 Orido, Shimizu 424, Japan. TEL 0543-34-0715. FAX 0543-35-9642. TELEX 03965689 FARSEA J. **Indexed:** Biol.Abstr.
Formerly (until 1990): Far Seas Fisheries Research Laboratory. S Series.

639.3 — CH
NATIONAL TAIWAN UNIVERSITY. INSTITUTE OF FISHERY BIOLOGY. REPORT. (Text and summaries in Chinese or English) 1956. irreg. (approx. biennial). exchange basis. National Taiwan University, Institute of Fishery Biology, Taipei, Taiwan 107, Republic of China. (back issues avail.) **Indexed:** Biol.Abstr.

353.9 — US — ISSN 0092-1696
SH35.N2
NEBRASKA. FISHERIES DIVISION. ANNUAL REPORT.
1971. a. Game and Parks Commission, Fisheries Division, Box 30370, Lincoln, NE 68503. TEL 402-471-0641. illus. **Document type:** government publication.

639 — CN — ISSN 0845-5562
NEW BRUNSWICK. DEPARTMENT OF FISHERIES AND AQUACULTURE. ANNUAL REPORT. (Text in English and French) 1964. a. free. Department of Fisheries and Aquaculture, Box 6000, Fredericton, NB E3B 5H1, Canada. TEL 506-453-2251. FAX 506-453-5210. **Document type:** government publication.
Formerly: New Brunswick. Department of Fisheries. Annual Report (ISSN 0077-8036)

NEW SOUTH WALES. DEPARTMENT OF AGRICULTURE. ANNUAL REPORT. see AGRICULTURE

FISH AND FISHERIES

639.2   AT   CODEN: FBNFEC
NEW SOUTH WALES FISHERIES. FISHERIES BULLETIN. 1984. irreg. price varies. N.S.W. Fisheries, Locked Bag 9, Pyrmont, N.S.W. 2009, Australia. TEL 02-566-7800. FAX 02-692-8299. Ed. P. Crew. circ. 750.
    Former titles: New South Wales. Department of Fisheries. Fisheries Bulletin; New South Wales. Department of Agriculture. Fisheries Bulletin (ISSN 0814-0545)
    Description: Discusses soundly designed and executed fisheries programs.

639.2   NZ   ISSN 0113-227X
NEW ZEALAND FISHERIES OCCASIONAL PUBLICATION. 1967. irreg. Ministry of Agriculture and Fisheries, Fisheries Greta Point, P.O. Box 297, Wellington, New Zealand. FAX 04-386-0574. (back issues avail.) **Indexed:** Deep Sea Res.& Oceanogr.Abstr.
    Supersedes in part (in 1987): New Zealand. Ministry of Agriculture and Fisheries. Fisheries Research Division Occasional Publication (ISSN 0110-1765)
    Description: Contains bibliographies and conference proceedings and monographs of various aspects of fisheries science.

639.3   NZ   ISSN 0113-2261
CODEN: NZFBEC
NEW ZEALAND FISHERIES RESEARCH BULLETIN. irreg. price varies. Ministry of Agriculture and Fisheries, Fisheries Greta Point, P.O. Box 297, Wellington, New Zealand. FAX 04-386-0574. illus. (back issues avail.) **Indexed:** Biol.Abstr. **Document type:** monographic series.
    Formerly: New Zealand. Ministry of Agriculture and Fisheries. Fisheries Research Division. Bulletin (ISSN 0110-1749)
    Description: Monographs on various aspects of fisheries science.

639.3   NZ   ISSN 0113-2180
NEW ZEALAND FISHERIES TECHNICAL REPORT. irreg. price varies. Ministry of Agriculture and Fisheries, Fisheries Greta Point, P.O. Box 297, Wellington, New Zealand. FAX 04-386-0574. (back issues avail.)
    Supersedes in part (in 1987): New Zealand. Ministry of Agriculture and Fisheries. Fisheries Research Division Occasional Publication (ISSN 0110-1765)
    Description: Reports on trawl surveys and other fisheries investigations in New Zealand waters.

NEW ZEALAND MARINE SCIENCES SOCIETY REVIEW. see *BIOLOGY*

639.2   NR
NIGERIA. FEDERAL DEPARTMENT OF FISHERIES. FEDERAL FISHERIES OCCASIONAL PAPER. (Continues occasional paper issued by the Dept. of Fisheries Research of Nigeria) 1969. irreg., latest 1974. price varies. Federal Department of Fisheries, P.M.B. 12529, Lagos, Nigeria. **Indexed:** Biol.Abstr.

639.3   SW   ISSN 1100-4096
SH287   CODEN: NJFREG
NORDIC JOURNAL OF FRESHWATER RESEARCH. (Text in English) 1933. a., no.68, 1993. SEK 250. Institute of Freshwater Research, S-178 93 Drottningholm, Sweden. FAX 46-87590338. Eds. Torbjoern Jaervi, Magnus Appelberg. circ. 1,800. **Indexed:** Anim.Breed.Abstr., Biol.Abstr., Curr.Adv.Ecol.Sci., Geo.Abstr., Sel.Water Res.Abstr. **Document type:** academic/scholarly publication.
—BLDSC (6117.926150); UnCover.
    Former titles (until vol.64, 1988): Institute of Freshwater Research, Drottningholm. Report (ISSN 0082-0032); (until vol.29, 1949): Meddelanden fraan Statens Undersoeknings- och Foersoeksanstalt foer Soetvattensfisket.
    Description: Concerned with all aspects of freshwater research in the northern hemisphere including anadromous and catadromous species. Specific topics covered include: ecology, ethology, evolution, genetics and limnology.

639.2 799.1   NO
NORSK FISKARALMANAKK. 1903. a. NOK 280. (Selskabet for de Norske Fiskeriers Fremme) A-S Nordanger Forlag, P.O. Box 731, N-5001 Bergen, Norway. TEL 47-55-31-13-11. FAX 47-55-31-13-13. adv. circ. 7,000. **Document type:** trade publication.
    Description: Prints information for Norwegian fishermen to help them with their daily tasks on board.

639.2   NO   ISSN 0803-5822
NORSK FISKEINDUSTRI. 1975. 8/yr. NOK 200 in Scandinavia; elsewhere NOK 400. Fiskerinaeringens Landsforening, Skippergt. 35-39, N-9005 Tromsoe, Norway. TEL 47-77-65-80-33. FAX 47-77-65-54-97. Ed. Eigill Fareth. adv.; bk.rev.; circ. 1,451 (controlled). **Document type:** trade publication.
    Former titles (until 1991): Fiskeindustrien & Fiskeprodusenten.

639.2   US   ISSN 0275-5947
SH221   CODEN: NAJMDP
NORTH AMERICAN JOURNAL OF FISHERIES MANAGEMENT. 1981. q. $30 (foreign $30) to members; libraries $400 (foreign $425) (includes all journals of the American Fisheries Society). American Fisheries Society, 5410 Grosvenor Ln., Ste. 110, Bethesda, MD 20814-2199. TEL 301-897-8616. FAX 301-897-8096. Eds. Phyllis Cahn, Steve Miranda. charts; illus.; stat.; index. circ. 3,300. (back issues avail.) **Indexed:** Aqua.Sci.& Fish.Abstr., Biol.Abstr., Chem.Abstr., Curr.Adv.Ecol.Sci., Curr.Cont., Deep Sea Res.& Oceanogr.Abstr., Environ.Abstr., Ind.Vet., Sel.Water Res.Abstr., Vet.Bull., W.R.C.Inf.
—BLDSC (6148.169000); Faxon; UnCover; SWETS. CCC.
    Description: Addresses the maintenance, enhancement, and allocation of fisheries resources. Its contents chronicle the development of practical monitoring and management programs for marine and freshwater fisheries.
Refereed Serial

639   CN
SH219.5.I5
NORTH PACIFIC ANADROMOUS FISH COMMISSION. ANNUAL REPORT. (Editions in English and Japanese) 1954. a. available on exchange. International North Pacific Fisheries Commission, 6640 N.W. Marine Dr., Vancouver, B.C. V6T 1X2, Canada. TEL 604-228-1128. FAX 604-228-1135. circ. 1,000. (also avail. in microfiche from CIS) **Indexed:** Aqua.Sci.& Fish.Abstr., Biol.Abstr., IIS, Ocean.Abstr.
    Former titles (until 1993): International North Pacific Fisheries Commission. Annual Report (ISSN 0074-7165); (until 1955): International North Pacific Fisheries Commission. Report of Meeting (ISSN 0258-5790)

639   US   ISSN 0094-128X
SH11
NORTHEAST PACIFIC PINK AND CHUM SALMON WORKSHOP. PROCEEDINGS. Key Title: Proceedings of the Northeast Pacific Pink Salmon Workshop. quadrennial. Department of Fish and Game, Division of Commercial Fisheries, Box 3-2000, Juneau, AK 99802-2000. TEL 907-465-4293. illus. **Document type:** proceedings.

639.2   CN   ISSN 1183-2428
SH33
NORTHERN AQUACULTURE. 1985. bi-m. Can.$20. Harrison House Publishers, 4611 William Head Rd., R.R. 1, Victoria, BC V9B 5T7, Canada. TEL 604-478-9209. FAX 604-478-1184. Ed. Peter Chettleburgh. adv. contact: Peter Chettleburgh. bk.rev. circ. 3,000. **Document type:** trade publication.
—BLDSC (6150.470000); UnCover.
    Formerly: Canadian Aquaculture (ISSN 0832-722X)

NORTHERN TERRITORY. DEPARTMENT OF PRIMARY INDUSTRY AND FISHERIES. AGNOTES. see *AGRICULTURE — Agricultural Economics*

639   NO
NORWAY. FISKERIDIREKTORATET. FISKEFLAATEN. (Subseries of Aarsberetning Vedkommende Norges Fiskerier) 1952. a. free. Fiskeridirektoratet - Directorate of Fisheries, Box 185, 5002 Bergen, Norway. **Document type:** academic/scholarly publication.

639 574.92   NO   ISSN 0802-488X
NORWAY. FISKERIDIREKTORATET. HAVFORSKNINGSINSTITUTTET. AARSMELDING. 1950. a. Fiskeridirektoratet, Havforskningsinstituttet - Directorate of Fisheries, Institute of Marine Research, P.O. Box 1870, N-5024 Bergen Nordnes, Norway. TEL 47-55-23-85-00. FAX 47-55-23-85-31. Ed.Bd.

639 574.92   NO   ISSN 0015-3117
CODEN: FDSHAJ
NORWAY. FISKERIDIREKTORATET. SKRIFTER. SERIE HAVUNDERSOEKELSER. (Text in English and Norwegian; summaries in English) 1900. irreg., vol.18, no.10, 1990. exchange basis. Fiskeridirektoratet, Havforskningsinstituttet - Directorate of Fisheries, Institute of Marine Research, Box 1870-72 Nordnes, N-5024 Bergen, Norway. TEL 47-55-23-85-00. FAX 47-55-23-85-31. TELEX 42297 OCEAN N. **Indexed:** Aqua.Sci.& Fish.Abstr., B.R.I., Biol.Abstr., Ocean.Abstr.
—UMI.
    Description: Report on Norwegian fishery and marine investigations.

799.1   AU   ISSN 0029-9987
OESTERREICHS FISCHEREI; Zeitschrift fuer die gesamte Fischerei. 1948. 8/yr. S.330. Oesterreichischer Fischereiverband, Scharfling, A-5310 Mondsee, Austria. FAX 06232-384733. Ed. Albert Jagsch. adv.; bk.rev.; bibl.; charts; illus.; index. circ. 2,500. **Indexed:** Aqua.Sci.& Fish.Abstr., Protozool.Abstr. **Document type:** consumer publication, trade publication.
—BLDSC (6312.100000).
    Description: Publication for both commercial and sports fishermen. Looks at many aspects of sports and nature, and includes a calendar of events.

OSEANOLOGI DI INDONESIA. see *EARTH SCIENCES — Oceanography*

639.3   FR
OSTREICULTEUR FRANCAIS. 10/yr. Publisaintonge, B.P. 22, Route de la Tremblade, 17920 Breuillet, France. TEL 46-22-61-61. FAX 46-22-77-00. Ed. Henri Lagarde. circ. 5,000.
    Description: Studies oyster farming.

639.2   US   ISSN 0195-6515
SH221.5.N65
PACIFIC FISHING. 1980. m. $24 in the U.S.; Canada $29 (Can.$ 34); elsewhere $72. Salmon Bay Communications, 1515 N.W. 51st St., Seattle, WA 98107. TEL 206-789-5333. FAX 206-784-5545. Ed. Steve Shapiro. adv.; index. circ. 10,000. (back issues avail.) **Indexed:** Can.B.P.I. **Document type:** trade publication.
    Description: Serves commercial fishing industry including boat owners and fishermen, seafood processors, traders and retailers on the Pacific Coast of the U.S. and British Columbia, Canada.

639   CN   ISSN 0842-2702
SH346
PACIFIC SALMON COMMISSION. ANNUAL REPORT. 1937. a. free. Pacific Salmon Commission, 1155 Robson St., Ste. 600, Vancouver, BC V6E 1B5, Canada. TEL 604-684-8061. (also avail. in microfiche from CIS) **Indexed:** Biol.Abstr., IIS, Ocean.Abstr. **Document type:** government publication.
    Formerly (until 1986): International Pacific Salmon Fisheries Commission. Annual Report (ISSN 0074-7254)

639   US   ISSN 1057-2538
SH11.A55   CODEN: PFCRAP
PACIFIC STATES MARINE FISHERIES COMMISSION. ANNUAL REPORT. 1949. a. free. Pacific States Marine Fisheries Commission, 45 S.E. 82nd Dr. Ste. 100, Gladstone, OR 97027. TEL 503-650-5400. FAX 503-650-5426. Ed. Al Didier. circ. 1,050. **Indexed:** Biol.Abstr., Deep Sea Res.& Oceanogr.Abstr., Ocean.Abstr. **Document type:** corporate report.
    Formerly: Pacific Marine Fisheries Commission. Annual Report (ISSN 0078-7574)

639   US
PACIFIC STATES MARINE FISHERIES COMMISSION. NEWSLETTER. 1962. q. free. Pacific States Marine Fisheries Commission, 45 S.E. 82nd Dr., Ste. 100, Gladstone, OR 97027. TEL 503-650-5400. FAX 503-650-5426. Ed. Al Didier. **Document type:** newsletter.
    Formerly: Pacific Marine Fisheries Commission. Newsletter (ISSN 0078-7590)

FISH AND FISHERIES

639.2   PK   ISSN 1010-3562
HD9466.P3
PAKISTAN SEAFOOD DIGEST. (Text in English) 1987. bi-m. $80. Press Associates Pvt. Ltd., Press Centre, Shahrah-e-Kamal Attaturk, Karachi, Pakistan. TEL 219262. FAX 2637754. TELEX 23868 PPI PK. Ed. Owais Aslam Ali. adv.; bk.rev. circ. 5,000.
Document type: trade publication.
    Description: Provides information on the seafood industry, fisheries, and other aquatic resources. Includes data of commercial significance regarding seafood exports from Pakistan, and news of recent advancements in technology affecting all sectors of the fishing industry.

PAPUA NEW GUINEA JOURNAL OF AGRICULTURE, FORESTRY AND FISHERIES. see *AGRICULTURE*

639.2   FR   ISSN 0031-3718
PECHE ET LES POISSONS. 1939. m. 255 F. (La Peche) Gerpresse, 8 rue Pierre Brossolette, 92300 Levallois-Perret, France. TEL 40-87-40-85. Ed. D. Maury. adv.; illus.

639.2   FR   ISSN 0031-3726
PECHE MARITIME. 1919. bi-m. 580 F. (foreign 750 F.) Moreux, 190 Bd. Haussmann, 75008 Paris, France. TEL 44-95-99-50. TELEX 290 131. adv.; bk.rev.; bibl.; charts; illus.; mkt.; stat.; tr.lit.; index. **Indexed:** Chem.Abstr.
—BLDSC (6416.950000).
    Description: Covers commercial fishing industry in France and the rest of the world.

639.2   BE
PECHEUR BELGE. Flemish edition: Belgische Visser. (Text in French) 1940. 10/yr. 650 Fr. 37-C rue A. Leveque, 1400 Nivelles, Belgium. FAX 67-21-75-08. TELEX 57944. adv.; bk.rev. circ. 26,000.

639.2   PO
PESCA E NAVEGACAO. 12/yr. Rua Conde Redondo, 76 4o Esq., 1100 Lisbon, Portugal. TEL 554543. FAX 53-24-41. TELEX 65874 REVMAR P. Ed. J. Morao de Campos. circ. 120,000.
    Description: Covers fishing, processing, maritime equipment, aquaculture and shipping activities.

639.2 799.1   IT
PESCA NOTIZIE. 1975. 6/yr. free. A.N.C.P., Via Guattani 13, 00161 Rome, Italy. TEL 6-844-393-51. FAX 6-844-39-50. TELEX 611346 LEGA. Ed. Ettore Iani. circ. 5,000.
Document type: corporate report.

639.2   US   ISSN 0258-5812
PESCA Y MARINA. (Text in Spanish) 1948. bi-m. $40 for 2 yrs. Editorial Pesca y Marina S.A., 2464 33rd Ave. W., Ste. 102, Seattle, WA 98199. TEL 206-285-3200. Ed. Guillermo Fisch. adv.; bk.rev.; charts; illus.; stat.; tr.lit. circ. 10,000. (also avail. in microform from UMI; reprint service avail. from UMI) **Indexed:** Biol.Abstr.

639.2   IT   ISSN 0394-2929
PESCE. 1984. 6/yr. L.30000 (foreign L.50000) (effective 1993). Pubblicita Italia s.a.s., Via Taglio 24, 41100 Modena, Italy. TEL 59-21-66-88. FAX 59-22-07-27. Ed. Onelio Benedetti. adv.; bk.rev.

639   PH   ISSN 0031-7543
PHILIPPINE FISHING JOURNAL. 1963. m. Business Masters International, 55 U.E. Tech. Avenue, University Hills, Subdivision Malabon, Rizal, Philippines. Ed. Emerito B. Torio. adv.; charts; illus.

639   PH   ISSN 0048-377X
SH1
PHILIPPINE JOURNAL OF FISHERIES. 1951. s-a. $3 per no. Bureau of Fisheries and Aquatic Resources, 860 Arcadia Building, Quezon Ave., Box 623, Quezon City, Metro Manila, Philippines. Ed. Felix R. Gonzales. circ. 3,000. **Indexed:** Chem.Abstr., Deep Sea Res.& Oceanogr.Abstr., Geo.Abstr.

639.3   FR   ISSN 0048-4237
PISCICULTURE FRANCAISE; d'eau vive et d'etang saumatre et marine. 1965. q. 65 F. Federation Nationale des Pisciculteurs-Salmoniculteurs de France, 10 rue Milton, 75009 Paris, France. TEL 42-80-30-31. FAX 42-80-51-48. TELEX 283 713. Ed. Alain Nogier. adv.; charts; illus.; stat. circ. 2,000. **Indexed:** Forest.Abstr., Nutr.Abstr.

639.2   FR   ISSN 0986-5675
PLAISANCE MER ET PECHE; en Mediterranee. 1987. 4/yr. 70 Fr. Editions Kerfan, 97-103 Av. Denis Semeria, B.P. 19, 06230 St. Jean Cap Ferrat, France. Ed. Daniel Garnier Gouguenheim.

639   FR   ISSN 0995-7111
PORT ALLIANCE. 1989. 11/yr. Societe Havraise d'Edition et de Communication Portuaires, Quai George V, 76600 Le Havre, France. TEL 35-21-46-45. FAX 35-21-73-08. Ed. Patrick Houmard. circ. 3,000.

PORTOS E NAVIOS; revista tecnica e informativa. see *TRANSPORTATION — Ships And Shipping*

PORTUGAL. INSTITUTO PORTUGUES DE INVESTIGACAO MARITIMA. BOLETIM. see *BIOLOGY — Zoology*

PORTUGAL. INSTITUTO PORTUGUES DE INVESTIGACAO MARITIMA. PUBLICACOES AVULSAS. see *BIOLOGY — Zoology*

639.3   UK
PRACTICAL FISHKEEPING. 1978. m. E M A P Pursuit Publishing Ltd., Bretton Court, Bretton, Peterborough, Cambs. PE3 8DZ, England. TEL 0733-264666. FAX 0733-267198. Ed. Steve Windsor. adv.; bk.rev.; illus.; tr.lit.; circ. 41,604 (paid). **Document type:** consumer publication.

639   CN
PRINCE EDWARD ISLAND. DEPARTMENT OF AGRICULTURE, FISHERIES AND FORESTRY. ANNUAL REPORT. 1960. a. free. Department of Fisheries and Aquaculture, P.O. Box 2000, Charlottetown, PE C1A 7N8, Canada. TEL 902-368-5240. FAX 902-892-3420. charts; stat.
    Former titles: Prince Edward Island. Department of Fisheries and Aquaculture. Annual Report; Prince Edward Island. Department of Fisheries. Annual Report; (until 1985): Prince Edward Island. Department of Fisheries and Labor. Annual Report; Prince Edward Island. Department of Fisheries. Annual Report (ISSN 0079-5143)

639.2   SP
PRODUCTOS DEL MAR. 1988. bi-m. 11000 ptas. (Europe 16000 ptas., elsewhere 18000 ptas.). Publicaciones Tecnicas Alimentarias, S.A., Triana 52, bajo izda., 28016 Madrid, Spain. TEL 1-350-53-19. FAX 1-350-78-80. Dir. Carlos Ayala. circ. 5,000. (reprint service avail.)
    Description: Covers all areas of the fish industry, including aquaculture.

PRODUITS DE LA MER. see *FOOD AND FOOD INDUSTRIES — Grocery Trade*

639.2   AT   ISSN 0156-403X
PROFESSIONAL FISHERMAN. 1978. m. Aus.$70. Baird Publications Pty. Ltd., 10 Oxford St., South Yarra, Vic. 3141, Australia. TEL 03-826-8741. FAX 03-827-0704. Ed. Neil Baird. circ. 4,500.
    Description: Publishes news, boat reviews, new gear and equipment reports and feature articles of interest to all commercial fishermen in Australia, New Zealand and S.W. Pacific.

597 639.3   US   ISSN 0033-0779
SH34   CODEN: PFCUAY
PROGRESSIVE FISH-CULTURIST. 1938. q. $25 (foreign $28) to individuals; libraries $400 (foreign $425) (includes all journals of the American Fisheries Society). American Fisheries Society, 5410 Grosvenor Lane, Ste. 110, Bethesda, MD 20814-2199. TEL 301-897-8616. FAX 301-897-8096. Ed. Robert Piper. charts; illus.; stat.; index. circ. 2,800. (also avail. in microform from MIM,UMI; reprint service avail. from UMI) **Indexed:** Anim.Breed.Abstr., Aqua.Sci.& Fish.Abstr., Biol.Abstr., Chem.Abstr., Curr.Adv.Ecol.Sci., Curr.Cont., Deep Sea Res.& Oceanogr.Abstr., Environ.Abstr., Environ.Per.Bibl., Excerp.Med., Geo.Abstr., Helminthol.Abstr., Ind.U.S.Gov.Per., Ind.Vet., Nutr.Abstr., Ocean.Abstr., Pollut.Abstr., Sel.Water Res.Abstr., Sugar Ind.Abstr., Vet.Bull.
—BLDSC (6924.660000); Faxon; UnCover; SWETS; UMI; CASDDS. **CCC.**
    Description: Melds new research with practical experience to advance all aspects of intensive and extensive aquaculture - freshwater and marine, vertebrates and invertebrates.
Refereed Serial

639.2   GW   ISSN 0438-4555
SH1   CODEN: PFTEA3
PROTOKOLLE ZUR FISCHEREITECHNIK. (Text and summaries in English and German) 1962. irreg. price varies. Bundesforschungsanstalt fuer Fischerei, Informations- und Dokumentationsstelle, Palmaille 9, 22767 Hamburg, Germany. FAX 040-38905129. stat.; circ. 400 (controlled). **Indexed:** Aqua.Sci.& Fish.Abstr., Biol.Abstr., Deep Sea Res.& Oceanogr.Abstr. **Document type:** government publication.

574   PR
PUERTO RICO. FISHERIES RESEARCH LABORATORY. TECHNICAL REPORT. (Text and summaries in English and Spanish) 1969. irreg. free. C O D R E M A R, Apdo. 3665 Marina Station, Mayaguez, PR 00708. TEL 809-833-2023. FAX 809-833-2410. Dir. Walter Padilla. abstr.; bibl.; charts; illus.; stat.; index. **Document type:** government publication.
    Former titles: Puerto Rico. Fisheries Research Laboratory. Contributions; Puerto Rico. Department of Agriculture. Agricultural and Fisheries Contributions.

639.3   CN
QUEBEC (PROVINCE). MINISTERE DE L'AGRICULTURE, DES PECHERIES ET DE L'ALIMENTATION. COMPTE RENDU. 1977. irreg. Ministere de l'Agriculture, des Pecheries et de l'Alimentation, 96 Montee Sandy Beach, C.P. 1070, Gaspe, PQ G0C 1R0, Canada. TEL 418-368-7615. FAX 418-368-8400.
    Formerly: Quebec (Province). Ministere de l'Agriculture, des Pecheries et de l'Alimentation. Cahier Special d'Information.

QUICK FROZEN FOODS INTERNATIONAL. see *FOOD AND FOOD INDUSTRIES*

QUINAULT NATURAL RESOURCES. see *CONSERVATION*

639.2   NL   ISSN 1018-094X
REGIONAL TUNA BULLETIN. 1988. q. South Pacific Commission, B.P. D5, Noumea, Cedex, New Caledonia. TEL 26-2000. FAX 687-263818. TELEX 3139 NM SOPACOM. (also avail. in microfiche from CIS) **Indexed:** IIS. **Document type:** newsletter.

RENEWABLE RESOURCES JOURNAL. see *ENVIRONMENTAL STUDIES*

639   US   ISSN 0083-7555
SH1   CODEN: UWRFAY
RESEARCH IN FISHERIES. (Represents the School's Annual Report) 1958. biennial. free. University of Washington, School of Fisheries WH-10, Seattle, WA 98195. TEL 206-543-4678. FAX 206-685-7471. Ed. Marcus Duke. index; circ. 3,000 (controlled). **Indexed:** Biol.Abstr.

338.3   FR   ISSN 0078-6241
SH334
REVIEW OF FISHERIES IN O E C D MEMBER COUNTRIES. 1967. a. price varies. Organization for Economic Cooperation and Development, 2 rue Andre-Pascal, 75775 Paris Cedex 16, France. (U.S. orders to: O.E.C.D. Publications and Information Center, 2001 L St., N.W., Ste. 700, Washington, D.C. 20036-4910. TEL 202-785-6323) (also avail. in microfiche from OEC) **Indexed:** IIS.

REVIEWS IN FISH BIOLOGY AND FISHERIES. see *BIOLOGY — Zoology*

639   CU
REVISTA CUBANA DE INVESTIGACIONES PESQUERAS. BOLETINES BIBLIOGRAFICOS. 1953. 3/yr. exchange basis. Direccion de Ciencia y Tecnica, Ministerio de la Industria Pesquera, 5ta Avda. y 248 Barlovento, Santa Fe, Playa, Havana, Cuba. FAX 0511345. TELEX 0511444 MIP. Eds. Hertensia Obregon, Armando Perez Lopez. circ. 900 (controlled). **Indexed:** Aquacult.Abstr., Biol.Abstr.
    Former titles: Revista Cubana de Investigaciones Pesqueras (ISSN 0138-8452); (until vol.2, no.3, 1977): Centro de Investigaciones Pesqueras. Revista de Investigaciones; Supersedes (in 1975) Centro de Investigaciones Pesqueras. Contribuciones (ISSN 0067-4656)
    Description: Publishes original works on subjects related to the research of marine resources.

REVISTA DE BIOLOGIA MARINA. see *BIOLOGY*

639.2 BU
RIBNO STOPANSTVO. 1955. 8/yr. $11. (Ministerstvo na Zemedelieto i Khranitelna Promishlenost) Izdatelstvo Profizdat, 82, Dondukov Blvd., Sofia, Bulgaria. (Dist. by: Hemus, 6, Rouski Blvd., 1000 Sofia, Bulgaria) (Co-sponsor: Durzhavno Stroitelno Obedinenie Ribno Stopanstvo) Ed. T. Antonova. circ. 1,300. **Indexed:** Nutr.Abstr.

639.3 IC ISSN 0484-9019
SH293.I2 CODEN: RIFIAM
RIT FISKIDEILDAR/MARINE RESEARCH INSTITUTE. JOURNAL. (Text in English and German; summaries in English and Icelandic) 1940. irreg., vol.12, no.3. exchange basis. Marine Research Institute - Hafrannsoknastofnunin, Skulagata 4, P.O. Box 1390, 121 Reykjavik, Iceland. FAX 354-1-623790. Ed. Unnsteinn Stefansson. circ. 400. (back issues avail.) **Indexed:** Biol.Abstr., Deep Sea Res.& Oceanogr.Abstr.
—BLDSC (7976.300000).

RURAL INDUSTRY DIRECTORY. see *AGRICULTURE*

799.1 XR ISSN 0373-675X
RYBARSTVI. 1968. m. 36. Kcs.($19.40) (Cesky Rybarsky Svaz) Statni Zemedelske Nakladatelstvi, Vaclavske nam. 47, 113 11 Prague 1, Czech Republic. TEL 26 59 51. (Subscr. to: Artia, Ve Smeckach 30, 111 27 Prague 1, Czech Republic) Ed. Bedrich Hala. adv.; abstr.; bibl.; illus.; tr.mkt.; index.

639.2 RU ISSN 0131-6184
RYBNOE KHOZYAISTVO. 1920. bi-m. $86. Izdatel'stvo Kolos, Sadovaya-Spasskaya 18, Moscow, Russia. TEL 207-26-67. FAX 207-28-70. (Subscr. to: Mezhdunarodnaya Kniga, Moscow, G-200, Russia) Ed. Sergei A. Studenetskii. adv.; bk.rev.; index. circ. 2,500. **Indexed:** Biol.Abstr., Chem.Abstr., Food Sci.& Tech.Abstr., Nutr.Abstr., Potato Abstr., Soyabean Abstr.
—BLDSC (0154.280000).

639.2 RU ISSN 0131-6672
RYBOVODSTVO I RYBOLOVSTVO. 1958. bi-m. $6. Izdatel'stvo Kolos, Sadovo-Spasskaya, 18, 107807 Moscow, Russia. (Co-sponsor: Ministerstvo Sel'skogo Khozyaistva) Ed. V.L. Kotov. illus. **Indexed:** Biol.Abstr., Nutr.Abstr.

639.2 US ISSN 0085-6592
S F I BULLETIN. 1951. 10/yr. free. Sport Fishing Institute, 1010 Massachusetts Ave., N.W., Ste.320, Washington, DC 20001. TEL 202-898-0770. Ed. Volfuer. adv.; bibl.; charts; illus. circ. 15,000. **Indexed:** Environ.Abstr. **Document type:** bulletin.
—CIS.
Formerly: Sport Fishing Institute. Bulletin (ISSN 0097-0492)

SAINT MARY'S UNIVERSITY. STUDIES IN MARINE AND COASTAL GEOGRAPHY. see *GEOGRAPHY*

639.2 333.7 799.1 CN
SALAR. 1971. q. membership. Atlantic Salmon Federation, P.O. Box 429, St. Andrews, NB E0G 2X0, Canada. TEL 506-529-4581. circ. 6,000. (back issues avail.)
—BLDSC (1765.931000).
Former titles: Atlantic Salmon Newsletter (ISSN 0225-7165); International Atlantic Salmon Foundation. Newsletter (ISSN 0703-5411)

SALMON - TROUT STEELHEADER. see *SPORTS AND GAMES — Outdoor Life*

SCHIFFAHRT INTERNATIONAL. see *TRANSPORTATION — Ships And Shipping*

SCIENTIA MARINA. see *EARTH SCIENCES — Oceanography*

639 UK
SH259
SCOTLAND. AGRICULTURE AND FISHERIES DEPARTMENT. MARINE LABORATORY. ABERDEEN ANNUAL REVIEW. 1968. a. The Scottish Office, Agriculture and Fisheries Department, Marine Laboratory, P.O. Box 101, Victoria Rd., Aberdeen AB9 8DB, Scotland. TEL 44-224-876544. FAX 44-224-295511.
—BLDSC (1520.268000).
Former titles: Scotland. Department of Agriculture and Fisheries. Marine Laboratory. Aberdeen Annual Review (ISSN 0951-3760); (until 1985): Scotland. Department of Agriculture and Fisheries. Marine Laboratory. Triennial Review of Research (ISSN 0140-5012); (until 1972): Scotland. Directorate of Fisheries Research. Annual Report (ISSN 0072-6141)

639 UK ISSN 0309-9105
SCOTTISH FISHERIES INFORMATION PAMPHLETS 1977 N.S. irreg., no.18, 1990. The Scottish Office, Agriculture and Fisheries Department, Marine Laboratory, P.O. Box 101, Victoria Rd., Aberdeen AB9 8DB, Scotland. TEL 44-224-876544. FAX 44-224-879156. TELEX 73587. **Indexed:** Aqua Sci.& Fish Abstr., Nutr.Abstr., Ocean.Abstr.
—BLDSC (8208.530000).

639 UK ISSN 0308-8022
SCOTTISH FISHERIES RESEARCH REPORTS. 1975. irreg., no.48, 1990. The Scottish Office, Agriculture and Fisheries Department, Marine Laboratory, P.O. Box 101, Victoria Rd., Aberdeen AB9 8DB, Scotland. TEL 44-224-876544. FAX 44-224-879156. TELEX 73587. charts. **Indexed:** Aqua Sci.& Fish Abstr., Biol.Abstr., Curr.Adv.Ecol.Sci., Nutr.Abstr., Ocean.Abstr.
—BLDSC (8208.550000).

639.2 UK
SCOTTISH FISHING FLEET AT DECEMBER 31 (YEAR). 1981. a. price varies. The Scottish Office, Agriculture and Fisheries Department, Pentland House, 47 Robb's Loan, Edinburgh EH14 1TW, Scotland. TEL 0224-876544. (Subscr. to: The Scottish Office Library, Rm 1-44, New St. Andrews House, Edinburgh EH1 3TG, Scotland) **Document type:** government publication.

639 UK ISSN 0080-8202
SCOTTISH SEA FISHERIES STATISTICAL TABLES. 1939. a. £11.50. Department of Agriculture and Fisheries, Pentland House, 47 Robbs Loan, Edinburgh EH14 1TW, Scotland. TEL 031-244-6438. FAX 031-244-6001. (Dist. by: Scottish Office Library, Rm. 1/44, New St Andrews House, Edinburgh EH1 3TG, Scotland) **Document type:** government publication.

639.2 US
SEA GRANT EXTENSION PROGRAM. NEWSLETTER. 1972. 5/yr. free. Sea Grant Extension Program, California Department of Wildlife and Fisheries Biology, University of California at Davis, Davis, CA 95616-8751. Ed. Christopher M. Dewees. circ. 4,500. **Document type:** newsletter.
Description: Covers news of fisheries worldwide.

639.34 CN ISSN 0700-9275
SEA PEN. 1956. 5/yr. membership. Vancouver Public Aquarium Association, Box 3232, Vancouver, BC V6B 3X8, Canada. TEL 604-685-3364. FAX 604-631-2529. Eds. Carmel Boerner, Marisa Nichini. charts; illus. circ. 24,000. **Document type:** newsletter, academic/scholarly publication.
Formerly (until 1976): Vancouver Public Aquarium Newsletter (ISSN 0042-2495)

639.2 US ISSN 0889-3217
HD9451 CODEN: SEFBEM
SEAFOOD BUSINESS. 1906. 7/yr. $30. Journal Publications (Rockland), Box 908, Rockland, ME 04841-0908. TEL 207-594-6222. Ed. Caroline Perkins. adv. circ. 15,500. (also avail. in microfiche from CIS) **Indexed:** SRI.
Formerly: Seafood Business Report (ISSN 0733-0464)

664.94 II ISSN 0037-010X
SH299
SEAFOOD EXPORT JOURNAL. (Text in English) 1968. m. Rs.180($30) Seafood Exporters Association of India, Seafood House, Willingdon Island, Cochin 682 003, India. TELEX 0885-6664 EXPO IN. Ed. R. Anirudhan. adv.: B&W page Rs.5000 ($600). bk.rev.; charts; illus.; stat.; tr.lit. circ. 2,000. **Indexed:** Food Sci.& Tech.Abstr. **Document type:** trade publication.
—BLDSC (8213.721000).

639 UK ISSN 0268-1293
SEAFOOD INTERNATIONAL. 12/yr. £30 (foreign £35). E M A P Heighway (Subsidiary of: E M A P Business Publishing Ltd.), Meed House, 21 John St., London WC1N 2BP. TEL 071-404-5513. FAX 071-831-9362. Ed. Michael Urch. adv.: B&W page £1858. color page £2983; trim 267 x 185; adv. contact: Lucie Mallett. circ. 5,500. **Document type:** trade publication.
—BLDSC (8213.721100); UnCover.
Description: Concerns the business of seafood retailers worldwide.

639.2 NZ ISSN 1172-4633
SEAFOOD NEW ZEALAND. 1980. m. NZ.$65 (foreign NZ.$155) (effective Aug. 1993). (New Zealand Fishing Industry Board) New Zealand Seafood Industry Magazine Ltd., Private Bag 24-901, Wellington, New Zealand. TEL 04-385-4005. FAX 04-385-2727. Ed. P. Stevens. adv. contact: Jackie Enright. bk.rev. circ. 6,500. **Document type:** trade publication.
Incorporates (1986-19??): New Zealand Professsional Fisherman (ISSN 0113-0927)
Description: For New Zealand commercial fisherman, fish processing companies, fish exporters, aquaculturalists, fish wholesalers.

639 UK
SEAFOOD NEWS. 12/yr. £30. MEED House, 21 John St., London WC1N 2BP. TEL 071-404-5513. FAX 071-831-9362. Ed. Ian Strutt. **Document type:** trade publication.

664 US ISSN 0270-417X
SEAFOOD PRICE-CURRENT. 1973. s-w. $252 (typically set in Sept.). Urner Barry Publications, Inc., Box 389, Toms River, NJ 08754. TEL 908-240-5330. FAX 908-341-0891. Ed. Paul B. Brown, Jr. adv. (tabloid format).

SEICHE. see *WATER RESOURCES*

639.2 CL
SERIE INVESTIGACION PESQUERA. (Text in Spanish; summaries in English) 1965. irreg., no.31, 1984. $5. Instituto de Fomento Pesquero, Seccion Edicion y Publicaciones, Jose Domingo Canas 2277, Casilla 1287, Santiago, Chile. abstr.; bibl.; charts; stat. circ. 600. (processed) **Indexed:** Biol.Abstr.
Formerly: Instituto de Fomento Pesquero. Boletin Cientifico (ISSN 0020-3882)

639.2 UK
SHETLAND FISHING NEWS. 1985. m. £8.40. Shetland Fishing News, 14 Alexandra Buildings, Lerwick, Shetland ZE1 0L., Scotland. TEL 0595-3622. FAX 0595-4637 (Subscr. to: The Shetland Times Ltd., Prince Alfred St., Lerwick, Shetland ZE1 0EP, Scotland) Ed. James Nicolson. adv.; bk.rev. circ. 1,600. (back issues avail.) **Document type:** trade publication.

SHIMA MARINELAND. SCIENCE REPORT. see *BIOLOGY*

SHIPPING AND MARINE INDUSTRIES JOURNAL; devoted to shipping and shipbuilding industries, fisheries and oceanography. see *TRANSPORTATION — Ships And Shipping*

639.2 CC ISSN 1001-1994
SHUICHAN KEJI QINGBAO/SCIENCE AND TECHNOLOGY INFORMATION ON AQUATIC PRODUCTS. (Text in Chinese) bi-m. Shanghai Shuichan Xuehui - Shanghai Society for Aquatic Products, 256 Jiamusi Lu, Shanghai 200433, People's Republic of China. TEL 5483215. (Co-sponsor: Shanghai Shuichan Yanjiusuo) Ed. Liu Fushun.

639 CC
SHUICHAN KEXUE. (Text in Chinese) q. Liaoning Sheng Shuichan Xuehui - Liaoning Aquatic Products Society, 50 Heishijiao Jie, Dalian, Liaoning 116023, People's Republic of China. TEL 491609. Ed. Wu Jingnan.

639.2   CC   ISSN 1000-6257
SHUICHAN WENZHAI. (Text in Chinese) bi-m. Zhongguo Shuichan Kexue Yanjiuyuan, Nanhai Shuichan Yanjiusuo, No. 231, Xingang Lu, Guangzhou, Guangdong 510300, People's Republic of China. TEL 451320. Ed. Yue Yongquan.

639.3   CC   ISSN 1000-0615
QH90.A1
SHUICHAN XUEBAO/JOURNAL OF AQUATIC PRODUCTS. (Text in Chinese) q. $2.50 per no. Zhongguo Shuichan Xuehui - Chinese Society of Aquatic Products, 334 Jungong Lu, Shanghai 200090, People's Republic of China. TEL 5432965. (Dist. overseas by: Guoji Shudian - China International Book Trading Corporation, P.O. Box 399, Beijing 100044, P.R.C.). **Indexed:** Anim.Breed.Abstr., So.Pac.Per.Ind.

SIMPLY SEAFOOD. see *HOME ECONOMICS*

639.2   SP   ISSN 0037-556X
SINDICATO NACIONAL DE LA PESCA BOLETIN DE INFORMACION. no.103, 1967. m. Sindicato Nacional de la Pesca, Paseo del Prado 18-20, Madrid, Spain. Ed. Francisco Muro De Iscar. charts; mkt.; stat.

SINGAPORE JOURNAL OF PRIMARY INDUSTRIES. see *AGRICULTURE*

639.2   IC   ISSN 1017-3609
SJAVARFRETTIR. (Supplement to: Fiskifrettir) (Text in Icelandic; summaries in English) a. ISK 2980 to non-subscribers to Fiskifrettir. Frodi Ltd., Armuli 18, 108 Reykjavik, Iceland. TEL 354-1-812300. FAX 1-812946. Ed. Gudjon Einarsson. adv. contact: Vaka Haraldsdottir. circ. 6,000. **Description:** Contains information on the Icelandic fishing industry, quota system, technological development.

639   SA
SOUTH AFRICA. SEA FISHERIES RESEARCH INSTITUTE. INVESTIGATIONAL REPORT. (Text in Afrikaans, English) 1934. irreg., no.133, 1990. exchange basis. Sea Fisheries Research Institute, Private Bag X2, Rogge Bay 8012, Cape Town, South Africa. TEL 27-21-4023911. FAX 27-21-252920. TELEX 5-20796 SA. Eds. H. Boonstra, A. Payne. circ. 1,300. **Indexed:** Biol.Abstr., GeoRef., Ocean.Abstr. **Document type:** government publication.
Former titles (until 1979): South Africa. Sea Fisheries Branch. Investigational Report (ISSN 0379-1084); South Africa. Sea Fisheries Institute. Investigational Report (ISSN 0081-2234).

639   SA   ISSN 1021-1055
SOUTH AFRICA. SEA FISHERIES RESEARCH INSTITUTE. RESEARCH HIGHLIGHTS. Afrikaans edition (ISSN 1021-1063) (Text in English) 1921. a. exchange basis. Sea Fisheries Research Institute, Private Bag X2, Rogge Bay 8012, Cape Town, South Africa. TEL 27-21-4023911. FAX 27-21-252920. TELEX 5-20796 SA. Eds. G.C. Pitcher, A.I.L. Payne. circ. 1,300. **Indexed:** Biol.Abstr.
Supersedes in part (in 1992): South Africa. Sea Fisheries Research Institute. Chief Directorate Sea Fisheries. Annual Report; Former titles: South Africa. Sea Fisheries Research Institute. Marine Development Branch. Annual Report (ISSN 1010-0830); (until 1983): South Africa. Sea Fisheries Institute. Department of Industries. Annual Report (ISSN 1010-1462); South Africa. Sea Fisheries Branch. Annual Report; South Africa. Division of Sea Fisheries. Annual Report (ISSN 0081-2218). **Description:** Selective review of completed and projected research at the institute.

639.2   SA   ISSN 0257-7631
SOUTH AFRICA. SEA FISHERIES RESEARCH INSTITUTE. SPECIAL REPORT. (Text in English) 1984. irreg., no.6, 1993. exchange basis. Sea Fisheries Research Institute, Private Bag X2, Rogge Bay 8012, Cape Town, South Africa. TEL 27-21-402-3911. FAX 27-21-252-920. TELEX 5-20796 SA. Eds. H. Boonstra, A. Payne. circ. 1,300. **Indexed:** Biol.Abstr., Ocean.Abstr. **Document type:** monographic series. **Description:** Monographs on marine science not meeting criteria for research papers.

639   SA   ISSN 1022-1093
SOUTH AFRICAN COMMERCIAL FISHERIES REVIEW. Afrikaans edition (ISSN 1022-1387) 1921. a. exchange basis. Sea Fisheries Research Institute, Private Bag X2, Rogge Bay 8012, Cape Town, South Africa. TEL 27-21-4023911. **Document type:** government publication.
Former titles: Commercial Sea Fisheries Review; Supersedes in part (in 1992): South Africa. Sea Fisheries Research Institute. Chief Directorate Sea Fisheries. Annual Report; Which was formerly: South Africa. Sea Fisheries Research Institute. Marine Development Branch. Annual Report (ISSN 1010-0830); (until 1983): South Africa. Sea Fisheries Institute. Department of Industries. Annual Report (ISSN 1010-1462); South Africa. Sea Fisheries Branch. Annual Report; South Africa. Division of Sea Fisheries. Annual Report (ISSN 0081-2218).
Description: Comparative annual review of the performance of the South African marine fishing industry.

639   SA   ISSN 0257-7615
SOUTH AFRICAN JOURNAL OF MARINE SCIENCE/SUID-AFRIKAANSE TYDSKRIF VIR SEEWETENSKAP. (Text in English; summaries in Afrikaans and English) 1935. irreg., no. 13, 1993. exchange basis. Sea Fisheries Research Institute, Private Bag X2, Rogge Bay 8012, Cape Town, South Africa. TEL 27-21-4023911. FAX 27-21-252920. TELEX. 5-20796 SA. Ed. A.I.L. Payne. circ. 1,300. (back issues avail.) **Indexed:** Biol.Abstr., Chem.Abstr., Curr.Adv.Ecol.Sci., Curr.Cont., Deep Sea Res.& Oceanogr.Abstr., Ind.S.A.Per., Ocean.Abstr., Sel.Water Res.Abstr. **Document type:** government publication, academic/scholarly publication.
—BLDSC (8338.958000); Faxon.
Former titles (until 1983): South Africa. Sea Fisheries Institute. Fisheries Bulletin (ISSN 0254-3559); South Africa. Sea Fisheries Branch. Fisheries Bulletin; South Africa. Division of Sea Fisheries. Fisheries Bulletin.

SOUTH AFRICAN SHIPPING NEWS AND FISHING INDUSTRY REVIEW. see *TRANSPORTATION — Ships And Shipping*

639.2   US
SOUTHEASTERN ASSOCIATION OF FISH AND WILDLIFE AGENCIES. PROCEEDINGS. 1947. a. $18.50. Southeastern Association of Fish and Wildlife Agencies, c/o Robert M. Brantly, Exec. Sec., 7221 Covey Trace, Tallahassee, FL 32308. TEL 904-893-0084. cum.index: vols. 1-39 (1947-1985). **Indexed:** Biol.Abstr. **Document type:** proceedings.
Formerly: Southeastern Association of Game and Fish Commissioners. Proceedings of the Annual Conference (ISSN 0081-2943)

639.2   CN   ISSN 0049-1705
SOU'WESTER; voice of Atlantic provinces fishing industry. 1968. bi-m. Can.$10. Fundy Group Publications, Box 128, 2 Second St., Yarmouth, N.S., Canada. TEL 902-742-7111. Ed. Alain Meuse. circ. 10,000. (tabloid format; back issues avail.) **Indexed:** Amer.Hist.& Life, Hist.Abstr.
Description: Coverage of Atlantic Canada's fishing and marine industry.

639.2   SP
SPAIN. DIRECCION GENERAL DE PESCA MARITIMA. PUBLICACIONES TECNICAS. irreg. Direccion General de Pesca Maritima, Madrid, Spain. illus.

SPORTFISKE. see *SPORTS AND GAMES — Outdoor Life*

799.1   DK   ISSN 0038-8211
SPORTSFISKEREN.* 1926. m. DKK 90. (Danmarks Sportsfiskerforbund - Federation of Danish Anglers) Harlang & Toksvig Bladforlag A-S, Vejle, Denmark. Ed. Tove Skjerbek. adv.; bk.rev.; circ. 20,637 (controlled).

639.2   JA   ISSN 0039-4866
SUISAN KAI/FISHERIES WORLD. (Text in Japanese) 1882. m. 2200 Yen($6.11) Japan Fisheries Association - Dainihon Suisankai, 9-13 Akasaka 1-chome, Minato-ku, Tokyo 107, Japan. Ed. Morita Hideo. adv.; bk.rev.; abstr.; charts; index. circ. 25,000. (looseleaf format)

639.2 620   JA   ISSN 0916-7617
SUISAN KOGAKU/FISHERIES ENGINEERING. (Text in English, Japanese) s-a. Nihon Suisan Kogakkai - Japanese Society of Fisheries Engineering, Suisancho Suisan Kogaku Kenkyujo, Ebida, Hasaki-machi, Kashima-gun, Ibaraki-ken 314-04, Japan.

623.8   JA   ISSN 0388-970X
SUISAN KOGAKU KENKYUJO GIHO. GYOSEN KOGAKU/NATIONAL RESEARCH INSTITUTE OF FISHERIES ENGINEERING. TECHNICAL REPORT. FISHING BOAT AND INSTRUMENT. (Text in Japanese; summaries in English) 1980. a. Suisancho, Suisan Kogaku Kenkyujo - Fisheries Agency, National Research Institute of Fisheries Engineering, 7620-1, Ebidai, Hasakimachi, Kashima-gun, Ibaraki-ken 314-04, Japan. **Indexed:** Agrindex.
—BLDSC (8717.445900).

639.2 620   JA   ISSN 0389-2344
SUISAN KOGAKU KENKYUJO GIHO. SUISAN DOBOKU/NATIONAL RESEARCH INSTITUTE OF FISHERIES ENGINEERING. TECHNICAL REPORT. AQUACULTURE AND FISHING PORT ENGINEERING. (Text in Japanese; summaries in English) 1980. a. Suisancho, Suisan Kogaku Kenkyujo - Fisheries Agency, National Research Institute of Fisheries Engineering, 7620-1, Ebidai, Hasaki-machi, Kashima-gun, Ibaraki-ken 314-04, Japan.
—BLDSC (8717.445800).

639.2 620   JA   ISSN 0388-9718
SH334.5   CODEN: SKKDER
SUISAN KOGAKU KENKYUJO KENKYU HOKOKU/NATIONAL RESEARCH INSTITUTE OF FISHERIES ENGINEERING. BULLETIN. (Text in Japanese; summaries in English) a. Suisancho, Suisan Kogaku Kenkyujo - Fisheries Agency, National Research Institute of Fisheries Engineering, 7620-1, Ebidai, Hasaki-machi, Kashima-gun, Ibaraki-ken 314-04, Japan. **Document type:** bulletin.
—BLDSC (2643.230000).

639.34   JA   ISSN 0371-4217
                      CODEN: SUZOAV
SUISANZOSHOKU/AQUACULTURE. (Text and summaries in English, Japanese) 1982. q. 6000 Yen($40) Japan Aquaculture Society, c/o Kochi University, Faculty of Agriculture, 200 Monobe, Nankoku, Kochi 783, Japan. TEL 81-0888-634141. FAX 81-0888-636492. Ed. Riichi Kusuda. adv.; bk.rev.; cum.index. circ. 1,350. (back issues avail.) **Document type:** bulletin.
—BLDSC (8514.965000); CASDDS. **CCC.**
Description: Journal presenting various research works in aquaculture.

639.2   FI   ISSN 0039-5528
SUOMEN KALASTUSLEHTI. 1892. 8/yr. FIM 170. Kalatalouden Keskusliitto - Federation of Finnish Fisheries Associations (Centraalfoerbundet foer Fiskerihushaallning), Koydenpunojankatu 7 B 23, 00180 Helsinki 18, Finland. TEL 358-0-640-126. FAX 358-0-608-309. Ed. Markku Myllyla. adv.; B&W page FIM 2900; trim 158 x 230; adv. contact: Jouko Poutanen. bk.rev.; bibl.; charts; illus.; index; circ. 4,392 (controlled). **Document type:** monographic series.
Description: Focuses on information dealing with fisheries. Directed to fish-water owners, commerical fishermen, fish farmers, scientists, fish jobbers and processers.

639   FI   ISSN 0085-6940
SH293.F5
SUOMEN KALATALOUS. (Text in Finnish; summaries in Swedish and English) 1912. irreg. exchange basis. Finnish Game and Fisheries Research Institute, Aquaculture Division, P.O. Box 202, SF-00151 Helsinki, Finland. TEL 358-0-624211. FAX 358-0-631513. TELEX 19101236 VDX SF. Ed. Kai Westman. circ. 1,300. **Indexed:** Biol.Abstr.

SURINAAMSE LANDBOUW/SURINAM AGRICULTURE. see *AGRICULTURE*

639.2   SP
SUSTRAI; revista agropesquera. 1985. q. free. Diputaciones Forales de Alava, Guipuzcoa y Vizcaya, Apdo. de Correos, 2044, 01080 Vitoria-Gasteiz, Spain. TEL (945)24 60 00. TELEX 35217-35218. Ed. Jesus Maria Oses Zurbano.

FISH AND FISHERIES   **2541**

639.34   639.34   GW   ISSN 0942-5160
T I. (Tatsachen, Informationen); Magazin fuer Aquaristik, Terristik, Naturgarten, Lebensraeume. 1968. q. DM.23.20 (foreign DM.24.40). (Tetra Werke) Tetra Verlag, Postfach 1580, 49304 Melle, Germany. TEL 05422-1050. FAX 05422-105266. TELEX 941520-TETRA-D. bk.rev. circ. 25,000. (back issues avail.) **Document type:** consumer publication.
    Formerly (until 1992): T I International (ISSN 0176-3660)

T S S A REPORT. (Tackle & Shooting Sports Agents Association) see *BUSINESS AND ECONOMICS*

639.2   UK
TACKLE TALK. 1987. m. £70($112) includes Who's Who in the Tackle Trade. Pendragon Publishing, 22 Nightingale Rd., Bushey, Watford, Herts WD2 3NJ, England. TEL 081-950-6360. FAX 081-420-4163. Ed. Ron Sorkin. adv.: B&W page £525, color page £950; trim 267 x 184. circ. 4,500. **Document type:** trade publication.
    Description: Business magazine covering angling trade worldwide.

639   JA
TANSUIGYO-HOGO/FRESHWATER FISH PROTECTION. 1975. a. 4000 Yen($20) Tansuigyo Hogo Kyokai, 2-38 Nichome Dojima, Kitaku, Osaka, Japan. Ed. Eizo Kimura. circ. 2,000.
    Formerly (until 1988): Tansuigyo (ISSN 0910-2078)

639.2   AT   ISSN 0817-3680
TASMANIA. DEPARTMENT OF PRIMARY INDUSTRY AND FISHERIES. SEA FISHERIES DIVISION. TECHNICAL REPORT (NO.). 1978. s-a. free to qualified personnel. Department of Primary Industry and Fisheries, Sea Fisheries Division, P.O. Box 619F, Hobart, Tas. 7001, Australia. FAX 002-278035. Ed. Jeremy M. Lyle. circ. 400 (controlled). **Indexed:** Biol.Abstr., Deep Sea Res.& Oceanogr.Abstr., Ocean.Abstr., Pollut.Abstr. **Document type:** government publication.
    —BLDSC (8715.196500).
    Incorporates (1967-1993): Tasmanin Fisheries Research (ISSN 0049-3015)
    Refereed Serial

THIS WEEK MAGAZINE. see *TRAVEL AND TOURISM*

639.34   JA   ISSN 0915-1605
TOBA SUIZOKUKAN NENPO/TOBA AQUARIUM. ANNUAL REPORT. (Text in English, Japanese) 1989. a. Toba Suizokukan, 3-6 Toba 3-chome, Toba-shi, Mie-ken 517, Japan.

639.2   JA   ISSN 0049-402X
                     CODEN: TSKHBZ
TOHOKU REGIONAL FISHERIES RESEARCH LABORATORY. BULLETIN/TOHOKU-KU SUISAN KENKYUJO KENKYU HOKOKU. (Text in Japanese; summaries in English) 1952. s-a. exchange basis. Tohoku National Fisheries Research Institute - Suisancho Tohokuku Suisan Kenkyujo, 3-27-5 Shinhama-cho, Shiogama-shi, Miyagi 985, Japan. Ed. Hisashi Kan-no. cum.index. circ. controlled. (processed) **Indexed:** Biol.Abstr., Deep Sea Res.& Oceanogr.Abstr.

639.2   JA   ISSN 0040-9014
SH1   CODEN: JTUFA9
TOKYO UNIVERSITY OF FISHERIES. JOURNAL/TOKYO SUISAN DAIGAKU KENKYU HOKOKU. (Text in English and Japanese) 1899. s-a. exchange basis. Tokyo University of Fisheries - Tokyo Suisan Daigaku, 4-5-7 Konan, Minato-ku, Tokyo 108, Japan. TEL 03-3471-1251. Ed. Seiichiro Ono. charts; illus. **Indexed:** Deep Sea Res.& Oceanogr.Abstr.
    —BLDSC (4909.000000); CASDDS.

338   JA   ISSN 0563-8372
AS552.T7172
TOKYO UNIVERSITY OF FISHERIES. REPORT/TOKYO SUISAN DAIGAKU RONSHU. (Text mainly in Japanese; summaries in English) 1966. a. Tokyo University of Fisheries - Tokyo Suisan Daigaku, 4-5-7 Konan, Minato-ku, Tokyo 108, Japan. TEL 03-3471-1251. Ed. Seiichiro Ono. illus.
    —BLDSC (7619.580000).

639   919.9   551.4   JA   ISSN 0388-0966
TOKYO UNIVERSITY OF FISHERIES. TRANSACTIONS. (Text in English or Japanese; summaries in English) 1974. irreg. Tokyo University of Fisheries - Tokyo Suisan Daigaku, 4-5-7 Konan, Minato-ku, Tokyo 108, Japan. TEL 03-3471-1251. Ed. Seiichiro Ono. **Indexed:** Biol.Abstr., Curr.Adv.Ecol.Sci., Deep Sea Res.& Oceanogr.Abstr., Vet.Bull.

639   AT   ISSN 0814-379X
TRAILERBOAT FISHERMAN. 1984. m. Aus.$45. Marine Publications Pty. Ltd., P.O. Box 668, Avalon Beach, N.S.W. 2107, Australia. TEL 61-2-973-2177. FAX 61-2-973-2257. Ed. James Hill. circ. 12,200. (back issues avail.)
    Description: News about recreational fishing and boating.

TROPICAL FISH HOBBYIST. see *HOBBIES*

574.92   NR   ISSN 0795-0101
TROPICAL FRESHWATER BIOLOGY. 1987. s-a. $25. Idodo Umeh Publishers Ltd., 52 Ewah Rd., P.O. Box 3441, Benin City, Nigeria. TEL 234-52-244404. TELEX 41303-IDOMEH-NG. Ed. Dr. Anthony E. Ogbeibu. adv.: B&W page $500; adv. contact: F. Opene. circ. 200 (controlled). **Document type:** academic/scholarly publication.
    —BLDSC (9056.164000).
    Description: Covers tropical freshwater biology in tropcial and subtropical regions.

TROUT. see *CONSERVATION*

639.2   UK
TROUT NEWS. 1987. q. free. (Directorate of Fisheries Research, Fisheries Laboratory) Lowestoft, Suffolk NR33 0HT, England. Ed. Dick Lincoln.
    Description: Examines the trout farming industry.

639.2   NL   ISSN 1018-0974
TUNA AND BILLFISH ASSESSMENT PROGRAMME TECHNICAL REPORT. French edition (ISSN 1018-0931) (Text in English or French) 1983. irreg., no.29, 1992. South Pacific Commission, B.P. D5, Noumea, Cedex, New Caledonia. TEL 26-2000. FAX 687-263818. TELEX 3139 NM SOPACOM.
    Formerly: Skipjack Survey and Assessment Programme Technical Report.

TUNISIA. INSTITUT NATIONAL SCIENTIFIQUE ET TECHNIQUE D'OCEANOGRAPHIE ET DE PECHE. BULLETIN. see *EARTH SCIENCES — Oceanography*

639.21   UG
UGANDA FRESHWATER FISHERIES RESEARCH ORGANIZATION. ANNUAL REPORT. 1948. a. $10. Uganda Freshwater Fisheries Research Organization, P.O. Box 343 (Nile Crescent), Jinja, Uganda. circ. 1,000. **Indexed:** Biol.Abstr.
    Formerly: East African Freshwater Fisheries Research Organization. Annual Report (ISSN 0070-7953)

639   BE
UITKOMSTEN VAN DE BELGISCHE ZEEVISSERIJ. 1957. a. free. Dienst voor de Zeevisserij, Bestuur voor de Economische Diensten, Administratief Centrum, Vrijhavenstr. 5, B-8400 Oostende, Belgium. TEL 32-59-508966. FAX 32-59-807693. TELEX 81075 DZVOST. Ed.Bd. stat. circ. 200. **Document type:** government publication.

639.3   US   ISSN 1042-6221
SH34
U.S. DEPARTMENT OF AGRICULTURE. SITUATION & OUTLOOK REPORT. AQUACULTURE. Key Title: Aquaculture Situation and Outlook. 1981. s-a. U.S. Department of Agriculture, Economic Research Service, Room 208, 1301 New York Ave., N.W., Washington, DC 20005. TEL 202-219-0515. (Dist. by: ERS-NASS, 341 Victory Dr., Herndon, VA 22070. TEL 800-999-6779) Ed. David Harvey. **Document type:** government publication.
    Formerly (until 1988): Aquaculture Outlook and Situation (ISSN 0278-131X)

639   US   ISSN 0565-0704
SH157.7   CODEN: IFCRAG
U.S. FISH AND WILDLIFE SERVICE. INVESTIGATIONS IN FISH CONTROL. Key Title: Investigations in Fish Control. no.25, 1969. irreg., no.91, 1982. U.S. Fish and Wildlife Service, Dept. of the Interior, Washington, DC 20240. TEL 202-653-7501. **Indexed:** Biol.Abstr., Chem.Abstr., Deep Sea Res.& Oceanogr.Abstr., Pollut.Abstr.
    —CASDDS.

639   US   ISSN 0083-0941
SH11
U.S. FISH AND WILDLIFE SERVICE. RESEARCH REPORTS. 1941. irreg., no.80, 1980. U.S. Fish and Wildlife Service, Dept. of the Interior, Washington, DC 20240. TEL 303-226-9403. (Orders to: Supt. Doc., Washington, DC 20402) **Indexed:** Biol.Abstr., Curr.Adv.Ecol.Sci., Weed Abstr.

639   US   ISSN 0094-7008
SH11
U.S. NATIONAL MARINE FISHERIES SERVICE. GRANT-IN-AID FOR FISHERIES: PROGRAM ACTIVITIES. a. free. U.S. National Marine Fisheries Service, National Oceanic and Atmospheric Administration, 1355 East-West Hwy., Silver Spring, MD 20910. TEL 301-713-2347. **Document type:** government publication.

639.2   US
U.S. NATIONAL MARINE FISHERIES SERVICE. IMPORTS AND EXPORTS OF FISHERY PRODUCTS. ANNUAL SUMMARY. a. U.S. National Marine Fisheries Service, Fisheries Statstics Division, National Oceanic and Atmospheric Administration, 1335 East-West Hwy., Silver Spring, MD 20910. TEL 301-713-2328. **Document type:** government publication.

639   US
U.S. NATIONAL MARINE FISHERIES SERVICE. TECHNICAL REPORT. 1940. irreg. price varies. U.S. National Marine Fisheries Service, Scientific Publications Office, 7600 Sandpoint Way, N.E., Bin C15700, Seattle, WA 98115. TEL 206-526-6107. FAX 206-526-6426. Ed. Ronald Hardy. index. circ. 2,000. (also avail. in microfiche from NTI) **Indexed:** Biol.Abstr., Ocean.Abstr. **Document type:** academic/scholarly publication, government publication.
    Former titles: U.S. National Marine Fisheries Service. Special Scientific Report: Fisheries; U.S Bureau of Commercial Fisheries. Special Scientific Report (ISSN 0082-8904)
    Description: Presents scientific investigations documenting long-term continuing programs of the service. Examines fishery problems, conservation, management, and economics.

639.34   JA   ISSN 0917-9631
UOZU SHUIZOKUKAN NENPO/UOZU AQUARIUM. ANNUAL REPORT. (Text in Japanese; summaries in English) 1990. a. Uozu Suizokukan, 1390 Sanga, Uozu-shi, Tayama-ken 937, Japan.

UPWELLINGS. see *WATER RESOURCES*

URUGUAY. MINISTERIO DE AGRICULTURA Y PESCA. PRECIOS DE PRODUCTOS E INSUMOS AGROPECUARIOS. see *AGRICULTURE — Agricultural Economics*

639.2   IC
VIKINGUR. 1939. 4/yr. $30. Farmanna og Fiskimannasamband, Borgartun 18, 105 Reykjavik, Iceland. TEL 354-1-62-40-67. FAX 354-1-62-99-34. Ed. Sigurjon Egilsson. adv.; bk.rev. circ. 5,000.

639.9   BE   ISSN 0776-6912
VISSERIJBLAD. (Text in Flemish) 1933. m. 2000 BEF (fl.112 in the Netherlands; £32 in UK; $63 in US). 2 Baelskaai, B-8400 Oostende, Belgium. TEL 32-59-32-5559. FAX 32-59-32-1752. Ed. V.Z.W. Liefkemores. adv. circ. 3,000. **Document type:** newspaper.

639.2   NE
VISSERIJNIEUWS; weekblad. 1934. w. fl.149.90 (foreign $185). Visserijnieuws B.V., Postbus 29, 8320 AA Urk, Netherlands. TEL 31-5277-4133. FAX 31-5277-4695. adv. contact: Jan Wildenberg. circ. 3,800. **Document type:** trade publication.
    Description: Covers the entire spectrum of the fish trade, including fisheries, fish-processing industries, wholesale and retail sales.

FISH AND FISHERIES — ABSTRACTING, BIBLIOGRAPHIES, STATISTICS

639.3 XR ISSN 0007-389X
VYZKUMNY USTAV RYBARSKY A HYDROBIOLOGICKY. BULLETIN. (Text in Czech; summaries in English) 1965. q. 25 Kcs. Vyzkumny Ustav Rybarsky a Hydrobiologicky - Research Institute of Fish and Hydrobiology, 38925 Vodnany, Czech Republic. TEL 342-905906. FAX 342-906208. Ed. Martin Flajshans. bk.rev.; bibl.; charts; illus.; index. circ. 180. (also avail. in diskette format) Indexed: Anim.Breed.Abstr., Aqua.Sci.& Fish.Abstr., Biol.Abstr., Protozool.Abstr., Ref.Zh.
Description: Covers culture of freshwater fishes, fisheries management of inland waters, hydrobiology, economy of aquaculture, fish diseases and fish toxicology.

639.2 US
WASHINGTON (STATE). DEPARTMENT OF FISHERIES. ANNUAL REPORT. 1985. a. Department of Fisheries, Box 43146, Olympia, WA 98504-3136. FAX 206-902-2947. *Document type:* government publication.

WER UND WAS IN DER DEUTSCHEN FLEISCH- FISCH- UND FEINKOST-INDUSTRIE. see *AGRICULTURE — Poultry And Livestock*

639.2 CN ISSN 0836-8600
WESTCOAST FISHERMAN. 1986. m. Can.$32.10($40) Westcoast Publishing Ltd., 1496 W. 72nd Ave., Vancouver, B.C. V6P 3C8, Canada. TEL 604-266-7433. FAX 604-263-8620. Ed. Peter Robson. adv. circ. 12,000.

639.2 639.9 AT
WESTERN AUSTRALIA. FISHERIES DEPARTMENT. REPORT. 1964. irreg., no.78, 1987. free. Fisheries Department, 108 Adelaide Terrace, Perth, W.A. 6000, Australia. Ed. Andrew Cribb. circ. 2,000. Indexed: Biol.Abstr. *Document type:* government publication.
—BLDSC (3939.541000).
Formerly: Western Australia. Department of Fisheries and Wildlife. Report (ISSN 0726-0733)

639.2 US ISSN 0270-160X
HD9453
WHO'S WHO IN THE FISH INDUSTRY. 1980. a. $85. Urner Barry Publications, Inc., Box 389, Toms River, NJ 08754. TEL 908-240-5330. Ed. Paul B. Brown, Jr. adv. circ. 3,500.

WHO'S WHO IN THE TACKLE TRADE. see *BUSINESS AND ECONOMICS — Trade And Industrial Directories*

WONDERFUL WEST VIRGINIA. see *CONSERVATION*

639.2 UK ISSN 0043-8480
SH1
WORLD FISHING. 1952. m. £35($85) (Europe £40; foreign £50). Oban Times Ltd., Royston House, Caroline Park, Edinburgh EH5 1QJ, Scotland. TEL 031-551-2942. FAX 031-551-2938. Ed. Martin Gill. adv.; bk.rev.; charts; illus.; index. circ. 6,500. (also avail. in microform from UMI) Indexed: BMT, Br.Tech.Ind., Ocean.Abstr., Pollut.Abstr. *Document type:* trade publication.
—BLDSC (9355.120000); UMI.
Description: Business and technical journal for fisheries management.

597 US ISSN 0194-3340
SH455 CODEN: WRGFE4
WORLD RECORD GAME FISHES. 1946. a. $9.75. International Game Fish Association, 1301 E. Atlantic Blvd., Pompano Beach, FL 33060-6744. TEL 305-941-3474. Ed. Ray Crawford. adv.; illus.; stat. circ. 25,000. *Document type:* bulletin.
Formerly: World Record Marine Fishes (ISSN 0084-2214)
Description: Presents game fish world records and articles on recreational fishing throughout the world.

639.3 US ISSN 1047-5672
SH380.6
WORLD SHRIMP FARMING. (Supplement avail.: Annual Report on World Shrimp Farming, Directory of Shrimp Farming in the Western Hemisphere) 1976. bi-m. $95 includes annual report and directory. Aquaculture Digest, 11057 Negley Ave., San Diego, CA 92131. TEL 619-271-6354. FAX 619-271-0324. (Subscr. to: 9434 Kearny Mesa Rd., San Diego, CA 92126) Ed. Robert Rosenberry. adv.; bk.rev.; abstr.; bibl.; charts; illus.; stat.; tr.lit. (back issues avail.) Indexed: W.R.C.Inf. *Document type:* consumer publication, newsletter, trade publication.
Supersedes in part (in 1989): Aquaculture Digest (ISSN 0193-3140)
Description: Reports on shrimp and prawn farming. Focuses on developments in Latin America, the United States and Southeast Asia.

639.3 CC
XIAMEN SHUICHAN XUEYUAN XUEBAO/XIAMEN INSTITUTE OF AQUATIC PRODUCTS. JOURNAL. (Text in Chinese) s-a. Y2.40. Xiamen Shuichan Xueyuan - Xiamen Institute of Aquatic Products, Jimei, Xiamen, Fujian 361021, People's Republic of China. TEL 48203. (Dist. overseas by: Jiangsu Publications Import & Export Corp., 56 Gao Yun Ling, Nanjing, Jiangsu, P.R.C.) Ed. Hong Huixin.
Description: Covers the breeding of aquatic products, natural resources, fishing facilities and environmental protection.

639.2 CC ISSN 1004-8340
XIANDAI YUYE XINXI/MODERN FISHERIES INFORMATION. (Text in Chinese) 1986. m. Y18 (foreign $40). Zhongguo Shuichan Kexue Yanjiuyuan, Donghai Shuichan Yanjiusuo - Chinese Academy of Fisheries Science, East China Sea Fisheries Research Institute, 300 Jungong Lu, Shanghai 200090, People's Republic of China. TEL 5434690. FAX 086-021-5432926. Ed. Lu Zhongkang. adv.; bk.rev.; index. circ. 3,000.

639.34 JA
YAMA NO UE NO SAKANATACHI/HIMEJI CITY AQUARIUM. NEWSLETTER. (Text in Japanese) 1969. irreg. Himeji Shiritsu Suizokukan - Himeji City Aquarium, 440 Nishinobusue, Himeji-shi, Hyogo-ken 670, Japan. *Document type:* newsletter.

332 SW ISSN 0347-4275
YRKESFISKAREN. Short title: Y F. 1977. fortn. SEK 300 (effective 1990). Sveriges Fiskares Riksfoerbund, Amerikaskjulet, Uppgang G, S-414 63 Goeteborg, Sweden. TEL 031-12-45-93. FAX 031-24-86-35. Eds. Bjoern Beckman, Bernt Andersson. adv.; bk.rev.; illus.; stat. circ. 8,500.
Formed by the merger of: Ostkusten (ISSN 0030-6495) & Svenska Vaestkustfiskaren & Insjoefisket (ISSN 0345-5408)

YUYE JIXIE YIQI/FISHERY MACHINERY AND INSTRUMENT. see *MACHINERY*

639.2 ZA
ZAMBIA. DEPARTMENT OF FISHERIES. ANNUAL REPORT. (Text in English) a. K.150. Zambia Government Printing Department, P.O. Box 30136, Lusaka, Zambia. *Document type:* government publication.
Supersedes in part (in 1974): Zambia. Department of Wildlife, Fisheries and National Parks. Annual Report.
Description: Presents the department's report on commercial fish farming.

639 ZA
ZAMBIA. DEPARTMENT OF FISHERIES. RESEARCH DIVISION. ANNUAL REPORT. (Text in English) 1958. a. Department of Fisheries, Research Division, P.O. Box 350100, Chilanga, Zambia. TEL 261-1-278680. circ. 2,000. Indexed: Biol.Abstr. *Document type:* government publication.
Supersedes (1963-1971): Fisheries Research Bulletin of Zambia (ISSN 0084-4713)

587 JA
ZENKOKU GYOKO KENSETSU GIJUTSU KENKYU. HAPPYOKAI KOENS HU. (Text in Japanese) 1956. a. Suisancho, Gyokobu - Fisheries Agency, Oceanic Fisheries Department, 2-1, Kasumigaseki 1-chome, Chiyoda-ku, Tokyo 100, Japan.

639.2 CC
ZHONGGUO SHUICHAN/CHINESE AQUATIC PRODUCTS. (Text in Chinese) m. Zhongguo Shuichan Zazhishe, 31 Minfeng Hutong, Xidan, Beijing 100032, People's Republic of China. TEL 666148. Ed. Yang Jian.

FISH AND FISHERIES — Abstracting, Bibliographies, Statistics

639.2 011 US ISSN 0739-814X
SH1
A S F A AQUACULTURE ABSTRACTS. (Aquatic Sciences & Fisheries Abstracts) (Text in English) 1984. bi-m. (plus a. index). $325 (foreign $355). (Food and Agriculture Organization of the U.N.) Cambridge Scientific Abstracts, 7200 Wisconsin Ave., 6th Fl., Bethesda, MD 20814. TEL 301-961-6750. FAX 301-961-6720. (Co-sponsors: U.N. Division for Ocean Affairs and the Law of the Sea; U.N. Environment Programme; Intergovernmental Oceanographic Commission) Ed.Bd. abstr.; index. (back issues avail.) Indexed: Cal.Tiss.Abstr., Chemorec.Abstr., Comput.& Info.Sys., Oncol.Abstr., Pollut.Abstr. *Document type:* abstracting/indexing.
●Also available online. Vendor(s): CISTI, DIMDI, DIALOG Information Services, Inc. (File no.44); European Space Agency, STN International. Also available on CD-ROM. Producer(s): SilverPlatter Information, Inc.
Description: Covers the science, practice, management and economics of aquaculture through an international network of aquatic science centers.

574.19 JA
ABSTRACTS OF SYMPOSIUM ON PEPTIDE CHEMISTRY/PEPUCHIDO KAGAKU TORONKAI KOEN YOSHISHU. (Text in English) 1963. a. Chemical Society of Japan - Nippon Kagakkai, 1-5, Kanda Surugadai, Chiyoda-ku, Tokyo 101, Japan. *Document type:* abstracting/indexing.

639.2 IC ISSN 0001-9038
SH1
AEGIR/SEA. (Text in Icelandic; summaries in English) 1905. s-m. $39 (effective 1993). Fiskifelag Islands - Fisheries Association of Iceland, P.O. Box 20, Hoefn v-Ingolfsstraeti, 101 Reykjavik, Iceland. TEL 354-1-10500. FAX 354-1-27969. Ed.Bd. adv.; charts; illus.; stat.; index. circ. 2,000.

639.3 US
AGRICULTURAL STATISTICS BOARD REPORTS: CATFISH. m. $31.25 (foreign $31.25) (subscr. includes q. Catfish Production). U.S. Department of Agriculture, Agricultural Statistics Board, Publications, Rm. 5829, South Bldg., Washington, DC 20250. (Subscr. to: Superintendent of Documents, U.S. Government Printing Office, Box 371954, Pittsburgh, PA 15250-7954. TEL 202-783-3238. FAX 202-512-2233) (back issues avail.) *Document type:* government publication.

639.3 US
AGRICULTURAL STATISTICS BOARD REPORTS: CATFISH PRODUCTION. q. $25 (foreign $31.25) (subscr. includes m. Catfish). U.S. Department of Agriculture, Agricultural Statistics Board, Publications, Rm. 5829, South Bldg., Washington, DC 20250. (Subscr. to: Superintendent of Documents, U.S. Government Printing Office, Box 371954, Pittsburgh, PA 15250-7954. TEL 202-783-3238. FAX 202-512-2233) (back issues avail.) *Document type:* government publication.

639.2 AG
ANUARIO ESTADISTICO PESQUERO. a. Subsecretaria de Agricultura Ganaderia y Pesca, Direccion Nacional de Pesca, Paseo Colon 922, 1o piso, Of. 146, 1063 Buenos Aires, Argentina. Dir. Jose Pellegrino. *Document type:* government publication.

AQUATIC SCIENCES & FISHERIES ABSTRACTS. PART 1: BIOLOGICAL SCIENCES AND LIVING RESOURCES. see *WATER RESOURCES — Abstracting, Bibliographies, Statistics*

AQUATIC SCIENCES & FISHERIES ABSTRACTS. PART 2: OCEAN TECHNOLOGY, POLICY AND NON-LIVING RESOURCES. see *WATER RESOURCES — Abstracting, Bibliographies, Statistics*

FISH AND FISHERIES — ABSTRACTING, BIBLIOGRAPHIES, STATISTICS

639 US ISSN 1045-6031
AQUATIC SCIENCES & FISHERIES ABSTRACTS. PART 3: AQUATIC POLLUTION AND ENVIRONMENTAL QUALITY. Variant title: Aquatic Pollution and Environmental Quality. 1990. bi-m. $245 (foreign $270). (Food and Agriculture Organization of the U.N.) Cambridge Scientific Abstracts, 7200 Wisconsin Ave., 6th Fl., Bethesda, MD 20814. TEL 301-961-6700. FAX 301-961-6720. (Co-sponsors: U.N. Division for Ocean Affairs and the Law of the Sea; Intergovernmental Oceanographic Commission; U.N. Environment Programme) Document type: abstracting/indexing.
●Also available online. Vendor(s): DIMDI, DIALOG Information Services, Inc. (File no.44), European Space Agency, STN International.
Also available on CD-ROM. Producer(s): SilverPlatter Information, Inc.
—BLDSC (1582.472000).
   Description: Devoted to contamination problems of oceans, seas, lakes, rivers, and estuaries. Examines a spectrum of current aquatic and environmental issues.

639.2 AT ISSN 1037-6879
AUSTRALIA. BUREAU OF AGRICULTURAL AND RESOURCE ECONOMICS. AUSTRALIAN FISHERIES STATISTICS (YEAR). a. Aus.$18. Australian Bureau of Agricultural and Resource Economics, G.P.O. Box 1563, Canberra, A.C.T. 2601, Australia. TEL 06-272-2211. FAX 06-272-2001. Document type: government publication, bulletin.
   Description: Provides production and trade data for the fishing industry of Australia.

AUSTRALIA. BUREAU OF STATISTICS. NORTHERN TERRITORY OFFICE. AGRICULTURE AND FISHING, NORTHERN TERRITORY. see *AGRICULTURE — Abstracting, Bibliographies, Statistics*

639.2 AT
AUSTRALIA. DEPARTMENT OF PRIMARY INDUSTRIES AND ENERGY. BACKGROUND FISHERIES STATISTICS. 1987. a. free. Department of Primary Industries and Energy, Fisheries Policy Branch, G.P.O. Box 858, Canberra, A.C.T. 2601, Australia. FAX 06-272-4215. Document type: government publication.
   Formerly: Australia. Department of Primary Industries and Energy. Basic Fish Statistics.

639.2 CN
BRITISH COLUMBIA COMMERCIAL CATCH STATISTICS: BY SPECIES, GEAR, MONTH AND AREA. a. Department of Fisheries and Oceans, Pacific Region, 410-555 W. Hastings St., Vancouver, B.C. V6B 5G3, Canada. TEL 604-666-3810. charts; illus.; stat.
   Formerly: British Columbia Commercial Catch Statistics: Herring, Groundfish, Shellfish and Other Fish.

388.3 310 CN
CANADA. DEPARTMENT OF FISHERIES AND OCEANS. PACIFIC REGION. ANNUAL SUMMARY OF BRITISH COLUMBIA CATCH STATISTICS. 1951. a. Department of Fisheries and Oceans, Pacific Region, 410-555 West Hastings St., Vancouver, B.C. V6B 5G3, Canada. TEL 604-666-3810.

639 CN
CANADIAN FISHERIES. STATISTICAL HIGHLIGHTS. 1984. a. Department of Fisheries & Oceans, Communications Directorate, 200 Kent St., Ottawa, Ont. K1A 0E6, Canada. Ed. Tim Hsu. circ. 2,400. (also avail. in microfiche from MML)

639.2 CC
CHINESE FISHERIES ABSTRACTS. (Text in Chinese) 1985. bi-m. $80. Zhongguo Shuichan Kexue Yanjiuyuan - Chinese Academy of Fishery Sciences, Fishery Scientific and Technical Information Institute, 150 Qingta Cun, Yongding Nanlu, Beijing 100039, People's Republic of China. TEL 8214442. Eds. Wang Minsheng, Lu Xueqi. adv. contact: Ningsheng Yang. bk.rev.; film rev.; software rev.; bibl.; illus. Document type: abstracting/indexing.
   Formerly: Zhongguo Nongye Wenzhai. Shuichan - Chinese Agriculture Abstracts. Aquatic Products (ISSN 1000-5978)
   Description: Covers fishery resource and environmental protection, fishing, marine aquaculture, disease control, feed and fertilizer, fishery machinery and fishery economics.

639.3 CC
CHINESE FISHERY ABSTRACTS (ENGLISH EDITION). (Text in English) 1988. a. $25. Zhongguo Shuichan Kexue Yanjiuyuan - Chinese Academy of Fishery Sciences, Fishery Scientific and Technical Information Institute, 150 Qingta Cun, Yongding Nanlu, Beijing 100039, People's Republic of China. TEL 8214442. FAX 8214685. Ed. Qiu Lijia. Document type: abstracting/indexing.
   Description: Covers fishery resource and environmental protection, fishing, marine aquaculture, freshwater aquaculture, disease control, feed and fertilizer, fishery products processing, fishery equipment and vessels, and fishery economics.

630 016 UN ISSN 0304-582X
F A O DOCUMENTATION - CURRENT BIBLIOGRAPHY. (Text in English, French, Spanish; summaries in English) 1967. bi-m. free. Food and Agriculture Organization of the United Nations, Sales & Distribution Section, Via delle Terme di Caracalla, 00100 Rome, Italy. abstr.; bibl.; index. circ. 4,500. (also avail. in microfiche)
   Formerly: F A O Documentation - Current Index (ISSN 0014-5580)

639 016 US ISSN 1042-6299
SH1
FISHERIES REVIEW; an abstracting service for fishery research and management. 1955. q. $14 (foreign $17.50). U.S. Fish and Wildlife Service (Ft. Collins), 1201 Oak Ridge Dr., Ste. 200, Ft. Collins, CO 80525-5589. TEL 303-223-9709. (Subscr. to: Superintendent of Documents, U.S. Government Printing Office, Box 371954, Pittsburgh, PA 15250-7954. TEL 202-783-3238. FAX 202-512-2233) Ed. Jeffrey Humphrey. bk.rev.; index. circ. 2,000. (back issues avail.) Document type: abstracting/indexing, government publication.
●Also available on CD-ROM. Producer(s): NISC (Wildlife Review/Fisheries Review; Fish & Fisheries Worldwide).
   Formerly: Sport Fishery Abstracts (ISSN 0038-786X)
   Description: Abstracts articles from the current literature in sport fishery research and management.

639.2 310 US ISSN 0162-6108
FROZEN FISHERY PRODUCTS. ANNUAL SUMMARY. a. U.S. National Marine Fisheries Service, National Oceanic and Atmospheric Administration, 1335 East-West Hwy., Silver Spring, MD 20910. TEL 301-713-2328. (Dist. by: Superintendent of Documents, U.S. Government Printing Office, Box 371954, Pittsburgh, PA 14250-7954. TEL 202-783-3238. FAX 202-512-2233) (also avail. in microfiche from CIS; reprint service avail. from CIS) Indexed: Amer.Stat.Ind. (1975-). Document type: government publication.

639 338.2 GW ISSN 0072-3673
HA1231
GERMANY. STATISTISCHES BUNDESAMT. FACHSERIE 3, LAND- UND FORSTWIRTSCHAFT, FISCHEREI; REIHE 4.5: FISCHEREI. (Includes subseries: Hochsee- und Kuestenfischerei; Bodenseefischerei) m. (plus a.). DM.49.20. 65180 Wiesbaden, Germany. TEL 0611-75-1. FAX 0611-724000. TELEX 61186-STBA-D. Document type: government publication.

639.2 UK ISSN 0953-8348
GREAT BRITAIN. SEA FISH INDUSTRY AUTHORITY. KEY INDICATORS. q. £35. Sea Fish Industry Authority, 18 Logie Mill, Logie Green Rd., Edinburgh EH7 4HG, Scotland. TEL 031-558-3331. FAX 031-558-1442. Document type: government publication.
   Description: Contains data and statistical analysis of UK fish landings, structure of the UK fishing fleet, and trade and consumption of fish commodities.

639.2 GR ISSN 0256-3584
SH273
GREECE. NATIONAL STATISTICAL SERVICE. RESULTS OF SEA FISHERY SURVEY BY MOTOR VESSELS. (Text in English and Greek) 1964. a. $3. National Statistical Service of Greece, Statistical Information and Publications Division, 14-16 Lycourgou St., 10166 Athens, Greece. TEL 3244-748. FAX 3222205. TELEX 216734 ESYE GR.

639 DK ISSN 1018-1571
SH253
I C E S FISHERIES STATISTICS/BULLETIN STATISTIQUE DES PECHES MARITIMES. (Text in English) 1906. a. price varies. International Council for the Exploration of the Sea, Palaegade 2-4, DK-1261 Copenhagen K, Denmark. FAX 33-934215. TELEX 22498 ICES DK. (Subscr. to: C.A. Reitzels Boghandel, Noerregade 20, DK-1165, Copenhagen K, Denmark) stat. circ. 350. (back issues avail.) Document type: bulletin.
   Formerly: International Council for the Exploration of the Sea. Bulletin Statistique (ISSN 0373-2045)

597 PH ISSN 0115-5997
I C L A R M BIBLIOGRAPHIES. 1980. irreg. price varies. International Center for Living Aquatic Resources Management, M.C.P.O. Box 2631, 0718 Makati, Metro Manila, Philippines. TEL 2-818-0466. FAX 2-816-3183. TELEX 64794-ICLARM-PN. Document type: bibliography.

639 016 II ISSN 0970-6879
INDIAN FISHERIES ABSTRACTS. 1962. q. exchange basis. Central Inland Capture Fisheries Research Institute, Barrackpore 743 101, West Bengal, India. TELEX 021-8552 CIFI IN. Ed. V.V. Sugunan. cum.index. circ. 210. (processed)
   Formerly: Bibliography of Indian Fisheries.

639.2 SP
INFORME DE LA PESQUERIA DE LA ANCHOA EN EL ANO (YEAR). 1991. a. Nekazaritza eta Arrantza Saila, Ozeanografi, Arrartza eta Elikadurarako Teknologia eta Ikerketa Erakundea - Departamento de Agricultura y Pesca, Instituto de Investigacion y Tecnologia para la Oceanografia, Pesca y Alimentacion) Eusko Juarlaritzaren Argitalpen-Zerbitzu Nagusia - Servicio Central de Publicaciones del Gobierno Vasco, Duque de Wellington, 2, 010˰ 1 Vitoria-Gasteiz, Spain. circ. 2,000.

639.2 310 SP
INTERNATIONAL COMMISSION FOR THE CONSERVATION OF ATLANTIC TUNAS. STATISTICAL BULLETIN. (Text in English, French and Spanish) 1971. a. 2500 ptas.($25) to qualified personnel or on exchange basis. International Commission for the Conservation of Atlantic Tunas, Principe de Vergara 17, 28001 Madrid, Spain. Ed. P.M. Miyake. circ. controlled. (also avail. in microfiche from CIS) Indexed: IIS.

574.192 JA
KOSO KOGAKU KENKYUKAI KOENKAI KOEN YOSHISHU/JAPANESE SOCIETY OF ENZYME ENGINEERING. ABSTRACTS OF ANNUAL MEETING. (Text in English, Japanese) s-a. Koso Kogaku Kenkyukai, Tanabe Seiyaku Oyo Seikagaku Kenkyujo, 16-89 Kashima 3-chome, Yodogawa-ku, Osaka 532, Japan. Document type: abstracting/indexing.

639 KU
KUWAIT. CENTRAL STATISTICAL OFFICE. FISHING STATISTICS BULLETIN/KUWAIT. AL-IDARAH AL-MARKAZIYYAH LIL-IHSA'. NASHRAH IHSA'AT AL-THARWAH AL-SAMAKIYYAH. (Text in Arabic) 1972. a., latest 1992. Central Statistical Office - Al-Idarah al-Markaziyyah il-Ihsa', P.O. Box 26188, Safat 13122, Kuwait. TEL 965-2428200. FAX 965-2430464. TELEX 22468 TAKHTET KT. Document type: government publication.
   Description: Provides statistical data at the wholesale and retail levels by quantity and type of fish.

639.2 MH
MACAO. DIRECCAO DOS SERVICOS DE ESTATISTICA E CENSOS. ESTATISTICAS DA PESCA/MACAO. CENSUS AND STATISTICS DEPARTMENT. STATISTICS OF FISHERY. (Text in Chinese, Portuguese) 1987. a. free. Direccao dos Servicos de Estatistica e Censos, Rua Inacio Baptista, No.4-6, P.O. Box 3022, Macao. TEL 3995311. FAX 307825. Document type: government publication.
   Description: Contains information on quantities and types of fish caught in the region.

FLORIST TRADE

639.2   MH
MACAO. DIRECCAO DOS SERVICOS DE ESTATISTICA E CENSOS. INQUERITO AS EMBARCACOES DE PESCA/MACAO. CENSUS AND STATISTICS DEPARTMENT. SURVEY OF FISHING VESSELS. (Text in Chinese, Portuguese) 1987. irreg. free. Direccao dos Servicos de Estatistica e Censos, Rua Inacio Baptista, No.4-6, P.O. Box 3022, Macao. TEL 3995311. FAX 307825. **Document type:** government publication.
   Description: Information on the structures and operating characteristics of fishing vessels and entrepeneurs.

MARINE SCIENCE CONTENTS TABLES. see *BIOLOGY — Abstracting, Bibliographies, Statistics*

MONTHLY STATISTICS ON AGRICULTURE, FORESTRY AND FISHERIES/NORIN SUISAN TOKEI GEPPO. see *AGRICULTURE — Abstracting, Bibliographies, Statistics*

639 011   CN   ISSN 0250-6394
SH1
N A F O STATISTICAL BULLETIN. 1952. a. price varies. Northwest Atlantic Fisheries Organization, P.O. Box 638, Dartmouth, NS B2Y 3Y9, Canada: TEL 902-469-9105. FAX 902-469-5729. TELEX 019-31475. Ed. T. Amaratunga. **Indexed:** Biol.Abstr., CS Ind., IIS.
   —BLDSC (8447.638000).
   Formerly (until 1980): International Commission for the Northwest Atlantic Fisheries. Statistical Bulletin (ISSN 0074-266X)
   Description: Fishery statistics for Northwest Atlantic region.

639.2 310   US   ISSN 1055-2766
HD9454
N M F S FISHERIES MARKET NEWS REPORT. (National Marines Fishery Service) 1981. 3/w. $269. Urner Barry Publications, Inc., Box 389, Toms River, NJ 08754. TEL 908-240-5330. FAX 908-341-0891. Ed. Joseph Soja. adv. circ. 700. (back issues avail.)
● Also available online.
   Formerly (until 1991): Weekly Statistical Fishery Report (ISSN 0734-9378)
   Description: National market report on fisheries.

574.19   JA
NIHON SEIKAGAKKAI KINKI SHIBU REIKAI YOSHISHU/JAPANESE BIOCHEMICAL SOCIETY. KINKI BRANCH OFFICE. ABSTRACTS OF MEETING. (Text in Japanese) a. Nihon Seikagakkai, Kinki Shibu, Kyoto Daigaku Kagaku Kenkyujo, Biseibutsu Kagaku Kenkyu Bumon, Gokanosho, Uji-shi, Kyoto 611, Japan. **Document type:** abstracting/indexing.

574.19   JA
NIHON TANPAKU KOGAKKAI NENKAI PUROGURAMU YOSHISHU/PROTEIN ENGINEERING SOCIETY OF JAPAN. ABSTRACTS OF THE MEETING. (Text in English, Japanese) 1990. a. Nihon Tanpaku Kogakkai, Tokyo Rika Daigaku Seimei Kagaku Kenkyujo, Tsugita Kenkyushitsu, 2669 Yamazaki, Noda-shi, Chiba-ken 278, Japan. **Document type:** abstracting/indexing.

639   CN
NORTH PACIFIC ANADROMOUS FISH COMMISSION. STATISTICAL YEARBOOK. 1970. a. exchange basis. North Pacific Anadromous Fish Commission, 6640 N.W. Marine Dr., Vancouver, B.C. V6T 1X2, Canada. TEL 604-228-1128. FAX 604-228-1135. circ. 500. (also avail. in microfiche from CIS) **Indexed:** IIS.
   Formerly: International North Pacific Fisheries Commission. Statistical Yearbook (ISSN 0535-1588)

639.3 310   NO   ISSN 0333-3728
NORWAY. STATISTISK SENTRALBYRAA. FISKERISTATISTIKK. (Text in English and Norwegian) 1868. a. NOK 70. Statistisk Sentralbyraa - Central Bureau of Statistics, P.O. Box 8131 Dep., N-0033 Oslo 1, Norway. TEL 47-22-864500. FAX 47-22-864973. circ. 1,150. **Indexed:** Biol.Abstr.
   Description: Statistics of fisheries in Norway.

PESCARE; la rivista dei pescatori. see *SPORTS AND GAMES*

639.2   BL   ISSN 0103-6181
PESQUISA DE ESTOQUES. 1974. s-a. Fundacao Instituto Brasileiro de Geografia e Estatistica, Av. Franklin Roosevelt 166, Centro, 20021-120 Rio de Janeiro, Brazil. TEL 021-284-7690. FAX 021-228-9575. **Document type:** government publication.
   Former titles (until 1988): Pesquisa Especial de Armazenagem; (until 1986): Armazenagem e Estocagem a seco e a Frio (ISSN 0101-028X)

639   PO
PORTUGAL. INSTITUTO NACIONAL DE ESTATISTICA. ESTATISTICAS DA PESCA - STATISTIQUES DE LA PECHE. CONTINENTE, ACORES E MADEIRA. (Text and summaries in French and Portuguese) 1969. a. Esc.1700. Instituto Nacional de Estatistica, Av. Antonio Jose de Almeida, 1078 Lisbon Codex, Portugal. (Subscr. to: Imprensa Nacional, Casa da Moeda, Direccao Comercial, Rua D. Francisco Manuel de Melo 5, 1000 Lisbon, Portugal) stat. (processed)
   Formerly: Portugal. Instituto Nacional de Estatistica. Estatisticas da Pesca - Statistiques de la Peche (ISSN 0377-225X)

QUEBEC (PROVINCE). BUREAU DE STATISTIQUE. STATISTIQUES DE L'AGRICULTURE, DES PECHES ET DE L'ALIMENTATION, EDITION (YEAR). see *AGRICULTURE — Abstracting, Bibliographies, Statistics*

639.2   UK   ISSN 0951-9882
SALMON FARMING; a monthly list of literature relating to the farming of Atlantic Salmon (Salmo salar L.), and related species. 1985. m. £30 to EC member countries; non EC member countries £40. The Scottish Office, Agriculture and Fisheries Department, Marine Laboratory, P.O. Box 101, Victoria Rd., Aberdeen AB9 8DB, Scotland. TEL 44-224-876544. FAX 44-224-295511. TELEX 73587.
   Description: Lists literature relating to the farming of Atlantic salmon and related species, divided into three sections: biology, ecology, economics.

315.61   TU
TURKEY. DEVLET ISTATISTIK ENSTITUSU. SU URUNLERI ISTATISTIKLERI/TURKEY. STATE INSTITUTE OF STATISTICS. FISHERY STATISTICS. (Text in English, Turkish) 1968. a., latest 1991. $25. Devlet Istatistik Enstitusu, Necatibey Caddesi No. 114, 06100 Ankara, Turkey. TEL 90-312-4185027. FAX 90-312-4170432. circ. 1,120. **Document type:** government publication.
   Supersedes: Turkey. Develet Istatistik Enstitusu. Su Urunleri Anket Sonuclari (ISSN 1013-6177)

639.2   NE   ISSN 0921-4283
VISSERIJ IN CIJFERS. (Text in Dutch; summaries in English) 1962. a. fl.13.50. Landbouw-Economisch Instituut, Conradkade 175, 2517 CL The Hague, Netherlands. TEL 31-70-3308330. FAX 31-70-3615624. Ed. W. Smit. **Document type:** government publication.

639 011   ZA   ISSN 0514-8731
ZAMBIA. CENTRAL STATISTICAL OFFICE. FISHERIES STATISTICS (NATURAL WATERS). 1965. a. $2. Central Statistical Office, P.O. Box 31908, Lusaka, Zambia. TEL 211-231.

FLORIST TRADE

see *Gardening and Horticulture–Florist Trade*

FOLKLORE

A N Q: A QUARTERLY JOURNAL OF SHORT ARTICLES, NOTES AND REVIEWS. see *LITERATURE*

ACADEMIA SCIENTIARUM HUNGARICA. ACTA ETHNOGRAPHICA. see *ANTHROPOLOGY*

398   SW   ISSN 0065-0897
ACTA ACADEMIAE REGIAE GUSTAVI ADOLPHI. (Text in English, German and Scandinavian languages; summaries in English) 1933. irreg., no.61, 1992. price varies. Kungliga Gustav Adolfs Akademien, Klostergatan 2, S-753 21 Uppsala, Sweden. (Dist. by: Almqvist & Wiksell International, P.O. Box 638, S-10128 Stockholm, Sweden) Ed. Lennart Elmevik.

AD MARGINEM; Randbemerkungen zur musikalischen Volkskunde. see *MUSIC*

398   US
AEROSTATICAL NOTES, ANVIL FIRERS SALUTES, AND CANNON SHOOTERS TARGET. (Text in Albanian, English, French, German, Serbo-Croatian) irreg. price varies. Advanced Anachronistic Anabiosis Associates Amalgamated, Box 234, Alviso, CA 95002-0234. Ed. J.J. Saxon-Gomez.

398 795.4   GW
AK EXPRESS; Internationalen Fachzeitschrift fuer Ansichtskarten-, Heimat-, Modir-, und Forschungssammler. 1976. q. DM.16($12) Verlag Pomp und Sobkowiak, Weidkamp 283, 45356 Essen, Germany. Ed. Guenter Sobrowiak. circ. 3,000. (back issues avail.)

398 949.5   GR
AKADEMIA ATHENON. KENTRON EREVNES TIS HELLENIKIS LAOGRAPHIAS. EPETERIS. (Text in English, French, German, Greek; summaries in English, French, Greek) 1939. irreg. price varies. Akademia Athenon, Kentron Erevnes tis Hellenikis Laographias, Leoforos Sygrou 129, 117 45 Athens, Greece. TEL 93-44-811. Ed. Anna Papamichael-Koutroubas. bibl.; cum.index. circ. 500. (back issues avail.) **Indexed:** Amer.Hist. & Life, Hist.Abstr., M.L.A.
   Formerly: Laographikon Archeion. Epeteris.

ALEMANNISCH DUNKT UES GUET. see *LINGUISTICS*

398   NE   ISSN 0927-1791
▼**ALLEDAAGSE DINGEN;** tijdschrift over volkscultuur in Nederland. 1992. 6/yr. fl.55. Stichting Nederlands Centrum voor Volkscultuur, Lucasbolwerk 11, 3512 EH Utrecht, Netherlands. TEL 31-30-319997. FAX 31-30-334047. Ed. Ineke Strouken.
   Description: Current information on traditional and popular culture in the Netherlands.

ALLEES ALL AROUND; includes Alley, Ally, Allie, Alyea. see *GENEALOGY AND HERALDRY*

398   GW
ALTES HANDWERK. 1972. irreg., no.60, 1993. price varies. (Gesellschaft fuer Volkskunde, Basel, Abteilung Film, SZ) Dr. Rudolf Habelt GmbH, Am Buchenhang 1, 53115 Bonn, Germany. TEL 0228-232016. FAX 0228-232017. Ed. Paul Hugger. **Document type:** monographic series.

AMERICAN DANCE CIRCLE. see *DANCE*

398   US   ISSN 0745-5178
GR105
AMERICAN FOLKLORE SOCIETY NEWSLETTER. 6/yr. $16. (American Folklore Society) American Anthropological Association, 4350 N. Fairfax Dr., Ste. 640, Arlington, VA 22203. TEL 703-528-1902. Ed. Shalom Staub. circ. 2,000. (looseleaf format; reprint service avail. from ISI,UMI) **Document type:** newsletter.
   Description: Covers folklore, material culture, music, art and local history.

AMERICAN INDIAN QUARTERLY. see *ANTHROPOLOGY*

AMERICAN UNIVERSITY STUDIES. SERIES 21. REGIONAL STUDIES. see *ETHNIC INTERESTS*

398   FR
LES AMIS DE CURNONSKY. 1970. q. 150 F.($15) 17, rue Coysevox B.P. 259, 75866 Paris Cedex 18, France. TEL 1-46-27-33-11. bk.rev. (back issues avail.)
   Formerly: Angevins de Paris.

398   RM
ANUARUL ARHIVEI DE FOLCLOR. (Text in Rumanian; summaries in English, French, German) 1980. a. 120 lei. (Institutul Arhiva de Folclor a Academiei Romane) Editura Academiei Romane, Bucharest, Str. Republicii 9, Cluj-Japoca, Rumania. Ed. Ion Cuceu. bk.rev.; abstr.; bibl.; charts; illus.; stat. circ. 1,000. (back issues avail.)
   Formerly: Anuarul de Folclor.

398   PE   ISSN 0255-4887
APACHETA; revista de las tradiciones populares del Peru. 1977. s-a. $2. Francisco Iriate Brenner, Ed. & Pub., Apdo. 1408, Lima, Peru. circ. 1,000.

APPELTJES VAN HET MEETJESLAND. see *HISTORY — History Of Europe*

ARCHIV FUER VOELKERKUNDE. see *ANTHROPOLOGY*

FOLKLORE

ARCHIVIO PER L'ALTO ADIGE; rivista di studi alpini. see LINGUISTICS

ARCHIVOS DE HISTORIA ANDINA. see HISTORY — History Of North And South America

ARMSTRONG NEWS. see ETHNIC INTERESTS

ARSTRYCK. see ARCHAEOLOGY

398   HU   ISSN 0139-4649
GN1
ARTES POPULARES. a. Lorand Eotvos University, Department of Folklore, Egyetem-ter 1-3, P.O.B. 109, 1364 Budapest, V, Hungary. Eds. Luiz Boglar, Geza Kezdi Nagy.

398   VE   ISSN 0254-1572
ARTESANIA Y FOLKLORE DE VENEZUELA. 1975. q. Bs.180($15) Apdo. 60935, Chacao, Caracas 1060, Venezuela. TEL 02-6623694. FAX 02-7629118. Ed. Fructuoso Pernia. adv.; charts; illus. circ. 10,000. **Document type:** academic/scholarly publication.
    Description: Covers the folklore and handicrafts of Venezuela and other Latin-American countries.

398   SW   ISSN 0066-8176
GR1
ARV; Scandinavian yearbook of folklore. (Text in English and German; summaries in English) 1945. a. SEK 210. (Kungliga Gustav Adolfs Akademien - Royal Gustavus Adolphus Academy) A W I International AB, Box 4627, S-116 91 Stockholm, Sweden. TEL 468-640-8800. FAX 468-641-1180. Ed. Dag Strombäck. bk.rev. circ. 500. **Indexed:** Amer.Hist.& Life, Anthropol.Lit., Hist.Abstr., M.L.A.

398   JA   ISSN 0385-2342
GR330
ASIAN FOLKLORE STUDIES. (Text in English) 1942. s-a. 3000 Yen($22) to individuals; institutions 6000 Yen ($40) (effective 1993). Nanzan University, Nanzan Anthropological Institute - Nanzan Daigaku Nanzan Jinruigaku Kenkyujo, 18, Yamazato-cho, Showa-ku, Nagoya 466, Japan. TEL 052-832-3111. FAX 052-833-6157. Ed. Peter Knecht. adv.; bk.rev.; bibl.; illus. circ. 350. (also avail. in microfiche from IDC; reprint service avail. from ISI,UMI) **Indexed:** A.I.C.P., Abstr.Pop.Cult., Arts & Hum.Cit.Ind., Curr.Cont., E.I., Hum.Ind., M.L.A., Rel.Ind.One. **Document type:** academic/scholarly publication. —UnCover; UMI.
    Formerly (until vol.22, 1963): Folklore Studies.
    Description: Contains articles on Asian oral tradition, belief, myth, medicine and art.

ASTRADO; revue bilingue de Provence. see LITERATURE

ATLAS POLSKICH STROJOW LUDOWYCH. see ANTHROPOLOGY

ATOKA; Yoruba photoplay series. see LITERATURE

398 369.4   AT   ISSN 0728-5531
AUSTRALIAN CHILDREN'S FOLKLORE NEWSLETTER. 1981. 2/yr. Aus.$6 (foreign Aus.$8). Australian Centre, University of Melbourne, Parkville, Vic. 3052, Australia. TEL 03-3447235. FAX 03-3477731. Eds. Gwenda Davey, June Factor. bk.rev. circ. 100. (back issues avail.) **Document type:** academic/scholarly publication, newsletter.

398 301   AT   ISSN 0819-0852
GR365
AUSTRALIAN FOLKLORE. 1987. s-a. Aus.$20 to individuals (foreign Aus.$25); institutions Aus.$30 (foreign Aus.$35) (effective 1994). Australian Folklore Association, c/o Prof. J.S. Ryan, Ed., Dept. of English & Communication Studies, University of New England, Armidale, N.S.W. 2351, Australia. TEL 067-732601. FAX 067-732623. bk.rev.; circ. 250 (paid). (back issues avail.)
    Description: Covers Australian folklore, folklife; contemporary and historical.

AVALON TO CAMELOT; issued quarterly on matters Arthurian. see LITERATURE

AYRSHIRE MONOGRAPHS. see ARCHAEOLOGY

B D A A NEWSLETTER. (Balalaika and Domra Association of America) see MUSIC

398 398   IT   ISSN 0067-9860
B R A D S. (Bollettino del Repertorio e dell'Atlante Demologico Sardo) (Text in Italian; summaries in English and German) 1966. irreg., no.15, 1992-93. L.25000 or exchange basis. Universita degli Studi di Cagliari, Cattedra di Storia delle Tradizioni Popolari, Cagliari, Italy. TEL 070-271573. FAX 070-291201. (Dist. by: Libreria CUEC, Via Is Mirrionis 12, 09123 Cagliari, Italy) Ed. Enrica Delitala. bk.rev. circ. 700. **Document type:** academic/scholarly publication.

398   CC
BANG JIN MEI DUO. (Editions in Chinese and Tibetan) q. Y3.60 for Chinese ed.; Tibetan ed. Y3. Zhongguo Minjian Wenyijia Xiehui, Xizang Fenhui - China Folk Artists Association, Xizang Chapter, Lhasa, Xizang (Tibet) 850001, People's Republic of China. (Dist. overseas by: Jiangsu Publications Import & Export Corp., 56 Gao Yun Ling, Nanjing, Jiangsu, P.R.C.)
    Description: Carries Tibetan folklores, legends, myths, ballads, proverbs and reviews of Tibetan folk art.

398 745   GW   ISSN 0067-4591
BAUERNHAEUSER DER SCHWEIZ. 1965. irreg., no.27, 1990. price varies. Dr. Rudolf Habelt GmbH, Am Buchenhang 1, 53115 Bonn, Germany. TEL 0228-232016. FAX 0228-232017. **Document type:** monographic series.

BAYERISCHE KRIPPENFREUND. see RELIGIONS AND THEOLOGY

398   GW   ISSN 0067-4729
BAYERISCHES JAHRBUCH FUER VOLKSKUNDE. 1950. a. DM.72. (Bayerische Akademie der Wissenschaften, Institut fuer Volkskunde) Prograph GmbH, Agnes-Bernauer-Str. 149e, Germany. TEL 089-282704. Ed. J. Bauer. bk.rev. circ. 800.

BAYERISCHES SONNTAGSBLATT FUER DIE KATHOLISCHE FAMILIE. see RELIGIONS AND THEOLOGY — Roman Catholic

BEND OF THE RIVER; the magazine of the historic Maumee Valley. see HISTORY — History Of North And South America

398   US   ISSN 1041-2212
PN982
BESTIA. 1989. a. fl.95($55) includes membership (effective 1994). (Beast Fable Society) John Benjamins Publishing Co., 821 Bethlehem Pike, Philadelphia, PA 19118. TEL 215-836-1200. FAX 215-836-1204. (And: Amsteldijk 44, P.O. Box 75577, 1070 AN Amsterdam, Netherlands. TEL 31-20-6738156. FAX 31-20-6792956) Ed. Benjamin Bennani. (back issues avail.) **Document type:** academic/scholarly publication, proceedings.
    Description: Presents articles dealing with the beast fable and its sister genres in all literatures, languages and periods

398 301.2   BL   ISSN 0104-060X
BIBLIOGRAFICA FOLCLORICA. 1977. a. Cr.$1000 (effective May 1994). Fundacao Nacional de Arte, Coordenacao de Folclore e Cultura Popular, Rua do Catete, 179, 22220 Rio de Janeiro RJ, Brazil. TEL 021-285-0441. FAX 021-262-4895. TELEX 31359. (Subscr. to: I.B.A.C., Rua da Imprensa 16, 20030 Rio de Janeiro RJ, Brazil. TEL 021-297-6116) (Co-sponsor: Instituto Brasileiro de Arte e Cultura) bk.rev. circ. 2,000. **Document type:** bibliography.

BIBLIOTECA DE LA TRADICION ORAL ANDINA. see HISTORY — History Of North And South America

398   UK
BLACK COUNTRY; tales of terror. 1984. q. £7.95. Mercia Publicity, Bugle House, 41 High St., Cradley Heath, Warley, W. Midlands B64 5HL, England. TEL 0384-67678. FAX 0384-410045. Ed. Bob Taylor. circ. 15,000. **Document type:** newsletter.
    Description: A backward glance at the darker side of Anglo Saxon heritage. Murders, hangings, folklore customs and the supernatural are drawn mostly from the 19th century.

398   UK   ISSN 1351-2447
BLACK COUNTRY BUGLE ANNUAL. 1973. a. £4.95. Mercia Publicity, Bugle House, 41 High St., Cradley Heath, Warley, W. Midlands B64 5HL, England. TEL 0384-67678. FAX 0384-410045. Ed. Aristotle Tump. adv. circ. 24,000. **Document type:** bulletin.
    Description: A Christmas compendium of life in the Midland shires of England. Old ghost stories, seasonal customs, legends, traditional pastimes.

398   UK
BLACK COUNTRY GHOSTS AND MYSTERIES. 1987. q. £8.95. Mercia Publicity, Bugle House, 41 High St., Cradley Heath, Warley, W. Midlands B64 5HL, England. TEL 0384-67678. FAX 0384-410045. Ed. Bob Taylor. circ. 15,000.
    Description: A selection of ghost stories and murder mysteries which possess a supernatural element. All based on actual cases and testimony.

BLAETTER FUER HEIMATKUNDE. see HISTORY

BLUE SMOKE. see LITERATURE

BLUES UNLIMITED. see MUSIC

398 914.40€   FR   ISSN 0991-532X
BOULITE. 3/yr. 550 F. Geste Editions, Maison des Ruralies, B.P. 1, 79230 Vouille, France. TEL 49-75-67-71. Ed. Jean-Louis Neveu.
    Description: Covers traditional life in the Poitou area.

BRIDGE (SALEM). see ETHNIC INTERESTS

398   US   ISSN 0749-0747
BUDSTIKKEN. (Text in English and Norwegian) 1970. s-a. $8 (foreign $10). Valdres Samband, P.O. Box 682, Hawley, MN 56549-0682. TEL 218-483-4461. Ed. June Adele Dolva. adv.; bk.rev. circ. 1,200.

398   BU   ISSN 0323-9861
BULGARSKI FOLKLOR. (Text in various languages) 1975. q. 1.50 lv. per issue. (Bulgarska Akademiia na Naukite) Publishing House of the Bulgarian Academy of Sciences, Acad. G. Bonchev St., Bldg. 6, 1113 Sofia, Bulgaria. Ed. P. Dinekov. circ. 1,380. (reprint service avail. from IRC)
—BLDSC (0018.538000).

398 954   II
C I I L. FOLKLORE SERIES. (Text in English, Hindi) 1975. irreg., latest 1987. Ministry of Human Resource Development, Central Institute of Indian Languages, Manasagangotri, Mysore 570 006, India. bibl.

398   BL   ISSN 0575-0075
CADERNOS DE FOLCLORE. 1975. irreg., no.35, 1986. Cr.$1000 (effective May 1994). Fundacao Nacional de Arte, Coordenacao de Folclore e Cultura Popular, Rua do Catete, 179, 22220 Rio de Janeiro RJ, Brazil. TEL 021-285-0441. FAX 021-262-4895. TELEX 31359. (Subscr. to: I.B.A.C., Rua da Imprensa 16, 20030 Rio de Janeiro RJ, Brazil. TEL 021-297-6116) (Co-sponsor: Instituto Brasileiro de Arte e Cultura) circ. 2,000. **Document type:** monographic series.

CAHIERS BRETONS/AR GWYR. see SOCIAL SCIENCES: COMPREHENSIVE WORKS

CALABRIA LETTERARIA. see LITERATURE

398 780   CN   ISSN 0708-4226
CANADA'S ATLANTIC FOLKLORE AND FOLKLIFE SERIES. 1979. a. Breakwater Books Ltd., P.O. Box 2188, St. John's, NF A1C 6E6, Canada. TEL 709-722-6680; 800-563-3333. FAX 709-753-0708.
    Description: Records and preserves a way of life peculiar to the Atlantic seaboard.

398   CN   ISSN 0225-2899
CANADIAN FOLKLORE/FOLKLORE CANADIEN. 1979. a. Can.$15. Folklore Studies Association of Canada, c/o Universite Laval, Cite Universitaire, Quebec, PQ G1K 7P4, Canada. TEL 418-656-7200. Ed. Laurier Turgeon. adv.; bk.rev. circ. 500. **Indexed:** Amer.Hist.& Life (1992-), Hist.Abstr. (1992-). **Document type:** academic/scholarly publication.

CANU GWERIN/FOLK SONG. see MUSIC

CAPE BRETON'S MAGAZINE; devoted to history, natural history & future of Cape Breton Island. see HISTORY — History Of North And South America

2546 FOLKLORE

CARINTHIA 1; Zeitschrift fuer geschichtliche Landeskunde von Kaernten. see HISTORY — History Of Europe

200 900 US ISSN 0528-1458
CARL NEWELL JACKSON LECTURES. irreg. price varies. Harvard University Press, 79 Garden St., Cambridge, MA 02138. TEL 617-495-2600. FAX 617-495-5898. **Document type:** monographic series.
Refereed Serial

CARPATHO-RUSYN AMERICAN. see ETHNIC INTERESTS

CATALOGO DANTE. see LITERATURE

CESKY LID/CZECH PEOPLE. see ANTHROPOLOGY

CHAR-KOOSTA NEWS; a weekly newspaper covering the Flathead Indian Reservation and the surrounding area. see ETHNIC INTERESTS

CHILDREN'S FOLKLORE REVIEW. see CHILDREN AND YOUTH — About

398 895.1 CC
CHU FENG. (Text in Chinese) bi-m. $21.20. Zhongguo Minjian Wenyijia Xiehui, Hunan Fenhui - China Folk Artists Association, Hunan Chapter, No. 35, Bayi Xilu, Changsha, Hunan 410000, People's Republic of China. TEL 47912. (Dist. in US by: China Books & Periodicals, Inc., 2929 24th St., San Francisco, CA 94110. TEL 415-282-2994) Ed. Ren Guangchun.
Description: Covers folk literature of Hunan Province.

CLANSMAN (HALIFAX). see ETHNIC INTERESTS

398 AU
COALDUST. 1978. m. Aus.$20. Tighes Hill Technical Union, Maitland Rd., Tighes Hill, N.S.W. 2297, Australia. TEL 049-67-4744. FAX 049-613692. circ. 150. (looseleaf format)
Description: Deals with folklore, music, education, and musical instruments.

398 BL
COLECAO ARQUIVOS DE FOLCLORE. 1969. irreg. Centro de Estudios Sociologicos de Juiz de Fora, Rua Halfeld 805-Sala 403, Caixa Postal 298, Juiz de Fora, Brazil.

398 BL
COLECAO PESQUISA. 1982. 4/yr. Comissao Estadual de Folclore e Artesanato, Secretaria de Estado da Cultura do Estado da Sao Paulo, Parque Ibirapuera, Sao Paulo, Brazil.

398 970 US ISSN 0736-6132
GR105
COME - ALL - YE; a review journal. 1977. q. $6 in U.S.; Canada $7; elsewhere $8. Legacy Books, 12 Meetinghouse Rd., Box 494, Hatboro, PA 19040-0494. TEL 215-675-6762. FAX 215-674-2826. Eds. Richard Burns, Lillian Krelove. adv.; bk.rev.; bibl. circ. 2,000. (back issues avail.) Indexed: Bk.Rev.Ind. (1983-), Child.Bk.Rev.Ind. (1983-). **Document type:** newsletter.
Description: Covers folklore and folklife, social history and community culture.

398 BL
COMISSAO GOIANA DE FOLCLORE. BOLETIM. 1977. q.? Comissao Goiana de Folclore, Rua 82, No. 455, Setor Sul, Goiana-Goias, Brazil.

398 FR ISSN 0413-9593
COMITE DU FOLKLORE CHAMPENOIS. BULLETIN. 1928. s-a. 100 F. Comite du Folklore Champenois, Biblioteheque Municipale, 1 passage H. Vendel, 51000 Chalons-sur-Marne, France. Ed.Bd. bk.rev.; index. circ. 500.

COMMUNITY HISTORY. see HISTORY — History Of Australasia And Other Areas

COMTE DE JETTE BULLETIN/GRAAFSCHAP JETTE BULLETIN. see ARCHAEOLOGY

COMUNIDADES Y CULTURAS PERUANAS. see ANTHROPOLOGY

COSTUME SOCIETY OF ONTARIO. NEWSLETTER. see CLOTHING TRADE — Fashions

COUNTRY DANCE AND SONG. see DANCE

COW NECK PENINSULA HISTORICAL JOURNAL. see HISTORY — History Of North And South America

CRITICAL STUDIES ON BLACK LIFE AND CULTURE. see ETHNIC INTERESTS

CROSSINGS. see GENEALOGY AND HERALDRY

398 PE
CUADERNOS DEL TALLER DE FOLKLORE. 1977. irreg. Universidad Nacional Federico Villareal, Direccion Universitaria de Proyeccion Social, Apdo. 1408, Lima, Peru. Ed. Francisco E. Iriarte Brenner. circ. 1,000.

398 CN ISSN 0701-0184
GR113
CULTURE & TRADITION. (Text in English and French) 1976. a. Can.$8. Memorial University of Newfoundland, Box 115, Arts and Admin. Bldg., St. John's, NF A1C 5S7, Canada. TEL 709-737-8402. E-mail: CULTURE@Kean.ucs.mun.ca. (Co-sponsor: Laval University) Ed.Bd. bk.rev.; illus. circ. 300. Indexed: M.L.A.
Description: Feature articles on Canadian folklore and related subjects.

398 AA ISSN 0257-6074
CULTURE POPULAIRE ALBANAISE. Albanian edition: Kultura Popullore (ISSN 0257-6082) (Text in French) 1981. a. Akademia e Shkencave e R P S S H, Instituti i Kultures Popullore - Academie des Sciences de la RPSA, Institut de Culture Populaire, Tirana, Albania. Ed. Alfred Uci. Indexed: Anthropol.Lit.

398 793.3 US ISSN 1048-972X
THE DAILY CLOG. 1984. m. $8. 95 E. Wayne Ave., Apt. 312, Silver Spring, MD 20901. TEL 301-495-0082. Ed. Julie Mangin. (back issues avail.) **Document type:** newsletter.
Description: Disseminates information on traditional Appalachian clogging and stringband music.

398 GW
DEUTSCHE GESELLSCHAFT FUER VOLKSKUNDE. D G V INFORMATIONEN. (Continues Its Mitteilungen) 1970. q. membership. Deutsche Gesellschaft fuer Volkskunde e.V., c/o Seminar fuer Volkskunde, University of Goettingen, Friedlaender Weg 2, 37085 Goettingen, Germany. bk.rev. circ. 1,100. Indexed: Dairy Sci.Abstr. **Document type:** newsletter.

398 GW
DEUTSCHE TRACHTENZEITUNG. 1947. bi-m. DM.22. Verband Deutscher Heimat- und Volkstrachtenvereine e.V., Dorotheenstr. 21, 81825 Munich, Germany. TEL 089-4394448. **Document type:** newsletter.
Formerly: Trachtenzeitung.

DITHMARSCHEN; Zeitschrift fuer Landeskunde und Heimatpflege. see HISTORY

DRACULA NEWS JOURNAL. see LITERATURE — Science Fiction, Fantasy, Horror

301.2 US ISSN 0888-3165
F1
DUBLIN SEMINAR FOR NEW ENGLAND FOLKLIFE. ANNUAL PROCEEDINGS. 1976. a. $10. (Dublin Seminar for New England Folklife) Boston University, Scholarly Publications, 985 Commonwealth Ave., Boston, MA 02215. TEL 617-353-4106. Ed. Peter Benes. adv.; bibl.; charts; illus.; index. circ. 2,000. (back issues avail.) Indexed: Anthropol.Lit., Avery Ind.Archit.Per. **Document type:** proceedings.
Refereed Serial

390 800 US ISSN 0882-2549
THE DUPLEX PLANET. 1979. m. $12. Box 1230, Saratoga Springs, NY 12866. TEL 518-692-7410. Ed. David B. Greenberger. circ. 800. (back issues avail.)
Description: Answers questions for senior citizens at nursing homes.

EAGLE (NAUGATUCK). see ETHNIC INTERESTS

398 GW
EBBES. 1979. bi-m. DM.22.00. W E K A - Verlag, Industriestr. 21, 86438 Kissing, Germany. Ed. Franz R. Miller. adv.; bk.rev. circ. 10,000.

EDICIONES DEL PUEBLO. see LITERATURE

ELLINIKA; philological, historical and folkloric review. see CLASSICAL STUDIES

ENGLISH DANCE AND SONG. see MUSIC

398 MX ISSN 0071-1683
ESTUDIOS DE FOLKLORE. 1961. irreg., latest 1987. price varies. Universidad Nacional Autonoma de Mexico, Instituto de Investigaciones Esteticas, Circuito Mtro. Mario de la Cueva, Zona Cultural, Ciudad de la Investigacion en Humanidades, 04000 Mexico, D.F., Mexico.

398 PY
ESTUDIOS FOLKLORICOS PARAGUAYOS. 1978. irreg. Casilla Postal 611, Asuncion, Paraguay.

ETNOFOLK. see ANTHROPOLOGY

572 398 PL
ETNOLOGIA I ANTROPOLOGIA KULTUROWA. (Text in Polish; summaries in various languages) 1961. irreg., no.17, 1994. price varies. Adam Mickiewicz University Press, Nowowiejskiego 55, 61-734 Poznan, Poland. TEL 527-380. FAX 61-526425. TELEX 413260 UAMPL. **Document type:** academic/scholarly publication.
—BLDSC (9120.451500).
Former titles (until no.17, 1994): Etnografia (ISSN 0209-2077); Uniwersytet im. Adama Mickiewicza w Poznaniu. Wydzial Filozoficzno-Historyczny. Seria Etnograficia.
Description: Contains current research results of the university scholars, their Ph.D. works and monographs. Each volume contains the work of one author.

ETNOLOGIA Y FOLKLORE. see ANTHROPOLOGY

ETNOLOSKA TRIBINA. see ANTHROPOLOGY

398 IT
ETNOSTORIA. 1984. 3/yr. L.40000. Bulzoni Editore, Via dei Liburni n.14, 00185 Rome, Italy. TEL 06-4455207. FAX 06-4450355. Ed. Aurelio Rigoli.

ETUDES BALKANIQUES. see HISTORY — History Of Europe

EULENSPIEGEL-JAHRBUCH. see LITERATURE

398 FI ISSN 0014-5815
F F COMMUNICATIONS. (Folklore Fellows) (Text mainly in English; occasionally in French and German) 1910. irreg. (2-5/yr.) price varies. Suomalainen Tiedeakatemia - Academia Scientiarum Fennica, Mariankatu 5, SF-00170 Helsinki, Finland. (Subscr. to: Bookstore Tiedekirja, Kirkkokatu 14, SF-00170 Helsinki, Finland) Ed. Lauri Honko. cum.index. circ. 200. (back issues avail.; reprint service avail. from UMI) Indexed: Abstr.Folk.Stud., Arts & Hum.Cit.Ind., Bull.Signal., Curr.Cont., M.L.A., Ref.Zh.

398 GW ISSN 0014-6242
GR1
FABULA/REVUE D'ETUDES SUR LE CONTE POPULAIRE; Zeitschrift fuer Erzaehlforschung - journal of folktale studies. (Supplements avail.) (Text English, German) 1958. s-a. DM.190. Walter de Gruyter und Co., Genthiner Str. 13, 10785 Berlin, Germany. TEL 030-26005-0. FAX 030-26005251. TELEX 184027. (U.S. addr.: Walter de Gruyter, 200 Saw Mill Rd., Hawthorne, NY 10532) Eds. Rolf Wilhelm Brednich, Hans-Joerg Uther. adv.; bk.rev. Indexed: Arts & Hum.Cit.Ind., Curr.Cont., Ind.Bk.Rev.Hum., M.L.A. **Document type:** academic/scholarly publication.
—UnCover; SWETS. **CCC.**

FEDERATION ARCHEOLOGIQUE ET HISTORIQUE DE BELGIQUE. ANNALES/FEDERATIE VAN NEDERLANDSTALIGE VERENIDENIS VOOR OUDHEIDKUNDE EN GESCHIEDENIS VAN BELGISCHE. JAARBOEKEN. see HISTORY — History Of Europe

398 914.603 SP
FLAMENCO; boletin de informacion. vol.5, 1975. irreg. (2-3/yr.) contribution. Tertulia Flamenca de Ceuta, P.O. Box 344, Ceuta, Spain. adv.; bk.rev.; illus.

745.5 US
FLORIDA FOLKLIFE RESOURCE DIRECTORY. 1977. irreg. free. Department of State, Bureau of Florida Folklife Programs, Box 265, White Springs, FL 32096. TEL 904-397-2192. FAX 904-397-2915. circ. 1,000.
  Former titles: Florida Festival Arts Directory; (until 1980): Florida Folk Arts Directory (ISSN 0162-5616)
  Description: Lists folk artists, ethnic associations, and interpreters and scholars active in preserving Florida's folk heritage.

398 US
FOAFTALE NEWS. 1985. q. £10($18) International Society for Contemporary Legend Research, c/o Paul Smith, Dept. of Folklore, Memorial University of Newfoundland, St. John's, NF A1C 5S7, Canada. TEL 709-737-8402. FAX 709-737-4569. TELEX 016-4101. Ed. Bill Ellis. bibl.; circ. 250 (paid). (back issues avail.) **Document type:** newsletter.
  Description: Reports and news items tracking currently active "urban" or contemporary legends worldwide. Intended for folklorists and other professionals interested in rumor or legend.

398 745.5 781.7 US
FOLK ARTS NOTES. s-a. free. Southern Arts Federation, 181 14th St., N.E., Ste. 400, Atlanta, GA 30309. illus. **Document type:** newsletter.
  Description: Informs the public on activities and news in the fields of southern folk arts and folk life.

389 RU
FOLK CREATIVITY. a. 2 Rub. Izdatel'stvo Muzyka, Ul. Neglinnaya 14, Moscow 103031, Russia. TEL 924-81-63. FAX 921-83-53.

FOLK IN KENT. see *DANCE*

398.097 CN ISSN 0842-2583
ML3544
FOLK-LORE. 1988. bi-m. Can.$13. Association Quebecoise des Loisirs Folkloriques, 4545 av. Pierre-de-Coubertin, C.P. 1000, Succ. M, Montreal, PQ H1V 3R2, Canada.
  Formerly: Loisirs Folkloriques (ISSN 0822-9295)

398 780 NE
FOLKBLAD PIBROCH. 1978. bi-m. fl.17.50. Stichting Pibroch, Uranuslaan 59, 4624 VP Bergen Op Zoom, Netherlands. Ed. P. van Wersch. adv.; bk.rev. circ. 600.

398 DK ISSN 0906-8988
FOLKEMINDER. 1974. q. membership. Foreningen Danmarks Folkeminder, Birketinget 6, 2300 Copenhagen S, Denmark. Ed. Else Marie Kofod. circ. 1,800.
  Formerly: M T M (Meddelelser til Medlemmerne) (ISSN 0107-0525)

398 UK
FOLKESTONE AND DOVER EXTRA. 1985. w. £16.64. Kent Messenger Group, 13 Queen St., Deal, Kent CT14 6EX, England. TEL 0304-365526. FAX 0304-374770. Ed. Brian Lewis. adv.; bk.rev.; film rev.; play rev. circ. 65,142. (tabloid format; also avail. in microform; back issues avail.)

390 US ISSN 0149-6840
GR105
FOLKLIFE CENTER NEWS. 1978. q. free. U.S. Library of Congress, American Folklife Center, Washington, DC 20540-8100. TEL 202-707-6590. FAX 202-707-2076. Ed. James Hardin. circ. 14,000. (tabloid format) **Indexed:** Ind.U.S.Gov.Per. **Document type:** government publication, newsletter.
  Description: Reports on the activities and programs of the center, along with articles about the traditional and expressive culture of the U.S.

398 SW ISSN 0071-6766
FOLKLIVSSKILDRINGAR OCH BYGDESTUDIER. 1934. irreg., no.12, 1987. price varies. Kungliga Gustav Adolfs Akademien, Klostergatan 2, S-753 21 Uppsala, Sweden. (Dist. by: Almqvist & Wiksell International, P.O. Box 638, S-101 28 Stockholm, Sweden) Ed. Lennart Elmevik.

398 RU
FOL'KLOR URALA. vol.2, 1976. irreg. 0.65 Rub. per issue. Ural'skii Gosudarstvennyi Universitet, Pr. Lenina 51, Sverdlovsk, Russia. circ. 600.

FOLKLORE 2547

398 FR ISSN 0015-5888
FOLKLORE; revue d'ethnographie meridionale. 1938. q. 5 F. Centre de Documentation et Musee Audois des Arts et Traditions Populaires, 24 rue du Palais, Carcassonne, France. Ed. Rene Nelli. bk.rev.; bibl.; illus.; cum.index. circ. 1,000. (also avail. in microform) **Indexed:** Arts & Hum.Cit.Ind.
  —BLDSC (3974.590000).

398 II ISSN 0015-5896
GR305
FOLKLORE; English monthly devoted to folk literature, folk arts & crafts, folk music & dance, tribal studies and related social science objects. (Text in English) 1956. m. Rs.45($15) to individuals; institutions Rs.60($20). (Indian Folklore Society) Indian Publications, 3 British Indian St., Calcutta 700 069, India. Ed. Sankar Sen Gupta. adv.; bk.rev.; charts; illus.; index. circ. 6,800. (also avail. in microfilm from UMI; reprint service avail. from ISI, UMI) **Indexed:** Abstr.Anthropol., Arts & Hum.Cit.Ind., M.L.A., RILM.
  —UMI.

398 UK ISSN 0015-587X
GR1
FOLKLORE. 1878. a. £24($55) (effective Jan. 1994). Folklore Society, c/o University College, Gower St., London WC1E 6BT, England. TEL 44-71-387-5894. Ed. Gillian Bennett. adv.; bk.rev.; bibl.; index, cum.index. circ. 1878-1958, 1959-1967. circ. 1,200. (also avail. in microform from PMC) **Indexed:** A.I.C.P., Arts & Hum.Cit.Ind., Br.Archaeol.Abstr., Br.Hum.Ind., Hum.Ind., Ind.Bk.Rev.Hum., M.L.A., Numis.Lit, RILM. **Document type:** academic/scholarly publication.
  —BLDSC (3974.600000); Faxon; UnCover; UMI.
  Description: Contains scholarly articles on all aspects of traditional British and European and related cultures.

398 CN ISSN 0824-3085
FOLKLORE. 1979. q. Can.$16.05. Saskatchewan History and Folklore Society Inc., 1860 Lorne Street, Regina, Sask. S4P 2L7, Canada. TEL 306-780-9204. FAX 306-781-6021. Ed. Richard J. Wood. adv.; bk.rev. circ. 2,000.
  —CCC.
  Description: Accounts the human history of Saskatchewan.

398 MX ISSN 0071-6774
FOLKLORE AMERICANO. (Text in English, French, Portuguese, Spanish) 1942. a. $34 (N. & C. America $38; S. America & Europe $43; Asia $48). Instituto Panamericano de Geografia e Historia, Servicios Bibliograficos, Ex-Arzobispado 29, Col. Observatorio, Deleg. Miguel Hidalgo, 11860 Mexico, D.F., Mexico. TEL 525-277-5888. FAX 525-271-6172. (Subscr. to: IPGH, Depto. de Distribucion y Ventas, Apdo. 18879, 11870 Mexico DF, Mexico) Ed. Celso Lara. bk.rev. circ. 1,000. (also avail. in microfilm; reprint service avail. from UMI) **Indexed:** A.I.C.P., Arts & Hum.Cit.Ind., Curr.Cont., Hisp.Amer.Per.Ind. **Document type:** academic/scholarly publication.
  —BLDSC (3974.620000).

398 US ISSN 0162-6280
GR1
FOLKLORE AND MYTHOLOGY STUDIES. 1977. a. $7.50. University of California, Los Angeles, Folklore Graduate Students' Association, Los Angeles, CA 90024. TEL 213-825-4321. Ed.Bd.
  —BLDSC (3974.621000).
  Description: Covers UCLA association news in folklore and mythological studies.

398 US
FOLKLORE & SOCIETY. irreg. price varies. University of Illinois Press, 1325 S. Oak St., Champaign, IL 61820. TEL 217-333-0950. FAX 217-244-8082. **Document type:** academic/scholarly publication.
  Refereed Serial

398 BE ISSN 0015-590X
FOLKLORE BRABANCON. Dutch edition: Brabantse Folklore (ISSN 0773-1426) 1921. 4/yr. 400 BEF. Service de Recherches Historiques et Folkloriques (SRHF), 61 rue du Marche-aux-Herbes, B-1000 Brussels, Belgium. TEL 32-2-5040430. FAX 32-2-5040495. Ed. G. Menne. bk.rev.; bibl.; charts; illus.; index. circ. 1,250. **Indexed:** Numis.Lit.
  —Faxon.

398 FR ISSN 0015-5918
FOLKLORE DE FRANCE. 1950. bi-m. 115 F. (foreign 170 F.)(effective 1991). Confederation Nationale des Groupes Folkloriques Francais, 8 av. General Leclerc, 30000 Nimes, France. TEL 66-84-87-77. Ed. J.C. Feybesse. adv.; bk.rev.; record rev.; illus. circ. 4,200.

398 BE
FOLKLORE DU MONDE. 1969. irreg., no.2, 1975. Librairie-Editions Thanh-Long, 34 rue Dekens, B-1040 Brussels, Belgium. **Document type:** monographic series.

398 II
FOLKLORE FELLOWS OF INDIA. NEWS BULLETIN. (Text in English) 1977. q. Rs.20($5) Folklore Fellows of India, Folklore Unit, Central Institute of Indian Languages, Mysore 570 006, India. Ed. Jawaharlal Handoo. adv.; bk.rev.; film rev.; play rev.; charts; illus.; stat.; index. circ. 2,000. (looseleaf format; back issues avail.)
  Description: Includes national and international news, views, and events of folkloric importance.

398 US ISSN 0015-5926
GR1
FOLKLORE FORUM. 1968. s-a. $8 to individuals; institutions $10; students $6; foreign $12. Folklore Forum, Inc., 504 N. Fess, Bloomington, IN 47405. TEL 812-855-1027. Eds. Ross Peterson-Veatch, Theresa Vaughan. adv.; bk.rev.; film rev.; rec.rev.; bibl.; cum.index: 1968-1978. circ. 300. (processed; back issues avail.) **Indexed:** Abstr.Folk.Stud., Amer.Bibl.Slavic & E.Eur.Stud., Amer.Hist.& Life, Hist.Abstr., M.L.A., Mid.East: Abstr.& Ind.
  —Faxon; UnCover.
  Description: Information on folklore. Includes one translation per issue.

398 US ISSN 1041-8644
GR1
FOLKLORE HISTORIAN. 1984. s-a. $7. (Indiana State University) Folklore and American Studies, Ozark Folk Center, Mountain View, AR 72560. Ed. Ronald L. Baker. **Indexed:** Amer.Hist.& Life (1991-), Hist.Abstr. (1991-).
  —BLDSC (3974.630500).

398 CE
FOLKLORE NEWS. (Text in English, Suihala) 1986. irreg. (Sri Lanka National Commission for Unesco) National Library of Sri Lanka, P.O. Box 1764, Colombo, Sri Lanka. Eds. N. Amarasinghe, S.J. Sumanasekera Banda. bk.rev. circ. 1,000.
  Description: Covers folklore activities and events of institutions and organizations.

398 US
FOLKLORE OF AMERICAN HOLIDAYS. 1986. quinquennial. $85. Gale Research Inc., 835 Penobscot Bldg., Detroit, MI 48226-4094. TEL 313-961-2242. FAX 313-961-6083. TELEX 810-221-7086. Eds. Hennig Cohen, Tristam Potter Coffin.
  Description: Illustrates the history and lore behind 133 holidays celebrated in the U.S.

398 US
FOLKLORE OF WORLD HOLIDAYS. 1991. irreg. $80. Gale Research Inc., 335 Penobscot Bldg., Detroit, MI 48226-4094. TEL 313-961-2242. FAX 313-961-6083. TELEX 810-221-7086. Ed. Margaret Read MacDonald.
  Description: Covers the folklore of over 375 holidays celebrated in over 150 countries, excluding the U.S. and Canada.

398 US ISSN 0015-5950
FOLKLORE SOCIETY OF GREATER WASHINGTON NEWSLETTER. 1964. 11/yr. $8. Folklore Society of Greater Washington, 307 Broadleaf Dr., N.E., Vienna, VA 22180. TEL 703-281-2228. Ed. Jennifer Woods. adv. circ. 3,000.

398 SZ ISSN 0015-5969
FOLKLORE SUISSE/FOLCLORE SVIZZERO. (Language edition of Schweizer Volkskunde) (Text in French, Italian) 1949. 4/yr. 40 SFr. (Schweizerische Gesellschaft fuer Volkskunde - Societe Suisse des Traditions Populaires) Reinhardt Media Service, Postfach 393, CH-4012 Basel, Switzerland. TEL 061-2613320. Ed.Bd. bk.rev.; illus.; index.

FOLKSONG IN THE CLASSROOM; a network of teachers of history, literature, music and the humanities - a newsletter. see *MUSIC*

FOLKLORE

398 US ISSN 0071-6804
FOLKTALES OF THE WORLD. 1963. irreg., no.13, 1980. price varies. University of Chicago Press, 5801 S. Ellis Ave., Chicago, IL 60637. TEL 312-702-7899. Ed. Richard M. Dorson. (reprint service avail. from ISI,UMI)
Refereed Serial

FORSCHUNGEN ZUR RECHTSARCHAEOLOGIE UND RECHTLICHEN VOLKSKUNDE. see *LAW*

396 RM ISSN 0015-7902
FORSCHUNGEN ZUR VOLKS- UND LANDESKUNDE. (Text in German) 1958. s-a. 70 lei($42) Editura Academiei Romane, Calea Victoriei 125, 79717 Bucharest, Rumania. (Dist. by: Rompresfilatelia, Calea Grivitei 64-66, P.O. Box 12-201, 78104 Bucharest, Rumania) Ed. G. Konnerth. bk.rev. **Indexed:** Amer.Hist.& Life, Anthropol.Lit., Bibl.Ling., Hist.Abstr., Numis.Lit.

398 US ISSN 0015-9220
PS1
FOXFIRE. 1967. s-a. $12.95 (foreign $24.95). Foxfire Fund, Inc., Box 541, Mountain City, GA 30562. TEL 404-746-5828. bk.rev.; illus. circ. 3,000. (processed; also avail. in microform from UMI; reprint service avail. from UMI) **Indexed:** Abstr.Folk.Stud., Access (1976-1987), M.L.A. —UnCover; UMI.
Description: Covers the Appalachian culture.

398 US
FOXFIRE BOOK SERIES. irreg., latest no.10. $14. Foxfire Fund, Inc., Box 541, Mountain City, GA 30562. TEL 404-746-5828.

398 AU ISSN 0016-156X
DER FROEHLICHE KREIS; Vierteljahresschrift fuer Volkstanz und Heimatpflege. 1947. q. free. Landesjugendreferat der Steiermaerkischen Landesregierung, Karmeliterplatz 2, A-8011 Graz, Austria. FAX 0316-877-2294. Ed. Heinz Kasparovsky. bk.rev.; rec.rev.; bibl. circ. 1,300. **Document type:** government publication.

FUNDACION DE ETNOMUSICOLOGIA Y FOLKLORE. ANUARIO. see *MUSIC*

398 JO
AL-FUNUN AL-SHA'BIYYAH. no.14, 1989. q. Ministry of Culture, Department of Culture and Arts, Folklore Section, P.O. Box 88, Amman, Jordan.

398 US
GARLAND FOLKLORE CASEBOOKS. 1981. irreg. Garland Publishing, Inc., 1000A Sherman Ave., Hamden, CT 06514. TEL 800-627-6273. (And: 717 Fifth Ave., New York, NY 10022. TEL 212-751-7447) Ed. Alan Dundes.

GESCHICHTSBLAETTER FUER WALDECK. see *HISTORY — History Of Europe*

398 943 GW
GUMBINNER HEIMATBRIEF. 1963. 2/yr. Kreisarchiv Gumbinnen e.V., Rohrteichstr. 19, 33602 Bielefeld, Germany. circ. 13,000. (back issues avail.) **Document type:** bulletin.

GYPSY LORE SOCIETY. NEWSLETTER. see *ANTHROPOLOGY*

HARVEST BOOK SERIES. see *SOCIOLOGY*

398 745.1 US
HEARTHSTONE COLLECTION OF FOLKLORE, NOSTALGIA AND HISTORY.* 1986. bi-m. $12. Infinity Press Publications, Box 1009, South Point, OH 45680-1009. TEL 614-377-4182. Ed. James R. Pack. adv. circ. 10,000. (back issues avail.)
Description: Contains articles by everyday people sharing their knowledge and experiences of the past, including people, places and events.

398 IS ISSN 0075-3661
HEBREW UNIVERSITY OF JERUSALEM. FOLKLORE RESEARCH CENTER. STUDIES. (Text in Hebrew and English) 1970. irreg., vol. 7, 1987. Magnes Press, Hebrew University, Jerusalem, P.O. Box 7695, Jerusalem 91076, Israel. TEL 972-2-660341. FAX 972-2-633370. Eds. Dov Noy, I. Ben-Ami. **Indexed:** Ind.Heb.Per. **Document type:** monographic series.

HECATE'S LOOM; Canada's national pagan magazine. see *RELIGIONS AND THEOLOGY — Other Denominations And Sects*

HEIMATBRIEF DER STADT GERMERSHEIM. see *HISTORY — History Of Europe*

398 781.7 GW ISSN 0177-2538
DER HEIMATPFLEGER; Zeitschrift fuer Volkstanz, Volksmusik, Brauchtum und Heimatpflege. 1984. q. DM.32. Verlag der Heimatzunft Baden-Wuerttemberg e.V., Maehringerstr. 8-1, 72770 Reutlingen, Germany. TEL 07121-59755. Ed. Markus Herrmann. adv.; bk.rev. circ. 1,000. (back issues avail.) **Document type:** bulletin.
Description: Research and teaching of traditional folk dance and music in Germany.

398 GW
HEIMATRECHT; Informationen fuer Freiheit und Selbstbestimmung. 1950. bi-m. DM.30($18.50) Bund der Vertriebenen, Kreisgruppe der Ortsverbaende, Beekstr. 17, Zimmer 220, 47051 Duisburg, Germany. Ed. Wolfgang Koska. bk.rev.; abstr. circ. 1,000. **Document type:** newsletter.

HESSISCHE BLAETTER FUER VOLKS- UND KULTURFORSCHUNG. see *ETHNIC INTERESTS*

HIAKA KHRONIKA. see *HISTORY — History Of Europe*

HISTORIC SCHAEFFERSTOWN RECORD. see *HISTORY — History Of North And South America*

HOUTLAND. see *HISTORY — History Of Europe*

398 CC ISSN 1002-0586
HUIZU YANJIU/RESEARCHES ON THE HUI. 1991. q. $12 (effective Jan. 1994). Ningxia Shehui Kexueyuan - Ningxia Academy of Social Sciences, Yinchuan, Ningxia 750021, People's Republic of China. TEL 0951-274593. Ed. Yang Huaizhong. adv.: page $600; adv. contact: Ding Jun. bk.rev. **Document type:** academic/scholarly publication.

398 SG
I C A INFORMATION.* (Text in English and French) 1975. q. free. African Cultural Institute, 13 av. President Habib Bourguiba, Dakar, Senegal. Ed. Basile Kossou. film rev.; play rev. circ. 2,000. (back issues avail.)

INDIAN - ARTIFACT MAGAZINE. see *ARCHAEOLOGY*

INDIAN MUSICOLOGICAL SOCIETY. JOURNAL. see *MUSIC*

INSTITUT ARCHEOLOGIQUE DU LUXEMBOURG. BULLETINS; archeologie-art-histoire-folklore. see *ARCHAEOLOGY*

398 AU
INSTITUT FUER GEGENWARTSVOLKSKUNDE. MITTEILUNGEN. (Issues also published in other series of the Akademie) 1973. irreg. price varies. Verlag der Oesterreichischen Akademie der Wissenschaften, Dr. Ignaz-Seipel-Platz 2, A-1010 Vienna, Austria. FAX 0222-5139541.

390 FR ISSN 0339-3275
INTERFOLK. 1975. 6/yr. 85 F. Inter-Groupe Folklore, Region Parisienne, 41 rue de la Butte aux Cailles, 75013 Paris, France. bk.rev. circ. 600. (processed)

INTERNATIONAL ARTHURIAN SOCIETY. NEWSLETTER. see *LITERATURE*

INUKTITUT. see *HISTORY — History Of North And South America*

IRISH MUSIC AND DANCE ASSOCIATION NEWSLETTER. see *MUSIC*

JAHRBUCH FUER MUSIKALISCHE VOLKS- UND VOELKERKUNDE. see *MUSIC*

398 301.2 GW ISSN 0075-2738
DD61.8
JAHRBUCH FUER OSTDEUTSCHE VOLKSKUNDE. 1962. a. price varies. (Deutsche Gesellschaft fuer Volkskunde e.V., Kommission fuer Ostdeutsche Volkskunde) N.G. Elwert Verlag, Reitgasse 7-9, 35037 Marburg, Germany. Ed. Peter Assion. circ. 1,000. **Document type:** academic/scholarly publication.

398 895.1 CC ISSN 1003-3327
JINGU CHUANQI/MODERN AND ANCIENT LEGENDS. (Text in Chinese) 1981. bi-m. Y25 (effective 1993). Hubei Sheng Wenlian, 1, Dongting 2 Lu, Donghu, Wuchang, Wuhan, Hubei 430071, People's Republic of China. TEL 86-027-612458. FAX 86-027-611973. (Dist. in US by: China Books & Periodicals, Inc., 2929 24th St., San Francisco, CA 94110. TEL 415-282-2994) Ed. Li Chuanfeng. circ. 380,000.
Description: Contains Chinese novles and short stories.

JONES COUNTY HISTORICAL REVIEW. see *HISTORY — History Of North And South America*

398 US ISSN 0191-1813
E169.1
JOURNAL OF AMERICAN CULTURE. 1978. q. $35 to individuals; institutions $65. (American Culture Association) Bowling Green State University, Popular Culture Center, Bowling Green, OH 43403. TEL 419-372-2981. Ed. Ray B. Browne. adv.; bk.rev.; illus.; index. circ. 1,200. (also avail. in microform from KTO,MIM,UMI) **Indexed:** Amer.Bibl.Slavic & E.Eur.Stud., Amer.Hist.& Life, Arts & Hum.Cit.Ind., Curr.Cont., Film Lit.Ind. (1988-), Hist.Abstr., Hum.Ind., Lang.& Lang.Behav.Abstr., Music Ind.
—BLDSC (4927.232000); Faxon; UnCover; UMI.
Refereed Serial

398 US ISSN 0021-8715
GR1
JOURNAL OF AMERICAN FOLKLORE. 1888. q. $50. (American Folklore Society) American Anthropological Association, 4350 N. Fairfax Dr., Ste. 640, Arlington, VA 22203. TEL 703-528-1902. Ed. Burt Feintuch. adv.; bk.rev.; film rev.; rec.rev. circ. 3,000. (also avail. in microform from MIM,UMI,PMC; reprint service avail. from ISI,KTO,UMI) **Indexed:** A.I.C.P., Acad.Ind., Amer.Bibl.Slavic & E.Eur.Stud., Amer.Hist.& Life, Anthropol.Lit., Arts & Hum.Cit.Ind., Bibl.Ling., Bk.Rev.Ind. (1965-), Chic.Per.Ind., Child.Bk.Rev.Ind. (1965-), Curr.Cont., Hist.Abstr., Hum.Ind., Ind.Bk.Rev.Hum., M.L.A., Mag.Ind., Music Ind., Ref.Sour., SSCI.
—BLDSC (4927.250000); Faxon; UnCover; SWETS; UMI.
Description: Articles on all areas of folklife and folklore.

398 US ISSN 0737-7037
GR1
JOURNAL OF FOLKLORE RESEARCH. 1964. 3/yr. $18 to individuals; institutions $25; students $15. Indiana University, Folklore Institute, 504 N. Fess, Bloomington, IN 47408. TEL 812-335-0043. FAX 812-855-5678. Ed. Mary Ellen Brown. adv.; bk.rev.; charts; illus.; index. circ. 700. (also avail. in microform from UMI) **Indexed:** A.I.C.P., Abstr.Folk.Stud., Amer.Hist.& Life, CERDIC, Curr.Cont., E.I., Hist.Abstr., M.L.A., Music Ind. **Document type:** academic/scholarly publication.
—Faxon; UnCover; SWETS; UMI. CCC.
Former titles: Folklore Institute. Journal (ISSN 0537-3131); Indiana University. Folklore Institute Journal (ISSN 0019-6819)
Description: Articles on the theoretical aspects of world folklore.

398 II
JOURNAL OF INDIA FOLKLORISTICS. (Text in English) 1978. s-a. Rs.50($15) Ministry of Human Resource Development, Central Institute of Indian Languages, Folklore Fellows of India, Manasagangotri, Mysore 570 006, India. Ed. J. Handoo. adv.; bk.rev.; bibl.; charts; illus.; stat.; index. circ. 1,100. (back issues avail.)
Description: A journal of folklore, ethnography, anthropology of the Indian sub-continent.

FOLKLORE

---

398   US   ISSN 0360-1927
GR114   CODEN: JLALEB
JOURNAL OF LATIN AMERICAN LORE. (Text in English and Spanish) 1975. s-a. $25 to individuals; institutions $35. University of California, Los Angeles, Latin American Center, 405 Hilgard Ave., Los Angeles, CA 90024. TEL 213-825-6634. Ed. Johannes Wilbert. adv.; bibl. circ. 325. (back issues avail.) Indexed: A.I.C.P., Amer.Hist.& Life, Anthropol.Lit., Arts & Hum.Cit.Ind., Bibl.Ling., Curr.Cont., Hisp.Amer.Per.Ind., Hist.Abstr.
—BLDSC (5010.105000); Faxon; UnCover.
  Description: Contains essays treating aspects of Latin American culture from a connotative viewpoint, and emphasizes the understanding of the symbolic value of cultural manifestations.

JOURNAL OF POPULAR CULTURE. see *LITERATURE*

398   AU   ISSN 0022-7560
DB283
KAERNTNER HEIMATLEBEN. 1959. irreg. price varies. Landesmuseum fuer Kaernten, Museumgasse 2, A-9010 Klagenfurt, Austria. TEL 0463-53630567. FAX 0463-53630540. circ. 600. Document type: bulletin.

KAILASH; journal of Himalayan studies. see *HISTORY — History Of Asia*

398   FI   ISSN 0355-0311
PH325
KALEVALASEURAN VUOSIKIRJA. 1921. a. FIM 160. Suomalaisen Kirjallisuuden Seura, Hallituskatu 1, FIN-00170 Helsinki, Finland. TEL 358-0-131231. FAX 358-0-1323220. Ed. Paivi Vallisaari. cum.index 1921-70. circ. 1,500. Indexed: M.L.A.
  Description: Contains articles on Finnish and Balto-Finnic folklife and cultural phenomena relating to an annually varying theme of research.

398   II
KHOJ DARPAN. (Text in Punjabi; summaries in English, Hindi, and Urdu) 1974. 2/yr. Rs.20 to individuals; institutions Rs.40 (foreign $30). Guru Nanak Dev University, Department of Punjabi Language, Literature & Culture, Amritsar 143 005, India. TEL 65728. Eds. K.S. Thind, Satinder Singh. adv.; bk.rev. circ. 500.

KOBIE, REVISTA DE BELLAS ARTES Y CIENCIAS: SERIE ANTROPOLOGIA CULTURAL. see *ANTHROPOLOGY*

398   RM
KORUNK; culture - homeland and the world. (Text in Hungarian) 1926. m. 144 lei($12) Intreprinderea de Stat Peutru Imprimate si Administrarea Publicatutor, 71341 Bucuresti, PTA - Presei Libere Nr. 1 Sect. I, Rumania. (Subscr. to: Redactia "Korunk," Str. Motilor Nr. 3, 3400 Cluj-Napoca, Rumania) Ed. Kantor Lajos. index. circ. 5,500. (back issues avail.)

398   FR   ISSN 0075-7160
KRYPTADIA: JOURNAL OF EROTIC FOLKLORE. (Text in English) 1883. irreg. (approx. a.). $15. La Cle des Champs, Valbonne (Alpes-Maritimes), France. Ed. G. Legman.

398   AA   ISSN 0257-6082
KULTURA POPULLORE. French edition: Culture Populaire Albanaise (ISSN 0257-6074) 1980. s-a. Akademia e Shkencave e RPSSH, Instituti i Kultures Popullore - Academie des Sciences de la RPSA, Institut de Culture Populaire, Tirana, Albania. Ed. Alfred Uci.

KULTUUR JA ELU/CULTURE AND LIFE. see *ETHNIC INTERESTS*

L C FOLK ARCHIVE FINDING AID. see *LIBRARY AND INFORMATION SCIENCES*

L C FOLK ARCHIVE REFERENCE AID. (U.S. Library of Congress) see *LIBRARY AND INFORMATION SCIENCES*

398   CY
LAOGRAPHIKE KYPROS. 1971. q. P.O. Box 1034, Leukosia, Cyprus.

398   IT   ISSN 0023-8503
LARES; trimestrale di studi demo-etno-antropologici. 1912-1915; resumed 1930-1943, N.S. 1949. q. L.75000 (foreign L.95000) (effective 1994). Casa Editrice Leo S. Olschki, Casella Postale 66, 50100 Florence, Italy. TEL 055-6530684. FAX 055-6530214. Ed. G. Battista Bronzini. adv.; bk.rev.; illus. circ. 1,000. **Document type:** academic/scholarly publication.

390   IT   ISSN 0075-8019
LARES. BIBLIOTECA. 1957. irreg., no.49, 1993. price varies. Casa Editrice Leo S. Olschki, Casella Postale 66, 50100 Florence, Italy. TEL 055-6530684. FAX 055-6530214. Ed. G. Battista Bronzini. adv.; bk.rev. circ. 1,000. **Document type:** monographic series.

LATAH LEGACY. see *HISTORY — History Of North And South America*

398   FR   ISSN 1159-098X
LEGENDES ET RUMEURS. a. 200 F. Geste Editions, Maison des Ruralies, B.P. 1, 79230 Vouille, France. TEL 49-75-67-71. Ed. Jean-Loic Le Quellec.
  Description: Covers contemporary legend, rumor, folktales, narratives and oral tradition.

398   GW
DER LICHTGANG. 1950. irreg. (3-4/yr.). DM.30. Bund "Heimat und Volksleben" e/V., c/o Ursula Huelse, Hauptstr. 157, 79211 Denzlingen, Germany. TEL 07666-2712. Ed. Heinz Bauer. adv.; bk.rev. circ. 3,000.

LIGHT BEARER. see *PARAPSYCHOLOGY AND OCCULTISM*

398   PL   ISSN 0024-4708
GR195
LITERATURA LUDOWA/FOLK LITERATURE; dwumiesiecznik naukowo-literacki. 1957. bi-m. $8.10. Polskie Towarzystwo Ludoznawcze, Ul. Szewska 36, 50-139 Wroclaw, Poland. (Dist. by: Ars Polona Krakowskie Przedmiescie 7, Warsaw, Poland) Ed. Czeslaw Hernas. bk.rev.; bibl.; illus.; index. circ. 1,500. Indexed: A.I.C.P., Bibl.Ling., M.L.A.

398   II
LOKABRITTA: HINDI FOLKLORE; devoted to the cause of the Indian Folklore Society. (Text in Hindi) 1986. bi-m. Rs.24($9) to individuals; institutions Rs.36($12). (Indian Folklore Society) Indian Publications, 3, British Indian St., Calcutta 700 069, India. Ed. Sankar Sen Gupta. adv.; bk.rev.; charts; illus.; index. circ. 4,000. (also avail. in microfilm from UMI; reprint service avail. from ISI,UMI)
  Formerly: Hindi Folklore.

LORE AND LANGUAGE. see *LINGUISTICS*

390   US   ISSN 0459-8962
LOUISIANA FOLKLORE MISCELLANY. 1958. a. $7 to individuals; institutions $10. Louisiana Folklore Society, c/o Dept. of English, Loyola University, 6363 St. Charles Ave., New Orleans, LA 70148. **Document type:** academic/scholarly publication.
  Description: Includes articles and other materials relating to the folklore of Louisiana.

398   HU   ISSN 0865-1906
Z5984.H8
MAGYAR NEPRAJZI BIBLIOGRAFIA/HUNGARIAN FOLKLORE BIBLIOGRAPHY. (Text in English, German or Hungarian) 1971. a. exchange basis. Neprajzi Muzeum - Library of the Ethnographical Museum, Kossuth Lajos ter 12, 1055 Budapest, Hungary. TEL 1-326-340. FAX 2-692-419. **Document type:** bibliography.

398   US
MAINE FOLKLORE CENTER NEWSLETTER. (Former name of issuing body: Northeast Folklore Society) 1962. s-a. Maine Folklore Center, South Stevens Hall, University of Maine, Orono, ME 04469. TEL 207-581-1891. Ed. Edward D. Ives. Indexed: M.L.A. **Document type:** newsletter.
  Formerly (until 1993): Northeast Folklore Society Newsletter (ISSN 0546-5370)

MAKEDONIKA. see *HISTORY — History Of Europe*

398   XN   ISSN 0542-2108
GR1
MAKEDONSK FOLKLOR. (Text in English, French, German, Macedonian, Russian, Serbo-Croatian, Slovenian) 1968. s-a. 1200 din.($12) Institut za Folklor Marko Cepenkov, Skopje, Ruzveltova 3, P.O. Box 319, 91000 Skopje, Macedonia. Ed. Blagoj Stojcovski. bk.rev. circ. 1,500. Indexed: A.I.C.P., M.L.A.
—BLDSC (0098.490000).

398   US   ISSN 1048-857X
GR1
MEDIEVAL FOLKLORE. a. $29.95. Edwin Mellen Press, 415 Ridge St., Box 450, Lewiston, NY 14092. TEL 716-754-2788. FAX 716-754-4056. Ed. Francesca Sautman. **Document type:** monographic series.

398 808   US   ISSN 0898-154X
MERVEILLES & CONTES/MARVELS & TALES/WUNDER & MAERCHEN/MARAVILLAS & CUENTOS/MERAVIGLIE & RACCONTI. (Text in English, French, German, Italian, Spanish) 1987. s-a. $20. Box 238, University of Colorado, Boulder, CO 80309. TEL 303-492-7226. FAX 303-492-8338. Eds. Jacques Barchilon, Francesca Sautman. bk.rev.; bibl.; illus. circ. 100. **Document type** academic/scholarly publication.
—UnCover.
  Description: Publishes in all disciplines concerned with folk and fairy tales.

MEXICO. DEPARTAMENTO DE INVESTIGACION DE LAS TRADICIONES POPULARES. BOLETIN. see *ANTHROPOLOGY*

398   US   ISSN 0275-6013
GR108
MID-AMERICA FOLKLORE. 1973. 2/yr. $10. Mid-America Folklore Society, c/o Arkansas College, Batesville, AR 72501. TEL 501-793-9813. Ed. George E. Lankford. bk.rev.; illus. circ. 300. (back issues avail.) Indexed: Abstr.Folk.Stud., Abstr.Pop.Cult., M.L.A. **Document type:** academic/scholarly publication.
—Faxon; UnCover.
  Formerly (until vol.7, 1979): Mid-South Folklore (ISSN 0099-2355)

398   US   ISSN 0894-4059
GR1
MIDWESTERN FOLKLORE. 1975. s-a. $7. Indiana State University, Department of English, Terre Haute, IN 47809. TEL 812-237-3160. (Co-sponsor: Hoosier Folklore Society) Ed. Ronald L. Baker. (back issues avail.)
—Faxon; UnCover.
  Formerly: Midwestern Journal of Language and Folklore.

301.2 915.16   CC
MIN SU/FOLK CUSTOMS. (Text in Chinese) m. $48.50. (Zhongguo Minjian Wenyijia Xiehui - China Folk Artists Association) Min Su Zazhishe, 39 Taipusi, Xidan, Beijing 100031, People's Republic of China. TEL 652188. (Dist. n US by: China Books & Periodicals, Inc., 2929 24th St., San Francisco, CA 94110. TEL 415-282-2994) Ed. Yang Liangcai.

398 959   PH   ISSN 0115-6853
DS688.M2
MINDANAO ART & CULTURE. (Text in English) 1979. irreg. Mindanao State University, Mamitua Saber Research Center, Folklore and History Section, P.O. Box 5594, Iligan City 9200, Philippines. Ed. Raymond Llorca. circ. 500 (controlled). **Document type:** academic/scholarly publication.

398   CC
MINJIAN GUSHI/FOLK TALES. (Text in Chinese) 1983. bi-m. Y7.20. Zhongguo Minjian Wenyi Yanjiuhui, Jilin Fenhui - Chinese Folk Arts Institute, Jilin Branch, 111 Sidalin Dajie, Changchun, Jilin 130021, People's Republic of China. TEL 884948. circ. 160,000. (back issues avail.)
  Description: Contains folktales, myths, legends, jokes, and narrative folk poetry.

FOLKLORE

398 895.1   CC   ISSN 0540-1151
PL2446
MINJIAN WENXUE. (Text in Chinese) 1955. m. Y15.60($61.20) Minjian Wenxue Zazhishe, Nongzhanguan Nanli 10, Rm. 1402, Beijing 100026, People's Republic of China. (Dist. outside China by: China International Book Trading Corp., P.O. Box 399, Beijing, P.R.C.; Dist. in US by: China Books & Periodicals, Inc., 2929 24th St., San Francisco, CA 94110. TEL 415-282-2994) Eds. Yang Zhijie, He Jia. adv.
  Description: Contains folk literature, stories, and jokes.

398   CC
MINJIAN WENXUE LUNTAN/TRIBUNE OF FOLK LITERATURE. (Text in Chinese; table of contents in English) bi-m. Y10.50. (Zhongguo Minjian Wenyijia Xiehui - Chinese Folk Literature and Art Workers' Association) Minjian Wenxue Zazhishe, Rm. 1402, No. 10, Nongzhanguan Nanli, Beijing 100026, People's Republic of China. (Dist. overseas by: China International Book Trading Corp., P.O. Box 399, Beijing, P.R.C.) Eds. Feng Junyi, Huang Bocang. adv.; bk.rev.
  Description: Contains studies of folk customs, folk literature, folk arts, and mythology.

398   US   ISSN 0026-6248
GR1
MISSISSIPPI FOLKLORE REGISTER. 1967. a. $5 to individuals; institutions $7. Mississippi Folklore Society, c/o Tom Rankin, Ed., Mississippi Folklore Register, Center for the Study of Southern Culture, University of Mississippi, University, MS 38677. TEL 601-232-5993. Ed. Tom Rankin. adv.; bk.rev.; bibl.; index. circ. 350. (back issues avail.) Indexed: M.L.A. Document type: academic/scholarly publication.
  —UnCover.

398   US   ISSN 0731-2946
GR110.M77
MISSOURI FOLKLORE SOCIETY. JOURNAL. 1979. a. $12. Missouri Folklore Society, Box 1757, Columbia, MO 65205. Ed. Donald M. Lance. bk.rev. circ. 450. Indexed: M.L.A.

MONDE ALPIN ET RHODANIEN; revue regionale d'ethnologie. see ANTHROPOLOGY

398   IT
MONDO POPOLARE. 1990. irreg., latest no.6. price varies. Angelo Longo Editore, Via Paolo Costa 33, P.O. Box 431, 48100 Ravenna, Italy. TEL 0544-217026. Ed.Bd. circ. 2,000. Document type: monographic series.

MUNDARTFREUNDE OESTERREICHS. MITTEILUNGEN. see LINGUISTICS

398   BO
MUSEO NACIONAL DE ETNOGRAFIA Y FOLKLORE. AVANCES DE INVESTIGACION. 1982. irreg. $10. Museo Nacional de Etnografia y Folklore, Calle Ingavi 916, Casilla 5817, La Paz, Bolivia. Ed.Bd. circ. 500.

MUSU PASTOGE/OUR HAVEN. see ETHNIC INTERESTS

MUZYKAL'NAYA FOL'KLORISTIKA. see MUSIC

915 592 398   II   ISSN 0047-8555
MYTHIC SOCIETY. QUARTERLY JOURNAL. (Text in English) 1909. q. Rs.60($15) (effective 1990). Mythic Society, Nrupatunga Rd., Bangalore 2, India. Ed. S.U. Kamath. bk.rev.; bibl.; charts; illus. circ. 340. Indexed: A.I.C.P.
  —BLDSC (7184.460000).
  Description: Deals with social research.

398   FI   ISSN 0355-0206
N I F NEWSLETTER. (Text in English) 1972. q. free. Nordic Institute of Folklore, c/o Turun Yliopisto, SF-20500 Turku, Finland. TEL 358-0-21-31-15-23. Ed. Reimund Kvideland. adv.; bk.rev.; bibl.; illus. circ. 2,200. Indexed: A.I.C.P. Document type: newsletter.

398   FI
N I F PUBLICATIONS. 1972. irreg. Nordic Institute of Folklore, c/o Turun Yliopisto, SF-20500 Turku, Finland. TEL 358-0-21-32-62-06. FAX 358-0-21-31015-23. circ. 300. Document type: academic/scholarly publication.
  Formerly: Nordic Institute of Folklore. Publications.

NAMIBIANA. see HISTORY — History Of Africa

NAPRSTKOVO MUZEUM ASIJSKYCH, AFRICKYCH A AMERICKYCH KULTUR. ANNALS. see ANTHROPOLOGY

NARODNA TVORCHIST' TA ETNOGRAFIYA; naukovo-populyarny zhurnal. see ANTHROPOLOGY

398   CI   ISSN 0547-2504
NARODNA UMJETNOST. (Text in Croatian; summaries in English) 1962. a. 200 din.($10) Institut za Etnologiju i Folkloristiku - Institut of Ethnology and Folklore Research, Ul. Kralja Zronimira 17-4, 41000 Zagreb, Croatia. TEL 041-440-880. Ed. Zorica Rajkvic. bk.rev.; charts; illus.; cum.index. circ. 1,000. (back issues avail.) Indexed: A.I.C.P., Bull.Signal.

398   YU   ISSN 0027-8017
GR259
NARODNO STVARALASTVO - FOLKLOR. (Text in Serbo-Croatian) 1952. q. 30 din.($11.60) Savez Udruzenja Folklorista Jugoslavije, Kneza Mihaila 35, Belgrade, Yugoslavia. Ed. Dusan Nedeljkovic. bk.rev. Indexed: M.L.A.

NEPRAJZI KOZLEMENYEK. see ANTHROPOLOGY

398   US   ISSN 0887-8048
F134
NEW JERSEY FOLKLIFE; a statewide publication. 1976. a. $12.50 to individuals; institutions $15; students $8.50 (includes New Jersey Folklore Society Review). New Jersey Folklore Society, Box 747, New Brunswick, NJ 08903. TEL 215-843-7184. Ed. William Westerman. adv.; bk.rev. circ. 300.
  Formerly: New Jersey Folklore.

398   US
NEW JERSEY FOLKLORE SOCIETY REVIEW. 3/yr. $12.50 to individuals; institutions $15; students $8.50 (includes New Jersey Folklife). New Jersey Folklore Society, Box 747, New Brunswick, NJ 08903. TEL 215-843-7184. Eds. Hugo A. Freund, Fred Thomsen.
  Formerly: New Jersey Folklore Society Newsletter.

398   US   ISSN 0361-204X
GR1
NEW YORK FOLKLORE. 1975. s-a. $35 to individuals (foreign $40); institutions $50 (foreign $55); students $20 (foreign $25). New York Folklore Society, Box 130, Newfield, NY 14867. TEL 607-273-9137. FAX 607-273-8225. Eds. Egle Zygas. bk.rev.; bibl.; index. circ. 650. (also avail. in microfilm from UMI; reprint service avail. from UMI) Indexed: Amer.Hist.& Life, Arts & Hum.Cit.Ind., Biol.Abstr., Chem.Abstr., Chic.Per.Ind., Curr.Cont., Hist.Abstr., Music Ind. Document type: academic/scholarly publication.
  —Faxon; UnCover; UMI.
  Supersedes: New York Folklore Quarterly (ISSN 0028-7229)
  Refereed Serial

398   US
NEW YORK FOLKLORE NEWSLETTER. 1980. q. free. New York Folklore Society, Box 130, Newfield, NY 14867. TEL 607-273-9137. FAX 607-273-8225. Ed. Janis Benincasa. adv.; bk.rev. circ. 3,200. Document type: newsletter.

NEW YORK PINEWOODS FOLK MUSIC CLUB NEWSLETTER. see MUSIC

NINNAU. see ETHNIC INTERESTS

390   DK   ISSN 0008-1345
NORD NYTT; Nordic periodical for folklife studies. (Text in English, Danish, Norwegian and Swedish) 1963. irreg. (4-8/yr.). $50 per 4 nos. N E F A-Norden, Institut for Arkaeologi og Etnologi, Vard hensten 5, DK-1467 Copenhagen K, Denmark. FAX 45-62-62-36-55. (Subscr. to: Museumstjenesten, Lysgaard, DK-8800 Viborg, Denmark) Ed. Joergen Burchardt. adv.; bk.rev.; bibl.; illus.; index. circ. 1,500. Indexed: Amer.Hist.& Life (until 1992), Hist.Abstr. (until 1992).
  —BLDSC (6117.650000).
  Description: Emphasizes ethnology and social anthropology.

398   US   ISSN 0090-5844
GR110.N8
NORTH CAROLINA FOLKLORE JOURNAL. 1948. 2/yr. $7.50 to individuals; institutions $10. North Carolina Folklore Society, c/o Department of English, Appalachian State University, Boone, NC 28608. TEL 704-262-2323. Ed. Thomas McGowan. bk.rev.; charts; illus.; cum.index: vols.1-8. circ. 700. Indexed: Abstr.Folk.Stud., Amer.Hist.& Life, Hist.Abstr., M.L.A., Music Ind.
  —BLDSC (6149.039600); Faxon; UnCover.
  Formerly (until 1972): North Carolina Folklore (ISSN 0029-246X)

NORTH GEORGIA JOURNAL. see TRAVEL AND TOURISM

398   US   ISSN 0078-1681
GR1
NORTHEAST FOLKLORE. (Text in English; occasionally in French) 1958. a. $25. Maine Folklife Center, South Stevens Hall, University of Maine, Orono, ME 04469. TEL 207-581-1891. Ed. Edward D. Ives. circ. 600. Indexed: Amer.Hist.& Life, Hist.Abstr. Document type: academic/scholarly publication.

NORTHEIMER JAHRBUCH. see ARCHAEOLOGY

398   US   ISSN 0029-3369
NORTHWEST FOLKLORE. 1960. s-a. $15 to individuals; institutions $30. c/o Scandinavian Dept., 318 Raitt Hall, DL20, University of Washington, Seattle, WA 98195. TEL 206-543-6884. Ed. Henning Sehmsdorf. bk.rev. circ. 750. Document type: academic/scholarly publication.
  —BLDSC (6151.750000); UnCover.
  Formerly (until 1965): Oregon Folklore Bulletin (ISSN 0474-4489)

398   NO   ISSN 0029-3601
NORVEG; tidsskrift for etnologi og folkloristikk. (Text in Norwegian; summaries in English or German) 1934. a. NOK 300 in the Nordic countries; elsewhere NOK 350. Scandinavian University Press, P.O. Box 2959-Toeyen, N-0608 Oslo, Norway. TEL 472-67-7600. FAX 472-67-7575. (U.S. addr.: Scandinavian University Press, 200 Meacham Ave., Elmont, NY 11003. TEL 516-352-7300) Ed.Bd. adv.; bk.rev.; index. circ. 650. (back issues avail.) Indexed: A.I.C.P.
  Formerly (until 1951): Ord og Sed.
  Description: Devoted to ethnology and folkloristic research.

NOTARIUS; a zalai honismereti mozgalom folyoirata. see HISTORY — History Of Europe

NOTRE COMTE/ONS GRAAFSCHAP. see HISTORY — History Of Europe

OBEROESTERREICHISCHE HEIMATBLAETTER. see HISTORY — History Of Europe

398   AU   ISSN 0029-9669
GR1
OESTERREICHISCHE ZEITSCHRIFT FUER VOLKSKUNDE. 1895. q. S.360. Verein fuer Volkskunde, Laudongasse 19, A-1080 Vienna, Austria. FAX 0222-4085342. Ed. Klaus Beitl. bk.rev.; bibl.; illus.; index. circ. 1,100. Indexed: Numis.Lit. Document type: newsletter.

398   AU
OESTERREICHISCHES MUSEUM FUER VOLKSKUNDE. VEROEFFENTLICHUNGEN. 1952. irreg. price varies. Verlag Ferdinand Berger und Soehne GmbH, Wienerstr. 21-23, A-3580 Horn, Austria. TEL 02982-2317-0. circ. 1,000. Document type: monographic series.

ONTARIO FOLKDANCER. see DANCE

398 800   US   ISSN 0883-5365
GR72
ORAL TRADITION. 1986. s-a. $20 to individuals; institutions $35. Slavica Publishers, Inc., Box 14388, Columbus, OH 43214. TEL 614-268-4002. Ed. John Miles Foley. bibl. Document type: academic/scholarly publication.
  —BLDSC (6277.803000); Faxon; UnCover.
  Description: Covers all aspects of oral literature, both historic and recent, with emphasis on slavic traditions.
  Refereed Serial

FOLKLORE 2551

133 200 398 800　　US　　ISSN 0362-1596
BL1
PARABOLA; the magazine of myth and tradition. 1976. q. $20. Society for the Study of Myth and Tradition, 656 Broadway, New York, NY 10012-2317. TEL 212-505-6200. FAX 212-979-7325. Eds. Ellen Draper, Virginia Baron. adv. contact: Beth Leonard. bk.rev.; cum.index; circ. 41,000 (paid). (also avail. in microform; back issues avail.) Indexed: Abstr.Engl.Stud., Amer.Hum.Ind., Arts & Hum.Cit.Ind., Bk.Rev.Ind. (1983-), CERDIC, Child.Bk.Rev.Ind. (1983-), Curr.Cont., Hum.Ind., Ind.Bk.Rev.Hum., Mid.East: Abstr.& Ind., Rel.& Theol.Abstr. (1989-), Rel.Ind.One. **Document type:** academic/scholarly publication.
—BLDSC (6404.600000); Faxon; UnCover; SWETS; UMI.
　Description: Devoted to the quest for meaning as expressed in the myths, symbols, and tales of the world's religious traditions.

398　　　　　US
PENNSYLVANIA DUTCH NEWS AND VIEWS. 1969. s-a. membership. Pennsylvania Dutch Folk Culture Society, Lenhartsville, PA 19534. TEL 215-562-4803. Ed. Florence Baver. circ. 250. (back issues avail.) Indexed: Amer.Hist.& Life, Hist.Abstr. **Document type:** newsletter.
　Description: Covers society news and folklore events.

PENNSYLVANIA FOLKLIFE. see HISTORY — History Of North And South America

398　　　　　IT　　ISSN 0031-9708
PIE/PIADA; rassegna d'illustrazione Romangnola. 1920. bi-m. L.20000. Ala Carini Spalliccy, Ed. & Pub., Via B. Flavio 17, Forli, Italy. adv.; bk.rev. circ. 1,000.

PIONEER AMERICA SOCIETY. NEWSLETTER. see HISTORY — History Of North And South America

PIONEER AMERICA SOCIETY TRANSACTIONS. see HISTORY — History Of North And South America

POLSKA PIESN I MUZYKA LUDOWA. ZRODLA I MATERIALY. see MUSIC

POMMERN; Kunst - Geschichte - Volkstum. see ART

398　　　　　II
PRAMPRA. (Text in Punjabi) 1977. q. Rs.12. Prampra Parkashan, J-11-80 Rajouri Garden Extn., New Delhi, 110027, India. Eds. S.S. Wanjara Bedi, Jatinder pal Singh Bedi. adv.; bk.rev.; illus. circ. 1,000. (back issues avail.)

PRILOZI ZA KNJIZEVNOST, JEZIK, ISTORIJU I FOLKLOR. see LINGUISTICS

398　　　　　TS
AL-QAFILAH (UMM AL-QUWAIN)/CARAVAN (UMM AL-QUWAIN). (Text in Arabic) 1977. q. exchange basis. Umm al-Quwain Folklore Society, P.O. Box 31, Umm al-Quwain, United Arab Emirates. TEL 665022. Ed. Yusuf Ali Fadil. circ. 500.
　Description: Covers folklore, traditional culture, and folk arts in the U.A.E.

QINGHAI MINZU XUEYUAN XUEBAO/QINGHAI INSTITUTE OF NATIONALITIES. JOURNAL. see ORIENTAL STUDIES

QUELLENWERKE ZUR ALTEN GESCHICHTE AMERIKAS. see HISTORY — History Of North And South America

398　　　　　AU
RAABSER MAERCHEN-REIHE. 1974. irreg., vol.9, 1992. price varies. Oesterreichisches Museum fuer Volkskunde, Laudongasse 15-19, A-1080 Vienna, Austria. TEL 0431-438905. FAX 0431-4085342. Ed. Klaus Beitl. adv. circ. 1,000. **Document type:** monographic series.

398 900　　US　　ISSN 1057-2368
REMINISCE. 1991. bi-m. $16.98 (foreign $25.98). Reiman Publications, Inc., 5400 S. 60th St., Greendale, WI 53129. TEL 414-423-0100. FAX 414-423-1143. (Subscr. to: Box 998, Greendale, WI 53129) Ed. Roy Reiman. illus.; circ. 2,000,000 (paid). **Document type:** consumer publication.
　Description: For people who love reliving the good times.

REVISTA DE DIALECTOLOGIA Y TRADICIONES POPULARES. see LINGUISTICS

REVISTA DE ETNOGRAFIE SI FOLCLOR. see ANTHROPOLOGY

398　　　　　BL
REVISTA PERNAMBUCANA DE FOLCLORE. exchange basis. Campanha de Defesa do Folclore Brasileiro, Instituto Joaquim Nabuco de Pesquisas Sociais, Av. 17 de Agosto 2187, Recife, Brazil. Dir. Valdemar Valente.

398　　　　　GW　　ISSN 0722-7671
RHEINISCH-BERGISCHER KALENDER; Heimatjahrbuch fur das Bergische Land. 1920. a. DM.17.80. Heider Verlag GmbH, Postfach 200540, 51435 Bergisch Gladbach, Germany. TEL 02202-95401. FAX 02202-21531. adv.; bk.rev.; index. circ. 12,000. (back issues avail.) **Document type:** bulletin.

RHEINISCHE HEIMATPFLEGE. see HISTORY — History Of Europe

398　　　　　GW　　ISSN 0080-2697
GR1
RHEINISCHES JAHRBUCH FUER VOLKSKUNDE. 1950. biennial. DM.60 to members; non-members DM.64. (Rheinische Vereinigung fuer Volkskunde) Volkskundliches Seminar der Universitaet Bonn, Am Hofgarten 22, 53113 Bonn, Germany. TEL 0228-737618. FAX 0228-737562. Ed. H.L. Cox. bk.rev. circ. 300. Indexed: M.L.A. **Document type:** academic/scholarly publication.

RIJKSUNIVERSITEIT TE GRONINGEN. NEDERSAKSISCH INSTITUUT. DRIEMAANDELIJKSE BLADEN; taal en volksleven in het oosten van Nederland. see LITERATURE

ROBIN. see ENVIRONMENTAL STUDIES

398　　　　　PL　　ISSN 0080-3561
ROCZNIK SADECKI. (Text in Polish; summaries in English, French, and Russian) 1938. a. 100 Zl. Polskie Towarzystwo Historyczne, Oddzial w Nowym Saczu, Rynek Ratusz, Nowy Sacz, Poland. Ed. Kazimierz Zajac. bk.rev. circ. 1,500.

398　　　　　SW　　ISSN 0586-5360
AS284.G87
SAGA OCH SED. (Text in English, German and Scandinavian languages; summaries in English) 1934. a. SEK 160 (effective 1992). Kungliga Gustav Adolfs Akademien, Klostergatan 2, S-753 21 Uppsala, Sweden. (Dist. by: Kungliga Gustav Adolfs Akademien, Klostergatan 2, S-753 21 Uppsala, Sweden) Ed. Lennart Elmevik. circ. 500. (back issues avail.) Indexed: M.L.A.

SAN YUE SAN. see LITERATURE

SAVIA ARGENTINA. see GENERAL INTEREST PERIODICALS — Argentina

SCHLERN; Zeitschrift fuer Suedtiroler Landeskunde. see ART

SCHWAELMER JAHRBUCH. see HISTORY — History Of Europe

398　　　　　SZ　　ISSN 0048-9522
GR1
SCHWEIZER VOLKSKUNDE. 1911. 4/yr. 40 SFr. (Schweizerische Gesellschaft fuer Volkskunde - Societe Suisse des Traditions Populaires) Reinhardt Media Service, Postfach 393, CH-4012 Basel, Switzerland. TEL 061-2613320. Ed.Bd. bk.rev.; illus.; index.

398　　　　　GW　　ISSN 0080-732X
GR240
SCHWEIZERISCHE GESELLSCHAFT FUER VOLKSKUNDE. SCHRIFTEN. 1902. irreg., no.75, 1993. price varies. (Schweizerische Gesellschaft fuer Volkskunde, SZ) Dr. Rudolf Habelt GmbH, Am Buchengang 1, 53115 Bonn, Germany. TEL 0228-232016. FAX 0228-232017. **Document type:** monographic series.
—BLDSC (8094.980000).

398　　　　　SZ　　ISSN 0036-794X
GR1
SCHWEIZERISCHES ARCHIV FUER VOLKSKUNDE. (Text in French, German and Italian) 1897. 4/yr. 60 SFr. (Schweizerische Gesellschaft fuer Volkskunde - Societe Suisse des Traditions Populaires) Reinhardt Media Service, Postfach 393, CH-4012 Basel, Switzerland. TEL 061-2613320. Ed. Ueli Gyr. bk.rev.; illus.; index. Indexed: A.I.C.P., Arts & Hum.Cit.Ind., M.L.A.
—Faxon.

SCOTTISH STUDIES. see HISTORY — History Of Europe

398　　　　　US　　ISSN 0037-0460
SEATTLE FOLKLORE SOCIETY NEWSLETTER.* 1969-1978 (vol.9); resumed 1984? q. $4. Seattle Folklore Society, BOx 30141, Seattle, WA 98103-0141. Ed. Vivian T. Williams. adv.; bk.rev.; index. circ. 900. (also avail. in microfilm from UMI; reprint service avail. from UMI) Indexed: Abstr.Folk.Stud.

398　　　　　BL
▼**SEMINARIO FOLCLORE E CULTURA POPULAR. SERIE ECONTROS E ESTUDOS.** 1992. irreg. Instituto Brasileiro de Arte e Cultura, Coordenacao de Folclore e Cultura Popular, Biblioteca Amadeu Amaral, Rua do Catete, 179, 22220 Rio de Janiero, RJ, Brazil. bibl. **Document type:** monographic series.
　Description: Provides information on seminars, debates, studies and research of the institute.

SERIE DE VOCABULARIOS Y DICCIONARIOS INDIGENAS "MARIANO SILVA Y ACEVES". see LINGUISTICS

SHAN CHA/CAMELLIA; minzu minjian wenxue shuangyuekan. see LITERATURE

398　　　　　CC
SHAN HAI JING/FOLKLORE. (Text in Chinese) 1981. bi-m. Y6($31.10) Zhongguo Minjian Wenyijia Xiehui, Zhejiang Fenhui - Chinese Folk Literature and Art Workers' Association, Zhejiang Branch, 9, Jiande Lu, Hangzhou, Zhejiang 310006, People's Republic of China, People's Republic of China. TEL 0571-778991. (Dist. in China by: Fuzhou City Post, Hua Lin Lu, Fuzhou, Fujian 350013, P.R.C.; Dist. outside China by: China International Book Trading Corporation (Guoji Shudian), P.O. Box 399, Beijing, P.R.C.; Dist. in US by: China Books & Periodicals, Inc., 2929 24th St., San Francisco, CA 94110. TEL 415-282-2994) Ed. Chen De-lai. circ. 920,000.
　Description: Contains stories and anecdotes from Chinese folklore. includes serial ghost stories, tales of the supernatural, city and town stories, "Three Kingdoms" stories, tales of city gods, and jokes and humor.

398　　　　　IT　　ISSN 0037-4563
SICILIA. (Text in Italian; summaries in English, French, German, Spanish) 1953. q. L.18000. S.F. Flaccovio Editore, Via Ruggero Settimo 37, 90139 Palermo, Italy. Ed. Giuseppe Orlanoli. charts; illus. circ. 5,000.

SING OUT!; the folksong magazine. see MUSIC

SLOVENSKO ETNOLOSKO DRUSTVO. GLASNIK. see HISTORY — History Of Europe

SLOVENSKY NARODOPIS/SLOVAK ETHNOGRAPHY. see ETHNIC INTERESTS

398　　　　　US
SMITHSONIAN FOLKLIFE STUDIES. irreg., no.6, 1991. free. Smithsonian Institution Press, 470 L'Enfant Plaza, Ste. 7100, Washington, DC 20560. TEL 202-287-3738. FAX 202-287-3637. Ed. Don Fisher. bibl.; charts; illus.; cum.index: 1978-1983. circ. 2,000. (back issues avail.) **Document type:** monographic series.

398　　　　　SP　　ISSN 0212-7547
GR237.P34
SOCIEDAD DE ESTUDIOS VASCOS. CUADERNOS DE SECCION. FOLKLORE. 1983. irreg. Eusko Ikaskuntza, Legazpi, 10-1, 20004 Donostia-San Sebastian, Spain. TEL 425 111.

SOCIEDAD DE EUSKO FOLKLORE. ANUARIO; etnografia y paletnografia. see ANTHROPOLOGY

FOLKLORE

398   FR   ISSN 0037-9077
GR150
SOCIETE DE MYTHOLOGIE FRANCAISE BULLETIN. 1950. 4/yr. 170 F. (effective Jan. 1991). Societe de Mythologie Francaise, 175 rue de Pontoise, 60000 Beauvais, France. bibl.

SOMERSET AND DORSET NOTES AND QUERIES. see HISTORY — History Of Europe

398   US   ISSN 0899-594X
GR1
SOUTHERN FOLKLORE. 1937. 3/yr. $25 (foreign $28). University Press of Kentucky, 663 S. Limestone St., Lexington, KY 40508-4008. TEL 606-257-8439. FAX 606-257-2984. Ed. Erika Brady. adv.; bk.rev.; bibl.; index. circ. 500. (also avail. in microform from UMI; reprint service avail. from UMI) Indexed: Amer.Hist.& Life, Curr.Cont., Hist.Abstr., Hum.Ind., Ind.Bk.Rev.Hum., M.L.A., Music Ind. Document type: academic/scholarly publication.
—BLDSC (8354.038000); Faxon; UMI.
    Formed by the 1988 merger of: Southern Folklore Quarterly (ISSN 0038-4127) & Kentucky Folklore Record (ISSN 0023-0227)
    Description: Articles on analytical, descriptive, comparative, and historical study of folklore. Examines recent developments in the discipline.
    Refereed Serial

SPELEO. see EARTH SCIENCES

398 028.5   US
SPOOFING. 1983. 2/yr. Creative With Words Publications, Box 223226, Carmel, CA 93922. Ed. Brigitta Geltrich. illus. (back issues avail.)
    Formerly: Are You Spoofing.
    Description: Each issue devotes to an individual theme, such as love, animal, nature and happiness.

398   IT
STROLIC. (Text in Italian and Friulian) 1920. a. L.50000($33) (Regione Friuli - Venezia - Giulia) GEAP Pordenone, Via Malignani 41, 33080 Fiume Veneto (PN), Italy. TEL 0432-501598. FAX 0432-511766. (Subscr. to: Societa Filologica Friulana, Via Manin 18, 33100 Udine, Italy) bk.rev. circ. 5,000. (back issues avail.)
    Description: Collection of folklore stories by various authors from the region Friuli Vezia Giulia.

398   FI   ISSN 1235-1946
STUDIA FENNICA. FOLKLORISTICA. 1933. irreg. Suomalaisen Kirjallisuuden Seura - Finnish Literature Society, Hallituskatu 1, P.O. Box 259, FIN-00170 Helsinki, Finland. TEL 358-0-131231. FAX 358-0-13123220. Ed.Bd.
    Supersedes in part (in 1992): Studia Fennica (ISSN 0085-6835).

SUEDOSTDEUTSCHES ARCHIV. see HISTORY — History Of Europe

398 949.12   IC
SULUR. 1971. a. ISK 1495. Soegufelag Eyfirdinga, Hafnarstraeti 90, IS-600 Akureyri, Iceland. TEL 354-6-24024. Ed. J.O. Halldorsson. circ. 900. (back issues avail.)

SVENSK VISARKIV. HANDLINGAR. see MUSIC

SVENSK VISARKIV. MEDDELANDEN. see MUSIC

SVENSK VISARKIV. SKRIFTER. see MUSIC

TAROT NETWORK NEWS. see NEW AGE PUBLICATIONS

TATRZANSKI ORZEL/TATRA EAGLE. see ETHNIC INTERESTS

398   US   ISSN 0040-3253
GR1
TENNESSEE FOLKLORE SOCIETY BULLETIN. 1935. q. $6. Tennessee Folklore Society, Box 201, Middle Tennessee State University, Murfreesboro, TN 37132. TEL 615-898-2576. bk.rev.; index.; cum.index: 1935-1972. circ. 425. (processed; also avail. in microfilm from TMI) Indexed: Abstr.Folk.Stud., Amer.Hist.& Life, Hist.Abstr., M.L.A., Music Ind.
—BLDSC (8790.620000); Faxon; UnCover.

398   US   ISSN 0082-3023
GR1
TEXAS FOLKLORE SOCIETY. PUBLICATIONS. 1916. a. $15. (Texas Folklore Society) University of North Texas Press, Box 13856, Denton, TX 76203-3856. TEL 817-565-2142. FAX 817-565-4590. Ed. Francis E. Abernethy. index. circ. 2,000. Document type: monographic series.

398 572 970   CN   ISSN 0381-6109
F1137
THEM DAYS. 1975. q. Can.$14.98($16) Them Days Inc., Box 939, Sta. B, Happy Valley, Goose Bay, NF A0P 1E0, Canada. TEL 709-896-8531. Ed. Doris Saunders. illus. circ. 3,000.
    Description: Oral history accounts of Labrador.

TIROLER HEIMATBLAETTER. see HISTORY — History Of Europe

398   UK   ISSN 0049-397X
TOCHER. (Text in English, Gaelic and Scottish) 1971. 2/yr. £6. University of Edinburgh, School of Scottish Studies, 27 George Square, Edinburgh EH8 9LD, Scotland. TEL 031-650-3060. Ed. A.J. Bruford. index every 6 yrs. circ. 1,000. (back issues avail.) Indexed: A.I.C.P. Document type: academic/scholarly publication.
    Description: Traditional tales, folksongs, oral history and other lore from the archives of the School of Scottish Studies, mostly transcribed from recent field recordings.

398   NO   ISSN 0332-5997
GR220
TRADISJON; tidsskrift for folkeminnevitskap. (Text in Norwegian; summaries in English) 1971. a. NOK 240 in the Nordic countries; elsewhere NOK 285. Scandinavian University Press, P.O. Box 2959-Toeyen, N-0608 Oslo, Norway. TEL 472-67-7600. FAX 472-67-7575. (U.S. addr.: Scandinavian University Press, 200 Meacham Ave., Elmont, NY 11003. TEL 516-352-7300) Ed. Reimund Kvideland. adv.; bk.rev.; index. circ. 800. (back issues avail.) Indexed: M.L.A.
    Description: Folkloristic science with perspectives to present times.

TRADITIONES. see ANTHROPOLOGY

TRICKSTER. see ANTHROPOLOGY

398   TR
TRINIDAD CARNIVAL; the world's most colourful festival. 1973. a. $12. Key Caribbean Publications Ltd., Corner Park St. & Ariapita Ave., Port-of-Spain, Trinidad & Tobago, W.I. Ed. Roy Boyke. adv. circ. 20,000.

TRISTANIA; a journal devoted to Tristan studies. see LITERATURE

398   IQ   ISSN 0002-4082
TURATH AL-SHA'BI;* folklore monthly magazine. (Text in Arabic; summaries in English) 1969. m. ID.3000. Ministry of Culture and Information, Nr au-Husoor Sq., Fitruly Qasr as-Salaam Bldg., Baghdad, Iraq. Ed. Lutfi El-Khouri. bk.rev.; index. circ. 15,000.

398 059.927   TS
TURATH WA FUNUN/HERITAGE AND ARTS. (Text in Arabic) 1980. q. Dubai Folklore Society - Jam'iyyat Dubai lil-Funun al-Sha'biyyah wal-Masrah, P.O. Box 1848, Dubai, United Arab Emirates. TEL 694222. circ. 1,000.
    Description: Covers all aspects of cultural heritage, folklore and popular culture in the U.A.E.

398   TU   ISSN 1015-4868
TURK FOLKLORU ARASTIRMALARI. 1981. a. Ministry of Culture, General Directorate of Monuments and Museums - Kultur Bakanligi, Anitlar ve Muzeler Genel Mudurlugu, Ankara, Turkey. Document type: academic/scholarly publication.
    Description: Scholarly studies of aspects of Turkish folklore and culture.

TURKEY TRACKS. see HISTORY — History Of North And South America

398   IT   ISSN 0390-4555
TUSCIA. 1973. q. L.10000. Ente Provinciale per il Turismo di Viterbio - Provincial Tourist Board of Viterbo, Piazza dei Caduti 16, 01100 Viterbo, Italy. TEL 0761-34-63-63. FAX 0761-32-62-06. Ed. Vincenzo Ceniti. adv.; cum.index: 1973-1983. circ. 5,000. (back issues avail.)

398   SA   ISSN 0049-4933
TYDSKRIF VIR VOLKSKUNDE EN VOLKSTAAL. (Text mainly in Afrikaans) 1944. s-a. R.25 (foreign R.30) (effective 1993). Genootskap vir Afrikaanse Volkskunde, P.O. Box 4585, Johannesburg 2000, South Africa. TEL 27-11-7823784. Ed. Willie Loots. adv.; bk.rev.; charts; illus. Indexed: Ind.S.A.Per. Document type: academic/scholarly publication.
    Description: Articles on folklore and folklife in South Africa.

UJ MAGYAR NEPKOLTESI GYUJTEMENY. see LITERATURE — Poetry

398   UK   ISSN 0082-7347
GR148.N6
ULSTER FOLKLIFE. 1955. a. £7. Ulster Folk and Transport Museum, Cultra, Holywood, County Down BT18 0EU, N. Ireland. TEL 428-428. FAX 02317-4786. Ed. Jonathan Bell. bk.rev. circ. 750. Indexed: A.I.C.P., Arts & Hum.Cit.Ind., Br.Archaeol.Abstr., Curr.Cont., M.L.A. Document type: academic/scholarly publication.
—BLDSC (9082.742500); UnCover.
    Description: Covers cultural, artistic, economic, and domestic heritage of this Northern Irish region.

UNE VILLE, UN PAYS. see HISTORY — History Of Europe

398 780   CK   ISSN 0067-9534
UNIVERSIDAD NACIONAL DE COLOMBIA. CENTRO DE ESTUDIOS FOLKLORICOS. MONOGRAFIAS. irreg., latest 1973. Universidad Nacional de Colombia, Facultad de Artes, Conservatorio de Musica, Bogota, Colombia. Ed. Guillermo Abadia Morales. circ. 2,000. Document type: monographic series.

398   CN   ISSN 0085-5243
UNIVERSITE LAVAL. ARCHIVES DE FOLKLORE. (Text and summaries in French) 1946. irreg., no.25, 1991. price varies. Presses de l'Universite Laval, Cite Universitaire, Quebec, PQ G1K 7P4, Canada. TEL 418-656-5106. FAX 418-656-2600. bibl. Indexed: M.L.A. Document type: monographic series.

398   US
UNIVERSITY FOLKLORE ASSOCIATION. COLLECTANEA. 1969. a. exchange basis. (University Folklore Association) University of Texas at Austin, Center for Intercultural Studies in Folklore and Ethnomusicology, E.P.S. 2140, Austin, TX 78712. TEL 512-471-5689. FAX 512-471-6535. bk.rev. circ. 500.
    Former titles: University Folklore Association. Folklore Papers; Folklore Annual (ISSN 0071-6782)

398   US   ISSN 0068-6247
UNIVERSITY OF CALIFORNIA, LOS ANGELES. CENTER FOR THE STUDY OF COMPARATIVE FOLKLORE AND MYTHOLOGY. PUBLICATIONS. irreg. University of California Press, 2120 Berkeley Way, Berkeley, CA 94720. TEL 415-642-4247. FAX 415-643-7127.
    Refereed Serial

398   US   ISSN 0731-1524
UNIVERSITY OF CALIFORNIA PUBLICATIONS. FOLKLORE & MYTHOLOGY STUDIES. 1953. irreg. vol.35, 1992. price varies. University of California Press, 2120 Berkeley Way, Berkeley, CA 94720. TEL 510-642-4247. FAX 510-643-7127. (Orders to: California-Princeton Fulfillment Services, 1445 Lower Ferry Rd., Ewing, NJ 08618. TEL 800-777-4726. FAX 800-999-1958) Ed.Bd. Document type: monographic series.
    Formerly: University of California Publications. Folklore Studies (ISSN 0068-6360)
    Description: Explores various mythological and folklore traditions.
    Refereed Serial

390 301.2   XO   ISSN 0083-4106
GN549.S6
UNIVERZITA KOMENSKEHO. FILOZOFICKA FAKULTA. ZBORNIK: ETHNOLOGIA SLAVICA; an international review of Slavic ethnology. (Text and summaries in various languages) 1969. a. exchange basis. Univerzita Komenskeho, Filozoficka Fakulta, c/o Ustredna Kniznica Filozofickej Fakulty, Gondova 2, 818 01 Bratislava, Slovakia. Ed. Jan Podolak. bk.rev.; illus. circ. 1,075. Indexed: Anthropol.Lit. Document type: academic/scholarly publication.
    Description: Contains scholarly papers, ethnological histories, biographical notes and reviews.

398　　　　　　　　AU
VEREIN FUER VOLKSKUNDE IN WIEN. SONDERSCHRIFTEN.. 1955. irreg., vol.3, 1978. Verein fuer Volkskunde, Laudongasse 19, A-1080 Vienna, Austria. FAX 0222-4085342. Ed. Klaus Beitl. bk.rev. circ. 600. **Document type:** monographic series.

VEREIN OBERPFAELZISCHES BAUERNMUSEUM. MITTEILUNGEN. see *AGRICULTURE*

398　　　　　　　　US　　ISSN 0042-6253
GR1
VILTIS; a folklore magazine. 1944. bi-m. $20. V.F. Beliajus, Ed. & Pub., 1337 Marion St., Denver, CO 80218. TEL 303-839-1589. adv.; bk.rev. circ. 2,500. (also avail. in microform from UMI)
　—Faxon; UnCover; UMI.

VOCE DELL'EMIGRANTE. see *ETHNIC INTERESTS*

VOCE DI FIUME. see *HISTORY*

398　　　　　　　　NE　　ISSN 0169-5614
VOLKSCULTUUR; Tydschrift over Tradities en Tydsverschynselen. (Text in Dutch) 1984. 2/yr. fl.35. Stichting Nederlands Centrum voor Volkscultuur, Lucasbolwerk 11, 3512 EH Utrecht, Netherlands. TEL 31-30-319997. FAX 31-30-334047. Ed. Ineke Strouken. bk.rev.; index. circ. 1,000. (back issues avail.)
　—SWETS.
　Formerly: Neerlands Volksleven.
　Description: Details traditional and popular culture.

398　　　　　　　　NE
VOLKSDANS. 1969. 8/yr. fl.70 membership. Landelijk Centrum Amateurdans, P.O. Box 452, 3500 AL Utrecht, Netherlands. FAX 31-30-332721. Ed. Willemijn in 't Veld. adv.; bk.rev.; illus.; circ. 3,000 (controlled).
　Former titles: Mei Plezant; Nevonieuws; Dansbalans (ISSN 0011-6165)

390　　　　　　　　GW
VOLKSKUENDLICHEN KOMMISSION FUER WESTFALEN. SCHRIFTEN. 1937. irreg. price varies. Aschendorffsche Verlagsbuchhandlung, Soesterstr. 13, 48155 Muenster, Germany. TEL 0251-690-0. FAX 0251-690143. **Document type:** monographic series.
　Former titles: Landschaftsverband Westfalen-Lippe (ISSN 0170-8090); Landschaftsverband Westfalen-Lippe. Volkskundliche Kommission. Schriften (ISSN 0075-7942)

398 943　　　　　　　GW　　ISSN 0176-1196
VOLKSKUNDE IN NIEDERSACHSEN. 1984. s-a. DM.10. Volker Schmerse Text- und Bildgestaltung, Postfach 110335, 37048 Goettingen, Germany. TEL 0551-46335. FAX 0551-47550. Ed. Gudrun Schwibbe. bk.rev.; illus. circ. 700. (back issues avail.) **Document type:** academic/scholarly publication.

398　　　　　　　　AU　　ISSN 0042-8531
VOLKSKUNDE IN OESTERREICH. 1966. m. S.250. Verein fuer Volkskunde, Laudongasse 19, A-1080 Vienna, Austria. FAX 0222-4085342. Ed. Klaus Beitl. adv.; film rev.; bibl.; index. circ. 1,300. (back issues avail.) **Document type:** bulletin.

VOLKSKUNDIG BULLETIN; tijdschrift voor Nederlandse cultuurwetenschap. see *ANTHROPOLOGY*

390　　　　　　　　GW
VOLKSKUNDLICHE STUDIEN. (Subseries of: Universitaet Innsbruck. Veroeffentlichungen) 1970. irreg. price varies. (Universitaet Innsbruck) Oesterreichische Kommissionsbuchhandlung, Maximilianstrasse 17, A-6020 Innsbruck, Austria. Ed. Karl Ilg.

398　　　　　　　GW　　ISSN 0083-6877
VOLKSTUM DER SCHWEIZ. 1941. irreg., no.12, 1979. price varies. Dr. Rudolf Habelt GmbH, Am Buchenhang 1, 53115 Bonn, Germany. TEL 0228-232016. FAX 0228-232017. **Document type:** monographic series.

WESTFAELISCHE FORSCHUNGEN. see *HISTORY — History Of Europe*

398　　　　　　　　SZ
WIR WALSER. 1963. 2/yr. 25 SFr. Internationale Vereinigung fuer Walsertum, Postfach 674, CH-3900 Brig-Glis, Switzerland. adv.; bk.rev.; bibl.; charts; illus. **Document type:** newsletter.

WISCONSIN WEST MAGAZINE. see *HISTORY — History Of North And South America*

WITTGENSTEIN. see *HISTORY — History Of Europe*

YEARBOOK FOR TRADITIONAL MUSIC. see *MUSIC*

ZALAI GYUJTEMENY; kozlemenyek zala megye kozgyujtemenyeinek kutatasaibol. see *HISTORY — History Of Europe*

398　　　　　　　GW　　ISSN 0044-3700
GR1
ZEITSCHRIFT FUER VOLKSKUNDE. 1905. s-a. DM.86 (students DM.54). (Deutsche Gesellschaft fuer Volkskunde e.V.) Verlag Otto Schwartz und Co., Annastr. 6, 37075 Goettingen, Germany. TEL 0551-31051. FAX 0551-372812. Ed. Gottfried Korff. adv.; bk.rev.; bibl.; illus.; index. **Indexed:** Arts & Hum.Cit.Ind., Curr.Cont., M.L.A., Music Ind. **Document type:** academic/scholarly publication.
　—Faxon; SWETS. **CCC**.

398 301.32　　　　BN　　ISSN 0581-751X
ZEMALJSKI MUZEJ BOSNE I HERCEGOVINE. GLASNIK. ETNOLOGIJA. Title also in French. (Vols. for 1965-66, 1969-70 issued in combined form) a. Zemaljski Muzej Bosne i Hercegovine, Vojvode Putnika 7, Sarajevo, Bosnia Hercegovina. Ed. Vlajko Palavestra. illus. **Indexed:** Anthropol.Lit.
　Continues the publication with the same title issued by the museum under its earlier name: Zemaljski Muzej u Sarajevu.

ZUMBERACKE NOVINE. see *ETHNIC INTERESTS*

398　　　　　　　GW　　ISSN 0514-8413
ZWISCHEN EIDER UND WIEDAU; Heimatkalender fuer Nordfriesland. a. price varies. (Nordfriescher Verein) Husum Druck- und Verlagsgesellschaft mbH, Postfach 1480, 25804 Husum, Germany. TEL 04841-6081. FAX 04841-61397. circ. 5,000. (back issues avail.) **Document type:** bulletin.

FOLKLORE — Abstracting, Bibliographies, Statistics

BIBLIOGRAPHIE ZUR SYMBOLIK, IKONOGRAPHIE UND MYTHOLOGIE. see *ANTHROPOLOGY — Abstracting, Bibliographies, Statistics*

398　　　　　　　　BL
BIBLIOTECA AMADEU AMARAL. SERIE REFERENCIA. irreg., no.3, 1992. Instituto Brasileiro de Arte e Cultura, Coordenacao de Folclore e Cultura Popular, Biblioteca Amadeu Amaral, Rua do Catete, 179, 22220 Rio de Janeiro, R.J., Brazil. **Document type:** bibliography.

398 016　　　　　　IT　　ISSN 0045-2432
BOLLETTINO BIBLIOGRAFICO SARDO E ARCHIVIO TRADIZIONI POPOLARI.* 1970. bi-m. L.4000. Via G. Giovanni 402, 09100 Cagliari, Italy. Ed. Giuseppe Della Maria. index.

INTERNATIONAL ARTHURIAN SOCIETY. BIBLIOGRAPHICAL BULLETIN/SOCIETE INTERNATIONALE ARTHURIENNE. BULLETIN BIBLIOGRAPHIQUE. see *LITERATURE — Abstracting, Bibliographies, Statistics*

390 016　　　　　　GW　　ISSN 0074-9737
INTERNATIONALE VOLKSKUNDLICHE BIBLIOGRAPHIE/INTERNATIONAL FOLKLORE BIBLIOGRAPHY/BIBLIOGRAPHIE INTERNATIONALE D'ETHNOLOGIE. (Entries in various languages) 1954. irreg., 1993. ann. Dr. Rudolf Habelt GmbH, Am Buchenhang 1, 53115 Bonn, Germany. TEL 0228-232016. FAX 0228-232017. Ed. R. Alsheimer. **Indexed:** A.I.C.P. **Document type:** monographic series.
　—BLDSC (4540.270000).

M L A DIRECTORY OF PERIODICALS; a guide to journals and series in languages and literatures. (Modern Language Association of America) see *LITERATURE — Abstracting, Bibliographies, Statistics*

398　　　　　　　　AU　　ISSN 0259-0778
OESTERREICHISCHE VOLKSKUNDLICHE BIBLIOGRAPHIE. 1966. irreg., no.23-24, 1992. price varies. Verband der Wissenschaftlichen Gesellschaften Oesterreichs, Verein fuer Volkskunde, Lindengasse 37, A-1070 Vienna, Austria. TEL 932166. Ed. Klaus Beitl.

FOOD AND FOOD INDUSTRIES

398　　　　　　　BE　　ISSN 0042-8523
VOLKSKUNDE, DRIEMAANDELIJKS TIJDSCHRIFT VOOR DE STUDIE VAN HET VOLKSLEVEN. (Text in Dutch) 1888. q. 6CO BEF (effective 1994). Centrum voor Studie en Documentatie, Jan de Voslei 37-6, B-2020 Antwerp, Belgium. adv.; bk.rev. **Document type:** academic/scholarly publication, abstracting/indexing, bibliography.

FOOD AND FOOD INDUSTRIES

see also Food and Food Industries—Bakers and Confectioners; Food and Food Industries—Grocery Trade; Agriculture; Fish and Fisheries; Home Economics; Hotels and Restaurants; Nutrition and Dietetics

664.028
A F F I LETTER. 1942. 20/yr. membership. American Frozen Food Institute, 1764 Old Meadow Ln., Ste. 350, McLean, VA 22102. TEL 703-821-0770. FAX 703-821-1350. Ed. Traci V. Carneal. charts; illus.; stat.; circ. 1,300 (controlled). (looseleaf format) **Document type:** trade publication.
　Former titles: American Frozen Food Institute. Weekly Report; American Frozen Food Institute. Newsletter; National Association of Frozen Food Packers. Newsletter.

664.9　　　　　　　GW　　ISSN 0170-0499
A F Z FLEISCH-LEBENSMITTEL-MARKT. (Allgemeine Fleischer Zeitung) 1950. m. DM.62.80 (foreign DM.72.10). Deutscher Fachverlag GmbH, Mainzer Landstr. 251, 60326 Frankfurt a.M., Germany. TEL 069-759501 FAX 069-75952999. (Subscr. to: Postfach 100606, 60006 Frankfurt a.M., Germany) adv.; bk rev.; charts; illus. circ. 28,866. **Document type:** trade publication.
　Formerly: Fleischer Offerten-Dienst (ISSN 0015-3605)

A I D VERBRAUCHERDIENST; Zeitschrift fuer Fach-, Lehr- und Beratungskraefte im Bereich Ernaehrung. (Auswertungs- und Informationsdienst fuer Ernaehrung, Landwirtschaft und Forsten e.V.) see *NUTRITION AND DIETETICS*

664　　　　　　　　US
A M I NEWSLETTER. 1959. w. membership only. American Meat Institute, 1700 N. Moore St., Ste. 1600, Arlington, VA 22209. TEL 703-841-2400. FAX 703-527-0938. Ed. Janet Riley. charts; illus. circ. 3,000. (back issues avail.) **Document type:** newsletter.
　Description: Covers issues related and relevant to the meat and poultry industry.

664.9　　　　　　　AT　　ISSN 1032-9560
A M L C NEWS. 1947. 10/yr. free to qualified personnel. Australian Meat and Livestock Corporation, P.O. Box 4129, Sydney, N.S.W. 2001, Australia. TEL 02-260-3111. FAX 02-267-6620. TELEX AA22887. Ed. Taffy Davies. circ. 27,000. **Document type:** newsletter.
　Former titles: Australian Meat and Livestock Corporation. Meat Producer and Exporter (ISSN 0815-3337); Australian Meat Board. Meat Producer and Exporter (ISSN 0045-0693)

664　　　　　　　　US
A S A E TRANSACTIONS. FOOD & PROCESS ENGINEERING. 1970. a. $45.50 to non-members; members $25.50. American Society of Agricultural Engineers, 2950 Niles Rd., St. Joseph, MI 49085-9659. TEL 616-429-0300. FAX 616-429-3852. Ed. Pamela DeVore-Hansen. circ. 150.
　Description: Addresses storage, packaging and handling of food products and more.
　Refereed Serial

664　　　　　　　　VE　　ISSN 0084-683X
A T A V E BOLETIN INFORMATIVO.* irreg. free. Asociacion de Tecnicos Azucareros de Venezuela, Estacion Experimental de Occidente, Yaritaguce, Yaracuy, Venezuela.

FOOD AND FOOD INDUSTRIES

664.9 636 AT ISSN 1030-8474
A U S - MEAT FEEDBACK. 1988. bi-m. Aus.$30 (foreign Aus.$45). Authority for Uniform Specifications Meat and Livestock (AUS-Meat), Attn: Ross Farmer, Business Manager, G.P.O. Box 4129, Sydney, N.S.W. 2001, Australia. TEL 02-261-2922. FAX 02-264-2321. Ed. Wendy Reiter. adv.: B&W page Aus.$1000, color page Aus.$1760; adv. contact: Lynda O'Leary. circ. 12,000. **Document type:** trade publication.
  Description: Features and news relevant to meat production, processing and retailing.

664 PL ISSN 0860-2859
   CODEN: AATAEX
ACTA ACADEMIAE AGRICULTURAE AC TECHNICAE OLSTENENSIS. TECHNOLOGIA ALIMENTORUM/AGRICULTURAL AND TECHNICAL ACADEMY IN OLSZTYN. FOOD TECHNOLOGY. (Supplement avail.: Technologia Alimentorum) (Text in Polish; summaries in English and Russian) 1956. irreg. price varies. (Akademia Rolniczo-Techniczna im. M. Oczapowskiego) Wydawnictwo A R T Olsztyn, Blok 21, 10-957 Olsztyn-Kortowo, Poland. TEL 48-89-273310. TELEX 0526419. (Distr. by: Ars Polona-Ruch, Krakowskie Przedmiescie 7, 00-901 Warsaw, Poland. TEL 48-22-265334) bibl.; charts; illus.; circ. 130 (controlled). **Indexed:** Chem.Abstr., Dairy Sci.Abstr., Field Crop Abstr., Poult.Abstr., Ref.Zh., Seed Abstr. **Document type:** academic/scholarly publication.
—CASDDS.
  Formerly: Akademia Rolniczo-Techniczna. Zeszyty Naukowe. Technologia Zywnosci (ISSN 0324-9212)

664 HU ISSN 0139-3006
   CODEN: ACALDI
ACTA ALIMENTARIA; an international journal of food science. (Text in English) 1972. q. $140 (effective 1992). (Magyar Tudomanyos Akademia) Akademiai Kiado, Publishing House of the Hungarian Academy of Sciences, P.O. Box 245, H-1519 Budapest, Hungary. TEL 181-2134. FAX 166-6466. TELEX 22-6228 AKNYO H. Eds. J. Hollo, I. Varsanyi. adv.; bk.rev.; index. **Indexed:** ASCA, Biodet.Abstr., Biotech.Abstr., Chem.Abstr., Curr.Adv.Ecol.Sci., Curr.Cont., Curr.Pack.Abstr., Dairy Sci.Abstr., Excerp.Med, Food Sci.& Tech.Abstr., Food Sci.& Tech.Abstr., Hort.Abstr., INIS Atomind., Rev.Med.& Vet.Mycol.
—BLDSC (0591.500000); Faxon; SWETS; CASDDS. CCC.
  Formerly (until 1975): Academiae Scientiarum Hungaricae. Acta Alimentaria (ISSN 0302-7368); Supersedes (1967-1970): Elelmiszertudomany (ISSN 0013-5917)

ADVANCES IN FOOD AND NUTRITION RESEARCH. see *NUTRITION AND DIETETICS*

AFRICAN FARMING AND FOOD PROCESSING. see *AGRICULTURE*

664 IE
AGRI BUSINESS. 12/yr. National & International Publications Ltd., 40 Fitzwilliam Sq., Dublin 2, Ireland. TEL 767018. FAX 767189. Ed. Linda Plunket. circ. 4,300.

AGRINDEX; international information system for the agricultural sciences and technology. see *AGRICULTURE*

AGRO FOOD INDUSTRY HI-TECH. see *AGRICULTURE*

AIRLINE, SHIP & CATERING ONBOARD SERVICES MAGAZINE; the international trade publication for the passenger service and duty free markets. see *TRANSPORTATION — Air Transport*

664 PL ISSN 0860-0627
AKADEMIA ROLNICZA IM. HUGONA KOLLATAJA W KRAKOWIE. ZESZYTY NAUKOWE. SERIA: TECHNOLOGIA ZYWNOSCI. (Text in Polish; summaries in English) 1985. a. price varies. Akademia Rolnicza im. Hugona Kollataja w Krakowie, Al. 29 Listopada 46, 31-425 Krakow, Poland. TEL 48-12-119144. FAX 48-12-336245. TELEX 322469 PL. Ed. Zdzislaw Piskornik. circ. 120 (paid). **Document type:** academic/scholarly publication.

664 PL
AKADEMIA ROLNICZA, POZNAN. ROCZNIKI. TECHNOLOGIA ZYWNOSCI. (Text in Polish; summaries in English and Russian) 1960. irreg. price varies. Akademia Rolnicza, Poznan, Ul. Wojska Polskiego 28, 60-637 Poznan, Poland. FAX 48-61-411022. TELEX 0413322 ARPL. **Indexed:** Bibl.Agri. **Document type:** academic/scholarly publication.
  Formerly: Akademia Rolnicza, Poznan. Roczniki. Technologia Rolno-Spozywcza (ISSN 0137-1762)
  Description: Works on microbiology, chemistry, physics, technology and biotechnology of food raw materials, food and fodder.

AKADEMIA ROLNICZA W SZCZECINIE. ZESZYTY NAUKOWE. RYBACTWO MORSKIE I TECHNOLOGIA ZYWNOSCI. see *FISH AND FISHERIES*

664 PL ISSN 0209-0503
AKADEMIA ROLNICZA WE WROCLAWIU. ZESZYTY NAUKOWE. TECHNOLOGIA ZYWNOSCI. (Subseries of: Akademia Rolnicza we Wroclawiu. Zeszyty Naukowe (ISSN 0867-7964)) (Text in Polish; summaries in English) 1979. irreg. price varies. Akademia Rolnicza we Wroclawiu, Ul. Norwida 25, 50-375 Wroclaw, Poland. FAX 22-95-76. (Subscr. to: Dzial Wydawnictw i Poligrafii Akademii Rolniczej, ul. Sopocka 23, 50-344 Wroclaw, Poland. TEL 21-12-77) circ. 320.

664 338 SP ISSN 0210-3168
ALFORJA; revista mensual de la produccion y distribucion moderna. 1978. m. 12500 ptas. (effective 1994). Grupo Arte y Cemento, S.A., Zancoeta, 9, 5 y 7, 48013 Bilbao, Spain. TEL 344-441-0766. FAX 344-441-9590. Ed. Ignacio Echevarria. adv. circ. 12,500. **Document type:** trade publication.
  Description: Covers retailing and general food and beverage industry.

630 SP
ALIMARKET; informe confidencial de alimentacion y bebidas. 1982. w. 83000 ptas. (foreign 115000 ptas.) includes Alimarket Revista and Alimarket Informe Anual (effective 1994). Publicaciones Alimarket, S.A., O'Donnell, 18, 2o, 28009 Madrid, Spain. TEL 91-577-82-25. FAX 91-431-37-27. Ed. Carlos Guerrero. adv.: B&W page 170000 ptas., color page 235000; trim 180 x 255. bk.rev.

664 630 SP
ALIMARKET INFORME ANUAL. (In 5 vols.: A. Alimentacion Perecedera, B. Alimentacion No Perecedera, C. Bebidas, D. No Alimentacion, E. Distribucion Alimentaria) a. 12500 ptas. per vol. (foreign 17500 ptas.) (effective 1994). Publicaciones Alimarket, S.A., O'Donnell, 18, 2o, 28009 Madrid, Spain. TEL 91-577-82-25. FAX 91-431-37-27. adv.: B&W page 170000 ptas., color page 235000 ptas.; trim 180 x 255. (also avail. in diskette format)

630 SP
ALIMARKET REVISTA. 1987. m. (11/yr.). 25000 ptas. (foreign 30000 ptas.) (effective 1994). Publicaciones Alimarket, S.A., O'Donnell, 18, 2o, 28009 Madrid, Spain. TEL 91-577-82-25. TELEX 91-431-37-27. Ed. Carlos Guerrero. adv.: B&W page 170000 ptas.; color page 235000 ptas.; trim 180 x 255. **Document type:** trade publication.
  Formerly: Alimarket Monografico.

664 SZ ISSN 0002-5402
   CODEN: ALMTBR
ALIMENTA. 1961. bi-m. 79 SFr. (foreign 95 SFr.). Cicero Verlag AG, Spindelstr. 2, CH-8021 Zurich, Switzerland. Ed. Urs von Arx. adv.; bk.rev.; abstr.; bibl.; charts; illus.; stat.; index. circ. 5,800. **Indexed:** Biol.Abstr., Chem.Abstr., Curr.Adv.Ecol.Sci., Curr.Cont., Dairy Sci.Abstr., Food Sci.& Tech.Abstr., Ind.Vet., Nutr.Abstr., Packag.Sci.Tech., Vet.Bull.
—BLDSC (0787.850000); UMI; CASDDS.

664 SP ISSN 0212-1689
   CODEN: AEQTDY
ALIMENTACION; equipos y tecnologia. 1982. m. (10/yr.). 11000 ptas.($220) (effective 1993). Editorial Alcion, S.A., Triana, 53, 28016 Madrid, Spain. TEL 341-457-39-45. FAX 341-457-39-45. TELEX 49236 QUMI E. Ed. Ramon R. Madrid. adv.; bk.rev.; index. circ. 6,000.
—BLDSC (0787.858000); CASDDS. CCC.

664 340 SP ISSN 0214-803X
ALIMENTALEX; international food law review - revue internationale de droit de l'alimentation - revista internacional de derecho alimentario. (Text in English, French, Spanish) 1987. s-a. 10000 ptas. (effective 1994). (Asociacion Iberoamericana para el Derecho Alimentario) Ediciones y Publicaciones Alimentarias, S.A., Sandoval, 12, 1o J, 28010 Madrid, Spain. TEL 91-446-96-59. FAX 91-593-37-44. Ed. C. Barros.

664 PO
ALIMENTAR. 1986. q. Esc.1200 (Europe Esc.3000; elsewhere Esc.4500) (effective 1994). Centro do Formacao Profissional do Sector Alimentar, Av. 25 de Abril, 32-B, Pontinha, 1675 Lisbon, Portugal. TEL 1-478-0149. FAX 1-479-6120. TELEX 64907 CFPSA. Ed. A. Fialho Silva. adv.: color page Esc.120000; 297 x 210. circ. 10,000.

664 642.5 SP ISSN 0300-5755
   CODEN: ALMNEC
ALIMENTARIA; revista de tecnologia e higiene de los alimentos. 1964. m. (10/yr.). 12000 ptas. (foreign 14500 ptas.) (effective 1994). (Asociacion Europea para el Derecho Alimentario, Seccion Espanola) Ediciones y Publicaciones Alimentarias, S.A., Sandoval, 12-1 J, 28010 Madrid, Spain. TEL 91-4469659. FAX 91-5933744. Ed. Carlos Barros Santos. adv.; bk.rev.; bibl.; illus. circ. 5,000. (reprint service avail.) **Indexed:** Biodet.Abstr., Dairy Sci.Abstr., Food Sci.& Tech.Abstr., Ind.SST, Soyabean Abstr.
—BLDSC (0787.880000); SWETS; CASDDS. CCC.
  Description: Covers foodstuff technology, microbiology and hygiene.

664 CK
ALIMENTARIA. 1984. bi-m. $20. Apdo. 85011, Bogota, Colombia. Ed. Julius Siefken. circ. 10,000.

664 IT
ALIMENTARISTA. fortn. L.70000. Agenzia Gestione Periodici s.r.l., Via Domenico Trentacoste 9, 20134 Milan, Italy. TEL 02-2640009. FAX 02-2640330. TELEX 351491 AGEPE I. adv.: color page L.27750000; trim 254 x 344. circ. 120,000. **Document type:** trade publication.

664 SZ
ALIMENTATION. 24/yr. Case Postale 105, CH-1001 Lausanne, Switzerland. TEL 021-201901. FAX 021-234413. circ. 1,200.

664 IT
ALIMENTAZIONE OGGI. m. L.5000. Federazione Italiana Dettaglianti Alimentazione, Comitato Piemontese Alimentaristi, Via Massena 20, 10128 Turin, Italy. TEL 11-55-161. FAX 11-551-62-89. Ed. Giovanni Perfumo. adv. circ. 3,000.

664 641.1 BL ISSN 0103-4235
   CODEN: ALNUE4
ALIMENTOS E NUTRICAO. (Text in Portuguese; abstracts in English, Portuguese) 1989. a. $30 or exchange basis. Universidade Estadual Paulista, Av. Vincente Ferreira, 1278, Caixa Postal 603, 17515-901 Marilia, SP, Brazil. TEL 0144-33-1844. FAX 0144-22-2504. TELEX 111-9016 UJME BR. abstr.; bibl. **Indexed:** Food Sci.& Tech.Abstr. **Document type:** academic/scholarly publication.
—CASDDS.

664 US ISSN 0744-625X
ALIMENTOS PROCESADOS. (Text in Spanish) 1982. 11/yr. $53 (foreign $131) (free to qualified personnel). Delta Communications Inc. (Subsidiary of: Cahners Publishing Company), Division of Reed Elsevier Inc., 455 N. Cityfront Plaza Dr., 24th Fl., Chicago, IL 60611. TEL 312-222-2000. FAX 312-222-2026. TELEX 210012 UR. Ed. Julia Gallo-Torres; Pub. Sally Schofield. adv.: B&W page $3440, color page $4820; trim 7 7/8 x 10 3/4; adv. contact: Michelle Wolfson. circ. 20,047. **Document type:** trade publication.
—UMI. CCC.
  Incorporates (1951-1985): Industrias Lacteas (ISSN 0019-8951); (1945-1985): Panadero Latinoamericano - Latin American Baker (ISSN 0031-0638)

ALLERGY HOTLINE. see *MEDICAL SCIENCES — Allergology And Immunology*

FOOD AND FOOD INDUSTRIES

664 910.202 GW ISSN 0175-8314
ALLES UEBER WEIN. 1983. bi-m. DM.72($42)
Woschek Verlag, Wilh.-Th.-Roemheld-Str. 34, 55130
Mainz, Germany. TEL 061311-81035.
FAX 06131-839898. Ed. Heinz-Gert Woschek. adv.
contact: Beata Kratz. bk.rev. circ. 33,000. (back
issues avail.) **Document type:** consumer publication.

664.9 GW ISSN 0170-9828
ALLGEMEINE FLEISCHER ZEITUNG. w. DM.440.10
(foreign DM.528.85). (Deutscher Fleischer-Verband)
Deutscher Fachverlag GmbH, Mainzer Landstr. 251,
60326 Frankfurt a.M., Germany. (Subscr. to:
Postfach 100606, 60006 Frankfurt a.M., Germany)
adv.; bk.rev.; illus. circ. 17,061. **Document type:**
newspaper.

641 SW ISSN 0002-6204
ALLT OM MAT/ALL ABOUT FOOD AND COOKING; & vin.
1970. 16/yr. Specialtidningsfoerlaget AB, P.O. Box
70452, S-107 26 Stockholm, Sweden. Ed. Thor
Wahlberg. index. circ. 154,300. (also avail. in audio
cassette)

664 SP
ALMIREZ. 12/yr. Ronda de la Universidad 14, 2o,
08007 Barcelona, Spain. TEL 3-412-38-00.
FAX 3-3188852. circ. 10,000.

664 DK ISSN 0906-0820
ALT OM MAD. 1991. 4/yr. DKK 32.50. Bonniers
Specialmagasiner A-S, Strandboulevarden 130,
2100 Copenhagen OE, Denmark. Ed. Dan Melchior.
Description: Features articles on food, with recipes
for weekdays and banquets, articles on wine and
ideas for kitchen and table.

664.9 NE ISSN 0926-0498
AMBACHT & INDUSTRIE. 1957. 6/yr. (Instituut
Slagersvakonderwijs (S.V.O.)) Audet Tijdschriften bv
(Subsidiary of: C. Misset B.V.), Postbus 9000, 6800
DA Arnhem, Netherlands. TEL 31-85-209911.
FAX 31-85-233007. adv.; illus.; tr.mk. circ. 8,870.
Indexed: Key to Econ.Sci. **Document type:** trade
publication.
Formerly (until 1990): Slagersambacht (ISSN
0037-671X)
Description: Provides latest product and industry
news to the Dutch Technical School for Butchers.

664.7 US ISSN 0065-7107
CODEN: ACHMBK
**AMERICAN ASSOCIATION OF CEREAL CHEMISTS.
MONOGRAPH SERIES.** irreg., no.9, 1988. $89
(foreign $107). American Association of Cereal
Chemists, Inc., 3340 Pilot Knob Rd., St. Paul, MN
55121. TEL 800-328-7560. FAX 612-454-0766.
TELEX 6502439657 (MCI UW). (also avail. in
microfilm from UMI) **Indexed:** Biol.Abstr. **Document
type:** monographic series.
—CASDDS.

**AMERICAN ASSOCIATION OF MEAT PROCESSORS. THE
GOLD BOOK MEMBERS.** see BUSINESS AND
ECONOMICS — Trade And Industrial Directories

664 US ISSN 0361-0888
TP493.5.A1
**AMERICAN FROZEN FOOD INSTITUTE. MEMBERSHIP
DIRECTORY AND BUYER'S GUIDE.** 1943. a. $100.
American Frozen Food Institute, 1764 Old Meadow
Ln., Ste. 350, McLean, VA 22102.
TEL 703-821-0770. FAX 703-821-1350. Ed. Traci
V. Carneal. adv.; circ. 3,500 (controlled). **Document
type:** directory, trade publication.
Formerly: American Frozen Food Institute.
Membership Directory (ISSN 0084-635X)

664 US
**AMERICAN INSTITUTE OF BAKING. TECHNICAL
BULLETIN.** 1979. m. $30. American Institute of
Baking, Research Department, 1213 Bakers Way,
Manhattan, KS 66502. TEL 913-537-4750.
FAX 913-537-1493. TELEX 881039 AIB MAN UD.
Ed. Gur Ranhotra. circ. 1,500. (looseleaf format;
back issues avail.) **Document type:** trade publication.
Description: Covers all areas of the baking
industry, including ingredients, products, processing,
equipment, packaging, nutrition and emerging
technologies.

641.53 663.2 US
**AMERICAN INSTITUTE OF WINE & FOOD. NEW YORK
AREA CHAPTER. NEWS.*** m. American Institute of
Wine & Food, New York Area Chapter, 1114 First
Ave., New York, NY 10021. TEL 212-838-2061.
Description: Provides an open forum for the
appreciation and discussion of all the relevant food
and wine subjects in order to improve their
awareness and quality.

636 US
**AMERICAN MEAT SCIENCE ASSOCIATION. RECIPROCAL
MEAT CONFERENCE. PROCEEDINGS.** 1948. a. $20.
National Live Stock and Meat Board, 444 N.
Michigan Ave., Chicago, IL 60611.
TEL 312-467-5520. Ed. H. Kenneth Johnson. circ.
650. (reprint service avail. from UMI) **Indexed:**
Chem.Abstr., Food Sci.& Tech.Abstr. **Document type:**
proceedings.

AMERICAN WINE & FOOD. see BEVERAGES

664.9 FR ISSN 0296-8746
AMI DU PROFESSIONNEL EN ALIMENTATION. 1946. m.
230 F. (outside Europe 300 F.)(effective Jan.
1992). Editions Bovidel s.a.r.l., 41 rue Etienne
Marcel, 75001 Paris, France. TEL 42-36-28-77.
adv.; tr.lit. circ. 2,300.
Formerly: Ami du Charcutier, du Boucher et du
Salaisonnier (ISSN 0044-8117)

664 613.2 SP ISSN 0003-2492
TX341 CODEN: ANBRAD
ANALES DE BROMATOLOGIA. (Text in Spanish;
summaries in English) 1949. q. 7844 ptas. (foreign
10000 ptas.). Sociedad Espanola de Bromatologia,
Edificio Facultad de Farmacia, Ciudad Universitaria,
28040 Madrid, Spain. TEL 91-394-17-99. bk.rev.;
bibl.; index, cum.index every 5 yrs. circ. 750.
Indexed: Biol.Abstr., Chem.Abstr., Dairy Sci.Abstr.,
Excerp.Med., Food Sci.& Tech.Abstr., Ind.SST, Mass
Spectr.Bull., Nutr.Abstr., Potato Abstr.
—BLDSC (0888.000000); CASDDS. **CCC**.

**ANNUAIRE DES EXPORTATEURS DE CAFES
AFRICAINS/EXPORTER DIRECTORY OF AFRICAN
COFFEE.** see BUSINESS AND ECONOMICS —
International Commerce

664 FR ISSN 1246-8371
ANNUAIRE DES INDUSTRIES DE LA CONSERVE. 1952. a.
652 F. Editions Comindus, 1 rue Descombes,
75017 Paris, France. TEL 1-43-80-79-16.
FAX 1-40-53-91-92.
Former titles: Annuaire National de la Conserve
(ISSN 0245-1301); Annuaire National des
Industries de la Conserve (ISSN 0084-652X)

ANNUAL EDITIONS: NUTRITION. see NUTRITION AND
DIETETICS

664 GW
CODEN: ALMHAO
**ARCHIV FUER LEBENSMITTEL HYGIENE, FLEISCH-, FISCH-
UND MILCHHYGIENE.** (Text in German; summaries in
English) 1950. 6/yr. DM.220. Verlag M. und H.
Schaper GmbH, Kalandstr. 4, 31061 Alfeld,
Germany. TEL 05181-8009-0.
FAX 05181-800933. (Subscr. to: Postfach 1642,
31046 Alfeld, Germany) Eds. Dr. G. Terplan, Dr. S.
Wenzel. adv.; bk.rev.; bibl.; charts; illus.; index. circ.
1,200. **Indexed:** Biodet.Abstr., Biol.Abstr.,
Chem.Abstr., Curr.Adv.Ecol.Sci., Dairy Sci.Abstr.,
Excerp.Med., Food Sci.& Tech.Abstr.,
Helminthol.Abstr., Ind.Vet., Sci.Cit.Ind., Vet.Bull.
Document type: trade publication.
—BLDSC (1615.870000); SWETS; CASDDS. **CCC**.
Formerly: Archiv fuer Lebensmittelhygiene,
Insbesondere fuer Fleisch-, Fisch- und Milchhygiene
(ISSN 0003-925X)

ARROW'S COMPLETE GUIDE TO MAIL ORDER FOODS. see
BUSINESS AND ECONOMICS — Marketing And
Purchasing

641.53 US ISSN 0892-1024
CODEN: ACULEH
ART CULINAIRE; the international magazine in good
taste. 1986. q. $59 (foreign $75). Box 9268,
Morristown, NJ 07963. TEL 201-993-5500.
FAX 201-993-8779. Ed. Mitchell Davis. adv. circ.
7,538. **Document type:** trade publication.

THE ART OF EATING. see HOME ECONOMICS

ARTE HELADERO. see AGRICULTURE — Dairying And
Dairy Products

664 SI ISSN 0218-2734
ASIA PACIFIC FOOD INDUSTRY; Asia Pacific food
industry business report. (Text in English) 1989. m.
$100. Asia Pacific Food Industry Publications Pte.
Ltd., 2 Shenton Way, No. 05-01/05 ICB Bldg.,
Singapore 0106, Singapore. TEL 222-3422.
FAX 222-5587. TELEX RS 28366 SAFAN. Ed. Hui
Kam Lin. adv. contact: Shirley Wong. circ. 6,500.
(back issues avail.)
Formerly: Asia Pacific Food Processing and
Packaging.

664 658 SI
ASIA PACIFIC FOOD INDUSTRY BUSINESS REPORT. (Text
in English) 1991. m. $120. Asia Pacific Food
Industry Publications Pte. Ltd., 2 Shenton Way, No.
05-01/05 ICB Bldg., Singapore 0106, Singapore.
TEL 222-3422. FAX 222-5587. TELEX RS 28366
SAFAN. Ed. Hui Kam Lin. adv. contact: Shirley Wong.
circ. 2,500.

ASIA PACIFIC FOODSERVICE PRODUCT NEWS. see
HOTELS AND RESTAURANTS

663.94 II ISSN 0004-4997
ASSAM REVIEW AND TEA NEWS. 1925. m.
Rs.1000($60) Assam Review Publishing Co., 29
Waterloo St., Calcutta 700 069, India. Ed. G.L.
Banerjee. adv.; bk.rev.; charts; illus.; stat. circ.
4,500. **Indexed** Chem.Abstr. **Document type:** trade
publication.

614 US
HD9000.9.U5
ASSOCIATION OF FOOD AND DRUG OFFICIALS. JOURNAL.
1937. 4/yr. $70 (foreign $85). Association of Food
and Drug Officials, Box 3425, York, PA 17402.
TEL 717-757-2888. FAX 717-755-8089. bibl. circ.
900. (also avail. in microfilm from PMC; reprint
service avail. from ISI) **Indexed:** Curr.Adv.Ecol.Sci.,
Curr.Cont., Curr.Pack.Abstr., Dairy Sci.Abstr., Food
Sci.& Tech.Abstr. **Document type:** academic/scholarly
publication.
—BLDSC (4704.160000); UnCover.
Former titles: Association of Food and Drug
Officials Quarterly Bulletin (ISSN 0195-4865);
Association of Food and Drug Officials of the United
States. Quarterly Bulletin (ISSN 0004-5721)
Description: Promotes and offers uniformity of
laws affecting foods, drugs, cosmetics, device, and
product safety.

AUSTRALASIAN TREE CROPS SOURCEBOOK. see
AGRICULTURE — Crop Production And Soil

664.028 AT
AUSTRALIAN DRIED FRUIT NEWS. N.S. 1973. 5/yr. not
avail. for overseas distribution. Australian Dried
Fruits Association, P.O.Box 1142, Mildura, Vic.
3502, Australia. FAX 050-233321. Ed. R. Skinner.
adv.; bk.rev.; charts; illus. circ. 5,500.

AUSTRALIAN GOURMET TRAVELLER. see TRAVEL AND
TOURISM

664.9 AT ISSN 0156-2681
AUSTRALIAN MEAT INDUSTRY BULLETIN. 1929. bi-m.
Aus.$30. Meat and Allied Trades Federation of
Australia, P.O. Box 1208, Crows Nest, N.S.W. 2065,
Australia. TEL 02-906-7767. FAX 02-906-8022.
Ed. Joy Allen. adv.; B&W page Aus.$850; color page
Aus.$1500; adv. contact: Joy Allen. bk.rev. circ.
5,500. **Document type:** trade publication.
Supersedes (in 1978): Meat Traddes Journal of
Australia (ISSN 0047-6366)
Description: Covers all aspects of the Australian
meat industry.

**AUSTRALIAN MEAT LIVESTOCK RESEARCH AND
DEVELOPMENT CORPORATION. ANNUAL REPORT.** see
AGRICULTURE — Poultry And Livestock

664.1 AT ISSN 0726-0822
CODEN: PAUTDL
**AUSTRALIAN SOCIETY OF SUGAR CANE
TECHNOLOGISTS. PROCEEDINGS.** 1930. a. Aus.$60.
Australian Society of Sugar Cane Technologists, c/o
Sugar Research Institute, P.O. Box 5611, Mackay
Mail Centre, Qld. 4741, Australia.
FAX 079-52-1734. Ed. B.T. Egan. cum.index every
5 yrs. circ. 1,000. **Indexed:** Biol.Abstr., Chem.Abstr.,
Hort.Abstr., Rev.Plant Path., So.Pac.Per.Ind., Soils &
Fert. **Document type:** proceedings.
—BLDSC (6656.750000); CASDDS.
Formerly (until Apr. 1978): Queensland Society of
Sugar Cane Technologists. Proceedings (ISSN
0079-8851)

FOOD AND FOOD INDUSTRIES

664　　　　　　UK
B B C GOOD FOOD MAGAZINE. 1989. m. £20. Redwood Publishing Ltd., 101 Bayham St., London NW1 0AG, England. TEL 071-331-8000. FAX 071-331-8001. (Subscr. to: P.O. Box 43, St. Leonards-on-Sea, E. Sussex TN38 9NB, England) Ed. Sarah-Jane Evans. circ. 543,694. **Document type:** consumer publication.

B B S R C BUSINESS. (Biotechnology and Biological Sciences Research Council) see *AGRICULTURE*

B B S R C NEWSLETTERS. (Biotechnology and Biological Sciences Research Council) see *AGRICULTURE*

B B S R C SCIENCE BRIEF. (Biotechnology and Biological Sciences Research Council) see *AGRICULTURE*

664.9　　　　　　GW
B G FORUM. (Berufsgenossenschaft) 4/yr. membership. (Fleischerei Berufsgenossenschaft) Deutscher Fachverlag GmbH, Mainzer Landstr. 251, 60326 Frankfurt a.M., Germany. TEL 069-759501. FAX 069-75952999. circ. 41,000. **Document type:** bulletin, trade publication.
　　Description: Provides information for employees of butchery trade associations.

B N F NUTRITION BULLETIN. (British Nutrition Foundation) see *NUTRITION AND DIETETICS*

664.6　658.8　　　UK
BABY FOODS: THE INTERNATIONAL MARKET. a. £1375($2750) Euromonitor, 87-88 Turnmill St., London EC1M 5QU, England. TEL 071-251-8024. FAX 071-608-3149. (Addr. in N. America: Euromonitor International, 111 W. Washington St., Chicago, IL 60602. TEL 312-541-8024. FAX 312-541-1567) (looseleaf format) **Document type:** trade publication.
　　●Also available online. Vendor(s): Data-Star, DIALOG Information Services, Inc.
　　Description: Analyzes the baby foods market for France, Germany, Italy, Spain, the U.K., the U.S., and Japan.

642.5　　　　　　AT
BAKING INDUSTRY REVIEW. 1937. m. Aus.$40 (effective Jan. 1993). Baking Industry Employers Association of N.S.W., 2-121 Alexander St., Crows Nest, N.S.W. 2065, Australia. TEL 02-439-6209. FAX 02-437-4717. Ed. Mark Crowe. adv.; bk.rev.; illus. circ. 400.
　　Formerly: Pastrycooks' Review.

664.1　　　　　　BG
BANGLADESH SUGAR MILLS CORPORATION. ANNUAL REPORT. (Text in English) a. Tk.20. Bangladesh Sugar Mills Corporation, Shilpa Bhaban, Motijheel Commercial Area, Dhaka 2, Bangladesh. stat.

642.5　633.2　　　US　　ISSN 1061-642X
BAY FOOD. 1988. m. $28. Berkeley Communications Inc., 5878 Doyle St., Emeryville, CA 94608. TEL 510-652-6115. FAX 510-652-4845. adv.: B&W page $1995, color page $2645; trim 10 x 13 1/4. bk.rev. circ. 35,000.
　　Description: Covers food and wine in Northern California. Includes coverage of the restaurant scene, food trends and preparation, and wine selection.

BEVERAGE AND FOOD WORLD. see *BEVERAGES*

BEVERAGE DIGEST. see *BEVERAGES*

BEVERAGE WORLD (ENGLISH EDITION); magazine of the beverage industry. see *BEVERAGES*

658.8　647.9　　　US　　ISSN 0892-5399
BILL OF FARE. 1986. bi-m. membership. Texas Restaurant Association, Box 1429, Austin, TX 78767-1429. TEL 512-472-3666. Ed. Julie Stephen Sherrier. circ. 5,600.
　　Formerly: Market Fare.
　　Description: Compendium of market research and statistics for Texas' foodservice and hospitality industries, and government legislation news.

664　607　　　　UK　　ISSN 0067-8651
BINSTED'S DIRECTORY OF FOOD TRADE MARKS AND BRAND NAMES. 1959. biennial. £60. Food Trade Press Ltd., Station House, Hortons Way, Westerham, Kent TN16 1BZ, England. TEL 0959-563944. FAX 0959-561285. Ed. Adrian Binsted. adv. circ. 2,500. **Document type:** directory.

664　　　　　　SZ
BIONA. (Editions in French, German) 1953. 6/yr. 12 SFr. (foreign 28 SFr.). (Verband Schweizer Reform- und Diaetfachgeschaefte) Vogt-Schild AG, Zuchwilerstr. 21, CH-4501 Solothurn, Switzerland. TEL 065-247247. FAX 065-247235. Eds. Thomas Gafner, Theo Veyre. adv.: B&W page 10250 SFr.; trim 184 x 266. circ. 260,000. **Document type:** trade publication.
　　Formerly (until 1992): Courrier Biona.

664.9　　　　　　GW　　ISSN 0941-3693
BLICK. 1965. m. DM.56. Bergmann und Lukullus Verlags GmbH, Max-Volmer-Str. 28, 40724 Hilden, Germany. TEL 02103-2040. FAX 02103-204204. Ed. Michael Jakobi. adv.: B&W page DM.5540, color page DM.9695; trim 297 x 210. bk.rev.; illus.; stat.; index. (tabloid format) **Document type:** trade publication.
　　Formerly: Blick ins Fleischer-Fachgeschaeft (ISSN 0006-4734)

BOLETIN DE PROMECAFE. see *AGRICULTURE — Crop Production And Soil*

BON APPETIT. see *HOME ECONOMICS*

644　910.09　　　FR
BONNE TABLE ET TOURISME; revue de la gastronomie et du tourisme dans le monde. 1950. 6/yr. 100 F.($12) 7 rue d'Aumale, 75009 Paris, France. TEL 42-81-30-12. FAX 40-16-81-85. TELEX 283 334 F. Dir. Jean Valby. adv.

664　　　　　　UK
BOOKER FITCH FOOD MAGAZINE. 1986. bi-m. C P R Publishing, Northern Rock House, 20 Market Place, Guisborough, Cleveland TS14 6HF, England. TEL 0287-639111. FAX 0287-637201. circ. 80,000. (controlled)
　　Formerly: Booker Food Magazine.

664　　　　　　BE
LA BOUCHERIE BELGE. Flemish edition: Belgische Beenhouwerij. (Text in French) 1894. fortn. 3100 BEF to non-members. Federation Nationale des Bouchers et Charcutiers Belgique, 116, Ave. de Cortenberg, B-1040 Brussels, Belgium. TEL 32-2-7352470. FAX 32-2-7366493. Ed. W. Van der Aa. adv.: B&W page 59400 BEF, color page 98200 BEF; trim 295 x 430. bk.rev. circ. 11,000 (7,000 Dutch ed.; 4,000 French ed.). **Document type:** trade publication.
　　Description: Publishes news and information on business, legislative, taxation and standards issues affecting the profession.

664.9　　　　　　FR
BOUCHERIE CHEVALINE DE FRANCE. 11/yr. 75 rue de Morillons, 75010 Paris, France. TEL 48-28-73-79. Ed. Genevieve Pinel. circ. 2,500.

664.9　　　　　　FR　　ISSN 0006-8284
BOUCHERIE FRANCAISE. 1948. m. 380 F. Societe d'Editions et de Publications Economiques et Techniques de l'Alimentation (S.E.P.E.T.A.), 98 Bd. Pereire, 75850 Paris Cedex 17, France. TEL 43-80-24-02. FAX 43-80-23-85. Ed. D. Unger. adv.; bibl.; film rev.; illus.; stat.; index. circ. 20,000. **Document type:** corporate report.

664　　　　　　GW
BRAU UND BRUNNEN BOTE; Magazin der Gruppe fuer Mitarbeiter und Freunde. 1890. q. Brau und Brunnen AG, Rheinische Str. 2, 44137 Dortmund, Germany. TEL 0231-1817633. FAX 0231-1817300. Ed. Bernd Weber. adv. circ. 10,000. (back issues avail.) **Document type:** trade publication.

BREAD PUDDING UPDATE. see *HOME ECONOMICS*

664.7　658.8　　　UK
BREAKFAST CEREALS: THE INTERNATIONAL MARKET. a. £1375($2750) Euromonitor, 87-88 Turnmill St., London EC1M 5QU, England. TEL 071-251-8024. FAX 071-608-3149. (Addr. in N. America: Euromonitor International, 111 W. Washington St., Ste. 920, Chicago, IL 60602. TEL 312-541-8024. FAX 312-541-1567) (looseleaf format) **Document type:** trade publication.
　　●Also available online. Vendor(s): Data-Star, DIALOG Information Services, Inc.
　　Description: Analyzes the breakfast cereals market for France, Germany, Italy, Spain, the U.K., the U.S., and Japan.

664　　　　　　CN　　ISSN 1188-8083
BRITISH COLUMBIA FOOD INDUSTRY DIRECTORY. biennial. Can.$10. DoMac Publications Ltd., 20316 56th Ave., Ste. 200, Langley, BC V3A 3Y7, Canada. TEL 604-532-8400. FAX 604-532-8401. **Document type:** directory.
　　Former titles: British Columbia Food and Beverage Processors Source Book (ISSN 1180-8233); British Columbia Food and Beverage Processors Directory (ISSN 0714-2234)

664　　　　　　UK　　ISSN 0007-070X
TX501　　　　　　　　CODEN: BFOJA9
BRITISH FOOD JOURNAL. 1899. 11/yr. $1979.95. M C B University Press Ltd., 60-62 Toller Ln., Bradford, W. Yorks BD8 9BY, England. TEL 0274-499821. FAX 0274-547143. TELEX 51317-MCBUNI-G. Ed. Brian Beharrell. bk.rev.; abstr.; charts; illus.; tr.lit.; index. (reprint service avail. from SWZ) **Indexed:** Art.Hosp.& Tour.; Biodet.Abstr.; Chem.Abstr.; Dairy Sci.Abstr.; Food Sci.& Tech.Abstr.; Sugar Ind.Abstr.; World Agri.Econ.& Rural Sociol.Abstr. **Document type:** trade publication.
　　—BLDSC (2300.800000); SWETS; UMI. **CCC.**
　　Incorporates: Food Marketing (ISSN 0267-4394);
　　Formerly: British Food Journal and Hygenic Review.
　　Description: Aims to foster a greater understanding of the methods and motives among all those involved in the food sector. Areas covered include food and sales law, consumer affairs, food marketing, production, nutrition and more.

BROILER INDUSTRY. see *AGRICULTURE — Poultry And Livestock*

664　　　　　　IT
BUONO E NATURALE; mensile di alimentazione naturale. 1989. m. L.50000 (foreign L.130000) (effective 1994). Tecniche Nuove s.p.a., Via C. Menotti, 14, 20129 Milan, Italy. TEL 02-75701. FAX 02-7610351. adv.: B&W page L.3320000, color page L.5320000; trim 180 x 250. circ. 34,248.
　　Formerly: Buono (ISSN 1120-5431)

664.9　　　　　　UK　　ISSN 0268-1781
BUTCHER AND PROCESSOR. 1984. 10/yr. £35. Smithfield Publishing Ltd., High St., Castle Camps, Cams CB1 6SN, England. TEL 0799-584879. FAX 0799-584883. Ed. Tony Pike. adv.; bk.rev. circ. 12,000. **Document type:** trade publication.
　　Description: Covers the industry from independent retailers and supermarket operators to meat processors and slaughterers.

BUTTERWORTHS LAW OF FOOD & DRUGS. see *LAW*

642　　　　　　CN
C C U F S A NEWSLETTER. 1987. q. membership. Canadian College & University Food Service Association, c/o University of Guelph, Drew Hall, Gordon St., Guelph, Ont. N1G 2W1, Canada. TEL 519-824-4120. FAX 519-837-9302. Ed. Shirley Louie. circ. 400. (looseleaf format; back issues avail.) **Document type:** newsletter.

664　382　　　　FR
C I E S COMMUNICATION. q. membership. International Center for Companies of the Food Trade and Industry - Comite International des Entreprise a Succursales, 61 Quai d'Orsay, 75015 Paris, France. TEL 47-05-48-43. FAX 33-1-45-51-59-83. bk.rev. **Document type:** trade publication.
　　Formerly: C.I.E.S. Quarterly Review.

664　　　　　　BL　　ISSN 0101-630X
**　　　　　　　　　　　　　CODEN: BECADK**
C T A A BOLETIM DE PESQUISA. (Text in Portuguese; summaries in English) 1970. irreg. Empresa Brasileira de Pesquisa Agropecuaria, Centro Nacional de Pesquisa de Tecnologia Agroindustrial de Alimentos, Av. das Americas, 29501 Guaratiba, 23020-470 Rio de Janeiro, R.J., Brazil. TEL 021-4101353. FAX 021-4101090. TELEX (021) 33267-EBPA-BR. circ. 1,000. (tabloid format; back issues avail.) **Indexed:** Chem.Abstr. **Document type:** academic/scholarly publication.
　　—BLDSC (2158.146300); CASDDS.

CAFE, CACAO, THE. see *AGRICULTURE*

663.93　　　　　　IV
CAFE D'AFRIQUE/AFRICAN COFFEE. q. Organisation Interafricaine du Cafe - Interafrican Coffee Organisation, BPV 210, Abidjan, Ivory Coast. TEL 216131. FAX 21-62-12. TELEX 22406 OICAFE.

663.93 GT
CAFETAL/COFFEE REVIEW. 1944. bi-m. Q.5 per no. Asociacion Nacional del Cafe, Edificio Etisa, Plazuela Espana, Zona 9, Ciudad de Guatemala, Guatemala. TEL 367487. Ed. Pta. Byron Dardon. adv.; charts; illus. circ. 5,000. **Indexed:** Biol.Abstr.
Formerly: Revista Cafetalera.

664 US
CALIFORNIA FOOD.* m. Ca Fo Publishing, Box 7495, Van Nuys, CA 91409-7495. TEL 818-703-6177. FAX 818-703-5005. Ed. Valerie Edgar. circ. 20,191.

CALIFORNIA FRESH FRUIT AND VEGETABLE SHIPMENTS BY RAIL, TRUCK, AND AIR. see TRANSPORTATION

CALORIE CONTROL COMMENTARY. see NUTRITION AND DIETETICS

642.5 US
CAMERON'S FOODSERVICE MARKETING REPORTER. 1982. s-m. $197. 5325 Sheridan Dr., Box 1160, Williamstown, NY 14231-1160. TEL 716-833-4369. FAX 716-834-4159. Ed. Nina Cameron. circ. 10,000. **Document type:** newsletter.
Formerly (until 1992): Cameron's Foodservice Promotions Reporter.
Description: Food service promotions and advertising newsletter for hotels, restaurants, military and country clubs.

CANADIAN FOOD AND PACKAGING DIRECTORY. see BUSINESS AND ECONOMICS — Trade And Industrial Directories

664 CN ISSN 0833-174X
CANADIAN FOOD TRADE DIRECTORY & BUYERS GUIDE. 1987. a. Can.$49.95. N C C Publishing, 222 Argyle Ave., Delhi, Ont. N4B 2Y2, Canada. TEL 519-582-2513. FAX 519-582-4040. adv.; charts; stat. **Document type:** directory.
Description: Lists food manufacturers, suppliers and their products. Lists food shows, associations, schools and franchises.

664 658.8 UK
CANNED FOODS: THE INTERNATIONAL MARKET. a. £1375($2750) Euromonitor, 87-88 Turnmill St., London EC1M 5QU, England. TEL 071-251-8024. FAX 071-608-3149. (Addr. in N. America: Euromonitor International, 111 W. Washington St., Ste. 920, Chicago, IL 60602. TEL 312-541-8024. FAX 312-541-1567) (looseleaf format) **Document type:** trade publication.
●Also available online. Vendor(s): Data-Star, DIALOG Information Services, Inc..
Description: Analyzes the markets for canned goods for France, Germany, Italy, Spain, the U.K., the U.S., and Japan.

664.9 IT
CARNE; dalla produzione al consumo. 1977. m. L.30000. Editoriale C.I.M., Via Aureliana 25, 00187 Rome, Italy. TEL 6-44-56-811. FAX 6-48-46-88. TELEX 613058 CIM ROM I. adv. circ. 10,000.

664 658.8 US
CAROLINA FOOD DEALER. 1938. m. $1. North Carolina Food Dealers Association, One Charlottetown Center, Charlotte, NC 28204. Ed. G. Everett Suddreth, Jr.

664 056.1 US
LA CARTA. (Text in Spanish) 1982. bi-m. Arturo Fortuno, Ed. & Pub., 12-12 37th Ave., Long Island City, NY 11101. TEL 718-482-1960. FAX 718-482-1964. adv. circ. 10,000. (tabloid format)

634.573 II ISSN 0008-7300
CASHEW BULLETIN. (Text in English) 1964. m. $35. Cashew Export Promotion Council, Chittoor Rd., Cochin 682 016, India. TELEX 885-6677 CEPC IN. Ed. K.G. Nayar. adv.; circ. 700 (controlled).

CAT INDUSTRY NEWSLETTER. see PETS

051 US
CATEGORY REPORTS. m. $1000. Marketing Intelligence Service Ltd., 33 Academy St., Naples, NY 14512. TEL 716-374-6326. FAX 716-374-5217. TELEX 469979. (back issues avail.)

664.9 UK
CATERING BUTCHER. Issued with: Meat & Poultry News (ISSN 0961-8139) 4/yr. 9 Vermont Pl., Tongwell, Milton Keynes MK15 8JA, England. TEL 44-908-613323. FAX 44-908-210656. Ed. Pamela Brook. bk.rev.

664.9 UK
CATERING BUYERS' GUIDE. 1964. a. £60. Benn Business Information Services Ltd. (Subsidiary of: Morgan-Grampian plc), Riverbank House, Angel Ln., Tonbridge, Kent TN9 1SE, England. TEL 0732-362666. FAX 0732-757829. TELEX 957829 BENTON G. Ed. Peter Bealing. adv.; bk.rev. circ. 5,000. **Document type:** directory.
Former titles: Hotel, Restaurant and Catering Supplies (ISSN 0142-1824); Sell's Hotel, Restaurant and Canteen Supplies (ISSN 0073-3504); Hotel, Restaurant and Canteen Supplies.
Description: Lists manufacturers and suppliers of products and services to the hotel supplies and catering business.

664 UK
CATERING SOUTH WEST. 10/yr. West of England Newspapers Ltd., Burrington Way, Plymouth, Devon PL5 3LN, England. TEL 0752-777151. FAX 0752-780680. Ed. George Harris. circ. 18,500.

658.9 642.47 US ISSN 0884-4984
CATERING TODAY.* 1985. bi-m. $18. ProTech Publishing and Communications, Box 1347, New Albany, IN 47151-1347. TEL 812-937-4464. FAX 812-937-4688. Ed. Paula Werne. adv.; bk.rev. circ. 40,000. (back issues avail.)
Description: Edited for all sectors of the catering industry, including on- and off-premises catering, social and institutional catering.

663.93 CK ISSN 0008-8951
CENICAFE. (Text in Spanish; summaries in English) 1949. q. free. (Centro Nacional de Investigaciones de Cafe, Seccion de Divulgacion Cientifica) Federacion Nacional de Cafeteros de Colombia, Chinchina, Caldas, Colombia. bk.rev.; bibl.; charts; illus.; index, cum.index: 1949-1959. circ. 2,500. **Indexed:** Agri.Eng.Abstr., Biol.Abstr., Chem.Abstr., Field Crop Abstr., Geo.Abstr., Herb.Abstr., Hort.Abstr., Meteor.& Geoastrophys.Abstr., Plant Breed.Abstr., Soils & Fert.

664 SP
CENTRA MARKET; para la formacion e informacion del detallista y el fabricante. 11/yr. 6000 ptas. (foreign 10000 ptas.). Centra S. Coop., O'Donnell 4, 28009 Madrid, Spain. TEL 1-431-85-00. FAX 1-577-78-05. Ed. F. Dominguez Ruz. circ. 25,000.

664 US ISSN 0009-0352
TP1 CODEN: CECHAF
CEREAL CHEMISTRY. 1924. bi-m. $200 (foreign $220). American Association of Cereal Chemists, Inc., 3340 Pilot Knob Rd., St. Paul, MN 55121-2097. TEL 800-328-7560. FAX 612-454-0766. TELEX 6502439657 (MCI UW). Ed. V. Rasper. adv.; bibl.; charts; illus.; index. circ. 3,666. (also avail. in microform from UMI,PMC; back issues avail.) **Indexed:** Agri.Eng.Abstr., Anal.Abstr., Biodet.Abstr., Biol.Abstr., Biol.& Agr.Ind., Cadscan, Chem.Abstr., Crop Physiol.Abstr., Curr.Adv.Ecol.Sci., Curr.Cont., Curr.Pack.Abstr., Dairy Sci.Abstr., Excerp.Med., Field Crop Abstr., Food Sci.& Tech.Abstr., Herb.Abstr., Ind.Sci.Rev., Lead Abstr., Maize Abstr., NRN, Nutr.Abstr., Plant Breed.Abstr., Rev.Med.& Vet.Mycol., Rev.Plant Path., Rice Abstr., Sci.Cit.Ind, Seed Abstr., Soils & Fert., Sorghum & Millets Abstr., Soyabean Abstr., Triticale Abstr., Weed Abstr., Zincscan.
—BLDSC (3120.000000); Faxon; UnCover; SWETS; UMI; CASDDS. **CCC.**
Description: Analytical procedures, technological tests and fundamental research in the cereal industry.

CEREAL FOODS WORLD. see AGRICULTURE — Feed, Flour And Grain

CEREAL POLICIES REVIEW. see AGRICULTURE — Feed, Flour And Grain

CEREVISIA AND BIOTECHNOLOGY. see BIOLOGY — Biotechnology

663.94 KE
CHAI MAGAZINE. (Text in English and Swahili) q. Kenya Tea Development Authority, Moi Ave., P.O. Box 30213, Nairobi, Kenya.

658.8 US ISSN 0009-0921
CHAIN MERCHANDISER; a national service & promotion publication & program. 1962. q. $12. Merchandising Publications Co., Rt. 1, Box 95C, Baker City, OR 97814. TEL 503-523-3642. FAX 503-523-2063. Ed. Henry von Morpurgo. adv. contact: Don Mayas. bk.rev.; illus. circ. 12,750. **Document type:** trade publication.
Formerly: Deli-Dairy World; Incorporates: Specialty Foods and Beverages.
Description: Devoted to improving merchandising methods at every level of the marketing and distributing process - from field and factory and warehouse to retail sales persons.

663.94 CC
CHAYE/TEA. (Text in Chinese) q. Zhejiang Chaye Xuehui - Zhejiang Tea Association, Zhejiang Nongye Daxue, Huajiachi, Hangzhou, Zhejiang 310029, People's Republic of China. TEL 42605. Ed. Wang Zhuocheng.

663.94 CC ISSN 1000-369X
CHAYE KEXUE/JOURNAL OF TEA SCIENCE. (Text in Chinese) s-a. $40. Chinese Academy of Agricultural Sciences, Tea Research Institute, 1 Yunqi Lu, Hangzhou, Zhejiang 310008, People's Republic of China. TEL 0571-7091258. FAX 0571-7091263. Ed. Chen Xindong. circ. 5,000. **Document type:** academic/scholarly publication.
Description: Covers the latest researches on tea science.

664 642.56 US
CHEF. 1932. 10/yr. $20. Talcott Communications Corporation, 20 N. Wacker Dr., Ste. 3230, Chicago, IL 60606-3102. TEL 312-849-2220. FAX 312-849-2184. Ed. Paul Clark; Pub. Daniel von Rabenau. adv.; illus. circ. 37,000. **Document type:** trade publication.
Former titles (until 1994): Chef Institutional (ISSN 0192-7116); Formerly (until 1971): Chef Magazine (ISSN 0009-2150)

642 FR ISSN 0980-8396
CHEF. 9/yr. 360 F. (foreign 530 F.). Editions Max Brezol, 9 rue Labie, 75338 Paris Cedex 17, France. TEL 45-74-21-62. FAX 45-74-01-03.

664 CN ISSN 0830-0895
CHEF DU SERVICE ALIMENTAIRE. English edition: Chef of the Foodservice Industry (ISSN 0833-2770) 1982. 6/yr. Can.$30. Chef du Service Alimentaire, 252 Route 171 S., P.O. Box 520, St-Etienne de Lauzon, Que. G0S 2L0, Canada. TEL 418-831-5317. FAX 418-831-5172. Ed. Maurice Leblanc. adv. circ. 18,506.

CHEMICAL BUSINESS BULLETINS: CHEMICALS AND THE FOOD INDUSTRY. see CHEMISTRY

664 658.8 UK
CHILLED FOODS, DELICATESSEN FOODS AND READY MEALS: THE INTERNATIONAL MARKET. a. £1375($2750) Euromonitor, 87-88 Turnmill St., London EC1M 5QU, England. TEL 071-251-8024. FAX 071-608-3149. (Addr. in N. America: Euromonitor International, 111 W. Washington St., Ste. 920, Chicago, IL 60602. TEL 312-541-8024. FAX 312-541-1567) (looseleaf format) **Document type:** trade publication.
●Also available online. Vendor(s): Data-Star, DIALOG Information Services, Inc.
Description: Analyzes the markets for delicatessen foods and prepared meals for France, Germany, Italy, Spain, the U.K., the U.S., and Japan.

FOOD AND FOOD INDUSTRIES

664 658 US ISSN 0193-323X
TX341 CODEN: CFENDJ
CHILTON'S FOOD ENGINEERING. 1928. m. $55. Chilton Co., Chilton Way, Box 2035, Radnor, PA 19089. TEL 215-964-4455. Ed. Charles J. Haberstroh, Jr. adv.; bk.rev.; abstr.; bibl.; charts; illus.; pat.; tr.lit.; index. circ. 60,300. (also avail. in microfilm from UMI; microfiche from UMI,CIS; reprint service avail. from UMI) Indexed: A.S.& T.Ind., Biol.Abstr., Chem.Abstr., Curr.Cont., Curr.Pack.Abstr., Dairy Sci.Abstr., Eng.Ind., Food Sci.& Tech.Abstr., Ind.Sci.Rev., Key to Econ.Sci., Nutr.Abstr., Packag.Sci.Tech., SRI, Tr.& Indus.Ind.
●Also available online. Vendor(s): DIALOG Information Services, Inc., Mead Data Central, Inc.
—BLDSC (3172.995200); Faxon; UnCover; SWETS; UMI. **CCC.**
Formerly: Food Engineering (ISSN 0015-637X)

664 US
CHILTON'S FOOD ENGINEERING DATABASE. s-a. $295 (effective Oct. 1993). Chilton Co., Chilton Way, Box 2035, Radnor, PA 19089. TEL 610-964-4416. Ed. Patrick O'Donnell. (reprint service avail.)

664 US ISSN 0148-4478
  CODEN: FEINDV
CHILTON'S FOOD ENGINEERING INTERNATIONAL. 6/yr. $65. Chilton Co., Chilton Way, Box 2035, Radnor, PA 19089. TEL 215-964-4440. Ed. Joyce Fassl. (also avail. in microform from UMI; microfiche from UMI; reprint service avail. from UMI) Indexed: A.S.& T.Ind., Dairy Sci.Abstr., Eng.Ind., Food Sci.& Tech.Abstr., Int.Packag.Abstr., Nutr.Abstr., Packag.Sci.Tech., PROMT, W.R.C.Inf.
●Also available online. Vendor(s): DIALOG Information Services, Inc..
—BLDSC (3172.995300); SWETS; UMI. **CCC.**
Formerly: Food Engineering International.

664 US
CHILTON'S FOOD ENGINEERING MASTER. a. $75 (effective Aug. 1993). Chilton Co., Chilton Way, Box 2035, Radnor, PA 19089. TEL 610-964-4416. Ed. Patrick O'Donnell. adv.: page $3460; adv. contact: Maryellen Murrin. (reprint service avail.)

663.92 US
CHOCOLATE NEWS;* the world's favorite flavor newsletter. 1980. bi-m. $15.95. Hampton International Communications, Inc., 211 E. 43rd St., Ste. 1306, New York, NY 10017. TEL 212-682-7320. Ed. Roberta Pliny. adv.; bk.rev.; illus. circ. 10,000. (looseleaf format; back issues avail.)
Description: Provides news and recipes from restaurants on chocolate.

663.92 US
CHOCOLATIER; the magazine for creative entertaining. 1984. bi-m. $19.95. Haymarket Group Ltd., 45 W. 34th St., Ste. 600, New York, NY 10001. TEL 212-239-0855. adv.; tr.lit. circ. 350,000. (reprint service avail.)

664 CU
CIENCIA Y TECNOLOGIA DE ALIMENTOS. s-a. $28 in S. America; N. America $30; elsewhere $34. Ediciones Cubanas, Obispo No. 527, Apdo. 605, Havana, Cuba.

CITROGRAPH; magazine of the citrus industry. see AGRICULTURE — Crop Production And Soil

664.8 US ISSN 0009-7594
CITRUS INDUSTRY MAGAZINE. 1920. m. $16. Associated Publications Corporation, 495 E. Summerlin St., Box 89, Bartow, FL 33830. TEL 813-533-4114. Ed. Richard Frisbie. adv.; charts; illus.; stat. circ. 7,800. (also avail. in microform from UMI) Indexed: Biol.Abstr., Chem.Abstr., Curr.Cont., Eng.Ind., Excerp.Med., Food Sci.& Tech.Abstr.
—UnCover.
Description: Gives fruit growing tips.

641.345 644.8 SZ
THE CLIPPER; the journal for the international trade in dried fruit and nuts. (Text in English, French, German, Spanish) 1986. 4/yr. 100 SFr. (foreign 150 SFr.). Agropress AG, Aeschengraben 16, CH-4051 Basel, Switzerland. TEL 061-2721170. FAX 061-2721126. TELEX 962185-IFWO-CH. Ed. G.H. Breuer. **Document type:** trade publication.
Formerly: Cracker (ISSN 1011-6060)

663.92 GH ISSN 0300-1385
SB267
COCOA RESEARCH INSTITUTE. ANNUAL REPORT. 1962. a. £10. Cocoa Research Institute, PO Box 8, Tafo, Ghana. **Indexed:** Biol.Abstr., Hort.Abstr., Rev.Appl.Entomol., Rev.Plant Path.
—BLDSC (1148.948000).

663.93 663.92 UK ISSN 0262-5938
HD9199.A1 CODEN: COCIEO
COFFEE & COCOA INTERNATIONAL. 1974. bi-m. £71($158) in the UK; overseas £86 (effective 1994). International Trade Publications Ltd., Queensway House, 2 Queensway, Redhill, Surrey RH1 1QS, England. TEL 0737-768611. FAX 0737-761989. TELEX 948669-TOPJNL-G. Ed. Michael Segal. adv.; charts; stat. circ. 4,000. (back issues avail.) **Indexed:** Food Sci.& Tech.Abstr., Packag.Sci.Tech. **Document type:** trade publication.
—BLDSC (3292.846000).
Formerly: Coffee International (ISSN 0309-331X)

663.93 US
COFFEE ANNUAL.* 1939. a. $9.50. George Gordon Paton & Co., Box 286, Old Greenwich, CT 06870-0286. TEL 212-619-2900. FAX 212-619-2902. Ed. W.J. Murphy. adv.; illus.; stat. circ. 4,000.

663.93 KE
COFFEE BOARD OF KENYA. ANNUAL REPORT, BALANCE SHEET AND ACCOUNTS. (Text in English and Swahili) a. Coffee Board of Kenya, Coffee Plaza, Haile Selassie Ave., Box 30566, Nairobi, Kenya.

663.93 631 US
COFFEE INTELLIGENCE.* vol.37, 1974. m. $95. George Gordon Paton & Co., Box 286, Old Greenwich, CT 06870-0286. TEL 212-619-2900. FAX 212-619-2902. charts; stat.

663.93 UK ISSN 0264-5378
COFFEE INTERNATIONAL DIRECTORY. 1981. a. £90($175) in the UK; overseas £100 (effective 1994). International Trade Publications Ltd., Queensway House, 2 Queensway, Redhill, Surrey RH1 1QS, England. TEL 0737-768611. FAX 0737-761989. TELEX 948669-TOPJNL-G. Ed. Stephen Wadey. adv. circ. 2,000. **Document type:** trade publication.

663 II ISSN 0010-0250
COFFEE MAZDOOR SAHAKARI. (Text and summaries in Hindi and Malayalam) 1968. q. Rs.2. All India Coffee Workers Cooperative Societies Federation Ltd., 10 U.B. Bungalow Rd., Jawahar Nagar, Delhi 7, India. Ed. Shyam Singh Negi. illus.; circ. controlled. (avail. on records)

COLLEGE - UNIVERSITY FOODSERVICE WHO'S WHO. see BUSINESS AND ECONOMICS — Trade And Industrial Directories

664 SP
COMESTIBLE. 1969. m. 1590 ptas.($35) c/o Arsenio Pardo Rodriguez, Ed., German Perez Carrasco, 63, 28027 Madrid, Spain. TEL (91)267 24 03. TELEX 43782. circ. 20,000. (back issues avail.) **Document type:** newspaper.

COMESTIBLES. see AGRICULTURE — Poultry And Livestock

COMMENTS ON AGRICULTURAL AND FOOD CHEMISTRY. see AGRICULTURE

664 AT
COMMONWEALTH SCIENTIFIC AND INDUSTRIAL RESEARCH ORGANIZATION. DIVISION OF FOOD SCIENCE AND TECHNOLOGY. REPORT OF RESEARCH. 1959. biennial. Aus.$10. C.S.I.R.O., Division of Food Processing, P.O. Box 52, North Ryde, N.S.W. 2113, Australia. circ. 500. **Indexed:** Agri.Eng.Abstr., Biol.Abstr., Chem.Abstr., Hort.Abstr.
Former titles: Commonwealth Scientific and Industrial Research Organization. Division of Food Processing. Report of Research (ISSN 1037-1052); (until 1989) Commonwealth Scientific and Industrial Research Organization. Division of Food Research. Report of Research (ISSN 0312-4975)
Description: Contains summaries of current research programs.

664 CN
COMPENDIUM OF ANALYTICAL METHODS. 4 base vols. (plus s-a. updates). Can.$180 for base vols.; updates Can.$60. (Health and Welfare Canada, Health Protection Branch) Polyscience Publications Inc., P.O. Box 148, 44 Seize Arpents, Morin Heights, PQ J0R 1H0, Canada. TEL 514-226-5870. FAX 514-226-5866. Ed. D. Warburton. **Document type:** government publication.
Description: Covers the microbiological analysis of foods and water and the detection of extraneous materials in foods.

663.93 US
COMPLETE COFFEE COVERAGE.* 1945. d. George Gordon Paton & Co., Box 268, Old Greenwich, CT 06870-0286. TEL 212-619-2900. FAX 212-619-2902. Ed. W.J. Murphy.

642.5 US
CONCESSIONAIRE. 1960. bi-m. membership only. National Association of Concessionaires, 35 E. Wacker Dr., Ste. 1545, Chicago, IL 60601. TEL 312-236-3858. FAX 312-236-7809. Ed. Susan M. Cross. circ. 1,000.

664 647.95 US
CONSULTANT (LOUISVILLE). (Former name of issuing body: International Society of Food Service Consultants) 1967. q. $28 (foreign $40). Foodservice Consultants Society International, 304 W. Liberty St., Ste. 201, Louisville, KY 40202-3011. TEL 502-583-3783. FAX 502-589-3602. bk.rev. circ. 1,000. **Indexed:** Tr.& Indus.Ind. **Document type:** trade publication.

664 658.8 UK
CONSUMER CATERING: THE INTERNATIONAL MARKET. a. £1375($2750) Euromonitor, 87-88 Turnmill St., London EC1M 5QU, England. TEL 071-251-8024. FAX 071-608-3149. (Addr. in N. America: Euromonitor International, 111 W. West Washington St., Ste. 290, Chicago, IL 60602. TEL 312-541-8024. FAX 312-541-1567) (looseleaf format) **Document type:** trade publication.
●Also available online. Vendor(s): Data-Star, DIALOG Information Services, Inc.
Description: Analyzes the international catering market for France, Germany, Italy, Spain, the U.K., the U.S., and Japan

664 US
▼**CONSUMER'S ORGANIC MAIL-ORDER DIRECTORY;** a guide to farmers and wholesalers who sell mail-order products. 1992. a. $9.95. Community Alliance with Family Farmers, Box 464, Davis, CA 95617. TEL 916-756-8518. FAX 916-756-7857. Ed. Candace L. Lampe. adv. circ. 2,000. (reprint service avail.) **Document type:** directory.
Description: National list of farmers and wholesalers who sell organic produce, meats and products direct to the public. Cross-reference index by subject, company and state name.

664 FR
CONTACT RUNGIS LE TRAIT D'UNION. m. 20 F. Relations Exterieures et Diffusion, 45, rue Richer, 75009 Paris, France. adv. circ. 10,000.

664 UK
▼**CONVIVIUM;** the journal of good eating. 1993. q. £25 (Europe £30; elsewhere £35). The Brynasground Press, Bryan's Ground, Stapleton, Herefordshire LD8 2LP, England. TEL 0544-260001. FAX 0544-260015. Ed. David Wheeler; Pub. David Wheeler. **Document type:** consumer publication.
Description: Devoted to the domestic (and occasional commercial) cultivation and preparation of vegetables and fruits.

641.53 US
COOKING CONTEST CHRONICLE. 1984. m. $19.95. Box 10792, Merrillville, IN 46411-0792. TEL 219-887-6983. Ed. Karen Martis. bk.rev. circ. 2,000. (looseleaf format) **Document type:** newsletter.
Description: Provides news and information on upcoming cooking contests, food trends, prize-winning recipes, helpful contesting tips, and guidelines.

FOOD AND FOOD INDUSTRIES

664 US
COOKING FOR PROFIT. 1932. m. $24 (Canada & Mexico $38; elsewhere $52). C P Publishing, Inc., Box 267, Fond du Lac, WI 54936-0267. TEL 414-923-3700. FAX 414-923-6805. Ed. Colleen Phalen. adv.; bk.rev.; charts; illus. (also avail. in microform from UMI). **Document type:** trade publication.
—Faxon; UnCover; UMI.
Description: Targeted to restaurant owners, managers, and institutional foodservice operators. Profiles successful foodservice operations, the latest in kitchen equipment use and maintenance, current food trends, and practical management techniques written by industry experts.

664 US ISSN 1068-2821
TX1 CODEN: CILLE2
COOK'S ILLUSTRATED. 1980-1990; resumed Nov. 1992. 6/yr. $24.95 (effective 1993). Natural Health L.P., 17 Station St., Box 1200, Brookline, MA 02147. TEL 617-232-1000. FAX 617-532-1572. (Subscr. to: Box 59048, Boulder, CO 80322-9048. TEL 303-447-9330) Eds. Christopher Kimball, Mark Bittman; Pub. Christopher Kimball. bk.rev.; illus. **Document type:** consumer publication.
Former titles (until 1992): Cook's (ISSN 0886-943X); (until 1985): Cook's Magazine (ISSN 0199-8978)
Description: Discusses practical home cooking techniques.

664 US
CO-OP NEWS (DAVIS). 1980. m. $6.50. Davis Food Cooperative, Inc., 620 G St., Ste. A, Davis, CA 95616-3753. TEL 916-758-2667. FAX 916-758-5941. Ed. Chris Laning. adv.; bk.rev. circ. 2,200. (tabloid format)
Description: Covers food, food politics, nutrition, and news of the Davis Food Co-op.

664 365 US
CORRECTIONAL FOODSERVICE MAGAZINE. (Includes Annual Industry Directory) 1991. bi-m. $25. International Publishing Company of America, 665 La Villa Dr., Miami Springs, FL 33166. TEL 305-887-1700. FAX 305-885-1923. Ed. Jim O'Neal. adv. circ. 10,193. **Document type:** trade publication.
Description: For foodservice professionals employed in prisons, jails and other correction institutions in the US and Canada.

COST OF PICKING AND HAULING FLORIDA CITRUS FRUITS. see AGRICULTURE — Agricultural Economics

COUNCIL FOR AGRICULTURAL SCIENCE AND TECHNOLOGY. SPECIAL PUBLICATIONS. see AGRICULTURE

COUNCIL FOR AGRICULTURAL SCIENCE AND TECHNOLOGY. TASK FORCE REPORTS. see AGRICULTURE

664 US
COUNTER CULTURE.* q. $4 per no. 633 Robinhood Dr., Yellow Springs, OH 45387-1932. Ed. Sean Wolf Hill.
Description: Covers restaurants and diners across the country.

664 CN ISSN 0822-3033
COUP DE POUCE. 1984. 13/yr. Can.$28($32) Editions Telemedia, 2001 Rue Universite, Ste. 900, Montreal, PQ H3A 2A6, Canada. TEL 514-499-0561. FAX 514-499-1844. Ed. Carole Schinck. circ. 146,772. **Indexed:** Pt.de Rep. (1991-).

664 CN ISSN 0831-0912
COUP DE POUCE EXTRA. 1984. 2/yr. $3.50. Editions Telemedia, 2001 University St., Ste. 900, Montreal, PQ H3A 2A6, Canada. TEL 514-499-0561. FAX 514-499-1844. Ed. Louise Faucher. circ. 38,202.
Description: Appeals to women and their families interested in food and who have a high cooking ability. Includes preparation techniques, new food and cooking trends, accessories, rush hour cooking, microwave menus, wine and cheese, and international cuisine.

COURRIER DE LA PLANETE; agriculture, environnement, alimentation, trois defis pour un monde solidaire. see AGRICULTURE — Agricultural Economics

641.53 US
CRACKER - SNACK WORLD. 1990. 3/yr. $24. Lott Publishing Co., Box 1107, Santa Monica, CA 90406. TEL 310-397-4217. Ed. D.M. Lott. adv. circ. 3,000. (tabloid format) **Document type:** trade publication, newspaper.

664.8 US ISSN 0011-0787
CRANBERRIES; the national cranberry magazine. 1936. m. (except Dec.-Jan. combined). $20. Box 858, S. Carver, MA 02366. TEL 508-866-5055. FAX 508-866-2970. Ed. Carolyn Gilmore. adv.; bk.rev.; charts; illus.; stat. circ. 800. **Indexed:** Chem.Abstr. **Document type:** trade publication.
●Also available online. Vendor(s): DIALOG Information Services, Inc.

664 US ISSN 1040-8398
TP368 CODEN: CRFND6
CRITICAL REVIEWS IN FOOD SCIENCE AND NUTRITION. 1970. 8/yr. $99.95 to individuals (foreign $107.90); institutions $389 (foreign $396.95). C R C Press, Inc., 2000 Corporate Blvd., N.W., Boca Raton, FL 33431. TEL 407-994-0555. FAX 407-998-9784. TELEX 568689-CRC PRESS. Ed. Fergus M. Clydesdale. bibl.; charts; illus. circ. 500. (back issues avail.) **Indexed:** Biol.Abstr., Chem.Abstr., Curr.Adv.Ecol.Sci., Curr.Cont., Curr.Pack.Abstr., Dairy Sci.Abstr., Dent.Ind., Diar.Dis.Res., Food Sci.& Tech.Abstr., Ind.Med., Ind.Sci.Rev., Ind.Vet., INIS Atomind., Sci.Cit.Ind., Soyabean Abstr.
—BLDSC (3487.475700); Faxon; UnCover; SWETS; CASDDS. CCC.
Former titles: C R C Critical Reviews in Food Science and Nutrition (ISSN 0099-0248); C R C Critical Reviews in Food Technology (ISSN 0007-9006)
Description: Presents critical viewpoints of current technology, food science, and human nutrition.

664 US
CROWLEY REVIEW. 1979. bi-m. free. Crowley Foods, Inc., 49 Court St., Metro Center, Box 549, Binghamton, NY 13902. TEL 607-722-6441. FAX 607-722-5298. Ed. Jeanne Walter. circ. 2,540. (back issues avail.)
Description: Covers news of the business of interest to employees.

CUBA AZUCAR. see AGRICULTURE — Crop Production And Soil

664 FR ISSN 0011-2704
CUISINE ET VINS DE FRANCE. 1947. m. 246 F. (foreign 348 F.). Groupe Marie Claire, 11 bis., rue Boissy d'Anglas, 75008 Paris, France. TEL 1-42-66-88-88. FAX 47-42-89-16. Ed. Evelyne Prouvost. adv.; bk.rev.; illus.; index; circ. 85,000 (controlled).
Description: Features recipes, wine and cuisine reviews, new products.

664.1 HU ISSN 0011-2720
CODEN: CUKOAI
CUKORIPAR. (Text in Hungarian; summaries in English, German and Russian) 1948. q. $18. (Magyar Elelmezesipari Tudomanyos Egyesulet) Lapkiado Vallalat, Lenin korut 9-11, 1073 Budapest 7, Hungary. TEL 222-408. (Subscr. to: Kultura, Box 149, H-1389 Budapest, Hungary) Ed. Albert Vigh. adv.; bk.rev.; charts. circ. 1,300. **Indexed:** Chem.Abstr., Field Crop Abstr., Herb.Abstr., Rural Recreat.Tour.Abstr., Sugar Ind.Abstr., World Agri.Econ.& Rural Sociol.Abstr.
—CASDDS.

D C A T DIGEST. (Drug, Chemical and Allied Trades Association) see PHARMACY AND PHARMACOLOGY

664 JM ISSN 0011-5428
DAILY GLEANER - FOOD SUPPLEMENT. w. J.$6. Gleaner Company Ltd., 7 North St., P.O. Box 40, Kingston, Jamaica, W.I. TEL 809-922-3400. FAX 809-922-6223. TELEX 2319 GLEANER JA. (US subscr. to: Eppok Co., 19-25 W. 44th St., New York, NY 10036, USA) Ed. Ken Allen. adv.; illus.; mkt. circ. 45,000.

664 US
DAIRY AND FOOD INDUSTRIES SUPPLY ASSOCIATION. REGULATORY UPDATE. q. Dairy and Food Industries Supply Association, 6245 Executive Blvd., Rockville, MD 20852-3938. TEL 301-984-1444. FAX 301-881-7832. **Document type:** newsletter.

664 US
DAIRY AND FOOD INDUSTRIES SUPPLY ASSOCIATION. REPORTER. 1958. m. free. Dairy and Food Industries Supply Association, 6245 Executive Blvd., Rockville, MD 20852-3938. TEL 301-984-1444. FAX 301-881-7832. Ed. Mary O'Dea. adv.; tr.lit. circ. 2,200. (back issues avail.) **Document type:** newsletter.
Description: Industry briefs, trends, trade shows, marketing information, Association news, and international trade opportunities.

664 US
DAIRY AND FOOD INDUSTRIES SUPPLY ASSOCIATION. TECHNICAL BULLETIN. s-a. Dairy and Food Industries Supply Association, 6245 Executive Blvd., Rockville, MD 20852-3938. TEL 301-984-1444. FAX 301-881-7832. **Document type:** newsletter.

664 US
DAIRY - DELI - BAKE DIGEST. 1986. m. membership. International Dairy - Deli - Bakery Association, 313 Price Pl., Ste. 202, Box 5528, Madison, WI 53705-0528. TEL 608-238-7908. FAX 608-238-6330. Ed. Carol Christison. bk.rev. circ. 11,000. **Document type:** newsletter.
Description: Covers management trends, new products and ideas, resources, legislation for dairy, deli and bakery professionals.

DAIRY, FOOD AND ENVIRONMENTAL SANITATION; a publication for sanitarians and fieldmen. see PUBLIC HEALTH AND SAFETY

637 US ISSN 0888-0050
DAIRY FOODS; leading the way to dairy profits. 1900. 13/yr. $82 (foreign $145). Delta Communications Inc. (Subsidiary of: Cahners Publishing Company), Division of Reed Elsevier Inc., 455 N. Cityfront Plaza Dr., 24th Fl., Chicago, IL 60611. TEL 312-222-2000. FAX 312-222-2026. TELEX 210012 UR. Ed. Mike Pehanich; Pub. Carolyn Dress. adv.: B&W page $4535, color page $6235; trim 7 7/8 x 10 3/4; adv. contact: Brana O'Bradovich. mkt.; stat.; tr.lit. circ. 20,105. (also avail. in microform from UMI; reprint service avail. from UMI) **Indexed:** Biodet.Abstr., Curr.Pack.Abstr., Dairy Sci.Abstr., Excerp.Med., Food Sci.& Tech.Abstr., Hlth.Ind., Tr.& Indus.Ind.
●Also available online. Vendor(s): DIALOG Information Services, Inc., Mead Data Central, Inc.
—BLDSC (3514.715000); UnCover; SWETS; UMI. CCC.
Former titles (until 1986): Dairy Record (ISSN 0011-5673); Incorporates (after vol.43, no.5, 1981): American Dairy Review (ISSN 0002-8169); Which was formerly (1960-1965): American Milk Review (ISSN 0098-7581); (1958-1959): American Milk Review and Milk Plant Monthly (ISSN 0096-0926); Which supersedes: Milk Plant Monthly (ISSN 0097-6903); (1939-1958): American Milk Review (Year) (ISSN 0096-0934); American Creamery and Poultry Produce Review; American Dairy Products Review; American Produce Review.
Description: Serves company and administrative management, plant operation, marketing and distribution personnel in the dairy industry. Covers the dairy processing industry in all its segments.

637 US ISSN 0888-0050
DAIRY FOODS MARKET DIRECTORY. 1984. a. $99. Delta Communications Inc. (Subsidiary of: Cahners Publishing Company), Division of Reed Elsevier Inc., 455 N. Cityfront Plaza Dr., 24th Fl., Chicago, IL 60611. TEL 312-222-2000. FAX 312-222-2026. Ed. Mike Pehenich. adv.; tr.lit. (also avail. in microfilm; back issues avail.) **Document type:** directory.
Description: Lists suppliers and distributors of equipment, services, ingredients and supplies to dairy food processors.

FOOD AND FOOD INDUSTRIES

664 UK ISSN 0308-8197
SF221 CODEN: DINIDD
DAIRY INDUSTRIES INTERNATIONAL. (Biennial Dairy & Ice Cream Industries Directory) 1936. m. £54($195) (foreign £125). Wilmington Publishing, Wilmington House, Church Hill, Dartford, Kent UA2 7EF, England. TEL 0322-277788. FAX 0322-276476. (Subscr. to: Ferrari House, 258 Field End Rd., Ruislip, Middx HA4 9AU. TEL 081-868-4499) Ed. Pauline Russell. adv.; bk.rev.; abstr.; bibl.; charts; illus.; stat.; index. circ. 5,681. **Indexed:** Biol.Abstr., Br.Tech.Ind., Chem.Abstr., Curr.Adv.Ecol.Sci., Curr.Cont., Curr.Pack.Abstr., Dairy Sci.Abstr., Excerp.Med., Food Sci.& Tech.Abstr., Key to Econ.Sci., Packag.Sci.Tech., PROMT, Rural Recreat.Tour.Abstr., Soyabean Abstr., World Agri.Econ.& Rural Sociol.Abstr.
—BLDSC (3515.050000); Faxon; UnCover; SWETS; CASDDS.
Formerly: Dairy Industries (ISSN 0011-5622); Incorporates: Dairy Engineering.

DAIRY PRODUCTS: THE INTERNATIONAL MARKET. see *AGRICULTURE — Dairying And Dairy Products*

DECANTER. see *BEVERAGES*

664 US
DELTA'S NEW PRODUCT NEWS. 1964. m. $359. Delta Communications Inc. (Subsidiary of: Cahners Publishing Company), Division of Reed Elsevier Inc., 455 N. Cityfront Plaza Dr., 24th Fl., Chicago, IL 60611. TEL 312-222-2000. FAX 312-222-2026. Ed. Martin J. Friedman. circ. 1,205. (back issues avail.) **Document type:** trade publication.
●Also available online. Vendor(s): Mead Data Central, Inc.
Former titles: Gorman's New Product News; New Product News.
Description: Provides information, indexes, and statistics on trends, companies, and the market on the latest retail food grocery product introductions in 20 different categories.

664 613 GW
DEMETER-BLAETTER. 1962. s-a. free. Demeter-Bund e.V., Postfach 710131, 70607 Stuttgart, Germany. TEL 0711-4411025. FAX 0711-4411690. Ed. Bruno Endlich. adv.; bk.rev. circ. 60,000. **Document type:** consumer publication.

664 DK ISSN 0107-0517
DENMARK. LEVNEDSMIDDELSTYRELSEN. PUBLIKATION. No.56, 1981. irreg. Sundhedsministeriet, Levnedsmiddelstyrelsen, Moerkhoej Bygade 19, DK-2860 Soeborg, Denmark.

664 GW ISSN 0012-0413
HD9013.1 CODEN: DLRUAJ
DEUTSCHE LEBENSMITTEL-RUNDSCHAU; Zeitschrift fuer Lebensmittelkunde und Lebensmittelrecht. (Text in German; summaries in English, German) 1903. m. DM.218.40 (students DM.148.80). (Bund fuer Lebensmittelrecht und Lebensmittelkunde e.V.) Wissenschaftliche Verlagsgesellschaft mbH, Postfach 101061, 70009 Stuttgart, Germany. TEL 0711-2582-0. FAX 0711-2582290. TELEX 723636-DAZ-D. Ed. Dr. K.G. Bergner. adv.; bk.rev.; abstr.; bibl.; illus.; pat.; tr.lit.; index. circ. 2,000. **Indexed:** Anal.Abstr., Biodet.Abstr., Biol.Abstr., Chem.Abstr., Curr.Adv.Ecol.Sci., Curr.Cont., Curr.Pack.Abstr., Dairy Sci.Abstr., Excerp.Med., Food Sci.& Tech.Abstr., Ind.Sci.Rev., Ind.Vet., INIS Atomind., Int.Packag.Abstr., Lead Abstr., Packag.Sci.Tech., Pig News & Info., Sci.Cit.Ind., Vet.Bull.; Zincscan. **Document type:** trade publication.
—BLDSC (3572.000000); SWETS; CASDDS. **CCC.**
Description: Discusses food chemistry, technology, and legislation.

658.8 GW ISSN 0012-1134
DEUTSCHER LEBENSMITTELGROSSHANDEL; der Supermarkt, der Cash- und Carry-Grosshandel. 1966. q. DM.48($20) Zeitungs- und Zeitschriftenverlag Heinrichs, Brueggekamp 1, 30890 Barsinghausen, Germany. TEL 05105-2289. Ed. G. Heinrichs. adv.; bk.rev.; charts; stat.; tr.lit. circ. 4,500. (tabloid format) **Document type:** trade publication.

658.8 664 GW ISSN 0012-1142
DEUTSCHER LEBENSMITTELHANDEL. 1966. q. DM.48($20) Zeitungs- und Zeitschriftenverlag Heinrichs, Brueggekamp 1, 30890 Barsinghausen, Germany. TEL 05105-2289. Ed. G. Heinrichs. adv.; bk.rev.; charts; stat.; tr.lit. circ. 7,900. (tabloid format) **Document type:** trade publication.

664 UK
DEVELOPMENTS IN FOOD PRESERVATION. 1981. irreg., vol.5, 1989. price varies. Elsevier Science Ltd., Books Division, P.O. Box 800, Kidlington, Oxford OX5 1DX, England. TEL 44-865-843000. FAX 44-865-843010. (Subscr. in U.S. and Canada to: Elsevier Science, 660 White Plains Rd., Tarrytown, NY 10591-5153. TEL 914-524-9200) Ed. S. Thorne. (back issues avail.) **Indexed:** Food Sci.& Tech.Abstr. **Document type:** monographic series.
Refereed Serial

664 UK
DEVELOPMENTS IN FOOD PROTEINS. 1982. irreg., vol.7, 1991. price varies. Elsevier Science Ltd., Books Division, P.O. Box 800, Kidlington, Oxford OX5 1DX, England. TEL 44-865-843000. FAX 44-865-843010. (Subscr. in U.S. and Canada to: Elsevier Science, 660 White Plains Rd., Tarrytown, NY 10591-5153. TEL 914-524-9200) Ed. B.J.F. Hudson. (back issues avail.) **Indexed:** Chem.Abstr., Dairy Sci.Abstr. **Document type:** monographic series.
Refereed Serial

664 MX
DICCIONARIO DE ESPECIALIDADES PARA LA INDUSTRIA ALIMENTARIA. 1990. a. Ediciones P L M, S.A. de C.V., San Bernadino 17, Col. del Valle, 03100 Mexico, D.F., Mexico. TEL 687-1766. FAX 536-5027. Ed. Beatriz Castaneda. circ. 5,000.

DIRECTORY OF COLLEGE & UNIVERSITY FOODSERVICE (YEAR). see *BUSINESS AND ECONOMICS — Trade And Industrial Directories*

642.5 338 CN
DIRECTORY OF RESTAURANT & FAST FOOD CHAINS IN CANADA (YEAR). 1980. a. Can.$270. Maclean Hunter Ltd., Business Publication Division, Maclean-Hunter Bldg., 777 Bay St., 5th Fl., Toronto, ON M5W 1A7, Canada. FAX 416-593-3166. Ed. Mary De Lisio. **Document type:** directory.
Description: Provides data on over 600 companies across Canada: Head office addresses and phone numbers; management names and titles; average number of seats per outlet; expansion plans for the year, locations and more.

DIRECTORY OF THE CANNING, FREEZING, PRESERVING INDUSTRIES. see *BUSINESS AND ECONOMICS — Trade And Industrial Directories*

DIRECTORY OF U.S. MEAT SUPPLIERS. see *BUSINESS AND ECONOMICS — Trade And Industrial Directories*

DISHWASHER. see *OCCUPATIONS AND CAREERS*

DOG INDUSTRY NEWSLETTER. see *PETS*

664 SP
DOSSIER OLEO. 1982. q. 5400 ptas. (foreign 8700 ptas.). Tecnipublicaciones, S.A., Fernando VI, 27, 28004 Madrid, Spain. TEL 91-319-7889. FAX 91-410-2041. Ed. Maria Dolores Penafiel Fernandez.
Description: Covers the oil and grease industries, especially olive oil production and business.

664 GW ISSN 0720-1249
CODEN: DRFSDW
DRAGOCO REPORT: FLAVORING INFORMATION SERVICE. (Editions in English, French, German and Spanish) 1956. q. free. Dragoco Gerberding & Co. AG, Dragocostr., 37601 Holzminden, Germany. TEL 05531-7040. FAX 05531-704391. TELEX 965336. (US addr.: Dragoco, Inc., Gordon Dr., Totowa, NJ 07512. TEL 201-256-3850) Eds. Katja Seibicke, Marlies Knirsch. index. circ. 12,000. (back issues avail.) **Indexed:** Chem.Abstr. **Document type:** trade publication.
—BLDSC (3622.350000); CASDDS.

664 FR ISSN 0221-0347
CODEN: CAENDI
ECOLE NATIONALE SUPERIEURE DE BIOLOGIE APPLIQUEE A LA NUTRITION ET A L'ALIMENTATION. CAHIERS. Cover title: E N S B A N A Cahiers. 1976. a. price varies. Ecole Nationale Superieure de Biologie Appliquee a la Nutrition et a l'Alimentation (ENSBANA), 11 rue Lavoisier, 75384 Paris Cedex 08, France. TEL 42-65-39-95. FAX 42-65-02-46. TELEX LAVOISI 649404 F. Ed. Denis Lozinet. adv.; bk.rev.; bibl.; charts; illus. circ. 3,000. **Indexed:** Bull.Signal., Chem.Abstr. **Document type:** monographic series.
—CASDDS.
Former titles: Amis de l'E.N.S.B.A.N.A. (ISSN 0221-0339); Amis de l'I.B.A.N.A. (Publication) (ISSN 0003-1801)

637 GW ISSN 0013-2500
EIER-WILD-GEFLUEGEL-MARKT. 3/w. DM.600($252) Heinrichs Verlag GmbH und Co. KG, Postfach 100550, 31105 Hildesheim, Germany. TEL 05121-53279. Ed. J. Heiber. adv.; illus. **Document type:** trade publication.

644 HU ISSN 0013-5909
CODEN: EMIPAB
ELELMEZESI IPAR/FOOD INDUSTRY. (Text in Hungarian; summaries in English, German and Russian) 1947. m. 1200 Ft.($48.50) (Magyar Elelmezesipari Tudomanyos Egyesulet - Scientific Society for Food Industry) Agroinform Kiado es Nyomda Kft., Kitaibal Pal u. 4, 1024 Budapest II, Hungary. TEL 135-1927. FAX 135-0344. Ed. Istvan Toth-Zsiga. adv. **Indexed:** Biodet.Abstr., Chem.Abstr., Curr.Cont., Dairy Sci.Abstr., Food Sci.& Tech.Abstr., INIS Atomind., Nutr.Abstr., Packag.Sci.Tech., Rural Recreat.Tour.Abstr., Soils & Fert., World Agri.Econ.& Rural Sociol.Abstr. **Document type:** newsletter.
—CASDDS.

664 614 HU ISSN 0422-9576
CODEN: EMKZAH
ELELMISZERVIZSGALATI KOZLEMENYEK. (Text in Hungarian; summaries in English, French, German and Russian) 1955. q. $37. Lapkiado Vallalat, Lenin korut 9-11, 1073 Budapest 7, Hungary. TEL 222-408. (Subscr. to: Kultura, P.O. Box 149, 1389 Budapest, Hungary) **Indexed:** Chem.Abstr., Dairy Sci.Abstr., Food Sci.& Tech.Abstr., INIS Atomind.
—CASDDS.

EMPIRE STATE FOOD SERVICE NEWS. see *HOTELS AND RESTAURANTS*

ENTREE; an uncompromising and confidential traveler's newsletter. see *TRAVEL AND TOURISM*

ENVIRONMENTAL NUTRITION; the newsletter of diet, nutrition and health. see *NUTRITION AND DIETETICS*

641.013 AT ISSN 0013-9548
EPICUREAN. 1966. irreg. Southdown Press, 32 Walsh St., Melbourne, Vic. 3000, Australia. Ed. Tony Fawcett. adv.; bk.rev.; charts.

664 AU
ERNAEHRUNG. 1977. m. S.1150. Fachzeitschriftenverlag GmbH, Schwarzenbergplatz 6, A-1030 Vienna, Austria. TEL 01-7153193. FAX 01-7154819. Ed. Klaus Smolka. adv. contact: Gerda Allacher. bk.rev. circ. 2,000. **Document type:** consumer publication.

664 SZ
ERNAEHRUNG. 26/yr. Case Postale 105, CH-1001 Lausanne, Switzerland. TEL 021-201901. FAX 021-234413. circ. 1,200.

664 GW ISSN 0343-9704
DIE ERNAEHRUNGSINDUSTRIE. Abbreviated title: D E I. 1972. m. (with 2 double issues/yr.). Konradin Verlag Robert Kohlhammer, Ernst-Mey-Str. 8, 70771 Leinfelden-Echterdingen, Germany. TEL 0711-7594-284. FAX 0711-7594397. Ed. Jochen Krueger. adv.: B&W page DM.5190, color page DM.7170; trim 190 x 270. bk.rev.; charts; illus.; stat. circ. 10,265. **Document type:** trade publication.
Description: Provides information on food technology as well as food and luxury food processing, including storage, ingredients, care, packaging, transport, and distribution.

FOOD AND FOOD INDUSTRIES

664 GW
ESSEN UND TRINKEN. 1972. m. DM.66 (Europe DM.108; elsewhere DM.168). Gruner und Jahr AG & Co., Am Baumwall 11, 20459 Hamburg, Germany. TEL 040-3703-0. FAX 040-37035606. Ed. Peter Ploog. adv.; illus. circ. 275,667. **Document type:** consumer publication.

664.9 IT ISSN 0394-2910
EUROCARNI. 1986. 12/yr. L.72000 (foriegn L.120000). Pubblicita Italia s.a.s., Via Taglio 24, 41100 Modena, Italy. TEL 59-216-688. FAX 51-220-727. Ed. Onelio Benedetti. adv.; bk.rev. circ. 10,000. **Document type:** trade publication.

664 UK ISSN 0955-5404
EUROFOOD. m. £186 in the UK and Europe; elsewhere £195. Agra Europe (London) Ltd., 25 Frant Rd., Tunbridge Wells, Kent TN2 5JT, England, England. TEL 44-892-533813. FAX 44-892-544895. TELEX 95114 AGRATW G. **Document type:** newsletter.
—BLDSC (3829.268320).
Description: Aimed at senior executives in the European food and drinks industry. Monitors the changing structure of the food industry in Europe and the development of the Single European Market.

664 UK ISSN 0960-7943
EUROFOOD MONITOR. irreg. £400($612) in the UK; elsewhere £460. Agra Europe (London) Ltd., 25 Frant Rd., Tunbridge Wells, Kent TN2 5JT, England. TEL 44-892-533813. FAX 44-892-544895. TELEX 95114 AGRATW G. (looseleaf format) **Document type:** trade publication.
●Also available online.
Description: Compiled by a European Community lawyer and expert in European food law.

EUROPA A TAVOLA. see HOME ECONOMICS

663.93 BE
EUROPEAN COFFEE REPORT. a. European Coffee Federation, Boudewijnlaan 21, B-1210 Brussels, Belgium. TEL 02-2230141. FAX 02-2231244.

664 UK ISSN 0955-4416
EUROPEAN FOOD AND DRINK REVIEW; quarterly review of food and drink technology. 1989. q. £65. Contract Communications Limited, Nestor House, Playhouse Yard, London EC4V 5EX, England. TEL 071-779-8714. FAX 071-779-8760. circ. 14,000. (back issues avail.) **Document type:** trade publication.
—BLDSC (3829.715100).

664 GW
EUROPEAN FOOD LAW REVIEW. (Text in English, French, German) q. DM.268 (foreign DM.272). Deutscher Fachverlag GmbH, Mainzer Landstr. 251, 60326 Frankfurt a.M., Germany. TEL 069-759501. FAX 069-75952999. circ. 600. **Document type:** trade publication.

EUROPEAN FOOD MARKETING DIRECTORY. see BUSINESS AND ECONOMICS — Trade And Industrial Directories

664 UK
EUROPEAN FOOD TRADES DIRECTORY. 1958. biennial. £130 (foreign £140). Newman Books Ltd., 32 Vauxhall Bridge Rd., London SW1V 2SS, England. TEL 071-973-6402. FAX 071-233-5056. Ed. David Ricketts. circ. 4,000. **Document type:** directory.
Incorporates: Food Industry Directory (ISSN 0264-4037); Formerly: Food Trades Directory and Food Buyer's Yearbook (ISSN 0309-0264)
Description: Lists U.K. food manufacturers, processors and suppliers, including retailers and other bulk purchasers.

664.9 FR
EUROVIANDE; le courrier des abattoirs viandes. 1960. bi-m. 60 F. 34, rue Laroche, 33-Bordeaux, France. Ed. Jean Cavignac. adv.; bk.rev.; charts; illus.; stat. circ. 6,500. **Indexed:** Food Sci.& Tech.Abstr.

664 US
EXPO (GREAT NECK); foodservice yearbook international. 1991. s-a. Keller International Publishing Corporation, 150 Great Neck Rd., Great Neck, NY 11021. TEL 516-829-9210. FAX 516-829-7265. circ. 15,700.
Description: Covers new products introduced at expositions.

664 615 US
F D A COMPLIANCE POLICY GUIDANCE. MANUAL. base vol. plus m. updates. $150 (foreign $300). (U.S. Food and Drug Administration) U.S. National Technical Information Service, 5285 Port Royal Rd., Springfield, VA 22161. TEL 703-487-4600. FAX 703-321-8547. TELEX 64617.
Formerly: F D A Compliance Policy Guide.

F D A CONSUMER. (U.S. Food and Drug Administration) see CONSUMER EDUCATION AND PROTECTION

F D A HOTLINE. see PUBLIC HEALTH AND SAFETY

664 615 US
F D A INSPECTION OPERATIONS MANUAL. (Supplement to: Basic Manual) 6/yr. $80 in U.S., Canada, Mexico; elsewhere $160. (Department of Health and Human Services, Food and Drug Administration) U.S. National Technical Information Service, 5825 Port Royal Rd., Springfield, VA 22161. TEL 703-487-4630.
Description: Provides a system for the issuance of Agency-wide operating standards for inspectors and investigators. Includes necessary instructions and references as well as excerpts of the authorities, responsibilities, objectives, policies and applicable guides.

641.1 615 US
F D C CONTROL NEWSLETTER. (Food, Drug, and Cosmetics) no.36, 1974. 3/yr. membership. American Society for Quality Control, Food, Drug and Cosmetic Division, 611 E. Wisconsin Ave., Box 3005, Milwaukee, WI 53201-3005. TEL 414-272-8575. Ed. James B. Kohnen. bk.rev.; charts. circ. 3,000.
Former titles: F D C Control; Food Quality Control (ISSN 0532-0941)

F F P SERIES IN FOOD PRODUCTS MARKETING. (Food Products Press) see BUSINESS AND ECONOMICS — Marketing And Purchasing

663.93 GW
F.O. LICHT'S INTERNATIONAL COFFEE REPORT. 1988. s-m. DM.575. F.O. Licht GmbH, Am Muehlengraben 22, 23902 Ratzeburg, Germany. FAX 04541-82145. **Document type:** trade publication.

664.122 GW ISSN 0014-6056
F.O. LICHT'S INTERNATIONAL MOLASSES REPORT. (Text in English and German) 1964. s-m. price varies. F.O. Licht GmbH, Am Muehlengraben 22, 23902 Ratzeburg, Germany. FAX 04541-82145. Ed. Helmut Ahlfeld. adv.; charts; stat. **Document type:** trade publication.

F.O. LICHT'S INTERNATIONAL SUGAR AND SWEETENER REPORT. see AGRICULTURE

FALVAK DOLGOZO NEPE. see AGRICULTURE

FARM AND FOOD. see AGRICULTURE

664 658.8 UK
FAST FOOD: THE INTERNATIONAL MARKET. a. £1375($2750) Euromonitor, 87-88 Turnmill St., London EC1M 5QU, England. TEL 071-251-8024. FAX 071-608-3149. (Addr. in N. America: Euromonitor International, 111 W. Washington St., Ste. 920, Chicago, IL 60602. TEL 312-541-8024. FAX 312-541-1567) (looseleaf format) **Document type:** trade publication.
●Also available online. Vendor(s): Data-Star, DIALOG Information Services, Inc.
Description: Analyzes the international fast-food market for France, Germany, Italy, Spain, the U.K., the U.S., and Japan.

FAVORITE BRAND NAME RECIPES. see HOME ECONOMICS

633 CK
FEDERACION NACIONAL DE CAFETEROS DE COLOMBIA. INFORME DE LABORES DE LOS COMITES DEPARTAMENTALES DE CAFETEROS. irreg. Federacion Nacional de Cafeteros de Colombia, Av. Jimenez 7-65, Bogota, Colombia. illus.

664.028 FR
FEDERATION DES INDUSTRIES ET COMMERCES UTILISATEURS DES BASSES TEMPERATURES. RAPPORT STATISTIQUE ANNUEL. 1976. a. 500 F. Ficur, 51-53 rue Fondary, 75739 Paris Cedex 15, France. TEL 45-79-10-49. FAX 45-79-61-29. TELEX 205705F.
Formerly: Federation Interprofessionnelle de la Congelation Ultra-Rapide. Rapport Statistique Annuel.

663 FR
FEDERATION INTERNATIONALE DES PRODUCTEURS DE JUS DE FRUITS. RAPPORT ANNUEL D'ACTIVITE. (Text in English) 1958. a. 50 F. Federation Internationale des Producteurs de Jus de Fruits - International Federation of Fruit Juice Producers, 10 rue de Liege, 75009 Paris, France.
Formerly: International Federation of Fruit Juice Producers. Proceedings. Berichte. Rapports (ISSN 0535-0182)

664 658.8 UK
FEEDBACK. 1914. 6/yr. membership. Food and Drink Federation, 6 Catherine St., London WC2B 5JJ, England. TEL 071-836-2460. FAX 071-379-0481. TELEX 299388. Ed. Denis Budge. adv.; bk.rev. circ. 3,500. **Document type:** trade publication.
Former titles (until 1992): F D F Feedback; F M F Feedback.

633.6 FJ
FIJI SUGAR YEAR BOOK. (Text in English, Fijian and Hindi) 1979. a. Fiji Sugar Industry, PO Box 644, Suva, Fiji. Ed. D.V. Tarte. charts; illus.; stat.; tr.lit. circ. 5,000.

664.9 IT
FILIERA CARNE. 12/yr. Via G. Galilei 14, 21024 Milan, Italy. TEL 2-29-00-38-14. Ed. Andrea Barbieri. circ. 15,000.

664.9 FR ISSN 1143-7375
FILIERES VIANDE ET PECHE; le magazine des professionels viande-charcuterie-volaille-poisson. 1978. 11/yr. 335 F. (foreign 420 F.). Groupe L S A, B.P. 142, 6 rue Marius Aufan, 92300 Levallois-Perret Cedex, France. TEL 47-58-20-00. FAX 47-58-77-00. circ. 10,500. (back issues avail.)
Formerly: Filiere Viande.

664 US
FINE FOODS. Bound with: Griffin Report of Food Marketing (ISSN 0192-4400) 1990. m. Griffin Publishing Company, Inc., 1099 Hingham St., Rockland, MA 02370. TEL 617-878-5300. FAX 617-871-4721. circ. 14,500 (controlled). **Document type:** trade publication.
Description: Covers industry news and new products and trends in the areas of prepared foods, wines and cheeses, and perishables.

664 UK ISSN 0969-2037
▼**FISH & CHIPS AND FAST FOOD.** 1993. q. £20($34) (foreign £22). F M J International Publications Ltd., Queensway House, 2 Queensway, Redhill, Surrey RH1 1QS, England. TEL 0737-768611. FAX 0737-761585. TELEX 948669-TOPJNL-G. Ed. Mick Witworth. **Document type:** trade publication.
Description: Geared toward managers of fish & chip establishments.

FLAVOUR & FRAGRANCE JOURNAL. see CHEMISTRY — Organic Chemistry

664.9 GW ISSN 0015-3575
CODEN: FLCHAT
FLEISCH; Fachzeitschrift fuer die Fleischgewinnung und Verarbeitung. (Text in German; index in English and Russian) 1947. m. DM.79 (foreign DM.101.50). Verlag Karlheinz Holz, Aarstr. 24, 65195 Wiesbaden, Germany. TEL 0611-9450751. FAX 0611-9450074. adv.; bk.rev.; charts; illus.; tr.lit.; index. **Indexed:** Chem.Abstr., Curr.Cont., Dairy Sci.Abstr., Food Sci.& Tech.Abstr., Helminthol.Abstr., Ind.Vet., Vet.Bull. **Document type:** trade publication.
—BLDSC (3950.380000); CASDDS.
Formerly: Fleischermeister.
Description: Trade publication for the meat industry. Covers meat quality, meat inspections and vocational training.

FOOD AND FOOD INDUSTRIES

664.9 GW ISSN 0930-6536
FLEISCH-MAGAZIN; internationale Fachzeitschrift fuer handwerkliche und industrielle Fleischverarbeitung Handel und Zulieferer. 1985. 11/yr. DM.130 (foreign DM.142). S N Verlag Michael Steinert, An der Alster 21, 20099 Hamburg, Germany. TEL 040-240852. FAX 040-2803788. TELEX 218138. Eds. Thomas Otto, Michael Reese. adv. (back issues avail.)

664.9 GW ISSN 0015-3613
CODEN: FLEIEC
DIE FLEISCHEREI. (Text in German; summaries in English, French and Spanish) 1950. m. DM.180 (foreign DM.205.20). Hans Holzmann Verlag GmbH, Gewerbestr. 2, 86825 Bad Woerishofen, Germany. TEL 08247-35401. FAX 08247-354170. Ed. Gudrun Reinhold. adv.; B&W page DM.4344, color DM.7410; trim 316 x 212; adv. contact: Walter Haeusl. bk.rev.; abstr.; charts; illus.; stat.; index. circ. 8,350. **Indexed:** Food Sci.& Tech.Abstr., Packag.Sci.Tech. **Document type:** trade publication. —BLDSC (3950.490000).
Formerly: Fleischereibedarf.

664.9 GW ISSN 0176-9502
FLEISCHEREI-TECHNIK; Zeitschrift fuer Ausstattung, Bau, Technik und Technologie im Fleischerhandwerk und der Fleischerwaren-Industrie. 1985. q. DM.75.50 (foreign DM.97.50). Verlag Karlheinz Holz, Aarstr. 24, 65195 Wiesbaden, Germany. TEL 0611-9450751. FAX 0611-9450074. Ed. Jutta Schmidt. circ. 15,000. (back issues avail.) **Document type:** trade publication.

664 AU
FLEISCHERMEISTER. m. Zeitungverlag Kuhn und Co., Kutschkergasse 42, A-1180 Vienna, Austria. TEL 01-34150307. FAX 01-3130121. TELEX 132741-KUHN-A. Ed. Gerd Volker Weege. circ. 5,400. **Document type:** trade publication.

664.9 GW ISSN 0015-363X
CODEN: FLEIA8
DIE FLEISCHWIRTSCHAFT. (Abstracts in English, French and German) 1920. m. DM.419 (foreign DM.441.70). (Bundesverband der Deutschen Fleischwarenindindustrie e.V.) Deutscher Fachverlag GmbH, Mainzer Landstr. 251, 60326 Frankfurt a.M., Germany. TEL 069-759501. FAX 069-75952999. (Subscr. to: Postfach 100606, 60006 Frankfurt a.M., Germany) adv.; bk.rev.; charts; illus.; stat. circ. 6,818. **Indexed:** Agri.Eng.Abstr., Anim.Breed.Abstr., Biodet.Abstr., Chem.Abstr., Curr.Cont., Curr.Pack.Abstr., Dairy Sci.Abstr., Excerp.Med., Food Sci.& Tech.Abstr., Helminthol.Abstr., Ind.Vet., INIS Atomind., Int.Packag.Abstr., Nutr.Abstr., Packag.Sci.Tech., Pig News & Info., Rural Recreat.Tour.Abstr., Soyabean Abstr., Vet.Bull., World Agri.Econ.& Rural Sociol.Abstr. **Document type:** trade publication. —BLDSC (3950.500000); SWETS; CASDDS.

664.9 GW ISSN 0722-7582
FLEISCHWIRTSCHAFT ESPANOL. (Text in Spanish) 1980. 2/yr. DM.63. Deutscher Fachverlag GmbH, Mainzer Landstr. 251, 60326 Frankfurt a.M., Germany. TEL 069-759501. FAX 069-75952999. (Subscr. to: Postfach 100606, 60006 Frankfurt a.M., Germany) Ed. Josef Kern. adv. circ. 2,500. (back issues avail.) **Document type:** trade publication.
Description: Reports on all aspects of meat production.

664.9 GW ISSN 0179-2415
FLEISCHWIRTSCHAFT INTERNATIONAL; journal of meat production and slaughterhouse practice, meat processing, preservation and supply. (Text in English) 1986. q. DM.93. Deutscher Fachverlag GmbH, Mainzer Landstr. 251, 60326 Frankfurt a.M., Germany. TEL 069-759501. FAX 069-75952999. (Subscr. to: Postfach 100606, 60006 Frankfurt a.M., Germany) Ed. Dr. Josef Kern. adv. circ. 9,033. (back issues avail.) **Document type:** trade publication. —BLDSC (3950.505000).

664 US ISSN 0886-5868
FLORIDA FOOD AND RESOURCE ECONOMICS. 1974. bi-m. University of Florida, Institute of Food and Agricultural Sciences, Food and Resource Economics Department, Box 110240 Gainesville, FL 32611-0240. TEL 904-392-6015. Ed. James R. Simpson. film rev.; charts; stat.

FLORIDA FOOD DEALER. see *FOOD AND FOOD INDUSTRIES — Grocery Trade*

330 US ISSN 1044-0364
FLORIDA RESTAURATEUR. 1965. 11/yr. $25 membership. Florida Restaurant Association, 2441 Hollywood Blvd., Hollywood, FL 33020. TEL 305-921-6300. FAX 305-925-6381. Ed. Hugh McLinden. adv.; bk.rev. circ. 16,441. **Document type:** trade publication.

664.7 UK ISSN 0071-6243
TS2120.F55
FLOUR MILLING AND BAKING RESEARCH ASSOCIATION. ANNUAL REPORT AND ACCOUNTS. 1968. a. membership. Flour Milling and Baking Research Association, Chorleywood, Herts. WD3 5SH, England. FAX 0923-284539. circ. 1,750. **Document type:** corporate report.
Issued formerly under name of one of its patent organizations: British Baking Industries Research Association. Annual Report.

664.1 UK ISSN 0263-2632
FLOUR MILLING AND BAKING RESEARCH ASSOCIATION. DIGEST. 1982. m. membership. Flour Milling and Baking Research Association, Chorleywood, Herts. WD3 5SH, England. FAX 0293-284539. Ed. Charlotte Stock. charts; illus. **Document type:** trade publication.

664 US ISSN 0272-9938
FOOD. (Subseries of: S I R S Social Issues (ISSN 0740-3127)) 1972. a. price varies. Social Issues Resources Series, Box 2348, Boca Raton, FL 33427-2348. TEL 407-994-0079; 800-232-7477. FAX 407-994-4704. (looseleaf format; also avail. in microfiche; back issues avail.) **Description:** Reprints articles that examine hunger, malnutrition, harmful food additives, the plight of the farmer, and government efforts to protect the food supply.

FOOD ADDITIVES AND CONTAMINANTS; analysis, surveillance, evaluation, control. see *PHARMACY AND PHARMACOLOGY*

664 UN ISSN 1014-8574
FOOD AID REVIEW. Spanish edition: Ayuda Alimentaria (ISSN 1014-8612); French edition: Aide Alimentaire (ISSN 1014-8604) 1987. a. World Food Programme, Via Cristoforo Colombo 426, 00145 Rome, Italy. TEL 57971. FAX 396-5133537. TELEX 626675 WFP 1.
Former titles (until 1990): World Food Programme. Annual Report (ISSN 1014-8515); (until 1988): World Food Programme ... in Review (ISSN 1014-1596).

664 UK
FOOD AID SHIPMENTS. 1980. a. £20($40) International Wheat Council, One Canada Sq., Canary Wharf, London E14 5AE, England. TEL 071-513-1122. FAX 071-712-0071. TELEX 8813241. stat. **Document type:** bulletin.
Formerly: Food Aid Convention.
Description: Contains statistical information about shipments of cereals food aid by members of the Food Aid Convention.

FOOD AND AGRICULTURAL LEGISLATION. see *LAW*

664 US
FOOD AND BEVERAGE JOURNAL. q. $10. 555 De Hard St., Ste. 240, San Francisco, CA 94107-2148. TEL 415-647-2890. FAX 415-647-2088. Ed. Katharine Micszkowski. adv.; bk.rev. circ. 30,000. **Document type:** trade publication.

664 663 US ISSN 0731-3799
HD9000.1 CODEN: FBEMDL
FOOD & BEVERAGE MARKETING; the national publication for food, beverage, beer, wine, liquor & tobacco marketing executives. 1982. 12/yr. $75. Springfield Publishing, 505 Eighth Ave., Ste. 1403, New York, NY 10018. TEL 212-695-0704. FAX 212-695-0748. Ed. Al Urbanski. adv.; tr.lit. circ. 18,077. (reprint service avail.) **Indexed:** Tr.& Indus.Ind.
●Also available online. Vendor(s): Mead Data Central, Inc.
—BLDSC (3977.026800).

FOOD & BEVERAGE MONITOR. see *BUSINESS AND ECONOMICS — Investments*

FOOD & BEVERAGE SPOTLIGHT. see *BUSINESS AND ECONOMICS — Investments*

664 SA ISSN 1012-7577
FOOD AND BEVERAGES (YEAR). (Text in English) a. (South African Foreign Trade Organisation) SAFTO, Publishing Division, P.O. Box 782706, Sandton 2146, South Africa. TEL 27-11-883-3737. FAX 27-11-883-6569. TELEX 4-24111 SA. adv. **Document type:** directory.

FOOD AND CHEMICAL TOXICOLOGY. see *ENVIRONMENTAL STUDIES — Toxicology And Environmental Safety*

FOOD & DRINK/BON VERRE, BONNE TABLE. see *BEVERAGES*

664 663 US ISSN 1056-8859
HD9000.1
FOOD & DRINK DAILY. 1985. d. $825. King Publishing Group, Inc., 627 National Press Bldg., Washington, DC 20045. TEL 202-638-4260. FAX 202-662-9744. Ed. Linda Gasparello. bk.rev. **Document type:** newsletter.
●Also available online. Vendor(s): Mead Data Central, Inc., NewsNet (FB03).
—BLDSC (3977.030090). CCC.
Incorporates (1989-1990): Daily Food and Drink Report (ISSN 1044-1433); **Formerly (until 1991):** World Food and Drink Report (ISSN 0885-7946); Which was formed by the 1985 merger of: World Food Report; World Drink Report.
Description: Covers all aspects of the food and beverage industry, its international markets, and its regulators. Reports on government agencies.

664 UK ISSN 0954-0431
FOOD & DRINK FROM BRITAIN BUYERS' GUIDE. (Text in English, French, German and Spanish) a. £70. William Reed Ltd., Broadfield Park, Crawley, W. Sussex RH11 9RT, England. TEL 0293-613400. FAX 0293-515174. adv.; illus. **Document type:** trade publication.

664 663 UK
FOOD AND DRINK TRADE HANDBOOK.* 1970. a. £5.50. (National Food and Drink Federation) Harrington Kilbride plc., The Publishing House, Highbury Sta. Rd., Islington, London N11 SE, England. Ed. L.E. Reeves-Smith.

FOOD AND DRUG ADMINISTRATION. see *LAW*

FOOD AND DRUG LAW JOURNAL. see *LAW*

FOOD AND DRUG LAW REPORTS. see *LAW*

FOOD & DRUGS INDUSTRY BULLETIN. see *LAW*

THE FOOD AND FIBER LETTER. see *AGRICULTURE*

664 US
FOOD AND HUNGER NOTES. q. donation. Mennonite Central Committee, 21 S. 12th St., Box 500, Akron, PA 17501-0500. TEL 717-859-1151. FAX 717-859-2171. TELEX 90-2210 MENCENCOM AKRP. Ed. David Schrock-Shenick. circ. 1,000. **Description:** Deals with food and environmental development issues.

664 UK
FOOD & NUTRITION UPDATE. m. £375. Leatherhead Food R.A., Randalls Rd., Leatherhead, Surrey KT22 7RY, England. TEL 0372-376761. FAX 0372-386228. TELEX 929846. **Document type:** bulletin.

FOOD & SERVICE. see *HOTELS AND RESTAURANTS*

641.5 US ISSN 0279-6740
TX341
FOOD & WINE. 1978. m. $26. (International Review of Food & Wine Associates) American Express Publishing Corp. (New York), 1120 Ave. of the Americas, New York, NY 10036. TEL 212-382-5600. FAX 212-768-1573. (Subscr. to: Box 3004, Harlan, IA 51537. TEL 800-333-6569) Ed. Mary Simons. adv. circ. 725,000. **Indexed:** Access (1985-).
Formerly: International Review of Food and Wine (ISSN 0149-6964)

FOOD ARTS; the magazine for professionals. see *HOTELS AND RESTAURANTS*

FOOD AND FOOD INDUSTRIES

664 AT ISSN 1032-5298
TP368 CODEN: FOAUEF
FOOD AUSTRALIA. 1949. m. Aus.$58 (foreign Aus.$90). Council of Australian Food Technology Associations, Inc., P.O. Box 1493, North Sydney, N.S.W. 2059, Australia. TEL 02-963-7672. FAX 02-9544327. (Co-sponsor: Australian Institute of Food Science and Technology) Ed. J. Kefford. adv.: B&W page Aus.$1090, color page Aus.$1740; trim 190 x 277; adv. contact: M. Mallaoch. bk.rev.; abstr.; bibl.; charts; illus.; tr.lit.; index. circ. 3,400. Indexed: Biodet.Abstr., Biol.Abstr., Chem.Abstr., Curr.Adv.Ecol.Sci., Curr.Cont., Curr.Pack.Abstr., Dairy Sci.Abstr., Excerp.Med., Food Sci.& Tech.Abstr., Hort.Abstr., Ind.Vet., Nutr.Abstr., Packag.Sci.Tech., Plant Breed.Abstr., Risk Abstr., So.Pac.Per.Ind. **Document type:** trade publication.
—BLDSC (3977.064000); UnCover; SWETS. **CCC**.
Formerly (until Sep. 1988): Food Technology in Australia (ISSN 0015-6647)
Description: Designed to promote the scientific and technical aspects of the food manufacturing industries in Australia.

FOOD BIOTECHNOLOGY. see *BIOLOGY — Biotechnology*

FOOD BOOKS REVIEW; the international journal for readers of books on food technology subjects. see *PUBLISHING AND BOOK TRADE*

664 US ISSN 1049-5568
HD9000.1 CODEN: FBUSEI
FOOD BUSINESS. 1988. s-m. Putman Publishing Co., 301 E. Erie St., Chicago, IL 60611. TEL 312-644-2020. Ed. Peggy Stath.
—UMI. **CCC**.

664 US ISSN 0015-6337
FOOD CHEMICAL NEWS. 1959. w. $945 (effective July 1993). Food Chemical News, Inc., 1101 Pennsylvania Ave., S.E., Washington, DC 20003. TEL 202-544-1980. FAX 202-546-3890. Ed. Natalie Pargas. index. (back issues avail.)
●Also available online. Vendor(s): Data-Star, DIALOG Information Services, Inc., NewsNet (FB07).
—BLDSC (3977.270000). **CCC**.
Description: Information service on government regulation of food and food additives.

664 US
FOOD CHEMICAL NEWS GUIDE; current status of food additives and color additives. 1964. w. $830 (effective Jan. 1994). Food Chemical News, Inc., 1101 Pennsylvania Ave., S.E., Washington, DC 20003. TEL 202-544-1980. FAX 202-546-3890. Ed. Louis Rothschild, Jr. (looseleaf format)
Description: Guide to the status of food additives and color additives updated weekly and referenced to federal regulations.

FOOD CHEMISTRY. see *CHEMISTRY*

664 UK ISSN 0956-7135
FOOD CONTROL. 1990. q. £145 in UK and Europe; elsewhere £155. Butterworth - Heinemann (Subsidiary of: Reed International PLC), Linacre House, Jordan Hill, Oxford OX2 8DP, England. TEL 0865-310366. FAX 0865-310898. TELEX 83111 BHPOXF G. (Subscr. to: Turpin Transactions Ltd., Distribution Centre, Blackhorse Rd., Letchworth, Herts SG6 1HN, England. TEL 0462-672555) Ed. G. Campbell-Platt. adv.; bk.rev.; pat. (also avail. in microform from UMI; back issues avail.; reprint service avail.) Indexed: Biodet.Abstr. **Document type:** academic/scholarly publication.
—BLDSC (3977.291500). **CCC**.
Description: Covers current research, technology, legislation and good practices in all area of food control.

664 658.8 US ISSN 1048-8197
FOOD DISTRIBUTION MAGAZINE. Short title: F D M. 1959. m. $49. National Food Distribution Network Inc., 406 Water St., Warren, RI 02885. TEL 401-245-4500. Ed. Ann Moore. adv.; bk.rev.; charts; illus.; stat.; tr.lit. circ. 36,000. (back issues avail.) **Document type:** trade publication.
Incorporates (1972-19??): Food Broker: Sales and Marketing; Former titles: Food Distributors News (ISSN 0015-6353); New England Grocery Magazine; N E G; New England Grocer Merchandiser.

380.14 US
FOOD DISTRIBUTION RESEARCH SOCIETY. NEWSLETTER. 1962. 3/yr. $50 includes Journal of Food Distribution Research. Food Distribution Research Society, 917 Cypress Lane, Greentown, PA 18426. TEL 717-857-1445. FAX 717-857-9211. Ed. Frank Gambino. adv.; bk.rev.; bibl.; charts; stat. circ. 282. (back issues avail.) **Document type:** newsletter.

FOOD, DRUG, COSMETIC, AND MEDICAL DEVICE LAW DIGEST. see *LAW*

664 UK ISSN 0956-6783
FOOD EUROPE; the European business magazine. 1985. q. £100. I M L Group plc, Blair House, High St., Tonbridge, Kent TN9 1BQ, England. TEL 0732-359990. FAX 0732-770049. Ed. Phil Dwyer. adv. (back issues avail.) **Document type:** trade publication.
Description: For senior management in European food industries.

FOOD FOR THOUGHT (LOS ANGELES). see *LIBRARY AND INFORMATION SCIENCES*

FOOD FROM GREECE; annual review for the Greek production of food and wines. see *BEVERAGES*

664 658.8 US
FOOD HERALD. 1947. m. $20 (effective 1994). Dallas-Fort Worth Grocers Association, 3001 LBJ FWY., Ste. 133, Dallas, TX 75234-7756. TEL 214-243-5885. Ed. Valerie A. Schenewerk. adv. circ. 1,000. **Document type:** trade publication.
Description: Reports on social and business activities of local, state and national grocers' associations. Covers food retailing, food safety, government regulations on food, grocery or convenience stores, as well as business trends and employee relations.

664 US ISSN 1067-1951
FOOD HISTORY NEWS. 1989. q. $12 (effective June 1992). HC 60, Box 354A, Islesboro, ME 04848. TEL 207-734-8140. FAX 207-734-8883. Ed. Sandra L. Oliver. bk.rev.; bibl.; circ. 525 (paid). (back issues avail.) **Document type:** newsletter.
Description: News and announcements of upcoming events in food history studies, history of specific dishes and or foods, practical information on reconstructing historic foods, and food history methodology.

664 UK ISSN 0268-005X
TP453.C65 CODEN: FOHYES
FOOD HYDROCOLLOIDS. 1986. bi-m. £155($255) (effective 1994). Oxford University Press, Oxford Journals, Walton St., Oxford OX2 6DP, England. TEL 0865-56767. FAX 0865-56646. TELEX 837330-OXPRES-G. (U.S. subscr. to: Oxford University Press Inc., 2001 Evans Rd., Cary, NC 27513. TEL 919-677-0977) Ed.Bd. adv.; bk.rev.; illus.; index. circ. 350. (reprint service avail. from SWZ) Indexed: Biol.Abstr., Curr.Abstr., Curr.Cont., Food Sci.& Tech.Abstr., Sci.Cit.Ind. **Document type:** academic/scholarly publication.
—BLDSC (3977.556000); SWETS; UMI; CASDDS. **CCC**.
Description: International journal for hydrocolloids research, from isolation and purification to use in food products. Includes chemical engineering and economic considerations.

664 664.752 CN ISSN 0015-6442
CODEN: FOCNAY
FOOD IN CANADA. 1941. 10/yr. Can.$49.99. Maclean Hunter Ltd., Business Publication Division, Maclean Hunter Bldg., 777 Bay St., Toronto, ON M5W 1A7, Canada. TEL 416-596-5884. FAX 416-596-5526. Ed. Cathie Wilson. adv.; charts; illus.; pat.; tr.lit. Indexed: Biol.Abstr., Can.B.P.I., Chem.Abstr., Curr.Pack.Abstr., Dairy Sci.Abstr., Food Sci.& Tech.Abstr., PROMT.
●Also available online. Vendor(s): Mead Data Central, Inc.
—BLDSC (3977.100000).
Incorporates: Canadian Baker; Canadian Food Industries.

664 UK ISSN 0071-7177
FOOD INDUSTRIES MANUAL. 1928. irreg., 23rd ed., 1993. £175. Blackie Academic & Professional, Wester Cleddens Rd., Bishopbriggs, Glasgow G64 2NZ, Scotland. TEL 041-762-2332. FAX 041-772-7524. (Dist. in U.S. and Canada by: Chapman and Hall, Inc., One Penn Plaza, 41st Fl., New York, NY 10019) Eds. M. Ranken, R.C. Kill. adv.; index. **Document type:** trade publication.

664 SA ISSN 0015-6450
CODEN: FISAAX
FOOD INDUSTRIES OF SOUTH AFRICA; processing, refrigeration, packaging. 1948. m. R.88.92 (foreign R.118) (effective 1994). Thomson Publications (Subsidiary of: Times Media Ltd.), P.O. Box 56182, Pinegowrie 2123, South Africa. TEL 27-11-789-2144. FAX 27-11-789-3196. Ed. Debbie Penrith. adv.; bk.rev.; charts; illus. circ. 3,138. (back issues avail.) Indexed: Dairy Sci.Abstr., Food Sci.& Tech.Abstr., Ind.S.A.Per., INIS Atomind. **Document type:** trade publication.
—BLDSC (3977.794000).

664 UK ISSN 0965-4682
FOOD INDUSTRY BULLETIN. Cover title: Leatherhead Food News. 1989. m. £330 to non-members. (International Centre for Information, Food and Technology) Leatherhead Food R.A., Randalls Rd., Leatherhead, Surrey KT22 7RY, England. TEL 0372-376761. FAX 0372-386228.
Description: Attempts to update members about the development of the Research Association with regular features regarding research activities, including highlights of panel work.

FOOD INDUSTRY DIRECTORY. see *BUSINESS AND ECONOMICS — Trade And Industrial Directories*

630 664 US ISSN 0046-4414
FOOD INDUSTRY FUTURES: A STRATEGY SERVICE. 1972. s-m. $150 (foreign $180). (Food Industry Futures) Cuthill Research Services, Inc., Box 430, Fayetteville, NY 13066. Ed. Ian D. Cuthill. bk.rev. (looseleaf format) **Document type:** newsletter.

664.9 NZ ISSN 0113-8901
FOOD INDUSTRY NEWS; the food and beverage business monthly. 1979. m. NZ.$35.75 (foreign NZ.$72) (effective 1994). Refer Liberty Publishing, P.O. Box 38046, Howick, Auckland, New Zealand. Ed. Allison Oosterman. adv.; illus. circ. 3,790. (tabloid format; back issues avail.) **Document type:** trade publication.
Formerly (until 1987): Food Industry (ISSN 0111-6843)
Description: Focuses on food processing and manufacturing. Special features on dairy, meat, seafood, packaging, milling and baking and beverages.

664 US
FOOD INDUSTRY NEWSLETTER; all the food news that matters. 1972. 22/yr. (plus irreg. updates). $245. Newsletters, Inc., Box 2730, Bethesda, MD 20827. TEL 301-469-6507. FAX 301-469-7271. Ed. Max Busetti. bk.rev. (looseleaf format; back issues avail.) **Document type:** newsletter.

664 US
FOOD INDUSTRY REPORT. vol.8, 1990. m. $57. Food & Nutrition Press, Inc., 2 Corporate Dr., Box 374, Trumbull, CT 06611. TEL 203-261-8587. FAX 203-261-9724. Ed. Gerald C. Melson. **Document type:** academic/scholarly publication.
Description: Covers career, financial and business news for food and related companies and food scientists.

664 US ISSN 0890-3263
FOOD INDUSTRY SKIRMISHER. 1926. bi-m. $9. Mid-Atlantic Food Dealers Association, 14 Commerce Street/Dundalk Center, Baltimore, MD 21222-6404. TEL 410-285-6777. FAX 410-285-6404. Ed. Jill I. Solimini. adv.; charts; illus.; stat. circ. 4,800. (back issues avail.)
Description: Serves food industry in Maryland, Delaware, Washington, DC and northern Virginia.

664 US
FOOD INGREDIENT NEWS. m. $295. Business Communications Co., Inc. (Norwalk), 25 Van Zant St., Ste. 13, Norwalk, CT 06855. TEL 203-853-4266. FAX 203-853-0348. Ed. Dorothy Kroll. **Document type:** newsletter.
Description: Covers product development, technology, patents, research and other news relating to the food industry.

FOOD AND FOOD INDUSTRIES

664.52   UK
TP418
FOOD INGREDIENTS & ANALYSIS INTERNATIONAL.
1970. bi-m. £70. Turret Group Plc., Turret House, 171 High St., Rickmansworth, Herts WD3 1SN, England. TEL 0923-777000. FAX 0923-771297. Ed. Alan Cartwright. adv.; bk.rev.; pat.; index. circ. 9,476. (also avail. in microform from PMC) **Indexed:** Anal.Abstr., Br.Tech.Ind., Chem.Abstr., Curr.Biotech.Abstr., Dairy Sci.Abstr., Excerp.Med., Food Sci.& Tech.Abstr., I.P.A., Nutr.Abstr., Packag.Sci.Tech. **Document type:** trade publication.
—UnCover.
    Former titles: Food Ingredients and Processing International (ISSN 0968-574X); (until 1990): Food; Flavouring, Ingredients, Processing, Packaging (ISSN 0143-8441); Food Flavours Ingredients and Processing; International Flavours and Food Additives (ISSN 0306-6517); Flavour Industry (ISSN 0015-3532); Incorporates: Perfumery and Essential Oil Record and Flavours.

664   595.7   US
FOOD INSECTS NEWSLETTER. 1987. s-a. University of Wisconsin - Madison, Department of Entomology, 545 Russell Laboratories, Madison, WI 53706. **Document type:** newsletter.

658.8   US   ISSN 0745-4503
FOOD INSTITUTE REPORT. 1928. w. $535. American Institute of Food Distribution, Inc., 28-12 Broadway, Fair Lawn, NJ 07410. TEL 201-791-5570. FAX 201-791-5222. Ed. Fredric Pfaff. bk.rev.; stat. **Document type:** newsletter.
    Formed by the 1982 merger of: Report on Food Markets (ISSN 0002-8940); Washington Food Report (ISSN 0162-5233); Food Distribution Digest; Which was formerly: American Institute of Food Distribution. Weekly Digest (ISSN 0002-8959)

664 658   US
▼**FOOD INVESTMENT REPORT.** 1993. 15/yr. $79. Food & Nutrition Press, Inc., 2 Corporate Dr., Box 374, Trumbull, CT 06611. TEL 203-261-8587. FAX 203-261-9724. Ed. Gerald C. Melson. **Document type:** academic/scholarly publication, newsletter.
    Description: Provides market analysis as well as the fundamentals and technical approach (charting). Deals with the food and related industries and all of the ramifications for the investor.

664   IE   ISSN 0790-0430
FOOD IRELAND. 11/yr. Irish Food Processing Industry, Poolbeg House, Poolbeg St., Dublin 2, Ireland. TEL 719244. FAX 719263. Ed. Fergus Farrell. bk.rev.; tr.lit. circ. 3,294.
—BLDSC (3980.100000).

664   UN   ISSN 1011-2588
FOOD IRRADIATION NEWSLETTER. (Text in English) 1977. irreg. free. International Atomic Energy Agency, Wagramerstr. 5, P.O. Box 100, A-1400 Vienna, Austria. (Co-sponsor: Food and Agriculture Organization) circ. 500. **Document type:** newsletter.
—BLDSC (3980.300000).

664 630   JA   ISSN 0583-1164
FOOD, ITS SCIENCE AND TECHNOLOGY. (Text in Japanese) 1958. a. National Food Research Institute, 2-1-2, Kannondai, Yatabe-Machi, Tsukuba-Gun, Ibaraki 305, Japan. circ. 1,500.
—BLDSC (8268.060000).

664.09   US
FOOD LABELING NEWS. w. $700. Food Chemical News, Inc., 1101 Pennsylvania Ave., S.E., Washington, DC 20003. TEL 202-544-1980. FAX 202-546-3890.
    Description: Provides in-depth, comprehensive information on dietary supplements labeling, advertising and packaging regulations for the food industry.

664   US
FOOD: LATIN AMERICAN INDUSTRIAL REPORT. (Avail. for each of 22 Latin American countries) 1985. a. $435 per country report. Aquino Productions, Box 15760, Stamford, CT 06901. TEL 203-325-3138. Ed. Andres C. Aquino.

FOOD LAW MONTHLY; the advisory service for the food, drug and cosmetics industries. see LAW

   340   AT
▼**FOOD LEGISLATION NEW SOUTH WALES.** 1994. 3/yr. Aus.$275 with updates. Law Book Co. Ltd., 44-50 Waterloo Rd., North Ryde, N.S.W. 2113, Australia. TEL 02-887-0177. FAX 02-888-9706. TELEX ASBOOK 27995. (looseleaf format)
    Description: Contains all comprehensively annotated and up-to-date legislation relating to food legislation in NSW.

   340   AT
FOOD LEGISLATION VICTORIA. 1990. 3/yr. Aus.$295 with updates. Law Book Co. Ltd., 44-50 Waterloo Rd., North Ryde, N.S.W. 2113, Australia. TEL 02-887-0177. FAX 02-888-9706. TELEX ASBOOK 27995. Ed.Bd. (looseleaf format)
    Description: Contains all comprehensively annotated and up-to-date legislation relating to food legislation in Victoria.

   642.5   US   ISSN 0091-018X
CODEN: FOMADE
FOOD MANAGEMENT; schools, colleges, hospitals, nursing homes contract services. 1972. m. $50. Penton Publishing (Subsidiary of: Pittway Company), 1100 Superior Ave., Cleveland, OH 44114. TEL 216-696-7000. FAX 216-696-7658. Ed. Donna Boss. adv.; illus.; tr.lit. circ. 52,000. (also avail. in microform) **Document type:** trade publication.
—BLDSC (3980.800000); Faxon; UnCover; UMI. CCC.
    Description: Discusses new products, legislation, and problems for institutional foodservice directors.

664   UK   ISSN 0015-6477
TX341   CODEN: FOMAAB
FOOD MANUFACTURE. 1927. m. $145. Morgan-Grampian (Process Press) Ltd. (Subsidiary of: Morgan-Grampian plc), Morgan-Grampian House, 30 Calderwood St., London SE18 6QH, England. TEL 081-855-7777. FAX 081-854-7476. Ed. Hugh Darrington. adv. contact: Derek Donovan. bk.rev.; abstr.; bibl.; charts; illus.; tr.lit. circ. 7,491. (also avail. in microform from UMI; reprint service avail. from UMI) **Indexed:** Biol.Abstr., Br.Tech.Ind., Chem.Abstr., Curr.Biotech.Abstr., Curr.Cont., Curr.Pack.Abstr., Dairy Sci.Abstr., Eng.Ind., Excerp.Med., Food Sci.& Tech.Abstr., Int.Packag.Abstr., Key to Econ.Sci., Nutr.Abstr., Packag.Sci.Tech., Risk Abstr. **Document type:** trade publication.
—BLDSC (3981.000000); UnCover; SWETS. CCC.
    Description: Technical coverage of processes, ingredients, machinery and packaging.

664 621.9   UK   ISSN 0268-1196
FOOD MANUFACTURE INGREDIENT AND MACHINERY SURVEY. (Supplement avail.) 1967. a. £26. Morgan-Grampian (Process Press) Ltd., 30 Calderwood St., Woolwich, London SE18 6QH, England. TEL 081-855-7777. FAX 081-854-7476. Ed. Hugh Darrington. adv. circ. 1,500.

664   UK   ISSN 0267-1506
CODEN: FMINEK
FOOD MANUFACTURE INTERNATIONAL. (Contents page in English, French, German, Italian) 1985. 6/yr. $130. Morgan-Grampian (Process Press) Ltd. (Subsidiary of: Morgan-Grampian plc), Morgan-Grampian House, 30 Calderwood St., London SE18 6QH, England. TEL 081-855-7777. FAX 081-854-7476. Ed. Hugh Darrington. adv. contact: Derek Donovan. circ. 8,000. **Indexed:** Food Sci.& Tech.Abstr., Packag.Sci.Tech. **Document type:** trade publication.
●Also available online. Vendor(s): Mead Data Central, Inc.
—BLDSC (3981.025500).
    Description: Technical coverage of European processes, ingredients, machinery and packaging.

664 659.1   AT   ISSN 0816-3634
FOOD MANUFACTURING NEWS. bi-m. Aus.$25 (foreign Aus.$65) (effective Jul. 1993). Yaffa Publishing Group, 17-21 Bellevue St., Surry Hills, N.S.W. 2010, Australia. TEL 02-281-2333. FAX 02-281-2750. Ed. Ken McGregor. adv.: B&W page Aus.$1700, color page Aus.$2470; trim 297 x 210. circ. 4,755. **Document type:** trade publication.
    Description: Provides the news and product information essential to keep management informed of new industry developments.

664.6   UK   ISSN 0268-0408
FOOD MARKET ABSTRACTS. bi-m. £325. Leatherhead Food R.A., Randalls Rd., Leatherhead, Surrey KT22 7RY, England. TEL 0372-376761. FAX 0372-386228. TELEX 929846. (back issues avail.) **Document type:** abstracting/indexing.

664   US
▼**FOOD MARKETER'S WEEKLY.** 1994. w. $600. Box 31292, Charleston, SC 29417. TEL 803-795-0961. FAX 803-795-2930. Ed. Max Busetti; Pub. Erik Schonher.
    Description: Provides information on the food industry, new products, marketing strategies and industry news.

664   GW   ISSN 0932-2744
CODEN: IFMTE8
FOOD MARKETING & TECHNOLOGY. (Text in English) 1986. bi-m. DM.112($66) Dr. Harnisch Verlags GmbH, Blumenstr. 15, 90402 Nuernberg, Germany. TEL 0911-203658. FAX 0911-204579. TELEX 179118103. Eds. Benno Keller, Ian Healey. adv.: B&W page DM.6680, color page DM.8930; trim 190 x 270. bk.rev. circ. 25,600. (back issues avail.) **Document type:** trade publication.
—BLDSC (3981.110000).
    Description: For the entire food industry, covering ingredients, processing technologies, packing and marketing aspects.

664   US   ISSN 0896-4203
FOOD MARKETING BRIEFS. 1987. m. $97 (effective 1993). Newsletters, Inc., Box 2730, Bethesda, MD 20827. TEL 301-469-8507. FAX 301-469-7271. Ed. Ray Marsili. (looseleaf format) **Document type:** newsletter.
    Description: National digest of food marketing information.

664   CN   ISSN 1188-4940
FOOD MART NEWS. 1991. 10/yr. Can.$14.95. Ishcom Publications Ltd., 169 The West Mall, Etobicoke, ON M9C 1C2, Canada. TEL 416-620-9900. FAX 416-622-6688. Ed. James W. Paine. adv. circ. 10,500. **Document type:** trade publication.

FOOD MICROBIOLOGY. see BIOLOGY — Microbiology

FOOD NEWS FOR CONSUMERS. see CONSUMER EDUCATION AND PROTECTION

664 641.1   US   ISSN 0160-8053
FOOD, NUTRITION & HEALTH NEWSLETTER. 1977. m. $74. Food & Nutrition Press, Inc., 2 Corporate Dr., Box 374, Trumbull, CT 06611. TEL 203-261-8587. FAX 203-261-9724. Eds. Paul A. Lachance, Michele C. Fisher. bk.rev.; charts; illus.; stat. (back issues avail.) **Document type:** academic/scholarly publication, newsletter.
    Description: Covers food, nutrition and health research, education, and policy issues.

664   US   ISSN 0194-2980
FOOD PACKAGING AND LABELING NEWSLETTER. 1977. m. $76. Food & Nutrition Press, Inc., 2 Corporate Dr., Box 374, Trumbull, CT 06611. TEL 203-261-8587. FAX 203-261-9724. Ed. Stanley Sacharow. bk.rev. (back issues avail.) **Document type:** academic/scholarly publication, newsletter.
    Description: Informs readers of the latest trends, emerging markets and legislation in food packaging and labeling.

FOOD PACKAGING BULLETIN. see PACKAGING

664   UK   ISSN 0957-5189
FOOD PACKER INTERNATIONAL. 1986. m. £34($90) Binsted Publications Ltd., Walton House, 90 London Rd., Hook, Hants. RG27 9LF, England. FAX 0256-766102. Ed. Edward C. Binsted. circ. 6,500. **Document type:** academic/scholarly publication.

FOOD PACKER INTERNATIONAL DIRECTORY (YEAR). see BUSINESS AND ECONOMICS — Trade And Industrial Directories

664   US
FOOD PEOPLE. 1989. every six wks. Associated Grocers Inc., Box 3763, Seattle, WA 98124. TEL 206-764-7585. FAX 206-763-7955. Ed. Robb Zerr. circ. 3,000.
    Description: Covers trends in the grocery business along with features on employee, retailers, new technology and industry issues.

FOOD AND FOOD INDUSTRIES 2565

664 628.5 US ISSN 1072-298X
▼**FOOD PLANT STRATEGIES**. 1993. m. $295 (outside N. America $345) (effective 1994). Packaging Strategies, Inc., 122 S. Church St., West Chester, PA 19382-3223. TEL 215-436-4220. FAX 215-436-6277. Ed. Mike Pehanich; Pub. William H. LeMaire. **Document type:** newsletter.
Description: Covers innovations and trends in the design and construction of new food factories, factory expansions and renovations. Also examines location strategies and new manufacturing technologies.

664 US ISSN 0015-6523
TP373 CODEN: FOPRA9
FOOD PROCESSING (CHICAGO). 1940. 13/yr. $35 (free to qualified personnel). Putman Publishing Co., 301 E. Erie St., Chicago, IL 60611. TEL 312-644-2020. Ed. Robert Swientek. adv.; bk.rev.; charts; illus.; tr.lit.; circ. 66,000 (controlled). (also avail. in microform from UMI) **Indexed:** B.P.I., Biol.Abstr., Bus.Ind., Dairy Sci.Abstr., Food Sci.& Tech.Abstr., Hlth.Ind., Int.Packag.Abstr., Key to Econ.Sci., Packag.Sci.Tech., Tr.& Indus.Ind.
—BLDSC (3981.810000); UnCover; SWETS; UMI. **CCC.**

664 UK ISSN 0264-9462
TP368
FOOD PROCESSING (TONBRIDGE). 1931. m. £55 in the UK; Europe £75; elsewhere £100. I M L Group plc, Blair House, High St., Tonbridge, Kent TN9 1BQ, England. TEL 0732-359990. FAX 0732-770049. Ed. Phil Dwyer. adv.; bk.rev.; charts; illus.; stat.; tr.lit. circ. 8,637. **Indexed:** Br.Tech.Ind., Chem.Abstr., Dairy Sci.Abstr., Excerp.Med., IIS, Nutr.Abstr.
—BLDSC (3981.809000); SWETS.
Former titles: Food Processing Industry (ISSN 0015-6531); Food Processing and Marketing.

FOOD PROCESSING FOOD PROCESSORS' RESOURCE. see BUSINESS AND ECONOMICS — Trade And Industrial Directories

664 AT ISSN 0816-309X
FOOD PROCESSOR. 1985. bi-m. Aus.$40 (free to qualified personnel). Reed Business Publishing Pty. Ltd. (Subsidiary of: Reed International PLC), 1-5 Railway St., Chatswood, N.S.W. 2067, Australia. TEL 02-372-5222. FAX 02-419-7533. Ed. Jennifer Larson. circ. 3,720.

664 US ISSN 1065-772X
FOOD PRODUCT DESIGN.* 1991. m. $60 (foreign $100) (effective Apr. 1991). Weeks Publishing Co., 3400 Dundee Rd., Ste. 100, Northbrook, IL 60062-2333. TEL 708-559-0385. FAX 708-559-0389. Ed. Scott Hegenbart. adv. circ. 26,000. **Document type:** trade publication.
—BLDSC (3981.859500); UnCover.
Description: Features articles and information on designing new and reformulated food products for the retail and foodservice markets.

664 US ISSN 0191-6181
TX599 CODEN: FPMNAN
FOOD PRODUCTION - MANAGEMENT; monthly publication of the canning, glass-packing, aseptic, and frozen food industry. 1878. m. $25 (foreign $40). C T I Publications Inc., 2619 Maryland Ave., Baltimore, MD 21218. TEL 410-467-3338. FAX 410-467-7434. Ed. Arthur I. Judge, II. adv.; bk.rev.; illus.; mkt.; tr.lit. circ. 5,000. (also avail. in microfilm from UMI) **Indexed:** Biol.Abstr., BPIA, Curr.Pack.Abstr., Food Sci.& Tech.Abstr., Int.Packag.Abstr., Packag.Sci.Tech.
—BLDSC (3981.864000); UMI.
Formerly: Canning Trade (ISSN 0008-560X)
Description: Preservation of fruits and vegetables.

664 US ISSN 1056-5078
FOOD PRODUCTS & EQUIPMENT. 1986. 10/yr. (includes end-of-year Food Products & Equipment Literature Review). $23. Gordon Publications, Inc., Part of Cahners Publishing Company, Division of Reed Elsevier Inc., 301 Gibraltar Dr., Box 650, Morris Plains, NJ 07950-0650. TEL 201-292-5100. FAX 201-898-9281. Ed. Dolly Grobstein. circ. 48,000. (tabloid format)
—**CCC.**
Description: For those responsible for buying and specifying equipment and instrumentation used in processing, handling and packaging; for processing plants engaged in meat, dairy, beverage, baked foods, preserved fruits, vegetables and other food product production.

FOOD PROTECTION REPORT. see PUBLIC HEALTH AND SAFETY

664 UK ISSN 0950-3293
CODEN: FQPRER
FOOD QUALITY AND PREFERENCE. 1988. 4/yr. £158($245) (effective 1994). Elsevier Science Ltd., Oxford Fulfilment Centre, P.O. Box 800, Oxford OX5 1DX, England. TEL 44-865-843000. FAX 44-865-843010. (Subscr. in U.S. and Canada to: Elsevier Science, 660 White Plains Rd., Tarrytown, NY 10591-5153. TEL 914-524-9200. FAX 914-333-2444) Ed.Bd. adv. **Document type:** academic/scholarly trade publication.
—BLDSC (3981.865400); SWETS. **CCC.**
Description: Multidisciplinary and international forum for researchers, industrialists and others involved with food and beverage production, distribution, marketing and promotion.
Refereed Serial

664 UK ISSN 0963-9969
TP368 CODEN: FORIEU
FOOD RESEARCH INTERNATIONAL. (Text and summaries in English or French) 1968. 6/yr. £272($420) (effective 1994). (Canadian Institute of Food Science and Technology, CN) Elsevier Science Ltd., Oxford Fulfilment Centre, P.O. Box 800, Kidlington, Oxford OX5 1DX, England. TEL 44-865-794141. FAX 44-865-60285. (Subscr. in U.S. and Canada to: Elsevier Science, 660 White Plains Rd., Tarrytown, NY 10591-5153. TEL 914-524-9200. FAX 914-333-2444) Ed. R.Y. Yada. adv.; bk.rev.; charts; illus.; index. circ. 3,000. (also avail. in microfilm from PMC; back issues avail.) **Indexed:** Biodet.Abstr., Biol.Abstr., Chem.Abstr., Curr.Adv.Ecol.Sci., Curr.Cont., Curr.Pack.Abstr., Dairy Sci.Abstr., Food Sci.& Tech.Abstr., Ind.Sci.Rev., Ind.Vet., INIS Atomind., Int.Packag.Abstr., Nutr.Abstr., Pig News & Info., Sci.Cit.Ind., Vet.Bull., World Agri.Econ.& Rural Sociol.Abstr. **Document type:** academic/scholarly publication.
—BLDSC (3982.120000); Faxon; UnCover; SWETS; UMI; CASDDS. **CCC.**
Former titles (until 1992): Canadian Institute of Food Science and Technology. Journal - Institut Canadien de Science et Technologie Alimentaires. Journal (ISSN 0315-5463); Canadian Institute of Food Technology Journal - Institut Canadien de Technologie Alimentaire Journal (ISSN 0008-3860)
Description: Provides an international forum for original research in the various disciplines encompassing the science and technology of food.
Refereed Serial

664 SA ISSN 0257-8867
CODEN: FORVDY
FOOD REVIEW. (Text in English) 1974. bi-m. R.78 (foreign R.159). (South African Association for Food Science and Technology) National Publishing (Pty) Ltd., P.O. Box 2735, Johannesburg 2000, South Africa. TEL 27-11-835-2221. FAX 27-11-835-1943. (Co-sponsor: South African Association of Industrial Flavour and Fragrance Manufacturer) Ed. Gill Loubser. adv.; B&W page R.3080; trim 297 x 210; adv. contact: Vanessa van der Mescht. bk.rev.; illus.; stat.; circ. 18,483. (back issues avail.) **Indexed:** Ind.S.A.Per., INIS Atomind., Sugar Ind.Abstr. **Document type:** trade publication.
—BLDSC (3982.600000); SWETS; CASDDS.
Formerly (until 1983): South African Food Review.
Description: Covers new techniques, laboratory and manufacturing equipment, materials, packaging technology, legislation and overseas developments affecting all sectors of the food and beverage manufacturing and distribution industries. Publishes association technical papers and project reports.

664 US ISSN 8755-9129
TX341 CODEN: FRINEL
FOOD REVIEWS INTERNATIONAL. 1985. 4/yr. $425. Marcel Dekker Journals, 270 Madison Ave., New York, NY 10016. TEL 212-696-9000. FAX 212-685-4540. TELEX 421419. (Subscr. to: Box 5017, Monticello, NY 12701) Eds. Roy Teranishi, Irwin Hornstein. (also avail. in microform from RPI) **Indexed:** Curr.Adv.Ecol.Sci., Food Sci.& Tech.Abstr. **Document type:** academic/scholarly publication.
—BLDSC (3982.620000); Faxon; UnCover; SWETS; CASDDS. **CCC.**

664 UK ISSN 0964-4164
▼**FOOD SAFETY & SECURITY**. 1992. m. £231($355) (effective 1994). Elsevier Science Ltd., Oxford Fulfilment Centre, P.O. Box 800, Kidlington, Oxford OX5 1DX, England. TEL 44-865-843000. FAX 44-865-843010. (Subscr. in U.S. and Canada to: Elsevier Science, 660 White Plains Rd., Tarrytown, NY 10591-5153. TEL 914-524-9200. FAX 914-333-2444) Ed. P. Barnes. **Document type:** newsletter.
—**CCC.**
Description: Provides the latest information on safety and security issues in food manufacture, distribution and sale, including chemical, biological and physical hazards.

FOOD SAFETY BRIEFING. see OCCUPATIONAL HEALTH AND SAFETY

664 UK
▼**FOOD SAFETY SERIES**. 1992. irreg., no.2, 1992. Chapman & Hall, 2-6 Boundary Row, London SE1 8HN, England. TEL 44-71-865-0066. FAX 44-71-522-9623. (U.S. addr.: 29 W. 35th St., New York, NY 10001-2291. TEL 212-244-3336) (Co-publisher: James & James Science Publishers Ltd.) Ed. M.H. Lessof. **Document type:** monographic series.

644 II ISSN 0532-0968
FOOD SCIENCE/AHARA VIJNANA. (Text in Kannada) 1956. 6/yr. Central Food Technological Research Institute, Mysore 570012, India. Ed. P.S. Balakrishnan. adv. circ. 3,000.

664 UK ISSN 0023-6438
TP368 CODEN: LBWTAP
FOOD SCIENCE AND TECHNOLOGY/SCIENCE ET TECHNOLOGIE ALIMENTAIRE/LEBENSMITTEL - WISSENSCHAFT UND TECHNOLOGIE. (Text and summaries in English, French, German) 1968. bi-m. £141 (effective 1994). (Swiss Society of Food Science and Technology, SZ) Academic Press Ltd. (Subsidiary of: Harcourt Brace & Company Ltd.), 24-28 Oval Rd., London NW1 7DX, England. TEL 44-71-267-4466. FAX 44-71-482-2293. TELEX 25775-ACPRES-G. (Subscr. to: Harcourt Brace & Company Ltd., Foots Cray High St., Sidcup, Kent DA14 5HP, England. TEL 44-81-300-3322. FAX 44-81-309-0807) Ed. A.T. Temperli. adv.; bk.rev.; charts; illus.; stat.; index. (back issues avail.) **Indexed:** Biol.Abstr., Chem.Abstr., Curr.Adv.Ecol.Sci., Curr.Cont., Curr.Pack.Abstr., Dairy Sci.Abstr., Field Crop Abstr., Food Sci.& Tech.Abstr., Herb.Abstr., Hort.Abstr., Ind Sci.Rev., Maize Abstr., Nutr.Abstr., Potato Abstr., Rev.Plant Path., Soyabean Abstr. **Document type:** academic/scholarly publication.
—BLDSC (3983.070000); Faxon; UnCover; SWETS; CASDDS. **CCC.**
Description: Pertains to all aspects of food sicence including the subject areas of chemistry, microbiology, biotechnology, food processing, and nutrition.

664 US ISSN 0891-8961
CODEN: FSTEEM
FOOD SCIENCE AND TECHNOLOGY SERIES. 1971. irreg., vol.58, 1993. price varies. Marcel Dekker, Inc., 270 Madison Ave., New York, NY 10016. TEL 212-696-9000. FAX 212-685-4540. TELEX 421419 MARDEEK. Ed. O. Fennema. **Indexed:** Biol.Abstr. **Document type:** monographic series.
—BLDSC (3983 065000); CASDDS.
Formerly (until 1984): Food Science Series (ISSN 0071-7223)
Refereed Serial

664 UK ISSN 0950-9623
FOOD SCIENCE AND TECHNOLOGY TODAY. 1987. q. £55($110) (effective 1994). Institute of Food Science and Technology, 210 Shepherd's Bush Rd., London W6 7NL, England. TEL 071-603-6317. FAX 071-602-9936. Ed. Heather Paine. adv.; bk.rev.; circ. 3,800 (controlled). **Indexed:** Art.Hosp.& Tour., Br.Tech.Ind , Dairy Sci.Abstr. **Document type:** trade publication.
—BLDSC (3983.090000); Faxon. **CCC.**
Description: Provides the food community with proceedings and symposia, articles, opinions, research, and review articles about food science and technology.

FOOD AND FOOD INDUSTRIES

664   GW
FOOD SERVICE; Markt - Systeme - Praxis. 1980. m. DM.141.95 (foreign DM.149.95). Deutscher Fachverlag GmbH, Mainzer Landstr. 251, 60326 Frankfurt a.M., Germany. TEL 069-7595-01. FAX 069-75952999. circ. 9,909. **Document type:** trade publication.
    Formerly (until 1988): Fast Food Praxis.

664   XR
FOOD SERVICE. (Text in Czech, Slovak) 1991. 8/yr. (Czech Hotel and Restaurant Association) Ceske a Slovenske Odborne Nakladatelstvi (Subsidiary of: Deutscher Fachverlag GmbH), Na Prikope 27, 11349 Prague 1, Czech Republic. TEL 02-268964. FAX 02-262893. circ. 7,000. **Document type:** trade publication.
    Description: Provides information concerning the hotel, restaurant, and industrial and institutional catering business.

664   HU
FOOD SERVICE MAGYARORSZAG. bi-m. Magyar Szakkiado Kft. (Subsidiary of: Deutscher Fachverlag GmbH), Pozsonyi Ut 54, 1133 Budapest, Hungary. TEL 01-203741. FAX 01-203741. circ. 7,000. **Document type:** trade publication.
    Description: Provides information on the catering and hotel trade.

FOOD SERVICE MANAGEMENT/GEKKAN SYOKUDO. see HOTELS AND RESTAURANTS

664   US   ISSN 0532-0992
FOOD SERVICE RESEARCH ABSTRACTS. 1971. a. $7.50. Society for the Advancement of Food Service Research, 304 W. Liberty St., Ste. 301, Louisville, KY 40202. TEL 813-465-7090. Ed. Helen M. Spencer. circ. 250. (back issues avail.)

648 664 331   AT
FOOD SHOP. 1971. m. Aus.$60. Retail Confectionery & Mixed Business Association, 250 Canterbury Rd., Surrey Hills, Vic. 3127, Australia. TEL 03-836-6566. FAX 03-836-3452. Ed. P. Judkins. adv.: page Aus.$650; trim 240 x 180; adv. contact: Sue Byrne. circ. 4,000. **Document type:** trade publication.
    Former titles (until 1990): Milk Bar; Food Shop.

FOOD STRUCTURE. see NUTRITION AND DIETETICS

664   GW   ISSN 0937-700X
FOOD TECHNOLOGIE MAGAZIN. 1990. q. DM.80($60) Dr. Harnisch Verlags GmbH, Blumenstr. 15, 90402 Nuernberg, Germany. TEL 0911-203658. FAX 0911-204579. TELEX 179118103. Eds. Benno Keller, Margot Baum. adv.: B&W page DM.4990, color page DM.7240; trim 190 x 270. bk.rev. circ. 13,400. (back issues avail) **Document type:** trade publication.
    Description: For decision makers in the food industry located in German-speaking areas of Europe

664   NZ   ISSN 0111-6606
    CODEN: FOTEDR
FOOD TECHNOLOGIST. 1970. q. NZ.$85 membership; foreign $50. New Zealand Institute of Food Science and Technology, P.O. Box 15-052, Christchurch, New Zealand. FAX 03-3889269. adv.; bk.rev. circ. 1,000. **Indexed:** Chem.Abstr., Curr.Cont., Food Sci.& Tech.Abstr.
    —BLDSC (3983.805000); CASDDS. **CCC.**
    Formerly: New Zealand Institute of Science and Technology. Newsletter.

664   US   ISSN 0015-6639
TP370   CODEN: FOTEAO
FOOD TECHNOLOGY. 1947. m. $82 to non-members. Institute of Food Technologists, 221 N. LaSalle St., Chicago, IL 60601. TEL 312-782-8424. Ed. John B. Klis. adv.; bk.rev.; bibl.; charts; illus.; pat.; stat.; tr.lit.; index. circ. 26,000. (also avail. in microfilm from UMI; reprint service avail. from UMI) **Indexed:** A.S.& T.Ind., Acad.Ind., Art.Hosp.& Tour., Biodet.Abstr., Biol.Abstr., Biol.& Agr.Ind., Chem.Abstr., Curr.Adv.Ecol.Sci., Curr.Cont., Curr.Pack.Abstr., Dairy Sci.Abstr., Excerp.Med., Food Sci.& Tech.Abstr., Gen.Sci.Ind., Hlth.Ind., Hort.Abstr., Ind.Sci.Rev., Ind.Vet., INIS Atomind., Int.Packag.Abstr., NRN, Nutr.Abstr., Packag.Sci.Tech., Sci.Cit.Ind., Sel.Water Res.Abstr., Sugar Ind.Abstr., Vet.Bull. **Document type:** trade publication.
    —BLDSC (3984.000000); EI; Faxon; UnCover; SWETS; UMI; CASDDS. **CCC.**

664   NZ   ISSN 1172-2460
    CODEN: FTNZAO
FOOD TECHNOLOGY IN NEW ZEALAND; production, processing, packaging, storage, distribution, marketing. 1964. m. NZ.$60 (including directory). (New Zealand Institute of Food Science & Technology) T.P.L. Media (Trade Publications), 308 Great South Rd., 1st Fl., Greenlane, Auckland, New Zealand. TEL 0064-09-529-3000. FAX 0064-09-529-3001. Ed. Rodney Fletcher. adv. contact: B&W page NZ.$1360, color page NZ.$1950; trim 297 x 210. illus.; index. circ. 2,531. **Indexed:** Chem.Abstr., Dairy Sci.Abstr., Food Sci.& Tech.Abstr.
    —BLDSC (3984.200000). **CCC.**
    Former titles (until 1992): Foodtech (ISSN 1171-1639); (until 1991): Food Technology in New Zealand (ISSN 0015-6655)
    Description: Publishes business news from the food processing and manufacturing industries; personality profiles; product news; technical articles; conference reports.

664   UK   ISSN 0950-4435
FOOD TECHNOLOGY INTERNATIONAL EUROPE. a. £25. Sterling Publications Ltd., 86-88 Edgware Rd., London W2 2YW, England. TEL 071-258-0066. Ed. Alan Turner.
    —BLDSC (3984.080000).

658.8 664   US   ISSN 0015-6663
FOOD TRADE NEWS. 1946. m. $36. Best-Met Publishing Co., 5737 Twin Knolls Rd., Ste. 438, Columbia, MD 21045-3240. FAX 215-642-0297. Ed. Meg Mejor. adv.; bk.rev. circ. 22,000. (tabloid format) **Indexed:** BPIA. **Document type:** trade publication.
    Description: Reports on the retail food industry in Pennsylvania, Delaware, southern New Jersey and northern Maryland.

664 658.8   UK   ISSN 0015-6671
HD9011.1   CODEN: FTRVAW
FOOD TRADE REVIEW. 1931. m. £40 (foreign £50). Food Trade Press Ltd., Station House, Hortons Way, Westerham, Kent TN16 1BZ, England. TEL 0959-563944. FAX 0959-561285. Ed. Howard Binsted. adv.; bk.rev.; abstr.; charts; illus.; tr.lit.; tr.mk.; index. circ. 5,164. **Indexed:** Br.Tech.Ind., Dairy Sci.Abstr., Food Sci.& Tech.Abstr., Int.Packag.Abstr., Key to Econ.Sci., Nutr.Abstr., PROMT. **Document type:** trade publication.
    ●Also available online. Vendor(s): Mead Data Central, Inc.
    —BLDSC (3984.300000). **CCC.**
    Incorporates: Impulse Foods (ISSN 0262-6616)

664   UK   ISSN 0260-1974
FOOD WORLD NEWS; the international news magazine of the food and drink, food ingredients and process plant industries. 1981. 6/yr. $120. World News Publications, 130 Wigmore St., London W1H OAT, England. FAX 071-487-5436. illus. (reprint service avail. from UMI) **Indexed:** PROMT.

664   CN   ISSN 0715-6421
FOODBORNE AND WATERBORNE DISEASE IN CANADA. French edition: Intoxications Alimentaires et Maladies d'Origine Hydrique au Canada (ISSN 0715-6405) (Editions in English, French) a. Can.$24. (Health and Welfare Canada, Health Protection Branch) Polyscience Publications Inc., 44 Seize Arpents, P.O. Box 148, Morin Heights, PQ J0R 1H0, Canada. TEL 514-226-5870. FAX 514-226-5866. Ed. E. Todd. circ. 1,000. **Document type:** government publication.
    Formerly (until 1974): Food-Borne Diseases in Canada (ISSN 0715-6413)
    Description: Summarizes information from federal, provisional and regional agencies on foodborne and waterborne disease occurring in Canada.

FOODINFO. see ABSTRACTING AND INDEXING SERVICES

FOODS BY MAIL. see BUSINESS AND ECONOMICS — Marketing And Purchasing

664   US
FOODS OF TOMORROW. 6/yr. Putman Publishing Co., 301 E. Erie St., Chicago, IL 60611. TEL 312-644-2020. TELEX 270258 EX PRSTLXCGO. Ed. Robert Sweintek. adv.: B&W page $6290; trim 8 x 10 7/8. circ. 67,633.

664   US   ISSN 0897-7208
FOODSERVICE DIRECTOR.* 1988. m. Bill Communications. Inc., 355 Park Ave. S., 3rd Fl., New York, NY 10010-1706. TEL 212-592-6200. Ed. Walter Schruntek. circ. 45,000. (tabloid format)
    Description: For foodservice professionals at schools, colleges, hospitals, nursing homes, airlines, business and incustry, penal institutions, military installations, and other non-commercial segments.

664   US   ISSN 0896-4505
HD9001   CODEN: FODIES
THE FOODSERVICE DISTRIBUTOR. 1987. m. $50 (free to qualified personnel). Penton Publishing (Subsidiary of: Pittway Company), 1100 Superior Ave., Cleveland, OH 44114-2543. TEL 216-696-7000. FAX 216-696-8765. (Subscr. to: Box 95759, Cleveland OH 44101) Ed. John Lawn. circ. 38,946 (controlled). (reprint service avail. from UMI) **Document type:** trade publication.
    —UMI. **CCC.**
    Description: Focuses on effective sales, marketing, merchandizing and promotional programs, and industry news, for foodservice distribution executives and sales representatives.

FOODSERVICE EAST. see HOTELS AND RESTAURANTS

642.5   US   ISSN 1040-4546
FOODSERVICE OPERATORS GUIDE. 1988. a. (plus s-a. update). $149. Foodservice Database Co., Inc., 5724 W. Diversey Ave., Chicago, IL 60639. TEL 312-745-9400. FAX 312-745-7432. Ed. Ray Mitchell. adv. **Document type:** directory.
    Description: Lists names and buyers for chain restaurants in the U.S.

FOODSERVICE PRODUCT NEWS. see HOTELS AND RESTAURANTS

664   US
FOODSERVICE REPORT. 1986. m. International Foodservice Distributors Association, 201 Park Washington Court, Falls Church, VA 22046. TEL 703-532-9400. Ed. John D. Thompson. adv. circ. 2,167.
    Description: Cover member companies' operations and buying-merchandising, sales warehouse design, distribution operations and industry trends.

FOODSERVICE YEARBOOK INTERNATIONAL. see BUSINESS AND ECONOMICS — Trade And Industrial Directories

664   US   ISSN 1065-0067
FOODTALK; the newsletter for people who enjoy food for the minc as well as the table. 1978. q. $18. Box 42-6543, San Francisco, CA 94142. TEL 415-386-3067. Ed. Elaine Douglas Cahn. bk.rev.; index, cum.index; circ. 10,000 (paid). (back issues avail.) **Document type:** newsletter.
    Description: Focuses on the cultural uses of food in ritual, history, folklore and ceremony.

FOODWEEK. see FOOD AND FOOD INDUSTRIES — Grocery Trade

664   CN   ISSN 1188-5211
▼**FRAIS DU JOUR.** 1992. 6/yr. Can.$30. Chef du Service Alimentaire, 252 Route 171 S., St-Etienne de Lauzon, Que. G0S 2L0, Canada. TEL 418-831-5317. FAX 418-831-5172. Ed. Maurice LeBlanc. adv. circ. 7,500.

FRANCIS - LEATHERHEAD FOOD RESEARCH ABSTRACTS. see FOOD AND FOOD INDUSTRIES — Abstracting, Bibliographies, Statistics

664.8   UK
FRESH PRODUCE JOURNAL. 1895. w. £72 (foreign £148). Lcckwood Press Ltd., 430-438 Market Towers, New Covent Garden Market, London SW8 5NN, England. TEL 071-622-6677. FAX 071-270-2047. Ed. Tessa Fox. adv.; bk.rev.; illus.; mkt.; stat.; tr.lit. circ. 7,000. **Document type:** trade publication.
    Former titles: Fruit Trades Journal (ISSN 0016-2256); Fruit, Flower and Vegetable Trades' Journal.

FOOD AND FOOD INDUSTRIES

664.8 658 US
FRESH PRODUCE WORKSHOP. Title varies: Spectacular Salads. irreg. price varies. Produce Marketing Association, 1500 Casho Mill Rd., Box 6036, Newark, DE 19714-6036. TEL 302-738-7100. FAX 302-731-2409.
  Description: Provides information on specific topics relating to the storing, receiving, handling and marketing of fresh produce.

664.8 658 US
FRESHLINE. s-m. membership. Produce Marketing Association, 1500 Casho Mill Rd., Box 6036, Newark, DE 19714-6036. TEL 302-738-7100. FAX 302-731-2409.
  Formerly (until 1991): P M A Newsletter.

664.94 UK
FRIERS CATERING ADVERTISER. no.2, 1980. m. £12.50. (Confederation of Fried Fish Caterers' Associations) G.R. Associates, 429 Meanwood Rd., Leeds 7, England. TEL 0532-458235. Ed. Owen Mackie Gillan. illus. circ. 5,000.
  Formerly: Fried Fish Caterer (ISSN 0261-2038)

664.028 658 UK ISSN 0265-6485
FROZEN AND CHILLED FOODS. 1948. m. £55.30($100.50) (foreign £60.70). F M J International Publications Ltd., Queensway House, 2 Queensway, Redhill, Surrey RH1 1QS, England. TEL 0737-768611. FAX 0737-761685. TELEX 948669-TOPJNL-G. Ed. Neil Murray. **Indexed:** Br.Tech.Ind., Dairy Sci.Abstr., Food Sci.& Tech.Abstr., Int.Packag.Abstr., Key to Econ.Sci., Packag.Sci.Tech. **Document type:** trade publication.
  —BLDSC (4042.230000).
  Formed by the merger of: Chilled Foods (ISSN 0262-7566); And: Frozen Foods (ISSN 0016-2205)
  Description: Features news and opinions on the latest products available in the U.L. frozen and chilled food industry.

664.028 641 UK ISSN 0267-8276
FROZEN AND CHILLED FOODS YEAR BOOK. 1957. a. £69.20($108) F M J International Publications Ltd., Queensway House, 2 Queensway, Redhill, Surrey RH1 1QS, England. TEL 0737-768611. FAX 0737-761685. TELEX 948669-TOPJNL-G. **Document type:** trade publication.
  —BLDSC (4042.240000).
  Formerly: Frozen Foods Year Book (ISSN 0071-9692)
  Description: Provides information on suppliers of all types of food products, from fish to poultry, pies, and deserts, as well as brand names, professional and trade associations, transport contractors, and retailers.

664.028 658.8 US ISSN 0016-2191
HD9001 CODEN: FFOADT
FROZEN FOOD AGE; the industry magazine of marketing and merchandising. 1952. m. $75. Frozen Food Age Publishing Corp., 263 Tresser Blvd., Stamford, CT 06901-3202. TEL 203-325-3500. FAX 203-325-8423. Ed. Warren Thayer. adv. contact: Steve Lichtenstein. charts; illus.; stat. circ. 19,400. (tabloid format) **Indexed:** Int.Packag.Abstr., Ref.Pt.Food Indus.Abstr. **Document type:** trade publication.

664.028 US ISSN 0889-5902
TP493.5
FROZEN FOOD DIGEST; the informative magazine of the frozen food industry. 1938. q. $30. Frozen Food Digest, Inc., 271 Madison Ave., New York, NY 10016. TEL 212-557-8600. FAX 212-986-9868. Ed. Jim McGuinness. adv.; bk.rev. circ. 15,000. (also avail. in microform from UMI; reprint service avail. from UMI) **Indexed:** B.P.I., Biol.Abstr., Bus.Ind., Curr.Pack.Abstr., Dairy Sci.Abstr., Food Sci.& Tech.Abstr., P.A.I.S., Packag.Sci.Tech., SRI, Tr.& Indus.Ind. **Document type:** trade publication.
  —UnCover.
  Formerly (until 1985): Quick Frozen Foods (ISSN 0033-6408)

664.028 US
FROZEN FOOD EXECUTIVE. 1983. m. $60. National Frozen Food Association, Inc., Box 6069, Harrisburg, PA 17112-0069. TEL 717-657-8601. FAX 717-657-9862. Ed. Lori B. Perle. adv.: B&W page $684; adv. contact: Joanne Myers. stat. circ. 4,142. (back issues avail.) **Document type:** trade publication.
  Description: News about the frozen food industry with information on NFFA, new products, legislation and statistics.

664.028 UK
FROZEN FOOD MANAGEMENT. 1983. 6/yr. £20. Winlove Publications Ltd., 4 High St., Croydon, Surrey CR0 1YA, England. TEL 081-688-2696. FAX 081-688-2726. Ed. Nick Tarry. adv. circ. 6,232. **Document type:** trade publication.
  Formerly: Fish Products.
  Description: Journal for suppliers of frozen food products and related services to the trade.

664.028 US ISSN 0192-0367
FROZEN FOOD REPORT. 1973. bi-m. membership. American Frozen Food Institute, 1764 Old Meadow Ln., Ste. 350, McLean, VA 22102. TEL 703-821-0770. FAX 703-821-1350. Ed. Traci V. Carneal. bk.rev. circ. 5,300. **Document type:** trade publication.
  Formerly: Monthly Frozen Food Report.

664.028 DK ISSN 0906-1649
FROZEN FOODS IN DENMARK. 1963. a. DKK 500. Dybfrostraadet - Council of Danish Frozen Food Industries, Vesterbrogade 6 D, 4, DK-1620 Copenhagen V, Denmark. TEL 33-33-95-00. FAX 33-33-95-05. adv.; stat. circ. 115. **Document type:** abstracting/indexing.
  Description: Annual statistical survey of the deep-frozen food consumption in Denmark, cold storage capacities, sales of ice cream, freezers, etc.

664.028 658.8 UK
FROZEN FOODS: THE INTERNATIONAL MARKET. a. £1375($2750) Euromonitor, 87-88 Turnmill St., London EC1M 5QU, England. TEL 071-251-8024. FAX 071-608-3149. (Addr. in N. America: Euromonitor International, 111 W. Washington St., Ste. 920, Chicago, IL 60602. TEL 312-541-8024. FAX 312-541-1567) (looseleaf format) **Document type:** trade publication.
  ●Also available online. Vendor(s): Data-Star, DIALOG Information Services, Inc.
  Description: Analyzes the frozen-foods market for France, Germany, Italy, Spain, the U.K., the U.S., and Japan.

FRUCHTHANDEL; internationale Fachzeitschrift fuer den Handel mit Fruechten und Gemuese. see AGRICULTURE — Crop Production And Soil

664.8 658.8 UK
FRUIT AND VEGETABLES: THE INTERNATIONAL MARKET. a. £1375($2750) Euromonitor, 87-88 Turnmill St., London EC1M 4QU, England. TEL 607-251-8024. FAX 071-608-3149. (Addr. in N. America: Euromonitor International, 111 W. Washington St., Ste. 920, Chicago, IL 60602. TEL 312-541-8024. FAX 312-541-1567) (looseleaf format) **Document type:** trade publication.
  ●Also available online. Vendor(s): Data-Star, DIALOG Information Services, Inc.
  Description: Analyzes the market for commercially and organically grown fruits and vegetables for France, Germany, Italy, Spain, the U.K., the U.S., and Japan.

664.8 NE ISSN 0016-2302
FRUITTEELT. 1911. w. fl.289.50 (effective 1994). Nederlandse Fruittelers Organisatie, Postbus 90607, 2509 LP The Hague, Netherlands. FAX 31-70-3453902. Ed.Bd. adv.; bk.rev.; charts; illus.; mkt.; stat.; tr.lit.; index. circ. 6,000. **Indexed:** Agri.Eng.Abstr., Biol.Abstr., C.I.S.Abstr., Chem.Abstr., Crop Physiol.Abstr., Hort.Abstr., Key to Econ.Sci., Plant Grow.Reg.Abstr., World Agri.Econ.& Rural Sociol.Abstr. **Document type:** trade publication.

FUMA/FOOD MACHINERY. see MACHINERY

664.028 GW
G V - PRAXIS; Zeitschrift fuer moderne Grossverpflegung. 1960. m. DM.179.90 (foreign DM.186.15). Deutscher Fachverlag GmbH, Mainzer Landstr. 251, 60326 Frankfurt a.M., Germany. TEL 069-759501. FAX 069-75952999. (Subscr. to: Postfach 100606, 60006 Frankfurt a.M., Germany) Ed. A. Bohl. adv.; bk.rev.; abstr.; bibl.; charts; illus.; stat. circ. 11,315. **Indexed:** Food Sci.& Tech.Abstr. **Document type:** trade publication.
  Former titles: G V - Praxis mit Tiefkuehlpraxis (ISSN 0342-376X); Tiefkuehl Praxis International (ISSN 0040-7259)

642.5 GW
G V: SWISS. (Grossverpflegung) 1988. 10/yr. Deutscher Fachverlag GmbH, Mainzer Landstr. 251, 60326 Frankfurt a.M., Germany. TEL 069-7595-01. FAX 069-75952999. (Subscr. to: Postfach 100606, 60006 Frankfurt a.M., Germany) Ed. B. Schmidt. circ. 5,100. (back issues avail.) **Document type:** trade publication.

GABONAIPAR. see AGRICULTURE — Feed, Flour And Grain

GASTRONOMIE & TOURISME. see TRAVEL AND TOURISM

GASTRONOMIE UND HOTEL IMPULSE. see HOTELS AND RESTAURANTS

664.1 PL ISSN 0016-5395
TP375 CODEN: GACUA2
GAZETA CUKROWNICZA. (Text in Polish; summaries in English, German) 1893. m. $51. (Stowarzyszenie Technikow Cukrownikow - Association of Polish Sugar Technicians) Wydawnictwo Czasopism i Ksiazek Technicznych SIGMA - NOT, Ul. Ratuszowa 11, P.O. Box 1004, 00-950 Warsaw, Poland. TEL 48-22-180918. FAX 48-22-192187. TELEX 814550 SIGMA PL. (Dist. by: Ars Polona- Ruch, Krakowskie Przedmiescie 7, Warsaw, Poland) Ed. Stanislaw Nikiel. adv.; bk.rev.; abstr.; illus. circ. 2,450. **Indexed:** Chem.Abstr., Field Crop Abstr., Food Sci.& Tech.Abstr., Herb.Abstr., Sugar Ind.Abstr.
  —CASDDS.

664 IT ISSN 0016-5999
GELATIERE ITALIANO; revista tecnico-professionale dei gelatieri italiani. vol.6, 1970. bi-m. L.20000. Residenza I Portici, 20090 Segrate, Milan 2, Italy. TEL 2-26-41-53-12. Ed. Paolo Bellavista. adv.; illus. circ. 13,000.

664.028 637.1 IT
GELATO ARTIGIANALE. 6/yr. Eta - Beta Gruppo Editoriale s.r.l., Centro Direzionale Colleoni Palazzo Astolabio, 20041 Agrate (MI), Italy. TEL 2-60-57-178. FAX 2-605-71-79. Ed. Eraldo Levati. circ. 20,000.

664 IC ISSN 1017-3552
GESTGJAFINN. 1981. bi-m. ISK 3414 (effective Jan. 1994). Frodi Ltd, Armuli 18, 108 Reykjavik, Iceland. TEL 354-1-812300. FAX 354-1-812946. Ed. Rut Helgadottir. adv.: B&W page ISK 60640, color page ISK 86880; trim 19 x 27; adv. contact: Anna Gunnarsdottir. circ. 15,000.
  Description: Publishes articles of interest to the food industry; bakers and confectioners, grocery trade, hotels and restaurants; articles on restaurants both in Iceland and elsewhere.

664 615.9 NE ISSN 0169-5959
THE GIST. q. Royal Gst-brocades nv., Corporate Communications, P.O. Box 1, 2600 MA Delft, Netherlands. Ed.Bd.

664 JA
GOCHISO-SAMA!; a culinary newsletter from Japan. (Text in English) q. 2500 Yen($20) Yagoto Fujimigaoka 13-2, Tenpaku-cho, Showa-ku, Nagoya 466, Japan. TEL 052-835-4458. Ed. Lucy Seligman Kanazawa. **Document type:** newsletter.
  Description: Covers the Japanese culinary treats.

LA GOLA. see HOTELS AND RESTAURANTS

664 UK
GOOD FOOD. 1973. bi-m. £15. John Edwards, 9 St. Mary's Garth, Church Rd., Buxted, Sussex, England. Ed. Heather Buckle. circ. 4,000.
  Formerly: Good 6500 (ISSN 0261-2534)

FOOD AND FOOD INDUSTRIES

664 GW ISSN 0017-2243
CODEN: GORDAM
GORDIAN; Internationale Zeitschrift fuer Lebensmittel und Lebensmittel-technologie. (Text and summaries in English and German) 1895. m. DM.103. Nahrungs- und Genussmittel-Fachverlag A.Gordian GmbH & Co. KG, Bellevue 24, 22301 Hamburg, Germany. Ed. U. Drevici-Kux. adv.; bk.rev.; bibl.; charts; illus.; mkt.; pat.; tr.mk.; stat.; index. circ. 3,100. **Indexed:** Biol.Abstr., Chem.Abstr., Dairy Sci.Abstr., Excerp.Med., Food Sci.& Tech.Abstr., Hort.Abstr., INIS Atomind., Key to Econ.Sci., Nutr.Abstr., Sugar Ind.Abstr.
—BLDSC (4201.500000); SWETS; CASDDS.

GOSPODARKA MIESNA. see AGRICULTURE — Poultry And Livestock

641.013 US ISSN 0017-2553
TX1 CODEN: GOUREF
GOURMET; the magazine of good living. 1941. m. $18. Conde Nast Publications Inc., Gourmet Magazine, 560 Lexington Ave., New York, NY 10022-6876. TEL 212-371-1330. FAX 212-753-2596. Ed. Gail Zweigenthal. adv.; illus.; index. circ. 906,299. (also avail. in microform from UMI) **Indexed:** Gard.Lit. (1992-), Mag.Ind., PMR, R.G. **Document type:** consumer publication.
—Faxon; UnCover; UMI.
Description: Includes articles, recipes and shopping tips on ethnicand gourmet cuisines; also restaurants and places of interest.

642.5 US ISSN 0199-0357
HD9321.1
GOURMET RETAILER.* 1979. m. $24. Sterling Southeast Inc., 3301 Ponce De Leon Blvd., No.300, Coral Gables, FL 33134-7273. TEL 305-893-8771. Ed. Nancy Moore. adv.; bk.rev.; circ. 17,389 (controlled).

664.028 FR ISSN 0769-6833
GRAND FROID. 1985. 11/yr. 340 F. (foreign 425 F.). Groupe L S A, B.P. 142, 6 rue Marius Aufan, 92300 Levallois-Perret Cedex, France. TEL 47-58-20-00. Ed. Sabine Carantino. adv.; bk.rev.; index. circ. 11,500.

664 658.8 US ISSN 0192-4400
GRIFFIN REPORT OF FOOD MARKETING. 1966. m. $36. Griffin Publishing Company, Inc., 1099 Hingham St., Rockland, MA 02370. TEL 617-878-5300. FAX 617-871-4721. adv. circ. 14,500. (tabloid format; back issues avail.) **Document type:** trade publication.
Formerly: Griffin Report of New England (ISSN 0017-422X); Incorporates: Yankee Grocer.

664 UK
▼**GROCER FOOD AND DRINK DIRECTORY.** 1992. a. £85. William Reed Ltd., Broadfield Park, Crawley, W. Sussex RH11 9RT, England. TEL 0293-613400. FAX 0293-613304. adv. **Document type:** directory, trade publication.

664 UK
▼**GROCER GUIDE TO THE U K'S TOP FOOD AND DRINK SUPPLIERS.** 1994. a. William Reed Ltd., Broadfield Park, Crawley, W. Sussex RH11 9RT, England. TEL 0293-613400. FAX 0293-613304. **Document type:** directory.

664 GW ISSN 0341-0498
GRUNDLAGEN UND FORTSCHRITTE DER LEBENSMITTELUNTERSUCHUNG UND LEBENSMITTELTECHNOLOGIE. 1953. irreg. price varies. Verlag Paul Parey (Berlin), Seelbuschring 9-17, 12105 Berlin, Germany. TEL 030-70784-0. FAX 030-70784199. Ed. Friedrich Kiermeier. bibl.; illus.; index. **Indexed:** Biol.Abstr., Food Sci.& Tech.Abstr. **Document type:** academic/scholarly publication.
—BLDSC (4223.222000).
Formerly: Grundlagen und Fortschritte der Lebensmitteluntersuchung (ISSN 0432-7454)

GUATEMALA. MINISTERIO DE AGRICULTURA, GANADERIA Y ALIMENTACION. DIRECCION GENERAL DE SERVICIOS AGRICOLAS. MEMORIA DE LABORES. see AGRICULTURE

664 MX
GUIA DE LA INDUSTRIA ALIMENTARIA/FEED INDUSTRY GUIDE. (Text in English, Spanish) 1963. a. $80. Informatica Cosmos, S.A. de C.V., Fernandez Arrieta 5-101, Col. Los Cipreses, 04830 Mexico D.F., Mexico. TEL 525-677-48-68. FAX 525-679-35-75. Ed. Raul Macazaga. adv.: B&W page $1000; trim 211 x 274. **Indexed:** Food Sci.& Tech.Abstr. **Document type:** directory.
Formerly: Alimentaria.
Description: Lists 1100 suppliers and 2400 products, ingredients and raw materials, machines for food manufacturing, services and materials. Indexes 1700 manufacturers of human and animal consumables.

GUIDE TO EATING ONTARIO SPORT FISH. see FISH AND FISHERIES

642.5 AU ISSN 1013-9478
GUSTO. 1983. m. S.380. O R A C Zeitschriftenverlag GmbH, Schoenbrunnerstr. 59-61, A-1050 Vienna, Austria. TEL 01-54621-0. FAX 01-5462178. Ed. Wolfgang Schlueter. circ. 173,000. (back issues avail.) **Document type:** trade publication.

664 636 US
H R I - BUYERS GUIDE. (Hotels, Restaurants, Institutions) 1970. w. $70 (typically set in Sept.). Urner Barry Publications, Inc., Box 389, Toms River, NJ 08754. TEL 908-240-5330. FAX 908-341-0891. Ed. Michael E. O'Shaughnessy. adv. (tabloid format)
Formerly: Restaurant Buyers Guide (ISSN 0270-4161)
Description: Gives reports about the perishable foods and their selling prices for hotels, restaurants, institutions, country clubs, caterers, and schools.

332.6 US
H R I MEAT PRICE REPORT. 1967. w. $150 (Fax delivery $225). Urner Barry Publications, Inc., Box 389, Toms River, NJ 08754. TEL 908-240-5330. FAX 908-341-0891. circ. 210 (paid). **Document type:** newsletter.
Former titles: Meat Price Report; Meat Service Report.
Description: Guide to current meat prices being paid to wholesalers and purveyors by hotels, restaurants, institutions, hospitals, clubs, and various commercial feeders.

664 NE
HANDBOOK OF AROMA RESEARCH. 1982. irreg. price varies. Kluwer Academic Publishers, Postbus 17, 3300 AA Dordrecht, Netherlands. TEL 31-78-334911. FAX 31-78-334254. TELEX 29245 KAPG NL. (Dist. by: Kluwer Academic Publishers Group, P.O. Box 322, 3300 AH Dordrecht, Netherlands. TEL 31-78-524400; N. America dist. addr.: Box 358, Accord Sta., Hingham, MA 02018-0358. TEL 617-871-6600) Ed. Michael Ruse. adv.; bk.rev. **Document type:** monographic series.
Refereed Serial

664 IS
AL-HASHULCHAN; Israeli restaurant business periodical. (Text in Hebrew) 1990. m. IS.150. El- Hayam Tikshoret Ltd., P.O. Box 32238, Tel Aviv 61321, Israel. TEL 972-3-6050060. Ed. Jeanne Gur. adv.; illus. circ. 15,000.

HEALTH FOODS BUSINESS; the business publication of the natural foods industry. see NUTRITION AND DIETETICS

664.6 658.8 UK
HEALTH, SLIMMING AND DIETETIC FOODS: THE INTERNATIONAL MARKET. a. £1375($2750) Euromonitor, 87-88 Turnmill St., London EC1M 5QU, England. TEL 071-251-8024. FAX 071-608-3149. (Addr. in N. America: Euromonitor International, 111 W. Washington St., Ste. 920, Chicago, IL 60602. TEL 312-541-8024. FAX 312-541-1567) (looseleaf format) **Document type:** trade publication.
●Also available online. Vendor(s): Data-Star, DIALOG Information Services, Inc.
Description: Analyzes the market for health and dietetic foods for France, Germany, Italy, Spain, the U.K., the U.S., and Japan.

664 642.59 US
HEALTHCARE FOODSERVICE MAGAZINE. (Includes Annual Industry Directory) 1991. m. $25. International Publishing Company of America, 665 La Villa Dr., Miami Springs, FL 33166. TEL 305-887-1700. FAX 305-885-1923. adv. circ. 29,215. **Document type:** trade publication.
Description: For foodservice professionals in hospitals, nursing homes, hospices and treatment centers, contract caterers and restaurant and cafeteria operators in healthcare facilities in the US and Canada.

HEALTHCARE FOODSERVICE WHO'S WHO. see BUSINESS AND ECONOMICS — Trade And Industrial Directories

664 613.2 US ISSN 1071-4499
▼**HEALTHY EATING.** 1993. m. $96. (National Academy of Medical Studies in Foods and Beverages) Paul Gillette Enterprises, 3284 Barham Blvd., Ste. 201, Los Angeles, CA 90068-1454. TEL 213-876-7590. FAX 213-876-4090. Ed. Dr. Norvelle A. Harris. bk.rev.; illus.; stat. (also avail. in diskette format; back issues avail.) **Document type:** newsletter.
Description: Presents the latest developments in nutrition and food safety, written entirely by physicians, for medical and general audiences.

HELPER TO TRADE UNION'S MEMBERS. see LABOR UNIONS

HIROSHIMA DAIGAKU SEIBUTSU SEISAN GAKUBU KIYO. see AGRICULTURE — Dairying And Dairy Products

HOKKAIDO EIYO SYOKURYO GAKKAISHI/HOKKAIDO SOCIETY OF FOOD AND NUTRITION. JOURNAL. see AGRICULTURE — Dairying And Dairy Products

658.8 647.95 BE
HORECA NEWS (BRUSSELS, 1971); hotels - restaurants - cafes - traiteurs - fast food - night-club - collectives. (Editions in Dutch, French) 1971. 9/yr. 1500 BEF (foreign 2900 BEF). Soprest S.A., 73 av. de l'Universite, bte. 2, B-1050 Brussels, Belgium. TEL 32-2-6476390. FAX 32-2-6460117. Ed. P. Van Reepinghen. adv.; illus.; stat. adv. circ. 21,600 (11,200 Dutch ed.; 10,400 French ed.). **Document type:** trade publication.
Description: Covers the food service, restaurant and catering trade in Belgium.

HOSPITAL FOOD & NUTRITION FOCUS. see HOSPITALS

HOSPITALITY FOODSERVICE; national monthly newspaper of the accommodation, food service and convention industries. see HOTELS AND RESTAURANTS

642.5 AT
HOST MAGAZINE; management magazine of food service, catering and accomodations. m. Aus.$35. Peter Isaacsons Publications, 45-50 Porter St., Prahran, Vic. 3181, Australia. TEL 520-5555. Ed. June Cummings. illus.; stat.; tr.lit. circ. 11,443. (back issues avail.)

HOTEL UND GASTGEWERBE; unabhaengiges Fachorgan fuer Hotellerie, Gastronomie, und Gemeinschaftsverpflegung. see HOTELS AND RESTAURANTS

HOTELS. see HOTELS AND RESTAURANTS

642.5 658 US
HOTLINE MAGAZINE. 1901. q. $90 membership. International Food Service Executives Association, Inc., 1100 S. State Rd. 7, Ste. 103, Margate, FL 33068. TEL 305-977-0767. FAX 305-977-0874. Ed. Ed Manley. adv.; bk.rev.; charts; illus. circ. 6,000.
Formerly (until 1989): Food Executive (ISSN 0015-6338)

664.9 HU ISSN 0018-800X
CODEN: HUSPAE
HUSIPAR. (Text in Hungarian; summaries in English, German and Russian) 1951. q. $18. (Magyar Elelmezesipari Tudomanyos Egyesulet) Lapkiado Vallalat, Lenin korut 9-11, 1073 Budapest 7, Hungary. TEL 222-408. (Subscr. to: Kultura, PO Box 149, H-1389 Budapest, Hungary) (Co-sponsor: Allatorgalmi es Husipari Troszt) Ed. Ferenc Lorincz. charts; illus.; index. **Indexed:** Chem.Abstr., Food Sci.& Tech.Abstr., Rural Recreat.Tour.Abstr., World Agri.Econ.& Rural Sociol.Abstr.
—CASDDS.

FOOD AND FOOD INDUSTRIES

664   HU   ISSN 0018-8085
HUTOIPAR. (Text in Hungarian; summaries in English and Russian) 1953. q. $24. (Magyar Elelmezesipari Tudomanyos Egyesulet) Lapkiado Vallalat, Lenin korut 9-11, 1073 Budapest 7, Hungary. TEL 222-408. (Subscr. to: Kultura, Box 149, H-1389 Budapest, Hungary) Ed. Laszlo B. Laczko. adv.; charts; illus. circ. 820. **Indexed:** Dairy Sci.Abstr., Food Sci.& Tech.Abstr., INIS Atomind.

663.92   UK
I C C O. ANNUAL REPORT. (Editions in English, French, Russian, Spanish) a. free. International Cocoa Organization, 22 Berners St., London W1P 3DB. TEL 071-637-3211. FAX 071-631-0114. TELEX 28173 ICOCOA G. **Document type:** corporate report.

663.92 631   UK
I C C O. COCOA NEWSLETTER. (Text in English, French, Spanish) 1990. s-a. free. International Cocoa Organization, 22 Berners St., London W1P 3DB, England. TEL 071-637-3211. FAX 071-631-0114. TELEX 28173 ICOCOA G. **Document type:** newsletter.
    Description: Provides economic, scientific and technical information of relevance to the world cocoa economy.

661.92 338.1   UK   ISSN 0308-4469
HD9200.A1
I C C O. QUARTERLY BULLETIN OF COCOA STATISTICS. (Editions in English, French, Russian, Spanish) 1974. q. £40 in Europe; elsewhere £50. International Cocoa Organization, 22 Berners St., London W1P 3DB, England. TEL 071-637-3211. FAX 071-631-0114. TELEX 28173 ICOCOA G. charts. circ. 1,000. (also avail. in microfiche from CIS; back issues avail.) **Indexed:** IIS. **Document type:** bulletin.
    —BLDSC (7178.120000).

663.92 338.1   UK
▼**I C C O WORLD COCOA DIRECTORY.** (Editions in English, French, Spanish) 1992. a. £75. International Cocoa Organization, 22 Berners St., London W1P 3DB, England. TEL 071-637-0114. FAX 071-631-0114. TELEX 28173 ICOCOA G. stat. (looseleaf format) **Document type:** directory.
    Description: Lists the names and addresses of more than 2,500 companies involved in the trade of cocoa and 100 organizations involved with cocoa research, trade, and manufacture. Also includes historical statistical data.

663.93   UK   ISSN 0144-6800
I C O LIBRARY MONTHLY ENTRIES - COFFEELINE. 1973. m. $58. International Coffee Organization, 22 Berners St., London W1P 4DD, England. FAX 071-580-6129. TELEX 267659. Ed. C.P.R. Dubois. circ. 600. **Document type:** newsletter.
    ●Also available online. Vendor(s): DIALOG Information Services, Inc. (File no.164).
    Description: Bibliographical journal about coffee.

664.1   UK
I C U M S A METHODS BOOK. a. plus irreg. updates. £110 (overseas £112). (International Commission of Uniform Methods of Sugar Analysis) I C U M S A Publications, c/o British Sugar plc., Technical Centre, Norwich Research Park, Colney, Norwich NR4 7UB, England. TEL 44-493-751678. FAX 44-493-751807. TELEX 32273-SUGPET-G. charts. (looseleaf format)

664   US
I D D A WRAP-UP. 1979. q. membership. International Dairy - Deli - Bakery Association, 313 Price Pl., Ste. 202, Box 5528, Madison, WI 53705-0528. TEL 608-238-7908. FAX 608-238-6330. Ed. Carol Christison. tr.lit. circ. 13,000. **Document type:** newsletter.
    Formerly: Dairy - Deli Wrap-Up.
    Description: Covers association news, products and services, seminars and awards.

I D HANDBOOK OF FOODSERVICE DISTRIBUTION (YEAR). (Institutional Distribution) see *BUSINESS AND ECONOMICS — Trade And Industrial Directories*

642.5   US
I F M A WORLD. 1970. 10/yr. free. (I F M A) International Foodservice Manufacturers Association, 180 N. Stetson Ave., Ste. 4400, Chicago, IL 60601. TEL 312-540-4400. Ed.Bd. bk.rev.; circ. controlled.
    Former titles: Foodservice Today; Business Barometer and Digest.

I F P R I RESEARCH REPORT. (International Food Policy Research Institute) see *AGRICULTURE — Agricultural Economics*

664   US
I F T BASIC SYMPOSIUM SERIES. 1986. irreg., vol.8, 1993. price varies. (International Food Technology) Marcel Dekker, Inc., 270 Madison Ave., New York, NY 10016. TEL 212-696-9000.
    FAX 212-658-4540. TELEX 421419.

334 658.8   UK
ICE CREAM, YOGHURTS AND CHILLED DESSERTS: THE INTERNATIONAL MARKET. a. £1375($2750) Euromonitor, 87-88 Turnmill St., London EC1M 5QU, England. TEL 071-251-8024. FAX 071-608-3149. (Addr. in N. America: Euromonitor International, 111 W. Washington St., Ste. 920, Chicago, IL 60602. TEL 312-541-8024. FAX 312-541-1567) (looseleaf format) **Document type:** trade publication.
    ●Also available online. Vendor(s): Data-Star, DIALOG Information Services, Inc..
    Description: Analyzes the markets for ice cream and other dairy desserts for France, Germany, Italy, Spain, the U.K., the U.S., and Japan.

663.93   US
IN GOOD TASTE. 1983. 10/yr. membership. Specialty Coffee Association of America, One World Trade Center, Ste. 800, Long Beach, CA 90831-0800. TEL 310-983-8090. FAX 310-983-8091. Ed. Ted R. Lingle. circ. 800.

664   II   ISSN 0019-4484
INDIAN CASHEW JOURNAL. (Text in English) 1964. q. $30. Cashew Export Promotion Council, Chittoor Rd., Cochin 682 016, India. TELEX 885-6677 CEPC IN. Ed. K.G. Nayar. adv. circ. 2,000. **Indexed:** Food Sci.& Tech.Abstr., Hort.Abstr.

664   II
INDIAN COCOA, ARECANUT & SPICES JOURNAL. (Text in English) 1969. q. Rs.4. Ministry of Agriculture, Directorate of Cocoa, Arecanut and Spices Development, 1-1143 Cannanore Rd., Calicut 673005, Kerala, India. Ed. E. Velappan. adv.; bk.rev.; charts; illus.; stat. circ. 2,000. **Indexed:** Agrindex, Agroforest.Abstr., Bio-Contr.News & Info., Food Sci.& Tech.Abstr., Hort.Abstr., Seed Abstr.
    Former titles: Arecanut and Spices Bulletin (ISSN 0044-8796); Indian Arecanut, Spices and Cocoa Journal.

663.93   II   ISSN 0019-4549
      CODEN: ICOFAJ
INDIAN COFFEE. (Editions in English, Kannada, Malayalam, Tamil) 1936. m. Rs.24 (foreign Rs.205). Ministry of Commerce, Coffee Board, Post Bag 5366, Bangalore 560 001, India. TEL 91-80-2265920. FAX 91-80-2265557. TELEX 0845-2221 COFI IN. Ed. A. Shahjahan. adv.; bk.rev.; bibl.; mkt.; stat.; index. circ. 5,000. **Indexed:** Biol.Abstr., Chem.Abstr., Curr.Adv.Ecol.Sci., Excerp.Med., Food Sci.& Tech.Abstr., Hort.Abstr. **Document type:** trade publication.
    —BLDSC (4394.200000).
    Description: Aims to promote India's coffee industry. Contains information on the latest researches on Indian coffee, new methods of controlling pests of coffee plants, and data on coffee marketing, development, and promotions.

INDIAN VEGETARIAN CONGRESS QUARTERLY. see *NUTRITION AND DIETETICS*

664   MX   ISSN 0187-7658
INDUSTRIA ALIMENTARIA. 1979. bi-m. $20. Alfa Editores Tecnicos S.A., Libertad No. 107-402, 03660 Mexico, D.F., Mexico. FAX 532-9504. Ed. Alejandro Garduno T. adv. circ. 4,000. **Indexed:** Curr.Pack.Abstr.

664   AG   ISSN 0326-9000
INDUSTRIA ALIMENTARIA. 1986. bi-m. $100. (Argentine Federation of Food Industries (COPAL)) Editora Tecnica Integral s.r.l., Av. Corrientes 2763, 2nd fl., Of. 9 y 10, 1046 Buenos Aires, Argentina. TEL 541-962-6100. Ed. Beatriz Liberatore. adv. circ. 4,000. **Document type:** trade publication.

664   CU   ISSN 0019-7459
INDUSTRIA ALIMENTICIA. (Text in Spanish; summaries in English, French and Spanish) 1968. q. $22 in N. America; S. America $24; Europe $28. (Ministerio de la Industria Alimenticia) Ediciones Cubanas, Obispo No. 527, Apdo. 605, Havana, Cuba. TEL 7-61-8453. Ed. Cesar Valdivia. adv.; bk.rev.; abstr.; bibl.; charts; illus.; stat. circ. 10,000. **Indexed:** Chem.Abstr., Curr.Cont.

664   US
INDUSTRIA ALIMENTICIA. (Text in Spanish) m. (except Dec.). $35 (foreign $70) (free to qualified personnel). Stagnito Publishing Company, 1935 Shermer Rd. Ste. 100, Northbrook, IL 60062. TEL 708-205-5660. FAX 708-205-5680. Ed. Elsa Torres; Pub. Mario Schacher. adv. contact: Laversia Dingle. circ. 20,000 (controlled). **Document type:** trade publication.
    Description: Contains material of interest to executives and department heads in the Latin American food-processing industry.

664.1   AG   ISSN 0325-0326
INDUSTRIA AZUCARERA. 1894. bi-m. $45. Reconquista 336, Piso 12, 1335 Buenos Aires, Argentina. Ed. Horacio Jose Bincaz. adv. **Indexed:** Food Sci.& Tech.Abstr., Sugar Ind.Abstr.

664   IT   ISSN 0019-7483
TX599   CODEN: ICOPAF
INDUSTRIA CONSERVE. 1926. q. L.15000. Stazione Sperimentale per l'Industria delle Conserve Alimentari, Viale F. Tanara 31 A, 43100 Parma, Italy. TEL 521-72-841. Ed. V. Castelli. adv.; bk.rev.; abstr.; bibl.; charts; illus.; mkt.; pat.; index. circ. 2,800. **Indexed:** Biol.Abstr., Chem.Abstr., Curr.Adv.Ecol.Sci., Curr.Cont., Curr.Pack.Abstr., Dairy Sci.Abstr., Food Sci.& Tech.Abstr., Packag.Sci.Tech.
    —BLDSC (4438.490000); SWETS; CASDDS.

664.028   SP   ISSN 0210-8674
INDUSTRIA CONSERVERA. 1934. m. 425 ptas.($16) Union de Fabricantes de Conservas de Galicia, Filipe Sanchez, 152, Vigo, Spain. adv.; bk.rev.; index. circ. 700.

664.9   IT
INDUSTRIA DELLE CARNI. 24/yr. Association of Meat Industries, Via C.G. Merlo 1, 20122 Milan, Italy. TEL 2-79-49-33. FAX 2-78-09-93. Ed. Roberto Barra. circ. 10,500.

664.1 663   IT   ISSN 0019-7734
      CODEN: INSIAN
INDUSTRIA SACCARIFERA ITALIANA. (Text in Italian; summaries in English) 1908. bi-m. L.60000 (effective 1993). Associazione Nazionale Tecnici Zucchero ed Alcole, Via Tito Speri, 5, Ferrara, Italy. TEL 39-532-205009. FAX 39-532-40709. Ed. Prof. Giorgio Mantovani. adv.; bk.rev.; abstr.; bibl.; charts; illus.; mkt.; pat. circ. 1,000. **Indexed:** Agri.Eng.Abstr., Chem.Abstr, Field Crop Abstr., Food Sci.& Tech.Abstr., Herb.Abstr., Soils & Fert., Sugar Ind.Abstr. **Document type:** bulletin, trade publication.
    —BLDSC (4442 000000); CASDDS.

664   IT   ISSN 0019-901X
      CODEN: INALBB
INDUSTRIE ALIMENTARI. (Text in Italian; summaries in English) 1962. m. L.120000($100) Chiriotti Editori S.p.A., Viale Rimembranza 60, P.O. Box 66, 10064 Pinerolo, Italy. TEL 121-794493. FAX 121-794480. Ed. Giovanni Chiriotti. adv.; bk.rev.; abstr.; bibl.; charts; illus.; pat. index. circ. 6,500. **Indexed:** Cadscan, Chem.Abstr., Curr.Adv.Ecol.Sci., Dairy Sci.Abstr., Food Sci.& Tech.Abstr., Lead Abstr., Nutr.Abstr., Packag.Sci.Tech., Rev.Med.& Vet.Mycol., Rural Recreat.Tour.Abstr., Sugar Ind.Abstr., Trop.Oil Seeds Abstr., World Agri.Econ.& Rural Sociol.Abstr., Zincscan. **Document type:** trade publication.
    —BLDSC (4464.780000); UMI; CASDDS. **CCC.**
    Description: Explores the problems concerning the technological, scientific, economic and legislative information in the food industry.

FOOD AND FOOD INDUSTRIES

664 630   FR   ISSN 0019-9311   CODEN: IALAA9
INDUSTRIES ALIMENTAIRES ET AGRICOLES. (Text in French; summaries in English, German) 1883. m. 690 F. (effective 1993). Association des Chimistes, 2 rue Oratoire, 75001 Paris, France. TEL 1-42-97-41-38. FAX 42-60-11-98. Ed. Guy Dardenne. adv.; bk.rev. circ. 8,000. (back issues avail.) **Indexed:** Chem.Abstr., Curr.Pack.Abstr., Dairy Sci.Abstr., Food Sci.& Tech.Abstr., Key to Econ.Sci., Nutr.Abstr., Sugar Ind.Abstr.
—BLDSC (4475.075000); SWETS; CASDDS.

664   FR   ISSN 0245-4505   CODEN: ICRLDL
INDUSTRIES DES CEREALES. 1980-1987; resumed 19?? bi-m. 400 F. (foreign 500 F.). (Association pour le Progres des Industries des Cereales) Arts Graphiques du Perche Edition, 1 rue du Coq-Heron, 75001 Paris, France. TEL 40-26-57-08. FAX 40-26-34-40. Ed. Claude Willm. adv.; bk.rev. circ. 2,500. **Indexed:** Food Sci.& Tech.Abstr., Plant Breed.Abstr.
—BLDSC (4475.206000); CASDDS.

664.1   YU   ISSN 0350-249X
INDUSTRIJA SECERA. (Supplement to: Hemijska Industrija (ISSN 0367-598X)) (Text in Serbo-Croatian; summaries in English) 1973. q. $50. Savez Hemicara i Tehnologa Jugoslavije, Kneza Milosa 9, P.O. Box 187, 11001 Belgrade, Yugoslavia. Ed. Milosav Dragojevic. adv.; bk.rev. circ. 1,000. **Indexed:** Chem.Abstr., Ref.Zh., Sugar Ind.Abstr.

664.9   IT   ISSN 0394-588X
INGEGNERIA ALIMENTARE - CONSERVE ANIMALI. 6/yr. L.45000 (Europe L.90000). G M Editoriale s.a.s., Via Lanzone 22, 20123 Milan, Italy. TEL 2-8055531. FAX 02-72010095. Ed. B.M. Moroni. circ. 13,000.
—BLDSC (4500.640000).

INGENIEURS DE LA VIE. see *AGRICULTURE — Crop Production And Soil*

THE INNKEEPERS' REGISTER. see *TRAVEL AND TOURISM*

INPAZ EN LAS AMERICAS. (Instituto Panamericano de Proteccion de Alimentos y Zoonosis) see *VETERINARY SCIENCE*

642.47   AT   ISSN 0814-5806
INSIDE DINING. m. Aus.$35 (foreign Aus.$90) (effective Jul. 1993). (Restaurant and Catering Association) Yaffa Publishing Group, 17-21 Bellevue St., Surry Hills, N.S.W. 2010, Australia. TEL 02-281-2333. FAX 02-281-2750. (Co-sponsor: Motor Inn and Motel Association) Ed. Scott Bolles. adv.; B&W page Aus.$2775, color page Aus.$3180; trim 273 x 210. circ. 14,411. **Document type:** trade publication.
Formerly (until 1984): *Restaurateur and Caterer* (ISSN 0812-9878); Incorporates: *Innews* (ISSN 0813-6793)
Description: Official voice of the food service industry.

642.5   US
INSITE (YEAR). 1980. a. $65 to non-members. National Association of Concessionaires, 35 E. Wacker Dr., Ste. 1545, Chicago, IL 60601. TEL 312-236-3858. FAX 312-236-7809. Ed. Susan M. Cross. adv.; charts; stat. circ. 3,500.

664.9   UK
INSTITUTE OF MEAT. BULLETIN. 4/yr. Institute of Meat, Langford, Bristol, Avon BS18 7DY, England. TEL 0934-85318. Ed. D.W. Leith. bk.rev. circ. 2,500. **Document type:** bulletin.

642.5   US   ISSN 0020-3572   HD9001
INSTITUTIONAL DISTRIBUTION.* 1965. 15/yr. Can.$100($80) others $110. Bill Communications, Inc., 355 Park Ave. S., 3rd Fl., New York, NY 10010-1706. TEL 212-592-6200. Ed. Joseph Angione. adv.; illus.; mkt.; pat.; stat.; tr.lit. circ. 44,000. (also avail. in microform from UMI; reprint service avail. from UMI) **Indexed:** Tr.& Indus.Ind.
●Also available online. Vendor(s): DIALOG Information Services, Inc., Mead Data Central, Inc. —UnCover; UMI.
Description: Directed to foodservice distribution executives and sales representatives.

664 641   BL   ISSN 0100-350X   TP368   CODEN: CITAC7
INSTITUTO DE TECNOLOGIA DE ALIMENTOS. COLETANEA. 1965. a. Cz.$2,500($25) Instituto de Tecnologia de Alimentos, Caixa Postal 139, Campinas SP, Brazil. circ. 500. **Indexed:** Biol.Abstr., Food Sci.& Tech.Abstr., Hort.Abstr., Nutr.Abstr.
—BLDSC (3297.800000); CASDDS.

664 658.8   BL   ISSN 0100-4964
INSTITUTO DE TECNOLOGIA DE ALIMENTOS. ESTUDOS ECONOMICOS. ALIMENTOS PROCESSADOS. 1975. irreg. $6. Instituto de Tecnologia de Alimentos, Caixa Postal 139, Campinas, S.P., Brazil.

664 641   BL   ISSN 0074-0144
INSTITUTO DE TECNOLOGIA DE ALIMENTOS. INSTRUCOES PRATICAS. 1968. irreg., no.3, 1970. $4.20 per no. Instituto de Tecnologia de Alimentos, C.P. 139, Campinas, S.P., Brazil.

664 641   BL   ISSN 0074-0152
INSTITUTO DE TECNOLOGIA DE ALIMENTOS. INSTRUCOES TECNICAS. 1968. irreg. Instituto de Tecnologia de Alimentos, C.P. 139, Campinas, S.P., Brazil.

INSTITUTO PANAMERICANO DE PROTECCION DE ALIMENTOS Y ZOONOSIS. PUBLICACION TECNICA. see *VETERINARY SCIENCE*

INSTITUTO SUPERIOR DE AGRONOMIA. ANAIS. see *AGRICULTURE*

INSTRUMENTATION IN THE FOOD AND PHARMACEUTICAL INDUSTRIES. see *INSTRUMENTS*

664   US
INTERIM (CHICAGO).* bi-m. free. Quaker Oats, Corporate Affairs Department, 321 N. Clark, Quaker Tower, Chicago, IL 60610. charts; illus. (tabloid format)

664   AU
INTERNATIONAL ASSOCIATION FOR CEREAL SCIENCE AND TECHNOLOGY. CONGRESS PROCEEDINGS. Title varies--Minutes of Meetings. 1958. biennial; 13th, Vienna, 1990. S.700. International Association for Cereal Science and Technology, P.O. Box 77, A-2320 Schwechat, Austria. **Document type:** proceedings.
Formerly: *International Association for Cereal Chemistry. Congress Proceedings* (ISSN 0074-1450)

641.53   US
INTERNATIONAL ASSOCIATION OF CULINARY PROFESSIONALS FOOD FORUM. 1978. bi-m. $30. International Association of Culinary Professionals, 304 W. Liberty St., Ste. 201, Louisville, KY 40202-3019. TEL 502-581-9786. Ed. Mary Goodbody. adv. circ. 2,080. **Document type:** newsletter.
Former titles: *International Association of Culinary Professionals Commentary*; *International Association of Cooking Professionals Commentary*.
Description: Covers international foods and the food industry.

INTERNATIONAL CENTER FOR COMPANIES OF THE FOOD TRADE AND INDUSTRY. CONGRESS REPORT. see *BUSINESS AND ECONOMICS — Marketing And Purchasing*

664.1   UK
INTERNATIONAL COMMISSION FOR UNIFORM METHODS OF SUGAR ANALYSIS. REPORT OF THE PROCEEDINGS OF THE SESSION (YEAR). 1936. quadriennially, 20th, 1990, Colorado Springs. £40 (foreign £48). (International Commission for Uniform Methods of Sugar Analysis) I C U M S A Publications, c/o British Sugar plc., Technical Centre, Colney, Norwich NR4 7UB, England. TEL 44-493-751678. FAX 44-493-751807. TELEX 32273-SUGPET-G. Ed. John V. Dutton. circ. 1,000. **Document type:** proceedings.
Description: Concerned with the analytical methods for the sugar industry.

664.1   GW   ISSN 0074-2708
INTERNATIONAL COMMISSION OF SUGAR TECHNOLOGY. PROCEEDINGS OF THE GENERAL ASSEMBLY. (Text in English, French, German) 1953. quadrennial, 19th, 1991, Cambridge. DM.100. International Commission of Sugar Technology - Commission Internationale Technique de Sucrerie, c/o Henk van Mailand, General Secretary-Treasurer, Donauwoertherstr. 50, 86861 Rain-Lech, Germany. TEL 09002-71210. FAX 09002-71346. circ. 800. **Indexed:** Chem.Abstr., Sugar Ind.Abstr. **Document type:** proceedings.

664   IO   ISSN 0074-3968
INTERNATIONAL CONGRESS OF SUGARCANE TECHNOLOGISTS. PROCEEDINGS. 1965. triennial, 1986, 19th, Indonesia. $110. International Society of Sugarcane Technologists, PO Box 86 JKWB, Jakarta 10270, Indonesia. Ed. John Clayton. circ. 3,000. **Document type:** proceedings.

664   FR   ISSN 0534-9257
INTERNATIONAL CONGRESS ON CANNED FOODS. TEXTS OF PAPERS PRESENTED AND RESOLUTIONS/CONGRES INTERNATIONAL DE LA CONSERVE. TEXTES DES COMMUNICATIONS. (Text in English and French; summaries in English, French and German) irreg., 10th, Paris, 1991. International Permanent Committee on Canned Foods - Comite International Permanent de la Conserve, c/o Yves Michelon, Sec.-Gen., 44 rue d'Alesia, 75682 Paris, France. TEL 33-1-43213821. FAX 33-1-43216839. **Document type:** proceedings.

664 670   US
INTERNATIONAL FOOD DIRECTORY. (Text in Arabic, English, French, Spanish) 1980. a. $250. Supermarket Productions, Box 6124, San Rafael, CA 94903. TEL 415-479-0211. Ed. Joan Adams. adv. contact: J.M. Adlman. bk.rev.; bibl. circ. 1,200. **Document type:** directory.
Description: Covers food and foodproducts worldwide.

664   UK   ISSN 0961-2831
INTERNATIONAL FOOD HYGIENE. 1989. bi-m. £30. Positive Action Publications Ltd., P.O. Box 4, Driffield, N. Humberside YO25 9DJ, England. TEL 0377-241724. FAX 0377-241910. Ed. Nigel Horrox; Pub. Nigel Horrox. adv. contact: Derrick Blunden. bk.rev. circ. 8,500. **Document type:** trade publication.
—BLDSC (4540.300800).
Description: Covers all aspects of food safety, hygiene and microbiology.

664   NE   ISSN 0924-5863
INTERNATIONAL FOOD INGREDIENTS; magazine on food ingredients and additives. 1989. bi-m. fl.120 in EC; fl.150 in rest of Europe; elsewhere $120 (effective 1994). Morgan Grampian Process Press Europe, P.O. Box 325, 3600 AH Maarssen, Netherlands. TEL 31-3465-73777. FAX 31-3465-73811. Ed. Jos van Haastrecht; Pub. Emile Blomme. adv. contact: Norbert Boutens. bk.rev.; illus.; mkt.; pat.; circ. 8,500 (controlled). **Document type:** trade publication.
—BLDSC (4540.301600).
Description: Covers research in food ingredients and additives, including new or novel applications, stabilizers, emulsifiers. Also covers food industry mergers, business trends, and new products.

664   UK   ISSN 0960-9784
▼**INTERNATIONAL FOOD SAFETY NEWS.** 1992. 10/yr. £180($297) (effective 1994). Churchill Livingstone Medical Journals, Robert Stevenson House, 1-3 Baxter's Pl., Leith Walk, Edinburgh EH1 3AF, Scotland. TEL 031-556-2424. FAX 031-459-1177. (Subscr. to: Longman Group, Journals Subscr. Dept., P.O. Box 77, Fourth Ave., Harlow, Essex CM19 5AA, England; U.S. subscr. to: Churchill Livingstone, 650 Ave. of the Americas, New York, NY 10011. TEL 212-206-5000) Ed. Gordon Paterson. adv. contact: David Dunnachie. circ. 150. **Document type:** newsletter.
Description: Contains current and international news and analysis of information on food pathogens and all aspects of food safety for public health labs, hospitals, environmental health officers and food industry professionals.

664.8 SZ ISSN 0250-944X
INTERNATIONAL FRUIT WORLD; review of the international fruit and vegetable wholesale trade. (Text in English, French, German, Spanish) 1942. 3/yr. 135 SFr. (foreign 270 SFr.). Agropress AG, Aeschengraben 16, CH-4051 Basel, Switzerland. TEL 061-2721170. FAX 061-2721126. adv.; bk.rev.; charts; illus.; stat.; tr.lit.; index. circ. 5,500. **Indexed:** Curr.Pack.Abstr., Food Sci.& Tech.Abstr., Packag.Sci.Tech. **Document type:** trade publication.
—BLDSC (4540.400000).

INTERNATIONAL JOURNAL OF FOOD MICROBIOLOGY. see BIOLOGY — Microbiology

664 UK ISSN 0950-5423
TX341 CODEN: IJFTEZ
INTERNATIONAL JOURNAL OF FOOD SCIENCE AND TECHNOLOGY. 1966. bi-m. £184 in Europe; elsewhere £202 ($300) (effective 1994). (Institute of Food Science and Technology of the United Kingdom) Blackwell Scientific Publications Ltd., Osney Mead, Oxford OX2 0EL, England. TEL 0865-240201. FAX 0865-721205. TELEX 83355-MEDBOK-G. Ed. D.G. Land. adv.; bk.rev.; charts; illus.; index. circ. 3,000. (also avail. in microform from UMI; back issues avail.; reprint service avail. from ISI) **Indexed:** ASCA, Br.Tech.Ind., Chem.Abstr., Curr.Adv.Ecol.Sci., Curr.Cont., Curr.Pack.Abstr., Dairy Sci.Abstr., Excerp.Med., Food Sci.& Tech.Abstr., Foul.Prev.Res.Dig., Hort.Abstr., Ind.Sci.Rev., Nutr.Abstr., Packag.Sci.Tech., Rice Abstr., Risk Abstr., Sci.Cit.Ind., Sugar Ind.Abstr. **Document type:** academic/scholarly publication.
—BLDSC (4542.253200); Faxon; UnCover; SWETS; UMI; CASDDS. **CCC.**
Formerly: Journal of Food Technology (ISSN 0022-1163)
Description: Research articles on the processing of food.
Refereed Serial

664 642.47 613
614 UK
INTERNATIONAL JOURNAL OF HYGIENE AND NUTRITION IN FOOD SERVICE AND CATERING. 1987. 4/yr. £79($159) A B Academic Publishers, P.O. Box 42, Bicester, Oxon. OX6 7NW, England. TEL 0869-320949. Eds. Drs. Robert Charles, Michael Kipps. **Indexed:** Art.Hosp.& Tour. **Document type:** trade publication.
—BLDSC (3092.885000).
Formerly: Catering and Health (ISSN 0267-3851)
Description: Concerned with the nutritional and hygienic aspects of foodservice.

664 II ISSN 0047-1151
INTERNATIONAL PRESS CUTTING SERVICE: PROCESSED FOOD PRODUCTS - SPICES. 1967. w. $65. International Press Cutting Service, Box 63, Allahabad 211001, India. Ed. N. Khanna. bk.rev.; index. circ. 1,200. (processed)

664.1 II ISSN 0047-1089
INTERNATIONAL PRESS CUTTING SERVICE: SUGAR - GUR - KHANDASARI. 1967. w. $65. International Press Cutting Service, PO Box 63, Allahabad 211001, India. Ed. N. Khanna. bk.rev.; index. circ. 1,200. (also avail. in processed)

663.9 II ISSN 0047-1100
INTERNATIONAL PRESS CUTTING SERVICE: TEA AND COFFEE NEWS. 1967. w. $65. International Press Cutting Service, Box 63, Allahabad 211001, India. Ed. N. Khanna. bk.rev.; index. circ. 1,200. (processed)

INTERNATIONAL PRESS CUTTING SERVICE: WHEAT & WHEAT PRODUCTS (RICE - FOOD GRAINS). see AGRICULTURE — Feed, Flour And Grain

664 640.73 US
INTERNATIONAL PRODUCT ALERT. 1983. s-m. $600. Marketing Intelligence Service Ltd., 33 Academy St., Naples, NY 14512. TEL 716-374-6326. FAX 716-374-5217. TELEX 469979. Ed. Sherie Meeker Barton. index. (back issues avail.)
●Also available online. Vendor(s): Data-Star, DIALOG Information Services, Inc.
Description: Introduces new products throughout 20 overseas countries.

664.1 UK ISSN 0020-8841
TP375 CODEN: ISUJA3
INTERNATIONAL SUGAR JOURNAL; a technical and commercial periodical devoted entirely to the sugar and sweetener industry. 1869. m. $155. International Media Ltd., P.O. Box 26, Port Talbot, W. Glamorgan SA13 1NX, Wales. TEL 44-639-887498. FAX 44-639-899830. Ed. N.J. Davies. adv.; bk.rev.; abstr.; charts; illus.; pat.; stat.; tr.lit. circ. 4,000. **Indexed:** Agri.Eng.Abstr., Anal.Abstr., Biol.Abstr., Br.Tech.Ind., Chem.Abstr., Crop Physiol.Abstr., Curr.Cont., Eng.Ind., Excerp.Med., Food Sci.& Tech.Abstr., Helminthol.Abstr., Herb.Abstr., Hort.Abstr., Key to Econ.Sci., Rural Recreat.Tour.Abstr., Soils & Fert., Sugar Ind.Abstr., Weed Abstr., World Agri.Econ.& Rural Sociol.Abstr. **Document type:** trade publication.
—BLDSC (4550.000000); Faxon; UnCover; SWETS; UMI; CASDDS.

664.1 319 UK
▼**INTERNATIONAL SUGAR ORGANIZATION. MARKET REPORT AND PRESS SUMMARY.** 1993. m. £20 (foreign £35). International Sugar Organization, 1 Canada Sq., Canary Wharf, London E14 5AA, England. TEL 071-513-1144. FAX 071-513-1146. TELEX 24143. stat. **Document type:** trade publication.
Description: Updates statistical reports and covers the world sugar market.

664.1 319 UK
INTERNATIONAL SUGAR ORGANIZATION. PROCEEDINGS. a. £20. International Sugar Organization, 1 Canada Sq., Canary Wharf, London E14 5AA, England. TEL 071-513-1144. FAX 071-513-1146. TELEX 24143. **Document type:** proceedings.

664.1 319 UK
INTERNATIONAL SUGAR ORGANIZATION. QUARTERLY MARKET REVIEW. 5/yr. £30. International Sugar Organization, 1 Canada Sq., Canary Wharf, London E14 5AA, England. TEL 071-513-1144. FAX 071-513-1146. TELEX 24143. **Document type:** trade publication.
Description: Reviews the status of the world sugar market.

664.1 UK
INTERNATIONAL SUGAR ORGANIZATION. SUGAR YEAR BOOK. a. £30. International Sugar Organization, 1 Canada Sq., Canary Wharf, London E14 5AA, England. TEL 071-513-1144. FAX 071-513-1146. TELEX 24143. **Indexed:** IIS. **Document type:** trade publication.

INTERNATIONAL UNION OF FOOD, AGRICULTURAL, HOTEL, RESTAURANT, CATERING, TOBACCO AND ALLIED WORKERS' ASSOCIATIONS. MEETING OF THE EXECUTIVE COMMITTEE. I. DOCUMENTS OF THE SECRETARIAT. II. SUMMARY REPORT. see LABOR UNIONS

INTERNATIONAL UNION OF FOOD, AGRICULTURAL, HOTEL, RESTAURANT, CATERING, TOBACCO AND ALLIED WORKERS' ASSOCIATIONS. NEWS BULLETIN. see LABOR UNIONS

IOWA PORK TODAY. see AGRICULTURE — Poultry And Livestock

664 IE ISSN 0047-1445
IRISH BACON NEWS.* 1967. q. free. Tara Publishing Co. Ltd., Poolbeg House, Poolbeg St., Dublin 2, Ireland. Ed. Colm Cronin. adv.; circ. 7,000 (controlled). (also avail. in microfilm from UMI; reprint service avail. from UMI)

664 IE
IRISH FOOD. 4/yr. 31 Deansgrange Rd., Blackrock, Co. Dublin, Ireland. TEL 893305. FAX 896406. Ed. Brian Gilsenan. circ. 3,500.

664 IE
IRISH MASTER BUTCHER. 6/yr. 31 Deansgrange Rd., Blackrock, Co. Dublin, Ireland. TEL 893305. FAX 896406. Ed. William Ryan. bk.rev. circ. 2,500.

664.9 IE
IRISH MEAT JOURNAL. 4/yr. Tara Publishing Co. Ltd., Poolbeg House, 1-2 Poolbeg St., Dublin 2, Ireland. TEL 719244. FAX 719283. Ed. Fergus Farrell. circ. 3,500.

664 IT ISSN 1120-1770
CODEN: ITFSEY
ITALIAN JOURNAL OF FOOD SCIENCE. (Text in English) 1989. q. L 150000($120) Chiriotti Editori, Viale Rimembranza, 60, PO Box 66, 10064 Pinerolo, Italy. TEL 121-794493. FAX 121-794480. Ed. Paolo Fantozzi.
—BLDSC (4588.340370); CASDDS. **CCC.**
Description: Publishes research articles, short communications and critical reviews in food science and technology and in related areas such as nutrition, microbiology and safety.

664 IT
ITALIAN MAGAZINE FOOD PROCESSING. (Text in English and French or German, Spanish) 4/yr. $63. Editrice Zeus, Corso Buenos Aires 47, 20124 Milan, Italy. TEL 29406225. FAX 29522168. Ed. Enrico Maffizzoni. circ. 6,500. **Document type:** trade publication.
Description: Covers machinery, plant components, and products for the food and drink industry.

651.43 US
J A C NEWSLETTER. q. J A C Creative Foods, Inc., 3050 E. 11th St., Los Angeles, CA 90023-3606. TEL 213-263-3344. FAX 213-263-3344. Ed. Terri Kishimoto.

664.3 US ISSN 0021-387X
JACOBSEN'S FATS & OILS BULLETIN. d. $288 (foreign $448). Jacobsen Publishing Co., 300 W. Adams St., Chicago, IL 60606. TEL 312-726-6600. FAX 312-726-6654. TELEX 190053. Ed. R. Everett Hodgson. adv.; mkt.; stat. **Document type:** bulletin.
Description: Daily market summary, highlighting vegetable oil, tallow and grease marketing.

664 630 JA ISSN 0301-9780
TX341 CODEN: SSKKCY
JAPAN. MINISTRY OF AGRICULTURE, FORESTRY AND FISHERIES. NATIONAL FOOD RESEARCH INSTITUTE. REPORT. (Text in English or Japanese) s-a. Ministry of Agriculture, Forestry and Fisheries, National Food Research Institute, 2-1-2, Kannondai, Yatabe-Cho, Tsukuba-Gun, Ibaraki-Ken 350, Japan.
—BLDSC (7560.650000); CASDDS.

664 JA
JAPAN. NATIONAL FOOD RESEARCH INSTITUTE. NEWS. (Text in Japanese) 1969. s-a. National Food Research Institute, 2-1-2, Kannondai, Yatabe-Machi, Tsukuba-Gun, Ibaraki 305, Japan. circ. 1,600.

664 JA ISSN 0386-2372
JAPAN MEAT PROCESSING JOURNAL. (Text in Japanese) m. 500 Yen($4) Japan Meat Processors Association, 5-6, 1-chome, Ebisu, Shibuya-ku, Tokyo 150, Japan. TEL 03-444-1211.

338.4 JA
JAPAN SUGAR YEARBOOK. (Text in English) 1958. a. free. Mitsui & Co., Ltd., C.P.O. Box 822, Tokyo 100-91, Japan. adv.; charts; illus.; stat. circ. 600.

664.2 JA ISSN 0021-5406
QP702.S75 CODEN: DPNKAV
JAPANESE SOCIETY OF STARCH SCIENCE. JOURNAL/DENPUN KAGAKU. (Text in Japanese or English; summaries in English) 1953. q. $40. Japanese Society of Starch Science, c/o National Food Research Institute, 2-1-2, Kannondai, Tsukuba 305, Japan. FAX 0298-38-7996. Ed. Susumu Hizukuri. adv.; bk.rev.; abstr.; charts; pat.; cum.index. circ. 1,200. (tabloid format) **Indexed:** Chem.Abstr., Curr.Adv.Biochem., Curr.Adv.Ecol.Sci., Curr.Cont., Food Sci.& Tech.Abstr.
—BLDSC (5066.680000); CASDDS.
Formerly: Technological Society of Starch. Journal.
Description: Covers chemistry and enzymology of starch and other carbohydrates.

664 UK ISSN 0264-3812
JAPANSCAN FOOD INDUSTRY BULLETIN. 1983. m. $475. Mitaka Ltd., 4-12 Morton St., Leamington Spa, Warwickshire CV32 5SY, England. TEL 0926-311126. FAX 0926-332990. (Subscr. to: Anville, Upper Quinton, Stratford-on-Avon CV37 8SX, England. TEL 0739-720395) Ed. Carole Burke. adv. circ. 200. (back issues avail.) **Document type:** bulletin, trade publication.
—BLDSC (4662.553000).
Description: Provides information on the Japanese food industry market including new products, market intelligence, legislation, trends and forecasts.

FOOD AND FOOD INDUSTRIES

JOINT F A O - W H O CODEX ALIMENTARIUS COMMISSION. REPORT OF THE SESSION. see *PUBLIC HEALTH AND SAFETY*

JOURNAL OF AGRICULTURAL & FOOD INFORMATION. see *AGRICULTURE*

664 US ISSN 1049-8850
SH334.9 CODEN: JAFPE5
JOURNAL OF AQUATIC FOOD PRODUCT TECHNOLOGY. 1991. q. $24 to individuals (foreign $33.60); institutions $36 (foreign $50.40); libraries $48 (foreign $67.20). Haworth Press, Inc., Food Products Press, 10 Alice St., Binghamton, NY 13904-1580. TEL 800-342-9678. FAX 607-722-1424. Ed. George M. Pigott. adv.: page $300. (also avail. in microfiche from HAW; reprint service avail. from HAW) **Indexed:** Biol.Dig., Environ.Abstr., Environ.Per.Bibl. (1991-), Food Sci.& Tech.Abstr., Sport Fish.Abstr. **Document type:** academic/scholarly publication.
—BLDSC (4947.159500); EI; UnCover; CASDDS.
Description: Disseminates international scientific information on aquatic food products.
Refereed Serial

664 US ISSN 1053-8739
TX946 CODEN: JCUFEU
▼**JOURNAL OF COLLEGE & UNIVERSITY FOODSERVICE.** 1993. q. $18 to individuals; institutions $24; libraries $36. Haworth Press, Inc., Food Products Press, 10 Alice St., Binghamton, NY 13904-1580. TEL 800-342-9678. FAX 607-722-1424. TELEX 49322599. Ed. Mahmood A. Khan. adv.; bk.rev. (also avail. in microfiche from HAW; reprint service avail. from HAW) **Indexed:** Educ.Admin.Abstr., Food Sci.& Tech.Abstr., Ref.Zh.
Description: Covers a broad spectrum of topics in institutional foodservice.
Refereed Serial

642.5 US ISSN 1052-9241
▼**JOURNAL OF CULINARY PRACTICE.** 1993. q. $28 to individuals; institutions $30; libraries $36. Haworth Press, Inc., 10 Alice St., Binghamton, NY 13904. TEL 607-722-5857; 800-342-9678. FAX 607-722-1424. TELEX 4932599. Ed. Darrell Gerdes. adv.; bk.rev. (also avail. in microfiche from UMI; reprint service avail. from HAW) **Indexed:** Food Sci.& Tech.Abstr. **Document type:** academic/scholarly publication.
Description: Devoted to research-based articles on food preparation and cooking.
Refereed Serial

612.3 US ISSN 0145-8884
TX545 CODEN: JFBIDW
JOURNAL OF FOOD BIOCHEMISTRY. 1977. 6/yr. $137. Food & Nutrition Press, Inc., 2 Corporate Dr., Box 374, Trumbull, CT 06611. TEL 203-261-8587. FAX 203-261-9724. Ed. J.R. Whitaker. bk.rev.; charts; illus.; index. (back issues avail.) **Indexed:** Chem.Abstr., Curr.Cont., Curr.Pack.Abstr., Dairy Sci.Abstr., Food Sci.& Tech.Abstr., Ind.Sci.Rev., Nutr.Abstr., Sci.Cit.Ind. **Document type:** academic/scholarly publication.
—BLDSC (4984.540000); Faxon; UnCover; SWETS; CASDDS.
Description: Devoted to original research on the effects of handling, storage and processing on the biochemistry of food tissues and syatems. Emphasizes the description of changes of chemical constituents, enzymes and cellular structures, and on the mechanisms that control these events.

664 US ISSN 0889-1575
TX501 CODEN: JFCAEE
JOURNAL OF FOOD COMPOSITION AND ANALYSIS. 1987. q. $110 (foreign $128). (United Nations University International Network of Foods Data Systems) Academic Press, Inc., Journal Division, 525 B St., Ste. 1900, San Diego, CA 92101-4495. TEL 619-230-1840. FAX 619-699-6800. (Subscr. to: Box 620000, Orlando, FL 32891-8340. TEL 800-543-9534) Ed. Kent K. Stewart. (back issues avail.) **Indexed:** Excerp.Med. **Document type:** academic/scholarly publication.
—BLDSC (4984.541000); Faxon; UnCover; SWETS; CASDDS. **CCC.**
Description: Covers all scientific aspects of the chemical composition of human foods.

658.8 US ISSN 0047-245X
HD9001
JOURNAL OF FOOD DISTRIBUTION RESEARCH. 1969. 2/yr. $50 (subscr. includes Newsletter). Food Distribution Research Society, 917 Cypress Lane, Greentown, PA 18426. TEL 717-857-9211. FAX 717-857-1445. Ed. Carl Toensmeyer. adv.; bibl.; charts; illus. circ. 300.
—BLDSC (4984.542000).
Description: Serves as an information clearinghouse for past, current, and future food distribution research, and provides channels for exchange of information.

664 UK ISSN 0260-8774
CODEN: JFOEDH
JOURNAL OF FOOD ENGINEERING. 1982. 12/yr. (in 3 vols., 4 nos./vol.). £507($780) (effective 1994). Elsevier Science Ltd., Oxford Fulfilment Centre, P.O. Box 800, Kidlington, Oxford OX5 1DX, England. TEL 44-865-843000. FAX 44-865-843010. (Subscr. in U.S. and Canada to: Elsevier Science, 660 White Plains Rd., Tarrytown, NY 10591-5153. TEL 914-524-9200. FAX 914-333-2444) Eds. B.M. McKenna, M.R. Okos. adv.; bk.rev.; illus. (also avail. in microform from UMI; back issues avail.) **Indexed:** Biol.Abstr., Chem.Abstr., Chem.Eng.Abstr., Dairy Sci.Abstr., Eng.Ind., Food Sci.& Tech.Abstr., Sci.Cit.Ind., T.C.E.A. **Document type:** academic/scholarly publication.
—BLDSC (4984.543000); EI; Faxon; UnCover; SWETS; CASDDS. **CCC.**
Description: Publishes papers on any subject at the interface between food and engineering, particularly those of relevance to industry.
Refereed Serial

664 US ISSN 1065-7258
CODEN: JFFLES
▼**JOURNAL OF FOOD LIPIDS.** 1993. q. $90 (effective 1993). Food & Nutrition Press, Inc., 2 Corporate Dr., Box 374, Trumbull, CT 06611. TEL 203-261-8587. FAX 203-261-9724. Ed. Fereidoon Shahidi.
—BLDSC (4984.544000); CASDDS.
Description: Provides an international forum for original research papers covering all aspects of food lipids: chemistry, analysis, methodology, nutrition, processing, stability and stabilization, and quality.

664 US ISSN 0145-8876
TP368 CODEN: JFPEDM
JOURNAL OF FOOD PROCESS ENGINEERING. 1977. 4/yr. $132. Food & Nutrition Press, Inc., 2 Corporate Dr., Box 374, Trumbull, CT 06611. TEL 203-261-8587. FAX 203-261-9724. Eds. D.R. Heldman, R.P. Singh. charts; illus.; index. (back issues avail.) **Indexed:** Curr.Pack.Abstr., Dairy Sci.Abstr., Food Sci.& Tech.Abstr., Int.Packag.Abstr. **Document type:** academic/scholarly publication.
—BLDSC (4984.545000); EI; Faxon; UnCover; SWETS; CASDDS.
Description: Specializes in the engineering aspects of equipment and process design for the food industry including packaging and sanitation.

664 US ISSN 0145-8892
TP368 CODEN: JFPPDL
JOURNAL OF FOOD PROCESSING AND PRESERVATION. 1977. 6/yr. $143. Food & Nutrition Press, Inc., 2 Corporate Dr., Box 374, Trumbull, CT 06611. TEL 203-261-8587. FAX 203-261-9724. Ed. Daryl B. Lund. bk.rev.; charts; illus.; index. (back issues avail.) **Indexed:** Biol.Abstr., Chem.Abstr., Curr.Cont., Curr.Pack.Abstr., Dairy Sci.Abstr., Food Sci.& Tech.Abstr., Ind.Sci.Rev., INIS Atomind., Int.Packag.Abstr., Packag.Sci.Tech., Sci.Cit.Ind., Sugar Ind.Abstr.
—BLDSC (4984.548000); Faxon; UnCover; SWETS; CASDDS.
Description: Covers chemistry, microbiology and engineering of food systems with respect to processing and preservation.

664 658 US ISSN 1045-4446
HD9000.1 CODEN: JFPMED
▼**JOURNAL OF FOOD PRODUCTS MARKETING.** 1992. q. $36 to individuals; institutions $48; libraries $75. Haworth Press, Inc., 10 Alice St., Binghamton, NY 13904. TEL 607-722-5857; 800-342-9678. FAX 607-722-1424. Ed. John L. Stanton. (also avail. in microform from UMI; reprint service avail. from HAW)
Description: Devoted to the full range of food product marketing, from food promotion and advertising through new food product development and consumer behavior research.
Refereed Serial

JOURNAL OF FOOD PROTECTION. see *PUBLIC HEALTH AND SAFETY*

664 US ISSN 0146-9428
TP372.5 CODEN: JFQUD7
JOURNAL OF FOOD QUALITY. 1977. 6/yr. $143. Food & Nutrition Press, Inc., 2 Corporate Dr., Box 374, Trumbull, CT 06611. TEL 203-261-8587. FAX 203-261-9724. Ed. John J. Powers. bk.rev.; charts; illus.; stat.; index. (back issues avail.) **Indexed:** Chem.Abstr., Curr.Adv.Ecol.Sci., Curr.Pack.Abstr., Dairy Sci.Abstr., Excerp.Med., Food Sci.& Tech.Abstr., Int.Packag.Abstr., Maize Abstr., Rev.Med.& Vet.Mycol., Rev.Plant Path., Sugar Ind.Abstr. **Document type:** academic/scholarly publication.
—BLDSC (4984.555000); Faxon; UnCover; SWETS; CASDDS.
Description: Covers all aspects of food quality assurance and regulations including environmental factors.

664 US ISSN 0149-6085
TX501 CODEN: JFSADP
JOURNAL OF FOOD SAFETY. 1977. q. $110. Food & Nutrition Press, Inc., 2 Corporate Dr., Box 374, Trumbull, CT 06611. TEL 203-261-8587. FAX 203-261-9724. Ed. T.J. Montville. bk.rev.; abstr.; charts; illus. (back issues avail.) **Indexed:** Chem.Abstr., Curr.Adv.Ecol.Sci., Curr.Cont., Curr.Pack.Abstr., Dairy Sci.Abstr., Ind.Sci.Rev., Ind.Vet., Rev.Med.& Vet.Mycol., Risk Abstr., Sci.Cit.Ind., Vet.Bull. **Document type:** academic/scholarly publication.
—BLDSC (4984.558000); Faxon; UnCover; SWETS; CASDDS.
Description: Emphasizes chemical and microbiological coverage of food safety. Includes toxicology, metabolism, and environmental conversion of materials entering the food supply.

641 664 US ISSN 0022-1147
TX1 CODEN: JFDSAZ
JOURNAL OF FOOD SCIENCE. 1936. bi-m. $100 to non-members; members $20. Institute of Food Technologists, 221 N. LaSalle St., Chicago, IL 60601. TEL 312-782-8424. Ed. Dr. Robert E. Berry. abstr.; bibl.; charts; illus.; index. circ. 12,000. (also avail. in microfilm from UMI; reprint service avail. from UMI) **Indexed:** Abstr.Hyg., Agri.Eng.Abstr., Anal.Abstr., Biol.& Agr.Ind., Biotech.Abstr., Cadscan, Chem.Abstr., Crop Physiol.Abstr., Curr.Adv.Ecol.Sci., Curr.Cont., Curr.Pack.Abstr., Dairy Sci.Abstr., Diar.Dis.Res., Environ.Per.Bibl., Excerp.Med., Field Crop Abstr., Food Sci.& Tech.Abstr., Gen.Sci.Ind., Helminthol.Abstr., Herb.Abstr., Hort.Abstr., Ind.Sci.Rev., Ind.Vet., INIS Atomind., Lead Abstr., Maize Abstr., Mass Spectr.Bull., Nutr.Abstr., Ocean.Abstr., Packag.Sci.Tech., Pig News & Info., Plant Grow.Reg.Abstr., Potato Abstr., Poult.Abstr., Psychol.Abstr., Rev.Med.& Vet.Mycol., Rice Abstr., Sci.Cit.Ind., Seed Abstr., Sel.Water Res.Abstr., Sorghum & Millets Abstr., Soyabean Abstr., Sugar Ind.Abstr., Triticale Abstr., Trop.Oil Seeds Abstr., Vet.Bull., VITIS, Zincscan. **Document type:** trade publication.
—BLDSC (4984.560000); Faxon; UnCover; SWETS; UMI; CASDDS. **CCC.**

FOOD AND FOOD INDUSTRIES

664   II   ISSN 0022-1155
TX341   CODEN: JFSTAB
JOURNAL OF FOOD SCIENCE AND TECHNOLOGY. (Text in English) 1964. bi-m. Rs.300($125) (effective 1991). Association of Food Scientists and Technologists (India), Central Executive Committee, CFTRI Campus, Mysore 570 013, India. TEL 21747. FAX 27697. TELEX 846241 FTRI IN. Ed. B.K. Lonsane. adv.; bk.rev.; charts; illus.; index. circ. 2,500. **Indexed:** Agri.Eng.Abstr., Anal.Abstr., Biol.Abstr., Chem.Abstr., Crop Physiol.Abstr., Curr.Adv.Ecol.Sci., Curr.Cont., Curr.Pack.Abstr., Dairy Sci.Abstr., Excerp.Med., Field Crop Abstr., Food Sci.& Tech.Abstr., Hort.Abstr., Ind.Vet., INIS Atomind., Int.Packag.Abstr., Mass Spectr.Bull., Nutr.Abstr., Packag.Sci.Tech., Plant Grow.Reg.Abstr., Poult.Abstr., Rev.Med.& Vet.Mycol., Rev.Plant Path., Rice Abstr., Seed Abstr., Sorghum & Millets Abstr., Triticale Abstr., Trop.Oil Seeds Abstr., Vet.Bull.
—BLDSC (4984.561000); UnCover; SWETS; CASDDS.
   Description: Stimulates research on various aspects of food science and technology.
   Refereed Serial

664   US   ISSN 0196-4283
JOURNAL OF FOODSERVICE SYSTEMS. 1980. 4/yr. $75. (Society of Foodservice Systems) Food & Nutrition Press, Inc., 2 Corporate Dr., Box 374, Trumbull, CT 06611. TEL 203-261-8587. FAX 203-261-9724. Ed. Carol A. Sawyer. adv.; bk.rev.; charts; illus.; index. (back issues avail.) **Indexed:** Food Sci.& Tech.Abstr. **Document type:** academic/scholarly publication.
—BLDSC (4984.571000); Faxon; UnCover; SWETS.
   Description: Devoted to original research pertaining to foodservice systems and the application to systems of the various disciplines required in their analysis, design and management, i.e., foodservice management, operations research and system analysis, food technology, nutrition, food microbiology, behavioral psychology, marketing, and process and facility engineering.

664   US   ISSN 1046-0756
TX556.M4   CODEN: JMFOEI
JOURNAL OF MUSCLE FOODS. 1990. q. $110. Food & Nutrition Press, Inc., 2 Corporate Dr., Trumbull, CT 06611. TEL 203-261-8587. FAX 203-261-9724. Ed. Norman G. Marriott. **Document type:** academic/scholarly publication.
—BLDSC (5021.110000).
   Description: Contains research and review manuscripts related to beef, lamb, veal, pork, seafood, poultry and muscle of other species that are consumed by humans.

JOURNAL OF RESTAURANT & FOODSERVICE MARKETING. see HOTELS AND RESTAURANTS

JOURNAL OF SENSORY STUDIES. see MEDICAL SCIENCES — Psychiatry And Neurology

615.1   US   ISSN 0022-4901
TX341   CODEN: JTXSBU
JOURNAL OF TEXTURE STUDIES; an international journal of rheology, psychorheology, physical and sensory testing of foods and pharmaceuticals. 1969. q. $148. Food & Nutrition Press, Inc., 2 Corporate Dr., Box 374, Trumbull, CT 06611. TEL 203-261-8587. FAX 203-261-9724. Ed. M.C. Bourne. adv.; bk.rev.; illus.; index. **Indexed:** Biol.Abstr., Chem.Abstr., Curr.Adv.Ecol.Sci., Curr.Cont., Dairy Sci.Abstr., Food Sci.& Tech.Abstr. **Document type:** academic/scholarly publication.
—BLDSC (5069.055000); Faxon; UnCover; SWETS; CASDDS.
   Description: Covers textural subjects for those interested in texture as part of commodity work and for rheologists attempting to relate fundamental measurements to textural attributes.

JOURNAL OF THE SCIENCE OF FOOD AND AGRICULTURE. see AGRICULTURE

663.93   ET   ISSN 1010-1616
KAFFA. 4/yr. Ethiopian Coffee & Haricot Beans Exporters' Association, P.O. Box 1982, Addis Ababa, Ethiopia. adv.

051   US
KANSAS FOOD NEWS. m. Kansas Food Dealers Association, 2809 W. 47th St., Shawnee Mission, KS 66205-1602. TEL 913-384-3838. FAX 913-384-3868. Ed. James G. Sheehan. circ. 1,400.

KANSAS RESTAURANT. see HOTELS AND RESTAURANTS

KANTINEN. see CLUBS

664 296   US
KASHRUS FAXLETTER. 1991. m. $30. Yeshiva Birkas Reuven, Box 204, Brooklyn, NY 11204. Ed. Rabbi Yosef Wikler. circ. 100.

664 338   CN   ISSN 0843-3402
KASHRUTH DIRECTORY. a. free. 4600 Bathurst St., Ste. 240, Willowdale, Ont. M2R 3V2, Canada. TEL 416-635-9550. **Document type:** directory.

663.93 630   KE
KENYA COFFEE; monthly bulletin. (Text in English) 1935. m. KShs.250($11) (foreign KShs.300). Coffee Board of Kenya, Coffee Plaza, Naile Selassie Ave., Box 30566, Nairobi, Kenya. (Co-sponsor: Coffee Research Foundation) Ed. P.M. Kivila. adv.; charts; illus. circ. 3,500. **Indexed:** Agri.Eng.Abstr., Agroforest.Abstr., Biotech.Abstr., Excerp.Med., Food Sci.& Tech.Abstr., Hort.Abstr., Plant Breed.Abstr., Rev.Plant Path., Rural Recreat.Tour.Abstr., Soils & Fert., World Agri.Econ.& Rural Sociol.Abstr. **Document type:** bulletin, trade publication.
   Description: Addresses activities of the coffee board of Kenya; discusses techniques and practices to improve coffee yield and quality.

663.94   KE
KENYA TEA DEVELOPMENT AUTHORITY. ANNUAL REPORT AND ACCOUNTS. (Text in English) a. Kenya Tea Development Authority, P.O. Box 30213, Nairobi, Kenya.

KEUKEN. see HOTELS AND RESTAURANTS

664   II   ISSN 0023-1037
KHADYA VIGYAN. (Text in Hindi) 1957. q. Central Food Technological Research Institute, Mysore 570 013, India. Ed. B. Anuradha. adv.; bk.rev.; charts; illus.; circ. 1,500 (controlled).

664.1   JA   ISSN 0023-138X
KIKAN TOGYO SHIHO/QUARTERLY INFORMATION OF SUGAR INDUSTRY. (Text in Japanese) 1964. q. membership. Japan Sugar Refiners' Association - Seito Kogyokai, 5-7 Sanbancho, Chiyoda-ku, Tokyo 102, Japan. circ. 800.

641.53   GW
KOCHEN UND GENIESSEN. 1985. m. DM.48 (foreign DM.81.60). Heinrich Bauer Verlag, Burchardstr. 11, 20095 Hamburg, Germany. TEL 040-3019-0. FAX 040-324879. Ed. Juergen Pietzker. adv. contact: Goesta Ahrweiler. circ. 143,247. **Document type:** consumer publication.

664.9   DK   ISSN 0906-2556
KOEDBRANCHEN. 1972. 10/yr. DKK 245. Danske Slagtermestres Landsforening, Postboks 709, DK-5230 Odense M, Denmark. TEL 66-128730. FAX 66-128794. Ed. Hanne Buhl. adv.: B&W page DKK 5700, color page DKK 10500; trim 297 x 210. bk.rev.; circ. 4,500 (controlled). **Document type:** trade publication.
   Former titles: Den Rigtige Slagter; Koedbranchen; Ugenyt; Slagtertidende.

664.9   SW   ISSN 0047-3510
KOETTBRANSCHEN. 1943. m. (10/yr). SEK 280. Koettbranschens Riksforbund, P.O. Box 5093, 121 16 Johanneshov, Sweden. FAX 08-6484668. Ed. Arne Frederiksson. adv.; bk.rev.; illus.; stat. circ. 4,500. **Document type:** trade publication.
   Formerly (until 1961): Svensk Slakteri- och Charkuteritidning.

KOMPASS PROFESSIONNEL. AGRICULTURE, ALIMENTATION. see BUSINESS AND ECONOMICS — Trade And Industrial Directories

KOMPASS PROFESSIONNELS. see BUSINESS AND ECONOMICS — Trade And Industrial Directories

664   AU   ISSN 0023-2432
KONDITOR ZEITUNG; Blaetter fuer die Suesswarenindustrie. 1872. m. DM.60. Zeitungsverlag Kuhn, Kutschkergasse 42, D-1180 Wien, Austria. adv.; bk.rev.; abstr.; stat.; tr.lit.; index. circ. 4,050.

664   RU   ISSN 0023-3587
TX599   CODEN: KOPRAU
KONSERVNAYA I OVOSHCHESUSHIL'NAYA PROMYSHLENNOST.* 1930. m. $19.80. (Gosudarstvennyi Nauchno-tekhnicheskii Komitet pri Sovete Ministrov) Izdatel'stvo Kolos, Sadovo-Spasskaya, 18, 107807 Moscow, Russia. bk.rev.; bibl. illus.; index. **Indexed:** Biol.Abstr., Chem.Abstr., Dairy Sci.Abstr., Food Sci.& Tech.Abstr., Nutr.Abstr., Packag.Sci.Tech.

KUECHE; Fachzeitschrift fuer aktuelle Kochkunst, Gastlichkeit und Ernaehrung. see HOTELS AND RESTAURANTS

664   GW
KUECHE IN KRANKENHAUS UND ALTENHEIM. Short title: K K A. 1975. 6/yr. DM.50 (foreign DM.64). Gastro Manuscript Verlag GmbH, Waldstr. 5, 65510 Huenstetten, Germany. TEL 06438-2027. FAX 06438-4190. Ed. Werner Gros. adv.; bk.rev. circ. 8,800. **Document type:** newsletter.

664   XR   ISSN 0023-5830
TP500   CODEN: KVPRAB
KVASNY PRUMYSL/FERMENTATION INDUSTRY; odborny mesicnik pro pracovniky v kvasnem a napojovem prumyslu. (Text in Czech; contents page and summaries also in English, German and Russian) 1955. m. $49.30. (Pivovary a Sladovny) Nakladatelstvi Technicke Literatury, Spalena 51, 113 02 Prague 1, Czech Republic. (Dist. by: Artia, Ve Smeckach 30, 111 27 Prague 1, Czech Republic) Ed. L. Sonkupova. adv.; abstr.; bibl.; charts; illus.; index. circ. 1,550. **Indexed:** Chem.Abstr., Dairy Sci.Abstr., Food Sci.& Tech.Abstr., Sugar Ind.Abstr.
—BLDSC (5134 500000); CASDDS.

664   AG   ISSN 0023-6217
L A M Y A REVISTA MENSUAL.* 1957. m. free. Liga de Almaceneros Minoristas y Afines, Independencia 10, 231 Berazategui, Argentina. adv.; charts; illus.

L P INTERNATIONAL. (Lebensmittel Praxis Verlag GmbH) see FOOD AND FOOD INDUSTRIES — Grocery Trade

664 613.2 615.9   DK   ISSN 0904-5198
L S T NYT. 1988. irreg. (4-6/yr.). DKK 60. Sundhedsministeriet, Levnedsmiddelstyrelsen, Moerkehoej Bygade 19, DK-2860 Soeborg, Denmark. TEL 39-69-66-00. Ed. Christian Rahbek.
   Description: Focuses on current activities of the National Food Agency of Denmark; features articles on toxicology, chemical contaminants in food, nutrition, and law dealing with food administration.

664   FR
LAMY - DEHOVE; reglementation des produits. (Supplements avail.) a. 1100 F. (with supplements 1520 F.)(effective 1993). Lamy S.A., 187-189 Quai de Valmy, 75490 Paris, France. TEL 44-72-13-43. FAX 44-72-13-95. index. (looseleaf format)
   Description: Covers law as it relates to food and the regulation of food products.

664   US
LATIN AMERICAN INTERNATIONAL FOOD INDUSTRY DIRECTORY. (Text in English, Portuguese, Spanish) 1985. a. $150 per m. Aquino Productions, Box 15760, Stamford, CT 06901. TEL 203-325-3138. Ed. Andres C. Aquino. **Document type:** directory.

LEBENSMITTEL PRAXIS; das Magazin fuer den Handel. see FOOD AND FOOD INDUSTRIES — Grocery Trade

664   AU
LEBENSMITTEL REPORT. m. Zeitungsverlag Kuhn und Co. GmbH, Kutschkergasse 42, A-1180 Vienna, Austria. TEL 01-47686. FAX 01-4768621. Ed. Gerd Volker Weege. circ. 5,400. **Document type:** trade publication.

664   SZ
LEBENSMITTEL - REVUE - ALIMENTAIRE. (Editions in French, German, Italian) 1892. m. 50 Fr. Schweizerischer Verband der Lebensmitteldetaillisten - Association Suisse des Detaillants en Alimentation, Falkenplatz 1, CH-3001 Berne, Switzerland. FAX 031-237646. Ec.Bd. adv.; bk.rev.; stat.; tr.lit.; index. circ. 5,270 (all eds.).
   Formerly: Lebensmittelhandel (ISSN 0023-9984)

FOOD AND FOOD INDUSTRIES

664   SZ   ISSN 0256-6575
LEBENSMITTEL-TECHNOLOGIE; Fachzeitschrift fuer Lebensmittel- und Genussmittel-Industrie Maschinen-Apparate-Geraete-Verfahren. Short title: L T. (Text in English, French and German; summaries in English and German) 1968. 10/yr. 92 SFr. (foreign 120 SFr.). Frieden Verlag AG, Guestr. 50, CH-8700 Kusnacht, Switzerland. TEL 01-9105054. FAX 01-9110189. Ed. Eva Frieden. adv.; bk.rev. circ. 6,000. **Indexed:** Curr.Cont. **Document type:** trade publication.

664   AU   ISSN 0254-9298
                    CODEN: LEBIEE
LEBENSMITTEL- UND BIOTECHNOLOGIE. 1984. 5/yr. S.625($57) (Verein Oesterreichischer Lebensmittel- und Biotechnolgen) Fachverlag Wien, Krottenbachstr. 31, A-1190 Vienna, Austria. TEL 0222-367973. FAX 0222-3691949. Ed. Dr. S.K. Fischer. adv.; bk.rev. circ. 2,000. (back issues avail.) **Indexed:** Chem.Abstr., Excerp.Med. **Document type:** trade publication.
—BLDSC (5179.624500); CASDDS.
Description: Examines the biotechnology methods, food industry, food analysis.

664   GW   ISSN 0342-9512
LEBENSMITTEL ZEITUNG. 1947. w. DM.299.80 (foreign DM.467.95). Deutscher Fachverlag GmbH, Mainzer Landstr. 251, 60326 Frankfurt a.M., Germany. TEL 069-759501. FAX 069-75952999. (Subscr. to: Postfach 100606, 60006 Frankfurt a.M., Germany) adv.; bk.rev; abstr.; charts; illus.; stat. circ. 41,991. **Indexed:** Key to Econ.Sci. **Document type:** trade publication.
—SWETS.

664 614.19   GW   ISSN 0937-1478
TP372.5   CODEN: LEBEE2
LEBENSMITTELCHEMIE. 1946. 6/yr. DM.344($235) (Lebensmittelchemie Gesellschaft - Fachgruppe in der Gesellschaft Deutscher Chemiker) V C H Verlagsgesellschaft mbH, Postfach 101161, 69451 Weinheim, Germany. TEL 06201-606-0. FAX 06201-606328. TELEX 465516-VCHWH-D. (US addr.: V C H Publishers Inc., 220 E. 23rd St., New York, NY 10010-4606. TEL 212-683-8333) Ed. K. Herrmann. circ. 3,420. (reprint service avail. from ISI) **Indexed:** Biol.Abstr. (1991-), Chem.Abstr., Excerp.Med., Food Sci.& Tech.Abstr., Sugar Ind.Abstr., VITIS, Weed Abstr. **Document type:** academic/scholarly publication.
—BLDSC (5179.626000); CASDDS. **CCC.**
Formerly (until 1990): Lebensmittel und Gerichtliche Chemie (ISSN 0341-5309)

664   GW   ISSN 0935-865X
LEBENSMITTELREPORT; Drogeriemarkt. 1984. 11/yr. DM.60. L F G Verlag, Ohlenschlagerstr. 6, 81369 Munich, Germany. TEL 089-783071. FAX 089-7809928. Ed. Frank J. Gindler. circ. 33,483. **Document type:** trade publication.

664   GW   ISSN 0047-4290
LEBENSMITTELTECHNIK. 1969. m. DM.70. Rhenania-Fachverlag GmbH, Possmoorweg 5, 22301 Hamburg, Germany. FAX 040-2717-2069. TELEX 213214. Ed. Voelker Herrmann. circ. 6,024. **Indexed:** INIS Atomind., Packag.Sci.Tech. **Document type:** trade publication.
—BLDSC (5179.635000).

LEGISLATIVE MEMORANDA. see HOTELS AND RESTAURANTS

LETTUCE CLUB. see HOME ECONOMICS

664   CC
LIANGSHI WENTI YANJIU/FOOD PROBLEMS RESEARCH.* (Text in Chinese) bi-m. Sichuan Liangshi Jingji Xuehui Yanjiusuo - Sichuan Society of Food Economy, 63 Dajie, Chengdu, Sichuan 610016, People's Republic of China. TEL 663456-254. Ed. Wu Kai.

664.1   XR
LISTY CUKROVARNICKE A REPARSKE. Abbreviated title: L C a R. (Text in Czech; summaries in English, German, Russian) 1882. m. 180 Kcs. Cukrspol Praha Modrany, Komoranska 39, 143 19 Prague 4 - Modrany, Czech Republic. Ed. Emile Wallova. adv.; bk.rev.; charts; illus.; pat.; index. circ. 1,050. (also avail. in microfilm) **Indexed:** Chem.Abstr., Curr.Adv.Ecol.Sci., Curr.Cont., Food Sci.& Tech.Abstr., Herb.Abstr., Ind.Sci.Rev., Nutr.Abstr., Sugar Ind.Abstr.
     Formerly (until 1992): Listy Cukrovarnicke (ISSN 0024-4449)

664   SW   ISSN 0024-5380
LIVS. 1951. 8/yr. SEK 470 (effective 1994). Sveriges Livsmedelshandlarefoerbund (SSLF), PO Box 1311, S-111 83 Stockholm, Sweden. TEL 08-141870. FAX 08-243506. Ed. Anita Helander. adv.; circ. 6,307 (controlled).
     Formerly (until vol.6, 1964): S S L F - Tidningen.

664   SW   ISSN 0024-5399
LIVSMEDELSTEKNIK. 1953-1957; resumed 1963. 9/yr. SEK 325. Stiftelsen Svensk Livsmedelsteknik, Katarinavaegen 20, 116 45 Stockholm, Sweden. FAX 08-6408045. Ed. Asa Leife. adv.: B&W page SEK 7150, color page SEK 12000; trim 185 x 270; adv. contact: Bo Eriksson. charts; illus.; stat.; circ. 2,500 (controlled). **Indexed:** Food Sci.& Tech.Abstr.
—BLDSC (5285.200000).
Description: Acts as a forum for information and contacts in all aspects for the processing and distribution of foodstuffs.

664 640.73   US
LOOKOUT - FOODS. 1978. s-m. $600. Marketing Intelligence Service Ltd., 33 Academy St., Naples, NY 14512. TEL 716-374-6326. FAX 716-374-5217. TELEX 469979. index. (back issues avail.)
    ●Also available online. Vendor(s): Data-Star, DIALOG Information Services, Inc.
     Supersedes in part: Lookout (Naples).

664   SW
MAAL OCH MEDEL. 1922. 20/yr. SEK 90 (effective 1991). Svenska Livsmedelsarbetarefoerbundet, PO Box 1156, 111 81 Stockholm, Sweden. adv. circ. 59,688.

664   UK
MCCANCE AND WIDDOWSON'S THE COMPOSITION OF FOODS. (Supplements avail.) irreg., 5th ed., 1993. £35. Royal Society of Chemistry, Thomas Graham House, Science Park, Milton Rd., Cambridge CB4 4WF, England. TEL 0223-420066. FAX 0223-423623. TELEX 818293. (Dist. by: Turpin Distribution Services Ltd., Blackhorse Rd., Letchworth, Herts. SG6 1HN, England. TEL 0462-672555. FAX 0462-480947) Ed.Bd.
Document type: trade publication.
Description: Contains revised and updated data on nearly 1,200 foods.

664   UK
MCCANCE AND WIDDOWSON'S THE COMPOSITION OF FOODS. SUPPLEMENTS. 1988. irreg., latest 1994. price varies. Royal Society of Chemistry, Thomas Graham House, Science Park, Milton Rd., Cambridge CB4 4WF, England. TEL 0223-420066. FAX 0223-423623. TELEX 818293. (Dist. by: Turpin Distribution Services Ltd., Blackhorse Rd., Letchworth, Herts. SG6 1HN, England. TEL 0462-672555. FAX 0462-480947)
Description: Discusses individual foods and dishes.

664.9   IT   ISSN 0024-9017
MACELLERIA ITALIANA. 1957. s-m. L.1500. Federazione Nazionale Macellai, Piazza G.G. Belli 2, 00153 Rome, Italy. Dr. Renzo Bauchiero. adv.; bk.rev. circ. 20,000. (looseleaf format)

664.9   FR
MAGAZINE DES ABATTOIRS. 1979. 6/yr. 300 F. 91 av. de la Republique, 75540 Paris Cedex 11, France. TEL 43-38-20-40. FAX 43-38-71-37. Ed. Jacques Pujol. adv. circ. 800.

641.53   US
MAGAZINE OF AMERICA'S BEST RECIPES. 1989. q. Blockbuster Periodicals, Inc., 2131 Hollywood Blvd., Hollywood, FL 33020. TEL 305-925-5242. Ed. Barbara Newman. circ. 30,000.
Description: Contains entries from the menus of the country's most celebrated restaurants. Each issue is devoted to a particular course.

664   US
▼**MAKE IT TASTY SPICE BLENDS;** food business newsletter. 1993. a. $22.95 (Canada $28.95; elsewhere $31.95). Make It Tasty Spice Co., c/o Prosperity & Profits Unlimited, Box 416, Denver, CO 80201. TEL 303-575-5676. **Document type:** newsletter.
Description: Contains recipes using various spice blends without salt.

664   US
MAPLE SYRUP DIGEST. 1961. q. $5 membership (Canada $7). North American Maple Syrup Council, c/o Roy Hutchinson, Box 240, Canterbury, NH 03224. adv.; illus.
     Formerly (until 1979): National Maple Syrup Digest.

637.2   RU   ISSN 0025-4649
                    CODEN: MZPYAE
MASLOZHIROVAYA PROMYSHLENNOST.* 1925. m. 27 Rub. Izdatel'stvo Kolos, Sadovo-Spasskaya, 18, 107807 Moscow, Russia. Ed. P.V. Naumenko. bk.rev.; bibl.; index. circ. 3,310. **Indexed:** Chem.Abstr., Dairy Sci.Abstr., Food Sci.& Tech.Abstr., Nutr.Abstr., Trop.Oil Seeds Abstr.
     Formerly: Masloboino-Zhirovaya Promyshlennost'

664.9   XR
MASO. bi-m. Ceske a Slovenske Odborne Nakladatelstvi (Subsidiary of: Deutscher Fachverlag GmbH), Na Prikope 27, 11349 Prague 1, Czech Republic. TEL 02-268964. FAX 02-262893. circ. 5,000.
Document type: trade publication.
Description: Provides information for the meat industry.

664   US
▼**MASTER CHOICE MAGAZINE.** 1992. q. Compass Foods Inc., 2 Paragon Dr., Montvale, NJ 07645. **Document type:** consumer publication.
Description: Contains recipes by famous chefs, and news and features about Master Choice line of food products.

664.1   MF
MAURITIUS SUGAR INDUSTRY RESEARCH INSTITUTE. ADVISORY BULLETIN. 1981. irreg. Mauritius Sugar Industry Research Institute, Reduit, Mauritius. FAX 230-454-1971. TELEX 4899 MSIRI IW.
Description: Covers food crop agronomy (maize, potatoes, tomatoes).

664.1   MF   ISSN 0369-2043
MAURITIUS SUGAR INDUSTRY RESEARCH INSTITUTE. ANNUAL REPORT. (Text in English) 1953. a., latest 1992. Mauritius Sugar Industry Research Institute, Reduit, Mauritius. FAX 230-454-1971. TELEX 4899 MSIRI IW. circ. 1,200. **Indexed:** Biol.Abstr., Food Sci.& Tech.Abstr., Herb.Abstr., Hort.Abstr., Rev.Appl.Entomol., Rev.Plant Path, Weed Abstr.
Description: Covers food crop agronomy and technology.

664.1   MF
MAURITIUS SUGAR INDUSTRY RESEARCH INSTITUTE. OCCASIONAL PAPER. 1958. irreg., latest 1993. price varies. Mauritius Sugar Industry Research Institute, Reduit, Mauritius. FAX 230-454-1971. TELEX 4899 MSIRI IW. circ. 500. (back issues avail.) **Indexed:** Biol.Abstr.

398   IS   ISSN 0334-1488
MAZONE UMITBACH/FOOD AND KITCHEN;* the magazine of the industrial kitchen. q. IS.25. Golden Pages Marketing and Management Ltd, P.O. Box 33023, Tel Aviv, Israel. TEL 03-7532222. Ed. Ester Shilo.

664.9   US   ISSN 0892-6077
HD9411   CODEN: MEAPE7
MEAT AND POULTRY; the business journal of the meat and poultry industry. 1955. m. $40 (foreign $75). Oman Publishing, Inc., 90 Throckmorton Ave., Box 1059, Mill Valley, CA 94942. TEL 415-388-7575. FAX 415-388-4961. (Subscr. to: Customer Service, Box 2129, Martinez, CA 94553-9889) Ed. Michael J. Alaimo; Pub. Michael J. Alaimo. adv.; bk.rev.; illus. circ. 18,250. **Indexed:** Curr.Pack.Abstr. **Document type:** trade publication.
—SWETS.
     Supersedes (as of Dec. 1986): Meat Industry (ISSN 0099-2011); **Formerly:** Western Meat Industry (ISSN 0043-3918)
Description: General business and technical industry information.

664.9   UK
MEAT & POULTRY NEWS. 12/yr. £35 europe £45; elsewhere £60. 9 Vermont Pl., Tongwell, Milton Keynes MK15 8JA, England. TEL 0908-613323. FAX 0908-210656. Ed. Pamela Brook. adv. contact: Deborah Brennan. circ. 14,000. **Document type:** trade publication.

FOOD AND FOOD INDUSTRIES 2575

664.9 658.8   UK
MEAT AND POULTRY: THE INTERNATIONAL MARKET. a. £1375($2750) Euromonitor, 87-88 Turnmill St., London EC1M 5QU, England. TEL 071-251-8024. FAX 071-608-3149. (Addr. in N. America: Euromonitor International, 111 W. Washington St., Ste. 920, Chicago, IL 60602. TEL 312-541-8024. FAX 312-541-1567) (looseleaf format) **Document type:** trade publication.
●Also available online. Vendor(s): Data-Star, DIALOG Information Services, Inc.
   Description: Analyzes the market for meat and poultry for France, Germany, Italy, Spain, the U.K., the U.S., and Japan.

664.9   US   ISSN 0025-6358
MEAT BOARD REPORTS. 1968. q. free. National Live Stock and Meat Board, 444 N. Michigan Ave., Chicago, IL 60611. TEL 312-467-5520. Ed. Lynn Heinze. circ. 13,000. **Document type:** trade publication.

664.9   US   ISSN 1049-5908
HD9410.1
MEAT BUSINESS MAGAZINE.* 1939. m. $19. ADmore, Inc., Box 28830, St. Louis, MO 63123-0030. TEL 800-451-0914. FAX 314-638-3880. Ed. Louise King. adv.; bk.rev.; index. circ. 9,100.
—UnCover.
   Former titles (until 1990): Meat Business (ISSN 1049-6688); (1973-1989): Meat Plant Magazine (ISSN 0192-2807)

664.9   UK   ISSN 0958-5141
                                      CODEN: MEAIEK
MEAT INDUSTRY. 1930. m. £27. International Thomson Business Publishing, 100 Avenue Road, London NW3 3TP, England. TEL 01-935-6611. Ed. Stephen Brennan. adv.; bk.rev.; illus.; mkt.; index. circ. 4,839. **Indexed:** Br.Tech.Ind., Food Sci.& Tech.Abstr.
   Former titles: Meat; Meat Industry (ISSN 0025-6366)

664.9   AT
MEAT INDUSTRY DIGEST. 1953. 10/yr. Aus.$22.50. Master Butchers Ltd., 432 Churchill Rd., Kilburn, S.A. 5084, Australia. TEL 61-8-2625433. FAX 61-8-3406043. Ed. T.K. Ford. adv.: page Aus.$150; trim 170 x 115; adv. contact: David Curtis. circ. 1,000. (back issues avail.)

MEAT INTERNATIONAL. see AGRICULTURE — Poultry And Livestock

664.9   UK
MEAT MANUFACTURING & MARKETING. 12/yr. 9 Vermont Pl., Tongwell, Milton Keynes MK15 8JA, England. TEL 0908-613323. FAX 0908-210656. Ed. Pamela Brook. circ. 5,000. **Document type:** trade publication.
   Description: Caters to directors and senior managers working in meatplant, meat manufacturing and curing, wholesaling and meat import-export services.

664.9   UK
MEAT MANUFACTURING & MARKETING INTERNATIONAL. 4/yr. 9 Vermont Pl., Tongwell, Milton Keynes MK15 8JA, England. TEL 0908-613323. FAX 0908-210656. Ed. Pamela Brook. circ. 8,469. **Document type:** trade publication.

664.9   US   ISSN 0025-6390
TS1950
MEAT PROCESSING. 1962. m. $48. Watt Publishing Co., 122 S. Wesley Ave., Mt. Morris, IL 60154-1497. TEL 815-734-4171. FAX 815-734-4201. Ed. Mark LeFens. adv.; charts; illus.; stat. circ. 17,407. **Indexed:** PROMT. **Document type:** trade publication.
—CCC.
   Formerly: Meat Processing International.
   Description: Directed to management and operating officials: news about meat packing, wholesaling, rendering establishments, foodservice chains, poultry and seafood processors.

664.9   UK   ISSN 0309-1740
                                      CODEN: MESCDN
MEAT SCIENCE. 1977. 9/yr. (in 3 vols., 3 nos./vol.) £544($840) (effective 1994). Elsevier Science Ltd., Oxford Fulfilment Centre, P.O. Box 800, Kidlington, Oxford OX5 1DX, England. TEL 44-865-843000. FAX 44-865-843010. (Subscr. in U.S. and Canada to: Elsevier Science, 660 White Plains Rd., Tarrytown, NY 10591-5153. TEL 914-524-9200. FAX 914-333-2444) Ed. R.A. Lawrie. adv.; bk.rev.; illus.; index. (back issues avail.) **Indexed:** Anim.Breed.Abstr., Biol.Abstr., Chem.Abstr., Curr.Cont., Excerp.Med., Food Sci.& Tech.Abstr., Ind.Sci.Rev., Ind.Vet., Int.Packag.Abstr., Nutr.Abstr., Packag.Sci.Tech., Sci.Cit.Ind., Vet.Bull. **Document type:** academic/scholarly publication.
—BLDSC (5413.796500); Faxon; UnCover; SWETS; CASDDS. **CCC.**
   Description: Provides an appropriate medium for the dissemination of interdisciplinary and international knowledge on all the factors which influence the properties of meat.
   Refereed Serial

664   JA   ISSN 0289-0542
MEAT SCIENCE. (Text in Japanese) s-a. Japanese Meat Processors Association, 5-6, 1-chome, Ebisu, Shibuya-ku, Tokyo 150, Japan. TEL 03-444-1211.

664   US   ISSN 0090-5631
TS1970   CODEN: PAMIDG
MEAT SCIENCE INSTITUTE. PROCEEDINGS. 1972. a. (National Meat Association) University of Georgia, Center for Continuing Education, Athens, GA 30602. TEL 404-542-1725. Ed. John A. Carpenter. **Document type:** proceedings.

664.9   UK
MEAT TRADER. 10/yr. National Federation of Meat Traders, High St., Castle Camps, Cambs CB1 6SN, England. TEL 0799-584879. FAX 0709-584883. Ed. John Fuller.

664.9 658.8   UK   ISSN 0025-6412
                                      CODEN: MTJOEI
MEAT TRADES JOURNAL. 1888. w. $96. International Thomson Business Publishing, 100 Avenue Road, London NW3 3TP, England. TEL 01-937-6611. adv.; bk.rev.; charts; illus.; mkt.; stat. circ. 16,047. (tabloid format)

664.9 331.88   AT   ISSN 0310-6721
MEATWORKER.* 1971. irreg. Australasian Meat Industry Employees Union, 62 Lygon St,, Carlton, Vic. 3053, Australia. Ed. R. Anear. **Document type:** newspaper.

664.9   SZ   ISSN 0026-1645
METZGER UND WURSTER/BOUCHER - CHARCUTIER/MACELLAIO - SALUMIERE. (Text in French, German & Italian) 1934. fortn. 28 F. Metzgereipersonal-Verband der Schweiz, Berninastr. 25, CH-8057 Zurich, Switzerland. adv.; abstr. circ. 5,500. (processed)

664.9   GW   ISSN 0005-7088
DER METZGERMEISTER. 1898. w. DM.296.40 (Europe DM.348.40). Richard Pflaum Verlag GmbH und Co. KG, Lazarettstr. 4, 80636 Munich, Germany. TEL 089-12607-0. FAX 089-12607-200. (Subscr. to: Postfach 190737, 80607 Munich, Germany) Ed. G. Kuehme. adv. circ. 7,200. **Document type:** newspaper.
—CCC.
   Formerly: Bayerishe Metzgermeister.

664   US   ISSN 0047-7117
MICHIGAN FOOD NEWS. 1958. m. $25. Michigan Grocers Association, 221 N. Walnut St., Lansing, MI 48933. TEL 517-372-6800. FAX 517-372-3002. Ed. Bobbie McKennon. adv.; bk.rev.; charts; illus.; circ. 6,000 (controlled)

MICHIGAN RESTAURATEUR. see HOTELS AND RESTAURANTS

664.8 658.8   US   ISSN 0096-7688
SB21
MICHIGAN STATE HORTICULTURAL SOCIETY. ANNUAL REPORT. 1870. a. $20. Michigan State Horticultural Society, Michigan State University, A388D Plant and Soil Science Bldg., East Lansing, MI 48824. TEL 517-355-5194. FAX 517-353-0890. Ed. Jerome Hull, Jr. circ. 2,500. (back issues avail.) **Indexed:** Crop Physiol.Abstr., Hort.Abstr., Plant Grow.Reg.Abstr. **Document type:** proceedings.

MICROWAVE TIMES. see HOME ECONOMICS

664   US   ISSN 0276-7961
TX657.064   CODEN: MIWOD5
MICROWAVE WORLD. 1980. q. $60 (foreign $80). International Microwave Power Institute, 10210 Leatherleaf Ct., Manassas, VA 22111-4245. TEL 703-257-1415. Ed. Brian T. Ford. bk.rev.; abstr.; illus.; pat. circ. 1,500. (back issues avail.)
—BLDSC (5761.240000); UnCover.
   Supersedes: Microwave Energy Applications Newsletter (ISSN 0026-2889)

664   US
MICROWAVES AND FOOD NEWSLETTER. 1991. m. $57. Food & Nutrition Press, Inc., 2 Corporate Dr., Box 374, Trumbull, CT 06611. TEL 203-261-8587. FAX 203-261-9724. Ed. Dr. Robert V. Decareau. **Document type:** academic/scholarly publication, newsletter.
   Description: Discusses new food products, production, packaging, quality assurance, microbiology, shelf-life, and microwave equipment.

664   LE
MIDDLE EAST AND WORLD FOOD DIRECTORY. 1987. biennial. $11C for two vols. Chatila Publishing House, P.O. Box 135121, Beirut, Lebanon. TEL 961-1-352413. FAX 961-1-352419. TELEX 23008 MIYAH LE. adv. circ. 5,000. **Document type:** directory.

664   LE   ISSN 0256-7032
MIDDLE EAST FOOD. 1985. 6/yr. $50. Chatila Publishing House, P.O. Box 135121, Chouran, Beirut, Lebanon. TEL 961-1-352413. FAX 961-1-352419. Ed. Saaddine Chihab. adv.; bk.rev. circ. 10,551. **Document type:** trade publication.
   Description: Covers articles to importers, wholesalers, and food distributors about catering, beverage products, and equipment in the Middle East, Anglophone Africa and other countries.

MIDWEST FOOD SERVICE. see HOTELS AND RESTAURANTS

MIELIES - MAIZE. see AGRICULTURE

664.9   PL
▼**MIESO I WEDLINY** 1993. 4/yr. Polskie Wydawnictwo Fachowe (Subsidiary of: Deutscher Fachverlag GmbH), Ul. Ratuszowa 11, 03-450 Warsaw, Poland. TEL 48-22-189622. FAX 48-22-192187. circ. 5,000. **Document type:** trade publication.
   Description: Provides information for the meat industry.

664 658.8   GW   ISSN 0026-3761
MILCH - FETTWAREN - EIER - HANDEL. 1948. 3/w. DM.708($266.40) Heinrichs Verlag GmbH und Co. KG, Postfach 100550, 31105 Hildesheim, Germany. TEL 05121-53279. Ed. J. Heiber. adv.; stat. (tabloid format) **Document type:** trade publication.

642.5   US   ISSN 0886-8832
MILITARY CLUB & HOSPITALITY. 1967. 8/yr. $27. Executive Business Media, Inc., 825 Old Country Rd., Box 1500, Westbury, NY 11590. TEL 516-334-3030. Ed. Robert Moran. adv.; charts; illus.; stat.; circ. 11,000 (controlled).
   Former titles (until 1986): Club and Food Service (ISSN 0192-7981); Clubmen Food Service; Club News (ISSN 0009-9619)

MILK AND LIQUID FOOD TRANSPORTER. see TRANSPORTATION — Trucks And Trucking

FOOD AND FOOD INDUSTRIES

658.8   NE   ISSN 0923-697X
MISSETS DISTRIFOOD; nieuwsblad voor de levensmiddelendetailhandel. 1896. w. fl.199.50. Uitgeversmaatschappij C. Misset B.V., Hanzestr. 1, 7006 RH Doetinchem, Netherlands. TEL 31-8340-49911. FAX 31-8340-43839. TELEX 45481. (Subscr. to: Postbus 4, 7000 RH Doetinchem, Netherlands) Ed. H. Weltje. adv.: B&W page fl.7815, color page fl.11465; trim 300 x 420; adv. contact: Cor van Nek. bk.rev.; charts; stat. circ. 14,350. (tabloid format) **Indexed:** Key to Econ.Sci. **Document type:** trade publication.
    Former titles (until 1985): Levensmiddelenmarkt (ISSN 0165-3008); H L (ISSN 0024-1555); **Incorporates:** Groothandel in Levensmiddelen (ISSN 0017-4572)
    Description: Aimed at owners, company managers, department heads and personnel of supermarkets, self-service food and specialty food shops.

664.9   NE
MISSET'S VLEES EN VLEESWAREN; onafhankelijk vakblad voor slagers. 1916. m. fl.165. Uitgeversmaatschappij C. Misset B. V., Hanzestr. 1, 7006 RH Doetinchem, Netherlands. (Subscr. to: Postbus 4, 7000 BA Doetinchem, Netherlands) Ed. E. Reuling. adv.: B&W page fl.3032; trim 215 x 285; adv. contact: Cor van Nek. bk.rev.; charts; illus.; mkt. circ. 5,610. **Indexed:** Key to Econ.Sci. **Document type:** trade publication.
    Former titles: Vlees en Vleeswaren (ISSN 0165-3407); Slagerij (ISSN 0037-6701)
    Description: Highlights production, handling, presentation and selling of meat and meat products.

MIXIN'. see *BEVERAGES*

664   US   ISSN 0888-7829
MODERN FOOD SERVICE NEWS. 1989. m. $30. Grocers Publishing Co., Inc., 15 Emerald St., Hackensack, NJ 07601. TEL 201-488-1800. adv. circ. 22,413. (tabloid format) **Document type:** trade publication.
    Description: Provides news and information to food service purchasing agents, buyers and end users in the states of New York, New Jersey and Connecticut.

664   US
MODERN GROCER EN ESPANOL. (Text in Spanish) 1921. m. $16. Grocers Publishing Co., Inc., 15 Emerald St., Hackensack, NJ 07601. TEL 201-488-1800. circ. 6,433. **Document type:** trade publication.
    Description: Services Hispanic retailers and wholesalers.

MODERN GROCER INDUSTRY DIRECTORY. see *BUSINESS AND ECONOMICS — Trade And Industrial Directories*

664.12   US   ISSN 0145-0662
MOLASSES MARKET NEWS. 1949. w. $40 (foreign $75). U.S. Department of Agriculture, 711 O St., Greeley, CO 80631-9540. TEL 303-353-9750. FAX 303-353-9790. (Alt. addr.: U S D A Livestock and Seed Division - LSAMS, South Bldg., Rm. 2623, Box 96456, Washington, DC 20090-6426. TEL 202-720-6231. FAX 202-690-3732) Ed. Keith Padgett. (also avail. in microfiche from CIS; back issues avail.; reprint service avail. from CIS) **Indexed:** Amer.Stat.Ind. (1984-). **Document type:** government publication.

DIE MOLKEREI-ZEITUNG WELT DER MILCH. see *AGRICULTURE — Dairying And Dairy Products*

664.028   FR
MONDE DE SURGELE. 1964. m. 509 F. Helios International, 14 bd. Montmartre, 75009 Paris, France. TEL 42-46-92-94. FAX 90-88-28-49. TELEX 432 845. Ed. C. Durrieu. adv. circ. 10,850. **Indexed:** Dairy Sci.Abstr., Food Sci.& Tech.Abstr., Packag.Sci.Tech. **Document type:** trade publication.
—BLDSC (8548.120000). **CCC.**
    Formerly (until 1993): Surgelation (ISSN 0049-2647)

658.8   US   ISSN 0047-7931
MONTANA FOOD DISTRIBUTOR. 1942. m. $10. Montana Food Distributors Association, 2700 Airport Rd., Box 5775, Helena, MT 59604-5775. TEL 406-449-6394. FAX 406-449-0647. Ed. Harry Black. adv.; bk.rev.; stat; tr.lit. circ. 1,400.

664 636   US   ISSN 0566-3628
MONTHLY PRICE REVIEW. m. (plus annual supplement). $108 (typically set in Sept.). Urner Barry Publications, Inc., Box 389, Toms River, NJ 08754. TEL 908-240-5330. FAX 908-341-0891. Ed. Paul B. Brown, Sr. (tabloid format) **Document type:** newspaper.

664   US
MOVING FOOD.* 6/yr. $24. Alliance of Warehouses & Federations, Box 8188, N. Brattleboro, VT 05304-8188.

664   AU
MUEHLEN MARKT. m. Millergasse 20, A-1060 Vienna, Austria. TEL 01-5976570. FAX 01-5976428.

642.5   US
N A C U F S JOURNAL. 1968. a. membership. National Association of College and University Food Services, 1405 S. Harrison, Ste. 303, Manly Miles Bldg., Michigan State University, E. Lansing, MI 48824. TEL 517-332-2494. FAX 517-332-8144. Ed. Thomas Walsh. bibl. circ. 1,600. **Document type:** trade publication.
    Supersedes: N A C U F S Technical Bulletin (ISSN 0027-5751)

642.5   US
N A C U F S NEWSWAVE. 1958. 5/yr. membership. National Association of College and University Food Services, 1405 S. Harrison, Ste. 303, Manly Miles Bldg., Michigan State Univ., E. Lansing, MI 48824. TEL 517-332-2494. Ed. Terry Cole. circ. 2,500. (back issues avail.) **Document type:** trade publication.
    Formerly: N A C U F S Newsletter - Digest.
    Description: Contains regional, conference and industry news and articles of interest to food service professionals.

664   US   ISSN 0883-6744
N A S F T SHOWCASE. 1967. bi-m. $30. National Association for Specialty Food Trade, Inc., 8 W. 40th St., New York, NY 10018-3902. TEL 212-921-1690. Ed. Ronald Tanner. adv.; bk.rev. circ. 26,000. **Document type:** trade publication.

664   US
N A W G A REVIEW. m. National-American Wholesale Grocers' Association, Inc., 201 Park Washington Court, Falls Church, VA 22046. TEL 703-532-9400. FAX 703-538-4673. Ed. John D. Thompson. circ. 4,034.

664   NO   ISSN 0040-7127
NAERINGSMIDDELINDUSTRIEN. 1947. m. NOK 360. Skarland Press A-S, Postboks 5042, Maj 0301 Oslo, Norway. TEL 47-22-60-13-90. FAX 47-22-69-36-50. Ed. Jan Helge Kalvik. adv.; bk.rev.; pat.; tr.lit.; index; circ. 4,500 (controlled).
    Formerly: Tidsskrift for Hermetikkindustri (ISSN 0040-7062)

664   AU
NAH UND FRISCH. m. Leopoldsgasse 4-1, Postfach 27, A-1025 Vienna, Austria. TEL 01-2161433. FAX 01-354942. TELEX 111386. Ed. Dieter Weihs. circ. 3,500.

664   GW
DIE NAHRUNGS- UND GENUSSMITTEL-INDUSTRIE UND IHRE HELFER/FOOD AND BEVERAGE INDUSTRY AND ITS SUPPLIERS. 1952. a. $40. Industrieschau-Verlagsgesellschaft mbH, Berliner Allee 8, 64295 Darmstadt, Germany. TEL 06151-38920. FAX 06151-33164. (U.S. subscr. to: Western Hemisphere Publishing Corp., Box 847, Hillsboro, OR 97123-0847. TEL 503-640-3736. FAX 503-640-2748) Ed. Margit Selka. circ. 6,000. **Document type:** directory.
•Also available online.
Also available on CD-ROM.

664   AU   ISSN 0027-7703
NAHRUNGSMITTEL. 3/w. S.350 per month. Austria Presse Agentur (APA), Gunoldstrasse 14, A-1199 Vienna, Austria. Ed. H. Jaros. (processed)

664.9 658
NATIONAL ASSOCIATION OF MEAT PURVEYORS. NEWSLETTER. s-m. membership. National Association of Meat Purveyors, 1920 Association Dr., Ste. 400, Reston, VA 22091-1547. TEL 703-758-1900. FAX 703-758-8001. circ. 420 (controlled). **Document type:** newsletter.

663.9   US
NATIONAL COFFEE ASSOCIATION OF U.S.A. NEWSLETTER. 1947. w. $30 (foreign $50). National Coffee Association of U.S.A. Inc., 110 Wall St., New York, NY 10005. TEL 212-344-5596. Ed. D.M. Brennan. bk.rev.; stat. circ. 550. **Document type:** newsletter.
    Formerly: National Coffee Association News Letter (ISSN 0027-9021)

051   US   ISSN 0747-7716
NATIONAL CULINARY REVIEW. 1932. m. $35 (effective Apr. 1992). American Culinary Federation, Inc., 10 San Bartola Dr., Box 3466, St. Augustine, FL 32085. TEL 904-824-4468. FAX 904-825-4758. Ed. Brent T. Frei. adv.; bk.rev. circ. 20,000. (also avail. in microfiche; back issues avail.) **Document type:** trade publication.
    Description: Covers food and industry issues; offers how-to preparation techniques; food histories.

641.374 658.87   US   ISSN 0895-9722
NATIONAL DIPPER; the magazine for ice cream retailers. 1985. 6/yr. $25. Lynda Utterback, Ed. & Pub., 1480 Renaissance Dr., No. 101, Park Ridge, IL 60068. TEL 708-390-6550. FAX 708-390-6558. adv.; bk.rev. circ. 20,000. (back issues avail.) **Document type:** trade publication.
    Description: Helps find new products for ice cream dipping store owners.

664.02 338.47   US   ISSN 0895-2043
HD9001
NATIONAL FROZEN FOOD ASSOCIATION DIRECTORY. 1948. a. $50. National Frozen Food Association, Inc., Box 6069, Harrisburg, PA 17112-0069. TEL 717-657-8601. FAX 717-657-9862. Ed. Lori B. Perle. adv.: B&W page $880; adv. contact: Joanne Myers. index. circ. 3,500. **Document type:** trade publication, directory.
    Formerly (until 1985): Frozen Food Factbook and Directory (ISSN 0071-9684)
    Description: Annual guide to membership of the National Frozen Food Association.

664.09   US
NATIONAL PACKING NEWS. m. $25. Box 1349, Murphys, CA 95247. TEL 209-728-1455. FAX 209-728-3277. Ed. Jack W. Soward. adv.; bk.rev.; stat.; tr.lit. circ. 2,400. **Document type:** newsletter.
    Incorporates (1989-1991): Eastern Packing News; (1937-1991): Western Packing News.
    Description: News about the food processing industry, including new products, plants, R&D, marketing, staff and line management personnel.

664.9   US   ISSN 0027-996X
    CODEN: NAPRAX
THE NATIONAL PROVISIONER. 1891. m. $50 (foreign $100) (free to qualified personnel). Stagnito Publishing Company, 1935 Shermer Rd., Ste. 100, Northbrook, IL 60062. TEL 708-205-5660. FAX 708-205-5680. Pub. Harry Stagnito. adv.; bk.rev.; charts; illus.; mkt.; pat.; tr.mk.; circ. 15,000 (controlled). **Indexed:** Chem.Abstr., Curr.Pack.Abstr., PROMT. **Document type:** trade publication.
—BLDSC (6029.800000); UnCover; UMI.
    Description: Contains articles of interest to executives and department heads in the meat, poultry and seafood processing industries.

NATIONAL RESEARCH INSTITUTE OF VEGETABLES, ORNAMENTAL PLANTS AND TEA. BULLETIN. SERIES B. see *AGRICULTURE*

NATURAL FOOD TRADER. see *NUTRITION AND DIETETICS*

641.4 664.9   GW
NEUE FLEISCHER-ZEITUNG. w. DM.435.60. Matthaes Verlag GmbH, Olgastr. 87, 70180 Stuttgart, Germany. TEL 0711-2133-0. adv. circ. 11,400. **Document type:** newspaper.

642.5   US   ISSN 8756-498X
NEW ORLEANS MENU; dining out and in. 1977. 10/yr. $20. New Orleans Big Bend & Pacific Co., Box 51831, New Orleans, LA 70151. TEL 504-524-0348. Ed. Thomas G. Fitzmorris. adv.; bk.rev. circ. 5,000. **Document type:** consumer publication.
    Description: Covers New Orleans restaurants, cooking, wine, and travel.

FOOD AND FOOD INDUSTRIES

664　　　　　　US　ISSN 0745-6239
NEWS AND FOOD REPORT. 1933. bi-w. $18 (effective 1994). New Hampshire Retail Grocers Association, 110 Stark St., Manchester, NH 03101-1777. TEL 603-669-9333. Ed. John M. Dumais. adv. contact: Patricia Houde. bk.rev. circ. 2,000.
Document type: trade publication.

NEWS & VIEWS OF LOCAL 23. see *LABOR UNIONS*

NIKKEI RESTAURANTS. see *HOTELS AND RESTAURANTS*

664　　　　　　JA　ISSN 0029-0394
　　　　　　　　　　CODEN: NSKGAX
NIPPON SHOKUHIN KOGYO GAKKAISHI/JOURNAL OF FOOD SCIENCE AND TECHNOLOGY. (Text in Japanese) 1953. m. 22440 Yen. Nippon Shokuhin Kogyo Gakkai - Japanese Society for Food Science and Technology, 2-1-2 Kannondai, Tsukuba City, Ibaraki-ken 305, Japan. FAX 0298-38-7153. Ed. H. Aokia. adv.; bk.rev.; charts; illus.; index. circ. 2,230. (reprint service avail. from ISI) **Indexed:** Chem.Abstr., Curr.Pack.Abstr., Food Sci.& Tech.Abstr., Triticale Abstr.
—BLDSC (4809.435000); SWETS; CASDDS.

664.1　　　　　　NR
NISUCO CHRONICLE. m. Nigerian Sugar Co., Bacita Estate, Pvt. Mail Bag 65, Jebba, Nigeria. adv.

NOETKOETT; aktuellt om svensk noetkoettsproduktion. see *AGRICULTURE*

664.8　　　　　　US
NORTH AMERICAN EXPORT DIRECTORY. a. Vance Publishing Corporation, 7950 College Blvd., Shawnee Mission, KS 66210. TEL 913-451-2200. Ed. Stephanie Wiemann. adv.; B&W page $2050. circ. 4,600. **Document type:** directory.

664　　　　　　US
NORTH COAST CO-OP NEWSLETTER.* 1975. 6/yr. $15. North Coast Cooperative, Inc., 977 9th St., Arcata, CA 95521-6112. TEL 707-445-3185. Ed. A.H. Labanca. adv.; illus. circ. 6,500. (tabloid format)
Description: Discusses food and cooperatives; food is covered through politics, agriculture, nutrition, consumer action alerts, and recipes.

663.93　　　　　　CR　ISSN 0550-1105
NOTICIERO DEL CAFE. 1964. m. free. Instituto del Cafe, Apartado 37, Calle 1, Avdas. 18 y 20, San Jose, Costa Rica. TEL 22-6411. TELEX 2279. Ed. Rocio Bogantes Madrigal. illus. circ. 5,500.

664　　　　　　SW
NOUVELLE FIPREGAZETTE. (Text in English, French, German) 1989. s-a. SEK 100($20) (Federation Internationale de la Presse Gastronomique) Nya Mediaplan AB, P.O. Box 6903, S-102 39 Stockholm, Sweden. TEL 08-669 0820. Ed. Alexander Scarlat. circ. 5,000.

NUTRITION FUNDING REPORT; a monthly guide to locating resources. see *NUTRITION AND DIETETICS*

NUTRITION LEGISLATION AND REGULATORY NEWS; a twice-monthly report of United States legislative, executive, and regulatory activities. see *NUTRITION AND DIETETICS*

613 641　　　　　　ZA　ISSN 0078-284X
NUTRITION NEWS IN ZAMBIA. (Text in English) 1969. q. free. National Food and Nutrition Commission, P.O. Box 32669, Lusaka, Zambia. bk.rev.; circ. 5,000 (controlled). (processed) **Document type:** government publication, newsletter.

NUTRITION SOCIETY OF INDIA. PROCEEDINGS. see *NUTRITION AND DIETETICS*

664　　　　　　AU　ISSN 0029-778X
OBST-GEMUESE. 1950. 2/w. S.260 per month. Austria Presse Agentur (APA), Gunoldstr. 14, A-1199 Vienna, Austria. Ed. H. Jaros. (processed)

OFFICIAL GUIDE TO FOOD SERVICE AND HOSPITALITY MANAGEMENT CAREERS. see *OCCUPATIONS AND CAREERS*

OIL WORLD WEEKLY; the weekly forecasting and information service for oilseeds, oilmeals, oils and fats. see *AGRICULTURE — Agricultural Economics*

664.3 658.8　　　　　　UK
OILS AND FATS: THE INTERNATIONAL MARKET. a. £1375($2750) Euromonitor, 87-88 Turnmill St., London EC1M 5QU, England. TEL 071-251-8024. FAX 071-608-3149. (Addr. in N. America: Euromonitor International, 111 W. Washington St., Ste. 920, Chicago, IL 60602. TEL 312-541-8024. FAX 312-541-1567) (looseleaf format) **Document type:** trade publication.
●Also available online. Vendor(s): Data-Star, DIALOG Information Services, Inc..
Description: Analyzes the market for oils and fats for France, Germany, Italy, Spain, the U.K., the U.S., and Japan.

OLSEN'S AGRIBUSINESS REPORT; monthly intelligence for agribusiness executives. see *AGRICULTURE*

664　　　　　　NE
ONDERNEMINGSANALYSES VOEDINGS- EN GENOTMIDDELEN-INDUSTRIE. a. fl.72. Delwel Uitgeverij B.V., Postbus 19110, 2500 CC The Hague, Netherlands. TEL 31-70-3624800. FAX 31-70-3605606.
Description: Financial and economic information on the food industries and luxury consumer goods market in the Netherlands.

664　　　　　　US
ORGANIC FOOD BUSINESS NEWS. 1989. m. $84. Hotline Printing and Publishing, Box 161132, Altamonte Springs, FL 32716. TEL 407-628-1377. FAX 407-628-9933. Ed. Dennis Blank. adv.; bk.rev. circ. 1,500. **Document type:** newsletter.

OUTPOST EXCHANGE; Milwaukee's food and wellness magazine. see *NUTRITION AND DIETETICS*

OVER THE GARDEN FENCE; natural living in North Texas. see *GARDENING AND HORTICULTURE*

664　　　　　　US
P - NUTTY NEWS AND NOTES. 1967. 4/yr. free (effective 1992). Virginia Carolina Peanut Promotions, 109 S. Main St., Box 1709, Rocky Mount, NC 27802. TEL 919-446-3097. FAX 919-972-8061. Ed. Betsy Owens. circ. 2,500. (back issues avail.)
Description: Covers news and information about peanuts, peanut products, and ideas for their use.

P P C. (Petits Propos Culinaires) see *HOME ECONOMICS*

633.6 664.1　　　　MF　ISSN 0254-5047
HD9117.M29
P R O S I. (Text in English, French) 1969. m. £150($20) Public Relations Office of the Sugar Industry, Plantation House, Port Louis, Mauritius. TEL 230-2123302. FAX 230-2128710. TELEX 4214 SUGMAUR IW. Ed. Jacques Dinan. adv.; bk.rev.; charts; illus.; stat. circ. 2,500.
Description: Covers articles on a wide range of subjects including agriculture, economy, industry, management, research, etc.

664.8　　　　　　US　ISSN 0030-8668
PACIFIC FRUIT NEWS. 1888. w. $40 (foreign $42). Frank Crawford, Ed. & Pub., Box 460, Copperopolis, CA 95228. TEL 209-785-3377. adv.; bk.rev.; stat. circ. 1,150. (tabloid format; back issues avail.)
Document type: trade publication.
Description: Covers events and market quotations in the processed fruit, vegetable, dried fruit and tree nut industries on the West Coast.

664.8 658.8　　　　US　ISSN 0030-9168
PACKER; devoted to the interest of commercial growers, packers, shippers, receivers and retailers of fruits, vegetables and other products. 1893. w. $45 (foreign $75). Vance Publishing Corporation, 7950 College Blvd., Shawnee Mission, KS 66210. TEL 913-451-2200. Ed. Bill O'Neill. adv.; illus.; mkt. circ. 15,388. (also avail. in microform from UMI; back issues avail.; reprint service avail. from UMI) —UMI. **CCC.**

664.8　　　　　　US
PACKER RED BOOK. a. Vance Publishing Corporation, 7950 College Blvd., Shawnee Mission, KS 66210. TEL 913-451-2200.

664.8　　　　　　US
PACKER'S PRODUCE AVAILABILITY AND MERCHANDISING GUIDE. a. Vance Publishing Corporation, 7950 College Blvd., Shawnee Mission, KS 66210. TEL 913-451-2200. FAX 913-451-5821. Ed. Bill O'Neill. circ. 16,000.

PAKISTAN SEAFOOD DIGEST. see *FISH AND FISHERIES*

642.5　　　　　　IT
PANIFICAZIONE E PASTICCERIA. 1973. m. (11/yr.). Antonio Cendali Expo C.T.S., Via Serbelloni 2, 20122 Milan, Italy. TEL 2-77181. FAX 2-781828. adv. circ. 19,000.
Formerly: Giornale degli Alimentaristi.

664　　　　　　US　ISSN 8750-9393
　　　　　　　　　　CODEN: PASJEG
PASTA JOURNAL. 1919. bi-m. $28 (foreign $38.50). National Pasta Association, 2101 Wilson Blvd, Ste. 920, Arlington, VA 22201-3008. TEL 703-841-0818. FAX 703-528-6507. Ed. Donna Chowning Reid. adv. circ. 900. **Document type:** trade publication.
—BLDSC (6409.203000).
Description: Covers the pasta industry for pasta manufacturing company executives and industry suppliers.

664.7 658.8　　　　UK
PASTA PRODUCTS: THE INTERNATIONAL MARKET. a. £1375($2750) Euromonitor, 87-88 Turnmill St., London EC1M 5QU, England. TEL 071-251-8024. FAX 071-608-3149. (Addr. in N. America: Euromonitor International, 111 W. Washington St., Ste. 920, Chicago, IL 60602. TEL 312-541-8024. FAX 312-541-1567) (looseleaf format) **Document type:** trade publication.
●Also available online. Vendor(s): Data-Star, DIALOG Information Services, Inc.
Description: Analyzes the pasta products market for France, Germany, Italy, Spain, the U.K., the U.S., and Japan.

664　　　　　　AT
PASTRYCOOKS & BAKERS NEWS MONTHLY. 1979. m. Aus.$80. Pastrycooks & Bakers Pty. Ltd., P.O. Box 270, Crows Nest, N.S.W. 2065, Australia. TEL 02-956-5155. FAX 02-954-4045. Ed. Norman Baxter. circ. 3,000. (back issues avail.) **Document type:** trade publication.
Incorporates: Australasian Baking; Which was formerly: Baker and Miller's Journal (ISSN 0311-1385) & Australasian Baker and Miller's Journal (ISSN 0004-8305).
Description: Directed to pastrycooks and bakers in Australia, New Zealand, South-East Asia and S. Pacific.

PEACH-TIMES. see *AGRICULTURE — Crop Production And Soil*

633.3　　　　　　US　ISSN 0031-3661
PEANUT JOURNAL AND NUT WORLD.* 1921. m. $8. (Virginia - Carolina Peanut Association) Peanut Journal Publishing Co., 2921 N. Radcliffe Ln., Chesapeake, VA 23321-4551. (Co-sponsor: National Peanut Council, Inc.) Ed. Terry Reel. adv.; bk.rev.; charts; illus.; stat. **Indexed:** Biol.Abstr.

PECAN GROWER. see *AGRICULTURE — Crop Production And Soil*

664　　　　　　US
PENGUIN PIPELINE. q. National Frozen Food Association, Inc., 4755 Linglestown Rd., No. 300, Harrisburg, PA 17112-8526. TEL 717-657-8601. FAX 717-657-9862. Ed. Cindi Rockwell. circ. 5,000. **Document type:** trade publication, newsletter.
Description: Industry news and information on promotions for March, the frozen food month.

664　　　　　　US　ISSN 0146-0501
　　　　　　　　　　CODEN: PTCNDC
PESTICIDE & TOXIC CHEMICAL NEWS. 1972. w. $780 (effective July 1993). Food Chemical News, Inc., 1101 Pennsylvania Ave., S.E., Washington, DC 20003. TEL 202-544-1980. FAX 202-546-3890. Ed. Cathy Cooper. index. (back issues avail.)
●Also available online. Vendor(s): Data-Star, DIALOG Information Services, Inc., NewsNet (CH18).
—BLDSC (6428.364000); CASDDS. **CCC.**
Formerly: Pesticide Chemical News.
Description: Contains information about regulatory and legislative activities governing pesticides, toxic chemicals, and hazardous wastes.

FOOD AND FOOD INDUSTRIES

664 US
PESTICIDE CHEMICAL NEWS GUIDE. 1974. m. $630 (effective Jan. 1994). Food Chemical News, Inc., 1101 Pennsylvania Ave., S.E., Washington, DC 20003. TEL 202-544-1980. FAX 202-546-3890. Ed. Reo Duggan. index. (looseleaf format; back issues avail.)
  Description: Lists all tolerances, administrative guidelines and exemptions for pesticide residues in food and feed.

PESTICIDRESTER I DANSKE LEVNEDSMIDLER/PESTICIDE RESIDUES IN DANISH FOOD. see AGRICULTURE — Crop Production And Soil

664.6 658.8 UK
PET FOODS AND PRODUCTS: THE INTERNATIONAL MARKET. a. £1375($2750) Euromonitor, 87-88 Turnmill St., London EC1M 5QU, England. TEL 071-251-8024. FAX 071-608-3102. (Addr. in N. America: Euromonitor International, 111 W. Washington St., Ste. 920, Chicago, IL 60602. TEL 312-541-8024. FAX 312-541-1567) (looseleaf format) **Document type:** trade publication.
● Also available online. Vendor(s): Data-Star, DIALOG Information Services, Inc.
  Description: Analyzes the pet food market for France, Germany, Italy, Spain, the U.K., the U.S., and Japan.

636 US ISSN 0031-6245
  CODEN: PEINE6
PETFOOD INDUSTRY. 1959. bi-m. $36 (typically set in Oct.; effective Jan.). Watt Publishing Co., 122 S. Wesley Ave., Mt. Morris, IL 61054. TEL 815-734-4171. FAX 815-734-4201. Ed. Tim Phillips. adv.: B&W page $1395, color page $1895. illus. circ. 5,500. (also avail. in microform from UMI; reprint service avail. from UMI; back issues avail.) **Indexed:** Curr.Pack.Abstr.
—UMI. **CCC.**
  Description: Serves individuals and firms manufacturing pet foods.

642.5
PIZZA & PASTA. 1988. 10/yr. $18. Talcott Communications Corporation, 20 N. Wacker Dr., Ste 3230, Chicago, IL 60606-3102. TEL 312-849-2220. Ed. Joseph Declan Moran. circ. 40,000. **Document type:** trade publication.
  Description: Informs commercial, independent and chain pizza operators, managers, distributors, equipment dealers, and restaurant operators.

642.5 US ISSN 0743-3115
TX770.P58
PIZZA TODAY. 1983. m. $18. (National Association of Pizza Operators) ProTech Publishing and Communications, Box 1347, New Albany, IN 47151-1347. TEL 812-937-4464. FAX 812-937-4688. Ed. Paula Werne. adv.; bk.rev.; tr.lit. circ. 40,000. (back issues avail.; reprint service avail.)
—Faxon; UnCover.
  Description: Informs pizza restaurant owners, operators and executives in the U.S. and Canada about industry news concerning sales and profits.

051 CN ISSN 0849-066X
PLAISIRS DE LA TABLE.* 6/yr. Publicor Inc., 7 Chemin Bates, Outremont, Que. H2V 1A6, Canada. TEL 514-270-1100. FAX 514-270-6900. Ed. Celine Tremblay. adv.: B&W & color, color page Can.$3395; trim 8 1/4 x 10 7/8. circ. 30,000.

663.94 633.72 II ISSN 0032-0978
PLANTERS' CHRONICLE. (Text in English) vol.68, 1973. m. United Planters' Association of Southern India, P.O. Box 11, Glenview, Coonoor 1, Nilgiris, Tamil Nadu, India. Ed. B. Sivaram. adv.; bk.rev.; charts. **Indexed:** Bio-Contr.News & Info., Forest.Abstr., Forest Prod.Abstr., Hort.Abstr., Plant Grow.Reg.Abstr., Rural Recreat.Tour.Abstr., Soils & Fert., World Agri.Econ.& Rural Sociol.Abstr.
—BLDSC (6525.200000).

664 DK ISSN 0902-5057
PLUS PROCES; process technology in food. 1987. 9/yr. DKK 350. Jante-Forlaget ApS, Box 15, Kongstrupvej 3, DK-4390 Vipperoed, Denmark. TEL 45-53-48-28-00. FAX 45-53-48-22-05. Ed. Terkel Spangsbo. circ. 7,137. **Document type:** trade publication.
  Description: Covers industrial research and development, new products, automation and computer control.

PODRAVKA; znanstveno-strucni casopis. see AGRICULTURE

641 543 PL ISSN 1230-0322
TP368 CODEN: PJFSE7
POLISH JOURNAL OF FOOD AND NUTRITION SCIENCES. (Text in English; summaries in Polish) 1957. q. $50. Polska Akademia Nauk, Centrum Agrotechnologii i Weterynarii, Ul. J. Tuwima 10, 10-718 Olsztyn-Kortowo, Poland. FAX 48-89-237824. TELEX 522621. (Dist. by: Ars Polona, Krakowskie Przedmiescie 7, 00-068 Warsaw, Poland) Ed. Adolf Horubala. circ. 500. **Indexed:** Biodet.Abstr., Biol.Abstr., Chem.Abstr., Curr.Adv.Ecol.Sci., Dairy Sci.Abstr., Excerp.Med., Field Crop Abstr., Food Sci.& Tech.Abstr., Herb.Abstr., Nutr.Abstr., Poult.Abstr. **Document type:** academic/scholarly publication.
—SWETS; CASDDS.
  Former titles (until 1992): Acta Alimentaria Polonica (ISSN 0137-1495); Roczniki Technologii i Chemii Zywnosci (ISSN 0080-374X)

664 PL ISSN 0528-9254
POLITECHNIKA LODZKA. ZESZYTY NAUKOWE. TECHNOLOGIA I. CHEMIA SPOZYWCZA. (Text in Polish; summaries in English and Russian) 1955. irreg. price varies. Wydawnictwo Politechniki Lodzkiej, Ul. Wolczanska 219, 93-085 Lodz, Poland. (Dist. by: Ars Polona-Ruch, Krakowskie Przedmiescie 7, Warsaw, Poland) Ed. Joanna Maslowska. circ. 206. **Indexed:** Chem.Abstr. **Document type:** academic/scholarly publication.
  Description: Analyzes the chemical technology of food, biotechnology, technology of fermentation, bio-inorganic and analytical chemistry.

PORC MAGAZINE. see AGRICULTURE — Poultry And Livestock

664 UK ISSN 0968-7661
▼**POTATO BUSINESS WORLD.** 1993. q. $180. Crier Publications Ltd., Arctic House, Rye Ln., Dunton Green, Sevenoaks, Kent TN14 5HB, England. TEL 44-732-451383. FAX 44-732-451383. Ed. Andrew Arnold. adv. circ. 4,250. (back issues avail.) **Document type:** trade publication.
  Description: Discusses all aspects pertaining to the processing of potatoes into finished food products.

POTATO MARKETS. see AGRICULTURE

POTPOURRI FROM HERBAL ACRES. see GARDENING AND HORTICULTURE

664 XR ISSN 0862-8653
  CODEN: POVEEC
POTRAVINARSKE VEDY/FOOD SCIENCES; vedecky casopis. (Text and summaries in Czech or Slovak and English) 1983. bi-m. $52. Ustav Zemedelskych a Potravinarskych Informaci, Slezska 7, 120 56 Prague 2, Czech Republic. TEL 257541. FAX 257090. Ed. Marcela Braunova. circ. 400. **Indexed:** Dairy Sci.Abstr., Food Sci.& Tech.Abstr. **Document type:** academic/scholarly publication.
—BLDSC (8084.851400); CASDDS.
  Formerly (until 1989): U V T I Z Sbornik - Potravinarske Vedy (ISSN 0232-0568)
  Description: Contains various articles on food chemistry, microbiology, food engineering, hygiene and nutrition.

664 US
PRAIRIE NEWS. 1976. 6/yr. $7.50. Blooming Prairie Warehouse Inc., 2340 Heinz Rd., Iowa City, IA 52240. TEL 319-337-6448. FAX 319-337-9940. Ed. Jodi DeMeulenaere. circ. 22,200.

PREHRAMBENO-TEHNOLOSKA I BIOTEHNOLOSKA REVIJA/FOOD TECHNOLOGY AND BIOTECHNOLOGY REVIEW. see BIOLOGY — Biotechnology

664.9 IT ISSN 1121-9068
PREMIATA SALUMERIA ITALIANA. 1988. 4/yr. Pubblicita Italia s.a.s., Via Taglio 24, 41100 Modena, Italy. TEL 59-216-753. FAX 59-220-727. Ed. Onelio Benedetti. adv.; bk.rev. circ. 18,000.

664.028 US ISSN 0747-2536
TP368 CODEN: PRFOEH
PREPARED FOODS. 1895. 13/yr. $84 (foreign $142). Delta Communications Inc. (Subsidiary of: Cahners Publishing Company), Division of Reed Elsevier Inc., 455 N. Cityfront Plaza Dr., 24th Fl., Chicago, IL 60611. TEL 312-222-2000. FAX 312-222-2026. TELEX 210012 UR. Ed. Mike Pehanich; Pub. Roy Hlavacek. adv.; charts; illus.; stat.; tr.lit.; index. circ. 71,815. (also avail. in microform from UMI; reprint service avail. from UMI) **Indexed:** Biol.Abstr., Bus.Ind., Chem.Abstr., Curr.Pack.Abstr., Dairy Sci.Abstr., Food Sci.& Tech.Abstr., Hlth.Ind., Int.Packag.Abstr., Key to Econ.Sci., PROMT, Tr.& Indus.Ind. **Document type:** trade publication.
● Also available online. Vendor(s): Mead Data Central, Inc.
—BLDSC (6607.876500); Faxon; UnCover; SWETS; UMI. **CCC.**
  Incorporates in 1986: Food Plant Equipment (ISSN 0015-6515); **Former titles (until 1984):** Processed Prepared Foods (ISSN 0192-7132); (1895-1977): Canner Packer; **Incorporates in 1981:** Food Development (ISSN 0279-0726); Which was formerly: Food Product Development (ISSN 0015-654X)

637 US
PREPARED FOODS FOOD INDUSTRY SOURCEBOOK. 1984. a. $69. Delta Communications Inc. (Subsidiary of: Cahners Publishing Company), Division of Reed Elsevier Inc., 455 N. Cityfront Plaza Dr., 24th Fl., Chicago, IL 60611. TEL 312-222-2000. FAX 312-222-2026. TELEX 210012 UR. Ed. Mike Pehanich. tr.lit. (also avail. in microform; back issues avail.) **Document type:** directory.
—BLDSC (6607.876500); Faxon; UnCover; SWETS; UMI. **CCC.**
  Formerly (until 1990): Prepared Foods Buyers' Guide (ISSN 0747-2536)
  Description: Lists manufacturers of equipment, ingredients, packaging, instruments, sanitation, maintenance, and services to food processors.

664 658.8 UK
PREPARED SOUPS: THE INTERNATIONAL MARKET. a. £1375($2750) Euromonitor, 87-88 Turnmill St., London EC1M 5QU, England. TEL 071-251-8024. FAX 071-608-3149. (Addr. in N. America: Euromonitor International, 111 W. Washington St., Ste. 920, Chicago, IL 60602. TEL 312-541-8024. FAX 312-541-1567) (looseleaf format) **Document type:** trade publication.
● Also available online. Vendor(s): Data-Star, DIALOG Information Services, Inc.
  Description: Analyzes the market for prepared soups for France, Germany, Italy, the U.K., the U.S., and Japan.

PREVENTION OF FOOD ADULTERATION CASES. see LAW

PROCESSED FOODS & BEVERAGES DIRECTORY (YEAR). see BUSINESS AND ECONOMICS — Trade And Industrial Directories

664 668.8 US
PRODUCE MARKETING ASSOCIATION MEMBERSHIP DIRECTORY & BUYER'S GUIDE. 1976. a. $100. Produce Marketing Association, 1500 Casho Mill Rd., Box 6036, Newark, DE 19714-6036. TEL 302-738-7100. FAX 302-731-2409. Ed. Kathy Means. adv. circ. 4,000.
  Former titles: Produce Marketing Almanac - Membership Directory; Produce Marketing Almanac; Produce Marketing Association Almanac; Supersedes (1968-1976): Produce Marketing Association. Yearbook (ISSN 0079-5860); Which was formerly titled: Produce Packaging and Marketing Association. Yearbook.

664.8 US
PRODUCE MERCHANDISING; the packer's retailing and merchandising magazine. 1988. m. $20 (foreign $35). Vance Publishing, 7950 College Blvd., Overland Park, KS 66210. TEL 913-451-2200. FAX 913-451-5821. TELEX 80-4294-SPEDEX-ATL. Ed. Bill O'Neill. adv.: B&W page $2990, color page $4515; 7 x 10. circ. 12,200. (back issues avail.)
  Description: Focuses on retailing fresh produce and related items. Contains information about handling, merchandising, and new trends for produce display and promotion for the produce trade.

FOOD AND FOOD INDUSTRIES

664.8 630 US ISSN 0032-969X
HD9001
PRODUCE NEWS. 1897. w. $35. Zim-Mer Trade Publications, Inc., 2185 Lemoine Ave., Fort Lee, NY 07024. TEL 201-592-9100. FAX 201-592-0809. Ed. Gordon Hochberg. adv.; charts; illus.; stat.; tr.lit. circ. 12,000.
Description: Covers commercial growing, marketing and distribution of fresh fruits.

664 US
PRODUCT ALERT. 1970. w. $600. Marketing Intelligence Service Ltd., 33 Academy St., Naples, NY 14512. TEL 716-374-6326. FAX 716-374-5217. TELEX 469979. Ed. Diane Beach. index. (back issues avail.)
●Also available online. Vendor(s): Data-Star, DIALOG Information Services, Inc.
Description: Highlights reports on new consumer products.

664 II ISSN 0030-8242
PROFODCIL BULLETIN. (Text and summaries in English) 1965. q. Rs.10($2.50) Processed Foods Exports Promotion Council, c/o Shri P.S. Srinivasan, Ed., 105 New Delhi House, Barakhamba Rd., New Delhi 110001, India. adv.; stat. circ. 1,000. **Indexed:** Food Sci.& Tech.Abstr.

338.1 US ISSN 1046-5332
HF5469.25
PROGRESSIVE GROCER'S DIRECTORY OF CONVENIENCE STORES. 1978. a. $220. Trade Dimensions, 263 Tresser Blvd., Stamford, CT 06901. TEL 203-977-7600. FAX 203-977-7645. Ed. Adrienne Toth. **Document type:** directory.
Former titles: Directory of Convenience Stores; Directory of Convenience Store Companies and Profile of the Industry; Directory of Convenience Store Companies (ISSN 0278-9698)
Description: Profiles chain companies with market area maps and demographic data.

PROGRESSIVE GROCER'S DIRECTORY OF MASS MERCHANDISERS. see *BUSINESS AND ECONOMICS — Trade And Industrial Directories*

664 658.8 US ISSN 0146-9223
HD9321.2
PROGRESSIVE GROCER'S MARKET SCOPE. 1975. a. $299. Trade Dimensions, 263 Tresser Blvd., Stamford, CT 06901. TEL 203-977-7600. FAX 203-977-7645. Ed. Adrienne Toth. index. (back issues avail.) **Document type:** trade publication.
Description: Contains retail market share information for over 1,200 chain supermarkets and wholesale buying offices; highlights the number of markets served and sales by product category, with selected demographic profiles of consumers.

338.1 US ISSN 0079-6921
HD9321.3
PROGRESSIVE GROCER'S MARKETING GUIDEBOOK. 1967. a. $320. Trade Dimensions, 263 Tresser Blvd., Stamford, CT 06901. TEL 203-977-7600. FAX 203-977-7645. Ed. Adrienne Toth. adv.; index. (back issues avail.)
Description: Profiles supermarket chains and wholesalers, including demographics, county statistics, and data on company buying and distribution policies.

664 XR ISSN 0033-1988
CODEN: PPOTAP
PRUMYSL POTRAVIN/FOOD INDUSTRY; technika a ekonomika prumyslove vyroby potravin. (Text in Czech or Slovak; summaries in English, French, German, Russian) 1950. m. 84 Kcs.($38.70) (Ministerstvo Zemedelstvi a Vyzivy Ceske Republiky) Statni Zemedelske Nakladatelstvi, Vaclavske nam. 47, 113 11 Prague 1, Czech Republic. TEL 26 59 51. (Subscr. to: Artia, Ve Smeckach 30, 111 27 Prague 1, Czech Republic) Ed. Jirina Safrova. adv.; bk.rev.; abstr.; bibl.; charts; illus.; pat.; stat.; tr.lit.; index. circ. 3,000. **Indexed:** Agri.Eng.Abstr., Anal.Abstr., C.I.S. Abstr., Chem.Abstr., Dairy Sci.Abstr., Food Sci.& Tech.Abstr., Nutr.Abstr., Rural Recreat.Tour.Abstr., World Agri.Econ.& Rural Sociol.Abstr.
—BLDSC (6938.400000); CASDDS.

663 PL ISSN 0137-2645
TP500 CODEN: PFOWDZ
PRZEMYSL FERMENTACYJNY I OWOCOWO WARZYWNY. 1952. m. $61. (Stowarzyszenie Naukowo-Techniczne Inzynierow i Technikow Przemyslu Spozywczego) Wydawnictwo Czasopism i Ksiazek Technicznych SIGMA - NOT, Ul. Ratuszowa 11, P.O. Box 1004, 00-950 Warsaw, Poland. TEL 48-22-180918. FAX 48-22-192187. TELEX 814550 SIGMA PL. (Dist. by: SIGMA NOT Ltd., Ul. Bartycka 20, 00-716 Warsaw, Poland) Ed. Maria Przegalinska. adv.; B&W page $1010. circ. 1,350. **Indexed:** Biol.Abstr., Nutr.Abstr., Sugar Ind.Abstr.
—BLDSC (6945.073000); CASDDS.
Formerly: Przemysl Fermentacyjny i Rolny (ISSN 0555-5264)
Description: Covers fruit and vegetable industry.

664 PL ISSN 0033-250X
CODEN: PRSPAD
PRZEMYSL SPOZYWCZY. (Text in Polish; summaries in English and German) 1947. m. $81.50. (Stowarzyszenie Naukowo-Techniczne Inzynierow i Technikow Przemyslu Spozywczego) Wydawnictwo Czasopism i Ksiazek Technicznych SIGMA - NOT, Ul. Ratuszowa 11, P.O. Box 1004, 00-950 Warsaw, Poland. TEL 48-22-180918. FAX 48-22-192187. TELEX 814550 SIGMA PL. (Dist. by: SIGMA NOT Ltd., Bartycka 20, 00-716 Warsaw, Poland) Ed. Karol Krajewski. adv.; B&W page $1010. bk.rev.; abstr.; bibl.; charts; illus.; pat.; stat.; index. circ. 1,750. **Indexed:** Chem.Abstr., Dairy Sci.Abstr., Food Sci.& Tech.Abstr., Nutr.Abstr., Packag.Sci.Tech., Rural Recreat.Tour.Abstr., Soyabean Abstr., Sugar Ind.Abstr., World Agri.Econ.& Rural Sociol.Abstr.
—BLDSC (6945.160000); CASDDS.
Description: Covers novelties of technics, machines, research, articles and trade fair.

664 IT
PUNTO D'ORO. 12/yr. Corso Re. Umberto 8, 10121 Turin, Italy. TEL 11-55-34-40. FAX 11-537040. Ed. Romualdo d'Antonio.

PURE FACTS. see *MEDICAL SCIENCES — Psychiatry And Neurology*

QUANDONG. see *AGRICULTURE — Crop Production And Soil*

664 FR
▼**QUICK FREEZE;** international guide to the frozen food industry. (Text in English, French, German, Spanish) 1992. a. 580 F. Helios International, 14 bd. Montmartre, 75009 Paris, France. TEL 90-89-33-00. FAX 90-88-28-49. TELEX 432 845. adv.; B&W page 10200 F., color page 18000 F.; trim 170 x 260; adv. contact: Claudie Seldran. circ. 9,000. **Document type:** directory.
Description: Manufacturers, exporters and importers of frozen food listed by country, brand name and product at the international level. Also includes transporters, coldstores, purchasing groups and subsidiary industries.

664.028 US ISSN 0890-5517
QUICK FROZEN FOODS ANNUAL PROCESSORS' DIRECTORY AND BUYERS' GUIDE. 1945. a. $98 (effective 1993). Frozen Food Digest, Inc., 271 Madison Ave., New York, NY 10016. TEL 212-557-8600. FAX 212-986-9868. circ. 4,993. **Document type:** directory.
Formerly (until 1985): Quick Frozen Foods Directory of Frozen Food Processors (ISSN 0079-9289)

664.028 US ISSN 0033-6416
TP493.5.A1 CODEN: QFFIAO
QUICK FROZEN FOODS INTERNATIONAL. (Text in English; summaries in French, German) 1959. q. $24 (foreign $50). E.W. Williams Publications Co., 2125 Center Ave., Ste. 305, Fort Lee, NJ 07024-5859. TEL 201-592-7007. FAX 201-592-7171. Ed. John M. Saulnier. adv.; bk.rev.; charts; illus.; stat. circ. 11,000. **Indexed:** Tr.& Indus.Ind. **Document type:** trade publication.
●Also available online. Vendor(s): Information Access Co.
—BLDSC (7216.407000); UnCover.

664 FR ISSN 0035-4244
TP368
R I A. (Revue de l'Industrie Agro-Alimentaire) 1953. fortn. 545 F. C E P Groupe France Agricole, 8 cite Paradis, 75493 Paris Cedex 10, France. TEL 40-22-70-60. FAX 40-22-70-70. TELEX 660 067 F. adv.; B&W page 14200 F., color page 20800 F.; trim 282 x 210; adv. contact: Muriel Case. circ. 10,000. (back issues avail.)
—BLDSC (7963.530000).
Formerly: R.T I A.
Description: Covers the meat, milk, grain, beverage, tinned food, bread and pastry industries.

664 IT
RASSEGNA ALIMENTARE. 5/yr. $63. Editrice Zeus, Corso Buenos Aires 47, 20124 Milan, Italy. TEL 29406225. FAX 29522168. Ed. Enrico Maffizzoni. circ. 5,500. **Document type:** trade publication.
Description: Covers machinery, plant components and products for the food and drink industry.

664 IT
RASSEGNA ALIMENTARE IN LINGUA RUSSA. (Text in Russian) 3/yr. $44. Editrice Zeus, Corso Buenos Aires 47, 20124 Milan, Italy. TEL 29406225. FAX 29522163. Ed. Enrico Maffizzoni. circ. 10,000. **Document type:** trade publication.
Formerly: Italia - U R S S Rassegna Alimentare.
Description: Covers machinery, plant components and products for the food and drink industry.

664 IT
RASSEGNA DI DIRITTO E TECNICA DELL'ALIMENTAZIONE. 1965. bi-m. L.110000 (foreign L.140000) (effective 1993). Franco Angeli Editore, Viale Monza 106, 20127 Milan, Italy. TEL 02-28-27-651. Ed. Renato Piccinino. adv. circ. 3,000.

RECIPE ANNUAL. see *HOME ECONOMICS*

RECIPE YEARBOOK (YEAR). see *HOME ECONOMICS*

641.53 540 US ISSN 0738-3932
RECIPES FOR SALE. 1986. a. $4. Cookbook Consortium, c/o Prosperity & Profits Unlimited, Distribution Services, Box 416, Denver, CO 80201-0416. TEL 303-575-5676. Ed. A. Doyle. circ. 1,500. (looseleaf format; also avail. in microform; back issues avail.) **Document type:** newsletter.
Description: Provides sources of finding recipes for sale.

664 US
REFERENCE SOURCE (YEAR). a. $30. Sosland Publishing Company, 4800 Main St., Ste. 100, Kansas City, MO 64112. TEL 816-756-1000.
Description: Factbook of statistical information for bakers. Includes product listings and troubleshooting sections for bread/cake and cookies/crackers.

664 US ISSN 1061-6152
REFRIGERATED AND FROZEN FOODS. 1990. m. $55 (foreign $110-$210) (free to qualified personnel). Stagnito Publishing Company, 1935 Shermer Rd., Ste. 100, Northbrook, IL 60062. TEL 708-205-5660. FAX 708-205-5680. Ed. Bob Harrison; Pub. Korry Stagnito. adv. contact: Sophia Giannapoulos. circ. 35,000 (controlled). **Document type:** trade publication.
Description: Aimed at management and employees in the U.S .and Canadian refrigerated and frozen food industries. Covers in-plant visits and news and analysis of business and consumer trends.

664 IT
REPERTORIO ITALIANO PER L'INDUSTRIA ALIMENTARE. a. $50. Editrice Zeus, Corso Buenos Aires, 47, 20124 Milan, Italy. TEL 29406225. FAX 29522168. Ed. Enrico Maffizzoni. **Document type:** catalog, trade publication.
Description: Lists 3000 companies in the Italian food and drink industry. Includes addresses and machines, plants and products.

642.5 US
REPORT ON INSTITUTIONAL FOODSERVICE. 1987. m. $195 (effective 1994) Information Central Inc., Box 3900, Prescott, AZ 86302. TEL 602-778-1513. Ed. Julie Woodman. stat.; index. (looseleaf format)
Description: Covers developments in and information on food service in schools, colleges, and healthcare and correctional institutions.

FOOD AND FOOD INDUSTRIES

RESTAURANT EXCHANGE NEWS. see *HOTELS AND RESTAURANTS*

RESTAURANT INTERNATIONAL. see *HOTELS AND RESTAURANTS*

630 338.19   CN
RETAIL FOOD PRICE REPORT; monthly bulletin. vol.11, 1971. m. free. Agriculture Canada, Policy Branch, Ottawa, ON K1A 0C5, Canada. TEL 613-995-5222. circ. 1,050. **Document type:** government publication.
   Formerly: Food Outlook (ISSN 0015-6507)

664   UK
THE REVIEW. 1925. m. £15. (Retail Fruit Trade Federation Ltd.) Millbrooke Publications, 44 Langford Green, Champion Hill, Camberwell, London SE5 8BX, England. TEL 071-274-8308. FAX 071-738-3767. Ed. Anna Pattie. adv.: B&W page £525, color page £950; trim 255 x 184. index. circ. 5,500. **Document type:** trade publication.
   Formerly: Retail Fruit Trade Review.

REVISTA BRASILEIRA DE BEBIDAS E ALIMENTOS. see *BEVERAGES*

633   CK   ISSN 0120-2278
REVISTA CAFETERA DE COLOMBIA. 1928. 3/yr. Federacion Nacional de Cafeteros de Colombia, Apdo. Aereo 3938, Bogota, Colombia. Ed. Jose Chalarca. bibl.; charts; illus.; stat. **Indexed:** Biol.Abstr.

REVISTA CUBANA DE ALIMENTACION Y NUTRICION. see *NUTRITION AND DIETETICS*

663.93   BL   ISSN 0034-9224
REVISTA DO COMERCIO DE CAFE. 1920. bi-m. $80. Centro do Comercio de Cafe do Rio de Janeiro, Rua da Quitanda 191, Andar 11, 20091 Rio de Janeiro, Brazil. FAX 21-253-4873. TELEX 21-22659. Ed. Adriano Barbosa. adv.; bk.rev.; illus.; charts; stat. circ. 9,200. **Document type:** trade publication.

664 668.6   SP   ISSN 1131-799X
TP368   CODEN: RCTAEU
REVISTA ESPANOLA DE CIENCIA Y TECNOLOGIA DE ALIMENTOS/SPANISH JOURNAL OF FOOD SCIENCE AND TECHNOLOGY. (Text in English, Spanish) 1961. bi-m. 9000 ptas.($125) (effective 1992). Consejo Superior de Investigaciones Cientificas (C.S.I.C.), Instituto de Agroquimica y Tecnologis de Alimentos, Vitruvio, 8, 28006 Madrid, Spain. TEL 96-369-08-00. TELEX 64197 AYTVE. Ed. Luis Duran Hidalgo. adv.; bk.rev.; abstr.; illus.; index. circ. 2,000. **Indexed:** Biol.Abstr., Bull.Signal., Chem.Abstr., Curr.Adv.Ecol.Sci., Curr.Cont., Dairy Sci.Abstr., Excerp.Med., Food Sci.& Tech.Abstr., Hort.Abstr., Ind.SST, Mass Spectr.Bull., Nutr.Abstr., Packag.Sci.Tech., Rice Abstr., Risk Abstr., Soils & Fert., Sugar Ind.Abstr.
   —BLDSC (7853.930500); SWETS; CASDDS.
   Formerly: Revista de Agroquimica y Tecnologia de Alimentos (ISSN 0034-7698)
   Description: Covers food science, technology and agricultural chemistry.

REVISTA INTERNACIONAL DE SOCIOLOGIA SOBRE AGRICULTURA Y ALIMENTOS/INTERNATIONAL JOURNAL OF SOCIOLOGY OF AGRICULTURE AND FOOD. see *SOCIOLOGY*

664   FR
REVUE CULINAIRE. 10/yr. Mutuelle des Cuisiniers, 45 rue Saint-Roch, 75001 Paris, France. TEL 42-61-52-75. Ed. Roger Peylet. circ. 5,000.

664   FR
REVUE DE L'INDUSTRIE ALIMENTAIRE. 1953. 10/yr. 550 F. Societe d'Edition et de Promotion Agro-Alimentaire Industrielle et Commerciales (SEPAIC), 8 cite Paradis, 75493 Paris Cedex 10, France. TEL 40-22-70-60. FAX 40-22-70-70. Ed. Jean-Luc Jicquel. circ. 4,000.

664   IT
TX341   CODEN: RSISAZ
RIVISTA DI SCIENZA DELL'ALIMENTAZIONE. 1955. q. L.130000 (foreign L.250000) (effective 1994). Societa Editrice Alimenti Alimentazione Nutrizione, Via Tiberio Imperatore 65, 00145 Rome, Italy. TEL 06-51600185. FAX 06-5137436. Ed. Riccardo Monacelli. adv.; bk.rev.; abstr.; illus.; index. circ. 5,000. **Indexed:** Biol.Abstr., Chem.Abstr., Food Sci.& Tech.Abstr., Sugar Ind.Abstr. **Document type:** academic/scholarly publication.
   —BLDSC (7992.801700).
   Former titles (until 1993): Societa Italiana di Scienza dell'Alimentazione. Rivista (ISSN 0391-4887); Scienza dell'Alimentazione (ISSN 0036-8865)

664 642 914.404   FR
ROBERT NOAH'S PARIS EN CUISINE NEWSLETTER; the insider's guide to gastronomic news of France. (Text in English) 1983. bi-m. $39 (effective 1992). Paris en Cuisine, Inc., 49 rue de Richelieu, 75001 Paris, France. TEL 33-1-42-61-35-23. FAX 33-1-42-60-39-96. (Subscr. to: Box 50099, St. Louis, MO 63105-5099) Ed. Robert S. Noah. bk.rev.; cum.index: 1983-1992. circ. 500. (looseleaf format; back issues avail.) **Document type:** newsletter.

664   GW
RUNDSCHAU FUER FLEISCHHYGIENE UND LEBENSMITTELUEBERWACHUNG. 1948. m. DM.67. Verlag M. und H. Schaper, Kalandstr. 4, 31061 Alfeld, Germany. (Subscr. to: Postfach 1642, 31046 Alfeld, Germany) Eds. Peter Habit, Josef Pueschner. adv.; bk.rev. circ. 3,000. (back issues avail.)
   Former titles (until 1993): Fleisch- und Lebensmittelhygiene (ISSN 0933-2758); Fleisch und Lebensmittelkontrolle (ISSN 0341-4558)

664   SW
S I K ANNUAL REPORT. (Text in English and Swedish) 1951. a. S I K - Swedish Institute for Food Research, P.O. Box 5401, S-402 29 Goeteborg, Sweden. circ. 2,000. **Indexed:** Dairy Sci.Abstr. **Document type:** corporate report.
   Formerly: Swedish Food Institute. Annual Report.

664.028   SW
S I K INFOOD. (Text in English) 1972. irreg. free. S I K - Swedish Institute for Food Research, P.O. Box 5401, S-402 29 Goeteborg, Sweden. circ. 700. **Document type:** newsletter.
   Formerly: S I K Information.

664 658.8   US
S N DISTRIBUTION STUDY OF GROCERY STORE SALES.* 1978. a. $60. Fairchild Books (Subsidiary of: Fairchild Publications Inc.), 7 W. 34th St., New York, NY 10001. TEL 212-630-4000. FAX 212-887-1946. TELEX 232666 FAPB. Ed. Sonja Yelenovic. circ. 1,500. (also avail. in microfiche from CIS; back issues avail.) **Indexed:** SRI.

664   GW
S P A R AKTUELL. 11/yr. DM.70.41 (foreign DM.120.80). (Handelsgruppe S P A R) Deutscher Fachverlag GmbH, Mainzer Landstr. 251, 60326 Frankfurt a.M., Germany. TEL 069-7595-01. FAX 069-75952999. circ. 23,817. **Document type:** trade publication.

SAFE FOOD NEWS. see *CONSUMER EDUCATION AND PROTECTION*

664.9   IT
SALUMAIO E IL GASTRONOMO. 12/yr. Via Fabio Filzi 41, 20124 Milan, Italy. TEL 2-60-80-378. FAX 2-688-77-40. Ed. Pietro Valentini. circ. 108,000.

SAMMLUNG LEBENSMITTELRECHTLICHER ENTSCHEIDUNGEN. see *LAW*

641.53   UK
SANDWICH & SNACK NEWS. 1990. 6/yr. £30. British Sandwich Association, 29 Market Pl., Wantage, Oxon. OX12 8BG, England. TEL 0235-772207. FAX 0235-769044. Ed. Jim Winship. circ. 7,000. **Document type:** trade publication.

664   UK
SAUCES AND SPREADS. 1987. every 18 mos. £155 per issue. Key Note Publications Ltd., Field House, Old Field Rd., Hampton TW12 2HQ, England. TEL 01 783-0755.
   Description: Provides an overview of the sauces and spreads industry (i.e jam, honey, savoury spreads, sandwich spreads) including industry structure, market size and trends, recent developments and prospects.

664.7 658.8   UK
SAVOURY SNACKS: THE INTERNATIONAL MARKET. a. £1375($2750) Euromonitor, 87-88 Turnmill St., London EC1M 5QU, England. TEL 071-251-8024. FAX 071-608-3149. (Addr. in N. America: Euromonitor International, 111 W. Washington St., Ste. 920, Chicago, IL 60602. TEL 312-541-8024. FAX 312-541-1567) (looseleaf format) **Document type:** trade publication.
   ●Also available online. Vendor(s): Data-Star, DIALOG Information Services, Inc.
   Description: Analyzes the market for chips, crackers, popcorn, and flavored nuts for France, Germany, Italy, Spain, the U.K., the U.S., and Japan.

664   GW
SCHOENER ESSEN. 1985. m. DM.42 (Europe DM.66; elsewhere DM.106.80). Gruner und Jahr AG & Co., Am Baumwall 11, 20459 Hamburg, Germany. TEL 040-3703-0. FAX 040-37035606. Ed. Angelika Jahr. circ. 200,133. **Document type:** consumer publication.

642.5   US   ISSN 0160-6271
LB3475.A1   CODEN: SFSJAC
SCHOOL FOOD SERVICE JOURNAL. 1946. 11/yr. $125 to non-members (foreign $160). American School Food Service Association, 1600 Duke St., 7th Fl., Alexandria, VA 22314-3436. TEL 703-739-3900. FAX 703-739-3915. Ed. Adrienne L. Gall. adv.; bk.rev.; tr.lit.; index. circ. 65,000.
   —Faxon; UnCover.
   Formerly: School Lunch Journal (ISSN 0036-6641)
   Description: Covers legislative and management issues concerning food service and child nutrition.

642.5   US   ISSN 0149-6808
SCHOOL FOOD SERVICE RESEARCH REVIEW. 1977. s-a. $24 (foreign $32). American School Food Service Association, 1600 Duke St., 7th Fl., Alexandria, VA 22314-3436. TEL 703-739-3900. FAX 703-739-3915. Ed. Deborah D. Canter. bk.rev.; index. circ. 250. (back issues avail.)
   —BLDSC (8092.744000); Faxon; UnCover.
   Description: Covers research and school food service and child nutrition.
   Refereed Serial

SCHOOL FOODSERVICE WHO'S WHO. see *BUSINESS AND ECONOMICS — Trade And Industrial Directories*

664.9   SZ   ISSN 0036-7680
SCHWEIZERISCHE METZGER-ZEITUNG/JOURNAL SUISSE DES BOUCHERS-CHARCUTIERS/GIORNALE SVIZZERO DEI MACELLAI. (Text in French, German and Italian) 1892. w. 160 Fr. to non-members; members 70 Fr. Verband Schweizer Metzgermeister - Swiss Master Butchers Federation, Postfach, CH-8028 Zurich, Switzerland. TEL 01-2527766. FAX 01-262874. Ed. Ulrich Amacher. adv.; bk.rev.; circ. 5,498 (controlled).

664   FR   ISSN 0240-8813
TX341   CODEN: SCALDC
SCIENCES DES ALIMENTS. (Text in English or French; summaries in English, French) 1981. bi-m. 1660 F. Lavoisier Abonnements, 11 rue Lavoisier, 75384 Paris Cedex 08, France. Ed. J.L. Multon. charts. circ. 1,000. **Indexed:** Biol.Abstr., Chem.Abstr., Curr.Adv.Biochem., Curr.Adv.Ecol.Sci., Curr.Cont., Dairy Sci.Abstr., Food Sci.& Tech.Abstr., Rev.Med.& Vet.Mycol., Sugar Ind.Abstr.
   —BLDSC (8165.660000); Faxon; SWETS; CASDDS. CCC.
   Description: Devoted to the various fields of food science and technology.

664.9   UK
SCOTTISH BUTCHER. (Supplement of: Butcher and Processor) 1984. 4/yr. Smithfield Publishing Ltd., High St., Castle Camps, Cambs CB1 6SN, England. TEL 0799-584879. FAX 0799-584883. Ed. Jeanne Gavin. adv.; bk.rev. circ. 2,000. **Document type:** trade publication.

FOOD AND FOOD INDUSTRIES 2581

SEAFOOD BUSINESS. see *FISH AND FISHERIES*

664   US
SEAFOOD CURRENT. 1987. q. free. North Carolina Sea Grant College Program, 105 1911 Bldg., Box 8605, North Carolina State University, Raleigh, NC 27695-8605. TEL 919-515-2454. FAX 919-515-7095. circ. 832. **Document type:** newsletter.

664   US   ISSN 0744-4664
SH334.9   CODEN: SELEDQ
SEAFOOD LEADER. 1981. 6/yr. $24. Waterfront Press Co., 1115 N.W. 46th St., Seattle, WA 98107. TEL 206-789-6506. Ed. Peter Redmayne. adv.; tr.lit. circ. 15,000.
—UnCover.
     Formerly: Ocean Leader.

SEAFOOD PRICE-CURRENT. see *FISH AND FISHERIES*

664   MX
SECTOR ALIMENTARIO EN MEXICO (YEAR). 1981. irreg., latest 1991. Mex.$6000($35) Instituto Nacional de Estadistica, Geografia e Informatica, Secretaria de Programacion y Presupuesto, Prol. Heroe de Nacozari, 2301, Sur, Puerta 11, Acceso, 20270 Aguascalientes, Ags., Mexico. TEL 91-49-18-19-48. FAX 91-491-80739. circ. 1,000.

641   IT
SELF MAGAZINE. 1966. m. (10/yr.). L.10000. Casa Editrice Edithema, Residenza I Portici Milano 2, 20090 Segrate (MI), Italy. TEL 2-26-41-53-12. FAX 2-26-40-989. Ed. Paolo Bellavista. adv. circ. 50,000. (tabloid format)

664   SP
SERIE DE COCINA POR LUIS RIPOLI. (Subject varies with each issue) irreg. price varies. Luis Ripoll Ed. & Pub., Calatrava 34, 07001 Palma de Mallorca, Spain.

664.1   II   ISSN 0037-332X
SHARKARA. (Text in English, Hindi) 1958. q. Rs.16($5.75) Ministry of Food and Civil Supplies, Department of Food, National Sugar Institute, Kalianpur, Kanpur 208 017, Uttar Pradesh, India. TEL 243016. TELEX 325-328-NSIK-IN. (Dist. by: Controller of Publications, Ministry of Urban Development, Civil Lines, Delhi 110 054, India) Ed. Shri N.C. Jain. adv.; bk.rev.; charts; illus.; tr.lit.; index. circ. 2,500. **Indexed:** Chem.Abstr.
     Description: Provides technical information about India's sugar industry.

664   US
SHELF ACTION. q. Meredith Corp., 750 Third Ave., 12th Fl., New York, NY 10017-2703. TEL 212-551-7157. Ed. Mary Rae. circ. 7,000.
     Description: Covers all food-related news.

SHIPIN KE-JI/FOOD SCIENCE. see *NUTRITION AND DIETETICS*

664   JA
SHOKUHIN KOGYO/FOOD INDUSTRY. 1958. s-m. 39000 Yen. Korin Publishing Co. Ltd., P.O. Box 41, Shitaya, Tokyo 110-91, Japan. Ed. Watanabe Masami. adv. circ. 25,000. **Indexed:** Chem.Abstr., Sugar Ind.Abstr. **Document type:** trade publication.

664   JA   ISSN 0037-4105
     CODEN: SHTKAY
SHOKUHIN TO KAGAKU. (Text in Japanese) 1959. m. 25,000 Yen. Food Science Co., Ltd. - Shokuhin to Kagakusha, Kosei Bldg., Bekkan 1-9-10, Uchikanda, Chiyoda-ku, Tokyo 101, Japan. TEL 03-3291-2081. FAX 03-3233-0478. Ed. Naokuni Kishi. adv.; bk.rev.; abstr.; bibl.; charts; illus.; pat.; stat.; index. circ. 27,500. **Indexed:** Chem.Abstr. **Document type:** academic/scholarly publication.
—BLDSC (3982.962000); CASDDS.

SHOPPER REPORT. see *BUSINESS AND ECONOMICS — Marketing And Purchasing*

664.1   CC
SICHUAN GANZHE/SICHUAN SUGAR CANE. (Text in Chinese) q. (Sichuan Zhitang Tangliao Gongye Yanjiusuo - Sichuan Sugar Manufacturing Industry Research Institute) Sichuan Ganzhe Bianjibu, 6 Yongxing Lu, Zizong Xian Chengguan, Sichuan 641200, People's Republic of China. TEL 2177. (Dist. overseas by: Jiangsu Publications Import & Export Corp., 56 Gao Yun Ling, Nanjing, Jiangsu, P.R.C.) Ed. Li Huafu.

664   US
SIMPLE COOKING. 1980. q. $16. John Thorne, Ed. & Pub., Box 88, Steuben, ME 04680-0088. bk.rev. circ. 2,000. (back issues avail.) **Document type:** newsletter.
     Description: Contains news and essays about gastronomy.

664.9   NE   ISSN 0037-6698
DE SLAGER; weekblad voor het slagersbedrijf. 1942. w. fl.159.50 (foreign fl.245). (Federatie van Nederlandse Slagerspatroonsbonden) Audet Tijdschriften bv (Subsidiary of: C. Misset B.V.), Postbus 9000, 6800 DA Arnhem, Netherlands. TEL 31-85-209911. FAX 31-85-233007. Eds. Wim Busser, Piet Verhamme. adv.: B&W page fl.3299, color page fl.4759; trim 230 x 300; adv. contact: Cor van Nek. charts; illus.; mkt.; pat.; stat.; tr.mk. circ. 6,970. **Indexed:** Key to Econ.Sci. **Document type:** trade publication.
     Description: Provides trade information and the latest developments for the retail meat business.

664 664.752   AT   ISSN 1038-5606
SMALL RETAILER. (Supplement avail.: Food-Grocery Price Guide) 1962. m. Aus.$78. Small Retailers Association of S.A. Inc., 321 Port Rd., P.O. Box 311, Hindmarsh, S.A. 5007, Australia. TEL 340-1722. FAX 340-1007. Ed. Dennis Harrison. circ. 1,200. **Document type:** trade publication.
     Former titles (until 1992): Independent Food Retailer (ISSN 0819-0712); (until 1986): South Australian Mixed Association Journal (ISSN 0819-0690)
     Description: Provides trade news for small retailers - awards, new products, business advice, members profiles.

664   NE
SNACK KOERIER; de vakkrant voor snackverkopend Nederland. 1987. fortn. fl.97.50 (1950 BEF). C. Misset B.V., Postbus 4, 7000 BA Doetinchem, Netherlands. TEL 31-8340-49911. FAX 31-8340-43839. adv.; B&W page fl.5796; 290 x 420; adv. contact: Cor van Nek. illus. circ. 12,530. (tabloid format) **Document type:** trade publication.
     Description: Covers the retail and wholesale snack trade in the Netherlands.

641.53   US   ISSN 0896-1670
TX803.P8   CODEN: SNWOE5
SNACK WORLD. 1941. m. $60 to non-members; members $30. International Snack Food Association, 1711 King St., No. 1, Alexandria, VA 22314. TEL 703-836-4500. FAX 703-836-8262. TELEX 704234. Ed. Al Rickard. adv.; illus.; mkt.; tr.lit. circ. 5,500. **Indexed:** Food Sci.& Tech.Abstr., Trop.Oil Seeds Abstr. **Document type:** trade publication.
—BLDSC (8313.750000).
     Former titles: Chipper - Snacker; Potato Chipper (ISSN 0032-5562)
     Description: Covers the snack industry around the world.

642   US   ISSN 0081-1483
SOCIETY FOR THE ADVANCEMENT OF FOOD SERVICE RESEARCH. PROCEEDINGS. 1959. a. Society for the Advancement of Food Service Research, 304 W. Liberty St., Ste. 301, Louisville, KY 40202. TEL 813-465-7090. Ed. Charles E. Eshbach. **Document type:** proceedings.

SODOBNO KMETIJSTVO. see *AGRICULTURE*

664.1   SA   ISSN 0038-2728
SB215
SOUTH AFRICAN SUGAR JOURNAL. (Text in English) 1917. m. R.60 (effective 1992). South African Sugar Association, Norwich Life House Bldg., 6th Fl., 6 Durban Club Place, Durban 4001, South Africa. TEL 031-305-6161. FAX 031-3044939. TELEX 6-22215. Ed. G.R. Dewey. adv.; bk.rev.; charts; illus.; mkt.; tr.lit.; index. circ. 4,000. **Indexed:** Bio-Contr.News & Info., Chem.Abstr., Field Crop Abstr., Herb.Abstr., Hort.Abstr., Ind.S.A.Per., Irr.& Drain.Abstr., Plant Breed.Abstr., Rural Recreat.Tour.Abstr., Soils & Fert., Weed Abstr., World Agri.Econ.& Rural Sociol.Abstr.

664 641.1   NL   ISSN 1018-0966
SOUTH PACIFIC FOODS LEAFLET. French edition: Aliments du Pacifique Sud (ISSN 1018-1296) (Text in English, French) 1980. irreg., no.18, 1992. South Pacific Commission, B.P. D5, Noumea, Cedex, New Caledonia. TEL 26-2000. FAX 687-263818. TELEX 3139 NM SOPACOM. **Document type:** monographic series.

664 642.5   US   ISSN 0199-2805
SOUTHEAST FOOD SERVICE NEWS. 1976. m. $4. Southeast Publishing Co., Inc., Box 47719, Atlanta, GA 30362. circ. 18,500. (tabloid format)

SPECIALTY COOKING; cookbook magazine. see *NUTRITION AND DIETETICS*

664   DK   ISSN 0906-7582
SPISEGUIDEN DANMARK.* 1978. a. Kr.20. N C C, Copenhagen, Denmark.
     Former titles (until 1991): Toyo Spiseguide (ISSN 0905-4812); (until 1989): Toyo (ISSN 0902-6444); (until 1983): Toyo Spiseguide (ISSN 0108-4992); (until 1981): Gode Spisemuligheder i Danmark (ISSN 0108-4984)

SPROUTLETTER. see *NUTRITION AND DIETETICS*

663.94 633.72   CE   ISSN 1010-4208
SRI LANKA JOURNAL OF TEA SCIENCE. (Text in English) 1928. s-a. $20. Tea Research Institute of Sri Lanka, St. Coombs, Talawakele, Sri Lanka. TEL 052-8385. FAX 052-8311. Eds. P. Sivapalan, A. Kathiravetpillai. adv.; bk.rev.; charts; illus.; index. circ. 2,000. **Indexed:** Biol.Abstr., Curr.Cont., Food Sci.& Tech.Abstr., Helminthol.Abstr., Hort.Abstr., Plant Breed.Abstr., Rev.Appl.Entomol., Rev.Plant Path., Soils & Fert., Sri Lanka Sci.Ind., Weed Abstr., World Agri.Econ.& Rural Sociol.Abstr.
—BLDSC (8425.116000).
     Formerly (until 1985): Tea Quarterly (ISSN 0040-036X)

664 340   US
STATE LEGISLATIVE UPDATE. 1990. 26/yr. membership. National Food Processors Association, 1401 New York Ave., N.W., Ste. 400, Washington, DC 20005. TEL 2C2-639-5900. FAX 202-627-8063. **Document type:** newsletter.

SUCRERIE BELGE. see *AGRICULTURE — Crop Production And Soil*

664.1   FR   ISSN 0039-4491
SUCRERIE FRANCAISE; revue de l'industrie sucriere francaise. 1860. 6/yr. 320 F. (foreign 360 F.). Arts Graphiques du Perche Edition, 1 rue du Coq-Heron, 75001 Paris, France TEL 40-26-57-08. FAX 40-26-34-40. Ed. Mme. Gueroult. adv.; charts; mkt.; stat.; index. **Indexed:** Chem.Abstr., Food Sci.& Tech.Abstr., Herb.Abstr., Soils & Fert., Sugar Ind.Abstr.
—BLDSC (8507.000000).

664.005   SJ
SUDAN JOURNAL OF FOOD SCIENCE AND TECHNOLOGY. (Text in English) 1968. a. $10. Food Research Centre, P.O. Box 213, Khartoum North, Sudan. Ed. S. Badi. bk.rev.; illus. **Indexed:** Biol.Abstr., Chem.Abstr., Dairy Sci.Abstr., Food Sci.& Tech.Abstr.

664   GW   ISSN 0081-9174
SUESSWAREN JAHRBUCH; Wer und Was in der deutschen Suesswarenindustrie. 1949. a. DM.149. B. Behr's Verlag GmbH, Averhoffstr. 10, 22085 Hamburg, Germany. **Document type:** directory.

664.1   US   ISSN 0039-4726
HD9100.1
SUGAR BULLETIN. 1922. s-m. $10 to non-members. American Sugar Cane League of the U.S.A., 201 N. Canal Blvd., Thibodaux, LA 70301. TEL 504-448-3707. Ed. J. Kelly Nix. adv.; illus. circ. 3,300. **Indexed:** Biol.Abstr., Plant Breed.Abstr., Sugar Ind.Abstr. **Document type:** bulletin.

SUGAR CANE; the only international journal devoted solely to sugarcane agriculture. see *AGRICULTURE*

ULRICH'S INTERNATIONAL PERIODICALS DIRECTORY 1994-95

FOOD AND FOOD INDUSTRIES

664.1　　　　　UK
SUGAR INDUSTRY JOURNAL BUYER'S GUIDE. 1974. s-a. $20 (free with subscription to International Sugar Journal and Sugar Cane). International Media Ltd., P.O. Box 26, Port Talbot, W. Glamorgan SA13 1NX, Wales. TEL 44-0639-887498.
FAX 44-639-899830. TELEX 21792-REF-869. Ed. N.J. Davies. adv.; tr.lit. circ. 10,600. **Document type:** directory.
　　Formerly (until 1983): International Sugar Journal Buyer's Guide.
　　Description: News and equipment, services and more for use in sugar growing and processing, plus suppliers directory.

664.1　　　　　US　　ISSN 0039-4734
HD9101　　　　　CODEN: SUJOAJ
SUGAR JOURNAL; covering the world's sugar industry. 1938. m. $33. Kriedt Enterprises, Ltd., 129 S. Cortez St., New Orleans, LA 70119-6118. TEL 504-482-3914. Eds. Lowell McCormick, Robert Oldemeyer. adv.; bk.rev.; bibl.; charts; illus.; tr.lit.; index. circ. 3,300. **Indexed:** ASCA, Biol.Abstr., Biotech.Abstr., Chem.Abstr., Curr.Adv.Ecol.Sci., Curr.Cont., Excerp.Med., Food Sci.& Tech.Abstr., Hort.Abstr., Soils & Fert., Sugar Ind.Abstr. —UnCover; CASDDS.

664.1 631　　　　　SA
SUGAR MILLING RESEARCH INSTITUTE. ANNUAL REPORT. (Text in English) 1950. a. $50 to non-members. Sugar Milling Research Institute, University of Natal, King George V Ave., 4001 Durban, South Africa. TEL 27-31-2616882. FAX 27-31-2616886. Ed. M.J. Kort. illus.; circ. 400 (controlled). **Indexed:** Sugar Ind.Abstr. **Document type:** corporate report.

664.1　　　　　NE
SUGAR SERIES. (Text in English) 1981. irreg., vol.12, 1990. price varies. Elsevier Science B.V., Books Division, P.O. Box 211, 1000 AE Amsterdam, Netherlands. TEL 31-20-5803911.
FAX 31-20-5803705. TELEX 18582 ESPA NL. (Subscr. in U.S. and Canada to: Elsevier Science Inc., Box 882, Madison Sq. Sta., New York, NY 10159. TEL 212-989-5800) (back issues avail.) **Document type:** monographic series.
　　Refereed Serial

664　　　　　TR　　ISSN 0302-4555
SUGAR TECHNOLOGISTS' ASSOCIATION OF TRINIDAD AND TOBAGO. PROCEEDINGS.* 1967. a. free. Sugar Manufacturers' Association of Trinidad & Tobago, Suite 402, 4th Level, Mecalfab's Building, 92 Queen St., Port-of-Spain, Trinidad & Tobago, W.I. Ed. M.Y. Khan. circ. controlled. (processed)

664.1 331.8　　　　　CN　　ISSN 0229-737X
SUGAR WORLD; a newsletter on issues of concern to sugar workers. (Editions in French, Portuguese, Spanish) 1977. 6/yr. Can.$15 to individuals; institutions Can.$30. I C C S A S W, 2084 Danforth Ave., Ste. 3, Toronto, ON M4C 1J9, Canada. TEL 416-467-8621. FAX 416-467-9143. Ed. Reg McQuaid. illus. **Indexed:** HR Rep. **Document type:** newsletter.

664.1　　　　　US　　ISSN 0039-4742
**　　　　　CODEN: SUAZA7**
SUGAR Y AZUCAR. (Text in English and Spanish) 1914. m. $75. Ruspam Communications, Inc., 452 Hudson Terr., Englewood Cliffs, NJ 07632. TEL 201-871-9200. FAX 201-871-9639. Ed. Richard Miller. adv.; charts; illus.; mkt.; stat.; index. circ. 5,491. (also avail. in microform from UMI; reprint service avail. from UMI) **Indexed:** ASCA, Biol.Abstr., Chem.Abstr., Curr.Adv.Ecol.Sci., Curr.Cont., Eng.Ind., Food Sci.& Tech.Abstr., Hort.Abstr., Rural Recreat.Tour.Abstr., Soils & Fert., Sugar Ind.Abstr., World Agri.Econ.& Rural Sociol.Abstr. **Document type:** trade publication. —BLDSC (8514.100000); UnCover; UMI; CASDDS.

664.1　　　　　US　　ISSN 0081-9212
SUGAR Y AZUCAR YEARBOOK. (Text in English and Spanish) a. $55. Ruspam Communications, Inc., 452 Hudson Terrace, Englewood Cliffs, NJ 07632. TEL 201-871-9200. FAX 201-871-9639. **Document type:** trade publication.

SUGARCANE FARMERS' BULLETIN. see AGRICULTURE

664.1　　　　　SJ
AL SUKARIA. 1977. a. £S20($2) Arab Sugar Federation, P.O. Box 195, Khartoum, Sudan. TEL 40498. Ed. Musa Awad Ballal. adv. circ. 1,000.
　　Former titles: Al Sukar al-Arabi; Al Sukaria.
　　Description: Covers sugar production and its by-products in the Arab world.

634.51　　　　　US
SUN-DIAMOND GROWER. vol.51, 1969. bi-m. Sun-Diamond Growers of California, Box 1727, Stockton, CA 95201. TEL 209-467-6219.
FAX 209-467-6357. Ed. Sandra J. McBride. adv.; bk.rev.; charts; illus.; circ. 12,000 (controlled). **Document type:** trade publication.
　　Formerly (until 1980): Diamond Walnut News (ISSN 0012-2319)
　　Description: Contains information for dried fruit, grape and nut growers about production techniques and industry affairs.

664 647　　　　　US
SUNBELT FOODSERVICE. 1984. m. $25. Shelby Publishing Co., Inc., 517 Green St., Gainesville, GA 30501. TEL 404-534-8380. FAX 404-535-0110. Ed. L. Griffith. adv. circ. 24,000. (tabloid format; back issues avail.)
　　Formerly: Shelby's Southwest Foodservice.

663.93　　　　　US
SUNBELT VENDING AND O C S. 1991. bi-m. $18. B G Group, 4016 Flowers Rd., Ste. 440A, Atlanta, GA 30360. TEL 404-451-2345. Ed. Ben Ginsberg. adv.; bk.rev. circ. 5,900.
　　Description: Assists management in the merchandise vending - coffee service industries to better operate and succeed in their businesses.

SUNFLOWER (BISMARCK). see AGRICULTURE — Crop Production And Soil

664　　　　　FR
SURGELATION; le magazine de la filiere glaces et surgeles. m. 200 F. (foreign 450 F.). Editions Max Brezol, 9 rue Labie, 75838 Paris Cedex 17, France. TEL 45-74-21-62. FAX 45-74-01-03. Ed. Georges Golan.

T C S & D YEARBOOK. (Temperature Controlled Storage and Distribution) see BUSINESS AND ECONOMICS — Trade And Industrial Directories

642.5　　　　　IE　　ISSN 0790-2042
T S N NEWS. (Tabacconists, Stationers, Newsagents News) 1975. 6/yr. £10. Clavis Press Ltd., Block 4, The Pye Centre, Dundrum, Dublin 14, Ireland. TEL 988055. FAX 988208. Ed. Alan Phelan. adv.; bk.rev. circ. 4,300.

338.1　　　　　CH　　ISSN 0492-1712
HD9116.T3　　　　　CODEN: TWSUA5
TAIWAN SUGAR.* 1954. irreg. $5. (Taiwan Sugar Corporation) Good Earth Press, c/o General Chamber of Commerce, 390 Fu Hsing South Rd., 6th Fl. Ste. 1, Taipei, Taiwan, Republic of China. illus. **Indexed:** Agri.Eng.Abstr., Anim.Breed.Abstr., Food Sci.& Tech.Abstr., Hort.Abstr., Pig News & Info., Plant Breed.Abstr., Poult.Abstr., Rice Abstr., Sugar Ind.Abstr.
—BLDSC (8598.650000); UnCover; CASDDS.
　　Formerly: Newsletter - Taiwan Sugar Corporation.

663.94　　　　　KE
TEA. 1980. s-a. KShs.280 (rest of Africa £5.75 or $11.10; Europe and India £5.90 or $11.40; elsewhere £6.05 or $11.70). Tea Research Foundation of Kenya, P.O. Box 820, Kericho, Kenya. TEL 254-361-20598. FAX 254-361-20575. Ed. C.O. Othieno. illus.; stat. circ. 700. **Indexed:** Agri.Eng.Abstr., Agroforest.Abstr., Food Sci.& Tech.Abstr., Hort.Abstr., P.L.E.S.A., Plant Breed.Abstr., Soils & Fert. **Document type:** academic/scholarly publication.
　　Supersedes: Tea in East Africa.

663.9 658.8　　　　　US　　ISSN 0040-0343
**　　　　　CODEN: TCTJA7**
TEA AND COFFEE TRADE JOURNAL. 1901-1984 (Jul.); resumed Jan.1985. m. $15. Lockwood Trade Journal Co., Inc., 130 W. 42nd St., New York, NY 10036-7802. TEL 212-391-2060.
FAX 212-827-0945. adv.; bk.rev.; charts; illus.; mkt.; tr.lit. circ. 8,000. **Indexed:** Chem.Abstr., Food Sci.& Tech.Abstr., Key to Econ.Sci., P.A.I.S., PROMT. ●Also available online. Vendor(s): Mead Data Central, Inc.
—BLDSC (8612.660000); UnCover.

663.94　　　　　II
TEA JOURNAL. (Text in English) 1988. m. $60. 30 Ripon St., Calcutta 700 016, India.
TEL 33-276231. (Subscr. to: 7 Old Court House St., Calcutta 700 001, India) Ed. S.C. Talukdar. adv.: B&W page $150, color page $300; adv. contact: Manabesh Talukder. circ. 30,000.

663.94　　　　　MW
TEA RESEARCH FOUNDATION. ANNUAL REPORT. 1966. a. $50. Tea Research Foundation, P.O. Box 51, Mulanje, Malawi. Ed. A.M. Whittle. circ. 200. **Indexed:** Hort.Abstr.
　　Formerly: Tea Research Foundation of Central Africa. Annual Report (ISSN 0258-4476)
　　Description: All aspects of tea growing and manufacture for regions with a single rainy season.

663.94　　　　　KE
TEA RESEARCH FOUNDATION OF KENYA. ANNUAL REPORT. 1950. a. KShs.180 (rest of Africa £5.45 or $10.50; Europe and India £5.60 or $10.80; elsewhere £5.75 or $11.10). Tea Research Foundation of Kenya, P.O. Box 820, Kericho, Kenya. Ed. C.O. Othieno. circ. 600. **Indexed:** Weed Abstr. **Document type:** corporate report, academic/scholarly publication.
　　Former titles: Tea Research Foundation. Annual Report; Tea Research Institute of East Africa. Annual Report.

663.94　　　　　US
TEA TALK; a newsletter on the pleasures of tea. 1989. q. $17.95. R & R Publications, 419 N. Larchmont, No. 225, Los Angeles, CA 90004-3000.
TEL 310-659-9650. Ed. Diana Rosen. adv. contact: Diana Rosen. bk.rev. circ. 2,500. **Document type:** newsletter.
　　Description: For tea fanciers, teapot collectors, and hosts of afternoon teas. Profiles restaurants, tearooms and hotels, new products, tea industry personnel and tea connoisseurship.

TEAGASC RESEARCH REPORT. see AGRICULTURE

TECNICA MOLITORIA. see AGRICULTURE — Feed, Flour And Grain

664　　　　　AG　　ISSN 0040-1943
TECNOLOGIA ALIMENTARIA.* 1967. bi-m. Arg.$23($18) 25 de Mayo 786, Buenos Aires, Argentina. Eds. Jose Gonzalez Ledo, Emma Zappettini. adv.; bk.rev.; bibl.; charts; illus.; stat.; tr.lit.; index. circ. 17,000. **Indexed:** Biol.Abstr., Chem.Abstr.

664　　　　　MX　　ISSN 0564-6758
TECNOLOGIA DE ALIMENTOS. (Text in Spanish; summaries in English) 1966. bi-m. $25. Asociacion de Tecnologos Alimentos de Mexico, Indianapolis No. 63-2, 03810 Mexico, D.F., Mexico. Ed. Hector Bourges. adv.; bk.rev.; bibl.; illus.; index. circ. 3,000. (back issues avail.) **Indexed:** Chem.Abstr., Dairy Sci.Abstr., Food Sci.& Tech.Abstr., Nutr.Abstr.

664　　　　　IT　　ISSN 1120-5334
TECNOLOGIE ALIMENTARI. 8/yr. L.140000. Stammer S.p.A., Via della Liberazione 1, 20068 Peschiera Borromeo (MI), Italy. TEL 02-55-30-26-06.
FAX 02-55-30-27-00. Ed. Girolamo Bellina. circ. 15,000.

664　　　　　IT
TECNORAMA ALIMENTARI E BEVANDE. 12/yr. Pubblicita Edizioni Associati s.r.l., Via Simone d'Orsenigo 22, 20135 Milan, Italy. TEL 2-551-18-42.
FAX 2-551-85-263. Ed. Ugo Caruti.

TEHNOLOGIJA MESA/MEAT TECHNOLOGY; casopis industrije mesa Jugoslavije. see AGRICULTURE — Poultry And Livestock

664　　　　　UK　　ISSN 0143-750X
TEMPERATURE CONTROLLED STORAGE & DISTRIBUTION. 1977. 7/yr. £48.40($94.50) (foreign £60.65). F M J International Publications Ltd., Queensway House, 2 Queensway, Redhill, Surrey RH1 1QS, England. TEL 0737-768611.
FAX 0737-761685. TELEX 948669-TOPJNL-G. Ed. Neil Murray. **Indexed:** Key to Econ.Sci. **Document type:** trade publication.
　　Incorporates: Frigoworld (ISSN 0961-3048); Which was formerly: Temperature Controlled Storage and Distribution International.
　　Description: Covers the latest equipment available for transport operators moving or storing perishable goods.

FOOD AND FOOD INDUSTRIES

664   JA
TEZUKAYAMA TANKI DAIGAKU SHOKUHIN KAGAKU KENKYUKAISHI/TEZUKAYAMA COLLEGE FOOD SCIENCES. (Text in English, Japanese) 1979. a. Shokuhin Kagaku Kenkyukai - Tezukayama Association for Food Sciences, Tezukayama Tanki Daigaku, 1-3, Gakuen Minami 3-chome, Nara-shi, Nara-ken 631, Japan.

664   US   ISSN 1061-284X
HD9321.3
THOMAS FOOD INDUSTRY REGISTER. (3-vol. set) 1898. a. $125. Thomas Publishing Company, One Penn Plaza, New York, NY 10119. TEL 212-290-7341. Ed. Dianne Johansson-Adams. adv. circ. 5,300.
Formerly (until 1990): Thomas Grocery Register (ISSN 0082-4151)
Description: Covers the entire grocery industry: distribution, sales, products, services, trade associations and events.

TIP; 't lekkerste blad. see HOME ECONOMICS

TOBAKK- OG KIOSK. see TOBACCO

664   IE
TODAY'S GROCER. 1985. 12/yr. I£30. Ashton Publications Ltd., 6 Martello Terr., Dun Laoghaire, Co. Dublin, Ireland. TEL 01-2809466. FAX 01-2806896. Ed. Carol-Anne O'Reilly. adv. contact: Frank Madden. circ. 8,500. **Document type:** trade publication.

TOOWOOMBA - QUEENSLAND'S GROWTH CENTRE. see BUSINESS AND ECONOMICS — Production Of Goods And Services

TORONTO LIFE EPICURE. see HOTELS AND RESTAURANTS

664 647.95   US
TOTAL FOOD SERVICE. 1991. m. $36. I D A Publishing Co., Inc., Box 2507, 282 Railroad Ave., Greenwich, CT 06830. TEL 203-661-9090. FAX 203-661-9325. adv.: B&W page $1980, color page $2365; trim 11 1/4 x 15. circ. 18,500.
Description: Reports tri-state news of the industry.

664   FR   ISSN 0758-5055
TOUTE L'ALIMENTATION. 1958. 11/yr. 100 Fr. (effective 1991). S E D I P A L, 15 rue de Rome, 75008 Paris, France. TEL 43-87-55-59. FAX 45-22-64-12. Ed. Dominique Perrot. adv. circ. 13,000.

664   UK   ISSN 0924-2244
TP368   CODEN: TFTEEH
TRENDS IN FOOD SCIENCE AND TECHNOLOGY. Library compendium: Trends in Food Science and Technology (Reference Edition) (ISSN 0968-0020) 1990. 12/yr. £65 to individuals; institutions £318($490) includes library compendium (effective 1994). Elsevier Science Ltd., Oxford Fulfilment Centre, P.O. Box 800, Kidlington, Oxford OX5 1DX, England. TEL 44-865-843000. FAX 44-865-843010. (Subscr. in U.S. and Canada to: Elsevier Science, 660 White Plains Rd., Tarrytown, NY 10591-5153. TEL 914-524-9200. FAX 914-333-2444) Ed. John O'Brien. adv.; index. **Document type:** academic/scholarly publication.
—BLDSC (9049.593000); ADONIS; EI; Faxon; SWETS; CASDDS. CCC.
Description: Information link between basic scientific research and its applications in the food industry.
Refereed Serial

664   UK   ISSN 0968-0020
TRENDS IN FOOD SCIENCE AND TECHNOLOGY (REFERENCE EDITION). 1990. a. £318($490) includes Trends in Food Science and Technology (effective 1994). Elsevier Science Ltd., Oxford Fulfilment Centre, P.O. Box 800, Kidlington, Oxford OX5 1DX, England. TEL 44-865-843000. FAX 44-865-843010. (Subscr. in U.S. and Canada to: Elsevier Science, 660 White Plains Rd., Tarrytown, NY 10591-5153. TEL 914-524-9200. FAX 914-333-2444) Ed. Gillian Griffith. (back issues avail.) **Document type:** academic/scholarly publication.
—CCC.
Description: Compendium of archival material from Trends in Food Science and Technology.
Refereed Serial

TROFIMA & POTA/FOOD & BEVERAGES; financial and technological monthly review for food, wines and packaging. see BEVERAGES

TWO AND A BUD. see BEVERAGES

U F C W ACTION. (United Food and Commercial Workers International Union) see LABOR UNIONS

U F C W LOCAL 27 REPORTER. (United Food & Commercial Workers) see LABOR UNIONS

664   UK
ULSTER FOOD TRADER. 1985. m. £7.50. Ralph Allen & Associates, 255A Upper Newtownards Rd., Belfast BT4 3JF, N. Ireland. Ed. Ralph Allen. circ. 8,000. (tabloid format)

UNITED FOOD & COMMERCIAL WORKERS UNION LOCAL 876. see LABOR UNIONS

U.S. DEPARTMENT OF AGRICULTURE. FOOD REVIEW. see AGRICULTURE — Agricultural Economics

U.S. DEPARTMENT OF AGRICULTURE. SITUATION & OUTLOOK REPORT. SUGAR & SWEETENERS. see AGRICULTURE — Agricultural Economics

664   US
U.S. FOOD SAFETY AND INSPECTION SERVICE. TECHNICAL INFORMATION. MEAT & POULTRY INSPECTION PROGRAM. a. free. U.S. Department of Agriculture, Food Safety and Inspection Service, Rm. 331E, Administration Bldg., Independence Ave. - 12th and 14th Sts., S.W., Washington, DC 20250. TEL 202-720-7025. (Subscr. to: USDA-FSIS-ILA Publications Office, Rm. 1165-South Bldg., Washington D.C. 20250) **Document type:** government publication.

UNIVERSITY OF SALAHADDIN. COLLEGE OF AGRICULTURE. SCIENTIFIC JOURNAL "ZANCO". see AGRICULTURE

URNER BARRY'S PRICE-CURRENT. see AGRICULTURE — Poultry And Livestock

664 636   US
URNER BARRY'S PRICE CURRENT (WEST COAST EDITION). vol.6, 1978. 2/wk. $121 (typically set in Sept.). Urner Barry Publications, Inc., P.O. Box 389, Toms River, NJ 08754. TEL 908-240-5330. FAX 908-341-0891. Eds. Michael E. O'Shaughnessy, Richard A. Brown. (tabloid format)
Formerly: Producer's Price Current (West Coast Edition) (ISSN 0273-5016)

664   GW
V I F GOURMET JOURNAL. m. DM.108 (foreign DM.119.40). Atlas Verlag und Werbung GmbH, Sonnenstr. 29, 80331 Munich, Germany. TEL 089-55241-0. FAX 089-55241271. Ed. Ulrich Metzner; Pub. Hajo Artope. adv. contact: Susanne Bertsch. circ. 50,610. **Document type:** consumer publication.

V W D - KAFFEE, KAKAO, TEE, SUESSWAREN. see BUSINESS AND ECONOMICS — Investments

V W D - ZUCKER. see BUSINESS AND ECONOMICS — Investments

664   US
VANGUARD (LA HABRA). 1937? bi-m. free to qualified personnel. Alpha Beta Company, 777 S. Harbor Blvd., La Habra, CA 90631. TEL 714-738-2000. Ed. Gary Stork. circ. 34,000 (controlled). **Indexed:** Avery Ind.Archit.Per.

VEGETARIAN JOURNAL. see NUTRITION AND DIETETICS

663.92   GW
VEREIN DER AM ROHKAKAOHANDEL BETEILIGTEN FIRMEN. GESCHAFTSBERICHT. a. Verein der am Rohkakaohandel Beteiligten Firmen e.V., Gotenstr. 21, 20097 Hamburg, Germany. TEL 040-236016-0. TELEX 02162388-WGA-D. **Document type:** trade publication.

664.9   FR
VIE DES METIERS BOUCHER CHARCUTER TRAITEUR. 10/yr. Practice Editions, 21 rue Baudin, 34000 Montpellier, France. TEL 67-58-61-09. FAX 67-58-26-87. Ed. Alain Vogel-Singer. circ. 6,800.

VINOHRAD. see GARDENING AND HORTICULTURE

664.94   US   ISSN 1064-4768
VIRGINIA AQUACULTURE MARKET NEWS REPORT. s-m. Department of Agriculture and Consumer Services, 1100 Bank St., Ste. 805, Richmond, VA 23219-3629. TEL 804-786-3947. FAX 804-371-7787. Ed. J.P. Welch. circ. 500. (back issues avail.) **Document type:** government publication.
Description: Provides wholesale aquaculture and seafood prices in Virginia and other East Coast markets to Virginia producers, agribusinesses and other readers.

664.9 658.8   NE   ISSN 0042-7691
VLEESDISTRIBUTIE EN VLEESTECHNOLOGIE; vakblad voor het management in de vleeswarenindustrie, grootslagerij, overige vleesverkopende bedrijven en de slachtpluimvee-sector. 1966. 11/yr. fl.139.50. Audet Tijdschriften bv (Subsidiary of: C. Misset B.V.), Postbus 9000, 6800 DA Arnhem, Netherlands. Ed. Wim Busser. adv.: B&W page fl.2510, color page fl.4605; trim 215 x 285; adv. contact: Cor van Nek. illus.; stat. circ. 2,300. **Document type:** trade publication.
Description: Covers managerial and technological aspects of the meat industry.

664.9   NE   ISSN 0922-2324
VLEESKRANT; Missets vakkrant voor de totale vleessektor. 1938. fortn. fl.150 (3000 BEF). C. Misset B.V., Postbus 4, 7000 BA Doetinchen, Netherlands. TEL 31-8340-49911. FAX 31-8340-43839. adv.: B&W page fl.5475; trim 290 x 420; adv. contact: Cor van Nek. circ. 12,130. **Document type:** trade publication, newspaper.
Description: Covers the meat industry in the Netherlands and abroad.

664   BE   ISSN 0011-0434
VOEDINGSBLAD. French edition: Alimentation et Distribution. 1951. bi-m (ca. alternate months). 350 BEF($6) Nationale Centrale voor Kleine en Middelgrote Levensmiddelenbedrijven - Central Nationale des Entreprises en Alimentation, Spastraat 8, 1040 Brussels, Belgium. TEL 32-2-2380511. FAX 32-2-2309354. Ed. F. de Ryck. adv.; bk.rev.; illus. circ. 9,400 (6,400 Dutch ed.; 3,000 French ed.). (also avail. in microform)

664   NE   ISSN 0042-7934
VOEDINGSMIDDELENTECHNOLOGIE. 1895. fortn. fl.192.50. Keesing Noordervliet B.V., De Molen 82-86, 3995 AX Houten, Netherlands. TEL 31-3403-58585. FAX 31-3403-58500. Ed. C. Grijspaardt-Vink. adv. circ. 3,496. **Indexed:** Biol.Abstr., Dairy Sci.Abstr., Excerp.Med., Food Sci.& Tech.Abstr., Int.Packag.Abstr., Key to Econ.Sci., Rural Recreat.Tour.Abstr., Sugar Ind.Abstr., World Agri.Econ.& Rural Sociol.Abstr. **Document type:** trade publication.
—BLDSC (9251.250000); SWETS.
Formerly: Voeding en Techniek.

664   NE
VOEDINGSTRENDS MAGAZINE. 1990. 2/yr. free to qualified personnel. C. Misset B.V., Postbus 4, 7000 BA Doetinchem, Netherlands. TEL 31-8340-49911. FAX 31-8340-43839. adv.: B&W page fl.7820; 182 x 257; adv. contact: Cor van Nek. illus.; circ. 75,000 (controlled). **Document type:** trade publication.
Description: Covers long-term developments in the food retailing and hotel and catering trades, focusing on the impact of the fast food industry.

W.A. MEAT WORKER. see LABOR UNIONS

641   UN   ISSN 0300-0923
TX553.A3
W H O FOOD ADDITIVES SERIES. (Text in English) 1972. irreg., vol.45, 1993. 45 SFr.($40.50) World Health Organization, 20, avenue Appia, 1211 Geneva 27, Switzerland. TEL 022-912111. FAX 022-788-0401. TELEX 27821 OMS. circ. 4,000 (3,000 English ed. 1,000 French ed.). **Indexed:** Biol.Abstr., Chem.Abstr., Excerp.Med., Food Sci.& Tech.Abstr., Nutr.Abstr.
—BLDSC (9311.905000).

FOOD AND FOOD INDUSTRIES — ABSTRACTING, BIBLIOGRAPHIES, STATISTICS

664 641.1 PL CODEN: AWAUEG
WARSAW AGRICULTURAL UNIVERSITY. S G G W. ANNALS. FOOD TECHNOLOGY AND NUTRITION. (Text mainly in English; occasionally in French, German or Russian; summaries in Polish) 1957. irreg. $10 per no. Szkola Glowna Gospodarstwa Wiejskiego (SGGW) - Warsaw Agricultural University, Ul. Nowoursynowska 166, 02-766 Warsaw, Poland. Ed. S. Zmarlicki. **Indexed:** Food Sci.& Tech.Abstr. **Document type:** academic/scholarly publication.
—BLDSC (1035.019000); CASDDS.
Former titles: Warsaw Agricultural University. S G G W - A R. Annals. Food Technology and Nutrition (ISSN 0208-5755); (until 1980): Akademia Rolnicza, Warsaw. Zeszyty Naukowe. Technologia Rolno-Spozywcza; Szkola Glowna Gospodarstwa Wiejskiego w Warszawie. Zeszyty Naukowe. Technologia Rolno-Spozywcza (ISSN 0137-7426)

WATER FARMING JOURNAL; America's aquaculture news monthly. see *WATER RESOURCES*

664 637 US ISSN 0270-4153
WEEKLY INSIDERS DAIRY & EGG LETTER. w. $142 (typically set in Sept.). Urner Barry Publications, Inc., Box 389, Toms River, NJ 08754. TEL 908-240-5330. FAX 908-341-0891. Ed. Richard A. Brown. (tabloid format)

664 636 US ISSN 0160-4872
WEEKLY INSIDERS POULTRY REPORT. w. $142 (typically set in Sept.). Urner Barry Publications, Inc., Box 389, Toms River, NJ 08754. TEL 908-240-5330. FAX 908-341-0891. Ed. Michael E. O'Shaughnessy. (tabloid format)

664 636 US ISSN 0160-4910
WEEKLY INSIDERS TURKEY LETTER. w. $142 includes Turkey Hatch Report. Urner Barry Publications, Inc., Box 389, Toms River, NJ 08754. TEL 908-240-5330. FAX 908-341-0891. Ed. Paul B. Brown. (tabloid format)

WEST AFRICA RICE DEVELOPMENT ASSOCIATION. OCCASIONAL PAPER. see *AGRICULTURE*

WEST AUSTRALIAN NUT AND TREE CROP ASSOCIATION YEARBOOK. see *AGRICULTURE — Crop Production And Soil*

664 US
WESTERN FOODSERVICE.* 1972. 12/yr. $24. Young - Conway Publications, 1101 Richmond Ave., Ste. 201, Point Pleasant Beach, NJ 08742-3049. adv.; bk.rev. circ. 25,000. (back issues avail.)
Formerly: Western Foodservice Operator and Foodservice Operator.

641.5 US
WINE & FOOD COMPANION.* bi-m. Context Communications, 43 W. 88th St., No. 4F, New York, NY 10024-3533. TEL 212-734-1961. FAX 212-737-7629. Ed. David Rosengarten. bk.rev.

642.5 UK
WINEPRESS; the monthly magazine for everyone in the wine bar trade. 1980. m. 16 Ennismore Ave., London W4 1SF, England. Ed. Helene Hodge. circ. 2,750.

664 US
WISCONSIN GROCER.* 1900. bi-m. free to qualified personnel. Wisconsin Grocers Association, 2601 Crossroads Sr., Ste. 185, Madison, WI 53704. TEL 608-222-4515. FAX 608-222-3111. Ed. Dianne Calgaro. adv. circ. 1,200.
Formerly: Wisconsin Food Dealer.

664 US
WORLD FOOD CHEMICAL NEWS. w. $1450. Food Chemical News, Inc., 1101 Pennsylvania Ave., S.E., Washington, DC 20003. TEL 202-544-1980. FAX 202-546-3890.
Description: Gathers the latest news from the many legislatures and regulatory agencies around the world.

664 UK ISSN 0963-4894
WORLD FOOD REGULATION REVIEW. 1991. m. $547 (effective 1994). B N A International, Inc. (Subsidiary of: The Bureau of National Affairs, Inc.), Heron House, 10 Dean Farrar St., London SW1H 0DX, England. TEL 44-71-222-8831. FAX 44-71-222-5550. (US subscr. to: 9435 Key West Ave., Rockville, MD 20850. TEL 202-452-4200) (back issues avail.)
—CCC.
Description: Information and analysis service, with emphasis to regulatory changes in the European Community and comprehensive coverage on international developments compiled by an expert advisory board.

664 UN ISSN 1010-1039
WORLD FOOD REPORT. Spanish edition: Informe Alimentario Mundial (ISSN 1014-2843); French edition: Rapport sur l'Alimentation (ISSN 0256-0879); Italian edition: Rapporto sull'Alimentazione (ISSN 1014-286X); German edition: Welternaehrungsbericht (ISSN 1014-2851) 1983. a. price varies (latest issue $10). Food and Agriculture Organization of the United Nations, c/o UNIPUB, 4611-F Assembly Dr., Lanham, MD 20706-4391. FAX 301-459-0056. (also avail. in microfiche from CIS) **Indexed:** IIS. **Document type:** monographic series.

WORLD GASTRONOMY. see *BEVERAGES*

WORLD SUGAR NEWS/KAIGAI SATO JOHO. see *AGRICULTURE — Crop Production And Soil*

YANKEE FOOD SERVICE. see *HOTELS AND RESTAURANTS*

613.1 CH ISSN 1021-9498 CODEN: YSFEEP
YAOWU SHIPIN FENXI/JOURNAL OF FOOD AND DRUG ANALYSIS. (Text in various languages) 1993. q. National Laboratories of Food and Drugs, 161-2 Kuen Yang St., Nankang, Taipei, Taiwan, Republic of China. TEL 2-7858283. **Indexed:** Excerp.Med. (1994-).
—BLDSC (4984.537500); CASDDS.

664 GW CODEN: ZIZVEF
Z F L - INTERNATIONALE ZEITSCHRIFT FUER LEBENSMITTEL-WIRTSCHAFT. (Text in German; summaries in English) 1949. 10/yr. DM.258 (foreign DM.275.40). Huethig GmbH, Postfach 102869, 69018 Heidelberg, Germany. TEL 06221-489281. FAX 06221-489205. TELEX 461727-HUEHDD. adv.: B&W page DM.4950; trim 210 x 297; adv. contact: Susanne Richert. charts; illus.; index. circ. 8,500. (back issues avail.) **Document type:** trade publication.
—BLDSC (9512.653200); CASDDS. **CCC.**
Former titles: Z F L - Internationale Zeitschrift fuer Lebensmittel-Technik, Marketing, Verpackung und Analytik; Z F L - Internationale Zeitschrift fuer Lebensmittel-Technologie und -Verfahrenstechnik (ISSN 0722-5733); (until 1982): Z F L - Zeitschrift fuer Lebensmittel-Technologie und -Verfahrenstechnik (ISSN 0341-2938); (until 1975): Z F L Deutsche Zeitschrift fuer Lebensmitteltechnologie (ISSN 0341-2946).
Description: Addresses topical questions, problems and trends from all areas of food technology in a practical and user-oriented manner.

Z L R - ZEITSCHRIFT FUER DAS GESAMTE LEBENSMITTELRECHT. see *LAW*

641 ZA ISSN 0084-4969
ZAMBIA. NATIONAL FOOD AND NUTRITION COMMISSION. ANNUAL REPORT. (Text in English) 1968. a. free. National Food and Nutrition Commission, P.O. Box 32669, Lusaka, Zambia. circ. 2,000. **Document type:** government publication.

ZEMIA. see *LABOR UNIONS*

663.94 CC
ZHONGGUO CHAYE/CHINESE TEA. (Text in Chinese) bi-m. Zhongguo Nongye Kexueyuan, Chaye Yanjiusuo - Chinese Academy of Agricultural Science, Tea Research Institute, 1 Yunxi Lu, Hangzhou, Zhejiang 310008, People's Republic of China. TEL 661824. Ed. Yu Yongming.

664 641.5 CC
ZHONGGUO SHIPIN BAO/CHINA'S FOOD NEWS. (Text in Chinese) 3/w. $139.38. China International Book Trading Corporation, P.O. Box 399, Beijing, People's Republic of China. TEL 8413063. FAX 8412023. TELEX 22496 CIBTC CN. (Dist. in US by: China Books & Periodicals, Inc., 2929 24th St., San Francisco, CA 94110. TEL 415-282-2994) **Document type:** newspaper.

664 CC ISSN 1000-9973 CODEN: ZHTIE7
ZHONGGUO TIAOWEIPIN/CHINESE SPICES. (Text in Chinese) m. Harbin Shipin Weisheng Gongye Yanjiusuo, 66, Shitoudao Jie, Daoli-qu, Harbin, Heilongjiang 150010, People's Republic of China. TEL 416701. Ed. Zhao Yi.
—CASDDS.

664 GW
ZUCKERWIRTSCHAFT/SUGAR ECONOMY/ECONOMIE SUCRIERE. 1954. a. DM.39. Verlag Dr. Albert Bartens, Lueckhoffstr. 16, 14129 Berlin, Germany. adv. circ. 2,200. **Document type:** directory.
Formerly: Zuckerwirtschaftliches Taschenbuch (ISSN 0084-5736)

664 SZ
ZUERI-OBST. 24/yr. Kantonale Zentralstelle fuer Obstbau, Strickhof Eschikon, CH-8315 Lindau, Switzerland. TEL 052-331821. Ed. Hans-Peter Berger.

FOOD AND FOOD INDUSTRIES — Abstracting, Bibliographies, Statistics

ABSTRACTS ON TROPICAL AGRICULTURE. see *AGRICULTURE — Abstracting, Bibliographies, Statistics*

664 AT ISSN 1036-0611
AUSTRALIA. BUREAU OF STATISTICS. MANUFACTURING PRODUCTION, AUSTRALIA: FOOD, DRINK, TOBACCO, STOCK AND POULTRY FOOD. 1977. m. Aus.$10.50 per no. Australian Bureau of Statistics, P.O. Box 10, Belconnen, A.C.T. 2616, Australia. **Document type:** government publication.
Formerly: Australia. Bureau of Statistics. Production of Food, Drink and Tobacco and Stock and Poultry Food, Australia.

BIBLIOGRAPHIE INTERNATIONALE DES INDUSTRIES AGRO-ALIMENTAIRES. see *AGRICULTURE — Abstracting, Bibliographies, Statistics*

664 016 YU ISSN 0351-2479
BILTEN DOKUMENTACIJE. PROIZVODNJA PREHRAMBENIH PROIZVODA. PROIZVODNJA PICA/BULLETIN OF DOCUMENTATION. MANUFACTURE OF FOOD PRODUCTS. MANUFACTURE OF BEVERAGES. 1950. bi-m. $264. Jugoslovenski Centar za Tehnicku i Naucnu Dokumentaciju - Yugoslav Center for Technical and Scientific Documentation (YCTSD), Sl. Penezica-Krcuna 29-31, Box 724, 11000 Belgrade, Yugoslavia. Ed. Ljiljana Kojic-Bogdanovic.
Formerly: Bilten Dokumentacije. Prehrambena Industrija (ISSN 0006-2669)

664 658.8 CN ISSN 0316-9537
BLUE BOOK OF FOOD STORE OPERATORS & WHOLESALERS. a. Can.$28. Sanford Evans Communications Ltd., 1700 Church Ave., P.O. Box 6900, Winnipeg, MB R3C 3B1, Canada. TEL 204-694-2022. FAX 204-694-3040. Ed. Gary Henry. **Document type:** directory.
Description: Lists all Canadian foodstore chains, cooperatives and food wholesalers with addresses and phone number of head office and branch offices. Executive and management of each listed by name and title.

664 MX ISSN 0186-9027
BOLETIN DE INFORMACION OPORTUNA DEL SECTOR ALIMENTARIO. 1988. m. Mex.$32($11) Instituto Nacional de Estadistica, Geografia e Informatica, Secretaria de Programacion y Presupuesto, Prol. Heroe de Nacozari 2301 Sur, Puerta 11, Acceso, 20270 Aguascalientes, Ags., Mexico. TEL 49-18-19-48. FAX 491-807-39. circ. 900.

FOOD AND FOOD INDUSTRIES — ABSTRACTING, BIBLIOGRAPHIES, STATISTICS

664   US   ISSN 0890-1813
CODEN: CSSWE4
C A SELECTS. ARTIFICIAL SWEETENERS. s-w. $210 (effective Jan. 1994). Chemical Abstracts Service (Subsidiary of: American Chemical Society), 2540 Olentangy River Rd., Box 3012, Columbus, OH 43210-0012. TEL 614-447-3600. FAX 614-447-3713. TELEX 6842086. **Document type:** abstracting/indexing.
Description: Covers preparation, properties, and uses of synthetic substances developed as sugar substitutes or supplements.

540   US   ISSN 0895-5913
CODEN: CSFAE9
C A SELECTS. FOOD & FEED ANALYSIS. 1988. s-w. $210 (effective Jan. 1993). Chemical Abstracts Service (Subsidiary of: American Chemical Society), 2540 Olentangy River Rd., Box 3012, Columbus, OH 43210-0012. TEL 614-447-3600. FAX 614-447-3713. TELEX 6842086. **Document type:** abstracting/indexing.
Description: Covers methodology for determining natural components (e.g., amino acids, fats, mineral elements, and sugars), additives, and contaminants in food and feed.

664 340   US   ISSN 1051-3914
CODEN: CAFAEJ
C A SELECTS. FOOD, DRUGS, & COSMETICS - LEGISLATIVE & REGULATORY ASPECTS. 1990. s-w. $210 (effective Jan. 1994). Chemical Abstracts Service (Subsidiary of: American Chemical Society), 2540 Olentangy River Rd., Box 3012, Columbus, OH 43210-0012. TEL 614-447-3600. FAX 614-447-3713. TELEX 6842086. **Document type:** abstracting/indexing.
Description: Covers government reports on food, drugs, and cosmetics, such as those found in the US Federal Register and those from governments of other countries. Includes information on standards of food, drugs, and cosmetics from non-government sources.

C A SELECTS. FOOD TOXICITY. see *CHEMISTRY — Abstracting, Bibliographies, Statistics*

338.4   CN   ISSN 0835-0000
HD9014.C2
CANADA. STATISTICS CANADA. FOOD INDUSTRIES. (Catalogue 32-250) (Text in English and French) 1918. a. Can.$20($42) (foreign $49). Statistics Canada, Publications Sales and Services, Ottawa, ON K1A 0T6, Canada. TEL 613-951-7277. FAX 613-951-1584. Ed. Peter Zylstra. circ. 500. (also avail. in microform from MML; back issues avail.) **Document type:** government publication.
Incorporates: Canada. Statistics Canada. Biscuit Industry (ISSN 0832-8455) & Canada. Statistics Canada. Bread and Other Bakery Products Industry (ISSN 0832-8463) & Canada. Statistics Canada. Confectionery Manufacturers (ISSN 0575-8246) & Canada. Statistics Canada. Dairy Products Industry (ISSN 0318-2711) & Canada. Statistics Canada. Cane and Beet Sugar Processors (ISSN 0384-2843); Canada. Statistics Canada. Feed Industry (ISSN 0700-0073); Canada. Statistics Canada. Fish Products Industry (ISSN 0527-5172); Canada. Statistics Canada. Flour and Breakfast Cereal Products Industry (ISSN 0700-0324); Canada. Statistics Canada. Fruit and Vegetable Processing Industries (ISSN 0384-4420); Canada. Statistics Canada. Meat and Poultry Industries (ISSN 0319-888X); Canada. Statistics Canada. Miscellaneous Food Processors (ISSN 0384-4420); Canada. Statistics Canada. Vegetabel Oil Mills (ISSN 0527-6403).
Description: Studies employment, inputs and outputs by commodities.

338.4   CN   ISSN 0527-5911
HD9490.C2
CANADA. STATISTICS CANADA. OILS AND FATS/HUILES ET CORPS GRAS. (Catalogue 32-006) (Text in English and French) 1950. m. Can.$50($60) (foreign $70). Statistics Canada, Publications Sales and Services, Ottawa, ON K1A 0T6, Canada. TEL 613-951-3511. FAX 613-951-3522. Ed. Peter Zylstra. circ. 300. pp./issue: 4. (looseleaf format; also avail. in microform from MML; diskette format; magnetic tape; back issues avail.) **Document type:** government publication.
Description: Shows domestic purchases and production of deodorized oils; manufacturers' sales of deodorized oils by type, packaged margarine, shortening and salad oils; oilseed crushings; production and stocks of vegetable oils meal.

664   US   ISSN 1068-1361
▼**CEREAL SOURCE (YEAR).** 1993. a. $250 to individuals (foreign $275); institutions, libraries $400 (foreign $440). American Association of Cereal Chemists, Inc., 3340 Pilot Knob Rd., St. Paul, MN 55121. TEL 800-328-7560. FAX 612-454-0766. TELEX 6502439657 (MCI UW). (diskette format) **Document type:** abstracting/indexing.
Description: Personal computer-based index of abstracts from articles published between 1960 and 1994 in the AACC journal Cereal Chemistry.

663.94   CC
CHAYE WENZHAI/TEA ABSTRACTS. (Text in Chinese) bi-m. Zhongguo Nongye Kexueyuan, Chaye Yanjiusuo - Chinese Academy of Agricultural Science, Tea Reseach Institute, 1 Yunxi Lu, Hangzhou, Zhejiang 310008, People's Republic of China. TEL 791258. Ed. Chen Zongfan. **Document type:** abstracting/indexing.

664.1   CU
CUBA. MINISTERIO DEL COMERCIO EXTERIOR. REPORTE MENSUAL DEL AZUCAR. 1981. m. C.$10. (Ministerio del Comercio Exterior (MINCEX)) Empresa Cubazucar, Calle 23 No. 55, Vedado, Havana, Cuba. TEL 70-9742. TELEX 51-1147.
Description: Covers markets and prices information on sugar.

664 310   US   ISSN 0145-5168
HD9490.U5   CODEN: CIFODE
CURRENT INDUSTRIAL REPORTS: FATS AND OILS. OILSEED CRUSHINGS. Key Title: Fats and Oils. Oilseed Crushings. (Series M2O-J) m. online only, plus printed a. supplement. price varies. U.S. Bureau of the Census, Data User Services Division, Washington, DC 20233. TEL 301-763-4100. (Subscr. to: Superintendent of Documents, U.S. Government Printing Office, Box 371954, Pittsburgh, PA 15250-7954. TEL 202-783-3238. FAX 202-512-2233) (also avail. in microfiche from CIS; reprint service avail. from CIS) **Indexed:** Amer.Stat.Ind. (1975-), Chem.Abstr. **Document type:** government publication.
●Available only online. Vendor(s): CompuServe, Inc., DIALOG Information Services, Inc.
—CASDDS.

664 310   US   ISSN 0273-4397
CODEN: CIFCDC
CURRENT INDUSTRIAL REPORTS: FATS AND OILS. PRODUCTION, CONSUMPTION, AND STOCKS. (Series M2O-K) m. online only, plus a. printed supplement. price varies. U.S. Bureau of the Census, Data User Services Division, Washington, DC 20233. TEL 301-763-4100. (Avail. through: Superintendent of Documents, U.S. Government Printing Office, Box 371954, Pittsburgh, PA 15250-7954. TEL 202-783-3238. FAX 202-512-2233) (also avail. in microfiche from CIS; reprint service avail. from CIS) **Indexed:** Amer.Stat.Ind. (1975-), Chem.Abstr. **Document type:** government publication.
●Available only online. Vendor(s): CompuServe, Inc., DIALOG Information Services, Inc.
—CASDDS.
Formerly: Current Industrial Reports: Fats and Oils. Production, Consumption, and Factory and Warehouse Stocks (ISSN 0145-5176)

011 664   IS
DAPAI TOCHEN VETAKTZERIM. (Text in English) 3/yr. Institute of Quality Control and Extension Services for the Food Industry, 76 Mazeh St., Tel Aviv 65789, Israel. TEL 03-622701.

664 011   GW
EXTRAKTE: NAHRUNG UND GENUSS. 1966. s-w. DM.566 (foreign DM.630). Extrakte-Team-Verlag GmbH, Postfach 180162, Wolfgang-Doering-Str. 2-4, 40595 Duesseldorf, Germany. TEL 0211-701011. FAX 0211-701013. Ed. Richard Leroch. adv.; charts; tr.lit.; index. circ. 5,700. (back issues avail.)

664.752 664.7 016   UK   ISSN 0430-7941
FLOUR MILLING AND BAKING RESEARCH ASSOCIATION. ABSTRACTS. 1948. bi-m. membership. Flour Milling and Baking Research Association, Chorleywood, Herts. WD3 5SH, England. FAX 0923-284539. Ed. Charlotte Stock. bk.rev.; abstr.; pat.; tr.lit.; index. circ. 1,500. **Document type:** abstracting/indexing.
—BLDSC (0553.080000).
Former titles: British Baking Industries Research Association. Abstracts (ISSN 0300-421X); Baking Research Association. Abstracts (ISSN 0005-4143)

658.8 310   UK   ISSN 0308-955X
FOOD INDUSTRY STATISTICS DIGEST. m. £139 to members; company members £90; non-members £120. Institute of Grocery Distribution, Business Publications, Letchmore Heath, Watford, Herts. WD2 8DQ, England. TEL 0923-857141. FAX 0923-352531. **Document type:** trade publication.
Formerly: Food Industry Statistics Digest Up-Date.
Description: Provides a wide range of data on all aspects of the food industry; includes more than 100 tables on economic environment, ggrocery markets, grocery retailing, grocery manufacturing, and grocery wholesaling, as well as consumer profiles.

FOOD MARKET ABSTRACTS. see *FOOD AND FOOD INDUSTRIES*

664 016   UK   ISSN 0015-6574
TP368
FOOD SCIENCE AND TECHNOLOGY ABSTRACTS. 1969. m. £785($1450) (effective 1994). International Food Information Service (IFIS Publishing), Lane End House, Shinfield, Reading RG2 9BB, England. TEL 734-883895. FAX 734-885065. (US and Canadian subscr. to: IFIS North American Desk, c/o National Food Lab., Inc., 6363 Clark Ave., Dublin, CA 94568. TEL 800-336-3782. FAX 510-833-8795) S. Hill, Managing Ed. bk.rev.; index. circ. 1,250. **Document type:** abstracting/indexing.
●Also available online. Vendor(s): CISTI, DIMDI, Data-Star (FSTA), DIALOG Information Services, Inc. (File no.51), European Space Agency (File no. 20/FSTA), JICST, Orbit Search Service (FSTA). Also available on CD-ROM. Producer(s): SilverPlatter Information, Inc. (COMPU-INFO).
—BLDSC (3983.080000).

664   US   ISSN 0146-9304
CODEN: FADLA3
FOODS ADLIBRA; key to the world's food literature. 1974. s-m. $200 (foreign $275) (effective 1994). (General Mills, Inc.) Foods Adlibra Publications, 9000 Plymouth Ave. N., Minneapolis, MN 55427. TEL 612-540-2720. FAX 612-540-3166. Ed. J.E. O'Connell. (also avail. in magnetic tape) **Document type:** abstracting/indexing.
●Also available online. Vendor(s): DIALOG Information Services, Inc. (File no.79).
Formerly: Food Industries Newsletter.

664   US
FOODS ADLIBRA FOODSERVICE EDITION. m. $100 (foreign $125) (effective 1994). (General Mills, Inc.) Foods Adlibra Publications, 9000 Plymouth Ave., N., Minneapolis, MN 55427. TEL 612-540-2720. FAX 612-540-3166. Ed. J.E. O'Connell. **Document type:** abstracting/indexing.
●Also available online. Vendor(s): DIALOG Information Services, Inc. (File no.79).

664   US
FOODS ADLIBRA SEAFOOD EDITION. m. $100 (foreign $125) (effective 1994). (General Mills, Inc.) Foods Adlibra Publications, 9000 Plymouth Ave., N., Minneapolis, MN 55427. TEL 612-540-2720. FAX 612-540-3166. Ed. J.E. O'Connell. **Document type:** abstracting/indexing.
●Also available online. Vendor(s): DIALOG Information Services, Inc. (File no.79).

664.752   US
FOODS ADLIBRA SNACK & CONFECTIONS EDITION. m. $100 (foreign $125) (effective 1994). (General Mills, Inc.) Foods Adlibra Publications, 9000 Plymouth Ave., N., Minneapolis, MN 55427. TEL 612-540-2720. FAX 612-540-3166. Ed. J.E. O'Connell. **Document type:** abstracting/indexing.
●Also available online. Vendor(s): DIALOG Information Services, Inc. (File no.79).

664   LS   ISSN 0890-4707
FOODSERVICE INFORMATION ABSTRACTS. 1983. s-m. $90 to non-members; members $45. National Restaurant Association, 1200 17th St., N.W., Washington, DC 20036. TEL 202-331-5900. FAX 202-331-2429. Ed. Laurence Himelfarb. circ. 300. (back issues avail.) **Document type:** abstracting/indexing.
Description: Summarized articles from 18 foodservice trade publications.

664 · UK
FRANCIS - LEATHERHEAD FOOD RESEARCH ABSTRACTS. 1965. m. Leatherhead Food R.A., Randalls Rd., Leatherhead, Surrey KT22 7RY, England. Ed. A. Pernet. index. circ. 400. **Document type:** abstracting/indexing.

FROZEN FOODS IN DENMARK. see *FOOD AND FOOD INDUSTRIES*

664 011 · GU
GUAM. DEPARTMENT OF COMMERCE. MONTHLY FOOD INDEX. (Supplement to its Quarterly Report on the Guam Consumer Price Index) m. free. Department of Commerce, Economic Research Center, 590 S. Marine Dr., GITC Bldg. Ste. 601, Tamuning 96911, Guam. FAX 671-646-7242.

HOSPITALITY INDEX; an index for the hotel, foodservice and travel industries. see *HOTELS AND RESTAURANTS* — *Abstracting, Bibliographies, Statistics*

I C O LIBRARY MONTHLY ENTRIES - COFFEELINE. (International Coffee Organization) see *FOOD AND FOOD INDUSTRIES*

658.8 310 · II
INDIAN RICE EXPORTERS' PERFORMANCE MONITOR. (Text in English, French, German, Italian) 1986. m. $500. Commercial Information Services, No. 1 Beena Building, 6th Road, T.P.S. 4, Bandra, Bombay 400 050, India. TEL 91-22-6426703. Ed. C. Moonjely. circ. 300.
Description: Statistics relating to quantity, prices and turnover of each participating rice exporter in India.

658.8 310 · II
INDIAN SPICES EXPORTERS' PERFORMANCE MONITOR. (Text in English, French, German, Italian) 1986. m. $500. Commercial Information Services, No.1 Beena Building, 6th Road, T.P.S. IV, Bandra, Bombay 400 050, India. TEL 91-22-6426703. Ed. C. Moonjely. circ. 300.
Description: Statistics relating to quantity, prices and turnover of each participating spice exporter in India.

663.94 310 · II
INDIAN TEA EXPORTERS' PERFORMANCE MONITOR. (Text in English, French, German, Italian) 1986. m. $500. Commercial Information Services, No.1 Beena Building, 6th Road, T.P.S. IV, Bandra, Bombay 400 050, India. TEL 91-22-6426703. Ed. C. Moonjely. circ. 300.
Description: Statistics relating to quantity, prices and turnover of each participating tea exporter in India.

664.1 338.19 · UK · ISSN 0020-885X
INTERNATIONAL SUGAR ORGANIZATION. STATISTICAL BULLETIN. 1937. m. £45 (overseas £69). International Sugar Organization, 1 Canada Sq., Canary Wharf, London E14 5AA, England. TEL 071-513-1144. FAX 071-513-1146. TELEX 24143. stat. circ. 3,500. (also avail. in microfiche from CIS) **Indexed:** IIS, P.A.I.S. **Document type:** bulletin.
—BLDSC (8447.540000).
Formerly: International Sugar Council. Statistical Bulletin.

664.1 · JA
JAPAN. POCKET SIZE STATISTICS OF SUGAR PRODUCTS. (Text in Japanese) 1963. a. membership. Japan Sugar Refiners' Association, 5-7, Sanbancho, Chiyoda-Ku, Tokyo 102, Japan. Ed. M. Baba.

664 · GW
LEBENSMITTELHANDEL IM SPIEGEL DER STATISTIK (YEAR). 1955. a. DM.85.60. Bundesverband des Deutschen Lebensmittel-Einzelhandels e.V., Ulrich-von-Hassell-Str. 64, 53123 Bonn, Germany. TEL 0228-919200. FAX 0228-9192010. Ed. H. Drexler. illus.; stat.; index. (back issues avail.) **Document type:** bulletin.
Formerly: Deutsche Lebensmittel-Einzelhandel im Spiegel der Statistik (Year) (ISSN 0720-1206)

MAGYAR MEZOGAZDASAGI BIBLIOGRAFIA. see *AGRICULTURE* — *Abstracting, Bibliographies, Statistics*

N T I S ALERTS: AGRICULTURE & FOOD. see *AGRICULTURE* — *Abstracting, Bibliographies, Statistics*

664 · NE · ISSN 0168-5287
NETHERLANDS. CENTRAAL BUREAU VOOR DE STATISTIEK. PRODUKTIESTATISTIEKEN: SUIKERINDUSTRIE. a. fl.12.50. Centraal Bureau voor de Statistiek, Prinses Beatrixlaan 428, Voorburg, Netherlands. (Orders to: SDU - Publishers, Christoffel Plantijnstraat, The Hague, Netherlands) **Document type:** government publication.

664 310 · FR
O E C D FOOD CONSUMPTION STATISTICS. (Text in English, French) every 5 yrs. price varies. Organization for Economic Cooperation and Development, 2 rue Andre-Pascal, 75775 Paris Cedex 16, France. (U.S. orders to: O.E.C.D. Publications and Information Center, 2001 L St., N.W., Ste. 700, Washington, D.C. 20036-4910. TEL 202-785-6323) (also avail. in microfiche)
Formerly: Food Consumption in the O E C D (ISSN 0474-537X)

664 016 · XR · ISSN 0032-7379
PREHLEDY POTRAVINARSKE LITERATURY/SURVEY OF FOOD LITERATURE. 1948. 6/yr. 400 Kcs.($13) (typically set in Nov.) Ustav Zemedelskych a Potravinarskych Informaci - Institute of Abricultural and Food Information, Londynska 55, 120 21 Prague 2, Czech Republic. FAX 422-207411. Ed. L. Benesova. bibl. circ. 1,200. **Document type:** abstracting/indexing.
Description: Publishes food and nutrition abstracts from original Czech and Slovak journals, books and other literature.

QUEBEC (PROVINCE). BUREAU DE STATISTIQUE. STATISTIQUES AGRO-ALIMENTAIRE. see *AGRICULTURE* — *Abstracting, Bibliographies, Statistics*

664 016 · RU · ISSN 0034-2521
REFERATIVNYI ZHURNAL. OBORUDOVANIE PISHCHEVOI PROMYSHLENNOSTI. 1956. m. 53.80 Rub. (including index 54.60 Rub.). Vsesoyuznyi Institut Nauchno-Tekhnicheskoi Informatsii (VINITI), Baltiiskaya ul., 14, Moscow A-219, Russia. (Subscr. to: Mezhdunarodnaya Kniga, Dimitrova ul. 39, 113095 Moscow, Russia) **Document type:** abstracting/indexing.

658.8 016 · US
REFERENCE POINT: FOOD INDUSTRY ABSTRACTS. 1971. m. $70 to non-members; members $50. Food Marketing Institute, 800 Connecticut Ave., N.W., Washington, DC 20006. TEL 202-452-8444. Ed. Barbara L. McBride. abstr.; bibl.; cum.index. circ. 300. **Document type:** abstracting/indexing.
Former titles: F M I Monthly Index Service (ISSN 0270-0352); S M I Monthly Index Service (Super Market Institute).

664 016 · UK · ISSN 0950-1789
SCIENCE & TECHNOLOGY ABSTRACTS. 1947. m. £340. Leatherhead Food R.A., Randalls Rd., Leatherhead, Surrey KT22 7RY, England. TEL 0372-376761. FAX 0372-386228. Ed. A. Pernet. pat. circ. 1,000. (back issues avail.) **Document type:** abstracting/indexing.
Formerly (until 1985): Abstracts from Current Scientific and Technical Literature (ISSN 0001-3439)

664.1 016 · UK · ISSN 0957-5022
TP375
SUGAR INDUSTRY ABSTRACTS. 1939. bi-m. £218($395) CAB International, Wallingford, Oxon. OX10 8DE, England. TEL 44-491-832111. FAX 44-491-833508. TELEX 847964-COMAGG-G. (U.S. subscr. to: CAB International, North American Office, 845 N. Park Ave., Tucson, AZ 85719. TEL 800-528-4841) adv.; bk.rev.; index. (back issues avail.) **Document type:** abstracting/indexing.
Former titles: Tate and Lyle's Sugar Industry Abstracts; Sugar Industry Abstracts (ISSN 0250-2887)
Description: Contains abstracts of current scientific and technical papers, patents, books, conference proceedings and reviews. Covers such topics as sugar processing, sugar factory equipment manufacture, sugar technology research, and other topics.

664 016 · GW · ISSN 0044-3026
CODEN: ZLUFAR
ZEITSCHRIFT FUER LEBENSMITTEL-UNTERSUCHUNG UND -FORSCHUNG; international journal of food research and technology. (Supplement avail.: Laws and Regulations and Legal Decisions Involving Food Stuffs) (Text in English, German) 1890. 12/yr. (in 2 vols., 6 nos./vol.) DM.1780($1113) (Federation of European Chemical Societies, Working Party on Food Chemistry) Springer-Verlag, Heidelberger Platz 3, 14197 Berlin, Germany. TEL 030-8207-1. FAX 030-8214091. (Subscr. in N. America to: Springer-Verlag New York, Inc., 44 Hartz Way, Secaucus, NJ 07096-2491. TEL 201-348-4033. FAX 201-348-4505) Ed. F. Kiermeier. adv.; bk.rev.; abstr.; bibl.; charts; illus.; index, cum.index: 1941-1955, 1956-1963. (also avail. in microform from UMI,PMC; back issues avail.; reprint service avail. from ISI) **Indexed:** Anal.Abstr., Biol.Abstr., Biotech.Abstr., Chem.Abstr., Curr.Adv.Ecol.Sci., Curr.Cont., Curr.Pack.Abstr., Dairy Sci.Abstr., Dent.Ind., Excerp.Med., Field Crop Abstr., Food Sci.& Tech.Abstr., Herb.Abstr., Hort.Abstr., Ind.Med., Ind.Vet., Maize Abstr., Mass Spectr.Bull., Nutr.Abstr., Packag.Sci.Tech., Pig News & Info., Poult.Abstr., Rev.Med.& Vet.Mycol., Rev.Plant.Path., Risk Abstr., Soils & Fert., Sugar Ind.Abstr., Triticale Abstr., Vet.Bull., VITIS, Weed Abstr. **Document type:** academic/scholarly publication.
—BLDSC (9469.000000); Faxon; SWETS; UMI; CASDDS. **CCC.**
Description: Experimental studies, preliminary reports, survey articles, and articles from other journals. Covers the analysis, composition, biological effects, storage, and related technical problems of all types of food. Each volume concludes with a subject index.

664.1 016 · GW · ISSN 0344-8657
TP375 · CODEN: ZUCKDI
ZUCKERINDUSTRIE; internationales Fachblatt fuer Technik, Anbau und Wirtschaft. (Text in German or English; summaries in English, French and Spanish) 1876. m. DM.289. Verlag Dr. Albert Bartens, Lueckhoffstr. 16, 14129 Berlin, Germany. Ed. J. Bruhns. adv.; bk.rev.; abstr.; bibl.; charts; illus.; mkt.; pat.; stat.; tr.lit.; index. circ. 2,500. **Indexed:** Chem.Abstr., Curr.Adv.Ecol.Sci., Curr.Cont., Field Crop.Abstr., Food Sci.& Tech.Abstr., Herb.Abstr., Key to Econ.Sci., Nutr.Abstr., Plant Breed.Abstr., Soils & Fert., Sugar Ind.Abstr. **Document type:** trade publication.
—BLDSC (9537.100000); CASDDS. **CCC.**
Former titles: Zeitschrift fuer die Zuckerindustrie (ISSN 0044-2623); (1948-1977): Zucker (ISSN 0044-538X)
Description: European journal covering beet and cane growing and production, European and German sugar economy, production of bioethanol and other renewable energy sources.

FOOD AND FOOD INDUSTRIES — Bakers And Confectioners

664.752 · US · ISSN 0001-2394
A S B E LETTER. no.31, 1970. q. membership. American Society of Bakery Engineers, Riverside Plaza Bldg., 2 N. Riverside Plaza, Ste. 1733, Chicago, IL 60606. TEL 312-332-2246. Ed. Robert A. Fischer. circ. 2,800.

A W M A BUYING GUIDE & ANNUAL MEMBERSHIP DIRECTORY. (American Wholesale Marketers Association) see *BUSINESS AND ECONOMICS* — *Trade And Industrial Directories*

664.752 · SP
ACTUALITAT FLEQUERA DE CATALUNYA. (Text in Catalan and Spanish) no.246, 1987. 12/yr. free. Gremi de Flequers de Barcelona, Pau Claris, 134, 08009 Barcelona, Spain. TEL 93-215-55-00. FAX 3-216-05-39. Ed. Xavier Vilamala i Vila. adv.; bk.rev.; charts; illus.; stat. circ. 8,500. **Document type:** trade publication.
Formerly: Actualidad Panadera de Cataluna.

664 · GW
ALLGEMEINE BAECKER-ZEITUNG. 1946. w. DM.357.60. Matthaes Verlag GmbH, Olgastr. 87, 70180 Stuttgart, Germany. TEL 0711-2133-0. Ed. Hugo Matthaes. circ. 15,400. **Indexed:** Food Sci.& Tech.Abstr. **Document type:** newspaper.

AMERICAN DELI-BAKERY NEWS. see *FOOD AND FOOD INDUSTRIES* — *Grocery Trade*

FOOD AND FOOD INDUSTRIES — BAKERS AND CONFECTIONERS

664.752 US ISSN 0066-0582
TX761
AMERICAN SOCIETY OF BAKERY ENGINEERS. PROCEEDINGS OF THE ANNUAL MEETING. 1925. a. free to members. American Society of Bakery Engineers, 2 N. Riverside Plaza, Ste. 1733, Chicago, IL 60606. TEL 312-332-2246. Ed. Robert A. Fischer. index, cum.index every 10 yrs. circ. 2,800. **Document type:** proceedings.

664.15 FR ISSN 0755-3110
ANNUAIRE SUCRIER. a. 580 F. Arts Graphiques du Perche Edition, 1 rue du Coq-Heron, 75001 Paris, France. TEL 40-26-57-08. FAX 40-26-34-40.

664.752 US ISSN 1065-190X
ATLANTIC BAKERS NEWS. 1988. 10/yr. $25. 661 N. Algiers St., Box 2728, Murphys, CA 95247. TEL 209-728-2061. FAX 209-728-2061. Ed. Pamela Abbott. adv.; bk.rev. circ. 2,750. (back issues avail.)
  Description: Written for bakers by bakers; contains information about retail bakery management; and covers new products and equipment, bakery trends.

664 GW
BACKJOURNAL. 1973. m. DM.60 (foreign DM.84). Gildefachverlag GmbH & Co. KG, Postfach 1351, 31043 Alfeld, Germany. TEL 05181-80040. Ed. Hildegard Maria Keil. adv.; illus. **Document type:** trade publication.

664.752 SZ
BAECKER KONDITOR ZEITUNG; Fachblatt fuer Baeckereien, Konditoreien und Tea-Rooms. 1889. w. 45 SFr. (members 35 SFr.). (Schweizerischer Baecker-Konditorenmeister-Verband) ASSA Schweizer Annoncen AG, Thunstrasse 22, CH-3000 Bern 6, Switzerland. TEL 031-434242. FAX 031-434252. adv. circ. 7,500. **Indexed:** Food Sci.& Tech.Abstr.
  Description: Covers news information and reports of events; includes calendar of events and exhibitions, positions available.

664 GW ISSN 0005-383X
CODEN: BAKOD6
BAECKER UND KONDITOR; Fachzeitschrift fuer Baeckerei, Konditorei, Dauerbackwarenproduktion und Speiseherstellung. (Text in German; contents page in English and Russian) 1953. 6/yr. DM.52 (foreign DM.70). Gildefachverlag GmbH & Co. KG, Postfach 1351, 31043 Alfeld, Germany. TEL 05181-80040. adv.; bk.rev.; charts; illus.; tr.lit.; index. **Indexed:** Food Sci.& Tech.Abstr., Nutr.Abstr. **Document type:** trade publication.
  —BLDSC (1854.750000); CASDDS.
  Description: Directed to bakers and confectioners; covering production, economics, industry news, and instruction. Includes reports and announcements of events and exhibitions, and classified ads.

664.752 SZ
BAECKER UND KONDITOR. 23/yr. Schweizerische Baeckerei und Konditorei Personalverband, Forschstr. 84, CH-8032 Zurich, Switzerland. TEL 01-535520. FAX 01-533806. circ. 6,900.

664.752 GW
BAECKER - WERK; Mitteilungsblatt der Baecker-Innung Nuernberg und deren wirtschaftlichen Einrichtungen. 1949. m. membership. Baecker - Innung Nuernberg, Ostendstr. 149-151, 90482 Nuernberg, Germany. adv.; circ. 3,000 (controlled).

664.752 GW
BAECKER - ZEITUNG; Betriebsfuehrung - Technik - Herstellung - Handel. 1947. w. DM.232 (foreign DM.273.80). Gildefachverlag GmbH & Co. KG, Postfach 1351, 31043 Alfeld, Germany. TEL 05181-80040. Ed. Mario Toepfer. adv.; bk.rev.; charts; illus.; mkt.; pat.; tr.lit. **Indexed:** Dairy Sci.Abstr., Food Sci.& Tech.Abstr. **Document type:** trade publication.
  Formerly: Archaeographie (ISSN 0005-3821)

646 GW
DER BAECKERMEISTER. 1946. w. DM.288.60 (foreign DM.338). Richard Pflaum Verlag GmbH und Co. KG, Lazarettstr. 4, 80636 Munich, Germany. TEL 089-12607-0. FAX 089-12607-200. (Subscr. to: Postfach 190737, 80607 Munich, Germany) Ed. G. Fassmann. circ. 7,200. **Indexed:** Food Sci.& Tech.Abstr. **Document type:** trade publication.

664.752 GW
BAEKO INFORMATIONEN. 1949. m. Verlag Chmieleorz GmbH & Co., Wilhelmstr. 42, 65183 Wiesbaden, Germany. Ed. Johannes Bornheim. adv. circ. 12,500.

664.752 GW
BAEKO MAGAZIN. m. Verlag Chmielorz GmbH, Marktplatz 13, 65183 Wiesbaden, Germany. TEL 0611-36098-0. FAX 0611-301303. adv.: B&W page DM.5094; trim 185 x 265; adv. contact: Reinhard Volkmer.

664 DK ISSN 0109-0038
BAGER-KONDITOR.* m. DKK 30. Danske Bagerstands Faellesorganisation, Valdemarsvej 12, Gershoej, DK-4050 Skibby, Denmark. (Co-sponsors: Danmarks Konditorforening; Koebenhavns Konditorlaug) Ed. Carl Einar Sovad. adv.; bk.rev. circ. 6,000.
  Formerly: Konditormestrenes Medlemsblad (ISSN 0047-3545)

664.7 NO ISSN 0005-4062
BAKER - KONDITOR. 1901. m. NOK 400. Baker- og Konditorbransjens Landsforening, P.O. Box 5472 Majorstuen, N-0305 Oslo, Norway. TEL 47-22-96-50-10. FAX 47-22-96-50-99. Ed. Knut Maroni. adv.; charts; illus.
  —CCC.

664.752 658.8 CN ISSN 0005-4097
BAKERS JOURNAL; the national business publication serving the Canadian bakery industry. 1938. 10/yr. Can.$15($20) N C C Publishing, 106 Lakeshore Rd. E., Ste. 209, Mississauga, Ont. L5G 1E3, Canada. TEL 416-271-8172. FAX 416-271-6188. Ed. Carol Lawless. adv.; bk.rev.; illus.; tr.lit. circ. 6,000. **Indexed:** Can.B.P.I. **Document type:** trade publication.

664.752 UK ISSN 0005-4100
CODEN: BAKREG
BAKERS REVIEW. 1887. m. £71. (National Association of Master Bakers, Confectioners & Caterers) Turret Group Plc., Turret House, 171 High St., Rickmansworth, Herts WD3 1SN, England. TEL 0923-777000. FAX 0923-771297. Ed. Debra Clay. adv.; illus.; pat. circ. 5,925. **Indexed:** Art.Hosp.& Tour., Biol.Abstr., Food Sci.& Tech.Abstr. **Document type:** trade publication.
  —BLDSC (1860.095000).
  Formerly: Baker, Confectioner, Caterer (ISSN 0005-4054)

664.752 US
BAKERS WAY. 1977. m. membership. American Institute of Baking, 1213 Bakers Way, Manhattan, KS 66502. TEL 913-537-4750. FAX 913-537-1493. TELEX 881039 AIB MAN UD. Ed. Martin Puntney. circ. 900. (tabloid format; back issues avail.)
  Former titles: American Institute of Baking. Institute News; American Institute of Baking. News.

664.752 US ISSN 1049-3174
BAKERY NEWSLETTER. w. (50/yr.). $245 (foreign $295). Delta Communications Inc. (Subsidiary of: Cahners Publishing Company), Division of Reed Elsevier Inc., 455 N. Cityfront Plaza Dr., 24th Fl., Chicago, IL 60611-5503. TEL 312-222-2000. FAX 312-222-2026. TELEX 210012 UR. pp./issue: 4. **Document type:** newsletter, trade publication.
  Description: Keeps readers on top of market and product trends, commodity reports, advertising and marketing strategies, mergers and acquisitions, competitive moves, government regulations.

664.752 658.8 US ISSN 0005-4127
TX761 CODEN: BPMKA4
BAKERY PRODUCTION AND MARKETING; management magazine of the bakery industry. 1966. 14/yr. $83 (foreign $146) (free to qualified personnel). Delta Communications Inc. (Subsidiary of: Cahners Publishing Company), Division of Reed Elsevier Inc., 455 N. Cityfront Plaza Dr., 24th Fl., Chicago, IL 60611-5503. TEL 312-222-2000. FAX 312-222-2026. TELEX 210012 UR. Ed. Dan Malovany; Pub. Peter Lachapelle. adv.: B&W page $4990, color page $6690; trim 7 7/8 x 10 3/4; adv. contact: Jeanne Sullivan. illus.; index. circ. 42,057. (also avail. in microform from UMI; reprint service avail from UMI) **Indexed:** Bus.Ind., Food Sci.& Tech.Abstr., Key to Econ.Sci., PROMT, Ref.Pt.Food Indus.Abstr., Tr.& Indus.Ind. **Document type:** trade publication.
  ●Also available online. Vendor(s): DIALOG Information Services, Inc., Mead Data Central, Inc. —Faxon; UnCover; UMI. **CCC**.
  Incorporates: Bakers Weekly (ISSN 0005-4119)

664.752 US
BAKERY PRODUCTION AND MARKETING RED BOOK. 1976. a. $255. Delta Communications Inc. (Subsidiary of: Cahners Publishing Company), Division of Reed Elsevier Inc., 455 N. Cityfront Plaza Dr., 24th Fl., Chicago, IL 60611. TEL 312-222-2000. FAX 312-222-2026. TELEX 210012 UR. Ed. Pat Reynolds. adv. circ. 30,043. (also avail. in microform; back issues avail.) **Document type:** directory.
  Description: Lists products sold by major wholesale bakers and confectioners.

664.752 658.8 UK
BAKERY PRODUCTS: THE INTERNATIONAL MARKET. a. £1375($2750) Euromonitor, 87-88 Turnmill St., London EC1M 5QU, England. TEL 071-251-8024. FAX 071-608-3149. (Addr. in N. America: Euromonitor International, 111 W. Washington St., Ste. 920, Chicago, IL 60602. TEL 312-541-8024. FAX 312-541-1567) (looseleaf format) **Document type:** trade publication.
  ●Also available online. Vendor(s): Data-Star, DIALOG Information Services, Inc.
  Description: Analyzes the market for bakery goods for France, Germany, Italy, Spain, the U.K., the U.S., and Japan.

664.752 IE
BAKERY WORLD. bi-m. £12. 22 Brookfield Ave., Blackrock, Co. Dublin, Ireland. TEL 886946. FAX 881098. (Subscr. to: P.O. Box 1973, Rathmines, Dublin 6, Ireland) Ed. Annette O'Meara. adv. circ. 1,609.
  Formerly: Master Baker.

664 US
BAKING & SNACK. 1979. m. free to qualified personnel. Sosland Publishing Company, 4800 Main St., Ste. 100, Kansas City, MO 64112. TEL 816-756-1000. FAX 816-756-0494. adv. circ. 8,800.
  Former titles: Baking and Snack Systems (ISSN 1040-9254) & Baking and Snack Equipment; (until 1987): Baking Equipment.

664.752 US
BAKING BUYER. (Supplement avail.: Baking Buyer Yearbook) 1985. 12/yr. free to qualified personnel. Sosland Publishing Company, 4800 Main St., Ste. 100, Kansas City, MO 64112. TEL 816-756-1000. FAX 816-756-0494. Ed. Kerrie Bertz. circ. 30,000 (controlled).
  Formerly: Buyer.
  Description: Provides information about new equipment, ingredients, packaging and serving.

664.752 UK ISSN 0957-4247
BAKING INDUSTRY DIRECTORY. a. E M A P Response Publishing Ltd., Wentworth House, Wentworth St., Peterborough PE1 1DS, England. TEL 0733-63100. FAX 0733-61313. TELEX 946665. adv.: B&W page £645, color page £1644; trim 185 x 126. circ. 10,291. **Document type:** trade publication, consumer publication.
  Former titles (until 1989): British Baker Directory (ISSN 0956-294x); (until 1988): British Baker Directory and Buyers Guide (ISSN 0142-3622); (until 1973): British Baker Classified Index and Directory.
  Description: Highlights bakeries and baker's goods.

FOOD AND FOOD INDUSTRIES — BAKERS AND CONFECTIONERS

664.752 NE ISSN 0924-9583
BAKKERIJ; weekblad voor de brood- en banketbakkerij. 1942. w. fl.169. (Nederlandse Bakkerij) Audet Tijdschriften bv (Subsidiary of: C. Misset B.V.), Postbus 9000, 6800 DA Arnhem, Netherlands. TEL 31-85-209911. FAX 31-85-233007. Ed. Ewald Lohmann. adv.: B&W page fl.3206, color page fl.4996; trim 215 x 285; adv. contact: Cor van Nek. charts; illus.; mkt.; stat. circ. 5,560. **Indexed:** Key to Econ.Sci. **Document type:** trade publication.
 Former titles (until 1990): Bakker (ISSN 0165-1595); (until 1976): Bakkersvakblad (ISSN 0005-4178)
 Description: Provides information on new products and methods as well as fiscal advice to bakers.

664.752 NE ISSN 0026-5934
BAKKERSWERELD. 1937. w. fl.160. Uitgeversmaatschappij C. Misset B. V., Hanzestr. 1, 7006 RH Doetinchem, Netherlands. TEL 31-8340-49911. FAX 31-8340-43839. TELEX 45481. (Subscr. to: Postbus 4, 7000 BA Doetinchem, Netherlands) Ed. H. Leyten. adv.: B&W page fl.3350; trim 230 x 300; adv. contact: Cor van Nek. illus. circ. 7,550. **Indexed:** Key to Econ.Sci. **Document type:** trade publication.
 Formerly: Misset's Bakkerswereld.
 Description: Directed to pastry cooks and bakers.

664.15 BE
BELGIAN KNITWEAR ASSOCIATION. REPORT. a. Belgian Knitwear Association - Federation de la Maille, Rode Beukendreef 14, 9831 Deurle, Belgium. TEL 091-82-21-11. FAX 091-82-40-21.
 Formerly: Comite Central de la Bonneterie Belge. Report.

664.752 US
BETTER HOMES AND GARDENS HOLIDAY COOKING. 1969. a. $3.50. Meredith Corporation, Special Interest Publications, 1716 Locust St., Des Moines, IA 50336. TEL 515-284-3000. Pub. Steve Levinson. adv.: B&W page $13450, color page $18350; adv. contact: Pat Tomlinson. circ. 600,000.
 Formerly: Better Homes and Gardens Baking Ideas.

664.752 658.8 UK
BISCUITS: THE INTERNATIONAL MARKET. a. £1375($2750) Euromonitor, 87-88 Turnmill St., London EC1M 5QU, England. TEL 071-251-8024. FAX 071-608-3149. (Addr. in N. America: Euromonitor International, 111 W. Washington St., Ste. 920, Chicago, IL 60602. TEL 312-541-8024. FAX 312-541-1567) (looseleaf format) **Document type:** trade publication.
 ●Also available online. Vendor(s): Data-Star, DIALOG Information Services, Inc.
 Description: Analyzes the market for biscuits in France, Germany, Italy, Spain, the U.K., the U.S., and Japan.

664.752 FR ISSN 0758-4164
BOULANGERIE FRANCAISE. (Text in French) 1904. 23/yr. 110 F. S.E.P.D.B.P., 7 quai d'Anjou, 75004 Paris, France. FAX 43-29-65-49. Ed. Patrice LeFrancois. adv.; bk.rev. circ. 4,500.

664.752 FR
BOULANGERIE RHONE-ALPES.* 1934. bi-m. 20 F. 108-110 bd. du Parc d'Artillerie, 69364 Lyon Cedex 07, France. TEL 78-72-29-70. Ed. Aime Charveyron. adv.; bk.rev. circ. 10,000.

664.752 SW ISSN 0284-9488
BREAD & CAKES; allt om broed. 1988. 10/yr. SEK 220 (effective 1990). Bread & Cakes, P.O. Box 21105, S-100 31 Stockholm, Sweden.

664.752 UK ISSN 0007-0300
CODEN: BRBAE5
BRITISH BAKER. 1885. w. £56. E M A P Maclaren Ltd., 19 Scarbrook Rd., Croydon, Surrey CR9 1QH, England. TEL 081-688 7788. FAX 081-688-8375. Ed. Martin Roebuck. adv.; illus.; mkt.; pat.; tr.mk. circ. 10,250. (also avail. in microfilm from UMI; reprint service avail. from UMI) **Document type:** trade publication.
 —BLDSC (2289.500000). CCC.
 Description: News and general information for all sectors of the baking industry.

664.752 SW ISSN 1100-0996
BROED; facktidskrift foer bagare och konditorer. 1900. m. (11/yr.). SEK 295. Sveriges Bageriofoerbund Service AB - Association of Swedish Master Bakers, Hovslagargatan 5, 111 48 Stockholm, Sweden. TEL 46-8-7626781. FAX 46-8-200244. Ed. Magnus Magnusson. adv.; bk.rev.; illus. circ. 2,799. **Document type:** trade publication.
 Former titles: Broed, Konditorn (ISSN 0345-181X); Broed (ISSN 0007-2168)

664.752 GW
BROT- UND BACKWAREN. 1952. m. DM.96. (Vereinigung Deutsche Backtechnik) Rhenania-Fachverlag GmbH, Possmoorweg 5, 22301 Hamburg, Germany. FAX 040-2717-2069. TELEX 213214. Ed. Volker Herrmann. circ. 4,247. **Indexed:** Food Sci.& Tech.Abstr., Packag.Sci.Tech. **Document type:** trade publication.
 Formerly: Backtechnik (ISSN 0344-4686)

664.15 US
BUBBLE AND CHEWING GUM WORLD. 1990. 3/yr. $24. Lott Publishing Co., Box 710, Santa Monica, CA 90406. TEL 310-397-4217. Ed. Dave Lott. adv.; circ. 3,000 (controlled). **Document type:** newspaper.
 Description: Covers trade news on all gum products of all types.

664.15 GW
BUNDESVERBAND DER DEUTSCHEN SUSSWARENINDUSTRIE. JAHRESBERICHT. a. Bundesverband der Deutschen Susswarenindustrie, Schumannstr 4-6, 53113 Bonn, Germany. TEL 0228-26007-0. FAX 0228-2600789. TELEX 886634.

664 UK ISSN 0007-8654
CODEN: CMMADZ
C M M. (Confectionery Manufacture & Marketing) 1955. 11/yr. £35. J.G. Kennedy & Co. Ltd., 12 Blackstock Mews, Blackstock Rd., London N4 2BT, England. TEL 071-226-3423. FAX 071-354-5372. Ed. Margaret Lang. adv.; bk.rev.; charts; illus.; mkt.; pat. circ. 7,800. **Indexed:** Food Sci.& Tech.Abstr., Int.Packag.Abstr., Packag.Sci.Tech. **Document type:** trade publication.
 Incorporates: Confectionery Buyer's Guide; I C M (Ice Cream Manufacture).
 Description: Information on candy and chocolate.

658.8 UK
C T N. (Confectioner, Tobacconist, Newsagent) 1887. w. $110.50. International Thomson Business Publishing, Greater London House, Hampstead Rd., London NW1 7SD, England. TEL 01-387-6611. Ed. Peter Arnott-Job. adv.; bk.rev.; charts; illus.; mkt.; tr.mk. circ. 25,096.
 Formerly: Confectionery and Tobacco News (ISSN 0010-5465); Incorporates: Smith's Trade News (ISSN 0037-7325); British Stationer (ISSN 0007-1811)
 Description: Directed to retailers providing magazines, candy, and cigarettes in neighborhood shops.

664.752 US
C W G E A NEWSLETTER. 1977. s-a. membership. Cooperative Whole Grain Education Association, 1019 Williamson, Madison, WI 53703. TEL 608-257-3649. adv. circ. 75. **Document type:** newsletter.

664.752 SZ
CANDIS. (Text in French, German) m. Candis Verlag GmbH, Muehlebachstr. 43, CH-8023 Zurich, Switzerland. TEL 01-2512592. Ed. Linus Drexler. circ. 6,200.

CANDY BUYERS DIRECTORY. see BUSINESS AND ECONOMICS — Trade And Industrial Directories

664.15 US
CANDY DISH.* m. National Candy Brokers and Salesmen's Association, 5216 Dundee Rd., Edina, MN 55346-2047.

664 US ISSN 0745-1032
HD9999.C72 CODEN: CANIDE
CANDY INDUSTRY. 1874. m. $25. (Magazines for Industry, Inc.) Advanstar Communications, Inc., 7500 Old Oak Blvd., Cleveland, OH 44130. TEL 216-826-2866. FAX 216-819-2651. (Subscr. to: 131 W. First St., Duluth, MN 55802. TEL 218-723-9477) Ed. Susan Tiffany. adv.; bk.rev.; illus.; index. circ. 4,000. (also avail. in microform) **Indexed:** Bus.Ind., Curr.Pack.Abstr., Dairy Sci.Abstr., Food Sci.& Tech.Abstr., PROMT, Tr.& Indus.Ind. **Document type:** trade publication.
 ●Also available online. Vendor(s): DIALOG Information Services, Inc.
 —BLDSC (3046.790000); Faxon. CCC.
 Former titles: Candy and Snack Industry; Baked Snack Industry (ISSN 0008-5537); Candy.
 Description: Company operations, technological advancements and other information for confectionery executives.

664.15 US
CANDY INDUSTRY BUYING GUIDE. 1945. a. $25. Advanstar Communications, Inc., 7500 Old Oak Blvd., Cleveland, OH 44130. TEL 216-826-2839. FAX 216-891-2726. (Subscr. to: 1 E. First St., Duluth, MN 55802. TEL 800-346-0085) Ed. Susan Tiffany. **Document type:** trade publication.
 Description: Annual publication for confectionary executives.

664.15 US ISSN 0886-3741
HD9330.C65 CODEN: CMARER
CANDY MARKETER (CLEVELAND). 1937. bi-m. $25. Advanstar Communications, Inc., 7500 Old Oak Blvd., Cleveland, OH 44130. TEL 216-826-2839. FAX 216-891-2726. (Subscr. to: 131 W. First St., Duluth, MN 55802. TEL 800-346-0085) Ed. Teresa Tarantino. adv. circ. 12,174. (also avail. in microfiche) **Document type:** trade publication.
 ●Also available online. Vendor(s): DIALOG Information Services, Inc.
 —CCC.
 Formerly: Candy Marketer Quarterly (ISSN 0733-9070)
 Description: Industry news, new products, features and promotions for candy, snack and tobacco buyers and merchandisers.

664.15 658.8 US ISSN 0162-5136
HD9999.C72
CANDY WHOLESALER; the magazine for candy, tobacco and snack food distributors. 1948. 10/yr. $36 (foreign $45). American Wholesale Marketers Association, 1128 16th St., N.W., Washington, DC 20036. TEL 202-463-2124. FAX 202-467-0559. adv.; charts; illus. circ. 11,400. **Document type:** trade publication.
 Formerly: National Candy Wholesaler (ISSN 0027-8882)
 Description: Industry advocate providing information on business issues and products of interest to wholesale distributors of consumer products.

658.8 US
CANDY WORLD ILLUSTRATED. 1914. 3/yr. $24. Lott Publishing Co., Box 1107, Santa Monica, CA 90406. Ed. Dave Lott. adv.; abstr.; illus.; stat. circ. 3,000. **Document type:** trade publication, newspaper.
 Former titles: American Buyer's Review; Western Buyer's Review; Western Confectioner and Tobacconist (ISSN 0043-3594); Western Tobacconist.

664 BE
CHOBISCO. (Editions in Dutch, French) 1938. m. (11/yr.). membership. Royale Chambre Syndicale des Grossistes en Confiserie, 22 rue de la Bourse, Bte. 3, B-1000 Brussels, Belgium. TEL 32-2-5110030. FAX 32-2-5126890. Ed. Paul de Backer.

663.92 641.345 US
CHOCOLATE AND NUT WORLD. 1989. 3/yr. $24. Lott Publishing Co., Box 710, Santa Monica, CA 90406. TEL 310-397-4217. Ed. Dave Lott. adv.; circ. 3,000 (controlled). **Document type:** trade publication, newspaper.
 Description: Covers trade news in the chocolate & nut world.

664.15 IT
CIOCCOLATA & C; il lato dolce della vita. 1991. q. L.8000 per no. Periodico Editore, Vis Piscane 16, 20129 Milan, Italy. TEL 02-7383532. FAX 02-70102517. Ed. Andreina Vanni. adv.

FOOD AND FOOD INDUSTRIES — BAKERS AND CONFECTIONERS

664.15   IT   ISSN 1120-5830
COMMERCIO BOMBONIERA ITALIANA. 6/yr. Editrice di Lombardo Giuseppa & C., Via Lombardia 83, 95045 Misterbianco (CT), Italy. TEL 095-399305. FAX 095-399398. adv.: B&W page L.3000000; color page L.3800000; trim 210 x 290. circ. 14,444.

664.15   UK   ISSN 0010-5473
                             CODEN: CNFPAF
CONFECTIONERY PRODUCTION. 1934. m. £45. Specialised Publications Ltd., 5 Grove Rd., Surbiton, Surrey KT6 4BT, England. TEL 081-390-0222. FAX 081-390-0126. Ed. Dennis Buckley. adv.: B&W page £472; trim 175 x 253. bk.rev.; charts; illus.; pat.; tr.lit.; tr.mk.; index. circ. 5,221. **Indexed**: Chem.Abstr., Curr.Cont., Food Sci.& Tech.Abstr., Int.Packag.Abstr., Key to Econ.Sci., Packag.Sci.Tech., Sugar Ind.Abstr. **Document type**: trade publication.
—BLDSC (3407.000000); CASDDS.

664.15 658.8   UK
CONFECTIONERY: THE INTERNATIONAL MARKET. a. £1375($2750) Euromonitor, 87-88 Turnmill St., London EC1M 5QU, England. TEL 071-251-8024. FAX 071-608-3149. (Addr. in N. America: Euromonitor International, 111 W. Washington St., Ste. 920, Chicago, IL 60602. TEL 312-541-8024. FAX 312-541-1567) (looseleaf format) **Document type**: trade publication.
● Also available online. Vendor(s): Data-Star, DIALOG Information Services, Inc.
    Description: Analyzes the confectionery market for France, Germany, Italy, Spain, the U.K., the U.S., and Japan.

664.15   FR
CONFISERIE. 1922. 8/yr. 500 Fr. (Salon International de la Confiserie Chocolaterie Biscuiterie) Editions de la Confiserie, 103 rue La Fayette, 75481 Paris Cedex 10, France. TEL 42-85-18-20. FAX 40-16-01-45. TELEX 633 166 PRCOM. Ed. Guy Urbain. adv.; illus.; stat.; circ. 4,000 (controlled).

664.15   SZ
CONFISEUR/CONFETTIERE. 11/yr. 65 SFr. (foreign 95 SFr.). Schweizerischer Konditor - Confiseurmeister - Verband, Wiesenstr. 7, CH-8032 Zurich, Switzerland. TEL 01-3834763. FAX 01-3832593. **Document type**: trade publication.

664.15   SP   ISSN 0210-1920
CONFITERIA ESPANOLA; revista profesional del dulce. 1930. m. 9850 ptas. (Europe $135; elsewhere $220). Montagud Editores, S.A., Ausias Marc, 25, 1, 08010 Barcelona, Spain. TEL 318-20-82. FAX 302-50-83. Ed. Federico Montagud Bosoms. adv.; index. circ. 8,000. **Indexed**: Ind.SST. **Document type**: trade publication.

664   NE   ISSN 0010-7042
CONSUDEL. vol.37, 1979. m. fl.65. Algemeen Publiciteitskantoor B.V., Keizersgracht 188, Amsterdam C, Netherlands. Ed. D.L. Broeder. adv.; bk.rev.; illus.; mkt.; pat.; tr.lit.; tr.mk.; index. circ. 2,400. **Indexed**: Key to Econ.SCi.

CONVENIENCE STORE. see FOOD AND FOOD INDUSTRIES — Grocery Trade

664.7   GW   ISSN 0046-0117
DEUTSCHE BAECKER ZEITUNG. 1913. w. DM.216. Deutscher Baecker Verlag GmbH, Postfach 102050, 44791 Bochum, Germany. TEL 0234-51841. FAX 0234-582630. Ed. Marlies Bootz. index. circ. 9,500. **Indexed**: Food Sci.& Tech.Abstr. **Document type**: trade publication.

664.15   GW
DEUTSCHE SUESSWARENINDUSTRIE (YEAR). a. Bundesverband der deutschen Suesswarenindustrie, Schumannstr. 4-6, 53113 Bonn, Germany. TEL 0228-260070. FAX 0228-2600789.

664.15   MX
DIRECTORIO DE CONFITERIA. a. Mex.$50. Producciones Manila, S.A., Baja California 32-A, Col. Roma, Deleg. Cuauhtemoc, 06760 Mexico, D.F., Mexico. TEL 525-564-7040. FAX 525-574-5696. Ed. Graciela Diaz Serrano. adv.

664.15   IT
DOLCE & GELATO ARTIGIANO.* 4/yr. Fratelli Vallardi Editori s.r.l., Corso Magenta 32, 20123 Milan, Italy. TEL 2-66-90-43-23. circ. 7,000.

664   MX
DULCELANDIA; industrias alimenticias. 1940. m. Mex.$70 (US $50; Europe $90). Producciones Manila, S.A., Baja California 32-A, Col. Roma, Deleg. Cuauhtemoc, 06760 Mexico, D.F., Mexico. TEL 525-564-7040. FAX 525-574-5696. Ed. Graciela Diaz Serrano. adv. circ. 5,000.

664.15   SP
DULCYPAS. 12/yr. Carmen 4 y 6, 08019 Sant Cugat del Valles (Barcelona), Spain. TEL 3-675-08-11. FAX 3-675-38-61. Ed. Ignacio Corbero. circ. 10,000.
    Description: Covers cake-making, confectionery, ice cream and related industries.

664   HU   ISSN 0013-0842
                             CODEN: EDESA5
EDESIPAR. (Contents page and summaries in German, Hungarian, Russian) 1950. q. $18. (Magyar Elelmezesipari Tudomanyos Egyesulet) Lapkiado Vallalat, Lenin korut 9-11, 1073 Budapest 7, Hungary. TEL 222-408. (Subscr. to: Kultura, Box 149, H-1389 Budapest, Hungary) Ed. Sandor Szanto. adv.; charts; illus. circ. 700. **Indexed**: Chem.Abstr., Food Sci.& Tech.Abstr., INIS Atomind.
—CASDDS.

EESTI NAINE; a magazine for women. see WOMEN'S INTERESTS

664.752   FR   ISSN 1140-5104
FILIERE FARINE. 11/yr. 360 F. (foreign 445 F.). Groupe L S A, B.P. 142, 6 rue Marius Aufan, 92304 Levallois-Perret Cedex, France. TEL 47-58-20-00. FAX 47-58-77-00. (Subscr. to: Filiere Farine, 46 rue de Clichy, 75009 Paris, France)

664.752   UK
FINANCIAL SURVEY COMPANY DATA FOR SUCCESS. BAKERY PRODUCTS MANUFACTURERS. a. I C C Financial Surveys Ltd., Field House, 72 Oldfield Rd., Hampton, Middlesex TW12 2HQ, England. TEL 081-783-0977. FAX 081-783-1940.
    Formerly (until 1991): Financial Survey Company Directory. Bakery Products Manufacturers (ISSN 0952-0058)

FINANCIAL SURVEY COMPANY DATA FOR SUCCESS. TOBACCO & CONFECTIONARY WHOLESALERS. see TOBACCO

FOOD HERALD. see FOOD AND FOOD INDUSTRIES

FOODS ADLIBRA SNACK & CONFECTIONS EDITION. see FOOD AND FOOD INDUSTRIES — Abstracting, Bibliographies, Statistics

664   CN   ISSN 0015-9158
LA FOURNEE. (Text in French) 1946. bi-m. Can.$25. Communications Vero Inc., 1600 Henri Bourassa Blvd., W., No. 420, Montreal, PQ H3M 3E2, Canada. TEL 514-332-8376. FAX 514-332-2666. Ed. Francoise Pittte. circ. 4,200. (back issues avail.)

664.752 658.8   US
FRESH BAKED. 1948. m. membership. Retail Bakers of America, 14239 Park Center Dr., Laurel, MD 20707-5261. TEL 301-725-2149. FAX 301-725-2187. bk.rev.; charts; stat. circ. 3,300. (back issues avail.) **Document type**: newsletter.
    Former titles: R B A Fresh Baked; A R B A Fresh Baked (Associated Retail Bakers of America).

641   JA
GATEAUX/GATOU. (Text in Japanese) 1952. m. exchange basis. Federation of Japan Confectionary Associations - Nihon Yogashi Kyokai Rengokai, 19-26 Ebisu 1-chome, Shibuya-ku, Tokyo 150, Japan. TEL 03-444-8711. FAX 03-444-8935. Ed. Kenji Nagao. adv.; bk.review. circ. 10,000. **Indexed**: Jap.Per.Ind.

637.4 664   FR   ISSN 1143-6352
GLACES MAGAZINE. 1948. m. (10/yr.). 350 F. (foreign 450 F.). (Confederation National de Glaciers de France) P H C Editions, 64 rue de la Rochefoucauld, 75009 Paris, France. TEL 40-16-03-88. FAX 40-16-04-60. adv.: B&W page 9500 F., color page 13500 F.; trim 260 x 180. bk.rev.; illus.; index, cum.index. circ. 8,000.
—BLDSC (4180.010000).
    Formerly (until 1989): Glacier Francais (ISSN 0017-0704)

664   US   ISSN 1052-4630
TX901   CODEN: GONEE9
GOURMET NEWS; the business newspaper for the gourmet industry. 1935. m. $35 (foreign $125). United Publications, Inc., Box 1056, Yarmouth, ME 04096. TEL 207-846-0600. Ed. Nancy H. Burnett. adv.; illus.; mkt.; tr.lit. circ. 20,000. **Document type**: newspaper.
    Former titles (until 1990): Gourmet Today (1986) (ISSN 0889-4515); (until 1986): Gourmet Today - Telefood (ISSN 8750-314X); Which was formed by the 1984 merger of: Gourmet Today (1979) (ISSN 0274-6263) Telefood (ISSN 0747-3540); Which was formerly: Telefood Magazine (ISSN 0040-2540).

664.752 338.1   SP   ISSN 0213-1021
HELADERIA INTERNACIONAL; revista profesional de heladeria y afines. 1984. bi-m. 6500 ptas. (Europe $70; elsewhere $85). Montagud Editores, S.A., Ausias Marc, 25, 1, 08010 Barcelona, Spain. TEL 318-20-82. FAX 302-50-83. Dir. Francisco Javier Antoia Girait. adv.; index. circ. 5,000. **Document type**: trade publication.

664.752 642.5   HU
HOSPITALITY. m. Magyar Szakacsok es Cukraszok Szovetsege, Rakocziuk 58, 1074 Budapest 7, Hungary. TEL 01-420709. TELEX 226209.

664.752   BL
I P: REVISTA DA INDUSTRIA DE PANIFICACAO/BAKING INDUSTRY REVIEW. 1935. m. Rua Ararquara 63, CEP 09900, Diadema, Sao Paulo, Brazil. Ed. Milton Coatti. circ. 10,000.

637.4 664   UK   ISSN 0019-106X
ICE CREAM & FROZEN CONFECTIONERY. 1949. m. £60 to Ice Cream Alliance members. Ice Cream Alliance, 90-94 Gray's Inn Rd., London WC1X 8AH, England. TEL 071-405-0712. FAX 071-404-5879. Ed. Lisa Grief. adv.; bk.rev., charts; illus.; pat.; stat.; tr.mk.; circ. 1,250 (controlled). **Indexed**: Dairy Sci.Abstr., Food Sci.& Tech.Abstr.

637.4   US   ISSN 0897-3261
ICE CREAM REPORTER; the newsletter for ice cream executives. 1987. m. $395. F I N D - S V P, Inc., 625 Avenue of the Americas, New York, NY 10011-2002. TEL 212-645-4500. FAX 212-645-7681. Ed. Howard Waxman. (back issues avail.) **Document type**: newsletter.
● Also available online. Vendor(s): NewsNet (FB04).
    Description: Offers news and analysis of events and decisions that affect frozen dessert industry: manufacturing, distribution, advertising and legislation.

664.752   US
INDEPENDENT (WASHINGTON, 1978). 1978. a. free. Independent Bakers Association, Box 3731, Washington, DC 20007. TEL 202-333-8190. Ed. Robert N. Pyle. circ. 3,000. (back issues avail.)

664.752   US
INDEPENDENT BAKERS ASSOCIATION NEWSLETTER. a. membership. Independent Bakers Association, Box 3731, Washington, DC 20007. TEL 202-333-8190. (Subscr. to: Box 3731, Washington, DC 20007) Ed. Robert N. Pyle. circ. 3,000. **Document type**: newsletter.

664.15   BE
INTERNATIONAL OFFICE OF COCOA, CHOCOLATE AND SUGAR CONFECTIONERY. ANNUAL STATISTICAL BULLETIN. Short title: I O C C C Annual Statistical Bulletin. a. 1200 Fr.($40) International Office of Cocoa, Chocolate and Sugar Confectionery (IOCCC), Av. de Cortenbergh 172 B-1040 Brussels, Belgium. TEL 735-1072. FAX 736-3623. TELEX 26246. **Document type**: bulletin.
    Formerly: International Office of Cocoa and Chocolate and the International Sugar Confectionery Manufacturers' Association. Periodic Bulletin (ISSN 0444-0978)
    Description: Provides international comparison of production, consumption as well as import and export in the chocolate, sugar confectionary and biscuit industries.

FOOD AND FOOD INDUSTRIES — BAKERS AND CONFECTIONERS

663 BE
INTERNATIONAL OFFICE OF COCOA, CHOCOLATE AND SUGAR CONFECTIONERY. REPORT OF THE GENERAL ASSEMBLY. quadrennial, latest 1988, Sydney. International Office of Cocoa, Chocolate and Sugar Confectionery (IOCCC), Av. de Cortenbergh 172, 1040 Brussels, Belgium. TEL 735-10-72. FAX 733-94-26. TELEX 26246.
 Formerly (until 1986): International Office of Cocoa and Chocolate and the International Sugar Confectionery Manufacturers' Association. Report of the General Assembly (ISSN 0535-1626)

664.752 FR
JOURNAL DU PATISSIER; confiseur, glacier, chocolatier, traiteur. (Quarterly supplement avail.) m. 290 F. (Europe 470 F.; elsewhere 570 F.). Editions des Patissiers de France, 4 rue de Hanovre, 75002 Paris, France. TEL 47-42-41-37. Ed. Robert Marty.

664 SP ISSN 0022-7218
JUVENTUD PANADERA. 1965. m. free. Club Juventud Panadera, Gobernador Viejo 9, 46003 Valencia, Spain. TEL 6-331-92-09. Ed. Dir. Antonio Flor Marti. adv.; illus. circ. 5,000.

664.15 GW ISSN 0022-7838
KAKAO UND ZUCKER; Technische Fachzeitschrift fuer die gesamte Suesswarenindustrie. 1948. m. DM.147 (foreign DM.157.20). Zeitschriftenverlag R B D V, Postfach 1135, 4000 Duesseldorf 1, Germany. TEL 0211-5050. FAX 0211-505-2555. Ed. Beate Henes-Karnahl. adv.; bk.rev.; abstr.; illus.; stat.; index, cum.index. circ. 1,600. **Indexed:** Dairy Sci.Abstr., Food Sci.& Tech.Abstr., Packag.Sci.Tech., Sugar Ind.Abstr. **Document type:** trade publication. —BLDSC (5081.700000). **CCC.**
 Description: Covers technology and production, marketing, new ideas, products and international news about the confectionery industry.

KHLEBOPRODUKTY. see *AGRICULTURE — Feed, Flour And Grain*

664 GW ISSN 0023-3234
KONDITOREI UND CAFE; die Konditorei, der Konditormeister. 1948. w. DM.426. (Deutscher Konditorenbund) Matthaes Verlag GmbH, Olgastr. 87, 70180 Stuttgart, Germany. TEL 0711-2133-0. adv.; bk.rev.; illus.; tr.lit.; index. circ. 9,000. **Indexed:** Food Sci.& Tech.Abstr. **Document type:** newspaper.

664.15 DK ISSN 0047-3553
KONFEKTUREHANDLEREN. 1915. m. membership. (Dansk Konfektureforening - Danish Confectionery Association) Ch. F. Mogensen I-S Bladforlag, Naestvedvej 12, 4160 Herlufmagle, Denmark. TEL 45-53-75-10-11. FAX 45-53-75-14-11. Ed. Benedikte Mogensen Nygaard. adv. circ. 1,200. **Document type:** trade publication.
 Formerly: Chokolade Konfekture og Sukkervare Industrien.

664 FI ISSN 0024-0699
LEIPURI. (Text in Finnish; summaries in Swedish) 1903. 8/yr. FIM 200. Suomen Leipuriliitto r.y., P.O. Box 115, SF-00241 Helsinki, Finland. TEL 358-0-14887304. FAX 358-0-14887301. Ed. Olli Kuhta. adv.; bk.rev.; illus. circ. 2,000.

LOCAL 3 BAKERY WORKERS NEWS. see *LABOR UNIONS*

664.15 US ISSN 0025-2573
MANUFACTURING CONFECTIONER. (Buying Guide; Purchasing Executives' Number) 1921. m. $25. Manufacturing Confectioner Publishing Co., 175 Rock Rd., Glen Rock, NJ 07452. TEL 201-652-2655. Ed. Allen Allured. adv.; bk.rev.; charts, illus.; index. circ. 3,489. (also avail. in microform from UMI) **Indexed:** Chem.Abstr., Curr.Pack.Abstr., Dairy Sci.Abstr., Food Sci.& Tech.Abstr.
 Formerly: Manufacturing Confectioner with International Confectioner.
 Description: Discusses financial information, marketing and candy making processes for the sweet goods industry.

664 UK ISSN 0025-4983
MASTER BAKER, CONFECTIONER & CATERER.* 1908. m. 20s. Irish Association of Master Bakers, 114 Somerton Rd., Belfast, N. Ireland. Ed. John Little. adv.

664.752 UK
MASTER BAKER'S HANDBOOK AND BUYER'S GUIDE. a. £29. Turret Group Plc., Turret House, 171 High St., Rickmansworth, Herts WD3 1SN, England. TEL 0923-777000. FAX 0923-771297. Ed. Marjorie Voss. **Document type:** trade publication.

664.72 US ISSN 0091-4843
HD9056.U4 CODEN: MBNEDH
MILLING & BAKING NEWS. 1922. w. $75. Sosland Publishing Company, 4800 Main St., Ste. 100, Kansas City, MO 64112. TEL 816-756-1000. FAX 816-756-0494. Ed. Gordon Davidson. adv.; illus.; stat.; index, cum.index. circ. 4,340. **Indexed:** PROMT, SRI. —BLDSC (5774.100000).
 Formerly: Southwestern Miller (ISSN 0038-4879)

664.752 658 US ISSN 0897-6201
 CODEN: MOBAE3
MODERN BAKING. 1987. m. free to qualified personnel. Donohue - Meehan Publishing Company (Des Plaines), 2700 River Rd., Des Plaines, IL 60018. TEL 708-299-4430. FAX 708-296-1968. Ed. Ed Lee. adv.; bk.rev.; circ. 27,000. (controlled). **Document type:** trade publication.

664.7 SP ISSN 0026-900X
MOLINERIA Y PANADERIA. 1906. m. 9850 ptas. (Europe $135; elsewhere $220) (includes Panaderia Noticias). Montagud Editores, S.A., Ausias Marc 25, 1, 08010 Barcelona, Spain. TEL 318-20-82. FAX 302-50-83. Ed. Federico Montagud Bosoms. adv.; bibl.; illus.; tr.lit.; index. circ. 7,000. **Indexed:** Ind.SST. **Document type:** trade publication.

NATIONAL HONEY MARKET NEWS. see *BUSINESS AND ECONOMICS — International Commerce*

664.752 GW
DIE NEUE BAECKEREI. 1955. 6/yr. DM.60. Verlag F.H. Kleffmann GmbH, Rottstr. 1-3, 44793 Bochum, Germany. Ed. F.H. Kleffmann. adv.; bk.rev. circ. 3,000. **Document type:** trade publication.
 Formerly: Neue Feinbaeckerei.

664.752 AU
DER NEUE KONDITOR. 26/yr. Jaegerstr. 63, A-1200 Vienna, Austria. TEL 0222-3307505. FAX 0222-3307505-10. circ. 2,000. **Document type:** trade publication.
 Formerly: Konditor.

664.752 FR
NOUVELLES DE LA BOULANGERIE. 1890. s-m. 200 F. Societe d'Edition et de Publication "las Talmeliers" (S O T A L), Avenue d'Eylau, 75782 Paris Cedex 16, France. FAX 47-27-65-71. Ed. Jean Labut. circ. 30,000.
 Formerly: Ami de la Boulangerie (ISSN 0044-8087)

664.752 AU
OESTERREICHISCHE BAECKER ZEITUNG. 1905. w. S.730 (foreign S.1000). Florianigasse 21, A-1080 Vienna, Austria. TEL 0222-425339-0. FAX 0222-42345175. Ed. Heinz Vagovics. adv.: B&W page S.13400, color page S.21600; trim 266 x 185. circ. 3,300. **Document type:** trade publication, newspaper.

664.752 US ISSN 0030-8528
PACIFIC BAKERS NEWS. 1961. m. $16 (foreign $50). C.W. Soward, Ed. & Pub., 180 Mendell St., San Francisco, CA 94124-1740. TEL 415-826-2664. FAX 415-821-1070. adv.; mkt.; stat. circ. 3,000.

664.752 MX ISSN 0187-8492
PAN. 1953. m. $60. Bravo Grupo Editorial, S.A., J. Ma. Bustillos 49, Col. Algarin, 06880 Mexico, D.F., Mexico. TEL 5-530-6062. FAX 5-538-86-79. Ed. Lazaro Bravo Bernabe. adv. circ. 10,000. (back issues avail.)

664.752 MX ISSN 0187-8506
PAN DIRECTORIO DE PROVEEDORES/BREAD CATERERS' DIRECTORY. 1967. a. $20. Bravo Grupo Editorial, S.A., Jose Maria Bustillos 49, Colonia Algarin, 06880 Mexico, D.F., Mexico. Ed. Lazaro Bravo Bernabe. adv. circ. 10,000. **Document type:** trade publication.
 Description: Covers the wheat, flour, bread, bakery, crackers and pasta industries.

664.752 SP ISSN 0214-3984
PANADERIA NOTICIAS. 1988. m. 9850 ptas. (Europe $135; elsewhere $220) (includes Molineria y Panaderia). Montagud Editores, S.A., Ausias Marc, 25, 1, 08010 Barcelona, Spain. TEL 318-20-82. FAX 302-50-83. Ed. Federico Montegud Bosoms. adv.; index. circ. 7,000. **Document type:** trade publication.

664.15 SP
PANORAMA CONFITERO. 12/yr. Almirante 9, 28004 Madrid, Spain. TEL 1-521-51-94. FAX 1-521-21-77. Ed. Julian Uceda. circ. 5,000.
 Description: Reviews the confectionery, pastry and ice cream industries.

664.752 SP
PANORAMA PANADERO. 12/yr. Almirante 9, 28004 Madrid, Spain. TEL 1-521-51-94. FAX 1-521-21-77. Ed. Julian Uceda. circ. 60,000.

664.752 IT ISSN 0392-4718
PASTICCERIA INTERNAZIONALE. 1978. bi-m. L.80000($70) Chiriotti Editori, Viale Rimembranza 60, Box 66, Pinerolo 10064, Italy. TEL 121-794493. FAX 121-794480. Ed. Emilia Coccolo Chiriotti. adv.; bk.rev. circ. 16,000. **Indexed:** Dairy Sci.Abstr. —CCC.
 Description: Forum for bakers, confectioners and ice-cream makers. Contains technical- practical articles on raw materials and processing in pastry, confectionery, chocolate making, and the culinary art. Also includes new suggestions in ice-cream making.

664 FR
PATISSERIE BOULANGERIE VIE PRATIQUE. 19/yr. 4 rue Santerre, 75012 Paris, France. TEL 43-45-03-33. FAX 43-44-51-41. TELEX 612 009 F. Ed. Serge Benard. circ. 20,000.

664.752 FR
PATISSIER MODERNE. 6/yr. 39 rue de Valois, 75001 Paris, France. TEL 42-61-49-88. Ed. Madeleine Garnavault. adv. circ. 5,000.

664.752 US
PENNSYLVANIA BAKER. 1933. m. $15. Pennsylvania Bakers Association, 100 State St., Harrisburg, PA 17101-1034. Ed. Morna McEver Golletz. adv. contact: Brad Wastler. bk.rev.; tr.lit. circ. 400. (back issues avail.) **Document type:** newsletter.
 Description: Covers member activities, industry news, governemntal regulations and upcoming events.

664 PL ISSN 0033-2313
PRZEGLAD PIEKARSKI I CUKIERNICZY. 1953. bi-m. $30.50. Wydawnictwo Czasopism i Ksiazek Technicznych SIGMA - NOT, Ul. Ratuszowa 11, P.O. Box 1004, 00-950 Warsaw, Poland. TEL 48-22-180918. FAX 48-22-192187. TELEX 8145500 SIGMA PL. (Dist. by: SIGMA NOT Ltd., Ul. Bartycka 20, 00-716 Warsaw, Poland) Ed. Magdalena Mart. adv.: B&W page $1000. bk.rev.; charts; illus.; stat.; index, cum.index. circ. 1,200. **Indexed:** Dairy Sci.Abstr., Food Sci.& Tech.Abstr.
 Description: Covers sugar industry, baking technics, technology, and trade.

664.15 US
QUICK TOPICS NEWSLETTER. 12/yr. membership only. American Wholesale Marketers Association, 1128 16th St., N.W., Washington, DC 20036. TEL 202.463-2124. FAX 202-467-0559. adv.; circ. 4,200. **Document type:** newsletter.
 Description: Industry and association news.

664 658 US
RETAIL BAKERS OF AMERICA. GOVERNMENT BULLETIN. 1947. irreg. membership. Retail Bakers of America, 14239 Park Center Dr., Laurel, MD 20707-5261. TEL 301-725-2149. FAX 301-725-2187. Ed. Gerard Panaro. circ. 3,400. (looseleaf format; back issues avail.) **Document type:** bulletin.
 Description: Provides pertinent legislative information for bakers.

FOOD AND FOOD INDUSTRIES — GROCERY TRADE

664 658 US
RETAIL BAKERS OF AMERICA. RESEARCH & MERCHANDISING BULLETIN. 1947. m. membership. Retail Bakers of America, 14239 Park Center Dr., Laurel, MD 20707-5261. TEL 301-725-2149. FAX 301-725-2187. adv.; tr.lit.; cum.index: 1947-1988. circ. 3,400. (looseleaf format; back issues avail.) Document type: bulletin.
   Description: Merchandising information for retail bakeries.

RETAIL NEWSAGENT TOBACCONIST CONFECTIONER. see TOBACCO

664.752 PO
REVISTA PORTUGUESA DE PANIFICACAO. 12/yr. Rua do Crucifixo 31, 1o, Lisbon 2, Portugal.

664 UK
S I. (Snackfood International) 1981. q. £15 (foreign £17.50). J.G. Kennedy & Co. Ltd., 12 Blackstock Mews, Blackstock Rd., London N4 2BT, England. TEL 01-226-3423. FAX 01-354-5372. Ed. Margaret Lang. adv. circ. 3,000. Indexed: Food Sci.& Tech.Abstr. Document type: trade publication.
   Formerly: S M M (Snackfood Manufacture and Marketing).

664.1 RU ISSN 0036-3340
CODEN: SAPRAK
SAKHARNAYA PROMYSHLENNOST. 1923. bi-m. $25. Izdatel'stvo Kolos, Sadovaya-Spasskaya 18, 107807 Moscow, Russia. TEL 207-16-31. FAX 207-28-70. Ed. Mikhail Ya. Puzikov. bk.rev.; bibl.; charts; illus.; stat.; index. circ 2,000. (tabloid format) Indexed: Biol.Abstr., Chem.Abstr., Food Sci.& Tech.Abstr., Nutr.Abstr.

664.752 SZ
SCHWEIZERISCHE KONDITOR CONFISEURMEISTER ZEITUNG. Dr. H. Dutsch Bahnhofstr. 37, P.O. Box 880, 8022 Zurich, Switzerland. adv. circ. 1,500.

664 UK ISSN 0080-7974
SCOTTISH BAKERS' YEAR BOOK. 1894. a. membership. Scottish Association of Master Bakers, Atholl House, 4 Torphichen St., Edinburgh EH3 8JQ, Scotland. TEL 031-229-1401. adv.; bk.rev. circ. 1,100. Document type: trade publication.

664.952 JA
SEIKA SEIPAN. 1931. m. 16080 Yen. Seika Jikkensha Co., Ltd., 2-13-11 Minamishinagawa, Shinagawa-Ku, Tokyo 140, Japan. FAX 03-471-7604. Ed. Yoshimasa Kaneko. circ. 35,000.

SMALL RETAILER. see FOOD AND FOOD INDUSTRIES

664.752 US ISSN 0037-7406
TX761 CODEN: SNFOAI
SNACK FOOD. 1912. m. $45 (foreign $70)-$210) (free to qualified personnel). Stagnito Publishing Company, 1935 Shermer Rd., Ste. 100, Northbrook, IL 60062. TEL 708-205-5660. FAX 708-205-5680. Ed. Bob Harrison; Pub. Glen Stout. adv. contact: Suzette Gorski. bk.rev.; charts; illus.; stat.; index. circ. 13,500. Indexed: Int.Packag.Abstr., PROMT. Document type: trade publication.
   —UnCover.
   Formerly: Biscuit and Cracker Baker.
   Description: Covers management methods, marketing, production and packaging in the snack food industry.

664 SA ISSN 0038-1993
SOUTH AFRICAN BAKERY AND CONFECTIONERY REVIEW. Abbreviated title: S.A. Bakery and Confectionery Review. (Text in English) 1949. bi-m. R.80. George Warman Publications (Pty) Ltd., P.O. Box 3847, Cape Town 8000, South Africa. TEL 27-21-245320. FAX 27-21-261332. Ed. Tony Walker. adv. circ. 2,250. Document type: trade publication.
   Description: Covers baking, confectionery and milling in South Africa.

664.752 AT
SOUTH AUSTRALIAN BAKER AND PASTRYCOOK. 1969. biennial. (Baking Trade Federation of Australia, South Australian Branch) Percival Publishing Co. Pty. Ltd., 17 Currie St., Adelaide, S.A. 5000, Australia. Ed. James Fryer.

664.752 US ISSN 0038-688X
SPECIALTY BAKER'S VOICE.* 1928. m. $25. (Specialty Bakery Owners of America, Inc.) Specialty Bakers of America, 1568 Ralph Ave., Brooklyn, NY 11236-3129. TEL 212-227-7754. Ed. Paulette Gingold. adv.; illus. circ. 650.

664.07 UK
STUDENT BAKER. 1934. 5/yr. membership. National Federation of Bakery Students Societies, 54 Occombe Valley Rd., Paignton, Devon TQ3 IQU, England. Ed. Raymond J. Lloyd. adv.; abstr. circ. 4,000.
   Formerly: New Student Baker (ISSN 0005-4135)

664 GW ISSN 0039-4653
SUESSWAREN. 1957. m. DM.120. Rhenania-Fachverlag GmbH, Possmoorweg 5, 22301 Hamburg, Germany. FAX 040-2717-2069. TELEX 213214. Ed. Volker Herrmann. adv.; bk.rev.; charts; illus.; mkt.; stat.; index. circ. 2,279. Indexed: Chem.Abstr., Dairy Sci.Abstr., Food Sci.& Tech.Abstr., Key to Econ.Sci. Document type: trade publication.

664 IT
TUTTODOLCE; rivista italiana dell'alimentazione dolciaria. 1981. m. L.65000 (foreign L.85000). Editrice Graphos sas di R. D'Antonio & C., Corso Re Umberto 8, 10121 Turin, Italy. FAX 011-537040. Ed. Romualdo D'Antonio. adv. circ. 18,000.
   Description: Deals with the Italian field of confectionery.

UNITED STATES DISTRIBUTION JOURNAL; the news publication of tobacco, confectionery, grocery distribution. see TOBACCO

UNITED STATES DISTRIBUTION JOURNAL SUPPLIER DIRECTORY. see TOBACCO

664.752 638.1 SP ISSN 0213-1005
VIDA APICOLA; revista de apicultura. 1982. bi-m. 4250 ptas.($55) (Europe $50). Montagud Editores, S.A., Ausias Marc, 25, 1, 08010 Barcelona, Spain. TEL 318-20-82. FAX 302-50-83. Dir. Silvia Canas Lloria. adv.; index. circ. 7,000. Document type: trade publication.

664.752 FR
VIE DES METIERS;* de la boulangerie, patisserie, confiserie. 10/yr. 385 F. 21 rue Baudin, 34000 Montpellier, France. TEL 67-58-61-09. FAX 67-58-26-87. Ed. Gerard Vogel-Singer. adv. circ. 13,500.

664.752 BE ISSN 0773-0047
VIE PROFESSIONNELLE. Dutch Edition: Beroepsleven (ISSN 0773-0004) (Text in French) 1888. 11/yr. 4455 BEF. Confederation Belge de la Boulangerie, Patisserie, Chocolaterie, Glacerie, Bd. Louis Mettewie 83, Bte. 42, B-1000 Brussels, Belgium. TEL 32-2-4692908. FAX 32-2-4692140. adv.; bk.rev. circ. 6,000. Document type: trade publication.
   Formed by the merger of: Boulanger Belge - Belgische Bakker; Notre Metier - Ons Beroep.
   Description: News and information for producers, merchants, wholesalers, professional organizations and schools connected with the baking, pastry and ice cream trade in Belgium.

664.15 UK
WHOLESALE CONFECTIONERS' ALLIANCE. YEARBOOK. a. Wholesale Confectioners' Alliance, 12 Northcliffe Close, Worcester Park, Surrey, England. TEL 01-3304080.

641.8 US
WILTON YEARBOOK OF BAKING AND CAKE DECORATING. 1975. a. $5.99. Wilton Enterprises, 2240 W. 75th St., Woodridge, IL 60517. TEL 708-963-7100. FAX 708-963-7299. Ed. Jeff Shankman. adv.; illus. circ. 600,000.
   Former titles: Wilton Cake Decorating Yearbook; Celebrate; The Annual for Cake Decorators (ISSN 0361-0896)

664 GW ISSN 0373-0204
HD9999.C73 CODEN: ZUSUAN
ZUCKER- UND SUESSWAREN WIRTSCHAFT; Fachzeitschrift fuer alle Bereiche der Suesswaren-Industrie. (Text in German; summaries in English, French, German) 1948. m. DM.174. Verlag Eduard F. Beckmann KG, Postfach 1120, 31251 Lehrte, Germany. TEL 05132-8591-0. FAX 05132-859125. Ed. Heiner Behre. adv.; bk.rev.; illus. circ. 2,100. Indexed: Dairy Sci.Abstr., Food Sci.& Tech.Abstr., Packag.Sci.Tech., Sugar Ind.Abstr. Document type: trade publication.
   —BLDSC (9537.078000).

FOOD AND FOOD INDUSTRIES — Grocery Trade

658.8 AU ISSN 0001-8112
A D E G - KAUFMANN. 1955. m. S.150. A D E G-Oesterreich Handelsaktiengesellschaft, Postfach 561, Gaudenzdorfer Guertel 41-45, 1120 Vienna, Austria. Ed. Gernot Urbaner. adv. circ. 3,000.

658.8 US
A G NEWS.* 1955. m. $12 to non-members. Associated Grocers of Colorado Inc., 707 17th St., Ste. 2800, Denver, CO 80202-3428. Ed. Colleen M. Kirk. adv.; circ. 2,000 (controlled). (tabloid format)

A L A WORLDWIDE DIRECTORY AND FACT BOOK. (American Logistics Association) see MILITARY

658.878 US
ADVANCE NEWS FOR SUPERMARKETERS. 1957. m. free to qualified personnel. Family Circle, Inc. (Subsidiary of: New York Times Co., Inc.), 110 Fifth Ave., New York, NY 10011. TEL 212-463-1673. Ed. Stephen Roche. circ. 19,000.
   Description: Updates for industry of future ad campaigns in Family Circle magazines.

658.8 US ISSN 0002-421X
ALABAMA FOOD MERCHANTS JOURNAL. 1919. bi-m. $2.50. (Alabama Food Council) Southeast Publishers, 1631 Pinevale, Jackson, MS 39211. Ed. David Marshall. adv.; illus.; tr.lit.; circ. 875 (controlled). Document type: trade publication.

658.8 US
ALABAMA - MISSISSIPPI GROCERS' DIGEST. bi-m. Southeast Publishers, 1631 Pinevale, Jackson, MS 39211. TEL 601-366-3940. Ed. David Marshall. circ. 800. Document type: trade publication.

658.8 CN ISSN 0002-5410
ALIMENTATION AU QUEBEC. (Text in French) 1961. m. Can.$30. Les Editions du Marchand Quebecois Inc., 1298 Saint-Zotique St., Montreal, PQ H2S 2N7, Canada. TEL 514-271-6922. FAX 514-271-1308. Ed. Francoise Pitt. circ. 14,636. (tabloid format)
   Incorporates: Le Depanneur (ISSN 0828-8720)

658.8 AG
ALMACENERO. 1953. m. Editorial Moreno S.R.L., Diag. Julio A. Roca 733, 1067 Buenos Aires, Argentina. TEL 541-334-8857. circ. 12,000.

658.8 664.752 US
AMERICAN DELI-BAKERY NEWS. 18/yr. Jenkins Communications, Inc., Box 194130, San Francisco, CA 94119-4130. TEL 415-777-0604. Ed. Richard Kanes. Document type: trade publication.

658.8 SP ISSN 1133-1364
ARAL PLUS. 1967. w. 11000 ptas. (foreign 17000 ptas.). Tecnipublicaciones, S.A., Fernando VI, 27, 28004 Madrid, Spain. TEL 91-319 78 89. FAX 91-319-70-89. Ed. Alfonso Claveria. adv. circ. 12,000. Document type: trade publication.
   Formerly (until 1993): Aral (ISSN 1130-8109)
   Description: Covers marketing, sales, and business in the food and non-food beverage industries.

658.8 US ISSN 0004-1505
ARIZONA GROCER. 1944. m. $50. (Retail Grocers Association of Arizona) Arizona Grocers Publishing Co., 120 E. Pierce, Phoenix, AZ 85004. TEL 602-252-9761. FAX 602-252-9021. Ed. Rodney K. Platt. adv.; illus.; circ. 2,300 (controlled). Document type: trade publication.

FOOD AND FOOD INDUSTRIES — GROCERY TRADE

658.8   US   ISSN 0004-1815
ARKANSAS GROCER. vol.20, 1975. bi-m. $3. Arkansas Grocer Publishing Co., Box 7806, Pine Bluff, AR 71601. TEL 501-534-8803. Ed. George T. Anderson. adv.; circ. 3,000 (controlled). **Document type:** trade publication.

658.8   US
ARKANSAS GROCERS AND RETAIL MERCHANTS NEWS. m. Arkansas Grocers Association, 1123 South University, Ste. 718, Little Rock, AR 72204. TEL 501-664-8680. Ed. J.D. Harper. circ. 4,500. **Document type:** trade publication.

658.8   AG
AUTOSERVICIOS, SUPERMERCADOS & ALMACENEROS. (Includes supplement: Noticias) 1953. m. $200. Editorial Moreno S.R.L., Diag. Julio A. Roca 733, 1067 Buenos Aires, Argentina. TEL 54-1-334-8857. adv.; bk.rev. circ. 12,000.
    Former titles: Autoservicios y Almaceneros; Almaceneros.

658.8   US
B F C FLYER. 1975. 12/yr. $5. Boston Food Co-Operative, 449 Cambridge St., Allston, MA 02134. TEL 617-787-1416. Ed. Elizabeth MacKenzie. adv.; illus. circ. 2,000. **Document type:** newsletter.
    Description: Newsletter for the Boston Food Co-operative grocery store.

310.663   US   ISSN 1060-9180
▼**BEVERAGE AISLE.** 1992. m. Keller International Publishing Corporation, 150 Great Neck Rd., Great Neck, NY 11021. TEL 516-829-9210. FAX 516-829-5414. adv. circ. 20,000. **Document type:** trade publication.
    Description: Provides information for increasing the volume and profitability of beverages sold through retail outlets.

658.8   US   ISSN 1057-0411
C S P; the magazine for C-store people. 1990. m. $48 (Canada $60; elsewhere $100). Associated Business Publications, 41 E. 42nd St., Ste. 921, New York, NY 10017-5391. TEL 212-490-3999. FAX 212-986-7864. Ed. Faye Brookman. circ. 20,000. **Document type:** trade publication.

658.8   US
CALIFORNIA GROCER. m. California Grocers Association, Box 2671, Sacramento, CA 95812-2671. TEL 916-488-3545. Ed. David L. Heylen. circ. 7,000. **Document type:** trade publication.

658.8   CN   ISSN 0008-3704
         CODEN: CAGRE7
CANADIAN GROCER. 1886. m. Can.$41. Maclean-Hunter Ltd., Business Publication Division, Maclean-Hunter Bldg., 777 Bay St., Toronto, ON M5W 1A7, Canada. TEL 416-596-5772. FAX 416-593-3162. TELEX 062-19547. Ed. George Condon. adv.; illus.; stat. circ. 19,500. **Indexed:** Can.B.P.I. **Document type:** trade publication.

CAROLINA FOOD DEALER. see *FOOD AND FOOD INDUSTRIES*

658.8   UK
CASH & CARRY MANAGEMENT. 1982. m. £60. Winlove Publications Ltd., 4 High St., Croydon, Surrey CR0 1YA, England. TEL 081-688-2696. FAX 081-688-2726. Ed. Kirsti Corbett. circ. 3,940. (back issues avail.) **Document type:** trade publication.
    Description: Covers grocery, catering, C.T.N. drinks equipment.

658.86   UK   ISSN 0262-4648
CASH & CARRY WHOLESALER. 1969. 10/yr. £46. Winlowe Publications Ltd., 4 High St., Croydon, Surrey CR0 1YA, England. Ed. Kirsti Corbett. adv. circ. 3,980. **Document type:** trade publication.

658.8   FR   ISSN 0222-0377
CHARCUTERIE ET GASTRONOMIE. 1951. m. 664 F. Societe d'Editions et de Publications de l'Alimentation, 15 rue Jacques Bingen, 75017 Paris, France. TEL 44-29-90-61. adv. circ. 18,000.
    Formerly (until 1979): Charcuterie de France.

658.8   UK
CHECKOUT. 1991. 12/yr. £33 (Europe £60). Quadrant House, The Quadrant, Sutton, Surrey SM2 5AS, England. TEL 081-652-3258. FAX 081-652-8925. Ed. Bernadette Donaldson. circ. 22,312. **Document type:** trade publication.
    Description: Directed to the grocery trade sector, especially multiples, independent grocers, off-licenses and cash and carry.

658.8   UK   ISSN 0961-6039
CHECKOUT FRESH. 1990. 8/yr. £18 (overseas £30). Blakebeck Magazines, Quadrant House, The Quadrant, Sutton, Surrey SM2 5AS, England. TEL 44-81-652-3261. Ed. Gary Kitchener. adv. contact: Debbie Atwell. circ. 12,500. **Document type:** trade publication.
    Description: Informs readers of retailers, wholesalers, and importers of all aspects of fresh produce sourcing, supply, and retail.

658.8   US   ISSN 0009-8817
CLEVELAND FOOD DEALER. 1915. m. $12. Cleveland Food Dealers Association, Inc., 4204 Detroit Ave., Cleveland, OH 44113. TEL 216-961-4836. FAX 216-961-9302. Dir. Alvin J. Palack. adv.; B&W page $155. illus. circ. 792. **Document type:** trade publication.

658.8   IT
COMMA. 1981. m. (11/yr.) L.50000($30) (Consorzio Nazionale Dettaglianti) E.T.A. Edizioni Tecniche Associate, Via Michelino 65, 40127 Bologna, Italy. TEL 51-50-81-11. FAX 51-50-83-12. TELEX 510880 CONAD I. Ed. Camilo de Berardinis. adv.; bk.rev. circ. 20,000. **Document type:** trade publication.
    Description: Presents articles on distribution, marketing and promotions in the food industry.

658.8   UK   ISSN 0267-9361
CONVENIENCE STORE. vol.3, 1970. fortn. £45 (foreign £60). William Reed Ltd., Broadfield Park, Crawley, W. Sussex RH11 9RT, England. TEL 0293-613400. FAX 0293-613156. Ed. Tony Hurren. adv.; illus.; stat. circ. 48,475. **Document type:** trade publication.
    Former titles: Independent Grocery News; Independent Retailer and Caterer (ISSN 0261-0833); (until Jan. 1981): Cash and Carry News (ISSN 0008-7270)

658.8   US
CONVENIENCE STORE DECISIONS. * m. Donohue - Meehan Publishing Company (Bensalem), 2 Greenwood Sq., Ste. 410, 3331 Street Rd., Bensalem, PA 19020-2023. TEL 215-579-9770. Ed. Joe Barks. circ. 42,000. **Document type:** trade publication.

658.8   US   ISSN 0045-8422
CONVENIENCE STORE NEWS; the information source for the industry. 1969. 16/yr. (every 3 wks.). $60. B M T Communications, Inc., 7 Penn Plaza, New York, NY 10001-3900. TEL 212-594-4120. FAX 212-714-0514. Ed. Maureen Azzato. adv.; bk.rev.; illus. circ. 118,000. **Document type:** trade publication.

658.8   US   ISSN 0194-8733
         HD9321.2
CONVENIENCE STORE NEWS INDUSTRY REPORT. (Supplement avail.: Industry Report (ISSN 0895-4666)) 1969. a. $30. B M T Communications, Inc., 7 Penn Plaza, New York, NY 10001-3900. TEL 212-594-4120. FAX 212-714-0514. Ed. Maureen Azzato. adv. **Document type:** trade publication.
    —BLDSC (3463.138690).
    Formerly: Convenience Store Industry Report (ISSN 0084-9294)

COUPON TREASURE HUNT NEWSLETTER. see *CONSUMER EDUCATION AND PROTECTION*

658.8   DK   ISSN 0045-9615
DANSK HANDELSBLAD. 1909. w. DKK 350. (Samvirkende Koebmandsforeninger i Danmark - Danish Retail Grocers Association) Dansk Handelsblad, Fenrisvej 11, 8230 Aabyhoej, Denmark. Ed. Frands Hansen. adv. circ. 10,800. (tabloid format) **Document type:** trade publication.
    Description: Provides topical news and information on assortments, shop-management and concepts, shop-developments, space management, marketing and technology. Laws and ordinance concerning the trade, national and international trends within the grocery business.

658.8   US   ISSN 0011-7862
DELI NEWS. 1964. m. $25. (Delicatessen Council of Southern California, Inc.) Pacific Rim Publishing Co. (Huntington Beach), P.O. Box 4533, Huntington Beach, CA 92605-4533. FAX 714-375-3906. Ed. Dave Daniel. adv.; illus. circ. 6,000. **Document type:** trade publication.

658.8   SP
DETALLISTA. 12/yr. Union of Food Retailers, Jorge Juan 19, 1a planta, 28001 Madrid, Spain. TEL 1-435-92-20. FAX 1-575-79-27. Ed. R. Argudo Richart. circ. 10,000. **Document type:** trade publication.

DEUTSCHER LEBENSMITTELGROSSHANDEL; der Supermarkt, der Cash- und Carry-Grosshandel. see *FOOD AND FOOD INDUSTRIES*

DIRECTORIO NACIONAL DE ABASTECIMIENTO E INSUMOS PARA SUPERMERCADOS. see *BUSINESS AND ECONOMICS — Trade And Industrial Directories*

DIRECTORY OF FOODSERVICE DISTRIBUTORS (YEAR); includes: full-line food, equipment, supplies, specialty distributors. see *BUSINESS AND ECONOMICS — Trade And Industrial Directories*

DIRECTORY OF SINGLE UNIT SUPERMARKET OPERATORS (YEAR). see *BUSINESS AND ECONOMICS — Trade And Industrial Directories*

DIRECTORY OF SUPERMARKET, GROCERY & CONVENIENCE STORE CHAINS (YEAR); includes: market share. see *BUSINESS AND ECONOMICS — Trade And Industrial Directories*

658.8   GW   ISSN 0722-6950
DYNAMIK IM HANDEL. 1957. m. DM.106.30. E H I - EuroHandelsinstitut e.V., Spichernstr. 55, 50672 Cologne, Germany. TEL 0221-57993-0. FAX 0221-5799345. Ed. Dr. Bernd Hallier. adv.; bk.rev.; charts; illus.; stat.; index. circ. 9,375. (back issues avail.) **Indexed:** Key to Econ.Sci. **Document type:** trade publication.
    —BLDSC (3637.145000).
    Former titles: Selbstbedienung-Dynamik im Handel (ISSN 0343-3226); Selbstbtbedienung und Supermarkt (ISSN 0582-4761)

658.8   FR
EPICERIE FRANCAISE. 1975. 22/yr. 290 F. Syndicat de l'Epicerie Francaise et de l'Alimentation Generale, 12 rue du Renard, 75004 Paris, France. TEL 42-72-25-51. FAX 42-72-05-54. Ed. Henri Zannettacci. circ. 13,664.

658.8   CN   ISSN 0013-9521
L'EPICIER. (Text in French) 1946. 10/yr. Can.$28. Magazines MacLean Hunter Ltee., 75 rue de Port-Royal E., Ste. 200, Montreal, Que. H3L 3T1, Canada. TEL 514-382-2411. FAX 514-382-4356. Ed. Stephane Bourbonnais. adv.; charts; illus.; stat.; tr.lit. circ. 13,383. (back issues avail.)

658.8   FR
EPICIER DU NORD. 11/yr. 120 F. 26 rue Paul Duez, 59800 Lille, France. TEL 20-52-11-45. Ed. Claude Triquet. circ. 3,500. **Document type:** bulletin.

658.8   GW   ISSN 0179-8812
ERNAEHRUNGSWIRTSCHAFT (GRAEFELFING). 1954. 6/yr. DM.120 (foreign DM.140). E. Albrecht Verlags KG, Freihamer Str. 2, 82166 Graefelfing, Germany. TEL 089-858530. FAX 089-8585320. Ed. Rainer Hauzeneder. adv.; B&W page DM.3120, color page DM.4980; trim 185 x 255; adv. contact: Arend Fock. bk.rev.; charts; illus.; stat. circ. 5,950. **Document type:** trade publication.
    —BLDSC (3810.740000).

658.8 634   UK
EUROFRUIT MAGAZINE. (Text in English, French, German, Italian, and Spanish) 1973. 11/yr. $150. Market Intelligence Ltd., Market Towers, New Covent Garden Market, London SW8 5NQ, England. TEL 071-498-6711. FAX 071-498-6472. TELEX 8950975. Ed. Linda Bloomfield. adv.; bk.rev. circ. 7,000. **Document type:** trade publication.
    Formerly: Eurofruit.
    Description: Covers the marketing of fresh fruit and vegetables from producer through to retailer.

FOOD AND FOOD INDUSTRIES — GROCERY TRADE

658.8   GW   ISSN 0936-9775
EUROMAGAZIN. 1951. m. DM.108. E. Albrecht Verlags KG, Freihamer Str. 2, 82166 Graefelfing, Germany. Ed. Rainer Hauzeneder. adv.; bk.rev.; charts; illus.; stat.; tr.lit. circ. 4,847. Indexed: Key to Econ.Sci. **Document type:** trade publication.
    Former titles (until 1989): Food and Nonfood (ISSN 0343-3927); Lebensmittel-Grosshandel - Susswaren-Zeitung (ISSN 0023-9976)

658.8   UK   ISSN 0961-1320
EUROPEAN FOOD RETAILER. q. £60($90) Crier Publications Ltd., Arctic House, Rye Ln., Dunton Green, Sevenoaks, Kent TN14 5HB, England. TEL 44-732-451515. FAX 44-732-451383. Ed. Heather Buckle. adv. circ. 9,241. (back issues avail.) **Document type:** trade publication.
    Description: Covers most aspects of large food retailing industries in Europe.

658   UK
EUROPEAN FROZEN FOOD BUYER. (Text in English; summaries in French, German, Italian, Spanish) 6/yr. £65 (N. American subscr. $90 ($135)) (effective 1993). Crier Publications Ltd., Arctic House, Rye Ln., Dunton Green, Sevenoaks, Kent TN14 5HB, England. TEL 0732-451515. FAX 0732-451383. TELEX 95645. Ed. Heather Buckle. adv. contact: David Brenchley. circ. 10,820. (Back issues avail.) **Document type:** trade publication.
    Description: Concentrates on matters of interest to the buying function, including market trends and relevant legislation.

658.8   UK   ISSN 0014-2948
EUROPEAN GROCERY LETTER. 1964. 3/yr. Colin Scott, Ed. & Pub., 1 St. Paul's Close, Clitheroe, Lancashire BB7 2NB, England. adv.; bk.rev.; abstr.; charts; illus.; stat.

658.8   FR
EURORUNGIS ACTUALITES. 1969. 7/yr. 400 F. B.P. 349, 94154 Rungis Cedex, France. TEL 46-75-99-96. FAX 46-86-36-22. Ed. Philippe Gautier. adv. contact: Gerard Galloula. bk.rev. circ. 20,000. **Document type:** trade publication.
    Formerly: Rungis Actualites.

658.8   US
EXPORT BUYER'S GUIDE. 1984. a. Vance Publishing Corporation, 7950 College Blvd., Shawnee Mission, KS 66210. TEL 913-451-2200. FAX 913-451-5821. adv. circ. 4,838. **Document type:** trade publication, consumer publication.
    Description: Guide to and for exporters of North American produce.

658.878   US
F M I ANNUAL FINANCIAL REVIEW. 1973. a. $30 to non-members; members $15. Food Marketing Institute, 800 Connecticut Ave., N.W., Washington, DC 20006. TEL 202-452-8444. Ed. Judith Kozacik. **Document type:** corporate report.

658.8   US   ISSN 0275-8059
F M I ISSUES BULLETIN. 1977. m. $35 to non-members. Food Marketing Institute, 800 Connecticut Ave., N.W., Washington, DC 20006. TEL 202-452-8444. Ed. Judy Smith. circ. 4,000. (back issues avail.) **Document type:** newsletter.
    Incorporates (in vol.10, no.8, 1989): Industry News Briefs.
    Description: Covers issues and ideas important to the food distribution industry. Includes industry trends, interviews with business and government leaders, and information on programs and services provided by the institute.

664 658.8   US   ISSN 0732-233X
HF5469
FACTS ABOUT STORE DEVELOPMENT. 1953. a. $30 to non-members; members $15. Food Marketing Institute, 800 Connecticut Ave., N.W., Washington, DC 20006. TEL 202-452-8444. Ed. Judith Kozacik. (also avail. in microfiche from CIS) Indexed: Ref.Pt.Food Indus.Abstr., SRI. **Document type:** trade publication.
    Formerly: Facts about New Supermarkets (ISSN 0081-9522).

658.8   US   ISSN 1046-2880
CODEN: FAFOEQ
FANCY FOOD. 1984. m. $26. Talcott Communications Corporation, 20 N. Wacker Dr., Ste. 3230, Chicago, IL 60606-3102. TEL 312-849-2220. Ed. Paul Clark; Pub. Daniel von Rabenau. adv. circ. 19,000. **Document type:** trade publication.
    Formerly: Fancy Food and Candy.
    Description: Written and researched for specialty food buyers.

658.8   UK
FAST FOOD FACTS. (In 5 parts) 24/yr. Hannington Rd., Walgrave, Northampton NN6 9QF, England. TEL 0604-781392. FAX 0604-781188. Ed. Ian Bruce.

FEEDBACK. see *FOOD AND FOOD INDUSTRIES*

658.8 664   US   ISSN 0191-9857
FLORIDA FOOD DEALER. 1977. bi-m. $12 to non-members; members $5. Retail Grocers Association of Florida, 105 Live Oak Gardens, Ste. 101, Casselberry, FL 32707. TEL 407-339-7423. Ed. Andy Williams. adv. contact: Teri Elias. bk.rev. circ. 2,500. **Document type:** trade publication.
    Description: Covers supermarkets, convenience stores, and wholesale food industries in Florida.

658.8   US   ISSN 0191-586X
FLORIDA GROCER. Includes Spanish section: Bodeguero. 1956. m. $29. Florida Grocer Publications, Inc., Box 430760, S. Miami, FL 33243. TEL 305-441-1138. FAX 305-661-6720. Ed. Dennis M. Kane. adv.; bk.rev. circ. 16,000. **Document type:** newspaper, trade publication.

658.8   US
FOCUS (OVERLAND PARK). 1979. a. Vance Publishing Corporation, 7950 College Blvd., Overland Park, KS 66210. TEL 913-451-2200. FAX 913-451-5821. adv. circ. 16,188.
    Description: Reviews the produce industry. Highlights consumer research on fresh fruit and vegetable consumption.

658.8   UK
FOOD & DRINK DAILY. 320/yr. 2 Chester Close, Chester Ave., Richmond, Surrey TW10 6NR, England. TEL 081-948-3181. Ed. Doreen King. circ. 1,000.

658.8   AT   ISSN 0156-0352
FOOD AND LIQUOR RETAILER. 1911. bi-m. Aus.$20. Master Grocers' Association of Victoria Ltd., 1464 Ferntree Gully Rd., Knoxfield 3180, Victoria, Australia. TEL 03-765-1318. FAX 03-764-9216. Ed. Keith Billington. adv.; bk.rev.; charts; illus.; stat. circ. 2,000. **Document type:** trade publication.
    Formerly: Australasian Grocer (ISSN 0004-8356)

FOOD BROKER QUARTERLY. see *BUSINESS AND ECONOMICS — Marketing And Purchasing*

658.8   US   ISSN 8756-8772
FOOD BUSINESS MERGERS & ACQUISITIONS. 1970. a. $370. American Institute of Food Distribution, Inc., 28-12 Broadway, Fair Lawn, NJ 07410. TEL 201-791-5570. FAX 201-791-5222. Ed. Frank Panyko. **Document type:** trade publication.

FOOD HERALD. see *FOOD AND FOOD INDUSTRIES*

658.8   US   ISSN 0746-0783
FOOD INDUSTRY ADVISOR. 1970. m. $10. Pennsylvania Food Merchants Association, Box 870, Camp Hill, PA 17011. FAX 717-731-0609. Ed. Ed Conley. adv. circ. 15,000. **Document type:** trade publication.
    Formerly: P F M A Advisor (ISSN 0199-6428)

658.8 642.5   US
FOOD INDUSTRY NEWS. (Buyer's guide avail.) 1983. m. $18. Foodservice Publishing Co., Inc., 3166 S. River Rd., No. 40-44, Des Plains, IL 60018-4204. TEL 708-699-3300. FAX 708-699-3307. Ed. April Love-Bailey. adv. circ. 20,000. (tabloid format) **Document type:** newspaper, trade publication.

658.8   UK   ISSN 0962-7235
FOOD INDUSTRY NEWS. 1991. 12/yr. £50 (Europe £75; elsewhere £150) (effective Jan. 1994). Beacon Publishing, 95 Bridger Way, Crowborough, E. Sussex TN6 2XD, England. TEL 44-892-668172. FAX 44-892-668173. Ed. Stephen Blake. adv.; bk.rev. circ. 9,878. **Document type:** trade publication.
    Description: News and information about the food industry.

FOOD INDUSTRY STATISTICS DIGEST. see *FOOD AND FOOD INDUSTRIES — Abstracting, Bibliographies, Statistics*

664 658.8   US   ISSN 0190-3349
HD9321.1
FOOD MARKETING INDUSTRY SPEAKS. 1949. a. $50 to non-members; members $25. Food Marketing Institute, 800 Connecticut Ave., N.W., Washington, DC 20006. TE_ 202-452-8444. FAX 202-429-4529. Ed. Judith Kozacik. Indexed: Ref.Pt.Food Indus.Abstr. **Document type:** trade publication.
—Faxon.
    Formerly: Supermarket Industry Speaks (ISSN 0081-9530)

658.8   US   ISSN 0279-3105
FOOD MERCHANDISING FOR NON-FOOD RETAILERS. 1981. q. Lebhar-Friedman, Inc., 425 Park Ave., New York, NY 10022. TEL 212-756-5000. Ed. Liz Parks. stat.; index. circ. 30,000. (back issues avail.)

658.8   US   ISSN 0015-6493
CODEN: FMADEI
FOOD MERCHANTS ADVOCATE. 1883. m. New York State Food Merchants Association, 130 Washington Ave., Albany, NY 12210. TEL 518-434-1900. Ed. Christopher Pellnat. adv.; bk.rev.; illus.; mkt. circ. 27,000. (tabloid format) **Document type:** trade publication.

658.8   UK
FOOD RETAILERS: THE INTERNATIONAL MARKET. a. £1375($2750) Euromonitor, 87-88 Turnmill St., London EC1M 5QU, England. TEL 071-251-8024. FAX 071-608-3149. (Addr. in N. America: Euromonitor International, 111 W. Washington St., Ste. 920, Chicago, IL 60602. TEL 312-541-8024. FAX 312-541-1567) (looseleaf format) **Document type:** trade publication.
    ●Also available online. Vendor(s): Data-Star, DIALOG Information Services, Inc.
    Description: Analyzes the food retail market for France, Germany, Italy, Spain, the U.K., the U.S., and Japan.

658.8   US
FOOD RETAILING REVIEW. 1985. a. $340. American Institute of Food Distribution, Inc., 28-12 Broadway, Fair Lawn, NJ 07410. TEL 201-791-5570. FAX 201-791-5222. Ed. Frank Panyko. **Document type:** trade publication.

658.8   UK   ISSN 0141-1446
FOOD WORKER. 1898. 6/yr. £10. Bakers, Food & Allied Workers Union, Stanborough House, Great North Rd., Stanborough, Welwyn Garden City AL8 7TA, England. TEL 0707-250150. FAX 0707-261570. Ed. Joe Marino. circ. 11,500. **Document type:** trade publication.

658.8   US   ISSN 0191-619X
FOOD WORLD. 1947. m. $36. Best-Met Publishing Co., Inc., 5537 Twin Knolls Rd., Ste. 438, Columbia, MD 21045-3240. FAX 301-740-4680. Ed. Shari Simmon. adv. circ. 21,000. (tabloid format) **Document type:** trade publication.
    Description: Reports on the retail food industry in Maryland, Delaware, Virginia, southern Pennsylvania and the District of Columbia.

FOOD AND FOOD INDUSTRIES — GROCERY TRADE

658.8 NE ISSN 0165-1641
FOODMAGAZINE; vakblad voor de gehele levensmiddelendistributie. Short title: F M. (Text in Dutch) 1944. 20/yr. fl.219.50. Audet Tijdschriften bv (Subsidiary of: C. Misset B.V.), Postbus 9000, 6800 DA Arnhem, Netherlands. TEL 31-85-209911. FAX 31-85-233007. Ed. L. Traas. adv.: B&W page fl.5350, color page fl.8640; trim 215 x 285; adv. contact: Cor van Nek. abstr.; illus.; mkt.; stat. circ. 10,470. **Indexed:** Key to Econ.Sci. **Document type:** trade publication.
  Formerly: Kruidenier (ISSN 0023-494X)
  Description: Analyzes market and product developments as well as relevant national and international news; for grocery store owners and managers.

658.8 NE ISSN 0925-8760
FOODMAGAZINE - INTERNATIONAL. Key Title: F M - International. 10/yr. fl.359. Audet Tijdschriften bv (Subsidiary of: C. Misset B.V.), Postbus 9000, 6800 DA Arnhem, Netherlands. TEL 31-85-209911. FAX 31-850233007. Ed. F. Koelling. adv. contact: Cor van Nek. circ. 800. **Document type:** trade publication.
  Former titles (until 1990): Food Analysis (ISSN 0925-8752); (until 1983): Marktanalytische Gegevens (ISSN 0166-5650)
  Description: Covers international developments in the food distribution and marketing industries for Dutch management and marketing executives.

658.8 UK ISSN 0951-130X
FOODNEWS. (Supplement avail.) 1973. w. £495. Foodnews Co., 22a Sidcup High St., Sidcup, Kent DA14 6EH, England. FAX 01-302-8121. TELEX 8954109 FN LDN G. Ed. Godfrey Brown. circ. 2,500.

658.8 664 AT
FOODWEEK. 1966. w. Aus.$365. Ian Huntley Pty. Ltd., 233 Military Rd., Cremorne, N.S.W. 2090, Australia. TEL 61-2-953-5788. FAX 61-2-953-2280. (Subscr. to: P.O. Box 99, Cremorne, N.S.W. 2090, Australia) Ed. Murray White. stat.; index. (back issues avail.) **Document type:** newsletter.
  Description: Covers fresh, processed food manufacturing, wholesaling and retailing.

658.8 US
FRESH PRODUCE REFERENCE MANUAL. 1974. irreg. $198 to non-members; members $134. Produce Marketing Association, 1500 Casho Mill Rd., Box 6036, DE 19714-6036. TEL 302-738-7100. FAX 302-731-2409. Ed. Steve Ahlberg. **Document type:** trade publication.
  Former titles: Food Service Guide to Fresh Produce; Buyers Guide for Fresh Produce; Food Service Directory and Buyers Guide for Fresh Produce.

658.8 SW ISSN 0016-1217
FRI KOEPENSKAP. (Supplement avail.: Fri Koepenskap Butik & Miljoe) 1943. w. SEK 560. (Dagab Detaljinvest) Fri Koepenskaps Foerlag AB, P.O. Box 1301, 171 25 Solna, Sweden. FAX 08-83-45-88. Ed. J. Svahnstrom. adv.; bk.rev. circ. 18,000. **Document type:** trade publication.
  Description: Weekly newspaper for food retailers in Sweden.

658.8 DK ISSN 0901-2745
FRIT KOEBMANDSKAB. 1960. q. DKK 350. (Samvirkende Koebmandsforeninger - Dansih Retail Grocers Association) Dansk Handelsblad, Fenrisvej 11, 8230 Aabyhoej, Denmark. TEL 86 15 80 11. FAX 86-158252. adv. circ. 11,800. **Document type:** trade publication.

658.8 NO ISSN 0016-1519
FRITT KJOEPMANNSKAP. 1960. fortn. NOK 120. Norges Colonialgrossisters Forbund, Karl Johansgt. 1, 0154 Oslo 1, Norway. Ed. Arne Giverholt. adv.; illus.; stat. circ. 14,000. (tabloid format) **Document type:** trade publication.
  —CCC.

FRONT LINES (PORTLAND). see CONSUMER EDUCATION AND PROTECTION

380 GW ISSN 0016-6243
GEMISCHTWARENHANDEL; der Feinkost- und Delikatessenhandel. 1966. q. DM.48($20) Zeitungs- und Zeitschriftenverlag Heinrichs, Brueggekamp 1, 30890 Barsinghausen, Germany. TEL 05105-2289. Ed. G. Heinrichs. adv.; bk.rev.; abstr.; stat.; tr.lit. circ. 4,800. (tabloid format) **Document type:** academic/scholarly publication.

658.8 US
GEORGIA GROCER. s-a. Georgia Grocers Association, 3200 Highlands Pkwy, No. 210, Smyrna, GA 30082-5192. TEL 404-934-7650. FAX 404-438-7744. Ed. Kathy M. Kuzava. circ. 2,000.

658.8 UK
GOOD FOOD RETAILING. 1986. 10/yr. £20. Stanshead Publications, 177 Stanshead Rd., Caterham, Surrey CR3 6AJ, England. TEL 0883-345481. FAX 0883-3448383. Ed. Nicola Grimes. adv. circ. 7,307. **Document type:** trade publication.
  Description: Grocery magazine targeted directly at the buyers of food and drink.

GOURMET NEWS; the business newspaper for the gourmet industry. see FOOD AND FOOD INDUSTRIES — Bakers And Confectioners

658.8 UK ISSN 0017-4351
GROCER. 1861. w. £45 (Europe £90; elsewhere £160). William Reed Ltd., Broadfield Park, Crawley, W. Sussex RH11 9RT, England. TEL 0293-613400. FAX 0293-613304. Ed. Clive Beddall. adv.; bk.rev.; charts; illus.; mkt. circ. 56,274. **Indexed:** Art.Hosp.& Tour., Int.Packag.Abstr., Mgmt.& Market.Abstr., PROMT, Rural Recreat.Tour.Abstr., World Agri.Econ. & Rural Sociol.Abstr. **Document type:** trade publication.
  ●Also available online.
  —BLDSC (4217.830000). **CCC.**

658.8 UK ISSN 0964-0371
GROCER MARKETING DIRECTORY. 1954. a. £35. William Reed Ltd., Broadfield Park, Crawley, W. Sussex RH11 9RT, England. TEL 0293-613400. FAX 0293-613304. adv. contact: Belinda Marston. circ. 5,000. circ. 5,000 (paid). **Document type:** directory.
  Former titles: Grocer Directory; Grocer Directory of Multiples and Co-Operatives (ISSN 0072-7695)

658.8 CN ISSN 1196-0817
GROCER TODAY MAGAZINE. 1987. 9/yr. Can.$27. Canada Wide Magazines Ltd., 4180 Lougheed Hwy., Ste. 401, Burnaby, BC V5C 6A7, Canada. TEL 604-299-7311. FAX 604-299-9188. Ed. Nancy Ryder. adv. circ. 4,300.
  Former titles (until 1993): British Columbia, Alberta, Saskatchewan and Manitoba Grocer (ISSN 1193-3658); (until 1992): British Columbia and Alberta Grocer (ISSN 1185-0035); (until 1990): British Columbia Grocer (ISSN 0841-7679)

658.8 US ISSN 0160-8894
GROCERS REPORT. 1978. m. Supermarket Productions, Box 6124, San Rafael, CA 94903-0124. TEL 415-479-0211. Ed. Joan Adams. adv.; circ. 15,000 (controlled). **Document type:** trade publication.

658.8 US ISSN 0017-4416
GROCERY COMMUNICATIONS; showcase of the Western food industry. 1970. bi-m. $25. National Food Distribution Network Inc., 406 Water St., Warren, RI 02885. TEL 401-245-4500. Ed. Steve Pasto. adv.; illus.; charts; stat. circ. 19,000. **Document type:** trade publication.

658.8 US ISSN 0361-4034
HD9320.1
GROCERY DISTRIBUTION; the magazine of physical distribution and plant development for the food industry. 1975. bi-m. $30 (foreign $75). Grocery Market Publications, 455 S. Frontage Rd., Ste. 116, Meadowbrook Office Center, Burr Ridge, IL 60521. TEL 708-986-8767. FAX 708-986-0206. Ed. Richard W. Mulville. adv.; bk.rev. circ. 15,000. **Indexed:** Ref.Pt.Food Indus.Abstr. **Document type:** trade publication.
  Description: Provides direct medium for marketing equipment, fixtures and services to the food industry.

658.8 US
THE GROCERY INDUSTRY: PAST, PRESENT, AND FUTURE. 1990. a. $395. Dun & Bradstreet Information Services (Murray Hill) (Subsidiary of: Dun & Bradstreet, Inc.), One Diamond Hill Rd., Murray Hill, NJ 07974. TEL 908-665-5224. FAX 908-771-7599. Eds. Vic Bongard, Sharon Cross.
  Description: Provides insight into the evolution of the grocery industry and financial analysis of individually-owned, medium-sized, or chain stores.

658.8 UK
GROCERY MARKET BULLETIN. m. £135 to personal members; company members £90; non-members £120. Institute of Grocery Distribution, Business Publications, Letchmore Heath, Watford, Herts. WD2 8DQ, England. TEL 0923-857141. FAX 0923-857141. **Indexed:** Cont.Pg.Manage. **Document type:** trade publication.
  Description: Includes features, business, financial and IGD news.

658.8 US ISSN 0888-0360
HD9321.1 CODEN: GRMAED
GROCERY MARKETING; the newspaper for the food industry. 1933. m. $68. Delta Communications Inc. (Subsidiary of: Cahners Publishing Company), Division of Reed Elsevier Inc., 455 N. Cityfront Plaza Dr., 24th Fl., Chicago, IL 60611. TEL 312-222-2000. FAX 312-222-2026. Ed. Ryan Mathews. adv. circ. 63,032. (tabloid format) **Indexed:** Ref.Pt.Food Indus.Abstr. **Document type:** trade publication.
  ●Also available online. Vendor(s): Mead Data Central, Inc.
  —UMI.
  Formerly: Grocers' Spotlight (ISSN 0017-4394)

658.8 US ISSN 1069-2568
GROCERY SERVICES REPORT. 1990. q. $10. 6401 Windsor Dr., Ste.104, Acworth, GA 30101. TEL 404-516-1124. FAX 404-516-0359. Ed. D. Lee Finch. adv.: B&W page $255; trim 8 x 10; adv. contact: Lynn Martis. circ. 5,000. **Document type:** trade publication.
  Description: Provides companies who provide a service or services to the food industry with pertinent information.

GUIDOR. (Guide Annuaire Officiel du Complexe de Rungis) see BUSINESS AND ECONOMICS — Trade And Industrial Directories

658.8 US
GULF COAST RETAIL GROCER; voice of the independent grocer. vol.27, 1972. m. $1. Retail Grocers Association of Houston, Inc., 1300 Sheperd Dr., Houston, TX 77007. TEL 713-862-3001. FAX 713-862-5296. Ed. Rick Johnson. adv.; tr.lit. circ. 2,000. **Document type:** trade publication.
  Formerly: Houston Retail Grocer.

658.8 UK
HEALTH RETAILER. 1989. m. £30. Freeway Publishing Services, The Old Auction Mart, Station Approach, Godalming, Surrey GU7 1EU, England. TEL 0483-860116. FAX 0483-860938. Ed. Sue Webb. adv.: 1550; adv. contact: Nigel Cross. bk.rev. circ. 3,000. (tabloid format; back issues avail.) **Document type:** trade publication.
  Description: Offers advice to independent retailers of natural health products.

658.8 US
HISPANIC MARKET NEWS. (Text in English, Spanish) 1987. m. free to qualified personnel. Productive Media Publishers, Inc., 9 W. Eighth St., Bayonne, NJ 07002-1201. TEL 201-795-4143. Ed. Mark Vila. adv. circ. 18,000. **Document type:** trade publication.
  Description: Addresses the food trade in the metro New York market. Contains information for business executives in manufacturing, retailing and distributing.

658.8 UK
HYPERMARKETS AND SUPERSTORES: THE INTERNATIONAL MARKET. a. £1375($2750) Euromonitor, 87-88 Turnmill St., London EC1M 5QU, England. TEL 071-251-8024. FAX 071-608-3149. (Addr. in N. America: Euromonitor International, 111 W. Washington St., Ste. 920, Chicago, IL 60602. TEL 312-541-8024. FAX 312-541-1567) (looseleaf format) **Document type:** trade publication.
  ●Also available online. Vendor(s): Data-Star, DIALOG Information Services, Inc.
  Description: Analyzes the market for large retail outlets in France, Germany, Italy, Spain, the U.K., the U.S., and Japan.

658.8 US ISSN 0018-9766
I G A GROCERGRAM. (Independent Grocers Alliance) 1926. m. $24. Pace Communications Inc., 1301 Carolina St., Greensboro, NC 27401. TEL 919-378-6065. FAX 919-275-2864. Ed. Mickey McLean. adv.; bk.rev. circ. 16,000. **Document type:** trade publication.

FOOD AND FOOD INDUSTRIES — GROCERY TRADE

I S. (Interservice) see *MILITARY*

658.8   UK   ISSN 0261-524X
INDEPENDENT GROCER; business magazine for all independent convenience and licensed grocers. 1981. 2/mo. £60 (foreign £72). Reed Business Publishing Group (Subsidiary of: Reed Elsevier group), Quadrant House, The Quadrant, Sutton, Surrey SM2 5AS, England. TEL 081-652-8754. Ed. Jim Muttram. circ. 40,425. (back issues avail.)
Document type: trade publication.
Description: Presents news, views and features for independent grocers running their own businesses.

658.8   US   ISSN 0895-4666
INDUSTRY REPORT (NEW YORK). (Supplement avail.: Convenience Store News Industry Report (ISSN 0194-8733)) s-a. $30. B M T Communications, Inc., 7 Penn Plaza, New York, NY 10001-3900. TEL 212-594-4120. FAX 212-714-0514. Ed. Maureen Azzato.

INSTITUTO DE TECNOLOGIA DE ALIMENTOS. ESTUDOS ECONOMICOS. ALIMENTOS PROCESSADOS. see *FOOD AND FOOD INDUSTRIES*

658.8   US   ISSN 1040-578X
INTERMOUNTAIN RETAILER. 1924. bi-m. $12. Utah Retail Grocers Association, 1578 West 1700 South, Salt Lake City, UT 84104. TEL 801-973-9517. FAX 801-972-8712. Ed. James V. Olsen. adv.; illus. circ. 1,500.
Formerly: Intermountain Food Retailer (ISSN 0020-5680)

658.8   UK   ISSN 0952-293X
INTERNATIONAL CHIPS SNACKS MANAGEMENT. 1986. 4/yr. Lion House, 4 Russell St., Leek, Staffs ST13 5JF, England. TEL 0538-399155. FAX 0538-382165. Ed. Chris Horton. bk.rev. circ. 2,000.

658.86 658   UK
INTERNATIONAL NEW PRODUCT REPORT. 1972. 24/yr. £550 (outside Europe £600). Mintel International Group Ltd., 18-19 Long Lane, London EC1A 9HE, England. TEL 071-606-4533. FAX 071-606-5932. Ed. David Jago. illus. **Document type:** consumer publication.
Former titles: New Product Report; European New Product Report.
Description: Report on new products worldwide.

658.8   US
IOWA GROCER. 1932. s-m. $25. Iowa Grocers Association, 2894 106th St., Ste. 102, Des Moines, IA 50322-3771. TEL 515-270-2628. Ed. Chris Killough. adv.: B&W page $510, color page $1110; trim 8 1/2 x 11. circ. 2,500.
Formerly: Iowa Food Dealer.
Description: For independent and chain grocers, convenience store owners and managers, key warehouse personnel servicing Iowa, food brokers, manufacturers and salespersons.

658.8   US   ISSN 0022-8516
KANSAS CITY GROCER.* 1913. m. $1. Retail Grocers Association, 2809 W. 47th St., Shawnee Mission, KS 66205. Ed. H.E. Richardson. adv.; illus. circ. 1,825.

658.8   US
KANSAS CITY GROCER ANNUAL FOOD INDUSTRY DIRECTORY.* 1957. a. $1.50. Retail Grocers Association, 2809 W. 47th St., Mission, KS 66205. adv. circ. 2,400.

658.8   US   ISSN 0022-8605
KANSAS FOOD DEALERS BULLETIN.* 1927. m. $5. Kansas Food Dealers Association, 2809 W. 47th St., Shawnee Mission, KS 67205. Ed. Lee E. Circle. adv.; illus. circ. 1,800.

658.8   NO   ISSN 0332-7078
KJOETTBRANSJEN. m. NOK 250. Kjoettbransjens Landsforbund, Postbox 6279, Etterstad, N-0603 Oslo, Norway. TEL 47-22-570-011. FAX 47-22-57-14-14. **Document type:** trade publication.

658.87   BE   ISSN 0046-2357
KRUIDENIER/EPICIER. (Text in Dutch and French) 1958. m. Misset Belgium, Savaanstraat 92, 9000 Ghent, Belgium. Ed. Mark DeBlock. adv. circ. 28,000.

658.8   GW   ISSN 0941-3537
L P INTERNATIONAL. 1991. fortn. DM.516. Lebensmittel Praxis Verlag GmbH, Postfach 1861, 56508 Neuwied, Germany. TEL 02631-879-0. FAX 02631-879175. TELEX 867731-ELPEE-D. Eds. Rainer Rutsche, Matthias Kersten. bk.rev.; illus.; index.; stat. **Document type:** newsletter.

658.8   IT   ISSN 0392-131X
LARGO CONSUMO. 1981. m. (11/yr.) L.220000 (foreign L.500000). Editoriale Largo Consumo s.r.l., Via Bodoni 2, 20155 Milan, Italy. TEL 02-3271646. FAX 02-3271840. TELEX 334497 LARCON I. Ed. Pier Carlo Garosci. adv. circ. 44,000.
Formerly: Largo Consumo Multicanale.

658.8   GW   ISSN 0023-9992
LEBENSMITTEL PRAXIS; das Magazin fuer den Handel. 1949. fortn. DM.105.60. Lebensmittel Praxis Verlag GmbH, Postfach 1861, 56508 Neuwied, Germany. TEL 02631-879-0. FAX 02631-879175. TELEX 867731-ELPEE-D. Eds. Rainer Rutsche, Matthias Kersten. adv. contact: Guenter Scheffel. bk.rev.; illus.; stat.; index; circ. controlled. **Indexed:** Key to Econ.Sci. **Document type:** trade publication.
—BLDSC (5179.623800).

658.8   AU   ISSN 0047-4282
DER LEBENSMITTELKAUFMANN. 1971. w. S.848. Oesterreichischer Wirtschaftsverlag, Nikolsdorfer Gasse 7-11, A-1051 Vienna, Austria. TEL 0222-555585. TELEX 1-11669. Ed. Dieter Koffler. circ. 21,200 (controlled). **Document type:** trade publication.
Incorporates: Lebensmittelhaendler (ISSN 0024-001X) & Lebensmittelpost (ISSN 0024-0036)

658.8   DK   ISSN 0105-6654
LEVNEDSMIDDELBLADET - SUPERMARKEDET/FOODSTUFF MAGAZINE - THE SUPERMARKET. 1962. m. (11/yr.). DKK 580. Forlaget Beilin og Johansen ApS, 1, Rosenborggade, 1130 Copenhagen K, Denmark. TEL 33 15 22 77. FAX 33-15-93-43. ED. Stig Juul Hesselaa. adv.; charts; illus.; circ. 7,063 (controlled). **Document type:** trade publication.
Formerly: Levnedsmiddelbladet (ISSN 0024-1571)
Description: Presents material of interest to individuals concerned with slaughterhouses and factories for canned meat and fish in Denmark, Norway and Sweden; supermarkets and minimarkets in Denmark; shops and other establishments in the food industry and trade, and associated suppliers, organizations and institutions.

658.8   US
LOSS PREVENTION NEWSLETTER FOR SUPERMARKET EXECUTIVES. m. $50 to non-members; members $25. Food Marketing Institute, 800 Connecticut Ave., N.W., Washington, DC 20006. TEL 202-452-8444. **Document type:** newsletter.

658.8   UK
▼**MARDEK GUIDE TO THE U K GROCERY TRADE.** 1993. a. £395. William Reed Ltd., Broadfield Park, Crawley, W. Sussex RH11 9RT, England. TEL 0293-613400. FAX 0293-613304. **Document type:** directory.

658.8   IT   ISSN 0391-7398
MARKET ESPRESSO; il giornale per gli operatori del commercio. 1973. fortn. L.50000 (foreign L.95000). Etas s.r.l., Via Mecenate, 89, 20138 Milan, Italy. TEL 02-58084-1. FAX 02-58012592. TELEX 331321 ETASPE I. Ed. Aldo Rotta. adv.: B&W page L.8833000; trim 266 x 388. abstr.; bibl.; charts; illus.; stat.; tr.lit. circ. 42,000.

658.8   IT
MARKET ESPRESSO FLASH. (Supplement to: Market Espresso; In 3 editions: Dettaglio Moderno, Operatori Intermedi, Dettaglio Tradizionale) a. Etas s.r.l., Via Mecenate, 89, 20138 Milan, Italy. TEL 02-58084-1. FAX 02-58012592. TELEX 331342 ETASPE I. adv. circ. 140,000.

664   MX
MAYOREO Y DISTRIBUCION. 1979. m. Mex.$70 (US $50; Europe $90). Producciones Manila, S.A., Baja California 32-A, Col. Roma, Deleg. Cuauhtemoc, 06760 Mexico, D.F., Mexico. TEL 525-564-7040. FAX 525-574-5696. Ed. Graciela Diaz Serrano. adv. circ. 5,000.

658.8   US   ISSN 0894-8097
MEXICAN AMERICAN GROCERS ASSOCIATION. MAGAZINE (Text in English, Korean, Spanish) 1987. m. $35 (typically set in Dec.). Mexican American Grocers Association, 405 N. San Fernando Rd., Los Angeles, CA 90031. TEL 213-227-1565. FAX 213-227-6935. Ed. Jerome Wilson Lloyd; Pub. Steven Soto. adv. contact: David Villafana. circ. 8,500. **Document type:** trade publication.
Description: Helps grocers in the Hispanic community to improve the operation of their outlets.

658.8   US   ISSN 1058-8620
MILITARY GROCER. 1991. bi-m. $40 (effective 1992). Downey Communications, 4800 Montgomery Ln., No. 710, Bethesda, MD 20814. TEL 301-718-7600. FAX 301-718-7652. Ed. C.J. Moore. adv.: E&W page $2850, color page $3350. circ. 12,000 (controlled). **Document type:** trade publication.
Description: Contains news and information about Defense Commissary Agency (DECA) issues, programs, policies and events. Features articles on how to enhance store management, improve merchandising and maintain customer service.

658.8   US
MINNESOTA GROCER. 1929. bi-m. $30 to non-members. Minnesota Grocers Council, Inc., 533 Saint Clair Ave., St. Paul, MN 55102-2857. FAX 612-228-1949. Ed. Randy Schubring. adv.; illus. circ. 4,500. **Document type:** trade publication.
Former titles: Minnesota Food Guide (ISSN 0026-5489)
Description: Informs people on issues of marketing trends in their industry.

658.8   US   ISSN 0026-6264
MISSISSIPPI GROCERS' GUIDE. 1954. q. $2.50. Mississippi Retail Grocers Association, 1631 Pinevale, Jackson, MS 39211. Ed. W.R. Read. adv.; stat.; tr.lit.; circ. 1,075 (controlled). (reprint service avail.)
Description: Edited for persons that sell products to consumers through retail grocery outlets.

658.8   US
MISSOURI GROCER. 1940. m. $15. Missouri Retail Grocers Association, Box 10223, Springfield, MO 65808. Ed. George Dillard.

658.8   US   ISSN 0026-7805
MODERN GROCER. 1921. s-m. $36. Grocers Publishing Co., Inc., 15 Emerald St., Hackensack, NJ 07601. TEL 201-488-1800. Ed. Howard Ackerman. adv.; illus.; mkt. circ. 19,712. (tabloid format) **Document type:** trade publication.
Incorporates: Snack Foods Merchandiser (ISSN 0037-7414)
Description: Provides news and information to chain store executives, buyers, wholesalers, distributors, manufacturers and brokers in the states of New York and New Jersey.

N A S F T SHOWCASE. (National Association for Specialty Food Trade, Inc) see *FOOD AND FOOD INDUSTRIES*

NATURAL HEALTH HANDBOOK; the retailer's guide to natural products. see *ALTERNATIVE MEDICINE*

658.8   NO
NORGES KJOEBMANNSBLAD. 1918. w. (45/yr.). NOK 180. (Norges Kolonial- og Landhandelforbund) Norges Kjoebmannsblad A-S, Drammensveien 30, Oslo 2, Norway. Ed. Leif B. Petersen. adv. circ. 9,190. **Document type:** trade publication.

658.8   UK
NORTH AMERICAN NEW PRODUCT REPORT. 24/yr. $495. I I S Galbraith, Inc., 13-19 Long Lane, London EC1A 9HE, England. TEL 4471-606-4533. FAX 4471-606-5932.

658.8   US
OKLAHOMA GROCERS JOURNAL. 1940. m. $5. Oklahoma Grocers Association, 25 N.E. 52, Box 18716, Oklahoma City, OK 73154. TEL 405-525-9419. Ed. Elden G. Roscher. adv. circ. 1,500.
Formerly (until Jan. 1989): Oklahoma Food Journal.

OPERATING RESULTS OF INDEPENDENT SUPERMARKETS. see *BUSINESS AND ECONOMICS — Small Business*

FOOD AND FOOD INDUSTRIES — GROCERY TRADE

658.8   US
OREGON FOOD JOURNAL. 1980. bi-m. $25 to non-members in Oregon; out-of-state $35. Association of Oregon Food Industries, Inc., Box 12847, Salem, OR 97309-0847. TEL 503-363-3768. FAX 503-363-5433. Ed. Dian Cox. adv. circ. 3,800. **Document type:** trade publication.

PRAIRIE NEWS. see *FOOD AND FOOD INDUSTRIES*

658.8   SW   ISSN 0345-9071
PRAKTISKT BUTIKSARBETE. 1941. m. SEK 475 (effective 1991). I C A -Foerlaget AB, 721 85 Vaesteraas, Sweden. Ed. Gunnar Holmberg. adv. circ. 17,500. **Document type:** trade publication.
   Formerly (until vol.10, 1969): I C A - Tidningen (ISSN 0347-3899)

PRIVATE LABEL; the magazine for house brands and generics. see *BUSINESS AND ECONOMICS — Production Of Goods And Services*

PRIVATE LABEL INTERNATIONAL; the magazine for store labels (own brands) and generics. see *BUSINESS AND ECONOMICS — Production Of Goods And Services*

658.8   US
PRODUCE AVAILABILITY AND MERCHANDISING GUIDE. 1893. a. $20 (foreign $25) with weekly newspaper Packer. Vance Publishing Corporation, 7950 College Blvd., Shawnee Mission, KS 66210. TEL 913-451-2200. FAX 913-451-5821. Ed. Bill O'Neill. adv. circ. 15,000.
   Description: Over 400 pages listing commodity and supply sources for fresh produce.

658.8 635.9   US   ISSN 0886-5663
                    CODEN: PRBSE9
PRODUCE BUSINESS; the international business magazine serving the fruit, vegetable and floral industries. 1985. m. $48 (effective Oct. 1988). Multipress International, Inc., 301 Yamato Rd., Ste. 4110, Boca Raton, FL 33431. TEL 407-241-4333. FAX 407-241-4486. Ed. James E. Prevor. adv.; bk.rev.; illus. circ. 19,000. (back issues avail.) **Document type:** trade publication.
   Description: Covers marketing, merchandising and management in the fresh fruit, vegetable, dried fruit, nut, floral and foliage industries.

658.8 639   FR
PRODUITS DE LA MER. 7/yr. 13 rue du Breil, B.P. 6305, Z I Rennes-Chantepie, 35063 Rennes Cedex, France. TEL 99-32-09-09. FAX 99-41-89-57. Ed. Patrick Bernard. circ. 9,000.
   Description: Covers the processing, marketing and distribution of fish and other seafood.

658.8   UK
PROFESSIONAL WHOLESALER. 12/yr. Federation of Wholesale Distributors, 36 The Gofts, Eastbourne, E. Sussex BN21 1HD, England. TEL 0323-24952. FAX 0323-32820. Ed. Alan Toft. **Document type:** trade publication.

658.8   US   ISSN 0033-0787
TX343
PROGRESSIVE GROCER; the magazine of supermarketing. 1922. m. $75. Trade Dimensions, 263 Tresser Blvd., Stamford, CT 06901. TEL 203-977-7600. FAX 203-977-7645. Ed. Michael Sansolo. adv.; charts; illus.; stat.; tr.lit. circ. 72,000. (also avail. in microform from UMI; microfiche from CIS; back issues avail.) **Indexed:** B.P.I., Bus.Ind., Hlth.Ind., Key to Econ.Sci., Ref.Pt.Food Indus.Abstr., SRI, Tr.& Indus.Ind. **Document type:** trade publication.
   ●Also available online. Vendor(s): DIALOG Information Services, Inc., Mead Data Central, Inc. —BLDSC (6924.661000); Faxon; UnCover; UMI.

658.8   US
PROGRESSIVE GROCER'S ANNUAL REPORT OF THE GROCERY INDUSTRY. a. $15. Maclean Hunter Publishing Company, 263 Tresser Blvd., Stamford, CT 06901. TEL 203-325-3500. FAX 203-325-4377. adv.; charts; circ. 70,049 (controlled).
   Formerly: Progressive Grocer's Annual Report of the Grocery Trade.

QUICK FROZEN FOODS INTERNATIONAL. see *FOOD AND FOOD INDUSTRIES*

658.8   UK
RETAIL GROCER. 12/yr. Northern Ireland Grocers Association, 9 Upper Crescent, Belfast BT7 1NT, N. Ireland. TEL 0232-230425. FAX 0232-243595. Ed. Elizabeth Gilpiw. circ. 4,200. **Document type:** trade publication.

658.8   AT   ISSN 0034-6136
RETAIL WORLD. 1947. fortn. Aus.$105. Retail World Pty. Ltd., 114 Terry St., Rozelle, N.S.W. 2039, Australia. TEL 02-555-1577. FAX 02-810-8004. Ed. Barry Flanagan. adv.; bk.rev.; charts; illus.; stat. circ. 15,936. (tabloid format; back issues avail.) **Document type:** trade publication.
   Description: Comprehensive coverage of developments in the food and beverage industries.

658.8   AT   ISSN 0034-6144
RETAILER OF QUEENSLAND. 1936. m. Aus.$60. Magazine Publishing Co., 2nd Fl., 4 Wandoo St., Fortitute Valley, Qld. 4006, Australia. TEL 07-252-4667. FAX 07-252-9677. Ed. I.F. Baldock. adv.; bk.rev. circ. 5,500. **Document type:** trade publication.
   Incorporates: Queensland Shopkeeper (ISSN 0033-622X)

658.8   US   ISSN 0035-7588
ROCKY MOUNTAIN FOOD DEALER.* 1907. m. $15. Rocky Mountain Food Dealers Association, 1370 Pennsylvania St., ste. 320, Denver, CO 80203-5022. TEL 303-830-7001. Ed. Gaylord Hanson. adv.; illus.; circ. 1,400 (controlled).

658.8   US
ROCKY MOUNTAIN FOOD DEALER ASSOCIATION. BULLETIN.* bi-m. Rocky Mountain Food Dealers Association, 1370 Pennsylvania St., Ste. 320, Denver, CO 80203-5022. **Document type:** trade publication, bulletin.

658.8   GW   ISSN 0939-6209
RUNDSCHAU; fuer den Lebensmittelhandel. 1935. m. DM.36 (foreign DM.42). E. Albrechts Verlags KG, Freihamer Str. 2, 82166 Graefelfing, Germany. TEL 089-85853-0. FAX 089-8585320. Ed. Rainer Hauzeneder. adv.: B&W page DM.13080, color page DM.22920; trim 185 x 255; adv. contact: Arend Fock. circ. 60,000. **Document type:** trade publication.

S N DISTRIBUTION STUDY OF GROCERY STORE SALES. see *FOOD AND FOOD INDUSTRIES*

658.8   UK   ISSN 0036-9233
SCOTTISH GROCER. 1928. m. £28.60. Peebles Publishing Group Ltd., Bergius House, Clifton St., Glasgow G3 7LA, Scotland. TEL 041-331-1022. FAX 041-331-1395. adv.; illus. **Document type:** trade publication.

658.8   US   ISSN 0194-1968
SHELBY REPORT OF THE SOUTHEAST. 1967. m. $25. Shelby Publishing Co., Inc., 517 Green St., Gainesville, GA 30501. TEL 404-534-8380. FAX 404-535-0110. Ed. L. Griffith. adv.; bk.rev. circ. 25,000.

658.8   US
SHELBY REPORT OF THE SOUTHWEST. 1977. m. $25. Shelby Publishing Co., Inc., 517 Green St., Gainesville, GA 30501. TEL 404-534-8380. Ed. L. Griffith. adv. circ. 20,000. (tabloid format; back issues avail.)

SMALL RETAILER. see *FOOD AND FOOD INDUSTRIES*

658.8 338   US
THE SOURCE (ABINGTON). 1986. bi-m. $12. P G A Services, Co. (Subsidiary of: Pennsylvania Grocers Development Fund Inc.), 1913 Guernsey Ave., Abington, PA 19001-3701. TEL 215-884-6006. Ed. John McNelis. adv. circ. 1,000. **Document type:** newsletter.
   Description: Provides information for retailers, with a focus on coupons and promotions.

658.8   US
SOUTH CAROLINA FOOD JOURNAL.* 1972. bi-m. $5. Food Retailers Association of South Carolina, 936 S. Stadium Rd., Columbia, SC 29201-4725. FAX 800-765-9854. Ed. William D. Platt. adv. circ. 1,000.

658.8   US
SOUTHERN SUPERMARKETING. 1968. q. $5. Southern Living, Inc., 2100 Lakeshore Dr., Birmingham, AL 35201. TEL 205-877-6320. Ed. Stephanie Duke. adv.: B&W page $970, color page $1370; trim 8 3/8 x 10 7/8. charts; illus.; stat.; circ. 6,500 (controlled). **Document type:** trade publication.

658.8   UK
SPAR TODAY. 12/yr. 32-40 Headstone Dr., Harrow, Middlesex HA3 5QT, England. TEL 081-863-5511. FAX 081-863-0603. TELEX 923215-SPAR-HA. Ed. Tina Carey. circ. 7,500.

658.86   SP
SPARCO; revista tecnica mensual de la distribucion. 1960. m. 1850 ptas. SPAR Espanola S.A., Apdo. 50878, Madrid, Spain.

658.8   US   ISSN 0194-1429
                    CODEN: SFMEE5
SPECIALTY FOOD MERCHANDISING.* 1971. m. $27. Tarter Communications, Inc., 28 Solar Ln., Albertson, NY 11507-1119. TEL 516-365-9088. Ed. Saul Tarter. adv. circ. 8,400. **Document type:** trade publication.
   Description: Directed to buyers and merchandisers of gourmet, ethnic, deli and natural foods in all distributor, supermarket and specialty store segments of the trade.

658.8 747 621.9   US
▼**STORE EQUIPMENT AND DESIGN**. 1992. bi-m. $25. S E D Publishing, Box 578249, Chicago, IL 60657-8429. TEL 312-281-4441. FAX 312-281-8275. Ed. Ed McKinley. adv.: B&W page $3980, color page $4980; trim 10 7/8 x 14 1/2. circ. 20,000. **Document type:** trade publication.
   Description: Covers design trends, new equipment introductions, remodeling, engineering and maintenance.

SUDAN JOURNAL OF FOOD SCIENCE AND TECHNOLOGY. see *FOOD AND FOOD INDUSTRIES*

658.8   UK   ISSN 0261-4251
SUPER MARKETING. 1951. w. £90. Reed Business Publishing Group (Subsidiary of: Reed Elsevier group), Quadrant House, The Quadrant, Sutton, Surrey SM2 5AS, England. TEL 081-652-8275. FAX 081-652-3958. Ed. Tracy Forrest. adv.; bk.rev.; illus. circ. 18,077. (tabloid format; back issues avail.) **Document type:** trade publication.
   ●Also available online.
   —BLDSC (8547.055400).
   Formerly (until 1972): Self Service and Supermarketing (ISSN 0037-1572)
   Description: Presents news, views and features on grocery retailing business.

658.8   SA   ISSN 0049-2590
SUPERMARKET AND RETAILER. 1953. m. R.260. Supermarket and Retailer CC, P.O. Box 46066, Orange Grove 2119, South Africa. TEL 011-728-7006. FAX 011-728-6182. Ed. Stephen R. Maister. adv.; bk.rev. circ. 7,000. **Indexed:** Ind.S.A.Per. **Document type:** trade publication.

658.8   US   ISSN 0196-5700
HD9321.1   CODEN: SUPBDD
SUPERMARKET BUSINESS. 1946. m. $70. Howfrey Communications, 1086 Teaneck Rd., Teaneck, NJ 07666-4838. TEL 201-833-1900. FAX 201-833-1273. Ed. Ken P. Partch. adv. circ. 73,535. (also avail. in microform from UMI; microfiche from CIS) **Indexed:** ABI Inform., Bus.Ind., Hlth.Ind., Key to Econ.Sci., PROMT, Ref.Pt.Food Indus.Abstr., SRI, Tr.& Indus.Ind. **Document type:** trade publication.
   ●Also available online. Vendor(s): Mead Data Central, Inc.
   —BLDSC (8547.078000); Faxon; UnCover; UMI. CCC.
   Former titles (until 1979): Supermarketing (ISSN 0039-5811); *(until 1973):* Food Topics (ISSN 0190-3748)
   Description: Pictures and analysis serving supermarket chains, wholesale headquarters, independent supermarkets, convenience stores, rack jobbers and food brokers.

SUPERMARKET FLORAL. see *GARDENING AND HORTICULTURE — Florist Trade*

658.8 US ISSN 0039-5803
HD9321.1
SUPERMARKET NEWS; the industry's weekly newspaper. 1952. w. $23 to retailers, food brokers, wholesalers; manufacturers $90; others $175 (effective 1992). Fairchild Fashion & Merchandising Group (Subsidiary of: Capital Cities - A B C, Inc.), 7 W. 34th St., New York, NY 10001. TEL 212-630-4199. FAX 212-630-4201. Ed. Daivd Merrefield. adv.; bk.rev.; illus.; mkt.; stat.; cum.index. circ. 58,000. (also avail. in microform from FCM,MIM) **Indexed:** Bus.Ind., Chic.Per.Ind., Hlth.Ind., PROMT, Ref.Pt.Food Indus.Abstr., Tr.& Indus.Ind. **Document type:** trade publication.
●Also available online. Vendor(s): DIALOG Information Services, Inc., Mead Data Central, Inc.
—BLDSC (8547.082000). **CCC.**

658.8 AT
SUPERMARKET NEWS. fortn. Aus.$80 (free to qualified personnel). Reed Business Pubishing Pty. Ltd., 1-5- Railway St., Chatswood, N.S.W 2067, Australia. TEL 02-372-5222. FAX 02-419-7399. Ed. Mike Kent. circ. 15,025. (tabloid format) **Indexed:** Tr.& Indus.Ind. **Document type:** trade publication.

658.8 US
SUPERMARKET SOFTWARE DIRECTORY. s-a. $60 to non-members; members $30. Food Marketing Institute, 800 Connecticut Ave., N.W., Washington, DC 20006. TEL 202-452-8444. **Document type:** directory.

658.878 US ISSN 1053-3648
SUPERMARKET STRATEGIC ALERT; the monthly update on the supermarket industry. 1990. m. $795 (effective 1993). Pollack Associates, 140 E. 81st St., Ste. 5E, New York, NY 10028. TEL 212-734-0753. FAX 212-988-9394. Ed. Mary Pollack. bibl.; index; circ. 300 (paid). (looseleaf format; back issues avail.) **Document type:** newsletter, trade publication.
—**CCC.**
Description: Provides an overview of the supermarket industry from articles in 85 daily to monthly general business and trade publications.

658.8 NZ ISSN 0112-949X
SUPERMARKETING; New Zealand's premier grocery magazine. 1985. 11/yr. NZ.$49.50 (effective 1994). Refer Liberty Publishing, P.O. Box 38046, Howick, Auckland, New Zealand. Ed. Maxine Wrennall. adv. circ. 4,077. (back issues avail.) **Document type:** trade publication.
Description: Covers grocery industry news and features.

SUPERMERCADO MODERNO. see BUSINESS AND ECONOMICS — Marketing And Purchasing

658.8 US ISSN 0040-4322
TEXAS FOOD MERCHANT. 1943. bi-m. $24. Texas Food Industry Association, 7333 Hwy. 290 E., Austin, TX 78723. TEL 512-926-9285. FAX 512-926-0917. Ed. Carla Jo Schaefer. adv.; B&W page $685, color page $1205; trim 8 1/2 x 11. bk.rev.; illus. circ. 3,000. **Document type:** trade publication.
Description: Provides information on business and marketing trends, and legislative issues affecting the food industry.

THREE HUNDRED THIRTY-EIGHT NEWS; labor monthly of the food service industry. see LABOR UNIONS

658.8 US ISSN 0278-6346
HC110.C6
TRENDS: CONSUMER ATTITUDES AND THE SUPERMARKET UPDATE. 1974. a. $50 to non-members; members $25. Food Marketing Institute, Research Division, 1750 K St., N.W., Washington, DC 20006. TEL 202-452-8444. FAX 202-429-4519. circ. 4,000. (also avail. in microfiche from CIS) **Indexed:** SRI. **Document type:** trade publication.
Formerly: Supermarket Trends (ISSN 0163-4488)

658.8 US ISSN 0041-249X
TRI-STATE FOOD NEWS. 1955. m. $10. Gateway Publications, Inc., 610 Beatty Rd., Monroeville, PA 15146-1502. TEL 412-856-7400. FAX 412-856-7954. Ed. David Smith. adv. contact: Beth Knizner. illus. circ. 26,341. (tabloid format)

658.8 SP
U D A PRESS. 26/yr. Union de Detallistas de Alimentacion, Departamento de Publicaciones - Union of Food Retailers, Publications Department, Jorge Juan 19, 1a planta, 28001 Madrid, Spain. TEL 1-578-22-22. FAX 1-575-79-27. Ed. Pilar Calleja.

658.8 UK
ULSTER GROCER. m. Jemma Publications (N.I.) Ltd., 151 University St., Belfast BT7 1HR, N. Ireland. Ed. Linda Giles. adv. circ. 4,216.

658.8 NE ISSN 0165-8883
VAKBLAD VOOR DE HANDEL IN AARDAPPELEN, GROENTEN EN FRUIT. 1947. w. fl.140. Stichting Vakblad voor de Groothandel in Aardappelen, Groenten en Fruit, Bezuidenhoutseweg 82, The Hague, Netherlands. TEL 070-3850500. FAX 070-3850220. Ed. J. Bunnik. adv.; bk.rev.; charts; illus.; stat. circ. 9,500. **Document type:** trade publication.
Formerly: Vakblad voor de Groothandel in Aardappelen, Groenten en Fruit.

658.8 US
▼**W G A UPDATE.*** 1992. irreg., approx. 5/yr. Wisconsin Grocers Association, 2601 Crossroads Sr., Ste. 185, Madison, WI 53704-7923. TEL 608-222-4515. FAX 608-222-3111. adv.: B&W page $1800; trim 8 1/2 x 11. circ. 1,500. **Document type:** newsletter.

658.8 US ISSN 0043-0560
WASHINGTON FOOD DEALER MAGAZINE. 1905. bi-m. $25. Washington State Food Dealers Association, 480 E. 19th, Tacoma, WA 98421. TEL 800-732-1889. FAX 206-272-2723. Ed. Bob Sheffels. adv.; charts; illus.; stat. circ. 4,300. **Document type:** trade publication.
Description: Features local and national articles of interest to Washington and Alaska grocers.

658.8 US
WE MAGAZINE (HAZELWOOD). 1972. q. Wetterau Incorporated, 8920 Pershall Rd., Hazelwood, MO 63042. TEL 314-595-4756. Ed. Amanda Newman. circ. 12,500. (back issues avail.)
Description: Features industry news, personnel information and company news.

658.8 CN ISSN 0705-906X
WESTERN GROCER MAGAZINE. 1916. bi-m. Can.$52. Mercury Publications Ltd., 945 King Edward St., Winnipeg, MB R3H 0P8, Canada. TEL 204-775-0387. FAX 204-775-7830. Ed. Kelly Gray. adv.; illus. circ. 10,700. **Document type:** trade publication.
Formerly: Western Grocer and Food Store Manager (ISSN 0043-3780)
Description: Trade publication for personnel in the grocery field-trade.

658.8 US
WESTERN GROCERY NEWS; a marketing publication from Sunset, the Magazine of Western Living. bi-m. free. Sunset Publishing Corp., 3055 Wilshire Blvd., Los Angeles, CA 90010. TEL 213-380-9680. FAX 213-380-4217. (Subscr. to: Sunset Publishing, Box 56656, Boulder, CO 80322-6656) Ed. Mark Hickling. circ. 9,000. (back issues avail.) **Document type:** trade publication.
Description: Covers product and retail issues, western trends, and marketing campaigns affecting the western grocery business.

658.8 US ISSN 0193-1504
HD9001 CODEN: WHFOEO
WHOLE FOODS; the natural foods business journal. 1977. m. $30. W F C, Inc., 3000 Hadley Rd., S. Plainfield, NJ 07080. TEL 908-769-1160. FAX 908-769-1171. Ed. Joseph S. King. adv. contact: Heather Wainer. bk.rev. circ. 11,000. **Document type:** trade publication.
Description: Covers the natural-products industry for retailers of these goods.

FORENSIC SCIENCES

see Medical Sciences–Forensic Sciences

FORESTS AND FORESTRY

see also Forests and Forestry–Lumber and Wood; Conservation

634.9 US
A F S E E E ACTIVIST; news for members, locally active in national forest issues. 1991. irreg. $25 includes membership. (Association of Forest Service Employees for Environmental Ethics) A F S E E E, Box 11615, Eugene, OR 97440. TEL 503-484-2692. FAX 503-484-3004. circ. 10,000. **Document type:** academic/scholarly publication.

634.9 UK
A P F NEWS. 1960. q. £29.37 to non-members; members £10. Association of Professional Foresters, 7-9 West St., Belford, Northumberland NE70 7QA, England. TEL 0668-213937. FAX 0668-213555. Ed. Jane Karthaus. adv.: Page £190 to non-members; members £95. bk.rev.; circ. 1,100 (controlled). **Document type:** newsletter.
Formerly: A P F Newsletter.
Description: Contains assocaiation news and articles by members, in addition to general U.K. forestry information.

634.9 SW
AARSRINGAR; en informationsskrift fraan Skogssaellskapet om Skogsfoervaltning, Skogs- och naturvaard. 1970. s-a. Skogssaellskapet, P.O. Box 5083, S-402 22 Goeteborg, Sweden. **Document type:** trade publication.

ACADEMIA DE STIINTE AGRICOLE SI SILVICE. BULLETIN.
see AGRICULTURE

634.9 IT ISSN 0515-2178
CODEN: ANLIA2
ACCADEMIA ITALIANA DI SCIENZE FORESTALI. ANNALI. (Text in Italian; summaries in English and Italian) 1953. a. L.50000 (foreign L.60000) (effective 1994). Accademia Italiana di Scienze Forestali, Piazza Edison, 11, 50133 Florence, Italy. TEL 055-570348. FAX 055-575724. Dir. Antonio Gabbrielli. circ. 400. **Indexed:** Biol.Abstr., Forest.Abstr., Forest Prod.Abstr., Irr.& Drain.Abstr., Plant Grow.Reg.Abstr., Seec Abstr., Soils & Fert. **Document type:** academic/scholarly publication.

634.9 PL ISSN 0860-4053
ACTA AGRARIA ET SILVESTRIA. SERIES SILVESTRIS. (Text in Polish; summaries in English and Russian) 1961. a. price varies. (Polska Akademia Nauk, Oddzial w Krakowie, Komisja Nauk Rolniczych i Lesnych) Ossolineum, Publishing House of the Polish Academy of Sciences, Rynek 9, 50-106 Wroclaw, Poland. TEL 48-71-386-25. FAX 48-71-448-103. TELEX 0712771 OSS PL. Ed. Jerzy Fabijanowski. bibl.; charts; illus. **Indexed:** Biol.Abstr., Excerp.Med., Forest.Abstr., Forest Prod.Abstr., Nutr.Abstr., Plant Breed Abstr., Seed Abstr. **Document type:** academic/scholarly publication.
Formerly (until 1965): Acta Agraria et Silvestria. Seria Lesna (ISSN 0065-0927)
Description: Papers on mountain forests, silviculture, forest management, forest genetics, dendrometry, forest entomology, wood techniques.

634.9 XO ISSN 0231-5335
QK474.8 CODEN: ACTDDL
ACTA DENDROBIOLOGICA. (Text in Slovak; summaries in English, German and Russian) a. Veda, Publishing House of the Slovak Academy of Sciences, Klemensova 19, 814 30 Bratislava, Slovakia. **Indexed:** Biol.Abstr., Forest.Abstr., Forest Prod.Abstr., Ornam.Hort.
—CASDDS.

FORESTS AND FORESTRY

634.9   XO
ACTA FACULTATIS FORESTALIS, ZVOLEN/VYSOKA SKOLA LESNICKA A DREVARSKA VO ZVOLENE. LESNICKA FAKULTA. ZBORNIK VEDECKYCH PRAC. (Text mainly in Slovak; occasionally in English, German; summaries in English, German, Russian) 1957. a. exchange basis. Technicka univerzita vo Zvolene - Technical University in Zvolen, T.G. Masaryka 2117-24, 960 53 Zvolen, Slovakia. TEL 0855-635. FAX 0866-20027. TELEX 72267. (Subscr. to: Slovenska Lesnicka a Drevarska Kniznica pri Technickej Univerzite, Miedzinarodna Wymena Publikacii, T.G. Masaryka 20, 961 02 Zvolen, Slovakia) Ed. Milan Hladik. charts; illus. circ. 400.
Indexed: Forest.Abstr., Forest Prod.Abstr., Helminthol.Abstr., Rev.Appl.Entomol., Soils & Fert.

634.9   FI   ISSN 0001-5636
SD1   CODEN: AFRFAZ
ACTA FORESTALIA FENNICA. (Text in English, Finnish) 1913. irreg. (2-6/yr.). FIM 70 per no. Suomen Metsatieteellinen Seura - Society of Forestry in Finland, Unioninkatu 40 B, SF-00170 Helsinki 17, Finland. (Subscr. to: Academic Bookstore, P.O. Box 23, SF-00371, Helsinki, Finland) (Co-sponsor: Metsaentutkimuslaitos (The Finnish Forest Research Institute)) Ed. Tommi Salonen. illus.; cum.index: 1913-1972; 1973-1984. circ. 1,700. (also avail. in microfiche from IDC) **Indexed:** Abstr.Bull.Inst.Pap.Chem., Agrindex, Biol.Abstr., Curr.Adv.Ecol.Sci., Curr.Adv.Plant Sci., Forest.Abstr., Forest Prod.Abstr., Irr.& Drain.Abstr., Rev.Plant Path., Soils & Fert. **Document type:** monographic series.
—BLDSC (0616.000000); UnCover.
Description: Monographs of forest science published in volumes comprising a single article.

634.9   XR   ISSN 0524-7438
            CODEN: AUAFAL
ACTA UNIVERSITATIS AGRICULTURAE. SERIES C. FACULTAS SILVICULTURAE. (Text and summaries in Czech, English) 1919. q. $20. Vysoka Skola Zemedelska, Zemedelska 1, 61300 Brno, Czech Republic. FAX 42-05-45211128. TELEX 62489. Ed. Jindrich Neruda. charts; stat.; index. circ. 350. **Indexed:** Biol.Abstr., Chem.Abstr., Curr.Cont., Forest.Abstr., Forest Prod.Abstr., Hort.Abstr., Soils & Fert. **Document type:** academic/scholarly publication.
—UMI; CASDDS.

ADVANCES IN HORTICULTURE & FORESTRY. see *GARDENING AND HORTICULTURE*

634.9   CN   ISSN 0225-6533
ADVENTURING IN CONSERVATION. 1919. 2/yr. free. Manitoba Forestry Association Inc., 900 Corydon Ave., Winnipeg, MB R3M 0Y4, Canada. TEL 204-453-3182. FAX 204-477-5765. circ. 850.
Description: Information on Association programs, articles related to forests, forestry, wildlife.

AGRINDEX; international information system for the agricultural sciences and technology. see *AGRICULTURE*

AGROFORESTRY SYSTEMS. see *AGRICULTURE*

634.9   PL   ISSN 0239-930X
AKADEMIA ROLNICZA IM. HUGONA KOLLATAJA W KRAKOWIE. ZESZYTY NAUKOWE. SERIA: LESNICTWO. (Text in Polish; summaries in English) 1966. a. price varies. Akademia Rolnicza im. Hugona Kollataja w Krakowie, Al. 29 Listopada 46, 31-425 Krakow, Poland. TEL 48-12-119144. FAX 48-12-336245. TELEX 322469 PL. Ed. Zdzislaw Piskornik. circ. 120 (paid). **Document type:** academic/scholarly publication.
Former titles (until 1979): Akademia Rolnicza w Krakowie. Zeszyty Naukowe. Lesnictwo (ISSN 0137-1851); (until 1972): Wyzsza Szkola Rolnicza w Krakowie. Zeszyty Naukowe. Lesnictwo (ISSN 0137-2076)

634.9 674   PL   ISSN 0137-172X
SD217.P7
AKADEMIA ROLNICZA, POZNAN. ROCZNIKI. LESNICTWO. (Text in Polish; summaries in English and Russian) 1957. irreg. price varies. Akademia Rolnicza, Poznan, Ul. Wojska Polskiego 28, 60-637 Poznan, Poland. FAX 48-61-411022. TELEX 0413322 ARPL. **Indexed:** Bibl.Agri., Forest.Abstr. **Document type:** academic/scholarly publication.
Description: Scientific and research works on forest botany, dendrometry forest organization, arrangement, breeding, utilization, mechanization, engineering and economics.

ALABAMA AGRICULTURAL EXPERIMENT STATION. RESEARCH REPORT SERIES. see *AGRICULTURE*

634.9   US   ISSN 0275-6625
ALABAMA FORESTS. 1958. bi-m. $24 to members. Alabama Forestry Association, Inc., 555 Alabama St., Montgomery, AL 36104. TEL 205-265-8733. FAX 205-262-1258. Ed. Rei Boyce. adv. circ. 3,400. **Document type:** trade publication.
Formerly: Alabama Forest Products (ISSN 0002-4228)

634.9   US   ISSN 0894-9654
ALABAMA'S TREASURED FORESTS. 1982. q. Alabama Forestry Commission, 513 Madison Ave., Montgomery, AL 36130-0601. TEL 205-240-9300. FAX 205-240-9390. Ed. Kim Gilliland. circ. 9,700 (controlled). **Document type:** government publication.
Description: Focuses on multiple-use management of forestland and promotion and support of Treasure Forest program.

634.9   US
ALASKA BRANCHING OUT. 1982. q. University of Alaska, Fairbanks, Alaska Cooperative Extension, Box 756180, Faribanks. TEL 907-474-6356. FAX 907-474-7439. Ed. Anthony F. Gasbarro. bk.rev. circ. 550.
Description: Covers forestry, environmental education, and natural history for the general public.

ALBERTA OIL & FORESTRY REVIEW. see *PETROLEUM AND GAS*

634.9   GW   ISSN 0002-5852
            CODEN: AFJZAL
ALLGEMEINE FORST- UND JAGDZEITUNG. (Summaries in English and French) 1838. m. DM.248. J.D. Sauerlaender's Verlag, Finkenhofstr. 21, 60322 Frankfurt a.M., Germany. TEL 069-555217. FAX 069-5964344. Eds. H. Steinlin, H. Kramer. adv.; bk.rev.; bibl.; charts; illus.; index. **Indexed:** Biol.Abstr., Chem.Abstr., Crop Physiol.Abstr., Curr.Adv.Ecol.Sci., Curr.Cont., Excerp.Med., Forest.Abstr., Forest Prod.Abstr., Irr.& Drain.Abstr., Plant Grow.Reg.Abstr., Rev.Plant Path., Soils & Fert. **Document type:** academic/scholarly publication.
—BLDSC (0791.740000).
Description: Forest preservation and research in Europe. Covers soil analysis and conservation, nutrition, and tree studies.

634.9   GW   ISSN 0002-5860
SD1
ALLGEMEINE FORST ZEITSCHRIFT; illustrierte Wochenzeitschrift fuer Waldwirtschaft und Umweltvorsorge. (Text in German; summaries in English) 1946. fortn. DM.293. B L V Verlagsgesellschaft mbH, Lothstr. 29, 80797 Munich, Germany. TEL 089-12705-0. FAX 089-12705354. Ed. Bernd Encke. adv.; bk.rev.; illus.; stat. **Indexed:** Apic.Abstr., Biol.Abstr., Chem.Abstr., Forest.Abstr., Forest Prod.Abstr., Rural Recreat.Tour.Abstr., World Agri.Econ.& Rural Sociol.Abstr. **Document type:** bulletin.
—CCC.

DER ALMBAUER; Mitteilungen fuer Alm-, Berg- und Gruenlandbauern und ueber Forstrechte. see *AGRICULTURE*

634.975   US
AMERICAN CONIFER SOCIETY. BULLETIN. 1983. q. $30. American Conifer Society, Box 5039, Bltmore Sta, Asheville, NC 28813. FAX 301-256-2208. Ed. Peter Loewer. adv.; bk.rev. circ. 900. **Document type:** academic/scholarly publication.

634.9   US   ISSN 0002-8541
SD1   CODEN: AMFOAH
AMERICAN FORESTS. 1895. bi-m. $30. American Forests, Box 2000, Washington, DC 20013. TEL 202-667-3300. FAX 202-667-7751. Ed. Bill Rooney. adv.; bk.rev.; illus.; index. circ. 30,000. (also avail. in microfilm from UMI; back issues avail.) **Indexed:** Abstr.Bull.Inst.Pap.Chem., Acid Pre.Dig., Acid Rain Abstr., Acid Rain Ind., Biol.Abstr., Biol.& Agr.Ind., Biol.Dig., Bk.Rev.Ind. (1965-), Bus.Ind., Chem.Abstr., Child.Bk.Rev.Ind. (1965-), Energy Rev., Environ.Abstr., Environ.Per.Bibl. (1972-), Farm & Garden Ind., Forest Abstr., Forest Prod.Abstr., Gen.Sci.Ind., GeoRef., Ind.Sci.Rev., Key Word Ind.Wildl.Res., Mag.Ind., Ocean.Abstr., PMR, Pollut.Abstr., R.G., Tr.& Indus.Ind. **Document type:** consumer publication.
—BLDSC (0815.395000); Faxon; UnCover; SWETS; UMI.

634.9   US
AMERICAN FORESTS' RESOURCE HOTLINE NEWSLETTER. (Former name of issuing body: American Forestry Association) 1985. bi-w. $36 to non-members; membership $45. American Forests, Box 2000, Washington, DC 20013. TEL 202-667-3300. FAX 202-667-7751. Ed. Gerald J. Gray. circ. 2,000. (back issues avail.) **Document type:** newsletter.
Formerly: A F A's Resource Hotline Newsletter.
Description: Publication on forest policy covering topics ranging from national forests to urban forestry.

634.9   FR   ISSN 0003-4312
SD1   CODEN: ANSFAS
ANNALES DES SCIENCES FORESTIERES. (Text mainly in French; summaries in English, French) 1923. 6/yr. 1125 F. (foreign 1375 F.) (effective 1994). (Institut National de la Recherche Agronomique) Editions Scientifiques Elsevier, 29, rue Buffon, 75005 Paris, France. TEL 33-1-47071122. FAX 33-1-43368093. TELEX 202400 F. (Subscr. in U.S. and Canada to: Elsevier Science Publishing Co., Inc., Box 882, Madison Sq. Sta., New York, NY 10159. TEL 212-989-5800) Ed. G. Aussenac. adv.; bk.rev.; charts; illus.; index. circ. 2,000. (also avail. in microform from UMI; reprint service avail. from ISI) **Indexed:** Abstr.Bull.Inst.Pap.Chem., Acid Pre.Dig., Bibl.Agri., Bio-Contr.News & Info., Biol.Abstr., Chem.Abstr., Curr.Adv.Ecol.Sci., Curr.Cont., Ecol.Abstr., Entomol.Abstr., Environ.Per.Bibl. (1990-), Excerp.Med., Forest.Abstr., Forest Prod.Abstr., Ind.Sci.Rev., Irr.& Drain.Abstr., Plant Grow.Reg.Abstr., Rev.Appl.Entomol., Sci.Cit.Ind., Seed Abstr., Soils & Fert. **Document type:** academic/scholarly publication.
—BLDSC (0995.750000); UnCover; CASDDS. **CCC.**
Description: Publishes research related to the forest, in particular: environmental factors - ecology, pedology, climatology; silviculture - dendrometry, growth laws, treatments; forest damage - entomology, pathology, atmospheric pollution, fire; genetics and improvement physiology and wood quality.
Refereed Serial

634.9   CI   ISSN 0351-2045
ANNALES FORESTALES/ANALI ZA SUMARSTVO. (Text and summaries in Croatian, English, French and German) vol.6, 1974. a. price varies. Jugoslavenska Akademija Znanosti i Umjetnosti, Razred za Prirodne Znanosti, Brace Kavurica 1, 41000 Zagreb, Croatia. Ed. Mirko Vidakovic. circ. 800. **Indexed:** Biol.Abstr., Forest.Abstr., Forest Prod.Abstr.

ARANETA RESEARCH JOURNAL. see *AGRICULTURE*

634.9   GW   ISSN 0003-7796
ARBEITSTECHNISCHE MERKHEFTE DER WALDARBEIT. 1950. irreg. (3-4/yr.). price varies. Wirtschafts- und Forstverlag Euting KG, Tannenstr. 1, 56587 Strassenhaus, Germany. adv.; charts; illus.

ARBOR AGE. see *BIOLOGY — Botany*

634.9   UK   ISSN 0307-1375
SB435   CODEN: ARJOD7
ARBORICULTURAL JOURNAL; the international journal of urban forestry. 1964. 4/yr. £89($179) to non-members. (Arboricultural Association) A B Academic Publishers, P.O. Box 42, Bicester, Oxon. OX6 7NW, England. TEL 0869-320949. Ed. T.H.R. Hall. adv.; bk.rev.; charts; illus.; index. circ. 2,000. (also avail. in microform) **Indexed**: Biol.Abstr., Curr.Adv.Ecol.Sci., Environ.Per.Bibl. (1985-), Forest.Abstr., Forest.Abstr, Forest Prod.Abstr., Geo.Abstr., Helminthol.Abstr., Hort.Abstr., Ornam.Hort., Soils & Fert. **Document type**: academic/scholarly publication.
—BLDSC (1593.810000). CCC.
Formerly: Arboricultural Association Journal (ISSN 0003-7931)

634.9   FR   ISSN 1164-9356
▼**ARBRE ACTUEL.** 1992. bi-m. 210 F. (foreign 265 F.). Institut pour le Developpement Forestier, 23 av. Bosquet, 75007 Paris, France. TEL 45-55-23-49. FAX 45-55-98-54. **Document type**: trade publication.

ARGENTINA FORESTAL. see FORESTS AND FORESTRY — Lumber And Wood

634.9   US   ISSN 0066-7404
ARIZONA FORESTRY NOTES.* 1966. irreg., no.21, 1984. free. College of Forest Research, Dept. of Forest Biology, 201 Mutting Hall, University of Maine, Oronol, ME 04469-0125. TEL 602-523-3031. Ed. Alan S. White. charts; stat. circ. 800. **Indexed**: Biol.Abstr., Forest.Abstr.

634.9   AT
ASIA - PACIFIC FOREST & TIMBER BULLETIN; resource management and timber export news. 1977. bi-m. Aus.$45 to individuals; institutions Aus.$85. R.L. Newman and Partners Pty. Ltd., P.O. Box 661, Mawson, A.C.T. 2607, Australia. TEL 06-286-2511. FAX 06-286-5653. Ed. Bob Newman. adv.: B&W page Aus.$320; trim 250 x 186. bk.rev. circ. 3,000. (back issues avail.) **Document type**: bulletin.
Former titles: Australasian Forest and Timber Bulletin; Forest and Timber Industries Bulletin.

634.9   AT
AUSTRALIAN FOREST GROWER.* 1977. q. Aus.$23. Australian Forest Development Institute, c/o Forest Industries House, 24 Napier Cl., Deakin, N.S.W. 2600, Australia. Ed. Jo Vondra. adv.; bk.rev. circ. 3,000. (back issues avail.)

634.9   AT   ISSN 0004-9158
SD1   CODEN: AUFOA5
AUSTRALIAN FORESTRY. 1936. q. Aus.$50. Institute of Foresters of Australia, Inc., P.O. Box E73, Queen Victoria, A.C.T. 2600, Australia. TEL 06-2813992. FAX 06-2814693. Ed. D. Doley. adv.; bk.rev.; abstr.; charts; illus.; stat.; index. circ. 1,500. **Indexed**: Abstr.Bull.Inst.Pap.Chem., Biodet.Abstr., Biol.Abstr., Chem.Abstr., Excerpt.Med., Forest.Abstr., Forest Prod.Abstr., Rev.Plant Path., Rural Recreat.Tour Abstr., Soils & Fert., World Agri.Econ.& Rural Sociol.Abstr.
—BLDSC (1800.000000); UnCover; SWETS.

B C NEWS. (Boise Cascade Corporation) see PAPER AND PULP

634.9   CN
B.C. PROFESSIONAL FORESTER. 1947. bi-m. Can.$45. Association of British Columbia Professional Foresters, 440-789 W. Pender St., Vancouver, BC V6C 1H2, Canada. TEL 604-687-8027. FAX 604-687-3264. Ed. Don Jepsen. adv. contact: Andwin Bryerton. bk.rev. circ. 3,000. (looseleaf format) **Document type**: newsletter.
Formerly (until 1987): Association of British Columbia Foresters. Highlights of Council Meetings.
Description: Newsletter to members of the Association and interested forestry groups on issues which impact foresters in their roles as professionals.

634.9   GW
B D F AKTUELL. 1960. m. DM.39.60. (Bund Deutscher Forstleute) Vereinigte Verlagsanstalten GmbH, Hoeherweg 278, 40231 Duesseldorf, Germany. Ed. Armin Ristau. adv.; charts; illus.; tr.lit. circ. 12,000. **Document type**: trade publication.
Formerly (until 1993): Deutsche Forstmann (ISSN 0012-012X)

634.9   MY   ISSN 0128-6471
BAMBOOS OF SABAH. (Text in English) irreg., no.14, 1993. price varies. Forest Research Centre, P.O. Box 1407, 90008 Sandakan, Sabah, Malaysia. TEL 089-531522. FAX 089-531068. **Document type**: monographic series.

634.9   BG   ISSN 1021-3279
BANGLADESH JOURNAL OF FOREST SCIENCE. (Text in English) 1969. s-a. free or exchange basis. Forest Research Institute, Chittagong, Bangladesh. TEL 031-212085. Ed. M.A. Sattar. bk.rev.; charts; illus.; stat. circ. 1,000. **Indexed**: Chem.Abstr., Forest.Abstr., Forest Prod.Abstr., Seed Abstr., Weed Abstr. **Document type**: academic/scholarly publication.
—BLDSC (1861.671500).
Former titles (until 1990): Bano Biggyan Patrika (ISSN 0254-4539); (until 1972): Forestdale News (ISSN 0046-4597)

634.9   US
BARK PRODUCERS REPORT. 1970. q. National Bark & Soil Producers Association, 10210 Leatherleaf Ct., Manassas, VA 22111-4245. TEL 703-257-0111. Dir. Robert C. LaGasse.

634.9   GW   ISSN 0177-5375
DER BAYERISCHE WALDBESITZER. 1963. bi-m. Bayerischer Waldbesitzerverband e.V., Postfach 210144, 80671 Munich, Germany. TEL 089-5803089. FAX 089-5807015. **Document type**: bulletin.

634.9   GW   ISSN 0067-4710
BAYERISCHES FORSTDIENST-TASCHENBUCH. 1966. 2/yr. DM.82. (Bund der Deutschen Forstmaenner, Landesverband Bayern e.V.) Walhalla Fachverlag, Dolomitenstr. 1, 93057 Regensburg, Germany. TEL 0941-696710. FAX 0941-68568. Ed. Klaus Baer. adv. circ. 1,000. **Document type**: corporate report.

634.9   NE   ISSN 0921-4275
BEDRIJFSUITKOMSTEN IN DE NEDERLANDSE PARTICULIERE BOSBOUW. 1974. a. fl.25. Landbouw-Economisch Instituut, Conradkade 175, 2517 CL The Hague, Netherlands. TEL 31-70-3308330. FAX 31-70-3615624. Ed. E.P. Berger, R.A.M. Schrijver. **Document type**: government publication.
Description: Data on income and profitability of Dutch forestry on the basis of a sample of holdings.

634.9   CC   ISSN 1000-1522
SD221   CODEN: BLDXE8
BEIJING LINYE DAXUE XUEBAO. English edition: Beijing University of Forestry. Journal (ISSN 1004-7301) (Text in Chinese) 1979. q. Y14. Beijing Linye Daxue, Xuebao Bianjibu, Qinghua Donglu, Beijing 100083, People's Republic of China. TEL 2568811. Ed. Yan Shuai. bk.rev. **Document type**: academic/scholarly publication.
—CASDDS.

634.9   CC   ISSN 1004-7301
▼**BEIJING UNIVERSITY OF FORESTRY. JOURNAL.** Chinese edition: Beijing Linye Daxue Xuebao (ISSN 1000-1522) (Text in English) 1992. s-a. $56. Beijing Linye Daxue, Xuebao Bianjibu - Beijing University of Forestry, Qinghua Donglu, Beijing 100083, People's Republic of China. TEL 2568811. Ed. Yan Shuai. **Document type**: academic/scholarly publication.

634.9   GW
    CODEN: BFORD2
BEITRAEGE FUER FORSTWIRTSCHAFT UND LANDSCHAFTSOEKOLOGIE. 1967. 4/yr. DM.88. (Forstliche Forschungsanstalt Eberswalde) D L V Deutscher Landwirtschaftsverlag Berlin GmbH, Thulestr. 7, 13189 Berlin, Germany. TEL 030-47800012. FAX 030-47800040. Ed. Dietmar Felden. charts; illus.; index. **Indexed**: Agri.Eng.Abstr., Bio-Contr.News & Info., Chem.Abstr., Crop Physiol.Abstr., Excerp.Med., Forest.Abstr., Forest Prod.Abstr., Seed Abstr., Soils & Fert. **Document type**: academic/scholarly publication.
—CASDDS.
Formerly: Beitraege fuer die Forstwirtschaft (ISSN 0323-4673)

634.9   IO   ISSN 0005-9145
    CODEN: BSELBN
BERITA SELULOSA. (Text in Indonesian; summaries in English) 1965. 4/yr. Rs.500 per no. Cellulose Research Institute - Lembaga Penelitian Selulosa, Jl. Tamansari 126, Bandung, Indonesia. Ed.Bd. adv.; bk.rev.; abstr.; bibl.; charts. circ. 500. **Indexed**: Abstr.Bull.Inst.Pap.Chem., Chem.Abstr.
—CASDDS.

634.9   SZ
BERNER WALD. 6/yr. Forstinspektion Oberland, Postfach 99, CH-3700 Spiez, Switzerland. TEL 033-544822. Ed. Adrian Meier. circ. 5,100.

634.9   AT   ISSN 0726-1268
BETWEEN THE LEAVES. 1981. s-a. Queensland Forest Service, G.P.O. Box 944, Brisbane, Qld. 4001, Australia. TEL 07-234-0157. circ. 5,000 (controlled).
Description: Staff news and activities of the Queensland Forest Service.

BIOLOGISCHE BUNDESANSTALT FUER LAND- UND FORSTWIRTSCHAFT, BERLIN-DAHLEM. MITTEILUNGEN. see AGRICULTURE

BIOTECHNOLOGY IN AGRICULTURE AND FORESTRY. see BIOLOGY — Biotechnology

BLICK INS HESSENLAND; Magazin fuer Landwirtschaft, Wald und Natur. see AGRICULTURE

634.9   FR   ISSN 0006-579X
SD1
BOIS ET FORETS DES TROPIQUES. (Text in French; summaries in English, Spanish) 1947. q. 250 F. (foreign 320 F.). C I R A D - Foret, 45 bis, Ave. de la Belle Gabrielle, 94736 Nogent-sur-Marne, France. TEL 43-94-43-00. FAX 43-94-43-81. TELEX CETEFO 264 653 F. Ed. Francois Grison. adv.; bk.rev.; charts; illus.; stat. circ. 1,500. **Indexed**: Abstr.Bull.Inst.Pap.Chem., Biol.Abstr., Chem.Abstr., Curr.Adv.Ecol.Sci., Forest.Abstr., Forest Prod.Abstr., Nutr.Abstr., Rural Recreat.Tour.Abstr., World Agri.Econ.& Rural Sociol.Abstr. **Document type**: academic/scholarly publication.
—UnCover; SWETS.
Description: Presents articles of general interest as well as scientific and research-development based articles; dossiers on a specific country or particular research field, reports of meetings.

634.9   BS   ISSN 0068-0486
BOTSWANA. FOREST DEPARTMENT. REPORT.* a. R.1($0.10) Government Printing Office, Forest Department, PB 0081, Gaborone, Botswana.

634.9   CN
BRITISH COLUMBIA. MINISTRY OF FORESTS. ANNUAL REPORT. 1912. a. price varies. Ministry of Forests, Public Affairs Branch, 1450 Government St., Victoria, B.C. V8W 3E7, Canada. FAX 604-386-0221. (Subscr. to: Crown Publication, 546 Yates Street, Victoria, B.C. V8W 1K8, Canada. TEL 604-386-4636) incex. circ. 3,000. **Indexed**: Biol.Abstr. **Document type**: government publication.
Former titles (until 1988): British Columbia. Ministry of Forests and Lands. Annual Report; British Columbia. Forest Service. Annual Report (ISSN 0068-1490)

634.9   CN   ISSN 0229-1622
BRITISH COLUMBIA. MINISTRY OF FORESTS. LAND MANAGEMENT HANDBOOKS. 1980. irreg. price varies. Ministry of Forests, 1450 Government St., Victoria, B.C. V8W 3E7, Canada. TEL 604-387-3484. (Subscr. to: Crown Publications, 546 Yates St., Victoria, B.C. V8W 1K8, Canada. TEL 604-386-4636) **Document type**: government publication.
Formerly: British Columbia. Ministry of Forests and Lands. Land Management Handbooks.

634.9   CN
BRITISH COLUMBIA. MINISTRY OF FORESTS. LAND MANAGEMENT REPORTS. 1975. irreg. price varies. Ministry of Forests, 1450 Government St., Victoria, B.C. V8W 3E7, Canada. TEL 604-387-3484. (Subscr. to: Crown Publications, 546 Yates St., Victoria, B.C. V8W 1K8, Canada. TEL 604-386-4636) **Indexed**: Herb.Abstr. **Document type**: government publication.
Formerly: British Columbia. Ministry of Forests and Lands. Land Management Reports (ISSN 0702-9861)

FORESTS AND FORESTRY

634.9 — CN — ISSN 0226-9368
BRITISH COLUMBIA. MINISTRY OF FORESTS. RESEARCH NOTES. 1938. irreg., no.105, 1991. price varies. Ministry of Forests, 1450 Government St., Victoria, B.C. V8W 3E7, Canada. TEL 604-387-3484. (Subscr. to: Crown Publications, 546 Yates Street, Victoria, B.C. V8W 1K8, Canada. TEL 604-386-4636) **Indexed:** Forest.Abstr., Forest Prod.Abstr. **Document type:** government publication.
—BLDSC (7747.820000).
Former titles: British Columbia. Ministry of Forests and Lands. Research Notes; British Columbia. Forest Service. Research Notes (ISSN 0068-1520)

635 — CN
BRITISH COLUMBIA. MINISTRY OF FORESTS. SPECIAL REPORT SERIES. 1989. irreg. price varies. Ministry of Forests, Parliament Bldgs., Victoria, B.C. V8V 1X4, Canada. (Subscr. to: Crown Publications, 546 Yates St., Victoria, B.C. V8W 1K8, Canada. TEL 604-386-4636) **Document type:** government publication.

634.9 — SZ
BUENDNERWALD. 6/yr. S E L V A, Postfach, CH-7000 Chur, Switzerland. TEL 081-222969. FAX 081-226789. Ed. Magnus Rageth. circ. 1,500. **Document type:** newsletter.

BUNDESFORSCHUNGSANSTALT FUER FORST- UND HOLZWIRTSCHAFT, HAMBURG. MITTEILUNGEN. see *FORESTS AND FORESTRY — Lumber And Wood*

354 — UV
BURKINA FASO. DIRECTION DES EAUX ET FORETS ET DE LA CONSERVATION DES SOLS. RAPPORT ANNUEL. a. Direction des Eaux et Forets et de la Conservation des Sols, Ouagadougou, Burkina Faso. stat. **Document type:** government publication.
Formerly: Upper Volta. Direction des Eaux et Forets et de la Conservation des Sols. Rapport Annuel.

C A L M SCIENCE. (Conservation and Land Management) see *CONSERVATION*

C A S A F A REPORT SERIES. (Committee on the Application of Science to Agriculture, Forestry and Aquaculture) see *AGRICULTURE*

634.9 — US
CALIFORNIA FORESTRY NOTE. 1960. irreg., no.105, 1991. free. Department of Forestry and Fire Protection, Box 944246, Sacramento, CA 94244-2460. TEL 916-445-5571. FAX 916-327-4980. Ed. Gary Brittner. cum.index: 1960-1991. circ. 1,500. **Indexed:** Forest.Abstr., Forest Prod.Abstr. **Document type:** government publication.
Formerly: California. Department of Forestry. State Forest Notes (ISSN 0068-5577)

634.9 — CN
CANADA. CANADIAN FOREST SERVICE. ONTARIO REGION. FORESTRY NEWSLETTER. French edition (ISSN 0825-1789) (Editions in English, French) 1971. q. free. Canadian Forest Service, Ontario Region, Box 490, Sault Ste. Marie, ON P6A 5M7, Canada. TEL 705-949-9461. FAX 705-759-7500. Ed. Sandra B. Burt. bibl. circ. 1,800. (back issues avail.) **Document type:** government publication.
Former titles: Canada. Forestry Canada. Ontario Region. Forestry Newsletter; Canada. Great Lakes Forestry Centre. Forestry Newsletter (ISSN 0825-1770); (until 1984): Canada. Great Lakes Forest Research Centre. Forestry Research Newsletter (ISSN 0705-520X)

634.96 — CN
CANADA. CANADIAN FOREST SERVICE. ONTARIO REGION. SURVEY BULLETIN; forest insect and disease conditions in Ontario. 1972. 3/yr. Canadian Forestry Service, Ontario Region, Box 490, Sault Ste. Marie, ON P6A 5M7, Canada. TEL 705-949-9461. FAX 705-759-7500. illus. **Document type:** government publication.
Former titles: Canada. Forestry Canada. Ontario Region. Survey Bulletin; Canada. Great Lakes Forestry Centre. Survey; Canada. Great Lakes Forest Research Centre. Survey Bulletin (ISSN 0705-503X)

634.9 595 — CN — ISSN 1195-3799
CANADA. CANADIAN FORESTRY SERVICE - MARITIMES REGION, FREDERICTON, NEW BRUNSWICK. INFORMATION REPORT M-X. French edition (ISSN 1195-3802) (Text in English) 1966. irreg. (5-8/yr.). free. Canadian Forest Service - Maritimes Region, Box 4000, Fredericton, NB E3B 5P7, Canada. TEL 506-452-3542. FAX 506-452-3525. Ed. C. Simpson. circ. 1,000. (also avail. in microform from MML) **Indexed:** Biol.Abstr., Forest.Abstr., Forest Prod.Abstr. **Document type:** government publication.
Former titles: Canada. Forestry Canada - Maritimes Region, Fredericton, New Brunswick. Information Report M-X; Canada. Canadian Forestry Service - Maritimes, Fredericton, New Brunswick. Information Report M-X (ISSN 0834-406X); Canada. Maritimes Forest Research Centre, Fredericton, New Brunswick. Information Report M-X (ISSN 0704-769X)

634.96 — CN
CANADA. FORESTRY CANADA. INSECT AND DISEASE CONDITIONS IN CANADA. (Editions in English and French) 1980. a. free. Forestry Canada, Place Vincent Massey, 21st Fl., Ottawa, Ont. K1A 1G5, Canada. TEL 819-997-1107. FAX 819-953-7048. (also avail. in microform from MML) **Document type:** government publication.
—BLDSC (3990.539400).
Former titles: Canada. Canadian Forestry Service. Insect and Disease Conditions in Canada; Canada. Environment Canada. Insect and Disease Conditions in Canada (ISSN 0226-9759); Supersedes: Canada. Department of the Environment. Forest Insect and Disease Survey. Annual Report (ISSN 0068-7588)

634.9 — CN — ISSN 0714-1181
CANADA. NORTHERN FORESTRY CENTRE. FOREST MANAGEMENT NOTE. 1980. irreg. (7/yr.). free. Northern Forestry Centre, 5320-122 St., Edmonton, AB T6H 3S5, Canada. TEL 403-435-7210. Ed. B. Laishley. circ. 750. (back issues avail.; reprint service avail. from MML) **Indexed:** Forest.Abstr. **Document type:** government publication.
—BLDSC (3991.260000).
Description: Brief technical note of forest management developments.

634.9 — CN — ISSN 0704-7673
CANADA. NORTHERN FORESTRY CENTRE. INFORMATION REPORT. 1971. irreg. (approx. 12/yr.). free. Northern Forestry Centre, 5320-122 St., Edmonton, AB T6H 3S5, Canada. TEL 403-435-7210. Ed. B. Laishley. bibl.; charts; illus.; stat. circ. 1,100. (back issues avail.; reprint service avail. from MML) **Indexed:** Chem.Abstr., Forest.Abstr., Forest Prod.Abstr. **Document type:** government publication.
—BLDSC (4493.991900).
Formerly: Canadian Forestry Service. Department of Fisheries and Forestry. Prairies Region. Information Report.
Description: Scientific and technical reports of forestry research studies.

634.9 — CN
CANADA. PACIFIC FOREST RESEARCH CENTRE. INFORMATION REPORT. Some issues called its Report. (Text in English and French) 1971. irreg. free. Pacific Forest Research Centre, 506 W. Burnside Rd., Victoria, B.C. V8Z 1M5, Canada. TEL 604-387-5985. abstr.; bibl.; charts; illus. **Document type:** government publication.

634.9 — CN
CANADA. PETAWAWA NATIONAL FORESTRY INSTITUTE ANNUAL SHAREHOLDER'S REPORT. (Editions in English, French) 1981. a. free. Petawawa National Forestry Institute, Chalk River, ON K0J 1J0, Canada. Ed.Bd. charts; stat. circ. 200. **Document type:** government publication.
Supersedes: Canada. Petawawa National Forestry Institute. Program Review (ISSN 0710-4251); Canada. Forest Management Institute. Program Review (ISSN 0071-7495)

634.9 — CN — ISSN 0228-0736
CANADA. PETAWAWA NATIONAL FORESTRY INSTITUTE. INFORMATION REPORTS/CANADA. INSTITUT FORESTIER NATIONAL DE PETAWAWA. RAPPORTS D'INFORMATION. (Editions in English, French) 1979. irreg. free. Petawawa National Forestry Institute, Chalk River, ON K0J 1J0, Canada. TEL 613-993-1210. Ed. Asoka C. Yapa. circ. 1,150 (750 English ed., 400 French ed.). (also avail. in microform from MML; reprint service avail. from MML) **Indexed:** Forest.Abstr., Forest Prod.Abstr. **Document type:** government publication.
Description: Technical reports containing results of research in forest genetics, biotechnology, forest inventory and forest management systems.

634.9 — CN
CANADIAN FOREST FIRE WEATHER INDEX. irreg. free. Pacific Forest Research Centre, 506 W. Burnside Rd., Victoria, B.C. V8Z 1M5, Canada. (back issues avail.)

634.9 — CN — ISSN 0068-8991
CANADIAN INSTITUTE OF FORESTRY. ANNUAL REPORT. Issued with: Forestry Chronicle (ISSN 0015-7546) a. Canadian Institute of Forestry - Institut Forestier du Canada, 1005-151 Slater St., Ottawa, ON K1P 5H3, Canada. TEL 613-234-2242. FAX 613-234-6181. adv.; bk.rev. circ. 3,000.

634.9 — CN — ISSN 0045-5067
SD255 — CODEN: CJFRAR
CANADIAN JOURNAL OF FOREST RESEARCH/REVUE CANADIENNE DE LA RECHERCHE FORESTIERE. (Text mainly in English; occasionally in French) 1971. m. Can.$98($102) to individuals; institutions Can.$297 (effective 1993). National Research Council of Canada, Research Journals - Conseil National de Recherches du Canada, Ottawa, Ont. K1A 0R6, Canada. TEL 613-993-9084. FAX 613-952-7656. TELEX 053-3145. Ed. W.M. Cheliak. adv.: B&W page Can.$550; trim 8 1/2 x 11; adv. contact: Hoda Jabbour. bibl.; illus.; index. circ. 1,000. (also avail. in microform from UMI; back issues avail.; reprint service avail. from UMI) **Indexed:** A.I.Abstr., Abstr.Bull.Inst.Pap.Chem., Acid Pre.Dig., Acid Pre.Dig., Acid Rain Abstr., Acid Rain Ind., Biodet.Abstr., Biol.Abstr., Chem.Abstr., Crop Physiol.Abstr., Curr.Adv.Ecol.Sci., Curr.Cont., Energy Ind., Energy Info.Abstr., Environ.Abstr., Environ.Per.Bibl. (1975-), Excerp.Med., Forest.Abstr., Forest Prod.Abstr., Geo.Abstr., Helminthol.Abstr., Ind.Sci.Rev., INIS Atomind., Irr.& Drain.Abstr., Plant Grow.Reg.Abstr., Rev.Plant Path., Risk Abstr., Sci.Cit.Ind., Seed Abstr., Sel.Water Res.Abstr., Soils & Fert., Telegen, Weed Abstr. **Document type:** academic/scholarly publication.
—BLDSC (3031.500000); CIS; Faxon; UnCover; SWETS; UMI; CASDDS. **CCC.**
Description: Discusses results of technical research studies in forestry.
Refereed Serial

CANADIAN SOCIETY OF PLANT PHYSIOLOGISTS. BULLETIN/SOCIETE CANADIENNE DE PHYSIOLOGIE VEGETALE. BULLETIN. see *BIOLOGY — Botany*

634.9 — PH
CANOPY INTERNATIONAL. (Text in English) 1975. bi-m. free. Department of Environmental and Natural Resources, Ecosystems Research and Development Bureau, College, Laguna 4031, Philippines. TELEX 6394-3628. Ed. Eliseo M. Baltazar. bibl.; charts; illus.; stat. **Indexed:** Abstr.Bull.Inst.Pap.Chem., Field Crop Abstr., Forest.Abstr., Forest Prod.Abstr., Herb.Abstr. **Document type:** newsletter.
Formerly: Canopy (ISSN 0115-0960)
Description: Promotes efficient use of natural resources and effective environmental management.

CAPITAL PRESS; regional Oregon, Idaho, Washington, N. California agricultural-forest weekly. see *AGRICULTURE*

634.9 — AU — ISSN 0008-9583
CENTRALBLATT FUER DAS GESAMTE FORSTWESEN. (Summaries in English and German) 1875. q. S.2120 (foreign S.2160). (Universitaet fuer Bodenkultur, Forstliche Abteilung) Oesterreichischer Agrarverlag GmbH, Bankgasse 1-3, A-1014 Vienna, Austria. TEL 5339676. FAX 5339656. (Co-sponsor: Forstliche Bundesversuchsanstalt Marianbrunn in Wien) Ed. W. Sagl. adv.; bk.rev.; bibl.; charts; illus.; stat.; index. circ. 2,000. **Indexed:** Biol.Abstr., Chem.Abstr., Excerp.Med., Forest.Abstr., Forest Prod.Abstr.

634.9 BE ISSN 0775-3446
CENTRE DE RECHERCHE ET DE PROMOTION FORESTIERES. DOCUMENTS. 1968-1990 (no.5). irreg. exchange basis. Centre de Recherche et de Promotion Forestieres, Section Ecologie, Passage des Deportes no. 2, B-5030 Gembloux, Belgium. TEL 32-81-622377. FAX 32-81-614544. TELEX 59482 FSAG B. **Indexed:** Forest.Abstr., Forest Prod.Abstr.
Formerly (until 1988): Centre d'Ecologie Forestiere et Rurale. Notes Techniques. A: Forestieres (ISSN 0770-1861); Supersedes in part: Centre d'Ecologie Forestiere. Notes Techniques (ISSN 0069-1801)

634.9 BE
CENTRE DE RECHERCHES SUR L'ELEVAGE ET LES PRODUCTIONS FOURRAGERES EN HAUTE BELGIQUE. NOTES TECHNIQUES. B: HERBAGERES. 1968. irreg., no.10, 1978. price varies. Centre de Recherches sur l'Elevage et les Productions Fourrageres en Haute Belgique, 75, rue Al'Roue, B-6921 Chanly, Belgium. **Indexed:** Forest.Abstr., Herb.Abstr.
Formerly: Centre d'Ecologie Forestrie et Rurale. Notes Techniques. B: Herbageres; Supersedes in part: Centre d'Ecologie Forestiere. Notes Techniques (ISSN 0069-1801)

634.9 CL ISSN 0716-1190
CHILE FORESTAL; la revista del sector forestal chileno. English edition: Chilean Forestry News (ISSN 0716-1344) 1975. m. (11/yr.). Esc.14000($85) (N. America $91; elsewhere $100). Corporacion Nacional Forestal, Avda. Bulnes 259, Ofc. 406, Santiago, Chile. TEL 6966724. FAX 6966724. Dir. Mariela Espejo S. adv. contact: Domingo Escobar. charts; illus.

634.9 CL ISSN 0716-1344
CHILEAN FORESTRY NEWS. Spanish edition: Chile Forestal (ISSN 0716-1190) (Text in English) m. Esc.11500($91) (N. America $100; elsewhere $110). Corporacion Nacional Forestal, Avda. Bulnes 259, Ofc. 406, Santiago, Chile. TEL 6966724. FAX 6966724. Ed. Roberto Rivadeneira. adv. contact: Domingo Escobar. illus.
—BLDSC (3172.993700).

CHISAN KENKYU HAPPYOKAI RONBUNSHU/FORESTRY CONSERVATION CONFERENCE, AICHI PREFECTURE. PROCEEDINGS. see CONSERVATION

634.9 US
CHRISTMAS TREE LOOKOUT. 1968. 3/yr. $18. Northwest Christmas Tree Association, 4093 12th St., S.E., Box 3366, Salem, OR 97302. TEL 503-364-2942. FAX 503-581-6819. Ed. Wally Hunter. adv.; B&W page $364; 7 x 10; adv. contact: Leann Williams. stat. circ. 1,698. **Document type:** trade publication.
Formerly: Northwest Lookout.

CHRISTMAS TREES MAGAZINE; a magazine of plantation management for Christmas tree growers. see AGRICULTURE

634.9 PL
CHRONOLOGY OF TREES AND SHRUBS IN SOUTH-WEST ASIA AND ADJACENT REGIONS. (Text in English) 1982. irreg. price varies. Polska Akademia Nauk, Instytut Dendrologii, Ul. Parkowa 5, 62-035 Kornik, Poland. (Dist. by: Ars Polona, Krakowskie Przedmiescie 7, 00-068 Warsaw, Poland) Ed. Kazimierz Browicz. **Document type:** academic/scholarly publication.

634.9 US
CITY TREES. 1964. bi-m. $20 (effective 1991). Society of Municipal Arborists, Box 364, Wellesley Hills, MA 02181-0403. TEL 617-235-7600. FAX 617-237-1936. Ed. Leonard E. Phillips. adv.; cum.index: 1984-1991. circ. 260. **Document type:** trade publication.
Description: Explores urban tree care and maintenance, forestry department management, and innovations in municipal aboriculture.

634.9 US
CLEMSON UNIVERSITY. DEPARTMENT OF FOREST RESOURCES. FOREST RESEARCH SERIES. irreg., no.46, 1989. Clemson University, Department of Forest Resources, Clemson, SC 29634-1003. TEL 803-656-3302. **Indexed:** Biol.Abstr. **Document type:** academic/scholarly publication.
Formerly: Clemson University. Department of Forestry. Forest Research Series.
Description: Contains results of major research projects in the Department.

634.9 US
CLEMSON UNIVERSITY. DEPARTMENT OF FOREST RESOURCES. FORESTRY BULLETIN. 1967. irreg., no.54, 1988. free. Clemson University, Department of Forest Resources, Clemson, SC 29634-1003. TEL 803-656-3302. charts; illus.; stat.; circ. 500 (controlled). (back issues avail.) **Indexed:** Biol.Abstr., Forest.Abstr. **Document type:** academic/scholarly publication.
Formerly: Clemson University. Department of Forestry. Forestry Bulletin (ISSN 0093-0083)
Description: Contains short progress reports and non-technical versions of major research studies.

634.9 US
CLEMSON UNIVERSITY. DEPARTMENT OF FOREST RESOURCES. TECHNICAL PAPER. irreg., no.18, 1987. Clemson University, Department of Forest Resources, Clemson, SC 29634-1003. TEL 803-656-3302. **Indexed:** Biol.Abstr., Forest.Abstr., Forest Prod.Abstr.
Formerly: Clemson University. Department of Forestry. Technical Paper.
Description: Non-research oriented reports, including lectures, annotated bibliographies and historical accounts.

634.9 UK ISSN 0010-3381
SD1
COMMONWEALTH FORESTRY REVIEW. (Text in English; summaries in English, French, Spanish) 1921. q. £50 to libraries; members £30; students £10 (effective 1994). Commonwealth Forestry Association, c/o Oxford Forestry Institute, South Parks Rd., Oxford OX1 3RB, England. TEL 0865-275072. FAX 0865-275074. Ed. Mrs. A.M.D. Okole. adv.: page £250. bk.rev.; abstr.; bibl.; charts; illus.; index. circ. 1,500. (also avail. in microfilm) **Indexed:** Agroforest.Abstr., Bio-Contr.News & Info., Biol.Abstr., Chem.Abstr., Curr.Adv.Ecol.Sci., Curr.Cont., Energy Ind., Energy Info.Abstr., Forest.Abstr., Forest Prod.Abstr., Geo.Abstr., I D A, Rev.Plant Path., Rural Devel.Abstr., Seed Abstr., So.Pac.Per.Ind., Soils & Fert. **Document type:** academic/scholarly publication.
—BLDSC (3340.200000); UnCover; SWETS.
Description: Covers forestry practice, research, and conservation within the Commonwealth with news, information, and discoveries worldwide.

COMMUNES FORESTIERES DE FRANCE. see PUBLIC ADMINISTRATION — Municipal Government

634.9 US ISSN 0010-6259
CONNECTICUT WOODLANDS. 1936. q. $10. Connecticut Forest and Park Association, Inc., Middlefield, 16 Meriden Rd., Rockfall, CT 06481-2961. TEL 203-346-2372. Ed. J.E. Hibbard. adv. circ. 2,800. **Indexed:** Biol.Abstr.

634.9 333.7 US
CONSERVATION NEWS DIGEST; news briefs for non-industrial private woodland owners across the nation. 1982. q. $15. American Resources, Inc., 374 Maple Ave., E., Ste. 210, Vienna, VA 22180. TEL 203-255-2700. Ed. Keith A. Argow. bk.rev. circ. 8,000. (back issues avail.) **Document type:** newsletter.

CONSTRUCTION EQUIPMENT BUYERS' GUIDE. see BUILDING AND CONSTRUCTION

634.9 US ISSN 0010-7085
CONSULTANT (COLUMBIA). 1956. q. $20. Association of Consulting Foresters of America, Inc., c/o Webb Forestry Consultants, 309 Church St., Columbia, MS 39429. TEL 601-736-4956. Ed. Micheal A. Webb. adv.; bk.rev. circ. 800. (also avail. in microform)

634.9 CN
COUNCIL OF FOREST INDUSTRIES OF BRITISH COLUMBIA. ANNUAL REPORT. a. Council of Forest Industries of British Columbia, Ste. 1200, 555 Burrard, Vancouver, B.C. V7X 1S7, Canada. TEL 604-684-0211. TELEX 04507752.

634.9 975 US
CRUISER. 1977. q. membership (includes Forest & Conservation History). Forest History Society, 701 Vickers Ave., Durham, NC 27701-3147. TEL 919-682-9319. Ed. Harold K. Steen. circ. 2,000. (tabloid format; back issues avail.; reprint service avail from UMI) **Document type:** newsletter.
Description: News and informational articles pertaining to the members and activities of the Forest History Society, with calendars of events, membership news, conferences and meetings, forthcoming articles in the society's magazine, and historical vignettes.

634.9 SP ISSN 0213-4128
CUADERNOS DE FITOPATOLOGIA; revista de fitopatologia terapeutica. 1984. q. 4837 ptas. (foreign 6058 ptas.). Ediciones y Promociones Lav, S.L., Apdo. 473, 46080 Valencia, Spain. TEL 96-372-02-61. FAX 96-371-05-16. Ed. Francisco Salvador Planes Planes.

634.9 CU ISSN 0138-7782
CUBA. CENTRO DE INFORMACION Y DOCUMENTACION AGROPECUARIO. BOLETIN DE RESENAS. SERIE: FORESTALES. (Abstracts in English) 1981. irreg. exchange basis. Centro de Informacion y Documentacion Agropecuario, Gaveta Postal 4149, Havana 4, Cuba. (Dist. by: Ediciones Cubanas, Obispo No. 461, Apdo. 605, Havana, Cuba) **Indexed:** Agrindex, Field Crop Abstr.
Formerly: Cuba. Centro de Informacion y Divulgacion Agropecuario. Boletin de Resenas. Serie: Forestales.

CURTIN UNIVERSITY OF TECHNOLOGY. MULGA RESEARCH CENTRE JOURNAL. see BIOLOGY

634.9 011 GW
D W J - INFO; Mitteilungen des Bundesverbandes. 1972. q. membersh p. Deutsche Waldjugend, Auf dem Hohenstein 3, 58675 Hemer, Germany. TEL 02372-6902. FAX 02372-62361. Ed.Bd. bk.rev. circ. 3,000. (back issues avail.) **Document type:** bulletin.

634.9 DK ISSN 0905-295X
DANSK SKOVBRUGS TIDSSKRIFT. 1916. q. DKK 190. Dansk Skovforening - Danish Forestry Society, Amalievej 20, 1875 Frederiksberg C, Denmark. TEL 31-244-266. FAX 31-240242. Ed. Soeren Fodgaard. bk.rev.; abstr.; charts; illus.; stat.; index. circ. 1,200. **Indexed:** Biol.Abstr., Chem.Abstr., Forest.Abstr., Forest Prod.Abstr., Soils & Fert. **Document type:** bulletin.
Formerly: Dansk Skovforenings Tidsskrift (ISSN 0011-6475)
Description: Comprehensive articles on research and development in biology and economy. Aimed at the professional forester.

DELTA. see AGRICULTURE

634.9 AG ISSN 0045-9895
DELTA DEL PARANA. (Text in Spanish; summaries in English) 1961. 2/yr. exchange basis. Estacion Experimental Delta del Parana, Casille Correo 14, Campana, Buenos Aires, Argentina.

634.96 DK
DENMARK. PLANT DIRECTORATE. ANNUAL REPORT. (Text in Danish; summaries in English) 1950. a. free. Plant Directorate, Skovbrynet 20, DK-2800 Hellerup, Denmark. Ed. Svend G. Pedersen. circ. 400. **Document type:** government publication.
Formerly: Danish Plant Protection Service. Annual Report (ISSN 0415-3944)

DEUTSCHE DENDROLOGISCHE GESELLSCHAFT. MITTEILUNGEN. see BIOLOGY — Botany

634.96 GW
DEUTSCHER FORSTVEREIN. JAHRESBERICHT. 1950. biennial. DM.15. Deutscher Forstverein e.V., Stresemannallee 61, 60596 Frankfurt a.M., Germany. TEL 069-638674. FAX 069-6312981. adv.; illus. circ. 6,000. **Document type:** proceedings.
Description: Minutes of the meeting of the Deutscher Forstverein.

FORESTS AND FORESTRY

630 634.9 NE ISSN 0166-2287
CODEN: DAMED8
DEVELOPMENTS IN AGRICULTURAL AND MANAGED FOREST ECOLOGY. 1975. irreg., vol.27, 1993. price varies. Elsevier Science B.V., Books Division, P.O. Box 211, 1000 AE Amsterdam, Netherlands. TEL 31-20-5803911. FAX 31-20-5803705. TELEX 18582 ESPA NL. (Subscr. in U.S. and Canada to: Elsevier Science Inc., Box 882, Madison Sq. Sta., New York, NY 10159. TEL 212-989-5800) (back issues avail.) **Document type:** monographic series.
—Faxon; CASDDS.
Refereed Serial

634.9 614 US
E S F QUARTERLY. (Environmental Science and Forestry) 1975. q. free. State University of New York, College of Environmental Science and Forestry, Office of News and Publications, 122 Bray Hall, One Forestry Drive, Syracuse, NY 13210. TEL 315-470-6644. FAX 315-470-6897. Ed. Jeri Lynn Smith. circ. 18,000. (back issues avail.) **Document type:** academic/scholarly publication.
Formerly: E S F (Year).
Description: Presents news of interest to the alumni of the College of Environmental Science and Forestry.

EAST AFRICAN AGRICULTURAL AND FORESTRY JOURNAL. see *AGRICULTURE*

338.1 630 IT ISSN 0012-9836
ECONOMIA MONTANA - LINEA ECOLOGICA. 1969. bi-m. L.80000. Agrifutura Editrice s.n.c., Casella Postale 5101, 00153 Rome Ostiense, Italy. TEL 06-540-32-24. FAX 06-70-30-00-38. Ed. Aldo Laureri. adv.; bk.rev. circ. 18,000. **Document type:** academic/scholarly publication.
Incorporates (in 1982): Arboricoltura da Legno; Pioppicoltura (ISSN 0032-0129)

634.9 HU ISSN 0014-0031
AZ ERDO. (Text in Hungarian; summaries in German and Russian) 1862. m. $30. (Orszagos Erdeszeti Egyesulet) Lapkiado Vallalat, Lenin korut 9-11, 1073 Budapest, Hungary. TEL 222-408. (Subscr. to: Kultura, Box 149, H-1389 Budapest, Hungary.) Ed. Dr. Bela Keresztesi. charts; illus. **Indexed:** Abstr.Bull.Inst.Pap.Chem., Agri.Eng.Abstr., Biol.Abstr., Forest.Abstr., Forest Prod.Abstr., Seed Abstr.

634.9 GW ISSN 0300-1237
CODEN: EJFPA9
EUROPEAN JOURNAL OF FOREST PATHOLOGY/JOURNAL EUROPEEN DE PATHOLOGIE FORESTIERE/EUROPAEISCHE ZEITSCHRIFT FUER FORSTPATHOLOGIE. (Text and summaries in English, French and German; abstracts in English) 1971. 7/yr. DM.638($425) Verlag Paul Parey (Hamburg), Spitalerstr. 12, 20095 Hamburg, Germany. TEL 040-33969-0. FAX 040-33969-199. TELEX 2161391-PARV-D. Ed. P. Schuett. index. (back issues avail.; reprint service avail. from ISI) **Indexed:** Acid Rain Abstr., Acid Rain Ind., Bio-Contr.News & Info., Biol.Abstr., Biotech.Abstr., Chem.Abstr., Curr.Adv.Ecol.Sci., Curr.Cont., Energy Ind., Energy Info.Abstr., Environ.Abstr., Environ.Per.Bibl. (1986-), Excerp.Med., Forest.Abstr., Forest Prod.Abstr., Helminthol.Abstr., Ind.Sci.Rev., Rev.Plant Path., Sci.Cit.Ind., Seed Abstr., Sel.Water Res.Abstr., Soils & Fert., Weed Abstr. **Document type:** academic/scholarly publication.
—BLDSC (3829.729100); UnCover; CASDDS. **CCC.**

634.9 II ISSN 0254-6426
EVERGREEN; newsletter of Kerala Forest Research Institute. 1977. 2/yr. free. Kerala Forest Research Institute, Peechi 680 653, Trichur District, Kerala State, India. TEL 22375. FAX 0487-40451. TELEX 887 275 KFRI IN. Ed. Dr. K.V. Sankaran. bk.rev.; abstr. circ. 600. (back issues avail.) **Indexed:** Forest.Abstr. **Document type:** academic/scholarly publication, newsletter.

634.9 US
F W S SERIES. 1972. irreg. price varies. Virginia Polytechnic Institute and State University, School of Forestry and Wildlife Resources, Blacksburg, VA 24061-0324. TEL 703-231-5481. FAX 703-231-3330. circ. 500. (back issues avail.)

FACULTAD NACIONAL DE AGRONOMIA MEDELLIN. REVISTA. see *AGRICULTURE*

634.9 GW
FANG; Fuehrungszeitschrift. 1973. 3/yr. membership. Deutsche Waldjugend, Auf dem Hohenstein 3, 58675 Hemer, Germany. TEL 02372-6902. FAX 02372-62361. Ed.Bd. circ. 3,000. (back issues avail.) **Document type:** bulletin.

FEDERAL PARKS & RECREATION. see *CONSERVATION*

634.9 BL ISSN 0015-3826
FLORESTA. (Text in Portuguese; summaries in English) 1969. s-a. $20. Fundacao de Pesquisas Florestais do Parana, Caixa Postal 4088, 82501-970 Curitiba, PR, Brazil. TEL 041-253-4616. FAX 041-253-2332. (Co-sponsor: Universidade Federal do Parana) Ed. Carlos Firkowski. adv.; page $300; 100 x 160. bibl.; charts; illus. circ. 500. **Indexed:** Forest.Abstr., Forest Prod.Abstr., Soils & Fert. **Document type:** academic/scholarly publication. **Description:** Articles on forests and forestry. Covers applied research, improvement of methods and techniques, general topics and principles, and bibliography reviews.
Refereed Serial

338.4 US
HD9757.F6
FLORIDA WOOD-USING INDUSTRY DIRECTORY. 1960. a. free. Department of Agriculture and Consumer Services, Division of Forestry, 3125 Conner Blvd., Tallahassee, FL 32399-1650. TEL 904-488-6358. Ed. Leon Irvin. stat. circ. 1,200. **Document type:** directory.
Incorporates: Commodity Drain Report of Florida's Primary Forest Industries (ISSN 0362-191X)

FOCUS (MOSCOW); on renewable natural resources. see *CONSERVATION*

582.16 634.9
635.977 XO ISSN 0139-9144
CODEN: FODEDF
FOLIA DENDROLOGICA. irreg., vol.3, 1977. price varies. (Slovenska Akademia Vied, Ustav Dendrobiologie) Veda, Publishing House of the Slovak Academy of Sciences, Klemensova 19, 814 30 Bratislava, Slovakia. (Dist. by: Slovart, Nam. Slobody 6, 817 64 Bratislava, Slovakia) (Co-sponsor: Arboretum Mlynany) Ed. Frantisek Bencat. **Indexed:** Biol.Abstr., Chem.Abstr., Forest.Abstr., Forest Prod.Abstr., Hort.Abstr., Irr.& Drain.Abstr., Soils & Fert. **Document type:** academic/scholarly publication.
—CASDDS.

634.9 FI ISSN 0015-5543
FOLIA FORESTALIA; metsatieteen aikakauskirja. (Text in English and Finnish) 1963. 4/yr. FIM 200 (or exchange basis). Metsantutkimuslaitos - Finnish Forest Research Institute, Unioninkatu 40 A, SF-00170 Helsinki, Finland. TEL 358-0-857051. FAX 358-0-625308. TELEX 121298 METLA SF. (Co-sponsor: Suomen Metsatieteellinen Seura r.y.) Ed. Eeva Korpilahti. bk.rev.; charts; illus.; stat. **Indexed:** Abstr.Bull.Inst.Pap.Chem., Bio-Contr.News & Info., Biol.Abstr., Curr.Adv.Ecol.Sci., Forest.Abstr., Forest Prod.Abstr., INIS Atomind., Soils & Fert. **Document type:** academic/scholarly publication.
—BLDSC (3969.900000).

634.9 PL ISSN 0071-6677
SD217.P7
FOLIA FORESTALIA POLONICA. SERIES A. LESNICTWO. (Text in Polish; summaries in English, German or Russian) 1958. a. price varies. (Polska Akademia Nauk, Komitet Nauk Lesnych) Wydawnictwo Naukowe P W N, Miodowa 10, 00-251 Warsaw, Poland. TEL 48-22-312738. FAX 48-22-267163. TELEX 813763 PWN PL. (Dist. by: Ars Polona, Krakowskie Przedmiescie 7, 00-068 Warsaw, Poland) Ed. Wieslaw Grochowski. circ. 720. **Indexed:** Abstr.Bull.Inst.Pap.Chem., Agri.Eng.Abstr., Biol.Abstr., Forest.Abstr., Forest Prod.Abstr., Soils & Fert. **Document type:** academic/scholarly publication.
—UnCover.

FOLIA VENATORIA; pol'ovnicky zbornik. see *VETERINARY SCIENCE*

634.9 US ISSN 1046-7009
SD140
FOREST & CONSERVATION HISTORY. 1957. q. $30 to individuals (foreign $36); institutions $50 (foreign $56). Forest History Society, 701 Vickers Ave., Durham, NC 27701-3147. TEL 919-682-9319. Ed. Kevin Foy. adv.; bk.rev.; bibl.; illus. circ. 1,700. (also avail. in microfilm from UMI; reprint service avail. from UMI) **Indexed:** Amer.Hist.& Life, Environ.Per.Bibl. (1972-), Forest.Abstr., Forest Prod.Abstr., Hist.Abstr. **Document type:** academic/scholarly publication.
—UnCover; UMI.
Former titles (until 1989): Journal of Forest History (ISSN 0094-5080); (until 1974): Forest History (ISSN 0015-7422)
Description: Research articles pertaining to the conservation, management, commercial use, history, environment, and artistic depiction of natural resources and landscapes, especially forests, throughout the United States and the world.
Refereed Serial

634.9 DK ISSN 0907-0362
SD191
FOREST & LANDSCAPE RESEARCH. (Text in English) 1905. irreg. (4-5 nos./vol.). DKK 100 per no. Danish Forest and Landscape Research Institute, Skovbrynet 16, DK-2800 Lyngby, Denmark. TEL 45-45-93-12-00. FAX 45-45-93-48-49. Ed. Niels Elers Koch. charts; illus. circ. 800. **Indexed:** Biol.Abstr., Forest.Abstr., Forest Prod.Abstr., Soils & Fert. **Document type:** academic/scholarly publication.
Formerly (until 1990): Forstlige Forsoegsvaesen i Danmark (ISSN 0367-2174)
Description: Forest, park and landscape research of relevance to Northern European conditions.
Refereed Serial

634.9 674 AT ISSN 0015-7392
CODEN: FOTIB3
FOREST AND TIMBER. 1963. a. (foreign Aus.$6). Forestry Commission, 95-99 York St., Sydney, N.S.W. 2000, Australia. Ed. Robert West. bk.rev.; charts; illus.; stat. circ. 15,000. **Indexed:** Aus.Sci.Ind., Biol.Abstr., Curr.Adv.Ecol.Sci., Forest.Abstr., Forest Prod.Abstr.

634.96 574.5 NE ISSN 0378-1127
SD1 CODEN: FECMDW
FOREST ECOLOGY AND MANAGEMENT; an international journal. (Text in English) 1978. 27/yr. (in 9 vols.; 3 nos./vol.). fl.2601($1406) (effective 1994). Elsevier Science B.V., P.O. Box 211, 1000 AE Amsterdam, Netherlands. TEL 31-20-5803911. FAX 31-20-5803598. TELEX 18582 ESPA NL. (Subscr. in U.S. and Canada to: Elsevier Science Inc., Box 882, Madison Sq. Sta., New York, NY 10159. TEL 212-989-5800. FAX 212-633-3990) Eds. R.F. Fisher, E.P. Farrell. adv.; bk.rev.; bibl.; illus.; index. (also avail. in microform from UMI; reprint service avail. from SWZ) **Indexed:** Acid Pre.Dig., Agroforest.Abstr., Biol.Abstr., Biol.& Agr.Ind., Chem.Abstr., Crop Physiol.Abstr., Curr.Adv.Ecol.Sci., Curr.Cont., Ecol.Abstr., Energy Ind., Energy Info.Abstr., Environ.Abstr., Environ.Per.Bibl. (1981-), Excerp.Med., Forest.Abstr., Forest Prod.Abstr., Herb.Abstr., Ind.Sci.Rev., Irr.& Drain.Abstr., Maize Abstr., Plant Grow.Reg.Abstr., Ref.Zh., Rev.Appl.Entomol., Rev.Plant Path., Risk Abstr., Seed Abstr., Sel.Water Res.Abstr., So.Pac.Per.Ind., Soils & Fert., Weed Abstr. **Document type:** academic/scholarly publication.
—BLDSC (3989.800000); Faxon; UnCover; SWETS; CASDDS. **CCC.**
Description: Publishes scientific articles concerned with forest management and conservation, and in particular the applications of biological, ecological and social knowledge to the management of man-made and natural forests.
Refereed Serial

634.9 US ISSN 0015-7406
FOREST FARMER. 1941. bi-m. $40. Forest Farmers Association, Box 95385, Atlanta, GA 30347. TEL 404-325-2954. FAX 404-325-2955. Ed. Jack Warren. adv.; bk.rev.; charts; illus. circ. 5,400. **Indexed:** Abstr.Bull.Inst.Pap.Chem., Environ.Abstr.
—BLDSC (3989.940000); UnCover.

634.9 US ISSN 0071-7452
FOREST FARMER. MANUAL EDITION. 1950. biennial. $20. Forest Farmers Association, Box 95385, Atlanta, GA 30347. TEL 404-325-2954. FAX 404-325-2955. Ed. Jack Warren. adv.; index. circ. 5,500.

FORESTS AND FORESTRY

634.9 KO ISSN 1225-6331
SD399.5 CODEN: IYYYA8
FOREST GENETICS RESEARCH INSTITUTE. RESEARCH REPORT. (Text in English, Korean; summaries in English) 1959. a. free. Forest Genetics Research Institute, P.O. Box 24, Suwon, Kyonggi-do 441-350, S. Korea. TEL 0331-290-1114. FAX 0331-292-4458. Ed. Bo-Sik Lee. film rev.; software rev.; bibl.; illus. circ. 1,000. **Indexed:** Biol.Abstr., Forest.Abstr., Forest Prod.Abstr., Seed Abstr.
—CASDDS.
Formerly: Institute of Forest Genetics. Research Report (ISSN 0073-9294)
Description: Covers different aspects of tree breeding, including selection, hybridization, early test and tissue culture.
Refereed Serial

FOREST INDUSTRIES NEWSLETTER. see *OCCUPATIONAL HEALTH AND SAFETY*

634.9 US ISSN 0015-7457
FOREST NOTES; New Hampshire's conservation magazine. 1936. 5/yr. $26 includes membership. Society for the Protection of New Hampshire Forests, 54 Portsmouth St., Concord, NH 03301. TEL 603-224-9945. FAX 603-228-0423. Ed. Richard Ober. adv.; bk.rev.; index. circ. 11,000. **Indexed:** Biol.Abstr.
—UnCover.

634.9 CN ISSN 0834-2008
FOREST PEOPLE. 1949. q. Can.$35 membership. 150 Consumers Rd., Ste. 502, Willowdale, ON M2J 1P9, Canada. TEL 416-493-4565. FAX 416-493-4608. Ed. Jim Coats. adv.; bk.rev. circ. 702. **Document type:** newsletter.
Formerly: Ontario Forestry Association. Newsletter.

634.9 US ISSN 0846-1007
FOREST PERSPECTIVES; new directions in resource management. 1991. q. $25. World Forestry Center, 4033 S.W. Canyon Rd., Portland, OR 97221. TEL 503-228-1367. FAX 503-228-3624. Ed. Lisa Cohn. adv.; bk.rev. circ. 3,000. (back issues avail.)
Description: Provides a forum for discussion by researchers and managers about policy and application of new forestry management.

634.9 595.7 CN ISSN 0833-5540
CODEN: RFFID4
FOREST PEST MANAGEMENT INSTITUTE. INFORMATION REPORT SERIES. French edition (ISSN 0833-5559) (Text in English and French) 1977. irreg. free. Forestry Canada, Forest Pest Management Institute, P.O. Box 490, 1219 Queen St. E., Sault Ste. Marie, Ont. P6A 5M7, Canada. TEL 705-949-9461. FAX 705-759-5700. Ed. K. Jamieson.
Description: Covers application technology, insecticide residue, buffer zone determination and herbicides.

634.9 595.7 CN ISSN 0714-1734
FOREST PEST MANAGEMENT INSTITUTE NEWSLETTER. (Text in English, French) 1982. q. free. Forestry Canada, Forest Pest Management Institute, 1219 Queen St. E., P.O. Box 490, Sault Ste. Marie, Ont. P6A 5M7, Canada. TEL 705-949-9461. FAX 705-459-5700. Ed. K.B. Jamieson. bibl. circ. 1,600. **Document type:** newsletter.
Description: Provides information on current issues and occurences in forest pest management to forest managers and researchers.

634.96 JA ISSN 0288-3740
FOREST PESTS/SHINRIN BOEKI. (Text in Japanese) 1952. m. $20. Forest Protection Association of Japan - Zenkoku Shinrinkumiai Rengokai, c/o Forest Protection National Federation of Forest Owners' Cooperative Association, Kopu Bldg., 1-1-12 Uchi-Kanda, Chiyoda-ku, Tokyo 100, Japan. Ed. K. Ito. adv.; bk.rev.; illus. circ. 3,000.
Former titles: Forest Protection - Shinrin Boeki; Shinrin Boeki Nyusu (ISSN 0559-8540)

634.96 CN ISSN 0832-1655
FOREST PLANNING CANADA; Canada's community forestry forum. 1985. 6/yr. Can.$30. Woodland Planning Publications Inc., P.O. Box 6234, Station "C", Victoria, B.C. V8P 5L5, Canada. TEL 604-727-6630. FAX 604-727-6630. Ed. Bob Nixon. adv.; bk.rev. circ. 1,700.
—CCC.
Description: News about community, forestry, politics and policy in Canada.

634.9 MY
FOREST RESEARCH BIENNIAL REPORT. (Text in English) 1973. biennial. M.$6. Forest Research Centre, P.O. Box 1407, 90008 Sandakan, Sabah, Malaysia. TEL 089-531422. FAX 089-531068. circ. controlled.

634.9 IO ISSN 0215-028X
CODEN: BPHUED
FOREST RESEARCH BULLETIN. (Text in Indonesian; summaries in English) 1948. irreg. exchange basis. Pusat Penelitian dan Pengembangen Hutan, Jalan Gunung Batu, P.O. Box 66, Bogor, Indonesia. Ed. Harun Alrasjid. circ. 500. (back issues avail.; reprint service avail. from UMI) **Indexed:** Biol.Abstr., Seed Abstr., VITIS. **Document type:** bulletin.
Former titles: Forest Research Institute. Report; Buletin Penelitian Hutan (ISSN 0216-4760); Pusat Penelitian dan Pengembangan Hutan. Laporan - Forest Research and Development Centre. Report.

634.9 II ISSN 0015-7481
FOREST RESEARCH INSTITUTE AND COLLEGES, DEHRA DUN. QUARTERLY NEWS LETTER. 1964. q. free. Forest Research Institute & Colleges, P.O. New Forest, Dehra Dun, India. Ed. S.K. Shukla. circ. 1,450.

634.9 MY ISSN 0126-8198
FOREST RESEARCH INSTITUTE: RESEARCH PAMPHLET. 1953. irreg., no.102, 1988. price varies. Forest Research Institute Malaysia - Institut Penyelidikan Perhutanan Malaysia, Kepong, 52109 Kuala Lumpur, Malaysia. TEL 03-6342633. FAX 603-6367753. TELEX FRIM MA 27007. Ed. Zakaria Ibrahim. bk.rev. circ. 300. (back issues avail.) **Indexed:** Biol.Abstr., Seed Abstr.

634.9 CN ISSN 0835-0752
SD146.B7 CODEN: FREPE7
FOREST RESOURCE DEVELOPMENT AGREEMENT REPORT. m. Ministry of Forests, 31 Bastion Square, Victoria, B.C. V8W 3E7, Canada. (Subscr. to: Crown Publications, 546 Yates St., Victoria, B.C. V8W 1K8, Canada. TEL 604-386-4636) (Co-sponsor: Forestry Canada)

634.9 US ISSN 0015-749X
SD1 CODEN: FOSCAD
FOREST SCIENCE; a journal of research and technical progress. 1955. q. $50 to individuals; institutions $100. Society of American Foresters, 5400 Grosvenor Ln., Bethesda, MD 20814. TEL 301-897-8720. FAX 301-897-3690. Ed. William F. Hyde. adv.; bk.rev.; bibl.; charts; illus.; index. circ. 1,641. (also avail. in microform from UMI; reprint service avail. from UMI) **Indexed:** Abstr.Bull.Inst.Pap.Chem., Biol.Abstr., Biol.& Agr.Ind., Chem.Abstr., Crop Physiol.Abstr., Curr.Adv.Ecol.Sci., Curr.Cont., Energy Ind., Energy Info.Abstr., Environ.Per.Bibl., Excerp.Med., Forest.Abstr., Forest Prod.Abstr., Geo.Abstr., Herb.Abstr., Hort.Abstr., Ind.Sci.Rev., INIS Atomind., Irr.& Drain.Abstr., Rev.Plant Path., Risk Abstr., Sci.Cit.Ind., Seed Abstr., Sel.Water Res.Abstr., Soils & Fert., Weed Abstr. **Document type:** academic/scholarly publication.
—BLDSC (3998.700000); Faxon; UnCover; SWETS; UMI.
Description: Comprehensive coverage of a full range of subjects fundamental to forestry: silviculture, soils, biometry, diseases, recreation, photosynthesis, tree physiology, all aspects of management and harvesting, and policy analysis.
Refereed Serial

634.9 US ISSN 0071-7568
FOREST SCIENCE MONOGRAPHS. 1959. irreg. (1-2/yr.), no.28, 1987. included in subscription to Forest Science. Society of American Foresters, 5400 Grosvenor Ln., Bethesda, MD 20814. TEL 301-897-8720. FAX 301-897-3690. Ed. William F. Hyde. bk.rev. circ. 1,670. **Indexed:** Abstr.Bull.Inst.Pap.Chem., Biol.Abstr., Biol.& Agr.Ind., Chem.Abstr., Forest.Abstr., Forest Prod.Abstr., Geo.Abstr., Soils & Fert. **Document type:** academic/scholarly publication.

634.9 CN ISSN 0706-7747
FOREST TIMES. 1979. 6/yr. m. Department of Natural Resources, Box 68, Truro, NS B2N 5B8, Canada. TEL 902-893-5660. FAX 902-893-6102. Ed. Sheena Masson. bk.rev.; charts; illus. circ. 16,000.

634.9 DK ISSN 0105-4120
CODEN: FTIPA3
FOREST TREE IMPROVEMENT. 1969. irreg. price varies. (Royal Agric.ltural University) DSR Booksellers, Thorvaldsensvej 40, DK-1871 Frederiksberg C, Denmark. illus. **Indexed:** Curr.Adv.Ecol.Sci., Forest.Abstr., Forest Prod.Abstr.

634.9 US ISSN 1069-2002
FOREST VOICE. 1989. q. $35 membership. Native Forest Counc l, Box 2171, Eugene, OR 97402. TEL 503-688-2600. FAX 503-461-2156. Ed. W.V. Rozek. circ. 10,000. **Document type:** newsletter.

634.9 333.7 US ISSN 1057-2724
SD143 CODEN: FOWAEV
FOREST WATCH; the citizens' forestry magazine. 1980. m. $27.50 (foreign $37.50). Cascade Holistic Economic Consultants (CHEC), 14417 S.E. Laurie, Oak Grove, OR 97267. TEL 503-652-7049. Ed. Jeff St. Clair. adv.; bk.rev.; index, cum.index. circ. 1,500. (back issues avail.)
—UnCover.
Formerly: Forest Planning (ISSN 0738-0585)
Description: News and articles on legislative, economic, environmental, and policy issues of interest to the national forest and its habitats.

634.9 CU ISSN 0426-9373
FORESTAL.* 1970. m. Federacion Nacional de Trabajadores de la Industria Madera, Muebles y sus Anexos, c/o Central de Trabajadores de Cuba, Pal. de Trabajadores, San Carlos y Penalver, Havana, Cuba. Ed. Jose Solis. circ. 12,000. **Indexed:** Forest.Abstr., Forest Prod.Abstr.

634.9 UK ISSN 0015-752X
SD1 CODEN: FRSTAH
FORESTRY. 1927. q. £90($170) (effective 1994). (Institute of Chartered Foresters of Great Britain) Oxford University Press, Oxford Journals, Walton St., Oxford OX2 6DP, England. TEL 0865-56767. FAX 0865-56646. TELEX 837330-OXPRES-G. (U.S. subscr. to: Oxford University Press Inc., 2001 Evans Rd., Cary, NC 27513. TEL 919-677-0977) Eds. J.A. Petty, I.R. Brown. adv.; bk.rev.; bibl.; charts; illus.; stat.; index. circ. 1,900. (also avail. in microform from UMI; reprint service avail. from UMI) **Indexed:** Biol.Abstr., Br.Hum.Ind., Chem.Abstr., Curr.Adv.Ecol.Sci., Curr.Cont., Environ.Per.Bibl. (1981-), Forest.Abstr., Forest Prod.Abstr., Geo.Abstr., Ind.Sci Rev., Irr.& Drain.Abstr., Plant Grow.Reg.Abstr., Rev.Appl.Entomol., Rev.Plant Path., Sci.Cit.Ind., Weed Abstr. **Document type:** academic/scholarly publication.
●Also available online. Vendor(s): European Space Agency (File nos.16 & 124/CAB).
—BLDSC (4000.000000); Faxon; UnCover; SWETS; UMI; CASDDS. **CCC.**
Description: Fundamental study of forestry, especially in its scientific aspects, in relation to its practice and to its impact on man and the environment.

634.9 UK ISSN 0308-7638
FORESTRY & BRITISH TIMBER. 1972. m. £40 (foreign £47). Benn Publications Ltd. (Subsidiary of: Morgan-Grampian plc), Benn House, Sovereign Way, Tonbridge, Kent TN9 1RW, England. TEL 0732-364422. FAX 0732-361534. Ed. Anthony Burt. adv. contact: Tim Oliver. bk.rev. circ. 4,756. **Indexed:** Agri.Eng.Abstr., Agroforest.Abstr., Forest.Abstr., Forest Prod.Abstr., Weed Abstr. **Document type:** trade publication.
—BLDSC (4001.290000).
Formerly: Forestry and Home Grown Timber (ISSN 0306-8129)

FORESTS AND FORESTRY

634.9   CN   ISSN 0015-7546
SD1   CODEN: FRCRAX
FORESTRY CHRONICLE. (Text in English and French) 1925. 6/yr. Can.$75 to individuals (US $88); institutions Can.$83 (US $100). Canadian Institute of Forestry - Institut Forestier du Canada, 1005-151 Slater St., Ottawa, ON K1P 5H3, Canada. TEL 613-234-2242. FAX 613-234-6181. Ed. J.H. Cayford. adv.; bk.rev.; illus.; charts; index, cum.index vols.1-44 (1925-1970). circ. 2,800. **Indexed:** Abstr.Bull.Inst.Pap.Chem., Bio-Contr.News & Info., Biol.Abstr., Chem.Abstr., Curr.Adv.Ecol.Sci., Curr.Cont., Environ.Abstr., Environ.Per.Bibl. (1972-), Forest.Abstr., Forest Prod.Abstr., Ind.Sci.Rev., Risk Abstr., Rural Recreat.Tour.Abstr., Sci.Cit.Ind., Soils & Fert., Weed Abstr., World Agri.Econ. & Rural Sociol.Abstr. **Document type:** academic/scholarly publication.
—BLDSC (4004.000000); Faxon; UnCover; SWETS; UMI. **CCC.**

634   US
FORESTRY: LATIN AMERICAN INDUSTRIAL REPORT. (Avail. for each of 22 Latin American countries) 1985. a. $435 per country report. Aquino Productions, Box 15760, Stamford, CT 06901. TEL 203-325-3138. Ed. Andres C. Aquino.

634.9   AT
FORESTRY LOG. 1968. a. Aus.$6. Australian National University, Forestry Department, Forestry Students Society, G.P.O. Box 4, Canberra, A.C.T. 2601, Australia. Ed.Bd. adv. circ. 600.

634.9   CN   ISSN 1185-9598
HD9764.C2
FORESTRY ON THE HILL. 1981. 6/yr. Can.$110. Canadian Forestry Association, 185 Somerset St. W., Ste. 203, Ottawa, ON K2P 0J2, Canada. TEL 613-232-1815. FAX 613-232-4210. Ed. Edwinna von Baeyer. adv. contact: Glen Blouin. bk.rev.; circ. 250 (paid). **Document type:** newsletter.
Formerly: What They Say about Forestry on the Hill (ISSN 0828-6299)
Description: Reports on forestry discussions in the House of Commons, Senate and federal departments and agencies; includes forest industry production and statistics.

634.9   MW
FORESTRY RESEARCH INSTITUTE OF MALAWI. RESEARCH RECORD. (Text in English) 1967. irreg. price varies. Forestry Research Institute, P.O. Box 270, Zomba, Malawi. TEL 265-522-866. FAX 265-522-782. TELEX 43533-FRIM-MI. Ed. Frederick P. Ziyabu. circ. 200. (back issues avail.) **Indexed:** Forest.Abstr. **Document type:** government publication.

634.9 674 614.7   US   ISSN 0195-5861
SD254.W4
FORESTRY RESEARCH WEST. 1973. q. free. U.S. Forest Service, Rocky Mountain Forest and Range Experiment Sta., 240 W. Prospect, Ft. Collins, CO 80526. TEL 303-498-1278. Ed. Rick Fletcher. bk.rev.; circ. 10,000. **Indexed:** Bio-Contr.News & Info., Environ.Abstr., Forest.Abstr. **Document type:** government publication.
—Faxon; UnCover.
Formerly (until 1979): Forestry Research (ISSN 0093-0148)
Description: Discusses a range of forestry-related topics for land managers.

634.9   NE   ISSN 0924-5480
FORESTRY SCIENCES. (Text in English) 1982. irreg., latest 1992. price varies. Kluwer Academic Publishers, Postbus 17, 3300 AA Dordrecht, Netherlands. TEL 31-78-334911. FAX 31-78-334254. TELEX 29245 KAPG NL. (Dist. by: Kluwer Academic Publishers Group, P.O. Box 322, 3300 AH Dordrecht, Netherlands. TEL 31-78-524400; N. America dist. addr.: Box 358, Accord Sta., Hingham, MA 02018-0358. TEL 617-871-6600) (back issues avail.) **Document type:** monographic series.

634.9   US
FORESTRY UPDATE. 1975. q. free. Oregon State University, Forestry Extension, Corvallis, OR 97331. TEL 503-737-3700. bk.rev.; abstr.; bibl. circ. 3,000.

634.9   US   ISSN 0015-7589
    CODEN: FOPEA4
FORESTS & PEOPLE. 1951. q. $11 to non-members (foreign $25) (effective 1993). Louisiana Forestry Association, Drawer 5067, Alexandria, LA 71307. TEL 318-443-2558. Ed. Georgiann Gullett. adv.; bk.rev.; illus.; index. circ. 7,500. **Indexed:** Chem.Abstr. **Document type:** trade publication.
Description: Covers all phases of Louisiana forestry and the people involved in it. Level ranges from technical to more general.

634.9 338.174   SZ   ISSN 0015-7597
FORET; revue de sylviculture et d'economie forestiere. 1947. m. 44 SFr. (foreign 49 SFr.). Economie Forestiere Association Suisse, Rosenweg 14, CH-4501 Solothurn, Switzerland. TEL 065-231011. FAX 065-233620. Ed. Veronique Salamin. adv.; B&W page 880 SFr.; trim 185 x 260. bk.rev.; charts; illus.; mkt.; stat.; index. circ. 2,421. **Indexed:** Forest.Abstr., Forest Prod.Abstr. **Document type:** academic/scholarly publication.

634.9   CN   ISSN 0380-321X
    CODEN: FRCVAB
FORET CONSERVATION; le magazine de la foret, de l'environnement et des sciences naturelles. 1939. 6/yr. Can.$27.73 (foreign Can.$38). Association Forestiere Quebecoise Inc., 175 rue St. Jean, 4e etage, Quebec, PQ G1R 1N4, Canada. TEL 418-529-2542. FAX 418-529-3021. Ed. Serge Beaucher. adv.; B&W page Can.$1230; trim 7 1/4 x 9 3/4. bk.rev.; charts; illus.; index. circ. 8,000. **Indexed:** Acid Pre.Dig., Biol.Abstr., Chem.Abstr., Curr.Adv.Ecol.Sci., Geo.Abstr., Periodex, Pt.de Rep. (1979-), RADAR. **Document type:** academic/scholarly publication.
Description: Covers subjects related to the forest, the environment and the natural sciences.

634.9   FR   ISSN 0992-955X
FORET DE GASCOGNE. 1932. m. 170 F. Maison de la Foret, 17 rue Esprit-des-Lois, 33080 Bordeaux Cedex, France. TEL 56-90-92-44. FAX 56-81-65-95. Ed. Jean Louis Martres. circ. 5,000. **Document type:** corporate report.

634.9 230   FR   ISSN 0150-6404
FORET - ENTREPRISE. 1982. 8/yr. 250 F. (foreign 330 F.). Institut pour le Developpement Forestier, 23 av. Bosquet, 75007 Paris, France. TEL 45-55-23-49. FAX 45-55-98-54. Ed. Patriu Devos. adv.; bk.rev.; illus. circ. 10,000. **Indexed:** Forest.Abstr.
Formerly (until 1982): Bulletin de la Vulgarisation Forestiere.
Description: Covers new techniques, recent research discoveries.

634.9   FR   ISSN 0153-0216
LA FORET PRIVEE; revue forestiere europeenne. 1958. bi-m. 320 F.($64) 61 av. de la Grande Armee, 75782 Paris Cedex 16, France. FAX 40-67-16-62. Ed. Lucile Decoufle; Pub. Charles Chavet. adv.; bk.rev.; bibl.; illus.; stat.; tr.lit.; index. circ. 4,000. **Indexed:** Forest.Abstr., Forest Prod.Abstr.
Former titles (until 1977): Foret Privee Francaise et Revues Forestiere Europeenne (ISSN 0153-0208); Foret Privee (ISSN 0046-4600)

634.9   FR   ISSN 0046-4619
FORETS DE FRANCE ET ACTION FORESTIERE. 1951. 10/yr. 280 F. (foreign 350 F.). Federation Nationale des Syndicats de Proprietaires Forestiers Sylviculteurs, 6 rue de la Tremoille, 75008 Paris, France. FAX 47-23-38-58. Ed. Guy de Selve. adv.; bk.rev.; bibl.; charts; illus.; stat.; index. circ. 8,000. **Indexed:** Acid Pre.Dig.

634.9   GW   ISSN 0344-1296
FORST, HOLZ UND JAGD TASCHENBUCH. 1947. a. DM.28. Verlag M. und H. Schaper GmbH, Kalandstr. 4, 31061 Alfeld, Germany. TEL 05181-8009-0. FAX 05181-800933. (Subscr. to: Postfach 1642, 31046 Alfeld, Germany) circ. 7,000. **Document type:** bulletin.

634.9 674   GW   ISSN 0932-9315
SD1   CODEN: FOHOEW
FORST UND HOLZ. 1946. 24/yr. DM.185. Verlag M. und H. Schaper GmbH, Kalandstr. 4, 31061 Alfeld, Germany. TEL 05181-8009-0. FAX 05181-800933. (Subscr. to: Postfach 1642, 31046 Alfeld, Germany) Ed. Dr. H.A. Guessone. adv.; bk.rev.; stat.; index, cum.index. circ. 3,000. **Indexed:** Agri.Eng.Abstr., Chem.Abstr., Forest.Abstr., Forest Prod.Abstr., Rural Recreat.Tour.Abstr., Seed Abstr., Soils & Fert., World Agri.Econ. & Rural Sociol.Abstr. **Document type:** trade publication.
—BLDSC (4012.880000). **CCC.**
Formerly: Forst- und Holzwirt (ISSN 0015-7961)

634.9   GW
FORST UND TECHNIK; Fachzeitschrift fuer Holztransport, Forst- und Umwelttechnik. m. DM.89 (foreign DM.112). (Bundesvereinigung des Holztransportgewerbes) D L V Deutscher Landwirtschaftsverlag Berlin GmbH, Thulestr. 7, 13189 Berlin, Germany. TEL 030-47800011. FAX 030-47800040. (Co-sponsor: Bundesarbeitsgemeinschaft Forstwirtschaftlicher Lohnunternehmer) Ed. Klaus Boehme. adv. **Document type:** trade publication.

634.9   GW   ISSN 0300-4112
SD1
FORSTARCHIV. (Text in German; summaries in English and German) 1925. 6/yr. DM.256. Verlag M. und H. Schaper GmbH, Kalandstr. 4, 31061 Alfeld, Germany. TEL 05181-8009-0. FAX 05181-800933. (Subscr. to: Postfach 1642, 31046 Alfeld, Germany) Eds. Dr. C. Wiebecke, Dr. Weidelt. adv.; bk.rev.; charts; illus.; stat. circ. 900. **Indexed:** Agri.Eng.Abstr., Chem.Abstr., Excerp.Med., Forest.Abstr., Forest Prod.Abstr., Rural Recreat.Tour.Abstr., Soils & Fert., World Agri.Econ. & Rural Sociol.Abstr. **Document type:** bulletin.
—**CCC.**

634.9   GW   ISSN 0015-797X
FORSTLICHE MITTEILUNGEN. 1947. s-m. DM.48($24) Gewerkschaft Gartenbau, Land- und Forstwirtschaft, Darmstaedterstr. 62, 64409 Messel, Germany. TEL 06159-656. FAX 06159-5795. Ed. Paul-Rudolf Haerle. adv.; bk.rev.; charts; illus.; stat. circ. 9,800. **Document type:** bulletin.

634.9   GW   ISSN 0015-7996
FORSTPFLANZEN-FORSTSAMEN. 1961. 4/yr. DM.36. Wirtschafts- und Forstverlag Euting KG, Tannenstr. 1, 56587 Strassenhaus, Germany. Ed. Helmut H. Euting. adv.; bk.rev.; bibl.; charts; illus.; stat.

634.9   GW   ISSN 0015-8003
FORSTWISSENSCHAFTLICHES CENTRALBLATT; Vereinigt mit Tharandter Forstliches Jahrbuch. (Text in German; summaries in English and German) 1879. bi-m. DM.244($163) Verlag Paul Parey (Hamburg), Spitalerstr. 12, 20095 Hamburg, Germany. TEL 040-33969-0. FAX 040-33969-199. TELEX 2161391-PARV-D. Ed. U. Ammer. adv.; bk.rev.; illus.; index. (reprint service avail. from ISI; back issues avail.) **Indexed:** Biol.Abstr., Chem.Abstr., Curr.Adv.Ecol.Sci., Curr.Cont., Excerp.Med., Forest.Abstr., Forest Prod.Abstr., INIS Atomind., Rural Recreat.Tour.Abstr., Seed Abstr., Soils & Fert., World Agri.Econ. & Rural Sociol.Abstr. **Document type:** academic/scholarly publication.
—BLDSC (4014.500000). **CCC.**

333.7 634.9   FR
FRANCE. DIRECTION DE L'ESPACE RURAL ET DE LA FORET. RAPPORT SUR LE FONDS FORESTIER NATIONAL; rapport au Comite de Controle pour l'annee. 1948. a. free. Ministere de l'Agriculture et de la Peche, Direction de l'Espace Rural et de la Foret (DERF), 1 ter, av. de Lowendal, 75007 Paris, France. stat. circ. 500. **Document type:** government publication.
Formerly: France. Direction des Forets. Rapport sur le Fonds Forestier National.

338.4 634.9   FR
FRANCE. MINISTERE DE L'AGRICULTURE ET DE LA FORET. PRODUCTIONS DE BOIS ET DE SCIAGES. a. Ministere de l'Agriculture et de la Foret, Service Central des Enquetes et Etudes Statistiques, 4, av. de Saint Mande, 75012 Paris, France. **Document type:** government publication.
Former titles: France. Ministere de l'Agriculture. Production de Bois et de Sciages; France. Direction des Forets. Production de la Branche Exploitation Forestiere et Production des Branches Science et Carbonisation en Foret.

FORESTS AND FORESTRY 2605

634.96 631.7 US
FRIENDS OF THE TREES SOCIETY NEWSLETTER. 1986. q. $10 (effective Jan. 1991). Friends of the Trees Society, Box 1064, Tonasket, WA 98855. TEL 509-485-2705. Ed. Michael Pilarski. bk.rev. circ. 3,000.
 Description: Explores sustainable agriculture and forestry worldwide.

634.9 MY
FRIM TECHNICAL INFORMATION. (Editions in Englisn, Malay) 1987. irreg. price varies. Forest Research Institute Malaysia, Kepong, 52109 Kuala Lumpur, Malaysia. TEL 03-6342633. Ed. Norhayati Nordin.

634.9 CC ISSN 1001-389X
FUJIAN LINXUEYUAN XUEBAO/FUJIAN COLLEGE OF FORESTRY. JOURNAL. (Text in Chinese; abstracts in English) 1960. q. Y4 (foreign $10) per no. Fujian Linxueyuan - Fujian Institute of Forestry, Xiqin, Nanping, Fujian 353001, People's Republic of China. TEL 0599-528080. FAX 0599-528085. Ed. Yu Xintuo. adv. contact: Yang Lunzeng. circ. 800 (paid); 400 (controlled). **Document type:** academic/scholarly publication.

634.9 CC
FUJIAN LINYE/FUJIAN FORESTRY. (Text in Chinese) bi-m. Y5.40. Fujiansheng Linye Ting - Forestry Bureau of Fujian Province, 25 Guping Lu, Fuzhou, Fujian 350003, People's Republic of China. TEL 535817. (Dist. overseas by: Jiangsu Publications Import & Export Corp., 56 Gao Yun Ling, Nanjing, Jiangsu, P.R.C).
 Description: Covers regional afforestation projects, forest protection, and national forestry policies, industries and environmental education.

634.9 JA ISSN 0288-8491
FUKUI PREFECTURAL GENERAL GREEN CENTER. FOREST RESEARCH DIVISION. ANNUAL REPORT. (Text in Japanese) 1961. a. free. Fukui Prefectural Green Center, Forest Research Division, 15, Rakuma, Manuoka-Cho, Sakai-Gun, Fukui 910-02, Japan. index. circ. 200. (back issues avail.)

634.9 FR ISSN 0761-3067
 CODEN: GAUSEM
GAUSSENIA; travaux du laboratoire forestier de toulouse. (Text in French; summaries in various languages) 1984. a. 20 F. Universite Paul Sabatier, Laboratoire Botanique et Forestier, 31062 Toulouse, France. Ed. G. Durrieu. bk.rev. circ. 250. **Indexed:** Biol.Abstr.
 Description: Original papers on botany and ecology of forest and forest trees or plants.

634.9 JA ISSN 0386-2321
GENDAI RINGYO/CURRENT FORESTRY. (Text in Japanese) 1964. m. 4200 Yen($33) (effective Apr. 1992). National Forestry Extension Association in Japan (NFEAJ), Sankaido Bldg., 1-9-13 Akasaka, Minato-ku, Tokyo, Japan. TEL 03-3583-8461. FAX 03-3583-8465. Ed. Hideo Abe. adv.; bk.rev. circ. 16,000.

634.9 US
GEORGIA FORESTRY. 1948. q. free to Georgia landowners. Forestry Commission, Forest Education Department, Box 819, Macon, GA 31298. TEL 912-751-3534. FAX 912-751-3465. Ed. Howard E. Bennett. bk.rev./ circ. 6,000 (controlled). **Document type:** government publication.
 Description: Features informational articles, success stories, progress reports and other material of interest to the forest community and the general public.

634.9 GW
GEWERKSCHAFT GARTENBAU, LAND- UND FORSTWIRTSCHAFT. FORSTLICHE MITTEILUNGEN. 1949. bi-m. Gewerkschaft Gartenbau, Land- und Forstwirtschaft, Druselstalstr. 51, 34063 Kassel, Germany. TEL 0561-93790. **Document type:** bulletin.

634.9 BU ISSN 0017-2286
 CODEN: GONAAR
GORSKOSTOPANSKA NAUKA/FORESTRY SCIENCE. (Summaries in English, French, German and Russian) 1964. 6/yr. 9.50 lv. (Akademiia na Selskostopanskite Nauki - Academy of Agricultural Sciences) Publishing House of the Bulgarian Academy of Sciences, Acad. G. Bonchev St., Bldg. 6, 1113 Sofia, Bulgaria. (Dist. by: Hemus, 6, Rouski Blvd., 1000 Sofia, Bulgaria) Ed.Bd. illus.; index. circ. 590. (reprint service avail. from IRC) **Indexed:** Biol.Abstr., BSL Biol., Chem.Abstr., Excerp.Med., Forest.Abstr., Forest Prod.Abstr., Rural Recreat.Tour.Abstr., World Agri.Econ. & Rural Sociol.Abstr. **Document type:** academic/scholarly publication.

634.9 XV ISSN 0017-2723
GOZDARSKI VESTNIK/SLOVENIAN JOURNAL OF FORESTRY; strokovna revija. (Text in Slovenian; summaries in English, German) 1938. m. $40. Zveza Drustev Inzenirjev in Tehnikov Gozdarstva in Lesarstva Slovenije, Erjavceva Cesta 15, Ljubljana, Slovenia. Ed. Zivan Veselic. circ. 2,000.

634.9 JA ISSN 0389-0988
GURIN PAWA/GREEN POWER. (Text in Japanese) 1979. m. Shinrin Bunka Kyokai - Forests Culture Association, c/o Asahi Shimbun Tokyo Honsha, 3-2 Tsukiji 5-chome, Chuo-ku, Tokyo 104-11, Japan. Ed. Ihara Shunichi.
 Description: Contains news of the association.

634.9 CN ISSN 0072-9140
H.R. MACMILLAN LECTURESHIP IN FORESTRY. 1950. irreg. free. University of British Columbia, Faculty of Forestry, 270-2357 Main Mall, Vancouver, BC V6T 1Z4, Canada. TEL 604-822-2727. FAX 604-822-8645. **Indexed:** Forest.Abstr. **Document type:** academic/scholarly publication.
 Description: Series of lectures on a variety of forestry topics.

HANNOVERSCHE LAND- UND FORSTWIRTSCHAFTLICHE ZEITUNG. see AGRICULTURE

634.9 DK ISSN 0017-9507
HEDESELSKABETS TIDSSKRIFT; tidsskrift for grundforbedring og skovbrug. 1879. 6/yr. DKK 75. Hedeselskabet, Viborg, Denmark. Ed. Jens Qvist. adv.; bk.rev.; charts; illus.; stat. circ. 16,600.

634.9 CN ISSN 0708-2169
HIBALLER FOREST MAGAZINE. 1948-1982; resumed 1983. m. Can.$20($18) H B Publishers Ltd., 117-534 Seymour St., Vancouver, B.C. V6B 3H6, Canada. TEL 604-669-7833. Ed. Paul Young. adv.; illus. circ. 10,600.
 Formerly: Hiballer Magazine (ISSN 0318-7632)

HIGHLIGHTS. see AGRICULTURE

634.9 GW ISSN 0724-6471
HOLZ AKTUELL. 1980. irreg. Karl Danzer Furnierwerke, Storlachstr. 1, 72760 Reutlingen, Germany. TEL 07121-307-0. FAX 07121-30783. Ed. Robert Matzek. adv. contact: Rolf Herzog. circ. 20,000. **Document type:** trade publication.

HOLZ - KURIER; forst- und holzwirtschaftlicher Wochendienst. see FORESTS AND FORESTRY — Lumber And Wood

HOLZFORSCHUNG; international journal of the biology, chemistry, physics and technology of wood. see FORESTS AND FORESTRY — Lumber And Wood

634.9 GW ISSN 0437-7168
DIE HOLZZUCHT. (Text in German; summaries in English) 1946. s-a. DM.18. Forschungsinstitut fuer Schnellwachsende Baumarten, Professor-Oelkers-Str. 6, 34346 Hann Muenden, Germany. TEL 05541-700446. bk.rev.; abstr.; cum.index. circ. 1,200. (back issues avail.) **Indexed:** Crop Physiol.Abstr., Field Crop Abstr., Forest.Abstr., Forest Prod.Abstr., Herb.Abstr., Soils & Fert. **Document type:** academic/scholarly publication.
 —BLDSC (4325.300000).
 Description: Research in the cultivation of fast growing broad leaved and coniferous tree species. Features propagation, disease control, economical and ecological aspects. Includes reports of events.

HORACE M. ALBRIGHT CONSERVATION LECTURESHIP. see CONSERVATION

634.9 BE
HOUTHANDEL EN NIJVERHEID. 1925. w. 4290 BEF($139) N.V. Drukkerij de Bouwkroniek, Zennestraat 37, B-1000 Brussels, Belgium. TEL 32-2-5138295. FAX 32-2-5117015. Ed. Paul Darmont. adv. contact: Leo van Hoorick. bk.rev.; charts; illus circ. 2,300. **Document type:** trade publication.

634.9 BL ISSN 0100-4557
SD1 CODEN: PSIFDB
I P E F JOURNAL. (Text in Portuguese; summaries in English) 1970. s-a. exchange basis only. Universidade de Sao Paulo, Instituto de Pesquisas e Estudos Florestais, Escola Superior de Agricultura "Luiz de Queiroz", Caixa Postal 530, 13400-970 Piracicaba SP, Brazil. TEL 0194-33-6155. FAX 0194-336081. TELEX 197881 IPEF BR. Ed. Walter de Paula Lima. adv.; bk.rev.; bibl.; tr.lit. circ. 1,000. **Indexed:** Abstr.Bull.Inst.Pap.Chem., Biol.Abstr., Forest.Abstr. **Document type:** academic/scholarly publication.
 —BLDSC (4567.283700); CASDDS.
 Description: Integrates research in silviculture, technology, environment, social economics and energy relating to forestry.

634.9 US ISSN 0276-2056
I S T F NEWS. Spanish edition: I S T F Noticias (ISSN 0743-5991); French edition: I S T F Nouvelles. 1980. q. $25 membership. International Society of Tropical Foresters - Sociedade Internacional de Forestales Tropicales, 5400 Grosvenor Ln., Bethesda, MD 20814. TEL 301-897-8720. FAX 301-897-3690. Ed. Frank H. Wadsworth. adv.; bk.rev.; bibl.; charts; illus. circ. 2,000.
 Description: Information about recent developments in tropical forestry, brief notes on programs and publications.

634.9 AU
I U F R O NEWS. 1973. q. membership. International Union of Forestry Research Organizations - Internationaler Verband Forstlicher Forschungsanstalten, Seckendorf-Gudent-Weg 8, A-1131 Vienna, Austria. TEL 0222-8770151. FAX 0222-8779355. TELEX 75312646-IUSC-A. bk.rev. circ. 7,000. **Indexed:** Forest.Abstr. **Document type:** newsletter.

634.9 AU ISSN 1016-3263
I U F R O WORLD SERIES. (Text mainly in English, French, German; occasionally in Italian, Russian) 1990. irreg. price varies. International Union of Forestry Research Organizations - Internationaler Verband Forstlicher Forschungsanstalten, Seckendorf-Gudert-Weg 8, A-1131 Vienna, Austria. TEL 0222-8770151. FAX 0222-8779355. **Document type:** monographic series.

ILLINOIS. DEPARTMENT OF CONSERVATION. OUTDOOR ILLINOIS. see CONSERVATION

634.9 US
IN FOCUS (WASHINGTON). m. $110 to non-members (foreign $133). National Forest Products Association, 1250 Connecticut Ave., N.W., Washington, DC 20036. TEL 202-463-2700. FAX 202-463-2785. Ed. Tim McCarthy. circ. 4,000.
 Formerly: Forest Industries Newsletter (Washington) (ISSN 0163-9129)

634.9 II ISSN 0073-635X
SD87 CODEN: IFOBAS
INDIAN FOREST BULLETIN (NEW SERIES). (Text in English) 1911. irreg., no.276, 1979. price varies. Forest Research Institute & Colleges, P.O. New Forest, Dehra Dun, India. circ. 500. **Indexed:** Biol.Abstr., Curr.Adv.Ecol.Sci., Forest.Abstr., Forest Prod.Abstr., Indian Sci.Abstr., Rev.Appl.Entomol., Rev.Plant Path.

634.9 II ISSN 0073-6368
INDIAN FOREST LEAFLETS (NEW SERIES). (Text in English) 1941. irreg., no.197, 1982. price varies. Forest Research Institute & Colleges, P.O. New Forest, Dehra Dun, India. circ. 500. **Indexed:** Biol.Abstr., Curr.Adv.Ecol.Sci., Forest.Abstr., Forest Prod.Abstr., Indian Sci.Abstr.

634.9 II
INDIAN FOREST RECORDS (NEW SERIES) FOREST MANAGEMENT AND MENSURATION. (Text in English) 1976. irreg., vol. 3, no.5, 1979. price varies. Forest Research Institute and Colleges, P.O. New Forest, Dehra Dun, India. circ. 500. **Indexed:** Biol. Abstr., Forest. Abstr., Indian Sci. Abstr.

FORESTS AND FORESTRY

634.9 II ISSN 0073-6406
INDIAN FOREST RECORDS (NEW SERIES) FOREST PATHOLOGY. (Text in English) 1950. irreg., vol.2, no.11, 1973. price varies. Forest Research Institute & Colleges, P.O. New Forest, Dehra Dun, India. circ. 500. **Indexed:** Biol.Abstr., Curr.Adv.Ecol.Sci., Forest.Abstr., Indian Sci.Abstr.
Formerly: Indian Forest Records (New Series) Mycology.

634.9 II ISSN 0073-6422
INDIAN FOREST RECORDS (NEW SERIES) SILVICULTURE. (Text in English) 1936. irreg., vol.13, no.1, 1974. price varies. Forest Research Institute & Colleges, P.O. New Forest, Dehra Dun, India. circ. 500. **Indexed:** Biol.Abstr., Curr.Adv.Ecol.Sci., Forest.Abstr., Indian Sci.Abstr.

634.9 II ISSN 0019-4816
SD1 CODEN: IFORA8
INDIAN FORESTER. (Text in English) 1875. m. Rs.100($50) Forest Research Institute & Colleges, P.O. New Forest, Dehra Dun, India. Ed. R.S. Mathur. adv.; bk.rev.; bibl.; charts; illus.; index. circ. 2,050. **Indexed:** Abstr.Bull.Inst.Pap.Chem., Agri.Eng.Abstr., Agroforest.Abstr., Bio-Contr.News & Info., Biol.Abstr., Chem.Abstr., Crop Physiol.Abstr., Curr.Adv.Ecol.Sci., Field Crop Abstr., Forest.Abstr., Forest Prod.Abstr., Herb.Abstr., Hort.Abstr., Ind.Vet., Irr.& Drain.Abstr., Plant Grow.Reg.Abstr., Rev.Plant Path., Rural Devel.Abstr., Seed Abstr., Soils & Fert., Trop.Oil Seeds Abstr., Weed Abstr. **Document type:** academic/scholarly publication.
—BLDSC (4409.200000); UnCover; SWETS; CASDDS.

634.9 II ISSN 0250-524X
CODEN: IJFODJ
INDIAN JOURNAL OF FORESTRY. (Text in English) 1978. q. Rs.130($15) Bishen Singh Mahendra Pal Singh, 23-A Connaught Pl., Dehra Ddun 248001, Uttar Pradesh, India. Ed. M.B. Raizada. adv.; bk.rev.; index. circ. 1,250. (back issues avail.) **Indexed:** Agroforest.Abstr., Bio-Contr.News & Info., Biol.Abstr., Chem.Abstr., Crop Physiol.Abstr., Curr.Adv.Ecol.Sci., Field Crop Abstr., Forest.Abstr., Forest Prod.Abstr., Herb.Abstr., Hort.Abstr., Irr.& Drain.Abstr., Plant Grow.Reg.Abstr., Potato Abstr., Rev.Plant Path., Rural Devel.Abstr., Seed Abstr., Soils & Fert., Triticale Abstr., Weed Abstr. **Document type:** academic/scholarly publication.
—Faxon; UnCover; CASDDS.

634.9 IO
INDONESIAN STATISTICS ON TRADE OF FOREST PRODUCTS. 1971. a. Rps.1500($4) Directorate General of Forestry, Forest Product Marketing Development Project, Jl. Salemba Raya 16, Jakarta, Indonesia. **Document type:** government publication.
Formerly (1971-1975): Forest Products Trade Statistics of Indonesia (ISSN 0302-203X)

634.9 RM
INDUSTRIA LEMNULUI & MOBILE. (Text mainly in Rumanian; occasionally in English, French, Hungarian; abstracts in English) 1949. q. $120. Forest - Infodoc S.A., Bd. Magheru Nr.31, sector 1, 70162 Bucharest, Rumania. TEL 659-68-65. adv.; bk.rev.; abstr.; bibl.; charts; illus.; stat.; index. circ. 4,300. (also avail. in microform) **Indexed:** Biol.Abstr., Chem.Abstr., Forest.Abstr., Forest Prod.Abstr., Hort.Abstr., Irr.& Drain.Abstr., Weed Abstr.
Incorporates (1964-1990): Mobila (ISSN 0026-7104); Former titles (until 199?): Industria Lemnului; (until 1986): Revista Padurilor-Industria Lemnului, Celuloza si Hirtie. Industria Lemnului; **Supersedes in part:** Revista Padurilor-Industria Lemnului-Celuloza si Hirtie (ISSN 0035-029X)

634.9 CU ISSN 0138-6735
INFORMACION EXPRESS. SERIE: FORESTALES. 1981. 2/yr. C.$0.60($5) in N. America; S. America and Europe $6; elsewhere $9; or exchange basis. Centro de Informacion y Documentacion Agropecuario, Gaveta Postal 4149, Havana 4, Cuba. TEL 301672. TELEX 0511007. (Dist. by: Ediciones Cubanas, Obispo No. 527, Apdo. 605, Havana, Cuba) stat. **Indexed:** Agrindex.

634.9 US ISSN 1062-9491
SD412
INNER VOICE; forest service employees speaking as concerned citizens. 1989. bi-m. $20 includes membership. (Association of Forest Service Employees for Environmental Ethics) A F S E E E, Box 11615, Eugene, OR 97440. TEL 503-484-2692. FAX 503-484-3004. Ed. Cheri Brooki. bk.rev.; index. circ. 20,000. (tabloid format; back issues avail.) **Document type:** newspaper.
Description: Looks at national forest management, with articles by forest service employees who are concerned with environmental ethics. Explores a variety of topic areas relating to public land management.
Refereed Serial

INSTITUTO NACIONAL DE INVESTIGACIONES FORESTALES. BOLETIN DIVULGATIVO. see *BIOLOGY — Entomology*

INSTITUTO NACIONAL DE INVESTIGACIONES FORESTALES. BOLETIN TECNICO. see *BIOLOGY — Entomology*

634.9 MX ISSN 0185-4445
INSTITUTO NACIONAL DE INVESTIGACIONES FORESTALES. CATALOGO. (Text in Spanish; summaries in English, Spanish) 1981-1985 (no.12); resumed. irreg. price varies. Instituto Nacional de Investigaciones Forestales y Agropecuarias, Centro de Documentacion Cientifica y Tecnologica, Av. Progreso No. 5, Col. Coyoacan, Delegacion Coyoacan, 04110 Mexico, D.F., Mexico. TEL 658-43-33. (back issues avail.) **Document type:** government publication.

634.9 MX ISSN 0185-2418
SD147
INSTITUTO NACIONAL DE INVESTIGACIONES FORESTALES. CIENCIA FORESTAL. (Text in Spanish; summaries in English, Spanish) 1976. s-a. $28. Instituto Nacional de Investigaciones Forestales y Agropecuarias, Centro de Documentacion Cientifica y Tecnologica, Av. Progreso No. 5, Col. Coyoacan, Delegacion Coyoacan, 04110 Mexico, D.F., Mexico. TEL 658-43-33. cum.index: 1976-1983, 1984-1985. (back issues avail.) **Indexed:** Agroforest.Abstr.

INSTITUTO NACIONAL DE INVESTIGACIONES FORESTALES. PUBLICACION ESPECIAL. see *BIOLOGY — Entomology*

634.9 NG ISSN 0534-4824
INTER-AFRICAN FORESTRY CONFERENCE. CONFERENCE FORESTIERE INTERAFRICAINE (COMMUNICATIONS). * (Text in English and French) 1951. irreg. Maison de l'Afrique, B.P. 878, Niamey, Niger.

INTERNATIONAL DIRECTORY OF WILDLAND FIRE. see *FIRE PREVENTION*

634.9 PR
INTERNATIONAL INSTITUTE OF TROPICAL FORESTRY. ANNUAL LETTER. (Text in English and Spanish) 1939. a. free. U.S. Department of Agriculture, International Institute of Tropical Forestry, Southern Forest Experiment Station, Call Box 25000, Rio Piedras, PR 00928-2500. TEL 809-766-5335. FAX 809-766-6302. TELEX 37401032. Dir. Ariel E. Lugo. bk.rev. circ. 3,000.

INTERNATIONAL JOURNAL OF WILDLAND FIRE. see *FIRE PREVENTION*

634.9 AT ISSN 1032-7290
INTERNATIONAL TREE CROPS. 1989. 2/yr. Aus.$25($30) (International Tree Crops Institute) Agrovision, P.O. Box 283, Caulfield South, Vic. 3162, Australia. TEL 61-3-211-6209. FAX 032118502. Ed. Geoff Wilson. circ. 2,500.
Description: Describes sustainable land use with multipurpose tree crops in agroforestry systems.

634.9 630 UK ISSN 0143-5698
CODEN: ITRJDW
INTERNATIONAL TREE CROPS JOURNAL; the journal of agroforestry. (Text in English; summaries in English, French and Spanish) 1980. q. £79($159) A B Academic Publishers, P.O. Box 42, Bicester, Oxon. OX6 7NW, England. TEL 0869-320949. Ed. Alan Grainger. adv.; bk.rev.; bibl.; illus.; index. (also avail. in microform) **Indexed:** Abstr.Rural Dev.Trop., Agroforest.Abstr., Biol.Abstr., Curr.Adv.Ecol.Sci., Energy Rev., Environ.Per.Bibl. (1989-), Forest.Abstr., Forest Prod.Abstr., Hort.Abstr., Irr.& Drain.Abstr., Maize Abstr., Rural Devel.Abstr., Seed Abstr., Soils & Fert., Trop.Oil Seeds Abstr., World Agri.Econ.& Rural Sociol.Abstr. **Document type:** academic/scholarly publication.
—BLDSC (4551.312000); Faxon; UnCover; SWETS. CCC.

634.9 AU ISSN 0074-9400
INTERNATIONAL UNION OF FORESTRY RESEARCH ORGANIZATIONS. CONGRESS PROCEEDINGS. 1893. quinquennial, 19th, 1990, Canada. price varies. International Union of Forestry Research Organizations - Internationaler Verband Forstlicher Forschungsanstalten, Seckendorf-Gudent-Weg 8, A-1131 Vienna, Austria. TEL 0222-8770151. FAX 0222-8779355. TELEX 75312646-IUSC-A. **Document type:** proceedings.

634.9 AU
INTERNATIONALER VERBAND FORSTLICHER FORSCHUNGSANSTALTEN. WELTKONGRESS BERICHTSWERK. (Text in English, French, German, Spanish) irreg. Can.$20 per vol. Internationaler Verband Forstlicher Forschungsanstalten - International Union of Forest Research Organizations, IUFRO Sekretariat, Seckendorf-Gudent-Weg 8, A-1131 Vienna, Austria. **Document type:** monographic series.

634.9 SP ISSN 1131-7965
▼**INVESTIGACION AGRARIA. SISTEMAS Y RECURSOS FORESTALES.** (Text in Spanish; summaries in English, Spanish) 1992. s-a. 5000 ptas. (foreign 7000 ptas.) (effective 1992). Ministerio de Agricultura, Pesca y Alimentacion, Instituto Nacional de Investigacion y Tecnologia Agraria y Alimentaria, Centro de Publicaciones, Paseo de la Infanta Isabel 1, 28071 Madrid, Spain. (I.N.I.T.A.A. addr.: Jose Abascal 56, 28003 Madrid, Spain. TEL 347-39-16) abstr.; bibl.; charts; stat.
—BLDSC (4557.717000).

634.9 IE ISSN 0021-1192
IRISH FORESTRY. 1944. s-a. £12 to non-members. Irish Forestry Society, Coillite Teoranta, Sidmonton Pl., Bray, Co. Dublin, Ireland. TEL 01-2867751. FAX 01-2868126. Ed. Alistair Pfeifer. adv.; bk.rev.; abstr.; charts; illus.; cum.index. circ. 750. **Indexed:** Biol.Abstr., Chem.Abstr., Forest.Abstr., Forest Prod.Abstr., Soils & Fert., Weed Abstr. **Document type:** academic/scholarly publication.
—BLDSC (4571.400000).

634.9 TU ISSN 0535-8418
CODEN: IUODA3
ISTANBUL UNIVERSITESI ORMAN FAKULTESI DERGISI, SERI A/UNIVERSITY OF ISTANBUL. FACULTY OF FORESTRY. REVIEW/UNIVERSITAT ISTANBUL. FORSTLICHEN FAKULTAET. ZEITSCHRIFT/UNIVERSITE D'ISTANBUL. FACULTE FORESTIERE. REVUE. (Text in Turkish, summaries in English, French, German) 1951. s-a. Istanbul Universitesi, Orman Fakultesi, Buyukdere, Istanbul, Turkey. Ed.Bd. abstr.; bibl.; charts; stat. **Document type:** academic/scholarly publication.
Description: Publishes research contributions on topics in forest science, including chemical analyses of materials, environmental issues, surveys of insect and microbial pests, park and forest management matters.

634.9 IT ISSN 0390-0010
SD201
ISTITUTO SPERIMENTALE PER LA SELVICOLTURA. ANNALI. (Text in Italian; summaries in English and French) 1970. a. price varies. Istituto Sperimentale per la Selvicoltura, Viale S. Margherita 80-82, 52100 Arezzo, Italy. TEL 39-575-353021. FAX 39-575-353490. Ed. Gianfranco Fabbio. circ. 1,200. (back issues avail.) **Indexed:** Biol.Abstr., Curr.Adv.Ecol.Sci., Forest.Abstr.
Description: Presents scientific reports.

FORESTS AND FORESTRY

634.9   IT   ISSN 0021-2776
ITALIA FORESTALE E MONTANA. (Text in Italian; summaries in English, Italian) 1946. bi-m. L.60000 (foreign L.70000) (effective 1994). Accademia Italiana di Scienze Forestali, Piazza Edison 11, 50133 Florence, Italy. TEL 055-570348. FAX 055-57524. Ed. Orazio Ciancio. bk.rev.; illus. circ. 1,000. **Indexed:** Bio-Contr.News & Info., Chem.Abstr., Forest.Abstr., Forest Prod.Abstr., Plant Grow.Reg.Abstr., Seed Abstr. **Document type:** academic/scholarly publication.
—BLDSC (4588.085000).

634.9   JA   ISSN 0286-4339
IWATE UNIVERSITY FORESTS. BULLETIN. (Text in Japanese) 1961. a. Iwate University, Faculty of Agriculture, University Forests - Iwate Daigaku Nogakubu, 3-18-8, Ueda, Morioka 020, Japan. TEL 0196-235 171. Ed. T. Ando. cum.index. circ. 420. (back issues avail.)

634.9   JA
JAPAN. FORESTRY AND FOREST PRODUCTS RESEARCH INSTITUTE. ANNUAL REPORT/NORINSHO RINGYO SHIKENJO NENPO. (Text in Japanese) 1961. a. Forestry and Forest Products Research Institute, P.O. Box 16, Tsukuba Norin Kenkyu Danchi-nai, Ibaraki 305, Japan. **Indexed:** Forest.Abstr. **Document type:** academic/scholarly publication.
Formerly: Japan. Government Forest Experiment Station, Tokyo. Annual Report (ISSN 0557-0352)
Description: Outline of activity of the Forest and Forest Products Research Institute.

634.9   JA
JAPAN. FORESTRY AND FOREST PRODUCTS RESEARCH INSTITUTE. BULLETIN. irreg. (5-6/yr.). Forestry and Forest Products Research Institute, P.O. Box 16, Tsukuba Norin Kenkyu Danchi-nai, Ibaraki 305, Japan. **Indexed:** Forest.Abstr. **Document type:** academic/scholarly publication, bulletin.
Description: Papers on forestry and forest products research.

634.9   JA   ISSN 0557-0395
JAPAN. GOVERNMENT FOREST EXPERIMENT STATION. KYUSHU BRANCH. ANNUAL REPORT/RINGYO SHIKENJO KYUSHU SHIJO NENPO. (Text in Japanese) 1960. a. Government Forest Experiment Station, Kyushu Branch - Rin'yama-cho Ringyo Shikenjo Kyushu Shijo, 4-11-16 Kurokami, Kumamoto 860, Japan. **Document type:** government publication.

JAPAN. NORIN-SHO NENPO/JAPAN. MINISTRY OF AGRICULTURE AND FORESTRY. ANNUAL REPORT. see *AGRICULTURE*

634.9   JA   ISSN 0021-485X
SD1   CODEN: NIRKAA
JAPANESE FORESTRY SOCIETY. JOURNAL/NIHON RINGAKKAISHI. (Text in Japanese or English) 1918. bi-m. 8000 Yen (foreign $60). Japanese Forestry Society, c/o Japan Forest Technical Association, 7, Rokuban-cho, Chiyoda-ku, Tokyo 102, Japan. FAX 03-3261-2766. Ed. Kimito Furuta. adv.; bk.rev.; bibl.; charts; illus.; index. circ. 4,000. **Indexed:** Agri.Eng.Abstr., Agroforest.Abstr., Bio-Contr.News & Info., Biol.Abstr., Chem.Abstr, Crop Physiol.Abstr., Forest.Abstr., Forest Prod.Abstr., Irr.& Drain.Abstr., Plant Breed.Abstr., Seed Abstr., Soils & Fert. **Document type:** government publication, academic/scholarly publication.

JARDIM BOTANICO DO RIO DE JANEIRO. ARQUIVOS. see *BIOLOGY — Botany*

634.9   CC   ISSN 1001-7380
JIANGSU LINYE KEJI. (Text in Chinese) 1974. q. Y10. Jiangsu Sheng Linye Kexue Yanjiusuo - Jiangsu Information Center of Forestry Science and Technology, Dongshanqiao, Zhonghua Menwai, Nanjing, Jiangsu 211153, People's Republic of China. TEL 86-25-6624515. Ed. Tu Zhongyu. adv. contact: Sun Tiru. circ. 3,000. **Document type:** academic/scholarly publication.

JORD OG VIDEN; agronomer - hortonomer - forstkandidater. see *AGRICULTURE*

JORDBRUG OESTJYLLAND (MIDT): SAMTLIGE LANDBRUG, SKOVBRUG OG GARTNERIER. see *AGRICULTURE*

JOURNAL OF DENDROLOGY. see *BIOLOGY — Botany*

634.9   US   ISSN 0022-1201
SD1   CODEN: JFUSAI
JOURNAL OF FORESTRY; a journal reporting on the science, practice and profession of forestry. 1902. m. $55 to individuals; institutions $100. Society of American Foresters, 5400 Grosvenor Ln., Bethesda, MD 20814. TEL 301-897-8720. FAX 301-897-3690. Ed. Rebecca N. Staebler. adv.; bk.rev.; video rev.; abstr.; bibl.; charts; illus.; stat.; index. circ. 18,650. (also avail. in microform from UMI,PMC; reprint service avail. from UMI) **Indexed:** Abstr.Bull.Inst.Pap.Chem., Biol.Abstr., Biol.& Agr.Ind., Biol.Dig., Chem.Abstr., Curr.Adv.Ecol.Sci., Curr.Cont., Energy Ind., Energy Info.Abstr., Eng.Ind., Environ.Abstr., Environ.Per.Bibl. (1972-), Excerp.Med., Forest.Abstr., Forest Prod.Abstr., Geo.Abstr., GeoRef., HRIS, Ind.Sci.Rev., INIS Atomind., P.A.I.S., Rev.Appl.Entomol., Sci.Cit.Ind., Sel.Water Res.Abstr. **Document type:** academic/scholarly publication.
—BLDSC (4985.000000); CIS; Faxon; UnCover; SWETS; UMI.
Description: Feature articles on the technology, practice and teaching of professional forestry. Regular columns include legislative, society, and news updates, opinion column.

634.9   US   ISSN 1054-9811
SD387.S87
▼**JOURNAL OF SUSTAINABLE FORESTRY.** 1993. q. $28 to individuals; institutions $36; libraries $48. Haworth Press, Inc., 10 Alice St., Binghamton, NY 13904. TEL 607-722-5857; 800-342-9678. FAX 607-722-1424. TELEX 4932599. Ed. Graeme P. Berlyn. adv.; bk.rev. (also avail. in microfiche from UMI; reprint service avail. from HAW) **Indexed:** Environ.Abstr., Environ.Per.Bibl (1992-).
Description: Contains topics from biotechnology, physiology, silviculture, wood science, economics, and forest management.
Refereed Serial

634.9   MY   ISSN 0128-1283
CODEN: JTFSEB
JOURNAL OF TROPICAL FOREST SCIENCE. (Text in English) 1988. q. M.$30 to individuals (foreign $30); institutions M$60 (foreign $60). Forest Research Institute Malaysia, Kepong, 52109 Kuala Lumpur, Malaysia. Eds. K.C. Khoo, Darus Hj. Ahmad. **Document type:** academic/scholarly publication.
—BLDSC (5070.675000).
Refereed Serial

634.9   UK   ISSN 0261-4286
SD1
JOURNAL OF WORLD FOREST RESOURCE MANAGEMENT; the journal of forest policy. 1984. s-a. £59($119) A B Academic Publishers, P.O. Box 42, Bicester, Oxon. OX6 7NW, England. TEL 0869-320949. Ed. Alan Grainger. adv.; bk.rev. (also avail. in microform) **Indexed:** Agroforest.Abstr., Curr.Adv.Ecol.Sci., Environ.Abstr., Environ.Per.Bibl. (1989-), Forest.Abstr., Forest Prod.Abstr., Rural Devel.Abstr. **Document type:** academic/scholarly publication.
—BLDSC (5072.671000); UnCover. CCC.
Description: Focuses on forest policy, economics, forecasting, ecology, resource assessment and all aspects of forests as a global resource.

KAERNTER BAUER. see *AGRICULTURE*

634.9   KO
KOREAN FORESTRY SOCIETY. JOURNAL. (Text in Korean; summaries in English) no.43, 1979. q. 5000 Won($10) Korean Forestry Society, c/o College of Agriculture, Seoul National University, Suwon 441-744, S. Korea. Ed. Joosang Chung. (back issues avail.) **Indexed:** Agroforest.Abstr., Crop Physiol.Abstr., Forest.Abstr., Forest Prod.Abstr., Plant Grow.Reg.Abstr., Seed Abstr. **Document type:** academic/scholarly publication.

KOREAN JOURNAL OF BREEDING. see *AGRICULTURE — Poultry And Livestock*

KUNGLIGA SKOGS- OCH LANTBRUKSAKADEMIENS TIDSKRIFT/ROYAL SWEDISH ACADEMY OF AGRICULTURE AND FORESTRY. JOURNAL/ACADEMIE ROYALE D'AGRICULTURE ET DE SYLVICULTURE DE SUEDE. ANNALES/KOENIGLICHE SCHWEDISCHE AKADEMIE DER LAND- UND FORSTWIRTSCHAFT. ZEITSCHRIFT. see *AGRICULTURE*

634.9   US
L S U FORESTRY NOTES. 1953. irreg., no.148, 1989. free. Louisiana State University, School of Forestry, Wildlife, and Fisheries, Baton Rouge, LA 70803. TEL 504-388-4131. Ed. Paul Y. Burns. circ. 250. **Document type:** academic/scholarly publication.

634.9   AU   ISSN 0023-7558
DER LAND- UND FORSTWIRTSCHAFTLICHE BETRIEB. 1954. m. S.540 (foreign S.660). (Verband Landwirtschaftlicher Gutsbetriebe in Oesterreich) Oesterreichischer Agrarverlag, Bankgasse 1-3, A-1014 Vienna, Austria. TEL 5339676. FAX 5339656. Ed. Arnold Kolterer. adv.; bk.rev.; bibl.; illus.; stat.; tr.lit.; index. circ. 3,500.

LANDBOTE; Fachblatt der Gewerkschaft Land-Forst-Garten. see *AGRICULTURE*

630 634.9   NO   ISSN 0801-1559
LANDBRUKETS AARBOK. 1962. a. NOK 268. Forlaget Tanum-Norli, Kr. Augustsgt. 7A, Oslo 1, Norway. TEL 02-110260. FAX 02-204583. Ed. A. Bruaset. circ. 2,000.
Formerly (1974-1980): Landbrukets Aarbok. Jordbruk, Hagebruk, Skogbruk (ISSN 0332-592X); **Formed by the merger of:** Landbrukets Aarbok. Jordbruk og Hagebruk (ISSN 0075-7853); Landbrukets Aarbok. Skogbruk (ISSN 0075-7861)

DIE LANDWIRTSCHAFT; Fachzeitschrift fuer die Gesamtinteressen der Land- und Forstwirtschaft. see *AGRICULTURE*

634.9 333.91   XO   ISSN 0323-0996
SD1   CODEN: LESBA6
LES. 1944. m. 36 Kcs. (Ministerstvo Lesneho a Vodneho Hospodarstva Slovenskej Republiky) Priroda, Krizkova 9, 815 34 Bratislava, Slovakia. TEL 472-41-45. (Subscr. to: Slovart, Gottwaldovo nam. 48, 80532 Bratislava, Slovakia)

634.9   CN   ISSN 0836-0618
LESLIE L. SCHAFFER LECTURESHIP IN FOREST SCIENCE. 1983. a. free. University of British Columbia, Faculty of Forestry, 270-2357 Main Mall, Vancouver, BC V6T 1Z4, Canada. TEL 604-822-2727. FAX 604-822-8645.

634.9   XR   ISSN 0322-9254
LESNICKA PRACE/FORESTRY. (Text in Czech; summaries in English, German and Russian) 1922. m. $21.20. Statni Zemedelske Nakladatelstvi, Vaclavske nam. 47, 113 11 Prague 1, Czech Republic. TEL 26 59 51. (Subscr. to: Artia, Ve Smeckach 30, 111 27 Prague 1, Czech Pupublic) Ed. Miroslav Poruba. illus. **Indexed:** Biol.Abstr., C.I.S. Abstr., Forest.Abstr., Forest Prod.Abstr.

634.9   XO   ISSN 0323-1046
LESNICKY CASOPIS/FORESTRY JOURNAL. (Text in Slovak) 1955. bi-m. 72 Kcs. (Vyskumny Ustav Lesneho Hospodarstva) Veda, Publishing House of the Slovak Academy of Sciences, Klemensova 19, 814 30 Bratislava, Slovakia. (Dist. by: Slovart, Nam. Slobody 6, 817 64 Bratislava, Slovakia) Ed. Jan Ilavsky. **Indexed:** Excerp.Med., Forest.Abstr., Forest Prod.Abstr., Soils & Fert.

634.9   XR   ISSN 0024-1105
SD83.C9   CODEN: LSNCAE
LESNICTVI/FORESTRY; vedecky casopis-scientific journal. (Text and summaries in Czech, English, Slovak) 1954. m. $112. Ustav Vedeckotechnickych Informaci pro Zemedelstvi, Slezska 7, 120 56 Prague 2, Czech Republic. TEL 257541. FAX 257090. (Co-sponsor: Ceskoslovenska Akademie Zemedelska) Ed. Radka Chlebeckova. adv.; bk.rev.; bibl.; charts; illus. circ. 700. (back issues avail.) **Indexed:** Abstr.Bull.Inst.Pap.Chem., Biol.Abstr., C.I.S. Abstr., Chem.Abstr., Excerp.Med., Forest.Abstr., Forest Prod.Abstr., Ornam.Hort., Ref.Zh., Rev.Appl.Entomol., Soils & Fert. **Document type:** academic/scholarly publication.
—CASDDS.
Description: Deales with the results of scientific work in the field of forestal biology, protection and amelioration of the forest soils, as well as with questions of timber output and hunting.

FORESTS AND FORESTRY

634.9   RU   ISSN 0024-1113
CODEN: LKHOAW
LESNOE KHOZYAISTVO. 1948. m. 19.20 Rub. Izdatel'stvo Lesnaya Promyshlennost', Ul. 25 Let Oktyabrya, 17, 103645 Moscow K-25, Russia. Ed. A.I. Mukhin. bk.rev.; bibl.; charts; illus.; stat.; index. circ. 31,932. **Indexed:** Abstr.Bull.Inst.Pap.Chem., Agri.Eng.Abstr., Agroforest.Abstr., Bio-Contr.News & Info., Biol.Abstr., Chem.Abstr., Field Crop Abstr., Forest.Abstr., Forest Prod.Abstr., Herb.Abstr., Hort.Abstr., Plant Grow.Reg.Abstr., Rev.Plant Path., Rural Recreat.Tour.Abstr., Seed Abstr., Soils & Fert., Triticale Abstr., Weed Abstr., World Agri.Econ.& Rural Sociol.Abstr.
—BLDSC (0097.130000).

634.9   RU   ISSN 0024-1148
SD1   CODEN: LESOAB
LESOVEDENIE. English translation: Russian Forest Sciences (US ISSN 1068-669X) 1966. bi-m. 31.20 Rub. (Rossiiskaya Akademiya Nauk) Izdatel'stvo Nauka, 90 Profsoyuznaya ul., 117864 Moscow, Russia. **Indexed:** Abstr.Bull.Inst.Pap.Chem., Agroforest.Abstr., Biol.Abstr., Chem.Abstr., Excerp.Med., Forest.Abstr., Forest Prod.Abstr.
—CASDDS.

634.9   AT   ISSN 0811-5400
LIANE NEWSLETTER. 1982. q. Aus.$25 (effective July, 1991). Rainforest Conservation Society Inc., 19 Colorado Ave., Bardon, Qld. 4065, Australia. TEL 07-368-13318. FAX 07-368-3938. bk.rev. circ. 1,000.

534.9   CC   ISSN 1001-1714
LIAONING LINYE KEJI/LIAONING FORESTRY TECHNOLOGY. (Text in Chinese) bi-m. Liaoning Sheng Linye Kexue Yanjiuyuan - Liaoning Institute of Forestry, 12 Yalujiang Jie, Congshan Donglu, Shenyang, Liaoning 110032, People's Republic of China. TEL 661401. Ed. Li Yansheng.

634.9 621.9   CC   ISSN 1001-4462
LINYE JIXIE/FORESTRY MACHINERY. (Text in Chinese) bi-m. Linye Bu, Harbin Linye Jixie Yanjiusuo - Ministry of Forestry, Harbin Institute of Forestry Machinery, 62, Xuefu Lu, Harbin, Heilongjiang 150086, People's Republic of China. TEL 61136. Ed. Shao Zhendong.

634.9   CC   ISSN 1001-7488
SD1   CODEN: LYKSAL
LINYE KEXUE/SCIENTIA SILVAE SINICA. (Text in Chinese; summaries in English) 1955. bi-m. $67.20. (Chinese Institute of Forestry) Science Press, Marketing and Sales Department, 16 Donghuangchenggen Beijie, Beijing 100707, People's Republic of China. TEL 4010642. FAX 4012180. TELEX 210247-SPBJ-CN. adv. circ. 21,000. **Indexed:** Agroforest.Abstr., Bio-Contr.News & Info., Biol.Abstr., Crop Physiol.Abstr., Curr.Adv.Ecol.Sci., Curr.Adv.Genetics & Molec.Biol., Forest.Abstr., Forest Prod.Abstr., Hort.Abstr., Plant Grow.Reg.Abstr.
—BLDSC (8173.810000); CASDDS.
Formerly (until 1979): Zhongguo Linye (ISSN 0250-3271); (until 1967): Lingye - Scientia Silvae Sinicae (ISSN 0459-441X)
Description: Covers silviculture, forest management, forest protection, forest industry, and forest economics. Emphasizes professional reports capable of creating new approaches to the development of forestry.
Refereed Serial

634.9   CC   ISSN 1000-839X
LINYE YUEKAN/FORESTRY MONTHLY. (Text in Chinese) m. Heilongjiang Sheng Linyeting, 1, Mujie Jie, Nangang-qu, Harbin, Heilongjiang 150001, People's Republic of China. TEL 37507. Ed. Ni Wanhua.

634.9 639.2   US
LOUISIANA STATE UNIVERSITY. SCHOOL OF FORESTRY, WILDLIFE AND FISHERIES. RESEARCH REPORTS. 1983. irreg., no.15, 1992. free. Louisiana State University, School of Forestry, Wildlife and Fisheries, 227 Forestry-Wildlife-Fisheries Bldg., Baton Rouge, LA 70803-6202. TEL 504-388-4131. Ed. Paul Y. Burns. circ. 200. **Document type:** monographic series.

634.9   CC
LUHUA YU SHENGHUO. (Text in Chinese) bi-m. Beijing Shi Linye Ju - Beijing Bureau of Forestry, 19 Beisanhuan Donglu, Dewai, Beijing 100029, People's Republic of China. TEL 2013339. Ed. Shan Conghui.

MAASEUTUTYOVAEN VIESTI. see *LABOR UNIONS*

634.9   MW   ISSN 0076-3071
MALAWI. DEPARTMENT OF FORESTRY AND GAME. REPORT. irreg. (approx. a.). Government Printer, Box 37, Zomba, Malawi. cum.index: 1960-65. **Document type:** government publication.

634.9   MY   ISSN 0302-2935
SD1
MALAYSIAN FORESTER. (Text and summaries in English) 1932. q. M.$40($20) Faculty of Forestry, Universiti Pertanian Malaysia, 43400 Serdang, Selangor, Malaysia. TEL 60-30-9486101. TELEX UNIPER MA 37454. Ed. Nik Muhamad Majid. adv.; bk.rev.; bibl.; charts; illus.; index. circ. 1,000. **Indexed:** Agroforest.Abstr., Bio-Contr.News & Info., Biol.Abstr., Crop Physiol.Abstr., Curr.Adv.Ecol.Sci., Excerp.Med., Forest.Abstr., Forest Prod.Abstr., Geo.Abstr., Hort.Abstr., Ornam.Hort., Plant Grow.Reg.Abstr., Rev.Appl.Entomol., Rev.Plant Path., Rural Ext.Educ.& Tr.Abstr., Seed Abstr., Weed Abstr.
—BLDSC (5356.066500).
Formerly: Malayan Forester (ISSN 0025-1275)

634.9   MF
MAURITIUS. FORESTRY SERVICE. ANNUAL REPORT. (Text in English) 1900. a. Rs.25. Ministry of Agriculture, Fisheries, and Natural Resources, Forestry Service, Botanical Gardens St., Curepipe, Mauritius.
Formerly (until 1968): Mauritius. Forest Department. Annual Report.
Description: Outlines activities of the Service.

MECANISATION FORESTIERE; activites forestieres internationales. see *TECHNOLOGY: COMPREHENSIVE WORKS*

634.9   FI   ISSN 0355-7596
METSANHOITAJA. 1951. 4/yr. membership. Suomen Metsanhoitajaliitto - Society of Finnish Foresters, Rautatielaisenkatu 6, 00520 Helsinki 52, Finland. TEL 358-1502-353. FAX 358-148-69-60. Ed. Jukka Sippola. adv.; bk.rev. circ. 3,300. (back issues avail.)

634.9 630   FI   ISSN 0359-968X
METSATILASTOLLINEN VUOSIKIRJA/YEARBOOK OF FOREST STATISTICS. (Portion of Official Statistics of Finland) (Text in English and Finnish) 1969. a. FIM 150. Metsantutkimuslaitos, Metsien Kaatyon Tutkimusosasto - Finnish Forest Research Institute, Forest Statistics Information Service, Unioninkatu 40 A, Fln-00170 Helsinki, Finland. TEL 358-0-857 051. FAX 358-0-85705-717. TELEX 121286 METLA SF. Ed. Martti Aarne. charts; stat. circ. 2,000. **Document type:** government publication.
Description: Submits up-to-date information about forestry and the forest industries in Finland.

634.9   US
MICHIGAN CHRISTMAS TREE JOURNAL. 1958. q. $12. Michigan Christmas Tree Association, Box 256, Okemos, MI 48805-0256. TEL 517-347-1010. FAX 517-349-3221. adv.; B&W page $200, color page $325; trim 7 1/2 X 10. circ. 1,500.

634.9   JA   ISSN 0916-8974
MIE DAIGAKU SEBUTSU SHIGEN GAKUBU ENSHURIN HOKOKU/MIE UNIVERSITY FORESTS. BULLETIN. (Text in Japanese) 1953. a. Mie University Forests, Kamihama-cho, Tsu-shi 514, Japan. TEL 81-592-32-1211. FAX 81-592-31-9634. Ed. Hiroshi Nagata. circ. 200. **Document type:** bulletin.
Formerly (until 1988): Mie Daigaku Nogakubu Enshurin Hokoku (ISSN 0544-1005)

MINNESOTA AGRICULTURAL EXPERIMENT STATION. STATION BULLETIN. see *AGRICULTURE*

634.96   US
MONTANA FOREST AND CONSERVATION EXPERIMENT STATION. BIENNIAL REPORT. biennial. (Montana Forest and Conservation Experiment Station) University of Montana, School of Forestry, Missoula, MT 59812. TEL 406-243-6582. FAX 406-243-4510. **Document type:** academic/scholarly publication.
Description: Contains forestry-related research conducted by the Montana Forest and Conservation Experiment Station.

634.9   SP   ISSN 0027-0105
MONTES. 1945. q. 200 ptas. Asociacion de Ingenieros de Montes, Joaquin Maria Lopez 23 4a, 28015 Madrid, Spain. TEL 1-543-61-48. FAX 1-544-75-70. adv.; bk.rev.; bibl.; charts; illus.; index. **Indexed:** Biol.Abstr., Chem.Abstr., Ind.SST.

634.9   IT
MONTI E BOSCHI. Short title: M B. 1949. bi-m. L.50000 (effective 1993). Edagricole S.p.A., Via Emilia Levante 31, 40139 Bologna, Italy. TEL 051-492211. FAX 051-493660. TELEX 510336. Ed. Umberto Bagnaresi. adv.: B&W page L.780000, color page L.1200000; 185 x 247. bk.rev. circ. 16,700. **Indexed:** Forest.Abstr.
—BLDSC (5966.071000).
Formerly: Montanaro d'Italia - Monti e Boschi (ISSN 0390-6736); Which was formed by the merger of: Monti e Boschi (ISSN 0027-0660); Montanaro d'Italia.
Description: Deals with forestry and mountain life, technical and economic problems concerning agriculture and animal husbandry in mountain regions.

MOUNTAIN CONSTRUCTOR & RECLAMATIONIST. see *BUILDING AND CONSTRUCTION*

N F P A: STATISTICAL ROUNDUP. (National Forest Products Association) see *BUSINESS AND ECONOMICS — Marketing And Purchasing*

N F R A NEWSLETTER. (National Forest Recreation Association) see *CONSERVATION*

634.9   AT
N S W FOREST PRODUCTS ASSOCIATION. PROLOGUE NOTES. (New South Wales) bi-m. Aus.$25 to non-members. N S W Forest Products Association, P.O. Box 903, Darlingurst, N.S.W. 2010, Australia. FAX 02-283-1467. Ed. W.J. Hurditch. circ. 700.

634.9   PL
NASZE DRZEWA LESNE. MONOGRAFIE POPULARNO NAUKOWE. (Text in Polish; summaries in English) 1970. irreg., vol.9, 1986. price varies. Polska Akademia Nauk, Instytut Dendrologii, Ul. Parkowa 5, 62-035 Kornik, Poland. (Dist. by: Ars Polona, Krakowskie Przedmiescie 7, 00-068 Warsaw, Poland) Ed. Stefan Bialobok. **Document type:** monographic series.

634.9   US
NATIONAL BARK & SOIL PRODUCERS ASSOCIATION. SPECIAL REGIONAL RELEASES. 1970. irreg. National Bark & Soil Producers Association, 10210 Leatherleaf Ct., Manassas, VA 22111-4245. TEL 703-257-0111. Dir. Robert C. LaGasse.

634.9   NE   ISSN 0028-2057
NEDERLANDS BOSBOUW TIJDSCHRIFT; voor het beheer van bos, natuur en landschap. Variant title: Bosbouw. (Text in Dutch; summaries in English) 1928. bi-m. Koninklijke Nederlandse Bosbouw Vereniging, Lovinklaan 1, 6800 Arnhem, Netherlands. adv.; bk.rev.; illus.; stat.; index. circ. 1,300. **Indexed:** Agri.Eng.Abstr., Bio-Contr.News & Info., Excerp.Med., Forest.Abstr., Forest Prod.Abstr., Key to Econ.Sci., Rev.Plant Path., Rural Devel.Abstr., Rural Recreat.Tour.Abstr., World Agri.Econ.& Rural Sociol.Abstr.
—BLDSC (6069.500000); SWETS.

634.9   DQ
THE NEW FORESTER. 1987. q. Ministry of Agriculture, Forestry & Wildlife Division, Botanical Gardens, Roseau, Dominica, W.I. Dir. Felix W. Gregoire.

FORESTS AND FORESTRY

634.9   NE   ISSN 0169-4286
SD409   CODEN: NEFOE6
NEW FORESTS. (Text in English) 1986. 4/yr. fl.334.($174.50) (effective 1994). Kluwer Academic Publishers, Postbus 17, 3300 AA Dordrecht, Netherlands. TEL 31-78-334911. FAX 31-78-334254. TELEX 29245 KAPG NL. (Dist. by: Kluwer Academic Publishers Group, P.O. Box 322, 3300 AH Dordrecht, Netherlands. TEL 31-78-524400. FAX 31-78-524474; N. America dist. addr.: Box 358, Accord Sta., Hingham, MA 02018-0358. TEL 617-871-6600. FAX 617-871-6528) Ed. M.L. Duryea. (also avail. in microform from UMI; back issues avail.; reprint service avail. from SWZ) **Indexed:** Biol.Abstr., Environ.Abstr., Environ.Per.Bibl., Geo.Abstr. **Document type:** academic/scholarly publication.
—BLDSC (6084.188000); CIS; UnCover; UMI. **CCC.**
    Description: Publishes papers dealing with fundamental and applied aspects of afforestation and reforestation, including related issues in biotechnology, economics and forest management.
    Refereed Serial

634.9   AT   ISSN 0085-3984
NEW SOUTH WALES. FORESTRY COMMISSION. RESEARCH NOTES. 1958. irreg. price varies. Forestry Commission, 95-99 York St., Sydney, N.S.W. 2000, Australia. circ. 500. **Indexed:** Aus.Sci.Ind., Forest.Abstr., Soils & Fert.
—BLDSC (7745.950000).

634.9   NZ   ISSN 0111-8129
                     CODEN: FRIBEJ
NEW ZEALAND. F R I BULLETIN. 1982. irreg. price varies. Forest Research Institute, Private Bag 3020, Rotorua, New Zealand. charts; illus. circ. 500. (back issues avail.) **Indexed:** Curr.Adv.Ecol.Sci., Forest.Abstr., Forest Prod.Abstr. **Document type:** monographic series.
—CASDDS. **CCC.**
    Description: Series includes technical reports, manuals and field guides dealing with forest practices and products.

634.9   NZ   ISSN 0077-9997
SD111.N7   CODEN: NZRFAC
NEW ZEALAND. FOREST RESEARCH INSTITUTE. REPORT. 1952. a. free. Forest Research Institute, Private Bag 3020, Rotorua, New Zealand. charts; illus. circ. 2,000. (back issues avail.) **Indexed:** Biol.Abstr., Forest.Abstr., Rev.Appl.Entomol., Rev.Plant Path., Weed Abstr.
    Description: Report includes lists of projects, staff and publications for the calendar year, and summary of main research events.

634.9   NZ   ISSN 0112-9597
SD1   CODEN: NZFOEH
NEW ZEALAND FORESTRY. 1925. q. NZ.$38 to individuals (foreign NZ.$53); institutions NZ.$60 (foreign NZ.$75). New Zealand Institute of Forestry Inc., P.O. Box 19-840, Christchurch, New Zealand. TEL 64-3-384-2432. Ed. C.J. Perley. adv.; bk.rev.; abstr.; charts; illus.; stat.; cum.index every 3 yrs. circ. 1,400. (also avail. in microfilm; back issues avail.) **Indexed:** Biol.Abstr., Chem.Abstr., Curr.Adv.Ecol.Sci., Forest.Abstr., Forest Prod.Abstr., Geo.Abstr., Rev.Plant Path., Soils & Fert. **Document type:** newsletter.
—BLDSC (6091.900000); UnCover. **CCC.**
    Formerly: New Zealand Journal of Forestry (ISSN 0028-8284)
    Description: Provides articles on forestry philosophy, policy, science, technology and practice. Fosters communication and debate within the Institute.

634.9   NZ   ISSN 0048-0134
SD111.N7   CODEN: NZFSAP
NEW ZEALAND JOURNAL OF FORESTRY SCIENCE. 1971. 3/yr. NZ.$50 individuals; institutions NZ.$100. Forest Research Institute, Private Bag 3020, Rotorua, New Zealand. TEL 64-7-347-5899. FAX 64-7-347-9380. Ed. J.A. Griffith. bk.rev.; charts; illus.; stat.; index. circ. 650. (back issues avail.; reprint service avail. from UMI) **Indexed:** Abstr.Bull.Inst.Pap.Chem., Biol.Abstr., Chem.Abstr., Curr.Adv.Ecol.Sci., Curr.Cont., Energy Ind., Energy Info.Abstr., Environ.Abstr., Forest.Abstr., Forest.Abstr., Forest Prod.Abstr., Geo.Abstr., Plant Breed.Abstr., Plant Grow.Reg.Abstr., Rev.Plant Path., Soils & Fert., VITIS. **Document type:** academic/scholarly publication.
—BLDSC (6094.100000); UnCover; UMI; CASDDS. **CCC.**
    Description: Covers a wide range of topics connected with forestry science, with particular reference to New Zealand and the south-west Pacific.

634.9   NR   ISSN 0300-2403
NIGERIA. FEDERAL DEPARTMENT OF FOREST RESEARCH. RESEARCH PAPER.* (Includes 3 series: Forest Series, Savanna Series, Forest Products Series) (Text and summaries in English) 1965. irreg. exchange basis. Federal Department of Forest Research, Private Mail Bag No. 5034, Ibadan, Nigeria. Ed.Bd. circ. 700. (back issues avail.) **Indexed:** Biol.Abstr.

634.9 674   NR
NIGERIAN JOURNAL OF FORESTRY. (Text in English) 1971. s-a. £N20. Forestry Association of Nigeria, Box 4185, Ibadan, Nigeria. TEL 022-411249. TELEX 31137 FORMECU NG. Ed. A.C. Omoluabi. adv.; bk.rev. circ. 500. **Indexed:** Biol.Abstr., Forest.Abstr., Forest Prod.Abstr., Soils & Fert.

634.9   NO   ISSN 0029-2087
SD203
NORSK SKOGBRUK. 1955. m. NOK 440. Norske Skogselskap, Wergelandsvn. 23 B, 0167 Oslo 1, Norway. FAX 02-604189. Ed. Johs Bjoerndal. adv.; bk.rev.; bibl.; charts; illus.; mkt.; stat.; index. circ. 5,900. (back issues avail.) **Indexed:** Agri.Eng.Abstr., Chem.Abstr., Forest.Abstr., Forest Prod.Abstr., Seed Abstr.
—BLDSC (6145.600000).

634.9   US
NORTH CAROLINA STATE UNIVERSITY. COLLEGE OF FOREST RESOURCES. TECHNICAL REPORT. 1950. irreg. (1-2/yr.). exchange basis. North Carolina State University, College of Forest Resources, Raleigh, NC 27695. circ. 160 (controlled). **Indexed:** Forest.Abstr., Forest Prod.Abstr. **Document type:** academic/scholarly publication.
    Formerly: North Carolina State University. School of Forest Resources. Technical Report (ISSN 0090-0664)

634.9   US   ISSN 0742-6348
SD144.A127   CODEN: NJAFEN
NORTHERN JOURNAL OF APPLIED FORESTRY. q. $40 to individuals; institutions $85. Society of American Foresters, 5400 Grosvenor Lane, Bethesda, MD 20814. TEL 301-897-8720. FAX 301-897-3690. Ed. H.V. Wiant. circ. 1,391. (also avail. in microform from UMI; reprint service avail. from UMI) **Indexed:** Agri.Eng.Abstr., Biol.Abstr., Chem.Abstr., Environ.Abstr., Forest.Abstr., Forest Prod.Abstr., Geo.Abstr., Rev.Plant Path., Seed Abstr., Sel.Water Res.Abstr., Weed Abstr. **Document type:** trade publication.
—BLDSC (6151.013530); UnCover; UMI.
    Refereed Serial

634.9   UK   ISSN 0269-5790
                      CODEN: OPOIEJ
O F I OCCASIONAL PAPERS. 1978. irreg. price varies. Oxford Forestry Institute, Department of Plant Sciences, University of Oxford, South Parks Rd., Oxford OX1 3RB, England. circ. 375. (also avail. in microform; back issues avail.) **Indexed:** Agroforest.Abstr., Biol.Abstr., Forest.Abstr.
—BLDSC (6244.490000).
    Formerly (until Oct. 1985): C F I Occasional Papers (ISSN 0141-8181)

634.9   AU   ISSN 1012-4667
                      CODEN: OEFOEH
OESTERREICHISCHE FORSTZEITUNG; Fachzeitschrift fuer das gesamt Forstwesen. 1889. m. S.985 (foreign S.1160). Oesterreichischer Agrarverlag, Bankgasse 1-3, A-1014 Vienna, Austria. TEL 5339676. FAX 5339656. Ed. F.W. Hillgarter. adv.; bk.rev.; index. circ. 2,500. (back issues avail.) **Indexed:** Biol.Abstr., C.I.S. Abstr., Chem.Abstr., Excerp.Med., Forest.Abstr., Forest Prod.Abstr., INIS Atomind., Key Word Ind.Wil.dl.Res., Rural Recreat.Tour.Abstr., World Agri.Econ.& Rural Sociol.Abstr. **Document type:** trade publication.
    Formerly (until 1988): Allgemeine Forstzeitung (ISSN 0002-5879)

634.9 674   FR
OFFICIEL DU BOIS (EDITION VERTE). 1930. w. 500 F. Societe "le Bois National", 3 rue Claude Odde, 42007 St. Etienne Cedex, France. TEL 77-74-33-99. FAX 77-93-11-26. TELEX 300 818. adv.
    Formerly: Bois National (Edition Verte).

OHIO STATE UNIVERSITY. AGRICULTURAL RESEARCH AND DEVELOPMENT CENTER, WOOSTER. SPECIAL CIRCULAR. see *AGRICULTURE*

634.9   US   ISSN 0030-123X
OHIO WOODLANDS; conservation in action. 1963. q. $8 (Canada $15; elsewhere $30). Ohio Forestry Association, Inc., 1335 Dublin Rd., No. 203D, Columbus, OH 43215-1000. TEL 614-486-6767. FAX 614-486-6769. Ed. Ronald C. Cornell. adv.; bk.rev.; illus. circ. 5,000. **Indexed:** Biol.Abstr.
    Formerly: Woodlands.

634.9   CN   ISSN 0381-3924
SD256.062
ONTARIO. MINISTRY OF NATURAL RESOURCES. FOREST RESEARCH REPORT. 1952. irreg. free. Ministry of Natural Resources, Ontario Forest Research Institute, P.O. Box 969 - 1235 Queen St. E., Sault Ste. Marie, Ont. P6A 5N5, Canada. TEL 705-946-2981. FAX 705-946-2030. circ. 1,000. **Indexed:** Forest.Abstr., Forest Prod.Abstr.
    Former titles: Ontario. Division of Forests. Research Library. Research Report (ISSN 0078-4753); Ontario. Department of Lands and Forests. Research Branch. Research Report.
    Description: Reports of various research programs carried out at the Institute.

634.9   CN
ONTARIO. MINISTRY OF NATURAL RESOURCES. ONTARIO FOREST RESEARCH INSTITUTE. FOREST RESEARCH NOTE. irreg. free. Ministry of Natural Resources, Ontario Forest Research Institute, P.O. Box 969 - 1235 Queen St. E. Sault Ste. Marie, Ont. P6A 5N5, Canada. TEL 705-946-2981. FAX 705-946-2030. circ. 1,000.
    Formerly: Ontario. Ministry of Natural Resources. Tree Improvement and Forest Biomass Institute. Forest Research Note (ISSN 0381-2650)
    Description: Publishes interim reports of various researched programs carried out at the Institute.

634.9   US
OREGON STATE UNIVERSITY. FOREST RESEARCH LABORATORY. BIENNIAL REPORT. 1958. biennial. free. Oregon State University, Forest Research Laboratory, Corvallis, OR 97331. TEL 503-737-4271. Ed. Ralph E. McNees. index. **Indexed:** Biol.Abstr.
    Formerly: Oregon State University. Forest Research Laboratory. Annual Report (ISSN 0078-5865)

634.9   US   ISSN 0078-5903
SD12
OREGON STATE UNIVERSITY. FOREST RESEARCH LABORATORY. RESEARCH BULLETIN. 1949. irreg., no.72, 1991. free. Oregon State University, Forest Research Laboratory, Corvallis, OR 97331. TEL 503-737-4271. Ed. Ralph E. McNees. circ. 2,000. (reprint service avail. from UMI) **Indexed:** Biol.Abstr., Forest.Abstr., Forest Prod.Abstr., Weed Abstr. **Document type:** bulletin.

634.9   US   ISSN 0078-5911
                      CODEN: OFRNBA
OREGON STATE UNIVERSITY. FOREST RESEARCH LABORATORY. RESEARCH NOTE. 1949. irreg., no.82, 1991. free. Oregon State University, Forest Research Laboratory, Corvallis, OR 97331. TEL 503-737-4271. Ed. Ralph E. McNees. (reprint service avail. from UMI) **Indexed:** Biol.Abstr., Forest.Abstr., Forest Prod.Abstr., Weed Abstr.

FORESTS AND FORESTRY

634.9   US   ISSN 0078-592X
SD12   CODEN: OUFPAQ
OREGON STATE UNIVERSITY. FOREST RESEARCH LABORATORY. RESEARCH PAPER. 1965. irreg., no.54, 1990. free. Oregon State University, Forest Research Laboratory, Corvallis, OR 97331. TEL 503-737-4271. Ed. Ralph E. McNees. circ. 2,000. (also avail. in microform from UMI; reprint service avail. from UMI) **Indexed:** Chem.Abstr., Forest.Abstr., Forest Prod.Abstr., Irr.& Drain.Abstr., Soils & Fert. **Document type:** academic/scholarly publication.

634.9   US   ISSN 0732-0981
ORIGIN TO DESTINATION. 1982. s-a. $20 (typically set in Oct.). Western Wood Products Association, Yeon Bldg., 522 S.W. Fifth Ave., OR 97204. TEL 503-224-3930. FAX 503-224-3934.

634.9   CN
PACIFIC FOREST RESEARCH CENTRE. PEST REPORT. irreg. free. Pacific Forest Research Centre, 506 W. Burnside Rd., Victoria, B.C. V8Z 1M5, Canada.

634.96
PACIFIC FORESTRY CENTRE. FOREST PEST LEAFLET. no.68, 1992. irreg. free. Pacific Forestry Centre, 506 West Burnside Rd., Victoria, B.C. V8Z 1M5, Canada. TEL 604-363-0600. FAX 604-363-0775. Ed. Alister McEwan. illus. (looseleaf format; back issues avail.) **Indexed:** Forest.Abstr.
   Formerly: Pacific Forest Research Centre. Pest Leaflet.

634.9   US
PACIFIC FORESTS. 1988. q. free. Pacific Logging Congress, 2300 S.W. Sixth Ave., Ste. 200, Portland, OR 97201. TEL 503-224-8406. FAX 502-224-7211. Ed. A. Wilson. adv.; circ. 8,500 (controlled). **Indexed:** Environ.Abstr. **Document type:** trade publication.
   Formerly: Pacific Logging Journal.
   Description: Covers issues facing the forestry industry in the western U.S., British Columbia and New Zealand.

634.92   PK   ISSN 0078-8147
PAKISTAN FOREST INSTITUTE, PESHAWAR. ANNUAL PROGRESS REPORT. Title varies: Pakistan Forest Institute, Peshawar. Progress Report. (Text in English) 1950. a. Pakistan Forest Institute, Peshawar, Pakistan. circ. 500. **Indexed:** Biol.Abstr., Chem.Abstr., Forest.Abstr. **Document type:** corporate report.

634.9   PK   ISSN 0030-9818
SD1   CODEN: PAJFAN
PAKISTAN JOURNAL OF FORESTRY. (Text in English) 1951. q. Rs.150($15) Pakistan Forest Institute, Peshawar, Pakistan. Ed. K.M. Siddiqui. adv.; bk.rev.; abstr.; charts; illus. circ. 400. **Indexed:** Agroforest.Abstr., Bio-Contr.News & Info., Biol.Abstr., Chem.Abstr., Field Crop Abstr., Forest.Abstr., Forest Prod.Abstr., Herb.Abstr., Plant Grow.Reg.Abstr., Rural Devel.Abstr., Rural Recreat.Tour.Abstr., Seed Abstr., Soils & Fert., Weed Abstr., World Agri.Econ.& Rural Sociol.Abstr. **Document type:** academic/scholarly publication.
—BLDSC (6341.000000); UnCover; CASDDS.

634.9   US   ISSN 1065-3651
PALLET ENTERPRISE. (Includes s-a. Buyer's Directory) 1981. 10/yr. $35 (Canada $45; elsewhere $75). Industrial Reporting, Inc., 1893 D-1 Billingsgate Circle, Richmond, VA 23233. TEL 804-740-1567. FAX 804-740-2826. Ed. Edward C. Brindley, Jr. adv. circ. 13,800. **Document type:** trade publication.

634.9   CN   ISSN 1192-1242
PARTNERS IN FORESTRY. 2/yr. Forestry Canada, Northwest Region, Northern Forestry Centre, 5320-122 St., Edmonton, AB T6H 3S5, Canada. TEL 403-435-7210. FAX 403-435-7359. **Document type:** newsletter.

634.9   US   ISSN 0031-4501
PENNSYLVANIA FORESTS. 1886. q. $20. Pennsylvania Forestry Association, 56 E. Main St., Mechanicsburg, PA 17055-3851. TEL 717-766-5371. Ed. Susan M. Haskins. adv.; illus. circ. 3,200. **Indexed:** Chem.Abstr.
   Formerly: Forest Leaves.

634.9   SP
PERIPLO. 1984. bi-m. 2750 ptas. Incafo, CastelIlo, 59, 28001 Madrid, Spain. TEL (91)431 34 60. TELEX 42491 CF-E. Ed. Luis Blas Aritio.

POWER EQUIPMENT AUSTRALASIA. see AGRICULTURE — Agricultural Equipment

POZNANSKIE TOWARZYSTWO PRZYJACIOL NAUK. KOMISJA NAUK ROLNICZYCH I KOMISJA NAUK LESNYCH. PRACE. see AGRICULTURE

634.9   US
PRODUCTION, PRICES, EMPLOYMENT AND TRADE IN NORTHWEST FOREST INDUSTRIES. q. free. U.S. Forest Service, Pacific Northwest Research Sta., Box 3890, Portland, OR 97208. TEL 503-326-7128. (also avail. in microfiche from CIS; reprint service avail. from CIS) **Indexed:** Amer.Stat.Ind. (1975-). **Document type:** government publication.

634.9   CN
PROFESSIONAL FORESTER. 1957. q. membership. Ontario Professional Foresters Association, 27 West Beaver Creek Rd., Richmond Hill, ON L4B 1M8, Canada. TEL 905-764-2921. FAX 905-764-2921. Ed. Mike Rosen. adv.; bk.rev.; circ. 1,300 (controlled). **Document type:** newsletter.

PROHORT. see GARDENING AND HORTICULTURE

PUBLIC LANDS NEWS. see CONSERVATION

PUUMIES. see BUILDING AND CONSTRUCTION — Carpentry And Woodwork

634.9   UK   ISSN 0033-5568
                  CODEN: QJFOA2
QUARTERLY JOURNAL OF FORESTRY. 1907. q. £42($128) (typically set in Jan.). (Royal Forestry Society of England, Wales & Northern Ireland) Hall - McCartney Ltd., P.O. Box 21, Unit 7, Campus 5, The Business Park, Letchworth, Herts. SG6 2JF, England. TEL 0462-675848. FAX 0462-679356. Ed. K.E. Stebbens. adv.; bk.rev.; illus.; index. circ. 5,000. **Indexed:** Biol.Abstr., Curr.Adv.Ecol.Sci., Curr.Cont., Forest.Abstr., Forest Prod.Abstr., Geo.Abstr., P.A.I.S., Rev.Appl.Entomol., Rev.Plant Path., RICS, Rural Recreat.Tour.Abstr., Soils & Fert., Weed Abstr., World Agri.Econ.& Rural Sociol.Abstr. **Document type:** academic/scholarly publication.
—BLDSC (7191.000000); UnCover.

QUEBEC (PROVINCE). CONSEIL DE LA CONSERVATION ET DE L'ENVIRONNEMENT. RAPPORT ANNUEL. see CONSERVATION

333.79   CN
QUEBEC (PROVINCE). MINISTERE DES FORETS. DIRECTION DE LA RECHERCHE. GUIDE. (Text in French; summaries in English, French) 1970. irreg. free. Ministere des Forets, Direction de la Recherche, 2700 rue Einstein, Sainte-Foy, PQ G1P 3W8, Canada. TEL 418-643-7994. FAX 418-643-2165. TELEX 051-31589 SDBCS QBC. circ. 900. **Document type:** government publication.
   Former titles: Quebec (Province). Ministere de l'Energie et des Ressources. Direction de la Recherche. Guide; Quebec (Province). Ministere de l'Energie et des Ressources. Direction de la Recherche et du Developpement. Guide; Quebec (Province) Ministere de l'Energie et des Ressources. Service de la Recherche Appliquee. Guide; Quebec (Province). Ministere de l'Energie et des Ressources. Service de la Recherche (Terres et Forets). Guide; Quebec (Province). Ministere de l'Energie et des Ressources. Service de la Recherche Forestiere. Guide.
   Description: Field handbooks or booklets to be used with field documents and instruments.

634.9 333.7   CN   ISSN 1183-3912
SD14.Q4   CODEN: MRFOEI
QUEBEC (PROVINCE). MINISTERE DES FORETS. DIRECTION DE LA RECHERCHE. MEMOIRE DE RECHERCHE FORESTIERE. (Text in French; summaries in English, French) 1970. irreg. free. Ministere des Forets, Direction de la Recherche, 2700 rue Einstein, Sainte-Foy, PQ G1P 3W8, Canada. TEL 418-643-7994. FAX 418-643-2165. TELEX 051-31589 SDBCS QBC. Ed. Fabien Caron. circ. 900. **Indexed:** Forest.Abstr. **Document type:** government publication, academic/scholarly publication, monographic series.
   Former titles: Quebec (Province). Ministere de l'Energie et des Ressources. Direction de la Recherche. Memoire; Quebec (Province). Ministere de l'Energie et des Ressources. Direction de la Recherche et du Developpement. Memoire; Quebec (Province). Ministere de l'Energie et des Ressources. Service de la Recherche (Appliquee). Memoire; Quebec (Province). Ministere de l'Energie et des Ressources. Service de la Recherche (Terres et Forets). Memoire; Quebec (Province). Ministere de l'Energie et des Ressources. Service de la Recherche Forestiere. Memoire; Quebec (Province). Ministere de l'Energie et des Ressources. Service de la Recherche. Memoire.
   Description: Partial or final research reports (includes theses).

634.9   CN   ISSN 0834-4833
                  CODEN: NRFOET
QUEBEC (PROVINCE). MINISTERE DES FORETS. DIRECTION DE LA RECHERCHE. NOTE DE RECHERCHE FORESTIERE. (Text in French; summaries in English, French) 1972. irreg. free. Ministere des Forets, Direction de la Recherche, 2700 rue Einstein, Sainte-Foy, PQ G1P 3W8, Canada. TEL 418-643-7994. FAX 418-643-2165. TELEX 051-31589 SDBCS QBC. Ed. Fabien Caron. charts; illus. circ. 900. **Document type:** government publication.
   Former titles: Quebec (Province). Ministere de l'Energie et des Ressources. Direction de la Recherche. Note de Recherche Forestiere; Quebec (Province). Ministere de l'Energie et des Ressources. Direction de la Recherche et du Developpement. Note de Recherche Forestiere; Quebec (Province). Ministere de l'Energie et des Ressources. Service de la Recherche (Appliquee). Note; Quebec (Province). Ministere de l'Energie et des Ressources. Service de la Recherche (Terres et Forets). Note; Quebec (Province). Ministere de l'Energie et des Ressources. Service de la Recherche Forestiere. Note.
   Description: Short research reports, commentaries, evaluations.

634.9   AT   ISSN 1035-977X
QUEENSLAND FOREST SERVICE. ADVISORY LEAFLET. 1938. irreg. Queensland Forest Service, G.P.O. Box 944, Brisbane, Qld. 4001, Australia. illus.
   Description: Advisory notes on use of timber and on control of timber pests in Queensland.

634.9   AT
SD111.Q8   CODEN: QFNRAV
QUEENSLAND FOREST SERVICE. DEPARTMENT OF PRIMARY INDUSTRIES. ANNUAL REPORT. 1916. a. Queensland Forest Service, Department of Primary Industries, G.P.O. Box 944, Brisbane, Qld. 4001, Australia. illus.
   Formerly: Queensland. Department of Forestry. Annual Report (ISSN 0480-9653)
   Description: Contains report to Parliament and statement of accounts.

634.9   AT   ISSN 1035-9788
                  CODEN: QFRNAV
QUEENSLAND FOREST SERVICE. RESEARCH NOTE. 1954. irreg. Queensland Forest Service, G.P.O. Box 944, Brisbane, Qld. 4001, Australia. TEL 07-877-9727. FAX 07-371-2217. TELEX QUFOR AA 43988. circ. 400 (controlled). **Indexed:** Biol.Abstr.
   Formerly: Queensland. Department of Forestry. Research Note (ISSN 0481-3219)
   Description: Brief scientific notes covering forest and timber research work carried out in the Forest Service.

FORESTS AND FORESTRY

634.9   AT   ISSN 1035-9796
SD111.Q8   CODEN: RPD@DK
QUEENSLAND FOREST SERVICE. RESEARCH PAPER.
1971. irreg. Queensland Forest Service, G.P.O. Box 944, Brisbane, Qld. 4001, Australia. TEL 07-877 9727. FAX 07-371-2217. TELEX QUEFOR AA 43988. circ. 400 (controlled). **Indexed:** Aus.Sci.Ind., Biol.Abstr., Forest.Abstr., Forest Prod.Abstr., Soils & Fert.
    Formerly: Queensland. Department of Forestry. Research Paper (ISSN 0157-809X)
    Description: Contains scientific papers covering major forest research projects of the Forest Service.

634.9   AT
QUEENSLAND FOREST SERVICE. RESEARCH REPORT.
1977. biennial. Queensland Forest Service, G.P.O. Box 944, Brisbane, Qld. 4001, Australia. illus. —BLDSC (7762.846500).
    Formerly: Queensland. Department of Forestry. Division of Technical Services. Report of Research Activities (ISSN 0311-0893)

634.9   AT   ISSN 1035-9818
QUEENSLAND FOREST SERVICE. TECHNICAL NOTE.
1978. irreg. Queensland Forest Service, G.P.O. Box 944, Brisbane, Qld. 4001, Australia.
    Description: Brief notes on research findings on forestry and timber subjects.

634.8   AT   ISSN 1035-9826
QUEENSLAND FOREST SERVICE. TECHNICAL PAPER.
1974. irreg. free to qualified personnel. Queensland Forest Service, G.P.O. Box 944, Brisbane, Qld. 4001, Australia. TEL 07-877-9727. FAX 07-371-2217. TELEX QUEFOR AA 43988. Ed. P. Nielsen. circ. 400. **Indexed:** Biol.Abstr., Forest.Abstr., Forest Prod.Abstr.
    Formerly: Queensland. Department of Forestry. Technical Paper (ISSN 0155-9664)
    Description: Reports experiments which have produced useful information in the forest and timber utilization research fields.

QUINAULT NATURAL RESOURCES. see *CONSERVATION*

634.9   CN   ISSN 0824-8818
REALISATIONS RECENTES A PETAWAWA/RECENT ACHIEVEMENTS AT PETAWAWA. (Text in English, French) 1983. q. free. Petawawa National Forestry Institute, Chalk River, ON K0J 1J0, Canada. FAX 613-589-2275. Ed. Asoka C. Yapa. circ. 1,750. (reprint service avail. from MMI) **Document type:** newsletter.
    Description: Contains results of recently completed or ongoing research on forest genetics, biotechnology and forest management systems.

634.9   GW
REGENWALD REPORT. 1986. q. DM.10. Rettet den Regenwald e.V., Poeseldorfer Weg 17, 20148 Hamburg, Germany. TEL 040-4103804. FAX 040-4500144. Ed. Reinhard Behrend. bk.rev. circ. 10,000. **Document type:** newsletter.
    Former titles: Regenwaelder Report; Regenwaelder Zeitung.

634.9   SP   ISSN 1130-958X
REVISTA FORESTAL ESPANOLA. 1991. 4/yr. 5000 ptas. Gran Via 31, 7o no., 28013 Madrid, Spain. TEL 91-532-38-75. FAX 91-522-73-20. Ed. Maria Angel Garcia Misol. **Document type:** trade publication.

634.9   VE   ISSN 0798-2437
REVISTA FORESTAL LATINOAMERICANA. (Text in Spanish; summaries in English, French) 1957. irreg. $20 per no. Instituto Forestal Latinoamericano, Apdo. 36, Merida, Venezuela. adv.; bk.rev. **Indexed:** Biol.Abstr., Forest.Abstr.
    Formerly (until 1981): Instituto Forestal Latinoamericano de Investigacion y Capitacion. Boletin (ISSN 0538-1126)
    Description: Publishes articles dealing with scientific, technical and industrial progresses and advancements carried out and achieved in the forestry sector of Latin America.

634.9   SP
REVISTA NATURA. 1983. m. 3120 ptas. (Europe 6500 ptas.; elsewhere 9300 ptas.). G y J Espana Ediciones, S.L. (Subsidiary of: Gruner & Jahr USA Publishing), Marques de Villamagna, 4, 28001 Madrid, Spain. TEL 91-435-8100. FAX 91-576-7881. TELEX 43419 ORBSA E. (And: Travesera de Gracia, 56, 08006 Barcelona, Spain) Ed. Alberto Huerta. adv. contact: Elena Sanchez Fabres. circ. 79,000. **Document type:** consumer publication.

634.9   RM
REVISTA PADURILOR. (Text in Rumanian; abstracts and summaries in English) 1885. q. $38. R.A. Romsilva, Bd. Magheru nr.31, etaj. 5, sector 1, 70162 Bucharest, Rumania. adv.; bk.rev. **Indexed:** Biol.Abstr., Forest.Abstr., Forest Prod.Abstr.
    Formerly (until 1986): Revista Padurilor-Industria Lemnului, Celuloza si Hirtie, Silvicultura si Exploatarea Padurilor; Which superseded in part: Revista Padurilor-Industria Lemnului-Celuloza si Hirtie (ISSN 0035-029X)

634.9   FR   ISSN 0035-2829
REVUE FORESTIERE FRANCAISE. 1949. bi-m. (plus special issue). 270 F. Ecole Nationale du Genie Rural, des Eaux et des Forets, 14 rue Girardet, 54042 Nancy, France. TEL 83-39-68-00. FAX 83-30-22-54. Eds. J. Parde, G. Blanchard. adv.; bk.rev.; abstr.; bibl.; charts; illus.; index, cum.index. circ. 3,000. **Indexed:** Abstr.Bull.Inst.Pap.Chem., Acid Pre.Dig., Biol.Abstr., Biol.& Agr.Ind., Bull.Signal., Curr.Adv.Ecol.Sci., Excerp.Med., Forest.Abstr., Forest Prod.Abstr., Rural Recreat.Tour.Abstr., World Agri.Econ.& Rural Sociol.Abstr.
—BLDSC (7902.000000); UMI. **CCC.**

634.9   IO   ISSN 0035-5372
SD1
RIMBA INDONESIA; * Indonesian journal of forestry. 1952. q. Rps.1600($8) Forest Research Institute, Box 66, Bogor, Indonesia. Ed. Dr. Ishemat Soerianegara. bk.rev.; bibl.; charts; illus.; index. circ. 750. (processed) **Indexed:** Biol.Abstr., Field Crop Abstr., Forest.Abstr., Forest Prod.Abstr., Herb.Abstr.

634.9 574.8   JA   ISSN 0387-9119
RINBOKU NO IKUSHU/FOREST TREE BREEDING. (Text in Japanese; summaries in English) 1957. q. 4000 Yen($35) Rinboku Ikushu Kyokai - Forest Tree Breeding Association, 7, Rokuban-cho, Chiyoda-ku, Tokyo 102, Japan. TEL 03-3261-3433. Ed. Ginsaku Nakada. adv.; bk.rev. circ. 1,200. **Indexed:** Forest.Abstr., Plant Grow.Reg.Abstr. **Document type:** bulletin.
    Description: Contains research and information on forest tree breeding.

634.9 674   JA
RINGYO TO KAKUZAI; forestry and forest chemicals. (Text in Japanese) nos.64-67, 1978. q. $38.25. Japan Publications Trading Co. Ltd., Box 5030, Tokyo International, Tokyo 100-31, Japan.

RURAL INDUSTRY DIRECTORY. see *AGRICULTURE*

634.9   US   ISSN 1068-669X
SD1
RUSSIAN FOREST SCIENCES. English translation of: Lesovedenie (RU ISSN 0024-1148) 1986. bi-m. $590. (Russian Academy of Sciences, RU) Allerton Press, Inc., 150 Fifth Ave., New York, NY 10011. TEL 212-924-3950. FAX 212-463-9684. Ed. A.S. Isaev. **Document type:** academic/scholarly publication. —**CCC.**
    Formerly: Soviet Forest Sciences (ISSN 0891-0324)

634.9   RW
RWANDA. PROJET PILOTE FORESTIER. PROGRAMME D'APPUI AU SERVICE FORESTIER PREFECTORAL DE KIBUYE. (Text in French) 1972. a. free. Projet Pilote Forestier, B.P. 1, Kibuye, Rwanda. TEL 68243.
    Formerly: Rwanda. Projet Pilote Forestier. Rapport Annuel.

634.9   US   ISSN 0080-5092
S.J. HALL LECTURESHIP IN INDUSTRIAL FORESTRY.
1959. a. free. University of California, Berkeley, Department of Forestry and Resource Management, 145 Mulford Hall, Berkeley, CA 94720. TEL 415-642-0376.

634.9   MY   ISSN 0080-5211
SABAH. FOREST DEPARTMENT. ANNUAL REPORT. (Text in English) 1951. a., latest 1990. M.$6. Forest Department - Jabatan Perhutanan, P.O. Box 311, 90007 Sandakan, Malaysia. TEL 089-660811. FAX 089-669170. TELEX MA 82016.

634.9   MY   ISSN 0128-5939
SANDAKANIA. (Text in English) irreg. price varies. Forest Research Centre, P.O. Box 1407, 90008 Sandakan, Sabah, Malaysia. TEL 089-531522. FAX 089-531068. Ed. K.M. Wong. **Document type:** monographic series.

634.9   NO   ISSN 0282-7581
SD217.S34   CODEN: SJFRE3
SCANDINAVIAN JOURNAL OF FOREST RESEARCH. (Text in English) 1986. q. NOK 915 in the Nordic countries; elsewhere NOK 955. (Nordic Forest Research Cooperation Committee) Scandinavian University Press, P.O. Box 2959 Toeyen, N-0608 Oslo, Norway. TEL 472-67-7600. FAX 472-67-7575. (U.S. addr.: Scandinavian University Press, 200 Meacham Ave., Elmont, NY 11003. TEL 516-352-7300) (Co-sponsor: Royal Swedish Academy of Agriculture and Forestry) Ed. Aake Barklund. index. **Indexed:** Environ.Per.Bibl. (1990-), Forest.Abstr., Irr.& Drain.Abstr., Plant Grow.Reg.Abstr., Soils & Fert. **Document type:** academic/scholarly publication.
—BLDSC (8087.506500); UnCover; SWETS.
    Description: Publishes original articles concerning forest research of relevance to Scandinavian conditions.

634.9 674.2 694   SZ
SCHWEIZER HOLZ-BOERSE; Fachblatt fuer alle Gebiete der Holzwirtschaft. (Text in German) 1919. w. 106 SFr. (foreign 160 SFr.). Schweizerische Handelsboerse, Bahnhofquai 7, Postfach 7075, CH-8023 Zurich, Switzerland. TEL 01-2112870. FAX 01-2112872. adv.; bk.rev. circ. 1,900. (back issues avail.) **Document type:** trade publication.

634.9   SZ
SCHWEIZER WALD. 11/yr. Winterhalde 12, CH-4572 Ammannsegg, Switzerland. TEL 065-471823. FAX 064-245760. TELEX 981195-SAG-CH. Ed. Rudolf Luterbacher. circ. 2,100.

634.9   SZ   ISSN 0036-7818
SD1
SCHWEIZERISCHE ZEITSCHRIFT FUER FORSTWESEN/JOURNAL FORESTIER SUISSE. (Text in French, German) 1850. m. 115 SFr. Schweizerischer Forstverein, ETH-Zentrum HG, FO21.1, CH-8092 Zurich, Switzerland. TEL 01-6325205. Ed. A. Schuler. adv.; bk.rev.; abstr.; bibl.; charts; illus.; index. circ. 1,900. (back issues avail.) **Indexed:** Biol.Abstr., Curr.Adv.Ecol.Sci., Excerp.Med., Forest.Abstr., Forest Prod.Abstr., Rural Recreat.Tour.Abstr., Soils & Fert., World Agri.Econ.& Rural Sociol.Abstr. **Document type:** academic/scholarly publication.

634.9   SZ
SCHWEIZERISCHE ZEITSCHRIFT FUER FORSTWESEN. BEIHEFTE. irreg. price varies. Schweizerischer Forstverein, ETH-Zentrum HG, FO21.1, CH-8092 Zurich, Switzerland. TEL 01-3625205. **Document type:** academic/scholarly publication.

634.9   UK   ISSN 0036-9217
SD1   CODEN: SFORAG
SCOTTISH FORESTRY. 1858. q. £40. Royal Scottish Forestry Society, Camsie House, Charlestown, Dunfermline, Fife KY11 3EE, Scotland. TEL 0383-873014. FAX 0383-872863. Ed. Jenny Johnson. adv.; bk.rev. circ. 1,500. **Indexed:** Biol.Abstr., Chem.Abstr., Curr.Adv.Ecol.Sci., Forest.Abstr., Forest Prod.Abstr., Geo.Abstr., Soils & Fert., Weed Abstr., World Agri.Econ.& Rural Sociol.Abstr. **Document type:** academic/scholarly publication, proceedings.
—BLDSC (8209.000000); UnCover.

SEEDLING NEWS. see *CONSERVATION*

SEIVA. see *AGRICULTURE*

634.9   CC
SENLIN FANGHUO/FIRE PREVENTION IN FORESTS. (Text in Chinese) q. Dongbei Linye Daxue - Northeast University of Forestry, 8, Hexing Lu, Harbin, Heilongjiang 150040, People's Republic of China. TEL 64911. Ed. Zheng Huanneng.

FORESTS AND FORESTRY

634.9   CC
SENLIN YU RENLEI/FOREST AND HUMAN KIND. (Text in Chinese) bi-m. Zhongguo Linxuehui - Chinese Society of Forestry, Yiheyuan, Wanshoushan Hou, Beijing 100091, People's Republic of China. TEL 2582211. Ed. Dong Zhiyong.

634.9 674   KO   ISSN 1010-8289
SEOUL NATIONAL UNIVERSITY FORESTS. RESEARCH BULLETIN/NYENSUBRIM NYENGU BOGO: SEOUL DAIHAGGYO NONGKWA DAIHAG. Key Title: Research Bulletin of the Seoul National University Forests. (Text in English and Korean) 1962. a. 10000 Won($15) Seoul National University Forests, College of Agriculture, Seoul National University, Suwon 441-744, S. Korea. FAX 0331-291-5830. Index. circ. 500. (also avail. in talking book) **Indexed:** Forest.Abstr. **Document type:** academic/scholarly publication.
    Formerly: Seoul National University Forests. Bulletin.

634.9   JA   ISSN 0389-2166
SHINRIN BUNKA KENKYU/REVIEW OF FORESTRY CULTURE. (Text in Japanese) 1980. a. Shinrin Bunka Kyokai - Forests Culture Association, Asahi Shimbun Tokyo Honsha, 3-2 Tsukiji 5-chome, Chuo-ku, Tokyo 104-11, Japan. Ed. Tsutsui Michio.

634.9   BE
SILVA BELGICA. 1893. 6/yr. 1400 Fr. Societe Royale Forestiere de Belgique - Koninklijke Belgische Bosbouwmaatschappij, Galerie du Centre, Bloc 2, 5e Etage, B-1000 Brussels, Belgium. TEL 2-223-07-66. FAX 2-223-01-45. Ed. M. Terlinden. adv.; bk.rev.; abstr.; charts; illus.; maps; mkt.; index. circ. 3,000. **Indexed:** Biol.Abstr., Excerp.Med., Forest.Abstr., Forest Prod.Abstr., Soils & Fert.
    Formerly: Societe Royale Forestiere de Belgique. Bulletin - Koninklijke Belgische Bosbouwmaatschappij. Tydschrift (ISSN 0037-9573)

634.9   FI   ISSN 0037-5330
SD1
SILVA FENNICA. (Text in English or Finnish) 1926. 4/yr. FIM 280. Suomen Metsatieteellinen Seura - Society of Forestry in Finland, Unioninkatu 40 B, SF-00100 Helsinki 17, Finland. (Subscr. to: Academic Bookstore, P.O. Box 23, SF-00371 Helsinki, Finland) Ed. Tommi Salonen. illus.; index, cum.index: (1926-1972 and 1973-1984). circ. 1,050. **Indexed:** Biol.Abstr., Curr.Adv.Ecol.Sci., Excerp.Med., Forest.Abstr., Forest Prod.Abstr.
—BLDSC (8281.000000); UnCover.
    Description: Covers all aspects of forest research, from basic to applied subjects.

SILVAE GENETICA; Zeitschrift fuer Forstgenetik und Forstpflanzenzuechtung. see *BIOLOGY — Genetics*

634.9   SW   ISSN 1101-9506
SD1   CODEN: SKFOEZ
SKOG & FORSKNING. (Text in Swedish) 1902. 4/yr. SEK 365 to non-members in Europe (elsewhere SEK 385); members in Europe SEK 320 (elsewhere SEK 340). Sveriges Skogsvaardsfoerbund - Swedish Forestry Association, Bragevaegen 30, Box 500, S-182 15 Danderyd, Sweden. TEL 46-8-753-03-90. FAX 46-8-755-86-02. Ed. Bengt Ek. bk.rev.; index. circ. 1,500. **Document type:** trade publication.
    Former titles (until 1991): Sveriges Skogsvaardsfoerbunds Tidskrift (ISSN 0371-2907); (until 1966): Svenska Skogsvaardsfoereningens Tidskrift (ISSN 0562-7605); (until 1927): Skogsvaardsfoereningens Tidskrift (ISSN 0039-730X)

634.9   NO   ISSN 0037-6396
SKOGEIEREN. 1914. 16/yr. NOK 270. Norges Skogeierforbund - Forest Owners' Federation, Stortingsgaten 30, P.O. Box 1438 Vika, 0115 Oslo 1, Norway. FAX 47-22-83-40-47. Ed. Kaare Wedul. adv. contact: Tor-Erling Pettersen. bk.rev.; charts; illus.; index. circ. 55,000. **Document type:** newsletter.
—CCC.

634.9   SW   ISSN 0037-640X
SKOGEN. 1914. 12/yr. SEK 500 to non-members (Europe SEK 535, elsewhere SEK 580); members (Europe SEK 495, elsewhere SEK 540). Sveriges Skogsvaardsfoerbund - Swedish Forestry Association, Bragevaegen 30, P.O. Box 500, 182 15 Danderyd, Sweden. TEL 46-08-753-0390. FAX 46-08-755-8602. Ed. Bo Lindevall. adv.; bk.rev. circ. 21,000. **Indexed:** Agri.Eng.Abstr., Chem.Abstr., Forest.Abstr., Forest Prod.Abstr.
    Incorporates (in 1979): Skogsaegaren.

634.9   NO   ISSN 0803-2866
        CODEN: MNISBE
SKOGFORSK. MEDDELELSER. (Text in English; summaries in Norwegian) 1920. irreg. NOK 100. Norsk Institutt for Skogforskning, Hoegskoleveien 12, N-1432 Aas, Norway. TEL 47-64-94-90-00. FAX 47-64-94-29-80. circ. 1,000. (back issues avail.) **Indexed:** Biol.Abstr., Curr.Adv.Ecol.Sci., Forest.Abstr., Forest Prod.Abstr., Rev.Plant Path., Soils & Fert. **Document type:** academic/scholarly publication.
    Former titles (until 1991): Norsk Institutt for Skogforskning. Meddelelser (ISSN 0332-5709); (1920-1974): Norske Skogsforsoeksvesen. Meddelelser.

634.9   NO   ISSN 0803-2858
SKOGFORSK. RAPPORT. (Text in Norwegian; summaries in English) 1980. irreg. NOK 80. Norsk Institutt for Skogforskning, Hoegskoleveien 12, N-1432 Aas, Norway. TEL 47-64-94-90-00. FAX 47-64-94-29-80. (back issues avail.) **Indexed:** Biol.Abstr., Forest.Abstr., Forest Prod.Abstr., Weed Abstr. **Document type:** academic/scholarly publication.
—BLDSC (7753.995000).
    Formerly (until 1991): Norsk Institutt for Skogforskning. Rapport (ISSN 0333-001X)

634.9   SW   ISSN 0346-1289
SKOGSMANNEN. 1891. m. SEK 120 (effective 1990). Sveriges Skogstjaenstemannafoerening, Klockaregatan 6, 360 23 Aalmeboda, Sweden. (Co-sponsors: Sveriges Kronojaegarefoerbund; S T - Skog) adv. circ. 5,000. **Document type:** trade publication.
    Formerly (until 1939): Skogvaktaren.

634.9   SW   ISSN 1102-1322
SKOGSVETENSKAP; nyheter om skogsforskning. 1991. q. S L U Info - Skog, S-901 83 Umeaa, Sweden.

634.9   IC
SKOGURINN. q. free. Skograektarfelag Reykjavikur - Reykjavik Forestry Association, Fossvogsbletti 1, IS-108 Reykjavik, Iceland. TEL 354-1-641770.
    Description: Publishes articles on forestry and the reforestation of Iceland.

634.9   DK   ISSN 0904-9207
SD57
SKOV OG NATUR/FOREST AND NATURE. 1982. a. DKK 60 free to libraries. Miljoeministeriet, Skov- og Natursyrelsen, Slotsmarken 13, DK-2970 Horsholm, Denmark. TEL 45-76--53-76. Ed.Bd. circ. 4,000. **Document type:** government publication.
    Former titles (until 1989): Miljoeministeriets Arealforvaltning (ISSN 0904-8863); (until 1988): Danske Statsskoves Udbytte af Ved og Penge (ISSN 0109-5234); (until 1983): Oversigt Over de Danske Statsskoves Udbytte af Ved og Penge for Finansaaret.

634.9   DK   ISSN 0900-6370
SKOVBRUGSTIDENDE.* 1914. m. DKK 190. (Danske Skovteknikeres Landsforening. D S L) Danske Skov- og Landskabsingenioerer, Albertslund, Denmark. Ed. Erik Sennels. adv.; bk.rev.; index. circ. 1,900.

634.9   DK   ISSN 0106-8539
SKOVEN. 1969. m. DKK 380. Dansk Skovforening - Danish Forestry Society, Amalievej 20, 1875 Frederiksberg C, Denmark. TEL 45-31-24-42-66. FAX 45-31-24-02-42. Ed. Soeren Fodgaard. adv.; B&W page DKK 3850. bk.rev.; abstr.; illus.; index; circ. 4,032. (controlled). **Document type:** trade publication.
    Description: Short articles on matters of current interest such as logging equipment, silviculture research results, forest policy, reports on events in forestry. Coverage is geared to all foresters.

634.9 634.96   UK
SLASHER. 1948. 6/yr. Forestry Commission, 231 Corstorphine Rd., Edinburgh EH12 7AT, Scotland. FAX 031-334-4473. TELEX 727879-FORCOM-G. Ed. Tracey Francis. bk.rev. circ. 11,500. (tabloid format) **Document type:** government publication, newspaper.

634.9   SW   ISSN 0348-2685
SMAASKOGSNYTT; forskningsinformation om smaaskaligt skogsbruk. 1977. bi-m. SEK 90 (effective 1991). S L U Info - Skog, S-770 73 Garpenberg, Sweden.

634.9   SW   ISSN 0283-1007
SMALL SCALE FORESTRY. (Text in English) 1986. s-a. SEK 100 (effective 1990). Swedish University of Agricultural Sciences, Department of Forest Extension, S-770 73 Garpenberg, Sweden.

634.9   SW   ISSN 0284-5776
SOEDRA SKOG. 1944. 6/yr. SEK 120 (effective 1991). Soedra Skogsaegarna, S-351 89 Vaexjoe, Sweden. FAX 470-21738. Ed. K-G Fridman. adv. circ. 35,000.
    Former titles: Soedra; Soedra-Kontakt.

634.9   SA   ISSN 0038-2167
SD1
SOUTH AFRICAN FORESTRY JOURNAL/SUID-AFRIKAANSE BOSBOUTYDSKRIF. (Text mainly in English; occasionally in Afrikaans) 1938. q. $80 (effective 1993). Southern African Institute of Forestry, P.O. Box 1022, Pretoria 0001, South Africa. TEL 27-12-473479. Ed. H.A. van der Sijde. adv.; bk.rev.; charts; illus.; bibl.; index. circ. 1,174. (back issues avail.) **Indexed:** Biol.Abstr., Curr.Adv.Ecol.Sci., Forest.Abstr., Forest Prod.Abstr., Herb.Abstr., Ind.S.A.Per., Rev.Plant Path, Seed Abstr., Soils & Fert., W.R.C.Inf., Weed Abstr. **Document type:** academic/scholarly publication.
—BLDSC (8337.190000); SWETS.

634.9   US   ISSN 0148-4419
SD144.A15   CODEN: SJAFD9
SOUTHERN JOURNAL OF APPLIED FORESTRY. q. $40 to individuals; institutions $85. Society of American Foresters, 5400 Grosvenor Ln., Bethesda, MD 20814. TEL 301-897-8720. FAX 301-897-3690. Ed. William Gladstone. adv. circ. 1,013. (also avail. in microform from UMI; reprint service avail. from UMI) **Indexed:** Abstr.Bull.Inst.Pap.Chem., Agri.Eng.Abstr., Biol.Abstr., Chem.Abstr., Curr.Adv.Ecol.Sci., Curr.Adv.Genetics & Molec.Biol., Energy Ind., Energy Info.Abstr., Environ.Abstr., Forest.Abstr., Forest Prod.Abstr., Geo.Abstr., Herb.Abstr., Rev.Plant Path., Seed Abstr., Sel.Water Res.Abstr., Weed Abstr.
—BLDSC (8354.245000); UnCover; UMI; CASDDS.
Refereed Serial

SPAIN. INSTITUTO NACIONAL DE INVESTIGACIONES AGRARIAS. COMUNICACIONES. SERIE: PROTECCION VEGETAL. see *AGRICULTURE — Crop Production And Soil*

SPAIN. INSTITUTO NACIONAL DE INVESTIGACIONES AGRARIAS. SERIE: PRODUCCION Y PROTECCION VEGETALES. see *AGRICULTURE — Crop Production And Soil*

634.9   US
SPRINGER SERIES IN WOOD SCIENCE. 1983. irreg. price varies. Springer-Verlag, 175 Fifth Ave., New York, NY 10010. TEL 212-460-1500.
FAX 212-473-6272. (Also: Berlin, Heidelberg, Tokyo and Vienna) Ed. T.E. Timell. **Document type:** monograph series.

634.9   CE
SRI LANKA FORESTER. (Text in English) 1953. s-a. Rs.15($10) Forest Department, Rajamalwatta Rd., Battaramulla, Sri Lanka. Ed. K. Vivekanandan. bk.rev. circ. 2,500. **Indexed:** Biol.Abstr., Forest.Abstr., Forest Prod.Abstr., Rev.Plant Path., Soils & Fert., Sri Lanka Sci.Ind.
    Formerly (until 1972): Ceylon Forester (ISSN 0045-6195)

FORESTS AND FORESTRY

634.9 — **IO**
STATISTIK KEHUTANAN INDONESIA. (Text in English and Indonesian) 1969. m. free. Bureau of Planning - Secretariat General of the Ministry of Forestry of the Republic of Indonesia, Manggala Wananakti Bldg. 3rd Fl., Jl. Gatot Subroto, Jakarta 10270, Indonesia. TEL 5803289. TELEX 45996-DEPHUT-IA. **Document type:** government publication.
Formerly: Forestry in Indonesia; **Supersedes:** Berita Hasil Hutan (ISSN 0303-2884)

634.9 — **SW** — **ISSN 0039-3150**
SD211 — **CODEN: SFSUAB**
STUDIA FORESTALIA SUECICA. (Text and summaries in English) 1963. irreg. no.167, 1985. price varies. Swedish University of Agricultural Sciences, Research Information Centre, Box 7057, S-750 07 Uppsala, Sweden. FAX 46-18-67-35-20. (Dist. by: A W I International AB, P.O. Box 4627, S-116 91 Stockholm, Sweden) Ed. Goeran Grant. charts. circ. 1,200. **Indexed:** Abstr.Bull.Inst.Pap.Chem., Biol.Abstr., Chem.Abstr., Curr.Adv.Ecol.Sci., Excerp.Med., Forest.Abstr., Forest Prod.Abstr., Rev.Appl.Entomol., Rev.Plant Path., Soils & Fert. **Document type:** academic/scholarly publication.
—BLDSC (8482.450000).

634.9 — **SJ**
SUDAN SILVA. (Text in English) no.13, 1962. a. $5. Sudan Forestry Society, Box 7089, Khartoum, Sudan. (Co-sponsor: National Council for Research) Ed. Hassan A. Musnad. adv. circ. 1,000. **Indexed:** Forest.Abstr., Forest Prod.Abstr., Soils & Fert.

SUO. see *AGRICULTURE*

634.9 — **CN**
SUPPLY POST. 1971. m. Can.$16($28) Ken Kenward Enterprises Ltd., 19329 Enterprise Way, No.108, Surrey, B.C. V3S 6J8, Canada. TEL 604-533-5577. FAX 604-533-9533. Ed. T.R.C. Kenward. adv. circ. 16,022.

634.9 674 — **SW** — **ISSN 0348-4599**
SVERIGES LANTBRUKSUNIVERSITET. INSTITUTIONEN FOER VIRKESLAERA. RAPPORTER. (Text in Swedish; summaries in English) 1955. irreg., no.240, 1993. SEK 400. Sveriges Lantbruksuniversitet, Institutionen foer Virkeslaera - Swedish University of Agricultural Sciences, Department of Forest Products, Box 7008, S-750 07 Uppsala, Sweden. TEL 46-18-67-10-00. FAX 46-18-67-34-90. Ed. Mats Nylinder. **Indexed:** Field Crop Abstr., Forest.Abstr., Forest Prod.Abstr., Herb.Abstr. **Document type:** academic/scholarly publication.
Formerly (until 1978): Kungliga Skogshoegskolan. Institutionen foer Virkeslaera. Rapporter (ISSN 0082-0040)

634.9 674 — **SW** — **ISSN 0349-8913**
SVERIGES LANTBRUKSUNIVERSITET. INSTITUTIONEN FOER VIRKESLAERA. UPPSATSER. (Text in English and Swedish) 1954. irreg., no.171, 1993. free. Sveriges Lantbruksuniversitet, Institutionen foer Virkeslaera - Swedish University of Agricultural Sciences, Department of Forest Products, Box 7008, S-750 07 Uppsala, Sweden. FAX 46-18-67-34-90. **Document type:** academic/scholarly publication.
Formerly (until 1978): Kungliga Skogshoegskolan. Institutionen foer Virkeslaera. Uppsatser (ISSN 0082-0059)

634.9 — **PH** — **ISSN 0115-0022**
CODEN: SYLVDD
SYLVATROP; the Philippine forest research journal. (Text in English, Filipino, Tagalog) 1976. 2/yr. P.50($15) Ecosystems Research and Development Bureau, College, Laguna 4031, Philippines. FAX 94-3628. Ed. Emilio A. Rosario. bk.rev.; abstr.; charts; illus.; pat.; stat.; tr.lit. (back issues avail.) **Indexed:** Biol.Abstr., Chem.Abstr., Forest.Abstr., Forest Prod.Abstr., Rev.Plant Path., Rural Recreat.Tour.Abstr., World Agri.Econ.& Rural Sociol.Abstr.
—CASDDS.
Supersedes (in Jan. 1976): Philippine Forest Research Journal.
Description: Contains scientific, technological, and descriptive articles, research notes, and reviews of forestry technical literature.

634.9 — **PL** — **ISSN 0039-7660**
CODEN: SYLWAD
SYLWAN.* (Text in Polish; summaries in English and Russian) 1820. m. 720 Zl. Polskie Towarzystwo Lesne, Ul. Bitwy Warszawskiej 1920 r. 3, 02-362 Warsaw, Poland. TEL 48-22-221470. bk.rev.; abstr.; bibl.; charts; illus.; index. circ. 2,200. **Indexed:** Biol.Abstr., Chem.Abstr., Forest.Abstr., Forest Prod.Abstr., Seed Abstr., Soils & Fert.
—CASDDS.

634.9 382 — **IV**
SYNDICAT DES EXPORTATEURS ET NEGOCIANTS EN BOIS DE COTE D'IVOIRE. BULLETIN DE LIAISON ET D'INFORMATION. (Text in French) 1963. q. 20000 Fr.CFA. Syndicat des Exportateurs et Negociants en Bois de Cote d'Ivoire, B.P. 1979, Abidjan 01, Ivory Coast. TEL 225-21-12-39. FAX 225-21-26-42. Ed. J.C. Bernard. charts; stat.

T U I A F P W INFORMATION. (Trade Union International of Agricultural, Forestry and Plantation Workers) see *LABOR UNIONS*

634.94 — **US**
TALL TIMBERS FIRE ECOLOGY CONFERENCE. PROCEEDINGS. 1969. a. price varies. Tall Timbers Research Station, Route 1, Box 678, Tallahassee, FL 32312. TEL 904-893-4153. (reprint service avail. from UMI) **Indexed:** Biol.Abstr., Excerp.Med., Forest.Abstr., Forest Prod.Abstr. **Document type:** proceedings.
Former titles (until no.16): Tall Timbers Ecology and Management Conference. Proceedings; Tall Timbers Fire Ecology Conference. Proceedings (ISSN 0082-1527)

634.9 — **US** — **ISSN 0496-7631**
TALL TIMBERS RESEARCH STATION. BULLETIN. 1962. irreg. price varies. Tall Timbers Research Station, Route 1, Box 678, Tallahassee, FL 32312. TEL 904-893-4153. **Indexed:** Forest.Abstr.
—BLDSC (2772.250000).

634.9 — **US** — **ISSN 0496-764X**
QH301
TALL TIMBERS RESEARCH STATION. MISCELLANEOUS PUBLICATION. 1961. irreg., vol.7, 1981. price varies. Tall Timbers Research Station, Rte. 1, Box 678, Tallahassee, FL 32312. TEL 904-893-4153. (back issues avail.; reprint service avail. from UMI)

634.9 613.62 — **CN** — **ISSN 0712-3094**
TALLYBOARD. (Text in English and French) 1955. bi-m. membership. Forest Products Accident Prevention Association, 128 McIntyre St. W., North Bay, Ont. P1B 8H2, Canada. TEL 705-472-4120. FAX 705-472-0207. Ed. David Dehaas. circ. 3,200 (controlled).
Description: Promotes health and safety in forest industries in Ontario.

634.9 674 — **FR**
TECHNIQUES FORESTIERES; le magazine professionnel du Machinisme Forestier. 1990. bi-m. 150 F. (foreign 245 F.)(effective Aug. 1990). Societe d'Edition et de Regie Specialisee (S.E.R.S.), (Subsidiary of: Masson), 5 et 7, rue Laromiguiere, 75005 Paris, France. TEL 1-45-87-29-99. FAX 1-45-87-29-99. Ed. Charles Celard. adv. **Document type:** trade publication.
Description: Information for those involved in forestry and lumber. Aimed at professionals interested in the latest equipment and technology available in the industry.

TEHO A. see *AGRICULTURE*

634.9 — **UN** — **ISSN 1014-2789**
QL84.5.A1
TIGER PAPER. 1974. q. $12. Food and Agriculture Organization of the United Nations, Regional Office for Asia and the Far East, Maliwan Mansion, Phra Atit Road, Bangkok 10200, Thailand. TEL 281-7844. FAX 662-2800445. TELEX 82815 FOODAG TH. Ed. J. Naewboonnien. bk.rev. circ. 2,000. **Document type:** bulletin.
—BLDSC (8835.040000).
Description: Dedicated to the exchange of information relating to wildlife and national parks management for the Asia-Pacific Region.

634.9 — **SW** — **ISSN 1100-8172**
TILL SKOGS; tidningen foer skogsbruk, fritid, och semester. 1987. irreg. Sveriges Skogsvaardsfoerbund, P.O. Box 273, S-182 52 Djursholm, Sweden. **Document type:** trade publication.

634.9 — **MY** — **ISSN 0126-9275**
TIMBER DIGEST. 1979. irreg. free. Forest Research Institute Malaysia - Institut Penyelidikan Perhutanan Malaysia, Kepong, 52109 Kuala Lumpur, Maylasia. TEL 03-6342633. FAX 03-6367753. Ed. Ashaari Amin.

634.9 674 — **UK** — **ISSN 0040-7763**
TIMBER GROWER. 1961. q. £15 (foreign £21). Timber Growers United Kingdom, 16c Market Pl., Diss, Norfolk IP22 3AB, England. Ed. David Steers. adv.; bk.rev.; charts; stat. circ. 4,000. **Indexed:** Forest.Abstr., Forest Prod.Abstr. **Document type:** trade publication.
Description: Covers policy development, current issues, silvicultural and woodland management, forest research, new forestry techniques and products, timber marketing, changes in law and taxation.

634.9 — **US**
THE TIMBER PRODUCER. 1959. m. $15. Box 39, Tomahawk, WI 54487. TEL 715-453-5159. Ed. Carl F. Theiler. adv. circ. 3,500. **Document type:** trade publication.

634.9 — **CN** — **ISSN 0833-0689**
TIMBERLINES. 1986. q. free. Forestry Canada, Northwest Region, Norhtern Forestry Centre, 5320-122 St., Edmonton, AB T6H 3S5, Canada. TEL 403-435-7210. FAX 403-435-7359. Ed. J. Samoil. circ. 5,000. **Document type:** newsletter.
Description: Covers federal forestry research and development for forest sector and targeted nonforestry audiences.

634.9 — **JA** — **ISSN 0082-4720**
SD226.039 — **CODEN: RSHKA6**
TOKYO METROPOLITAN AGRICULTURAL EXPERIMENT STATION, ITSUKAICHI OFFICE. FORESTRY EXPERIMENTAL BULLETIN/RINGYO SHIKEN KENKYU HOKOKU. (Text and summaries in English, French, German and Japanese) 1904. irreg. (8-10/yr.). exchange basis. Tokyo Metropolitan Agricultural Experiment Station, Itsukaichi Office - Tokyo-to Nogyo Shikenjo Itsukaichi Bunjo, 853 Tokura, Itsukaichi-machi, Nishitama-gun, Tokyo 190-01, Japan.

634.9 — **US** — **ISSN 0563-9093**
TOPS. 1967. a. membership. Georgia Forestry Association, Inc., 500 Pinnacle Way, Ste. 505, Norcross, GA 30071-3634. Ed. Laura Newbern. adv. circ. 3,500. **Document type:** trade publication.

634.9 — **JA** — **ISSN 0082-5379**
TOTTORI DAIGAKU NOGAKUBU FUZOKU ENSHURIN HOKOKU/TOTTORI UNIVERSITY FORESTS. RESEARCH BULLETIN. (Text in Japanese; summaries in English) 1958. biennial. Tottori Daigaku, Nogakubu Fuzoku Enshurin - Tottori University Forests, 1-1 Koyama-cho, Tottori 680, Japan. Ed. Tetuzo Kurimura. **Indexed:** Biol.Abstr., Forest.Abstr., Forest Prod.Abstr., Ind.Vet., Plant Breed.Abstr.
Formerly: Tottori University Forests. Bulletin.

TOWN AND COUNTRY FARMER. see *AGRICULTURE*

634.9 — **RU**
TRADE UNIONS INTERNATIONAL OF AGRICULTURAL, FORESTRY AND PLANTATION WORKERS. BULLETIN. 1949. bi-m. Trade Unions International of Agricultural, Forestry and Plantation Workers, c/o Christian Alliaume, Sec.-Gen., Bolshaya Serpukhovskaia 44, 113093 Moscow M-93, Russia. TEL 7-095-2302370. FAX 7-095-2302263. **Document type:** bulletin.

634.96 — **SW** — **ISSN 0284-8457**
TRAESKYDD; aktuellt fraan Traeskyddsinstitutet. 1974. q. Svenska Traeskydosinstitutet, P.O. Box 5607, S-114 86 Stockholm, Sweden. **Document type:** newsletter.
Former titles (until vol.3-4, 1987): Traeskydd. Aktuellt; (until vol.3, 1979): Aktuellt fraan Traeskyddsinstitutet.

634.9 — **US**
TREE CARE INDUSTRY. 1990. m. $30. National Arborist Association, Box 1094, Amherst, NH 03031-1094. TEL 603-673-8952. FAX 603-672-2613. Ed. Peter Gerstenberger. adv. circ. 16,000. **Document type:** trade publication.
Description: For commercial and institutional arborists, municipal and utility foresters, and landscape contractors.

FORESTS AND FORESTRY

634.9   US
TREE FARMER. 1932. bi-m. $15 includes membership. American Forest Council, 1250 Connecticut Ave., N.W., Washington, DC 20036. TEL 202-463-2455. FAX 202-463-2461. **Document type:** trade publication.
    Formerly (until 1991): American Tree Farmer.

TREE PHYSIOLOGY. see *BIOLOGY — Botany*

634.9 333.750   CN   ISSN 0847-9224
TREELINES. 1982. q. free. Saskatchewan Forestry Association, Box 400, Prince Albert, SK S6V 5R7, Canada. Ed. Marie Grono. (looseleaf format; back issues avail.) **Document type:** newsletter.
    Description: Covers association activities and updates, articles on forest management, and resource topics from all sides of controversial topics.

TREES; structure and function. see *BIOLOGY — Botany*

TREES IN SOUTH AFRICA/BOME IN SUID-AFRIKA. see *BIOLOGY — Botany*

634.9   US
TREEWORKER. 1984. m. $14.50. National Arborist Association, Box 1094, Amherst, NH 03031-1094. TEL 603-673-3311. FAX 603-672-2613. Ed. Brian H. Barnard. circ. 1,800. (looseleaf format) **Document type:** trade publication.
    Description: Deals with safety and educational issues pertinent to arboriculture: the care of trees.

TROPENLANDWIRT; Zeitschrift fuer die Landwirtschaft in den Tropen und Subtropen. see *AGRICULTURE*

634.9   TU
TURKISH FORESTRY, LAND IRRIGATION, AGRICULTURE AND AGRICULTURAL INDUSTRY WORKERS' UNION. TARIM-IS/TURKIYE ORMAN, TOPRAKSU, TARIM VE TARIM SANAYII ISCILERI SENDIKASI. TARIM-IS. 1961. m. Necatibey Caddesi, Ankara, No. 22, 9-10-12, Sihhiye, Ankara, Turkey. TEL 90-312-2317856. FAX 90-312-2298592. bk.rev. circ. 1,000.

TURKISH JOURNAL OF AGRICULTURE AND FORESTRY/TURK TARIM VE ORMANCILIK DERGISI. see *AGRICULTURE*

634.9   UG   ISSN 0082-7177
UGANDA. FORESTRY DEPARTMENT. ANNUAL REPORT. 1904. a. Sh.3000. Forestry Department, Box 7124, Kampala, Uganda. cum.index. **Indexed:** Forest.Abstr.

634.9   UG   ISSN 0082-7193
UGANDA. FORESTRY DEPARTMENT. TECHNICAL NOTES. 1953. irreg., latest no.222, 1979. free. Forestry Department, Box 7124, Kampala, Uganda. cum.index: 1953-79. **Indexed:** Biol.Abstr., Forest.Abstr. **Document type:** government publication.

634.9 674   UN   ISSN 0041-6436
SD1
UNASYLVA; international journal of forestry and forest products. Spanish edition (ISSN 0251-1584); French edition (ISSN 0251-1053) 1947-1971; resumed 1974. q. $24 (effective 1994). Food and Agriculture Organization of the United Nations (Rome), Via delle Terme di Caracalla, 00100 Rome, Italy. TEL 57974350. FAX 57975155. TELEX 610181 FAQ I. Ed. Stephen A. Dembner. bk.rev. circ. 11,000 (6,500 English ed.; 2,500 French ed.; 2,000 Spanish ed.). (also avail. in microfiche from CIS) **Indexed:** Abstr.Bull.Inst.Pap.Chem., Abstr.Rural Dev.Trop., Asian-Pac.Econ.Lit., Biol.Abstr., Biol.& Agr.Ind., Biol.Dig., Curr.Adv.Ecol.Sci., Deep Sea Res.& Oceanogr.Abstr., Forest.Abstr., Forest Prod.Abstr., Geo.Abstr., I D A, IIS, Int.Lab.Doc., PROMT, Rural Devel.Abstr., Rural Ext.Educ.& Tr.Abstr., Rural Recreat.Tour.Abstr., World Agri.Econ.& Rural Sociol.Abstr.
—BLDSC (9085.000000); UnCover; SWETS.
    Description: Covers forest planning and policy, administration, education, genetics, hydrology, wildlife.

634.9   BU
UNION OF FORESTRY AND TIMBER INDUSTRY WORKERS. BULLETIN. 1964. q. Union of Forestry and Timber Industry Workers, Dimo Hadjidimov St. 29, Sofia 1606, Bulgaria. **Document type:** bulletin, trade publication.

634.9   US
U.S. DEPARTMENT OF AGRICULTURE. FOREST SERVICE. VOLUNTEER OPPORTUNITIES (YEAR). a. free. U.S. Department of Agriculture, Forestry Service, Volunteer Program, Union Sta., 2501 Wall Ave., Ogden, UT 84401. TEL 801-625-5306. (Subscr. to: Superintendent of Documents, U.S. Government Printing Office, Box 371954, Pittsburgh, PA 15250-7954. TEL 202-783-3238. FAX 202-512-2233) **Document type:** government publication.
    Description: Lists volunteer opportunities in all aspects of forest management.

634.9   US   ISSN 0092-9654
U.S. FOREST SERVICE. GENERAL TECHNICAL REPORT I N T. 1966. irreg. free. U.S. Forest Service, Intermountain Research Sta., 324 25th St., Ogden, UT 84401. TEL 801-625-5437. bibl. (also avail. in microfiche) **Indexed:** Biol.Abstr., Curr.Adv.Ecol.Sci., Forest.Abstr., Forest Prod.Abstr. **Document type:** government publication.

634.9   US
U.S. FOREST SERVICE. GENERAL TECHNICAL REPORT N C. 1966. 8/yr. free. U.S. Forest Service, North Central Forest Experiment Sta., 1992 Folwell Ave., St. Paul, MN 55108. TEL 612-649-5276. Ed. Robert D. Wray. charts; illus.; index; circ. 1,000 (controlled). (looseleaf format; also avail. in microform from NTI) **Indexed:** Bibl.Agri., Biol.Abstr., Curr.Adv.Ecol.Sci., Forest.Abstr. **Document type:** government publication.

634.9   US   ISSN 0083-2480
SD356.52.P42
U.S. FOREST SERVICE. GENERAL TECHNICAL REPORT N E. 1927. irreg. free. U.S. Forest Service, Northeastern Forest Experiment Sta., 359 Main Rd., Delaware, OH 43015. TEL 614-363-0023. circ. 1,800. **Indexed:** Biol.Abstr., Curr.Adv.Ecol.Sci., Forest.Abstr., Forest Prod.Abstr., Rev.Plant Path. **Document type:** government publication.

634.9   US
U.S. FOREST SERVICE. INTERMOUNTAIN RESEARCH STATION. RECENT REPORTS. 1956. q. free. U.S. Forest Service, Intermountain Research Sta., 324 25th St., Ogden, UT 84401. TEL 801-625-5437. circ. 8,000. **Document type:** government publication.
    Former titles: U.S. Forest Service. Intermountain Forest and Range Experiment Station. Recent Reports; U.S. Forest Service. Annual Report (ISSN 0083-1468)

634.9   US   ISSN 0196-2094
SD11   CODEN: GTRSD3
U.S. FOREST SERVICE. PACIFIC SOUTHWEST FOREST AND RANGE EXPERIMENT STATION. GENERAL TECHNICAL REPORT P S W. Key Title: General Technical Report P S W. 1972. irreg. free. U.S. Forest Service, Pacific Southwest Research Sta., Box 245, Berkeley, CA 94701-0245. TEL 510-559-6324. FAX 510-559-6440. Ed. Vincent Y. Dong. (also avail. in microfiche) **Indexed:** Biol.Abstr., Forest.Abstr., Forest Prod.Abstr., Herb.Abstr., Soils & Fert. **Document type:** government publication.
—CASDDS.
    Formerly: U.S. Forest Service. General Technical Report PSW (ISSN 0092-9662)

634.9   US
U.S. FOREST SERVICE. RESEARCH NOTE I N T. irreg. U.S. Forest Service, Intermountain Research Sta., 324 25th St., Ogden, UT 84401. TEL 801-625-5437. **Indexed:** Biol.Abstr., Curr.Adv.Ecol.Sci., Excerp.Med., Meteor.& Geoastrophys.Abstr. **Document type:** government publication.

634.9   US   ISSN 0361-2449
SD11   CODEN: XAFNBE
U.S. FOREST SERVICE. RESEARCH NOTE N C. Key Title: Research Note N C. 1966. 12/yr. free. U.S. Forest Service, North Central Forest Experiment Sta., 1992 Folwell Ave., St. Paul, MN 55108. TEL 612-649-5276. Ed. Robert D. Wray. charts; illus.; stat.; index; circ. 2,000 (controlled). (looseleaf format) **Indexed:** Bibl.Agri., Biol.Abstr., Curr.Adv.Ecol.Sci., Excerp.Med., Forest.Abstr., Forest Prod.Abstr., Irr.& Drain.Abstr., Rev.Plant Path., Rural Recreat.Tour.Abstr., Soils & Fert., World Agri.Econ.& Rural Sociol.Abstr. **Document type:** government publication.

634.9   US   ISSN 0502-4994
SD11
U.S. FOREST SERVICE. RESEARCH NOTE R M. Supersedes Its Research Notes. 1963. irreg., no.456, 1985. free. U.S. Forest Service, Rocky Mountain Forest and Range Experiment Sta., 240 W. Prospect, Fort Collins, CO 80526. TEL 303-498-1719. **Indexed:** Biol.Abstr., Curr.Adv.Ecol.Sci., Excerp.Med., Forest.Abstr., Forest Prod.Abstr., Pollut.Abstr., Seed Abstr. **Document type:** government publication.
    Description: Research findings and techniques on various forestry-related topics.

634.9   US
U.S. FOREST SERVICE. RESEARCH PAPER I N T. irreg. U.S. Forest Service, Intermountain Research Sta., 324 25th St., Ogden, UT 84401. TEL 801-625-5437. **Indexed:** Biol.Abstr., Curr.Adv.Ecol.Sci., Forest.Abstr., Forest Prod.Abstr., Meteor.& Geoastrophys.Abstr. **Document type:** government publication.

634.9   US   ISSN 0565-8721
U.S. FOREST SERVICE. RESEARCH PAPER N C. 1966. 10/yr. free. U.S. Forest Service, North Central Forest Experiment Sta., 1992 Folwell Ave., St. Paul, MN 55108. TEL 612-649-5276. Ed. Robert D. Wray. charts; illus.; stat.; index; circ. 2,000 (controlled). (looseleaf format; also avail. in microform from NTI) **Indexed:** Bibl.Agri., Biol.Abstr., Curr.Adv.Ecol.Sci., Forest.Abstr., Forest Prod.Abstr., Rural Recreat.Tour.Abstr., Soils & Fert., World Agri.Econ.& Rural Sociol.Abstr. **Document type:** government publication.

634.9   US   ISSN 0502-5001
SD11
U.S. FOREST SERVICE. RESEARCH PAPER R M. Supersedes the Station's Paper. 1963. irreg., no.261, 1975. free. U.S. Forest Service, Rocky Mountain Forest and Range Experimenet Sta., 240 W. Prospect, Fort Collins, CO 80526. TEL 303-498-1719. **Indexed:** Agri.Eng.Abstr., Biol.Abstr., Curr.Adv.Ecol.Sci., Forest.Abstr., Forest Prod.Abstr. **Document type:** government publication.

634   US
U.S. FOREST SERVICE. RESOURCE BULLETIN I N T. irreg. U.S. Forest Service, Intermountain Research Sta., 324 25th St., Ogden, UT 84401. TEL 801-625-5437. **Indexed:** Biol.Abstr. **Document type:** bulletin, government publication.

634.9   US   ISSN 0565-873X
U.S. FOREST SERVICE. RESOURCE BULLETIN N C. 1966. 5/yr. free. U.S. Forest Service, North Central Forest Experiment Sta., 1992 Folwell Ave., MN 55108. TEL 612-649-5276. Ed. Robert D. Wray. charts; illus.; index; circ. 4,000 (controlled). (looseleaf format; also avail. in microform from NTI) **Indexed:** Bibl.Agri., Biol.Abstr., Forest.Abstr. **Document type:** bulletin, government publication.

634.9   US   ISSN 0748-1284
SD11
U.S. FOREST SERVICE. RESOURCE BULLETIN P N W. 1963. irreg. free. U.S. Forest Service, Pacific Northwest Research Sta., Box 3890, Portland, OR 97208. TEL 503-326-7128. **Indexed:** Biol.Abstr., Forest.Abstr., Soils & Fert. **Document type:** government publication.

634.9   US
U.S. FOREST SERVICE. SOUTHERN FOREST EXPERIMENT STATION. RECENT PUBLICATIONS. 1976. q. free. U.S. Department of Agriculture, Forest Service, Southern Forest Experiment Sta., 701 Loyola Ave., New Orleans, LA 70113. TEL 504-589-3935. FAX 504-589-3961. Ed. Carol Lowe. bk.rev. circ. 7,010. **Indexed:** Agri.Eng.Abstr. **Document type:** government publication.
    Formerly: U.S. Forest Service. Southern Forest Experiment Station. Research Accomplished; Which was formed by the merger of: Forest Research News for the South (ISSN 0071-7541); U.S. Forest Service. Southern Forest Experiment Station. Recent Publications.
    Description: Lists publications available to the public.

UNIVERSITAET FUER BODENKULTUR IN WIEN. DISSERTATIONEN. see *AGRICULTURE*

634.9   RM   ISSN 1220-9422
UNIVERSITATEA TRANSILVANIA DIN BRASOV. BULETINUL. SERIA B1. ECONOMIA FORESTIERA/TRANSYLVANIA UNIVERSITY OF BRASOV. BULLETIN. SERIES B1. SILVICULTURA. (Text in English, French, German) 1956. a. price varies. Universitatea Transilvania din Brasov - Transylvania University of Brasov, Bd. Eroilor, Nr. 29, 2200 Brasov, Rumania. Ed. Darie Parascan. bibl.; illus.; stat. **Indexed:** Forest.Abstr., Forest Prod.Abstr. **Document type:** bulletin.
—BLDSC (2782.303000).
     Supersedes in part: Universitatea din Brasov. Buletinul. Seria B. Economia Forestiera.

UNIVERSITY OF DAR ES SALAAM. FACULTY OF AGRICULTURE, FORESTRY AND VETERINARY SCIENCE. ANNUAL RECORD OF RESEARCH. see *AGRICULTURE*

634.9 575.1   US
UNIVERSITY OF FLORIDA. SCHOOL OF FOREST RESOURCES & CONSERVATION. COOPERATIVE FOREST GENETICS RESEARCH PROGRAM. PROGRESS REPORT. (Subseries of its Research Report) 1957. irreg., no.29, 1987. free. University of Florida, School of Forest Resources & Conservation, Gainesville, FL 32601. TEL 904-392-1792. Ed. R.E. Goddard. circ. 300. **Document type:** academic/scholarly publication.
     Formerly: University of Florida. School of Forestry. Cooperative Forest Genetics Research Program. Progress Report (ISSN 0071-6146)
     Refereed Serial

UNIVERSITY OF IDAHO. FOREST, WILDLIFE AND RANGE EXPERIMENT STATION, MOSCOW. STATION BULLETIN. see *CONSERVATION*

UNIVERSITY OF IDAHO. FOREST, WILDLIFE AND RANGE EXPERIMENT STATION, MOSCOW. STATION NOTE. see *CONSERVATION*

UNIVERSITY OF MINNESOTA. CENTER FOR NATURAL RESOURCE POLICY AND MANAGEMENT. WORKING PAPERS. see *WATER RESOURCES*

634.9   US   ISSN 0888-6229
                        CODEN: MFCBAC
UNIVERSITY OF MONTANA. FOREST AND CONSERVATION EXPERIMENT STATION, MISSOULA. MISCELLANEOUS PUBLICATIONS. 1968. irreg., no.53, 1993. price varies. University of Montana, School of Forestry, Montana Forest and Conservation Experiment Sta., Missoula, MT 59812. TEL 406-243-6655. FAX 406-243-4510. Ed. Robert Prister. **Document type:** academic/scholarly publication.
     Formerly: University of Montana. Forest and Conservation Experiment Station, Missoula. Bulletin (ISSN 0077-1155)

634.9   US   ISSN 0077-1163
UNIVERSITY OF MONTANA. FOREST AND CONSERVATION EXPERIMENT STATION, MISSOULA. RESEARCH NOTES. 1964. irreg., no.25, 1992. $1. University of Montana, School of Forestry, Montana Forest and Conservation Experiment Sta., Missoula, MT 59812. TEL 406-243-6655. FAX 406-243-4510. Ed. Robert Pfister. **Document type:** academic/scholarly publication.
     Description: Provides brief descriptions of new forestry research in Montana.

634.9   US
UNIVERSITY OF MONTANA. FOREST AND CONSERVATION EXPERIMENT STATION. RESEARCH REPORTS. 1987. irreg., no.2, 1988. price varies. University of Montana, School of Forestry, Montana Forest and Conservation Experiment Sta., Missoula, MT 59812. TEL 406-243-6655. FAX 406-243-4510. **Document type:** academic/scholarly publication.
     Description: Provides longer descriptions of new forestry research in Montana

UNIVERSITY OF SALAHADDIN. COLLEGE OF AGRICULTURE. SCIENTIFIC JOURNAL "ZANCO". see *AGRICULTURE*

634.9 550 574   CN
UNIVERSITY OF TORONTO. FACULTY OF FORESTRY. RESEARCH REPORT. 1980. irreg. free. University of Toronto, Faculty of Forestry, 33 Willcocks St., Toronto, ON M5S 3B3, Canada. TEL 416-978-6152. FAX 416-978-3834. circ. 1,500. **Document type:** academic/scholarly publication.

634.9   GW   ISSN 0935-7017
UNSER WALD. 1948. bi-m. DM.25. Schutzgemeinschaft Deutscher Wald, Meckenheimer Allee 79, 53115 Bonn, Germany. TEL 0228-658462.
FAX 0228-656980. **Document type:** newsletter.

634.9   CN   ISSN 0048-1858
URBAN FOREST. 1965. 6/yr. membership. Ontario Shade Tree Council, 5 Shoreham Dr., North York, Ont. M3N 1S4, Canada. TEL 416-699-1213. FAX 416-851-9610. Ed. Eric C. Oakleaf. adv.; circ. 300 (controlled).
     Formerly: Ontarion Shade Tree Council. Newsletter.
     Description: Covers tree preservation, propagation, urban forestry and arboriculture. Includes list of publications avail through the Council and upcoming events.

634.9   US   ISSN 1052-2484
SB436
URBAN FORESTS. 1980. bi-m. free to qualified personnel. American Forests, Box 2000, Washington, DC 20013-2000. TEL 202-667-3300. FAX 202-667-7751. **Indexed:** Environ.Abstr., Gard.Lit. (1992-). **Document type:** consumer publication.
—CIS; UnCover.
     Formerly (until June 1990): Urban Forests Forum.

635   BE   ISSN 0771-3851
VERBONDSNIEUWS VOOR DE BELGISCHE SIERTEELT; vakblad van het A.V.B.S. (Text in Dutch) 1956. s-m. (A.V.B.S.) Belgische Boerenbond, Minderbroedersstraat 8, B-3000 Leuven, Belgium. TEL 32-16-242246. Ed. F. Hofkens. adv.; bk.rev.; tr.lit.; index. circ. 2,500. (back issues avail.) **Indexed:** Hort.Abstr., Ornam.Hort., Rice Abstr., Seed Abstr.
—BLDSC (9155.762000).

634.9   SW   ISSN 1101-2722
VI SKOGSAEGARE; foer et fritt, loensamt och aktivt skogsbruk. (Supplements avail.: Paa Skogssidan; Nytt i Norrskog) 1990. bi-m. SEK 150 (effective 1991). Vi Skogsaegare, P.O. Box 1144, S-251 11 Helsingborg, Sweden.

634.9   AT
VICTORIA, AUSTRALIA. DEPARTMENT OF CONSERVATION, FORESTS AND LANDS. LANDS AND FORESTS BULLETIN. 1937. irreg. free. Department of Conservation, Forests and Lands, 240 Victoria Parade, East Melbourne, Vic. 3002, Australia. Ed. David Meagher. circ. 1,200. **Indexed:** Aus.Sci.Ind., Biol.Abstr., Forest.Abstr., Forest Prod.Abstr.
     Former titles: Victoria, Australia. Department of Conservation, Forests and Lands. Bulletin; Victoria, Australia. Forest Commission. Bulletin (ISSN 0085-7742)

634.9   US   ISSN 0740-011X
VIRGINIA FORESTS. 1946. q. Virginia Forestry Association, 1205 E. Main St., Richmond, VA 23219-3627. FAX 804-644-8466. Ed. Charles F. Finley, Jr. adv.; B&W page $460. bk.rev.; index, circ. 4,000. (back issues avail.)

634.9 574   XO
VYSKUMNY USTAV LESNEHO HOSPODARSTVA VO ZVOLENE. LESNICKE STUDIE. (Text in Slovak; summaries in English, German, Russian) 1960. irreg. price varies. (Vyskumny Ustav Lesneho Hospodarstva vo Zvolene) Priroda, Krizkova 9, 815 34 Bratislava, Slovakia. TEL 472-41-45. charts; illus ; index. **Indexed:** Biol.Abstr.

634.9   XO   ISSN 0232-0029
VYSOKA SKOLA LESNICKA A DREVARSKA VO ZLOVENE. DREVARSKA FAKULTA. ZBORNIK VEDECKYCH PRAC. (Text in Slovak; a part of science articles and summaries in English, German, Russian) 1957. a. exchange basis. Vysoka Skola Lesnicka a Drevarska vo Zvolene, Drevarska Fakulta - College of Forestry and Wood Technology, Zvolen, Marxova 24, 960-53 Zvolen, Slovakia. TELEX 72267. (Subscr. to: Ustredna Lesnicka a Drevarska Kniznica SSR pri VSLD vo Zvolene - Central Library of Forestry and Wood Technology at the University College, Marxova 20, 961 02 Zvolen, Slovakia) Ed. Imrich Melcer. illus. circ. 300. **Document type:** academic/scholarly publication.

634.9   GW
WALBAUERNVERBAND NORDRHEIN-WESTFALEN. MITTEILUNGSBLATT. m. membership. Landwirtschaftsverlag GmbH, Huelsebrockstr. 2, 48165 Muenster, Germany. TEL 02501-8010. FAX 02501-801-204. (Subscr. to: Postfach 480249, 48079 Muenster, Germany) circ. 3,300. (back issues avail.) **Document type:** bulletin.

634.9   GW   ISSN 0863-4807
SD1
DER WALD; Fachzeitschrift fuer Oekologie, Bewirschaftung und Schutz des Waldes. 1969. m. DM.70 (foreign DM.95). D L V Deutscher Landwirtschaftsverlag Berlin GmbH, Thulestr. 7, 13189 Berlin, Germany. TEL 030-47800021. FAX 030-47800040. Ed. Waldemar Roempler. adv.; bk.rev.; charts; illus. **Indexed:** Excerp.Med., Forest.Abstr. **Document type:** academic/scholarly publication.
—BLDSC (9261.459000).
     Formerly (until 1990): Sozialistische Forstwirtschaft (ISSN 0038-6154)

634.9   GW   ISSN 0043-0048
DIE WALDARBEIT; Forstbetrieb, Forsttechnik, Forstarbeit. 1950. m. DM.34. Wirtschafts- und Forstverlag Euting KG, Tannenstr. 1, 56587 Strassenhaus, Germany. Ed. Helmut Heinz Euting. adv.; bk.rev.; bibl.; charts; illus.; stat. **Indexed:** Forest.Abstr., Forest Prod.Abstr.

634.9   TH   ISSN 0043-0196
WANASAN. (Text in Thai; summaries in English) 1936. q. $10. Royal Forest Department, Vanasarn Forest Journal Office, Bangkok, Thailand. Ed. Tem Smitinand. adv. bk.rev.; abstr.; bibl.; charts; stat.; index; circ. 5,400 (controlled). (processed) **Indexed:** Forest.Abstr.

WASHINGTON (STATE). DEPARTMENT OF REVENUE. FOREST TAX SECTION. FOREST TAX ANNUAL REPORT. see *BUSINESS AND ECONOMICS — Public Finance, Taxation*

WATER, WOODS & WILDLIFE. see *BIOLOGY — Botany*

WEST VIRGINIA. AGRICULTURAL AND FORESTRY EXPERIMENT STATION. ANNUAL REPORT. see *AGRICULTURE*

WEST VIRGINIA. AGRICULTURAL AND FORESTRY EXPERIMENT STATION. BULLETIN. see *AGRICULTURE*

WEST VIRGINIA. AGRICULTURAL AND FORESTRY EXPERIMENT STATION. CIRCULAR. see *AGRICULTURE*

WEST VIRGINIA. AGRICULTURAL AND FORESTRY EXPERIMENT STATION. CURRENT REPORT. see *AGRICULTURE*

634.9   US   ISSN 0197-1387
                        CODEN: WVFNDG
WEST VIRGINIA FORESTRY NOTES. 1973. irreg. (approx. 1/yr.). West Virginia University, Agricultural and Forestry Experiment Station, Morgantown, WV 26506-6108. TEL 304-293-3411.
FAX 304-293-3740. Ed. Debbie Fast. circ. 2,500. **Document type:** academic/scholarly publication.
—CASDDS.

634.9   US   ISSN 0885-6095
SD144.A18   CODEN: WJAFEK
WESTERN JOURNAL OF APPLIED FORESTRY. q. $35 to individuals; institutions $80. Society of American Foresters, 5400 Grosvenor Lane, Bethesda, MD 20814. TEL 301-897-8720. FAX 301-897-3690. Ed. R.M. Lanner. adv. circ. 900. (also avail. in microform from UMI; reprint service avail. from UMI) **Indexed:** Environ.Abstr., Forest.Abstr., Forest Prod.Abstr., Seed Abstr., Weed Abstr.
—BLDSC (9300.828600); UnCover.

634.9   NZ   ISSN 0110-1048
WHAT'S NEW IN FOREST RESEARCH; semi-technical newsletter. 1973. m. free. Forest Research Institute, Private Bag 3020, Rotorua, New Zealand. TEL 64-7-347-5899. FAX 64-7-347-9380. charts; illus. circ. 2,000. (back issues avail.) **Indexed:** Agroforest.Abstr., Forest.Abstr., Forest Prod.Abstr., Geo.Abstr., Rev.Plant Path., Rural Recreat.Tour.Abstr., World Agri.Econ.& Rural Sociol.Abstr. **Document type:** monographic series.
—CCC.
     Description: Each issue describes, in semi-technical language, one aspect of current forestry research.

FORESTS AND FORESTRY — ABSTRACTING, BIBLIOGRAPHIES, STATISTICS

WILDERNESS NEWS. see *ENVIRONMENTAL STUDIES*

WILDFIRE. see *FIRE PREVENTION*

634.9   US   ISSN 0511-9723
WILLIAM L. HUTCHESON MEMORIAL FOREST. BULLETIN. irreg. price varies. Rutgers University, Department of Biological Sciences, New Brunswick, NJ 08903. TEL 908-932-2075. (Co-Sponsor: William H. Hutcheson Memorial Forest Committee) Eds. Charles Leck, Helen F. Buell. **Document type:** bulletin. —BLDSC (9318.915000).

634.9   US   ISSN 0743-5231
WOOD MACHINING NEWS. 1984. bi-m. $72 in N. America; elsewhere $78. Wood Machining Institute, Box 476, Berkeley, CA 94701. TEL 510-943-5240. FAX 510-945-0947. Ed. Ryszard Szymani. bk.rev.; abstr.; bibl.; illus.; pat.; stat.; tr.lit.; index. circ. 600. (back issues avail.) **Document type:** newsletter.
Description: Provides news and technical information about the latest worldwide developments in the field of wood machining, inlcuding the technology of saws and sawing, planning, and molding plus other operations and equipment associated with wood machining.

634.9 674   SA
WOOD S A & TIMBER TIMES. (Text in English) 1975. m. R.185. Malnor (Pty) Ltd., Nedbank East City, South Block, 120 End St., P.O. Box 10469, Johannesburg 2000, South Africa. TEL 27-11-402-5022. FAX 27-11-402-7587. Ed. Kerry Manning. adv. contact: Ken Nortje. bk.rev. circ. 4,000. **Indexed:** Forest.Abstr., Forest Prod.Abstr., Ind.S.A.Per. **Document type:** trade publication.
Formed by the merger of: Wood Southern Africa (ISSN 0256-7172) & Timber Times (ISSN 1017-432X)

WOOD TECHNOLOGY. see *FORESTS AND FORESTRY — Lumber And Wood*

634.9   US
WOODLAND REPORT; late breaking news on private forestry issues from Washington D.C. and state capitals. 1984. 8/yr. $15 includes National Woodlands Magazine. National Woodland Owners Association, 374 Maple Ave., E., Ste. 204, Vienna, VA 22180. TEL 703-255-2700. Ed. Keith A. Argow. circ. 3,000. **Document type:** newsletter.
Description: Contains practical forestry information for woodland owners.

639.9   UG
WOODSMAN NEWSLETTER. 1962. a. free. Forestry Department, Box 7124, Kampala, Uganda. **Indexed:** Forest.Abstr.
Formerly: Woodsman.

634.9   US   ISSN 0148-5741
SD254
YALE FOREST SCHOOL NEWS. 1913. 4/yr. free to qualified personnel. (Yale Forestry Alumni Association) Yale University, School of Forestry and Environmental Studies, 205 Prospect St., New Haven, CT 06511. TEL 203-432-5130. FAX 203-432-5942. Ed. Gordon Geballe. bibl.; illus. circ. 2,200. (reprint service avail. from ISI)

634.9   US   CODEN: BYSSDM
YALE UNIVERSITY. SCHOOL OF FORESTRY AND ENVIRONMENTAL STUDIES. BULLETIN. 1912. a. price varies. Yale University, School of Forestry and Environmental Studies, New Haven, CT 06511. TEL 203-432-5130. FAX 203-432-5942. **Indexed:** Biol.Abstr., Forest.Abstr., Forest Prod.Abstr. **Document type:** bulletin.
Formerly: Yale University. School of Forestry. Bulletin (ISSN 0361-4425)

634.9   US
YANKEE WOODLOT. 1942. irreg. free. University of Maine at Orono, Cooperative Extension Service, 107 Nutting Hall, Orono, ME 04469. TEL 207-581-2890. FAX 207-581-3466. (Co-sponsor: United States Department of Agriculture) c/o Bud Blumenstock. bk.rev. circ. 4,500.
Formerly (until 1982): Maine Cooperative Extension Service. Forestry Facts.

634.9   IS
YEDIOT KEREN KAYEMIT LEYISRAEL. s-a. Keren Kayemit Leyisrael, Information Department, P.O. Box 283, Jerusalem, Israel. Ed. Avi Goren.

634.9   ZA   ISSN 0084-4616
ZAMBIA. DEPARTMENT OF FORESTRY. REPORT. 1964. a. K.150. Zambia Government Printing Department, P.O. Box 30136, Lusaka, Zambia. **Document type:** government publication.

634.9   CC   ISSN 1000-5692
CODEN: ZHLXEC
ZHEJIANG LINXUEYUAN XUEBAO/ZHEJIANG INSTITUTE OF FORESTRY. JOURNAL. (Text in Chinese) q. Zhejiang Linxueyuan - Zhejiang Institute of Forestry, Lin'an Xian (County), Zhejiang 311300, People's Republic of China. TEL 22567. Ed. Liu Maochun. —CASDDS.

634.9   CC
ZHEJIANG LINYE/ZHEJIANG FORESTRY. (Text in Chinese) q. Zhejiang Sheng Linye-ting - Zhejiang Provincial Bureau of Forestry, 168 Kaixuan Lu, Hangzhou, Zhejiang 310004, People's Republic of China. TEL 43891. Ed. Fan Fusheng.

634.9   CC   ISSN 1001-3776
SD222.C479
ZHEJIANG LINYE KEJI. (Text in Chinese) bi-m. Zhejiang Linye Kexue Yanjiusuo, Liuxia, Hangzhou, Zhejiang 310023, People's Republic of China. TEL 529277. Ed. Fan Fusheng.

634.9   CC   ISSN 1000-0623
ZHONGGUO LINYE/FORESTRY IN CHINA. (Text in Chinese) 1950. m. $0.90 per no. Zhongguo Linye Zazhishe, Linye Bu - Ministry of Forestry, Hepingli, Beijing 100013, People's Republic of China. TEL 4217381. (Dist. overseas by: China International Book Trading Corp., P.O. Box 339, Beijing, P.R.C.) Ed. Zhao Shengtie.

634.9   CC
ZHONGGUO LINYE JIAOYU/CHINA FORESTRY EDUCATION. (Text in Chinese) bi-m. Beijing Linye Daxue - Beijing University of Forestry, Qinghua Donglu, Beijing 100083, People's Republic of China. TEL 2568811. Ed. Zhang Guanli.

FORESTS AND FORESTRY —
Abstracting, Bibliographies, Statistics

ABSTRACTS OF BULGARIAN SCIENTIFIC LITERATURE. AGRICULTURE AND FORESTRY. VETERINARY MEDICINE. see *AGRICULTURE — Abstracting, Bibliographies, Statistics*

634.9 630   UK   ISSN 0952-1453
AGROFORESTRY ABSTRACTS. (Annual Author and Subject Index avail.) 1988. q. £85($149) (International Council for Research in Agroforestry (ICRAF)) CAB International, Wallingford, Oxon. OX10 8DE, England. TEL 44-491-832111. FAX 44-491-833508. TELEX 847964 COMAGG G. (U.S. subscr. to: CAB International, North American Office, 845 N. Park Ave., Tucson, AZ 85719. TEL 800-528-4841) R.E.H. Haynes. (also avail. in diskette format) **Document type:** abstracting/indexing.
●Also available online. Vendor(s): BRS Online Products, DIMDI, Data-Star, DIALOG Information Services, Inc., European Space Agency, STN International.
Also available on CD-ROM.
Description: Covers all aspects of agroforestry. Includes agroforestry components and processes - trees, animals and crops; production, service, conservation, human ecology, and social and economic aspects; development issues; research and methodology.

634.9   AT   ISSN 1038-4243
AUSTRALIA. BUREAU OF AGRICULTURAL AND RESOURCE ECONOMICS. QUARTERLY FOREST PRODUCTS STATISTICS. 1992. q. Aus.$48. Australian Bureau of Agricultural and Resource Economics, G.P.O. Box 1563, Canberra, A.C.T. 2601, Australia. TEL 06-272-2211. (Subscr. to: A B A R E Publications, G.P.O. Box 1563, Canberra, A.C.T. 2601, Australia) bk.rev. **Indexed:** Forest.Abstr. **Document type:** government publication. —BLDSC (7181.332500).
Formed by the merger of (1984-1992): Australia. Bureau of Agricultural and Resource Economics. Monthly Forest Products Trade Statistics; (1975-1992): Australia. Department of Primary Industry. Forestry and Timber Bureau. Australian Forest Resources (ISSN 0157-8189); (1950-1992): Australia. Department of Primary Industry. Forestry and Timber Bureau. Quarterly Timber Statistics; Which was formerly (until June 1992): Timber Supply Review (ISSN 0040-778X).
Description: Contains statistics on forest products production, supply, imports and exports, and commentaries on the economic outlook for the industry.

674   AT   ISSN 1036-0093
AUSTRALIA. BUREAU OF STATISTICS. MANUFACTURING PRODUCTION, AUSTRALIA: WOOD AND WOOD PRODUCTS. 1990. m. Aus.$6 per no. Australian Bureau of Statistics, P.O. Box 10, Belconnen, A.C.T. 2616, Australia. **Document type:** government publication.
Description: Contains production statistics for sawn Australian grown timber, woodchips, wood pulp, paper and paperboard, and wooden framed doors.

634.9   AT   ISSN 1034-179X
AUSTRALIA. BUREAU OF STATISTICS. TASMANIAN OFFICE. FOREST PRODUCTS, TASMANIA. 1980. q. Aus.$5 per no. Australian Bureau of Statistics, Tasmanian Office, G.P.O. Box 66A, Hobart, Tas. 7001, Australia. **Document type:** government publication.
Formerly: Australia. Bureau of Statistics. Tasmanian Office. Sawmilling, Woodchipping, etc., Statistics, Tasmania.
Description: Covers sawmilling, plywood milling, chipping, grinding and flaking.

674 310   US   ISSN 0511-8255
BAROMETER (PORTLAND). w. $48 (typically set in Jan.) Western Wood Products Association, 522 S.W. Fifth Ave., Portland, OR 97204-2122. TEL 503-224-3930. FAX 503-224-3934. stat. **Document type:** trade publication.
Description: Explores softwood lumber production techniques, shipments, new and unfilled orders, and inventory for the U.S. Western region.

634.9   VE   ISSN 0798-1945
BIBLIOGRAFIA FORESTAL LATINOAMERICANA. 1975. q. $20 per no. Instituto Forestal Latinoamericano, Apdo. 36, Merida, Venezuela. FAX 58-74-448906. **Document type:** bibliography.
Supersedes: Instituto Forestal Latinoamericano de Investigacion y Capacitacion. Boletin Bibliografico. (ISSN 0046-9971); **Formerly (until 1981):** Instituto Forestal Latinoamericano de Investigacion y Capacitacion. Bibliographical Bulletin.
Description: Contains bibliographical references on tropical forestry, forest products and the forest industry.

634.9   IT
BOLLETTINO DELLA BIBLIOGRAFIA FORESTALE ITALIANA. 1981. a. L.30000 (foreign L.35000) (effective 1994). Accademia Italiana di Scienze Forestali, Piazza Edison, 11, 50133 Florence, Italy. TEL 055-570348. FAX 055-575724. **Document type:** bibliography.

DE BOOMKWEKERIJ (THE HAGUE); beschouwingen over economische ontwikkelingen. see *AGRICULTURE — Abstracting, Bibliographies, Statistics*

FORESTS AND FORESTRY — ABSTRACTING, BIBLIOGRAPHIES, STATISTICS

634.9 016   UK
CAB INTERNATIONAL. FORESTRY BUREAU. ANNOTATED BIBLIOGRAPHIES. 1966. irreg. price varies. CAB International, Forestry Bureau, Wallingford, Oxon. OX10 8DE, England. TEL 44-491-832111. FAX 44-491-833508. TELEX 847964 COMAGG G. (U.S. subscr. to: CAB International, North American Office, 845 N. Park Ave., Tucson, AZ 85719. TEL 800-528-4841) **Indexed:** Forest.Abstr. **Document type:** bibliography.
   Formerly: Commonwealth Forestry Bureau Annotated Bibliographies (ISSN 0069-7052)

634.9   CN   ISSN 1183-7918
CANADA. FORESTRY CANADA. PUBLICATIONS DIGEST - ABREGE DES PUBLICATIONS. (Text in English and French) 1980. q. free. Forestry Canada, Place Vincent Massey, 21st Fl., Ottawa, Ont. K1A 1G5, Canada. TEL 819-997-9390. FAX 819-953-7048. circ. 4,000. **Document type:** abstracting/indexing.
   Formerly (until 1991): Canada. Environment Canada. Information Reports Digest - Digest des Rapports d'Information (ISSN 0226-6342)
   Description: Abstracts of reports published by Forestry Canada, along with listings of journal articles and symposium proceedings, available as reprints.

CANADA. STATISTICS CANADA. PAPER AND ALLIED PRODUCTS INDUSTRIES. see *PAPER AND PULP — Abstracting, Bibliographies, Statistics*

338.4   CN   ISSN 0835-0078
HD9764.C2
CANADA. STATISTICS CANADA. WOOD INDUSTRIES. (Catalogue 35-250) (Text in English and French) 1917. a. Can.$49($59) (foreign $69). Statistics Canada, Publications Sales and Services, Ottawa, Ont. K1A 0T6, Canada. TEL 613-951-7277. FAX 613-951-1584. stat. (also avail. in microform from MML) **Document type:** government publication.
   Supersedes: Canada. Statistics Canada. Sawmills and Planing Mill and Shingle Mill Products Industries (ISSN 0828-9867); **Formerly:** Canada. Statistics Canada. Sawmills and Planing Mills and Shingle Mills (ISSN 0318-7128)
   Description: Annual census of manufactures.

674 016   FR
CENTRE TECHNIQUE DU BOIS ET DE L'AMEUBLEMENT. PROFILS. 1950. bi-m. 1200 F. Centre Technique du Bois et de l'Ameublement, 10 av. de Saint Mande, 75012 Paris, France. TEL 40-19-49-19. FAX 43-40-85-65. bibl. circ. 700.
   Former titles (until 1990): Centre Technique du Bois et de l'Ameublement. Revue Documentaire (ISSN 0295-5717); (until 1985): Centre Technique du Bois et de l'Ameublement. Bulletin Bibliographique (ISSN 0008-9869)
   Description: Abstracting journal on international wood literature.

634.9 613.1   II   ISSN 0971-443X
▼**CURRENT INDIAN FORESTRY, ENVIRONMENT & WILDLIFE ABSTRACTS.** (Text in English) 1993. q. $35. Agrim Publishers, Anekant Palace, 29 Rajpur Rd., Dehra Dun 249 001, India. TEL 0135-25845. FAX 0135-22727. Ed. Sudhir K. Arora. index. **Document type:** abstracting/indexing.
   Description: Presents abstracts of published Indian researches in the field of forestry, environmental science and wildlife.

CURRENT TITLES IN WILDLAND FIRE. see *FIRE PREVENTION — Abstracting, Bibliographies, Statistics*

674 310   US   ISSN 0195-9336
DESTINATION OF SHIPMENTS OF WESTERN WOOD SPECIES BY STATE. q. $20 (typically set in Jan.). Western Wood Products Association, 522 S.W. Fifth Ave., Portland, OR 97204-2122. TEL 503-224-3930. FAX 503-224-3934. (back issues avail.) **Document type:** trade publication.

674   US
DIVIDENDS FROM WOOD RESEARCH; recent publications of the Forest Products Laboratory. 1974. s-a. U.S. Forest Service, Forest Products Laboratory, Madison, WI 53705. FAX 608-231-9592. (Subscr. to: Supt. of Documents, Washington, DC 20402.) **Document type:** government publication, catalog.

634.9 574   SP   ISSN 0212-226X
ESCUELA TECNICA SUPERIOR DE INGENIEROS DE MONTES. BIBLIOTECA. BOLETIN BIBLIOGRAFICO Y DOCUMENTAL. INFORMACION FORESTAL. SERIE A: MONOGRAFIAS. 1969. q. 1600 ptas. (foreign 2000 ptas.). (Universidad Politecnica de Madrid, Escuela Tecnica Superior de Ingenieros de Montes, Biblioteca) Fundacion Conde del Valle de Salazar, Ciudad Universitaria, s-n, 28040 Madrid, Spain. TEL 91-336 70 85. FAX 91-453-95-57. Ed. Rosario Martin-Montalvo San Gil. bk.rev. **Document type:** monographic series, bibliography.
   Supersedes in part: Escuela Tecnica Superior de Ingenieros de Montes. Biblioteca. Boletin Bibliografico y Documental (ISSN 0210-1297)

634.9 574   SP   ISSN 0212-2278
ESCUELA TECNICA SUPERIOR DE INGENIEROS DE MONTES. BIBLIOTECA. BOLETIN BIBLIOGRAFICO Y DOCUMENTAL. INFORMACION FORESTAL. SERIE B: PUBLICACIONES PERIODICAS. 1969. q. 1600 ptas. (foreign 2000 ptas.). (Universidad Politecnica de Madrid, Escuela Tecnica Superior de Ingenieros de Montes, Biblioteca) Fundacion Conde del Valle de Salazar, Ciudad Universitaria, s-n, 28040 Madrid, Spain. TEL 91-336 70 85. FAX 91-543-95-57. Ed. Rosario Martin-Montalvo y San Gil. **Document type:** bibliography.
   Supersedes in part: Escuela Tecnica Superior de Ingenieros de Montes. Biblioteca. Boletin Bibliografico y Documental.

F A O DOCUMENTATION - CURRENT BIBLIOGRAPHY. see *FISH AND FISHERIES — Abstracting, Bibliographies, Statistics*

634.9 016   UK   ISSN 0140-4784
FOREST PRODUCTS ABSTRACTS. 1978. bi-m. £170($311) CAB International, Forestry Bureau, Wallingford, Oxon. OX10 8DE, England. TEL 44-491-832111. FAX 44-491-833509. TELEX 847964 COMAGG G. (U.S. subscr. to: CAB International, North American Office, 845 N. Park Ave., Tucson, AZ 85719. TEL 800-528-4841) (also avail. in diskette format; back issues avail.; reprint service avail.) **Indexed:** Abstr.Bull.Inst.Pap.Chem., Agri.Eng.Abstr., Forest.Abstr. **Document type:** abstracting/indexing.
   ●Also available online. Vendor(s): BRS Online Products (CABA), CISTI, DIMDI, DIALOG Information Services, Inc., European Space Agency (File nos.16 & 124/CAB).
   Description: Covers all aspects of wood processing from harvesting to marketing.

634.9 016   UK   ISSN 0015-7538
SD1
FORESTRY ABSTRACTS; compiled from world literature. 1939. m. £388($627) CAB International, Forestry Bureau, Wallingford, Oxon. OX10 8DE, England. TEL 44-491-832111. FAX 44-491-833508. TELEX 847964 COMAGG G. (U.S. subscr. to: CAB International, North American Office, 845 N. Park Ave., Tucson, AZ 58719. TEL 800-528-4841) Ed. C.A.D. Elbourn. index, cum.index: vols.1-5. circ. 1,200. (also avail. in diskette format; back issues avail. reprint service avail.) **Indexed:** Abstr.Bull.Inst.Pap.Chem., Chem.Abstr., Field Crop Abstr., Forest Prod.Abstr., Rev.Appl.Entomol., Rural Recreat.Tour.Abstr., Seed Abstr., Weed Abstr., World Agri.Econ.& Rural Sociol.Abstr. **Document type:** abstracting/indexing.
   ●Also available online. Vendor(s): BRS Online Products (CABA), CISTI, DIMDI, DIALOG Information Services, Inc., European Space Agency.
   —BLDSC (4001.000000).
   Description: Covers world literature on all aspects of forestry, including land use and conservation.

634.9 016   UK   ISSN 0071-7584
FORESTRY ABSTRACTS. LEADING ARTICLE REPRINT SERIES. 1942. irreg. price varies. CAB International, Wallingford, Oxon. OX10 8DE, England. TEL 44-491-832111. FAX 44-491-833508. TELEX 847964 COMAGG G. (U.S. subscr. to: CAB International, North American Office, 845 N. Park Ave., Tucson, AZ 85719. TEL 800-528-4841) **Indexed:** Forest.Abstr. **Document type:** abstracting/indexing.
   ●Also available online. Vendor(s): BRS Online Products, CISTI, DIMDI, DIALOG Information Services, Inc., European Space Agency.

674   FR
FRANCE. SERVICE D'ETUDE DES STRATEGIES ET DES STATISTIQUES INDUSTRIELLES. RESULTATS MENSUELS DES ENQUETES DE BRANCHE. TRAVAIL MECANIQUE DU BOIS. m. 260 F. (foreign 310 F.) (effective 1991). Service d'Etude des Strategies et des Statistiques Industrielles (SESSI), 85 bd. du Montparnasse, 75270 Paris Cedex 06, France. TEL 45-56-42-34. FAX 45-56-40-71.
   Description: Follows developments in the woodworking industry through the performance of selected ind cators.

674   FR
FRANCE. SERVICE D'ETUDE DES STRATEGIES ET DES STATISTIQUES INDUSTRIELLES. RESULTATS TRIMESTRIELS DES ENQUETES DE BRANCHE. TRAVAIL MECANIQUE DU BOIS. q. 180 F. (foreign 210 F.) (effective 1991). Service d'Etude des Strategies et des Statistiques Industrielles (SESSI), 85 bd. du Montparnasse, 75270 Paris Cedex 06, France. TEL 45-56-42-34. FAX 45-56-40-71.
   Description: Provides detailed industry-wide performance statistics for comparative evaluations.

634.9   SZ
HOLZPREISE/PRIX DU BOIS. (Text in French and German) 1987. 4/yr. Bundesamt fuer Statistik, Schwarztorstr. 96, CH-3003 Bern, Switzerland. TEL 031-323€011. FAX 031-3236061. **Document type:** government publication.
   Formerly: Ho zpreisstatistik.

634.9   II   ISSN 0073-6430
INDIAN FOREST RECORDS (NEW SERIES) STATISTICAL. (Text in English) 1960. irreg., vol.3, no.1, 1983. price varies. Forest Research Institute & Colleges, P.O. New Forest, Dehra Dun, India. circ. 500. **Indexed:** Biol.Abstr., Forest.Abstr., Indian Sci.Abstr.

634.9   IT
ITALY. ISTITUTO NAZIONALE DI STATISTICA. STATISTICHE FORESTALI. 1955. a. L.18000 (effective 1993). Istituto Nazionale di Statistica, Via Cesare Balbo 16 00100 Rome, Italy. FAX 06-46735198. circ. 1,050. **Document type:** government publication.
   Formerly: Italy. Istituto Centrale di Statistica. Annuario di Statistica Forestale (ISSN 0075-1707)

634.9 314   GW
JAHRESBERICHT DER LANDESFORSTVERWALTUNG. 1953. a. DM.48. Ministerium fuer Laendlichen Raum, Ernaehrung, Landwirtschaft und Forsten, Kernerplatz 10, 70182 Stuttgart, Germany. FAX 0711-1262255. **Document type:** government publication.
   Formerly (until 1983): Forststatistisches Jahrbuch (ISSN 0084-7690)

674 310   US   ISSN 0195-9395
LUMBER PRICE INDEX. INLAND INDEX. Variant title: Lumber Price Trends. Inland Index. m. $28 (typically set in Jan.). Western Wood Products Association, Yeon Bldg., 522 S.W. Fifth Ave., Portland, OR 97204-2122. TEL 503-224-3930. FAX 503-224-3934. (back issues avail.) **Document type:** trade publication.

634.9   US   ISSN 0735-066X
LUMBER PRICE INDEX. F N W COAST INDEX. 1982. q. $28 (typically set in Jan.). Western Wood Products Association, Yeon Bldg., 522 S.W. Fifth Ave., OR 97204. TEL 503-224-3930. FAX 503-224-3934.

MAGYAR MEZOGAZDASAGI BIBLIOGRAFIA. see *AGRICULTURE — Abstracting, Bibliographies, Statistics*

MONTHLY STATISTICS ON AGRICULTURE, FORESTRY AND FISHERIES/NORIN SUISAN TOKEI GEPPO. see *AGRICULTURE — Abstracting, Bibliographies, Statistics*

NORIN TOSHO SHIRYO GEPPO. see *AGRICULTURE — Abstracting, Bibliographies, Statistics*

634.9   NO   ISSN 0468-8155
NORWAY. STATISTISK SENTRALBYRAA. SKOGSTATSTIKK. (Subseries of Norges Offisielle Statistikk) 1952. a. NOK 75. Statistisk Sentralbyraa, P.O. Box 8131 Dep., N-0033 Oslo 1, Norway. TEL 47-22-864500. FAX 47-22-864973. circ. 1,050. **Document type:** government publication.

FORESTS AND FORESTRY — LUMBER AND WOOD

634.9 314   PL
POLAND. GLOWNY URZAD STATYSTYCZNY. ROCZNIK STATYSTYCZNY LESNICTWA I GOSPODARKI DREWNEM. (Issued in its Seria Roczniki Branzowe) irreg., latest 1981. Zaklad Wydawnictw Statystycznych, Al. Niepodleglosci 208, 00-925 Warsaw, Poland. TEL 48 22 25-03-45.
   Formerly: Poland. Glowny Urzad Statystyczny. Rocznik Statystyczny Lesnictwa (ISSN 0079-2721)

333.7   II   ISSN 0377-3302
SD88.R3
RAJASTHAN FOREST STATISTICS. (Text in English) irreg. Forest Department, Jaipur, Rajasthan, India.

674   US   ISSN 1055-0895
RANDOM LENGTHS YARDSTICK; monthly measure of forest products statistics. 1991. m. $190 (foreign $230). Random Lengths Publications, Inc., Box 867, Eugene, OR 97440-0867. TEL 503-686-9925. FAX 800-874-7979. Ed. Joseph Heitz. charts. circ. 760. (back issues avail.) **Document type:** newsletter. —CCC.
   Description: Statistical update for the forest products industry, including prices, production, shipment, order totals, housing starts, and exports.

674   US   ISSN 0485-9960
RANDOM LENGTHS YEARBOOK. 1965. a. $34.95. Random Lengths Publications, Inc., Box 867, Eugene, OR 97440-0867. TEL 503-686-9925. FAX 800-874-7979. charts.
   Description: Price histories for lumber and panel items, plus data relating to wood products markets.

634.9 016   RU   ISSN 0034-2440
REFERATIVNYI ZHURNAL. LESOVEDENIE I LESOVODSTVO. 1962. m. 31.60 Rub. (42 Rub. including index). Vsesoyuznyi Institut Nauchno-Tekhnicheskoi Informatsii (VINITI), Baltiiskaya ul., 14, Moscow A-219, Russia. (Subscr. to: Mezhdunarodnaya Kniga, Dimitrova ul. 39, 113095 Moscow, Russia) **Indexed:** Biol.Abstr., Chem.Abstr., Forest.Abstr., Forest Prod.Abstr. **Document type:** abstracting/indexing.

674 310   SQ
SWAZILAND. CENTRAL STATISTICAL OFFICE. TIMBER STATISTICS. 1970. a., latest 1991. free. Central Statistical Office, Box 456, Mbabane, Swaziland. TEL 43765. charts; stat. circ. 500. **Document type:** government publication.
   Formerly: Swaziland. Central Statistical Office. Commercial Timber Plantation and Wood Products Statistics.

634.9 016   US
U.S. FOREST SERVICE. NORTH CENTRAL FOREST EXPERIMENT STATION. LIST OF PUBLICATIONS. 1966. a. free. U.S. Forest Service, North Central Forest Experiment Sta., 1992 Folwell Ave., St. Paul, MN 55108. TEL 612-649-5276. Ed. Robert D. Wray. circ. 1,500 (controlled). **Indexed:** Agri.Eng.Abstr. **Document type:** government publication.
   Supersedes: U.S. Forest Service. North Central Forest Experiment Station, St. Paul. Annual Report (ISSN 0083-2472)

634.9   SZ
WALD- UND HOLZWIRTSCHAFT DER SCHWEIZ. JAHRBUCH/L'ECONOMIE FORESTIE ET L'INDUSTRIE DU BOIS EN SUISSE. ANNUAIRE. (Text in French and German) 1930. a. 19 SFr. Bundesamt fuer Statistik, Schwarztorstr. 96, CH-3003 Bern, Switzerland. TEL 031-3236011. FAX 031-3236061. **Document type:** government publication.
   Formerly: Schweizerischen Wald- und Holzwirtschaft. Jahrbuch.

674 310   US   ISSN 0511-7704
HD9757.A4
WESTERN LUMBER FACTS. m. $36 (typically set in Jan.). Western Wood Products Association, 522 S.W. Fifth Ave., Portland, OR 97204-2122. TEL 503-224-3930. FAX 503-224-3934. **Document type:** trade publication.
   Description: Reviews industry statistics, prices, trade, and housing starts.

674 310   US   ISSN 0730-5176
WESTERN WOOD PRODUCTS ASSOCIATION. EXPORT REPORT. 1981. m. (plus q. summaries). $28 (typically set in Jan.). Western Wood Products Association, Yeon Bldg., 522 S.W. Fifth Ave., Portland, OR 97204. TEL 503-224-3930. FAX 503-224-3934. **Document type:** trade publication.
   Description: Shows softwood lumber exports by species and major country destinations.

674 310   US   ISSN 0511-8298
HD9757.A5
WESTERN WOOD PRODUCTS ASSOCIATION. MONTHLY F.O.B. PRICE SUMMARY, PAST SALES. COAST MILLS. m. $45 (typically set in Jan.). Western Wood Products Association, Yeon Bldg., 522 S.W. Fifth Ave., Portland, OR 97204-2122. TEL 503-224-3930. FAX 503-224-3930. (back issues avail.) **Document type:** trade publication.

674 310   US   ISSN 0195-9409
WESTERN WOOD PRODUCTS ASSOCIATION. MONTHLY F.O.B. PRICE SUMMARY, PAST SALES. INLAND MILLS. 1933. m. $45 (typically set in Jan.). Western Wood Products Association, Yeon Bldg., 522 S.W. Fifth Ave., Portland, OR 97204-2122. TEL 503-224-3930. FAX 503-224-3930. (back issues avail.) **Document type:** trade publication.

674 310   US   ISSN 0195-931X
HD9757.A17
WESTERN WOOD PRODUCTS ASSOCIATION. STATISTICAL YEARBOOK. 1968. a. $20. Western Wood Products Association, 522 S.W. Fifth Ave., Portland, OR 97204-2122. TEL 503-224-3930. FAX 503-224-3934. (back issues avail.) **Document type:** trade publication.
   Formerly: Statistical Supplement to Facts.

FORESTS AND FORESTRY — Lumber And Wood

see also Paper and Pulp

694 674   SP   ISSN 0044-9261
A I T I M BOLETIN DE INFORMACION TECNICA. 1964. bi-m. 7000 ptas. (foreign 12500 ptas.) (effective 1994). Asociacion de Investigacion Tecnica de las Industrias de la Madera, Flora, 3, 2o Dcha., 28013 Madrid, Spain. TEL 91-542-58-64. FAX 91-559-05-12. Ed. Ricardo Velez Munoz. adv.: B&W page 70000 ptas., color page 120000 ptas.; adv. contact: Pilar Zapata Ruiz. bk.rev.; bibl.; charts; illus. circ. 5,000. **Indexed:** Ind.SST. **Document type:** bulletin.
   Description: Covers aspects of the lumber industry from the science of the living tree to its transformation into a finished product. Also covers the cork industry, architecture and carpentry, furniture and decorative arts.

AFFICHES D'ALSACE ET DE LORRAINE - MONITEUR DES SOUMISSIONS ET DES VENTES DE BOIS DE L'EST. see *BUILDING AND CONSTRUCTION*

674 634.9   PL
AKADEMIA ROLNICZA, POZNAN. ROCZNIKI. CHEMICZNA TECHNOLOGIA DREWNA. (Text in Polish; summaries in English and Russian) 1961. irreg. price varies. Akademia Rolnicza, Poznan, Ul. Wojska Polskiego 28, 60-637 Poznan, Poland. FAX 48-61-411022. TELEX 0413322 ARPL. circ. 1,960. **Indexed:** Bibl.Agri., Forest.Abstr. **Document type:** academic/scholarly publication.
   Formerly: Akademia Rolnicza, Poznan. Roczniki. Technologia Drewna (ISSN 0137-1797)
   Description: Works on wood chemistry, cellulose and paper technology, hardboards technology, hydrolysis and pyrolysis, protection and conservation of wood, utilization and processing of wood by-products, chemical modification of wood.

674 690   SZ
AKTIV. fortn. Christlicher Holz- und Bauarbeiterverband der Schweiz, Zeughausstr. 39, 8026 Zurich, Switzerland. TEL 2415442.

674   US
ALASKA FOREST PRODUCTS NEWSLETTER. 1966. q. free. University of Alaska, Fairbanks, Alaska Cooperative Extension, Box 756180, Fairbanks, AK 99775-6180. TEL 907-474-6356. FAX 907-474-7439. Ed. Tony Gasbarro. bk.rev.; bibl. circ. 700. (looseleaf format)

674   US
AMERICAN TIMBERMAN AND TRUCKER. m. Bill Lund Advertising, Box 1006, Chehalis, WA 98532-0130. TEL 206-748-0206. FAX 206-748-0244. Ed. Vi Lund.

674   US
AMERICAN WOOD - PRESERVERS' ASSOCIATION. BOOK OF STANDARDS. a. $42 to non-member; members $32. American Wood - Preservers' Association, Box 286, Woodstock, MD 21163-0286. TEL 410-465-3169. FAX 410-465-3195. Ed. John F. Hall. circ. 2,000. **Document type:** trade publication.
   Description: Contains all 88 of AWPA's standards for Preservatives, Treated Wood Commodities, Analytical Methods, Evaluation and Miscellaneous Standards along with Conversion Factors and Correction Tables.

674   US
AMERICAN WOOD - PRESERVERS' ASSOCIATION. PROCEEDINGS. 1905. a. $55 paper; cloth $70. American Wood - Preservers' Association, Box 286, Woodstock, MD 21163-0286. TEL 410-465-3169. FAX 410-465-3195. Ed. John F. Hall. adv. circ. 2,000. **Indexed:** Chem.Abstr., Forest.Abstr., Forest Prod.Abstr. **Document type:** proceedings.
   Description: Contains all papers and reports presented at AWPA's annual meeting along with a list of AWPA committee members and committee regulations, AWPA's membership list, and the plant list.

ANNUAL BOOK OF A S T M STANDARDS. VOLUME 04.09. WOOD. see *ENGINEERING — Engineering Mechanics And Materials*

674   US   ISSN 0193-8495
HD9769.H393
ANNUAL HARDWOOD SYMPOSIUM. PROCEEDINGS. 1972. a. $10 to non-members; members $5. Hardwood Research Council, Box 34518, Memphis, TN 38184-0518. TEL 901-377-1824. FAX 901-382-6419. circ. 400. **Indexed:** Forest.Abstr. **Document type:** proceedings.
   Description: Presents current developments in forest management, processing, and manufacturing of hardwoods. Emphasizes the practical application of research results.

674   AG
ARGENTINA FORESTAL. 1942. 6/yr. Camara Argentina de Aserradores de Maderas, Depositos y Afines, Alsina 440, 1087 Buenos Aires, Argentina. circ. 3,000. **Indexed:** Forest.Abstr., Forest Prod.Abstr.

674.2   SI   ISSN 0217-4421
ASIAN TIMBER; for the forestry, woodworking, panels & furniture industries. (Text in English) 1982. m. $140. Toucan Publications Pte Ltd., 322-C King George's Ave., Singapore 0820, Singapore. TEL 65-299-7121. FAX 65-299-7545. (Dist. in U.S. by: Roy McDonald Associates, 2094 S.E. Gerhard Dr., Hillsboro, OR 97123. TEL 503-640-2011) Ed. Andrew Y.C. Loh. adv.: B&W page $2860, color page $3510; trim 210 x 297. circ. 10,094. (back issues avail.) **Document type:** trade publication.
   Formerly: Asian Timber Trades Journal (ISSN 0264-4134)
   Description: Covers the latest developments of the forestry, woodworking, panels and furniture industries.

AUSTRALIA. BUREAU OF STATISTICS. MANUFACTURING PRODUCTION, AUSTRALIA: WOOD AND WOOD PRODUCTS. see *FORESTS AND FORESTRY — Abstracting, Bibliographies, Statistics*

674   AT
AUSTRALIAN TIMBERMAN. 1977. m. Aus.$48. Marabridge Pty Ltd., P.O. Box 552, Fortitude Valley, Qld. 4006, Australia. TEL 07-252-8511. FAX 07-2528921. Ed. Bill Wilkie; Pub. Jim Bowden. adv.; bk.rev. circ. 8,500. **Indexed:** Biol.Abstr. **Document type:** trade publication, newspaper.
   Formerly: Timberman.

674   BG
BANGLADESH FOREST INDUSTRIES DEVELOPMENT CORPORATION. ANNUAL REPORT. (Text in English) a. Bangladesh Forest Industries Development Corporation, 186 Circular Rd., Motijheel, Dhaka 2, Bangladesh. **Document type:** corporate report.

FORESTS AND FORESTRY — LUMBER AND WOOD

674 AU
BAU HOLZ. 11/yr. Ebendorferstr. 7, A-1082 Vienna, Austria. TEL 01-423641. FAX 01-423641258. TELEX 114833. Ed. Alexander Czauderna.

674.2 UK ISSN 0306-4123
TS875
BOARD MANUFACTURE & PROCESSING; the only journal exclusively covering board materials and finishes for architects, builders, importers and distributors of fibreboard, chipboard, plywood and allied products. 1958. bi-m. £25($70) (overseas £35) (effective 1994). Chandler Publications Ltd., 10 South St., Totnes, Devon TQ9 5DZ, England. TEL 44-803-864668. FAX 44-803-865649. Ed. Jack R.D. Heming. adv.; bk.rev.; bibl.; charts; illus.; mkt.; tr.lit. circ. 2,000. **Document type:** consumer publication, trade publication.
  Formerly: Board Manufacture Practice (ISSN 0006-534X)
  Description: Contains articles of interest to manufacturers and converters of wood-based sheet materials, plastic finishes, and appropriate machinery.

674 FR
BOIS DU SUD. 6/yr. 8 rue Pierre Rameil, 66000 Perpignan, France. TEL 68-35-34-34. FAX 68-35-09-61. Ed. M. Raymond Saleta.

674 FR
BOIS HEBDO; scierie-menuiserie-batiment. 1895. w. 100 F. Publicite Claude Larrey, 73 bis, av. de Wagram, 75017 Paris, France. adv.

BUILDING PRODUCTS DIGEST. see BUILDING AND CONSTRUCTION

634.9 674 GW ISSN 0007-5892
BUNDESFORSCHUNGSANSTALT FUER FORST- UND HOLZWIRTSCHAFT, HAMBURG. MITTEILUNGEN. (Text in English and German) 1947. irreg., no.171, 1992. price varies. Kommissionverlag Max Wiedebusch, Dammtorstr. 20, 20354 Hamburg, Germany. TEL 040-345001. FAX 040-3480117. Eds. S. Schrader, H.R. Schoenwald. bk.rev. **Indexed:** Abstr.Bull.Inst.Pap.Chem., Geo.Abstr. **Document type:** monographic series.

674 US
C I N T R A F O R NEWS. 1985. q. free. Center for International Trade in Forest Products, University of Washington, College of Forest Resources, AR-10, Seattle, WA 98195. TEL 206-543-8684. FAX 206-685-0790. Ed. John Dirks. circ. 2,700. **Document type:** newsletter.
  Description: Provides information and statistics about forest products and international trade to large and small businesses, government and the public.

674 FR ISSN 0296-8541
TS800
C T B INFO. bi-m. 420 F. Centre Technique du Bois et de l'Ameublement, 10 av. Saint-Mande, 75012 Paris, France. TEL 40-19-49-19. FAX 43-40-85-65. circ. 1,400. **Indexed:** Forest.Abstr., Forest Prod.Abstr.
  Incorporates (in 1985): Centre Technique du Bois et de l'Ameublement. Bulletin d'Informations Techniques (ISSN 0008-9877); Courrier de l'Industriel du Bois et de l'Ameublement (ISSN 0335-5276); Courrier de l'Exploitant et du Scieur (ISSN 0396-0595)
  Description: Study results and CTBA activities.

674 US ISSN 0008-1094
CALIFORNIA FORESTRY AND FOREST PRODUCTS; technical notes. 1957. irreg., no.60, 1985. exchange basis. University of California, Berkeley, Department of Forestry and Resource Management, 47th St. & Hoffman Blvd., Richmond, CA 94804. TEL 415-231-4561. Ed.Bd. charts; illus.; stat. circ. 775. **Indexed:** Chem.Abstr., Forest.Abstr. **Document type:** academic/scholarly publication.

674 CN ISSN 0318-4277
TS800
CANADIAN FOREST INDUSTRIES; Canada's only national publication serving saw and pulpwood logging, sawmilling and allied activities. (Directory number avail.) 1888. 8/yr. Can.$25 (US Can.$36, elsewhere Can.$68). J C F T Forest Communications, 1 rue Pacifique, Ste.-Anne-de-Bellevue, PQ H9X 1C5, Canada. TEL 514-457-2211. Ed. Scott Jamieson. adv.; illus.; stat.; tr.lit.; index. circ. 18,000. (also avail. in microfiche from UMI) **Indexed:** Can.B.P.I., Can.Per.Ind., Curr.Adv.Ecol.Sci., Curr.Cont., Forest.Abstr., Forest Prod.Abstr., PROMT. **Document type:** trade publication.
  ●Also available online. Vendor(s): Southam Electronic Publishing.
  —BLDSC (3024.100000); Faxon; UnCover. **CCC.**
  Formed by the merger of: Canada Lumberman; Timber of Canada.
  Description: Serves the Canadian forest industry's harvesting sector reporting on activities taking place from the stump to the mill gate, including logging, transportation, roadbuilding, equipment maintenance, forest management and silviculture.

674 CN ISSN 1183-9139
CANADIAN WOOD PRODUCTS; the sawmilling and remanufacturing magazine. 1991. 6/yr. Can.$22.47 (US Can.$38, elsewhere Can.$55). J C F T Forest Communications, 1 rue Pacifique, Ste.-Anne-de-Bellevue, PQ H9X 1C5, Canada. TEL 514-457-2211. Ed. Scott Jamieson. adv.: B&W page Can.$2355, color page Can.$3550; trim 8 1/8 x 10 7/8. circ. 300 (paid); 6,187 (controlled).

674 US
CAPITAL COMMENTS. 1979. m. National Lumber and Building Material Dealers Association, 40 Ivy St., S.E., Washington, DC 20003. TEL 202-547-2230. FAX 202-547-7640. circ. 800. **Document type:** newsletter.

674 IT ISSN 0008-8765
  CODEN: CLCAA9
CELLULOSA E CARTA. (Text in Italian; summaries in English, French and German) 1953. bi-m. L.40000. R.E.S.S., Via Assisi 163, 00181 Rome, Italy. TEL 06-78051-242. FAX 06-78051368. Dir. Matteo Renato Pistone. adv.; bk.rev.; bibl.; charts; illus.; stat.; index. circ. 8,000. **Indexed:** Abstr.Bull.Inst.Pap.Chem., Biol.Abstr., Chem.Abstr., ELLIS, Forest.Abstr., Forest Prod.Abstr.
  —CASDDS.
  Incorporates: Indicatore Cartario (ISSN 0392-9108)

674 FR
CENTRE TECHNIQUE DU BOIS ET DE L'AMEUBLEMENT. PUBLICATIONS. 1954. irreg. price varies. Centre Technique du Bois et de l'Ameublement, 10 av. de St Mande, 75012 Paris, France. TEL 40-19-49-19. FAX 43-40-85-65. charts; illus. circ. 4,000. **Indexed:** Forest.Abstr., Forest Prod.Abstr. **Document type:** monographic series.
  Formerly: Centre Technique du Bois et de l'Ameublement. Cahiers (ISSN 0008-9885)
  Description: Monographs on wood technology and wood products.

674 SP
COMERCIO E INDUSTRIA DE LA MADERA. 8/yr. 16000 ptas.($150) Elsevier Prensa S.A., Avda. Parallel, 180, 08015 Barcelona, Spain. TEL 3-325-53-50. FAX 3-425-28-80. Ed. Marcel Lleal Galceran. circ. 7,000.

674 BE
COURRIER DU BOIS. Dutch edition: Houtnieuws. 1961. 4/yr. free. Bureau Nationale de Documentation sur le Bois - Nationaal Houtvoorlichtingsbureau, 109-111 rue Royale, 1000 Brussels, Belgium. Ed.Bd. adv.; bk.rev.; bibl.; charts; illus. circ. 32,000.

674 US
CROW'S WEEKLY REPORT OF LUMBER & PANEL PRODUCTS - FOREST INDUSTRY JOURNAL. w. $225. C.C. Crow Publications, Inc., Box 25749, Portland, OR 97225-0749. TEL 503-646-8075. FAX 503-646-9971. Ed. Sam Sherrill. circ. 2,000. **Document type:** newsletter.
  Formerly: Crow's Weekly Letter.
  Description: Contains species-product information, market analysis, industry news and price guides.

674 US
DEALERS (WASHINGTON). m. National Lumber and Building Material Dealers Association, 40 Ivy St., S.E., Washington, DC 20003. TEL 202-547-2230. **Document type:** consumer publication.

DESTINATION OF SHIPMENTS OF WESTERN WOOD SPECIES BY STATE. see FORESTS AND FORESTRY — Abstracting, Bibliographies, Statistics

DIRECTORY OF ONTARIO LUMBER & BUILDING MATERIALS RETAILERS. BUYER'S GUIDE & PRODUCT DIRECTORY. see BUSINESS AND ECONOMICS — Trade And Industrial Directories

DIRECTORY OF THE FOREST PRODUCTS INDUSTRY. see BUSINESS AND ECONOMICS — Trade And Industrial Directories

DIRECTORY OF TIMBER TRADE. see BUSINESS AND ECONOMICS — Trade And Industrial Directories

674 XV
DOLENJSKI GOZDAR; glasilo delavcev Gozdnega Gospodarstva Novo Mesto. (Text in Slovenian) 1964. bi-m. free. Gozdno Gospodarstvo Novo Mesto, Gubceva 15, Novo Mesto, Slovenia. TEL 068 21-065. illus. circ. 1,100. (looseleaf format; back issues avail.)

674 XO ISSN 0012-6136
  CODEN: DRVYAP
DREVARSKY VYSKUM/WOOD RESEARCH. (Text in English, German, Russian, Slovak or Czech; summaries in English, German, Russian) 1956. q. $112. Statny Drevarsky Vyskumny Ustav - State Forest Products Research Institute, Lamacska cesta 1, 833 30 Bratislava, Slovakia. FAX 427-374460. charts; illus.; stat. circ. 700. (also avail. in microfilm) **Indexed:** Abstr.Bull.Inst.Pap.Chem., Biol.Abstr., Chem.Abstr., Forest.Abstr., Forest Prod.Abstr.
  —CASDDS.
  Description: Wood and forestry research.

674 621.9 CI ISSN 0012-6772
TS800 CODEN: DRINAT
DRVNA INDUSTRIJA. (Text in Croatian) 1950. m. 1400000 din.($6) Tehnicki Centar za Drvo, Ul. 8 Maja 82, 41001 Zagreb, Croatia. TELEX 22-367-YU IDZG. Ed. Stanislav Badjun. adv.; bk.rev.; bibl.; illus. circ. 2,000. **Indexed:** Abstr.Bull.Inst.Pap.Chem., Chem.Abstr., Forest.Abstr., Forest Prod.Abstr.
  —CASDDS.

674 BE
ECHO DES BOIS. 1909. w. 4550 BEF. S.A. l' Echo des Bois, Rue de l'Abattoir 29, B-1000 Brussels, Belgium. FAX 32-2-5118641. Ed. C. Castelo. adv.; bk.rev.; bibl.; pat.; stat.; tr.lit. circ. 3,500. **Document type:** trade publication.

674 634.9 HU ISSN 0014-0066
ERDOGAZDASAG ES FAIPAR. 1947. m. $26. (Magyar Elelmezesipari Tudomanyos Egyesulet) Lapkiado Vallalat, Lenin korut 9-11, 1073 Budapest 7, Hungary. TEL 222-408. (Subscr. to: Kultura, Box 149, H-1389 Budapest, Hungary) Ed. Pal Kiraly. bk.rev.; charts; illus. circ. 5,000.

674 GW
EUROPAEISCHER WIRTSCHAFTSDIENST. EILDIENST HOLZ. 1926. w. DM.310. Casimir Katz Verlag, Bleichstr. 20-22, 76593 Gernsbach, Germany. TEL 07224-9397-0. FAX 07224-939750. TELEX 78915-DBV-D. Ed. Casimir Katz. circ. 480. **Document type:** trade publication.

674 GW
EUROPAEISCHER WIRTSCHAFTSDIENST. LAUBHOLZ-DIENST. 1926. fortn. DM.310. Casimir Katz Verlag, Bleichstr. 20-22, 76593 Gernsbach, Germany. TEL 07224-9397-0. FAX 07224-939750. TELEX 78915-DBV-D. Ed. Fr. Steinmetz. circ. 650. **Document type:** trade publication.

674 GW
EUROPAEISCHER WIRTSCHAFTSDIENST. TIMBER-SERVICE. (Text in English) 1926. w. DM.820. Casimir Katz Verlag, Bleichstr. 20-22, 76593 Gernsbach, Germany. TEL 07224-9397-0. FAX 07224-939750. TELEX 78915-DBV-D. Ed. Annette Steinmetz. circ. 480. **Document type:** trade publication.

FORESTS AND FORESTRY — LUMBER AND WOOD

674   PH
F P R D I JOURNAL; magazine for forest products research and industries development. (Text in English) 1972. s-a. P.23. Forest Products Research and Industries Development Commission, College, Laguna 4031, Philippines. Ed. Emerita R. Barile. charts; illus. circ. 1,000. **Indexed:** Abstr.Bull.Inst.Pap.Chem., Chem.Abstr, Forest.Abstr., Forest Prod.Abstr.
— BLDSC (4029.408000).
    Formerly (until 1982): Forpride Digest (ISSN 0115-0456); Which incorporates: FORPRIDECOM Technical Notes; Which was formerly: F P R I Technical Notes.

674   HU   ISSN 0014-6897
FAIPAR. (Summaries in German and Russian) 1950. m. $25.50. (Faipari Tudomanyos Egyesulet) Lapkiado Vallalat, Lenin korut 9-11, 1073 Budapest 7, Hungary. TEL 222-408. (Subscr. to: Kultura, Box 149, H-1389 Budapest, Hungary) Ed. Pal Rdka. adv.; charts; illus. **Indexed:** Agri.Eng.Abstr., Chem.Abstr., Forest.Abstr., Forest Prod.Abstr., Hung.Build.Bull.

674   UK
FINANCIAL SURVEY COMPANY DATA FOR SUCCESS. TIMBER MERCHANTS. a. I C C Financial Surveys Ltd., Field House, 72 Oldfield Rd., Hampton, Middlesex TW12 2HQ, England. TEL 081-783-0977. FAX 081-783-1940.
    Formerly (until 1991): Financial Survey Company Directory. Timber Merchants (ISSN 0953-5934)

674.8   PL   ISSN 0071-6685
    CODEN: FFPBAY
FOLIA FORESTALIA POLONICA. SERIES B. DRZEWNICTWO. (Text in Polish; summaries in English and Russian) 1959. irreg., no.21, 1991. price varies. (Polska Akademia Nauk, Komitet Technologii Drewna) Wydawnictwo Naukowe P W N, Miodowa 10, 00-251 Warsaw, Poland. TEL 48-22-312738. FAX 48-22-267163. TELEX 813763 PWN PL. Ed. M. Lawniczak. circ. 610. **Indexed:** Abstr.Bull.Inst.Pap.Chem., Biol.Abstr., Forest.Abstr., Forest Prod.Abstr.

FOREST AND TIMBER. see FORESTS AND FORESTRY

674   US
FOREST INDUSTRY AFFAIRS; information for decision. 1968. s-m. $175. Ahlfeld & Associates, Inc., Box 19187, Washington, DC 20036. Ed. Bill Ahlfeld. circ. 500. (looseleaf format)
    Former titles: Forest Industry Affairs Letter; Dean Sherman's Forest Industry Affairs Letter (ISSN 0011-7234)

674   US
▼**FOREST PRODUCTS EQUIPMENT.** 1992. m. $35. L & W Publishing Co., Box 789, Hwy. 1 S., Swainsboro, GA 30401. TEL 912-237-6778. FAX 912-237-6878. adv.: B&W page $1420, color page $1915; trim 8 3/8 x 10 7/8. circ. 30,500.

674   US   ISSN 0015-7473
TS800   CODEN: FPJOAB
FOREST PRODUCTS JOURNAL. 1947. 10/yr. $115 in Canada and Mexico $125; elsewhere $155 (effective Jan. 1992). Forest Products Research Society, 2801 Marshall Ct., Madison, WI 53705. TEL 608-231-1361. FAX 608-231-2152. Ed. Arthur Brauner. adv.; abstr.; bibl.; charts; illus.; stat.; tr.lit. circ. 5,000. (also avail. in microform from UMI,PMC; reprint service avail. from UMI) **Indexed:** Abstr.Bull.Inst.Pap.Chem., Agri.Eng.Abstr., Agri.Ind., Art & Archaeol.Tech.Abstr., Biol.Abstr., Chem.Abstr., Curr.Adv.Ecol.Sci., Curr.Cont., Energy Info.Abstr., Eng.Ind, Environ.Abstr., Excerp.Med., Forest.Abstr., Forest Prod.Abstr., Geo.Abstr., Ind.Sci.Rev., INIS Atomind., Sci.Cit.Ind, Soils & Fert.
— BLDSC (3992.000000); CIS; Faxon; UnCover; SWETS; UMI; CASDDS. **CCC.**

674   US
FOREST PRODUCTS RESEARCH SOCIETY. TECHNICAL NEWSLETTER SERIES. vol.5, 1991. q. $52 to non-members; members $20. Forest Products Research Society, 2801 Marshall Ct., Madison, WI 53705-2295. TEL 608-231-1361. FAX 608-231-2152. Ed. Arthur B. Brauner. **Document type:** newsletter.
    Description: Includes information on the production of primary timber products from standing trees.

674   CN
FOREST SERVICE CRUISING PROCEDURES AND CRUISE COMPILATION MANUAL. base vol. (plus irreg. suppl.) Can.$28. Ministry of Forests, Victoria, B.C., Canada. (Subscr. to: Crown Publications, 546 Yates St., Victoria, B.C. V8W 1K8, Canada. TEL 604-386-4636) (back issues avail.)
    Description: Outlines the cruising procedures acceptable to the Ministry in the sale of merchantable timber on Crown Lands in B.C.

674.8   RM   ISSN 0015-7503
FORESTA; Rumanian wood and furniture review. (Editions in English, French and German) 1969. q. $22. Chamber of Commerce and Industry of the Socialist Republic of Rumania, Bd. N. Balcescu Nr. 22, Bucharest, Rumania. (Dist. by: Rompresfilatelia, P.O. Box 12-201, Calea Grivitei 64-66, Bucharest, Rumania) adv. circ. 3,000. **Indexed:** PROMT.

FORESTRY RESEARCH WEST. see FORESTS AND FORESTRY

FORET - ENTREPRISE. see FORESTS AND FORESTRY

674   CN   ISSN 0824-2119
    CODEN: SPCCDI
FORINTEK CANADA CORP., WESTERN LABORATORY. SPECIAL PUBLICATIONS. 1979. irreg. membership. Forintek Canada Corp., Western Laboratory, 2665 East Mall, Vancouver, BC V6T 1W5, Canada. TEL 604-224-3221. FAX 604-222-5690. circ. 1,100. (also avail. in microfiche from MML; reprint service avail. from MML) **Indexed:** Forest.Abstr., Forest Prod.Abstr. **Document type:** academic/scholarly publication.
    Description: Provides technical information about forest products.

FORST UND HOLZ. see FORESTS AND FORESTRY

GIDROLIZNAYA I LESOKHIMICHESKAYA PROMYSHLENNOST'. see CHEMISTRY

GREAT BRITAIN. BUILDING RESEARCH ESTABLISHMENT. REPORTS. see FIRE PREVENTION

GUIDE FOR BUYERS OF QUALITY HARDWOODS. see BUSINESS AND ECONOMICS — Trade And Industrial Directories

674 621.9   GW   ISSN 0018-3822
H O B - DIE HOLZBEARBEITUNG. 1954. 10/yr. DM.101.10 (foreign DM.231.10). A.G.T. Verlag Thum GmbH, Postfach 109, 71601 Ludwigsburg, Germany. TEL 07141-223156. FAX 07141-223131. Ed. Lothar Friedrich. circ. 10,931. **Document type:** trade publication.
    Description: Design and operation of machines, systems and tools for working and processing wood, wood materials, plastics and materials processed like wood.

H P V A EXECUTIVE BRIEF. (Hardwood Plywood & Veneer Association) see BUILDING AND CONSTRUCTION — Carpentry And Woodwork

674   SW   ISSN 0072-9922
HANDBOOK OF THE NORTHERN WOOD INDUSTRIES. (Text in English) 1887. biennial. SEK 475. AB Svensk Traevarutidning, Midskogsgraend 5, S-115 43 Stockholm, Sweden. TEL 46-8-664-34-00. FAX 46-8-664-30-05. Ed. Rune Liudqvist. adv.; index. circ. 3,500. **Document type:** consumer publication, trade publication.

674   GW   ISSN 0518-0147
HANDBUCH HOLZ. 1950. a. DM.15. Wirtschafts- und Forstverlag Euting KG, Tannenstr. 1, 56587 Strassenhaus, Germany.

674   US
HARDWOOD EXPRESSIONS. 1990. q. free to qualified personnel. Hardwood Manufacturers Association, 400 Penn Center Blvd., Ste. 530, Pittsburgh, PA 15235. TEL 412-829-0823. Ed. Susan M. Regan. circ. 30,000.
    Description: Showcases solid US hardwood furniture, cabinetry, flooring, and architectural woodwork.

HARDWOOD PLYWOOD & VENEER NEWS. see BUILDING AND CONSTRUCTION — Carpentry And Woodwork

674   GW   ISSN 0018-3768
TA419.A1   CODEN: HOZWAS
HOLZ ALS ROH- UND WERKSTOFF; European journal of wood and wood industries. 6/yr. DM.498($311) (Deutsche Gesellschaft fuer Holzforschung) Springer-Verlag, Heidelberger Platz 3, 14197 Berlin, Germany. TEL 030-8207-1. FAX 030-8214091. (Subscr. in N. America to: Springer-Verlag New York, Inc., 44 Hartz Way, Secaucus, NJ 07096-2491. TEL 201-348-4033. FAX 201-348-4505) (Co-sponsor: Federation Europeenne des Syndicates de Fabricants de Paneaux de Particules) Ed. H. Schultz. (also avail. in microform from UMI; back issues avail.; reprint service avail. from ISI) **Indexed:** Abstr.Bull.Inst.Pap.Chem., Appl.Mech.Rev., Art & Archaeol.Tech.Abstr., Chem.Abstr., Curr.Adv.Ecol.Sci., Curr.Cont., Excerp.Med., Forest.Abstr., Forest Prod.Abstr., Ind.Sci.Rev., INIS Atomind., Sci.Cit.Ind., Soils & Fert.
— BLDSC (4323.000000); UnCover; SWETS; UMI; CASDDS. **CCC.**

674 634.9   AU   ISSN 0018-3784
HOLZ - KURIER; forst- und holzwirtschaftlicher Wochendienst. 1946. w. S.1830 (foreign S.2250). (Bundesholzwirtschaftsrat) Oesterreichischer Agrarverlag GmbH, Bankgasse 1-3, A-1014 Vienna, Austria. TEL 5339676. FAX 5339656. Ed. Kurt Gadenz. adv.; bk.rev.; abstr.; illus.; pat.; stat.; index. circ. 4,500. **Indexed:** Chem.Abstr.

674   AU
HOLZ UND AGRAR IM SPIEGEL. q. Heinestr. 3, A-1020 Vienna, Austria. TEL 01-2143344. FAX 01-2167929. Ed. Johannes Vater. circ. 10,400.

674   SZ
HOLZ ZEITUNG. w. Schueck Soehne AG, Bahnhofstr. 24, CH-8803 Rueschlikon, Switzerland. TEL 01-7241044. FAX 01-7242258. Ed. Curt Mayer. circ. 2,560.

674   GW   ISSN 0018-3792
HOLZ-ZENTRALBLATT; unabhaengiges Organ fuer die Forst und Holzwirtschaft. (Monthly suppl.: Bausortiment und Heimwerkerbedarf) 1874. 3/wk. DM.340.80 per no. D R W-Verlag Weinbrenner GmbH & Co., Fasanenweg 18, 70771 Leinfelden-Echterdingen, Germany. TEL 0711-7591-1. adv.; bk.rev.; illus.; stat.; index. circ. 19,000. **Indexed:** Agri.Eng.Abstr., Chem.Abstr., Forest.Abstr., Forest Prod.Abstr., Key to Econ.Sci., Packag.Sci.Tech., Soils & Fert. **Document type:** newspaper.
— **CCC.**

674 634.9   GW   ISSN 0018-3830
    CODEN: HOLZAZ
HOLZFORSCHUNG; international journal of the biology, chemistry, physics and technology of wood. (Text in English) 1947. bi-m. DM.998. Walter de Gruyter und Co., Genthiner Str. 13, 10785 Berlin, Germany. TEL 030-26005-0. FAX 030-26005251. TELEX 184027. (U.S. addr.: Walter de Gruyter, Inc., 200 Saw Mill Rd., Hawthorne, NY 10532) Eds. G. Stegmann, H. Nimz. adv.; bk.rev.; abstr.; illus.; index. circ. 450. **Indexed:** Abstr.Bull.Inst.Pap.Chem., Art & Archaeol.Tech.Abstr., Biol.Abstr., Chem.Abstr., Curr.Adv.Biochem., Curr.Adv.Ecol.Sci., Curr.Cont., Excerp.Med., Forest.Abstr., Forest Prod.Abstr., Ind.Sci.Rev., INIS Atomind., Paper & Bd.Abstr., Rev.Plant Path., Sci.Cit.Ind., Sugar Ind.Abstr. **Document type:** academic/scholarly publication.
— BLDSC (4324.000000); Faxon; UnCover; SWETS; CASDDS. **CCC.**

674   AU   ISSN 0018-3849
    CODEN: HOZVAP
HOLZFORSCHUNG UND HOLZVERWERTUNG; Mitteilungen der Oesterreichischen Gesellschaft fuer Holzforschung. (Text in English and German) 1948. 6/yr. S.1830 (foreign S.2250). (Bundesministerium fuer Wissenschaft und Forschung) Oesterreichischer Agrarverlag, Bankgasse 1-3, A-1014 Vienna, Austria. TEL 5339676. FAX 5339656. Ed. Josef Kisser. adv.; bk.rev.; abstr.; index. circ. 2,000. **Indexed:** Abstr.Bull.Inst.Pap.Chem., Biol.Abstr., Chem.Abstr, Curr.Cont., Excerp.Med., Forest.Abstr., Forest Prod.Abstr., Hort.Abstr., Maize Abstr., Soils & Fert.
— BLDSC (4324.500000); CASDDS

674 GW ISSN 0018-3865
DIE HOLZSCHWELLE. 1907. a. DM.40.
Studiengesellschaft fuer Holzschwellenoberbau e.V., Bayerstr. 57-59, 80335 Munich, Germany. TEL 089-5389057. FAX 089-531657. Eds. Ursula Giese, J. Tebbe. adv.; bk.rev.; charts; illus.; stat. circ. 2,000. **Document type:** trade publication.

674 NE
HOUTADRESBOEK. 1979. a. fl.100 (free with subscr. to Houtwereld). Nijgh Periodieken B.V., Postbus 122, 3100 AC Schiedam, Netherlands. TEL 31-10-4274100. FAX 31-10-4739911. adv.: B&W page fl.2215, color page fl.4145; trim 210 x 297; adv. contact: Bert Niewold. circ. 3,200. **Document type:** directory.

HET HOUTBLAD; vaktijdschrift voor het houtvak en de bouwsector. see BUILDING AND CONSTRUCTION — Carpentry And Woodwork

674 NE ISSN 0018-6732
HOUTWERELD. 1947. fortn. fl.156 includes Houtadresboek. Nijgh Periodieken B.V., Postbus 122, 3100 AC Schiedam, Netherlands. TEL 31-10-4274100. FAX 31-10-4739911. adv.: B&W page fl.1820, color page fl.3165; trim 210 x 297; adv. contact: Bert Niewold. circ. 2,567. **Indexed:** Excerp.Med., Key to Econ.Sci. **Document type:** trade publication.

HYDROLYSIS AND WOOD CHEMISTRY. see CHEMISTRY

I A W A JOURNAL. (International Association of Wood Anatomists) see BIOLOGY — Botany

674 US
I H P A NEWS. m. membership. International Hardwood Products Association, 4214 King St. W., Alexandria, VA 22302-1507. TEL 703-836-6696. FAX 703-836-6370. (Subscr. to: Box 1308, Alexandria, VA 22313) Ed. W. Baer. circ. 250.
Formerly: International Hardwood Products Association. News.

674 II ISSN 0046-9033
CODEN: IPIJDR
I P I R I JOURNAL. (Text in English) 1971. s-a. Rs.20. Indian Plywood Industries Research Institute, Box 2273, Tumkur Rd., Bangalore 560022, India. Ed. Joseph George. bk.rev.; abstr.; cum.index. **Indexed:** Forest.Abstr.

ILLINOIS BUILDING NEWS. see BUILDING AND CONSTRUCTION

674 II
INDIAN ACADEMY OF WOOD SCIENCE. JOURNAL. (Text in English) 1970. s-a. Rs.100. Indian Plywood Industries Research Institute, Box 2273, Tumkur Rd., Bangalore 560022, India. Ed. C.N. Deshprabhu. **Indexed:** Chem.Abstr., Forest.Abstr., Forest Prod.Abstr. **Document type:** academic/scholarly publication.

674 II ISSN 0073-6384
INDIAN FOREST RECORDS (NEW SERIES) COMPOSITE WOOD. (Text in English) 1952. irreg., vol.1, no.2, 1964. price varies. Forest Research Institute & Colleges, P. O. New Forest, Dehra Dun, India. circ. 500. **Indexed:** Biol.Abstr., Forest.Abstr., Indian Sci.Abstr.

674 II ISSN 0073-6414
INDIAN FOREST RECORDS (NEW SERIES) LOGGING. (Text in English) 1966. irreg., vol.1, no.3, 1972. price varies. Forest Research Institute & Colleges, P.O. New Forest, Dehra Dun, India. circ. 500. **Indexed:** Biol.Abstr., Forest.Abstr., Indian Sci.Abstr.

674 II ISSN 0073-6449
INDIAN FOREST RECORDS (NEW SERIES) TIMBER MECHANICS. (Text in English) 1952. irreg., vol.4, no.1, 1981. price varies. Forest Research Institute & Colleges, P.O. New Forest, Dehra Dun, India. circ. 500. **Indexed:** Biol.Abstr., Forest.Abstr., Indian Sci.Abstr.

674 II ISSN 0442-6827
INDIAN FOREST RECORDS WOOD ANATOMY. (Text and summaries in English) 1950. irreg. price varies. Forest Research Institute & Colleges, P.O. New Forest, Dehra Dun 248 006, India. circ. 500. **Indexed:** Biol.Abstr., Forest.Abstr., Indian Sci.Abstr.
Formerly: Indian Forest Records Wood Technology.

674 MX
INFORMADOR; noticias y comentarios de la industria mueblera y maderera. 1969. s-m. Playa Caleta No. 359, Col. Reforma Iztaccihuatl, Mexico 08810 D.F., Mexico. Dir. Jose Luis Melgar Ayala. circ. 15,000. (back issues avail.)

674 MX
INSTITUTO DE ECOLOGIA. NOTA TECNICA. 1982. irreg. $10. Instituto de Ecologia, Apdo. 63, 91000 Xalapa, Veracruz, Mexico D.F., Mexico. FAX 281-69-10. bibl.; charts; illus. circ. 2,500. (back issues avail.) **Indexed:** Forest.Abstr., Forest Prod.Abstr.
Formerly (until 1988): Instituto Nacional de Investigaciones sobre Recursos Bioticos. Nota Tecnica.

INSTYTUT TECHNOLOGII DREWNA. PRACE. see BUILDING AND CONSTRUCTION — Carpentry And Woodwork

674 CN ISSN 1194-5745
INTERLOG QUARTERLY REVIEW. 1991. q. Can.$23.60($27) Image Fast Productions Inc., Box 601, Vancouver, BC V6C 2N5, Canada. TEL 604-683-1515. FAX 604-683-4142. Ed. Bob Beattie; Pub. Bob Beattie. adv.: B&W page Can.$1028, color page Can.$1523; trim 8 1/4 x 11; adv. contact: Bob Beattie. circ. 4,145. **Document type:** trade publication.
Description: Focuses on the common good and economic health of full-phase logging contractors, owner-operators and haulers.

674.8 II ISSN 0047-1054
INTERNATIONAL PRESS CUTTING SERVICE: PLYWOOD - TIMBER - PARTICLE BOARD. 1967. w. $65. International Press Cutting Service, Box 63, Allahabad 211001, India. Ed. N. Khanna. bk.rev.; index. circ. 1,200. (processed)

674 JA ISSN 0021-4477
JAPAN LUMBER JOURNAL. 1960. s-m. 28000 Yen($280) (effective Jan. 1994). Japan Lumber Journal, Inc., No.2 YH Bldg. 8-F, 1-36-1, Higashi-Ikebukuro, Toshima-ku, Tokyo 170, Japan. FAX 03-5950-2253. Ed. Satoshi Ogawa. mkt. circ. 9,500.

674 634.9 JA ISSN 0021-4795
CODEN: MKZGA7
JAPAN WOOD RESEARCH SOCIETY. JOURNAL/MOKUZAI GAKKAISHI. (Text in English, Japanese) 1955. m. 10500 Yen. Japan Wood Research Society - Nippon Mokuzai Gakkai, 21-4-407 Hongo 6, Bunkyo-ku, Tokyo 113, Japan. TEL 03-3816-0396. FAX 03-3818-6568. Ed. Nakatsubo Fumiaki. adv.; bk.rev.; abstr.; bibl.; charts. circ. 1,750. **Indexed:** Abstr.Bull.Inst.Pap.Chem., Biol.Abstr., Chem.Abstr., Forest.Abstr., Forest Prod.Abstr., Hort.Abstr., Plant Grow.Reg.Abstr., Sugar Ind.Abstr. **Document type:** academic/scholarly publication.
—BLDSC (4808.500000); Faxon; SWETS; CASDDS. CCC.
Description: Covers wood sciences and forest products.

L B M A O REPORTER. (Lumber & Building Materials Association of Ontario) see BUILDING AND CONSTRUCTION

674 US ISSN 0076-1109
L S U WOOD UTILIZATION NOTES. 1960. irreg., no.39, 1986. free. Louisiana State University, School of Forestry, Wildlife, and Fisheries, 227 Forestry-Wildlife-Fisheries Bldg., Baton Rouge, LA 70803-6202. TEL 504-388-4131. Ed. E.T. Choong. circ. 350. **Document type:** academic/scholarly publication.

764 684 IT ISSN 0024-0532
IL LEGNO (MILAN). 1922. m. (10/yr.). L.80000 (foreign L.160000) (effective 1994). Industria del Mobile s.r.l., Via Giambologna 21, 20136 Milan, Italy. TEL 02-8394780. FAX 02-8372547. circ. 10,000.

674 XV ISSN 0024-1067
LES; revija za lesno gospodarstvo. (Text in Slovenian; summaries in English and German) 1948. bi-m. $40. Zveza Drustev Inzenirjev in Tehnikov Gozdarstva in Lesarstva Slovenije, Erjavceva 15, Ljubljana, Slovenia. Ed. Joze Kovac. bk.rev.; abstr.; bibl.; charts; illus.; stat.; index. circ. 2,800.

674 RU
LESNAYA PROMYSHLENNOST. 1926. 3/w. Vokzal'naya pl. 3, 125047 Moscow, Russia. TEL (095) 250-46-23. Ed. V.A. Alekseev.

674 US ISSN 0194-150X
LOG TRUCKER. vol.4, 1979. m. $10. Loggers World Publications, 4206 Jackson Hwy., Chehalis, WA 98532. TEL 206-262-3376. Ed. Bill Palmroth. circ. 12,000. **Document type:** trade publication.
Description: Logging information in Western U.S., including items for sale, news of log truck drivers, truck parades and logging conferences.

634.982 CN ISSN 1193-5855
LOGGER. 1990. bi-m. Can.$10.70($20) Westcoast Publishing Ltd., 1496 West 72nd Ave., Vancouver, BC V6P 3C8, Canada. TEL 604-266-7433. FAX 604-263-8620. Ed. Robert Allington. adv. circ. 12,000.
Formerly (until 1992): Westcoast Logger (ISSN 1189-3575)

634.9 674.2 US ISSN 0192-7124
LOGGER AND LUMBERMAN. 1952. m. $20. Dixie Publications, 257 N. Main St., Box 489, Wadley, GA 30477. TEL 912-252-5237. FAX 912-252-1140. Ed. Jack D. Smith. adv.; bk.rev.; tr.lit. circ. 24,000. **Document type:** trade publication.
Incorporates (1984-199?): Timber Equipment Trader; Former titles: Dixie Logger and Lumberman (ISSN 0046-0435); Dixie Machinery and Lumberman.

634.982 US ISSN 0047-4983
SD538.2.W4
LOGGERS WORLD. 1964. m. $10. Loggers World Publications, 4206 Jackson Hwy, Chehalis, WA 98532. TEL 206-262-3376. Ed. Michael P. Crouse. adv.; bk.rev. circ. 16,000. **Document type:** trade publication.
Description: Covers the logging industry in Western U.S., including items for sale and news of logging camps.

674 CN ISSN 0225-7572
LOGGING & SAWMILLING JOURNAL. 1968. m. Can.$28. Rob Starhope, Ed. & Pub., 622 W. 22nd St., North Vancouver, BC V7M 2A7, Canada. Ed. Norm Poole. adv.; bk.rev. circ. 16,700. **Document type:** trade publication.
—CCC.
Incorporates: Silviculture (ISSN 0827-7583); Supersedes in part (as of 1982): Canadian Pulp and Paper Industry (ISSN 0008-4867)

674 658.8 US ISSN 0024-7294
LUMBER CO-OPERATOR. 1917. m. $20 to non-members; members $15. Northeastern Retail Lumber Association, nc., 339 East Ave., Rochester, NY 14604. TEL 716-325-1626. FAX 716-325-6179. Ed. Ellen Rye; Pub. John J. Brill. adv. contact: Christine Mattke. film rev.; illus. circ. 3,900. **Document type:** trade publication.

LUMBER PRICE INDEX. INLAND INDEX. see FORESTS AND FORESTRY — Abstracting, Bibliographies, Statistics

674 332 US
LUMBERMENS RED BOOK; reference book of the Lumbermens Credit Association. 1876. s-a. (plus w. supplements). $1630. Lumbermens Credit Association, Inc., 111 W. Jackson Blvd., Chicago, IL 60604-3596. TEL 312-427-0733. FAX 312-427-9323. Ed. William J. Clancy. stat.; cum.index. **Document type:** trade publication.
Description: Mercantile credit information for wood industry.

674 CN ISSN 0024-8231
M L B LOG. 1941. q. Can.$45. Maritime Lumber Bureau, Box 459, Amherst, N.S. B4H 4A1, Canada. TEL 902-667-3889. FAX 902-667-0401. Ed. Diana Blenkhorn. adv.; stat. circ 425.

674 747 SP
LA MADERA. 1973. 11/yr. 8000 ptas. (foreign 14000 ptas.). Rosellon 186 4o, 08008 Barcelona, Spain. TEL 3-323-14-91. FAX 3-45-48-565. Ed. Julio Cayuela Tormo. adv. contact: Susana Cayuela. bk.rev.

FORESTS AND FORESTRY — LUMBER AND WOOD

674 690   MX
MADERA Y SU USO EN LA CONSTRUCCION. 1976. irreg. $10. Instituto de Ecologia, Apdo. 63, 9100 Xalapa, Veracruz, Mexico D.F., Mexico. FAX 281-69-10. bibl.; charts; illus. circ. 2,500. (back issues avail.)

674   SP
MADERPRESS. 6/yr. Elsevier Prensa S.A., Av. Paral.lel 180, 08015 Barcelona, Spain. TEL 3-325-53-50. FAX 3-425-28-80. Ed. Marcel Lleal. circ. 5,000.
    Description: Covers new products for the wood industry.

MADISON'S CANADIAN LUMBER DIRECTORY. see *BUSINESS AND ECONOMICS — Trade And Industrial Directories*

674   CN   ISSN 0715-5468
MADISON'S CANADIAN LUMBER REPORTER. w. Can.$165 (outside N. America Can.$210). Madison's Canadian Lumber Reporter (1973) Ltd., Box 2486, Vancouver, BC V6B 3W7, Canada. TEL 604-681-6838. FAX 604-681-6585. Ed. L. Ward Johnson. mkt. **Document type:** consumer publication, trade publication.
    Description: Devoted to North American lumber market activity.

674   SP
MAQUINARIA FORESTAL. 6/yr. 3850 ptas. Tredita Editores S.L., Orellana 10, 28004 Madrid, Spain. TEL 1-308-18-98. FAX 1-319-20-06.

674   MY   ISSN 0126-771X
MASKAYU; a news bulletin on the timber industry in Malaysia. (Text in English) 1972. m. M.$96($42) Malaysian Timber Industry Board - Lembaga Perindustrian Kayu Malaysia, P.O. Box 10887, 50728 Kuala Lumpur, Malaysia. FAX 03-2929834. TELEX MALTIM MA 30993. circ. 2,000. **Document type:** bulletin.
    Description: Provides up-to-date news on the Malaysian timber industry as well as excerpts of the world timber industry. Also features monthly export statistics, information on wood utilization, and market analysis.

MEISTERBETRIEB. see *PLASTICS*

MEMBERS. see *BUILDING AND CONSTRUCTION — Hardware*

674 691.1 658.8   US   ISSN 0739-9723
MERCHANT MAGAZINE. 1922. m. $11. Merchant Magazine, Inc., 4500 Campus Dr., Ste. 480, Newport Beach, CA 92660. TEL 714-852-1990. Eds. Juanita Lovret, David Cutler. adv.; bk.rev.; illus.; tr.lit. circ. 5,022. **Document type:** trade publication.
    Former titles: Western Lumber and Building Materials Merchant (ISSN 0043-3888); California Lumber Merchant.
    Description: Covers industry news, how-to, new products, association news, new publications, and business trends for home centers and the lumber and building materials retailer and wholesalers in the 13 western states.

674   US   ISSN 0076-9509
MISSISSIPPI STATE UNIVERSITY. FOREST PRODUCTS UTILIZATION LABORATORY. INFORMATION SERIES. 1965. irreg. Mississippi State University, Forest Products Laboratory, Box 9820, Mississippi State, MS 39762. TEL 601-325-2116. **Document type:** academic/scholarly publication.

674   US   ISSN 0026-640X
MISSISSIPPI STATE UNIVERSITY. FOREST PRODUCTS UTILIZATION LABORATORY. RESEARCH REPORT. 1966. irreg. free. Mississippi State University, Forest Products Laboratory, Box 9820, Mississippi State, MS 39762. TEL 601-325-2116. **Document type:** academic/scholarly publication.

674 658.8   IT
MONDOLEGNO. 1977. m. L.72000($123) Editoriale P E G SpA, Via Fratelli Bressan, 2, 20126 Milan, Italy. TEL 02-25-79-841. FAX 02-25-52-779. TELEX 323088 PEGMOS I. Ed. Almerico Ribera. adv.; B&W page L.1380000, color page L.2208000; trim 175 x 273. illus. circ. 4,000.
    Supersedes (1922-1977): Legno (Lainate).

MOTOCULTURE MAGAZINE. see *GARDENING AND HORTICULTURE*

N F P A: STATISTICAL ROUNDUP. (National Forest Products Association) see *BUSINESS AND ECONOMICS — Marketing And Purchasing*

674   US
N H L A NEWSLETTER. m. membership only. National Hardwood Lumber Association, Box 34518, Memphis, TN 38184-0518. TEL 901-377-1818. FAX 901-382-6419. **Document type:** newsletter, trade publication.

N V R - INFORMATIEF. (Nederlandse Vereniging van Rubber- en Kunststoffabrikanten) see *PLASTICS*

NATIONAL HARDWOOD LUMBER ASSOCIATION MEMBERSHIP DIRECTORY. see *BUSINESS AND ECONOMICS — Trade And Industrial Directories*

634.9   US   ISSN 0279-9812
NATIONAL WOODLANDS MAGAZINE. 1979. q. $15 includes Woodland Report newsletter. National Woodland Owners Association, 374 Maple Ave. E., Ste. 204, Vienna, VA 22180. TEL 703-255-2700. Ed. Eric Johnson. circ. 3,000.

674   NZ   ISSN 0113-3128
                                CODEN: NZFIEX
NEW ZEALAND FOREST INDUSTRIES. 1969. m. NZ.$55 (foreign NZ$85). Profile Publishing Ltd., P.O. Box 5544, Wellesley St., Auckland, New Zealand. TEL 09-358-5455. FAX 09-358-5462. Ed. Vicki Jayne. adv.; bk.rev.; charts; illus. circ. 2,000. **Indexed:** Agri.Eng.Abstr., Forest.Abstr., Forest Prod.Abstr.
    Formerly: Forest Industries Review (ISSN 0110-7844)
    Description: For timber industry professionals in New Zealand.

NIGERIAN JOURNAL OF FORESTRY. see *FORESTS AND FORESTRY*

674   SW   ISSN 0283-2631
TS1080   CODEN: NPPJEG
NORDIC PULP & PAPER RESEARCH JOURNAL. (Text in English) 1986. q. SEK 2300. Arbor Publishing AB, Midskogsgraend 5, S-115 43 Stockholm, Sweden. TEL 46-8-664-34-00. FAX 46-8-664-30-05.
    —BLDSC (6117.927800); Faxon; CASDDS.

674   US   ISSN 0029-3156
TS800
NORTHERN LOGGER AND TIMBER PROCESSER. 1952. m. $10. N L Publishing, Inc., Box 69, Old Forge, NY 13420. TEL 315-369-3078. FAX 315-369-3736. Ed. Eric A. Johnson. adv.; bk.rev.; charts; illus.; stat.; tr.lit.; cum.index: 1959-1971. circ. 13,800. (back issues avail.) **Indexed:** Abstr.Bull.Inst.Pap.Chem., Agri.Eng.Abstr., Forest.Abstr., Forest Prod.Abstr. **Document type:** trade publication.
    —BLDSC (6151.016000); Faxon; UnCover.
    Formerly: Northern Logger.

674 380.1   US
NORTHWESTERN LUMBER ASSOCIATION DEALER REFERENCE MANUAL. a. $75. Northwestern Lumber Association, 1405 Lilac Dr. N., Ste. 130, Minneapolis, MN 55422-4505. TEL 612-544-6822. FAX 612-544-0820. (Co-sponsor: Iowa Lumber Association) Ed. Lori Kyllo. adv.; index. circ. 2,050. **Document type:** trade publication, directory.
    Former titles: Northwestern Lumbermen's Association Dealer Reference Manual; Northwestern-Iowa Dealer Reference Manual (ISSN 0078-1800)

674   AU   ISSN 0029-9154
OESTERREICHISCHE GESELLSCHAFT FUER HOLZFORSCHUNG. SCHRIFTTUMSKARTEIDIENST - CARD INDEX SERVICE. (Text in English, French and German; summaries in German) 1950. s-m. S.3460. Oesterreichische Gesellschaft fuer Holzforschung, Franz-Grill-Str. 7, A-1030 Vienna, Austria. FAX 0222-782623-50. Ed. Udalfried Krames. bk.rev.; abstr. circ. 100. (cards) **Document type:** bulletin.

OFFICIEL DU BOIS (EDITION VERTE). see *FORESTS AND FORESTRY*

634.982 674.22   CN   ISSN 0030-3631
OPERATIONS FORESTIERES ET DE SCIERIE. 1966. 4/yr. Can.$21.40($34) (foreign $53). J C T Forest Communications, 1 rue Pacifique, Ste-Anne-de-Bellevue, PQ H9X 1C5, Canada. TEL 514-457-2211. FAX 514-457-2558. TELEX 058-24168. Ed. Guy Fortin. adv.; illus.; stat.; tr.lit.; index. circ. 6,219.
    Description: Serves French-speaking logging and sawmilling operators in eastern Canada.

674.2   US
HD9769.P5
PANEL WORLD. 1960. bi-m. $18. Hatton-Brown Publishers, Inc., 225 Hanrick St., Montgomery, AL 36104. TEL 205-834-1170. FAX 205-834-4525. (Subscr. to: Box 2268, Montgomery, AL 36102-2268) Ed. David E. Knight. adv.; bk.rev.; charts; illus.; stat.; index. circ. 10,000. **Indexed:** Forest.Abstr., Forest Prod.Abstr.
    —CCC.
    Former titles: Plywood and Panel World (ISSN 0744-6853); Plywood and Panel (ISSN 0032-177X); Plywood Magazine.

674   US
PAPER TREE LETTER; independent analysis of forest products economics. 1981. m. $329. Miller Freeman, Inc. (Subsidiary of: United Newspapers), 600 Harrison St., San Francisco, CA 94107. TEL 415-905-2200. FAX 415-905-2232. TELEX 278273. Ed. Will Mies. (back issues avail.)
    —CCC.
    Formerly (until 1990): Hay Roe's Paper Tree Letter (ISSN 0822-8094)
    Description: Analysis of paper and forest products industries.

PAPERI JA PUU/PAPER AND TIMBER. see *PAPER AND PULP*

PAPIRIPARI ES NYOMDAIPARI SZAKIRODALMI TAJEKOZTATO/PAPER INDUSTRY & PRINTING ABSTRACTS. see *PAPER AND PULP — Abstracting, Bibliographies, Statistics*

674 558.8   US
PENNSYLVANIA MARKETING BULLETIN. 1948. m. free. Department of Environmental Resources, Bureau of Forestry, Box 8552, Harrisburg, PA 17105-8552. TEL 717-787-2105. FAX 717-783-5109. Ed. David H. Holt. adv. circ. 8,000. (looseleaf format) **Document type:** government publication, bulletin.
    Formerly: Pennsylvania. Department of Environmental Resources. Bureau of Forestry. Marketing Bulletin.

674   US   ISSN 1063-0414
TS851
POWER EQUIPMENT TRADE. 1952. m. (11/yr.). $30. Hatton-Brown Publishers, Inc., 225 Hanrick St., Montgomery, AL 36104. TEL 205-834-1170. FAX 205-834-4525. (Subscr. to: Box 2268, Montgomery, AL 36102-2268) Ed. Rich Dunnell. adv.; bk.rev.; illus.; mkt.; tr.lit. circ. 20,500. (also avail. in microform from UMI; reprint service avail. from UMI) **Indexed:** Abstr.Bull.Inst.Pap.Chem.
    —UMI.
    Former titles (until 1992): Chain Saw Age and Power Equipment Trade (ISSN 1055-4734); (until 1990): Chain Saw Age (ISSN 0009-093X)
    Description: Contains technical, marketing, and business management information edited for those who sell outdoor power equipment, related components and accessories.

674   PL   ISSN 0079-4724
POZNANSKIE TOWARZYSTWO PRZYJACIOL NAUK. KOMISJA TECHNOLOGII DREWNA. PRACE. (Text in Polish; summaries in English) 1968. a. price varies. Poznanskie Towarzystwo Przyjaciol Nauk, Komisja Technologii Drewna, Ul. Mielzynskiego 27-29, 61-725 Poznan, Poland. (Dist. by: Ars Polona-Ruch, Krakowskie Przedmiescie 7, Warsaw, Poland) Ed. Jerzy Wislocki. **Indexed:** Biol.Abstr.
    —BLDSC (6588.149500).

674   BN   ISSN 0350-1256
PREGLED (SARAJEVO, 1964); nausnotehnickih radova i informacija. (Text in Serbo-Croatian; summaries in English and German) 1964. s-a. free. S I P A D - I R C Sumaprojekt, Omladinsko Setaliste 10, 71000 Sarajevo, Bosnia Hercegovina. TEL 071 615-149. FAX 071-616-744. TELEX 41711. Ed. Zoran Georgijevic. circ. 300. (back issues avail.)

FORESTS AND FORESTRY — LUMBER AND WOOD

PREVISIONS GLISSANTES DETAILLEES EN PERSPECTIVES SECTORIELLES (VOL.4): INDUSTRIES DU BOIS ET DE L'AMEUBLEMENT. see *BUSINESS AND ECONOMICS — Economic Situation And Conditions*

674   PL   ISSN 0373-9856
PRZEMYSL DRZEWNY. 1950. m. $81.50. (Stowarzyszenie Inzynierow i Technikow Lesnictwa i Drzewnictwa) Wydawnictwo Czasopism i Ksiazek Technicznych SIGMA - NOT, Ul. Ratuszowa 11, P.O. Box 1004, 00-950 Warsaw, Poland. TEL 48-22-180918. FAX 48-22-192187. TELEX 814550 SIGMA PL. (Dist. by: SIGMA NOT Ltd., Ul. Bartycka 20, 00-716 Warsaw, Poland. Ed. Andrzej Paszkiewicz. adv.; B&W page $1010. circ. 1,650. **Indexed:** Forest.Abstr., Forest Prod.Abstr.

674   DK   ISSN 0106-2018
PUFF; fagtidsskrift for traelast- og byggemarkeder. 1977. 10/yr. Odsgard Reklame - Marketing ApS, Roenvej 10, 2600 Glostrup, Denmark. adv. circ. 3,100.

PUUMIES. see *BUILDING AND CONSTRUCTION — Carpentry And Woodwork*

674   US   ISSN 0483-9420
RANDOM LENGTHS; the weekly report on North American forest products markets. (Supplement avail.: Random Lengths Midweek Market Report) 1944. w. $193.50 (foreign $210). Random Lengths Publications, Inc., Box 867, Eugene, OR 97440-0867. TEL 503-686-9925. FAX 800-874-7979. Ed. Burrle Elmore; Pub. Jon P. Anderson. charts; stat. circ. 12,400. (looseleaf format; back issues avail.) **Document type:** trade publication, newsletter.
●Also available online.
—CCC.
Description: Prices on softwood lumber and panel products with analysis of trading patterns and industry trends.

674   US   ISSN 0891-7833
RANDOM LENGTHS BIG BOOK. 1987. a. $150. Random Lengths Publications, Inc., Box 867, Eugene, OR 97440-0867. TEL 503-686-9925. FAX 800-874-7979. **Document type:** directory.
—CCC.
Description: Provides information on the North American wood products industry.

674 382   ISSN 8756-288X
RANDOM LENGTHS EXPORT; a bi-weekly report on export markets for forest products. 1968. fortn. $102.50 (foreign $130). Random Lengths Publications, Inc., Box 867, Eugene, OR 97440-0867. TEL 503-686-9925. FAX 800-874-7979. Ed. Jessie Taylor; Pub. Jon P. Anderson. stat. circ. 1,450. (looseleaf format) **Document type:** newsletter.
Formerly: Random Lengths Export Market Report.
Description: Prices and market summaries covering North American lumber and panel items sold in international markets.

674   US   ISSN 1044-4912
RANDOM LENGTHS LOCATOR. 1983. m. $30. Random Lengths Publications, Inc., Box 867, Eugene, OR 97440-0867. TEL 503-686-9925. FAX 503-686-9629. Ed. Nancy Jodoin. adv. circ. 12,400. (looseleaf format; back issues avail.) **Document type:** trade publication.
—CCC.
Description: For the forest products industry.

674   US
RANDOM LENGTHS MIDWEEK MARKET REPORT. (Supplement to: Random Lengths (ISSN 0483-9420)) 1974. w. $150 (effective 1994). Random Lengths Publications, Inc., Box 867, Eugene, OR 97440. TEL 503-686-9629. Ed. Burrle Elmore. (looseleaf format; back issues avail.) **Document type:** newsletter.
●Also available online.
—CCC.
Description: Forest products price and market updates.

674   JA
RESEARCH REPORT OF FOREIGN WOOD. 1972. irreg., latest 1986. free. Shimane Daigaku, Nogakubu - Shimane University, Faculty of Agriculture, 1060 Nishi-Kawazu-machi, Matsue-shi, Shimane-ken 690, Japan. circ. 200. **Document type:** academic/scholarly publication.

674.2   BL   ISSN 0034-7582
TS800
REVISTA DA MADEIRA. 1952. m. $35. IPSIS Grafica E Editora S.A., Rua Dr. Licio de Miranda 451, Box 5632, Sao Paulo, Brazil. Ed. Luiz Carlos de Almeida. adv.; illus. circ. 12,500. **Indexed:** Biol.Abstr.

674 676   CU   ISSN 0138-6441
REVISTA FORESTAL BARACOA. (Table of contents and abstracts in English) 1971. 3/yr. $22 in S. America; N. America $24; elsewhere $28. Centro de Informacion y Documentacion Agropecuario, Gaveta Postal 4149, Havana 4, Cuba. (Dist. by: Ediciones Cubanas, Obispo No. 527, Apdo. 605, Havana, Cuba) (back issues avail.) **Indexed:** Agrindex.

674   FR   ISSN 0035-2519
REVUE DU BOIS ET DE SES APPLICATIONS. 1946. 9/yr. 399 F. (foreign 524 F.) S O P R O G E, S.A., 7 ter, Cour des Petites-Ecuries, 75010 Paris, France. FAX 47-70-33-94. Ed. Nell Boix. adv.; bk.rev.; charts; illus.; pat. circ. 4,000. **Indexed:** Excerp.Med., Forest.Abstr., Forest Prod.Abstr., Key to Econ.Sci.
—CCC.

RINGYO TO KAKUZAI; forestry and forest chemicals. see *FORESTS AND FORESTRY*

674   US
S F NEWSLETTER. w. $25. Southern Forest Products Association, Box 641700, Kenner, LA 70064-1700. TEL 504-443-4464. FAX 504-443-6612. Ed. David Kellogg. circ. 1,500. **Document type:** newsletter.

674.2   SW   ISSN 0347-0555
SAAGVERKEN/SAWMILLS. 1915. 10/yr. SEK 500 within the Nordic countries; elsewhere SEK 530. (Saagverkens Riksfoerbund) Arbor Publishing AB, Midskogsgraend 5, S-115 43 Stockholm, Sweden. TEL 46-8-664-34-00. FAX 46-8-664-30-05. Ed. Lennart Johansson. adv.; charts; illus.; circ. 3,319.
Formerly (until 1974): Saagverken, Traevaruindustrien (ISSN 0041-1892); Formed by the 1970 merger of: Saagverken (ISSN 0036-259X); Traevaruindustrien (ISSN 0372-2791)
Description: Directed to the Swedish sawmill industry, timber trade, wood industry.

SCHWEIZER HOLZ-BOERSE; Fachblatt fuer alle Gebiete der Holzwirtschaft. see *FORESTS AND FORESTRY*

674   SZ
SCHWEIZER HOLZ REVUE. 1972. q. 32 SFr. Verlag Laupper AG, Postfach 659, CH-4142 Muenchenstein 1, Switzerland. TEL 061-4113646. FAX 061-4119020. circ. 10,000.

674   SZ
SCHWEIZER HOLZBAU. 1935. m. 85 SFr. Hoch und Tiefbau Verlag AG, Postfach 7039, CH-8023 Zurich, Switzerland. TEL 0258-8333. FAX 0261-0324. TELEX 816350. Ed. Walter Bogusch. adv. circ. 8,100. **Document type:** trade publication.

674   CC   ISSN 1001-005X
SENLIN CAIYUN KEXUE/LUMBERING SCIENCE. (Text in Chinese) q. Zhongguo Linxuehui, Senlin Caiyun Xuehui, Dongbei Linye Daxue, Hexing Lu, Harbin, Heilongjiang 150040, People's Republic of China. Ed. Wang Zhongxing.

SEOUL NATIONAL UNIVERSITY FORESTS. RESEARCH BULLETIN/NYENSUBRIM NYENGU BOGO: SEOUL DAIHAGGYO NONGKWA DAIHAG. see *FORESTS AND FORESTRY*

SIA; skogsindustriarbetaren. see *PAPER AND PULP*

674   SW   ISSN 1101-8003
SKOG & SAAG; tidskrift foer skogsbruk och traefoeraedling. 1966. q. free. (Saagverksfoereningen Saabi - Sawmill Association Saabi) Saabi AB, P.O. Box 394, S-551 15 Joenkoeping, Sweden. TEL 036-198603. FAX 036-128610. (Subscr. to: P.O. Box 394, S-551 15 Jonkoping, Sweden) Ed. Henrik Asplund. adv.; bk.rev.; illus. circ. 78,000. **Document type:** trade publication.
Formerly (until 1991): Saagrevyn (ISSN 0347-0547)

674   SW   ISSN 1101-3354
SKOGSINDUSTRIERNA. 1989. bi-m. Skogsindustrierna, P.O. Box 26210, S-100 41 Stockholm, Sweden.
Supersedes: S C P F Information.

634.982   US   ISSN 0744-2106
SOUTHERN LOGGIN' TIMES. 1972. m. $20. Hatton-Brown Publishers, Inc., 225 Hanrick St., Montgomery, AL 36104. TEL 205-834-1170. FAX 205-834-4525. (Subscr. to: Box 2268, Montgomery, AL 36102-2268) Ed. David K. Knight. adv. circ. 11,000. (tabloid format)
—CCC.
Formerly: Loggin' Times.

674   US   ISSN 0038-4313
TS800
SOUTHERN LUMBERMAN. 1881. m. $18. Greysmith Publishing, Inc., Box 681629, 128 Holiday Ct., Ste. 116, TN 37058-1629. TEL 615-791-1961. FAX 615-790-6188. Ed. Nanci P. Gregg. adv.; bk.rev.; charts illus.; mkt.; stat.; tr.lit. circ. 12,000. **Indexed:** Biol.Abstr., Chem.Abstr. **Document type:** trade publication.
Incorporates: Lumber Journal.
Description: Informs owners and managers of sawmills in North America, as well as the end users of the sawmill's product.

674   IT
SPAZIOLEGNO. 10/yr. Viale Mugello 6, 20137 Milan, Italy. TEL 2-761-08-78. FAX 2-749-00-37. TELEX 322210 MILLA. Ed. Silvia Buchi. circ. 9,000.

674   SW   ISSN 0346-7090
CODEN: MSTRDZ
SVENSKA TRAESKYDDSINSTITUTET. MEDDELANDEN/SWEDISH WOOD PRESERVATION INSTITUTE. REPORTS. (Text in English and Swedish) 1952. irreg., no.168, 1993. $60. Svenska Traeskyddsinstitutet - Swedish Wood Preservation Institute, Box 5607, S-114 86 Stockholm, Sweden. FAX 08-108081. Ed. Joeran Jermer. circ. 1,000. **Indexed:** Forest Prod.Abstr. **Document type:** monographic series.
—CASDDS.

674   US   ISSN 0082-089X
SYMPOSIUM ON PARTICLEBOARD - COMPOSITE MATERIALS. PROCEEDINGS. 1967. a. $79 (Canada and Mexico $82.50; Latin America $87.50; Europe $97.50; Elsewhere $102.50). Washington State University, Wood Materials Laboratory, Pullman, WA 99164-1806. TEL 509-335-4916. (Orders to: Forest Products Society, 2801 Marshall Ct., Madison, WI 53705-2295. TEL 608-231-1361. FAX 608-231-2152) Ed. Tom Maloney. **Document type:** proceedings.
Description: Publishes papers on the manufacture of particleboard and other composite materials.

TECHNIQUES FORESTIERES; le magazine professionnel du Machinisme Forestier. see *FORESTS AND FORESTRY*

674   SP
TECNIMADERA. 12/yr. 6500 ptas. (foreign 10300 ptas.). Tecnipublicaciones, S.A., Fernando VI 27, Apdo. Correos 14526, 28080 Madrid, Spain. TEL 1-319-78-89. FAX 1-310-20-41.

674   FR
TELEX BOIS. 11/yr. Groupe Alain Thirion, 6 rue Jean Viriot, 88000 Epinal, France. TEL 29-82-26-01. FAX 29-35-07-97. TELEX 960 432. Ed. Alain Thirion. circ. 35,000.

674   UN   ISSN 0259-4323
TIMBER BULLETIN. 1948. 10/yr. Economic Commission for Europe (ECE), Palais des Nations, 1211 Geneva 10, Switzerland. TEL 917-1234. FAX 917-0123. TELEX 412962.
—BLDSC (8848.050000).
Former titles (until 1984): Timber Bulletin for Europe (ISSN 0040-7747); (until 1955): Timber Statistics (ISSN 1010-318X)

674   II   ISSN 0040-7755
TIMBER DEVELOPMENT ASSOCIATION OF INDIA. JOURNAL. (Text in English) 1953. q. $20 (effective 1992). Timber Development Association of India, P.O. New Forest, Dehra Dun 248 006, Uttar Pradesh, India. FAX 91-135-23258. Ed. Satish Kumar. adv.; bk.rev.; charts; illus. circ. 325. **Indexed:** Agroforest.Abstr., Art & Archaeol.Tech.Abstr., Chem.Abstr., Forest.Abstr., Forest Prod.Abstr., Sugar Ind.Abstr.
—BLDSC (4908.650000).
Formerly: Timber Dryers' and Preservers' Association of India. Journal.

FORESTS AND FORESTRY — LUMBER AND WOOD

676   US   ISSN 0160-6433
TS1171   CODEN: TIHAEY
TIMBER HARVESTING. 1953. m. $30. Hatton-Brown Publishers, Inc., 225 Hanrick St., Montgomery, AL 36104. TEL 205-834-1170. FAX 205-834-4525. (Subscr. to: Box 2268, Montgomery, AL 36102-2268) Ed. David E. Knight. adv.; illus.; stat. circ. 22,000. **Indexed:** Abstr.Bull.Inst.Pap.Chem.
—CCC.
     Former titles (until 1978): Pulpwood Production and Timber Harvesting (ISSN 0097-7357); Pulpwood Production and Sawmill Logging; (until 1956): Pulpwood Production (ISSN 0033-4154)

674   US   ISSN 0194-5955
TIMBER MART-SOUTH. 1976. q. $225 (foreign $300). Timber Marts, Inc., Box 1278, Highlands, NC 28741. TEL 704-526-3653. FAX 704-526-3683. Ed. F.W. Norris. stat. circ. 800. **Document type:** trade publication.
     Description: Market price survey and report of raw forest products.

674   US   ISSN 0885-906X
TIMBER PROCESSING. 1976. m. (10/yr.). $30. Hatton-Brown Publishers, Inc., 225 Hanrick St., Montgomery, AL 36104. TEL 205-834-1170. FAX 205-834-4525. (Subscr. to: Box 2268, Montgomery, AL 36102-2268) Ed. David E. Knight. adv.; illus.; stat. circ. 15,000.
—CCC.
     Formerly (until 1985): Timber Processing Industry.

674   UK   ISSN 0967-8093
TIMBER TRADES ADDRESS BOOK. 1921. a. £52 (overseas £62). Benn Business Information Services Ltd., Riverbank House, Angel Ln., Tonbridge, Kent TN9 1SE, England. TEL 0732-362666. FAX 0732-767301. TELEX 957892 BENTON G. Ed. Gwen Young. circ. 5,000. **Document type:** directory.
     Formerly: T T J Timber Telephone Address Book (ISSN 0141-5735)
     Description: Contains information on more than 6,000 manufacturers, agents, and distributors in the U.K. timber industry.

674   UK   ISSN 1351-7716
▼**TIMBER TRADES ADDRESS BOOK. SHIPPING MARKS - SOFTWOOD.** 1994. a. £35. Benn Business Information Services Ltd., Riverbank House, Angel Ln., Tonbridge, Kent TN9 1SE, England. TEL 0732-362666. FAX 0732-367601. TELEX 957829 BENTON G. Ed.Bd. circ. 1,000. **Document type:** directory.
     Description: Contains information on producers of softwood based in Canada, the Commonwealth of Independent States, Finland, Norway, Poland, Sweden, and the UK, providing details of their shipping marks, grades, mills, loading ports, and UK sales contacts.

674   UK   ISSN 0082-4364
TIMBER TRADES JOURNAL. ANNUAL SPECIAL ISSUE. 1879. a. Benn Publications Ltd., Sovereign Way, Tonbridge, Kent TN9 1RW, England. TEL 0732 364422. adv. circ. 5,865.

674 621.9   UK   ISSN 0262-6071
TIMBER TRADES JOURNAL AND WOOD PROCESSING. 1873. w. £80 (foreign £98). Benn Publications Ltd. (Subsidiary of: Morgan-Grampian plc), Benn House, Sovereign Way, Tonbridge, Kent TN9 1RW, England. TEL 0732-364422. FAX 0732-361534. Ed. Audrey Dixon. adv. contact: Laurie Wedd. bk.rev.; illus.; mkt.; stat. circ. 6,500. (also avail. in microform from UMI) **Indexed:** Br.Tech.Ind., Chem.Abstr., Key to Econ.Sci. **Document type:** trade publication.
—SWETS.
     Formerly (until Nov. 1980): Timber Trades Journal and Woodworking Machinery (ISSN 0040-7798); Incorporates: Timber Trades Journal and Saw Mill Advertiser & Timber and Plywood (ISSN 0040-7739) & Wood (ISSN 0043-762X)

674   US   ISSN 0192-0642
TIMBER - WEST. 1975. m. $20. Timber - West Publications, Inc., Box 610, Edmonds, WA 98020. TEL 206-778-3388. FAX 206-771-3623. Ed. John L. Nederlee. adv. contact: Don Pravitz. circ. 10,000 (controlled). **Document type:** trade publication.
     Incorporates (in 1992): Western Mills Today.
     Description: Reports on the logging and lumber segment of the forest industry in the western US with emphasis on Alaska, Washington, Oregon, Idaho, Montana and northern California.

674   US   ISSN 1065-7010
▼**TIMBERTIMES;** logging & lumbering history & modeling. 1993. q. Box 219, Hillsboro, OR 97123. TEL 503-648-6530. Ed. Steven R. Gatke. **Document type:** consumer publication.

TRAE NYTS LEVERANDOERREGISTER. see *BUILDING AND CONSTRUCTION — Carpentry And Woodwork*

674.2   DK   ISSN 0105-8738
TRAE OG INDUSTRI/DANISH WOOD INDUSTRY. 1974. m. (10/yr.). (Traeindustriens Fabrikantforening) Teknisk Forlag A-S, Skelbaekgade 4, DK-1780 Copenhagen V, Denmark. TEL 45-31-21068-01. FAX 45-31-21-04-01. adv.; bk.rev.; charts; illus.; mkt.; pat.; stat.; tr.lit.; index. circ. 9,536.
     Formerly: Traeindustrien (ISSN 0041-0632)
     Description: Focuses on providing the wood-working industry with information on new machinery and equipment. Reports and reviews important trade exhibitions at home and abroad.

674.2   DK
TRAELAST-TIDENDE. m. Sixtusvej 2, 2300 Copenhagen S, Denmark. adv. circ. 1,000.

674   UG
UGANDA. FORESTRY DEPARTMENT. TIMBER LEAFLET. 1953. irreg., latest no.53, 1972. free. Forestry Department, Box 7124, Kampala, Uganda. cum.index: 1953-72.

UNASYLVA; international journal of forestry and forest products. see *FORESTS AND FORESTRY*

UNION REGISTER. see *LABOR UNIONS*

674   RM   ISSN 1220-9430
UNIVERSITATAE TRANSILVANIA DIN BRASOV. BULETINUL. SERIE B2. INDUSTRIALIZAREA LEMNULUI/TRANSYLVANIA UNIVERSITY OF BRASOV. BULLETIN. SERIES B2. WOOD INDUSTRY. (Text in English, French, German) 1956. a. price varies. Universitatea Transilvania din Brasov - Transylvania University of Brasov, Bd. Eroilor no. 29, 2200 Brasov, Rumania.
—BLDSC (2782.303100).
     Supersedes in part: Universitatea din Brasov. Buletinul. Seria B. Economie Forestiera.

674   CN   ISSN 0079-8355
UNIVERSITE LAVAL. DEPARTEMENT D'EXPLOITATION ET UTILISATION DES BOIS. NOTE DE RECHERCHES. (Text in French) 1967. irreg. free. Universite Laval, Departement Sciences du Bois, Quebec, PQ G1K 7P4, Canada. TEL 418-656-3493. Ed. Marcel Goulet. circ. 1,000. **Indexed:** Forest.Abstr. **Document type:** academic/scholarly publication.

674   CN   ISSN 0079-8363
UNIVERSITE LAVAL. DEPARTEMENT D'EXPLOITATION ET UTILISATION DES BOIS. NOTE TECHNIQUE. (Text in English and French) 1967. irreg. free. Universite Laval, Departement Sciences du Bois, Quebec, PQ G1K 7P4, Canada. TEL 418-656-3493. Ed. Pierre Laforest. circ. 1,000. **Indexed:** Forest.Abstr. **Document type:** academic/scholarly publication.

674.1 690   US
VIRGINIA POLYTECHNIC INSTITUTE AND STATE UNIVERSITY. SARDO PALLET AND CONTAINER RESEARCH LABORATORY. LABORATORY REPORT. 1949. irreg. price varies. Virginia Polytechnic Institute and State University, Sardo Pallet and Container Research Laboratory, c/o M.S. White, Blacksburg, VA 24061-0503. TEL 703-231-7134. FAX 703-231-8868. circ. 1,000. **Document type:** academic/scholarly publication.
     Formerly: Virginia Polytechnic Institute and State University. Wood Research and Wood Construction Laboratory. Special Report (ISSN 0083-6508)

674   SZ
WALD UND HOLZ. 16/yr. 58 SFr. (foreign 77 SFr.). Waldwirtschaft Verband Schweiz, Rosenweg 14, CH-4501 Solothurn, Switzerland. TEL 065-231011. FAX 065-233620. adv.: B&W page 1300 SFr.; trim 185 x 260. circ. 11,000. **Document type:** trade publication.
     Incorporates: Waldarbeit.

674   PL   CODEN: AWATDC
WARSAW AGRICULTURAL UNIVERSITY. S G G W. ANNALS. FORESTRY AND WOOD TECHNOLOGY. (Text mainly in English; occasionally in French, German or Russian; summaries in Polish) 1957. irreg., no.12, 1980. $10 per no. Szkola Glowna Gospodarstwa Wiejskiego (SGGW) - Warsaw Agricultural University, Ul. Nowoursynowska 166, 02-766 Warsaw, Poland. Ed. T. Dudzinska. illus. **Document type:** academic/scholarly publication.
—BLDSC (1035.020000); CASDDS.
     Former titles: Warsaw Agricultural University. S G G W - A R. Annals. Forestry and Wood Technology (ISSN 0208-5704); (until 1980): Akademia Rolnicza, Warsaw. Zeszyty Naukowe. Technologia Drewna.

WESTERN CANADIAN LUMBER WORKER. see *LABOR UNIONS*

674   US
WESTERN DRY KILN ASSOCIATION. PROCEEDINGS. 1948. a. $6.50 or membership. West Coast Dry Kiln Association, 2290 S.W. Westchester Ave., Portland, OR 97225-4460. TEL 503-643-2829. Ed. Charles Kozlik. circ. 700. **Indexed:** Forest.Abstr., Forest Prod.Abstr. **Document type:** proceedings.
     Formerly: Western Dry Kiln Clubs. Proceedings.

674 658.7   US
WESTERN LUMBER (YEAR) BUYERS MANUAL. 1972. a. (typically set in Oct.). Western Wood Products Association, Yeon Bldg., 522 S.W. Fifth Ave., Portland, OR 97204-2122. TEL 503-224-3930. FAX 503-224-3934. circ. 20,000. **Document type:** trade publication.
     Description: Guide to the products and services of the Association's member mills.

WESTERN LUMBER FACTS. see *FORESTS AND FORESTRY — Abstracting, Bibliographies, Statistics*

674   CN
WESTERN RED CEDAR LUMBER BUYERS GUIDE. a. Western Red Cedar Lumber Association, 1200 - 555 Burrard St., Vancouver, BC V7X 1S7, Canada. TEL 604-684-0266. FAX 604-687-4930. **Document type:** directory.
     Formerly: Where to Buy Western Red Cedar Lumber Products.

WESTERN WOOD PRODUCTS ASSOCIATION. EXPORT REPORT. see *FORESTS AND FORESTRY — Abstracting, Bibliographies, Statistics*

WESTERN WOOD PRODUCTS ASSOCIATION. MONTHLY F.O.B. PRICE SUMMARY, PAST SALES. COAST MILLS. see *FORESTS AND FORESTRY — Abstracting, Bibliographies, Statistics*

WESTERN WOOD PRODUCTS ASSOCIATION. MONTHLY F.O.B. PRICE SUMMARY, PAST SALES. INLAND MILLS. see *FORESTS AND FORESTRY — Abstracting, Bibliographies, Statistics*

WESTERN WOOD PRODUCTS ASSOCIATION. QUARTERLY INJURY & ILLNESS INCIDENCE REPORT. see *OCCUPATIONAL HEALTH AND SAFETY — Abstracting, Bibliographies, Statistics*

WESTERN WOOD PRODUCTS ASSOCIATION. STATISTICAL YEARBOOK. see *FORESTS AND FORESTRY — Abstracting, Bibliographies, Statistics*

674   US
WEYERHAEUSER TODAY. 1970. bi-m. free to qualified personnel. Weyerhaeuser Company, Tacoma, WA 98477. TEL 206-924-2882. FAX 206-924-3332. charts; illus. circ. 50,000. (tabloid format) **Document type:** newspaper.
     Formerly: Weyerhaeuser News; Which supersedes: Weyerhaeuser World (ISSN 0042-6938)

WHERE TO BUY HARDWOOD PLYWOOD AND VENEER. see *BUILDING AND CONSTRUCTION — Carpentry And Woodwork*

674   CN   ISSN 1183-6652
WOOD/BOIS. 4/yr. Canadian Wood Council, 1730 St. Laurent Blvd., Ste. 350, Ottawa, ON K1G 5L1, Canada. TEL 613-731-7800. FAX 613-731-7899. circ. 18,000.
     Formerly (until 1991): Wood Post.
     Description: Technical publication covering wood structural products and buildings constructed of wood.

674 **US** **ISSN 0735-6161**
TA419.A1   CODEN: WFSCD4
WOOD AND FIBER SCIENCE. 1969. q. $110. Society of Wood Science and Technology, One Gifford Pinchot Dr., Madison, WI 53705. TEL 608-231-9347. Ed. Arno Schneiwind. adv.; bk.rev.; abstr.; charts; illus.; index. circ. 800. (back issues avail.) **Indexed:** Abstr.Bull.Inst.Pap.Chem., Chem.Abstr., Curr.Adv.Ecol.Sci., Curr.Cont., Forest.Abstr., Forest Prod.Abstr., Risk Abstr., Soils & Fert., Sugar Ind.Abstr.
—BLDSC (9345.021000); Faxon; UnCover; SWETS; UMI; CASDDS.
Formerly: Wood and Fiber (ISSN 0043-7654)

674 **US** **ISSN 0043-7662**
WOOD & WOOD PRODUCTS; furniture, cabinets, woodworking and allied products management and operations. 1896. m. $35 (foreign $100). Vance Publishing Corporation, 400 Knightsbridge Parkway, Lincolnshire, IL 60069. Ed. Harry Urban. adv.; charts; illus.; mkt.; pat.; tr.lit.; tr.mk. circ. 51,500. (also avail. in microform from UMI) **Indexed:** A.S.& T.Ind., Eng.Ind., Excerp.Med., Forest.Abstr., Forest Prod.Abstr., Tr.& Indus.Ind.
—Faxon; UnCover; UMI. **CCC.**

674 **US**
WOOD & WOOD PRODUCTS REFERENCE BUYING GUIDE. 1963. a. $10. Vance Publishing Corporation, 400 Knightsbridge Parkway, Lincolnshire, IL 60069. Ed. Harry Urban. circ. 51,500. (also avail. in microform from UMI)
—**CCC.**
Formerly: Wood & Wood Products Reference Data - Buying Guide (ISSN 0084-1080)

674 621.9 **UK** **ISSN 0144-7238**
WOOD BASED PANELS INTERNATIONAL. 1980. 6/yr. £46 (foreign £55). Benn Publications Ltd. (Subsidiary of: Morgan-Grampian plc), Benn House, Sovereign Way, Tonbridge, Kent TN9 1RW, England. TEL 0732-364422. FAX 0732-361534. Ed. Brian Williams. adv. contact: John Dent. circ. 7,845. **Document type:** trade publication.
—**CCC.**
Description: Covers the plywood, panel veneer and value-added surfacing industry.

674 **US** **ISSN 1066-5757**
WOOD DESIGN FOCUS; a newsletter of contemporary wood engineering. 1989. q. $25 (foreign $40). Wood Products Center, 4033 S.W. Canyon Rd., Portland, OR 97221. TEL 503-228-0819. FAX 503-228-3624. Ed. Robert Leichti. adv.; bk.rev. circ. 1,000. (back issues avail.) **Document type:** newsletter.
Description: Covers the design and application of solid timber and structural wood engineered products.

674 **US** **ISSN 1045-7348**
TS840
WOOD DIGEST. 1984. m. $50 (Canada and Mexico $65; elsewhere $120). Johnson Hill Press, Inc., 1233 Janesville Ave., Ft. Atkinson, WI 53538. TEL 414-563-6388. FAX 414-563-1701. Ed. Steve Ehle. adv.; illus.; circ. 52,000 (controlled). (tabloid format) **Indexed:** Tr.& Indus.Ind.
Formerly: Furniture-Wood Digest (ISSN 0746-1089)
Description: Provides productivity solutions for manufacturers of furniture, cabinets, millwork and specialty wood products.

WOOD FINISHER. see *BUILDING AND CONSTRUCTION — Carpentry And Woodwork*

338.1 **US**
WOOD INDUSTRIES OF NEW MEXICO. 1973. irreg. free. State Forestry Division, Box 1948, Santa Fe, NM 87504-1948. TEL 505-827-5830. FAX 505-827-3903. Ed. David D. Brown. circ. 300. **Document type:** government publication.
Formerly: New Mexico Forest Products Directory (ISSN 0094-2782)

338.4 **CN**
WOOD LEADER. 1975. 6/yr. free. Canadian Wood Council, 1730 St. Laurent Blvd., Ste. 350, Ottawa, ON K1G 5L1, Canada. TEL 613-731-7800. FAX 613-731-7899. Ed. Don Griffith. circ. 1,800. (back issues avail.)
Former titles (until 1987): U S A C Communique; U S Activities Report (ISSN 0700-3986)

674 621.9 **US**
WOOD MACHINERY MANUFACTURERS OF AMERICA. BUYER'S GUIDE AND DIRECTORY. (Text in Chinese, English, French, German, Spanish) 1976. a. membership. Wood Machinery Manufacturers of America, 1900 Arch St., Philadelphia, PA 19103. TEL 215-564-3484. FAX 215-564-2175. circ. 10,000. **Document type:** directory.
Description: Resource guide for the woodworking industry.

674 694 **II**
WOOD NEWS. (Text in English) 1991. q. Ganesh Publications Pvt.Ltd., 57, 10th Cross, West of Chord Rd. II Stage, Mahalakshmipurm P.O., Bangalore 560 086, India. TEL 080-3322207. FAX 080-3345014. TELEX 0845-2020 APPU IN. Ed. Joseph George; Pub. Gouri Ramakrishnan. **Document type:** trade publication.

WOOD PRODUCTS: INTERNATIONAL TRADE AND FOREIGN MARKETS. see *AGRICULTURE — Agricultural Economics*

674 **JA** **ISSN 0049-7916**
WOOD RESEARCH/MOKUZAI KENKYU. (Text in English) 1949. irreg. (1-2/yr.). exchange basis. Wood Research Institute, Kyoto University, Gokanosho, Uji, Kyoto 611, Japan. Ed.Bd. charts; stat. circ. 800. **Indexed:** Abstr.Bull.Inst.Pap.Chem., Biol.Abstr., Chem.Abstr., Forest.Abstr., Forest Prod.Abstr.
—BLDSC (9345.600000).

WOOD S A & TIMBER TIMES. see *FORESTS AND FORESTRY*

674 **GW** **ISSN 0043-7719**
TA419   CODEN: WOSTBE
WOOD SCIENCE AND TECHNOLOGY. 1966. 6/yr. DM.688($430) (International Academy of Wood Science) Springer-Verlag, Heidelberger Platz 3, 14197 Berlin, Germany. TEL 030-8207-1. FAX 030-8214091. (Subscr. in N. America to: Springer-Verlag New York, Inc., 44 Hartz Way, Secaucus, NJ 07096-2491. TEL 201-348-4033. FAX 201-348-4505) Ed.Bd. (also avail. in microform from UMI; back issues avail.; reprint service avail. from ISI) **Indexed:** Abstr.Bull.Inst.Pap.Chem., Art & Archaeol.Tech.Abstr., Chem.Abstr., Curr.Adv.Ecol.Sci., Curr.Cont., Forest.Abstr., Forest Prod.Abstr.
Document type: academic/scholarly publication.
—BLDSC (9345.850000); Faxon; UnCover; SWETS; UMI; CASDDS. **CCC.**
Description: Covers all aspects of the biology, physics, chemistry, and technology of wood.

634.9 674 **US**
TS800   CODEN: FOINBV
WOOD TECHNOLOGY. 1889. bi-m. $75 (free to qualified personnel). Miller Freeman, Inc. (Subsidiary of: United Newspapers), 600 Harrison St., San Francisco, CA 94107. TEL 415-905-2200. FAX 415-905-2232. TELEX 278273. Ed. David A. Pease. adv.: B&W page $2145, color page $3420; trim 8 1/8 x 10 7/8. charts; illus.; mkt.; tr.lit.; circ. 20,600 (controlled). (also avail. in microform from UMI; microfiche from CIS; reprint service avail. from UMI) **Indexed:** Abstr.Bull.Inst.Pap.Chem., B.P.I, Biol.& Agr.Ind., Bus.Ind., Chem.Abstr., Excerp.Med., Forest.Abstr., Forest Prod.Abstr., Geo.Abstr., PROMT, Soils & Fert., SRI, Tr.& Indus.Ind.
●Also available online. Vendor(s): DIALOG Information Services, Inc.
—Faxon; UnCover. **CCC.**
Former titles (until 1992): Forest Industries (ISSN 0015-7430); (1961-1962): Lumberman and Wood Industries (ISSN 0360-1560)

WOODWORKING; Canada's leading magazine serving the producers of wood and wood products. see *BUILDING AND CONSTRUCTION — Carpentry And Woodwork*

674 **GW** **ISSN 0177-7114**
WOODWORKING INTERNATIONAL. (Text in English) 1983. q. DM.80($50) Dr. Harnisch Verlags GmbH, Blumenstr. 15, 90402 Nuernberg, Germany. TEL 0911-203658. FAX 0911-204579. TELEX 179118103. Ed. Adrian Alecu. adv.; B&W page DM.5950, color page DM.7900; trim 190 x 270. bk.rev. circ. 12,000. (back issues avail.) **Document type:** trade publication.
Description: For the wood processing industries.

674 **CN**
YARDSTICK. 1988. bi-m. free. (Western Retail Lumberman's Association) Craig Kelman & Associates Ltd., 3C - 2020 Portage Ave., Winnipeg, MB R3J 0K4, Canada. TEL 204-885-7798. FAX 204-889-3576. Ed. Jim E. Watson. adv. contact: Lawrence Bujokas. bk.rev. circ. 1,336. **Document type:** trade publication.
Description: For retail lumber dealers and others in the building supply industry in Manitoba, Saskatchewan, Alberta, Yukon and NWT.

674 **UN** **ISSN 0084-3768**
HD9750.4
YEARBOOK OF FOREST PRODUCTS/ANNUAIRE DES PRODUITS FORESTIERS/ANUARIO DE PRODUCTOS FORESTALES. (Text in English, French and Spanish) 1947. a. $50. Food and Agriculture Organization of the United Nations, c/o UNIPUB, 4611-F Assembly Dr., Lanham, MD 20706-4391. FAX 301-459-0056. (also avail. in microfiche from CIS) **Indexed:** Forest.Abstr., Forest Prod.Abstr., IIS.
—BLDSC (9412.200000).

674 **CC**
ZHONGGUO MUCAI/CHINESE LUMBER. (Text in Chinese) bi-m. Zhongguo Mucai Zong Gongsi - Chinese Lumber Corporation, No. 385, Donghanyang Lu, Shanghai 200080, People's Republic of China. TEL 5454788. Ed. Zhou Shumin.

674 **CN** **ISSN 0824-0868**
2 X 4. 1985. 5/yr. Can.$45. Editions C.R. Inc., P.O. Box 1010, Victoriaville, Que. G6P 8Y1, Canada. TEL 819-752-4243. FAX 819-758-8812. Ed. Claude Roy. adv. circ. 8,052 (controlled). (tabloid format; back issues avail.)
Description: Covers the wood products industries in Canada.

FUNERALS

AMERICAN BLUE BOOK OF FUNERAL DIRECTORS. see *BUSINESS AND ECONOMICS — Trade And Industrial Directories*

614.61 **US** **ISSN 0002-7804**
AMERICAN CEMETERY. 1928. m. $15. Kates - Boylston Publications, Inc., 1501 Broadway, New York, NY 10036. TEL 212-398-9266. Ed. Charles O. Kates. adv.; bk.rev.; illus.; tr.lit. circ. 5,066.

AMERICAN CEMETERY ASSOCIATION. MEMBERSHIP DIRECTORY. see *BUSINESS AND ECONOMICS — Trade And Industrial Directories*

393.1 **US** **ISSN 0002-8576**
AMERICAN FUNERAL DIRECTOR. 1877. m. $20. Kates - Boylston Publications, Inc., 1501 Broadway, New York, NY 10036. TEL 212-398-9266. FAX 212-768-9140. Ed. Charles O. Kates. adv.; bk.rev.; charts; illus. circ. 11,725.

393 **GW**
BESTATTUNGSGEWERBE. 1949. m. Bundesverband des Deutschen Bestattungsgewerbes e.V., Schirmerstr. 76, 40211 Duesseldor, Germany. TEL 0211-675036. FAX 0211-357140. circ. 3,300. **Document type:** trade publication.

393
C F S A NEWSLETTER. (Former name of issuing body: Casket Manufacturers Association of America) 1953. m. $30. Casket & Funeral Supply Association of America, 708 Church St., Evanston, IL 60201. TEL 708-866-8383. FAX 708-866-0901. Ed. George Lemke. circ. 550. (looseleaf format; back issues avail.) **Document type:** newsletter.
Formerly: C M A Newsletter.

393.1 **CN** **ISSN 0319-3225**
CANADIAN FUNERAL DIRECTOR. 1923. m. $50 (foreign $55). Halket Publishing Ltd., 174 Harwood Ave. S., Ste. 206, Ajax, Ont. L1S 2H7, Canada. TEL 416-427-6121. Ed. Ray Halket. adv.; bk.rev.; charts; illus.; tr.lit.
Formerly: Canadian Funeral Service (ISSN 0008-364X)

614.6 **US**
CATHOLIC CEMETERY. 1949. m. $30 to non-members. National Catholic Cemetery Conference, 710 N. River Rd., Des Plaines, IL 60016. TEL 708-824-8131. Ed. Leo A. Droste. adv. circ. 1,951.

FUNERALS — ABSTRACTING, BIBLIOGRAPHIES, STATISTICS

614.6 US ISSN 0162-4237
KF3781.A15
CEMETERY BUSINESS & LEGAL GUIDE. 1973. m. (10/yr.). $110. C B Legal Publishing Corp., 555 Skokie Blvd., Ste. 500, Northbrook, IL 60062-2845. TEL 708-480-1020. FAX 708-509-1027. Ed. Harvey Lapin. index every 3 yrs. circ. 500. (looseleaf format; back issues avail.) **Document type:** newsletter.

393 US ISSN 0270-5281
RA626
CEMETERY MANAGEMENT. 1974. m. $45. American Cemetery Association, Three Skyline Pl., Ste. 1111, Falls Church, VA 22041. TEL 703-379-5838. Ed. Lee Shaw. adv. circ. 2,822.

614.62 US
CREMATIONIST OF NORTH AMERICA. 1965. q. $7.50. Cremation Association of North America, Box 7047, Incline Village, NV 89450. TEL 702-831-6555. FAX 702-831-9359. Ed. Jean M. Scribner. adv.; bk.rev.; charts; illus.; stat. circ. 1,000. (reprint service avail.)
Formerly: National Cremation (ISSN 0027-9080)

393 US ISSN 0199-3186
DIRECTOR. 1930. m. $24 (foreign $30). (National Funeral Directors Association) N F D A Publications, Inc., 11121 W. Oklahoma Ave., Box 27641, Milwaukee, WI 53227-0641. TEL 414-541-2500. FAX 414-541-1909. Ed. Sue Simon. adv.: B&W page $1115, color page $2025; trim 8 1/4 x 10 7/8; adv. contact: Kellie Schilling. bk.rev.; circ. 14,913 (paid); 433 (controlled).
Indexed: ABI Inform., Tr.& Indus.Ind. **Document type:** trade publication.
Description: Informs the funeral service profession about the role of the funeral director in contemporary America.

DIRECTORY OF CREMATORIA. see BUSINESS AND ECONOMICS — Trade And Industrial Directories

393 UK
EMBALMER. 1932. 4/yr. membership. British Institute of Embalmers, 21C Station Rd., Knowle, Solihull, West Midlands B93 0HL, England. TEL 0564-778991. FAX 0564-770812. Ed. D.L. Kaye. adv.; bk.rev. circ. 1,450.

393 US
FACTS FROM THE FOUNDATION. q. National Foundation of Funeral Service, 2250 E. Devon Ave., Rm. 250, Des Plaines, IL 60018. TEL 708-827-6337. Ed. Howard Raether. circ. 3,000.

393 US ISSN 0273-9747
FLORIDA FUNERAL DIRECTOR. bi-m. $12. (Florida Funeral Directors Association) Florida Funeral Directors Services, Inc., Box 6009, Tallahassee, FL 32314. TEL 904-224-1969. Ed. Jan Scheff. adv. circ. 1,000. **Document type:** trade publication.
Description: Focuses on the profession of funeral directing.

393.1 SA ISSN 1016-7250
FORUM. (Text in Afrikaans, English) 1948. q. free. National Funeral Directors' Association of Southern Africa, Box 18, Observatory 7935, South Africa. FAX 27-21-475433. Ed. Chris Molyneux. adv.; bk.rev. circ. 800. **Document type:** trade publication.
Formerly: Funeral Forum (ISSN 0016-2787)

393 GW
FRIEDHOF UND DENKMAL. 1956. q. DM.16. Arbeitsgemeinschaft Friedhof und Denkmal e.V., Weinbergstr. 25-27, 34117 Kassel, Germany. TEL 0561-91893-0. FAX 0561-9188310. Ed. Eberhard Haase. circ. 4,500. **Document type:** bulletin.

FRONTIERES; les vivants et les morts. see PSYCHOLOGY

614.6 FR
FUNERAIRE MAGAZINE. 11/yr. B.P. 8, 69702 Givors Cedex, France. TEL 72-24-89-33. FAX 72-24-61-93. circ. 6,000.

614.6 FR
FUNERAL INTERNATIONAL. 11/yr. 7 rue Georges-Pitard, 75015 Paris, France. TEL 42-50-03-02. FAX 42-50-90-06. TELEX 203 624. Ed. Claude Dyan. circ. 12,000.

393 US ISSN 0148-6705
FUNERAL SERVICE INSIDER.* 1963. w. $255. Atcom, Inc., 1541 Morris Ave., Bronx, NY 10457-8702. Ed. Jean De Sapio. circ. 1,500. (reprint service avail. from UMI)
—CCC.
Formerly: Directors Newsletter.
Description: For owners and managers of funeral homes and related services.

393.1 UK ISSN 0016-2809
FUNERAL SERVICE JOURNAL. 1885. m. £9.50. Middlesex County Press Ltd., Cricketfield Rd., Uxbridge, Middlesex, England. Ed. R.H. Wilson. adv.; bk.rev.; abstr.; charts; illus.; tr.lit.; index.
—BLDSC (4056.600000).

614.6 UK ISSN 0020-2762
INSTITUTE OF BURIAL AND CREMATION ADMINISTRATION. JOURNAL.* 1913. q. 50p. Institute of Burial & Cremation Administration Inc., Chesterfield & District Crematorium, Brimington, Chesterfield, Derbyshire, England. Ed. A.L. Wallace.

614.6 DK ISSN 0907-8541
KIRKEGAARDSKULTUR.* 1923. a. DKK 90. Foreningen for Kirkegaardskultur, Aalborg, Denmark. Ed. Axel Andersen. illus.
Formerly (until 1992): Vore Kirkegaarde (ISSN 0108-2302)

614.61 DK ISSN 0107-9123
KIRKEGAARDSLEDEREN. 1981. bi-m. DKK 100. Foreningen af Danske Kirkegaardsledere, c/o Kirkegaardsinspektoer Claes Foghmoes, Figenvej 109, DK-4700 Naestved, Denmark. TEL 53-729300. FAX 45-53-73-97-01. adv.; illus. circ. 1,250.

614.62 SW ISSN 0282-0595
KYRKOGAARDEN. (Text in Swedish; summaries in German) 1929. 8/yr. SEK 220 to non-members; members SEK 188. Sveriges Kyrkogaards och Krematoriefoerbund, P.O. Box 19071, S-104 32 Stockholm 19, Sweden. TEL 46-8-15-05-40. FAX 46-8-612-80-36. Ed. Magnus Magnusson. adv. contact: Jan Arvidsson. circ. 3,000. **Document type:** trade publication.
—BLDSC (5134.981500).
Formerly: Ignis (ISSN 0019-1698)

393 UK
M A B BULLETIN. 1983. bi-m. £12 (foreign £15). Memorial Advisory Bureau, 139 Kensington High St., London W8 6SX, England. TEL 071-937-0052. FAX 071-937-1393. Ed. Sam Weller. adv.; bk.rev.; circ. 2,500 (controlled). (tabloid format; back issues avail.) **Document type:** bulletin.

MARKERS. see ART

MASKINENTREPRENOEREN. see BUILDING AND CONSTRUCTION

614.6 US ISSN 0739-0289
MORTICIANS OF THE SOUTHWEST. 1947. m. $18 (effective Sep. 1991). Farring Inc., 2514 National Dr., Garland, TX 75041. TEL 214-840-1060. Ed. Nancy E. Farrell. adv.; bk.rev. circ. 3,600. **Document type:** trade publication.
Description: Reports on activities, products and services, state and national regulatory trends, business and financial news, and personal involvement for funeral industry practitioners throughout the Southwest, including the Republic of Mexico.

614.62 US ISSN 0027-1268
RA622
MORTUARY MANAGEMENT. 1914. m. (11/yr.). $27 (foreign $30). Berg Publications Inc., 315 Silverlake Blvd., Los Angeles, CA 90026. TEL 213-665-0101. FAX 213-665-3068. Ed. Ronald A. Hast. adv.; bk.rev.; illus. circ. 7,100. (also avail. in microform from UMI) **Document type:** trade publication.
—UMI.
Description: Trade publication designed for funeral directors and others related to the funeral service industry, including manufacturers, suppliers and dealers of funeral merchandise and equipment, embalmers, cemeteries and mortuary science students and colleges.

614 UK ISSN 0953-3567
PHAROS INTERNATIONAL. 1934. q. £15.50($40) (Europe £17; elsewhere £22). Cremation Society of Great Britain, Brecon House, 16-16a Albion Pl., 2nd Fl., Maidstone, Kent ME14 5DZ, England. TEL 0622-688292. FAX 0622-686698. (Co-sponsor: International Cremation Federation) Ed. R.N. Arber. adv.; illus.; stat. circ. 750. **Document type:** trade publication.
—BLDSC (6449.123000).
Formerly: Pharos (ISSN 0048-3672)

614.61 US ISSN 0038-397X
SOUTHERN CEMETERY. 1958. bi-m. $21. John W. Yopp Publications, Inc., Box 1147, Beaufort, SC 29901. TEL 800-849-9677. Ed. Mary Cronley. adv.; illus. circ. 2,293.

393.1 US ISSN 0038-4135
SOUTHERN FUNERAL DIRECTOR; a business and professional journal devoted to the interests of funeral directors in the South and Southwest. 1919. m. $25. John W. Yopp Publications, Inc., Box 1147, Beaufort, SC 29901. TEL 800-849-9677. adv.; illus. circ. 6,110.

393 US
TEXAS DIRECTOR. 1964. m. (Texas Funeral Directors Association) Rector - Duncan & Associates, Box 14667, Austin, TX 78761. TEL 512-454-5262. FAX 512-451-9556. Ed. Jeannette Brown. adv.: B&W page $325, color page $875; trim 8 1/2 x 11; adv. contact: Larry Hanners. bk.rev.; circ. 1,000 (controlled). **Document type:** trade publication.

155.937 US ISSN 0160-8681
THANATOS. 1975. q. $16 (foreign $21). (Florida Funeral Directors Association) Florida Funeral Directors Services, Inc., c/o Jan Scheff, Ed., Box 6009, Tallahassee, FL 32314. bk.rev. circ. 5,000. **Document type:** consumer publication.
—UMI.
Description: Offers a sensitive and educational approach to the issues of dying, death and bereavement.

393 NE
HET VIJFDE ZEGEL. q. Federatie van Katholieke Begrafenisiatellingen Zonder Winstoogmerk, Velkenkamp 211, 3607 LK Maarssen, Netherlands. adv.; bk.rev.

363.7 US
YELLOW BOOK NEWS. 1979. m. $10. Nomis Publications, Inc., Box 5122, Youngstown, OH 44514. TEL 216-788-9608; 800-321-7479. FAX 216-788-1112. Ed. Margaret Rouzzo. adv. circ. 21,000. **Document type:** trade publication.
Description: Covers news affecting the funeral home industry.

YELLOW BOOK OF FUNERAL DIRECTORS. see BUSINESS AND ECONOMICS — Trade And Industrial Directories

FUNERALS — Abstracting, Bibliographies, Statistics

363.7 316.8 SA
SOUTH AFRICA. CENTRAL STATISTICAL SERVICE. CENSUS OF SOCIAL, RECREATIONAL AND PERSONAL SERVICES - UNDERTAKERS AND CREMATORIUM SERVICES. (Report No. 95-03-01) irreg., latest 1988. R.4.40 (foreign R.5.50). Central Statistical Service - Sentrale Statistiekdiens, Private Bag X44, Pretoria 0001, South Africa. TEL 27-12-310-8911. FAX 27-12-310-8500. (Orders to: Government Printing Works, Private Bag X85, Pretoria 0001, South Africa) **Document type:** government publication.

FURNITURE AND HOUSE FURNISHINGS

see Interior Design and Decoration—Furniture and House Furnishings

GARDENING AND HORTICULTURE

see also Gardening and Horticulture—Florist Trade; Agriculture—Crop Production and Soil; Biology—Botany

635   US   ISSN 0569-2423
A A B G A NEWSLETTER. 1975. m. membership. American Association of Botanical Gardens & Arboreta, Inc., 786 Church Rd., Wayne, PA 19087. TEL 215-688-1120. FAX 215-293-0149. adv.; bk.rev. circ. 2,400. **Indexed:** Gard.Lit. (1992-). **Document type:** newsletter.

A A N TODAY. (American Association of Nurserymen) *see AGRICULTURE*

635 712   IT
A C E R. 4/yr. Via Bolchini 12, 21100 Varese, Italy. TEL 332-45-72-88. FAX 331-45-77-45. Ed. Giovanni Sala. circ. 11,500.

635   US
A C G A MULTILOGUE. 1983. bi-m. $25 to individuals; institutions $50. American Community Gardening Association, 325 Walnut St., Philadelphia, PA 19106. TEL 206-684-0264. Ed. Barbara Donnette. bk.rev. circ. 300. (looseleaf format; back issues avail.) **Document type:** newsletter.
Description: Exchange of current member information including: job notices, notices of conferences, minutes of board meetings, resources, referrals and requests.

635   UK
A G S GUIDES. irreg. price varies. Alpine Garden Society, The A G S Centre, Avonbank, Pershore, Worcs. WR10 3JP, England. TEL 44-386-554790. FAX 44-386-554801. Ed. C Grey Wilson. illus.; cum.index. circ. 9,500. (back issues avail.)

635   US   ISSN 0747-3109
A O S AWARDS QUARTERLY. 4/yr. $18 (foreign $21). American Orchid Society, 6000 S. Olive Ave., W. Palm Beach, FL 33405. TEL 407-585-8666. FAX 407-585-0654.

634   SA   ISSN 0303-1918
A P G A ANNUAL/A P K V JAARBLAD. (Text in Afrikaans and English) a. Apricot, Peach and Pear Growers' Association, P.O. Box 414, Paarl 7620, Cape Province, South Africa. Ed. J.F. van den Berg. adv. circ. 2,000.

635   US   ISSN 0882-8024
A S H S NEWSLETTER. 1985. m. membership. American Society for Horticultural Science, c/o Christine A. Radiske, Exec. Dir., 113 S. West St., Ste. 400, Alexandria, VA 22314-2824. TEL 703-836-4606. FAX 703-836-2024. Ed. Michael W. Neff. adv. circ. 5,000. (back issues avail.) **Document type:** newsletter.
Description: News of horticultural science and of the Society's activities. Includes dissertations and information on job opportunities in the field.

635   US
A S T A NEWSLETTER. 12/yr. membership only. American Seed Trade Association, Inc., 601 13th St., N.W., Ste. 570 S., Washington, DC 20005-3807. TEL 202-638-3128. FAX 202-638-3171. **Document type:** newsletter.

635 580.7   RM   ISSN 0068-3329
ACTA BOTANICA HORTI BUCURESTIENSIS. (Text and summaries in English, French, German, and Rumanian) 1958. a. exchange basis. Universitatea Bucuresti, Gradina Botanica, Soseaua Cotroceni Nr. 32, 76258 Bucharest, Rumania. **Indexed:** Biol.Abstr.

635   NE   ISSN 0567-7572
SB13   CODEN: AHORA2
ACTA HORTICULTURAE. 1963. irreg., latest no.350. price varies. International Society for Horticultural Science, Englaan 1, 6703 ET Wageningen, Netherlands. TEL 31-8370-21747. FAX 31-8370-21586. TELEX 45760 ISHS NL. **Indexed:** Agri.Eng.Abstr., Agroforest.Abstr., Bio-Contr.News & Info., Biodet.Abstr., Biol.Abstr., Chem.Abstr., Crop Physiol.Abstr., Fababean Abstr., Field Crop Abstr., Food Sci.& Tech.Abstr., Forest.Abstr., Helminthol.Abstr., Hort.Abstr., Irr.& Drain.Abstr., Maize Abstr., Nutr.Abstr., Ornam.Hort., Plant Breed.Abstr., Plant Grow.Reg.Abstr., Potato Abstr., Rev.Plant Path., Rice Abstr., Rural Ext.Educ.& Tr.Abstr., Rural Recreat.Tour.Abstr., Seed Abstr., Soils & Fert., Soyabean Abstr., Weed Abstr., World Agri.Econ.& Rural Sociol.Abstr. **Document type:** monographic series.
—BLDSC (0624.330000); UnCover; SWETS; CASDDS.

635   XR   ISSN 0862-2558
ACTA UNIVERSITATIS AGRICULTURAE. SERIES B. FACULTAS HORTICULTURAE. (Text and summaries in Czech, English) 1987. s-a. $20. Vysoka Skola Zemedelska, Zemedelska 1, 613 00 Brno, Czech Republic. FAX 05-578-427. TELEX 62489. Ed. Jan Golias. charts; stat.; index. circ. 170. **Document type:** academic/scholarly publication.

ADELAIDE BOTANIC GARDENS. JOURNAL. *see BIOLOGY — Botany*

635   IT   ISSN 0394-6169
ADVANCES IN HORTICULTURAL SCIENCE. (Text and summaries in English) 1876. 4/yr. L.50000 (foreign L.60000) (effective 1994). Universita degli Studi di Firenze, Dipartimento di Ortoflorofrutticoltura, Via Donizetti 6, 50144 Florence, Italy. TEL 055-333462. FAX 055-331497. Ed. P.L. Pisani. adv.; bk.rev.; abstr.; index. circ. 1,500. (processed; also avail. in cards) **Indexed:** Biol.Abstr., Chem.Abstr., Crop Physiol.Abstr., Field Crop Abstr., Food Sci.& Tech.Abstr., Forest.Abstr., Herb.Abstr., Hort.Abstr., Ornam.Hort., Plant Breed.Abstr., Plant Grow.Reg.Abstr., Rev.Plant Path., Seed Abstr., Soils & Fert., VITIS, Weed Abstr.
—BLDSC (0709.062000); SWETS.
Formerly (until 1986): Rivista della Ortoflorofrutticoltura Italiana (ISSN 0035-5968)

634   II   ISSN 0971-0507
ADVANCES IN HORTICULTURE & FORESTRY. (Text and summaries in English) a. Rs.360($50) (typically set in June). Scientific Publishers, 5A, New Pali Rd., P.O. Box 91, Jodhpur 342 001, India. Ed. S.P. Singh. circ. 400. **Document type:** academic/scholarly publication.
—BLDSC (0709.062500).

635.933 583.81   US   ISSN 0002-0265
AFRICAN VIOLET MAGAZINE. 1947. 6/yr. $13.50. African Violet Society of America, Inc., Box 3609, Beaumont, TX 77704-3609. Ed. Jane Birge. adv.; bk.rev.; illus. circ. 16,000. **Indexed:** Biol.Abstr.
—UnCover.

635   II
AGRI HORTICULTURAL SOCIETY OF INDIA. HORTICULTURAL BULLETIN.* vol.5, 1972. q. Agri Horticultural Society of India, 1 Alipore Rd., Calcutta 27, India. Ed.Bd.

AGRICOLA VERGEL; fruticultura, horticultura, floricultura, citricultura, vid, arroz. *see AGRICULTURE — Crop Production And Soil*

AGRICULTURE AND HORTICULTURE/NOKO TO ENGEI. *see AGRICULTURE*

635   PL   ISSN 0239-9326
AKADEMIA ROLNICZA IM. HUGONA KOLLATAJA W KRAKOWIE. ZESZYTY NAUKOWE. SERIA: OGRODNICTWO. (Text in Polish; summaries in English) 1970. a. price varies. Akademia Rolnicza im. Hugona Kollataja w Krakowie, Al. 29 Listopada 46, 31-425 Krakow, Poland. TEL 48-12-119144. FAX 48-12-336245. TELEX 322469 PL. Ed. Zdzislaw Piskornik. circ. 120 (paid). **Document type:** academic/scholarly publication.
Former titles (until 1980): Akademia Rolnicza w Krakowie. Zeszyty Naukowe. Ogrodnictwo (ISSN 0137-1878); (until 1974): Wyzsza Szkola Rolnicza w Krakowie. Zeszyty Naukowe. Ogrodnictwo (ISSN 0137-2084)

635   PL   ISSN 0137-1738
AKADEMIA ROLNICZA, POZNAN. ROCZNIKI. OGRODNICTWO. (Text in Polish; summaries in English and Russian) 1959. irreg. price varies. Akademia Rolnicza, Poznan, Ul. Wojska Polskiego 28, 60-637 Poznan, Poland. FAX 48-61-411022. TELEX 0413322 ARPL. **Indexed:** Bibl.Agri. **Document type:** academic/scholarly publication.
Description: Focuses on orcharding, nurserymanship, market gardening, edible mushrooms, decorative plants, breeding and seed production of gardening plants, garden engineering.

635   US
AKRON ROSE RAMBLER. m. (except Jan.). $10. Akron Rose Society, c/o Peter Schneider, Ed., Box 16035, Rocky River, OH 44116. bk.rev. **Document type:** newsletter.
Description: Contains articles about exhibition, new varieties, importing, non-dogmatic cultural advice and news from the world of roses.

ALABAMA AGRICULTURAL EXPERIMENT STATION. RESEARCH REPORT SERIES. *see AGRICULTURE*

ALEXANDRIA JOURNAL OF AGRICULTURAL RESEARCH. *see AGRICULTURE*

ALLERTONIA; a series of occasional papers. *see BIOLOGY — Botany*

634.55   US
ALMOND FACTS. 1922. bi-m. $25 (foreign $45). Blue Diamond Growers, Box 1768, Sacramento, CA 95812. TEL 916-442-0771. FAX 916-325-2880. TELEX 494-9933. Ed. Susan Brauner. adv.; B&W page $1020, color page $1545. circ. 7,857.

ALOE, CACTUS & SUCCULENT SOCIETY OF ZIMBABWE. INGENS BULLETIN. *see BIOLOGY — Botany*

635   CN   ISSN 0836-320X
ALPINE GARDEN CLUB OF BRITISH COLUMBIA. BULLETIN. 1956. 5/yr. Can.$15 membership only. Alpine Garden Club of British Columbia, Box 5161, Main Post Office, Vancouver, B.C. V6B 4B2, Canada. Ed. Linda Verbeek. bk.rev. circ. 700. **Document type:** bulletin.
Formerly: Alpine Garden Club of British Columbia. Monthly Bulletin (ISSN 0701-1652)
Description: Articles on plants, especially alpines, occurrence in wild, club news, plant culture and more.

635   UK   ISSN 0002-6476
ALPINE GARDEN SOCIETY QUARTERLY BULLETIN. 1930. q. £16($32) Alpine Garden Society, The A G S Centre, Avonbank, Pershore, Worcs. WR10 3JP, England. TEL 44-386-554790. FAX 44-386-554801. Ed. C. Grey-Wilson. adv.; bk.rev.; illus.; index, cum.index vols.1-15; vols.31-40; vols.41-50. circ. 12,000. **Indexed:** Curr.Adv.Ecol.Sci., Gard.Lit. (1992-). **Document type:** bulletin.
—BLDSC (7171.000000).
Incorporates: Alpine Gardening (ISSN 0952-8598)
Description: Contains detailed description of plant cultivation as well as journeys to mountain regions in search of plants.

635   UK
ALPINE GARDEN SOCIETY QUARTERLY NEWSLETTER. 1932. a. Alpine Garden Society, The A G S Centre, Avonbank, Pershore, Worcs. WR10 3JP, England. TEL 44-386-554790. FAX 44-386-554801.
Formerly (until 1993): Alpine Garden Society Year Book (ISSN 0269-5200)

AMARANTH TODAY. *see AGRICULTURE — Crop Production And Soil*

635   US
AMARYLLIS. a. $1. Amaryllis Inc., Box 318, Baton Rouge, LA 70821. TEL 504-924-5560. Ed. Ed Beckham. (tabloid format) **Document type:** catalog.
Description: Catalog of Amaryllis bulbs.

GARDENING AND HORTICULTURE

635 UK ISSN 0002-6832
AMATEUR GARDENING. 1884. w. £34. I P C Magazines, Specialist Magazine Group (Subsidiary of: Reed International PLC), King's Reach Tower, Stamford St., London SE1 9LS, England. TEL 0202-680586. FAX 0444-440619. TELEX 892084 REEDBP G. (Dist. by: Quadrant Subscription Services, Oakfield House, Perrymount Rd., Haywards Heath, W. Sussex RH16 3DH, England. TEL 0444-440421) Ed. Graham Clarke. adv. contact: David Gannicott. illus. circ. 84,935. **Document type:** consumer publication.
—CCC.

635 NE ISSN 0002-6875
AMATEURTUINDER. 1927. 6/yr. fl.25. Algemeen Verbond van Volkstuindersverenigingen in Nederland, Kemphaanweg 1, 1358 AA Almere, Netherlands. TEL 31-36-5318536. FAX 31-36-5315927. Ed. H.B.J.A.G. Vroklage. adv.; bk.rev.; illus.; index. circ. 30,000.
Description: Covers cultivation and the growing of usual and unusual vegetation and crops in the average allotment garden, the planning and maintenance of a garden, greenhouses, and the use of various tools. Targeted to the amateur gardener.

712 UK ISSN 0957-8870
AMENITY MANAGEMENT. 1989. m. £20 (rest of Europe £40; N. America, S. America, Africa, Asia £50; Australia, New Zealand, Japan £60). Haymarket Trade and Leisure Publications Ltd., 38-42 Hampton Rd., Teddington, Middx. TW11 OJE, England. TEL 081-943-5023. FAX 081-943-5673. Ed. Lesley Turner. adv.; bk.rev.; illus.; stat.; tr.lit. circ. 5,320. **Document type:** trade publication.
Description: Covers new machines, new techniques, business management for the landscape and grounds maintenance industry.

712 UK
AMENITY POWER. 10/yr. Baranite House, 13 Whitehorse St., Baldock, Herts SG7 6QB, England. TEL 0642-892608. FAX 0462-490066. Ed. Jane Undery. circ. 5,250.
Description: Industry information about garden machinery and power equipment for specialists.

AMERICAN ASSOCIATION OF NURSERYMEN UPDATE. see *AGRICULTURE*

AMERICAN ASSOCIATION OF NURSERYMEN WHO'S WHO IN THE NURSERY INDUSTRY MEMBER DIRECTORY. see *AGRICULTURE*

AMERICAN BAMBOO SOCIETY. JOURNAL. see *BIOLOGY — Botany*

AMERICAN BAMBOO SOCIETY NEWSLETTER. see *BIOLOGY — Botany*

635.9 US ISSN 0065-762X
SB413.C18
AMERICAN CAMELLIA YEARBOOK. 1946. a. $8. American Camellia Society, 1 Massee Lane, Fort Valley, GA 31030. TEL 912-967-2358. Ed. Ann B. Brown. index, cum.index from 1946. circ. 5,200. **Indexed:** Hort.Abstr.
—BLDSC (0811.800000).

634.98 US ISSN 0569-3845
SB428 CODEN: ACTJB3
AMERICAN CHRISTMAS TREE JOURNAL. 1956. q. $45 to non-members. National Christmas Tree Association, 611 E. Wells St., Milwaukee, WI 53202. TEL 414-276-6410. FAX 414-276-3349. Ed. Dennis Tompkins. adv.; bk.rev.; illus.; mkt.; tr.lit. circ. 2,700.
—Faxon; UnCover.
Formerly: American Christmas Tree Growers' Journal (ISSN 0002-7901)

AMERICAN CONIFER SOCIETY. BULLETIN. see *FORESTS AND FORESTRY*

635.933 US ISSN 0002-8150
AMERICAN DAHLIA SOCIETY. BULLETIN. Key Title: Bulletin of the American Dahlia Society, Inc. 1915. q. $20 includes membership (foreign $24.50). (American Dahlia Society, Inc.) Norman Hines, Ed. & Pub., 364 S. 600 West, Hebron, IN 46341. TEL 219-988-3721. (Subscr. to: c/o Alan Fisher, Memb.Chr., 1 Rock Falls Ct. Rockville, MD 20854) adv.: B&W page $100. illus. circ. 1,700. **Document type:** bulletin.

634 US ISSN 0002-8568
CODEN: AMFGAR
AMERICAN FRUIT GROWER. 1880. m. $14. Meister Publishing Co., 37733 Euclid Ave., Willoughby, OH 44094. TEL 216-942-2000. Ed. Gary Acuff. adv.; bk.rev.; charts; illus.; mkt.; tr.lit. circ. 54,388. (also avail. in microform from UMI) **Indexed:** Agri.Eng.Abstr., Biol.Abstr., Chem.Abstr, Farm & Garden Ind., Hort.Abstr., Weed.Abstr. **Document type:** trade publication.
—BLDSC (0815.500000); Faxon; SWETS; UMI. CCC.

635 US ISSN 0194-3456
AMERICAN FUCHSIA SOCIETY BULLETIN. 1938. bi-m. $15 membership only (subscr. includes Update). American Fuchsia Society, San Francisco County Fair Bldg., 9th Ave. & Lincoln Way, San Francisco, CA 94122. TEL 707-643-0449. Ed. Elsie A. Sydnot. bk.rev. circ. 1,200. **Document type:** bulletin.
Formerly: American Fuchsia Society. Monthly Bulletin.
Description: Issues the latest fuchsia culture information including summaries and descriptions of new, yearly cultivation introductions, a list of fuchsia nurseries, and culture publications. Provides news about society activities.

635 615.19 US
AMERICAN HERB ASSOCIATION NEWSLETTER. 1981. q. $20 (foreign $28). American Herb Association, Box 1673, Nevada City, CA 95959-1673. Ed. Kathi Keville. adv.; bk.rev.; film rev.; abstr.; bibl.; charts; illus. circ. 800. (looseleaf format; back issues avail.) **Document type:** newsletter.

635 US ISSN 0096-4417
SB1
AMERICAN HORTICULTURIST. 1922. 6/yr. membership. American Horticultural Society, 7931 E. Boulevard Dr., Alexandria, VA 22308. TEL 703-768-5700. Ed. Kathleen Fisher. adv.; bk.rev.; illus.; index. circ. 20,000. (also avail. in microform from UMI; back issues avail.; reprint service avail. from UMI) **Indexed:** Biol.& Agr.Ind., Biol.Dig., Farm & Garden Ind., Gard.Lit. (1992-), Hort.Abstr., Ind.Sci.Rev., Intl.Polym.Sci.& Tech., Plant Breed.Abstr., Rev.Plant Path. **Document type:** consumer publication.
—Faxon; UnCover; SWETS; UMI.
Formerly: American Horticultural Magazine (ISSN 0002-8800); Incorporates: American Horticultural Society News and Views (ISSN 0002-8819); Gardeners Forum.
Description: Covers garden design, plant selection, the environment, horticultural history and personalities, and issues in horticultural science.

635 US
AMERICAN HORTICULTURIST NEWS EDITION. 6/yr. membership only. American Horticultural Society, 7931 E. Boulevard Dr., Alexandria, VA 22308. TEL 703-768-5700. **Indexed:** Gard.Lit. (1992-). **Document type:** newsletter.
Description: Covers horticultural research, gardening tips, environmental information.

635 US
AMERICAN HOSTA SOCIETY JOURNAL. 2/yr. membership only. American Hosta Society, 5300 Whiting Ave., Edina, MN 55435.

635 US
AMERICAN IRIS SOCIETY. BULLETIN. 4/yr. membership only. American Iris Society, 7414 E. 60th St., Tulsa, OK 74145. TEL 918-627-0706. **Document type:** bulletin.

635.969 US ISSN 0003-0198
SB354
AMERICAN NURSERYMAN. 1904. s-m. $45 (foreign $75). American Nurseryman Publishing Co., 77 Washington St., Ste. 2100, Chicago, IL 60602-2904. TEL 312-782-5505. FAX 312-782-3232. Ed. Julie S. Higginbotham. adv. contact: Tim Hill. bk.rev.; charts; illus.; pat.; tr.lit.; index; circ. 14,689 (paid). (also avail. in microform from UMI; reprint service avail. from UMI) **Indexed:** Bio-Contr.News & Info., Biol.& Agr.Ind., Chem.Abstr., Farm & Garden Ind., Forest.Abstr., Gard.Lit. (1992-), Hort.Abstr., Ornam.Hort., Plant Grow.Reg.Abstr. **Document type:** trade publication.
—BLDSC (0847.130000); Faxon; UnCover; UMI.
Description: Presents management and technical articles for growers of trees, shrubs and woody ornamental plants; landscape professionals; and retail garden center operators.

635.934 US ISSN 0003-0252
SB409.A1
AMERICAN ORCHID SOCIETY BULLETIN. 1932. m. $30 (foreign $36). American Orchid Society, 6000 S. Olive Ave., W. Palm Beach, FL 33405. TEL 407-585-8666. FAX 407-585-0654. Dir. Lee S. Cooke. adv.; bk.rev.; charts; illus.; index. circ. 26,500. **Indexed:** Biol.Abstr., Chem.Abstr., Hort.Abstr., Ornam.Hort. **Document type:** bulletin.
—UnCover.

635.9 US
AMERICAN PENSTEMON SOCIETY BULLETIN. s-a. $10. American Penstemon Society, 1569 S. Holland Ct., Lakewood, CO 80232. TEL 303-986-8096. Ed. Jack Ferreri. adv. circ. 400. **Document type:** bulletin.

635 US
AMERICAN PEONY SOCIETY. BULLETIN. 1912. 4/yr. membership only. American Peony Society, 250 Interlachen Rd., Hopkins, MN 55343. TEL 612-938-4706. adv. **Document type:** bulletin.

635.967 US ISSN 0003-0864
AMERICAN ROCK GARDEN SOCIETY BULLETIN. (Supplement: A R G S Bulletin Board) 1934. q. $25 (effective Jan. 1994). American Rock Garden Society, c/o Jacques Mommens, Box 67, Millwood, NY 10546. Ed. Gwen Kelaidis. adv.; bk.rev.; illus.; index, cum.index: vols.1-50, 1943-1992. circ. 4,500. **Indexed:** Gard.Lit. (1992-). **Document type:** bulletin.

635.9 US ISSN 0066-0000
SB411
AMERICAN ROSE ANNUAL. 1916. a. $10. American Rose Society, Box 30000, Shreveport, LA 71130-0030. TEL 318-938-5402. Ed.Bd. index, cum.index: 1916-1993. **Document type:** bulletin.

635.9 US ISSN 0003-0899
SB411
AMERICAN ROSE MAGAZINE. 1933. m. $32. American Rose Society, Box 30000, Shreveport, LA 71130-0030. TEL 318-938-5402. Ed.Bd. adv.; bk.rev.; illus.; charts; cum.index every 2 yrs. circ. 22,000. **Document type:** bulletin.

635 581 US ISSN 0003-1062
SB1 CODEN: JOSHB5
AMERICAN SOCIETY FOR HORTICULTURAL SCIENCE. JOURNAL. 1903. bi-m. $165. American Society for Horticultural Science, c/o Christine A. Radiske, Exec. Dir., 113 S. West St., Alexandria, VA 22314-2824. TEL 703-836-4606. FAX 703-836-2024. Ed. Werner J. Lipton. charts; illus.; stat.; index, cum.index: 1903-1951, 1952-1961, 1962-1968, 1969-1976, 1977-1981, 1982-1986, 1987-1991. circ. 5,000. (also avail. in microform from WWS; reprint service avail. from KTO) **Indexed:** Agri.Eng.Abstr., Agroforest.Abstr., Biol.Abstr., Biol.& Agr.Ind., Biotech.Abstr., Chem.Abstr., Crop Physiol.Abstr., Curr.Adv.Ecol.Sci., Curr.Adv.Genetics & Molec.Biol., Excerp.Med., Field Crop Abstr., Food Sci.& Tech.Abstr., Forest.Abstr., Forest Prod.Abstr., Helminthol.Abstr., Herb.Abstr., Hort.Abstr., Irr.& Drain.Abstr., Maize Abstr., Ornam.Hort., Plant Breed.Abstr., Plant Grow.Reg.Abstr., Potato Abstr., Rev.Plant Path., Sci.Cit.Ind., Seed Abstr., Sel.Water Res.Abstr., Soils & Fert., Sorghum & Millets Abstr., Trop.Oil Seeds Abstr., VITIS, Weed Abstr.
—BLDSC (4692.850000); Faxon; UnCover; SWETS; CASDDS.
Formerly: American Society for Horticultural Science. Proceedings.
Description: Repository for detailed papers of completed basic or fundamental research in horticultural science.

635 US
AMERIGOLD NEWSLETTER. 1978. q. $12 includes membership. Marigold Society of America, Inc., 807 Sierra Madre Way, Davis, CA 95616. TEL 916-756-8099. (Subscr. to: Box 112, New Britain, PA 18901) Ed. William R. Morris. circ. 350. (tabloid format; back issues avail.) **Document type:** newsletter.
Description: Provides specific information on the marigold and its use. Deals with the promotion of the marigold as an international friendship flower.

GARDENING AND HORTICULTURE

635   BE   ISSN 0772-1099
AMI DES FLEURS. 1962. q. 800 BEF. Publivog b.v.b.a., Rozenlaan 17, B-9111 Belsele, Belgium. TEL 03-7723791. FAX 03-7725085. Ed. Wilfried Delforge. adv.; bibl.; illus.; tr.lit.; index. circ. 25,000.
    Supersedes (in 1976): Jardin et Logis (ISSN 0021-5503); Formerly: Vieux Jardinier (ISSN 0042-5796)

635 747   FR   ISSN 0044-8095
AMI DES JARDINS ET DE LA MAISON. 1930. m. 180 F. Ami des Jardins, S.A., 8-10 rue Pierre Brossolette, 92300 Levallois Perret, France. adv.; bk.rev.; illus.; tr.lit.; index; circ. 200,000 (controlled).
    Description: Articles for the flower, plant and tree enthusiast. Also features recipes and general household information.

635.933   FR   ISSN 0003-1844
AMIS DES ROSES. 1896. q. 110 F. Societe Francaise des Roses, Parc de la Tete d'Or, 69459 Lyon Cedex 3, France. adv.; illus. circ. 4,500.
    Description: Information of interest to botanists, gardners, and all lovers of flowers. Offers useful tips in flower growing. Features articles centering around a variety of notable gardens worldwide.

635   FR   ISSN 0998-7738
ANNUAIRE OFFICIEL DE LA FEDERATION NATIONALE DES PRODUCTEURS DE L'HORTICULTURE ET DES PEPINIERES. 1973. biennial, latest 1990. 450 F. Federation Nationale des Producteurs de l'Horticulture et des Pepinieres, 19 bd. Magenta, 75010 Paris, France. TEL 42-40-99-22. FAX 42-40-92-53. adv.; bk.rev.; cum.index. circ. 6,000. **Document type:** catalog.
    Former titles: Annuaire Federal de l'Horticulture et des Pepinieres (ISSN 1141-5975); Annuaire Professionnel de l'Horticulture et des Pepinieres (ISSN 0517-9130)

635 712
ANNUAL GARDEN. a. $19.95. Rodale Press, Inc., 33 E. Minor St., Emmaus, PA 18098. TEL 215-967-5171.

ANTHOS; vierteljahres-Zeitschrift fuer Freieusgestaltung, Gruen und Landschaftsplannung. see ARCHITECTURE

635   SP
APUNTES DE JARDINERIA. 1986. q. 1800 ptas. Glosa, S.A., Ronda San Pedro 22, pral. 2, 08010 Barcelona, Spain. TEL 93 3012433. Ed. Maria Munne-Pericall. adv.; bk.rev. circ. 25,000.

635 581   CN
THE AQUATIC GARDENER. Short title: T A G. 1985. bi-m. $15 (foreign $28). Aquatic Gardeners Association, c/o Dorothy Reimer, Membership Sec., 83 Cathcart St., London, ON N6C 3L9, Canada. (And: 6205 Lookout Loop, Raleigh, NC 27612) Ed. Neil Frank. bk.rev.; bibl.; illus. circ. 500.
    Description: Contains articles on experiences with specific aquatic plants, aquascaping, culture techniques and the general mechanics of aquatic gardening.

AQUATIC PLANT NEWS. see BIOLOGY — Botany

AQUILEGIA. see CONSERVATION

ARBORETUM LEAVES. see BIOLOGY — Botany

ARBORICULTURAL JOURNAL; the international journal of urban forestry. see FORESTS AND FORESTRY

635   US
ARBORICULTURE CONSULTANT. 1968. 6/yr. membership only. American Society of Consulting Arborists, 5130 W. 101st Circle, Westminster, CO 80031. TEL 303-466-2722. FAX 303-466-7401. adv.; bk.rev. circ. 200. **Document type:** trade publication.
    Description: Aides the professional consulting arborist.

635   FR
ARBORICULTURE EN VAL DE LOIRE. 4/yr. 105 F. Ouest Publicite, 11 impasse Ambroise-Croizat, B.P. 136, 37701 Saint Pierre des Corps, France. TEL 47-44-21-85. FAX 47-32-02-55. Ed. Aubard. circ. 2,500.

635   US
ARIL SOCIETY INTERNATIONAL NEWSLETTER. s-a. membership only. Aril Society International, 111 W. Magna Vista, Arcadia, CA 91006. (Subscr. to: Wanda Smith, 3020 N. Anderson Rd., Garden City, KS 67846) Ed. Lin Flanagan. circ. 500. **Document type:** newsletter.
    Description: Information on the aril and aril-bred iris.

635   US
ARIL SOCIETY INTERNATIONAL YEARBOOK. 1958. a. membership only. Aril Society International, 111 W. Magna Vista, Arcadia, CA 91006. (Subscr. to: Wanda Smith, 3020 N. Anderson Rd., Garden City, KS 67846) Eds. Carole Vossen, Marilyn Harlow. adv.; index every 10 yrs. circ. 500. (back issues avail.)

635   US   ISSN 0197-4033
AROIDEANA. 1958. a. membership only. International Aroid Society, Box 43-1853, S. Miami, FL 33143. TEL 305-271-3767. Ed. Amy Donovan. (back issues avail.)
    Description: Provides information on members of the arum family (Araceae).

712   SP   ISSN 1132-3493
▼**ARQUITECTURA DEL PAISAJE.** 1992. q. 5500 ptas. (foreign 6500 ptas.) (effective 1994). Ediciones de Horticultura, S.L., Apdo. de Correos, 48, 1o, 43205 Rues (Tarragona), Spain. TEL 77-750402. FAX 77-753056. adv.; B&W page 74000 ptas., color page 125000 ptas.; trim 210 x 280. circ. 3,300. **Document type:** trade publication.
    Description: Contains commercial and technical information on all aspects of landscape gardening: including public parks and golf courses.

ASKLEPIOS. see BIOLOGY — Botany

635   AT   ISSN 0812-9495
AUSTRALIAN GARDEN JOURNAL. 1981. 5/yr. Aus.$23 (foreign Aus.$36) (effective 1992). Australian Garden Journal Pty. Ltd., P.O. Box 588, Bowral, N.S.W. 2576, Australia. TEL 048-61-4999. FAX 048-61-4356. Ed. Tim North. adv.; bk.rev.; circ. 6,000 (paid). **Indexed:** Gard.Lit. (1992-).

635   AT
AUSTRALIAN GARDENER. 1983. m. Aus.$26.40. H.J. Holdings Pty. Ltd., 33 Nundah St., Nundah, Qld. 4012, Australia. TEL 07 260-5622. Ed. Heather Jeffery. adv.; bk.rev.; index. circ. 50,000. (back issues avail.)
    Formerly: Queensland Gardener.

635   AT
AUSTRALIAN GERANIUM SOCIETY. JOURNAL. 4/yr. membership only. Australian Geranium Society, 118 Thorney Rd., Fairdield West, N.S.W. 2165, Australia.

635 581   AT
AUSTRALIAN HOME GARDENER'S HANDBOOK AND DIARY. 1980. a. Aus.$12.95 plus postage. Royal Horticultural Society of Victoria, P.O. Box 2000, Glen Waverley, Vic. 3150, Australia. TEL 03-803-0133. FAX 03-803-0556. adv.; charts; illus.; index. circ. 20,000. (back issues avail.) **Document type:** consumer publication.
    Description: How-to tips on gardening.

635   AT
AUSTRALIAN HORTICULTURE. 1903. m. Aus.$54. Rural Press - Victoria, P.O. Box 1386, Collingwood, Vic. 3066, Australia. TEL 03-287-0900. FAX 03-287-0999. Ed. Anita Boucher. circ. 7,000. **Indexed:** Hort.Abstr., Weed Abstr.
    Incorporates: Seed and Nursery Trader (ISSN 0037-0770)

635   AT   ISSN 1032-5646
AUSTRALIAN NURSERY MAGAZINE. q. Aus.$28($48) Nursery Industry of Australia (NIAA), P.O. Box 907, Epping, N.S.W. 2121, Australia. TEL 61-2-876-5200. Ed. N. Weatherly. adv. contact: D. Clancey. bk.rev. circ. 2,000. (back issues avail.) **Document type:** newsletter, trade publication.
    Formerly (until 1988): Australian Nurseryman (ISSN 0155-3801)

635.9   AT   ISSN 0045-0782
AUSTRALIAN ORCHID REVIEW. 1936. bi-m. Aus.$41. (Orchid Society of New South Wales) Graphic World Pty. Ltd., 14 McGill St., Lewisham, N.S.W. 2049, Australia. FAX 61-2-560-6677. Ed. David Wallace. adv.; bk.rev. circ. 10,000.

AUSTRALIAN PLANTS. see BIOLOGY — Botany

635   AT
AUSTRALIAN SUNFLOWER ANNUAL. 1976. q. Aus.$12. Australian Sunflower Association, P.O. Box 337, Toowoomba, Qld. 4350, Australia. Ed. Chris Warmingtor. adv. circ. 6,000.
    Formerly: Sunflower.

635   US   ISSN 0005-1926
AVANT GARDENER. 1968. m. $18. Horticultural Data Processors, Box 489, New York, NY 10028. Ed. Thomas Powell. bk.rev.; index. (also avail. in microform from UMI) **Indexed:** Gard.Lit. (1992-). —UMI.
    Description: Information on new plants, products and techniques.

635   US
AZALEAN. 1978. 4/yr. $20 membership. Azalea Society of America, Box 24536, W. Bethesda, MD 20827-0536. TEL 301-855-5269. Ed. Robert Hobbs. adv.; bk.rev. circ. 950.
    Description: Contains articles on all aspects of growing azalean; recent azalean introductions and culture; plus news on chapter activities.

635   UK   ISSN 0961-7477
B B C GARDENERS' WORLD MAGAZINE. 1991. m. £17.95. (British Broadcasting Corporation) Redwood Publishing Ltd., 101 Bayham St., London NW1 0AG, England. TEL 071-331-8000. (Subscr. to: P.O. Box 25, Wetherby, W. Yorkshire LS23 7EW, England) Ed. Adam Pasco. adv.; bk.rev. circ. 371,000. (back issues avail.)

635.9   US
B C I MAGAZINE. bi-m. $18. Bonsai Clubs International, 2636 W. Mission Rd., Ste. 277, Tallahassee, FL 32304. Ed. Jean C. Smith. adv. circ. 3,400.
    Description: Articles on the fine art of Bonsai.

635   US
BAER'S GARDEN NEWSLETTER. 1979. 4/yr. $4. John Baer's Sons, Box 328, Lancaster, PA 17603. Ed. Gerald S. Lestz. bk.rev. circ. 200. **Document type:** newsletter.

BAILEYA; a journal of horticultural taxonomy. see BIOLOGY — Botany

BAMBOO JOURNAL. see BIOLOGY — Botany

635   BG   ISSN 0379-4288
                              CODEN: BAHODP
BANGLADESH HORTICULTURE. 1973. s-a. $10. Bangladesh Society for Horticultural Science, Bangladesh Agricultural Research Institute, Dhaka, Joydebpur, Bangladesh. Ed. Mofizul Hoque. adv.; bk.rev.; charts. circ. 1,000. **Indexed:** Biol.Abstr., Chem.Abstr., Field Crop Abstr., Food Sci.& Tech.Abstr., Herb.Abstr., Hort.Abstr., Ornam.Hort., Plant Breed.Abstr., Plant Grow.Reg.Abstr. —CASDDS.

BAY OF PLENTY FARMER. see AGRICULTURE

635 583.46   US   ISSN 0096-8684
BEGONIAN. 1934. bi-m. $17 (overseas $25). American Begonia Society, Box 231129, Encinitas, CA 92023-1129. TEL 707-764-5407. (Subscr. to: John Ingles, Jr., 157 Monument, Rio Dell, CA 95562-1617) Ed. Tamsin Boardman. adv.; bk.rev.; illus.; index; circ. 2,000 (controlled). (processed) **Indexed:** Biol.Abstr., Hort.Abstr., Ornam.Hort.
    Description: Stimulates and promotes interest in begonias and other shade-loving plants. Encourages the introduction and development of new types of plants, and conservation of the species.

635   CC   ISSN 1001-0009
BEIFANG YUANYI/NORTHERN HORTICULTURE. (Text in Chinese) 1977. bi-m. Y21.60 (foreign Y108). (Heilongjiang Sheng Nongkeyuan, Yuanyisuo = Heilongjiang Academy of Agricultural Sciences, Horticultural Institute) Beifang Yuanyi Bianjibu, Yifayuan, Haping Lu, Harbin, Heilongjiang 150069, People's Republic of China. TEL 0451-6663603. FAX 0451-6662358. (Co-sponsor: Heilongjiang Society of Horticultural Sciences) Ed. Liu Enchen. adv. circ. 20,000. **Document type:** academic/scholarly publication.
    Description: Covers all areas of horticulture, including fruits, vegetables, melons, flowers and plant protection. Also introduces methods of home gardening, chemical fertilizing and pest control.

GARDENING AND HORTICULTURE

634　　　　　BE　　ISSN 0005-8467
BELGISCHE FRUITREVUE. 1948. m. 1400 BEF (foreign 2144 BEF). Prov. Pomologische Vereniging Van Oost-Vlaanderen v.z.w., c/o M. Georges Storme, Krommehamlaan, 27, B-9031 Drongen, Belgium. TEL 32-9-2272401. FAX 32-9-2279896. charts; illus.; stat.

635　　　　　BE　　ISSN 0005-8483
BELGISCHE TUINBOUW. (Text in Dutch) 1919. fortn. (m. Jul.-Aug.). 3000 BEF($20) Syndicale Kamer Belgische Tuinbouw, Kasteellaan 66, B-9000 Ghent, Belgium. TEL 32-9-2257460. FAX 32-9-2334411. Ed. A. Tollenaere. adv.; bk.rev.; charts; illus.; mkt.; stat. circ. 2,000.

635　　　　　AU　　ISSN 0005-9609
BESSERES OBST. 1956. m. S.595 (foreign S.690). (Bundesobstbauverband Oesterreichs) Oesterreichischer Agrarverlag GmbH, Bankgasse 1-3, A-1014 Vienna, Austria. TEL 5339676. FAX 5339656. Ed. Gerlinde Ferenz. adv.; bk.rev.; illus.; index. circ. 4,000. **Indexed:** Hort.Abstr.

635　　　　　GW　　ISSN 0303-1241
BETRIEBS- UND MARKTWIRTSCHAFT IM GARTENBAU. 1974. irreg. price varies. Verlag Paul Parey (Berlin), Seelbuschring 9-17, 12105 Berlin, Germany. TEL 030-70784-0. FAX 030-70784199. bibl.; illus.; index. **Indexed:** Rural Recreat.Tour.Abstr., World Agri.Econ. & Rural Sociol.Abstr. **Document type:** consumer publication.

635 643.7　　　US　　ISSN 1069-3084
▼**BETTER HOMES AND GARDENS GARDEN, DECK AND LANDSCAPE PLANNER.** Key Title: Garden, Deck and Landscape Planner. 1992. s-a. Meredith Corporation, Special Interest Publications, 1716 Locust St., Des Moines, IA 50309. TEL 515-284-3000. FAX 515-284-2700. Pub. Steve Levinson. adv.: B&W page $20025, color page $28775; trim 8 x 10 1/2; adv. contact: Pat Tomlinson. circ. 450,000. **Document type:** consumer publication.
  Description: Offers dozens of project and product ideas for landscaping and outdoor living projects.

635 640　　　US　　ISSN 0733-0340
BETTER HOMES AND GARDENS GARDEN IDEAS AND OUTDOOR LIVING. Key Title: Garden Ideas and Outdoor Living. 1940. 3/yr. newsstand price: $3.50. Meredith Corporation, Special Interest Publications, 1716 Locust St., Des Moines, IA 50336. TEL 515-284-3000. adv.: B&W page $20025, color page $28775. illus. circ. 500,000. **Document type:** consumer publication.

635　　　　　US
BETTER HOMES AND GARDENS GARDEN PRODUCTS AND PLANNING GUIDE. 1991. a. Meredith Corporation, Special Interest Publications, 1716 Locust St., Des Moines, IA 60309. TEL 515-284-3000. FAX 515-284-2700. Pub. Steve Levinson. adv.: B&W page $20025, color page $28775; trim 8 x 10 1/2; adv. contact: Pat Tomlinson. circ. 450,000.
  Description: Contains new products sections devoted to tools, power equipment, lighting, furniture, structures, pool and patio.

BETTER HOMES AND GARDENS HOME PLAN IDEAS. see HOME ECONOMICS

635　　　　　US　　ISSN 1051-8959
BETWEEN THE VINES. 1989. 3/yr. $15 includes membership. American Ivy Society, Box 2123, Naples, FL 33939-2123. TEL 513-862-4700. Ed. Ann Speanburg; Pub. Rachel Cobb. circ. 375. **Document type:** newsletter.
  Description: Contains short pieces with news, research, and growing tips.

BIBLIOGRAPHY ON SOILLESS CULTURE. see AGRICULTURE — Abstracting, Bibliographies, Statistics

635　　　　　GW　　ISSN 0173-9832
BIO-LAND. 1980. bi-m. DM.48. Bioland e.V., Barbarossastr. 14, 73066 Uningen, Germany. TEL 07161-31012. FAX 07161-37819. Ed. Susanne Erhardt. adv.; bk.rev. circ. 10,500. (back issues avail.)
  Description: Features organic agriculture and nutrition.

BIOLOGICAL AGRICULTURE AND HORTICULTURE; an international journal of sustainable production systems. see AGRICULTURE

635　　　　　SZ
BIOTERRA - BIOLOGISCHE LAND UND GARTENBAU. 7/yr. 45 SFr. Obere Wildeggstr. 9, CH-9000 St. Gallen, Switzerland. TEL 071-228266. Ed. Anita Doerler. adv.; bk.rev. circ. 10,000. **Document type:** consumer publication.
  Formerly: Biologische Land und Gartenbau.
  Description: Covers organic gardening and agriculture.

635.9　　　　NE　　ISSN 0165-6406
BLOEMBOLLENCULTUUR. 1889. fortn. fl.280. (Koninklijke Algemeene Vereeniging voor Bloembollencultuur) Uitgeversmaatschappi C. Misset B.V., Postbus 4, 7000 BA Doetinchem, Netherlands. TEL 31-8340-49911. FAX 31-8340-33939. (Editorial addr.: P.O. Box 20, 2180 AA Hillegom, Netherlands. TEL 31-2520-25224. FAX 31-2520-25304) adv.: B&W page fl.1436; trim 215 x 285; adv. contact: Cor van Nek. bk.rev.; abstr.; illus.; mkt. circ. 4,830. **Indexed:** Chem.Abstr., Hort.Abstr., Key to Econ.Sci., Ornam.Hort., Plant Grow.Reg.Abstr., Weed Abstr. **Document type:** trade publication.
  Formerly: Weekblad voor Bloembollencultuur (ISSN 0043-1788)
  Description: Provides information on flower bulb cultivation and production, including techniques, business and marketing operations, useful new products, and other news of interest to commercial bulb growers, wholesalers, exporters and suppliers.

635　　　　　BE　　ISSN 0006-4920
BLOEMENVRIEND. 1966. q. 800 BEF. Publivog b.v.b.a, Rozenlaan 17, B-9111 Belsele, Belgium. TEL 03-7723791. FAX 03-7725085. Ed. Wilfried Delforge. illus. circ. 15,000.

635.9　　　　GW　　ISSN 0006-5226
BLUMENFREUNDIN BLUMENPOST. 1958. m. free. Ernst Gerdes Verlag, Wakendorfer Str. 61, 24211 Preetz, Germany. TEL 04342-82393. FAX 04342-86288. illus. circ. 150,000. **Document type:** consumer publication.

BOLETIN DEL REGISTRO DE VARIEDADES. see AGRICULTURE — Crop Production And Soil

635　　　　　GW
BONSAI. 1982. q. DM.40 (foreign DM.45). Bonsai-Club Deutschland e.V., Trifelsstr. 15, 67269 Gruenstadt, Germany. TEL 06359-84941. FAX 06359-86896. adv.; bk.rev.; bibl.; film rev.; play rev.; illus.; index; cum.index. circ. 40,000. (back issues avail.) **Document type:** bulletin.
  Formerly: Bonsai-Magazin (ISSN 0177-1612)

635　　　　　CN
BONSAI CANADA. YEARBOOK. a. membership only. Bonsai Canada, 12 Beardmore Cres., Willowdale, Ont. M2K 2P5, Canada.

635.965　　　　IT　　ISSN 1121-2950
BONSAI ITALIANO. 1991. m. (10/yr.) L.35000 (effective 1993). Zanfi Editori s.r.l., Via Emilia Ovest 954, ang. Via T. Livio 1, 41100 Modena, Italy. TEL 059-891700. FAX 059-891701. **Document type:** consumer publication.
  Description: Contains information on bonsai plants for beginners and experts.

635.9　　　　US　　ISSN 0149-9726
BONSAI JOURNAL. 1966. q. $20 (foreign $25). American Bonsai Society, Inc., Box 358, Keene, NH 03431. TEL 603-352-9034. Ed. Arch Hawkins. adv.; bk.rev. circ. 1,400.
  Incorporates (1967-199?): A B Stracts.
  Description: Information on growing bonsai trees for both novice and expert.

635　　　　　US　　ISSN 1044-2529
BONSAI TODAY. 1989. bi-m. $42 (Canada $48; overseas $52.50) (effective 1994). Stone Lantern Publishing Co., 75 Union Ave., Sudbury, MA 01776. TEL 508-443-7110. FAX 508-443-9115. (Subscr. to: Box 816, Sudbury, MA 01776) Ed. W. John Palmer. adv.; circ. 8,300 (paid). (back issues avail.) **Document type:** consumer publication.
  Description: Presents a forum for the art and technique of growing miniature trees and landscapes.

635　　　　　NE　　ISSN 0923-2443
DE BOOMKWEKERIJ (DOETINCHEM). 1988. 44/yr. fl.182.50. (Nederlandse Bond van Boomkwekers) C. Misset B.V., Postbus 4, 7000 BA Doetinchem, Netherlands. TEL 31-8340-49911. FAX 31-8340-48839. (Editorial addr.: P.O. Box 9324, 2300 PH Leiden, Netherlands. TEL 31-71-161171. FAX 31-71-161200) adv.: B&W page fl.1942; trim 215 x 285; adv. contact: Cor van Nek. circ. 5,290. **Document type:** trade publication.
  Supersedes (1888-1988): Plantenbeurs (ISSN 0165-8972)
  Description: Information on the growing and selling of young trees and ornamental plants, including growing techniques and issues in business operation and management.

635　　　　　US
BOREALIS. 1982. 8/yr. $10 to individuals (foreign $25); students $5. Alaska Native Plant Society, Box 141613, Anchorage, AK 99514. TEL 907-333-8212. Ed. Lynn Balogh. adv.: B&W page $25; adv. contact: Verna Pratt. bk.rev. circ. 180. **Document type:** newsletter.
  Formerly: Alaska Native Plant Society. Newsletter.

634.9 635.9　　　US　　ISSN 0006-8535
BOXWOOD BULLETIN. 1961. q. $15 membership. American Boxwood Society, Box 85, Boyce, VA 22620. TEL 703-837-1758. Ed. Johns McCarthy. bk.rev.; illus.; cum.index vols. 1-25, 26-30; circ. 800 (paid). (back issues avail.) **Document type:** bulletin.

635　　　　　US
BOXWOOD BUYER'S GUIDE. irreg., 3rd ed., 1990. $15 membership. American Boxwood Society, Box 85, Boyce, VA 22620. TEL 703-837-1758.
  Description: List Boxweed nurseries.

635　　　　　UK
BRITISH AND EUROPEAN GERANIUM SOCIETY. GAZETTE. 3/yr. £5 (includes Yearbook) (membership only). British and European Geranium Society, 26 Crabtree Ln., Sheffield S5 7AY, England. TEL 0742-426200. FAX 0742-425379. circ. 4,000 (controlled). **Document type:** newsletter.

635　　　　　UK
BRITISH AND EUROPEAN GERANIUM SOCIETY. YEARBOOK. a. $5 (includes 3/yr Gazette) (membership only). British and European Geranium Society, 26 Crabtree Ln., Sheffield S5 7AY, England. TEL 0742-426200. FAX 0742-425379. circ. 4,000 (controlled). **Document type:** consumer publication.

635.933　　　　UK　　ISSN 0264-3405
BRITISH CACTUS & SUCCULENT JOURNAL. 1945. q. £12($28) in the UK and EC nations; elsewhere £13 (effective 1994). British Cactus & Succulent Society, 71 Lakes Ln., Newport Pagnell, Bucks. MK16 8HT, England. TEL 0908-611650. Ed. G.E. Cheetham. adv.; bk.rev.; illus.; index; circ. 5,600 (controlled). (back issues avail.) **Indexed:** Biol.Abstr., Hort.Abstr., Ornam.Hort. **Document type:** academic/scholarly publication.
  —BLDSC (2292.230000).
  Formerly (until 1982): National Cactus and Succulent Journal (ISSN 0027-8858)
  Description: Contains scholarly and popular discussions of classification, history of succulents, geographic and travel articles, and descriptions of collections.

BRITISH COLUMBIA. MINISTRY OF AGRICULTURE FISHERIES AND FOOD. FIELD CROP PRODUCTION GUIDE TO WEED, DISEASE, INSECT, BIRD AND RODENT CONTROL. see AGRICULTURE

635.8　　　　CN　　ISSN 0706-4292
BRITISH COLUMBIA. MINISTRY OF AGRICULTURE FISHERIES AND FOOD. MUSHROOM PRODUCTION GUIDE. 1983. irreg. Ministry of Agriculture Fisheries and Food, Extension Systems Branch, Parliament Bldgs., Victoria, BC V8W 2Z7, Canada.

GARDENING AND HORTICULTURE

635 CN ISSN 1181-9820
BRITISH COLUMBIA. MINISTRY OF AGRICULTURE FISHERIES AND FOOD. NURSERY CROP PRODUCTION GUIDE FOR COMMERCIAL GROWERS. biennial. Ministry of Agriculture Fisheries and Food, Extension Systems Branch, Parliament Systems Branch, Victoria, BC V8W 2Z7, Canada.
 Supersedes in part: British Columbia. Ministry of Agriculture Fisheries and Food. Nursery, Greenhouse Vegetable and Ornamental Production Guide for Commercial Growers (ISSN 0840-8068); Which was formed by the merger of: British Columbia. Ministry of Agriculture and Food. Greenhouse Vegetable Production (ISSN 0835-0760); British Columbia. Ministry of Agriculture. Nursery Production Guide (ISSN 0705-5757)

BRITISH COLUMBIA. MINISTRY OF FORESTS. SPECIAL REPORT SERIES. see FORESTS AND FORESTRY

634 CN
BRITISH COLUMBIA FRUIT GROWERS ASSOCIATION. HORTICULTURAL FORUM PROCEEDINGS. 1969. a. British Columbia Fruit Growers Association, 1473 Water St., Kelowna, B.C. V14 1J6, Canada. **Document type:** proceedings.
 Formerly: British Columbia Fruit Growers Association. Horticultural Conference Proceedings (ISSN 0068-1555)

634 CN ISSN 0068-1563
BRITISH COLUMBIA FRUIT GROWERS ASSOCIATION. MINUTES OF THE PROCEEDINGS OF THE ANNUAL CONVENTION. 1890. a. British Columbia Fruit Growers Association, 1473 Water St., Kelowna, B.C. V14 1J6, Canada. **Document type:** proceedings.

634 CN ISSN 0007-0572
BRITISH COLUMBIA ORCHARDIST. 1959. m. Can.$3($4) Box 423, Salmon Arm, BC V1E 4N6, Canada. TEL 604-763-1116. FAX 604-860-5002. Ed. E.W. Noonan; Pub. Jim Hayward. adv.; charts; illus.; stat.; circ. 2,728 (controlled).

635 UK
BRITISH IVY SOCIETY. JOURNAL. 2/yr. British Ivy Society, 66 Corwall Rd., Ruislip, Middlesex HA4 6AN, England.

635 UK
BRITISH IVY SOCIETY. OCCASIONAL PAPERS. irreg. membership only. British Ivy Society, 66 Corwall Rd., Ruislip, Middlesex HA4 6AN, England.

635 UK
BRITISH PELARGONIUM & GERANIUM SOCIETY. YEARBOOK. 1958. a. £5. British Pelargonium & Garanium Society, 23 Beech Cres., Kidlington, Oxford OX5 1DW, England. Ed. J. Morbey. adv.; bk.rev. circ. 2,000.

635 700 US ISSN 0884-8815
BROOKGREEN JOURNAL. 1971. q. membership. Brookgreen Gardens, 1931 Brookgreen Gardens Dr., Murrells Inlet, SC 29576-5101. TEL 803-237-4218. FAX 803-237-1014. Ed. Robin Salmon. bk.rev.; illus. circ. 4,600. **Indexed:** Gard.Lit. **Document type:** academic/scholarly publication.
 Formerly: Brookgreen Bulletin.
 Description: Articles pertaining to sculpture, history, wildlife, and horticulture.

632.97 US
BUG BULLETIN; integrated pest management for ornamental plants. w. (Mar.-Oct.). $100. Nursery I P M, Inc., Box 1619, Westminister, MD 21158. TEL 410-857-0343. Ed. Chuck Cornell. **Document type:** newsletter.

635 630 SI
BULLETIN OF AGRI-HORTICULTURE. (Text in Chinese, English) 1965. irreg. S.$1.50 per no. Tri-Products Private Ltd., Block 1006, Eunos Avenue 7, No. 01-44, Singapore 1440, Singapore. TEL 7492028. FAX 7492113. TELEX RS 24200 TMSR. Ed. Low Siew-Liap. adv.; charts; illus.; stat. circ. 5,000. **Document type:** bulletin.

635 658 US ISSN 0736-9050
BUSINESS OF HERBS. 1983. 6/yr. $20 (Canada $23; elsewhere $28) (effective 1994). Northwind Farm Publications, Rte. 2, Box 246, Shevlin, MN 56676. TEL 218-657-2478. FAX 318-657-2447. Eds. Paula and David Oliver. adv.; bk.rev.; circ. 2,200 (paid). **Indexed:** Gard.Lit. (1992-). **Document type:** trade publication.
 Description: Provides marketing and production techniques, covers government regulatory issues and research on medicinal herbs, profiles successful herb growers and business owners and lists useful resources and news for the small herb business.

635.9 CN
C O P F NEWS. q. Can.$25. Canadian Ornamental Plant Foundation, P.O. Box 21083, North Bay, ON P1B 7N8, Canada. TEL 705-495-2563. FAX 705-495-1449. Ed. Peggy Walsh Craig. circ. 700. (back issues avail.) **Document type:** newsletter.
 Description: Offers updated plant information, new registration information, profiles of members.

635 US
C S S A NEWSLETTER. 1929. 6/yr. membership only. Cactus & Succulent Society of America (Lawndale), c/o Eleanor E. Barker, 3602 W. 157th St., Lawndale, CA 90260. TEL 213-556-1923. (Subscr. to: c/o Mindy Fusaro, Box 35034, Des Moine, IA 50315-0301) circ. 4,000. **Document type:** newsletter.
 Description: Includes club news, calendar of shows and exhibits, and brief articles on growing cactus and succulents.

635 US ISSN 0008-1116
CALIFORNIA GARDEN. 1909. bi-m. $7 (foreign $10). San Diego Floral Association, Casa del Prado, Rm. 105, Balboa Park, San Diego, CA 92101-1619. TEL 619-232-5762. adv.; bk.rev.; bibl.; charts; illus.; stat.; index. circ. 3,000. **Indexed:** Cal.Per.Ind. (1980-), Geo.Abstr. **Document type:** consumer publication.
 Description: Covers climate, soils and general plant care. Lists officers and affiliates.

635 US
CALIFORNIA HORTICULTURAL SOCIETY. NEWSLETTER. 1972. m. $35 to members (foreign $40). California Horticultural Society, 1847 34th Ave., San Francisco, CA 94122. TEL 415-566-5222. bk.rev. circ. 700. **Document type:** bulletin.
 Description: Reports the society's activities, gives notice of future meetings, and gives a brief description and botanical identification of plants discussed at the previous meeting.

712 US
CALIFORNIA LANDSCAPING. 9/yr. $25. (California Landscape Contractors Association) Adams Publishing, 68860 Perez Rd., Ste. J, Cathedral City, CA 92234. TEL 619-770-4370. Ed. Marc Greg. bk.rev. circ. 13,474.

CAMBRIDGESHIRE FARMERS. see AGRICULTURE

635.933 US ISSN 0008-204X
CAMELLIA JOURNAL. 1946. 4/yr. (plus Yearbook). $20. American Camellia Society, 1 Massee Lane, Fort Valley, GA 31030. TEL 912-967-2358. FAX 912-967-2083. Ed. Ann B. Brown. adv.; bk.rev.; index; cum.index. circ. 5,000. **Indexed:** Hort.Abstr., Ornam.Hort., Plant Grow.Reg.Abstr.
—BLDSC (3016.040000).

634 CN ISSN 0045-4885 CODEN: CAFRAW
CANADIAN FRUITGROWER. 1929. 9/yr. Can.$14. N C C Publishing, 222 Argyle Ave., Delhi, ON. N4B 2Y2, Canada. TEL 519-582-2510. FAX 519-582-4040. Ed. Ben Steidman. adv.; B&W page Can.$901; trim 8 x 11; adv. contact: Ben Countryman. circ. 4,000 (controlled).

635 CN
CANADIAN GARDEN NEWS. 1983. 9/yr. Can.$8($14) Larking, Inc., 514 Kortright Rd. W., Guelph, Ont. N1G 3Y6, Canada. TEL 519-822-3126. Ed. Ken Larke. adv.

635 CN ISSN 0847-3463
CANADIAN GARDENING. 6/yr. Camar Publications Ltd., 130 Spy Ct., Markham, Ont. L3R 5H6, Canada. TEL 416-475-8440. FAX 416-475-9246. Ed. Liz Primeau. circ. 95,000. **Indexed:** Gard.Lit. (1992-).

635 CN ISSN 0068-8908
CANADIAN HORTICULTURAL COUNCIL. ANNUAL MEETING REPORTS. 1922. a. Can.$40. Canadian Horticultural Council, 310-1011 Prince of Wales Drive, Ottawa, ON K2C 3W7, Canada. TEL 613-226-4187. **Document type:** proceedings.
 Description: Contains a summary of the recent crop year for a number of commodities, as well as a regulatory update and overview on trade issues.

635 CN ISSN 0068-8916
CANADIAN HORTICULTURAL COUNCIL. COMMITTEE ON HORTICULTURAL RESEARCH. ANNUAL REPORTS. 1963. a. Canadian Horticultural Council, 310-1011 Prince of Wales Drive, Ottawa, ON K2C 3W7, Canada. TEL 613-226-4187. Eds. C.J. Bishop, S. Whitney. **Document type:** proceedings.
 Description: Summarizes research carried out in Canada by federal, provincial and private institutions in the area of horticulture.

635 CN ISSN 0828-8259
CANADIAN HORTICULTURAL HISTORY/HISTOIRE DE L'HORTICULTURE AU CANADA. (Text in English, French) 1985. irreg. Can.$30 per vol. to individuals (foreign Can.$33); institutions Can.$35 (foreign Can.$38). Royal Botanical Gardens, P.O. Box 399, Hamilton, ON L8N 3H8, Canada. TEL 905-527-1158. FAX 905-577-0375. Ed. Ina Vrugtman. **Indexed:** Gard.Lit. (1992-). **Document type:** academic/scholarly publication.
—Faxon.

635 CN ISSN 0715-3775
CANADIAN IRIS SOCIETY. NEWSLETTER. 1956. 4/yr. membership only. Canadian Iris Society, 199 Florence Ave., Willowdale, ON M2N 1G5, Canada. TEL 416-225-1088. Ed. Marie Dowson. **Document type:** newsletter.

635 CN
CANADIAN PRAIRIE LILY SOCIETY. NEWSLETTER. 1973. irreg. (3-4/yr.). Can $5. Canadian Prairie Lily Society, 22 Red River Rd., Saskatoon, SK S7K 1G8, Canada. circ. 200. **Document type:** newsletter.
 Description: Concerned with growing the genus Lilium and its hybridization.

635 CN ISSN 0068-9602
CANADIAN ROSE ANNUAL. 1955. a. $18. Canadian Rose Society, 10 Fairfax Crescent, Scarborough, ON M1L 1Z8, Canada. Ed. Ethel Freeman. bk.rev. circ. 1,500.
 Formerly: Canadian Rose Society. Yearbook.

635 CN
CANADIAN SOCIETY FOR HORTICULTURAL SCIENCE. NEWSLETTER. 1956. a. membership. Canadian Society for Horticultural Science, Ste. 907, 151 Slater St., Ottawa, Ont. K1P 5H4, Canada. Ed. J.B. Price. bk.rev. circ. 250. **Document type:** newsletter.
 Formerly: Canadian Society for Horticultural Science. Journal (ISSN 0315-6877)

635 US ISSN 1063-7451
CAROLINA GARDENER. 1988. 6/yr. $14.95. Carolina Gardener, Inc., Box 4504, Greensboro, NC 27404. TEL 919-294-8199. FAX 919-294-8290. Ed. L.A. Jackson. adv. circ. 25,000. (back issues avail.)
 Description: Articles on gardening, landscaping and horticulture for gardeners in both North and South Carolina.

CASA E JARDIM. see INTERIOR DESIGN AND DECORATION — Furniture And House Furnishings

CATALOGUS FLORAE AUSTRIA. see BIOLOGY — Botany

CHATAR. see ARCHITECTURE

635 CN
CHATTER. 1950. 4/yr. membership only. African Violet Society of Canada, 1573 Arbordale Ave., Victoria, B.C. V8N 5J1, Canada. Ed. Bob McCabe. adv. circ. 1,000.
 Description: International magazine for amateur growers which promotes the growing and showing of African Violets

GARDENING AND HORTICULTURE

635   JA   ISSN 0069-3227
SB317.5   CODEN: CDEGAF
CHIBA UNIVERSITY. FACULTY OF HORTICULTURE. TECHNICAL BULLETIN/CHIBA DAIGAKU ENGEIGAKUBU GAKUJUTSU HOKOKU. (Text in Japanese, English; summaries, tables of contents in English) 1953. a. free. Chiba University, Faculty of Horticulture - Chiba Daigaku Engeigakubu, 648 Matsudo, Matsudo-shi, Chiba 271, Japan. FAX 0473-66-2234. circ. 750. **Indexed:** Bio-Contr.News & Info., Biol.Abstr., Field Crop Abstr., Helminthol.Abstr., Herb.Abstr., Hort.Abstr., INIS Atomind., Ornam.Hort., Rev.Plant Path, Rice Abstr., Seed Abstr., Soils & Fert., World Agri.Econ.& Rural Sociol.Abstr. **Document type:** bulletin.

635   UK
CHILEANS. 1960. a. £16($33) 5 Lyons Ave., Hetton-le-Hole DH5 OHS, England. TEL 091-526-3324. (Subscr. to: R. Purvis, 19 Brooks Dr., Fairlands, Guilford GU3 3ND, England) Ed. H. Middleditch. bk.rev.; illus. circ. 500. (back issues avail.)
Description: Cacti and succulents of South America: cultivation, identification, conservation.

635   NE   ISSN 0578-039X
CHRONICA HORTICULTURAE. 1961. 4/yr. fl.88. International Society for Horticultural Science, Englaan 1, 6703 ET Wageningen, Netherlands. TEL 31-8370-21747. FAX 31-8370-21586. Ed. J.J.M.G. Van Assche. adv. circ. 3,500. **Indexed:** Agri.Eng.Abstr., Biol.Abstr., Hort.Abstr. **Document type:** bulletin.
—SWETS.
Description: Bulletin for members of the Society.

635   US   ISSN 0090-5771
SB413.C55
CHRYSANTHEMUM. 1945. q. $12.50. National Chrysanthemum Society, Inc., c/o Galen L. Goss, Sec., 10107 Homar Pond Dr., Fairfax Station, VA 22039-1650. TEL 703-978-7981. Ed. Robert Knox. circ. 1,800. (back issues avail.) **Document type:** bulletin.
Description: How-to information on growing chrysanthemums.

CIENCIA Y TECNICA EN LA AGRICULTURA. SERIE: VIANDAS TROPICALES. see *AGRICULTURE — Crop Production And Soil*

635   NZ   ISSN 0009-7705
CITY BEAUTIFUL. 1928. 2/yr. (plus a. suppls.). NZ.$15 to non-members. Canterbury Horticultural Society, Inc., P.O. Box 369, Christchurch, New Zealand. Ed. Jean Grierson. adv.; bk.rev. circ. 2,600. (processed; avail. on records)
—CCC.

635.9   UK
CLASSIFIED DIRECTORY OF DAHLIAS AND GUIDE TO JUDGING. 1946. biennial. £1.75. National Dahlia Society, c/o A.G. Winkless, Gen. Sec., 8 Station Rd., Kirby Muxloe, Leicester LE9 9EJ, England. TEL 0533-387717. adv. circ. 4,000.
Description: Guide to classified dahlias and to current rules for judging dahlias.

635   CN
COGNITION. 4/yr. membership only. Canadian Organic Growers, 146 Elveston Dr., Toronto, Ont. M4A 1N6, Canada. TEL 416-848-9345.

COLORADO HOMES & LIFESTYLES. see *INTERIOR DESIGN AND DECORATION*

635   IT   ISSN 0390-0444
COLTURE PROTETTE. Short title: C P. 1972. m. (11/yr.). L.68000 (effective 1993). Edagricole s.p.a., Via Emilia Levante 31, 40139 Bologna, Italy. TEL 051-492211. FAX 051-493600. Ed. Ranieri Favilli. adv.: B&W page L.950000, color page L.1550000; 185 x 247. circ. 21,850. **Indexed:** Agri.Eng.Abstr., Crop Physiol.Abstr., Field Crop Abstr., Forest.Abstr., Forest Prod.Abstr., Hort.Abstr., Irr.& Drain.Abstr., Ornam.Hort., Plant Grow.Reg.Abstr., Potato Abstr., Seed Abstr., Soils & Fert., Weed Abstr., World Agri.Econ.& Rural Sociol.Abstr.
—BLDSC (3322.940000).
Description: Deals with all problems concerning production methods and equipment for flower and vegetable growing.

634 635   SP
COMERCIALIZACION HORTOFRUTICOLA. 12/yr. Plaza del Runto, Edificio Anton 8o, 21003 Huelva, Spain. TEL 955-26-27-30. FAX 955-243-769. Ed. Francisco Mampel.

635   AT
SB317.65.A8
COMMONWEALTH SCIENTIFIC AND INDUSTRIAL RESEARCH ORGANIZATION. DIVISION OF HORTICULTURE. REPORT. 1962. biennial. free. C.S.I.R.O., Division of Horticulture, G.P.O. Box 350, Adelaide, S.A. 5001, Australia. TEL 08-303-8600. FAX 618-303-8601. TELEX 82406. Ed. A. Brennan. circ. 1,000 (controlled). **Indexed:** Biol.Abstr., Field Crop Abstr., Herb.Abstr., Hort.Abstr. **Document type:** corporate report.
Formerly: Commonwealth Scientific and Industrial Research Organization. Division of Horticultural Research. Report (ISSN 0069-7435)

635   US
COMMUNITY GREENING REVIEW. a. membership. American Community Gardening Association, 325 Walnut St., Philadelphia, PA 19106. Ed. Marc Breslav. circ. 300. (back issues avail.)
Former titles: Journal of Community Gardening; A C G A Journal.
Description: Provides a forum to stimulate discussion stressing community and expanding the gardening to include all types of greening efforts. Highlights programs and resources from around the country, legislative developments related to community gardening, land acquisition and funding techniques, horticultural topics, activities for youth, seniors and handicapped.

COMPOSTING NEWS. see *ENVIRONMENTAL STUDIES — Waste Management*

632.97   US   ISSN 0742-1516
CONNECTICUT GREENHOUSE NEWSLETTER. bi-m. c/o Richard J. McAvoy, Dept. of Plant Science, U-67, 1276 Storrs Rd., University of Connecticut, Storrs, CT 06269. **Document type:** newsletter.
—BLDSC (3417.640000).

635 643.7   NZ   ISSN 0113-6739
CONSUMER HOME AND GARDEN. 1988. q. NZ.$32.50 (effective 1994). Consumers' Institute, Private Bag 6996, Te Aro, Wellington 6035, New Zealand. TEL 64-4-384-7963. FAX 64-4-385-8752. adv.; circ. 35,000 (paid). **Document type:** consumer publication.
Description: Covers consumer testing and research: gardening, home improvements, do-it-yourself.

CORNELL PLANTATIONS. see *COLLEGE AND ALUMNI*

635   UK
THE COTTAGE GARDENER. 1982. 4/yr. £5 single membership ($20); joint membership £8 ($30). Cottage Garden Society, 5 Nixon Close, Thornhill, Dewsbury, W. Yorks. WF12 0JA, England. TEL 0924-468469. Ed. Pat Taylor. adv. contact: Pat Taylor. bk.rev.; circ. 7,000 (controlled). **Document type:** newsletter.
Formerly: Cottage Garden Society. Newsletter.
Description: Contains articles on gardening, letters, quizzes, and local group information.

COUNTRY GARDEN. see *AGRICULTURE*

635   US
COUNTRY GARDENS. a. $3.95 per no. Meredith Magazine Group, 70 W. 36th St., 15th Fl., New York, NY 10018. TEL 212-594-9044. FAX 212-594-2389.

COUNTRY LIVING (OWEGO). see *CONSERVATION*

CROSSOSOMA. see *BIOLOGY — Botany*

CROSSWORDS. see *BIOLOGY — Botany*

CRUCIFERAE NEWSLETTER. see *AGRICULTURE*

635   US   ISSN 1060-1236
CRYPTANTHUS SOCIETY. JOURNAL. 1986. 4/yr. $10 (foreign $15). Cryptanthus Society, 2355 Rusk, Beaumont, TX 77702. TEL 409-835-0644. FAX 409-835-5265. adv.; bk.rev. circ. 750.

CULTIVAR. see *AGRICULTURE*

CYCAD SOCIETY NEWSLETTER. see *BIOLOGY — Botany*

635   UK   ISSN 0143-3571
CYCLAMEN JOURNAL. 1976. 2/yr. $15 membership only. Cyclamen Society, Little Pilgrims, 2 Pilgrims Way East, Otford, Sevenoaks, Kent TN14 5QN, England. TEL 44-959-522322. adv.; bk.rev. circ. 900. **Document type:** academic/scholarly publication.
Description: Contains articles on propagation and cultivation, cyclamen in the wild, new strains of pot-plant cultivars and breeding reports.

635.934   US   ISSN 0011-5290
DAFFODIL JOURNAL. 1964. q. $20 membership. American Daffodil Society, Inc., 1686 Grey Fox Trails, Milford, OH 45150. Ed. Katherine Frank. adv.; bk.rev.; index. circ. 1,400. **Document type:** bulletin.

635.9   UK   ISSN 0070-2544
DAFFODILS. 1913. a. £4.99. Royal Horticultural Society, Vincent Sq., London SW1P 2PE, England. TEL 01-834-4333. Ed. Susanne Mitchell. circ. 1,000. **Indexed:** Rev.Plant Path. **Document type:** bulletin.
Formerly (until 1970): Daffodil and Tulip Year Book.

635   US
DAHLIAS OF TODAY. 1981. a. $15 membership only. Puget Sound Dahlia Association, Box 5602, Bellevue, WA 98006. adv. circ. 3,000.
Formerly: Puget Sound Dahlia Association. Bulletin.

635   LV   ISSN 0132-6457
DARZS UN DRAVA/GARDENING AND BEEKEEPING. (Text in Latvian; summaries in Russian) 1958. m. $160. Izdevejs Darzs un Drava Ltd., Balasta Dambis, 3, Riga LV-1081, Latvia. TEL 371-2-465-758. adv.; bk.rev. circ. 12,000. (back issues avail.)

635.9   US   ISSN 0744-0219
SB413.D3
DAYLILY JOURNAL; daylily gardener's magazine. 1946. q. $18 includes membership. American Hemerocallis Society, Inc., 6635 Highway E, Edgerton, MO 64444. TEL 816-227-3384. (Subscr. to: c/o Elly Launius, 1454 Rebel Dr., Jackson, MS 39211) Ed. Frances L. Gatlin. adv. contact: Frances L. Gatlin. bk.rev.; charts; illus. circ. 7,200.
Formerly: Hemerocallis Journal (ISSN 0018-0297)

634   SA   ISSN 0011-7285
DECIDUOUS FRUIT GROWER/SAGTEVRUGTEBOER. (Text in Afrikaans and English) 1951. m. R.64.98 (foreign R.85) (effective 1994). Deciduous Fruit Board, Parc du Cap, P.O. Box 1801, 7535 Bellville, South Africa. TEL 27-21-9461066. FAX 27-21-9461967. TELEX 555025. Ed. H. Wenhold. adv.; bk.rev.; charts; illus.; mkt.; stat.; index. circ. 4,500. **Indexed:** Agri.Eng.Abstr., Agroforest.Abstr., Biodet.Abstr., Crop Physiol.Abstr., Excerpt.Med., Hort.Abstr., Ind.S.A.Per., INIS Atomind., Plant Breed.Abstr., Plant Grow.Reg.Abstr., W.R.C.Inf.

635   UK
DELPHINIUM SOCIETY YEARBOOK. 1929. a. £6($10) (effective 1994). Delphinium Society, c/o Mrs. Shirley Bassett, Takakkaw, Ice House Wood, Oxted, Surrey RH8 9DW, England. Ed. L. Cooper. adv.; bk.rev. circ. 1,500.

635   GW   ISSN 0011-992X
DEUTSCHE BAUMSCHULE. 1949. m. DM.189. Verlag Dr. Rudolf Georgi GmbH und Co. KG, Theaterstr. 77, Postfach 407, 52062 Aachen, Germany. TEL 0241-477-910. FAX 0241-477-9160. Ed. Helmut Maethe. adv.; bk.rev.; abstr.; charts; illus.; stat.; index. circ. 3,700. **Indexed:** Biol.Abstr., Forest.Abstr., Hort.Abstr., Irr.& Drain.Abstr., Ornam.Hort., Rural Recreat.Tour.Abstr., Soils & Fert., Weed Abstr., World Agri.Econ.& Rural Sociol.Abstr.
—BLDSC (3563.400000). **CCC.**

GARDENING AND HORTICULTURE 2633

635   GW   ISSN 0341-2091
DEUTSCHER GARTENBAU; ueberregionale Fachzeitschrift fuer alle Sparten des Gartenbaus. 1947. w. DM.338. Verlag Eugen Ulmer GmbH, Wollgrasweg 41, 70599 Stuttgart, Germany. TEL 0711-4507-0. FAX 0711-4507-120. TELEX 723634-ULMER-D. (Subscr. to: Postfach 700561, 70574 Stuttgart, Germany) Ed. Gerd Heinrichs. adv.; bk.rev.; charts; illus.; stat. circ. 9,300. **Indexed:** Excerp.Med., Hort.Abstr., Irr.& Drain.Abstr., Ornam.Hort., Plant Grow.Reg.Abstr., Rural Recreat.Tour.Abstr., Seed Abstr., Soils & Fert., Weed Abstr., World Agri.Econ.& Rural Sociol.Abstr. **Document type:** consumer publication.
—CCC.
   Formerly: Erwerbsgaertner.

DEVELOPMENTS IN LANDSCAPE MANAGEMENT AND URBAN PLANNING. see *HOUSING AND URBAN PLANNING*

DOEHETZELF. see *HOME ECONOMICS*

635   US
DWARF CONIFER NOTES. irreg. Theophrastus, Box 458, Little Compton, RI 02837-0458.
   Description: Presents news on conifers and other subjects.

635.9   US   ISSN 0418-2057
DWARF IRIS SOCIETY PORTFOLIO.* 1952. a. $2. American Iris Society, Dwarf Iris Society, c/o James W. Fry, 1052 Cardinal Way, Palo Alto, CA 94303-3540. TEL 316-686-8734. illus. circ. 300. (processed)

635.9   AT   ISSN 1033-0003
EARLY MORN AFRICAN VIOLET GROUP NEWSLETTER. 1975. m. Aus.$12. Early Morn African Violet Group Inc., 48 Haig St., Burwood, Vic. 3125, Australia. TEL 03-807-9642. (Subscr. to: Alice Steadson, Membership Sec., 1-217 Blackburn Rd., Doncaster East, Vic. 3109, Australia) Ed. Marhorie Lambert. circ. 240 (paid).
   Description: Studies Gesneriads; African violets and others.

635   US
▼**EASY GARDENING.** 1993. a. newsstand price: $2.95. New York Times Women's Magazines, Special Interest Publications, 110 Fifth Ave., New York, NY 10011. TEL 212-463-1275. FAX 212-463-1912. adv.: B&W page $16440, color page $21000; trim 8 x 10 1/2. circ. 600,000. **Document type:** consumer publication.

635   US
▼**EASY LAWN & GARDEN.** 1994. bi-m. plus a. supplement. $15; newsstand price: 295. Aqua-Field Publishing Company, 66 W. Gilbert St., Shrewsbury, NJ 07702. TEL 908-842-8300. FAX 908-842-0281. (Subscr. to: National Gardening Magazine, Box 51106, Boulder, CO 80321-1106) Ed. Edward Montague; Pub. Stephen Ferber. adv. contact: Susan Bernard. **Document type:** consumer publication.
   Description: Offers gardening and fertilizing tips aimed primarily at the beginner.

635   UA   ISSN 1110-0206
EGYPTIAN JOURNAL OF HORTICULTURE. (Text in English; summaries in Arabic and English) 1966. s-a. $57 (effective 1994). (Egyptian Horticultural Society, Research Department) National Information and Documentation Centre (NIDOC), Tahrir St., Dokki, Awqaf P.O., Cairo, Egypt. TEL 20-2-701696. Ed. Y.A. Wally. charts; illus. circ. 2,000. (back issues avail.; reprint service avail. from IRC) **Indexed:** Biol.Abstr., Chem.Abstr., Field Crop Abstr., Food Sci.& Tech.Abstr., Herb.Abstr., Hort.Abstr., Packag.Sci.Tech., Rev.Plant Path., Soils & Fert. **Document type:** academic/scholarly publication.

635   AU
EIPELDAUERS GARTENMAGAZIN. m. Hugo H. Hitschmann Verlag GmbH, Inkustr. 1-7, A-3400 Klosterneuburg, Austria. TEL 02243-8868626. FAX 02243-8868656. Ed. Herta Eipeldauer. adv.: B&W page S.15900, color page S.28500; trim 191 x 273; adv. contact: Evelyne Hampel. circ. 26,000. **Document type:** consumer publication.

635   GW   ISSN 0013-2772
EISENBAHN-LANDWIRT. 1917. m. (Hauptverband der Bundesbahn-Landwirtschaft e.V.) Druckhaus Karlsruhe GmbH, Ostring 6, 76131 Karlshue, Germany. adv. circ. 120,000.

635   JA
ENGEI GAIDO/GUIDE TO GARDENING. (Text in Japanese) 1973. q. 5000 Yen. Shufunotomo Co. Ltd., 2-9 Kanda Surugadai, Chiyoda-ku, Tokyo 101, Japan. Ed. Masuo Tabuchi. adv.; bk.rev. circ. 150,000. **Document type:** consumer publication.

333.7 712   US
ENVIRONMENTAL LANDSCAPE NEWS. q. $25. California Xeriscape Foundation, 16176 Mesa Robles Dr., Hacienda Heights, CA 91745. **Document type:** newsletter.

635   US
ENVIRONMENTARIAN. 1988. m. $25. Wild Food Inc., 3531 Glendale Ave., Ste. 369, Phoenix, AZ 85051. Ed. Linda Runyon. circ. 180.
   Description: Provides information about wild food identification, and foraging techniques.

L'ERBORISTA. see *PHARMACY AND PHARMACOLOGY*

634   GW   ISSN 0014-0309
ERWERBSOBSTBAU. 1959. m. DM.188($125) Verlag Paul Parey (Berlin), Seelbuschring 9-17, 12105 Berlin, Germany. TEL 030-70784-0. FAX 030-70784199. Ed.Bd. adv.; bk.rev.; charts; illus.; index. (back issues avail.) **Indexed:** Agri.Eng.Abstr., Crop Physiol.Abstr., Food Sci.& Tech.Abstr., Hort.Abstr., Plant Breed.Abstr., Plant Grow.Reg.Abstr., Rural Recreat.Tour.Abstr., Weed Abstr., World Agri.Econ.& Rural Sociol.Abstr. **Document type:** consumer publication.
—SWETS. CCC.

712   CN   ISSN 0846-5339
ESPACES VERTS. 1988. 7/yr. Can.$33. Editions Versicolores Inc., 1320 Saint-Joseph Blvd., Quebec, PQ G2K 1G2, Canada. TEL 418-628-8690. FAX 418-628-0524. Ed. Francois Bertrand; Pub. Francois Bernatchez. adv. contact: Paul Poisson. circ. 2,290. **Document type:** trade publication.
   Formerly: Bulletin d'Information sur l'Entretien et l'Amenagement des Espaces Verts (ISSN 0840-7428)

ESSEX HOMES & LIVING. see *INTERIOR DESIGN AND DECORATION*

635   US   ISSN 0737-8823
SB413.E95
EUPHORBIA JOURNAL. 1982. a. $45. Strawberry Press, 227 Strawberry Dr., Mill Valley, CA 94941. TEL 415-388-5017. FAX 415-381-9628. Ed. Dr. Herman Schwartz. index, cum.index. circ. 5,000. (back issues avail.) **Document type:** academic/scholarly publication.
   Description: Contains articles by world authorities and encyclopedic descriptive and photographic studies of all the world's euphorbias.

634   IT
EUROFRUTTA. 1965. m. L.3500. Associazione Grossisti Ortofrutticoli, Via Lombroso 54, Milan, Italy. Ed. Mario Invernizzi. adv. circ. 8,000.

EXCELSA. see *BIOLOGY — Botany*

F P I: FLOWERING PLANT INDEX. see *BIOLOGY — Abstracting, Bibliographies, Statistics*

635   GW   ISSN 0014-6315
FACHBERATER FUER DAS DEUTSCHE KLEINGARTENWESEN.* 1951. q. DM.8. (Bundesverband Deutscher Kleingaertner e.V.) Druckhaus Karlsruhe, Ostring 6, Postfach 2026, 7500 Karlsruhe 1, Germany. Ed. Johann Dreyer. adv.; bk.rev.; illus. circ. 5,000.

635.95   US   ISSN 0014-6943
QK73.U62
FAIRCHILD TROPICAL GARDEN BULLETIN. 1945. q. $10 (foreign $14). Fairchild Tropical Garden, 10901 Old Cutler Rd., Miami, FL 33156. TEL 305-667-1651. FAX 305-661-8953. Ed. Karen Nagle. bk.rev.; charts; illus. circ. 5,000. **Indexed:** Gard.Lit. (1992-). **Document type:** bulletin.
   Description: Articles geared to amateur gardeners, horticulturists and botanists.

635   GW   ISSN 0170-5512
FAMILIENHEIM UND GARTEN. 1949. m. DM.20.40. Familienheim und Garten Verlagsgesellschaft mbH, Neefestr. 2a, 53115 Bonn, Germany. TEL 0228-695254. FAX 0228-695255. Ed. Manfred Rosenthal. adv.: B&W page DM.7700, color page DM.13300; trim 269 x 191; adv. contact: Gerd Boeker. circ. 314,503. **Document type:** consumer publication.
   Formerly (until 1978): Siedler (ISSN 0170-5520)

FARMING UNCLE; periodical for natural people and mother nature lovers. see *AGRICULTURE*

635   US   ISSN 0733-8015
FIDDLEHEAD FORUM. 1974. 6/yr. $8 (foreign $10). American Fern Society (Bronx), c/o Dr. John Mickel, Ed., New York Botanical Garden, Bronx, NY 10458-5126. TEL 718-817-8636. bk.rev. circ. 1,400. **Document type:** bulletin.
—BLDSC (3918.825000); SWETS.
   Description: Contains horticultural and botanical notes, regarding ferns, and society business.

635   US
FIG LEAFLET. 4/yr. membership only. Friends of the Fig, 5715 W. Paul Bryant Dr., Crystal River, FL 32629. TEL 904-795-0439.
   Description: Promotes the propagation of figs, and provides a medium for the exchange of information, fig plants, and scions.

635   US   ISSN 0896-6281
FINE GARDENING. 1988. bi-m. $26. Taunton Press, Inc., 63 S. Main St. Box 5506, Newton, CT 06470-5506. TEL 203-426-8171. FAX 203-426-3434. Ed. Nancy Beaubaire. circ. 150,000. **Indexed:** Access (1994-), Gard.Lit. (1992-), Ind.How To Do It (1988-). **Document type:** consumer publication.
—UnCover.
   Description: Articles featuring "hands-on" knowledge aimed at experienced and novice gardeners, with an emphasis on landscape design.

632   BU   ISSN 0324-0290
QK710   CODEN: FIRADV
FIZIOLOGIIA NA RASTENIIATA. (Text in Bulgarian; summaries in English and Russian) 1974. q. 2.70 lv. per no. (Bulgarska Akademiia na Naukite) Publishing House of the Bulgarian Academy of Sciences, Acad. G. Bonchev St., Bldg. 6, 1113 Sofia, Bulgaria. (Dist. by: Hemus, 6, Rouski Blvd., 1000 Sofia, Bulgaria) (Co-sponsor: Akademiia na Selskostopanskite Nauk) Ed. Todor Kadrev. bibl.; illus. circ. 470. (reprint service avail. from IRC) **Indexed:** Biol.Abstr., BSL Biol., Excerp.Med., Fababean Abstr., Field Crop Abstr., Irr.& Drain.Abstr., Maize Abstr., Plant Grow.Reg.Abstr., Soils & Fert., VITIS.
—CASDDS.
   Formerly: Bulgarska Akademiia na Naukite. Institut po Fiziologiia na Rasteniiata "Metodii Popov." Izvestiia (ISSN 0007-3970)

635   CN   ISSN 1180-159X
FLEURS, PLANTES ET JARDINS. 1990. a. Can.$28.95. Editions Versicolores Inc., 1320 St-Joseph Blvd., Quebec, PQ G2K 1G2, Canada. TEL 418-628-8690. FAX 418-628-0524. Ed. Larry Hodgson; Pub. Francois Bernatchez. adv. contact: Paul Poisson. circ. 50,000. **Document type:** consumer publication.

635   GW
FLORA (HAMBURG). Schoene Pflanzen fuer Haus und Garten. 1985. m. DM.44.40 (Europe DM.74.40; elsewhere DM.120). Gruner und Jahr AG & Co., Am Baumwall 11, 20459 Hamburg, Germany. TEL 040-3703-0. FAX 040-37035606. adv.; bk.rev.; charts; illus.; index. circ. 302,364. (back issues avail.) **Document type:** consumer publication.
   Description: Information about indoor and garden plants for leisure gardeners.

635   US   ISSN 1051-9076
FLORACULTURE INTERNATIONAL. 1990. 8/yr. $51. International Horticulture Publications, Box 9, 335 N. River St., Batavia, IL 61510-0009. TEL 708-208-9080. FAX 708-208-9350. Ed. D.J. Hamrick. circ. 11,000 (controlled). **Document type:** trade publication.
   Description: Covers floriculture production worldwide.

2634 GARDENING AND HORTICULTURE

635 US ISSN 0741-1448
FLORIDA FOLIAGE.* (Annual directory and buyer's guide avail.: Florida Foliage Locator) 1977. m. $30 (foreign $50). Florida Foliage Association, 5401 S. Kirkman Rd., Ste. 650, Orlando, FL 32819-7911. TEL 407-886-1036. FAX 407-886-9585. Ed. Barbara Hollerand. adv.; bk.rev. circ. 2,500. **Indexed:** Hort.Abstr.
—UnCover.

FLORIDA HOME & GARDEN. see *INTERIOR DESIGN AND DECORATION*

635 US ISSN 1065-1683
FLORIDA NURSERYMAN.* 1952. m. $18 (effective 1993). Harvest Publications, Box 9125, Winter Harvest, FL 33883-9125. TEL 813-666-3184. FAX 813-665-8251. adv.; bk.rev.; tr.lit. circ. 9,959. (back issues avail.)
Description: Features research, marketing and business trends for industry professionals.

635 IT
FLORTECNICA. 12/yr. Ace International, Via Mocomero 26, 29010 Vernasca (PC), Italy. TEL 39-50-93-52. Ed. Arturo Croci. circ. 6,500.

635 US ISSN 0162-3249
FLOWER AND GARDEN; the world's gardening magazine. 1957. bi-m. $12.95. K C Publishing Inc., 700 47th St., Ste. 310, Kansas City, MO 64112. TEL 816-531-5730. FAX 816-531-3873. Ed. Kay M. Olson. adv.: B&W page $10500, color page $14735. bk.rev.; charts; illus.; index. circ. 738,311. (also avail. in microfilm from UMI; reprint service avail. from UMI) **Indexed:** Consum.Ind., Gard.Lit. (1992-), Ind.How To Do It (1979-), Mag.Ind., PMR, R.G. **Document type:** consumer publication.
●Also available online. Vendor(s): DIALOG Information Services, Inc.
Supersedes: Flower and Garden. Southern Edition (ISSN 0162-3230); Flower and Garden. Northern Edition; Flower and Garden. Western Edition.
Description: Covers gardening and home lawn care. Contains important information, helpful advice and timely tips on planting and caring for flowers vegetables, trees, shrubbery and lawns.

THE FLOWER ARRANGER. see *ARTS AND HANDICRAFTS*

FOLIA DENDROLOGICA. see *FORESTS AND FORESTRY*

712
FOLIA DI ACER; rivista di architettura del paesaggio, cultura dell'ambiente e informazione editoriale. q. L.40000. Verde Editoriale, Via Bolchini 12, 21100 Varese, Italy. TEL 0332-457288. Ed. Giovanni Sala.

FOUR SEASONS (BERKELEY). see *BIOLOGY — Botany*

635 PL ISSN 0015-931X
QK1 CODEN: FRFGAF
FRAGMENTA FLORISTICA ET GEOBOTANICA. (Text in Polish; summaries in English) 1954. q. price varies. Polska Akademia Nauk, Instytut Botaniki - Polish Academy of Sciences, Institute of Botany, Ul. Lubicz 46, 31-512 Krakow, Poland. (Dist. by: Ars Polona, Krakowskie Przedmiescie 7, 00-068 Warsaw, Poland) Ed. Adam Jasiewicz. bibl.; charts; illus. circ. 680. **Indexed:** Biol.Abstr., Field Crop Abstr., GeoRef, Herb.Abstr., Plant Breed.Abstr., Rev.Plant Path.
—BLDSC (4032.100000).

635 GW ISSN 0016-0946
DER FREIZEITGAERTNER; Fachzeitschrift fuer Gartenfreunde und Siedler. 1963. m. DM.29. Verlag Huesken, Am Ellenbogen 12, Postfach 110664, 45355 Essen, Germany. adv. circ. 12,000.

634 US ISSN 1072-2831
▼**FRESH CUT**; the magazine for value-added produce. 1993. 6/yr. $15 (Canada & Mexico $30; elsewhere $45). Columbia Publishing and Design, 2809-A Fruitvale Blvd., Box 1467, Yakima, WA 98907-1467. TEL 509-248-2452; 800-900-2452. FAX 509-248-4056. Ed. Ken Hodge. circ. 5,984. (back issues avail.) **Document type:** trade publication.

635 DK ISSN 0046-5224
FRUGT, GROENT OG BLOMSTER; gartner nyt. 1914. m. membership. Landsorganisation Danmarks Frugthandlere Frugthandlerforeningen af 1889, Hambros Alle 3, 2900 Hellerup, Denmark. Ed. O. Lyngbaek. adv. circ. 1,200.
Formerly: Frugthandlerbladet.

634 US ISSN 1049-4545
FRUIT GARDENER. 1969. 6/yr. $16 (Canada and Mexico $25; elsewhere $30). California Rare Fruit Growers, Inc., c/o Sue Irvine, 9872 Aldgate Ave., Garden Grove, CA 92641. TEL 714-638-1796. FAX 714-744-1705. Ed. Clytia M. Chambers. adv. contact: Jane Bainter. bk.rev. circ. 3,000. **Document type:** consumer publication.
Description: For better understanding on growing sub-tropical fruits, and unusual vegetables.

634 UK ISSN 0953-2188
FRUIT GROWER. 1985. m. £16 (foreign £25.60). A.C.T. Publishing, Lamberhurst Rd., Horsmonden, Kent TN12 8DP, England. TEL 0892-724277. FAX 0892-722516. Ed. John R. Jarrett. bk.rev. circ. 3,200. (back issues avail.) **Indexed:** Agri.Eng.Abstr., Hort.Abstr. **Document type:** trade publication.
Description: Publishes research articles, industry news and company profiles geared to European fruit growers and packers.

634 581 PL ISSN 0137-1479
CODEN: FSREDB
FRUIT SCIENCE REPORTS. (Text in English) 1974. q. 100000 Zl.($16) Research Institute of Pomology and Floriculture - Instytut Sadownictwa i Kwiaciarstwa, Ul. Pomologiczna 18, 96-100 Skierniewice, Poland. TEL 48-40-20-21. FAX 01148-40-3228. TELEX 886659 INSAD. Ed. L. Michalczuk. circ. 1,000. **Indexed:** Agrindex, Biol.Abstr., Chem.Abstr, Crop Physiol.Abstr., Curr.Adv.Ecol.Sci., Helminthol.Abstr., Hort.Abstr., Plant Grow.Reg.Abstr., Ref.Zh., Seed Abstr., Soils & Fert., VITIS, Weed Abstr. **Document type:** academic/scholarly publication.
—BLDSC (4042.960000); CASDDS.

635 634 US ISSN 0091-3642
SB354 CODEN: FVRJAA
FRUIT VARIETIES JOURNAL. 1946. q. $20 (foreign $32). American Pomological Society, c/o Dr. Robert M. Crassweller, Bus. Mgr., 103 Tyson Bldg., University Park, PA 16802. TEL 814-863-6163. FAX 814-863-6139. Ed. David C. Ferree. adv.; bk.rev.; abstr.; charts; illus.; index. circ. 1,000. (also avail. in microform from UMI; reprint service avail. from UMI,ISI) **Indexed:** Biol.Abstr., Curr.Adv.Ecol.Sci., Curr.Cont., Hort.Abstr., Plant Breed.Abstr., Soils & Fert., Weed Abstr.
—BLDSC (4043.100000); Faxon; UnCover; UMI; CASDDS.
Formerly (until 1972): Fruit Varieties and Horticultural Digest (ISSN 0016-2272)
Description: Reports introductions and evaluations of fruit varieties and rootstocks of interest to professional horticulturists and fruit breeders, fruit growers, amateur fruit breeders and testers, nurserymen and gardeners.

635 FR ISSN 0248-1294
CODEN: FRUIAS
FRUITS; fruits tropicaux, culture, industrie, economie. (Text in French, summaries in English, French, Spanish) 1945. bi-m. 400 F. (foreign 500 F.) (effective Jan. 1994). C I R A D, Departement des Productions Fruitiers et Horticoles, Avenue du Val-de-Montferrand, B.P. 5035, 34032 Montpellier Cedex, France. TEL 67-61-58-65. FAX 67-61-55-13. TELEX 485 631 IFRAMON F. Ed. Chantal Loison. adv.; bk.rev.; bibl.; illus. circ. 2,500. (also avail. in microfilm) **Indexed:** Agri.Eng.Abstr., Agri.Ind., Bibl.Agri., Bio-Contr.News & Info., Biol.Abstr., Biotech.Abstr., Chem.Abstr., Crop Physiol.Abstr., Curr.Cont., Dairy Sci.Abstr., Field Crop Abstr., Food Sci.& Tech.Abstr., Hort.Abstr., Irr.& Drain.Abstr., Maize Abstr., Plant Grow.Reg.Abstr., Seed Abstr., Soils & Fert., Sugar Ind.Abstr., Trop.Oil Seeds Abstr., World Agri.Econ.& Rural Sociol.Abstr.
—BLDSC (4045.000000); SWETS; CASDDS.
Formed by the 1978 merger of: Fruits A (ISSN 0248-1308); Fruits B (ISSN 0248-1316); Which supersedes: Fruits (ISSN 0016-2299); Which was formerly: Fruits d'Outre-Mer (ISSN 0367-2816).
Description: Focuses on the botany, ecology, plantation management, plant protection and use of tropical fruits.

635 UK ISSN 0071-9730
FUCHSIA ANNUAL. 1938. a. £5. British Fuchsia Society, 20 Brodawel Llannon, Llanelli, Dyfed SA14 6BJ, Wales. TEL 0269-843798. adv.; bk.rev. circ. 5,000.

635 US
FUCHSIA FAN. 1951. bi-m. $15 membership. National Fuchsia Society, 11507 E. 187th St., Artesia, CA 90701. TEL 310-865-1806. Ed. Robin Whitecotton. adv.; bk.rev. circ. 600. **Document type:** bulletin.

635 US
FUCHSIA FLASH. 1983. 10/yr. $10 (foreign $12). Northwest Fuchsia Society, Box 33071, Bitter Lake Sta., Seattle, WA 98133-0071. TEL 202-364-7735. Ed. Joan Hampton. adv.; bk.rev. circ. 400. **Document type:** bulletin.
Formerly: Northwest Fuchsia Society. Bulletin.

FUJI TAKERUI SHOKUBUTSUEN HOKOKU/FUJI BAMBOO GARDEN. REPORTS. see *BIOLOGY — Botany*

645 JA
FURORA FUKUSHIMA/FLORA FUKUSHIMA. (Text in Japanese) a. Fukushimaken Shokubutsu Kenkyukai - Botanical Society of Fukushima, c/o Mr. Toshio Higuchi, 3-16 Yachinaka, Sasaya, Fukushima-shi, Fukushima-ken 960-02, Japan.

FUTURE FARMERS OF AMERICA. NEWSLETTER. see *AGRICULTURE*

635.95 US ISSN 0016-3627
G S N. GESNERIAD SAINTPAULIA NEWS.* 1964. bi-m. $12.75 (foreign $15.75). Gesneriad Society, c/o Stoehr, 2206 Queen Elizabeth Ct., Ste. 8, Indianapolis, IN 46227-6577. TEL 317-862-4695. (Co-sponsor: Saintpaulia International) Ed. Walter Maurus. adv.; bk.rev.; charts; illus.; index. circ. 9,000.

635 AU
GAERTNER KURIER. 25/yr. Bankgasse 1-3, A-1014 Vienna, Austria. TEL 01-5330461. FAX 01-533967656. TELEX 114030. circ. 4,500.

635 GW ISSN 0936-3734
GAERTNERBOERSE UND GARTENWELT; Gb und Gw. 1900. w. DM.208($139) Verlag Paul Parey (Hamburg), Spitalerstr. 12, 20095 Hamburg, Germany. TEL 040-33969-0. FAX 040-33969-199. TELEX 2161391-PARV-D. Ed. Walter Fikuart. adv.; bk.rev.; abstr.; bibl.; charts; illus.; stat.; index. circ. 7,400. (back issues avail.) **Indexed:** Agri.Eng.Abstr., Chem.Abstr., Hort.Abstr., Ornam.Hort., Plant Grow.Reg.Abstr., Rural Recreat.Tour.Abstr., World Agri.Econ.& Rural Sociol.Abstr. **Document type:** consumer publication.
—SWETS.
Formerly: G B und G W - Gaertnerboerse und Gartenwelt; Which was formed by merger of: Deutsche Gaertnerboerse (ISSN 0012-0138); Gartenwelt (ISSN 0016-4798)

635 GW ISSN 0301-2719
GAERTNERISCHE BERUFSPRAXIS. (Series A: Produktionsgartenbau; Series B: Landschafts- und Sportplatzbau) 1937. irreg. price varies. Verlag Paul Parey (Berlin), Seelbusching 9-17, 12105 Berlin, Germany. TEL 030-70784-0. FAX 030-70784199. bibl.; illus.; index. **Document type:** bulletin.

635 GW ISSN 0724-7281
GAFA - GARTENFACHHANDEL SAATGUTWIRTSCHAFT. m. DM.90. Hortus Zeitschriften Coellen und Bleeck GbR, Rheinallee 4A, 53173 Bonn, Germany. TEL 0228-353030. FAX 0228-353033. **Document type:** trade publication.
Description: For the German and international green market.

635 FR ISSN 0768-7516
GAMMES JARDIN. 1986. 6/yr. Bureau Europeen de Presse et de Publicite, 59 rue du Faubourg-Poissonniere, 75009 Paris, France. TEL 47-70-94-62. FAX 45-23-36-81. Ed. Michel Chansiaux. circ. 9,000.

635 712 IS ISSN 0016-4402
SB403
GAN V'NOF/GARDEN AND LANDSCAPE. (Text in Hebrew; contents page in English and Hebrew) 1945. 10/yr. $60. Israel Landscape and Gardening Association, P.O. Box 40035, Tel Aviv, Israel. TEL 972-3-9429993. FAX 972-3-5429996. Ed. Tair Zvulun. adv.; bk.rev.; illus. circ. 4,000.

GARDENING AND HORTICULTURE

635 UK
SB4
THE GARDEN. 1804. m. £19. Maxwell International Contract Publishing, Greater London House, Hampstead Rd., London NW1 7QQ, England. Ed. Suzanne Mitchell. bk.rev.; illus.; index; cum.index every 10 yrs: 1956-1965. circ. 133,599. (back issues avail.) **Indexed:** Biol.Abstr., Biol.& Agr.Ind., Chem.Abstr., Hort.Abstr., Ornam.Hort.
—BLDSC (4070.220000); UnCover; UMI.
Former titles: Royal Horticultural Society. Garden Journal (ISSN 0308-5457); Royal Horticultural Society Journal (ISSN 0035-8924)

635
GARDEN ANSWERS. 1982. m. £8.50. Frontline Ltd. (Subsidiary of: E M A P - Haymarket Ltd.), Park House, 117 Park Rd., Peterborough PE1 2TR, England. TEL 0733-555161. FAX 62788. TELEX 329292 FRONT G. Ed. Adam Pasco. circ. 71,945.
Incorporates: Greenhouse.

635
GARDEN CENTER BULLETIN. 1937. m. $12.50. Garden Center of Greater Cleveland, 11030 East Blvd., Cleveland, OH 44106. TEL 216-721-1600. Ed. Marilyn R. Sommer. adv.; bk.rev. circ. 4,000. **Document type:** bulletin.

635 US
GARDEN CENTER NEWSLETTER. 6/yr. membership only. Garden Centers of America, 1250 I St., N.W., Ste. 500, Washington, DC 20005. TEL 202-789-2900. Ed. Clint Albin. circ. 1,000. **Document type:** newsletter.
Formerly: G C A Newsletter.

635 US
▼**GARDEN CENTER PRODUCTS AND SUPPLIES.** 1994. bi-m. $48. Branch-Smith Inc., 120 St. Louis St., Ft. Worth, TX 76104. TEL 817-332-8236. FAX 817-877-1862. Ed. Yale Youngblood. adv.; B&W page $1450. circ. 20,000. **Document type:** trade publication.

635 US
GARDEN CLUB OF AMERICA. NEWSLETTER. 6/yr. membership only. Garden Club of America, 598 Madison Ave., New York, NY 10022. TEL 212-753-8287. FAX 212-753-0134. **Document type:** newsletter.
Description: Civic improvement and education to promote the love of gardening.

635 US ISSN 0733-4923
SB469
GARDEN DESIGN; the fine art of residential landscape architecture. 1982. bi-m. $20. Meigher Communications, 399 Park Ave., New York, NY 10022. TEL 212-522-2073. circ. 58,000. **Indexed:** Avery Ind.Archit.Per., Gard.Lit. (1992-), Search (1993-).
—Faxon; UnCover.
Description: Covers specific gardens, trends, profiles, history, and essays.

635 US
GARDEN GLORIES. q. Garden Clubs of Illinois, Inc., Old Nichols Library, 110 S. Washington St., Naperville, IL 60540. TEL 708-968-5552. Ed. Frank Folk. bk.rev.; film rev. circ. 10,000.

635.9 UK ISSN 0307-1243
SB451
GARDEN HISTORY. 1973. s-a. £18 (subscr. includes Garden History Society Newsletter). Garden History Society, 5 The Knoll, Hereford HR1 1RU, England. TEL 0432-354479. Eds. Jane Crawley, Elizabeth Whittle. bibl.; illus. circ. 1,700. **Indexed:** Avery Ind.Archit.Per., Br.Tech.Ind., Gard.Lit. (1992-), RILA. **Document type:** academic/scholarly publication.
—BLDSC (4070.800000); SWETS.

635 UK
GARDEN HISTORY SOCIETY. NEWSLETTER. 3/yr. (included in subscr. to Garden History). Garden History Society, 5 The Knoll, Hereford HR1 1RU, England. TEL 0432-354479. **Document type:** newsletter.

635 JA ISSN 0433-0919
GARDEN LIFE/GADEN RAIFU. (Text in Japanese) 1962. m. 17620 Yen. Seibundo Shinkosha Publishing Co. Ltd, 1-5-5 Kanda Nishiki-Cho, Chiyoda-Ku, Tokyo 101, Japan. Ed. Kiyoko Takuma.

635 UK ISSN 0016-4593
GARDEN NEWS. 1958. w. £35. Frontline Ltd. (Subsidiary of: E M A P - Haymarket Ltd.), Park House, 117 Park Rd., Peterborough PE1 2TR, England. TEL 0733-555161. FAX 62788. TELEX 329292 FRONT G. Ed. Adam Pasco. adv.; bk.rev.; illus. circ. 125,477. **Document type:** newspaper.
—CCC.

635 US
GARDEN NEWSLETTER. 1972. q. $25. Friends of the Seattle Botanical Garden, 2450 S. Milledge Ave., Athens, GA 30605. TEL 706-542-1244. FAX 706-542-3091. Ed. Mollie B. Henry. adv. circ. 1,300. (back issues avail.) **Document type:** newsletter.
Formerly: Garden Leaflet.
Description: Informs members of news and events. Includes information on the latest developments and plant profiles.

635 US ISSN 0016-4607
GARDEN PATH. 1930. q. $5. Ohio Association of Garden Clubs, c/o Mrs. Dean Wells, 2185 Woodville Rd., No. R10, Mansfield, OH 44903. TEL 419-756-6863. Ed. Mrs. Karl Roller. adv.; bk.rev.; illus. circ. 8,000. **Document type:** newsletter.

635 AT ISSN 1030-0392
GARDEN PESKEM; the Australian directory of garden pesticides. 1987. irreg. Aus.$25. University of Queensland, Gatton College, Lawes (via Gatton), Qld. 4343, Australia. TEL 074-601-291. FAX 074-601-283. TELEX QUCOL AA40866. circ. 400. **Document type:** directory.
Description: Lists of products (their uses and rates) which are registered pesticides for use in the home garden. Listings of uses are sorted by both crop and pest.

GARDEN RAILWAYS. see *HOBBIES*

635 US ISSN 0195-1386
GARDEN SUPPLY RETAILER GREEN BOOK. (Special issue of: Garden Supply Retailer) 1950. a. $10. Chilton Co., 201 King of Prussia Rd., Radnor, PA 19089. TEL 215-964-4269. adv.; bk.rev.; index; circ. 27,000. (also avail. in microfilm from UMI; reprint service avail. from UMI) **Document type:** directory.
Formerly: Home and Garden Supply Merchandiser Green Book.

635 UK ISSN 0261-3816
GARDEN TRADE NEWS INTERNATIONAL. m. £20($88) E M A P Apex Publications Ltd., Apex House, Oundle Rd., Peterborough PE2 9NP, England. TEL 0733-898100. FAX 0733-898418. Ed. Mike Wyatt. adv.: B&W page $2090, color page $3300; adv. contact: David W. Cook. bk.rev.; illus.; tr.lit.; circ. 7,201 (controlled). (tabloid format; back issues avail.) **Document type:** trade publication.
—CCC.
Description: Covers all aspects of garden product retailing. Contains in-depth features on major market sectors and new products.

635 US ISSN 0016-464X
THE GARDENER. 1958. bi-m. $15. Gardeners of America, Inc., 5560 Merle Hay Rd., Box 241, Johnston, IA 50131-0241. TEL 515-278-0295. FAX 515-278-6245. Ed. Carol Donovan. adv.; bk.rev. circ. 10,000.

635 CN ISSN 0832-6509
GARDENER'S GUIDE TO PEST PREVENTION AND CONTROL IN THE HOME AND GARDEN. 1986. irreg. Can.$10.65. Ministry of Agriculture Fisheries and Food, Extension Systems Branch, Parliament Bldgs., Victoria, BC V8V 1X4, Canada. (Subscr. to: Crown Publications, 546 Yates St., Victoria, BC V8W 1K8, Canada. TEL 604-386-4636) illus. **Document type:** government publication.
Former titles: Pest Control for the Home Garden (ISSN 0708-1723); Pest Control for the Home Gardener (ISSN 0714-3745)

635 IT
GARDENIA. m. L.62000 (foreign L.140000). Editoriale Giorgio Mondadori S.p.A., Via A. Ponti, 10, 20143 Milan, Italy. TEL 02-891661. FAX 02-89125888. Ed. Mary Annovazzi. adv.; illus. circ. 120,000.

635 US
GARDENIA SOCIETY OF AMERICA. q. membership only. Gardenia Society of America, Box 879, Atwater, CA 95301. TEL 209-385-4251.

635 US ISSN 0270-3041
SB450.9
GARDENING. 1979. a. Conde Nast Publications Inc., Gardening Magazine, 350 Madison Ave., New York, NY 10017. TEL 212-880-8800.
Former titles (until 1981): House and Garden Gardening Guide (ISSN 0270-9899); Gardens (ISSN 0147-8591)

635 US
GARDENING & OUTDOOR LIVING. s-a. Hachette Magazines, Inc., 1633 Broadway, 45th Fl., New York, NY 10009. TEL 212-767-6811. Ed. Marion Lyons. bk.rev.

635 581 AT
GARDENING NEWS. 1980. bi-m. Aus.$18. Royal Horticultural Society of Victoria, P.O. Box 2000, Glen Waverley, Vic. 3150, Australia. TEL 03-803-0133. FAX 03-803-0556. Ed. Rosemary Davies. adv.; bk.rev.; charts; illus.; index. circ. 7,000. (back issues avail.) **Document type:** consumer publication.
Description: How-to tips on gardening. Includes recipes and information on landscaping.

635 AT
GARDENING NEWS AND SCHEDULE. 1982. q. membership. Box Hill Horticultural Society Inc., P.O. Box 287, Box Hill, Vic. 3128, Australia. TEL 03-890-3941 FAX 03-878-6761. Ed. Flora Miller. adv.; illus. circ. 350. (back issues avail.) **Document type:** newsletter.

635 658.8 UK
GARDENING: THE INTERNATIONAL MARKET. a. £1375($2750) Euromonitor, 87-88 Turnmill St., London EC1M 5QU, England. TEL 071-251-8024. FAX 071-608-3149. (Addr. in N. America: Euromonitor International, 111 W. Washington St., Ste. 920, Chicago, IL 50602. TEL 312-541-8024. FAX 312-541-1567) (looseleaf format) **Document type:** trade publication.
●Also available online. Vendor(s): Data-Star, DIALOG Information Services, Inc.
Description: Analyzes the market for gardening tools and supplies for France, Germany, Italy, Spain, the U.K., the U.S., and Japan.

635 UK ISSN 0264-1917
GARDENING WHICH?. 10/yr £47. Consumers' Association, 2 Marylebone Rd., London NW1 4DF, England. TEL 071-830-6000. FAX 071-830-6220. (Subscr. to: Consumers' Association, Castlemead, Gascoyne Way, Hertford SG14 1LH, England) Ed. A. Ayres. circ. 153,000.
Description: Focuses on gardening techniques, goods and services. Caters to all levels of expertise.

635 AT ISSN 1035-655X
GARDENS & BACKYARDS. 1985. bi-m. Aus.$21. Magazine House Pty. Ltd., P.O. Box 706, Crows Nest, N.S.W. 2065, Australia. TEL 02-438-2399. FAX 61-2-4363014. Ed. Carol Fallows. adv.; bk.rev. circ. 17,276. (back issues avail.) **Document type:** consumer publication.
Formerly (until 1990): Garden Scene (ISSN 0818-2833)
Description: Practical consumer magazine for Australian gardeners.

790 UK
GARDENS OF ENGLAND AND WALES. 1927. a. £3. National Gardens Scheme Charitable Trust, Hatchlands Park, East Clandon, Guildford, Surrey GU4 7RT, England. TEL 0483-211535. FAX 0483-211537. Ed. D.G. Carpenter. adv.; index. circ. 165,000. **Document type:** consumer publication, directory.
Former titles (until 1983): Gardens Open to the Public in England and Wales (ISSN 0141-2361); (until 1979): Gardens of England and Wales Open to the Public (ISSN 0072-0186)

635 CN ISSN 0863-4947
CODEN: PHSREL
GARDENS WEST. 1987. 9/yr. Can.$20. Cornwall Publishing Company Ltd., Box 268C, Vancouver, BC V6B 3V7, Canada. TEL 604-879-4591. FAX 604-879-5110. Ed. Dorothy Horton. adv.; bk.rev. circ. 50,000. (back issues avail.) **Indexed:** Gard.Lit. (1992-).
—BLDSC (6475.990000); CASDDS.
Description: Information for the home gardener in western Canada.

GARLIC TIMES; the newsletter of lovers of the stinking rose. see *NUTRITION AND DIETETICS*

GARDENING AND HORTICULTURE

635   AU
GARTEN MAGAZIN FUER ALLE. 11/yr. Parkring 12, A-1010 Vienna, Austria. TEL 01-5128416. Ed. Alfred Blazek. circ. 10,000.

635   GW   ISSN 0342-4650
GARTEN- UND FREIZEITMARKT. 1962. m. DM.93. Patzer Verlag GmbH und Co. KG, Koenigsallee 65, 14193 Berlin, Germany. TEL 030-8959030. FAX 030-89590317. adv.; bk.rev. circ. 4,000. **Document type:** bulletin.
Formerly: Gaertnerischer Fachhandel.

635 712   GW   ISSN 0016-4720
GARTEN UND LANDSCHAFT; journal of landscape architecture and landscape planning. 1890. m. DM.176.40 (students DM.135.60). (Deutsche Gesellschaft fuer Gartenkunst und Landschaftspflege) Callwey Verlag, Postfach 800409, 81604 Munich, Germany. TEL 089-436005-0. FAX 089-436005-13. Ed.Bd. bk.rev.; bibl.; charts; illus.; stat.; index. circ. 8,800. (back issues avail.) **Indexed:** Avery Ind.Archit.Per., Excerp.Med., Geo.Abstr. **Document type:** trade publication.
—BLDSC (4072.420000). CCC.

635   GW
GARTEN ZEITUNG. m. Deutscher Bauernverlag GmbH, Reinhardtstr. 14, 10117 Berlin, Germany. TEL 030-2893-0. FAX 030-2893205. Ed. Christian Gehler. adv. contact: Hans-Juergen Henze. circ. 230,000. **Document type:** consumer publication.

333.78   GW   ISSN 0016-4739
DAS GARTENAMT. 1952. m. DM.147. Patzer Verlag GmbH und Co. KG, Koenigsallee 65, 14193 Berlin, Germany. TEL 030-8959030. FAX 030-89590317. adv.; bk.rev.; abstr.; index. circ. 2,200. **Indexed:** Excerp.Med., Hort.Abstr., Ornam.Hort. **Document type:** bulletin.

635   SZ   ISSN 0016-4747
GARTENBAU/HORTICULTURE. (Text in French and German) 1879. w. 142 SFr. Gartenbau Verlag, Gaertnerstr., Postfach, CH-4501 Solothurn, Switzerland. TEL 065-226622. FAX 065-228162. adv.; bk.rev.; illus.; stat.; tr.lit.; index. circ. 7,070. **Indexed:** Biol.Abstr., Chem.Abstr., Food Sci.& Tech.Abstr., Ornam.Hort. **Document type:** bulletin.
Formerly: Schweizer Gartenbau-Blatt.

635   GW
GARTENBAU IN BADEN. 1948. fortn. DM.25. Verband Badischer Gartenbaubetriebe, Seminarstr. 10, 76133 Karlsruhe, Germany. adv.; bk.rev. circ. 1,240.

635   GW   ISSN 0942-0118
                     CODEN: GTNBAV
GARTENBAU MAGAZIN. 1954. m. DM.73.20 (foreign DM.89.40). Bernhard Thalacker Verlag GmbH, Postfach 3361, 38023 Braunschweig, Germany. TEL 0531-380040. FAX 0531-3800425. adv.; B&W page DM.4243.20, color page DM.5983.20; trim 272 x 186. circ. 30,533. **Indexed:** Agri.Eng.Abstr., Biol.Abstr., Food Sci.& Tech.Abstr., Hort.Abstr., INIS Atomind., Ornam.Hort., Soils & Fert. **Document type:** trade publication.
—CCC.
Formed by merger of: Gartenbau (ISSN 0323-4835) & T A S P O - Magazin (ISSN 0177-5014).

635   GW   ISSN 0016-4763
DER GARTENBAUINGENIEUR; Zeitschrift fuer Fuehrungskraefte im Gartenbau und Landespflege. 1955. 6/yr. DM.50. (Bund der Ingenieure des Gartenbaues und der Landespflege) Klette Druck und Verlag Euroflora-Verlag GmbH, Freunder Landstr. 25, 52078 Aachen, Germany. FAX 0241-523333. Ed. Wolfgang Lutz. adv.; charts; illus. circ. 3,500. **Document type:** academic/scholarly publication.

635   AU
GARTENBAUWIRTSCHAFT. 1946. s-m. S.890 (foreign S.1077). (Bundesverband der Erwerbsgaertner Oesterreichs) Oesterreichischer Agrarverlag GmbH, Bankgasse 1-3, A-1014 Vienna, Austria. TEL 5339676. FAX 5339656. Ed. W. Leiter. adv.; bk.rev.; charts; illus.; index. circ. 4,000. **Indexed:** Chem.Abstr., Forest.Abstr., Sci.Cit.Ind.
Formerly: Gartenbauwirtschaft mit Gartenbau Nachrichten (ISSN 0016-4771)

635   GW   ISSN 0016-478X
SB10   CODEN: GTBWAY
GARTENBAUWISSENSCHAFT. (Summaries in English and French) 1955. 6/yr. DM.657.60. (Deutsche Gartenbauwissenschaftliche Gesellschaft e.V.) Verlag Eugen Ulmer GmbH, Wollgrasweg 41, 70599 Stuttgart, Germany. TEL 0711-4507-0. FAX 0711-4507-120. TELEX 723634-ULMER-D. (Subscr. to: Postfach 700561, 70574 Stuttgart, Germany) Ed. J. Grunewaldt. bk.rev.; bibl.; charts; illus.; index. circ. 650. **Indexed:** Agri.Eng.Abstr., Biol.Abstr., Chem.Abstr., Crop Physiol.Abstr., Curr.Adv.Ecol.Sci., Curr.Cont., Excerp.Med., Food Sci.& Tech.Abstr., Forest.Abstr., Hort.Abstr., Ind.Sci.Rev., Irr.& Drain.Abstr., Ornam.Hort., Plant Breed.Abstr., Plant Grow.Reg.Abstr., Rev.Plant Path., Rural Recreat.Tour.Abstr., Soils & Fert., World Agri.Econ.& Rural Sociol.Abstr. **Document type:** consumer publication.
—BLDSC (4072.500000); Faxon; UnCover; SWETS; CASDDS. CCC.

635   SZ
GARTENFREUND. m. Postfach 61, CH-4132 Muttenz 1, Switzerland. TEL 061-4612375. Ed. Max Glinz. circ. 32,800. **Document type:** consumer publication.

635   GW   ISSN 0341-2105
GARTENPRAXIS. m. DM.130.80. Verlag Eugen Ulmer GmbH, Wollgrasweg 41, 70599 Stuttgart, Germany. TEL 0711-4507-0. FAX 0711-4507-120. TELEX 723634-ULMER-D. (Subscr. to: Postfach 700561, 70574 Stuttgart, Germany) Ed. K. Ruecker. adv.; bk.rev.; illus. circ. 15,000. **Document type:** consumer publication.
—CCC.

635   DK   ISSN 0106-8393
GARTNER TIDENDE. 1885. w. DKK 945. Dansk Erhvervsgartnerforening, Hvidkaervej 29, DK-5250 Odense SV, Denmark. TEL 45-66-17-17-14. FAX 45-66-17-17-15. Ed. Palle Dahl. adv.; bk.rev. circ. 3,493. **Indexed:** Agri.Eng.Abstr., Bio-Contr.News & Info., Crop Physiol.Abstr., Forest.Abstr., Hort.Abstr., Maize Abstr., Ornam.Hort., Plant Grow.Reg.Abstr., Seed Abstr., Weed Abstr., World Agri.Econ. & Rural Sociol.Abstr.
—BLDSC (4072.700000).
Description: Presents information for potted plant, flower, vegetable and fruit growers, plus nurserymen, and market gardeners.

635   DK   ISSN 0109-2324
GARTNEREN. 1975. q. DKK 40 to individuals; libraries free. Gartnernes Landsklub, Sjaelsoevej 51, DK-3460 Birkeroed, Denmark. TEL 42-81-05-80. Ed. Hans Melgaard. illus. circ. 9,500.

630   NO   ISSN 0046-5437
                     CODEN: GARTA6
GARTNERYRKET. (Text in Norwegian) 1910. 20/yr. NOK 500. Norsk Gartnerforbund - Norwegian Horticultural Growers Association, Motzfeldtsgate 1, 0187 Oslo 1, Norway. TEL 02-173444. FAX 02-174488. Ed. Asbjoerg Roeneid-Hansen. adv.; illus.; tr.lit.; index. circ. 3,100. **Indexed:** Chem.Abstr., Hort.Abstr., Ornam.Hort., Plant Grow.Reg.Abstr., World Agri.Econ.& Rural Sociol.Abstr.
—BLDSC (4072.750000). CCC.

635.9   NE
GAZONGIDS. 1990. a. fl.14.50. M Xpress vof, P.O. Box 66, 5258 ZH Berlicum, Netherlands. TEL 31-4103-4347. Ed. F.X. van Miert. adv. contact: E. Cammelbeeck. circ. 10,000. **Document type:** trade publication.
Description: Covers data on lawnmowers and instructions on sowing seeds, fertilizing, sprinkling and maintenance.

635   GW   ISSN 0016-6286
GEMUESE; Spezialblatt fuer den Feld- und Intensivgemuesebau. 1965. m. DM.106.80. B L V Verlagsgesellschaft mbH, Lothstr. 29, 80797 Munich, Germany. TEL 089-12705-0. FAX 089-12705354. Ed. H.D. Hartmann. adv.; bk.rev.; illus.; index. circ. 5,000. **Indexed:** Hort.Abstr., Ornam.Hort., Plant Breed.Abstr., Weed Abstr. **Document type:** trade publication.
—SWETS. CCC.

635   SZ
GEMUESEBAU. 20/yr. 60 SFr. Verband Schweizerischer Gemueseproduzenten - Union Maraichere Suisse - Unione Svizzera Produttori di Verdura, Route du Jura 29, Case Postale 912, CH-1701 Fribourg, Switzerland. TEL 037-831151. FAX 037-266050. adv. circ. 4,000. **Document type:** bulletin.

635   US
GEORGIA GREEN INDUSTRY ASSOCIATION NEWSLETTER. 1990. m. membership. Georgia Green Industry Association, Inc., Box 369, Hwy. 5 N., Epworth, GA 30541. TEL 706-492-4664. FAX 706-492-4668. Ed. Sherry Loudermilk. adv.; charts; illus.; stat.; tr.lit. circ. 475. (back issues avail.) **Document type:** newsletter.
Description: Provides new plant cultivar information, business and management tips, pesticide information and industry happenings.

635.933   US   ISSN 0016-8599
GERANIUMS AROUND THE WORLD. 1953. q. $12.50 membership. International Geranium Society, Box 92734, Pasadena, CA 91109-2734. Ed. Michael Vassar. adv.; bk.rev.; illus. circ. 1,100.

635 631   US
GERMINATIONS; newsletter of the Butterbrooke Farm seed co-op. 1980. q. $12.50. Butterbrooke Farm, 78 Barry Rd., Oxford, CT 06478-1529. TEL 203-888-2000. Ed. Tom Butterworth. bk.rev. circ. 200. **Document type:** newsletter.
Description: Contains articles on gardening, horticulture and sustainable agriculture.

635.9   IT
GIARDINI. 1981. m. (11/yr.) L.120000 (effective 1993). Zanfi Editori s.r.l., Via Emilia Ovest 954, ang. Via T. Livio 1, P.O. Box 433, 41100 Modena, Italy. TEL 059-891700. FAX 059-891701. TELEX 522272 ZANFI I. adv. circ. 80,000. **Document type:** consumer publication.
Description: Contains ideas, practical suggestions for flowers, vegetables and nurseries.

635.9   IT   ISSN 0016-965X
GIARDINO FIORITO. 1931. m. (10/yr.). L.73000 (effective 1993). (Societa Italiana Amici dei Fiori) Edagricoie S.p.A., Via Emilia Levante 31, 40139 Bologna, Italy. TEL 051-492211. FAX 051-493660. Ed. Alessandro Chiusoli. adv.; B&W page L.1700000, color page L.2600000; 185 x 247. illus.; index. circ. 44,300. **Indexed:** Chem.Abstr.
—UMI.
Description: Covers flower growing, gardening and country life.

GILDEA REVIEW. see ENVIRONMENTAL STUDIES

635.9   CN   ISSN 1187-8673
GLADIOLUS, DAHLIAS. 1921. a. Can.$10. Canadian Gladiolus Society, 1274 129 A St., Surrey, BC V4A 3Y4, Canada. TEL 604-536-8200. Ed. Grant Wilson. adv.
Formerly (until 1990): Canadian Gladiolus Society. Annual (ISSN 0319-1915)

GLOXINIAN; the magazine for gesneriad growers. see BIOLOGY — Botany

635   US
GOING AND GROWING. 3/yr. membership only. National Junior Horticultural Association, c/o Joe Maxson, Ed., 401 N. Fourth St., Durant, OK 74701.

GOLF COURSE MANAGEMENT. see SPORTS AND GAMES — Ball Games

635   US
GOOD EARTH ASSOCIATION. NEWSLETTER. 1984. bi-m. $10 membership. Good Earth Association, 202 E. Church St., Pocohontas, AR 72455-2899. TEL 501-892-8329. FAX 501-892-5399. Ed. Gladys Nelson. adv. circ. 500. (tabloid format) **Document type:** newsletter.

634   US   ISSN 0046-6174
GOOD FRUIT GROWER. 1946. s-m. $30 (foreign $55) (effective 1993). Fruit Commission, 1005 Tieton Dr., Yakima, WA 98902-3587. TEL 509-457-2315. FAX 509-453-4880. (Subscr. to: Box 9219, Yakima, WA 98909-0219) Ed. Jim Black. adv.; bk.rev.; charts; illus. circ. 12,371. (tabloid format) **Indexed:** Hort.Abstr. **Document type:** government publication.
—BLDSC (4201.332380).

GARDENING AND HORTICULTURE

635   US   ISSN 0888-5672
GOURD. 1970. 4/yr. $5 (foreign $8). American Gourd Society Inc., Box 274, Mt. Gilead, OH 43338. TEL 419-946-3302. Ed. Ted Modrowski. bk.rev. circ. 2,500. (back issues avail.) **Document type:** bulletin.
   Description: Information on gourds and gourdcraft.

635   SZ
G'PLUS. (Text in German) 1897. fortn. 92 SFr. Verband Schweizerischer Gaertnermeister, Forchstr. 287, CH-8029 Zurich, Switzerland. TEL 01-3813700. FAX 01-4227037. Ed. Felix Kappeli. adv.; bk.rev. circ. 5,000. **Indexed:** Ornam.Hort. **Document type:** consumer publication.
   Former titles: G'phis; Gaertnermeister; Schweizerische Gaertnerzeitung.

635 634.8   BU   ISSN 0436-2624
        CODEN: GRLNA9
GRADINARSKA I LOZARSKA NAUKA/HORTICULTURAL AND VITICULTURAL SCIENCE. (Text in Bulgarian; summaries in English, French, Russian) 1964. 8/yr. 1.40 lv. per no. (Akademiia na Selskostopanskite Nauki) Publishing House of the Bulgarian Academy of Sciences, Acad. G. Bonchev St., Bldg. 6, 1113 Sofia, Bulgaria. (Dist. by: Hemus, 6, Rouski Blvd., 1000 Sofia, Bulgaria) Ed. M. Kondarev. circ. 1,080. (reprint service avail. from IRC) **Indexed:** Agri.Eng.Abstr., Biol.Abstr., BSI Bsl., Chem.Abstr, Curr.Adv.Ecol.Sci., Excerp.Med., Hort.Abstr., Rev.Appl.Entomol., Rev.Plant Path., VITIS, Weed Abstr.

712 796.352   FR
GREEN KEEPER. 4/yr. Egerie Golf, 13 rue des Harias, B.P. 5, 78124 Mareil-sur-Mauldre, France. TEL 34-75-87-90. FAX 34-75-87-89. Ed. Jean-Luc Duclos. circ. 2,000.

635   US   ISSN 0149-5569
GREEN MARKETS. 1977. w. $795 (foreign $1030). Pike & Fischer, Inc., 4600 East-West Hwy., Ste. 200, Bethesda, MD 20814. TEL 301-654-6262. FAX 301-654-6297. Ed. Kevin Wiggins. **Document type:** newsletter.
   ●Also available online.

635   US   ISSN 0895-772X
GREEN MARKETS DEALER REPORT. w. $267. Pike & Fischer, Inc., 4600 East West Hwy., Ste. 200, Bethesda, MD 20814. TEL 301-654-6262. FAX 301-654-6297. Ed. Carolyn Rhodes. **Document type:** newsletter.

635   US   ISSN 1064-0118
GREEN PRINTS; the weeder's digest. 1990. q. $14 (Canada and Mexico $17; England $23). Green Prints, Box 1355, Fairview, NC 28730. TEL 704-628-1902. Ed. Pat Stone. adv. circ. 6,000. (back issues avail.) **Document type:** consumer publication.
   Description: Explores the personal, not how-to, side of gardening with humorous and heartfelt stories and art.

635   US   ISSN 0190-9789
THE GREEN SCENE. 1972. 6/yr. $9.75. Pennsylvania Horticultural Society, 325 Walnut St., Philadelphia, PA 19106. TEL 215-625-8250. FAX 215-625-9392. Ed. Jean Byrne. circ. 13,500 (paid). **Indexed:** Gard.Lit. (1992-).
   Description: Publishes articles on horticultural and related topics of local interest.

635   US
GREEN THUMB GARDENING NEWSLETTER. 1985. s-a. free to buyers of Spray-N-Grow. Spray-N-Grow, 20 Hwy. 35 S., Box 2137, Rockport, TX 78382. TEL 512-790-9033. FAX 512-790-9313. Ed. Melanie Lyon. circ. 270,000 (controlled). **Document type:** newsletter.
   Description: Contains information for Spray-N-Grow gardeners, including uses of the product, results, and general gardening tips.

635   US
GREEN WORLD NEWS. 1989. m. $25 (effective Jan. 1992). Bonsai and Orchid Association, 26 Pine St., Dover, DE 19901. TEL 302-736-6781. FAX 302-736-6763. Ed. Le Roy Rench. circ. 3,500. (back issues avail.)
   Description: Covers world trade, regulation effecting the industry, trade inquiries, growing information, cost control and trade exposition.

635   CN   ISSN 0712-4996
GREENHOUSE CANADA. 1980. 12/yr. Can.$24($36) N C C Publishing, 222 Argyle St., Delhi, Ont. N4B 2Y2, Canada. TEL 519-582-2510. FAX 519-582-4040. Ed. Ben Steidman. adv.: B&W page Can.$673; trim 8 x 10 7/8; adv. contact: Mark Crandon. circ. 4,270. (back issues avail.)
   Description: Directed to commercial greenhouse growers of flowers and vegetables.

635   US   ISSN 0745-7324
GREENHOUSE GROWER. (Supplements avail. in June and Sept.) 1983. m. $25. Meister Publishing Co., 37733 Euclid Ave., Willoughby, OH 44094. TEL 216-942-2000. Ed. Jane A. Lieberth. adv. circ. 22,158. **Indexed:** Farm & Garden Ind. **Document type:** trade publication.
   —CCC.

635.98   US   ISSN 0744-8988
        CODEN: GMANEP
GREENHOUSE MANAGER. 1982. m. $24. Branch-Smith Inc., 120 St. Louis St., Ft. Worth, TX 76104. TEL 817-332-8236. FAX 817-877-1862. Ed. Dave Kuack. adv. circ. 20,000.
   —BLDSC (4214.943080).

635.98   US
GREENHOUSE NEWSLETTER. 1964. bi-m. $9. U.S. Department of Agriculture, University of Connecticut, Storrs, College of Agriculture and Natural Resources, Connecticut Cooperative Extension System, Box U-67, Storrs, CT 06268. TEL 203-486-3435. Ed. Richard McAvoy. charts; illus.; stat. circ. 1,000. **Indexed:** Hort.Abstr.
   Formerly: Connecticut Florists' Newsletter.

GREENMASTER. see SPORTS AND GAMES — Ball Games

635   IC   ISSN 1017-3560
GRODUR OG GARDAR. 1984. 2/yr. ISK 1042 (effective 1994). Frodi Ltd., Armuli 18, 108 Reykjavik, Iceland. TEL 354-1-812300. FAX 1-812946. Ed. Eirikur S. Eiriksson. adv.: B&W page ISK 45520, color page ISK 70320; trim 19 x 27; adv. contact: Ragnar Petersen. circ. 6,000.
   Description: Focuses on gardening and the raising of indoor plants.

635   DK   ISSN 0108-8920
GROENNE FAG; fagblad for gartnere og groensagsproducenter. 1982. fortn. DKK 600 (typically set in Jan.) Forlaget Groenne Fag, P.O. Box 85, Oestervang 33, DK-4000 Roskilde, Denmark. TEL 45-42-36 88 76. FAX 45-46-32-16-26. Ed. Eigil Bisgaard. adv. contact: Bente Dietz. bk.rev.; illus. circ. 1,800. (back issues avail.)
   Description: Directed to nurserymen and commercial growers of fruits and vegetables both outdoors and under glass.

712   DK   ISSN 0108-4755
GROENT MILJOE. 1951. irreg. (approx. 8/yr) DKK 123 (typically set in Nov.) Landsforeningen Danske Anlaegsgartnermestre, Linde Alle 16, DK-2720 Vanloese, Denmark. TEL 45-31-74-94-00. FAX 45-31-74-15-00. Ed. Soeren Holgersen. adv. contact: Steen Lykke Madsen. bk.rev.; cum.index; 1983-1990. circ. 6,000.
   Formerly (until 1983): Anlaegsgartneren (ISSN 0108-7770)
   Description: Technical subjects for people involved with construction and maintenance of recreational grounds.

635 634   NE   ISSN 0925-9708
GROENTEN & FRUIT. Key Title: Groenten en Fruit. Algemeen. (Supplements avail.: Fruit (ISSN 0925-9694); Glasgroenten (ISSN 0925-9686); Paddestoeler (ISSN 0925-9716); Vollegrondsgroenten (ISSN 0925-9678)) 1945. w. fl.259.70 (includes supplements). (Centraal Bureau van de Tuinbouwveilingen in Nederland) Uitgeversmaatschappij C. Misset B.V, Hanzestr. 1, 7006 RH Doetinchem, Netherlands. TEL 31-8340-49911. FAX 31-8340-43839. Ed. Henk van Esch adv.: B&W page fl.3295; trim 215 x 285; adv. contact: Cor van Nek. bk.rev.; bibl.; charts; illus.; stat.; index. circ. 19,500. (tabloid format) **Indexed:** Agri.Eng.Abstr., Chem.Abstr, Crop Physiol.Abstr., Hort.Abstr., Irr.& Drain.Abstr., Key to Econ.Sci., Ornam.Hort., Plant Grow.Reg.Abstr., Rice Abstr., Rural Recreat.Tour.Abstr., World Agri.Econ.& Rural Sociol.Abstr. **Document type:** trade publication.
   Supersedes (in 1991): Groenten en Fruit (ISSN 0017-4491)

635   NE   ISSN 0925-9694
GROENTEN & FRUIT - VAKDEEL FRUIT. 1991. w. fl.137.80 (effective 1992). Uitgeversmaatschappij C. Misset B.V., Hanzestr. 1, 7006 RH Doetinchem, Netherlands. TEL 31-8340-49911. FAX 31-8434-43839. adv.: B&W page fl.1202; trim 215 x 285; adv. contact: Cor van Nek. illus. circ. 4,150. **Document type:** trade publication.
   Description: Provides specialized information on all aspects of commercial fruit growing.

635   NE   ISSN 0925-9686
GROENTEN & FRUIT - VAKDEEL GLASGROENTEN. 1991. w. fl.206.70. Uitgeversmaatschappij C. Misset B.V., Hanzestr. 1, 7006 RH Doetinchem, Netherlands. TEL 31-8340-49911. FAX 31-8340-43839. adv.: B&W page fl.2394; trim 215 x 285; adv. contact: Cor van Nek. illus. circ. 13,280. **Document type:** trade publication.
   Description: Provides specialized information of interest to commercial greenhouse farmers.

635   NE   ISSN 0925-9716
GROENTEN & FRUIT - VAKDEEL PADDESTOELEN. 1991. w. fl.159. Uitgeversmaatschappij C. Misset B.V., Hanzestr. 1, 7006 RH Doetinchem, Netherlands. TEL 31-8340-49911. FAX 31-8340-43839. adv.: B&W page fl.572; trim 215 x 285; adv. contact: Cor van Nek. illus. circ. 3,990. **Document type:** trade publication.
   Description: For the commerical mushroom growing industry in the Netherlands.

635   NE
GROENTEN & FRUIT - VAKDEEL VOLLEGRONDSGROENTEN. (Supplement to: Groenten & Fruit (ISSN 0925-9708)) 1980. w. fl.190.80 (effective 1992). Uitgeversmaatschappij C. Misset B.V., Hanzestr. 1, 7006 RH Doetinchem, Netherlands. TEL 31-8340-49911. FAX 31-8340-43839. TELEX 45481. (Subscr. to: Postbus 4, 7000 BA Doetinchem, Netherlands) Ed. J.S. Horsting. adv.: B&W page fl. 2073; trim 215 x 285; adv. contact: Cor van Nek. bk.rev.; charts; illus. circ. 11,070. **Document type:** trade publication.
   Former titles (until 1991): Vollegrond (ISSN 0922-3576); (until 1983): Tuinderij Vollegrond (ISSN 0167-2835)
   Description: Information on growing techniques, mechanization and trade of field vegetables.

635 637   US   ISSN 0017-4688
SB469
GROUNDS MAINTENANCE. 1966. m. free to qualified personnel; others $30. Intertec Publishing Corp., 9800 Metcalf, Overland Park, KS 66212-2215. TEL 913-341-1300. FAX 913-967-1898. Ed. Mark Welterlen. adv.; bk.rev.; charts; illus.; index; circ. 45,521 (controlled). (also avail. in microform from UMI; reprint service avail. from UMI.) **Indexed:** Sportsearch. **Document type:** trade publication.
   —BLDSC (4220.145000); UnCover; UMI. **CCC.**

635   US
GROUNDS MANAGEMENT FORUM. 1973. m. membership. Professional Grounds Management Society, 120 Cockeysville Rd., Ste.1C4, Hunt Valley, MD 21031. TEL 410-584-9754. FAX 410-584-9756. Ed. John Gillan. adv.; bk.rev. circ. 1,700. **Document type:** newsletter.
   Former titles: P G M S Newsletter; Manager's Memo; Professional Gardener (ISSN 0033-0116)

2638 GARDENING AND HORTICULTURE

635.9   UK
GROW DAHLIAS WITH US. 1976. irreg. £1.50. National Dahlia Society, c/o Gen. Sec. A.G. Winkless, 8 Station Rd., Kirby Muxloe, Leicester LE9 9EJ, England. TEL 0533-387717.
Description: Information for the beginner about growing dahlias.

635.98   US
GROW LETTER. 1974. q. $65 (effective Jan. 1990) (free to qualified personnel). Sheldon Fredericks Adv., Inc., 655 Washington Blvd., Stamford, CT 06901. TEL 203-324-0010. FAX 203-324-0520. bk.rev.; bibl.; charts; illus.; tr.lit. circ. 28,100. (looseleaf format; back issues avail.)

635 634   CN   ISSN 0017-4777
GROWER. 1879. m. $25 (foreign $35). Ontario Fruit and Vegetable Growers Association, 355 Elmira Rd., No. 103, Guelph, ON N1K 1S5, Canada. TEL 519-763-8728. FAX 519-763-6604. Ed. Blair Adams. adv.; bk.rev.; charts; illus.; mkt.; stat. circ. 11,600. (tabloid format) **Indexed:** Agri.Eng.Abstr., PROMT. **Document type:** newspaper, trade publication.

635   UK   ISSN 0017-4785
GROWER. 1923. w. £45 (students £30). Grower Publications Ltd., 50 Doughty St., London WC1N 2LP, England. TEL 071-405-0364. FAX 071-831-2230. TELEX 8954111. Ed. Peter Rogers. adv.; bk.rev.; abstr.; charts; illus.; mkt.; stat.; tr.lit.; index. circ. 13,656. **Indexed:** Agri.Eng.Abstr., Biol.Abstr., Curr.Adv.Ecol.Sci., Hort.Abstr., PROMT. —BLDSC (4220.700000); SWETS.

635   US   ISSN 0276-9433
GROWER TALKS MAGAZINE. 1937. m. $22 (Canada and Mexico $28; elsewhere $54). Ball Publishing, Box 9, Batavia, IL 60510. TEL 708-208-9080. FAX 708-208-9350. Ed. Vic Ball. adv. circ. 10,000. (back issues avail.) **Indexed:** Gard.Lit. (1992-). **Document type:** trade publication.
Description: Trade magazine for the commercial grower of horticultural plants.

635   US   ISSN 1043-2906
GROWING EDGE MAGAZINE; indoor & outdoor gardening for today's grower. 1989. q. $24.95 (foreign $45) (effective 1994). New Moon Publishing, Inc., 215 S.W. Second St., Box 1027, Corvallis, OR 97339-1027. TEL 507-757-0027. FAX 503-757-0028. Ed. Don Parker; Pub. Tom Alexander. adv. contact: Teresa Nikkila. circ. 25,000. **Indexed:** Gard.Lit. (1992-). **Document type:** consumer publication, trade publication.
●Also available online.
Description: Covers high-tech gardening, including hydroponics, controlled environments, greenhouses, drip irrigation, water conservation and organic gardening.

635   US   ISSN 1060-9296
▼**GROWING FOR MARKET;** news and ideas for market gardeners. 1992. m. $26 (Canada $30). Fairplain Publications, Box 3747, Lawrence, KS 66046. TEL 913-841-2559. Ed. Lynn Byczynski. bk.rev.; abstr.; cum.index. (looseleaf format; back issues avail.) **Document type:** newsletter.
Description: Serves the needs of diversified small-scale growers committed to sustainable farming.

GROWING NATIVE. see *BIOLOGY — Botany*

635   SZ
DIE GRUENE. w. Haltenbachstr. 2, CH-8006 Zurich, Switzerland. TEL 01-2617680. Ed. Carlo Sacchetto. circ. 43,000.

635.9   IT
GUIDA VERDE.* m. L.30000. Curcio Periodici S.p.A., Via Arno 64, 00198 Rome, Italy. Ed. Rosanna Falconi. adv. circ. 82,500.

635 581   US
H S I BULLETIN. 1985. 4/yr. $20 includes membership. Heliconia Society International, c/o Flamingo Gardens, 3750 Flamingo Rd., Ft. Lauderdale, FL 33330. TEL 317-251-7343. FAX 317-251-9071. Eds. Gilbert S. Daniels, Rudolf M. Sterkel. adv.; bk.rev. circ. 700. **Document type:** bulletin.

635   JA
HAPPO SANSO/WILD FLOWER LOVER'S SOCIETY OF NORTHERN BLOCK. JOURNAL. (Text in Japanese) 1980. a. Happo Sansokai - Wild Flower Lover's Society of Northern Block, c/o Mr. Eiji Takano, 5-10, 9-chome, Nishino 11-jo, Nishi-ku, Sapporo-shi, Hokkaido 060, Japan.

HARDWARE AND GARDEN REVIEW. see *BUILDING AND CONSTRUCTION — Hardware*

635   UK   ISSN 0969-1901
HARDY PLANT JOURNAL. 2/yr. £8.50 membership only. Hardy Plant Society (UK), Little Orchard, Great Cumberton, Pershore, Worcs. WR10 3DP, England. TEL 0386-710317. **Document type:** academic/scholarly publication.
Formerly: Hardy Plant Society. Bulletin.

635   UK
HARDY PLANT SOCIETY. NEWS LETTER. 3/yr. membership only. Hardy Plant Society (UK), Little Orchard, Great Cumberton, Pershore, Worcs. WR10 3DP, England. TEL 0386-710317. **Document type:** newsletter.

635   US
HARDY PLANT SOCIETY OF OREGON. BULLETIN.* 1985. a. membership only. Hardy Plant Society of Oregon, c/o HANNI, 2148 N.E. 16th Dr., Portland, OR 97230-5562. Ed. Sharon Streeter. bk.rev. circ. 750.

635   US   ISSN 1049-4618
S521
HARROWSMITH COUNTRY LIFE. 1986. bi-m. $16. Camden House Publishing, Ferry Rd., Charlotte, VT 05445. TEL 802-425-3961. FAX 802-425-3307. Ed. John Barstow; Pub. Fred Laflamme. adv. contact: Jennifer Jolley. bk.rev. circ. 200,000. **Indexed:** Access (1986-), Gard.Lit. (1992-), Ind.How To Do It (1979-). **Document type:** consumer publication. —UnCover.
Formerly: Harrowsmith (U.S. Edition).

635   US
HARVESTS.* 1955. q. $15 (foreign $25). Better Lawn and Turf Institute, 1509 Johnson Ferry Rd., Ste. 190, Marietta, GA 30062-8122. TEL 615-277-3722. Ed. Eliot C. Roberts. bk.rev. circ. 1,500. (tabloid format; back issues avail.)

635   DK   ISSN 0017-8497
HAVEBLADET. 1920. bi-m. DKK 40. Kolonihaveforbundet for Danmark, Frederikssundsvej 304 A, 2700 Broenshoej, Denmark. TEL 01-288750. Eds. Ivan Larsen, Eyvind Thorsen. adv.; charts; illus. circ. 47,000.

635   DK   ISSN 0017-8500
HAVEN. 1900. 11/yr. DKK 270 (effective Nov. 1993). Det Danske Haveselskab, Jaegersborgvej 47, DK-2800 Lyngby, Denmark. TEL 45-93-60-00. FAX 45-93-51-44. Ed. Johan Damgaard Jensen. adv.; bk.rev.; charts; illus.; circ. 80,000 (controlled).

635   US   ISSN 1041-6838
HEATHER NEWS. 1982. 4/yr. $10 membership. North American Heather Society, c/o Pauline Croxton, 3641 Indian Creek Rd., Placerville, CA 95667. adv.; bk.rev. circ. 500. **Document type:** newsletter.
Description: Promotes the advancement of knowledge of the several botanical genera of heaths and heathers.

635   US
HEATHER NOTES. 1985. 4/yr. $5 membership. Northeast Heather Society, Box 101, Highland View, Alstead, NH 03602-0101. TEL 603-835-6165. Ed. Walter K. Wornick. **Document type:** newsletter.

635   UK
HEATHER SOCIETY. BULLETIN. 3/yr. $16 membership. Heather Society, Denbeigh, All Saints Rd., Creeting St. Mary, Ipswich, Suffolk 1P6 8PJ, England. TEL 0449-711220. Ed. A.W. Jones. **Document type:** bulletin.

635   UK   ISSN 0440-5757
HEATHER SOCIETY. YEARBOOK. 1963. a. $14 membership. Heather Society, Denbeigh, All Saints Rd., Creeting St. Mary, Ipswich, Suffolk LIP6 8PJ, England. TEL 0449-711220. Ed. A.W. Jones. adv.; bk.rev.; bibl.; cum.index: 1963-1972. circ. 1,500.

635   GW
HEIM UND GARTEN. 1947. m. DM.49.80. Landbuch Verlag GmbH, Kabelkamp 6, 30179 Hannover, Germany. TEL (0511)67806-0.
Description: Informative (non-technical) publication about all aspects of gardening. Features horticulture, landscaping, vegetable gardening, tips. Includes readers' opinions and ideas.

635   SW   ISSN 0018-0343
HEMTRAEDGAARDEN. 1945. 4/yr. SEK 90 to members (effective 1991). Riksfoerbundet Svensk Traedgaard, Nytorpsv. 34, 102 46 Stockholm, Sweden. Ed. Daniel Nordlund. adv.; bk.rev.; illus. circ. 24,500.
Formerly (until 1946): Tidskrift foer Nordsvensk Traedgaardsodling.

635   US   ISSN 1040-581X
THE HERB COMPANION; in celebration of the useful plants. 1988. bi-m. $21 (foreign $26). Interweave Press, Inc., 201 E. Fourth St., Loveland, CO 80537. TEL 303-669-7672. FAX 303-667-8317. Ed. Linda Ligon. circ. 125,000. **Indexed:** Gard.Lit. (1992-), Ind.How To Do It (1989-). **Document type:** consumer publication.
Description: Covers growing herbs in all climates and situations, appreciating their rich and varies history and using them in cooking, crafts and daily life.

635   US   ISSN 0163-9900
SB351.H5
HERB QUARTERLY. 1979. q. $24. Long Mountain Press, Box 689, San Anselmo, CA 94979-0689. TEL 415-455-9540. FAX 415-455-9541. Ed. Linda Sparrowe; Pub. James Keough. adv.; bk.rev.; abstr.; charts; illus.; index. circ. 35,000. (back issues avail.) **Indexed:** Gard.Lit. (1992-). **Document type:** consumer publication.
Description: All the garden lore of the ages as well as new crafts, medicinals, recipes and herb garden know-how.

635   US   ISSN 1048-3160
HERB, SPICE AND MEDICINAL PLANT DIGEST. 1983. 4/yr. $10. University of Massachusetts, Department of Plant and Soil Science, Stockbridge Hall, Amherst, MA 01003. TEL 412-545-2347. FAX 413-545-1242. bk.rev. circ. 1,500. **Indexed:** Gard.Lit. (1992-). **Document type:** newsletter. —BLDSC (4296.865000).
Description: For herb growers and those interested in herbs. Includes cultural information, surveys of current literature, and technical material.

635   US
HERBARIST. 1935. a. $5. Herb Society of America, Inc., 9019 Kirtland Chardon Rd., Mentor, OH 44060. TEL 216-256-0514. Ed. Dorothy Fish. adv. contact: Linda Wells. bk.rev.; illus.; cum.index: 1934-1981. circ. 3,000. (back issues avail.) **Indexed:** Gard.Lit. (1992-).

635   UK
HERBARIUM. 1990. q. £14 (N. America £18). The Herb Society, 134 Buckingham Palace Rd., London SW1W 9SA, England. TEL 071-823-5583. Ed. Penelope Ody. adv.; bk.rev. (back issues avail.) **Document type:** newsletter.
Description: Appeals to those sharing an interest in cultivating and cooking with herbs.

HERBERTIA. see *BIOLOGY — Botany*

635   US
HERITAGE ROSE LETTER. 1975. 5/yr. membership only. Heritage Roses Group, c/o Leonie Bell, Ed., 101 Cedar Grove Rd., Conshohocken, PA 19428. circ. 2,000.

635   II   ISSN 0970-2326
HIMALAYAN PLANT JOURNAL. (Not published 1987-1988) 1982. q. $25 to individuals; institutions $35. Primulaceae Books, Abhijit Villa, B.P.O. Ecchey, Kalimpong-Darjeeling 734 301, West Bengal, India. TEL 673. Ed. Udai C. Pradhan. adv.; bk.rev. circ. 500.
—BLDSC (4315.008000).
Description: Deals with conservation, culture, history, hybridization and identification of Himalayan flora.

HIROSHIMASHI SHOKUBUTSU KOEN KIYO/HIROSHIMA BOTANICAL GARDEN. BULLETIN. see *BIOLOGY — Botany*

GARDENING AND HORTICULTURE

HIROSHIMASHI SHOKUBUTSU KOEN SAIBAI KIROKU/HIROSHIMA BOTANICAL GARDEN. INVESTIGATION. see *BIOLOGY — Botany*

635 US ISSN 1040-6212
HOBBY GREENHOUSE. 1975. q. $12 (Canada & Mexico $14; foreign $15). Hobby Greenhouse Association, 8 Glen Terr., Bedford, MA 01730-2048. TEL 617-275-0377. (Subscr. to: 18517 Kingshill Rd., Germantown, MD 20874-2211) Ed. Janice L. Hale. adv.; bk.rev.; illus.; index. circ. 2,500. (back issues avail.)
 Description: Promotes greenhouse gardening as a hobby or avocation; disseminates practical and instructive information on management and growing techniques.

635.9 US ISSN 0738-2421
CODEN: HSOJEY
HOLLY SOCIETY JOURNAL. 1947. 4/yr. $10. Holly Society of America, Inc., 304 North Wind Rd., Baltimore, MD 21204. Ed. Mrs. Macpherson Raymond. bk.rev.; cum.index: 1947-1980. circ. 1,000. **Indexed:** Hort.Abstr., Ornam.Hort., Soils & Fert.
—BLDSC (4322.406500).
 Incorporates (1947-1983): Holly Society of America. Proceedings (ISSN 0273-043X); **Formerly:** Holly Letter (ISSN 0046-774X)

HOME FLAIR. see *INTERIOR DESIGN AND DECORATION*

635 US
HOMEOWNER'S RESOURCE GUIDE TO A BEAUTIFUL LAWN. 8/yr. $10. Lawn Institute, 1509 Johnson Ferry Rd., Ste. 190, Marietta, GA 30062-8122. TEL 404-977-5492. FAX 404-977-8205. Ed. James R. Brooks. **Document type:** consumer publication.
 Formerly (until 1992): Harvests Newsletter.
 Description: To enhance lawn grass quality; proper lawn care maintenance practices.

HOMES AND GARDENS. see *INTERIOR DESIGN AND DECORATION*

635.969 CN ISSN 0847-9763
HORT WEST. 1982. bi-m. $15. British Columbia Nursery Trades Association, 101 - 5830 176 A St., Surrey, BC, Canada. TEL 604-574-7772. FAX 604-574-7773. Ed. Phil Pearsall. adv.; bk.rev. circ. 1,200. (back issues avail.) **Document type:** trade publication.
 Formerly: Nursery Trades B.C. (ISSN 0823-7867)

635 SZ
HORTICULTEURS ET MARAICHERS ROMANDS. 1939. m. 36 SFr. Association des Horticulteurs de la Suisse Romande, Gd-rue 82, P.O. Box 454, CH-1110 Morges, Switzerland. FAX 021-8010617. (Co-sponsors: Association Romande des Fleuristes; Union Maraichere Romande; Groupement des Paysagistes Romands) Ed. M. Jacques Cartier. adv.; bk.rev.; illus.; mkt. circ. 2,000. **Document type:** consumer publication.
 Former titles: Journal des Horticulteurs et Maraichers Romands; Journal des Horticulteurs et Maraichers. (ISSN 0021-8057)

635.9 RM ISSN 1017-155X
HORTICULTURA. (Text in Rumanian; summaries in English, French and Russian) m. Ministerul Agriculturii si Alimentatiei, Calea Serban Voda, nr. 30-32, Sector 4, Bucharest, Rumania. TEL 41-32-30. Ed. Valeriu Cernat. adv.; charts; illus. circ. 7,000. **Indexed:** Chem.Abstr.
 Formerly (until 1990): Productia Vegetala. Horticultura (ISSN 0254-5756); Incorporates (in 197?): Revista de Horticultura si Viticultura (ISSN 0556-6010); Which was formerly (1952-1967): Gradina, Via si Livada (ISSN 0367-4118)

635 SP ISSN 1132-2950
HORTICULTURA; revista de hortalizas, flores y plantas ornamentales. (Supplements avail.) 1982. 8/yr. 6000 ptas. (foreign 7500 ptas.) (effective 1994). Ediciones de Horticultura, S.L., Apdo. de Correos 48, 43200 Reus (Tarragona), Spain. TEL 77-750402. FAX 77-753056. TELEX 56876. adv.: B&W page 102000 ptas., color page 168000 ptas.; trim 210 x 280. circ. 6,500.
 Description: Contains news, cultural and economic information covering all aspects of horticulture: crops under glass, field vegetables, flowers and cut flowers, nurseries, and commercial products.

635 UK
HORTICULTURAL BUSINESS DATA. a. £6. University of Reading, Department of Agricultural Economics & Management, 4 Earley Gate, Whiteknights Rd., P.O. Box 237, Reading RG5 2AR, England. TEL 0734-875123. FAX 0734-756467. TELEX 847813-RULIB-G. Eds. R.L. Vaughn, R.C. Crane. circ. 500. (back issues avail.) **Document type:** bulletin.
 Formerly: Financial Results of Horticultural Holdings.

635 AT
HORTICULTURAL GUIDE TO AUSTRALIAN PLANTS. 1975. a. Aus.$6. Society for Growing Australian Plants, Queensland Region, Box 809, Fortitude Valley, Qld. 4006, Australia.

635 US
HORTICULTURAL HANDBOOKS.* 1982. 3/yr. $9. Kevin A. Cappo, Ed. & Pub., 1018 Sunrise Trail Dr., Mahomet, IL 61853. bk.rev.

635 US ISSN 0886-5779
HORTICULTURAL NEWS. 1875. q. $20 membership. New Jersey State Horticultural Society, Box 116, Clayton, NJ 08312-0116. TEL 609-863-0110. FAX 609-881-4191. Ed. Linda Vorsa. adv. circ. 475. (back issues avail.) **Document type:** trade publication.

635 RH
HORTICULTURAL QUARTERLY REVIEW. q. (Horticultural Promotion Council) Modern Farming Publications Trust, Agriculture House, Leopold Takawira St., P.O. Box 1622, Harare, Zimbabwe. TEL 263-4-753278. FAX 263-4-750754. TELEX 22084 CFU ZW. adv.: B&W page Z.$3486, color page Z.$4686; adv. contact: Michael Rook.

380 635 NE ISSN 0441-7461
HORTICULTURAL RESEARCH INTERNATIONAL; directory of horticultural research institutes and their activities in 74 countries. irreg., 5th ed., 1993. fl.345 (effective 1993). International Society for Horticultural Science, Englaan 1, 6703 ET Wageningen, Netherlands. TEL 31-8370-21747. FAX 31-8370-21586. maps. **Document type:** directory.
 Description: Lists 2500 horticultural research institutes throughout the world, with personnel, main fields of interest and activity, addresses, telephone and fax numbers.

635 US ISSN 0163-7851
SB317.5 CODEN: HORED5
HORTICULTURAL REVIEWS. 1979. a. price varies. (American Society for Horticultural Science) John Wiley & Sons, Inc., 605 Third Ave., New York, NY 10158-0012. TEL 212-850-6000. FAX 212-850-6088. Ed. Jules Janick. **Indexed:** Biol.Abstr., Chem.Abstr., Crop Physiol.Abstr., Curr.Adv.Genetics & Molec.Biol., Field Crop Abstr., Hort.Abstr., Ornam.Hort., Rev.Plant Path., Soils & Fert.
—BLDSC (4331.247300); Faxon; UnCover; CASDDS.

635 CN
HORTICULTURAL SOCIETIES' NEWSLETTER. 4/yr. membership only. Ministry of Agriculture and Food, Guelph Agriculture Centre, Rural Organizations and Services Branch, P.O. Box 1030, Guelph, Ont. N1H 6N1, Canada. TEL 519-767-3540. (Co-sponsor: Ontario Horticultural Association) **Document type:** newsletter.
 Description: Publishes information regarding Ontario Horticultural Associations and Horticultural Societies.

635 ET
HORTICULTURAL SOCIETY OF ETHIOPIA. BULLETIN. (Text in English) irreg. Horticultural Society of Ethiopia, Box 1261, Addis Ababa, Ethiopia.

635 US
HORTICULTURAL SOCIETY OF NEW YORK. NEWSLETTER. 1945. q. membership. Horticultural Society of New York, 128 W. 58th St., New York, NY 10019. TEL 212-757-0915. FAX 212-246-1207. Ed. Jim Doyle. bk.rev. circ. 1,500. **Document type:** newsletter.

635 US ISSN 0018-5329
SB1
HORTICULTURE;* the magazine of American gardening. 1904. m. $26 (foreign $30). Horticulture Limited Partnership, 98 N. Washington St., Boston, MA 02114-1913. TEL 617-742-5600. FAX 617-367-6364. (Subscr. to: Box 53880, Boulder, CO 80322. TEL 800-234-2415) Ed. Thomas C. Cooper. adv.; bk.rev.; charts; illus.; index. circ. 330,000. (also avail. in microform from UMI,MIM; talking book; reprint service avail. from UMI) **Indexed:** Access (1978-), Biol.Abstr., Biol.& Agr.Ind., Biol.Dig., Bk.Rev.Ind. (1965-), Child.Bk.Rev.Ind. (1965-), Consum.Ind., Curr.Adv.Ecol.Sci., Excerp.Med., Farm & Garden Ind., Gard.Lit. (1992-), Gen.Sci.Ind., Ind.How To Do It (1990-), Ind.Sci.Rev., Mag.Ind., R.G., Ref.Sour. —Faxon; UnCover; UMI.
 Description: Provides news, views, articles, and how-to on gardening and gardening techniques.

635 FR ISSN 0395-8531
HORTICULTURE FRANCAISE. 1970. m. 345 F. (foreign 445 F.)(effective 1993). Lien Horticole, B.P. 30, 34471 Perols Cedex, France. adv.; bk.rev. circ. 5,000. **Indexed:** Hort.Abstr., Weed Abstr.
—BLDSC (4331.295000).

635 NZ ISSN 1170-1803
SB4
HORTICULTURE IN NEW ZEALAND (LINCOLN). 1973. s-a. NZ.$60 (includes Newsletter). Royal New Zealand Institute of Horticulture, Box 12, Lincoln University, Canterbury, New Zealand. Ed. R. Davison. bk.rev.; illus. circ. 500. **Indexed:** Gard.Lit. (1992-), Hort.Abstr., Soils & Fert.
—UnCover.
 Former titles (until 1990): Royal New Zealand Institute of Horticulture. Annual Journal (ISSN 0110-5760); (until 1989): Royal New Zealand Institute of Horticulture. Journal (ISSN 0557-6601)

635 NZ ISSN 0110-8530
HORTICULTURE NEWS. 1979. m. NZ.$45. New Zealand Rural Press Ltd., 300 Great South Rd., P.O. Box 4233, Auckland, New Zealand. TEL 0064-09-5209451. Ed. Alex Stone. adv.; illus. circ. 6,425.

HORTICULTURE RESEARCH INTERNATIONAL. see *AGRICULTURE — Crop Production And Soil*

635 CN ISSN 0823-8472
HORTICULTURE REVIEW. 18/yr. Can.$32.10. Landscape Ontario Horticultural Trade Association, 1293 Matheson Blvd., E., Mississauga, ON L4W 1R1, Canada. TEL 905-629-1184. FAX 905-629-4438. adv.: B&W page Can.$640; trim 8 1/8 x 10 7/8; adv. contact: Steve Moyer. bk.rev.
 Description: Provides the industry with timely, up-to-date information on all provincial happenings.

635 UK
HORTICULTURE WEEK. 1841. w. $250. Haymarket Magazines Ltd., 38-42 Hampton Rd., Teddington, Middx. TW11 0JE, England. TEL 081-943-5000. TELEX 895-2440-HAYMRT-G. Ed. Jim Deen. adv.; illus. circ. 10,213. **Indexed:** Forest.Abstr., Hort.Abstr., Rev.Plant Path.
 Formerly: Gardeners Chronicle - Horticultural Trade Journal (ISSN 0016-4682)
 Description: Trade news for nurserymen, landscapers, garden center managers and park managers.

635 UK ISSN 0964-8992
▼**THE HORTICULTURIST;** journal of the Institute of Horticulture. 1992. q. £39.50($72.50) Institute of Horticulture, 80 Vincent Sq., London SW1P 2PE, England. TEL 071-976-5951. FAX 071-976-5951. Ed. D.F. Day. adv.; bk.rev.; illus.; index. circ. 2,400. (back issues avail.) **Document type:** academic/scholarly publication.
—BLDSC (4331.319000); UMI.
 Incorporates (1987-1994): Professional Horticulture (ISSN 0950-0928); (1932-1987): Scientific Horticulture (ISSN 0080-7737)
 Refereed Serial

GARDENING AND HORTICULTURE

635 US ISSN 0742-8219
HORTIDEAS. 1984. m. $15. HortIdeas Publishing, 460 Black Lick Rd., Gravel Switch, KY 40328. TEL 606-332-7606. FAX 606-332-7606. Ed. Gregory Williams; Pub. Patricia Y. Williams. bk.rev.; s-a. index. circ. 1,600. (looseleaf format; back issues avail.) **Indexed:** Excerp.Med., Gard.Lit. **Document type:** newsletter.
Description: Contains reports on the latest research, methods, tools, plants, and books of interest to food and ornamental gardeners, from hundreds of worldwide sources.

635 CI ISSN 0018-5337
HORTIKULTURA/HORTICULTURAL MAGAZIN YUGOSLAVIJE. (Text in Croatian) 1934. q. 200 din.($15.15) Drustvo za Uredjenje Pejzaza i Vrtlarstvo SR Hrvatske, Savska c. 120, 41000 Zagreb, Croatia. Ed. Stjepan V. Letinic. adv.; bk.rev. circ. 1,250.

634 635 SP ISSN 1130-1678
HORTOFRUTICULTURA. 11/yr. 6000 ptas. (foreign 10000 ptas.). Edagricole Espana S.A., Castello 32, Dcha. 3o, 28001 Madrid, Spain. TEL 1-5780534. FAX 1-575-32-97. Eds. Nicolas Castilla, Rafael Gella. adv.; B&W page 89000 ptas., color page 120000 ptas.; adv. contact: Julia Dominguez. circ. 9,000.
Description: For fruit and vegetable cooperatives, young agriculturists, flower grocers, researchers, and agricultural extension centers.

635 US ISSN 0018-5345
SB317.5 CODEN: HJHSAR
HORTSCIENCE. 1966. m. $165. American Society for Horticultural Science, c/o Christine A. Radiske, Exec. Dir., 113 S. West St., Alexandria, VA 22314-2824. TEL 703-836-4606. FAX 703-836-2024. Ed. Wermer J. Lipton. adv.; bk.rev.; charts; illus.; index; cum.index: 1966-1976, 1977-1981, 1982-1986, 1987-1991. circ. 6,000. (also avail. in microform from WWS) **Indexed:** Agri.Eng.Abstr., Biol.Abstr., Biol.& Agr.Ind., Biol.Dig., Biotech.Abstr., Cadscan, Chem.Abstr., Cott.& Trop.Fibr.Abstr., Crop Physiol.Abstr., Curr.Adv.Ecol.Sci., Curr.Adv.Genetics & Molec.Biol., Curr.Cont., Excerp.Med., Farm & Garden Ind., Field Crop Abstr., Food Sci.& Tech.Abstr., Forest.Abstr., Forest Prod.Abstr., Helminthol.Abstr., Herb.Abstr., Hort.Abstr., I D A, Ind.Sci.Rev., INIS Atomind., Irr.& Drain.Abstr., Lead Abstr., Maize Abstr., Nutr.Abstr., Ornam.Hort., Plant Breed.Abstr., Plant Grow.Reg.Abstr., Potato Abstr., Rev.Plant Path., Sci.Cit.Ind., Seed Abstr., Sel.Water Res.Abstr., Soils & Fert., Sorghum & Millets Abstr., Soyabean Abstr., VITIS, Weed Abstr., World Agri.Econ.& Rural Sociol.Abstr., Zincscan.
—BLDSC (4331.360000); Faxon; UnCover; SWETS; CASDDS.
Description: Provides horticultural information of interest to a broad array of horticulturists; serves the communication needs of all levels of ASHS membership.

635 US ISSN 1063-0198
HORTTECHNOLOGY. 1991. q. $40. American Society for Horticultural Science, c/o Christine A. Radiske, Exec. Dir., 113 S. West St., Ste. 400, Alexandria, VA 22314-2824. TEL 703-836-4606. FAX 703-836-2024. Ed. John F. Kelly. adv.; bk.rev.; charts; illus.; index. circ. 6,000. **Document type:** academic/scholarly publication.
—UnCover; SWETS.
Description: Provides applied science-based information to professional horticulturists and practitioners; includes original research reports on technologically based subjects of potential or immediate value to horticultural practitioners.

635 UK ISSN 0950-1657
HORTUS; a gardening journal. 1987. 4/yr. £25 (Europe £30; elsewhere £35). The Bryansground Press, Bryan's Ground, Stapleton, Herefordshire LD8 2LP, England. TEL 0544-260011. FAX 0544-260015. Ed. David Wheeler; Pub. David Wheeler. adv.; bk.rev.; index. **Indexed:** Gard.Lit. (1992-). **Document type:** consumer publication.
—BLDSC (4331.364000).
Description: Privately published journal devoted to the decorative aspects of horticulture: history, design and ornament, plants, books and people.

HOUJYOU. see AGRICULTURE

HOUSE & GARDEN (LONDON). see INTERIOR DESIGN AND DECORATION

635 US ISSN 1061-4079
HOUSEPLANT MAGAZINE. (Text in English) 1987. 4/yr. $19.95 in US; Canada Can.$24.95. HousePlant Inc., Rt 1, Box 271-2, Elkins, WV 26241. TEL 304-636-1212. FAX 304-636-9723. Ed. Larry Hodgson. adv. contact: Todd Goldman. bk.rev.; illus. circ. 50,000. **Indexed:** Gard.Lit. (1992-). **Document type:** consumer publication.
Formerly (until 1992): Houseplant Forum (ISSN 0833-031X)
Description: Provides information on indoor gardening.

635.9 US
HUAMU PENJING/FLOWERS, TREES & POTTED LANDSCAPES. (Text in Chinese) bi-m. $35.75. China Books & Periodicals, Inc., 2929 24th St., San Francisco, CA 94110. TEL 415-282-2994. FAX 415-282-0994.

635 AT ISSN 0018-7909
HUON NEWS. 1964. w. Aus.$5. Huon Newspaper Co. Pty. Ltd., Franklin, Tasmania 7113, Australia. Ed. L.K. Geeves. circ. 2,268.

635 AT
HYDROPONIC SOCIETY OF VICTORIA. NEWSLETTER. 1982. 6/yr. Aus.$15 (foreign Aus.$25). Hydroponic Society of Victoria, P.O. Box 212, Monbulk, Vic. 3793, Australia. TEL 03-756-7532. FAX 03-558-0382. adv. circ. 225. **Document type:** newsletter.
Description: To encourage hobbyist and commercial growers in hydroponics. Provides local and overseas information to members.

635 SA
I B S A BULLETIN. 1963. a. $10. Indigenous Bulb Growers Association of South Africa, 3, The Bend, Edgemead 7441, South Africa. Ed.Bd. bk.rev. circ. 250. **Document type:** bulletin.
Formerly (until June 1974): I B S A Newsletter.
Description: Devoted to the conservation of South African bulbous plants by means of cultivation and propagation.

I E S NEWSLETTER. (Institute of Ecosystem Studies) see ENVIRONMENTAL STUDIES

I P M PRACTITIONER; monitoring the field of pest management. (Integrated Pest Management) see AGRICULTURE

635 NE
I S O S C PROCEEDINGS. Represents: International Congress on Soilless Culture. Proceedings. (Text in English) 1969. quadrennial, 8th, South Africa, 1992. fl.150 to non-members. International Society of Soilless Culture, P.O. Box 52, 6700 AB Wageningen, Netherlands. TEL 31-8370-13809. FAX 31-8370-23457. Ed.Bd. (back issues avail.) **Document type:** proceedings.

IDE-NYT: TIL VILLA, RAEKKEHUSE OG JORDBRUGERE. see INTERIOR DESIGN AND DECORATION

635.9 581 GW ISSN 0170-8414
IMMERGRUENE BLAETTER. 1961. a. DM.40. Deutsche Rhododendron Gesellschaft, Am Steinberg 3, 31157 Sarstedt, Germany. TEL 05066-826114. FAX 05066-42601. Ed. Prof. Dr. Wolfgang Spethmann. bk.rev.; index. circ. 1,300. (back issues avail.) **Document type:** consumer publication.

635 US
IN HOUSE HORT.* 1990. m. $15 (foreign $18). 270 Park Ave. S., Ste. 9A, New York, NY 10010-6105. TEL 212-228-0222. Ed. Joan Shelton Stover.

712 US ISSN 1042-7562
IN-SITE. 1987. bi-m. $49. Jame Martin Associates, Inc., 24380 N. Hwy. 45, Vernon Hills, IL 60061. TEL 708-634-8888. Ed. Cathy Walker. circ. 700.

635 II ISSN 0019-4875
CODEN: INHOAK
INDIAN HORTICULTURE. (Text in English) 1956. q. Rs.28($10) Indian Council of Agricultural Research, Krishi Anusandhan Bhaven, Pusa, New Delhi 110012, India. Ed. Neelam Chhabra. bk.rev.; charts; illus.; index. circ. 12,000. **Indexed:** Biol.Abstr., Field Crop Abstr., Food Sci.& Tech.Abstr., Forest.Abstr., Helminthol.Abstr., Herb.Abstr., Hort.Abstr., INIS Atomind., Nutr.Abstr., Packag.Sci.Tech., Plant Breed.Abstr.
Description: Deals with fruits, vegetables, and flowers.

635 II ISSN 0019-5251
SB13 CODEN: IJHOAQ
INDIAN JOURNAL OF HORTICULTURE. (Text in English) 1943. q. Rs.150($45) Horticultural Society of India, 255 Upper Palace Orchards, Bangalore 566006, India. Ed. K.L. Chadha. adv.; bk.rev.; charts; illus.; stat. circ. 800. **Indexed:** Agroforest.Abstr., Biol.Abstr., Chem.Abstr., Crop Physiol.Abstr., Field Crop Abstr., Food Sci.& Tech.Abstr., Hort.Abstr., Ornam.Hort., Plant Grow.Reg.Abstr., Potato Abstr., Seed Abstr., Soyabean Abstr., Sugar Ind.Abstr., Trop.Oil Seeds Abstr., Weed Abstr., World Agri.Econ.& Rural Sociol.Abstr.
—Faxon; CASDDS.

635 II ISSN 0970-2970
INDIAN JOURNAL OF MUSHROOMS. 1973. s-a. Rs.60($30) to individuals; institutions Rs.150($75). Indian Mushroom Growers Association, Mushroom Research Laboratory, College of Horticulture & Forestry, Chambaghat, Solan 173 230, H.P., India. Ed. T.R. Shandilya. adv. circ. 400. (back issues avail.) **Indexed:** Rev.Plant Path.
Description: Articles on mushroom research and on the domestication of other edible fungi.

635 II ISSN 0970-2172
INDIAN ORCHID JOURNAL. 1985. 4/yr. $15. c/o Ganesh Mani Pradhan and Udai C. Pradhan, Ganesh Villa, Kalimpong 734-301, WB, India.

INFORMATION SOURCES IN AGRICULTURE AND HORTICULTURE. see AGRICULTURE

INSTITUTUL AGRONOMIC CLUJ-NAPOCA. BULETINUL. SERIA AGRICULTURA. see AGRICULTURE

635 RM ISSN 0379-8372
INSTITUTUL AGRONOMIC ION IONESCU DE LA BRAD. LUCRARI STIINTIFICE. SERIA HORTICULTURA. 1957. a. Institutul Agronomic "Ion Ionescu de la Brad", Aleea M. Sadoveanu, nr. 3, Jassy, Rumania. **Indexed:** Biol.Abstr., Chem.Abstr., Crop Physiol.Abstr., Field Crop Abstr., Herb.Abstr., Hort.Abstr., Plant Breed.Abstr., Plant Grow.Reg.Abstr.
—BLDSC (5303.405500).
Supersedes in part: Institutul Agronomic Ion Ionescu de la Brad. Lucrari Stiintifice. Seria Agronomie-Horticultura (ISSN 0075-3505)

634 PL ISSN 0208-5925
INSTYTUT SADOWNICTWA I KWIACIARSTWA W SKIERNIEWICACH. PRACE. SERIA B: ROSLINY OZDOBNE/ORNAMENTAL PLANTS. 1975. irreg. 40000 Zl.($12) Research Institute of Pomology and Floriculture - Instytut Sadownictwa i Kwiaciarstwa, Ul. Pomologiczna 18, 96-100 Skierniewice, Poland. TEL 48-40-20-88. FAX 01148-40-3228. TELEX 886659 INSAD. Ed. K. Mynett. circ. 1,000. **Indexed:** Plant Grow.Reg.Abstr., Seed Abstr. **Document type:** academic/scholarly publication.

634 PL ISSN 0208-5933
CODEN: PSKSDQ
INSTYTUT SADOWNICTWA I KWIACIARSTWA W SKIERNIEWICACH. SERIA A: PRACE DOSWIADCZALNE Z ZAKRESU SADOWNICTWA/FRUIT RESEARCH. (Text in Polish; summaries in English) 1955. irreg. 40000 Zl.($12) Research Institute of Pomology and Floriculture - Instytut Sadownictwa i Kwiaciarstwa, Ul. Pomologiczna 18, 96-100 Skierniewice, Poland. TEL 20-21. FAX 01148-40-3228. TELEX 886659 INSAD. Ed. E. Niemczyk. circ. 1,000. **Indexed:** Biol.Abstr., Hort.Abstr., Plant Grow.Reg.Abstr., Ref.Zh., Weed Abstr. **Document type:** academic/scholarly publication.
—BLDSC (6582.365000); CASDDS.

635 US ISSN 0254-2528
INTERAMERICAN SOCIETY FOR TROPICAL HORTICULTURE. PROCEEDINGS. (Former name of issuing body: American Society for Horticultural Science, Tropical Region) (Text and summaries in English and Spanish) 1957. a. $20. Interamerican Society for Tropical Horticulture, c/o Carl W. Campbell, 18905 S.W. 280th St., Homestead, FL 33031. FAX 305-247-3597. Ed. Richard J. Campbell. bk.rev.; index, cum.index: vols.1-12 (1957-1968). circ. 500. **Indexed:** Hort.Abstr., Ornam.Hort., Trop.Abstr., Weed Abstr. **Document type:** proceedings.
—BLDSC (6727.200000).
Former titles: American Society for Horticultural Science, Tropical Region, Proceedings of the Annual Meeting; American Society for Horticultural Science. Caribbean Region. Proceedings of the Annual Meeting (ISSN 0066-0116)

GARDENING AND HORTICULTURE

635 747   US   ISSN 1063-1607
INTERIOR LANDSCAPE. 1984. q. $16 (foreign $24). American Nurseryman Publishing Co., 77 Washington St., Ste. 2100, Chicago, IL 60602-2904. TEL 312-782-5505. FAX 312-782-3232. Ed. Cynthia C. Urbano. adv. contact: Tim Hill. bk.rev.; charts; illus.; stat.; tr.lit. circ. 4,500. (also avail. in microform from UMI; back issues avail.; reprint service avail. from UMI) **Indexed:** Hort.Abstr. **Document type:** trade publication.
—UMI.
    Formerly: Interior Landscape Industry (ISSN 0742-1648)
    Description: Presents business and technical articles for professionals who design, install and maintain interior landscape projects, and foliage buyers.

635.977   US   ISSN 0198-9561
INTERNATIONAL BONSAI. 1979. q. $24 (foreign $32). International Bonsai Arboretum, Box 23894, Rochester, NY 14692-3894. TEL 716-334-2595. FAX 716-334-6239. Ed. Wm. N. Valavanis. adv.; bk.rev.; circ. 5,000 (paid). (back issues avail.)

635   US   ISSN 0159-656X
INTERNATIONAL CAMELLIA JOURNAL. a. membership only. International Camellia Society, Box 750, Brookhaven, MS 39601-0750. TEL 601-833-7351. **Indexed:** Ornam.Hort.

635
INTERNATIONAL CAMELLIA SOCIETY. MID-YEAR NEWSLETTER. a. membership only. International Camellia Society, Box 750, Brookhaven, MS 39601-0750. TEL 601-833-7351. **Indexed:** Hort.Abstr.

635   NE   ISSN 0074-6231
INTERNATIONAL HORTICULTURAL CONGRESS. PROCEEDINGS. 1899. quadrennial; 23rd, 1990, Florence, Italy. avail. on request. International Society for Horticultural Science, Englaan 1, 6703 ET Wageningen, Netherlands. TEL 31-8370-21747. FAX 31-8370-21586. **Indexed:** Biol.Abstr., Weed Abstr. **Document type:** proceedings.
    Description: Publishes papers and reports presented at the congress.

634.3   US   ISSN 0074-7203
SB608.C5
INTERNATIONAL ORGANIZATION OF CITRUS VIROLOGISTS. PROCEEDINGS OF THE CONFERENCE. 1961. triennial. price varies. International Organization of Citrus Virologists, c/o Dr. L.W. Timmer, Univ. of Florida, CREC, 700 Experiment Station Rd., Lake Alfred, FL 33850. TEL 813-956-1151. FAX 813-956-4631. Ed.Bd. (back issues avail.) **Document type:** proceedings.
—BLDSC (6842.981000).

581   US   ISSN 0538-9143
INTERNATIONAL PLANT PROPAGATORS' SOCIETY. COMBINED PROCEEDINGS OF ANNUAL MEETINGS. 1950. a. price varies. International Plant Propagators' Society, Inc., Washington Park Arboretum, University of Washington, XD-10, Seattle, WA 98195. TEL 209-543-8602. FAX 206-685-2692. Ed. John A. Wott. circ. 3,000. **Indexed:** Ornam.Hort. **Document type:** proceedings.
—BLDSC (3325.040000).
    Description: Information on the art and science of plant propagation. Contains papers presented in 7 regional meetings.

635   UK   ISSN 0075-0700
IRIS YEAR BOOK. 1924. a. £9. British Iris Society, Copper Beeches, N. End Ln., Downe, Orpington, Kent BR6 7HG, England. TEL 44-689-853646. FAX 44-689-861593. Ed. B.C. Baughen. adv.; bk.rev. circ. 800. **Document type:** academic/scholarly publication.

635   CN   ISSN 0827-2824
ISLAND GROWER. 1984. 11/yr. Can.$18. Greenheart Publications, 7007 Richview Dr., RR 4, Sooke, B.C. VOS 1N0, Canada. Ed. Phyllis Kusch. adv.; bk.rev.; index. circ. 8,000. (back issues avail.)

635   IS
ISRAEL INSTITUTE OF HORTICULTURE. SCIENTIFIC ACTIVITIES. triennial. $20 (effective 1993). Agricultural Research Organization, Israel Institute of Horticulture, Volcani Centre, P.O. Box 6, Bet Dagan 50250, Israel. TEL 972-3-9683215. FAX 972-3-993998. TELEX 381476. **Indexed:** Biol.Abstr. **Document type:** government publication.

635   US   ISSN 0882-4142
IVY JOURNAL. 1975. a. $15 includes membership. American Ivy Society, Box 2123, Naples, FL 33939-2123. TEL 513-862-4700. Ed. Ann Speanburg; Pub. Rachel Cobb. adv.; bk.rev.; illus. circ. 375. **Indexed:** Hort.Abstr., Ornam.Hort. **Document type:** academic/scholarly publication.
    Description: Includes articles on ivy culture, hardiness, and uses; profiles old and new varieties.

635.9   UK
JANUARY BULLETIN. a. £8. National Dahlia Society, c/o General Sec. A.G. Winkless, 8 Station Rd., Kirby Muxloe, Leicester LE9 9EJ, England. TEL 0533-387717. Ed. E. Pitt. circ. 3,500.
    Description: Information about new developments in dahlias. Includes results from dahlia shows.

635   JA   ISSN 0013-7626
    CODEN: EGKZA9
JAPANESE SOCIETY FOR HORTICULTURAL SCIENCE. JOURNAL/ENGEI GAKKAI ZASSHI. (Text in English, Japanese) 1925. q. 7000 Yen (effective since 1989). Japanese Society for Horticultural Science - Engei Gakkai, c/o Kyoto University, Faculty of Agriculture, Sakyo-ku, Kyoto 606, Japan. TEL 075-753-6053. FAX 075-753-6068. Ed. Ken-ichi Arisumi. adv.; charts; index. circ. 3,000. **Indexed:** Biol.Abstr., Chem.Abstr., Crop Physiol.Abstr., Curr.Adv.Ecol.Sci., Curr.Adv.Genetics & Molec.Biol., Curr.Cont., Excerp.Med., Field Crop Abstr., Food Sci.& Tech.Abstr., Helminthol.Abstr., Herb.Abstr., Hort.Abstr., INIS Atomind., Irr.& Drain.Abstr., Ornam.Hort., Plant Breed.Abstr., Plant Grow.Reg.Abstr., Rev.Plant Path., Rice Abstr., Seed Abstr., Soils & Fert., VITIS, Weed Abstr. **Document type:** academic/scholarly publication.
—BLDSC (4809.450000); SWETS; CASDDS. CCC.

JARDIM BOTANICO DO RIO DE JANEIRO. ARQUIVOS. see BIOLOGY — Botany

635.9   CN
JARDIN BOTANIQUE DE MONTREAL. LEGUMES: RESULTATS DES CULTURES D'ESSAI. (Text in French) 1969. a. free to botanical and horticultural institutions. Jardin Botanique de Montreal, Bibliotheque, 4101 est, rue Sherbrooke, Montreal, Que. H1X 2B2, Canada. TEL 514-872-1824. FAX 514-872-3765. illus. circ. 600.
    Former titles: Jardin Botanique de Montreal. Annuelles et Legumes: Resultats des Cultures d'Essai (ISSN 0319-3098); Jardin Botanique de Montreal. Annuelle (ISSN 0319-3101)

635   SZ
JARDIN FAMILIAL. m. 12 rue Samuel Cornut, CH-1860 Aigle, Switzerland. TEL 025-261807. Ed. Jean-David Christinat.

635   FR   ISSN 0240-5024
JARDIN FAMILIAL DE FRANCE. 1934. bi-m. 30 F. Ligue Francaise du Coin de Terre et du Foyer, 11 rue Saint Romain, 75006 Paris, France. Ed. Raymond Mondet. circ. 20,000.
    Formerly: Jardin Familial; Incorporates: Jardin Ouvrier de France (ISSN 0021-5465)

635   FR
JARDINERIES VEGETAL. 1976. s-m. 600 F. Editions J, B.P. 30, 78511 Rambouillet Cedex, France. TEL 34-84-70-60. FAX 34-84-70-55. TELEX 695589. Ed. Francois Langendorff. adv. circ. 9,500. **Document type:** newspaper, trade publication.
—CCC.
    Formerly: Jardineries (ISSN 0151-4695); Incorporates (in Oct. 1987): Vegetal.

635   FR   ISSN 0021-5481
JARDINS DE FRANCE. 1827. 10/yr. 190 F. (foreign 275 F.). Societe Nationale d'Horticulture de France, 84 rue de Grenelle, 75007 Paris, France. Ed. M. Leduc. adv.; bk.rev.; bibl.; illus. circ. 10,000. **Indexed:** Chem.Abstr., Hort.Abstr.

635   US
JOHN E. BRYAN GARDENING NEWSLETTER. 1978. 12/yr. $30. John E. Bryan, Ed. & Pub., 300 Valley St., Ste. 206, Sausalito, CA 94965-2480. TEL 415-331-7848. FAX 415-331-5725. bk.rev. circ. 250. **Document type:** newsletter.
    Description: Focuses on Northern California growing conditions and includes general information.

JORD OG VIDEN; agronomer - hortonomer - forstkandidater. see AGRICULTURE

635.933   US   ISSN 0745-7839
SB413.R47
JOURNAL AMERICAN RHODODENDRON SOCIETY. 1947. q. $25. American Rhododendron Society, Box 1380, Gloucester, VA 23061. TEL 804-693-4433. Ed. Sonja Nelson. adv.: B&W page $300. bk.rev.; illus.; index, cum.index: 1947-1970, 1971-1980, 1981-1990. circ. 5,800. (back issues avail.) **Indexed:** Hcrt.Abstr., Ornam.Hort., Plant Grow.Reg.Abstr.
    Formerly (until 1982): American Rhododendron Society. Quarterly Bulletin (ISSN 0003-0821)
    Description: Covers all aspects of Rhododendron culture, gardens, development - scientific and educational for serious gardeners and novices.

JOURNAL OF AQUATIC PLANT MANAGEMENT. see BIOLOGY — Botany

634.9   US   ISSN 0278-5226
JOURNAL OF ARBORICULTURE. 1975. bi-m. $55 (membership $70). International Society of Arboriculture, Box GG, Savoy, IL 61874. Ed. Dan Neely. adv.; bk.rev.; bibl.; illus.; index. circ. 5,500. **Indexed:** Bio-Contr.News & Info., Biol.Abstr., Biol.& Agr.Ind., Farm & Garden Ind., Forest.Abstr., Forest Prod.Abstr., Gard.Lit. (1992-), Hort.Abstr., Ornam.Hort., Soils & Fert.
—BLDSC (4947.174000); UnCover.
    Supersedes: Arborist's News (ISSN 0003-7958); International Shade Tree Conference. Proceedings (ISSN 0074-834X)

712 635   UK   ISSN 0144-5170
SB451
JOURNAL OF GARDEN HISTORY. 1981. q. £114($191) Taylor & Francis Ltd., Rankine Rd., Basingstoke, Hants RG24 8PR, England. TEL 0256-840366. FAX 0256-479438. TELEX 858540. Ed. John Dixon Hunt. adv.; bk.rev.; illus. **Indexed:** Amer.Hist.& Life, Art & Archaeol.Tech.Abstr., Artbibl.Mod., Arts & Hum.Cit.Ind., Avery Ind.Archit.Per., Br.Archaeol.Abstr., Br.Hum.Ind., Br.Tech.Ind., Curr.Cont., Environ.Per.Bibl., Gard.Lit. (1992-), Hist.Abstr., RILA **Document type:** newsletter.
—BLDSC (4987.300000); Faxon; UnCover; SWETS. CCC.
    Description: Main emphasis is on documentation of individual gardens in all parts of the world; articles on other topics: iconography, aesthetics, botany and horticulture, technology, social and economic history, conservation and restoration of historic gardens.
    Refereed Serial

610   US   ISSN 1049-6475
SB351.H5   CODEN: JHEPEF
JOURNAL OF HERBS, SPICES & MEDICINAL PLANTS. 1991. q. $28 to individuals; institutions $32; libraries $42. Haworth Press, Inc., 10 Alice St., Binghamton, NY 13904. TEL 607-722-5857; 800-342-9678. FAX 607-722-1424. Ed. Lyle Craker. adv.; bk.rev.; illus. (also avail. in microfiche from UMI; reprint service avail. from HAW) **Document type:** academic/scholarly publication.
    Description: Features original articles and short reviews associated with the production and development of herbs, spices, and medicinal plants. Includes information related to such areas as physiology, breeding, productivity, commercial applications, and marketing.
    Refereed Serial

635   US   ISSN 1054-4682
SB317.5   CODEN: JHCHEF
▼**JOURNAL OF HOME & CONSUMER HORTICULTURE.** 1993. q. $28 to individuals; institutions $36; libraries $48. Haworth Press, Inc., 10 Alice St., Binghamton, NY 13904. TEL 607-722-5857; 800-342-9678. FAX 607-722-1424. TELEX 4932599. Ed. Ray Poincelot. adv.; bk.rev. (also avail. in microfiche from UMI; reprint service avail. from HAW) **Indexed:** Food Sci.& Tech.Abstr. **Document type:** academic/scholarly publication.
    Description: For academics and business professionals concerned with home and consumer horticulture.
    Refereed Serial

GARDENING AND HORTICULTURE

635 UK ISSN 0022-1589
CODEN: JHSCA8
JOURNAL OF HORTICULTURAL SCIENCE. 1919. bi-m. £85($148.75) (Horticultural and Agricultural Research Station) Headley Bros. Ltd, Invicta Press, Ashford, Kent TN24 8HH, England. Ed. A.R. Rees. bibl.; charts; illus.; index, cum.index: vols.1-10, 11-20. circ. 1,150. (reprint service avail. from SWZ) **Indexed:** Agri.Eng.Abstr., Bio-Contr.News & Info., Biol.Abstr., Biol.& Agr.Ind., Biotech.Abstr., Cadscan, Chem.Abstr., Crop Physiol.Abstr., Curr.Adv.Ecol.Sci., Curr.Cont., Energy Ind., Energy Info.Abstr., Excerp.Med., Field Crop Abstr., Food Sci.& Tech.Abstr., Forest.Abstr., Helminthol.Abstr., Herb.Abstr., Hort.Abstr., Ind.Sci.Rev., Irr.& Drain.Abstr., Lead Abstr., Nutr.Abstr., Ornam.Hort., Plant Breed.Abstr., Plant Grow.Reg.Abstr., Rev.Appl.Entomol., Rev.Plant Path., Sci.Cit.Ind., Seed Abstr., Sel.Water Res.Abstr., Soils & Fert., VITIS, Zincscan. **Document type:** academic/scholarly publication.
—BLDSC (5003.000000); Faxon; UnCover; SWETS; CASDDS.

635 US
JOURNAL OF THERAPEUTIC HORTICULTURE. 1986. a. $15 to non-members. American Horticultural Therapy Association, 362A Christopher Ave., Gaithersburg, MD 20879-3660. TEL 301-948-3010. FAX 301-869-2397. circ. 1,000. **Indexed:** Gard.Lit. (1992-). **Document type:** trade publication.
Description: Devoted to using horticulture to enhance the lives of special populations through therapy and vocational rehabilitation.

634 YU ISSN 0350-2155
CODEN: JUVODH
JUGOSLOVENSKO VOCARSTVO/JOURNAL OF YUGOSLAV POMOLOGY. (Text in Serbo-Croatian; summaries in English, French and German) 1967. q. $30. Jugoslovensko Naucno Vocarsko Drustvo, Vojvode Stepe 9, Cacak, Serbia, Yugoslavia. FAX 032-47-406. TELEX 13866 VOVINST YU. Ed. Asen Stancevic. adv.; bk.rev.; abstr.; bibl. circ. 2,000. **Indexed:** Chem.Abstr., Hort.Abstr., Plant Breed.Abstr., Ref.Zh., Seed Abstr.
—BLDSC (5073.855000); CASDDS.

635 GW
K T B L ARBEITSBLAETTER GARTENBAU. irreg., no.670, 1993. DM.2.50. Kuratorium fuer Technik und Bauwesen in der Landwirtschaft e.V., Bartningstr. 49, 64289 Darmstadt, Germany. TEL 06151-7001-0. FAX 06151-7001123. **Document type:** monographic series.

635 XR ISSN 0862-4372
KAKTUSY. (Text in Czech, Slovak; summaries in English) 1965. bi-m. $25 per vol. Spolecnost Ceskych a Slovenskych Pestitelu Kaktusu aj Sukulentu, se Dilem v Brne, Pivovarska 861, 289 22 Lysa n.L., Czech Republic. TEL 325-972-407. Ed. Jan Riha. adv.; bk.rev.; illus.; index.
Description: Includes articles about botany, observations in ecology, cultivation, propagation, ornamental use of cacti and other succulents.

635 GW ISSN 0931-380X
KALENDER FUER DEN BIOGARTEN. 1986. a. DM.14.80. Pala-Verlag GmbH, Rheinstr. 37, 64283 Darmstadt, Germany. TEL 06151-23028. FAX 06151-292713. Ed. Dettmer Gruenefeld. adv.; bk.rev. circ. 15,000. (back issues avail.) **Document type:** consumer publication.

635 JA ISSN 0374-8731
CODEN: KESKAM
KANAGAWA HORTICULTURAL EXPERIMENT STATION. BULLETIN. (Text in Japanese; summaries in English) 1952. a. free. Prefectural Horticultural Experiment Station, 1217 Ninomiya, Ninomiya-machi, Kanagawa, Japan. **Indexed:** Biodet.Abstr., Biol.Abstr., Hort.Abstr., Plant Breed.Abstr.

635 US
KANSAS WILDFLOWER SOCIETY NEWSLETTER. 1978. 4/yr. $15 membership. (Kansas Wildflower Society) Hall Publishing Co., Mulvane Arts Center, Washburn University, Topeka, KS 66621. TEL 913-231-1010. FAX 913-233-2780. Ed. Sheldon H. Cohen. bk.rev.; circ. 550 (controlled). **Document type:** newsletter.
Description: Deals with the flora of the Great Plains.

635 634 HU ISSN 0023-0677
CODEN: SZBODH
KERTESZET ES SZOLESZET/GARDENING AND VINICULTURE. 1951. w. $52. (Szoleszetti es Boraszati Kutato Intezet) Agricola Kft., P.O. Box 14, 1355 Budapest, Hungary. TEL 361-1122-237. FAX 361-1530-518. (Subscr. to: Kultura, Box 149, H-1389 Budapest, Hungary) Ed. Klara Biza. adv.; bk.rev. circ. 30,000. **Indexed:** Agri.Eng.Abstr., Chem.Abstr., Field Crop Abstr., Hort.Abstr., Seed Abstr., Soils & Fert., VITIS. **Document type:** trade publication.
—CASDDS.
Formerly: Szoleszet es Boraszat (ISSN 0133-381X)

635 HU ISSN 0133-3410
KERTGAZDASAG/HORTICULTURE. (Text in English, Hungarian) 1956. bi-m. 1200 Ft. (Ministry of Agriculture) Agroinform Kiado es Nyomda Kft., Kitaibel Pal u. 4, 1024 Budapest II, Hungary. TEL 135-1927. FAX 135-0344. Ed. Molnar Bela. **Document type:** newsletter.
●Also available online.
—BLDSC (5090.275000).

635 333.78 UK ISSN 0265-3842
QK1 CODEN: KEWMEI
KEW MAGAZINE. 1787. q. £27.50($56.50) to individuals; institutions or libraries £63($118). (Royal Botanic Gardens) Basil Blackwell Ltd., 108 Cowley Rd., Oxford OX4 1JF, England. TEL 0865-791100. FAX 0865-791347. TELEX 837022-OXBOOK-G. (Co-sponsor: Bentham-Moxon Trust) Ed. Victoria Matthews. adv.; bk.rev.; illus. circ. 1,400. (also avail. in microform; microfiche from IDC; back issues avail.) **Indexed:** Gard.Lit. (1992-), Ornam.Hort.
—UnCover; SWETS; UMI. **CCC**.
Incorporates: Curtis's Botanical Magazine (ISSN 0011-4073)

635.9 JA
KIBI NO KUSABANA/ASSOCIATION OF WILD PLANT IN KURASHIKI. JOURNAL. (Text in Japanese) 1981. a. Kurashiki Yaso no Kai - Association of Wild Plant in Kurashiki, c/o Mr. Isamu Komatsubara, 20-23, Kanda 1-chome, Kurashiki-shi, Okayama-ken 712, Japan.

635 US
KIWIFRUIT ENTHUSIASTS JOURNAL. 1985. a. $14.95. Friends of the Trees Society, Box 1064, Tonasket, WA 98855. TEL 509-485-2705. bk.rev. (back issues avail.) **Document type:** academic/scholarly publication.
Formerly (until 1992): Actinidia Enthusiasts Newsletter (ISSN 1052-8911)
Description: Provides information on available species, growing suggestions, sources, and propagation.

635 NE ISSN 0166-3704
KLEINE AARDE. 1972. q. fl.25. Postbus 151, 5280 AD Boxtel, Netherlands. Ed. H. Kleijburg. adv.; bk.rev.; illus. circ. 20,000. (back issues avail.)

KOREAN JOURNAL OF BREEDING. see AGRICULTURE — Poultry And Livestock

635 GW ISSN 0178-0166
KRAUT UND RUEBEN; das Magazin fuer biologischen Gaertnern und naturgemaesses Leben. 1985. m. DM.92. B L V Verlagsgesellschaft mbH, Lothstr. 29, 80797 Munich, Germany. TEL 089-12705-0. FAX 089-12705354. Ed. Wolfram Franke. adv.; bk.rev. **Document type:** trade publication.
—**CCC**.
Description: Focuses on organic gardening and holistic health.

635 US
L A I F S JOURNAL. (Supplement avail.: Monthly Fern Lesson) bi-m. $18. Los Angeles International Fern Society, Box 90943, Los Angeles, CA 91109-0943.

635 II ISSN 0023-7388
LAL-BAUGH. (Text in English) 1956. q. Rs.10. Mysore Horticultural Society, Lalbaugh, Bangalore 560004, India. TEL 603781. Ed. Y.S. Nagaraju. illus. circ. 3,000. **Indexed:** Biol.Abstr., Hort.Abstr.

712 CN ISSN 0843-459X
LANDMARK. 1989. bi-m. Can.$25 (foreign $25). Charlton Communications Inc., 807 Manning Rd. N.E., Ste. 200, Calgary, AB T2E 7M8, Canada. TEL 403-569-8520. FAX 403-569-9590. Ed. Stacy Cohen; Pub. Mary-Lynn Charlton. adv. contact: John Batiuk. **Document type:** trade publication.
Description: Covers land management, land care and design professionals, services and suppliers.

712 UK
LANDSCAPE & GARDEN CONTRACTOR. 1987. 6/yr. £30. (Landscape Industry International) Peter Neale & Associates, Maltravers House, 28 London Rd., Cheltenham, Glos. GL52 6DX, England. TEL 0242-221456. FAX 0242-576452. Ed. Brent Krefield. circ. 5,300.
Description: News and features for the smaller landscape and garden contractor.

LANDSCAPE ARCHITECTURE. see ARCHITECTURE

712 AT ISSN 0310-9011
LANDSCAPE AUSTRALIA. 1979. q. Aus.$36 (New Zealand Aus.$42; elsewhere Aus.$45). (Australian Institute of Landscape Architects) Landscape Publications, 17 Carlyle Cres., Mont Albert, Vic. 3127, Australia. TEL 03-890-5764. FAX 03-899-6789. Ed. Ralph P. Neale. adv.; bk.rev.; index. circ. 2,952. **Indexed:** Avery Ind.Archit.Per., Br.Tech.Ind., Gard.Lit. (1992-).
—BLDSC (5153.143000).
Description: Provides information about design of open space in all its aspects - both within Australia and in overseas countries.

712 US ISSN 0194-7257
CODEN: LACOE9
LANDSCAPE CONTRACTOR; official publication of the Illinois Landscape Contractors Association. 1965. m. $65. (Illinois Landscape Contractors Association) Maury Boyd and Associates, Inc., 2200 S. Main St., Lombard, IL 60148. TEL 708-932-8443. Ed. Deborah Slott. adv.: B&W page $630, color page $1235; trim 7 3/8 x 9 7/8; adv. contact: Esther Baricza. bk.rev.; circ. 2,200 (controlled). **Document type:** trade publication.
Supersedes (1959-1978): Midwest Landscaping (ISSN 0026-3400)
Description: Dedicated to educating, advising and informing members of the industry and furthering the goals of the Association.

LANDSCAPE DESIGN. see ARCHITECTURE

712 US
LANDSCAPE DESIGN.* 1988. bi-m. $25. Gold Trade Publications, Inc., 68-860 Perez Rd., Ste. J, Cathedral City, CA 92234-7248. TEL 818-781-8300. Ed. Matthew Trulio. adv.; bk.rev.; charts; stat. circ. 13,000. **Indexed:** Gard.Lit. (1992-). **Document type:** trade publication.

712 UK
LANDSCAPE DIRECTORY. biennial. Peter Neale & Associates, Maltravers House, 28 London Rd., Cheltenham, Glos. GL52 6DX, England. TEL 0242-221456. FAX 0242-576452. **Document type:** directory.

712 UK ISSN 0266-9455
LANDSCAPE INDUSTRY INTERNATIONAL. 1982. bi-m. £40. Peter Neale & Associates, Maltravers House, 28 London Rd., Cheltenham, Glos. GL52 6DX, England. TEL 0242-221456. FAX 0242-576452. Ed. Peter Neale. adv.; bk.rev. circ. 7,135.
—BLDSC (5153.146130).
Description: All aspects of landscape design and construction, from the private garden to the reclamation project.

LANDSCAPE JOURNAL; design, planning, and management of the land. see ARCHITECTURE

635 US
LANDSCAPE MANAGEMENT'S SEED POCKET GUIDE. a. Advanstar Communications, 7500 Old Oak Blvd., Cleveland, OH 44130. TEL 216-826-2839. FAX 216-891-2726. adv.: B&W page $4580, color page $5940; trim 6 x 8 3/16. circ. 44,680. **Document type:** trade publication.
Description: Covers how to specify and select seed mixtures by location and climate zone, varietal seeds, shade factors and more.

LANDSCAPE RESEARCH. see ARCHITECTURE

GARDENING AND HORTICULTURE   2643

712 UK ISSN 0960-3328
LANDSCAPE SHOWCASE. 1990. bi-m. 3-5 Church St., Brierley Hill, W. Midlands DY5 3PT, England. TEL 0384-481989. FAX 0384-481447. Ed. Charles Smart. circ. 4,000. **Document type:** trade publication.
Description: Guide to materials and services for landscaping.

712 CN ISSN 0225-6398
LANDSCAPE TRADES. 1979. 9/yr. Can.$32.10. Landscape Ontario Horticultural Trades Association, 1293 Matheson Blvd. E., Mississauga, ON L4W 1R1, Canada. TEL 905-629-1184. FAX 905-629-4438. Ed. Rita Weerdenberg. adv.: B&W page Can.$1050, color page Can.$1750; trim 8 1/8 x 10 7/8; adv. contact: Steve Moyer. bk.rev.; illus. circ. 8,500.
Description: Reaches all realms of the industry and communicates information and ideas for management, middle management and the workers.

712 US
LANDSCAPING HOMES & GARDENS. bi-m. $24.95. Arden Communications, Inc., 340 E. 93rd St., Ste. 14C, New York, NY 10128-5552. TEL 212-722-7508. FAX 212-722-7508. Ed. Jamie Gibbs. bk.rev. circ. 250,000. **Document type:** consumer publication.

712 DK ISSN 0023-8066
LANDSKAB. (Text in Danish; summaries and captions in English) 1923. 8/yr. DKK 440. (Association of Danish Landscape Architects) Arkitektens Forlag, Nyhavn 43, DK-1051 Copenhagen K, Denmark. TEL 33-13-62-00. FAX 33-91-27-70. Ed. Annemarie Lund. adv.; bk.rev.; charts; illus.; index. circ. 1,400. (reprint service avail. from UMI) **Indexed:** Avery Ind.Archit.Per., Br.Tech.Ind., Geo.Abstr. —BLDSC (5153.159000); UMI.
Formerly (1923-1968): Havekunst.
Description: Journal on garden and landscape planning.

712 UK
LAWN & GARDEN EQUIPMENT. m. 25A New St., Salisbury, Wilts. SP1 2PH, England. TEL 0722-414245. FAX 0722-414165. Ed. Chris Biddle. bk.rev. circ. 2,400.

LAWN & GARDEN TRADE. see BUSINESS AND ECONOMICS — Marketing And Purchasing

635 US ISSN 1046-154X
LAWN & LANDSCAPE MAINTENANCE. 1979. 12/yr. $25 (foreign $82) (effective Jan. 1994). (Group Interest Enterprises) G.I.E., Inc. Publishers, 4012 Bridge Ave., Cleveland, OH 44113. TEL 216-961-4130. FAX 216-961-0364. Ed. Cindy Code. adv.; bk.rev. circ. 45,000. **Document type:** trade publication.
—UnCover.
Former titles (until July 1989): A L A Lawn and Landscape Maintenance; (until Nov. 1988): American Lawn Applicator; (until 1984): Lawn Care Professional.

635
LEAFLET (BOSTON). 1980. bi-m. membership. Massachusetts Horticultural Society, Horticultural Hall, 300 Massachusetts Ave., Boston, MA 02115. TEL 617-536-9280. FAX 617-262-8780. Ed. Terry Cronin. adv.; bk.rev. circ. 11,000.
Description: News and announcements and items of interest to members of the society.

635 FR ISSN 0293-6852
LIEN HORTICOLE. 1964. w. 347.70 F. (foreign 680 F.). Editions du Lien, B.P. 30, 34471 Perols Cedex, France. TEL 67-50-06-18. FAX 67-50-19-02. adv.; bk.rev. circ. 13,000.

635 US ISSN 1046-9761
LILACS QUARTERLY JOURNAL. 1971. 4/yr. $15 to individuals; institutions $35. International Lilac Society, c/o David P. Gressley, Membership Secy., The Holden Arboretum, 9500 Sperry Rd., Mentor, OH 44060-8199. TEL 216-946-4400. FAX 216-256-1655. Ed. Owen Rogers. adv.; bk.rev.; cum.index: 1974-1983. circ. 600. (back issues avail.) **Document type:** directory, monographic series, proceedings.
Formerly: International Lilac Society. Newsletter.
Description: Covers lilac culture, inventories, close-up illustrations, and a membership directory. Includes proceedings from annual convention.

635 NZ ISSN 0069-3820
LINCOLN COLLEGE. DEPARTMENT OF HORTICULTURE. BULLETIN. 1967. irreg. price varies. Lincoln College, Department of Horticulture, Canterbury, New Zealand. circ. 2,750. **Indexed:** Bibl.Agri., Hort.Abstr., Rural Recreat.Tour.Abstr., World Agri.Econ.& Rural Sociol.Abstr. **Document type:** bulletin.

635 US ISSN 0889-258X
LINDLEYANA. 4/yr. $24 (foreign $26). American Orchid Society, 6000 S. Olive Ave., W. Palm Beach, FL 33405. TEL 407-585-8666. FAX 407-585-0654. **Indexed:** Hort.Abstr., Ornam.Hort., Plant Grow.Reg.Abstr., Seed Abstr. —BLDSC (5221.035000); UnCover.

635 IT ISSN 0394-3704
LINEA VERDE; periodico per il vivaismo e l'impiantistica. 1975. m. L.160000 foreign (effective 1994). (Associazione dei Orticultori Professionali di Italia) Aquarius Editrice, Via A. Gramsci 803, Sesto Fiorentino, 50019 Florence, Italy. TEL 055-4250271. FAX 055-452504. (Co-sponsor: Nuovo Consorzio Florovivaisti Comaschi) Ed. Mauro Bonciani. adv.: color page L.1500000. bk.rev. circ. 6,800. (back issues avail.)

635 631 US ISSN 0897-9561
LIVING AMONG NATURE DARINGLY!; how to for trappers, farmers, and homesteaders. Short title: L A N D. 1986. 5/yr. $9. Bill Anderson, Ed. & Pub., 4466 Ike Mooney Rd., Silverton, OR 97381. TEL 503-873-8829. adv.; bk.rev.; index. circ. 1,000. (back issues avail.) **Document type:** trade publication.

635 US ISSN 0738-7687
LIVING OFF THE LAND; a subtropic newsletter. 1975. 5/yr. $14 (foreign $15). Geraventure, Box 2131, Melbourne, FL 32902-2131. TEL 305-723-5554. Ed. Marian Van Atta. adv.; bk.rev.; illus. circ. 850. (looseleaf format; back issues avail.)
Description: Advice on growing subtropical foodstuffs for domestic consumption, with recipes and seed exchanges, and with each issue devoted to a particular fruit, vegetable, or herb.

LONGWOOD GRADUATE PROGRAM SEMINARS. see BIOLOGY — Botany

LOZARSTVO I VINARSTVO. see BEVERAGES

635 US ISSN 0738-3053
SB413.M34
MAGNOLIA (HAMMOND). 1966. 2/yr. $18 (foreign $20). Magnolia Society, 907 S. Chestnut St., Hammond, LA 70403-5102. TEL 504-542-9477. Ed. Larry W. Langford. adv.; cum.index. circ. 550. (back issues avail.) **Document type:** monographic series.

635 US ISSN 1054-9153
MAGNOLIA (WINSTON-SALEM). 1980. 4/yr. membership only. Southern Garden History Society, c/o Old Salem, Inc., Drawer F, Salem Sta., Winston-Salem, NC 27108. TEL 919-724-3125. bk.rev. **Indexed:** Gard.Lit. (1992-). **Document type:** newsletter, bulletin.
Formerly: Southern Garden History Society. Bulletin.
Description: Encourages research and preservation of materials on the history of gardens in the South with annual meetings and conferences.

MAINE ORGANIC FARMER AND GARDENER. see AGRICULTURE

635.9 US
MALUS. 1985. 2/yr. $20 membership. International Ornamental Crabapple Society, c/o Dr. Thomas L. Green, Agriculture Dept., Western Illinois University, Macomb, IL 61455. TEL 309-298-1160. FAX 309-298-2880. **Document type:** bulletin.
Formerly: Crab Gab.

635.9 UK ISSN 0464-8072
QK495.C11
MAMMILLARIA JOURNAL. 1960. q. £6.50($14) Mammillaria Society, 26 Glenfield Rd., Banstead, Surrey SM7 2DG, England. TEL 0737-354036. Ed. W.F. Maddams. adv.; bk.rev. circ. 600. **Document type:** academic/scholarly publication.

635 FR
MARAICHER DE FRANCE. m. Societe Languedoc Presse Publicite, 32 av. Georges Clemenceau, B.P. 162, 34003 Montpellier, France. TEL 67-92-50-27. FAX 67-58-85-29. Ed. Marty Maxel. circ. 14,500.

MARKET BULLETIN FRUIT AND VEGETABLES. see BUSINESS AND ECONOMICS — Cooperatives

MARKT IN GRUEN. see BUSINESS AND ECONOMICS — Marketing And Purchasing

634 US ISSN 0025-4223
MARYLAND FRUIT GROWER. (Supplement incl.: Maryland Orchardist) 1931. a. $15 to U.S. and Canada only (including supplement). Maryland State Horticultural Society, Department of Horticulture, University of Maryland, College Park, MD 20742-5611. TEL 301-405-4351. Ed. C.S. Walsh. abstr.; charts; mkt.; stat.; tr.lit. circ. 200. (processed)

635.934 US ISSN 0025-6927
MEDIANITE. 1960 q. $5.50 includes membership. (Median Iris Society) Sheldon Butt, Ed. & Pub., 1904 Arrowhead Lane, Godfrey, IL 62035-1501. TEL 618-466-1342. adv.: B&W page $45. bk.rev.; illus.; index. curr.index: 1960-1974. circ. 450. **Document type:** newsletter.
Description: Fosters the interest in scientific research and horticulture development of the median class of bearded irises.

635 712 GW ISSN 0178-1308
MEIN SCHOENER GARTEN. 1972. m. $60. Burda Verlag GmbH, Postfach 1230, 77602 Offenburg, Germany. TEL 089-9250-0. FAX 089-92503519. (Dist. in U.S. by: GLP International, 153 S. Dean St., Englewood, NJ 07631. TEL 201-871-1010. FAX 201-871-0870) Ed. Gert Spiegel. adv.; illus. circ. 374,800. **Document type:** consumer publication.

635 US
MENZELIA. irreg. membership only. Northern Nevada Native Plant Society, Box 8965, Reno, NV 89507. TEL 702-358-7759.

MESEMB STUDY BULLETIN. see BIOLOGY — Botany

635.9 UK ISSN 0144-6916
MIDLAND BONSAI SOCIETY JOURNAL. 1976. 3/yr. membership. Midland Bonsai Society, c/o G. Rushforth, 24 Gracemere Cresc., Hall Green, Birmingham 28, England.

635 JA ISSN 0285-211X
MINAMI-KYUSHU DAIGAKU ENGEIGAKUBU KENKYU HOKOKU. SHIZEN KAGAKU, JINBUN SHAKAI KAGAKU/MINAMI KYUSHU UNIVERSITY. FACULTY OF HORTICULTURE. BULLETIN. NATURAL SCIENCE, CULTURAL SCIENCE, AND SOCIAL SCIENCE. (Text and summaries in English and Japanese) 1968. a. Minami-Kyushu Daigaku, Engeigakubu - Minami Kyushu University, Faculty of Horticulture, Hibarigaoka, Takanabe-cho, Koyu-gun, Miyazaki-ken 884, Japan. TEL 0983-23-0793. FAX 0983-22-3444. circ. 500. **Indexed:** Agrindex, Jap.Per.Ind. **Document type:** academic/scholarly publication, bulletin.
—BLDSC (2508.530000).
Formerly (until 1972): Minami Kyushu University. Faculty of Horticulture. Bulletin.

635.9 US
MINIATURE ROSE GROWERS BULLETIN. q. $5. American Rose Society, Box 30000, Shreveport, LA 71130-0030. TEL 318-938-5402. **Document type:** bulletin.
Description: Includes information on miniatures, new varieties, their availability, suggestions on landscaping use, growing indoors and outdoors, and articles by experienced growers.

635 US ISSN 0026-5500
MINNESOTA HORTICULTURIST. 1873. 9/yr. $25. Minnesota State Horticultural Society, 1755 Prior Avenue N, Falcon Heights MN 55113. TEL 612-624-7752. Ed. Lynn Steiner. adv.; illus.; index. circ. 16,000. **Indexed:** Gard.Lit. (1992-), Hort.Abstr.
Description: Gardening magazine written specifically for northern gardeners. Covers all aspects of home horticulture.

GARDENING AND HORTICULTURE

635 634.96 US
MISSISSIPPI NATIVE PLANT QUARTERLY. 1980. 4/yr. $7.50. Mississippi Native Plant Society, Box 2151, Starkville, MS 39759. TEL 601-324-0430. Ed. Victor A. Rudis. bk.rev. circ. 300. **Document type:** newsletter.
  Former titles: Mississippi Native Plant Society Quarterly; Mississippi Native Plant Society Newsletter; Mississippi N.P.S. Newsletter.
  Description: Focuses on activities and people associated with Mississippi indigenous and naturalized plants. Contains a calendar of upcoming events, notes on plant propagation and identification, plant and seed exchanges, landscape designs, and habitat preserves.

635 581 US ISSN 0026-6507
QK1
MISSOURI BOTANICAL GARDEN BULLETIN. 1913. 6/yr. membership. Missouri Botanical Garden, Box 299, St. Louis, MO 63166-0299. TEL 314-577-5123. FAX 314-577-9599. Ed. Susan Caine. illus. circ. 30,000. **Indexed:** Forest Prod.Abstr. **Document type:** bulletin.

635 US
MONTHLY FERN LESSON. Issued with: L A I F S Journal. m. membership only. Los Angeles International Fern Society, Box 90943, Pasadena, CA 91109-0943. TEL 619-436-1419. Ed. Phyllis Bates.

635 IE ISSN 0332-4273
MOOREA. 1982. a. £7.50 membership. Irish Garden Plant Society, c/o National Botanical Gardens, Glasnevin, Dublin 9, Ireland. FAX 337329. Ed.Bd. bk.rev.; circ. 600 (controlled).

MORTON ARBORETUM QUARTERLY. see BIOLOGY — Botany

631.3 FR ISSN 1245-3609
MOTEURS LOISIRS ET PAYSAGES. (Text in French) 1979. m. 300 F. Editions J, B.P. 30, 78511 Rambouillet Cedex, France. TEL 34-84-70-60. FAX 34-84-70-55. TELEX 695589. Ed. Francois Langendorff. adv.; illus.; stat. circ. 6,000. (back issues avail.) **Document type:** trade publication, newspaper.
  —CCC.
  Formerly: Moteurs Loisirs (ISSN 0241-8622)

635 674 FR ISSN 0998-495X
MOTOCULTURE MAGAZINE. 1972. m. (11/yr.). 280 F. (foreign 380 F.). Societe d'Edition et de Regie Specialisee (S.E.R.S.), (Subsidiary of: Masson), 5 et 7, rue Laromiguiere, 75005 Paris, France. TEL 1-46-34-21-60. FAX 1-45-35-56-70. (Subscr. to: Zone Industrielle, B.P. 22, 41350 Vineuil, France. TEL 54-43-89-94) Ed. F. Magarian. adv. circ. 6,000.
  Former titles: Special Scies a Moteur et Techniques Forestieres; Special Scies a Moteur et Accessoires (ISSN 0240-3803)
  Description: Information for those involved in landscaping. Aimed mainly at professionals interested in latest equipment and technology available in the industry.

MURATOR. see ARCHITECTURE

635 US ISSN 0740-8161
MUSHROOM; the journal. 1983. q. $16. Box 3156, University Sta., Moscow, ID 83843. TEL 208-882-8720. Eds. Don H. Coombs, Maggie Rogers. adv.; bk.rev.; charts; illus. circ. 2,150. (back issues avail.) **Document type:** consumer publication.
  Description: News and features about wild mushrooming and the growing of exotic mushrooms.

635.8 589.2 UK ISSN 0144-0551
CODEN: MUSJDK
MUSHROOM JOURNAL. 1945. m. membership. Mushroom Growers' Association, 2 St. Pauls St., Stamford, Lincs. PE9 2BE, England. TEL 01-235-5077. adv.; bk.rev.; charts; illus.; mkt.; stat.; index; circ. 1,000 (controlled). **Indexed:** Cott.& Trop.Fibr.Abstr., Food Sci.& Tech.Abstr., Hort.Abstr., Nutr.Abstr., Rev.Plant Path., Rural Recreat.Tour.Abstr., Triticale Abstr., World Agri.Econ.& Rural Sociol.Abstr. **Document type:** bulletin.
  —BLDSC (5990.150000); CASDDS.
  Formerly: M G A Bulletin (ISSN 0024-8150)
  Description: News and information on all aspects of the industry in the UK and worldwide.

635 UK
N.C.S. BULLETIN. q. £9. National Chrysanthemum Society, 2 Lucas House, Craven Rd., Rugby, Warwickshire, England. Ed. H.B. Locke. adv. circ. 11,000.

635 UK
N.C.S. YEARBOOK. 1930. a. membership. National Chrysanthemum Society, 2 Lucas House, Craven Rd., Rugby, Warwickshire, England. Ed. H. Randall. adv. circ. 6,000.

N T C WORKSHOP REPORT SERIES. (National Turfgrass Council) see BIOLOGY — Botany

635.934 US ISSN 0099-8745
SB409.5.U6 CODEN: OKHAAN
NA OKIKA O HAWAII/HAWAII ORCHID JOURNAL. 1972. q. $15. Honolulu Orchid Society, 1710 Pali Hwy., Honolulu, HI 96813. TEL 808-988-3177. FAX 808-988-4231. (Co-sponsor: Pacific Orchid Society) Ed. Yoneo Sagawa. adv.; bk.rev.; abstr.; illus. circ. 750. (back issues avail.) **Indexed:** Biol.Abstr., Hort.Abstr.
  Formed by the merger of: Pacific Orchid Society of Hawaii. Bulletin (ISSN 0030-8838); Na Pua Okika o Hawaii Nei - Orchids of Hawaii (ISSN 0027-7304)
  Description: Orchid culture, classification and breeding.

635 UK ISSN 0027-8726
NATIONAL AURICULA & PRIMULA SOCIETY (NORTHERN) YEAR BOOK. 1872. a. £5.75. National Auricula & Primula Society, c/o R. Taylor, 8 Larkfield Terrace, Thwaites Brow, Keighley, W. Yorks. BD21 4SX, England. TEL 0535-665619. adv.; bk.rev.; illus.; index, cum.index every 3 yrs. circ. 500. (back issues avail.) **Document type:** newsletter.
  Description: Provides information on all aspects of interest to growers of auriculas and primulas.

635 UK ISSN 0077-4189
NATIONAL DAHLIA SOCIETY ANNUAL. a. £5.75. National Dahlia Society, c/o Gen. Sec. A.G. Winkless, 8 Station Rd., Kirby Muxloe, Leicester LE9 9EJ, England. TEL 0533 387717. Ed. E. Pitt. adv.; bk.rev. circ. 5,500.
  Description: Information about the activities of the Society.

NATIONAL FEDERATION OF FRUIT & POTATO TRADES. FEDERATION NEWS. see AGRICULTURE

635 US ISSN 0027-9331
SB1
NATIONAL GARDENER. 1930. 6/yr. $4. National Council of State Garden Clubs, Inc., 4401 Magnolia Ave., St. Louis, MO 63110. TEL 314-776-7574. FAX 314-776-5108. Ed. Susan Davidson. adv.; bk.rev.; illus. circ. 30,000. **Indexed:** Gard.Lit. (1992-).

635 658 US ISSN 0887-8447
NATIONAL GARDENING. 1977. bi-m. $18 (foreign $24). National Gardening Association, 180 Flynn Ave., Burlington, VT 05401. TEL 802-863-1308. FAX 802-863-5962. index. circ. 200,000. (back issues avail.) **Document type:** consumer publication.
  Formerly: Gardens for All.
  Description: Provides complete, current and useful information about growing vegetables, fruit and flowers for the backyard gardener as well as advanced techniques for the more experienced gardener.

635 658 US ISSN 0270-0816
NATIONAL GARDENING SURVEY (YEAR); an exclusive market research report for the lawn and garden industry. 1977. a. $350. National Gardening Association, 180 Flynn Ave., Burlington, VT 05401. TEL 802-863-1308. Ed. Bruce W. Butterfield. circ. 500. (back issues avail.)
  Formerly: G F A - Gallup National Gardening Survey (Year).

635 US ISSN 0077-5088
NATIONAL JUNIOR HORTICULTURAL ASSOCIATION. NEWSLETTER. 1940. irreg. free. National Junior Horticultural Association, c/o Joe Maxson, Ed., 401 N. Fourth St., Durant, OK 74701. bk.rev. circ. 6,000. **Document type:** newsletter.

635 UK
NATIONAL SWEET PEA SOCIETY. ANNUAL. a. £12 membership. National Sweet Pea Society, 3 Chalk Farm Rd., Stokenchurch, High Wycombe, Bucks HP14 3TB, England. TEL 0494-482153. **Document type:** corporate report.

635 UK
NATIONAL SWEET PEA SOCIETY. BULLETIN. 2/yr. £12 membership. National Sweet Pea Society, 3 Chalk Farm Rd., Stokenchurch, High Wycombe, Bucks HP14 3TB, England. TEL 0494-482153. **Document type:** bulletin.

NATIONAL TROPICAL BOTANICAL GARDEN. BULLETIN. see BIOLOGY — Botany

NATIVE PLANT SOCIETY OF NEW MEXICO. NEWSLETTER. see BIOLOGY — Botany

635 GW ISSN 0944-4564
NATUERLICH GAERTNERN; mit der Natur leben. 8/yr. DM.46. Organischer Landbau Verlag, Postfach 1123, 53895 Bad Muensterifel, Germany. TEL 02484-1558. FAX 02484-2558. Ed. Kurt Walter Lau. adv.; bk.rev. **Document type:** consumer publication.
  —CCC.
  Former titles (until 1993): Garten Organisch (ISSN 0170-5385); (until 1988): Naturgemaesser Land- und Gartenbau (ISSN 0028-0933)

NATUR UND LANDSCHAFT; Zeitschrift fuer Naturschutz, Landschaftspflege und Umweltschutz. see CONSERVATION

NATURAL SOLUTIONS. see AGRICULTURE — Crop Production And Soil

NATUREN OG HJEMMET. see PETS

NAUKA U PRAKSI. see AGRICULTURE

635 790.1 IT
NEGOZIANTE GARDEN & GRILL. 10/yr. Piazza S. Camillo de Lellis 1, 20124 Milan, Italy. TEL 2-66-984-880. FAX 2-66-98-47-71. Ed. Roberto Galimberti.

635 US ISSN 1061-3994
NEIL SPERRY'S GARDENS. 1987. 10/yr. $21.50. Gardens South, Box 864, McKinney, TX 75069. TEL 214-562-5050. FAX 214-562-5053. adv. contact: Shelley Pace. circ. 27,000 (paid).
  Former titles (until 1992): Gardens and More (ISSN 1052-3243); Neil Sperry's Gardens and More (ISSN 0893-1887)
  Description: Covers Texas home, gardener and landscaping news.

635 US
NERIUM NEWS. 1986. 4/yr. membership only. International Oleander Society, Box 3431, Galveston, TX 77552-0431. TEL 409-762-9334. Ed. Elizabeth S. Head. circ. 250. **Document type:** newsletter.

712 GW ISSN 0548-2836
NEUE LANDSCHAFT. m. DM.145.80. Patzer Verlag GmbH und Co. KG, Koenigsallee 65, 14193 Berlin, Germany. TEL 030-8959030. FAX 030-89590317. circ. 5,700. **Indexed:** Dok.Str., Excerp.Med. **Document type:** bulletin.

635.9 US
NEW ENGLAND WILD FLOWER SOCIETY NEWSLETTER. 1980. 3/yr. $35 membership. New England Wild Flower Society, Inc., Garden-in-the-Woods, 180 Hemenway Rd., Framingham, MA 01701. TEL 508-877-7630. Ed. Ginger Carr. adv. circ. 4,000. **Document type:** newsletter.
  Description: Current information on society activities, conservation, rare plants, research and horticulture.

635 US
▼**THE NEW GARDEN JOURNAL;** an organic gardening guide for home gardeners. 1993. m. $18. Zimmerman & Associates, Box 6121, San Antonio, TX 78209. (Ed. addr.: Box 913, Georgetown, TX 78627. TEL 512-863-5062. FAX 512-863-5062) Ed. Judy Barrett. circ. 5,000 (paid). **Document type:** consumer publication.

NEW IDEA. see HOME ECONOMICS

GARDENING AND HORTICULTURE

635   JA
NEW INFORMATION ON HORTICULTURE: FLOWERS/ENGEI SHIN CHISHIKI: HANA NO GO. (Text in Japanese) 1951. m. 4200 Yen. Takii Shubyo Co. Ltd., 180 Umekoji-Inokuma, C.P.O. Box 7, Kyoto 600-91, Japan. TEL 75-365-0123. FAX 75-365-0110. adv.; bk.rev.; charts; illus.; mkt.; stat.; tr.lit.; index. (processed)
    Supersedes in part: New Information on Horticulture (ISSN 0013-7634)

636   JA
NEW INFORMATION ON HORTICULTURE: VEGETABLES/ENGEI SHIN CHISHIKI: YASAI NO GO. (Text in Japanese) 1951. m. 3840 Yen. Takii Shubyo Co. Ltd., 180 Umekoji-Inokuma, C.P.O. Box 7, Kyoto 600-91, Japan. TEL 75-365-0123. FAX 75-365-0110. adv.; bk.rev.; charts; illus.; stat.; tr.lit.; index.
    Supersedes in part: New Information on Horticulture (ISSN 0013-7634)

635   UK   ISSN 1352-4186
THE NEW PLANTSMAN. 1979. q. £25 (foreign £29). (Royal Horticultural Society) H H L Publishing, 80 Vincent Sq., London SW1P 2PE, England. TEL 071-834-4333. FAX 071-3630-6060. (Subscr. to: R H S Subscription Serivices. P.O. Box 38, Ashford, Kent TN25 6PR, England) Ed. Victoria Matthews. illus. circ. 1,200. **Indexed:** Forest.Abstr., Gard.Lit. (1992-), Hort.Abstr., Ornam.Hort. **Document type:** academic/scholarly publication.
    —BLDSC (6528.100000).
    Formerly (until Feb. 1994): Plantsman (ISSN 0143-0106)
    Description: Surveys all aspects of cultivated plants, including taxonomy, physiology, conservation, and history.
    Refereed Serial

635   NZ
NEW ZEALAND FUCHSIA SOCIETY. NEWS LETTER. 1953? 11/yr. membership only. New Zealand Fuchsia Society, P.O. Box 11-082, Ellerslie, Auckland 872-118, New Zealand. Ed. Mrs. P. Anderson. bk.rev. circ. 175. **Document type:** newsletter.

635   NZ   ISSN 0028-8136
NEW ZEALAND GARDENER. 1944. m. NZ.$52.50. New zealand Gardener Publications Ltd., P.O. Box 6341, Wellesley St., Auckland, New Zeland. TEL 09-3777889. Ed. Julian Matthews. adv.; bk.rev.; illus.; index. circ. 60,000. **Indexed:** Gard.Lit. (1992-).
    —CCC.

NEW ZEALAND HOME AND BUILDING. see *BUILDING AND CONSTRUCTION*

635   US   ISSN 0029-1641
NORFOLK BOTANICAL GARDEN SOCIETY BULLETIN. 1940. m. membership. Norfolk Botanical Garden Society, 5302 Lakeside Ave., Virginia Beach, VA 23451. TEL 804-425-5344. Ed. William Genz. adv.; bk.rev.; charts; illus. circ. 500.

635   NO   ISSN 0029-1986
NORSK HAGETIDEND. 1885. m. NOK 350 (typically set in Jan.). Norske Hageselskap - Norwegian Horticultural Society, Motzfeldtsgt. 1, Oslo 1, Norway. FAX 47-22-172-319. Ed. Knut Loenoe. adv.; bk.rev.; charts; illus.; index. circ. 41,878. (back issues avail.) **Indexed:** Biol.Abstr.
    —CCC.

635.934   US   ISSN 0029-2370
SB413.G5
NORTH AMERICAN GLADIOLUS COUNCIL BULLETIN. 1945. q. $10.50 (foreign $12.50). North American Gladiolus Council, 4344 Vera St., Boise, ID 83204. TEL 208-376-2024. (Subscr. to: NAGC, 701 S. Hendricks Ave., Marion, IN 46953) Ed. Arlen De Meyer. adv.; charts; illus.; stat. circ. 1,200. **Indexed:** Biol.Abstr., Chem.Abstr.
    —BLDSC (6013.550000).
    Description: Discusses all aspects of gladiolus cultivation, from backyard growing to hybridizing, research, commercial production, and cultivar classification.

635 016   US
NORTH AMERICAN HORTICULTURE: A REFERENCE GUIDE. irreg. $60. American Horticultural Society, 7931 E. Boulevard Dr., Alexandria, VA 22308. TEL 703-768-5700. (reprint service avail. from UMI) **Document type:** directory.
    Formerly: Directory of American Horticulture (ISSN 0417-5522)
    Description: Information about horticultural and conservation societies.

635   US
NORTH AMERICAN LILY SOCIETY. QUARTERLY BULLETIN. q. membership only. North American Lily Society, Inc., Box 272, Owatonna, MN 55060. TEL 507-451-2170. **Document type:** bulletin.

635   US   ISSN 0741-9910
NORTH AMERICAN LILY SOCIETY. YEARBOOK. a. $12.50. North American Lily Society, Inc., Box 272, Owatonna, MN 55060. TEL 507-451-2170.
    —BLDSC (5218.900000).

635   US
NORTH CAROLINA WILD FLOWER PRESERVATION SOCIETY. NEWSLETTER. 2/yr. membership only. North Carolina Wild Flower Preservation Society, 900 W. Nash St., Wilson, NC 27893.

635   UK
NORTHERN GARDENER. q. Northern Horticulture Society, Harlow Carr Botanical Gardens, Crag Ln., Harrogate HG3 1QB, England. TEL 0423-565418. **Document type:** bulletin.

635   US
NORTHERN NEVADA NATIVE PLANT SOCIETY. NEWSLETTER. 9/yr. membership only. Northern Nevada Native Plant Society, Box 8965, Reno, NV 89507. TEL 702-358-7759. **Document type:** newsletter.

635   US
NORTHERN NUT GROWERS ASSOCIATION. ANNUAL REPORT. 1911. a. $15 membership. Northern Nut Growers Association (Chetopa), Pecan Experiment Field, Box 247, Chetopa, KS 67336-0247. Ed. William Reid. circ. 2,000. **Indexed:** Hort.Abstr. **Document type:** academic/scholarly publication, proceedings.
    Description: Contains articles presented at annual meetings, dealing with nut trees.

635   US
NORTHERN TURF MANAGEMENT. 1990. m. $25. Argus Agronomics (Subsidiary of: Argus Inc.), Box 1420, Clarksdale, MS 38614. TEL 601-624-8502. FAX 601-627-1977. Ed. Ed Phillips. adv. circ. 25,200. (tabloid format) **Document type:** trade publication.
    Description: For the northern turf market including golf course superintendents, professional lawn care operators, municipal parks and recreational areas, sod producers, sports turf managers and others.

635   US   ISSN 1050-6217
SB118.73
NURSERY BUSINESS GROWER. bi-m. Brantwood Publications, 3023 Eastland Blvd., Ste. 103, Clearwater, FL 34621-4106.
    Supersedes in part (in 1990): Nursery Business (ISSN 0029-6406)

635.73   US   ISSN 1048-8189
SB118.73
NURSERY BUSINESS RETAILER. bi-m. Brantwood Publications, 3023 Eastland Blvd., Ste. 103, Clearwater, FL 34621-4106.
    —UnCover.
    Supersedes in part (in 1990): Nursery Business (ISSN 0029-6406)

635 658.8   US
NURSERY MANAGER. 1915. m. $24. Branch-Smith Inc., 120 St. Louis St., Ft. Worth, TX 76101. TEL 817-332-8236. FAX 817-877-1862. Ed. David Morgan. adv. circ. 15,000.
    Formerly: Southern Florist and Nurseryman (ISSN 0038-4119)

635   US
NURSERY NEWS. 1986. m. $15 (effective Jan. 1990). Cenflo, Inc. 120 S. Riverside Plaza, Ste. 464, Chicago, IL 60606. TEL 312-258-8500; 800-732-4581. FAX 312-258-8558. Ed. Rosemary Baldwin. adv.; bk.rev. circ. 19,466. (tabloid format; back issues avail.) **Document type:** newspaper, trade publication.
    Description: For growers, wholesalers, rewholesalers, retailers, landscapers using trees, shrubs, plants for exterior ornamentation.

635.969   UK   ISSN 0029-6430
NURSERYMAN & GARDEN CENTRE. 1894. fortn. £44 (foreign £59). Bouverie Publishing Company Ltd., 131-151 Temple Chambers, Temple Ave., London EC4Y 0DT, England. TEL 071-583-3030. FAX 071-583-4068. Ed. Peter Dawson. adv.; bk.rev.; illus.; mkt.; index. circ. 4,243. (processed) **Indexed:** Hort.Abstr., Ornam.Hort. **Document type:** trade publication.

635   US
NUTSHELL (NEW CARLISLE). 4/yr. $15 (foreign $20). Northern Nut Growers Association, 9870 S. Palmer Rd., New Carlisle, OH 45344. TEL 513-878-2610. **Document type:** newsletter.

635   US
O A N DIGGER. 1956. m. free. Oregon Association of Nurserymen, 2780 S.E. Harrison, Ste. 102, Milwaukie, OR 97222. TEL 503-653-8723. FAX 503-653-1528. Ed. Don Grey. adv.; bk.rev.; illus.; circ. 4,500 (controlled). (back issues avail.) **Document type:** trade publication.
    Description: News, features, and research information for the Northwest nursery and landscape industries.

O A N DIRECTORY & BUYER'S GUIDE. (Oregon Association of Nurserymen) see *BUSINESS AND ECONOMICS — Trade And Industrial Directories*

635   GW   ISSN 0029-7798
OBST UND GARTEN. vol.92, 1973. m. DM.59.10. (Landesverband fuer Obstbau, Garten und Landschaft Baden-Wuerttemberg e. V.) Verlag Eugen Ulmer GmbH, Wollgrasweg 41, 70599 Stuttgart, Germany. TEL 0711-4507-0. FAX 0711-4507-120. TELEX 723634-ULMER-D. (Subscr. to: Postfach 700561, 70574 Stuttgart, Germany) Ed. H. Kuhnhaeuser. adv.; bk.rev.; charts; index. circ. 21,000. **Document type:** consumer publication.
    —CCC.

635 634.8   AU
OBST - WEIN - GARTEN. 1950. m. S.180 to non-members. Landes Obst- und Weinbauverein fuer Steiermark, Kindermanngasse 8-2, A-8020 Graz, Austria. Ed. D. Altmann. adv.; bk.rev.; illus.; index. circ. 10,000.
    Former title: Obst- und Weinbau (ISSN 0029-7771)
    Description: Covers fruits and viticulture.

635   PL   ISSN 0030-0756
                      CODEN: OGRDAK
OGRODNICTWO.* 1964. m. Wydawnictwo Hortpress, Spolka z o.o., Ul. Zielna, paw. 106, 00-108 Warsaw, Poland. (Dist. by: Ars Polona- Ruch, Krakowskie Przedmiescie 7, Warsaw, Poland) bibl.; charts; illus.; stat. circ. 4,500.
    —CASDDS.

635   US
ON THE FRINGE. 1983. 6/yr. $10. Ohio Native Plant Society, 6 Louise Dr., Chagrin Falls, OH 44022. TEL 216-338-6622. Ed. A.K. Malmquist. bk.rev. circ. 300.

635   CN
ONTARIO REGIONAL LILY SOCIETY. NEWSLETTER. 3/yr. Can.$7 membership only. Ontario Regional Lily Society, c/o Michael Hornick, Secy., R.R. 2, Tillsonburg, ON N4G 4G7, Canada. circ. 200. **Document type:** newsletter.

635   CN   ISSN 0838-1674
OPTION SERRE. 1988. 10/yr. Can.$33. Editions Versicolores Inc., 1320 Blvd. Saint-Joseph, Quebec, PQ G2K 1G2, Canada. TEL 418-628-8690. FAX 418-628-0524. Ed. Georges O'Shaughnessy; Pub. Francois Bernatchez. adv. contact: Paul Poisson. circ. 1,580. **Document type:** trade publication.

GARDENING AND HORTICULTURE

635.9   AT   ISSN 0474-3342
ORCHADIAN. 1963. q. Aus.$26 includes membership (effective July 1993). Australasian Native Orchid Society, P.O. Box C106, Clarence St., Sydney, N.S.W. 2000, Australia. Ed. N.J. Grundon. adv.; bk.rev.; index. circ. 800. **Indexed:** Biol.Abstr.

ORCHARDIST OF NEW ZEALAND. see *AGRICULTURE — Crop Production And Soil*

635.9   US   ISSN 0097-9546
SB409.A1
ORCHID ADVOCATE. 1975. bi-m. $20. Cymbidium Society of America, Inc., c/o Don Burkey, Ed., Box 1289, Carpinteria, CA 93014. TEL 805-684-8066. adv.; bk.rev.; charts; illus.; tr.lit. circ. 1,500. (back issues avail.)
    Description: Covers cool growing orchid genera, principally cymbidiums and paphiopedilums.

635   US
ORCHID DIGEST. 1938? 4/yr. $18 (effective 1993). Orchid Digest Corporation, c/o Mrs. N.H. Atkinson, Memb. Secy., Box 916, Carmichael, CA 95609-0916. Ed. J.A. Fowlie. adv.; bk.rev. circ. 4,400.
    Description: For orchid growers.

635   UK   ISSN 0030-4476
ORCHID REVIEW. 1893. bi-m. £19.95. Royal Horticulture Society, 21B Chudleigh Rd., Kingsteignton, Newton Abbot, Devon TQ12 3JT, England. TEL 0626-66648. Ed. W. Rittershausen. adv.; bk.rev.; illus.; index. circ. 2,000. **Indexed:** Hort.Abstr., Ornam.Hort. **Document type:** newsletter. —BLDSC (6277.940000); UnCover.

635   GW   ISSN 0473-1425
SB409.A1
DIE ORCHIDEE. 1949. bi-m. DM.70. Deutsche Orchideen Gesellschaft e.V., Bornemannstr. 2, 60599 Frankfurt, Germany. TEL 08405-686. (Subscr. to: Deutsche Orchideen-Gesellschaft e.V., Jahnstr. 4, D-8071 Stammham, Germany) adv.; bk.rev.; index. circ. 7,500. (back issues avail.) **Indexed:** Hort.Abstr.

ORCHIDEEEN. see *BIOLOGY — Botany*

635 614.7   AT   ISSN 0157-2601
ORGANIC GROWER. 1977. q. Aus.$16. Organic Growers Association, W.A., P.O. Box 213, Wembley, W.A. 6014, Australia. Ed. Caroline Smith. adv.; bk.rev. circ. 700. (back issues avail.) **Document type:** bulletin.
    Description: Information on how to grow foods without the use of artificial fertilizers, pesticides, etc.

631.8   AT   ISSN 0816-6668
ORGANIC GROWING (ULVERSTONE). 1976. q. Aus.$18 (foreign Aus.$26). Organic Gardening and Farming Society of Tasmania Inc., P.O. Box 228, Ulverstone, Tas. 7315, Australia. FAX 003-950331. Ed. Chris A. Payn. adv.; bk.rev. circ. 2,000. (also avail. in diskette format; back issues avail.) **Indexed:** Pinpointer.
    Formerly (until 1980): Organic Gardener and Farmer.

635   DK   ISSN 0109-4262
ORGANISATIONER OG TAL I GARTNERIET. (Supplement to: Gartner-Tidende) 1983. a. (included in subscr. to: Gartner-Tidende). Dansk Erhvervsgartnerforening, Hvidkaervej 29, DK-5250 Odense SV, Denmark. FAX 45-66-17-17-15.
    Formerly: D E G.

635.9   US
ORNAMENTALS NORTHWEST NEWSLETTER. Cover title: Ornamentals NorthWest. 1975-1990; resumed 1992. bi-m. $10 (foreign $15). Oregon State University, Cooperative Extension Service, Department of Horticulture, Corvallis, OR 97331. TEL 503-737-5452. FAX 503-737-3479. (Co-sponsors: Washington State University; University of Idaho; British Columbia Ministry of Agriculture) Ed. James L. Green. bk.rev.; index. circ. 5,000. **Indexed:** Bibl.Agri., Gard.Lit. (1992-). **Document type:** newsletter.
    Supersedes: Oregon Ornamental and Nursery Digest (ISSN 0030-4778).

634   FR
OUEST HORTICOLE ET MARAICHER. 1947. m. 10 F. Comite Horticole et Maraicher, 3 place de la Petite-Hollande, 44000 Nantes, France. adv. circ. 12,000.

643.6   US   ISSN 0192-7558
OUTDOOR POWER EQUIPMENT. 1959. m. $14. Chilton Co., One Chilton Way, Radnor, PA 19089. TEL 215-964-4270. FAX 215-964-4284. Ed. Terry Gallagher. adv.; illus. circ. 15,000.
—CCC.
    Formerly: Lawn Equipment Journal (ISSN 0023-9410)

642 664 635   US
OVER THE GARDEN FENCE; natural living in North Texas. 1972. 4/yr. $10. Over the Garden Fence, Inc., Box 386, Lake Dallas, TX 75065. TEL 817-497-4634. Ed. Emile Gilutin. adv.; bk.rev.; charts; illus.; tr.lit.; index, cum.index. circ. 10,000.

635   FR   ISSN 0758-1688
P H M, REVUE HORTICOLE. 1959. 11/yr. 295 F. (foreign 395 F.). Societe d'Edition et de Documentation Agricole (SEDA), SARL, 1 place de la Republique, 75003 Paris, F-87020 Limoges Cedex, France. TEL 33-1-48-04-90-82. FAX 33-1-48-04-85-75. Ed. Jean Mardikian. adv.; illus.; stat.; index. circ. 15,000. **Indexed:** Agri.Eng.Abstr., Bio-Contr.News & Info., Forest.Abstr., Hort.Abstr., Irr.& Drain.Abstr., Ornam.Hort., Plant Grow.Reg.Abstr., Rev.Plant Path., Soils & Fert. —SWETS.
    Formed by the 1974 merger of: Revue Horticole (ISSN 0035-3302); Pepinieristes Horticulteurs Maraichers (ISSN 0031-5087)

635   US   ISSN 0479-947X
P H S NEWS. 11/yr. $9.75. Pennsylvania Horticultural Society, 325 Walnut St., Philadelphia, PA 19106. TEL 215-625-8250. FAX 215-625-8288. **Document type:** newsletter.

635.969 658.8   US   ISSN 0192-7159
PACIFIC COAST NURSERYMAN AND GARDEN SUPPLY DEALER. 1941. m. $20. Cox Publishing Co., 306 W. Foothill Blvd., Box 1477, Glendora, CA 91740. TEL 818-914-3916. FAX 818-914-3751. Ed. Harold R. Young. adv.; bk.rev.; illus.; tr.lit.; circ. 10,500 (controlled). **Document type:** trade publication.
    Former titles: Pacific Coast Nurseryman; (until 1977): Pacific Coast Nurseryman and Garden Supply Dealer (ISSN 0030-8587)

635   US   ISSN 0163-7843
SB453.2.P33
PACIFIC HORTICULTURE. 1940. q. $12 (Canada and Mexico $14; elsewhere $16). Pacific Horticultural Foundation, Box 22609, San Francisco, CA 94122. TEL 415-524-1914. (Subscr. to: Circulation Dept., Box 485, Berkeley, CA 94701. TEL 510-526-2853) Ed. W.G. Waters. adv.; bk.rev.; illus.; biennial index. circ. 15,000. **Indexed:** Biol.Abstr., Cal.Per.Ind. (1980-), Gard.Lit. (1992-). —UnCover.
    Formerly (until 1975): California Horticultural Journal.

635   US
PACIFIC NORTHWEST LILY SOCIETY. BULLETIN. 1979. irreg. (2-3/yr.). $8 membership only. Pacific Northwest Lily Society, 19766 S. Impala Lane, Oregon City, OR 97045. TEL 503-656-1575. Ed. Mary Hoffman. bk.rev. circ. 400. **Document type:** bulletin, newsletter.
    Description: Publishes society news, and information on lily culture, propagation and marketing.

635   US   ISSN 0276-4164
PALMETTO. 1981. q. $20 to individuals; institutions $50; libraries $10. Florida Native Plant Society, Box 680028, Orlando, FL 32868. TEL 407-299-1472. Ed. Peggy S. Lantz. adv.; bk.rev.; circ. 2,500 (controlled). **Document type:** academic/scholarly publication.

580.744   CN   ISSN 0710-0469
PAPPUS. 1981. q. membership. Royal Botanical Gardens, Box 399, Hamilton, ON L8N 3H8, Canada. TEL 905-527-1158. FAX 905-577-0375. Ed. J. Lord. circ. 6,000. (back issues avail.) **Indexed:** Gard.Lit. (1992-). **Document type:** newsletter.

712   SA
PARKS AND GROUNDS; technical magazine for landscape design, construction and maintenance. 1977. bi-m. R.58. Avonwold Publishing Co. (Pty) Ltd., Avonwold House, 24 Baker St., Rosebank, Johannesburg 2196, South Africa. TEL 27-11-788-1610. FAX 27-11-880-2732. (Subscr. to: P.O. Box 52068, Saxonwold 2132, Transvaal, South Africa) Ed. Christine Johnson. adv. circ. 3,944. (back issues avail.) **Indexed:** Ind.S.A.Per. **Document type:** trade publication.
    Description: Provides technical information on landscape design, construction, and maintenance for the landscaping and horticulture industries in South Africa.

635   SA
PARKS AND GROUNDS BUYER'S GUIDE. (Text in English) 1988. a. R.50. Avonwold Publishing Co. (Pty.) Ltd., Avonwold House, 24 Baker St., Rosebank, Johannesburg 2196, South Africa. TEL 27-11-788-1610. FAX 27-11-880-2732. (Subscr. to: P.O. Box 52068, Saxonwold 2132, Transvaal, South Africa) Ed. Christine Johnson. adv.; bk.rev. circ. 3,000. (back issues avail.) **Document type:** trade publication.
    Description: Discusses nurseries, machinery and equipment, chemicals and fertilizers as well as allied trades.

635 790.01   SP
PARQUES Y JARDINES. 1991. 6/yr. 3850 ptas. Tredita Editores, S.L., C. Orellana 10 bajo dcha., 28004 Madrid, Spain. TEL 1-308-18-98. FAX 1-319-20-06. Dir. Julian Mendieta Guerrero. circ. 15,000.
    Formerly: Linea Verde.

PAYSAGE ACTUALITES. see *ARCHITECTURE*

PEELINGS (WASHINGTON). see *HISTORY — History Of North And South America*

635   UK   ISSN 0267-1891
PELARGONIUM NEWS. 1967. 3/yr. (plus annual year book). £3. British Pelargonium and Geranium Society, 66 Sundridge Ave., Chislehurst, Kent BR7 5LU, England. Ed. Leslie A. Cross. adv.; bk.rev.; illus. circ. 1,800.

635.9   US   ISSN 0031-448X
PENNSYLVANIA FLOWER GROWERS. BULLETIN. 1950. 6/yr. $30 (foreign $40). Pennsylvania Flower Growers, 16 Hertzel St., Warren, PA 16345-2588. TEL 814-726-3779. Ed. Gary E. Olsen. adv.; bk.rev.; illus.; index, cum.index: nos.1-150 (1950-1963). circ. 600. (looseleaf format) **Indexed:** Gard.Lit. (1992-), Hort.Abstr., Ornam.Hort., Soils & Fert. **Document type:** bulletin.
    Description: Research in all areas of flower and plant growing.

635   US
PEPEROMIA AND EXOTIC PLANT SOCIETY. GAZETTE. Cover title: P E P S Gazette. 1977. 3/yr. $7.50 membership only. Peperomia and Exotic Plant Society, c/o Anita Baudeau, 100 Neil Ave., New Orleans, LA 70131. Ed. Gregory R. Sytch. adv.; circ. 200 (controlled). **Document type:** bulletin.
    Formerly: Peperomia Society International. Gazette.
    Description: Informs members of growing methods, where to obtain Peperomias and other exotic plants and supplies, and presents other information of interest.

635   US
PERENNIAL PLANT ASSOCIATION. NEWSLETTER. 1985. 4/yr. membership only. Perennial Plant Association, 3383 Schurtzinger Rd., Hilliard, OH 43026. TEL 614-771-8431. FAX 614-771-8431. adv.; bk.rev. circ. 1,400. **Document type:** newsletter.
    Description: Promotes the development of the perennial plant industry.

635   US
PESTICIDE PROGRESS. 1964. q. $150 membership. Interstate Professional Applicator's Association, Box 1377, Milton, WA 98354. TEL 206-848-3407. FAX 206-922-9437. Ed. Mary Ellen Smith. adv. circ. 400. (back issues avail.)

635 II
PHAL PHOOL. (Text in Hindi) 1977. q. Rs.28($10) Indian Council of Agricultural Research, Krishi Anusandhan Bhavan, Pusa, New Delhi 110012, India. Ed. Kuldeep Sharma. adv.; bk.rev.; charts; illus.; index. circ. 7,000.
 Description: Caters to the needs of horticulturists, vegetable growers, nurserymen, and orchardists.

PHOENIX HOME & GARDEN. see *INTERIOR DESIGN AND DECORATION*

635 US
PLANT PRESS. 1980. irreg. (approx. 4/yr.). membership only. Arizona Native Plant Society, Box 41206, Sun Sta., Tucson, AZ 85717. bk.rev. **Document type:** bulletin.

635.9 US ISSN 0362-5850
SB1 CODEN: PLGAA
PLANTS & GARDENS: BROOKLYN BOTANIC GARDEN RECORD. 1945. q. $25 (includes Plants & Gardens News). Brooklyn Botanic Garden, 1000 Washington Ave., Brooklyn, NY 11225. TEL 718-941-4044. Ed.Bd. illus.; index. circ. 25,000. **Indexed:** Biol.Abstr., Biol.& Agr.Ind., Chem.Abstr., Forest.Abstr., Gard.Lit. (1992-), Hort.Abstr.
 —Faxon; UnCover.
 Formerly: Plants and Gardens (ISSN 0032-101X)
 Description: Provides how-to, basic gardening and horticultural information.

635 US
PLANTS & GARDENS NEWS. 1986. 4/yr. (includes Plants & Gardens: Brooklyn Botanic Garden Record). Brooklyn Botanic Garden, 1000 Washington Av., Brooklyn, NY 11225. TEL 718-941-4044. FAX 718-857-2430. Ed. Betsy Kissam. bk.rev. circ. 25,000. (tabloid format; back issues avail.) **Indexed:** Gard.Lit. (1992-). **Document type:** newsletter.

635 US
PLUMERIA SOCIETY OF AMERICA. NEWSLETTER. 4/yr. membership only. Plumeria Society of America, Inc., Box 22791, Houston, TX 77227-2791. TEL 713-780-8326.

635 US
POME NEWS. 1976. 4/yr. $10. Home Orchard Society, Box 230192, Tigard, OR 97281-0192. TEL 503-630-3392. Eds. Winnifred Fisher, Ken Fisher. circ. 1,000.
 Description: Covers care of fruit-producing plants in the home, including landscaping, variety selection, grafting, and pruning.

634 US ISSN 0748-6510
POMONA. 1967. q. $8 membership. North American Fruit Explorers (NAFEX), RR 1, Box 94, Chapin, IL 62628. Ed. John English. adv.; bk.rev. circ. 3,000.
 Description: Devoted to the discovery, cultivation, and appreciation of superior varieties of fruit and nuts. Contains short articles by NAFEX members about their fruit-related endeavors.

635 SP
PONIENTE. 52/yr. Velazquez 2, 04700 El Ejido (Almeria), Spain. TEL 51-48-39-76. FAX 51-48-39-38. Ed. Jose A. Canton Mira. circ. 8,000.

635 664 US ISSN 0197-4084
POTPOURRI FROM HERBAL ACRES. 1979. q. $18. Pine Row Publications, Box 428, Washington Crossing, PA 18977. Ed. Phyllis V. Shaudys. adv.; bk.rev.; charts; index. circ. 2,000.
 Description: Provides a forum to herbal experts for sharing their knowledge, crafts, culinary recipes, and the latest news about the world of herbs.

635.9 FR
POUR NOS JARDINS. 1876. bi-m. 35 F. (effective 1992). Societe d'Horticulture et des Jardiniers de France, 97 bd Saly, 59308 Valenciennes Cedex, France. TEL 27-46-37-50. FAX 27-29-08-12. Dir. Patrick Masquelier. adv. circ. 650,000.

635 UK ISSN 0032-6399
PRACTICAL GARDENING. 1960. m. £19. Frontline Ltd. (Subsidiary of: E M A P - Haymarket Ltd.), Park House, 117 Park Rd., Peterborough PE1 2TR, England. TEL 0733-55161. FAX 62788. TELEX 329292 FRONT G. Ed. Mike Wyatt. adv.; bk.rev.; charts; illus. circ. 90,382.
 —CCC.

635 CN
PRAIRIE GARDEN; Western Canada's only gardening annual. 1938. a. Can.$5.50. Winnipeg Horticultural Society, Box 517, Winnipeg, Man. R3C 2J3, Canada. Ed. Frances Wershler. cum.index. circ. 8,000.
 Description: Aims to promote horticulture and provide information for amateur and professional gardeners.

635.933 US ISSN 0162-6671
SB413.P7
PRIMROSES.* 1941. q. $10. American Primrose, Primula, and Auricula Society, c/o White Horse Village, 535 Gradyville, Rt. 1, Ste. G153, Newtown Sq., PA 19073-2815. Ed. Richard Critz. adv.; bk.rev.; charts; illus. circ. 800.
 Former titles: American Primrose Society. Quarterly; American Primrose, Primula and Auricula Society, Quarterly (ISSN 0003-0619)

635 US ISSN 1041-5610
PRO. 1988. bi-m. $24 (Canada and Mexico $55; elsewhere $120). Johnson Hill Press, Inc., 1233 Janesville Ave., Ft. Atkinson, WI 53538. TEL 414-563-6388. FAX 414-563-1701. Ed. Karla Cuculi. adv.; circ. 40,000 (controlled). (tabloid format)
 Description: For owners and operators of lawn maintenance service firms. Includes features on management, new products, operator profiles, and industry news.

635 NE
PRODUKTSCHAP VOOR SIERGEWASSEN. JAARVERSLAG - STATISTIEK. 1947. a. fl.100. Produktschap voor Siergewassen, Bezuidenhoutse Weg 153, Postbus 930 99, 2509 AB The Hague, Netherlands. circ. 1,500.
 Formed by the merger of: Produktschap voor Siergewassen. Jaarverslag (ISSN 0077-7609) & Produktschap voor Siergewassen. Statistiek (ISSN 0556-543X)

712 UK
PROFESSIONAL LANDSCAPER. 1987. bi-m. £12. Albatross Publications, P.O. Box 193, Dorking, Surrey RH5 5YF, England. Ed. Carol Andrews. adv. circ. 4,000. (back issues avail.) **Document type:** trade publication.

712 634.9 US
PROHORT. 1982. q. Center for Urban Horticulture, University of Washington, Seattle, WA 98195. TEL 206-543-8616. FAX 206-685-2692. Ed. Dave Stockdale. circ. 1,500. (looseleaf format) **Document type:** newsletter.
 Description: Covers technical, topical information for landscape industry, urban forestry, and urban ecology professionals.

635 NE ISSN 0921-5506
PROPHYTA; vakblad voor teeltmateriaal. (Text in Dutch; International edition in Dutch, English, French, Spanish) 1949. 8/yr. (international ed. 4/yr.). fl.175 (International edition $45). Uitgeversmaatschappij C. Misset B.V., Postbus 4, 7000 BA Doetinchem, Netherlands. TEL 31-8340-49911. FAX 31-8340-43839. (Co-sponsors: Nederlandse Vereniging van Tuinzaad Bedrijfsleven, Ciopora Nederland, Nederlandse Vereniging van Plantenkwekers) Ed. Mrs. M.E. Hoffman-Viersma. adv.: B&W page fl.1388, international ed. fl.3035; trim 210 x 297; adv. contact: Cor van Nek. bk.rev.; illus.; pat.; stat.; tr.lit. circ. 2,340 (International ed. 7,000). **Indexed:** Field Crop Abstr., Herb.Abstr., Hort.Abstr., Ind.Vet., Maize Abstr., Ornam.Hort., Plant Breed.Abstr., Plant Grow.Reg.Abstr., Potato Abstr., Seed Abstr., Triticale Abstr. **Document type:** trade publication.
 Formerly (until 1987): Zaadbelangen (ISSN 0165-618X)
 Description: Articles of interest to plant breeders, producers and dealers in seeds, members of research institutes and government agricultural and horticultural agencies.

PTERIDOLOGIST. see *BIOLOGY* — Botany

635.9 US ISSN 0885-3894
PUBLIC GARDEN. 1950. q. $24. American Association of Botanical Gardens and Arboreta, Inc., 786 Church Rd., Wayne, PA 19087. TEL 215-688-1120. FAX 215-293-0149. Ed. Sharon Lee. adv.; bk.rev. circ. 2,400. **Indexed:** Bibl.Agri., Gard.Lit. (1992-). **Document type:** trade publication.
 —UnCover.
 Former titles (until 1986): American Association of Botanical Gardens and Arboreta. Bulletin; Arboretum and Botanical Garden Bulletin; American Association of Botanical Gardens and Arboreta. Newsletter.
 Description: Themed issues on topics of current concern to those working in public horticulture.

634 PK ISSN 0033-4316
PUNJAB FRUIT JOURNAL. (Text and summaries in English and Urdu) 1937. q. Rs.100($20) (£10). Punjab Cooperative Fruit Development Board, Faisalabad, Pakistan. TEL 92-411-32830. Ed. Muhammad Hussan. adv.; bk.rev.; charts; illus.; mkt.; stat. circ. 3,000. **Document type:** academic/scholarly publication.

635 II ISSN 0033-4324
PUNJAB HORTICULTURAL JOURNAL. (Text in English) 1961. q. Rs.30($10) Punjab State Cooperative Fruit Development Federation Ltd, S.C.O. No. 15, Sector 17, 3rd Fl., Chandigarh, India. Ed. B.S. Dhillon. adv.; bk.rev.; charts; illus. circ. 300. **Indexed:** Crop Physiol.Abstr., Food Sci.& Tech.Abstr., Hort.Abstr., Ornam.Hort., Plant Grow.Reg.Abstr., Soils & Fert.

635 CN ISSN 0705-6923
QUEBEC VERT. (Text in French) 1981. m. Can.$38. Editions Vers.colores Inc., 1320 Blvd. Saint-Joseph, Quebec, PQ G2K 1G2, Canada. TEL 418-628-8690. FAX 418-628-0524. Ed. Bertrand Dumont; Pub. Francois Bernatchez. adv. contact: Paul Poisson. bk.rev. circ. 3,888. **Indexed:** Ornam.Hort. **Document type:** trade publication.

635 634 658.8 AT ISSN 0033-6122
QUEENSLAND FRUIT AND VEGETABLE NEWS. 1951. fortn. Aus.$40 (Asia & Pacific Aus.$60; elsewhere Aus.$70). Queensland Fruit and Vegetable Growers, Box 19, Brisbane Market, Brisbane, Qld. 4106, Australia. TEL 07-213-2464. FAX 07-213-2467. Ed. S. Heaton. adv.; bk.rev.; circ. 500 (paid); 8,000 (controlled). **Document type:** trade publication.

635 US
QUILL & TROWEL NEWSLETTER. 1953. bi-m. membership. Garden Writers Association of America, 10210 Leatherleaf Ct., Manassas, VA 22111-4245. TEL 703-257-1032. Ed. Robert C. LaGasse. adv.; bk.rev. circ. 1,400. **Document type:** newsletter.
 Former titles: Garden Writers Newsletter; Garden Writers Bulletin (ISSN 0016-4631)
 Description: Contains organization news.

635 UK ISSN 0080-441X
R.H.S. GARDENER'S DIARY. 1912. a. £4.99. Royal Horticultural Society, Vincent Sq., London SW1P 2PE, England. TEL 01-834-4333. Ed. Susanne Mitchell. circ. 66,000. **Document type:** bulletin.

635 US
R S F NEWSLETTER. 1974. 4/yr. $30 membership only. Rhododendron Species Foundation, Box 3798, Federal Way, WA 98063-3798. TEL 206-927-6960. Ed. Renee Hill. circ. 1,200. **Document type:** newsletter.

635 GW ISSN 0341-9789
CODEN: RASNDF
RASEN - TURF - GAZON. (Supplement avail.: Greenkeepers Journal) q. DM.54. Hortus Zeitschriften Coellen und Bleeck GbR, Rheinallee 4A, 53173 Bonn, Germany. TEL 0228-353030. FAX 0228-353033. **Document type:** trade publication.
 —CASDDS.
 Description: International multi-language journal focusing on vegetation techniques.

380.14 FR ISSN 0249-1605
RAYONS JARDIN. 1973. 10/yr. 190 F. 14 rue Chaptal, 92300 Levallois Perret, France. TEL 47-57-31-66. FAX 47-57-21-57. Ed. Marie-Helene Loae'c. adv.; bk.rev. circ. 6,000.
 Formerly (until 1982): Circuits Jardin.

GARDENING AND HORTICULTURE

635   US
THE REVIEW (UPPERCO). 1969. 2/yr. $3.50 membership only. Society for Japanese Irises, 16815 Falls Rd., Upperco, MD 21155. TEL 410-374-4788. Ed. Evelyn J. White.
Description: Contains articles about iris varieties, culture, hybridizing, and exhibiting. Contains reports about the tour gardens visited, convention information and the results of popularity polls.

635   SZ
REVUE HORTICOLE SUISSE. bi-m. 45 SFr. (foreign 60 SFr.). Centre Horticole de Lullier, CH-1254 Jussy, Switzerland. TEL 022-7591814. FAX 022-7591887. Ed. Jean Schneider. circ. 2,000. **Document type:** bulletin.

634.8 634.9   SZ
REVUE SUISSE DE VITICULTURE, ARBORICULTURE ET HORTICULTURE. (Text in French; summaries in English, German and Italian) 1969. 6/yr. 35 SFr. Association par la Mise en valeur des Travaux de la Recherche Agronomique, Case Postale 190, CH-1260 Nyon, Switzerland. TEL 022-3634151. FAX 022-3621325. Ed. Michel Magnenat. adv.: B&W page 1312 SFr.; trim 180 x 250. bk.rev.; illus.; stat. circ. 6,800. **Indexed:** Agri.Eng.Abstr., Bio-Contr.News & Info., Biol.Abstr., Chem.Abstr., Crop Physiol.Abstr., Excerp.Med., Food Sci.& Tech.Abstr., Hort.Abstr., Plant Breed.Abstr., Plant Grow.Reg.Abstr., Rev.Appl.Entomol., Rev.Plant Path., Soils & Fert., VITIS, Weed Abstr. **Document type:** academic/scholarly publication.
Formerly: Revue Suisse de Viticulture et Arboriculture (ISSN 0035-4171)

635   GW
RHEINISCHE MONATSSCHRIFT FUER GEMUESE OBST ZIERPFLANZEN. 1912. m. DM.80. Rheinischer Landwirtschafts Verlag GmbH, Rochusstr. 18, 53123 Bonn, Germany. TEL 0228-5200636. FAX 0228-5200660. Ed. Hans-W. Peters. circ. 6,000. **Document type:** newsletter.

635   AT
THE RHODODENDRON. 1959. a. Aus.$20. Australian Rhododendron Society, P.O. Box 21, Olinda, Vic. 3788, Australia. TEL 61-3-803-4434. Ed. B. Davidson. adv.; bk.rev. circ. 1,000. **Document type:** bulletin.
Formerly: Australian Rhododendron Society. Journa.
Description: Advance and disseminate knowledge on the Genus Rhododendron.

635   GW   ISSN 0482-9905
RHODODENDRON UND IMMERGRUENE LAUBGEHOELZE. a. Deutsche Rhododendron Gesellschaft e.V., Marcusallee 60, 28359 Bremen, Germany.

635.9   UK   ISSN 0269-5561
SB413.R47
RHODODENDRONS, WITH CAMELLIAS AND MAGNOLIAS. 1946. a. £4.99. Royal Horticultural Society, Vincent Sq., London SW1P 2PE, England. TEL 01-834-4333. Ed. Susanne Mitchell. index. circ. 1,250. **Document type:** bulletin.
Formerly (until 1972): Rhododendron and Camellia Yearbook (ISSN 0080-2891)

LE RICHELIEU DIMANCHE. see *AGRICULTURE*

635 581   BE   ISSN 0374-7867
RIJKSSTATION VOOR SIERPLANTENTEELT. ACTIVITEITSVERSLAG. (Text in Dutch) 1965. a. free. Rijksstation voor Sierplantenteelt, Caritasstraat 21, B-9090 Melle, Belgium. TEL 32-9-2521052. FAX 32-9-2525075. (Subscr. to: C L O Gent, Burg. Van Gansebergehelaan 96, B-9820 Merelbeke, Belgium) Ed. Dr. J. Heursel. circ. 200. **Document type:** academic/scholarly publication, bulletin, government publication.
Description: Covers research activities in the breeding, cultivation and propagation of ornamental plants.

RIVISTA DI FRUTTICOLTURA E DI ORTOFLORICOLTURA. see *AGRICULTURE — Crop Production And Soil*

635   UK   ISSN 0265-5500
ROCK GARDEN. 1937. s-a. £7($20) Scottish Rock Garden Club, 3 Woodhouselee, Easter Howgate, Penicuik, Midlothian EH26 0PG, Scotland. TEL 031-445-3268. (Subscr. to: I.M. Aitchison, 20 Gorse Way, Formby, Merseyside L37 1PB, England. TEL 07048-76382) Eds. C.A. & I.P. Bainbridge. adv.; bk.rev.; bibl.; charts; illus.; index. circ. 4,000. **Document type:** bulletin.
Formerly (until 1983): Scottish Rock Garden Club Journal.
Description: Information on species and genera, cultivation, plant and seed expeditions, plants in the wild.

631 635   US   ISSN 0884-3252
S605.5
RODALE'S ORGANIC GARDENING. 1942. 9/yr. $25 (foreign $37). Rodale Press, Inc., 33 E. Minor St., Emmaus, PA 18098. TEL 800-441-7761. Ed. Mat Dansker. adv.; bk.rev.; charts; illus. circ. 1,333,836. (also avail. in microform from UMI; reprint service avail. from UMI) **Indexed:** Bibl.Agri., Biol.Dig., Environ.Per.Bibl., Hlth.Ind., Ind.How To Do It (1977-), Mag.Ind., MELSA, PMR, R.G.
—UnCover.
Former titles (until Aug. 1985): Organic Gardening (ISSN 0163-3449); (until July 1978): Organic Gardening and Farming (ISSN 0030-4913)

635   CN
ROSARIAN. 3/yr. membership only. Canadian Rose Society, 10 Fairfax Crescent, Scarborough, ON M1L 1Z8, Canada. **Document type:** newsletter.
Description: Promotes knowledge of rose-growing in northern climates.

635   UK
THE ROSE. 1907. q. £14.50. Royal National Rose Society, Chiswell Green, St. Albans A22 3NR, England. TEL 0727-850461. FAX 0727-850360. Ed. Peter Harkness. adv.; bk.rev. circ. 19,000. **Indexed:** Hort.Abstr., Ornam.Hort. **Document type:** newsletter.
Supersedes (as of 1985): Rose Annual (ISSN 0483-3686)

635.9   US
ROSE ARRANGER'S BULLETIN. q. $5. American Rose Society, Box 30000, Shreveport, LA 71130-0030. TEL 318-938-5402. **Document type:** bulletin.
Description: Includes information on rose shows, judging schools, and workshops.

635.9   US
ROSE EXHIBITORS FORUM. 4/yr. $10. American Rose Society, Box 30000, Shreveport, LA 71130-0030. TEL 318-938-5402. **Document type:** bulletin.
Formerly: A R S Rosaceae.
Description: Promotes the skill and art of growing and exhibiting roses; provides a forum for exchange of information.

635   US
ROSE HYBRIDIZERS ASSOCIATION NEWSLETTER. 1969. 4/yr. $7 membership. Rose Hybridizers Association, 3245 Wheaton Rd., Horseheads, NY 14845. TEL 607-562-8592. Ed. Barbara Maas. circ. 500. **Document type:** newsletter.

581 635   CN   ISSN 0046-6751
ROYAL BOTANICAL GARDENS, HAMILTON, ONT. GARDENS' BULLETIN. 1947. q. membership. Royal Botanical Gardens, Box 399, Hamilton, ON L8N 3H8, Canada. TEL 905-527-1158. FAX 905-577-0375. Ed. J. Lord. circ. 6,000. (back issues avail.) **Document type:** bulletin.

580.744   CN   ISSN 0072-9647
ROYAL BOTANICAL GARDENS, HAMILTON, ONT. SPECIAL BULLETIN. 1947. a. membership. Royal Botanical Gardens, Box 399, Hamilton, Ont. L8N 3H8, Canada. TEL 905-527-1158. FAX 905-577-0375. Ed. Helen Yantsis. circ. 6,100. (back issues avail.) **Document type:** bulletin.
Description: Review of the year's activities and financial statements.

ROYAL BOTANICAL GARDENS, HAMILTON, ONT. TECHNICAL BULLETIN. see *BIOLOGY — Botany*

635   NZ   ISSN 0114-1481
ROYAL NEW ZEALAND INSTITUTE OF HORTICULTURE. NEWSLETTER. q. NZ.$60 (includes Journal). Royal New Zealand Institute of Horticulture, P.O. Box 12, Lincoln University, Canterbury, New Zealand. **Document type:** newsletter.
—CCC.
Formerly (until 1989): Horticulture in N.Z. (Wellington) (ISSN 0110-1153)

RURAL DELIVERY. see *GENERAL INTEREST PERIODICALS — Canada*

635   US
S L I NEWSLETTER. 1952. q. $7.50 to individuals; institutions $10. Society for Louisiana Irises, c/o Elaine Bourque, 1812 Broussard Rd. E., Lafayette, LA 70508. TEL 318-856-5859. (Alt. addr.: Box 40175, University of Southern Louisiana, Lafayette, LA 90504. TEL 318-856-5859) Eds. Dennis Vercher, Farron Campbell. adv.: Page $40. illus. circ. 400. (processed)

635   US
S P C N I ALMANAC. 2/yr. membership only. Society for Pacific Coast Native Iris, c/o Mrs. Dorothy Foster, 977 Meredith Ct., Somoma, CA 95476.

635   RU   ISSN 0235-2591
SADOVODSTVO I VINOGRADARSTVO. 1898. bi-m. $45. Izdatel'stvo Kolos, Sadovaya-Spasskaya 18, 107807 Moscow, Russia. TEL 207-18-80. FAX 207-28-70. Ed. Vasilii I. Sergeev. bk.rev.; bibl.; illus.; index. circ. 9,400. **Indexed:** Agri.Eng.Abstr., Agroforest.Abstr., Biol.Abstr., Chem.Abstr., Hort.Abstr., Irr.& Drain.Abstr., Nutr.Abstr., Ornam.Hort., Plant Breed.Abstr., Plant Grow.Reg.Abstr., Seed Abstr., Weed Abstr.
Formerly: Sadovodstvo (ISSN 0131-3568)

635   US
SAGE NOTES. 1981. 6/yr. $10 membership. Idaho Native Plant Society, Box 9451, Boise, ID 83707. Ed. Laura Bond. adv.; bk.rev. circ. 400. **Document type:** newsletter.

SAN DIEGO HOME - GARDEN LIFESTYLES. see *INTERIOR DESIGN AND DECORATION*

635   CN
SASKATCHEWAN ORCHID SOCIETY. NEWSLETTER. 1986. 6/yr. membership only. Saskatchewan Orchid Society, P.O. Box 411, Saskatoon, SK S7K 3L3, Canada. TEL 306-249-1073. Ed. Mary Jane Eley. adv. circ. 60. **Document type:** newsletter.

635   SZ
SCHWEIZER GARTEN. m. Villa Mueslischreck, CH-6042 Dietwil, Switzerland. TEL 041-912950. Ed. Elsi Wepf. circ. 17,600.

635   SZ
SCHWEIZERISCHER BERUFSGAERTNER. 11/yr. Mittelstr. 5, Postfach 854, CH-3000 Bern 9, Switzerland. TEL 031-3012616. Ed. K. Schwab. circ. 1,600. **Document type:** trade publication.

635   SZ
SCHWEIZERISCHER PFLANZENFREUND. m. Ernst Meier AG, CH-8630 Tann Rueti, Switzerland. TEL 055-317171. Ed. Erwin Meier. circ. 5,000.

GARDENING AND HORTICULTURE

635   NE   ISSN 0304-4238
SB4   CODEN: SHRTAH
SCIENTIA HORTICULTURAE; an international journal. 1973. 20/yr. (in 5 vols.; 4 nos./vol.). fl.1700($919) (effective 1994). (International Society for Horticultural Science) Elsevier Science B.V., P.O. Box 211, 1000 AE Amsterdam, Netherlands. TEL 31-20-5803911. FAX 31-20-5803598. TELEX 18582 ESPA NL. (Subscr. in U.S. and Canada to: Elsevier Science Inc., Box 882, Madison Sq. Sta., New York, NY 10159. TEL 212-989-5800. FAX 212-633-3990) Eds. M. Reid, G. Germing. adv.; bk.rev.; bibl.; illus.; index. **Indexed:** Agri.Eng.Abstr., ASCA, Biol.Abstr., Biotech.Abstr., Cadscan, Chem.Abstr., Crop Physiol.Abstr., Curr.Adv.Ecol.Sci., Curr.Cont., Excerp.Med., Field Crop Abstr., Food Sci.& Tech.Abstr., Helminthol.Abstr., Hort.Abstr., Irr.& Drain.Abstr., Lead Abstr., Ornam.Hort., Packag.Sci.Tech., Plant Breed.Abstr., Plant Grow.Reg.Abstr., Potato Abstr., Ref.Zh., Rev.Plant Path., Seed Abstr., Soils & Fert., Sugar Ind.Abstr., VITIS, Weed Abstr., Zincscan. **Document type:** academic/scholarly publication.
—BLDSC (8172.400000); Faxon; UnCover; SWETS; CASDDS. **CCC.**
Description: Publishes research related to horticultural crops, covering both open-air and protected production of vegetables, fruits, edible fungi and ornamentals under temperate, sub-tropical and tropical conditions.
Refereed Serial

635   US   ISSN 0745-3590
THE SEED POD. 1956. 4/yr. membership only. American Hibiscus Society, Box 12073, St. Petersburg, FL 33733-2073. TEL 813-896-1081. Ed. Katie McClain. adv. circ. 1,800. **Document type:** consumer publication.
Description: Provides news and current information to members of the society regarding the hibiscus plant; includes calendar of events.

635   US
SEED SAVERS EXCHANGE. (Comes in three annual editions: Yearbook (in Jan.); Summer Edition (in July-Aug.); Harvest Edition (in Oct.-Nov.)) 1976. 3/yr. $25 in U.S.; Can. $30; elsewhere $40. 3076 N. Winn Rd., Decorah, IA 52101. TEL 319-382-5990. FAX 319-382-5872. Ed. Kent Whealy. bk.rev. circ. 6,000. **Indexed:** Gard.Lit. (1992-).
Formerly: True Seed Exchange.
Description: Directed to backyard gardeners and others interested in the preservation and propagation of non-commercial, heirloom and traditional varieties of vegetables, fruits, grains, and nuts.

631.521   US   ISSN 0037-0789
SEED TRADE NEWS. 1923. 14/yr. $25 includes International Seed Directory. Dean Enterprises Inc., 9995 W 69th St., Eden Prairie, MN 55344-3497. TEL 612-941-5820. FAX 612-941-1708. Ed. Frank Zaworski. adv.; charts; mkt.; stat. circ. 3,400. **Document type:** trade publication.

SEEDHEAD NEWS. see *BIOLOGY — Botany*

635   UK
SEMPERVIVUM SOCIETY. NEWSLETTER. irreg. £2.50 for 3 issues. Sempervivum Society, 11 Wingle Tye Rd., Burgess Hill, W. Sussex RH15 9HR, England. TEL 0444-236848. adv.; bk.rev. **Document type:** newsletter.
Formerly: Sempervivum Society. International Newsletter; Supersedes (in 1986): Houseleeks (ISSN 0140-0304).

634.9   US   ISSN 0037-3133
SHADE TREE. 1928. 6/yr. membership. New Jersey Shade Tree Federation, Box 231, Cook College, Rutgers University, New Brunswick, NJ 08903. TEL 908-246-3210. Ed. Donald Lacey. adv.; index. circ. 1,200. **Indexed:** Forest.Abstr., Forest Prod.Abstr., Hort.Abstr. **Document type:** bulletin.

635.9   JA   ISSN 0037-3737
SHIN KAKI/NEW FLOWERS. (Text in Japanese) 1954. q. 4720 Yen. Takii Shubyo Co. Ltd., 180 Umekoji-Inokuma, C.P.O. Box 7, Kyoto 600-91, Japan. TEL 75-365-0123. FAX 75-365-0110. adv.; bk.rev.; bibl.; charts; illus.; stat.; tr.lit.; index. cum.index.

635   JA   ISSN 0037-4407
SHUBYO TO ENGEI. (Text in Japanese) 1947. a. free. Tokita Seed Co. Ltd., 1069 Nakagawa, Omiya, Saitama-ken, Japan. FAX 048-684-5042. Ed. Tsutomu Tokita. bk.rev.; mkt.

635   SP
SOCIEDAD ESPANOLA DE HORTICULTURA. REVISTA. 1935. m. 3000 ptas. Sociedad Espanola de Horticultura, Arrieta, 7-5, 28013 Madrid, Spain. TEL (91)248 31 24. FAX 91-247-55-56. TELEX 47530 SEH-E. Ed. Jose Luis Lopez Vilches. adv.; bk.rev.

635   US
SOILLESS GROWER. 1979. bi-m. $30 includes membership (foreign $40). Hydroponic Society of America, Box 3075, San Ramon, CA 94583. TEL 510-743-9605. FAX 510-743-9302. Ed. Maynard Bates. adv.; bk.rev. circ. 700. (looseleaf format)
Former titles: Hydroponic - Soilless Grower; Hydroponic Society of America Newsletter.
Description: How-to tips on hydroponic - soilless growing for the hobbyist to the multi-acre commercial grower.

SONORAN QUARTERLY. see *BIOLOGY — Botany*

635 747   SA   ISSN 0038-2183
SOUTH AFRICAN GARDEN & HOME. 1946. m. R.70.79 (overseas R.120.56) (effective 1993). Republican Press (Pty) Ltd., P.O. Box 32083, Mobeni 4060, Natal, South Africa. TEL 27-31-422041. FAX 27-31-921231. Ed. Margaret Wasserfall. adv.; bk.rev.; illus. circ. 180,000. **Document type:** consumer publication.
Description: Covers decor and gardening.

635   II   ISSN 0038-3473
SOUTH INDIAN HORTICULTURE. (Text in English) 1953. bi-m. $50. South Indian Horticultural Association, Tamil Nadu Agricultural University, Coimbatore 641 003, India. Ed. Dr. Abdul Khader. adv.; bk.rev.; bibl.; charts; illus.; stat. circ. 1,000. **Indexed:** Agroforest.Abstr., Biol.Abstr., Crop Physiol.Abstr., Hort.Abstr., Irr.& Drain.Abstr., Ornam.Hort., Plant Breed.Abstr., Plant Grow.Reg.Abstr., Rice Abstr., Seed Abstr., Soils & Fert.
—BLDSC (8352.070000).

SOUTHERN ACCENTS. see *INTERIOR DESIGN AND DECORATION*

635   US
SOUTHERN CALIFORNIA HORTICULTURAL INSTITUTE. MONTHLY BULLETIN.* m. membership only. Southern California Horticultural Institute, Box 41080, Los Angeles, CA 90041-0080. **Document type:** bulletin.

712   US
SOUTHERN GOLF - LANDSCAPE & RESORT MANAGEMENT.* 1955. bi-m. $9. Brantwood Publications, Inc., 3023 Eastland Blvd., Ste. 103, Clearwater, FL 34621-4106. TEL 813-796-3877. Ed. Richard W. Morey. adv.; bk.rev.; charts; illus. circ. 8,500. (also avail. in microform from UMI; reprint service avail. from UMI) **Indexed:** Sportsearch.
Formerly: Southern Golf - Landscape and Turf Industry (ISSN 0146-8251); Formed by the merger of: Landscape and Turf Industry (ISSN 0274-5941); Southern Golf; Landscape and Turf Industry (ISSN 0274-5941); Which was formed by the 1980 merger of: Turf-Grass Times; (1969-1980): Landscape Industry (ISSN 0023-804x); Which was formerly titled (1961-1968): Landscape Design and Construction; (1955-1961): Landscaping.

635.969 658.8   US   ISSN 8755-2256
SB118.73
SOUTHERN LANDSCAPE & TURF.* 1955. m. $15. Brantwood Publications, 3023 Eastland Blvd., Ste. 103, Clearwater, FL 34621-4106. TEL 813-796-3877. Ed. Richard W. Morey. adv.; bk.rev.; illus.; stat.; circ. 18,000 (controlled). (reprint service avail. from UMI) **Indexed:** Farm & Garden Ind.
Supersedes in part (in 1990): Nursery Business (ISSN 0029-6406)

635   US
SOUTHERN LIVING GARDEN GUIDE. 1989. a. $3.95. Southern Progress Corp. (Subsidiary of: Time, Inc. Magazine Co.), c/o H. Jahnson, V.P. Circulation, 2100 Lakeshore Dr., Birmingham, AL 35209. TEL 205-877-6000. FAX 205-877-6422. adv.: B&W page $5680, color page $8000; trim 8 1/8x 10 7/8. circ. 400,000.

635   US
SOUTHERN TURF MANAGEMENT. 1990. m. $25. Argus Agronomics (Subsidiary of: Argus Inc.), Box 1420, Clarksdale, MS 38614. TEL 601-624-8503. FAX 601-627-1977. circ. 19,800. (tabloid format) **Document type:** trade publication.
Description: Covers the production and maintenance of turf in the southern states.

SPAZIO CASA. see *INTERIOR DESIGN AND DECORATION — Furniture And House Furnishings*

635   GW   ISSN 0178-837X
DER STAUDENGARTEN. 1973. q. DM.50 (students DM.25). Gesellschaft der Staudenfreunde e.V., Meiseweg 1, 65795 Hattersheim, Germany. TEL 06190-3642. Eds. Hermann Hald, Martel Hald. adv.; bk.rev. circ. 3,500. **Indexed:** Hort.Abstr. **Document type:** consumer publication.
Formerly: Iris- und Lilien.
Description: Promotes knowledge of hardy perennial plants for gardens.

635   US
SUBTROPICAL PLANT SCIENCE. 1946. a. $15. Rio Grande Valley Horticultural Society, Box 600, Edinburg, TX 78540-0600. Ed. Gene Lester. charts; illus.; stat.; index. cum.index: vols.1-25 (1946-1971). circ. 400. (back issues avail.) **Indexed:** Biol.Abstr., Chem.Abstr., Food Sci.& Tech.Abstr., Hort.Abstr., Nutr.Abstr., Ornam.Hort., Soils & Fert.
Formerly (until vol.44, 1991): Rio Grande Valley Horticultural Society. Journal.

635   NE   ISSN 0039-4467
SUCCULENTA. (Text in Dutch; summaries in English) 1919. m. fl.50. Nederlands-Belgische Vereniging van Liefhebbers van Cactussen en Andere Vetplanten - Dutch Society for Amateurs of Succulent Plants, Punter 26-10, 8242 EA Lelystad, Netherlands. Ed. F. Robert de Groot. adv.; bk.rev.; illus.; index. circ. 3,800.

635   HU   ISSN 0230-2241
SB396.5
SZOLOTERMESZTES ES BORASZAT/VINE-GROWING AND VITICULTURE. 1979. q. University of Horticulture, Research Institute for Viticulture and Enology, P.O. Box 25, Kisfai 182, Kecskemet 6000, Hungary. Ed. Bako Zoltanne. circ. 2,000.

635   GW   ISSN 0177-5006
T A S P O. (Thalacker's Allgemeiner Samen- und Pflanzen-Offerte); groesste unabhaengige Fachzeitung fuer Europas Gartenbau. 1867. w. DM.175.20 (foreign DM.231). Bernhard Thalacker Verlag GmbH, Postfach 3361, 38023 Braunschweig, Germany. TEL 0531-380040. FAX 0531-3800425 Ed. Renate Veth. adv.; B&W page DM.7998, color page DM.8578; trim 430 x 280. circ. 25,000. (tabloid format; back issues avail.) **Document type:** trade publication. —CCC.

635   GW   ISSN 0177-6126
T A S P O GARTENKURIER. (Thalackers Allgemeiner Samen- und Pflanzen-Offerte) 1984. bi-m. DM.45. Bernhard Thalacker Verlag, Hamburgerstr. 277, Postfach 3361, 38114 Braunschweig, Germany. TEL 0531-380040. FAX 0531-3800425. Ed. Gabi Friedrichs. adv.; circ. 120,000 (controlled). (back issues avail.)

T I; Magazin fuer Aquaristik, Terristik, Naturgarten, Lebensraeume. (Tatsachen, Informationen) see *FISH AND FISHERIES*

635   CN   ISSN 0835-3271
T L C...FOR PLANTS. (Tender Loving Care) 1988. q. Can.$14.95($16.95) Gardenvale Publishing Co., Ltd., One Pacific, St. Anne de Bellevue, PQ H9X 1C5, Canada. TEL 514-457-2744. FAX 514-457-6255. Ed. Kathryn Spracklin. adv. contact: Barbara Paul. bk.rev.; index. circ. 30,000. (back issues avail.) **Document type:** consumer publication.

GARDENING AND HORTICULTURE

634 630   AT   ISSN 0039-9787
TASMANIAN FRUITGROWER & FARMER.* 1915. m. Aus.$1. Huon Newspaper Co. Pty. Ltd., Franklin, Huon, Tasmania, Australia. Ed. Donald M. Yeates. adv.; bk.rev.; charts; illus.; mkt. circ. 2,000.

635   GW
TECHNISCHE UNIVERSITAET MUENCHEN. INSTITUT FUER WIRTSCHAFTSLEHRE DES GARTENBAUES. FORSCHUNGSBERICHTE ZUR OEKONOMIE IN GARTENBAU. 1968. irreg. Technische Universitaet Muenchen, Institut fuer Wirtschaftslehre des Gartenbaues, Weihenstephan, 81673 Munich, Germany.

635   US   ISSN 0744-0987
TEXAS GARDENER; the magazine for Texas gardeners. 1981. bi-m. $15. Suntex Communications, Inc., Box 9005, Waco, TX 76710-9005. Ed. Chris S. Corby. adv. circ. 35,000. **Indexed:** Gard.Lit. (1992-). **Document type:** consumer publication.

635   US
TEXAS HORTICULTURIST. 1973. m. $12. Texas Pecan Growers Association, Inc., Box C C, College Sta., TX 77841. TEL 409-846-1752. FAX 409-846-1752. Ed. Cindy Wise. adv. circ. 2,700.
   Description: Covers horticulture, fruit, vegetable, rose and greenhouse growing.

635   US
TEXAS NATIVE PLANT SOCIETY NEWS. 1986. 6/yr. $15 membership (effective 1993). Native Plant Society of Texas, Box 891, Georgetown, TX 78627. TEL 512-863-9685. FAX 513-869-0393. Eds. Melinda Larson, Dana Tucker. adv.; bk.rev. circ. 1,750. **Document type:** newsletter.

635   US   ISSN 0040-6619
THRU THE GARDEN GATE. 1941. bi-m. $5 to non-members. Federated Garden Clubs of Michigan, Inc., 343 Wildwood Dr., Holland, MI 49423-6920. TEL 616-392-4406. Ed. Judy Nykamp. adv. contact: Betty Miller. bk.rev.; illus.; circ. 7,000 (paid). **Document type:** newsletter.
   Description: Presents news items on the members and activities of the clubs, with announcements of competitions, seminars, conferences, and informative articles on horticultural and handicraft techniques.

635   GW
▼**TOPOS;** European landscape magazine. (Text in English and German) 1992. q. DM.206. Callwey Verlag, Postfach 800409, 81604 Munich, Germany. TEL 089-436005-0. FAX 089-43600513. circ. 3,000. **Document type:** trade publication.

TOWN AND COUNTRY FARMER. see AGRICULTURE

635   FI   ISSN 0049-4356
TRAEDGAARDSNYTT. (Text in Swedish) 1946. s-m. Fmk.265. Svenska Traedgaardsfoerbundet, Spannmaalsvaegen 4D, 00700 Helsinki, Finland. TEL 90-354881. FAX 90-3513675. Ed. Nina Holmlund. adv.; bk.rev. circ. 2,500. **Indexed:** Sci.Abstr.

635   SA   ISSN 0041-1744
TRANSVAAL GARDENER. 1952. q. R.35 (effective 1994). Transvaal Horticultural Society, 10 Tyrone Ave., Parkview 2193, South Africa. TEL 011-646-1136. Ed. Helen Bloom. adv.; bk.rev. circ. 1,000.

TREES IN SOUTH AFRICA/BOME IN SUID-AFRIKA. see BIOLOGY — Botany

635   CN   ISSN 0380-1470
TRELLIS. 1974. 10/yr. membership. Civic Garden Centre, 777 Lawrence Ave. E., Don Mills, Ont. M3C 1P2, Canada. TEL 416-445-1552. Ed. Aldona Satterthwaite. adv.; bk.rev. circ. 3,000.

635   US
TROPICAL FRUIT NEWS. (Text in English, occasionally in Spanish) 12/yr. $35. Rare Fruit Council International, Inc., Box 561914, Miami, FL 33156. TEL 813-474-6133. Ed. Bobby Cannon. **Document type:** academic/scholarly publication, consumer publication.
   Supersedes: Rare Fruit Council International. Newsletter.
   Description: Covers fruit culture, horticulture, preservation, usage and marketing of tropical and sub-tropical fruits.

635   RU   ISSN 0041-4905
CODEN: TSVTAN
TSVETOVODSTVO. 1958. bi-m. $56. Izdatel'stvo Kolos, Sadovaya-Spasskaya 18, 107807 Moscow, Russia. TEL 207-55-13. FAX 207-28-70. Ed. Inna K. Artamonova. bk.rev.; bibl.; illus.; index. circ. 65,000. **Indexed:** Biol.Abstr., Chem.Abstr.
—BLDSC (0396.480000).

635 630   BE
TUINBOUW VISIE. (Text and summaries in Dutch) 1989. w. 1200 BEF. Editions Rurales, 92 Leon Grosjeanlaan, B-1140 Brussels, Belgium. TEL 02-730-3300. FAX 02-736-0414. TELEX 25882. Ed.Bd. circ. 10,000.
   Formerly: Tuinbouw Leven.

635   US   ISSN 1045-6503
TURF. 1988. m. N E F Publishing Co., 50 Bay St., Box 391, St. Johnsbury, VT 05819. TEL 802-748-8908. Ed. Daniel Hurley. adv. circ. 17,200. **Document type:** trade publication.
   Description: For turf grass professionals. Covers the green space industry with information on developments in technology.

712   CN   ISSN 1186-0170
TURF & RECREATION. 1988. 6/yr. $25 (foreign $35). Turf & Recreation Publishing Inc., 19469 - 92nd Ave., Surrey, BC V4N 4G6, Canada. TEL 604-888-8843. FAX 604-888-8734. Ed. Rud Kendall. adv. contact: Richard Savage. bk.rev. circ. 13,143. **Document type:** trade publication.
   Description: Emphasis on new products, developments, trends and topics.

635   US   ISSN 1059-6348
TURF CENTRAL. 1990. m. $12. N E F Publishing, Co., Box 391, 50 Bay St., St. Johnsbury, VT 05819. TEL 802-748-8908. Ed. Dan Hurley. adv. circ. 16,000. **Document type:** trade publication.
   Description: Focuses on practical aspects of the greenspace industry and on developing research and technology.

712   UK   ISSN 0262-0669
TURF MANAGEMENT. 1982. m. £20 (rest of Europe £40; N. America, S. America, Africa, Asia £50; Austrialia, New Zealand, Japan £60). Haymarket Trade and Leisure Publications Ltd., 38-42 Hampton Rd., Teddington, Middx. TW11 OJE, England. TEL 081-943-5023. FAX 081-943-5673. Ed. Richard Garlick. adv.; bk.rev. circ. 5,283.

TURF NEWS. see AGRICULTURE — Crop Production And Soil

635   US   ISSN 1058-3254
TURF SOUTH. 1989. m. N E F Publishing Co., Box 391, 50 Bay St., St. Johnsbury, VT 05819. TEL 802-748-8908. FAX 802-748-1866. adv. circ. 17,100. **Document type:** trade publication.
   Description: Focuses on the greenspace industry, including research developments and new technology.

635   US   ISSN 1071-4995
TURF WEST. 1991. m. N E F Publishing Co., Box 391, 50 Bay St., St. Johnsbury, VT 05819. TEL 802-748-8908. FAX 802-748-1866. adv. circ. 11,100. **Document type:** trade publication.
   Description: Focuses on the practical aspects of the greenspace industry and on developing research and technology.

U K PESTICIDE GUIDE. see AGRICULTURE — Crop Production And Soil

635   US   ISSN 0073-3075
TX7   CODEN: XAHGA2
U.S. DEPARTMENT OF AGRICULTURE. HOME AND GARDEN BULLETIN. 1950. irreg. U.S. Department of Agriculture, Washington, DC 20250-1300. TEL 202-720-2791. (also avail. in microfiche from UPD) **Indexed:** Biol.Abstr., Forest.Abstr., Nutr.Abstr. **Document type:** government publication.

712   NO   ISSN 0333-1555
UTEMILJOE.* 1981. 8/yr. NOK 280. Sameiet Utemiljo, Skippergt. 21, 0152 Oslo 1, Norway. Ed. Trond Kamperud. adv.; bk.rev. circ. 2,000.
   Description: Concerns landscape architecture.

635   CN
VEGETABLES SPECIALIST. 1967. irreg. free. Department of Agriculture & Rural Development, Plant Industry Branch, Fredericton, N.B. E3B 5H1, Canada. TEL 506-453-2666. FAX 506-453-7978. bk.rev. circ. 200.
   Formerly: Vegetables Newsletter (ISSN 0042-3092)

VERBONDSNIEUWS VOOR DE BELGISCHE SIERTEELT; vakblad van het A.V.B.S. see FORESTS AND FORESTRY

635   XO   ISSN 0042-6326
CODEN: VINOAM
VINOHRAD. (Text in Czech, Slovak) 1962. m. 30 Kcs.($20) (Ministry of Agriculture and Nourishment) Priroda, Krizkova 9, 815 34 Bratislava, Slovakia. TEL 472-41-45. (Subscr. to: Slovart, Gottwaldovo nam. 48, 805 32 Bratislava, Slovakia) **Indexed:** Chem.Abstr., Food Sci.& Tech.Abstr., VITIS.
—BLDSC (9236.910000); CASDDS.

635   SW   ISSN 0042-6407
VIOLA;* Traedgaardsvaerlden. 1895. s-w. SEK 483 (effective 1991). (Traedgaardsnaeringens Riksfoerbund) Traedgaardsnaeringens Konsult AB, P.O. Box 66, S-121 22 Johanneshov, Sweden. (Co-sponsor: Sveriges Traedgaardsanlaeggningsfoerbund) Ed. Susanne Linde; Pub. Nils Viktorsson. adv.: B&W page SEK 12700, color page SEK 16750. bk.rev.; index. circ. 8,500. cols./p.: 5.
   Incorporates (in 1959): Traedgaardsvaerlden.

635   IT   ISSN 1120-3005
VITA IN CAMPAGNA. 1983. m. L.45000. Informatore Agrario S.r.l., Largo Caldera 11, 37122 Verona, Italy. TEL 045 597855. Ed. Alberto Rizzotti. adv.; bk.rev.; charts; illus.; mkt.; stat.; index; circ. 78,206 (controlled). (tabloid format)
   Description: Articles for part-time farmers, gardeners.

635   UK
VITIS; journal of the Society of Garden Designers. 1984. q. £25 (foreign £40). Society of Garden Designers, 6 Borough Rd., Kingston-upon-Thames, Surrey KT2 6BD, England. TEL 081-974-9483. (Dist. by: Stanhope Press, 61 Grafton Rd., Kentish Town, London NW5 3EN, England. TEL 071-387-0041) Ed. Andrew Wilson. adv. contact: Julia Fogg. circ. 500. **Document type:** newsletter.

W N P S NEWSLETTER. (Wyoming Native Plant Society) see BIOLOGY — Botany

635   PL
CODEN: AWAHEB
WARSAW AGRICULTURAL UNIVERSITY. S G G W. ANNALS. HORTICULTURE. (Text in English; summaries in Polish) 1957. irreg. $10 per no. Szkola Glowna Gospodarstwa Wiejskiego (SGGW) - Warsaw Agricultural University, Ul. Nowoursynowska 166, 02-766 Warsaw, Poland. Ed. J.R. Starck. **Indexed:** Hort.Abstr., Weed Abstr. **Document type:** academic/scholarly publication.
—CASDDS.
   Former titles: Warsaw Agricultural University. S G G W - A R. Annals. Horticulture (ISSN 0208-5747); (until 1980): Akademia Rolnicza, Warsaw. Zeszyty Naukowe. Ogrodnictwo (ISSN 0083-7288)

WASHINGTON NATIVE PLANT SOCIETY. OCCASIONAL PAPERS. see BIOLOGY — Botany

635   US   ISSN 1046-8749
SB1
WASHINGTON PARK ARBORETUM BULLETIN. q. $35. Arboretum Foundation, University of Washington XD-10, Seattle, WA 98195. TEL 206-325-4510. FAX 206-325-8893. Ed. Jan Silver. adv. circ. 3,000. **Indexed:** Bibl.Agri.
—UnCover.

635   US   ISSN 1069-5982
WATER GARDEN JOURNAL. 1985. 4/yr. membership only. International Water Lily Society, c/o Santa Barbara Botanic Garden, 1212 Mission Canyon Rd., Santa Barbara, CA 93105. TEL 805-682-4726. FAX 805-563-0352. Ed. Edward L. Schneider. bk.rev. circ. 800. **Document type:** academic/scholarly publication.
   Formerly: Water Lily Journal.
   Description: Dedicated to the furtherance of all aspects of water gardening.

GARDENING AND HORTICULTURE — ABSTRACTING, BIBLIOGRAPHIES, STATISTICS

WEED CONTROL MANUAL. see *AGRICULTURE — Crop Production And Soil*

WESTERN FRUIT GROWER. see *AGRICULTURE — Crop Production And Soil*

635 US
WESTERN TURF MANAGEMENT. 1990. m. $25. Argus Agronomics (Subsidiary of: Argus Inc.), Box 1420, Clarksdale, MS 38614. TEL 601-624-8503. FAX 601-627-1977. Ed. Ed Phillips. circ. 10,600. (tabloid format) **Document type:** trade publication.
  Description: For golf course superintendents, professional lawn care service operators, supervisors of municipal parks and other recreational areas, sod producers and sports turf managers in the ten Western states. Covers the production and maintenance of turf.

WILD FLOWER NOTES. see *BIOLOGY — Botany*

635 US ISSN 1065-8912
SB450.9
WOMAN'S DAY GARDENING & OUTDOOR LIVING IDEAS. 1988. a. $3.25 per no. Hachette Magazines, Inc., Woman's Day Special Publications, 1633 Broadway, 45th Fl., New York, NY 10019.
TEL 212-767-6000. adv. circ. 450,000.

635 US
WORLD PUMPKIN CONFEDERATION. JOURNAL. 1983. irreg. membership only. World Pumpkin Confederation, 14050 Gowanda State Rd., Collins, NY 14034. FAX 716-532-5690. adv. circ. 3,000.
  Formerly: World Pumpkin Confederation. Newsletter.
  Description: Unites people with a common interest in giant pumpkins, giant squash, and giant watermelons.

635 US ISSN 0896-6834
YARD AND GARDEN. 1977. 9/yr. $40 (Canada $55; elsewhere $120). Johnson Hill Press, Inc., 1233 Janesville Ave., Ft. Atkinson, WI 53538.
TEL 414-563-6388. FAX 414-563-1701. Ed. Elliott Maras. circ. 35,000 (controlled). (tabloid format)
  Formerly: Yard and Garden Product News.
  Description: Serves retailers of yard and garden equipment by providing sales strategies, marketing ideas and product information that will assist them in becoming more successful business people.

635 AT ISSN 0085-8382
YOUR AUSTRALIAN GARDEN. 1965. irreg. Aus.$2.50 per no. David G. Stead Memorial Wildlife Research Foundation of Australia, Box 4840, Sydney, N.S.W. 2001, Australia. Ed. Thistle Y. Stead. bk.rev. circ. 3,000.

635 AT ISSN 0044-1031
YOUR GARDEN. 1947. m. Aus.$36 (foreign Aus.$45). Southdown Press, 32 Walsh St., Melbourne, Vic. 3000, Australia. TEL 03-320-7000. Ed. Tony Fawcett. adv.; bk.rev.; illus.; index. circ. 90,000.
  Indexed: Pinpointer.

635 UK ISSN 0969-1332
▼**YOUR GARDEN.** 1993. m. £17.40($43.70) I P C Magazines, Specialist Magazine Group (Subsidiary of: Reed Elsevier plc), King's Reach Tower, Stamford St., London SE1 9LS, England. TEL 071-261-5000. FAX 0444-440619. TELEX 892084 REEDBP G. (Subscr. to: YG Subscriptions, Freepost, Haywards Heath, W. Sussex RH16 3ZA, England. TEL 0622-721555) Ed. Graham Clark. adv. contact: David Gannicott. (back issues avail.) **Document type:** consumer publication.
  Description: Contains garden news, garden plants, product guides, hints and tips, step-by-step guides, house plants, and questions and answers.

635 CC
YUANLIN. (Text in Chinese) bi-m. Shanghai Yuanlin Guanli-ju - Shanghai Gardens Administration, No.4, Lane 195, Fujian Zhonglu, Shanghai 200001, People's Republic of China. TEL 3225453. Ed. Yan Lingzhang.

635 CC ISSN 0513-353X
CODEN: AHTSAU
YUANYI XUEBAO/ACTA HORTICULTURAE SINICA. (Text in Chinese) 1962. q. $4 per no. (effective 1994). Zhongguo Nongye Kexueyuan, Shucai Huahui Yanjiuyuan - Chinese Academy of Agriculture, Chinese Society for Horticultural Science, 30 Baishiqiao Lu, Beijing 100081, People's Republic of China. TEL 86-1-8314433. FAX 86-1-8316374. TELEX 222720 CAAS CN. circ. 4,000. **Indexed:** Curr.Adv.Ecol.Sci., Hort.Abstr., Ornam.Hort., Seed Abstr. **Document type:** academic/scholarly publication.
—BLDSC (0624.340000).
  Description: Covers fruits, vegetables, melons and ornamentals in temperate, subtropical and tropical areas.

635 XR ISSN 0139-7761
ZAHRADKAR. 1968. m. 30 Kcs.($15) Cesky Zahradkarsky Svaz, Ustredni Vybor, Ckalova 22, 160 41 Prague 6, Czech Republic. TEL 26 59 51. (Subscr. to: Artia, Ve Smeckach 30, 111 27 Prague 1, Czech Republic) Ed. Oto Zouplna.

635 XR ISSN 0862-867X
ZAHRADNICTVI/HORTICULTURE. vedecky casopis. (Text and summaries in zech, English, Slovak) 1974. q. $34. Ustav Zemedelskych a Potravinarskych Informaci, Slezska 7, 120 56 Prague 2, Czech Republic. TEL 257541. FAX 257090. Ed. Zdena Radosova. circ. 700. **Indexed:** Agri.Eng.Abstr., Crop Physiol.Abstr., Forest.Abstr., Hort.Abstr., Ornam.Hort., Plant Grow.Reg.Abstr., Seed Abstr. **Document type:** academic/scholarly publication.
  Formerly (until 1989): U V T I Z Sbornik - Zahradnictvi (ISSN 0231-567X)

635 XO ISSN 0139-9470
ZAHRADNICTVO. (Text in Czech, Slovak) 1962. m. 60 Kcs. (Ministry of Agriculture and Nourishment) Priroda, Krizkova 9, 815 34 Bratislava, Slovakia. TEL 472-41-45. (Subscr. to: Slovart, Gottwaldovo nam. 48, 805 32 Bratislava, Slovakia)
  Formed by the 1982 merger of: Zahradnik (ISSN 0139-7818); Zahradnicke Listy (ISSN 0044-1694); Formerly: Ovocnarstvi a Zelinarstvi.

ZHIWU BAOHU/PLANT PROTECTION. see *BIOLOGY — Botany*

635.9 US
ZHONGGUO HUAHUI BAO/CHINESE JOURNAL OF FLOWERS. (Text in Chinese) s-w. $76. China Books & Periodicals, Inc., 2929 24th St., San Francisco, CA 94110. TEL 415-282-2994.
FAX 415-282-0994. **Document type:** newspaper.

635.9 US
ZHONGGUO HUAHUI PENJING/CHINESE FLOWERS - POTTED LANDSCAPE. (Text in Chinese) m. $42.50. China Books & Periodicals, Inc., 2929 24th St., San Francisco, CA 94110. TEL 415-282-2994.
FAX 415-282-0994.

635 US
ZINGIBER.* 2/yr. membership only. American Ginger Society, Box 100, Archer, FL 32618-0100. TEL 904-495-9168.

GARDENING AND HORTICULTURE — Abstracting, Bibliographies, Statistics

634 016 GW ISSN 0302-4601
AKTUELLE LITERATURINFORMATIONEN AUS DEM OBSTBAU. (Text in English and German) 1972. irreg. free. Technische Universitaet Berlin, Universitaetsbibliothek, Str. des 17. Juni 135, 10623 Berlin, Germany. TEL 030-31423980. FAX 030-31424743. Ed. Gudrun Weiland. circ. 350. **Indexed:** VITIS. **Document type:** monographic series.

338.1 635 CN ISSN 0318-5184
SB29.C2
CANADA. STATISTICS CANADA. SURVEY OF CANADIAN NURSERY TRADES INDUSTRY. (Catalogue 22-203) (Text in English and French) 1919. a. Can.$22($26) (foreign $31). Statistics Canada, Publications Sales and Services, Ottawa, Ont. K1A 0T6, Canada. TEL 613-951-7277.
FAX 613-951-1584. (also avail. in microform from MML)
  Description: Provides an overview of the industry including estimates of the total land used for growing nursery stock or sod, labor costs and employment, purchases and sales of plant materials and sod.

635 US ISSN 1061-3722
Z5996.A1
▼**GARDEN LITERATURE;** an index to periodical articles and book reviews. 1992. q. $50 to individuals (foreign $70); nstitutions $75 (foreign $95). Garden Literature Press, 398 Columbus Ave., Ste. 181, Boston, MA 02116. TEL 617-424-1784. FAX 617-424-1712. Ed. Sally Williams. **Document type:** abstracting/indexing.
  Description: Indexes over 100 journals, newsletters, newspapers and annuals of interest to gardeners, garden designers, growers and retailers, historians, horticulturists, landscape architects, and preservationists.

635 US ISSN 0897-5175
Z5996.A1
GARDENER'S INDEX. 1986. a. $18. CompuDex Press, Box 27041, Kansas City, MO 64110.
TEL 816-931-1334. **Document type:** abstracting/indexing.
  Description: Presents combined annual index to Fine Gardening, Flower and Garden, Horticulture, National Gardening and Organic Gardening magazines.

GERMANY. STATISTISCHES BUNDESAMT. FACHSERIE 3: LAND- UND FORSTWIRTSCHAFT, FISCHEREI; REIHE 3: LANDWIRTSCHAFTLICHE BODENNUTZUNG UND PFLANZLICHE ERZEUGUNG. see *AGRICULTURE — Abstracting, Bibliographies, Statistics*

635 016 UK ISSN 0018-5280
SB1
HORTICULTURAL ABSTRACTS; compiled from world literature on temperate and tropical fruits, vegetables, ornaments, plantation crops. 1931. m. £484($904) CAB International, Bureau of Horticulture and Plantation Crops, Wallingford, Oxon. OX10 8DE, England. TEL 44-491-832111. FAX 44-491-833508. TELEX 847964 COMAGG G. (U.S. subscr. to: CAB International, North American Office, 845 N. Park Ave., Tucson, AZ 85719. TEL 800-528-4841) adv. bk.rev.; abstr.; index, cum.index: vols.1-30 (1931-1960) in 5 vols. circ. 1,650. (also avail. in diskette format; back issues avail.) **Indexed:** Biol.Abstr., Forest.Abstr., Forest Prod.Abstr., Helminthol.Abstr., Nutr.Abstr., Rev.Appl.Entomol., VITIS. **Document type:** abstracting/indexing.
  ●Also available online. Vendor(s): BRS Online Products (CABA), CISTI, DIMDI, DIALOG Information Services, Inc., European Space Agency (File nos.16 & 124/CAB).
—BLDSC (4330.000000).

635 PO
INSTITUTO DE INVESTIGACAO CIENTIFICA TROPICAL. INDEX SEMINUM QUAE HORTUS ET MUSAEUM AGRICOLUM TROPICUM. 1949. a. free. Instituto de Investigacao Cientifica Tropical, Jardim - Museu Agricola Tropical, Rua Jua, 54, 1300 Lisbon, Portugal. TEL 364-5321 FAX 363-1640. (Subscr. to: Centro de Documentacao e Informacao, Rua Jau 47, 1300 Lisbon, Portugal) circ. 1,200. **Document type:** catalog.

ONTARIO. MINISTRY OF AGRICULTURE AND FOOD. SEASONAL FRUIT AND VEGETABLE REPORT. see *AGRICULTURE — Abstracting, Bibliographies, Statistics*

GARDENING AND HORTICULTURE — FLORIST TRADE

635.9 016 UK ISSN 0305-4934
ORNAMENTAL HORTICULTURE. 1975. bi-m. £127($230) CAB International, Wallingford, Oxon. OX10 8DE, England. TEL 44-491-832111. FAX 44-491-833508. TELEX 847964 COMAGG G. (U.S. subscr. to: CAB International, North American Office, 845 N. Park Ave., Tuscon, AZ 85719. TEL 800-528-4841) circ. 300. (also avail. in diskette format; back issues avail.) **Document type:** abstracting/indexing.
●Also available online. Vendor(s): BRS Online Products, CISTI, DIMDI, DIALOG Information Services, Inc., European Space Agency (File nos.16 & 124/CAB).
—SWETS.
Description: Aimed at horticultural scientists dealing with ornamentals; horticulturalists concerned with public parks, gardens, and other amenities; nursery workers; students; and serious amateur gardeners.

631.53 016 UK ISSN 0032-0803
PLANT BREEDING ABSTRACTS. 1930. m. £487($912) CAB International, Wallingford, Oxon. OX10 8DE, England. TEL 44-491-832111. FAX 44-491-833508. TELEX 847964 COMAGG G. (U.S. subscr. to: CAB International, North American Office, 845 N. Park Ave., Tucson, AZ 85719. TEL 800-528-4841) adv.; bk.rev.; abstr.; index. circ. 1,600. **Indexed:** Anim.Breed.Abstr., Apic.Abstr., Biol.Abstr., Field Crop Abstr., Forest.Abstr., Helminthol.Abstr., Herb.Abstr., Rev.Plant Path., Rice Abstr., Rural Recreat.Tour.Abstr., World Agri.Econ.& Rural Sociol.Abstr. **Document type:** abstracting/indexing.
●Also available online. Vendor(s): BRS Online Products (CABA), CISTI, DIMDI, DIALOG Information Services, Inc., European Space Agency (File nos.16 & 124/CAB).
—BLDSC (6514.000000).
Description: Covers world literature on crop breeding and genetics. All species of economic importance are included.

RECENT LITERATURE ON MEDICINAL PLANTS. see MEDICAL SCIENCES — Abstracting, Bibliographies, Statistics

635 310 NE ISSN 0440-0771
SB319.N4
TUINBOUWCIJFERS. 1968. a. fl.35. Landbouw-Economisch Instituut, Conradkade 175, 2517 CL The Hague, Netherlands. TEL 31-70-3308330. FAX 31-70-3615624. Ed. W. van Veen. **Document type:** government publication.
Description: Statistical data on income, production, sales, inputs, acreage and other features of Dutch horticulture.

635 GW ISSN 0940-9920
ZANDERA. (Text in German; summaries in English) 1982. s-a. DM.30. Buecherei des Deutschen Gartenbaues e.V., Thaerstr. 7, 14469 Potsdam, Germany. Ed. Clemens Alexander Wimmer. bk.rev. circ. 200. **Document type:** bibliography.

634 RH
ZIMBABWE. CENTRAL STATISTICAL OFFICE. CENSUS OF REGISTERED DECIDUOUS FRUIT GROWERS. a. Central Statistical Office, P.O. Box 8063, Causeway, Harare, Zimbabwe. circ. 600. (looseleaf format; back issues avail.) **Document type:** government publication.

GARDENING AND HORTICULTURE — Florist Trade

635.9 NE ISSN 0165-2591
BLOEM EN BLAD. 1979. fortn. fl.180. Uitgeversmaatschappij C. Misset B.V., Hanzestr. 1, 7006 RH Doetinchem, Netherlands. TEL 31-8340-49911. FAX 31-8340-43839. TELEX 45481. (Subscr. to: Postbus 4, 7000 BA Doetinchem, Netherlands) Ed. E. v.d Berg. adv.; B&W page fl.2259; trim 210 x 297; adv. contact: Hans Dijcker. bk.rev.; charts; illus. circ. 8,890. **Document type:** trade publication.
Description: Covers all aspects of the retail trade in potted plants, purchase and sale of cut flowers, floral arrangement.

635.9 NE ISSN 0929-8223
BLOEMENBUSINESS; vakblad voor de totale sierteelt. (Text in Dutch) 1983. q. fl.75. Flora Media, Postbus 155, 6500 AD Nijmegen, Netherlands. TEL 31-80-784646. Ed. Bas Meisters. circ. 8,700. (back issues avail.) **Document type:** trade publication.
Formerly (until 1993): Bloemenvak (ISSN 0925-3580)

635.9 658.8 DK ISSN 0006-4955
BLOMSTER; Nordisk tidsskrift for binderi og blomster. (Text in Danish and Norwegian) 1918. 10/yr. DKK 250. (Dansk Blomsterhandlerforening) Blomster ApS, P.O. Box 100, Storegade 26, DK-4550 Asnaes, Denmark. TEL 45-53-45-10-24. FAX 45-53-45-08-17. (Co-sponsor: Norsk Blomsterhandlerforbund) Ed. Jens Poulsen. adv.: B&W page DKK 4600, color page DKK 9600; adv. contact: Lars Erigsson. bk.rev.; illus. circ. 2,200. **Document type:** trade publication.
Formed by the 1980 merger of: Blomster & Blomsterbinderen.

635.9 658.8 SW ISSN 0006-4963
BLOMSTER-BRANSCHEN. 1926. m. (10/yr.). SEK 360. Swedish Florist's Association, Box 808, S-161 24 Bromma, Sweden. TEL 46-8-25-97-31. FAX 46-8-26-96-06. TELEX 13403. Ed. Ewa Kohlstrom. adv.; bk.rev.; circ. 3,000 (controlled). **Document type:** trade publication.
Description: Provides current information of interest to florists.

635.9 GW ISSN 0341-2075
BLUMEN EINZELHANDEL. 1972. m. DM.157.80. Verlag Eugen Ulmer.GmbH, Wollgrasweg 41, 70599 Stuttgart, Germany. TEL 0711-4507-0. FAX 0711-4507-120. TELEX 7-23634-ULMER-D. (Subscr. to: Postfach 700561, 70574 Stuttgart, Germany) Ed. G. Heinrichs. adv.; bk.rev.; illus. circ. 7,200. **Document type:** trade publication.
—BLDSC (2115.200000). **CCC.**

635.9 658.8 GW ISSN 0007-5973
BUNTE BLUMENWELT. 1961. m. membership. Fleurop GmbH, Lindenstr. 3-4, 12207 Berlin, Germany. TEL 030-713710. FAX 030-71371198. adv.; bk.rev. circ. 580,000. **Document type:** trade publication.

635.9 658.8 CN ISSN 0008-3585
CANADIAN FLORIST, GREENHOUSE AND NURSERY. 1905. m. Can.$12($18) Horticulture Publications Ltd., 1090 Aerowood Dr., Unit 1, Mississauga. Ont. L4W 1Y5, Canada. TEL 416-625-2730. FAX 416-625-1355. Ed. Peter Heywood. adv.; bk.rev.; charts; illus.; tr.lit. circ. 3,000.

635 UK
THE COMPLETE FLORIST. m. Unit D8, Pinetrees Rd., Salhouse Rd., Norwich, Norfolk NR7 9BB, England. TEL 0603-700006. FAX 0603-300409. Ed. Kate Morely.

635.9 US
CORNELL RECOMMENDATIONS FOR COMMERCIAL FLORIST CROPS. (Part 2: Pest Control - Diseases, Insects and Weeds) a. price varies. Cornell University, Media Services, 7-8 Business and Technology Park, Ithaca, NY 14850. TEL 607-255-2080. FAX 607-255-9946.

635.9 IT
DATA & FIORI. 6/yr. Ace International, Via Mocomero 26, 29010 Vernasca (PC), Italy. TEL 39-50-93-52. Ed. Arturo Croci. circ. 25,000.

EDGAR BROOKES ACADEMIC AND HUMAN FREEDOM LECTURE. see EDUCATION — Higher Education

635.9 US
F T D FAMILY. m. Florists' Transworld Delivery Association, 29200 Northwestern Hwy., Box 2227, Southfield, MI 48037. TEL 313-355-9300. FAX 313-948-6415. Ed. William P. Golden. bk.rev. circ. 24,000. **Document type:** newspaper.

635.9 CN ISSN 0827-150X
FLEUR DESIGN. 1985. 7/yr. Can.$27. (Association Professionelle des Fleuristes Detaillants du Quebec, Inc.) Editions Versicolores Inc., 1320 boul. St.-Joseph, Quebec, PQ G2K 1G2, Canada. TEL 418-628-8690. FAX 418-628-0524. Ed. Caty Berube; Pub. Francois Bernatchez. adv. contact: Paul Poisson. bk.rev. circ. 1,850. **Document type:** trade publication.

635.9 GW
FLEUROP MAGAZIN. 1951. m. membership. Fleurop GmbH, Lindenstr. 3-4, 12207 Berlin, Germany. TEL 030-713710. FAX 030-71371198. circ. 10,500. **Document type:** bulletin.

635.9 FR ISSN 0339-8390
FLEURS DE FRANCE; revue mensuelle d'information professionnelle. m. 290 F. 33 rue du Pont Neuf, 75001 Paris, France. TEL 42-33-46-32. FAX 45-08-87-23. Ed. Bernard Hirsch. adv. circ. 5,495. **Document type:** trade publication.
Formerly: Fleuriste de France.

745.92 UK
FLORA INTERNATIONAL. 1974. bi-m. £18.95. The Fishing Lodge Studio, 77 Bulbridge Rd., Wilton, Salisbury, Wilts. SP2 OLE, England. TEL 0722-743207. Ed. Russell Bennett. adv.: B&W page £245, color page £324; trim 270 X 175. bk.rev. circ. 20,000. **Indexed:** Sci.Cit.Ind. **Document type:** consumer publication.
Formerly: Flora (ISSN 0306-882X)
Description: Provides articles and features on flower arranging, floristry, and flower crafts for the international florist and flower arranger industry.

635.9 US ISSN 0046-4082
FLORAFACTS. 1961. m. $15. Florafax International, Inc., Box 45745, Tulsa, OK 74145. TEL 918-622-8415. Ed. Angela H. Caruso. adv.; bk.rev. circ. 22,500.

635.9 US
FLORAL AND NURSERY TIMES. 1979. s-m. $35. XXX Publishing Enterprises Ltd., 436 W. Frontage Rd., Northfield, IL 60025. TEL 708-441-0300. FAX 708-441-0308. Ed. Barbara Gilbert. adv. circ. 17,500. (tabloid format; back issues avail.) **Document type:** trade publication.

FLORAL EDITION; buyer's guide. see BUSINESS AND ECONOMICS — Trade And Industrial Directories

635.9 US
FLORAL MANAGEMENT; business news for the floral industry. 1984. m. $24. Society of American Florists, 1601 Duke St., Alexandria, VA 22314. TEL 703-836-8700. Ed. Butch Kinerney. adv.; charts; illus. circ. 15,000. **Document type:** newsletter.
Formerly: S A F.
Description: Business information for retailers, wholesalers, and growers in the floral industry.

635.9 US
FLORAL MARKETING ASSOCIATION DIRECTORY AND BUYER'S GUIDE. 1975. a. $70 to non-members; members $45. Produce Marketing Association, 1500 Casho Mill Rd., Box 6036, Newark, DE 19714-6036. TEL 302-738-7100. FAX 302-731-2409. Ed. Terry Humfeld. **Document type:** directory.
Formerly: Floral Marketing Directory and Buyer's Guide.

635.9 US
FLORAL MASS MARKETING. 1982. bi-m. $15. Cenflo, Inc., 120 S. Riverside Plaza, Ste. 464, Chicago, IL 60606. TEL 312-258-8500. FAX 312-258-8558. Ed. Rosemary Baldwin. circ. 12,162. (tabloid format) **Document type:** trade publication, newspaper.
Description: For floral and nursery buyers at supermarket chains, discount store chains, variety store, depertment store and convenience store chains; top volume garden center buyers.

635.9 IT ISSN 0015-3834
FLORICOLTURA PESCIATINA. 1958. m. (10/yr.). L.10000 (foreign L.30000) (effective 1992). Comune di Pescia, Comitato Biennale del Fiore, Via Fratelli Rosselli, 2, 51017 Pescia, Italy. TEL 572-47-68-97. FAX 572-47-086. Ed. Antonio Natali. adv.: B&W page L.300000. bk.rev.; charts; illus.; stat. circ. 2,000.

635.9 658.8 GW ISSN 0015-4393
FLORIST. 1948. s-m. DM.112.80. (Fachverband Deutscher Floristen e.V) Appel-Druck, Donau-Verlag GmbH, Augsburgerstr. 82, Postfach 1154, 8870 Guenzburg, Germany. FAX 08221-34527. adv.; bk.rev. circ. 12,800.

GARDENING AND HORTICULTURE — FLORIST TRADE

635.9 658.8   US   ISSN 0015-4385
FLORIST. 1967. m. $28. Florists' Transworld Delivery Association, 29200 Northwestern Hwy., Box 2227, Southfield, MI 48037. TEL 313-355-9300. FAX 313-948-6415. Ed. William P. Golden. adv.; bk.rev.; charts; illus.; stat. circ. 29,300. **Document type:** trade publication.

635.9   SZ
DER FLORIST/FLEURIST. (Text in French, German) 1920. s-m. 86 Fr. to non-members; members 76 Fr. Schweizerischer Floristenverband, Postfach 380, CH-8042 Zurich, Switzerland. TEL 01-3621530. FAX 01-3638873. Eds. Bruno Braun, Gabi Hophan. adv.; bk.rev.

635.9 658.8   UK   ISSN 0015-4415
FLORIST TRADE MAGAZINE. 1949. m. £25 (foreign £60). Lonsdale Publications Ltd., 86-90 Richmond Rd., Kingston-upon-Thames, Surrey KT2 5EW, England. TEL 081-546-1535. FAX 081-547-3682. Ed. Caroline Marshall-Foster. adv. contact: Claudia Hull. bk.rev.; illus.; tr.lit. circ. 10,000. **Document type:** trade publication.
    Incorporates (1981-199?): Florists' News.
    Description: News briefs and informational items on the operational and marketing aspects of the industry, oriented toward shopkeepers, wholesalers, and floristry tutors. Provides technical advice and equipment reviews.

635.9 658.8   US   ISSN 0015-4423
FLORISTS' REVIEW. 1897. m. $36 (foreign $46). Florists' Review Enterprises, 3641 S.W. Plass, Topeka, KS 66611. TEL 913-266-0888. FAX 913-266-0333. Ed. Marge Nichols Sullivan. adv. contact: Rick Nesbitt. bk.rev.; charts; illus.; mkt.; pat.; tr.lit.; index. circ. 32,000. (also avail. in microfilm from UMI; reprint service avail. from UMI) **Indexed:** Biol.Abstr., Farm & Garden Ind. **Document type:** trade publication.
—UnCover; UMI.

635.9   US   ISSN 0015-4490
FLOWER NEWS. 1947. w. $20. Cenflo, Inc., 120 S. Riverside Plaza, Ste. 464, Chicago, IL 60606. TEL 312-258-8500. FAX 312-258-8558. Ed. Rosemary Baldwin. circ. 18,724. (tabloid format) **Document type:** trade publication, newspaper.
    Description: For retail and wholesale florists, florist suppliers and growers.

635.9   CN   ISSN 0836-3749
FLOWER SHOP. 1986. 12/yr. Can.$24. N C C Publishing, 22 Argyle Ave., Delhi, ON N4B 2Y2, Canada. TEL 519-582-4040. FAX 519-582-4040. Ed. Ben Steidman. adv.: B&W page Can.$764; trim 8 x 11; adv. contact: Jim Dillon. circ. 5,700. (back issues avail.) **Document type:** trade publication.
    Description: For the Canadian retail florist: profiles of designers and businesses, new products.

635.9   UK
FLOWER TRADES JOURNAL. 1978. m. £40 (Europe £52; elsewhere £73). Yewtree Publishing Co. Ltd., 17 Wickham Rd., Beckenham, Kent BR3 2JS, England. TEL 081-658-8688. FAX 081-658-2250. Ed. Margarette Worsfold. adv.; bk.rev. circ. 3,000. **Document type:** trade publication.
    Description: Presents news, calendar of events, advertisements, and services on the international floricultural industry, with advice columns on import/export, wholesale and retail handling and care.

635.9 658.8   US   ISSN 0199-4751
FLOWERS&; the beautiful magazine about the business of flowers. 1934. m. $38.95 (foreign $48.95) (typically set in Jan.). Teleflora, 12233 W. Olympic Blvd., Ste. 118, Los Angeles, CA 90064. TEL 310-826-5253. FAX 310-477-0229. Ed. Marie Moneysmith. adv.; bk.rev.; illus.; circ. 33,000 (paid). **Document type:** trade publication.
    Former titles (until 1980): Teleflorist; (until 1977): Teleflora Spirit (ISSN 0040-2532)

367
GLADIOLUS ANNUAL. 1926. a. £8 to non-members (foreign £9) (effective 1993). British Gladiolus Society, 1 Naginton Dr., Penkridge, Staffordshire, ST19 5TA, England. TEL 0785-715813. Ed. Mrs. E. Anderson. adv.; bk.rev. circ. 500. **Indexed:** Hort.Abstr. **Document type:** trade publication.
    Description: Covers the work of the society and results of research by Gladiolus growers in the U.K. and throughout the world.

635.9   US   ISSN 1053-7104
GREENHOUSE PRODUCT NEWS. 1990. m. free to growers. Scranton Gillette Communications, Inc., 380 E. Northwest Hwy., Des Plaines, IL 60016. TEL 708-298-6622. FAX 708-390-0408. Ed. Lisa S. Osborne. adv.; circ. 20,000 (controlled). **Document type:** trade publication.
—CCC.

635.9   FR   ISSN 0290-683X
INFORMATIONS FLEURISTES. 8/yr. 59 rue du Faubourg-Poissonniere, 75009 Paris, France. TEL 47-70-94-62. FAX 45-23-36-81. Ed. Michel Chansiaux. circ. 10,000.
    Formerly (until 1975): Inf. F (ISSN 0290-6821)

635.9   SP
INTERFLORA. 6/yr. Asociacion Espanola Interflora, Torrelaguna 125, 28043 Madrid, Spain. TEL 1-413-10-43. FAX 1-519-35-83. Ed. J. Luis Delgado Garcia. circ. 10,000.

635.9   GW   ISSN 0022-6262
DER JUNGE FLORIST. 1952. m. DM.14.40. (Fachverband Deutscher Floristen e.V.) Appel-Druck, Donau-Verlag GmbH, Augsburgerstr. 82, 89312 Guenzburg, Germany. FAX 08221-34527. adv.; bk.rev.; index. circ. 4,000.
    Formerly: Bindestube.

635.9   US
LINK MAGAZINE. 1977. m. $30. Wholesale Florists & Florist Suppliers of America, 5313 Lee Hwy., Box 7308, Arlington, VA 22207. TEL 703-241-1100. FAX 703-237-6438. Ed. Lisa Mickey. adv. circ. 1,500. (back issues avail.)
    Description: News and articles on business and sales topics relevant to the floral industry.

635.9   UK
MERCURY. 1932. m. £15.84. (Florists Telegraph Delivery Association) Interflora British Unit Ltd., Interflora House, Sleaford, Lincolnshire, England. FAX 0529-304394. Ed. Ken Neighbour. adv.; bk.rev.; illus. circ. 2,500. (tabloid format)

635.9 658.8   US   ISSN 0026-217X
MICHIGAN FLORIST. 1942. bi-m. membership. Michigan Floral Association, Box 24065, Lansing, MI 48909-4065. TEL 517-394-2900. FAX 517-394-3011. Ed. Sue Ann Stuever; Pub. Marsha Gray. adv. contact: Barbara Doyal. illus. circ. 1,700. **Document type:** trade publication.

635.9   UK
NEWSLETTER (ARUNDEL). m. Yapton Ln., Walberton, Arundel, W. Sussex BN18 0AS, England. TEL 0243-554320. FAX 0243-554316. Ed. P.D. Grieves. bk.rev. circ. 300.

635.9 658.8   US   ISSN 0030-090X
OHIO FLORISTS ASSOCIATION. BULLETIN. 1929. m. membership. Ohio Florists Association, 2130 Stella Ct., No. 200, Columbus, OH 43215-1033. TEL 614-487-1117. FAX 614-487-1216. Ed. Jane Lieberth. charts; illus.; tr.lit.; index. circ. 3,400. **Indexed:** Hort.Abstr., Ornam.Hort., Plant Grow.Reg.Abstr., Weed Abstr. **Document type:** bulletin.
—BLDSC (6246.400000).

635.9   US   ISSN 1064-6558
ORNAMENTAL OUTLOOK. 10/yr. $25 (out-of-state $45; free to qualified personnel). F G R Incorporated, 1331 N. Mills Ave., Orlando, FL 32803-2598. TEL 407-894-6522. FAX 407-894-6511. adv. circ. 12,500. **Document type:** trade publication.
—UnCover.
    Description: Covers growing and media supplies, irrigations systems, packaging, carrier services, greenhouse structures, chemical and environmental concerns, shipping and marketing of foliage and ornamentals.

635.9   SP   ISSN 0213-6414
OROPHRYS; revista del florista profesional. 1986-1988; resumed 1991. q. 3972 ptas. (foriegn 4240 ptas.). Ediciones y Promociones Lav, S.L., Apdo. 473, 46080 Valencia, Spain. TEL 96-372-02-61. FAX 96-3710516. Ed. Francisco Salvador Planes Planes.

635.9   UK   ISSN 0961-2599
PLANT FINDER. 1978. a. £11.99. Headmain, Lakeside, Gaines Rd., Whitbourne, Worcs. WR6 5RD, England. TEL 0886-21119. FAX 0886-21853. Eds. Tony Lord, Chris Philip. adv.; index. circ. 25,000. **Document type:** directory.
    Formerly: Hardy Plant Directory.
    Description: Lists some 60,000 available from more than 600 nurseries in England.

PRODUCE BUSINESS; the international business magazine serving the fruit, vegetable and floral industries. see *FOOD AND FOOD INDUSTRIES — Grocery Trade*

745.92   US
PROFESSIONAL FLORAL DESIGNER. bi-m. American Floral Services, 3737 N.W. 34th St., Oklahoma City, OK 73112. TEL 405-947-3373.

635.9   US   ISSN 1054-9552
ROCKY MOUNTAIN GARDENER. 1990. q. $12. Westwind Publishing, Box 1230, Gunnison, CO 81230. TEL 303-641-5091. FAX 303-641-4329. Ed. Susan Martineau. adv.; bk.rev.; illus.; circ. 2,500 (paid). **Document type:** consumer publication.
—UnCover.
    Description: Offers a regional forum for the Rocky Mountain states. Covers general gardening, botany, and natural history.

635.9 658.8   US
SUPERMARKET FLORAL. 1988. m. free to qualified personnel. Vance Publishing Corporation, 7950 College Blvd., Shawnee Mission, KS 66210. TEL 913-451-2200. FAX 913-451-5821. (Subscr. to: Box 2939, Shawnee Mission, KS 66201) Ed. Kirsten Bosnak. adv. circ. 10,000. (tabloid format; back issues avail.) **Document type:** trade publication.
    Description: Educational articles for supermarket floral department buyers and managers.

TODAY'S HOSPITAL GIFT SHOP BUSINESS. see *BUSINESS AND ECONOMICS — Marketing And Purchasing*

TOKYO NO IKEBANA. see *ARTS AND HANDICRAFTS*

635.9   NE   ISSN 0165-3350
TUIN & LANDSCHAP. 1979. fortn. fl.170. (Kring Tuin- en Landschapsvoorziening) Uitgeversmaatschappij C. Misset B.V., Postbus 4, 7000 BA Doetinchem, Netherlands. TEL 31-8340-49911. FAX 31-8340-43839. TELEX 45481. (Editorial addr.: P.O. Box 9324, 2300 PH Leiden, Netherlands. TEL 31-71-161161. FAX 31-71-161200) Ed. E. v.d. Berg. adv.: B&W page fl.2242; trim 215 x 285; adv. contact: Cor van Nek. bk.rev.; charts; illus. circ. 8,910. **Document type:** trade publication.
    Description: Information on the layout and maintenance of gardens, parks and other green spaces, material used, machinery and tools.

635   NE   ISSN 0042-2223
VAKBLAD VOOR DE BLOEMISTERIJ. Variant title: Bloemisterij. 1945. w. fl.191.50. (Vereniging Bloemenveilingen Nederland) C. Misset B.V., Postbus 4, 7000 BA Doetinchem, Netherlands. TEL 31-8340-49911. FAX 31-8340-43839. TELEX 45481. (Editorial addr.: P.O. Box 9324, 2300 PH Leiden, Netherlands. TEL 31-71-16171. FAX 31-71-161200) Ed. V.D. Berg. adv.: B&W page fl.3790; trim 215 x 285; adv. contact: Cor van Nek. bk.rev.; charts; illus.; mkt. circ. 17,880. **Indexed:** Agri.Eng.Abstr., Crop Physiol.Abstr., Hort.Abstr., Key to Econ.Sci., Ornam.Hort., Plant Grow.Reg.Abstr., Rural Recreat.Tour.Abstr., World Agri.Econ.& Rural Sociol.Abstr. **Document type:** trade publication.
—SWETS.
    Description: Information on all aspects of growing potted plants and cut flowers.

VERBONDSNIEUWS VOOR DE BELGISCHE SIERTEELT; vakblad van het A.V.B.S. see *FORESTS AND FORESTRY*

WHO'S WHO IN FLORICULTURE. see *BIOGRAPHY*

GASTROENTEROLOGY

see Medical Sciences—Gastroenterology

GENEALOGY AND HERALDRY

929 US
A G L L NEWS. q. American Genealogical Lending Library, Box 244, Bountiful, UT 84011. TEL 801-298-5358.

929.6 US ISSN 0892-4201
A M S STUDIES IN THE EMBLEM. 1987. irreg., no.12, 1994. price varies. A M S Press, Inc., 56 E. 13th St., New York, NY 10003. TEL 212-995-5413. FAX 212-995-5413. Eds. Peter M. Daly, Daniel S. Russell. (back issues avail.)
Description: Monographs and reference works on the tradition, art and cultural significance of the emblem in history.

A T M REUNION REGISTRY. (Adoption Triangle Ministries) see *SOCIAL SERVICES AND WELFARE*

929 US
ABER BULLETIN. 1971. s-a. $6. Aber Family of America, 1216 Lillie Circle, Salt Lake City, UT 84121. TEL 801-262-4586. Eds. Catherine Greenberg, Hugh T. Law. circ. 95. (back issues avail.)
Description: Researches common ancestry and descendants of ancestors.

929 UK
ABERDEEN AND NORTH EAST SCOTLAND FAMILY HISTORY SOCIETY. JOURNAL. 1979. q. £12. Aberdeen and North East Scotland Family History Society, 164 King St., Aberdeen AB2 3BD, Scotland. TEL 44-224-646323. adv.; bk.rev. circ. 3,500.
Formerly: Aberdeen and North East Scotland Family History Society. Newsletter (ISSN 0143-4500)

929 US ISSN 0883-1173
ABOUT ALFORDS. 1982. q. $15. 1403 Kingsford Dr., Florissant, MO 63031. TEL 314-831-8648. Ed. Gilbert K. Alford, Jr. circ. 100.

929 GT ISSN 0065-0463
ACADEMIA GUATEMALTECA DE ESTUDIOS GENEALOGICOS, HERALDICOS E HISTORICOS. REVISTA. 1967. irreg., no.9, 1987. price varies. Academia Guatemalteca de Estudios Genealogicos, Heraldicos e Historicos, 12 Calle 11-51, Zona 1, Guatemala City, Guatemala. Ed. Ramiro Ordonez Jonama. circ. 400.

929 US ISSN 0199-9591
ACADIAN GENEALOGICAL EXCHANGE NEWSLETTER. 1972. q. $15. 863 Wayman Branch Rd., Covington, KY 41015. TEL 606-356-9825. Ed. Janet B. Jehn. bk.rev.; index. **Document type:** newsletter.
Description: Dedicated to Acadian, Cajun and French Canadian genealogy and history.

929 US ISSN 8755-5026
ADAMS FAMILY CHRONICLE. 1979. q. membership. Adams Family Association, Inc., 939 Sotu Comet Ave., Panama City, FL 32404. Ed. Lowell T. Adams. bk.rev. circ. 900. **Document type:** newsletter.
Formerly: Adams Family Newsletter.

ADAY TO REMEMBER. s-a. Mildred Y. Aday, Ed. & Pub., 8174 Vanguard Dr., Denver, CO 80221-4652. TEL 303-428-9221.

929 AU ISSN 0001-8260
CS1
ADLER; review for genealogy and heraldry. 1881; N.S.1947. q. S.480. Heraldisch-Genealogische Gesellschaft Adler, Haarhof 4a, A-1014 Vienna, Austria. adv.; bk.rev.; bibl.; illus.; cum.index every 3 yrs. circ. 850. **Indexed:** Amer.Hist.& Life, Hist.Abstr. **Document type:** academic/scholarly publication.

ADOPTION REFORM ORGANIZATIONS. see *SOCIAL SERVICES AND WELFARE*

AFRICAN-AMERICAN FAMILY HISTORY ASSOCIATION NEWSLETTER. see *ETHNIC INTERESTS*

929 US ISSN 0272-1937
AFRO-AMERICAN HISTORICAL AND GENEALOGICAL SOCIETY. JOURNAL. 1980-1992; N.S. 1994. q. $25 to individuals; institutions $35. Afro-American Historical and Genealogical Society, Box 73086, Washington, DC 20056-3086. TEL 202-234-5203. adv.; bk.rev.; illus.; index; institutions 1980-1989. circ. 500. **Indexed:** Amer.Hist.& Life, Geneal.Per.Ind., Hist.Abstr. **Document type:** academic/scholarly publication.
—UnCover.

929 US
AFRO-AMERICAN HISTORICAL AND GENEALOGICAL SOCIETY. NEWSLETTER. q. membership only. Afro-American Historical and Genealogical Society, Box 73086, Washington, DC 20056-3086. **Document type:** newsletter.

929 GW ISSN 0170-2653
AHNENLISTEN KARTEI. irreg. Verlag Degener und Co., Nuernbergerstr. 27, 91413 Neustadt, Germany. FAX 09161-1378. **Document type:** monographic series.

929 US
ALABAMA FAMILY HISTORY AND GENEALOGY NEWS.* 1980. 4/yr. $8.50. (North Central Alabama Genealogical Society) Briarwood Press, c/o Joyce Davis, 546 Haralson Ave., Gadsden, AL 35901. circ. 250.

929 US
ALABAMA GENEALOGICAL EXCHANGE QUARTERLY.* 1984. q. $20. Wood Publishing Co., 13200 Woodrose Dr., Brookwood, AL 35444-9227. TEL 205-758-4507. Ed. Thomas Harold Wood. adv.; bk.rev.; abstr.; bibl.; charts; illus.; stat.; index. circ. 500. (back issues avail.)

929 CN
ALBERTA GENEALOGICAL SOCIETY. ANCESTOR INDEX. (Supplement to: Relatively Speaking) 1975. a. Alberta Genealogical Society, Box 12015, Edmonton, AB T5J 3L2, Canada. Ed. F. Siemens. circ. 200.
Formerly: Alberta Genealogical Society. Surnames Register (ISSN 0704-9145)

ALBURY & DISTRICT HISTORICAL SOCIETY. BULLETIN. see *HISTORY — History Of Australasia And Other Areas*

929 US
ALEXANDER NEWSLETTER. bi-m. $12. 3601H Bent Oak Trail, Elkhart, IN 46517. circ. 50.
Formerly: Alexander Tree.

929 398 325 US ISSN 0883-5926
CS71
ALLEES ALL AROUND; includes Alley, Ally, Allie, Alyea. 1984. q. $15. Box 347, Friendswood, TX 77546. Ed. Ginger Rae Allee. bk.rev.; abstr.; bibl.; charts; illus.; stat.; cum.index. circ. 100. (back issues avail.)

929 US
ALLEN COUNTY LINES. 1976. q. $10. Allen County Genealogical Society of Indiana, Box 12003, Ft. Wayne, IN 46862. index. circ. 280. (also avail. in microform) **Document type:** newsletter.

929 US ISSN 0885-3215
ALLEN FAMILY CIRCLE. a. $2.30. 4906 Ridgeway, Kansas City, MO 64133. Ed. Lois Allen. circ. 200. (looseleaf format; back issues avail.) **Document type:** newsletter.
Description: Attentive to, and clearinghouse for researchers of Allen surname.

929 US ISSN 0002-8592
F104.N6
AMERICAN GENEALOGIST. Abbreviated title: T A G. 1922. q. $20. David L. Greene, Ed. & Pub., Box 398, Demorest, GA 30535-0398. TEL 206-865-6440. bk.rev.; index. circ. 1,650. (also avail. in microform from UMI; reprint service avail. from UMI) **Indexed:** Geneal.Per.Ind. **Document type:** academic/scholarly publication.
—BLDSC (0816.200000); UnCover; UMI.
Formerly (until 1932): New Haven Genealogical Magazine.
Description: Documented analyses of genealogical problems. Includes short compiled genealogies.
Refereed Serial

929 CN
AMIS DE L'HISTOIRE DE LA PERADE. COLLECTION "NOS VIEILLES FAMILLES". (Text in French) no.2, 1973. irreg. Can.$3.90. Amis de l'Histoire de la Perade, Case Postale 157, Ste.-Anne de la Perade, Que. G0X 2J0, Canada. illus. circ. 1,000. **Document type:** monographic series.

929 AT ISSN 0044-8222
CS2008.V53
ANCESTOR. 1961. q. Aus.$33 (effective June 1993). Genealogical Society of Victoria, Inc., 5th Fl., Curtin House, 252 Swanston St., Melbourne, Vic. 3000, Australia. TEL 03-663-7033. Ed. Joy Roy. adv.; bk.rev. circ. 6,000.
Description: Contains articles and titbits on tracing family history, genealogy and heraldry which generally include reproductions of old documents and photographs.

929 US ISSN 0736-9115
F497.A73
ANCESTOR HUNT; gateway to the western reserve. 1973. q. $10 membership. Ashtabula County Genealogical Society, Inc., Henderson Library, 54 E. Jefferson St., Jefferson, OH 44047. Ed. Marion Holmes. bk.rev. circ. 310.
Description: Devoted to genealogical material relating to Ashtabula County.

929 US ISSN 0272-0426
CS1
ANCESTORING. 1980. s-a. $25. Augusta Genealogical Society, Inc., Box 3743, Augusta, GA 30904. TEL 404-738-2241. Ed. Carrie M. Adamson. abstr.; bibl.; illus.; stat. circ. 1,400. (back issues avail.) **Indexed:** Geneal.Per.Ind.
—UnCover.

929 US
ANCESTORS - DESCENDANTS OF FUTRAL - CLIFFORD, WATKINS - WOOD; with allied families: Boyd, Echolas, Gay, Glass, Henry, McClanahan, McClurkin, McDaniel, Pinson, Reynolds, Smith. 1978. s-a. $15. Futral Genealogy Trails, Rt. 2, Box 427B, Carthage, TN 37030. TEL 615-735-0093. Ed. Jenny Futral. bk.rev. circ. 20. (back issues avail.) **Document type:** newsletter.
Description: Contains family information as contributed with writers' permission.

929 US ISSN 0734-4988
F868.S23
ANCESTORS WEST. 1974. q. $10. Santa Barbara County Genealogical Society, Box 1303, Santa Barbara, CA 93116. TEL 805-967-8954. Ed. Beatrice McGrath. adv.; bk.rev. circ. 450. (back issues avail.)

929 AT ISSN 0313-251X
CS2000
ANCESTRAL SEARCHER. 1976. q. Aus.$30. Heraldry and Genealogy Society of Canberra, Inc., G.P.O. Box 585, Canberra, A.C.T. 2601, Australia. TEL 06-295-1141. Ed. June McKenzie. adv.; bk.rev. circ. 1,300. (back issues avail.) **Document type:** newsletter.

929 US
ANCESTRY. 1966. q. $15. Palm Beach County Genealogical Society, Inc., Box 1746, W. Palm Beach, FL 33402. TEL 407-832-3279. Ed.Bd. adv.; bk.rev.; bibl.; index. circ. 400. (back issues avail.) **Indexed:** Geneal.Per.Ind. **Document type:** bulletin.
Description: Covers topics relating to Florida and Palm Beach genealogy.

929 US ISSN 0749-5927
CS1
ANCESTRY NEWSLETTER. 1983. bi-m. $18. Ancestry, Box 476, Salt Lake City, UT 84110-0476. TEL 801-531-1790. Ed. Loretto Szucs. adv. circ. 9,500. **Document type:** newsletter.
Description: Presents historical and how-to genealogical research techniques.

929 CN ISSN 0316-0513
L'ANCETRE. 1974. m. (10/yr.). Can.$25 (foreign $30). Societe de Genealogie de Quebec, C.P. 9066, Ste-Foy, PQ G1V 4A8, Canada. TEL 418-651-9127. Ed. Jacques Saintonge. bk.rev. circ. 1,100. **Document type:** bulletin.

929.9 GW
ANDERUNGEN UN ERGAENZUNGEN. a. World Vexillological Research Institute, Postfact 200 828, 53138 Bonn, Germany. Ed. Roman Klimes.

GENEALOGY AND HERALDRY

929   US   ISSN 0889-1680
ANSON NEWSLETTER. 1986. q. $12. 789 Rt. 44-55, Highland, NY 12528. TEL 914-883-6118. Ed. Shirley V. Anson. adv.; bk.rev. circ. 90. (looseleaf format; back issues avail.) **Document type:** newsletter.

ANTIQUEWEEK - CENTRAL. see *ANTIQUES*

ANTIQUEWEEK - EASTERN EDITION; weekly antique, auction & collectors' newspaper. see *ANTIQUES*

929
ANY AMSBAUGH ANCESTORS?. 1986. irreg. $5 per vol. Ancestor Seminar Library, c/o Sally Seaman Williams, Ed., Box 1035, N. Highlands, CA 95660-1035. TEL 916-991-4165. circ. 50. (back issues avail.)
Description: Covers genealogy and history of any Amsbaugh family (and spelling variations).

929   US   ISSN 1041-8466
APPALACHIAN FAMILIES. 1988. q. $15. Mountain Press (Signal Mountain), Box 400, Signal Mountain, TN 37377-0400. TEL 615-886-6369. Ed. James L. Douthat. adv.; bk.rev. circ. 350.
Description: Traces migration patterns of families moving around the mid-Atlantic states.

929   US   ISSN 0888-6814
APPALACHIAN ROOTS. 1983. m. $16. Box 4004, Parkersburg, WV 26104. TEL 304-489-2325. Ed. Mary Jo Brown. adv.; bk.rev. circ. 450. (looseleaf format; back issues avail.) **Document type:** newsletter.
Description: Features source reviews, meeting notices, and questions and answers, of interest to family and professional historians of the Appalachian area of the U.S.

929   US   ISSN 0736-0800
APPLELAND BULLETIN. 1972. q. $10 membership; libraries $7.50. Genealogical Society of North Central Washington, Box 5280, Wenatchee, WA 98807-5280. TEL 509-664-5989. bk.rev.; index. circ. 212. (back issues avail.) **Indexed:** Geneal.Per.Ind. **Document type:** bulletin.
Description: Historical information, research notes, abstracts of marriage and cemetery records, and bible records pertaining to the genealogies of local families in North Central Washington State.

929   US   ISSN 1047-689X
APPLER FAMILY NEWSLETTER. 1982. q. $6. 10417 New Bedford Ct. S.E., Lehigh Acres, FL 33936-7253. TEL 813-368-6373. (Alt. addr. (June - Oct.): Box 1897 Hillsbord, NH 03244-1897) circ. 130. (back issues avail.) **Document type:** newsletter.
Description: Covers family history of past and present generations including births, marriages, deaths, and family achievements.

ARCHAEOLOGIA. see *ARCHAEOLOGY*

929   GW   ISSN 0003-9470
CS680
ARCHIV OSTDEUTSCHER FAMILIENFORSCHER. 1952. bi-m. DM.65. Arbeitsgemeinschaft Ostdeutscher Familienforscher e.V., c/o Heike Brachwitz, Am Muehlenhof 5, 26180 Rastede, Germany. TEL 04402-81662. Ed. Rolf Brachwitz. illus.; index. circ. 1,100.

929   US
AREA FOOTPRINTS. 1978. s-a. $17 (effective Jan. 1991). Genealogical Society of Butler County, Inc., Box 426, Poplar Bluff, MO 63901. TEL 314-686-8426. Ed. Helen Sparkman. bk.rev. circ. 100.
Description: The purpose of preserving and making available the genealogical records of Butler Co. and surrounding area of S.E. Missouri and N.E. Arkansas.

929   US   ISSN 1067-8638
F265.S3
ARGYLL COLONY PLUS. 1986. 3/yr. $25 membership. North Carolina Scottish Heritage Society, c/o Glenn H. McGugan, Treas., 1235 E. Hedgelawn Way, Southern Pines, NC 28387. Ed. Victor Clark. bk.rev.
Description: Genealogical information and historical items on the Scots in North Carolina and their descendants.

929   US   ISSN 0571-0472
F410
ARKANSAS FAMILY HISTORIAN. 1962. q. $15. Arkansas Genealogical Society, Inc., Box 908, Hot Springs, AR 71902-0908. Ed. Margaret Harrison Hubbard. bk.rev.; index. circ. 1,600. (also avail. in microfiche) **Document type:** bulletin.

929   US
ARKANSAS HISTORICAL AND GENEALOGICAL MAGAZINE. 1988. bi-m. $12. Professional Genealogists of Arkansas, Inc., Box 1807, Conway, AR 72032. TEL 501-470-1120. Ed. Desmond Walls Allen. index; circ. 678 (paid). **Document type:** academic/scholarly publication, newsletter.
Formerly (until 1994): Professional Genealogists of Arkansas Newsletter (ISSN 1040-4430)
Description: Publishes scholarly material on genealogy and historical research, with particular emphasis on Arkansas and the Southern U.S.

929   SA   ISSN 0004-2145
ARMA. 1958. q. $10. Heraldry Society of Southern Africa, P.O. Box 44245, Claremont 7735, South Africa. Ed. C. Pama. adv.; bk.rev. circ. 200. **Indexed:** Ind.S.A.Per., Resour.Ctr.Ind.

ARMAS E TROFEUS; revista de historia, heraldica, genealogia e arte. see *HISTORY — History Of Europe*

929.6   US
ARMIGER'S NEWS. 1979. q. $25 to individuals; libraries $10 (effective 1992). American College of Heraldry, Inc., Drawer CG, Tuscaloosa, AL 35486-2870. Ed. Thomas Paul Westgaard. adv.; bk.rev.; illus.; circ. 250 (paid). (looseleaf format; also avail. in microfiche; back issues avail.) **Document type:** newsletter.
Description: Contains news related to heraldry, coats of arms borne in the Americas and biographies of the Armigers.

929   BE
ARMORIAL FRANCAIS; ou repertoire alphabetique des notices des familles nobles, patriciennes bourgeoises de France. 1977. q. 330 Fr. per no. 2 rue Emmanuel Hiel, 1030 Brussels, Belgium. Ed. J.H. Willems. bibl.

929   US
ARMSTRONG BULLETIN BOARD. 1986. q. $6. c/o Fred Field, Ed. & Pub., 1516 Avenida Selva, Fullerton, CA 92633-1531. TEL 714-871-5767. circ. 160 (paid). **Document type:** bulletin.

ARMSTRONG NEWS. see *ETHNIC INTERESTS*

929   US   ISSN 0890-4014
ARNOLD ANCESTRY. 1986. q. $7.50. Kinseeker Publications, Box 184, Grawn, MI 49637. Ed. Victoria Wilson. bk.rev. circ. 80. (looseleaf format; back issues avail.) **Document type:** newsletter.

929   US   ISSN 0749-517X
F392.F7
AROUND THE BEND. 1981. q. membership. Fort Bend County Genealogical Society, Box 274, Richmond, TX 77469-0274. Ed. Bitsy Barr. bk.rev.; index. circ. 100.

929   US   ISSN 0004-4377
ASHTREE ECHO. 1966. s-a. $12 (effective 1993). Fresno Genealogical Society, Box 1429, Fresno, CA 93716-1429. adv.; bk.rev.; index. circ. 240. (processed) **Document type:** newsletter.

929   UK   ISSN 0261-8850
ASPECTS OF EDENBRIDGE. 1980. irreg. £0.95 per no. Edenbridge and District Historical Society, c/o J. Willsmer, Little Hatch, Crouch House Rd., Edenbridge TN8 5EL, England. illus.; charts.

ASSOCIATION FOR GRAVESTONE STUDIES. NEWSLETTER. see *ART*

929   US
ASSOCIATION OF PROFESSIONAL GENEALOGISTS QUARTERLY. 1979. q. $35. Association of Professional Genealogists, 3421 M St. N.W., Ste. 236, Washington, DC 20007. TEL 504-766-3018. Ed. Sharon DeBartolo Carmack. adv.; bk.rev.; abstr.; bibl. circ. 700. **Document type:** academic/scholarly publication.
—UnCover.
Former titles (until 1991): A P G Quarterly (ISSN 0890-3816); A P G Newsletter; Supersedes (1975-1979, vol.5, no.3): Professional Genealogists News Bulletin.

ATLANTIC COUNTY HISTORICAL SOCIETY YEARBOOK. see *HISTORY — History Of North And South America*

929   US
ATWOOD ANCESTORS. 4/yr. $5. c/o Claudette Maerz, Ed., Box 37010, Bloomington, MN 55431. index.

929.9   US   ISSN 0004-7988
AUGUSTAN. q. Augustan Society, Box P, Torrence, CA 90507.

929   US
AUGUSTAN SOCIETY NEWSLETTER. irreg. membership. Augustan Society, Inc., Box P, Torrance, CA 90508. TEL 310-320-7766. Ed. Rodney Hartwell. **Document type:** newsletter.

929   US
AUGUSTAN SOCIETY OMNIBUS; an international journal of history, genealogy & heraldry. (Text in English) 1957. q. $40. Augustan Society, Inc., Box P, Torrance, CA 90508. TEL 310-320-7766. Ed. Rodney Hartwell. adv.; bk.rev.; charts; illus.; cum.index: 1959-1975. circ. 2,000. (back issues avail.) **Indexed:** Geneal.Per.Ind. **Document type:** academic/scholarly publication.
Former titles: Agustan Society Information Bulletin; Forbears Augustan (ISSN 0004-7988); Incorporates: Royalty and Monarchy; Genealogical Library Journal; Colonial Genealogist; English Genealogist (ISSN 0145-6059); Which was formerly: English Genealogist Helper (ISSN 0361-7157); Incorporates: Germanic Genealogist (ISSN 0363-9169); Which was formerly: Germanic Genealogist Helper (ISSN 0361-3062); Incorporates: Heraldry; Chivalry.

929 920 374   US
AUSTIN GENEALOGICAL SOCIETY QUARTERLY. 1960. q. $15 to individuals; families $17. Austin Genealogical Society, Box 1507, Austin, TX 78767-1507. Ed. William M. Koehler. bk.rev.; charts; index. circ. 500. **Indexed:** Geneal.Per.Ind.

929   AT
▼**AUSTRALASIAN FEDERATION OF FAMILY HISTORY. NEWSLETTER.** 1992. s-a? Australasian Federation of Family History, 120 Kent St., Sydney, N.S.W. 2000, Australia.

929 296   US   ISSN 0882-6501
DS101
AVOTAYNU. 1985. 4/yr. $24 in US and Canada; elsewhere $32. Avotaynu Inc., Box 900, Teaneck, NJ 07666. TEL 201-837-8300. FAX 201-837-6272. Ed. Sallyann Admur Sack. adv.; bk.rev. circ. 2,000. (back issues avail.) **Document type:** academic/scholarly publication.
—UnCover.
Description: International review of Jewish genealogy. Correspondents in 16 countries regularly contribute articles of interest to persons tracing their Jewish family history.

929   US   ISSN 0094-6915
F410
BACKTRACKER. 1971. q. $10 (effective 1993). Northwest Arkansas Genealogical Society, Box 796, Rogers, AR 72757. Ed. George Crabtree. bk.rev.; bibl.; charts; circ. 400 (paid).
—UnCover.
Description: Aid to genealogical research in Benton, Carroll, Madison and Washington Counties, Arkansas.

929   US   ISSN 8756-7237
CS71
BALL BEGINNINGS.* 1984. 3/yr. $12. Claudette Maerz, Pub., Box 3101C, Bloomington, MN 55431.

GENEALOGY AND HERALDRY

929.9   SP   ISSN 0213-0955
BANDERAS. q. 2000 ptas.($20) Sociedad Espanola de Vexilologia, Mineria, 17, 3-9, 08004 Barcelona, Spain. Eds. Adolfo Duran Rodriguez, Sebastian Herreros Agui.

929   UK   ISSN 0140-8623
BANYAN TREE. 1977. q. £5 to members; non-members 75p each. East Yorkshire Family History Society, 5 Ryde St., Hull, N. Humberside, England. Ed. S. Dixon. adv.; bk.rev. circ. 1,000.

929   US
BAREFOOT PRINTS. 1991. q. Drawer D, Gilcrest, CO 80623. TEL 303-737-2692. Ed. Rex K. Barefoot. circ. 55. (looseleaf format)
   Description: Information on the Barefoot family and its history.

929   US
BARKER-JOSLYN FAMILY TREE CLIMBER. irreg. Jonathan Bacon, Ed.& Pub., 9615 England, Overland Park, KS 66212. TEL 913-383-9116. circ. 150.

929   US   ISSN 1062-6859
BARNES BULLETIN 2.0. 1986. irreg. $7 per no. K A R D Files, 19305 S.E. 243rd Pl., Kent, WA 98042-4820. TEL 206-432-1659. Ed. Judy K. Dye. adv.; bk.rev.; stat. (back issues avail.) **Document type:** bulletin.
   Formerly (until 1992): Barnes Bulletin.

929   US   ISSN 0888-4625
CS71
BARNETT SOURCE.* 1986. q. $12. Craig Junction Publishers, c/o Marsha Wilson Bovey, Ed., Box 310, Craigmont, ID 83523-0310. TEL 208-924-5740. bk.rev.; index. circ. 100. (back issues avail.)

929   US   ISSN 0899-1367
CS71
BARRETT BRANCHES. 1982. irreg. $7.25 per no. McNeill Enterprises, Box 779, Napavine, WA 98565-0779. TEL 509-922-4521. adv.; bk.rev. circ. 75. (back issues avail.)
   Description: Miscellaneous data on the surname, including bible records, wills, marriage records, county histories, census records, family records, and obituaries; accepts lineage sheets from families for permanent recording.

929   US   ISSN 0882-8202
CS71
BARRON FAMILY NEWSLETTER. 1975. irreg. (6/vol.) $17 (effective 1994). (Barron Family Association) Family Heritage Publications, 11475 Holiday Way, Hillsboro, OH 45133-9368. TEL 513-393-3925. Ed. William P. Barron, Jr. adv.; bk.rev. circ. 50. **Indexed:** Geneal.Per.Ind. **Document type:** newsletter.
   Description: Aims to further family history research and foster preservation of that history.

929   US
BARTHMES FAMILY ASSOCIATION; dedicated to the search for descendants of the Barthmes family. 1984. q. $7 includes membership. Barthmes Family Association, Inc., Box 954, Bridgeport, CA 93517-0954. TEL 916-495-2775. FAX 916-495-2320. Ed. Brenda Musil. adv. circ. 175.

929 978   US
BARTON COUNTY GENEALOGICAL SOCIETY. QUARTERLY. 1980. q. $12.50. Barton County Genealogical Society, Inc., Box 425, Great Bend, KS 67530. Ed. Karen P. Neuforth. bk.rev. circ. 60. **Indexed:** Geneal.Per.Ind. **Document type:** newsletter.
   Formerly: Barton County Genealogical Society. Newsletter.

929   US
BATEMAN DATUM. 1980. a. $3. Bateman Family Association, Box 211, Lebo Rt., West Plains, MO 65775. Ed. Mary Jo Burroughs. bk.rev. circ. 50.

929   GW   ISSN 0005-7118
BAYERISCHER LANDESVEREIN FUER FAMILIENKUNDE. BLAETTER. 1923-1942; N.S. 1958. a. DM.39. Bayerischer Landesverein fuer Familienkunde e.V., Ludwigstr.14, 80539 Munich, Germany. TEL 028638-398. bk.rev. circ. 1,000.
   —CCC.

929   US
THE BEALL NEWS. 1991. q. $10. Beall Family Association, 326 S.E. 82nd Ave., Portland, OR 97216. Ed. William Ryland Beall, III.
   Description: Publishes new research and corrections to the printed record regarding families with the Beale surname (including variations), as well as genealogical queries and other information.

929   US
BEAN STALK.* q. membership. Southern Bean Association, c/o Hood, 114 Crossline Ln., Florence, AL 35633.

929   US
BEECH GROVE; newsletter of Familie Hagenbuch. 1982. s-a. $4. Hagenbuch Press, 821 W. Siddonsburg Rd., Dillsburg, PA 17019. TEL 717-432-8911. Ed. Mark O. Hagenbuch. circ. 100. (looseleaf format; back issues avail.) **Document type:** newsletter.
   Description: Past, present and future information on Hagenbuch and allied families.

929   GW   ISSN 0067-5261
BEITRAEGE ZUR WESTFAELISCHEN FAMILIENFORSCHUNG. irreg. price varies. (Westfaelische Gesellschaft fuer Genealogie und Familienforschung) Aschendorffsche Verlagsbuchhandlung, Soesterstr. 13, 48155 Muenster, Germany. TEL 0251-690-0. FAX 0251-690143. Ed. Werner Frese. bk.rev. **Document type:** monographic series.
   —BLDSC (1887.560000).

929.6 976   US
BELCHER BULLETIN. 1986. m. $20 (foreign $25). (Belcher History Center) Belcher Bulletin, Inc., Box 10, Belcher, KY 41513. Ed. Fon R. Belcher. bk.rev.; illus. **Indexed:** Geneal.Per.Ind. **Document type:** bulletin.
   Description: Features history and biography of Belcher family in America, Nova Scotia, and Great Britain.

BELGIAN LACE. see *ETHNIC INTERESTS*

929   US   ISSN 1041-231X
CS71
BELL CHIMES; published for Bells, their relatives, and descendants. 1980. bi-m. $15. Clan Bell Descendants, Inc., Box 451, Springfield, VT 05156. TEL 802-885-3151. Ed. Irving Bell. adv.; bk.rev.; illus. circ. 828. **Document type:** newsletter.
   Description: Published for Bells whose ancestors were believed to have been born in Great Britain. Includes news, features, queries, genealogies.

BEND OF THE RIVER; the magazine of the historic Maumee Valley. see *HISTORY — History Of North And South America*

929   US   ISSN 0884-6510
CS71.B469a
BENNETT EXCHANGE. 1980. q. $10.50. Beverly Bennett Baumann, Ed. & Pub., 17 Breeman St., Albany, NY 12205-4928. TEL 518-869-5260. bibl.; charts. circ. 120. (looseleaf format; back issues avail.) **Document type:** newsletter.
   Description: Objective is to establish connections in the Bennett family branches.

929   US
BERKS COUNTY GENEALOGICAL SOCIETY. JOURNAL. 1980. q. $15. Berks County Genealogical Society, Box 14774, Reading, PA 19612. Ed.Bd. adv.; bk.rev.; index. circ. 950. (also avail. in microfiche)

929   US
BERMUDA BEACON; a quarterly for people of Bermuda ancestry. 1983. q. $4. 564 Poppy Ln., Santa Maria, CA 93455. TEL 805-937-4406. Ed. Alva M. Hamilton. charts; index. circ. 100. (back issues avail.)
   Description: Covers family histories, excerpts of Bermuda wills, pedigree and family tree charts.

BERNER ZEITSCHRIFT FUER GESCHICHTE UND HEIMATKUNDE. see *HISTORY — History Of Europe*

929   US
BEST NEST.* 1981. s-a. $3. Best Family Genealogical Society, 628 US Hwy. 12 E, Garrison, MT 59731-9704. Ed. Joan Best. bk.rev.

929   US
BIRDSALL BULLETIN. 1984. 3/yr. $12. Birdsall-Birdsell Family Association, Box 11154, Greenwich, CT 06831. Ed. Barbara Kollhoff. circ. 32.

929   US
BISHOP GET-TOGETHER NEWSLETTER. vol.3, 1986. 4/yr. c/o William G. Bishop, Jr., 1329 Lakeview Dr., Virginia Beach, VA 23455. circ. 300.

929   UK
BLACK COUNTRY BUGLE. 1972. m. £15.95. Mercia Publicity, Bugle House, 41 High St., Cradley Heath, Warley, West Midlands B64 5HL, England. TEL 0384-67678. FAX 0384-410045. Ed. H. Taylor. adv.; bk.rev. circ. 53,000. **Document type:** newsletter.
   Description: Anglo-Saxon heritage publication with regular emphasis on trans-Atlantic links between American citizens today, and their ancestral connections with 19th-century pioneers of English stock. Includes the back-tracking of family trees in Europe for subscribers.

929   US   ISSN 1056-6953
BLAIR COUNTY GENEALOGICAL SOCIETY. NEWSLETTER. 1981. q. membership. Blair County Genealogical Society, Inc., Box 855, Altoona, PA 16603-0855. TEL 814-942-3681. Ed. William R. Anslinger. index. circ. 500. **Document type:** newsletter.

929   US
BOGGS NEWSLETTER QUARTERLY.* 1978. q. $17. 1421 Chablis Ct., N., Orange Park, FL 32073-5209. Ed. R.J. Boggs. adv. circ. 125.

929   US   ISSN 0743-0957
CS71
BONNET-T-E'S AND KIN. 1973. irreg. donation basis. Howard E. Bonnett, Ed.& Pub., 314 E. Glenwood Road, Lake Forest, IL 60045. TEL 708-234-4804. circ. 450. **Document type:** newsletter.

929   US   ISSN 0733-6764
BORGO FAMILY HISTORIES. 1983. irreg., no.3, 1993. price varies. Borgo Press, Box 2845, San Bernardino, CA 92406. TEL 909-884-5813. FAX 909-888-4942. Ed. Michael Burgess.
   Description: Genealogies, compendia, census indexes, and family records.

929   US   ISSN 0885-1247
BORN YOUNG NEWSLETTER. 1984. q. $10. Vicki Young Albu, Ed. & Pub., 347 12th Ave., N., S. St. Paul, MN 55075-1957. TEL 612-455-3626. adv.; bk.rev.; abstr.; illus.; index. circ. 250. (looseleaf format; back issues avail.) **Document type:** newsletter.
   Description: Information exchange for genealogists researching ancestors named Young, Jung, Yonge.

929   US
BOURLAND - BULLETIN. vol.2, 1978. q. $15. Bourland - Society, Rt. 3, Box 5206, Galena, MO 65656. TEL 417-538-4133. bk.rev.; illus. circ. 500. **Document type:** newsletter.
   Former titles: Bourland - Loving Bulletin; Bourland Bulletin - Loving Letter; Bourland Bulletin.

929   US
BOYER ROOTS. a. membership. Association of American Boyers, Inc., Box 1547, Frederick, MD 21702.

929   US
BOYLE FAMILY LETTER.* 1983. q. $10 (foreign $12.50). Joan Semona Boyle, Ed. & Pub., R.R. 3, Box 136 ., Stover, MO 65078-9420. TEL 314-671-4265. circ. 100.

929   US   ISSN 1045-862X
BOZARTH BEACON. 1985. q. $10. Bozarth Beacon, 38518 Kickbush Ln., Springfield, OR 97478-9641. TEL 503-746-9736. Ed. Gayle Mark. bk.rev. circ. 126. (back issues avail.) **Document type:** newsletter.
   Description: Promotes research involving Bozarth family lines.

929   NE   ISSN 0006-8632
DE BRABANTSE LEEUW. 1950. 4/yr. fl.42.50. Noordbrabants Genootschap, P.O. Box 1104, 5200 BD 's-Hertogenbosch, Netherlands. TEL 31-73-139484. Ed. L. Adriaenssen. bk.rev. circ. 600.
   —SWETS.
   Description: Articles on genealogy, heraldry and onomastics regarding families rooted mainly in the northern port of the duchy of Brabant, a province of the Netherlands.

GENEALOGY AND HERALDRY

929 US ISSN 0892-9238
BRADFORD COMPACT NEWSLETTER. 1946. a. $8 (effective 1991). Governor William Bradford Compact, 5204 Kenwood Ave., Chevy Chase, MD 20815-6604. TEL 301-654-7233. (Subscr. to: Herbert Giffin, Treas., 3712 Harrison St., N.W., Washington, DC 20015) Ed. John M. Pogue. circ. 570 (paid).
Description: Informs on meetings, current events, new books, projects, genealogical and other information on members. Includes essays, artwork, photographs, news notes and a president's letter.

929 US
BRADSHAW - BRATCHER QUARTERLY.* q. $20. Genealogical & Historical News, c/o Robert Bradshaw, Box 779, Saipan, CM 96950, Mariana Islands.
Formerly: Bradshaw - Bratcher Letter.

929 US ISSN 0742-9851
BRANCHES AND TWIGS. 1972. q. $20 (effective Oct. 1994). Genealogical Society of Vermont, RFD 3, Box 986, Putney, VT 05346. TEL 802-387-5797. Ed. Mrs. Lloyd E. Church. bk.rev.; circ. 11,300 (paid). **Document type:** bulletin.
—UnCover.

929 US
BRANCHES OF BERKS. 4/yr. $15 to individuals; families $20 (includes B C G S Journal). Berks County Genealogical Society, Box 14774, Reading, PA 19612.

929 US ISSN 1044-5552
BRASHEAR FAMILY BRANCHES. 1985. m. 817 Stratford Dr., Bedford, TX 76021-5321. TEL 817-268-1581. Ed. Arzella Brashear Spear. circ. 128. (looseleaf format; back issues avail.) **Document type:** newsletter.

929 US
BRASWELL BRANCHES. q. $12. Nona Williams, Ed. & Pub., Box 225, Ben Lomond, CA 95005. TEL 408-475-3114. adv.; bk.rev. (also avail. in microfiche) **Document type:** newsletter.

929 US
BRAY NOSTALGIA. 3/yr. $10. Box 325, Elwood, NE 68937. TEL 308-785-2046. Ed. Cheryl L. Clark.

929 US ISSN 0743-8958
CS71
BRIDGE BUILDER. 1968. s-a. $7.50 (includes Newsletter). Pontius Family Association, 2009 Garden Dr., Niskayuna, NY 12309-2309. TEL 518-374-1965. FAX 518-374-4453. (Subscr. to: Janet E. Pontius, Sec., 126 Maplewood Estates, Scott Depot, WV 25560-9744. TEL 304-757-6361) Ed. James W. Pontius. charts; illus.; index; circ. 380 (paid). (back issues avail.)
Description: Dedicated to research, education and preservation of family history and genealogy.

929 CN ISSN 0840-7738
BRIDGING THE GAP. 1988. irreg. (4-6/yr.). Can.$16.05($15.50) Highland Heritage, c/o Alex W. Fraser, Alington Rd. R.R.1, Lancaster, Ont. K0C 1N0, Canada. TEL 613-347-2363. Ed. Rhoda Ross. adv.; bk.rev. circ. 100. (looseleaf format; back issues avail.)
Description: Covers genealogy, local history, book notices and queries.

929 US
BRINGIN' HOME THE BACON. 1981. irreg. Jonathan Bacon Ed.& Pub., 9615 England, Overhead Park, KS 66212. TEL 913-383-9116. circ. 150.

929 UK ISSN 0308-4183
BRISTOL AND AVON FAMILY HISTORY SOCIETY. JOURNAL. 1975. q. £4 membership. Bristol and Avon Family History Society, 29 High St., Staple Hill, Bristol BS16 4HB, England. Ed. Ian Haddrell. adv.; bk.rev. circ. 1,200.
Description: Official publication of the Bristol and Avon History Society, research into family history, society news.

929 CN ISSN 0229-527X
BRITISH COLUMBIA GENEALOGICAL SOCIETY. NEWSLETTER. vol.3, 1978. q. Can.$30 to individuals; seniors Can.$20; studenst Can.$15. British Columbia Genealogical Society, Box 88054, Richmond, BC V6X 3T6, Canada. **Document type:** newsletter.
—UnCover.

929 CN ISSN 0315-3835
CS88.B74
BRITISH COLUMBIA GENEALOGIST. 1971. q. Can.$30 to individuals; seniors Can.$15; students Can.$15. British Columbia Genealogical Society, Box 88054, Richmond, BC V6X 3T6, Canada. bk.rev.; charts. circ. 900.
—UnCover.

929 US
BROOKS FAMILY QUERY EXCHANGE.* q. Brooks Family Historical Society and Library, c/o Karen D. Rocher, Ed., 2902 Rocher Rd., Ft. Scott, KS 66701.

929 US
CS71
BROWN FAMILY NEWS & GENEOLOGICAL SOCIETY; a genealogical triannual on the surname Brown. 1972. q. $5. Tactical Edge, Inc., 19 Terrace St., Keene, NH 03431. Ed. Hal Gordon Brown. adv.; bk.rev.; index. circ. 250. (looseleaf format)
Formerly: Brown Family (ISSN 0147-0019)

929 US ISSN 1044-856X
BROYLES FAMILY NEWSLETTER. 1982. 6/yr. $12. c/o John K. Broyles, Sr., Ed., Rt. 3, Box 178, Clinton, TN 37716. TEL 615-457-5866. adv.; bk.rev. circ. 135. (reprint service avail.) **Document type:** newsletter.

929 US
BRYAN COUNTY HERITAGE ASSOCIATION QUARTERLY. 1984. q. $12.50. Bryan County Heritage Association, Inc., Box 153, Calera, OK 74730. TEL 405-434-5848. Ed. Marie Hawthorne. (back issues avail.)
Description: To preserve yesterday for tomorrow.

929 974 US ISSN 1047-2770
BUCKS COUNTY GENEALOGICAL SOCIETY. NEWSLETTER. 1981. q. $12. Bucks County Genealogical Society, Box 1092, Doylestown, PA 18901. circ. 750. **Document type:** newsletter.
Description: To promote and encourage the study of genealogy and family history in the Bucks County area by providing educational opportunities through meetings, workshops, seminars, publications and other educational programs.

929 US
BULLRUSH. 1985. q. membership. Innes Clan Society, 129 Ravenna Dr., Long Beach, CA 90803. TEL 310-438-6331. Ed. Joseph J. Innes. charts; illus.; circ. 200 (controlled). **Document type:** newsletter.
Formerly: Innes Clan Society Newsletter.
Description: Disseminates historical information about clan Innes and the current activities of the society.

929 US
BURKE JOURNAL. vol.10, no.3, 1992. q. membership. Burke County Genealogical Society, Box 661, Morgantown, NC 28680-0661.

928 UK
BURKE'S FAMILY INDEX. 1976. irreg. £9.50. Burke's Peerage, 205 St. John's Hill, Battersea, London SW11 1TH, England. TEL 071-924-5132. FAX 071-978-5732. Ed. Hugh Montgomery-Massingberd.

929 UK
BURKE'S ROYAL FAMILIES OF THE WORLD. VOL. 2: AFRICA AND THE MIDDLE EAST. 1979. irreg. £47.50. Burke's Peerage, 205 St. John's Hill, Battersea, London SW11 1TH, England. TEL 071-924-5132. FAX 071-978-5732. Ed. H. Montgomery-Massingberd.

929 US ISSN 0730-4978
CS71
BURNETT FAMILY NEWSLETTER. 1981. q. $15 (foreign $20). Burnett Family Genealogical Association, Inc., 3891 Commander Dr., Chamblee, GA 30341-0016. TEL 404-455-6445. Ed. Thomas R. Burnett. bk.rev.; index. circ. 100. (looseleaf format; also avail. in microform; audio cassette; back issues avail.) **Document type:** newsletter.

929 US ISSN 1071-0523
BUSH - MEETING DUTCH; a quarterly newsletter of local history and genealogy of the former Evangelical United Brethren Church, its predecessors and sister churches. 1984. q. $5. c/o David Koss, Ed., Illinois College, Jacksonville, IL 62650. TEL 217-245-3460. bk.rev. circ. 60. (looseleaf format; back issues avail.) **Document type:** newsletter.

929 US ISSN 1054-9560
BUSHONG BULLETIN. 1985. q. $10. c/o Carol Willsey Bell, Ed., 4649 Yarmouth Ln., Youngstown, OH 44512. TEL 216-782-8380. (Subscr. to: J.W. Bushong, 504 E. 52nd St., Odessa, TX 79762) index. circ. 100. (looseleaf format; back issues avail.) **Document type:** bulletin.
Description: Genealogical research on the Bushong family.

929 US ISSN 1058-5133
F865
C G S NEWS. (Supplement to: The Nugget (ISSN 1059-9711)) vol.18, 1987. bi-m. $30. California Genealogical Society, 300 Brannan St., Ste. 409, Box 77105, San Francisco, CA 94107-0105. TEL 415-777-9936. Ed. Jan Keiser. adv. circ. 750. (looseleaf format; back issues avail.) **Document type:** newsletter.
Formerly: California Genealogical Society. Newsletter (ISSN 8756-694X)
Description: Covers past and forthcoming events, library acquisitions, and current genealogical news.

929 US ISSN 0899-1375
CS71
CAIN CONNECTIONS. 1982. irreg. $7.25 per no. McNeill Enterprises, Box 79, Napavine, WA 98565-0779. TEL 509-922-4521. circ. 50. (back issues avail.)
Description: Miscellaneous data on branches of the surname, including bible records, marriage records, county histories, census records, family records, wills, and obituaries; accepts lineage sheets from families for permanent recording.

929 US ISSN 0895-8939
F187.C15
CALVERT COUNTY GENEALOGY NEWSLETTER. 1985. m. $12. Calvert County Genealogical Society, Box 9, Sunderland, MD 20689. TEL 410-535-0839. Ed. Mildred O'Brien. adv.; bk.rev. circ. 150. (looseleaf format; back issues avail.) **Document type:** newsletter.

929 US ISSN 1055-1018
CAMPBELL CONTACTS IN AMERICA. 1979. q. $15. 416 JF Townline Rd., Rt. 8, Janesville, WI 53545. TEL 608-756-2495 Ed. Chris A. Campbell. bk.rev.; index, cum.index: 1979-1992 (vol.1-11). circ. 325. (looseleaf format; back issues avail.) **Document type:** newsletter.
Description: Publishes all forms of Campbell surname genealogical information from early America. Maintains regis & tree compiler database of Campbell surname genealogical data.

929 US
CANFIELD FAMILY ASSOCIATION. PUBLICATION. 1982. q. $8 to individuals (foreign $14); libraries $4. Canfield Family Association, 1144 N. Gordon, Wichita, KS 67203-6611. TEL 316-942-7120. Ed. Genevieve (Canfield) Martinson. circ. 130.
Description: Articles dealing with persons named Canfield, family charts, queries, vital records, census records, and Bible records.

929 US ISSN 0885-4718
F127.A3
THE CAPITAL. 1986. q. $14 (typically set in Oct.). Valley Quarterlies, c/o Arthur Kelly, Ed., 60 Cedar Heights Rd., Rhinebeck, NY 12572. TEL 914-876-4592. bk.rev.; index. circ. 150. (back issues avail.) **Document type:** monographic series.

929 US ISSN 1057-9435
CAROLINA HERALD AND NEWSLETTER. 1972. q. $10. South Carolina Genealogical Society, P.O. Box 492, SC 29202-0492. TEL 803-276-8209. Ed. Glenda Bundrick. bk.rev. circ. 3,000. (back issues avail.)
Formerly: Carolina Herald (ISSN 0736-3400)
Description: Aims to raise standards of genealogical research in South Carolina and promote the preservation of early records.

929 US ISSN 0363-440X
F253
CAROLINAS GENEALOGICAL SOCIETY. BULLETIN. (Yearbook avail.) 1964. q. $15 to individuals; families $18 (yearbook included). Carolinas Genealogical Society, c/o Virginia Kindricks, Pres., Box 397, Monroe, NC 28111 TEL 704-289-6737. bk.rev. circ. 300. **Document type:** newsletter.

GENEALOGY AND HERALDRY

929 US
CAROLINAS GENEALOGICAL SOCIETY. YEARBOOK. a. Carolinas Genealogical Society, c/o Virginia Kindricks, Pres., Box 397, Monroe, NC 28111-0397. TEL 704-289-6737.

929 US
CARPENTER AND RELATED FAMILY HISTORICAL JOURNAL. 1981. q. $4. Carpenter and Related Family Association, Box 1356, Bowling Green, KY 42101-1004. TEL 502-842-7803. Ed. James Ausie Carpenter. circ. 280.

929 US ISSN 0892-2152
CARROLL CABLES. 1987. q. $10. Kinseeker Publications, Box 184, Grawn, MI 49637. Ed. Victoria Wilson. bk.rev. circ. 50. (looseleaf format; back issues avail.) **Document type:** newsletter.

929 US
CELTIC KNOT. 1978. 3/yr. $12 (foreign $18). (Irish Family Names Society) Ellen Mulderig, Ed. & Pub., 6114 Madra Ave., San Diego, CA 92120-3906. TEL 619-583-0826. bk.rev. circ. 400. **Document type:** newsletter.
  Formerly: Irish Family Names Society News Letter.
  Description: Reports on origin of Irish surnames, queries from Society members, and lists members names, addresses and surnames being searched.

929 NE
CENTRAAL BUREAU VOOR GENEALOGIE. JAARBOEK. 1947. a. $45 includes Mededelingen. Centraal Bureau voor Genealogie, Prins Willem-Alexanderhof 22, Postbus 11755, 2502 AT The Hague, Netherlands. TEL 31-70-3814651. illus.; index. circ. 10,000.
  Description: Annual containing articles on genealogy, heraldry and iconography.

949.2 NE ISSN 0165-6473
CENTRAAL BUREAU VOOR GENEALOGIE. MEDEDELINGEN. 1947. 4/yr. $45 includes Jaarboek. Centraal Bureau voor Genealogie, Prins Willem Alexanderhof 22, Postbus 11755, 2502 AT The Hague, Netherlands. TEL 31-70-3814651. adv.; bk.rev.; abstr. circ. 10,000.
  Description: News on the subjects of genealogy, archival records, biography, and bibliography.

929 US
CENTRAL GEORGIA GENEALOGICAL SOCIETY. NEWSLETTER. 1979. m. $20 membership. Central George Genealogical Society, Inc., Box 2024, Warner Robins, GA 31099-2024. TEL 912-923-7662. **Document type:** newsletter.

929 US
CENTRAL GEORGIA GENEALOGICAL SOCIETY. QUARTERLY. 1979. q. $20 includes mambership. Central Georgia Genealogical Society, Inc., Box 2024, Warner Robins, GA 31099-2024. TEL 912-923-7662. Ed. William R. Henry. adv.; bk.rev.; abstr.; index. circ. 380.
  Description: Genealogical interest articles, membership-research directory and computer tips for genealogists.

929 US ISSN 0095-1439
F457.T25
CENTRAL KENTUCKY RESEARCHER. 1971. q. $7.50. Taylor County Historical Society, Box 14, Campbellsville, KY 42719. Eds. Aileen McKinley, Gwynette Sullivan. bk.rev.; cum.index: 1971-1984; 1985-1989. circ. 290. **Indexed:** Amer.Hist.& Life, Hist.Abstr.

929 US ISSN 1050-1339
CENTRAL NORTH CAROLINA JOURNAL. 1990. q. $20 (effective 1993). Box 219, Cameron, NC 28326-0219. TEL 910-245-7664. FAX 919-775-5763. Ed. James Vann Comer. bk.rev. circ. 400. (back issues avail.)

929 970 FR
CENTRE DE GENEALOGIE ET D'HISTOIRE DES ILES D'AMERIQUE. 1982. q. 140 F. Centre de Genealogie et d'Histoire des Iles d'Amerique, 30 rue Boissiere, 75016 Paris, France. Ed. Etienne de Serville. bk.rev. circ. 200.

929 FR
CENTRE GENEALOGIQUE DE L'ESSONNE. BULLETIN. q. Centre Genealogique de l'Essonne, Le Coudreau, 91490 Milly-la-foret, France.

929 FR ISSN 0753-4183
CENTRE GENEALOGIQUE DE L'OUEST. REVUE TRIMESTRIELLE. 1969. q. 200 F. (foreign 230 F.). Centre Genealogique de l'Ouest, 26, rue Leon Jamin, 44000 Nantes, France. TEL 40-20-32-93. bk.rev.
  Formerly (until 1981): Centre Genealogique de l'Ouest. Bulletin de Liaison (ISSN 0183-6242)

929 AG ISSN 0327-7941
CENTRO DE ESTUDIOS GENEALOGICOS DE CORDOBA. BOLETIN. 1972. a. $15 (effective 1993). Centro de Estudios Genealogicos de Cordoba, Chicoana 330, 5000 Cordoba, Argentina. TEL 212541. Ed. Alejandro Moyano Aliaga. bk.rev. circ. 300. **Document type:** bulletin.
  Description: Contains genealogical research and documental sources in relation to families in the American continent.

929.9 AG
CENTRO INTERDISCIPLINARIO DE ESTUDIOS CULTURALES. BOLETIN DE LA FUNDACION. 1991. bi-m. Centro Interdisciplinario de Estudios Culturales, Via Rivadavia 1321, Piso 2 of. 6, Buesos Aires, Argentina.

929 RE
CERCLE GENEALOGIQUE DE BOURBON. BULLETIN TRIMESTRIEL. no.26, 1989. q. Cercle Genealogique de Bourbon, Archives Departementales de la Reunion, Le Chaudron, 97490 Sainte Clotilde, Reunion. **Indexed:** P.L.E.S.A. (1989-).

920 US ISSN 0749-5684
CERTIFIED COPY. 1972. q. $9. Greater Cleveland Genealogical Society, Box 40254, Cleveland, OH 44140-0254. Eds. Dianne Young, Carolyn Corcoran. bk.rev.; bibl.; index. circ. 200. (also avail. in microfilm) **Indexed:** Geneal.Per.Ind.
  —UnCover.
  Formerly: Greater Cleveland Genealogy Society. Newsletter.

929 US
CHALICE. 1980. s-a. $10. (National Blue Family Association) John Gray, Ed.& Pub., Box 86, 107 N. Main St., Mt. Victory, OH 43340. TEL 513-354-2351. bk.rev.; index. circ. 100. (looseleaf format; back issues avail.) **Document type:** newsletter.

929 US ISSN 1041-6579
CS71
CHAMBERLAIN CHAIN. 1985. irreg., vol.14, 1992. $6.50 per no. Weidner Words, 2206 W. Borden Rd., Spokane, WA 99204-9668. TEL 509-448-9263. Ed. Carolyn Weidner. index. (back issues avail.)
  Description: Surname series with lineages and queries.

929 US ISSN 0277-2086
F547.C4
CHAMPAIGN COUNTY GENEALOGICAL SOCIETY NEWSLETTER. q. $10 membership. Champaign County Genealogical Society, c/o Champaign County Historical Archives, 201 S. Race St., Urbana, IL 61801-3283. TEL 217-367-4025. Ed. Jean Evans. circ. 300. **Indexed:** Geneal.Per.Ind. **Document type:** newsletter.

929 US ISSN 0277-2086
F547.C4
CHAMPAIGN COUNTY GENEALOGICAL SOCIETY QUARTERLY. 1979. q. $10 membership. Champaign County Genealogical Society, c/o Champaign County Historical Archives, 201 S. Race St., Urbana, IL 61801-3283. TEL 217-367-4025. Ed. Joan B, Lund. bk.rev.; charts; stat.; index. circ. 300. (processed; back issues avail.) **Indexed:** Geneal.Per.Ind.
  —UnCover.

929 US ISSN 1046-5901
CHARBONNEAU CONNECTION. (Text in English, French) 1984. q. $5. Milton E. Charbonneau, Ed. & Pub., 9040 Farley Rd., Pickney, MI 48169. TEL 313-878-3680. bk.rev.; cum.index. circ. 60. (looseleaf format; back issues avail.) **Document type:** newsletter.
  Description: Genealogical and historical data on all Charbonneau families in US and Canada, includes all variations of the name.

929 US ISSN 0887-1132
CHARTER CONNECTIONS.* 1986. q. $10. Charter, Charter, and Baughman, 514 S. Maple, McPherson, KS 67460. Ed. Gary L. Charter. index, cum.index. circ. 50. (looseleaf format; back issues avail.)

929 US
CHAUTAUQUA GENEALOGIST. q. $9 includes membership. Chautauqua County Genealogical Society, Box 404, Fredonia, NY 14063.

929 US
CHEROKEE ANCESTOR DIRECTORY FOR RESEARCH. 1977. q. $10. Oklahoma Yesterday, 8745 E. 9th St., Tulsa, OK 74112. TEL 918-835-4118. Ed. Dorothy J. Mauldin. index. (back issues avail.)

929 US
CHESTER DISTRICT GENEALOGICAL SOCIETY. BULLETIN. 1978. q. $16 to individuals; institutions $7. Chester District Genealogical Society, Box 336, Richburg, SC 29729. Ed. Jean Hicklin Nichols. bk.rev. circ. 770 (paid); 150 (controlled). **Document type:** bulletin.
  Formerly: Chester County Genealogical Society. Bulletin.

929 US ISSN 0193-8770
CHICAGO GENEALOGICAL SOCIETY. NEWSLETTER. 11/yr. $16 (includes Chicago Genealogist). Chicago Genealogical Society, Box 1160, Chicago, IL 60690. **Document type:** newsletter.

929 US ISSN 0009-3556
CS1
CHICAGO GENEALOGIST. 1968. q. $16 (includes newsletter). Chicago Genealogical Society, Box 1160, Chicago, IL 60690. bk.rev.; illus.; index, cum.index; circ. 900 (controlled). (processed) **Indexed:** Geneal.Per.Ind.
  —UnCover.

929 976 US
CHICKASAW TIMES PAST. 1982. q. $15. Chickasaw County Historical & Genealogical Society, Box 42, Houston, MS 38851. Ed. Kay Griffin. bk.rev. circ. 150.

929 US
CHISHOLM TRAIL. 1980. q. membership. Williamson County Genealogical Society, Box 585, Round Rock, TX 78680. TEL 512-255-7057. Ed. Linda Emry. bk.rev. circ. 250.

929 US
CHRISTIAN MARKS SOCIETY NEWSLETTER. 1981. irreg. $1. Christian Marks Society, North Rd., S. Ryegate, VT 05069. TEL 802-429-2346. Ed. Vivian G. Nemhauser. circ. 100. (looseleaf format; back issues avail.) **Document type:** newsletter.
  Description: Trace a family from Pennsylvania, 1800, to Minnesota today.

929 US ISSN 0741-8264
F547.S3
CIRCUIT RIDER (SPRINGFIELD). 1969. q. $12 membership. Sangamon County Genealogical Society, Box 1829, Springfield, IL 62705-1829. TEL 217-546-9238. Ed. Manford White. adv.; bk.rev.; index. circ. 425. (back issues avail.) **Document type:** newsletter.
  Supersedes: Sangamon County Genealogical Society of Illinois. Quarterly.

917.306 929 US
CLAN GUTHRIE NEWS. 1984. q. $18. Clan Guthrie - U S A, Inc., 4911 W. 101 Terrace, Overland Park, KS 66207. TEL 913-491-4485. (Subscr. to: c/o Billy Guthrie, Box 8184, Gadsden, AL 35902. TEL 205-546-1064) Ed. Peggy G. Wink. circ. 778. (tabloid format; back issues avail.)
  Description: Genealogical information and announcements on the activities of and literature pertaining to this nonprofit corporation that represents the Scottish clan surname.

CLAN HUNTER NEWS. see CLUBS

929 US
CLAN MACLEOD SOCIETY U S A. NEWSLETTER. membership. 2/yr. Clan MacLeod Society U S A, 7909 Loch Ave., Columbia, SC 29223. adv.; bk.rev. circ. 1,300. **Document type:** newsletter.

929 US ISSN 0163-9951
CS71
CLAN MACNEIL ASSOCIATION OF AMERICA. GALLEY. 1973. 2/yr. $15 to non-members. Clan MacNeil Association of America, c/o R.N. McNeill, Pres., 1824 Stoneyridge Dr., Charlotte, NC 28214. Ed. Nellie McNeill Sanders. bk.rev.; illus. circ. 900.

GENEALOGY AND HERALDRY

929   CN
CLAN MACTAVISH - THOMPSON WORLDWIDE. 1983. q. Clan MacTavish Association, P.O. Box 27072, Ottawa, ON K1J 9L9, Canada. TEL 613-523-6004. Ed. Tim Skinner; Pub. D. Mactavish. circ. 120 (controlled). **Document type:** newsletter.
Formerly: Clan MacTavish Association Newsletter.
Description: Covers the history of the Clan MacTavish as well as Thompson, Thomson, Thomas, Todd and desendants.

929   US   ISSN 0009-8213
CS71
CLAN MCLAREN SOCIETY, U S A. QUARTERLY. 1969. q. membership. Clan McLaren Society, U S A, 5843 Royalcrest, Dallas, TX 75230. Ed. Banks McLaurin, Jr. circ. 145 (controlled). (processed)

CLAN ROSS NEWSLETTER. see ETHNIC INTERESTS

929   CN   ISSN 0226-2436
CLANDIGGER. 1979. q. Can.$8. Alberta Genealogical Society, Box 754, Edmonton, AB T5J 2L2, Canada. TEL 403-424-4429. Ed. Pamela Forsyth. circ. 400. (looseleaf format; back issues avail.)

CLANSMAN (HALIFAX). see ETHNIC INTERESTS

929   US
CLARK CLARION. 1977. q. $8. Rugh Lanphear, Ed.& Pub., 633 E. 13th St., Bowling Green, KY 42101-2531. bk.rev. circ. 100. (back issues avail.)

CLOGHER RECORD. see HISTORY — History Of Europe

929   US   ISSN 0883-0940
CS71
CLOUD FAMILY JOURNAL. 1978. q. $20 to individuals. Cloud Family Association, c/o Linda Boose, Sec., 508 Crestwood Dr., Eastland, TX 76448. TEL 805-965-7423. Ed. Janice Cloud. bk.rev.; index. circ. 200. (back issues avail.) **Document type:** newsletter.
—UnCover.
Formerly (until 1984): Cloud Family Newsletter.

929 917.306   US
CLUES (LINCOLN). 1973. a. membership only. American Historical Society of Germans From Russia, 631 D St., Lincoln, NE 68502. TEL 402-474-3363. FAX 402-474-7229. Ed. Jo Ann Kuhr. circ. 6,000. **Indexed:** Amer.Bibl.Slavic & E.Eur.Stud.
Description: Articles pertinent to the genealogy of Germans from Russia who started to immigrate to the Americas in the 1870s.

929.6   UK   ISSN 0010-003X
THE COAT OF ARMS; a heraldic quarterly magazine. 1950. q. £14.50 to non-members. Heraldry Society, 44-45 Museum St., London WC1A 1LY, England. TEL 071-430-2172. Ed. J.P. Brooke-Little. adv.; bk.rev.; illus.; index approx. every 2 yrs. circ. 1,400. **Indexed:** Br.Hum.Ind., M.L.A. **Document type:** academic/scholarly publication.
—BLDSC (3292.460000); UnCover.

929   US   ISSN 0749-758X
COFFEY COUSINS' CLEARINGHOUSE. 1981. q. $8. 1416 Green Berry Rd., Jefferson City, MO 65101. TEL 314-635-9057. Ed. Bonnie R. Culley. cum.index: 1981-85. circ. 200. (looseleaf format) **Document type:** newsletter.
Description: Publishes querries and information on all Coffey-Coffee families.

929   US
COGGESHALL HISTORICAL ASSOCIATION BULLETIN.* 1980. q. free. Coggeshall Historical Association, 3645 Kiowa Rd., Youngstown, OH 44511. circ. 800. (back issues avail.)

929 976   US   ISSN 0887-1264
COLE CHRONICLE; a genealogical journal for family historians. 1986. q. $15. Clovis Byars Herring, Ed.& Pub., Rt. 1, Box 123A, Buffalo, TX 75831.

929   US
COLEMAN WORLD. 1980. q. $6. c/o Fred Field, Ed. & Pub., 1516 Avenida Selva, Fullerton, CA 92633-1531. TEL 714-871-5767. circ. 175 (paid). **Document type:** bulletin.

929   US
COLLIER QUARTERLY. 1974. q. $20. Collier Research, c/o Timothy Biarnesen, Ed., Box 371883, El Paso, TX 79937. TEL 915-595-2725. adv.

929   US   ISSN 1060-0949
COLLIN CHRONICLES. 1981. q. $15. Collin County Genealogical Society, Box 865052, Plano, TX 75086-5052. TEL 214-596-3567. Ed. Aurora H. Chancy. adv.; bk.rev.; index. circ. 225. (back issues avail.)

929   US   ISSN 0010-1435
COLONIAL COURIER. 1956. q. $4. Daughters of American Colonists, National Society, 2205 Massachusetts Ave. N.W., Washington, DC 20008. TEL 202-667-3076. Ed. Mrs. Charles W. Miles. bk.rev.; illus.
Description: Covers historical and educational subjects, as well as genealogy.

929   US   ISSN 0892-077X
COLORADO COLLECTIONS. 1981. irreg., vol.11, 1990. price varies. Foothills Genealogical Society, Box 15382, Lakewood, CO 80215. Ed. Kay R. Merrill.

929   US
COLORADO COUNCIL OF GENEALOGICAL SOCIETIES. NEWSLETTER. 1983. q. membership. Colorado Council of Genealogical Societies, Box 24379, Denver, CO 80224-0379. TEL 303-781-8864. Ed. C.E. Schmeckpeper. bk.rev. circ. 100. **Document type:** newsletter.

929   US   ISSN 0892-0788
COLORADO GENEALOGICAL CHRONICLES. 1985. irreg., vol.15, 1993. price varies. Foothills Genealogical Society, Box 15382, Lakewood, CO 80215.

929   US   ISSN 0010-1613
COLORADO GENEALOGIST. 1939. q. $20 to family members and institutions; individuals $15. Colorado Genealogical Society, Box 9218, Denver, CO 80209. TEL 303-571-1535. Ed. Birdie Monk Holsclaw. adv. contact: Barbara Henritze. bk.rev.; index, cum.index. circ. 650. (also avail. in microfiche) **Indexed:** Geneal.Per.Ind.
—UnCover.

929   US   ISSN 0896-9590
CS71
COLTON CLARION. 1988. s-a. $10. Surname Publications, 900 Todhunter Ave., No. 4, West Sacramento, CA 95605-1934. TEL 916-375-0160. Ed. Verna Ellis. adv. **Document type:** newsletter.

929   US   ISSN 8755-2914
F127.C8
THE COLUMBIA (RHINEBECK). 1985. q. $14 (typically set in Oct). Valley Quarterlies, c/o Arthur Kelly, Ed., 60 Cedar Heights Rd., Rhinebeck, NY 12572. TEL 914-876-4592. index. circ. 200. (back issues avail.) **Document type:** monographic series.

929.9   NZ
COMMONWEALTH HERALDRY BULLETIN. 1969. a. Commonwealth Heraldry Board, P.O. Box 23-056, Papatoetoe, New Zealand.

COMMUNITY HISTORY. see HISTORY — History Of Australasia And Other Areas

929.9   FR
CONFEDERATION INTERNATIONALE DE GENEALOGIE ET D'HERALDIQUE. BULLETIN. (Text in English, French) 1971. q. Confederation Internationale de Genealogie et d'Heraldique - International Confederation of Genealogy and Heraldry, 24 rue St. Louis en l'Ile, 75004 Parisq, France.

929   US   ISSN 0197-2103
CS42
CONNECTICUT ANCESTRY. 1958. q. $20. Connecticut Ancestry Society, Inc., Box 249, Stamford, CT 06904. Ed. Pat Lorrabee. bk.rev.; bibl.; index. circ. 400. (also avail. in microfiche; back issues avail.) **Indexed:** Geneal.Per.Ind.
—UnCover.
Formerly (until 1971): Stamford Genealogical Society. Bulletin (ISSN 0561-7979)

929   US
CONNECTICUT MAPLE LEAF. vol.4, 1990. s-a. $20 (students $10). French-Canadian Genealogical Society of Connecticut, Inc., Box 45, Tolland, CT 06084. Ed. Susan Paquette. circ. 500. (also avail. in microfiche)
Description: Information source for members tracing their roots from Connecticut to Canada, Acadia and France.

929   US   ISSN 0045-8120
F93
CONNECTICUT NUTMEGGER. 1969. q. $12 to libraries. Connecticut Society of Genealogists Inc., Box 435, Glastonbury, CT 06033. TEL 203-569-0002. adv.; bk.rev. circ. 4,500. **Indexed:** Geneal.Per.Ind.
Formerly: Nutmegger.

929   CN   ISSN 0707-7130
CS88.Q4
CONNECTIONS (POINTE CLAIRE). 1978. 4/yr. Can.$30 individual membership; institutions Can.$20. Quebec Family History Society, P.O. Box 1026, Pointe Claire, PQ H9S 4H9, Canada. TEL 514-695-1502. Ed. Carol Truesdell. adv.; bk.rev. circ. 750.

929   US   ISSN 0890-0639
CONNECTIONS: KIMBALL FAMILY ASSOCIATION NEWSLETTER. 1969. q. $7.50. Kimball Family Association, 14 Manson Road, Kittery, ME 03904-5534. TEL 207-439-2747. Ed. Judith A. Kimball. circ. 700. (looseleaf format) **Document type:** newsletter.
Formerly: Kimball Family Association Newsletter.

THE CONSTANTIAN. see POLITICAL SCIENCE

929   US
COOK'S CRIER. 1969. q. $5. c/o Carl A. Patin, Box 993, Castle Berry, FL 32707. (Subscr. to: c/o Betty Harvey Williams, 118 Fairview Ave., Warrensburg, MO 64093) bk.rev.; bibl.

929   US   ISSN 1058-4021
COOPER COLLECTION (GRAWN). 1990. q. $10. Kinseeker Publications, Box 184, Grawn, MI 49637. Ed. Marie Kezeli. bk.rev. circ. 25. (looseleaf format) **Document type:** newsletter.

929   US   ISSN 0098-4841
F810
COPPER STATE BULLETIN. 1965. q. $10. Arizona State Genealogical Society, Box 42075, Tucson, AZ 85733-2075. Ed. Floyd R. Necley. adv.; bk.rev.; charts. circ. 500. (back issues avail.) **Indexed:** Geneal.Per.Ind.
—UnCover.

300   US
CORNERSTONE CLUES. 1976. q. $12. Cornerstone Genealogical Society, Box 547, Waynesburg, PA 15370. Ed. Norma T. Bell. bk.rev.; bibl. circ. 700.

929   US   ISSN 0731-8375
F547.D3
CORNSILK FROM DEKALB COUNTY, IL. 1975. q. $10. DeKalb County Historical - Genealogical Society, Box 295, Sycamore, IL 60178. Ed. Florence Marshall. bk.rev. circ. 250. (looseleaf format) **Indexed:** Geneal.Per.Ind.

929   US
CORSTORPHINE JOURNAL. 1986. q. membership. Clan Forrester Society, Inc., 3070 Georgia Hwy. 81 S.W., Loganville, GA 30249. TEL 404-466-8134. circ. 100. (looseleaf format) **Document type:** newsletter.

929   US
COUSINS ET COUSINES. vol.4, 1981. q. $4. Northwest Territory Canadian and French Heritage Center, Box 29397, Brooklyn Center, MN 55429-0397. TEL 612-645-3671. (Affiliate: Minnesota Genealogical Society) Ed. Judith Bougie. adv.; bk.rev. circ. 1,200. **Document type:** newsletter.

929   US   ISSN 0090-6093
CS71
COWAN CLAN UNITED. NEWSLETTER.* Key Title: Newsletter Cowan Clan United. 1977. 4/yr. $5. Genealogical Reference Builders, 760 Pine St., Rathdrum, ID 83858. Ed. Elaine Walker. index. **Document type:** newsletter.

929   US
COWARD FAMILY NEWSLETTER. 1972. 2/yr. donation. 2140 Marion St., Birmingham, AL 35226-3012. TEL 205-822-2446. (And: c/o Jo Ann Smith, Box 30093, Raleigh, NC 27622) Ed. Trudy Adams. bk.rev.; circ. 300 (controlled). **Document type:** newsletter.

929   US
COWETA COUNTY GENEALOGICAL SOCIETY MAGAZINE. 1981. q. membership. Coweta Genealogical Society, Box 1014, Newnan, GA 30264. bk.rev. circ. 250.

2660 GENEALOGY AND HERALDRY

929 US ISSN 0895-4062
COX HERITAGE. 1987. irreg., no.15, 1992. $5 per issue. Palouse Publications, SE 310 Camino, Pullman, WA 99163-2206. TEL 509-334-1732. Ed. Janet Margolis Damm. (back issues avail.) **Document type:** newsletter.

929 US
CRACKER CRUMBS. 1978. q. $10 to non-members; members $5. Manasota Genealogical Society, Inc., 1405 Fourth Ave. W., Bradenton, FL 34205-7507. TEL 813-758-3584. Ed. Peg Wetsel. adv.; bk.rev. circ. 300. **Document type:** newsletter.
Formerly: Manasota Genealogical Society. Newsletter.

929 US
CRAIG - LINKS; uniting the Craigs of America. 1980. q. $15.50 (effective 1990). Glyndwr Resources, 43779 Valley Rd., Decatur, MI 49045-8905. TEL 616-423-8639. Ed. Ann Burton. bk.rev.; abstr.; bibl.; charts; illus.; index. circ. 200. (looseleaf format; back issues avail.) **Document type:** newsletter.

929 UK ISSN 0265-5705
CRAWFORD CHRONICLE. 1983. a. $15. Irish Heritage Association, 162a Kingsway, Dunmury, Belfast BT17 9AD, Northern Ireland. Kathleen Neill. **Document type:** newsletter.
Description: Covers genealogies of the Crawford clan worldwide.

929 US ISSN 1043-7401
CS71
CRAWFORD EXCHANGE. 1979. bi-a. $15 (foreign $19). Whisler Creations, 121 South 168th St., Seattle, WA 98148-1611. TEL 206-244-9277. Ed. Wilton M. Whisler. index. circ. 200. (looseleaf format; back issues avail.) **Indexed:** Geneal.Per.Ind.
Formerly (until 1987): Crawford Families Exchange (ISSN 0736-2102)
Description: Covers family history and provides genealogical information pertaining to the Crawford name.

929 US
CRISP NEWSLETTER. 1981. a. $5. Phillip Heritage House, 605 Benton Ave., Missoula, MT 59801. TEL 406-543-3495. (back issues avail.) **Document type:** newsletter.

929 UK ISSN 0261-1104
CRONICL POWYS/POWYS CHRONICLE. 1981. 3/yr. £7 membership (foreign £10). Powys Family History Society - Cymdeithas Hanes Teuluoedd Powys, c/o Mike Hall, Ed., Pleasant View, Erwood, Builth Wells, Powys LD2 3EJ, Wales. adv.; bk.rev. circ. 550. **Document type:** bulletin.

929 664 US
CROSSINGS. 1975. bi-m. $17 to individuals; institutions $100. Stearns County Historical Society, 235 33rd Ave. S., Box 702, St. Cloud, MN 56302-0702. TEL 612-253-8424. FAX 612-253-2172. Ed. Ann Brown. bk.rev.; circ. 1,250 (paid). **Document type:** newsletter.
Description: Intends to nurture a knowledge of and an appreciation for the history of Stearns County and the State of Minnesota.

929 US
CROSSROAD TRAILS. 1980. q. $10. Effingham County Genealogical Society, Box 1166, Effingham, IL 62401. TEL 217-739-2447. Ed. Eleanor Bounds. adv.; bk.rev.; illus. circ. 260. (back issues avail.) **Indexed:** Geneal.Per.Ind.
Description: Covers statistics, stories, queries, how to do research, and family history-ancestor charts.

929.9 AT ISSN 0814-5008
CRUX AUSTRALIS. q. Aus.$45. Flag Society of Australia, Box 142 Collins St. P.O., Melbourne, Vic 3000, Australia. Ed. Tony Burton.

CUMBERLAND AND WESTMORLAND ANTIQUARIAN AND ARCHAEOLOGICAL SOCIETY. TRANSACTIONS. see ARCHAEOLOGY

929 970.1 US
CWY YE: CHEROKEE BLOOD NEWSLETTER. 1984. s-a. $15. Cherokee Research, Box 22261, Chattanooga, TN 37422. Ed. Shirley C. Hoskins. **Document type:** newsletter.

929 976 US
CYPRESS BASIN GENEALOGICAL AND HISTORICAL SOCIETY REPORTER. 1979. 3/yr. $10 includes membership. Cypress Basin Genealogical and Historical Society, Box 403, Mt. Pleasant, TX 75455. Ed. Ardelia Gauntt. adv.; bk.rev.
Formerly: Cypress Basin Genealogical and Historical Society Quarterly.

929 CN ISSN 0824-7730
DADSWELL FAMILY BULLETIN. 1982. s-a. Can.$6 for 4 nos. 1310 Brydges St., London, ON N5W 2C4, Canada. TEL 519-451-7594. Ed. Barbara Balch Nethercott. index; circ. 100 (paid). (back issues avail.) **Document type:** bulletin.
Description: Includes additions, corrections, updates to family lines, new connections, family stories and anecdotes, current births, deaths, marriages.

929 US
DAKOTA HOMESTEAD NEWSLETTER. 1972. q. $8. Bismarck-Mandan Historical and Genealogical Society, Box 485, Bismarck, ND 58502-0485. TEL 901-222-4066. Ed. Don J. Mueller. adv.; bk.rev. circ. 250. **Document type:** newsletter.

929 US
DALEE NEWSLETTER. 1985. q. $10 (foreign $12). 1810 Linwood Blvd., Oklahoma City, OK 73106-2626. TEL 405-232-8843. FAX 405-232-8844. Ed. Martha DaLee Haidek. circ. 40. (looseleaf format; back issues avail.) **Document type:** newsletter.

929 US
DALLAS QUARTERLY. 1955. q. $18 (including DGS Newsletter) (effective 1993). Dallas Genealogical Society, Box 12648, Dallas, TX 75225. Ed. Adrienne B. Jamieson. bk.rev. circ. 1,100. (also avail. in microform) **Indexed:** Geneal.Per.Ind. **Document type:** bulletin.
Formerly: Dallas Genealogical Society. Quarterly.

929 US
DAVENPORT NEWSLETTER. 1979. q. $9. 3510 McMillan, Tyler, TX 75701. Ed. Gene Davenport. circ. 165. **Document type:** newsletter.
Description: Features queries, bible records, cemetary inscriptions and other genealogical leads. Maintains computer files on Davenport surnames.

DAWSON COUNTY HISTORICAL & GENEALOGICAL NEWSLETTER. see HISTORY — History Of North And South America

929 UK
DEBRETT'S PEERAGE & BARONETAGE. 1976. quinquennial. £120. (Debrett's Peerage Ltd.) MacMillans, Brunel Rd., Houndsmill Estate, Basingstoke, Hamps RG21 2XS, England. Eds. Charles Kidd, David Williamson. adv.

929 920 UK
DEBRETT'S PEOPLE OF TODAY. 1982. a. £93.50. Debrett's Peerage Ltd., 73-77 Britannia Rd., Fulham, London SW6 2JR, England. TEL 071-736-6524. FAX 071-731-7768. Ed.Bd. circ. 10,000.
Former titles: Debrett's Distinguished People of Today & Debrett's Handbook.

929 US
DEEP SOUTH GENEALOGICAL QUARTERLY. 1962. q. $18. Mobile Genealogical Society, Box 6224, Mobile, AL 36660. TEL 205-626-6573. Ed. Dee Rhodes. bk.rev.; charts; index. circ. 450.

929 US ISSN 0731-3896
F163
DELAWARE GENEALOGICAL SOCIETY. JOURNAL. 1980. 2/yr. $13. Delaware Genealogical Society, 505 Market St. Mall, Wilmington, DE 19801. TEL 302-475-3616. FAX 302-656-5036. Ed. Mary Fallon Richards. adv.; index. circ. 2,400. (back issues avail.)
Description: Provides raw data-bible records, cemetery readings, indexes to early records, military men, school records, and some compiled genealogies.

929 US
DESCENDANTS OF DANIEL COLE SOCIETY. 1987. q. $10. Box 367, Mahopac Falls, NY 10542. TEL 914-628-0912. Ed. Dorothy Kelsey. adv. circ. 30. (back issues avail.)

929 US
DESCENDANTS OF JAMES BINGHAM OF COUNTY DOWN, NORTHERN IRELAND. NEWSLETTER. 1980. a. free. James Barry Bingham, Ed.& Pub., 2226 Kehrsglen Ct., Chesterfield, MO 63017. circ. 500. (looseleaf format) **Document type:** newsletter.

929 US ISSN 1044-7873
DESCENDANTS OF PETER SHAKLEE (1756-1834) NEWSLETTER. 1980. q. $7 (effective 1992). Peter Shaklee Family Organization, 14901 N. Pennsylvania Ave., No. 369, Oklahoma City, OK 73134-6072. TEL 405-755-8921. index. (back issues avail.) **Document type:** newsletter.
Description: Examines the family history and records of descendants of Peter Shaklee, who came to America at the age of 17 and fought in the Revolutionary War.

929 US ISSN 1048-8901
CS71
DESCENDANTS OF RICHARD RISLEY IN AMERICA. 1983. a. membership only. Risley Family Association, Box 552, Clarkson, NY 14430. Ed. Roy Goold.
Description: Contains articles of biographical, historical and genealogical content concerning members of the Risley (Wrisley, Rizley) family in America and England.

929 US ISSN 1046-4220
CS71
DESCENDANTS OF RICHARD RISLEY SENIOR. 1989. a. membership only. Risley Family Association, Box 552, Clarkson, NY 14430. Ed. Roy Goold. **Document type:** monographic series.
Description: Publishes the comprehensive genealogy of the Risley family in America.

929 AT ISSN 0084-9731
CS2000
DESCENT. 1961. q. membership. Society of Australian Genealogists, Richmond Villa, 120 Kent St., Sydney, N.S.W. 2000, Australia. TEL 02-247-3953. FAX 02-241-4872. Eds. E.C. Best, H.E. Garnsey. adv.; bk.rev.; circ. 7,500 (paid). **Indexed:** Aus.P.A.I.S.

929 US
DESPENCER. q. $13. Spencer Family Association, 915 White Gate Dr., Mt. Prospect, IL 60056. Ed. Frances Spencer Powell.

929 US ISSN 0011-9687
DETROIT SOCIETY FOR GENEALOGICAL RESEARCH. MAGAZINE. 1937. q. $15. Detroit Society for Genealogical Research, Inc., c/o Detroit Public Library, Burton Historical Collection, 5201 Woodward Ave., Detroit, MI 48202. TEL 313-833-1000. Ed. Ruth Kennedy. bk.rev.; index. circ. 1,000. (also avail. in microfilm from UMI; reprint service avail. from UMI) **Indexed:** Geneal.Per.Ind., Mich.Mag.Ind.
—UnCover; UMI.

929 GW ISSN 0012-1193
DEUTSCHES ADELSBLATT. 1945. m. DM.80. (Vereinigung der Deutschen Adelsverbaende) Verlag Deutsches Adelsblatt GmbH, Westerbrak 10, 37619 Kirchbrak, Germany. FAX 05533-3389. Ed.Bd. adv. contact: Christina von Flotow. bk.rev.; illus. circ. 5,000. **Document type:** newsletter.

929 GW
DEUTSCHES GESCHLECHTERBUCH; genealogisches Handbuch buergerlicher Familien. 1889. irreg., no.195, 1989. C.A. Starke Verlag, Frankfurter Str. 51-53, 65549 Limburg, Germany. TEL 06431-42033. FAX 06431-43927. **Document type:** directory.

929 US ISSN 0890-4456
DEWITT COUNTY GENEALOGICAL SOCIETY. QUARTERLY. 1975. q. $11. Dewitt County Genealogical Society, Box 632, Clinton, IL 61727. TEL 217-935-3493. Ed. Betty Adcock. bk.rev.; bibl. circ. 200. (back issues avail.) **Indexed:** Geneal.Per.Ind.
—UnCover.

929 US
DIABLO DESCENDENTS NEWSLETTER. 1975. m. membership. Contra Costa County Genealogical Society, Box 910, Concord, CA 94522-0910. Ed. Paul Graham. bk.rev.; index, cum.index: 1977-1986. circ. 270. (looseleaf format) **Document type:** newsletter.

GENEALOGY AND HERALDRY 2661

929 US
DICK DOCUMENTS; family quarterly newsletter. 1985. bi-m. Legacy, Box 2040, Pinetop, AZ 85935. (back issues avail.) **Document type:** newsletter.

929 US
DIRECTORY OF FAMILY ASSOCIATIONS. a.? Genealogical Publishing Co., 1001 N. Calvert St., Baltimore, MD 21202. Ed. Elizabeth Petty Bentley. **Document type:** directory.

929 US
DIRECTORY OF PROFESSIONAL GENEALOGISTS (YEAR). 1979. biennial. $12 to non-members. Association of Professional Genealogists, 3421 M St., N.W., Ste. 236, Washington, DC 20007. adv. circ. 700. **Document type:** directory.
Former titles: Association of Professional Genealogists. List of Professional Genealogists and Related Services; Directory of Professional Genealogists and Related Services (ISSN 0272-3387)

929 US ISSN 0736-2854
CS71
DODD DIGGINGS. 1980. q. $10. Avlyn Dodd Conley, Ed. & Pub., 8177 Turn Loop Rd., Glen Burnie, MD 21061-1113. TEL 301-766-8564. circ. 100. (looseleaf format; back issues avail.)
Description: Genealogical research information on surname Dodd, Dodds anywhere.

929 US
DOHNER FAMILY NEWSLETTER; Doner, Donner, Danner and allied families. 1980. q. $5. Dudley Dohner, Ed. & Pub., 40701 Rancho Vista Blvd., No. 68, Palmdale, CA 93551. TEL 805-943-3416. adv. circ. 40. (looseleaf format; back issues avail.) **Document type:** newsletter.

929 UK ISSN 0144-459X
DONCASTER ANCESTOR. 1980. q. £7.50 to individuals; families and libraries £10. Doncaster Family History Society, 25 Sunningdale Close, Bessacarr Grange, Doncaster, S. Yorks. DN4 6UR, England. TEL 0302-530805. Ed. T.E. Bowman. bk.rev.; illus. circ. 400. **Document type:** newsletter.

929 US ISSN 8755-2353
F187.D6
DORCHESTER COUNTY GENEALOGICAL MAGAZINE. 1981. bi-m. $14. 1058 Taylors Island Rd., Madison, MD 21648. Ed. Debra Smith Moxey. adv.; bk.rev. circ. 250. (looseleaf format; also avail. in microfiche from LDS; back issues avail.)

929 US ISSN 0886-2796
CS31
DOROT. 1979. q. $12 to non-members. Jewish Genealogical Society, Inc., Box 6398, New York, NY 10128. TEL 212-330-8257. Ed. Alex E. Friedlander. adv.; bk.rev. circ. 1,000. (back issues avail.) **Document type:** newsletter.
Description: Jewish genealogy and family history from New York area sources.

929 US ISSN 0897-3350
CS71
DOUGHTY TREE. 1977. 4/yr. $10. Doughty Family Association, Box 203, Mays Landing, NJ 08330. Ed. Clarence E. Doughty. bk.rev.; index, cum.index. circ. 250. (also avail. in Braille; microfiche) **Document type:** newsletter.

929 US
DOUTHIT FAMILY TREE.* vol.2, 1982. s-a. Lauck & Lee Enterprise, Box 2085, McKinleyville, CA 95521-2085. TEL 707-839-4180.

929 US ISSN 0882-5874
DURCH DIE FENSTERSCHEIBE; Scheib-Shipe-Shive family. 1981. q. $17.50. B G M Publications, 28635 Old Hideaway Rd., Cary, IL 60013. TEL 708-639-2400. Ed. Betty G. Massman. circ. 675.
Description: Genealogical information on the surname Scheib, Shipe, Shive, and variations.

929 US ISSN 0892-208X
DURKEE FAMILY NEWSLETTER. 1982. q. $7.50 (foreign $15). Society of Genealogy of Durkee, 3753 E. 15th St., Long Beach, CA 90804-2943. TEL 310-494-2836. Ed. Bernice B. Gunderson. charts; illus.; stat.; index. circ. 430. (back issues avail.) **Document type:** newsletter.
Description: Covers the history of the Durkee family. Each issue features a specific family group.

920 US
DUSTY TRAILS. q. $10. Genealogical Institute of Oklahoma, 3813 Cashion Place, Oklahoma City, OK 73112. Eds. Sybil C. Barker, Patty W. Eubanks. bibl. (back issues avail.)

929 284 US
DUTCH CHURCH TRANSCRIPTS. 1985. s-a. $15. Reformed Church Archives, 21 Seminary Place, New Brunswick, NJ 08901. TEL 908-296-1779. Ed. Russell L. Gasero. circ. 125. (looseleaf format; back issues avail.)
Formerly: Dutch American Genealogist.
Description: Transcriptions of Dutch Reformed Church records in the United States.

929 US ISSN 0732-1007
EAGLET. 1981. 3/yr. $15 membership. Polish Genealogical Society of Michigan, Burton Historical Collection, Detroit Public Library, 5201 Woodward Ave., Detroit, MI 48202. Ed. Jan Zaleski. bk.rev. circ. 800. Indexed: Geneal.Per.Ind., Mich.Mag.Ind. **Document type:** academic/scholarly publication.

929 US ISSN 0424-107X
F450
EAST KENTUCKIAN; journal of genealogy and heraldry. 1965. q. $12. Box 24202, Lexington, KY 40524. Ed. Clayton R. Cox. bk.rev. circ. 740. (back issues avail.)
—UnCover.

929 US ISSN 0885-4025
EAST TENNESSEE ROOTS; historical - genealogical quarterly. q. East Tennessee Heritage Foundation, Inc., 1345 Oak Ridge Tpke., No. 318, Oak Ridge, TN 37830. Ed. Paula Gammell.
—UnCover.
Description: Includes county records, family histories, cemetery inscriptions and other items of interest to genealogical researchers.

929 US
ECK FAMILY NEWSLETTER. 4/yr. $7. c/o Shirley E. Buirch, Ed., 520 Forest Ave., Lodi, CA 95240. **Document type:** newsletter.

929 US
EDMONDSON FAMILY ASSOCIATION BULLETIN. 1968. q. $6. Edmondson Family Association, 1028 Glendon Way, S. Pasadena, CA 91030. TEL 818-799-8266. Ed. William Edmundson. circ. 800. (back issues avail.) **Document type:** bulletin.
Description: Covers family lines, land records, censuses, and cemetery records.

929 US ISSN 1045-2605
EDWARD HOWELL FAMILY ASSOCIATION. NEWSLETTER.* 1979. 3/yr. $10. Edward Howell Family Association, c/o Carol Morton, Ed., 22723 Rio Gusto Ct., Valencia, CA 91354-2355. TEL 818-359-8427. circ. 450. (looseleaf format; back issues avail.) **Document type:** newsletter.

929 US ISSN 0743-8591
CS71
EDWARDS JOURNAL. 1983. q. $12. Conley Publications, Box 2617, Laurel, MD 20708. Ed. Elaine Nelson. bk.rev. (back issues avail.)

929 976 US ISSN 0887-1299
ELKINS EAGLE; a genealogical research journal for family historians. 1986. q. $15. Clovis Byars Herring, Ed.& Pub., Rt. 1, Box 123A, Buffalo, TX 75831.

929 US ISSN 0740-1477
ELLIS COUSINS NEWSLETTER. 1979. q. $15 (foreign $19). Ellis Publishers Inc., 1201 Maple St., Friona, TX 68935. TEL 806-247-3053. Eds. Bill & Carol Ellis. circ. 600 (controlled). (back issues avail.) **Document type:** newsletter.
Description: Covers family histories, old photos, and news of ongoing research on the Ellis surname.

929 US
ELY HERITAGE.* q. c/o Theresa Ryan, Ed., 1704 Ross Rd., Forest Hill, MD 21050-2852. (back issues avail.)

EMBLEMATICA; an interdisciplinary journal for emblem studies. see HISTORY — History Of Europe

929.9 FR ISSN 0769-7864
EMBLEMES ET PAVILLONS. q. 100 F. Societe Francaise de Vexillologie, c/o Lucien Philippe, Ed., 28 rue F. Chopin, 34920 Le Cres, France. **Document type:** newsletter.

929 US ISSN 0887-5693
EMERICK FAMILY NEWSLETTER. 1984. q. $18. Ohio Connection, Box 14296, Dayton, OH 45413. TEL 513-279-0385. Ed. Ann Fenley. circ. 70. (back issues avail.) **Document type:** newsletter.
Description: Genealogical inquiries and articles pertaining to the various lines of Emerick descent.

929 971 CN ISSN 0226-6245
CS88.C27
ENTRAIDE GENEALOGIQUE. 1978. q. Can.$20. Societe de Genealogie des Cantons de l'Est Inc., 275 Dufferin, local 211, Sherbrooke, PQ J1M 4M5, Canada. TEL 819-821-5414. Ed.Bd. bk.rev. circ. 400.

929 AT ISSN 0046-2489
ESCUTCHEON. 1966. q. Aus.$6. Heraldry Society of Australia, 201 Spring St., Melbourne, Vic. 3000, Australia. adv. circ. 200.
Formerly: Tabard Talk.

929 UK ISSN 0140-7503
CS435.E7
ESSEX FAMILY HISTORIAN. 1974. 4/yr. membership only. Essex Society for Family History, The Old Granary, Justice Wood, Polstead, Suffolk CO6 5DH, England. TEL 0787-211361. Ed. P.E. Moore. adv.: B&W page £40. bk.rev.; circ. 1,850 (controlled).

929 US ISSN 0279-067X
F72.E7
ESSEX GENEALOGIST. 1981. q. $13. Essex Society of Genealogists, Box 313, Lynnfield, MA 01940-0313. Ed. Marcia W. Lindberg. circ. 100. Indexed: Geneal.Per.Ind.
—UnCover.

929.9 AG
ESTANDARTE. 1991. bi-m. $35. Asociacion Argentina de Vexillologia, c/o Alberto R. Perazzo, Costa Rica 5595 (1414), Buenos Aires, Argentina.

929 US ISSN 0737-481X
CS71
ESTES TRAILS; for and about Estes everywhere. 1980. q. $15. Historic Trails Library, Rt. 1, Box 373, Philadelphia, MS 39350-9762. TEL 601-656-3506. Ed. Mary Estes Beckhan. adv.; bk.rev.; circ. 550 (paid). **Document type:** newsletter.
Description: Covers U.S. and other countries; maintains card files; collects lineage charts; and publishes source records.

929 CN ISSN 0824-4936
CS88.Q4
L'ESTUAIRE GENEALOGIQUE. 1982. 4/yr. Can.$15($17) Societe Genealogique de l'Est du Quebec (S.G.E.Q.), P.O. Box 253, Rimouski, PQ G5L 7C1, Canada. Ed.Bd. bk.rev. circ. 400. **Document type:** bulletin.

929 US ISSN 0747-5810
ESWAU HUPPEDAY. 1981. q. $12.50. Broad River Genealogical Society, Inc., Box 2261, Shelby, NC 28150. Ed. Mike Allen. bk.rev. circ. 450. **Document type:** bulletin.
—UnCover.
Description: Contains historical and genealogical information from the Broad River Basin.

929 US
EVANS ANCESTORY. 1986. 3/yr. $15. Lathrop Enterprises (Sheldon), Rt. 2, Box 280, Sheldon, MO 64784. TEL 417-884-2619. Ed. Wilma Lathrop. adv.; bk.rev. circ. 200.

929 US ISSN 0892-2144
EWING EXCHANGE. 1987. q. $10. Kinseeker Publications, Box 184, Grawn, MI 49637. Ed. Victoria Wilson. bk.rev. circ. 35. (looseleaf format; back issues avail.) **Document type:** newsletter.

929 US
F G S DELEGATE DIRECTIONS.* 1991. irreg. Federation of Genealogical Societies, Box 3385, Salt Lake City, UT 84110-3385. **Document type:** newsletter.

GENEALOGY AND HERALDRY

929   SA   ISSN 0014-7117
FAMILIA. (Text in Afrikaans, Dutch, English) 1963. q. $18. Genealogical Society of South Africa, Box 44245, Claremont 7735, South Africa. Ed. C. Pama. adv.; bk.rev.; index every 3 yrs. circ. 1,300. **Indexed:** Ind.S.A.Per.

929   GW
FAMILIENGESCHICHTLICHE BLAETTER DER FAMILIE SCHREIBER-SCRIBA. (Text in English, German) 1900. q. DM.20($10) Familienbund Scriba, Dieburger Str. 199-E-10, 64287 Darmstadt, Germany. TEL 06151-74397. Ed. O.A. Scriba. circ. 580.

929   GW   ISSN 0427-9522
FAMILIENGESCHICHTLICHE BLAETTER UND MITTEILUNGEN. 1903. irreg. DM.50. Verein zur Foerderung der Zentralstelle fuer Personen- und Familiengeschichte e.V., Archivstr. 12-14, 14195 Berlin, Germany. TEL 030-83901100. Ed. Johann Karl von Schroeder. **Document type:** bulletin. **Former titles:** Familiengeschichtliche Blaetter; Verein zur Erhaltung der Zentralstelle fuer Deutsche Personen-und Familiengeschichte, Rundschreiben. Mitteilungen.

929   GW   ISSN 0430-0440
FAMILIENKUNDLICHES JAHRBUCH SCHLESWIG-HOLSTEIN. 1962. a. membership. Schleswig-Holsteinische Gesellschaft fuer Familienforschung und Wappenkunde e.V., Postfach 3809, 24037 Kiel, Germany. Ed. Friedrich Schmidt-Sibeth. circ. 700. (back issues avail.) **Document type:** bulletin.

929   GW   ISSN 0014-7176
FAMILIENVERBAND AVENARIUS. FAMILIENZEITSCHRIFT. 1961. irreg. DM.25. Familienverband Avenarius e.V., Eschersheimer Landstr. 460, 60433 Frankfurt a.M., Germany. Ed. Gert Avenarius. charts; illus.; stat. circ. 200. (tabloid format)

929   CN   ISSN 0030-2945
FAMILIES. 1962. q. Can.$35 (foreign $35) includes "Newsleaf". Ontario Genealogical Society, Suite 251, 40 Orchard View Blvd., Toronto, ON M4R 1B9, Canada. TEL 416-489-0734. FAX 416-489-0938. Ed. Ryan Taylor. adv.; bk.rev.; index. circ. 5,500. (back issues avail.) **Indexed:** Amer.Hist.& Life, Can.Per.Ind., Geneal.Per.Ind., Hist.Abstr.
—UnCover.
Formerly: Ontario Genealogical Society. Bulletin.
Description: Covers society projects, branch and member activities, a queries section and matters of concern to genealogy and heritage enthusiasts.

929   US   ISSN 0890-0353
FAMILIES OF WYOMING COUNTY, WV. 1986. q. $10. Ancestor Seminars Library, c/o Sally Seaman Williams, Ed., Box 1035, N. Highlands, CA 95660-1035. TEL 919-991-4165. circ. 190. (back issues avail.)
Description: Covers genealogy and history of any family from Wyoming County.

929   US   ISSN 0890-0361
FAMILIES OF YANCEY COUNTY, NV. 1984. q. $10. Ancestor Seminars Library, c/o Sally Williams, Ed., Box 1035, N. Highlands, CA 95660-1035. TEL 916-991-4165. adv.; bk.rev.; charts; index. circ. 190. (back issues avail.)
—UnCover.

929   US
FAMILY ASSOCIATIONS, SOCIETIES & REUNIONS. 1981. a. $8. Ye Olde Gelealogie Shoppe, Box 39128, Indianapolis, IN 46239. TEL 317-862-3330. Ed. J. Konrad.

929   US   ISSN 0735-682X
FAMILY BACKTRACKING. 1976. q. $12. Puget Sound Genealogical Society, Box 601, Tracyton, WA 98393-0601. TEL 206-871-0202. Ed. Cindy Spove. adv.; bk.rev.; circ. 200 (controlled).

300   US   ISSN 0533-0939
FAMILY FINDINGS. 1969. q. $12. Mid-West Tennessee Genealogical Society, Box 3343, Jackson, TN 38303-0343. Ed. Darlene Wiggins. adv.; bk.rev.; charts; index. circ. 250-300.

929   CN   ISSN 0227-0994
CS80
FAMILY GENEALOGIES. 1981. irreg., latest 1986. Highland Heritage, Arlington Rd. R.R.1, Lancaster, Ont. K0C 1N0, Canada. TEL 613-347-2363. (back issues avail.)
Description: Contains a variety of obituaries, family tree charts with some notes, many surname queries of interest to the researcher.

929   US
FAMILY HISTORIAN. 1981. q. $15. Madison County Genealogical Society, Box 26, Madisonville, TX 77864. FAX 714-247-0209. Ed. Audrey Johnson Stevens. circ. 85.
Formerly: Past and Present.

929   UK   ISSN 0014-7265
CR1
FAMILY HISTORY. 1962. 4/yr. £12($18) Institute of Heraldic and Genealogical Studies, Northgate, Canterbury, Kent CT1 1BA, England. TEL 0227-768664. FAX 0227-765617. Ed. Cecil R. Humphery-Smith. adv.; bk.rev.; charts; illus. circ. 1,300. (also avail. in microform from UMI; reprint service avail. from UMI) **Indexed:** Amer.Hist.& Life, Br.Hum.Ind., Hist.Abstr. **Document type:** academic/scholarly publication.
—BLDSC (3865.564100); UMI.
Description: Offers scholarly articles about matters geneological and heraldic.

929 977   US   ISSN 0742-1419
F572.W3
FAMILY HISTORY CAPERS. 1974. q. $14 individual membership; families $15. Genealogical Society of Washtenaw County, Michigan, Inc., Box 7155, Ann Arbor, MI 48107-7155. TEL 313-668-6422. Ed. Nancy H. Krohn. circ. 293. **Indexed:** Geneal.Per.Ind.
Former titles (until 1979): Tombstone Connections; Genealogical Society of Washtenaw County, Michigan. Newsletter.
Description: Contains county records, Bible records, naturalizations, genealogy of local settlers, family histories of members and queries.

929   US   ISSN 0884-3716
FAMILY HISTORY WORLD. RESEARCH NEWS. 1982. irreg. $3.50 per issue. (Genealogical Institute) Family History World, Box 22045, Salt Lake City, UT 84122. TEL 801-257-6174. Ed. Arlene H. Eakle. adv.; bk.rev. circ. 10,000. (back issues avail.)
Indexed: Geneal.Per.Ind.
Description: Provides new sources for research; published and unpublished indexes; professional techniques; reviews of newly printed guides and source books.

929   AT   ISSN 0812-3136
FAMILY LOCAL HISTORY SOURCES IN VICTORIA. 1983. biennial. Aus.$10. Custodians of Records, P.O. Box 30, Blackburn, Vic. 3130, Australia. TEL 03-878-0711. Ed.Bd. circ. 2,000.
Description: Lists addresses, prices, opening times and addresses of major resources and lists main holdings for family and local history.

929   GW
FAMILY NOTES: A JOURNAL OF THE HUECK FAMILIES. 1968. a. $10 to libraries. Hueck Family Association, 4030 Ratingen-Hosel, 40883 Am Rennbaum, Germany. Ed. Edward Hueck. circ. 200.

929   US   ISSN 0014-7389
CS42
FAMILY PUZZLERS. 1964. w. $30. Heritage Papers, Box 7776, Athens, GA 30604-7776. TEL 706-613-0030. Ed. Mary Bondurant Warren. bk.rev.; bibl.; charts; illus.; index, cum.index. circ. 2,200. (back issues avail.)
Description: Provides free queries for subscribers, features, and editor's notes on special research problems.

929   US   ISSN 0736-1858
CS42
FAMILY RECORDS TODAY; the journal of American family records. 1980. q. membership. American Family Records Association, 311 E. 12th St., Box 15505, Kansas City, MO 64106. TEL 816-373-6570. Ed. Nita B. Neblock. adv.; bk.rev. circ. 500. **Indexed:** Geneal.Per.Ind.
Description: Contains general genealogical research information, and ethnic research information such as Indian, Black, Jewish, English, and German. Includes books of the AFRA inter-library loan, and queries.

929   US
FAMILY TIES. vol.2, 1976. q. $7.50. Holland Genealogical Society, 300 River Ave., Holland, MI 49423. Ed. Bill Robertson. circ. 150.

929   US
FAMILY TREE DIGEST. 1979. m. $7.50. Family Tree Genealogical Society, 450 Potter St., Wauseon, OH 43567. TEL 419-335-6485. Ed. Howard V. Fausey. circ. 250. (looseleaf format)

929   US
FAMILY TREE EXCHANGE. 1985. 3/yr. $5. Jackie Puffenberger, Ed.& Pub. Rt. 1, Box 330, Fulks Run, VA 22830. TEL 703-896-8857. adv.; index. circ. 200. (looseleaf format; back issues avail.)

929   UK   ISSN 0267-1131
FAMILY TREE MAGAZINE. 1984. m. £18.60 (overseas £30.72). Family Tree Magazine, 61 Great Whyte, Ramsey, Huntington, Cambs. PE17 1HR, England. TEL 0487-814050. Ed. Avril Cross. adv.; bk.rev.; charts; illus.; index. circ. 31,500. (microfiche; back issues avail.) **Document type:** consumer publication.

529   US
FAMILY TREE NEWSLETTER. 1979. m. (except Dec.). $20 includes membership. Cobb County Genealogical Society, Inc., Box 1413, Marietta, GA 30061-1413. Ed. Bette Hochman. bk.rev. circ. 300. **Indexed:** Geneal.Per.Ind. **Document type:** newsletter.

529   US   ISSN 1059-0803
F292.C6
FAMILY TREE QUARTERLY. 1991. q. $20 includes membership (Family Tree Newsletter). Cobb County Genealogical Society, Inc., Box 1414, Marietta, GA 30061-1413. Eds. Mimi Jo Butler, Mary Hancock. circ. 300.
Description: Features Cobb County records, land, tax, marriage, family data, and miscellaneous related data.

929   US
FAMILY TREEBUNE. vol.2, 1978. q. $5.50. Thomas Nash Descendants Association, c/o D. Roberts, 2733 Running Brook, Dallas, TX 75228. TEL 214-328-4973.

929   US
FANNIN COUNTY GENEALOGICAL QUARTERLY; Bonham 52 years ago. 1982. q. $15. 605 Agnew, Bonham, TX 75418. TEL 214-583-5215. Ed. Pat Stephens. adv.; bk.rev.; index. circ. 100.

929   US   ISSN 0892-5194
FAYETTE COUNTY (KY.) GENEALOGICAL SOCIETY QUARTERLY. 1986. q. $10 to individuals; families $15. Fayette County (Ky.) Genealogical Society, Box 8113, Lexington, KY 40533. Ed. Melvin Hurst. bk.rev. circ. 200.
—UnCover.
Description: Contains birth and marriage records, history of cemeteries and listings of those buried there.

929   US
FEDERATION OF GENEALOGICAL SOCIETIES FORUM. 1976. q. $9 to members; non-members $15; institutions $25. Federation of Genealogical Societies, Box 3385, Salt Lake City, UT 84110-3385. TEL 801-254-2785. (And: Box 271, Western Springs, IL 60558-0271) Ed. Sandra H. Luebking. adv.; bk.rev. circ. 25,000. **Document type:** newsletter.
—UnCover.
Formerly (until 1989): Federation of Genealogical Societies Newsletter (ISSN 0894-3265)
Description: Designed to expand readers' knowledge of genealogical research and inform on important events.

929   US   ISSN 1040-2276
CS71
FERGUSON FILES. 1987. q. $10. Kinseeker Publications, Box 184, Grawn, MI 49637. Ed. Victoria Wilson. bk.rev. circ. 40. (looseleaf format; back issues avail.) **Document type:** newsletter.

929   US   ISSN 0890-9458
CS71
FISHER FAMILIES. 1986. a. $6.50 (effective Mar. 1991). c/o Susan Gallyon Dechant, Ed., 3960E German Rd., Kettle Falls, WA 99141-9402. TEL 509-738-6731. bk.rev.

GENEALOGY AND HERALDRY

929   AT   ISSN 0157-8804
FITZHARDINGE'S NOBILIARY; information concerning the gentry and nobility. 1980. quadrennial. $45. C.D. FitzHardinge-Bailey, 15 Dutton St., Bankstown, N.S.W. 2200, Australia. FAX 61-2-796-7473. Ed. Charles Bailey of Baileville. adv.; bk.rev. circ. 2,000. (also avail. in microform; back issues avail.)

929.9   CN   ISSN 0835-8346
FLAG & BANNER. 1987. q. Can.$6.42 (US Can.$7; elsewhere Can.$8). J. Braverman Incorporated, 1755 W. 4th, Vancouver, BC V6J 1M2, Canada. TEL 604-732-7586. FAX 604-736-6439. Ed. Doreen Braverman. adv.: page Can.$185; adv. contact: Doreen Braverman. circ. 6,000. (back issues avail.) **Document type**: newspaper.
   Description: Aims to enhance the public understanding of vexillology, the study of flags. Covers the protocol, history, controversy, manufacture of flags.

929.9   US   ISSN 0015-3370
FLAG BULLETIN. 1961. bi-m. $34. Flag Research Center, Box 580, Winchester, MA 01890. TEL 617-729-9410. FAX 617-721-4817. Ed. Whitney Smith. adv.; bk.rev.; bibl.; charts; illus.; index. circ. 1,150. (also avail. in microfilm) **Indexed**: Abstr.Folk.Stud., Amer.Hist.& Life, Hist.Abstr., Int.Polit.Sci.Abstr. **Document type**: academic/scholarly publication.
   Description: Covers all types of flags and state heraldry from all eras and countries.

929.9   GW
FLAGGENFORUM. (Text in English, German) q. DM.36($18) Archiv fuer Flaggenkunde, c/o Ralf Stelter, Ed., Im Muehlenwinkel 7a, 45525 Hattingen, Germany.

929.9   SZ
FLAGGENMITTEILUNG. (Text in German, occasionally English, French) irreg. (3-6/yr.) c/o Dr. Gunter Mattern, Sichternstr. 35, 4410 Liestal, Switzerland. **Document type**: newsletter.

929.9   UK   ISSN 0142-1271
FLAGMASTER. bi-m. £15. Flag Institute, 10 Vicarage Rd., Chester CH2 3HZ, England. Dir. William Crampton. **Document type**: newsletter.

929.9   CN   ISSN 0833-1510
FLAGSCAN. 1986. q. Can.$20. Canadian Flag Association - Association Canadienne de Vexillologie, 50 Heathfield Dr., Scarborough, ON M1M 3B1, Canada. TEL 416-267-9618. Ed. Kevin Harrington. **Document type**: newsletter.

FLEMISH AMERICAN HERITAGE. see *ETHNIC INTERESTS*

929 970   US
FLINTLOCK & POWDERHORN. 1976. s-a. membership. General Society Sons of the Revolution, Editorial Office, Fraunces Tavern, 54 Pearl St., NY 10004-2429. TEL 212-245-1776. FAX 212-509-3467. Ed. Richard Farmer Hess. bk.rev. circ. 6,500. **Document type**: academic/scholarly publication.
   Description: Reports speeches and articles given at state society meetings.

929   US   ISSN 0893-5041
FLIPPING FLIPPINS. 1987. q. $12.50. Flippin Family Association, 12206 Brisbane Ave., Dallas, TX 75234-6528. TEL 214-241-2739. Ed. Nova A. Lemons. adv.; bk.rev.; index; circ. 65 (controlled). (looseleaf format)
   Description: Gathers information on all the Flippen-Flippin and allied lines.

920   US   ISSN 0374-6240
FLORIDA GENEALOGICAL SOCIETY JOURNAL. 1958. 2/yr. $15 membership; family $20; libraries $10. Florida Genealogical Society, Box 18624, Tampa, FL 33679-8624. Ed. Ceta Armitage. adv.; bk.rev. circ. 390.
   Description: Family histories, lineage charts and surname index.

920   US
FLORIDA GENEALOGICAL SOCIETY NEWSLETTER. 5/yr. $15 membership; family $20; libraries $10. Florida Genealogical Society, Box 18624, Tampa, FL 33679-8624. **Document type**: newsletter.

929   US   ISSN 0161-4932
F310
FLORIDA GENEALOGIST. 1977. q. $18. Florida State Genealogical Society, Box 10249, Tallahassee, FL 32302. TEL 904-328-4321. (Subscr. to: c/o Leslie J. Maddocks, 606 Nelson Point Rd., Niceville, FL 32578) Ed. Linda Pazics Kleback. bk.rev.; index, cum.index: 1978-1988. circ. 600. **Indexed**: Geneal.Per.Ind.
—UnCover.
   Description: Publishes manuscripts and source materials pertaining to the history and genealogy of the territory and state of Florida.

929   US   ISSN 8756-2316
F368
FLORIDA PARISHES GENEALOGICAL NEWSLETTER. 1979. bi-m. $10. 20011 Will Hughes Rd., Livingston, LA 70754-2642. Ed. Donna Adams. bk.rev. circ. 110. (looseleaf format; back issues avail.) **Document type**: newsletter.

929   US   ISSN 0738-159X
FLOWER OF THE FOREST BLACK GENEALOGICAL JOURNAL. 1982. a. $5. Mullac Publishing, 822 Bonaparte Ave., Baltimore, MD 21218. TEL 301-235-6697. Ed. Agnes Kane Callum. adv.; bk.rev. circ. 300. (back issues avail.)

929 011   US   ISSN 0748-0970
F782.J4
FOOTHILLS INQUIRER. 1980. q. $10. Foothills Genealogical Society, Box 15382, Lakewood, CO 80215. Ed. Pat Kemper. adv.; index. circ. 300. (back issues avail.)
—UnCover.
   Description: Church, bible, county, death, and marriage records etc. pertaining to genealogical research in four Colorado counties (Jefferson, Clear Creek, Gilpin and Park), with historical vignettes, queries, and creative work.

929   US   ISSN 0426-8261
CS42
FOOTPRINTS (FORT WORTH). 1957. q. $12. Ft. Worth Genealogical Society, Box 9767, Fort Worth, TX 76147. Ed. Barbara Knox. adv.; bk.rev.; bibl.; stat.; index. circ. 850. (also avail. in microfilm) **Indexed**: Geneal.Per.Ind.
—UnCover.

929   UK   ISSN 0143-3601
FOOTPRINTS (NORTHAMPTON). 1979. q. £4.50. Northampton Family History Society, 294 Birchfield Rd. E., Northampton NN3 2SY, England.

929   US
FOOTPRINTS IN TIME. 1987. q. membership only. Gaston - Lincoln Genealogical Society, Box 584, Mount Holly, NC 28120. Ed. Annette Williams.

929   US   ISSN 0071-7738
FORT BELKNAP GENEALOGICAL ASSOCIATION. BULLETIN.* 1962. a. $4. Fort Belknap Genealogical Association, H.C. 60, Box 409, Graham, TX 76450. TEL 817-549-1856. Ed. Barbara Ledbetter. circ. 100.

929   US
FOUR FLAGS TRACER. 1981. q. $14. Four Flags Area Genealogical Society, Box 414, Nile, MI 49120. Ed. Waneta Batten. circ. 130.

129   US
FOX FAMILY FACTS. 1988. irreg. $6 per vol. Ancestor Seminars Library, c/o Sally Seaman Williams, Box 1035, N. Highlands, CA 95660-1035. TEL 916-991-4165. circ. 50. (back issues avail.)
   Description: Covers genealogy and history of any Fox family (and spelling variations).

929   US
FRANCIS - KING BULLETIN.* 1980. q. Rev. David H. Francis, Ed. & Pub., 1618 W. Grantham St., Goldsboro, NC 27530. circ. 75.
   Formerly: France - Francis Family.

929   US   ISSN 1060-5312
▼**FRANKLIN PIERCE TIMES**. 1992. q. $11.50. 79 Elm St., Springfield, VT 05156.

929   US   ISSN 1059-4051
FRANKLINTONIAN. 1979. 6/yr. $14 membership. Franklin County Genealogical Society, Box 2503, Columbus, OH 43216-2503. TEL 614-469-1300. adv.; bk.rev.; index. circ. 625.
   Formerly (until Apr. 1980): Ohio Genealogical Society. Franklin County Chapter. President's Message.

929   US   ISSN 0887-6320
FRARY FAMILY JOURNAL. 1970. a. membership. Frary Family Association, 12 Lohmann Place, Dumont, NJ 07628. Ed. Grace L. Frary. circ. 1,000.

929   US   ISSN 0887-6312
FRARY FAMILY NEWSLETTER. 1970. s-a. $6 membership. Frary Family Association, 12 Lohman Place, Dumont, NJ 07628. TEL 201-384-2111. Ed. Grace L. Frary. **Document type**: newsletter.
   Description: Contains news of interest to descendents of John and Prudence Frary.

929   US   ISSN 0899-4188
FREDERICK FINDINGS. 1988. q. $21 to individuals; libraries $18 (Canada $25) (effective 1994). Lineage Search Associates, 6419 Colts Neck Rd., Mechanicsville, VA 23111-4233. TEL 804-730-7414. index.
—UnCover.

929   US   ISSN 0887-2139
CS71
FREDERICK FORERUNNERS; a surname newsletter. 1983. q. $10. c/o Jean Nathan, Ed., 3803 MacNicholas Ave., Cincinnati, OH 45236. TEL 513-791-2240. cum.index vols.1-5. circ. 60. (back issues avail.) **Indexed**: Geneal.Per.Ind. **Document type**: newsletter.
—UnCover.
   Description: Provides information on all types of genealogical sources for the Frederick and Frederickson surnames and variant spellings.

929   US
FREELAND AND ALLIED FAMILIES. 1971. a. $3.50 per issue. Freeland Family Association, 220 4 St., Del Mar, CA 92014. TEL 619-755-1284. Ed. Bernard French Freeland. bibl.; charts; illus. circ. 300.
   Formerly: Freeland Quarterly and Allied Families.

929   US   ISSN 0899-1626
CS71
FREEMAN FOOTNOTES. 1983. irreg. $7.25 per no. McNeill Enterprises, Box 779, Napavine, WA 98565-0779. TEL 509-922-4521. (back issues avail.)
   Description: Miscellaneous data on branches of the surname; accepts lineage sheets from families for permanent recording.

929   US
FREESTONE FRONTIERS. 1981. q. $12.50 (effective 1991). Freestone County Genealogical Society, Box 14, Fairfield, TX 75840. Ed. Margaret Tolar. bk.rev. circ. 150.

929   US   ISSN 8756-8446
F767.F8
FREMONT COUNTY NOSTALGIA NEWS. 1981. 4/yr. $10. Fremont County Genealogical Society, c/o Riverton Branch Library, 1330 W. Park, Riverton, WY 82501. TEL 307-856-3556. Ed. Marlys A. Bias. bk.rev. circ. 75. (back issues avail.)
   Description: Index to vital records, funeral home records, censuses, cemeteries.

929   US
FRENCHLINE. 1984. q. $15. French Family Association, 521 River View Dr., San Jose, CA 95111. TEL 408-227-4411. Ed. Mara French. bk.rev. circ. 600. (looseleaf format; back issues avail.)
   Description: Covers immigrants to the U.S. from England with the surname French, mostly from 1630-1640.

929   US
FRISBE - FRISBEE FAMILY ASSOCIATION OF AMERICA. BULLETIN. 1950. q. $20. Frisbe - Frisbee Family Association of America, 630 W. Bonita, Apt. 11-H, Claremont, CA 91711. TEL 714-626-5898. Ed. Nora G. Frisbee. index. circ. 350. (looseleaf format; also avail. in microfilm; back issues avail.)
   Description: Records births deaths and marriages of family members and stories about family members past and present.

GENEALOGY AND HERALDRY

929 US
FRITTS-FRITZ FAMILY NEWSLETTER.* 1981. a. $2. Fritts Cousins, c/o Gregory & Patti Fritts, Eds., 2801 Park Center Rd., Ste. A-900, Alexandria, VA 22302. circ. 1,200. **Document type:** newsletter.

929 US ISSN 0882-2514
FROST ON THE VINE. 1984. q. membership. Frost Family Association, c/o Debbie Fuller, Ed., 2665 Orchard St., Soquel, CA 95073. TEL 408-475-8638. index. circ. 135.

FULTON COUNTY (ILLINOIS) HISTORICAL & GENEALOGICAL SOCIETY NEWSLETTER. see HISTORY — History Of North And South America

929 US
FULTON COUNTY FOLK FINDER. 1982. q. $6. Fulton County Historical Society, Inc., 37 E, 375 N, Rochester, IN 46975. TEL 219-223-4436. Ed. Shirley Willard. adv.; bk.rev. circ. 150. **Document type:** newsletter.

929 977 US
FULTON COUNTY IMAGES. 1963. a. $15. Fulton County Historical Society, Inc., 37 E, 375 N, Rochester, IN 46975. TEL 219-223-4436. Ed. Shirley Willard. adv.; bk.rev. circ. 750. **Indexed:** Amer.Hist.& Life, Hist.Abstr. **Document type:** academic/scholarly publication.
Formerly (until 1991): Fulton County Historical Society Quarterly.

929.6 US
FUNDAMENTA. 1979. irreg. National Flag Foundation, Flag Plaza, Pittsburgh, PA 15219-3630. FAX 412-261-1776.

929 US ISSN 0882-8377
F869.S12
G A S LITES. 1977. q. membership. Genealogical Association of Sacramento, Inc., Box 28297, Sacramento, CA 95828. Ed. Ann Saunders Hulbert. adv.; bk.rev.; index. circ. 400. (looseleaf format; back issues avail.)
Formerly: Genealogical Association of Sacramento. Quarterly.

929 US
▼**G S O C NEWS.** 1992. q. Genealogical Society of Okaloosa County, Florida, Box 1175, Fort Walton Beach, FL 32549. TEL 904-689-1535. Ed. Florence Lembeck. **Document type:** newsletter.

929 US
GABLER FAMILY ASSOCIATION NEWSLETTER & RECORD. (Supplement avail.: What Did You Do in WWII Grandpa?) (Text in English, German) 1978. biennial. $7. Gabler Family Association, Box 721, Lake Havasu, AZ 86403. TEL 602-855-8185. Ed. David H. Gabler. circ. 100.
Description: News and information provided for the exchange and record of the genealogy of Michael Gabler.

929.9 SP
GACETA. irreg. Sociedad Espanola de Vexilologia, Mineria, 17, 3-9, 08004 Barcelona, Spain. (Co-sponsor: Cetnre Belgo-Europeen d'Etudes des Drapeaux) **Document type:** newsletter.

929 AG
GACETA GENEALOGICA. 1989. irreg. $7 (effective 1993). Centro de Estudios Genealogicos de Cordoba, Chicoana 330, 5000 Cordoba, Argentina. TEL 212541. Ed. Alejandro Moyano Aliaga. bk.rev. circ. 200.
Description: Contains short studies in genealogical and heraldic subjects.

929 US
GAGE FAMILY NEWSLETTER. 1985. q. $8. 29 Seminole Ct., Winter Haven, FL 33881. TEL 813-294-2496. Ed. John A. Gage. (looseleaf format; back issues avail.) **Document type:** newsletter.
Description: Contains genealogical information concerning the Gage family.

929 US
GAITHER CONNECTION. 1984. s-a. $15. Society of John Gaither Descendants, Inc., 9107 Split Rail Dr., Louisville, KY 40272. Ed. Eva Gaither Thornberry. circ. 1,000.

929 US ISSN 0893-3162
GATHERING GIBSONS. 1987. q. $10. Kinseeker Publications, Box 184, Grawn, MI 49637. Ed. Victoria Wilson. bk.rev. circ. 40. (looseleaf format; back issues avail.)

929 054.1 FR ISSN 0754-9725
GE MAGAZINE; genealogie aujourd'hui. 1982. 11/yr. 308 F. Editions Christian, B.P. 99, 75522 Paris Cedex 11, France. Ed. Francis Christian. adv.; bk.rev. circ. 8,000.

929 US
▼**GEBHARD FAMILY SOCIETY INTERNATIONAL. NEWSLETTER.** 1992. q. $6 (foreign $8). Gebhard Family Society of America, 5821 Rowland Hill Rd., Cascade, MD 21719. TEL 301-241-3312. Ed. Victor Gebhart. (back issues avail.) **Document type:** newsletter.

929 US
GEBHARD FAMILY SOCIETY OF AMERICA. NEWSLETTER. 1980. q. $6. Gebhard Family Society of America, 5821 Rowland Hill Rd., Cascade, MD 21719. TEL 301-241-3312. Ed. Victor Gebhart. **Document type:** newsletter.
Description: Brings together all people searching the Gebhard family.

929 917.306 US ISSN 1052-3189
GEBORENER DEUTSCHER; a newsletter for German-born adoptees and their birth-adoptive families. 1988. q. free. William L. Gage, Ed. & Pub., 805 Alvarado Dr. N.E., Albuquerque, NM 87108-1648. TEL 505-268-1310. adv.; bk.rev.; illus. circ. 800. **Document type:** newsletter.
●Also available online.
Description: Covers adoption-related search and reunion stories related to German-born adoptees. Includes general interest on Germany, Germans and German - American relations.

929 US
GEER FAMILY ASSOCIATION NEWSLETTER (GEAR GEER GEERE GERE). vol.3, 1986. q. $15. Geer Family Association, Box 6335, Harrisburg, PA 17112. adv. circ. 400. **Document type:** newsletter.

929 US
GEMS OF GENEALOGY. 1975. 6/yr. $6 includes membership. Bay Area Genealogical Society, Inc., c/o Myra Michaletz, Pres., Box 283, Green Bay, WI 54305. bk.rev. circ. 305. **Document type:** newsletter.

929 US
GENEAGRAM. 1976. m. $10. Charlotte County Genealogical Society, Box 2682, Port Charlotte, FL 33949. Ed. Nita Groh. bk.rev. circ. 150. **Document type:** newsletter.

929 US
GENEALOGIA. 1977. q. included in subscr. to Pioneer Times. Mid-Missouri Genealogical Society, Inc., Box 715, Jefferson City, MO 65102. TEL 314-896-8117. (processed)

929 US
GENEALOGICAL & HISTORICAL NEWS.* (Editions for different states) 1985. bi-m. $15. c/o Robert Bradshaw, Box 779, Saipan, CM 96950, Mariana Islands. Ed. R.D. Bradshaw. adv.; bk.rev. circ. 1,000.

929 US
GENEALOGICAL FORUM OF OREGON. BULLETIN. (Membership directory avail.) 1951. 4/yr. $10. Genealogical Forum of Portland Oregon, Neighbors of Woodcraft Bldg. 812, 1410 S.W. Morrison St., Portland, OR 97205. TEL 503-227-2398. Ed. Ruth C. Bishop. adv.; bk.rev.; bibl.; charts. circ. 900. **Indexed:** Geneal.Per.Ind.
Former titles: Genealogical Forum of Portland, Oregon. Quarterly Bulletin (ISSN 0433-3179); (1961-1967): Genealogical Society of Portland, Oregon. Monthly Bulletin (ISSN 0163-0539); Genealogical Forum of Portland, Oregon. Bulletin (ISSN 0163-0504)
Description: Family histories, study materials, census and vital records, passenger and immigration lists, and general periodicals pertaining to genealogical research in all states, with an emphasis on the state of Oregon.

929 US ISSN 0882-1623
GENEALOGICAL GEMS. 1982. q. $10 membership. Fox Valley Genealogical Society, Box 1592, Appleton, WI 54913-1592. Ed. Mary Klein. circ. 250.
Incorporates (1982-199?): Nuggets.
Description: Contains items concerning Wisconsin's Outagamie, Calumet and Waupaca counties.

929 US ISSN 0738-3770
GENEALOGICAL GOLDMINE. 1968. 2/yr. $3.50 donation. Paradise Genealogical Society, Inc., Box 460, Paradise, CA 95967-0460. TEL 916-877-2330. Ed. Carllene Marek. adv. circ. 275.
Description: Promotes interest in genealogy of Butte County, California.

929 US ISSN 0016-6359
CS1
GENEALOGICAL HELPER; for those who wish to do their own genealogical research. Variant title: Everton's Genealogical Helper. 1947. bi-m. $21. Everton Publishers Inc., Box 368, Logan, UT 84323-0368. TEL 800-443-6325. FAX 801-752-0425. Ed. Valarie N. Chambers. adv.; bk.rev.; bibl.; illus.; index, cum.index. circ. 48,000. (also avail. in microform from UMI; reprint service avail. from UMI) **Indexed:** Geneal.Per.Ind.
—UnCover.

929 US ISSN 1045-8166
F127.J4
GENEALOGICAL JOURNAL OF JEFFERSON COUNTY, NEW YORK. 1989. q. $15 (effective Jan. 1992). Family Tree, Box 4311, Boise, ID 83711. TEL 208-939-9136. Ed. Patricia R. James. bk.rev.; index. circ. 225. (looseleaf format; back issues avail.) **Indexed:** Geneal.Per.Ind.
Description: Publishes records and indexes vital to the family researcher of Jefferson County.

929 US ISSN 0016-6367
F131
GENEALOGICAL MAGAZINE OF NEW JERSEY. 1925. 3/yr. $15 for non-members. Genealogical Society of New Jersey, Box 1291, New Brunswick, NJ 08903. Eds. Roxanne K. Carkhuff, Janet T. Riemer. bk.rev.; index. subject ind. for vols.1-35. circ. 875. **Indexed:** Geneal.Per.Ind.
—UnCover.

929 AT
GENEALOGICAL RESEARCH DIRECTORY. 1981. a. Aus.$26($24) c/o K. Johnson, 17 Mitchell St., N. Sydney, N.S.W. 2060, Australia. (U.S. subscr. to: Jan Jennings, 3324 Crail Way, Glendale, CA 91206) Eds. K.A. Johnson, M.R. Sainty. adv.; bk.rev. circ. 10,000. (back issues avail.)

929 900 US
GENEALOGICAL SOCIETIES & HISTORICAL SOCIETIES IN THE UNITED STATES. a. $8. Ye Olde Genealogie Shoppe, Box 39128, Indianapolis, IN 46239. TEL 317-862-3330.
Formerly: Genealogical Societies and Historical Societies.

929 US ISSN 0148-6616
F317.O3
GENEALOGICAL SOCIETY OF OKALOOSA COUNTY, FLORIDA. JOURNAL. 1977. 3/yr. $12. Genealogical Society of Okaloosa County, Florida, Box 1175, Fort Walton Beach, FL 32549. TEL 904-897-4801. Ed. Marsha G. Cox. bk.rev. circ. 275.

929 US ISSN 0092-7953
F253
GENEALOGICAL SOCIETY OF OLD TRYON COUNTY. BULLETIN. Key Title: Bulletin - Genealogical Society of Old Tryon County. 1973. q. $15. Genealogical Society of Old Tryon County, Inc., Box 938, Forest City, NC 28043. Ed. Blanche W. Culberth. bk.rev.; index. circ. 925. (processed) **Document type:** bulletin.
Description: Purposes of the Society are the gathering, compiling, publishing and permanent preservation of the genealogical and historical records and materials of the general area of the original old Tryon county and immediately adjoining areas.

929 US
GENEALOGICAL SOCIETY OF SARASOTA. NEWSLETTER. 1979. 4/yr. $10 membership. Genealogical Society of Sarasota, Box 1917, Sarasota, FL 34230-1917. **Document type:** newsletter.

GENEALOGY AND HERALDRY

929   GW   ISSN 0016-6383
GENEALOGIE; Deutsche Zeitschrift fuer Familienkunde. 1952. 6/yr. DM.48. Verlag Degener und Co., Nuernbergerstr. 27, 91413 Neustadt, Germany. FAX 09161-1378. Ed. Manfred Dreiss. **Document type:** bulletin.

929   FR
GENEALOGIE FRANC - COMTOISE. 1980. 4/yr. 150 F. Centre d'Entraide Genealogique de Franche-Comte, 3 rue Beauregard, 25000 Besancon, France. Ed. Daniel Foltete. adv.; bk.rev. **Document type:** bulletin.
    Formerly (until Dec.1990): Centre d'Entraide Genealogique de Franche-Comte. Bulletin (ISSN 0247-1086)

929   FR
GENEALOGIE LORRAINE. 1970. q. 190 F. Archives de Meurthe et Moselle, Union des Cercles Genealogiques Lorrains, B.P. 8, 54131 St. Max Cedex, France. Ed. Jacques Chamagne. bk.rev.; bibl. circ. 1,500.
    Formerly (until 1984): Cercle Genealogique de Lorraine. Revue.

929   US   ISSN 1056-3571
E184.L7
GENEALOGIJA. 1990. 2/yr. $10. Balzekas Museum of Lithuanian Culture, Lithuanian American Genealogy Society, 6500 S. Pulaski Rd., Chicago, IL 60629. TEL 312-582-6500. circ. 750.

929   GW   ISSN 0085-0934
GENEALOGISCHES HANDBUCH DES BAYERISCHEN ADELS. 1950. biennial. DM.96. (Vereinigung des Adels in Bayern) Verlag Degener und Co., Nuernbergerstr. 27, 91413 Neustadt, Germany. FAX 09161-1378. **Document type:** directory.

929   GW   ISSN 0514-3292
CS1
GENEALOGISCHES JAHRBUCH. 1961. a. (Zentralstelle fuer Personen und Familiengeschichte) Verlag Degener und Co., Nuernbergerstr. 27, 91413 Neustadt, Germany. FAX 09161-1378. **Document type:** bulletin.

929   US   ISSN 0197-1468
CS1
GENEALOGIST (SALT LAKE CITY). 1980. 2/yr. $25 (foreign $28). Association for the Promotion of Scholarship in Genealogy, Ltd., 255 N. Second W., Salt Lake City, UT 84103-4545. TEL 801-521-4732. Ed. Neil D. Thompson. adv.; bk.rev. circ. 500. Indexed: Geneal.Per.Ind. **Document type:** academic/scholarly publication.

929   UK   ISSN 0016-6391
GENEALOGISTS' MAGAZINE. 1925. q. £12($19.80) Society of Genealogists, 14 Charterhouse Buildings, Goswell Rd., London EC1M 7BA, England. TEL 071-251-8799. Ed. Frank Leeson. adv.; bk.rev.; charts; illus.; cum.index at end of each vol. circ. 12,500. (also avail. in microform from UMI; reprint service avail. from UMI) Indexed: Br.Hum.Ind., Geneal.Per.Ind. **Document type:** academic/scholarly publication, newsletter.
—BLDSC (4096.430000); UnCover; UMI.

929   US
GENEALOGY AMERICA. m. $18. Press America, Box 1076, Provo, UT 84603. Eds. Julia P. Schiffman, Preston J. Owens.

929 979   US   ISSN 1049-9571
GENEALOGY BULLETIN. 1984. 4/yr. $10 (free to libraries or genealogical and historical societies). Dollarhide Systems, 203 W. Holly St., Ste. M1, Bellingham, WA 98225. TEL 206-671-3808. FAX 206-676-5805. Ed. Bill Dollarhide. adv.; bk.rev.; circ. 10,000. (controlled). **Document type:** bulletin.
    Formerly: Bill's Bulletin.
    Description: Publication for genealogical exchange. Includes approximately 3,000 surnames with information which will allow for contact between genealogists researching the same family name.

929   US
GENEALOGY CLUB OF ALBUQUERQUE QUARTERLY. 1978. q. $10. Genealogy Club of Albuquerque, 423 Central N.E., Albuquerque, NM 87102. TEL 505-848-1376. Ed. Jone Chappell. bk.rev.; index. circ. 275. **Document type:** newsletter.
    Former titles: Genealogy Club of Albuquerque Newsletter; Genealogy Club Newsletter.

929   US
GENEALOGY TIMES & SEASONS. 1988. 4/yr. $12. A.G.E.S., Box 2127, Salt Lake City, UT 84110-2127. Ed. Ronald V. Jackson.
    Formerly: Accelerated Indexing Systems International. Journal of Genealogy.

929   US
GENEALOGY WORKSHOP BULLETIN. 1975. 5/yr. $9 membership. Genealogy Workshop, c/o Brooklyn Historical Society, 128 Pierrepont St., Brooklyn, NY 11201. TEL 718-783-6779. Ed. Elizabeth A. Feldhusen. circ. 180. **Document type:** bulletin.
    Description: Keeps members informed of scheduled meetings, summaries of past meetings, hints on genealogy resources and newer finds in the field.

929   NE
GENEALOGYSK JIERBOEKJE. (Text in Dutch and Frisian) 1951. a. Fryske Akademy, Doelestrjitte 8, 8911 DX Ljouwert-Leeuwarden, Netherlands. TEL 31-58-131414. FAX 31-58-131409.

929   XR   ISSN 0139-8741
GENEOLOGICKA A HERALDICKA SPOLECNOST PRAGUE. ZPRAVODAJ. ACTA GENEOLOGICA AC HERALDICA. 1969. 4/yr. (Geneologicka a Heraldicka Spolecnost v Prague) Artia, Ve Smeckach 30, 111 27 Prague 1, Czech Republic. FAX 42-2-231-5206. TELEX 121065 ARTA C.

929   CN   ISSN 0821-5359
CS88.N63
GENERATIONS (FREDERICTON). 1979. q. Can.$20 membership to individuals; institutions Can.$25. New Brunswick Genealogical Society, P.O. Box 3235, Sta. "B", Fredericton, NB E3A 5G9, Canada. Ed. Carman Williston. adv.; bk.rev.; cum.index. circ. 800. (back issues avail.)

929   CN   ISSN 0226-6105
GENERATIONS (WINNIPEG). 1976. q. Can.$25 membership. Manitoba Genealogical Society Inc., 885 Notre Dame Ave., Winnipeg, MB R3E 0M4, Canada. TEL 204-783-9139. Ed. Joyce S. Elias. adv.; bk.rev.; abstr.; bibl.; charts; illus.; index. circ. 800. (back issues avail.) Indexed: Geneal.Per.Ind. **Document type:** academic/scholarly publication.
    Incorporates (in 1987): M G S News (ISSN 0710-2852)
    Description: Provides articles on genealogical research, methods and sources, results of members' individual research and information relating to society business and events.

929   US
GENIE. 1967. q. $12.50 membership. Ark-La-Tex Genealogical Association, Inc., Box 4462, Shreveport, LA 71134. TEL 318-746-3125. Ed. Ethel Krause. bk.rev. circ. 450. **Document type:** newsletter.

929   FI   ISSN 0016-6898
CS884
GENOS. (Text in Finnish, Swedish) 1930. q. FIM 140. Suomen Sukututkimusseura - Genealogiska Samfundet i Finland (Genealogical Society of Finland), Mariankatu 7, 00170 Helsinki 17, Finland. TEL 90-179189. Ed. Terhi Nallinmaa-Luoto. adv.; bk.rev.; bibl. circ. 2,700.

929   NE   ISSN 0016-6936
GENS NOSTRA, "ONS GESLACHT". 1945. m. fl.50. Nederlandse Genealogische Vereniging, P.O. Box 976, 1000 AZ Amsterdam, Netherlands. Ed. C.H. van Wijngaarden. bk.rev.; bibl.; charts; illus.; index. circ. 10,500.
    Description: Covers genealogical topics.

929   US   ISSN 0435-5385
GEORGIA GENEALOGICAL MAGAZINE; a magazine of genealogical source material concerning Georgians. 1961. q. $25. Rev. Emmett Lucas, Jr., Ed. & Pub., Box 1267, Greenville, SC 29602-1267. TEL 803-233-2346. FAX 803-233-2349. bk.rev.; index, cum.index 1961-72. circ. 900. (back issues avail.) Indexed: Geneal.Per.Ind.
—UnCover.

929   US
GEORGIA GENEALOGICAL SOCIETY QUARTERLY. 1964. q. $18. Georgia Genealogical Society, Inc., Box 54575, Atlanta, GA 30308-0575. TEL 404-656-2350. Ed. Joye Quinn. adv.; bk.rev. circ. 1,100. (back issues avail.) **Document type:** academic/scholarly publication.
    Description: Provides readers with previously unpublished source material from Georgia.

929   US   ISSN 8755-1756
E184.G3
GERMAN CONNECTION. 1977. q. $18 (effective Jan. 1992). German Research Association, Inc., Box 711600, San Diego, CA 92171-1600. TEL 619-454-7046. Ed. Joan Lowrey. bk.rev.; index. circ. 650. (back issues avail.) **Document type:** newsletter.
    Description: Cultural and how-to articles on genealogy for families from German-speaking areas in the US and Europe.

929   US
▼**GERMAN GENEALOGICAL SOCIETY OF AMERICA. NEWSLETTER.** 1992. 10/yr. $18 membership. German Genealogical Society of America, Box 291818, Los Angeles, CA 90029. TEL 714-621-7399. Ed. Lois Burlo. bk.rev. circ. 1,500. (back issues avail.) **Document type:** newsletter.

929   US   ISSN 1049-2313
E184.G3
GERMAN RESEARCH ASSOCIATION SURNAME BOOK. 1990. biennial. German Research Association, Inc., Box 711600, San Diego, CA 92171-1600. TEL 619-454-7046. **Document type:** academic/scholarly publication.

929   US   ISSN 1058-8736
CS71
GEST-GUEST QUARTERLY; a historical & genealogical newsletter for Gest, Gist, Guess & Guest Families. 1982. 3/yr. $9.60 (for 2 yrs.). 2101 Hayes Rd., Ste. 1409, Houston, TX 77077. TEL 713-784-6130. Ed. Henry G. Guest, Jr. circ. 200. **Document type:** newsletter.
    Description: Annotated bibliography on publications available on genealogical history and research, with announcements of selected family reunions throughout the country.

929   US
GIDEON'S TRUMPET. 1979. bi-m. 15. Granger Homestead Society, Inc. 295 N. Main St., Canandaigua, NY 14424. circ. 850.

929   US
GILA HERITAGE. 1983. q. $4. Northern Gila County Genealogical Society, Inc.. Box 952, Payson, AZ 85547-0952. Ed. Barbara Sparks. bk.rev. circ. 100.
    Formerly: Tonto Trails.

929   US   ISSN 0890-2372
CS71
GILBERT GALLERY. 1986. irreg. $6 per no. Family Quest, 2204 W. Houston, Spokane, WA 99208-4440. TEL 509-326-2089. Ed. Donna Potter Phillips. (back issues avail.)
    Description: Serves as a "clearinghouse" on Gilbert surname.

929   US   ISSN 0890-4022
GILLET GILLETTE GILLETT PRIDE 'N' JOY. vol.2, 1987. q. $10. 1103 W. First, McCook, NE 69001. TEL 308-345-5358. Ed. B.E. Gillett. adv.; bk.rev. circ. 100. **Document type:** newsletter.
    Description: Provides information for people searching the same common ancestor, preserves family stories, and shows how history affected the Gilletts and how they affected history.

929   US
GILMORE GENEALOGICAL NEWSLETTER. 1985. a. $5. Master Copy Printing, 3522 Twin City Highway, Groves, TX 77169. FAX 409-962-9535. Ed. Wm. R. Gilmore. bk.rev. circ. 200. **Document type:** newsletter.
    Description: Genealogical publication for the Gilmore family.

GENEALOGY AND HERALDRY

929 UK ISSN 0141-8009
GLASGOW & WEST OF SCOTLAND FAMILY HISTORY SOCIETY. NEWSLETTER. 1978. 2/yr. £7 (foreign £10) membership. Glasgow & West of Scotland Family History Society, c/o Strathclyde Regional Archives, The Mitchell Library, North St., Glasgow G3 7DN, Scotland. adv.; bk.rev. circ. 1,000. **Document type:** newsletter.

929 US ISSN 1059-1664
F627.L4
GLEANINGS (KEOKUK). 1985. q. $5. Lee County Genealogical Society of Iowa, Box 303, Keokuk, IA 52632-0303. TEL 319-524-1633. (Ed. addr.: 518 Fulton St., Keokuk, IA 52632-5632) Ed. Mary G. Hull. bk.rev. circ. 115.
Formerly: Lee County Genealogical Society Newsletter.
Description: Informs of material available in the County Court Houses and the Public Libraries of Lee County.

929 US
GOINGSNAKE MESSENGER. 1984. q. $10. Goingsnake District Heritage Association, Box 180, Westville, OK 74965. Ed. Virgil Talbot. bk.rev. circ. 400.
Description: Preserves the history of the area.

929 US ISSN 8755-3023
F868.T9
GOLDEN ROOTS OF THE MOTHER LODE. 1969. q. $12 membership. Tuolumne County Genealogical Society, Box 3956, Sonora, CA 95370. TEL 209-532-1317. Ed. Anne Williams. circ. 250. (back issues avail.)
—UnCover.
Description: Explores genealogy, country, and state history, and genealogical research information.

929 GW ISSN 0176-1900
GOLDMANN-NACHRICHTEN. 1969. s-a. DM.20($12.50) Richard Goldmann Verlag, Pfarrer-Kneipp-Str. 4, 44141 Dortmund, Germany. Ed. Richard Goldmann. adv.; illus.; index; 1969-1977. circ. 200. (back issues avail.) **Document type:** newsletter.

929.6 CN ISSN 1183-2827
GONFANON. (Text in English, French) q. Heraldry Society of Canada - Societe Heraldique du Canada, P.O. Box 8467, Sta. T, Ottawa, ON K1G 3H9, Canada. Ed. Jean McPhee. **Document type:** newsletter.

929 US
GOODENOWS' GHOSTS. 1980. q. $20. Goodenow Family Association, 3756 Knox St., St. Joseph, MI 49085. TEL 616-429-2654. circ. 225. (back issues avail.)
Formerly: Goodenough's Ghosts.
Description: For all people with Goodenough, Goodenow, Goodnow, Goodno, related spellings and allied family lines.

929 US
GOODRICH GOSPEL. 1980. q. $6 to libraries. Goodrich Family Association, c/o Ginny & George Farrell, Eds., 7 Lake Shore Dr., Cary, IL 60013. bk.rev. circ. 200.

929 US ISSN 0892-1423
GOODWIN NEWS. 1979. s-a. $15 to individuals; libraries $9.50. (Goodwin Family Organization) Goodwin Family Publications, 39 Lost Trail Rd., Roswell, NM 88201-9509. TEL 505-625-0961. Ed. Murray H. Sharp. bk.rev.; index; circ. 200 (paid). (looseleaf format; back issues avail.) **Document type:** newsletter.
Description: Apprises members of latest research findings on Goodwins and related lines.

929 US ISSN 1062-7219
▼**THE GOOSE**; Gantz - Ganse - Gans genealogy. (Text in English, German) 1993. s-a. $10. Crystal Educational Counselors, 62 E. Boehms Rd., Willow Street, PA 17584-9721. TEL 717-464-4201. Eds. James D. and Peg L. Raibley Beissel. (looseleaf format)

929 US ISSN 1057-8218
GRAHAM GROUP. 1990. q. $10. Kinseeker Publications, Box 184, Grawn, MI 49637. Ed. Marie Kezeli. bk.rev. circ. 25. (looseleaf format) **Document type:** newsletter.

929 US
▼**GRANVILLE COUNTY QUERIES.*** 1992. q. $10. c/o Frances Wheeler, 9920 N.E. 120th St., Okeechobee, FL 34972-7453.
Description: For researchers of Granville County, North Carolina.

929 US
GRAPEVINE (RED BANK); Kniffen-Sniffen family newsletter. 1983. s-a. Reunions U S A, Box 124, Red Bank, NJ 07701. TEL 908-530-2065. Ed. Paul Sniffen. circ. 50. (looseleaf format) **Document type:** newsletter.
●Also available online.

929 US ISSN 0146-0269
CS71
GRAVES FAMILY NEWSLETTER. 1976. 6/yr. $20 (foreign $30). Graves Family Association, 261 South St., Wrentham, MA 02093-1504. TEL 508-384-8084. Ed. Kenneth V. Graves. bk.rev. circ. 400. **Document type:** newsletter.
—UnCover.
Description: For descendants of ancestors named Graves, Grave, or Greaves.

929 US
GRAWUNDER AND GRAFFUNDER CONNECTION. s-a. $5. Grawunder Technical Services, 13108 Penn Ave., Burnsville, MN 55337. TEL 612-890-3240. Eds. Linnea Grovender, Gladys Grovender. index. **Document type:** newsletter.
Formerly: Grawunder Connection.
Description: To locate and identify family clans with these and related surnames.

929 US ISSN 1049-8087
GREAT MIGRATION NEWSLETTER. 1990. q. $8. New England Historic Genealogical Society, 101 Newbury St., Boston, MA 02116. Ed. Robert Charles Anderson.

929 US ISSN 0743-2828
GREEN COUNTRY QUARTERLY. 1980. q. $10. Broken Arrow Genealogical Society, Box 1244, Broken Arrow, OK 74013-1244. TEL 918-455-8619. Ed. Marmie Apsley. bk.rev. circ. 50. (back issues avail.)
Description: Presetns information and records of the Green Country (Northeastern area) of Oklahoma, as well as genealogical information.

929 US
GREEN FAMILY QUARTERLY. 1986. 4/yr. $15. Ann Gregath, Ed. & Pub., Box 1045, Cullman, AL 35056-1045. bk.rev. circ. 80.

GREENBRIER HISTORICAL SOCIETY. JOURNAL. see HISTORY — History Of North And South America

929 UK ISSN 0261-1139
GREENTREES. 1978. q. membership. Central Middlesex Family History, c/o Mrs. E.V. Pirie, 44 Dorchester Ave., North Harrow, Middlesex HA2 7AU, England. Ed. E. Whittleton. adv.; bk.rev. circ. 150.

929 US
GRISWOLD FAMILY OF ENGLAND & AMERICA. 1983. irreg., vol.7, 1983. $35. Griswold Family Association, Inc., c/o Esther L. French, RD Box 139, Chatham, NY 12037. Eds. Charles and Edna Townsend.

929 US ISSN 0738-4866
CS71
GUNN SALUTE. 1970. q. membership. Clan Gunn Society of North America, 5323 Split Rail Rd., Dayton, OH 45429. TEL 513-293-3636. FAX 513-293-9955. Ed. Jane Mitakides. bk.rev. circ. 1,200.

929 UK ISSN 0262-4672
GWENT FAMILY HISTORY SOCIETY. JOURNAL. 1981. 3/yr. £7 (foreign £10). Gwent Family History Society, c/o Mrs. A. Marshall, 37 Buttercup Court, Ty Canol, Cwmbran, Gwent NP4r 6JY, Wales. adv.; bk.rev. circ. 750.

929 US
HALE HERITAGE. no.2, 1985. q. Sources Publishing, Box 6282, Norfolk, VA 23508.

929 CN ISSN 1185-2135
CS88.H37
HAMILTON BRANCH. 1970. q. membership. Ontario Genealogical Society, Hamilton Branch, Box 904, LCD-1, Hamilton, ON L8N 3P6, Canada. TEL 905-529-0039. Ed. Gloria Oakes. bk.rev. circ. 588. **Document type:** newsletter.

929 UK ISSN 0306-6843
HAMPSHIRE FAMILY HISTORIAN. 1974. q. £10 (typically set in Apr.). Hampshire Genealogical Society, 21 Abbotts Ann Rd., Harestock, Winchester, Hants. SO22 6ND, England. TEL 0962-884543. (Dist. by: J. Kimber, 21 The Towers, Victoria Rd., Netley Abbey, Hants. SO3 5DR, England. TEL 0703-454295) Ed. L.E. Ruffell. adv.; bk.rev.; index; circ. 3,000 (paid). **Document type:** newsletter.
Formerly: South East Hampshire Genealogical Society. Journal (ISSN 0305-2303)

929 US
HANCOCK HERITAGE. 1983. q. $10. Ohio Genealogical Society, Hancock County Chapter, Box 672, Findlay, OH 45839-0672. Ed. Bev Kelly. index. (looseleaf format; back issues avail.)

929 US
HARDEN-IN-ING NEWSLETTER. 1984. q. $15. Harden (Hardin, Harding) Family Association, c/o John Hardin, Dir., Rt.1, Box 2290, Crewe, VA 23930. TEL 804-645-8595. (Subscr. to: Terry Parks, Trustee, 7049 Balcom Ave., Reseda, CA 91335) Ed. J. Oran Hardin. circ. 400. (back issues avail.) **Document type:** newsletter.
Formerly: Harden Newsletter.

929 UK ISSN 0268-1021
HARDS FAMILY NEWSLETTER. 1984. s-a. £2 (foreign £3). Hards Family Society, Venusmead, Congresbury, Bristol BS19 5EZ, England. TEL 0934 834780. Ed. Roger Hards. circ. 140. **Document type:** newsletter.
Description: Reports of Hards Family Society activities and genealogical news.

929 US
HARGROVE NEWSLETTER.* q. Hargrove Family Association, c/o Neal Hartgrove, Ed., 822 Oakwater Dr., Garner, NC 27529-4100.

929 UK ISSN 0307-0298
CS439
HARRINGTON FAMILY MISCELLANY. 1975. q. £10. Harrington Miscellany Press, Ashton Lodge, Church Rd., Lyminge, Folkestone, Kent CT18 8JA, England. Ed. Duncan W. Harrington L.H.G. bk.rev. circ. 100. (also avail. in microfiche; back issues avail.)

929 US
HARRISONBURG-ROCKINGHAM HISTORICAL SOCIETY NEWSLETTER; preserving our heritage. 1978. q. membership. Harrisonburg-Rockingham Historical Society, Box 716, Dayton, VA 22821. TEL 703-897-2616. Ed. Mary Mullen. **Document type:** newsletter.

929 US
HART FORUM;* for Hart surname and associated spellings. 1984. q. $14. Bob & Marian Breyer, Eds. & Pubs., 8004 Clearbrook Dr., Raleigh, NC 27615. TEL 219-834-7249.

929 US ISSN 0898-543X
CS71
HASTINGS HERALD. 1985. irreg., vol.12, 1992. $7.25. Name Game Enterprises, S. 4204 Conklin St., Spokane, WA 99203-6235. TEL 509-747-4903. Ed. E. Dale Hastin Smith. bk.rev.; abstr.; stat.; index. (back issues avail.)
Description: Covers genealogy and lineage. Includes biographies, wills, marriages, family records, queries, and obituary records.

HATCHER REVIEW. see HISTORY — History Of Europe

929 US ISSN 0440-5234
F620
HAWKEYE HERITAGE. 1966. q. membership. Iowa Genealogical Society, Box 7735, Des Moines, IA 50322. TEL 515-276-0287. Ed. Larry Allen. adv.; page $90; adv. contact: Rhonda Q. Riordan. circ. 3,000. (back issues avail.) **Indexed:** Geneal.Per.Ind. **Document type:** bulletin.
—UnCover.

GENEALOGY AND HERALDRY

929 US ISSN 0736-9557
CS71
HAYES OF AMERICA HERALD. 1981. q. $14 (Canada $17). Culver Publications, 840 Mesman Dr., Grants Pass, OR 97527-6018. TEL 503-471-0387. Ed. Lois H. Culver. bk.rev.; abstr.; bibl.; charts; index. circ. 200. Document type: newsletter.
Incorporates (in 1989): Hayes Maze (ISSN 8756-4726)
Description: Dedicated to untangling the Hayes, Hays, and Hay families in America.

929 US ISSN 0885-4823
HAYNES FAMILY ASSOCIATION. CHRONICLE. 1982. q. $10. Haynes Family Association, 330 Gralake, Ann Arbor, MI 48103-2025. TEL 313-769-4437. Ed. Paul D. Haynes. circ. 190.

929 301 US ISSN 0149-5046
F292.H7
HEARD HERITAGE; Heard County, Georgia - a history of its people. 1976. s-a. $7.50. Genealogical Researcher, c/o Lynda S. Eller, Box 249, Lanett, AL 36863. bk.rev. circ. 150.

929 US ISSN 0093-9854
F385
HEART OF TEXAS RECORDS. 1958. q. $10 to individuals; institutions $8. Central Texas Genealogical Society, Waco - McLennan County Library, 1717 Austin Ave., Waco, TX 76701. TEL 817-754-0189. Ed. Peggy S. Duty. adv.; bk.rev. circ. 335. (back issues avail.). **Indexed:** Geneal.Per.Ind.
—UnCover.
Formerly: Family Tree (Waco).

929 NO ISSN 0046-7170
HEDMARK SLEKTSHISTORIELAGS TIDSSKRIFT. 1941. s-a. NOK 30. Hedmark Slektshistorielag, Box 2, 2314 Espa, Norway. Ed. Odd Stensrud. bk.rev.
—CCC.

929 US
HEIR LINES. 1982. q. $10. Warren County Genealogical Society, 300 E. Silver St., Lebanon, OH 45036. FAX 513-933-1144. Ed. Harriet E. Foley. index. circ. 250. **Document type:** bulletin.
Former titles: Warren County Genealogical Society Quarterly (ISSN 0742-4779); Warren County Genealogical Society. Newsletter.
Description: Contains membership addresses, queries, deed index, Civil War Discharges, obituary indexes, plus geneological and historical articles about Warren County Ohio families.

929 UK ISSN 0260-1753
HEL ACHAU; the Clwyd family historian. (Text in English and Welsh) 1980. 3/yr. £6 (foreign £8). Clwyd Family History Society, c/o Miss J. Thomas, Ed., 27 Mile Barn Rd., Wrexham, Clwyd LL13 9LX, Wales. TEL 0978-350716. adv.; bk.rev. circ. 1,000. (also avail. in microfiche) **Document type:** academic/scholarly publication, newsletter.
Description: Covers genealogy and family history of the county of Clwyd.

929 US ISSN 0882-5882
HELLER HELPER. 1983. q. $17.50. B G M Publications, 28635 Old Hideaway Rd., Cary, IL 60013. TEL 708-639-2400. Ed. Betty G. Massman. circ. 700. (back issues avail.)
Description: Genealogical information on Heller surname.

929 US
HENDERSON HERITAGE.* 1984. q. $14. c/o Mary K. Hubbard, Ed., 2005 Parkview Blvd., Colorado Springs, CO 80906-1631. TEL 703-777-3787. cum.index. circ. 120.

929 977 US
HENRY COUNTY HISTORICALOG. 1973. s-a. $6. Henry County Historical Society, 614 S. 14th St., New Castle, IN 47362. TEL 317-529-4028. Ed. Richard P. Ratcliff. bk.rev.; bibl.; charts. circ. 1,200. **Document type:** bulletin.

929 US ISSN 0730-6520
F392.M7
HERALD. 1978. q. $18. Montgomery County Genealogical & Historical Society, Inc., Box 867, Conroe, TX 77305-0867. TEL 409-756-8625. Ed. Vera M. Wimberly. adv.; bk.rev.; index. circ. 300. (back issues avail.) **Indexed:** Geneal.Per.Ind.
—UnCover.
Description: Summarizes Montgomery County, Texas, civil records and seeks their preservation. Provides research tools and articles pertaining to genealogy.

929.6 XR ISSN 0139-5009
HERALDIKA; bulletin pro Pomocne Vedy Historicka. 1968. 4/yr. (Pomocne Vedy Historicka) Artia, Ve Smeckach 30, 111 27 Prague 1, Czech Republic. FAX 42-2-231-5206. TELEX 121065 ARTA C.

929 AU ISSN 0073-1897
HERALDISCH - GENEALOGISCHE GESELLSCHAFT ADLER. JAHRBUCH. 1874. irreg., 3rd series, vol.13, 1988. S.650. Heraldisch-Genealogische Gesellschaft Adler, Haarhof 4a, A-1014 Vienna, Austria. **Document type:** monographic series.

929.6 UK ISSN 0437-2980
HERALDRY GAZETTE. bi-m? Heraldry Society, 44-45 Museum St., London WC1A 1LY, England. Ed. E.N. Taylor.

929 CN ISSN 0441-6619
HERALDRY IN CANADA/HERALDIQUE AU CANADA. (Text in English, French) 1966. q. Can.$50 to individuals; institutions Can.$40; students Can.$25. Heraldry Society of Canada - La Societe Heraldique du Canada, 106 Doucet, Hull, PQ J8Y 5P1, Canada. TEL 819-776-2818. Ed. Daniel Cogne. adv.; bk.rev. circ. 500. **Document type:** academic/scholarly publication.

929.6 IE
HERALDRY SOCIETY OF IRELAND. NEWSLETTER. q. Heraldry Society of Ireland - Cumann Araltais na hEirann, Castle Matrix, Rathale, Limerick, Ireland.

929.6 UK ISSN 0141-4534
HERALDRY SOCIETY OF SCOTLAND. JOURNAL. 1977. a. Heraldry Society of Scotland, 25 Craigentinny Cres., Edinburgh EH7 6QA, Scotland.

929 UK ISSN 0260-1044
HEREFORDSHIRE FAMILY HISTORY SOCIETY. JOURNAL. 1980. q. £1.32 (U.S. and Canada £1.85; elsewhere £1.94) to non-members. Herefordshire Family History Society, 14a Tillington Rd., Hereford HR4 9QJ, England. Ed. M. Beavan. bk.rev. circ. 500.

929 US
L'HERITAGE. 1978. q. $17.95. St. Bernard Genealogical Society, Inc., Box 271, Chalmette, LA 70044. Ed. Shirley C. Bourquard. bk.rev.; index. circ. 300.

929 US
HERITAGE OF STONE. 1971. s-a. $10. Stone County Historical Society, Box 284, Mountain View, AR 72560. TEL 501-585-2256. (back issues avail.)

929 US ISSN 0886-0262
HERITAGE QUEST. 1985. bi-m. $28. Box 329, Bountiful, UT 84011-0329. TEL 801-298-5358. FAX 801-298-5468. Ed. Leland K. Meitzler. adv.; bk.rev. circ. 12,000. (also avail. in microfiche) **Document type:** consumer publication.
—UnCover.
Description: Includes articles on how to find and record genealogical data; international in scope.

929 US
HERITAGE SEEKER. 1979. q. $5. Harrison County Genealogical Society, 2243 Central St., Bethany, MO 64424-1335. TEL 816-425-2459. Ed. Pearl James. bk.rev.; circ. 150 (paid). **Document type:** newsletter.

929.1 CN ISSN 0707-0780
HERITAGE SEEKERS. 1978. q. Can.$7 membership. Alberta Genealogical Society, Grande Prairie and District Branch, Box 1257, Grande Prairie, AB T8V 4Z1, Canada. Ed.Bd. adv.; bk. rev. circ. 95. **Document type:** newsletter.

929 GW ISSN 0018-0793
HEROLD (BEPLIN). 1873; N.S.1959. q. membership. Verein fuer Heraldik, Genealogie und Verwandte Wissenschaften, Archivstr. 12-14, 14195 Berlin, Germany. TEL 030-83901100. Ed. Johann Karl von Schroeder. adv.; bk.rev.; bibl.; illus.; index. circ. 1,200. **Indexed:** Numis.Lit. **Document type:** bulletin.

929 UK ISSN 0309-913X
HERTFORDSHIRE PEOPLE. 1977. 3/yr. £5. Hertfordshire Family and Population History Society, 6 The Crest, Ware, Herts. SG12 ORR, England. Ed. Alan Ruston. bk.rev.; index. circ. 500. (back issues avail.)

929 US
HERVEY FAMILIES OF AMERICA BULLETIN.* 1984. q. $12. Donald G. Hervey, Ed. & Pub., 8910 Brae Acres Rd., Houston, TX 77074-4110. TEL 713-432-0881. adv.; bk.rev. index. circ. 60. (looseleaf format; back issues avail.)

929 GW ISSN 0018-1064
CS627.H42
HESSISCHE FAMILIENKUNDE.* 1948. q. DM.30 membership. Arbeitsgemeinschaft der Familienkundlichen Gesellschaften in Hessen, c/o C.W. Schmidt, Postfach 1660, 8530 Neustadt, Germany. adv.; bk.rev.; bibl.; charts; illus.; index. circ. 1,700.

929 US ISSN 0737-7258
CS71
HEYDON - HAYDEN - HYDEN FAMILIES QUARTERLY. 1978. q. $15 (typically set in Jan.). Heydon - Hayden - Hyden Families Association, Box 6575, New Orleans, LA 70174. TEL 504-834-3632. Ed. Gene Hyden. bibl.; charts; illus.; index, cum.index: 1978-1986. circ. 150. (back issues avail.)
Description: Genealogical, biographical, historical research on all spelling variations of Heydon, Hayden, Hyden, Haden, Hiden, Haydon.

929 SP ISSN 0018-1285
HIDALGUIA; revista de genealogia, nobleza y armas. 1953. bi-m. 6500 ptas. (foreign 8000 ptas.) (effective 1993). Instituto Salazar y Castro, Calle de Aniceto Marinas, 114, 28008 Madrid, Spain. TEL 542-81-46. FAX 542-85-23. Dir. Vicente De Cadenas Y Vicent. bk.rev.; bibl.; illus.; index, cum.index: 1953-1977. circ. 3,000. **Indexed:** Amer.Hist.& Life, Hist.Abstr.

929 US
HIDDEN VALLEY JOURNAL. 1978. a. $15 includes membership. Escondido Genealogical Society, Box 2190, Escondido, CA 92025. Ed. Jean Brown. circ. 150.
Supersedes (May, 1982): Hidden Valley Quarterly.
Description: Includes biographies of members, pedigree charts, information genealogical sources.

929 US ISSN 0739-3199
CS71
HIGDON FAMILY NEWSLETTER. 1972. m. $15 membership. Higdon Family Association, Inc., Box 26008, Alexandria, VA 22313. TEL 919-781-7240. Ed. Frank B. Higdon. bk.rev. circ. 200. (processed)

929 UK ISSN 0262-6659
HIGHLAND FAMILY HISTORY SOCIETY JOURNAL. 1981. q. £8 membership. Highland Family History Society, c/o The Reference Room, Public Library, Farraline Park, Inverness IV1 1NH, Scotland. Ed. Jonathan McColl. adv.; bk.rev.; charts. circ. 500. (back issues avail.)

929 CN ISSN 0707-2554
HIGHLAND HERITAGE. 1979. irreg., latest 1989. Arlington Rd. R.R. 1, Lancaster, Ont. K0C 1N0, Canada. TEL 613-347-2363. Ed. Alex W. Fraser. adv. circ. 350. (back issues avail.)
Description: Features articles, tidbits, surname queries for researchers of Glen-Garry regional history and families.

929 US ISSN 1062-7200
E184.G3
▼**THE HIGHWAYMAN;** Raible - Raibley genealogy. (Text in English, German) 1992. s-a. $10. Crystal Educational Counselors, 62 E. Boehms Rd., Willow Street, PA 17584-9721. TEL 717-464-4201. Eds. James D. and Peg L. Raibley Beissel. (looseleaf format) **Document type:** newsletter.
Formerly (until 1992): German Ancestry (ISSN 1061-0529).

GENEALOGY AND HERALDRY

929   US   ISSN 0885-2367
HINMAN HERITAGE. 1976. q. membership only. Hinman Family Association, 2263 E. Leonora St., Mesa, AZ 85213-2260. TEL 602-890-2827. Ed. Milton E. Hinman. circ. 195. (looseleaf format; back issues avail.) **Document type:** newsletter.
   Description: Provides information, family history, family events, notices of meetings, and reunions.

929   US
HISTORICAL TIDINGS. q. membership. Franklin County (Tennessee) Historical Society, Box 130, Winchester, TN 37398.

HISTORICAL TIME CAPSULES OF MONROE COUNTY. see HISTORY — History Of North And South America

HISTORISCHER VEREIN DES KANTONS BERN. ARCHIV. see HISTORY — History Of Europe

929   US
HITCHCOCK FAMILY ASSOCIATION NEWSLETTER. 1990. q. membership. Hitchcock Family Association, 05445 E. Harbor Dr., Fruitland Park, FL 34731. Ed. Robert E. Hedgcock. circ. 100.
   Description: Concerned with all lines of the Hitchcock Family and adopted spellings: Hedgcock; Hedgcock, Hedgcoe, Hedgecough, Hedgecoke.

929   US
HOBBS FAMILY ASSOCIATION NEWSLETTER. 1977. q. $7. Hobbs Family Association of the U.S., Rt. 4, Box 318-H, Winnsboro, SC 29180. TEL 803-635-5219. Ed. Ralph L. Hobbs. bk.rev.; circ. 200 (paid). (looseleaf format) **Document type:** newsletter.
   Description: Covers genealogical news of interest only to Hobbs and related families.

929   US
HOGAN FAMILY ASSOCIATION RESEARCH QUARTERLY. 1979. q. $5. Hogan Family Association, 6212 Vista Verde, Las Vegas, NV 89102. TEL 702-871-7241. Ed. Carol A. Hogan. circ. 50. (looseleaf format; back issues avail.)
   Description: Covers the Hogan ancestors from 1690 to present.

929.9   CN   ISSN 1183-1766
HOGTOWN HERALDRY. q. Can.$10 membership. Heraldry Society of Canada, Toronto Branch - Societe Heraldique du Canada, c/o Rev. Dr. R. Black, 1231 Gerrard St. E., Toronto, ON M4L 1Y5, Canada. **Document type:** newsletter.

929   US   ISSN 0018-3636
HOLLINGSWORTH REGISTER. 1965. q. $12. Harry Hollingsworth, Ed. & Pub. (Inglewood), 3250 W. 108th St., Inglewood, CA 90303. illus.; index. circ. 75. (processed) **Indexed:** Geneal.Per.Ind.

929   US   ISSN 0891-270X
HOLLOWELL HERITAGE. 1987. irreg., no.6, 1992. $5 per no. Palouse Publications, SE 310 Camino, Pullman, WA 99163-2206. TEL 509-334-1732. Ed. Janet Margolis Damm. **Document type:** newsletter.

929 900   US   ISSN 0887-3135
HOLSTON PASTFINDER. 1982. q. $18 to non-members. Holston Territory Genealogical Society, Box 433, Bristol, VA 24203. Ed. Shelby Ireson Edwards. bk.rev. circ. 350.

929   US
HOLT HAPPENINGS. 1921. a. membership. Holt Association of America, 79 Diamond Hill Rd., Candia, NH 03034-2512. TEL 603-483-8293. Ed. Robert L. Holt. circ. 400. **Document type:** newsletter.
   Description: Family news, some genealogy.

929   US
HOMESTEADER. 1978. q. membership. Southeast Nebraska Genealogical Society, Box 562, Beatrice, NE 68310. circ. 150.

929   US
HOOD COUNTY GENEALOGICAL SOCIETY NEWSLETTER. 1984. q. $10 membership. Hood County Genealogical Society, Box 1623, Granbury, TX 76048. TEL 817-573-2840. Ed. Merle E. McNeese. bk.rev.; circ. 200 (paid). (looseleaf format; back issues avail.) **Document type:** newsletter.
   Description: Provides information about the pioneer families of Hood County, Texas; answers questions from people who are researching the area.

929   US   ISSN 0018-4756
HOOSIER GENEALOGIST. 1961. q. $20 membership. Indiana Historical Society, 315 W. Ohio St., Indianapolis, IN 46202. TEL 317-232-1884. FAX 317-233-3109. Ed. Ruth Dorrel. bk.rev.; index. circ. 6,900. **Indexed:** Geneal.Per.Ind.
   Description: Publishes original records of Indiana, including family bibles, marriage, wills, court record and cemeteries.

929   US   ISSN 0147-1228
F525
HOOSIER JOURNAL OF ANCESTRY. 1969-1972, resumed 1977 (vol.4). 3/yr. $15. Box 33, Little York, IN 47139. TEL 812-752-2051. FAX 707-826-3717. Ed. Sing Chew. adv. contact: Linda Hall-Martin. bk.rev. circ. 700. **Indexed:** Geneal.Per.Ind. **Document type:** academic/scholarly publication.
   Description: Publishes mostly source records from 30 counties in southeastern Indiana, from the time each county was formed.

929   US   ISSN 0886-9103
HOWARD HISTORIAN; genealogical newsletter of the Howard surname. 1986. 3/yr. $12. Curt Howard, Ed. & Pub., 4441 Ormond Trace, Marietta, GA 30066. TEL 404-926-4010. FAX 404-926-4013. bk.rev.; circ. 225 (paid). **Document type:** newsletter.
   Description: Articles of interest to Howard lineage researchers. Includes queries and family histories.

929   US
HUBBELL FAMILY HISTORICAL SOCIETY. ANNUAL. a. $15 (subscr. includes Family Notes). Hubbell Family Historical Society, 2051 E. McDaniel St., Box 3813 GS, Springfield, MO 65808-3813. TEL 708-969-4208. Ed. Robert L. Hubbell. circ. 500.

929   US
HUBBELL FAMILY HISTORICAL SOCIETY. FAMILY NOTES. 1982. s-a. Hubbell Family Historical Society, 2051 E. McDaniel St., Box 3813 GS, Springfield, MO 65808-3813. TEL 708-969-4208. Ed. Robert L. Hubbell. **Document type:** newsletter.

929   US
HUDSON FAMILY ASSOCIATION. BULLETIN. 1974. q. $20. Hudson Family Association (South), 232 Loop Dr., Slidell, LA 70458. TEL 504-643-0633. Ed. William A. Shull, Jr. (back issues avail.) **Document type:** bulletin.
   Incorporates (1978-1989): Hudsoniana.

929   US   ISSN 0747-5675
CS71
HUGHES FAMILY LETTER.* 1982. q. $10. Donna Adams, Ed. & Pub., 20011 Will Hughes Rd., Livingston, LA 70754-2642. bk.rev.
   Description: Genealogical data and queries on any Hughes family in the Southeastern states.

HUGUENOT SOCIETY OF GREAT BRITAIN AND IRELAND. PROCEEDINGS. see HISTORY — History Of Europe

HUGUENOT SOCIETY OF GREAT BRITAIN AND IRELAND. QUARTO SERIES. see HISTORY — History Of Europe

HUGUENOT TRAILS. see HISTORY — History Of North And South America

929   US
HUMPHREY FAMILY QUARTERLY. 1984. q. $12. Humphrey Family Association, 701 Mountian Tr., Warrior, AL 35180. TEL 205-647-3485. Ed. Robert L. Humphrey. bk.rev.; index. circ. 300. (back issues avail.) **Document type:** newsletter.
   Description: Publishes material and queries on the Humphrey family worldwide.

929   US   ISSN 0018-7852
HUNTERDON HISTORICAL NEWSLETTER. 1965. 3/yr. $12 to non-members; institutions $50; students $3. Hunterdon County Historical Society, 114 Main St., Flemington, NJ 08822. TEL 201-782-1091. Ed. Roxanne K. Carkhuff. bk.rev.; illus. circ. 600.

929   US   ISSN 0747-8445
F285
HUXFORD GENEALOGICAL SOCIETY. MAGAZINE. 1974. q. $25 membership. Huxford Genealogical Society, Inc., Box 595, Homerville, GA 31634. TEL 912-487-2310. Ed.Bd. bk.rev. circ. 1,200. (back issues avail.)

929   UK
I'ANSON TIMES. 1976. irreg. membership. c/o Thomas Henry Wolstencroft, 29 Meadowfield, Whaley Bridge, Stockport, Cheshire, England.

929   US   ISSN 0019-1809
ILLIANA GENEALOGIST. 1965. q. $15. Illiana Genealogical & Historical Society, Box 207, Danville, IL 61834-0207. TEL 217-431-8733. Ed. Sally Powell. bk.rev.; index. circ. 600. **Indexed:** Geneal.Per.Ind. **Document type:** bulletin.

929   US   ISSN 0046-8622
ILLINOIS STATE GENEALOGICAL SOCIETY QUARTERLY. 1969. q. $20 individual membership. Illinois State Genealogical Society, Box 10195, Springfield, IL 62791. TEL 217-789-1968. Ed. Fonda D. Baselt. adv.; bk.rev.; bibl.; charts; stat.; index, cum.index: 1969-1976; circ. 2,500 (controlled). (processed) **Indexed:** Geneal.Per.Ind.
   Description: Publishes articles on Illinois settlers, genealogies, research aids and sources, computer genealogy, and free queries to members.

IMMIGRATION DIGEST. see POPULATION STUDIES

929   US
IMPRINTS. 1982. q. $12. Genealogical Society of Broward County, Inc., Box 485, Ft. Lauderdale, FL 33302. bk.rev.; circ. 200 (paid).

929   US
IN SEARCH OF THE GUIBORD-CHOPP FAMILY. irreg. Jonathan Bacon, Ed. & Pub., 9615 England, Overland Park, KS 66212. TEL 913-383-9116. circ. 150.

929   AG   ISSN 0579-3599
INSTITUTO ARGENTINO DE CIENCIAS GENEALOGICAS. BOLETIN INTERNO. 1969. m. Instituto Argentino de Ciencias Genealogicas, Circulo Militar, Av. Santa Fe 750, Buenos Aires, Argentina.

553.8   SP   ISSN 0210-7228
INSTITUTO GEMOLOGICO ESPANOL. BOLETIN. 1972. 2/yr. $30. Instituto Gemologico Espanol, Victor Hugo 1, 28004 Madrid, Spain. TEL 091-5326267. Ed.Bd. adv.; bk.rev. circ. 4,500. **Indexed:** Ind.SST.

929   VE
INSTITUTO VENEZOLANO DE GENEALOGIA. BOLETIN. no.7, May 1992. irreg. Instituto Venezolano de Genealogia, Apdo. de Correos 60706, Carcaras 1060, Venezuela.

929   BE   ISSN 0020-5621
INTERMEDIAIRE DES GENEALOGISTES/MIDDELAAR TUSSEN DE GENEALOGISCHE NAVORSERS. 1946. bi-m. 1200 Fr.($40) Service de Centralisation des Etudes Genealogiques et Demographiques de Belgique, Maison des Arts, 147 Chaussee de Haecht, B-1030 Brussels, Belgium. bk.rev.; bibl.; index, cum.index every 5 yrs. circ. 1,600.

929.9   NE
INTERNATIONAL DIRECTORY OF VEXILLOLOGISTS. a. $2. Geyaartsborg 11, 6228 AG Maastricht, Netherlands. Ed. Jos Poels.

929   US   ISSN 0736-8054
INTERNATIONAL SOCIETY FOR BRITISH GENEALOGY AND FAMILY HISTORY. NEWSLETTER. 1979. q. $15 membership. International Society for British Genealogy and Family History, Box 3115, Salt Lake City, UT 84110-3115. Ed. Joy Wade Moulton. bk.rev. circ. 1,000. **Document type:** newsletter.

929   US
IOWA GENEALOGICAL SOCIETY NEWSLETTER. 1978. bi-m. $20 membership. Iowa Genealogical Society, 6000 Douglas, Box 7735, Des Moines, IA 50322. TEL 515-276-0287. Ed. Elizabeth McKray. bk.rev. circ. 2,700. (looseleaf format; back issues avail.)
   Description: Covers events and activities of the IGS and fellow societies.

GENEALOGY AND HERALDRY

929   US   ISSN 0740-5006
F262.I7
IREDELL COUNTY TRACKS (NC). 1978. q. $10 membership. Genealogical Society of Iredell County, NC, Box 946, Statesville, NC 28677. TEL 704-878-5384. Ed. Mildred J. Miller. adv.; bk.rev. circ. 297.
—UnCover.
    Formerly: Genealogical Society of Iredell County, NC Quarterly.
    Description: Historical and biographical sketches on the ancestors of local families in Iredell County, North Carolina, with genealogical inquiries, list of archives, cemetary records, and an index of surnames.

929   IE   ISSN 0047-1437
IRISH ANCESTOR. 1969. s-a. £5($12) c/o Rosemary Folliott, Ed., The Glebe House, Fethard, Co. Tipperary, Ireland. bk.rev.; illus. circ. 800. (tabloid format; back issues avail.)

929   US
IRISH GENEALOGY.* 1978. q. $12. Irish Genealogical Society, 21 Hanson Ave., Somerville, MA 02143-3714. Ed. Joseph M. Glynn. adv.; bk.rev. circ. 500. **Indexed:** Geneal.Per.Ind.
    Formerly (until 1983): Irish Family History.

929.9   IE
IRISH HERALD. a. Heraldry Society of Ireland - Cumann Araltais na hEirann, Castle Matrix, Rathale, Limerick, Ireland.

929   UK
IRISH HERITAGE LINKS. 1981. 4/yr. $40 first year; renewals $30. Irish Heritage Association, 162a Kingsway, Dunmurry, Belfast BT17 9AD, Northern Ireland. Kathleen Neill. adv.; bk.rev.; illus.; index. circ. 5,000. **Document type:** newsletter.
    Former titles: Irish Family Links; Family Links: Past and Present (ISSN 0260-7816)
    Description: Covers all aspects of Irish heritage.

929   AT   ISSN 0814-5482
IRISH LINK; Irish family history magazine. 1984. q. Aus.$30 for two years. Irish Link, P.O. Box 135, South Melbourne, Vic. 3205, Australia. Ed. H.W. Coffey; Pub. H.W. Coffey. bk.rev.; cum.index. circ. 2,000. (back issues avail.) **Document type:** academic/scholarly publication.
    Incorporates (as of 1988): Ulster Link.
    Description: Family history magazine devoted to finding relatives of Irish ancestry in Ireland, Australia and New Zealand.

929 977   US   ISSN 0743-7579
F547.I7
IROQUOIS STALKER. 1971. q. $8. Iroquois County Genealogical Society, 103 W. Cherry St., Watseka, IL 60970. TEL 815-432-2215. Ed. Cheryl Gocken. bk.rev.; index. circ. 375.
    Description: Covers family histories, newspaper extractions, and index of cemeteries.

976   US   ISSN 0737-7932
F347.I8
ITAWAMBA SETTLERS. 1981. q. $20. Itawamba Historical Society, Box 7, Mantachie, MS 38855. Eds. Bob Franks, Roy Turner. bk.rev. circ. 600.
    Description: Devoted to the preservation of the county's genealogical and historical records.

929   US
J.W. DAWES FAMILY NEWSLETTER. 1968. q. $8. (John W. Dawes Family Association) Pres Xpress, 843 Third St., Crescent City, CA 95531. TEL 707-464-3026. Ed. Irene B. Knudsen. cum.index: 1968-1980. circ. 225. **Document type:** newsletter.
    Formerly: Dawes Family Newsletter.

929   US   ISSN 0149-6867
CS42
JACKSONVILLE GENEALOGICAL SOCIETY QUARTERLY. (Includes newsletter) 1973. q. $20 membership. Jacksonville Genealogical Society, Box 60756, Jacksonville, FL 32205-0756. TEL 904-388-0253. Ed. Grace H. Jarvis. adv.; bk.rev. circ. 200.
    Formerly: Jacksonville Genealogical Society. Magazine. (ISSN 0092-8704)

929   US
JACOB'S LADDER. (Text in English, occasionally some German) 1983. irreg. (approx. 3/yr.). $10. Christlieb - Crislip - Crislip Family Association, Ridge Rd., R.D. 1, Box 57, Queensbury, NY 12804-9717. TEL 518-793-6869. Ed. Ned Crislip. circ. 300. (back issues avail.) **Document type:** newsletter.
    Description: Covers family history and genealogy; births, deaths, marriages; Clan reunion information.

929   US
JASPER COUNTY MISSOURI JOURNAL. 1979. q. $4. Jasper County Historical Society, 1718 Garrison, Carthage, MO 64836. Ed. Eleanor Coffield. index. circ. 130.

929   US   ISSN 0195-7384
E184.F85
JE ME SOUVIENS. 1978. s-a. $20 to individuals (foreign $22.50); institutions $25 (foreign $27.50). American-French Genealogical Society, Box 2113, Pawtucket, RI 02861-0113. Ed. Paul Delisle. adv.; bk.rev. circ. 700. **Document type:** newsletter.

929   DK   ISSN 0105-8347
JEG ARBEJDER MED; Dansk Slaegtsforskerfortegnelse. 1978. a. DKK 50. Dansk Historisk Haandbogsforlag ApS, Buddingevej 87 A, DK-2800 Lyngby, Denmark. TEL 45-93-48-00. FAX 45-93-47-47. Eds. Henning Jensen, Ole Hesselberg-Borgqvist. adv.; circ. 2,400 (controlled).

929   US   ISSN 1056-5590
JENNINGS NEWSLETTER. 1987. 3/yr. $10 (foreign $13). Janet E. Thomas, Ed. & Pub., Box 245, Novinger, MO 63554. TEL 816-488-6616. FAX 816-488-6885. adv.; bk.rev. (back issues avail.) **Document type:** newsletter.
    Description: Consists of genealogical information pertaining to the Jennings-Jenkins lineage including, birth, death, marriage, census, biblical, and ship records. Discusses early Jenningses and Jenkinses from all over the world and includes a cross-index of indivuduals.

929   US   ISSN 0893-2921
JEWISH GENEALOGICAL SOCIETY OF PHILADELPHIA. CHRONICLES. 1982. q. $20 (foreign $15) membership. Jewish Genealogical Society of Philadelphia, 332 Harrison Ave., Elkins Park, PA 19117-2662. TEL 215-635-3263. Ed. Harry D. Boonin. adv.; bk.rev. circ. 450. (back issues avail.) **Document type:** newsletter.
    Description: Forum covering Jewish genealogy and research. Includes Jewish religion, traditions, activities and various genealogical information.

929   US   ISSN 0749-6850
JOHNSON COUNTY GENEALOGIST. 1972. q. $12.50 (family membership $17.50). Johnson County Genealogical Society & Library, Inc., Box 12666, Shawnee Mission, KS 66282-2666. Ed. Charlene Mischlich. adv. circ. 300. **Indexed:** A.I.P.P. **Document type:** newsletter.

929   US
JOHNSON HERALD. 1982. s-a. $4. Johnson Family Historical Society, Inc., 5271 Chapman St. South, Salem, OR 97306. FAX 503-238-1652. Ed. Gerald G. Johnson. circ. 100.

929   CN   ISSN 0731-8979
JOHNSON REPORTER; relatively speaking. 1981. q. Can.$10($10) Johnson Family Niagra Peninsula Region, R.R.1, 504 Kilman Rd., Ridgeville, Ont. L0S 1M0, Canada. TEL 416-892-2390. Eds. David Johnson, Roy Johnson. adv. circ. 200. (tabloid format; back issues avail.)

929   US   ISSN 0749-1522
JONES JOURNEYS. 1973. q. $17. Ancestor's Attic, 4041 Pedley Rd., No. 18, Riverside, CA 92509. TEL 714-685-8936. Ed. Frances R. Nelson. adv.; index. (back issues avail.)

929   US
JONES OF VIRGINIA LETTER.* q. $10. Genealogical & Historical News, c/o Robert Bradshaw, Box 779, Saipan, CM 96950, Mariana Islands.

929   US
JOSEPH & MARY RAY REUNIONS NEWSLETTER; Fouts, Phouts. 1972. q. $12.50 (effective 1991). Fran Hoerster, Ed. & Pub., 2606 Culver, Midland, TX 79705. TEL 915-694-0101. circ. 145. **Document type:** newsletter.
    Description: Collects and disseminates data on this family and descendants of North Carolina, South Carolina, Kentucky, Tennessee, Alabama, and Texas from 1770-1860, as well as current events in the family.

929   US   ISSN 0277-4909
JOTS FROM THE POINT. 10/yr. $20 (subscr. includes Western Pennsylvania Genealogical Quarterly) (membership). Western Pennsylvania Genealogical Society, 4338 Bigelow Blvd., Pittsburgh, PA 15213-2695. TEL 412-681-5533. Ed. Jean S. Morris. circ. 1,600 (paid). **Document type:** newsletter.

929   CN   ISSN 0021-8006
JOURNAL HISTORIQUE DES BERNIER; voix des Bernier d'Amerique. (Text mainly in French, occasionally in English) 1962. q. $15. Association des Familles Berniers, C.P. 82, 133 est, du Manoir, Cap-St-Ignace, Que. J0B 2P0, Canada. Ed. Cyril Bernier. adv.; bk.rev.; bibl.; illus. circ. 1,000. (processed)
    Formerly: Journal des Bernier.

JOURNAL OF AMERICAN INDIAN FAMILY RESEARCH. see *ETHNIC INTERESTS*

JOURNAL OF AMERICAN INDIAN FAMILY RESEARCH MONTHLY NEWSLETTER. see *ETHNIC INTERESTS*

JOURNAL OF ANCIENT AND MEDIEVAL STUDIES. see *HISTORY*

929.9   US
JOURNAL OF HERALDIC STUDIES. a. Heraldry Society of the United States of America, 1617 W. 261 St., Harbor City, CA 90710.

929 410 325   UK   ISSN 0262-4842
JOURNAL OF ONE-NAME STUDIES. 1980. q. £8. Guild of One-Name Studies, Box G, 14 Charterhouse Bldgs., Goswell Rd., London EC1M 7BA, England. Ed. Mary Rumsey. bk.rev.; cum.index. circ. 1,500. (back issues avail.) **Document type:** academic/scholarly publication.

929   US   ISSN 0451-3991
F465
KANSAS CITY GENEALOGIST 1959. q. $15. Heart of America Genealogical Society, c/o Kansas City Public Library, 311 E. 12th St., Kansas City, MO 64106. Ed. Joanne C. Eakin. adv.; bk.rev. circ. 450. (back issues avail.) **Indexed:** Geneal.Per.Ind.
—UnCover.

929   US   ISSN 1043-7657
F680
KANSAS REVIEW. 1975. 4/yr. $10 (typically set in July). Kansas Council of Genealogical Societies, Box 3858, Topeka, KS 66604-6858. Ed. Ruth Sanderson. adv.; bk.rev. circ. 215. **Document type:** newsletter.

929   US   ISSN 0741-2045
CS71
KATES KIN; Kates/Cates family. 1978. q. free to qualified personnel. 1395 Main St., Box 8, Rarden, OH 45671. TEL 614-372-6705. Ed. Anna Kates Gardner. bk.rev.; index; circ. 800 (controlled). (looseleaf format; also avail. in microfiche; back issues avail.)
    Description: Covers family histories in the U.S. Includes a census information service and bible records.

929   GW   ISSN 0943-5905
DIE KEMENATE. (Text in English, German) 1979. s-a. DM.28($20) Familienverband Berneburg - Werneburg - Family Association Berneberg - Werneburg, Trettachstr. 60, 87561 Oberstdorf, Germany. TEL 08322-4914. (U.S. addr.: c/o Frank Berneburg, Box 1026, Osborn, ID 83846. TEL 208-752-3921) Ed. Edmund Berneburg. circ. 250. (back issues avail.) **Document type:** newsletter.

2670 GENEALOGY AND HERALDRY

929 976   US   ISSN 0023-0103
F450
KENTUCKY ANCESTORS. 1965. q. $35. Kentucky Historical Society, Old State Capitol, Box H, Frankfort, KY 40602-2108. TEL 502-564-3016. FAX 502-564-4701. Ed. Cheryl Conover. abstr.; illus.; index. circ. 4,800. **Indexed:** Amer.Hist.& Life, Hist.Abstr.
—UnCover.
    Description: Family history publication featuring genealogical research and records from private and public sources throughout the State and the Nation.

929   US   ISSN 0899-1359
F450
KENTUCKY QUERIES. 1986. irreg. $7.25 per no. McNeill Enterprises, Box 779, Napavine, WA 98565-0779. TEL 509-922-4521. bk.rev.
    Description: Accepts Kentucky related queries.

929   US   ISSN 0736-0886
CS71
KERSHNER KINFOLK. 1982. q. $14 membership. Kershner Family Association, 1449 Fox Run Dr., Charlotte, NC 28212. TEL 704-535-6025. Ed. William E. Kershner, Jr. circ. 100.
    Description: German-American family history, particularly that of the Kirschner - Kershner family; descendants of three brothers who emigrated from Hessen to Philadelphia in the years 1731-1742.

929   US
KEY FAMILY NEWSLETTER.* 1980. q. $100. Lance E. Key, Ed. & Pub., Box 364, Lipan, TX 76462. circ. 100. (looseleaf format; back issues avail.) **Document type:** newsletter.

929   US
KEYHOLE. 1971. q. $12 membership. Genealogical Society of Southwestern Pennsylvania, Box 894, Washington, PA 15301. index. circ. 1,000. (processed) **Indexed:** Geneal.Per.Ind.

929   US   ISSN 1069-207X
KIN KOLLECTING. 1986. q. $4 per no. Ashley County Genealogical Society, Box R, Crossett, AR 71635. Ed. Rebecca Brown. **Document type:** bulletin.

929   CN   ISSN 0823-8367
VK808
KINDRED SPIRITS. 1982. q. Can.$12. Ontario Genealogical Society, Whitby - Oshawa Branch, P.O. Box 174, Whitby, ON L1N 5S1, Canada. TEL 416-668-1362. Ed. Dorothy Brown. bk.rev. circ. 450. (back issues avail.) **Document type:** newsletter.

929   US
KINFOLKS AND CONNECTIONS OF ALEXANDER COUNTY, N.C. 1983. 4/yr. $10 includes membership. Alexander County Genealogical Society, Box 241, Hiddenite, NC 28636. Ed. Linda R. Correll. bk.rev.; circ. 240 (paid). **Document type:** newsletter.
    Supersedes (in Sep. 1986): Alexander County Genealogical Society Newsletter.

929   CN
KINGS COUNTY HISTORICAL AND ARCHIVAL SOCIETY, INC. NEWSLETTER. 1961. 7/yr. Can.$10. Kings County Historical and Archival Society, Inc., c/o W. Harvey Dalling, Sussex Corner, N.B. E0E 1R0, Canada. TEL 506-433-3244. Eds. W. Harvey Dalling, Ernest Friars. adv.; bk.rev. circ. 300. (back issues avail.) **Document type:** newsletter.
    Formerly: Kings County Historical Society. Newsletter.

026   US   ISSN 0882-9802
KINSHIP KRONICLE. 1976. q. $6.50 (typically set in Jan.). Rockingham Society of Geneologists, Box 81, Exeter, NH 03833-0081. TEL 603-436-5824. Ed. Carl W. Brage. rec.rev.; charts; index; circ. 250 (paid). (looseleaf format; back issues avail.) **Document type:** newsletter.
—UnCover.

929.9   GW
KLEEBLATT. q. Herladischer Verein "Zum Kleeblatt", Berlinerstr. 14, E, 30457 Hannover, Germany.

929   US   ISSN 1063-4142
CS71.K72873
KNARR, KNERR, KNORR FAMILY NEWSLETTER. 1979. bi-m. $7.50. Knarr, Knerr, Knorr Family Association, 7657 Squirrel Creek Dr., Cincinnati, OH 45247-3614. TEL 513-385-3422. Ed. Larry Knarr. circ. 150. (looseleaf format; also avail. in microform; back issues avail.) **Document type:** newsletter.

929   US   ISSN 0454-8973
CS71
KNIGHT LETTER; communication for Knight and Knecht family researchers. 1968. q. $8. Merle Ganier, Ed.& Pub., 2108 Grace Ave., Fort Worth, TX 76111-2816. bk.rev. circ. 200. (also avail. in microfiche; back issues avail.)

929   US   ISSN 0741-7284
F547.K7
KNOX COUNTY ILLINOIS GENEALOGICAL SOCIETY. QUARTERLY. 1973. q. $10. Knox County Illinois Genealogical Society, Box 13, Galesburg, IL 61402-0013. Ed.Bd. bibl.; stat.; index. circ. 280. **Indexed:** Geneal.Per.Ind.
—UnCover.

929   NE   ISSN 0921-013X
KONINKLIJK NEDERLANDSCH GENOOTSCHAP VOOR GESLACHT- EN WAPENKUNDE. WERKEN UITGEGEVEN. 1974. a. price varies. (Koninklijk Nederlandsch Genootschap voor Geslacht- en Wapenkunde) Walburg Pers BV, Postbus 4159, 7200 BD Zutphen, Netherlands. TEL 31-5750-10522.
FAX 31-5750-41025. **Document type:** monographic series.

929   US   ISSN 0883-7961
KREFELD IMMIGRANTS AND THEIR DESCENDANTS. 1984. s-a. $14. Links Genealogy Publications, 7677 Abaline Way, Sacramento, CA 95823. TEL 916-428-2245. Ed. Iris Carter Jones. adv.; bk.rev. circ. 200. **Document type:** newsletter.
    Description: Researches the early Germantown, PA pioneers from Krefeld, Germany.

929   US
KRIEGBAUM HERITAGE.* vol. 3, 1977. q. 613 SW Medford Ave., Topeka, KS 66606-1829. Ed. Michael Malone.

KRONOS; journal of Cape history. see HISTORY — History Of Africa

929   US
LA FAYETTE; history and genealogy of Fayette County, Pa. 1981. 4/yr. $16. Southwest Pennsylvania Genealogical Services, Box 253, Laughlintown, PA 15655. Ed. William L. Iscrupe. (back issues avail.)
    Description: Covers wills, deeds, marriages, deaths, tax lists, cemetary-church-census records, naturalizations, and news items.

929   US   ISSN 0883-7708
LAMB'S PASTURES. 1985. s-a. $15. Stephen A. Lamb, Ed. & Pub., 2983 Bayside Ct., Wantagh, NY 11793. adv.; bk.rev. circ. 150. (looseleaf format; back issues avail.) **Document type:** newsletter.

929   US   ISSN 0748-1071
F157.L2
LANCASTER COUNTY CONNECTIONS. 1983. q. $17.50 membership. Box 207, Hershey, PA 17033. Ed. Gary T. Hawbaker. adv.; bk.rev. circ. 700. **Indexed:** Geneal.Per.Ind.
—UnCover.
    Description: Genealogical information on the ethnicity of the Pennsylvania county area.

LANCASTER COUNTY HISTORICAL SOCIETY. JOURNAL. see HISTORY — History Of North And South America

LAND AN DER MIESA. see HISTORY — History Of Europe

929   US   ISSN 8756-7067
F572.L3
LAPEER LEGACY. 1983. q. $12 to individuals; families $15; foreign $15. Lapeer County Genealogical Society, DeAngeli Branch Library, 921 W. Nepessing, Lapeer, MI 48446. TEL 313-664-6971. Ed. Alice J. Bohnsack. index. circ. 220. (back issues avail.)
—UnCover.

THE LAST LEAF. see HISTORY — History Of North And South America

929   US   ISSN 0747-6663
F752.L3
LATAH COUNTY GENEALOGICAL SOCIETY. QUARTERLY. 1981. q. $8 membership. Latah County Genealogical Society, 110 S. Adams, Moscow, ID 83843. Ed. Dorothy Viets Schell. index. circ. 80. **Document type:** newsletter.

974.8   US   ISSN 0023-8988
F157.S6
LAUREL MESSENGER. 1960. q. $15 membership. Historical & Genealogical Society of Somerset County, Inc., R F D No. 2, Box 238, Somerset, PA 15501. TEL 814-445-6077. Ed. Jeanne Coleman. bk.rev. circ. 1,000. **Indexed:** Geneal.Per.Ind. **Document type:** newsletter.

929   US
LAVENDER LINE. 1982. q. $20. Lavender Agency, Box 884, Bay Minette, AL 36507. Ed. Dess Lavender-Sangster. adv.; bk.rev. circ. 300.

929   US   ISSN 0748-1691
CS71
LAWSON LETTERS. 1979. 4/yr. $15. League of Lawsons, International, 1760 Jack Pine Ln., Redding, CA 96003-8724. TEL 916-549-5182. Ed. Mary Alice Lawson.

929   CN
LEAF OF THE BRANCH. 1989. q. Manitoba Genealogical Society, South West Branch, 53 Almond Cres., Brandon, MB R7B 1A2, Canada.
TEL 204-728-2857. FAX 204-725-1719. Eds. Elizabeth M. Wall, Margaret Goodman. circ. 150. **Document type:** newsletter.
    Description: Short articles and notices of interest to those researching family history.

929   UK   ISSN 0262-7574
LEICESTERSHIRE FAMILY HISTORY SOCIETY. NEWSLETTER. 1974. 4/yr. membership. Leicestershire Family History Society, 33 Garland Crescent, Leicester LE3 9BN, England. Ed. Joyce Billings. adv.; bk.rev. circ. 700. **Document type:** newsletter.
    Formerly: Leicestershire Family History Circle. Newsletter (ISSN 0140-9301)

LEICESTERSHIRE HISTORIAN. see HISTORY

929   UK   ISSN 0262-4435
LEITHEAD FAMILY NEWSLETTER. s-a. Dave Leithead, Ed. & Pub., 87 Chatsworth Dr., Mansfield, Nottinghamshire NG18 4QU, England. **Document type:** newsletter.

929   US   ISSN 0887-2856
F157.W8
LEST WE FORGET. 1981. s-a. $10 individual membership; families $15. Wyoming County Historical Society, Box 309, Tunkhannock, PA 18657. Eds. Jean Brewer, Paula Radwanski. bk.rev. circ. 500. **Document type:** newsletter.

929   US   ISSN 0748-1012
F497.L6
LICKING LANTERN; a light into the past. 1976. q. $12 membership (effective Jan.). Licking County Genealogical Society, 743 E. Main St., Box 4037, Newark, OH 43058-4037. TEL 614-345-3571. Ed. Kathy Dean. index. circ. 750. (back issues avail.) **Document type:** newsletter.
    Description: Contains early Licking County, Ohio records and information: deaths, obituaries, marriages, old newspaper articles, queries, programs available, and library acquisitions.

929.9   FI   ISSN 0357-1432
LIEHUVAN VARIT. 1970. 6/yr. Maamiehentie 1 C, SF 1630 Vaanta 63, Helsinki, Finland.

929   US   ISSN 0047-4630
CS42
LIFELINER (RIVERSIDE). 1965. q. $10. Genealogical Society of Riverside, Box 2557, Riverside, CA 92516. TEL 909-682-4998. Ed. Georgia Harris. adv.; bk.rev.; index. circ. 200. (processed) **Indexed:** Geneal.Per.Ind.

929   US   ISSN 1047-8655
F472.L85
LIFELINES (CHILLICOTHE). 1987. q. $12 to individuals; family $15. Livingston County Library, Livingston County Genealogical Society, 450 Locust St., Chillicothe, MO 64601. TEL 816-646-2168.

LIFESTORY; America's only magazine of writing personal and family history. see JOURNALISM

929 976   US
LINCOLN COUNTY TENNESSEE PIONEERS. 1970. s-a. $8. c/o Jane Warren Waller, Ed., 238 Point Clear, Conroe, TX 77304. bk.rev. circ. 450.

GENEALOGY AND HERALDRY

929 US
LIPSCOMB NEWSLETTER. 1981. a. $5. Phillip Heritage House, 605 Benton Ave., Missoula, MT 59801. TEL 406-543-3495. (back issues avail.) **Document type:** newsletter.

929 US
LITTELL'S LIVING AGE.* 1972. a. $7.50. Littell Families of America, Inc., 220 Hoover Blvd., Holland, MI 49423-3719. Ed. Ted Littell. bk.rev. circ. 500.

929 UK ISSN 0260-759X
LIVERPOOL FAMILY HISTORIAN. 1976. q. £1. (Liverpool Family History Society) Alt Press, c/o Dr. R. A. Yorke, Ed., 3 Wicks Lane, Formby, Liverpool, England. adv.; bk.rev. circ. 1,000.
Formerly (until Apr. 1981): Liverpool Family History Society (ISSN 0260-7557)

929 US ISSN 0732-7595
CS71
LOGSDON CONNECTIONS. q. $10. Gloria Logsdon Lucas, Ed. & Pub., 21056 Niagara River Dr., Sonora, CA 95370.

929 CN
LONG POINT GENEALOGIST. (Supplement to: Norfolklore) 1978. irreg. (4-5/yr.). membership. Norfolk Historical Society, 109 Norfolk St. S., Simcoe, Ont. N3Y 2W3, Canada. TEL 519-426-1583.

929 US
LOOKING; a Look family newsletter. q. $5. Ruth Harrison Janes, Ed. & Pub., 2816 Sloat Rd., Pebble Beach, CA 93953.

929.1 US ISSN 0362-4293
CS42
LOST IN CANADA?; Canadian-American genealogical journal. 1975. q. $14. Northwest Territory Canadian and French Heritage Center, Box 29397, Brooklyn Center, MN 55429-0397. TEL 608-269-6361. Ed. Joy Reisinger. adv.; bk.rev. circ. 1,000. **Indexed:** Geneal.Per.Ind.
—UnCover.

929 US
LOST PALATINE.* 1982. m. $12. 20290 Happy Dale Ln., Estero, FL 33928. Ed. Gail Breitband. adv.; bk.rev. circ. 125.

929 US
A LOT OF BUNKUM. 1980. m. $18. Old Buncombe County Genealogical Society, Box 2122, Asheville, NC 28802. TEL 704-253-1894. Ed. Doris Ward. circ. 500. (looseleaf format) **Document type:** newsletter.

929 US
LOTT LINEAGES. 1988. irreg. $5.50 per vol. Ancestor Seminars Library, c/o Sally Seaman Williams, Ed., Box 1035, N. Highlands, CA 95660-1035. TEL 916-991-4164. circ. 50. (back issues avail.)
Description: Covers genealogy and history of any Lott family.

LOUISIANA ARCHIVES AND MANUSCRIPTS ASSOCIATION. NEWSLETTER. see *LIBRARY AND INFORMATION SCIENCES*

929 US ISSN 0148-7655
F366
LOUISIANA GENEALOGICAL REGISTER. 1954. q. $25. Louisiana Genealogical and Historical Society, Box 3454, Baton Rouge, LA 70821. Ed. Nell T. Boersma. bk.rev.; index. circ. 525.
—UnCover.

929 US
LOVE LETTERS. 1984. q. $10. Roots 'n Things, 11910 Windmill Rd., Colorado Springs, CO 80908-4169. Ed. Pat Love Stubblefield Warner. circ. 175. (looseleaf format) **Document type:** newsletter.

929 US
LOW COUNTRY COURIER. 1960. 10/yr. $12 for individual membership; families $18; associations $8. South Carolina Genealogical Society, Charleston Chapter, Box 20266, Charleston, SC 29413-0266. Ed. Doris O'Brian. bk.rev. circ. 250.

LOYALIST GAZETTE. see *HISTORY — History Of North And South America*

929 US
LUCKY MEE FAMILY ASSOCIATION; news and notes from Mee to Mee. 1977. q. $12 to non-members. Lucky Mee Family Association, Drawer 4487, El Paso, TX 79914. TEL 915-751-7233. Ed. Joseph W. Mee. circ. 180. (looseleaf format; back issues avail.)
Formerly: News and Notes from Mee to Mee.

929 US
LUCKY MEE FAMILY ASSOCIATION. YEARBOOK. a. membership only. Lucky Mee Family Association, Drawer 4487, El Paso, TX 79914. TEL 915-751-7233. Ed. Joseph W. Mee. circ. 180 (controlled).

929 US ISSN 0099-1791
CS71
LUPTONIAN. 1974. irreg. free. David Walker Lupton, Ed. & Pub., Box 443, Bayboro, NC 28515-0443. TEL 919-745-7037. bk.rev.; bibl.; charts; illus.; stat.; index. circ. 300. (back issues avail.) **Document type:** newsletter.

929 975 US ISSN 0896-4602
LUTHER FAMILY NEWSLETTER; devoted to the interest of the descendants of Captain John Luther, Mass. Bay Colony 1630. 1987. q. $10. Luther Family Association, 2531 Lakeview St., Lakeland, FL 33801. TEL 813-665-5788. Ed. George Luther. bk.rev. circ. 875. (looseleaf format; back issues avail.) **Document type:** newsletter.

929 US ISSN 0887-9354
LYBARGER LINKAGES. 1985. 2/yr. 10. Lybarger Memorial Association, Box 7792, West Trenton, NJ 08628. TEL 609-396-1099. Ed. Lee H. Lybarger. circ. 800. (back issues avail.) **Document type:** newsletter.

929 US ISSN 0892-418X
CS71
LYNN - LINN LINEAGE QUARTERLY. 1987. q. $18. (Genealogical Research) Phyllis J. Bauer, Ed. & Pub., 3510 Turnberry Dr., McHenry, IL 60050-7557. TEL 815-385-9626. bk.rev. circ. 100. (back issues avail.)

929 SZ ISSN 1011-4009
DS135.S9
MAAJAN - DIE QUELLE. (Text in German) 1986. q. 65 SFr. Schweizerische Vereinigung fuer Juedische Genealogie, Postfach 876, CH-8021 Zurich, Switzerland. TEL 01-4627883. FAX 01-4635288. Eds. Rene Loeb, Raymond M. Jung. adv.; bk.rev. circ. 500. (back issues avail.) **Document type:** bulletin.

929 US ISSN 1066-8446
MCCLAIN COUNTY OKLAHOMA HISTORICAL AND GENEALOGICAL SOCIETY. QUARTERLY. 1984. q. $8 to members. McClain County Historical & Genealogical Society, 203 Washington St., Purcell, OK 73080. TEL 405-527-5894. Ed. Joyce A. Rex. bk.rev.; cum.index. circ. 200. **Document type:** newsletter.
Description: Covers the history of the county from its early days as the Pontotoc Co. of Indian Territory of Chicksaw Nation to the present, as well as family histories.

929 US
MCCOWM - COLQUHOUN QUARTERLY. 1987. q. $20. Collier Research, c/o Timothy P. Biarnesen, Box 371883, El Paso, TX 79937. TEL 915-595-2725.

929 US
MCCRARY (MCCREARY) "CLAN" NEWSLETTER. 1977. 5/yr. $7.95. 406 Jefferson Dr., Charlotte, NC 28270-5344. TEL 704-366-3474. Ed. Ms. Leslie McCrary. bk.rev. circ. 200. (back issues avail.)

929 US
MCCURRY KITH & KIN.* 1983. q. membership. McCurry Family Organization, 2295 Bedford Ct., Jonesboro, GA 30236-2502. circ. 50.

929 US
MAC'S TRACS. 1981. q. $9. McJunkin Journal, c/o Katherine L. McJunkin, Ed., 7736 Idlewood Ln., Dallas, TX 75230-3202.

929 US ISSN 0883-556X
MADDEN FAMILY NEWSLETTER. 1984. q. $15. 1101 Wilmington Ave., Apt. A, Dayton, OH 45420. TEL 513-293-0779. Ed. Mariam W. Schaefer. adv.; bk.rev.; index. circ. 132. **Document type:** newsletter.

929 US ISSN 1071-1937
MADISON COUNTY MUSINGS. 1980. q. $12.50 membership. Madison County Genealogical and Historical Society, Box 427, Huntsville, AR 72740. TEL 501-738-6408. Ed. Lucille Simpson. bk.rev. circ. 600. **Document type:** newsletter, directory.
Description: Covers family histories, group sheets, courthouse records, cemetery enumerations and general history of Madison County.

929 US ISSN 0743-8095
F225
MAGAZINE OF VIRGINIA GENEALOGY. 1962. q. $20 includes V G S Newsletter. Virginia Genealogical Society, 5001 W. Broad St., Ste. 115, Richmond, VA 23230-3023. adv. circ. 2,800. **Indexed:** Geneal.Per.Ind.
—UnCover.
Formerly (until 1984): Virginia Genealogy Society. Quarterly.
Description: Provides primary source material for Virginia genealogy and local history, with emphasis on 18th century vital statistics, court, and land records.

929 UK ISSN 0265-5691
MAGUIRE BULLETIN. 1983. a. $15. Irish Heritage Association, 162a Kingsway, Dunmurry, Belfast BT17 9AD, Northern Ireland. Kathleen Neill. **Document type:** newsletter.
Description: Covers the history and genealogy of the Maguire clan worldwide.

929 US ISSN 1064-6086
THE MAINE GENEALOGIST. 1976. q. $15. Maine Genealogical Society, Box 221, Farmington, ME 04938. Eds. Joseph C. Anderson, Lois Ware Thurston. bk.rev.; index; circ. 900 (paid). (back issues avail.) **Document type:** academic/scholarly publication.

929 US ISSN 0885-307X
F18
MAINE SEINE. 1978. q. $7.50. Maine Genealogical Society, 14 Adelbert St. S. Portland, ME 04106. TEL 207-799-4661. Ed. Alan H. Hawkins. bk.rev. circ. 1,200. (looseleaf format; back issues avail.)
—UnCover.

929.6 UK ISSN 0144-6932
MAJESTY. 1980. m. £20($49) (Canada $60; elsewhere £37). Grove Ash, Bletchley, Milton Keynes, Bucks. MK1 1BZ, England. TEL 071-436-4006. FAX 071-436-3458. (N. American subscr. to: Majesty Subscriptions, Box 301070, Escondido, CA 92030. TEL 619-747-8327) Ed. Ingric Seward; Pub. Peter King. adv. contact: Anthony Edwards. bk.rev. circ. 55,365. **Document type:** consumer publication.
Description: Covers the lives and activities of members of the British royal family.

929 US ISSN 0890-8192
MAN FROM MAINZ AND HIS DESCENDANTS. 1986. q. $17.50. B G M Publications, 28635 Old Hideaway Rd., Cary, IL 60013. TEL 708-639-2400. Ed. Betty G. Massman. circ. 278. (back issues avail.)
Description: Genealogical information on the surnames Mansker, Minsker, Mentzer, Mencer, and variations.

929 US ISSN 0883-7805
MANLEY FAMILY NEWSLETTER. 1983. 2/yr. $15. Manley Family Association, 171 Nathan Dr., Bohemia, NY 11716. TEL 516-567-0386. Ed. Trudi Manley. adv.; bk.rev.; bibl.; charts; illus. circ. 250. (back issues avail.) **Indexed:** Geneal.Per.Ind.
Document type: newsletter.
Description: Documents Manley family history, genealogy and heritage both past and present.

929 UK ISSN 0308-6380
CS439
MARFLEET SOCIETY NEWSLETTER. 1976. q. £2.50. Marfleet Society, 4 Robotham Close, Huncote, Leics. LE9 6BB, England. Ed. J.K. Marfleet. circ. 150. **Document type:** newsletter.

929 CN ISSN 0821-3275
MARKWICK MIDDEN. (Text in English) 1982. s-a. Can.$5($5) Valerie Ann Melanson, Ed. & Pub., 3506 Swansacre, Vancouver, B.C. V5S 4J8, Canada. TEL 604-435-9806. charts; illus. circ. 100. (back issues avail.) **Indexed:** Geneal.Per.Ind.

GENEALOGY AND HERALDRY

929 US
MARSHLAND TO HEARTLAND. 1987. q. $8. Ohio Genealogical Society, Ottowa County Chapter, Box 193, Port Clinton, OH 43452. TEL 419-734-7396. Ed. Martha A. Grindstaff. index. (back issues avail.)
 Description: Publishes items of genealogical interest relating to Ottowa County, Ohio.

929 US
MARTIN NEWSLETTER. a. $5. Phillip Heritage House, 605 Benton Ave., Missoula, MT 59801. TEL 406-543-3495. (back issues avail.) **Document type:** newsletter.

929 US ISSN 0542-8351
MARYLAND GENEALOGICAL SOCIETY BULLETIN. 1960. q. $18. Maryland Genealogical Society, 201 W. Monument St., Baltimore, MD 21201. TEL 410-685-3750. Ed. F. Edward Wright. adv.; bk.rev. circ. 1,500. **Indexed:** Geneal.Per.Ind. **Document type:** bulletin.

929 US
MARYLAND GENEALOGICAL SOCIETY NEWSLETTER. 1973. q. membership. Maryland Genealogical Society, 201 W. Monument St., Baltimore,.MD 21201. TEL 410-685-3750. Ed. Ella Rowe. (looseleaf format; back issues avail.) **Document type:** newsletter.

929 US ISSN 0895-4496
MASON FAMILY NEWSLETTER. 1987. 4/yr. $10. Compu - Chart, c/o Mrs. Paula Perkins Mortensen, 363 S. Park Victoria Dr., Milpitas, CA 95035-5708. adv. **Indexed:** Geneal.Per.Ind. **Document type:** newsletter.
 Description: Information on the surname and allied lines, accepting queries, family group sheets, ancestor charts, and other items of genealogical interest.

929 974 US
MATTANAWCOOK OBSERVER; a magazine of local history and genealogy of Lincoln, Penobscot County, Maine and the surrounding towns. 1982. q. $15. 14 Adelbert St., S. Portland, ME 04106-6512. Ed. Alan H. Hawkins. bk.rev. circ. 250. **Indexed:** Geneal.Per.Ind.

929 US ISSN 8756-3959
MAYFLOWER DESCENDANT; a magazine of Pilgrim genealogy and history. 1985. s-a. $18 (Canada $23; foreign $28). Massachusetts Society of Mayflower Descendants, 376 Boylstun St., 2 Fl., Boston, MA 02116-3812. FAX 617-266-1624. Ed. Alicia Crane Williams. bk.rev.; index. circ. 600. **Document type:** academic/scholarly publication.
 —UnCover.

929 917.4 US ISSN 0148-5032
F68
MAYFLOWER QUARTERLY; a journal of family history in colonial New England. 1935. q. $10. General Society of Mayflower Descendants, Box 3297, Plymouth, MA 02361. (Subscr. to: c/o Mildred Ramos, 3800 Montrose Ave., Richmond, VA 23222) Ed. Richard L. Husband. bk.rev.; charts; illus. circ. 22,000. **Indexed:** Geneal.Per.Ind.
 —UnCover.

929 US ISSN 0730-5214
E184.M45
MENNONITE FAMILY HISTORY. 1982. q. $17. Box 171, Elverson, PA 19520. TEL 215-286-0258. FAX 215-286-6860. Eds. Lois Ann Mast, J. Lemar Mast. adv.; bk.rev.; charts; illus.; index. circ. 1,850. (back issues avail.) **Indexed:** Geneal.Per.Ind. **Document type:** trade publication.
 —Faxon; UnCover.
 Description: Covers Mennonite, Amish, and Brethren genealogy and family history.

929 US ISSN 0732-3395
CS44
MEYER'S DIRECTORY OF GENEALOGICAL SOCIETIES IN THE U S A & CANADA. 1976. biennial. $23 (effective 1994). Libra Publications, 5179 Perry Rd., Mt. Airy, MD 21771. TEL 410-875-2824. FAX 410-875-2824. Ed. Mary K. Meyer. adv. circ. 1,500. **Document type:** directory.
 Formerly: Directory of Genealogical Societies in the U S A and Canada.

929 977 US ISSN 0889-3640
MIAMI MEANDERINGS. 1986. q. $7 to individuals; families $10. Miami County Historical & Genealogical Society, Box 305, Troy, OH 45373. Ed. Marion Clark. circ. 300. **Document type:** newsletter.

929 US
MICK FAMILY NEWSLETTER. 1979. q. $5. c/o Emma L. Smith, Ed., 6555 Manson Dr., Waterford, MI 48329. bk.rev. circ. 262. **Indexed:** Geneal.Per.Ind. **Document type:** newsletter.

929.1 US
MID-HUDSON GENEALOGICAL JOURNAL.* 1975. q. $6. Box 4436, West Columbia, SC 29171-4436. TEL 803-755-9568. Ed. Nancie Davis. adv.; bibl. circ. 100.

920 UK ISSN 0307-2851
CS435.M53
MIDLAND ANCESTOR. vol.4, 1975. q. £8($18) Birmingham and Midland Society for Genealogy and Heraldry, Executive Committee, 92 Dimmingsdale Bank, Birmingham B32 1ST, England. Ed. J. Gilmore. bk.rev.; bibl. circ. 3,200.

929 US
MIDLAND GENEALOGICAL SOCIETY. NEWSLETTER. 1972. m. membership. Midland Genealogical Society, Box 1191, Midland, TX 79702. TEL 915-688-8991. **Document type:** newsletter.
 Description: Provides information on meetings and other activities of the society, as well as other information of genealogical interest. Includes a bibliography of new acquisitions in the genealogy section of the Midland County Public Library.

929.3 US ISSN 0271-8685
CS42
MIDWEST HISTORICAL AND GENEALOGICAL REGISTER. QUARTERLY. 1966. q. $20 to individuals; institutions $17 (effective 1993). (Midwest Historical and Genealogical Society, Inc.) Rand Publishing Company, Box 1121, Wichita, KS 67201. TEL 316-264-3611. FAX 316-264-3611. Ed. Jane Murray. adv.; bk.rev. circ. 800. (back issues avail.) **Indexed:** Geneal.Per.Ind.
 —UnCover.
 Formerly: Midwest Genealogical Society. Surname Index (ISSN 0091-6439)
 Description: Genealogical and historical articles pertaining to Kansas, especially Sedgwick County.

929 US ISSN 1068-0756
MILESTONES. 1957. 3/yr. $12.50. Miles Merwin (1623-1697) Association, Inc., 1733 Blue Bell Rd., Blue Bell, PA 19422-2117. TEL 215-646-0231. Ed. Merwyn R. Buchanan. circ. 700. (looseleaf format; back issues avail.) **Document type:** newsletter.
 Description: Covers descendants of Miles and current activities of the association.

929 US
MILLER MONITOR. 1978. q. $17. Ancestor's Attic, c/o Frances R. Nelson, 4041 Pedley Rd., No. 18, Riverside, CA 92509. TEL 714-685-8936.

929 US
MILLER OF VIRGINIA LETTER.* q. $10. Genealogical & Historical News, c/o Robert Bradshaw, Box 779, Saipan, CM 96950, Mariana Islands.

929 US
MILLS QUARTERLY. 1987. q. $20. Collier Research, c/o Timothy P. Biarnesen, Ed., Box 371883, El Paso, TX 79937. TEL 915-595-2725.

929 UK ISSN 0261-3158
MILNHOLM CROSS NEWSLETTER. (Text in English, Scottish) 1981. s-a. £13($26) Clan Armstrong Trust Ltd., 87 Inskip Terrace, Gateshead NE8 4AJ, England. (Subscr. to: 4 Oakland Rd., West Monkseaton, Whitley Bay, Tyne and Wear NE25 8LS, England) Ed. Joseph Armstrong. adv.; bk.rev. circ. 300. (looseleaf format) **Document type:** newsletter.
 Description: Provides a mixture of history, heraldry and genealogy.

929 US ISSN 0741-3599
MINNESOTA GENEALOGICAL JOURNAL. 1984. 2/yr. $16 (effective 1993). Park Genealogical Books, 3601 78th Ave. N., Brooklyn Park, MN 55443. Ed. Alfred J. Dahlquist, Mary Hawker Bakeman. adv.; bk.rev.; cum.index. circ. 600. (also avail. in microfiche)
 —UnCover.
 Description: Covers early Minnesota area records.

929 US
MINNESOTA GENEALOGICAL SOCIETY. NEWSLETTER. 1969. 4/yr. membership. Minnesota Genealogical Society, Box 16069, St. Paul, MN 55116-0069. TEL 612-645-3671. circ. 1,600. **Document type:** newsletter.

929 US ISSN 0581-0086
MINNESOTA GENEALOGIST. 1969. q. membership. Minnesota Genealogical Society, Box 16069, St. Paul, MN 55116-0069. TEL 612-645-3671. circ. 1,600. **Indexed:** Geneal.Per.Ind. **Document type:** academic/scholarly publication.
 —UnCover.

929 CN
MISSISQUOI HISTORICAL SOCIETY REPORTS. (Text in English and French) 1960. a. Can.$15. Missisquoi Historical Society, 2 River St., Stanbridge East, PQ J0J 2H0, Canada. TEL 514-248-3153. Ed. Paige A. Knight. circ. 750. (back issues avail.) **Document type:** monographic series.

929 US ISSN 0747-5667
F465
MISSOURI STATE GENEALOGICAL ASSOCIATION JOURNAL. 1981. q. $15. Missouri State Genealogical Association, Box 833, Columbia, MO 65205-0833. TEL 314-364-1275. Ed. Robert M. Doerr. bk.rev. circ. 1,000. (also avail. in diskette format) **Indexed:** Geneal.Per.Ind.
 —UnCover.
 Description: Offers previously unpublished resource materials from all over the state, brief family history articles and queries.

929 US ISSN 0740-9699
F127.M55
THE MOHAWK. 1984. q. $14 (typically set in Oct.). Valley Quarterlies, c/o Arthur Kelly, Ed., 60 Cedar Heights Rd., Rhinebeck, NY 12572. TEL 914-876-4592. index. circ. 200. (back issues avail.) **Document type:** monographic series.
 —UnCover.

929 US
MONROE COUNTY GENEALOGICAL SOCIETY NEWS. 1982. q. $5 membership. Monroe County Genealogical Society, c/o Vivian Shelquist, Ed., Rt. 3, Albia, IA 52531. TEL 515-932-5477. circ. 250. **Document type:** newsletter.

929 US
MONTGOMERY COUNTY GENEALOGICAL JOURNAL. 1971. q. $9.50. c/o Ann Evans Alley, Rt. 1, Box 71, Adams, TN 37010.

929 US
MOORE FAMILY REGISTER. 4/yr. Ophelia Wade, Ed. & Pub., Rte. 1, Box 26, Bragg City, MO 63827.

MORASHA/HERITAGE. see ETHNIC INTERESTS

929 US
THE MORELAND MUSTER. q. $12. Nona Williams, Ed. & Pub., Box 225, Ben Lomond, CA 95005. TEL 408-475-3114. adv.; bk.rev. (also avail. in microfiche) **Document type:** newsletter.

929 US ISSN 0883-3605
CS71
MORGAN MIGRATIONS; the research aid for Morgan, Morgen, Moughon, etc. families. 1977. 3/yr. $15. Lineage Search Associates, 6419 Colts Neck Rd., Mechanicsville, VA 23111-4233. TEL 804-730-7414. Ed. Michael E. Pollock. bk.rev.; index.

929 US ISSN 1059-3705
MORRIS MEMBERS. 1990. q. $10. Kinseeker Publications, Box 184, Grawn, MI 49637. Ed. Marie Kezeli. bk.rev. circ. 25. (looseleaf format) **Document type:** newsletter.

929 US ISSN 0882-4266
MOUNTAIN EMPIRE GENEALOGICAL QUARTERLY. 1982. q. $20. Mountain Empire Genealogical Quarterly, c/o Gregory Lynn Vanover, Box 628, Pound, VA 24279. TEL 703-796-5233. Eds. Gregory L. Vanover, Joan S. Vanover. adv.; bk.rev. circ. 800.
 Formerly (until 1983): Mountain Empire Quarterly (ISSN 8756-0704)

929 US ISSN 8756-4327
MUDDY ROOTS. q. membership. Mississippi County Genealogy Society, Box 5, Charleston, MO 63834.

GENEALOGY AND HERALDRY

929   GW
MULOT'SCHEN FAMILIENVERBAND. ZEITSCHRIFT; genealogische Mitteilungen fuer Hugenotten- und Waldensernachkommen. 1955. s-a. DM.24($12) Mulot'scher Familienverband, c/o Heinz Mulot, Steineshof-Zell, 36329 Romrod, Germany. TEL 06636-555. Ed. Heinz Mulot. circ. 250. (looseleaf format; back issues avail.)

929 051   US
MUNRO EAGLE. 1971. a. $2. Clan Munro Association U S A, Inc., 11 Las Huertas Ridge Rd., Placitas, NM 87043. Ed. Frances E. Stephens. circ. 650 (controlled). (back issues avail.)

929   US   ISSN 1059-3713
MURPHY MATES. 1991. q. $10. Kinseeker Publications, Box 184, Grawn, MI 49637. Ed. Marie Kezeli. bk.rev. circ. 25. (looseleaf format) **Document type:** newsletter.

929 069.6   US
MUSEUM RECORD. 1982. m. $5. Bay County Historical Society, 321 Washington Ave., Bay City, MI 48708. TEL 517-893-5733. (Co-sponsor: Historical Museum of Bay County) Ed. Rodrick Ramsay. circ. 500. (back issues avail.)
Formerly: Bay County Crier.

929.9   US   ISSN 1053-3338
N A V A NEWS. 6/yr. $30 to individuals; students $15. North American Vexillological Association, 1977 N. Olden Ave., Ste. 225, Trenton, NJ 08618. Ed. Grace R. Cooper. **Document type:** newsletter.

929   US   ISSN 0747-9891
F3
N E H G S NEXUS. 1984. 5/yr. $35 (includes New England Historical and Genealogical Register). New England Historic Genealogical Society, 101 Newbury St., Boston, MA 02116. TEL 617-536-5740. Eds. Robert Shaw, Julie Helen Otto. abstr.; bibl.; charts; illus.; index. circ. 13,500. (back issues avail.)
—UnCover.
Description: Membership publication specializing in genealogy, demographics and social history.

929   US   ISSN 0887-1353
N G S NEWSLETTER. 1975. bi-m. $35 includes National Genealogical Society Quarterly; free to members. National Genealogical Society, 4527 17th St., N., Arlington, VA 22207. TEL 703-525-0050. Ed. Ann Crowley. circ. 13,000. (looseleaf format) **Document type:** newsletter.
—UnCover.
Formerly (until 1987): National Genealogical Society. Newsletter (ISSN 0197-4831)

929   US   ISSN 8756-4718
NASH NOTATIONS. 1983. q. $14 (Canada $17). Culver Publications, 840 Mesman Dr., Grants Pass, OR 97527-6018. TEL 503-471-0387. Ed. Lois H. Culver. abstr.; bibl.; charts; index. circ. 100. **Document type:** newsletter.
Description: Researches all Nash names in the US.

929   US   ISSN 0738-985X
F325
NATCHEZ TRACE TRAVELER. 1981. q. $20 (effective 1994). Natchez Trace Genealogical Society, Box 420, Florence, AL 35631. Ed. Darrell A. Russel. bk.rev.; index; circ. 450 (paid); 150 (controlled). (back issues avail.) **Indexed:** Geneal.Per.Ind.

929   US   ISSN 0742-9045
CS44
NATIONAL DIRECTORY OF LOCAL RESEARCHERS. 1981. a. $10. Family Tree Genealogical Society, 450 Potter St., Wauseon, OH 43567. TEL 419-335-6485. Ed. Howard V. Fausey. adv. circ. 200. **Document type:** directory.

929   UK   ISSN 0951-9521
NATIONAL GENEALOGICAL DIRECTORY. 1979. a. £7($14.50) Hollow Hole Farm, Binegar Lane, Binegar, Somerset BA3 4TR, England. TEL 0749-840184. Ed. Iris Louise Caley. adv. circ. 2,000. **Document type:** directory.
—BLDSC (6024.028000).
Description: International research aid for all family, local and special interest historians.

929   US   ISSN 0027-934X
CS42
NATIONAL GENEALOGICAL SOCIETY QUARTERLY. 1912. q. $35 (includes Newsletter). National Genealogical Society, 4527 17th St., N., Arlington, VA 22207. TEL 703-525-0050. Eds. Elizabeth Shown Mills, Gary Bernard Mills. adv.; bk.rev.; charts; index. circ. 13,000. (also avail. in microfiche from PMC)
Indexed: Amer.Hist.& Life, Bk.Rev.Ind. (1977-), Child.Bk.Rev.Ind. (1977-), Geneal.Per.Ind., Hist.Abstr. **Document type:** academic/scholarly publication.
—UnCover.

973   US
NATIONAL SOCIETY OF UNITED STATES DAUGHTERS OF 1812. NEWSLETTER. 1923. 3/yr. membership only. National Society of United States Daughters of 1812, 1461 Rhode Island Ave., N.W., Washington, DC 20005. TEL 202-332-3181. circ. 5,000. **Document type:** newsletter.
Description: Genealogical snd historical news from the national office and state chapters, with news of activities and topics of interest to members.

929   US
NAVARRO LEAVES AND BRANCHES. 1978. 4/yr. membership. Navarro County Genealogical Society, Box 2278, Corsicana, TX 75151. Ed. Elizabeth Gillispie. bk.rev. circ. 225. (back issues avail.)

929   US   ISSN 1064-0894
THE NAVIGATOR. 1981. 6/yr. $12 membership. Norfolk Genealogical Society, Box 12813, Thomas Corner, Norfolk, VA 23541-0813. Ed. Katherine Partridge. adv.; bk.rev. circ. 200.
Description: Bi-monthly publication of the Norfolk Genealogical Society.

929   NE   ISSN 0921-9021
NEDERLAND'S ADELSBOEK. a. $62. Centraal Bureau voor Genealogie, Prins Willem-Alexanderhof 22, P.O. Box 11755, 2502 AT The Hague, Netherlands. TEL 31-70-3814651. illus.; index.
Description: Genealogies of the nobility of the Netherlands.

929   NE   ISSN 0928-0979
NEDERLAND'S PATRICIAAT. 1910. a. $60. Centraal Bureau voor Genealogie, Prins Willem Alexanderhof 22, Postbus 11755, 2502 AT The Hague, Netherlands. TEL 31-70-3814651. illus.; cum.index.
Description: Genealogies of prominent Dutch families.

929   NE
NEDERLANDS REPERTORIUM VAN FAMILIENAMEN. 1963. a. price varies. (Koninklijke Nederlandse Academie van Wetenschappen) Walburg Pers BV, Postbus 4159, 7200 BD Zutphen, Netherlands. TEL 31-5750-10522. FAX 31-5750-41025.

929   NE   ISSN 0028-226X
DE NEDERLANDSCHE LEEUW. (Supplements avail.) 1883. m. fl.65. (Koninklijk Nederlandsch Genootschap voor Geslacht- en Wapenkunde) Centraal Bureau voor Genealogie, P.O. Box 11755, 2502 AT The Hague, Netherlands. TEL 31-70-814651. Ed. J.G. Smit. bk.rev. circ. 1,400. **Document type:** academic/scholarly publication.
—SWETS.

929.6   US   ISSN 1048-7980
THE NEW CONSTELLATION. 1970. 3/yr. membership. National Flag Foundation, Flag Plaza, Pittsburgh, PA 15219-3630. TEL 412-261-1776. Ed. George F. Cahill. circ. 3,000. **Document type:** newsletter.
Formerly (until 1990): Flag Plaza Standard (ISSN 0882-2220)
Description: Resource for flag etiquette, history and news of activities related to the U.S. flag.

929 974   US   ISSN 0028-4785
F1
NEW ENGLAND HISTORICAL AND GENEALOGICAL REGISTER. 1847. q. $35 (includes N E H G S Nexus). New England Historic Genealogical Society, 101 Newbury St., Boston, MA 02116. TEL 617-536-5740. Ed. Jane Fletcher Fiske. adv.; bk.rev.; bibl.; illus.; index. circ. 14,000. (also avail. in microform from UMI; reprint service avail.) **Indexed:** Amer.Hist.& Life, Geneal.Per.Ind., Hist.Abstr.
—Faxon; UnCover.
Description: Archival quality material on genealogy, with emphasis on New England families and their English or European origins.

NEW GLEANINGS. see *MUSEUMS AND ART GALLERIES*

929   US   ISSN 1055-0763
F33
NEW HAMPSHIRE GENEALOGICAL RECORD. 1903. q. $20 to non-members; members free. New Hampshire Society of Genealogists, Box 2316, Concord, NH 03302-2316. TEL 603-432-8317. FAX 603-437-1808. Ed. George F. Sanborn, Jr. adv.; bk.rev. circ. 925. **Document type:** academic/scholarly publication.
—SWETS.
Description: Publishes genealogies, source records and book reviews that touch upon New Hampshire families.

NEW JERSEY HISTORY; a magazine of New Jersey history. see *HISTORY — History Of North And South America*

929   US   ISSN 0899-1340
NEW JERSEY QUERIES. 1986. irreg. $7.25. McNeill Enterprises, Box 779, Napavine, WA 98565-0779. TEL 509-922-4521. bk.rev.
Description: Forum of communication for research of New Jersey ancestral names. Accepts queries.

929   US
NEW RACE. a. $10. Phillip Heritage House, 605 Benton Ave., Missoula, MT 59801. TEL 406-543-3495. (back issues avail.) **Document type:** newsletter.

929   US   ISSN 0028-7237
F116
NEW YORK GENEALOGICAL AND BIOGRAPHICAL RECORD. 1869. q. $25. New York Genealogical and Biographical Society, 122 E. 58th St., New York, NY 10022-1939. TEL 212-755-8532. Ed. Henry B. Hoff. adv.; bk.rev.; illus.; index. circ. 2,000. (also avail. in microform from MCA,UMI; back issues avail.; reprint service avail. from UMI) **Indexed:** Geneal.Per.Ind. **Document type:** academic/scholarly publication.
—UnCover.
Description: Source material and compiled genealogies for New York State families.

929   US   ISSN 1051-5887
NEW YORK PEDIGREES. 1990. irreg $5 per no. Family Tree, Box 4311, Boise, ID 83711. TEL 208-939-9136. Ed. Patricia R. James. index. circ. 250. (looseleaf format; back issues avail.)
Description: Circulates pedigree charts concerning New York as submittec by researchers.

929   US   ISSN 1041-6560
F118
NEW YORK STATE QUERIES. 1987. irreg., vol.9, 1992. $6.50 per no. Weidner Words, 2206 W. Borden Rd., Spokane, WA 99204-9668. TEL 509-448-9263. Ed. Carolyn Weidner. bk.rev.; index. (back issues avail.)
Description: Contains anectdotes on New York state.

929   NZ   ISSN 0110-4012
NEW ZEALAND GENEALOGIST. 1970. 6/yr. NZ.$31 membership. New Zealand Society of Genealogists Inc., P.O. Box 8795, Symonds St., Auckland 1035, New Zealand. TEL 09-689-019. Ed. Vivienne Parker. adv.; bk.rev.; charts; index. circ. 6,000. (back issues avail.)
—CCC.

929   CN   ISSN 0838-049X
NEWFOUNDLAND ANCESTOR. 1984. q. Can.$25. Newfoundland and Labrador Genealogical Society Inc., Colonial Bldg., Military Rd., St. John's, NF A1C 2C9, Canada. TEL 709-754-9525. Ed. Elsa Hochwald. bk.rev.; index; circ. 1,100 (controlled).
Description: Provides members with a means in which to share information and exchange ideas on the subject of family history research in the province of Newfoundland.

929   US   ISSN 0747-8739
F548.25
NEWS FROM THE NORTHWEST. 1977. bi-m. membership. Northwest Suburban Council of Genealogists, Box AC, Mt. Prospect, IL 60056. Ed. Evelyn Koons. bk.rev.; s-a. index. circ. 250. (looseleaf format; back issues avail.) **Indexed:** Geneal.Per.Ind. **Document type:** newsletter.

GENEALOGY AND HERALDRY

929   UK   ISSN 0260-695X
NEWTH-NUTH FAMILY HISTORY SOCIETY. NEWSLETTER. 1979. irreg. (approx. a.). membership. Newth-Nuth Family History Society, c/o Mrs. Janet D. Nuth, Ed., 27 Charville Lane, Hayes, Middlesex, England.
Formerly (until 1980): Newth Nuth News.

929   US
NICHOLS NOSTALGIA. 1984. q. $18. Nickleodeon, Box 365, Byron, CA 94514. Ed. Jeannie Gordon Vaughan. bk.rev.; index. circ. 250. (back issues avail.)
Description: Provides data relating to the surname Nichols, Nicholas, Nickle, Nicol, Nicholl, etc. Lists marriages, births, deaths, military records, Bible records, family histories, pictures, queries and ancestor file listing.

929   NE   ISSN 0166-2767
NIET ZO BENAUWD. (Summaries in English) 1959. a. fl.12.50($7) Stichting Familieclub Johannes van der Linden - Foundation Family Club Johannes van der Linden, Salomeschouw 61, 2726 JP Zoetermeer, Netherlands. TEL 31-79-411955. Ed. M.E. Leegwater-van der Linden. adv.; bk.rev.; illus.; circ. 150 (controlled). (processed)

929   NR
NIGERIAN NAMES. 1972. irreg. Daystar Press, Box 1261, Ibadan, Nigeria.

929   FR   ISSN 0755-7469
NORD GENEALOGIE. 1971. bi-m. 240 F. Groupement Genealogique de la Region du Nord, B.P. 62, 59118 Wambrechies, France. Ed. Edmond Derreumaux. bibl. circ. 1,500. **Document type:** bulletin.

929   GW
NORDDEUTSCHE FAMILIENKUNDE IN VERBINDUNG MIT DER ZEITSCHRIFT FUER NIEDERDEUTSCHE FAMILIENKUNDE. 1919. 4/yr. DM.40 to non-members. (Genealogische Gesellschaft, Sitz Hamburg e.V.) H. Scherer Verlag GmbH, Boothstr. 21A, 12207 Berlin, Germany. Ed. Georg W. Jahn. bk.rev.; bibl.; index. circ. 800.
Formed by the 1986 merger of: Zeitschrift fuer Niederdeutsche Familienkunde (ISSN 0044-3190); Norddeutsche Familienkunde (ISSN 0468-3390)

929.9   NO   ISSN 0109-7539
NORDISK FLAGKONTAKT. 2/yr. Vest-Agder Fylkesmuseum, Postboks 4048, Kongsgaard, 4602 Kristiansand, Norway. Ed. Jan Henrik Munksgaard.

929   CN
NORFOLKLORE. q. membership. Norfolk Historical Society, 109 Norfolk St. S., Simcoe, Ont. N3Y 2W3, Canada. TEL 519-426-1583.
Formerly: Eva Brook Donly Museum News.

929   NO   ISSN 0029-2141
CS910
NORSK SLEKTSHISTORISK TIDSSKRIFT. 1926. s-a. 180($35) Norsk Slektshistorisk Forening, P.O. Box 9562, Egertorvet, N-0128 Oslo 1, Norway. Ed.Bd. adv.; bk.rev. circ. 1,800.

929.1   US   ISSN 0360-1056
F253
NORTH CAROLINA GENEALOGICAL SOCIETY JOURNAL. 1975. q. $25 to individuals; institutions $22 (includes Newsletter). North Carolina Genealogical Society, Box 1492, Raleigh, NC 27602. Ed. Raymond A. Winslow, Jr. bk.rev.; charts; illus.; index. circ. 2,375.
—UnCover.
Description: Articles of general genealogical value, source data from original documents, and other material from previously unpublished sources.

929   US
NORTH CAROLINA GENEALOGICAL SOCIETY NEWSLETTER. Cover title: N C G S News. 1974. 6/yr. $25 includes North Carolina Genealogical Society Journal. North Carolina Genealogical Society, Box 1492, Raleigh, NC 27602. Ed. Timothy Kearney. bk.rev.; bibl.; charts. (back issues avail.) **Document type:** newsletter.
Description: Coverage of the Society's meetings with a message from the president of the Society.

929   UK   ISSN 0306-9206
NORTH CHESHIRE FAMILY HISTORIAN. 1969. q. £5. North Cheshire Family History Society, 24 Palatine House, Edgeley, Stockport, Cheshire SK3 9HT, England. Eds. M.N. Hollings, S.M. Crossley. adv.; bk.rev.; illus. circ. 800. **Document type:** bulletin.

929   US
NORTH LOUISIANA GENEALOGICAL SOCIETY JOURNAL. 1981. q. membership. North Louisiana Genealogical Society, Box 324, Ruston, LA 71273. Ed.Bd. adv.; bk.rev. circ. 125.

929   US   ISSN 0743-1341
F548.25
NORTH SUBURBAN GENEALOGICAL SOCIETY. NEWSLETTER. 1975. bi-m. $12. North Suburban Genealogical Society, c/o Winnetka Public Library, 768 Oak St., Winnetka, IL 60093. TEL 312-446-7220. Ed. Allison Childs. bk.rev. circ. 250. **Indexed:** Geneal.Per.Ind. **Document type:** newsletter.

929   UK   ISSN 0309-8486
NORTHAMPTONIANA. 1977. q. £1. Northampton Family History Society, 294 Birchfield Rd. E., Northampton NN3 2SY, England. Ed. Christopher J. Glazebrook. bk.rev.

NORTHEAST MISSISSIPPI HISTORICAL AND GENEALOGICAL SOCIETY QUARTERLY. see HISTORY — History Of North And South America

929   UK   ISSN 0307-8140
NORTHUMBERLAND & DURHAM FAMILY HISTORY SOCIETY. JOURNAL. 1975. q. £10 (foreign £14). Northumberland & Durham Family History Society, c/o J.A. Ashburner, Sec., 10 Melrose Grove, Jarrow, Tyne & Wear NE32 4HP, England. Ed. J.A. Readdie. bk.rev. circ. 2,000. **Document type:** bulletin.

929   US   ISSN 0887-588X
NORTHWEST GEORGIA HISTORICAL & GENEALOGICAL QUARTERLY.* 1966. q. $15. Northwest Georgia Historical and Genealogical Society, Inc., Box 951, Rome, GA 30162-0951. Ed. Terrell Shaw. adv.; bk.rev.; charts. circ. 400. (back issues avail.)

929   UK   ISSN 0263-6506
NORTH WEST KENT FAMILY HISTORY. 1978. q. £8. North West Kent Family History Society, 3 Mereside, Orpington, Kent BR6 8ET, England. Ed. Ron Anthony. bk.rev.; index. circ. 1,400. (back issues avail.) **Document type:** consumer publication.

929   UK
NORTH WEST SOCIETIES. COMBINED REGISTER OF MEMBERS' INTERESTS. 1977. irreg. (approx. every 2-3 yrs.). £2.50 to non-members. Lancashire Family History and Heraldry Society, c/o A.A. Todd, 78 Albert St., Ramsbottom, Bury, Lancs BL0 9EL, England. (Co-sponsors: Family History Society of Cheshire; North Cheshire Family History Society; Liverpool Family History Society) bk.rev. circ. 2,000.
Formerly (until 1981): Inquisition (ISSN 0144-7211)

929   US
NORTON COUNTY TRACER.* q. $7.50. Norton County Genealogical Society, Box 446, Norton, KS 67654-0446. TEL 913-877-2481. circ. 100.

929   US   ISSN 1049-1821
CS71
NORTON NOTES. 1987. q. $10. Kinseeker Publications, Box 184, Grawn, MI 49637. Ed. Victoria Wilson. bk.rev. circ. 35. (looseleaf format; back issues avail.) **Document type:** newsletter.

929   US
NORWEGIAN TRACKS. 1710. q. $16. Vesterheim Genealogical Center, 415 W. Main St., Madison, WI 53703. TEL 608-262-2504. (Subscr. to: 502 W. Water St., Decorah, IA 52101) Ed. Gerhard B. Naeseth. circ. 1,630. (back issues avail.) **Document type:** newsletter.
Description: Provides information on Norwegian genealogy.

929   CN   ISSN 0714-3672
CS88.N64
NOVA SCOTIA GENEALOGIST. 1972. 3/yr. Can.$20($20) Genealogical Association of Nova Scotia, P.O. Box 641, Sta."M", Halifax, NS B3J 2T3, Canada. Ed. Freda Withrow. bk.rev.; index. circ. 1,200. (tabloid format; back issues avail.) **Document type:** newsletter.
Formerly: Royal Nova Scotia Historical Society. Genealogical Newsletter.

929   US   ISSN 1059-9711
F860
THE NUGGET. (Supplement avail.: C G S News (ISSN 1058-5133)) 1991. s-a. California Genealogical Society, 300 Brannan St., Ste. 409, Box 77105, San Francisco, CA 94107-0105. TEL 415-777-9936. Ed. Marje Kelt. adv.
Description: Includes genealogical information, queries, and memoirs.

929   US   ISSN 1055-8632
NUGGETS FROM PARADISE. 1982. m. $20 membership. Paradise Genealogical Society, Inc., Box 460, Paradise, CA 95967-0460. TEL 916-877-2330. Eds. Thomasene Pierro, Earl Cowden. bk.rev. circ. 325. (looseleaf format; back issues avail.) **Document type:** newsletter.

929   US
NYANDO ROOTS. 1984. q. $10. Nyando Roots Genealogical Club, Box 175, Massena, NY 13662. Ed.Bd. circ. 800.
Description: Contains information concerning the first settlers in St. Laurence and Franklin Counties, New York. Covers cemetaries, newspapers, histories and other material related to this area.

929   US
NYE FAMILY NEWSLETTER. 1966. 2/yr. $10. Nye Family of America Association, Box 134, E. Sandwich, MA 02537. TEL 508-888-2368. Ed. Andrea Leonard. bk.rev.; illus.; circ. 2,500 (controlled). **Document type:** newsletter.
Description: Provides news of the Benjamin Nye Homestead Museum activities, family news and genealogical information.

929   US   ISSN 0740-8013
F392.M4
OAK LEAVES. 1982. q. $15. Matagorda County Genealogical Society, Box 264, Bay City, TX 77404-0264. TEL 409-245-6931. Eds. Carol Sue Gibbs, Shirley Brown. bk.rev. circ. 200.

929   US   ISSN 0473-9825
OHIO GENEALOGICAL SOCIETY. REPORT. 1960. q. $25. Ohio Genealogical Society, 34 Sturges Ave., Box 2625, Mansfield, OH 44906-0625. TEL 419-522-9077. Ed. Phyllis Brownmiller. adv.; bk.rev.; index. circ. 6,350.
—UnCover.

929   US   ISSN 0893-1593
OHIO GENEALOGICAL SOCIETY. WOOD COUNTY CHAPTER. NEWSLETTER. 1981. bi-m. $8 includes membership. Ohio Genealogical Society, Wood County Chapter, Box 722, Bowling Green, OH 43402. TEL 419-352-4940. Ed. Lolita Guthrie. bk.rev.; abstr.; charts; stat.; index; circ. 450 (paid); 150 (controlled). (looseleaf format) **Document type:** newsletter.
—UnCover.
Description: Covers Wood County historical and family data from the 1820s to the 1950s, from church, school, town and township sources, with news of meetings and projects.

929   US   ISSN 1052-858X
OHIO GENEALOGICAL SOCIETY NEWSLETTER. 1970. m. $25 (effective Jan. 1991). Ohio Genealogical Society, Box 2625, Mansfield, OH 44906-0625. TEL 419-522-9077. Ed. Sunda Peters. circ. 6,350. **Document type:** newsletter.

929   US   ISSN 1063-4649
F490
OHIO RECORDS & PIONEER FAMILIES; the cross road of our nation. 1960. q. $19 to non-members; members $18. Ohio Genealogical Society, Box 2625, Mansfield, OH 44906-0625. Ed. Susan Dunlap Lee. circ. 1,200. (processed) **Indexed:** Geneal.Per.Ind.

929   US   ISSN 0474-0742
OKLAHOMA GENEALOGICAL SOCIETY QUARTERLY. 1955. q. membership. Oklahoma Genealogical Society, Box 12986, Oklahoma City, OK 73157. Eds. Mrs. Sharron Ashton, Mrs. Dorothy Paul. bk.rev.; index. circ. 1,150.
—UnCover.

OKLAHOMA PONTOTOC COUNTY QUARTERLY. see HISTORY — History Of North And South America

929 US ISSN 0895-4070
OKLAHOMA QUERIES. 1988. irreg., no.8, 1991. $5 per issue. Palouse Publications, SE 310 Camino, Pullman, WA 99163-2206. TEL 509-334-1732. Ed. Janet Margolis Damm. (back issues avail.) **Document type:** newsletter.

929 942 UK
OLD CORNWALL. 1925. s-a. £1.50 per no. Federation of Old Cornwall Societies, 8 Avenue Rd., Falmouth, Cornwall, England. TEL 0326-316782. Ed. A. Pearson. bk.rev.; bibl.; charts; illus. circ. 1,000. **Indexed:** Br.Hum.Ind.
Description: Contains items of local interest.

929 US
OLD FORT GENEALOGICAL SOCIETY: QUARTERLY. 1982. q. $5. Old Fort Genealogical Society, Inc., Box One, Fort Madison, IA 52627. Ed. Connie Street. circ. 170 (paid). **Document type:** newsletter.
Formerly (until 1988): Old Fort Genealogical Society. Newsletter.

929 US ISSN 0098-4760
F680
OLD FORT LOG. 1974. q. $8. Old Fort Genealogical Society of Southeastern Kansas, 201 S. National, Fort Scott, KS 66701. Ed. Margie E. Williams. illus.; index. circ. 200.
Description: Contains minutes of monthly meetings, queries, surname exchange, vital records and other genealogical related material of interest to researchers interested in Bourbon County, Kansas.

929 US
OLD WESTMORELAND; the history and genealogy of Westmoreland County, Pennsylvania. 1980. q. $16. Southwest Pennsylvania Genealogical Services, Box 253, Laughlintown, PA 15655. Ed. William L. Iscrupe. (back issues avail.)
Description: Includes wills, deeds, marriages, deaths, tax lists, cemetery-church-census records, naturalizations, and news items.

929 US
OLDE MECKLENBURG GENEALOGICAL SOCIETY QUARTERLY. 1983. q. $10 to individuals (family $15). Mecklenburg Genealogical Society, Box 32453, Charlotte, NC 28232. Dir. Ronald Touchstone. adv.; bk.rev.; index. circ. 500. **Document type:** newsletter.
Formerly: Mecklenburg Genealogical Society Quarterly.

929 GW ISSN 0030-2074
OLDENBURGISCHE FAMILIENKUNDE. 1959. q. DM.30. Oldenburgische Gesellschaft fuer Familienkunde, Lerigauweg 14, 26131 Oldenburg, Germany. Ed. Wolfgang Buesing. **Document type:** bulletin.

929 914 US ISSN 1056-0378
O'LOCHLAINNS IRISH FAMILY JOURNAL. Key Title: O'Lochlainns Personal Journal of Irish Families. 1986. bi-m. $49. Irish Genealogical Foundation, Box 7575, Kansas City, MO 64116. TEL 816-454-2410. FAX 816-454-2410. Ed. Michael C. O'Laughlin. adv.; bk.rev.; bibl.; charts; illus.; stat.; index. circ. 3,000. (back issues avail.) **Document type:** academic/scholarly publication, newsletter.
Description: Covers Irish genealogy, history and Irish America.

929 US ISSN 0882-1933
CS71
OLSCHWANGER JOURNAL.* 1983. a. $15. Anna Olswanger, Ed. & Pub., 7117 Harps Mill Rd., Raleigh, NC 27615-5323. TEL 901-327-4341. circ. 250.

929 US
OLYMPIA GENEALOGICAL SOCIETY. QUARTERLY. 1975. q. $10. Olympia Genealogical Society, c/o Olympia Timberland Library, 8th and Franklin, Olympia, WA 98501. TEL 206-352-0595. Ed. Jerri McCoy. bk.rev.; index. circ. 300. (back issues avail.) **Indexed:** Geneal.Per.Ind. **Document type:** bulletin.

929 US ISSN 1066-5382
ON THE RAMAGE TRAIL. 1991. q. free. 7570 E. Speedway, No. 509, Tucson, AZ 85710. TEL 602-296-4377. Eds. Bill & Ann Ramage. circ. 200. **Document type:** newsletter.

929 UK ISSN 0265-5683
O'NEILL CLAN NEWS. 1982. a. $15. Irish Heritage Association, 162a Kingsway, Dunmurry, Belfast BT17 9AD, Northern Ireland. Ed. Kathleen Neill. **Document type:** newsletter.
Description: Covers all aspects of O'Neill history and genealogy worldwide.

929 CN ISSN 1188-1089
ONTARIO GENEALOGICAL SOCIETY. KINGSTON BRANCH. KINGSTON RELATIONS. 1974. 5/yr. Can.$20. Ontario Genealogical Society, Kingston Branch, P.O. Box 1394, Kingston, ON K7L 5C6, Canada. Ed. Stephanie Stone. bk.rev. circ. 580. (back issues avail.) **Document type:** newsletter.
Formerly (until Jan. 1992): Ontario Genealogical Society. Kingston Branch. Newsletter (ISSN 0316-5183)
Description: Genealogical news of Frontenac, Lennox and Addington Counties, Ontario.

929 CN ISSN 0708-5583
CS88.06
ONTARIO GENEALOGICAL SOCIETY. OTTAWA BRANCH NEWS. 1970. 6/yr. $10. Ontario Genealogical Society, Ottawa Branch, P.O. Box 8346, Ottawa, ON K1G 3H8, Canada. TEL 613-745-0200. Ed. Bill Tufts. bk.rev. circ. 1,055.
Formerly: Ontario Genealogical Society. Ottawa Branch. Publication.
Description: An aid in learning more of local genealogies and local history, includes queries.

929 CN ISSN 0380-1616
ONTARIO GENEALOGY SOCIETY. NEWSLEAF. 1971. 4/yr. Can.$35 (foreign $35) includes "Families". Ontario Genealogical Society, Ste. 251, 40 Orchard View Blvd., Toronto, ON M4R 1B9, Canada. TEL 416-489-0734. Ed. Alfreda Veenstra. adv.; bk.rev. circ. 5,500. (back issues avail.)

929 US
ORANGE COUNTY CALIFORNIA GENEALOGICAL SOCIETY QUARTERLY. 1964. q. $15. Orange County California Genealogical Society, Box 1587, Orange, CA 92668. Ed. J.G. Weissgerber. adv.; bk.rev.; bibl.; charts; illus.; index. circ. 600. **Indexed:** Geneal.Per.Ind. **Document type:** academic/scholarly publication.
Formerly: Orange County Genealogical Society. Quarterly (ISSN 0030-4263)
Description: Original articles, reprints and recasts using family histories, Bible records, old letters, vital statistics, census, county and cemetery records. Local history, queries and book reviews.

929 US
ORANGEBURGH GERMAN-SWISS NEWSLETTER. 1983. q. $15. Orangeburgh German-Swiss Genealogical Society, Box 974, Orangeburgh, SC 29116-0974. TEL 803-534-6000. Ed. Beverly Shuler. index. circ. 400. (looseleaf format; back issues avail.) **Document type:** newsletter.

929.817 CN ISSN 0845-9304
ORDER OF ONTARIO/ORDRE DE L'ONTARIO. 1987. a. Ministry of Citizenship, c/o Ontario Honours & Awards Secretariat, 77 Bloor St. W., Toronto, ON M7A 2R9, Canada.

929 US ISSN 0738-1891
F875
OREGON GENEALOGICAL SOCIETY QUARTERLY. 1962. q. $18. Oregon Genealogical Society, Inc., Box 10306, Eugene, OR 97440-2306. TEL 503-746-7924. adv.; bk.rev. circ. 475. —UnCover.

929 UK
ORIGINS. 1977. q. £6.50 to non-members (foreign £7.25). Buckinghamshire Family History Society, Varneys, Rudds Lane, Haddenham, Bucks HP17 8JP, England. Ed. Eve McLaughlin. bk.rev. circ. 1,000.

929 GW ISSN 0472-190X
OSTDEUTSCHE FAMILIENKUNDE. 1953. 4/yr. DM.40. Verlag Degener and Co., Nuernbergerstr. 27, 91413 Neustadt, Germany. FAX 09161-1378. **Document type:** bulletin.

929 US ISSN 0890-2631
OSWALD OUTLINES. 1984. irreg. $6. Family Quest, 2204 W. Houston, Spokane, WA 99208-4440. TEL 509-326-2089. Ed. Donna Potter Phillips. bk.rev. circ. 25. (looseleaf format; back issues avail.)
Description: Serves as "clearinghouse" on Oswald surname.

929 US ISSN 0733-4559
F392.V2
OUR HERITAGE. 1980. q. $10 membership. Genealogical Society of Van Zandt County, Box 716, Canton, TX 75103-0716. TEL 903-567-5012. Ed. (Mary) Jane Gamon. bk.rev.; circ. 387 (controlled).

929 US
OUR MISSING LINKS. 1976. q. $10. Kosciusko County Historical Society, Box 1071, Warsaw, IN 46580. TEL 219-269-1078. Ed. Anne Laurie Smith. adv.; bk.rev.; index. circ. 230. (back issues avail.)

929 US ISSN 0742-8472
CS71
OVERHOLSER FAMILY ASSOCIATION. BULLETIN. 1979. s-a. membership. Overholser Family Association, 313 Henry Ln., Wallingford, PA 19086. Ed. Barbara B. Ford. bk.rev. circ. 400. **Indexed:** Geneal.Per.Ind. **Document type:** newsletter.

929 CN
OXFORD TRACER. m. Can.$8 (membership). Ontario Genealogical Society, Oxford County Branch, Box 1092, Woodstock, Ont. N4S 8P6, Canada. Ed. Mary Evans.

929 UK ISSN 0309-2275
OXFORDSHIRE FAMILY HISTORIAN. 1976. 3/yr. £7 to individuals; institutions £8. Oxfordshire Family History Society, 19 Mavor Close, Woodstock, Oxon OX20 1YL, England. TEL 0993-812258. Ed. Carole Newbigging. bk.rev. bibl. circ. 1,000. **Document type:** newsletter.
Incorporating: Oxfordshire Family History Society. Newsletter.

929 US
P G S COUNTRY. 1978. 3/yr. $6. Plains Genealogical Society, Kimball Public Library, 208 S. Walnut St., Kimball, NE 69145. TEL 308-235-2008. Ed. Marcia Buescher. adv.; bk.rev. circ. 65. **Document type:** newsletter.
Formerly: Plains Genealogical Society. Newsletter.

929 US
PALATINE LEAVES.* 1980. q. $5. Barry Tracy, Ed. & Pub., Box 159, Dryden, ME 04225. adv.; bk.rev. circ. 25.

PANORAMA. see HISTORY — History Of Europe

929 EE
LE PARCHEMIN. (Text in French) 1936. bi-m. 1300 BEF. Office Genealogique et Heraldique de Belgique, c/o Musees Royaux d'Art et d'Histoire, Parc du Cinquantenaire 10, B-1040 Brussels, Belgium. TEL 32-2-74-17-300. Ed. Patrick d'Hose. adv.; bk.rev.; charts; illus.; index, cum.index 1936-1973. circ. 1,000.

929 BE
LE PARCHEMIN. RECUEIL GENEALOGIQUE ET HERALDIQUE.. 1952. a. price varies. Office Genealogique et Heraldique de Belgique, c/o Musees Royaux d'Art et d'Histoire, Parc du Cinquantenaire 10, B-1040 Brussels, Belgium. TEL 32-2-74-17-300. Ed. Jean-Francois de Montigny. charts; illus.; index, cum.index: 1952-1960, 1961-1973, 1973-1980. circ. 1,000. **Indexed:** Numis.Lit.

929 US ISSN 0148-3994
CS71
PARKE SOCIETY NEWS LETTER. 1963. 3/yr. $15 membership (effective 1992). Parke Society, Inc., 805 Evergreen Dr., Reading, PA 19610. TEL 610-670-2909. Ed. David L. Parke. bk.rev.; bibl.; charts. circ. 900. (also avail. in microfiche; back issues avail.) **Document type:** newsletter.
Formerly (until 1977): Park(e)(s) Family News.
Description: Emphasis is on research for records and lineages of those named Park, Parks or Parkes.

GENEALOGY AND HERALDRY

929   US   ISSN 0898-5456
CS71
PARKER PAPERS. 1985. irreg., vol.12, 1992. $7.25. Name Game Enterprises, S. 4204 Conklin St., Spokane, WA 99203-6235. TEL 509-747-4903. Ed. E. Dale Hastin Smith. bk.rev.; index. (back issues avail.)
   Description: Covers genealogy and lineage and queries. Includes biographies, wills, marriages, family records, queries, and obituary records.

929   UK   ISSN 0142-9388
PARLEY PAPERS. 1979. s-a. membership. Parley Family History Society, c/o 36 Duchy Rd., Harrogate, N. Yorks. HG1 2ER, England. Ed. M.D. Griffiths. circ. 60.

929   US   ISSN 0093-9811
CS71
PARROTT TALK. 1973. q. $8. c/o E.P. Scott, Box 446, Sudan, TX 79371. Eds. Evelyn P. Scott, Roberta L. Robinson. bk.rev.; charts; index. circ. 75. (processed; back issues avail.)

929   CN   ISSN 0710-5185
PASQUIN. vol.11, 1979. q. Can.$15. Association des Familles Paquin Inc., 41, Des Cantons, Charlesbourg, PQ G1H 7B1, Canada. Ed. Charles-Henri Paquin. **Document type:** bulletin.
   Formerly: Origine des Familles Paquin au Canada.

929   US   ISSN 0736-8267
PASSENGER AND IMMIGRATION LISTS INDEX SUPPLEMENT. 1982. a. $170. Gale Research Inc., 835 Penobscot Bldg., Detroit, MI 48226. TEL 313-961-2242. FAX 313-961-6083. Eds. P. William Filby, Paula K. Woolverton.
   Description: Enables researchers to locate people who emigrated to the New World between the 16th and early 20th centuries.

929   US
PASTFINDER. q. $12 membership. Hemet - San Jicinto Genealogical Society, Box 2516, Hemet, CA 92546. TEL 714-652-3011. **Document type:** newsletter.

929   US
▼**PASTIME.** 1992. q. American Genealogical Lending Library, Box 244, Bountiful, UT 84010. TEL 801-298-5358. bk.rev. **Document type:** newsletter.

929   US   ISSN 0887-1280
PATE PIONEERS. 1986. 4/yr. $15. Clovis Byars Herring, Ed. & Pub., Rt 1. Box 123A, Buffalo, TX 75831.

929   US   ISSN 1057-3445
CS71
PATTERSON PEOPLE. 1990. q. $10. Kinseeker Publications, Box 184, Grawn, MI 49637. Ed. Marie Kenezi. bk.rev. circ. 25. (looseleaf format) **Document type:** newsletter.

929   US   ISSN 0885-5749
PATTERSON POST. 1985. q. $11. 3635 Arbolado Dr., Las Vegas, NV 89121-2901. Ed. Mary Patterson Ingebretsen. circ. 265. (back issues avail.)
   Description: Provides a vehicle for the exchange of information between researchers of the Patterson surname.

PEABODY ESSEX MUSEUM COLLECTIONS. see *HISTORY*

929   US   ISSN 8756-4238
PECK PIONEERS. 1983. 3/yr. $15. 204 S. Howard, Moscow, ID 83843. TEL 208-882-1309. Ed. Kathleen Peck Probasco. **Document type:** newsletter.
—UnCover.
   Description: Collects genealogical information on the name Peck and variant spellings.

929.6   US
PEEK AT PIKE. 1982. q. $10. Pike & Calhoun Counties Genealogical Society, Box 104, Pleasant Hill, IL 62366. Ed. Virginia Hart.

929   US
PELLISSIPPIAN. 1980. q. $16. Pellissippi Genealogical and Historical Society, 118 Hicks St., Clinton, TN 37716. Ed. Mary S. Harris. adv.; bk.rev. circ. 140. **Document type:** bulletin, newsletter.

929   US   ISSN 0882-3685
PENNSYLVANIA GENEALOGICAL MAGAZINE. 1895. s-a. $8 to non-members. Genealogical Society of Pennsylvania, 1300 Locust St., Philadelphia, PA 19107. TEL 215-545-0391. bk.rev.; abstr.; index, cum.index. circ. 1,600. **Indexed:** Geneal.Per.Ind.
—Faxon; UnCover.

929 974   US   ISSN 0148-4036
F160.M45
PENNSYLVANIA MENNONITE HERITAGE. 1978. q. $25 includes membership. Lancaster Mennonite Historical Society, 2215 Millstream Rd., Lancaster, PA 17602-1499. TEL 717-393-9745. Ed. David J. Rempel Smucker. bk.rev.; illus.; stat.; cum.index: 1978-1982, 1983-1987, 1988-1992. circ. 3,200. **Indexed:** Amer.Hist.& Life, Geneal.Per.Ind., Hist.Abstr. **Document type:** academic/scholarly publication.
—Faxon; UnCover.
   Supersedes (1960-1977): Mennonite Research Journal (ISSN 0025-9381)
   Description: Focuses on the historical background, religious thought and expression, culture, and genealogy of the Mennonite-related groups originating in Pennsylvania.

929   US   ISSN 0895-4488
PERKINS FAMILY NEWSLETTER. 1986. 4/yr. $10. Compu - Chart, c/o Paula Perkins Mortensen, Ed., 363 S. Park Victoria Dr., Milpitas, CA 95035-5708. adv. **Indexed:** Geneal.Per.Ind. **Document type:** newsletter.
   Description: Information on the surname and allied lines, accepting queries, family group sheets, ancestor charts, and other items of genealogical interest.

929   US   ISSN 0898-1574
CS71
PERKINS PRESS. 1987. irreg. $7. Jennifer A. Perkins Publications, N. 5803 Ash, Spokane, WA 99205-6807. TEL 509-325-5919. Ed. Jennifer Ann Henley Perkins. circ. 50. (back issues avail.)
   Description: Covers Perkins' birth, marriage, probate, military records. Includes Perkins branches, lineages and queries.

929   US
PERPETUAL FLAME. 1973. a. $5. Cantwell - Conteville Family Association, 12006 Meadowview, Cypress, TX 77429. Ed. Ann Billings. circ. 75. (looseleaf format) **Document type:** newsletter.
   Formerly (until 1989): Cantwell - Conteville Family Association Newsletter.

929   DK   ISSN 0300-3655
PERSONALHISTORISK TIDSSKRIFT. 1880. s-a. DKK 160($20) Samfundet for Dansk Genealogi og Personalhistorie, c/o Birgit Flemming Larsen, Klostermarken 13, DK-9000 Aalborg, Denmark. TEL 45-98-16-11-35. FAX 45-98-10-22-48. Ed. Tommy P. Christensen. adv.; bk.rev.; bibl.; index, cum.index. circ. 1,500. **Document type:** academic/scholarly publication.

929   UK   ISSN 0262-4427
PETERBOROUGH & DISTRICT FAMILY HISTORY SOCIETY JOURNAL. 1982. q. £6. Peterborough & District Family History Society, 7 Teasles, Deeping St. James, Peterborough PE6 8SJ, England. TEL 0733-341290. Ed. Jan Johnson. adv.; bk.rev. circ. 300. (back issues avail.) **Document type:** bulletin.

929   US
PHARR QUARTERLY. 1987. q. $20. Collier Research, c/o Timothy P. Biarnesen, Ed., Box 371883, El Paso, TX 79937. TEL 915-595-2725.

929   US
PHELPS COUNTY GENEALOGICAL SOCIETY QUARTERLY. 1985. 4/yr. $18 membership. Phelps County Genealogical Society, Box 571, Rolla, MO 65401. bk.rev. circ. 150.
   Description: Genealogical and historical data concerning Phelps County, Mo., and the surrounding area.

929   US
PHELPS FAMILY NEWS. 1987. m. $20 membership. Phelps Family Association, 1002 Queen St., Camden, SC 29020-3113. TEL 803-432-8432. Ed. Dallas L. Phelps. circ. 200. **Document type:** newsletter.
   Description: News and genealogical information regarding the Phelps surname (including variants such as Felts, Phipps).

929   US
PIATT COUNTY HISTORICAL AND GENEALOGICAL SOCIETY QUARTERLY. 1981. q. $8. Piatt County Historical and Genealogical Society, Courthouse Annex, Box 111, Monticello, IL 61856. Ed. Lisa Winters. circ. 200. (looseleaf format; back issues avail.) **Document type:** newsletter.

929   US   ISSN 0741-0360
CS71
THE PIED COW. 1983. s-a. $10 membership. Chadbourne Family Association, HCR 72, Box 8350, Chadbourne's Ridge, North Waterboro, ME 04061. Ed. Marjorie Chadbourne Barden. circ. 450.

929 917.7   US
PINE, THE PLOW AND THE PIONEER; histories of Three Lakes, Clearwater Lake, Gagen & Hiles areas. 1984. triennial. $12 per no. Three Lakes Historical Society, Box 250, Three Lakes, WI 54562. TEL 715-546-3529. Ed. Walt Goldsworthy. adv.; bk.rev. circ. 1,000. (back issues avail.)

929   US
PIONEER BRANCHES. 1986. q. $12. Northeast Washington Genealogical Society, c/o Colville Public Library, 195 S. Oak St., Colville, WA 99114. TEL 509-684-4092. Eds. Lorraine Best, Ora Kitt. adv.; bk.rev. circ. 100.
   Description: Includes genealogical information about Stevens, Ferry counties and Washington state. Features calendar of events, club happenings, feature articles, queries, newspaper extracts, genealogical gleanings.

929   US   ISSN 0739-6155
PIONEER TIMES. 1977. q. $14. Mid-Missouri Genealogical Society, Inc., Box 715, Jefferson City, MO 65102. TEL 314-896-8117. Ed.Bd. adv.; bk.rev. circ. 600.
—UnCover.

929   US   ISSN 0735-309X
F472.J2
PIONEER WAGON. 1980. q. $15. Jackson County Genealogical Society, Box 2145, Independence, MO 64055. TEL 816-252-8128. Ed. Verna Gail Johnson. bk.rev. circ. 350. (back issues avail.)

929   US
PLATTE COUNTY HISTORICAL AND GENEALOGICAL SOCIETY BULLETIN. 1947. q. $15. Platte County Historical Society, Box 103, Platte City, MO 64079. TEL 816-431-5121. Ed. Betty Soper. bk.rev. circ. 1,000. (tabloid format) **Document type:** bulletin.
   Description: Examines the history, architecture and genealogy of Platte County.

PLUM CREEK ALMANAC. see *HISTORY — History Of North And South America*

929   US   ISSN 0735-9349
CS49
POLISH GENEALOGICAL SOCIETY NEWSLETTER. 1979. s-a. $15 to individuals; libraires $7.50. Polish Genealogical Society, Inc., 984 N. Milwaukee Ave., Chicago, IL 60622. Ed. Edward A. Peckwas. adv.; bk.rev.; bibl.; charts; illus.; index. circ. 1,000. (back issues avail.) **Indexed:** Amer.Bibl.Slavic & E.Eur.Stud., Geneal.Per.Ind.

929   US   ISSN 1062-7855
▼**POLLOCK POTPOURRI.** 1992. q. $10 (effective 1994). Lineage Search Associates, 6419 Colts Neck Rd., Mechanicsville, VA 23111-4233. TEL 804-730-7414. index.

DIE POMMERSCHEN LEUTE. see *ETHNIC INTERESTS*

929   US
PONTIUS FAMILY ASSOCIATION. NEWSLETTER. 1981. q. $7.50 (includes Bridge Builder). Pontius Family Association, 2009 Garden Dr., Niskayuna, NY 12309-2309. TEL 518-374-1965. FAX 518-374-4453. (Subscr. to: Janet E. Pontius, Sec., 126 Maplewood Estates, Scott Depot, WV 25560-9744. TEL 304-757-6361) Eds. Philip W. Pontius, Janet E. Pontius. circ. 380 (paid). (back issues avail.) **Document type:** newsletter.
   Description: Contains announcements and minutes of association meetings. Reports activities of association.

POWESHIEK COUNTY, IOWA SEARCHER. see *HISTORY — History Of North And South America*

GENEALOGY AND HERALDRY

929 US ISSN 0032-6623
PRAIRIE GLEANER. 1969. q. membership. West Central Missouri Genealogical Society and Library, Inc., c/o Mrs. J. Eldon Yung, 705 Broad, Warrensburg, MO 64093. Ed. A.J. Heck, Jr. adv.; bk.rev.; index. circ. 650. (processed)
—UnCover.

929 US
PRAIRIE PIONEER. 1981. q. $9. Warren County Illinois Genealogical Society, Box 761, Monmouth, IL 61462-0761. Ed.Bd. bk.rev. circ. 225.

929 US
PRATHER BULLETIN. 1973. 6/yr. $5. Ellsberry Records, c/o Elizabeth P. Ellsberry, Box 206, Chillicothe, MO 64601. TEL 816-646-4409.

929 US
PREDMORE, PRIDEMORE, PRIDMORE, PRIGMORE ASSOCIATION. JOURNAL. 1986. 4/yr. $20. 545 Jefferson, Kimberley, ID 83341. Ed. Howard Johnston. bk.rev. circ. 100.

929 US
PRESTON SCOOP. 1987. bi-m. $10. Doris J. O'Brien, Ed. & Pub., 106 Mikel Ct., Summerville, SC 29485. TEL 803-873-7897. adv. (looseleaf format; back issues avail.) **Document type:** newsletter.
Description: Publishes family history and genealogical research.

929 US
PRIDDY PRESS. q. $15. Folk Family Printers, Box 52048, Knoxville, TN 37950. Ed. Hester E. Stockton.
Description: Open forum for those who seek information on the Priddy surname or any variants.

929 US ISSN 1052-1380
F187.P9
PRINCE GEORGE'S COUNTY GENEALOGICAL SOCIETY. BULLETIN. 1969. 10/yr. $12. Prince George's County Genealogical Society, Inc., Box 819, Bowie, MD 20718-0819. TEL 301-779-1457. Eds. Roberta Pohl, Robert Clark. bk.rev.; index. circ. 600. **Indexed:** Geneal.Per.Ind. **Document type:** newsletter.
Description: Covers genealogical matters, including queries, transcriptions, local activities, with emphasis on Prince George's County and the State of Maryland.

929 AT
PROGENITOR. 1982. q. Aus.$25. Genealogical Society of the Northern Territory, P.O. Box 37212, Winnellie, N.T. 5789, Australia. Ed. Digby Tomlinson. adv.; bk.rev.; index. circ. 350. (back issues avail.)

929 US
PROSPECTORS, DIGGERS & DOERS. q? Four State Genealogy Club, 922 Galena Ave., Galena, KS 66739.

929 FR ISSN 1169-1808
PROVENCE GENEALOGIE. 1976. q. 120 F. (foreign 200 F.). Centre Genealogique de Midi-Provence, 13110 Port-De-Bouc, France. bk.rev.; circ. 500 (controlled). (processed) **Document type:** bulletin.
Description: Articles relative to geneological researches, especially in the south of France.

929 US ISSN 0899-1332
E184.F89
QUAKER QUERIES. 1986. irreg. $7.25 per no. McNeill Enterprises, Box 779, Napavine, WA 98565-0779. TEL 509-922-4521. bk.rev. circ. 300. (back issues avail.)
Description: Accepts Quaker-related queries.

929 200 US ISSN 0737-8246
E184.F89
QUAKER YEOMEN. 1974. q. $17 (typically set in Apr.). James E. Bellarts, Pub. & Ed., 2330 S.E. Brookwood Ave., Ste. 108, Hillsboro, OR 97123-8168. FAX 503-640-2217. bk.rev.; bibl.; charts; index. circ. 300. (back issues avail.) **Indexed:** Geneal.Per.Ind.
—UnCover.
Description: Newsletter of Quaker and related genealogy.

929 AT ISSN 0811-3394
QUEENSLAND FAMILY HISTORIAN. 1980. q. membership; libraries Aus.$15. Queensland Family History Society Inc., P.O. Box 171, Indooroopilly, Qld. 4068, Australia. TEL 07-376-4339. Ed. D. Montgomery. adv.; bk.rev.; index. circ. 1,000.

929 US
RABBIT TRACKS. 1983. q. $10 includes membership. Conejo Valley Genealogical Society, Inc., Box 1228, Thousand Oaks, CA 91358. Ed. Delores V. Pederson. bk.rev. circ. 350.

929 US ISSN 0892-2071
RAGSDALES OF AMERICA. 1987. q. $12. (Ragsdales of America) Nona Williams, Ed. & Pub., Box 225, Ben Lomond, CA 95005. TEL 408-475-3114. adv.; bk.rev. (looseleaf format) **Document type:** newsletter.

929 US ISSN 0734-2055
CS71
RAINEY TIMES. 1981. a. $20. Rt. 4, Box 56, Sulphur Springs, TX 75482. TEL 903-885-3523. FAX 903-439-1081. Ed. Marynell Bryant. adv.; index; circ. 300 (controlled). (back issues avail.) **Document type:** academic/scholarly publication.
Description: Publishes genealogical records pertaining to all spellings of the Rainey name.

RAMPANT LION. see HISTORY — History Of Europe

929 US ISSN 0890-2968
CS42
REDWOOD RESEARCHER. 1968. q. $9 membership. Redwood Genealogical Society, Box 645, Fortuna, CA 95540. Ed. Patricia Madsen. bk.rev.; cum.index: 1968-1986. circ. 210. (back issues avail.)
Description: Deals mainly with Humboldt County genealogical records.

300 CN ISSN 0701-8878
CS80
RELATIVELY SPEAKING. (Includes: Ancestor Index) 1973. q. Can.$22. Alberta Genealogical Society, Box 12015, Edmonton, AB T5J 3L2, Canada. Ed. Judy Bradley. bk.rev.
—UnCover.

929 US
RESEARCHIN' OUACHITA - CALHOUN COUNTIES, AR.. 1981. 2/yr. $10. Ouachita - Calhoun Genealogical Society, Box 2092, Camden, AR 71701. bk.rev. circ. 200.

929 US ISSN 1050-7914
REUNION TALKS ON RISLEYS. irreg., latest no.3. membership. Risley Family Association, Box 552, Clarkson, NY 14430. Ed. Roy Goold. **Document type:** monographic series.
Description: Records biographical and genealogical information about prominent members of the Risley family.

REUNIONS - THE MAGAZINE. see SOCIAL SERVICES AND WELFARE

929 FR ISSN 0222-6782
REVUE FRANCAISE DE GENEALOGIE. 1979. 6/yr. 105 F. (foreign 140 F.). S E P S, 12 rue Poincare, 55800 Revigny, France. adv.; bk.rev.

929 FR ISSN 0294-7382
REVUE GENEALOGIQUE NORMANDE; histoire et monographie des familles, heraldique, documentation. 1978. q. 180 F. (effective Jan. 1991). Union des Cercles Genealogiques et Heraldiques de Normandie, 10 rue de Torigni, 76130 Mt. St.-Aignan, France. adv.; bk.rev. circ. 1,400.
Formerly: Cercle Genealogique et Heraldique de Normandie (ISSN 0222-6766)

929 US ISSN 1057-6010
REYNOLDS RECORDS. 1991. q. $10. Kinseeker Publications, Box 184, Grawn, MI 49637. Ed. Marie Kezeli. bk.rev. circ. 25. (looseleaf format) **Document type:** newsletter.

929 US ISSN 0190-3055
F78
RHODE ISLAND GENEALOGICAL REGISTER. 1978. a. $35 to individuals (effective Jan.1991). Nellie M.C. Beaman, Ed. & Pub., Box 585, Princeton, MA 01541. TEL 508-464-5588. bk.rev.

RHODE ISLAND HISTORY. see HISTORY — History Of North And South America

929 US ISSN 0147-2488
CS71
RICHARDSON FAMILY RESEARCHER AND HISTORICAL NEWS. 1975. q. $10 (free to qualified personnel). (Richardson Heritage Society) R T S, Inc., 944 South G. St., Box 123, Broken Bow, NE 68822-0123. TEL 308-872-2167. FAX 308-872-2167. Ed. Harry Marcus Richardson. adv.; bk.rev.; charts. circ. 1,000. **Document type:** newsletter.
Incorporates: Moore Family Inquirer.
Description: For researchers of the Richardson, Moore and allied families.

929 GW
RIEBELING - NACHRICHTEN DER FAMILIE RIEBELING AUF DER SCHWALM. 1930. a. Familienverband Riebeling auf der Schwalm, Beethovenstr. 52, 36304 Alsfeld, Germany. TEL 06631-5218. circ. 300. (back issues avail.) **Document type:** newsletter.
Description: Histories of several Riebeling families, in Germany and the United States.

929 US ISSN 1050-7922
RISLEY RECORD. 1978. q. membership only. Risley Family Association, Box 552, Clarkson, NY 14430-0552. Ed. Roy Goold, Pres. **Document type:** newsletter.
Description: Publishes historical and genealogical articles about the descendants of Richard Risley.

929 975 US
RITCHIE COUNTY HISTORICAL SOCIETY NEWSLETTER. 1973. q. $3. Ritchie County Historical Society, c/o David M. Scott, Ed., 200 S. Church St., Harrisville, WV 26362. circ. 125. (processed)

929.6 IT ISSN 0035-5771
RIVISTA ARALDICA. 1903. m. $50. Collegio Araldico, Via S. Maria dell'Anima 16, Rome, Italy. Dir. Roberto C. Bertini Frassori. bk.rev.; index. circ. 1,000.

929 US
ROBB RELATIVES; descendants of William Robbe (1692-1769) of Peterborough, New Hampshire. 1985. 2/yr. $5. 421 Kemmerer Rd., State College, PA 16801. TEL 814-237-6447. Ed. Barbara Robb Kabel. (looseleaf format; back issues avail.) **Document type:** newsletter.
Description: Publishes genealogical research, Robb-Robbe-Rabb queries, short articles and letters.

929 US
ROBERT MCKAY CLAN NEWSLETTER. 1965. a. $10. 5319 Manning Pl., N.W., Washington, DC 20016-5311. TEL 202-363-3663. Eds. Wallace & Dorothy Shipp. **Document type:** newsletter.
Description: Family history and reunion news.

929 US ISSN 8756-7741
ROBERTS REGISTER. 1982. 3/yr. $10. Roma Publishing, 5560 Gibson Rd., Vicksburg, MS 39180. TEL 601-638-6334. Ed. M. Roberts. adv.; bk.rev. circ. 450.

929 US ISSN 0898-5448
ROBERTSON REPORT. 1984. irreg., vol.19, 1992. $7.25. Name Game Enterprises, S. 4204 Conklin, Spokane, WA 99203-6235. TEL 509-747-4903. Ed. E. Dale Hastin Smith. bk.rev.; stat.; index. (back issues avail.)
Description: Covers genealogy and lineage. Includes biographies, wills, marriages, family records, queries, and obituary records.

929 975 US ISSN 0888-3807
ROBESON COUNTY REGISTER. 1986. q. $25. Dr. Morris F. Britt, Ed. & Pub., Doctor's Bldg., Ste. 901, 1012 S. Kings Dr., Charlotte, NC 28283. FAX 704-333-1443. adv.; bk.rev. circ. 100. (back issues avail.)
Description: Genealogical and historical magazine for those interested in Robeson County, North Carolina.

929 US
ROBINSON, ROBERSON, ROBISON, ROBERTSON OF VIRGINIA LETTER.* q. $10. Genealogical & Historical News, c/o Robert Bradshaw, Box 779, Saipan, CM 96950, Mariana Islands.

929 US
ROCKINGHAM RECORDER. 1945. irreg. $6. Harrisonburg-Rockingham Historical Society, Box 716, Dayton, VA 22821. TEL 703-897-2616.

GENEALOGY AND HERALDRY

929 900 US ISSN 0048-8534
F882.R6
ROGUE DIGGER. 1966. q. $20. Rogue Valley Genealogical Society, Inc., 133 S. Central Ave., Medford, OR 97501. TEL 503-770-5848. Ed. Jean Maack. adv.; bk.rev.; charts; illus.; stat.; index. circ. 300. (processed; back issues avail.)
—UnCover.

929.6 US
ROLL OF ARMS. 1928. irreg. $12.50. New England Historic Genealogical Society, Committee on Heraldry, 101 Newbury St., Boston, MA 02116. illus. circ. 500.

929 US ISSN 0748-6251
ROOT CELLAR PRESERVES. 1979. q. $12.50. Root Cellar, Sacramento Genealogical Society, Box 265, Citrus Heights, CA 95611. TEL 916-723-4768. Ed. Mary Anne McDaniel. adv.; bk.rev.; index. circ. 335,223. (back issues avail.) **Indexed:** Geneal.Per.Ind. **Document type:** newsletter.
Formerly: From the Shelves of the Root Cellar (ISSN 0748-6243)
Description: Genealogical periodical with articles and records covering Sacramento, the foothills, and the greater Sacramento Valley.

929 US
ROOTING AROUND. 1980? q. $10 membership. Leavenworth County Genealogical Society, Box 362, Leavenworth, KS 66048. Ed. Rita Spindler.

929 US ISSN 0737-9242
ROOTS AND BRANCHES. vol.14, 1991. q. $15 membership. Garfield County Genealogists, Inc., Box 1106, Enid, OK 73702-1106. TEL 405-234-6086. Ed. Gail J. Roberts. adv.; bk.rev.

929 US ISSN 0748-2485
F665
ROOTS & LEAVES. 1974. q. $6.50 for non-members. Eastern Nebraska Genealogical Society, Box 541, Fremont, NE 68025. TEL 402-721-9553. Ed. Claire Mares. adv.; bk.rev.; bibl.; cum.index: 1977-1988, 1989-1992. circ. 325. (back issues avail.)
—UnCover.
Formerly: Eastern Nebraska Genealogical Society Quarterly.
Description: Covers five counties of Nebraska-Dodge, Cuming, Colfax, Washington, & Saunders.

929 US
ROSENBERRY NEWSLETTER. q. Box 112, Plainfield, PA 17081. Ed. Edward Rosenberry.

929 US ISSN 0730-5168
CS1
ROTA GENE; international genealogical magazine. 1979. bi-m. $15. (International Genealogy Fellowship of Rotarians) Aceto Bookmen, 5721 Antietam Dr., Sarasota, FL 34231. TEL 813-924-9170. Ed. Charles D. Townsend. adv.; bk.rev. circ. 300. **Indexed:** Geneal.Per.Ind. **Document type:** newsletter.
—UnCover.

929 976 US ISSN 0896-0712
ROUGE. 1980. q. $15 to members. Baton Rouge Genealogical and Historical Society, Box 80565, S.E. Sta., Baton Rouge, LA 70898-0565. Ed. Karen Strawn. bk.rev. circ. 300.
Formerly (until 1988): Baton Rouge (ISSN 0279-0416)

929 US
ROWE REGISTER. 1985. q. $35. Richard Herbert Tivey, Ed. & Pub., RFD 1, Box 605, Ctr. Barnstead, NH 03225. TEL 603-776-6996. adv.; bk.rev. circ. 2,000.

ROYAL AUSTRALIAN HISTORICAL SOCIETY. TECHNICAL INFORMATION SERVICE. see HISTORY — History Of Australasia And Other Areas

ROYAL SOCIETY OF ANTIQUARIES OF IRELAND. JOURNAL. see ARCHAEOLOGY

929.6 UK ISSN 0950-3439
ROYALTY. 1981. m. $5.95 per issue. Bacall Ltd., 581 Finchley Rd., London NW3 7B5, England.
—UnCover.
Description: Covers the lives and activities of members of European royal families.

929.6 UK
ROYALTY COLLECTOR'S EDITION. 1990. q. $5.95 per issue. Bacall Ltd., 581 Finchley Rd., London NW3 7B5, England.
Description: Focuses on the life and activities of a specific member of a European royal family.

929 US
RUSHING PAST.* 1979. q. $5. (Rushing Family Association of the United States) Jack Rushing, Ed. & Pub., Box 15, Liberty Corner, NJ 07938. bk.rev. circ. 500.

929 US
RUSSELL REGISTER. 1978. q. $17. Ancestor's Attic, 4041 Pedley Rd., No. 18, Riverside, CA 92509. TEL 714-685-8936. Ed. Frances R. Nelson. index. (back issues avail.)

929 US ISSN 1049-1848
RYAN RAMBLINGS. 1990. q. $10. Kinseeker Publications, Box 184, Grawn, MI 49637. Ed. Victoria Wilson. bk.rev. circ. 30. (looseleaf format; back issues avail.) **Document type:** newsletter.

929.9 SA
S A V A NEWSLETTER. 1990. q. Southern Africa Vexillological Association, P.O. Box 836, Pinegowrie 2123, South Africa.

525 977 US ISSN 0896-4408
S S G H S NEWSLETTER. vol.5, 1977. m. $15 membership (includes Where the Trails Cross). South Suburban Genealogical and Historical Society, Box 96, South Holland, IL 60473-0096. TEL 312-708-9474. Ed. Rea Reed. circ. 500.
Document type: newsletter.
Formerly: Southsubkin.

525 US
S S G H S RESEARCH SERIES. 1990. irreg., vol.4, 1992. $10. South Suburban Genealogical and Historical Society, Box 96, South Holland, IL 60473-0096. TEL 312-708-9474. **Document type:** monographic series.
Description: Covers censuses, burial records, and other demographic research in Illinois.

929 US ISSN 0882-6528
F547.S2
ST. CLAIR COUNTY GENEALOGICAL SOCIETY QUARTERLY. 1978. q. $15 includes membership. St. Clair County Genealogical Society, Box 431, Belleville, IL 62222-0431. TEL 618-277-7705. Ed. Mardy Eisloeffel. bk.rev. circ. 500.

929 US ISSN 1065-5255
ST. LOUIS GENEALOGICAL SOCIETY. NEWS AND NOTES. vol.8, 1975. m. St. Louis Genealogical Society, 9011 Manchester Rd., Ste. 3, St. Louis, MO 63144. TEL 314-968-2763. Ed.Bd. bibl.

929 US ISSN 0036-2956
F474.S253
ST. LOUIS GENEALOGICAL SOCIETY QUARTERLY. 1968. q. $15. St. Louis Genealogical Society, 9011 Manchester Rd., Ste. 3, St. Louis, MO 63144. TEL 314-968-2763. Ed. Maryhelen Wilson. adv.; bk.rev.; index, cum.index: 1968-1977, 1978-1987. circ. 2,500. (processed; back issues avail.)
—UnCover.

929 US ISSN 0893-3057
SALINE. 1986. q. $15 to individuals; couples $22.50; institutions and libraries $25. Saline County History & Heritage Society, Inc., Box 221, Bryant, AR 72089-0221. TEL 501-847-0402. Ed. Leon Rowland Moore. bk.rev.; index. circ. 220. (back issues avail.)
Description: Covers the history of the communities and families of Saline county.

929 US
SANS TACHE. 1985. s-a. membership. Clan Napier in North America, Kilmahew, Rt. 2, Box 614, Ramer, AL 36069-9245. TEL 205-281-0505. Ed. Lt.Col. John H. Napier, III. bk.rev. circ. 225. (back issues avail.)

929 US ISSN 0895-6103
F868.S25
SANTA CLARA COUNTY CONNECTIONS. 1964. s-a. $5. Santa Clara County Historical and Genealogical Society, City Library, 2635 Homestead Rd., Santa Clara, CA 95051. TEL 408-299-4321. Ed. Dorothy Wuss. adv.; bk.rev.; bibl.; charts; index. circ. 450. (processed) **Indexed:** Geneal.Per.Ind.
—UnCover.
Formerly: Santa Clara County Historical and Genealogical Quarterly (ISSN 0036-4517)
Description: Deals with local information: census, records, tax lists, and early settlers for genealogical and historical researchers.

929 US ISSN 0740-9702
F127.S26
THE SARATOGA. 1984. q. $14 (typically set in Oct.). Valley Quarterlies, c/o Arthur C.M. Kelly, Ed., 60 Cedar Heights Rd., Rhinebeck, NY 12572. TEL 914-876-4592. bk.rev.; index. circ. 150. (back issues avail.) **Document type:** monographic series.

929 US
SARGENT NEWSLETTER. 1991. a. $5. Phillip Heritage House, 605 Benton Ave., Missoula, MT 59801. TEL 406-543-3495. (back issues avail.) **Document type:** newsletter.

929 CN ISSN 0048-9182
SASKATCHEWAN GENEALOGICAL SOCIETY. BULLETIN. 1969. q. Can.$32.50 (senior citizens Can.$27.50. Saskatchewan Genealogical Society, Box 1894, Regina, SK S4P 3E1, Canada. TEL 306-780-9207. FAX 306-781-6021. Ed. Norman Wilson. bk.rev.; index. circ. 1,250. (back issues avail.)
—UnCover.

929 US
SAVAGE FAMILY DEPOSITORY NEWSLETTER.* 1983. q. $8. c/o Jean Savage Lichtenwald, 2510 E. Juliet Dr., Orange City, FL 32738-2430.

929 US
SCANDINAVIAN SAGA. vol.2, 1981. 2/yr. membership. Scandinavian-American Genealogical Society, Box 16069, St. Paul, MN 55116. (Affiliate: Minnesota Genealogical Society) Ed. Barbara Sexton. bk.rev. circ. 350.

929 US
SCHALE (WESTFALEN) NEWSLETTER. 1984. q. $5. c/o David Koss, Ed., Illinois College, Jacksonville, IL 62650. TEL 217-245-3460. circ. 40. (looseleaf format; back issues avail.) **Document type:** newsletter.
Description: Studies German and American families from Schale, Westphalia.

929 US ISSN 0882-5890
SCHARTZER - SCHERTZER CONNECTION. 1984. q. $17.50. B G M Publications, 28635 Old Hideaway Rd., Cary, IL 60013. TEL 708-639-2400. Ed. Betty G. Massman. circ. 380. (back issues avail.)
Description: Genealogical information on the surnames Schartzer, Schertzer, Schatzer, and variations.

929 US ISSN 0882-5904
SCHNEIDER CONNECTIONS. 1984. q. $17.50. B G M Publications, 28635 Old Hideaway Rd., Cary, IL 60013. TEL 708-639-2400. Ed. Betty G. Massman. circ. 1,005. (back issues avail.)
Description: Genealogical information on the surname Schneider and variations.

929 US
SCHWACHAMER DU FORD GENEALOGICAL SOCIETY. BULLETIN. q. Schwachamer Du Ford Genealogical Society, 4 Brentwood Terrace, New Monmouth, NJ 07748. TEL 908-671-1888. Ed. Ruth Hartman. **Document type:** bulletin.

929.9 GW
SCHWARZER LOEWE. 2/yr. Herladik-Fachgruppe, Harnackstr. 9, 04317 Leipzig, Germany. Ed. Ulrich Zeiler.

929.9 SZ
SCHWEIZER WAPPEN UND FAHNEN. a. Stiftung Schweizer Wappen und Fahnen, Lutzelmattstr. 4, Luzerne 6006, Switzerland. Ed. Joseph Melchoir Galliker.

929 CN ISSN 0701-3272
SCOTIAN. 1966. q. free. Sons of Scotland Benevolent Association, 90 Eglinton Ave. E., 4th fl., Toronto, ON M4P 2Y3, Canada.

929 — AT — ISSN 1030-7788
SCOTS LINK; the Scottish family history magazine Australia and New Zealand. 1987. q. Aus.$20 (effective May 1994). P.O. Box 135, S. Melbourne, Vic. 3205, Australia. (New Zealand addr.: P.O. Box 370, Thames, New Zealand) adv.; bk.rev. circ. 1,000. **Document type:** academic/scholarly publication.

929.1 — UK — ISSN 0300-337X
CS460
SCOTTISH GENEALOGIST. 1955. q. £12. Scottish Genealogy Society, 16 Charlotte Sq., Edinburgh EH2 4YS, Scotland. TEL 031-225-8585. FAX 031-225-1110. Ed. Ivor R. Guild. bk.rev.; cum.index every 4 yrs. circ. 1,360. **Indexed:** Br.Hum.Ind. **Document type:** academic/scholarly publication.

929 — ISSN 1059-9843
SEARCH LIGHT. 1980. q. $5 (typically set in Mar.). Rte. 8, Carmel, NY 10512. Ed. Betty Light Behr. bk.rev.; charts; illus.; circ. 200 (paid). (tabloid format; back issues avail.) **Document type:** newsletter.
  Description: Communicates and maintains direct contact with family and descendants of the many Lights and variants worldwide. Contains previously unpublished genealogies and biographic articles, along with census, church, and cemetary records.

929 — ISSN 0037-0401
SEARCHER. 1965. m. membership. Southern California Genealogical Society Inc., Box 4377, Burbank, CA 91503. TEL 818-843-7247. Ed. Pamela A. Myers. adv.; bk.rev.; charts; illus.; index. circ. 1,500. **Indexed:** Geneal.Per.Ind. **Document type:** newsletter.

929 — US
SEARCHING FOR SCRUGGS. 1982. q. $5 to non-members. Scruggs Family Association, Ottawa Hill, Rt. 1, Box 154, Miami, OK 74354-9370. Ed. Patricia Scruggs Trolinger. bk.rev. circ. 150.

929 — US
SEATTLE GENEALOGICAL SOCIETY BULLETIN. 1952. q. $20. Seattle Genealogical Society, Box 1708, Seattle, WA 98111-1708. TEL 206-522-8658. adv.; bk.rev.; bibl.; charts. circ. 1,700. **Indexed:** Geneal.Per.Ind. **Document type:** bulletin.

929 — US — ISSN 0274-6441
CS42
SECOND BOAT. 1980. bi-m. $25 (effective 1994). Pentref Press, Box 398, Machias, ME 04654. TEL 207-255-4114. Ed. Rosemary Bachelor. adv.; bk.rev.; index. circ. 3,000. (back issues avail.)
—UnCover.
  Description: Specializes in colonial American genealogy with an emphasis on pre-1650 immigrants and descendants to 1800; publishes ancestors queries on persons born before 1800.

929 — US — ISSN 0363-4590
F687.C9
SEEKER (PITTSBURG). 1971. q. $8. Crawford County Genealogical Society of Southeast Kansas, 211 W. Fourth St., Pittsburg, KS 66762. TEL 316-231-8110. Ed. Elaine Sauer. illus. circ. 140.

929 — US
SEEKING 'N SEARCHING ANCESTORS. 1985. bi-m. $7 membership. c/o Peggy Smith Hake, Ed., Rt. 1, Box 52, St. Elizabeth, MO 65075. adv.; bk.rev. circ. 250.

929 — US — ISSN 1046-5545
CS42
SENECA SEARCHERS. 1981. bi-m. $10 to individuals; families $12 (foreign $12) (membership) (effective 1994). Seneca County Genealogical Society, Box 157, Tiffin, OH 44883-0157. Ed. Ruth Brill. adv.; index. circ. 375. (back issues avail.) **Document type:** newsletter.
  Description: Genealogical newsletter intended to promote genealogy and inform members of the availability of records in Seneca County, Ohio.

929 — US — ISSN 1049-1783
THE SEPTS. 1990. q. $10 individual membership. Irish Genealogical Society, c/o Minnesota Genealogical Society, Box 16069, St. Paul, MN 55116.

929 — US
SEQUOIA GENEALOGICAL SOCIETY. NEWSLETTER. 1975. 8/yr. membership (typically set in Mar.). Sequoia Genealogical Society, Inc., Tulare City Library, Genealogy Dept., 113 N. "F" St., Tulare, CA 93274. TEL 209-685-2342. Ed. V. Smallwood. circ. 250. (processed; back issues avail.)

929 312 — BE
SERVICE DE CENTRALISATION DES ETUDES GENEALOGIQUES ET DEMOGRAPHIQUES DE BELGIQUE. NOUVELLES BREVES. bi-m. Service de Centralisation des Etudes Genealogiques et Demographiques de Belgique, Maison des Arts, 147 Chaussee de Haecht, B-1030 Brussels, Belgium.

929 — US
SHELBY EXCHANGE. 1988. 4/yr. $12.50. Box 536, Freeman, SD 57029. TEL 605-925-7186. Ed. Carol Peterson. circ. 50.

929 — US — ISSN 1063-956X
CS71
SHELDON FAMILY ASSOCIATION QUARTERLY. 1986. q. $25 (renewals $15). Sheldon Family Association, c/o Rose Sheldon Newton, President, 4409 Bridgetown Run, Ft. Wayne, IN 46804-4808. FAX 219-432-8834. bk.rev. **Document type:** newsletter.
  Formerly (until Jan. 1991): Sheldon Family Association Newsletter (ISSN 1041-5637)

929 — CN — ISSN 0843-6924
SHEM TOV. 1988. q. Can.$30 (effective 1993). Jewish Genealogical Society of Canada, Box 446, Sta. A, Willowdale, ON M2N 5T1, Canada. TEL 416-638-3280. adv.; bk.rev.; circ. 300 (paid). (back issues avail.) **Document type:** newsletter.
  Description: Aims to promote an awareness in the Jewish community of possibilities of tracing ancestry; shares research techniques and disseminates information on Jewish general research for beginners and advanced researchers.

929 — US — ISSN 8755-0547
CS71
SHERBONDY BEACON. 1984. a. membership. Sherbondy Family Association, 6509 W. 102nd St., Overland Park, KS 66212-1723. TEL 913-341-8641. Ed. Jeffrey D. Sherbondy. circ. 100. (back issues avail.)
  Description: Historical, biographical and current event information and photos on the descendants of any and all Sherbondy ancestors.

929 — US — ISSN 1073-4503
"SHOW ME" STATE GENEALOGICAL NEWS. 1980. q. $15. Missouri State Genealogical Association, Box 833, Columbia, MO 62505-0833. TEL 314-634-4511. Ed. Barbara Pugh. circ. 850. (looseleaf format; back issues avail.) **Document type:** newsletter.
  Description: Directed to Missouri state residents who are interested in researching their genealogical history.

929 — UK — ISSN 0261-135X
SHROPSHIRE FAMILY HISTORY JOURNAL. 1980. q. £6. Shropshire Family History Society, c/o Michael J. Hulme, 19 Brook Rd., Bomere Heath, Shrewsbury, Shropshire SY4 3PU, England. TEL 0939-290516. Ed. Gillian Thompson. adv.; bk.rev. circ. 1,400. **Document type:** newsletter.

929 — GW — ISSN 0175-761X
SIEBENBUERGISCHE FAMILIENFORSCHUNG. 1984. s-a. DM.30. Arbeitskreis fuer Siebenbuergische Landeskunde e.V., Schloss Horneck, 74831 Gundelsheim, Germany. TEL 06269-8476. FAX 06269-8397. Ed. Balduin Herter. bk.rev. circ. 400. (back issues avail.) **Document type:** academic/scholarly publication.
—CCC.

929 — US — ISSN 0899-1618
CS71
SIMONSON MISCELLANEOUS RESEARCH DATA. 1978. irreg. price varies. McNeill Enterprises, Box 779, Napavine, WA 98565-0779. TEL 509-922-4521. circ. 50. (back issues avail.)
  Description: Miscellaneous data on branches of the surname, including bible records, marriage records, county histories, census records, family records, wills and obituaries. Accepts lineage sheets from families for permanent recording.

929 — US
THE SIMPSON CLAN. q. $12. Nona Williams, Ed. & Pub., Box 225, Ben Lomond, CA 95005. TEL 408-475-3114. (also avail. in microfiche) **Document type:** newsletter.

929 — US — ISSN 1045-9987
CS71
SIMS SEEKER. 1989. q. $17.50. B G M Publications, 28635 Old Hideaway Rd., Cary, IL 60013. TEL 708-639-2400. Ed. Betty G. Massman. circ. 150. (back issues avail.)
  Description: Genealogical information on the surnames Sims, Simms, Syms, Symes, and variations.

929 — US — ISSN 0895-0202
SKINNER KINSMEN UPDATE. 1983. q. $16.50. (Skinner Family Association) Brandywine Press, 1936 E. Fifth St., Ontario, CA 91764. TEL 909-941-3877. Ed. Gregg Legutki. adv.; bk.rev. circ. 100. (looseleaf format; back issues avail.)

929 — DK — ISSN 0107-539X
SLAEGT OG STAVN. 1981. 4/yr. DKK 40. Slaegtshistorisk Forening for Storkoebenhavn, c/o Lone Wredstroem, Store Kongensgade 89, DK-1264 Copenhagen, Denmark. adv.; bk.rev.; illus. circ. 570. **Document type:** newsletter.

929 — DK — ISSN 0108-3880
SLAEGTEN FISKER; aarsskrift. 1973. a. membership. (Slaegten Fisker Forening) Anders Fisker, Moellegaardsvej 15, Resenbro, 8600 Silkeborg, Denmark. illus.

929 — FI — ISSN 0780-8763
SLAEKT OCH BYGD. (Text in Swedish) 1957. a. Jakobstadsnejdens Slaekt och Bygdeforskare, Ankarvagen 7, 68600 Jakobstad, Finland. circ. 500.

929 948 — SW — ISSN 0280-3984
SLAEKTHISTORISKT FORUM. 1977. 5/yr. SEK 225($35) membership. Sveriges Slaektforskarfoerbund, P.O. Box 15222, S-161 15 Bromma, Sweden. TEL 46-8-659-31-10. FAX 46-8-659-85-00. Ed. Elisabeth Thorsell. adv.; bk.rev.; illus. circ. 5,000. (back issues avail.)
  Formerly (until 1982): Genealogisk Ungdoms Tidskrift.

929 — US — ISSN 0278-3134
CS71
SMITH PAPERS.* 1980. irreg. Sims Genealogical Publishing, Box 161984, Sacramento, CA 95816-1984. FAX 916-457-8247. Ed. Mary Sims. adv.; bk.rev. circ. 1,000.

929 — US
SMOKY MOUNTAIN HISTORICAL SOCIETY. NEWSLETTER. 1977. q. $10 membership. Smoky Mountain Historical Society, Box 5078, Sevierville, TN 37864. Ed. James E. Shular. bk.rev. circ. 500.
  Description: Dedicated to preserving the history as well as the pre-history of the East Tennessee counties of Blount, Cocke and Sevier.

929 — US — ISSN 1062-3000
CS71
SNYDER-SNIDER-SCHNEIDER DATA LETTER. 1980. m. $8 for 10 nos. Robert A. Longbottom, Ed.& Pub., 1164 Catherine St., Suffield, OH 44260. TEL 216-628-4435. circ. 350.

929 — CN — ISSN 0037-9387
SOCIETE GENEALOGIQUE CANADIENNE-FRANCAISE. MEMOIRES. 1944. q. $30. Societe Genealogique Canadienne-Francaise, Case Postale 335, Station Place d'Armes, Montreal, PQ H2Y 3H1, Canada. TEL 514-729-8366. Ed. Normand Robert. adv.; bk.rev.; index. circ. 3,300. **Indexed:** Periodex, Pt.de Rep. (1983-).

SOCIETE HISTORIQUE DE SAINT-BONIFACE. BULLETIN. see HISTORY — History Of North And South America

SOMERSET AND DORSET NOTES AND QUERIES. see HISTORY — History Of Europe

GENEALOGY AND HERALDRY

929 US
SOMERSET PAST; history and genealogy of Somerset County, Pa. 1981. 4/yr. $13. Southwest Pennsylvania Genealogical Services, Box 253, Laughlintown, PA 15655. Ed. William L. Iscrupe. (back issues avail.)
   Description: Covers wills, deeds, births, marriages, deaths, tax lists, cemetery--church-census records, naturalizations, and news items.

929 970 US
SONS AND DAUGHTERS OF THE SODDIES. REPORTS;* sod houses and dugouts in North America. 1955. irreg. (1-2/yr.). $2 for 2 yrs. Sod House Society of America, Sod House Survey, Colby, KS 67701. TEL 913-462-2021. illus.; stat.; tr.lit. circ. 10,000. (processed)

SONS OF THE AMERICAN REVOLUTION MAGAZINE. see HISTORY — History Of North And South America

929 AT ISSN 0311-2756
SOUTH AUSTRALIAN GENEALOGIST. 1974. q. Aus.$16. South Australian Genealogy & Heraldry Society, Inc., G.P.O. Box 592, Adelaide, S.A. 5001, Australia. TEL 08-272-4222. FAX 08-272-4910. Ed. A.G. Peake. adv.; bk.rev. circ. 3,000.
   Description: To assist people with the tracing of their families' histories.

SOUTH CAROLINA HISTORICAL MAGAZINE. see HISTORY — History Of North And South America

929 US
SOUTH CAROLINA MAGAZINE OF ANCESTRAL RESEARCH. 1973. q. $25. Brent H. Holcomb, Ed. & Pub., Box 21766, Columbia, SC 29221. TEL 803-772-6919. bk.rev. circ. 750. (back issues avail.) Indexed: Geneal.Per.Ind.

929 US
SOUTH DAKOTA GENEALOGICAL SOCIETY QUARTERLY. q. $15 to individuals; institutions $18. South Dakota Genealogical Society, Box 1101, Pierre, SD 57501. Ed. Judy Huber; Pub. Marilyn Heesch. **Document type:** newsletter.

929 US ISSN 0735-6870
F294.A9
SOUTHERN ECHOES. 1979. m. $25 includes Ancestoring. Augusta Genealogical Society, Inc., Box 3743, Augusta, GA 30904. TEL 404-738-2241. Ed. Carrie M. Adamson. bk.rev.; bibl.; index. circ. 1,000. (looseleaf format; back issues avail.) Indexed: Geneal.Per.Ind.

929 US ISSN 0584-4487
CS42
SOUTHERN GENEALOGICAL EXCHANGE QUARTERLY. 1957. q. $16. Box 2801, Jacksonville, FL 32203-2801. Ed. Mary Louise Howard. bk.rev.; illus.; index. circ. 367.
   —UnCover.
   Description: Promotes genealogical pursuits.

929 US ISSN 8755-1748
Z1251.S7
SOUTHERN GENEALOGICAL INDEX. 1984. a. $10. Mountain Press (Signal Mountain), Box 400, Signal Mountain, TN 37377-0400. TEL 615-886-6369. Ed. James L. Douthat. adv.; bk.rev. circ. 400.
   Formerly: Southern Genealogy and Heraldry.

929 US ISSN 1048-8057
F208
SOUTHERN QUERIES. 1990. bi-m. $24 (effective through Dec. 1995). PerroBlanco Publications, Box 726, Durham, NC 27702-0726. TEL 919-687-4818. Ed. Steve Smith. bk.rev.; software rev.; circ. 2,100 (paid). **Document type:** consumer publication.
   Description: For people researching ancestors and families in the South. Includes queries, how-to articles, calendar of family reunions and genealogical events.

929 US ISSN 0895-2876
SOUTHERN ROOTS & SHOOTS. 1985. q. $12 to individuals; families $15. Delta Genealogical Society, c/o Rossville Public Library, 504 McFarland Ave., Rossville, GA 30741. Ed. J.E. Couch. bk.rev. circ. 300.

929 US
THE SOUTHSIDE VIRGINIAN; a journal of genealogy and history. 1982. q. $22 (effective Mar. 1994). Southside Virginian Publishing Co., Box 3684, Richmond, VA 23235-7584. TEL 804-272-4875. FAX 804-272-4930. Eds. C.M. & K.S. Hooper. bk.rev.; illus.; maps; cum.index: 1982-1990. circ. 900. (back issues avail.) **Document type:** academic/scholarly publication.
   —UnCover.
   Description: Provides transcriptions and abstracts of genealogical source materials, previously unpublished, for the counties of Southside Virginia.

929 US ISSN 0736-5683

929 US
SPEAKING RELATIVELY. 1975. bi-m. membership. Ohio Genealogical Society, East Cuyahoga County Chapter, 6808-C Colonial Dr., Mentor, OH 44060. Ed. Francis N. Slack. circ. 275.

929 US ISSN 0899-1596
CS71
STAFFORD DATA. 1982. irreg. $7.25 per no. McNeill Enterprises, Box 779, Napavine, WA 98565-0779. TEL 509-922-4521. circ. 50. (back issues avail.)
   Description: Miscellaneous data on branches of the surname, including bible records, marriage records, county histories, census records, family records, wills, and obituaries; accepts lineage sheets from families for permanent recording.

929 UK
STAFFORDSHIRE BUGLE. 1991. m. £15.95. Mercia Publicity, Bugle House, 41 High St., Cradley Heath, Warley, W. Midlands B64 5HL, England. TEL 0384-67678. FAX 0384-410045. Ed. Abel Rowley. adv.; bk.rev. circ. 7,500. **Document type:** newsletter.
   Formerly: Birmingham Bugle.

929 US ISSN 0893-3359
STANLY COUNTY GENEALOGICAL SOCIETY. JOURNAL. 1981. q. $7 membership (effective 1993-1994). Stanly County Genealogical Society, Box 31, Albemarle, NC 28002-0031. Ed. Zelma Eudy. circ. 210. **Document type:** academic/scholarly publication.

929 US
STEFFEL CHRONICLE. 1981. q. Richard S. Steffel, Ed. & Pub., 16 Fairway Dr., Eustis, FL 32726. TEL 904-357-9806.

929 US
STEPHENSON COUNTY SWOGHEN. 1983. q. membership. Stephenson County Genealogical Society, Box 514, Freeport, IL 61032. Ed. Lois De Garmo. adv. circ. 250.

929 US ISSN 0894-8313
STEPPING BACK IN TIME. 1987. q. $30 (effective March 1994). Sherrill Investigations, Box 5, Sherrills Ford, NC 28673-0005. TEL 704-478-2469. Ed. Elizabeth Bray Sherrill. adv.; bk.rev.; abstr.; charts; illus.; index. (back issues avail.) **Document type:** newsletter.
   —UnCover.
   Description: Covers genealogy in eastern Catawba County, NC.

929 US ISSN 1059-4019
CS71
STEWART CONNECTION. (Supplement to: Stewart Newsletter (ISSN 1056-5582)) 1991. q. $5 (combined subscr. $10; foreign $13). Janet E. Thomas, Ed. & Pub., Box 245, Novinger, MO 63554. TEL 816-488-6616. FAX 816-488-6885. (back issues avail.)
   Description: Query publication for subscribers to newsletter.

929 US ISSN 1056-5582
CS71
STEWART NEWSLETTER. 1987. 3/yr. $10 including Connection (foreign $13). Janet E. Thomas, Ed. & Pub., Box 245, Novinger, MO 63559. TEL 816-488-6616. FAX 816-488-6885. adv.; bk.rev. (back issues avail.) **Document type:** newsletter.
   Description: Consists of genealogical information on the Stewart lineage including census, biblical, ship, marriage, and death records. Contains information on early Stewarts throughout the world; includes cross-index of individuals.

929 US ISSN 0895-8483
STILWELL - STILLWELL WHAT THE 'L' 1986. bi-m. $16. Box 2623, Weaverville, CA 96093. FAX 916-623-3929. Ed. Alice Stillwell. circ. 200. (looseleaf format; back issues avail.)
   Description: Examines obituaries, background sketches, general family information, group or military records, wills, and other queries, as well as pedigree charts in the evaluation of genealogical charts.

929 US
STIRES FAMILY NEWSLETTER. 1977. m. $10. RD, No. 2, Box 3249, Livermore Falls, ME 04254. TEL 207-897-4222. Ed. W. Dennis Stires. bk.rev.; bibl.; charts; illus.; index. circ. 45. (looseleaf format; also avail. in microform from LDS; back issues avail.) **Document type:** newsletter.

929 US ISSN 0039-1522
CS1
STIRPES. 1961. q. $22 (subscr. includes TSGS Newsletter). Texas State Genealogical Society, 204 Glentower, San Antonio, TX 78213. Ed. Frances Condra. adv.; bk.rev.; cum.index: 1961-1985; circ. 700 (controlled). **Document type:** academic/scholarly publication.
   Description: Includes material on Texas families, histories, cemetery listings, queries, county records, state records, and research centers.

929 US ISSN 0883-9050
THE STOCKTON FAMILY NEWSLETTER. 1985. q. Robert Stockton, Ed. & Pub., 14067 La Forge St., Whittier, CA 90605. **Document type:** newsletter.

929 US
▼**STOUT BRANCHES.** 1992. q. $18. Family Scribe, Box 32, Sierra Vista, AZ 85636-0032. Ed. Neva Jane Stout Bryant. bk.rev.; index.
   Description: Provides data relating to the surname Stout-Stoudt-Staudt etc. Lists marriages, births, deaths, military records, Bible records, family histories, pictures, queries and ancestor file listings.

929 US
STRANGE BRANCHES AND TWIGS. 1968. q. $10. 5373 Sunset Ave., Indianapolis, IN 46208. Ed. Clover A. (Strange) Haskins. **Document type:** newsletter.
   Description: Describes members of the Strange family past and present; provides detailed genealogical information.

929 UK ISSN 0143-8859
STRAYS. 1979. irreg. £2. Cumbria Family History Society, c/o Mrs. M.M. Russell, 32 Granada Rd., Denton, Manchester M38 2LJ, England. TEL 061 336 6553.

929 US
THE STUDEBAKER FAMILY. 1966. q. $10. Studebaker Family National Association, 6555 S. State Rt. 202, Tipp City, OH 45371-9444. TEL 513-667-4451. FAX 513-667-4798. Ed. Ruth E. Studebaker. circ. 1,587. (back issues avail.) **Document type:** newsletter.

STUDIA ANTHROPONYMICA SCANDINAVICA; tidskrift foer nordisk personnamnsforskning. see LINGUISTICS

SUKUVIESTI. see HISTORY — History Of Europe

929 US
SUTHERLAND QUARTERLY. 1986. q. $20. Collier Research, c/o Timothy Biarnesen, Ed., Box 371883, El Paso, TX 79937. TEL 915-595-2725.

929 US ISSN 1059-6976
F465
SUTLER. 1986. 3/yr. $13.50. Lathrop Enterprises (Sheldon), Rt. 2, Box 280, Sheldon, MO 64784. TEL 417-884-2619. Ed. Wilma Lathrop. bk.rev. circ. 200.
   Formerly: Bushwhackers and Rock Thumpers.

929 SW ISSN 0349-1714
SVENSKA ANTAVLOR. (Text in Swedish) 1980. s-a. SEK 225. Sveriges Slaektforskarfoerbund, P.O. Box 15222, S-161 15 Bromma, Sweden. Ed. Bengt Hjord. index. circ. 5,000. (back issues avail.)

GENEALOGY AND HERALDRY

929   US   ISSN 0275-9314
E184.S23
SWEDISH AMERICAN GENEALOGIST; a quarterly journal devoted to Swedish American biography, genealogy and personal history. 1981. q. $20. Swenson Swedish Immigration Research Center, Augustana College, 639 38th St., Rock Island, IL 61201-2273. TEL 309-794-7204. FAX 306-794-7443. Ed. Nils William Olsson. adv.; bk.rev.; bibl.; charts; illus.; index. circ. 1,200. **Indexed:** Geneal.Per.Ind.
—UnCover.

929   US
SYCAMORE LEAVES.* 1973. q. $10. Wabash Valley Genealogical Society, Inc., 2906 E. Morris Ave., Terre Haute, IN 47805-2123. Ed. Betty Hatfield. adv. circ. 250. (processed)

929   US
T U NEWS. 1964. q. $3. Tingley's United, R.D. No. 2, Stoneboro, PA 16153. TEL 412-376-3572. Ed. George Tingley. circ. 1,200.

929   US   ISSN 1052-7753
CS71
TACKETT FAMILY JOURNAL. 1964. q. $12.50. Tackett Family Association, 1830 Johnson Dr., Concord, CA 94520. TEL 510-680-0383. Ed. Jim W. Tackitt. bk.rev. circ. 350. (also avail. in microfilm) **Indexed:** Geneal.Per.Ind.
Former titles: Tackett Journal; (until Jan. 1989): America Pioneers: Tackett - Tacket - Tackitt Families of America (ISSN 0517-4376)

929   UK   ISSN 0141-3589
TALBOTANIA. 1977. s-a. 50p. per no. Talbot Research Organisation, 142 Albemarle Ave., Elson, Gosport, Hants PO12 4HY, England. Eds. Mary & Michael Talbot. bk.rev. circ. 100.

929   US   ISSN 0899-160X
CS71
TALBOTT TREE. 1982. irreg. $7.25 per no. McNeill Enterprises, Box 779, Napavine, WA 98565-0779. TEL 509-922-4521. bk.rev. circ. 80. (back issues avail.)
Description: Miscellaneous data on branches of the surname, including bible records, marriage records, county histories, census records, family records, wills, and obituaries; accepts lineage sheets from families for permanent recording.

929   US
TALLEY...TALLY RESEARCHER. 1979. q. $7.50. Midwestern Enterprises, 5412 Raytown Rd., Kansas City, MO 64133. TEL 816-356-5100. Ed. Hugh M. Burton. index. circ. 84.

929.3761   US   ISSN 0494-6944
F325
TAP ROOTS.* q. Southern Genealogical Institute, 9418 Shartel Dr., Shreveport, LA 71108.

929   AT   ISSN 0159-0677
TASMANIAN ANCESTRY. 1980. q. Aus.$25. Genealogical Society of Tasmania Inc., P.O. Box 60, Prospect, Tas. 7250, Australia. Ed. Anne Bartlett. adv.; bk.rev.; index. circ. 1,300. (back issues avail.)
Description: Includes articles on genealogy and dissemination of genealogical information.

929 976   US   ISSN 0893-309X
TATE TRAILS. 1983. q. $15 to individuals; families $18. Tate County Mississippi Genealogical and Historical Society, Box 974, Senatobia, MS 38668. TEL 601-562-0390. Ed. Gail Shepard Tomlinson. bk.rev. circ. 275.

929   US   ISSN 0735-9144
CS71
TAYLOR QUARTERLY (ALEXANDRIA). 1983. q. $8.50. 5911 Brookview Dr., Alexandria, VA 22310-1818. Ed. Antoinette Condo. bk.rev. circ. 400.

929   US
TAYLOR QUARTERLY (EL PASO). 1987. q. $20. Collier Research, c/o Timothy P. Biarnesen, Ed., Box 3718833, El Paso, TX 79937. TEL 915-595-2725.

929   US   ISSN 0882-0635
F435
TENNESSEE ANCESTORS. 1985. 3/yr. $15. East Tennessee Historical Society, 500 W. Church Ave., Knoxville, TN 37902-2505. TEL 615-544-5732. Ed. Rene Jordan. bk.rev.; index. circ. 2,000. (back issues avail.) **Document type:** academic/scholarly publication.
—UnCover.

929   US
TENNESSEE GENEALOGICAL MAGAZINE, "ANSEARCHIN'" NEWS. 1954. q. $20. Tennessee Genealogical Society, Box 111249, Memphis, TN 38111-1249. FAX 901-327-3273. Ed. Betsy West. bk.rev.; stat.; index. circ. 2,100.
Formerly: Ansearchin' News (ISSN 0003-5246)

929   US
TENNESSEE - KENTUCKY QUERIES. 1987. irreg., vol.11, 1992. $7.25. Name Game Enterprises, S. 4204 Conklin St., Spokane, WA 99203-6235. TEL 509-747-4903. Ed. E. Dale Hastin Smith. bk.rev.; index. (back issues avail.)
Formerly: Tennessee Queries (ISSN 0898-5472)
Description: Serves as a forum for genealogical queries and communication relating to the states of Tennessee and Kentucky.

929   US   ISSN 0735-2794
F377.T5
TERREBONNE LIFE LINES. 1981. q. $20 to individuals; libraries $18. Terrebonne Genealogical Society, Box 295, Sta. 2, Houma, LA 70360. Ed. Audrey B. Westerman. bk.rev. circ. 500. **Document type:** newsletter.
Description: Genealogical information for Assumption, Lafourche and Terrebonne parishes in Louisiana and related areas.

929   US   ISSN 0884-2108
TERRELL TRAILS. 1985. q. $12. Terrell Society of America, Inc., c/o Pat Terrell, Secy., Rt.5, Box 211, Reed Creek Dr., Bassett, VA 24055. TEL 704-541-1857. Ed. Dan Brinson. bk.rev.; charts; cum.index: 1985-1990. circ. 200. (looseleaf format; back issues avail.)
—UnCover.
Description: Covers news of the Terrell Society of America. Includes genealogical information and queries.

929   US
TERRY FAMILY HISTORIAN.* 1982. q. $16. c/o Robert M. Terry, Ed., 1518 Skyline Cir., Sapulpa, OK 74066. adv.; bk.rev. circ. 300.
●Also available online.

929   US   ISSN 0741-6105
F385
TEXARKANA U S A QUARTERLY. 1974. q. $10 individual membership; couples $12.50. Texarkana U S A Genealogical Society Inc., 2404-A Briar Rose Dr., Texarkana, AR 75502. TEL 501-772-3955. Ed. Geraldine Meador Johnson. adv.; bk.rev. circ. 307. (also avail. in Braille; back issues avail.)
Description: Contains data on mostly Bowie County, Texas and Miller County, Arkansas.

929   US   ISSN 0091-1607
F532.K2
THE-A-KI-KI. 1970. q. $12 membership (typically set in Jan.). Kankakee Valley Genealogical Society, Box 442, Bourbonnais, IL 60914. FAX 815-933-2516. Ed. Marcia Stang. index. circ. 125. **Indexed:** Geneal.Per.Ind.

929   US   ISSN 1066-601X
THINK ON. 1983. q. $15 membership. Clan MacLellan in America, Inc., 8636 Don Carol Dr., El Cerrito, CA 94530. TEL 510-527-6867. (Subscr. to: 5230 Angelita Ave., Dayton, OH 45424-2709) Ed. A.L. McClellan. bk.rev.; cum.index: 1981-1991. circ. 500. (back issues avail.) **Document type:** newsletter.
Description: Deals with the genealogy and exploits of the MacLellan families and Scotland as it relates to the MacLellan name in all its spellings.

929   US   ISSN 0094-0844
CS42
THE THORNY TRAIL. 1972. s-a. membership. Midland Genealogical Society, P.O. Box 1191, Midland, TX 79702. TEL 915-697-1721. adv.; bk.rev.; charts; index. circ. 225. (processed; back issues avail.) **Indexed:** Geneal.Per.Ind.
Description: Helps develop and maintain ancestral charts and records. Includes queries.

THREE RIVERS CHRONICLE. see HISTORY — History Of North And South America

929.7 340   SW   ISSN 0280-9257
TIDNING FOER KUNGOERELSER OM EFTERNAMN. 1964. fortn. SEK 50 (effective 1991). Patent- och Registreringsverket, Patentverket, P.O. Box 5005, S-102 42 Stockholm, Sweden. **Document type:** government publication.
Formerly (until 1983): Tidning om Kungoerelser om Slaektnamn.

929   US
TIMBER TRAILS. 1980. q. $10 membership. Yamhill County Genealogical Society, Box 568, McMinnville, OR 97128. Ed. Ruth Stoller.
Description: Covers early Yamhill County public records, County cemetery listings, family records and other genealogical material on mostly Yamhill County families.

929   US
TIMMONS FAMILY NEWSLETTER. 1980. q. Box 262 Montrose, Montrose, MN 55363. TEL 612-675-3457. Ed. Bunnie Runman. adv.; index. circ. 125. (looseleaf format; back issues avail.) **Document type:** newsletter.
Description: Details the census records, births, marriages, deaths, and biographies of the Timmons family.

929   US
TINNEY-GREEN(E) FAMILY ORGANIZATION NEWSLETTER. 1972. irreg. $50 per no. Tinney GenSearch Consultants, 1221 Pacific Ave., Salt Lake City, UT 84104-2314. TEL 801-596-7004. Ed. Thomas Milton Tinney, Sr. adv.; bk.rev. circ. 50. (also avail. in microfilm; back issues avail.)
Formerly: Tinney-Green(e) Family Organization Quarterly.

929   US
TOLLE FAMILY EXCHANGE. 1984. bi-m. $6. c/o Thoren Tolle Meyers, 10351 16th St., Garden Grove, CA 92643.

929   US   ISSN 0893-7664
THE TOMBSTONE. 1983. q. $7.50. Cochise Genealogical Society, Box 68, Pirtleville, AZ 85626. TEL 602-364-3156. Ed. Charles Riley. adv.; circ. 87 (paid). (back issues avail.) **Indexed:** Geneal.Per.Ind. **Document type:** newsletter.

929   US   ISSN 0734-8495
F680
TOPEKA GENEALOGICAL SOCIETY QUARTERLY. 1970. q. $15 (effective Jan. 1992). Topeka Genealogical Society, Box 4048, Topeka, KS 66604-0048. TEL 913-233-5762. Ed. Helen L. King. adv.; bk.rev.; bibl.; charts; index. circ. 845. (microform; also avail. in microfiche; back issues avail.) **Indexed:** Geneal.Per.Ind. **Document type:** academic/scholarly publication.

929   US
TOWNSEND NEWSLETTER. 1976. q. membership. Townsend Society of America, Inc., 107 E. Main St., Oyster Bay, NY 11771. Ed. Martha J. Burke. circ. 700. (back issues avail.)
Formerly (until 1975): Townsend Topics.

929 976   US   ISSN 0882-2158
F450
TRACES (GLASGOW). 1973. q. $10 membership. South Central Kentucky Historical and Genealogical Society, Inc., Box 157, Glasgow, KY 42142-0157. Ed. Martha P. Reneau. bk.rev. circ. 400. **Document type:** bulletin.
—UnCover.

929   US
TRACES IN THE SAND. 1982. q. Vista P. Setters, Ed. & Pub., 3545 Bear Hollow Rd., Whites Creek, TN 37189.

TRACES OF INDIANA AND MIDWESTERN HISTORY. see HISTORY — History Of North And South America

929   US
TRACINGS. 1981. s-a. $10. Anderson County Genealogical Society, Box 2045, Palestine, TX 75802. circ. 145. (back issues avail.)

929   US
TRACKS AND TRACES. 1977. 2/yr. $10. Union County Genealogical Society, c/o Barton Library, 200 E. Fifth St., El Dorado, AR 71730. TEL 501-862-3944.

GENEALOGY AND HERALDRY

929 979   US   ISSN 0362-0344
F897.C6
TRAIL BREAKERS. 1974. q. $12. Clark County Genealogical Society, Library 1511 Main St., Box 2728, Vancouver, WA 98668. TEL 206-256-0977. Ed. Jane Germann. adv.; bk.rev. circ. 500. (back issues avail.)
—UnCover.

929   US   ISSN 0740-4999
F478
TRAIL TRACER. 1980. q. $8 membership. Vincennes University, Northwest Territory Genealogical Society, Lewis Historical Library - LRC 22, Vincennes, IN 47591. TEL 812-885-4330. Ed. Donna Beeson. adv.; bk.rev. circ. 250. (back issues avail.) **Document type:** academic/scholarly publication.

929   CN   ISSN 1195-4906
TRAILS. 1980. q. Can.$15. Ontario Genealogical Society (Windsor), Essex County Branch, Box 2, Sta. "A", Windsor, ON N9A 6J5, Canada. Ed. Larry Monkhouse. bk.rev.; bibl.; charts; tr.lit.; index. circ. 300. (looseleaf format) **Document type:** newsletter.

929   US   ISSN 1060-0337
F739.G7
TREASURE STATE LINES. 1976. q. $20. Great Falls Genealogical Society, 1400 First Ave. N., Great Falls, MT 59401. TEL 406-727-3922. adv.; B&W page $50. bk.rev.; index. circ. 200. **Document type:** newsletter.
Description: Discusses local and family history, genealogical research, and queries.

929   US   ISSN 0893-2069
TREE SHAKER. 1977. q. $6. Eastern Kentucky Genealogical Society, Inc., Box 1544, Ashland, KY 41105-1544. TEL 606-329-0090. Ed. Evelyn S. Jackson. bk.rev.; abstr.; charts; cum.index 1977-1985. circ. 958. (back issues avail.) **Indexed:** Geneal.Per.Ind. **Document type:** newsletter.
Description: Covers genealogical subjects such as wills, marriages, deeds, cemeteries, bible record and queries from members.

929   US   ISSN 0041-2201
TREE TALKS. 1961. q. $18. Central New York Genealogical Society, Box 104 Colvin Sta., Syracuse, NY 13205. Ed. David K. Martin. bk.rev.; abstr.; stat.; index. circ. 1,000. **Indexed:** Geneal.Per.Ind.
Incorporates: Cousin Huntin'

929   US   ISSN 0162-1440
F693
TREE TRACERS. 1976. q. $12 to individuals; families $15; non-profit organizations $10. Southwest Oklahoma Genealogical Society, Tree Tracers Committee, Box 148, Lawton, OK 73502-1048. FAX 405-248-0243. Ed. Donna Irwin. bk.rev. circ. 400. (processed) **Indexed:** Geneal.Per.Ind.
—UnCover.
Description: Includes records of Southwest Oklahoma and research suggestions for the U.S.

929   US
TREESEARCHER. 1959. q. $15 to individuals; libraries $12. Kansas Genealogical Society, Inc., P.O. Box 103, Village Square Mall, Lower Level, 2601 Central, Dodge City, KS 67801.
TEL 316-225-1951. (Subscr. to: Mrs. Dan Schaffer, Rte. 1 Box 49, Spearville, KS 67876) Ed. Gay Rooney. bk.rev.; index. circ. 500. **Indexed:** Geneal.Per.Ind.

929   US   ISSN 0496-1803
F897.B4
TRI-CITY GENEALOGICAL SOCIETY. BULLETIN. 1961. s-a. $10 (typically set in Jan.). Tri-City Genealogical Society, Box 1410, Richland, WA 99352-9758. Ed. Leona Wilson George. adv.; bk.rev.; index. circ. 200. **Indexed:** Geneal.Per.Ind. **Document type:** bulletin.
Description: Provides information useful for genealogical research.

929   US   ISSN 0740-896X
F525
TRI-STATE PACKET. 1977. q. $12 membership. Tri-State Genealogical Society, c/o Willard Library, 21 First Ave., Evansville, IN 47710.
TEL 812-425-4309. Ed. Brenda Joyce Jerome. bk.rev.; bibl.; stat.; tr.lit.; index. circ. 600. (back issues avail.) **Indexed:** Geneal.Per.Ind.
—UnCover.

920   US   ISSN 0149-2438
CS71
TUFTS KINSMEN. 1975. q. $10. Tufts Kinsmen Association, Inc., Box 571, Dedham, MA 02026-0806. Ed. Herbert F. Adams. illus. circ. 1,000. (back issues avail.)

929   US   ISSN 0564-4437
F693
TULSA ANNALS. 1966. 3/yr. $15. Tulsa Genealogical Society, Box 585, Tulsa, OK 74101-0585. TEL 918-742-3893. Ed. Ken Wade. adv.; bk.rev.; index. circ. 500. (back issues avail.)

929 900   US   ISSN 0740-4409
F868.M5
UNDER CONSTRUCTION. 1977. q. $6. Mendocino Coast Genealogical Society, Box 762, Fort Bragg, CA 95437. TEL 707-937-5482. FAX 707-937-5482. Ed. Alice Holmes. adv.; bk.rev. circ. 50. **Document type:** newsletter.

929   US
UNDER THE RUNYON TREE. 1982. 4/yr. $9. c/o G.J. Halstead, Ed., Box 491, Pocono Pines, PA 18350.

929   FR   ISSN 1240-4489
UNION GENEALOGIQUE DU CENTRE. INFORMATIONS GENEALOGIQUES DU CENTRE. 1975. q. 110 F. Union Genealogique du Centre, B.P. 147, 18003 Bourges Cedex, France. TEL 48-65-72-58. adv. circ. 1,600.
Formerly (until 1992): Union Genealogique du Centre. Informations Genealogiques (ISSN 0337-6680)

929   US   ISSN 0270-465X
UPCHURCH BULLETIN. 1980. q. $15. Michael Enterprises, Box 35804, Tucson, AZ 85740. Ed. Robert Phillip Upchurch. bk.rev. circ. 200.

929   US   ISSN 0146-2229
CS1
UTAH GENEALOGICAL ASSOCIATION. GENEALOGICAL JOURNAL. 1971. q. $25 membership (foreign $30). Utah Genealogical Association, Box 1144, Salt Lake City, UT 84110. Ed. RoseMari Finter. adv.; bk.rev.; index. circ. 700. (also avail. in microfilm from UMI) **Indexed:** Geneal.Per.Ind. **Document type:** academic/scholarly publication.
—UnCover.
Description: Contains genealogical and local history articles of local, national, and international scope on treating source materials, methodology, preservation, and research techniques.

929   US
UTAH GENEALOGICAL ASSOCIATION. NEWSLETTER. q. $25 membership (foreign $30). Utah Genealogical Association, Box 1144, Salt Lake City, UT 84110. TEL 801-531-2091. Ed. RoseMari Finter. adv.; bk.rev. circ. 700. **Document type:** academic/scholarly publication.
Description: Contains articles on developments and events in the field of genealogy and lists new acquisitions at the Salt Lake Family History Library.

929   US
V G S NEWSLETTER. 6/yr. $20 includes Magazine of Virginia Genealogy. Virginia Genealogical Society, 5001 W. Broad St., Ste. 115, Richmond, VA 23230-3023. bk.rev. **Document type:** newsletter.
Description: Provides news of local historical societies, libraries, celebrations and points of interest. Includes query column for those seeking family information for members.

929   US
VALLEY QUARTERLY. 1962. q. $10 to individual members; family $15. San Bernardino Valley Genealogical Society, Box 2220, San Bernardino, CA 92406. TEL 714-887-3762. Ed. Virginia R. Harshman. adv.; bk.rev. circ. 200. (back issues avail.) **Document type:** monographic series.
Description: Contains primarily San Bernardino Co., CA genealogical data, surnames indexed annually in 4th issue.

VALOR. see HISTORY — History Of North And South America

929.6   SW   ISSN 0349-0602
VAPENBILDEN. 1976. s-a. SEK 60 (membership) (1990). Svenska Heraldiska Foereningen, c/o O. Wennerholm, Haesthovsstigen 14, S-430 33 Fjaeraas, Sweden.

929   US   ISSN 1059-4655
VEALE HERITAGE. 1978. q. membership. Veale Family Association, 1003 Ave. B, Redondo Beach, CA 90277. Ed. Carl W. Veale.

929.9   BE   ISSN 0772-3261
VEXILLA BELGICA. (Text in French) 1977. a. Societas Vexillologica Belgica, Rue Martin Lindekens, 57, 1150 Brussels, Belgium. Ed. Hugh Robert Boudin.

929.9   SZ
VEXILLA HELVETICA. (Text in French, German) a. Societe Suisse de Vexillologie, c/o Dr. Emil Dreyer, Flurweg 43, 3052 Zollikofen, Switzerland.

929.9   IT
VEXILLA ITALICA. 2/yr. Centro Italiano di Studi Vessillologici, Via Luigi Bravo 7, 21026 Gavirate (VA), Italy. Ed. Aldo Ziggioto.

929.9   NE
VEXILLA NOSTRA. 6/yr. fl.35 membership. Nederlandse Vereniging voor Vlaggenkunde, Johan Wagenaarkade 84-11, 3533 TM Utrect, Netherlands. Ed. J.F. van Heyningen.

929.9   XR
VEXILOLOGIE. q. c/o Ales Brozek, Post Prihradka 1, CS-400, 12 Usti na Laba, Czech Republic.

929   US
VICK FAMILY NEWSLETTER. 1985. q. $5. Vick Family Association, c/o James M. Perrin, Ed., 219 Randall Ave., Hammond, LA 70403. TEL 504-386-4476. bk.rev. circ. 100. **Document type:** newsletter.

929   US
VIERS-VEIRS QUARTERLY NEWSLETTER. 1981. q. $10. Viers-Veirs Family Organization, 1867 Robertson Dr., No.14, Omaha, NE 68114. Ed. Richard L. Anderson. circ. 115. **Document type:** newsletter.

929   US   ISSN 0739-3482
F225
VIRGINIA APPALACHIAN NOTES. 1977. q. $15 individual membership; institutions $12.50. Southwestern Virginia Genealogical Society, Box 12485, Roanoke, VA 24026. Ed. Vicie "Babe" Fowler. bk.rev. circ. 625. (also avail. in microfilm)
—UnCover.
Description: Publishes genealogical material from the area.

929   US   ISSN 0300-645X
F221
VIRGINIA GENEALOGIST. 1957. q. $20. John Frederick Dorman, Ed. & Pub., Box 5860, Falmouth, VA 22403-5860. TEL 703-371-9115. Ed. John Frederick Dorman. bk.rev.; index. circ. 1,200. (also avail. in microfiche; back issues avail.) **Indexed:** Geneal.Per.Ind.
—UnCover.

929   US   ISSN 0890-9423
VIRGINIA, WEST VIRGINIA QUERIES. Short title: VA - W. VA Queries. (In 7 vols.) 1987. irreg. $5.50 per issue. Topp of the Line, W. 1304 Cliffwood Ct., Spokane, WA 99218-2917. Ed. Bette Butcher Topp. bk.rev.

929   BE
VLAAMSE STAM; tijdschrift voor familiegeschiedenis. 1965. m. (10/yr.). 850 Fr. (foreign 1200 Fr.). Vlaamse Vereniging voor Familiekunde - Flemish Society of Genealogy, Nieuwoortsteenweg 20, 8400 Oostende, Belgium. Ed. E. van Haverbeke. adv.; bk.rev.; bibl. circ. 3,500.

929.9   NE
VLAGGEN. 6/yr. fl.25. Vlaggen, Papaverhof 34, 2565 CB - Den Haag, Netherlands. Ed. A. Jansen. **Document type:** newsletter.

929.9   NE
VLAGGEN DOKUMENTIE CENTRUM. INFO-BULLETIN. (Text in Dutch, English) 2/yr. fl.20. Vlaggen Dokumentie Centrum, De Kempenaerstraat 163, 1051 CM Amsterdam, Netherlands.

929   US   ISSN 0743-1848
LA VOIX DES PRAIRIES. 1980. q. $10 (effective 1993). Evangeline Genealogical & Historical Society, Box 664, Ville Platte, LA 70586. Ed. John Young. bk.rev.; index. circ. 250. **Document type:** newsletter.

929   US
W.I. GENEALOGICAL COUNCIL NEWSLETTER. 1989. q. $5 to individuals; libraries $10 (typically set in May). Wisconsin Genealogical Council Newsletter, Rte. 3, Box 253, Black River Falls, WI 26115. TEL 608-378-4388. FAX 608-378-3006. (Subscr. to: Emil Kraus, WI Gen. Council, 6083 Co. Trk., S. Rapids, WI 54495) Ed. Pat Kell. adv.; bk.rev. circ. 200. (looseleaf format; back issues avail.) **Document type:** newsletter.

929   US   ISSN 8755-2167
F680
WACONDA ROOTS AND BRANCHES. 1979. q. $8 to individuals; families $9. North Central Kansas Genealogical Society and Library, Inc., Box 251, Cawker City, KS 67430. Ed. Dorothy Reling. adv.; bk.rev. circ. 150.
    Formerly: North Central Kansas Genealogical Society. Newsletter.

929   US   ISSN 0898-5421
CS71
WADE WORLD. 1985. irreg., vol.13, 1992. $7.25. Name Game Enterprises, S. 4204 Conklin St., Spokane, WA 99203-6235. TEL 509-747-4903. Ed. E. Dale Smith. bk.rev.; abstr.; stat.; index. (back issues avail.)
    Description: Covers genealogy and lineage. Includes biographies, wills, marriages, family records, queries, and obituary records.

929   US
WAGONER JOURNAL. 1978. s-a. $12.50 to individuals; institutions $5. Northwest Genealogical Society, Box 6, Alliance, NE 69301. Ed. Patricia Pinney. adv.; bk.rev. circ. 300. (looseleaf format) **Indexed:** Geneal.Per.Ind.
    Formerly (until 1982): Wagoner.

929   US   ISSN 1055-7857
WAKE TREASURES; a journal. 1982. q. $20. Wake County Genealogical Society, Inc., Box 17713, Raleigh, NC 27619. TEL 919-772-6899. Ed. Lynne White Belvin. adv.; bk.rev.; index. circ. 260. (back issues avail.)
    Formerly (until 1991): Wake County Genealogical Society Newsletter (ISSN 1041-6536)
    Description: Provides "how-to" information on research and genealogical hints, free queries to members, news of seminars and workshops in area, abstracting of Wake County records, and announcement of monthly meetings.

929   US   ISSN 1056-7321
CS71
WALKER FOOTPRINTS.* 1986. irreg. $6 per no. Pence Publications, 11009 E. Third Ave. No. 93, Spokane, WA 99206-6501. TEL 509-235-8614. Ed. Maxine E. Pence. bk.rev.; abstr.; charts; illus.; stat.; index. circ. 35. (back issues avail.)
    Description: Only Walker related material: from all over the U.S. and foreign. Purpose is to connect researchers and help others.

929   US   ISSN 0887-3860
WANDERING WOLFS. 1986. q. $10. Kinseeker Publications, Box 184, Grawn, MI 49637. Ed. Victoria Wilson. bk.rev. circ. 50. (looseleaf format; back issues avail.) **Document type:** newsletter.

929   US
WARE QUARTERLY. 1987. q. $20. Collier Research, c/o Timothy P. Biarnesen, Ed., Box 371883, El Paso, TX 79937. TEL 915-595-2725.

929   US   ISSN 1047-6628
WASHINGTON (MARIETTA). 1983. q. $8 membership. Ohio Genealogical Society, Washington County Chapter, Box 2174, Marietta, OH 45750. Ed. Sharon Cory Gardner. bk.rev. circ. 250. **Document type:** newsletter.
    Description: Provides source material and other information pertaining to the genealogy and early history of Washington County, Ohio.

929   US   ISSN 0091-8857
WATAUGA ASSOCIATION OF GENEALOGISTS. UPPER EAST TENNESSEE. BULLETIN. 1972. s-a. $12 membership (typically set in May). Watauga Association of Genealogists - Upper East Tennessee (WAGS), Box 117, Johnson City, TN 37605-0117. Ed. Dessie Little Simmons. adv.; bk.rev. circ. 650. **Indexed:** Geneal.Per.Ind. **Document type:** bulletin.
    Description: Concerned with preserving all types of earlyu records; encourages genealogical and historical research.

929   US
WEATHERBEE ROUND-UP, a genealogy & family history newsletter for Weatherbee descendants. 1977. bi-m. contribution. 1360 West Mason St., Decatur, IL 62522-2704. TEL 217-423-9081. Ed. Carl Weatherbee. bk.rev. circ. 350. **Document type:** newsletter.

929   US   ISSN 1067-523X
F457.W5
WEBSTER'S WAGON WHEEL. 1980. q. $10. Webster County Historical and Genealogical Society, Box 215, Dixon, KY 42409. TEL 502-639-5170. Ed. Betty J. Branson. bk.rev. circ. 125.

929   US   ISSN 1060-4650
THE WEDGE; Beisel - Beissel international genealogy. (Text in English, German) 1980. s-a. $10. Crystal Educational Counselors, 62 E. Boehms Rd., Willow Street, PA 17584-9721. TEL 717-464-4201. Eds. James D. & Margaret L. Beissel. circ. 99. (looseleaf format; back issues avail.) **Document type:** newsletter.

929   US
WEST CENTRAL KENTUCKY FAMILY RESEARCH ASSOCIATION. BULLETIN. 1968. q. $15 includes Kentucky Family Records. West Central Kentucky Family Research Association, Box 1932, Owensboro, KY 42302. Ed.Bd. bk.rev.; bibl. circ. 500. **Indexed:** Geneal.Per.Ind.

WEST COAST STUDIES. see HISTORY — History Of North And South America

929   US   ISSN 1059-4272
WESTCHESTER CONNECTIONS. 1990. biennial. Westchester County Genealogical Society, Box 518, White Plains, NY 10603. Ed. Laura J. LeBarron.
    Description: Contains genealogical articles and material on Westchesterites.

929   GW   ISSN 0172-1879
WESTDEUTSCHE GESELLSCHAFT FUER FAMILIENKUNDE. MITTEILUNGEN. 1913. q. DM.50. Westdeutsche Gesellschaft fuer Familienkunde, Postfach 100822, 51608 Gummersbach, Germany. TEL 02261-66993. FAX 02261-61632. bk.rev. circ. 1,600. **Document type:** academic/scholarly publication.
    —BLDSC (5875.800000).

970 929   US   ISSN 1072-6756
▼**WESTERN KENTUCKY JOURNAL.** 1994. q. $20. Brenda Joyce Jermome, Ed. & Pub., 300 W. Water St., Newburgh, IN 47630-1158. TEL 812-853-5562. bk.rev.; circ. 250 (paid). **Document type:** academic/scholarly publication.
    Description: Contains articles on various aspects of genealogy and genealogic research.

929   US   ISSN 0747-7805
F186.9
WESTERN MARYLAND GENEALOGY. 1985. q. $17 (foreign $30). Catoctin Press, 709 E. Main St., Middletown, MD 21769-7802. Ed. Donna Valley Russell. bk.rev. circ. 700. **Indexed:** Geneal.Per.Ind. **Document type:** academic/scholarly publication.
    Description: Includes genealogical records for Frederick, Washington, Allegany, Carroll, Montgomery, and Garrett Counties.

929   US   ISSN 0890-6858
F118
WESTERN NEW YORK GENEALOGICAL SOCIETY JOURNAL. 1974. q. $20. Western New York Genealogical Society, Box 338, Hamburg, NY 14075. Ed.Bd. bk.rev.; bibl.; charts; tr.lit. circ. 700.

929   US   ISSN 0278-7431
F148
WESTERN PENNSYLVANIA GENEALOGICAL SOCIETY QUARTERLY. 1974. q. $20 (subscr. includes Jots from the Point) (membership). Western Pennsylvania Genealogical Society, 4338 Bigelow Blvd., Pittsburgh, PA 15213-2695. TEL 412-681-5533. Ed. Jean S. Morris. **Indexed:** Geneal.Per.Ind.
    Formerly: Western Pennsylvania Genealogical Quarterly (ISSN 0095-0866)

929   US
WETZEL COUNTY GENEALOGICAL SOCIETY. NEWSLETTER. 1979. q. $7. Wetzel County Genealogical Society, Box 464, New Martinsville, WV 26155-0464. Ed.Bd. circ. 200.

929   US
WEYMOUTH SURNAME NEWSLETTER. 1985. q. $5. Al Weymouth, Ed.& Pub., c/o Don Weymouth, 119 Winthrop Ln., Holden, ME 01520. circ. 40. **Document type:** newsletter.

929.1   US   ISSN 0092-4164
F547.C7
WHERE THE TRAILS CROSS. 1970. q. $15 membership (includes S S G H S Newsletter). South Suburban Genealogical and Historical Society, Box 96, South Holland, IL 60473-0096. TEL 708-333-9474. Ed. Jan Helge. bk.rev. circ. 550. (back issues avail.) **Document type:** academic/scholarly publication.
    —UnCover.

WHITE COUNTY HERITAGE. see HISTORY — History Of North And South America

929   US   ISSN 0887-6959
WHITMAN COUNTY GENEALOGICAL SOCIETY. NEWSLETTER. 1984. 10/yr. $12 membership. Whitman County Genealogical Society, Box 393, Pullman, WA 99163-0393. Ed. Judy Standar McMurray. adv.; bk.rev. circ. 140. **Document type:** newsletter.
    Description: Keeps members informed and updated on genealogical matters in the area and provides information on genealogy.

929   US
WHO, WHEN & WHERE OF LINCOLN COUNTY, WEST VIRGINIA. 1981. q? Lincoln County Genealogical Society (Griffithsville), Box 92, Griffithsville, WV 25521.

929   US
WIGFIELD NEWSLETTER. 1971. a. $5. Phillip Heritage House, 605 Benton Ave., Missoula, MT 59801. TEL 406-543-3495. abstr.; bibl.; charts; illus.; stat.; tr.lit. (looseleaf format; back issues avail.) **Document type:** newsletter.

929   US   ISSN 0899-1634
CS71
WILEY WORLD. 1985. irreg. $7.25 per no. McNeill Enterprises, Box 779, Napavine, WA 98565-0779. TEL 509-922-4521. bk.rev. (back issues avail.)
    Description: Miscellaneous data on branches of the surname, including bible records, marriage records, county histories, census records, family records, wills, and obituaries; accepts lineage sheet from families for permanent recording.

929   US   ISSN 1042-6884
F547.W5
WILL - GRUNDY COUNTIES GENEALOGICAL SOCIETY NEWS. 1982. m. $15. Will - Grundy Counties (IL) Genealogical Society, Box 24, Wilmington, IL 60481-0024. TEL 815-436-4140. Ed. Marilyn Boehner. circ. 300. (looseleaf format; back issues avail.)

929   US   ISSN 8756-6931
F547.W5
WILL - GRUNDY COUNTIES GENEALOGICAL SOCIETY QUARTERLY. 1982. q. $15. Will - Grundy Counties (IL) Genealogical Society, Box 24, Wilmington, IL 60481-0024. TEL 815-478-3715. Ed. Delilah Kuse. bk.rev. circ. 300. (back issues avail.)

WILLIAM AND MARY QUARTERLY; a magazine of early American history and culture. see HISTORY — History Of North And South America

929   US
WILLIAMS KISSIN COUSINS NEWSLETTER.* 6/yr. $10. Williams Kissin Cousins, Box 3056, Wichita Falls, TX 76309. (back issues avail.)

929   US
WILLIAMS OF VIRGINIA LETTER.* q. $10. Genealogical & Historical News, c/o Robert Bradshaw, Box 779, Saipan, CM, 96950, Mariana Islands.

929   US   ISSN 0897-6686
WILSON COURIER.* 1988. q. $15. Craig Junction Publishers, Box 310, Craigmont, ID 83523-0310. TEL 208-924-5740. Ed. Marsha Bovey. circ. 200. (back issues avail.)

929   US
WILSON OF VIRGINIA LETTER.* q. $10. Genealogical & Historical News, c/o Robert Bradshaw, Box 779, Saipan, CM 96950, Mariana Islands.

GENEALOGY AND HERALDRY — ABSTRACTING, BIBLIOGRAPHIES, STATISTICS

929   UK   ISSN 0260-7174
WILTSHIRE FAMILY HISTORY SOCIETY. JOURNAL. 1981. q. £7. Wiltshire Family History Society, 21 Elizabeth Dr., Devizes, Wiltshire SN10 3SB, England. Ed. Beryl Hurley. bk.rev. circ. 2,100. (back issues avail.) **Document type:** bulletin.

929   US
WINE PRESS. 1975. m. $25. Napa Valley Genealogical & Biographical Society, Box 385, Napa, CA 94559. TEL 707-252-2252. circ. 315. **Document type:** newsletter.
    Description: News and information of interest to society members.

929   US
WISCONSIN STATE GENEALOGICAL SOCIETY NEWSLETTER. 1954. q. $14. Wisconsin State Genealogical Society, Inc., 2109 20 Ave., Monroe, WI 53566. Ed. Virginia V. Irvin. bk.rev.; stat.; index, cum.index: 1954-1960, 1964-1971. circ. 1,800. (looseleaf format) **Indexed:** Geneal.Per.Ind.

929   US   ISSN 0091-6706
CS71
WOOD - WOODS FAMILY MAGAZINE.* 1973. q. $20. Wood Publishing Co., 13200 Woodrose Dr., Brockwood, AL 35444-9227. TEL 205-758-4507. Ed. Thomas Harold Wood. adv.; bk.rev.; abstr.; bibl.; charts; illus.; stat.; index. circ. 500. (back issues avail.)

929   US   ISSN 0741-6881
WOODSON WATCHER PLUS ALLIED LINES. 1982. q. $15. Lineage Research Associates, c/o Mary McGraw Harland, 1750 Allegro Dr., Richmond, VA 23231. TEL 800-730-7414. Eds. Felix Earle Luck, Mary McCraw Harland. bk.rev.; index. circ. 75.

929   US   ISSN 0513-6776
YAKIMA VALLEY GENEALOGICAL SOCIETY BULLETIN. 1967. q. $12. Yakima Valley Genealogical Society, Box 445, Yakima, WA 98907. TEL 509-248-1328. Ed. Ellen Brzoska. bk.rev.; index. (back issues avail.) **Indexed:** Geneal.Per.Ind. **Document type:** bulletin.
    —UnCover.
    Description: Contains local records, family lineage and vital records and researches.

929   US
YARBOROUGH FAMILY MAGAZINE. 1966-1968; 1979-1982; resumed 1984. m. Charles D. Yarborough, Ed. & Pub., 1001 Bedford Rd., Bedford, TX 76022. TEL 817-282-9999. bk.rev.; bibl.; illus.; index. circ. 125. (processed)

929   US
YELL COUNTY HISTORICAL & GENEALOGICAL ASSOCIATION. 1981. 3/yr. $15 (effective 1992). Yell County Historical Society, Box 622, Dardanelle, AR 72834. bk.rev. circ. 500. (back issues avail.)

929 976   US   ISSN 1050-7361
YELLOWED PAGES. 1971. q. $14 (foreign $20). Southeast Texas Genealogical & Historical Society, Box 3827, Beaumont, TX 77704-3827. Ed. Margie M. Boyd. bk.rev.; cum.index: 1971-1988. circ. 360. (back issues avail.)

929   US   ISSN 0277-9668
F540
YELLOWJACKET. 1975. q. $10. Great River Genealogical Society, c/o Quincy Public Library, 526 Jersey, Quincy, IL 62301. TEL 217-222-0226. Ed.Bd. adv.; bk.rev.; index. circ. 300. (looseleaf format; back issues avail.)
    —UnCover.

YESTERYEARS; a quarterly magazine for the appreciation and study of New York State history and genealogy. see HISTORY — History Of North And South America

929   US
YORK COUNTY GENEALOGICAL SOCIETY. JOURNAL. 1986. q. $12. York County Genealogial Society, Box 2242, Ogunquit, ME 03907. TEL 207-646-3753. Ed. Dorothy A. Seaman. index. circ. 200.

YORKER PALATINE NEWSLETTER. see POPULATION STUDIES

929   UK
YORKSHIRE ARCHAEOLOGICAL SOCIETY PARISH REGISTER SERIES. 1899. a. £15. Yorkshire Archaeological Society, Claremont, 23 Clarendon Rd., Leeds LS2 9NZ, England. TEL 0532-457910. Ed. C.S. Preston. index. circ. 300. **Document type:** bulletin.

929   US
YUCAIPA VALLEY FAMILY FINDERS. 1982. m. $7.50. Yucaipa Valley Genealogical Society, Box 32, Yucaipa, CA 92399. **Document type:** newsletter.

929   US   ISSN 0887-3046
CS71
ZINGSHEIM TIMES. 1986. q. $3. Kinseeker Publications, Box 184, Grawn, MI 49637. Ed. Denise Wilson. bk.rev. circ. 20. (looseleaf format; back issues avail.) **Document type:** newsletter.

GENEALOGY AND HERALDRY — Abstracting, Bibliographies, Statistics

929   US
CURRENT GENEALOGICAL PUBLICATIONS. 1984. irreg., vol.9, 1993. Claudette Maerz, Ed. & Pub., Box 31010, Bloomington, MN 55431.
    Description: Annotated listings of family histories and genealogical reference books.

929   US
DIRECTORY OF FAMILY 'ONE-NAME' PERIODICALS. 1983. a. $8. Ye Olde Genealogie Shoppe, Box 39128, Indianapolis, IN 46239. TEL 317-862-3330. Ed. J. Konrad. circ. 1,000.

929   US
GENEALOGICAL PERIODICAL ANNUAL INDEX; key to the genealogical literature. 1962. a. $20. Heritage Books, Inc., 1540 E. Pointer Ridge Pl., Bowie, MD 20716. TEL 301-390-7708. Ed. Elaine Fiehrer. bk.rev. circ. 1,000. (back issues avail.) **Document type:** abstracting/indexing.

929   US
GRASSROOTS CATALOG. 1983. a. $20. C O M G E N E S, Box 1581, Silver City, NM 88062. Ed. Barbara Holley Rock. adv.; bk.rev. circ. 150.
    Former titles (until 1989): Genealogical Abstracts; **(until 1984):** Genealogical Abstracter.
    Description: Presents information on local genealogical resources and family group sheets organized by state, county, and contributor to show resources available and research fees.

PERIODICAL SOURCE INDEX. see HISTORY — Abstracting, Bibliographies, Statistics

GENEALOGY AND HERALDRY — Computer Applications

929   UK   ISSN 0263-3248
CS14   CODEN: CGENER
COMPUTERS IN GENEALOGY. 1982. q. £7($11.55) to non-members; members £6($9.90). Society of Genealogists, 14 Charterhouse Buildings, Goswell Rd., London EC1M 7BA, England. TEL 071-251-8799. Ed. Eric Probert. circ. 1,700. **Document type:** academic/scholarly publication, newsletter.
    —BLDSC (3394.920300).

929 001.6   US   ISSN 0277-5913
CS14
GENEALOGICAL COMPUTING. 1981. q. $25 (Canada $30; elsewhere $35). Ancestry, Box 476, Salt Lake City, UT 84110-0476. TEL 801-531-1790. FAX 801-531-1798. Ed. Dennis Sampson. adv.; bk.rev. circ. 4,800. **Indexed:** Geneal.Per.Ind.
    —UnCover.
    Description: For genealogists interested in applying personal computing to their genealogical research. Provides how-to articles, views on the future of the field, software review and descriptions of useful electronic bulletin boards and data bases.

GENERAL INTEREST PERIODICALS — Africa

see also General Interest Periodicals–Egypt; General Interest Periodicals–Ethiopia; General Interest Periodicals–Ghana; General Interest Periodicals–Kenya; General Interest Periodicals–Libya; General Interest Periodicals–Malagasy Republic; General Interest Periodicals–Malawi; General Interest Periodicals–Mozambique; General Interest Periodicals–Nigeria; General Interest Periodicals–South Africa; General Interest Periodicals–Sudan; General Interest Periodicals–Tanzania; General Interest Periodicals–Uganda; General Interest Periodicals–Zambia; General Interest Periodicals–Zimbabwe

052   UK   ISSN 0267-6362
DT1
AFRICA EVENTS.* 1984. m. £18($51) Dar Es Salaam Ltd., 55 Banner St., London EC1Y 8PX, England. Ed. Abdilatif Abdalla. adv.; bk.rev.; illus. circ. 22,000. **Indexed:** Per.Islam. (1991-).
    —UnCover.
    Description: Features articles and regular columns on African political and business affairs, as well as latest developments in the arts and sports.

056.9   PO
AFRICA HOJE. 1985. m. Rua Joaquim Antonio de Aguiar 45-5o Esq., 1000 Lisbon, Portugal. TEL 01-557175. FAX 01-557667. circ. 30,000.

051   AU   ISSN 0259-5796
AFRICA PRESS CLIPS. (Text in English) 1987. q. S.200($20) A P C Communications, Postfach 88, A-1000 Vienna, Austria. TEL 0222-2902487. FAX 0222-2902489. TELEX 111010-TZST-A. Ed. Sam Chukwudi. adv.; film rev.; play rev.; charts; illus. circ. 15,000.
    Description: Contains articles derived from a variety of the printed media on African social and economic conditions. Includes section on resources available from industrialized nations.

496   US   ISSN 1045-2303
DT1
AFRICAN COMMENTARY.* 1989. m. African Commentary Corp., 60 Platinum Circle, Northampton, MA 01002-9903.
    —UMI.

052   UK   ISSN 0268-0432
DT515
AFRICAN CONCORD; premier Pan-African weekly. 1984. w. £N390($182) African Concord Ltd., Aare Abiola House, 26-32 Whistler St., London N5 INJ, England. TEL 071-359-5335. FAX 071-359-9173. Ed. Bayo Onanuga. adv.; bk.rev.; illus. circ. 85,000. (back issues avail.)

AFRICAN STUDY MONOGRAPHS. see ANTHROPOLOGY

057.85   PL   ISSN 0208-8010
Z3503
AFRYKA, AZJA, AMERYKA LACINSKA. (Text in Polish; summaries in English, French, German) 1972. irreg., no.67, 1989. price varies. (Uniwersytet Warszawski, Wydzial Geografii i Studiow Regionalnych, Instytut Krajow Rozwijajacych Sie) Wydawnictwa Uniwersytetu Warszawskiego, Ul. Obozna 8, 00-032 Warsaw, Poland. (Dist. by: Ars Polona-Ruch, Krakowskie Przedmiescie 7, Warsaw, Poland) bk.rev. circ. 500. **Indexed:** Curr.Cont.Africa.
    —BLDSC (0735.546000).
    Formerly (until 1979): Przeglad Informacji o Afryce (ISSN 0208-8002)

052   GW   ISSN 0342-0396
AKTUELLER INFORMATIONSDIENST AFRIKA. (Text in English, French) 1974. fortn. DM.160. Institut fuer Afrika Kunde, Neuer Jungfernstieg 21, 20354 Hamburg, Germany. TEL 040-3562523. FAX 040-3562547. Ed. Klaus Hemstedt. circ. 180. **Document type:** abstracting/indexing.
    Description: Reprints of press reports from all major African countries covering economic and political developments.

AMINA. see WOMEN'S INTERESTS

GENERAL INTEREST PERIODICALS — AFRICA

055.1   IT
ARGOS (MILAN, 1987). 1987. m. L.85000. Editoriale Albero S.r.l., Via Branda Castiglioni, 2-A, 20156 Milan, Italy. TEL 02-38-00-29-01. FAX 02-38-00-34-67.

052   TZ   ISSN 0856-3349
AZANIA NEWS. (Text in English) m. Pan Africanist Congress of Azania, Box 2412, Dar es Salaam, Tanzania. TEL 27937. FAX 25324. TELEX 41578.

054.1   DM
BENIN - MAGAZINE. m. B.P. 1210, Cotonou, Benin. circ. 5,000.
    Description: Covers social and economic affairs.

054.1   DM
BENIN - PRESSE INFORMATION. w. Agence Benin - Presse, B.P. 72, Cotonou, Benin. TEL 31-26-55.

054.1   FR   ISSN 0005-6499
BINGO; le mensuel du monde noir. 1953. m. 210 F. Farafina Communications, 12 rue Quincampois, 75005 Paris, France. Ed. Pauline Joachim. adv.; bk.rev.; film rev.; play rev.; illus. circ. 52,400. **Indexed:** Curr.Cont.Africa.

056.9   CV
BOLETIM OFICIAL DA REPUBLICA DE CABO VERDE. w. Imprensa Nacional, C P 113, Praia, Sao Tiago, Cape Verde Islands.

052   LB
BONG CRIER. 1982. w. Ministry of Information, Gbarnga City, Bong City, Liberia. TEL 707032. Ed. Henrie H. Thomson.

054.1   ZR
CAHIERS ZAIROIS DE LA RECHERCHE ET DU DEVELOPPEMENT.* 1967. irreg. $8.00. Office National de la Recherche et du Developpement, B.P. 16706, Kinshasa, Zaire. bk.rev.; illus. circ. 2,000.
    Supersedes: Cahiers Congolais de la Recherche et du Developpement.

052   CM
CAMEROON TIMES. 1960. 3/wk. B.P. 200, Limbe, Cameroon. Ed. Jerome F. Gwellem. circ. 12,000.

056.9   CV
CAPE VERDE. MINISTRY OF FOREIGN AFFAIRS. BOLETIM INFORMATIVO. 1976. w. Ministry of Foreign Affairs, C P 126, Praia, Sao Tiago, Cape Verde Islands. circ. 1,500. **Document type:** government publication, bulletin.

054.1   UV
CARREFOUR AFRICAIN. 1960. m. B.P. 507, Ougadougou, Burkina Faso. Ed. Babou Paulin Bamouni. circ. 6,000.

054.1   TI
DIALOGUE; hebdomadaire politique et d'informations generales. (Text in French) 1974. w. Dar al Amal, 2 rue Mars 1934, Tunis, Tunisia. adv.
    Formerly: Dialogue pour le Progres.

054.1   RW   ISSN 0257-0017
DIALOGUE. 1967. m. 1800 F.($50) B.P. 572, Kigali, Rwanda. TEL 250-74178. Ed. J.B. Mbonabucya. adv.; bk.rev.; bibl.; illus.; stat.; index. circ. 3,000. (back issues avail.) **Indexed:** P.L.E.S.A.
    Description: All economic, social, cultural, political and religious subjects concerning Rwanda with a Christian perspective.

059   SJ
AL DIMUQRATI/DEMOCRATE. w. £S0.25 per no. Dar Al Arabi Lil Tibaa, P.O. Box 2280, Khartoum, Sudan.

960   IV   ISSN 0046-1024
EBURNEA; le premier mensuel ivoirien d'information. 1967. m. 5000 Fr.CFA. Agence Ivoirienne de Presse, 11 Ave. Bir Hakeim, B.P. V 138, Abidjan, Ivory Coast. TELEX 23781. adv.; charts; illus.

054.1   778.5   CM
LE GRIOT; hebdomadaire des spectacles, du cinema et de la culture. no. 6, 1976. w. 01 B.P. 495, Abidjan 01, Ivory Coast. TEL 35-72-23. TELEX 42258. illus. circ. 20,000.

057.85   PL
INFORMATORY REGIONALNE. 1968. irreg. Uniwersytet Warszawski, Instytut Geografii Krajow Rozwijajacych sie, Al. Zwirki i Wigury 93, 00-089 Warsaw, Poland. Ed. Zygmunt Komorowski.

059   SJ
AL ITTIHADI/UNIONIST. w. £S0.25 per no. Democratic Unionist Party, P.O. Box 1981, Khartoum II, Sudan.

054.1   IV   ISSN 0047-1674
IVOIRE DIMANCHE. 1971. w. (Societe de Presse et d'Edition de Cote d'Ivoire) Inter Afrique Presse, 01 B.P. 1807, Abidjan 01, Ivory Coast. Ed. Justin Vieyra. adv.; bk.rev.; film rev.; charts; illus. circ. 75,000.

054.1   ML
JAMANA; revue culturelle malienne. q. B.P. 2043, Bamako, Mali. Ed. Alpha Oumar Konare.

JAMES S. COLEMAN MEMORIAL PAPERS SERIES. see HISTORY — History Of Africa

054.1   FR   ISSN 0757-116X
DT1
JEUNE AFRIQUE PLUS. (Supplement to: Jeune Afrique (ISSN 0021-6089)) 1983. bi-m. J A Press, 57 bis rue d'Auteuil, 75016 Paris, France.

054.1   RE   ISSN 0395-8876
JOURNAL DE L'ILE DE LA REUNION. 1950. d. 3700 F.; newsstand price: 5 F. Ste. France Antilles, 42 rue Alexis-de-Villeneuve, B.P. 166, 97463 Saint-Denis, Reunion. TEL 21-32-64. FAX 262-20-08-37. TELEX 916453. Owner(s): France Antilles, 12 rue de Presbourg, 75016 Paris, France. TEL 45-00-15-55. FAX 45-01-80-29. Ed. Jacques Tillier; Pub. Philippe Baloukjy. adv. contact: Stephane Estival. bk.rev.; circ. 26,000 (controlled). cols./p.: 6; pp./issue: 40. **Document type:** newspaper.

059   RW
KANGURA. fortn. Kigali, Rwanda. Ed. Hassan Ngeze.

059   KE
KENYA YETU. (Text in Swahili) 1965. m. Ministry of Information & Broadcasting, P.O. Box 8053, Nairobi, Kenya. TEL 28411. TELEX 22244. Ed. M. Ndavi. circ. 10,000.

052   LB
THE KPELLE MESSENGER. (Text in English and Kpelle) m? Kpelle Literacy Center, Lutheran Church, P.O. Box 1046, Monrovia, Liberia. Ed. John J. Manawu.

059   LO
LENTSOE LA BASOTHO. (Text in Sesotho) 1986. w. Ministry of Foreign Affairs and Information Broadcasting, P.O. Box 36, Meseru 100, Lesotho. TEL 326561. FAX 310003. TELEX 4450. Ed. M. Mokomeng.

059   LO
LESOTHO TODAY. (Text in English) 1986. w. Ministry of Foreign Affairs and Information Broadcasting, P.O. Box 36, Maseru 100, Lesotho. TEL 323561. FAX 310003. TELEX 4450. Ed. K.M. Kotsokoane. circ. 2,500.

052   LB
LIBERIA: POLITICAL, ECONOMICS AND SOCIAL MONTHLY.* (Text in English) vol.2, 1973. m. $12. Ministry of Information, Cultural Affairs and Tourism, Monrovia, Liberia. Ed. Bill Frank. adv.; bk.rev.; film rev.; illus.

052   LB
LIBERIAN STAR. 1954. m. P.O. Box 691, Monrovia, Liberia. Ed. Henry Cole.

052   LB
LORMA WEEKLY. (Text in English and Lorma) w. P.O. Box 1046, Monrovia, Liberia.

054.1   NG
MARCHE. 1989. m. Naimey, Niger. Ed. Abdoulaye Moussa Massalatchi.

052 054.1   MF   ISSN 0025-6064
MAURITIUS TIMES. (Text in English, French) 1954. w. $100. Mauritius Times Publication, 23 Bourbon St., Port-Louis, Mauritius. TEL 2121313. FAX 2302121743. Ed. B. Ramlallah. adv.; bk.rev. circ. 15,000.

052   LB
MIRROR. d. Logan Town, P.O. Box 891, Monrovia, Liberia. Ed. David E.M. Acheampong.

960   FT   ISSN 0255-9617
NATION DJIBOUTI. (Text in French) 1948. w. 6500 F. Secretariat General a l'Information, P.O. Box 32, Djibouti, Djibouti. TEL 352201. Ed. Ismael H. Tani. adv.; bk.rev.; illus.; tr.lit. circ. 4,000. **Document type:** government publication.
    Supersedes: Reveil de Djibouti (ISSN 0034-6276)

052   LB
THE NEW LIBERIAN. 1978. 4/wk. E.J. Roye Bldg., Capitol Hill, POB 9021, Monrovia, Liberia. Ed. Mike James. circ. 15,000.

052   KE
NEWS FROM KENYA. m. Ministry of Information & Broadcasting, P.O. Box 8053, Nairobi, Kenya. TEL 28411. TELEX 22244.

054.1   NG   ISSN 0550-6891
DT547.A2
NIGER. 1967. q. 3000 Fr.CFA. Ministere de l'Information, B.P. 368, Niamey, Niger. illus. (also avail. in microfilm from KTO) **Indexed:** Curr.Cont.Africa.

059   NG
NIGERAMA. q. Agence Nigerienne de Presse, Naimey, Niger.

054.1   NR   ISSN 0029-0076
QH195.N5   CODEN: NIFIAC
NIGERIAN FIELD. 1931. q. £N50 to individuals; institutions £N100. Nigerian Field Society, P.O. Box 30385, Secretariat Post Office, Ibadan, Nigeria. TEL 234-22-714338. (Subscr. to: Chief Roy Carrington, Treasurer, Nigerian Field Society, c/o Nigerian Gas Cylinders, Km. 22 Iwo Rd., Ibadan, Nigeria) Ed. Pat Oyelola. adv.; bk.rev.; illus. circ. 1,000. **Indexed:** Biol.Abstr., Chem.Abstr., Curr.Adv.Ecol.Sci., Curr.Cont.Africa, Forest.Abstr., Forest.Prod.Abstr., GeoRef., M.L.A. **Document type:** academic/scholarly publication.
    Description: Provides a forum for academics to exchange information on all aspects of science and culture in Nigeria. Also contains society news.

054.1   SG
OUEST AFRICAIN.* w. 10000 Fr.CFA. Societe Nationale de Presse, d'Edition et de Publicite, c/o Sonapresse, Dakar, Senegal. illus. **Document type:** newspaper.

052   LB
PALM. 6/yr. Johnson & Carey Sts., P.O. Box 1110, Monrovia, Liberia. Ed. James C. Dennis.

056.1   EG
POTOPOTO. (Text in Fang and Spanish) irreg. Apdo. 236, Bata, Equatorial Guinea. Dir. Francisco de Anta Franco.

054.1   SG
REPUBLIQUE.* 1989. w. c/o Agence Havas Afrique, B.P. 503, Dakar, Senegal.

960 956   CU
REVISTA AFRICA Y MEDIO ORIENTE. (Editions in English, Spanish) s-a. $12 in S. America; N. America $14; elsewhere $18 (add $2 for English edition). Ediciones Cubanas, Obispo No. 527, Apdo. 605, Havana, Cuba.

054.1   MG
REVUE DE L'OCEAN INDIEN. (Text in French) 1980. m. $97. Communication et Media Ocean Indien, Rue H. Rabesahala, B.P. 46, Antsakaviro, 101 Antananarivo, Malagasy Republic. TEL 22536. FAX 34534. TELEX 22225. Ed. Georges Ranaivosoa. adv.; bk.rev. circ. 5,000.

079.69   MF
RODRIGUAIS. (Text in Creole, English, French) 1989. w. Rs.156($25) Rodrigues Developpement Ltee, Saint Gabriel, Rodrigues, Mauritius. TEL 8311 613. FAX 8311-484. Ed. Jacques Edouard. adv. contact: Louis Gonzaque Martin. bk.rev.; illus. cols./p.: 4; pp./issue: 4. (back issues avail.) **Document type:** newspaper.

054.1   FR   ISSN 0581-2976
LE SAHARIEN. 1927. q. 180 F. (foreign 220 F.) (effective 1992). Rahla, 4 rue Coetlogon, 75006 Paris, France. TEL 42-22-67-41. Ed. Louis LePrieur. bk.rev.; charts; illus. circ. 1,600. **Indexed:** Documentatieblad. **Document type:** bibliography, bulletin.
    Formerly: Eurafrique.

GENERAL INTEREST PERIODICALS — ALBANIA

059   KE
SAUTI NYKANI. (Text in Swahili) 1964. bi-m. free. Evangel Publishing House, P.O. Box 28963, Nairobi, Kenya. TEL 254-2-802033. FAX 254-2-802034. circ. 20,000.

059   SJ
SAWT AL SUDAN/VOICE OF SUDAN. w. £S0.25 per no. Dar Al Sudan Lil Tibaa, P.O. Box 197, Khartoum, Sudan.

059   SJ
SAWT AL UMMAH/VOICE OF THE NATION. w. £S0.25 per no. Ummah Party, P.O. Box 3619, Khartoum, Sudan.

059   SL
SEME LOKOI. (Text in Mende) 1939. m. $2. U.C.C. Provincial Literature Bureau, Box 28, Bo, Sierra Leone. Ed. David Amara Lamin. adv.; illus. circ. 500. (back issues avail.)

052   SL
SIERRA LEONE NEWSLETTER. 1974. m. Ministry of Information and Broadcasting, Government Information Services, Lightfoot Boston St., Freetown, Sierra Leone.

054.1   SG
SUD HEBDO. 1987. w. 18 rue Raffenel, B.P. 4130, Dakar, Senegal. TEL 22-75-09. FAX 22-52-90. Ed. Babacar Toure. circ. 15,000.

052   SJ
SUDAN NEWS AGENCY. WEEKLY REVIEW/WAKATLAT AL-SUDAN LIL-ANBA. WEEKLY REVIEW. (Text in English) 1972. w. Sudan News Agency - Wakatkat al-Sudan Lil-Anba, P.O. Box 1506, Elgamhouria St., Khartoum, Sudan.

052   LB
SUNDAY EXPRESS. w. Mamba Point, P.O. Box 3029, Monrovia, Liberia. Ed. John F. Scotland. circ. 5,000.

052 054.1   MF
SUNDAY NATION. (Text in English or French) w. Independent Publications Ltd., B.P. 647, Port Louis, Mauritius.

052   LB
SUNDAY PEOPLE. 2/wk. P.O. Box 3366, Monrovia, Liberia. Ed. D.G. Pyne-Draper.

059   ML
SUNJATA. m. B.P. 141, Bamako, Mali. Ed. Soumeylou Maiga. circ. 3,000.

960   CD   ISSN 0049-3066
TCHAD ET CULTURE. no. 55, 1971. bi-m. 450 Fr.CFA. B.P. 907, N'djamena, Chad. TEL 235-51-54-32. FAX 235-51-61-50. Ed. Sabine Laplane; Pub. Albert Lorent. circ. 3,000. (back issues avail.)

059   SJ
AL THAWRAH AL SHAABIYAH. w. £S0.25 per no. Revolutionary Committees in Sudan, P.O. Box 2860, Khartoum, Sudan.

054.1   FR
TITRA; le journal des journaux africains. 1991. m. 350 F. (outside Europe 400 F.). Periscoop, 12 rue Gilodes, 34080 Montpellier, France. TEL 67-75-32-29. FAX 67-75-28-82. Ed. Charles-Albert Ryng. adv. circ. 6,000. (back issues avail.) **Document type:** newspaper.
   Former titles (until Aug. 1993): Libertitres; (until May 1991): Intertitres (ISSN 1157-2973)
   Description: Provides a press resume of African media.

059   TG
TOGO DIALOGUE. m. 5500 Fr.CFA. (Ministry of Information) Etablessement National des Editions du Togo, EDITOGO, B.P. 891, Lome, Togo. TEL 21-37-18. TELEX 5294. Ed. Kokou Amedegnato. adv.; illus. circ. 5,000.

052   US   ISSN 0730-8876
DT38.7
TRANSAFRICA FORUM; a quarterly journal of opinion on Africa and the Caribbean. (Supplement avail.: Transafrica Forum Issues Briefs) 1982. q. $32 to individuals (foreign $56); institutions $60 (foreign $84). (TransAfrica: The Black American Lobby for Africa & the Caribbean) Transaction Publishers, Transaction Periodicals Consortium, Department 3092, Rutgers University, New Brunswick, NJ 08903. TEL 908-932-2280. FAX 908-932-3138. Ed. Randall Robinson. adv.; bk.rev. circ. 1,000. (back issues avail.) **Indexed:** Amer.Hist.& Life, Hist.Abstr., HR Rep. **Document type:** academic/scholarly publication.
  —BLDSC (9020.564600); UMI. CCC.
   Description: Information on political, economic and cultural affairs affecting black communities worldwide. Devoted to a better understanding of policy issues and their impact internationally.

052   US   ISSN 0730-188X
TRANSAFRICA FORUM ISSUES BRIEFS.* 1981. q. included in subscription to TransAfrica Forum. TransAfrica Forum, 1744 R. St., N.W., Washington, DC 20009-2410. TEL 202-547-2550. Ed. Niikwao Akuetteh. circ. 1,500. (back issues avail.)
  —CCC.
   Description: Covers political and social issues related to U.S. foreign policy toward Africa and the Caribbean.

054.1   GO
UNION; quotidien Gabonais d'information. 1974. d. 41000 Fr.CFA. SONAPRESSE, B.P. 3849, Libreville, Gabon. TEL 73-21-84. TELEX 5391. Ed. Albert Yangari. adv.; illus. (tabloid format)

UNIVERSITY OF CALIFORNIA AT LOS ANGELES. JAMES S. COLEMAN AFRICAN STUDIES CENTER. NEWSLETTER. see HISTORY — History Of Africa

UNIVERSITY OF CALIFORNIA AT LOS ANGELES. JAMES S. COLEMAN AFRICAN STUDIES CENTER. OCCASIONAL PAPERS SERIES. see HISTORY — History Of Africa

059   SJ
AL WATANI AL ITTIHADI/NATIONAL UNIONIST. w. £S025 per no. National Unionist Party, P.O. Box 1096, Khartoum, Sudan.

GENERAL INTEREST PERIODICALS — Albania

079.4965   AA
BASHKIMI. 1943. d. Fronti Demokratik i Shqiperise - Democratic Front of Albania, Bulevardi Stalin, Tirana, Albania. TEL 42-28110. Ed. Hamit Borici. circ. 30,000. (also avail. in microfilm from NRP) **Document type:** newspaper.

079.4965   AA
ZERI I POPULLIT. 1942. d. (except Mon.). Partia Socialist e Shqiperise - Socialist Party of Albania, Bulevardi Deshmoret e Kombit, Tirana, Albania. TEL 355-42-27409. FAX 355-42-27417. TELEX 4151. Ed. Thoma Gellci. circ. 120,000. **Document type:** newspaper.

GENERAL INTEREST PERIODICALS — Andorra

076.7   AN
DIARI D'ANDORRA. (Supplement included monthly: L'Estudiant) (Text in Catalan) 1991. 6/wk. 25000 ptas. Prensa Andorrana S.A., Avinguda Riberaygua 39, Andorra La Vella, Andorra. TEL 63700. FAX 63800. Ed. Ignazi Planells; Pub. Manuel Pujadas. adv. contact: Josep Martinez. bk.rev.; film rev.; music rev.; play rev.; illus. cols./p.: 5; pp./issue: 36. (tabloid format; back issues avail.; reprint service avail.) **Document type:** newspaper.
   Description: Covers politics, opinion, society, economics, sports, culture, and entertainment.

GENERAL INTEREST PERIODICALS — Argentina

056.1   AG
AL MARGEN. m. Carlos Pellegrini 465, psio 10, Depto. 77, 1009 Buenos Aires, Argentina. TEL 568-4798. **Document type:** consumer publication.

056.1   AG   ISSN 0003-2581
F2801
ANALISIS - CONFIRMADO. 1961. w. $208. Condor S.R.L., Independencia 2744, Buenos Aires, Argentina. Ed. Fernando M. Morduchowicz. bk.rev.; film rev.; play rev.; illus. circ. 40,000.
   Formed by the merger of: Confirmado; Analisis.

056.1   AG
AQUAS VIVAS. 1983. bi-m. Malabia 696, 2 A., Buenos Aires, Argentina. Ed. Rogelio Blumengarten.

056.1   AG   ISSN 0004-0983
ARGENTINA.* (Text in Portuguese, Spanish) 1957. q. Arg.$120. Estrada 6647, Santa Fe, Argentina. Ed. Manuel Marcos Roman. adv.; illus. circ. 3,000. (tabloid format)

056.1   AG
ARGENTINA EN POSTIVO; al encuentro de soluciones para todos los argentinos. 1985. m. Agencia Periodistica Argentina, Casilla de Correo 1236, 1000 Correo Central, Buenos Aires, Argentina. Ed. Ricardo Duro.

056.1   AG   ISSN 0006-1611
BIBLIOTECA;* revista mensual de interes general. 1968. m. Arg.$2800. c/o Carlos A. Brandon, O'Higgins 2470, Buenos Aires, Argentina.

056.1   AG
EL BUEN GURKA. 1991. fortn. Arg.$10000 per no. Lavalle 1494, 4o piso, Buenos Aires, Argentina. Ed. Raul Jassen.

079.82   AG
LA CIUDAD. 1959. 5/wk. Arg.$10 per mo. (foreign Arg.$25); newsstand price: Arg.$1. Lamadrid 125, 1870 Avellaneda, B.A., Argentina. TEL 203-9402. FAX 203-6705. Pub. Roberto Persico. adv. contact: Alejandra Persico. illus. cols./p.: 5; pp./issue: 16. (tabloid format) **Document type:** newspaper.
   Description: Contains local news of Avellaneda, with sections dedicated to women, food, politics, sports, education, and literature.

056.1   AG
CLARIN INTERNACIONAL. 1945. w. $52. Arte Grafico Editorial Argentino S.A., Piedras 1743, Buenos Aires, Argentina. Ed. Ernestina Laura Herrera de Noble. circ. controlled. (tabloid format)

079.82   AG
CRONICA. 1962. d. $25 per mo.; newsstand price: $1. Impresa Patagonia, Namuncura 122, Comodoro Rivadavia, 9000 Chubut, Argentina. TEL 0967-30229. FAX 0967-31780. Ed. Daniel Zamit; Pub. Diego Zamit. adv. contact: Eduardo Mirando. bk.rev.; film rev.; music rev.; play rev.; illus. circ. 12,500. cols./p.: 6; pp./issue: 60. (tabloid format) **Document type:** newspaper.

056.1   AG
CUADERNOS DE MAIPU; informar para servir. 1985. irreg. Centro de Estudios de Relaciones Internacionales y de Estrategia Nacional, Maipu 889, Segundo Poso, 1006 Buenos Aires, Argentina. Ed. Antonio Rodriguez Villar.

056.1   AG
DIA. 1884. d. Arg.$650000 per trimester. El Dia S A I C F, Diagonal 80 No. 815-21, 1900 La Plata, Argentina. TEL 54-21-210101. FAX 54-21-251533. TELEX 31165. Ed. Raul E. Kraiselburd. adv.; bk.rev.; film rev.; play rev.; charts; illus.; stat.; tr.lit. circ. 60,000. (back issues avail.)

056.1   AG
DIGNIDAD. 1991. fortn. Dean Funes 871, Buenos Aires, Argentina. Ed. Osvaldo E. Mendez. (tabloid format)

056.1   AG
DOCUMENTO DE PROTAGONISTAS; la otra forma de leer noticias. m. Bege Producciones s.r.l., Corrientes 1922, 6o, 64, 1045 Buenos Aires C.F., Argentina. TEL 953-4739. Ed. Alejandro Morales.

056.1   AG
ETICA; periodismo para la gente. 1991. w.? Editorial Etica, Periodismo para la Gente S.A., Sarmiento 1889 6o B, Buenos Aires, Argentina. TEL 46-4408. Ed. Ramon Roque Cuello. (tabloid format)

056.1 AG
FIN DE SIGLO. m.? Arg.$48000 per no. Comite de Periodistas LatinoAmericanos (Copel), Juan Naon 637, 1406 Buenos Aires C.F., Argentina. TEL 9813446. Ed. Vincente Zito Lema.

056.1 AG ISSN 0016-3325
FUTURO.* vol.4, 1970. m. Arg.$240($1) Hipolito Yrigoyen 521, Pilar, Argentina. Eds. Jose Bernado Domenech, Santiago Sanguinetti. adv.; illus. (tabloid format)

056.1 AG ISSN 0326-4378
GENERACION. Key Title: Generacion '83. 1984. m. Piedras 730, 1070 Buenos Aires, Argentina. Ed. Daniel Sario.

056.1 AG
GENTE. 1965. w. $169. Editorial Atlantida, S.A., Azopardo 579, 3o, 1307 Buenos Aires, Argentina. TEL 33-4591. TELEX 21163. (In U.S and Canada subscr. to: Interamerican Network, Box 364, Scarsdale, NY 10583. TEL 914-793-9764) Dir. Jorge de Lujan Gutierrez. adv.; illus. circ. 133,000.

056.1 AG
ORIGENES. 1990. bi-m. Arg.$12000 per no. Riobamba 7037, 3000 Santa Fe, Argentina. TEL 68191.

056.1 AG
▼**PANORAMA.** 1992. m. Arg.$6 per no. Grupo Editorial Brasil - Argentina S.A., Avda. Cordoba 1345, piso 12, 1055 Buenos Aires C.F., Argentina. TEL 42-3275. FAX 054-1-41-8835. Ed. Enrique Szewach. Document type: consumer publication.

056.1 AG
PLEAMAR. 1977. m. Arg.$1200 for 6 nos. Ediciones Pleamar, Cordoba 1690, 3000 Santa Fe, Argentina. film rev.; illus.

056.1 AG ISSN 0032-8375
PRIMERA PLANA;* la revista de noticias de mayor circulacion. 1962. w. Arg.$105($55) Editorial Primera Plana s.r.l., Peru 367, Floor 12, Buenos Aires, Argentina. Ed. Victorio I.S. Dalle Nogare. adv.; illus. circ. 70,000.

056.1 AG
PUNTO DE VISTA: revista de cultura. 1978. q. $40 for 6 nos. Casilla de Correo 39, Sucursal 49 (B), Buenos Aires, Argentina. TEL 854-6857. Ed. Beatriz Sarlo. adv.; bk.rev.; index. circ. 3,000. Document type: academic/scholarly publication.
Description: Covers literature, literary history, cultural history, the arts, Argentine and Latin American politics, and debates.

056.1 AG
▼**QUINTO PODER.** 1992. m. Opinion Publica S.A., Peru 590, 3o B, Buenos Aires, Argentina. TEL 343-1967. Ed. Miguel Angel Diez. Document type: consumer publication.

056.1 AG
RETORNO DEL PUEBLO. fortn. Los Federales, S.A., Bacacay 1951, 1 piso, Buenos Aires, Argentina. TEL 631-2311. Ed. Luis Barroso.

056.1 AG
REVISTA LA NACION. w. Bouchard 557, Buenos Aires, Argentina. adv. circ. 365,000.

056.1 398 AG
SAVIA ARGENTINA. Corrientes 1955 3E, 1045 Buenos Aires, Argentina. Ed. Diana Maglio.

056.1 AG ISSN 0037-1866
SEMBRADOR.* s-m. Arg.$350($1) Parroquia Santisima Trinidad Rufino, La Misma del Punto (8), Italia 62, Rufino, Argentina. adv.; illus.; tr.lit.; index; circ. controlled. (tabloid format)

056.1 AG ISSN 0037-4784
SIETE DIAS ILUSTRADOS. 1967. w. $113. Editorial Abril S.A., Avenida Leandro N. Alem 896, 1001 Buenos Aires, Argentina. Dir. Ricardo Camara. adv.; bk.rev.; film rev.; play rev.; illus. circ. 110,000.

056.1 AG
SOMOS. 1976. w. $169. Editorial Atlantida, S.A., Azopardo 579, 1307 Buenos Aires, Argentina. TEL 331-4591. (In U.S and Canada subscr. to: Interamerican Network, Box 364, Scarsdale, NY 10583. TEL 914-793-9764) adv.; illus. circ. 21,000.

056.1 AG ISSN 0326-3681
VIDA SILVESTRE. bi-m. $30. (Fundacion Vida Silvestre Argentina) Fernando Garcia Cambeiro (Dist.), Cochabamba 244, 1150 Buenos Aires, Argentina. Ed. Miguel A. Reynal.

GENERAL INTEREST PERIODICALS — Australasia

see also General Interest Periodicals–Australia; General Interest Periodicals–New Zealand; General Interest Periodicals–Oceania

052 AT ISSN 0004-8437
AUSTRALASIAN POST. 1850. w. Aus.$104 (foreign Aus.$143). Southdown Press, 32 Walsh St., W. Melbourne, Vic. 3000, Australia. TEL 03-320-7000. FAX 03-320-7410. Ed. Terry Carroll. adv.; bk.rev.; film rev.; illus. circ. 180,000.

050 301.2 US ISSN 1043-898X
DU1 CODEN: COPAEV
THE CONTEMPORARY PACIFIC; a journal of island affairs. 1989. s-a. $17 to individuals in Pacific Islands (non-Pacific $30); institutions in Pacific Islands $25 (non-Pacific $40). (Center for Pacific Islands Studies) University of Hawaii Press, Journals Department, 2840 Kolowalu St., Honolulu, HI 96822. TEL 808-956-8833. FAX 808-988-6052. Ed. David Hanlon. adv.; bk.rev.; illus. circ. 675. (back issues avail.; reprint service avail. from UMI) Indexed: Abstr.Rural Dev.Trop. Document type: academic/scholarly publication.
—BLDSC (3425.197700); UnCover; UMI.
Description: Covers a wide range of current issues in the Pacific Islands.
Refereed Serial

050 AT ISSN 0011-3182
CURRENT AFFAIRS BULLETIN. 1947. bi-m. Aus.$40 to individuals; schools and students Aus.$30; WEA members Aus.$27 (foreign Aus.$57). Worker's Educational Association, 72 Bathurst St., Sydney, N.S.W. 2000, Australia. TEL 02-264-5726. FAX 02-267-7900. Ed. Bob Howard. adv.; bk.rev.; illus.; circ. 3,500 (paid). (also avail. in microfilm from UMI; reprint service avail. from UMI) Indexed: AESIS, Aus.P.A.I.S., Gdlns., INIS Atomind. Document type: academic/scholarly publication.
—BLDSC (3494.075000); Faxon; UnCover; UMI.
Description: Publishes original manuscripts which deal with issues of public and current interest in a wide range of areas - politics, international relations, economics, law, industrial relations, education, social issues, science, the arts and sport.

050 790 AT
KABAR COCOS. (Text in English and Cocos Malay (a dialect of Bahusa Malayu)) 1961. m. Aus.$15 in Asia and Pacific; elsewhere Aus.$35 (effective 1991). Office of the Administrator, Cocos (Keeling) Islands, Indian Ocean, 6799, Via Western Australia, Australia. TEL 6722-6677. FAX 0011-6722-6668. Ed. Alan Whykes. adv.; bk.rev. circ. 200. Document type: newsletter.
Supersedes (in 1987): Cocos Clarion.
Description: Covers the history, people, religion, culture, development, environment and current affairs of the Cocos (Keeling) Islands.

GENERAL INTEREST PERIODICALS — Australia

052 CN ISSN 0045-0170
A N Z A NEWS. 1961. m. Can.$9 to non-members. (Australia - New Zealand Association) Down-Under Publications, 3 W. 8th Ave., Vancouver, B.C. V5Y 1M8, Canada. TEL 604-876-7128. Ed. W. Walker. adv.; illus. circ. 3,800.
Description: Covers news from Australia and New Zealand.

052 AT
ADVERTISER. 1966. w. Standard Newspapers Ltd., 10-14 Park Rd., Cheltenham, Vic. 3192, Australia. Ed. Garry Barker. adv. circ. 26,337. (back issues avail.)
Formerly: Sandringham-Brighton Advertiser.

052 919.404 UK ISSN 0301-5785
AUSTRALIAN OUTLOOK; the original and leading newspaper for migrants and visitors to Australia. 1970. m. £13.50 (US £20). Consyl Publishing, 3 Buckhurst Rd., Bexhill-on-Sea, E. Sussex TN40 1QF, England, England. TEL 44-424-223111. FAX 44-424-224992. Ed. N. Deacon. adv. contact: Sandra Melvin. bk.rev.; illus. circ. 30,000. (tabloid format) Indexed: A.B.C.Pol.Sci., Br.Hum.Ind., SSCI. Document type: newspaper.
Description: Contains information for the potential migrant or visitor to Australia.

052 AT
AUSTRALIAN SPECTATOR.* 1970. w. free. 17 Hollywood Ave., Bondi Junction, N.S.W. 2022, Australia. Ed. Jeff O'Sullivan. circ. 40,000. (back issues avail.)
Formerly: Bondi Spectator.

052 990 AT ISSN 1033-131X
AUSTRALIAN STUDIES. 1984. s-a. Aus.$25. Australian Studies Association, Centre for Australian Studies, Curtin University, G.P.O. Box 1987U, Perth, W.A. 6001, Australia. TEL 09-350-7211. FAX 61-9-351-7726. Eds. Stephen Alomes, Don Grant. bk.rev. circ. 320. (back issues avail.) Document type: academic/scholarly publication.
Formerly: Australian Studies Bulletin (ISSN 0815-2500)

052 AT
BANKSTOWN - CANTERBURY TORCH. 1920. bi-w. Torch Publishing Co. Pty. Ltd., 47 Allingham St., Bankstown, N.S.W. 2200, Australia. Ed. P.C.L. Engisch. circ. 78,414.

052 790.1 659.1 AT
BEGA DISTRICT NEWS. 1864. s-w. Aus.$70. Southern Publishers Pty. Ltd., 34 Auckland St., Bega, N.S.W., Australia. FAX 064-921178. Ed. Anna Glover. adv.; bk.rev. circ. 3,000. (back issues avail.)

052 AT
BINGARA ADVOCATE. 1934. w. Aus.$45. R.J. & J.A. Lewis, 34 Maitland St., Bingara, N.S.W. 2404, Australia. TEL 067-241-127. FAX 067-241-127. Ed. Robert J. Lewis. adv. circ. 950.

052 AT ISSN 0812-5864
BLACKALL LEADER. 1983. w. Aus.$41. 85 Shamrock St., Blackall, Qld. 4472, Australia. Ed. W. Grover. circ. 900. (back issues avail.)

052 AT
BLUE MOUNTAINS GAZETTE. 1963. w. free. Mountain Press Pty. Ltd., 274 Macquarie Rd., Springswood, N.S.W. 2777, Australia. Ed. M.E. Ticehurst. play rev. circ. 31,200. (back issues avail.)

079.943 AT
BOWEN INDEPENDENT. 1903. s-w. Aus.$156. 28 George St., Bowen, Qld. 4805, Australia. TEL 077-861888. FAX 077-862273. Ed. David Anthony. circ. 4,700. (back issues avail.) Document type: newspaper.
Description: Provides a local chronicle of topical events and issue.

052 AT
AP7
THE BULLETIN WITH NEWSWEEK. 1880. w. Aus.$99. A C P Publishing Pty. Ltd., 54-58 Park St., Sydney, N.S.W. 2000, Australia. TEL 02-282-8200. FAX 02-267-4359. Ed. Lyndall Crisp; Pub. Richard Walsh. adv.; B&W page $4025, color page $6200; adv. contact: Peter Miller. bk.rev.; film rev.; play rev.; charts; illus.; mkt. circ. 110,000. Indexed: Child.Lit.Abstr., Gdlns., INIS Atomind., PROMT, Rehabil.Lit., So.Pac.Per.Ind. Document type: consumer publication.
●Also available online.
Formed by the 1984 merger of: Bulletin (ISSN 0007-4039); Newsweek; Incorporates: Australian Financial Times.

079.9429 AT
CENTRALIAN ADVOCATE. 1947. 2/w. Aus.$91 for 6 mos. Nationwide News Pty. Ltd. (Subsidiary of: News Ltd.), 2 Gap Rd., Alice Springs, N.T. 0871, Australia. TEL 089-52-1711. FAX 089-52-4218. (Subscr. to: P.O. Box 2254, Alice Springs, N.T. 5750, Australia) Ed. Gary E. Shipway. adv.; bk.rev.; film rev.; play rev. circ. 6,695. (back issues avail.) Document type: newspaper.

GENERAL INTEREST PERIODICALS — AUSTRALIA

051 US
CHURINGA. m. free. Australian Consulate General, Office of Public Arrairs, 630 Fifth Ave., New York, NY 10111. TEL 212-245-4000.
Description: Reports on cultural events in and around New York concerning Australia.

079.945 AT
COMMUNITY NEWS. 1978. w. Aus.$48. R.E.N. Nominees Pty. Ltd., P.O. Box 182, Moonee Ponds, Vic. 3039, Australia. TEL 370-9222. FAX 370-3437. Ed. Owight Smith. adv. contact: Marija Newbolo. circ. 107,271. (back issues avail.)
Document type: newspaper.
Formerly: Community and Real Estate News (ISSN 0157-5783)

COURRIER AUSTRALIEN; French monthly/mensuel Francais. see GENERAL INTEREST PERIODICALS — France

659.1 052 AT
EASTERN SUBURBS REPORTER. 1981. w. Aus.$60. Community Newspaper Group, 120 Roe St., Northbridge, W.A. 6003, Australia. FAX 09-227-9487. (Subscr. to: P.O. Box 543, Morley, W.A. 6062, Australia) Ed. Hartley Joynt. adv. circ. 54,300. (looseleaf format; back issues avail.)

079.945 AT
EMERALD HILL, SANDRIDGE & ST. KILDA TIMES. 1978. w. Aus.$49. Peter Isaacson Publications Pty. Ltd., 45-50 Porter St., Prahran, Vic. 3181, Australia. TEL 03-245-7777. FAX 03-245-7700. Ed. Linda Wayman. adv. contact: Roberta Davis. bk.rev.; illus. circ. 45,000. (also avail. in microfilm; back issues avail.) **Document type:** newspaper.
Formerly (until 1979): Emerald Hill and Sandridge Times (ISSN 0156-7624)
Description: Broad-based commercial newspaper serving the southern, inner-metropolitan bayside suburbs of Melbourne, Australia.

ENVIRONMENT; exploring the social and physical environments of W.A. see ENVIRONMENTAL STUDIES

052 AT
EUROA GAZETTE. 1897. w. Aus.$0.50. Euroa Gazette Newspapers, 31, Binney St., Euroa, Vic. 3666, Australia. TEL 057-935041. FAX 057-953063. Ed. Helen Donaldson. adv. circ. 2,525.
Description: Features news, sports and farming topics.

640 AT ISSN 1036-6083
FAMILY CIRCLE. 1973. m. Aus.$2.50 per no. Murdoch Magazines Pty. Ltd., P.O. Box 1545, N. Sydney, N.S.W. 2060, Australia. Ed. Sue Short. adv. circ. 326,000.
Formerly (until 1981): Australian Family Circle (ISSN 0310-1118)

052 AT
FREMANTLE GAZETTE. 1977. bi-w. Aus.$19.20. Community Newspapers (Fremantle), 7 High St, Fremantle, W.A. 6160, Australia. (Subscr. to: P.O. Box 1094, Fremantle, W.A. 6160, Australia) Ed. Simon Madfield. film rev.; play rev. circ. 27,000. (tabloid format; back issues avail.)

052 AT
GOSFORD AND PENINSULA TIMES. 1984. w. Aus.$41.60. Central Coast Publications, 97 Donnison Street, Gosford, N.S.W. 2250, Australia. Ed. Dallas Sherringham. film rev. circ. 23,000. (tabloid format; back issues avail.)

079.944 AT
GREAT LAKES ADVOCATE. 1952. w. Aus.$36. Regional Publishers (N.S.W.) Pty. Ltd., 41 Helen St., Forster, N.S.W. 2428, Australia. TEL 065-546688. FAX 065-556399. (Subscr. to: P.O. Box 138, Forster, N.S.W. 2428, Australia) Ed. Susan Gogarty. adv.; bk.rev. circ. 5,200. **Document type:** newspaper.
Description: Features local news, sports and letters.

052 AT
GREEN PLACE MAGAZINE. 1972. m. Aus.$9. Green Place Pty. Ltd., 3 Ormsby Grove, Toorak, Vic. 3142, Australia. TEL 03-826-1503. Ed. Beverley Will. adv.; bk.rev. circ. 20,000. (back issues avail.)
Description: Covers life and commerce in Toorak region.

052 AT ISSN 1321-9820
H Q. 1983. bi-m. A C P Publishing Pty. Ltd., 54-58 Park St., Sydney, N.S.W. 200, Australia. TEL 02-282-8131. FAX 02-267-3616. Ed. S. Martyn; Pub. Richard Walsh. adv. contact: Peter Miller. circ. 400,000. **Document type:** consumer publication.
Formerly: Good Housekeeping.

052 AT
HARDEN MURRUMBURRAH EXPRESS. w. Harden Murrumburrah Express Pty Ltd, 181 Parker St, Cootamundra, N.S.W. 2590, Australia. Ed. Barry Clarke. circ. 1,200. (back issues avail.)

052 AT
HERVEY BAY OBSERVER. 1980. s-w. free. Maryborough Newspaper Co., Pty. Ltd., Bazaar St., Maryborough, Qld. 4650, Australia. TEL 071 22 2222. FAX 071-224734. (Subscr. to: P.O. Box 216, Maryborough, Qld. 4650, Australia) Ed. Phillip Deem. adv. contact: Bruce Becker. circ. 12,600. (tabloid format; back issues avail.)
Incorporates: Hervey Bay Fraser Island Sun (ISSN 0810-9788)

079.944 AT
INNER WESTERN SUBURBS COURIER. 1884. w. Eastern Suburbs Newspapers, 170 Bourke St., Alexandria, N.S.W. 2015, Australia. TEL 02-693-9999. FAX 02-317-5780. Ed. B. Doyle. adv. contact: T. Pullinger. film rev.; play rev.; illus. circ. 81,825.
Document type: newspaper.
Formerly: Western Suburbs Courier.
Description: Focuses on women, entertainment, real estate and sports in the area.

052 PH ISSN 0047-2336
DS1
JOURNAL OF CONTEMPORARY ASIA. 1970. q. $45. P.O. Box 592, Manila 1099, Philippines. Ed. Peter Limqueco. adv.; bk.rev.; bibl.; index. circ. 3,500. (also avail. in microfilm from UMI; reprint service avail. from SCH,UMI) **Indexed:** Abstr.Rural Dev.Trop., Amer.Hist.& Life, Asian-Pac.Econ.Lit., ASSIA, Curr.Cont., E.I., Hist.Abstr., Int.Lab.Doc., Mid.East: Abstr.& Ind., Rural Recreat.Tour.Abstr., Soc.Sci.Ind., SSCI, World Agri.Econ.& Rural Sociol.Abstr. —BLDSC (4965.225000); Faxon; UnCover; SWETS; UMI.

079.9423 AT
LEADER. 1918. w. Aus.$65. Leader Newspapers Pty. Ltd., Barossa Valley, 34 Dean St., Angaston, S.A. 5353, Australia. TEL 085-642035. Ed. A.R.K. Robinson. adv.; bk.rev. circ. 6,600. (back issues avail.) **Document type:** newspaper.
Description: Regional publication covering local products such as wine and fruit, as well as marble quarries, cement, window extrusion and electrical manufacturing plants, sheep, wool, cattle, pigs, wheat, flour mills, and poultry raising.

079.9423 AT
LOXTON NEWS. 1960. w. Aus.$50. Loxton News Pty. Ltd., Box 352, Loxton, S.A. 5333, Australia. TEL 085-847271. FAX 085-847547. Ed. Denis Hann. adv.; bk.rev.; circ. 2,650 (paid). **Document type:** newspaper.
Description: Covers regional news and sports of the Loxton, Australia area.

079.945 AT
MACEDON RANGES TELEGRAPH. 1977. w. Aus.$52. Telegraph News Pty. Ltd., 52 Aitken St., Gisborne, Vic. 3437, Australia. TEL 054-282-600. FAX 054-282917. Ed. Carol Job. adv. circ. 18,893. **Document type:** newspaper.

079.941 AT
MANDURAH TELEGRAPH. 1983. w. Aus.$47. South West Printing and Publishing Co. Ltd., Proffit St., Bunbury, W.A. 6230, Australia. (Subscr. to: P.O. Box 353, Cannington, W.A. 6107, Australia) Ed. A. Van Dyk. circ. 11,320. **Document type:** newspaper.
Formerly: Mandurah Telegraph and Murray Telegraph.

079.944 AT
MOSMAN AND LOWER NORTH SHORE DAILY. 1917. w. Aus.$0.40. Cumberland Newspapers, Level 1, 2-6 Spit Rd., Spit Junction 2088, Sydney, Australia. TEL 960-222. FAX 969-6031. Ed. Barry Laws. adv. contact: Sue Chambers. circ. 32,628. (also avail. in microfiche; back issues avail.) **Document type:** newspaper.
Former titles: Mosman Daily; Mosman and Lower North Shore Daily.

052 AT
NARACOORTE HERALD. 1875. s-w. Aus.$52.52($68) Naracoorte Herald Pty Ltd, 93 Smith St, Naracoorte, S.A. 5271, Australia. Ed. Richard Peake. circ. 2,850. (back issues avail.)

NATIONAL COUNTRY LIFE. see AGRICULTURE

052 AT
NEWS WEEKLY. 1943. fortn. Aus.$45 (foreign Aus.$79). Freedom Publishing Co., 582 Queensberry St., N. Melbourne, Vic. 3051, Australia. TEL 03-326-5757. FAX 03-328-2877. Ed. Peter Westmore. adv.; bk.rev.; film rev. circ. 16,000.
Description: A current affairs magazine covering politics both Australian and international, economics, world affairs and more.

052 AT
NORTH QUEENSLAND REGISTER. 1876. w. Aus.$42. Rural Press North Queensland Pty. Ltd., 155 Denham St., Townsville, Qld. 4810, Australia. TEL 077-213344. FAX 077-213059. Ed. J. Andersen. adv.; bk.rev.; film rev.; bibl.; charts; illus.; tr.lit.; stat. circ. 6,000. (also avail. in microfilm)
Formerly: Register.

079.945 AT
NORTH EASTERN AND GOULBURN VALLEY FARMER. 1982. m. Aus.$15. Wangaratta Newspapers Pty., Ltd., 37 Rowan St., Wangaratta, Vic. 3677, Australia. TEL 057-219856. FAX 057-219447. (Subscr. to: P.O. Box 221, Wangaratta, Vic. 3677, Australia) Ed. Philip Nolan. adv. circ. 14,000. **Document type:** newspaper.
Formed by the merger of: North Eastern Farmer & Goulburn Valley Farmer.
Description: News and features of interest to readers in the region.

052 AT
NORTH WEST TELEGRAPH.* 1968. w. Aus.$60($40) Albany Advertiser Ltd., 165 York St., P.O. Box 168, Albany, W.A. 6330, Australia. TEL 09 362 5699. (Subscr. to: P.O. Box 353, Cannington, W.A. 6107, Australia) Ed. John Brown. circ. 17,200.

630 079.945 AT
PAKENHAM GAZETTE BERWICK GAZETTE. 1910. w. Aus.$56. 100-106 Main St., Pakenham, Vic. 3810, Australia. TEL 059-412-666. FAX 059-412-515. (Subscr. to: P.O. Box 9, Pakenham, Vic. 3810, Australia) Ed. Dorothy Thomas. adv. circ. 8,300. (back issues avail.) **Document type:** newspaper.
Formerly: Pakenham Gazette and Berwick City News.

052 AT ISSN 1321-9847
PEOPLE. w. Aus.$130. A C P Publishing Pty. Ltd., 54-58 Park St., Sydney, N.S.W. 2000, Australia. TEL 02-282-8743. FAX 02-267-4365. Ed. David Naylor; Pub. Richard Walsh. adv. contact: Peter Miller. bk.rev.; film rev.; play rev.; illus. circ. 260,200. **Document type:** consumer publication.
Formed by the merger of: Pix (ISSN 0032-0390); People; **Formerly:** Pix - People.

052 AT
PORT LINCOLN TIMES. 1927. s-w. Aus.$70. Port Lincoln Times Pty. Ltd., 2 Washington Street, Port Lincoln, S.A., Australia. Ed. Brian Barnett. adv.; bk.rev. circ. 6,600. (also avail. in microfilm; back issues avail.)

052 AT ISSN 0034-0391
READER'S DIGEST (AUSTRALIAN EDITION). 1945. m. Aus.$32.95. Reader's Digest (Australia) Pty. Ltd., G.P.O. Box 4353, Sydney, N.S.W. 2001, Australia. TEL 699-0111. Ed. Hugh Vahghan-Williams. adv.; bk.rev.; illus. circ. 480,000. **Indexed:** GdIns.

079.941   AT
SOUND TELEGRAPH. 1969. w. Aus.$50. South West Printing and Publishing Co. Ltd., Proffit St., Bunbury, W.A. 6230, Australia. (Subscr. to: P.O. Box 353, Cannington, WA 6107, Australia) Ed. John Brown. circ. 22,600. **Document type:** newspaper.
  Formerly: Midlands Telegraph.

052   AT
SOUTHERN WEEKLY MAGAZINE. 1975. w. Weekly Magazine Partnership, 181 Parker St, Cootamundra, N.S.W. 2590, Australia. Ed. B.A. Clarke. adv.; bk.rev. circ. 50,000. (back issues avail.)

052   AT
SPENCER GULF PICTORIAL. 1969. w. Aus.$35. Northern Newspapers Pty. Ltd., 21 Forsyth Street, Whyalla, S.A. 5600, Australia. Ed. Lindy McCallum. adv. circ. 11,500. (back issues avail.)

079.94   AT
THE STANDARD. (Quarterly supplements avail.: South West Tourist News; Goldfields Tourist News) 1872. 6/w. (Mon.-Sat.). 170-176 Koroit St., Warrnambool, Vic. 3280, Australia. TEL 055-61-4000. FAX 055-62-0389. Owner(s): John Fairfax Group Pty. Ltd., 235-243 Jones St., Broadway, Sydney, N.S.W. 2007, Australia. TEL 02-282-2833. FAX 02-282-3208. Ed. I.W. Pech; Pub. E.N. Cavey. adv. contact: G.C. Rollinson. bk.rev.; film rev.; music rev.; play rev.; tele.rev.; illus. Wire service(s): AAP. circ. 12,893 (paid); 146 (controlled). cols./p.: 7; pp./issue: 32. (tabloid format; also avail. in microfilm; reprint service avail.) **Document type:** newspaper.

079.946   AT
SUNDAY EXAMINER. 1984. w. Aus.$0.80 per no. Examiner Newspaper Pty. Ltd., 71-75 Paterson St., Launceston, Tas. 7250, Australia. TEL 003-31-5111. FAX 003-320-300. Ed. Rod Scott. adv. contact: Peter Cooper. bk.rev. circ. 42,000. **Document type:** newspaper.

079.943   AT   ISSN 0039-5226
SUNDAY MAIL. 1916. w. Aus.$1.50 per no. Queensland Newspapers Pty. Ltd., Campbell St., Bowen Hills, Brisbane, Qld., Australia. FAX 07-252-6692. Ed. Bob Gordon. adv. contact: John Banks. bk.rev. circ. 566,925. **Document type:** newspaper.
•Also available online.

079.943   AT
SUNDAY SUN. 1901. w. Aus.$123 for 3 mos. Sun Newspapers, 367 Brunswick St., Fortitude Valley, Qld. 4006, Australia. FAX 2533103. TELEX 40105. adv.; bk.rev.; film rev.; play rev.; mkt. circ. 388,179. (tabloid format) **Document type:** newspaper.
  Formerly: Sunday Truth (ISSN 0039-5358)

079.943   AT
SUNSHINE COAST WEEKLY. 1983. w. free. Sunshine Coast Newspaper Co., Aerodrome Rd., P.O. Box 56, Maroochydore, Qld. 4558, Australia. TEL 074-308000. FAX 074-435150. Ed. Peter Owen. adv.; film rev.; play rev.; charts; illus.; stat.; tr.lit. circ. 40,000. (tabloid format; back issues avail.) **Document type:** newspaper.

079.943   AT
THE TABLELANDER NEWSPAPER. 1982. w. Aus.$30. North Queensland Newspaper Co. Pty. Ltd., P.O. Box 20, 53 Mabel St., Ste. 4, Atherton, Qld. 4883, Australia. TEL 070-911977. FAX 070-912913. Ed. Wally Coutts. adv. circ. 15,400. (back issues avail.) **Document type:** newspaper.
  Description: Concentrates on local news & issues of particular interest to Far Northerners.

052   AT
TABLELANDS ADVERTISER. 1961. w. Aus.$23.40. Tablelands Advertiser, 109 Byrnes St., Marreba, Qld. 4880, Australia. TEL (070)921334. Ed. B.J. Simpson. adv.; bk.rev.; film rev.; play rev. circ. 15,110. (back issues avail.)
  Description: News and advertising media for the entire Cairns Hinterland, Gulf and Coastal areas of Far North Queensland.

052   AT   ISSN 0726-4690
THIS IS NEWCASTLE AND THE HUNTER REGION. 1960. a. Aus.$10. Hunter Valley Research Foundation, P.O. Box 23, Tighes Hill, N.S.W. 2297, Australia. TEL 049-694566. FAX 049-614-981. (Co-sponsor: Newcastle City Council) charts; illus.; stat. circ. 5,000.

079.943   AT
TWIN CITIES ADVERTISER. 1976. w. Aus.$0.70 per no. North Queensland Newspaper Company Ltd., 442-446 Flinders St., Townsville, Qld. 4810, Australia. Ed. Ned Makim. adv.; bk.rev. circ. 35,000. **Document type:** newspaper.
  Formerly: Townsville Advertiser.
  Description: Community weekly paper.

052   AT   ISSN 0727-6745
VOGUE ENTERTAINING GUIDE. 1978. bi-m. Aus.$30 (foreign Aus.$45) (effective Jan. 1992). Conde Nast Publications Pty. Ltd., 170 Pacific Highway, Greenwich, N.S.W. 2065, Australia. TEL 02-964-3888. FAX 02-864-3882. (U.S. and Canada subscr. to: International Subscriptions Inc., 30 Montgomery St., 7th Fl., Jersey City, NJ 07302) Ed. Sharyn Storrier-Lyneham. adv.; bk.rev. circ. 71,730. **Document type:** consumer publication.

079.945   AT
WARRAGUL GAZETTE. 1898. w. Aus.$72.80. Warragul Regional Newspaper Pty. Ltd., 97 Queen St., Warragul, Vic. 3820, Australia. TEL 056-235666. FAX 056-232367. (Subscr. to: P.O. Box 305, Warragul, Vic., 3820, Australia) Ed. Carolyn Lurner. circ. 9,200. **Document type:** newspaper.

079.944   AT
WEEKLY SOUTHERN COURIER. 1955. w. Aus.$6 per no. Eastern Suburbs Newspapers, 170 Bourke Rd., Alexandria, Sydney, N.S.W. 2015, Australia. TEL 02-693-9999. FAX 02-317-5780. Ed. Graham Harris. adv. bk.rev. circ. 46,254. **Document type:** newspaper.
  Former titles (until 1989): Weekly-Courier; (until 1986): Bondi Weekly-Courier.

079.944   AT
WENTWORTH COURIER. 1946. w. Eastern Suburbs Newspapers, 170 Bourke St., Alexandria, N.S.W. 2015, Australia. TEL 02-693-9999. FAX 02-317-5780. Ed. B. Doyle. adv. contact: T. Pullinger. bk.rev.; film rev.; play rev.; charts; illus. circ. 48,669. **Document type:** newspaper.
  Description: Focuses on women, entertainment, travel, real estate and sports in the area.

079.945   AT
WEST GIPPSLAND TRADER. 1981. w. Warragul Regional Newspaper Pty. Ltd., 97 Queen St., Warragul, Vic. 3820, Australia. TEL 056-235666. FAX 056-232367. (Subscr. to: P.O. Box 305, Warragul, Vic. 3820, Australia) Ed. Carolyn Lurner. circ. 9,700. **Document type:** newspaper.

052   AT
WHEATBELT MERCURY. 1912. w. Aus.$45. Merredin Advertiser, P.O. Box 283, Merredin, W.A. 6415, Australia. FAX 090-412577. Ed. H.J. Ventris. adv. circ. 3,200.

052   AT
3D WORLD MAGAZINE. 1989. fortn. Aus.$56. Jonathan Morris, 44 Reservoir St., Ste. 8, Surry Hills, N.S.W. 2010, Australia. TEL 02-211-1222. FAX 02-281-4193. Ed. Mary Gillespie. circ. 25,000.
  Description: Covers all areas of entertainment in Sydney including music, clubs, theater, film, arts, fashion and lifestyle.

GENERAL INTEREST PERIODICALS — Austria

943   US
AUSTRIA KULTUR; news from Austria (science, culture, education). 1962. m. free. Austrian Cultural Institute, 11 E. 52nd St., New York, NY 10022-5390. TEL 212-759-5165. FAX 212-319-9636. bk.rev. circ. 10,000. **Document type:** newsletter.
  Former titles (until 1992): Austrian Institute Calendar of Events; Austrian Institute Newsletter.

052   AU   ISSN 0304-8713
DB17
AUSTRIA TODAY; news, events, trends from Austria. (Text in English) 1975. q. S.330. Austria Today Verlag GmbH KG, Hofburg Schweizertor, Postfach 47, A-1014 Vienna, Austria. TEL 0222-5872184. FAX 0222-566159. Ed.Bd. adv.; bk.rev.; charts; illus.; index. circ. 20,000. **Document type:** consumer publication.
  —UnCover.

053.1   AU
BASTA; Magazin am Puls der Zeit. 1983. m. S.480. R E V Zeitschriften Verlagsgesellschaft mbH, Seidengasse 5, A-1072 Vienna, Austria. TEL 01-52146-0. FAX 01-521461640. Eds. Robert Sterk, Brigitta Perner. circ. 130,000. **Document type:** consumer publication.

943.6   AU   ISSN 0007-6228
BURGENLAENDISCHE GEMEINSCHAFT. 1956. m. membership. Burgenlaendische Gemeinschaft - Burgenland Society, Mogersdorf 178, A-7540 Guessing, Austria. Ed. Julius Gmoser. adv.; illus.

053.1   AU   ISSN 0007-6252
BURGENLAENDISCHES LEBEN. 1948. 2/yr. S.120. Burgenland Verlag GmbH, Postfach 14, A-7001 Eisenstadt, Austria. TEL 02682-2015. Ed. Dr. Fritz Zimmermann. adv.; bk.rev.; illus. circ. 6,000.

053.1   AU   ISSN 0013-2470
EHE UND FAMILIE. 1967. m. S.14 per issue. (Katholischer Familienverband Oesterreichs) Ehe und Familie Zeitschriftenverlagsgesellschaft mbH, Spiegelgasse 3-3-9, A-1010 Vienna, Austria. TEL 0222-51552-201. adv.; bk.rev.; abstr.; charts; illus.; tr.lit. circ. 70,000. (tabloid format) **Document type:** consumer publication.

943.6   AU   ISSN 0016-2469
FUERSTENFELDER GRENZLANDECHO. 1963. fortn. S.130. Verein fuer Heimatpflege Fuerstenfeld, Postbox 89, A-8280 Fuerstenfeld, Austria. TEL 03382-3388. Ed. Helmut Mayer. adv.; bk.rev.; illus.
  Description: Covers regional news and information, including cultural news and events, societies, sports and entertainment.

943.6   AU   ISSN 0016-6146
GEMEINDEKURIER; Mitteilungsblatt der Stadt Berndorf. 1963. m. S.40. Stadtgemeinde Berndorf, Karl Kislingerplatz 2, A-2560 Berndorf, Austria. Ed. Alfred Hauer. adv.
  Description: Covers local interests.

053.1   AU   ISSN 0017-5781
GUTE NACHRICHTEN. 1960. 4/yr. free. Brunner Verlag, Ringelschmiedgasse 5, A-8600 Bruck-Mur, Austria. TEL 03862-51266. FAX 03862-51266. Ed. Wilfrid M. Brunner. adv.; bk.rev.; illus.; stat. circ. 4,000. **Document type:** consumer publication.

079.94   AT
GYMPIE TIMES. 5/w. (Tue.- Sat.). newsstand price: Aus.$0.60. 197 Mary St., Gympie, Qld. 4570, Australia. TEL 074-821011. FAX 074-826969. Owner(s): Rural Press Ltd., Bells Line of Road, N. Richmond, N.S.W. 2754, Australia. TEL 045-704444. FAX 045-704663. Ed. Michael Roser. adv. contact: John Kelly. bk.rev.; film rev.; music rev.; play rev.; tele.rev.; illus. Wire service(s): AAP. circ. 5,555 (paid). pp./issue: 24. (tabloid format) **Document type:** newspaper.

ILLUSTRIERTE NEUE WELT; Unabhaengige internationale Zeitschrift. see *ETHNIC INTERESTS*

053.1 943.6   AU   ISSN 0023-5210
KULTURBERICHTE AUS TIROL. 1948. q. free. Tiroler Landesregierung, Kulturabteilung, Sillgasse 8, A-6020 Innsbruck, Austria. Ed. Magdalena Hoermann. bk.rev.; bibl.; cum.index: 1948-1970. circ. 2,800. **Document type:** government publication.
  Description: Information about cultural events in the Tyrol.

053.1   AU   ISSN 0027-5131
MUTTER. 1948. m. S.125. Panorama Verlagsgesellschaft mbH, Dominikanerbastei 19, A-1011 Vienna, Austria. TEL 01-5353274. adv.; bk.rev.; illus.

053.1   AU   ISSN 0028-3223
NEUE ILLUSTRIERTE WOCHENSCHAU; das Blatt fuer Alle. 1908. w. S.536($37) Verlag A. Kirsch, Kaiserstr 8-10, A-1072 Vienna, Austria. Ed. Peter Lang. adv.; bk.rev.; film rev.; play rev.; illus.; tr.lit. circ. 172,000.

GENERAL INTEREST PERIODICALS — AZERBAIJAN

073 AU
NEUE KRONEN ZEITUNG. 1959. d. S.188 per wk. Krone Verlag GmbH und Co. KG, Muthgasse 2, A-1190 Vienna, Austria. TEL 01-36010. FAX 01-3698896. (Dist. by: Mediaprint, Richard-Strauss-Str. 16, A-1232 Vienna, Austria. TEL 01-61010) Ed. Hans Dichand. circ. 1,475,803. (tabloid format) **Document type:** newspaper.

052 AU
NIEDEROESTERREICH-PERSPEKTIVEN; Vierteljahresschrift fuer Kultur, Wirtschaft, und Planung im Bundesland Niederoesterreich. 4/yr. S.30 per no. Niederoesterreichische Landesregierung, Presseabteilung, Herrengasse 11-13, A-1014 Vienna, Austria. Ed. Gottfried Kapf. circ. 7,116.

053.1 AU ISSN 0029-7542
OBEROESTERREICHISCHE GEMEINDEZEITUNG. 1947. m. S.142. (Oberoesterreichischer Gemeindebund) Landesverlag (Ried), An der Riedauer Str., A-4910 Ried, Austria. Ed. Dr. Hans Neuhofer. adv.; bk.rev.; index. circ. 10,000.

053 AU
PROFIL; das unabhaengige Nachrichtenmagazin Oesterreichs. 1970. w. S.1150 (foreign S.1670). Wirtschafts-Trend Zeitschriftenverlagsgesellschaft mbH, Marc-Aurel-Str. 10-12, A-1010 Vienna, Austria. TEL 0222-53470-0. FAX 0222-53470349. Eds. Herbert Lackner, Josef Votzi; Pub. Hubertus Czernin. adv. contact: Gottfried Satek. bk.rev.; illus. circ. 115,000. **Document type:** consumer publication.

943 AU
ROTWEISSROT.* fortn. S.160. Auslandsoesterreicherwerk, Herrengasse 6, A-1010 Vienna, Austria. illus.
  Former titles: Auslandsoesterreicher; Stimme Oesterreichs.

053.1 AU ISSN 0038-139X
SONNTAGSPOST;* die illustrierte unabhaengige Wochenzeitung. 1950. w. S.456. Oesterreichischer Verlag, Giselastrasse 3, A-6300, Wirgl, Tirol, Austria. Ed. Paul Kaufmann. adv.; bk.rev.; film rev.; play rev.; illus.; circ. 28,300 (controlled). (tabloid format)

053.1 AU
TENDENZ. m. S.240. Tendenz Verlag, Vogelsanggasse 25-27, A-1050 Vienna, Austria. TEL 0222-547094. FAX 0222-547094. Ed. Amir Bayati. adv. contact: Walburga Barta.

053.1 AU
ULTIMO; das Salzburg Magazin mit Programm. m. S.99. (Landesjugendreferat Salzburg) Akzente Salzburg, Nonntaler Hauptstr. 1, A-5020 Salzburg, Austria. TEL 0662-849291. FAX 0662-84929122. adv.; B&W page S.20000, color page S.32000; trim 165 x 248; adv. contact: Sieglinde Trunkenpolz. circ. 30,000 (controlled). **Document type:** consumer publication.
  Formerly: Blizz.

073 AU
▼**VOLKSSTIMME;** Wochenzeitung fuer Politik, Gesellschaft und Kultur. 1994. w. (Thu.). S.960; newsstand price: S.25. Zeitungsgesellschaft mbH, Kaiserstr. 67-1-DG, A-1070 Vienna, Austria. TEL 0222-52166. FAX 0222-5236885. Ed. Ulrich Perzinger; Pub. Brigitte Loew-Radeschnig. adv.: page S.20000; trim 265 x 363; adv. contact: Johanna Riegler. bk.rev.; film rev.; music rev.; tele.rev.; tr.lit. cols./p.: 5; pp./issue: 24. **Document type:** newspaper.

073 AU
VORARLBERGER. 1978. w. S.350. Logos Medienverlagsgesellschaft mbH, Anton-Schneider-Str. 32, Postfach 371, A-6901 Bregenz. TEL 05574-43671. FAX 05574-47171. Ed. Jutta Michaud. adv.: B&W page S.13860; 210 x 275. bk.rev.; film rev. circ. 110,000. **Document type:** newspaper.

053.1 AU
WIENER. 1980. m. S.630. Metro Zeitschriften Verlags GmbH, Donaustr. 102, A-3400 Klosterneuburg, Austria. TEL 02243-88600. FAX 02243-88600199. adv. circ. 158,000. **Document type:** consumer publication.

053.1 AU
WIENERIN. 1985. 10/yr. S.590. Metro Zeitschriften Verlags GmbH, Donaustr. 102, A-3400 Klosterneuburg, Austria. TEL 02243-88600. FAX 02243-88600199. circ. 85,000. **Document type:** consumer publication.

073.6 AU
WOCHEN RUNDSCHAU; unabhaengige Zeitung fuer Badischl und das Salzkammergut. 1980. w. S.350. Druckerei Wimmer, Kaiser-Franz-Joseph-Str., 4820 Bad Ischl, Austria. TEL 06132-2714314. FAX 06132-2714318. Ed. Peter Huemer. circ. 8,000. (back issues avail.) **Document type:** newspaper.

053.1 AU
WOCHENPRESSE; das Oesterreichische Nachrichtenmagazin. 1946. w. S.940. Kurier AG, Lindengasse 52, 1070 Vienna, Austria. TEL 0222-93-75-21. Ed. Hans Magenschab. circ. 50,000.

053.1 AU
WORTMUEHLE; Literaturblaetter aus dem Burgenland. 1978. q. S.160. Edition Roetzer GmbH, Mattersburger Str. 25, A-7000 Eisenstadt, Austria. TEL 02682-62494. adv.; bk.rev. circ. 800. **Document type:** bulletin.

GENERAL INTEREST PERIODICALS — Azerbaijan

077 AJ ISSN 0233-3112
BAKINSKII RABOCHII; obshchestvenno-politicheskaya gazeta Azerbaidzhanskoi Respubliki. (Text in Russian) 1906. 6/w. Metbuat pr., 529-i, 370146 Baku, Azerbaijan. TEL 38-68-08. FAX 38-00-29. Ed. E. Abaskuliev. adv.; illus. circ. 13,944. (broadsheet format) **Document type:** newspaper.

GENERAL INTEREST PERIODICALS — Bahrain

059.927 BA
AL-ADHWAA'. 1965. w. Arab Printing and Publishing House, P.O. Box 250, Manama, Bahrain. TEL 245251. FAX 293166. TELEX 8564. Ed. Muhammad Qassim Shirawi. circ. 7,000.

059.927 BA
GULF PANORAMA. m. P.O. Box 1122, Manama, Bahrain. TEL 277677. Ed. Ibrahim Bashmi. circ. 15,000.

052 BA
INSIDE BAHRAIN. (Text in English) fortn. Inside Bahrain Promotions, P.O. Box 102435, Manama, Bahrain. TEL 291110. FAX 294655. Ed. Isa bin Khalifa al-Khalifa. circ. 11,000.

956 BA
MAWAKEF WEEKLY MAGAZINE/AL-MAWAQIF. w. 10 BD. Box 1083, Manama, Bahrain. illus.

059.927 BA
AL-MAWAKIF. 1973. w. P.O. Box 1083, Manama, Bahrain. TEL 231231. FAX 271720. Ed. Mansoor Radhi. circ. 4,000.

059.927 BA
AL-MURSHID/GUIDE. (Text in Arabic, English) m. Arab Printing and Publishing House, P.O. Box 553, Manama, Bahrain. FAX 293145. Ed. M. Soliman.

059.927 BA
SADA AL-USBOU'; majallah usbu'iyyah siyasiyyah jami'ah. 1969. w. (Tues.). 50000 din.($140) Ali A. Sayyar, Ed. & Pub., P.O. Box 549, Manama, Bahrain. TEL 291234. FAX 290507. TELEX 8880 SAYAR BN. adv.: B&W page 300 din., color page 500 din; bleed 285 x 210; adv. contact: Ali A. Sayyar. bk.rev.; film rev.; play rev.; tele.rev.; illus. circ. 30,000. (back issues avail.) **Document type:** consumer publication.
  Description: Covers general and political news, cultural topics and business issues of interest.

052 BA
THIS IS BAHRAIN AND WHAT'S ON. (Text in English) 1975. q. Gulf Advertising and Marketing Co., P.O. Box 726, Manama, Bahrain. TEL 250014. FAX 230025. TELEX 8494. Ed. Fenella Flanagan. circ. 15,000.

GENERAL INTEREST PERIODICALS — Bangladesh

059.914 BG
AD-DAWAT. (Text in Bengali) 1976. m. Rajshahi Town, Bangladesh. Ed. Mohammad Abul Qasem.

059.914 BG
AMOD. (Text in Bengali) 1955. w. Comilla Sadar, Comilla, Bangladesh. TEL 81-5193. Ed. Shamsun Nahar Rabbi. circ. 6,000.

059.914 BG
ANANDA BICHITRA. (Text in Bengali) 1986. fortn. 1 DIT Ave., Dhaka, Bangladesh. TEL 2-241639. Ed. Shahadat Chowdhury. circ. 32,000.

059.914 BG
ANANDA PATRA. (Text in Bengali) w. 188 Motijheel Circular Rd., Dhaka 1000, Bangladesh. TEL 2-406988. Ed. Mostafa Jabbar.

052 BG
BANGLADESH. (Text in English) fortn. 112 Circuit House Rd., Dhaka 1000, Bangladesh. TEL 2-402013. Ed. A.B.M. Abdul Matin.

052 BG
BANGLADESH GAZETTE. (Text in English) 1947. w. Bangladesh Government Press, Tejgaon, Dhaka, Bangladesh. Ed. M. Huda.

079.5492 052 BG
BANGLADESH OBSERVER. (Text in English) d. Al-Helal Printing & Publishing Co. Ltd., Observer House, 33 Toynbee Circular Rd., Motijheel Commercial Area, Dhaka 1000, Bangladesh. TEL 880-2-235105. FAX 880-2-833563. Ed. K.M.A. Munim. adv. (broadsheet format) **Document type:** newspaper.

059.914 BG
BICHITRA. (Text in Bengali) 1972. w. Dainik Bangla Bhaban, 1 DIT Ave., Dhaka 1000, Bangladesh. TEL 2-232086. Ed. Shahadat Chowdhury. circ. 42,000.

059.914 BG
CHITRA BANGLA. (Text in Bengali) w. 137 Shanti Nagar, Dhaka, Bangladesh. TEL 2-407601. Ed. Fullora Begum Flora. circ. 46,000.

059.914 BG
CHITRA DESH. (Text in Bengali) w. 24 Ramkrishna Mission Rd., Dhaka 1000, Bangladesh. Ed. Hena Akhtar Chowdhury.

059 BG ISSN 0009-4870
CHITRALI. (Text in Bengali) 1963. w. $70. Al-Helal Printing & Publishing Co. Ltd., Observer House, 33 Toynbee Circular Rd., Motijheel Commercial Area, Dhaka 1000, Bangladesh. TEL 880-2-235105. FAX 880-2-411989. Ed. Ahmed Z. Chowdhury. bk.rev.; film rev.; play rev.; tele.rev.; illus. circ. 25,000. (also avail. in microform)

059.914 BG
CHUTTI. (Text in Bengali) w. 87 Bijoy Nagar, Dhaka 1000, Bangladesh. TEL 2-231112. Ed. Jawadul Karim. circ. 18,000.

079.5492 BG
DAILY INQILAB. (Text in Bengali) 1986. d. Tk.1700 (India Tk.6405; Asia Tk.10690; Europe Tk.13630; America Tk.16580). Inqilab Enterprise & Publications Ltd., 2-1 R.K. Mission Rd., Dhaka 1203, Bangladesh. TEL 880-2-240147. FAX 880-2-833122. Ed. A.M.M. Bahauddin; Pub. A.S.M. Baqibillah. adv.; bk.rev.; film rev.; music rev.; play rev.; tele.rev.; illus.; circ. 205,000 (paid); 5,000 (controlled). cols./p.: 8; pp./issue: 12. (back issues avail.) **Document type:** newspaper.

079.5492 BG
DAILY PURBANCHAL. (Text in Bengali) 1978. d. Tk.800. Purbanchal Publishers, 38 Iqbal Nagar, Khulna 9100, Bangladesh. TEL 880-41-21013. FAX 880-41-21432. Ed. Liaqat Ali; Pub. Alhaj Liaqat Ali. adv. contact: Zakir Hossain. illus.; circ. 32,000 (paid); 3,000 (controlled). cols./p.: 8; pp./issue: 8. (standard format) **Document type:** newspaper.
  Description: Covers local, national and international news.

079.5492 052 BG
DAILY TRIBUNE. (Text in English) 1979. d. Tk.900($450) Purbanchal Publishers, 38 Iqbal Nagar, Khulna 9100, Bangladesh. TEL 880-41-21013. FAX 880-41-21432. Ed. Begum Ferdousi Ali; Pub. Alhaj Liaqat Ali. adv. contact: Tarun Kanti. bk.rev.; film rev.; music rev.; illus. circ. 24,000. cols./p.: 8; pp./issue: 8. (broadsheet format) Document type: newspaper.
   Description: Covers local, regional, national and international news and events.

079.5493 BG
DAINIK MEILLAT. Variant title: Daily Meillat. (Publication suspended from Dec. 1989 to April 1990) (Supplements avail.) (Text in Bengali) 1987. newsstand price: Tk.4. Daily Meillat, 28 Toyenbee Circular Rd., Motijheel Commercial Area, Dhaka 1000, Bangladesh. TEL 880-2-240026. FAX 880-2-863797. Ed. Chowdhury Mohammad Farouque; Pub. Chowdhury Mohammad Farouque. adv. contact: M.A. Qauder. bk.rev.; illus.; circ. 30,000. (paid); 10,000. (controlled). cols./p.: 8; pp./issue: 8. (broadsheet format; back issues avail.) Document type: newspaper.

051 BG
DHAKA BISVABIDYALAYA PATRIKA. Added title: Dacca Visva Vidyalaya Patrika. (Text in Bengali) 1973. a. University of Dhaka, Ramna, Dhaka 2, Bangladesh.

052 BG
DHAKA COURIER. (Text in English) w. 62-61 Purana Paltan, Dhaka, Bangladesh. TEL 2-238222. Ed. Enayet Ullah Khan. circ. 5,000.

059.914 BG
DHAKA DIGEST. (Text in Bengali) 1974. m. 34 Topkhana Rd, Dhaka, Bangladesh. Ed. Rashid Chowdhury. circ. 7,000.

059.914 BG
EKOTA. (Text in Bengali) w. 15 Larmini St., Wari, Dhaka, Bangladesh. TEL 2-257854. Ed. Matiur Rahman. circ. 25,000.

059.914 BG
THE FORTNIGHTLY AHMADI. (Text in Bengali) 1925. fortn. Ahmadyya Art Press, 4 Bakshi Bazar Rd., Dhaka 1211, Bangladesh. TEL 501379. Ed. Maqbul Ahmad Khan. circ. 1,000.
   Description: Contains religious and moral articles.

052 BG
HERALD. (Text in English) 1981. w. 87 Bijoy Nagar, Dhaka, Bangladesh. TEL 2-231533. Ed. Jaqadul Karim. circ. 4,000.

052 BG
HOLIDAY. (Text in English) 1965. w. $40 for S. Asia; Europe & Africa $68; N. America $80. Holiday Building, 30 Tejgaon Industrial Area, Dhaka 1208, Bangladesh. TEL 2-329163. FAX 02-833650. Ed. Enayetullah Khan. adv.; bk.rev. circ. 19,000.
   Description: A broadsheet political weekly on trade and aviation.

059.914 BG
ISPAT (KUSHTIA). (Text in Bengali) 1976. w. Majampur, Kushtia, Bangladesh. TEL 71-3676. Ed. Waliur Bari Choudhury. circ. 3,000.

059.914 BG
JUGABHERI. (Text in Bengali) 1931. w. Rasheedistan, Rai Hussain, Amberkhana, Sylhet, Bangladesh. TEL 821-5461. Ed. Fahmeeda Rasheed Choudhury. circ. 6,000.

059.914 BG
KALANTAR. (Text in Bengali) 1971. w. 87 Khanjahan Ali Rd., Khulna, Bangladesh. TEL 41-61424. Ed. Noor Mohammad. circ. 12,000.

059.914 BG
KANAK. (Text in Bengali) w. 144 DIT Extension Rd., Dhaka, Bangladesh. TEL 2-415110. Ed. Amir Hossain.

059.914 BG
KANKAN. (Text in Bengali) 1974. w. Nawab Bari Rd, Bogra, Bangladesh. TEL 51-6424. Ed. Mrs. Sufia Khatun. circ. 6,000.

059.914 BG
KRISHI KATHA.* (Text in Bengali) 1957. m. Faircim Giet, Dhaka 1230, Bangladesh. Ed. Nurjahan Koreshi. circ. 6,000.

052 BG
MOTHERLAND. (Text in English) 1974. w. Khanjahan Ali Rd., Khulna, Bangladesh. TEL 41-61685. Ed. M.N. Khan.

059.914 BG
MUKTIBANI. (Text in Bengali) 1972. w. Toyenbee Circular Rd., Motijheel C-A, Dhaka 1000, Bangladesh. TEL 2-253712. TELEX 642474. Ed. Nizam Uddin Ahmed. circ. 35,000.

079.5492 BG
NATUN BANGLA. (Text in Bengali) 1971. w. Tk.100. 44A Hatirpul, Sonargaon Rd., Dhaka 1205, Bangladesh. TEL 880-2-863794. Ed. Mujibur Rahman. adv.; bk.rev. circ. 20,000. Document type: newspaper.

059.914 BG
NATUN KATHA. (Text in Bengali) w. 31E Topkhana Rd., Dhaka, Bangladesh. Ed. Hajera Sultana. circ. 4,000.

059.914 BG
NIPUN. (Text in Bengali) m. 520 Peyarabag, Magbazar, Dhaka 11007, Bangladesh. TEL 2-312156. Ed. Shajahan Chowdhury.

059.914 BG
THE PAKSHIK PROTIRODH. (Text in Bengali) 1977. fortn. Tk.48. Ministry of Home Affairs, Dept. of Answer and V.D.P., School Bldg., 2nd Fl., Bangladesh Secretariat, Dhaka, Bangladesh. TEL 2-405606. Ed. Jahangir Habibullah. circ. 25,000.
   Formerly: Monthly Protirodh.

059.914 BG
REPORTER. (Text in Bengali) 1976. w. 28J Toyenbee Circular Rd., Motijheel C/A, Dhaka, Bangladesh. TEL 2-257589. Ed. Ershad Mazumdar. circ. 5,000.

059.914 BG
SANDIP. (Text in Bengali) w. 28-A-3 Toyenbee Circular Rd., Dhaka, Bangladesh. TEL 2-235542. Ed. Mohsen Ara Rahman.

052 BG
SUNDAY STAR. (Text in English) 1981. w. 149A DIT Extension Ave., Dhaka, Bangladesh. TEL 2-403980. Ed. Mohiuddin Ahmed.

059.914 BG
SWADESH. (Text in Bengali) w. 19 B.B. Ave., Dhaka, Bangladesh. TEL 2-256946. Ed. Zakiuddin Ahmed. circ. 8,000.

059.914 BG
TAROKALOK. (Text in Bengali) w. 8-3 Neelkhet, Babupura, Dhaka 1205, Bangladesh. TEL 2-507952. Ed. Sajjad Kadir.

052 BG
VOICE FROM THE NORTH. (Text in English) 1981. w. Dinajpur Town, Dinajpur, Bangladesh. TEL 531-3256. Ed. Muhammad Mohsin. circ. 5,000.

GENERAL INTEREST PERIODICALS — Belarus

057.99 BW ISSN 0320-7544
BELARUS'. (Text in Byelorussian) 1930. m. 4.60 Rub. (Sayuz Pismennikaw Belarusi) Belarus', Ul. Zakharova 19, Minsk, Belarus. TEL 33-20-01. Ed. A.A. Shabalin. index. circ. 18,500.

079.77 BW ISSN 0017-1948
GOLOS RADZIMY. (Text in Byelorussian) 1955. w. (Thur.) $60. Pr. F. Skaryna, 44, 22060 Minsk, Belarus. TEL 0172-330315. Ed. Vaslav G. Matskevich. adv. contact: Taisa Bondarenko. bk.rev.; film rev.; music rev.; play rev.; illus. cols./p.: 5; pp./issue: 16. (tabloid format) Document type: newspaper.
   Description: For Belarussians living abroad. Covers social and political processes in Belarus; cultural, historical religious events, literature etc.

077 BW
ZVYAZDA; belaruskaya gazeta. (Text in Byelorussian) 1917. 5/yr. 240 Rub.($120) (Council of Ministers of Byelarus) Zvyazda, Francisk Skorina pr. 77, 220041 Minsk, Belarus. TEL 0172-325105. FAX 0172-322203. Ed. Vladimir Narkevich. adv.; bk.rev.; film rev.; play rev.; bibl.; illus.; stat.; circ. 81,098 (controlled). (back issues avail.) Document type: newspaper.
   Formerly: Zvezda.
   Description: Covers economy, culture, social services and welfare.

GENERAL INTEREST PERIODICALS — Belgium

053.932 079.493 BE
BELANG VAN LIMBURG. (Text in Dutch) 1879. d. (Mon.-Sat.). 6545 BEF($760); newsstand price: 26 BEF. Concentra Uitgeversmaatschappij, Herckenrodesingel 10, 3500 Hasselt, Belgium. TEL 32-11-878111. FAX 32-11-878204. Eds. Mark Platel, Richard Swartenbroekx. adv. contact: Erna Viaene. bk.rev.; film rev.; play rev.; tele.rev.; illus. Wire service(s): AP. circ. 109,290 (paid). cols./p.: 8; pp./issue: 32. (broadsheet format) Document type: newspaper.

053.932 BE ISSN 0005-8386
HET BESTE UIT READER'S DIGEST (BELGIAN - FLEMISH EDITION). (Text in Dutch) 1968. m. 117 BEF. N.V. Reader's Digest S.A., 29 Quai du Hainaut, 1080 Brussels, Belgium. Ed. Joe H. Beauduin. adv.; bk.rev.; illus. circ. 80,416.

053.932 BE
DE BOND; weekblad voor het gezin. (Text in Dutch) 1921. w. (Fri.). 800 BEF. (Bond van Grote en Jonge Gezinnen) Publicarto N.V., Langestraat 170, B-1150 Brussels 15, Belgium. TEL 32-2-7790000. FAX 31-2-7791616. adv.; bk.rev. circ. 337,085. (tabloid format) Document type: newspaper.
   Description: Covers topics relating to families with children, including housing, education, travel, and food.

053.931 BE
BRUGSCH HANDELSBLAD. (Text in Dutch) 1906. w. 2000 Fr. NV Drukkerij Herreboudt, Eekhoutstraat 4, 8000 Brugge, Belgium. TEL 050-330-661. circ. 40,000. (back issues avail.)

949.3 BE ISSN 0007-4047
THE BULLETIN; THE NEWSWEEKLY OF THE CAPITAL OF EUROPE. (Supplements avail.) 1962. w. 3500 BEF($104) (includes Supplements). Ackroyd Publications, 329 Av. Moliere, B-1060 Brussels, Belgium. TEL 32-2-3439909. Ed. Monique Ackroyd. adv.; bk.rev.; abstr.; bibl.; illus.; circ. 16,000 (controlled).
   Description: General information about Belgium.

CAHIERS WALLONS. see LITERARY AND POLITICAL REVIEWS

940 BE
CONFLUENT; revue du Centre de la Wallonie. (Text in French) 1971. 10/yr. 750 Fr. Editions du Confluent (Edico), 35 rue Mazy, B-5100 Namur, Belgium. TEL 081-302835. FAX 081-302835. Ed. Pierre Dulieu. adv.; bk.rev.; play rev.; illus.; tr.lit. circ. 4,000.

079.493 BE ISSN 0770-9021
COURRIER DE GAND. (Text in French) 1975. w. 3300 BEF. Editions E R E L B.V.B.A., 16 St. Sebastiaanstraat, B-8400 Oostende, Belgium. TEL 32-59-701308. FAX 32-59-803451. Ed. Monique Lanoye. adv.; bk.rev. circ. 28,000. Document type: newspaper.
   Description: Covers local news of the area surrounding Ghent.

079.493 BE
COURRIER DU LITTORAL ET DE BRUGES. (Text in French) 1944. w. 3300 BEF. Editions E R E L B.V.B.A., 16 St. Sebastiaanstraat, B-8400 Oostende, Belgium. TEL 32-59-701308. FAX 32-59-803451. Ed. Monique Lanoye. adv.; bk.rev. circ. 12,200. Document type: newspaper.
   Formerly: Courrier du Littoral (ISSN 0011-054X); (until 1947): Courrier du Littoral la Flandre (ISSN 0770-9129)
   Description: Local news of the Belgian coastal area and the city of Bruges.

GENERAL INTEREST PERIODICALS — BELIZE

054.1 BE
LA DERNIERE HEURE. 1906. d. 4950 Fr. Editions de la Derniere Heure, 127 Blvd. Jacqumain, B-1000 Brussels, Belgium. TEL 211-27-11. Ed. Patrice le Modey. circ. 95,000.

054.1 BE
L'EVENEMENT. Variant title: Magazine de l'Evenement. 1910. m. 980 BEF. Groupe R. Dupuis, Rue de Stalle 70-82, B-1180 Brussels, Belgium. TEL 32-2-332-04-05. FAX 32-2-332-05-98. TELEX 64-168 DUPUIS B. Ed. Violaine Muuls. adv.; bk.rev.; illus.; circ. 30,000 (controlled).

054.1 BE ISSN 0777-7302
L'INSTANT. (Text in French) 1990. w. 4400 BEF. Newsco S.A., Rue de Joncker 46, 1060 Brussels, Belgium. TEL 32-2-537-08-00. FAX 32-2-534-02-38. adv.; B&W page 70000 BEF, color page 105000 BEF; trim 203 x 265. circ. 26,369.

330 320 BE ISSN 0025-9934
MERCURE; hebdomadaire financier, economique et politique. 1944. w. 205 bd. Charles Michiels, 1160 Brussels, Belgium. bk.rev.; pat.; stat.; tr.lit. circ. 8,000.

050 BE
NEWCOMER; an introduction to life in Belgium. s-a. Ackroyd Publications, 329 Av. Moliere, B-1060 Brussels, Belgium. TEL 32-2-3439909. Ed. Vicky Whenham. circ. 25,000.
   Description: Introduction to life in Belgium. Service information.

053.931 BE ISSN 0030-2651
ONS ERFDEEL; algemeen Nederlands tweemaandelijks kultureel tijdschrift. 1957. 5/yr. 2000 BEF (effective 1994). Stichting Ons Erfdeel v.z.w., Murissonstraat 260, B-8931 Rekkem, Belgium. TEL 32-56-411201. FAX 32-56-414707. Ed. Jozef Deleu. adv.; bk.rev.; film rev.; music rev.; play rev.; bibl.; charts; illus. circ. 10,000. **Indexed:** Bibl.Ling.; E.I., M.L.A. —SWETS.

054.1 BE
PANORAMA - DE POST. (Text in Dutch) 1957. w. 2860 BEF. Tijdschriften Uitgevers Maatschappij N.V.I.U.M., Jan Blockxstraat 7, 2018 Antwerp, Belgium. TEL 32-3-247-45-11. (U.S. address: Interactive Market Systems, 55 Fifth Ave., New York, NY 10003) Ed. L. Moolenaar. adv. contact: Patrick de Borchgrave. illus. circ. 73,070.
   Former titles: Panorama; T V Panorama (ISSN 0034-3285); Panorama - Ons Land.

054.1 BE
POURQUOI PAS?; le grand hebdomadaire Belge d'information. (Text in French) 1910. w. 1976 BEF. Roularta Media Group, 33 Place Jamblline de Meux, 1040 Brussels, Belgium. Ed. Jacques Schepmans. adv. circ. 80,000.

053.932 BE ISSN 0037-1408
SELECTION DU READER'S DIGEST (BELGIAN - FRENCH EDITION). (Text in French) 1947. m. 117 BEF. N.V. Reader's Digest S.A., 29 Quai du Hainaut, 1080 Brussels, Belgium. Ed. Joe H. Beauduin. adv.; bk.rev.; illus. circ. 88,768.

SEPTENTRION; revue de culture neerlandaise. see GENERAL INTEREST PERIODICALS — Netherlands

050 BE
LE SOIR ILLUSTRE. (Text in French) w. Rossel, Reg. Publishing, Rue Royale 112, B-1000 Brussels, Belgium. TEL 32-2-2255555. FAX 32-2-2255911. Ed. Steve Polus; Pub. Robert Hurbain. circ. 101,067. **Document type:** consumer publication.

079.493 054.1 BE
VERS L'AVENIR. Arlon regional edition: Avenir du Luzembourg. Charleroi regional edition: Rappel. Tournai regional edition: Courrier de l'Escaut. (Text in French) 1918. d. (Mon.-Sat.). 6000 BEF; newsstand price: 25 BEF. S.A. Vers L'Avenir, Bd E. Merlot, 12, 5000 Namur, Belgium. TEL 32-81-248811. FAX 32-81-226024. Ed. Yvon Lambert; Pub. Jacques de Thysebaert. adv.; bk.rev.; film rev.; music rev.; play rev.; tele.rev.; illus. Wire service(s): RN. circ. 119,423 (paid). cols./p.: 7; pp./issue: 26. (broadsheet format; also avail. in microfilm) **Document type:** newspaper.

054.1 BE
LE VIF - L'EXPRESS. 1983. w. 3990 Fr. Le Vif S.A., Place du Jamblienne de Meuse, 33, B-1040 Brussels, Belgium. TEL 02-736-7900. FAX 02-734-3040. circ. 125,000.
   Formerly: Vif.

079.493 053.932 BE
HET VOLK. (Published in 16 regional editions: Gent; Gent - Rand; Meetjesland - Leie - Gent; Vlaamse Ardennen; Dender; Waas; Roeselare - Tielt; Kortrijk - Waregem; Westhoek; Brugge - Oostkust; Kempen; Brabant; Oostende - Westkust; Antwerpen - Mechelen; Limburg; De Nieuwe Gids) (Text in Dutch) 1891. d. (Mon.-Sat.). 6545 BEF; newsstand price: 26 BEF. Het Volk N.V., Forelstraat 22, 9000 Gent, Belgium. TEL 32-9-2656111. FAX 32-9-2252071. Ed. Johan Velge; Pub. Jaki Louage. adv. contact: Monique Moonen. bk.rev.; film rev.; music rev.; play rev.; tele.rev.; illus.; circ. 130,000 (paid). cols./p.: 5; pp./issue: 40. (also avail. in microfilm; back issues avail.) **Document type:** newspaper.

050 BE
WHAT'S ON. w. Ackroyd Publications, 329 Av. Moliere, B-1060 Brussels, Belgium. TEL 32-2-3439909. **Document type:** consumer publication.
   Description: Guide to entertainment providing a listing of all cultural events and television programming in Brussels and the provinces.

GENERAL INTEREST PERIODICALS — Belize

079.728 BH
PEOPLE'S PULSE. 1988. w. $40 (typically set in Jan.). (United Democratic Party) People's Pulse Ltd., 7 Tanoomah St., Box 1104, Belize City, Belize. TEL 501-2-77035. FAX 501-2-76012. Ed. Richard Stuart. adv.; bk.rev. circ. 5,000. **Document type:** newspaper.
   Description: Carries national, regional and international news.

GENERAL INTEREST PERIODICALS — Benin

079.6683 DM
GAZETTE DU GOLFE. 1987. fortn. Carre 961 J Etoile Rouge, B.P. 03-1624, Cotonou, Benin. TEL 31-35-58. FAX 30-01-99. TELEX 5053. Ed. Ismael Y. Soumanou. circ. 33,000. **Document type:** newspaper.

GENERAL INTEREST PERIODICALS — Bermuda

051 BM ISSN 0005-9382
THE BERMUDIAN. 1930. m. $30 (foreign $36). Bermudian Publishing Company Limited, P.O. Box HM 283, Hamilton HM AX, Bermuda. TEL 809-295-0695. FAX 809-292-6727. Ed. Kevin Stevenson. adv.; bk.rev.; illus. circ. 7,500. (also avail. in microfilm from KTO)
   Description: Dedicated to recording social events, news and sports.

GENERAL INTEREST PERIODICALS — Bhutan

079.5498 059.9541 BT
KUENSEL (DZONGKHA EDITION). (Text in Dzongkha) 1986. w. Ministry of Communications, Department of Information, P.O. Box 204, Thimphu, Bhutan. TEL 22134. TELEX 890212. Ed. Goembo Dorji. circ. 1,441. **Document type:** newspaper.

079.5498 052 BT
KUENSEL (ENGLISH EDITION); Bhutan's national newspaper. 1986. w. rs.400 in India, Bangladesh, Nepal; Asia & Australia $60; Europe $70; U.S. & Canada $80 (effective 1994). (Ministry of Communications, Department of Information) Sangay Agency, P.O. Box 285, Thimphu, Bhutan. TEL 22134. TELEX 890212. Ed. Kinley Dorji. adv. contact: Pratap Rai. circ. 6,023. **Document type:** newspaper.

079.5498 BT
KUENSEL (NEPALI EDITION). (Text in Nepali) 1986. w. Ministry of Communications, Department of Information, P.O. Box 204, Thimphu, Bhutan. TEL 22134. TELEX 890212. Ed. R.N. Mishra. circ. 253. **Document type:** newspaper.

GENERAL INTEREST PERIODICALS — Bolivia

056.1 BO
AQUI; semanario del pueblo. 1979. w. Bol.$300($150) Asociacion Aqui - Avance, Casilla 10937, La Paz, Bolivia. TEL 34-35-24. FAX 35-24-55. Ed. Remberto Cardenas M. adv.; bk.rev.; circ. 5,000 (controlled). (tabloid format; back issues avail.)

053.1 GW ISSN 0945-201X
BOLIVIA SAGO INFORMATIONSBLATT; Analysen - Berichte. 1978. bi-m. DM.18. Sago Informationszentrum Bolivien e.V., Kottbusser Damm 101, 10967 Berlin, Germany. bk.rev.; illus. circ. 500. **Document type:** newsletter.

056.1 BO
VISION BOLIVIANA. bi-m. Bol.$7 per no. Calle Loavza 420, Casilla 2870, La Paz, Bolivia. adv.; bk.rev.; film rev.; illus.

GENERAL INTEREST PERIODICALS — Botswana

079.6883 BS
BOTSWANA DAILY NEWS/TSA DIKANG GOMPIENO. Variant title: Daily News (Botswana). (Text in English and Setswana) 1965. d. free (foreign P.6). Department of Information and Broadcasting, Private Bag 0060, Gaborone, Botswana. TEL 352541. FAX 352541. TELEX 2409 BD. Ed. Itumeleng Sabone. adv.; circ. 45,000 (paid). (tabloid format) **Document type:** newspaper, government publication.
   Former titles (until 1978): Dikang tsa Gompieno tsa Botswana; (until 1969): Bechuanaland Daily News; Bechuanaland News Flashes.
   Description: Covers national and international events, emphasizing parliamentary proceedings and other national political activities.

079.6883 BS
BOTSWANA GAZETTE. (Text in English) 1985. w. P.30 (southern Africa $46; rest of Africa $56; elsewhere $72). News Company Botswana Pty. Ltd., Box 1605, Gaborone, Botswana. TEL 3128333. FAX 312774. TELEX 2631 BD. Ed. Alfred P. Mulenga. adv.; circ. 14,000 (paid). (tabloid format) **Document type:** newspaper.
   Description: Fosters debate on national political and economic issues.

079.6883 BS
BOTSWANA GUARDIAN. (Text in English) 1982. w. P.200. Pula Printing & Publishing, P.O. Box 1641, Gaborone, Botswana. TEL 3252077. FAX 374381. Ed. Joel O.B. Sebonego; Pub. William Jones. adv.; circ. 17,500 (paid). (tabloid format) **Document type:** newspaper.
   Description: Covers news and events in Gaborone and Francistown.

052 BS ISSN 0301-9020
DT790
BOTSWANA HANDBOOK. (Text in English) 1974. quinquennial. P.1 per no. Department of Information and Broadcasting, Private Bag 0060, Gaborone, Botswana. TEL 352541. TELEX 2409 BD. Ed. Itumeleng Sabone. circ. 30,000. **Indexed:** Ind.S.A.Per. **Document type:** government publication.
   Description: Traces the country's development activities by all government ministries and departments, and parastatal organizations, functions, achievements, and the role of the private sector in the economy.

052 BS
BOTSWANA IN PICTURES. 1986. irreg. P.1 per no. Information and Broadcasting, Private Bag 0060, Gaborone, Botswana. Ed. Itumeleng Sabone. circ. 16,000. **Document type:** government publication, consumer publication.
   Description: Pictorial magazine designed to show and publicize the country and its people, culture, and economic activities.

052 BS
FACTS ON BOTSWANA. 1990. irreg. free. Department of Information and Broadcasting, Private Bag 0060, Gaborone, Botswana. Ed. Itumeleng Sabone. circ. 20,000. **Document type:** government publication.
   Description: Includes information on various topics concerning Botswana: social, political, historical, economic, educational, cultural, and geographical.

052 BS
THE GAZETTE. w. POB 1605, Gaborone, Botswana. TEL 312822. TELEX 2631. circ. 16,000.

079.6883
MIDWEEK SUN. 1989. w. P.33.20 (foreign P.200.25). Sun Publishing, Bag 00153, Gaborone, Botswana. TEL 314937. FAX 374381. Ed. Joel O.B. Sebonego; Pub. William Jones. adv.; circ. 15,000 (paid). (tabloid format) **Document type:** newspaper.
  Description: Provides news analysis and investigative reports of national events.

079.6883 BS
MMEGI. (Text in English, Setswana) 1984. w. P.98 to individuals (southern Africa P.110; elsewhere $130); institutions P.110 ($150) (effective 1994). Mmegi Publishing Trust, Private Bag BR50, Gaborone, Botswana. TEL 374784. FAX 305508. Ed. Titus Mbuya. adv.; bk.rev. circ. 20,000. (tabloid format) **Document type:** newspaper.

052 BS
NEWS LINK. w. Private Bag 40063, Gaborone, Botswana. TEL 372852. FAX 374558.

052 BS
NORTHERN ADVERTISER/MOANAMESI WA BOKONE. 1985. w. free. Premier Investments (Pty) Ltd., P.O. Box 402, Francistown, Botswana. TEL 212365. FAX 212265. Ed. M.G. Fish. adv.; film rev.; play rev. circ. 6,000. (looseleaf format; back issues avail.) **Document type:** consumer publication.
  Description: Contains information about news and local sports.

052
SCOPE MAGAZINE. 1983. s-a. P.50. University of Botswana, Private Bag 0022, Gaborone, Botswana. TEL 351151 ext. 2050. FAX 356591. TELEX 2429 BD. Ed. Tekane Tekane. adv.: B&W page P.200. illus. circ. 1,500. **Document type:** consumer publication, academic/scholarly publication.
  Description: Covers socioeconomic and political affairs at the local, national, regional, and international levels.

GENERAL INTEREST PERIODICALS — Brazil

056.9 BL
ATLANTE. (Text in English, Portuguese) 1990. q.? Cz.$40 per no. Pointer Editores Associados Ltda., Av. Sabia 641, 04515 Sao Paulo, Brazil. TEL 11-542-2499. FAX 11-542-2614. Ed. Casimiro Xavier de Mendonca.

056.9 BL
BRASIL AGORA. 1991. s-m. Cr.$600 per no. Alameda Glete 1049, 01215 Sao Paulo, Brazil. TEL 220-7198. Dir. Joao Periera. circ. 50,000.

056.9 GW ISSN 0173-6582
BRASILIEN NACHRICHTEN. 1976. q. DM.28. An der Illoshoehe 30, 49078 Osnabrueck, Germany. Ed.Bd. adv.; bk.rev. circ. 1,000. **Indexed:** HR Rep.

056.7 BL ISSN 0104-396X
▼**CARAS.** 1993. w. Editora Caras Ltda., Av. Eng. Luis Carlos Berrini 1253, 12o andar, 04571-010 Sao Paulo SP, Brazil. TEL 011-531-2177. FAX 011-531-2895. Ed. Edgardo Martolio. adv.; bk.rev.; film rev.; play rev.; rec.rev.; illus. circ. 148,000. **Document type:** consumer publication.
  Description: Articles, interviews and photographs of celebrities, news makers and ordinary people doing extraordinary things.

056.9 BL ISSN 0010-2105
COMARCA DE SUZANO.* 1961. w. Cr.$10($10) Empresa Jornalistica a Comarca de Suzano, Travessa Mirambawa 408, Suzano, Sao Paulo, Brazil. Ed. Thadeu Jose De Moraes. circ. 5,000. (looseleaf format)

079.81 BL
COMERCIO DA FRANCA. (Supplement included w.: Domingo, Carro) 1915. d. (except Mon.). Cr.$50000($200); newsstand price: Cr.200. Ouvidor Freire, 1986, 14400-630 Franca, SP, Brazil. TEL 016-721-3731. FAX 016-722-8916. Ed. Sonia Machiavelli. adv. contact: Sulce Xavier. bk.rev.; film rev.; music rev.; illus.; circ. 18,000 (morn. ed.); 24,000 (Sun. ed.) (paid). cols./p.: 6; pp./issue: 28. (standard format; also avail. in microfilm; back issues avail.) **Document type:** newspaper.

056.9 BL ISSN 0011-2216
CRUZEIRO. 1908? w. Cr.$34000. Rua do Livramento 179-203, Rio de Janeiro, Brazil. Ed. Accioly Netto.

056.9 BL
EXAME VIP. (Supplement to: Exame) 1981-1983; resumed. bi-w. Editora Abril, S.A., Rua Geraldo Flausino Gomes 61, 04573-900 Sao Paulo, SP, Brazil. TEL 011-877-1322. Ed. Victor Civita. adv.; bk.rev.; charts; illus.; stat. circ. 76,000.

056.9 BL
GEOGRAFICA UNIVERSAL. 1974. m. $59. Bloch Editores S.A., Rua do Russel 766-804, 22210-000 Rio de Janeiro, RJ, Brazil. TEL 021-5554000. FAX 021-2059998. TELEX 2121525 BLOC. Ed. Lincoln Martins. circ. 100,000. **Document type:** consumer publication.
  Description: Covers adventure, science, technology, tourism, art, history and geography.

056.9 BL
LAVRA: IDEIAS E LETRAS. 1990. 3/yr. Lavralibro - Processamento Editorial Ltda., SHIS QI 23, Conj. 8, Casa 11, 71600 Brasilia DF, Brazil. TEL 061-366-1002. Eds. Murilo Moreira Veras, Maria Vilma Muniz. **Document type:** consumer publication.

056.9 BL
LEGENDA. vol.11, 1989. q. Cz.$15 per no. Editora Legenda Ltda., Rua Guarara 174, Casa 3, Jardim Paulista, 01425 Sao Paulo SP, Brazil. TEL 885-0620. **Document type:** consumer publication.

056.9 BL
MANCHETE. 1952. w. $225. Bloch Editores S.A., Rua do Russel 766-804, 22210-000 Rio de Janeiro, RJ, Brazil. TEL 021-5554000. FAX 021-2059998. TELEX 2121525 BLOC. Ed. R. Muggiatti. circ. 150,000. **Document type:** consumer publication.
  Description: Covers current events, people and leisure.

056.9 BL
REVISTA DO PENSAMENTO BRASILEIRO. 1989. q.? 652184 BTN. Centro de Documentacion do Pensamento Brasileiro, Rua Alfredo Brito 39, Pelourinho, 40025 Salvador, Bahia, Brazil.

▼**REVISTA DO RIO DE JANEIRO - U E R J.** 1993. s-a. Universidade do Estado do Rio de Janeiro, Rua Sao Francisco Xavier 524, Maracana, 20550 Rio de Janeiro RJ, Brazil. (Co-publisher: Ayuri Editorial Ltda.) Ed. Luiz Eduardo Rezende.

056.1 BL ISSN 0036-4657
SAO PAULO. 1956. w. Cr.$200. Arquidiocese de Sao Paulo, Av. Higienopolis, 890, CEP 01238 Sao Paulo, Brazil. TEL 66-9660. TELEX 23151 MFNA BR. Ed. Antonio Aparecido Pereira. adv.; bk.rev.; film rev.; bibl.; illus. circ. 10,000. (back issues avail.)

056.9 PO
SELECOES DO READERS DIGEST (BRAZIL EDITION). 1942. m. $23.40. Selecoes do Readers Digest S.A.R.L., Rua Joaquim Antonio de Aguiar no.43 r-c, Lisbon, Portugal. FAX 3511-659203. TELEX 12410 DIGEST P. Ed. Margarida Sarda. adv. circ. 100,000.

056.9 BL ISSN 0104-1789
SUPERINTERESSANTE. 1987. m. $70. Editora Abril, S.A., R. Geraldo Flausino Gomez, 61, 04573-900 Sao Paulo SP, Brazil. TEL 011-534-5344. FAX 011-534-5638. (Subscr. to: Rua do Curtume, 769, 05065-900 Sao Paulo SP, Brazil. TEL 011-823-9100) Ed. Almir Gajardoni. adv.; bk.rev.; charts; illus. circ. 310,000. **Document type:** consumer publication.
  Description: Covers scientific subjects, putting all the latest discoveries and new technologies within the reader's reach.

056.9 BL
TEMA; revista das faculdades de Teresa Martin. 1987? 3/yr. Centro de Estudos e Pesquisas de Artes e Letras Teresa Martin, Rua Antonieta Leitao 129, 02925 Sao Paulo SP, Brazil. TEL 011-876-2755. Ed. Zenaide Bassi Ribeiro Soares. **Document type:** academic/scholarly publication.

079.81 BL
TRIBUNA DE PETROPOLIS. 1902. d. $8.54 per mo. R. Alencar Lima 26, Petropolis, RJ, Brazil. TEL 55242425122. Ed. Luis Bogo; Pub. Mariano D'Almeida. adv. contact: Wilson Nogueira. film rev.; music rev.; illus. cols./p.: 10; pp./issue: 30. (standard format) **Document type:** newspaper.

056.9 BL ISSN 0100-7122
AP66
VEJA. (Regional supplements for Sao Paulo and Rio de Janeiro avail.) 1968. w. $280. Editora Abril, S.A., R. Otaviano Alves de Lima 4400, 02909-900 Sao Paulo SP, Brazil. TEL 011-877-1322. FAX 011-877-1640. (Subscr. to: Rua do Curtume, 769, CEP 05065-900 Sao Paulo SP, Brazil. TEL 011-823-9100) Ed. Mario Sergio Conti. adv.; bk.rev.; dance rev.; film rev.; music rev.; play rev.; rec.rev.; video rev.; charts; illus.; stat. circ. 850,000. (also avail. in microfilm from UMI) **Indexed:** World Agri.Econ.& Rural Sociol.Abstr. **Document type:** consumer publication.
  —UMI.
  Formerly: Veja e Leia (ISSN 0042-3165)
  Description: Covers Brazilian and world politics, economics, science and technology, education, arts, sports, medicine and religion.

056.9 BL ISSN 0042-3955
AS80 CODEN: VERIEY
VERITAS. 1955. 4/yr. Cz.$15($16) (Pontificia Universidade Catolica do Rio Grande do Sul) Editora da P U C R S, c/o Antoninho M. Naime, Caixa Postal 12001, 90620 Porto Alegre RS, Brazil. bk.rev.; charts; index. circ. 1,000.
  —BLDSC (9170.120000).
  Supersedes: Pontificia Universidade Catolica do Rio Grande do Sul. Anais.

056.9 BL ISSN 0042-6873
AP66
VISAO. 1952. w. $325. Editora Visao Ltda., Alvaro de Carvalho, 350, 2o andar, C.P. 3082 Paulo, 01050 Sao Paulo, Brazil. TEL 256-5011. FAX 258-1919. TELEX 11-21-436. Ed. Hamilton Lucas de Oliveira. adv.; bk.rev.; film rev.; play rev.; charts; stat. circ. 149,000. (also avail. in microfilm)

GENERAL INTEREST PERIODICALS — Bulgaria

057.8 YU ISSN 0006-9272
BRATSTVO; vestnik na bulgarskata narodnost v SFR Jugoslavija. (Text in Bulgarian) 1960. w. 60 din.($7.58) Kej 29 Dekemvri 8, Nis, Serbia, Yugoslavia. Ed. Stojan Stankov.

949.77 BU ISSN 0007-3903
BULGARIA TODAY; social politics. (Editions in Arabic, English, French, German, Italian, Portuguese, Russian, Spanish) 1952. m. 12 lv.($8) Sofia Press Agency, 29 Slavyanska Str., 1040 Sofia, Bulgaria. TEL 88-5831. TELEX 22622. (Dist. by: Hemus, 6, Rouski Blvd., 1000 Sofia, Bulgaria) Ed. Boznko Bogdanov. adv.; bk.rev.; illus. circ. 6,190 (English ed.).

059.918 BU ISSN 0204-4218
CODEN: GVPSD7
SHUMEN. PEDAGOGICHESKI INSTITUT. GODISHNIK.. (Text in Bulgarian) irreg., vol.12, 1988. 1.20 lv. (Pedagogicheski Institut, Prirodomatematicheski Fakultet) Izdatelstvo Pedagogicheski Institut "Konstantin Preslavski", 9700 Shumen, Bulgaria. TEL 63151. FAX 63171. Ed.Bd. **Document type:** academic/scholarly publication.
  —CASDDS.

079.77 BU ISSN 0861-797X
STANDART; Bulgarian national daily. (Supplements avail.) (Text in Bulgarian; summaries in English) 1992. d. 1200 lv.($540); newsstand price: 5 lv. Standart Daily, 53 Atnim I Str., 1303 Sofia, Bulgaria. TEL 359-2-325-000.
FAX 359-2-465-009. Owner(s): New Holding, 53 Atnim I Str., 1303 Sofia, Bulgaria. Ed. Valeri Zapryanov; Pub. Krassimir Stojcheff. adv.: B&W page $2808; adv. contact: Maxim Behar. film rev.; music rev.; play rev.; tele.rev.; illus. Wire service(s): AP, AFP, RN. circ. 120. cols./p.: 6; pp./issue: 36. (tabloid format; also avail. in microform) **Document type:** newspaper.
  Description: Provides comprehensive information about domestic and international events. Includes sports and cultural news, entertainment guide.

GENERAL INTEREST PERIODICALS — Burundi

054.1 BD
BURUNDI MAGAZINE. (Text in French) no.120, 1990. m. B.P. 2573, Bujumbura, Burundi. **Indexed:** P.L.E.S.A. (1990-).

GENERAL INTEREST PERIODICALS — Cameroon

079.6711 052 CM
CAMEROON TRIBUNE. (Text in English) 1974. w. B.P. 1218, Yaounde, Cameroon. TEL 22-27-00. TELEX 8311. Ed. Abui Mama Eloundou. adv.; bk.rev. circ. 25,000. **Document type:** newspaper.

GENERAL INTEREST PERIODICALS — Canada

051 CN ISSN 0840-657X
ACTIF; l'encyclopedie juridique des biens personnels. 1988. 11/yr. Can.$39.50 (foreign Can.$68.50). Editions Edibec, Inc., 4316 Boul. St. Laurent, Ste. 301, Montreal, Que. H2W 1Z3, Canada. TEL 514-843-9191. FAX 514-842-2422. Ed. Carolle Piche-Burton. adv. circ. 15,000. **Indexed:** Pt.de Rep. (1990-).

054.1 CN ISSN 0383-8714
AP21
L'ACTUALITE. English edition: Maclean's (ISSN 0024-9815) (Text in French) 1961. bi-m. Can.$25. Magazines Maclean Hunter Quebec Ltee., 1001 Boul. de Maisonneuve Ouest, 11th fl., Montreal, Que. H3A 3E1, Canada. TEL 514-845-2543.
FAX 514-845-4393. (Subscr. to: Maclean Hunter Ltd., Magazine Division, Maclean Hunter Bldg., 777 Bay St., Toronto, Ont. M5W 1A7, Canada) Ed. Jean Pare. adv.: B&W page Can.$8950, color page Can.$11475. bk.rev.; film rev.; play rev.; illus. circ. 240,000. **Indexed:** Acad.Ind., Can.Per.Ind., Can.Wom.Per.Ind., Pt.de Rep. (1979-).
  Description: Current affairs magazine covering issues and trends in Canada and around the world.

071 CN
ADVERTISER POST. 1932. w. $104. W.R. Warwick - Turner Publications, Inc., P.O. Box 1029, N. Battleford, SK S9A 3E6, Canada.
TEL 306-445-7231. FAX 306-445-3223. Ed. Lois A. Walsh. adv.; bk.rev. circ. 19,444. **Document type:** newspaper.

051 CN
THE AFFILIATE (ONTARIO). 1987. m. $50. Reveal, 777 Barb Rd., RR 1, Vankleek Hill, ON K0B 1R0, Canada. TEL 613-678-3453. Ed. Peter Riden. adv.: B&W page $150. (back issues avail.)
  Description: Carries poetry, articles, art, photos, cartoons, interviews, reviews, music and news items.

071.1 CN
AGINCOURT NEWS. 1950. w. Can.$15; newsstand price: Can.$.40. Watson Publishing Company Limited, 150 Milner Ave., Unit 35, Scarborough, ON M1S 3R3, Canada. TEL 416-291-2583. Ed. Robert M. Watson; Pub. Robert M. Watson. adv.; illus. cols./p.: 6; pp./issue: 12. (tabloid format; back issues avail.) **Document type:** newspaper.

051 CN ISSN 0002-4775
LAW
ALBERTA GAZETTE. 1905. s-m. Can.$50. Publication Services Alberta, 11510 Kingsway Ave., Edmonton, Alta. T5G 2Y5, Canada. TEL 403-427-4952.
FAX 403-452-0668. Ed. Jane Grimstead. charts; illus. circ. 1,400. (also avail. in microform from KTO,MML)

051 US ISSN 0225-0519
CODEN: ALRPE9
ALBERTA REPORT. w. Can.$79. United Western Communications, 17327-106A Ave., Edmonton, Alta. T5S 1M7, Canada. TEL 403-484-8884.
FAX 403-486-1690. Ed. Stephen Hopkins. adv. contact: Lisa Murphy. bk.rev.; film rev.

051 CN
ALBERTA REPORT - WESTERN REPORT. 1979. w. Can.$59. Interwest Publications, 17327 - 106 A Ave., Edmonton, Alta. T5S 1M7, Canada.
TEL 403-489-8884. FAX 403-489-3280. circ. 52,000. (also avail. in microform from MML) **Indexed:** Can.Per.Ind.
  Formerly: Western Report.

071.1 CN
AMHERST DAILY NEWS; Cumberland county's daily newspaper. 1893. d. (Mon.-Fri.). Cumberland Publishing Ltd., P.O. Box 280, Amherst, NS B4H 3Z2, Canada. TEL 902-667-5102.
FAX 902-667-0419. Ed. John B. Conrad; Pub. Earl J. Gouchie. adv. contact: Richard Spicer. Wire service(s): AP, CanP. (broadsheet format) **Document type:** newspaper.

071.1 CN
ANCASTER NEWS. 1967. w. Can.$52 (in US Can.$104); newsstand price: Can.$.50. 4 Cameron Dr., Ancaster, ON L9G 2L3, Canada.
TEL 905-648-4464. FAX 905-648-7458. Ed. Debra Downey; Pub. John Young. adv. contact: Linda Wilkinson. illus.; circ. 8,257 (controlled). cols./p.: 5; pp./issue: 24. (tabloid format; also avail. in microfiche; reprint service avail.) **Document type:** newspaper.
  Formerly: Ancaster News Journal.

054.1 CN ISSN 0834-1443
L'AQUILON. 1985. w. Can.$20 to individuals; institution Can.$35. P.O. Box 1325, Yellowknife, NT X1A 2N9, Canada. TEL 403-873-6603. FAX 403-873-2158. circ. 1,000 (controlled).

071.1 CN
ARGENTEUIL. 1952. w. newsstand price: Can.$.80. Cie. d'Edition Andre Paquette, 52 Principale, Lachute, PQ J8H 3A8, Canada. TEL 514-562-6875.
FAX 514-562-2494. Ed. Ann St-Jacques. adv. contact: Pierre Desrosiers. bk.rev.; circ. controlled. cols./p.: 7; pp./issue: 28. (tabloid format; back issues avail.) **Document type:** newspaper.

054.1 CN ISSN 0383-2554
AUJOURD'HUI CREDO. 1953. 10/yr. Can.$14 (in U.S. Can.$18)(effective Sep. 1990). Eglise du Canada, 132, Victoria, Greenfield Park, PQ J4V 1L8, Canada. TEL 514-466-7733. Ed. Gerard Gautier. circ. 1,000. (back issues avail.)
  Description: Provides a French Protestant perspective on the religious life in Canada and throughout the world as well as cultural, social, economic and political and ecumenical issues.

071.1 CN
AYR NEWS. 1854. w. Can.$15($40); newsstand price: Can.$.40. Ayr News Ltd., 40 Piper St., Ayr, ON N0B 1E0, Canada. TEL 519-632-7432.
FAX 519-632-7743. Ed. John P. Schmidt; Pub. James W. Schmidt. adv. contact: John P. Schmidt. illus.; circ. 4,350 (paid). cols./p.: 6; pp./issue: 16. (broadsheet format; also avail. in microfilm from GCS) **Document type:** newspaper.

071.1 CN
BEACON HERALD. (Supplements avail.) 1854. d. (Mon.-Sat.). Can.$243.96 (in US Can.$435); newsstand price: Can.$.50. Beacon Herald of Stratford Limited, 108 Ontario St., Stratford, ON N5A 6T6, Canada. TEL 519-271-2220.
FAX 519-271-1026. Ed. Ron Carson; Pubs. Charles W. Dingman, Stanford H. Dingman. adv. contact: David B. Nickel. illus. Wire service(s): CanP. circ. 13,500. cols./p.: 6; pp./issue: 24. (broadsheet format; also avail. in microfilm from GCS) **Document type:** newspaper.

051 CN ISSN 0005-7517
F1060.1
THE BEAVER; exploring Canada's history. 1920. bi-m. Can.$22.50($22.50) (effective 1994). Hudson's Bay Co., 450 Portage Ave., Winnipeg, MB R3C 0E7, Canada. TEL 204-786-7048. FAX 204-774-8624. Ed. Christopher Dafoe. adv.; bk.rev.; charts; illus.; index. circ. 43,000. (back issues avail.; reprint service avail. from MML) **Indexed:** Amer.Hist.& Life, Anthropol.Lit., Can.Per.Ind., CMI, Hist.Abstr., Ind.Child.Mag., Mag.Ind.
  —UnCover.

071.1 CN
BEETON - SCHOMBERG RECORD SENTINEL. 1978. w. Can.$28.89($87); newsstand price: Can.$.75. 34 Main St. W., Beeton, ON L0G 1A0, Canada. TEL 905-729-2287. FAX 905-729-2541. Ed. Bruce R. Haire. adv. contact: John H. Archibald. illus.; circ. 2,500 (paid). cols./p.: 5; pp./issue: 28. (tabloid format) **Document type:** newspaper.

051 CN
BLISS. m. 11207-103 Ave., Edmonton, AB T5K 2V9, Canada. TEL 403-420-0709. FAX 403-426-0632. Eds. Karen Unland, Christopher Spencer. adv.: B&W page Can.$350. circ. 10,000.

071.1 CN
BOISSEVAIN RECORDER. 1899. w. Can.$20($50) Box 220, Boissevain, MB R0K 0E0, Canada. Ed. Miles G. Phillips; Pub. Miles G. Phillips. adv.; circ. 1,800 (paid). cols./p.: 5; pp./issue: 24. **Document type:** newspaper.

051 CN ISSN 0847-2998
BRITISH COLUMBIA REPORT. 1989. w. Can.$69. British Columbia Report Magazine Ltd., 103-1161 Melville St., Vancouver, BC V6E 2X7, Canada.
TEL 604-682-8202. FAX 604-682-0963. Ed. Terry O'Neill. adv.; bk.rev. circ. 20,000.
  Supersedes in part (in Sep. 1989): Western Report.

071.1 CN
CALEDON CITIZEN. 1982. w. Can.$37.45; newsstand price: Can.$.75. 25 Queen St. N., Bolton, ON L7E 1C1, Canada. TEL 905-857-6626.
FAX 905-857-6363. Ed. Mark Pavilons; Pub. Bruce R. Haire. adv. contact: John Archibald. cols./p.: 5; pp./issue: 28. (tabloid format; back issues avail.) **Document type:** newspaper.

071.1 CN ISSN 0828-1815
CALGARY HERALD. 1883. d. 215-16 St. S.E., Calgary, AB T2P 0W8, Canada. TEL 403-235-7361.
FAX 403-235-7379. Ed. Crosbie Cotton; Pub. Kevin Peterson. adv. contact: Peter Baillie. bk.rev.; illus. (broadsheet format; also avail. in microform) **Document type:** newspaper.
  ●Also available online. Vendor(s): Southam Electronic Publishing.

071.1 CN
CAMBRIDGE TIMES. 1949. s-w. (Wed., Sat.). newsstand price: Can.$.50. 240 Holiday Inn Dr., Cambridge, ON, Canada. TEL 519-623-7793.
FAX 519-623-7337. Owner(s): Southam Newspaper Group, 1450 Don Mills Rd., Don Mills, ON M3B 2X7, Canada. TEL 416-445-6641. FAX 416-442-2261. Ed. Rick Drennan; Pub. Peter Winkler. adv. contact: Deb Gregory. illus.; circ. 30,700 (controlled). (tabloid format; back issues avail.) **Document type:** newspaper.

071.1 CN
CAMROSE BOOSTER. 1952. w. Can.$75($150); newsstand price: free. Camrose Booster Ltd., 4925 48th St., Camrose, AB T4V 1L7, Canada.
TEL 403-672-3142. FAX 403-672-2518. Ed. Berdie Fowler; Pub. Blain Fowler. adv. contact: Ron Pilger. circ. 20 (paid); 12,026 (controlled). cols./p.: 5; pp./issue: 60. **Document type:** newspaper.

051 CN
CANADA JOURNAL. q. Can.$24 (foreign Can.$45). Ruland Communications Inc., 427 Mount Pleasant Rd., Toronto, Ont. M4S 2L8, Canada.
TEL 416-485-5795. FAX 416-485-6354. Ed. Yuri Klugman. circ. 20,000.

GENERAL INTEREST PERIODICALS — CANADA 2695

051   CN   ISSN 0829-4380
CANADA REPORTS. French edition: Reportage Canada. Spanish edition: Reportaje Canada. 1945. q. free. External Affairs and International Trade Canada, Foreign Policy Communications Division, 125 Sussex Dr., Ottawa, Ont. K1A 0G2, Canada. TEL 613-992-9280. TELEX 053-3745. Ed. Mary Anne Dehler. illus. circ. 18,500. **Indexed:** Geo.Abstr. —UnCover.
  Supersedes (in 1985): Canada Weekly (ISSN 0384-2312); Which was formerly (until 1972): Canadian Weekly Bulletin.

CANADIAN ALMANAC AND DIRECTORY. see *BIBLIOGRAPHIES*

051   CN   ISSN 0706-2168
G1   CODEN: CGEJAB
CANADIAN GEOGRAPHIC. 1930. bi-m. Can.$23.95 (foreign Can.$29.95). Royal Canadian Geographical Society, 39 McArthur Ave., Vanier, ON K1L 8L7, Canada. TEL 613-745-4629. FAX 613-744-0947. Ed. Ian Darragh. adv.; bk.rev. circ. 250,000. (also avail. in microfilm; back issues avail.) **Indexed:** Amer.Hist.& Life, Bk.Rev.Ind. (1965-), Can.Per.Ind., Child.Bk.Rev.Ind. (1965-), Hist.Abstr., Mag.Ind. Document type: consumer publication.
  —BLDSC (3025.900000); Faxon; UMI. **CCC.**
  Formerly (until 1978): Canadian Geographical Journal (ISSN 0315-1824)
  Description: Aim is to advance geographical knowledge in the Canadian context by serving as a bridge between the academic-scientific community and the public. Primary subjects of interest include: people, places, resources, environment, heritage, and science.

917.1   CN   ISSN 0382-4624
CANADIAN LIVING. 1975. 13/yr. Can.$21.98. Telemedia Publishing Inc., 50 Holly St., Toronto, Ont. M4S 3B3, Canada. TEL 416-482-8600. FAX 416-482-2252. (Subscr. to: 797 Don Mills Rd., 13 Fl., Don Mills, Ont. M3C 1V2, Canada) Ed. Bonnie Cowan. adv. circ. 573,060. **Indexed:** Can.Per.Ind., CMI.

971   CN   ISSN 0008-4565
CANADIAN NEWS FACTS; the indexed digest of Canadian current events. 1967. bi-m. Can.$259. M P L Communications Inc., 700-133 Richmond St. W., Toronto, ON M5H 3M8, Canada. TEL 416-869-1177. FAX 416-869-0456. Eds. Barrie Martland, Stephen D. Pepper. stat.; index, q. cum.index. (back issues avail.)
  Description: Details the major issues in Canadian news. For researchers or institutions.

051   CN   ISSN 0045-5334
CANADIAN SCENE. 1951. fortn. Can.$45 (foreign Can.$65)(free to Canadian ethnic media). Canadian Scene Inc., 73 Simcoe St., Ste. 7, Toronto, ON M5J 1W9, Canada. TEL 416-523-0439. FAX 416-593-0448. Ed. Ben Viccari. bk.rev. circ. 500.

CANADIAN SOCIAL TRENDS. see *STATISTICS*

071   CN   ISSN 1192-8301
▼**CAPE BRETONER.** 1992. 8/yr. Can.$19.95. P.O. Box 220, Sydney, Cape Breton Island, NS B1P 6H1, Canada. TEL 902-567-6400. FAX 902-567-6200. Ed. John Hanratty; Pub. Roger LeBlanc. adv.; bk.rev.; illus.; circ. 9,500 (paid). (tabloid format) Document type: newspaper.
  Description: Offers current news and activities on the island for residents as well as those who have moved away.

071   CN
CARDSTON CHRONICLE - GLOBE. 1979. w. Can.$30. Brad Flickinger, Ed. & Pub., Bag 8, Cardston, Alta. T0K 0K0, Canada. TEL 403-653-2222. FAX 403-653-2240. adv.; bk.rev.; illus. circ. 2,250. **Indexed:** Bibl.Cart.
  Former titles: Chronicle (ISSN 0227-1192); Cardston Chronicle.

071.1   CN
CARILLON (STEINBACH). 1946. w. Can.$26($120); newsstand price: Can.$.70. Box 1209, Steinbach, MB R0A 2A0, Canada. TEL 204-326-3421. FAX 204-326-4860. Ed. Peter Dyck; Pub. Rick Derksen. adv.; adv. page Can.$1060; adv. contact: John Wiebe. bk.rev.; circ. 13,000 (paid). cols./p.: 6; pp./issue: 44. (broadsheet format; also avail. in microfiche; back issues avail.; reprint service avail.) Document type: newspaper.

051   CN
THE CATALYST (EDMONTON). 1974. q. Celanese Canada Inc., P.O. Box 99, Edmonton, AB T5J 2H7, Canada. TEL 403-471-3246. Ed. Bob Leman. circ. 1,200.

971   CN
CHETWYND ECHO. 1959. w. Can.$21($24) Echo Publishing, Ste. 205-4717 51 St., Pioneer Place Bldg., Box 750, Chetwynd, B.C. V0C 1J0, Canada. TEL 604-788-2246. FAX 604-788-9988. Ed. Maureen Gammon. adv.; bk.rev.; charts; illus. circ. 2,134.
  Formerly: Chetwynd Reporter (ISSN 0009-3408)

071.1   CN
CHETWYND PIONEER. 1979. w. Can.$32.10($70); newsstand price: Can.$.50. Box 600, 5021 49th Ave., Chetwynd, BC V0C 1J0, Canada. Ed. Randy Hill; Pub. Ruth Torgerson. adv. contact: Ruth Torgerson. circ. 1,262 (paid); 105 (controlled). cols./p.: 5; pp./issue: 20. Document type: newspaper.

051   CN
CITY DWELLER. bi-m. 2733 Lakeshore Blvd., W., Ste. 16, Toronto, Ont. M8V 1G9, Canada. TEL 416-255-5485. Ed. Roslyn Anna Rosen. circ. 25,000.

071.1   CN
CLEARWATER NORTH THOMPSON TIMES. (Supplement avail.) 1964. w. Can.$19 (foreign Can.$40). Robicon Publishing Inc., RR 1, Box 1102, Clearwater, BC V0E 1N0, Canada. TEL 604-674-3343. FAX 604-674-3777. Ed. Nancy Chappell; Pubs. Bruce & Nancy Chappell. adv. contact: Bruce Chappell. bk.rev.; illus.; circ. 1,615 (paid); 1,848 (controlled). cols./p.: 6; pp./issue: 20. (broadsheet format) Document type: newspaper.

051   CN   ISSN 0826-4260
COMMUNITY DIGEST. 1983. w. Can.$25. Community Digest Publications, 216-1755 Robson St., Vancouver, BC V6Y 3B7, Canada. TEL 604-875-8313. FAX 604-875-0336. Ed. S. Bowell. adv.; bk.rev. circ. 25,000.
  Description: Serves the South Asian, East African, Middle Eastern, aboriginal and black Canadian ethnic communities.

914.5   CN
COMUNITA VIVA. 1971. m. Can.$20. Photo Press Publishing Co., Box 429, Station D, Toronto, Ont. M6P 3K1, Canada. FAX 658-9727. Ed. Rino Citarella. adv.; bk.rev. circ. 22,450.
  Description: All news concerning community with reference to the Italian community.

071.1   CN
CONTACT (LAVAL). (Est and Oeust editions avail.) 1945. w. Hebdos du Bloc Nord, 189 ave. Laval, Laval, PQ H7N 3V8, Canada. TEL 514-667-4360. FAX 514-667-9498. Owner(s): Hebdos Telemedia, 6455 Jean Talon E., Montreal, PQ H1S 1M8, Canada. TEL 514-257-6494. FAX 514-257-6585. Ed. Jacques Dion. illus. cols./p.: 7. (tabloid format) Document type: newspaper.

051   CN   ISSN 0832-7556
CONTACT (QUEBEC). 1986. 3/yr. free. Communications Services, Pavillon Felix A. Savard, Local 214, Laval University, Quebec, PQ G1K 7P4, Canada. TEL 418-656-2571. FAX 418-656-2809. Ed. Diane Dontigny. adv.; bk.rev.; circ. 90,000 (controlled). Document type: academic/scholarly publication.

051   CN   ISSN 0838-2395
COTTAGE LIFE. 1988. 6/yr. Can.$17.50($23.50) (foreign $27.50). Quarto Communications, 111 Queen St. E., Ste. 408, Toronto, ON M5C 1S2. TEL 416-360-6880. FAX 416-360-6814. Ed. Ann Vanderhoof. adv.: B&W page Can.$4585, color page Can.$5470; adv. contact: Patricia Moylan. bk.rev. circ. 70,000. (also avail. in microform from MML) Document type: consumer publication.
  Description: Magazine for and about cottagers, aims to enhance the quality of cottage life through articles on boating, watersports, cooking, fishing, building, renovating, entertaining and enjoying life at the cottage.

051   CN   ISSN 1057-3372
COUNTRYSIDE. 1989. q. Can.$12.84. Norby Publishing, R.R. 1, Fifth Line W., Terra Cotta, Ont. L0P 1N0, Canada. TEL 416-838-2800. FAX 416-838-3697. Ed. Mike Pembry. adv. circ. 10,000. **Indexed:** Gard.Lit. (1992-).

971.3   CN   ISSN 0826-3035
COUNTY MAGAZINE. 1976. q. Can.$15. County Magazine Printshop Ltd., P.O. Box 30, 71 Main St., Bloomfield, Ont. K0K 1G0, Canada. TEL 613-393-3355. Ed. Steve Campbell. adv. circ. 2,500.

071.1   CN
COURRIER. (Regional editions avail. for Ahuntsic, Bordeaux-Cartierville, De Groulx, Des Moulins, Deux-Montagnes, Laval) 1945. w. Hebdos du Bloc Nord, 189 ave. Laval, Laval, PQ H7N 3V8, Canada. TEL 514-667-7360. Owner(s): Hebdos Telemedia, 6455 Jean Talon E., Montreal, PQ H1S 1M8, Canada. TEL 514-257-6494. FAX 514-257-6585. Ed. Jacques Dion. adv. contact: Raymond Fortin. illus. cols./p.: 7. (tabloid format) Document type: newspaper.

071   CN
COURRIER DE LA NOUVELLE-ECOSSE. (Text in French) 1937. w. Can.$25 (foreign Can.$40). Societe de Presse Acadienne, 4 rue Alma, C.P. 402, Yarmouth, N.S. B5A 4B3, Canada. TEL 902-742-9119. FAX 902-742-9110. circ. 3,800. Document type: newspaper.
  Description: Covers Francophone interest.

051   CN
CROC. m. Ludcom Inc., 5800 Ave. Monkland, Montreal, Que. H4A 1G1, Canada. TEL 514-483-6320. FAX 514-483-6329. Ed. Pierre Huet.
  Description: Contains humor, photographs and cartoons which contribute to create a subtle sense of humor mixed with the French "ironie" and the English sense of parody.

051   CN   ISSN 0822-6016
F1021.2
CULTURE COMMUNIQUE. 1978. irreg. Can.$49($59) (foreign $69). Statistics Canada, Publications Division, Ottawa, Ont. K1A 0T6, Canada. TEL 613-951-7276.
  Description: Used to release advanced, timely data on cultural activities, institutions and industries in Canada.

071.1   CN
DAILY GRAPHIC. 1896. d. (Mon.-Sat.). Can.$108.30($216); newsstand price: Can.$.50. P.O. Box 130, 1941 Saskatchewan Ave. W., Portage la Prairie, MB R1N 3B4, Canada. TEL 204-857-3427. FAX 204-239-1270. Owner(s): Bowes Publishers Ltd., P.O. Box 7400, London, ON N5Y 4X3, Canada. TEL 807-468-5555. FAX 807-468-4318. Ed. Simon Blake; Pub. Tom Tenszen. adv. contact: B.R. Clayton. bk.rev.; illus. Wire service(s): CanP. circ. 4,136 (paid). cols./p.: 6; pp./issue: 12. (broadsheet format; also avail. in microfilm from CML; back issues avail.) Document type: newspaper.

071.1   CN
DAILY MINER AND NEWS. d. (Mon.-Fri.). Can.$104($480) Bowes Publishers Ltd., P.O. Box 7400, London, ON N5Y 4X3, Canada. TEL 807-468-5555. FAX 807-468-4318. Ed. Ross Ponter; Pub. Theodore A. Weiss. adv. contact: Jim Blight. circ. 5,000 (paid). (broadsheet format; also avail. in microfiche) Document type: newspaper.

071.1   CN
DAILY PRESS. 1934. d. (Mon.-Sat.). 187 Cedar St., S., Timmins, ON P4N 7G1, Canada. TEL 705-268-5050. FAX 705-268-7373. Ed. Dave McGee; Pub. John A. Farrington. adv. contact: Sue Downs. Wire service(s): CanP. cols./p.: 6; pp./issue: 12. (broadsheet format; also avail. in microform) Document type: newspaper.

051   CN   ISSN 0317-7076
DECKS AWASH. 1968. bi-m. Can.$20. Aardvark Communications Ltd., P.O. Box 9548, Sta. B, St. John's, Nfld. A1A 2Y4, Canada. TEL 709-753-8871. FAX 709-722-3335. Ed. Roger Burrows. adv.; bk.rev. circ. 2,500. Document type: consumer publication.
  Description: Covers rural Newfoundland lifestyle, including history and current affairs on a regional basis.

G

ULRICH'S INTERNATIONAL PERIODICALS DIRECTORY 1994-95

GENERAL INTEREST PERIODICALS — CANADA

071.1 CN
DELTA OPTIMIST. Sunday edition: South Delta Today. 1922. 3/wk. (Wed., Fri., Sun.). newsstand price: Can.$.25. Today Publishing Ltd., 5485 48th Ave., Delta, BC V4K 1X2, Canada. TEL 604-946-4451. FAX 604-946-5680. Owner(s): Lower Mainland Publishing Ltd., 1970 Alberta St., Vancouver, BC V5Y 3X4, Canada. TEL 604-872-8255. FAX 604-879-1483. Ed. Ted Murphy; Pub. Tom Siba. adv.: page Can.$683.55; adv. contact: Dave Hamilton. illus.; circ. 15,000 (controlled). cols./p.: 5; pp./issue: 32. (tabloid format) **Document type:** newspaper.

054.1 071.1 CN
DEVOIR. 1910. d. (Mon.-Sat.) Can.$699.17. 2050 rue de Bleury, 9e etage, Montreal, PQ H3A 3M9, Canada. Ed. Lise Bissonnette. adv. contact: Lucie Pinsonneault. bk.rev. Wire service(s): AFP, CanP, RN. (standard format; back issues avail. in microform from SOC; back issues avail.; reprint service avail.) **Document type:** newspaper.
●Also available online. Vendor(s): Southam Electronic Publishing.
Also available on CD-ROM.

071.1 CN
DIDSBURY REVIEW. 1986. w. Can.$24; newsstand price: Can.$.65. 2017A - 19 Ave., Didsbury, AB T0M 0W0, Canada. TEL 403-335-3301. FAX 403-335-8143. Ed. Janice Harrington; Pub. Gene Hartmann. adv. contact: Alison Wright. bk.rev.; illus.; circ. 2,007 (paid). cols./p.: 5; pp./issue: 28. (tabloid format) **Document type:** newspaper.

051 CN
DISTRICT NEWS. w. Can.$19.50. Robert Axford, Ed. & Pub., P.O. Box 328, Red Lake, ON P0V 2M0, Canada. TEL 807-727-2619. FAX 807-727-3717. adv. contact: Donna Spence. circ. 2,700. **Document type:** newspaper.

971 CN ISSN 0012-6721
DRUM. 1966. w. Can.$35. Drum Publishers Ltd., Box 2719, Inuvik, N.W.T. X0E 0T0, Canada. TEL 403-979-4545. Ed. Dan Holman. adv. circ. 2,000.

071.1 CN
DRYDEN OBSERVER. 1897. w. Can.$26.75($70); newsstand price: Can.$.50. Alex Wilson Coldstream Ltd., Colonization St., Dryden, ON P8N 2Y9, Canada. FAX 807-223-2907. Ed. Sylvia Veal; Pub. Jacqueline Saville. adv. contact: Susan Kereliuk. bk.rev.; illus. cols./p.: 6; pp./issue: 22. (broadsheet format; also avail. in magnetic tape; microfiche; back issues avail.) **Document type:** newspaper.
●Also available on CD-ROM.

071.1 CN
EAST END NEWS. 1950. w. Can.$15; newsstand price: Can.$.40. Watson Publishing Company Limited, 150 Milner Ave., Unit 35, Scarborough, ON M1S 3R3, Canada. TEL 416-291-2583. Ed. Robert M. Watson. adv.; illus. (tabloid format; back issues avail.) **Document type:** newspaper.

051 CN
EASY LIVING. (In 3 editions: Fraser Valley, Surrey, Victoria) 1979. m. Can.$28. Eagle Promotions Ltd., Ste. 201, 30272 Simpson Rd., R.R. 1, Clearbrook, BC V2S 1M3, Canada. TEL 604-852-9360. FAX 604-852-2894. Ed. Colleen McLaughlin. adv.; bk.rev.; illus. circ. 150,000 (controlled). **Document type:** consumer publication.
   Description: Contains upbeat, humorous articles about family, home and lifestyles.

071 054.1 CN ISSN 0046-1016
L'EAU VIVE; Saskatchewan's only French weekly newspaper. (Text in French) 1971. w. Can.$30. Publications Fransaskoises, 2606 rue Central, Regina, SK S4N 2N9, Canada. TEL 306-347-0481. FAX 565-3450. adv.; bk.rev.; illus. **Document type:** newspaper.
   Former titles: (until 1978) Ficelle (ISSN 0705-0798); (until 1977): Eau Vive.

071.1 CN
ECHO. 1963. w. 18 Barker Walk, Manitouwadge, ON P0T 2C0, Canada. TEL 807-826-3788. FAX 807-826-3910. Ed. B.J. Schermann; Pub. B.J. Schermann. adv. contact: Francine Levesque. illus. cols./p.: 5; pp./issue: 12. (standard format) **Document type:** newspaper.

071.1 CN
ECHO DE FRONTENAC. 1929. w. Can.$24 (foreign Can.$60). 5040 boul. Veterans, Lac Megantic, PQ G6B 2G5, Canada. TEL 819-583-1630. FAX 819-583-1124. Ed. Gaetan Poulin. adv. contact: Remi Tremblay. bk.rev.; illus.; circ. 4,700 (paid); 4,450 (controlled). cols./p.: 7; pp./issue: 32. (tabloid format; reprint service avail.) **Document type:** newspaper.

071.1 CN
ECLAIREUR - PROGRES. 1987. w. Hebcor, 12625 1ere Ave., St-Georges, PQ G5Y 2E4, Canada. TEL 418-228-8858. FAX 418-228-0268. Owner(s): Quebecor, 612 St-Jacques, Montreal, PQ H3C 4M8, Canada. TEL 514-877-9777. FAX 514-877-9757. Ed. Simon Busque; Pub. Andre Bolduc. adv. contact: Robert Quirion. cols./p.: 8; pp./issue: 60. (tabloid format; also avail. in microfilm; diskette format; back issues avail.; reprint service avail.) **Document type:** newspaper.

051 CN ISSN 0711-589X
EDMONTON. 1979. m. $18. Comac Communications Ltd., 10301 108th St., Ste. 100, Edmonton, Alta. T5J 1L7, Canada. TEL 403-423-3807. Ed. Kate Hildebrandt. adv. circ. 43,000.

971 CN ISSN 0046-1296
EDMONTON NATIVE NEWS. 1963. bi-m. membership. Canadian Native Friendship Centre, 11205 101st St., Edmonton, AB T5G 2A4, Canada. TEL 403-479-1999. Ed. Yvonne Allen. circ. 500.
   Description: Contains items of local interest.

071.1 CN ISSN 0705-405X
EDMONTON SUN. (Supplements avail.) 1978. d. (Mon.-Fri., Sun.). 4900 92 Ave., No. 250, Edmonton, AB T6B 3A1, Canada. TEL 403-468-0100. FAX 403-468-0128. Owner(s): Toronto Sun Publishing Corp., 333 King St. E., Toronto, ON M5A 3X5, Canada. TEL 416-946-2222. FAX 416-947-3119. Ed. Paul Stanway; Pub. Ronald W. Mitchell. adv. contact: Heather McKie. bk.rev.; illus. (tabloid format; also avail. in microfiche) **Document type:** newspaper.

051 CN ISSN 0013-8657
ENTERPRISE. (Text mainly in English, occasionally in French) 1963. w. Can.$18.19 (foreign Can.$40). Cavell Enterprises Ltd., Box 834, Iroquois Falls A, Ont. P0K 1G0, Canada. TEL 705-232-4081. FAX 705-232-4235. Ed. Sandra Dewar. adv.; bk.rev.; rec.rev.; charts; illus. circ. 2,988.
   Description: Community newspaper with news on Iroquois Falls, Matheson and the surrounding areas.

051 CN
▼**ENTERTAINER.** 1992. 6/yr. Can.$15($22) Q C S Publishing & Marketing, 238 Davenport Rd., Ste. 265, Toronto, Ont. M5R 1J6, Canada. TEL 416-761-7940. FAX 416-771-8415. adv.: B&W & color, B&W page Can.$3200; trim 8 1/4 x 10 3/4. circ. 100,000.

071.1 CN
ESTON PRESS. 1916. w. Can.$26.80($52) 112 Main St., Eston, SK S0L 1A0, Canada. TEL 306-962-3221. FAX 306-962-4445. Owner(s): MT Publishing Co. Ltd., Box 99, Eston, SK S0L 1A0, Canada. Ed. Verna D. Thompson; Pubs. Grant & Verna D. Thompson. adv.; bk.rev.; illus. cols./p.: 5; pp./issue: 16. (tabloid format; back issues avail.) **Document type:** newspaper.

071.1 CN
EXPRESS (MEAFORD). 1906. w. Can.$26($54); newsstand price: Can.$.60. 68 Sykes St. N., Meaford, ON N4L 1R2, Canada. TEL 519-538-1421. FAX 519-538-5028. Ed. S. Woodhouse; Pub. R.J. Brebner. adv. contact: N. Haldane. illus. cols./p.: 6; pp./issue: 16. (also avail. in microform; back issues avail.) **Document type:** newspaper.

051 CN ISSN 0845-8715
FALSE CREEK NEWS. 1988. w. Can.$25. Creek Slopes Publications, 661A Market Hill, Vancouver, BC V5Z 4B5, Canada. TEL 604-876-6770. FAX 604-875-0336. Ed. S. Bowell. adv. circ. 25,000.
   Formerly (until 1989): Creek Slopes Magazine (ISSN 0843-1868)

071.1 CN
FEUILLE D'ERABLE. 1945. w. Can.$17($65); newsstand price: Can.$.63. Publications Appalaches Ltee., 1717 St. Calixte, No. 5, Plessisville, PQ G6L 1R2, Canada. TEL 819-362-7049. FAX 819-362-2216. Ed. Jean Fontaine; Pub. Andree Wright. adv. contact: Slyvie Tremblay. illus. circ. 5,000. cols./p.: 7; pp./issue: 40. (tabloid format; also avail. in microform from SOC; back issues avail.) **Document type:** newspaper.

071.1 CN ISSN 0840-4496
FIFTY-FIVE PLUS. 1988. bi-m. Can.$12.84. Limestone City Publications, RR 1, Battersea, ON K0H 1H0, Canada. TEL 613-353-2060. FAX 613-353-2060. Ed. Sharon Freeman. adv. contact: Josie Peras Walsh. bk.rev. circ. 30,000. **Document type:** consumer publication.

071.1 CN
FLAMBOROUGH REVIEW. 1918. w. Can.$24; newsstand price: Can.$.50. 30 Main St. N., P.O. Box 20, Waterdown, ON L0R 2H0, Canada. TEL 905-689-4841. FAX 905-689-3110. circ. 3,600. cols./p.: 5; pp./issue: 40. **Document type:** newspaper.

051 054.1 CN ISSN 0015-6957
F1051
FORCES.* (Text in English and French; multi-lingual inserts) 1967. q. Can.$15. Societe d'Edition de la Revue Forces, 500 rue Sherbrooke Ouest, Bur. 430, Montreal, Que. H3A 3C6, Canada. TEL 514-286-7600. Ed. Dir. Jean Sarrazin. adv.; charts; illus.; stat; cum.index every 2 yrs.; circ. controlled. **Indexed:** Can.Per.Ind., Pt.de Rep. (1979-). —UnCover.

071.1 CN ISSN 0046-6743
THE FOUR SEASONS. 1968. s-a. free. Halifax Wildlife Association, P.O. Box 593, Halifax, NS B3J 2R7, Canada. Ed. A.B. Inglis. adv. circ. 900. **Document type:** newsletter.
   Formerly: Wildlife News.

051 US
FOUR SEASONS HOTELS AND RESORTS MAGAZINE.* 1983. q. New York Times Custom Publishing, 590 Madison Ave., 32nd Fl., New York, NY 10022. Ed. Jennifer Luckacs. adv. circ. 36,000. **Document type:** consumer publication.
   Description: Lifestyle magazine for guests at Four Seasons hotels.

051 CN
FRANK.* fortn. Great Central Publishing Co. Ltd., Box 2462, Sta. D, Ottawa, Ont. K1P 5W6, Canada. TEL 613-232-2125. FAX 613-238-7784.

051 CN ISSN 0838-603X
NX513.A1F88
FUSE MAGAZINE. 1976. 5/yr. Can.$20 to individuals (foreign Can.$24); institutions Can.$32 (foreign Can.$38). Arton's Publishing, 183 Bathurst St., 1st Fl., Toronto, ON M5T 2R7, Canada. TEL 416-367-0159. FAX 416-360-0781. Ed.Bd. adv.: B&W page Can.$400; 7 x 9 3/4. bk.rev. circ. 5,000. (also avail. in microfilm from MML; back issues avail.) **Indexed:** Alt.Press Ind., Artbibl.Mod., Can.Per.Ind., Can.Wom.Per.Ind., CMI. **Document type:** consumer publication.
—UnCover. **CCC.**
   Former titles: Fuse (ISSN 0226-8086); Centerfold.
   Description: Provides direct access to the vital and diverse arts culture which exists outside of major museums and galleries. Reaches cultural communities through its hybridization of arts journalism, investigative features and regular reviews of visual art, film, video, alternative press and independent music.

071.1 CN
GAZETTE. 1778. d. Can.$154. 250 rue St-Antoine O., Montreal, PQ H2Y 3R7, Canada. Owner(s): Southam Newspaper Group, 1450 Don Mills Rd., Toronto, ON M3B 2X7, Canada. TEL 416-445-6641. FAX 416-442-3378. Ed. Joan Fraser; Pub. David Perks. adv. contact: Jean Sanche. Wire service(s): CanP, KR, LAT WP, NYT. circ. 165,000. cols./p.: 6. (broadsheet format; also avail. in microform from CML) **Document type:** newspaper.
●Also available online. Vendor(s): Southam Electronic Publishing.
Also available on CD-ROM.

GENERAL INTEREST PERIODICALS — CANADA

071.1   CN
GAZETTE DU MANIWAKI. 1929. w. Can.$35; newsstand price: free. 93 Notre Dame, Maniwaki, PQ J9E 2H5, Canada. TEL 819-449-2233. FAX 819-449-7067. Ed. Pascal Chausse; Pub. Denise Carriere. adv. contact: Georges Lafontaine. cols./p.: 7; pp./issue: 40. (tabloid format; back issues avail.) **Document type:** newspaper.

051   CN   ISSN 0016-8432
GEORGIA STRAIGHT. 1967. w. Can.$40($60) Vancouver Free Press Publishing Corp., 1235 West Pender St., 2nd Fl., Vancouver, BC V6E 2V6, Canada. TEL 604-681-2000. FAX 604-681-0272. Ed. Dan McLeod. adv. contact: David Mochuk. bk.rev.; film rev.; play rev. circ. 93,000. **Document type:** consumer publication.
Formerly: Vancouver Free Press.

051   CN   ISSN 0849-5696
GEORGIAN BAY TODAY; the seasonal newsletter linking recreationists, residents and tourists...with nature. 1988. q. Can.$19.95($14) for 3 yrs. Heisey Publishing, c/o 29 Bernard Ave., Toronto, ON M5R 1R3, Canada. TEL 416-944-1217. FAX 416-944-0133. Ed. Mark Kubisz. adv. circ. 1,376. (tabloid format) **Document type:** newsletter.

071.1   CN
GLENGARRY NEWS. (Supplements avail.) 1892. w. Can.$26($99) Box 10, 3 Main St., Alexandria, ON K0C 1A0, Canada. Ed. Greg Kielec; Pub. Joe Banks. adv. contact: Lindsay Cameron. illus.; circ. 7,500 (paid). cols./p.: 6; pp./issue: 26. (broadsheet format; also avail. in microfiche; back issues avail.) **Document type:** newspaper.

054.1   CN
▼**GLOBE.** (Text in French) 1991. 6/yr. Editions Globe Magazine Inc., 422 chemin du Roy, St. Augustin-de-Desmaures, PQ G3A 1W8, Canada. TEL 418-878-1800. FAX 418-878-4506. Ed. Florian Chasse. adv.: B&W page Can.$2950, color page Can.$4200; trim 8.38 x 12. circ. 43,000. **Document type:** consumer publication.

071.1   CN
GLOBE AND MAIL. 1844. d. (Mon.-Sat.). Globe and Mail Ltd., 444 Front St., W., Toronto, ON M5V 2S9, Canada. TEL 416-585-5000. FAX 416-585-5275. Ed. William Thorsell; Pub. A. Roy Megarry. (broadsheet format) **Document type:** newspaper.

071.1   CN
GULF ISLANDS DRIFTWOOD. 1960. w. Can.$27.82; newsstand price: Can.$.75. Driftwood Publishing, 328 Lower Ganges Rd., Ganges V0S 1E0, Canada. TEL 604-537-9933. FAX 604-537-2613. Ed. Tony Richards; Pub. Joyce Carlson. adv. contact: Joyce Carlson. cols./p.: 5; pp./issue: 48. (tabloid format) **Document type:** newspaper.

051   CN   ISSN 0829-1373
HAMILTON THIS MONTH. 1984. 6/yr. Can.$12.95. Town Publishing Group Inc., 361 King St. W., Hamilton, ON L8P 1B4, Canada. TEL 416-522-6117. FAX 416-529-2242. Ed. Elizabeth Kelly. adv. contact: Heather Rose. bk.rev.; film rev.; play rev. circ. 40,000. (back issues avail.) **Document type:** consumer publication.
Description: Includes investigative insights and analysis on issues facing the Hamilton, Burlington and Oakville region, as well as regular service features that reflect lifestyle trends and encourage readers to enjoy the best of their city.

071.1   CN
HANOVER POST. 1880. w. Can.$31.20; newsstand price: Can.$.65. 413 18th Ave., Hanover, ON N4N 3S5, Canada. Ed. Michael Turner; Pub. Marie David. adv. contact: Marie David. illus.; circ. 4,800 (paid). cols./p.: 6; pp./issue: 26. (broadsheet format; also avail. in microfilm from GCS; back issues avail.) **Document type:** newspaper.

071.1   CN
HERALD (HERBERT). 1911. w. Can.$16.05($25); newsstand price: Can.$.45. P.O. Box 399, Herbert, SK S0H 2A0, Canada. TEL 306-784-2422. FAX 306-784-2620. Ed. Cynthia Firus; Pub. Rhonda J. Ens. adv. contact: Rhonda J. Ens. illus. cols./p.: 6; pp./issue: 16. (tabloid format; back issues avail.) **Document type:** newspaper.

071.1   CN
HERALD LEADER PRESS. (Supplement avail.) 1988. w. Can.$31.03($62); newsstand price: Can.$.58. P.O. Box 130, 1941 Saskatchewan Ave., Portage la Prairie, MB R1N 3B4, Canada. TEL 204-857-3427. FAX 204-239-1270. Owner(s): Bowes Publishers Ltd., P.O. Box 7400, London, ON N5Y 4X3, Canada. TEL 807-468-5555. FAX 807-468-4318. Ed. Simon Blake; Pub. Tom Tenszen. adv. contact: B.R. Clayton. bk.rev.; illus. Wire service(s): CanP. circ. 6,303. cols./p.: 6; pp./issue: 16. (broadsheet format; also avail. in microform from CML; back issues avail.) **Document type:** newspaper.

051   CN   ISSN 0820-2893
HERITAGE LINK. 1986. 5/yr. Can.$15. 10110-82 Avenue, Suite 205, Edmonton, Alta. T6E 1Z4, Canada. TEL 403-432-1510. FAX 403-939-6276. Ed. Mike Pawlus. adv.; bk.rev. circ. 5,000. (back issues avail.)
Description: News for and about Alberta.

051   CN
HERITAGE NEWS.* m. Box 81076, Fiddlers Green Outlet, Ancaster, Ont. L9G 1N1, Canada. TEL 416-648-0093. FAX 416-648-8799. Ed. Donald Bowles.

051   CN   ISSN 0715-5948
HI-RISE. 1980. 11/yr. Can.$10. Val Publications Ltd., 95 Leeward Glenway, Unit 121, Don Mills, Ont. M3C 2Z6, Canada. TEL 416-424-1393. FAX 416-467-8262. Ed. Valerie M. Dunn. adv.; bk.rev. circ. 35,000.
Description: Lifestyle publication for residents of apartments and townhouses; subjects covered include psychology, cooking, politics, health, business and community news.

071.1   CN
HIGHWAY 40 COURIER. 1959. w. Can.$16($32); newsstand price: Can.$.40. Roger Manegre, Ed. & Pub., 200 Steele St., Cut Knife, SK S0M 0N0, Canada. TEL 306-398-4901. FAX 306-398-4909. adv. contact: Roger Manegre. illus.; circ. 800 (paid). cols./p.: 5; pp./issue: 8. (tabloid format; back issues avail.) **Document type:** newspaper.

051 054.1   CN   ISSN 0704-2965
HORIZONS (MONTREAL). French edition (ISSN 0704-2973) (Text in English) 1939. s-m. free. Air Canada, Employee Communications, Air Canada Centre, 261, P.O. Box 14000, St. Laurent, Que. H4Y 1H4, Canada. TEL 514-422-5915. FAX 514-422-5914. charts; illus.; tr.lit. circ. 30,000. Indexed: Curr.Cont.
Formerly (until 1972): Between Ourselves (ISSN 0006-0291)

051   CN
▼**HOUR.** 1993. w. Can.$50 (foreign Can.$75). Communications Voir Inc., 4126 Saint-Denis St., Ste. 302, Montreal, PQ H2W 2M5, Canada. TEL 514-848-0777. FAX 514-848-0360. adv. contact: Claudia Pharand. circ. 50,000. (tabloid format) **Document type:** consumer publication.

071   CN   ISSN 0714-5810
HUB. 1973. w. Can.$40 (foreign Can.$80). P.O. Box 1250, Hay River, NT X0E 0R0, Canada. TEL 403-874-6577. FAX 403-874-2678. Ed. Vicky Latour. adv. contact: Chris Brodeur. bk.rev. circ. 4,000. **Document type:** newspaper.

071.1   CN
HUDSON GAZETTE. 1950. w. Can.$18 (in U.S. Can.$35); newsstand price: Can.$.50. 397 Main Rd., Hudson, PQ J0P 1H0, Canada. TEL 514-458-5482. FAX 514-458-3337. Owner(s): CREG Investments, P.O. Box 70, Hudson, PQ J0P 1H0, Canada. TEL 514-458-5482. Ed. Greg Jones. adv. contact: Greg Jones. circ. 2,160 (paid); 1,115 (controlled). cols./p.: 7; pp./issue: 16. (tabloid format) **Document type:** newspaper.

051   CN
HURONIA LIFESTYLE.* 10/yr. 24 Dunlop St. W., Barrie, Ont. L4M 1A2, Canada. TEL 705-721-1450. Ed. Wally Moran. circ. 27,000.

051   CN   ISSN 0828-1289
THE IDLER. 1985. 6/yr. Can.$28.50 (effective Jan. 1994). The Idler Society, 255 Davenport Rd., Toronto, ON M5R 1J9, Canada. TEL 416-962-6001. FAX 416-962-4279. Ed. David Warren. adv. contact: Karen O'Reilly. bk.rev.; circ. 8,000 (paid). (also avail. in microfilm from MML) **Document type:** consumer publication.

054.1   CN
IMPORTANT. (Text in French) 1991. 4/yr. Groupe Magazines, 877 rue St. Pierre, Terrebonne, PQ J6W 1E6, Canada. TEL 514-964-1978. FAX 514-964-2327. Ed. Alex Leblanc; Pub. Denis Clermont. adv.: B&W page Can.$2100, color page Can.$2995; adv. contact: Nicole Michaud. circ. 35,000.

051 054.1   CN
▼**IN MONTREAL.** (Text in English, French) 1993. 10/yr. Can.$10. Federation C J A, 515 Cote St.-Catherine Rd., Montreal, PQ H3W 1M6, Canada. TEL 514-345-2624. FAX 514-346-2643. Ed. Robin Charney. adv.: color page Can.$2500. circ. 30,000. (tabloid format)

071.1   CN
INDEPENDENT (ELMIRA). 1974. w. Can.$26 (in U.S. Can.$50); newsstand price: Can.$.75. North Waterloo Publishing, 15 King St., Elmira, ON N3B 2R1, Canada. TEL 519-669-5155. FAX 519-669-5928. Ed. Bob Verdun. adv.: page Can.$592; adv. contact: Hugh Weltz. circ. 6,900 (paid). cols./p.: 5; pp./issue: 28. (tabloid format; also avail. in microfiche; back issues avail.) **Document type:** newspaper.

071.1   CN
INDEPENDENT (GRIMSBY). Variant title: Grimsby Independent. 1885. w. Can.$25; newsstand price: Can.$.75. 19 Adelaide St., Grimsby, ON L3M 4G5, Canada. Ed. Julie Hendriks. adv. contact: Robert Van Wyngaarden. circ. 4,673 (paid). cols./p.: 5; pp./issue: 24. (back issues avail.; reprint service avail.) **Document type:** newspaper.

971   CN   ISSN 0019-722X
INDO-CANADIAN. (Text in Punjabi) 1964. q. Can.$60. Indo-Canadian Times Inc., P.O. Box 2296, Vancouver, BC V6B 3W5, Canada. FAX 604-599-5415. Ed. Tara Singh Hayer. adv. contact: Harjit Singh Bains. bk.rev.; illus. **Document type:** newspaper.

071.1   CN
INNISFAIL BOOSTER. w. 4932 4th St., Innisfail, AB T4G 1N2, Canada. TEL 403-227-3477. Pub. R.L. Brinson. adv. contact: R.L. Brinson. circ. 7,500 (controlled). cols./p.: 6; pp./issue: 24. (tabloid format) **Document type:** newspaper.

071.1   CN
INNISFIL SCOPE. 1978. w. Can.$20.33($87); newsstand price: Can.$.50. 34 Main St., Beeton, ON L0G 1A0, Canada. TEL 705-729-4441. FAX 905-729-2541. Ed. Bruce R. Haire. adv. contact: John H. Archibald. illus.; circ. 2,850 (paid). cols./p.: 6; pp./issue: 16. (tabloid format) **Document type:** newspaper.

071.1   CN
JOURNAL LA VOIX. 1960. w. Can.$88. Journal la Voix Nouvelle Inc., 38 A Augusta, Sorel, PQ J3P 1A3, Canada. TEL 514-743-8466. FAX 514-742-8567. **Document type:** newspaper.

071.1   CN
KERROBERT CITIZEN. 1910. w. Jamac Publishing Ltd., 919 Main St., Kindersley, SK S0L 1S0, Canada. TEL 306-463-4611. FAX 306-463-6505. Ed. Timothy Crump; Pub. James Crump. adv. contact: Stewart Crump. illus. cols./p.: 5. (tabloid format) **Document type:** newspaper.

071.1   CN
▼**KIRKLAND LAKE GAZETTE.** (Supplements avail.) 1993. w. 1 Duncan Ave., Kirkland Lake, ON P2N 2N8, Canada. TEL 705-568-NEWS. FAX 705-568-4444. Ed. Walter Francyk; Pub. Dave Armstrong. adv. contact: Lois Perry. illus.; circ. 7,479 (controlled). cols./p.: 5; pp./issue: 20. (tabloid format; reprint service avail.) **Document type:** newspaper.

GENERAL INTEREST PERIODICALS — CANADA

051 CN
KOOTENAY REVIEW. m. Can.$8.50. R.R. No.1, Nelson, B.C. V1L 5P4, Canada. TEL 604-825-4663. FAX 604-352-3013. Ed. Lorna Lynch. adv.: B&W page Can.$290; 9 3/4 x 7 1/4. circ. 11,352.
Description: Covers unique stories of local history, characters, businesses, wildlife, events and entertainment, opinion and commentary.

071.1 CN
LANGLEY ADVANCE. 1931. 2/wk. (Wed., Fri.). Can.$24($120); newsstand price: Can.$.50. 20488 Fraser Hwy., Langley, BC V3A 4G2, Canada. TEL 604-534-8641. FAX 604-534-3383. Owner(s): Mrs. N. Schatz, 72 Ave., Langley, BC V3A 6H4, Canada. TEL 604-888-6381. Ed. Bob Groenezeld; Pub. Ian Schatz. adv. contact: Irene Lousier. illus.; circ. 10,000 (paid); 34,500 (controlled). cols./p.: 5; pp./issue: 32. (tabloid format; also avail. in microfilm from CML; back issues avail.) **Document type:** newspaper.

071.1 CN
LAST MOUNTAIN TIMES. 1907. w. Can.$16.05; newsstand price: Can.$.80. Last Mountain Times Ltd., 103 First Ave. W., Nokomis, SK S0G 3R0, Canada. TEL 306-528-2020. FAX 306-528-2090. Ed. L.W. Emmons; Pub. Lyle Emmons. adv. contact: L.W. Emmons. bk.rev.; illus.; circ. 1,800 (paid). cols./p.: 5; pp./issue: 20. (tabloid format; back issues avail.) **Document type:** newspaper.

071.1 CN
LEADER (MORRISBURG). 1863. w. Can.$19; newsstand price: Can.$.47. Morrisburg Leader Limited, Morrisburg Shopping Plaza, Morrisburg, ON K0C 1X0, Canada. TEL 613-543-2987. FAX 613-543-3643. Ed. A.B. Laurin. adv. contact: Sam Laurin. illus. circ. 2,850. cols./p.: 8; pp./issue: 12. (broadsheet format) **Document type:** newspaper.

071.1 CN
LEADER NEWS. 1946. w. Jamac Publishing Ltd., 919 Main St., Kindersley, SK S0L 1S0, Canada. TEL 306-463-4611. FAX 306-463-6505. Ed. Timothy Crump; Pub. James Crump. adv. contact: Stewart Crump. illus. cols./p.: 5; pp./issue: 14. (tabloid format) **Document type:** newspaper.

071.1 CN ISSN 1192-2915
▼**LEFTY'S LETTER**; news, views and reviews for the left-hander. 1992. 10/yr. Can.$18.19. Richard W. Unger, Ed.& Pub., Box 212, Spiritwood, SK S0J 1M0, Canada. TEL 306-883-2462. (Subscr. to: 610 4th St. E., Spiritwood, SK S0J 2M0, Canada) bk.rev. (back issues avail.) **Document type:** newsletter.
Description: Aimed at the Canadian left-handers, but also covers American personalities.

051 CN
LEISUREWAYS. 1982. 6/yr. Can.$6. Canada Wide Magazines Ltd. (Toronto), 2 Carlton St., Ste. 801, Toronto, ON M5B 1J3, Canada. TEL 416-595-5007. Ed. Deborah Milton. adv.; circ. 600,000 (controlled).
Description: Travel and leisure articles for members of the Canadian Automobile Association in Ontario.

051 CN ISSN 0821-5278
LETHBRIDGE MAGAZINE. 1981. 7/yr. Can.$10. Byrne Publishing Group, Inc., Box 1203, Lethbridge, AB T1J 4A4, Canada. TEL 403-327-3200. FAX 403-320-6049. Ed. Suzanne Zintel. adv. contact: Sherry Wieland. bk.rev.; illus. circ. 16,375. (back issues avail.) **Document type:** consumer publication.
Description: Covers general interest subjects for the Lethbridge area.

051 CN
LIFESTYLES 5749. 1973. 6/yr. Can.$18. A T E Publishing Co. Ltd., PO Box 175, Downsview, Ont. M3M 3A3, Canada. TEL 416-881-3070. FAX 416-731-6000. Ed. Ron Csillag. adv. circ. 87,820.

071.1 CN
LISTOWEL BANNER. 1866. w. Can.$29($80) Newfoundland Capital Corporation (NCC), 25 Townline Rd., Tillsonburg, ON, Canada. TEL 519-688-6397. FAX 519-842-3511. circ. 5,800 (paid). (broadsheet format) **Document type:** newspaper.

051 CN
THE LOG. 1948. m. $12.50. Lantzville Log Society, Box 268, Lantzville, B.C. V0R 2H0, Canada. TEL 604-390-2847. adv. circ. 2,743.

051 CN ISSN 0711-6233
LONDON MAGAZINE (LONDON). (Supplement avail.: London Magazine Business Annual (ISSN 1194-4005)) 1980. 9/yr. $16. Blackburn Group, 231 Dundas St., Ste. 203, London, ON N6A 1H1, Canada. TEL 519-679-4901. FAX 519-434-7842. Ed. Jackie Skender. adv. circ. 35,000. (also avail. in microfiche from MML)
●Also available online.
Formerly: Ontario Living.
Description: Covers homes, leisure and city issues for upscale audience in London and southwestern Ontario.

051 CN ISSN 0024-9262
AP5
MACLEAN'S; Canada's weekly newsmagazine. French edition: L'Actualite (ISSN 0383-8714) 1905. w. Can.$39.95. Maclean Hunter Ltd., Maclean Hunter Bldg., 777 Bay St., Toronto, ON M5W 1A7, Canada. TEL 416-596-5386. FAX 416-596-7730. TELEX 065-24196. Ed. Kevin Doyle. adv.; bk.rev.; illus. circ. 560,000. (also avail. in microform from MML)
Indexed: Acad.Ind., Bk.Rev.Ind. (1978-), Can.Lit.Ind., Can.Per.Ind., Child.Bk.Rev.Ind. (1978-), CMI, Energy Ind., Energy Info.Abstr., Hlth.Ind., Mag.Ind., R.G.
●Also available online. Vendor(s): Mead Data Central, Inc., Southam Electronic Publishing.
—BLDSC (5330.392000); Faxon; UnCover. **CCC**.

051 054.1 CN
▼**MAGAZINE PROVIGO.** (Text in English, French) 1993. s-m. Quebecor Inc., 7 Bates Rd., Outremont, PQ H2V 1A6, Canada. TEL 514-270-1100. FAX 514-276-5120. Ed. Denyse Sisto. adv.: Color page Can.$23100; trim 8 x 10 7/8. circ. 2,160,604. **Document type:** consumer publication.

071.1 CN
MAIDSTONE MIRROR. 1911. w. Can.$23.54. Turner Warwick Publications, 892 104th St. N., Battleford, SK S9A 3E6, Canada. TEL 306-893-2251. FAX 306-893-4707. Ed. Susan Sandberg; Pub. W.R. Warwick. circ. 1,878. **Document type:** newspaper.

071.1 CN
MANITOBA BEAVER. w. newsstand price: Can.$.50. Box 1148, Beausejour, MB R0E 0C0, Canada. TEL 204-268-1155. FAX 204-268-1084. adv.: page Can.$350. **Document type:** newspaper.

071.1 CN
▼**MARKET CONNECTION.** 1993. m. Last Mountain Times Ltd., 103 First Ave. W., Nokomis, SK S0G 3R0, Canada. TEL 306-528-2020. FAX 306-528-2090. Ed. L.W. Emmons; Pub. Lyle Emmons. adv.: B&W page Can.$375; adv. contact: L.W. Emmons. circ. 6,410 (controlled). cols./p.: 5; pp./issue: 16. (tabloid format; back issues avail.) **Document type:** newspaper.

051 CN ISSN 1192-1692
▼**MARKETPLACE.** 1992. m. Can.$28($25) Nepean Marketplace, 1891 Merivale Rd., Nepean, ON K2G 1G5, Canada. TEL 613-225-1934. FAX 613-225-7499. Ed. Kelly Nolan. adv.: B&W page Can.$1440, color page Can.$1940; trim 8 1/4 x 10 1/2. circ. 34,300. **Document type:** consumer publication.

051 CN
MARKHAM MONTH.* 1979. m. Can.$25. Thornhill Publications Ltd., 3335 - 14th Ave., Ste. 1, Markham, ON L3R 0H3, Canada. TEL 416-475-1743. circ. 20,781.

051 CN
THE MERCURY. 1917. w. Can.$13 (US Can.$55). Tofield Mercury Publishing Ltd., Box 150, 5312 50 St., Tofield, AB T0B 4J0, Canada. TEL 403-662-4046. FAX 403-662-3735. Ed. Anne Francoeur; Pub. Anne Francouer. adv. contact: Charlotte Munkedal. bk.rev.; illus. cols./p.: 5. (tabloid format; reprint service avail.) **Document type:** newspaper.

071 CN ISSN 1182-5812
MIRROR. 1985. w. $45. Communications Gratte-Ciel, Ltee., 400 McGill St., 2nd Fl., Montreal, PQ H2Y 2G1, Canada. TEL 514-393-1010. Ed. Peter Scowen. adv.: B&W page $1520, color page $1795. circ. 80,000. (tabloid format) **Document type:** newspaper.
Formerly (until 1990): Montreal Mirror (ISSN 0833-8086)

071.1 CN
MONITEUR & THE ECHO EXPRESS. Variant title: Hawkesbury Express. (Text in English, French) 1978. w. Can.$100($160) 88 Main St. E., Hawkesbury, ON K6A 1A3, Canada. TEL 613-632-0191. FAX 613-632-6383. adv. contact: Andre Cayer. illus. cols./p.: 7; pp./issue: 28. (tabloid format; back issues avail.) **Document type:** newspaper.

051 CN ISSN 1183-2142
MONTREAL PASSIONS. 1991. 6/yr. Les Editions M.P. Inc., 4112 Sainte-Catherine St. W., Montreal, Que. H3Z 1P2, Canada. TEL 514-932-1739. Ed. Lynn Suderman.

051 CN
MONTREAL SCOPE. (Text in English, French) 1976. m. Can.$15. Metro Plaza Ltd., Rm. 232, 1253 McGill College, Montreal, PQ H3B 2Y5, Canada. TEL 514-933-3333. FAX 514-931-9581. Ed. Nicolas Evreinow. adv.; circ. 40,000 (controlled).

071.1 CN
MORINVILLE AND DISTRICT GAZETTE. w. Can.$25. 9920 - 103 St., Morinville, AB T0G 1P0, Canada. TEL 403-939-7443. FAX 403-460-9364. Ed. Sue Gawlak; Pub. Duff Jamison. adv. contact: Mary Jamison. bk.rev.; illus.; circ. 29 (paid); 6,400 (controlled). (broadsheet format) **Document type:** newspaper.

071.1 CN
MOUNTAINEER. 1922. w. Can.$21; newsstand price: Can.$.75. Mountaineer Publ. Co. Ltd., 4814 49 St., Rocky Mountain House, AB T0M 1T1, Canada. TEL 403-845-3334. FAX 403-845-5570. Ed. Brian Mazza; Pub. L.O. Mazza. adv. contact: Ernest Murias. circ. 4,480 (paid). cols./p.: 6; pp./issue: 32. (broadsheet format; back issues avail.) **Document type:** newspaper.

051 CN ISSN 0820-876X
MUSKOKA LIFE. 1982. 7/yr. Muskoka Publications Group, 27 Dominion St., Box 1600, Bracebridge, Ont. P0B 1C0, Canada. TEL 705-645-4463. FAX 705-645-3928. Ed. Susan Pryke. adv. circ. 9,515.

071.1 CN
NELSON DAILY NEWS. 1902. d. News Publishing Co., 266 Baker St., Nelson, BC V1L 4H3, Canada. TEL 604-352-3552. FAX 604-352-2418. Owner(s): Sterling Newspapers Ltd., 1827 W. 5th Ave., Vancouver, BC V6J 1P5, Canada. TEL 604-352-3552. FAX 604-732-3961. Ed. Dave Howe; Pub. L.R. (Verne) Shaull. adv. contact: Lesley Peters. bk.rev.; illus. circ. 5,000. cols./p.: 6; pp./issue: 16. (broadsheet format; also avail. in microfilm) **Document type:** newspaper.

051 CN ISSN 1189-6256
NETWORK. 1987. 6/yr. Can.$15($18) Canadian Controlled Media Communications, 287 MacPherson Ave., Toronto, ON M4V 1A4, Canada. TEL 416-928-2909. FAX 416-966-1181. Ed. Maureen Littlejohn. adv. contact: Harvey Wolfe. circ. 150,000 (controlled). (back issues avail.) **Document type:** consumer publication.
Formerly: Network Entertainment.
Description: Canadian and international content includes popular music and film personality interviews and profiles, a broad range of in-depth features, nostalgia, photo essays, audio-video, charts and news section.

051 CN
NEW PACIFIC. 1991. 4/yr. Can.$20 (foreign $20). New Pacific Communications Inc., 1155 Robson St., Ste. 401, Vancouver, BC V6E 1B5, Canada. TEL 604-688-0753. FAX 604-688-8239. Ed. Carol Berger; Pub. Charles Kelly. adv.: B&W page Can.$3420, color page Can.$4930; trim 8 1/2 x 11 1/4. circ. 25,000. **Document type:** consumer publication.

GENERAL INTEREST PERIODICALS — CANADA 2699

051 CN ISSN 0835-9423
NEW WEEKLY MAGAZINE. 1987. w. Can.$90. New Magazine Publishing Company Ltd., P.O. Box 390, Station "A", Ottawa, Ont. K1N 8V4, Canada. TEL 613-230-1644. Ed.Bd. adv.; bk.rev. circ. 130,000.
Formerly: New Magazine.

051 CN ISSN 0028-8888
CODEN: NEGAE3
NEWFOUNDLAND GAZETTE. 1807. w. Can.$75. Queen's Printer, Newfoundland, Confederation Bldg., St. John's, NF A1B 4J6, Canada. TEL 709-729-3649. FAX 709-729-1900. Ed. David C.B. Dawe. illus.; stat. circ. 1,200. (also avail. in microfilm from KTO) **Document type:** government publication.

051 CN
NEWFOUNDLAND LIFESTYLE. 1982. 4/yr. Can.$12.84 (US Can.$18, elsewhere Can.$25). Communications Ten Ltd., 197 Water St., P.O. Box 2356, Sta. C, St. John's, NF A1C 6E7, Canada. TEL 709-726-9300. FAX 709-726-3013. Ed. Mr. Adrian D. Smith. circ. 17,500.
Description: Editorial package of subjects and topics related to Newfoundland and its people.

051 CN
NEWFOUNDLAND QUARTERLY. Abbreviated title: N Q. 1900. q. Can.$12 (foreign Can.$15). Newfoundland Quarterly Association, P.O. Box 13486, Sta. A, Kenmount Rd., St. John's, NF A1B 4B8, Canada. Ed. Harry Cuff. bk.rev.
Former titles (until 1971): New Newfoundland Quarterly (ISSN 0380-5824); (until 1966): Newfoundland Quarterly (ISSN 0380-5816); (until 1901): Newfoundland Magazine (ISSN 0380-5808)

051 054.1 CN
NEWFOUNDLAND STUDIES. (Text in English, French) 1985. s-a. Can.$25. Memorial University, Department of English, St. John's, Nfld. A1C 5S7, Canada. TEL 709-737-8000. FAX 709-737-4000. Ed. Patrick O'Flaherty. circ. 500.

051 CN
NEWS - NORTH. 1945. w. Can.$30($50) Northern News Services, Box 2820, Yellowknife, N.W.T. X1A 2R1, Canada. FAX 403-873-2661. TELEX 034-45508. Ed. Craig Harper. adv.; bk.rev. circ. 9,200. (tabloid format; also avail. in microfilm from CML)
Formerly: News of the North.

071 CN ISSN 0382-8843
LE NORD. 1976. w. Can.$25($40) (effective Jan. 1993). Le Nord, C.P. 2320, 905 rue Georges, Hearst, ON P0L 1N0, Canada. TEL 705-372-1233. FAX 705-362-5954. Ed. Omer Cantin. adv. contact: Francine Pouliot. bk.rev. circ. 3,500. (tabloid format; also avail. in microfiche; back issues avail.) **Document type:** newspaper.
Description: Covers items of local and regional interest.

051 CN
NORTHERN JOURNAL. 1983. a. Can.$26($30) (foreign Can.$45). Motherlode Publications, 204 A Main St., P.O. Box 5215, Whitehorse, Y.T. Y1A 4Z1, Canada. TEL 403-668-7336. FAX 403-633-4425. Ed. Roc E. Lachance. adv.; bk.rev.; illus. circ. 60,000.
Description: Covers sporting, mining, business, leisure, art, environmental and social life in the North.

071.1 CN
NORTHERN LIGHT. 1913. w. Box 416, Bathurst, NB E2A 3Z3, Canada. TEL 506-546-4491. FAX 506-546-1491. Owner(s): Thompson Newspapers, 65 Queen St. W., Toronto, ON M5H 2M8, Canada. TEL 416-864-1710. FAX 416-864-1697. Ed. Greg Mulock; Pub. Al McCarthy. adv. contact: Maurice Aube. bk.rev.; illus. cols./p.: 6; pp./issue: 36. (broadsheet format; also avail. in microfilm from GCS) **Document type:** newspaper.

071.1 CN
NORTHERN PEN. 1980. w. Can.$48.15. Bebb Publishing, 10-12 North St., Box 520, St. Anthony, NF A0K 4S0, Canada. TEL 709-454-2191. FAX 709-454-3718. Ed. Allan Bock; Pub. Bernard Bromley. adv. contact: Andrea Quinlan. illus. circ. 6,580. (broadsheet format; also avail. in microfilm; back issues avail.) **Document type:** newspaper.
Description: Serves the residents of the Great Northern Peninsula of Newfoundland and the Southern Labrador coast.

071.1 CN
NORTHERNER. (Supplement avail.: Heading North) w. Can.$35 (US Can.$70); newsstand price: Can.$.50. Timberline Publishing, 715 La Ronge Ave., La Ronge, SK S0J 1L0, Canada. TEL 306-425-3344. FAX 306-425-2827. Ed. Scott Boyes; Pub. Scott Boyes. adv. contact: Mero Sayers. circ. 2,000 (paid). cols./p.: 5; pp./issue: 24. (tabloid format; back issues avail.) **Document type:** newspaper.
Formerly: Northland News.

392 CN
NOUS FIANCES. (Text in French) 1966. 4/yr. Can.$4. Publications Cousin Poupart-Turmel Inc., 6285 Cairns Ave., Anjou, Montreal, Que., Canada. Ed. Guy Cousin. adv.

051 700 CN ISSN 0712-1326
NOW. (Text in English) 1981. w. Can.$45 (foreign Can.$103). Now Communications Inc., 150 Danforth Ave., Toronto, Ont. M4K 1N1, Canada. TEL 416-461-0871. FAX 416-461-2886. Ed. Michael Hollett. adv.; bk.rev.; film rev.; play rev.; illus. circ. 96,061. (tabloid format; also avail. in microfilm; back issues avail.)
Description: Toronto's news and entertainment voice, covering issues and events in the city. Covers comedy, dance, theatre, restaurant reviews, music features.

071 CN ISSN 0702-7915
NUNATSIAQ NEWS. (Supplements avail.) (Text in English and Inuktitut) 1972. w. Can.$30($30) NorText, Box 8, Iqaluit, NT X0A 0H0, Canada. TEL 819-979-5357. FAX 819-974-4763. Ed. Todd Phillips. circ. 6,000. (tabloid format) **Document type:** newspaper.
Formerly: Inuksuk (ISSN 0702-7923)

071.1 CN
OAKVILLE BEAVER. (Supplements avail.) 1963. 3/wk. (Wed., Fri., Sun.). 467 Speers Rd., Oakville, ON L9H 3X9, Canada. TEL 905-845-3824. FAX 905-845-3085. Ed. Norm Alexander; Pub. Ian Oliver. adv. contact: Bob Glasbey. pp./issue: 42. **Document type:** newspaper.

051 CN ISSN 0840-5492
OKANAGAN LIFE MAGAZINE. 1988. 7/yr. Can.$10. Byrne Publishing Group, Inc., Box 1479, Sta. A, Kelowna, BC V1Y 7V8, Canada. TEL 604-861-5399. FAX 604-868-3040. Ed. J. Paul Byrne. adv. circ. 17,499. **Document type:** consumer publication.
Description: Covers general interest subjects for the Okanagan Valley.

071.1 CN
OLDS GAZETTE. w. Can.$17. Box 3860, 5030 51st St., Olds, AB T4H 1P6, Canada. Ed. Mary Jane Harper; Pub. Brian Leatherdale. adv. contact: Brian Leatherdale. bk.rev.; illus. (standard format; back issues avail.) **Document type:** newspaper.

071.1 CN
OLIVER CHRONICLE. (Supplements avail.) 1937. w. Can.$18 (local; elsewhere in Canada Can.$30; foreign Can.$75); newsstand price: Can.$.50. Tydeman Publishing, 36083 97th St., Oliver, BC V0H 1T0, Canada. TEL 604-498-3711. FAX 604-498-3966. Ed. Kathleen Connolly; Pub. Michael Newman. adv. contact: Vance Potter. illus. circ. 3,348. cols./p.: 6; pp./issue: 22. (broadsheet format) **Document type:** newspaper.

051 CN ISSN 0030-2937
J2 CODEN: ONGAE9
ONTARIO GAZETTE. 1867. w. Can.$110. Ministry of Government Services, 50 Grosvenor St., Toronto, Ont. M7A 1N8, Canada. TEL 416-326-5310. adv.; s-a. index. circ. 2,229. (also avail. in microform from UMI,BHP; microfilm from KTO) **Indexed:** C.I.S.Abstr.

071.1 CN
OSOYOOS TIMES. (Supplements avail.) 1947. w. Can.$18($75); newsstand price: Can.$.50. Box 359, Osoyoos, BC V0H 1V0, Canada. TEL 604-495-7725. FAX 604-495-6616. Ed. Patrick Turner; Pubs. Patrick Turner, Chris Stodola. adv. contact: Patrick Turner. illus.; circ. 2,610 (paid). cols./p.: 5; pp./issue: 40. (tabloid format) **Document type:** newspaper.

051 CN ISSN 0824-9075
OTTAWA MAGAZINE. 1981. 8/yr. Can.$14($19) Pegasus Publishing Inc., 192 Bank St., Ottawa, ON K2P 1W8, Canada. TEL 613-234-7751. FAX 613-234-9226. Ed. Rosa Harris-Adler. adv. contact: Duncan Weir. circ. 40,000. (back issues avail.)

071.1 CN ISSN 0843-2570
OTTAWA SUN. (Supplement avail.) 1988. d. 380 Hunt Club Rd., Ottawa, ON K1G 5H7, Canada. TEL 613-739-7000. FAX 613-739-8041. Ed. Richard Vansickle; Pub. Hartley Steward. adv. contact: Lise Desgroseilliers. bk.rev.; illus. Wire service(s): AP, CanP. circ. 52,000 (paid). cols./p.: 4. (tabloid format; also avail. in microfilm from GCS) **Document type:** newspaper.

071.1 CN
OYEN ECHO. 1973. w. Can.$18($30) 109 6 Ave. E., P.O. Box 210, Oyen, AB T0J 2J0, Canada. TEL 403-664-3622. FAX 403-664-3622. Owner(s): Holmes Publishing Ltd., 1577 Dunmore Rd. S.E., Medicine Hat, AB T1A 1Z8, Canada. TEL 403-526-5937. FAX 403-526-5678. Ed. Diana M. Walker; Pub. Ron Holmes. adv. contact: Helen Ball. illus. cols./p.: 5; pp./issue: 12. (tabloid format; back issues avail.; reprint service avail.) **Document type:** newspaper.

071.1 CN
PASS HERALD LTD.. 1930. w. Can.$30. Crowsnest Mall, Blairmore, AB T0K 0E0, Canada. TEL 403-562-2248. FAX 403-562-8379. Ed. Trevor Slapak; Pub. Gail Sygutek. adv. contact: Trevor Slapak. illus.; circ. 1,545 (paid); 1,255 (controlled). cols./p.: 5; pp./issue: 20. (tabloid format) **Document type:** newspaper.

071.1 CN
PELHAM HERALD. 1955. w. Can.$52. Box 550, 1477 Pelham St. S., Fonthill, ON L0S 1E0, Canada. Owner(s): Brabant Newspapers, 333 Arvin Ave., Stoney Creek, ON L8E 2M6, Canada. TEL 905-523-5800. FAX 905-523-4014. Ed. Laurie Miladin; Pub. Martha Cepuch. adv. contact: Martha Cepuch. cols./p.: 5; pp./issue: 16. (tabloid format) **Document type:** newspaper.

071.1 CN
PEMBROKE OBSERVER. (Supplements avail.) 1857. d. Can.$133. 186 Alexander St., Pembroke, ON K8A 4L9, Canada. TEL 613-732-3691. FAX 613-732-2645. Owner(s): Thomson Newspapers, 65 Queen St., Toronto, ON M5H 2M8, Canada. TEL 416-864-1710. FAX 416-864-0109. Ed. Mike Walsh; Lois Hornby. adv. contact: Neal O'Donoghue. Wire service(s): CanP. circ. 8,000 (paid). cols./p.: 6; pp./issue: 16. (broadsheet format; also avail. in microfilm from GCS) **Document type:** newspaper.

071.1 CN
PENTICTON HERALD. (Supplements avail.) 1906. d. (Mon.-Sat.). Can.$117. Penticton Herald, 186 Nanaimo Ave., W., Penticton, BC V2A 1N4, Canada. TEL 604-492-4002. FAX 604-492-2403. Owner(s): Thomson Newspapers Co. Ltd., 65 Queen St. W., Toronto, ON M5H 2M8, Canada. TEL 416-864-1710. FAX 416-864-0109. Ed. Randall O'Donnell; Pub. Jane Howard. adv. contact: Andre Martin. bk.rev.; illus. Wire service(s): CanP. circ. 10,000 (paid). cols./p.: 6; pp./issue: 18. (broadsheet format; also avail. in microfilm; back issues avail.) **Document type:** newspaper.

071.1 CN
PICKERING POST. 1950. w. Can.$15; newsstand price: Can.$.40. Watson Publishing Company Limited, 150 Milner Ave., Unit 35, Scarborough, ON M1S 3R3, Canada. TEL 416-291-2583. Ed. Robert M. Watson; Pub. Robert M. Watson. adv.; illus. cols./p.: 6; pp./issue: 12. (tabloid format; back issues avail.) **Document type:** newspaper.

G

GENERAL INTEREST PERIODICALS — CANADA

071.1   CN
PICTOU ADVOCATE. 1893. w. Can.$20 (foreign Can.$95); newsstand price: Can.$.75. 11 George St., Box 1000, Pictou, NS B0K 1H0, Canada. TEL 902-485-8014. FAX 902-752-4816. Owner(s): Advocate Printing & Publishing, Browns Point Rd., Box 1000, Pictou, NS B0K 1H0, Canada. TEL 902-485-1990. FAX 902-485-6353. Ed. Gordon Stiles; Pub. Sean Murray. adv. contact: Judy Ferguson. illus.; circ. 4,709 (paid); 188 (controlled). (broadsheet format; also avail. in microform; back issues avail.; reprint service avail.) **Document type:** newspaper.

051   CN
THE PLANET TODAY.* 1989. 10/yr. Planet Newspapers Ottawa Inc., 350 Harry Walker Pkwy., Ste. 15, Newmarket, Ont. L3Y 8E2, Canada. TEL 416-727-2300. FAX 416-853-3754. Ed. Liane Macrae. adv.: B&W page Can.$4831, color page Can.$5581; trim 11 3/8 x 14. circ. 102,826.

071.1   CN
PORTAGE. (Supplements avail.) 1978. w. Can.$45($78) Editions de l'Est, 16 du Domaine, Riviere-du-Loup, PQ G5R 2P5, Canada. TEL 418-862-1774. FAX 418-862-4387. Owner(s): Quebecor, 612 St-Jacques, Montreal, PQ H2C 4M8, Canada. TEL 418-877-9777. FAX 418-877-9790. Ed. Georges Fraser. adv. contact: Colber Lebel. illus. cols./p.: 7; pp./issue: 36. (tabloid format) **Document type:** newspaper.

071.1   CN
PRINCE RUPERT DAILY NEWS. 1910. d. (Mon.-Fri.). Can.$165. Sterling Newspapers Limited, 801 Second Ave., W., Prince Rupert, BC V8J 1H6, Canada. TEL 604-624-6781. FAX 604-624-2851. Ed. Scott Crowson. adv. contact: Karen Myers. circ. 3,450 (paid). (broadsheet format) **Document type:** newspaper.

071.1   CN
QUEBEC CHRONICLE - TELEGRAPH. 1764. w. Can.$23($50); newsstand price: Can.$0.75. Karen MacDonald, Ed. & Pub., 3484 chemin Ste-Foy, Sainte-Foy, PQ G1X 1S8, Canada. TEL 418-650-1764. FAX 418-650-1764. adv. contact: Yves St.Germain. bk.rev. circ. 5,000. cols./p.: 5; pp./issue: 12. (tabloid format) **Document type:** newspaper.
    Description: Covers local news and community events for the English-speaking community in the greater Quebec city region.

051   CN   ISSN 0316-2052
QUEBEC FRANCAIS. 1973. q. Can.$24($30) Publications Quebec Francais, C.P. 9185, Sainte-Foy, PQ G1U 4B1, Canada. TEL 418-527-0809. FAX 418-527-4765. adv.; bk.rev. circ. 8,000. (also avail. in microfilm from BNQ; back issues avail.)

051   CN   ISSN 0033-6041
AP5
QUEEN'S QUARTERLY; a Canadian review. 1893. q. Can.$20($25) Queen's Quarterly, Queen's University, Kingston, ON K7L 3N6, Canada. TEL 613-545-2667. FAX 613-545-6822. Ed. Boris Castel. adv.; bk.rev.; charts; index, cum.index: 1893-1953, 1954-1968, 1969-1978. circ. 3,000. (also avail. in microform from UMI; back issues avail.; reprint service avail. from UMI) **Indexed:** Abstr.Engl.Stud., Amer.Bibl.Slavic & E.Eur.Stud., Amer.Hist.& Life, Arts & Hum.Cit.Ind., Can.Lit.Ind., Can.Per.Ind., CMI, Curr.Cont., Hist.Abstr., Ind.Bk.Rev.Hum., Int.Polit.Sci.Abstr., Lang.& Lang.Behav.Abstr., M.L.A., Mid.East: Abstr.& Ind., P.A.I.S.
    —BLDSC (7211.700000); Faxon; UnCover; UMI. CCC.
    Refereed Serial

051   CN   ISSN 0034-0413
READER'S DIGEST (CANADIAN-ENGLISH EDITION). (Text in English) 1948. m. Can.$32.06. Periodicals Reader's Digest Ltee. - Reader's Digest Magazines Ltd., 215 Redfern Ave., Westmount, PQ H3Z 2V9, Canada. TEL 514-934-0751. Ed. Alexander Farrell. adv.; illus. circ. 1,307,394. (also avail. in microform from UMI; reprint service avail. from UMI) **Indexed:** Can.Per.Ind., CMI, Hlth.Ind., Mag.Ind.
    —UMI.

051   CN   ISSN 0829-4399
REPORTAGE CANADA. English edition: Canada Reports. Spanish edition: Reportaje Canada. (Text in French) 1947. q. free. External Affairs and International Trade Canada, Foreign Policy Communications Division, 125 Sussex Dr., Ottawa, Ont. K1A 0G2, Canada. TEL 613-992-9280. TELEX 053-3745. illus. circ. 9,500.
    Supersedes: Hebdo Canada (ISSN 0384-2304)

071.1   CN
REVIEW. 1893. w. Can.$22($80); newsstand price: Can.$.55. 41 High St., Vankleek Hill, ON K0B 1R0, Canada. TEL 613-678-3327. FAX 613-678-2700. Ed. Louise Sproule; Pub. Louise Sproule. adv. contact: Perthena McFall. circ. 3,358 (paid). (broadsheet format) **Document type:** newspaper.

071.1   CN
RIDGETOWN DOMINION. 1895. w. Can.$23.50($37) 11 Ebenezer St. W., Ridgetown, ON N0P 2C0, Canada. TEL 519-674-3700. FAX 519-674-5131. Ed. Shelia McBrayne; Pub. Barb Brown. adv. contact: Jim Brown. bk.rev.; illus. circ. 2,850. cols./p.: 5; pp./issue: 24. (tabloid format; back issues avail.) **Document type:** newspaper.

071.1   CN
RIVERS BANNER; gazette-reporter. 1993. w. Can.$20($50); newsstand price: free. 526 2nd Ave., Rivers, MB R0K 1X0, Canada. TEL 204-328-7494. FAX 204-328-5212. Owner(s): Ken & Chris Waddell, 272 Hamilton St., Neepawa, MB R0J 1H0, Canada. Ed. Sheila Szapko; Pubs. Ken & Chris Waddell. adv.: B&W page Can.$125; adv. contact: Sheila Szapko. illus. cols./p.: 4; pp./issue: 8. (back issues avail.) **Document type:** newspaper.

071.1   CN
RODNEY MERCURY. 1892. w. Can.$45; newsstand price: Can.$.45. 11 Ebenezer St. W., Ridgetown, ON N0P 2C0, Canada. TEL 519-674-3232. FAX 519-674-5131. Ed. Sheila McBrayne; Pub. Barb Brown. adv. contact: Jim Brown. illus. circ. 1,300. cols./p.: 5; pp./issue: 16. (tabloid format; back issues avail.) **Document type:** newspaper.

051   CN   ISSN 0035-8908
ROYAL GAZETTE. 1874. w. Can.$48.15. Queen's Printer, Prince Edward Island, Charlottetown, P.E.I., Canada. TEL 902-368-5190. FAX 902-368-5544. Ed. P.J. Murphy. adv. circ. 700. (also avail. in microfilm from KTO)

051 635   CN   ISSN 0703-7724
RURAL DELIVERY. 1976. 10/yr. Can.$13.75 (foreign Can.$20.75). D v L Publishing, Box 1509, Liverpool, NS B0T 1K0, Canada. Ed. Dirk van Loon. adv.; bk.rev. circ. 10,000. **Document type:** consumer publication.
    Description: Provides information and support for rural residents in Atlantic Canada.

071   CN   ISSN 0049-4658
SACKVILLE TRIBUNE-POST. 1902. w. Can.$23($85) Tribune Post Ltd., Sackville, NB E0A 3C0, Canada. TEL 506-536-2500. FAX 506-536-4024. Ed. H. Smith. adv. circ. 3,451. (also avail. in microfilm) **Document type:** newspaper.

051   CN   ISSN 0835-7919
SAFARIR. 1987. 12/yr. Can.$39. Artistocrates, Inc., 549 Grande Allee Est, Quebec, PQ G1R 2J5, Canada. TEL 418-522-1062. FAX 418-522-3597. adv. circ. 61,711.

071.1   CN
ST. ALBERT GAZETTE. 1961. s-w. Can.$30. Jamison Newspapers, Inc., 25 Chisholm Ave., Box 263, St. Albert, AB T8N 1N3, Canada. TEL 403-460-5500. FAX 403-460-8220. Ed. Sue Gawlak; Pub. Duff Jamison. adv. contact: Mary Jamison. bk.rev.;. Wire service(s): SHNA. circ. 8,500 (paid); 14,000 (controlled). (tabloid format; back issues avail.) **Document type:** newspaper.

071.1   CN
ST. LAURENT ECHO. (Supplements avail.) 1895. w. Can.$45($78) Editions de l'Est, 16 du Domaine, Riviere-du-Loup, PQ G5R 2P5, Canada. TEL 418-862-1774. FAX 418-862-4387. Owner(s): Quebecor, 612 St-Jacques, Montreal, PQ H2C 4M8, Canada. TEL 418-877-9777. FAX 418-877-9790. Ed. Georges Fraser. adv. contact: Colbert Lebel. illus. cols./p.: 7; pp./issue: 36. (tabloid format) **Document type:** newspaper.

051   CN
SALMON ARM OBSERVER. 1907. w. Can.$32($40) Box 550, Salmon Arm, B.C. V1E 4N7, Canada. TEL 604-832-2131. FAX 604-832-5140. Ed. Brian Smart. adv. circ. 5,500. (also avail. in microfilm; back issues avail.)

051   CN   ISSN 0036-4975
SATURDAY NIGHT; Canada's leading magazine of comment and opinion. 1887. 10/yr. Can.$19.95($31.45) Saturday Night, 184 Front St., E., Toronto, ON M5A 4N3, Canada. TEL 416-368-7237. FAX 416-368-5112. Ed. John Fraser. adv.; bk.rev.; illus.; stat. circ. 405,000. (also avail. in microform from MML,UMI; **Indexed:** Bk.Rev.Ind. (1965-), Can.Lit.Ind., Can.Per.Ind., Can.Wom.Per.Ind., Child.Bk.Rev.Ind. (1965-), CMI, Mag.Ind., P.A.I.S. **Document type:** consumer publication.
    —UnCover; UMI.

071.1   CN
SCARBOROUGH NEWS. 1950. w. Can.$15; newsstand price: Can.$.40. Watson Publishing Company Limited, 150 Milner St., Unit 35, Scarborough, ON M1S 3R3, Canada. TEL 416-291-2583. Ed. Robert M. Watson; Pub. Robert M. Watson. adv.; illus. cols./p.: 6; pp./issue: 12. (tabloid format; back issues avail.) **Document type:** newspaper.

054.1   CN   ISSN 0037-1378
SELECTION DU READER'S DIGEST (CANADIAN-FRENCH EDITION). (Text in French) 1947. m. Can.$32.06. Periodiques Reader's Digest Ltee. - Reader's Digest Magazines Ltd., 215 Redfern Ave., Westmount, PQ H3Z 2V9, Canada. TEL 514-934-0751. FAX 514-932-3637. Ed. Lise Verschelden. adv.; bk.rev.; illus. circ. 326,774. (also avail. in microform from UMI; reprint service avail. from UMI) **Indexed:** Can.Per.Ind., Periodex, Pt.de Rep. (1979-).
    —UMI.

SENIOR WORLD; Canada's national magazine for the mature reader. see GERONTOLOGY AND GERIATRICS

051   CN   ISSN 0228-9091
SIGNAL. (Text in English, French) 1989. 4/yr. Can.$1.50 per no. Ligue Securite du Quebec, 2536 La Pierre, La Salle, Que. H8N 2W9, Canada. TEL 514-595-9110. FAX 514-595-3398. Ed. Diane Des Autels. adv. circ. 10,000. **Document type:** newsletter.

051   CN   ISSN 0707-4964
SLAVE RIVER JOURNAL. 1978. w. Can.$37.45. P.O. Box 990, Fort Smith, N.W.T. X0E 0P0, Canada. TEL 403-872-2784. FAX 403-872-2754. adv. contact: Sandra Jaque. circ. 2,118.
    Description: Serves the South Slave Region in the NWT as well as Fort Chipewyan, Alberta.

071.1   FR
SOLEIL. (Supplements avail.) 1896. d. 390 rue Saint-Vallier E., Quebec, PQ G1K 7J6, Canada. TEL 418-647-3233. FAX 418-647-3260. Owner(s): UniMedia Inc., 600 boul. de Maisonneuve O., Bur. 3200, Montreal, PQ H3A 3J2, Canada. TEL 514-284-2500. FAX 514-284-1129. Ed. J. Jacques Samson; Pub. Gilbert Lacasse. adv. contact: Denis Dube. bk.rev.; illus. Wire service(s): AFP, AP, NYT, PC, RN. cols./p.: 6. (broadsheet format; also avail. in microform from SOC) **Document type:** newspaper.
    ●Also available on CD-ROM.

071.1   CN
SOLEIL DE COLOMBIE BRITANNIQUE. (Supplements avail.) 1968. w. Can.$25($55); newsstand price: Can.$.60. 1645 W. 5th Ave., Vancouver, BC V5N 1S4, Canada. TEL 604-730-9575. FAX 604-730-9576. Ed. Pierre Longnus; Pub. Jacques Baillaut. adv.: page Can.$979; adv. contact: Alain Barillaud. circ. 2,800 (controlled). cols./p.: 5; pp./issue: 16. (back issues avail.) **Document type:** newspaper.

071   CN
SOOKE NEWS MIRROR; a community newspaper. 1959. w. Can.$40. Island Publishers Ltd., Box 339, Sooke, B.C. V0S 1N0, Canada. TEL 604-642-5752. FAX 604-642-4767. Ed. Mitch Moned. adv.; bk.rev.; illus. circ. 4,800. **Document type:** newspaper.
    Formerly: Sooke Mirror (ISSN 0026-5837)

GENERAL INTEREST PERIODICALS — CANADA   2701

071.1   CN
SOUTHWEST BOOSTER. 1966. w. Can.$98; newsstand price: free. 30-4th Ave. N.W., Swift Current, SK S9H 3X4, Canada. TEL 306-773-9321. FAX 306-773-9136. Ed. Peter Godfrey; Pub. Bill Mann. adv. contact: Bob Watson. illus.; circ. 19,100 (controlled). cols./p.: 5; pp./issue: 44. (tabloid format) **Document type:** newspaper.

071.1   CN
SPECTATOR. (Supplements avail.) 1846. d. (Mon.-Sat.). Can.$139. 44 Frid St., Hamilton, ON L8N 3G3, Canada. TEL 905-526-3333. FAX 905-522-1696. Owner(s): Southam Newspaper Group, 1450 Don Mills Rd., Don Mills, ON M3B 2X7, Canada. TEL 416-445-6641. FAX 416-442-3386. Ed. Rob Austin; Pub. Jake Doherty. adv. contact: Dave Weber. bk.rev.; illus. Wire service(s): CanP, KR, LAT WP. circ. 130,818 (paid). cols./p.: 6. (broadsheet format) back issues avail.; reprint service from CML) **Document type:** newspaper.

071.1   CN
STAR & TIMES. 1900. w. Can.$42.80($96); newsstand price: Can.$.50. Swan Valley Star & Times, 704 Main St., Box 670, Swan River, MB R0L 1Z0, Canada. TEL 204-734-3858. FAX 204-734-4935. Ed. Robert F. Gilroy; Pub. Robert F. Gilroy. adv. contact: Brian Gilroy. illus. cols./p.: 6; pp./issue: 28. (broadsheet format) **Document type:** newspaper.

051   CN   ISSN 0226-9686
SUBURBAN. (Text in English and French) 1962. w. Can.$105. La Cie de Publications Michael Inc., 8170 Wavell Rd., Cote St. Luc, Que. H4W 1M3, Canada. FAX 514-484-7284. Ed. Michael A. Wollock. adv.; bk.rev.; film rev.; play rev. circ. 101,000. (tabloid format; back issues avail.)

071.1   CN
SUN TIMES. 1853. d. (Mon.-Sat.). $668.80. 290 9th St. E., Owen Sound, ON N4K 1N7, Canada. TEL 519-376-2250. FAX 519-376-7190. Owner(s): Southam Newspaper Group, 1450 Don Mills Rd., Don Mills, ON M3B 2X7, Canada. TEL 416-445-6641. FAX 416-442-3386. Ed. Jim Merriam; Pub. Alex Beer. adv. contact: Warren Elder. bk.rev.; illus.; circ. 22,144 (paid). cols./p.: 6; pp./issue: 23. (broadsheet format; also avail. in microform from CML; back issues avail.; reprint service avail. from CML) **Document type:** newspaper.

071.1   CN
SWIFT CURRENT SUN. (Supplements avail.) 1903. 2/wk. Can.$40.66($118) 55 1st Ave. N.E., Swift Current, SK S9H 2A9, Canada. TEL 306-773-3116. FAX 306-773-2653. Ed. John Morran; Pub. Michael J. Hertz. adv. contact: Garth Hordenchuk. bk.rev.; illus. cols./p.: 5; pp./issue: 24. (tabloid format; also avail. in microfiche from GCS) **Document type:** newspaper.

071.1   CN
TELEGRAPH (BATTLEFORD). (Supplement avail.: Advertiser Post) 1979. s-w. Can.$37.45. Turner Warwick Publications, 892 104th St. N., Battleford, SK S9A 3E6, Canada. TEL 306-445-7231. FAX 306-445-3223. Ed. Lois Walsh; Pub. W.R. Warwick. adv. contact: Chad Charbonneau. circ. 2,500 (paid). cols./p.: 6; pp./issue: 12. **Document type:** newspaper.

071.1   CN
TELEGRAPH (SASKATOON). see SPORTS AND GAMES — Outdoor Life

071.1   CN
TEMISKAMING SPEAKER. (Supplements avail.) 1906. w. Can.$28.08; newsstand price: Can.$.65. 18 Wellington St., New Liskeard, ON P0J 1P0, Canada. TEL 705-647-6791. FAX 705-647-9669. Ed. Gord Brock; Pub. Dave Armstrong. adv. contact: Lois Perry. illus.; circ. 7,600 (paid). cols./p.: 6; pp./issue: 30. (broadsheet format) **Document type:** newspaper.

051   CN   ISSN 0823-6542
THUNDER BAY MAGAZINE. 1983. bi-m. Can.$16.95. White Oaks Publishing, 1184 Roland St., Thunder Bay, ON P7B 5M4, Canada. TEL 807-623-7110. FAX 807-623-7110. Ed. John P. Mallon. adv.; bk.rev. circ. 28,000. (back issues avail.; reprint service avail.)

071.1   CN
TILBURY TIMES. 1884. w. Can.$42.25($57) McConnell Publishing Inc., P.O. Box 490, 9 Prospect St., Tilbury, ON N0P 2L0, Canada. TEL 519-682-0411. FAX 519-682-3633. Ed. Gerry Harvieux; Pub. Terry McConnell. adv. contact: Victoria Charron. illus.; circ. 3,012 (paid); 288 (controlled). cols./p.: 5; pp./issue: 24. (tabloid format; also avail. in microfiche) **Document type:** newspaper.

051   CN
TORONTO EVENTS PLANNER. 1990. 3/yr. Can.$70. Pearl Publishing Inc., 99 Kimbark Blvd., Toronto, ON M5N 2Y3, Canada. TEL 416-782-3322. FAX 416-787-9299. Ed. Sybil Levine. adv.: B&W page Can.$1200, color page Can.$1600; trim 8 1/2 x 11. **Document type:** consumer publication.

971.3   CN   ISSN 0049-4194
TORONTO LIFE. 1966. m. (plus q., s-a. & a. supplements). Can.$22. Toronto Life Publishing Co. Ltd., 59 Front St. E., 3rd fl., Toronto, Ont. M5E 1B3, Canada. TEL 416-364-3333. FAX 416-585-5275. Ed. Marq de Villiers. adv.; bk.rev. circ. 96,000. **Indexed:** Can.Lit.Ind., Can.Per.Ind., CMI.

071.1   CN
TOTTENHAM TIMES. 1978. w. Can.$35($87); newsstand price: Can.$.75. 34 Main St. W., Beeton, ON L0G 1A0, Canada. TEL 905-729-2287. FAX 905-729-2541. Ed. Bruce R. Haire. adv. contact: John H. Archibald. circ. 2,850 (paid). cols./p.: 5; pp./issue: 24. (tabloid format) **Document type:** newspaper.

071.1   CN
TRANSCRIPT & FREE PRESS. 1870. w. Can.$25($78); newsstand price: Can.$.75. Box 400, 240 Main St., Glencoe, ON N0L 1M0, Canada. adv.; circ. 2,720 (paid). cols./p.: 5; pp./issue: 24. (tabloid format) **Document type:** newspaper.

071.1   CN
TRENTONIAN & TRI-COUNTY NEWS. 1956. 3/wk. (Mon., Wed., Fri.). Can.$138.17; newsstand price: Can.$.50. 41 Quinte St., P.O. Box 130, Trenton, ON K8V 5R3, Canada. TEL 613-392-6501. FAX 613-392-0505. Owner(s): Thomson Newspapers Ltd., 65 Queen St., W., Toronto, ON M5H 2M8, Canada. TEL 416-864-1710. FAX 416-864-0234. Ed. Paul Hageman; Pub. Garry Gordon. adv. contact: Bob Crowther. cols./p.: 6; pp./issue: 14. (broadsheet format; also avail. in microfiche; back issues avail.) **Document type:** newspaper.

071.1   CN
TRI-CITY NEWS. 1985. s-w. Meadowridge Publications, 1405 Broadway, Port Coquitlam, BC V3C 5W9, Canada. TEL 604-525-6397. FAX 604-944-0703. Ed. Mark Hamilton. adv. contact: Karla Pearson. bk.rev.; circ. 45,458 (controlled). (tabloid format; back issues avail.) **Document type:** newspaper.

071.1   CN
TRURO DAILY NEWS. (Sunday ed. is tabloid) d. P.O. Box 220, 6 Louise St., Truro, NS B2N 5C3, Canada. Ed. Joe Wallace; Pub. Milton S. Ellis. adv. contact: Bruce Pearson. bk.rev.; illus. Wire service(s): CanP. cols./p.: 6. (broadsheet format; also avail. in microfilm) **Document type:** newspaper.

054   CN
UNION DES CANTONS DE L'EST. (Text in French) 1866. w. Can.$33($60) Journal l'Union Inc., C.P. 130, Victoriaville, Que. G6P 6S8, Canada. TEL 819-357-8232. FAX 819-357-3623. Ed. Richard Lacoursiere. adv.; bk.rev.; film rev.; play rev.; illus. circ. 12,000. (also avail. in microform)

054.1   CN   ISSN 0316-6368
UNIVERSITE DE MONCTON. REVUE. Key Title: Revue de l'Universite de Moncton. 1968. s-a. Can.$18. Universite de Moncton, Moncton, NB E1A 3E9, Canada. TEL 506-858-4062. FAX 506-8584534. Ed. Michel Saint-Louis. bk.rev.; circ. 650 (controlled). **Indexed:** Pt.de Rep. (1983-). **Document type:** academic/scholarly publication.
Description: Contains articles and book reviews on all subjects, treated in a scholarly manner.

051   CN   ISSN 1180-9906
UPTOWN MAGAZINE. 1987. fortn. $25. Canadian Publishers, 1465 St. James St., Winnipeg, MB R3H 0W9, Canada. Ed. Heidi Quiring. adv. circ. 10,500. (tabloid format)
Formerly (until 1989): Uptown Gazette (ISSN 0847-8031)

054.1   CN   ISSN 0849-035X
V O, VIE OUVRIERE. 1951. 6/yr. Can.$20 (foreign Can.$25) to individuals; institutions Can.$28 (foreign Can.$33). Revue Vie Ouvriere Inc., 1212 Rue Panet, Montreal, PQ H2L 2Y7, Canada. TEL 514-523-5998. FAX 514-527-3403. Ed.Bd. adv.; bk.rev.; illus.; index. circ. 3,000. (back issues avail.) **Indexed:** CERDIC, Pt.de Rep. (1983-).
Formerly (until 1990): Vie Ouvriere (ISSN 0229-3803)
Description: Looks at conditions of work and life of the working class, their organizations, culture and struggles.

071.1   CN
VALLEYVIEW VALLEY VIEWS. (Supplements avail.) 1963. w. Can.$35($80); newsstand price: Can.$.70. Box 787, Valleyview, AB T0H 3N0, Canada. Ed. Joan Plaxton; Pub. Joan Plaxton. adv. contact: Wayne Plaxton. bk.rev. circ. 1,571. cols./p.: 5; pp./issue: 24. (tabloid format; back issues avail.) **Document type:** newspaper.

051   CN
▼**VALUE PLUS MAGAZINE.** 1993. m. Can.$24. Value Plus Magazine Ltd., 105 Kenneth St., Duncan, BC V9L 1N5, Canada. TEL 604-746-6463. FAX 604-746-7445. Ed. Frank Hird-Rutter. adv.: B&W page Can.$1290, color page Can.$3230; trim 8 1/2 x 11. circ. 11,000.

051   CN   ISSN 0831-4039
VEN'D'EST. 1985. q. Can.$15 to individuals (foreign Can.$25); institutions Can.$20 (foreign Can.$30). Editions Cooperatives du Ven'd'Est, Ltee., P.O. Box 430, Petit Rocher, NB E0B 2E0, Canada. TEL 506-783-4097. FAX 506-783-8386. Ed. Loie Vennin. adv. contact: Micheline Trempe. bk.rev. circ. 4,500. **Document type:** consumer publication.
Description: General interest publication for the Acadian population of the maritime provinces. Themes are education, peace, fishing, forestry, feminism. Also includes international sections on art and culture, ecology and politics.

071.1   CN
VERMILION STANDARD. 1909. w. Can.$20 (foreign Can.$100); newsstand price: Can.$.50. 4917 50 Ave., Box 750, Vermilion, AB T0B 4M0, Canada. TEL 403-853-5344. FAX 403-853-5203. Ed. Steven Dills; Pub. Steven Dills. adv. contact: Steven Dills. circ. 3,506 (paid); 82 (controlled). cols./p.: 5; pp./issue: 36. (tabloid format; also avail. in microfilm from CML; back issues avail.) **Document type:** newspaper.

051   CN   ISSN 1182-6142
VICTORIA AND VANCOUVER ISLAND VISITOR. 1969. w. Visitor Publications, 770 Enterprise Cresc., Victoria, BC V8Z 6R4, Canada. TEL 604-727-3469. FAX 604-727-6344. adv. circ. 34,094. (tabloid format)

051   CN   ISSN 1182-0438
VICTORIA TODAY. 1988. m. Island Publishers, 770 Enterprise Cresc., Victoria, BC V8Z 6R4, Canada. TEL 604-727-3469. FAX 604-727-6344. adv. circ. 53,000.

051   CN   ISSN 0832-4719
VICTORIA'S MONDAY MAGAZINE. 1975. w. Can.$74.90 (foreign Can.$85). Monday Publications Ltd., 1609 Blanshard St., Victoria, B.C. V8W 2J5, Canada. TEL 604-382-6188. FAX 604-381-2662. Ed. Sid Tafler. adv.; bk.rev. circ. 40,000.

054.1   CN
VOYAGEUR (SUDBURY). 1968. w. Can.$15($60) Hebdo le Voyageur Inc., 1314 bvd. Lasalle, Sudbury, Ont. P3A 1Y8, Canada. TEL 705-560-3355. FAX 705-560-9420. Ed. Pierre Giroux. circ. 10,000. (tabloid format; also avail. in microfilm

2702 GENERAL INTEREST PERIODICALS — CENTRAL AFRICAN REPUBLIC

071.1   CN
WATROUS MANITOU. 1933. w. Can.$18; newsstand price: Can.$.75. 309 Main St., Watrous, SK S0K 4T0, Canada. TEL 306-946-3343. FAX 306-946-2026. Pubs. Frank W. & Isabel F. Wilson. adv.; circ. 2,100 (paid). cols./p.: 5; pp./issue: 24. (tabloid format) **Document type:** newspaper.

071.1   CN
WEST HILL NEWS. 1950. w. Can.$15; newsstand price: Can.$.40. Watson Publishing Company Limited, 150 Milner Ave., Unit 35, Scarborough, ON M1S 3R3, Canada. TEL 416-291-2583. Ed. Robert M. Watson. adv.; illus. (tabloid format; back issues avail.) **Document type:** newspaper.

051   US
WESTCHESTER SPOTLIGHT. m. Meadow Publications, Inc., 126 Library Lane, Mamaroneck, NY 10543-3608. TEL 914-381-4740. FAX 914-381-4641. Ed. Susan Meadow. bk.rev.; film rev.

071.1   CN
WESTERN CANADIAN. 1900. w. Can.$30($48); newsstand price: Can.$.50. B K S Publishing Ltd., 424 Ellis Ave., Manitou, MB R0G 1G0, Canada. TEL 204-242-2555. FAX 204-242-3137. Ed. Bryan Klippenstein. adv. contact: Bryan Klippenstein. illus. circ. 2,000. cols./p.: 5; pp./issue: 16. (tabloid format) **Document type:** newspaper.

051   CN   ISSN 0049-7444
WESTERN LIVING. 1971. 10/yr. Can.$18. Telemedia West, 300 Southeast Twr., 555 W. 12th Ave., Vancouver, BC V5Z 4L4, Canada. TEL 604-877-7732. FAX 604-877-4848. Ed. Paula Brook. adv.; bk.rev. circ. 252,000. **Indexed:** CMI.

071.1   CN
WESTMOUNT EXAMINER. 1928. w. Can.$25.92($90) 210 Victoria St., Westmount, PQ H3Z 2M4, Canada. TEL 514-484-5610. FAX 514-484-6028. Owner(s): Publications Dumont, 9216 Boivin, La Salle, PQ H8R 2E7, Canada. TEL 514-363-3223. FAX 514-363-9772. Ed. Craig McKee; Pub. Bruce Stevenson. adv. contact: Patrick Frye. illus.; circ. 375 (paid); 9,625 (controlled). cols./p.: 5; pp./issue: 28. (tabloid format)

051   CN   ISSN 1185-345X
WHAT'S HAPPENING MAGAZINE. 1984. 7/yr. Can.$15. Susan K. Bailey Enterprises Ltd., 135 Main St., Box 171, Foxboro, ON K0K 2B0, Canada. TEL 613-969-8896. FAX 613-969-1836. Ed. JoAnne Lewis. adv.; bk.rev. circ. 15,000.
Former titles (until 1991): In Touch with What's Happening (ISSN 0845-7611); (until 1988): What's Happening Magazine (ISSN 0820-4691)
Description: Designed to inform residents of the Quinte area about local happenings.

051   CN
WHAT'S ON MAGAZINE. 1988. w. free. Kootenay Weekly Express, P.O. Box 922, Nelson, B.C. V1L 6A5, Canada. TEL 604-354-3910. FAX 604-352-5075. Ed. Margaret Chrumka. adv. circ. 17,191. (tabloid format) **Document type:** newspaper.

051   CN   ISSN 1187-1539
WHAT'S UP NIAGARA MAGAZINE. 1981. m. Can.$24. Rannie Printing and Publishing Ltd. (Subsidiary of: Burgoyne Community Newspapers Ltd.), P.O. Box 3044, St. Catharines, Ont. L2R 7E3, Canada. TEL 905-682-2683. FAX 905-682-3603. (Subscr. to: 140 Welland Ave., Ste. 1, St. Catharines, ON L2R 2N6, Canada) Ed. Molly Harding. adv. contact: Chris Alderson. bk.rev. circ. 30,000. (back issues avail.)
Formerly: What's Up Niagara (ISSN 0712-3892)

051   CN   ISSN 0838-4096
WINTER CITIES. 1982. 4/yr. Can.$40. Winter Cities Association, 1933 5th St. S.W., Calgary, Alta. T2S 2B2, Canada. FAX 403-245-9701. adv.; bk.rev. circ. 600.
Formerly: Winter Cities News.

051   CN
YELLOWKNIFER. w. P.O. Box 2820, Yellowknife, N.W.T. X1A 2R1, Canada. TEL 403-873-4031. Ed. Brian Jones. circ. 6,000. (also avail. in microfilm from CML)

971   CN   ISSN 0044-1376
YUKON NEWS. 1960. s-w. Can.$210. Media North Ltd., c/o D.S. Robertson, 211 Wood St., Whitehorse, Yukon Y1A 2E4, Canada. TEL 403-667-6285. FAX 403-668-3755. Ed. P. Leshiak. adv.; bk.rev.; charts; illus. circ. 8,900.

051   CN
7 JOURS. 1989. w. Can.$2 per no. Trustar Ltd., 10000 Lajeunesse St., Ste. 200, Montreal, Que. H3L 2E1, Canada. TEL 514-383-3400. FAX 514-383-4353. adv. circ. 200,000.

GENERAL INTEREST PERIODICALS — Central African Republic

UNITE - DIGNITE - TRAVAIL: PROGRAMME TRIENNAL D'INVESTISSEMENT DE L'ETAT. see BUSINESS AND ECONOMICS — Abstracting, Bibliographies, Statistics

GENERAL INTEREST PERIODICALS — Central America

see also General Interest Periodicals–Bermuda; General Interest Periodicals–Cuba; General Interest Periodicals–Dominican Republic; General Interest Periodicals–Guatemala; General Interest Periodicals–Mexico; General Interest Periodicals–Panama

056.1   SP
CENTROAMERICA ANUARIO. 1990. a. Centro Espanol de Estudios de America Latina, Avda. Reyes Catolicos, 4, planta 5a, 28040 Madrid, Spain.

056.1   BH
FUN & GAMES. m. $15. Cream Ltd., 3304 Partridge St., Lake Independence, Belize City, Belize.

052   BH
GOVERNMENT GAZETTE. w. B.$24. Government Printery, Power Lane, Belmopan, Belize. TEL 08-22293. FAX 08-23367. adv. circ. 2,000. **Document type:** government publication.

LATINA. see GENERAL INTEREST PERIODICALS — South America

053.1   GW
NICARAGUA HEUTE. 1982. s-a. Christliche Initiative Romero, Kardinal-von-Galen-Ring 45, 48149 Muenster, Germany. TEL 0251-89503. circ. 20,000. (back issues avail.)

056.1   GT
PANORAMA INTERNACIONAL; revista semanal centroamericana. 1989. w. I C A N, S.A., 6ta. Avda., 15-48 Zona 1, Guatemala City, Guatemala. TEL 005022-51-8555. FAX 005022-52-8475. Ed. Vittorugo Mangiavillani. **Document type:** consumer publication.

053.1   GW
PRESENTE. 1983. s-a. Christliche Initiative Romero, Kardinal-von-Galen-Ring 45, 48149 Muenster, Germany. TEL 0251-89503. circ. 6,000. (back issues avail.)

052   BH
REPORTER. 1968. w. 147 Allenby St., crnr. West St., POB 707, Belize City, Belize. TEL 2-72503. Ed. Harry Lawrence. circ. 6,500.

056.1   CR
RUMBO. 1981. w. $75 for 6 mos. Nacion S.A., Apartado 10138, San Jose, Costa Rica. TEL 87-43-70. FAX 40-64-80. TELEX 376-2358. Ed. Roxana Zuniga Quesada. adv.; bk.rev. circ. 8,000. (reprint service avail. from L.A.Times Syndicate)
Former titles (until 1987): Rumbo Centroamericano; (until 1984): Nacion Internacional.

079.728   CR
TICO TIMES. (Text in English) 1956. w. $45 (foreign $70). Tico Times S.A., Av. 8, Calle 15, San Jose, Costa Rica. TEL 506-22-89-52. FAX 506-33-63-78. (Subscr. to: P.O. Box 4632, San Jose, Costa Rica; U.S. subscr. to: Box 025216, Miami, FL 33102) Ed. Dery Dyer. adv.; circ. 14,600 (paid). (back issues avail.) **Document type:** newspaper.
Description: Covers Costa Rica and Central America, as well as Panama.

051   US   ISSN 0040-7917
THE TIMES OF THE AMERICAS. 1956. fortn. $25. Times of the Americas, Inc., 910 17th St., N.W., Ste. 321, Washington, DC 20006. FAX 202-429-5570. adv.; bk.rev. circ. 3,000. (also avail. in microform from UMI,MIM; microfilm from KTO)
Description: Political and economic news and informed opinion and analysis pieces on Latin America and the Carribean.

051   US   ISSN 1068-5332
WEEKLY NEWS UPDATE ON NICARAGUA AND THE AMERICAS. w. $25. Nicaragua Solidarity Network, 339 Lafayette St., New York, NY 10012. TEL 212-674-9499. E-mail: nicanet%transfer@blythe.org. index. **Document type:** newsletter.
●Also available online.
Description: Up-to-date news from a variety of sources covering Central and South America and the Caribbean.

GENERAL INTEREST PERIODICALS — Chile

056.1   CL
ANALISIS. 1977. w. Emision Ltda., Manuel Montt 425, Santiago, Chile. TEL 223-4386. Dir. Juan Pablo Cardenas. circ. 30,000.
Description: Covers political, economic and social affairs.

056.1   CL
LA EPOCA. m? Impresiones y Comunicaciones S.A., Olivares 1229 piso 5,6 y 9, Santiago, Chile. TEL 6990087. Ed. Emilio Filippi.

056.1   CL
QUE PASA?. 1971. w. Esc.11250. Editorial Portada Ltda., Europa 2020, Providencia, Santiago, Chile. TEL 2-225-5817. FAX 2-225-3201. TELEX 341029. Ed. Roberto Pulido Espinosa. adv. circ. 30,000.

056.1   CL   ISSN 0037-1203
SELECCIONES DEL READER'S DIGEST (CHILEAN EDITION). (Text in Spanish) 1940. m. Reader's Digest Chile Limitada, Calle Huelen 95, Casilla 3141, Santiago, Chile. adv.; bk.rev.; illus. circ. 48,000.

GENERAL INTEREST PERIODICALS — China

915.122   CC   ISSN 0517-659X
ANHUI HUABAO/ANHUI PICTORIAL. (Text in Chinese) 1958. bi-m. Y18. Anhui Huabao Publishing House, 1, Chenghuang Miao Qianjie, Hefei, Anhui 230061, People's Republic of China. TEL 273312. Eds. Tang Pushen, Chen Yuzhong. illus. (tabloid format)
Description: Introduces the economics, customs, culture, art and scenic spots in Anhui Province.

059.951   CC
BA XIAOSHI YIWAI/AFTER WORK HOURS. (Text in Chinese) 1980. m. Y13.20 (foreign $26.10). Tianjin Renmin Chubanshe, Qikan Bu - Tianjin People's Publishing House, 10 Changde Dao, Tianjin 300050, People's Republic of China. (Dist. outside China by: China International Book Trading Corp., P.O. Box 399, Beijing, P.R.C.; Dist. in US by: China Books & Periodicals, Inc., 2929 24th St., San Francisco, CA 94110) Ed. Yuan Xin. adv.; illus. circ. 100,000.

GENERAL INTEREST PERIODICALS — CHINA

050   CC   ISSN 1000-9140
DS701
BEIJING REVIEW; a magazine of Chinese news and views. Japanese edition: Pekin Shuho (ISSN 1000-9353); Spanish edition: Beijing Informa (ISSN 1000-9159); German edition: Beijing Rundschau (ISSN 1000-9167); Chinese edition: Beijing Zhoubao. (Text in English; French edition also avail.) 1958. w. $30.50 to individuals; institutions $35.50. (Ministry of Culture, Foreign Language Bureau) Beijing Review Publishing Co., 24 Baiwanzhuang Lu, Beijing 100037, People's Republic of China. TEL 8315599. FAX 01-8314318. (Dist. by: China International Book Trading Corp. (Guoji Shudian), Box 399, Beijing, P.R.C.; Dist. in US by: China Books and Periodicals Inc., 2929 24th St., San Francisco, CA 94110) adv.; bk.rev.; stat.; s-a. index. circ. 100,000. (also avail. in microform from BLH,MIM) **Indexed:** CLOSS, Excerp.Med., Geo.Abstr., Int.Lab.Doc., Key to Econ.Sci., Mid.East: Abstr.& Ind., Soc.Sci.Ind.
—BLDSC (1878.332000); Faxon; UnCover; SWETS.
Formerly (until 1979): Peking Review (ISSN 0031-4129)
Description: Covers political, economic, and social developments in China today. Discusses international questions and presents the official views of the Chinese Communist Party. Prints full texts of official documents and statements.

059.959   CC
CHIN - NITAYASARNPAP. (Thai edition of: China Pictorial) (Editions in various languages) 1987. m. $24. China Pictorial, Huayuan Cun, Xi Jiao, Beijing 100044, People's Republic of China. FAX 8413023. TELEX 22496-CIBTC-CN. (Dist. overseas by: China International Book Trading Corp., P.O. Box 399, Beijing, P.R.C.) adv.; illus.; index.

055.91   CC   ISSN 1000-9299
CHINA. (Rumanian edition of: China Pictorial) (Editions in various languages) 1977. m. $24. (Ministry of Culture, Foreign Language Bureau) China Pictorial, Huayuan Cun, Xi Jiao, Beijing 100044, People's Republic of China. FAX 8413023. TELEX 22496-CIBTC-CN. (Dist. overseas by: China International Book Trading Corp., P.O. Box 399, Beijing, P.R.C.) adv.; illus.; index.

059.951   US
CHINA BRIEFING. 1980. a. Westview Press, 550 Central Ave., Boulder, CO 80301. TEL 303-444-3541. FAX 303-449-3356. **Document type:** academic/scholarly publication.
Description: Assesses contemporary politics, economics, and culture in China.

059.96   CC   ISSN 1000-9302
CHINA GAZETA LA PICHA. (Swahili edition of: China Pictorial) (Editions in various languages) 1964. m. $24. (Ministry of Culture, Foreign Language Bureau) China Pictorial, Huayuan Cun, Xi Jiao, Beijing 100044, People's Republic of China. FAX 8413023. TELEX 22496-CIBTC-CN. (Dist. overseas by: China International Book Trading Corp., P.O. Box 399, Beijing, P.R.C.) adv.; illus.; index.

059.951 910.202   US   ISSN 0734-6549
DS712
CHINA GUIDEBOOK.* 1979. a. $18.95. Eurasia Press Inc., 18-20 Jordan Rd., Fair Lawn, NJ 07410-5229. FAX 201-837-1378. TELEX 668916 EURASIA. (Dist. in U.S. and Canada by: Houghton Mifflin Co., 2 Park St., Boston, MA 02108) Ed. Fredric M. Kaplan. adv. circ. 55,000.
Description: Travel and reference guide to People's Republic of China.

053.1   CC   ISSN 1000-9264
CHINA IM BILD. (German edition of: China Pictorial) (Editions in various languages) 1956. m. $24. (Ministry of Culture, Foreign Language Bureau) China Pictorial, Huayuan Cun, Xi Jiao, Beijing 100044, People's Republic of China. TEL 8415118. FAX 8413023. TELEX 22496-CIBTC-CN. (Dist. overseas by: China International Book Trading Corp., P.O. Box 399, Beijing, P.R.C.; Dist. in US by: China Books and Periodicals, Inc., 2929 24th St., San Francisco, CA 94110) adv.; illus.; index.

951   HK   ISSN 0009-4404
DS777.55
CHINA NEWS ANALYSIS. 1953. s-m. HK.$1450 (foreign $195) (effective 1994). C.N.A., G.P.O. Box 3225, Hong Kong. TEL 852-559-9620. FAX 852-521-8814. Ed. Yves Nalet. bk.rev.; stat.; index. (back issues avail.)
—BLDSC (3180.210000); UnCover; SWETS.
Description: Analyzes data from over 50 magazines and 20 dailies published in the People's Republic of China. Also surveys medium- and long-term developments in China. Each issue covers a major topic.

052   HK
CHINA NEWSLETTER. (Text in English) q. K P M G Peat Marwick China, 8F Princes Bldg., P.O. Box 50, Central, Hong Kong. TEL 5226022. FAX 8452588.
Description: Covers selected economic and legal news on recent situations in China.

052   CC   ISSN 0009-4420
DS777.55
CHINA PICTORIAL. (Chinese edition: Renmin Huabao (ISSN 0448-9373); French edition: La Chine (ISSN 1000-9272); German edition: China im Bild (ISSN 1000-9264); Italian edition: La Cina (ISSN 1000-9272); Japanese edition: Chugoku Gaho (ISSN 1000-9337); Rumanian edition: China (ISSN 1000-9299); Spanish edition: China Revista Ilustrada (ISSN 1000-9280); Swahili edition: Chin a Gazeta la Picha (ISSN 1000-9302); Swedish edition: Kina (ISSN 1000-9329); Thai edition: Chin - Nitayasarnpap) (Editions also in Arabic, Hindi, Korean, Russian, Tibetan, Urdu) 1950. m. $35. (Ministry of Culture, Foreign Language Bureau) China Pictorial, Huayuan Cun, Beijing 100044, People's Republic of China. FAX 8415118. TELEX 22496-CIBTC-CN. (Dist. overseas by: China International Book Trading Corp., P.O. Box 399, Beijing, P.R.C.; Dist. in US by: China Books and Periodicals, Inc., 2929 24th St., San Francisco, CA 94110. TEL 415-282-2994) Ed. Zhang Jiahua. adv.; illus.; index. circ. 500,000. (tabloid format; also avail. in microform from UMI,MIM) **Indexed:** GeoRef.
—UnCover.
Description: Contains short articles and color photography. Presents China's magnificent scenery, the life of its people, and its works of art.

059.951   US   ISSN 1069-5834
▼**CHINA REVIEW INTERNATIONAL**; a journal of reviews of scholarly literature in Chinese studies. 1994. s-a. $25 to individuals; institutions $30 (effective 1994). University of Hawaii Press, Journals Department, 2840 Kolowalu St., Honolulu, HI 96822. TEL 808-956-8833. FAX 808-988-6052. E-mail: CHINA@UHUNIX.UHCC.HAWAII.EDU. Ed. Roger T. Ames. adv.; bk.rev. (back issues avail.; reprint service avail. from UMI) **Document type:** academic/scholarly publication.
Description: Serves the Sinological community by publishing timely reviews in English of published scholarship in all areas of Chinese studies, with an interdisciplinary, international perspective. Also publishes "state of the art" articles on selected topics of interest.

056.1   CC   ISSN 1000-9280
CHINA REVISTA ILUSTRADA. (Spanish edition of: China Pictorial) (Editions in various languages) 1954. m. $24. (Ministry of Culture, Foreign Language Bureau) China Pictorial, Huayuan Cun, Xi Jiao, Beijing 100044, People's Republic of China. FAX 8413023. TELEX 22496-CIBTC-CN. (Dist. overseas by: China International Book Trading Corp., P.O. Box 399, Beijing, P.R.C.; Dist. in US by: China Books & Periodicals, Inc., 2929 24th St., San Francisco, CA 94110. TEL 415-282-2994) adv.; illus.; index.

951   CC   ISSN 1003-0905
DS701
CHINA TODAY. Chinese edition: Xiandai Zhongguo (ISSN 1003-0891); French edition: Chine au Present (ISSN 1003-0921); German edition: China Heute (ISSN 1003-093X); Portuguese edition: China Hoje (ISSN 1003-0913); Spanish edition: China Hoy (ISSN 1003-0948) (Text in English (British); Arabic and N. American editions also avail.). 1952. m. (Portuguese edition bi-m.). $26. (China Welfare Institute) Jinri Zhongguo Zazhishe, 24 Baiwanzhuang Lu, Beijing 100037, People's Republic of China. TEL 8326037. FAX 8328338. (Dist. by: China International Book Trading Corporation (Guoji Shudian), P.O. Box 399, Beijing, P.R.C. TEL 8412027; English ed. dist. in U.S. by: China Books and Periodicals, Inc., 2929 24th St., San Francisco, CA 94110. TEL 415-282-2994) Ed. Meng Jiqing. adv.: color page $2,000; adv. contact: Sanshi Wang. bk.rev.; illus. (also avail. in microform from UMI,MIM) **Indexed:** Bibl.& Ind.Geol., Geo.Abstr., Int.Lab.Doc., Peace Res.Abstr.
●Also available online. Vendor(s): DIALOG Information Services, Inc.
—Faxon; UnCover; SWETS.
Formerly (until 1990): China Reconstructs (ISSN 0009-4447)
Description: Introduces various aspects of life in the People's Republic of China, through articles and photography.

CHINA TRIBUNE/CHUNG-KUO LUN T'AN. see GENERAL INTEREST PERIODICALS — Taiwan

059.951   CC
CHINAFRICA; a monthly magazine of news and views. (Text in English) m. $26. Guoji Shudian, Qikan Bu - China International Book Trading Corp., P.O. Box 399, Beijing 100044, People's Republic of China. TEL 8413063. FAX 8412023.
Description: Published especially for readers in Africa. Highlights new developments in various aspects of China's life as well as the achievements of African countries.

054.1   CC   ISSN 1000-9272
LA CHINE. (French edition of: China Pictorial) (Editions in various languages) 1954. m. $24. (Ministry of Culture, Foreign Language Bureau) China Pictorial, Huayuan Cun, Xi Jiao, Beijing 100044, People's Republic of China. FAX 8415118. TELEX 22496-CIBTC-CN. (Dist. overseas by: China International Book Trading Corp., P.O. Box 399, Beijing, P.R.C.; Dist. in US by: China Books & Periodicals, Inc., 2929 24th St., San Francisco, CA 94110. TEL 415-282-2994) adv.; illus.; index.

059.956   CC   ISSN 1000-9337
CHUGOKU GAHO. (Japanese edition of: China Pictorial) (Editions in various languages) 1956. m. $24. (Ministry of Culture, Foreign Language Bureau) China Pictorial, Huayuan Cun, Xi Jiao, Beijing 100044, People's Republic of China. FAX 8413023. TELEX 22496-CIBTC-CN. (Dist. overseas by: China International Book Trading Corp., P.O. Box 399, Beijing, P.R.C.) adv.; illus.; index.

055.1   CC   ISSN 1000-9310
LA CINA. (Italian edition of: China Pictorial) (Editions in various languages) 1964. m. $24. (Ministry of Culture, Foreign Language Bureau) China Pictorial, Huayuan Cun, Xi Jiao, Beijing 100044, People's Republic of China. FAX 8413023. TELEX 22496-CIBTC-CN. (Dist. overseas by: China International Book Trading Corp., P.O. Box 399, Beijing, P.R.C.) adv.; illus.; index.

059.9   CC   ISSN 1000-7296
DONG XI NAN BEI/EAST - WEST - SOUTH - NORTH. (Text in Chinese) 1983. m. $41.30. Jinlin Ribao She - Jilin Daily, 68 Stalin Dajie, Changchun, Jilin 130051, People's Republic of China. (Dist. in US by: China Books & Periodicals, Inc., 2929 24th St., San Francisco, CA 94110. TEL 415-282-2994)
Description: Publishes articles from a variety of publications. Subjects including culture and art, personalities, social life, natural sciences, moral education, health and hygiene, and interesting anecdotes.

053.1   GW
DUESSELDORFER DRACHEN-POST. 1981. q. Haus-Endt-Str. 96, 40593 Dusseldorfer, Germany. TEL 0211-719684. Eds. Dieter Boening, Gisela Beste-Rueckert. circ. 1,500.
Description: News about China.

GENERAL INTEREST PERIODICALS — CHINA

059.951 CC ISSN 1000-0453
DUZHE WENZHAI/READER'S DIGEST. (Text in Chinese) m. Gansu Renmin Chubanshe, Qikan Bu - Gansu People's Publishing House, 81, Di-1 Xincun, Lanzhou, Gansu 730030, People's Republic of China. TEL 466321. (Dist. overseas by: Jiangsu Publications Import & Export Corp., 56 Gao Yun Ling, Nanjing, Jiangsu, P.R.C.) Ed. Zhou Dun. circ. 2,000,000.

499.992 CC ISSN 0032-4361
EL POPOLA CINIO/ZHONGGUO BAODAO. (Text in Esperanto) 1950. m. $15. Ministry of Culture, Foreign Language Bureau - Wenhua-bu, Waiwen-ju, 23, Baiwanzhuang Lu, Fuwai, Beijing 100037, People's Republic of China. TEL 896180. Ed. Zhou Dongyuan. bk.rev.; illus. circ. 14,000.

915.124 CC ISSN 0429-8020
FUJIAN HUABAO/FUJIAN PICTORIAL. (Text in Chinese) m. Y42 (foreign $106.20). Fujian Sheng Chuban Zongshe, 27 Degui Xiang, Hedong Lu, Fuzhou, Fujian 350001, People's Republic of China. TEL 552209. (Dist. in US by: China Books & Periodicals, Inc., 2929 24th St., San Francisco, CA 94110. TEL 415-282-2994) Ed. Chen Songdu. illus.

059.951 CC
FUJIAN XIANGTU. (Text in Chinese) q. Y2.80 (HK.$28). Min Meng Fujian Sheng Weiyuanhui, Zhengxie Dalou, No.6, Wusi Lu, Fuzhou, Fujian 350001, People's Republic of China. TEL 556741. (Dist. overseas by: Jiangsu Publications Import & Export Corp., 56 Gao Yun Ling, Nanjing, Jiangsu, P.R.C.) Ed. Yang Yi.
Description: Provides local news of Fujian to overseas Chinese, and promotes the culture of South China.

915.145 CC ISSN 0451-3118
GANSU HUABAO/GANSU PICTORIAL. (Text in Chinese) m. Y18. Gunsu Huabao She, 81, Di-1 Xincun, Lanzhou, Gansu 730030, People's Republic of China. TEL 466321. Ed. Chen Shaoquan. illus. (tabloid format)

915.127 CC
GUANGDONG HUABAO/GUANGDONG PICTORIAL. (Text in Chinese) m. $106.20. Guangdong Huabao She, Guangzhou, Guangdong, People's Republic of China. (Dist. in US by: China Books & Periodicals, Inc., 2929 24th St., San Francisco, CA 94110. TEL 415-282-2994) illus.

059.951 CC
GUANGXI HUABAO/GUANGXI PICTORIAL. (Text in Chinese) bi-m. Guangxi Xinwen Tupian She - Guangxi News Photo Press, 41 You'ai Lu, Nanning, Guangxi 530001, People's Republic of China. TEL 33175. Ed. Tang Li.

915.115 CC
HEBEI HUABAO/HEBEI PICTORIAL. (Text in Chinese) q. $35.40. Hebei Huabao She, Shijiazhuang, Hebei, People's Republic of China. (Dist. in US by: China Books & Periodicals, Inc., 2929 24th St., San Francisco, CA 94110. TEL 415-282-2994) illus.

915.184 CC
HEILONGJIANG HUABAO. (Text in Chinese) bi-m. Y2.50($41.90) 21, Liaoyang Jie, Nangang Qu, Harbin, Heilongjiang 150001, People's Republic of China. TEL 31037. (Dist. outside China by: China Internation Book Trading Corp., P.O. Box 2820, Beijing, P.R.C.; Dist. in US by: China Books & Periodicals, Inc., 2929 24th St., San Francisco, CA 94110. TEL 415-282-2994) Ed. Wang Jian. illus.

915.118 CC
HENAN HUABAO. (Text in Chinese) bi-m. Y15. Henan Huabao She, No. 1, Wei 5 Lu, Zhengzhou, Henan 450003, People's Republic of China. TEL 552670. Ed. Xu Kuidong. illus.

059.951 CC
HUANGJIN SHIDAI/GOLDEN TIMES. (Text in Chinese) m. Gongqingtuan Guangdong Shengwei, No. 1, Beitongjing, Dongshan Si, Guangzhou, Guangdong 510080, People's Republic of China. TEL 777586. Ed. Lai Jihuang.

059.591 CC
HUAREN ZHI SHENG/VOICE OF THE CHINESE. (Text in Chinese) bi-m. Y6.08. Fujian Renmin Chubanshe, Qikan Bu - Fujian People's Publishing House, 27 Degui Xiang, Fuzhou, Fujian, 350001, People's Republic of China. TEL 538622. (Dist. overseas by: Jiangsu Publications Import And Export Corp., 56 Gao Yun Ling, Nanjing, Jiangsu, P.R.C.) Ed. Guo Meijuan.
Description: Focuses on developments in the special economic zones and cities of South China, and issues including emigration, China's economic policies, and China's policies regarding the status of Taiwan and the overseas Chinese.

059.951 CC
JIANGXI HUABAO/JIANGXI PICTORIAL. (Text in Chinese) 1983. bi-m. Y30 (foreign Y120). Jiangxi Huabao She - Jiangxi Pictorial Agency, 125 Guangchang East Rd., Nanchang, Jiangxi 330002, People's Republic of China. TEL 225902. FAX 218147. (Dist. by: China International Book Trading Corporation, P.O. Box 399, Beijing, P.R. China) Ed. He Fulin. adv.: page Y20000; adv. contact: Chen Hong. circ. 5,000.
Description: Contains pictures that reflect the latest development in Jiangxi's economy, tourism, art, and science and technology.

059.962 CC
JILIN HUABAO/JILIN PICTORIAL. (Text in Chinese) bi-m. Jilin Huabao She, 28, Chongqing Lu, Changchun, Jilin 130041, People's Republic of China. TEL 828019. Ed. Chen Xuewen.

059.956 CC ISSN 0449-0312
JINMIN CHUGOKU/RENMIN ZHONGGUO/PEOPLE'S CHINA. (Text in Japanese) 1953. m. $12. (Ministry of Culture, Foreign Language Bureau - Wenhua-bu, Waiwen-ju) Renmin Zhongguo Zazhishe, 3, Chegongzhuang, Fuwai, Beijing 100044, People's Republic of China. TEL 890491. (Dist. overseas by: China International Book Trading Corp., P.O. Box 399, Beijing, P.R.C.) Ed. Yang Zhesan. illus.

059.951 770 CC ISSN 1003-417X
JINRI SHENGHUO/TODAY'S LIFE. (Text in Chinese) bi-m. $41.90. Zhejiang Renmin Meishu Chubanshe - Zhejiang People's Fine Art Publishers, 125 Wulin Lu, Hangzhou, Zhejiang 310006. TEL 552931. (Dist. in US by: China Books & Periodicals, Inc., 2929 24th St., San Francisco, CA 94110. TEL 415-282-2994) illus.

059.951 CC
JINTIAN/TODAY. (Text in Chinese) m. Jilin Sheng Zonggonghui, Fu 126, Stalin St., Changchun, Jilin 130022, People's Republic of China. TEL 882084. Ed. Lu Zongsheng.

058.7 CC ISSN 1000-9329
KINA. (Swedish edition of: China Pictorial) (Editions in various languages) 1960. m. $24. (Ministry of Culture, Foreign Language Bureau) China Pictorial, Huayuan Cun, Xi Jiao, Beijing 100044, People's Republic of China. FAX 8413023. TELEX 22496-CIBTC-CN. (Dist. overseas by: China International Book Trading Corp., P.O. Box 399, Beijing, P.R.C.)

059.951 CC ISSN 0457-6306
LIAONING HUABAO/LIAONING PICTORIAL. (Text in Chinese) 1945. m. Liaoning Huabao She, No. 29, Minzu Beijie, Heping-qu, Shenyang, Liaoning, People's Republic of China. TEL 332589. Ed. Wang Chuanjiang.

059.951 CC ISSN 8755-9358
AP95.C4
LIAOWANG/OUTLOOK. (Text in Chinese) 1981. w. Y44.2 for Chinese ed.; Overseas ed. Y104 ($139). (Xinhua News Agency) Liaowang Zazhishe, No. 57, Xuanwumen Xidajie, Beijing 100803, People's Republic of China. TEL 3074423. (Dist. in US by: China Books & Periodicals, Inc., 2929 24th St., San Francisco, CA 94110. TEL 415-282-2994) Ed. Chen Dabin. circ. 400,000.
Description: Covers political, intellectual, and news events in China and the world through reportage, observation, and analysis. Includes first-hand accounts and interviews. Reports the policies of the Chinese Communist Party, observes societal trends, and reflects the views and needs of the masses.

059.951 CH ISSN 0257-9456
MAINLAND CHINA MONTHLY. Key Title: Zhongguo Dalu. (Text in Chinese) 1974. m. NT.$600 in ROC; Hong Kong HK.$120; elsewhere $30. Institute of Mainland China Affairs - Chung-kuo Ta Lu Wen T'i Yen Chiu So, 16, Hangchow S. Rd. Sec. 1, Taipei, Taiwan, Republic of China. TEL 02-391-3064. FAX 02-394-1374. Ed. Lin Yen-wen. adv.; charts; illus.; maps.

059.951 CC ISSN 1004-0641
NAN FENG CHUANG/WINDS FROM THE SOUTH. (Text in Chinese) 1985. m. $35.90. Guangzhou Shiwei Xuanchuan Bu, No. 512, Dongfeng Donglu Rd., Guangzhou, Guangdong 510050, People's Republic of China. TEL 3806155. FAX 3800777. (Dist. overseas by: China International Book Trading Corp., P.O. Box 399, Beijing, P.R. China) Ed. Wu Xun. circ. 500,000.
Description: Reflects the social life of Chinese people in the midst of economic development.

320 CC
NEXUS: CHINA IN FOCUS. Chinese edition: Qiao. (Editions in Chinese, English, Russian) 1987. q. $15.50 for Eng. ed.; Chinese ed. $36; Russian ed. $16. Zhongguo "Qiao" Zazhishe - China Bridge Magazine Company, Minzu Wenhua Gong, 5th Floor, Beijing, People's Republic of China. TEL 6024433. (Dist. outside China by: Guoji Shudian - China International Book Trading Corp., P.O. Box 399, Beijing, P.R.C.. TEL 8413063; Dist. in US by: China Books & Periodicals, Inc., 2929 24th St., San Francisco, CA 94110. TEL 415-282-2994) Ed. Mu Guangren. illus.
Description: Covers contemporary Chinese society. Topics include new types of work, relationships, and the changes occurring in urban China today.

059.951 CC
QILU XIANGQING. (Text in Chinese) q. Shandong Sheng Guiguo Huaqiao Lianhehui, No. 278, Quancheng Lu, Jinan, Shandong 250011, People's Republic of China. TEL 612892. Ed. Niu Qishan.

059.951 CC
QITAN/STRANGE TALES. (Text in Chinese) bi-m. Sichuan Kexue Jishu Xiehui - Sichuan Science and Technology Society, No. 11, Renmin Nanlu 4 Duan, Chengdu, Sichuan 610041, People's Republic of China. TEL 551713. Ed. Yang Xiao.

059.951 CC
QUNZHONG WENHUA/MASS CULTURE; wenhua yishu zonghexing yuekan. (Text in Chinese) m. Y13.20($35) Wenhua-bu, Shehui Wenhua Yishu Shiye Guanlisi, 2, Shatan Beijie, Beijing 100722, People's Republic of China. TEL 4012255. (Dist. outside China by: China International Book Trading Corp., P.O. Box 399, Beijing, P.R.C.; Dist. in US by: China Books & Periodicals, Inc., 2929 24th St., San Francisco, CA 94110. TEL 415-282-2994) Ed. Feng Junyi.

059.951 CC ISSN 0448-9373
RENMIN HUABAO. English edition: China Pictorial (ISSN 0009-4420) (Editions in various languages) 1950. m. $24. (Ministry of Culture, Foreign Language Bureau) China Pictorial, Huayuan Cun, Xi Jiao, Beijing 100044, People's Republic of China. FAX 8415118. TELEX 22496-CIBTC-CN. (Dist. overseas by: China International Book Trading Corp., P.O. Box 399, Beijing, P.R.C.; Dist. in US by: China Books & Periodicals, Inc., 2929 24th St., San Francisco, CA 94110. TEL 415-282-2994) adv.; illus.; index. (tabloid format)

079.51 CC
RENMIN RIBAO/PEOPLE'S DAILY. (Semi-monthly supplement avail.: Humor & Satire; Overseas edition avail.) (Text in Chinese) 1948. d. Y13.80($460) (Overseas Edition Y13) per mo. Renmin Ribao Chubanshe - People's Daily Publishing House, 2 Jintai Xilu, Beijing 100733, People's Republic of China. TEL 86-1-509-1006. FAX 861-509-1982. (Dist. in US by: China Books & Periodicals, Inc., 2929 24th St., San Francisco, CA 94109. TEL 415-282-2994. FAX 415-282-0994) Ed. Fan Jingyi. adv.: page $80000. bk.rev.; film rev.; music rev.; play rev.; illus. circ. 2,900,000. (also avail. in microfilm; back issues avail.; reprint service avail.)
Document type: newspaper.

915.143　　　CC　　ISSN 1001-0440
SHAANXI HUABAO/SHAANXI PICTORIAL. (Text in Chinese) bi-m. $47.30. Shaanxi Xinwen Chuban-ju - Shaanxi Journalism and Publishing Bureau, 92 Zhuque Dajie, Xi'an, Shaanxi 710068, People's Republic of China. TEL 54596. (Dist. in US by: China Books & Periodicals, Inc. 2929 24th St., San Francisco, CA 94110. TEL 415-282-2994) illus.

915.114　　　CC
SHANDONG HUABAO/SHANDONG PICTORIAL. (Text in Chinese) 1943. m. Y36. Shandong Sheng Chuban Zongshe, Shandong Huabao She, 89, Kuanhousuo Jie, Jinan, Shandong 250011, People's Republic of China. TEL 610691. (Dist. outside China by: China International Book Trading Corp., P.O. Box 399, Beijing, P.R.C.; Dist. in US by: China Books & Periodicals, Inc., 2929 24th St., San Francisco, CA 94110. TEL 415-282-2994) Ed. Zhang Shuyong. illus.
Description: Comprehensive news photo magazine that covers politics, economics and culture in Shandong Province.

915.113 770　　　CC
SHANGHAI PICTORIAL. Chinese edition: Shanghai Huabao. (Text in English) bi-m. $22. Shanghai Pictorial Publisher, 20 Fenyang Lu, Shanghai 200031, People's Republic of China. TEL 4335973. (Dist. outside China by: China International Book Trading Corp., P.O. Box 399, Beijing, P.R.C.; Dist. in US by: China Books & Periodicals, 2929 24th St., San Francisco, CA 94110. TEL 415-282-2994) Ed. Zhu Yanling. (back issues avail.)
Description: Shows cultural, social, and economic changes, and the unique characteristics of this huge metropolis.

059.951　　　CC　　ISSN 0559-717X
SHANXI HUABAO/SHANXI PICTORIAL. (Text in Chinese) q. Shanxi Huabao She, 46 Jiefang Lu, Taiyuan, Shanxi 030002, People's Republic of China. TEL 223751. Ed. Wang Bugui.

059.951　　　CC
SHEHUI - JIANTING/SOCIETY - FAMILY. (Text in Chinese) bi-m. Zhejiang Renmin Chubanshe, Qikan Bu - Zhejiang People's Publishing House, 125 Wulin Lu, Hangzhou, Zhejiang 310006, People's Republic of China. TEL 552931. Ed. Shen Tuqi.

059.951　　　CC
SHENGHUO - CHUANGZAO/LIFE - CREATION. (Text in Chinese) m. Y9.60. Fujian Sheng Zonggonghui, Fujiansheng Zonggonghui Dasha, Wusi Lu Zhongduan, Fuzhou, Fujian 350003, People's Republic of China. TEL 553292. (Dist. overseas by: Jiangsu Publications Import & Export Corp., 56 Gao Yun Ling, Nanjing, Jiangsu, P.R.C.)
Description: Covers topics of popular interest.

059.951　　　CC
SHENZHEN FENGCAI. (Supplement to: Shenzhen Special Zone Daily) (Text in Chinese) 1982. m. Shenzhen Tequ Baoshe - Shenzhen Special Zone Daily, No. 4, Shennan Zhonglu, Shenzhen, Guangdong 518009, People's Republic of China. TEL 2241428. FAX 2243919. Ed. Tong Jiahuan.

079.51　　　CC
SHENZHEN SPECIAL ZONE DAILY. (Monthly supplement avail.: Shenzhen Fengcai) (Text in Chinese) d. Shenzhen Tequ Baoshe, No. 4, Shennan Zhonglu, Shenzhen, Guangdong 518009, People's Republic of China. TEL 2241428. FAX 2243919. adv.
Document type: newspaper.

059.951　　　CC
SHIDAI. (Text in Chinese) m. Zhongguo Gongren Chubanshe, Liupukang, Dewai, Beijing 100011, People's Republic of China. TEL 4215296. Ed. Guo Chen.

059.951　　　CC　　ISSN 1003-0271
SHIJIE BOLAN/WORLD EXPO. (Text in Chinese) m. $47.20. Shijie Zhishi Chubanshe - World Affairs Press, 31-A Waijiaobu Jie, Dongcheng Qu, Beijing 100005, People's Republic of China. TEL 5125544. (Dist. in US by: China Books & Periodicals, Inc., 2929 24th St., San Francisco, CA 94110. TEL 415-282-2994) Ed. Wu Miaofa.

059.951　　　CC
SHIJIE ZHI CHUANG/WINDOW ON THE WORLD. (Text in Chinese) 1979. bi-m. Y8.40. Shanghai Translation Publishing House - Shanghai Yiwen Chubanshe, No.14, Lane 955, Yan'an Zhonglu, Shanghai, People's Republic of China. TEL 2472890. Eds. Luo Zhaotian, Xu Dizhou. circ. 150,000.
Description: Publishes general articles from a variety of publications.

059.951　　　CC　　ISSN 1003-028X
SHIJIE ZHISHI HUABAO/WORLD AFFAIRS PICTORIAL. (Text in Chinese) 1983. m. $35.30. Shijie Zhishi Chubanshe - World Affairs Press, 31-A, Waijiaobu Jie, Dongcheng Qu, Beijing 100005, People's Republic of China. (Dist. in US by: China Books & Periodicals, Inc., 2929 24th St., San Francisco, CA 94110. TEL 415-282-2994) Ed. Wu Kaiqin. illus.
Description: Introduces many parts of the world. Examines ethnic customs, famous sites, culture and art, economics and science, sports, history and geography, famous people, strange and unusual wildlife, and political struggle.

915.138　　　CC　　ISSN 1004-2210
SICHUAN HUABAO/SICHUAN PICTORIAL. (Text in Chinese) 1972. bi-m. Y5. Sichuan Huabao She, No. 7 Zhongfu Rd., Chengdu, Sichuan 610016, People's Republic of China. TEL 6615454. (Dist. outside China by: China Publications Foreign Trade Corp., P.O. Box 614, Beijing, P.R.C.) Ed. Liu Chunsheng. bk.rev.; illus. (tabloid format)

059.951　　　CC
WENHUA GUANGCHANG. (Text in Chinese) bi-m. Y15($44.61) Huacheng Chubanshe, No. 11, Shuiyin Lu, Huanshi Donglu, Guangzhou, Guangdong 510075, People's Republic of China. TEL 768688. Ed. Yang Guangzhi.

059.951　　　CC
WENHUA YU SHENGHUO/CULTURE & LIFE. (Text in Chinese) bi-m. $27.50. Shanghai Wenyi Chubanshe - Shanghai Literature and Art Press, 74 Shaoxing Lu, Shanghai 200020, People's Republic of China. TEL 4372608. (Dist. in US by: China Books & Periodicals, Inc., 2929 24th St., San Francisco, CA 94110. TEL 415-282-2994) Ed. Li Zhongfa.

059.951　　　CC
XIANDAI HUABAO/MODERN PICTORIAL. (Text in Chinese) q. Guangzhou Shi Wenlian, No. 170, Wende Lu, 4th Fl., Guangzhou, Guangdong 510030, People's Republic of China. Ed. Zhou Jinyao.

011　　　CC　　ISSN 1001-6651
XINHUA WENZHAI. (Text in Chinese) 1979. m. Y43.20($130.90) Renmin Chubanshe, Qikan Bu - People's Publishing House, 166 Chaonei Dajie, Beijing 100706, People's Republic of China. TEL 55-2654. (Dist. outside China by: China International Book Trading Corp., P.O. Box 399, Beijing, P.R.C.; Dist. in US by: China Books & Periodicals, 2929 24th St., San Francisco, CA 94110) Ed. Zhang Zuoyao. bk.rev.; index. circ. 300,000. (back issues avail.)
Description: Covers politics, philosophy, economics, social sciences, the humanities, science, technology, and recent academic information.

011　　　CC　　ISSN 1001-666X
XINHUA YUEBAO/XINHUA MONTHLY REPORT. Variant English title: Xinhua Monthly. (Text in Chinese) 1949. m. Y36($117.40) Renmin Chubanshe, Qikan Bu - People's Publishing House, 166 Chaonei Dajie, Beijing 100706, People's Republic of China. TEL 555571. (Dist. outside China by: China International Book Trading Corp., P.O. Box 399, Beijing, P.R.C.; Dist in US by: China Books & Periodicals, Inc., 2929 24th St., San Francisco, CA 94110) Eds. Dai Hesheng, Zhang Xiaoping. bk.rev.; index. circ. 50,000. (back issues avail.)
Description: Reprints selected articles from Chinese newspapers on politics, philosophy, economics, culture, science, foreign relations, and international news.

915.16　　　CC
XINJIANG HUABAO/XINJIANG PICTORIAL. (Text in Chinese) bi-m. $41.90. Xinjiang Ribao She - Xijiang Daily Publishers, 1 Yangzijiang Lu, Wulumuqi, Xijiang 8300051, People's Republic of China. TEL 43701. (Dist. in US by: China Books & Periodicals, Inc., 2929 24th St., San Francisco, CA 94110. TEL 415-282-2994) illus.

059.951　　　CC
XINXI HUABAO/INFORMATION PICTORIAL. (Text in Chinese) q. Qingdao Ribao She - Qingdao Daily, No. 33, Taiping Lu, Qingdao, Shandong 266001, People's Republic of China. TEL 284612. Ed. Zhang Bingshan.

059.951　　　US
YANHUANG ZISUN/CHINESE DESCENDANTS. (Text in Chinese) bi-m. $21.20. China Books & Periodicals, Inc., 2929 24th St., San Francisco, CA 94110. TEL 415-282-2994. FAX 415-282-0994.

915.135　　　CC
YUNNAN HUABAO/YINNAN SUMLA SHI LAIKA/YUITNAT HUAQBOQ/YIRNAR AWHA LIRSHATAD/LAI RANG YING NANG. (Text mainly in Chinese; occasionally in various languages) bi-m. Y15($61) Yunnan Huabao She, 601 Beijing Lu, Kunming, Yunnan 650011, People's Republic of China. TEL 25677. (Dist. outside China by: China International Book Trading Corp., P.O. Box 399, Beijing, P.R.C.; Dist. in US by: China Books & Periodicals, Inc., 2929 24th St., San Francisco, CA 94110. TEL 415-282-2994) Eds. Ke Xiaoping, Baduma Gaishuang. illus. (tabloid format)

059.951　　　CC　　ISSN 1001-1730
ZHILI/INTELLIGENCE. (Text in Chinese) m. Zhili Zazhishe, 287 Heping Lu, Tianjin 300041, People's Republic of China. TEL 315526. Ed. Rong Jiaxing.

059.951　　　CC
ZHISHI WENKU. (Text in Chinese) m. Xue Lilun Zazhishe, 121, Zhaolin Jie, Daoli-qu, Harbin, Heilongjiang 150010, People's Republic of China. TEL 414788. Ed. Zhan Shuquan.

059.951　　　CC
ZHISHI YU SHENGHUO/KNOWLEDGE AND LIFE. (Text in Chinese) bi-m. Shandong Kexue Jishu Chubanshe - Shandong Science and Technology Publishers, No. 16, Yuhan Lu, Jinan, Shandong 250002, People's Republic of China. TEL 615315. Ed. Zhao Weidong.

059.951　　　US
ZHONGGUO WENHUA BAO/CHINA CULTURE NEWSPAPER. (Text in Chinese) 3/w. $95.60. China Books & Periodicals, Inc., 2929 24th St., San Francisco, CA 94110. TEL 415-282-2994. FAX 415-282-0994. *Document type:* newspaper.

951　　　CC　　ISSN 1002-9591
ZHONGGUO XIZANG. English edition: China's Tibet. (Editions in Chinese, English, Tibetan) 1989. bi-m. (Tibetin ed. q.). $17.40 for Chinese ed.; English ed. $11.60. (Tongzhanbu 2 Ju) China's Tibet, 135 Fuyoujie St., Beijing 100031, People's Republic of China. TEL 3096107. (Overseas subscr. to: China International Book Trading Corp., P.O. Box 399, Beijing, P.R. China) Ed. Liao Dongfan. adv.: B&W page Y5000; adv. contact: Lha Mo. circ. 25,000.
Description: Covers Tibet's politics, economics, culture and education, public health, science and technology, and regional autonomy.

059.951　　　CC
ZHONGHUA YINGCAI. (Editions in Chinese, English) bi-m. Zhonghua Yingcai Huabaoshe, No. 27, Luoxian Huton, Fuyou Jie, Beijing 100031, People's Republic of China. TEL 664682. Ed. Wang Xiaopeng.

059.951　　　CC
ZHUIQIU/PURSUIT. (Text in Chinese) bi-m. $19.80. Zhongguo Qingnian Chubanshe, Qikan Bu - China Youth Press, 21, Dongsi 12 Tiao, Beijing 100708, People's Republic of China. TEL 442125. (Dist. in US by: China Books & Periodicals, Inc., 2929 24th St., San Francisco, CA 94110. TEL 415-282-2994) Ed. Lin Junxiong.

GENERAL INTEREST PERIODICALS — Colombia

056.1　　　CK　　ISSN 0008-235X
CAMPESINO; semanario para la cultura y dignificacion del pueblo rural. 1958. w. $20. (Accion Cultural Popular) Editora Dosmil, Carrera 39 A No 15-11, Bogota D.E., Colombia. Ed. Joaquin Gutierrez Macias. adv.; bk.rev.; charts, illus.; circ. 70,000 (controlled). (tabloid format)

051 US ISSN 0010-1397
COLOMBIA TODAY. 1965. m. free. Colombia Information Service, Colombian Center, 140 E. 57th St., New York, NY 10022. TEL 212-421-8300. charts; illus.; stat. circ. 13,000. (tabloid format) Indexed: Int.Lab.Doc., Key to Econ.Sci.

056.1 CK ISSN 0011-1708
CROMOS; la actualidad ilustrada. 1916. w. Col.45000($200) Inversiones Cromos S.A., Calle 70A No. 7-81, Apdo. Aereo 59317, Bogota D.E., Colombia. TEL 217-17-54. FAX 211-26-42. Dir. Alberto Zalamea. adv.; bk.rev.; illus. circ. 68,000.

056.1 CK
NUEVA FRONTERA. 1974. w. Carrera 7A, No. 17-01, 5o, Bogota, Colombia. TEL 334-3763. Dir. Carlos Lleras Restrepo. circ. 23,000.
   Description: Covers politics, society, arts and culture from a liberal point of view.

079.861 CK
LA OPINION. (Includes weekly supplements: Imagenes (Sun.), Infantil (Sat.)) 1960. d. Avda. 4, 16-12, Cucuta, N. de S., Colombia. TEL 75-719999. FAX 75-717869. Ed. Rafael Pabon; Pub. Jose Eustorgio Colmenares. adv. contact: Ciceron Florez. bk.rev.; film rev.; music rev.; illus.; circ. 15,000 (paid); 1,500 (C. cols./p.: 6; pp./issue: 28. (standard format) Document type: newspaper.

056.1 CK ISSN 0121-0211
REVISTA DINERS. 1963. m. $1.10 per no. (Diners Club de Colombia S.A.) Ediciones Gamma, Carrera 10 No. 64-65, Piso 3, Bogota DF, Colombia. TEL 212-2893. FAX 212-8931. Ed. Jose Fernando Lopez. adv.: color page $2995. bk.rev. circ. 130,000.

056.1 CK
SEMANA. 1982. w. $100. Editorial Caribe S.A., Calle 93A-13A, 6-10, Bogota, Colombia. TEL 257-5400. FAX 257-9471. TELEX 42106 EDICA CO. Dir. Felipe Lopez Caballero. adv.; bk.rev. circ. 60,000.

056.1 CK
VEA. w. Calle 20, No. 4-55, Bogota, Colombia. circ. 90,000.

056.1 CK
VOZ PROLETARIA. 1957. w. Carrera 34, No. 9-28, Bogota, Colombia. TEL 247-2346. TELEX 45152. Dir. Manuel Cepeda Vargas.

GENERAL INTEREST PERIODICALS — Congo

079.672 CF
AUJOURD'HUI. 1990. d. 2 bis, Pual Kamba Poto Poto, Brazzaville, Congo. TEL 83-77-44. FAX 83-77-44. Ed. Fyllaoifua Oisassa. adv. contact: Paul Moutou-Nombault. bk.rev.; illus. pp./issue: 16. (tabloid format) Document type: newspaper.

GENERAL INTEREST PERIODICALS — Cuba

056.1 CU
ACTUALIDAD CULTURAL. irreg. Ministerio de Cultura, 4 No. 251 esq. a 11, Vedado, Havana, Cuba.

056.1 CU ISSN 0523-8579
BOHEMIA. 1908. w. $86 in N. America; S. America $90; elsewhere $100. Ediciones Cubanas, Obispo No. 527, Apdo. 605, Havana, Cuba. TEL 7-7-2833. Dir. Caridad Miranda Martinez. illus. circ. 312,000. (also avail. in microfilm from UMI; reprint service avail. from UMI) Indexed: Amer.Hist.& Life, Hist.Abstr.

056.1 CU
COMICOS. m. $20 in N. America; S. America $26; Europe $29; elsewhere $41. (Union de Periodistas y Escritores de Cuba) Ediciones Cubanas, Obispo No. 527, Apdo. 605, Havana, Cuba. TEL 7-22-5892. circ. 70,000.

056.1 CU
COMPILACIONES TEMATICAS. s-a. Academia de Ciencias, Instituto de Documentacion e Informacion Cientifico-Tecnica (I D I C T), Capitolio Nacional Prado y San Jose, La Habana 2, Havana, Cuba.

056.1 CU ISSN 0864-1331
DEL CARIBE. 1983. s-a. $12 in S. America; N. America $14; elsewhere $16. Casa del Caribe en Santiago de Cuba, Calle 13 No. 154 esq. 8, Vista Alegre, Zona Postal 4, Santiago de Cuba, Cuba. TEL 809-42285. TELEX 061-228 CARIBE CU. (Dist. by: Ediciones Cubanas, Obispo No. 527, Apdo. 605, Havana, Cuba) Ed. Jose M. Fernandez Pequeno. circ. 3,500.

056.1 US
▼**GIBARENO.** 1993. q. Municipio de Gibara en el Exilio, Box 557354, Miami, FL 33255-7354. Ed. Manuel Diaz-Piferrer.
   Description: For people originally from Gibara, Cuba, who now live in exile.

056.1 CU
INTER PRESS SERVICE. REVISTA MENSUAL. (Text in English, Spanish) m. Inter Press Service, Edif. Fosca, Apto. 2-G, 17 y M, Vedado, Havana, Cuba. TEL 30-4030. Ed. Claude Hackin.

056.1 CU
INTER PRESS SERVICE. REVISTA SEMANAL. (Text in English, Spanish) w. Inter Press Service - Tercer Mundo, Edif. Focsa, Apto. 2-G, 17 y M, Vedadeo, Havana, Cuba. TEL 30-40-30. Ed. Claude Hackin.

056.1 CU
MINISTERIO DE CULTURA. TABLAS. 1982. q. $14 in N. and S. America; Europe $15; elsewhere $16. Ministerio de Cultura, Calle 6 no. 111, e-rra. y 3ra, Miramar, Playa, Havana, Cuba. TELEX 511400 MINCULT CU. (Dist. by: Ediciones Cubanas, Obispo No. 527, Apdo. 605, Havana, Cuba) circ. 4,000.

056.1 CU
MONCADA. 1966. m. Ministerio del Interior, Belascoain No. 452, Zanja, Decimo Piso, Centro Habana, Havana, Cuba. TEL 7-79-7109. Dir. Ricardo Martinez. circ. 70,000.

056.1 CU
NACION CUBANA. q. $8 in N. America; S. America $10; Europe $12; elsewhere $14. (Asamblea Nacional) Ediciones Cubanas, Obispo N. 527, Apdo. 605, Havana, Cuba.

056.1 CU
NOVEDADES CUBANAS. q. Ministerio de Cultura, Obispo No. 461, Apdo. 605, Havana, Cuba.

056.1 052 CU
PRISMA LATINOAMERICANO. (Editions in English, Portuguese, Spanish) 1979. m. $30 in S. America; N. America $34; elsewhere $38. Ediciones Cubanas, Obispo No. 527, Apdo. 605, Havana, Cuba. Dir. Jesus Hernandez Perez. bk.rev.; illus. circ. 60,000 (20,000 English ed.; 15,000 Portuguese ed.; 25,000 Spanish ed.).

056.1 CU
TEMAS. q. $10 in N. and S. America; Europe $12; elsewhere $14. (Ministerio de Cultura) Ediciones Cubanas, Obispo No. 527, Apdo. 605, Havana, Cuba.

056.1 CU ISSN 0041-8420 AP63
UNIVERSIDAD DE LA HABANA. DEPARTMENTO DE ACTIVIDADES CULTURALES. REVISTA. 1928. 3/yr. C.$120($11) in N. America; S. America $12; Europe $15; elsewhere $19. Universidad de la Habana, Departamento de Actividades Culturales, Calle San La Zaro esq. L, Vedado, Havana 4, Cuba. (Dist. by: Ediciones Cubanas, Obispo No. 527, Apdo. 605, Havana, Cuba) Ed. Ambrosio Fornet. bk.rev. circ. 5,000.

GENERAL INTEREST PERIODICALS — Cyprus

059.89 CY
ANEXARTITOS/INDEPENDENT. (Text in Greek) 1973. w. Ethniki Demokratiki Enosi Kyprou, P.O. Box 1064, A. Karyos St., Egnomi, Nicosia, Cyprus. TEL 02-449766. Ed. Antonis Markrides.

052 CY ISSN 1012-2559
THE BLUE BERET. (Text in English) m. P.O. Box 1642, HQ, United Nations Forces in Cyprus, Nicosia, Cyprus. TEL 02-359000. circ. 1,100.

079.5645 CY
CYPRUS. OFFICIAL GAZETTE. (Text in Greek) 1960. w. £C45($110) Government Printing Office, Nicosia, Cyprus. TEL 357-2-302202. FAX 357-2-302205. cols./p.: 2. (back issues avail.) Document type: government publication, newspaper.
●Also available online.
   Description: Reports on statute and amendment laws, invitations to tenders, and vacant positions within each department of the government of Cyprus.

079.5645 052 TU
CYPRUS TODAY. (Text in English) 1991. w. £17.50 in Europe & UK; USA & Far East £22; Australia & NZ £25 (effective 1994). A N Graphics Ltd., P.O. Box 831, Dr. Fazil Kucuk Bulvari, Lefkosa, Mersin 10, Turkey. TEL 90-392-227-6433. FAX 90-392-229-1934. pp./issue: 16. Document type: newspaper.
   Supersedes (1989-1990): Cyprus Times.
   Description: Covers Turkish Cypriot economic and social issues, politics and cultural topics.

052 CY
CYPRUS WEEKLY. (Text in English) 1979. w. 216 Mitsis 3 Bldg., Archbishop Makarios Ave., P.O. Box 1992, Nicosia, Cyprus. TEL 02-441433. TELEX 2260. Eds. A. Efthyvoulos, A. Hadjipapas. circ. 15,000.
   Description: Greek-Cypriot independent.

059.89 CY
EKLOYI/CHOICE. (Text in Greek) 1989. m. A. Kaissis, 16 Stassikratous, 1st Fl., Nicosia, Cyprus. TEL 02-474168. circ. 2,000.

059.89 CY
ENDOSKOPISI. (Text in Greek) 1984. bi-m. 4 Annis Komninis, 6th Fl., Nicosia, Cyprus. TEL 02-458541. FAX 02-450370. Ed. Nikos Hadjicostis. circ. 3,000.

059.89 CY
ENIMEROSSI/BRIEFING. (Text in Greek) 1982. w. Makriros & Agapinoros Sts., P.O. Box 1417, Nicosia, Cyprus. TEL 02-477181. Ed. Panayotis Papademetris. circ. 10,000.

058.89 CY
EPIKERI/CURRENT AFFAIRS. (Text in Greek) 1987. w. 19 Boumboulinas St., P.O. Box 3786, Nicosia, Cyprus. TEL 02-455788. Ed. Lazaros Mavros. circ. 2,500.

079.5645 CY
EPISIMOS EPHIMERIS TIS KYRIAKES DEMOKRATIAS. (Text in Greek) w. £C45($108) Printing Office of the Republic of Cyprus, Director's Office, Nicosia, Cyprus. TEL 357-2-302202. FAX 357-2-302205. Ed. I. Ioannis. index. circ. 5,000. (back issues avail.) Document type: newspaper, government publication.
   Description: Covers statute laws, amendment laws, invitiations to tenders, and job vacancies in the government of Cyprus.

059.89 CY
ESO - ETIMOS/EVER - READY. (Text in Greek) 1913. q. Cyprus Scouts Association, P.O. Box 4544, Nicosia, Cyprus. TEL 02-443587. Ed. Takis Neophyton.

059.89 CY
EXORMISI/STARTING LINE. (Text in Greek) 1989. w. 87b Ag. Phylaxeos, P.O. Box 1697, Limassol, Cyprus. TEL 05-332814. Ed. G. Erotokritou. circ. 2,500.

059.89 CY
FLASH. (Text in Greek) 1978. w. 11 Kolokotronis St., P.O. Box 4626, Kaimakli, Nicosia, Cyprus. TEL 02-437887. Ed. Loucas Barbas. circ. 12,000.

052 330 CY
HERMES INTERNATIONAL; the new regional force in the world of business, finance and politics. (Text in English) 1985-1992; resumed 1994. m. £C12 (Australia Aus.$60; Canada Can.$56; Greece Dr.11000; Middle East US$42; South Africa R.165; U.S. $42). P.O. Box 4706, Nicosia, Cyprus. TEL 357-2-365656. FAX 357-2-461470. Ed. Alan Gathergood. adv.; bk.rev. circ. 7,000. Document type: consumer publication.
   Supersedes: Success (ISSN 1010-1195)
   Description: Covers upscale life-style and business in Cyprus and elsewhere in the eastern Mediterranean.

059.8   CY   ISSN 0023-611X
KYPROS; Pancyprian newspaper. (Text and summaries in Greek) 1952. w. £C2.60. Cosmos Press Ltd., Cosmos Press Bldg., Apostolos Varnavas St., P.O. Box 1491, Nicosia, Cyprus. Ed. John Kyriakides. adv.; bk.rev.; film rev.; play rev.; bibl.; illus.; cum.index. circ. 15,200. **Document type:** newspaper.

059.89   CY
KYRIATIKIS ORES/SUNDAY HOURS. (Text in Greek) w. 7 Androkleon St., P.O. Box 1450, Nicosia, Cyprus. TEL 02-448548. Ed. Phivos Morides.

052   CY
NICOSIA THIS MONTH. (Text in English) 1984. m. P.O. Box 1015, Nicosia, Cyprus. TEL 357-2-473124. FAX 357-2-463363. TELEX 5374. Ed. Ellada Sophocleous. circ. 3,000. **Document type:** consumer publication, government publication.

059.89   CY
PARASKINO/BEHIND THE SCENES. (Text in Greek) 1987. w. 39 Kennedy Ave., Nicosia, Cyprus. TEL 02-313334. Ed. D. Michael. circ. 4,500.

059.89   CY
PERIODIKO/PERIODICAL. (Text in Greek) 1986. w. 31 Archangelos Ave., Nicosia, Cyprus. TEL 02-353646. FAX 02-352298. TELEX 3826. Ed. Phillippos Stylianon. circ. 23,500.

059.89   CY
TO PROSSOPO/FACE. 1989. m. 105 Boumboulinas St., Nicosia, Cyprus. TEL 02-454222. Ed. Christos Styliandes.

052   CY
SYNERGATIKO VIMA/CO-OPERATIVE ROSTRUM. 1982. m. Pan-Cyprian Co-operative Federation, Ltd., Shanteclair Bldg., 4th Fl., No. 401, 2 Sofoulis St., Nicosia, Cyprus. TEL 357-2-458757. FAX 357-2-446833. circ. 7,000.

GENERAL INTEREST PERIODICALS — Czech Republic

052   XR   ISSN 0011-4634
DB191
CZECHOSLOVAK LIFE. French edition: Vie Tchecoslovaque. German edition: Tschechoslowakisches Leben. Italian edition: Vita Cecoslovacca. Spanish edition: Vida Checoslovaca. (Text in English) 1946. m. $6. (Federalni Ministerstvo Kultury) Orbis Press Agency, Vinohradska 46, 120 41 Prague 2, Czech Republic. TEL 2-257741. FAX 2-254385. Ed. Eva Maisnerova. adv.; illus. circ. 90,000.

052   XR
DAILY NEWS AND PRESS SURVEY. (Text in English) 1965. d. $540. Ceska Tiskova Kancelar - Czech News Agency, Opletalova 5, Prague 1, Czech Republic. Ed. Alexandr Kramer. (processed) Former titles: Information from Czechoslovakia; (until 1988): Czechoslovak Information Bulletin; (until 1985): Czechoslovak Digest.

057.86   XR   ISSN 0023-5849
AP52
KVETY. 1951. w. 104 Kcs.($80) Kvety Ceske, Na Florenci 3, 117 14 Prague 1, Czech Republic. TEL 2-2323451. TELEX 12184. (Subscr. to: Artia, Ve Smeckach 30, 111 27 Prague 1, Czech Republic. TEL 42-2-246041) Ed. Jiri Blahota. illus. circ. 401,000.

073.7   XR   ISSN 0862-5921
LIDOVE NOVINY. 1893. 6/w. (Mon.- Sat.) 1272 Kc. (Europe $202; U.S. $355); newsstand price: 4.50 Kc. Narodni 11, 111 21 Prague 1, Czech Republic. Owner(s): Lidove Novine Corp., Narodni 11, 111 21 Prague 1, Czech Republic; Ringier AG, Dufourstr. 23, Zurich, Switzerland. TEL 41-1-2596111. FAX 41-1-2596840. Ed. Libor Sevcik; Pub. Michal Klima. adv.; page 98000 Kc.; trim 256 X 378; adv. contact: Iva Sladka. Wire service(s): R. (tabloid format; also avail. in microfilm from NRP; Braille; back issues avail., reprint service avail.) **Document type:** newspaper.
● Also available online.

073.7   XR   ISSN 1210-3934
THE PRAGUE POST. (Text in English) 1991. w. $170. Lion's Share Group Ltd., Na Porci 12, 115 30 Prague 1, Czech Republic. TEL 42-2-2487-5000. FAX 42-2-2487-5050. Ed. Alan Levy; Pub. Lisa L. Fankengerg. adv.; B&W page $2000, color page $3175; adv. contact: Kristin Spirkova. circ. 14,000. (also avail. in microfilm from NRP) **Document type:** newspaper.
Description: Covers general news, financial and economic developments, culture, and the arts from the Czech Republic's capital city.

057.86   XR   ISSN 0322-998X
PRAHA. m. 24 Kcs.($44.90) (Narodni Vybor Hlavniho Mesta Prahy) Panorama, Halkova 1, 120 72 Prague 2, Czech Republic. Ed. Josef Molin. illus. circ. 12,000.
Supersedes (in 1970): Nova Praha.

073.7   XO   ISSN 0231-7427
SMENA. 1949. d. 89.70 Kcs. per quarter. Smena Publishing House, Dostojewskieto rad 1, 812 84 Bratislava, Slovakia. (Subscr. to: P N S, Gottwaldovo nam. 6, 813 31 Bratislava, Slovakia) Ed. Lubomir Chorvatovic. circ. 125,000. (also avail. in microfiche from IDC) **Document type:** newspaper.

073.7   XR   ISSN 0231-732X
SVOBODNE SLOVO. 1907. 6/w. (Mon.-Sat.) $280; newsstand price: 3.80 Kc. Melantrich, Inc., Vaclavske nam. 36, 112 12 Prague 1, Czech Republic. Ed. Jaroslav Fridrich. adv. contact: Karel Klouda. bk.rev.; film rev.; music rev.; play rev.; tele.rev.; illus.; tr.lit.; circ. 155,000 (paid); 137,000. cols./p.: 5; pp./issue: 12. (standard format) **Document type:** newspaper.

GENERAL INTEREST PERIODICALS — Denmark

078.9   DK
AALBORG STIFTSTIDENDE. 6/w. Lanagervej 1, P.O. Box 8000, DK-9220 Aalborg Oest, Denmark. TEL 45-98-15-15-15. FAX 45-98-15-6-7-11. Eds. Erling Broendum, Uffe Riis Soerensen. circ. 73,242. **Document type:** newspaper.

078.9   DK
AARHUS STIFTSTIDENDE. 6/w. Olof Palmes Alle 39, DK-8200 Aarhus, Denmark. TEL 45-86-78-40-00. FAX 45-86-78-44-00. Eds. Aage Holm-Pedersen, Aage Lundgaard. adv. circ. 64,348. cols./p.: 8; pp./issue: 32. **Document type:** newspaper.

078.9   DK
AMTS AVISEN. 6/w. Noerregade 7, DK-8900 Randers, Denmark. TEL 45-86-42-75-11. FAX 45-86-41-81-50. Eds. Ole C. Joergensen, Ib Sleimann. circ. 29,939. cols./p.: 8; pp./issue: 24. **Document type:** newspaper.

078.9   DK
B.T. d. Kr. Bernikowsgade 6, DK-1116 Copenhagen K, Denmark. TEL 45-33-75-75-33. FAX 45-33-75-20-20. Eds. Peter Dall, Henning Laessoe. circ. 192,743. cols./p.: 6; pp./issue: 48. **Document type:** newspaper.

053.981   DK
DET BEDSTE FRA READER'S DIGEST (DANISH EDITION). 1946. m. DKK 269. Det Bedste fra Reader's Digest A-S, Forlaget Det Bedste, Jagtvej 169, P.O. Box 810, 2100 Copenhagen, Denmark. TEL 31-181213. FAX 31-181236. Ed. Ole Knudsen. adv.; bk.rev.; illus. circ. 136,000.

078.9   DK   ISSN 0106-4223
BERLINGSKE TIDENDE. (Supplements avail.) 1749. d. newsstand price: DKK 7.50. Berlingske Dagblade, Pilestraede 34, DK-1147 Copenhagen K, Denmark. TEL 45-33757500. FAX 45-33752072. Ed. Hans Dam. adv. contact: Emilia Hoejbjeg. bk.rev.; film rev.; music rev.; play rev.; tele.rev.; video rev.; illus.; circ. 135,128 (controlled). **Document type:** newspaper.

053.981   DK   ISSN 0006-2537
BILLEDBLADET. Variant title: Billed - Bladet. 1938. w. Bladforlaget af Foerste Oktober 1987 A-S, Vesterbrogade 16, DK-1506 Copenhagen V, Denmark. Ed. Anders Thisted. adv.; bk.rev.; dance rev.; film rev.; music rev.; play rev.; rec.rev.; illus. circ. 220,000.

078.9   DK
BLAA AVIS. 1981. 3/w. newsstand price: DKK 14. Den Blaa Avis, Generatorvej 8 D, DK-2730 Herlev, Denmark. TEL 45-44-92-44-44. FAX 45-44-92-77-17. Ed. Karsten Ree; Pub. Karsten Ree. adv. contact: Jasper Madsen. cols./p.: 6; pp./issue: 80. (tabloid format) **Document type:** newspaper.

078.9   DK
BORNHOLMEREN. 6/w. P.O. Box 140, Snellemark 26, DK-3700 Roenne, Denmark. TEL 45-56-95-25-26. FAX 45-56-95-84-49. Ed. Bo Schriver. circ. 6,000. cols./p.: 6; pp./issue: 32. **Document type:** newspaper.

078.9   DK
BORNHOLMS TIDENDE. 1866. 6/w. DKK 298($43) Bornholms Tidende A-S, Noerregade 11-19, DK-3700 Roenne, Denmark. TEL 45-56-95-14-00. FAX 45-56-95-31-19. Ed. Joergen Baungaard. adv.; bk.rev. circ. 11,204. cols./p.: 8; pp./issue: 20. (back issues avail.)

052   DK   ISSN 0011-6084
HF211
DANISH JOURNAL. French edition: Revue Danoise (ISSN 0035-0982); German edition: Daenische Rundschau (ISSN 0414-9262); Spanish edition: Informaciones Danesas (ISSN 0107-1335) 1920. irreg. Udenrigsministeriet - Ministry of Foreign Affairs, Asiatisk Plads 2, DK-1448 Copenhagen K, Denmark. Eds. Preben Hansen, Flemming Andre Larsen. illus. Indexed: Key to Econ.Sci.
Formerly: Danish Foreign Office Journal.

052   DK   ISSN 0011-6157
DANMARKSPOSTEN; a magazine for Danes abroad. 1920. 10/yr. DKK 275. Dansk Samvirke - Association of Danes Abroad, Koebmagergade 67, DK-1150 Copenhagen K, Denmark. TEL 33-32-09-13. FAX 33-32-53-52. Ed. Jens Witthoefft Nielsen. adv.; bk.rev.; illus. circ. 6,500.

053.981   DK   ISSN 0106-5726
DANSK NATUR - DANSK SKOLE. 1961. a. DKK 50. Landsforeningen Dansk Natur - Dansk Skole, Gaerdebred 20, 2300 Copenhagen S, Denmark. Ed. Henner Bahnson. illus.

078.9   DK
EKSTRA BLADET. d. Raadhuspladsen 37, DK-1595 Copenhagen V, Denmark. TEL 45-33-11-13-13. FAX 45-33-14-10-00. Eds. Sven Ove Gade, Bent Falbert. adv.; B&W page DKK 30100, color page DKK 48650. circ. 198,000. cols./p.: 6; pp./issue: 64. **Document type:** newspaper.

058.981   DK   ISSN 0014-7133
FAMILIE JOURNALEN. 1877. w. DKK 845. Aller Press A-S, Vigerslev Alle 18, 2500 Valby, Denmark. TEL 45-36-30-33-33. FAX 45-36-30-24-40. Ed. Anker Tune. adv.; bk.rev.; illus. circ. 306,853.

078.9   DK
FOLKEBLADET (SYDJYLLAND). 6/w. Jernbanegade 35, DK-6000 Kolding, Denmark. TEL 45-75-52-20-00. FAX 45-75-53-21-44. Ed. Tage Rasmussen. circ. 17,000. cols./p.: 8; pp./issue: 24. **Document type:** newspaper.

078.9   DK
FOLKETIDENDE. 6/w. Tvaergade 14, DK-4800 Nykoebing F, Denmark. TEL 45-54-85-20-66. FAX 45-54-85-38-52. Ed. P. Westergaard-Andersen. circ. 23,500. cols./p.: 8; pp./issue: 22. **Document type:** newspaper.

078.9   DK
FREDERICIA DAGBLAD. 6/w. Danmarksgade 28, DK-7000 Fredericia, Denmark. TEL 45-75-92-26-00. FAX 45-75-92-33-55. Ed. Mogens Soerensen. circ. 7,500. **Document type:** newspaper.

078.9   DK
DET FRI AKTUELT. 6/w. Raadhuspladsen 45-47, DK-1595 Copenhagen V, Denmark. TEL 45-33-32-40-01. FAX 45-33-12-26-41. Ed. Lisbeth Knudsen. circ. 47,255. **Document type:** newspaper.

GENERAL INTEREST PERIODICALS — DOMINICAN REPUBLIC

078.9   DK
FUENS STIFTSTIDENDE. d. Blangstedgaardsvej 2-6, DK-5220 Odense SOe, Denmark. TEL 45-66-11-11-11. FAX 45-65-93-25-74. Eds. Bent A. Koch, Egon Toettrup. adv.: B&W page DKK 31200, color page DKK 39000. circ. 66,000. cols./p.: 8; pp./issue: 22. **Document type:** newspaper.

078.9   DK
FYNS AMTS AVIS. 5/w. Sct. Nicolai Gade 3, DK-5700 Svendborg, Denmark. TEL 45-62-21-46-21. FAX 45-62-22-06-10. Ed. Arne Mariager. circ. 22,663. **Document type:** newspaper.

053.981   DK   ISSN 0107-9840
GRENZLAND; Informationen und Hinweise zu aktuellen Fragen des Grenzlandes aus der Sicht der deutschen Volksgruppe. (Text in German) 1980. a. (Bund deutscher Nordschleswiger) Deutsches Generalsekretariat, Vestergade 30, 6200 Aabenraa, Denmark. illus.
Description: Information about the German minority in Denmark.

078.9   DK
HELSINGOER DAGBLAD. 6/w. Klostermosevej 101, DK-3000 Helsingoer, Denmark. TEL 45-42-22-21-10. FAX 45-42-22-11-08. Ed. John Bech. circ. 6,947. cols./p.: 6; pp./issue: 32. **Document type:** newspaper.

078.9   DK
HERNING FOLKEBLAD. 6/w. Oestergade 25, DK-7400 Herning, Denmark. TEL 45-97-12-37-00. FAX 45-97-22-36-00. Eds. Gorm Albrechtsen, Flemming Larsen. circ. 16,500. cols./p.: 8; pp./issue: 29. **Document type:** newspaper.

053.981   DK   ISSN 0046-7626
HJEMMET. 1904. w. DKK 845. Egmont Magasiner, Vognmagergade 10, 1145 Copenhagen K, Denmark. Ed. Kaj Dorph-Petersen. adv.; bk.rev.; illus. circ. 285,000.

078.9   DK
HOLBAEK AMTS VENSTREBLAD. 6/w. Ahlgade 1, DK-3400 Holbaek, Denmark. TEL 45-53-43-20-48. FAX 45-59-44-50-34. Ed. Alfred Hansen. circ. 21,257. cols./p.: 8; pp./issue: 24. **Document type:** newspaper.

078.9   DK
HORSENS FOLKEBLAD. 6/w. Soendergade 47, DK-8700 Horsens, Denmark. TEL 45-75-62-45-00. FAX 45-76-61-07-97. Ed. Mogens Ahrenkiel. circ. 22,900. cols./p.: 8; pp./issue: 28. **Document type:** newspaper.

078.9   DK
INFORMATION (COPENHAGEN). St. Kongensgade 40C, P.O. Box 188, DK-1006 Copenhagen K, Denmark. TEL 45-33-14-14-26. FAX 45-33-93-80-83. Ed. Lasse Ellegaard. adv. circ. 25,524. cols./p.: 8; pp./issue: 24. **Document type:** newspaper.

078.9   DK
JYDSKE VESTKYSTEN. d. Banegaardspladsen, DK-6700 Esbjerg, Denmark. FAX 45-75-13-62-62. Ed. Nils Thostrup. circ. 32. cols./p.: 8. **Document type:** newspaper.

078.9   DK
KALUNDBORG FOLKEBLAD OG SAMSOE FOLKETIDENDE. 6/w. Skibbrogade 40-42, DK-4400 Kalundborg, Denmark. TEL 45-53-51-24-60. FAX 45-53-51-02-80. Ed. Joergen Jensen. circ. 9,746. cols./p.: 8. **Document type:** newspaper.

078.9   DK
KJERTEMINDE AVIS. 6/w. Ndr. Ringvej 54, DK-5300 Kerteminde, Denmark. TEL 45-65-32-10-04. FAX 45-65-32-27-04. Ed. J. Wind-Hansen. circ. 1,800. cols./p.: 8; pp./issue: 4. **Document type:** newspaper.

078.9   DK
KRISTELIGT DAGBLAD. 6/w. Fanoegade 15, DK-2100 Copenhagen Oe, Denmark. TEL 45-39-27-12-35. FAX 45-39-27-08-00. Ed. Gunnar Rytgaard. adv.: B&W page DKK 23296, color page DKK 26346. circ. 14,568. cols./p.: 8; pp./issue: 12. **Document type:** newspaper.

078.9   DK
LOEGSTOER AVIS. 6/w. Torvegade 2, DK-9670 Loegstoer, Denmark. TEL 45-98-67-12-11. FAX 45-98-67-12-11. Ed. Ejnar Damsgaard. circ. 2,776. cols./p.: 6; pp./issue: 12. **Document type:** newspaper.

078.9   DK
MIDDELFART VENSTREBLAD. 6/w. Algade 48, DK-5500 Middelfart, Denmark. TEL 45-64-41-13-03. FAX 45-64-41-13-07. Ed. Lars Bech Nielsen. circ. 6,200. **Document type:** newspaper.

078.9   DK
MIDTJYLLANDS AVIS. 6/w. P.O. Box 317, Vestergade 30, DK-8600 Silkeborg, Denmark. TEL 45-86-82-13-00. FAX 45-86-81-35-77. Ed. Viggo Soerensen. circ. 22,500. **Document type:** newspaper.

078.9   DK   ISSN 0109-1182
MORGENAVISEN JYLLANDS-POSTEN. Variant title: Jyllands-Posten. 1871. d. Groendalsvej 3, DK-8260 Viby J, Denmark. TEL 45-87-38-38-38. FAX 45-87-38-34-89. Ed. Joergen Ejboel. adv.; bk.rev. circ. 142,538. cols./p.: 8. (broadsheet format) **Document type:** newspaper.

078.9   DK
MORSOE FOLKEBLAD. 6/w. Elsoevej 105, DK-7900 Nykoebing M., Denmark. TEL 45-97-72-10-00. FAX 45-97-72-10-10. Ed. Leif Kristiansen. circ. 6,600. **Document type:** newspaper.

078.9   DK
NAESTVED TIDENDE - SJAELLANDS TIDENDE. 6/w. Ringstedgade 13, DK-4700 Naestved, Denmark. TEL 45-53-72-45-11. FAX 45-55-77-01-57. Ed.Bd. circ. 38,000. **Document type:** newspaper.

078.9   DK   ISSN 0905-8567
NORDSCHLESWIGER; Der Nordschleswiger. (Text in German) Bund Deutscher Nordschleswiger, Skibbroen 4, DK-6200 Aabenraa, Denmark. TEL 45-74-62-38-80. FAX 45-74-62-94-30. Ed. Siegfried Matlock. circ. 4,000. cols./p.: 7; pp./issue: 14. **Document type:** newspaper.

078.9   DK
NY DAG. 6/w. Hoejevej 15, DK-4900 Nakskov, Denmark. TEL 45-53-92-14-00. FAX 45-53-92-11-09. Ed. Klaus Sivebaek. circ. 9,500. **Document type:** newspaper.

053.981   DK   ISSN 0107-4687
NYT FRA DANMARK. 1981. 4/yr. DKK 190. Forlaget Nyt fra Danmark ApS, 20.012 Ny Oestergade 5, DK-1101 Copenhagen K, Denmark. TEL 45-33-91-25-66. FAX 45-33-91-24-99. Ed. Allan Alstrup. adv.; bk.rev. circ. 10,411.
Description: Directed to Danish expatriates.

078.9   DK
POLITIKEN. d. Dagbladet Politiken Ltd., Raadhuspladsen 37, DK-1595 Copenhagen V, Denmark. TEL 45-33-11-85-11. FAX 45-33-15-41-17. circ. 148.900. **Document type:** newspaper.

078.9   DK
RINGKJOEBING AMTS DAGBLAD. 6/w. St. Blichersvej 5, DK-6950 Ringkoebing, Denmark. TEL 45-97-32-07-22. FAX 45-97-32-05-46. Ed. Kristian Sand. circ. 17,048. cols./p.: 8; pp./issue: 22. **Document type:** newspaper.

053.981   DK   ISSN 0109-0429
SAMSPIL; tidskrift om invandrere. 1983. 8/yr. DKK 200. Ministry of Interior, Invandrerbladet, Samspil, P.O. Box 1098, 1009 Copenhagen K, Denmark. FAX 33-150343. Ed. Arly Christensen. bk.rev.; illus. circ. 2,500.

053.981   DK
SE OG HOER. 1953. w. DKK 897. Aller Press A-S, Vigerslev Alle 18, 2500 Copenhagen Valby, Denmark. TEL 45-36-30-33-33. FAX 45-36-30-01-60. Ed. Mogens E. Pedersen. adv.; film rev.; play rev.; illus. circ. 306,361.

078.9   DK
SKAGENS AVIS. 6/w. Skolevej 8, DK-9990 Skagen, Denmark. TEL 45-98-44-11-55. FAX 45-98-45-05-70. Ed. Johs. Bruun-Bindslev. circ. 4,472. **Document type:** newspaper.

078.9   DK
SKIVE FOLKEBLAD. 6/w. Gemsevej 7-9, DK-7800 Skive, Denmark. TEL 45-97-51-34-11. FAX 45-97-51-28-35. Ed. Ole Dall. circ. 13,959. cols./p.: 8; pp./issue: 18. **Document type:** newspaper.

053.981   DK   ISSN 0905-4774
SOENDAG. Variant title: Spis og Drik. Variant title: Ugemagasinet Soendag. 1921. w. DKK 767. Vesterbrogade 16, P.O. Box 424, DK-1505 Copenhagen V, Denmark. TEL 45-31-23-16-11. FAX 45-33-25-30-34. (Subscr. to: Vigerslev Alle 18, DK-2500 Valby, Denmark) Ed. Johnny Johansen. adv.: B&W page DKK 15100, color page DKK 22800. circ. 114,000.
Formerly (until 1989): Soendags - B.T. (ISSN 0038-0512)

053.981   DK   ISSN 0107-2072
SPANSK SKANDINAVISK FORENING. MEDLEMSINFORMATION. 1976. q. free. Spansk Skandinavisk Forening, c/o Arne Rasborg, Hellerupvej 46, 2900 Hellerup, Denmark. illus.

078.9   DK
THISTED DAGBLAD. 6/w. Jernbanegade 15-17, DK-7700 Thisted, Denmark. TEL 45-97-92-33-22. FAX 45-97-91-10-16. Ed. Hans Peter Kragh. circ. 11,200. cols./p.: 8; pp./issue: 18. **Document type:** newspaper.

053.981   DK
THYRAS VOLD. 1920. m. (11/yr.). DKK 60. Slesvig-Ligaen, Prinsessegade 9, DK-7000 Frederiksberg, Denmark. Ed. Joergen Gjedsted. adv. circ. 3,000.

053.981   DK   ISSN 0041-5669
UDE OG HJEMME. 1927. w. DKK 421. Aller Press A-S, Vigerslev Alle 18, 2500 Valby, Denmark. TEL 45-36-30-33-33. FAX 45-36-30-24-40. Ed. Hans Herman. adv.; film rev.; illus. circ. 144,972. (tabloid format)

078.9   DK
VEJLE AMTS FOLKEBLAD. 6/w. Bugattivej 8, DK-7100 Vejle, Denmark. TEL 45-75-85-77-88. FAX 45-75-85-74-76. Ed. Vagn Nygaard. adv. circ. 28,000. cols./p.: 8; pp./issue: 32. **Document type:** newspaper.

078.9   DK
VENDSYSSEL TIDENDE. d. Frederikshavnsvej 81, DK-9800 Hjoerring, Denmark. TEL 45-98-92-17-00. FAX 45-98-92-66-01. Ed. Claus Dindler. circ. 23,726. cols./p.: 8; pp./issue: 20. **Document type:** newspaper.

078.9   DK
VIBORG STIFTS FOLKEBLAD. 1877. d. DKK 1740. Viborg Stifts Folkeblad, Sct. Mathiasgade 7, DK-8800 Viborg, Denmark. TEL 45-86-62-68-00. FAX 45-86-62-22-20. Ed. Per Sunesen. adv.; bk.rev.; film rev.; music rev.; play rev.; tele.rev.; video rev.; illus.; circ. 12,720 (controlled). (broadsheet format; also avail. in microfilm) **Document type:** newspaper.

078.9   DK   ISSN 0106-4142
WEEKENDAVISEN. 1971. w. Pilestraede 34, DK-1785 Copenhagen K, Denmark. TEL 45-33-75-75-75. FAX 45-33-75-20-50. circ. 47,000. **Document type:** newspaper.

053.981 055.1   DK   ISSN 0108-2795
ZIBALDONE; serie disordinata e incoerente di pensieri, motivi, idee, ed immagini, periodico senza pretese. (Text in Danish and Italian) 1982. bi-m. DKK 5 per no. c/o Ezio Pace, Hesselvej 6, 8240 Risskov, Denmark. illus.

GENERAL INTEREST PERIODICALS — Dominican Republic

056.1   DR   ISSN 0002-2047
AP63
AHORA. 1962. w. RD.$14.($40) Publicaciones Ahora, Apdo. Postal 1402, San Martin 236, Santo Domingo, Dominican Republic. TEL 565-5581. TELEX 346-0423. Dir. Mario Alvarez Dugan. adv.; film rev.; illus.

GENERAL INTEREST PERIODICALS — Ecuador

056.1   EC
CALLE. 1956. w. Casilla 2010, Quito, Ecuador. Dir. Carlos Enrique Carrion. circ. 20,000.

056.1   EC
IMPACTO INTERNACIONAL; revista del Ecuador para el mundo. 1977. m. Gran Pasaje, Apdo. 5644, Guayaquil, Ecuador. Ed.Bd. film rev.; illus.

079.866   EC
EL UNIVERSO. 1921. d. S/140400; newsstand price: S/350. Escobedo 1204 y 9 de Octubre, Guayaquil, Guayas, Ecuador. TEL 593-4-490000. FAX 593-4-491034. Ed. Maria Teresa Perez; Pub. Carlos Perez. adv. contact: Cesar Perez. bk.rev.; film rev.; music rev.; illus. Wire service(s): AP, RN. circ. 145,000 (morn. ed.); 280,000 (Sun. ed.). cols./p.: 10; pp./issue: 44. (standard format) **Document type:** newspaper.

056.1   EC   ISSN 0042-7128
VISTAZO. 1957. fortn. $65. Editores Nacionales S.A., Aguirre 730, Casilla 1239, Guayaquil, Ecuador. TEL 4-328505. TELEX 3423. Ed. Xavier Alvarado Roca. circ. 85,000.

GENERAL INTEREST PERIODICALS — Egypt

059.927   UA
AL-AHAD AL-GEDID. (Text in Arabic) 1936. w. 88 Sharia Said M. Koraim, Alexandria, Egypt. TEL 807874. Ed. Galal M. Koraitem.

079.62   UA
AL-AHRAM. Evening edition: Al-Ahram al-Masa'i. International edition (London): Al-Ahram al-Dawli. N. American edition (ISSN 0891-673X); Weekly edition (Friday). English edition: Al-Ahram Weekly. (Supplements avail.) (Text in Arabic) 1875. d. $300 for N. American ed.; Friday ed. $100 (effective 1994). Mu'assasat al-Ahram, Sharia al-Galaa, Cairo, Egypt. TEL 02-758333. FAX 02-745888. TELEX 20185 AHRAM UN. (In N. America: Al-Ahram International, 405 Lexington Ave., 39th Fl. New York, NY 10174. TEL 212-972-6440. FAX 212-286-0285) Pub. Hamzi Fuad. adv.; bk.rev.; film rev.; illus.; circ. 900,000 (paid). **Document type:** newspaper.

059.927   UA
AL-AHRAM AL-IQTISADI. (Text in Arabic) w. $140 in N. America (effective 1994). Mu'assasat al-Ahram, Sharia Al-Galaa, Cairo, Egypt. TEL 02-758333. FAX 02-745888. TELEX 20185 AHRAM UN. (In N. America: Al-Ahram International, 405 Lexington Ave., New York, NY 10174. TEL 212-972-6440. FAX 212-286-0285) Ed. Issam Rifaat. adv. circ. 100,000. **Document type:** consumer publication.
Description: Covers economic and political affairs in Egypt and the world.

079.62 052   UA
AL-AHRAM WEEKLY. (Text in English) 1991. w. $150 in N. America (effective 1994). Mu'assasat al-Ahram, Sharia al-Galaa, Cairo, Egypt. TEL 02-758333. FAX 02-745888. (In N. America: Al-Ahram International, 405 Lexington Ave., 39th Fl., New York, NY 10174. TEL 212-972-6440. FAX 212-286-0285) adv. (broadsheet format) **Document type:** newspaper.

079.62   UA
AL-AKHBAR. (Text in Arabic) 1952. d. Dar Akhbar al-Yawm, 6 Sharia as-Sahafa, Cairo, Egypt. TEL 02-574-8400. FAX 02-574-8178. bk.rev.; illus. (broadsheet format) **Document type:** newspaper.

059.927   UA
AKHBAR AL-YAWM. (Text in Arabic) 1944. w. Dar Akhbar al-Yawm, 6 Sharia as-Sahafa, Cairo, Egypt. TELEX 92215. circ. 1,087,177.

059.927   UA   ISSN 0002-3655
AKHER SAA. (Text in Arabic) 1934. w. Dar Akhbar al-Yawm, 6 Sharia as-Sahafa, Cairo, Egypt. TEL 02-574-8100. FAX 02-574-8178. Ed. Muhammad Wajdi Kandil. circ. 130,367. **Document type:** consumer publication.

059.927 054.1   UA
AMITIE INTERNATIONALE. (Text in Arabic, French) 1957. q. Association Egyptienne d'Amitie Internationale, 59 Av. Hourriya, Alexandria, Egypt. TEL 23639. Ed. Zaki Badaoui.

079.62 052   UA
EGYPTIAN GAZETTE. (Text in English) 1879. d. Dar al-Tahrir, 24 Sharia Zakaria Ahmed, Cairo, Egypt. TEL 02-574-9494. FAX 02-574-9797. TELEX 92475 TAHRIR UN. Ed. Mohamed el-Ezabi. circ. 35,000. **Document type:** newspaper.

079.62 052   UA
EGYPTIAN MAIL. (Text in English) w. Dar al-Tahrir, 24 Sharia Zakaria Ahmed, Cairo, Egypt. TEL 02-741611. FAX 02-749949. TELEX 92475 TAHRIR UN. Ed. Mohamed el-Ezabi. adv. circ. 35,000. **Document type:** newspaper.

059.927   UA
EL-ARABI. m. $24. Dar Akhbar al-Yawm, 6 Sharia as-Sahafa, Cairo, Egypt. TELEX 92215.

079.62   UA
AL-GOMHOURIA. (Text in Arabic) 1953. d. Dar al-Tahrir, 24 Sharia Zakaria Ahmed, Cairo, Egypt. TEL 02-574-9090. FAX 02-574-9191. Ed. Mahfouz al-Ansari. adv. circ. 650,000. **Document type:** newspaper.

059.927   UA
HORREYATI/MY LIBERTY. Variant romanisation: Hurriyyati. (Text in Arabic) 1990. w. Dar al-Tahrir, 24 Sharia Zakaria Ahmad, Cairo, Egypt. TEL 02-741611. FAX 02-749949. TELEX 92475 TAHRIR UN. circ. 250,000.

059.927   UA
KITAB AL-HILAL. (Text in Arabic) m. Dar al- Hilal, 16 Sharia Muhammad Ezz el-Arab, Cairo, Egypt. TEL 02-27954. TELEX 92703. Ed. Moustafa Nabil.

059.927   UA
KITAB EL YOM. m. $14. Dar Akhbar al-Yawm, 6 Sharia as-Sahafa, Cairo, Egypt. TELEX 92215.

MIDDLE EAST OBSERVER. see *GENERAL INTEREST PERIODICALS — Middle East*

059.92   UA
AL-MISSA. (Text in Arabic) 1956. d. Dar al-Tahrir, 24 Sharia Zakaria Ahmed, Cairo, Egypt. TEL 02-741611. FAX 02-749949. TELEX 92475 TAHRIR UN. Ed. Samir Ragab. circ. 105,000. **Document type:** newspaper.

059.927   UA
AL-MUSAWWAR. 1924. w. $180 in N. America (effective 1994). Dar Al-Hilal, 16 Sharia Muhammad Ezz Al-Arab, Cairo, Egypt. TEL 02-362-5450. FAX 02-362-5469. (In N. America: Al-Ahram International, 405 Lexington Ave., New York, NY 10174. TEL 212-972-6440. FAX 212-286-0285) Ed. Makram Mohammed Ahmed. adv.; illus. circ. 130,423. **Document type:** consumer publication.

059.927   UA
NISF AL-DUNYA. (Text in Arabic) 1990. w. Mu'assasat al-Ahram, Sharia al-Galaa, Cairo, Egypt. TEL 02-758333. FAX 02-745888. TELEX 20185 AHRAM UN. adv.; illus.

059.927   UA
OCTOBER. 1976. w. Dar al-Maaref, 1119 Sharia Corniche en-Nil, Cairo, Egypt. TEL 02-777-077. FAX 02-574-4999. TELEX 92199. (In N. America: Al-Ahram International, 405 Lexington Ave., New York, NY 10174. TEL 212-972-6440. FAX 212-286-0285) Ed. Salah Montassir. adv. circ. 140,500. Indexed: RILA. **Document type:** consumer publication.

962   UA
PRISM; quarterly of Egyptian culture. q. £4. Foreign Cultural Relations, Foreign Press and Information Department, 44, Mesaha St., Giza, Egypt. Ed. Rawheya Tawfik.

079.62 054.1   UA
LE PROGRES EGYPTIEN. (Text in French) 1897. d. Dar al-Tahrir, 24 Sharia Zakaria Ahmed, Cairo, Egypt. TEL 02-741611. FAX 02-749949. TELEX 92475 TAHRIR UN. Ed. Khaled Anwar Bakir. circ. 22,000. **Document type:** newspaper.

059.927   UA
RIWAYAT AL-HILAL. (Text in Arabic) m. Dar al- Hilal, 16 Sharia Muhammad Ezz el-Arab, Cairo, Egypt. TEL 02-27954. TELEX 92703. Ed. Husain Mones.

059.927   UA
SABAH AL-KHAYR. (Text in Arabic) w. $180 in N. America (effective 1994). Mu'assasat Ruz al-Yusuf, 89A Sharia Qasr el-Aini, Cairo, Egypt. (Subscr. in N. America to: Al-Ahram International, 405 Lexington Ave., New York, NY 10174. TEL 212-972-6440. FAX 212-286-0285) **Document type:** consumer publication.

059.927   UA
SAMIR. (Text in Arabic) w. Dar al- Hilal, 16 Sharia Muhammad Ezz el-Arab, Cairo, Egypt. TEL 02-27954. TELEX 92703.

GENERAL INTEREST PERIODICALS — Estonia

079.474   ER   ISSN 1018-7286
DK502.3
THE BALTIC INDEPENDENT. (Text in English) 1990. w. $75 to individuals; institutions $96 (effective 1994). Baltic Independent Ltd., P.O. Box 45, Parnu mnt. 67a, 0090 Tallinn, Estonia. TEL 372-2-683074. FAX 372-2-311232. TELEX 173193 ETA. Ed. Tarmu Tammerk. adv.: B&W page $999; trim 360 x 250; adv. contact: Reet Maran. bk.rev. circ. 9,500. **Document type:** newspaper.
Formerly (until June 1990): Estonian Independent.
Description: Presents news from an independent viewpoint on Estonian, Latvian and Lithuanian politics, business, and culture.

059   ER
EESTI ELU/ESTONIAN LIFE. (Text in English, Estonian) 1989. m. $78 (effective 1994). Narva mnt. 5, 1st Fl., 0090 Tallinn, Estonia. TEL 0142-422244. FAX 0142-449558. Ed. Maris Makko; Pub. Sirje Endre. circ. 7,500. **Document type:** newspaper.

077   ER
PAEVALEHT. 1905. d. (Mon.-Sat.). 400 EEK ($30). Paevaleht Ltd., Parnu mnt 67a, 0090 Tallinn, Estonia. TEL 3722-681-235. FAX 3722-442-762. Ed. Margus Mets. adv.; bk.rev.; film rev.; music rev.; play rev.; tele.rev.; illus.; tr.lit. circ. 30,000. (tabloid format) **Document type:** newspaper.
Description: News and columns on politic, culture, sport, business and life.

GENERAL INTEREST PERIODICALS — Ethiopia

059.928   ET   ISSN 0047-3391
KESTE DAMENA/RAINBOW;* illustrated monthly. (Text in Amharic and English) 1967. m. Novosti Press Agency in Ethiopia, Box 239, Addis Ababa, Ethiopia. Ed. Vadim Rozov. adv.; illus. Indexed: Comput.Dtbs.

059.928   ET
YEZARIETU ETHIOPIA. w. Ministry of Information, P.O. Box 30232, Meskel Sq., Addis Ababa, Ethiopia. Ed. Shiferaw Mengeshaw. adv. circ. 25,000.

GENERAL INTEREST PERIODICALS — European Communities

055.1   IT
▼**BELL'EUROPA;** alla scoperta del contiente piu bello del mondo. 1993. m. L.58000 (foreign L.130000). Editoriale Giorgio Mondadori S.p.A., Via A. Ponti 10, 20143 Milan, Italy. TEL 02-891661. FAX 02-89125888. Ed. Salvatore Giannella. illus. circ. 140,000. **Document type:** consumer publication.
Description: Presents the art, architecture, geography, history, culture and traditions of Europe.

058.8   NO   ISSN 0332-5806
ERGO; tidsskrift for kultur- og samfunnsspoersmaal. 1970. q. NOK 195. Solum Forlag, P.O. Box 140 Skoeyen, N-0212 Oslo 2, Norway.
Description: Devoted to cultural and social questions of a more or less general nature.

072.1 052 UK ISSN 0959-9061
THE EUROPEAN. 1990. w. $135. The European Ltd., Orbit House, 5 New Fetter Ln., London EC4A 1AP, England. TEL 071-822-2020. FAX 071-377-4910. Ed. Charles A. Garside. adv.; bk.rev.; film rev.; illus.; circ. 167,500 (paid). (broadsheet format; also avail. in microfilm; back issues avail.) **Document type:** newspaper.
●Also available online.
  Description: Covers the news, financial and economic developments, the arts, life-style, and sports of Europe.

055.1 IT ISSN 1121-8851
EUROS. (Text in Italian; contents page in Italian, Spanish) 1991. m. L.80000 (foreign L.130000). Euros Editrice s.r.l., Via Francesco Crispi 1, 00187 Rome, Italy. TEL 06-6787402. FAX 06-6840597. Ed. Vittorio Nistico.

GENERAL INTEREST PERIODICALS — Falkland Islands

052 FK
PENGUIN NEWS. 1979. fortn. £20. Penguin News, Box 178, Ross Rd., Port Stanley, Falkland Islands. FAX 22238. Ed. James Stevens. circ. 1,000.

GENERAL INTEREST PERIODICALS — Finland

078.97 FI ISSN 0785-398X
AABO UNDERRETTELSER. (Text in Swedish) 1824. 5/w. Aabo Tidnings och Tryckeri, Auragatan 1 B, FIN-20100 Aabo, Finland. TEL 358-921-333-886. FAX 358-921-333-964. Ed. Torbjoern Kevin. circ. 8,000. **Document type:** newspaper.

078.97 FI ISSN 0355-6913
AAMULEHTI. 1881. d. FIM 865; newsstand price: FIM 7. Kustannus Oy Aamulehti, P.O. Box 327, Patamaenkatu 7, FIN-33101 Tampere, Finland. TEL 358-31-266-6111. FAX 358-31-266-6259. Ed. Raimo Seppala; Pub. Raimo Seppala. adv. contact: Jaana Pauhu. bk.rev.; film rev.; music rev.; play rev.; tele.rev.; video rev.; illus. Wire service(s): RN. circ. 135,000. cols./p.: 8; pp./issue: 36. (broadsheet format; also avail. in microfilm) **Document type:** newspaper.

059.945 FI ISSN 0355-3051
APU. 1933. w. FIM 1002. A-Lehdet Oy, Hitsaajankatu 7, 00810 Helsinki 81, Finland. FAX 0-781911. Ed. Jorma K. Virtanen. illus. circ. 255,113. **Document type:** consumer publication.
  Description: General interest weekly for the whole family.

078.97 FI ISSN 0358-6294
BORGAABLADET. (Text in Swedish) 1860. 6/w. Tryckeri- och Tidnings, P.O. Box 24, FIN-06101 Borgaa, Finland. TEL 358-915-173-333. FAX 358-915-173-348. Ed. Rolf Gabrielsson. circ. 11,100. **Document type:** newspaper.

078.97 FI ISSN 1235-9246
DEMARI. Key Title: Poliittinen Uutislehti Demari. 1988. 5/w. Demari, P.O. Box 338, FIN-00531 Helsinki, Finland. TEL 358-90-701-041. FAX 358-753-4688. TELEX 124433 SSDEM SF. Ed. Jukka Halonen. circ. 40,000. **Document type:** newspaper.

053.1 GW ISSN 0176-8751
DEUTSCH - FINNISCHE RUNDSCHAU. 1968. q. membership. Deutsch - Finnische Gesellschaft e.V., Kleistsr. 37, 70736 Fellbach, Germany. TEL 0711-513289. FAX 0711-5181750. adv.; bk.rev. circ. 10,000. (back issues avail.) **Document type:** newsletter.

059.945 FI ISSN 0355-7227
ET-LEHTI. m. FIM 205. Sanoma Corporation, PL 113, SF-00381 Helsinki, Finland. TEL 358-0-1221. Ed. Marjukka Luomala. circ. 135,467.
  Description: For retired and retirement-aged people.

078.97 FI ISSN 0356-1682
ETELA - POHJANMAA. 1926. 5/w. FIM 360. Etela - Pohjanmaa, PL 10, Keskuskatu 10, FIN-60101 Seinajoki, Finland. TEL 964-4142142. FAX 964-4144905. Ed. Paula Hamalainen. adv. contact: Aapo Viitala. bk.rev.; film rev.; music rev.; play rev.; tele.rev.; video rev.; illus.; circ. 11,754 (controlled). cols./p.: 7; pp./issue: 12. (tabloid format) **Document type:** newspaper.

078.97 FI ISSN 0357-0975
ETELA-SAIMAA. 1914. d. Etel-Saimaan Kustannus, Lauritsalantie 1, FIN-53100-Lappeenranta, Finland. TEL 358-953-5591. FAX 358-16936. TELEX 58217 SAIMA SF. Ed. Lauri Sarhimaa. circ. 36,022. **Document type:** newspaper.
  Formerly: It-Suomen Sanomat.

078.97 FI ISSN 0359-5056
ETELA-SUOMEN SANOMAT. 1914. d. Esan Kirjapaino, P.O. Box 80, FIN-15101 Lahti, Finland. TEL 358-918-57-511. FAX 358-918-575-466. TELEX 16132 ESA SF. Ed.Bd. circ. 71,018. **Document type:** newspaper.

078.97 FI ISSN 0356-2751
HAMEEN SANOMAT. 1879. d. Hameen Sanomat, P.O. Box 530, FIN-13111 Hameenlinna, Finland. TEL 358-917-1511. FAX 358-917-151-492. Ed. Esko Ojala. circ. 33,344. **Document type:** newspaper.

078.97 FI ISSN 0355-2047
HELSINGIN SANOMAT. (Supplement avail.: Helsingin Sanomat. Kuukausiliite (ISSN 0780-0096)) 1904. Sanoma, Ludviginkatu 6-8, FIN-00130 Helsinki, Finland. TEL 358-1221. FAX 358-605-709. TELEX 124897 HELSA SF. Ed. Janne Virkkunen; Pub. Seppo Kievari. circ. 482,453. **Document type:** newspaper.

059.945 FI ISSN 0780-0096
HELSINGIN SANOMAT. KUUKAUSILIITE. (Supplement to: Helsingin Sanomat) 1983. s-m. Sanoma Corporation, P.O. Box 240, SF-00101 Helsinki, Finland. TEL 90-1221. FAX 90-1223229. Ed.Bd. circ. 574,900.

078.97 FI ISSN 0356-0724
HUFVUDSTADSBLADET. (Text in Swedish) 1864. d. Hufvudstadsbladet, Mannerheimvaegen 18, PB 217, FIN-00101 Helsinki, Finland. TEL 358-12-531. FAX 358-642-930. TELEX 124402 HBL SF. Eds. Bo Stenstroem, Rafael Paro. circ. 67,230. **Document type:** newspaper.

059.945 FI ISSN 0355-4317
HYMY. 1959. m. FIM 225. Yhtyneet Kuvalehdet Oy, Maistraatinportti 1, FIN-00240 Helsinki, Finland. TEL 358-0-156-6524. FAX 358-0-156-6505. TELEX 121364. Ed. Esko Tulusto. adv.: B&W page FIM 10000, color page FIM 14700. illus. circ. 111,661.
  Formerly: Hymylehti (ISSN 0018-8298)

078.97 FI ISSN 0356-1674
HYVINKAAN SANOMAT. 1924. 6/w. Hyvinkaan Sanomalehti, P.O. Box 106, FIN-05801 Hyvinkaa, Finland. TEL 358-914-555-100. FAX 358-914-555-117. Ed. Pentti Kiiski. circ. 15,203. **Document type:** newspaper.

078.97 FI ISSN 0356-2298
IISALMEN SANOMAT. 1926. d. Iisalmen Sanomat, P.O. Box 11, FIN-74101 Iisalmi, Finland. TEL 358-977-15-511. FAX 358-977-155-1401. Ed. Risto Ylitalo. circ. 20,019. **Document type:** newspaper.

078.97 FI ISSN 0356-1283
ILKKA. 1906. d. Ilkka, P.O. Box 60, FIN-60101 Seinajoki, Finland. TEL 358-964-186-555. FAX 358-186-500. TELEX 72130 ILKKA SF. Ed. Kari Hokkanen. circ. 57,536. **Document type:** newspaper.

078.97 FI ISSN 0355-2055
ILTA - SANOMAT. 1932. 6/w. Sanoma, Korkeavuorenkatu 34, FIN-00130 Helsinki, Finland. TEL 358-1221. FAX 358-1223419. TELEX 124897 HELSA SF. Eds. Vesa-Pekka Koljonen, Hannu Savola. circ. 223,815. **Document type:** newspaper.

078.97 FI ISSN 0783-0025
ILTALEHTI. 1980. 6/w. Uusi Suomi, P.O. Box 3, FIN-00101 Helsinki, Finland. FAX 358-533-512. TELEX 124898 UUSIS SF. Ed. Veli-Antti Savolainen. circ. 113,544. **Document type:** newspaper.

078.97 FI ISSN 0356-4444
ITA - SAVO. 1907. d. Savonlinnan Kirjapaino, P.O. Box 35, FIN-57101 Savonlinna, Finland. TEL 358-957-29-171. FAX 358-957-20240. TELEX 5611 ITASA SF. Ed. Esko Suikkanen.

078.97 FI ISSN 0782-5528
JAKOBSTADS TIDNING. (Text in Swedish) 1937. 6/w. Jakobstads Tryckeri och Tidnings AB, Jakobsgatan, FIN-68600 Jakobstad, Finland. TEL 358-967-235-5555. FAX 358-967-18277. Ed. Alf Snellman. circ. 12,122. **Document type:** newspaper.

078.97 FI ISSN 0356-3502
KAINUUN SANOMAT. 1917. d. Kainuun Sanomat, Viestitie 2, FIN-87700 Kajaani, Finland. TEL 358-986-1661. FAX 358-986-23013. Ed. Keijo Korhonen. circ. 30,408. **Document type:** newspaper.

059.945 FI ISSN 0355-4252
KAKS PLUS. m. FIM 270. Yhtyneet Kuvalehdet Oy, Maistraatinportti 1, FIN-00240 Helsinki, Finland. TEL 358-0-156-6524. FAX 358-0-156-6505. TELEX 121364. Ed. Sanna Wirtavuori. adv.: B&W page FIM 12400, color page FIM 18300. circ. 58,988.
  Description: For young families with babies.

078.97 FI ISSN 0356-1356
KALEVA. 1899. d. FIM 860. Kaleva, Postilokero 70 Ahjotie 1, FIN-90150 Oulu, Finland. TEL 981-5377111. FAX 981-5377248. TELEX 32112 KALEV SF. Ed. Tervo Mallinen; Pub. Martti Ursin. adv.: B&W page FIM 58572, color page FIM 71232; adv. contact: Harri Kesti. circ. 95,955 (controlled). cols./p.: 8; pp./issue: 27. (broadsheet format) **Document type:** newspaper.

078.97 FI ISSN 0789-0265
KANSAN LEHTI. 1898. 5/w. Kansan Lehti, P.O. Box 16, FIN-33540 Tampere, Finland. TEL 358-931-591-1111. FAX 358-931-591-190. Ed. Vesa Karvinen. circ. 11,000. **Document type:** newspaper.

078.97 FI ISSN 0356-1380
KANSAN TAHTO. 1917. 4/w. Kansan Tahto, P.O. Box 61, FIN-90101 Oulu, Finland. TEL 358-981-221-722. Ed. Eero Matero. circ. 14,596. **Document type:** newspaper.

078.97 FI ISSN 0357-1521
KANSAN UUTISET. 1957. 4/w. Suomen Kansan Demokraattinen Liitto, Niittaajankatu 8, FIN-00810 Helsinki, Finland. TEL 358-75-881. FAX 358-758-8301. TELEX 124663 KU HKI. Eds. Yrjo Rautio, Pertti Jokinen. circ. 43,454. **Document type:** newspaper.

078.97 FI ISSN 0357-2021
KESKI - UUSIMAA. 1918. d. Keski - Uusimaa, P.O. Box 52, FIN-04301 Tuusula, Finland. TEL 358-90-255-255. FAX 358-90-255-247. Ed. Auvo Kantola. circ. 24,674. **Document type:** newspaper.

078.97 FI ISSN 0788-8325
KESKIPOHJANMAA. 1917. d. Keski - Pohjanmaan Kirjapaino, P.O. Box 45, FIN-67101 Kokkola, Finland. TEL 358-968-28-511. FAX 358-968-20208. Ed. Lassi Jaakkola. circ. 35,121. **Document type:** newspaper.

078.97 FI ISSN 0356-1402
KESKISUOMALAINEN. 1918. d. Keskisuomalainen, Aholaidantie 3, FIN-40320 Jyvaskyla, Finland. TEL 358-941-622-000. FAX 358-941-622-272. TELEX 28211 KSM SF. Ed. Erkki Laatikainen. circ. 81,852. **Document type:** newspaper.

059.945 FI ISSN 0023-2610
KODIN KUVALEHTI. 1950. s-m. FIM 337. (Sanomaprint) Sanoma Corporation, PL 113, SF-00381 Helsinki, Finland. TEL 358-0-1221. Ed. Eija Ailasmaa. adv.; bk.rev.; illus. circ. 166,697.

078.97 FI ISSN 0356-1135
KOTIMAA. 1905. s-w. Kotimaa, Pohjoiskaari 15, FIN-00200 Helsinki, Finland. FAX 358-674417. Ed. Tuomo Korteniemi. circ. 70,000. **Document type:** newspaper.

078.97 FI ISSN 0356-3101
KOUVOLAN SANOMAT. d. Kouvolan Sanomat, P.O. Box 40, FIN-45101 Kouvola, Finland. TEL 358-951-28-911. FAX 358-951-28-911. Ed. Juha Oksanen. circ. 34,414. **Document type:** newspaper.

078.97 FI ISSN 0356-3545
KRISTITYN VASTUU. 1964. w. Suomen Kristillinen Liitto - Finnish Christian Union, Toolonkatu 50 D, FIN-00250 Helsinki, Finland. TEL 358-440-791. Ed. Ulla Riutta. circ. 10,000. **Document type:** newspaper.

059.945 FI
KURIREN. 1959. 20/yr. FIM 260 (typically set in June). Kurirenforlaget, Box 12, 65101 Vasa 10, Finland. FAX 961-173158. Ed. Frejvid Weegar. adv.; bk.rev. circ. 20,437.

078.97 FI ISSN 0782-5730
KYMEN SANOMAT. 1955. d. Kymen Sanomien Kirjapaino, P.O. Box 114, FIN-48100 Kotka, Finland. TEL 358-952-16-300. Ed. Jukka Vehkasalo. circ. 33,980. **Document type:** newspaper.

078.97 FI ISSN 0356-4541
LALLI. 1917. 5/w. Keskustan Kustannus, FIN-32800 Kokemaki, Finland. TEL 358-939-364-855. FAX 358-939-364-276. Ed. Seppo Keranen. circ. 10,431. **Document type:** newspaper.

078.97 FI ISSN 0356-1623
LANSI - SAVO. 1917. d. Lansi Savo, Teollisuuskatu 2, FIN-50130 Mikkeli, Finland. TEL 358-955-3501. FAX 358-955-350-337. Eds. Ilkka Juva, Seija Rasila. circ. 29,182. **Document type:** newspaper.

078.97 FI ISSN 0782-6419
LANSI - SUOMI. 1905. d. Oy Lansi Suomi, Kaivopuistontie 1, FIN-26100 Rauma, Finland. TEL 358-938-3361. FAX 358-938-240-959. Ed. Mikko Uola. circ. 20,200. **Document type:** newspaper.

078.97 FI ISSN 0359-6753
LAPIN KANSA. 1928. d. Lapin Kansa, Veitikantie 8, FIN-96100 Rovaniemi, Finland. TEL 358-960-2911. FAX 358-960-291-345. TELEX 37213 LKROV SF. Ed. Heikki Tuomi-Nikula. circ. 43,759. **Document type:** newspaper.

078.97 FI ISSN 0355-3787
MAASEUDUN TULEVAISUUS. 1916. 3/w. Maataloustuottajain Keskusliitto, P.O. Box 440, FIN-00101 Helsinki, Finland. TEL 358-131-151. FAX 358-6943717. Ed. Mikko Vesa. circ. 122,343. **Document type:** newspaper.

059.945 FI ISSN 0355-9637
NYKYPOSTI. m. FIM 220. Yhtyneet Kuvalehdet Oy, Maistraatinportti 1, FIN-00240 Helsinki, Finland. TEL 0-15661. FAX 358-0-156-6505. TELEX 121364. Ed. Irma Karama. adv.; B&W page FIM 13500, color page FIM 19900. circ. 133,253.

078.97 FI ISSN 0789-0737
POHJALAINEN. 1984. d. Vaasa, P.O. Box 37, FIN-65101 Vaasa, Finland. TEL 358-961-249-111. FAX 358-961-249-351. TELEX 74212 PONEN SF. Ed. Jaakko Elenius. circ. 65,000. **Document type:** newspaper.

078.97 FI ISSN 0782-372X
POHJOLAN SANOMAT. 1915. d. Pohjolan Sanomat, Sairaalakatu 2, FIN-94100 Kemi, Finland. TEL 358-9698-2911. TELEX 3643 POHSA SF. Eds. Matti Lammi, Reijo Alatormanen. circ. 42,203. **Document type:** newspaper.
  Formerly: Tornion Laakso.

078.97 FI ISSN 0782-5404
SALON AEUDUN SANOMAT. 1943. d. Salon Seudun Sanomalehti, P.O Box 117, FIN-24101 Salo, Finland. TEL 358-924-30-021. FAX 358-924-3002300. Eds. Jarmo Vahasilta, Seppo Suominen. circ. 21,758. **Document type:** newspaper.

078.97 FI ISSN 0355-8746
SATAKUNNAN KANSA. 1918. d. Satakunnan Kirjateollisuus, P.O. Box 58, FIN-28101 Pori, Finland. TEL 358-939-328-111. TELEX 66102 NEWSP SF. Ed. Erkki Teikari. circ. 62,620. **Document type:** newspaper.

078.97 FI ISSN 0356-3510
SAVON SANOMAT. 1907. d. Savon Sanomain Kirjapaino, Vuorikatu 21 - 23, FIN-70100 Kuopio, Finland. TEL 358-971-303-111. FAX 358-971-303-111. TELEX 42111 SASAN SF. Eds. Tapani Lepola, Raimo Ylinen. circ. 90,609. **Document type:** newspaper.

059.945 FI ISSN 0358-8017
SEURA (1979). 1935. w. FIM 598. Yhtyneet Kuvalehdet Oy, Maistraatinportti 1, FIN-00240 Helsinki, Finland. TEL 358-0-156-6524. FAX 358-0-156-6505. TELEX 121364. Ed. Jouni Flinkkila. adv.: B&W page FIM 26500, color page FIM 38900; trim 217 x 280. illus. circ. 272,950. **Document type:** consumer publication.
  Former titles: Suur-Seura (ISSN 0355-189X); Seura (ISSN 0037-2943)

059.945 FI ISSN 0039-5552
AP80
SUOMEN KUVALEHTI. 1917. w. FIM 580. Yhtyneet Kuvalehdet Oy, Maistraatinportti 1, FIN-00240 Helsinki, Finland. TEL 358-0-156-6524. FAX 358-0-156-6505. TELEX 121364. Ed. Martti Backman. adv.: B&W page FIM 20300, color page FIM 29800. bk.rev.; charts; illus.; stat.; index. circ. 104,326. **Document type:** consumer publication.

078.97 FI ISSN 0356-3588
SUOMENMAA. 1965. 4/w. Maakansa, P.O. Box 86, FIN-00371 Helsinki, Finland. TEL 358-562-5044. FAX 358-562187. Ed.Lauri Kontro. circ. 18,000. **Document type:** newspaper.

078.97 FI ISSN 0355-9149
TIDNINGEN AALAND. (Text in Swedish) 1891. 5/w. Aalands Tidnings-Tryckeri, P.O. Box 50, FIN-22101 Mariehamn, Finland. TEL 358-928-26-026. FAX 358-928-15-755. Ed. Ray Soederholm. circ. 11,502. **Document type:** newspaper.

078.97 FI ISSN 0356-1631
TIEDONANTAJA. 1968. w. Tiedonantajayhdistys, Jarrumiehenkatu 2 B, FIN-00520 Helsinki, Finland. FAX 358-146-3520. Ed. Erkki Susi. circ. 13,000. **Document type:** newspaper.

078.97 FI ISSN 0782-5846
TURUN PAIVALEHTI. 1951. 5/w. Turun Paivalehti, P.O. Box 230, FIN-20101 Turku, Finland. TEL 358-921-353-900. FAX 358-921-353-580. Ed. Antti Vuorenrinne. circ. 11,012. **Document type:** newspaper.

078.97 FI
TURUN SANOMAT. 1904. d. Turun Sanomat, Kauppiaskatu 5, FIN-20100 Turku, Finland. TEL 358-921-693-311. FAX 358-921-693274. TELEX 62213 TUSAN SF. Ed. Ari Valjakka. circ. 134,705. **Document type:** newspaper.

078.97 FI ISSN 0357-1858
UUSIMAA. 1894. 6/w. Uusimaa, P.O. Box 15, FIN-06151 Porvo, Finland. TEL 358-915-172-322. FAX 358-915-174-736. Ed. Reijo Hirvonen. circ. 14,492. **Document type:** newspaper.

078.97 FI ISSN 0782-6559
VAESTRA NYLAND. (Text in Swedish) 1881. 6/w. Ekens Tryckeri, P.O. Box 26, FIN-10602 Ekenaes, Finland. TEL 358-911-62-800. FAX 358-911-15179. Ed. Olle Spring. circ. 12,500. **Document type:** newspaper.

059.945 FI ISSN 0042-2290
VALITUT PALAT/READER'S DIGEST (FINNISH EDITION).*
(Text in Finnish) 1945. m. FIM 162. Reader's Digest AB, Sentnerikuja 5, 00441 Helsinki, Finland. Ed. Raimo Moysa. adv.; film rev.; illus. circ. 320,000.

078.97 FI ISSN 0356-1844
VASABLADET. (Text in Swedish) 1856. 6/w. Vasabladet, Sandoegatan 6, FIN-65100 Vasa, Finland. TEL 358-961-129-003. FAX 358-961-129-003. TELEX 74269 VABLA SF. Ed. Birger Thoelix. circ. 27,485. **Document type:** newspaper.

078.97 FI
VIIKKO - ETEENPAIN. w. Kymenlaaksonkatu 10, FIN-48100, Finland. TEL 358-952-181-777. FAX 358-181-157. Ed. Risto Tuominen. circ. 10,000. **Document type:** newspaper.

078.97 FI ISSN 0357-2463
YLA - VUOKSI. 1927. 6/w. Yla - Vuoksi, Lappeentie 24, FIN-55100 Imatra, Finland. TEL 358-954-66-066. FAX 358-954-68447. Ed. Markku Soikkeli. circ. 15,622. **Document type:** newspaper.

GENERAL INTEREST PERIODICALS —
France

054.1 053.1 FR ISSN 0003-1704
AMI DU PEUPLE/VOLKSFREUND. (Text in French, German) 1858. w. 216 F. (foreign 398 F.). 30 rue Thomann, 67082 Strasbourg, France. TEL 88-32-79-08. FAX 88-22-51-66. Ed. B. Deck. adv.; bk.rev.; film rev.; illus.

054.1 FR ISSN 0044-8966
ARMOR; magazine de la Bretagne. 1969. m. 225 F. (foreign 300 F.). Societe de Presse, de Publicite et d'Edition de Landehen, 7 rue St. Jacques, B.P. 419, 22404 Lamballe, France. FAX 96-31-22-12. Ed. Yann Poilvet. adv.; bk.rev.; charts; illus.; tr.lit. circ. 40,000. **Indexed:** Amer.Bibl.Slavic & E.Eur.Stud., Ind.U.S.Gov.Per., PROMT.

054.1 FR ISSN 1165-3973
ATLANTICA; aquitaine - euskadi revue transfrontaliere d'information regionale et europeenne. m. 250 F. Office des Nouvelles Internationales, 18 rue de Folin, 64200 Biarritz, France. TEL 59-43-80-35. FAX 59-43-80-41. Eds. Jean Pousset, Andoni Ortuzar. adv.; illus.

054.1 FR
AUVERGNE MAGAZINE; magazines de France. m. 280 F. Editions Rene Dessagne, B.P. 90, 11 rue Pierre Leroux, 87000 Limoges, France. circ. 2,125. **Description:** Contains items of local interest.

054.1 600 FR ISSN 0243-1335
CA M'INTERESSE. 1981. m. 204 F. Prisma Presse, 6 rue Daru, 75008 Paris, France. TEL 44-15-30-00. FAX 47-64-10-42. TELEX 616076. Ed. Corinne Allavena. adv. circ. 327,000. **Indexed:** Pt.de Rep. (1991-).
  Description: Examines the daily environment, explains current events and investigates man's behavior.

054.1 FR ISSN 0008-0217
DC1
CAHIERS FRANCAIS. 1956. 5/yr. 230 F. (Europe 290 F., elsewhere 390 F.). Documentation Francaise, 29-31 Quai Voltaire, 75340 Paris Cedex 07, France. TEL 1-40-15-70-00. FAX 40-15-72-30. TELEX 215 666 DOCFRAN. (Subscr. to: 124 rue Henri Barbusse, 93308 Aubervilliers Cedex, France. TEL 48-39-56-00. FAX 48-39-56-01) Dir. Jean Jenger. charts; illus.; maps. circ. 25,000. (also avail. in microfiche from DFR) **Indexed:** Key to Econ.Sci., P.A.I.S.For.Lang.Ind., P.A.I.S., Pt.de Rep. (1979-).
Document type: government publication.
  —BLDSC (2948.945000); SWETS.

054.1 US ISSN 0886-005X
CHAMPS-ELYSEES. (Text in French) 1984. m. $118. Champs-Elysees Inc., Box 158067, Nashville, TN 37215-8067. TEL 800-824-0829. FAX 615-297-3138. (audio cassette; with printed transcription)

054.1 FR
CORREZE MAGAZINE; magazines de France. m. 280 F. (foreign 400 F.). Editions Rene Dessagne, B.P. 90, 11 rue Pierre Leroux, 87003 Limoges, France. TEL 55-77-25-97.
  Description: Contains items of local interest.

052 054.1 AT ISSN 0011-0442
COURRIER AUSTRALIEN; French monthly/mensuel Francais. (Text mainly in French; occasionally in English) 1892. m. Aus.$45. 506-149 Castlereagh, Sydney, N.S.W. 2000, Australia. Ed. Jean-Pierre Sourdin. bk.rev.; film rev.; play rev.; bibl. circ. 7,000.
  Description: Non-political publication covering news of France and Australia, for the French and Francophone community in Australia, New Zealand and New Caledonia.

074 FR ISSN 0220-8261
LE DAUPHINE LIBERE. 1945. d. Les Iles Cordees, 38113 Veurey-Voroize Cedex, France. TEL 76-88-71-00. FAX 76-88-70-96. Ed. Hubert Perrin. circ. 384,100. **Document type:** newspaper.

GENERAL INTEREST PERIODICALS — FRANCE

074   FR   ISSN 0181-7981
LA DEPECHE DU MIDI. 1870. d. Avenue Jean Baylet, 31095 Toulouse Cedex, France. TEL 61-41-11-49. FAX 61-44-74-74. Ed. Guy-Michel Empociello. circ. 228,068. **Document type:** newspaper.
   Former titles (until 1948): Democratie (ISSN 1155-6196); (until 1945): Depeche (ISSN 1155-6188)

053.1   FR
DERNIERES NOUVELLES D'ALSACE. (Text in French and German) 1877. d. Imprimerie et Edition des Dernieres Nouvelles de Strasbourg, 17-21 rue de la Nuee-Bleue, 67000 Strasbourg, France. TEL 88-23-31-23. Ed. Jacques Puymartin.

054.1   FR
DERNIERES NOUVELLES DU LUNDI. 1952. w. Imprimerie et Editions des Dernieres Nouvelles de Strasbourg, 17-21 rue de la Nuee-Bleue, 67000 Strasbourg, France. TEL 88-21-31-23. Ed. Jacques Puymartin.

054.1   FR
DOSSIERS ET DOCUMENTS. 1973. m. 120 F. (foreign 156 F.). Monde, 13 - 15 rue Falguiere, 75015 Paris, France. TEL 40-65-29-30. FAX 40-65-25-99. (Subscr. to: Immeuble Sirius, 1 place Hubert-Beuve-Mery, 94852 Ivry-sur-Seine Cedex, France. TEL 49-60-32-90) (also avail. in microfiche)

054.1   GW
ECOUTE. m. Spotlight Verlag GmbH, Freihamerstr. 4b, 82166 Graefelfing, Germany. TEL 09221-3982. FAX 09221-84681. Ed. Daniele Janovsky. adv. contact: Elke Pohl. circ. 40,225. **Document type:** consumer publication.

054.1   FR   ISSN 0013-0710
AP20
ECRITS DE PARIS; revue des questions actuelles. 1945. m. 350 F. (Centre d'Etudes des Questions Actuelles) Societe Parisienne d'Editions et de Publications, 9 Passage des Marais, 75010 Paris, France. TEL 1-42-01-40-51. Ed. Madeleine Malliavin. adv.; bk.rev.; film rev.; play rev.; rec.rev. circ. 20,000. **Indexed:** Amer.Hist.& Life, Hist.Abstr.

074   FR   ISSN 0240-4958
L'EST REPUBLICAIN. 1889. d. Rue Theophraste Reneudot, Houdemont, 54185 Heillecourt Cedex, France. TEL 83-59-80-54. FAX 83-59-80-13. Ed. Pierre Taribo. circ. 242,328. **Document type:** newspaper.

054.1   FR   ISSN 0765-412X
EVENEMENT DU JEUDI. 1984. w. 2 rue Christine, 75006 Paris, France. TEL 1-43-54-84-80. FAX 1-46-34-69-36. TELEX 205 802. Ed. Jean-Marcel Bouguereau. circ. 260,000.

054.1   FR   ISSN 0014-6285
FACETTES; lien des curieux, chercheurs. 1967. q. 200 F.($24) Facettes, 56, rue de Tassigny, 94700 Maisons Alfort, France. TEL 43-68-47-76. Dir. Anny Barroyer. bk.rev.; bibl, illus. circ. 3,600.

054.1   FR
FAMILLE CHRETIENNE. 1978. w. 260 F. Societe d'Editions pour la Famille, 52 rue Taitbout, 75440 Paris Cedex 09, France. Ed. Andre Jozan. adv.; illus.

054.1   FR   ISSN 0988-5757
FAMILLE MAGAZINE. 1954. m. 196 F. Societe de Publications et d'Editions Reunies, 21 rue du Faubourg St. Antoine, 75550 Paris Cedex 11, France. Dir. J Guespereau. adv.; illus.
   Formerly: Clair Foyer.

074   FR   ISSN 0182-5852
LE FIGARO. 1854. d. 37 rue du Louvre, 75002 Paris, France. TEL 42-21-62-00. FAX 42-21-64-05. Ed. Daniel Seguin. circ. 410,330. **Document type:** newspaper.

052   UK   ISSN 0958-8213
FRANCE; the quarterly magazine for Francophiles. 1989. q. 126 F.($29.75) France Magazine Ltd., Dormer House, The Square, Stow-on-the-Wold, Glos. GL54 1BN, England. TEL 451-831398. FAX 0451-830869. adv. circ. 63,000.
   Description: Covers the heritage, arts, culture, history, politics, cuisine, wine and regions of France.

074   FR   ISSN 0015-9549
FRANCE DIMANCHE. w. 118 F. (foreign 510 F.). Hachette Filipacchi Publications, 6 rue Ancelle, 92525 Neuilly sur Seine Cedex, France. TEL 40-88-72-59. FAX 40-88-72-62. (Subscr. to: 90 rue de Flandre, 75947 Paris Cedex 19, France. TEL 40-34-35-00) adv.; illus. **Document type:** newspaper.

052   US   ISSN 0886-2478
FRANCE MAGAZINE. 1985. q. free. Maison Francaise, 4101 Reservoir Rd., N.W., Washington, DC 20007. TEL 202-944-6069. FAX 202-944-6072. Ed. Jean Mendelson. adv. contact: Rebecca Rubin. bk.rev.; illus.; circ. 67,000 (controlled).
   Description: A collection of feature articles on France.

054.1   FR   ISSN 0015-9670
FRANCE MUTUALITE. 1959. m. 30 F. (Association Nationale de la Presse Mutualiste) Cooperative d'Information et d'Edition Mutualiste (C.I.E.M.), 67 rue Blomet, 75015 Paris, France. Ed. G. Quittard. illus.
   —CCC.

074   FR   ISSN 0182-5860
FRANCE-SOIR. 1944. d. 37 rue du Louvre, 75081 Paris Cedex 02, France. TEL 44-82-87-00. FAX 44-82-88-45. Ed. Bernard Morrot. circ. 231,753. **Document type:** newspaper.

051   US   ISSN 0888-8663
FRANCE TODAY. French edition: Journal Francais d'Amerique (ISSN 0195-2889) 1984. 10/yr. $27. France Press, Inc., 1051 Divisadero St., San Francisco, CA 94115. TEL 415-921-5100. FAX 415-921-0213. Ed. Anne Prah-Perochon. adv.; bk.rev.; film rev.; play rev. circ. 30,000.

054.1   MC
GAZETTE MONACO - COTE D'AZUR. 1976. m. 25 blvd Albert 1er, MC 98000, Monaco. TEL 93-25-20-36. FAX 93-25-14-64. Ed. Michel Daner. circ. 10,000. **Document type:** newspaper.

054.1   FR   ISSN 0220-8245
GEO; un nouveau monde: la terre. (Text in French) 1979. m. 298 F. Prisma Presse, 6 rue Daru, 75008 Paris, France. TEL 44-15-30-00. FAX 47-64-10-42. TELEX 644 403. Ed. Yan Meot. adv.; bk.rev.; illus. circ. 585,000. **Indexed:** Pt.de Rep. (1981-). **Document type:** consumer publication.
   Description: Explores the planet and those who live on it.

074   FR
ICI PARIS. 1945. w. 510 F. Hachette Filipacchi Publications, 6 rue Ancelle, 92525 Neuilly sur Seine Cedex, France. TEL 40-88-72-59. FAX 40-88-72-62. (Subscr. to: 90 rue de Flandre, 75947 Paris Cedex 19, France. TEL 40-34-35-00) Ed. Louis Balaye. adv.; film rev.; illus. circ. 372,386. **Document type:** newspaper.

054.1   FR   ISSN 0019-9893
INFORMATEUR DE LA QUINZAINE. 1920. s-m. 375 F. Societe d'Etudes, 5 bd. Beaumarchais, 75180 Paris Cedex 04, France. circ. 1,500.

054.1 800   FR   ISSN 0294-4308
INSTITUT CATHOLIQUE DE PARIS. REVUE. q. 210 F. Institut Catholique de Paris, 21 rue d'Assas, 75270 Paris Cedex 06, France. TEL 44-39-52-00. FAX 45-44-27-14. **Document type:** academic/scholarly publication.
   —BLDSC (7878.700000).
   Formerly: Institut Catholique de Paris. Nouvelles.
   Description: Quarterly journal with contributions on subjects taught in the Institut Catholique de Paris.

052   FR   ISSN 0294-8052
INTERNATIONAL HERALD TRIBUNE. 1887. d. (6/wk.). $350. International Herald Tribune, 181 Ave. Charles de Gaulle, 92521 Neuilly Cedex, France. TEL 46-37-06-51. FAX 46-37-93-38. TELEX 612718. (And: 850 Third Ave., 8th Fl., New York, NY 10022. TEL 212-752-3890) Ed. John Vinocur. adv.; bk.rev.; illus. circ. 195,000. **Document type:** newspaper.
   Description: Global daily newspaper.

054.1   US   ISSN 0195-2889
JOURNAL FRANCAIS D'AMERIQUE. English edition: France Today (ISSN 0888-8663) (Text in French) 1979. fortn. $35. France Press, Inc., 1051 Divisadero St., San Francisco, CA 94115. TEL 415-921-5100. FAX 415-921-0213. Ed. Anne Prah-Perochon. adv.; bk.rev. circ. 35,000.
   Description: Provides current news from France and covers travel, arts, cinema, business, and French-related events in the United States.

054.1   FR   ISSN 0022-5681
JOURS DE FRANCE.* 1954. w. 265 F. Societe de Presse Jours de France, 12 rue du Mail, 75002 Paris, France. TEL 40-70-15-15. Ed. Marcel Dassault. adv.; bk.rev.; illus. circ. 673,000.

054.1   FR   ISSN 0395-1081
DC611.C8
KYRN; magazine de la Corse. 1969. m. 800 F. Editions Corse Mediterranee, 7 rue Cesar-Campinchi, 20200 Bastia, Corsica, France. FAX 95-31-36-71. circ. 25,000.

054.1   FR   ISSN 0988-5226
LIGNES. 1987. q. 300 F. (foreign 315 F.) (effective 1991). Librairie Seguier, 3 rue Seguier, Paris 75006, France. TEL 46-34-15-16. FAX 40-46-95-15. Dir. Michel Surya. adv.; bk.rev. circ. 2,000.
   Description: Covers politics, philosophy, debates, history.

054.1   FR
LIMOUSIN MAGAZINE; magazines de France. Variant title: Limousin-Marche Magazine. m. 280 F. Editions Rene Dessagne, B.P. 90, 11 rue Pierre Leroux, 87000 Limoges, France. TEL 55-77-25-97. circ. 23,100.
   Description: Contains items of local interest.

054.1   FR   ISSN 1148-425X
MAINTENANT. 1990. bi-m. 30 F. per no. N.S.P., 38 rue Servan, 75544 Paris Cedex 11, France. TEL 43-70-11-05. FAX 43-70-05-15. Ed. Frederic Taddei.

054.1   FR   ISSN 0542-1594
MAISON DE MARIE CLAIRE. 1967. m. 529 F. Marie-Claire-Album, 11 bis, rue Boissy-d'Anglas, 75008 Paris, France. TEL 1-42-66-88-88. TELEX 240 387. (U.S. subscr. to: INSA, 10 Wedgewood Lane, Voorheesville, NY 12186-9769) Ed. Jean Prourost. illus.

054.1   FR   ISSN 0026-024X
MESSAGER. 1897. w. 200 F. 22 av. General de Gaulle, 74201 Thonon, France. FAX 50-71-15-16. adv.; charts; illus.

074   FR   ISSN 0026-0258
MESSAGER DE LA HAUTE SAVOIE. 1897. w. 660 F. Imprimerie du Messager S.A., 22 av. General de Gaulle, 74201 Thonon les Bains, Haute-Savoie, France. TEL 50-71-10-14. FAX 50-71-15-16. Ed. Bernard Mossu. adv.; bk.rev. circ. 50,000. **Document type:** newspaper.

074   FR   ISSN 0395-2037
LE MONDE. 1944. d. Le Monde s.a.r.l., 15 rue Falguiere, 75105 Paris, France. TEL 40-65-25-25. FAX 40-65-25-99. Ed. Bruno Frappat. **Document type:** newspaper.

074 320   FR   ISSN 0026-9360
LE MONDE. SELECTION HEBDOMADAIRE. (Supplement avail.: Liber) 1950. w. 1890 F. (foreign 2960 F.). Le Monde s.a.r.l., 15 rue Falguieres, 75501 Paris Cedex 15, France. TEL 40-65-25-25. FAX 40-65-25-99. TELEX 206 806F. (Subscr. to: 1 place Hubert-Beuve-Mery, 94852 Ivry-sur-Seine Cedex, France. TEL 40-65-25-25) Ed. Andre Fontaine. adv.; bk.rev. circ. 23,524. **Indexed:** Key to Econ.Sci., Pt.de Rep. (1988-). **Document type:** newspaper.
   —CCC.

074   FR   ISSN 0767-4007
MONTAGNE. 1919. d. 28 rue Morel Ladeuil, 63003 Clermont Ferrand Cedex, France. TEL 73-34-69-00. FAX 73-34-69-85. Ed. Paul Saigne. **Document type:** newspaper.

GENERAL INTEREST PERIODICALS — FRANCE 2713

054.1 MC
MONTE CARLO COTE D'AZUR. m. Europa Residence, Place des Moulins, MC 98000, Monaco. TEL 93-25-07-77. FAX 93-25-76-57. TELEX 469 567. Ed. Michel Pastor.

054.1 FR ISSN 0756-192X
NEWLOOK. 1983. m. 220 F. (foreign 319 F.). Editions Filipacchi, 63-65 Champs Elysees, 75008 Paris, France. TEL 40-74-70-00. FAX 40-74-73-71. TELEX 651 294 F. (Subscr. to: 99 rue d'Amsterdam, 75008 Paris, France. TEL 42-80-68-55) Ed. Maxime Chavanne. adv.; bk.rev.; illus. circ. 180,000. (back issues avail.) **Document type:** consumer publication.

051
NEWS FRANCE; France's English language newspaper. (Text in English, some French) 1987. m. 80 F.($30) Association The News, B.P. 59, 24500 Eymet, France. TEL 53-23-84-30. FAX 53-27-33-55. Ed. Clin Bond. adv. contact: Clin Bond. bk.rev.; bibl.; illus.; stat. (tabloid format; back issues avail.) **Document type:** newspaper.
  Description: Aids Anglophiles in their efforts to integrate in France.

074 FR ISSN 0224-5477
NICE MATIN. 1945. d. 214 Route de Grenoble, 06290 Nice Cedex 3, France. TEL 93-18-28-38. FAX 93-83-93-97. Ed. Charles Buchet. circ. 252,835. **Document type:** newspaper.

074 FR ISSN 0755-379X
NORD MATIN. 1944. d. 15 rue du Caire, 59052 Roubaix Cedex 1, France. TEL 20-75-92-56. FAX 20-82-36-41. Ed. Pierre Pinson. circ. 252,835. **Document type:** newspaper.

054.1 FR ISSN 0029-4632
NOUS DEUX PRESENTE. 1951. m. 120 F. Editions Mondiales, 2 rue des Italiens, 75009 Paris, France. circ. 823,397.

054.1 FR ISSN 0029-4713
AP20
NOUVEL OBSERVATEUR. 1964. w. 760 F. Nouvel Observateur du Monde, 14 rue Dussoubs, 75081 Paris Cedex 02, France. FAX 42-36-19-63. TELEX 680 729. (Subscr. to: 25 rue d'Hauteville, 75010 Paris, France) Ed. Laurent Joffrin. adv.; bk.rev.; film rev.; music rev.; play rev.; illus. circ. 324,200. (also avail. in microform from UMI; reprint service avail. from UMI) **Indexed:** Pt.de Rep. (1979-).
—BLDSC (6176.706000); UnCover; SWETS; UMI.

074 FR ISSN 0152-2590
LA NOUVELLE REPUBLIQUE DU CENTRE OUEST. 1944. d. 232 av. de Grammont, 37048 Tours Cedex, France. TEL 47-31-70-00. FAX 47-31-70-70. Ed. Herve Gueneron. circ. 267,098. **Document type:** newspaper.

054.1 052 056.1 FR ISSN 0398-9682
NOUVELLES DE FRANCE. (Text in French; summaries in English and Spanish) 1947. bi-m. 240 F. Association pour la Diffusion de la Pensee Francaise, 12 rue Pierre et Marie Curie, 75005 Paris, France. TEL 43-26-41-59. FAX 46-34-52-65. Ed.Bd. bk.rev.; charts.
  Formerly: Breves Nouvelles de France (ISSN 0045-2785)

054.1 FR
NOUVELLES RICARD. no.382, 1978. q. free. Societe Ricard, 4-6 rue Berthelot, 13014 Marseille, France. Ed. Andre Perrichon. charts; illus.; stat. circ. 100,000.

054.1 FR
O K - PODIUM. s-m. 170 F. (foreign 308 F.). Publications Filipacchi, 63-65 Champs Elysees, 75008 Paris, France. TEL 40-74-70-00. TELEX 651 294. (Subscr. to: 99 rue d'Amsterdam, 75008 Paris, France. TEL 42-80-68-55)
  Formerly: Podium.

074 FR
OUEST FRANCE. 1944. d. 35051 Rennes Cedex, France. TEL 99-32-60-00. FAX 99-32-60-25. Ed. Didier Pillet. circ. 792,182. **Document type:** newspaper.

054.1 FR
PARIS - COTE D'AZUR. 1959. bi-m. 5 F. per no. (Paris - Cote d'Azur International) Fernard Dartigues, 2, rue Auber, 06400 Cannes, France. TEL 93-68-22-77. adv.; bk.rev. circ. 10,000.

054.1 FR
PARIS - COTE D'AZUR INTERNATIONAL. 1959. m. 200 F. Fernard Dartigues, 2 rue Auber, 06400 Cannes, France. TEL 93-68-22-77. adv.
  Description: Cultivates links between Paris and the Cote d'Azur.

054.1 FR ISSN 0397-1635
AP20
PARIS MATCH. 1949. w. 580 F.($140) (foreign 855 F.). Publications Filipacchi, 63-65 Champs Elysees, 75008 Paris, France. TEL 40-74-70-00. TELEX 651 294. (Subscr. to: 99 rue d'Amsterdam, 75008 Paris, France. TEL 42-80-68-55; In U.S.: Box 0007, Rouses Point, NY 12979. TEL 800-363-1310) Ed. Michel Sola. adv. contact: Philippe Sechet. illus. circ. 690,000. **Indexed:** Pt.de Rep. (1979-).
  Former titles (until 1976): Nouveau Paris Match (ISSN 0337-8721); (until 1972): Paris Match (ISSN 0031-2029)
  Description: Covers French and world affairs.

054.1 FR ISSN 0031-2045
PARIS-SUD; organe d'information des arrondissements sud de Paris. 1961. m. 25 F.($2) Editions Municipales S.A.R.L., 38, rue Croix-des-Petits-Champs, 75001 Paris, France. TEL 42-36-34-47. FAX 1-40-39-01-23. Ed. R. Dubail. adv.; bk.rev.
  Incorporates: Vaugirard-Grenelle (ISSN 0042-2894)

074 FR ISSN 0767-3558
LE PARISIEN. 1944. d. 25 av. Michelet, 93408 St. Ouen Cedex, France. TEL 40-10-33-51. FAX 40-12-90-90. Ed. Jacques Lallain. circ. 393,920. **Document type:** newspaper.

054.1 FR
PERIGORD MAGAZINE; magazines de France. m. 280 F. Editions Rene Dessagne, B.P. 90, 11 rue Pierre Leroux, 87000 Limoges, France. TEL 55-77-29-97. circ. 6,500.
  Description: Contains items of local interest.

054.1 FR
PLANETE SURVIE. Variant title: Document Survie. 1980. w. 250 F. Daniel Fargeas, Ed. & Pub., Vingrau, 66600 Rivesaltes, France. charts; illus.

054.1 FR
LE POINT. 1972. w. 499 F. Societe d'Exploitation de l'Hebdomadaire "le Point" (S E B D O), 140 rue de Rennes, 75006 Paris, France. TEL 1-45-44-39-00. FAX 1-45-49-30-20. TELEX 202 784. Ed. Claude Imbert. adv.; bk.rev. circ. 329,658. **Indexed:** Avery Ind.Archit.Per. **Document type:** consumer publication.

054.1 FR ISSN 0048-5004
POURQUOI. 1964. 10/yr. 225 F. to individuals; libraries 205 F. Ligue Francaise de l'Enseignement et de l'Education Permanente, 3 rue Recamier, 75341 Paris Cedex 07, France. TEL 43-58-96-93. Ed. Marc Sebille. adv.; bk.rev.; film rev.; illus. circ. 37,000. (tabloid format)

074 FR
LE PROGRES. 1859. d. 93 av. du Progres, 69680 Chassieu Cedex, France. TEL 72-22-23-23. FAX 72-22-23-46. Ed. Jean-Louis Dousson. circ. 383,126. **Document type:** newspaper.

054.1 FR
QUERCY MAGAZINE; magazines de France. m. 280 F. Editions Rene Dessagne, B.P. 90, 11 rue Pierre Leroux, 87000 Limoges, France. TEL 55-77-29-97. circ. 4,000.
  Description: Contains items of local interest.

054.1 FR ISSN 0246-9405
REVOLUTION. 1980. w. 670 F. (foreign 830 F.). 15 rue Montmartre, 75001 Paris, France. TEL 42-33-61-26. Eds. Jean-Paul Jouary, Gerard Streiff.
—SWETS.
  Supersedes (in 1980): France Nouvelle.
  Description: Covers current revolutionary activity worldwide.

054.1 FR
ROUERGUE MAGAZINE; magazines de France. m. 280 F. Editions Rene Dessagne, B.P. 90, 11 rue Pierre Leroux, 87000 Limoges, France. TEL 55-77-29-97. circ. 2,300.
  Description: Contains items of local interest.

054.1 FR ISSN 0048-9018
SAISONS D'ALSACE; toute la vie culturelle de l'Alsace. 1948. q. 240 F. (foreign 275 F.). Dernieres Nouvelles d'Alsace, 17-21, rue de la Nuee-Bleue, 67000 Strasbourg Cedex, France. TEL 88-23-30-83. FAX 88-75-16-21. Ed. Bernard Reumaux. adv.; bk.rev.; charts; illus.
  Description: Relates Alsatian history, arts, literature, sociology and fine arts.

054.1 FR ISSN 0037-1386
SELECTION DU READER'S DIGEST (FRENCH EDITION). (Text in French) 1947. m. 240 F. Selection du Reader's Digest, S.A., 212 bd. Saint Germain, 75007 Paris, France. TEL 1-46-64-16-16. TELEX 200 882. (Subscr. to: 1-7 av. Louis Pasteur, 92220 Bagneux, France) Ed. C. de Villeneuve. adv.; bk.rev.; illus. circ. 1,164,260. (also avail. in microform from UMI; reprint service avail. from UMI) **Document type:** consumer publication.
—UMI.

074 FR
SUD OUEST. 1944. d. newsstand price: 4 F. 8 rue de Cheverus, 33000 Bordeaux, France. TEL 56-00-33-33. FAX 56-44-64-61. Ed. J. Aubert; Pub. J.F. Lemoine. adv. contact: M. Annic. bk.rev.; illus.; circ. 351,631 (paid); 14,795 (controlled). cols./p.: 8; pp./issue: 28. (also avail. in microfiche; back issues avail.) **Document type:** newspaper.

050 FR ISSN 0985-1798
UNIR. (Text in Interlingua) 1960. q. 25 F. Union Interlinguiste de France, 75 Allee Danielle Casanova, 93320 les Pavillons Sous Bois, France. TEL 48-49-67-95. Ed. Rene Jacobs; Pub. Rene Jacobs. bk.rev. circ. 100. **Document type:** bulletin.

054.1 FR ISSN 0049-5794
VALEURS ACTUELLES. 1966. w. 875 F. (foreign 1107 F.). Valmonde & Cie, 54 rue Martre, 92586 Clichy Cedex, France. TEL 1-49-68-18-18. FAX 1-47-35-85-00. Ed. Francois d'Orcival. adv.; bk.rev.; film rev.; play rev.; charts; illus. circ. 150,000.

054.1 FR
VELAY MAGAZINE; magazines de France. m. 280 F. Editions Rene Dessagne, B.P. 90, 11 rue Pierre Leroux, 87000 Limoges, France. TEL 55-77-29-79. circ. 2,125.
  Description: Contains items of local interest.

054.1 FR
VIE; hebdomadaire chretien d'actualite. 1945. w. Malesherbes Publications, 163 bd. Malesherbes, 75859 Paris Cedex 17, France. TEL 48-88-46-00. FAX 48-88-46-01. TELEX 649 333 F. adv. circ. 396,094.

054.1 659.152 FR
VOGUE. 1921. 10/yr. 350 F.($159) (foreign 520 F.) (effective Aug. 1990). Publications Conde Nast S.A., 4 Place du Palais-Bourbon, 75341 Paris Cedex 07, France. TEL 40-62-00-11. FAX 40-62-02-55. TELEX 260 752. (Subscr. to: 60732 Sainte-Genevieve Cedex, France. TEL 16-44-03-44-00; Subscr. in U.S. to: International Subscriptions Inc., 1305 Paterson Plank Rd, N. Bergen, NJ 07047-1890. TEL 201-867-9381) Ed. Jean Poniatowski. adv. circ. 80,020. **Indexed:** Consum.Ind. **Document type:** consumer publication.

074 FR ISSN 0999-2189
VOIX DU NORD. 1945. d. 1108 F. Voix du Nord, 8 place du General de Gaulle, B.P. 549, 59023 Lille Cedex, France. TEL 20-78-40-40. FAX 20-78-42-44. Ed. Andre Soleua. adv. contact: Michel Marin. circ. 400,000. (looseleaf format; also avail. in microfilm; back issues avail.) **Document type:** newspaper.
  Description: Covers regional and local news, national and international politics and finance.

G

GENERAL INTEREST PERIODICALS — French Polynesia

079 FP
DEPECHE DE TAHITI. 1964. d. (Mon.-Sat.). newsstand price: 120 FCP. B.P. 50, Papeete, Tahiti. **Document type:** newspaper.

079 FP
NOUVELLES DE TAHITI. d. (Mon.-Sat.). newsstand price: 110 FCP. Place de la Cathedrale, B.P. 629, Papeete, Tahiti. **Document type:** newspaper.

GENERAL INTEREST PERIODICALS — Gambia

079.6651 GM ISSN 0796-0832
▼**DAILY OBSERVER.** (Text in English) 1992. d. D.884.80($238) (W. Africa $215; Europe and Asia $227); newsstand price: D.4. Observer Co. (Gambia) Ltd., New Town - Sait Matty Junction, Bakau, P.O. Box 131, Banjul, Gambia. TEL 220-496608. FAX 220-496878. Pub. Kenneth Y. Best. adv. contact: Mae Gene Best. bk.rev.; film rev.; music rev.; illus. Wire service(s): AP. circ. 4,000. cols./p.: 6; pp./issue: 12. (tabloid format; back issues avail.; reprint service avail.) **Document type:** newspaper.
Description: Seeks to improve the flow of information from the government to the people, from the people to the government, and among the people of Gambia.

052 GM
FOROYAA/FREEDOM. w. Bundunka Kunda, POB 2306, Serrekunda, Gambia. Eds. Halifa Sallah, Sam Sarr.

052 GM
THE GAMBIA ONWARD. w? 48 Grant St., Banjul, Gambia. Ed. Rudolph Allen.

052 GM
THE GAMBIA OUTLOOK. w? 29 Grant St., Banjul, Gambia.

079.6651 GM
GAMBIA WEEKLY. (Text in English) 1943. w. D.104($30); newsstand price: D.2. Ministry of Information, Department of Information and Broadcasting, 14 Hagan St., Banjul, Gambia. TEL 220-226621. FAX 220-227230. TELEX 2204-GW-PRESOFF. Ed. Alien Sagnia. adv.; charts; illus. Wire service(s): LAT WP. circ. 1,500. cols./p.: 4; pp./issue: 10. (back issues avail.) **Document type:** newspaper, government publication.
Formerly (until 1989): Gambia News Bulletin (ISSN 0046-5380)

052 GM
THE GAMBIAN. w? 60 Lancaster St., Banjul, Gambia. Ed. Ngaing Thomas.

052 GM
THE GAMBIAN TIMES. 1981. fortn. People's Progressive Party, 21 Leman St., POB 698, Banjul, Gambia. TEL 445. Ed. Momodou Gaye.

052 GM ISSN 0796-000X
THE NATION. fortn. People's Press, 3 Boxbar Rd., POB 334, Banjul, Gambia. Ed. W. Dixxen Colley.

052 GM
THE TOILER. w? 31 Leman St., POB 698, Banjul, Gambia. Ed. Pa Modou Fall.

052 GM
THE TORCH. 1984. w? 59 Gloucester St., Banjul, Gambia. Ed. Sana Manneh.

052 GM
THE WORKER. w? Gambia Labour Congress, 6 Albion Pl., POB 508, Banjul, Gambia. Ed. M.M. Ceesay.

GENERAL INTEREST PERIODICALS — Germany

053.1 GW
A Z - DIE ANDERE ZEITUNG; Frankfurter Stadtillustrierte. m. DM.40. Medien Service Verlagsgesellschaft mbH, Musikantenweg 28, 60316 Frankfurt a.M., Germany. TEL 069-4960054. FAX 069-435405. Ed. Willi Hau. adv. contact: Harald Joachim. circ. 21,385. **Document type:** consumer publication.

053.1 GW
A Z KARLSRUHER ANZEIGEN ZEITUNG. 1983. w. A Z Verlag GmbH, Zaehringerstr. 43, 7500 Karlsruhe 1, Germany. TEL 0721-376082. Ed. Maria Hock. adv. circ. 223,322.

053.1 GW
AACHEN LIVE. m. free. Verlag Aachen Live, Augustastr. 55, 52072 Aachen, Germany. TEL 0241-532079. FAX 0241-532070. Eds. Estella Kuehmstedt, Peter Wagner. circ. 19,870. **Document type:** consumer publication.

073 GW
AACHENER NACHRICHTEN. (Editions avail. for: Eifel, Stolberg, Eschweil, Rur-Wurm, Erkelenz, Dueren, Juelich) d. Zeitungsverlag Aachen GmbH, Dresdner Str. 3, 52068 Aachen, Germany. TEL 0241-5101-0. FAX 0241-5101399. Ed. Dieter Maetschke. adv. contact: Hans-Werner Ast. circ. 65,986. **Document type:** newspaper.

073 GW
AACHENER VOLKSZEITUNG. d. Zeitungsverlag Aachen GmbH, Dresdner Str. 3, 52068 Aachen, Germany. TEL 0241-5101-0. FAX 0241-5101399. Ed. Ottmar Braun. adv. contact: Hans-Werner Ast. circ. 167,218. **Document type:** newspaper.

073 GW
ABENDZEITUNG. d. Abendzeitung GmbH und Co. KG, Sendlingerstr. 10, 80331 Munich, Germany. TEL 089-2377-0. FAX 089-2377729. Ed. Uwe Zimmer; Pubs. Anneliese Friedmann, Johannes Friedmann. adv. contact: Bernd Obermeier. circ. 217,138. **Document type:** newspaper.

053.1 GW
ACCENT. m. Accent Verlag GmbH, Huetlinstr. 39, 78462 Konstanz, Germany. TEL 07531-23494. FAX 07531-29120. Ed. Daniel Hirschler. adv. contact: Markus Hotz. circ. 11,614. **Document type:** consumer publication.

053.1 GW ISSN 0341-7212
AESTHETIK UND KOMMUNIKATION; Beitraege zur politischen Erziehung. 1970. q. DM.58. Elefanten Press, Am Treptower Park 28-30, 12435 Berlin, Germany. TEL 030-68834100. FAX 030-68834159. adv.; bk.rev.; cum.index. circ. 15,000. **Document type:** bulletin.

053.1 GW
AKTSCHEN. 1988. bi-m. Aktschen Verlag, Goldenes Horn 10B, 12159 Berlin, Germany. TEL 030-7042432. Ed. Torsten Friebe. circ. 600. (tabloid format; back issues avail.)

053.1 GW
DIE AKTUELLE. 1979. w. (Mon.). Gong Verlag GmbH, Innere Cramer-Klett-Str. 6, 90403 Nuernberg, Germany. TEL 0911-5325-0. FAX 0911-5325494. Ed. Patrick Engel. adv. contact: Walter Krey. **Document type:** consumer publication.

053.1 FR
ALLEMAGNE D'AUJOURD'HUI; politique, economie, societe, culture. N.S. 1966. q. 165 F. (foreign 200 F.). Association pour la Connaissance de l'Allemagne d'Aujourd'hui, 8 rue Faraday, 75017 Paris, France. TEL 1-42-27-41-55. Ed. Jerome Vaillant. adv.; bk.rev.; index. circ. 2,000. **Indexed:** P.A.I.S.For.Lang.Ind. **Document type:** academic/scholarly publication.
—BLDSC (0789.900000).
Formerly (until 1993): Allemanges d'Aujourhui (ISSN 0002-5712)
Description: Information and analysis about political, social, economic and cultural events and realities in Germany today.

053.1 GW
ALLES IN UND UM HAMBURG. fortn. Alles Verlag GmbH, Gruendgensstr. 16, 22309 Hamburg, Germany. TEL 040-6328050. FAX 040-63280555. Ed. Peter Prior. adv. contact: Hannes Bergner. circ. 50,000. **Document type:** bulletin.

073 GW
ALLGAEUER ZEITUNG. d. Allgaeuer Zeitungsverlag GmbH, Kotternerstr. 64, 87435 Kempten, Germany. TEL 0831-2061. FAX 0831-29001. Eds. Gernot Roemer, Helmut Hojer. adv. contact: Manfred Mueller. circ. 116,386. **Document type:** newspaper.

073 GW
DIE ALLGEMEINE SONNTAGSZEITUNG. w. (Sun.). Johann Wilhelm Naumann GmbH und Co., Juliuspromenade 64, 97070 Wuerzburg, Germany. TEL 0931-30863-0. FAX 0931-3086333. Ed. Carl-Heinz Pierk; Pubs. Heinrich Naumann, Theodor Herr. adv. contact: Karina Elbert. circ. 18,948. **Document type:** newspaper.

073 GW ISSN 0935-0063
ALLGEMEINE ZEITUNG. 1968. d. Wiesbadener Kurier GmbH und Co., Grosse Bleiche 44-50, 55116 Mainz, Germany. TEL 06131-1441. FAX 06131-144577. Ed. Hermann Dexheimer. adv. contact: Walter Daehn. circ. 132,010. **Document type:** newspaper.

073 GW
ALTBAYERISCHE HEIMATPOST. w. (Sun.). Druck- und Verlagshaus Alois Erdl KG, Gabelsbergerstr. 4-6, 83308 Trostberg, Germany. TEL 08621-80817. FAX 08621-80843. Ed. Alois Weichsgartner. adv. contact: Erwin Huber. circ. 19,300. **Document type:** bulletin.

073 GW
ALTMARK-ZEITUNG. d. Verlag Renner und Meineke GmbH, Vor-dem-Neuperver-Tor 4, 29410 Salzwedel, Germany. TEL 03901-25041. FAX 03901-25042. Ed. Hans-Joachim Wicht; Pub. Ulrike Meineke. circ. 38,008. **Document type:** newspaper.

053.1 GW
AMTLICHES BEKANNTMACHUNGSBLATT FUER DIE GEMEINDE METTLACH. 1970. w. Herzberger GmbH, Hubertusstr. 22, 66697 Mettlach-Weiten, Germany.

053.1 GW
AMTSBLATT DES BISTUMS LIMBURG. 1827. bi-m. DM.30. Verlag des Bischoflichen Ordinariates Limburg, Postfach 1355, 64459 Limburg, Germany. TEL 06431-295228. **Document type:** bulletin.

052 375.4 GW ISSN 0723-0206
ANGLO-AMERICAN SPOTLIGHT. (Text in English) 1982. m. Spotlight Verlag, Freihamerstr. 4b, 82166 Graefelfing, Germany. TEL 089-8548221. FAX 089-8548223. TELEX 522934. Ed. Kevin Perryman. adv.; bk.rev. circ. 78,000. (back issues avail.) **Document type:** consumer publication.
Description: General news about English-speaking countries, travel and politics for Germans who are learning English.

053.1 GW
ASCHAFFENBURGER STADTZEITUNG. 1986. m. Kasper Verlagsgesellschaft bR, Bayernstr. 36, 63739 Aschaffenburg, Germany. TEL 06021-20770. FAX 06021-20770. Ed. Thomas Kasper. adv. contact: Thomas Kasper. bk.rev. circ. 24,972. **Document type:** bulletin.

053.1 GW
AUF EINEN BLICK; Freizeit- und Fernsehillustrierte. 1983. w. (Thu.). DM.78 (foreign DM.209). Heinrich Bauer Verlag, Burchardstr. 11, 20095 Hamburg, Germany. TEL 040-3019-0. FAX 040-326922. Ed. Hartmut Klemann; Pub. Heinz Bauer. adv. contact: Guenther Granzow. circ. 2,840,252. **Document type:** consumer publication.

053.1 GW
AUGSBURG LIVE. m. free. Verlag Bruno Marcon, Ravenspurgerstr. 41, 86150 Augsburg, Germany. TEL 0821-252960. FAX 0821-2529615. Ed. Bruno Marcon. circ. 13,720. **Document type:** bulletin.

073 GW
AUGSBURGER ALLGEMEINE. d. Presse Druck- und Verlagsgesellschaft mbH, Curt-Frenzel-Str. 2, 86167 Augsburg, Germany. TEL 0821-777-0. FAX 0821-704471. Eds. Gernot Roemer, Winfried Striebel; Pub. Guenter Holland. adv. contact: Karl Kammerer. circ. 368,649. **Document type:** newspaper.

073 GW
B Z. d. Ullstein Verlag GmbH, Kochstr. 50, 10969 Berlin, Germany. TEL 030-25910. FAX 030-2516071. Ed. Wolfgang Kryszohn; Pub. Wilhelm Pannier. adv. contact: Norbert Wendt. circ. 312,335. **Document type:** newspaper.

GENERAL INTEREST PERIODICALS — GERMANY

073 GW
B Z AM SONNTAG. w. (Sun.). Ullstein Verlag GmbH, Kochstr. 50, 10969 Berlin, Germany. TEL 030-25910. FAX 030-2516071. Owner(s): Axel Springer Verlag AG, Axel-Springer-Platz 1, 20355 Hamburg, Germany. TEL 040-3470-0. FAX 040-340581. Ed. Wolfgang Kryszohn; Pub. Wilhelm Pannier. adv. contact: Norbert Wendt. circ. 132,152. **Document type:** newspaper.

053.1 GW
BAD AACHEN; die Zeitschrift fuer Aachener. m. free. Bad Aachen Verlagsgesellschaft mbH, Dresdnerstr. 1, 52068 Aachen, Germany. TEL 0241-5199201. FAX 0241-5199209. Ed. Heike Vollert-Stueber; Pub. Hanne Kelsch-Schmitz. adv. contact: Ferdinand Vijgen. circ. 22,000. **Document type:** bulletin.

073 GW
BADISCHE NEUESTE NACHRICHTEN. d. Badendruck GmbH, Linkenheimer Landstr. 133, 76149 Karlsruhe, Germany. TEL 0721-789-0. FAX 0721-789155. Ed. Edwin Kraus; Pub. Hans Wilhelm Baur. adv. contact: Holger Hinrichs. circ. 167,560. **Document type:** newspaper.

073 GW
BADISCHE ZEITUNG. 1946. d. Badischer Verlag GmbH, Baslerstr. 88, 79115 Freiburg, Germany. TEL 0761-496-0. FAX 0761-41098. Ed. Ansgar Fuerst. circ. 176,000. **Document type:** newspaper.

073 GW
BADISCHES TAGBLATT. d. Badisches Tagblatt GmbH, Stefanienstr. 1-3, 76530 Baden-Baden, Germany. TEL 07221-215-0. FAX 07221-215240. Ed.Bd. adv. contact: Wolfgang Hoffarth. circ. 41,219. **Document type:** newspaper.

053.1 GW ISSN 0005-7045
BAYERISCHE GEMEINDEZEITUNG. 1949. fortn. DM.125.40. Verlag Bayer Kommunalpresse GmbH, Postfach 190737, 80607 Munich, Germany. Ed. Annemarie Scherieble-von Hassel. adv.; bk.rev.; illus. circ. 9,000. (tabloid format) **Document type:** consumer publication.

073 GW ISSN 0341-3993
BAYERISCHE STAATSZEITUNG. 1950. w. (Fri.). Bayerische Staatszeitung GmbH, Sendlingerstr. 80, 80331 Munich, Germany. TEL 089-2183-0. FAX 089-299562. Ed. Carl Schmoeller. adv. contact: Klaus Jaeger. circ. 18,860. **Document type:** newspaper.

BAYERISCHES SONNTAGSBLATT FUER DIE KATHOLISCHE FAMILIE. see RELIGIONS AND THEOLOGY — Roman Catholic

073 GW ISSN 0340-2673
BAYERNKURIER. 1950. w. Bayernkurier GmbH, Nymphenburgerstr. 64, 80335 Munich, Germany. TEL 089-120040. FAX 089-1293050. Ed. Wilfried Scharnagl. adv. contact: Ute Magg. circ. 153,511. **Document type:** newspaper.

053.1 GW
BAYERNSPIEGEL. 1956. bi-m. DM.40. Bayerische Einigung e.V., Residenzstr. 27, 80333 Munich, Germany. TEL 089-294143. Ed. Florian Besold. circ. 800. **Document type:** consumer publication.

073 GW
BERLINER KURIER. d. (except Sun.). Gruner und Jahr Berliner Zeitung Verlag GmbH, Karl-Liebknecht-Str. 29, 10178 Berlin, Germany. TEL 030-23275975. FAX 030-23275254. Owner(s): Gruner und Jahr AG & Co., Am Baumwall 11, 20459 Hamburg, Germany. TEL 040-3703-0. FAX 040-37035607. Ed. Wieland Sandmann. adv. contact: Heinz Schlosser. circ. 175,504. **Document type:** newspaper.

073 GW
BERLINER KURIER AM SONNTAG. w. (Sun.). Gruner und Jahr Berliner Zeitung Verlag GmbH, Karl-Liebknecht-Str. 29, 10178 Berlin, Germany. TEL 030-23275975. FAX 030-23275254. Ed. Wieland Sandmann. adv. contact: Heinz Schlosser. circ. 142,300. **Document type:** newspaper.

073 GW
BERLINER MORGENPOST. d. Ullstein Verlag GmbH, Kochstr. 50, 10969 Berlin, Germany. TEL 030-25910. FAX 030-2516071. Owner(s): Axel Springer Verlag, Axel-Springer-Platz 1, 20355 Hamburg, Germany. Ed. Bruno Waltert. adv. contact: Norbert Wendt. circ. 198,563. **Document type:** newspaper.

073 GW
BERLINER ZEITUNG. d. Gruner und Jahr Berliner Zeitung Verlag GmbH, Karl-Liebknecht-Str. 29, 10178 Berlin, Germany. TEL 030-23279. FAX 030-23275581. Owner(s): Gruner und Jahr AG & Co., Am Baumwall 11, 20459 Hamburg, Germany. TEL 040-3703-0. FAX 040-37035604. Ed. Hans Eggert; Pub. Erich Boehme. adv. contact: Harald Wahls. circ. 258,125. **Document type:** newspaper.

053.1 GW
BESCHEID; Koelner Jugendzeitschrift. 1986. q. DM.10($15) Bescheid, Dreifelder Weg 13, 50767 Cologne, Germany. TEL 0221-791893. Ed. Thomas Haendel. adv.; bk.rev.; film rev.; play rev. circ. 2,000. (back issues avail.) **Document type:** academic/scholarly publication.
   Description: Provides adolescents in the Cologne region with information about local activities, school, politics, and cultural life.

053.1 GW ISSN 0176-8816
BESSERES LEBEN; Magazin fuer natuerliche Lebensfuehrung. 1983. bi-m. Access Marketing GmbH, Feldbergstr. 2, 61462 Koenigstein, Germany. TEL 06174-9263-0. **Document type:** consumer publication.

073 GW
BILD. d. (except Sun.). Axel Springer Verlag AG, Axel-Springer-Platz 1, 20355 Hamburg, Germany. TEL 040-3470-0. FAX 040-345811. Ed.Bd. adv. contact: Hannelore Dietzsch. circ. 4,493,076. **Document type:** newspaper.

053.1 GW ISSN 0341-4906
BILD AM SONNTAG. 1956. w. (Sun.). Axel Springer Verlag AG, Axel-Springer-Platz 1, 20355 Hamburg, Germany. TEL 040-3470-0. FAX 040-345811. Ed. Michael Spreng. adv. contact: Ruediger Kurtz. circ. 2,649,860. **Document type:** newspaper.

053.1 GW
BILD UND FUNK. w. Burda Verlag Gmbh, Postfach 1230, 77602 Offenburg, Germany. TEL 089-9250-0. FAX 089-92503519. circ. 1,192,788. **Document type:** consumer publication.

053.1 GW
BILDWOCHE. 1983. w. (Thu.). Axel Springer Verlag AG, Axel-Springer-Platz 1, 20355 Hamburg, Germany. FAX 040-340224. Ed. Peter Haferland. adv. contact: Dieter Koering. illus. circ. 543,312. **Document type:** consumer publication.

053.1 GW
BLITZ; Leipzig, Dresden, Halle, Chemnitz. m. free. City Werbeverlags GmbH, Uferstr. 19, 04105 Leipzig, Germany. TEL 0341-209735. FAX 0341-284188. Ed. Torsten Reineck. adv. contact: Norbert Meyer. circ. 35,000. **Document type:** bulletin.

053.1 GW
BLIZZ. m. DM.30. PubliCom Verlag GmbH, Staendeplatz 13, 34117 Kassel, Germany. TEL 0561-1080101. FAX 0561-103014. Ed. Dirk Steinbach. adv. contact: Michael Schmelich. circ. 22,000. **Document type:** bulletin.

053.1 GW
BONNER ILLUSTRIERTE. m. DM.39. Bouvier Verlag, Am Hof 28, 53113 Bonn, Germany. TEL 0228-7290141. FAX 0228-7290179. Ed. Heinz Dietl; Pub. Thomas Grundmann. adv. contact: Ursula Goebbels. circ. 6,400. **Document type:** consumer publication.

053.1 GW
BOULEVARD. m. free. Boulevard Illustrierten Verlag GmbH, Rheinallee 7, 55118 Mainz, Germany. TEL 06131-676071. FAX 06131-675466. Ed. Conny Becker; Pub. Axel Wenzel. adv. contact: Horst Franke. **Document type:** consumer publication.

073 GW
BRAUNSCHWEIGER ZEITUNG. (Editions avail.: Gifhorner Rundschau, Helmstedter Nachrichten, Peiner Nachrichten, Salzgitter Zeitung, Wolfenbuetteler Anzeiger, Wolfsburger Nachrichten, Bad Lauterberger Tageblatt, Goslarsche Zeitung, Osteroder Kreis-Anzeiger) d. Braunschweiger Zeitungsverlag GmbH, Hamburgerstr. 277, 38114 Braunschweig, Germany. TEL 0531-3900-0. FAX 0531-3900610. Ed. Arnold Rabbow. adv. contact: Clas Schilling. circ. 219,861. **Document type:** newspaper.

053.1 GW
BREMER. m. DM.40. Bremer Blatt Verlag GmbH, Humboldtstr. 56, 28203 Bremen, Germany. TEL 0421-79007-0. FAX 0421-7900777. Ed. Lothar Bienkowski. adv. contact: Christina Barkhorn. circ. 19,571. **Document type:** consumer publication.

073 GW
BREMER NACHRICHTEN. d. Bremer Tageszeitungen AG, Martinistr. 43-45, 28195 Bremen, Germany. TEL 0421-3671-0. FAX 0421-328327. Ed. Dietrich Ide. adv. contact: Egon Hoppe. circ. 211,838. **Document type:** newspaper.

053.1 GW ISSN 0171-1644
BROMBERG. 1959. 3/yr. DM.7.50($5) per no. c/o G. Ohlhoff, Nordstr. 4, 49207 Bad Rothenfelde, Germany. **Document type:** consumer publication.

053.1 GW
BUNTE. 1948. w. $170. Burda Verlag GmbH, Postfach 1230, 77602 Offenburg, Germany. TEL 089-9250-0. FAX 089-92503519. (U.S. subscr.: GLP International, 153 S. Dean St., Englewood, NJ 07631. TEL 201-871-1010. FAX 201-871-0870) Ed. Peter Boenisch. circ. 1,800,000. (back issues avail.) **Document type:** consumer publication.
   Incorporates: Bunte Oesterreich (ISSN 0007-5981); **Formerly:** Bunte Illustrierte (ISSN 0407-923X)

BURGENLAENDISCHES LEBEN. see GENERAL INTEREST PERIODICALS — Austria

053.1 GW
BUTLER PARKER. 1965. fortn. DM.1.50 per no. Zauberkreis Verlag, Karlsruher Str. 22, 76437 Rastatt, Germany. Ed. R. Greiser.

053.1 GW ISSN 0008-7440
CASSELLA-RIEDEL ARCHIV. 1966. 3/yr. free. Cassella-Riedel Pharma GmbH, Hanauer Landstr. 521, 60386 Frankfurt a.M., Germany. Ed. Friedrich Enders. adv. circ. 45,000. **Document type:** consumer publication.
   —BLDSC (3062.700000).

073 GW
CELLESCHE ZEITUNG. d. Schweiger und Pick Verlag, Bahnhofstr. 1-3, 29221 Celle, Germany. TEL 05141-279-0. FAX 05141-279191. Ed. Michael Rothfuchs; Pub. Ernst Pfingsten. adv. contact: Juergen Raduenz. circ. 33,406. **Document type:** newspaper.

053.1 GW
CHARAKTER; Goettingens City-Magazin. 1986. m. Charakter Medien Verlag GmbH, Lotzestr. 29, 37083 Goettingen, Germany. TEL 0551-507510. FAX 0551-73047. Ed. Axel Schueler-Bredt; Pub. Mathias Mueller-Using. adv. contact: Remsy Bahra. bk.rev.; film rev.; play rev.; illus.; circ. 14,700 (controlled). **Document type:** bulletin.

053.1 GW
CITY-ZEITUNG (HANNOVER). 1975. bi-m. Regional Medien, Lenaustr. 12, 30169 Hannover, Germany. TEL 0511-1319919. Ed. Ingeburg Peters. (back issues avail.)

053.1 GW ISSN 0941-6374
COCKTAIL. bi-m. DM.18. Esdes Design und Medien KG, Theodor-Heuss-Str. 3, 38122 Braunschweig, Germany. TEL 0531-890000. FAX 0531-890089. Ed. Sven Freiwald; Pub. Bernd Elmenthaler. adv. contact: Michael Till. circ. 15,000. **Document type:** consumer publication.

GENERAL INTEREST PERIODICALS — GERMANY

073   GW   ISSN 0939-2807
DARMSTAEDTER ECHO. 1945. d. Darmstaedter Echo Verlag und Druckerei GmbH, Holzhofallee 25-31, 64295 Darmstadt, Germany. TEL 06151-3871. FAX 06151-387307. Ed. Roland Hof. adv. contact: Werner Isenbuegel. circ. 113,390. **Document type:** newspaper.

073   GW
DEISTER- UND WESERZEITUNG. d. Verlag C.W. Niemeyer, Baustr. 44, 31785 Hameln, Germany. TEL 05151-200-0. FAX 05151-200305. Ed. Hermann Griesser; Pubs. Guenther Niemeyer, Hans Niemeyer. adv. contact: Horst Koerber. circ. 38,171. **Document type:** newspaper.

073   GW   ISSN 0012-0510
DEUTSCHE NATIONAL-ZEITUNG. 1951. w. (Fri.). DM.1.80 per no. D S Z Druckschriften- und Zeitungsverlag GmbH, Paosostr. 2, 81243 Munich, Germany. TEL 089-8347007. FAX 089-8341534. Ed. Erik Janus; Pub. Gerhard Frey. adv. contact: Aurelia Dietsch. bk.rev. circ. 120,000. (also avail. in microfilm from NRP) **Document type:** newspaper.
  Formerly: Soldaten-Zeitung.

073   GW   ISSN 0341-9371
DEUTSCHE TAGESPOST. 3/wk. (Tue., Thu., Sat.). Johann Wilhelm Naumann GmbH und Co., Juliuspromenade 64, 97070 Wuerzburg, Germany. TEL 0931-30863-0. FAX 0931-3086333. Ed. Carl-Heinz Pierk; Pubs. Heinrich Naumann, Theodor Herr. adv. contact: Karina Elbert. circ. 16,500. **Document type:** newspaper.

073   GW   ISSN 0302-7503
DEUTSCHE WOCHEN-ZEITUNG. 1959. w. DM.1.80. D S Z Druckschriften- und Zeitungsverlag GmbH, Paosostr. 2, 81243 Munich, Germany. TEL 089-8347007. FAX 089-8341534. Ed. Erik Janus; Pub. Gerhard Frey. adv. contact: Aurelia Dietsch. illus. circ. 40,000. **Document type:** newspaper.

053.1   GW
DEUTSCHER HAUSKALENDER; der Hausfreund Hessische Volkskalender. 1883. a. DM.11.80. Verlag Thiele und Schwarz, Werner-Heisenberg-Str. 7, 34123 Kassel, Germany. TEL 0561-589090. Ed. Juergen Weishaupt. circ. 10,000. **Document type:** bulletin.

320.9   GW
DEUTSCHER KURIER. 1969. m. DM.6. D V G-Deutsche Verlagsgesellschaft mbH, Brueckenstr. 1, Postfach 270, 83022 Rosenheim, Germany. adv.; illus.

073   GW   ISSN 0341-9398
DEUTSCHES ALLGEMEINES SONNTAGSBLATT. 1948. w. (Fri.). Hansisches Druck- und Verlagshaus GmbH, Mittelweg 11, 20149 Hamburg, Germany. TEL 040-414190. FAX 040-41419111. Ed. Arnd Brummer. circ. 90,657. **Document type:** newspaper.
  Formerly (until 1967): Sonntagsblatt (ISSN 0932-7355)

053.1   GW
DEUTSCHES MONATSMAGAZIN. 1973. s-a. Union GmbH und Co., Schanzenstr. 82, 40549 Duesseldorf, Germany. TEL 0211-5502-0. FAX 0211-574116. Ed. Dieter Preuss. adv. contact: Annemarie Puetz. circ. 49,500. **Document type:** bulletin.

052   GW
DEUTSCHLAND. (Editions in Arabic, English, French, German, Japanese, Portuguese, Spanish) 1961. bi-m. Frankfurter Societaets-Druckerei GmbH, Frankenallee 71-81, 60327 Frankfurt a.M., Germany. TEL 069-7501-0. FAX 069-7306965. TELEX 411655. Ed. Peter Hintereder. adv.; bk.rev.; charts; illus. circ. 500,000. (back issues avail.) **Document type:** bulletin.
  Former titles (until 1993): Scala (ISSN 0340-0441); (until 1974): Scala International (ISSN 0581-9385)
  Description: Reports for readers abroad on events in Germany in the political, economic and cultural fields.

053   GW
DEUTSCHLAND-JOURNAL. 1972. m. DM.18. Nordwestdeutscher Zeitungsverlag, Parkallee 86, 20144 Hamburg, Germany. Ed. H. Wellems. adv.; bk.rev. circ. 30,000.

073   GW
DITHMARSCHER LANDESZEITUNG. d. Westholsteinische Verlagsanstalt Boyens und Co., Am Wulf-Isebrand-Platz, 25746 Heide, Germany. TEL 0481-6886-0. FAX 0481-6886462. Ed. Guenter Wolf; Pub. Uwe Boyens. adv. contact: Klaus Boehlke. circ. 25,869. **Document type:** newspaper.

053.1   GW
DOKUMENT UND ANALYSE. 1972. m. DM.69.60($40) Dokument-Verlag, Barer Str. 43, 80799 Munich, Germany. TEL 089-2720-100. Ed. Bogislaw von Randow. (back issues avail.) **Document type:** bulletin.

053.1   GW   ISSN 0012-5172
H5
DOKUMENTE; Zeitschrift fuer den deutsch-franzoesischen Dialog. 1945. bi-m. DM.37 (foreign DM.41.20). (Gesellschaft fuer Uebernationale Zusammenarbeit e.V.) Europa Union Verlag GmbH, Bachstr. 32, 53115 Bonn, Germany. TEL 0228-7290010. FAX 0228-695734. TELEX 8-86822. Ed.Bd. adv.; bk.rev.; film rev.; index. circ. 3,500. (back issues avail.) Indexed: Amer.Hist.& Life, Hist.Abstr., P.A.I.S.For.Lang.Ind.
  —CCC.
  Description: Studies French-German connections in politics, economics, culture and literature.

073   GW
DONAUKURIER. (Editions avail.: Aichacher Zeitung, Eichstaetter Kurier, Geisenfelder Zeitung, Hilpoltsteiner Kurier, Pfaffenhofener Kurier, Schrobenhausener Zeitung, Wolznacher Anzeiger) d. Donaukurier Verlagsgesellschaft, Stauffenbergstr. 2a, 85051 Ingolstadt, Germany. TEL 0841-9666-0. FAX 0841-9666551. Ed. Friedrich Kraft. adv. contact: Irmgard Kammerer. circ. 83,399. **Document type:** newspaper.

053.1   GW
DURLACH AM WOCHENENDE. 1969. w. DM.90. Verlag am Wochenende, Hauptstr. 93, 76327 Pfinztal, Germany. TEL 07240-1071. FAX 07240-8113. Ed. Frank Armbruster. adv. contact: circ. 19,960. **Document type:** consumer publication.
  Formerly (until 1991): Turmberg-Rundschau.

053.1   GW   ISSN 0343-0405
ECHO AUS DEUTSCHLAND. 1964. 6/yr. DM.30. (Carl Duisburg Gesellschaft) Nomos Verlagsgesellschaft mbH und Co. KG, Waldseestr. 3-5, 76530 Baden-Baden, Germany. TEL 07221-21040. FAX 07221-210427. (Subscr. to: Postfach 610, 76484 Baden-Baden, Germany) Ed. Eva-Maria Regenhardt-Dein. (back issues avail.) **Document type:** consumer publication.

053.1   GW   ISSN 0013-2241
EGERER ZEITUNG; fuer die Heimatvertriebenen aus dem Stadt- und Landkreis Eger. 1950. m. DM.24. (Egerer Landtag e.V.) Verlag Egerer Zeitung, Herrnstr. 14, 86854 Amberg, Germany. Ed. Josef Voit. adv.; bk.rev.; index. circ. 6,500.

053.1   GW
ELBE WOCHENBLATT. 1963. w. free. Elbe-Wochenblatt Verlagsgesellschaft MbH, Luneburger Str. 25, 21073 Hamburg, Germany. FAX 040-76600024. Ed. Joern Legahn. adv.; illus. circ. 249,000.
  Formerly: Elbe Wochenblatt fuer Sued Hamburg (ISSN 0015-2374)

073   GW
EMDER ZEITUNG. d. Gerhard Verlag, Postfach 1453, 26694 Emden, Germany. TEL 04921-8900-0. FAX 04921-32440. Ed. Herbert Kolbe; Pub. Edzard Gerhard. adv. contact: Gert Janssen. circ. 11,530. **Document type:** newspaper.

073   GW
ERZGEBIRGS RUNDSCHAU. w. (Thu.). Erzgebirgs Rundschau GmbH, Scheibnerstr. 1, 09456 Annaberg-Buchholz, Germany. TEL 03733-2834. FAX 03733-2834. Ed. Axel Scheibe; Pub. Manfred Riesche. adv. contact: Elke Grundig. circ. 50,000. **Document type:** newspaper.

053.1   GW
ESSLINGER ZEITUNG. d. Richard Bechtle Verlagsgesellschaft, Zeppelinstr. 116, 73730 Esslingen, Germany. TEL 0711-9310-0. FAX 0711-316769124. Ed. Dietrich Simmert; Pubs. Otto Bechtle, Friedrich Bechtle. adv. contact: Norbert Kindler. circ. 48,808. **Document type:** newspaper.

EVANGELISCHER DIGEST. see RELIGIONS AND THEOLOGY

073   GW
EXPRESS (COLOGNE). d. M. DuMont Schauberg, Breitestr. 70, 50667 Cologne, Germany. TEL 0221-224-0. FAX 0221-2242524. Ed. Rainer Gefeller; Pub. Alfred DuMont. adv. contact: Bodo Almert. circ. 410,857. **Document type:** newspaper.

053.1   GW   ISSN 0342-2739
DER FEINSCHMECKER. 1974. m. Jahreszeiten Verlag GmbH, Possmoorweg 5, 22301 Hamburg, Germany. TEL 040-2717-0. FAX 040-27172056. Ed. Wolf Thieme; Pub. Jochen Karsten. adv. contact: Jens Brockmann. circ. 55,796. (back issues avail.) **Document type:** consumer publication.

053.1   GW   ISSN 0939-2505
FERNSEHWOCHE; aktuell und vielseitig. 1969. w. (Fri.). DM.83.20 (foreign DM.218). Heinrich Bauer Verlag, Burchardstr. 11, 20095 Hamburg, Germany. TEL 040-3019-0. FAX 040-336391. Ed. Peter Roppilez. adv. contact: Guenther Granzow. circ. 2,131,433. **Document type:** consumer publication.

073   GW
FLENSBURGER TAGEBLATT. d. Schleswig - Holsteinischer Zeitungsverlag GmbH, Nikolaistr. 7, 24937 Flensburg, Germany. TEL 0461-808-0. FAX 0461-808246. Ed. Stefan Lipsky. adv. contact: Reinald Meyer. circ. 166,351. **Document type:** newspaper.

053.1   GW
▼**FOCUS (OFFENBURG).** 1993. w. $230. Burda Verlag GmbH, Postfach 1230, 77602 Offenburg, Germany. TEL 089-9250-0. FAX 089-92503519. (U.S. dist.: GLP International, 153 S. Dean St., Englewood, NJ 07631. TEL 201-871-1010. FAX 201-871-0870) adv. circ. 700,000. **Document type:** consumer publication.

053.1   GW
FORSCHUNGSBERICHTE DES LANDES NORDRHEIN-WESTFALEN. irreg. price varies. Westdeutscher Verlag GmbH, Postfach 5829, 65048 Wiesbaden, Germany. TEL 0611-160225. FAX 0611-160229. Indexed: Dok.Str., Forest.Abstr., INIS Atomind., Met.Abstr. **Document type:** monographic series.

073   GW
FRAENKISCHER TAG. d. Fraenkischer Tag GmbH und Co. KG, Gutenbergstr. 1, 96050 Bamberg, Germany. TEL 0951-188-0. FAX 0951-188112. Pub. Bernhard Wagner. adv. contact: Edwin Wagner. circ. 76,025. **Document type:** newspaper.

073   GW
FRAENKISCHES VOLKSBLATT; Tageszeitung fuer Unterfranken. Variant title: Fraenkische Volkszeitung. (Supplement avail.: R T V) 1868. 6/wk. DM.32.50 per mo. Volksblatt Verlagsgesellschaft mbH, Juliuspromenade 64, 97070 Wuerzburg, Germany. TEL 0931-3091-0. FAX 0931-13270. Ed. Klaus Hoeynck. adv. contact: Paul Zoeller. bk.rev.; film rev.; music rev.; tele.rev.; circ. controlled. (standard format) **Document type:** newspaper.

073   GW
FRANKENPOST. d. Frankenpost Verlag GmbH, Poststr. 9-11, 95028 Hof, Germany. TEL 09281-816-0. FAX 09281-816283. Owner(s): Sueddeutscher Verlag GmbH, Thomas-Dehler-Str. 27, 81737 Munich, Germany. TEL 089-678040. FAX 089-678014192. Ed. Malte Buschbeck. adv. contact: Hans Niederlaender. circ. 103,533. **Document type:** newspaper.

053.1   GW
FRANKENTHAL, EINST UND JETZT. 1959. 2/yr. DM.7.50. Stadtverwaltung Frankenthal, Kulturamt, Kanalstr. 1, 67227 Frankenthal, Germany. FAX 06233-89553. TELEX 0465232. circ. 1,200. (back issues avail.) **Document type:** government publication.

053.1   GW   ISSN 0935-8994
FRANKFURT MAGAZIN. 1987. m. (11/yr.). DM.36. Frankfurt Magazin Verlags GmbH, Postfach 100851, 60008 Frankfurt a.M., Germany. TEL 069-289863. FAX 069-291355. Ed. Johannes Theissen; Pub. Bernhard Mihm. adv.: page DM.2200. bk.rev.; index. circ. 10,000. (back issues avail.) **Document type:** consumer publication.

GENERAL INTEREST PERIODICALS — GERMANY

053.1 GW
FRANKFURTER. 1986. s-a. DM.10. Skyline Medien Verlags GmbH, Wolfsgangstr. 88, 60322 Frankfurt, Germany. TEL 069-550891. FAX 069-5971434. Eds. Erk Walter, Heinz Meffert. adv.; bk.rev.; bibl.; illus.; film rev. circ. 15,000. (back issues avail.)

073 GW ISSN 0174-4909
FRANKFURTER ALLGEMEINE. (Other edition avail.: Rhein-Main-Zeitung) d. Frankfurter Allgemeine Zeitung GmbH, Hellerhofstr. 2-4, 60327 Frankfurt a.M., Germany. TEL 069-7591-0. FAX 069-75911743. Ed.Bd. adv. contact: Dieter Droell. **Document type:** newspaper.

053.1 GW
FRANKFURTER ALLGEMEINE MAGAZIN. (Supplement to: Frankfurter Allgemeine Zeitung) 1980. w. (Fri.). Frankfurter Allgemeine Zeitung GmbH, Hellerhofstr. 2-4, 60327 Frankfurt a.M., Germany. TEL 069-7591-0. FAX 069-75911171. Ed. Thomas Schroeder. adv. contact: Wolf-Dietrich Auerbach. circ. 394,760. (back issues avail.) **Indexed:** INIS Atomind. **Document type:** newspaper.

073 GW
FRANKFURTER NEUE PRESSE. d. Frankfurter Societaets-Druckerei GmbH, Frankenallee 71-81, 60327 Frankfurt a.M., Germany. TEL 069-7501-0. FAX 069-7306965. Ed. Peter Fischer. circ. 109,670. **Document type:** newspaper.

073 GW ISSN 0940-6980
FRANKFURTER RUNDSCHAU. 1945. d. Druck- und Verlagshaus Frankfurt am Main GmbH, Grosse Eschheimerstr. 16-18, 60313 Frankfurt a.M., Germany. TEL 069-21991. FAX 069-2199521. Ed. Roderich Reifenrath. adv. contact: Peter Schwalm. circ. 189,070. **Document type:** newspaper.

053.1 GW ISSN 0171-9289
AP30
FREIBEUTER; Vierteljahreszeitschrift fuer Kultur und Politik. 1979. q. DM.50. Verlag Klaus Wagenbach, Ahornstr. 4, 10787 Berlin, Germany. TEL 030-2115069. FAX 030-2116140. Ed.Bd. adv.; bk.rev. circ. 14,000. **Document type:** consumer publication.
—Faxon.

073 GW
FREIE PRESSE. d. Chemnitzer Verlag und Druck GmbH, Brueckenstr. 15-19, 09111 Chemnitz, Germany. TEL 0371-6560. FAX 0371-643042. Owner(s): Medien Union GmbH. Ed. Hannes Koehler. adv. contact: Rainer Beier. circ. 516,931. **Document type:** newspaper.

073 GW
FREIES WORT. d. Suhler Verlagsgesellschaft mbH, Friedrich-Koenig-Str. 6, 98527 Suhl, Germany. TEL 03681-5130. FAX 03681-21400. Owner(s): Sueddeutscher Verlag GmbH, Thomas-Dehler-Str. 27, 81737 Munich, Germany. TEL 089-678040. FAX 089-67804192. Ed. Gerd Schwinger. adv. contact: Manfred Eich. circ. 123,198. **Document type:** newspaper.

073 GW
FREITAG (BERLIN). w. (Fri.). Zeitungsverlag Freitag GmbH, Am Treptower Park 28-30, 12435 Berlin, Germany. TEL 030-6883440-0. FAX 030-68834420. Ed. Bernd Mansel. circ. 18,874. **Document type:** newspaper.

053.1 GW
FREIZEIT UND KULTUR; Stadtmagazin fuer Freiburg und die Region. 1986. bi-m. DM.48. Freizeit und Kultur Verlag, Dorfstr. 28, 79249 Merzhausen, Germany. TEL 0761-405333. FAX 0761-405341. Ed. Guenter Lorenz; Pub. Brigitte Hrabe-Lorenz. adv. contact: Carmen Lorenz. circ. 14,700. (back issues avail.) **Document type:** consumer publication.

053.1 GW
FREIZEITSPIEGEL. 1983. m. free. Infoterm Verlag GmbH, Kueferstr. 32-34, 73728 Esslingen, Germany. TEL 0711-356637. FAX 0711-3508901. Ed. Joerg Bleyhl. adv. contact: Thomas Scheerer. circ. 39,459. (back issues avail.) **Document type:** consumer publication.

053.1 GW ISSN 0016-2450
FUER SIE. 1948. fortn. Jahreszeiten Verlag GmbH, Possmoorweg 5, 22301 Hamburg, Germany. TEL 040-2717-0. FAX 040-27172059. TELEX 213214. Ed. Andreas Millies; Pub. Heinz Scheibenpflug. adv. contact: Helma Spieker. circ. 769,633. **Document type:** consumer publication.

073 GW
FULDAER ZEITUNG. d. Verlag Parzeller GmbH & Co. KG, Postfach 409, 36004 Fulda, Germany. TEL 0661-280-0. FAX 0661-280259. Ed. Hermann-Joseph Konze; Pub. Thomas Schmitt. circ. 51,986. **Document type:** newspaper.

053.1 GW
FUNK UHR. 1952. w. (Fri.). Axel Springer Verlag AG, Axel-Springer-Platz 1, 20355 Hamburg, Germany. FAX 040-343180. Ed. Imre Kusztrich. adv. contact: Dieter Koering. circ. 2,005,446. **Document type:** consumer publication.

053.1 GW
GEMEINDE CLEEBRONN. MITTEILUNGSBLATT. w. Walter Druck und Verlag GmbH, Raiffeisenstr. 55, 74336 Brackenheim, Germany. TEL 07135-104-0. adv.: B&W page DM.513; trim 185 x 270. circ. 900. **Document type:** newspaper.

053.1 GW
GEMEINDE LEINGARTEN. AMTSBLATT. w. Walter Druck und Verlag GmbH, Raiffeisenstr. 55, 74336 Brackenheim, Germany. TEL 07135-104-0. FAX 07135-10439. adv.: B&W page DM.604.80; trim 185 x 270. circ. 3,300. **Document type:** newspaper.

053.1 GW
GEMEINDE TALHEIM. MITTEILUNGSBLATT. w. Walter Druck und Verlag GmbH, Raiffeisenstr. 55, 74336 Brackenheim, Germany. TEL 07135-104-0. FAX 07135-10439. adv.: B&W page DM.626.40; trim 185 x 270. circ. 1,500. **Document type:** newspaper.

053.1 GW
GEMEINDE ZABERFELD. MITTEILUNGSBLATT. w. Walter Druck und Verlag GmbH, Raiffeisenstr. 55, 74336 Brackenheim, Germany. TEL 07135-104-0. FAX 07135-10439. adv.: B&W page DM.513; trim 185 x 270. circ. 1,200. **Document type:** newspaper.

073 GW
GENERAL-ANZEIGER. d. Bonner Verlagsanstalt Hermann Neusser, Justus-von-Liebig-Str. 15, 53121 Bonn, Germany. TEL 0228-6688-0. FAX 0228-6688411. Ed. Helmut Herles; Pubs. Hermann Neusser, Martin Neusser. adv. contact: Guenter Berk. circ. 85,084. **Document type:** newspaper.

052 GW ISSN 0722-883X
GERMAN COMMENTS; review of politics and culture. 1983. q. DM.36. Verlag A. Fromm, Postfach 1948, 49009 Osnabrueck, Germany. TEL 0541-310334. FAX 0541-310440. Ed. Peter Hopen. circ. 3,000. **Document type:** bulletin.

052 II ISSN 0016-8793
GERMAN NEWS. (Text in English and Hindi) vol.19, 1977. m. Rs.15. Embassy of the Federal Republic of Germany, Press and Information Office, No. 6 Shanti Path, Chanakyapuri, New Delhi 21, India. TEL 604861. FAX 6873111. TELEX 3182077. Ed. Martin Kobler. bk.rev.; charts; illus.; stat.; index. circ. 100,000.
Formerly: German News Weekly.

053.1 GW
GEROLDSECKER LAND; Jahrbuch einer Landschaft. 1958. a. DM.17.80. Landkreis Ortenau, Badstr. 20, 77652 Offenburg, Germany. circ. 4,000.

073 GW
GIESSENER ALLGEMEINE. d. Mittelhessische Druck- und Verlags GmbH, Marburgerstr. 35, 35390 Giessen, Germany. TEL 0641-3003-0. FAX 0641-32916. Ed.Bd; Pub. Christian Rempel. adv. contact: Wilfried Kaempf. circ. 63,862. **Document type:** newspaper.

053.1 GW
GIG; Muenster-Osnabrueck. 1986. m. Gig Verlags GmbH, Hafenweg 48, 48155 Muenster, Germany. TEL 0251-60105. FAX 0251-60117. adv.: B&W page DM.3200, color page DM.5300; trim 190 x 270. adv. contact: Hubert Steinert. bk.rev. circ. 30,900. **Document type:** consumer publication.

073 GW
DIE GLOCKE. d. Verlag Engelbert Holterdorf, Ruggstr. 27, 59302 Oelde, Germany. TEL 02522-73-0. FAX 02522-73166. Eds. Fried Gehring, Ulrich Gehre; Pubs. Engelbert Holterdorf, Fried Gehring. adv. contact: Dieter Schoenbeck. circ. 64,387. **Document type:** newspaper.

073 GW
GLUECKSREVUE. w. (Wed.). Burda Verlag GmbH, Postfach 1230, 77602 Offenburg, Germany. TEL 0781-8401. FAX 0781-842983. Ed. Peter Saller. adv. contact: Herbert Scherer. circ. 451,568. **Document type:** consumer publication.

073 GW
GMUENDER ANZEIGER. 1977. w. free. Gmuender Tagespost, Vordere Schmiedgasse 18, 73525 Schwaebisch Gmuend, Germany. FAX 07171-600155. adv. circ. 51,083. **Document type:** newspaper.

053.1 GW
GRUENBERGER WOCHENBLATT. m. DM.40.20 (foreign DM.51). P. Keppler Verlag GmbH und Co. KG, Industriestr. 2, 63150 Heusenstamm, Germany. TEL 06104-6060. FAX 06104-606145. **Document type:** consumer publication.

057.1 GW ISSN 0172-4525
GUTEN TAG. (Text in Russian) 1979. m. DM.48. Friedrich Reinecke Verlag GmbH, Hartwicusstr. 3-4, 22087 Hamburg, Germany. TEL 040-228070. FAX 040-22807260. Ed. Peter Dvorak. circ. 165,000. (also avail. in microfiche) **Document type:** consumer publication.

073 GW
H N A SONNTAGSZEIT. (Hessische - Niedersaechsische Allgemeine) (Sunday edition of: Hessische-Niedersaechsische Allgemeine) w. (Sun.). Dierichs GmbH und Co. KG, Frankfurterstr. 168, 34121 Kassel, Germany. TEL 0561-2030-0. FAX 0561-20306. Ed. Lothar Orzechowski. adv. contact: Horst Prehm. circ. 228,760. **Document type:** newspaper.

053.1 GW
HAMBRUECKER WOCHENBLATT. w. Primo Verlagsdruck, Neurottstr. 19, 69190 Walldorf, Germany. TEL 06227-62033. FAX 06227-30247. **Document type:** consumer publication.

053.1 GW
HAMBURG FUEHRER. 1976. m. DM.66. Hamburg Fuehrer Verlag GmbH, Rothenbaumchaussee 195, 20149 Hamburg, Germany. TEL 040-448185. FAX 040-452368. Ed. Susan Kunst-Elliot. circ. 45,000. (back issues avail.) **Document type:** consumer publication.

073 GW
HAMBURGER ABENDBLATT. d. Axel Springer Verlag AG, Axel-Springer-Platz 1, 20355 Hamburg, Germany. TEL 040-3470-0. FAX 040-340581. Ed. Peter Kruse. adv. contact: Annette Budesheim. circ. 308,470. **Document type:** newspaper.

073 GW
HAMBURGER MORGENPOST. d. Morgenpost Verlag GmbH, Griegstr. 75, 22763 Hamburg, Germany. TEL 040-88303-0. FAX 040-88303295. Owner(s): Gruner und Jahr AG & Co., Am Baumwall 11, 20459 Hamburg, Germany. TEL 040-3703-0. FAX 040-37035607. Eds. Wolf Heckmann, Manfred von Thien; Pub. Hans Dichand. adv. contact: Hans-Joachim Eggers. circ. 168,315. **Document type:** newspaper.

073 GW
HAMBURGER RUNDSCHAU. w. (Thu.). Neue Hamburger Rundschau GmbH, Lange Reihe 29, 20099 Hamburg, Germany. TEL 040-280148-0. FAX 040-2803058. Ed. Joachim Mueller. adv. contact: Axel Franken. circ. 7,996. **Document type:** newspaper.

073 GW
HANAUER ANZEIGER. d. (except Sun.). Hanauer Anzeiger GmbH und Co., Hammerstr. 9, 63450 Hanau, Germany. TEL 06181-2903-0. FAX 06181-253999. Ed. Dieter Groos; Pub. Horst Bauer. adv. contact: Heidi Sickenberger. circ. 22,794. **Document type:** newspaper.

GENERAL INTEREST PERIODICALS — GERMANY

053.1 GW
HANDBUCH STIL UND ETIKETTE; Sicher auftreten bei allen Geschaeftlichen, offiziellen und privaten Anlaessen. 1990. q. DM.198. Verlag Norman Rentrop, Theodor-Heuss-Str. 4, 53177 Bonn, Germany. TEL 0228-8205-0. FAX 0228-364411. Ed. Norman Rentrop. (looseleaf format) **Document type:** bulletin.
  Formed by the merger of: Stil- und Etiketteberater & Stil und Etikette (ISSN 0939-0286)
  Description: How to behave correctly in society.

073 GW
HANNOVERSCHE ALLGEMEINE ZEITUNG. d. Verlagsgesellschaft Madsack GmbH, Bemeroderstr. 58, 30559 Hannover, Germany. TEL 0511-518-0. FAX 0511-513175. Ed. Wolfgang Mauersberg; Pub. Luise Madsack. adv. contact: Helga Pieplow. circ. 230,983. **Document type:** newspaper.

073 GW
HARBURGER ANZEIGEN UND NACHRICHTEN. d. Luehmanndruck G. Schroeter und Soehne GmbH, Sand 20, 21073 Hamburg, Germany. TEL 040-76694-0. FAX 040-7650262. Ed. Hans-Joachim Elwenspoek. adv. contact: Knut Leissner. circ. 27,567. **Document type:** newspaper.

073 GW
HEILBRONNER STIMME. d. Heilbronner Stimme GmbH, Allee 2, Hochhaus, 74072 Heilbronn, Germany. TEL 07131-615-0. FAX 07131-615200. Eds. Uwe Jacobi, Siegfried Schilling. adv. contact: Hans-Juergen Klein. circ. 101,763. **Document type:** newspaper.

053.1 GW ISSN 0933-5358
HEIMAT OSTBAYERN; fuer und ueber Land und Leute in Niederbayern-Oberpfalz. 1987. s-a. DM.35. c/o Fritz Markmiller, Ed. & Pub., Steinweg 4, 84124 Dingolfing, Germany. adv. **Document type:** academic/scholarly publication.

053.1 GW ISSN 0179-8790
HEIMATGEMEINSCHAFT ECKERNFOERDE. JAHRBUCH; Schwansen, Huetten, Daenischwohld. 1936. a. DM.25. Heimatgemeinschaft Eckernfoerde e.V., Ringstr. 25, 24354 Rieseby, Germany. TEL 04355-291. Ed. Detlef Redderbek. index. circ. 3,800. (back issues avail.)

HEIMATJAHRBUCH KREIS AHRWEILER. see *LITERATURE*

053.1 GW
HEIMATJAHRBUCH LANDKREIS ALZEY-WORMS. 1961. a. DM.8.50. Kreis-Volkshochschule Alzey-Worms, Geschaeftsstelle, Peterspforte 12, 55232 Alzey, Germany. TEL 06731-7432. adv.; bk.rev. circ. 4,000.

053.1 GW ISSN 0933-5498
HERR SCHMIDT; mit Pupille: das Magazin aus Wuerzburg. 1987. m. DM.33. Weissbach Verlag HandbH, Sophienstr. 15, 97072 Wuerzburg, Germany. TEL 0931-884344. FAX 0931-887371. Ed. Wolf-Dietrich Weissbach. circ. 8,000.

073 GW
HESSISCHE - NIEDERSAECHSISCHE ALLGEMEINE. d. Dierichs GmbH und Co. KG, Frankfurterstr. 168, 34121 Kassel, Germany. TEL 0561-2030-0. FAX 0561-20306. Ed. Lothar Orzechowski; Pubs. Rainer Dierichs, Dietrich Batz. adv. contact: Horst Prehm. **Document type:** newspaper.

053.1 GW
HIGH SCORE; Magazin fuer Spiel & Freizeit. 1987. bi-m. Edit Lind GmbH, Am Suedhang 5, 55127 Mainz, Germany. TEL 06131-478100. Eds. Manfred Schloesser, Stefan Dreizehnter. circ. 80,000.

053.1 GW
HIGHLIGHTS; Glanzlichter vom Reise und Modemarkt. 1987. m. DM.40. Christian Schmiedl Verlag, St. Paulsplatz 6, 80336 Munich, Germany. TEL 089-535778. FAX 089-531099. circ. 50,000. **Document type:** consumer publication.

053.1 GW ISSN 0018-3113
HOERZU. 1946. w. (Fri.) Axel Springer Verlag AG, Axel-Springer-Platz 1, 20355 Hamburg, Germany. TEL 040-3470-0. FAX 040-34722628. Ed. Klaus Stampfuss. adv. contact: Dieter Koering. tele.rev.; illus.; tr.lit. circ. 2,707,179. (reprint service avail.) **Document type:** consumer publication.

053.1 GW
HOLLFELDER BLAETTER; Studien zur Heimatforschung auf der noerdlichen Frankenalb. 1976. q. DM.16. Arbeitskreis fuer Heimatforschung, Badstr. 3, 96142 Hollfeld, Germany. TEL 09274-652. cum.index. circ. 650.

073 GW
HOLSTEINISCHE COURIER. d. Karl Wachholtz Verlag, Am Gaensemarkt 1-3, 24534 Neumuenster, Germany. TEL 04321-946-0. FAX 04321-946224. Eds. Holger Loose, Klaus Lutter; Pubs. Gisela Wachholtz, Ulrich Wachholtz. adv. contact: Jens Kalkowski. circ. 18,510. **Document type:** newspaper.

073 GW
HONNEFER VOLKSZEITUNG. d. H V Z Druckerei- und Verlagsgesellschaft mbH, Hauptstr. 38f, 53604 Bad Honnef, Germany. TEL 02224-2075. FAX 02224-79494. Ed. Victor Francke; Pub. Franz Josef Kayser. adv. contact: Wolfgang Kuendgen. circ. 5,900. **Document type:** newspaper.

073 GW
ISERLOHNER KREISANZEIGER UND ZEITUNG. d. Zeitungsverlag Iserlohn, Theodor-Heuss-Ring 4-6, 58636 Iserlohn, Germany. TEL 02371-29045. FAX 02371-29044. Ed. Eduard Grueber; Pub. Gertrud Wichelhoven. adv. contact: Leo Plattes. circ. 31,358. **Document type:** newspaper.

053.1 GW
JAHRBUCH DER STADT WEINSBERG. 1955. a. DM.12. Jahrbuch Verlag, Schwabstr. 20, 74183 Weinsberg, Germany. circ. 1,500. **Document type:** bulletin.

053.1 GW ISSN 0342-5835
JAHRBUCH DES KREISES DUEREN. 1963. a. DM.12. Verlag des Eifelvereins, Stuertzstr. 2-6, 52349 Dueren, Germany. TEL 02421-13121. Ed. Edgar Manz.

059.919 GW ISSN 0931-9921
JAHRESTAGUNG (YEAR) SUVAZIAVIMO DARBAI. (Text in German, Lithuanian) a. Litauisches Kulturinstitut, 68623 Lampertheim, Germany.

053.1 GW ISSN 0940-6530
JOURNAL FRANKFURT. 1982. s-m. DM.54. Presse Verlagsgesellschaft fuer Zeitschriften und Neue Medien mbH, Ludwigstr. 37, 60388 Frankfurt a.M., Germany. TEL 069-756181-0. FAX 069-75618191. Ed. Helmut Ortner. adv.; bk.rev. circ. 33,550. **Document type:** consumer publication.
  Formed by 1990 merger of: Auftritt & Pflasterstrand.

073 GW
JUNGE WELT. d. Verlagsanstalt in Berlin GmbH, Am Treptower Park 28-30, 12435 Berlin, Germany. TEL 030-68834301. FAX 030-68834398. Ed. Jens Koenig. adv. contact: Dagmar Ludwig. circ. 48,547. **Document type:** newspaper.

053.1 GW ISSN 0931-2854
JUNI; Magazin fuer Kultur und Politik. 1986. 3/yr. DM.50 for 4 nos. Juni Verlag, Malmedyerstr. 41, 41066 Moenchengladbach, Germany. TEL 02161-664245. FAX 02161-661556. Eds. Walter Delabar, Horst Winz. adv.; bk.rev.

053.1 GW ISSN 0936-6547
KIEL; das Stadtmagazin. 1987. m. Koerner Verlag GmbH, Eckernfoerderstr. 259, 2300 Kiel-Kronshagen, Germany. TEL 0431-542072. adv.; bk.rev.; film rev.; illus.; play rev. circ. 12,700.

073 GW
KIELER NACHRICHTEN. d. Kieler Nachrichten GmbH, Fleethoern 1-7, 24103 Kiel, Germany. TEL 0431-903-0. FAX 0431-903935. Ed. Juergen Heinemann. adv. contact: Thomas Brammer-Tuerck. circ. 166,279. **Document type:** newspaper.

053 GW
KIELS FEINE ADRESSEN. 1983. q. DM.27. Ewald Schwarzer Verlag, Wallbergstr. 3, 82024 Taufkirchen, Germany. TEL 089-612020. Ed. Ewald Schwarzer. circ. 6,000. (back issues avail.)

053.1 GW
KLAPPE AUF. 1987. m. DM.55. Belschner und Godulla GdbR, Adlerstr. 22, 76133 Karlsruhe, Germany. TEL 0721-606093. FAX 0721-607121. Pub. Bernd Belschner. adv. contact: Guenter Kromer. circ. 20,401. (back issues avail.) **Document type:** newsletter.

053.1 GW ISSN 0023-222X
DIE KLUGE HAUSFRAU; Kundenzeitschrift der Edeka. 1925. w. free. Verlagsgruppe Hilden Werberuf GmbH, Beethovenstr. 55-59, 40724 Hilden, Germany. Ed. Dr. Wolfgang Oehme. adv.; bk.rev.; illus. circ. 500,000.

053.1 GW
KOCHERBURGBOTE. 1956. w. DM.14. Bezirksamt Aalen-Unterkochen, Rathausplatz 7, 73432 Aalen, Germany. TEL 07361-9880-11. FAX 07361-9880-21. adv. circ. 1,450. (back issues avail.) **Document type:** newsletter.

053 GW ISSN 0178-5540
KOELN - BONNS FEINE ADRESSEN. 1983. q. DM.27. Ewald Schwarzer Verlag, Wallbergstr. 3, 82024 Taufkirchen, Germany. TEL 089-612020. Ed. Ewald Schwarzer. circ. 8,000. (back issues avail.)

073 GW
KOELNER STADT-ANZEIGER. d. (except Sun.). M. DuMont Schauberg, Breitestr. 70, 50667 Cologne, Germany. TEL 0221-224-0. FAX 0221-2242524. Ed. Dieter Jepsen-Foege; Pub. Alfred DuMont. adv. contact: Bodo Almert. circ. 287,531. **Document type:** newspaper.

073 GW
KOELNISCHE RUNDSCHAU. d. Heinen Verlag GmbH, Stolkgasse 25-45, 50667 Cologne, Germany. TEL 0221-1632-0. FAX 0221-1632491. Ed. Dieter Breuers; Pub. Helmut Heinen. adv. contact: Horst Litsch. circ. 157,941. **Document type:** newspaper.

053.1 GW
KOENIGSTEINER WOCHE. q. Gerichtstr. 12, 61462 Koenigstein, Germany. circ. 9,000.

053.1 GW
KONKRET. 1974. m. Gremliza Verlags GmbH, Schulterblatt 58c, 20357 Hamburg, Germany. TEL 040-431085. FAX 040-4302211. Ed. Wolfgang Schneider; Pub. Hermann Gremliza. adv. contact: Bettina Fischer. bk.rev.; illus. circ. 40,000. **Document type:** consumer publication.

073 GW
KREISZEITUNG. (Editions avail. for: Bassum, Bruchhausen-Vilsen, Harpstedt, Hoya, Stuhr-Weyhe, Syke, Twistringen, Weyhe-Leeste, Wildeshausen) d. Kreiszeitung Verlagsgesellschaft mbH, Ristedter Weg 17, 28857 Syke, Germany. TEL 04242-58-0. FAX 04242-5839. Ed. Hartmut Bigalke. adv. contact: Arnim Wollschlaeger. circ. 81,257. **Document type:** newspaper.

053.1 GW ISSN 0935-6436
KULTUR VORSCHAU INTERNATIONAL. 1923. q. Verlag Horst Deike KG, Postfach 100452, 78404 Konstanz, Germany. TEL 07531-8155-0. FAX 07531-815581. Ed. Wolfgang Deike. (back issues avail.) **Document type:** consumer publication.

073 GW
KURIER AM SONNTAG. (Sunday edition of: Weser-Kurier, Bremer Nachrichten) w. (Sun.). Bremer Tageszeitungen AG, Martinistr. 43-45, 28195 Bremen, Germany. TEL 0421-3671-0. FAX 0421-328327. Ed. Dietrich Ide. adv. contact: Egon Hoppe. circ. 211,219. **Document type:** newspaper.

053.1 GW ISSN 0023-5652
AP30
KURSBUCH. 1965. 4/yr. DM.48. Rowohlt-Berlin Verlag GmbH, Einsteinufer 63A, 10587 Berlin, Germany. TEL 030-3410723. FAX 030-3410824. Ed. Ingrid Karsunke, Karl-Markus Michel. adv. circ. 20,000. **Indexed:** Phil.Ind. **Document type:** consumer publication.
—Faxon; SWETS.

GENERAL INTEREST PERIODICALS — GERMANY

053.1 GW
L V R - REPORT. 1980. m. free. Landschaftsverband Rheinland, Kennedyufer 2, 50663 Cologne, Germany. TEL 0221-8092781. FAX 0221-8092888. Ed. Klaus Jacobi. circ. 18,000. **Document type:** consumer publication.
Description: General interest publication for the Rheinland region, featuring current events, culture, politics and history.

053.1 GW
LAHN-DILL ANZEIGER. 1977. w. Anzeigerblatt Verlag Lahn-Dill, Elsa-Brandstroem-Str. 18, 35578 Wetzlar, Germany. TEL 06441-75166. FAX 06441-74588. Eds. Winfried Brandhoff, Christian Reiche. adv.; circ. 720,000 (controlled). **Document type:** consumer publication.

053.1 GW
LANDES-TROST; Zeitung fuer Neustadt. 1983. q. DM.20. Verein der Freunde der alternativen Provinzpresse, c/o Hubert Brieden, Im Dorn 7, 31535 Neustadt, Germany. TEL 05032-61705. circ. 1,000. **Document type:** newspaper.

073 GW
LANDESZEITUNG. d. Landeszeitung Lueneburger Heide GmbH, Am Sande 16-20, 21335 Lueneburg, Germany. TEL 04131-740-0. FAX 04131-740213. Ed. Christoph Steiner. adv. contact: Dieter Borchardt. circ. 36,036. **Document type:** newspaper.

073 GW
LAUFFENER BOTE. w. Walter Druck und Verlag GmbH, Raiffeisenstr. 55, 74336 Brackenheim, Germany. TEL 07135-104-0. adv.: B&W page DM.642.60; trim 185 x 270. circ. 4,200. **Document type:** newspaper.

073 GW
LAUSITZER RUNDSCHAU. d. L R Medienverlag GmbH, Str. der Jugend 54, 03050 Cottbus, Germany. TEL 0355-481-0. FAX 0355-481293. Owner(s): Saarbruecker Zeitung Verlag GmbH, Gutenbergstr. 11-23, 66117 Saarbruecken, Germany. TEL 0681-502-0. FAX 0681-5022500. Ed. Wolfgang Nagorske. adv. contact: Monika Langenickel. circ. 209,333. **Document type:** newspaper.

053.1 GW
LEICHTER LEBEN. 1970. 3/yr. free. Versorgung u. Verkehr Kiel, Knooper Weg 75, 24116 Kiel, Germany. adv.; bk.rev. circ. 170,000.

073 GW
LEIPZIGER VOLKSZEITUNG. d. Leipziger Druck- und Verlagsgesellschaft mbH, Emilienstr. 3, 04107 Leipzig, Germany. TEL 0341-2181-0. FAX 0341-311948. Owner(s): Verlagsgesellschaft Madsack GmbH, Bemeroderstr. 58, 30559 Hannover, Germany. TEL 0511-518-0. FAX 0511-513175; Axel Springer Verlag AG, Axel-Springer-Platz 1, 20355 Hamburg, Germany. TEL 040-3470-0. FAX 040-340581. Ed. Hartwig Hochstein. adv. contact: Andreas Mueller. circ. 380,505. **Document type:** newspaper.

053.1 GW ISSN 0932-318X
LICHTENRADER RUNDSCHAU; Monatszeitung von und fuer Menschen in Lichtenrade Ost. 1978. m.(11/yr.). free. Nahariyastr. 33, 12309 Berlin, Germany. TEL 030-7467574. circ. 2,700. **Document type:** newsletter.

053.1 GW ISSN 0177-8390
LIVE; Essen - das Stadtmagazine. 1982. m. DM.25($80) (in EC countries DM.40). Doterner GmbH, Westfalenstr. 98, 45136 Essen, Germany. TEL 0201-85111-1. FAX 0201-8511155. Ed. Bodo F. Schmischke. adv.; bk.rev. circ. 25,000. (back issues avail.) **Document type:** newsletter.
Description: Local news and events in the city of Essen.

073 GW
LUDWIGSBURGER KREISZEITUNG. d. Ungeheuer und Ulmer GmbH und Co., Koernerstr. 14-18, 71634 Ludwigsburg, Germany. TEL 07141-130-0. FAX 07141-921426. Ed. Wilfried Simonis; Pub. Konrad Ulmer. adv. contact: Heinz Killinger. **Document type:** newspaper.

053.1 GW
LUDWIGSTEINER BLAETTER. q. DM.18($18) Vereinigung Jugendburg Ludwigstein e.V., Burg Ludwigstein, 37214 Witzenhausen, Germany. TEL 05542-1912.

073 GW
LUEBECKER NACHRICHTEN. d. (except Mon.). Luebecker Nachrichten GmbH, Herrenholz 10-12, 23556 Luebeck, Germany. TEL 0451-144-0. FAX 0451-1441022. Owner(s): Axel Springer Verlag AG, Axel-Springer-Platz 1, 20355 Hamburg, Germany. TEL 040-3470-0. FAX 040-340581. Ed. Thomas Lubowski; Pub. Juergen Wessel. adv. contact: Jochen Ruehmling. **Document type:** newspaper.

053.1 GW ISSN 0932-3325
M I T MITTELSTANDSMAGAZIN. m. DM.60. Mittelstands Verlagsgesellschaft mbH, Heussallee 40, 53113 Bonn, Germany. TEL 0228-915280. FAX 0228-9152822. Ed. Cosima Ningelgen. adv. contact: Karl-Heinz Schulte. circ. 35,525. **Document type:** bulletin.

073 GW
MACH MAL PAUSE. w. (Wed.). Heinrich Bauer Verlag, Burchardstr. 11, 20095 Hamburg, Germany. TEL 040-3019-0. FAX 040-335830. Ed. Juergen Pietzker. adv. contact: Goesta Ahrweiler. circ. 446,097. **Document type:** consumer publication.

073 GW
MAERKISCHE ALLGEMEINE. d. Maerkische Verlags- und Druckgesellschaft mbH, Friedrich-Engels-Str. 24, 14473 Potsdam, Germany. TEL 0331-324-0. FAX 0331-324310. Eds. Hans-Ulrich Conrad, Peter Mugay; Pub. Alexander Gauland. adv. contact: Peter Nitsch. circ. 242,673. **Document type:** newspaper.

073 GW
MAERKISCHE ODERZEITUNG. d. Maerkisches Verlags- und Druckhaus GmbH, Kellenspring 6, 15230 Frankfurt a.O., Germany. TEL 0335-55300. FAX 0335-5530538. Owner(s): Neue Pressegesellschaft, Frauenstr. 77, 89070 Ulm, Germany. TEL 0731-15601. FAX 0731-156308. Ed. Heinz Kannenberg. adv. contact: Werner Noll. circ. 166,521. **Document type:** newspaper.

053.1 GW ISSN 0460-5047
HD3340.5
DAS MAGAZIN. 1954. m. Das Magazin Verlagsgesellschaft mbH, Franz-Mehring-Platz 1, 13189 Berlin, Germany. TEL 030-58314433. FAX 030-58314444. Ed. Hartmut Berlin. adv. contact: Juergen Nowak. circ. 92,000. **Document type:** consumer publication.

073 GW
MAIN-ECHO. (Editions avail. for: Alzenau, Dieburg-Erbach, Gemuenden, Marktheidenfeld, Obernburg) d. Main-Echo Kirsch GmbH, Goldbacherstr. 25-27, 63739 Aschaffenburg, Germany. TEL 06021-396-0. FAX 06021-20641. Ed.Bd. adv. contact: Reinhard Fresow. circ. 90,695. **Document type:** newspaper.

073 GW
MAIN-POST. d. Mainpresse Zeitungsverlagsgesellschaft mbH, Bernerstr. 2, 97084 Wuerzburg, Germany. TEL 0931-6001-0. FAX 0931-6001242. Ed. David Brandstaetter. adv. contact: Paul Zoeller. circ. 156,021. **Document type:** newspaper.

073 GW
MANNHEIMER MORGEN. d. Mannheimer Morgen Verlag GmbH, Am Marktplatz, 68159 Mannheim, Germany. TEL 0621-39201. FAX 0621-3921376. Eds. Sigmar Heilmann, Horst-Dieter Schiele; Pubs. Karl Ackermann, Rainer von Schilling. adv. contact: Gerhard Haeberle. circ. 99,355. **Document type:** newspaper.

053.1 GW
MARESIANER. 1952. q. DM.2. Maresianer SV, Maria-Theresia-Gymnasium Regerplatz 1, 81675 Munich, Germany. Ed. Marcus Roth. adv.; bk.rev. circ. 600. (back issues avail.)

053.1 GW
MARIENBAD - TEPLER HEIMATBRIEF. 1948. m. DM.26. Heimatverband der Marienbader Stadt und Land e.V., Abensbergstrasse 3a, 80993 Munich, Germany. TEL 089-1417366.

DAS MARKGRAEFLERLAND. see HISTORY — History Of Europe

059.927 GW
MATSCHALLA. (Text in Arabic) m. Verlag Zeit im Bild, Julian-Grimau-Allee 10, DDR-8010 Dresden, E. Germany (D.D.R.). (Orders to: Buchexport, Leninstr. 160, DDR-7010 Leipzig, E. Germany (D.D.R.))

073 GW
MEINE FAMILIE UND ICH. m. $50. Burda Verlag GmbH, Postfach 1230, 77602 Offenburg, Germany. TEL 089-9250-0. FAX 089-92503519. (U.S. dist.: GLP International, 153 S. Dean St., Englewood, NJ 07631. TEL 201-871-1010. FAX 201-871-0870) Ed. Peter Schneider. circ. 997,667. **Document type:** consumer publication.

073 GW
MEININGER TAGEBLATT. d. Gesellschaft fuer Werbung, Presse, Vertrieb mbH, Sachsenstr. 2a, 98617 Meiningen, Germany. TEL 03693-4403-0. FAX 03693-440335. Ed. Ulrich Lutz. adv. contact: Detlev Koch. circ. 9,964. **Document type:** newspaper.

943 GW ISSN 0026-0029
DD3
MERIAN; Monatsheft der Staedte und Landschaften. 1948. m. DM.10.95. Hoffmann und Campe Verlag, Harvestehuder Weg 42, 20149 Hamburg, Germany. Ed. Volker Skierka. adv.; bk.rev.; illus.; maps. circ. 200,000. **Document type:** consumer publication. —UnCover.
Description: Information on the political, economic and cultural aspects of cities and counties.

073 GW
MINDENER TAGEBLATT. d. J.C.C. Bruns GmbH und Co. KG, Obermarktstr. 26-30, 32423 Minden, Germany. TEL 0571-882-0. FAX 0571-882157. Ed. Christophe Pepper; Pub. Rainer Thomas. adv. contact: Heinz Bornemann. circ. 37,212. **Document type:** newspaper.

073 GW
MITTELBAYERISCHE ZEITUNG. d. Mittelbayerische Druck- und Verlagsgesellschaft mbH, Margaretenstr. 4, 93047 Regensburg, Germany. TEL 0941-207-0. FAX 0941-207437. Eds. Kurt Hofner, Gerd Otto; Pub. Karl Heinz Esser. adv. contact: Stefan Kolleth. circ. 123,878. **Document type:** newspaper.

073 GW
MITTELDEUTSCHE ZEITUNG. 1990. 6/wk. DM.15.40; newsstand price: DM.0.70. Mitteldeutsches Druck- und Verlagshaus GmbH, Postfach 531, 06075 Halle, Germany. TEL 0345-565-0. FAX 0345-5652351. Ed. Stefan Lehnebach; Pub. Alfred-Neven Dumont. adv. contact: Dieter Koetter. bk.rev.; film rev.; music rev.; tele.rev. circ. 435,465. cols./p.: 6; pp./issue: 20. (standard format) **Document type:** newspaper.

073 GW
MITTELDEUTSCHER EXPRESS. d. Mitteldeutscher Express GmbH, Delitzscherstr. 65, 06112 Halle, Germany. TEL 0345-565-0. FAX 0345-5655248. Ed. Thomas Groeger; Pub. Alfred DuMont. adv. contact: Dietger Koetter. circ. 66,098. **Document type:** newspaper.

053.1 GW
MUEHLHEIMER MONAT. 1962. q. free. Magistrat der Stadt Muehlheim, Presseamt, Friedensstr. 20, 48145 Muehlheim, Germany. FAX 06108-601125. cum.index. circ. 10,500. (back issues avail.)

073 GW
MUENCHENER KULTURFUEHRER MIT THEATERPLAN. m. DM.20. Ewald Schwarzer Verlag, Wallbergstr 3., 82024 Taufkirchen, Germany. TEL 089-61202-0. Ed. Ewald Schwarzer. circ. 12,300.

053 GW ISSN 0178-5516
MUENCHENS FEINE ADRESSEN. 1980. m. DM.62. Ewald Schwarzer Verlag, Wallbergstr. 3, 82024 Taufkirchen, Germany. TEL 089-612020. Ed. Ewald Schwarzer. circ. 9,000.

073 GW
MUENCHNER MERKUR. d. Muenchener Zeitungsverlag GmbH, Paul-Heyse-Str. 2-4, 80336 Munich, Germany. TEL 089-5306-0. FAX 089-5306651. Ed. Werner Giers. adv. contact: Rainer Liebelt. circ. 192,302. **Document type:** newspaper.

GENERAL INTEREST PERIODICALS — GERMANY

073 GW
MUENSTERSCHE ZEITUNG. d. Verlag Lensing - Wolff GmbH, Neubrueckenstr. 8-11, 48143 Muenster, Germany. TEL 0251-5920. FAX 0251-592212. Ed. Ralf Koerner. adv. contact: Alexander Neetzow. circ. 64,168. **Document type:** newspaper.

053.1 GW
NACHRICHTENBLATT DER GEMEINDE BISINGEN. 1953. w. DM.52.80. (Gemeindeverwaltung Bisingen) A. Conzelmann & Co., Untere Koppenhalde 13, Postfach 127, 7457 Bisingen, Germany. TEL 07476-360.

053.1 GW
NACHRICHTENBLATT DER GEMEINDE GROSSELFINGEN. 1954. w. DM.52.80. (Gemeindeverwaltung Grosselfingen) A. Conzelmann & Co., Untere Koppenhalde 13, Postfach 127, 7457 Bisingen, Germany. TEL 07476-1360. FAX 07476-2502.

053.1 GW
NACHRICHTENBLATT FUER DIE GEMEINDEN SINZHEIM UND HUGELSHEIM. 1949. w. DM.26. Buergermeisteramt Sinzheim, Hauptstr. 71, 76547 Sinzheim, Germany. TEL 07221-80624. FAX 07221-80666. adv. circ. 28,000. (tabloid format) **Document type:** government publication.
  Description: Informs people about local news and performances.

053.1 GW
NECKARWESTHEIMER GEMEINDEBLATT. w. Walter Druck und Verlag GmbH, Raiffeisenstr. 55, 74336 Brackenheim, Germany. TEL 07135-104-0. FAX 07135-10439. adv.: B&W page DM.626.40; trim 185 x 270. circ. 1,000. **Document type:** newspaper.

053.1 GW
DAS NEUE. 1952. w. (Mon.). DM.109.20 (foreign DM.240). Heinrich Bauer Verlag, Burchardstr. 11, 20095 Hamburg, Germany. TEL 040-3019-0. FAX 040-330984. Ed. Ralf Schoppe. adv. contact: Sven Schrader. circ. 509,422. **Document type:** consumer publication.

053.1 GW
DAS NEUE BLATT. 1950. w. (Wed.). DM.114.40 (foreign DM.246). Heinrich Bauer Verlag, Burchardstr. 11, 20095 Hamburg, Germany. TEL 040-3019-0. FAX 040-327817. Ed. Ralf Schoppe. adv. contact: Goesta Ahrweiler. illus. circ. 1,268,514. **Document type:** consumer publication.

053.1 GW ISSN 0934-4713
NEUE KRONSTAEDTER ZEITUNG; Nachrichten fuer Kronstaedter und Burzenlaender in aller Welt. 1985. q. DM.20($15) Verlag Neue Kronstaedter Zeitung, Waldstr. 10, 82319 Starnberg, Germany. TEL 08151-16619. Ed. Hermann W. Schlandt. bk.rev. circ. 1,600. (back issues avail.) **Document type:** newspaper.

053.1 GW
NEUE ODERZEITUNG. 1981. q. DM.20. Werner Bader Verlag, Insterburgerstr. 10, 50997 Cologne, Germany. TEL 02233-21050.

073 GW
NEUE OSNABRUECKER ZEITUNG. d. Neue Osnabruecker Zeitung GmbH, Breiter Gang 10-14, 49074 Osnabrueck, Germany. TEL 0541-3100. FAX 0541-310234. Ed. Franz Schmedt; Pubs. Leo Frmm, Hermann Elstermann. adv. contact: Friedhelm Henschen. circ. 196,756. **Document type:** newspaper.

073 GW
NEUE PRESSE (COBURG). d. Druck- und Verlagsanstalt Neue Presse GmbH, Friedrich-Rueckert-Str. 73, 96450 Coburg, Germany. TEL 09561-647-0. FAX 09561-647110. Ed. Lutz Hegenberg. adv. contact: Joerg Stark. circ. 34,979. **Document type:** newspaper.

073 GW
NEUE PRESSE (HANNOVER). d. Verlagsgesellschaft Madsack GmbH und Co., Bemeroderstr. 58, 30559 Hannover, Germany. TEL 0511-518-0. FAX 0511-513175. Ed. Erwin Lutz. circ. 56,000.

053.1 GW
NEUE REVUE. 1946. w. (Fri.). DM.150.80 (foreign 274). Heinrich Bauer Verlag, Burchardstr. 11, 20095 Hamburg, Germany. TEL 040-3019-0. FAX 040-335830. Ed. Juergen Pietzker. adv. contact: Guenther Granzow. illus. circ. 701,741. **Document type:** consumer publication.
  Formed by the 1966 merger of: Revue; Neue Illustrierte.
  Description: Focuses on enjoyment of life, entertainment, topical information, partnerships, leisure time and travel, activities and environmental issues.

073 GW
NEUE RUHR ZEITUNG. d. Zeitungsverlag Niederrhein GmbH, Friedrichstr. 34-38, 45128 Essen, Germany. TEL 0201-2064-0. FAX 0201-2064621. Ed. Richard Kiessler; Pub. Dietrich Oppenberg. adv. contact: Manfred Kraemer. circ. 1,177,502. **Document type:** newspaper.

073 GW
DER NEUE TAG. d. Neue Tag Druck- und Verlagshaus GmbH, Weigelstr. 16, 92637 Weiden, Germany. TEL 0961-85-0. FAX 0961-46925. Ed. Gustav Kaiser. adv. contact: Dietrich Eckert. circ. 87,417. **Document type:** newspaper.

050 GW
NEUE WELT. 1932. w. (Wed.). Welt am Sonnabend GmbH, Adlerstr. 22, 40211 Duesseldorf, Germany. TEL 0211-3666-0. FAX 0211-3666339. Ed. Martina Luederitz. adv. contact: Josef Wolter. bk.rev.; illus. circ. 502,195. **Document type:** consumer publication.

073 GW
NEUE WESTFAELISCHE. d. Zeitungsverlag Neue Westfaelische GmbH, Niedernstr. 21-27, 33602 Bielefeld, Germany. TEL 0521-555-0. FAX 0521-555348. Ed. Reiner Kirst. adv. contact: Wolfgang Geese. circ. 217,813. **Document type:** newspaper.

053.1 GW ISSN 0138-5011
NEUE ZEIT. 1945. d. (Christlich-Demokratische Union Deutschlands) Verlag Neue Zeit, Mittelstr. 2-4, 10117 Berlin, Germany. TEL 030-20314-0. FAX 030-2004757. Owner(s): Frankfurter Allgemeine Zeitung GmbH, Hellerhofstr. 2-4, 60327 Frankfurt a.M., Germany. TEL 069-7591-0. FAX 069-75911743. Ed. Monika Zimmerman. adv. contact: Frank Hoernig. circ. 37,000. (also avail. in microfilm from BHP, KTO) **Document type:** newspaper.

073 GW ISSN 0323-3375
NEUES DEUTSCHLAND. 1946. d. Neues Deutschland Druckerei und Verlag GmbH, Franz-Mehring-Platz 1, 10243 Berlin, Germany. TEL 030-5831-0. FAX 030-58312625. Ed. Reiner Oschmann. adv. contact: Manfred Ibold. circ. 83,244. **Document type:** newspaper.

073 GW
DER NORD-BERLINER. w. (Thu.). Moeller Druck und Verlag GmbH, Oraniendamm 48, 13469 Berlin, Germany. TEL 030-4190942. FAX 030-4025071. Ed. Lutz Lange; Pubs. Adolf Moeller, Wolfgang Moeller. adv. contact: Joern Zessler. circ. 37,000. **Document type:** newspaper.

073 GW
NORDHEIMER MITTEILUNGEN. w. Walter Druck und Verlag GmbH, Raiffeisenstr. 55, 74336 Brackenheim, Germany. TEL 07135-104-0. FAX 07135-10439. adv.: B&W page DM.626,40; trim 185 x 270. circ. 2,300. **Document type:** newspaper.

073 GW
NORDKURIER. d. Kurierverlag und Druck GmbH, Woldeckerstr. 27, 17033 Neubrandenburg, Germany. TEL 0395-585-0. FAX 0395-585334. Ed. Gerhard Deckl. adv. contact: Andreas Poeller. circ. 153,690. **Document type:** newspaper.

073 GW
NORDSEE-ZEITUNG. d. Ditzen Druck- und Verlagsgesellschaft mbH, Hafenstr. 140, 27576 Bremerhaven, Germany. TEL 0471-597-0. FAX 0471-597555. Ed. Joerg Jung; Pub. Joachim Ditzen-Blanke. adv. contact: Uwe Katenkamp. circ. 76,372. **Document type:** newspaper.

073 GW
NORDWEST-ZEITUNG. d. Nordwest-Zeitung Druck- und Pressehaus GmbH, Peterstr. 28-34, 26121 Oldenburg, Germany. TEL 0441-23901. FAX 0441-239249. Ed. Rolf Seelheim. adv. contact: Peter Bremer. circ. 324,040. **Document type:** newspaper.

073 GW
NUERNBERGER NACHRICHTEN. d. Nuernberger Presse Druckhaus GmbH, Marienstr. 9-11, 90402 Nuernberg, Germany. TEL 0911-216-0. FAX 0911-2162432. Ed. Felix Hartlieb; Pub. Bruno Schnell. adv. contact: Klaus Kreissel. circ. 344,101. **Document type:** newspaper.

073 GW
NUERNBERGER ZEITUNG. d. Nordbayerische Verlagsgesellschaft mbH, Marienstr., 90402 Nuernberg, Germany. TEL 0911-2351-0. FAX 0911-2418295. Eds. Martin Doebert, Rainer Hajeck. adv. contact: Klaus Kreissel. circ. 30,140. **Document type:** newspaper.

073 GW
OBERBAYERISCHES VOLKSBLATT. d. Oberbayerisches Volksblatt GmbH, Hafnerstr. 5-13, 83022 Rosenheim, Germany. TEL 08031-181-0. FAX 08031-118216. Ed. Willi Boersch. adv. contact: Max Breu. circ. 77,126. **Document type:** newspaper.

073 GW
OBERHESSISCHE PRESSE. d. Verlag Johann August Koch, Postfach 1829, 35007 Marburg, Germany. TEL 06421-409-0. FAX 06421-409302. Ed. Paul-Josef Raue; Pub. Wolfram Hitzeroth. adv. contact: Eberhard Wilms. circ. 32,701. **Document type:** newspaper.

053.1 GW
OBERMENZINGER HEFTE. 1967. q. membership. (Verein der Freunde Schloss Blutenburg) Erasmus Grasser - Verlag GmbH, Lipperheidestr. 1, 81245 Munich, Germany. TEL 089-8345704. Ed. Wolfgang Vogelsgesang. adv.; index. circ. 1,500. (back issues avail.)
  Description: Cultural aspects of the west of Munich.

053.1 GW
OBERSTDORFER MAGAZIN; information in words and pictures for guests and local people. 1987. bi-w. DM.69 (foreign DM.184). Kurverwaltung Oberstdorf, Postfach 1320, 87553 Oberstdorf, Germany. TEL 08322-7000. FAX 08322-700236. TELEX 054444. Ed. Michael Schmidl. adv. contact: circ. 11,000. (back issues avail.) **Document type:** consumer publication.

053.1 GW ISSN 0029-8360
DER ODENWALD; Zeitschrift des Breuberg-Bundes. 1953. q. DM.30. Breuberg-Bund, Am Wittumsacker 7, 64401 Gross-Bieberau, Germany. TEL 06162-2470. Ed. W. Wackerfuss. bk.rev.; charts; illus.; cum.index (1953-1983). circ. 1,500. **Document type:** consumer publication.
  Description: Contains news and items of local interest.

073 GW
OFFENBACH-POST. d. Pressehaus Bintz Verlag GmbH, Grosse Marktstr. 36-44, 63065 Offenbach, Germany. TEL 069-80630. FAX 069-8063386. Ed. Ulrich Jung. adv. contact: Wilhelm Huesemann. circ. 54,124. **Document type:** newspaper.

073 GW
OFFENBLATT. 1966. s-m. DM.30. Stadt Offenburg, Amt fuer Presse- und Oeffentlichkeitsarbeit, Postfach 2450, 77614 Offenburg, Germany. TEL 0781-82271. FAX 0781-82582. circ. 27,000. **Document type:** newspaper.
  Formerly (until 1992): Offene Tor.

073 GW
OFFENBURGER TAGEBLATT. d. Reiff Verlagsgesellschaft mbH, Marlenerstr. 9, 77656 Offenburg, Germany. TEL 0781-504-0. FAX 0781-504207. Ed. Tim Arnold; Pub. Peter Reiff. adv. contact: Angelika Kleinfelder. **Document type:** newspaper.

GENERAL INTEREST PERIODICALS — GERMANY

073 GW
OLDENBURGISCHE VOLKSZEITUNG. d. Oldenburgische Volkszeitung Verlag KG, Neuer Markt 2, 49377 Vechta, Germany. TEL 04441-88031. FAX 04441-88032. Ed. Cornelius Riewerts. adv. contact: Gerd Beil. circ. 24,189. **Document type:** newspaper.

073 GW
OSTSEE-ZEITUNG. d. Ostsee-Zeitung GmbH, Richard-Wagner-Str. 1a, 18055 Rostock, Germany. TEL 0381-365-0. FAX 0381-365373. Owner(s): Axel Springer Verlag AG, Axel-Springer-Platz 1, 20355 Hamburg, Germany. TEL 040-3470-0. FAX 040-340581; Luebecker Nachrichten GmbH, Herrenholz 10-12, 23556 Luebeck, Germany. TEL 0451-144-0. FAX 0451-1441022. Ed. Gerd Spilker; Pub. Helmut Reinke. adv. contact: Michael Schottmann. circ. 221,048. **Document type:** newspaper.

073 GW
OSTTHUERINGER ZEITUNG. d. Ostthueringer Zeitungsverlag GmbH, Altestr. 1, 04626 Loebichau, Germany. TEL 03447-525911. FAX 03447-525914. Ed. Ullrich Erzigkeit. adv. contact: Robert Lentes. circ. 522,332. **Document type:** newspaper.

053.1 GW
PAPA JOE'S KUNST UND BIERBLATT. 1979. m. free. c/o Hanns Buschmann, Ed., Im Wielpuetzfeld 9, 51503 Roesrath, Germany. TEL 02205-81633. circ. 20,000. (back issues avail.)

073 GW
PASSAUER NEUE PRESSE. d. Neue Presse Verlags GmbH, Dr.-Hans-Kapfinger-Str. 30, 94032 Passau, Germany. TEL 0851-502-0. Ed. Rudolf Kollboeck. adv. contact: Wolfgang Lichtenegger. circ. 161,565. **Document type:** newspaper.

073 GW
PFAELZISCHER MERKUR. d. Zweibruecker Druckerei und Verlagsgesellschaft mbH, Hauotstr. 66, 66482 Zweibruecken, Germany. TEL 06332-9242-0. FAX 06332-924239. Owner(s): Saarbruecker Zeitung Verlag und Druckerei GmbH, Gutenbergstr. 11-23, 66117 Saarbruecken, Germany. TEL 0681-502-0. FAX 0681-5022500. Ed. Edgar Steiger. adv. contact: Wolfgang Heller. circ. 12,211. **Document type:** newspaper.

053.1 GW
PFINZTAL AN WOCHENENDE; Die Lokalzeitung zwischen Karlsruhe und Pforzheim. 1990. w. DM.90. Verlag am Wochenende, Hauptstr. 93, 76327 Pfinztal, Germany. TEL 07240-1071. FAX 07240-8113. Ed. Frank Armbruster. adv. contact: 25,487. **Document type:** consumer publication.

073 GW
PFORZHEIMER ZEITUNG. d. J. Esslinger GmbH und Co., Poststr. 5, 75172 Pforzheim, Germany. TEL 07231-32001. FAX 07231-353120. Ed. Horst Pieper; Pub. Rosa Esslinger. adv. contact: Albert Esslinger-Kiefer. circ. 44,856. **Document type:** newspaper.

073 GW
PIRMASENSER ZEITUNG. d. Pirmasenser Zeitung Verlag und Druck Adolf Deil AG, Gaertnerstr. 20, 66953 Pirmasens, Germany. TEL 06331-8005-0. FAX 06331-800529. Ed. Hans Frieder Baisch; Pub. Hilde/Becker-Baisch. adv. contact: Volker Baisch. circ. 15,773. **Document type:** newspaper.

073 GW
POTSDAMER NEUESTE NACHRICHTEN. d. Potsdamer Zeitungsverlagsgesellschaft mbH, Lindenstr. 29, 14467 Potsdam, Germany. TEL 0331-376146. FAX 0331-2800850. Ed. Michael Erbach. adv. contact: Niels Mester. circ. 14,163. **Document type:** newspaper.

053.1 GW ISSN 0032-6828
PRALINE. 1954. w. (Thu.). DM.114.40 (foreign DM.245). Heinrich Bauer Verlag, Burchardtstr. 11, 20095 Hamburg, Germany. TEL 040-3019-0. FAX 040-326589. Ed. Sabine Sandfort; Pub. Heinz Bauer. adv. contact: Guenther Granzow. illus. circ. 521,913. **Document type:** consumer publication.

053.1 GW ISSN 0937-0927
PRISMA (HAMBURG); Revista Republicii Federale Germania. (Text in German and Romanian) 1969. 6/yr. DM.24. Friedrich Reinecke Verlag GmbH, Hartwicusstr. 3-4, 22087 Hamburg, Germany. TEL 040-228070. FAX 040-22807260. Ed. Peter Dvorak. circ. 23,000. **Document type:** consumer publication.

059.945 GW ISSN 0344-7065
PROFIL (HAMBURG); folyoirat a Nemetorszagi Szoevetsegi Koeztarsasagbol. Polish edition (ISSN 0344-7057) (Text in Hungarian) 1976. 6/yr. DM.24. Friedrich Reinecke Verlag GmbH, Hartwicusstr. 3-4, 22087 Hamburg, Germany. TEL 040-228070. FAX 040-22807260. Ed. Peter Dvorak. circ. 33,000. (also avail. in microfiche) **Document type:** consumer publication.

053.1 GW
QUINTESSENZ (KASSEL); die Schuelerzeitung am Friedrichsgymnasium. 1980. q. DM.6($5) Friedrichsgymnasium Kassel, Humboldtstr. 5, 34117 Kassel, Germany. TEL 0561-772031. Ed. Thomas Habbe. adv.: B&W page DM.200; adv. contact: Mario Westmeier. film rev.; play rev.; abstr.; stat. circ. 1,750. (back issues avail.) **Document type:** newsletter.

READER'S DIGEST - DAS BESTE (GERMAN BRAILLE EDITION). see *HANDICAPPED — Visually Impaired*

053.1 GW
READER'S DIGEST - DAS BESTE (GERMAN EDITION); eine internationale Lesezeitschrift. 1948. m. DM.49.90. Verlag das Beste GmbH, Augustenstr. 1, 70178 Stuttgart, Germany. TEL 0711-6602-0. FAX 0711-6602547. Ed. Renate Wriedt. adv. contact: Max Bieniussa. bk.rev.; illus.; index. circ. 1,628,834. **Document type:** consumer publication. Formerly: Beste aus Reader's Digest (German Edition) (ISSN 0005-9668)

073 GW
RECKLINGHAEUSER ZEITUNG. d. J. Bauer KG, Kampstr. 84b, 49448 Marl, Germany. TEL 022365-107-0. FAX 022365-107274. Ed. Kurt Bauer; Pub. Kurt Bauer. adv. contact: Heiner Roer. circ. 77,932. **Document type:** newspaper.

053.1 GW ISSN 0170-6802
AN REMS UND MURR; halbjahreshefte fuer Heimat und Kultur im Rems-Murr-Kreis. 1974. s-a. DM.17. Einhorn Verlag GmbH, Sebaldstr. 9-11, 73525 Schwaebisch-Gmuend, Germany. Ed. Otto Heuschele. circ. 3,000. (back issues avail.) **Document type:** bulletin.

073 GW
REUTLINGER GENERAL-ANZEIGER. d. Zeitungsverlag GmbH, Burgstr. 1-7, 72764 Reutlingen, Germany. TEL 07121-302-0. FAX 07121-302677. Ed. Erpo von Droste; Pub. Valdo Lehari. adv. contact: Karl-Heinz Zeller. circ. 46,584. **Document type:** newspaper.

073 GW
RHEIN-NECKAR-ZEITUNG. d. Rhein-Neckar-Zeitung GmbH, Hauptstr. 23, 69117 Heidelberg, Germany. TEL 06221-519-1. FAX 06221-519217. Ed.Bd. adv. contact: Walter Silberzahn. circ. 106,275. **Document type:** newspaper.

073 GW
RHEIN-ZEITUNG. d. Mittelrhein-Verlag GmbH, August-Horch-Str. 28, 56070 Koblenz, Germany. TEL 0261-89200. FAX 0261-892476. Ed. Horst Schilling. adv. contact: Karl-Heinz Muckelbauer. circ. 239,180. **Document type:** newspaper.

073 GW
RHEINISCHE POST. d. Rheinisch-Bergische Druckerei und Verlagsgesellschaft mnH, Zuelpicherstr. 10, 40196 Duesseldorf, Germany. TEL 0211-505-0. FAX 0211-5047562. Ed. Joachim Sobotta; Pubs. Gottfried Arnold, Esther Betz. adv. contact: Lutz Schreiner. circ. 396,293. **Document type:** newspaper.

073 GW ISSN 0173-3028
RHEINISCHER MERKUR; Christ und Welt. 1814; N.S. 1946. w. (Fri.). Verlag Rheinischer Merkur GmbH, Godesberger Allee 91, 53175 Bonn, Germany. TEL 0228-884-0. FAX 0228-884199. Ed. Thomas Kielinger. adv. contact: Helmut Dippel. circ. 110,833. (also avail. in microform from NRP)

073 GW
DIE RHEINPFALZ. d. Rheinpfalz Verlag und Druckerei GmbH, Amtstr. 5-11, 67059 Ludwigshafen, Germany. TEL 0621-590201. FAX 0621-5902297. Ed. Michael Grathe. adv. contact: Emil Erbacher. circ. 243,723. **Document type:** newspaper.

073 GW
RUHR-NACHRICHTEN. d. Ruhr-Nachrichten Verlag GmbH, Westenhellweg 86-88, 44137 Dortmund, Germany. TEL 0231-9059-0. FAX 0231-9059407. Ed. Florian Lensing-Wolff; Pub. Florian Lensing-Wolff. adv. contact: Franz Pieper. circ. 219,657. **Document type:** newspaper.

053.1 GW
RUNDBRIEF HEIMATKREIS FRIEDEBERG (NEUMARK). 1975. s-a. Heinrich-Specht-Weg 1, 25421 Pinneberg, Germany. Ed. Erich Schulz.

073 GW
SAALE-ZEITUNG. d. T.A. Schachenmayer GmbH, Theresienstr. 17-21, 97688 Bad Kissingen, Germany. TEL 0971-8040-0. FAX 0971-804041. Ed. Ulrich Lutz; Pubs. Kuno Schachenayer, Bernd Schachenmayer. adv. contact: Erich Krueger. circ. 16,112. **Document type:** newspaper.

073 GW
SAARBRUECKER ZEITUNG. d. Saarbruecker Zeitung Verlag GmbH, Gutenbergstr. 11-23, 66117 Saarbruecken, Germany. TEL 0681-502-0. FAX 0681-5022500. Ed. Rudolph Bernhard. adv. contact: Manfred von Ackern. circ. 183,011. **Document type:** newspaper.

073 GW
SAECHSISCHE ZEITUNG. 1945. d. (except Sun.) DM.15.80 per mo.; newsstand price: DM.0.80. Dresdner Druck- und Verlagshaus GmbH, Ostra-Allee 20, 01067 Dresden, Germany. TEL 0351-4864-0. Owner(s): Gruner und Jahr AG und Co., Am Baumwall 11, 20459 Hamburg, Germany. TEL 040-3703-0. FAX 040-37035607. Ed. Wolfgang Schuetze; Pub. Karl Helesic. adv.: B&W page DM.60045.23, color page DM.96097.96; trim 457 x 329; adv. contact: Karl-Heinz Kesting. Wire service(s): AP,RN. circ. 439,070. cols./p.: 6; pp./issue: 32. **Document type:** newspaper.

053.1 US ISSN 1041-2018
SCHAU INS LAND. (Text in German) 1987. m. $118. Champs-Elysees Inc., Box 158067, Nashville, TN 37215-8067. TEL 800-824-0829. FAX 615-297-3138. (audio cassette; with printed transcription)

053.1 GW
SCHLESISCHER KULTURSPIEGEL. 1966. q. Stiftung Kulturwerk Schlesien, Kardinal-Doepfner-Platz 1, 97070 Wuerzburg, Germany. TEL 0931-53696. Ed. Ulrich Schmilewski. bk.rev.; illus. **Document type:** newsletter.

053.1 GW
DAS SCHOENE ALLGAEU. 1935. m. DM.85.60. Agrarverlag Allgaeu GmbH, Porschestr. 2, 87437 Kempten, Germany. TEL 0831-79008. adv.; bk.rev. circ. 20,000.

053.1 GW ISSN 0941-7052
SCHOENER BAYERISCHER WALD; Zeitschrift fuer Kultur Freizeit Erholung und Unterhaltung. 1978. bi-m. DM.36. B W Z Verlags GmbH, Postfach 1262, 94476 Grafenau, Germany. TEL 08552-4200. FAX 08552-42050. Ed. Erich Stecher. adv.; bk.rev. **Document type:** consumer publication.

053.1 GW ISSN 0937-6356
SCHOENHENGSTER HEIMAT. 1952. m. DM.54. Schoenhengster Heimatbund e.V., Postfach 1180, 73011 Goeppingen, Germany. TEL 07161-69922. circ. 7,000. **Document type:** bulletin.

053.1 GW ISSN 0487-6598
SCHOENHENGSTER JAHRBUCH. 1956. a. DM.11.80. Schoenhengster Heimatbund e.V., Postfach 1180, 73011 Goeppingen, Germany. TEL 07161-69922. circ. 7,000. **Document type:** bulletin.

073 GW
SCHWAEBISCHE ZEITUNG. d. Schwaebischer Verlag KG, Rudolf-Roth-Str. 16-18, 88299 Leutkirch, Germany. TEL 07561-80-0. FAX 07561-80134. Ed. Hanns Funk. adv. contact: Franz Wunden. circ. 198,806. **Document type:** newspaper.

GENERAL INTEREST PERIODICALS — GERMANY

073 GW
SCHWARZWAELDER BOTE. d. Schwarzwaelder Bote GmbH, Kirchtorstr. 14, 78727 Oberndorf, Germany. TEL 07423-78-0. FAX 07423-7873. Ed. Joerg Bischoff. adv. contact: Heinz-Ludwig Giebel. circ. 139,325. **Document type:** newspaper.

073 GW
SCHWERINER VOLKSZEITUNG. d. Landesverlag Mecklenburg GmbH, Von-Stauffenberg-Str. 27, 19061 Schwerin, Germany. TEL 0385-63780. FAX 0385-375140. Ed. Christoph Hamm; Pub. Helmut Markwort. adv. contact: Joerg Stark. circ. 176,824. **Document type:** newspaper.

SECHZIG - NA UND?. see *GERONTOLOGY AND GERIATRICS*

053.1 GW
SENIOREN-ZEITSCHRIFT. 1974. q. Sozialamt, Abteilung Altenhilfe, Eschenheimer Landstr. 42-44, 60322 Frankfurt a.M., Germany. (Co-sponsor: Presse- und Informationsamt der Stadt Frankfurt am Main) Ed. Maria Schuster. (back issues avail.) **Document type:** government publication.

073 GW
SIEGENER ZEITUNG. d. Vorlaender und Rothmaler GmbH, Obergraben 39, 57072 Siegen, Germany. TEL 0271-5941. FAX 0271-594318. Ed. Eberhard Winterhager; Pub. Wolfgang Rothmaler. adv. contact: Christ Plitsch. circ. 63,909. **Document type:** newspaper.

053.1 GW
SILENCE COURIER; Gaestezeitschrift der Silencehotels Deutschland. (Text in English, French, German) 1981. q. DM.15.20. Sisu Steinschulte Verlag, Bismarckstr. 10, 53113 Bonn, Germany. TEL 0228-361063. circ. 50,000.
Description: For guests at Silence Hotels in Germany.

053.1 GW
SKYLINE (FRANKFURT). 1984. m. Skyline Medien Verlag GmbH, Wolfsgangstr. 88, 60322 Frankfurt a.M., Germany. TEL 069-550891. FAX 069-5971434. Eds. Heinz Meffert, Erk Walter. adv. contact: Joachim Heinricht. bk.rev.; film rev.; play rev. circ. 73,308. (back issues avail.) **Document type:** bulletin.
Description: Information about what's going on in Frankfurt.

053.1 GW
SONDERTHEMA. (Editions in English, French, German and Spanish) 9/yr. Inter Nationes e.V., Kennedyallee 91-103, 53175 Bonn, Germany. TEL 0228-880-0. FAX 0228-880457. TELEX 17228308-IND-D. Ed. Helmut Nagelschmitz. **Document type:** consumer publication.
Formerly: Sonderdienst.
Description: Background information on German politics and economics.

073 GW
SONNTAG AKTUELL. w. (Sun.). Stuttgarter Presseunion GmbH, Plieningerstr. 150, 70567 Stuttgart, Germany. TEL 0711-7205-0. FAX 0711-7205930. Ed. Hans-Joachim Schlueter. adv. contact: Guenter Kaluza. circ. 878,575. **Document type:** newspaper.

053.1 GW
SONNTAGSANZEIGER. 1985. m. Power Print Druck und Verlags KG, Holtenklinkerstr. 88-92, Postfach 800806, 21029 Hamburg Bergedorf, Germany. TEL 040-724040-0. Ed. Ulrich Lohmann. adv.; bk.rev.; circ. 3,200 (controlled). (back issues avail.)

DER SONNTAGSBRIEF. see *GERONTOLOGY AND GERIATRICS*

073 GW
SPANDAUER VOLKSBLATT. w. (Fri.). Erich Lezinsky Verlag GmbH, Neuendorferstr. 101, 13585 Berlin, Germany. TEL 030-330006-0. FAX 030-3333666. Ed. Peter Bolm. adv. contact: Gerhard Duennhaupt. circ. 40,000. **Document type:** newspaper.

053.1 GW ISSN 0178-6830
SPEX. m. DM.66 (foreign DM.72). Spex Verlagsgesellschaft mbH, Aachenerstr. 40-44, 50674 Cologne, Germany. TEL 0221-515015. FAX 0221-511139. Ed. Christoph Gurk. adv. contact: Doris Volk. circ. 16,237. **Document type:** consumer publication.

053.1 GW ISSN 0038-7452
AP30
DER SPIEGEL. 1947. w. DM.260. Spiegel-Verlag Rudolf Augstein GmbH und Co. KG, Brandstwiete 19, 20457 Hamburg, Germany. TEL 040-30070. FAX 040-30072247. Ed. R. Augstein. adv.: B&W page DM.48000, color page DM.87320; trim 178 x 252; adv. contact: Horst Goerner. bk.rev.; film rev.; charts; illus.; stat. circ. 1,179,452. (also avail. in microform from RPI,PMC) **Indexed:** Dok.Arbeitsmed., Key to Econ.Sci., Packag.Sci.Tech. **Document type:** consumer publication.
—SWETS.
Description: Deals with politics, business, current affairs and culture.

053.1 GW
STADT BRACKENHEIM. AMTS- UND MITTEILUNGSBLATT. w. Walter Druck und Verlag GmbH, Raiffeisenstr. 55, 74336 Brackenheim, Germany. TEL 07135-104-0. FAX 07135-10439. adv.: B&W page DM.691.20; trim 185 x 270. circ. 4,500. **Document type:** newspaper.

053.1 GW
STADTBLATT; Osnabruecker. 1978. m. DM.33. B V W Verlag GmbH, Grosse Rosenstr. 34, 49074 Osnabrueck, Germany. TEL 0541-26475. FAX 0541-24602. Eds. Dagmar Nottbusch, Martin Willmann. adv. contact: Karin Vinke. bk.rev.; film rev.; play rev. circ. 6,264. (back issues avail.) **Document type:** newsletter.
Description: Local and cultural news and dates in the Osnabruck area.

053.1 GW
STADTZEITUNG BRAUNSCHWEIG. 1978. m. DM.32. Gerstaeckerstr. 25, 38102 Braunschweig, Germany. TEL 0531-340129. FAX 0531-347122. Ed. Hans-Guenther Eggers. adv.; bk.rev.; film rev.; play rev. circ. 3,500. **Document type:** bulletin.

053.1 GW
STAECKBRIEF. 1974. q. DM.2. Steidl Publishers, Dustere Str. 4, 37073 Goettingen, Germany. TEL 0551-496060. FAX 0551-4960649. Ed. Gerhard Steidl. adv.; bk.rev. circ. 50,000. **Document type:** consumer publication.

053.1 028.5 GW ISSN 0177-4913
STATION TO STATION. 1979. m. Station to Station Verlagsgesellschaft mbH, Werftbahnstr. 8, 24143 Kiel, Germany. TEL 0431-7057161. FAX 0431-7057100. adv. contact: Karin Hansen. film rev.play rev. circ. 11,125. (back issues avail.) **Document type:** bulletin.

053.1 GW
STERN MAGAZIN. 1948. w. DM.208 (Europe DM.384.80; elsewhere DM.734.24). Gruner und Jahr AG & Co., Am Baumwall 11, 20459 Hamburg, Germany. TEL 040-3703-0. FAX 040-37035604. Ed. Rolf Schmidt-Holtz. adv. contact: Rolf Grimm. illus. circ. 1,613,846. (also avail. in microform from UMI; reprint service avail. from UMI) **Document type:** consumer publication.
—SWETS.
Formerly: Stern (ISSN 0039-1239)

073 GW
STRAUBINGER TAGBLATT. d. Attenkofer'sche Buch- und Kunstdruckerei, Ludwigplatz 30, 94315 Straubing, Germany. TEL 09421-940-0. FAX 09421-940206. Ed. Ottmar Guggeis; Pub. Hermann Balle. adv. contact: Hubert Lauer. circ. 133,048. **Document type:** newspaper.

073 GW
STUTTGARTER NACHRICHTEN. d. Stuttgarter Nachrichten Verlagsgesellschaft mbH, Plieningerstr. 150, 70567 Stuttgart, Germany. TEL 0711-7205-0. FAX 0711-7205747. Ed. Juergen Offenbach. adv. contact: Manfred Scholl. circ. 220,910. **Document type:** newspaper.

073 GW
STUTTGARTER ZEITUNG. d. Stuttgarter Zeitung Verlagsgesellschaft mbH Eberle AG, Plieningerstr. 150, 70567 Stuttgart, Germany. TEL 0711-7205-0. FAX 0711-7205516. Ed. Thomas Loeffelholz. circ. 220,910. **Document type:** newspaper.

073 GW ISSN 0174-4917
SUEDDEUTSCHE ZEITUNG. d. Sueddeutscher Verlag GmbH, Sendlingerstr. 8, 80331 Munich, Germany. TEL 089-2183-0. FAX 089-2183787. Eds. Dieter Schroeder, Gernot Sittner. adv. contact: Hans-Joachim Grossman. circ. 402,866. **Document type:** newspaper.

073 GW
SUEDKURIER. d. Suedkurier GmbH, Max-Stromeyer-Str. 178, 78467 Konstanz, Germany. TEL 07531-999-0. FAX 07531-26785. Ed. Gerd Appenzeller. circ. 140,457. **Document type:** newspaper.

053.1 GW
SUEDOSTDEUTSCHE. 1949. m. DM.35. Verlag der Suedostdeutsche, Alter Postweg 97A, 86159 Augsburg, Germany. TEL 0821-594719. FAX 0821-582650. Ed. Rudolf Wagner. adv.; bk.rev. circ. 7,000. **Document type:** bulletin.

073 GW
SUEDTHUERINGER ZEITUNG. d. Suedthueringer Verlag GmbH, Postfach 1225, 36453 Barchfeld, Germany. TEL 036961-470-0. FAX 036961-47023. Ed. Berthold Duecker. circ. 20,623. **Document type:** newspaper.

073 GW
SUEDWEST PRESSE; Schwaebische Donauzeitung. 6/wk. Neue Pressegesellschaft, Frauenstr. 77, 89070 Ulm, Germany. TEL 0731-15601. FAX 0731-156308. Ed. Ulrich Wildermuth. adv. contact: Elke Philipsen. bk.rev.; film rev.; music rev.; tele.rev. Wire service(s): AP, RN. circ. 120,000. (tabloid format) **Document type:** newspaper.

053.1 GW
SUPER ILLU. w. (Thu.). DM.83.20. Magazin Verlag Berlin GmbH, Mollstr. 1, 10178 Berlin, Germany. TEL 030-238760. FAX 030-23876496. Ed. Jochen Wolff. adv. contact: Heinz Scheiner. circ. 583,951. **Document type:** consumer publication.

053.1 GW
SZENE HAMBURG. 1973. m. DM.55. Szene Verlag Klaus Heidorn KG, Heilwigstr. 24, 20249 Hamburg, Germany. TEL 040-41904-0. FAX 040-443577. Ed. Klaus Heidorn, Kirstin Ruge; Pub. Klaus Heidorn. adv. contact: Silke Laube. circ. 25,589. **Document type:** consumer publication.

053.1 GW
T I P DER WOCHE. (Trends Infos Praktisches); Neckarsulm - Heilbronn. 1984. w. T I P Werbeverlag GmbH und Co. KG, Karl-Wuest-Str. 15, 74076 Heilbronn, Germany. TEL 07131-1572-0. adv.; film rev. circ. 229,530.

T V ANZEIGER; das regionale Fernsehmagazin. see *COMMUNICATIONS — Television And Cable*

073 GW
T Z. d. Zeitungsverlag T Z Muenchen GmbH, Paul-Heyse-Str. 2-4, 80336 Munich, Germany. TEL 089-53060. FAX 089-5306522. Eds. Hans Riehl, Helmut Stegmann; Pubs. Dirk Ippen, Alfons Doeser. adv. contact: Rainer Liebelt. circ. 160,968. **Document type:** newspaper.

053.1 GW
TAG. 1976. q. DM.3.20. (Bundesknappschaft, Bochum) Wirtschaftsdienst Gesellschaft fuer Medien & Kommunikation mbH & Co. OHG, Lange Str. 13, 60311 Frankfurt a.M., Germany. Ed. Ruediger Wirth. adv. contact: Hubert Lauer. circ. 1,250,000. **Document type:** bulletin.

073 GW
DER TAGESSPIEGEL. d. Tagesspiegel GmbH, Potsdamerstr. 77-87, 10785 Berlin, Germany. TEL 030-26009-0. FAX 030-26009332. Ed. Hermann Rudolph. adv. contact: Jens Robotta. circ. 130,745. **Document type:** newspaper.

053.1 GW ISSN 0931-9085
DIE TAGESZEITUNG. Short title: T A Z. 1978. 6/wk. DM.474. T A Z Verlagsgenossenschaft e.G., Kochstr. 18, 10969 Berlin, Germany. TEL 030-25902-0. FAX 030-2518095. Ed. Arno Widman. adv. contact: Gerd Thomas. bk.rev.; cum.index: 1984-1991. circ. 61,710. (also avail. in microfilm; diskette format; back issues avail.) **Document type:** newspaper.
●Also available online.

053.1 GW
TELEGRAPH. m. DM.3 per no. Umwelt Bibliothek Berlin e.V., Schliemannstr. 22, 10437 Berlin, Germany. TEL 030-4483687. FAX 030-4481035. E-mail: telegrapg@vlberlin.zer. Ed. Wolfgang Rueddenklau. **Document type**: bulletin.

053.1 GW
TEMPO (HAMBURG). 1986. m. DM.60. Jahreszeiten Verlag GmbH, Possmoorweg 5, 22301 Hamburg, Germany. TEL 040-27170. FAX 040-27172056. TELEX 213214-JAG-D. Ed. Walter Mayer. adv. contact: Michael Koerner. bk.rev.; charts; film rev.; illus.; play rev. circ. 120,000. **Document type**: consumer publication.

053.1 NO ISSN 0802-7323
N3128
TERSKEL/THRESHOLD. 1990. s-a. NOK 90 per no. Museet for Samtidskunst, Bankplassen 4, P.O. Box 8191, Dep 0034, Oslo, Norway. TEL 47-22-33-58-20. FAX 47-22-33-57-90. Ed. Jan Brockmann. **Document type**: academic/scholarly publication, catalog.

073 GW
THUERINGER ALLGEMEINE. d. Thueringer Allgemeine Verlag GmbH, Juri-Gagarin-Ring 113-117, 99084 Erfurt, Germany. TEL 0361-530-0. FAX 0361-530499. Ed. Sergej Lochthofen. adv. contact: Robert Lentes. circ. 535,337. **Document type**: newspaper.

073 GW
THUERINGISCHE LANDESZEITUNG. d. Thueringische Landeszeitung Verlag GmbH, Marienstr. 14, 99423 Weimar, Germany. TEL 03643-3201. FAX 03643-64046. Ed. Hans Hoffmeister. adv. contact: Robert Lentes. circ. 521,424. **Document type**: newspaper.

053.1 GW
TOUK TOUK. 1986. irreg. c/o Rainer Kocherscheidt, Schwanenstr. 5, 42551 Velbert, Germany. TEL 02051-54741. bk.rev. circ. 150.

053.1 GW
TRANSATLANTIK; das Kulturmagazin. 1980. m. DM.84. TransAtlantik Verlagsgesellschaft mbH, Brandstwiete 19, 20457 Hamburg, Germany. TEL 040-3007717. FAX 040-3007247. Eds. Marianne Schmidt, Reinhard Hesse. adv.; bk.rev.; illus. circ. 60,000. (back issues avail.)

073 GW
TRAUNSTEINER WOCHENBLATT. d. Zeitungsverlag Anton Miller GmbH, Marienstr. 12, 83278 Traunstein, Germany. TEL 0861-64061. FAX 0861-8305. Ed. Martin Miller; Pub. Anton Miller. adv. contact: Marianne Schoenbrunn. circ. 15,791. **Document type**: newspaper.

053.1 GW
TREND. 1976. m. Hertlein Verlag, Ludwigstr. 8a, 97070 Wuerzburg, Germany. TEL 0931-14091. FAX 0931-14094. Ed. Angela Say; Pub. Lothar Steigerwald. adv. contact: Ruediger Schade. bk.rev. circ. 29,600. (back issues avail.) **Document type**: bulletin.

073 GW
TRIERISCHER VOLKSFREUND. d. Trierischer Volksfreund GmbH, Nikolaus-Koch-Platz 1-3, 54290 Trier, Germany. TEL 0651-7199-0. FAX 0651-7199990. Ed. Norbert Kohler. adv. contact: Winfried Blass. circ. 99,338. **Document type**: newspaper.

073 GW
TROSTBERGER TAGBLATT. d. (except Sun.). Alois Erdl KG, Gabelsbergerstr. 4-6, 83308 Trostberg, Germany. TEL 08621-808-0. FAX 08621-80868. Ed. Thomas Grabmueller; Pubs. Oskar Erdl, Wigbert Schacht. adv. contact: Erwin Huber. circ. 17,880. **Document type**: newspaper.

053.1 GW
ULTIMO (KIEL); Kiel's Stadtmagazin. 1968. m. DM.41. Ultimo-Verlag GmbH, Bluecherplatz 9, 24105 Kiel, Germany. TEL 0431-86757. FAX 0431-82330. Ed. Rainer Langholz. adv. contact: Avni Mahnoli. circ. 12,848. **Document type**: consumer publication.
    Description: Information about cultural events in the city, with emphasis on New Age events.

053.1 GW ISSN 0566-2575
UNSER BOCHOLT; Zeitschrift fuer Kultur und Heimatpflege. (Text in Dutch, German, Plattdeutsch) 1950. 4/yr. DM.20. Stadtarchiv, Verein fuer Heimatpflege Bocholt e.V., Muensterstr. 76, 46397 Bocholt, Germany. TEL 02871-953349. FAX 02871-953222. TELEX 813709. Ed. Hans D. Oppel. adv.; bk.rev.; illus. circ. 1,700. (back issues avail.)

053.1 GW ISSN 0937-1508
UNSERE HEIMAT. 1958. a. DM.8. Kreis Borken, Burloerstr. 93, 46325 Borken, Germany. TEL 02861-821348. FAX 02861-63320. circ. 8,000. (back issues avail.)

053.1 GW
UNSERE ILLUSTRIERTE. 1991. w. DM.28. Heinrich Bauer Verlag, Burchardstr. 11, 20095 Hamburg, Germany. TEL 040-3019-0. FAX 040-326589. Ed. Juergen Koepcke. circ. 350,000.

053.1 GW
UNTER DER DORFLINDE IM ODENWALD. 1913. bi-m. DM.12. Odenwaldklub e.V., Postfach 1270, 64734 Hoechst, Germany. TEL 06163-4785. bk.rev. circ. 15,000. (back issues avail.)

073 GW
VOLKSSTIMME. d. (except Sun.). Magdeburger Verlags- und Druckhaus GmbH, Bahnhofstr. 17, 39104 Magdeburg, Germany. TEL 0391-388-0. FAX 0391-32694. Owner(s): Heinrich Bauer Verlag, Burchardstr. 11, 20095 Hamburg, Germany. TEL 040-3019-0. FAX 040-326589. Ed. Heinzgeorg Oette. adv. contact: Ulrich Levenig. circ. 331,137. **Document type**: newspaper.

073 GW
VOLKSSTIMME AM SONNTAG. w. (Sun.). Magdeburger Verlags- und Druckhaus GmbH, Bahnhofstr. 17, 39104 Magdeburg, Germany. TEL 0391-388-0. FAX 0391-32694. Owner(s): Heinrich Bauer Verlag, Burchardstr. 11, 20095 Hamburg, Germany. TEL 040-3019-0. FAX 040-324879. Ed. Reinhold Stimpert. adv. contact: Ulrich Levenig. circ. 327,832. **Document type**: newspaper.

053.1 GW
VORSICHT; das Rhein-Nahe Journal. m. Verlag Matthias Ess, Bleichstr. 25, 55543 Bad Kreuznach, Germany. TEL 0671-300267. FAX 0671-30028. Ed.Bd. adv. contact: Andreas Rabsch. circ. 11,152. **Document type**: consumer publication.

053.1 GW ISSN 0017-4874
DIE WAAGE; Zeitschrift der Gruenenthal. 1959. bi-m. DM.7. Gruenenthal GmbH, Steinfeldstr. 2, 52222 Stolberg, Germany. Ed. I. Sievers. adv.; bk.rev.; illus.; index; circ. 35,000 (controlled).
    Formerly: Gruenenthal Waage.

053.1 GW ISSN 0931-2889
WAELLER HEIMAT; Jahrbuch des Westerwaldkreises. 1987. a. DM.11.50. Kreisverwaltung des Westerwaldkreises, Postfach 1162, 56409 Montabaur, Germany. TEL 02602-124400. FAX 02602-124394. TELEX 869-619-KVMO-D. (Subscr. to: Verlag Linus Wittich KG, Rheinstr. 41, 56203 Hoehr, Germany) Ed. Karl Kahn. adv.; bk.rev. circ. 7,000. **Document type**: bulletin.

073 GW
WALDECKISCHE LANDESZEITUNG. d. Wilhelm Bing Verlag, Lengefelderstr. 6, 34497 Korbach, Germany. TEL 05631-33376. FAX 05631-560069. Ed. Wilhelm Bing; Pub. Hermann Bing. circ. 27,888. **Document type**: newspaper.

073 GW
WANDSBEKER WOCHENBLATT. 1976. w. Hamburger Wochenblatt Verlag, Curslacker Neuer Deich 44, 21029 Hamburg, Germany. TEL 040-7256040. FAX 040-7247786. Ed. Manfred R. Heinz. adv.: B&W page DM.9828, color page DM.11028; trim 280 x 420. circ. 126,479. (tabloid format; back issues avail.) **Document type**: newspaper.

053.1 780.904 831 GW
DIE WEBEREIZEITUNG. 1984. m. DM.15($10) Verein Alte Weberei e.V., Bogenstrasse 1-8, PF 1103, 33330 Guetersloh, Germany. TEL 05241-26033. Ed. Patrick Poch. adv.; bk.rev.; film rev. (back issues avail.)
    Description: General entertainment news, especially for the Alte Weberei section of Guetersloh.

053.1 US
THE WEEK IN GERMANY. 1972. w. free. German Information Center, 950 Third Ave., New York, NY 10022. TEL 212-888-9840. FAX 212-752-6691. Ed. Susan Steiner. circ. 38,000. **Document type**: government publication, newsletter.
●Also available online. Vendor(s): Mead Data Central, Inc., NewsNet (IT65).

073 GW ISSN 0173-8437
DIE WELT. 1946. d. (except Sun.). Axel Springer Verlag AG, Axel-Springer-Platz 1, 20355 Hamburg, Germany. TEL 040-3470-0. FAX 040-340581. Eds. Peter Gillies, Gerhard Mumme; Pub. Claus Jacobi. adv. contact: Hans Biehl. circ. 223,710. **Document type**: newspaper.

073 GW
WELT AM SONNTAG. w. (Sun.). Axel Springer Verlag AG, Axel-Springer-Platz 1, 20355 Hamburg, Germany. TEL 040-3470-0. FAX 040-345811. Eds. Manfred Geist, Guenter Boeddeker; Pub. Ernst Cramer. adv. contact: Hans Biehl. circ. 423,355. **Document type**: newspaper.

053.1 GW ISSN 0049-7126
WELTBILD. 1948. fortn. Weltbild Verlag GmbH, Frauentorstr. 5, 86152 Augsburg, Germany. TEL 0821-3257-0. FAX 0821-3257201. Ed. Albert Herchenbach. adv. contact: Kurt Telschig. bk.rev.; charts; illus. circ. 252,592. **Document type**: consumer publication.

073 GW
WESER-KURIER. d. (except Sun.). Bremer Tageszeitungen AG, Martinistr. 43-45, 28195 Bremen, Germany. TEL 0421-3671-0. FAX 0421-328327. Eds. Volker Weise, Juergen Bettmann. adv. contact: Egon Hoppe. circ. 211,219. **Document type**: newspaper.

073 GW
WESTDEUTSCHE ALLGEMEINE. d. Westdeutsche Allgemeine Verlagsgesellschaft mbH, Friedrichstr. 34-38, 45128 Essen, Germany. TEL 0201-804-0. FAX 0201-22642285. Ed. Ralf Lehrmann; Pub. Erich Brost. adv. contact: Manfred Kraemer. circ. 1,177,502. **Document type**: newspaper.

073 GW
WESTDEUTSCHE ZEITUNG. d. Verlag W. Giradet, Koenigsallee 27, 40212 Duesseldorf, Germany. TEL 0211-8382-0. FAX 0211-8382392. Ed. Paulheinz Grupe; Pub. Michael Giradet. adv. contact: Dankward Sobottke. circ. 184,487. **Document type**: newspaper.

053.1 GW ISSN 0179-6100
WESTEN. 1950. bi-m. DM.30. Erwin von Steinbach Gesellschaft e.V., Wiesenstr. 110, 70794 Filderstadt, Germany. TEL 0711-701645. Eds. Eduard Haug, Dietrich Pfaehler. bk.rev. circ. 850.

073 GW
WESTFAELISCHE NACHRICHTEN. d. Aschendorffsche Verlagsbuchhandlung, Soesterstr. 13, 48155 Muenster, Germany. TEL 0251-690-0. FAX 0251-690143. Ed. Jost Springensguth. adv. contact: Josef Hoppe. circ. 228,058. **Document type**: newspaper.

073 GW
WESTFAELISCHE RUNDSCHAU. d. Zeitungsverlag Westfalen GmbH, Bruedeweg 9, 44135 Dortmund, Germany. TEL 0231-9573-0. FAX 0231-9573202. Ed. Frank Buente. adv. contact: Manfred Kraemer. circ. 1,172,502. **Document type**: newspaper.

073 GW ISSN 0177-5804
WESTFAELISCHER ANZEIGER. d. Emil Griebsch Graphische Betriebe GmbH, Gutenbergstr. 1, 59065 Hamm, Germany. TEL 02381-105-0. FAX 02381-105239. Eds. Josef Surholt, Heinz-Juergen Ziller; Pub. Dirk Ippen. adv. contact: Burckhardt Schmidt. circ. 49,870. **Document type**: newspaper.

073 GW
WESTFALEN-BLATT. d. Westfalen-Blatt Vereinigte Zeitungsverlage GmbH, Sudbrackstr. 14-18, 33611 Bielefeld, Germany. TEL 0521-585-0. Eds. Carl Busse, Rolf Dressler; Pub. Carl Busse. adv. contact: Gabriele Foerster. circ. 142,987. **Document type**: newspaper.

GENERAL INTEREST PERIODICALS — GHANA

073 GW
WESTFALENPOST. d. Westfalenpost GmbH, Schuermannstr. 4, 58097 Hagen, Germany. TEL 02331-917-0. FAX 02331-9174263. Ed. Dieter Soika; Pub. Dorita Straeter. adv. contact: Manfred Kraemer. circ. 1,205,593. **Document type:** newspaper.

053.1 GW ISSN 0043-4418
DER WESTPREUSSE. 1949. s-m. DM.90 (foreign DM.96). Landsmannschaft Westpreussen e.V., Norbertstr. 29, 48151 Muenster, Germany. TEL 0251-523424. FAX 0251-533830. adv.; bk.rev.; film rev.; play rev.; abstr.; bibl.; illus.; stat.; index, cum.index. circ. 15,000.
   Description: News about local history, politics, and reports about the Landsmannschaft and its members.

053.1 GW
WESTRICHER HEIMATBLAETTER; heimatkundliche Mitteilungen aus dem Landkreis Kusel. 1937. q. DM.17. Kreisverwaltung Kusel, Triererstr. 49, 66869 Kusel, Germany. TEL 06381-44176. FAX 06381-44117. TELEX 0451431.

073 GW
WETZLARER NEUE ZEITUNG. d. Wetzlardruck GmbH, Elsa-Brandstroem-Str. 18, 35578 Wetzlar, Germany. TEL 06441-701-0. FAX 06441-71684. Ed. Wulf Eigendorf. adv. contact: Peter Rother. circ. 75,519. **Document type:** newspaper.

053.1 GW
WIENER. 1988. m. $60. Heinrich Bauer Verlag (Munich), Charles-de-Gaulle-Str. 8, 81737 Munich, Germany. TEL 089-6786455. FAX 089-6378657. (Dist. in U.S. by: GLP International, Inc., 153 S. Dean St., Englewood, NJ 07631-3513. TEL 201-871-1010. FAX 201-871-0870) Ed. K. Weichler. circ. 106,795. **Document type:** consumer publication.

073 GW
WIESBADENER KURIER. d. Wiesbadener Kurier GmbH, Grosse Bleiche 44-50, 55116 Mainz, Germany. TEL 06131-144-1. FAX 06131-144577. Ed. Hilmar Boersing. adv. contact: Ruediger Vogt. circ. 86,455. **Document type:** newspaper.

943 GW ISSN 0049-7622
WIESBADENER LEBEN. 1951. m. DM.40. Verlag Chmielorz GmbH und Co., Wilhelmstr. 42, 65185 Wiesbaden, Germany. Ed. Kurt Thomas. adv.; bk.rev.; film rev.; play rev.; abstr.; illus. circ. 6,000.
   Description: Covers local cultural interests.

073 GW
WINTERHUDER WOCHENBLATT. 1976. w. Hamburger Wochenblatt Verlag, Curslacker Neuer Deich 44, 21029 Hamburg, Germany. TEL 040-72506040. FAX 040-7247786. Ed. Manfred R. Heinz. circ. 118,187. (tabloid format; back issues avail.) **Document type:** newspaper.

073 GW
DIE WOCHE. w. (Thu.). Woche Zeitungsverlag GmbH, Harvestehuder Weg 41, 20149 Hamburg, Germany. TEL 040-2717-0. FAX 040-27172081. Ed. Manfred Bissinger. adv. contact: Michael Wittke. circ. 300,000. **Document type:** newspaper.

053.1 GW
WOCHENBLATT FUER KAISERSLAUTERN. w. Suwe, Postfach 1316, 6800 Mannheim 1, Germany.

053.1 GW
WOCHENBLATT FUER LANDAU. w. Suwe, Postfach 1316, 6800 Mannheim 1, Germany.

053.1 GW
WOCHENBLATT FUER LUDWIGSHAFEN. w. Suwe, Postfach 1316, 6800 Mannheim 1, Germany.

053.1 GW
WOCHENBLATT FUER MANNHEIM. w. Suwe, Postfach 1316, 6800 Mannheim 1, Germany.

053.1 GW
WOCHENBLATT FUER NEUSTADT. w. Suwe, Postfach 1316, 6800 Mannheim 1, Germany.

053.1 GW
WOCHENBLATT FUER SPEYER. w. Suwe, Postfach 1316, 6800 Mannheim 1, Germany.

050 GW
WOCHENEND. 1948. w. (Thu.). DM.114.40 (foreign DM.246). Heinrich Bauer Verlag, Burchardstr. 11, 20095 Hamburg, Germany. TEL 040-3019-0. FAX 040-330985. Ed. Marion Horn. adv. contact: Guenther Granzow. illus. circ. 360,522. **Document type:** consumer publication.

073 GW ISSN 0509-0652
WOCHENPOST; Zeitung fuer Politik, Kultur, Wirtschaft, Unterhaltung. 1953. w. DM.114.40; newsstand price: DM.2.50. Berliner Verlag GmbH, Mauerstr. 86-88, 10117 Berlin, Germany. TEL 030-23101-0. FAX 030-23101159. Ed. Mathias Greffrath. adv. contact: Heinz Kirchner. bk.rev.; film rev.; music rev.; tele.rev. circ. 114,697. cols./p.: 5; pp./issue: 52. (back issues avail.) **Indexed:** World Agri.Econ.& Rural Sociol.Abstr. **Document type:** newspaper.

053.1 GW
WUPPERBRUECKE. 1980. s-a. Stadt Wuppertal, Presse- und Informationsamt, Wegnerstr. 7, Postfach 201414, 5600 Wuppertal 2, Germany. TEL 0202-5636528. FAX 0202-5635353. TELEX 8591871-SKW-D. Ed. Kurt Schnoering. circ. 1,500.

053.1 GW ISSN 0044-2070
AP30
DIE ZEIT; Wochenzeitung fuer Politik, Wirtschaft, Handel und Kultur. 1946. w. Zeitverlag Gerd Bucerius GmbH, Speersort 1, 20095 Hamburg, Germany. TEL 040-32800. FAX 040-327111. (U.S. subscr. to: German Language Publications, Inc., 560 Sylvan Ave., Englewood Cliffs, NJ 07632. TEL 212-736-7455) Ed. Robert Leicht. adv. contact: Wolfgang Stamer. bk.rev.; illus. circ. 493,463. (also avail. in microfilm from NRP) **Indexed:** Key to Econ.Sci. **Document type:** newspaper.
—SWETS.

053.1 GW
DAS ZEITBILD; Themen aus Politik, Wirtschaft, Umwelt und Technik. 1959. m. Zeitbild Verlag GmbH, Mainzerstr. 255, 53179 Bonn, Germany. TEL 0228-857011. FAX 0228-856823. circ. 960,000. (back issues avail.)

053.1 GW
ZWISCHEN VOGELSBERG UND SPESSART. 1949. a. DM.4. Main-Kinzig-Kreises, Barbarossastr. 20-24, 63571 Gelnhausen, Germany. TEL 06051-85278. FAX 06051-85399. Ed. Magda Reiter. adv.; index. circ. 10,000. (back issues avail.) **Document type:** bulletin.

053.1 GW ISSN 0037-461X
7 TAGE. a. DM.104. Klambt-Verlag GmbH, Im Neudeck 1, 67346 Speyer, Germany. Ed. Herbert Hofner, Angelika Haug. circ. 299,466.

053.1 GW
21 ZWANZIG. m. free. 21 Zwanzig Verlag, Am Berge 38, 21335 Lueneburg, Germany. TEL 04131-391162. FAX 04131-391163. Ed. Oliver Schneider; Pub. Roman Reimer. adv. contact: Sandra Holstein. circ. 14,731. **Document type:** consumer publication.

GENERAL INTEREST PERIODICALS — Ghana

059.96 GH
AKWANSOSEM. m. Information Services Department, P.O. Box 745, Accra, Ghana. Ed. Foster Appiah.

052 GH
CHIT CHAT. m. P.O. Box 7043, Accra, Ghana. Ed. Rosemond Adu.

052 GH
DRUM. m. P.O. Box 1197, Accra, Ghana.

052 320 GH
GHANA DIGEST. (Text in English) 1973. m. Information Services Department, P.O. Box 745, Accra, Ghana. Ed. S. Ikoi-Kwaku. illus. circ. 12,000.
   Description: Contains United Nations, OAU and other agency reports.

052 GH
GHANA NEWS BULLETIN. (Text in English) 1974. m. Information Services Department, P.O. Box 745, Accra, Ghana. TEL 228011. Ed. E.A. Afro. circ. 8,000. **Document type:** bulletin.

052 GH ISSN 0016-9587
GHANA REVIEW. m. NC.0.30. Information Services Department, P.O. Box 745, Accra, Ghana. TEL 228011. Ed. J. Oppong-Agyare. adv.; illus. circ. 18,000.
   Former titles: Ghana Builds; Ghana Reconstructs.
   Description: Examines economic, political, and social reports.

052 GH
INSIGHT PUBLICATION; quarterly for current African thinking. 1966. q. $7. Nananom Publishers, Box 5446, Accra, Ghana. Ed. W.B. Ohene. bk.rev.; film rev.; play rev. circ. 20,000.
   Formerly: Insight and Opinion (ISSN 0020-1960)

059.96 GH
KABAARE. 1967. m. Information Services Department, P.O. Box 745, Accra, Ghana. TEL 228011. circ. 2,000.

059.96 GH
KASEM LIBIE. m. Information Services Department, P.O. Box 745, Accra, Ghana. TEL 228011. Ed. A.C. Aziiba.

052 GH
KPODOGA. (Editions in English, Ewe) 1976. m. (Ewe); 3/yr. (English). Institute of Adult Education, University of Ghana, P.O. Box 31, Legon, Ghana. Ed. Yao Aduamah. circ. 2,000. **Document type:** newspaper.
   Description: Rural community paper promoting literacy and rural development.

059.96 GH
LAHABILI TSUGU. m. Information Services Department, P.O. Box 745, Accra, Ghana. TEL 2288011. Ed. T.T Sulemana.

059.96 GH
MANSRALO. m. Information Services Department, P.O. Box 745, Accra, Ghana. TEL 228011. Ed. Martin Nii-Moi.

052 GH
MIRROR. 1952. w. $35 (effective Feb. 1992). Graphic Rd., P.O. Box 742, Accra, Ghana. FAX 669886. adv.; bk.rev. circ. 126,000. **Indexed:** HR Rep.

059.96 GH
MOTABIALA. m. Information Services Department, P.O. Box 745, Accra, Ghana. TEL 228011. Ed. K. Gropone. circ. 10,000.

052 GH
NEW GHANA. 1957. m. 30p. per no. Information Services Department, P.O. Box 745, Accra, Ghana. illus. circ. 10,000.
   Formerly: Ghana Today (ISSN 0016-9609)
   Description: Examines cultural, political, and economic affairs.

059.96 GH
NKWANTABISA. m. Information Services Department, P.O. Box 745, Accra, Ghana. TEL 228011. Eds. F. Appiah, E. Eduful.

052 GH
THE POST. 1980. m. Information Services Department, P.O. Box 745, Accra, Ghana. TEL 228011.
   Description: Current affairs and analysis.

052 GH
THE SCOPE. m. P.O. Box 8162, Tema, Ghana. Eds. E. Emmanuel, D. Ziorklui. circ. 10,000.

GENERAL INTEREST PERIODICALS — Gibraltar

079.468 GI
GIBRALTAR CHRONICLE. 1801. d. £160; newsstand price: £0.40. Gibraltar Chronicle Ltd., 2 Library Gardens, Gibraltar. TEL 78589. FAX 79927. Ed. F. Cantos. adv.: B&W page £460; color page £800. bk.rev.; film rev.; illus.; music rev.; play rev.; tele.rev.; illus.; circ. 6,000 (paid). cols./p.: 5; pp./issue: 24. (tabloid format) **Document type:** newspaper.

079.468 GI
PANORAMA; the Gibraltar newsweekly. 1975. w. £33 (overseas £45); newsstand price: £0.40. Mediterranean Sun Publishing Co. Ltd., 93-97 Irish Town, Gibraltar. TEL 79797. FAX 74664. Ed. Joe Garcia. adv.: B&W page £300; adv. contact: Douglas Cumming. tele.rev.; illus. cols./p.: 4. **Document type:** newspaper.
   Description: Reports on local news and covers current affairs.

GENERAL INTEREST PERIODICALS — Great Britain

052 UK ISSN 0965-8289
ACTIVE LIFE. 1989. bi-m. £7.99. (Christ Church) Aspen Specialist Media, Cosway St., London NW1 5NJ, England. TEL 071-262-2622. FAX 071-706-4811. Ed. Helene Hodge. adv.; bk.rev.; film rev.; play rev.; illus. circ. 300,000. (back issues avail.) **Document type:** consumer publication.
   Description: Publishes general-interest for articles for senior citizens.

072 UK
AMERICAN; the only newspaper for all Americans in Britain. 1976. fortn. $40. British American Newspapers Ltd., 114-115 West St., Farnham, Surrey GU9 7HL, England. FAX 0252-716792. Ed. Bob Pickens. adv.; bk.rev.; illus. circ. 15,000. (tabloid format) **Document type:** newspaper.

051 US
ANGLOFILE. 1988. m. $12. Goody Press, Box 33515, Decatur, GA 30033. TEL 404-633-5587. FAX 404-377-8829. Ed. W.P. King. bk.rev.; film rev.; music rev.; video rev. circ. 3,000.
   Description: News coverage of British entertainment and pop culture.

072.916 UK
ANTRIM GUARDIAN. 1970. w. (Wed.). newsstand price: £0.45. Antrim Guardian, 83-85 Wellington St., Ballymena BT43 6AD, N. Ireland. TEL 0266-41221. FAX 0266-653920. Owner(s): Northern Newspaper Group, Railway Rd., Coleraine, Co. Londonderry, N. Ireland. TEL 0265-43344. Ed. Maurice O'Neill. adv. contact: Lesley Lynn. bk.rev.; film rev.; circ. 24,000 (paid). pp./issue: 44. (broadsheet format) **Document type:** newspaper.

052 UK
ASHFORD EXTRA. 1967. w. £16.64 per no. Kent Messenger Group, 13 Queen St., Deal, Kent CT14 6EX, England. TEL 0304-365526. FAX 0304-374770. Ed. Brian Lewis. adv.; bk.rev. circ. 32,834.
   Incorporating (after 1983): Ashford Advertiser (ISSN 0004-4334)

072.916 UK
BALLYMENA GUARDIAN. 1970. w. newsstand price: £0.45. 83-85 Wellington St., Ballymena, Co. Antrim BT43 6AD, N. Ireland. TEL 0266-41221. FAX 0266-653920. Owner(s): Northern Newspaper Group, Railway Rd., Coleraine, Co. Londonderry, Northern Ireland. TEL 0265-43344. Ed. Maurice O'Neill. adv. contact: Lesley Lynn. bk.rev.; film rev.; tele.rev.; illus.; circ. 24,000 (paid). (broadsheet format) **Document type:** newspaper.

072.916 UK
BANBRIDGE CHRONICLE. 1870. w. newsstand price: £0.45. Banbridge Chronicle Press Ltd., 14 Bridge St., N. Banbridge BT32 3JS, N. Ireland. Ed. R. Hooks. adv. contact: Edward Stodgett. illus.; circ. 7,800 (paid). cols./p.: 7; pp./issue: 40. **Document type:** newspaper.

072.916 UK ISSN 0951-0370
BELFAST GAZETTE. 1922. w. £65 (includes supplements) (effective 1994). H.M.S.O., 16 Arthur St., Belfast BT1 4GD, Northern Ireland. TEL 0232-238451. FAX 0232-230782. Ed. Roy Dubois. adv. contact: 240. **Document type:** newspaper, government publication.
   —BLDSC (1887.884000).

072.8 UK
BERWICK ADVERTISER. 1808. w. (Thu.). £37.70 (Europe £44.72; elsewhere £65.78). Tweeddale Press Group, 90 Marygate, Berwick-upon-Tweed, Northumberland TD15 1BW, England. TEL 0289-306677. FAX 0289-307377. Ed. A.R. Langmark. adv. contact: G. Bell. bk.rev.; film rev.; music rev. cols./p.: 9; pp./issue: 24. (broadsheet format) **Document type:** newspaper.

072.2 UK
BEXHILL-ON-SEA OBSERVER. 1896. w. newsstand price: £0.25. Bexhill Observer, 18 Sackville Rd., Bexhill, E. Sussex BN25 4PZ, England. TEL 0424-730555. FAX 0424-730832. Owner(s): 1066 Newspapers, Telford Rd., St. Leonards, E. Sussex TN38 9LZ, England. TEL 0424-854242. FAX 0424-852850. Ed. Andrea Hargreaves. adv. contact: Steve Etheridge. bk.rev.; illus. cols./p.: 8; pp./issue: 40. (tabloid format) **Document type:** newspaper.

072.7 UK
BIDDULPH CHRONICLE. 1983. w. £34; newsstand price: £0.26. Heads (Congleton) Ltd., 11 High St., Congleton, Ches. CW12 1BW, England. TEL 0260-273737. FAX 0260-280687. Ed. A.J. Condliffe. adv. contact: P. Austen. bk.rev.; film rev.; music rev.; play rev.; illus. (tabloid format; back issues avail.) **Document type:** newspaper.

072.7 UK
BOLTON JOURNAL. 1985. w. Reed Northern Newspapers, Newspaper House, Churchgate, Bolton BL1 1DE, England. TEL 0204-22345. FAX 0204-363222. **Document type:** newspaper.

BRAILLE NEWS SUMMARY. see *HANDICAPPED — Visually Impaired*

072.6 UK
BRENTWOOD GAZETTE; A12 Group. w. £46 (effective 1992). Essex Chronicle Series Ltd., Westway, Chelmsford, Essex CM1 3BE, England. TEL 0245-262421. Ed. Peter Smith. adv.; illus. circ. 15,186. (tabloid format; back issues avail.) **Document type:** newspaper.

072.929 UK
BRIDGEND AND DISTRICT RECORDER. (Text in English) 1984. w. free. Recorder (Wales) Ltd., Cambria House, Wyndham St., Bridgend CF31 1EY, Wales. TEL 0656-669330. FAX 0656-656894. Ed. R.A. David. adv. contact: Jan Styles. bk.rev.; tr.lit. circ. 47,000. cols./p.: 9; pp./issue: 28. (tabloid format) **Document type:** newspaper.

072.2 UK
BRIGHTON AND HOVE LEADER. 1987. w. free. Southern Publishing Co., 89 North Rd., Brighton BN1 4AU, England. TEL 0273-606799. FAX 0273-607215. Ed. Mike Ward. adv. circ. 123,659. (tabloid format) **Document type:** newspaper.

072.5 UK ISSN 0144-784X
BUCKS ADVERTISER. w. (Fri.). £32. Central Counties Newspapers Ltd., 2-4 Exchange St., Aylesbury, Bucks HP20 1UJ, England. TEL 0296-24444. FAX 0296-393451. Owner(s): E M A P Newspapers Ltd. Ed. C. East. adv.: B&W page £912.60. illus. circ. 54,814. cols./p.: 9; pp./issue: 82. **Document type:** newspaper.
   Incorporating: Thames Gazette; Aylesbury News.

072.5 UK
BUCKS FREE PRESS. w. (Fri.). Bucks Free Press Group, Gomm Rd., High Wycombe, Bucks HP13 7DW, England. TEL 0494-521212. FAX 0494-441977. Owner(s): Westminster Press Ltd., Newspaper House, 8-16, Great New St., London EC4P 4ER, England. TEL 071-353-1030. FAX 071-353-7526. adv.; circ. 33,000 (paid). **Document type:** newspaper.

072.5 UK
BUCKS FREE PRESS MIDWEEK. w. (Tue.). Bucks Free Press Group, Gomm Rd., High Wycombe, Bucks HP13 7DW, England. TEL 0494-521212. FAX 0494-441977. Owner(s): Westminster Press Ltd., Newspaper House, 8-16, Great New St., London EC4P 4ER, England. TEL 071-353-1030. FAX 071-353-7526. adv. contact: Becky Jones. circ. 9,037 (paid). **Document type:** newspaper.

072.7 UK
BURY JOURNAL. 1987. w. newsstand price: free. Reed Northern Newspapers (Bury) (Subsidiary of: Reed Regional Newspapers Ltd.), 10 Boulton St., Bury, Nr. Manchester BL9 0LQ, England. TEL 061-763-1583. FAX 061-761-5330. Ed. Brian Caven. adv. contact: Marilyn Hart. music rev. cols./p.: 8; pp./issue: 40. (tabloid format; also avail. in microfiche; back issues avail.) **Document type:** newspaper.

052 UK
CAMBRIDGE TOWN, GOWN & COUNTY SERIES. 1976. irreg., latest vol.29. price varies. Oleander Press, 17 Stansgate Ave., Cambridge CB2 2QZ, England. (U.S. address: 80 Eighth Ave., Ste. 303, New York, N.Y. 10011) Eds. Audrey Ward, Philip Ward. circ. 2,500. **Document type:** monographic series.

052 UK
CAMBRIDGESHIRE LIFE MAGAZINE. 1966. m. £12. County Life Ltd., P.O. Box 81, Lincoln, Lincolnshire LN5 7DY, England. TEL 0522-77567. FAX 0522-77463. Ed. Hilary Hammond. adv.; illus.
   Formerly: Cambridgeshire, Huntingdon and Peterborough Life (ISSN 0008-2023)
   Description: Describes the best of the county in words and pictures.

052 UK
CAMBRIDGESHIRE PRIDE. 1982. m. £8. Pride Publications Ltd., 14 Middletons Rd., Yaxley, Peterborough PE7 3LR, England. TEL 0733-242312. FAX 0733-244035. Ed. Ralph Braybrook. adv.; bk.rev.; film rev.; play rev. circ. 17,500. (back issues avail.)

072.5 UK
CASTLE DONINGTON, KEGWORTH AND MELBOURNE NUNEWS. 1967. w. newsstand price: £0.10. NuNews Ltd., St. Annes Ln., Castle Donington, Derbys. DE74 2JH, England. TEL 0332-810329. FAX 0332-810329. Owner(s): Echo Press (1983) Ltd., Jubilee Dr., Loughborough, Leics. LE11 OXS, England. TEL 0509-232632. FAX 0509-610090. Ed. P.J. Riprin. adv. contact: J. Black. illus. cols./p.: 7; pp./issue: 20. (tabloid format) **Document type:** newspaper.

052 UK
CHALLENGE (WORTHING). 1958. m. £4.92. Challenge Publishing, Revenue Bldgs., Chapel Rd., Worthing, W. Sussex BN11 1BQ, England. TEL 44-903-214198. FAX 44-903-217663. Ed. Donald Banks. circ. 80,000.

052 UK ISSN 0009-3289
CHESHIRE LIFE. 1934. m. £22.80 (foreign £32.80). Town and County Magazines (Subsidiary of: Oyston Publications PLC), Oyston Mill, Strand Rd., Preston PR1 8UR, England. TEL 0772-722022. FAX 0772-736496. Ed. Peter Williams. adv.: B&W page £925, color page £1325; trim 200 x 295; adv. contact: Liz Wareing. bk.rev.; illus. circ. 11,000. **Document type:** consumer publication.
   Formerly: Cheshire Life and Border Counties Magazine.

072.5 UK
CHRONICLE & ECHO. 1931. w. (except Sun.). newsstand price: £0.25. Northampton Mercury Co., Upper Mounts, Northampton NN1 3HR, England. TEL 0604-231122. FAX 0604-233000. Owner(s): E M A P Newspaper Division, 1 Lincoln Court, Peterborough, Cambs. PE1 2RF, England. Ed. Robin Fletcher. adv. contact: Joanne Shaw. bk.rev.; film rev.; music rev.; play rev.; tele.rev.; illus. Wire service(s): RN, UK News. circ. 30,324 (paid). cols./p.: 8; pp./issue: 44. (tabloid format; back issues avail.) **Document type:** newspaper.

052 UK ISSN 0261-3964
CITY NEWS (NEWCASTLE UPON TYNE). 1981. 8/yr. Newcastle City Council, Media Relations Unit, Civic Centre, Newcastle upon Tyne NE99 1BN, England. FAX 091-261-6191. Ed. Lynda Fothergill. adv.; illus. circ. 137,000. **Document type:** bulletin.
   Description: Promoting the work of Newcastle City Council.

GENERAL INTEREST PERIODICALS — GREAT BRITAIN

072.1 — UK
CITY OF LONDON AND DOCKLAND TIMES. s-m. £12.60. 44-46 Fleet St., London EC4Y 1BN, England. TEL 071-353-2562. FAX 071-353-2060. Ed. Dennis Delderfield. adv.; circ. 10,000 (paid). **Document type:** newspaper.
 Description: Contains information on events for those who live and work in the City of London and the Docklands area.

052 — UK
CITY OF LONDON RECORDER.* 1976. w. £27.05. City of London Recorder, Capital Newspapers, 250/256 Kingsland Rd., London E8 4DJ, England. Ed. Dennis Delderfield. adv.; bk.rev. circ. 10,000.
 Formerly: City Recorder.

072.3 — UK
CLEVEDON PORTISHEAD NEALSEA ADMAG. 1979. w. newsstand price: £0.65. Admag Newspapers (Subsidiary of: Community Media Ltd.), 11 Beacons Field Rd., Weston-super-Mare, Avon BS23 1YE, England. TEL 0934-417921. FAX 0934-635031. adv.; tr.lit.; circ. 73,215 (controlled). cols./p.: 8; pp./issue: 28. **Document type:** newspaper.
 Description: Contains local advertisements.

072.3 — UK
CLIFTON DIGEST GRAPEVINE. 13/yr. Community Media Ltd., Journal House, Hartcliffe Way, Bristol BS3 5RJ, England. TEL 0272-68000. FAX 0272-639944. Ed. Carolyn Burdet. adv.: page £495; adv. contact: Kimara Balloch. bk.rev.; film rev.; play rev.; circ. 10,000 (paid). **Document type:** newspaper.
 Formerly (until Feb. 1992): Clifton Digest.
 Description: Contains business and life-style articles of interest to persons living and doing business in the Clifton area.

072.914 — UK
CLYDEBANK POST. 1983. w. £27. Craig M. Jeffrey Ltd., Clyde Weekly Press (Subsidiary of: Clyde and Forth Press Ltd.), 15 Colquhoun Sq., Helensburgh, Dunbartonshire G84 8SE, Scotland. TEL 0436-73434. FAX 0436-71241. Ed. A. McGinley. circ. 8,354. (tabloid format) **Document type:** newspaper.

072.6 — UK
COASTAL EXPRESS. w. Essex County Newspapers, Oriel House, North Hill, Colchester, Essex CO1 1TZ, England. TEL 0206-761212. FAX 0206-769523. (Dist. by: Brunel Court, Brunel Way, Colchester, Essex CO4 4XP, England. TEL 0206-754310) Ed. R.A. Winward. adv. contact: Andy Marshall. illus. (tabloid format) **Document type:** newspaper.

072.6 — UK
COLCHESTER EXPRESS. w. Essex County Newspapers, Oriel House, North Hill, Colchester, Essex CO1 1TZ, England. TEL 0206-761212. FAX 0206-769523. (Dist. by: Brunel Court, Brunel Way, Colchester CO4 4XP, England. TEL 0206-754310) Ed. R.A. Winward. adv. contact: Andy Marshall. illus. (tabloid format) **Document type:** newspaper.

072.7 — UK
CONGLETON CHRONICLE. 1893. w. £34; newsstand price: £0.26. Heads (Congleton) Ltd., 11 High St., Congleton, Ches. CW12 1BW, England. TEL 0260-273737. FAX 0260-280687. Ed. A.J. Condliffe. adv. contact: P. Austen. bk.rev.; film rev.; music rev.; play rev.; illus. (tabloid format; back issues avail.) **Document type:** newspaper.

052 — UK
CONTACT (CRAWLEY, 1947). 1947. 3/yr. free. Bowthorpe plc, Gatwick Rd., Crawley, W. Sussex RH10 2RZ, England. TEL 0293-528888. FAX 0293-541905. Ed. P.R. Ramage. bk.rev.; circ. 7,000 (controlled). (back issues avail.) **Document type:** newsletter.
 Description: Covers company news of Bowthorpe Group worldwide.

640 — UK — ISSN 0141-0555
COSMOPOLITAN (BRITISH EDITION). 1972. m. £21.60. National Magazine Co. Ltd., 72 Broadwick St., London W1V 2BP, England. TEL 071-439-5000. FAX 071-439-5179. Ed. Marcelle D'Argy Smith. adv. circ. 456,703. (reprint service avail. from UMI) **Document type:** consumer publication.
 —UMI.

052 — UK — ISSN 0010-9746
COTSWOLD LIFE. 1967. m. £14. Cotswold Life Ltd., West One House, St. George's Rd., Cheltenham, Glos., England. TEL 0242-226373. Ed. J. Drinkwater. bk.rev.; illus. circ. 10,000.

052 — UK
COUNTDOWN MAGAZINE. 1970. q. free to Countdown cardholders. Countdown PLC, 88-92 Earls Court Rd., Kensington, London W.8, England. TEL 938-1041. FAX 937-8968. Ed. Gail Somers. adv.; bk.rev. circ. 50,000.
 Formerly (until 1983): Countdown Today.

052 — UK — ISSN 0045-8856 S3
COUNTRY LIFE. 1897. w. $175. I P C Magazines, Specialist Magazine Group (Subsidiary of: Reed International PLC), King's Reach Tower, Stamford St., London SE1 9LS, England. TEL 071-261-7070. FAX 0444-440619. TELEX 892084 REEDBP G. (Dist by: Quadrant Subscription Services, Oakfield House, Perrymount Rd., Haywards Heath, W. Sussex RH16 3DH, England. TEL 0444-440421) Ed. Clive Aslet. adv. contact: Lesley Bilton. bk.rev.; illus.; index. cum.index. circ. 51,830. (also avail. in microform from UMI; reprint service avail. from UMI) Indexed: Art & Archaeol.Tech.Abstr., Art Ind., Artbibl.Mod., Avery Ind.Archit.Per., Br.Hum.Ind., Br.Tech.Ind., Geo.Abstr., RILA, Rural Recreat.Tour.Abstr., So.Pac.Per.Ind., World Agri.Econ.& Rural Sociol.Abstr. **Document type:** consumer publication.
 —BLDSC (3481.890000); UnCover; UMI. **CCC**.

052 — UK
COUNTRY LIVING. m. £23.40. National Magazine Co. Ltd., 72 Broadwick St., London W1V 2BP, England. TEL 071-439-5000. FAX 071-439-5179. (Subscr. to: Quadrant Subscription Services, Oakfield House, Perrymount Rd., Haywards Heath, W. Sussex RH16 3DH, England. TEL 0444-445577) Ed. Francine Lawrence. adv. contact: Vivien Cotterill. circ. 186,059. **Document type:** consumer publication.

052 — UK — ISSN 0011-0213
COUNTRY QUEST; the magazine for Wales and the border. 1960. m. £14. North Wales Newspapers, Mold, Clwyd, Wales. FAX 0248-354793. Ed. Ray Bower. adv.; bk.rev.; illus. circ. 8,000.

052 — UK — ISSN 0011-0272
COUNTRYMAN; a bi-monthly illustrated magazine of the British countryside and its people, past & present. 1927. bi-m. $25. Countryman Ltd., Sheep St., Burford, Oxford OX18 4LH, England. TEL 099382258. Ed. Christopher Hall. adv.; bk.rev.; illus.; index. circ. 68,000. (also avail. in microform from UMI; reprint service avail. from UMI) Indexed: Biol.Abstr. **Document type:** consumer publication.
 —BLDSC (3481.904000).

052 — UK — ISSN 0263-015X
COUNTY BORDER TIMES. Running title: Surrey and Hants. County Border Times & News. 1981. w. 104A West St., Farnham, Surrey GU9 7EN, England. Ed. Guy Bellamy. adv.; bk.rev.; illus. circ. 18,000.

072.916 — UK
COUNTY DOWN SPECTATOR. 1904. w. newsstand price: £0.38. Spectator Newspapers, Main St., Bangor, Co. Down BT20 4AF, N. Ireland. TEL 0247-270270. FAX 0247-271544. Ed. Paul Flowers. adv. contact: Brian Sloan. bk.rev.; film rev.; music rev.; play rev.; tele.rev.; illus.; circ. 16,980 (paid). cols./p.: 10; pp./issue: 38. (broadsheet format) **Document type:** newspaper.

072.4 — UK
COVENTRY CITIZEN. 1982. w. Coventry Newspapers Ltd., Corporation St., Coventry, W. Midlands CV1 1FP, England. TEL 0203-633633. FAX 0203-533820. Ed. Peter Jeal. adv. contact: Derek Stone. film rev.; music rev.; tele.rev.; illus. cols./p.: 7; pp./issue: 44. (tabloid format) **Document type:** newspaper.

072.3 — UK
CREDITON COUNTRY COURIER. 1974. fortn. £14.56. Sue Read, Ed. & Pub., 012 High St., Crediton, Devon EX17 3LF, England. TEL 0363-774263. FAX 0363-773545. adv. contact: Alan Quick. film rev.; circ. 3,500 (paid). (tabloid format; also avail. in audio cassette; back issues avail.) **Document type:** newspaper.
 Description: Covers news about local people and places.

072.7 — UK
CREWE & NANTWICH GUARDIAN. 1987. w. newsstand price: £0.26. Reed Regional Newspapers (Cheshire - Merseyside) (Subsidiary of: Reed Regional Newspapers Ltd.), 136 Nantwich Rd., Crewe, Ches. CW2 6AX, England. TEL 0270-258858. FAX 0270-583321. Ed. Anne Loader. adv. contact: Simon Boynton. bk.rev.; film rev.; music rev.; play rev.; illus.; circ. 41,330 (paid). cols./p.: 8; pp./issue: 54. (reprint service avail.) **Document type:** newspaper.

052 — UK
CREZ; the Grove Cresent gazette. q. (Kingston Polytechnic Students' Union) K & N Press, E. Molesey, Surrey, England. TEL 01-979-5999. Ed. Daren Luscombe. film rev.; play rev.; bibl.; illus.; tr.lit. circ. 4,000. (back issues avail.)
 Description: Covers internal sports, general welfare advice, internal news, films and local entertainments.

072.1 — UK — ISSN 0011-2089
CROYDON ADVERTISER. 1869. w. (Fri.). £29.12. Croydon Advertiser Group Ltd., Advertiser House, Brighton Rd., South Croydon CR2 6UB, England. TEL 44-81-668411. FAX 44-81-6609442. Owner(s): Portsmouth & Sunderland Newspapers Plc. Ed. Malcolm Starbrook. adv.; bk.rev.; film rev.; play rev.; tele.rev. cols./p.: 10. (also avail. in microfilm) **Document type:** newspaper.
 Incorporates: Croydon Times; Former titles: Croydon Guardian; Croydon Express.

072.913 — UK — ISSN 0964-3885
CUMBERLAND NEWS AND KILSYTH CHRONICLE. w. (Wed.). Johnston (Falkirk) Ltd., 1 Newmarket Centre, Falkirk FK1 1JZ, Scotland. TEL 0324-624959. FAX 0324-629792. Ed. G. Guthrie. adv. contact: M. Gillies. cols./p.: 8; pp./issue: 36. (tabloid format) **Document type:** newspaper.

052 — UK — ISSN 0011-2984
CUMBRIA; a magazine of Lakeland life. 1951. m. £9.95 (foreign £14.50). Dalesman Publiishing Co. Ltd., Clapham, Lancaster LA2 8EB, England. TEL 05242-51225. FAX 05242-51708. Ed. Terry Fletcher. adv. contact: John Sullivan. bk.rev.; illus.; index. circ. 15,856. **Document type:** consumer publication.

072.1 — UK — ISSN 0307-7578
DAILY MAIL. 1896. d. Mail Newspapers, Carmelite House, London EC4Y 0JA, England. adv.; bk.rev.; illus. (tabloid format; also avail. in microfilm from LCP; reprint service avail.) **Document type:** newspaper.

072.1 — UK — ISSN 0956-8050
DAILY MIRROR. 1903. d. (Mon.-Sat.). Mirror Group Newspapers Ltd., Holborn Circus, London EC1P 1DQ, England. (tabloid format; also avail. in microfilm) **Document type:** newspaper.

072.1 — UK — ISSN 0307-1235
DAILY TELEGRAPH. d. Daily Telegraph Ltd., 1 Canada Sq., Canary Wharf, London E14 5AT, England. cum.index. (broadsheet format; also avail. in microfilm) Indexed: PROMT. **Document type:** newspaper.
 Formerly (until 1969): Daily Telegraph and Morning Post.

052 — UK — ISSN 0011-5800
DALESMAN; a monthly magazine of Yorkshire and its people. 1939. m. £10.95 (foreign £14.50). Dalesman Publishing Co. Ltd., Clapham, Lancaster LA2 8EB, England. TEL 05242-51225. FAX 05242-51708. Ed. Terry Fletcher. adv. contact: John Sullivan. bk.rev.; illus.; index. circ. 58,711. **Document type:** consumer publication.
 —BLDSC (3517.200000).

052 — UK — ISSN 0011-8990
DERBYSHIRE LIFE AND COUNTRYSIDE. 1931. m. £18 (foreign £23). Derbyshire Countryside Ltd., Lodge Lane, Derby DE1 3HE, England. TEL 0332-47087. FAX 0332-290688. Ed. Vivienne Irish. adv.; bk.rev.; illus.; play rev. circ. 11,658.

GENERAL INTEREST PERIODICALS — GREAT BRITAIN

072 UK
DINNINGTON & MALTBY TRADER NEWS. 1971. w. free. Four Counties Newspapers, 50 Laughton Rd., Dinnington, Nr. Sheffield, Nottinghamshire S80 2AS, England. TEL 0909-564800. FAX 0909-550619. Ed. Richard Bacon; Pub. Michael Williams. adv. contact: Audrey Ridge. bk.rev.; music rev. circ. 27,250. cols./p.: 8; pp./issue: 36. (tabloid format; back issues avail.) **Document type:** newspaper.

072.1 UK
DOCKLANDS NEWS. 1983. m. £12. 20 Mastmaker Court, Mastmaker Rd., Isle of Dogs, London E14 9TU, England. TEL 071-512-8420. FAX 071-538-4414. Ed. Carole Lyders. adv.; B&W page £1388; adv. contact: Simon Haithwaite. bk.rev. circ. 145,000. (tabloid format; back issues avail.) **Document type:** newspaper.
Description: Covers business and recreational activities in the Docklands area of eastern London.

072.3 UK
DORSET EVENING ECHO. d. (Mon.-Fri.). Dorset Evening Echo Ltd., 57 St. Thomas St., Weymouth, Dorset DT4 8EU, England. TEL 0305-784804. FAX 0305-782593. Owner(s): Southern Newspapers plc., 45 Above Bar, Southampton SO9 7BA, England. TEL 0703-634134. Ed. Michael Woods. adv.: B&W page £735, color page £885; adv. contact: David Johnston. bk.rev.; film rev.; music rev.; tele.rev.; circ. 22,425 (paid). cols./p.: 7; pp./issue: 32. (tabloid format; back issues avail.) **Document type:** newspaper.

052 UK ISSN 0959-1079
DORSET LIFE. 1976. m. £16.95 (foreign £21.50). Dorset County Magazine Ltd., 95 North St., Wareham, Dorset BH20 4AE, England. adv.; bk.rev. circ. 7,000. **Document type:** consumer publication.
Superseded in part: Somerset and West Monthly.
Description: News of local interest.

052 UK
DORSET PLUS. 1985. w. Western Gazette, Sherborn Rd., Yeovil, Somerset, England. circ. 46,670.

072.914 UK
DUMBARTON AND VALE OF LEVEN REPORTER. 1964. w. £24. Craig M. Jeffrey Ltd., Clyde Weekly Press (Subsidiary of: Clyde and Forth Press Ltd.), 15 Colquhoun Sq., Helensburgh, Dunbartonshire G84 8SE, Scotland. TEL 0436-73434. FAX 0436-71241. Ed. T. Kemp. circ. 6,134. (tabloid format) **Document type:** newspaper.

072.912 UK
DUNFERMLINE HERALD AND POST. 1991. w. (Thu.). free. Dunfermline Herald and Post, 19-23 High St., 2nd Fl., Dunfermline, Fife KY11 7DL, Scotland. TEL 0383-621818. FAX 0383-621211. Owner(s): Thomson Regional Newspapers. adv. contact: Ray Watt. cols./p.: 8; pp./issue: 36. (tabloid format) **Document type:** newspaper.

942 UK
DUNMOW BROADCAST & DISTRICT ADVERTISER. 1952. m. £2. May & Brett Ltd., 23 High St., Dunmow, Essex, England. Ed.Bd. adv.; bk.rev. circ. 6,000. (tabloid format)

072.1 UK
EALING & ACTON GAZETTE. Regional editions: Greenford & Northolt Gazette. Hammersmith, Fulham & Shepherd's Bush Gazette. Southall Gazette. 1860. w. (Fri.). Middlesex County Press Ltd., 134-136 Broadway, London W13 0TL, England. TEL 081-579-3131. FAX 081-566-1201. Ed. John Moore. adv. contact: Sue O'Brien. bk.rev. circ. 33,000. (tabloid format) **Document type:** newspaper.
Formerly: Gazette - Ealing, Hammersmith and Fulham.

072.2 UK
EAST KENT MERCURY. w. Kent Messenger Group, 13 Queen St., Deal, Kent CT14 6EX, England. TEL 0304-365526. FAX 0304-374770. Ed. Malcolm Mitchell. bk.rev. circ. 11,500. (tabloid format; back issues avail.) **Document type:** newspaper.
Description: Local and county news.

052 UK
EAST LOTHIAN LIFE. 1989. q. £10. P J Design, 2 Beveridge Row, Belhaven, Dunbar, E. Lothian EH42 1TP, Scotland. TEL 0368-863593. Ed. Pauline Jaffray. bk.rev. circ. 3,000. (back issues avail.) **Document type:** consumer publication.

052 UK ISSN 0012-8791
EASTERN EVENING NEWS.* 1882. d. £149.76. Eastern Counties Newspaper Ltd., Rm. 120, Temple Chambers, Temple Ave., London EC4Y 0DT, England. FAX 0603-612930. TELEX 975276-ECNNCH-G. Ed. P. Ware. adv.; bk.rev.; illus. circ. 50,000. (also avail. in microfilm)

072.913 UK
EDINBURGH GAZETTE. 2/w. £76 (with Company Law and Official Notification Supplement £140) (effective 1993). H.M.S.O., 71 Lothian Rd., Edinburgh EH3 9AZ, Scotland. (Subscr. to: H.M.S.O. Books, Publications Centre, 51 Nine Elms Ln., London S.W. 5DR, England. TEL 44-71-873-0011. FAX 44-71-873-8463) **Document type:** newspaper, government publication.

052 UK
ESHER AND LEATHERHEAD COURIER. 1966. m. free. Surrey Advertiser Group, 134 High St., Esher, Surrey KT10 9QJ, England. TEL 0372-463553. FAX 0372-469045. Ed. Ian Tait. circ. 34,000. **Document type:** bulletin.

072.6 UK
ESSEX CHRONICLE; A12 Group. w. £46 (effective 1992). Essex Chronicle Series Ltd., Westway, Chelmsford, Essex CM1 3BE, England. TEL 0245-262421. Ed. Peter Smith. adv.; illus. circ. 41,300. (tabloid format; back issues avail.) **Document type:** newspaper.

052 UK ISSN 0014-0910
ESSEX COUNTRYSIDE. 1952. m. £11.50. William Carling & Co., Market Place, Hitchin, Herts, England. Ed. E. V. Scott. adv.; illus. circ. 15,321.

THE EUROPEAN. see GENERAL INTEREST PERIODICALS — European Communities

072.3 UK
EVENING ECHO, BOURNEMOUTH. 1900. d. (except Sun.). newsstand price: £0.26. Richmond Hill, Bournemouth, Dorset BH2 6HH, England. TEL 0202-554601. FAX 0202-293676. Owner(s): Southern Newspapers plc., 45 Above Bar, Southampton SO9 7BA, England. TEL 073-634134. Ed. Gareth Weekes; Pub. Mike Emsley. adv. contact: Ken WHiffin. circ. 51,293 (paid). cols./p.: 8; pp./issue: 52. (tabloid format; also avail. in microfiche; back issues avail.; reprint service avail.) **Document type:** newspaper.

072.4 UK
EVENING SENTINEL (STOKE-ON-TRENT). 1873. d. (except Sun.). £174.20. Sentinel House, Etruria, Stoke-on-Trent, Staffs. ST1 5SS, England. TEL 0782-289800. FAX 0782-260516. Ed. S. Dooley. adv. contact: R. Apsey, G. White. bk.rev.; film rev.; music rev.; play rev.; tele.rev.; illus. cols./p.: 8; pp./issue: 56. (tabloid format; back issues avail.; reprint service avail.) **Document type:** newspaper.

072.1 UK
EVENING TIMES (LONDON). d. Grays Inn House, 127 Clerkenwell Rd., London EC1R, England. TEL 071-405-2121. FAX 071-405-1888. **Document type:** newspaper.

052 UK
EVERGREEN. 1985. q. £11 (foreign £12.95). This England Ltd., P.O. Box 52, Cheltenham, Glos. GL50 1YQ, England. TEL 0242-577775. FAX 0242-222034. **Document type:** bulletin.

052 UK ISSN 0268-7801
EXPRESSION. 1984. bi-m. (American Express Europe Ltd.) Redwood Publishing Ltd., 101 Bayham St., London NW1 0AG, England. TEL 071-331-8000. FAX 071-331-8001. Ed. Sue Thomas. circ. 300,500 (controlled). **Document type:** consumer publication.

072.3 UK
FALMOUTH PACKET. 1856. w. (Thu.). newsstand price: £0.30. Packet Newspapers (Cornwall) Ltd., Ponsharden, Falmouth, Cornwall TR10 8AP, England. TEL 0326-373791. FAX 0326-373887. Owner(s): Yattendon Investment Trust Ltd., Harbourne Ct., 67 Harbourne Rd., Edgbaston, Birmingham B15 3BU, England. TEL 021-456-4004. FAX 021-454-6937. Ed. John Marquis. adv.; bk.rev.; film rev.; music rev.; play rev.; circ. 14,647 (paid). cols./p.: 7; pp./issue: 40. (tabloid format; also avail. in microfiche; back issues avail.) **Document type:** newspaper.

072.912 UK
FIFE HERALD. 1822. w. £38.48. Strachan and Livingston Ltd., 23 Kirk Wynd, Kirkcaldy, Fife KY1 1EP, Scotland. TEL 0592-261451. FAX 0592-204180. Ed. Duncan Stewart Campbell. **Document type:** newspaper.

052 UK
FORTE. 1986. q. £10. Jermyn Publications (Subsidiary of: Forte PLC), Regent Palace Hotel, 3rd Fl., Piccadilly Circus, London WA1 4BZ, England. TEL 071-437-7777. FAX 071-734-8489. Ed. Delia Cooke. circ. 75,000. **Document type:** consumer publication.
Description: General interest publication covering theatre, restaurants, health, events, and fashion.

072 UK
GAINSBOROUGH TRADER NEWS. 1973. w. free. Four Counties Newspapers, 5-7 Church St., Gainsborough, Lincs. DN21 2JJ, England. TEL 0427-615800. FAX 0427-616912. Ed. Gail Salabank. adv.; bk.rev.; music rev. circ. 12,997. cols./p.: 8; pp./issue: 20. (tabloid format; back issues avail.) **Document type:** newspaper.
Formerly: Gainsborough Journal.

072.914 UK ISSN 0016-4178
GALLOWAY NEWS. 1858. w. £39.50. Scottish & Universal Newspapers Ltd., 144 King St., Castle Douglas, Scotland. TEL 0556-504141. FAX 0556-504159. Ed. Allan Phin. adv.; bk.rev.; illus. circ. 9,306. **Document type:** newspaper.
Description: Contains items of local interest.

072.8 UK
GAZETTE AND HERALD. 1790. w. £42.64 (foreign £70.72). York & County Press, P.O. Box 29, 76-86 Walmgate, York YO1 1YN, England. TEL 0904-653051. FAX 0904-611488. Ed. Dorothy Brundell. adv.; bk.rev.; circ. 12,300 (paid). (back issues avail.) **Document type:** newspaper.

072.5 UK
GRANTHAM AND MELTON TRADER NEWS. 1978. w. free. Four Counties Newspapers, 5-7 Welby St., Grantham, Lincs NG31 6JZ, England. TEL 0476-74433. FAX 0476-66704. Ed. Richard Bacon; Pub. Michael Williams. adv. contact: Audrey Ridge. bk.rev.; music rev. circ. 30,026. cols./p.: 8; pp./issue: 40. (tabloid format; back issues avail.) **Document type:** newspaper.

072.7 UK ISSN 0261-3077
THE GUARDIAN (MANCHESTER). Key Title: Guardian (London). (Weekly edition avail.: Manchester Guardian Weekly (ISSN 0959-3608)) 1821. d. (Mon.-Sat.). £388 (N. America £782). Guardian Newspapers, 164 Deansgate, Manchester M60 2RR, England. TEL 44-61-832-7200. FAX 44-61-831-7308. Owner(s): Guardian Newspapers Ltd., 119 Farringdon Rd., London EC1R 3ER, England. TEL 44-71-278-2332. FAX 44-71-837-2114. (Subscr. in U.S. and Canada to: Manchester Guardian, 19 W. 44th St., Ste. 1613, New York, NY 10036-6101. TEL 212-944-1333. FAX 212-944-1179) Ed. Peter J. Preston. adv.; bk.rev.; illus.; index, cum.index; circ. 450,000 (paid). (broadsheet format; also avail. in microfilm from UMI; diskette format; back issues avail.; reprint service avail. from UMI) **Indexed:** Br.Hum.Ind. **Document type:** newspaper.
●Also available online.
Formerly (until 1959): Manchester Guardian (ISSN 0307-756X)

GENERAL INTEREST PERIODICALS — GREAT BRITAIN

072.1 UK ISSN 0958-9996
GUARDIAN WEEKLY. Overseas edition: Manchester Guardian Weekly (ISSN 0959-3608) 1919. w. £72($78) (in Canada Can.$89). Guardian Publications Ltd., Abney Hall, Manchester Rd., Cheadle, Ches. SK8 1PD, England.
FAX 061-428-2108. (U.S. and Canadian subscr. to: Manchester Guardian, 19 W. 44th St., Ste. 1613, New York, NY 10036-6101. TEL 212-944-1333. FAX 212-944-1179) Ed. Patrick Ensor. adv. contact: Suzanne Francis. bk.rev.; film rev.; illus.; play rev. circ. 108,776. (also avail. in microform from UMI; reprint service avail. from UMI) **Document type:** newspaper.
●Also available online. Vendor(s): Mead Data Central, Inc.
—SWETS; UMI.
Formerly (until 1968): Manchester Guardian Weekly (ISSN 0025-200X)

072.913 UK
HAMILTON ADVERTISER. w. Scottish & Universal Newspapers Ltd., Press Bldgs., Campbell St., Hamilton ML3 6AX, Scotland. TEL 0698-283200. FAX 0698-891151. Ed. Graham Isdale. adv. contact: Colin Gilchrist. circ. 31,886. (tabloid format; back issues avail.) **Document type:** newspaper.

052 UK
HARLOW AND BISHOP'S STORTFORD CITIZEN. w. free. London & Essex Guardian Newspapers Ltd., News Centre, Fulbourne Rd., London E17 4EW, England. FAX 0279-450259. Ed. Steve Donnelly. adv. circ. 26,000. (back issues avail.)
Former titles: Harlow and Bishop's Stortford Gazette; Harlow Gazette.

072.1 UK
HARROW OBSERVER. Regional editions: Pinner Observer. Stanmore Observer. Wembley Observer. 1855. w. (Thu.). £37.44. Middlesex County Press Ltd. (Harrow), 326 Station Rd., Harrow, Middx HA1 2DR, England. TEL 081-424-0024.
FAX 081-863-0932. Ed. John Moore. adv. circ. 30,000. (back issues avail.) **Document type:** newspaper.

072.6 UK
HARWICH AND MANNINGTREE STANDARD. 1877. w. newsstand price: £0.28. Essex County Newspapers (Subsidiary of: Reed Regional Newspapers Ltd.), 28 Jackson Rd., Clacton, Essex CO15 1QL. TEL 0255-221221. FAX 0255-432824. Ed. Peter Laurie. adv. contact: Jane Powell. illus.; circ. 6,400 (paid). (tabloid format) **Document type:** newspaper.

072.914 UK
HELENSBURGH ADVERTISER. 1957. w. £25. Craig M. Jeffrey Ltd., Clyde Weekly Press (Subsidiary of: Clyde and Forth Press Ltd.), 15 Colguhoun Sq., Helensburgh, Dunbartonshire G84 8SE, Scotland. TEL 0436-73434. FAX 0436-71241. Ed. Fiona Howard. circ. 6,659. (tabloid format) **Document type:** newspaper.

052 UK
HELLO!. 1988. w. £85 (Europe £99; elsewhere £135 to £178). Hello! Ltd., 69-71 Upper Groond, London SE1 9PQ, England. TEL 071-334-7404.
FAX 071-334-7412. Ed. Maggie Koumi. adv. circ. 453,746. **Document type:** consumer publication.
Description: Contains features about royalty, celebrities, society, and world figures.

072.5 UK
HENLEY STANDARD. (Supplements avail.) 1885. w. Higgs & Co., Reading Rd., Henley, Oxon. RG9 1AD, England. TEL 0491-572178. FAX 0491-573571. Ed. George Tuckfield. adv.: B&W page £329; adv. contact: Sue Hutchinson. bk.rev.; film rev.; music rev.; illus.; circ. 13,400 (paid). cols./p.: 7; pp./issue: 48. (tabloid format; also avail. in microfilm; audio cassette; back issues avail.) **Document type:** newspaper.

072.1 UK
THE HERALD (LONDON). d. Grays Inn House, 127 Clerkenwell Rd., London EC1R, England.
TEL 071-405-2121. FAX 071-405-1888. Ed. William Russell. adv.; bk.rev.; illus. **Document type:** newspaper.

072.3 UK
HERALD EXPRESS. (Supplements avail.: Poperty, Drive-In) 1926. d. £1; newsstand price: £0.26. Herald Express Publications Ltd., Barton Hill Rd., Torquay, Devon TQ2 8JN, England.
TEL 0803-213213. FAX 0803-313093. Owner(s): Northcliffe Newspapers, 31 St. John St., London WC1N 2QB, England. 071-242-7070. Ed. Jim Mitchell. adv.: Page £1037.40; adv. contact: Tony Aspinall. bk.rev.; film rev.; music rev.; play rev.; tele.rev.; illus. Wire service(s): UK News. circ. 31,200 (paid). cols./p.: 7; pp./issue: 32. (tabloid format; also avail. in microfilm; back issues avail.) **Document type:** newspaper.
●Also available online.
Also available on CD-ROM.
Description: Covers news and events in Torquay, Newton Abbot, Totnes, and other communities in southern Devon.

052 US
HERITAGE. 1984. bi-m. $24.95. British Connection, R.D. 1, Box 812, Landisburg, PA 17040. (U.K. addr.: 4 The Courtyard, Denmark St., Wokingham, Berks. RG11 2AZ, England; U.K. subscr. to: Unit C, Challenge House, Sherwood Dr., Bletchley, Bucks. MK3 6DP, England) Ed. Paul Dobson. adv. circ. 32,877. **Document type:** consumer publication.
Description: Focuses on Britain's history, traditions, castles, cottages, crafts and incomparable countryside.

052 UK ISSN 0306-672X
HERTFORDSHIRE COUNTRYSIDE. 1946. m. £10. William Carling & Co., Hitchin, Herts, England. Ed. E.V. Scott. adv.; illus. circ. 5,827.
Formerly: Hertfordshire Countryside Illustrated (ISSN 0018-0904)

052 UK ISSN 0019-2422
AP4
ILLUSTRATED LONDON NEWS. 1842. bi-m. $39. Illustrated London News & Sketch Ltd., 20 Upper Ground, London SE1 9PF, England.
FAX 01-620-1594. Ed. James Bishop. adv.; bk.rev.; film rev.; play rev.; illus.; cum.index. circ. 53,970. (also avail. in microform from UMI; reprint service avail. from UMI) **Indexed:** Bk.Rev.Ind. (1977-), Br.Archaeol.Abstr., Br.Hum.Ind., Br.Tech.Ind., Child.Bk.Rev.Ind. (1977-), Geo.Abstr., Numis.Lit. **Document type:** consumer publication.
—BLDSC (4367.150000); SWETS; UMI.

052 910.09 UK ISSN 0951-8932
IN CORNWALL MAGAZINE. 1986. a. £1.50($2.50) M & M Publications, The Cabin, Cove Road, Mullion, Cornwall TR12 7DH, England. TEL (0326) 240176. Ed. Michael H. George. adv. circ. 15,000. (back issues avail.)

072.1 UK
INTERNATIONAL EXPRESS. U.S. Edition. 1990. w. £85($104) Express Newspapers plc., Ludgate House, 245 Blackfriars Rd., London SE1 9UX, England. TEL 071-922-7463. FAX 071-922-7461. Ed. Ray Hills. adv.; illus. **Document type:** newspaper.

072.911 UK ISSN 0020-9929
INVERNESS COURIER. 1817. s-w. £70.72. Carruthers & Sons, Box 13, 9-11 Bank Lane, Inverness IV1 1QW, Scotland. FAX 0463-243439. Ed. J. MacDonald. adv.; bk.rev.; play rev. circ. 35,233. **Document type:** newspaper.

072.4 UK
KENILWORTH CITIZEN. w. Coventry Newspapers Ltd., Corporation St., Coventry, W. Midlands CV1 1FP, England. TEL 0203-634343. FAX 0203-553820. Ed. Peter Jeal. adv. contact: Derek Stone. film rev.; music rev.; tele.rev.; illus.; circ. 138,315 (paid). cols./p.: 7; pp./issue: 48. (tabloid format) **Document type:** newspaper.

052 UK ISSN 0023-0030
KENT LIFE. 1962. m. £16. Datateam Publishing Ltd., Datateam House, Tovil Hill, Maidstone, Kent ME15 6QS, England. TEL 0622-687031.
FAX 0622-757646. Ed. Rod Cooper. adv.; bk.rev.; illus. circ. 7,151. **Document type:** bulletin.
Description: Contains features, profiles, and photography on arts and culture, history, fashion and design, and leisure activities in this county.

052 UK ISSN 0023-0049
KENT MESSENGER; county paper of Kent. 1859. w. £49.40. Kent Messenger Group, 13 Queen St., Deal, Kent CT14 6EX, England. TEL 0304-365526. FAX 0304-374770. Ed. John Evans. adv.; bk.rev.; abstr.; bibl.; charts; film rev.; illus.; play rev.; mkt.; stat.; tr.lit. circ. 43,486.

072.914 UK
KIRKINTILLOCH & BISHOPBRIGGS HERALD. 1883. w. £26. D. MacLeod Ltd., Luggiebank House, Redbrae Rd., Kirkintilloch, Glasgow G66 2DD, Scotland. TEL 041-775-0040. FAX 041-776-2218. Ed. Christine McPherson. adv. circ. 11,329. (tabloid format) **Document type:** newspaper.

052 UK ISSN 0023-7167
THE LADY. 1885. w. £43.50. 39-40 Bedford St., Strand, London WC2E 9ER, England.
TEL 071-379-4717. FAX 071-497-2137. Ed. Arlene Usden. adv.; bk.rev.; play rev. circ. 65,000. **Document type:** consumer publication.
—CCC.

072.913 UK ISSN 0964-3893
LANARK GAZETTE. 1973. w. (Fri.). Johnston (Falkirk) Ltd., 1 Newmarket Centre, Falkirk FK1 1JZ, Scotland. TEL 0324-624959. FAX 0324-629792. Ed. J.M. Bell. adv. cols./p.: 11; pp./issue: 14. (broadsheet format) **Document type:** newspaper.

052 UK ISSN 0023-7469
LANCASHIRE LIFE. 1947. m. £22.80 (foreign £32.80). Town and County Magazines (Subsidiary of: Oyston Publications PLC), Oyston Mill, Strand Rd., Preston PR1 8UR, England. TEL 0772-722022.
FAX 0772-736496. Ed. Peter Williams. adv.: B&W page £965, color page £1350; trim 200 x 295; adv. contact: Liz Wareing. bk.rev. circ. 12,500. **Document type:** consumer publication.

942 052 UK
LANCASHIRE MAGAZINE. 1977. bi-m. £10.50. Ridings Publishing Co., 33 Beverley Rd., Driffield, Yorkshire YO25 7SD, England. Ed. Winston Halstead. adv.; bk.rev.; illus.; index. circ. 14,250. **Document type:** consumer publication.
Description: English county periodical with focus on Lancashire.

052 UK ISSN 0140-6981
LEICESTER TOPIC.* 1964. m. £10. John Ball Publications Ltd., Topic House, Beechale Rd., Wenter Blvd., Nottingham. Notts. NG8 3LH, England. adv.

072.5 UK
LEIGHTON BUZZARD AND LINSLADE CITIZEN. 1987. w. newsstand price: £0.20. Premier Newspapers Ltd., Napier House, Auckland Park, Bletchley, Milton Keynes MK1 1BU, England. TEL 0908-374033. FAX 0908-37145. Ed. Jan Henderson; Pub. S mon Abra. adv. contact: Kerry Drucker. bk.rev.; film rev.; music rev.; tele.rev. circ. 18,000. cols./p.: 9; pp./issue: 36. (tabloid format) **Document type:** newspaper.

052 UK ISSN 0024-371X
LINCOLNSHIRE LIFE. 1961. m. £15 (foreign £17.50). County Life Ltd., P.O. Box 81, Lincoln LN5 7DY, England. TEL 0522-77567. FAX 0522-77463. Ed. Hilary Hammond. adv.; bk.rev.; illus. circ. 8,000.

072.913 UK ISSN 0964-3540
LINLITHGOWSHIRE JOURNAL AND GAZETTE. 1989. w. (Fri.). Johnston (Falkirk) Ltd., 1 Newmarket Centre, Falkirk FK1 1JZ, Scotland. TEL 0324-624959. FAX 0324-629792. Ed. Colin Mailer. adv. contact: J. Young. cols./p.: 8; pp./issue: 32. (tabloid format) **Document type:** newspaper.

LIVING. see *HOME ECONOMICS*

072.929 UK
LLANELLI STAR. Regional editions: Burry Port Star. Lanelli Star (Gwendraeth). Llanelli Star (Bont & Estuary). (Text in English, Welsh) 1809. w. (Thu.). £36.40; newsstand price: £0.25. Llanelli Star, 10 Station Rd., Llanelli, Dyfed SA15 1BJ, Wales.
TEL 0554-774809. FAX 0554-775456. Owner(s): Northcliffe Group Ltd., 31 John St., London WC1N 2QB, England. TEL 071-242-7070. FAX 071-400-1111. Ed. R. Lloyd. adv. contact: P. Rees. bk.rev.; film rev.; music rev. circ. 18,113. cols./p.: 7; pp./issue: 52. (tabloid format; also avail. in microfiche) **Document type:** newspaper.

GENERAL INTEREST PERIODICALS — GREAT BRITAIN

052 UK ISSN 0264-9497
LONDON PORTRAIT. 1981. 12/yr. free. I P C Magazines, Specialist Magazine Group (Subsidiary of: Reed International P.L.C.), King's Reach Tower, Stamford St., London SE1 9LS, England. TEL 071-261-7214. FAX 0444-440619. TELEX 892084 REEDBP G. (Dist. by: Quadrant Subscription Services, Oakfield House, Perrymount Rd., Haywards Heath, W. Sussex RH16 3DH, England. TEL 0444-440421) Ed. Maggi O'Sullivan. adv. contact: Penny Churchill. film rev.; play rev.; circ. 90,000 (controlled). (back issues avail.) **Document type:** consumer publication.
Description: Lifestyle magazine aimed at top London residential market.

072.1 UK ISSN 0958-9600
LONDON WEEKLY ADVERTISER. 1939. w. newsstand price: £0.60. Brittain Publications, 137 George Ln., South Woodford, London E18 1AJ, England. TEL 081-530-7555. FAX 081-530-7609. adv. **Document type:** newspaper.
Former titles: London and Local Advertiser; London Weekly Advertiser (ISSN 0024-6182)

072.5 UK
LONG EATON HERALD AND POST. 1973. w. free. Long Eaton Herald and Post, 5-7 Stanford St., Nottingham NG1 7BQ, England. FAX 0602-240626. Owner(s): Midland Independent Newspapers, Birmingham Post and Mail, Colmore Circus, Birmingham B4 6AX, England. Ed. Mike Astill. adv. contact: Barbara Buckle. bk.rev.; film rev.; music rev.; tele.rev. circ. 52,000. cols./p.: 9; pp./issue: 48. (tabloid format) **Document type:** newspaper.

072.2 UK
MAIDSTONE STAR. 1981. w. free. Star Publishing Ltd., Maidstone Press Centre, Bank St., Maidstone, Kent ME1H 1PZ, England. TEL 0622-678556. FAX 0622-675071. Ed. Peter Edwards. adv. contact: Jan Smith. cols./p.: 8; pp./issue: 28. (tabloid format) **Document type:** newspaper.

052 UK
MANX LIFE. bi-m. £7.50. Isle of Man Times Ltd., Myrtle St., Douglas, Isle of Man, U.K. Ed. Robert Kelly. adv.

052 UK
MANX POST. 1987. 5/yr. Ronague Enterprises Ltd., Ronague Chapel, Ronague, Castletown, Surrey, England. TEL 0624-823355. FAX 0624-825577. Ed. Annie Lowey. adv.; bk.rev. circ. 2,000. (tabloid format; back issues avail.)

052 UK ISSN 0047-5823
MANX STAR. 1971. w. £24. Isle of Man Times Ltd., Myrtle St., Douglas, Isle of Man, U.K. Ed. Kathy Crebbin. adv.; bk.rev.; illus. circ. 10,000.
Formerly: Woman's Magazine.

072.3 UK
MELKSHAM INDEPENDENT NEWS. 1990. fortn. £24. Wiltshire Media Ltd., 31 Market Pl., Melksham, Wiltshire SN12 6EV, England. TEL 0225-704761. FAX 0225-708081. Ed. Ian Drew; Pub. Ian Drew. circ. 10,500. (tabloid format) **Document type:** newspaper.

072.3 UK
MID DEVON GAZETTE. 1856. w. £10.40 for 3 mos.; newsstand price: £0.30. 29 Brampton St., Tiverton, Devon EX16 6AG, England. TEL 0884-242500. FAX 0884-258527. TELEX 49010 TIVERTON G. Owner(s): Northcliffe Newspapers, 31 John St., London WC1N 2QB, England. TEL 071-242-7070. FAX 071-242-4089. Ed. Ron Hill. adv.; B&W page £677.04; adv. contact: Jo Carey. film rev.; tele.rev.; play rev.; illus. cols./p.: 8; pp./issue: 52. (tabloid format; also avail. in magnetic tape; back issues avail.) **Document type:** newspaper.
Formed by the Sep. 1993 merger of: Gazette (South Molton Edition) & Gazette (Culm Valley Edition) & Gazette (Crediton Edition) & Gazette (Tiverton Edition).

072.6 UK
MID ESSEX EXPRESS. w. Essex County Newspapers, Oriel House, North Hill, Colchester, Essex CO1 1TZ, England. TEL 0206-761212. FAX 0206-769523. (Dist. by: Brunel Court, Brunel Way, Colchester CO4 4XP, England. TEL 0206-754310) Ed. R.A. Winward. adv. contact: Andy Marshall. illus. (tabloid format)

052 UK
MIDWEEK; free thinking. 1988. w. free. 7-9 Rathbone St., London W1P 1AF, England. TEL 071-636-6651. FAX 071-872-0806. Ed. Bill Williamson. adv.; bk.rev. circ. 128,000. **Document type:** consumer publication.
Description: General interest publication providing news and information on films, theatre, restaurants and TV personalities.

072.5 UK
MILTON KEYNES CITIZEN. 1982. w. (Thu.). newsstand price: £0.40. Citizen Newspaper, Napier House, Auckland Park, Bletchley, Milton Keynes MK1 1BU, England. TEL 0908-374033. FAX 0908-371115. Ed. Jan Henderson; Pub. Simon Abra. adv. contact: Kerry Drucker. film rev.; music rev.; tele.rev.; circ. 89,700. cols./p.: 9; pp./issue: 208. (tabloid format) **Document type:** newspaper.

052 UK
MOTORING & HOME - LIFE. 1988. m. free. Motoring & Home - Life Magazines Ltd., 42A High St., Lurgan, Co. Armagh BT66 8AU, N. Ireland. TEL 0762-324006. FAX 0762-325213. Ed. Margaret Kinsella. adv. circ. 25,000. **Document type:** consumer publication.

052 UK ISSN 0047-956X
NEW CHISLEHURST ANNOUNCER.* 1967. m. free. Premier Publicity Service Ltd., 14 High St., Chislehurst, Kent, England. Ed. N.L. Roper. adv.; illus. circ. 25,000. (tabloid format)

072.2 UK
NEW FOREST POST. 1981. w. free. New Forest Post, 41 Gosport St., Lymington SO41 9PA, England. TEL 0590-671122. FAX 0590-678727. Owner(s): Southern Newspapers, 45 Above Bar, Southampton, Hampshire SO9 7BA, England. TEL 0703-634134. FAX 0703-631911. Ed. Neal Butterworth. adv.; page £873; adv. contact: Pamela Davidson. bk.rev.; film rev.; music rev. circ. 37,064. cols./p.: 7; pp./issue: 40. (tabloid format) **Document type:** newspaper.

052 UI ISSN 0047-987X
DA880.S5
NEW SHETLANDER. (Text in English and Shetland dialect) 1947. q. £4.50 (foreign £5). Shetland Council of Social Service, 5 Harbour St., Lerwick ZE1 0LR, Shetland Islands, U.K. TEL 0595-3816. Eds. John Graham, Laurence Graham. adv.; bk.rev.; illus. circ. 2,400.

072.5 UK
NEWARK TRADER NEWS. 1983. w. free. Four Counties Newspapers, 48 Barnbygate, Newark, Notts. NG24 1QD, England. TEL 0636-640650. FAX 0636-605547. Ed. Richard Bacon; Pub. Michael Williams. adv. contact: Audrey Ridge. bk.rev.; music rev. circ. 18,848. cols./p.: 8; pp./issue: 40. (tabloid format; back issues avail.) **Document type:** newspaper.

072.1 UK ISSN 0028-9280
NEWS OF THE WORLD. 1843. w. £67. News Group Newspapers Ltd., 1 Virginia St., London EC1 9XR, England. TEL 071-782-4000. FAX 071-782-9504. Ed. Patricia Chapman. adv.; bk.rev.; illus. circ. 4,857,000. **Document type:** newspaper.

052 200 UK
NEWS SPECIAL; & the messenger. 1968. m. £3.72. Challenge Publishing, Revenue Bldgs., Chapel Rd., Worthing, W. Sussex BN11 1BQ, England. TEL 44-903-214198. FAX 44-903-217663. Ed. Donald Banks. circ. 70,000. (tabloid format)

052 UK
NEWSWEEK INTERNATIONAL. 1933. w. £39. Newsweek Inc., 18 Park St., London W1Y 4HH, England. TEL 071-629-8361. FAX 071-629-0050. **Document type:** consumer publication.

052 UK
NINE TO FIVE. 1982. w. $2. London House, 9A Margaret St., London W1A 4LR, England. TEL 071-637-1377. FAX 071-636-4694.

072.8 UK
NORMANTON ADVERTISER. 1890. w. (Fri.). free. Normanton Advertiser, West St., Normanton, W. Yorkshire WF6 2AP, England. TEL 0924-892117. FAX 0924-892117. Ed. Peter Warrender; Pub. Peter Warrender. cols./p.: 6; pp./issue: 12. (tabloid format) **Document type:** newspaper.

072.3 UK
NORTH DEVON JOURNAL. w. £10.40; newsstand price: £0.30. 96 High St., Barnstaple, Devon EX31 1HT, England. TEL 0271-43064. FAX 0271-23165. TELEX 34983 BARNSTAPLE G. Owner(s): Northcliffe Newspapers, 31 John St., London WC1N 2QB, England. TEL 071-242-7070. FAX 071-242-4089. Ed. Ron Hill. adv.; bk.rev.; film rev.; play rev.; tele.rev.; illus. cols./p.: 8; pp./issue: 52. (tabloid format; also avail. in magnetic tape; back issues avail.) **Document type:** newspaper.

942 UK
NORTHAMPTONSHIRE IMAGE. 1905. m. £1.50 per no. Northampton Mercury Co. Ltd., Upper Mounts, Northampton NN1 3HR, England. TEL 0604-231122. FAX 0604-232434. Ed. Peter R. Hall. adv.; B&W page £649, color page £873; trim 270 x 194. bk.rev. circ. 28,000. **Document type:** bulletin.
Former titles (until 1986): Independent Image; (until 1985): Northampton and County Independent (ISSN 0048-0711)

052 UK
NOTTINGHAM ARROW. 1974. bi-m. free. Nottingham City Council, Public Relations Office, Exchange Buildings South, Smithy Row, Nottingham NG1 2HU, England. TEL 0602-483500. FAX 0602-350864. Ed. Tim Jones. circ. 115,500. **Document type:** newsletter.

072.5 UK
NOTTINGHAM EVENING POST. 1878. d. (Mon.-Sat.). newsstand price: £0.27. Forman Hardy Holdings, Forman St., Nottingham NG1 4AB, England. TEL 0602-482000. FAX 0602-484753. Ed. B. Williams; Pub. L.C. Simmons. adv. contact: C. Oskwarek. bk.rev.; film rev.; music rev.; tele.rev.; tr.lit.; circ. 114,971 (paid). cols./p.: 10. (broadsheet format; back issues avail.) **Document type:** newspaper.

072.5 UK
NOTTINGHAM HERALD AND POST. 1983. w. free. Nottingham Herald and Post, 5-7 Stanford St., Nottingham NG1 7BQ, England. FAX 0602-240626. Owner(s): Midland Independent Newspapers, Birmingham Post and Mail, Colmore Circus, Birmingham B4 6AX, England. Ed. Mike Astill. adv. contact: Barbara Buckle. bk.rev.; film rev.; music rev.; tele.rev. circ. 136,000. cols./p.: 9; pp./issue: 48. (tabloid format) **Document type:** newspaper.

052 UK ISSN 0048-0940
NOTTINGHAM TOPIC.* 1964. m. £10. John Ball Publications Ltd., Topic House, Beechale Rd., Wenter Blvd., Nottingham, Notts NG8 3LH, England. adv.; charts; illus.
Incorporating: Nottingham Countryside.

072.1 UK ISSN 0029-7712
OBSERVER. 1791. w. £95. Observer Ltd., Chelsea Bridge House, Queenstown Rd., London SW8 4NN, England. Ed. Donald Trelford. adv.; bk.rev. circ. 600,000. (also avail. in microfilm) **Indexed:** Bk.Rev.Ind. (1965-), Br.Hum.Ind., Child.Bk.Rev.Ind. (1965-), Child.Lit.Abstr., Peace Res.Abstr. **Document type:** newspaper.
—BLDSC (6206.150000).

052 UK ISSN 0030-199X
OLD LADY OF THREADNEEDLE STREET. 1921. q. £5. Bank of England, Old Lady Office, Threadneedle St., London EC2R 8AH, England. TEL 071-601-4703. Ed. S. Young. bk.rev.; illus.; index. circ. 4,500.
Description: Covers news of the Bank of England, with features and review articles.

072.7 UK
OLDHAM EVENING CHRONICLE. 1880. 5/wk. (Mon.-Fri.). newsstand price: £0.26. Hirst, Kidd & Rennie Ltd., 172 Union St., Oldham, Lancs OL1 1EQ, England. TEL 061-633-2121. FAX 061-627-0905. Ed. Philip Hirst; Pub. Hubert Hirst. adv. contact: Jim Whittingham. film rev.; music rev.; tele.rev.; circ. 37,110 (paid). cols./p.: 6; pp./issue: 32. (tabloid format; also avail. in microfilm; back issues avail.) **Document type:** newspaper.

GENERAL INTEREST PERIODICALS — GREAT BRITAIN

052 UK ISSN 0965-2507
▼**OLDIE.** 1992. fortn. £35 (Europe £45; elsewhere £60). Oldie Publications Ltd., 26 Charlotte St., London W1P 1HJ, England. TEL 071-636-3686. FAX 071-636-3685. Ed. Richard Ingrams. adv. contact: Hamish Miller. circ. 30,000. **Document type:** consumer publication.

072.911 UK
ORCADIAN. 1854. w. £45. Orcadian Limited, Kirkwall, Orkney KW15 1DW, Scotland. Ed. J.E. Miller. adv.; bk.rev. circ. 11,343. **Document type:** newspaper.

052 UK ISSN 0031-160X
PARADE. 1915. m. 70s.($12.) P.O. Box 171, London E11, England. Ed. L Holsworth. illus. circ. 250,000. (tabloid format) **Indexed:** PMR.

052 UK
PEERAGE. 1986. q. £15. Peerage Publications, 9 Mortlake Terr., Kew Green, Richmond, Surrey TW9 3DT, England. TEL 081-747-0385. Ed. Sara Marden-King; Pub. Bruce Duncan. adv. circ. 125,000. **Document type:** consumer publication.

052 UK ISSN 0048-3605
PETTS WOOD POST.* 1970. m. free. Premier Publicity Service Ltd., 14 High St., Chislehurst, Kent, England. Ed. N.L. Roper. adv.; illus. circ. 25,000. (tabloid format)

052 UK ISSN 0034-0405
READER'S DIGEST (BRITISH EDITION). 1938. m. £25.95. Reader's Digest Association Ltd., Berkeley Square House, London W1X 6AB, England. TEL 071-629-8144. FAX 071-499-9751. Ed. Russell Twisk. adv.; illus. circ. 1,651,820. (also avail. in microform from UMI; reprint service avail. from UMI) **Indexed:** GdIns. **Document type:** consumer publication.
—UMI.

052 UK ISSN 0260-8499
REFLECTIONS. 1981. m. free. Peerage Publications, 9 Mortlake Terr., Kew Green, Richmond, Surrey TW9 3DT, England. TEL 081-747-0385. Ed. Sara Marden-King; Pub. Bruce Duncan. adv.; circ. 100,000. (back issues avail.) **Document type:** consumer publication.

072.5 UK
RETFORD AND BAWTRY TRADER NEWS. 1973. w. free. Four Counties Newspapers, 18 Carolgate, Retford, Notts DN22 6BU, England. TEL 0777-706969. FAX 0777-706825. Ed. Richard Bacon; Pub. Michael Williams. adv. contact: Audrey Ridge. bk.rev.; music rev. circ. 21,508. cols./p.: 8; pp./issue: 44. (tabloid format; back issues avail.) **Document type:** newspaper.

072.6 UK
ROMFORD OBSERVER. w. £46 (effective 1992). Essex Chronicle Series Ltd., Westway, Chelmsford, Essex CM1 3BE, England. TEL 0245-262421. Ed. Peter Smith. adv.; illus. circ. 59,439. (tabloid format; back issues avail.) **Document type:** newspaper.

052 UK
ROTHMILL QUARTERLY. 1929. s-a. free. Tullis Russell & Co. Ltd., Auchmuty & Rothes Paper Mills, Markinch, Glenrothes, Fife KY7 6PB, Scotland. Ed. Thomas D. Murray. circ. 3,000.

072.2 UK
RYE & BATTLE OBSERVER. 1991. w. newsstand price: £0.25. Bexhill Observer, 18 Sackville Rd., Bexhill, E. Sussex BN25 4PZ, England. TEL 0424-730555. FAX 0424-730832. Owner(s): 1066 Newspapers, Telford Rd., St. Leonards, E. Sussex TN38 9LZ, England. TEL 0424-854242. FAX 0424-852850. Ed. Andrea Hargreaves. adv. contact: Steve Etheridge. illus. cols./p.: 8; pp./issue: 40. (tabloid format) **Document type:** newspaper.

052 UK
ST. ANDREWS CITIZEN. 1870. w. £27.04 (foreign £38.48). Strachan and Livingston Ltd., 5A Greyfriars Garden, St. Andrews, Fife KY16 9HG, Scotland. FAX 0334-55400. (Subscr. to: Strachan and Livingston Ltd. 23-25 Kirk Wynd, Kirkcaldy, Fife KY1 1EP, Scotland) Ed. Duncan S. Campbell. adv.; bk.rev. circ. 13,700. (tabloid format; also avail. in talking book; back issues avail.)

072.3 UK
ST. AUSTELL BODMIN AND NEWQUAY PACKET. w. (Thu.). free. Packet Newspapers (Cornwall) Ltd., Ponsharden, Falmouth, Cornwall TR10 8AP, England. TEL 0326-373791. FAX 0326-373887. Owner(s): Yattendon Investment Trust Ltd., Harbourne Ct., 67 Harbourne Rd., Edgbaston, Birmingham B15 3BU, England. TEL 021-456-4004. FAX 021-454-6937. Ed. John Marquis. adv.; bk.rev.; film rev.; music rev.; play rev.; circ. 23,843. cols./p.: 7; pp./issue: 20. (tabloid format) **Document type:** newspaper.

072.7 UK
SALE AND ALTRINCHAM MESSENGER. 1975. w. (Thu.). newsstand price: £0.20. Sale and Altrincham Messenger Ltd., 46 Washway Rd., Sale, Manchester M33 1QZ, England. TEL 061-969-8411. FAX 061-976-3703. Owner(s): Reed Regional Newspapers, The Academy, Bridge St., Warrington WA1 2RU, England. TEL 0925-33033. Ed. Philip Fleming. adv. contact: Nuala O'Rourke. bk.rev.; film rev.; music rev.; tr.lit.; circ. 1,508 (paid); 54,575. cols./p.: 8; pp./issue: 88. **Document type:** newspaper.

072.7 UK
SANDBACH CHRONICLE. 1893. w. £34; newsstand price: £0.26. Heads (Congleton) Ltd., 11 High St., Congleton, Ches. CW12 1BW, England. TEL 0260-273737. FAX 0260-280687. Ed. A.J. Condliffe. adv. contact: P. Austen. bk.rev.; film rev.; music rev.; play rev.; illus. (tabloid format; back issues avail.) **Document type:** newspaper.

072.911 UK ISSN 0955-8756
SCOTLAND ON SUNDAY. 1988. w. £124.80. Scotsman Publications Ltd., 20 North Bridge, Edinburgh EH1 1YT, Scotland. TEL 031-225-2468. FAX 031-220-2443. Ed. Andrew Jaspan. adv.; bk.rev. circ. 84,769. (back issues avail.) **Document type:** newspaper.

942 UK ISSN 0048-9751
SCOTS MAGAZINE. 1739. m. D.C Thomson & Co. Ltd., 7-25 Bank St., Dundee DD1 9HU, Scotland. Ed. Maurice Fleming. adv.; bk.rev.; illus. **Indexed:** Br.Hum.Ind.
—BLDSC (8205.977500).

052 UK ISSN 0036-9209 DA750
SCOTTISH FIELD. 1902. m. £28. George Outram & Co. Ltd., The Plaza Tower, East Kilbride, Glasgow G74 1LW, Scotland. TEL 03552-46444. FAX 03552-63013. Ed. Peter Evans. adv.; bk.rev.; illus. circ. 17,150. **Document type:** consumer publication.

052 UK
SHEFFIELD CITY PRESS. 1982. fortn. free. Sheffield City Press, 49 Broomgrove Rd., Sheffield S10 2NA, England. TEL 0742-683199. FAX 0742-532471. Ed. Simon Regan. adv.; bk.rev.; film rev.; play rev. circ. 10,000. (back issues avail.)

052 UK ISSN 0260-5732
SHETLAND LIFE. 1980. m. £20.16. Shetland Times Ltd., Prince Alfred St., Lerwick, Shetland, Scotland. TEL 0595-3622. FAX 0595-4637. Ed. James R. Nicolson. adv.; bk.rev.; charts. circ. 3,000. **Document type:** bulletin.
Description: Covers the economy and domestic life of this island region of Northern Scotland.

079.1135 UK
SHETLAND TIMES. 1872. w. £56.68. Shetland Times Ltd., Prince Alfred St., Lerwick, Shetland, Scotland. TEL 0595-3622. FAX 0595-4637. Ed. Vaila Wishart. adv.; bk.rev. circ. 11,201. **Document type:** newspaper.

072.3 UK
SIDMOUTH HERALD. 1849. w. (Sat.). £21.84. Sidmouth Herald, Caxton House, East St., Sidmouth, Devon EX10 8BL, England. TEL 0395-515191. FAX 0395-579159. Ed. Trevor Vanstone. adv.; bk.rev.; film rev.; play rev. circ. 7,000. (tabloid format; back issues avail.) **Document type:** newspaper.

072.5 UK
SKEGNESS STANDARD. (Other editions for: Boston, Sleaford, Maldethorpe, Alford, Horncastle, Spilsby, Gainsborough, Lincoln) 1922. w. £52; newsstand price: £0.33. Skegness Standard, The Hildreds Centre, Skegness, Lincolnshire PE25 3NR, England. TEL 0754-610362. FAX 0754-610987. Owner(s): Lincolnshire Standard Group, The Newspaper Centre, Redstone Rd., Boston, Lincolnshire PE21 8EA, England. TEL 0205-311433. FAX 0205-369827. Ed. John Coupe. adv. contact: Jane Parker. bk.rev.; film rev.; music rev.; tele.rev. cols./p.: 8; pp./issue: 68. (tabloid format; back issues avail.) **Document type:** newspaper.

052 UK ISSN 0961-9364
SOMERSET MAGAZINE. 1991. m. £16.95 (foreign £21.50). Smart Print Publications Ltd., 23 Market St., Crewkerne, Somerset TA18 7JU, England. TEL 0460-78000. FAX 0460-76718. Ed. Jack Rayfield. adv.; bk.rev. circ. 7,000. **Document type:** consumer publication.
Description: Local news and features concerning the county of Somerset.

072.5 UK
SOUTH BUCKS STAR. Regional editions: Wycombe Star, Thame & Chinnor Star, Chiltern Star. 1981. w. (Fri.). free. Bucks Free Press Group, Gomm Rd., High Wycombe, Bucks HP13 7DW, England. TEL 0494-521212. FAX 0494-441977. Owner(s): Westminster Press Ltd., Newspaper House, 8-16, Great New St., London EC4P 4ER, England. TEL 071-353-1030. FAX 071-353-7526. Ed. Alan Cleaver; Pub. Hew Stevenson. adv. contact: Becky Jones. bk.rev.; film rev.; music rev.; tele.rev.; circ. 94,000. cols./p.: 8; pp./issue: 88. (tabloid format) **Document type:** newspaper.

072.1 UK
SOUTH LONDON GUARDIAN. 1977. w. (Thu.). free. South London Guardian, 34-44 London Rd., Morden, Surrey SM4 5BR, England. TEL 081-646-6336. FAX 081-770-2266. Ed. Roger Mills; Pub. Paul Davidon. adv. contact: Sue Bebber. bk.rev.; film rev.; music rev.; tele.rev. cols./p.: 8. (tabloid format; back issues avail.)

072.1 UK
SOUTH LONDON PRESS (FRIDAY). 1865. w. £25. South London Press Ltd., 2-4 Leigham Court Rd., London SW16 2PD, England. TEL 081-769-4444. Ed. Robert Bowden. circ. 47,205. (back issues avail.) **Document type:** newspaper.
Description: Covers news in Lambeth, Lewisham, Southwark, Wandsworth and Greenwich.

072.1 UK
SOUTH LONDON PRESS (TUESDAY). 1865. w. £15.60. South London Press Ltd., 2-4 Leighan Court Rd., London SW16 2PD, England. TEL 081-769-4444. Ed. Robert Bowden. circ. 30,506. (back issues avail.) **Document type:** newspaper.
Description: Covers news in Lewisham, Lambeth, Southwark, Wandsworth and Greenwich.

052 UK ISSN 0038-3422
SOUTH EAST LONDON & KENTISH MERCURY. 1833. w. £10.92. Westminster Press Ltd., 116 Deptford High St., London SE8 4NX, England. Ed. Roger Norman. adv.; bk.rev.; film rev.; play rev. circ. 39,513.

072.8 UK
SOUTHERN REPORTER. w. £38.74 (Europe £45.76; elsewhere £66.82). Tweeddale Press Group, 90 Marygate, Berwick-upon-Tweed, Northumberland TD15 1BW, England. TEL 0289-306677. FAX 0289-307377. Ed. A.R. Langmark. adv. contact: G. Bell. bk.rev.; film rev.; music rev. (broadsheet format) **Document type:** newspaper.

072.1 UK ISSN 0039-5196
SUNDAY EXPRESS. 1918. w. £31.20. Express Newspapers PLC, Ludgate House, 245 Blackfriars Rd., London SE1 9U4X, England. TEL 71-928-8000. Ed. Robin Morgan. bk.rev.; film rev.; play rev. circ. 2,390,000. (also avail. in microform from UMI) **Document type:** newspaper.

072.4 UK ISSN 0039-5242
SUNDAY MERCURY. 1848. w. 40p. per no. Birmingham Post & Mail Ltd., 28 Colmore Circus, Queensway, Birmingham B4 6AX, England. FAX 021-233-0271. Ed. Peter Whitehouse. adv.; bk.rev.; film rev.; illus.; play rev.; tele.rev. circ. 151,000. (tabloid format; also avail. in microfilm) **Document type:** newspaper.

GENERAL INTEREST PERIODICALS — GREAT BRITAIN

072.8 UK ISSN 0039-5315
SUNDAY SUN. 1919. w. Newcastle Chronicle and Journal Ltd., Thomson House, Groat Market, Newcastle Upon Tyne, Tyne & Wear NE1 1ED, England. TEL 091-2327500. FAX 091-2304144. Owner(s): Thomson Regional Newspapers Ltd. Ed. Chris Rushton. adv.; bk.rev.; illus. circ. 116,814. (also avail. in microform from UMI) **Document type:** newspaper.

052 UK ISSN 0039-6397
SUSSEX LIFE. 1965. m. £13.50. Dateteam Publishing Ltd., Dateteam House, Tovil Hill, Maidstone, Kent ME15 6QS, England. Ed. Rod Cooper. adv.; bk.rev.; illus. circ. 6,870.
   Description: Contains features, profiles, and photography on arts and culture, history, fashion and design, and leisure activities in the area.

052 UK
T N T MAGAZINE. 1983. w. free. 52 Earls Court Rd., London W8 6EJ, England. TEL 071-936-3985. FAX 071-937-6279. Ed. David Moase. adv. contact: Wayne Holmes. circ. 57,395 (controlled). **Document type:** consumer publication.
   Description: Provides news and information on entertainment and travel.

052 UK
TATLER. m. £30 (Europe and N. America £42; elsewhere £48). Conde Nast Publications Ltd., Vogue House, Hanover Sq., London W1R 0AD, England. TEL 071-499-9080. FAX 071-493-1345. (Subscr. to: Quadrant Subscription Services, Oakfield House, Perrymount Rd., Haywards Heath, W. Sussex RH16 3DH, England) Ed. Jane Procter; Pub. Anne Holcroft. circ. 73,262. **Document type:** consumer publication.

072.8 UK
TEESDALE MERCURY. 1854. w. (Wed.). newsstand price: £0.20. Teesdale Mercury Ltd., 24 Market Pl., Barnard Castle, Durham DL12 8NB, England. TEL 0833-37140. FAX 0833-38633. Ed. Jim McTaggert. adv.: page £600; adv. contact: Maggie Banner. cols./p.: 7; pp./issue: 14. (back issues avail.) **Document type:** newspaper.

072.8 UK
TELEGRAPH & ARGUS. (Supplements avail: Yorkshire Observer, Weekend Planner) 1868. d. newsstand price: £0.27. Bradford and District Newspapers (Subsidiary of: Pearsons), Hall Ings, Bradford, W. Yorks. BD1 1JR, England. TEL 0274-729511. FAX 0274-726901. Owner(s): Westminster Press, 8-16 Great New St., London EC4P 4ER, England. TEL 071-353-1030. Ed. Perry Austin-Clerk. adv.: B&W page £1850; adv. contact: Trevor Lee. bk.rev.; film rev.; music rev.; play rev.; tele.rev.; illus. circ. 66,649. cols./p.: 7; pp./issue: 64. (tabloid format; reprint service avail.) **Document type:** newspaper.

052 UK
TELEGRAPH MAGAZINE. (Included in: Daily Telegraph (London)) 1976. w. Daily Telegraph Ltd., One Canada Sq., Canary Wharf, London E14 5DT, England. TEL 071-538-5000. Ed. F. Lawrence. adv.; illus. circ. 733,899. (also avail. in microform) **Indexed:** Br.Hum.Ind.; High.Educ.Curr.Aware.Bull.
   Former titles: Telegraph Sunday Magazine; Daily Telegraph Magazine (ISSN 0011-5495); Weekend Telegraph.

052 UK
TEMPO (LONDON, 1947). 1947. m. free. Department of Employment, Caxton House, Tothill St., London SW1H 9NF, England. TEL 071-273-4997. FAX 071-273-5633. Ed. David Mattes. adv. circ. 51,000. (tabloid format)

052 UK
THAMES VALLEY BUSINESS. q. free. Windsor Newspaper Co. Ltd., 256 Ipswich Rd., Slough, Berks SL1 4EP, England. adv. circ. 26,000. **Document type:** consumer publication.
   Formerly: Thames Valley Life Style.

052 UK
THANET EXTRA. 1980. w. £16.64. Kent Messenger Group, 13 Queen St., Deal, Kent CT14 6EX, England. TEL 0304-365526. FAX 0304-374770. Ed. Malcolm Mitchell. film rev.; play rev. circ. 54,767. (tabloid format; back issues avail.)

072.2 UK ISSN 0962-0966
THANET GAZETTE. Variant title: Isle of Thanet Gazette. 1879. w. £12.75 for 3 mos.; newsstand price: £0.32. Associated Kent Newspapers (A K N) Ltd. (Subsidiary of: E M A P Newspaper Division), Union Row, Margate, Kent CT9 1PP, England. TEL 0843-221313. FAX 0843-291799. Owner(s): Senews Ltd., Woods House, Telford Rd., St. Leonards-on-Sea, E. Sussex, England. TEL 0424-854458. FAX 0424-850800. Ed. Mike Pearce. adv.: B&W page £1095; adv. contact: Peter Edwards. illus. cols./p.: 8; pp./issue: 56. (tabloid format) **Document type:** newspaper.

072.2 UK ISSN 0962-0974
THANET TIMES. 1960. w. £12.75 for 3 mos.; newsstand price: £0.32. Associated Kent Newspapers (A K N) Ltd. (Subsidiary of: E M A P Newspaper Division), Union Row, Margate, Kent CT9 1PP, England. TEL 0843-221313. FAX 0843-291799. Owner(s): Senews Ltd., Woods House, Telford Rd., St. Leonards-on-Sea, E. Sussex TN38 9LZ, England. TEL 0424-854458. FAX 0424-850800. Ed. Mike Pearce. adv.: B&W page £1095; adv. contact: Peter Edwards. illus. cols./p.: 8; pp./issue: 56. (tabloid format) **Document type:** newspaper.

052 UK
THIS IS BRISTOL AND BATH. 1977. m. free. Brunel Press Ltd., Temple Way, Old Market, Bristol BS99 7HD, England. TEL 0272-277319. FAX 0272-279568. Ed. Anthony Lewis. adv.; bk.rev. circ. 22,500. (also avail. in microfilm)
   Formerly: Bristol and West Country Illustrated.

052 UK ISSN 0040-652X
THREE CROWNS. 1962. 3/yr. free. Coutts and Company, 440 Strand, London W.C.2, England. Ed. J.L. Hooper. charts; illus. circ. 2,000.

072.3 UK
TORBAY WEEKENDER. 1980. w. Harmsworth House, Barton Hill Rd., Torquay, Devon TQ2 8JN, England. TEL 0803-213213. FAX 0803-316770. Ed. David Scott. **Document type:** newspaper.

052 UK
TOWER HAMLETS NEWS. 1972. fortn. Patriot Sq., London E2 9LN, England. TEL 081-980-3286. Ed. Ashley Gibbins. adv.; bk.rev.; film rev.; play rev. circ. 80,000. (tabloid format) **Document type:** consumer publication.

072.916 UK
TYRONE COURIER. 1880. w. £59.80. Tyrone Courier Ltd., 58 Scotch St., Dungannon BT70 1BD, N. Ireland. TEL 08687-22271. FAX 08687-26171. Ed. R.G. Montgomery. circ. 13,490. (tabloid format) **Document type:** newspaper.

914.2 US ISSN 8750-1082
U K MAGAZINE. 1982. bi-m. $16. M D Enterprises, Inc., Box 25, 111 Clayton Rd., Hatboro, PA 19040. TEL 215-230-9448. FAX 215-230-9449. Ed. Paul Simon; Pub. Hannibal Graves. adv.; bk.rev. circ. 38,000. (back issues avail.) **Document type:** consumer publication.
   Description: Promotes the connection between the United Kingdom and the U.S. through business, food, travel, events, clubs, organizations, genealogy and mail order.

072.916 UK
ULSTER GAZETTE AND ARMAGH STANDARD. 1844. w. £62.40. Ulster Gazette (Armagh) Ltd., 56 Scotch St., Armagh BT61 7DF, N. Ireland. TEL 0861-522639. FAX 0861-527029. Ed. Eric Villiers. adv. circ. 11,078. **Document type:** newspaper.

052 UK ISSN 0049-5107
ULSTER TATLER. 1966. m. £15. Ulster Journals Ltd., 39 Boucher Rd., Belfast BT12 6UT, N. Ireland. Ed. R.M. Sherry. **Document type:** consumer publication.

072.8 UK
WASHINGTON STAR. Regional editions: Hartlepool Star. Houghton Star. Peterlee Star. Seaham Star. South Tyne Star. Sunderland Star. 1985. w. (Thu.). free. Northeast Press Ltd., Coniston House, Ste. 14, Washington, Tyne and Wear NE38 7SH, England. TEL 091-4170050. FAX 091-4173291. Owner(s): Northeast Press Ltd., Hind Court, 149 Fleet St., London EC4A 3DL, England. TEL 071-583-2100. Ed. Mike Wedge; Pub. Steve Gascoigne. adv. contact: Chris Grieveson. bk.rev.; film rev.; music rev.; tele.rev. circ. 250,000 (all editions). cols./p.: 7. (tabloid format) **Document type:** newspaper.

072.3 UK
WELLINGTON WEEKLY NEWS. w. newsstand price: £0.25. 26 High St., Wellington, Somerset TA21 8RA, England. TEL 0823-662439. FAX 0823-665793. TELEX 49010 TIVERTON G. Owner(s): Northcliffe Newspapers, 31 John St., London WC1N 2QB, England. TEL 071-242-7070. FAX 071-242-4089. Ed. Ron Hill. adv.: B&W page £483; adv. contact: Jo Carey. bk.rev.; film rev.; play rev.; tele.rev.; illus. (tabloid format) (also avail. in magnetic tape; back issues avail.) **Document type:** newspaper.

052 UK
WESSEX NEWS. 1936. 11/yr. free. (Southampton University, Students Union) S U S U, University Rd., Highfield, Southampton, England. Ed.Bd. adv.; bk.rev.; film rev.; play rev. circ. 3,000. (tabloid format)

072.911 UK
WEST HIGHLAND FREE PRESS. (Text in English, Gaelic) 1972. w. £37. West Highland Publishing Co., Industrial Estate, Broadford, Isle of Skye IV49 9AP, Scotland. TEL 0471-822464. FAX 0471-822694. Ed. Ian McCormack. adv. contact: Bob Wilson. circ. 9,611. **Document type:** newspaper.

072.2 UK
WEST SUSSEX GAZETTE. 1853. w. (Thu.). £34.84; newsstand price: £0.24. West Sussex Gazette, 53 High St., Arundel, W. Sussex BN18 0SD, England. TEL 0903-882201. FAX 0903-884368. Owner(s): Portsmouth Publishing, News Centre, Hilshea, Hants PO2 9SX, England. TEL 0705-664488. Ed. Gary Shipton; Gary/Shipton. adv. contact: Paul Robins. bk.rev.; film rev.; music rev.; tele.rev. circ. 15,350 (paid). cols./p.: 10; pp./issue: 28. (broadsheet format; back issues avail.) **Document type:** newspaper.

052 UK
WESTENDER. 1988. m. 108-110 Camden High St., London NW1 0LU, England. TEL 071-485-6050. Ed. Danny Connolley. adv.; bk.rev.; film rev.; play rev.; charts; illus. circ. 40,000 (controlled). (tabloid format; back issues avail.)

052 UK
WESTERN SUNDAY INDEPENDENT. 1808. w. 45p. per no. West of England Newspapers Ltd., Burrington Way, Plymouth, Devon Pl5 3LN, England. FAX 0752-780680. Ed. John Noble. adv.; bk.rev.; film rev.; play rev. circ. 46,000. (tabloid format)
   Formerly: Independent (ISSN 0019-3631)

072.3 UK
WESTON-SUPER-MARE ADMAG. 1979. w. newsstand price: £0.65. Admag Newspapers (Subsidiary of: Community Media Ltd.), 11 Beacons Field Rd., Weston-super-Mare, Avon BS23 1YE, England. TEL 0934-417921. FAX 0934-635031. adv.; tr.lit.; circ. 73,215 (controlled). cols./p.: 8; pp./issue: 44. **Document type:** newspaper.

072.3 UK
WEYMOUTH, PORTLAND AND DORCHESTER ADVERTISER. 1988. w. £17.68; newsstand price: £0.15. Southern Newspapers, 3 St. Nicholas St., Weymouth, Dorset DT4 8AD, England. TEL 0305-776226. FAX 0305-760773. (Dist. by: ADS, 71-73 High St., Poole, Dorset BH15 1BB, England. TEL 0202-666633) Ed. Nick Rowe. adv. contact: Dave Silk. film rev.; play rev. circ. 37,000. (tabloid format) **Document type:** newspaper.

072.3 UK
WHITE HORSE NEWS. 1990. fortn. £24. Wiltshire Media Ltd., 31 Market Pl., Melksham, Wiltshire SN12 6EV, England. TEL 0225-704761. FAX 0225-708081. Ed. Ian Drew; Pub. Ian Drew. circ. 8,500. (tabloid format) **Document type:** newspaper.

2732 GENERAL INTEREST PERIODICALS — GREECE

072.7 UK
WHITEHAVEN NEWS. 1852. w. newsstand price: £0.25. Cumbrian Newspapers Ltd., Newspaper House, Dalston Rd., Carlisle CA2 5UA, England. adv.; bk.rev.; film rev.; music rev.; play rev.; tele.rev.; illus.; circ. 20,000 (paid). (broadsheet format) **Document type:** newspaper.

072.3 UK
WILTSHIRE GAZETTE AND HERALD. 1816. w. (Thu.). £40.72; newsstand price: £0.35. Media in Wessex, 100 Victoria Rd., Swindon, Wiltshire SN1 3BE, England. TEL 0793-528144. FAX 0793-542434. Owner(s): Westminster Press Ltd., 8-16 Great New St., London EC4P 4ER, England. TEL 071-353-1030. FAX 071-353-7526. Ed. Peter Gawthorpe. adv. contact: Lynda Winfield. bk.rev.; film rev.; music rev.; tele.rev.; circ. 24,000. cols./p.: 8; pp./issue: 22. (broadsheet format; back issues avail.) **Document type:** newspaper.

072.5 UK
WOBURN SANDS AND CRANFIELD CITIZEN. 1982. w. newsstand price: £0.40. Premier Newspapers Ltd., Napier House, Auckland Park, Bletchley, Milton Keynes MK1 1BU, England. TEL 0908-374033. FAX 0908-37145. Ed. Jan Henderson; Pub. Simon Abra. adv. contact: Kerry Drucker. film rev.; music rev.; tele.rev.; tr.lit. circ. 89,700. cols./p.: 9; pp./issue: 180. (tabloid format) **Document type:** newspaper.

072.5 UK
WORKSOP TRADER. 1970. w. (Wed.). free. Four Counties Newspapers, Westbourne House, Newcastle St., Worksop, Notts. S80 2AS, England. TEL 0909-483333. FAX 0909-501080. Ed. Richard Bacon; Pub. Michael Williams. adv. contact: Audrey Ridge. circ. 30,917. cols./p.: 8; pp./issue: 48. (tabloid format; back issues avail.) **Document type:** newspaper.

072.2 UK
WORTHING GUARDIAN. Regional editions: Littlehampton Guardian. Pulborough, Storrington & Steyning Guardian. Shoreham Guardian. 1982. w. £26 (foreign £35). Worthing Guardian Series, 56a Chapel Rd., Worthing, W. Sussex BN11 0HJ, England. TEL 0903-209025. FAX 0903-201481. Owner(s): Johnson Press, 53 Manor Pl., Edinburgh EH3 7EG, Scotland. TEL 031-225-3361. Ed. Tony Mayes. adv. contact: Yvette Mayes. circ. 102,000. cols./p.: 7; pp./issue: 34. **Document type:** newspaper.

072.9 UK
Y CYMRO. (Text in Welsh) 1932. w. £24.44. North Wales Newspapers Ltd., Mold Industrial Park, Wrexham Rd., Mold, Clwyd CH7 1XY, Wales. TEL 0352-700022. FAX 0352-752180. Ed. Glyn Evans. adv.; bk.rev. circ. 4,600. (tabloid format; back issues avail.) **Document type:** newspaper.

052 UK ISSN 0044-0620
YORKSHIRE LIFE. 1947. m. £18 (foreign £23). Town and County Magazines (Subsidiary of: Oyston Publications PLC), Oyston Mill, Strand Rd., Preston PR1 8UR, England. TEL 0772-722022. FAX 0772-736496. Peter Williams. adv.: B&W page £720, color page £1065; trim 200 x 295; adv. contact: Liz Wareing. bk.rev.; illus. circ. 10,000. **Document type:** consumer publication.
—BLDSC (9421.235800).

052 UK ISSN 0044-0639
YORKSHIRE RIDINGS MAGAZINE. 1964. bi-m. £10.50. Ridings Publishing Co., 33 Beverley Rd., Driffield, Yorkshire YO25 7SD, England. Ed. Winston Halstead. adv.; bk.rev.; illus.; index. circ. 12,000. **Document type:** consumer publication.
Formerly: Ridings.
Description: English county periodical with focus on Yorkshire.

052 UK
YOURS. 1973. m. Choice Publications Ltd., Apex House, 5th Floor, Oundle Rd., Peterborough PE2 9NP, England. adv.; play rev. circ. 130,704. (tabloid format; back issues avail.)

052 UK ISSN 0044-4340
ZERO ONE. 1975. s-a. £5($7) Zero One Publications, 39 Minford Gardens, W. Kensington, London W14 0AP, England. Ed. Arthur Moyse. adv.; bk.rev.; film rev.; play rev.; illus.; circ. 600 (controlled) **Document type:** bulletin.
Description: Anarchist-oriented publication.

052 UK
20-20. 1989. m. Time Out Group ltd., Tower House, Southampton row, London WC2E 7HD, England. FAX 071-836-7118. (Subscr. to: Unit 8, Grove Ash, Bletchley, Milton Keynes, MK1 1BZ, England) Ed. Stephen Wood. bk.rev. circ. 41,260.
Description: Features and listings of art, film, theatre, dance, sport, TV.

GENERAL INTEREST PERIODICALS — Greece

079.495 GR
I ALLAGHI; kathimerini ephimerida trodeftikon archon. 1961. d. (except Mon.). Dr.21000($400); newsstand price: Dr.70. E. Karelli & Co., Kazani Str. 4, Iraklion 71202, Crete, Greece. TEL 30-81-280022. FAX 30-81-243370. Ed. K. Trigonis; Pub. M. Karellis. adv. contact: G. Chatzidaki. film rev.; music rev.; play rev.; tele.rev.; illus.; circ. 1,300 (paid); 3,100 (controlled). cols./p.: 6; pp./issue: 24. **Document type:** newspaper.
Description: Espouses progressive principles.

059.8 GR
AUTO-EXPRESS. (Text in Greek) 1967. m. Dr.2160($10) Hellenews Ltd., 39 Halandriou St., 151 25 Amaroussion, Athens, Greece. TEL 682.7582. Ed. John A. Koutelierise. adv. circ. 45,000. (back issues avail.)

052 949.5 938 UK ISSN 0068-2454
DF11
BRITISH SCHOOL AT ATHENS. ANNUAL. (Text in English; abstracts in English, Greek) 1894. a. £35 (effective Mar. 1993). British School at Athens, 31-34 Gordon Sq., London WC1H 0PY, England. TEL 071-387-8029. FAX 071-383-0781. Ed. Graham J. Shipley. index. circ. 950. (also avail. in microfilm from BHP; reprint service avail. from KTO) **Indexed:** A.I.C.P., Art & Archaeol.Tech.Abstr., Avery Ind.Archit.Per., Bibl.Ling., Br.Archaeol.Abstr., Br.Hum.Ind., Br.Tech.Ind., Numis.Lit. **Document type:** academic/scholarly publication.
—BLDSC (1073.675000).
Description: Includes the work of B.S.A. members on cultural, historical, artistic, or geographic aspects of Greece in classical, medieval, and modern times.
Refereed Serial

059.8 US ISSN 0577-5574
PA5273
CHARIOTEER; an annual review of modern Greek culture. (Text in English, Greek) 1960. a. $15 to individuals (foreign $20); institutions $20 (foreign $25) (effective 1993). Pella Publishing Company, 337 W. 36th St., New York, NY 10018. TEL 212-279-9586. Ed. Carmen Capri-Karka. adv.; bk.rev.; illus. circ. 1,500. (back issues avail.) **Indexed:** Amer.Bibl.Slavic & E.Eur.Stud.

059.8 GR
EIKONES. w. Bobolas Ed. & Pub., Benaki Str., Metamorfossi, 152 35 Halandri, Athens, Greece. circ. 87,000.

059.8 GR
EMBROS/FORWARD. (Text in Greek) 1896. w. Odos Christou Lada 7, Athens, Greece. TEL 30-1-322-8565. Ed. A.E. Paraschos.

079.495 GR
ESTIA. 1984. d. (except Sun.). Dr.460000; newsstand price: Dr.150. 7 Anthimou Gazi, Athens 105 61, Greece. TEL 30-1-3220481. FAX 30-1-3243071. Ed. Spyros Papageorgiou; Pub. Adonis Kyrou. adv. contact: Elias Kontaktsis. bk.rev.; music rev.; play rev.; illus.; circ. 100 (paid); 5,000 (controlled). cols./p.: 8; pp./issue: 6. **Document type:** newspaper.

059.8 GR
KAI. 1984. w. $150. Grammi S.A., 15 Voukourestiou Str., 106 71 Athens, Greece. TEL 01 3643821-4, 3644151-5. Ed. George Tsoutsias. adv. circ. 135,000.

059.8 GR
KLIK. (Text in Greek) 1987. m. Dr.8000 in Europe; in U.S. Dr.8500. Special Publications Aris Terzopoulos S.A., 7 Fragoklisias Str., 151 25 Marousi, Greece. TEL 68979411-8. Ed. Petros Kostopoulos. adv.; bk.rev.; film rev. circ. 90,000. (back issues avail.) **Document type:** consumer publication.
Description: Greek general interest consumer-oriented magazine.

059.8 GR
MAKEDONIKI ZOI/MACEDONIAN LIFE. m. Odos Mitropoleos 70, 546 22, Thessaloniki, Greece. TEL 051-277700. Ed. N.J. Mertzos.

059.8 GR
MIA. 1986. fortn. $90. Grammi S.A., 15 Voukourestiou Str., 106 71 Athens, Greece. TEL 01 3643821-4, 3644151-5. Ed. Eleana Kirkili. adv. circ. 79,037.

079.495 GR
TA NEA. (Supplement avail.: Afto Nea) 1946. d. Dr.47700; newsstand price: Dr.150. Lambrakis Press S.A., 3 Christou Lada, Athens 102 37, Greece. TEL 30-1-333355. FAX 30-1-3241112. Ed. Leon Karapanagiotis; Pub. Christos Cambrakis. adv.: Page Dr.1650000; adv. contact: Nikos Biliris. illus. cols./p.: 6; pp./issue: 90. (tabloid format) **Document type:** newspaper.

059.8 GR ISSN 0040-8255
NISAKI MAS I KEA;* periodikon tou syndesmou ton Kion. 1952. q. Dr.80($15) K. Hartofylakadis, Ed. & Pub., Fotiou Patriarchou 21, Athens 706, Greece. illus. circ. 1,500.

059.8 GR
ROMANTZO.* w. Theofanidis Nicolaos S.A., 5 Anazagora St., 105 52 Athens, Greece. circ. 120,000.

059.8 GR ISSN 0039-8888
TACHYDROMOS/COURIER. 1953. w. $112. Lambrakis Press S.A., 3 Christou Lada, 102 37 Athens, Greece. TEL 01-3250810. TELEX 215904. Ed. Roula Mitropoulou. adv.; bk.rev.; illus. circ. 177,182.

059.8 700 GR
TO TETARTO. 1985. m. $50. Grammi S.A., 15 Voukourestiou Str., 106 71 Athens, Greece. TEL 01 3643821-4, 3644151-5. Ed. Nikos Sotiriadis. adv. circ. 15,000.

079.495 GR
TO VIMA/TRIBUNE. 1922. w. Dr.8500($86) in U.S.; Cyprus $52; Europe and Turkey $76. Odos Christou Lada, 102 37 Athens, Greece. TEL 30-1-322-0221. FAX 30-1-322-8797. TELEX 215904. Ed. Stavros Psycharos. circ. 190,000. **Document type:** newspaper.

GENERAL INTEREST PERIODICALS — Greenland

079.82 GL ISSN 0904-2458
A G - ATIUAGAGDLIUTIT - GROENLANDSPOSTEN. (Text in Danish and Greenlandic) 1861. s-w. Selvejende Institution Atuagagdliutit - Groenlandsposten, P.O. Box 39, 3900 Nuuk, Greenland. Ed. Joergen Fleischer. adv.; bk.rev.; illus. circ. 5,000. **Document type:** newspaper.
Formerly (until 1988): Atuagagdliutit (ISSN 0901-9103)

058.398 DK ISSN 0017-4556
G725 CODEN: GRGSAX
GROENLAND (CHARLOTTENLUND). 1953. 8/yr.. DKK 300. Groenlandske Selskab - Greenland Society, L.E. Bruunsvej 10, DK-2920 Charlottenlund, Denmark. TEL 45-31-63-57-33. FAX 45-31-63-55-43. Ed. Keld Hansen. adv.: B&W page DKK 2500. bk.rev.; index. circ. 2,000. **Indexed:** Biol.Abstr.

GENERAL INTEREST PERIODICALS — Guatemala

056.1 972 GT
REVISTA 13 GRAFICO. a. free. Ministerio de Educacion, Centro Nacional de Libros de Texto y Material Didactico (CENALTEX), 35 Calle Final, Zona 11, Finca Las Charcas, Guatemala. Ed. Adolfo Lopez Alfaro. circ. 4,000.

056.1 GT
▼**TIEMPO.** 1992. fortn. Q.5 per no. 14 Calle "A", 11-49, Zona 1, 01001 Guatemala, Guatemala. Dir. Adolfo Barrera. **Document type:** consumer publication.

GENERAL INTEREST PERIODICALS — Guyana

052   GY
MIRROR. 1962. w. $52.00. New Guyana Co. Ltd., 8 Industrial Estate, Ruimveldt, Greater Georgetown, Guyana. TEL 02-624-712. Ed. Janet Jagan. circ. 25,000.

052   GY
NEW NATION. 1955. w. People's National Congress, Sophia Exhibition Site, Georgetown, Guyana. TEL 2-68520. Ed. Adam E. Harris. circ. 26,000.

GENERAL INTEREST PERIODICALS — Haiti

054.1   HT   ISSN 0304-5757
CONJONCTION; revue franco-haitienne. 1946. q. $25. Institut Francais d'Haiti, Boite Postale 131, Port au Prince, Haiti. Dir. Christian Burgue. adv.; bk.rev.; bibl.; charts; illus.; stat.; index. circ. 1,200. (back issues avail.) **Indexed:** Hisp.Amer.Per.Ind. (until 1993).
—BLDSC (3417.563000).

054.1   HT
HAITI PROGRES. w. 11 rue Capois, Port-au-Prince, Haiti. Ed. Ben Dupuy.

054.1   HT
MESSAGER DU NORD-OUEST. w. Port de Paix, Haiti.

054.1   HT
MONITEUR. 2/w. B.P.214 bis, Port-au-Prince, Haiti. TEL 1-2-1026. Ed. Marcel Elibert. circ. 2,000.

054.1   HT
SEPTENTRION. w. Cap Haitien, Haiti. Ed. Nelson Bell. circ. 2,000.

GENERAL INTEREST PERIODICALS — Hong Kong

079.5125 052   HK   ISSN 0004-4474
ASIA MAGAZINE. (Text in English) 1961. w. $25. Asia Magazine Ltd., 6F Morning Post Bldg., Tong Chong St., Quarry Bay, Hong Kong. TEL 853-565-2331. FAX 852-565-9441. (U.S. address: 122 E. 42nd St., New York, NY 10017) Ed. Peter Cordingley. adv.; bk.rev.; illus. circ. 669,210. **Document type:** newspaper.
—UnCover.
Description: Sunday supplement for English language newspapers for Asia's well-educated, affluent and internationally-oriented people.

959   HK   ISSN 1012-6244
ASIAWEEK; the Asian news weekly. (Text in English) 1975. w. HK$270($34.93) (effective Jan. 1994). Asiaweek Ltd., 34F CitiCorp Centre, 18 Whitfield Rd., Causeway Bay, Hong Kong. TEL 852-508-2688. FAX 852-571-0916. TELEX 83540-AWEEK-HX. (Subscr. to: P.O. Box 60280, Tsat Tze Mui Post Office, Hong Kong.) Ed. Salman W. Morrison. adv.; bk.rev.; charts; illus. circ. 103,012. (also avail. in microfilm)
—UnCover; SWETS.

059.951   HK
B INTERNATIONAL. (Text in English) 1971. m. HK$306. Z Y C Holding Ltd. (Subsidiary of: Yongder Hall Group), 10th Fl., Cheung Kong Bldg., 661 King's Rd., Quarry Bay, Hong Kong. TEL 852-565-1313. FAX 852-565-8217. Ed. Mirja Muncy. adv. circ. 20,000. **Document type:** consumer publication.
Description: A lifestyle magazine for upper-class Chinese in Hong Kong. Covers beauty, culture, fashions, sports, travel, wine and cuisine, business profiles, parties and social events.

059.95   HK
CHENG MING MONTHLY. (Text in Chinese) 1977. m. $46. Hennessy Rd., P.O. Box 20370, Hong Kong. TEL 5740664. Ed. 5740664. adv.; bk.rev.

059.95   HK
CHOIFUNG. (Text in Chinese) w. Choifung News Agency, 12, Kowloon City Rd., Flat C, 11-F, P.O. Box 9370, Kowloon, Hong Kong.

059.951   HK
CONTEMPORARY/TANG TAI; shih shih chou k'an. (Text in Chinese) fortn. $75. Hsin Mei Chia Co., Ltd., 2nd Fl., 27 Yeow-wah St., Wanchai, Hong Kong. TEL 838-9688. FAX 838-8167. (U.S. orders to: World Journal Bookstore, 141-07 20th Ave., Whitestone, NY 11357. TEL 718-746-8889) Ed. Cheng Hsiang. adv.
Description: Covers political and social issues in China and Hong Kong.

059.95   HK
CONTEMPORARY MONTHLY. (Text in Chinese) 1989. m. $52. Ideal Wisdom Ltd., 27 Yiu Wa St., 1st Fl., Wanchai, Hong Kong. TEL 8389789. FAX 8389688. Ed. Ching Cheong. circ. 50,000.
Formerly (until 1991): Contemporary News Weekly.

052   UK
DATELINE HONG KONG. 1981. m. free. Hong Kong Government Office, 6 Grafton St., London W1X 3LB, England. TEL 071-499-9821. FAX 071-493-1964. Ed. Ranjit Peiris. circ. 1,750.

052   HK
HONG KONG TATLER. 1977. m. HK$250. (Communication Management Ltd.) Communication Management Ltd., 1811 Hong Kong Plaza, 188 Connaught Rd. West, Hong Kong. TEL 547-7117. FAX 858-2671. Ed. Linda Ross. adv.; bk.rev.; illus. circ. 22,264. **Document type:** consumer publication.

059.95   HK
LIFE OVERSEAS/HUA JEN. (Text in Chinese) m. HK$144 in Hong Kong; PRC, ROC, Macao HK$170.40; elsewhere $28. Rm. 1102, Kai Wong Commercial Bldg., 222-226 Queen's Rd., Central, Hong Kong. TEL 542-3811. FAX 541-7189. (Overseas orders to: 245-151 Sai Yee St., G-F, Mong Kok, Kowloon, Hong Kong) adv.
Description: Covers world news and developments in China and Hong Kong.

059.95   HK
METROPOLITAN WEEKLY. (Text in Chinese) 1983. w. Rm. 1008, 10-F, Toppan Bldg., 22A Westlands Rd., Quarry Bay, Hong Kong. TEL 8113811. FAX 852-5-8113822. Ed. Charles You. circ. 130,000.
Description: Covers entertainment and social news.

059.95   HK
THE MIRROR/CHING PAO. (Text in Chinese) m. HK$18 per no. Mirror Post Cultural Enterprises Co. Ltd., Flat D, 10th Fl., Waldorf Mansion, 2-6 Causeway Rd., Causeway Bay, Hong Kong. TEL 576-9288. (US orders to: Mrs. Li Ya Mo, 149-60 Ash Ave., Flushing, NY 11355; Eur. orders to: Mr. Han Tien Chin, 46 rue des Gravilliers, 75003 Paris, France) adv.
Description: Covers international news, plus the situation in China.

059.951   HK
NEWSDOM/SINWEN TIENTI. (Text in Chinese) 1945. w. HK$312 (foreign HK$410). Rm.903, Yat Fat Bldg., 44 Des Voeux Rd., Central, Hong Kong. TEL 5-247738. FAX 5-218390. (Dist. in ROC by: Far East Book Co., 24 Aikuo E. Rd., Taipei, Taiwan, R.O.C.) adv.
Description: Covers news of China and the world.

059.95   HK
THE NINETIES MONTHLY/JIU SHI NIAN DAI. 1970. m. HK$220($58) (foreign $58). Going Fine Ltd., Southward Mansion 1A & 1B, 3 Lau Li St., Causeway Bay, Hong Kong. TEL 887-3997. FAX 887-3897. (Dist. in US by: Chinese Periodicals Distribution, 507 S. Stoneman Ave., Alhambra, CA 91801. TEL 818-282-0361) Ed. Lee Yee. adv. circ. 40,000. **Indexed:** HR Rep.
Formerly (until 1984): Seventies Monthly.
Description: Provides information and analysis on the political, economic and social conditions of P.R. China, Taiwan and Hong Kong.

059.95   HK
OPEN MAGAZINE. (Text in Chinese) 1990. m. Hennessy Rd., P.O. Box 20558, Hong Kong. TEL 5296926. Ed. Kam Chong. circ. 10,000.

059.95   HK
THE PERSPECTIVE/NAN PEI CHI. (Text in Chinese) 1970. m. P.O. Box 9-6306, Tsimshatsui, Kowloon, Hong Kong. TEL 3-676364. adv.; illus.
Description: Covers world news and economics.

052   HK   ISSN 0034-0383
READER'S DIGEST (ASIAN EDITION). (Text in English) 1963. m. HK$393($30) (typically set in Jan.). Reader's Digest Association Far East Ltd., 3 Ah Kung Ngam Village Rd., Shaukiwan, Hong Kong. TEL 852-884-5678. FAX 852-568-9024. TELEX 74700 DIGST HX. Ed. Janie Couch. adv.; bk.rev.; illus. circ. 250,000. **Document type:** consumer publication.

052   HK
SINGAPORE EVE MODE. (Text in English) 1988. q. S.$10 per no. Communication Management Ltd., 1811 Hong Kong Plaza, 188 Connaught Rd. W., Hong Kong. TEL 547-7117. FAX 852-8582671. TELEX 61758 TATCO HX. Ed. Linda Ross. circ. 74,800. **Document type:** consumer publication.
Formerly: Singapore Eve.

079.51   HK
SOUTH CHINA MORNING POST. (Text in English) d. South China Morning Post Ltd., Morning Post Bldg., 6th Fl., Quarry Bay, Hong Kong. TEL 0852-565-2435. FAX 0852-565-2435. adv.
Document type: newspaper.

052   HK
SUNDAY MORNING POST MAGAZINE. (Text in English) 1989. w. South China Morning Post Bldg., Tong Chong St., Quarry Bay, Hong Kong. TEL 565-2515. FAX 565-5608. Ed. Peter Cordingley. circ. 77,248.
Description: Covers fashion, travel, food and lifestyle.

052   HK   ISSN 0039-8675
TA KUNG PAO. (English Edition) w. $16. Fei Yi-Ming, 342 Hennessy Rd., Hong Kong, Hong Kong. adv.; illus. (tabloid format)

059.95   HK   ISSN 0041-3836
AP95.C4
TU CHER WEN CHER READER'S DIGEST (CHINESE EDITION). (Text in Chinese) 1965. m. HK$393($30) Reader's Digest Association Far East Ltd., 3 Ah Kung Ngam Village Rd., Shaukiwan, Hong Kong. TEL 852-884-5678. FAX 852-567-1479. TELEX 74700 DIGST HX. Ed. Janie Couch. adv. contact: Leo U. Murray. bk.rev.; illus. circ. 300,000.

059.95   HK
WIDE ANGLE/KUANG CHIAO CHING. (Text in Chinese) 1972. m. HK$10. Wide Angle Press, 195-197 Johnston Rd., 7-F Wanchai, Hong Kong. Ed. K.K. Lee. adv.; bk.rev.; illus. circ. 30,000.

079.5125   HK
XIN WAN BAO/NEW EVENING POST. (Text in Chinese) 1950. d. HK$4; newsstand price: HK$4. New Evening Post Ltd., 342, Hennessy Rd., G-F, Wanchai, Hong Kong. TEL 852-8383312. FAX 853-5752706. Ed. Li Zhuxing; Pub. Huang Guohua. adv.: B&W page HK$29240, color page HK$49300; adv. contact: Michael Kwong. bk.rev.; film rev.; music rev.; play rev.; illus. circ. 95,000. cols./p.: 17; pp./issue: 24. **Document type:** newspaper.

059.95   HK   ISSN 1015-5015
YAZHOU ZHOUKAN. (Text in Chinese) 1987. 51/yr. $152.60. Asiaweek Ltd., 13th Fl., South, Somerset House, 28 Tong Chong St., Quarry Bay, Hong Kong. TEL 5630232. FAX 5657730. TELEX 83540-AWEEK-HX. (Subscr. to: P.O. Box 60280, Tsat Tze Mui Post Office, Hong Kong, Hong Kong; Dist. in Japan by: Intercontinental Marketing Corp., I.P.O. Box 5056, Tokyo 100-31, Japan. TEL 81-3-3661-7458. FAX 81-3-3667-9646) Ed. Thomas Hon Wing Polin. adv.; bk.rev. circ. 85,000. (back issues avail.) **Document type:** consumer publication.

GENERAL INTEREST PERIODICALS — Hungary

073.9   HU   ISSN 0865-4093
BESZELO. 1989. w. $84 (effective Jan. 1993). Ab-Beszelo Kiado Kft., Deri Miksa u. 10, Budapest 8, Hungary. TEL 331-1137574. FAX 331-1343504. (Subscr. to: Kultura, P.O. Box 149, 1389 Budapest, Hungary) Ed. Koszeg Ferenc. adv.; bk.rev. circ. 14,000. **Document type:** newspaper.
Description: Focuses on events in Parliament, on the political parties, and on events in former communist countries. Covers fundamentalism, human rights, trade unions and economics.

GENERAL INTEREST PERIODICALS — ICELAND

059.945 HU ISSN 0007-2885
BUDAPEST. 1966. m. $28. Lapkiado Vallalat, Lenin korut 9-11, 1073 Budapest 7, Hungary. TEL 222-408. (Subscr. to: Kultura, Box 149, H-1389 Budapest, Hungary) Ed. Vargha Balazs. **Indexed:** Hung.Build.Bull.

053.1 HU ISSN 0007-2893
BUDAPESTER RUNDSCHAU. (Text in German) 1967. w. $37. Lapkiado Vallalat, Lenin korut 9-11, 1073 Budapest 7, Hungary. TEL 222-408. (Subscr. to: Kultura, Box 149, H-1389 Budapest, Hungary) Ed. Janos Nemes. adv.; bk.rev. circ. 10,000. (also avail. in microfilm from NRP)

059.945 RM
CONTEMPORANUL IDEEA EUROPEANA. 1881. w. Ministry of Culture, Piata Presei Libere 1, 71341 Bucharest, Rumania. TEL 177413. Ed. Nicolae Breban.
Description: Cultural, political and scientific review.

073.9 HU ISSN 0133-0306
DAILY NEWS; weekly edition. (Text in English) 1967. w. 2400 Ft.($80); newsstand price: 49 Ft. Magyar T - Hungarian News Agency, Naphegy ter. 8, 1016 Budapest, Hungary. TEL 361-1756928. FAX 361-1188384. Ed. Sandor Korospataki Kiss; Pub. Dezso Kopreda. adv.: B&W page 120000 Ft.($1500); 432 x 282; adv. contact: Agnes Muhi. film rev.; music rev.; play rev.; illus.; circ. 10,000 (controlled). cols./p.: 6; pp./issue: 8. (standard format) **Document type:** newspaper.
Former German parallel title: Nueste Nachrichten.

059.945 HU ISSN 0016-240X
FULES. 1957. w. $39. Erasmuspress Ltd., Dozsa Gyorgy ut. 150, 1138 Budapest, Hungary. (Subscr. to: Kultura, P.O. Box 149, 1389 Budapest, Hungary) Ed. Laszlo Tiszai.

052 HU ISSN 0209-5386
HUNGARIAN DIGEST. French edition: Revue de Hongrie. German edition: Ungarland. (Text in English) 1980. bi-m. $6. Lapkiado Vallalat, Lenin krt. 9-11, 1073 Budapest 7, Hungary. TEL 222-408. (Subscr. to: Kultura, P.O. Box 149, H-1389 Budapest, Hungary) Ed. Tibor Zador. adv.; illus. circ. 50,000. **Indexed:** Key to Econ.Sci.
Incorporates: Hungarian Review (ISSN 0018-7763)
Description: Covers political, economic and cultural issues.

052 HU ISSN 0238-9932
DB901
HUNGARIAN OBSERVER. (Text in English) m. $43. Pallas Lap-es Konyvkiado Vallalat, Lenin korut 9-11, H-1906 Budapest, Hungary. TEL 36-1-2210285. (Subscr. to: Kultura, P.O. Box 149, H-1389 Budapest, Hungary) Ed. Tomas Zala.
●Also available online. Vendor(s): Mead Data Central, Inc.
—BLDSC (4337.038000).

059.945 HU ISSN 0451-7490
KEPES UJSAG/ILLUSTRATED NEWS. 1960. w. 35 Ft (effective 1993). Factum '90 Kft., Gyulai Pal u. 14, 1085 Budapest, Hungary. TEL 138-4644. FAX 118-8503. (Dist. by: Kultura, P.O. Box 149, 1389 Budapest 62, Hungary. TEL 361-180-3194) Ed. Mihaly Kovacs. circ. 200,000.

059.918 HU
L'UDOVE NOVINY. (Text in Slovak) w. Nagymezo u. 49, 1065 Budapest, Hungary. TEL 131-9184. Ed. Pal Kondacs. circ. 1,700.

052 HU ISSN 0133-9788
M T I DAILY BULLETIN. (Text in English) 1966. d. $810 in Europe; elsewhere $888. Magyar Tavirati Iroda - Hungarian News Agency, Pl. Naphegy ter. 8, 1016 Budapest, Hungary. TEL 361-175-6722. FAX 361-228-8204. TELEX 061-22-4373. Ed. Andras Lontai. circ. 20. **Document type:** bulletin.
Description: Reports on the most important political, economic, cultural and sports events of Hungary.

059.945 052 CN
MAGYAR NAPLO (TORONTO, 1979). (Text in English and Hungarian) 1979. m. Can.$10($10) Victor Szabo, Ed. & Pub., P.O. Box 771, Sta. A, Toronto, Ont. M5W 1G3, Canada. TEL 416-921-6161. FAX 416-283-2357. adv.; bk.rev. circ. 10,000.

059.945 HU ISSN 0864-8646
DS135.H9
MULT ES JOVO. 1988. q. Szerkesztoseg Cime, Marvany u. 17, 1012 Budapest, Hungary. TEL 156-3211. FAX 156-9773. Ed. Janos Kobanyai.

073.9 HU
NEPSZAVA. 1873. 6/w. 4680 Ft.; newsstand price: 19.50 Ft. Topokvesz ut 30-A, 1022 Budapest, Hungary. TEL 361-202-7788. FAX 361-202-7798. Ed. Andras Kereszty; Pub. Janos Fenyo. adv. contact: Andras Szocs. circ. 120,000 (controlled). cols./p.: 6; pp./issue: 16. (broadsheet format) **Document type:** newspaper.

059.945 HU ISSN 0238-9037
REFORM. 1988. w. $93. P.O. Box 222, 1443 Budapest, Hungary. TEL 142-4350. FAX 122-4240. Ed. Peter Toke. circ. 385,000. (tabloid format)

943.8 HU ISSN 0133-0950
SZABAD FOLD. 1945. w. $27. Konyves Kalman krt. 76, 1087 Budapest, Hungary. FAX 1-133-6794. TELEX 22-5554. (Subscr. to: Kultura, P.O. Box 149, 1389 Budapest, Hungary) Ed. Gyula Eck. adv.; bk.rev. circ. 600,000.

059.945 HU ISSN 1216-092X
SZABOLCS - SZATMAR-BEREGI SZEMLE. 1956. 4/yr. 35 Ft. Moricz Zsigmond Konyvtar, Szabadsag ter 2, 4400 Nyiregyhaza, Hungary. Ed. Mezo Andras. adv.; bk.rev.; illus. circ. 1,300. **Indexed:** World Agri.Econ.& Rural Sociol.Abstr.
Formerly: Szabolcs - Smatmari Szemle (ISSN 0133-2465)

059.945 HU ISSN 0133-090X
UJ MAGYAR HIREK/NEW HUNGARIAN NEWS. 1948. fortn. 1200 Ft.($19) Magyar Vilag Kiado Kft., Benczur utca 15, 1068 Budapest, Hungary. TEL 122-5616. FAX 122-2421. TELEX 22-3317. (U.S. subscr. to: c/o Leslie J. Dus, Box 26244, Cleveland, OH 44126) Ed. Eva Arokszallasi. adv.; bk.rev. circ. 52,000. (back issues avail.)
Description: Hungarian history, news about life in Hungary and in Hungarian communities worldwide.

053.1 HU
UNGARISCHE WOCHENSCHAU. (Text in German) w. $240 in Europe; elsewhere $258 (effective 1993). Magyar Tavirati Iroda - Hungarian News Agency, Naphegy ter 8, 1016 Budapest, Hungary. TEL 361-175-6722. TELEX 061-22-4373. Ed. Andras Lontai. circ. 200.
Description: Publishes background materials and summaries, important articles, government standpoints, laws, directions.

052 054.1 057.1 HU ISSN 0024-8495
WEEKLY BULLETIN. French edition: Bulletin Hebdomadaire (ISSN 0133-9931); Spanish edition: Boletin Semanal (ISSN 0133-9885); Russian edition: Jezsenyegyelnij Bjuletiny (ISSN 0133-9834) (Text in English) 1962. w. $222 in Europe; elsewhere $234 (effective 1993). Magyar Tavirati Iroda - Hungarian News Agency, Pl. Naphegy ter. 8, 1016 Budapest, Hungary. TEL 361-175-6722. TELEX 061-22-4373. (Subscr. to: P.O. Box 3, 1426 Budapest, Hungary) Ed. Andras Lontai. index. circ. 563 (186 English ed.; 144 French ed.; 172 Russian ed.; 61 Spanish ed.). (looseleaf format; back issues avail.) **Indexed:** PROMT. **Document type:** bulletin.
Former titles (until 1970): Fortnightly Bulletin (ISSN 0324-3044); (until 1968): Weekly Bulletin (ISSN 0200-2396)
Description: Publishes background materials and summaries, important articles, government standpoints, and laws from Hungary.
Refereed Serial

GENERAL INTEREST PERIODICALS — Iceland

079.4912 IC ISSN 1021-8203
ALTHYDUBLADID. 1919. d. ISK 1400 per m.; newsstand price: ISK 140. Alprent hf., Hverfisgoetu 8-10, Reykjavik, Iceland. TEL 354-1-625-566. FAX 354-1-629-244. Ed. Sigurdur Tomas Bjoergvinsson. adv. contact: Amundi Amundason. **Document type:** newspaper.

079.4912 IC ISSN 1021-8254
D V; frjalst, ohad dagblad. Variant title: Dagbladid Visir. 1987. d. ISK 16800; newsstand price: ISK 140. Frjals Fjoelmidlun hf., Thverholt 14, 105-Reykjavik, Iceland. TEL 354-96-25013. FAX 354-96-11605. Eds. Jonas Kristjansson, Ellert B. Schram. adv. contact: Pall Stefansson. bk.rev.; film rev.; music rev.; play rev.; tele.rev.; video rev.; illus. circ. 45,000. **Document type:** newspaper.

079.4912 IC
DAGUR. d. ISK 1400 per m.; newsstand price: ISK 125. Dagsprent hf., Strandgata 31, P.O. Box 60, Akureyri, Iceland. TEL 354-96-24222. FAX 354-96-27639. Eds. Johann Olafur Halldorsson, Oskar Thor Halldorsson. adv. contact: Frimann Frimannsson. **Document type:** newspaper.

059.396 IC ISSN 1021-8270
FAXI. 1939. 7-8/yr. ISK 1900($35) (effective Jan. 1992). (Malfundafelagid Faxi) Manadarbladid Faxi, Vallargata 17, 230 Keflavik, Iceland. TEL 354-2-11114. FAX 354-2-11114. Ed. Helgi Holm. adv.; index. circ. 460. (back issues avail.)

058.396 IC ISSN 0017-9698
HEIMA ER BEZT. 1951. m. $25. Gudjon Baldvinsson, Ed. & Pub., Armula 23, IS-108 Reykjavik, Iceland. bk.rev.; charts; illus. circ. 2,800.

052 IC ISSN 0019-1094
DL301
ICELAND REVIEW. (Text in English) 1963. q. $29.50. Iceland Review, P.O. Box 12122, IS-132 Reykjavik, Iceland. TEL 354-1-675-700. FAX 354-1-674-066. Eds. Haraldur J. Hamar, Asgeir Fridgeirsson. adv.; bk.rev.; illus.
—BLDSC (4361.450000); UnCover.
Description: Focuses on Icelandic nature, culture, politics, economy, art and literature.

053.1 949.12 GW
ISLAND - BERICHTE DER GESELLSCHAFT DER FREUNDE ISLANDS HAMBURG. 1960. q. DM.80 to individuals; institutions DM.150. Gesellschaft der Freunde Islands e.V., Raboisen 5, 20095 Hamburg, Germany. TEL 040-336696. FAX 040-331347. Ed. Guenter Papendick. bk.rev. circ. 375. **Document type:** newsletter.

058.396 IC ISSN 1017-3587
MANNLIF. 1984. 10/yr. ISK 5290 (effective Jan. 1994). Frodi Ltd., Armuli 18, 108 Reykjavik, Iceland. TEL 354-1-812300. FAX 1-812946. Eds. Bjarni Brynjolfsson, Kristjan Thorvaldsson. adv.: B&W page ISK 60640, color page ISK 86880; trim 20.5 x 27.5; adv. contact: Ragnar Petersen. illus. circ. 15,000.
Description: Publishes articles of interest to both men and women on such subjects as literature, politics, motion pictures and theater.

079.4912 IC ISSN 1021-7266
MORGUNBLADID. (Supplement avail.: Lesbok) 1913. d. ISK 16800; newsstand price: ISK 125. Arvakur h.f., Kringlan 1, 103-Reykjavik, Iceland. TEL 354-691100. Eds. Matthias Johannessen, Styrmir Gunnarsson. adv.; bk.rev.; film rev.; music rev.; play rev.; tele.rev.; video rev.; illus. circ. 52,077. **Document type:** newspaper.

052 949.12 IC ISSN 0253-8083
NEWS FROM ICELAND. (Includes special supplement on business and travel) (Text in English) 1975. m. $28. Iceland Review, P.O. Box 12122, IS-121 Reykjavik, Iceland. TEL 354-1-675-700. FAX 354-1-674-066. Ed. Haraldur J. Hamar. adv.; illus.
Description: Directed to international readership, containing general news and summaries of development in the economy, fisheries, trade, tourism and industry in Iceland.

058.396 IC ISSN 1021-7592
SAMUEL. 1968. 6/yr. ISK 3200($45) Frodi Ltd., Armuli 18, 108 Reykjavik, Iceland. TEL 354-1-812300. FAX 354-1-812946. Ed. Thorarinn J. Magnusson. adv. contact: Helgi Runar Oskarsson. index. circ. 10,000. (back issues avail.)
Description: Concerned with issues of interest to young men such as leisure, hobbies, technology, automobiles and sports.

079.4912 IC ISSN 1021-8459
TIMINN. 1917. d. ISK 16800; newsstand price: ISK 125. Timamot hf., Stakkholti 4, P.O. Box 5210, 125 Reykjavik, Iceland. TEL 354-631600. FAX 354-16270. Ed. Jon Kristjansson. adv.; bk.rev.; film rev.; music rev.; play rev.; tele.rev.; video rev.; illus. circ. 14,000. **Document type:** newspaper.

058.396 IC ISSN 0042-1197
URVAL; timarit fyrir alla. 1942. bi-m. ISK 2420($36) Frjals Fjoelmidlun HF - Independent Media, Inc., Thverholt 11, Reykjavik, Iceland. TEL 1-63-27-00. FAX 1-63-29-99. Ed. Gudrun Hergils. adv. contact: Jon Vikingur. bk.rev.; tr.lit. circ. 5,300.

058.396 IC ISSN 0042-6105
VIKAN. 1938. m. ISK 8070($153) Samutgafan Korpus hf, Armula 20-22, 108 Reykjavik, Iceland. TEL 354-1-813122. FAX 354-1-680102. Ed. Thorarinn J. Magnusson. adv. contact: Helga Benediktsdottir. bk.rev.; illus. circ. 11,500.

GENERAL INTEREST PERIODICALS — India

059.914 II
AASPAS. (Text in Gujarati) 1976. w. NR Khanpur Gate, Khanpur, Ahmedabad 380 001, India. TEL 272-391131. Ed. Gunvant C. Shah. circ. 100,373.

059 II
ABHAYADUTA. (Text in Hindi) vol.11, 1972. w. Rs.15. High Court Rd., Jodhpur, India. adv.
Description: Contains local news and current affairs.

059.914 II
ABHIYAAN. (Text in Gujarati) 1986. w. Shakti Publications Pvt. Ltd., Shakti House, Ashok Rd., Kandivli E., Bombay 400 101, India. TEL 022-888-4435. FAX 022-8893519. TELEX 011-74542 ASHA-IN. Ed. Sheela Bhatt; Pub. Ketan Sanghvi. circ. 112,400.

079.54 II
THE AFTERNOON DESPATCH & COURIER. (Supplements avail.: Business Extra (Tue.); Sports Extra (Wed.); Woman's Extra (Thu.)) (Text in English) 1985. d. (except Sun.). newsstand price: Rs.1.50. Courier Publications Pvt. Ltd., Afternoon House, 6, Nanabhai Lane, Fort, Bombay 400 001, India. TEL 2871616. FAX 2870371. TELEX 011-2075 ADC IN. Ed. Behram Contractor; Pub. Shashikant Jadav. adv. contact: Rozina Gaziyani. bk.rev.; film rev.; music rev.; illus.; circ. 70,000 (paid); 500 (controlled). cols./p.: 5; pp./issue: 28. (back issues avail.; reprint service avail.) **Document type:** newspaper.

079.54 II
▼**AFTERNOON ON SUNDAY.** (Text in English) 1992. w. newsstand price: Rs.3.50. Courier Publications Pvt. Ltd., Afternoon House, 6 Nanabhai Lane, Fort, Bombay 400 001, India. TEL 2871616. FAX 2870371. TELEX 011-2075 ADC-IN. Ed. Behram Contractor; Pub. Shashikant Jadav. adv. contact: Rozina Gaziyani. bk.rev.; film rev.; music rev.; illus.; circ. 80,000 (paid); 1,000 (controlled). cols./p.: 4; pp./issue: 40. (back issues avail.) **Document type:** newspaper.

059.91 II ISSN 0002-3639
AKHAND ANAND. (Text in Gujarati) 1947. m. Rs.60. Sastu Sahitya Mudranalaya Trust, Swami Akhandanand Marg, Bhadra, Box 50, Ahmedabad 380001, India. TEL 391798. Ed. R.M. Bhatt. circ. 30,878.
Description: Presents literary and cultural items.

079.54 II
AKKAS DAILY. (Weekly supplements avail.: Sports - Films; Literary - Women) (Text in Urdu) 1966. d. Rs.300; newsstand price: Rs.1. Akkas Daily, 1-1, Khetra Das Lane, West Bengal 700012, India. TEL 91-33-261187. FAX 91-33-269644. Ed. Karim Raza Monghyri. bk.rev.; film rev.; illus.; circ. 43,105 (paid); 44,000 (controlled). cols./p.: 8; pp./issue: 4. (back issues avail.) **Document type:** newspaper.

052 II
ALL INDIA APPOINTMENT GAZETTE. (Text in English) 1973. fortn. 7 Old Court House St., Calcutta 700 001, India. TEL 33-206663. Ed. S.C. Talukdar. circ. 170,000.

059.914 II
ALOKPAAT. (Text in Bengali) 1986. m. Mitra Prakashan (Pvt) Ltd., 281 Muthiganj, Allahabad 211 003, India. TEL 532-51042. TELEX 540280. Ed. Aloke Mitra. circ. 62,500.

052 II
ALPHA DIGEST. (Text in English) 1963. m. Rs.30($1.50) Bharatiya Vidya Bhavan, Bhavan's College of Mass Communication, Kulapati K.M. Munshi Marg, Bombay 400007, India. Ed. M.K.B. Nair. adv.; bk.rev.; illus. circ. 1,750.
Formerly: Alpha News Digest (ISSN 0002-6409)

079.54 II
AMAR UJALA. (Weekly supplement avail.: Raviwasari (Sun.); regional editions avail. for Agra, Bareilly, Meerut, Moradabad, and Kanpur) (Text in Hindi) 1948. d. Rs.750; newsstand price: Rs.2. Amar Ujala Prakashan, Sikandra Rd., Agra, Uttar Pradesh 282 007, India. TEL 0562-361600. FAX 0562-361600. Ed. Ashok Kumar Agarwal; Pub. Atul Kumar Maheshwari. adv.; bk.rev.; film rev.; illus. cols./p.: 8; pp./issue: 16. (back issues avail.) **Document type:** newspaper.

059.948 II
AMBULIMAMA. (Text in Tamil) 1947. m. 188 N.S.K. Salai, Vadapalani, Madras 600 026, India. Ed. Nagi Reddi. circ. 68,000.

059.914 II
AMRUTA/CINE WEEKLY. (Text in Gujarati) 1967. w. Rs.104 (foreign Rs. 260). Jai Hind Press Bldg., Near Sharda Baug, Rajkot 360 001, India. TEL 0091-281-48816. FAX 0091-281-48677. Ed. Y.N. Shah. circ. 28,000.
Description: Aims to promote and popularize cine-art, films and dramas.

059.914 II
ANDHRA JYOTI SACHITRA VARA PATRIKA. (Text in Telugu) 1967. w. Vijayawada 520 010, India. TEL 866-74532. Ed. Puranam Subramanya Sarma. circ. 71,000.

059.914 II
ANDHRA PATRIKA. d. Andhra Patrika, 14-14-21 Mallikarjuna Rao St., Gandhinagar, Vijayawada 520 003, India. TEL 61247. adv.

079.54 II
ANDHRA PRABHA. (Supplement avail.: Adivaram Anubhandham (Sun.)) (Text in Telugu) 1938. d. Rs.646($170); newsstand price: Rs.1.50. Andhra Prabha Ltd., Domalaguda, Hyderabad 500029, India. TEL 040-233586. FAX 040-234632. Ed. V. Vasudeva Deekshitulu; Pub. H.R.S. Manian. adv. contact: C. Kuppuswamy. bk.rev.; film rev.; music rev.; illus. circ. 60,000. cols./p.: 8; pp./issue: 12. (back issues avail.) **Document type:** newspaper.

059.914 II
ANDHRA PRABHA ILLUSTRATED WEEKLY. (Text in Telugu) 1952. w. Express Estates, Mount Rd., Madras 600 002, India. Ed. Potturi Venkateswara Rao. circ. 57,500.

059.914 II
ASAM BANI. (Text in Assamese) 1955. w. Tribune Bldg., Guwahti 781 003, India. TEL 23251. Ed. Tilak Hazarika. circ. 29,400.

050 II ISSN 0004-4644
DS1
ASIAN RECORDER; weekly record of Asian events with index. (Text in English) 1955. w. $175. Asian Recorder & Publications (Private) Ltd., A-126, Niti Bagh, New Delhi 110 049, India. TEL 011-652622. FAX 011-6862857. TELEX 031-73137 KRAK IN. Ed. A.K.B. Menon. q. index, cum.index. circ. 3,000.
Description: Culled from newspapers of many Asian countries and of the leading newspapers of the world. Provides news events taking place in Asia.

052 II ISSN 0403-4457
AS472.A85
ASIATIC SOCIETY. ANNUAL REPORT. (Text in English) a. Asiatic Society, 1 Park St., Calcutta 16, India.

052 II ISSN 0004-4989
ASSAM INFORMATION. (Text in English) vol.24, 1973. m. Rs.3. Directorate of Information and Public Relations, Silpukhuri, Gauhati 3, Assam, India. Ed. Shri Satya Prasad Barua. illus.

915 II
AVAKASH. (Text in Hindi) 1979. s-m. Rs.3 per no. Jnanamandal Ltd., A J Bhavan Box 1007, Sant Kabir Rd., Varanasi 221001, India. Ed. S.V. Gupta. adv.; bk.rev. circ. 60,000.

059.914 II
BALA JYOTI. (Text in Telugu) 1980. m. Labbipet, Vijayawada 520 010, India. TEL 866-474532. TELEX 475217. Ed. A. Sasikant Satakarni. circ. 32,600.

059.914 II
BHARATHI. (Text in Telugu) m. Andhra Patrika, 14-14-21 Mallikarjuna Rao St., Gandhinagar, Vijiyawada 520 003, India. TEL 61247. adv.

079.54 II
BIJNOR TIMES; Hindi daily. (Text in Hindi) 1963. d. newsstand price: Rs.1.50. Ram Ganga Prakshan, Bijnor Times Rd., Uttar Pradesh 246701, India. TEL 01342-62602. Ed. C.M. Raghuwanshi; Pub. B.S. Chauhan. adv. contact: S.D. Sharma. bk.rev.; film rev.; illus.; circ. 51,750 (paid); 52,000 (controlled). cols./p.: 8; pp./issue: 8. **Document type:** newspaper.

059.91 II ISSN 0006-3827
BISMOI. (Text and summaries in Assamese) 1969. bi-m. Rs.7.50. Shashi Phukan, Ed. & Pub., Bismoi Prakash, Maligaon, Gauhati 11, Assam, India. adv.; bk.rev.; film rev.; play rev. circ. 10,000. (processed; avail. on records)

059.914 II
BISWIN SADI. (Text in Urdu) 1937. m. 3583 Netaji Subash Marg, Darya Ganj, P.O. Box 7013, New Delhi 110 002, India. TEL 11-271637. Ed. Z. Rehman Nayyar. circ. 36,000.

050 II ISSN 0006-4882
BLITZ. (Text in English, Hindi, Manathi and Urdu) 1941. w. Rs.250 (foreign Rs.458). Blitz Publications Private Ltd., 17-17H, Cawasji Patel St., Fort, Bombay 400 001, India. TEL 2047166. FAX 2047984. TELEX 011-6801 BLTZ IN. Ed. R.K. Karanjia. adv.; bk.rev.; film rev.; play rev.; illus. circ. 381,800. (tabloid format)

059.914 II
BLITZ NEWS MAGAZINE. (Editions in English, Hindi, Urdu) 1941. w. Blitz Publications Private Ltd., 17-17H Cawasji Patel St., Bombay 400 001, India. TEL 2047166. FAX 2047984. TELEX 011-86801 BLTZ-IN. Ed. R.K. Karanjia. circ. 245,000.

052 II
BOMBAY. (Text in English) 1979. s-m. Rs.64. 28 A&B Jolly Maker Chambers - II, Nariman Point, Bombay 400 021, India. TEL 22-2026152. FAX 22-2026164. TELEX 1185373. Ed. Arun Katiyar. circ. 18,851.

052 II ISSN 0045-3846
AP8
CALCUTTA REVIEW. 1842. q. Rs.7.50. (University of Calcutta) Calcutta University Press, Sri Sibendra Nath Kanjilal, 48 Hazra Rd., Calcutta 19, West Bengal, India. Ed. Amalendu Bose. index. (also avail. in microfilm from UMI; reprint service avail. from UMI) **Indexed:** M.L.A.

059.914 II
CHANDOBA. (Text in Marathi) 1952. m. 188 N.S.K. Salai, Vadapalani, Madras 600 026, India. Ed. Nagi Reddi. circ. 110,000.

059.91 II
CHITRALEKHA. (Text in Gujarati) 1950. w. Rs.175($60) Madhuri Kotak, Ed. & Pub., 62 Vaju Kotak Marg, Bombay 400001, India. TEL 91-22-2611526. FAX 22-2615895. TELEX 011-78298 JEE IN. (Subscr. to: 132 Andheri Industrial Estate, Veera Desai Road, Andheri, Bombay 400 058) adv.; illus. circ. 325,000. **Document type:** consumer publication.

052 II ISSN 0011-3123
CURRENT WEEKLY. (Text in English) 1949. w. Rs.31($4) Current Publications Private Ltd., Nariman Bhavan, 15th Floor, Nariman Point, Bombay 400 021, India. Ed. Ayub Syed. adv.; bk.rev.; film rev.; play rev. circ. 80,000. **Indexed:** G.Soc.Sci.& Rel.Per.Lit.

GENERAL INTEREST PERIODICALS — INDIA

079.54 ‖
DAILY HINDI MILAP. (Text in Hindi) 1929. d. Rs.500($160); newsstand price: Rs.1.50. Daily Milap, Milap Rd., Jalandhar, Punjab 144001, India. TEL 56834. FAX 56836. Ed. Vishwa Kirti Yash. adv. contact: Bharat Bhushan. bk.rev.; film rev.; music rev.; illus. cols./p.: 8; pp./issue: 8. (back issues avail.) **Document type:** newspaper.

079.54 ‖
DAILY JAGRAN. (Regional editions avail. for Varanasi, Kanpur, Lucknow, Gorakhpur, Jhansi, Bareilly, Meerut, Agra, and New Delhi) (Text in Hindi) 1981. d. newsstand price: Rs.2.20. Jagran Prakashan (Varanasi) Pvt. Ltd., S-14-1, Andhara Pul, Varanasi 221 002, India. TEL 91-542-44646. FAX 91-542-323700. (Alt. addr.: 362 Civil Lines, Jhansi, U.P. 284001, India. TEL 91-517-440022. FAX 91-517-440011) Ed. Narendra Mohan; Pub. Virendra Kumar. adv.; bk.rev.; film rev.; music rev.; illus.; circ. 86,000 (paid). cols./p.: 8; pp./issue: 12. **Document type:** newspaper.

079.54 ‖
DAILY MILAP. (Text in Urdu) 1923. d. Rs.500($160); newsstand price: Rs.1.50. Daily Milap, Milap Rd., Jalandhar, Punjab 144001, India. TEL 56834. FAX 56836. Ed. Vishwa Kirti Yash. adv. contact: Bharat Bhushan. bk.rev.; film rev.; music rev.; illus.; circ. 15,265 (paid). cols./p.: 8; pp./issue: 8. **Document type:** newspaper.

079.54 ‖
DAINIK GANADOOT. (Text in Bengali) 1968. d. $1.50 per mo.; newsstand price: Rs.1.50. Oalace Compound, Agartala 799001, India. TEL 03815018. FAX 03814157. Ed. Sushil Chaudhuri. adv.; bk.rev.; illus. circ. 35,000. cols./p.: 8; pp./issue: 7. **Document type:** newspaper.

079.54 ‖
DAINIK JAGRAN. (Text in Hindi) 1947. d. Rs.720; newsstand price: Rs.2. Hazaratganz, Lucknow, U.P. 226001, India. TEL 0522-234176. FAX 0522-234176. Ed. Narendra Mohan Gupta; Pub. Vinod Shukla. adv. contact: Sona Avasthi. bk.rev.; film rev.; music rev.; illus.; circ. 485,238 (paid). cols./p.: 8; pp./issue: 14. (also avail. in microfilm; back issues avail.) **Document type:** newspaper.

079.54 ‖
DAINIK NAVAJYOTI. (Regional editions avail. for Ajmer, Jaipur and Kota) (Text in Hindi) 1936. d. newsstand price: Rs.1.50. Dainik Navajyoti, Kaisarganj, Ajmer, Rajasthan 305 001, India. TEL 0145-21636. FAX 0145-50873. TELEX 303-234 NJTI-IN. Ed. D.B. Chaudhary. adv. contact: Arvind Agrawal. bk.rev.; film rev.; music rev.; illus. circ. 283,000. cols./p.: 8; pp./issue: 12. **Document type:** newspaper.

079.54 ‖
DAINIK SAMBAD. (Text in Bengali) 1966. d. Rs.360($15); newsstand price: Rs.2. Dainik Sambad, P.O. Box 2, 11 Jagannath Bari Rd., Agartala, Tripora 799001, India. TEL 91-381-6676. FAX 91-381-4845. Ed. Bhupen Datta Bhaumik; Pub. Malina Das. adv.: page Rs.31000; trim 23 x 16.5; adv. contact: B. Datta. bk.rev.; film rev.; music rev.; illus.; circ. 52,000 (paid). cols./p.: 8; pp./issue: 8. (back issues avail.; reprint service avail.)

052 320 ‖ ISSN 0377-6832
DS401
DATA INDIA. (Text in English) no.42, 1974. w. $480. Press Institute of India, Sapru House Annexe, Barakhamba Rd., New Delhi 110 001, India. TEL 11-3318646. (Co-sponsor: Research Institute for Newspaper Development) Ed. K.S. Ramakrishnan. charts; stat. (looseleaf format)

052 ‖ ISSN 0011-698X
DATELINE DELHI. (Text in English) 1968. m. Rs.6. Neighbourhood Publications Cooperative Society Ltd., 21 Northend Complex, Ramakrishna Ashram Marg off Panchkuin Rd., New Delhi 110001, India. Ed. Aruna Dasgupta. adv.; bk.rev.; charts; illus. circ. 10,000. (tabloid format)

079.54 ‖
DELHI MID DAY. (Weekly supplement avail.: Specials) (Text in English) 1989. d. newsstand price: Rs.1.50. Special Protection Services Ltd., 411, World Trade Centre, Barakhamba Ln., New Delhi 110001, India. TEL 81-11-371-5581. FAX 81-11-332-5335. Ed. John Dayal. adv. contact: Madan Sachdeva. bk.rev.; film rev.; music rev.; illus. circ. 30,000. cols./p.: 5; pp./issue: 12. (tabloid format) **Document type:** newspaper.

052 ‖ ISSN 0301-9055
DEMOCRATIC FORUM. (Text in English) m. Rs.6. 19 Dharmatala St., Calcutta 13, India. illus.

079.54 ‖
DESHBANDHU. (Text in Hindi) 1959. d. Patrakar Prakashan Pvt. Ltd., Raipur 492001, India. TEL 91-771-534911. FAX 91-771-534955. Ed. M.R. Surjan; Pub. Lalit Surjan. adv.; bk.rev.; film rev.; music rev.; illus. cols./p.: 8; pp./issue: 16. (also avail. in microfilm; back issues avail.) **Document type:** newspaper.

059.948 ‖
DEVI. (Text in Tamil) 1983. w. 727 Anna Salai, Madras 600 006, India. TEL 44-861428. Ed. B.Ramachandra Adityan. circ. 117,800.

059 ‖ ISSN 0417-3937
DHARMAYUG. (Text in Hindi) 1950. w. $20. Bennett, Coleman & Co., Ltd. (Bombay), Times Bldg., Dr Dadabhai Naoroji Rd., Bombay 400001, India. TEL 22-2620271. FAX 22-2620401. TELEX 1173504. (U.S. subscr. addr.: M-s. Kalpana, 42-75 Main St., Flushing, NY 11355) Ed. Ganesh Mantri. adv.; illus. circ. 70,700.

079.54 ‖
DINA SUDAR. (Text in Tamil) 1964. d. Dina Sudar, 11-2 Queen's Rd., Bangalore 560 052, India. TEL 566213. Ed. B.S. Mani. adv. contact: V. Gandhi. film rev.; circ. 35,000 (paid). cols./p.: 8; pp./issue: 4. **Document type:** newspaper.

059.914 ‖ ISSN 0012-3005
DINAMAN; weekly Hindi news magazine. (Text in Hindi) w. 10 Daryganj, New Delhi 110 002, India. TEL 11-271911. Ed. Ghanbhyam Pankanj. adv.; bk.rev.; illus. **Document type:** newspaper.

052 ‖ ISSN 0013-9815
EQUALS ONE. (Text in English) 1965. q. Rs.16.($6.) Sri Aurobindo Society, Pondicherry 605002, India. Eds. Medhananda & Maude Pickett Smith. adv.; bk.rev.; illus. circ. 1,000.

051 ‖
FIRST CITY; Delhi's city magazine. (Text in English) 1990. m. Rs.10 per no. First City Magazine, A-11 Chittaranjan Park, New Delhi 110 019, India. TEL 6410474. Ed. Probir Dasgupta.

059.914 ‖ ISSN 0970-1710
FRONTLINE. 1984. fortn. $74. Kasturi & Sons Ltd., Kasturi Bldgs., 859-860 Anna Salai, Madras 600 002, India. FAX 44-835325. TELEX 41-6655. Ed. G. Kasturi. adv. circ. 68,365. (also avail. in microfilm)
  Description: Covers politics and culture in India. Includes economics, entertainment, and environmental issues.

052 ‖
GENTLEMAN. (Text in English) 1980. m. 920 Tulsiani Chambers, Nariman Point, Bombay 400 021, India. TEL 22-2872142. Ed. Maneck Danar. circ. 82,000.

052 ‖ ISSN 0017-1484
DS498
GOA TODAY. (Text in English) 1966. m. Rs.72 (foreign Rs.250). Goa Publications Pvt. Ltd., 3-C Shivkrupa Apts., St. Inez, Panjim Goa 403 001, India. TEL 44554. Ed. Manohar Shetty. adv.; bk.rev.; illus. circ. 10,000.

059.914 ‖
GRIHALAKSHMI. (Text in Malayalam) 1979. m. The Mathrubhumi Bldg., Kozhikode 673 001, India. TEL 63651. Ed. M.T. Vasudevan Nair. circ. 90,900.

079.54 ‖
GUJARATMITRA & GUJARATDARPAN. (Text in Gujarati) 1863. d. Rs.514 (US Rs.7551); newsstand price: Rs.1. Gujaratmitra Pvt. Ltd., Sonifalia, Surat, Gujarat 395003, India. TEL 099-262-53437. FAX 099-261-652151. Ed. Shri B.P. Reshamwala. adv. contact: Shri A.P. Jhaveri. bk.rev.; film rev.; music rev.; illus.; circ. 81,978 (paid). cols./p.: 8; pp./issue: 14. (also avail. in microfilm; back issues avail.) **Document type:** newspaper.

052 ‖ ISSN 0018-1625
HIGHLIGHTS.* w. Rs.0.35 per no. c/o E. H. Tippoo, Ed., Wachel Molla Mansion, 8 Lenin Sarani, Calcutta 13, India. adv.; illus.

052 ‖ ISSN 0046-7456
HIMALAYAN OBSERVER. (Text in English) vol. 7, 1973. w. $20. (Hill People League) Himalayan Observer Press, 9th Mile, Kalimpong, India. Ed. B.D. Basnet. adv.; bk.rev. circ. 2,500.

059.914 ‖
HINDU INTERNATIONAL EDITION. (Text in English) 1975. w. $55. 859-860 Anna Salai, Madras 600 002, India. TEL 44-835067. FAX 44-835325. TELEX 416655. Ed. N. Ravi. adv.; bk.rev. circ. 5,000.

052 ‖ ISSN 0018-8336
HYPHEN.* 1957. m. Rs.10.($6) C. Ramakrishna, Ed. & Pub., Strand Hotel, 25 Strand Rd., Apollo Bunder, Bombay 1, India. adv.; bk.rev.; film rev.; illus. circ. 5,000.

079.54 052 ‖ ISSN 0019-2430
ILLUSTRATED WEEKLY OF INDIA. (Text in English) 1880. w. $32. Bennett, Coleman & Co., Ltd. (Bombay), Times Bldg., Dr. D.N. Rd., Bombay 400001, India. TEL 4150271. (U.S. subscr. addr.: M-s. Kalpana, 42-75 Main St., Flushing, NY 11355) Ed. K.C. Khanna. adv.; bk.rev.; film rev.; illus. **Document type:** newspaper.
—UnCover.

052 ‖ ISSN 0027-4690
IMPULSE. (Text in English) 1970. fortn. Rs.2. Cosmopolitan Institute of Public Affairs, c/o Shiv Prasad "Muflis", L.I.G. 115, Harshwardhan Nagar, Bhopal 462 003, India. Ed. Suresh Mehrotra. adv.; bk.rev.; film rev.; play rev.; illus. circ. 2,000. (tabloid format)

059.914 ‖ US
INDIA BRIEFING. 1987. a. Westview Press, 550 Central Ave., Boulder, CO 80301. TEL 202-444-3541. FAX 303-449-3356. **Document type:** academic/scholarly publication.
  Description: Assesses contemporary politics, economics, and culture in India.

052 ‖
INDIA MAGAZINE; of her people and culture. (Text in English) 1980. m. Rs.180($60) Business India Group of Publications, Wadia Bldg., 17-19 Dalal St., Bombay 400 023, India. TEL 22-274161. FAX 22-2875671. TELEX 118-3557-BZIN-IN. Ed. Malvika Singh. adv.; film rev.; play rev. circ. 10,500. (back issues avail.)

052 ‖ ISSN 0970-5074
INDIA PERSPECTIVES. (Text in mainly in English) 1988. m. Room 149B, 'A' Wing, Shastri Bhavan, New Delhi 110 001, India. TEL 11-388873. Ed. Bharat Bhushan. bk.rev. circ. 50,000.
—UnCover.
  Description: Covers Indian economy, science and technology, with a focus on Indian cultural heritage.

052 ‖ ISSN 0537-0922
INDIA TODAY. (Editions in English, Hindi, Tamil, Telugu, Malyalam) 1975. fortn. Rs.125. Living Media India Pvt. Ltd., F-14-15 Connaught Place, New Delhi 110 001, India. TEL 11-3315801. FAX 11-3316180. TELEX 3161245. Ed. Aroon Purie. adv.; bk.rev.; film rev.; illus. circ. 600,000 (Eng. & Hindi eds.). **Indexed:** Br.Tech.Ind.

052 ‖ ISSN 0019-4972
INDIAN INSTITUTE OF WORLD CULTURE. TRANSACTIONS. (Text in English) 1945. 4/yr. Rs.30. Indian Institute of World Culture, 6 Shri B.P. Wadia Rd., P.O. Box 402, Basavangudi, Bangalore 560 004, India. bk.rev.

GENERAL INTEREST PERIODICALS — INDIA

052
INDIAN OBSERVER. (Text in English) 1958. m. 26F Connaught Pl., Delhi 110 001, India. TEL 11-3312329. Ed. Harbhajan Singh. circ. 26,500.

050
▼**INDIAN RECORDER.** (Text in English) 1994. w. $250. Asian Recorder & Publications (Private) Ltd., A-126, Niti Bagh, New Delhi 110 049, India. TEL 011-652622. FAX 011-6862857. Ed. A.K.B. Menon.

954 ‖ ISSN 0019-6509
INDIANA. N.S. 1975. q. Rs.25.($15) Information Research Academy, 37 Amir Ali Ave., Calcutta 700019, India. Ed. Partha Subir Guha. adv.; bk.rev.; index. circ. 2,700.

052
INTELLECTUALS' RENDEZVOUS. (Text in English) 1976. m. Heritage Publishers, 4C Ansari Rd.ht Circus, Darya Ganj, New Delhi 110 002, India. TEL 11-3266258. bk.rev. circ. 4,500.

052 ‖ ISSN 0020-8493
INTERNATIONAL REPORTER. (Text in English) 1963. w. Rs.15.($2) Baldev Raj, Ed. & Pub., M-48A Malviyanagar, New Delhi 17, India. bk.rev.; film rev.; illus.; music rev.; play rev. circ. 10,000. (tabloid format)

059.914 ‖
JAGAT (HINDI) MONTHLY. (Text in Hindi) 1958. m. 8-818 Ajmeri Gate, Delhi 110 006, India. Ed. Prem Chand Verma. circ. 18,000.
Description: Popular and family magazine

059.914 ‖
JAGAT WEEKLY. (Text in Urdu) 1956. w. 8-818 Ajmeri Gate, Delhi 110 006, India. TEL 11-664847. Ed. Prem Chand Verma. circ. 11,000.

079.54 059.914 ‖
JAI HIND. (Text in Gujarati) 1948. d. Rs.625 (foreign Rs.1670). Jai Hind Publications, Jai Hind Press Bldg., Babubhai Shah Marg, Rajkot 360 001, India. TEL 0281-40511. FAX 0091-281-48677. Ed. Y.N. Shah. adv. circ. 100,000. Document type: newspaper.
Description: Provides information and knowledge pertaining to socio-economic development, art, economics, science and technology, business and management.

079.54 ‖
JANASHAKTI NEWS WEEKLY. (Text in Malayalam) 1940. w. Rs.30. A.V. Vasavan, Ed. & Pub., Cochin 682001, India. adv.; bk.rev.; illus. Document type: newspaper.

079.54 ‖
JANMABHOOMI. (Text in Gujarati) 1934. d. (except Sunday). Rs.540 (foreign Rs.3670) (effective 1991). (Janmabhoomi Bhavan) Saurashtra Trust, Janmabhoomi Marg, Fort, Bombay 400 011, India. TEL 2870831. TELEX 11-86859 BHOO IN. Ed. Harinda Dave. adv.; bk.rev.; film rev.; illus. circ. 37,875. Document type: newspaper.
Description: Daily newspaper with general interests.

059.914 ‖
JANMABHOOMI PRAVASI. (Text in Gujarati) 1939. w. Rs.125 (foreign Rs.860)(effective 1991). Saurashtra Trust, Janmabhoomi Bhavan, Janmabhoomi Marg, Fort, Bombay 400 001, India. TEL 2870831. TELEX 11-86859 BHOO IN. Ed. Harinda Dave. adv.; bk.rev.; film rev.; illus. circ. 101,192.
Description: Covers current affairs, editorials, general interest articles on sports, films, literature, politics, drama, book review, etc.

059.914 ‖
JASOOSI DUNIYA. (Editions in Hindi, Urdu) 1953. m. 5 Kolhan Tola St., Allahabad, India. Ed. S. Abbas Husainy. circ. 70,000.

059.914 052 ‖
JUNIOR POST. (Text in Tamil) w. Rs.143 (foreign Rs.975). Vasan Publications Pvt., Ltd., 757, Anna Salai, Madras 600 002, India. TEL 91-44-8264054. FAX 91-44-8267619. TELEX 041-7358 VASN IN. Ed. S. Balasubramanian. circ. 80,000. (tabloid format)

059.914 ‖
JUNIOR VIKATAN; Tamil weekly. (Text in Tamil) 1983. w. Rs.182 (foreign Rs.1014). Vasan Publications Pvt. Ltd., 757 Anna Salai, Madras 600 002, India. TEL 91-44-8264054. FAX 91-44-8267619. TELEX 041-7358 VASN IN. Ed. S. Balasubramanian. circ. 225,000.
Description: News magazine.

059.914 ‖
JYOTI CHITRA. (Text in Telugu) 1977. w. Andhra Jyoti Buildings, Vijayawada 520 010, India. Ed. T. Kutumba Rao. circ. 52,600.

059.914 ‖
JYOTSANA. 1947. m. Rajendranagar, Patna, India. Ed. S. Narayan. circ. 11,000.

059.948 ‖
KADAMBINI. (Text in Hindi) 1960. m. Rs.510. Hindustan Times House, Kasturga Gandhi Marg, New Delhi 110 001, India. TEL 11-3318201. FAX 011-3321189. TELEX 3166310. Ed. Rajendra Awasthy. adv. contact: Ved Poakash. bk.rev. circ. 150,000.

059.914 ‖
KALKANDU. (Text in Tamil) 1948. w. $25. Kumudam Publications Pvt. Ltd., 151 Purasawalkam High Rd., Madras 600 010, India. TEL 44-642-2146. FAX 91-44-642-5041. TELEX 41-24122 KMDM IN. Ed. S.A.P. Annamalai. circ. 125,000.

059.914 ‖
KARALA SABDAM. (Text in Malayalam) 1962. w. Thevally, Quilon 691 009, India. TEL 2403. TELEX 886296. Ed. B.A. Rajakrishnan. circ. 84,200.

059.914 ‖
KARMASANGSTHAAN. (Text in Bengali) 1988. w. 7 Old Court House St., Calcutta 700 001, India. TEL 33-207618. Ed. S.C. Talukdar. circ. 40,000.

954 ‖ ISSN 0022-9261
KASTURI; Kannada digest. (Text in Kannada) 1956. m. Rs.14. Karnataka Patrika Private Limited, Koppikar Rd., Hubli, Karnataka, India. Ed. Khadri Shamanna. circ. 30,500.

059.91 ‖ ISSN 0022-9539
KAVIAMUTHU. (Text in Tamil) 1969. m. Rs.12. A. Sivasubramonia Pillai, Ed. & Pub., 7-4-1 Meiyagam Vadivee Swaran, Nagercoil 2, Kanyakumari District, Tamil Nadu 629 007, India. Ed. A. Sivasubramania Pillai. adv.; bk.rev.; film rev.; abstr.; illus. circ. 1,000.

059.914 ‖ ISSN 0023-0537
KERALA SREE. (Text in Malayalam) 1956. d. Rs.60. Ed. S. Kakanatt, Mullakkal, Alleppey 10, Kerala, India. (Subscr. to: P.B. 333, Alleppey 688001, Kerala, India) adv.; bk.rev.; film rev.; play rev.; illus. circ. 10,000.

059.914 ‖
KUMUDAM. (Text in Tamil) 1947. w. $52. Kumudam Publications Pvt. Ltd., 151 Purasawalkam High Rd., Madras 600 010, India. TEL 44-642-2146. FAX 91-44-642-5041. TELEX 41-24122 KMDM IN. Dir. P. Varadarajan. circ. 375,000.

052 ‖
LINK INDIAN NEWS MAGAZINE. (Text in English) 1958. w. Link House, Bahadurshah Zafar Marg, New Delhi 110 002, India. TEL 11-3311056. TELEX 3162384. Ed. Sitanshu Das. circ. 11,000.

059 ‖
MADHYA PRADESH VIKAS VARSHIKI. (Text in Hindi) 1973. a. Rs.115. Shri Radhika Prakashan Pvt. Ltd., Swadesh Bhawan 26-A, Press Complex, Maharana Pratap Nagar, Bhopal 462 011, India. TEL 552077. Ed. O. Prakash Kundra. adv.; B&W page Rs.6000. circ. 5,000.
Former titles: Madhya Pradesh Yearbook; Madhya Pradesh Varshiki.
Description: Reference book serving as a window on Madhya Pradesh with authentic data.

059 ‖
MAGHREBI BENGAL. (Text in Urdu) 1952. fortn. Rs.3. Department of Information and Cultural Affairs, Writers' Bldgs., Calcutta 700001, India. Ed. Uttam Ghosh. circ. 3,000.

059.91 ‖ ISSN 0025-0392
MAHARASHTRA. (Text and summaries in Marathi) 1936. w. Rs.15($3.) P. R. Ambike, Ed. & Pub., 1398 Sadashiv Peth, Poona, India. adv.; bk.rev. circ. 2,000.

052 ‖ ISSN 0542-1462
MAINSTREAM. (Text in English) 1962. w. Rs.150 (Asia $60, Europe $77, America $88). Perspective Publications Pvt. Ltd., F-24 Bhagat Singh Market, New Delhi 110001, India. TEL 344772. Ed. Nikhil Chakravartty. adv.; bk.rev. circ. 11,500.
Description: Focuses on current affairs.

079.54 ‖
MAKKAL KURAL. (Text in Tamil) 1973. d. Rs.576($290) Newsmen Associates Ltd., 1, First Main Rd., United India Colony, Kodambakkam, Madras 600 024, India. TEL 044-4831188. FAX 044-4832833. Ed. M. Shanmu Gavel. adv. contact: K. Sitha Ran Jan. music rev.; circ. 61,840 (paid); 1,900 (controlled). cols./p.: 6; pp./issue: 12. (also avail. in diskette format; back issues avail.; reprint service avail.) Document type: newspaper.

059.914 ‖
MALAIMATHI. (Text in Tamil) bi-w. $104. Kumudam Publications Pvt. Ltd., 151 Purasawalkam High Rd., Madras 600 010, India. TEL 44-642-2146. FAX 91-44-642-5041. TELEX 41-24122 KMDM IN. Ed. S.A.P. Annamalai. circ. 78,000.

059.91 ‖ ISSN 0025-1399
MALLIGE. (Text in Kannada) 1961. m. Rs.18. Mallige Printers & Publishers (Pvt.) Ltd., 28, Sirsi Rd., Bangalore 560018, India. Ed. H.C. Ramanna. adv.; bk.rev. (looseleaf format)

059.914 ‖
MANOHAR KAHANIYAN. (Text in Hindi) 1940. m. Mitra Prakashan (Pvt) Ltd, 281 Muthiganj, Allahabad 211 003, India. TEL 532-41042. TELEX 540280. Ed. Aloke Mitra. circ. 368,600.

059 ‖
MANOHARA. (Text in Marathi) vol.39, 1972. w. Rs.24. Kirloskar Press, Veer Savarkar Marg, Poona 411009, India. Ed. M.S. Kirloskar. adv.

059.914 ‖
MANORAMA. (Editions in Bengali, Hindi) 1924. fortn.(Hindi), m.(Bengali). Mitra Parkashan (Pvt) Ltd., 281 Muthiganj, Allahabad 211 003, India. TEL 532-51042. TELEX 540280. Ed. Aloke Mitra. circ. 276,200.

059.91 ‖ ISSN 0025-4096
MARUEE. (Text in Sindhi) 1967. m. Rajni Hamsraj Panjabi, F-19 Kubernagar, Ahmedabad, India. adv.; bk.rev.; film rev. circ. 2,000.

059.914 ‖
MATHRUBHUMI ILLUSTRATED WEEKLY. (Text in Malayalam) 1923. w. Mathrubhumi Bldg., K.P. Kesava Menon Rd., Kozhikode 673 001, India. TEL 63651. Ed. N.V. Krishna Worrior. circ. 78,600.

059.914 ‖
MAYA. (Text in Hindi) 1929. fortn. Mitra Prakashan (Pvt) Ltd, 281 Muthiganj, Allahabad 211 003, India. TEL 532-51042. TELEX 540280. Ed. Aloke Mitra. circ. 224,000.

059.914 ‖
MAYURA. (Text in Kannada) 1968. m. 66 Mahatma Gandhi Rd., Bangalore 560 001, India. TEL 812-573291. TELEX 8452339. Ed. K.N. Hari Kumar. circ. 76,300.

059.915 ‖
MERI SAHELI. (Text in Hindi) 1987. m. 160 D.N. Rd., Bombay 400 001, India. Ed. Hema Malini. circ. 89,600.

079.54 ‖
MID-DAY. (Text in English) 1979. d. (Mon.-Sat.) Rs.560 (US Rs.8385); newsstand price: Rs.1.75. Mid-Day Publications Ltd., 156 D.J. Dadajee Rd., Tardeo, Bombay 400 034, India. TEL 4942586. FAX 4938734. Ed. Tarique Ansari. adv.; bk.rev.; film rev.; music rev.; illus. circ. 96,000. cols./p.: 5; pp./issue: 32. (tabloid format) Document type: newspaper.

GENERAL INTEREST PERIODICALS — INDIA

052 ‖
MIRROR. 1961. m. Rs.120. Eve's Weekly Ltd., J.K. Somani Bldg., Bombay Samachar Marg, Bombay 400 023, India. TEL 22-271444. Ed. Prabha Govind. adv.; bk.rev. circ. 57,000.

052 ‖ ISSN 0026-8380
AP8
MODERN REVIEW. (Text in English) 1907. m. Rs.40.($14) Prabasi Press Private Ltd., 77-2-1 Lenin Sarani, Calcutta 13, India. TEL 40-1738. Ed. Lakshmi Chatterji. adv.; bk.rev.; charts; illus. circ. 6,000. **Indexed:** P.A.I.S.

059.948 ‖
MUTHTHARAM. (Text in Tamil) 1980. w. 93A Kogambakkam High Rd., Madras 600 034, India. TEL 44-476306. Ed. Sri Parasakthi. circ. 60,300.

059.914 ‖
NABA KALLOL. (Text in Bengali) 1960. m. 11 Jhamapookur Lane, Calcutta 700 009, India. TEL 33-354294. Ed. P.K. Mazumdar. circ. 43,000.

052 ‖
NAGALAND TIMES. (Text in English) 1970. w. Rs.13. Nagaland Nationalist Cooperative Society Ltd., Box 12, Dimapur, Nagaland, India. Ed. T.P. Bhattacharjee. adv.; bk.rev. circ. 2,000.
Description: Covers news and current affairs.

059.914 ‖
NAR NARI. (Text in Hindi) 1949. m. Nari Prakashan, Patna 800 004, India. Ed. V. Vatsyayan. circ. 10,000.

052 ‖ ISSN 0027-9145
NATIONAL DIARY; a weekly record of Indian events with index. (Text in English) 1964. w. Rs.75. S. B. Chaudhuri, Ed. & Pub., 59 Ballygunge Gardens, Calcutta 19, India. index.

079.54 059.91 ‖ ISSN 0028-1506
NAVBHARAT TIMES; daily Hindi newspaper. (Text in Hindi) 1950. d. $80. Bennett Coleman & Co. Ltd. (Bombay), Times Bldg., Dr. D.N. Rd., Bombay 400001, India. TEL 4150271. (U.S. subscr. addr.: M-s. Kalpana, 42-75 Main St., Flushing, NY 11355) Ed. Rajendra Mathur. circ. 52,259. **Document type:** newspaper.

052 ‖
NEETEE. (Text in English) 1955. w. 4 Sukhlal Johari Lane, Calcutta 700 001, India. Ed. M.P. Poddar.

052 ‖
NEW DELHI. (Text in English) 1978. s-m. Rs.5 per no. Anand Bazar Patrika Ltd., P.T.I. Bldg., Parliament St., New Delhi 110001, India.

079.54 052 ‖ ISSN 0047-9969
NEW WAVE; India's national newsweekly. (Text in English) 1971. w. Rs.70($70) New Wave Society, c/o Ganesh Shukla, Ed., 285 Defence Colony Flyover, New Delhi 110024, India. adv.; bk.rev.; illus. circ. 10,000. (tabloid format; also avail. in microfilm from UMI; reprint service avail. from UMI) **Document type:** newspaper.

052 ‖ ISSN 0028-9094
NEWS FROM PONDY.* (Text in English) 1968. q. free. Home (Plan Publicity and Tourism) Department, Pondicherry, India. adv.; illus.

059.91 ‖ ISSN 0029-0688
NIRANJAN; children's fortnightly magazine. (Text in Gujarati) 1969. fortn. Rs.96 (foreign Rs. 175). Niranjan Publications, Jai Hind Press Bldg., Near Sharda Baug, Rajkot 360 001, India. TEL 0091-285-45640. FAX 0091-281-48677. Ed. N.R. Shah. adv.; bk.rev. circ. 19,000.
Description: Carries interesting, thought provoking stories, puzzles, and comic strips.

052 ‖ ISSN 0029-5345
NOW. (Text in English) 1964. w. Rs.15. Nation Trust, 54 Ganesh Chandra Ave., Calcutta 13, India. Ed. Ajit Roy Mukherjee. bk.rev.; film rev.; play rev. **Indexed:** Nutr.Abstr.

059.914 ‖
NUTAN KAHANIYAN. (Text in Hindi) 1975. m. 15 Sheocharan Lal Rd., Allahabad 211 003, India. TEL 532-56612. Ed. N.P. Singh. circ. 167,500.

052 ‖
OH CALCUTTA. (Text in English) 1971. a. $10. Aditi Nath Roy, Ed. & Pub., CB-168, Sector 1, Salt Lake, Calcutta 700 064, India. TEL 374502. adv.; bk.rev.; film rev.; charts; illus. circ. 25,000.
Description: Features Indian heritage and culture.

052 ‖ ISSN 0030-2619
ONLOOKER. (Text in English) 1939. s-m. Rs.12.($2.50) Free Press House, 215 Free Press Journal Marg, Nariman point, Bombay 400 021, India. TEL 22-2874566. TELEX 112570. Ed. K. Gopalakrishnan. adv.; bk.rev.; illus. circ. 61,000.
Description: News and current affairs.

052 ‖
ORACLE. (Text in English) 1979. q. Netaji Research Bureau, Netaji Bhawan, 38-2 Lala Lajpat Rai Road, Calcutta-700 020, India.

052 ‖ ISSN 0030-5014
ORGANISER. (Text in English) 1947-1975; resumed. w. Rs.25. 29 Rani Jhansi Rd., Delhi 110 055, India. TEL 11-529595. Ed. V.P. Bhatia. adv.; bk.rev.; charts; illus. circ. 44,100.

059 ‖
PACHIM BANGLA. (Text in Santhali) 1968. fortn. Rs.2.50. Department of Information and Cultural Affairs, Writers' Bldgs., Calcutta 700001, India. Ed. Uttam Ghosh. circ. 3,200.

079.54 ‖
PANCHAJANYA. (Text in Hindi) 1947. w. Rs.225. 29 Rani Jhansi Marg, New Delhi 110 055, India. TEL 11-529595. FAX 11-7514876. Ed. Tarun Vijay. bk.rev. circ. 130,000. **Document type:** newspaper.

052 ‖
PANCHAYATI RAJ (CALCUTTA). 1961. m. Rs.1.80. Department of Information and Cultural Affairs, Writers' Bldgs., Calcutta 700001, India. Ed. Uttam Ghosh. circ. 5,000.

052 ‖
PARADE. (Text in English) 1988. m. Esperanca, Shahid Bhagat Singh Rd., Bombay 400 039, India. TEL 22-202-4181. TELEX 112029. Ed. Rajendra Menon. circ. 77,400.

050 ‖
PASCHIM BANGA. (Text in Bengali) 1967. w. Rs.24. Department of Information and Cultural Affairs, Writers' Bldgs., Calcutta 700001, India. Eds. A. Bhattacharya, D.J. Majumdar. circ. 10,000.

059 ‖
PASCHIM BONGAL. (Text in Hindi) 1959. fortn. Rs.5. Department of Information and Cultural Affairs, Writers' Bldgs., Calcutta 700001, India. Ed. Uttam Ghosh. circ. 4,200.
Formerly: Sramik Barta.

059.914 ‖
PHULWADI; children's weekly. (Text in Gujarati) 1967. w. Rs.104 (foreign 495). Jai Hind Press Bldg., Near Sharda Baug, Rajkot 360 001, India. TEL 0091-285-48816. FAX 0091-281-48677. circ. 28,000.
Description: Carries interesting, thought provoking stories, puzzles, comic strips.

059.914 ‖ ISSN 0971-2097
HC431
▼**POLITICAL ECONOMY JOURNAL OF INDIA.** (Text and summaries in English) 1992. 2/yr. Rs.80 to individuals; institutions Rs.120; foreign $20. Centre for Indian Development Studies, 206, Sector 9-C, Chandigarh 160 017, India. TEL 0172-95362. Ed. V.S. Mahajan. adv.; bk.rev.; bibl. circ. 450. **Document type:** academic/scholarly publication.
Description: Covers Indian economic developments and their relations with the world economy.

059 ‖
PRAJAMATA ILLUSTRATED WEEKLY. (Text in Kannada) 1931. w. Rs.170. M-S Newspapers and Periodicals, North Anjaneya Temple Rd., Basavangudi, Bangalore 560 004, India. TEL 812-60. G.V. Anji. adv.; bk.rev.; film rev.; charts; illus. circ. 58,500.

079.54 ‖
PRAVASI. 1979. d. (except Sunday). Rps.3625. Saurashtra Trust, Janmabhoomi Bhavan, Janmabhoomi Marg., Fort, Bombay 400 001, India. TEL 2870831. TELEX 11-86859 BHOO IN. Ed. Harindra Dave. adv.; bk.rev.; film rev.; illus. circ. 22,284. **Document type:** newspaper.
Description: Daily newspaper with news, view and general interest articles.

059.91 ‖ ISSN 0032-7239
PREET LARI. (Text and summaries in Punjabi) 1933. m. Rs.40. Preet Lari Publishers, c/o S. Rati Singh, Preet Nagar, Amritsar, Punjab, India. Ed. Poonam Singh. adv.; bk.rev.; film rev.; illus. circ. 19,648. (tabloid format)

052 ‖
PROBE INDIA. (Text in English) 1979. m. Mitra Prakashan (Pvt) Ltd., 281 Muthiganj, Allahabad 211 003, India. TEL 532-53681. TELEX 540280. Ed. Aloke Mitra. circ. 35,600.

059.91 ‖
PUNJABI DIGEST. (Text in Gurmukhi, Punjabi) 1971. m. Rs.30($20) (Sher-I-Punjab Publication) Sardar Amar Singh & Sons, 209 Hemkunt House, 6 Rajendra Place, P.O. Box 2549, New Delhi 110 008, India. Ed. Sardar H.B. Singh. adv.; bk.rev.; illus. circ. 75,600.

079.54 ‖
RANCH EXPRESS. (Text in Hindi) 1963. d. Ranchi Prakashan Pvt. Ltd., 55 Baralal St., Ranchi 834001, India. TEL 0651-3012110. FAX 0651-303466. Ed. Pawan Maroo. adv. contact: Rajesh Chabra. bk.rev.; film rev.; music rev.; illus. circ. 63,000. cols./p.: 8; pp./issue: 10. (broadsheet format; back issues avail.) **Document type:** newspaper.

059.948 ‖
RANI MUTHU. (Text in Tamil) 1969. m. Rani Syndicate, 1091 Periyar E.V.R. High Road, Madras 600 007, India. TEL 44-5324771. Ed. A.MA. Samy. circ. 121,584.

052 ‖ ISSN 0034-0421
READER'S DIGEST (INDIAN EDITION). (Text in English) 1954. m. Rs.199. Reader's Digest Association Private Ltd., Orient House, 2nd Fl., Mangalore St., Ballard Estate, Bombay 400 038, India. TEL 22-2617291. FAX 91-22-2613347. TELEX 1183406. Ed. Ashok Mahadevan. adv.; bk.rev.; illus. circ. 388,000.

059.914 ‖
SAKHI. (Text in Gujarati) 1984. m. Rs.60 (foreign Rs.120). Sakhi Publications, Jai Hind Press Bldg., nr Gujarat Chamber, Ashram Rd., Navrangpura, Ahmedabad 380 009, India. TEL 0091-281-48816. FAX 0091-281-48677. Ed. Y.N. Shah. circ. 11,000.
Description: Provides interesting and thought-provoking stories for housewives.

059.914 ‖
SANANDA. (Text in Bengali) 1986. fortn. 6 Prafulla Sarkar St., Calcutta 700 001, India. TEL 33-278000. TELEX 215468. Ed. Aparna Sen. circ. 74,400.

079.54 ‖
SANCHAR. (Regional editions avail. for Sanchar, and Solapur; supplements avail.: Share Market Review (Mon.); Agricultural Supplement (Mon.); Ladies Special "Priyamvada" Supplement (Tue.); Health Guide (Thu.); Entertainment Supplement (Fri.); Literary Supplement (Sun.)) (Text in Marathi) 1961. d. Rs.500. Sanchar Paper Corporation, Sanchar Bldg., Hotgi Rd., Solapur, Maharashtra 413003, India. TEL 29481. FAX 27759. TELEX 795 243 SANC IN. Ed. Ranganath Madhav Vaidya. adv. contact: Meghraj Kadadi. bk.rev.; film rev.; music rev.; illus.; circ. 34,577 (paid); 563 (controlled). cols./p.: 8; pp./issue: 10. (back issues avail.; reprint service avail.) **Document type:** newspaper.

079.54 ‖
▼**SANDHYA RANCHI EXPRESS.** (Text in Hindi) 1992. d. Ranchi Prakashan Pvt. Ltd., 55 Baralal St., Ranchi 834001, India. TEL 0651-301211. FAX 0651-303466. Ed. Pawan Maroo. adv. contact: Rajesh Chabra. bk.rev.; film rev; music rev.; illus. circ. 10,000. (tabloid format; back issues avail.) **Document type:** newspaper.

059.914 ‖
SAPTAHIK HINDUSTAN. (Text in Hindi) 1950. w. 18-20 Kasturba Bandhi Marg, Delhi 110 001, India. TEL 11-3318201. TELEX 3166130. Ed. Mrinal Pande. circ. 32,100.

059.91 ‖ ISSN 0036-4754
SARASVAT; literary and cultural. (Text in Bengali) 1968. q. Rs.2. Saraswat Library, 206 Bidhan Sarani, Calcutta 700006, India. Ed. Amiya Kumar Bhatta-Charjee. adv.; bk.rev.; film rev.; play rev.; illus.; index. circ. 1,000.

059 ‖
SARATHI GUJARATI WEEKLY. (Text in Gujarati) vol.8, 1972. w. Rs.15. Sarathi Karyalaya, Box 276, Rajkot, India. adv.; illus.

079.54 ‖ ISSN 0036-4991
SATYA PRAKASH; Bengali weekly. (Text in Bengali) 1875. w. Rs.30. P.K. Kar, Ed. & Pub., P.O. Navapalli 743203, 24 Parganas, W. Bengal, India. adv.; bk.rev.; film rev.; play rev.; illus. circ. 15,000. (tabloid format; avail. on records) Document type: newspaper.
 Description: A socio-economic newspaper.

059.914 ‖
SATYAKATHA. (Text in Hindi) 1974. m. Mitra Prakashan (Pvt) Ltd, 281 Muthiganj, Allagabad 211 003, India. TEL 532-51042. Ed. Aloke Mitra. circ. 150,500.

052 ‖
SAVVY. (Text in English) 1984. m. Esperanca, 7th Fl., Shahid Bhagat Singh Rd., Bombay 400 039, India. TEL 22-2024135. TELEX 112029. Ed. Ingrid Albuquerque. circ. 77,630.

059.914 ‖
SCREEN (CALCUTTA). (Text in English) 1960. w. India Express, P-5 Kalakar St., Calcutta 700 001, India. Ed. M.P. Poddar. circ. 93,740.

052 ‖ ISSN 0970-8324
SEVARTHAM; Indian culture in a Christian context. (Text in English and Hindi; summaries in English) 1976. a. Rs.35($6) St. Albert's College, P.O. Box 5, Ranchi 834 001, India. Ed. J. Feys. bk.rev.; cum.index. circ. 550. (back issues avail.) Document type: academic/scholarly publication.

059.91 ‖ ISSN 0037-3273
SHAMA. (Text in Urdu) 1939. m. Rs.135 (foreign $1150). Shama Magazine, 13-14 Asaf Ali Rd., New Delhi 110002, India. TEL 11-732666. FAX 11-7521130. TELEX 3161601-SHAMA-IN. Eds. Idrees Dehlvi, M. Yunus Dehlvi. adv.; film rev.; illus. circ. 80,000. (tabloid format) Document type: consumer publication.

059 ‖
SHER-I-PUNJAB. (Text in Urdu) 1911. w. Rs.24($30) Sardar Amar Singh & Sons, Hemkunt House, 6 Rajindra Place, New Delhi 110008, India. TEL 11-5715225. Ed. Sardar Jang Bahadur Singh. adv. circ. 15,000. (tabloid format)

059.914 ‖
SHREE. (Text in Marathi) 1967. w. 40 Cawasji Patel St., Bombay 400 023, India. TEL 22-2044171. TELEX 1176844. Ed. Kamlesh D. Mehta. circ. 91,700.

059.914 ‖
SHREEWARSHA. (Text in Hindi) 1980. w. 40 Cawasji Patel St., Bombay 400 023, India. TEL 22-2044171. Ed. R.M. Bhutta. circ. 50,000.

052 ‖
STARDUST. (Text in English) 1971. m. Esperanca, 7th Floor, Shahid Bhagat Singh Rd., Bombay 400 039, India. TEL 22-2024181. TELEX 112029. Ed. Nishi Prem. circ. 160,900.

079.54 ‖
THE STATESMAN. (Regional editions avail. for Culcutta and New Delhi) (Text in English) 1875. d. Rs.650. Statesman Ltd., Statesman House, Connaught Circus, New Delhi 110 001, India. TEL 91-11-331-5911. FAX 91-11-331-5296. Ed. C.R. Irani; Pub. Ravindra Kumar. adv. contact: B.B. Sachdeva. bk.rev.; film rev.; music rev.; illus. Wire service(s): AP, RN. circ. 147,000. cols./p.: 8; pp./issue: 18. (broadsheet format; back issues avail.) Document type: newspaper.

STATESMAN WEEKLY; news and comments from "The Statesman" of New Delhi and Calcutta. see POLITICAL SCIENCE

059.914 ‖
STREE. (Text in Gujarati) 1962. w. Rs.175 (foreign Rs.352). Sandesh Bhavan, Gheekanta, P.O. Box 151, Ahmedabad 380 001, India. TEL 272-24243. FAX 91-272-24392. TELEX 1216532. Ed. Lilaben Patel. circ. 65,986.

052 ‖ ISSN 0039-2340
STRIDE. (Text in English) 1966. m. Rs.6. 49 Milan Park, Garia, Calcutta 32, India. Ed. Amalendu Dutta Gupta. adv.; bk.rev.; bibl. circ. 3,500. (tabloid format)

059.914 ‖
SUDHA. (Text in Kannada) 1965. w. 66 Mahatma Gandhi Rd., Bangalore 560 001, India. TEL 080-588999. FAX 080-587675. Ed. K.N. Hari Kumar. circ. 150,781.

052 ‖
THE SUN. (Text in English) 1977. w. Rs.312. 8B Bahadur Shah Zafar Marg, P.O. Box 7164, Delhi 110 002, India. TEL 11-3319286. TELEX 3165931. Ed. V.B. Gupta. adv.; bk.rev. circ. 22,400.

079.54 052 ‖
SUNDAY. (Text in English) 1973. w. 6 Prafulla Sarkar St., Calcutta 700 001, India. TEL 33-274880. TELEX 215468. Ed. Vir Singhvi. circ. 126,500. Document type: newspaper.

079.54 052 ‖
SUNDAY MAIL (ENGLISH EDITION). (Also published in Bombay, Calcutta, Madras) (Hindi edition avail.) 1986. w. Mercantile House, 6th Fl., 15 Kasturba Gandhi Marg, New Delhi 110 001, India. TEL 642-2039. FAX 643-5871. TELEX 70067 MAIL IN. Ed. A.S. Abraham. circ. 55,000. Document type: newspaper.
 Formerly: Mail Sunday.

059.914 ‖
SUNDAY MAIL (HINDI EDITION).* (English edition avail.) 1989. w. Mercantile House, 15 Kasturba Gandhi Marg, New Delhi 110 01, India. TEL 11-3317878. (Also published in Calcutta) Ed. K.L. Nandan. circ. 155,000.

079.54 ‖
THE SUNDAY OBSERVER. (Editions in English, Hindi) 1981. w. Rs.60. Vijaya, 17 Barakhamba Rd., New Delhi 110 001, India. TEL 11-3713200. FAX 11-3327065. TELEX 3166893. Ed. Chandan Mitra. adv.; bk.rev. circ. 61,800. Document type: newspaper.

052 954 ‖
SURYA INDIA. (Text in English) 1976. m. Rs.60. Youngman Printers & Publishers Pvt. Ltd., Kanchanjunga, 18 Barakhamba Rd., New Delhi 110001. TEL 3310202. Ed. Dr. J.K. Jain. adv.; bk.rev.; illus.; stat. circ. 47,000.

915.4 ‖ ISSN 0039-9280
TAMIL ARASU. (Editions in English and Tamil) 1970. m. (English ed.); fortn. (Tamil ed.). Rs.12 for Tamil ed.; Rs.6 for English ed. Director of Information and Public Relations, Fort St. George, Madras 600009, Tamil Nadu, India. adv.; charts; illus. circ. 48,000.

059.914 ‖
TARANGA. (Text in Kannada) 1983. w. Udayavani Building, Press Corner, Manipal 576 119, India. TEL 20841. Ed. S.K. Gulvadi. circ. 148,500.

059.948 ‖
THUGLAK. (Text in Tamil) 1970. fortn. Viveka Publishers, 5 Bishops Wallers Ave., C.I.T. Colony, Madras 600 004, India. TEL 44-74222. Ed. Cho S. Ramaswamy. circ. 197,300.

079.54 ‖
UTTAR BHARAT TIMES. (Weekly supplements avail.: Parivariya Parishisht; Rajnetik Jagat) (Text in Hindi) 1981. d. Rs.300($20); newsstand price: Rs.1. Paresh Kumar Kashyap, Ed. & Pub., Court Rd., Bijnor 246 701, U.P., India. TEL 01342-62664. adv. contact: Jaideep Kashyap. bk.rev.; film rev.; music rev.; illus.; circ. 23,000 (paid); 2,200 (controlled). cols./p.: 7; pp./issue: 6. (back issues avail.) Document type: newspaper.

352 954 ‖ ISSN 0303-5395
DS485.U6
UTTAR PRADESH. (Text in Hindi) m. Rs.70. Information and Public Relations Department, Lucknow, Uttar Pradesh, India.

079.54 ‖
VAARAANTARI RANI; Rani weekly. (Text in Tamil) 1964. w. Rs.145 (US Rs.1080). Rani Syndicate, 1091 Periyar E.V.R. High Rd., Madras 600 007, India. TEL 44-5324771. Ed. A.M. Samy. adv.; B&W page Rs.12000, color page Rs.24000; trim 24 x 18; adv. contact: G. Srinivasan. film rev.; illus.; circ. 262,689. circ. 262,689 (paid). cols./p.: 4; pp./issue: 44. (tabloid format) Document type: newspaper.

052 ‖ ISSN 0042-5303
VIDURA. (Text in English) 1963. bi-m. $50. Press Institute of India, Sapru House Annexe, Barakhamba Rd., New Delhi 110 001, India. TEL 11-3318066. (Co-sponsor: Research Institute for Newspaper Development) Ed. S. Nihal Singh. adv.; bk.rev.; charts; illus.; stat. circ. 2,000. (processed) Indexed: Ind.India.

059.914 ‖
VISWARACHANA/WORLD DEVELOPMENT; illustrated fortnightly. (Text in Telugu) fortn. Pothukuchi Sambasiva Rao, Viswasahithi 6-3-195, New Bhoiguda, Secunderabad-3, India. TEL 823177.

059.914 ‖
YUVDARHSAN. (Text in Gujarati) 1975. w. c/o Warsha Publications Pvt Ltd., Warsha House, 6 Zakaria Bunder Rd., Sewri, Bombay 400 015, India. TEL 22-441843. Ed. R.M. Bhutta. circ. 23,800.

052 ‖
2001. (Text in English) 1966. m. Times of India Bldg., Dr. Dadabhai Naoroji Rd., Bombay 400 001, India. TEL 22-2621692. FAX 22-2620144. TELEX 1182699. Ed. Mukul Sharma. circ. 20,600.

GENERAL INTEREST PERIODICALS — Indonesia

059.992 IO
BERITA NEGARA. 1951. s-w. Jalan Pertjetakan Negara 21, Kotakpos 2111, Jakarta, Indonesia. TEL 021-4207251. (also avail. in microfilm from KTO)

059.992 IO
BUANA MINGGU. w. Jalan Tanah Abang Dua 33, Jakarta Pusat 10110, Indonesia. TEL 021-364190. TELEX 46472. Ed. Winoto Parartho. circ. 193,450.

052 ‖
DEPTHNEWS INDONESIA. (Text in English) 1972. w. Press Foundation of Indonesia, Jalan Jatinegara barat III/6, Jakarta 13310, Indonesia. TEL 021-8194994. FAX 021-8195501. Ed. Sumono Mustoffa.

059.992 ‖
GEMA JUSAN. 1981. m. Corps of Invalids, Jalan Salemba Tengah 47, Jakarta Pusat, Indonesia. Ed. H. Anwan Bey. circ. 20,000.

052 ‖
INDONESIA MAGAZINE. (Text in English) 1969. m. 20 Jalan Merdeka Barat, Jakarta, Indonesia. TEL 021-352015. TELEX 46655. Ed. Hadely Hasibuan. circ. 15,000.

052 ‖ IO ISSN 0216-1974
INDONESIA TODAY. (Text in English) 1974. q. Department of Information, Jl. Merdeka Barat 7, Jakarta, Indonesia. illus.

059.992 052 AT ISSN 0812-7131
J A I A. (Text in English, Indonesian) 1977. a. Aus.$7. Australian-Indonesian Association of Victoria, c/o Hilary Da Costa, President, 10 Kent Rd., Box Hill, Vic. 3128, Australia. (Subscr. to: P.O. Box 515, Mt. Waverley, Vic. 3149, Australia) Ed. Dewi Anggraeni. adv.; bk.rev. circ. 500. (back issues avail.) Indexed: Mid.East: Abstr.& Ind. Document type: academic/scholarly publication.
 Formerly: A I A Journal.

059.992 IO
MANGLE. (Text in Sundanese) 1957. w. Jalan Lodaya 19-21, 40262 Bandung, Indonesia. TEL 022-411438. Ed. Oejang Darajatoen. circ. 74,000.

2740 GENERAL INTEREST PERIODICALS — IRAN

059.992   IO
MIMBAR KABINET PEMBANGUNAN. 1966. m. Department of Information, Jalan Merdeka-Barat 7, Jakarta, Indonesia.

051   IO   ISSN 0126-270X
HC446
PRISMA; the Indonesian indicator. (Text in English) 1975. irreg. (2-3/yr.). Rps.12000 for 4 nos.; in US $40 to individuals; institutions $45. (Institute for Economic and Social Research, Education and Information - Lembaga Penelitian, Pendidikan dan Penerangan Ekonomi dan Sosial (LP3ES)) P.T. Pustaka LP3ES, Jalan S. Parman 81, Slipi, Jakarta 11420, Indonesia. TEL 21-597211. Ed. Aswab Mahasin. adv.; bk.rev.; abstr.; bibl.; charts. circ. 1,300. Indexed: Bibl.Ling., E.I. —UnCover.
    Former titles: Indonesian Indicator (ISSN 0301-6269); Prisma.
    Description: Each issue is thematic, covering a subject concerned with social and economic developments in Indonesia.

059.992   IO
PRISMA: MAJALAH PEMIKIRAN SOSIAL EKONOMI. 1971. m. (Institute for Economic and Social Research, Education, and Information - Lembaga Penelitian, Pendidikan dan Penerangan Ekonomi dan Sosial (LP3ES)) P.T. Pustaka LP3ES, Jalan S. Parman 81, Slipi, Jakarta 11420, Indonesia. TEL 21-597-211.

059.992   IO
SELECTA. fortn. Kebon Kacang 29-4, Jakarta, Indonesia. Ed. Samsudin Lubis. circ. 80,000.

059   ISSN 0126-4273
TEMPO; the Indonesian weekly news magazine. (Text in Indonesian) 1971. w. $17. (Pusat Perdagangan Senen) P.T. Grafiti Pers, Lantai 8, Jl. H.R. Rasuna Said Kav. C-17 Kuningan, Jakarta 12940, Indonesia. TEL 021-5201022. FAX 021-5200092. TELEX 62797-IA. (Singapore Addr.: Media Link, 1 Sophia Rd., No. 04-26, Peace Centre, Singapore 0922. TEL 65-3361725; Japan Addr.: Raira Enterprise Co., Ltd., 1-6-8-402, Shimoochiai, Shinjuku-ku, Tokyo 161, Japan. TEL 03-3360-9171) Ed. Goenawan Mohamad. adv.: B&W page $2315, color page $5158; trim 190 X 257; adv. contact: Hendrix K. Hidayat. bk.rev.; film rev.; charts; illus. circ. 168,033. (also avail. in microfiche; reprint service avail. from UMI)

GENERAL INTEREST PERIODICALS — Iran

059.915   IR
ARMAN. irreg., vol.2, 1990. Rs.250 per no. P.O. Box 11365-818, Teheran, Iran.

059.915   IR
ETTELA'AT HAFTEGI. w. $400 to N. America (effective 1994). Ettela'at Publications, P.O. Box 11365-9365, Khayyam Ave., Tehran 11144, Iran. TEL 98-21-328404. FAX 98-21-3111223. TELEX 212336. Ed. Fathollah Javadi. circ. 200,000.
    Document type: consumer publication.

059.915   IR
FARJAD. 1991. m. Rs.250 per no. Razi Ave., P.O. Box 5166-11365, Teheran, Iran.

059.915   IR   ISSN 1021-450X
GOZARESH; iqtisadi, ilmi, ijtimai. (Text in Persian, summaries in English) 1990. m. IRl.1000 (foreign IRI.25000). P.O. Box 14155-5467, Tehran, Iran. TEL 98-21-6417293. FAX 98-21-6417294. Ed. A. Golbaf. adv.; illus. circ. 30,000. Document type: consumer publication.
    Description: Covers political, business and economic issues in Iran and the world, scientific news, health concerns, urban issues, and literary and cultural topics.

059.915   IR   ISSN 0075-0476
IRAN ALMANAC AND BOOK OF FACTS. (Text in English) 1961. a. $50. Echo Publications, Av. Hafez, Kuche Hurtab No. 4, P.O. Box 11365-5551, Teheran, Iran. adv.

059.915 051   US
IRAN POST. (Text in English and Iranian) w. $30. Iran Post, Box 3765, Beverly Hills, CA 90212. TEL 213-464-5335.

059.915   IR
JAVANEH. q. Soroush Press, 228 Mottahhari Ave., P.O. Box 15875-1163, Teheran, Iran. TEL 021-830771.

079.55 059.915   IR   ISSN 0885-8179
KAYHAN. (Text in Persian; editions also avail. in Arabic, English) 1941. d. $1022 to N. America (effective 1994). Kayhan Publications, Ferdowsi Ave., P.O. Box 11365-9631, Tehran, Iran. TEL 98-21-3110251. FAX 98-21-3114228. TELEX 212467. adv.; bk.rev.; illus. circ. 350,000. (broadsheet format; also avail. in microfilm from LCP) Document type: newspaper.

079.55 059.9435   IR
KAYHAN (TURKISH EDITION). (Text in Turkish) 1984. m. $53 to N. America (effective 1994). Kayhan Publications, Ferdowsi Ave., P.O. Box 11365-9631, Teheran, Iran. TEL 98-21-3110251. FAX 98-21-3114228. TELEX 212467. Document type: newspaper.

KAYHAN AL-ARABI. see GENERAL INTEREST PERIODICALS — Middle East

079.55 059.915   IR   ISSN 1044-6141
KAYHAN-I HAVA'I. (Text in Persian) 1950. w. $131 to N. America (effective 1994). Kayhan Publications, Ferdowsi Ave., P.O. Box 11365-9631, Tehran, Iran. FAX 98-21-3114228. Document type: newspaper.

079.55 052   IR   ISSN 0885-8160
KAYHAN INTERNATIONAL. (Daily edition also avail.) (Text in English) 1959. w. $131 to N. America (d. ed. $351) (effective 1994). Kayhan Publications, Ferdowsi Ave., P.O. Box 11365-9631, Tehran, Iran. TEL 98-21-3110251. FAX 98-21-3114228. TELEX 212467. Ed. Hossein Raghfar. Document type: newspaper.

059.914   IR
KAYHAN URDU. (Text in Urdu) 1991. m. $53 to N. America (effective 1994). Kayhan Publications, Ferdowsi Ave., P.O. Box 11365-9631, Tehran, Iran. TEL 98-21-3110251. FAX 98-21-3114228. TELEX 212467. Document type: newspaper.

079.55 059.915   IR
KHURASAN. (Text in Persian) 1948. d. S.A. Musaviyan, P.O. Box 91735-511, Meshed, Iran. (broadsheet format) Document type: newspaper.

059.915   IR
KHVURJIN. no.55, 1990. m. Rs.250 per no. F. Gulafra, Vali Asar Rd., Opp Fatimi Rd., Blk.4, Teheran, Iran. illus.
    Description: Humor magazine.

059.915   US
DS251
RAHAVARD PERSIAN JOURNAL. 1982. q. $36 (foreign $44). Hassan Shahbaz, Ed. & Pub., Box 24640, Los Angeles, CA 90024. adv.; bk.rev. circ. 5,000. Document type: academic/scholarly publication.
    Formerly: Rahavard (ISSN 0742-8014)
    Description: Aims to preserve Persian culture among Iranian immigrants.

059.927   IR
SOROUSH (MONTHLY). (Editions in Arabic, English, French; weekly edition in Farsi) m. Soroush Press, 228 Mottahhari Ave., P.O. Box 15875-1163, Teheran, Iran. TEL 021-830771. Ed. Mahdi Firoozan.

059.915   IR
SOROUSH (WEEKLY). (Text in Farsi; monthly editions in Arabic, English, French) 1972. w. $100. Soroush Press, 228 Mottahhari Ave., P.O. Box 15875-1163, Teheran, Iran. TEL 021-830771. Ed. Mahdi Firoozan. adv.; bk.rev. circ. 60,000.
    Formerly (until 1981): Tamasha.

GENERAL INTEREST PERIODICALS — Iraq

052   IQ   ISSN 0005-3902
BAGHDAD OBSERVER.* (Text in English) 1967. d. $300. (Ministry of Information and Culture) Dar Al-Ma'mum for Translation and Publishing, Kholafa St., Baghdad, Iraq. Ed. Naji S. Al-Hadithi. adv.; bk.rev. circ. 7,000. (tabloid format)

GENERAL INTEREST PERIODICALS — Ireland

052   IE
BRAY PEOPLE. (Text in English) w. £8.44 for 3 months. People Newspapers Ltd., 1 North Main St., Wexford, Ireland. TEL 053 22155. FAX 053-23801. Ed. Ger Walsh. circ. 37,141. (tabloid format; also avail. in microfilm from IMI)

052   IE
CILL DARA AND LIFFEY VALLEY NEWS. (Text in English) 1984. fortn. free. Enterprise Publications, Enterprise Centre, Melitta Rd., Kildare, Ireland. TEL 045-21132. FAX 045-21560. TELEX 60699. Ed. Martin Dempsey. adv. circ. 32,000. (tabloid format; back issues avail.)
    Incorporates: Cill Dara News & Liffey Valley News.

072.915   IE
DERRY PEOPLE DONEGAL NEWS. 1900. w. newsstand price: I£0.55. Derry People Donegal News Ltd., Crossview House, High Rd., Letterkenny, Co. Donegal, Ireland. TEL 21014. FAX 22881. Owner(s): N W of I Printing and Publishing Co., 10 John St., Omagh, Co. Tyrone, Ireland. TEL 0662-243444. Ed. E.J. Quigley; Pub. Austin Lynch. adv. contact: Eunan McGlynn. circ. 11,500 (paid). cols./p.: 10; pp./issue: 26. (broadsheet format; back issues avail.) Document type: newspaper.

072.919   IE
EAST CORK NEWS. (Text in English) 1981. w. £32.76. Waterford News & Star, Michael St., Waterford, Ireland. TEL 051-74951. FAX 051-55281. Ed. Peter Doyle. circ. 18,645. Document type: newspaper.

059.916   IE   ISSN 0014-8946
FEASTA. (Text in Irish) 1948. m. £11($35) Conradh na Gaeilge - Gaelic League, 13 Dyke Parade, Cork, Ireland. Ed. Seamas Ruiseal. adv.; bk.rev.; illus.; index, cum.index every 5 yrs. circ. 2,000.

052   IE
GUARDIAN. (Text in English) 1853. w. £8.44 for 3 months. People Newspapers Ltd., 1 North Main St., Wexford, Ireland. TEL 053-22155. FAX 053-23801. Ed. Ger Walsh. circ. 37,141. (tabloid format)

052   IE
I T MAGAZINE. (Irish Tatler) 1890. m. Noelle Campbell Sharp, Campenella, Killiney Ave., Marino Ave. West, Dublin, Ireland. adv.; bk.rev.; charts; illus.; index, cum.index. circ. 25,630.
    Formerly: Irish Tatler and Sketch (ISSN 0021-1397); Incorporating: Irish Bride and Home.

052   IE   ISSN 0790-6862
IN DUBLIN. 1976. fortn. $30. Tribune Publications Plc, 15 Lower Baggot St., Dublin 2, Ireland. TEL 01-615555. FAX 01-615302. Ed. Fiona Looney. adv.; bk.rev.; film rev. circ. 10,083.
    Description: Listings: current affairs; arts and entertainment; review.

052   IE
IRELAND. 1980. q. $5. (Workers' Party of Ireland) Repsol Publications, 30 Gardiner Pl., Dublin 1, Ireland. Ed. Sean Cionnaith. circ. 2,000.
    Description: Gives an insight into the country from a working class perspective. Keeps the reader in touch with the struggle against terrorism and for peace, work, democracy and class politics.

IRELAND: A DIRECTORY (YEAR). see BUSINESS AND ECONOMICS — Trade And Industrial Directories

052   IE   ISSN 0021-0951
IRELAND'S OWN. 1902. w. $56.95. Ireland's Own, Main St., Wexford, Ireland. TEL 053-22155. FAX 053-23801. Ed. Austin Channing. adv.; bk.rev.; illus. circ. 51,500. Document type: consumer publication.

052   IE
IRISH BYSTANDER. 1977. m. £8. Sports Enterprises Ltd., Box 14, Dun Laoire, Co. Dublin, Ireland. Ed. Pat Ruddy. adv.

GENERAL INTEREST PERIODICALS — ISRAEL

072.917   IE   ISSN 0021-1222
IRISH INDEPENDENT. 1905. d. Independent Newspapers plc, 90 Middle Abbey St., Dublin, Ireland. TEL 353-1-731333. FAX 353-1-731787. Ed. Vincent Doyle. adv.; bk.rev.; bibl.; charts; illus.; stat. circ. 144,000. (also avail. in microfilm from IMI) **Document type:** newspaper.

052   IE
IRISH WEEKLY EXAMINER. 1898. w. £5.20. Thomas Crosbie & Co. Ltd., 95 Patrick St., Cork, Ireland. Ed. Tim Cramer. adv.; bk.rev. circ. 20,000.
    Incorporating: Cork Weekly Examiner and Weekly Herald (ISSN 0010-874X)

072.915   IE
KILKENNY PEOPLE NEWSPAPER. 1892. w. I£94.20. Kilkenny People, 34 High St., Kilkenny, Ireland. TEL 056-21015. FAX 056-21414. Ed. John Keane. circ. 18,600. **Document type:** newspaper.

072.915   IE
LEITRIM OBSERVER. 1890. w. (Wed.). I£55; newsstand price: I£0.80. Leitrim Observer Ltd., St. George's Terrace, Carrick-on-Shannon, Co. Leitrim, Ireland. TEL 078-20025. FAX 078-20112. Ed. Anthony Hickey; Pub. Patrick Dunne. adv. contact: Willie Donnellan. cols./p.: 9; pp./issue: 20. (broadsheet format) **Document type:** newspaper.

072.915   IE
LONGFORD LEADER. 1897. w. (Wed.). I£60; newsstand price: I£0.75. Longford Leader Ltd., Market Sq., Longford, Ireland. TEL 01-45241. FAX 01-41489. Owner(s): Midland Publishing Ltd., Market Sq., Longford, Ireland. Ed. Eugene McGee; Pub. Eugene McGee. adv. contact: Margaret Faughnan. bk.rev.; circ. 21,500 (paid). cols./p.: 9; pp./issue: 22. (broadsheet format; also avail. in microfilm; back issues avail.) **Document type:** newspaper.

052   IE
MAGILL: IRELAND'S CURRENT AFFAIRS MONTHLY MAGAZINE. 1977. m. $50. Magill Publications Ltd., 15 Lower Baggot St., Dublin 2, Ireland. TEL 615555. TELEX 90995. Ed. Vincent Browne. adv.; bk.rev.; film rev.; play rev. circ. 40,000.

072.918   IE
MEATH CHRONICLE. 1897. w. I£51.84; newsstand price: I£0.80. Meath Chronicle Ltd., Market Sq., Navan, Co. Meath, Ireland. TEL 046-21442. FAX 046-23565. Ed. James Davis. adv.; B&W page I£2550, color page I£2805; trim 540 x 348; adv. contact: Mary Dunne. bk.rev.; film rev.; music rev.; tele.rev.; tr.lit. circ. 19,635. cols./p.: 9; pp./issue: 24. (broadsheet format; also avail. in microfilm from IMI; back issues avail.) **Document type:** newspaper.

072.919   IE
NATIONALIST AND MUNSTER ADVERTISER. (Text in English) 1890. w. $260; newsstand price: I£0.75. Nationalist Newspaper Ltd., Queen St., Clonmel, Co. Tipperary, Ireland. TEL 052-22211. FAX 052-25248. Ed. Tom Corr. adv. contact: Philip Corby. bk.rev.; film rev.; music rev.; tele.rev. circ. 15,578. cols./p.: 9; pp./issue: 28. (broadsheet format; also avail. in microfilm from IMI) **Document type:** newspaper.

052   IE
PEOPLE. (Text in English) w. £98. People Newpapers Ltd., 1 N. Main St., Wexford, Ireland. Ed. Dermot Walsh. circ. 37,393. (tabloid format; also avail. in microfilm from IMI)

052   IE
STANDARD. (Text in English) w. £8.44 for 3 mos. People Newpapers Ltd., 1 N. Main St., Wexford, Ireland. TEL 053-22155. FAX 053-23801. Ed. Ger Walsh. circ. 37,141. (tabloid format)

072.917   IE   ISSN 0039-5218
SUNDAY INDEPENDENT. (Text in English; occasionally in Gaelic) 1905. w. Independent Newspapers Ltd., 90 Middle Abbey St., Dublin 1, Ireland. TEL 353-1-731333. FAX 353-1-731787. adv.; bk.rev.; film rev.; illus.; play rev. circ. 252,500. **Document type:** newspaper.

072.919   IE   ISSN 0040-8034
TIPPERARY STAR. (Text in English and Gaelic) 1909. w. $260; newsstand price: I£0.75. Nationalist Newspaper Ltd., Friar St., Thurles, Co. Tipperary, Ireland. TEL 0504-21122. FAX 0504-21100. Ed. Michael Dundon. adv. contact: Pat Kelly. bk.rev.; charts; illus.; mkt.; stat. circ. 10,434. cols./p.: 9; pp./issue: 26. (broadsheet format; also avail. in microfilm from IMI) **Document type:** newspaper.

072.917   IE
TUAM HERALD AND WESTERN ADVERTISER. (Text in English and Irish) 1837. w. £45. Herald Printing & Publishing Co., Ltd., Dublin Rd., Tuam, Co. Galway, Ireland. TEL 093-24183. FAX 093-24478. Ed. David Burke. adv.; bk.rev. circ. 12,000. (back issues avail.) **Document type:** newspaper.
    Description: Includes news, sports, features, local historical items, art and reviews.

072.918   IE
WESTMEATH EXAMINER. (Text in English) 1882. w. I£50.96. Westmeath Examiner Ltd., 19 Dominick St., Mullingar, Co. Westmeath, Ireland. TEL 044-48426. FAX 044-40640. Ed. Nicholas Nally. adv. contact: Nicholas Nally. bk.rev.; film rev.; music rev.; tele.rev. circ. 13,325. cols./p.: 9; pp./issue: 20. (broadsheet format; back issues avail.) **Document type:** newspaper.

052   IE
WICKLOW PEOPLE. (Text in English) w. £98. People Newspaper Ltd., 1 N. Main St., Wexford, Ireland. TEL 053 22155. Ed. Dermot Walsh. circ. 37,393. (tabloid format; also avail. in microfilm from IMI)

GENERAL INTEREST PERIODICALS — Israel

052   IS
A A C I NORTH. 1970. bi-m. membership. Association of Americans and Canadians, P.O. Box 6535, Haifa 31060, Israel. TEL 972-4-387140. Eds. Myrna Bennett, Laurie Wolberg. adv. circ. 1,800. **Document type:** newsletter.

059.945   IS
A HET TURKE. (Text in Hungarian) w. P.O. Box 2026, Bnei Brak, Israel. TEL 03-794736.
    Description: Weekly of national news and events.

059.92   IS
AL EL. m. free. Merchavim Regional Municipal Council, D.N. Negev 85400, Israel. TEL 057-923337.

052   IS
ALAWDAH. (Text in English) m. P.O. Box 19563, Jerusalem, Israel. Ed. Raymonda Tawil.

057.1   IS   ISSN 0736-8518
ALEF. (Text in Russian) 1981. w. IS.130($55) Chamah, 53 Nachmani St., Tel Aviv, Israel. TEL 03-621682. FAX 03-624897. (U.S. addr.: 78 Pearl St., New York, NY 10004. TEL 212-943-9690) adv.; bk.rev.

059.92   IS
ALEI MERCHAVIM. m. Merchavim Regional Municipal Council, D.N. Negev 85400, Israel.

059.92   IS   ISSN 0569-163X
AM VEADAMATO. 1967. s-a. Keren Kayemet Leyisrael, P.O. Box 283, Jerusalem, Israel.

079.5694   IS
HA'ARETZ. (Text in Hebrew) 1918. d. 21 Salman Shocken St., P.O. Box 233, Tel Aviv 61001, Israel. TEL 972-3-5121212. FAX 972-3-6810012. adv.; bk.rev.; illus. circ. 55,000. (broadsheet format; also avail. in microfilm from UMI) **Document type:** newspaper.

059.92   IS
ASSOCIATION OF AMERICANS AND CANADIANS IN ISRAEL. CENTRAL REGION. NEWSLETTER. (Text in English) bi-m. membership. Association of Americans and Canadians in Israel, Central Region, 22 Mazeh St., Tel Aviv 65213, Israel. TEL 03-299799. Ed. Miriam Selove. adv. circ. 3,000. **Document type:** newsletter.

056.1   IS   ISSN 0334-8954
AURORA; semanario Israeli de actualidad. (Text and summaries in Spanish) 1963. w. $100. Editorial "Aurora" Ltd. Israel, P.O. Box 18066, Tel Aviv, Israel. TEL 972-3-5625216. FAX 972-3-5625082. Ed. Arie Avidor. adv.; B&W page $1980; adv. contact: Gabriel Sverdlik. bk.rev.; film rev.; play rev.; illus.; stat.; tr.lit. circ. 25,000. (tabloid format)

059.92   IS   ISSN 0334-3170
DS101
BAERETZ YISRAEL. 1973. m. IS.15. Hayam Ltd., P.O. Box 23178, Tel Aviv 61231, Israel. TEL 03-287330. Ed. Haim Kaufman.

059.92   IS
BAGALIL HAELYON. 1970. m. free. Upper Galilee Regional Municipal, Kiryat-Shmona 10200, Israel. TEL 06-945635. FAX 06-949444. Ed. Ora Lipetz. adv.; bk.rev. circ. 4,000.

059.92   IS
DAPAI TAMAR. irreg. Regional Council Tamar, D.N. Dead Sea 86910, Israel. TEL 057-84184.

079.5694   IS
AL-FAJR. English edition: Al-Fajr Jerusalem Palestinian Weekly (ISSN 1066-3479) (Text in Arabic) 1972. d. $200 in U.S. (effective 1993). 7 Antara Ben Shaddad, P.O. Box 19315, East Jerusalem, Via Israel. TEL 972-2-894508. FAX 972-2-273521. (Subscr. in U.S. to: Omar International, Inc., 16 Crowell St., Hempstead, NY 11550. TEL 516-485-5905) Ed. Hanna Siniora. adv. contact: Paul Ajlouni. (also avail. in microfilm from IDC) **Document type:** newspaper.
    Description: Covers political and social issues affecting Palestinians under Israeli occupation and in exile.

059.92   IS
GHETTO FIGHTERS HOUSE; activities and events. (Text in Hebrew) q. free. Ghetto Fighters House, Kibbutz Lochamei Haghetaot, D.N. Asherat 25220, Israel. Dir. Simcha Stein. bk.rev. **Document type:** newsletter.

052   IS
IN ENGLISH MAGAZINE; the voice of the English-speaking community. (Text in English) 1986. m. $50. P.O. Box 592, Raanana, Israel. TEL 052-913608. FAX 052-913088. Ed. Dov Sydney. adv.; bk.rev. circ. 20,000.
    Formerly: In English (ISSN 0792-0679)

052   IS
ISRAEL. GOVERNMENT PRESS OFFICE. DAILY NEWS AND EDITORIAL SURVEY. (Text in English) 1949. d. free. Government Press Office, Agron House, 37 Hillel St., Jerusalem 94581, Israel. Ed. Ralph Mandel. circ. controlled.
    Formerly (until 1977): Israel. Government Press Office. Weekly News Bulletin.

059.92   IS
ISRAEL NEWS BULLETIN. 1983. 3/m. $60. P.O. Box 24269, Mount Scopus, Jerusalem, Israel. Ed. Rafael Medoff. bk.rev. circ. 3,000.

079.5694   IS   ISSN 0199-7424
DS101
ISRAEL SCENE. (Supplement to: Jerusalem Post - International Edition) 1979. bi-m. $15. World Zionist Organization, Department of Information, P.O. Box 92, Jerusalem 91920, Israel. TEL 972-2-527156. FAX 972-2-513542. (U.S. office: 110 E. 59th St., New York, NY 10022. TEL 212-339-6020) Ed. Lisa Gann-Perkal. adv.; bk.rev. circ. 55,000. (back issues avail.) **Indexed:** Ind.Jew.Per. **Document type:** newspaper.

056.1   IS   ISSN 0792-9560
▼**ISRAEL Y MEDIO ORIENTE.** (Text in Spanish) 1993. m. $60 (effective 1994). Editorial "Aurora" Ltd. Israel, P.O. Box 18066, Tel Aviv 61180, Israel. TEL 972-3-5625216. FAX 972-3-5625082. Ed. Arie Avidor. adv. contact: Gabriel Sverdlik. film rev.; play rev.; illus. **Document type:** consumer publication.
    Description: Covers news and events in Israel and the Middle East for a Spanish-speaking audience.

GENERAL INTEREST PERIODICALS — ITALY

059.92   IS
ISRAEL YEARBOOK AND ALMANAC (YEAR). 1946. a. $35. I B R T Ltd., 8 Hata'asiya St., Ste. 207, Jerusalem 93420, Israel. TEL 972-2-720107. FAX 972-2-719128. Ed. Naftali Greenwood. adv.; illus. (back issues avail.) **Document type:** academic/scholarly publication, consumer publication.
— BLDSC (4583.952000).
    Formerly (until 1992): Israel Yearbook (ISSN 0075-1413)
    Description: Provides comprehensive statistical and chronological coverage of major events and issues affecting Israel during the preceding year, with commercial directories and tourist information.

079.5694 052   IS   ISSN 0792-822X
THE JERUSALEM POST. French edition (ISSN 0792-8211) (International edition avail.) (Text in English) 1925. d. $470 (effective 1994). Jerusalem Post, P.O. Box 81, Jerusalem 91000, Israel. TEL 972-2-315666. FAX 972-2-389017. Owner(s): American Publishing, 111 S. Emma, West Frankfort, IL 62896. (And: Jerusalem Post, 211 E. 433rd St., Ste. 601, New York, NY 10017. TEL 212-599-3666. FAX 212-599-4743) Ed. David Bar-Illan; Pub. Yehuda Levy. adv. contact: Ari Golan. illus.; circ. 45,000 (paid). (broadsheet format; also avail. in microfilm from IDC) **Document type:** newspaper.
  • Also available online. Vendor(s): Mead Data Central, Inc.
  Also available on CD-ROM.
    Former titles (until 1950): Palestine Post; Which supersedes in 1932): Palestine Bulletin; (1919-1931): Palestine Weekly.

079.5694 054.1   IS   ISSN 0792-8211
THE JERUSALEM POST (EDITION FRANCAISE). (Text in French) 1990. w. 650 F. (effective 1994). Jerusalem Post, P.O. Box 81, Jerusalem 91000, Israel. TEL 972-2-315666. FAX 972-2-389017. Owner(s): American Publishing, 111 S. Emma, West Frankfort, IL 62896. (And: Jerusalem Post, 211 E. 43rd St., Ste. 601, New York, NY 10017. TEL 212-599-3666. FAX 212-599-4743) Ed. David Bar-Illan. adv. contact: Ari Golan. circ. 7,500 (paid). (tabloid format) **Document type:** newspaper.
  • Also available online. Vendor(s): Mead Data Central, Inc.
  Also available on CD-ROM.

079.5694 052   IS
THE JERUSALEM POST (INTERNATIONAL EDITION). (Text in English) w. $79.95. Jerusalem Post, P.O. Box 81, Jerusalem 91000, Israel. TEL 972-2-315666. FAX 972-2-389017. Owner(s): American Publishing, 111 S. Emma, West Frankfort, IL 62896. (And: Jerusalem Post, 211 E. 43rd St., Ste. 601, New York, NY 10017. TEL 212-599-3666. FAX 212-599-4743) Ed.David Bar-Illan; Pub. Yehuda Levy. adv. contact: Ari Golan. bk.rev.; circ. 65,000 (paid).
  • Also available online. Vendor(s): Mead Data Central, Inc.
  Also available on CD-ROM.

052   IS
JERUSALEM VOICE. (Text in English) 1970. bi-m. membership. Association of Americans and Canadians in Israel, Jerusalem Region, P.O. Box 30018, Jerusalem 91300, Israel. TEL 972-2-617151. FAX 972-2-661186. Ed. Lee Glassman. adv. contact: Shalva Davies. circ. 4,500. **Document type:** bulletin.

059.92   IS
LAHAVOT. 1988. m. Kibbutz Lahavot ha-Bashan, D.N. Galil Elyon 12 125, Israel.

053.1   IS
M B. (Mitteilungsblatt) (Text in German) 1932. m. $24. (Irgun Oley Merkaz Europa) Bitaon Publishing Co. Ltd., 15 Rambam St., P.O. Box 1480, Tel Aviv 61014, Israel. FAX 972-3-664461. Ed. Zeev Estreicher. adv.; bk.rev.; circ. 4,000 (controlled).

079.5694   IS
MA'ARIV. (Text in Hebrew) 1948. d. $948 in U.S. Modiin Publishing House Ltd., Carlebach St. 2, P.O. Box 20010, Tel Aviv 61200, Israel. TEL 972-3-5632111. FAX 972-3-5610614. (Subscr. in U.S. to: Ma'ariv, 60 E. 42nd St., New York, NY 10165. TEL 212-687-1632) Ed. Jacob Erez. adv.; bk.rev.; illus. circ. 130,000. **Document type:** newspaper.

059.92   IS
MAARIV LANOAR. 1957. w. IS.240($96) Modiin Publishing House Ltd., 2 Carlebach St., P.O. Box 20010, Tel Aviv 61200, Israel. TEL 972-3-5632111. FAX 972-3-5632030. TELEX 33735. Ed. Amnon Beirav. adv. circ. 100,000.

059.92   IS
MONITIN. m. 127 Igal Alon St., Tel Aviv, Israel. TEL 03-253211.

956.94   IS   ISSN 0027-2892
MOZNAYIM. 1929. m. $75. Hebrew Writers Association in Israel, P.O. Box 7098, Tel Aviv, Israel. FAX 972-3-6919681. Eds. Ortsion Bartana, Moshe Ben-Shaul. adv.; bk.rev.; index. circ. 3,000. **Indexed:** Ind.Heb.Per., M.L.A.

956.940 296 070   AG   ISSN 0327-5930
MUNDO ISRAELITA; actualidad de la semana en Israel y en el mundo judio. 1923. w. $150. Editorial Mundo Israelita, Lavalle 2615, 1r Piso, 1052 Buenos Aires, Argentina. TEL 1-961-7999. FAX 1-961-0763. Ed. Jose Kestelman. adv.; bk.rev.; illus. (tabloid format) **Document type:** newspaper.

052   IS   ISSN 0334-374X
NEGEV; journal of Ben Gurion University of the Negev. (Text in English) 1975. s-a. free. Ben Gurion University, Department of Public Affairs, P.O. Box 653, Beersheva 84105, Israel. TEL 972-57-39943. FAX 972-57-270656. circ. 11,000.

059.92   IS
NEKUDA. 1979. m. IS.110($85) Nekuda Ktav-et, Ofra, Mizrach Benjamin Mobile Post 90906, Israel. TEL 972-2-810488. FAX 972-2-810388. Ed. Israel Harel. adv.; bk.rev. circ. 10,000. **Document type:** newspaper.

059.92   IS
REMENY; irodalmi, kulturalis es tarsadalmi zsido folyoirat - Jewish magazine of literature, culture and society. (Text in Hungarian) m. $50. P.O. Box 251, Tel Aviv, Israel. TEL 03-701090. Ed. Nafalti Kraus.

059.92   IS
REVISTA MEA. (Text in Rumanian) m. 52 Harakevet St., Tel Aviv, Israel. TEL 03-370011.

056.1   IS
REVISTA W I Z O. English edition: W I Z O Review (ISSN 0042-9732) (Text in Spanish; German ed. also avail.) 1930. q. $5. Women's International Zionist Organization, 38 David Hamelech Blvd., Tel Aviv 64237, Israel. TEL 972-3-5421805. FAX 972-3-6958267. Ed. Hillel Schenker. bk.rev.
    Description: Contains the latest news about the organization's policies and activities in Israel and around the world, as well as coverage of Israeli cultural and political issues.

059.92   IS
SHAARIM; bulletin of the workers of the municipality of Tel Aviv - Yafo. m. Rehov Fumbreita 4, Tel Aviv 64234, Israel. TEL 03-241231. Ed. Teddy Kaufman.

059.92   IS   ISSN 0503-146X
DS101
HAUMAH. 1962. q. IS.50 (effective 1993). Misdar Jabotinsky, P.O. Box 21174, Tel Aviv 61211, Israel. TEL 972-52-583949. Ed. Joseph Chrust. adv.; bk.rev. circ. 2,000.

059.92   IS
YIDDISH ZEITUNG. (Text in Yiddish) w. 52 Harakevet St., Tel Aviv, Israel. TEL 03-370011.

GENERAL INTEREST PERIODICALS — Italy

055.1   US
ACQUERELLO ITALIANO. (Text in Italian) 1990. bi-m. $89. Champs-Elysees Inc., Box 158067, Nashville, TN 37215-8067. TEL 800-824-0829. FAX 615-297-3138. (audio cassette; with printed transcription)

055.1   IT
ALLEANZA MONARCHICA. 1967. m. L.30000($52.50) Alleanza Monarchica, P.O. Box 1, 10100 Turin, Italy. FAX 011-539548. Ed. Roberto Vittucci Righini. adv.; bk.rev. circ. 20,000. (tabloid format)

055.1   IT   ISSN 0002-6492
ALPINO. 1919. m. L.15000. Associazione Nazionale Alpini, Via Marsala 9, 20121 Milan, Italy. TEL 02-6552692. FAX 02-6592364. Dir. Arturo Vita. adv.; bk.rev.; bibl.; illus.; stat.; tr.lit.; circ. controlled. (tabloid format)

055.1   IT
ALTA VAL TANARO. 1945. w. L.8000. Tipografia Odello, Via Marenco, 95, 12073 Ceva, Italy.

055.1   IT
L'AMICO DEL POPOLO. 1909. w. L.35000($17) Amico del Popolo S.R.L., Piazza Piloni 11, I-32100 Belluno, Italy. FAX 0437-940661. TELEX 440147 AMPOP. adv.; bk.rev. circ. 25,000.

055   IT   ISSN 0391-5131
ANNALI D'ITALIA. 1961. m. L.25000. Istituto Publiaci, Corso Vittorio Emanuele 326, 00186 Rome, Italy. Ed. Marcello Vazio. adv. circ. 40,000.
    Description: Presents activities in Italy and at the Vatican.

065   IT   ISSN 0393-6368
L935
ANNUARIO D E A DELLE UNIVERSITA E ISTITUTI DI STUDIO E RICERCA IN ITALIA/D E A DIRECTORY OF UNIVERSITIES, SCIENTIFIC AND CULTURAL INSTITUTIONS IN ITALY. 1983. a. $135. D E A Editrice, Via Lima, 28, 00198 Rome, Italy. TEL 06-8551441. FAX 06-8543228. TELEX 622492. Ed. Anna Ligi. adv.; bk.rev. circ. 2,000. **Document type:** directory.

055.1   IT
APE DEL CONCA. 1883. q. free. Via Pascoli, 12, 47047 Morciano di Romagna, Italy. Ed. Quadrio Muratori. circ. 2,000.

055.1   IT
ARETUSA. 1969. fortn. (22/yr.) L.10000. A.I.S.A. Agenzia Informazioni Stampa Aretusa, Via Tucidide 44, 96100 Siracusa, Italy. Ed. Salvatore Xibilia Panusa. adv. circ. 800.

055   IT
ARRINGA. 1968. fortn. L.15000. (Associazione Nazionale dei Procuratori e Patrocinatori Legali) Emilio Ponticello, Ed. & Pub., Via Sampiero di Bastelica 93, 00176 Rome, Italy. adv.; bk.rev. circ. 5,000.

055   IT
ATENEO BRUZIO. 1954. m. (9/yr.) L.3000. Via Nicola Serra 52, 87100 Cosenza, Italy. Ed. Luigi Pellegrini. adv.

075   IT   ISSN 1120-6020
AVVENIRE. 1968. d. Mauro Macchi 61, 20124 Milan, Italy. TEL 02-67801. FAX 02-6780345. Ed. Dino Boffo; Pub. Livio Gualerzi. adv. contact: Giuseppe Costa. bk.rev.; film rev.; play rev. circ. 88,260. cols./p.: 8; pp./issue: 28. (standard format; back issues avail.) **Document type:** newspaper.

055.1 320   IT
BARBINELLA. 1980. m. L.6000. Via Ceschelli 16, 80047 San Giuseppe Vesuviano, Italy. Ed. G. Romano Artolo. adv.; illus.

055.1   IT   ISSN 0392-2561
BEST BOOMERANG. 1977. m. L.8000($15) Editrice Sopi s.r.l., Via dei Serpenti 164, 00184 Rome, Italy. Ed. Elisabetta Ponti. adv. circ. 115,000.

055.1   IT
CAGLIARITANO. m. G.I.A. Editrice, Viale Regina Margherita 26, 09100 Cagliari, Italy. TEL 070-66-59-18. FAX 070-66-4095.

005.1   IT
CAPITALE OGGI. 1991. m. free. Amorosino Editore Roma, Via Francesco Salata, 18, 00177 Rome, Italy. TEL 06-274040.
    Description: Covers news, art, music and sports.

055   IT
CASA NOSTRA. 1952. bi-m. L.2000. Casa Cardinale Maffi, Via Aurelia Nord 9, Cecina (Livorno), Italy. Ed. Rido Creatini. adv. circ. 1,500.

GENERAL INTEREST PERIODICALS — ITALY

055.1   IT
CASA OGGI. 1972. m. (10/yr.). L.52000. Di Baio Editore s.r.l., Via Settembrini 11, 20124 Milan, Italy. Ed. Giuseppe Maria Jonghi Lavarini. adv.; bk.rev. circ. 71,000.
    Former titles: Milano Casa Oggi; Milanocasa.

055.1   IT   ISSN 0008-719X
CASANA. 1958. q. free. Banca Carige S.p.A, Via Cassa di Risparmio, 15, 16123 Genoa, Italy. TEL 010-5792255. Ed. Nino Gotta. bk.rev.; bibl.; illus.; stat. circ. 50,000. **Indexed:** Numis.Lit.

055.1   IT   ISSN 0008-7491
IL CASTELLO; periodico cavese di vita cittadina. 1947. m. L.10000. c/o Prof. Domenico Apicella, Ed., 84013 Cava dei Tirreni, Italy. TEL 441625. Ed. Domenico Apicella. adv.; bk.rev.; illus. circ. 2,000. (tabloid format)
    Description: Publication concerned with political and administrative life in Cava and Salerno. Also promotes cultural and artistic development of its people.

055.1   IT
CHIAZZE. 1979. q. L.4000. Tipografo Fiorino-Ruvo, Casella Postale 45, I-70037 Ruvo di Puglia, Italy. Ed.Bd. (tabloid format; back issues avail.)

055.1   IT
CITTA (LATINA); quindicinale di informazione, sport, cultura e spettacolo. 1981. s-m. price varies. La Citta S.r.l., c/o Ardetti, Casella Postale 128, 04100 Latina, Italy. adv.; bk.rev. circ. 5,000. (tabloid format)

055   IT
CITTA NUOVA (ROME). 1956. 23/yr. L.48000 (foreign L.120000). Citta Nuova Editrice, Via degli Scipioni 265, 00192 Rome, Italy. TEL 06-3216212. FAX 06-3251410. Ed. Guglielmo Boselli. adv.; bk.rev. circ. 70,000.
    Description: Opinion oriented, emphasizes dialogue and culture. Explores all paths toward a united world.

055.1 052   IT
CITTA OGGI. (Text in English, Italian) 1991. m. free. Amorosino Editore Roma, Via Francesco Salata, 18, 00177 Rome, Italy. TEL 06-274040.
    Description: Covers politics, news, style and sports.

055.1   IT
COMUNE DI CERVIA. 1971. bi-m. free. Amministrazione Comunale di Cervia, Piazza Garibaldi 1, 48015 Cervia, Italy. TEL 0544-973444. FAX 0544-970912. Ed. Tolmino Baldassari. illus.; stat. circ. 10,000. (tabloid format)
    Description: Contains information about the city regarding political, cultural, ambiental and administrative news.

055.1   IT
CONTROLUCE. 1977. m. L.10000. Associazione Amici della Storia e della Cultura, Via Brusimpiano 2, 21037 Lavena Ponte, Italy.

055   IT
COPPIA MODERNA.* 1970. w. L.500 per. no. Pop, Via Braga 9, 20125 Milan, Italy. Ed. Pietro Granelli. adv. circ. 150,000.

075   IT
CORRIERE DELLA SERA. 1876. d. L.320000 (foreign L.696950). R C S Editoriale Quotidiani S.p.A., Via Solferino 28, 20121 Milan, Italy. Ed. Paolo Mieli. **Document type:** newspaper.

055.1   IT
CORRIERE DI ROMA. 1948. bi-w. L.50000 (foreign L.100000) (effective 1994). Gruppo Editoriale Gesualdi, Via IV Novembre 152, 00187 Rome, Italy. TEL 06-6784964. FAX 06-6782994. Ed. Giuseppe Gesualdi. adv.: page L.6000000; 280 x 430. circ. 305,000. **Document type:** newspaper.

055.1   IT
CORRIERE DI TRECATE. 1955. w. L.700. Pastore Augusto, Piazza Cavour 2, 28069 Trecate, Italy. circ. 700.

055.1   IT
CORTINA. 1933. s-a. Giovanna Mariotti, Ed. & Pub., 32043 Cortina d'Ampezzo, Italy. TEL 0436-861684. adv.; bk.rev.; illus. circ. 7,500. **Document type:** monographic series.

055.1   IT
CRONACA VERA. 1969. w. L.1200 per no. Edizioni Wilson S.R.L., Via Carlo Ravizza, 53-A, 20149 Milan, Italy. Ed. Antonio Perria. adv. circ. 350,000.

055.1   IT
CROTONESE. 1980. s-m. (Alfabeta Coop. s.r.l.) Editoriale Crotonese s.r.l., Via 25 Aprile, 17, 88074 Crotone, Italy. circ. 6,000. (back issues avail.)

055.1   IT
DOCUMENTI. m? Comune di Parma, Piazza Garibaldi No 1, Parma, Italy. TEL 218327. FAX 0521-282913. TELEX 532233. Ed. Francesca Carra. charts; illus.; stat.
    Description: Features articles on current events. Each issue focuses on a single topic.

055.1   IT
DOMANI DI NOI RAGAZZI. q. Editirce Pellegrini, Via Roma, 74, 87100 Cosenza, Italy.

055.1   IT   ISSN 0012-5296
DOMENICA DEL CORRIERE. 1899. w. L.78000. Rizzoli Editore-Corriere della Sera, Via A. Rizzoli 2, 20132 Milan, Italy. Ed. P. Magnaschi.

056.1   UY   ISSN 0012-9534
ECO D'ITALIA. unico settimanale Italiano dell'Uruguay. (Text in Italian and Spanish) 1963. w. L.700($4.) Ituzaingo 1482, Montevideo, Uruguay. Ed. Gaetano Cario. adv.; bk.rev.; film rev.; play rev.; charts; illus.; stat.; tr.lit. circ. 3,000. (looseleaf format)

059.956   IT
ENDAS PIEMONTE; organo di informazione dell'Endas Piemontese. 1979. bi-m. free. Via Giolitti 19, 10121 Turin, Italy. TEL 8396977.

055.1   IT   ISSN 0013-9718
EPOCA. 1950. w. L.140400 (foreign L.205900). Arnoldo Mondadori Editore S.p.A., Casella Postale 1833, 20101 Milan, Italy. TEL 3199345. Ed. Carlo Rognoni. adv.; bk.rev.; film rev.; music rev.; play rev.; record rev.; illus. circ. 204,000.
—SWETS.

055   IT   ISSN 0423-4243
AP37
ESPRESSO. 1955. w. L.32000. Editoriale l' Espresso S.p.A., Via Po 12, 00198 Rome, Italy. TEL 06-84781. TELEX 610629. Ed. Giovanni Valentini. adv.; bk.rev. circ. 373,900. (also avail. in microfilm from UMI; reprint service avail. from UMI) —SWETS; UMI.

055.1   IT
L'ETICHETTA. q. L.35000 (foreign L.55000). Via Barozzi, 7, 20122 Milan, Italy. TEL 798933. Ed. Luigi Veronelli. circ. 17,500.

055.1   IT
EUROPA 2000; rivista bimestrale di cultura europea. bi-m. L.30000. Antonio Iodice, Via Vallarsa, 31, 00141 Rome, Italy. TEL 398047. Ed. Giacomo Cesario.

940   IT   ISSN 0014-3189
EUROPEO; settimanale politico di attualita. 1945. w. L.78000. Rizzoli Editore-Corriere della Sera, Via A. Rizzoli 2, 20132 Milan, Italy. TEL 02-2588. Ed. Lamfranco Vaccari. adv.; bk.rev.; film rev.; illus.; tele.rev. circ. 172,000.

055.1   IT   ISSN 0014-3308
EVA EXPRESS. 1933. w. L.91500 (foreign L.158000). Rusconi Editori S.p.A., Servizio Abbonamenti, Viale Sarca 235, 20126 Milan, Italy. TEL 02-66191. FAX 02-6619-2737. Ed. Paolo Mosca. adv.; bk.rev.; film rev.; illus.; tr.lit. circ. 326,391.
    Formerly: Eva.

F A V L; attualita, gente, storia e cultura della Tuscia. 1989. m.? Faul Edizioni Artistiche s.r.l., Via Cavour, 67, Viterbo, Italy. TEL 0761-224560. Ed. Bruno Barbini.

055.1   IT
F F - SUDTIROLER ILLUSTRIERTE. (Text in German) w. F F - Sudtiroler Illustrierte S.r.l., Via della Rena, 3, 39100 Bolzano, Italy. TEL 0471-971701. FAX 0471-981460.

F M R. (Franco Maria Ricci S.p.A.) see *ART*

055.1   IT
FERRARA. 1960. m. free. Comune di Ferrara, Palazzo Comunale, I-44100 Ferrara, Italy. TEL 419263. Dir. Gian Pietro Testa. adv.; bk.rev.

055   IT
FIAMMA NOVA. 1935. m. L.1500. Centro Nazionale Ordine Francescano Secolare, Via delle Mura Aurelie 9, 00165 Rome, Italy. Ed. Eliodoro Mariani. adv. circ. 120,000.

055.1   IT   ISSN 0015-2536
FIORISCE UN CENACOLO.* vol.28, 1967. m. L.2000. Eremo Italico, 84085 Mercato S. Severino, Salerno, Italy.

055   IT   ISSN 0391-769X
FIUGGI. 1905. m. L.4000. Maria Martini Editore, Via della Loggetta 5, 03014 Fiuggi, Italy. Ed. Pietro Martini. adv.; bk.rev.; illus. circ. 4,000. **Document type:** newspaper.

055.1   IT
▼**FOCUS**; scopire e capire il mondo. 1992. m. L.38400 (foreign L.64200). Gruner und Jahr - Mondadori S.p.A., Corso Monforte 54, 20122 Milan, Italy. Ed. Remo Guerrini. **Document type:** consumer publication.

055.1   IT   ISSN 0531-9870
FONDAZIONE LUIGI EINAUDI. ANNALI. 1966. a. L.50000 (effective 1993). Fondazione Luigi Einaudi, Via Principe Amedeo 34, 10123 Turin, Italy. TEL 11-83-56-56. FAX 011-8179093. Ed. Franco Venturi. circ. 1,000. **Document type:** corporate report.
    Description: Reports on the scientific activities of the foundation. Includes papers on the social sciences from grant recipients.

075   IT
GAZZETTA DEL LUNEDI. 1945. w. Via Varese 2, Genoa, Italy. TEL 010-517851. Dir. Mimmo Angeli. circ. 150,000. **Document type:** newspaper.

055.1   IT   ISSN 0016-6944
GENTE. 1956. w. L.112300 (foreign L.230000). Rusconi Editori S.p.A., Servizio Abbonamenti, Viale Sarca 235, 20126 Milan, Italy. TEL 02-66191. FAX 02-6619-2737. Ed. Sandro Mayer. adv.; bk.rev.; film rev.; play rev.; illus. circ. 915,114.
    Description: Covers political, cultural and current events.

055.1 320   IT   ISSN 0393-7941
GENTE MESE; mensile di politica, attualita, cultura. 1986. m. L.48000 (foreign L.75000). Rusconi Editori S.p.A., Viale Sarca 235, 20126 Milan, Italy. TEL 02-66191. FAX 02-6619-2630. Ed. Sandro Mayer. circ. 135,327. (back issues avail.)

055.1   IT   ISSN 0393-7925
GENTE MONEY; mensile di economia attualita, cultura e politica. m. L.67200 (foreign L.115000). Rusconi Editori S.p.A., Viale Sarca 235, 20126 Milan, Italy. TEL 02-66191. FAX 02-6619-2206. Ed. Enrico Cisnetto. circ. 117,527.

055.1   IT   ISSN 0017-0259
GIORNALE DI BARGA; voce indipendente di unita ideale con i barghigiani all'estero. 1949. m. L.22000 (foreign L.50000). Umberto Sereni, Ed. & Pub., Casella Postale No. 33, Lucca 55051, Italy. TEL 0583-73003. adv.; charts; illus. circ. 1,700. (looseleaf format; back issues avail.)
    Description: Provides news of local events in the Tuscan district of Barga for former residents who have emigrated to other parts of the world.

055.1   IT
LA GRINTA; periodico di attualita, cultura, turismo e sport. 1971. m. L.20000. Edizioni La Grinta s.r.l., Via G.B. Viotti, 32, 13100 Vercelli, Italy. TEL 0161-393-395. Dir. Stefano Di Tano. adv.; bk.rev. circ. 3,000. (back issues avail.)

055.1   IT
ICHNUSA;* rivista della Sardegna. 1982. bi-m. L.5000 per no. Editrice Democratica Sarda, Via dei Conversi 48, 09129 Cagliari, Italy. (Dist. by: Libreria Dessi, Largo Cavallotti 17, 07100 Sassari, Italy) Ed.Bd. illus.

055.1   IT
ILLUSTRAZIONE ITALIANA. 1873. q. L.80000 (foreign L.120000). Media Presse S.r.l., Via Nino Bixio, 30, 20129 Milan, Italy. TEL 2043941. Ed. Massimo Caprara. illus. circ. 47,250.

G

GENERAL INTEREST PERIODICALS — ITALY

055.1 IT ISSN 0019-3410
INCIDENZA;* rivista bimestrale di cultura e ricerche. vol.8, 1966. bi-m. L.4000($8.) Via Giordano Bruno, 30, Catania, Italy. Ed. Antonio Corsaro.

055.1 IT
INFORMATORE. 1965. s-w. L.150000($75) Via Giulia di Barolo, 22, 10124 Turin, Italy. Ed. Giuseppe Paolo Muratori. adv.; bk.rev. circ. 70,876. (tabloid format; also avail. in microform)

055.1 IT
▼**L'ITALIA SETTIMANALE.** 1992. w. L.100000 (foreign L.150000) (effective 1992). Editoriale L' Italia S.p.A., Via Gorizia 53, 00198 Rome, Italy. TEL 85301081. FAX 06-85301091. Ed. Marcello Veneziani. illus. **Document type:** consumer publication.

055.1 IT ISSN 0393-5469
ITINERARIO; rivista bimestrale di analisi e proposte dal Mezzogiorno per l'Italia che cambia. 1985. bi-m. L.60000. Via Vittoria Coconna 16, 80121 Naples, Italy. Ed. Sevip.

055.1 IT
JESUS. 1979. m. L.86000 (effective until July 1993). Societa San Paolo, Gruppo Periodici S.r.l., Via Liberazione, 4, 12051 Alba (CN), Italy. TEL 0173-317356. FAX 0173-317423. Ed. D. Stefano Andreatta.

055.1 IT ISSN 0393-6457
DG451
LETTERA DALL'ITALIA. vol.3, 1988. q. L.25000 (foreign L.35000). Istituto della Enciclopedia Italiana, Piazza Paganica 4, 00186 Rome, Italy. TEL 06-67311-6712646. TELEX ITALEN-1-623620. Eds. Vincenzo Cappelletti, Francesco Schino.
Description: News on cultural life and events in Italy.

055.1 IT
LETTURE TRENTINE E ALTOATESINE. bi-m. L.35000($35) Editriche Panarama, Via Anzoletti 3, Trento, Italy. Ed. Pinnuccia di Gesaro. film rev.; play rev.

055.1 IT
LIGURIA. 1933. m. (11/yr.). L.5000. Liguria-Sabatelli Editori, Via Cairoli 8, 16124 Genova, Italy. Ed. Paolo E. Taviani. adv. circ. 9,500.

005.1 IT
LUOGO COMUNE. 1990. bi-m. L.30000. Associazione General Intellect, Via Cernaia 32, Rome, Italy. Ed. Marco Bascetta.

055.1 IT
MANI-FESTA; il diverso della scrittura. 1988. q. L.14000 (foreign L.28000). Via F. Giordani 23, 80121 Naples, Italy. TEL 081-7611295. Ed. Carmela Mangiacapre.

055.1 IT ISSN 0025-8717
MEGLIO. 1959. bi-m. L.6000. Viale Giuseppe di Vittorio, 205-C, 71100 Foggia, Italy. Ed. Mario Romano. adv.; bk.rev.; abstr.; bibl.; charts; film rev.; illus.; tr.lit. circ. 750. (tabloid format; also avail. in cards)

055.1 IT
METICCIA; rivista bimestrale multimediale volta al superamento della mentalita etnocentrica tramite la valorizzazione delle culture. bi-m. L.50000. Libertel s.r.l., Via Ampere 45, 20131 Milan, Italy. TEL 02-70602691. FAX 02-70602698. Ed. Roberto Lazzeri.

075 IT
MONITORE VALDOSTANO/MONITEUR VALDOTAIN. (Text in French and Italian) 1950. w. L.30000. Ennio Pedrini, Corso Novara, 125, 10154 Turin, Italy. **Document type:** newspaper.

055.1 IT
NEVESOLE.* 1967. m. (7/yr.). L.400 per no. Via Moute Madonna 27, 00060 Formello, Rome, Italy. Ed. Giancarlo Calzolari. adv.; bk.rev. circ. 16,500.

055.1 IT
LA NOSTRA DOMENICA. 1921. w. L.60000. (Opera Buona Stampa) Editrice Sesaab, Viale Papa Giovanni XXIII, 118, 24100 Bergamo, Italy. TEL 035-249120. adv.; bk.rev. circ. 10,000.
Formerly (until 1978): Domenica del Popolo.

055.1 IT ISSN 0029-3768
NOSTRA VOCE. 1947. m. (11/yr.). L.5000. Federazione Italiana Dipendenti Enti Locali, Casella Postale N.35, Piazza Caduti 26-5, 31021 Mogliano Veneto (Treviso), Italy. Dir. Giacomo Sandri. adv.; illus.; stat.; tr.lit. circ. 90,000. (tabloid format; also avail. in cards)

055.1 IT
NOTIZIARIO CULTURALE. 1955. m. Universita Popolare Sestrese, Ptta. dell'Universita Popolare, 16154 Genoa Sestri, Italy. Ed. Silvano Motti. adv.; bk.rev. circ. 1,200. (back issues avail.)

055.1 052
▼**NUOVA CITTA OGGI.** 1992. m. free. Amorosino Editore Roma, Via Francesco Salata 18, 00177 Rome, Italy. TEL 06-274040.
Description: Covers politics, news, information, sports and shows.

055.1 IT ISSN 0029-6198
NUOVA GAZZETTA DI CALABRIA; settimanale d'informazione. w. L.10000. Editrice Pellegrini, Via Roma 74, Casella Postale 158, 87100 Cosenza, Italy. Ed. Luigi Pellegrini-Cosenza.
Description: Covers news and items of local interest.

055.1 IT ISSN 0029-6260
NUOVA VENEZIA;* bimestrale di attualita culturale. vol.6, 1967. bi-m. L.1000. Presso Galleria S. Giorgio, Via Casavorgnan 12, Mestre, Italy. Ed. Angelo Scarpa. adv.; bibl.; charts; illus.; stat.

055.1 IT
NUOVO BORGHESE. w. L.45000. Societa Editrice Periodici Illustrati, Viale Regina Margherita 7, 20122 Milan, Italy. Ed. Mario Tedeschi. adv. circ. 93,000.

055.1 IT ISSN 0030-0705
OGGI. 1945. w. L.78000. Rizzoli Editore-Corriere della Sera, Via A. Rizzoli 2, 20132 Milan, Italy. TEL 02-665941. Dir. Willy Molco. adv.; illus. circ. 696,000.

055.1 IT
PANORAMA. 1962. w. L.140400 (foreign L.205900). Arnoldo Mondadori Editore S.p.A., Casella Postale 1833, 20101 Milan, Italy. TEL 3199345. Ed. Andrea Monti. adv.; bk.rev.; film rev.; charts; illus. circ. 529,000.

055.1 IT
PENINSULA. 1977. m. L.15000. Lorenzo Piras Editore, Via delle Rose, 8, 80063 Piano di Sorrento (Naples), Italy. TEL 081-8286428. Dir. Lorenzo Piras. circ. 1,000.

055.1 IT
PER LUI. 1982. 11/yr. Edizioni Conde Nast, Piazza Castello 27, 20121 Milan, Italy. circ. 130,000.

055.1 IT
PETTINE. 1985. bi-m. L.2000. Pastore Augusto, Piazza Cavour 2, 28069 Trecate, Italy. circ. 500.

055.1 IT
PIAZZA GRANDE; mensile di annuci economici, cultura e informazione. 1985. m. L.20000. Piazza Grande, Via G. Monaco, 25E, Arezzo, Italy. TEL 0575-302277. FAX 0575-350327. Ed. Ivo Brocchi.

055.1 IT
POLIORAMA; rivista di ricerche filologiche e interdisciplinari. s-a. L.60000 (effective 1990). Licosa S.p.A., Via Duca di Calabria 1-1, 50125 Florence, Italy.

005.1 IT
POLITICA E AMICIZIA; rivista trimestrale di cultura, politica, sindacalismo, problemi sociali. 1990. q. L.50000. Via N. Sauro 61, Cassago Brianza (Co), Italy. TEL 02-2440121. Ed. Luca Rossetti. **Document type:** consumer publication.

055 IT
POP.* 1971. w. L.10000. Pop, Via Braga 9, 20125 Milan, Italy. Ed. Pietro Granelli. adv. circ. 150,000.

055 IT ISSN 0394-4247
POPOLI. 1915. 10/yr. L.35000 (foreign L.45000). Missioni della Compagnia di Gesu, Piazza S. Fedele 4, 20121 Milan, Italy. FAX 02-72271224. Ed. Giuseppe Bellucci. adv.; bk.rev. circ. 150,000.
Formerly: Popoli e Missioni.

055.1 IT
PRESTIGE; motori, moda, costume. 1984. m. L.80000 (foreign L.160000) (effective 1994). Ediauto S.r.l., Via G.B. Cassinis, 23, 20139 Milan, Italy. TEL 02-57408813. FAX 02-57408859. Ed. Silvana Casarotto. circ. 45,000.

055.1 IT
PROGETTO (ROME);* bimestrale della Cisl di politica del lavoro. 1981. bi-m. L.14,000. (Confederazione Italiana Sindacati Lavoratori) Edizioni del Lavoro s.r.l., Via G.B. Martini 6, 00198 Rome, Italy. Ed. Alberto Cuevas. adv.; bk.rev. circ. 6,000. **Indexed:** Int.Lab.Doc.

055.1 IT ISSN 0391-5514
PROGETTO (TURIN). 1978. m. (10/yr.). L.22000 (foreign L.32000) (effective 1994). (Servizio Missionario Giovanile) Editrice Elle Di Ci, Corso Francia 214, 10096 Leumann (Turin), Italy. TEL 011 95-91-091. Ed. Ernesto Olivero. circ. 4,500.

055.1 IT ISSN 0033-4286
PUNGOLO DEL SUD; periodico di cronache mediterranee. 1958. m. L.5000. Via F.9(Piazza Leoni), Palermo, Italy. Ed. Vito Vaiarelli. illus.; stat. circ. 18,000. (looseleaf format)
Description: Covers news of the Mediterranean.

QUI TOURING. see *TRAVEL AND TOURISM*

055.1 IT
REALTA NUOVA. 1927. bi-m. donation. Istituto Culturale Rotariano, Via Morozzo della Rocca, 9, 20123 Milan, Italy. TEL 02-4818683. FAX 02-4819130. Ed. Alessandro Ubertone. adv. circ. 33,000.

055.1 IT
RISVEGLIO; settimanale indipendente del Canavese e delle valli di Lanzo. 1921. w. L.4000. Via Garibaldi 1, 10073-Cirie, Italy. Ed. Carlo Brizio. adv.; illus.

055.1 IT
ROMAGNA SERA; settimanale indipendente. w. L.50000 (foreign L.100000). Romagna Sera, Corso Garibaldi, 256, 47100 Forli, Italy. TEL 0543-33596. Ed. Enzo Fasoli. adv. (back issues avail.)
Description: Covers current events, culture, sports and general Italian interests.

055.1 IT
IL RUBASTINO. 1969. bi-m. L.25000. Associazone Turistica "Pro-Loco", P-zza Bovio 41, 70037 Ruvo di Puglia, Italy. (back issues avail.)

055.1 IT
IL SABATO. vol.14, 1991. w. L.117000. Editoriale Italiana s.r.l., Via Lucrezio Caro 38, 00193 Rome, Italy. TEL 06-3211792. FAX 06-3210997. Ed. Paolo Ligouri.

055.1 IT
SCIENZA & VITA. 1979. m. L.67200 (foreign L.112000). Rusconi Editori S.p.A., Servizio Abbonamenti, Viale Sarca 235, 20126 Milan, Italy. TEL 02-66191. FAX 02-6619-2737. Ed. Giancarlo Pini. circ. 84,112.
Formerly: Scienza e Vita Nuova (ISSN 0393-7917)

055.1 IT ISSN 0037-1483
SELEZIONE DAL READER'S DIGEST (ITALIAN EDITION). 1948. m. L.3700 per no. Selezione Dal Reader's Digest S.p.A., Via Alserio 10, 20173 Milan, Italy. TEL 02-69871. FAX 66800070. TELEX 330378. Ed. Pietro Mariano Benni. adv.; bk.rev.; illus. circ. 1,000,000.

055 IT
SKEMA. 1969. m. L.10000. Skema s.r.l., Via Marzabotto 10-3, 40133 Bologna, Italy. adv. circ. 76,000.

075 IT ISSN 0391-786X
SOLE 24 ORE. 1865. d. L.450000 (foreign L.880000). Editrice Il Sole - 24 Ore, S.p.A., Via Lomazzo 52, 20154 Milan, Italy. TEL 02-31031. FAX 02-312055. Pub. Salvatore Carrubba. **Document type:** newspaper.

GENERAL INTEREST PERIODICALS — JAPAN

052
SPEAK UP. (Text in English) 1985. m. L.76800($60) (Istituto Geografico de Agostini) Rizzoli Editore, Via Gaspere Gozzi 5, 20129 Milan, Italy. TEL 02-700231. FAX 02-70100319. TELEX 200290. Ed. Jason Vella. adv.; bk.rev.; film rev.; play rev. circ. 120,000. (back issues avail.)

054.1   IT   ISSN 0039-0348
STATI UNITI D'EUROPA; rivista internazionale indipendente economica, sociale, culturale, tecnica, scientifica, industriale, turistica. (Text in French and Italian) 1962. bi-m. L.20000. Casa Editrice G.D., Via Aldrovandi, 5, 20129 Milan, Italy. Ed. Giuseppe Hurle. adv.; bk.rev.; play rev.; illus.; index.

055   IT   ISSN 1121-1288
STOP. 1963. w. L.74900 (effective 1990). Industrie Grafiche Cino del Duca S.p.a, Via Borgogna 5, 20122 Milan, Italy. TEL 781-051. Ed. Sandro Orlini. adv.; B&W page L.8200000, color page L.14760000; trim 210 x 271. circ. 343,965.

055.1   IT
SUBWAY. s-m. Edizioni Lakota, Via Pietro Mascagni 3, 00199 Rome, Italy. TEL 06-837879. Ed. Max Stefani.

005.1   IT
TEMPO IMMAGINE; mensile di attualita, cultura, turismo. 1989. m. L.40000 (foreign L.80000). Edizioni Tempo ed Immagine s.r.l., Viale Bruno Buozzi 77, 00197 Rome, Italy. TEL 872038. FAX 878214. Ed. Tarquinio Maiorino. **Document type:** consumer publication.

055.1   IT
TEMPO POLLINO; mensile politico-culturale e d'informazione. 1978. m. $25. Tempo Pollino, Via Telesio 12, 87012 Castrovillari, Italy. TEL 0981-21759. Ed. Angelo Silvio Rotondaro. cum.index: 1978-1987. circ. 1,000. (tabloid format; back issues avail.)

055.1   IT   ISSN 1121-0532
IL TERRITORIO; quadrimestrale del Monfalconese. (Text in Italian; summaries in Italian, Slovenian) 1978. q. L.25000. Centro Culturale Pubblico Polivalente, Via XXIV Maggio, 8, 34077 Ronchi dei Legionari (Go), Italy. TEL 0481-778605. FAX 0481-474589. Ed. Aldo Buccarella. adv.; bk.rev.; abstr.; bibl.; charts; illus.; stat.; cum.index. circ. 1,500. (back issues avail.)

055.1   IT
TESTI DELLA CULTURA ITALIANA. 1983. s-a. Costa & Nolan, Via Peschiera 21, 16122 Genova, Italy. Ed. Edoardo Sanguineti. circ. 1,500. (back issues avail.)

055.1   IT
TOP MAGAZINE. 1987. m. L.4500 per no. (Coop Athena 2001 a.r.l.) Edizioni L.E.T.I. s.r.l., Via E.Q. Visconti, 20, 00193 Rome, Italy. TEL 06-386353. Ed. Francesco Puzzo. adv.

055   IT
TRASUMENUS. 1967. m. L.10000. Corso Vannucci 66, 06062 Citta della Pieve (Perugia), Italy. Ed. Mario Villani. adv. circ. 10,000.

055.1   IT
UNA CITTA; mensile d'informazione, cultura e politica. 1991. m. Piazza Dante Alighieri 21, 47100 Forli, Italy. TEL 0543-21422. (tabloid format)

055.1   IT
UOMO CITTA TERRITORIO; rivista di cultura e societa. 1976. m. L.50000($18.30) Uomo Citta Territorio Gruppo Culturale, Via Dietro le Mura B-5, 38100 Trento, Italy. TEL 0461-983496. FAX 0461-983496. adv.; bk.rev.; cum.index: 1976-1986. (back issues avail.)

055.1   IT   ISSN 1120-7639
VENETO: IERI, OGGI, DOMANI; attualita, storia, arte, curiosita, miti e personaggi della regione piu bella d'Italia. 1990. m. Newton Stocchiero Periodici s.r.l., Via dell'Industria 51, 36100 Vicenza, Italy. TEL 0444-562963. Ed. G.A. Cibotto.

055.1   IT
VIA EMILIA; notiziario santilariese. 1979. bi-m. L.10000. Via Indipendenza 2-B, 42049 Santi Ilario d'Enza (RE), Italy. TEL 0522-671079. circ. 500. (tabloid format; back issues avail.)

055.1   IT
VISTO. 1989. w. Via Rizzoli 4, 20132 Milan, Italy. TEL 02-2588. FAX 02-25843683. Ed. Marcello Minerbi. circ. 350,000.

075   IT
VITA TRENTINA; settimanale diocesano di informazione. 1926. w. L.50000 (effective Jan. 1993). Vita Trentina Editrice - Coop., s.r.l., Via S. Giovanni Bosco, 5, 38100 Trento, Italy. TEL 0461-982143. FAX 0461-233446. Dir. Agostino Valentini. adv. contact: Gianni Franceschini. bk.rev.; film rev.; play rev.; circ. 15,000 (controlled). (tabloid format; also avail. in microfilm; back issues avail.) **Document type:** newspaper.

055.1 261   IT   ISSN 0042-7780
LA VOCE; settimanale di informazione. 1953. w. L.50000 (effective 1994). Chiesa di San Severo a Porta Sole, Via della Gabbia 7, 06123 Perugia, Italy. TEL 075-5727871. FAX 075-5731066. Ed. Elio Bromuri. adv.; B&W page L.1300000; adv. contact: Mrs. L. Mezzetti. bk.rev.; circ. 7,000 (paid). (tabloid format) **Document type:** newspaper.
   Description: Covers regional information: politics, society, religion and the Catholic Church.

055.1   IT
VOCE DELLA REGIONE. 1968. m. L.6000. Silvio Panaro Editore, Via G. Gentile 53-C, 70126 Bari, Italy. TEL 080-5583477. FAX 080-5580326. Ed. Silvio Panaro. adv.; bk.rev. circ. 22,000.
   Formerly: Voce Nuova (ISSN 0042-787X)

055.1   IT
LA VOCE LIBERA; settimanale della lista per Trieste. 1978. w. L.25000. Associazione per la Zona Franca Integrale e Trieste e la sua Provincia, Corso Caba 6, Trieste, Italy. TEL 041 744840. Ed. Carlo Ventura. adv.; bk.rev.; cum.index. circ. 4,000. (back issues avail.)

055.1   IT   ISSN 0390-4539
30 GIORNI. 1974. m. (11/yr.). L.50000. Edit Editoriale Italiana S.r.l., Via M. Malpighi 2, 00161 Rome, Italy. **Document type:** consumer publication.

GENERAL INTEREST PERIODICALS — Ivory Coast

054.1   IV
GAZETTE DU CENTRE. s-m. 150 Fr.CFA. (Mairie Bouake) Edipresse, 08 B.P. 254, Abidjan 08, Ivory Coast. TEL 37-17-27. (back issues avail.)

GENERAL INTEREST PERIODICALS — Japan

952   AG   ISSN 0001-768X
ACTUALIDADES DE JAPON.* s-m. free. Embassy of Japan in Argentina, Azcuenaga 1035, Buenos Aires, Argentina. Ed. Tatsuo Takashima. illus. circ. 3,500.

059.956   JA   ISSN 0914-8833
AERA. (Text in Japanese) 1988. w. $193. Asahi Shimbunsha - Asahi Shimbun Publishing Co., 3-2 Tsukiji 5-chome, Chuo-ku, Tokyo 104-11, Japan. (Subscr. to: Japan Publications Trading Co., Ltd., Box 5030, Tokyo International, Tokyo, Japan) Ed. Hidetoshi Nishimura.
   ●Also available online.
   Description: Covers current national and international news, including political, economic, business, cultural, and social events.

052   JA   ISSN 0002-0753
AGE OF TOMORROW. 1961. q. Hitachi, Ltd., Advertising Dept., 6, Kanda-Surugadai 4 chome, Chiyoda-ku, Tokyo, Japan. Ed. Shozaburo Kobayashi. illus. circ. 20,000.
   —UnCover.

059.956   JA
ANGLE. (Text in Japanese) 1977. m. 2400 Yen. Shufu-to-Seikatsusha Ltd., 5-7, 3-chome, Kyobashi, Chuo-ku, Tokyo 104, Japan. Ed. Kanichi Sugawara.

079.52   JA
ASAHI EVENING NEWS. (Text in English) 1954. d. 3300 Yen (US 8370 Yen) per mo.; newsstand price: 120 Yen. Asahi Shimbun, 5-3-2, Tsukiji, Chuo-ku, Tokyo 104-11, Japan. TEL 03-5540-7641. FAX 03-3542-6172. Ed. Yasunori Asai; Pub. Toshitada Nakae. adv. contact: Ryoichi Sato. bk.rev.; music rev.; illus. Wire service(s): AP, RN, NYT. circ. 34,000 (controlled). cols./p.: 8; pp./issue: 12. **Document type:** newspaper.

059.956   JA
ASAHI GRAPH. (Text in Japanese) 1923. w. $274.50. Asahi Shimbunsha - Asahi Shimbun Publishing Co., 3-2, Tsukiji 5-chome, Chuo-ku, Tokyo 104, Japan. TEL 03-3545-0131. TELEX 22226. (Subscr. to: Japan Publications Trading Co., Ltd., Box 5030, Tokyo International, Tokyo, Japan) Ed. Yasushi Sato. adv.; bk.rev.; illus. circ. 125,000.

059.956   JA   ISSN 0571-2378
AP95.J2
ASAHI JANARU/ASAHI JOURNAL. (Text in Japanese) 1959. w. $190.50. Asahi Shimbunsha - Asahi Shimbun Publishing Co., 3-2, Tsukiji 5-chome, Chuo-ku, Tokyo 104-11, Japan. (Subscr.to: Japan Publications Trading Co., Ltd., Box 5030, Tokyo International, Tokyo, Japan) Ed. Mitsuko Shimomura.

059.956   JA
ASAHI SHIMBUN SHUKUSATUBAN/REDUCED SIZE ASAHI SHIMBUN. (Text in Japanese) 1919. m. $573. Asahi Shimbunsha - Asahi Shimbun Publishing Co., 3-2 Tsukiji 5-chome, Chuo-ku, Tokyo 104-11, Japan. (Subscr. to: Japan Publications Trading Co., Ltd., Box 5030, Tokyo International, Tokyo, Japan) Ed. Takenori Oikawa.
   ●Also available online.

059.956   JA
BUNGEI SHUNJU. (Weekly supp. avail.: Shukan Bunshun) 1923. m. 12480 Yen. Bungei Shunju Ltd., 3-23, Kioi-cho, Chiyoda-ku, Tokyo 102, Japan. TEL 03-3265-1211. FAX 03-3221-4878. Ed. Kohji Shirakawa. circ. 574,987. **Document type:** consumer publication.
   Description: Contains investigative reporting, travel articles, essays, fictions, world affairs and cultural activities.

059.956   JA
CENTRAL PUBLIC OPINION/CHUOKORON. Variant title: Central Review. (Text in Japanese) 1887. m. 9250 Yen. Chuokoron-Sha, Inc., 2-8-7 Kyobashi, Chuo-ku, Tokyo 104, Japan. TEL 03-3563-1866. FAX 03-3561-5920. Ed. Takashi Hirabayashi. circ. 180,000.

059.956   JA
DIAMOND BOX (YEAR). (Text in Japanese) 1980. m. 6000 Yen($40) Diamond, Inc., 4-2 Kasumigaseki, 1-chome, Chiyoda-ku, Tokyo 100, Japan. TEL 03-504-6282. Ed. Wada Masaki. circ. 200,000. (back issues avail.)
   Description: Intellectual lifestyle magazine for Yuppies.

059.956   JA
DON DON. (Text in Japanese) 1976. m. 5390 Yen. Nihon Journal Press, 11-8, 2-Chome, Higashi-Shimbashi, Minato-ku, Tokyo, Japan. Ed. Satoshi Mita.

052 DS801   JA   ISSN 0012-8295
EAST. (Text in English) 1964. 6/yr. 4800 Yen($70) East Publications, Inc., 19-7, Minami-Azabu 3, Minato-ku, Tokyo 106, Japan. TEL 03-3446-7721. FAX 03-3441-9793. (Subscr. to: P.O. Box 591360, San Francisco, CA 94159-1360) Ed. Tohru Morita. adv.; bk.rev.; illus.; index. circ. 65,000. (also avail. in microfilm from UMI; reprint service avail. from UMI) **Indexed:** Arts & Hum.Cit.Ind., Curr.Cont., SSCI.
   —UnCover; UMI.
   Description: Covers all aspects of Japan with emphasis on culture, arts, and history.

059.956   JA
FOCUS. (Text in Japanese) w. Shincho-Sha, 71 Yaraicho, Shinjuku-ku, Tokyo, Japan. TEL 03-3266-4211. FAX 03-3266-5235. Ed. Akio Goto. circ. 850,000.

GENERAL INTEREST PERIODICALS — JAPAN

059.956   JA
FRIDAY. (Text in Japanese) 1984. w. Kodansha Ltd., 12-12 Otowa 2-chome, Bunkyo-ku, Tokyo 112, Japan. TEL 03-5395-3440. FAX 03-3943-8582. TELEX J34509 KODANSHA. Ed. Tetsu Suzuki. circ. 950,000. **Document type:** consumer publication.
   Description: Photo magazine.

059.956   JA
FUTARI NO HEYA/PLUS ONE. (Text in Japanese) 1978. q. 7920 Yen. Shufunotomo Co., Ltd., 2-9 Kanda Surugadai, Chiyoda-ku, Tokyo 101, Japan. Ed. Yasuko Makino. circ. 180,000. **Document type:** consumer publication.
   Formerly: Room for Two.

059.956   JA
GEIBUN MOOKS. (Text in Japanese) 1978. m. 14,400 Yen. Geibunsha, 5, 3-chome, Kanda-Surugadai, Chiyoda-ku, Tokyo, Japan. Ed. Keizo Takanashi.

059.956   JA
GEKKAN ASAHI/MONTHLY ASAHI. (Text in Japanese) 1989. m. $125. Asahi Shimbunsha - Asahi Shimbun Publishing Co., 3-2 Tsukiji 5-chome, Chuo-ku, Tokyo 104-11, Japan. (Subscr.to: Japan Publications Trading Co., Ltd., Box 5030, Tokyo International, Tokyo, Japan) Ed. Naoaki Yano.

059.956   JA
GENDAI. (Text in Japanese) 1966. m. Kodansha Ltd., 12-21, Otowa 2-chome, Bunkyo-ku, Tokyo 112, Japan. TEL 03-5395-3517. TELEX 22570. Ed. Shunkichi Yabuki. circ. 190,000.
   Description: Cultural and political journal.

059.956   JA
HIRA-GANA TIMES. 12/yr. 3000 Yen. Yano Research Institute Ltd., 2-10-1 Hamacho Nihonbashi, Nisshin Bldg. 7F, Chuo-ku, Tokyo 103, Japan. TEL 03-667-9188. FAX 03-667-0269. Ed. Hataru Nomura.

059.956   JA
ICHIMI. 1989. q. 450 Yen per no. S.S. Communications Inc., SSC Bldg., 11, Niban-cho, Chiyoda-ku, Tokyo 102, Japan. TEL 03-5276-2123. FAX 03-5276-2129. Ed. Takuji Hatano. adv. circ. 300,000. **Document type:** consumer publication.
   Formerly (until Sep. 1993): LoFt.
   Description: Provides information about innovative products, fashion and specialty stores.

053.1   GW
JAPAN AKTUELL. 1984. bi-m. DM.30 (Europe DM.35, elsewhere DM.45). Aspekte Verlag, Meckenheimer Allee 110, 53115 Bonn, Germany. TEL 0228-634262. FAX 0228-693249. Ed. Hans-Henning Derpa. adv.; bk.rev. circ. 5,000. (back issues avail.)

059.956   JA   ISSN 0912-6317
JAPAN FREE PRESS. 1986. 50/yr. 30000 Yen($228) C T Whipple Co., Riverside E. 4, 1-9-11 Saga, Koto-ku, Tokyo 135, Japan. FAX 03-3643-3091. Ed. Charles T. Whipple.
   ●Also available online. Vendor(s): NewsNet (IT66).
   Description: Presents a varied mix of synopses from the Japanese press.

952   US
DS889
JAPAN INFO. 1966. bi-m. free. Consulate General of Japan, New York, Japan Information Center, 299 Park Ave., 18th Fl., New York, NY 10171. TEL 212-371-8222. Ed. Kenneth Clark. bk.rev.; illus. circ. 2,500. **Indexed:** Sage Fam.Stud.Abstr. **Document type:** newsletter.
   Formerly: Japan Report (New York) (ISSN 0021-4604)

059.856   JA
JAPAN INFORMATION RESOURCES IN THE UNITED STATES. (Text in English) irreg., latest 1990. 1000 Yen($6.50) Keizai Koho Center, Otemachi Bldg., 6-1 Ote-machi 1-chome, Chiyoda-ku, Tokyo 100, Japan. FAX 03-3201-1418. Ed. Michihisa Nabeshima.
   Description: Guide to research sources about Japan in the US. Contains sections on Japanese government organizations, chambers of commerce, industrial associations, research institutes, universities, and libraries.

052   JA
JAPAN INTERNATIONAL JOURNAL. (Text in English) 1991. m. 700 Yen. Business World Corp., 2-8-6 Shiroganedai, Minatoku, Tokyo 108, Japan. TEL 81-3-3442-0211. FAX 81-3-3442-0217. Ed. Hiro Miyata. adv. contact: Catherine Clinchard. **Document type:** consumer publication.
   Description: General interest magazine covering business, politics, culture and lifestyles.

052   JA   ISSN 0388-6115
JAPAN PICTORIAL. (Text in English) 1978. q. $22. Japan Graphic, Inc., Palaceside Bldg., 1-1-1 Hitotsubashi, Chiyoda-ku, Tokyo, Japan. Ed. Toyoji Watanabe. adv.; illus. circ. 200,000.

059.956   JA   ISSN 0287-7112
JAPAN PRESS WEEKLY: NEWS & COMMENTS. (Text in English) 1956. w. 15000 Yen. Japan Press Service, Shinnihon Bldg., 4-25-6 Sendagaya, Shibuya-ku, Tokyo 151, Japan. TEL 03-3423-2381. FAX 03-3423-2383. Ed. Shinchiro Omura. **Document type:** newsletter.
   Description: Introduces the movements of Japanese progressive forces and their views on political, economic and social issues.

052   JA   ISSN 0289-1956
JAPAN TIMES. (Supplement avail.: The Japan Times Weekly) (Text in English) d. 11380 Yen. Japan Times Ltd., 5-4 Shibaura 4-chome, Minato-ku, Tokyo 108, Japan. TEL 03-3453-2013. FAX 03-3452-8023. **Indexed:** CAD CAM Abstr. (until 1992), Environ.Abstr., Robomat. (until 1992), Telegen (until 1989).
   Description: General interest periodical covering topics concerning the environment, society, women, business, and trade.

079.52   JA
THE KOCHI. (Text in Japanese) 1904. d. 3500 Yen set (morning & evening eds.) per mo. Kochi Shimbun, 3-2-15 Honmachi, Kochi 780-70, Japan. TEL 0888-22-2111. FAX 0888-73-3267. Ed. Toshio Twai; Pub. Shoroku Hashii. adv. contact: Yoshtaki Matsuda. bk.rev.; film rev.; music rev.; illus.; circ. 228,700 (morning ed.); 142,000 (evening ed.) (paid). cols./p.: 15. (also avail. in diskette format; microfilm; back issues avail.; reprint service avail.) **Document type:** newspaper.

059.956   JA
LET'S LOVE OITA. a. Oita Prefecture Planning Department, Public Information Division, 1-1 Ote-machi 3-chome, Oita-ken 870, Japan. TEL 0975-361111. FAX 0975-342142. Ed. Kiyoshi Tomonaga.

059.956   JA
LINK-UP: HIROSHIMA PREFECTURE NEWS. 6/yr. Hiroshima Prefecture Government, Public Relations Section, 10-52 Moto-machi, Naka-ku, Hiroshima 730, Japan.

059.956   JA   ISSN 0913-8102
LIVING IN JAPAN. (Text in English) 1961. irreg., every 3-4 yrs. $39. American Chamber of Commerce in Japan, Bridgestone Toranomon Bldg., 5-F, 3-25-2 Toranomon, Minato-ku, Tokyo 105, Japan. TEL 03-3433-5381. FAX 03-3436-1446. adv. circ. 10,000.
   Description: For families anticipating a move to Japan. Provides information on what to bring, schools, health care, buseinss and finance, working women, children, culture, legal affairs and the Kansai area.

051   JA
LIZZENGREASY. (Text in English) 1988. m. $2 per no. Dai Ni Kuroda Kopo 203, Funabashi 5-30-6, Setagaya-ku, Tokyo 156, Japan. Eds. Liz Stumps, Greasy Fletcher. bk.rev. **Document type:** newsletter.
   Description: Covers different aspects of Japanese culture such as tradition, society, and public transportation.

059.956 052   JA   ISSN 0025-0813
MAINICHI GRAPHIC. (Text in Japanese; captions in English) w. 300 Yen per no. Mainichi Newspapers, 1-1-1 Hitotsubashi, Chiyoda-ku, Tokyo 100-51, Japan. TEL 03-3212-0321. FAX 03-3211-0895. TELEX 22324. (Dist. by: Oversea Courier Service Inc., Osaka Branch Office, 3-28 Nozatonishi, Nishiyodogawa-Ku, Osaka 541, Japan) Ed. Masuichiro Akagi. illus.

059.956   JA
MARCO POLO. (Text in Japanese) 1991. m. 8640 Yen. Bungei Shunju Ltd., 3-23, Kioi-cho, Chiyoda-ku, Tokyo 102, Japan. TEL 03-3265-1211. FAX 03-3221-5323. Ed. Tadashi Saito. circ. 180,000. **Document type:** consumer publication.

059.956   JA
MORNING STAR/MYOJO. (Text in Japanese) 1952. m. Shueisha Inc., 5-10, 2-chome, Hitotsubashi, Chiyoda-ku, Tokyo 101-50, Japan. TEL 03-3230-6300. Ed. Norio Akiyama. circ. 750,000.

053.1   GW
NEUES AUS JAPAN. 1954. bi-m. Japanische Botschaft, Godesberger Allee 102-104, 53175 Bonn, Germany. TEL 0228-8191-251. FAX 0228-8191-210. circ. 4,500. **Document type:** newsletter.

059.956   JA
NEWSWEEK NIHON BAN; the international magazine. (Text in Japanese) 1986. w. 14900 Yen. Newsweek International, Sumitomo Seimei, Aoyama Bldg., 3rd Fl., 3-1-30 Minami Aoyama, Minato-ku, Tokyo 107, Japan. TEL 813-238-5711. (Co-publisher: T B S - Brittanica Co.) Ed. Shinyoku Sei. adv.: B&W page $6080, color page $9600. bk.rev.; film rev.; play rev.; charts; illus.; index. circ. 160,000. (back issues avail.) **Document type:** consumer publication.
   Description: Overview of world events, politics, economics, social issues and arts.

059.956   JA
ONE WORLD. a. 200 Yen. One World Press, No. 2, 107-1 Mamiya Kannami, Tagata-gun, Shizuoka-ken 419-01, Japan. FAX 0559-790886. Ed. Otsushi Endo. maps.
   Description: Introduces the cities, festivals and scenic spots of Shizuoka prefecture.

059.956   JA
SERAI. (Text in Japanese) 1974. bi-w. 8400 Yen. Shogakukan Inc., 3-1, 2-chome, Hitotsubashi, Chiyoda-ku, Tokyo, Japan. FAX 03-3230-5768. Ed. Bin Iwamoto.
   Formerly (until 1989): Goro.
   Description: Lifestyle magazine that aims to help readers lead more enriching lives.

059.956   JA
SHUKAN ASAHI/WEEKLY ASAHI. (Text in Japanese) 1922. w. $221. Asahi Shimbunsha - Asahi Shimbun Publishing Co., 3-2, Tsukiji 5-chome, Chuo-ku, Tokyo 104-11, Japan. (Subscr. to: Japan Publications Trading Co., Ltd., Box 5030, Tokyo International, Tokyo, Japan) Ed. Makoto Takeuchi.

059.956   JA
SHUKAN BUNSHUN. (Supplement to: Bungei Shunju Magazine) 1959. w. 29120 Yen. Bungei Shunju Ltd., 3-23, Kioi-cho, Chiyoda-ku, Tokyo 102, Japan. TEL 03-3265-1211. FAX 03-3234-3964. Ed. Kazuyoshi Hanada. circ. 7,766,900. **Document type:** consumer publication.

059.956   JA
SHUKAN POST/WEEKLY POST. (Text in Japanese) 1969. w. 25920 Yen. Shogakukan Publishing Inc., 3-1, 2-chome, Hitotsubashi, Chiyoda-ku, Tokyo, Japan. TEL 03-3230-5271. TELEX 22192. Ed. Akira Yamamoto.

059.956   JA
SHUKAN SHINCHO. (Text in Japanese) 1956. w. Shincho-Sha, 71, Yarai-cho, Shinjuku-ku, Tokyo 162, Japan. TEL 03-3266-5211. FAX 03-3266-5235. Ed. Hikoya Yamada. circ. 599,000.

059.956   JA
SHUKAN SPA!. (Text in Japanese) 1952. w. Fuso-Sha Co., 6 Ichigaya-daimachi, Shinjuku-ku, Tokyo 162-80, Japan. TEL 03-3226-8880. Ed. Naoki Watanabe. circ. 400,000.

059.956   JA
SHUKAN YOMIURI. (Text in Japanese) 1938. w. 270 Yen. Yomiuri Shimbun Publication Dept., 1-7-1, Ohtemachi, Chiyoda-ku, Tokyo 100-55, Japan. TEL 03-3242-1111. TELEX 22228. Ed. Shinji Kageyama. adv.; bk.rev. circ. 300,000.

059.956   JA
SHUPPAN NEWS; Shuppan news, publications news and reviews. (Text in Japanese) 1973. 3/m. Shuppan News Co. Ltd., 3-2-4 Misaki-cho, Chiyoda-ku, Tokyo 101, Japan. adv.; illus.

059.956   JA   ISSN 0039-5080
SUN. (Text mainly in Japanese) 1963. m. 15468 Yen. Heibonsha Ltd., 5 Sanban-cho, Chiyoda-ku, Tokyo 102, Japan. TEL 03-3265-0465. FAX 03-3265-0477. Ed. Keichi Kadosaki. adv.; bk.rev.; illus. circ. 250,000.
Description: Centers on culture and the arts. Each issue carries a feature article exploring one subject in depth.

059.956   JA   ISSN 0039-5234
SUNDAY MAINICHI. (Text in Japanese) 1922. w. 150 Yen per no. Mainichi Newspapers, 1-1-1 Hitotsubashi, Chiyoda-ku, Tokyo 100-51, Japan. TEL 03-3212-0321. FAX 03-3211-0895. TELEX 22324. (Dist. by: Oversea Courier Service Inc., Osaka Branch Office, 3-28 Nozatonishi, Nishoyodogawa-ku, Osaka 541, Japan) Ed. Taro Maki. circ. 258,000. (tabloid format)

079.52   JA
TENJI MAINICHI. (Text in Japanese) 1922. w. 20000 Yen. Mainichi Newspapers, Osaka, Braille Mainchi Section, 3-4-5, Umeda, Kita-ku, Osaka, Japan. TEL 06-346-8386. FAX 06-346-8385. Ed. Tadamitsu Morioka. adv. circ. 12,000. (also avail. in Braille) **Document type**: newspaper.

059.956   JA
TOKYO TIME OUT. 1990. 12/yr. 5000 Yen. Paradigm, Vickie Paradise Green, Kamiyama Ambassador 209, 18-6 Kamiyama-cho, Shibuya-ku, Tokyo 150, Japan. TEL 03-5478-7941. FAX 03-5478-7942. adv. circ. 24,000.
Description: Covers city entertainment, celebrities, travel, dining, sports, fashion, music and film.

059.956   JA
TOKYO TODAY. 1987. 12/yr. 5000 Yen($71) Ueno & Associates Co. Ltd., No. 505, 14-12 Roppongi 3-chome, Minato-ku, Tokyo 106, Japan. TEL 03-3423-0660. FAX 03-3403-0993. Ed. Allan Lars Gruhl. adv.; bk.rev. circ. 18,000.
Description: For Western residents of Tokyo.

952 370   JA   ISSN 0041-6576
UNDERSTANDING JAPAN. 1960. s-a. 1950 Yen free to qualified educational organizations. International Society for Educational Information, Inc. - Kokusai Kyoiku Joho Senta, Royal Wakaba 504, 22 Wakaba 1-chome, Shinjuku-ku, Tokyo 160, Japan. TEL 03-3358-1138. FAX 03-3359-7188. Ed. Michiko Kaya. adv. circ. 10,000.

059.956   JA
UNESCO ASIA BUNKA NEWS BULLETIN. 1972. m. Asian Cultural Centre for Unesco, Publishers Bldg., 6 Fukuro-machi, Shinjuku-ku, Tokyo 162, Japan. TEL 03-269-4435. FAX 03-269-4510.
Description: Introduces the cultures of Asia and the Pacific and includes the activities of the center.

059.956   US
UNIVERSITY OF CALIFORNIA AT BERKELEY. CENTER FOR JAPANESE STUDIES. SERIES. no.3, 1969. irreg., no.24, 1990. price varies. (Center for Japanese Studies) University of California Press, 2120 Berkeley Way, Berkeley, CA 94720. TEL 510-642-4247. FAX 510-643-4247. (Subscr. to: California-Princeton Fulfillment Services, 1445 Lower Ferry Rd., Ewing, NJ 08618. TEL 800-777-4726. FAX 800-999-1958) (back issues avail.) **Document type**: monographic series.
Description: Publishes papers on the history, politics, art, and culture of Japan.
Refereed Serial

059.956   JA
USHIO/TIDE. (Text in Japanese) 1960. m. 7200 Yen. Ushio Shuppansha, 1-3, Iidabashi 3-chome, Chiyoda-ku, Tokyo 102, Japan. TEL 03-3230-0771. FAX 03-3230-0658. Ed. Kentaro Nishihara. adv.; bk.rev. circ. 330,000.
Description: Opinions on the human condition, ideas, and thoughts on the future of Japan for middle management level readers.

059.956   JA
WEEKLY FOR THE MASSES/SHUKAN TAISHU. (Text in Japanese) 1958. w. 8460 Yen. Futabasha Publishers, 3-28, Higashi-Gokecho, Shinjuku-ku, Tokyo, Japan. Ed. Toul Korenaga.

GENERAL INTEREST PERIODICALS — Jordan

059.92   JO
AKHBAR AL-USBOU/NEWS OF THE WEEK; jaridah siyasiyya intiqadiyya. (Text in Arabic) 1959. w. 1.00 din. per no. Abdul Hafeed Mohammad, Ed. & Pub., P.O. Box 605, Amman, Jordan. TEL 677881. FAX 677882. TELEX 21644. Ed. Abdul Hafeed Mohammad. adv.; bk.rev. circ. 100,000.

059   JO
AMMAN IN THE EVENING/AMMAN-AL MASA'A. (Text in Arabic) 1961. w. Box 522, Amman, Jordan. Ed. Yasser Hijazi.

079.5695   JO
AD-DUSTOUR. (Supplements avail.) (Text in Arabic) 1967. d. 60 din.($100) includes Sports supplement. Jordan Press and Publishing, University St., P.O. Box 591, 11118 Amman, Jordan. TEL 667170. Ed. Nabeel al-Shareef. adv. contact: Yosef Ammars. bk.rev.; tele.rev.; illus. Wire service(s): AFP, RN. circ. 100,000. cols./p.: 8; pp./issue: 32. **Document type**: newspaper.

059   JO
JORDAN/URDON. (Text in Arabic) 1909. w. Box 6194, Amman, Jordan. Ed. Hadna Khalil Nasr.

059.92   US
JORDAN ISSUES AND PERSPECTIVES. 1990. bi-m. free. Jordan Information Bureau, 2319 Wyoming Ave., N.W., Washington, DC 20008. TEL 202-265-1606. FAX 202-667-0777. illus.; stat. (back issues avail.)

059.927   JO
AL-SABAH/MORNING. (Text in Arabic) 1972. w. P.O. Box 2396, Amman, Jordan. Ed. Arafat Higazi. circ. 6,000.

052   JO
STAR. (Text in English) 1982. w. Media Services International, P.O. Box 9313, Amman, Jordan. TEL 648298. TELEX 21392. Ed. Osama ash-Sharif. circ. 10,000. **Document type**: consumer publication.
Formerly: Jerusalem Star.

GENERAL INTEREST PERIODICALS — Kazakhstan

077   KZ   ISSN 0233-3414
KAZAKHSTANSKAYA PRAVDA; republikanskaya obshchestvenno-politicheskaya gazeta. (Text in Russian) 1920. 6/w. Ul. Gogolya 39, 480055 Alma-Ata, Kazakhstan. TEL 32-72-630586. FAX 32-72-637677. Owner(s): Kabinet Ministrov Respubliki Kazakhstan. Ed. V.M. Srybnykh. adv.; illus. circ. 114,900. (broadsheet format) **Document type**: newspaper.

GENERAL INTEREST PERIODICALS — Kenya

079.6762 052   KE
DAILY NATION. Coast Edition. Western Kenya Edition. City Edition. (Includes yearly supplement: Nation Economic Report) (Text in English) 1960. d. KShs.9200 for 3 mos.; newsstand price: KShs.15. Nation Newspapers Ltd., P.O. Box 49010, Nairobi, Kenya. TEL 254-2-221222. FAX 254-2-214531. Owner(s): Nation Printers & Publishers. Ed. Wangethi Mwangi; Pub. A.A.A. Ekirapa. adv. contact: Cyrille Nabutola. bk.rev.; film rev.; music rev.; play rev.; tele.rev.; abstr.; bibl.; charts; illus.; stat.; tr.lit. Wire service(s): AFP, AP, RN. circ. 165,000. cols./p.: 6; pp./issue: 32. (back issues avail.) **Document type**: newspaper.

052   KE   ISSN 0020-1863
INSIDE KENYA TODAY. 1968. q. EAs.210($18) Ministry of Information and Broadcasting, POB 8053, Nairobi, Kenya. TEL 28411. TELEX 22244. Ed. M. Ndavi. adv.; illus. circ. 10,000.
Formerly: Kenya Today.

052   KE
JOE MAGAZINE; Africa's entertainment monthly. 1973. m. Joe Publications Ltd., Victoria House, Tom Mboya St., P.O. Box 30362, Nairobi, Kenya. Ed. Terry Hirst.

KENYA EXPORT DIRECTORY. see BUSINESS AND ECONOMICS — International Commerce

079.6762 350   KE
KENYA GAZETTE. (Includes supplement avail. in 3 parts: Acts, Bills, Legislative Supplement) (Text in English) 1898. w. KShs.558. Office of the President, Government Press, Haile Selaissie, P.O. Box 30128, Nairobi, Kenya. TEL 254-2-334075-9. index. circ. 8,000. (also avail. in microfilm from KTO; back issues avail; document delivery service avail.)
Document type: newspaper, government publication.

059   KE
KENYA LEO. (Text in Kiswahili) 1983. d. Kanu, P.O. Box 30958, Nairobi, Kenya. TEL 337798. Ed. Joram Amadi.

052 967.62   KE   ISSN 0454-949X
DT434.E2
KENYA NEWSLETTER; a fortnightly review. 1969. fortn. Ministry of Information and Broadcasting, P.O. Box 30025, Nairobi, Kenya.

052   KE
KENYA RECORD; the monthly news and opinion magazine. 1978. m. Research, Editorial and Design Services Ltd., P.O. Box 57881, Nairobi, Kenya. Ed. Joel Mbogo. adv.

052   KE
KENYA TIMES. (Text in English) 1983. d. Kanu, P.O. Box 30958, Nairobi, Kenya. TEL 24251. TELEX 25008. Ed. Phillip Ochieng. circ. 36,000.
Description: Party newspaper.

052   KE
PEOPLE. 1978. m. Research, Editorial and Design Services Ltd., P.O. Box 57881, Nairobi, Kenya. Ed. Odhiambo Okite. adv.

079.6762   KE
THE STANDARD. (Text in English) 1902. d. P.O. Box 30080, Likoni Rd., Nairobi, Kenya. TEL 254-2-540280. FAX 254-2-553939. TELEX 24032. Ed. Ali S. Hafedh. adv.; illus. circ. 7,000. (also avail. in microfilm from UMI) **Document type**: newspaper.
Formerly (until Jul. 1974): East African Standard; *Incorporates*: Leader; Mombasa Times.

079.6762   KE
SUNDAY NATION. 1960. w. EAs.2574. Nation Newspapers Ltd., Nation House, Tom Mboya St., POB 49010, Nairobi, Kenya. TEL 540280. TELEX 24032. Ed. George Mbugguss. adv.; bk.rev.; film rev.; play rev.; abstr.; bibl.; charts; illus.; stat.; tr.lit. circ. 170,000. **Document type**: newspaper.

079.6762   KE
THE SUNDAY STANDARD. (Text in English) w? P.O. Box 30080, Likoni Rd., Nairobi, Kenya. TEL 254-2-540280. FAX 254-2-553939. TELEX 24032. Ed. Francis M'thaiya Awaniki. adv.; illus. circ. 65,000. (also avail. in microfilm from UMI) **Document type**: newspaper.

052   KE
SUNDAY TIMES. w? P.O. Box 30958, Nairobi, Kenya. TEL 337798. TELEX 25008.

059   KE
TAIFU JUMAPILI. (Text in Kiswahili) 1987. w. P.O. Box 49010, Nairobi, Kenya. Ed. Robert K. Mwangi.

059.96   KE
UTAMADUNI. 1982. m. Arts and Cultural Consultants, P.O. Box 22529, Nairobi, Kenya. Ed. Nyakundi John Peter.

052   KE   ISSN 1016-9717
WAJIBU; a journal of social and religious concern. (Text in English) 1985. q. $25 in Africa; elsewhere $35. P.O. Box 32440, Nairobi, Kenya. TEL 720400. Ed. G. Wakuraya Wanjohi. circ. 600. Indexed: P.L.E.S.A.
Description: Seeks to foster a dialogue between people of different ethnic and religious groups for peace and understanding.

GENERAL INTEREST PERIODICALS — KOREA

079.6762 330 KE
THE WEEKLY REVIEW. (Text in English) 1975. w. $240. Weekly Review Ltd., P.O. Box 42271, Nairobi, Kenya. TELEX 25137 ESB. Ed. Amboka Andere. adv. contact: Bernadette Otiato. bk.rev. circ. 40,000. **Document type:** newspaper.
  Description: Political and business review of mainly Kenyan events.

052 KE
WHAT'S ON. w? Rehema House, P.O. Box 49010, Nairobi, Kenya. TEL 27651. Ed. Nancy Kairo. circ. 10,000.

059.96 KE
Y M C A REVIEW. (Young Men's Christian Association) 1983. q. O.F.E. P.R. Services, P.O. Box 62620, Nairobi, Kenya. Ed. J.O. Okoko.

GENERAL INTEREST PERIODICALS — Korea

059.957 KO
DONG-A NYONKAM. 1967. a. Dong-A Ilbo, 139 Sejongno, Chongno-gu, Seoul, S. Korea. TEL 02-721-7114. Ed. Kwon O-Kie. circ. 30,000.

052 US ISSN 1053-4806
DS922.46
KOREA BRIEFING. 1990. a. Westview Press, 5500 Central Ave., Boulder, CO 80301. TEL 303-444-3541. FAX 303-449-3356. **Document type:** academic/scholarly publication.
—BLDSC (5113.451700).
  Description: Assesses contemporary politics, economics, and culture in India.

079.5195 052 KO ISSN 0023-3897
KOREA HERALD. (Text in English) 1953. d. (except Mondays). 4000 Won per mo.; Hong Kong $23.80; Japan 3000 Yen; SE Asia $28.50; Canada, Europe $36.40; Africa, S. America $39.50. Korea Herald Inc., 1-12, 3-ga, Hoehyon-dong, Chung-gu, Seoul 100-771, S. Korea. TEL 02-756-7711. FAX 02-755-4894. TELEX HERALD-K26543. (Or: C.P.O. Box 6479, Seoul, S. Korea) Ed. Min Dae-ki. adv.; bk.rev.; charts; illus.; stat. circ. 55,000. **Document type:** newspaper.

052 KO ISSN 0023-3900
DS901 CODEN: KOJODS
KOREA JOURNAL. (Text in English) 1961. q. $30. Korean National Commission for Unesco, Box Central 64, Seoul, S. Korea. FAX 82-2-774-3956. TELEX MOCNDM-K23231-2 EXT.6364. Ed. Lee Seung-Hwan. adv.; bk.rev.; charts; illus.; stat. circ. 3,500. **Indexed:** Asian-Pac.Econ.Lit., M.L.A., RILM. —Faxon; UnCover.
  Description: Quarterly of the Korean National Commission for Unesco.

079.5195 052 KO ISSN 0023-3935
KOREA TIMES. (Text in English) 1950. d. 22300 Won($31.85) per month. Kang-Jae Chang, 14 Chunghak-Dong, Chongno-Gu, Seoul, S. Korea. Ed. Il-yon Yu. adv.; bk.rev.; film rev.; play rev.; abstr.; illus. circ. 150,000. **Document type:** newspaper.

052 KO
READER'S DIGEST (SOUTH KOREAN EDITION). (Text in Korean) 1978. m. 12000 Won($17) (Yonkang Scholarly Foundation) Dong-A Publishing Co. Ltd., 295-15 Doksan-dong, Guro-gu, Seoul, S. Korea. TEL 02-866-8800. FAX 02-862-0410. Ed. Man-Ki Kim. circ. 150,000.

059.957 KO
WEEKLY CHOSUN. (Text in Korean) w. 61 Taepyong-no 1, Chung-ku, Seoul, S. Korea. circ. 350,000.

059.957 KO
WEEKLY HANKOOK. (Text in Korean) 1964. w. 14 Chunghak-dong, Chongno-ku, Seoul, S. Korea. Ed. Hong Yoo-Sun. circ. 400,000.

GENERAL INTEREST PERIODICALS — Kuwait

079.536 052 KU
ARAB TIMES. (Text in English) 1977. d. $200. Dar al-Seyassah Printing, Publishing and Distributing House, P.O. Box 2270, 13023 Safat, Kuwait. TEL 965-4813566. FAX 965-4816236. TELEX 22332. Ed. Ahmad Abd al-Aziz al-Jarallah. **Document type:** newspaper.

059.927 KU ISSN 0258-3941
AL-ARABI; majallah thiqafiyyah musawwarah. (Text in Arabic) 1952. m. Ministry of Information - Wizarat al-'Ilam, P.O. Box 748, Safat, 13008 Kuwait, Kuwait. TEL 965-2427141. FAX 965-2424370. TELEX 44041 MITR KT. Ed. Muhammad Al-Ramaihiy. adv.; bk.rev.; illus. **Document type:** government publication.
  Description: Covers issues affecting the Arab nation, and other items of interest to all Arabic speakers throughout the world.

665.5 KU
KUWAITI DIGEST. (Text in English) 1972. q. free. Kuwait Oil Company (K.S.C.), Supdt. Press and Publications Division, P.O. Box 9758 Ahmadi, 61008 Ahmadi, Kuwait. TEL 965-3989111. FAX 965-3983661. TELEX 44226 KUOKO. Ed. Salem R. Al Roomi. circ. 8,500. **Indexed:** Mid.East: Abstr.& Ind.
  Formerly (1946-1972): Al-Kuwaiti.
  Description: Articles on economic, cultural, educational and other fields of development in Kuwait.

059.927 KU
NAHDA. w. International Airport St., Industrial Area, Shuwaikh, P.O. Box 695, Al Kuwait, Kuwait. adv. circ. 96,000.

079.536 059.927 KU
AL-SEYASSAH. (Text in Arabic) 1965. d. Dar al-Seyassah Printing, Publishing and Distributing House, P.O. Box 2270, 13023 Safat, Kuwait. TEL 965-4813566. FAX 965-4816326. TELEX 22332. Ed. Ahmad Abd al-Aziz al-Jarallah. circ. 80,000. **Document type:** newspaper.

GENERAL INTEREST PERIODICALS — Latvia

079.474 LV
AVIZITE. 1990. s-m. Degoles 6, 3104 Tukums, Latvia. TEL 8-231-29240. Ed. Arvis Grods. bk.rev. **Document type:** newspaper.

079.474 052 LV
▼**THE BALTIC OBSERVER;** news from Estonia, Latvia and Lithuania. (Monthly supplement avail.: Informnews) (Text in English) 1991. w. $85. Baltic News Ltd., Balasta Dambis 3, LV 1081 Riga, Latvia. TEL 371-2-462-119. FAX 371-2-463-387. E-mail: bo@mii.lu.lv. (Subscr. to: Communicate with the Baltics, Akadeemia tee 21-G, EE 0026 Tallinn, Estonia; Dist. in U.S by: Copyland - BO, 558 Pilgrim Dr., Ste. A, Foster City, CA 94404. TEL 415-341-2679) Ed. Karlis Freibergs. adv. contact: Einars Vitols. bk.rev.; illus. Wire service(s): BNS. circ. 8,700. cols./p.: 6; pp./issue: 16. (tabloid format; also avail. in microfiche from NRP; back issues avail.) **Document type:** newspaper.
  Description: Brings the latest news from Estonia, Latvia and Lithuania. Covers the week's biggest stories, business and economy, weekly legislation reviews, profiles, commentaries and political cartoons.

077 LV
DO VOSTREBOVANIYA. 1990. 26/yr. Ul. Mariyas 1, Daugavpils, Latvia. TEL 39468. Ed. Lyudmila Kuz'mina. circ. 3,000. **Document type:** newspaper.

059.9193 LV ISSN 0132-6449
LIESMA. 1958. m? 1 Ganibu dambi 12, 226810 Riga, Latvia. TEL 328889. Ed. Dainis Caune. circ. 138,000.

S A L - NEWS. see *ETHNIC INTERESTS*

GENERAL INTEREST PERIODICALS — Lebanon

079.569 059.927 LE
AL-ANWAR. (Text in Arabic) 1960. d. Dar Assayad S.A.L., P.O. Box 1038, Hazmieh, Beirut, Lebanon. TEL 961-1-456373. FAX 961-1-456373. Dir. Bassam Freiha. adv. **Document type:** newspaper.

059.92 LE
MONDAY MORNING. 1971. w. Tewfik Abou Khater Bldg., Wardieh Sq., P.O. Box 1812, Beirut, Lebanon. Ed. Fawaz C. Najia. adv. circ. 20,000.

054.1 LE
REVUE DU LIBAN. (Text in French) 1928. w. $200. Societe pour le Developpement de la Presse, Rue Issa Maalouf, Imm. Dimitri Trad., Quartier Sioufi, Beirut, Lebanon. TELEX REVRAK 42121 LE. Ed. Melhem Karam. adv.; bk.rev. circ. 25,000.

059.927 LE
SAMAR. (Text in Arabic) w. $150. Dar Assayad S.A.L., P.O. Box 1038, Hazmieh, Beirut, Lebanon. FAX 961-1-456373. (U.K. addr.: c/o Contact PR & Mgt. (UK) Ltd., 3 Park Pl., 12 Lawn Ln., Vauxhall, London SW8 1UA, England. TEL 44-71-582-2220) **Document type:** consumer publication.

GENERAL INTEREST PERIODICALS — Lesotho

079.6885 LO
THE MIRROR. d. Maseru, Lesotho. Ed. Mike Pitso. circ. 4,000. **Document type:** newspaper.

GENERAL INTEREST PERIODICALS — Liberia

079.6662 LB
DAILY LISTENER. m. P.O. Box 35, Monrovia, Liberia. Ed. Charles C. Dennis. circ. 3,500. **Document type:** newspaper.

079.6662 LB
DAILY OBSERVER. 1981. d. 117 Broad St., P.O. Box 1858, Crown Hill, Monrovia, Liberia. TEL 223545. Ed. Stanton B. Peabody. circ. 30,000. **Document type:** newspaper.

GENERAL INTEREST PERIODICALS — Libya

059.927 LY
AL-BAIT. (Text in Arabic) fortn. Press Service, P.O. Box 4845, Tripoli, Libya.

059.927 LY
AL-JAMAHIRIYA. (Text in Arabic) 1980. w. P.O. Box 4814, Tripoli, Libya. TEL 49294.

059.927 LY
AL-THAQAFAH AL-ARABIYYAH. (Text in Arabic) 1973. w. P.O. Box 4587, Tripoli, Libya. circ. 25,000.

059.927 LY
AL-USBU' AL-SIYASI. (Text in Arabic) w. Press Service, P.O. Box 4845, Tripoli, Libya.

059.927 LY
AL-USBU' AL-THAQAFI. (Text in Arabic) w. Press Service, P.O. Box 4845, Tripoli, Libya. Ed. Mustafa al-Misullati.

059.927 LY
AL-ZAHF AL-AKHDAR. (Text in Arabic) w. Press Service, P.O. Box 4845, Tripoli, Libya.

GENERAL INTEREST PERIODICALS — Lithuania

059.919 LI
ATGIMIMAS. 1988. w. Zigimantu 26, Vilnius 232600, Lithuania. TEL (0122) 224-406. FAX 0122-227-531. Ed. Rimvydas Valatka. circ. 30,000.

059.919 LI
GIMTASIS KRASTAS. 1967. w. Teviske Society for Cultural Relations with Lithuanians Living Abroad, Tilto g-ve 8-2, Vilnius 232600, Lithuania. TEL (0122) 623-881. Ed. Kazys Zhilenas. circ. 100,000. (also avail. in microfilm from NRP)

059.919 LI
KRANTAI. 1989. m. P.O. Box 511, 232000 Vilnius ARP-3, Lithuania. TEL (0122) 224-743. Ed. Vaidotas Daunys.

GENERAL INTEREST PERIODICALS — MALTA 2749

077 LI
LIETUVOS RYTAS. (Supplements. avail.: Motorway; TV Antenna) (Editions in Lithuanian and Russian) 1990. d. (except Sun.- Mon.) Lithuanian ed., w. Russian ed. $149 74.25 Lit. for 9 mos.; newsstand price: 0.80 Lit. Lietuvos Rytas, Gedimino Av. 12A, 2001 Vilnius, Lithuania. TEL 370-2-226272. FAX 370-2-227656. Ed. Gedvydas Vainauskas. adv.; bk.rev.; film rev.; music rev.; play rev.; tele.rev.; illus.; tr.lit.; circ. 85,000 (paid); 40,000 (controlled). cols./p.: 5; pp./issue: 40. (tabloid format) **Document type:** newspaper.

051 LI
LITHUANIA INFOSERVICE. (Text in English) irreg. (4-6/yr.) $10. P.O. Box 673, Klaipeda 5815, Lithuania. Ed. Igor Balenko. circ. 10,000. **Document type:** consumer publication.

059.919 LI
MAZOJI LIETUVA. 1932. w. H. Manto 2, Klaipeda 235800, Lithuania. Ed. Kestutis Oginskas.

059.9192 LI
AP95.L5
NAUJASIS ZIDINYS - AIDAI. m. 22 Rub. per no. Kataliku Pasauliu, Pylimo 27, 2001 Vilnius, Lithuania. TEL 0122-222-363. Ed. Petras Kinbrys. bk.rev.; film rev.; play rev.; abstr.; bibl.; charts; illus.; stat.; index. Indexed: Amer.Bibl.Slavic & E.Eur.Stud. (until 1992), M.L.A.
Incorporates (1945 - Jan. 1992): Aidai-Echoes (ISSN 0002-208X); Which was formerly: Aidai Menesinis.

800 LI
SLUOTA. 1934. fortn. Bernardinu 8-8, Vilnius 232722, Lithuania. TEL (0122) 613-171. Ed. Rytis Tilvytis.

059.919 LI ISSN 0132-6546
SVYTURYS. 1949. m. $36. Maironio 1, Vilnius 232600, Lithuania. TEL 0122-627488. Ed. Juozas Bausys. adv.

GENERAL INTEREST PERIODICALS — Luxembourg

074.935 LU
LETZEBURGER LAND. (Supplements avail.) (Text in English, French, German, Luxembourgish) 1954. w. 2030 Fr.; newsstand price: 54 Fr. Rue de Strasbourg, 2560 Luxembourg, Luxembourg. TEL 48-57-57. FAX 49-63-09. Dir. Jean-Paul Hoffmann. bk.rev.; illus. (standard format; back issues avail.) **Document type:** newspaper.

074.94 LU
LUXEMBOURG NEWS. (Text in English) 1981. w. 2450 Fr.($205) International City Magazines, 31 allee Scheffer, 2520 Luxembourg, Luxembourg. TEL 352-47-00-53. FAX 352-47-00-56. Ed. Wendy Winn; Pub. Pol Wirtz. adv.; B&W page 25500 Fr.; 185 x 270; adv. contact: Michele Gosselin. bk.rev.; illus. circ. 2,200. cols./p.: 4; pp./issue: 28. **Document type:** newspaper.

GENERAL INTEREST PERIODICALS — Malagasy Republic

054.1 MG
ECLAIR; mensuel independant d'information, d'analyse et d'opinion. 1976. m. FMG.9000. Latimer Rangers, Ed. & Pub., P.O. Box 4392, Antananarivo, Malagasy Republic.

059.553 MG ISSN 1019-7737
GAZETINAO. (Text in French, Malagasy) 1975. bi-m. FMG.1200. Agence de Presse Evangelique et Culturelle, Box 1758, 101 Antananarivo, Madagascar. TEL 331-77. (Subscr. to: IPA 37, Anosimasina, Antananarivo, Madagascar) Ed. Etienne Marie Rakotomahanina. adv. circ. 3,000.

054.1 MG
MADAGASCAR RENOUVEAU; magazine d'information politique, economique, social et culturelle. q. FMG.900. Direction de l'Information, B.P. 271, Antananarivo, Malagasy Republic. **Indexed:** Curr.Cont.Africa.

054.1 MG
OCEAN INDIEN ACTUEL; magazine mensuel d'informations. 1977. m. FMG.250. 15 rue Ratsimilaho, B.P. 3464, 101 Antananarivo, Malagasy Republic. TEL 25634. Ed. Richard Claude Ratovonarivo. circ. 10,000. **Indexed:** Curr.Cont.Africa.
Description: Reports on events in Southeast Africa.

GENERAL INTEREST PERIODICALS — Malawi

052 MW
BLANTYRE HANDBOOK. (Text in English) 1978. q. Centraf Associates Ltd., P.O. Box 30462, Chichiri, Blantyre 3, Malawi.

052 MW
LOOK 'N READ. (Text in English) 1980. m. Centraf Associates Ltd., P.O. Box 30463, Chichiri, Balantyre 3, Malawi.

052 MW
MALAWI NEWS. (Text in English and Chichewa) 1958. w. Blantyre Newspapers Ltd., POB 39, Ginnery Corner, Malawi. Ed. Samuel Chunga. bk.rev. circ. 13,500.

059.96 052 MW
MONI. (Text in Chichewa and English) 1964. m. K.45. (Archdiocese of Blantyre) Montfort Press and Popular Publications, P.O. Box 5592, Limbe, Malawi. TEL 651139. TELEX 44814. Ed. B.L. Ng'ombe. adv.; bk.rev. circ. 40,000.

059.96 MW ISSN 0378-4703
MOYO. (Text in English) 1969. m. Ministry of Health, POB 3, Blantyre, Malawi.

GENERAL INTEREST PERIODICALS — Malaysia

059.992 MY
DEWAN MASYARAKAT. 1963. m. Dwan Bahasa dan Pustaka, Jalan Wisma Putra, P.O. Box 10803, 50926 Kuala Lumpur, Malaysia. TEL 03-2481011. Ed. Nik Zainal Abidin Hassan. circ. 65,000.

052 HK
MALAYSIA TATLER. 1989. m. M.$6 per no. Communication Management Ltd., 1811 Hong Kong Plaza, 188 Connaught Rd. W., Hong Kong. TEL 547-7117. FAX 858-2671. Ed. Lina Ross. circ. 20,000. **Document type:** consumer publication.

052 MY ISSN 0126-527X
DS591
MALAYSIAN PANORAMA. 1971. q. free. Ministry of Foreign Affairs - Kementerian Luar Negeri, Jalan Wisma Putra, Kuala Lumpur, Malaysia. illus. circ. 15,000.

059.992 MY
MASTIKA. m. 46M Jalan Lima, Off Jalan Chan Sow Lin, Kuala Lumpur, Malaysia. TEL 03-487055. Ed. Azizah Ali. circ. 40,000.

059.951 MY
MISTER MAGAZINE.* (Text in Chinese) 1976. m. Life Publishing Sdn. Bhd., 80M, Jalan 21-39, Damansara Utama, 47400 Petaling Jaya, Selangor, Malaysia. Ed. Chew Sung. circ. 60,000.

059.951 MY
NEW LIFE POST. (Text in Chinese) 1972. fortn. 80M Jalan SS21-39, Damansara Utama, 47400 Petaling Jaya, Selangor, Malaysian. TEL 03-7190355. FAX 03-7172163. Ed. Low Beng Chee. circ. 160,000.

079.595 MY
NEW TONG BAO (NATIONAL EDITION). Night edition avail. for Klang Valley. (Supplements avail.: World News & Business; Entertainment & Leisure) (Text in Chinese) 1957. d. newsstand price: M.$0.70. Malayan Thung Pau Daily News Sdn Bhd, No. 13, Jalan 13-6, 46200 Petaling Jaya, Malaysia. TEL 60-3-757-9911. FAX 60-3-757-7641. Owner(s): Sin Heap Lee Media Sdn Bhd, 346 Jalan Tun Razak, 50400 Kuala Lumpur, Malaysia. TEL 60-3-263-7788. FAX 60-3-263-1391. Ed. Teo Bak Kim. adv. contact: Loo Phan Kooi. bk.rev.; film rev.; music rev.; illus. circ. 35,000. cols./p.: 10; pp./issue: 36. **Document type:** newspaper.

059.992 MY
PEDOMAN MASYARAKAT. 1961. m. Malaysian Information Services, Mosque Rd., 93612 Kuching, Sarawak, Malaysia. TEL 082-240141. FAX 082-247917. TELEX MA 70113. Eds. Hamka Othman, Hadi Hj. Bibi. circ. 3,000.

059.992 MY
PEDOMAN RAKYAT. 1956. m. Malaysian Information Services, Mosque Rd., 93612, Kuching, Sarawak, Malaysia. TEL 082-240141. FAX 082-247917. TELEX MA 70113. Eds. Hamka Othman, Hadi Bibi. circ. 30,000.

059.992 MY
PEMBRITA. (Text in Iban) 1950. m. Malaysian Information Services, Mosque Rd., 93612 Kuching, Sarawak, Malaysia. TEL 082-240141. FAX 082-247917. TELEX MA 70113. Ed. Alban Jawa. circ. 6,500.

059.992 MY
PENGASOH. 1918. m. Majlis Ugama Islam, Jita Bahru, Kelantan, Malaysia. Ed. Yusoff Zaky Yacob. circ. 15,000.

079.595 MY
SABAH TIMES. (Christmas supplement avail.) (Text in English, Malay) 1952. d. Sabah Times Sdn. Bhd., No. 76, Saya St., P.O. Box 10525, 88805 Kote Kinabalu, Malaysia. TEL 60-88-249111. FAX 60-88-249222. Ed. Lee Weng Chung. adv. contact: Priscilla Majambun. film rev.; music rev.; tele.rev.; illus. cols./p.: 9; pp./issue: 24. (broadsheet format; back issues avail.) **Document type:** newspaper.

079.595 MY
SANDAKAN JIH PAO. (Text in Chinese) 1960. d. Sandakan Jih Pao & Printing Co. Sdn. Bhd., Lot 12, Hock Seng Industrial Estate, Mile 3, North Rd., P.O. Box 337, 90007 Sandakan, Malaysia. TEL 60-89-212566. FAX 60-89-212750. Ed. Lin Yi Boo; Pub. Chong Chang Hing. adv. contact: Pang Thou Chong. bk.rev.; film rev.; music rev.; play rev.; tele.rev.; illus. cols./p.: 10; pp./issue: 20. (broadsheet format) **Document type:** newspaper.

052 059.992 MY ISSN 0036-4762
J8
SARAWAK GAZETTE. (Text in English, Iban, Malay; summaries in English) 1870. q. M.$16. (State Government) Sarawak Museum, 93566 Kuching, Sarawak, Malaysia. TEL 082-244232. FAX 082-246680. Ed. Ybhg. Datuk Hj. Taha Ariffin. adv.; bk.rev.; bibl.; charts; illus. circ. 600. (tabloid format; also avail. in microform; microfilm from KTO) **Indexed:** Forest.Abstr., Rural Devel.Abstr.

079.595 MY
UTUSAN SARAWAK. 1949. s-w. Abell Rd., Kuching, Sarawak, Malaysia. Ed. Abdul Aziz Haji Malim. circ. 2,000. **Document type:** newspaper.

059.992 MY
WATAN. (Text in English, Malay) 1977. every 3 weeks. Kumpulan Akhbar Watan (KJ) Sdn Bhd, 50-52 Lorong Rahim Kajai 14, Taman Tun Dr Ismail, 60000 Kuala Lumpur, Malaysia. Ed. Encik Hishamuddin Haji Yaacub. circ. 80,000.

GENERAL INTEREST PERIODICALS — Malta

079.9458 059.9277 MM
IL-GENS. (Text in Maltese) 1988. w. £7.50. Media Centre, National Rd., Blata L-Bajda HMR 02, Malta. TEL 353-246677. FAX 353-234057. Ed. Carmel Attard. adv.; bk.rev.; film rev.; play rev.; tele.rev.; illus.; circ. 1,000 (paid); 12,000 (controlled). cols./p.: 5; pp./issue: 28. (tabloid format; back issues avail.) **Document type:** newspaper.

079.9458 MM
SUNDAY TIMES. (Supplements avail.) 1929. w. £8.84($25); newsstand price: $.40. Allied Newspapers Ltd., 341 St. Paul St., Valletta VLT 07, Malta. TEL 356-241464. FAX 356-247901. Ed. Laurence Grech; Pub. Austin Bencini. adv.; B&W page £222, color page £370; adv. contact: Joseph Urry. bk.rev.; illus. Wire service(s): RN. cols./p.: 5; pp./issue: 68. (tabloid format) **Document type:** newspaper.

GENERAL INTEREST PERIODICALS — Mexico

056.1   MX   ISSN 0010-7581
CONTENIDO. 1963. m. Mex.$220($15) Editorial Contenido, S.A., Darwin 101, Anzures, 11590 Mexico D.F., Mexico. TEL 5-531-3162. Ed. Armando Ayala Anguiano. adv.; bk.rev.; charts; illus. circ. 200,000.

056.1   MX   ISSN 0010-910X
CORREO DEL SUR; semanario regional. 1961. w. $7. Heladio G. Camacho, Gutenberg 303 O, Apdo. Postal 334, Cuernavaca, Mor., Mexico. adv.; bk.rev.; illus.; index. circ. 4,000. (tabloid format)

079.72   MX
CRONICA DE BAJA CALIFORNIA. (Supplements included: Sahvaro, Travesura) 1990. d. newsstand price: Mex.$1.80. Grupo Editorial de Baja California, Ave. Heroes de la Patria 952, 2100 Mexicali, Baja California, Mexico. TEL 52-65-57-48-01. FAX 52-65-57-04-24. Ed. Adolfo Sanchez Rodriguez; Pub. Jose Santiago Healy. adv. contact: Diego Monteverede Woolfolk. film rev.; music rev.; play rev.; illus. Wire service(s): AP, Notimex, Inforsel. circ. 17,095 (morn. ed.); 18,453 (Sun. ed.). cols./p.: 8; pp./issue: 42. (standard format; back issues avail.) **Document type:** newspaper.
    Description: Covers politics, sports, finance, social news and entertainment.

056.1   MX   ISSN 0185-2477
CUENTO; revista de imaginacion. 1964. q. $40. G.V. Editores, S.A. de C.V., Popocatepetl 510, Col. General Anaya, 03330 Mexico, D.F., Mexico. Ed. Edmundo Valades Mendoza. adv.; illus.; index. circ. 17,000.

056.1   MX
CUESTION. 1980. d. Mex.$300000($100) Editorial Hara S.A., 410 Laguna de Mayran, Mexico D.F., Mexico. TEL 250-4055. Ed. Alberto Gonzalez Parra. circ. 22,000. (back issues avail.)

056.1   MX   ISSN 0188-4816
CULTURA SUR. 1989. bi-m. Mex.$7($5) per no. Consejo Nacional para la Cultura y las Artes, Programa Cultural de las Fronteras, Alvaro Obregon 273, Col. Roma, 06700 Mexico D.F., Mexico. TEL 5-11-12-61. circ. 5,000 (paid).

056.1   MX
DE LOS CUATRO VIENTOS. bi-m. Editorial Huiznahuac s. de c.v. y r.l., Magdalena 51, Col. del Valle, 03100 Mexico D.F., Mexico. TEL 652-75-28. Ed. Margarita Montalvo.

079.72   MX
DIARIO 17. English edition: New York Times - Acapulco. (Supplements included: Deportivo 17, Ejecutivo) 1989. d. Mex.$200($66.70); newsstand price: Mex.$1.50. Calz. Pie de la Cuesta No. 90, Acapulco, Gro., Mexico. TEL 82-46-01. FAX 83-13-87. Pub. Victor Manuel Garcia Garcia. adv.: B&W page Mex.$3600 first section; Mex.$3000 other sections; adv. contact: J. Francisco Medina Rivera. film rev.; music rev.; play rev. circ. 18,000. cols./p.: 8; pp./issue: 26. (tabloid format; also avail. in diskette format; back issues avail.) **Document type:** newspaper.

056.1   MX   ISSN 0012-9445
ECO DE NAYARIT; bisemanario popular portavoz de la region. 1917. s-w. $8. Calle Allende Num. 12 Pte., Acaponeta, Nayarit, Mexico. Ed. Antonio Saizar Quintero. adv.; illus. (tabloid format)
    Description: Contains items of local interest.

079.72   MX
ECO DEL MANTE. 1939. d. Mex.$100($100); newsstand price: $.40. Guerrero 701 Ote., 89800 Mante, Tamaulipas, Mexico. TEL 91-123-22420. FAX 91-123-20040. Ed. Antolin Sierra Ayala; Ed. Manuel Nunez Rangel. film rev.; music rev.; illus. circ. 5,000. cols./p.: 8; pp./issue: 8. (standard format; also avail. in diskette format) **Document type:** newspaper.

056.1   MX
FIESTA. 1974. w. Novedades Editores, S.A. de C.V., Morelos 16, 3er Piso, C.P. 06040, Mexico, D.F., Mexico. adv.; illus.

056.1   MX   ISSN 0015-0835
FIGARO; semanario popular. 1952. w. Mex.$2. Ave. Morelos 45, Mexico City, Mexico. Ed. Salvador Acevedo Lopez. adv.; film rev.; play rev.; illus. circ. 85,000. (tabloid format)

056.1   MX
FIN DE SIGLO. m. Mex.$3,600($40) Espartza Oteo, No. 144-108, Col. Guadalupe Inn, CP 01020, Mexico, D.F., Mexico.

056.1   MX
FOCA ROMANTICA. 1982. w. $43. Editorial La Foca, S.A. de C.V., Plomo no.25, Col. Valle Gomez, C.P. 06240, Mexico, D.F., Mexico. adv.; illus.

056.1   MX   ISSN 0016-6952
GENTE. 1965. m. $65 (foreign $95) (effective 1993). Editorial Gente S.A., 890 Palmas, 11000 Lomas, Mexico, D.F., Mexico. TEL 252-520-2414. FAX 252-282-4678. (U.S. subscr. to: 2554 Lincoln Blvd., Ste. 1043, Marina del Rey, CA 90291) Ed. Raul Azcarraga. adv.; bk.rev. circ. 50,000.
    Description: General news coverage of Mexican and international current events. Subjects include economics, art, religion, business, economics, science, medicine, politics and more.

079.72   MX
HERALDO DE SALTILLO. (Supplements avail: Dominical, Gente) 1963. d. Mex.$180($40); newsstand price: $.50. Cia. Editora de Coahuila, Abasolo 228, 25000 Saltillo, Coahuila, Mexico. TEL 52-84-14-22-50. FAX 52-84-14-88-74. Ed. Eduardo De la Pena; Pub. Martin Salazar. adv. contact: Alicia De La Pena. bk.rev.; film rev.; illus.; circ. 5,000 (controlled). cols./p.: 6; pp./issue: 12. (standard format; back issues avail.) **Document type:** newspaper.

079.72   MX
HERALDO DE SAN LUIS POTOSI. 1942. d. newsstand price: Mex.$1.50. Villerias 305, 78000 San Luis Potosi, Mexico. TEL 48-12-33-12. FAX 48-12-20-81. Ed. Alejandro Villasana Mena; Pub. Rodrigo Villasana Lopez. adv. contact: Ricardo Pinto Turnbull. bk.rev.; film rev.; music rev.; play rev.; illus. (tabloid format; also avail. in microfilm; back issues avail.; reprint service avail.) **Document type:** newspaper.
    •Also available online.

056.1   MX   ISSN 0018-2192
HISPANO AMERICANO; seminario de la vida y la verdad. (Distributed in Mexico as Tiempo) vol.55, 1970. w. Mex.$180($20) Tiempo S.A. de C.V., Barcelona 32, Mexico 6 D.F., Mexico. Ed. Ovidio Gondi. adv.; bk.rev.; film rev.; play rev.; charts; illus.
    —Faxon.

056.1   MX
HISTORIA ILUSTRADA.* 1976. m. Mex.$450($36) Corporacion Editorial S.A., Lucio Blanco 435, Col. San Juan Tlihuaca, 02400 Mexico D.F., Mexico. adv. circ. 100,000.
    Formerly: Genesis.

056.1   MX   ISSN 0019-2880
AP63
IMPACTO. 1950. w. Mex.$8 per no. Av. Ceylan 517, Apdo. 2986, 23000 Mexico D.F., Mexico. TEL 5-587-3855. FAX 5-567-7781. Ed. Carlos Moncada Ochoa. adv.; bk.rev.; film rev. circ. 115,000.

056.1   MX   ISSN 0021-261X
ISTMO; revista del pensamiento actual. 1959. bi-m. Mex.$84($52) (effective July 1993). Centros Culturales de Mexico, A.C., Goya 73-303, 03910 Mexico D.F., Mexico. TEL 5631963. FAX 5636435. Ed. Patricia Montelongo de Galindo. adv. contact: Armando Raimond. bk.rev.; index. circ. 10,000.

056.1   MX   ISSN 0185-6596
JUEVES DE EXCELSIOR. 1922? w. Excelsior, Compania Editorial, S.C.L., Bucareli 17, 2o piso, Mexico DF, Mexico. 535-66-08. FAX 535-36-86. Ed. Leon Garcia Soler. **Document type:** consumer publication.

056.1   MX
KENA. 1964. fortn. Mex.$15 per no. Grupo Juventud S.A., Avda. Insurgentes Sur 605-906, Naples, 03810 Mexico D.F., Mexico. TEL 5-536-6654. FAX 5-682-3037. Ed. Liliana Moreno. adv.; bk.rev. circ. 86,349.

056.1   MX   ISSN 0034-9844
MANANA. 1943. w. Mex.$200. Amberes 38, Mexico 6, D.F., Mexico. Ed. Luis J. Solana Morales. adv.; charts; illus.

079.72   MX
MOMENTO. (Supplement avail.: Septimo Dia) 1975. d. Cia. Editora Regional del Centro, S.A. de C.V., Zenon Fernandez 800, 78280 San Luis Potosi, Mexico. TEL 14-44-44. FAX 12-20-20. Pub. Ramon Pedroza Langarica. adv. contact: Rosa Delia Duenas Martinez. film rev.; music rev.; play rev.; illus. cols./p.: 5; pp./issue: 44. (standard format) **Document type:** newspaper.

079.72   MX
PERIODICO ZOCALO. (Supplement included: Zocalito) 1965. d. $200; newsstand price: $.55. Zocalo Newspapers, Cuauhtemoc 714 Norte, 26000 Piedras Negras, Coahuila, Mexico. TEL 011-52878-21090. FAX 011-52878-23352. (And: Box 7368, Eagle Pass, TX 78853. TEL 210-703-0832) Ed. Francisco Juaristi Santos; Pub. Francisco Juaristi Septien. adv. contact: Jose Luis Rodales Plata. bk.rev.; film rev.; music rev.; play rev.; illus. Wire service(s): AP, UPI, KR, LAT, Notimex, Proceso, Universal, Excelsior. circ. 21,000. cols./p.: 6; pp./issue: 50. (standard format)

079.72   MX
POR ESCRITO; el semanario de Guadalajara. 1988. w. (Fri.) Mex.$104($260); newsstand price: Mex.$2. Editorial Unidifusion, Av. Mexico 3150, Monraz, 44670 Guadalajara, Jalisco, Mexico. TEL 3-813-1415. FAX 3-813-1465. Ed. Guillermo Camacho Perez; Pub. Alejandro Diaz Romo. adv.: B&W page Mex.$2448; adv. contact: Yolanda Hernandez. film rev.; music rev.; illus.; circ. 14,000 (paid), 1,500 (controlled). cols./p.: 4; pp./issue: 64. (tabloid format) **Document type:** newspaper.
    Description: Covers politics, sports, and economics, and includes features.

079.72   MX
LA PRENSA. (Includes fortn. supplements: Salvavidas; Detras de Tu Cara) 1928. d. Mex.$300; newsstand price: Mex.$2. Editora la Prensa, S.A. de C.V., Basilio Badillo 40, 06030 Mexico, D.F., Mexico. TEL 905-228-9977. FAX 905-512-5296. Pub. Carlos Abedrop Davila. adv. contact: Benjamin Salmon Salazar. film rev.; music rev.; play rev.; illus. Wire service(s): AP, AFP, RN, Notimex. circ. 198,500 (paid); 3,500 (controlled). cols./p.: 5; pp./issue: 64. (tabloid format; back issues avail.) **Document type:** newspaper.

056.1   MX   ISSN 0033-1929
PROVINCIA SOCIAL.* 1961. m. Mex.$60.($4.80) Impresiones, S.A., Matamoros 813 Ote, Apdo. No. 44, Monterrey N.L., Mexico. Ed. Guadalupe Gomez De Puertas. adv.; illus. circ. 3,000.

079.72   MX
LA RAZON. (Regional w. eds. for Cadereyta, Montemorelos) 1979. 6/w. newsstand price: Mex.$1. Cia. Editorial Tijerina, S.A., J.M. Rojo No. 440 Sur, 6400 Monterrey, N.L., Mexico. TEL 342-96-97. FAX 342-96-98. Ed. Benjamin Castro Guzman; Pub. Francisco Tijerina Gonzalez. adv.: B&W page Mex.$1000; adv. contact: Jose Luis Campos Martinez. film rev.; music rev.; play rev.; illus. Wire service(s): Notimex, Excelsior. circ. 8,300 (paid). cols./p.: 6; pp./issue: 32. (tabloid format; also avail. in diskette format; back issues avail.; reprint service avail.) **Document type:** newspaper.
    Description: Contains local, national and international information. Covers sports, finance and economics.

056.1   MX   ISSN 0035-0486
REVISTA TAMAULIPAS. 1947. m. Mex.$100($19) Editora Revista Tamaulipas, Juarez y F.l. Madero, Apdo. Postal 460, Tampico, Tam., Mexico. Ed. Silvio Lattuada. adv.; bk.rev.; film rev.; play rev.; charts; illus.; tr.lit. circ. 30,000.

056.1   MX
SELECCIONES DEL READER'S DIGEST (MEXICAN EDITION). 1940. m. Mex.$25 per no. Reader's Digest Mexico, S.A. de C.V., Avda. Lomas de Sotelo 1102, Col. Lomas Hermosa, Apdo. 552, Naucalpan, 11200 Mexico D.F., Mexico. TEL 5-358-9155. TELEX 1774213. Ed. Audon Coria Mendez. circ. 587,828.

GENERAL INTEREST PERIODICALS — MIDDLE EAST

079.72   MX
SOL DE PARRAL. 1981. d. Sol de Parral, S.A., Colegio No. 20, 33800 Hgo. del Parral, Chihuahua, Mexico. TEL 2-52-50. FAX 2-53-40. illus.; circ. 5,400 (controlled). cols./p.: 8; pp./issue: 20. (standard format) **Document type:** newspaper.

079.72   MX
SOL DE TAMPICO. 1950. d. $15 per mo.; newsstand price: $.35. Cia. Periodistica del Sol de Tampico, S.A. de C.V., Altamira 311 Pte., 89000 Tampico Tamaulipas, Mexico. TEL 12-10-67. FAX 12-68-21. Ed. Ruben Diaz de la Garza; Pub. Mario Vazquez Rana. adv. contact: Leobardo Puebla G. bk.rev.; film rev.; music rev.; illus.; circ. 67,000 (morn. ed.); 27,000 (eve. ed.); 25,000 (Sun. ed.) (paid). cols./p.: 8; pp./issue: 90. (standard format) **Document type:** newspaper.
    Description: Covers national and international news, sports, entertainment, business, and society.

056.1   MX   ISSN 0040-7275
TIEMPO; semanario de la vida y la verdad. (Distributed in the U.S. as Hispano-Americano) vol.46, 1965. w. Mex.$180($20) Tiempo S.A. de C.V., Barcelona No. 32, Mexico 6, D.F., Mexico. Ed. Martin Luis Guzman. adv.; bk.rev.; illus.

056.1   US
VISION (NEW YORK); la revista latinoamericana. (Text in Spanish) 1950. s-m. $124. Vision, Inc., 310 Madison Ave., No. 1412, New York, NY 10017-6000. TEL 212-953-1308. FAX 212-953-1619. Ed. M. bk.rev.; film rev. circ. 180,000.

GENERAL INTEREST PERIODICALS — Middle East

059.927   QA
AKHBAR AL-USBU'. (Text in Arabic) 1986. w. Ali bin Ali Printing and Publishing Establishment, P.O. Box 4896, Doha, Qatar. TEL 445561. FAX 433778. TELEX 4234. Ed. Adil Ali bin Ali. circ. 15,000.

059.927   UK
AL-ALAM. (Text in Arabic) 1984. w. £125. Unistage Ltd., 55-57 Banner St., London EC1Y 8PX, England. TEL 071-608-3454. FAX 071-608-3581. Ed. Saed Shehabi. circ. 20,000. **Document type:** consumer publication.

072.1 052   UK
ARAB NEWS. 1974. d. £125($267) Saudi Research and Marketing, Arab Press House, 184 High Holborn, London WC1V 7AP, England. TEL 071-831-8181. FAX 071-831-2310. TELEX 889272. (And: P.O. Box 4556, Jeddah 21412, Saudi Arabia. TEL 966-2-6691888. FAX 966-2-6671650; Subscr. in U.S. to: Attache International, 3050 Broadway, Boulder, CO 80304-3154. TEL 303-442-8900. FAX 303-442-7979) Ed. Farouk Lukman. adv.: B&W page $6400; 14 x 21 3/16. illus. circ. 57,000. cols./p.: 6. (broadsheet format) **Document type:** newspaper.
    Description: Covers world news, business and events affecting the Arab world.

059.927   MK
AL-BARA'IM. (Text in Arabic) w. Dar al- Usrah, P.O. Box 7440, Muttrah, Sultanate of Oman. TEL 794922. FAX 795348. TELEX 3266. circ. 1,800.

052   QA
GULF TIMES. (Text in English) 1978. w. Gulf Publishing and Printing Organization, P.O. Box 533, Doha, Qatar. TEL 329424. FAX 601808. TELEX 4600. Ed. Ahmad Abd al-Malik. circ. 15,000.

059.927 072.1   UK   ISSN 0967-5590
AL-HAYAH. (In 3 editions: International; Arabian Peninsula; Levant) (Text in Arabic) 1946. d. $700. Media Communications plc, Kensington Centre, 66 Hammersmith Rd., London W14 8AT, England. TEL 44-71-602-9988. FAX 44-71-602-4963. (And: Media Force, Ivoire Centre, Sin El-Fil, Beirut, Lebanon. TEL 961-1-493246. FAX 961-1-498967) Ed. Jihad Khazen. adv.: B&W page $9320 in international ed.; 530 x 555. film rev.; illus.; cum.index: 1990-; circ. 120,000 (paid). cols./p.: 8; pp./issue: 20. (broadsheet format; also avail. in microfilm; back issues avail.) **Document type:** newspaper.
    ●Also available on CD-ROM.

051   US   ISSN 1073-6697
DS51.K7
INTERNATIONAL JOURNAL OF KURDISH STUDIES. 1986. s-a. $30 to individuals; institutions $50. Kurdish Library, 345 Park Pl., Brooklyn, NY 11238. TEL 718-783-7930. FAX 718-398-4365. Ed. Wheeler Thackston. adv.; bk.rev. circ. 1,000. (back issues avail.) **Document type:** academic/scholarly publication.
    Formerly: Kurdish Times (ISSN 0885-386X)
    Description: Presents articles by and about Kurds.

052   IS   ISSN 0792-6049
DS101
THE JERUSALEM REPORT. 1990. bi-w. $69. 22 Yosef Rivlin St., P.O. Box 1805, Jerusalem 91017, Israel. (Subscr. in U.S. to: Box 580, Mt. Morris, IL 61054. TEL 800-827-1119) Ed. Hirsh Goodman. adv.; bk.rev. **Document type:** consumer publication.
    Description: International coverage and commentary on issues and events pertaining to Israel, the Middle East and the Jewish world.

079.55 059.927   IR   ISSN 0885-8187
KAYHAN AL-ARABI. (Daily edition also avail.) (Text in Arabic) 1980. w. $131 to N. America (d. ed. $351) (effective 1994). Kayhan Publications, Ferdowsi Ave., P.O. Box 11365-9631, Teheran, Iran. TEL 98-21-3110251. FAX 98-21-3114228. TELEX 212467. **Document type:** newspaper.

059.927   TS
AL-KHALIJ. (Text in Arabic) 1970-1972; resumed 1980. d. Dar al- Khalij lil-Sahafah wal-Tiba'ah wal-Nashr, P.O. Box 30, Sharjah, United Arab Emirates. TEL 350883. FAX 599336. TELEX 68055 KHALIJ EM. Ed. Rashid Umran Turaim. circ. 58,870.

059.927 915.3   QA
AL-KHALIJ AL-JADID. (Text in Arabic) m. Ministry of Information, P.O. Box 1968, Doha, Qatar.

051   US
KURDISH LIFE. 1991. q. $20 (foreign $25). Kurdish Library, Center for Research, 345 Park Pl., Brooklyn, NY 11238. TEL 718-783-7930. FAX 718-398-4365. Ed. Wheeler Thackston.
    Description: Publishes analysis of events and issues behind the headlines, news from Kurdish organizations around the world, announcements of new reports and publications.

059.927   UK   ISSN 0261-0876
AP95.A6
AL-MAJALLA. (Text in Arabic) 1980. w. $166 (effective 1994). Saudi Research and Marketing, Arab Press House, 184 High Holborn, London WC1V 7AP, England. TEL 071-831-8181. FAX 071-831-2310. TELEX 889272. (And: P.O. Box 4556, Jeddah 21441, Saudi Arabia. TEL 966-2-6691888. FAX 966-2-6671650; Subscr. in U.S. to: Attache International, 3050 Broadway, Ste. 300, Boulder, CO 80304-3154. TEL 303-442-8900. FAX 303-442-7979) Ed. Abdulrahman Al-Rashid. adv. contact: B&W page $3467, color page $5733; trim size 220 x 285. illus.; circ. 144,691 (paid). **Document type:** consumer publication.
    Description: Publishes news of the Arab world, including business, financial, cultural, social and political issues.

079.62 052   UA   ISSN 0047-7257
MIDDLE EAST OBSERVER. (Text in English) 1954. w. £E10($25) 8 Sharia Chawarby, Cairo, Egypt. Ed. Ahmad Sabry. adv.; illus. circ. 30,000. Indexed: Key to Econ.Sci. **Document type:** newspaper.
    Description: Covers economic conditions in the Middle East and Africa, focusing on markets, foreign trade, and relevant laws and contracts.

052 956   GR   ISSN 0259-9627
MIDDLE EAST TIMES; the region's weekly. (In 2 editions: International, Egypt) (Text in English) 1983. w. $90 to individuals in Europe, the Middle East, and Africa (N. America and Asia $120); institutions in Europe, the Middle East, and Africa $150 (N. America and Asia $180) (effective 1993). P.O. Box 30183, Athens 100 33, Greece. TEL 30-1-361-4505. FAX 30-1-360-9673. TELEX 226-180 FPC. **Document type:** newspaper.
    Description: Reports and comments on political, social, economic, financial, and business news in the Middle East

059.927   SU
AL-MUJTAMA'. (Text in Arabic) 1964. w. P.O. Box 354, Riyadh, Saudi Arabia. Dir. Saleh Salem.

059.927   MK
AL-NAHDAH.* (Text in Arabic) w. P.O. Box 979, Muscat, Sultanate of Oman. TEL 707849. TELEX 3161. Ed. Talib Said al-Meawaly. illus. circ. 1,570.

NEWS CIRCLE/HALQAT AL-AKHBAR; Arab-American monthly. see ETHNIC INTERESTS

059.927   MK
OMAN TODAY. Variant title: Sultanate of Oman Today. 1980. q. Apex Publishing, P.O. Box 5616, Ruwi, Muscat, Sultanate of Oman. TEL 799388. FAX 793316. TELEX 5515. Ed. Janet Allison. adv.; bk.rev. circ. 10,000.
    Description: Features and listings periodical, includes day trips, car tests and more.

059.927   TS
RAS AL-KHAIMAH. (Text in Arabic) 1969. m. free. Municipal Government, Department of Tourism and Information, P.O. Box 200, Ras al-Khaimah, United Arab Emirates. TEL 21333. Ed. Ahmad al-Tadmuri. circ. 1,000.
    Description: News and information about activities and local cultural events in the Emirate.

059.927 915.3   QA
AL-RAYAH. (Text in Arabic) 1979. w. Gulf Publishing and Printing Organization, P.O. Box 533, Doha, Qatar. TEL 810450. FAX 601808. TELEX 4600. Ed. Ahmad Ali. circ. 18,000.

059.927   UK
SAYIDATI. (Text in Arabic) 1981. w. $166 (effective 1994). Saudi Research and Marketing, Arab Press House, 184 High Holborn, London WC1V 7AP, England. TEL 071-831-8181. FAX 071-831-2310. TELEX 889272. (And: P.O. Box 4556, Jeddah 21441, Saudi Arabia. TEL 966-2-6691888. FAX 966-2-6671650; Subscr. in U.S. to: Attache International, 3050 Broadway, Ste. 300, Boulder, CO 80304-3154. TEL 303-442-8900. FAX 303-442-7979) Ed. Mattar Al-Ahmadi. adv.: B&W page $3067, color page $5000; trim 220 x 285. circ. 163,594 (paid). **Document type:** consumer publication.
    Description: Covers beauty, international fashion, health and exercise, social issues, education, child care, medical news, travel and the arts. For the Arab family.

059.927   QA
AL-SHARQ. (Text in Arabic) 1985. d. Al- Sharq Printing, Publishing and Distribution House, P.O. Box 3488, Doha, Qatar. TEL 662444. FAX 662450. TELEX 5103. Ed. Nasser al-Othman. circ. 20,000.

072.1 059.927   UK   ISSN 0265-5772
AL-SHARQ AL-AWSAT; the international daily newspaper of the Arabs. Variant title: Asharq Al-Awsat. (Magazine supplement avail.) (Text in Arabic) 1978. d. £200($300) Saudi Research and Marketing, Arab Press House, 184 High Holborn, London WC1V 7AP, England. TEL 071-831-8181. FAX 071-831-2310. TELEX 889272. (And: P.O. Box 4556, Jeddah 21412, Saudi Arabia. TEL 966-2-6691888. FAX 966-2-6671650; U.S. subscr. to: Attache International, 3050 Broadway, Ste. 300, Boulder, CO) 80304-3154. TEL 303-442-8900. FAX 303-442-7979) Ed. Othman Al-Omeir. adv.: B&W $9333; 14 x 21 3/16. circ. 211,702. cols./p.: 8. (broadsheet format) **Document type:** newspaper.
    Description: Covers international politics, business, finance, education and sports.

059.927   UK
AL-SHARQ AL-AWSAT MAGAZINE. (Supplement to: Al-Sharq al-Awsat (ISSN 0265-5772) (Text in Arabic) w. $75. Saudi Research and Marketing, Arab Press House, 184 High Holborn, London WC1V 7AP, England. TEL 071-831-8181. FAX 071-404-6311. (And: P.O. Box 4556, Jeddah 21421, Saudi Arabia. TEL 966-2-6691888. FAX 966-2-6671650; Subscr. in U.S. to: Attache International, 3050 Broadway, Ste. 300, Boulder, CO 80304-3154. TEL 303-442-8900. FAX 303-442-7979) adv.: color page $4667; trim 220 x 285. circ. 162,706 (paid). **Document type:** consumer publication.
    Description: Entertainment magazine for an Arabic speaking audience.

GENERAL INTEREST PERIODICALS — MOLDOVA

059.927   MK
TRIBUTE TO OMAN. 1982. a. Apex Publishing, P.O. Box 5616, Ruwi, Muscat, Sultanate of Oman. TEL 799388. FAX 793316. TELEX 5515. Ed. Janet Allison. circ. 18,000.
    Description: Documents Oman's people.

059.927   QA
AL-URUBAH/ARABISM. Variant spelling: Al-Ourubah. (Text in Arabic) 1970. w. Dar al- Urubah Press and Publishing, P.O. Box 1115, Doha, Qatar. TEL 325874. TELEX 4497. Ed. Abdullah Hussain Naama. circ. 25,000.

059.927   MK
AL-USRAH. (Text in Arabic) 1974. w. Dar al- Usrah, P.O. Box 7440, Muttrah, Sultanate of Oman. TEL 794922. FAX 795348. TELEX 3266. Ed. Sadek Abdowani. illus. circ. 12,585.

052   UK   ISSN 0964-6280
VOICE INTELLIGENCE REPORT. 1972. q. £72. Morris International Associates Ltd., 15 A Lowndes St., London SW1X 4EY, England. (U.S. dist. addr.: Box 976, New York, NY 10272) Ed. Claud Morris. bk.rev.; stat. circ. 5,000. (back issues avail.)
    Formerly: Voice of the Arab World (ISSN 0954-5697)

059.927   TS
AL-WAHDAH. (Text in Arabic) 1973. d. Dar Suhuf al-Wahdah, P.O. Box 12488, Abu Dhabi, United Arab Emirates. TEL 478100. TELEX 23850 JALDI EM. Ed. Rashid bin Uwaidah.

GENERAL INTEREST PERIODICALS — Moldova

077   MV
NEZAVISIMAYA MOLDOVA. 1991. 5/w. Ul. Pushkina 22, 277012 Kishiniev, Moldova. TEL 0422-233605. FAX 0422-233608. Owner(s): Parlament Respubliki Moldova. adv.; illus. (broadsheet format) Document type: newspaper.

GENERAL INTEREST PERIODICALS — Monaco

054.1   MC
SOCIETY. (Text in English, French) 1980. s-a. free. Societe des Bains de Mer, Sporting d'Hiver, Place du Casino, MC 98000, Monaco. TEL 010-33-93-30-99-31. Ed. June Benas-Quin. circ. 25,000.

GENERAL INTEREST PERIODICALS — Morocco

054.1   MR   ISSN 0047-2174
JOURNAL DE TANGER.* (Text in French) 1904. w. DH.200. 11 ave Moulay Abd al-Aziz, B.P. 420, Tangier, Morocco. Ed. Abdelhak Bakhat. adv.; bk.rev. circ. 10,000.

GENERAL INTEREST PERIODICALS — Mozambique

052   UK   ISSN 0969-7802
▼**A I M REPORTS.** 1993. 24/yr. £14 to individuals (Europe £23; elsewhere £28); institutions £22 (Europe £35; elsewhere £48). Agencia de Informacao de Mocambique - Mozambique News Agency, 7 Old Bailey, London EC4M 7NB, England. TEL 071-329-8842. FAX 071-329-8845. Ed. Americo Xavier. circ. 600. Document type: bulletin, newsletter.
    Description: Disseminates information about the economic, social and political development of Mozambique.

056.9   MZ
BOLETIM DA REPUBLICA. 3/w. $262. Imprensa Nacional de Mocambique, Avda. Vladimir Lenine, C.P. 275, Maputo, Mozambique.
    Description: Contains government and official notices.

052   MZ
MOZAMBIQUE FILE. (Text in English) 1976. m. 65000 mt($14) to individuals (foreign $24); institutions $25 (foreign $35) (effective 1994). Agencia de Informacao de Mocambique - Mozambique News Agency, C.P. 896, Maputo, Mozambique. TEL 428603. FAX 421906. TELEX 6430. Dir. Ricardo Malate. adv. circ. 1,200. (back issues avail.) Document type: newsletter.
    Former titles: Mozambique News; A.I.M. Information Bulletin.
    Description: Contains information on the country's political, economic, social and military situation.

079.679   MZ
NOTICIAS. 1926. d. (except Sun.). 131460 mt($552) Sociedade do Noticias, S.a.r.l., Rua Joaquim Lapa 55, 327 Maputo, Mozambique. TEL 420119. FAX 420575. Ed. Bernardo Mavanga. illus. cols./p.: 9; pp./issue: 8. (standard format) Document type: newspaper.

056.9   MZ
TEMPO. (Text in Portuguese) 1970. w. $86. Tempografica, S.A.R.L., Av. Ahmed Sekou Toure 1078, Box 2917, Maputo, Mozambique. TEL 426191. TELEX 6486. Ed. Simeao Cachamba. adv.; bk.rev.; illus. circ. 20,000. Document type: consumer publication.

GENERAL INTEREST PERIODICALS — Namibia

079.68 053.1   SX
ALLGEMEINE ZEITUNG. (Text in German) 1915. d. Deutscher Verlag (Pty) Ltd., P.O. Box 2127, Windhoek, Namibia. TEL 061-225411. FAX 061-224843. Ed. Hans Feddersen. circ. 6,000. Document type: newspaper.

360 079.6881   SX
BRICKS COMMUNITY NEWSPAPER. (Text in English) 1989. bi-m. Bricks Community Project, 4 Katatura Community Centre, P.O. Box 20642, Windhoek 9000, Namibia. TEL 264-61-62726. FAX 264-61-63510. film rev. circ. 2,000. (tabloid format; back issues avail.) Document type: newspaper.
    Description: Covers local development issues, civil enablement and other matters of concern to Namibians.

052   SX   ISSN 0378-7826
NAMIBIA TODAY. w. South West Africa People's Organization, P.O. Box 24669, Windhoek, Namibia. TEL 061-229150.
    Formerly: Namibia (ISSN 0027-7754)

079.68   SX
THE NAMIBIAN. (Text mainly in English, occasionally in Afrikaans) 1989. d. (5/wk.). Free Press of Namibia (Pty) Ltd., P.O. Box 20783, Windhoek, Namibia. TEL 061-216186. Ed. Gwen Lister. adv. circ. 14,000. Document type: newspaper.

079.68   SX
TEMPO. (Leisure supplement avail.) (Text in Afrikaans, English, German) w. (Sun.). n.$165; newsstand price: N.$3. P.O. Box 1794, Windhoek, Namibia. TEL 061-225822. FAX 061-223110. Owner(s): Democratic Media Holdings, Marconi Str., Windhoek, Namibia. TEL 061-225411. FAX 061-35674. Ed. G. Cloete; Pub. N. Kruger. adv. contact: Ms. M. Roets. illus. circ. 8,000. (tabloid format) Document type: newspaper.
    Formed by the 1992 merger of: Namibia Nachrichten & Sondag Republikein & Times of Namibia.

079.6881   SX
WINDHOEK ADVERTISER. 1919. d. John Meinert (Pty) Ltd., P.O. Box 2255, Windhoek 9000, Namibia. Document type: newspaper.

GENERAL INTEREST PERIODICALS — Nepal

059.914   NP
ARPAN; Nepali weekly. (Text in Nepali) 1964. w. $20. Nepal Economic and Commerce Research Centre, P.O. Box 285, 7-358 Kohity Bahal, Kathmandu, Nepal. TEL 977-1-220531. FAX 977-1-225544. TELEX 2634 ONZA NPL. Ed. Manju Ratna Sakya. adv.; bk.rev. circ. 16,000.
    Description: Provides new and commentaries.

079.5496 052   NP
THE COMMONER. (Text in English) 1956. d. (Sun.-Fri.). Rs.600($12) Commoner, P.O. Box 203, Naradevi, Kathmandu, Nepal. TEL 977-1-228236. Ed. Gopal Dass Shrestha; Pub. Gopal Dass Shrestha. adv. contact: Ms. Usha Shrestha. illus.; circ. 6,000 (paid). cols./p.: 6; pp./issue: 8. (tabloid format; back issues avail.) Document type: newspaper.

079.5496   NP
DAILY NEWS. (Text in English, Nepali) 1983. d. (Sun.-Fri.). Rs.1500($25) 7-358 Kohity Bahal, P.O. Box 171, Kathmandu, Nepal. TEL 977-1-220531. FAX 977-1-225544. Ed. Mrs. Subha Luxmi Sakya; Pub. Manju Ratna Sakya. bk.rev.; illus. cols./p.: 4; pp./issue: 4. (standard format; back issues avail.; reprint service avail.) Document type: newspaper.

059.914   NP
JANMABHUMI. (Text in Nepali) 1970. w. Rs.1501($3) (effective 1993). Janmabhumi Press, Tahachal, Kathmandu, Nepal. TEL 271485. Ed. Ganesh Ballav Pradhan. adv.: page $40; adv. contact: Shirish B. Pradhan. bk.rev. circ. 271,485.

059.914   NP
MATRIBHOOMI/NEPALI WEEKLY. (Text in Nepali) w. GA 2-549. Kamal Pokhai at Police Station, Kathmandu, Nepal. TEL 412501. Ed. Govinda Biyogi.

052   NP
NEPAL CHRONICLE. (Text in English) w. Chandra Lal Jha, Ed. & Pub., Maruhiti, Nepal.

052   NP   ISSN 0028-2723
DS485.N4
NEPAL PRESS DIGEST. (Text in English) 1957. w. Rs.720($50) Nepal Press Digest (Pvt) Ltd., Lazimpat, Kathmandu, Nepal. Ed. Mahesh Chandra Regmi.

052   NP   ISSN 0028-2731
DS485.N4
NEPAL PRESS REPORT. (Text in English) 1957. d. Rs.3600($250) Regmi Research (Pvt) Ltd., Lazimpat, Kathmandu, Nepal. TEL 4-11927. Ed. Suresh C. Regmi.
    Description: Translations of news reports, editorial comments and special articles from the non-English press.

079.5496   NP
SAMAJ DAILY. (Text in Nepali) 1954. d. Rs.500($20) (effective 1987). P.O. Box 4149, Dilli Bazar, Kathmandu, Nepal. TEL 977-1-412840. Ed. Mani Raj Upadhyaya. circ. 5,000. (back issues avail.) Document type: newspaper.

052   NP   ISSN 0042-2878
VASUDHA MONTHLY. (Text in English) vol.12, 1968. m. Rs.3($18) Vasudha Publication, 8-535 Makhangali New Rd., Kathmandu, Nepal. Ed. T.L. Shrestha. adv.; bk.rev. circ. 3,000.

GENERAL INTEREST PERIODICALS — Netherlands

053.931   NE
A O. (Aktuele Onderwerpen) 1938. w. fl.88. Stichting I V I O, Postbus 37, 8200 AA Lelystad, Netherlands. TEL 31-3200-76411. FAX 31-3200-33756. Ed. A.L. Greiner. bk.rev.; bibl.; charts; illus.; stat.; cum.index; circ. 7,000 (controlled).
    Formerly: Actuele Onderwerpen-Reeks (ISSN 0001-7841)

079.492   NE
ALGEMEEN DAGBLAD. 1946. d. Algemeen Dagblad, P.O. Box 241, 3000 DB Rotterdam, Netherlands. TEL 31-10-4066077. FAX 31-10-4066969. Owner(s): Dagbladunie (Subsidiary of Reed Elsevier plc), Marten Meesweg 35, 3068 AV Rotterdam, Netherlands. Ed. A.I. Abram. adv.; illus. circ. 414,000. Document type: newspaper.

053.931   NE   ISSN 0003-5718
ANTILLIAANSE NIEUWSBRIEF. 1959. m. free. Kabinet van de Gevolmachtigde Minister van de Nederlandse Antillen, Afdeling Voorlichting, Badhuisweg 173-175, 2597 JP The Hague, Netherlands. FAX 31-70-3512722. Ed. R.A. Capriles Martina. adv.; bk.rev. circ. 9,500. (tabloid format) Indexed: Key to Econ.Sci. Document type: government publication.

053.931 NE ISSN 0005-9692
HET BESTE UIT READER'S DIGEST (DUTCH EDITION).
(Text in Dutch) 1957. m. fl.6.75 per no.
Uitgeversmaatschappij The Reader's Digest N.V.,
Hogehilweg 17, 1101 CB Amsterdam ZO,
Netherlands. FAX 31-20-6976422. Ed. Jan Walta.
adv.; illus. circ. 395,000.

949.2 NE ISSN 0006-7571
BOOM-PERS COMBINATIE.* d. Uitgeverij Boom, P.O. Box
400, 7940 AK Meppel, Netherlands.
TEL 31-5220-57012. FAX 31-5220-53864. Eds.
M.J. Boom, J.H. Boom. circ. 48,670.

079.492 NE
BRABANTS NIEUWSBLAD. d. (6/wk.). newsstand price:
fl.1.75. Postbus 1052, 4700 BB Roosendaal,
Netherlands. TEL 31-1650-35970. Ed. G.
Bielderman; Pub. W.J.C. Bouman. adv.; bk.rev.; film
rev.; music rev.; tele.rev.; illus. Wire service(s): AP,
ANP, NPA, RN. cols./p.: 8; pp./issue: 28. (also avail.
in microform; back issues avail.) **Document type:**
newspaper.

079.492 NE ISSN 0007-2648
BRUG; weekblad voor Nijmegen en omgeving. 1959. w.
free. Gelderlander Weekbladpers, Postbus 205,
6500 AE Nijmegen, Netherlands.
FAX 31-80-240620. Ed. W. Mulder. adv.; bk.rev.
circ. 109,000. **Document type:** newspaper.

053.931 NE
D C - MAGAZINE/D C - NEWSBRIEF. 1971. q. fl.15. A-Z
Publicity C.V., Postbus 5107, 6802 EC Arnhem,
Netherlands. Ed. J.M.G. Withagen. adv. circ. 64,000.
Formerly (until 1987): Drivers Club Magazine.

949.2 NE ISSN 0024-8592
DRENTHE. 1929. m. (10/yr.). fl.33. Drents
Genootschap, Postbus 174, 9400 AD Assen,
Netherlands. illus.

052 UK
DUTCH CROSSING. 2/yr. University College, London,
Centre for Low Countries Studies, Gower St., London
WC1E 6BT, England. illus. **Document type:**
academic/scholarly publication.

053.931 NE ISSN 0922-3444
AP15
ELSEVIER. 1944. w. fl.224.50. Bonaventura B.V.
(Subsidiary of: Elsevier N.V.), Hoogoorddreef 60,
1101 BE Amsterdam, Netherlands.
TEL 31-20-5674911. FAX 31-20-5674629. TELEX
14013 BONAV NL. Ed. J.V.D. Bossche. adv.; bk.rev.;
film rev.; play rev.; charts; illus. circ. 125,000.
Indexed: Key to Econ.Sci. **Document type:** consumer
publication.
—SWETS.
Formerly (until 1987): Elseviers Magazine (ISSN
0013-6395)

053.931 NE ISSN 0023-7698
LAND VAN VALKENBURG.* 1948. w. fl.6.40. Postbus
909, 6300 AX Valkenburg, Netherlands. Ed. L.
Pluymaekers. adv.; bk.rev.
Description: Contains items of local interest.

079.492 NE
N R C - HANDELSBLAD. 1970. d. N R C Handelsblad,
P.O. Box 824, 3000 DL Rotterdam, Netherlands.
TEL 31-10-4066111. FAX 31-10-4066967.
Owner(s): Dagbladunie (Subsidiary of: Reed Elsevier
plc), Marten Meeseweg 35, 3068 AV Rotterdam,
Netherlands. Ed. B. Knapen. adv.; illus. circ.
242,000. **Document type:** newspaper.

059 NE ISSN 0165-4411
NIEUWE REVUE. 1953. w. fl.124.80. Geillustreerde
Pers B.V., Stadhouderskade 85, 1073 AT
Amsterdam, Netherlands. TEL 31-20-5734811.
FAX 31-20-5734406. Eds. Hans Verstraaten, Jean
Mentens. adv.; illus. circ. 160,000. **Document type:**
consumer publication.

053.931 NE ISSN 0031-0867
AP15
PANORAMA. 1913. w. fl.2.85 per no. Uitgeverij
Spaarnestad B.V. (Haarlem), P.O. Box 1, 2000 MA
Haarlem, Netherlands. TEL 31-23-304304.
FAX 31-23-304213. TELEX 41371 NL. Ed. Juke
Wartenbergh. adv.: color page fl.18830. bk.rev.;
illus. circ. 195,000. **Indexed:** Intl.Ind.TV. **Document
type:** consumer publication.

079.492 NE
HET PAROOL. 1945. d. P.O. Box 433, 1000 AK
Amsterdam, Netherlands. TEL 31-20-5629333.
FAX 31-20-5622822. Ed. S. van der Zee. circ.
100,000. **Document type:** newspaper.

053.931 NE ISSN 0165-5574
PRIVE. 1977. w. fl.91. De Telegraaf Tijdschriftengroep
B.V., P.O. Box 127, 1000 AC Amsterdam,
Netherlands. TEL 31-20-5853375.
FAX 31-20-5854111. Ed. W.P.J. Smitt. adv.; circ.
500,000 (paid). **Document type:** consumer
publication.
Description: Publishes human interest stories,
medical and health news, and news and gossip
about celebrities from the worlds of politics, TV, film
and show business.

079.492 NE
REFORMATORISCH DAGBLAD. 1971. d. (Mon.-Sat.).
fl.334. Reformatorisch Dagblad, Postbus 613, 7300
AP Apeldoorn, Netherlands. TEL 31-55-495222.
FAX 31-55-417450. Owner(s): Erdee-Holding B.V.
Ed. C.S.L. Janse; Pub. J. Koetsier. adv. contact: J.
Alderliesten. bk.rev.; music rev.; illus. circ. 5,500.
cols./p.: 7; pp./issue: 30. (standard format; also
avail. in microform) **Document type:** newspaper.

054.1 BE ISSN 0771-8934
SEPTENTRION. revue de culture neerlandaise. 1972.
4/yr. 1200 BEF (effective 1994). Stichting Ons
Erfdeel v.z.w., Murissonstraat 260, B-8931 Rekkem,
Belgium. TEL 32-56-411201. FAX 32-56-414707.
Ed. Jozef Deleu. film rev.; play rev.; charts; illus. circ.
10,000. **Indexed:** Br.Archaeol.Abstr.
Description: Covers all cultural history relevant to
Belgium and the Netherlands.

079.492 NE
DE TELEGRAAF. 1893. d. De Telegraaf, P.O. Box 376,
1000 EB Amsterdam, Netherlands.
TEL 31-20-5859111. FAX 31-20-5852113. circ.
780,000. **Document type:** newspaper.

079.492 NE
TROUW. 1943. d. P.O. Box 859, 1000 AW
Amsterdam, Netherlands. TEL 31-20-5629444.
FAX 31-20-6680389. Ed. J. Greven. adv. circ.
121,000. **Document type:** newspaper.

079.492 NE
DE VOLKSKRANT. 1919. d. De Volkskrant, P.O. Box
1002, 1000 BA Amsterdam, Netherlands.
TEL 31-20-5629222. FAX 31-20-5626289. Ed. H.
Lockefeer. circ. 342,100. **Document type:** newspaper.

053.931 056.1 NE ISSN 0042-9902
WACHT TE KOOI; seaman's digest. 1962. w. fl.100.
Stichting Nederlands Studiecentrum voor
Zeevarenden, Veerkade 9, 3016 DE Rotterdam,
Netherlands. TEL 31-10-4138114. Ed. E.J. Moojen.
adv.; bk.rev.; film rev.; play rev.; illus. circ. 3,800.
Document type: newspaper.
Description: Covers national and international
shipping news, current events, politics, finance,
economics, sports, culture and entertainment.

GENERAL INTEREST PERIODICALS — New Zealand

079.93 NZ ISSN 0002-3612
AKAROA MAIL. 1876. bi-w. NZ.$25. Akaroa Mail and
Banks Peninsula Advertiser, P.O. Box 9, Akaroa, New
Zealand. TEL 03-3277-622. Ed. M. de Hamel. adv.;
bk.rev.; circ. 5,800 (controlled). (tabloid format; also
avail. in microfilm) **Document type:** newspaper.
—CCC.
Description: Contains items of local interest.

079.93 NZ ISSN 1170-0025
ASHBURTON GUARDIAN. 1877. 6/w. (Mon.- Sat.).
newsstand price: NZ.$0.50. Ashburton Guardian Co.
Ltd., 199-205 Burnell St., Ashburton, New Zealand.
TEL 64-033083089. FAX 64-033089855.
Owner(s): Ashburton Guardian Holdings Ltd.,
199-205 Burnell St., Ashburton, New Zealand. Ed.
Sue Newman; Pub. Bruce Bell. adv. contact: N. Pitt.
film rev.; music rev.; illus.; circ. 300 (paid); 6,000
(controlled). cols./p.: 10; pp./issue: 16. (broadsheet
format; also avail. in microfiche; back issues avail.)
Document type: newspaper.

079.93 NZ ISSN 1170-1277
CHRISTCHURCH MAIL. 1985. s-w. (Mon.& Thur.). 1st
Fl., Paxus House, Cnr. Tuam & High Sts.,
Christchurch, Canterbury, New Zealand.
TEL 03-366-1622. FAX 03-365-6623. Owner(s):
Christchurch Press Co. Ltd., Cathedral Sq., Colombo
St., Christchurch, Canterbury, New Zealand. TEL
03-379-0940. FAX 03-364-8496. Ed Glyn
Clayton. adv. contact: Trevor Laplanche. music rev.;
illus.; circ. 124,000 (controlled). cols./p.: 7;
pp./issue: 36. (tabloid format; back issues avail.)
Document type: newspaper.
Formerly (until 1990): Christchurch Mid-week Mail
(ISSN 1170-0157)

052 NZ ISSN 1171-0179
DIRECTIONS. 1936. bi-m. New Zealand Automobile
Association, 342 Lambton Quay, P.O. Box 1,
Wellington, New Zealand. TEL 04-4738-738.
FAX 04-4712-080. Ed. Dick Smithies. adv. contact:
Annette McGrevy. circ. 533,341. **Document type:**
consumer publication.
Former titles (until 1991): Motoring Today (ISSN
0113-5090); (until 1988): Motor World (ISSN
0112-8094)

079.93 NZ ISSN 1170-036X
THE ENSIGN. 1878. 6/w. (Mon.-Sat.). newsstand price:
NZ.$0.45. P.O. Box 182, Gore, New Zealand.
bk.rev.; film rev.; music rev.; play rev.; tele.rev.; illus.;
tr.lit. cols./p.: 10; pp./issue: 12. (broadsheet format)
Document type: newspaper.

079.93 NZ ISSN 0113-9428
EVENING POST. 1865. d. (Mon.- Sat.). newsstand price:
NZ.$0.60. Wellington Newspapers Ltd., 40 Boulcott
St., Wellington, New Zealand. TEL 74-0444.
FAX 474-0237. Owner(s): Independent Newspapers
Ltd., 25-33 Victoria St., Wellington, New Zealand.
TEL 496-9800. FAX 496-9841. Ed. Paul Cavanagh;
Pub. Ian Wells. adv. contact: Ty Dallas. bk.rev.; film
rev.; music rev.; play rev.; tele.rev.; illus. Wire
service(s): NPA. cols./p.: 8; pp./issue: 36.
(broadsheet format) **Document type:** newspaper.

052 NZ
LISTENER. 1939. w. NZ.$95 (effective Feb. 1994).
New Zealand Listener Ltd., P.O. Box 7, Auckland,
New Zealand. TEL 64-9-623-1002.
FAX 64-9-623-1011. (Subscr. to: P.O. Box
100-741, North Shore Mail Centre, Auckland 10,
New Zealand) Ed. Terry Snow; Pub. Graham Billings.
adv. contact: Trish Turney. bk.rev.; film rev.; music
rev.; play rev.; illus.; circ. 115,660 (paid). (back
issues avail.)
—CCC.
Former titles: Listener T V and Radio Times;
Listener (ISSN 0110-5787); New Zealand Listener
(ISSN 0028-839X)
Description: General features, current affairs,
entertainment, TV and radio programme listings.

052 NZ ISSN 0027-7274
N.Z. TRUTH.* 1901. w. NZ.$59.15($10.40) News
Media Ownership Ltd., 27-35 Mercer St., Wellington,
New Zealand. Ed. A. Hitchens. adv. circ. 154,000.
(tabloid format)
—CCC.

052 NZ ISSN 0028-8489
NEW ZEALAND MONTHLY REVIEW. 1959. bi-m. NZ.$30.
New Zealand Monthly Review Society Inc., P.O. Box
13-483, Armagh, Christchurch, New Zealand. Ed.
Steven Cowan. adv.; bk.rev. circ. 600. (also avail. in
microform from UMI; reprint service avail. from UMI)
Indexed: So.Pac.Per.Ind.
—CCC.
Description: Provides an independent, left wing
analysis at New Zealand and overseas events.

993 UK ISSN 0028-8500
DU400
NEW ZEALAND NEWS U.K. 1927. w. £28 (Europe
£38.50; elsewhere £57.75). Tweeddale Press
Group, 25 Royal Opera Arcade, London SW1Y 4UY,
England. TEL 071-930-6451. FAX 071-930-8780.
(Subscr. to: P.O. Box 10, Berwick-upon-Tweed,
Northumberland TD15 1BW, England. TEL
0289-306677) Ed. Kevin McMenamin. adv. contact:
Ana Hensley. bk.rev. circ. 20,000. **Document type:**
newspaper.

GENERAL INTEREST PERIODICALS — NICARAGUA

052   UK   ISSN 0962-2918
NEW ZEALAND OUTLOOK; the original and leading newspaper for migrants and visitors to New Zealand. m. £7.50 (overseas £15). Consyl Publishing, 3 Buckhurst Rd., Bexhill-on-Sea, E. Sussex TN40 1QF, England. TEL 0424-223111. FAX 0424-224992. Ed. Sandra Melvin. adv.; bk.rev.; illus. circ. 30,000. (tabloid format) **Document type:** newspaper.

052   NZ
NEW ZEALAND TURF DIGEST. s-w. News Media Ltd., Glenside Crescent, P.O. Box 1327, Auckland, New Zealand. TEL 09-778-630. FAX 09-778-782. Ed. Bob Lovett. circ. 22,000.

079.93   NZ   ISSN 1170-1013
THE NORTHLAND TIMES. (Monthly supplement avail.: Agriculture in the Community) 1904. d. (except Sun.). NZ.$90; newsstand price: NZ.$0.30. 45 Normanhy St., Dargaville 0300, Northland, New Zealand. TEL 64-9-439-8209. FAX 64-0-439-6505. Owner(s): The North Auckland Times Co. Ltd., 45 Normanhy St., Darbaville 0300, New Zealand. Ed. Robert Maxted; Pubs. Robert & Rosalie Maxted. adv. contact: Helen Murdoch. film rev.; music rev.; play rev.; tele.rev.; illus. Wire service(s): NPA, RN. circ. 3,040 (paid). cols./p.: 10; pp./issue: 8. (broadsheet format; back issues avail.) **Document type:** newspaper.

079.93   NZ   ISSN 0114-426X
OTAGO DAILY TIMES. 1861. d. (except Sun.). newsstand price: NZ.$0.60. Lower Stuart St., Dunedin, New Zealand. TEL 03-477-4760. Owner(s): Allien Press Ltd., P.O. Box 181, Dunedin, New Zealand. TEL 03-477-4760. Ed. Geoff Adams; Pub. Julian Smith. adv. contact: Nicholas Smith. bk.rev.; film rev.; music rev.; play rev.; tele.rev.; illus.; tr.lit. Wire service(s): AAP, AFP, AP, NPA, RN. circ. 50,000. (broadsheet format; back issues avail.) **Document type:** newspaper.

052   AT   ISSN 0034-0448
READER'S DIGEST (NEW ZEALAND EDITION). (Text in English) 1950. m. NZ.$40.95. Reader's Digest (Australia) Ptu. Ltd., G.P.O. Box 4353, Sydney, N.S.W. 2001, Australia. TEL 09-3600434. FAX 09-3600584. Ed. Hugh Vaughan-Williams. adv.; bk.rev.; illus. circ. 151,000.

052   NZ
STRAIGHT FURROW. 1933. fortn. NZ.$35. P.O. Box 715, Wellington, New Zealand. TEL 04-737-269. FAX 04-731-081. Ed. Susan Grant. circ. 86,000.

079.93   NZ   ISSN 1172-0743
SUNDAY TIMES. 1965. w. NZ.$130.90. Wellington Newspapers Ltd., 40 Boulcott St., Wellington, New Zealand. TEL 474-0000. FAX 474-0350. Ed. Karl du Fresne. adv.; bk.rev.; film rev.; play rev.; illus. circ. 86,310. **Document type:** newspaper.
—CCC.
   Former titles (until 1992): Dominion Sunday Times (ISSN 1170-0289); (until 1987): New Zealand Times (ISSN 0111-5782); (until Apr. 1981): Sunday Times (ISSN 0039-5323)

052   NZ
TIME NEW ZEALAND. w. Guardian Assurance Bldg., Queen St., P.O. Box 198, Auckland, New Zealand. circ. 38,000.

079.93   NZ   ISSN 1170-0688
WAIKATO TIMES. (Weekly supplements avail.: MotorTimes; Racing Times) 1872. 6/w. (Mon.- Sat.). newsstand price: NZ.$0.60. Waikato - King Country Press, Foreman Rd., Hamilton, Waikato, New Zealand. TEL 07-8496180. FAX 07-8496180. Ed. Syzanne Carty. adv. contact: Delwyn Knight. bk.rev.; film rev.; music rev.; play rev.; tele.rev.; illus.; tr.lit. Wire service(s): AAP, RN. circ. 41,000 (paid). cols./p.: 10; pp./issue: 24. (back issues avail.; reprint service avail.) **Document type:** newspaper.

079.93   NZ   ISSN 1170-0009
WAIRARAPA TIMES-AGE. 1878. 6/w. (Mon.-Sat.). newsstand price: NZ.$0.60. 70-74 Chapel St., Masterton, Wairarapa, New Zealand. TEL 06-378-9999. FAX 06-378-2371. Ed. A.G. Wyatt. adv. contact: G.N. Kavidson. bk.rev.; film rev.; music rev.; play rev.; tele.rev.; illus.; tr.lit. Wire service(s): NPA. circ. 9,200 (paid). cols./p.: 10; pp./issue: 22. (broadsheet format; back issues avail.) **Document type:** newspaper.

GENERAL INTEREST PERIODICALS — Nicaragua

056.1   NQ
CAMBIO; revista para los exigentes. 1991. bi-m. Publicaciones Cambio, Villa 9 de Junio C-387, Puente 1 c. arriba 5 vrs. sur, Apdo. 1068, Managua, Nicaragua. TEL 94095. Ed. Clementina Rivas Franco. circ. 3,000. **Document type:** consumer publication.

056.1   HO
CAMBIO EMPRESARIAL. m. Apdo. 4, Tegucigalpa, Honduras. Ed. Joaquin Medina Oviedo.

056.1   CR
DIARIO EXTRA. 1978. d. Col.6240($52) (typically set in Jan.). Sociedad Periodista Extra Ltda., Calle 4, Av. 4, piso 2, Apdo. 177-1009, Fecosa, San Jose, Costa Rica. TEL 506-23-95-05. FAX 506-23-61-01. Ed. William Gomez V. circ. 97,000. (tabloid format)

056.1 051   NQ   ISSN 0259-4374
F1521
ENVIO. (Editions in English, Spanish) 1982. m. $32 (Europe $40). Universidad Centroamericana, Revista Envio, Apdo. A-194, Managua, Nicaragua. TEL 782557. FAX 72583. Eds. Maria Lopez Vigil, Judy Butler. circ. 4,000. (also avail. in microfilm)
Indexed: HR Rep.
—UnCover.
   Incorporates (in 1988): Central American Historical Institute. Update (ISSN 0259-4382)
   Description: Contains analysis of political, economic and social situation in Nicaragua and Central America.

056.1   HO
EXTRA. 1965. m. Apdo. 54, Tegucigalpa, Honduras. TEL 37-2533. Ed. Vincente Machado Valle.

056.1   HO   ISSN 0046-7359
HIBUERAS; revista de informacion y divulgacion general. 1970. q. free. Prohisa, Grupo 12, Bloque 27, No. 15 Colonia Presidente Kennedy, Tegucigalpa, Honduras. Dir. Raul Lanza Valeriano. adv.; charts; illus. circ. 3,000.

056.1   HO
HONDURAS (YEAR). 1979. bi-m. free. Junta Militar de Gobierno, Secretaria de Prensa, Apdo. Postal 403, Tegucigalpa, D.C., Honduras. Ed. Juan R. Ardon. illus.; stat.

052 056.1   HO
HONDURAS AL DIA; boletin internacional. (Text in English and Spanish) 1978. irreg. free. Junta Militar de Gobierno, Secretaria de Prensa, Apdo. Postal 403, Tegucigalpa, D.C., Honduras. Ed.Bd.

056.1   NQ
NICARAGUA. SECRETARIA DE INFORMACION Y PRENSA. CARTA INFORMATIVA. 1976. m. Secretaria de Informacion y Prensa, Managua, Nicaragua.

056.1   NQ
NICARAGUA GRAFICA. bi-m. Apdo. 2791, Managua, Nicaragua. TEL 75107. Ed. Francisco Rivas Quijano.

056.1   NQ
▼**EL PAIS**. 1992. m. C.$10 per no. China Palace, 1c. al sur, 1c. arriba, 1c. as sur, 50 Vrs. arriba, Managua, Nicaragua. TEL 71306. Ed. Luis Hernandez Bustamante. **Document type:** consumer publication.

056.1   CR
PENSAMIENTO COSTARRICENSE. 1977. irreg. free (not for international distribution). Ministerio de Cultura, Juventud y Deportes, Dept. de Publicaciones, Apdo. 10227, San Jose, Costa Rica.

056.1   HO   ISSN 0034-6926
REVISTA A P H.* 1969. m. L.60. Asociacion de Prensa Hondurena, Tegucigalpa, D.C., Honduras. Ed. Nora Landa Blanco. adv.; bk.rev.; charts; illus.

056.1   NQ
▼**REVISTA NICARAGUENSE**. 1992. irreg. Apdo. Postal 3514 y 3269, Managua, Nicaragua. TEL 44-589. FAX 622953. Ed. Jorge Eduardo Arellano.

056.1   HO
SECTANTE. (Supplements avail.) 1975. q. Secretaria de Cultura, Turismo e Informacion, Comision Publicitaria, 2 Avda. y 3 Calle no. 101, Tegucigalpa, Honduras.

056.1   CR
TIEMPO ACTUAL. q. Col.30. Junta de Pensiones y Jubilaciones del Magisterio Nacional, Apartado 3974, San Jose, Costa Rica. Dir. Enrique Vargas Soto.

056.1   NQ
VIA CIVICA; unica salida. no.6, Feb. 1992. bi-m. Parque El Carmen 1C. al N. y 1/2c. al Oriente, Managua, Nicaragua. TEL 22413. FAX 26676. Ed. Jaime Briceno. **Document type:** consumer publication.

GENERAL INTEREST PERIODICALS — Niger

079.6   NG
HASKE. (Supplement avail.) 1990. w. 600 F.($160) Sahel Media Contact, B.P. 297, Niamey, Niger. TEL 227-74-10-53. FAX 227-73-20-06. Pub. Ibrahir Check Diop. adv. contact: Daniel Gay. bk.rev.; illus. cols./p.: 4; pp./issue: 16. (tabloid format)

GENERAL INTEREST PERIODICALS — Nigeria

069.96   NR   ISSN 0795-2031
ABOKIYAR HIRA. (Text in Hausa) 1987. m. Albah Publishers, POB 6177, Bompai-Kano, Nigeria. Ed. B. Foukbah. circ. 35,000.
   Description: General interest, cultural publication.

052   NR
THE ANALYST. (Text in English, Hausa, Igbo and Yoruba) 1986. m? Kaduna, Nigeria. Ed. Rufa'i Ibrahim.

052   NR
CHAMPION. s-w. Calabar Advertising Co., 31 Eyo Edem St., Calabar, Nigeria.

079.669   NR   ISSN 0331-2739
DAILY TIMES. (Text in English) 1949. d. $1362. Daily Times of Nigeria Ltd., Mew Isheri Rd., Agidingbi, P.M.B. 21340, Ikeja, Nigeria. TEL 234-900850. Ed. Farouk Umar Muhammed. adv.; bk.rev.; illus.; circ. 250,000 (controlled). **Document type:** newspaper.
   Formerly: Nigerian Daily Times.

052   NR   ISSN 0189-9228
FUN TIMES; a leisure, light-hearted magazine. 1984. m. £N24. Daily Times of Nigeria Ltd., Publications Division, New Isheri Rd., Agidingbi - Ikeja, P.M.B. 21340, Lagos, Nigeria. TEL 900850-9. Ed. David Lasekan. circ. 12,000.

079.669   NR
GASKIYA TA FI KWABO. (Text in Hausa) 1939. w. Ahmadu Bello Way, P.O. Box 254, Kaduna, Nigeria. TEL 234-62-401420. TELEX 71120. Ed. Muhammad Sabanzara Hassan. adv.; bk.rev.; illus. circ. 66,000. **Document type:** newspaper.
   Description: Reports on local culture, farming, and sports events and covers regional and foreign news.

059.96   NR
GBOUNGBOUN. (Text in Yoruba) w. Sketch Publishing Co. Ltd., New Ct. Rd., PMB 5067, Ibadan, Nigeria. TEL 414851. Ed. A.O. Adebanjo. circ. 80,000.

052   NR   ISSN 0189-3963
HEADLINES. (Text in English) 1973. m. £N52. Daily Times of Nigeria Ltd., Publications Division, New Isheri Rd., PMB 21340, Ikeja, Lagos, Nigeria. TEL 900850-9. Ed. Adams Aliu. circ. 40,000. (tabloid format; also avail. in microfilm; back issues avail.)
   Description: Created to arouse human interest via headline news.

052   NR
HOME STUDIES. 1964. m. Daily Times Publications, 3-7 Kakawa St., Lagos, Nigeria. Ed. G. Odusanya. circ. 40,000.

052   NR   ISSN 0020-1936
INSIGHT.* q. $4. Daily Times of Nigeria Ltd., New Isker Rd., Agidingbi, P.M.B. 21340, Ikeja, Nigeria. adv.; bk.rev.; charts; illus.

GENERAL INTEREST PERIODICALS — NORWAY

059.963 NR ISSN 0021-1494
IROHIN YORUBA. (Text in Yoruba) 1945. w. African Newspapers of Nigeria Ltd., 212 Broad St., Box 2416, Ibadan, Nigeria. TEL 234-4108806. Ed. S.A. Ajibade. adv.; bk.rev.; play rev.; charts; illus. circ. 85,000. (tabloid format) **Document type:** newspaper.

052 059 NR
KANO STATE COURIER. (Editions in English, Hausa) 1971. q. free. Ministry of Home Affairs and Information, Information Division, Kano, Nigeria. Ed.Bd. illus. circ. 5,000.
Formerly (until 1984): Kano State of Nigeria Today.

052 NR
KWARA NEWS. (Text in English) q. Ministry of Home Affairs and Information, Information Division, Governor's Office, P.M.B. 1378, Lorin, Kwara State, Nigeria. circ. 2,500.

052 NR
LAGOS LIFE. 1985. w. Guardian Newspapers Ltd., Rutam House, Isolo Expwy., PMB 1217, Oshodi, Lagos, Nigeria. Ed. B. Ogunbadejo. circ. 100,000.

052 NR
LAGOS STATE TODAY.* 1974. m. 24A Oil Mill St., P.O. Box 3738, Lagos, Nigeria. Ed. Adebimpe Afunku. adv.; charts; illus.

052 NR ISSN 0023-7272
LAGOS WEEKEND. 1965. w. £N52($49.74) Daily Times of Nigeria Ltd., Publications Division, New Isheri Rd., Agidingbi - Ikeja, P.M.B. 21340, Lagos, Nigeria. TEL 900850-9. Ed. Chinaka Fynecontry. adv.; bk.rev.; film rev.; play rev. circ. 288,874.

052 966.9 NR
MIDWEST BULLETIN. q. Ministry of Home Affairs and Information, Printing and Stationery Division, P.M.B. 1099, Benin City, Nigeria. illus.

052 NR
MID-WEST THIS WEEK. w. Arin Associates, 50B New Lagos Rd., Benin City, Lagos, Nigeria. Eds. T. Okuduwa, Prince A.R. Nwoko.

052 NR
MONTHLY LIFE. 1984. m. West African Book Publishers, POB 3445, Lagos, Nigeria. TEL 900760. TELEX 26144. Ed. W. Olaoye. circ. 40,000.

052 NE
THE NEW NATION. m. 52 Iwaya Rd., Onike, Yaba, Surulere, POB 896 Lagos, Nigeria. TEL 863629. TELEX 26517.
Description: News magazine.

079.669 NR ISSN 0331-2755
NEW NIGERIAN. (Text in English) 1966. d. New Nigerian Newspaper Ltd., Ahmadu Bello Way, P.O. Box 254, Kaduna, Nigeria. TEL 234-62-214389. adv.; illus. **Document type:** newspaper.

052 NR
NEWBREED. w. £N276. New Breed Organisation Ltd., Plot 14, Western Ave., 1 Rafiu Shittu St., Alaka Estate, P.O. Box 5414, Surulere, Lagos, Nigeria. TEL 802-6909. FAX 831175. Ed. Chris Okolia. illus.
Formerly (until 1978): New Times.
Description: Examines the Nigerian economy, finance and world business.

052 NR ISSN 0189-8892
AP9
NEWSWATCH; Nigeria's weekly newsmagazine. 1985. w. £N3 per no. Newswatch Communications Ltd., 62 Oregun Rd., P.M.B. 21499, Ikeja, Nigeria. FAX 962887. TELEX 27847-NEWCOM-NG. (Dist. in U.S. by: Medialink International, Inc., 191 Atlantic Ave., Brooklyn, NY 11201) Ed. Ray Ekpu. adv.; bk.rev.; illus. circ. 150,084. (also avail. in microfilm) —Faxon; UnCover.

052 NR ISSN 0048-0363
NIGERIA CONFIDENTIAL;* so that the people may know. 1969. w. L.24($66.20) Nigeria Confidential Co., 83 Palm Ave., Mushin, Lagos, Nigeria. Ed. Abiodun Aloba. circ. 1,000. (processed)

079.669 NR ISSN 0331-2712
NIGERIAN TRIBUNE. (Text in English) 1950. d. African Newspapers of Nigeria, 212 Broad St., Box 2416, Ibadan, Nigeria. TEL 234-4108806. adv.; illus. **Document type:** newspaper.

052 NR
NORTHERN STATES REVIEW;* review of life in the North. (Text in English) 1973. q. £N50($1) per copy. Rota Publishing Co. Ltd., A.C. 5 Lagos St. (2nd Floor), P.O. Box 497, Kaduna, Nigeria. Ed. Jacob M.T. Ovuorie. adv.; charts.

052 NR ISSN 0030-218X
OMA.* (Text in English) 1962. q. 5s.($1.25) Oma Press, Orlu Division, Awo-Omamma, Nigeria. Ed. G.K. Obioha. adv.; bk.rev.; illus. circ. 4,000.

052 NR ISSN 0048-329X
PEOPLE. 1969. m. £N1.6($10.) People's Publishing Co. Ltd., P.O. Box 3121, Lagos, Nigeria. Ed. Olu Akinsanya. adv.; bk.rev.; illus. circ. 20,000. (also avail. in microfilm from UMI; reprint service avail. from UMI)

052 NR
QUALITY. 1987. m. Ultimate Publications, Oregun Rd., Lagos, Nigeria. Ed. Bala Dan Musa.

052 NR
RIVERS STATE. MINISTRY OF INFORMATION. QUARTERLY JOURNAL. (Text in English) a. free. Ministry of Information, Port Harcourt, Rivers State, Nigeria. charts; illus.
Description: Provides briefs and information about the Rivers State of Nigeria.

052 NR ISSN 0038-6634
SPEAR. (Text in English) 1962. m. £N24. Daily Times of Nigeria Ltd., Publications Division, New Isheri Rd., Agidingbi - Ikeja, P.M.B. 21340, Lagos, Nigeria. TEL 900850-9. Ed. Coker Onita. adv.; bk.rev.; illus. circ. 10,000.
Description: General interest review of government, and African events.

079.669 NR ISSN 0331-2658
SUNDAY TIMES. (Text in English) 1953. w. Daily Times of Nigeria Ltd., New Isheri Rd., Agidingbi, P.M.B. 21340, Ikeja, Nigeria. TEL 234-9000850. Ed. Farouk Umar Muhammed. **Document type:** newspaper.

079.669 NR ISSN 0331-2569
SUNDAY TRIBUNE. (Text in English) 1978. w. $227. African Newspapers of Nigeria, 212 Broad St., Box 2416, Ibadan, Nigeria. TEL 234-4108806. (Dist. overseas by: Distrinews, P.O. Box 61, 1040 Etterbeek 1, Belgium) adv. **Document type:** newspaper.

052 NR
TIMES INTERNATIONAL. 1974. w. £N36. Daily Times of Nigeria Ltd., 3-7 Kakawa St., POB 139, Lagos, Nigeria. TEL 900850-9. Ed. Hezy Idowu. bk.rev.; film rev.; play rev. circ. 50,000.
Description: General interest review of world events, economy, government, literature and health.

079.669 NR
TRIUMPH. 1982. d. newsstand price: £N10. (Kano State Government) Triumph Publishing Co., Gidan Sa'adu Zungur, P.M.B. 3155, Kano, Nigeria. TEL 234-64-649592. FAX 234-64-633875. Ed. Garba Shehu. bk.rev.; film rev.; music rev.; play rev.; tele.rev.; illus. circ. 5,000. cols./p.: 6; pp./issue: 16. (back issues avail.; reprint service avail.; document delivery service avail.) **Document type:** newspaper.

052 NR
WESTERN NIGERIA ILLUSTRATED. q. Ministry of Information, Ibadan, Nigeria.

069.96 NR
YANCIN DAN ADAM/FREEDOM FOR MAN. (Text in Hausa) w. PMB 2112, Jos, Nigeria. Ed. D.D. Dinka.

GENERAL INTEREST PERIODICALS — Norway

078.1 NO
ADRESSEAVISEN. 1767. 6/w. NOK 1315; newsstand price: NOK 10. Adresseavisen A-S, P.O. Box 6070, N-7003 Trondheim, Norway. TEL 47-72-50-00-00. FAX 47-72-58-06-23. Eds. K.E. Amdahl, Gunnar Flikke. adv. contact: O.E. Drilsvik. bk.rev.; film rev.; music rev.; play rev.; tele.rev.; video rev.; illus. circ. 90,002. cols./p.: 8. (broadsheet format; reprint service avail.) **Document type:** newspaper.

078.1 NO
AFTENPOSTEN. 1860. d. NOK 1788; newsstand price: NOK 10. P.O. Box 1178, Sentrum, N-0107 Oslo, Sweden. TEL 47-22-86-30-00. FAX 47-22-42-63-25. Ed. Einar Hanseid. adv.: B&W page NOK 94500, color page NOK 151200; adv. contact: Clas Malm. circ. 278,669. cols./p.: 8; pp./issue: 44. **Document type:** newspaper.

058.398 NO ISSN 0002-5771
ALLERS. 1876. w. NOK 1586. A-S Allers Familie-Journal, Persveien 20, Postboks 250, Oslo 5, Norway. Ed. Stig Fossum. adv.; illus. circ. 160,893.
—CCC.

078.1 NO
ALTAPOSTEN. 1969. 6/yr. NOK 870; newsstand price: NOK 8. (Nord Norge Samkjoeringen) P.O. Box 1193, N-9501 Alta, Norway. TEL 47-78-43-50-88. FAX 47-78-43-61-47. Ed. Ulf Joergensen. adv.: B&W page NOK 8850, color page NOK 15750; adv. contact: Magnar Leinan. circ. 5,198. cols./p.: 5; pp./issue: 24. **Document type:** newspaper.

078.1 NO
ARBEIDERBLADET. 1884. 6/w. NOK 1550; newsstand price: NOK 8. P.O. Box 1183 Sentrum, N-0107 Oslo, Norway. TEL 47-22-72-60-00. FAX 47-22-64-92-82. Ed. Arvid Jakobsen. adv.: B&W page NOK 21000, color page NOK 21000; adv. contact: Ingar Mortensen. circ. 43,528. cols./p.: 5; pp./issue: 54. **Document type:** newspaper.

078.1 NO
AVISA TRONDHEIM. 1924. 6/w. NOK 1140; newsstand price: NOK 8. Troendersamkjoeringen, P.O. Box 5440 Lade, N-7002 Trondheim, Norway. TEL 47-73-92-11-22. FAX 47-92-14-10. Ed. Tom Hansen. adv.: B&W page NOK 11380, color page NOK 15880. circ. 13,766. cols./p.: 5; pp./issue: 37. **Document type:** newspaper.

078.1 NO
BERGENS TIDENDE. (Supplement avail.: B T - Eiendomsmagasin) 1868. 6/w. NOK 1404; newsstand price: NOK 8. Bergens Tidende A-S, P.O. Box 87, N-5015 Bergen, Norway. TEL 47-55-21-4500. FAX 47-55-31-2306. Ed. Magne Gaasemyr. adv.: B&W page NOK 54000, color page NOK 81700; adv. contact: Boerre Liland. film rev.; music rev.; play rev.; tele.rev.; video rev.; illus. circ. 95,708. cols./p.: 8; pp./issue: 48. (broadsheet format) **Document type:** newspaper.

058.398 NO ISSN 0005-9684
DET BESTE FRA READER'S DIGEST (NORWEGIAN EDITION). (Text in Norwegian) 1947. m. NOK 150($20) Det Beste AS, Postboks 1160, Sentrum, 0107 Oslo 1, Norway. Ed. Gunnar Arneson. adv.; illus.; index. circ. 171,000.
—CCC.

078.1 NO
DAG OG TID. 1962. w. NOK 445; newsstand price: 10. Karl Johansgt. 13, N-0154 Oslo, Norway. TEL 47-22-11-14-55. FAX 47-22-41-42-10. Ed. Audun Skjervoey. adv.: B&W page NOK 12700; adv. contact: Kjell Arve Straumsvaag. circ. 6,263,007. cols./p.: 5; pp./issue: 21. **Document type:** newspaper.

078.1 NO
DAGBLADET. 1869. 5/w. NOK 2500; newsstand price: NOK 8. P.O. Box 1184 Sentrum, N-0107 Oslo, Norway. TEL 47-22-31-06-00. FAX 47-22-42-95-48. Ed. Bjoern Siemensen. adv.: B&W page NOK 61625, color page NOK 94125. circ. 227,796. cols./p.: 5; pp./issue: 60. **Document type:** newspaper.

078.1 NO
DAGENS NAERINGSLIV. 1890. 6/w. NOK 2150; newsstand price: 15. TEL 47-22-00-20-00. FAX 47-22-00-20-20. adv.: B&W page NOK 57350, color page NOK 89000; adv. contact: Karin Bugge. circ. 52,422. **Document type:** newspaper.

058.398 NO ISSN 0014-7141
FAMILIEN. Key Title: Familien (Oslo). 1920. 26/yr. NOK 189($36) Hjemmet Mortensens Forlag AS, Soerkedalsvejen 10 A, N-0369 Oslo, Norway. TEL 47-22-961-500. FAX 47-2-961-382. Ed. Kaare Lunde. adv.: B&W page NOK 14000, color page NOK 23400. circ. 162,778 (controlled).
Former titles (until 1959): Kristen Ungdom (ISSN 0804-1733); (until 1938): Ungdomsfaklen (ISSN 0804-175X)

GENERAL INTEREST PERIODICALS — OCEANIA

078.1 NO
FINNMARK DAGBLAD. 1913. 6/w. NOK 1090; newsstand price: NOK 8. Finnmarksamkjoeringen, P.O. Box 360, N-9601 Hammerfest, Norway. TEL 47-78-41-14-22. FAX 47-78-41-34-36. Ed. Magne Nedregaard. adv. contact: Bjoerg Hansen. circ. 11,659. cols./p.: 5; pp./issue: 32. (tabloid format) **Document type:** newspaper.

078.1 NO
FINNMARKEN. 1899. 6/yr. NOK 1090; newsstand price: NOK 8. Finnmarksamkjoeringen, P.O. Box K, N-9801 Vadsoe, Norway. TEL 47-78-95-35-55. FAX 47-78-95-22-22. adv.: B&W page NOK 9700, color page NOK 17150. circ. 8,327. cols./p.: 5; pp./issue: 26. **Document type:** newspaper.

078.1 NO
FIRDA. 1917. 6/w. NOK 990; newsstand price: NOK 8. Fylkessamkj. for Sogn og Fjordane, P.O. Box 160, N-6801 Foerde, Norway. TEL 47-57-82-95-00. FAX 47-57-82-38-18. Ed. Rune Timberlid. adv.: B&W page NOK 8100, color page NOK 16200; adv. contact: Roar Tomassen. circ. 13,321. cols./p.: 5; pp./issue: 30. **Document type:** newspaper.

078.1 NO
FREDRIKSSTAD BLAD. 1889. 6/w. NOK 1126; newsstand price: NOK 8. P.O. Box 143, N-161 Fredrikstad, Norway. TEL 47-69-31-90-00. FAX 47-69-31-81-01. Ed. Truls Velgaard. adv.: B&W page NOK 16750, color page NOK 26125. circ. 21,341. cols./p.: 5; pp./issue: 49. **Document type:** newspaper.

078.1 NO
FREDRIKSTAD - AVISA DEMOKRATEN. 1906. 6/w. NOK 925; newsstand price: NOK 8. P.O. Box 83, N-1601 Fredrikstad, Norway. TEL 47-69-31-99-99. FAX 47-69-31-34-70. Ed. Ole K. Arvesen. adv.: B&W page NOK 15100, color page NOK 20300; adv. contact: Marit Melleby. circ. 10,313. cols./p.: 5; pp./issue: 45. **Document type:** newspaper.

078.1 NO
FREMOVER. 1903. 6/w. NOK 1000; newsstand price: NOK 8. Nordlandssamkjoeringen, P.O. Box 324, N-8501 Narvik, Norway. TEL 47-76-94-10-90. FAX 47-76-94-22-10. Ed. Henry Arne Hansen. adv.: B&W page NOK 13600, color page NOK 18375; adv. contact: Kirsti Kvitvik Lund. circ. 10,923. cols./p.: 5; pp./issue: 31. (tabloid format) **Document type:** newspaper.

078.1 NO
HARSTAD TIDENDE. 1887. d. Harstad Tidende A-S, P.O. Box 85, Storgaten 11, Harstad, N-9401 Troms, Norway. TEL 47-770-18000. FAX 47-770-18005. Ed. Odd Rikard Olsen. adv. contact: Stein Fossen. bk.rev.; film rev.; music rev.; play rev.; tele.rev.; video rev.; illus.; circ. 16,448 (controlled). cols./p.: 5; pp./issue: 37. (tabloid format) **Document type:** newspaper.

078.1 NO
HAUGESUNDS AVIS. 1895. 6/w. NOK 1172; newsstand price: NOK 8. P.O. Box 2024, N-5501 Haugesund, Norway. TEL 47-52-71-95-95. FAX 47-52-71-94-94. Ed. Rune Hallheim. adv.: B&W page NOK 20500, color page NOK 29100; adv. contact: Else Vedoe.

058.398 NO ISSN 0018-2842
HJEMMET. 1911. w. NOK 1066. Hjemmet Mortensen AS, P.O Box 5001 Jordstuen, N-0301 Oslo, Norway. Ed. Roennaug Greaker. adv.; illus. circ. 260,000. —CCC.

078.1 NO
HORDALAND. 1883. 3/w. NOK 470; newsstand price: NOK 7. P.O. Box 38, N-5701 Voss. TEL 47-56-51-12-17. FAX 47-56-51-01-80. Ed. Sigmund Midttun. adv.: B&W page NOK 16112; adv. contact: Magnhild Steine. circ. 10,809. cols./p.: 8; pp./issue: 12. **Document type:** newspaper.

078.1 NO
INDRE SMAALENENES AVIS. 1899. 3/w. NOK 760; newsstand price: NOK 8. P.O. Box 25, N-1851 Mysen, Norway. TEL 47-69-89-00-44. FAX 47-69-89-24-04. Ed. David Koht-Norbye. adv.: B&W page NOK 14000, color page NOK 18425; adv. contact: Liv Reidun Jenssen. circ. 7,692. cols./p.: 7; pp./issue: 18. **Document type:** newspaper.

078.1 NO
KARJALAINEN. 1874. d. newsstand price: FIM 5. Pohjois - Karjalan Kirjapaino Oy, PL 99, Kosti Aaltosen tie 9, FIN-80140, Finland. TEL 358-73-1551. FAX 358-73-155-363. Ed. Pekka Sitari; Pub. Jorma Norppa. adv. contact: Raimo Koskivirta. circ. 53,479. **Document type:** newspaper.

078.1 NO
KLASSEKAMPEN. 1969. 6/w. NOK 1640; newsstand price: NOK 10. P.O. Box 83 Bryn, N-0611 Oslo, Norway. TEL 47-22-64-93-20. FAX 47-22-63-93-20. Ed. Sigurd Allern. adv.: B&W page NOK 15600, color page NOK 24600; trim 380 x 293; adv. contact: Eli Benedikte Skorpen. circ. 9,692. cols./p.: 6; pp./issue: 22. **Document type:** newspaper.

078.1 NO
LOFOTPOSTEN. 1896. 6/w. NOK 1040; newsstand price: NOK 8. Nord Norge Samkjoeringen, P.O. Box 85, N-8301 Svolvaer, Norway. TEL 47-76-07-00-11. FAX 47-76-07-00-09. (Co-sponsor: Vestfjord Samkjoeringen) Ed. Brynjar Tollefsen. adv.: B&W page NOK 9653, color page NOK 17723; adv. contact: Harald Karlsen. circ. 11,397. cols./p.: 5; pp./issue: 34. (tabloid format) **Document type:** newspaper.

078.1 NO
MOSS AVIS. 1876. 6/w. NOK 1060; newsstand price: NOK 8. P.O. Box 248 - 250. TEL 47-69-25-30-40. FAX 47-69-25-56-73. Ed. Svein E. Hildonen. adv.: B&W page NOK 11800, color page NOK 16800; adv. contact: Kari Beatten Loekken. circ. 14,349. **Document type:** newspaper.

058.398 NO
NAA. 1952. w. NOK 915. Hjemmet Mortensen Forlag, Soerkedalsveien 10 A, 0369 Oslo, Norway. TEL 22-95-15-00. FAX 22-96-13-83. Ed. Gunnar Holm. adv.; illus. circ. 83,217.

078.1 NO
NAMDAL ARBEIDERBLAD. 1917. 6/w. NOK 1100; newsstand price: NOK 8. Media - Riks, P.O. Box 158, N-7801 Namsos, Norway. TEL 47-74-27-25-33. FAX 47-74-27-17-95. Ed. Morten Nordmeland. adv.: B&W page NOK 8900, color page NOK 13850; adv. contact: Torfinn Flak. circ. 11,911. cols./p.: 5; pp./issue: 30. **Document type:** newspaper.

078.1 NO
NORDLANDS FRAMTID. 1910. 6/w. NOK 1100; newsstand price: NOK 8. Nordlandssamkjoeringen, P.O. Box 313, N-8001 Bodoe, Norway. TEL 47-75-52-01-60. FAX 47-75-52-47-95. Ed. Thor Woje. adv.: B&W page NOK 16740, color page NOK 19000; adv. contact: Karin Berg. circ. 20,751. cols./p.: 5; pp./issue: 48. **Document type:** newspaper.

078.1 NO
NORDLANDSPOSTEN. 1862. 6/w. NOK 975; newsstand price: NOK 8. Nord-Norge Samkjoeringen, P.O. Box 44, N-8001 Bodoe, Norway. TEL 47-75-52-72-00. FAX 47-75-52-72-22. Ed. Iver Hammeren. adv.: B&W page NOK 8910, color page NOK 16762; adv. contact: Astrid Bangaas. circ. 17,653. cols./p.: 5; pp./issue: 40. **Document type:** newspaper.

078.1 NO
NORDLYS. 1902. 6/w. NOK 1140; newsstand price: NOK 8. Nordlyssamkjoeringen, P.O. Box 656, N-9001 Tromsoe, Norway. TEL 47-77-62-35-00. FAX 47-77-62-35-02. Ed. Ivar Kristoffersen. adv.: B&W page NOK 13000, color page NOK 24950; adv. contact: Bodil Nilsen. circ. 32,285. cols./p.: 5; pp./issue: 50. **Document type:** newspaper.

058.398 NO ISSN 0029-2257
NORSK UKEBLAD. 1933. w. NOK 988. Hjemmet Mortensen Forlag AS, Soerkedalsveien 10 A, 0369 Oslo, Norway. TEL 22-96-15-00. FAX 22-96-13-81. Ed. Tor Erik Solberg. adv.; illus. circ. 259,383. —CCC.

078.1 NO
RINGERIKES BLAD. 1845. 6/w. NOK 1180; newsstand price: 8. P.O. Box 68, N-3501 HOenefoss, Norway. TEL 47-32-12-80-00. FAX 47-32-12-17-74. Ed. Trond Hjerpseth. adv.: B&W page NOK 19400, color page NOK 41600. circ. 13,453. cols./p.: 8; pp./issue: 14. **Document type:** newspaper.

078.1 NO
SOENDAGS - B A. 1990. w. newsstand price: NOK 10. P.O. Box 824, N-5002 Bergen, Norway. TEL 47-55-32-16-00. FAX 47-55-31-00-30. Ed. Olav Terje Bergo. adv.: B&W page NOK 11500, color page NOK 15500; adv. contact: Turid Naess. circ. 23,889. cols./p.: 6. **Document type:** newspaper.

078.1 NO
SOGN AVIS. 1896. 5/w. NOK 795; newsstand price: NOK 8. Fylkessamkj. for Sogn og Fjordane, P.O. Box 187, N-5842 Leikanger, Norway. TEL 47-57-65-30-22. FAX 47-57-65-35-43. Ed. Gerhard Haugland. adv.: B&W page NOK 7200, color page NOK 16200; adv. contact: Ingmaar Fosshagen. circ. 11,155. cols./p.: 5; pp./issue: 28. **Document type:** newspaper.

078.1 NO
SOGNDAGBLAD. 1938. 6/w. NOK 830; newsstand price: NOK 8. Vestlandssamkjoeringen, P.O. Box 129, N-5901 Hoeyanger, Norway. TEL 47-57-71-29-33. FAX 47-57-71-29-17. Ed. Johs B. Thue. adv.: B&W page NOK 7500, color page NOK 14850; adv. contact: Odd Rune Foersund. circ. 5,477. cols./p.: 5; pp./issue: 22. **Document type:** newspaper.

078.1 NO
TOENSBERGS BLAD. 1870. 6/w. NOK 1250; newsstand price: 10. P.O. Box 2003, Postterminalen, N-3103 Toensberg, Sweden. TEL 47-33-31-00-00. FAX 47-33-31-06-48. Ed. Svein Doevle Larssen. adv.: B&W page NOK 21635, color page NOK 30455; adv. contact: Ragnhild Abrahamsen. circ. 32,641. cols./p.: 8; pp./issue: 28. **Document type:** newspaper.

078.1 NO
TROENDER - AVISA. 6/w. NOK 1200; newsstand price: NOK 8. P.O. Box 2520, N-7701 Steinkjer, Norway. TEL 47-74-16-30-00. FAX 47-74-16-48-77. Eds. Johs. Brandzaeg, Paul Ole Kjerkreit. adv.: B&W page NOK 13600, color page NOK 20050; adv. contact: Bjoern Saether. circ. 23,243. cols./p.: 6; pp./issue: 31. **Document type:** newspaper.

078.1 NO
TROMS FOLKEBLAD. 1965. 6/w. NOK 1095; newsstand price: NOK 8. Nord Norge Samkjoeringen, P.O. Box 308, N-9301 Finnsnes, Norway. TEL 47-77-84-05-11. FAX 47-84-19-00. Ed. Rolf A. Erstad. adv. contact: Raymond Lind. circ. 6,867. cols./p.: 5; pp./issue: 23. **Document type:** newspaper.

078.1 NO
TROMSOE. 1898. 6/yr. NOK 980; newsstand price: NOK 8. Nord Norge Samkjoeringen, P.O. Box 1028, N-9001 Tromsoe, Norway. TEL 47-77-65-66-00. FAX 47-77-65-51-17. Ed. Yngve Nielssen. adv.: B&W page NOK 8990, color page NOK 14690; adv. contact: Svanhild Hansen. circ. 9,143. cols./p.: 5; pp./issue: 40. (tabloid format) **Document type:** newspaper.

078.1 NO
VERDENS GANG. Short title: V G. 1945. d. NOK 2136. Verdens Gang A-S, Akersgt. 34, N-0107 Oslo, Norway. TEL 47-2-11-40-40. FAX 47-2-42-58-11. TELEX 71306 VGN. Ed. Einar Hanseid. adv.; bk.rev. circ. 367,038. **Document type:** newspaper.

GENERAL INTEREST PERIODICALS — Oceania

052 XE ISSN 0892-2098
MARSHALL ISLANDS JOURNAL. (Text in English and Marshallese) 1970. w. $77. Micronitor News and Printing Co., Majuro, Marshall Islands. TEL 011-692-9-3143. FAX 011-692-9-3136. Ed. Giff Johnson. adv.; bk.rev.; illus. circ. 3,300. (tabloid format)
 Formerly: Micronesian Independent.
 Description: News and comment on Marshall Islands and Pacific, general readership newspaper.

052 PP
P N G BUSINESS. (Papua New Guinea) 1977. m. K.30. Word Publishing Co., P.O. Box 1982, Boroko, Papua New Guinea. FAX 252579. Ed. Sam Valum. adv.; illus. circ. 10,000.
 Formerly (until 1984): New Nation.

052 059.99   WS   ISSN 0036-3839
SAMOA TIMES. (Text in English and Samoan) 1964. w. $30. Samoa Times Ltd., Box 1160, Apia, Western Samoa. Ed. Leulu Felise Va'A. adv.; bk.rev.; illus. circ. 7,000. (tabloid format)
  Incorporates: Samoa Bulletin.

052   PP
TIMES OF PAPUA NEW GUINEA. 1980. w. K.180. Word Publishing Co., Box 1982, Boroko, Papua New Guinea. FAX 252579. Ed. Anna Solomon. adv.; illus. circ. 10,000.

059.99   PP
WANTOK. (Text in Tok Pisin) 1970. w. K.180. Word Publishing Co., P.O. Box 1982, Boroko, Papua New Guinea. FAX 252579. Ed. Francis Uliau. adv.; illus. circ. 15,000. Indexed: So.Pac.Per.Ind.

THE WASHINGTON PACIFIC REPORT. see *POLITICAL SCIENCE*

GENERAL INTEREST PERIODICALS — Pakistan

059.914   PK
AHANG. (Text in Urdu) vol.17, 1964. s-m. Rs.45. Pakistan Broadcasting Corporation, 81A Satellite Town, Rawalpindi, Pakistan.

079.5491   PK
DAWN (WEEKEND EDITION). (Text in English) 1975. w. (Fri.). $67 to North America. Pakistan Herald Publications (Pvt.) Ltd., Haroon House, Dr. Ziauddin Ahmed Rd., G.P.O. Box 3740, Karachi 4, Pakistan. TEL 529671. FAX 513188. TELEX 23623-PHPL-PK. Ed. Ahmad Ali Khan. adv.; bk.rev.; film rev.; illus. **Document type:** newspaper.
  Description: National and international news of Pakistan.

059.914   PK
FAMILY. (Text in Urdu) 1989. w. $145 in U.S. Nida-i-Millat (Pvt) Ltd., NIPCO House, 4 Sharae Fatima Jinnah, Lahore, Pakistan. TEL 92-42-302050. FAX 92-42-367005. Ed. Majid Nizami. adv.; bk.rev.; illus.; circ. 60,000. (paid). (tabloid format; back issues avail.) **Document type:** consumer publication.
  Description: Covers political events, social issues, and matters of general and domestic interest.

052   PK   ISSN 0018-0467
HERALD. (Text in English) 1970. m. Rs.295($37) Pakistan Herald Publications (Pvt.) Ltd., Haroon House, Dr. Ziauddin Ahmed Rd., G.P.O. Box 3740, Karachi 1, Pakistan. TEL 529671. FAX 513188. TELEX 24167-PHPL-PK. Ed. Sherry Rahman. adv.; bk.rev.; film rev.; charts; illus.
  Description: General interest and national news of Pakistan.

079.5491 059.914   PK
JIHAD. (Peshawar and Rawalpindi - Islamabad editions avail.) (Text in Urdu, Pushto, occasional articles in English) 1975. d. Rs.1095($70) Daily Jihad, 15-A Islamia Club Bldg., Khyber Bazaar, Peshawar, Pakistan. TEL 210522. (And: Daily Jihad, Chowk Waris Khan, Murree Rd., Rawalpindi, Pakistan. TEL 553979) Ed. Sharif Farooq; Pub. Sharif Farooq. adv.; bk.rev.; film rev.; illus. cols./p.: 8; pp./issue: 8. (broadsheet format) **Document type:** newspaper.

079.5491   PK
MASHAL. Variant title: Daily Mashal Bahawalpur. (21 special editions avail.: Agriculture; Banking; Industrial; Religious Holidays; National Days) (Text in Urdu) 1989. d. Rs.1000. Daily Mashal, Circular Rd., Bahawalpur 63104, Pakistan. TEL 92-621-7288. FAX 92-621-4722. Ed. Robeena Majeed Hashmi; Pub. Syed Majeed Hashmi. adv.; bk.rev.; film rev.; music rev.; play rev.; tele.rev.; illus. circ. 8,000. cols./p.: 8; pp./issue: 4. (standard format; back issues avail.) **Document type:** newspaper.

079.5491 052   PK
THE MUSLIM. Regional edition: Karachi and Southern Region. Regional edition: Lahore and Punjab Region. Regional edition: Peshawar and Northern Region. (Supplement avail.: Friday Magazine) (Text in English) 1979. d. newsstand price: Rs.5. Islamabad Publications (Private) Ltd., 9 Hameed Chambers, 44000 Islamabad, Pakistan. TEL 92-51-218922. FAX 92-51-218928. Ed. Agha Murtaza Pooya; Pub. S. Tahir Hussain Mashhadi. adv. contact: Mudassar Raza Bokhari. Wire service(s): APP, PPI, PNI. circ. 40,000. cols./p.: 8; pp./issue: 14. **Document type:** newspaper.
  Description: Covers national and international news.

079.5491   PK
NARA-E-HAQ. (Text in Urdu) 1939. d. Rs.720; newsstand price: Rs.3. Daily Nara-e-Haq, Osman Rd., Quetta, Pakistan. TEL 72016. Ed. M. Iftikhar Yousaf; Pub. M. Iftikhar Yousaf. adv.; bk.rev.; film rev.; music rev.; tele.rev.; illus. circ. 15,000. cols./p.: 8; pp./issue: 6. (standard format) **Document type:** newspaper.

059.914 052   PK   ISSN 0030-9591
PAK JAMHURIAT. (Text in Bengali, English and Urdu) 1960. w. Rs.10. Pak Publishers, 33-A Habibullah Rd., Lahore, Pakistan. Ed. Anwar Hussain. adv.; bk.rev.; charts; illus.; tr.lit. circ. 40,000.

954   US   ISSN 1061-6101
▼**PAKISTAN (BOULDER).** 1992. biennial. Westview Press, 5500 Central Ave., Boulder, CO 80301. TEL 303-444-3541. FAX 303-449-3356. **Document type:** academic/scholarly publication.
  Description: Assesses contemporary politics, economics, and culture in Pakistan.

052   US   ISSN 0030-963X
DS376
PAKISTAN AFFAIRS. 1947. fortn. free. Embassy of Pakistan, Information Division, 2315 Massachusetts Ave., N.W., Washington, DC 20008. TEL 202-939-6225. Ed. Parvaiz Ahmed. bk.rev.; illus. circ. 17,000.
  Description: Focuses on politics, government and economics.

052   PK
PAKISTAN DIGEST. 1974. m. Rs.60. Tareen & Tareen Ltd., 4 Amil St., off Robson Rd., G.P.O. Box 671, Karachi, Pakistan. adv.; bk.rev.; illus. circ. 12,000.

052   PK   ISSN 0377-2586
DS376
PAKISTAN PICTORIAL. (Text in English) 1973. bi-m. Rs.9($3) Pakistan Publications, Box 183, Shahrah Iraq, Karachi 1, Pakistan. charts; illus.

079.5491 052   PK   ISSN 1010-1632
PAKISTAN TIMES OVERSEAS WEEKLY. Key Title: Pakistan Times. (Text in English) 1983. w. $27 in Middle East; Europe & Far East $35; U.S., Canada & Australia $45 (effective 1993). (Progressive Papers Limited) Pakistan Times, Zero Point, Islamabad, Pakistan. TEL 825893. TELEX 44811 TIMES PK. Eds. Khan A. Majid, S.K. Durrani. adv.; illus.; stat. (tabloid format) **Document type:** newspaper.
  Description: Domestic and international news of Pakistan.

052   PK
PAKISTAN YEAR BOOK. (Text in English) 1973. biennial. $33. East-West Publishing Company, 22 Corner Chambers, I.I. Chundrigar Rd., Karachi 74200, Pakistan. Ed. Rafique Akhtar. circ. 5,000.
  Description: Reviews the nation's life; progress achieved and problems encountered therein.

052   PK   ISSN 0033-6386
QUETTA TIMES. (Text in English) 1924. w. Albert Press, Jinnah Rd., Quetta, Baluchistan, Pakistan. Ed. S. Rustomji. adv.; illus.

079.5491   PK
SADA-E-PAKISTAN. (Special Holiday & Festival editions avail.) (Text in Urdu) 1988. d. Daily Sada-e-Pakistan, Sada-e-Pakistan Rd., Model Town B, Bahawalpur, Pakistan. TEL 92-621-4360. Ed. Rana Abdul Salam; Pub. Rana Abdul Salam. adv.; illus.; circ. 9,000 (paid); 500 (controlled). cols./p.: 8; pp./issue: 4. (broadsheet format) **Document type:** newspaper.
  Description: Covers news at the local, national and international level.

079.9541 059.914   PK
SHAM. (Text in Urdu) 1991. d. newsstand price: Rs.3. Daily Sham, Bldg. No.1, Bazar-7, I-102, Islamabad, Pakistan. TEL 415511. Ed. Imtiaz Ali; Pub. Imtiaz Ali. adv.; film rev.; music rev.; tele.rev.; illus. Wire service(s): AFP, APP, PPI, RN, UPI. circ. 10,000. pp./issue: 6. **Document type:** newspaper.

052   PK   ISSN 0039-0313
AP8
STATESMAN; week-end review. (Text in English) 1955. w. Rs.200. Mohammad Owais, Ed. & Pub., 260-C, Commercial Area, P.E.C.H.S., Karachi 29, Pakistan. TEL 435627. adv.; bk.rev.; illus. circ. 5,000.
  Indexed: Mid.East: Abstr.& Ind.

052   PK   ISSN 0039-5277
SUNDAY POST. (Text in English) 1957. w. Rs.12($4). 4-5 Amil St., Off Robson Rd., Karachi 1, Pakistan. Ed. Ameen K. Tareen. adv.; bk.rev.; illus. circ. 11,300.
  Description: Social and cultural magazine of general interest.

052   PK
VIEWPOINT. (Text in English) 1975. w. Rs.395($60) Forum Publications Ltd., 4 Lawrence Rd., Lahore, Pakistan. TEL 301285. Ed. Mazhar Ali Khan. adv.; bk.rev. circ. 5,000.

GENERAL INTEREST PERIODICALS — Panama

056.1   PN   ISSN 0024-662X
F1561
LOTERIA. Cover title: Revista Cultural Loteria. 1941. bi-m. free (foreign $10). Loteria Nacional de Beneficencia, Departamento de Beneficencia Cultural, Apdo. 21, Panama 1, Panama. TEL 27-2202. FAX 27-3710. Ed. Javier A. Comellys. adv.; bibl.; charts; illus.; cum.index: 1969-1977, 1978-1988. circ. 10,000. (back issues avail.) Indexed: Amer.Hist.& Life, Hisp.Amer.Per.Ind., Hist.Abstr.
● Also available online.
  Description: Covers literature, history, psychology, philosophy, sociology and more.

056.1   PN
PUNTO Y APARTE. bi-m. Bl.1.95 per no. Ediciones Letra Impresa, S.A., Apdo. Postal 604268, El Dorado, Panama. TEL 60-9383. Ed. Viviane Nathan.

079.7287   PN
EL SIGLO. (Supplement included w.: Entre Nos) 1985. d. $7500; newsstand price: $.25. Corporacion Universal de Informacion S.A., Santo Domingo, Panama W4, Panama. TEL 506-69-3311. FAX 506-69-6954. Pub. Jaime Padilla Beliz. adv. contact: Tatiana Padilla G. bk.rev.; film rev.; music rev.; play rev.; illus.; circ. 30,000 (morn. ed.); 16,000 (Sun. ed.) (paid). cols./p.: 5; pp./issue: 72. (tabloid format) **Document type:** newspaper.

GENERAL INTEREST PERIODICALS — Paraguay

056.1   PY
A B C REVISTA. w. Yegros 745, CC 1421, Asuncion, Paraguay. circ. 90,000.

056.1   PY
NUESTRO TIEMPO; publicacion paraguaya de actualidad. m. 6000 g. (foreign $50). Centro de Investigacion y Documentacion, Paraguari 1546, Asuncion, Paraguay. TEL 71122. Ed. Mons. Mario Melanio Medina.

056.1 052   PY   ISSN 0049-0598
SINTESIS;* revista Paraguaya. (Text in English and Spanish) 1969. m. 50 g. per no. Eladio Gonzalez Nunez, Ed. & Pub., Anotado Punto 4, Casilla de Correo 1056, Asuncion, Paraguay. adv.; bk.rev.; film rev.; play rev.; abstr.; bibl.; illus. circ. 5,000. Indexed: HR Rep.

GENERAL INTEREST PERIODICALS — Peru

056.1   PE   ISSN 0567-753X
ACTA HEREDIANA. 1968. a. Universidad Peruana Cayetano Heredia, Direccion de Biblioteca Publicaciones y Museos, Avda. Honorio Delgado 932, Apdo. 2563, Lima 100, Peru.

GENERAL INTEREST PERIODICALS — PHILIPPINES

056.1   PE   ISSN 0253-0015
F3401   CODEN: BLIMEY
BOLETIN DE LIMA; revista cientifica y cultural. (Text in Spanish; summaries in English, German and Spanish) 1979. bi-m. $100 (foreign $150). Editorial Los Pinos E.I.R.L., Casilla 18-1027, Lima 18, Peru. TEL 460031. Ed. Fernando Villiger. adv.; bk.rev. circ. 2,500. **Document type:** consumer publication.
—BLDSC (2207.480000); Faxon. **CCC**.
    Description: Presents research relating to Peru in the fields of biology, ecology, geography, history, archaeology, folklore, medicine, oceanography, and natural sciences.

056.1   PE
GENTE; la gran revista del Peru. 1957. w. S/16000($180) Editora de Publicaciones Gente, S.A., Eduardo de Habich, 170, Miraflores, Lima 18, Peru. TEL 451747. FAX 46-1173. Ed. Enrique Escardo Vallejo-Gallo. circ. 52,000. (back issues avail.)

079.85   PE
EL IMPARCIAL; el decano de la prensa regional. 1891. d. S/14 per mo. Editora Radar, Av. Grau 203, Huacho, Peru. TEL 034-32-4410. Ed. Gustavo Martinez Padilla. adv. contact: Ana Adrianzen Molero. film rev.; music rev.; play rev.; illus. cols./p.: 4; pp./issue: 6. (tabloid format; back issues avail.; reprint service avail.) **Document type:** newspaper.

079.85 052   PE
LIMA TIMES. (Text in English) 1975. w. S.50($95) Andean Air Mail & Peruvian Times S.A., Apdo. 2484, Lima, Peru. TEL 453-761. FAX 5114-467-888. Ed. Eleanor Zuniga. adv. **Document type:** newspaper.
    Description: News on Peruvian economy, politics, tourism and archeology.

079.85   PE
EL PUEBLO; decano de la prensa del sur. 1905. d. newsstand price: S/1. Editorial Arequipa, Sucre 213, Arequipa 035, Peru. TEL 211500. FAX 213361. Eds. William Cornejo, Daniel Macedo; Pub. Eduardo Laime Valdivia. adv.; bk.rev.; film rev.; music rev.; play rev.; illus. Wire service(s): AFP. cols./p.: 10; pp./issue: 16. (standard format) **Document type:** newspaper.
    Description: Contains local, regional and national news and commentary.

GENERAL INTEREST PERIODICALS — Philippines

052   PH
EXPRESSWEEK. 1973. w. Philippines Daily Express Publishing Corp., 371 Bonifacio Dr., Port Area, Manila, Philippines. charts; illus.

052   PH   ISSN 0115-2971
HOMELIFE; the Philippines' family magazine. 1954. m. P.120. Society of St. Paul, Inc., MCPO 525, Makati, Metro Manila, Philippines. FAX 632-817-8955. Ed. Anders R. Arboleda. adv.; bk.rev.; illus. circ. 50,000.

059.9921   PH   ISSN 0116-2187
KAPAWA NEWS. (Text and summaries in English and Hiligaynon) 1966. w. P.200($30) (effective 1991). L.V. Moles - J.A. Stantos Sts., Tangub, Bacolod City 6100, Philippines. TEL 2-10-73. FAX 034-2-70-17. (Subscr. to: P.O. Box 365, Bacolod City 6100, Philippines) Ed. Natalio V. Sitjar. circ. 26,400. (tabloid format; back issues avail.)

059.992   PH
LIFESTYLE ASIA. 1987. m. P.1080($80) Lifestyle Asia Publishing Co., Inc., 25 Tolentino St., San Lorenzo Village, Makati, Metro Manila, Philippines. TEL 817-729191. FAX 817-3999. Ed. Julie Yap Daza. adv. circ. 31,424.
    Description: Chronicles the lifestyles and preferences of Asia's wealthy class.

052   PH
MANILA JOURNAL.* (Text in English) 1973. w. $17. Philippine Journalists, Inc., Journal Building, Railroad St. & 20th St., Port Area, Manila, Philippines. Ed. Eugene Ramos. adv.; bk.rev.; charts; illus. circ. 16,924.
    Formerly: Times Journal of Manila (International Edition).

079.599 052   PH
MANILA TIMES. (Publication suspended from Sep. 1972 to Feb. 1986) (Supplements avail.) (Text in English) 1945. d. P.1564. Metromedia Times Corporation, No. 30 Pioneer St., Corner EDSA, Mandaluyong, Philippines. TEL 631-89-71. FAX 631-77-88. Ed. Frederick K. Agcaoili. adv. contact: Alda N. Iglesia. bk.rev.; film rev.; music rev.; play rev.; tele.rev.; illus. circ. 193,200. pp./issue: 20. (back issues avail.) **Document type:** newspaper.

079.599   PH   ISSN 0300-3906
MINDANAO MAIL. vol.23, 1977. s-w. P.30($12) Emilio L. Abarico, Ed. & Pub., Lozano Bldg., 2nd Fl., Rm. 203, C. M. Recto Ave., Davao City 1901, Philippines. adv.; illus.; pat.; stat.; tr.lit.; index. circ. 9,875. **Document type:** newspaper.

052 059.992   CN   ISSN 0845-8669
MOSAIK; multicultural news and views. (Text in English, Filipino, Spanish) 1984. m. Can.$25($20) Ted Alcuitas, Ed. & Pub., 1080 Pacific St., Ste. 108, Vancouver, B.C. V6E 4C2, Canada. TEL 604-682-7559. adv.; bk.rev. circ. 3,500. (back issues avail.)
    Formerly: Mosaic (Winnipeg, 1984); Incorporating: Kalayaan (ISSN 0827-5343)

052   PH   ISSN 0038-1160
AP8
SOLIDARITY; current affairs, ideas and the arts. 1965. bi-m. $16 in Asia; Americas and Europe $18. Solidaridad Publishing House, 531 Padre Faura, Ermita, Manila, Philippines. TEL 586581. (Subscr. to: P.O. Box 3959, Manila, Philippines.) Ed. F. Sionil Jose. adv.; bk.rev. circ. 3,000. **Indexed:** Abstr.Engl.Stud., E.I., M.L.A.
—UnCover.
    Description: Presents ideas and viewpoints of leading writers and intellectuals of Asian society, government, politics, economics, culture and the arts.

GENERAL INTEREST PERIODICALS — Poland

073.8   PL
A B C. 1990. 5/w. Leszczynska Oficyna Wydawnicza, Ul. Slowianskiego 63, 64-100 Leszno, Poland. TEL 48-65-207061. FAX 48-65-208055. Ed. Antoni Neczynski. adv.; illus. circ. 100,000. **Document type:** newspaper.

073.8   PL
A - Z DZIENNIK OBYWATELSKI. 1990. 5/yr. Pl. Wolnosci 2, 35-061 Rzeszow, Poland. TEL 48-17-39491. FAX 48-17-36831. TELEX 633321. Ed. Andrzej Potocki. adv. circ. 100,000. **Document type:** newspaper.

073.8   PL   ISSN 0867-0374
CZAS KRAKOWSKI. (Supplement avail.: Ex Libris (ISSN 0867-1958)) 1990. 5/w. Wydawnictwo Arka Press S.A., Rynek Kleparski 4, IV p., 31-150 Krakow, Poland. Ed. Jan Polkowski. circ. 55,000. **Document type:** newspaper.

073.8   PL   ISSN 1230-3739
DAILY NEWS. (Text in English) 1949. 5/w. Polska Agencja Prasowa (P.A.P.) - Polish Press Agency, P.O. Box 898, 00-950 Warsaw, Poland. TEL 48-22-297167. FAX 48-2-6286707. Ed. Miroslaw Luniewski. circ. 50,000. **Document type:** newspaper.
    Description: Covers politics, economics, social matters and cultural life.

073.8   PL   ISSN 1230-7203
DZIENNIK. 1916. Kadex - Edytor S.C., P.O. Box 178, 20-601 Lublin, Poland. TEL 48-81-558010. FAX 48-81-558010. Ed. Leszek Alojzy Gzella. adv.; illus. circ. 84,000. **Document type:** newspaper.
    Former titles (until 1993): Dziennik Lubelski (ISSN 0867-5090); (1945-1990): Sztandar Ludu (ISSN 0137-9313)

073.8   PL   ISSN 0137-9062
DZIENNIK BALTYCKI. 1945. 5/w. Prasa Gdanska sp. z o.o., P.O. Box 419, 80-886 Gdansk, Poland. TEL 48-58-315041. FAX 48-58-313560. Ed. Jan Jakubowski. adv.; illus. circ. 75,000. **Document type:** newspaper.

073.8   PL   ISSN 0208-7707
DZIENNIK LODZKI. 1945. 5/w. Prasa Lodzka, Ul. W. Sienkiewicza 3-15, 90-113 Lodz, Poland. TEL 48-42-329300. FAX 48-42-322832. Ed. Zdzislaw Szczepanski. adv.; illus. circ. 62,000. **Document type:** newspaper.
    Former titles (until 1980): Dziennik Popularny (ISSN 0137-947X); (until 1974): Dziennik Lodzki (ISSN 0867-4639); (until 1956): Lodzki Express Illustrowany (ISSN 0867-4620)

073.8   PL
DZIENNIK POJEZIERZA. 1983. 5/w. POL ska z o.o., Al. J. Pilsudskiego 54, 10-557 Olsztyn, Poland. TEL 48-89-336140. FAX 48-89-333751. Ed. Pawel Krupa. adv.; illus. circ. 37,500. **Document type:** newspaper.

073.8   PL   ISSN 0137-9089
DZIENNIK POLSKI. 1945. 6/w. Wydawnictwo Jagiellonia S.A., Ul. Wielopole 1, II p., 31-072 Krakow, Poland. TEL 48-12-226304. FAX 48-12-228249. Ed. Czeslaw T. Niemczynski. adv.; illus. circ. 83,000. **Document type:** newspaper.

073.8   PL   ISSN 1230-8722
DZIENNIK POZNANSKI. 1991. 5/w. Express Polfrost, Ul. Mlynska 5, 61-279 Poznan, Poland. TEL 48-61-523681. FAX 48-61-525879. Ed. Kanrad Napierala. adv.; illus. circ. 100,000. **Document type:** newspaper.

073.8   PL
DZIENNIK RADOMSKI - 24 GODZINY. 1991. 5/w. Drogowiec sp. z o.o., Ul. J. Slowackiego 1, 26-600 Radom, Poland. Ed. Marek Oleszczuk. adv.; illus. circ. 50,000. **Document type:** newspaper.

073.8   PL
DZIENNIK SLASKI. 1992. 5/w. Fibak Noma Press S.A., Ul. Plebiscytowa 36, 40-041 Katowice, Poland. TEL 48-32-512681. FAX 48-32-516475. Ed. Ewelina Sykulska. adv.; illus. circ. 100,000. **Document type:** newspaper.

073.8   PL   ISSN 0137-9046
DZIENNIK WIECZORNY. 1959. 5/w. De-Wu-Press, Ul. Dworcowa 110, 85-010 Bydgoszcz, Poland. TEL 48-52-224600. FAX 48-52-227117. Ed. Zbigniew Gulewicz. adv.; illus. circ. 57,000. **Document type:** newspaper.

073.8   PL   ISSN 0137-9038
DZIENNIK ZACHODNI. 1945. 5/w. Prasa Slaska sp. z o.o., P.O. Box 338, 40-925 Katowice, Poland. TEL 48-32-537241. FAX 48-32-538196. Ed. Wlodzimierz Pazniewski. adv.; illus. **Document type:** newspaper.

073.8   PL   ISSN 0137-902X
ECHO DNIA. 1971. 5/w. Echo Press sp. z o.o., P.O. Box 163, 25-953 Kielce, Poland. TEL 48-41-43943. FAX 48-41-45820. Ed. Jerzy Gierszewski. adv.; illus. circ. 54,000. **Document type:** newspaper.

073.8   PL   ISSN 0137-9011
ECHO KRAKOWA. 1946. 5/w. Wydawnictwo Echo, P.O. Box 64, 31-072 Krakow, Poland. TEL 48-12-227588. Ed. Witold Grzybowski. adv.; illus. circ. 49,000. **Document type:** newspaper.

073.8   PL
EXPRESS BYDGOSKI. 1990. 5/w. Wydawnictwo Express, Ul. Warszawska 13, 85-058 Bydgoszcz, Poland. TEL 48-52-222614. FAX 48-52-222615. Ed. Marek Zagorski. adv.; illus. circ. 40,000. **Document type:** newspaper.

073.8   PL
▼**EXPRESS FAKTY.** 1992. 5/w. Wydawnictwo Prasowe Multico, P.O. Box 386, 20-950 Lublin, Poland. TEL 48-81-25017. Ed. Stanislaw Jadczak. adv.; illus. circ. 100,000. **Document type:** newspaper.

073.8   PL   ISSN 0137-9097
EXPRESS ILUSTROWANY. 1923. 5/w. Prasa Ilustrowana ska z o.o., Ul. Sienkiewicza 3-5, 90-113 Lodz, Poland. TEL 48-42-329390. FAX 48-42-320637. Ed. Julian Bek. adv.; illus. circ. 66,000. **Document type:** newspaper.

073.8   PL   ISSN 0137-9100
EXPRESS POZNANSKI. 1946. 5/w. Wydawnictwo Express, Ul. Grunwaldzka 19, 60-762 Poznan, Poland. TEL 48-61-661443. FAX 48-61-665848. Ed. Dariusz Nowaczyk. adv.; illus. circ. 50,000. **Document type:** newspaper.

GENERAL INTEREST PERIODICALS — POLAND

073.8   PL   ISSN 0137-9119
EXPRESS WIECZORNY. 1946. 5/w. Fundacja Prasowa Solidarnosci, Al. Jerozolimskie 125-127, 02-017 Warsaw, Poland. Ed. Krzysztof Czubanski. adv. circ. 150,000. **Document type:** newspaper.
   Description: Covers politics, social life, cultural life, criminal stories.

073.8   PL
GAZETA KIELECKA - 24 GODZINY. 1989. 5/w. Ul. Zlota 3, 25-015 Kielce, Poland. TEL 48-41-57248. FAX 48-41-56197. Ed. Anna Krawiecka. adv.; illus. circ. 50,000. **Document type:** newspaper.

073.8   PL   ISSN 0208-7693
GAZETA KRAKOWSKA. 1949. 6/w. Wydawnictwo Gazeta Krakowska ska z o.o., Ul. Wielopole 1, 31-072 Krakow, Poland. TEL 48-12-227588. FAX 48-12-21563. Ed. Jerzy Sadecki. adv.; illus. circ. 150,000. **Document type:** newspaper.
   Former titles (until 1980): Gazeta Poludniowa (ISSN 0137-9496); (until 1975): Gazeta Krakowska (ISSN 0867-468X)

073.8   PL
GAZETA LUBUSKA. 1952. 5/w. Lubpress, P.O. Box 120, 65-042 Zielona Gora, Poland. TEL 48-68-4661. FAX 48-68-3707. Ed. Miroslaw Rataj. adv.; illus. circ. 93,100. **Document type:** newspaper.

057.85   UK
GAZETA NIEDZIELNA. (Text in Polish) 1949. w. £32 (Europe £37). Veritas Foundation Publication Centre, 63 Jeddo Rd., London W12 9EE, England. TEL 081-749-4957. FAX 081-749-4965. Ed. Z.E. Walaszewski. adv.; bk.rev.; film rev.; play rev. circ. 3,000. (back issues avail.) **Document type:** newspaper.

073.8   PL
GAZETA NOWA. 1990. 5/w. Alpo S.C., Ul. Niepodleglosci 22, 65-048 Zielona Gora, Poland. TEL 48-68-71077. FAX 48-68-72255. Ed. Andrzej Buck. adv.; illus. circ. 168,000. **Document type:** newspaper.

073.8   PL   ISSN 0860-908X
GAZETA WYBORCZA. (Saturday issue: Gazeta Swiateczna; Includes weekly supplements: Gazeta Televizyjna, Magazyn Gazety Wyborczej, Gazeta - The Wall Street Journal Europe, Gazeta o Ksiazkach; Also 18 regional editions avail.) 1989. d. (except Sunday). foreign $25 per mo.; newsstand price: 4000 Zl. Agora - Gazeta Ltd., Nowy Swiat 27, 00-029 Warsaw, Poland. TEL 48-22-269084. FAX 48-22-261434. Ed. Adam Michnik. adv.; bk.rev.; film rev.; music rev.; play rev.; tele.rev.; illus. Wire service(s): AFP, EPA, RN, TASS, PAP. circ. 550,000. cols./p.: 5; pp./issue: 56. (tabloid format; also avail. in microfilm from NRP; diskette format) **Document type:** newspaper.

073.8   PL
GONIEC POMORSKI. 1989. 5/w. Ul. Grundwaldzaka 8-10, 75-241 Koszlin, Poland. TEL 48-94-24760. FAX 48-94-26807. Ed. Jozef Banasiak. circ. 150,000. **Document type:** newspaper.
   Description: Paper of the regione of Pomerania. Covers politics, social life, sport, culture.

073.8   PL   ISSN 0137-9232
KURIER POLSKI. 1957. 6/w. Kurier Polski ska z o.o., Ul. Zgoda 11, 00-018 Warsaw, Poland. TEL 48-22-272483. FAX 48-22-270552. Owner(s): Stronnictwo Demokratyczne - Democratic Party. Ed. Andrzej Nierychlo. **Document type:** newspaper.

057.85   PL   ISSN 0867-2237
NIE. 1990. w. $19.50. U R M A Spolka z o.o., Ul. Poznanska 3, 00-680 Warsaw, Poland. TEL 48-22-296360. FAX 48-22-259833. (Subscr. to: Centrala Kolportazy Prasy i Wydawnictw, Ul. Towarowa 28, 00-839 Warsaw, Poland) Ed. Jerzy Urban. circ. 500,000.

073.8   PL   ISSN 0867-8405
NOWA EUROPA; dziennik niezalezny. 1992. 5/w. Nowa Europa sp. z o.o., Ul. Miedziana 11, 00-958 Warsaw, Poland. TEL 48-22-206161. FAX 48-22-206166. Ed. Witold Gadomski. **Document type:** newspaper.
   Description: Covers politics, finance, business, social life, sport and culture.

057.85   PL
PANORAMA. 1954. w. Fibak Noma Press S.A., Ul. Plebiscytowa 36, 40-003 Katowice, Poland. TEL 48-32-611880. Ed. Andrzej Wrazidlo. illus. circ. 165,000.
   Formerly: Panorama Slaska.

057.85 052   PL   ISSN 0137-2955
PANORAMA POLSKA (NASZA OJCZYZNA). (Text in Polish; supplement in English and French) 1956. m. $13. (Towarzystwo Lacznosci z Polonia Zagraniczna "Polonia") Polska Agencja Interpress, Ul. Bagatela 12, 00-585 Warsaw, Poland. (Dist. by: Ars Polona-Ruch, Krakowskie Przedmiescie 7, Warsaw, Poland) Ed. Tadeusz Lachowicz. adv.; bk.rev.; charts; film rev.; illus.
   Formerly (until 1971): Nasza Ojczyzna (ISSN 0027-8327)

057.85   PL   ISSN 0032-244X
POLAND. (Editions in English, French, German, Spanish) 1954. q. $14. Polska Agencja Interpress, Bagatela 12, 00-585 Warsaw, Poland. (Dist. by: Ars Polona-Ruch, Krakowskie Przedmiescie 7, Warsaw, Poland) Ed. Ryszard Wasita. adv.; illus.

943.8 DK4010   US   ISSN 0032-2970
POLISH REVIEW. 1956. q. $30 (foreign $35). Polish Institute of Arts and Sciences of America, Inc., 208 E. 30th St., New York, NY 10016. TEL 212-686-4164. Ed. Joseph W. Wieczerzak. adv.; bk.rev.; bibl.; index, cum.index: 1956-1980. circ. 1,500. (also avail. in microform from UMI; reprint service avail. from UMI) **Indexed:** Amer.Hist.& Life, Hist.Abstr., M.L.A., Mid.East: Abstr.& Ind., P.A.I.S., Polit.Sci.Abstr.
—Faxon; UnCover; UMI.

073 AP54   PL   ISSN 0032-3500
POLITYKA. (Supplements avail.: Import - Export; Prywatyzacja; Mieszkania; Finanse; Kultura) 1957. w. 34000 Zl. per no. Spoldzielnia Pracy "Polityka", Ul. Dubois 9, 00-182 Warsaw, Poland. TEL 48-22-635-3491. FAX 48-22-635-1797. TELEX 812546. (Dist. by: RSW "Prasa-Ksiazka-Ruch" Centrala Koportazy Prasy i Wydawnictw, ul. Towarowa 28, 00-958 Warsaw, Poland. TEL 48-22-201019) Ed. Jan Bijak. adv.; B&W page 65000000 Zl.; trim 289 x 442; adv. contact: Krystyna Jarosz. bk.rev.; charts; illus.; stat. circ. 300,000. (also avail. in microfilm) **Indexed:** M.L.A. **Document type:** newspaper.
   Description: For politicians, business executives, intellectuals.

057.85   PL
PRZEGLAD TYGODNIOWY. 1982. w. Capital Press, Spolka z o.o., Ul. Bracka 22, 00-028 Warsaw, Poland. TEL 48-22-276294. FAX 48-22-279128. TELEX 816400. Ed. Waclaw Zurek. circ. 210,600.
   Description: Covers political, social, historical, cultural, scientific and artistic interest.

057.85   PL   ISSN 0033-2488
PRZEKROJ. 1945. w. $148. Ul. Reformacka 3, 31-012 Krakow, Poland. TEL 48-12-225954. FAX 48-12-214929. TELEX 0322733. (Dist. by: Ars Polona Ruch, Krakowskie Przedmiescie 7, Warsaw, Poland) Ed. Mieczyslaw Czuma. adv.; bk.rev.; illus. circ. 150,000. **Document type:** consumer publication.
   Description: Covers all subjects of general interest with emphasis on literature, art, astrology, education.

057.85   PL
REPORTER. 1985. m. Wydawnictwo Interpress, Ul. Bagatela 12, 00-585 Warsaw, Poland. TEL 48-22-219376. Ed. Wojciech Pielecki. circ. 100,000.

073.8   PL   ISSN 0208-9130
RZECZYPOSPOLITA. 1982. 6/w. Presspublica sp. z o.o., Pl. Starynkiewicza 7, 02-015 Warsaw, Poland. TEL 48-2-628-3401. FAX 48-2-628-0588. Ed. Dariusz Fikus. adv.; illus. circ. 230,000. **Document type:** newspaper.

057.85   PL   ISSN 0867-6070
SLASK OPOLSKI. 1991. q. 80000 Zl. Instytut Slaski w Opolu, Ul. Piastowska 17, 45-082 Opole, Poland. TEL 364-41. FAX 330-81. TELEX 073-3736 ISLPL. adv.; bk.rev. circ. 300. **Document type:** bulletin.

057.85   PL   ISSN 0867-3403
SPOTKANIA (WARSAW). 1990. w. 5600 Zl. per issue. Spotkania Press, Ul. Przasnyska 6, 01-756 Warsaw, Poland. TEL 48-22-399022. FAX 48-22-399724. Ed. Maciej Ilowiecki. adv.; bk.rev.; illus. circ. 150,000.
   Description: Political, social, economic, cultural and scientific magazine.

073.8   PL   ISSN 0867-8723
SUPER EXPRESS. 1990. 3/w. Z P R - Express sp. z o.o., P.O. Box 19, 00-835 Warsaw, Poland. TEL 48-22-243265. FAX 48-22-203687. Ed. Grzegorz Lindenberg. adv. circ. 110,000. **Document type:** newspaper.
   Formerly (until 1991): Express (ISSN 0867-549X)

073.8   PL   ISSN 0867-0536
TRYBUNA. 1948. 6/w. 238000 Zl.($66) for 3 mos.; newsstand price: 4000 Zl. Ad Novum, Ul. Miedziana 11, 00-835 Warsaw, Poland. TEL 48-2-625-3015. FAX 48-22-204100. Ed. Dariusz Szymczycha; Pub. Dariusz Szymczycha. adv.; bk.rev.; film rev.; music rev.; play rev.; tele.rev.; illus.; circ. 55,000 (paid); 100,000 (controlled). **Document type:** newspaper.
   Former titles: Trybuna Kongresowa (ISSN 0867-0099); (until 1990): Trybuna Ludu (ISSN 0137-9348)
   Description: Provides news and comments on political, economic, social, and cultural affairs in Poland and abroad.

057.85   PL   ISSN 0041-4808
TYGODNIK POWSZECHNY; katolickie pismo spoleczno-kulturalne. 1945. w. $52. Spoleczny Instytut Wydawniczy "Znak", Ul. Kosciuszki 37, 30-105 Krakow, Poland. TEL 48-12-221372. FAX 48-12-224548. TELEX 0325707 TYPO PL. (Subscr. to: SIW Znak, Wislna 12, 31-007 Krakow, Poland) Ed. Jerzy Turowicz. adv.; bibl.; film rev.; illus.; play rev. circ. 70,000. **Indexed:** M.L.A.

057.85   PL   ISSN 0860-7591
WARSAW VOICE; Polish and Central European review. (Includes weekly insert: Voice Business; and monthly inserts: The Financial Voice, The Real Estate Voice, Privatization Updated, The Green Voice) (Text in English) 1988. w. $98 (Europe $78). Warsaw Voice S.A., Ksiecia Janusza 64, 01-452 Warsaw, Poland. TEL 48-22-366377. FAX 48-22-371995. Ed. Andrzej Jonas. adv. contact: Anna Kolendarska. circ. 15,000.
   •Also available online. Vendor(s): Mead Data Central, Inc.
   Description: Covers business, politics, culture, social affairs, sports and tourism.

057.85   PL   ISSN 0209-1747
WPROST. 1982. w. $91. Publishing and Advertising Agency "Wprost", Ul. Grunwaldzka 104, 60-307 Poznan, Poland. TEL 48-61-699371. FAX 48-61-668097. TELEX 414486. (Subscr. to: Wprost Agency's Subscription Department, ul. Sniadeckich 23, 60-773 Poznan, Poland) Ed. Marek Krol. adv. contact: Anna Borowiak. circ. 100,000.
   Description: Provides general information on national and international politics, social issues and culture.

057.85   PL   ISSN 0044-1538
ZA I PRZECIW; tygodnik ilustrowany. 1957. w. $32. Chrzescijanskie Stowarzyszenie Spoleczne - Christian Social Association, Ul. Marszalkowska 4, 00-590 Warsaw, Poland. (Dist. by: RSW "Prasa-Ksiazka-Ruch" Centrala Kolportazu Prasy i Wydawnictw, Ul. Towarowa 28, 00-958 Warsaw) Ed. Kazimierz Morawski. adv.; illus. circ. 50,000.

073.8   PL   ISSN 0137-9437
ZYCIE WARSZAWY. (Supplement avail.: Auto i Zycie (ISSN 0867-7352); Ex Libris (ISSN 0867-1958); Historia i Zycie (ISSN 0860-6099); Kultura i Zycie (ISSN 0860-6528);) 1944. 5/w. Zycie - Press ska z o.o., Armii Ludowej 3-5, 00-575 Warsaw, Poland. TEL 48-2-624-6990. FAX 48-2-625-2426. Ed. Kazimierz Wojcicki. adv.; illus. **Document type:** newspaper.

GENERAL INTEREST PERIODICALS — Portugal

076.9   PO
ACORIANO ORIENTAL. 1835. d. Esc.31199; newsstand price: Esc.100. Impracor, S.A., Dr. Bruno Tavares Carreiro, Ponta Delgada, 9500 Acores, Portugal. TEL 351-96-629700. FAX 351-96-629018. Ed. Gustavo Moura. adv. contact: Vasco Pinto. bk.rev.; film rev.; music rev.; play rev.; illus. cols./p.: 8; pp./issue: 28. (tabloid format) **Document type:** newspaper.

056.9   PO   ISSN 0300-4368
CHARADISTA. 1922. q. Esc.500. Tertulia Edipica, Sociedade Charadistica, Rua de Arroios 11, r.c.-E, 1100 Lisbon, Portugal. bk.rev.; illus. circ. 1,000.

076.9   PO
CORREIO DA HORTA. 1930. d. $4 per mo.; newsstand price: Esc.25. R. Comendador E. Rebelo 5, 9900 Horta, Acores, Portugal. TEL 22496. Ed. Fernando Santos; Pub. Francisco Gomes. bk.rev.; illus.; circ. 1,320 (paid). cols./p.: 5; pp./issue: 8. **Document type:** newspaper.

076.9   PO
DIARIO DE VISEU. (Supplement included weekly: Beira Alta Press) 1981. d. Gaveto da Av. Jose Relvas 1, 3502 Viseu codex, Portugal. TEL 424062. FAX 25827. adv.; bk.rev.; film rev.; music rev.; play rev.; illus. (tabloid format; also avail. in diskette format) **Document type:** newspaper.

076.9   PO
DIARIO DO ALENTEJO; jornal regionalista independente. 1932. w. Esc.4000. Praca da Republica 12, 7800 Beja, Alentejo, Portugal. TEL 323111. FAX 084-321398. Ed. Carlos Pereira; Pub. Antonio Alexandre Raposo. adv. contact: Leopoldo Santos. bk.rev.; film rev.; music rev.; play rev.; illus. cols./p.: 6; pp./issue: 28. (also avail. in diskette format) **Document type:** newspaper.

056.9   PO
ELES & ELAS. 1983. m. Esc.5000($35) (effective Jan. 1994). Gabinete 1, Imprensa, Promocao e Relacoes Publicas, Ltd., Rua de Sao Bento, 311, 3o Esq., 1200 Lisbon, Portugal. TEL 01-3961771. FAX 01-605688. Dir. Maria da Luz de Braganca. adv. contact: Alexandra Rosario. circ. 64,000. (microform; back issues avail.)
   Supersedes in part: Eles e Elas - a Revista (ISSN 0870-8932)
   Description: Contains information on public events concerning distinguished politicians, artists, and financiers, and their families.

056.9   PO
EPOCA. w. Impala Sociedade Editorial, Lda., Rua Cristino da Silva, 1 r-c, 2745 Queluz, Portugal. TEL 439-02-34. FAX 439-02-33.

056.9   PO
NOVA GENTE. w. Impala Sociedade Editorial, Lda., Rua Cristino da Silva 1, r-c, 2745 Queluz, Portugal. TEL 439-02-34. FAX 439-02-33. **Document type:** consumer publication.

056.9   PO
OPCAO.* 1976. w. Frente - Sociedade de Publicacoes Lda., Rua Artur Paiva 38, Lisbon, Portugal. Ed. Jose M. Teixeira. circ. 21,500.

056.9   PO
SABADO. 1988. w. Esc.230. Invesmedia, S.A., Rua Newton 5, 1100 Lisbon, Portugal. TEL 01-8151633. FAX 01-835291. Dir. Wilton Fonseca. circ. 53,900.

056.9   PO
SELECCOS DO READER'S DIGEST. m. Rua Francisco Manuel de Melo 21, 1000 Lisbon, Portugal. TEL 01-6831121. Dir. Margarida Sarga. circ. 177,000.

056.9   PO
SETE. w. Av. da Liberdade 190-2o Dto., 1298 Lisbon Codex, Portugal. TEL 01-766062. Dir. Caceres Montiero. circ. 54,300.

056.9   PO   ISSN 0049-335X
TEMPO. 1930. s-m. $40. Tempografica, S.A.R.L., Av. Ahmed Sekou Toure, 1078, C.P. 2917, Penafiel, Portugal. Ed. Antonio Pimentel. circ. 40,000.

TRANVIA; Revue der Iberischen Halbinsel. see *GENERAL INTEREST PERIODICALS — Spain*

056.9   US
VOZ DE PORTUGAL/VOICE OF PORTUGAL. (Text mainly in Portuguese; occasionally in English) 1960. s-m. $10. Voz de Portugal, 370 A St., Hayward, CA 94541. TEL 510-537-9503. Ed. Lourenco Costa Aguiar. adv. circ. 4,300. (tabloid format; back issues avail.)

GENERAL INTEREST PERIODICALS — Puerto Rico

056.1   PR   ISSN 0890-6548
AP63
IMAGEN; nuestra revista. 1986. m. $24. Casiano Communications Inc., 1700 Fernandez Juncos Ave., Stop 25, San Juan, PR 00909-2999. TEL 809-728-3000. FAX 809-728-7325. TELEX WU 380239 CARIBUS US. Ed. Norma Borges. adv.: B&W page $3930, color page $5661; trim 8 1/8 x 10 3/4. bk.rev. circ. 100,000. **Document type:** consumer publication.
   Description: Focuses on fashion, beauty, personalities and timely information.

051   PR   ISSN 0033-4049
F1951
PUERTO RICO LIVING. 1963. a. $5.50. Martin Wittstein, 54 Caleta de San Juan, Old San Juan, PR 00901. Ed. Barbara Dimando. circ. 12,000.
   Description: Guide to island living, recreation and business. Includes official tour guide to Old San Juan.

056.1 052   PR   ISSN 0360-7917
AS74.A1
REVISTA - REVIEW INTERAMERICANA. (Text in English and Spanish) 1971. s-a. $18 (foreign $20). Universidad Interamericana de Puerto Rico, San German Campus, Call Box 5100, San German, PR 00753. TEL 809-264-1912. Ed. Dr. Juan R. Gonzalez Mendoza. adv.; bk.rev.; bibl.; illus.; index. circ. 1,500. (also avail. in microform from UMI; reprint service avail. from UMI) **Indexed:** Abstr.Engl.Stud.; Amer.Hist.& Life, ERIC, Hisp.Amer.Per.Ind., Hist.Abstr. **Document type:** academic/scholarly publication.
   —UnCover. **CCC**.
   Formerly: Revista Interamericana (ISSN 0196-1373)

051   PR
VIEQUES TIMES; what's happening on the Isla Nena. 1987. m. $20. Vieques News-Info, 153 Flamboyan St., Esperanza Beach, Vieques, PR 00765. TEL 809-741-8508. Ed. Charlie Connelly. adv.; bk.rev. circ. 4,000.

GENERAL INTEREST PERIODICALS — Rumania

079.498   RM   ISSN 1220-7489
ADEVARUL/TRUTH; cotidian independent. (Supplement avail. m.: Salonul Literar (ISSN 1221-1710)) 6/w. S.C. Adevarul s.r.l., Bul. Revolutiei 81, 2900 Arad, Rumania. TEL 057-213302. FAX 057-16854. Ed. Tristan Mihuta. adv.; bk.rev.; film rev.; music rev.; play rev.; illus. cols./p.: 5; pp./issue: 12. **Document type:** newspaper.
   Formerly (until 1989): Flacara Rosie - Red Flame.
   Description: Covers news, information, politics, social problems, economics, culture, sports, and world events.

079.498   RM   ISSN 1221-5775
AGENDA. (Supplement avail. s-a.: Almanah Agenda) 1990. w. (Sat.). newsstand price: 200 lei. S.C. Agenda s.r.l., 1 Mai Nr. 2, 1900 Timisoara, Timis, Rumania. TEL 190835. FAX 190839. Pub. Zoltan Kovacs. adv.; bk.rev.; film rev.; music rev.; play rev.; illus. Wire service(s): Rompres. circ. 100,000. cols./p.: 5; pp./issue: 44. (tabloid format) **Document type:** newspaper.
   Description: Contains general interest information, national and local news, and features.

055.91   RM
ALBINA. 1897. m. Piata Presei Libere 1, 71341 Bucharest, Rumania. TEL 173627. Ed. Spiridon Stanel. circ. 130,000.

079.498   RM
ALLGEMEINE DEUTSCHE ZEITUNG FUER RUMAENIEN. (Supplement included: Banaten Zeitung) (Text in German) d. (except Mon.). 6000 lei; newsstand price: 50 lei. A D I International Press, Piata Presei Libere 1, 79777 Bucharest, Rumania. TEL 01-6181723. FAX 01-6183758. Ed. Emmerich Reichrath. adv.; bk.rev.; music rev.; play rev.; illus. cols./p.: 6; pp./issue: 8. (tabloid format) **Document type:** newspaper.
   Formerly (until 1993): Neuer Weg.
   Description: Contains general news and reports.

055.91   RM
ARGES. 1966. m. Bd. RSE 88, Pitesti, Rumania. Ed. Sergiu Nicolaescu. circ. 3,000.

055.91   RM
ATENEU. 1964. m. Str. Eliberarii 63, Bacau, Rumania. Ed. George Genoiu. circ. 7,000.

079.498   RM   ISSN 1220-577X
AZI. (Supplements included weekly: Petele Culturii, Carusel) 1990. d. (except Sun.). 2600 lei per mo. (Europe $223; US $305); newsstand price: 100 lei. Romania Azi S.A., Calea Victoriei 39A, 70101 Bucharest, Rumania. TEL 614-19-98. FAX 312-01-28. TELEX 11054. Ed. Octavian Stireanu. adv. contact: Mrs. Viorica Dumitrescu. bk.rev.; film rev.; music rev.; play rev.; illus. circ. 40,000. cols./p.: 7; pp./issue: 16. **Document type:** newspaper.

055.91   US   ISSN 0197-1441
DR212
COMUNIUNEA ROMANEASCA/RUMANIAN COMMUNION. (Text in English, French, Rumanian) 1973. irreg. contributions. 19965 Riopelle, Detroit, MI 48203. TEL 313-893-9237. Ed. George Alexe. bk.rev. circ. 500.
   Description: Promotes Romanian Orthodox faith and literature as a cultural bridge between the US and Romania.

055.91   RM   ISSN 1220-4560
CRONICA; renastere romaneasca, integrare europeana. 1966. s-m. 52 lei($96) (America and Australia $108). Comitetul de Cultura - Ministry of Culture, Str. V. Alecsandri Nr. 8, Iasi, Rumania. TEL 98-146433. Ed. Ioan Holban. adv.; bk.rev.; film rev.; play rev.; illus. circ. 8,000. (tabloid format)
   Description: Covers culture, arts, literature, philosophy, science, religion and personalities.

079.498   RM
CUGET LIBER/FREE THINKING; independent daily newspaper. (Supplement included: Litoral - Seacoast) 1989. d. (except Wed.). newsstand price: 150 lei. S.C. Cuget Liber S.A., No. 5 I.C. Bratianu, 8700 Constantza, Rumania. TEL 665606. FAX 665759. Ed. Arcadie Strahilevici. bk.rev.; film rev.; music rev.; play rev.; illus. cols./p.: 6; pp./issue: 8. (standard format) **Document type:** newspaper.

079.498   RM   ISSN 1220-9597
CURIERUL DE VILCEA; ziar independent. 1990. d. (except Mon.). 46800 lei($29.80); newsstand price: 150 lei. S.C. Curier s.r.l., Calea lui Traian 127, 1000 Vilcea, Rumania. TEL 004-050-712326. FAX 004-050-718265. Ed. Mircea Monu. adv. contact: Maria Stoian. bk.rev.; film rev.; music rev.; play rev.; illus. cols./p.: 6; pp./issue: 4. (standard format) **Document type:** newspaper.
   Description: Contains news and articles of opinion and information from Vilcea.

079.498   RM
CUVANTUL LIBER. 1989. w. newsstand price: 50 lei. 1 Decembrie 1918, Nr. 60A, 8375 Giurgiu, Rumania. TEL 221227. Ed. Ion Gaghii. bk.rev.; film rev.; play rev.; illus. cols./p.: 7; pp./issue: 6. (broadsheet format) **Document type:** newspaper.

055.91   RM
ERDEYI FIGYELO. 1958. fortn. Str. Primariei 1, 4300 Tirgu Mures, Rumania. Rumanian. TEL 954-26780. Ed. Elteto Kozsef. illus. circ. 15,000.
   Formerly (until 1989): Uj Elet.

055.91   RM
FAMILIA. 1865; N.S. 1965. m. Str. Romana 3, 3700 Oradea, Rumania. TEL 991-14129. Ed. Ioan Moldovan. circ. 4,000.

055.91   RM   ISSN 0015-3362
AP86
FLACARA. 1911. w. 10400 lei($7) S C Publicatiile
Flacara S.A., Piata Presei Libere 1, 71341
Bucharest, Rumania. TEL 401-6174763.
FAX 401-3218289. Ed. Liviu Timbus. adv. contact:
Mihai Sandoiu. illus. circ. 50,000.

079.498   RM   ISSN 1221-0110
GAZETA DE TRANSILVANIA; cotidian independent.
(Supplements avail.: Magazine G T; Foaie pentru
Minte, Inima si Literatura) 1838. d. (except Mon.).
newsstand price: 100 lei. 3 Mihail Sadoveanu St.,
2200 Brasov, Romania. TEL 0040-68-142029.
FAX 0040-68-152927. Ed. Eduard Huidan. adv.
contact: Cornelius Popa. bk.rev.; film rev.; music rev.;
play rev.; illus.; circ. 30,000 (paid); 10,000
(controlled). cols./p.: 7; pp./issue: 6. (standard
format) **Document type:** newspaper.
  Description: Covers social problems, politics, arts,
and sports.

059.396   RM
HET. (Text in Hungarian) 1970. w. $52 in Europe;
elsewhere $62 (effective Nov. 1991). Piata Presei
Libere 1, 71554 Bucharest, Rumania. TEL 184939.
Ed. Galfalvi Zsolt. circ. 4,000.
  Description: Review of society, culture, science and
ecology.

059.951   RM
LUOMANIYA. (Text in Chinese) 1957. q. Foreign
Languages Press Group, Piata Presei Libere 1,
71341 Bucharest, Rumania. TEL 173836. circ.
10,000.

052   RM   ISSN 0028-9116
NEWS FROM RUMANIA.* (Text in English) vol.12,
1970. fortn. Agerpres, the Romanian News Agency,
Piata Scinteii Nr. 1, Bucharest, Rumania.

057.91   RM
NOVII VIK. (Text in Ukrainian) 1949. s-m. Piata Presei
Libere 1, 71341 Bucharest, Rumania. Ed. Ion
Colesnic. circ. 1,600.

055.91   RM
RAMURI. 1964. m. Bis Str. Savinesti 3, Craiova,
Rumania. Ed. Marin Sorescu. circ. 4,000.

079.498   RM   ISSN 1221-4051
REATEREA BANATEANA. (Supplement avail.: O K
Week-end Magazin (ISSN 1221-4035)) d. (except
Sun.). newsstand price: 100 lei. Tim-Press S.A., Bd.
Revolutiei 1989, Nr. 8, 1900 Timisoara, Timis,
Rumania. TEL 096-190145. FAX 190370. Ed.
George Boieru. adv. contact: Stefan Vartiade. bk.rev.;
film rev.; music rev.; play rev.; illus. pp./issue: 16.
(tabloid format) **Document type:** newspaper.
  Formerly (until 1990): Drapelul Rosu.
  Description: Covers local, regional and national
news concerning politics, economics, social life,
commentary, and international policy.

052   RM
ROMANIA: ARTICLES - FEATURES - INFORMATION.
(Editions in English, French, German, Russian,
Spanish) vol.27, 1976. m. Agerpres, the Romanian
News Agency, Piata Scinteii Nr. 1, Bucharest,
Rumania. illus.; charts.

052   RM   ISSN 0048-8658
DR267
ROMANIA: DOCUMENTS-EVENTS. (Editions in English,
French, German, Russian and Spanish) vol.6, 1976.
w. Agerpres, the Romanian News Agency, Piata
Scinteii Nr. 1, Bucharest, Rumania.

052   RM   ISSN 1220-5028
ROMANIAN PANORAMA. Chinese edition (ISSN
1220-5052); French edition: Panorama Roumain
(ISSN 1220-501X); German edition: Rumaenisches
Panorama (ISSN 1220-5036); Spanish edition:
Panorama Rumano (ISSN 1220-5044); Russian
edition: Rumunskaya Panorama (ISSN 1221-3365)
(Text in English) 1955. m. 480 lei($52) Foreign
Languages Press Group "Romania" - Redactia
Publicatiilor pentru Strainatate "Romania", Piata
Presei Libere Nr. 1, P.O. Box 33-28, 71341
Bucharest, Rumania. TEL 6173836. FAX 3110526.
Ed. Dorin Iancu. adv.: page $500. bk.rev.; illus. circ.
40,000. (back issues avail.)
  Former titles (until 1991): Romania; Romania
Today (ISSN 0035-9815)
  Description: Publishes articles on Rumania's
history, economy, home and foreign policy, lifestyle,
culture, literature, arts, sports and miscellania.

057.1   RM
RUMUNSKAYA PANORAMA. English edition: Romanian
Panorama (ISSN 1220-5028) (Text in Russian)
1950. m. Foreign Languages Press Group, Piata
Presei Libere 1, 71341 Bucharest, Rumania.
TEL 173836. circ. 54,000.
  Formerly: Rumunia.

079.498   RM
SZABADSAG. (Text in Hungarian) 1989. 5/w.
(Tue.-Sat.). 2315 lei($22) per mo.; newsstand price:
100 lei. Szabadsag Ltd., Str. Napoca Nr. 16, P.O.
Box 340, 3400 Cluj, Rumania. TEL 40-64-118985.
FAX 40-64-197206. Ed. Zoltan Tibori Szabo. adv.:
B&W page $510; trim 252 x 368. bk.rev.; film rev.;
music rev.; play rev.; illus.; circ. 29,500 (paid); 500
(controlled). **Document type:** newspaper.

055.91   RM
TOMIS. 1966. m. 100 lei. Cultural Department of
Rumania, Str. Ion Lahovari 87, Constantza, Rumania.
TEL 611079. (Subscr. to: 54 Tomis Blvd., 8700
Constantza, Rumania) Ed. Constantin Novac. adv.
circ. 3,000. **Document type:** consumer publication.
  Description: Covers literature, art, history, culture
and science.

055.91   RM
TRIBUNA. 1884. w. Str. Universitatii 1, Cluj-Napoca,
Rumania. Ed. Vasile Salajan. circ. 6,000. (also avail.
in microfilm from NRP)

055.91   RM
UNIVERSUL CARTII. 1991. m. Ministerul Culturii, Piata
Presei Libere nr. 1, 71341 Bucharest 1, Rumania.
TEL 617-33-06.

GENERAL INTEREST PERIODICALS — Russia

057.1 320   UK
BRITAIN - RUSSIA. (Former name of issuing body: Great
Britain - U S S R Association) 1962. 3/yr. Britain -
Russia Centre, 14 Grosvenor Pl., London SW1X
7HW, England. TEL 071-235-2116.
FAX 071-259-6254. Ed. Helen O'Connor. bk.rev.
circ. 1,600. (back issues avail.) **Document type:**
academic/scholarly publication.
  Formerly: Britain - U S S R.
  Description: Covers topics on Russia and the other
former Soviet republics, except Estonia, Latvia, and
Lithuania.

077   RU
▼**CHAS PIK.** (Text in Russian) 1993. w. Izdatel'skii
Dom Chas Pik, Nevskii pr. 81, 191040 St.
Petersburg, Russia. TEL 7-812-289-2565.
FAX 7-812-277-1340. E-mail:
news@chaspik.spb.su. Ed. Nataliya Chaplina. adv.;
illus. circ. 105,981. (broadsheet format) **Document
type:** newspaper.

057.1   RU
DEPUTATSKII VESTNIK. 1990. w. Fond Deputatskikh i
Grazhdanskikh Initsiativ, Ul. Vainera 9A, 620219
Sverdlovsk, GSP 940, Russia. Ed. E.I. Kolezeev. circ.
34,000.

077   RU
DUMA; nezavisimaya gazeta Ural'skogo
gornozavodskogo regiona. (Text in Russian) 1990.
m. 30 Rub. per issue. Vozrogdenie, Ul. Uchitelskaya,
7-38, Nizhny Tagil, 6220036 Sverdlovskaya
Oblast', Russia. TEL 25-08-30. Ed. Vera Davidenko.
adv.: page 20000 Rub. circ. 10,000. **Document type:**
newspaper.

057.1   RU   ISSN 0234-1670
EKHO PLANETY. 1988. w. T.A.S.S., Tverskoi Bul'var
10-12, 103009 Moscow, Russia.
TEL 095-290-66-45. FAX 095-203-30-49. Ed.
Nikolai Setunskii. circ. 750,000.

077   RU
GOSPODIN NAROD; Rossiiskaya respublikanskaya
gazeta. (Text in Russian) 1990. w.? Ul.
Lobachevskogo 66, A, 117454 Moscow, Russia.
TEL 432-96-66. **Document type:** newspaper.

057.1   RU   ISSN 0454-5508
KRUGOZOR. 1964. m. $124. Gosteleradio S.S.S.R., Ul.
Pyatnitskaya, 25, Moscow, Russia. Ed. B.L.
Tikhonenko. illus. circ. 500,000.

077   RU   ISSN 0027-1306
MOSCOW NEWS. (Editions in English, German, Russian)
1930. w. (English & Russian eds.); m. (German ed.)
$75 for English ed.; $150 for Russian ed. 16-2
Tverskaya ul., Moscow, Russia.
TEL 7095-209-1984. FAX 7095-209-0267. Eds.
Len Karpinsky (Russian ed.), Yegor Bykovsky
(English ed.). adv.; bk.rev. circ. 45,000 (English ed.);
800,000 (Russian ed.). (tabloid format; also avail. in
microform) **Document type:** newspaper.
● Also available online. Vendor(s): DIALOG
Information Services, Inc., GBI.
  Description: Covers politics, economy and cultural
issues.

057.1   RU   ISSN 0868-5975
MOYA MOSKVA. 1991. m. $103. Ul. Tverskaya 13,
103032 Moscow, Russia. TEL 292-17-50. (Dist. in
U.S. by: Victor Kamkin Inc., 4956 Boiling Brook
Pkwy, Rockville, MD 20852. TEL 301-881-5973)
Ed. Vadim Istomin. circ. 60,000.

077   RU
NEZAVISIMAYA GAZETA. Selected semi-monthly English
translation: Independent Newspaper from Russia (US
ISSN 1064-4431) (Selected semi-monthly Russian
language version published in U.S. avail.:
Nezavisimaya Gazeta (ISSN 1064-444X)) (Text in
Russian) 1991. 5/w. $270. (Moskovskoi Gorodskoi
Sovet Narodnykh Deputatov) Nezavisimaya Gazeta,
Myasnitskaya, 13, 101000 Moscow, Russia.
TEL 095-928-4850. (301-881-5973) Ed. Vitalii
Tretyakov. adv.: B&W page $4200; 14 1/4 x 10.
circ. 225,000 (paid). **Document type:** newspaper.

057.1   RU
PRESS-KUR'ER. 1990. w. Novokuznetskii Gorodskoi
Rabochii Komitet, Ul. Tsiolkovskogo 23, kab. 6,
654041 Novokuznetsk, Russia. TEL 54-42-89. Ed.
S. Kamashevskii. circ. 22,500.

057.1   RU
RADIKAL. (Supplement to: Delovoi Mir) 1990. w.
24 Rub. (effective 1992). Delovoi Mir, Kutuzovskii
prosp., 39, 103051 Moscow K-51, Russia.
TEL 923-76-94. Ed. Aleksandr Malinov. adv. circ.
40,000.

051   US
▼**RUSSIAN LIFE.** 1993. bi-m. $25. Rich Frontier
Publishing Co., 1706 18th St., N.W., Washington,
DC 20009. TEL 202-232-3343.
FAX 202-232-6020. Ed. Vladimir Belyakov. adv.:
B&W page $7500; trim 8 3/8 x 10 7/8. circ.
33,623. **Document type:** consumer publication.

077   RU
SLOVO; chastnaya svobodnaya gazeta. 1990. w. 0.10
per issue. Ul. Lenina 33, 184200 Apatity,
Murmanskaya Oblast', Russia. TEL 3-17-20. Ed. N.V.
Dobrotvor. circ. 5,000. **Document type:** newspaper.

052   II   ISSN 0038-5786
SOVIET REVIEW. (Text in English) vol.7, 1970. 5/mo.
Rs.4. U.S.S.R. Embassy in India, Information
Department, 25 Barakhamba Rd., New Delhi
110001, India. Ed. G.L. Kolokolov. **Indexed:** M.L.A.

057.1   RU   ISSN 0131-8748
SPUTNIK; monthly digest of Russian press and
literature. English edition (ISSN 0131-8721); French
edition (ISSN 0131-8756); German edition (ISSN
0131-873X); Spanish edition (ISSN 0201-4394)
(Text in Russian) 1967. m. $63. Novosti Press
Agency, 4 Zubovsky Boulevard, Moscow, Russia.
TEL 095-201-2424. FAX 095-201-2119. TELEX
411321. (Dist. in U.S. by: Victor Kamkin Inc., 4956
Boiling Brook Pkwy., Rickville, ND 20852. TEL
301-881-5973) Ed. B. Krotkov. adv.; bk.rev.; film
rev.; play rev.; charts; illus. stat. circ. 300,000.

077.1   RU
SVOBODNYI KURS; nezavisimaya gazeta. 1991. 26/yr.
0.40 Rub. (Altaiskaya Regional'naya Assotsiatsiya
Ekonomicheskogo Sotrudnichestva) Altaiiskaya
Pravda, Ul. Korolenko 105, 656099 Barnaul,
Russia. Ed. Vladimir Ovchinnikov. **Document type:**
newspaper.

056.9   PO   ISSN 0870-9467
VIDA SOVIETICA. m. $200. Editora Vida Sovietica, Lda.,
Praca Andrade Caminha, 3-1700 Lisbon, Portugal.
adv.

052   RU
VOSKRESENIE (ENGLISH EDITION). (Editions in 21 languages) 1930. m. $84. Voskresenie, Ul. Moskvina, 8, 103772 Moscow, Russia. TEL 095-924-5689. (Dist. in U.S: by: Victor Kamkin Inc., 4956 Boiling Brook Pkwy., Rockville, MD 20852. TEL 301-5973) Ed. A.N. Misharin.
    Former titles: Soviet Union (ISSN 0206-510X); (until 1950): U.S.S.R. in Construction.

057.1   RU
VOSKRESENIE (RUSSIAN EDITION). (Editions in 21 languages) 1930. m. $84. Voskresenie, Ul. Moskvina, 8, 103772 Moscow, Russia. TEL 095-924-5689. (Dist. in U.S: by: Victor Kamkin Inc., 4956 Boiling Brook Pkwy., Rockville, MS 20852. TEL 301-881-5973) Ed. A.N. Misharin. bk.rev.; charts; illus. **Indexed:** RILM.
    Formerly: Sovetskii Soyuz (ISSN 0132-1234)
    Description: Covers international affairs, national politics, sports, farming, crafts, leisure, religion, arts, nature and ecology, health and education. Includes special section for children plus large "mailbag" with letters to the editor from all over the world.

GENERAL INTEREST PERIODICALS — Saint Vincent

079   US
▼**INDEPENDENT WEEKLY.** 1993. w. EC$120 (EC.$144 international). Independent Weekly Publishing Company Ltd., Stoney Ground, Kingstown, St. Vincent, W.I. TEL 809-457-9379. Ed. Conley Rose. adv.; illus. cols./p.: 7; pp./issue: 16. **Document type:** newspaper.
    Description: News and commentary on local and regional issues, with coverage of sports and entertainment.

GENERAL INTEREST PERIODICALS — Saudi Arabia

059.927   QA
AL-ARAB. (Text in Arabic) 1972. d. Dar al- Urubah Press and Publishing, P.O. Box 1115, Doha, Qatar. TEL 325874. TELEX 4497. Ed. Khalid Naama. circ. 25,000.

ARAB NEWS. see *GENERAL INTEREST PERIODICALS — Middle East*

052   SU
ARABIAN SUN.* (Text in English) 1945. w. Saudi Arabian Oil Co., P.O. Box 5000, Dhahran 31311, Saudi Arabia. TEL 966-38743856. FAX 966-38738490.

079.538 059.927   SU
BILAD. (Text in Arabic) 1934. d. P.O. Box 7095, Jeddah 21462, Saudi Arabia. TEL 966-2-6711000. FAX 966-2-6711222. Ed. Abdulaziz Mohammad Al-Nahari. adv.; illus. **Document type:** newspaper.

059.927   SU
AL-FAISAL. (Text in Arabic) 1976. m. P.O. Box 3, Riyadh 11411, Saudi Arabia. TEL 966-2-4653026. FAX 966-2-4647851. Ed. Zaid Al-Hussein. adv.

059.927   SU
AL-HARAS AL-WATANI. (Text in Arabic) m. P.O. Box 6819, Riyadh 11452, Saudi Arabia. TEL 966-2-4829524. Ed. Abdul Rahman Al-Shatry. **Document type:** consumer publication.

059.927   SU
IQRAA. (Text in Arabic) w. P.O. Box 9486, Jeddah 21413, Saudi Arabia. TEL 966-2-6711000. FAX 966-2-6716555. Ed. Yahya Bajnaid. **Document type:** consumer publication.

079.538 059.927   SU
AL-JAZIRAH. (Text in Arabic) d. Mu'assasat al-Jazirah lil-Sihafah wal-Tiba'ah wal-Nashr, Nassiria Rd., P.O. Box 354, Riyadh 11411, Saudi Arabia. TEL 966-1-4021440. FAX 966-1-4021795. Ed. Mohamed Bin Abbas. adv.; illus. (broadsheet format) **Document type:** newspaper.

079.538 059.927   SU
AL-MADINAH. (Text in English) 1937. d. Mu'assasat al-Madinah lil-Sihafah, P.O. Box 807, Jeddah 21421, Saudi Arabia. TEL 966-2-6985168. adv. **Document type:** newspaper.

AL-MAJALLA. see *GENERAL INTEREST PERIODICALS — Middle East*

079.538 059.927   SU
AL-MASSAIYAH. (Text in Arabic) d. Mu'assasat al-Jazirah lil-Sihafah wal-Tiba'ah wal-Nashr, P.O. Box 354, Riyadh 11411, Saudi Arabia. TEL 966-1-4021440. FAX 966-1-4021795. adv. **Document type:** newspaper.

079.538 059.927   SU
NADWAH. (Text in Arabic) 1958. d. P.O. Box 5803, Mecca, Saudi Arabia. TEL 966-2-5200111. FAX 966-2-5203055. Ed. Yusuf Damanhoori. adv. **Document type:** newspaper.

079.538 059.927   SU
AL-RIYADH. (Text in Arabic) 1963. d. P.O. Box 851, Riyadh, Saudi Arabia. TEL 966-1-4774610. FAX 966-1-4794167. Ed. Turki Al-Sudairi. adv.; illus. (broadsheet format) **Document type:** newspaper.

079.538 052   SU
RIYADH DAILY. (Text in English) d. P.O. Box 61466, Riyadh 11585, Saudi Arabia. TEL 966-1-4782000. FAX 966-1-4784333. Ed. Talaat Wafa. adv.; illus. **Document type:** newspaper.

SAYIDATI. see *GENERAL INTEREST PERIODICALS — Middle East*

059.927   SU
AL-SHARQ. w. P.O. Box 2662, Dammam 31461, Saudi Arabia. TEL 966-2-8570943. FAX 966-2-8578011. Ed. Abdullah Bin Turki Al-Towergy. **Document type:** consumer publication.
    Description: Covers cultural news and topics.

AL-SHARQ AL-AWSAT; the international daily newspaper of the Arabs. see *GENERAL INTEREST PERIODICALS — Middle East*

AL-SHARQ AL-AWSAT MAGAZINE. see *GENERAL INTEREST PERIODICALS — Middle East*

079.538 059.927   SU
UKAZ. (Text in Arabic) 1960. d. Mu'assasat 'Ukaz lil-Sihafah wal-Nashr, P.O. Box 1508, Jeddah 21441, Saudi Arabia. TEL 966-2-6722630. FAX 966-2-6728150. Ed. Hashim Abdo Hashim. adv. **Document type:** newspaper.

059.927   SU
AL-YAMAMAH. (Text in Arabic) 1952. w. 270. Al-Yamamah Press Establishment, P.O. Box 25848, Riyadh 11476, Saudi Arabia. TEL 966-2-4764442. FAX 966-2-4775162. Ed. Abdul Aziz Al-Mansour. adv.: B&W page SRI. 3000; color page SRI. 4500. circ. 35,000. **Document type:** consumer publication.

079.538 059.927   SU
AL-YAWM. (Text in Arabic) 1965. d. Dar al-Yawm lil-Sihafah wal-Tiba'ah wal-Nashr, P.O. Box 565, Dammam 31421, Saudi Arabia. TEL 966-3-8333333. FAX 966-3-8433337. Ed. Sultan Al-Bazzie. adv. **Document type:** newspaper.

GENERAL INTEREST PERIODICALS — Scandinavia

see also *General Interest Periodicals–Denmark; General Interest Periodicals–Finland; General Interest Periodicals–Norway; General Interest Periodicals–Sweden*

640.73   SW   ISSN 0035-7235
RAAD & ROEN/ADVICE AND RESULTS. (Text in Swedish; summaries in English) 1958. m. SEK 135. Konsumentverket - National Swedish Board for Consumer Policies, P.O. Box 503, S-162 15 Vaellingby, Sweden. TEL 08-759-8300. FAX 08-7598529. Ed. Gudrun Hjelte. illus.; index. circ. 175,000. (also avail. in audio cassette) **Document type:** consumer publication.
    Formerly (until 1973): Sweden. Statens Institut foer Konsumentfraagor. Meddelar (ISSN 0082-0121)

GENERAL INTEREST PERIODICALS — Senegal

059.927   SG   ISSN 0850-1378
BARIDOU - IFRIKHIA; mensuel culturel politique islamique. (Text in Arabic) 1991. m. 50000 Fr.CFA. Dar Senegalia, B.P. 2283, 58 av. de la Republique, Dakar, Senegal. TEL 23-10-65. FAX 35-20-78. TELEX 51-445 SG. Ed. El Hadj Sylla. circ. 3,500. **Document type:** newspaper.

OUEST AFRICAIN. see *GENERAL INTEREST PERIODICALS — Africa*

GENERAL INTEREST PERIODICALS — Seychelles

052   SE
THE SEYCHELLES NATION. (Text in Creole, English, French) d. Ministry of Information, Culture & Sports Division, POB 321, Victoria, Seychelles. TEL 24161. FAX 21006. TELEX 2320. Ed. R. Jumeau. circ. 1,500. **Document type:** government publication.

054.1
SEYCHELLES TODAY. (Text in English and French) q. Seychelles Agence de Presse, Information Division, POB 321, Victoria, Seychelles. TEL 24161. FAX 21006. TELEX 2322. circ. 4,000. **Document type:** government publication.

052   SE
SEYCHELLES WEEKEND NATION. (Text in Creole, English, French) w. Ministry of Information, Culture & Sports Division, POB 321, Victoria, Seychelles. TEL 24161. FAX 21006. TELEX 2322. Ed. R. Jumeau. **Document type:** government publication.

GENERAL INTEREST PERIODICALS — Sierra Leone

052
THE GLOBE. w? 40 Rowdon St., Freetown, Sierra Leone. TEL 26272. Ed. Sam Tumoe.

052
LEONEAN SUN. 1974. m. 49 Main Rd., Wellington, Freetown, Sierra Leone. TEL 023363. Ed. Rowland Martyn.

052   SL
NEW CITIZEN. w? Freetown, Sierra Leone. Ed. I.B. Kargbo.

052   SL
THE NEW SHAFT. s-w. 60 Old Railway Line, Brookfields, Freetown, Sierra Leone. TEL 41093. Ed. Franklin Bunting-Davies. circ. 10,000.

052   SL
PROGRESS. w. 1 Short St., Freetown, Sierra Leone. TEL 23588. Ed. Fode Kandeh. circ. 7,000.

052   SL
THE VISION. w? Freetown, Sierra Leone. Ed. Sika Massaquoi.

052   SL
WEEKEND SPARK. 1983. w. 7 Lamina Sankoh St., Freetwon, Sierra Leone. TEL 23397. Ed. Rowland Martyn. circ. 20,000.

GENERAL INTEREST PERIODICALS — Singapore

059.951
THE CITIZEN. (Text in Chinese, English) m. People's Association, Kallang, Singapore 1439, Singapore. TEL 3448222.

079.54   SI
LIANHE ZAOBAO. (Text in Chinese) 1923. d. S.$199.10; newsstand price: S.$0.55. Singapore Press Holdings Ltd., Corporate Relations Department, 82 Genting Lane, Singapore 1334, Singapore. TEL 7438800. Ed. Lim Jim Koon. adv.; color page S.$18184.20; adv. contact: Lawrence Loh. bk.rev.; film rev, music rev.; illus.; circ. 205,000 (paid). (broadsheet format; also avail. in microfilm; back issues avail.) **Document type:** newspaper.

GENERAL INTEREST PERIODICALS — SOUTH AFRICA

052   SI
MIRROR OF OPINION. (Text in English) 1965. d. (6/w.). S.130. Ministry of Information & the Arts, Media Division, PSA Bldg., 36th Fl., 460 Alexandra Rd., Singapore 0511, Singapore. Ed. Siew Lock Fai. circ. 400. (looseleaf format)
Description: Highlights of Malay, Chinese and Tamil press.

079.54   SI
THE NEW PAPER. (Text in English) 1988. d. (Mon.-Sat.). newsstand price: S.$0.50. Singapore Press Holdings Ltd., Corporate Relations Department, 82 Genting Lane, Singapore 1334, Singapore. TEL 7438800. FAX 7492221. (Subscr. to: 390 Kim Seng Rd., Singapore 0923, Singapore. TEL 7305544. FAX 7375375) Ed. P.N. Balji. adv. contact: Lawrence Loh. film rev.; music rev.; illus. Wire service(s): AFP, AP, RN, NYT, UPI. circ. 106,000 (paid). cols./p.: 10; pp./issue: 48. (also avail. in microfilm; back issues avail.; reprint service avail.) **Document type:** newspaper.

052   SI   ISSN 0129-766X
SINGAPORE. (Text in English) 1946. a. S.7. Ministry of Information and the Arts, Publicity Division, PSA Bldg., 30th Fl., 460 Alexandra Rd., Singapore 0511, Singapore. TEL 65-2799835. FAX 65-2799860. Ed. TLaw Chiew Mee. circ. 12,000. (back issues avail.) **Document type:** government publication.
Formerly (until 1968): Singapore Year Book.

052   SI   ISSN 0303-7169
HC445.8
SINGAPORE BULLETIN. (Text in English) 1972. m. Ministry of Information and the Arts, Publicity Division, PSA Bldg., 30th Fl., 460 Alexandra Rd., Singapore 0511, Singapore. TEL 2799825. FAX 2799860. TELEX RS22428 MITA SI. Ed. Ng Poey Siong. bk.rev. circ. 8,500. **Document type:** government publication.
—BLDSC (8285.461500).

052   HK
SINGAPORE TATLER. (Text in English) 1984. m. S.$5 per no. Communications Management Ltd., 1811 Hong Kong Plaza, 188 Connaught Rd. West, Hong Kong. TEL 547-7117. FAX 852-8582671. TELEX 61758 TATCO HX. Ed. Linda Ross. circ. 85,860. **Document type:** consumer publication.

079.5957   SI
STRAITS TIMES; weekly overseas edition. w. $76.50. Singapore Press Holdings Ltd., Corporate Relations Department, 82 Genting Lane, News Centre, Singapore 1334, Singapore. TEL 743-8800. FAX 747-3835. TELEX RS 55050 SPHNC. **Document type:** newspaper.

GENERAL INTEREST PERIODICALS — Slovakia

057.87   XO   ISSN 0323-0643
KRASY SLOVENSKA/BEAUTY OF SLOVAKIA. (Text in Slovak; summaries in English, German, Russian) 1921. m. 60 Kcs.($42) (Slovak Central Committee of Czechoslovak Union of Physical Training) Sport, Vajnorska 100A, 832 58 Bratislava, Slovakia. Ed. Milan Kubis. circ. 19,000.

057.87   XO
MATICNE CITANIE. KALENDAR. 1990. a. 20 Kcs. Matica Slovenska, Slovenska Narodna Kniznica, UL. L. Novomeskeho 32, 036-52 Martin, Slovakia. TEL 0842-331-71. FAX 0842-324-54. TELEX 075331. Ed. Cyril Zuffa.

073.7   XO
NARODNA OBRODA; nezavisly dennik obcansky Slovenska. (Supplements avail.) 1990. 6/w. (except Sun.). 1209 SK.; newsstand price: 3.90 SK. Nofra, Inc, Trnavska cesta 112, 830 00 Bratislava, Slovakia. TEL 42-7-220433. FAX 42-7-296281. Owner(s): Narodna Obrada, tranavska cesta 112, 830 00 Bratislava, Slovakia; SOCPRESS, 17, av. du General Mangin, 750 16 Paris, France. bk.rev.; film rev.; music rev.; play rev.; tele.rev.; illus. circ. 6,500. cols./p.: 5; pp./issue: 13. (standard format; also avail. in microfilm from NRP) **Document type:** newspaper.

073.7   XO
NOVY CAS; nezavisly dennik. (Weekly supplements avail.: T I P; Saturday TV Magazine) 1949. 6/w. (Mon.- Sat.). Cas, a.s., Gorkeho 5, 812 78 Bratislava, Slovakia. TEL 42-7-363070. FAX 42-7-363104. Ed. Zuzana Rackova; Pub. Jozef Vido. adv.: page 25600 SK.; trim 200 X 265; adv. contact: Marcela Mrovova. bk.rev.; film rev.; music rev.; play rev.; tele.rev.; illus.; circ. 250,000 (paid). cols./p.: 4; pp./issue: 32. (tabloid format; also avail. in diskette format; back issues avail.) **Document type:** newspaper.
Former titles (until 1991): Cas (ISSN 0862-9579); (until 1990): Lud (ISSN 0323-1348)

057.87   US
SLOVAK AMERICAN CULTURAL SOCIETY OF THE MIDWEST. NEWSLETTER. 1991. 3/yr. $15 to individuals; non-profit organizations $25 (membership). Slovak American Cultural Society of the Midwest, Box 5398, Naperville, IL 60567. TEL 815-838-9877. Ed. Thomas Klimek Ward. **Document type:** newsletter.
Description: Discusses Slovak history, culture, current events, and cuisine in the U.S. and Slovakia.

073.7   XO   ISSN 0862-8823
SLOVENSKE NARODNE NOVINY. (Text in Slovak) 1990. w. 156 Kcs. Matica Slovenska, Mudronova 26, 036-52 Martin, Slovakia. TEL 42-842-38706. FAX 42-842-32454. Ed. Milos Majer. **Document type:** newspaper.

GENERAL INTEREST PERIODICALS — South Africa

079.62 052   SA   ISSN 1017-6128
THE ARGUS. Weekend edition: Weekend Argus (ISSN 1016-7161) (Supplements avail.: Tonight (d.); Weekend) (Text in English) 1857. d. R.291.20. 122 St. George's St., P.O. Box 56, Cape Town 8000, South Africa. TEL 27-21-488-4911. FAX 27-21-488-4075. Owner(s): Argus Newspapers, 47 Salem St., Johannesburg 2000, South Africa. Ed. Andrew Drysdale; Pub. John Featherstone. adv. contact: Greg Brophy. bk.rev.; film rev.; music rev.; play rev.; tele.rev.; illus. Wire service(s): AFP, AP, RN. circ. 105,000 (paid). cols./p.: 10; pp./issue: 24. (broadsheet format; also avail. in microfiche; back issues avail.) **Document type:** newspaper.

079.68 053.936   SA   ISSN 1016-3905
BEELD. (Text in Afrikaans) 1974. d. (Mon.-Sat.). P.O. Box 5425, Johannesburg 2000, South Africa. TEL 27-11-4021460. FAX 27-11-4021871. Owner(s): National Media. Ed. S. de Swardt. adv. circ. 62,000. **Document type:** newspaper.

052   SA   ISSN 0302-7244
BONA (ENGLISH EDITION). Sotho edition: Bona (Sepedi Kgatiso) (ISSN 0302-9239); Xhosa edition: Bona (Xhosa Uhlelo) (ISSN 0302-9212); Zulu edition: Bona (Zulu Ukucindezelwa) (ISSN 0302-9220) 1956. m. R.30.78 (overseas R.74) (effective 1993). Republican Press (Pty) Ltd., P.O. Box 32083, Mobeni 4060, Natal, South Africa. TEL 27-31-422041. FAX 27-31-921231. TELEX 62-4422. Ed. Red Baker. adv.; bk.rev. circ. 320,000. **Document type:** consumer publication.
Supersedes: Bona (ISSN 0006-7016)
Description: Variety of articles for younger black adults.

035.1 052   SA   ISSN 0259-0115
BRUCKA; 'n brug na buite. (Text in Afrikaans, English, German) 1963. q. membership. South African-German Cultural Association - Suid Afrikaans - Duitse Kultuurvereniging, P.O. Box 70944, Die Wilgers, Pretoria 0041, South Africa. TEL 27-12-8071280. FAX 27-12-8071281. Ed. Jens Kruger. adv.; illus.; charts; stat. circ. 6,000.
Description: Aim is to promote cultural ties between Southern Africa and the German-speaking countries in Europe.

079.68 053.936   SA
DIE BURGER. Cape Town edition: Burger (Wes-Kaap). Port Elizabeth edition: Burger (Oos-Kaap). (Text in Afrikaans) 1915. d. P.O. Box 692, Cape Town 8000, South Africa. TEL 27-21-4062222. FAX 27-21-4062913. Owner(s): National Media. Ed. Ebbe Dommisse. adv. Wire service(s): RN, SAPA. circ. 78,000. (also avail. in microfilm) **Document type:** newspaper.

079.68 053.936   SA
DIE BURGER (OOS-KAAP). (Weekly supplements avail.: Jonge Burger; Wongids) (Text in Afrikaans) 1937. d. (Mon.-Sat.). newsstand price: R.0.90. Cawood St. 52, Port Elizabeth 6001, South Africa. TEL 27-41-542431. FAX 27-41-545166. Owner(s): National Media. Ed. Jean LeRoux; Pub. Jonathan Crowther. adv. contact: Stefan Engelbrecht. Wire service(s): RN, SAPA. circ. 11,500 (paid). cols./p.: 7; pp./issue: 16. (broadsheet format; also avail. in microfiche; back issues avail.) **Document type:** newspaper.
Formerly (until 1993): Oosterlig.

079.68 052   SA   ISSN 1016-3948
CAPE TIMES. (Text in English) 1898. d. P.O. Box 11, Cape Town 8000, South Africa. TEL 27-21-4884911. FAX 27-21-4884717. Owner(s): Times Media Ltd. Ed. J.C. Viviers. adv. circ. 56,500. **Document type:** newspaper.

052   SA
CAPETONIAN. (Text in English) m. R.6. Carl Momberg, 66 Loop St., Box 1796, Cape Town 8000, South Africa. adv.

053.93 052   SA   ISSN 0008-7866
CATHCART CHRONICLE.* (Text in Afrikaans and English) 1877. w. R.2. Box 29, Cathcart, Cape Province, South Africa. Ed. M.G. Kidson. adv. circ. 400.

079.68 052   SA   ISSN 1016-3956
THE CITIZEN. (Text in English) 1976. d. The Citizen (Pty) Ltd., P.O. Box 7712, Johannesburg 2000, South Africa. TEL 27-11-4022900. FAX 27-11-4026862. Ed. M.A. Johnson. adv. circ. 242,000. **Document type:** newspaper.

079.68 052   SA   ISSN 1016-3964
CITY PRESS. (Text in English) 1983. w. P.O. Box 3413, Johannesburg 2000, South Africa. TEL 27-11-4021632. FAX 27-11-4026501. Owner(s): National Media. Ed. K. Sibiya. adv. circ. 150,000. **Document type:** newspaper.

052   SA
COMMUNITY NEWSPAPERS. (Text in English) 1969. w. free. Newspaper House, 4th Fl., 122 St. George's St., Cape Town 8000, South Africa. Ed. H. Arendse. adv. circ. 138,000. (also avail. in microfilm)
Formerly (until 1986): Cape Herald.

053.93 052   SA   ISSN 0011-0426
COURIER (BEAUFORT WEST). (Text in Afrikaans and English) 1869. w. R.4. Courier Printing and Publishing Co., Bank St., Box 64, Beaufort West, South Africa. Ed. Rufus Dercksen. adv. circ. 1,800. (tabloid format)

079.68
DAILY DISPATCH. (Text in English) 1872. d. (6/wk.). R.155.10. Dispatch Media Limited, 33 Caxton St., P.O. Box 131, East London 5200, South Africa. TEL 27-431-430010. FAX 27-431-4351. Ed. J.G. Williams. adv.; illus. circ. 33,581. (also avail. in microfilm from PSL) **Document type:** newspaper.
Formerly (until 1898): East London Dispatch.

079.68 052   SA   ISSN 1016-8184
DAILY NEWS. Weekend edition: Saturday News (ISSN 1018-6980) (Text in English) 1915. d. (Mon.-Fri.). P.O. Box 47549, Greyville, Durban 4023, South Africa. TEL 27-31-3082911. FAX 27-31-3082111. Owner(s): Natal Newspapers Ltd. Ed. M.J. Green. adv. circ. 100,000. **Document type:** newspaper.

079.68 052   SA
DIAMOND FIELDS ADVERTISER. (Text in English) 1885. d. P.O. Box 610, Kimberley 8300, South Africa. TEL 27-531-26261. FAX 27-53125881. Owner(s): Argus Printing & Publishing. Ed. Charles Guild. adv. circ. 8,100. **Document type:** newspaper.

053.93 052   SA   ISSN 0012-4028
DISTRICT MAIL/DISTRIKSPOS. (Text in Afrikaans and English) 1928. w. R.7.50. Modern Newspapers (Pty) Ltd., Box 58, 1B Victoria St., Somerset West, South Africa. Ed. M. Sadie. adv. (tabloid format)
Description: Contains items of local interest.

GENERAL INTEREST PERIODICALS — SOUTH AFRICA

052 910.3   SA   ISSN 0419-7674
DRUM; Africa's leading magazine beating to the pulse of the times. (Editions in English, Zulu) 1951. m. R.27.16 (foreign R.32.76). Drum Publications, National Magazines (Subsidiary of: National Media Limited), 2nd Fl., Eaton Place, Norwich Park, Sandton 2199, South Africa. TEL 011-783-7227. FAX 011-783-8822. (Subscr. to: P.O. Box 1802, Cape Town 8000, South Africa) Ed. Barney Cohen. adv.; bk.rev. circ. 150,000. **Document type:** consumer publication.
    Description: Reflects black trends and thinking in South Africa.

079.68 052   SA
EASTERN PROVINCE HERALD. (Text in English) 1845. d. P.O. Box 1117, Port Elizabeth 6000, South Africa. TEL 27-41-5047911. FAX 27-41-554966. Owner(s): Times Media Ltd. Ed. D. Smith. adv. circ. 26,309. **Document type:** newspaper.
    Formerly (until 1898): Eastern Province Herald and Port Elizabeth Commercial News.

053.93 052   SA   ISSN 0011-7161
ECHO (DE AAR). (Text in Afrikaans, English) 1921. w. R.2.20. I.J.A. Wood, Pub., Box 44, 12 Miller St., De Aar, South Africa. (Co-publishers: C. Wood, R.E. Wood) Ed. M. Venter. circ. 1,800.

079.62   SA
EIKESTADNUUS. (Text in Afrikaans, English) 1946. w. Eikestadnuus (Pty) Ltd., Alexanderstr. 44, Stellenbosch 7600, South Africa. TEL 27-21-8872840. FAX 27-21-8839538. Ed. Riaan Gerber. adv. contact: Marida Smit. bk.rev.; film rev.; music rev.; play rev.; illus. (tabloid format) **Document type:** newspaper.

079.68 052   SA
EVENING POST. (Text in English) 1950. d. P.O. Box 1121, Port Elizabeth 6000, South Africa. TEL 27-41-5047911. FAX 27-41-554966. Owner(s): Times Media Ltd. Ed. N.M. Woudberg. adv. circ. 20,234. **Document type:** newspaper.

053.93   SA
FISH HOEK ECHO. (Text in Afrikaans and English) 1951. s-m. R.15($30) U M L (Pty) Ltd., 1 Somerset House, Recreation Road, Fish Hoek 7975, South Africa. Ed. Barry D. Lotz. adv.; bk.rev. circ. 15,500. (back issues avail.)

053.93   SA
HANDHAAF. 1963. m. R.15. Federasie van Afrikaanse Kultuurverenignge, 91050 Aucklandpark 2006, Johannesburg, South Africa. Eds. A.M.Vd. Berg, J.G. du Plessis. adv.; bk.rev.; illus. circ. 24,500.

052   SA   ISSN 0018-1722
HIGHWAY MAIL. 1949. w. R.6. Highway Mail (Pty.) Ltd., 174-176 Old Main St., Box 16, Pinetown, Natal 3600, South Africa. Ed. G.D.G. Oliver. adv.; bk.rev.; illus. circ. 3,886. (tabloid format)

052   SA
HIGHWAY REPORTER. 1976. m. R.2.50. Highway Mail (Pty.) Ltd., 174-176 Old Main Rd., Box 16, Pinetown, Natal 3600, South Africa. Ed. G.D.G. Oliver. adv.; illus.

052   SA
HORIZON; your family paper. 1979. w. R.80. Hakim Publications, P.O. Box 200, Kliptown 1812, Johannesburg 2001, South Africa. TEL 011-857-2053. FAX 011-857-1591. Ed. Adam A. Kola. adv.; bk.rev. circ. 30,000. (tabloid format)

053.93   SA   ISSN 0018-7089
HUISGENOOT. (Text in Afrikaans) 1916. w. R.271. National Magazines (Subsidiary of: National Media Ltd.), P.O. Box 1802, Cape Town 8000, South Africa. TEL 27-21-4062100. FAX 27-21-4062936. Ed. Niel Hammann. bk.rev.; film rev.; illus. circ. 514,818. **Indexed:** Ind.S.A.Per. **Document type:** consumer publication.

079.68 059.968   SA   ISSN 0019-1779
ILANGA. (Text in Zulu) 1903. s-w. P.O. Box 2159, Durban 4000, South Africa. TEL 27-31-3094350. FAX 27-31-309-3489. Ed. T.G. Mthembu. adv.; illus. circ. 106,000. **Document type:** newspaper.

079.68 059.968   SA
IMVO ZABANTSUNDU. (Text in Xhosa) 1909. w. P.O. Box 190, King William's Town 5600, South Africa. TEL 27-433-23550. FAX 27-433-333865. Owner(s): Perskorporasie van Suid-Afrika Bpk. Ed. D. du Plessis. adv. circ. 51,000. **Document type:** newspaper.
    Formerly (until 1912): Imvo Zabantsundu Bomzzantsi Afrika.

053.93   SA   ISSN 0256-0488
KEUR. (Text in Afrikaans) 1967. w. R.160.06 (overseas R.271.24) (effective 1993). Republican Press (Pty) Ltd., P.O. Box 32083, Mobeni 4060, Natal, South Africa. TEL 27-31-422041. FAX 27-31-921231. Ed. Gerhard Badger. circ. 127,000. **Document type:** consumer publication.
    Description: Entertainment and news reviews.

052   SA
THE MAIL. (Text in English) 1898. w. R.40. Text Publications (Pty) Ltd., P.O. Box 102, 37C Carrington St., Mafeking 8670, South Africa. TEL 0140-811330. FAX 0140-812886. TELEX 8-4832 BP. Ed. Leslie Sehume. adv.; bk.rev.; play rev.; illus. circ. 10,000. (tabloid format) **Document type:** newspaper.
    Incorporates: Mirror; Former titles: Mafeking Mail and Botswana Guardian (ISSN 0024-9718); (until 1966) Mafeking Mail and Protectorate Guardian.

053.93   SA   ISSN 0048-119X
MIDLAND NEWS. (Text in Afrikaans, English) 1892. w. Rs.25.90. W B Printers C.C., Box 224, Cradock, South Africa. Ed. R.E. Wood. adv.; bk.rev.; film rev.; illus. circ. 1,500. (tabloid format)
    Formerly: Nuwe Afrikaner.

053.93   SA   ISSN 0027-7746
NAMIB TIMES. (Text in Afrikaans, English, German) 1958. s-w. R.10. Box 706, Walvis Bay, South Africa. Ed. Paul Vincent.

079.68 052   SA   ISSN 1016-8214
NATAL MERCURY. Weekend edition: Weekend Mercury (ISSN 1018-7006) (Text in English) 1852. d. P.O. Box 950, Durban 4000, South Africa. TEL 27-31-3082300. FAX 27-31-3082333. Owner(s): Natal Newspapers Ltd. Ed. John Patten. adv. circ. 64,000. **Document type:** newspaper.

079.68   SA
NATAL WITNESS. (Text in English) 1846. d. Natal Witness (Pty) Ltd., P.O. Box 362, Pietermaritzburg 3200, South Africa. TEL 27-331-942011. FAX 27-331-940468. Ed. David Willers. adv. circ. 23,000. **Document type:** newspaper.

079.68   SA   ISSN 0030-8447
PAARL POST. (Text in Afrikaans, English) 1904. w. R.90. P.O. Box 248, Paarl 7620, South Africa. TEL 27-211-611170. FAX 27-211-22753. Ed. Anne Kruger; Pub. Lambert Retief. adv.; circ. 10,000 (paid). (tabloid format) **Document type:** newspaper.

052   SA   ISSN 0259-126X
PERSONALITY. w. R.160.06 (overseas R.271.24) (effective 1993). Republican Press (Pty) Ltd., P.O. Box 32083, Mobeni 4060, Natal, South Africa. TEL 27-31-422041. FAX 27-31-921231. Ed. Wendy Christopher. adv.; bk.rev.; film rev.; play rev.; bibl.; charts; illus.; stat. circ. 127,000. **Document type:** consumer publication.
    Former titles (until 1986): Family Radio and T V (ISSN 0256-0305); Personality (ISSN 0031-5648); S A U K - S A B C Bulletin (ISSN 0036-0988)
    Description: Entertainment and news reviews.

079.68 052   SA   ISSN 1016-8230
POST NATAL. (Text in English) 1971. w. P.O. Box 733, Durban 4000, South Africa. TEL 27-31-3082400. FAX 27-31-3082427. Owner(s): Natal Newspapers Ltd. Ed. B. Ranguthee. adv. circ. 42,581. **Document type:** newspaper.

079.68 052   SA   ISSN 1016-3654
PRETORIA NEWS. (Text in English) 1898. d. P.O. Box 439, Pretoria 0001, South Africa. TEL 27-12-3255382. FAX 27-12-3257300. Owner(s): Argus Printing & Publishing. Ed. Deon du Plessis. adv.; illus. circ. 27,465. **Document type:** newspaper.

079.68 053.936   SA   ISSN 1017-1657
RAPPORT. (Text in Afrikaans) 1970. w. Rapport Uitgewers Bpk., P.O. Box 8422, Johannesburg 2000, South Africa. TEL 27-11-4022620. FAX 27-11-4020562. Ed. B. van Walsem. adv. circ. 360,000. **Document type:** newspaper.

052   SA   ISSN 0034-0456
READER'S DIGEST (SOUTH AFRICAN EDITION). (Text in English) 1948. m. R.62.81. Reader's Digest Association (Pty) Ltd., P.O. Box 4494, Cape Town 8000, South Africa. FAX 27-21-211283. Ed. Wendy Morgenrood. adv.; bk.rev.; illus. circ. 370,000.

052 059.96   SA
SEIPONE. 1979. m. free. Nasionale Streekkoerante Ltd., Box 515, Potchefstroom 2520, South Africa. TEL 0148-3916. FAX 0148-930148. Ed. D. Dhlamini. adv.; bk.rev. circ. 6,000. (tabloid format)

053.93   SA   ISSN 0258-8951
SKIPPER. (Text in Afrikaans, English) 1981. m. free. Department of Environment Affairs, Private Bag X447, Pretoria 0001, South Africa. FAX 012-322-2682. Ed. Nicolene Botha. bk.rev. circ. 70,000. (back issues avail.)
    Description: Children's magazine on the environment.

079.62 052   SA
SOUTH; news for new times. (Supplements avail.: Southeaster (w.); Chalkline (m.)) (Text in English) 1987. w. (Wed.). R.80($150) South Press Services Ltd., P.O. Box 13096, Sir Lowry Rd., Woodstock 7900, South Africa. TEL 27-21-4622012. FAX 27-21-4615407. Ed. Rafiq Rohan; Pub. Ebrahim Bhorat. adv.; B&W page R.5323.50; adv. contact: Yvette Johnson. bk.rev.; film rev.; music rev.; play rev.; tele.rev.; illus. Wire service(s): AFP,RN. circ. 12,000 (paid). cols./p.: 5; pp./issue: 28. (tabloid format; back issues avail.) **Document type:** newspaper.
    Description: Independent, liberal perspective on community news and political issues in the Cape.

053.93 052   SA   ISSN 0038-3228
SOUTH COAST HERALD. (Text in Afrikaans and English) 1945. w. R.17. South Coast Herald (Pty) Ltd., 36 Reynolds St, Port Shepstone, Natal, South Africa. Ed. Mrs. T. Moss. circ. 8,500. (tabloid format)

079.68   SA   ISSN 0049-1519
SOUTH COAST SUN. 1970. w. R.90 (effective 1993). Amanzimtoti Printing & Publishing Co. (Pty) Ltd., 33 Main Rd., Doonside 4126, Natal, South Africa. TEL 27-31-9032341. FAX 27-31-9035756. Ed. Heather Butler. adv.; bk.rev.; play rev. circ. 5,882. (tabloid format) **Document type:** newspaper.

052   SA
SOUTHERN AFRICA REPORT. (Text and summaries in English) 1983. w. $550. Southern Africa Report Association, Dept. 9B, P.O. Box 261579, Excom 2023, South Africa. Ed. Raymond Louw. charts. (back issues avail.)

079.68 052   SA   ISSN 1016-3697
THE SOWETAN. (Text in English) 1980. d. P.O. Box 6663, Johannesburg 2000, South Africa. TEL 27-11-4740128. FAX 27-11-4740652. Owner(s): Argus Printing & Publishing. Ed. A. Klaaste. adv. circ. 200,000. **Document type:** newspaper.

079.62   SA   ISSN 0038-8629
SPRINGS & BRAKPAN ADVERTISER. (Text in Afrikaans and English) 1916. w. (Fri.). R.78. Springs Advertiser (Pty) Ltd., 88 Third St., P.O. Box 138, Springs 1560, South Africa. TEL 27-11-812-1600. FAX 27-11-812-1908. Owner(s): M.O. Dannheisser, P.S. Dannheisser. Ed. C. Stagg; Pub. M.O. Dannheisser. adv. contact: L. Pretorius. play rev.; illus.; circ. 11,500 (paid). cols./p.: 7; pp./issue: 52. (tabloid format; also avail. in microfilm from PSL) **Document type:** newspaper.

079.68 052   SA   ISSN 1016-3700
STAR. (Text in English) 1881. d. (Mon.-Sat.). P.O. Box 1014, Johannesburg 2000, South Africa. TEL 27-11-6339111. FAX 27-11-8366186. Owner(s): Argus Printing & Publishing. Ed. Richard Steyn. adv. circ. 377,000. **Document type:** newspaper.

079.68 052   SA   ISSN 1016-3727
SUNDAY STAR. Key Title: Sunday Star (Late Final Edition). Regional edition: Sunday Star (Africa Edition) (ISSN 1016-3719) (Text in English) 1984. w. P.O. Box 1014, Johannesburg 2000, South Africa. TEL 27-11-6339111. FAX 27-11-8384714. Owner(s): Argus Printing & Publishing. Ed. Dave Hazelhurst. adv. circ. 101,761. **Document type:** newspaper.

079.68 052   ISSN 0039-5331
SUNDAY TIMES. (Text in English) 1906. w. (Sun.) P.O. Box 1090, Johannesburg 2000, South Africa. TEL 27-11-4972711. FAX 27-11-4972664. Owner(s): Times Media Ltd. Ed. Ken Owen. adv. circ. 530,000. **Document type:** newspaper.
—BLDSC (8533.555360).

079.68 052   SA   ISSN 1016-6939
SUNDAY TRIBUNE. (Text in English) 1972. w. P.O. Box 47549, Greyville, Durban 4023, South Africa. TEL 27-31-3082100. FAX 27-31-3082111. Owner(s): Natal Newspapers Ltd. Ed. D. Wightman. adv. circ. 124,249. **Document type:** newspaper.

079.68 053.936   SA   ISSN 1016-3735
TRANSVALER. (Johannesburg & Pretoria editions avail.) (Text in Afrikaans) 1937. d. P.O. Box 845, Johannesburg 2000, South Africa. TEL 27-11-7769111. FAX 27-11-402-0037. Owner(s): Perskorporasie van Suid-Afrika Bpk. Ed. Gerhard Burger. adv. circ. 42,000. **Document type:** newspaper.

079.68   SA
VENSTER VAN DIE OVERBERG. (Text in Afrikaans and English) 1907. w. R.10.73($16) Caledon Venster Printing Works, Box 40, Caledon 7230, South Africa. TEL 27-281-23074. FAX 27-281-23075. Ed. F. Du Plessis. adv.; illus. circ. 3,000. **Document type:** newspaper.
Description: Contains items of local interest.

079.68 053.936   SA   ISSN 1018-6999
DIE VOLKSBLAD. (Text in Afrikaans) 1916. d. P.O. Box 267, Bloemfontein 9300, South Africa. TEL 27-51-473351. FAX 27-51-4777363. Owner(s): National Media. Ed. Johan de Wet. adv. circ. 27,268. **Document type:** newspaper.

079.68 053.936   SA   ISSN 1015-9649
VRYE WEEKBLAD. (Text in Afrikaans) 1988. w. P.O. Box 177, Newtown, Johannesburg 2113, South Africa. TEL 27-11-836-2151. FAX 27-11-8385901. Ed. Max du Preez. adv. circ. 13,000. **Document type:** newspaper.

079.68 052   SA   ISSN 1016-3751
WEEKLY MAIL. (Text in English) 1985. w. P.O. Box 260425, Excom, Johannesburg 2023, South Africa. TEL 27-11-3342400. FAX 27-11-3342905. Eds. Anton Harber, Irwin Manoim. adv. circ. 31,000. **Document type:** newspaper.

GENERAL INTEREST PERIODICALS — South America

see also General Interest
 Periodicals–Argentina; General Interest
 Periodicals–Bolivia; General Interest
 Periodicals–Brazil; General Interest
 Periodicals–Chile; General Interest
 Periodicals–Colombia; General Interest
 Periodicals–Ecuador; General Interest
 Periodicals–Guyana; General Interest
 Periodicals–Paraguay; General Interest
 Periodicals–Peru; General Interest
 Periodicals–Uruguay; General Interest
 Periodicals–Venezuela

ECOS DE ESPANA. see *GENERAL INTEREST PERIODICALS — Spain*

056.1 051   US
LATINA. (Text in English, Spanish) 1990. m. free. Box 581546, Minneapolis, MN 55458-1546. TEL 612-623-4305. Ed. Sally Lund. adv.: B&W page $800, color page $1275; trim 8 x 10. circ. 10,000. **Document type:** consumer publication.

056.1   VE   ISSN 0379-6922
F1401
MUNDO NUEVO; revista de estudios latinoamericanos. 1978. q. Bs.240($24) Universidad Simon Bolivar, Instituto de Altos Estudios de America Latina, Apdo. Postal 17.271, Caracas 1015-A, Venezuela. Ed. Miguel Angel Burelli Rivas. adv.; bk.rev. circ. 2,000. **Indexed:** Hisp.Amer.Per.Ind.

056.9 056.1   BL   ISSN 0103-6777
NOSSA AMERICA. Spanish edition: Nuestra America (ISSN 0103-6785) 1989. bi-m. Cr.$5300 per no. Memorial de America Latina, Avda. Mario de Andrade, 664, 01156 Sao Paulo SP, Brazil. TEL 011-823-9611. FAX 011-825-7545. TELEX 1124190. Ed. Eric Nepomuceno. **Document type:** consumer publication.

GENERAL INTEREST PERIODICALS — Spain

056.1   SP   ISSN 0569-9789
ANALECTA CALASANCTIANA; publicacion semestral religioso-cultural y de investigacion historica. 1959. s-a. 1500 ptas.($20) (Colegio Teologado P. Felipe Scio) Escuelas Pias de Espana, Delegacion Generel, Canalejas 129, Apdo. 206, 37080 Salamanca, Spain. Dir. Jose P. Burgues. bk.rev.; bibl.; index. circ. 400. (back issues avail.) **Indexed:** Amer.Hist.& Life, Hist.Abstr.

054   SP
ASSOCIACO "OMNIUM CULTURAL." BUTLLETI INTERIOR INFORMATIU. (Text and summaries in Catalan) 1972. q. membership. Associacio "Omnium Cultural", Montcada 20 Pral (Palau Dalmases), Barcelona 3, Spain. play rev.; bibl. circ. 19,000.
Description: Explores Catalan culture and language.

056.1   SP   ISSN 0211-6200
LA BICI. 1982. m. Moredi, S.A., Rafael Herrera, 3-1, 28036 Madrid, Spain. TEL 7339713. FAX 7339673.

056.1   SP
BIERZO 7. 1984. w. Avda. del Ferrocarril 18, 24400 Ponferrada, Spain. TEL 987-404855. Ed. Maria Angeles Calvo Diez. circ. 3,000.

056.1   SP
CARTA DE ESPANA; revista de emigracion e inmigracion. 1960. m. $20. Ministerio de Trabajo y Seguridad Social, Instituto Espanol de Emigracion, Paseo del Pintor Rosales 44-46, 28008 Madrid, Spain. TEL 07-34-1-547-6305. Ed. Amparo Fernandez Nunez. adv.; bk.rev. circ. 20,000.
Description: Covers immigration to Spain and emigration to foreign countries.

056.1 052   SP   ISSN 0213-7534
CATALONIA CULTURE. English edition (ISSN 0214-266X); French edition (ISSN 0214-2678) 1987. bi-m. 5000 ptas.($50) Center Unesco de Catalunya, Mallorca, 285, 08037 Barcelona, Spain. FAX 457-58-51. TELEX 98314 CUNC. Ed.Bd. circ. 8,000.
Formerly: Catalonia.
Description: Offers data about the Catalan culture in its different aspects; literature, arts, science and technology.

056.1   SP   ISSN 0045-6896
AP60
CIERVO. 1951. m. 6000 ptas. (foreign 6800 ptas.). Publicaciones de el Ciervo, S.A., Calvet 56, entresuelo 3, Apdo. 12121, 08021 Barcelona, Spain. TEL 93-2005145. FAX 93-2011015. Eds. Lorenzo Gomis Sanahuja, Rosario Bofill. adv.; bk.rev.; film rev.; play rev. circ. 5,000.
Description: Forum for free Christian thought in the world of culture.

056.1   SP
CIUDAD NUEVA INTERNACIONAL. 1958. m. 3000 ptas. (foreign 5000 ptas.). Focolare Movimiento, Andres Tamayo, 4, bajos, 28028 Madrid, Spain. TEL 255-95-30. FAX 361-14-12. adv.; bk.rev; film rev.; bibl. circ. 10,000. (back issues avail.)

CONSUMER SPAIN. see *BUSINESS AND ECONOMICS — Marketing And Purchasing*

054 052   SP
CORT; revista mallorquina. (Text in Catalan, English) 1947. s-m. 400. Miguel Ferrer Sureda, Troncoso, 9, Palma de Mallorca, Spain. Ed. Gaspar S. Serra. illus.

056.1   SP
CRONICA DE ALBACETE Y DE CASTILLA LA MANCHA; semanario regional de informacion general. 1972. w. 4500 ptas. Ediciones Cronica, S.L., Teodoro Camino 2, 6o, 02002 Albacete, Spain. TEL 3497-214387. FAX 3497-240536. Ed. Demetrio Gutierrez Alarcon. adv.; bk.rev.; film rev.; abstr.; bibl.; illus.; pat.; tr.lit. circ. 18,900.
Formerly (until 1985): Cronica de Albacete.

056.1   GW
ECOS DE ESPANA. m. Spotlight Verlag GmbH, Freihamerstr. 4b, 82166 Graefelfing, Germany. TEL 089-85482-0. FAX 089-8548223. Ed. Manuel Moral. adv. contact: Elke Pohl. circ. 14,800. **Document type:** consumer publication.

076   SP
EGIN. (Regional editions avail. for: Araban Zehar, Bizkaia, Gipuzkoa, Natarroa; Weekly supplements avail.: Gaztegin, Igandegin) (Text in Basque and Spanish) 1977. d. 25000 ptas. for 6 mos. Orain, S.A., Poligono Eziago 10B, 20120 Hernani, Gipuzkoa, Spain. TEL 554712. FAX 551207. Ed. Jabier Salutregi. adv. contact: Hector Senosiain. bk.rev.; film rev.; music rev.; play rev.; illus. circ. 51,366. cols./p.: 5; pp./issue: 82. (standard format; back issues avail.) **Document type:** newspaper.
Description: Covers general news, mostly of the Basque region.

056.1   SP
EUROPEO. 1988. m. 6300 ptas. (foreign 9900 ptas.). Ediciones Detursa, Serrano, 6 2o izda., 28001 Madrid, Spain. TEL 57717535. FAX 4311550. Ed. Antonio S. Idzikowski. adv.; bk.rev.; index. circ. 30,000. (back issues avail.)
Description: Covers architecture, art, music, theater, photography, fashion, books, museums and art galleries.

056.1   SP
EL FARO; decano de la prensa de Granada. w. C. Fray Vicente Pinilla, 17, 18600 Motril, Spain. TEL 958-82-06-19. FAX 958-82-34-18.

076   SP
FARO ASTORGANO. 1980. 5/w. 6000 ptas.($60) (effective Jan. 1992). Edypsa, Prensa Astorgana 2, 24700 Astorga, Leon, Spain. TEL 987-61-70-12. FAX 987-61-70-25. Ed. Isidro Martinez. adv.; bk.rev.; circ. 2,200. (paid). (tabloid format) **Document type:** newspaper.

056.1   SP
FUNDACION JUAN MARCH. ANALES. a. free. Fundacion Juan March, Servicio de Informacion y Prensa, Castello, 77, 28006 Madrid, Spain. TEL 435-42-40. FAX 576-34-20.

056.1   SP   ISSN 0210-4148
FUNDACION JUAN MARCH. BOLETIN INFORMATIVO. (Text in Spanish) 1971. m. free. Fundacion Juan March, Servicio de Informacion y Prensa, Castello, 77, 28006 Madrid, Spain. TEL 435-42-40. FAX 5763420. Ed. Andres Berlanga. illus. circ. 12,000. **Indexed:** GeoRef.

056.1   SP
GARBO. 1953. w. 1560 ptas.($22) M. Fernanda G. de Nadal, Tallers 62, Barcelona 1, Spain. adv.; bk.rev.; film rev.; bibl.; illus. circ. 103,000.

056.1   SP
GEO. m. 4800 ptas. (Europe 10700 ptas.; elsewhere 14700 ptas.). G y J Espana Ediciones, S.L. (Subsidiary of: Gruner & Jahr USA Publishing), Marques de Villamagna 4, 28001 Madrid, Spain. TEL 341-435-8100. Dir. Javier Rubio. adv. contact: Elena Sanchez Fabres. circ. 38,932. **Document type:** consumer publication.
Description: Explores the world we live in. Covers countries, cities, expeditions, travel and scientific and technical discoveries.

056.1   SP   ISSN 0018-330X
HOJA DEL LUNES DE ORENSE.* w. 360 ptas. Region, Cardenal Quiroga 11 y 15, Orense, Spain. adv.; play rev.; bibl.; illus.; tr.lit.; circ. controlled.

GENERAL INTEREST PERIODICALS — SRI LANKA

056.1 SP
HOLA. w. 17000 ptas. Empresa Editora Hola, S.A., Apdo. de Correo 14707, 28006 Madrid, Spain. Ed. Eduardo Sanchez Junco.

056.1 SP
INTERVIU. 1976. w. Ediciones Zeta, O'Donnell 12, 5a planta, 28009 Madrid, Spain. TEL 91-522-0072. FAX 91-577-6188. Ed. D. Eduardo Alvarez Puga. circ. 494,347.

056.1 SP ISSN 0210-8496
JABEGA. 1973. q. 1700 ptas. (foreign 2000 ptas.) (effective 1993). Diputacion Provincial, Servicio de Publicaciones, Palacio Provincial, Plaza de la Marina, Malaga, Spain. TEL 95-222-42-01. FAX 95-221-77-79. Ed. Victoria Rosado. bk.rev. circ. 3,000. (also avail. in microfiche; back issues avail.)

056.1 SP ISSN 0047-4304
LECTURAS. 1921. w. $401.20. H Y M S.A., Aribau 28, 08011 Barcelona, Spain. TEL 323-70-63. FAX 454-13-22. Ed. Julio Bou Gibert. adv. circ. 350,000.

052 SP ISSN 0024-6433
LOOKOUT. (Text in English) 1963. m. 3975 ptas.($40) Lookout Publications S.A., Puebla Lucia, Fuengirola (Malaga), Spain. TEL 52-460950. FAX 52-461022. Ed. Ken Brown. adv. contact: Steve Cameron. bk.rev.; illus. circ. 25,000.

076 SP
MAJORCA DAILY BULLETIN. (Text in English) 1962. d. (except Mon.). 2000 ptas.($15) per mo.; newsstand price: 100 ptas. Gruppo Serra, Palau de la Prensa, Passeig Mallorca 9A, 07011 Palma de Mallorca, Spain. TEL 788400. FAX 719706. Ed. Tom Sweeney; Pub. Pedro Serra. adv.: B&W page 77000 ptas., Sun. 87000 ptas.; adv. contact: Carmen Serra. music rev, play rev, illus. Wire service(s): RN. circ. 5,000. cols./p.: 6; pp./issue: 24. (tabloid format; back issues avail.) **Document type:** newspaper.

076 SP
MENORCA, DIARIO INSULAR. (Includes supplements: Teletodo, Antena Semanal) (Text in Catalan, Spanish) 1941. d. 33600 ptas. (in U.S. 13350 ptas. per mo.). Editorial Menorca, S.A., Avda. Central 5, 07714 Mahon, Baleares, Spain. TEL 971-35-16-00. FAX 971-35-38-35. Ed. Joan-Bosco Marques Bosch; Pub. Marcos Carreras Carreras. adv.: B&W page 113400 ptas. Tue.-Fri., 135980 ptas. Sat.-Mon.; 257 x 355; adv. contact: Rosa Pons Olives. bk.rev.; film rev.; play rev.; music rev.; illus. Wire service(s): EFE, OTR. circ. 5,219 (paid); 328 (controlled). cols./p.: 5; pp./issue: 32. (tabloid format; also avail. in microfiche; back issues avail.) **Document type:** newspaper.

076 SP
EL PAIS; panorama semanal. (Supplement avail.: Liber) 1983. w. $50. Prisa, Miguel Yuste, 40, Madrid-17, Spain. Ed. Juan Luis Cebrian. adv. circ. 27,000. **Document type:** newspaper.

056.1 SP
PRONTO. 1972. w. Publicaciones Heres, S.A., Gran Via de Carlos 3, 124-5o, 08034 Barcelona, Spain. TEL 93-2805555. FAX 93-205-2658. Ed. Antonio G. Abad. circ. 925,108.

076 SP
REGIO 7. (Text in Catalan) 1978. d. (except Sun.). newsstand price: 100 ptas. Edicions Intercomarcals, S.A., St. Antoni M. Claret, 32, 08240 Manresa (Barcelona), Spain. TEL 874-64-54. FAX 874-03-52. Ed. Joan Montraveta Montraveta. adv. contact: Jordi Guals Gorgues. bk.rev.; film rev.; music rev.; illus.; circ. 8,177 (paid). cols./p.: 5; pp./issue: 40. (tabloid format) **Document type:** newspaper.
Description: Contains local and general information.

056.1 054 SP
REUS; semanario de la ciudad. (Text in Catalan and Spanish) 1952. w. 520 ptas. Editorial Reddis S.A., Baja del Carmen, 23, Reus (Tarragona), Spain. Ed. Carlos Giro Puig.

054.9 SP ISSN 0213-5876
REVISTA DE CATALUNYA. (Text in Catalan) 1986. m. (except Aug.). 8600 ptas. (Europe 11500 ptas.; elsewhere $120) (effective 1993). Fundacion Revista de Catalunya, Bisbe Cacador, Num. 3, 08002 Barcelona, Spain. TEL 93-310-23-49. (Dist. by: Publicaciones de L'Abadia de Montserrat, C. Ausias Marc 92-98, 08013 Barcelona, Spain) Ed. Max Cahner. adv.; bk.rev.; index. (back issues avail.)

056.1 SP ISSN 0210-2854
DP302.E83
REVISTA DE ESTUDIOS EXTREMENOS. 1927. 3/yr. 1000 ptas.($12) Centro de Estudios Extremenos, Servicio de Publicaciones, Felipe Checa 15, 06071 Badajoz, Spain. Ed. Manuel Pecellin Lancharro. bk.rev. circ. 1,000. (back issues avail.) **Indexed:** Amer.Hist.& Life, Hist.Abstr.
● Also available online.

056.1 SP ISSN 0037-1793
SEMANA; revista grafica. 1940. w. 5600 ptas.($11.60) Semana, S.A., Cuesta de San Vicente, 26, Aptdo. 383, 28008 Madrid, Spain. TEL 91-2472300. adv.; bk.rev.; illus. circ. 340,590.

056.1 SP ISSN 0495-5773
TIERRAS DE LEON. 1961. q. 2400 ptas. Institucion "Fray Bernardino de Sahagun", Edificio Fierro, Puerta de la Reina, 1, Leon, Spain. illus.

053.1 GW ISSN 0930-0724
TRANVIA; Revue der Iberischen Halbinsel. 1986. q. DM.36. Postfach 303626, 10707 Berlin, Germany. TEL 030-8832561. Eds. Walter Frey, Brunhilde Wehinger. adv.; bk.rev.; film rev.; play rev.; illus. circ. 2,000. (back issues avail.) **Document type:** consumer publication.
Description: Covers the culture and politics of the Iberian Peninsula.

076 SP
LA VOZ DE AVILES. 1908. d. 32301 ptas.($230) Avda. Gijon 70, 33400 Aviles, Spain. TEL 98-5540000. FAX 98-5544340. Ed. Juan Manuel Lopez Wes. adv. contact: Juan Carlos Grande Palomares. bk.rev.; film rev.; music rev.; play rev.; illus. circ. 8,500 (morn. ed.); 10,500 (Sun. ed.). cols./p.: 5; pp./issue: 36. (tabloid format; also avail. in microfilm) **Document type:** newspaper.

GENERAL INTEREST PERIODICALS — Sri Lanka

079.5493 CE
JANATHA; daily evening newspaper. (Text in Sinhala) 1953. d. newsstand price: Rs.3.50. Associated Newpapers of Ceylon Ltd., Lake House, D.R. Wijewardena Mawatha, Colombo 10, Sri Lanka. TEL 94-1-421181. FAX 94-1-449069. Ed. M. Newton Pinto. adv.; bk.rev.; film rev.; illus. circ. 35,000. (tabloid format; also avail. in microfilm; back issues avail.; reprint service avail.) **Document type:** newspaper.

079.5493 052 CE
THE SRI LANKA NEWS. (Text in English) w. Associated Newspapers of Ceylon Ltd., Lake House, D.R. Wijewardene Mawatha, Colombo 10, Sri Lanka. TEL 94-1-421181. FAX 94-1-449069. TELEX 22262 CE. **Document type:** newspaper.
Formerly: Ceylon News.

052 CE ISSN 0490-6381
SRI LANKA.* 1972. m. Government Information Department, 7 Sir Baron Jayatilleke Mawatha, Colombo 1, Sri Lanka. Ed.Bd. charts; illus.

079.5493 052 CE
SUNDAY TIMES. (Text in English) 1923. w. Rs.9 per no. Wijeya Newspapers (Pvt.) Ltd., 47 W.A.D. Ramanayake Mawatha, Colombo 2, Sri Lanka. FAX 423922. TELEX 21266 LAK EXPO CE. Ed. Sinha Ratnatunga. adv.; bk.rev. circ. 60,000. **Indexed:** Fuel & Energy Abstr.; High.Educ.Curr.Aware.Bull. **Document type:** newspaper.
Supersedes: Times of Ceylon Sunday Illustrated.
Description: Covers news and current affairs of interest to Sri Lanka.

GENERAL INTEREST PERIODICALS — Sudan

052 SJ
NILE MIRROR. (Text in English) irreg. Ministry of Southern Affairs, Khartoum, Sudan.

052 SJ
S U N A. Variant title: S U N A Daily Bulletin. (Text in English) 1958. d. Sudan News Agency, Box 1506, Elgamhouria St., Khartoum, Sudan.
Supersedes: Sudan News Agency. English Daily Bulletin (ISSN 0562-5092)

GENERAL INTEREST PERIODICALS — Sultanate Of Oman

079.536 052 MK
OMAN DAILY OBSERVER. (Supplement avail.) (Text in English) 1981. d. (Sat.-Thu.). Oman Newspaper House, P.O. Box 3002, Ruwi, Muscat 112, Sultanate of Oman. TEL 701555. FAX 790524. Ed. Said Bin Khalfan Al-Harthy; Pub. Abdul Wahab Al-Mantheri. adv. contact: Mohammed Al-Kamali. bk.rev.; film rev.; music rev.; tele.rev.; illus. Wire service(s): RN. cols./p.: 8; pp./issue: 20. (broadsheet format) **Document type:** newspaper.

079.9535 052 MK
TIMES OF OMAN. (Text in English) 1975. d. Essa Mohammad Essa al-Zedjali, Ed. & Pub., P.O. Box 770, Ruwi 112, Sultanate of Oman. TEL 701953. FAX 799153. TELEX 3352. adv.; bk.rev. circ. 15,000. **Document type:** newspaper.

079.536 MK
UMAN. (Supplements avail.) (Text in Arabic) 1972. d. Oman Newspaper House, P.O. Box 3002, Ruwi, Muscat 112, Sultanate of Oman. TEL 701555. FAX 790524. Ed. Hamood Al-Siyabi; Pub. Abdul Wahab Al-Mantheri. adv. contact: Mohammed Al-Kamali. bk.rev.; film rev.; music rev.; tele.rev.; illus. cols./p.: 8; pp./issue: 20. (broadsheet format) **Document type:** newspaper.

GENERAL INTEREST PERIODICALS — Surinam

053.931 SR
SURINAAMS NIEUWS AGENTSCHAP. BULLETIN. (Editions in Dutch, English) d. Surinaams Nieuws Agentschap, Gravenstraat 39C, Paramaribo, Surinam. TELEX 258. Dir. E.G.J. deMees.

GENERAL INTEREST PERIODICALS — Swaziland

052 SQ
NEWS FROM SWAZILAND. w. Swaziland Broadcasting and Information Service, Allister Miller St., POB 464, Mbabane, Swaziland. TEL 42771. TELEX 2035.

052 SQ
SWAZI LIFE. 1984. m. Mbabane House, POB 592, Mbabane, Swaziland. TEL 44408. TELEX 2191. Eds. A. Mbuli, E. Stephens.

052 SQ
THE SWAZI NEWS. 1983. w. (Sat. in English). The Times of Swaziland, POB 156, Mbabane, Swaziland. TEL 42211. TELEX 2097. Ed. Jabu E. Matsebula. circ. 7,000.

079.6887 SQ
SWAZILAND OBSERVER. (Text in English) 1981. d. Swazi Plaza, POB A385, Mbabane, Swaziland. TEL 23383. TELEX 2322. Ed. Timothy Shongwe. circ. 8,000. **Document type:** newspaper.

052 SQ
SWAZIVIEW. 1988. m. POB 1532, Mbabane, Swaziland. TEL 42716. circ. 3,500.

079.6887 SQ
THE TIMES OF SWAZILAND. 1897. d. The Times of Swaziland, Allister Miller St., POB 156, Mbabane, Swaziland. TEL 42211. TELEX 2097. Ed. Norman Sowerby. circ. 11,000. (also avail. in microfilm from PSL) **Document type:** newspaper.
Incorporates: Business in Swaziland.

052 SQ
TINDZABA NEWS. (Text in English, siSwati) m. Swaziland Broadcasting and Information Service, Allister Miller St., POB 464, Mbabane, Swaziland.

GENERAL INTEREST PERIODICALS — SWEDEN

059.968 SQ
UMBIKI. (Text in siSwati) m. Swaziland Broadcasting and Information Service, Allister Miller St., POB 464, Mbabane, Swaziland. TEL 42761. TELEX 2035.

GENERAL INTEREST PERIODICALS —
Sweden

058.7 SW ISSN 0400-2334
AARET RUNT. 1946. w. SEK 695. Aaret Runt Foerlaget, S-105 44 Stockholm, Sweden. TEL 08-7365200. FAX 08-304900. TELEX 10043 BONMAGS. (Subscr. to: P.O. Box 3217, S-103 64 Stockholm, Sweden) Ed. Arne Winerdal. adv.; illus. circ. 310,000.
   Incorporates (in 1952): Vaart Hem.

078.5 SW
AFTONBLADET. 1830. d. Tidningen Aftonbladet AB, Arenavaegen 63, Globen, S-105 18 Stockholm, Sweden. TEL 46-8-725-20-00. FAX 46-8-600-01-82. TELEX 100 65. Eds. Rolf Alsing, Thorbjoern Larsson. adv.; B&W page SEK 62000, color page SEK 75000; trim 252 x 380; adv. contact: Mart Nurk. circ. 342,500. cols./p.: 5. **Document type:** newspaper.

058.7 SW ISSN 0345-0759
ALLAS VECKOTIDNING. 1931. w. SEK 587. Allers Foerlag AB, S-251 85 Helsingborg, Sweden. Ed. T. Jansson. adv.; film rev.; charts; illus. circ. 222,087.

058.7 SW ISSN 0002-578X
ALLERS. 1877. w. SEK 587. Allers Foerlag AB, 251 85 Helsingborg, Sweden. TEL 46-42-17-35-00. FAX 46-42-17-35-68. Ed. Chris Bergendorff. circ. 279,211. (also avail. in audio cassette)

078.5 SW
ARBETARBLADET. 1902. 6/w. AB Arbetarbladet, Hattmakargatan 12, P.O. Box 287, S-801 04 Gaevle, Sweden. TEL 46-026015093-00. FAX 46-026-18-52-70. TELEX 47033. Ed. Rune Sjoegren. adv. contact: Leif Larsson. circ. 29,600. **Document type:** newspaper.

078.5 SW ISSN 0345-0961
ARBETAREN; veckotidning for frihetlig politik ekonomi och kultur. vol.69, 1922. w. SEK 432. Sveriges Arbetares Centralorganisation, P.O. Box 6507, S-113 83 Stockholm, Sweden. TEL 46-8-16-08-90. FAX 46-8-673-03-45. Ed. Martin Nilsson. adv. contact: Birgitta Ekengren. bk.rev.; charts; illus. (tabloid format; also avail. in microform) **Document type:** newspaper.
   Formerly (until 1958): Dagstidningen Arbetaren.
   Description: Publishes news on politics, economy, culture and union affairs.

078.5 SW
ARVIKA NYHETER. 1895. d. AB Arvika Nyheter, P.O. Box 925, S-671 29 Arvika, Sweden. TEL 46-0570-170-00. FAX 46-0570-198-80. Ed. Ove Ekloef. adv. contact: Pia Forslund. circ. 13,400. **Document type:** newspaper.

058.7 SW ISSN 1100-4843
DET BAESTA/READER'S DIGEST. Spine title: D B. 1943. m. SEK 269 (foreign SEK 319). Reader's Digest AB, P.O. Box 25, 164 93 Kista, Sweden. TEL 46-8-752-03-60. FAX 46-8-752-87-01. Ed. Ullastina Oestberg. adv.; bk.rev.; illus.; circ. 200,700 (controlled).
   Formerly (until 1988): Baesta ur Reader's Digest (ISSN 0005-3864)
   Description: General interest family magazine with international contents covering subjects from science, medicine and health, to travel, culture, art-of-living and humor.

078.5 SW
BORAAS TIDNING. 1826. d. AB Boraas Tidning, Allegatan 67, P.O. Box 224, S-501 04 Boraas, Sweden. TEL 46-033-17-80-00. FAX 46-033-10-14-36. TELEX 36051. Ed. Jan Oejmertz. adv.; B&W page SEK 36750, color page SEK 42200; adv. contact: Kjell Hemmaroe. circ. 57,100. **Document type:** newspaper.

058.7 052 SW ISSN 1101-6345
HN571
CURRENT SWEDEN. 1970. irreg. (8-10/yr.). free. Svenska Institutet - Swedish Institute, P.O. Box 7434, S-103 91 Stockholm, Sweden. TEL 46-8-789-20-00. FAX 46-8-20-72-48. TELEX 10025 SWEDINS S. (Dist. in U.S. by: Swedish Information Service, One Dag Hammarskjold Plaza, New York, NY 10017-2201) Ed. Gabrielle Sjoestedt. index. circ. 4,500 (English ed.); 2,000(French ed.); 2,500(German ed.); 2,000(Spanish ed.). (processed) **Indexed:** Biol.Dig.
   —BLDSC (3504.056000).
   Incorporates (1973-1978): Environment Planning and Conservation in Sweden.
   Description: Publishes articles about issues in the Swedish public debate.

078.5 SW
DAGEN. d. Dagengruppen AB, Gammelgaardsvaegen 38-42, S-105 36 Stockholm, Sweden. TEL 46-8-619-24-00. TELEX 10888. Ed. Olof Djurfeldt. adv.; B&W page SEK 15480, color page SEK 20880; adv. contact: Runo Bergstroem. circ. 20,200. **Document type:** newspaper.

078.5 SW
DAGENS NYHETER. d. Dagens Nyheter AB, Raalambsvaegen 17, S-105 15 Stockholm, Sweden. TEL 46-8-738-10-00. FAX 46-8-54-57-90. Eds. Christina Juttestroem, Svante Nycander. adv.; B&W page SEK 148488, color page SEK 203000. circ. 407,126. **Document type:** newspaper.

058.7 SW ISSN 0011-5916
DAMERNAS VAERLD. Variant title: Nya Damernas Vaerld. 1934. m. SEK 390. Bonniers Maanads Tidningar, Sveavaegen 53, S-105 44 Stockholm, Sweden. FAX 46-8-315916. (Subscr. to: Box 6422, S-113 82 Stockholm, Sweden) Ed. Eva Birmann. adv.; illus. circ. 131,000.
   Formerly (until 1946): Flitiga Haender.

078.5 SW
ESKILSTUNA - KURIREN; med Strengnaes Tidning. 1890. 6/w. Eskilstuna-Kurirens AB, Rademachergatan 14-16, P.O. Box 120, S-631 02 Eskilstuna, Sweden. TEL 46-16-15-60-00. FAX 46-16-11-98-37. Ed. Jerker Norin. adv.: B&W page SEK 22300, color page SEK 31975; adv. contact: Jan Zachrisson. circ. 34,000. **Document type:** newspaper.

▼078.5 SW
EXPRESSEN. d. Kvaellstidningen Expressen AB, Gjoerwellsgatan 30, S-105 16 Stockholm, Sweden. TEL 46-8-738-30-00. FAX 46-8-619-00-50. TELEX 17480 EXPRES S. Ed. Olle Waestberg. adv.: B&W page SEK 46000, color page SEK 48000; adv. contact: Stefan Seboe.

058.7 SW ISSN 0283-0647
FIB-AKTUELLT. 1962. w. SEK 690. Baltic Press AB, Box 30204, 104 25 Stockholm, Sweden. Ed. Jan Toernqvist. circ. 55,000.

078.5 SW
GOETEBORGS - POSTEN. 1858. d. Tidnings AB Stampen, Polhemsplatsen 5, S-405 02 Goeteborg, Sweden. TEL 46-31-624-000. FAX 46-31-157-918. Ed. Peter Hjoerne. circ. 276,000. **Document type:** newspaper.

078.5 SW
GOTLANDS ALLEHANDA. 1872. 6/w. Gotlands Allehandas Tryckeri AB, Brovaeg. 21, P.O. Box 1284, S-621 23 Visby, Sweden. TEL 46-498-20-25-00. FAX 46-498-21-00-03. Ed. Goeran Mattsson. adv. contact: Jan Klingsell. circ. 12,400. **Document type:** newspaper.

078.5 SW
GOTLANDS TIDNINGAR. 1884. 6/w. Gotlands Tidningar AB, Brovaeg. 10, P.O. Box 1223, S-621 23 Visby, Sweden. TEL 46-498-21-52-30. FAX 46-498-21-11-97. Eds. Haakan Ericsson, Hans E. Andersson. adv.; B&W page SEK 11875, color page SEK 13629; adv. contact: Goeran Haellstroem. circ. 13,200. **Document type:** newspaper.
   Formed by the merger of (1928-1983): Gotlands Folkblad; (1884-1983): Gotlaenningen.

078.5 SW
HAELSINGE KURIREN. 1895. 6/w.(plus w. supplement). SEK 1495; newsstand price: SEK 7. Haelsinge Kuriren AB, Braedgaardsgatan 6, S-826 27 Soederhamn, Haelsingland, Sweden. TEL 46-270-70-000. FAX 46-270-103-25. Ed. Soeren Thunell; Pub. Bo Praentarje. adv. contact: Oerjan Faelth. circ. 12,200. cols./p.: 5; pp./issue: 40. (tabloid format; also avail. in magnetic tape) **Document type:** newspaper.

058.7 SW ISSN 0345-4843
HAENT I VECKAN. 1964. w. SEK 587. Allers Foerlag AB, S-251 85 Helsingborg, Sweden. Ed. Bengt Gustavsson. circ. 176,648.

078.5 SW
HELSINGBORGS DAGBLAD. d. Helsingborgs Dagblad AB, Vasatorpsvaegen 1, P.O. Box 822, S-251 08 Helsingborg, Sweden. TEL 46-42-17-51-16. FAX 46-42-17-51-56. TELEX 722 41 HDPRESS. Ed. Sven-Aake Olofsson. adv.; B&W page SEK 36565, color page SEK 47377; adv. contact: Jonas Wahlbeck. circ. 50,800. **Document type:** newspaper.

058.7 SW ISSN 0345-4630
HEMMETS VECKOTIDNING. 1929. w. SEK 695. Allers Foerlag AB, S-251 85 Helsingborg, Sweden. Ed. Ulla Cocke. circ. 285,000.

058.7 SW ISSN 1101-9581
HENNES SERIER. 1945-1981; resumed 1990. q. SEK 15 per no. Hemmets Journal AB, Fack, S-200 22 Malmoe 3, Sweden. Ed. Meta Andersson. circ. 100,000.
   Former titles (until 1981): Hennes (ISSN 0018-0394); (until vol.17, 1964): Hennes Aelsklingstidning Fick; (until vol.27, 1963): Fick; (until 1961): Fickjournalen.

058.7 SW ISSN 0345-4991
INVANDRARTIDNINGEN (WEEKLY); Easy Swedish edition. English edition (ISSN 0349-5515); Finnish edition (ISSN 0346-3923); Greek edition (ISSN 0345-9055); Serbo-Croatian edition (ISSN 0345-8288); Spanish edition (ISSN 0349-5523) Polish edition (SW ISSN 0349-5531) 1967. w. (44/yr.). SEK 190 in Sweden; other Nordic countries SEK 240; elsewhere SEK 490 (effective Nov.1993). Stiftelsen Invandrartidningen, P.O. Box 1352, S-111 83 Stockholm, Sweden. TEL 08-787-87-00. FAX 08-723-08-69.
   Description: News and information to immigrants in Sweden.

058.7 SW ISSN 0345-6471
KONTAKTEN. 1939. 10/yr. free. L.M. Ericsson AB, HF-LME-1, 12625 Stockholm, Sweden. FAX 46-87-19-19-76. Ed. Lars-Goeran Hedin. adv.; illus. circ. 47,000.
   Description: Internal magazine of the Ericsson Corporation.

078.5 SW
KRISTIANSTADSBLADET. (Supplement avail.: T V - Bladet.) d. Kristianstadsbladet Larson & Olofson KB, V. Vallgatan 2, P.O. Box 537, S-291 25 Kristianstad, Sweden. TEL 46-44-18-55-00. FAX 46-44-12-89-84. Ed/Bd. adv.; B&W page SEK 40000, color page SEK 44600; adv. contact: Stefan Isberg. circ. 32,300. **Document type:** newspaper.

058.7 SW ISSN 0023-5822
KVAELLSSTUNDEN. 1938. w. SEK 360. Lantmaennens Tryckeri-Forening, P.O. Box 1080, S-721 27 Vaesteraas 1, Sweden. TEL 190-400. FAX 188-434. Ed. Aake Lindberg. adv.; bk.rev.; illus. circ. 72,000.

058.7 SW ISSN 0345-7109
LEKTYR.* 1923. m. SEK 326 (effective 1991). Baltic Press, P.O. Box 30204, S-104 25 Stockholm, Sweden. Eds. Jan Bard, Alex Odelius.

058.7 SW
LUNDIAN. (Text in English) 1988. m. $50. (English International Association) M. Arthur Diakite, P.O. Box 722, S-220 07 Lund, Sweden. TEL 46-111322. FAX 46-111322. Ed. M. Robinson. bk.rev.; circ. 10,000 (controlled). (back issues avail.) **Document type:** newsletter.

058.7 SW ISSN 1100-0589
MAANADENS STOPP. 1963. m. SEK 327 (effective 1991). Baltic Press AB, Box 30204, 104 25 Stockholm, Sweden. Ed. Jan Toernqvist. adv.; illus. circ. 50,000.

GENERAL INTEREST PERIODICALS — SWITZERLAND

058.7 SW ISSN 0349-4225
MAANADSJOURNALEN. 1980. m. SEK 474 (effective 1991). Bonniers Maanads Tidningar, Sveavaagen 53, S-105 44 Stockholm, Sweden. FAX 46-8-32-78-40. (Subscr. to: P.O. Box 3263, S-103-65 Stockholm, Sweden) Ed. Stefan Mehr. adv.; bk.rev.; charts; illus. circ. 64,000. (also avail. in audio cassette)
Supersedes (1910-1980): Veckojournalen (ISSN 0042-2940)

078.5 SW
NORRLAENDSKA SOCIALDEMOKRATEN. 1919. d. Tryckeri AB Norrlaendska Socialdemokraten, Robertsviksgatan 5, S-951 83 Luleaa, Sweden. TEL 46-920-360-00. FAX 46-920-171-42. TELEX 68301. Ed. Aake Haerdfeldt. adv. contact: Roland Lindgren. circ. 43,400. **Document type:** newspaper.

058.7 320 SW ISSN 0345-8350
NY SOLIDARITET; internationell veckotidning foer politik, industri, vetenskap och kultur. 1974. 24/yr. SEK 250 (effective 1990). Ny Solidaritet, P.O. Box 5846, S-102 48 Stockholm, Sweden.

078.5 SW
OERNSKOELDSVIK ALLEHANDA. 1894. 6/w. AB Allehanda, Centralgatan 18, P.O. Box 110, S-891 23 Oernskoeldsvik, Sweden. TEL 46-660-100-60. FAX 46-660-184-46. TELEX 6056. Ed. Jerry Erixon. adv.: B&W page SEK 14900, color page SEK 17600; adv. contact: Bernt Gideonsson. circ. 22,200. **Document type:** newspaper.

078.5 SW
OESTERSUNDS - POSTEN. 1877. 6/w. Oestersunds-Postens Tryckeri AB, Kyrkgatan 32, P.O. Box 720, S-831 28 Oestersund, Sweden. TEL 46-63-16-16-00. FAX 46-63-11-60-07. Ed. Haakan Larsson. adv.: B&W page SEK 21627, color page SEK 24827; adv. contact: Per-Aake Einarsson. circ. 30,000. **Document type:** newspaper.

078.5 SW
OESTGOETA CORRESPONDENTEN. 1838. 6/w. AB Oestgoeta Correspondenten, Badhusgatan 5, S-581 89 Linkoeping, Sweden. TEL 46-13-28-00-00. FAX 46-13-11-42-40. TELEX 50054 CORRE S. Ed. Ernst Klein. adv.: B&W page SEK 37904, color page SEK 44984. circ. 66,400. **Document type:** newspaper.

078.5 NP
OESTRA SMAALAND - NYHETERNA. 1928. 6/w. Tidningen Oestra Smaaland, Amerikavaegen 1, P.O. Box 612, S-391 26 Kalmar, Sweden. TEL 46-480-613-00. FAX 46-480-877-60. TELEX 43005. adv.: B&W page SEK 21714, color page SEK 25498; adv. contact: Evert Baeckstroem. circ. 13,200. **Document type:** newspaper.

078.5 SW
SKAANSKA DAGBLADET. 1888. d. AB Skaanska Dagbladet, Oestergatan 11, P.O. Box 165, S-201 21 Malmoe, Sweden. TEL 46-40-738-00. FAX 46-40-30-48-23. TELEX 32 312 SKDAN S. Ed. Jan A. Johansson. adv.: B&W page SEK 30000, color page SEK 39400; adv. contact: Stig Nilsson. circ. 30,000. **Document type:** newspaper.

078.5 SW
SMAALANDS - TIDNINGEN; med Smaalands Dagblad, Vetlanda Posten och Tranaas Tidning. 1899. d. Smaalands-Tidningens Tryckeri AB, Stora Torget 4, P.O. Box 261, S-575 23 Eksjoe, Sweden. TEL 46-381-132-00. FAX 46-381-151-90. Ed. Margaretha Nilsson. adv.: B&W page SEK 37100, color page SEK 45400; adv. contact: Bror-Gunnar Andersson. circ. 37,659. **Document type:** newspaper.

078.5 SW
SOEDERMANLANDS NYHETER. 1893. 6/w. Soedermanlands Nyheter AB, St. Annegatan 3, S-611 79 Nykoeping, Sweden. TEL 46-155-767-00. FAX 46-155-26-86-82. Ed. Lars J. Eriksson. adv. contact: Yngve Fredriksson. circ. 24,500. **Document type:** newspaper.

078.5 SW
SVENSKA DAGBLADET. 1884. d. Svenska Dagbladet AB & Co., Gjoerwellsgatan 28, S-105 17 Stockholm, Sweden. TEL 46-8-13-50-00. FAX 46-8-618-60-04. Ed. Mats Svegfors. adv.: B&W page SEK 132200, color page SEK 181000; adv. contact: Tomas Waktel. circ. 215,491. **Document type:** newspaper.

058.7 SW ISSN 0346-2315
SVENSKA JOURNALEN; foer hemmet och familjen. 1925. fortn. SEK 294 (effective 1990). Siktgatan 8, 162 88 Vaellingby, Sweden. adv. circ. 71,300.
Formerly (until vol.51, 1956): Svenska Journalen, Hemmet och Familjen; Formed by the 1953 Merger of: Hemmet och Familjen; Svenska Journalen.

058.7 SW ISSN 0039-6958
SVERIGE-NYTT/SWEDISH DIGEST. (Text in Swedish) 1948. w. SEK 990($86.50) Aktiebolaget Sverige-Nytt, P.O. Box 47307, S-100 74 Stockholm, Sweden. FAX 08-457666. (Subscr. to: P.O. Box 12345, 200 23 Malmoe, Sweden) Ed. Mats Ahlsen. adv.; bk.rev.; illus. circ. 4,500. (tabloid format)

058.7 SW ISSN 0346-2439
SVERIGEKONTAKT; en tidning foer all vaerldens svenskar. 1914. q. SEK 100 membership (effective 1991). Riksfoereningen Sverigekontakt, P.O. Box 53066, S-400 14 Goeteborg, Sweden. FAX 031-209902. Ed. Lennart Limberg. adv.; bk.rev.; illus. circ. 5,000.
Formerly (until 1972): Allsvensk Samling (ISSN 0002-6174)

052 SW
HC371
SWEDEN NOW. German edition: Schweden Heute (ISSN 0346-0789); Italian edition: Svezia Oggi. 1967. bi-m. SEK 235 (effective 1989). Ingenjoersfoerlaget AB, P.O. Box 27315, S-102 54 Stockholm, Sweden. TEL 08-665-1700. TELEX 17191-TECNEWS-S. Ed. Helene Tuerk. adv.; bk.rev.; film rev.; play rev. circ. 33,000. Indexed: AESIS, Key to Econ.Sci., P.A.I.S.
Supersedes: Featuring Sweden; Incorporates: Industria International (ISSN 0073-7283)

078.5 SW
SYDOESTRAN; sydoestra Sveriges dagblad. 1903. 6/w. Sydoestran, Landbrogatan 17, S-371 88 Karlskrona, Sweden. TEL 46-455-190-00. FAX 46-455-111-09. Ed. Haakan Quisth. adv.: B&W page SEK 18050, color page SEK 19940; adv. contact: Inge Pettersson. circ. 23,900. **Document type:** newspaper.

078.5 SW
SYDSVENSKA DAGBLADET SNAELLPOSTEN. 1848. d. Sydsvenska Dagbladets AB, Krusegatan 19, S-205 05 Malmoe, Sweden. TEL 46-040-28-12-00. FAX 46-040-28-14-60. Eds. Jan Wifstrand, Per T. Ohlsson. adv.: B&W page SEK 80704, color page SEK 108964; adv. contact: Lennart Andersson. circ. 119,500. **Document type:** newspaper.

078.5 SW
TIDNINGEN IDAG RIKS. d. Tidningbolaget G T - Kvaellposten K B, Exportgatan 2, P.O. Box 417, S-401 26 Goeteborg, Sweden. TEL 46-31-63-90-00. FAX 46-8-618-84-05. TELEX 2505 GTPRESS S. Ed. Bengt Hansson. adv.: B&W page SEK 62310, color page SEK 86900; adv. contact: Torbjoern Wittstroem. circ. 250,000. **Document type:** newspaper.

078.5 SW
TRELLEBORGS ALLEHANDA. 1876. 6/w. Tryckery AB Allehanda Syd, Algatan 27, P.O. Box 73, S-231 21 Trelleborg, Sweden. TEL 46-410-545-00. FAX 46-410-174-10. Ed. Mats Wickstroem. adv.: B&W page SEK 28900, color page SEK 34900; adv. contact: Lars Holst. circ. 10,400. **Document type:** newspaper.

078.5 SW
TROLLHAETTANS TIDNING; med Lilla Edet - Posten. 1906. d. Tvaastads Tidnings AB, Staveredsgatan 18, P.O. Box 54, S-461 22 Trollhaettan, Sweden. TEL 46-520-126-70. FAX 46-520-374-08. Ed. Torbjoern Haakansson. adv.: B&W page SEK 16031, color page SEK 20812; 255 x 375; adv. contact: Lennart Larsson. circ. 17,799. **Document type:** newspaper.

078.5 SW
UPSALA NYA TIDNING. 1890. 6/w. SEK 1290; newsstand price: SEK 8. (Axel Johansson Foundation) AB Upsala Nya Tidning, P.O. Box 36, S-751 03 Uppsala, Sweden. TEL 46-18-170000. FAX 46-18-170204. Ed. Folke Johansson. adv.: B&W page SEK 38640, color page SEK 49640; adv. contact: Soeren Axelsson. bk.rev.; film rev.; music rev.; play rev.; tele.rev.; video rev. Wire service(s): AP. circ. 65,200. cols./p.: 8; pp./issue: 38. (broadsheet format; also avail. in microfilm) **Document type:** newspaper.

078.5 SW
VAERMLANDS FOLKBLAD. 1918. 6/w. Vaermlands Folkblad AB, Saeteriveagen 7, P.O. Box 67, S-651 03 Karlstad, Sweden. TEL 46-54-19-05-00. FAX 46-54-19-01-10. TELEX 66067 VFKSTAD. Ed. Rolf Jansson. adv.: B&W page SEK 23800, color page SEK 28480; trim 372 x 528; adv. contact: Ragnar Hermansson. circ. 27,805. **Document type:** newspaper.

078.5 SW
VAESTERBOTTENS FOLKBLAD. 1917. 6/w. Nya Vaesterbottens Folkblad AB, Formvaegen 16, P.O. Box 6104, S-906 04 Umeaa. TEL 46-90-17-00-00. FAX 46-90-17-02-50. Ed. Lennart Andersson. adv.: B&W page SEK 15884, color page SEK 19214; adv. contact: Michael Olofsson. circ. 20,100. **Document type:** newspaper.

078.5 SW
VAESTERBOTTENS - KURIREN. 1900. 6/w. Vaesterbottens-Kurirens AB, Foerraadsvaegen 9, S-901 70 Umeaa, Sweden. TEL 46-90-15-10-00. FAX 46-90-14-31-22. TELEX 54070. Eds. Olof Kleberg, Lars Westerlund. adv.: B&W page SEK 31416, color page SEK 37842; adv. contact: Jan Jonsson. circ. 46,300. **Document type:** newspaper.

078.5 SW
VAESTERBOTTINGEN. 1979. w. Tidningsfoereningen Vaesterbottingen Ekonomisk Foerening, Riddargatan 2A, P.O. Box 3053, S-903 02 Umeaa, Sweden. TEL 46-90-14-14-65. FAX 46-90-14-01-71. Ed. Anders Oehberg. adv.: B&W page SEK 12440, color page SEK 13940; adv. contact: Johagen Erland. circ. 5,100. **Document type:** newspaper.

078.5 SW
VAESTERNORRLANDS ALLEHANDA. 1874. 6/w. Haernoesands Boktryckeri AB, Nybrogatan 13, P.O. Box 208, S-871 24 Haernoesand, Sweden. TEL 46-611-150-00. FAX 46-611-154-98. TELEX 71023 ANKARET S. Ed. Bo Oestman. adv. contact: Ulf Aakerlund. circ. 15,500. **Document type:** newspaper.

058.7 SW ISSN 0346-4105
VECKO-REVYN. Variant title: Nya Veckorevyn. (Supplement avail.: Svepet) 1935. w. SEK 860 (effective 1991). Aahlen och Aakerlunds Foerlags AB, Torsgatan 21, 105 44 Stockholm, Sweden. FAX 8-325228. TELEX 10043 BONMAGS. (Subscr. to: P.O. Box 3217, 105 44 Stockholm, Sweden) Ed. Bengt Holenquist. adv.; film rev.; illus. circ. 101,500.
Formerly (until vol. 32, 1937): Vecko-Revyn med Damernas Vaerld.

058.7 SW ISSN 0346-4180
VI. Variant title: Tidningen Vi. (Includes Bild-Vi) 1913. 40/yr. SEK 855. Kooperativa Foerbundet, P.O. Box 15210, S-104 65 Stockholm, Sweden. Ed. Mats Ekdahl. adv.; bk.rev.; illus. circ. 175,000.

052 US ISSN 1066-9116
VIEWPOINT SWEDEN. 1990. irreg., 15-20/yr. free. Consulate General of Sweden, One Dag Hammarskjold Plaza, New York, NY 10017-2201. TEL 212-751-5900. FAX 212-752-4789. Ed. Kjersti Board.
Formed by the merger of (1977-1990): Working Life in Sweden; (1977-1990): Social Change in Sweden; (1982-1990): Cultural Life in Sweden; (1980-1990): Political Life in Sweden; (1977-1990): Human Environment in Sweden (ISSN 0890-9628)

078.5 SW
YSTADS ALLEHANDA. 1873. 6/w. Tidnings AB Allehanda Syd, Lilla Norregatan 9, S-271 81 Ystad, Sweden. TEL 46-411-645-00. FAX 46-411-160-85. TELEX 32 341. Ed. Staffan Bjoernberg. adv. contact: Inge Liljenberg. circ. 25,100. **Document type:** newspaper.

GENERAL INTEREST PERIODICALS — Switzerland

073 SZ ISSN 0003-6315
ANZEIGER SOLOTHURN-LEBERN. 1895. w. 60 SFr. Vogt-Schild AG, Zuchwilerstr. 21, CH-4501 Solothurn 1, Switzerland. TEL 065-247247. FAX 065-247235. adv. circ. 33,899. (tabloid format) **Document type:** newspaper.

GENERAL INTEREST PERIODICALS — TAIWAN 2769

053.5 SZ ISSN 0005-9676
DAS BESTE AUS READER'S DIGEST (SWISS-GERMAN EDITION). (Text in German) 1948. m. 50 Fr. Das Beste aus Reader's Digest AG, Raeffelstr. 11, CH-8021 Zurich, Switzerland. Ed. Hans Bosshard. adv.; bk.rev.; illus. circ. 250,000.

072 SZ
L'EXPRESS; feuille d'avis de Neuchatel. (Text in French) 1738. 6/wk. 242 SFr. Case Postale 561, CH-2001 Neuchatel, Switzerland. TEL 038-256501. FAX 038-247736. Ed. Jean-Luc Vautravers; Pub. Fabien Wolfrath. adv. contact: Raymond Aeby. bk.rev.; film rev.; tele.rev.; circ. 33,428. cols./p.: 5; pp./issue: 32. Document type: newspaper.
● Also available online.

053.5 SZ
FACTUM; das wissenschaftliche Magazin zum Verstaendnis der heutigen Zeit. (Text in German) 1979. 9/yr. 59.80 Fr. Foerderung christlicher Publizistik, Postfach 263, CH-9435 Heerbrugg, Switzerland. TEL (071)724358. FAX 071-725665. Ed.Bd. bk.rev. circ. 6,500.

053.5 SZ ISSN 0016-5867
GEGENWART. 1939. bi-m. 50 SFr. (foreign 55 SFr.). Baerenplatz 2, CH-3011 Bern, Switzerland. Ed.Bd. adv.: B&W page 250 SFr. bk.rev.; index. circ. 1,800. Document type: bulletin.

052 SZ
GENEVA NEWS AND INTERNATIONAL REPORT. (Text in English) 1980. m. 50 SFr. (foreign 60 SFr.). Geneva News Publishing Co. S.A., 14 Rue Du-Roveray, CH-1207 Geneva, Switzerland. TEL 022-7360136. FAX 022-7863517. Ed. Padma de Mello. adv.; bk.rev. circ. 20,000. Document type: consumer publication.

073.5 SZ
DAS GOETHEANUM. 1921. w. 90 SFr. (Allgemeine Anthroposophische Gesellschaft) Wochenschrift "Das Goetheanum", Postfach 134, CH-4143 Dornach, Switzerland. TEL 061-7017230. FAX 061-7017468. Eds. Martin Barkhoff, Manfred Krueger. adv.; bk.rev. circ. 11,000. Document type: newspaper.

055.1 SZ
L'HEBDO. 1981. w. Ringier AG, CH-4800 Zofingen, Switzerland. TEL 062-503111. FAX 062-503571. circ. 36,766. Document type: bulletin.

055.1 SZ
ILLUSTRE. 1921. w. Ringier AG, CH-4800 Zofingen, Switzerland. TEL 062-503111. FAX 062-503571. circ. 117,284. Document type: consumer publication.

055.1 SZ
PARIS MATCH (SWITZERLAND). w. Regie Publicitaire Reymond Forestier, 14 Chemin du Grand Communal, CH-1222 Vesenaz, Switzerland. circ. 33,680.

PFIFF. see CHILDREN AND YOUTH — For

053.5 SZ
REVUE SCHWEIZ SUISSE SVIZZERA. 1927. 8/yr. 59 SFr. (foreign 71 SFr.). Schweizerische Verkehrszentrale, Bellariastr. 38, CH-8027 Zurich, Switzerland. FAX 01-2881205. TELEX 815391. (U.S. subscr. addr.: Swiss National Tourist Office, 608 Fifth Ave., New York, NY 10020) Ed. Roland Baumgartner. adv.; bk.rev.; illus. circ. 15,000. Document type: consumer publication.
Former titles: Schweiz, Suisse, Svizzera, Svizra, Switzerland; Schweiz, Suisse, Svizzera, Switzerland (ISSN 0036-7230)

055.1 914.309 SZ ISSN 0035-628X
RIVISTA DI LUGANO; rassegna settimanale illustrata per le famiglie. (Text in Italian) 1937. w. 50 SFr. F. Maerk, P.O. Box 2958, CH-6901 Lugano, Switzerland. TEL 091-235631. FAX 091-213043. Ed. Armando Libotte. adv.; bk.rev.; illus. circ. 6,500.
Description: Covers local interests.

053.5 SZ ISSN 0036-7362
SCHWEIZER ILLUSTRIERTE. 1911. w. Ringier AG, CH-4800 Zofingen, Switzerland. TEL 062-503111. FAX 062-503571. adv.; bk.rev.; charts;film rev.; illus. circ. 207,901. Document type: consumer publication.

053.5 SZ ISSN 0036-7532
SCHWEIZERISCHE BEOBACHTER. 1927. s-m. 49 SFr. (Europe 69 SFr.; rest of world 89 SFr.). Jean Frey AG, Edenstr. 20, CH-8021 Zurich, Switzerland. FAX 01-2078282. Ed.Bd. adv.; bk.rev. circ. 381,611. Document type: consumer publication.

055.1 SZ ISSN 0037-1394
SELECTION DU READER'S DIGEST (SWISS-FRENCH EDITION). (Text in French) 1947. m. 50 Fr. Selection du Reader's Digest AG, Raeffelstr. 11, CH-8021 Zurich, Switzerland. Ed. Hans Bosshard. adv.; bk.rev.; illus. circ. 80,000.

073 SZ ISSN 0038-1195
SOLOTHURNER-ZEITUNG; Tageszeitung. 1907. d. 224 SFr. Vogt-Schild AG, Zuchwilerstr. 21, CH-4501 Solothurn 1, Switzerland. TEL 065-247247. FAX 065-247335. TELEX 934646. Ed. Werner Hunziker. adv.; bk.rev. circ. 45,307. Document type: newspaper.

073 SZ
SONNTAGS BLICK. w. (Sun.). Ringier AG, Dufourstr. 23, CH-8008 Zurich, Switzerland. TEL 01-2596262. FAX 01-2518006. Ed. Fridolin Luchsinger. adv. contact: Urs Schneider. circ. 362,745. Document type: newspaper.

052 US ISSN 0039-7474
SWISS JOURNAL/SCHWEIZER JOURNAL; the official voice of the Swiss in America. (Text mainly in English; summaries in French, German, Italian) 1918. b-m. $26 (foreign $32). Swiss Journal Co., Inc., 548 Columbus Ave., San Francisco, CA 94133. TEL 415-362-8072. Eds. Louis Muschi, Achille Muschi. adv. circ. 10,000. (back issues avail.)
Description: Covers news of persons and events of interst to Swiss residents of the U.S. and to Americans of Swiss descent.

052 SZ ISSN 0039-7490
D839
SWISS REVIEW OF WORLD AFFAIRS. 1951. m. $57. Neue Zuercher Zeitung, Box 660, CH-8021 Zurich, Switzerland. TEL 01-2581111. FAX 01-2521329. Ed. Hugo Buetler. adv.; bk.rev.; charts; illus. circ. 4,400. Indexed: Int.Lab.Doc., Mid.East: Abstr.& Ind.—Faxon; UnCover; SWETS.
Description: Collection of articles and comments from the Neue Zuercher Zeitung.

073 SZ
TAGES ANZEIGER. 1893. d. newsstand price: 1.70 SFr. Tages Anzeiger AG, Werdstr. 21, CH-8004 Zurich, Switzerland. TEL 01-2484111. FAX 01-2484191. circ. 273,466. Document type: newspaper.

TOASTER. see CHILDREN AND YOUTH — For

055.1 SZ
TRENTE JOURS. 1949. 9/yr. Editions Trente Jours S.A., 23 rue du Pre du Marche, CH-1004 Lausanne, Switzerland. Ed. F.-L. De Senger. adv.; bk.rev.; film rev.; charts; illus. circ. 399,954. Document type: consumer publication.
Description: Leisure magazine covering current topics in entertainment, art, culture, human interest, society, travel, hobbies, literature, home, health and food.

053.5 SZ
TURICUM; kultur, wissenschaft und wirtschaft. 1970. q. 64 SFr. Zuerichsee Medien AG, Seestr. 86, CH-7612 Staefa, Switzerland. Ed. Walter Baumann, Antonino Orlando. adv.; bk.rev.; film rev.; play rev.; illus. circ. 22,000.

053.5 SZ
WELTRUNDSCHAU. 1956. a. 97 SFr. Weltrundschau Verlag AG, Oberneuhofstr. 1, Postfach 427, 6340 Baar, Switzerland. FAX 042-314404. Ed. G. Braun. circ. 100,000.

072 SZ
ZOFINGER TAGBLATT. (Text in German) 1872. 6/wk. 219 SFr. Zofinger Tagblatt AG, Henzmannstr. 18, CH-4800 Zofingen, Switzerland. TEL 062-509393. FAX 062-509349. Ed. Paul Ehringer. bk.rev.; film rev.; music rev.; tele.rev. circ. 16,777. Document type: newspaper.

073 SZ
ZUERCHER OBERLAENDER. 1852. d. (except Sun.). 220 SFr. Zuercher Oberlaender, Rappperswilerstr. 1, CH-8620 Wetzikon, Switzerland. TEL 01-9333333. FAX 01-9323232. Ed. Oscar Fritschi. adv. contact: Konrad Mueller. film rev.; music rev.; play rev.; tele.rev.; circ. 36,355 (paid); 800 (controlled). cols./p.: 4; pp./issue: 36. (standard format) Document type: newspaper.

GENERAL INTEREST PERIODICALS — Syria

059 SY
ARAB PALESTINIAN RESISTANCE. vol.6, 1974. m. $36. P.O.B. 3577, Damascus, Syria. Ed. T. Kamleh.

079.5691 SY
AL-BA'ATH. (Text in Arabic) 1953. d. P.O. Box 9389, Damascus, Syria. TEL 963-11-6664600. FAX 963-11-6622099. adv.; illus. (broadsheet format) Document type: newspaper.

GENERAL INTEREST PERIODICALS — Taiwan

079.512 CH
THE CHINA NEWS. (Supplements avail.: Weekend (Fri.); Student News (Sun.)) (Text in English) 1949. d. NT.$560 per mo.; newsstand price: NT.$12. China News, 110 Yenping S. Rd., 11F, Taipei, Taiwan 106, Republic of China. TEL 02-388-7931. FAX 02-381-5859. Ed. Ong Hock Chuan; Pub. Simone Wei. adv.: B&W page NT.$64000, color page NT.$96000; trim 36.6 x 51; adv. contact: Ada Ong. bk.rev.; film rev.; music rev.; illus. Wire service(s): AP, RN. circ. 100,000. cols./p.: 8; pp./issue: 20. (back issues avail.; reprint service avail.) Document type: newspaper.

079.512 CH
THE CHINA POST. (Irregular supplements avail.) (Text in English) 1952. d. NT.$360($12) per mo. China Post, No.8, Fu Shun St., Taipei, Taiwan 104, Republic of China. TEL 02-596-9971. FAX 02-595-7962. adv. contact: Heidi Chen. bk.rev.; film rev.; music rev.; illus. Wire service(s): AP, LAT WP, RN, UPI. circ. 150,000. cols./p.: 8; pp./issue: 16. (also avail. in microfiche; back issues avail.) Document type: newspaper.

059.951 CH
CHINA TRIBUNE/CHUNG-KUO LUN T'AN. (Text in Chinese) 1975. s-m. NT.$1020 (students NT.$870) in ROC; Hong Kong $76; Asia $88; elsewhere $99. 6F, No. 561, Chung Hsiao E. Rd., Sec. 4, Taipei, Taiwan, Republic of China. TEL 02-767-2444. (US subscr. to: World Journal Bookstore, 141-07 20th Ave., Whitestone, NY 11357. TEL 718-746-8889) Ed. Tsai Shih-ping. adv.

059.951 CH
CROWN/HUANG KUAN. (Text in Chinese) 1954. m. NT.$1000 in ROC; Hong Kong HK.$325; elsewhere $50. Crown Magazine, P.O. Box 3300, Taipei, Taiwan, Republic of China. TEL 02-716-8888. FAX 02-713-3422. (Or: 50, Lane 120, Tunhwa N. Rd., Taipei, Taiwan, R.O.C.; Dist. in US by: World Journal Bookstore, 141-07 20th Ave., Whitestone, NY 11357) adv.

059.951 CH ISSN 0012-9135
ECHO/HAN SHENG. (Text in Chinese) 1971. q. $159.23. Echo Magazine Co., Pa-Teh Rd., Sec. 4, Lane 72, Alley 16, No. 5-2, Taipei, Taiwan, Republic of China. Ed. Linda Wu. adv.; illus.; index. circ. 10,000.

GENERAL INTEREST PERIODICALS — TANZANIA

079.512 052   CH   ISSN 0255-9870
FREE CHINA JOURNAL; a leading information source about the Republic of China on Taiwan. (Supplement avail.: Documentary Supplement) (Text in English) 1964. 2/w. NT.$600($24) Kwang Hwa Publishing Co., 2 Tientsin St., Taipei, Taiwan 10041, Republic of China. TEL 02-397-0180. FAX 02-356-8233. TELEX 11636-INFORM. (US subscr. to: Kwang Hwa Publishing (USA) Inc., 900 N. Western Ave., Ste. 101, Los Angeles, CA 90029. TEL 213-461-4918) Ed. Chang Ying. bk.rev.; charts; illus. circ. 68,000. (also avail. in microform from UMI; reprint service avail. from UMI) **Document type:** newspaper.
—UMI.
   Formerly (until 1983): Free China Weekly (ISSN 0016-0318)
   Description: International news coverage of cultural and socio-economic events affecting the Republic of China.

052   CH   ISSN 0016-030X
DS701
FREE CHINA REVIEW. (Editions in English, French, Spanish, German) 1951. Eng. ed. m.; other eds. bi-m. NT.$600 in ROC; Hong Kong HK.$65; U.S. $18; elsewhere $25. Kwang Hwa Publishing Co., 2 Tientsin St., Taipei, Taiwan 10041, Republic of China. TEL 02-351-6419. FAX 02-351-6227. TELEX 11636-INFORM. (U.S. subscr. to: Kwang Hwa Publishing (USA) Inc., 900 N. Western Ave., Ste. 101, Los Angeles, CA 90029. TEL 213-461-4918) Ed. Jiang Ping-lun. adv.; bk.rev.; charts; illus.; index. circ. 49,800. (also avail. in microfilm from UMI; microfiche from UMI) **Indexed:** Key to Econ.Sci., M.L.A., P.A.I.S.
—Faxon; UMI.
   Description: Commentary on and analysis of the political, economic, social, and cultural issues that affect modern life in the Republic of China, as well as issues affecting Hong Kong, Macao, and the Chinese mainland.

059.951 052   US   ISSN 0256-9043
SINORAMA/KUANG HUA HUA PAO. Chinese-Japanese edition (ISSN 0256-9051); Chinese-Spanish edition (ISSN 0256-906X) (Text in Chinese and English) 1976. m. Kwang Hwa Publishing Co., 900 N. Western Ave., Ste. 101, Los Angeles, CA 90029. TEL 213-461-4918. Ed. Sunny Hsiao. adv.; bk.rev.; illus. circ. 110,000.

059.951 352   CH   ISSN 0039-9051
TAIPEI PICTORIAL/TAIPEI HUA K'AN. (Text in Chinese) 1968. m. free to Taipei citizens and foreign governments. Taipei City Government, Department of Information, 39 Chang An W. Rd., P.O. Box 59052, Taipei, Taiwan, Republic of China. TEL 02-551-0143. FAX 02-537-4087. Ed. Hsu Chih-chung. charts; illus.; stat. circ. 27,000. **Document type:** government publication.

059.951 052   CH
TAIWAN PICTORIAL. 1954. m. NT.$240. Taiwan Pictorial Society, Box 1919, 20 Chungking S. Rd., Sec. 2, Taipei, Taiwan 10741, Republic of China. TEL 3111196. adv.; illus.
   Formerly: Taiwan (ISSN 0039-9086)

GENERAL INTEREST PERIODICALS — Tanzania

059.96   TZ
ELIMU HAINA MWISHO. m. POB 1986, Mwanza, Tanzania. circ. 45,000.

059.96   TZ
HABARI ZA WASHIRIKA. m. Cooperative Union of Tanzania, POB 2567, Dar es Salaam, Tanzania. TEL 23346. TELEX 41809. Ed. H.V.N. Chibulunje. circ. 40,000.

059.96   TZ
KWEUPE. (Text in Swahili) w. Information Broadcasting Services, POB 222, Zanzibar, Tanzania.

059.96   TZ
MFANYAKAZI/WORKER. w. POB 15359, Dar es Salaam, Tanzania. TEL 28128. Ed. Hamidu Nzowa. circ. 100,000.

059.96   TZ   ISSN 0856-1265
MUISLAMU. 1981. m. National Muslim Council of Tanzania, POB 16250, Dar es Salaam, Tanzania. TEL 37609. Ed. Y. Sadik. circ. 10,000.

059.96   TZ   ISSN 0856-0188
NCHI YETU/OUR COUNTRY. (Text in Swahili) 1964. m. POB 9142, Dar es Salaam, Tanzania. TEL 25375. TELEX 41419. circ. 50,000.

079.678   TZ   ISSN 0856-4051
▼**SHABA NEWSPAPER.** (Text in Swahili) 1992. w. $20. Oliprint Ltd., P.O. Box 16250, Dar es Salaam, Tanzania. TEL 30272. Ed. Yassin N. Sadik. adv.: page Sh.240. film rev.; circ. 40,000 (controlled). **Document type:** newspaper.
   Description: Covers politics, health, the environment, and sports and entertainment.

052   TZ
SPOTLIGHT ON SOUTH AFRICA. q. African National Congress, POB 2239, Dar es Salaam, Tanzania.

052   TZ   ISSN 0856-017X
TANZANIA NEWS REVIEW. Some issues called News Review Tanzania. (Text in English) 1964. m. $10. National Directorate of Information Services, Box 9142, Dar es Salaam, Tanzania. TELEX 41419 INFORM TZ. adv.; bk.rev. circ. 10,000. (back issues avail.)

052   TZ   ISSN 0039-9485
DT436
TANZANIA NOTES & RECORDS. 1936. a. $18 to individuals; institutions $22. Tanzania Society, c/o Mrs. Carol Sharp, Ex. Sec., Box 511, Dar es Salam, Tanzania. Ed. I.N. Kimambo. adv.; bk.rev.; bibl.; charts; illus.; index. circ. 1,200. **Indexed:** Amer.Hist.& Life, Anthropol.Lit., Curr.Cont.Africa, Hist.Abstr.
   Formerly: Tanganyika Notes and Records.

059.96   TZ
URUSI LEO. (Text in Swahili) 1968. w. Informatsionnoye Agentstvo Novosti (IAN), POB 2271, Dar es Salaam, Tanzania. TEL 23897. TELEX 41095. Ed. V. Sharayev. circ. 25,000.

059.96   TZ
WELA. (Text in Swahili) q? POB 180, Dodoma, Tanzania.

GENERAL INTEREST PERIODICALS — Thailand

079.593   TH
BANGKOK POST WEEKLY REVIEW. (Text in English) 1989. w. B.1500($60) in Thailand; other Asian B.2550 ($102); elsewhere B.3550 ($147); (including Bangkok Post Economic Review). Post Publishing Co., Ltd., Bangkok Post Bldg., 136 Nanong Rd., Off Sunthorn Kosa Rd., Klong Toey, Bangkok 10110, Thailand. TEL 662-240-3700. FAX 662-240-3790. TELEX 82833 TICALBK TH. Ed. Anussorn Thavisin. adv.: B&W page B.11250; trim 10 x 12 1/2; adv. contact: Supachai Yurawan. circ. 11,538. (tabloid format) **Document type:** newspaper.
   Description: Consolidates the most important political, business and social news reported that week by the Bangkok Post Newspaper.

059.959   TH
BANGKOK WEEKLY. (Text in Thai) w. 533-539 Sri Ayutthaya Rd., Bangkok, Thailand. Ed. Vichit Rojanaprabha.

059.959   TH
CHAO KRUNG. (Text in Thai) m. 12 Mansion 6, Rajdamnern Ave., Bangkok 10200, Thailand. Ed. Nopphorn Bunyarit.

059.9591   TH
DARATHAI. (Text in Thai) 1954. w. (Thu.). newsstand price: 10 baht. Siam Offset Co. Ltd., 9-1 Soi Sri Ak-Surn, Bangkok 10120, Thailand. TEL 662-249-1575. FAX 662-249-5415. Ed. Mrs. Usa Bukkavesa. adv. contact: Ms Apirai Bukkavesa. film rev.; music rev.; tele.rev.; illus. **Document type:** consumer publication.

059.959   TH
DICHAN. (Text in Thai) fortn. 1400 Thai Bldg., Thanon Phra Ram Si, Bangkok, Thailand. TEL 02-243-0351. Ed. Pee Malakul Na Aytthaya.

059.959   TH   ISSN 0125-5584
GRAND PRIX. (Text in Thai) 1969. m. B.600. Grand Prix International Co., Ltd., 129-133 Rim Klong Prapar, Prachachuen Rd., Bangsue, Bangkok 10800, Thailand. TEL 662-02-587-0101. FAX 662-02-587-6567. Ed. Prachin Eamlumnow. circ. 60,000. **Document type:** consumer publication.

059.959   TH
LALANA. (Text in Thai) 1972. fortn. 44 Moo 10, Bangna-Trad, Bangna, Bangkok 10260, Thailand. TEL 02-317-1400. FAX 02-317-1409. Ed. Nantawan Yoon. circ. 65,000.

059.959   TH
LIVING IN THAILAND. (Text in English) 1972. m. B.40($1.70) per no. Media Transasia (Thailand) Ltd., Orakarn Bldg., 14th Fl., 26 Chidlom Rd., Bangkok 10330, Thailand. FAX 2535335. TELEX 84003-MEDTRAN-TH. Ed. V. Uberoi. adv.; bk.rev.; rec.rev.; illus. circ. 17,355.
   Supersedes: Impact; Bangkok Standard (ISSN 0028-940X)

059.959   TH
LOOK. (Text in Thai) m. 1-54 Sukhumvit 30, Pra Khanong, Bangkok 10110, Thailand. TEL 02-258-1265. Ed. Kanokwan Milindavanij.

059.959   TH
MATHICHON WEEKLY REVIEW. (Text in Thai) w. 12 Thedsaban Naruban Rd., Bangken, Bangkok, Thailand. Ed. Ruangchai Sabnirand.

059.959   TH
SAEN SANUK. (Text in Thai) m. 50 Soi Saeng Chan, Sukhumvit 42, Bangkok 10110, Thailand. TEL 02-392-0052. FAX 02-391-1486. Ed. Somtawin Kongsawatkiat. circ. 85,000.

059.959   TH
SATAWA LIANG. (Text in Thai) m. 689 Wang Burapa Rd., Bangkok, Thailand. Ed. Thamrongsak Srichand.

059.959   TH
SIAM RATH WEEKLY REVIEW. (Text in Thai) w. Mansion 6, Rajdanmern Ave., Bangkok 10200, Thailand. Ed. Prachuab Thongural.

059.959   TH
SKUL THAI. (Text in Thai) w. 58 Soi 36, Sukhumvit Rd., Bangkok 10110, Thailand. TEL 02-258-5861. FAX 02-258-9130. Ed. Prayoon Songsermsawas.

052   HK
THAILAND TATLER. 1991. m. B.70 per no. Communication Management Ltd., 1811 Hong Kong Plaza, 188 Connaught Rd. W., Hong Kong. TEL 547-7117. FAX 858-2671. Ed. Lina Ross. adv. circ. 18,200. **Document type:** consumer publication.

GENERAL INTEREST PERIODICALS — Tonga

052   TO   ISSN 0113-0374
DU880
MATANGI TONGA. (Text in English; summaries in Tongan) 1986. bi-m. $27.60 (effective 1993). Vava'u Press Ltd., P.O. Box 427, Nuku'alofa, Tonga. TEL 676-23-101. FAX 676-23-101. Ed. Pesi Fonua. adv.; bk.rev. circ. 3,000. (back issues avail.)
   Description: News on Tongan-related topic of current interest.

079   TO
THE TONGA CHRONICLE. Tongan edition: Ko e Kolonikali. (Editions in English, Tongan (Malayo-Polynesian)) 1964. w. (Thur.). $T.20.80; newsstand price: $T.0.40. Tungi Arcude, Taufa'ahau Rd., Nuku'alofa, Tongatapu, South Pacific, Tonga. TEL 676-23302. FAX 676-23336. Owner(s): Government of the Kingdom of Tonga, Prime Minister's Office, Nuku'alofa, South Pacific, Tonga. TEL 676-23300. Ed. Paua Manu'atu. adv.: page $T.360 (single ed), $T.720 (both eds.); adv. contact: Mohameti Afu. bk.rev.; illus. cols./p.: 6; pp./issue: 10. (tabloid format) **Document type:** newspaper.

GENERAL INTEREST PERIODICALS — Turkey

059.9435   TU
AKTUEL. 1991. w. Medya Plaza Basin, Ekspress Yolu, 34540 Gunesli - Istanbul, Turkey. TEL 90-212-5504870. FAX 90-212-5028373. adv. **Document type:** consumer publication.

059.9435   TU
BAB-I ALI MAGAZIN. 1989. w. Alemdar Cad., Guzel Sanatler Sokak 11 Kat. 2, Sultanahmet - Istanbul, Turkey. TEL 90-212-5194707. FAX 90-212-5194221. **Document type:** consumer publication.

059.9435   TU
BAROMETRE. 1991. w. Mesrutlyet Caddesi 164-3, 80050 Sishane - Istanbul, Turkey. TEL 90-212-2527200. FAX 90-212-2526420. **Document type:** consumer publication.

059.943   TU
BELGE/DOCUMENT. (Text in Turkish) m. 6 Hurriyet Cad., Girne, Mersin 10, Turkey. Ed. Erdal Andiz.

079.56 059.9435   TU
BUGUN. 1989. d. Medya Plaza Basin, Ekspress Yolu, 34540 Gunesli - Istanbul, Turkey. TEL 90-212-5504900. FAX 90-212-5028340. adv.; illus. **Document type:** newspaper.

059.943   TU
CENGEL. (Text in Turkish) m? Erdal Andiz, Ed. & Pub., Lefkosa - Nicosia, Mersin 10, Turkey. TEL 520-75225.

079.56 059.9435   TU
CUMHURIYET. 1924. d. newsstand price: 8000 TL. Yeni Gun Haber Ajansi, Basin ve Yayincilik A.S., P.K. 246, 34334 Cagaloglu - Istanbul, Turkey. TEL 90-212-5120505. FAX 90-212-5138595. Ed. Ozgen Acar. adv.; illus. **Document type:** newspaper.

CYPRUS TODAY. see GENERAL INTEREST PERIODICALS — Cyprus

079.56 059.9435   TU
DUNYA. 1953. d. Narlibahce Sokak 15, 34440 Cagaloglu - Istanbul, Turkey. TEL 90-212-5120190. FAX 90-212-5140687. TELEX 23822. adv. **Document type:** newspaper.

079.56 059.9435   TU
FOTOMAC. 1991. d. Medya Plaza Basin, Ekspres Yolu, 34540 Gunesli - Istanbul, Turkey. TEL 90-212-5504890. adv.; illus. **Document type:** newspaper.

059.9435   TU
GOLGE ADAM. 1986. w. Alaykosku Cad. 11, Cagaloglu - Istanbul, Turkey. TEL 90-212-5123800. FAX 90-212-5111100. TELEX 30418. adv. **Document type:** consumer publication.

079.56 059.9435   TU
▼**GUN.** 1993. d. Medya Plaza Basin, Ekspres Yolu, 34540 Gunesli - Istanbul, Turkey. TEL 90-212-5504810. adv. **Document type:** newspaper.

059.943   TU
HABER. (Text in Turkish) w. Lefkosa - Nicosia, Mersin 10, Turkey. TEL 520-78188. Ed. Mehmet Akar.

079.56 059.9435   TU
HURRIYET. 1948. d. Babiali Caddesi 15-17, 34360 Cagaloglu - Istanbul, Turkey. TEL 90-212-5120000. FAX 90-212-5156705. Ed. Ertugrul Ozkok. adv.; illus. circ. 545,000. **Document type:** newspaper.

059.943   TU
KOOPERATIF/CO-OPERATIVE. (Text in Turkish) 1970. m. Department of Co-operative Development, Lefkosa - Nicosia, Mersin 10, Turkey. TEL 520-71207. circ. 2,000.

059.943   TU
KUZEY KIBRIS. English edition: Kibris - Northern Cyrpus Monthly. (Text in Turkish) 1963. m. free. K.K.T.C. Enformasyon Dairesi - Turkish Republic of Northern Cyprus, Press and Information Office, P.K. 828, Lefkosa Kibris, Mersin 10, Turkey. TEL 90-392-2284133. FAX 90-392-2284847. TELEX 571577. Eds. Mustafa Kortun (Turkish); Ms Beraat Mustafaoglu (English); Pub. Hakki Yazgan. circ. 8,000 (4,500 Turkish ed.; 3,500 English ed.). **Document type:** government publication, newspaper.
Description: Covers issues relating to the Turkish Republic of Northern Cyprus, its people and their life and culture.

059.943   TU
KUZY KIBRIS KULTUR DERGISI/NORTHERN CYPRUS CULTURAL JOURNAL. (Text in Turkish) m. P.O. Box 157, Lefkosa - Nicosia, Mersin 10, Turkey. Ed. Gunsel Dogasal.

059.9435   TU
MEDYA. 1987. w. Halaskargazi Cad. Ilbay Apt. 252-14 Kat. 5, 80230 Sisli - Istanbul, Turkey. TEL 90-212-2307233. FAX 90-212-2411641. adv.

079.56 059.9435   TU
MEYDAN. 1990. d. c/o Prof. Kazim Ismail Gurkan Cad. 10, 34410 Cagaloglu - Istanbul, Turkey. TEL 90-212-5134972. FAX 90-212-5269908. adv.; illus. **Document type:** newspaper.

079.56 059.9435   TU
MILLI GAZETE. 1973. d. Cayhane Sokak 1, 34020 Topkapi - Istanbul, Turkey. TEL 90-212-5674775. FAX 90-212-55674024. TELEX 23373. Ed. Hasan Karakaya. adv.; illus. **Document type:** newspaper.

079.56 059.9435   TU
MILLIYET. 1950. d. Yuzyil Mah. Mahmutbey Vlyadugu Alti, Ikitalli - Istanbul, Turkey. TEL 90-212-5056111. FAX 90-212-505-6233. TELEX 22251. adv.; illus. circ. 335,000. **Document type:** newspaper.

059.943   TU
NEW CYPRUS. Turkish edition: Yeni Kibris. (Text in English) North Cyprus Research and Publishing Centre, P.O. Box 327, Lefkosa - Nicosia, Mersin 10, Turkey. TEL 520-78194. FAX 520-72592. TELEX 2585. Ed. Ahmet C. Gazioglu.

059.94   TU   ISSN 0259-6911
NEWSPOT; Turkish digest. (Text in English) 1981. fortn. free. Directorate General of Press and Information, Ataturk Blvd. 203, 06688 Ankara, Turkey. TEL 90-4-4671180. FAX 90-4-4684966. circ. 7,500. (back issues avail.) Indexed: Per.Islam.
Description: Addresses economic, political, and cultural events from the Turkish perspective.

059.9435   TU
AP95.T8
NOKTA. 1983. w. Nokta Yayinlari A.S., Buyukdere Cad. Ali Kaya Sok. 8, 80720 Levent - Istanbul, Turkey. TEL 90-212-2819916. FAX 90-212-4183527. TELEX 26510. adv.; illus. **Document type:** consumer publication.

059.9199 079.56   TU
NOR MARMARA. (Text in Armenian) 1940. d. (Mon.-Sat.). TL.3000000($270); newsstand price: TL.7000. Solakzade Sok. No. 5, Istanbul. TEL 90-212-2491989. FAX 90-212-2444736. Ed. Rober Haddeler. adv. contact: Ari Haddeler. bk.rev.; film rev.; music rev.; play rev.; tele.rev.; illus.; circ. 400 (paid); 1,700 (controlled). cols./p.: 8; pp./issue: 4. **Document type:** newspaper.

059.943   TU
OZURLUK. (Text in Turkish) m? Hurrem Tulga, Ed. & Pub., P.O. Box 327, Lefkosa - Nicosia, Mersin 10, Turkey.

059.9435   TU
PANORAMA. 1987. w. Interpress Basin ve Yayincilik A.S., Buyukdere Cad. Ali Kaya Sokak 8, 80720 Levent - Istanbul, Turkey. TEL 90-212-2815539. FAX 90-212-2683291. adv. **Document type:** consumer publication.

079.56 059.9435   TU
SABAH. 1950. d. Medya Plaza Basin, Ekspress Yolu, 34540 Gunesli - Istanbul, Turkey. TEL 90-212-5504900. FAX 90-212-5028590. TELEX 28851. Ed. Zafer Mutlu. adv.; illus. circ. 507,000. **Document type:** newspaper.

059.943   TU
SPECIAL NEWS BULLETIN - DIGEST. (Text in English) w. Turkish Republic of Northern Cyprus, Public Relations Office, Lefkosa - Nicosia, Mersin 10, Turkey. TEL 520-75773. TELEX 57169.

079.56 059.9435   TU
AP95T8 T46
TEMPO. 1989. w. Hurguc Gazetcilik A.S., Gunesli - Istanbul, Turkey. TEL 90-212-5500081. FAX 90-212-5503474.

079.56 059.9435   TU
TERCUMAN. 1961. d. Serckale Sokak 4, 34370 Topkapi - Istanbul, Turkey. TEL 90-212-5016263. FAX 90-212-5446562. TELEX 22253. adv.; illus. **Document type:** newspaper.

079.56 052   TU
TURKISH DAILY NEWS. (Text in English) 1961. d. Tunus Cad. 50-A-7, 06680 Kavaklidere - Ankara, Turkey. TEL 90-312-4282956. FAX 90-312-4278890. Ed. Ilnur Cevlik. adv.; illus. **Document type:** newspaper.
Formerly: Daily News.

052   TU   ISSN 1010-8874
TURKISH REVIEW. (Text in English) 1985. q. Directorate General of Press and Information, Ataturk Blvd. 203, 06688 Ankara, Turkey. TEL 90-4-4671180. FAX 90-4-4684966. Ed. K. Ahmet Parla.
Description: Covers international and domestic policy issues affecting Turkey.

079.56 059.9435   TU
TURKIYE. 1970. d. Catalcesme Sokak 17, 34410 Cagaloglu - Istanbul, Turkey. TEL 90-212-5139900. FAX 90-212-5138973. TELEX 22000. adv.; illus. **Document type:** newspaper.

059.943   TU
ULUSLARARASI KUZY KIBRIS MAGAZIN/INTERNATIONAL NOTHERN CYPRUS MAGAZINE. (Text in English and Turkish) 1987. q. Yorum Publishing House, Cengiz Han St., Yuva Apt. Kosliuciftlik, Lefkosa - Nicosia, Mersin 10, Turkey. Ed. Tansu Konuralp.

079.56 059.9435   TU
YENI ASIR. 1895. d. Gaziosmanpasa Bulvar 5, Cankaya - Izmir, Turkey. TEL 90-232-4415000. FAX 90-232-4252200. TELEX 52312. Ed. Cemil Devren. adv.; illus. **Document type:** newspaper.

059.9435   TU
YENI DUSUNCE. 1981. w. Binektasi Soka 18-9, 06660 Kocatepe - Ankara, Turkey. TEL 90-312-4173756. FAX 90-312-4187180.

079.56 059.9435   TU
YENI GUNAYDIN. 1968. d. Alaykosku Caddesi, Eryilmaz Sokak 13, Cagaloglu - Istanbul, Turkey. TEL 90-212-5117072. FAX 90-212-5125659. Ed. Rahmi Turan. adv.; illus. circ. 300,000. **Document type:** newspaper.

079.56 059.9435   TU
ZAMAN. 1962. d. Cobancesme Kaledner Sokak 21, 34530 Yenibosna - Istanbul, Turkey. TEL 90-212-6523351. FAX 90-212-6522423. TELEX 28994. Ed. Halit Esendir. adv.; illus. **Document type:** newspaper.

GENERAL INTEREST PERIODICALS — Tuvalu

052   TV
TUVALU ECHOES. (Text in English) 1983. s-m. Aus.$30 (outside Pacific region $60). Department of Broadcasting & Information, Auala o Tuvalu, Box 92, Funafuti, Tuvalu. TEL 688-20731. FAX 688-20732. Ed. Ruby Bruce; Pub. Mr. Pusinelli Laafai. adv. contact: Ruby Bruce. (A4 format; back issues avail.; reprint service avail.) **Document type:** government publication.
Description: Publishes government news, community news and other regional and international news of interest.

GENERAL INTEREST PERIODICALS — Uganda

079.6761   UG
DAILY TOPIC. (Text in English) 1979. d. Sh.3000; newsstand price: Sh.3000. Progressive Publishing House, Katwe Rd., Kampala, Uganda. TEL 256-41-237854. FAX 256-41-231854. Ed. Wasswa John Baptist. adv.: Page $460. bk.rev.; film rev.; music rev.; play rev.; tele.rev.; illus. circ. 10,000. cols./p.: 6; pp./issue: 20. (tabloid format; back issues avail.; reprint service avail.) **Document type:** newspaper.

059.96   UG
DBEMBE. fortn. EAs.40. Freedom Press, Box 14089, Kampala, Uganda.

059.96   UG   ISSN 0419-8735
DWON LWAK/PEOPLE'S VOICE. no.600, 1976. w. EAs.18.40($3) Ministry of Information, Broadcasting and Tourism, Box 7142, Kampala, Uganda. Ed. George Alele. circ. 5,100.

052   UG
FOCUS. (Text in English) 1983. 4/wk. Islamic Information Service and Material Centre, P.O. Box 268, Kampala, Uganda. TEL 255696. FAX 255698. TELEX 62247. Ed. Hajji Katende. circ. 8,500.

079.6761   UG
▼**THE MONITOR.** 1992. s-w. Sh.46800($199) (rest of Africa Sh.189800; Europe and N. America Sh.218000); newsstand price: Sh.500. Monitor Publications Ltd., P.O. Box 12141, Kampala, Uganda. TEL 041-236939. FAX 041-251352. Ed. Wafula Orguttu. adv.: Page Sh.360000 ($); adv. contact: Serugo James. bk.rev.; film rev.; play rev.; tele.rev.; illus. circ. 34,000. cols./p.: 6; pp./issue: 20. (back issues avail.) **Document type:** newspaper.

059.96   UG
MULENGERA. (Text in Luganda) w. P.O. Box 6787, Kampala, Uganda.

079.6761   UG
THE NEW VISION. The Sunday Vision. (Supplements avail.: Straight Talk, Weekend) 1986. d. P.O. Box 9815, Kampala, Uganda. TEL 235209. FAX 235221. Ed. William Pike. adv.: Full page Sh.566000 ($480); adv. contact: Perez Owori. bk.rev.; music rev.; play rev. illus. Wire service(s): RN. circ. 500 (paid); 33,000 (controlled). cols./p.: 6; pp./issue: 32. **Document type:** newspaper.

052   UG
NEWSDESK. (Text in English) 1990. bi-m.? Newsdesk Publishers, P.O. Box 1515, Kampala, Uganda. **Indexed:** P.L.E.S.A. (1990-).

059.96   UG
TAIFA UGANDA EMPYA. (Text in Luganda) 1953. w. POB 1986, Kampala, Uganda. TEL 254652. TELEX 61064. Ed. A. Semboga. adv. circ. 23,800.

079.6761   UG
UGANDA CONFIDENTIAL; the paper that splits the atom. (Text in English) 1991. w. $110 to individuals; institutions $150. P.O. Box 9948, Kampala, Uganda. FAX 256-41-245580. Eds. Gerald Mwaita, John Kateeba. bk.rev.; film rev. circ. 40,000 (paid). (back issues avail.) **Document type:** newspaper.
Description: Provides a forum for the popular discussion of national issues.

079.6761   UG
WEEKLY TOPIC. 1986. w. Sh.320. Progressive Publishing House, Katwe Rd., Kampala, Uganda. TEL 256-41-231854. FAX 256-41-231854. Ed. Wasswa John Baptist. adv.: Page $460. bk.rev.; film rev.; music rev.; play rev.; tele.rev.; illus. circ. 15,000. cols./p.: 6; pp./issue: 20. (tabloid format; back issues avail.; reprint service avail.) **Document type:** newspaper.

GENERAL INTEREST PERIODICALS — Ukraine

077   KR
GOLOS UKRAINY/HOLOS UKRAINY. (Text in Russian, Ukrainian) 1991. 5/w. Ul. Nesterova, 4, 252047 Kiev, Ukraine. TEL 044-441-8823. FAX 044-224-7254. Owner(s): Verkhovnyi Sovet Ukrainy. Ed. S. Pravdenko. adv.; illus. circ. 312,077. (tabloid format) **Document type:** newspaper.

057.917   KR   ISSN 0024-7871
LYUDYNA I SVIT. (Text in Ukrainian) 1960. m. 10 Rylsky provulok, 254025 Kiev, Ukraine. TEL 044-228-2387. Ed. Mikola Rubanets. index. circ. 46,000.
Formerly: Voiovnychyi Ateyist.

057.917   US
NARODNA VOLYA/PEOPLE'S WILL. w. $10. Ukrainian Fraternal Association, 440 Wyoming Ave., Scranton, PA 18509-0350. TEL 717-342-0937. FAX 717-347-5649. Ed. Nicholas Duplak. circ. 3,000.

057.917   PL   ISSN 0027-8254
NASHE SLOVO. (Includes monthly supplements: Nasha Kultura (ISSN 0209-3170); Switanok (ISSN 0239-5460)) (Ukrainian) 1958. w. $11.70. Ukrainskie Towarzystwo Spoleczno-Kulturalne - Ukrayins'ke Suspil'no-Kul'turne Tovarystvo, Ul. Nowogrodzka 15, 00-511 Warsaw, Poland. Ed. Grzegorz Bojarski. illus.

077 052   KR   ISSN 0549-110X
NEWS FROM THE UKRAINE. (Text in English) 1964. w. $19 (typically set in Jan.). Society for Cultural Relations with Ukrainians Abroad, 6 Zoloti Vorota St., Kiev 252601, Ukraine. TEL 224-80-81. FAX 228-04-38. Ed. Volodymyr Kanash. adv.; bk.rev.; illus. **Document type:** newspaper.
Description: Provides cultural and political news (home and foreign) as well as sports new, historical reviews.

077   KR
RABOCHAYA GAZETA/ROBITNICHA GAZETA. (Text in Russian, Ukrainian) 1057. 5/w. (Tue.-Sat.). Prospect Pobedu, 50, 252047 Kiev, Ukraine. TEL 44-441-8657. FAX 44-446-0298. Ed. Evelina Babenko-Pivtoradni. adv.; bk.rev.; film rev.; music rev.; play rev.; tele.rev.; illus.; tr.lit. cols./p.: 8; pp./issue: 4. (standard format; also avail. in Braille) **Document type:** newspaper.

057.917   KR   ISSN 0041-6088
UKRAINA; hromads'ko-politychnyi, literaturno-khudozhnii ilyustrovanyi tyzhnevyk. 1941. w. Peremohy pr. 50, 252047 Kiev, Ukraine. TEL 044-441-88-31. Ed. Anatoly Mikhailenko. bk.rev.; dance rev.; illus. circ. 70,000.

052   KR
UKRAINE. (Text in English) 1959. q. $0.80. Peremohy pr. 50, 252047 Kiev, Ukraine. TEL 044-441-8831. Ed. Mikola Podolyan. bk.rev.; charts; illus.

077
URYADOVII KUR'ER; gazeta organiv derzhavnoi vikonavchoi vladi Ykraini. (Text in Ukrainian) 3/w. (Verkhovna Rada - Supreme Council) Uryadovii Kur'er, Vul. Sadova 1, 252008 Kiev, Ukraine. TEL 044-293-6828. FAX 044-226-2447. Ed. Mikhailo Soroka. adv.; illus. circ. 218,841. (tabloid format) **Document type:** newspaper.

GENERAL INTEREST PERIODICALS — Union Of Myanmar

059.958 052   BR
DO KYAUNG THA. (Text in Burmese, English) 1965. m. Myawaddy Press, 181-3 Sule Pagoda Rd., Yangon, Union of Myanmar. circ. 17,000.

059.958 052   BR
MOETHAUKPAN/AURORA. (Text in Burmese, English) 1980. m. Myawaddy Press, 181-3 Sule Pagoda Rd., Yangon, Union of Myanmar. circ. 27,500.

059.958   BR
MYAWADDY JOURNAL. (Text in Burmese) 1989. fortn. Myawaddy Press, 181-3 Sule Pagoda Rd., Yangon, Union of Myanmar. circ. 8,700.

059.958   BR
NGWETARYI MAGAZINE. (Text in Burmese) 1961. m. Myawaddy Press, 181-3 Sule Pagoda Rd., Yangon, Union of Myanmar. TEL 01-82669. circ. 3,400.

GENERAL INTEREST PERIODICALS — United Arab Emirates

079.5357   TS
AL-BAYAN. (Text in Arabic) 1980. d. Mu'assasat al-Bayan, P.O. Box 2710, Dubai, United Arab Emirates. TEL 444000. FAX 282267. TELEX 47707 PRESS EM. Ed. Khalid M. Ahmed. bk.rev. circ. 70,000. **Document type:** newspaper.
Description: Business news coverage of the U.A.E., the Arab world, and the international economic situation.

059.927   TS
BILADI. (Text in Arabic) 1989. q. Al- Saqr Publishing House, P.O. Box 198, Ajman, United Arab Emirates. TEL 425135. FAX 421876. Ed. Khalifa al-Galaf. circ. 2,000.

059.927   TS
AL-DHAFRA. (Text in Arabic) 1974. w. Dar Suhuf al-Wahda, Majallat al-Dhafra, P.O. Box 2488, Abu Dhabi, United Arab Emirates. TEL 478400. FAX 478930. TELEX 23850. Ed. Rashid bin Ewaidah. adv. circ. 60,000.
Description: Covers local, Gulf, and international events.

079.536   TS
EMIRATES NEWS. (Text in English) 1971. d. Al- Ittihad Press, Publishing and Distribution Corp., P.O. Box 791, Abu Dhabi, United Arab Emirates. TEL 451600. FAX 461801. TELEX 22984 ITTPRESS EM. Ed. Abdullah al-Nuwais. **Document type:** newspaper.
Description: Covers events in the U.A.E. and the Gulf.

079.536   TS
AL-FAJR. (Text in Arabic) 1975. d. Dar al- Fajr lil-Sahafah wal-Tab'a wal-Nashr, P.O. Box 505, Abu Dhabi, United Arab Emirates. TEL 478300. FAX 478436. Ed. Obaid Humaid al-Mazrawi. **Document type:** newspaper.
Description: Covers news and events in the U.A.E. and the Gulf.

052   TS
GULF WEEKLY. (Text in English) 1979. w. Al- Nisr Corporation, P.O. Box 6519, Dubai, United Arab Emirates. TEL 447100. FAX 449139. TELEX 47030 GNEWS EM. Ed. Alan Almas.

079.5357   TS
AL-ITTIHAD. (Text in Arabic) 1969. d. Al- Ittihad Press, Publishing and Distribtuion Corp., P.O. Box 791, Abu Dhabi, United Arab Emirates. TEL 451600. FAX 461801. TELEX 22984 ITPRESS EM. Ed. Abdullah al-Nuwais. circ. 60,000. **Document type:** newspaper.
Description: Covers political, social and cultural news and developments in the U.A.E.

079.5357   TS
AL-ITTIHAD AL-USBU'I. (Text in Arabic) 1969. w. Al-Ittihad Press, Publishing and Distribution Corp, P.O. Box 791, Abu Dhabi, United Arab Emirates. TEL 451600. FAX 461801. TELEX 22984 ITPRESS EM. Ed. Abdullah al-Nuwais. circ. 60,000. **Document type:** newspaper.

079.536 052   TS
KHALEEJ TIMES. (Includes supplements: Young Times, Lifestyle, Weekend) (Text in English) 1979. d. Mu'assasat Galadari lil-Tiba'ah wal-Nashr, P.O. Box 11243, Dubai, United Arab Emirates. TEL 582400. FAX 582238. TELEX 46820 NEWS EM. Ed. Abd al-Latif Galadari. circ. 55,620. **Document type:** newspaper.
Description: Covers financial, social and cultural news in the U.A.E., the Gulf, and the world.

059.927   SU
AL-LIQA. (Text in Arabic) m. P.O. Box 812, Riyadh, Saudi Arabia. Ed. Ibrahim al-Ulai al-Maiman.

079.5357   TS
WEEK END. (Text in English) 1986. w. Mu'assasat Galadari lil-Tiba'ah wal-Nashr, P.O. Box 11243, Dubai, United Arab Emirates. TEL 582400. FAX 582238. TELEX 48620 NEWS EM. Ed. Abdul Latif Galadari. **Document type:** newspaper.

GENERAL INTEREST PERIODICALS — UNITED STATES

052   TS
WHAT'S ON. (Text in English) 1979. m. Motivate Publishing, P.O. Box 2331, Dubai, United Arab Emirates. TEL 246060. TELEX 48366 MAM EM. Ed. Ubaid Humaid al-Tayir.
    Description: News of the Emirates and suggestions for travel, social and cultural activities.

GENERAL INTEREST PERIODICALS — United Kingdom Miscellaneous Islands

052   UI
ALDERNEY MAGAZINE. 1989. q. £5.50($17.50) Island Publishing, P.O. Box 123, Alderney, Channel Islands. TEL 0481-822137. FAX 0481-822110. Ed. Robert Godfrey. adv.; bk.rev.; film rev. (back issues avail.)
    Description: Covers topical and historical material that relates to the British Channel Islands, including Alderney, Guernsey, Jersey, Sark and Herm.

GENERAL INTEREST PERIODICALS — United States

051   US   ISSN 0001-4397
F380.F8
ACADIANA PROFILE. 1969. q. $9. Acadian News Agency, Inc., Box 52247, Oil Center Sta., Lafayette, LA 70505. TEL 800-200-7919. Ed. Trent Angers. adv.; bk.rev.; bibl.; charts; illus. circ. 10,000.

051   US
ACTION LINKAGE NETWORKER. 1969. m. $50. Action Linkage, Box 684, Bangor, ME 04401. TEL 207-945-4330. Ed. Carl Pease. bk.rev. circ. 1,100.
    Description: Provides network of connection between people concerned about creating a positive future. Includes sections on learning, economics, community, computer and society, libraries, and religious values.

051   US   ISSN 1045-4969
AGENDA NEW YORK.* 1989. q. $40. Agenda U S A, Inc., 155 E. 55th At., No. NN, New York, NY 10022-4038. TEL 212-286-8633. FAX 212-286-0986. Ed. Pamela von Nostitz. circ. 10,000.
    Description: Provides information on how to run events more creatively and professionally for events planners in New York, New Jersey, Connecticut and Palm Beach, Florida.

051   US   ISSN 0002-4562
SK1
ALASKA; the magazine of life on the last frontier. 1935. m. $24. Alaska Publishing Properties, Inc., 808 E St., Ste. 200, Anchorage, AK 99501. TEL 907-272-6070. FAX 907-272-2552. Ed. Tobin Morrison. adv.; bk.rev.; illus.; cum.index: 1935-1972. circ. 249,000. (back issues avail.) **Indexed:** Abstr.Anthropol., Access (1975-), GeoRef., Mag.Ind., PMR. **Document type:** consumer publication.
—Faxon; UnCover.
    Formerly: Alaska Sportsman.

051   US   ISSN 1040-4279
ALBUQUERQUE MONTHLY. 1983. m. $20. Starlight Publishing, Inc., Box 928, Albuquerque, NM 87103. TEL 505-768-7008. FAX 505-255-7359. Ed. Gregor Krause. adv.; bk.rev. circ. 20,000. **Document type:** consumer publication.

051   US   ISSN 8750-8257
ALPINE SUN. 1952. w. $15. H & H Publications, Inc., 2144-B Alpine Blvd., Alpine, CA 91901. TEL 619-445-3288. Ed. Ellen B. Holzman. adv. circ. 2,100. (tabloid format; back issues avail.)
    Description: Covers information and entertainment news for Alpine, California (East of San Diego).

071
ALTERNATIVES (MYRTLE BEACH). 1987. fortn. $21.95. Alternative Publications, Ltd., Drawer 2485, Myrtle Beach, SC 29578. TEL 803-444-5556. FAX 803-444-5558. Ed. Valerie Graham. adv.; bk.rev. circ. 20,000. (tabloid format) **Document type:** newspaper.
    Description: Contains regional news and lifestyle features for residents of the coastal areas of North and South Carolina.

051   US
AMERICA ENTERTAINS; a celebration of home, family and friends. 1988. q. Working Woman, McCall's Group, 110 Fifth Ave., New York, NY 10011. TEL 212-463-1000.

051   US
AMERICAN PUBLIC OPINION DATA. a. $174.50. Opinion Research Service, 4948 St. Elmo Ave., No. 207, Bethesda, MD 20814-6013.
    Description: Companion to the American Public Opinion Index. Provides responses to questions listed in the Index.

051   US   ISSN 0192-5717
ANN ARBOR OBSERVER. 1976. m. $14. Ann Arbor Observer Company, 201 Catherine, Ann Arbor, MI 48104. TEL 313-769-3175. FAX 313-769-3375. Ed. John Hilton. adv. circ. 56,000. (also avail. in microfiche from UMI,UNM) **Document type:** consumer publication.

051   US   ISSN 0192-5725
ANN ARBOR SCENE MAGAZINE. vol.8, 1979. q. $4. Box 1988, Ann Arbor, MI 48106. TEL 313-769-2084.
    Description: Covers items of local interest.

051   US
ANNAPOLIS. m. $28. Thomas Gorsline Publisher, 419 Fourth St., Annapolis, MD 21403. TEL 301-263-7400. FAX 301-268-4825. bk.rev. circ. 12,000.
    Formerly: Annapolitan (ISSN 0899-2320)

051   US   ISSN 0003-617X
ANTWERP BEE-ARGUS; Paulding County Eagle. 1883. w. $18. 113 N. Main St., Box 278, Antwerp, OH 45813. TEL 419-258-8161. FAX 419-258-8161. Ed. Sandra Kay Temple. adv.; bk.rev. circ. 1,350.
    Description: Focuses on court statistics, local government issues, social and athletic events and farm news.

051 917.6   US   ISSN 0363-2318
PS553
APPALACHIAN HERITAGE; a magazine of southern Appalachian life and culture. 1973. q. $18. Berea College, Hutchins Library, CPO Library, Berea, KY 40404. TEL 606-986-9341. FAX 606-986-9494. Ed. Sidney Saylor Farr. bk.rev.; index. circ. 1,000. (also avail. in microform from UMI)
—Faxon; UnCover; UMI.

051   US   ISSN 0044-8788
AREAS OF CONCERN. 1971. q. $5. Concerned Citizens of the Delaware Valley, Box 47, Bryn Mawr, PA 19010. TEL 610-525-1129. Ed. Harry Hyde Jr. adv.; bk.rev.; charts; illus. circ. 200. (processed; also avail. in microform from UMI; back issues avail.) **Document type:** newsletter.

051   US
ARGUS MAGAZINE. vol.6, 1971. w. free. Maryland Media, Inc., Box U, College Park, MD 20742. Ed. Michael Fribush. adv.; bk.rev. circ. 21,000.
    Former titles: Argus - Dimension; Argus (College Park) (ISSN 0044-8826)

051   US
ARKANSAS HOMES & LIFESTYLES. a. Arkansas Writers' Project, Inc., Box 34010, Little Rock, AR 72203-4010. TEL 501-375-2985. FAX 501-375-3623. Ed. Audrey M. Coleman. circ. 30,000.

051   US   ISSN 0164-6273
ARKANSAS TIMES. 1974. m. $16. Arkansas Writer's Project, Inc., Box 34010, 201 E. Markham, 200 Heritage Center West, Little Rock, AR 72203. TEL 501-375-2985. FAX 501-375-2985. adv.; bk.rev. circ. 31,586. **Indexed:** Access (1986-1992).
    Description: Profiles business, political and social culture in Arkansas. Includes investigative reporting, recreation and entertainment guides.

051   US
AROUND SAN DIEGO. 1989. m. McKinnon Enterprises, Box 719001, San Diego, CA 92171-9001. TEL 619-571-1818. FAX 619-571-1889. Ed. Dirk Sutro; Pub. Lawrence Bame. adv. circ. 66,088. **Document type:** consumer publication.
    Description: Contains the latest information on performing arts, concerts, festivals, art galleries, museums, outing ideas, classes, and garden shows.

051   US
AROUND TOWN PUBLICATION.* bi-w. $19.50. Around Town Publication, 880 S.W. Tenth Ave., no. BAY7, Pompano Beach, FL 33069-4633. Ed. Patrick G. Mascola. adv.; film rev.; play rev.; illus. circ. 25,000. (tabloid format; back issues avail.)
    Description: For the age group 35-65. Covers fine dining and traveling.

051   US   ISSN 1043-5085
ASPEN MAGAZINE. 1973. bi-m. $24. Ridge Publications, Box G-3, Aspen, CO 81612. TEL 303-920-4040. FAX 303-920-4044. Ed. Janet O'Grady. adv. circ. 16,000. **Indexed:** Access (1975-). **Document type:** consumer publication.
—UnCover.
    Description: For Aspen residents and visitors. Covers sports, business, the arts, culture, and local politics.

051   US   ISSN 1053-623X
F294.A7
ATHENS MAGAZINE. 1989. 6/yr. $12.95. Athens Newspapers Inc., 1 Press Pl., Athens, GA 30601. TEL 706-549-0123. FAX 706-543-5234. (Subscr. to: Box 912, Athens, GA 30603-0192) Ed. Elaine Kalber. adv.; bk.rev. circ. 5,500. **Document type:** consumer publication.
    Description: Articles about people and issues in Athens and Northeast Georgia; includes short fiction, essays, photographs, and visual art.

071   US
ATLANTA INQUIRER. 1960. w. $18.20. Atlanta Inquirer, Inc., 947 Martin Luther King Jr. Dr. N.W., Box 92367, Morris Brown Sta., Atlanta, GA 30314. TEL 404-523-6086. Ed. David L. Stanley. adv.; bk.rev.; circ. 60,000 (paid). (back issues avail.) **Document type:** newspaper.

051   US   ISSN 0004-6701
HF296
ATLANTA MAGAZINE. 1961. m. $15. Emmis Publishing Corp., 950 N. Meridian St., Ste. 1200, Indianapolis, IN 46204-3908. TEL 404-872-3100. FAX 404-876-2748. Ed. Lee Walburn. bk.rev.; circ. 61,000 (paid). (also avail. in microform from BLH,UMI) **Indexed:** Access (1975-), P.A.I.S. **Document type:** consumer publication.
—UMI.

051   US
ATLANTIC CITY MAGAZINE. 1977. 12/yr. $19.95. Abarta Metro Publishing, 1000 W. Washington Ave., Pleasantville, NJ 08232. TEL 609-272-7900. FAX 609-272-7910. Ed. Deborah Ein; Pub. John Bitzer. adv. contact: Jane Thompson. circ. 50,000. **Document type:** bulletin.

051   US   ISSN 0004-797X
AUGUSTA MAGAZINE. 1966. bi-m. $12.95. Augusta Magazine, Inc., 1164 Broad St., Box 1405, Augusta, GA 30903-0517. FAX 706-722-8901. Ed. Beth Siciliano. adv.; bk.rev. circ. 14,000.
    Description: Features the people, places and events of the Augusta area.

917.6   US   ISSN 1054-5441
AURA OF FORT WORTH AND TARRANT COUNTY. 1985. bi-m. $16.95. LeWay - Aura, Inc., 2917 Morton St., Fort Worth, TX 76107-2925. TEL 817-332-3548. FAX 817-336-8409. Ed. John Paschal. adv. contact: Maureen Jones. bk.rev. circ. 20,000. (back issues avail.) **Document type:** consumer publication.
    Formerly: Aura of Fort Worth.
    Description: Contains features, personality profiles and subjects of interest to the upscale market in the DFW area as well as a broader market.

051   US
AVENTURA LIFESTYLES.* q. G S & J Publishing, Inc., 5212 N.W. 54th Ave., Pompano Beach, FL 33073-3755. TEL 305-977-5901. circ. 15,000 (controlled).

051   US
AVENUE. vol.2, 1978. 11/yr. $100. Avenue Magazine, Inc., 145 E. 57th St., New York, NY 10022-2141. TEL 212-758-9517. FAX 212-758-7395. Ed. Andy Port. illus. circ. 80,000.

051   US
AZALEA CITY NEWS & REVIEW.* 1974. w. $8. 8333 Douglas Ave., Dallas, TX 75225-5811. adv.; bk.rev.; film rev.; play rev.; illus.; circ. 10,000 (controlled). (tabloid format; back issues avail.)
    Formerly (until 1979): Azalea City News.

2774 GENERAL INTEREST PERIODICALS — UNITED STATES

051   301.4157   US
B W M T - ATLANTA NEWSLETTER. 1981. m. $18. Black & White Men Together - Atlanta, Box 1334, Atlanta, GA 30301-1334. TEL 404-892-2968. Ed. John Nicholson. bk.rev.; film rev.; play rev. circ. 200. (tabloid format; back issues avail.) **Document type:** newsletter.
   Description: Contains articles, announcements, calendar of events, and discussion topics.

640   US   ISSN 1051-323X
AP2
BACK HOME; hands on and down to earth. 1990. q. $16. Box 370, Mountain Home, NC 28758-0370. TEL 704-696-3838. FAX 704-696-0700. Ed. Terry Krautwurst. adv.; bk.rev. circ. 20,000. **Document type:** consumer publication.

051   US   ISSN 0199-6290
F446
BACK HOME IN KENTUCKY. 1977. bi-m. $12 (effective Oct. 1991). Greysmith Publishing, Inc., Box 6811629, 128 Holiday Ct., Ste. 116, Franklin, TN 37068-1629. TEL 615-794-4338. FAX 615-790-6188. Ed. Nanci Gregg. adv.; bk.rev. circ. 10,000. (back issues avail.)
   Description: Provides a glimpse of Kentucky's scenery, history, personalities, literature, cooking, gardening and wildlife.

640   US   ISSN 1050-9712
BACKWOODS HOME MAGAZINE. 1989. 6/yr. $17.95. David J. Duffy, Ed. & Pub., 1257 Siskiyou Blvd., Ste. 213, Ashland, OR 97520. TEL 503-488-2053. FAX 503-488-2063. bk.rev. circ. 60,000.

051   US   ISSN 0746-9888
BAKER VALLEY NEWS. 1982. fortn. $15. Baker Valley News Publishing Co., Box 84, Baker, CA 92309. TEL 619-733-4300. FAX 619-733-4615. Eds. Carolyn Jacobson, Lois Clark. adv. circ. 540.
   Supersedes (in 1984, no.23): Mojave Road Report.

051   US
BALTIMORE SCENE MAGAZINE.* q. GuestInformant Quick Guide, 400 E. Pratt St., 8th Fl., Baltimore, MD 21202. TEL 301-783-7520. FAX 301-783-7520. Ed. Jennifer LaFleur.

051   US
BAY WINDOW. 1951. m. $18. Balboa Bay Club, 1221 W. Coast Hwy., Newport Beach, CA 92663. TEL 714-645-5000. FAX 714-642-6947. Ed. Jim Felton. adv. circ. 4,269.
   Description: Contains items of club member interest.

051   US
BELLAIRE - S W. m. Creneau Media Group, Box 3388, Houston, TX 77253. TEL 713-880-4611. FAX 713-880-4644. Ed. Cristina Adams. circ. 10,500.

051 974   US   ISSN 1042-587X
BERKSHIRE MAGAZINE.* 1982. bi-m. Berkshire Publishing, Inc., Box 97, Jay, NY 12941-0097. TEL 413-298-3791. Ed. William Hutchinson. bk.rev. circ. 17,000.

051   US   ISSN 0273-6160
BETTER LIVING. 1981. q. $10. Avant-Garde Media, Inc., 80 Central Park W., Ste. 16B, New York, NY 10023. Ed. Ralph Ginzburg. adv.; bk.rev. circ. 1,000,000. (tabloid format)

051   US
BEVERLY HILLS (213). 1983. w. $2 per no. Baker Communications, Inc. (Beverly Hills), 9465 Wilshire Blvd., Ste. 307, Beverly Hills, CA 90212. TEL 213-275-8850. Ed. Brian Boye; Pub. Seth Baker. adv.
   Description: Focuses on fashion, beauty, interior design, people, places, social events, finances, foods, wines, liquor, exotic and classic automobiles and new products. Reports on restaurants, films, society and personalities.

051   US   ISSN 0006-0410
BEVERLY REVIEW. 1904. w. $16. T R Communications, 1739 W. 99th St., Chicago, IL 60643. TEL 312-238-3366. Ed. Robert M. Olszewski, Jr. adv.; bk.rev. circ. 5,500.
   Description: Contains items of local interest.

051   US
BIG APPLE PRESS.* 1991. m. $15. Vocall Communications Corp., 70 E. 55th St., New York, NY 10022-3222. TEL 212-754-2118. FAX 212-465-1123. Eds. Peg Dardenne, Leo J. Northart.

051   US
BIG BEANS. m. Just Publications, 8 Alton Place, No. 2, Brookline, MA 02146. TEL 617-739-5878. Ed. Marc Malkin. circ. 30,000.

051   US   ISSN 0006-3754
BIRMINGHAM WORLD.* 1930. w. $12.50. 407 15th St. N., Birmingham, AL 35203-1844. TEL 205-251-6523. (Affiliate: Scott Newspaper Syndicate) Ed. Marcel Mepson. adv.; bk.rev. (also avail. in microform)

051   US
▼**BIZ (HOUSTON).** 1992. m. American City Business Journals, Inc. (Houston), 1 W. Loop S., Ste. 650, Houston, TX 77027. TEL 713-688-8811. Ed. Mark Pawlosky. adv. contact: Deborah Sanders. circ. 70,000 (controlled).

051   US
▼**BIZ (ST. LOUIS).** 1992. m. free to qualified personnel. American City Business Journals, Inc. (St. Louis), 1 Metropolitan Sq., Ste. 2170, St. Louis, MO 63102. TEL 314-421-6200. Ed. Mark Pawlosky. adv. contact: Carol Stolze. circ. 70,000 (controlled).

051   US
BLOOMINGTON MONTHLY. 1987. m. $18. Bloomington Monthly, Inc., 663 N. Walnut, Bloomington, IN 47404-3846. TEL 812-336-4774. FAX 812-332-4774. Ed. Tom Coleman. adv.: B&W page $450; adv. contact: Jeff Huston. bk.rev.; film rev. circ. 10,000.
   Description: Community-oriented with feature articles on local people and events plus an arts and entertainment calendar.

051   US   ISSN 1041-3456
BLUE RIDGE COUNTRY. 1988. bi-m. $14.95. Leisure Publishing Co. (Roanoke), Box 21535, 3424 Brambleton Ave., S.W., Roanoke, VA 24018. TEL 703-989-6138. FAX 703-989-7603. Ed. Kurt Rheinheimer. adv. circ. 75,000. **Document type:** consumer publication.
   Description: Covers profiles on towns, photographs and recipes, history, heritage and beauty of Southern Appalachians.

051   US   ISSN 0894-1386
BLUM'S FARMERS & PLANTERS ALMANAC AND TURNER'S CAROLINA ALMANAC. 1828. $2.25. Blum's Almanac Company, 3301 Healy Dr., S.W., Winston-Salem, NC 27103. TEL 910-765-5811. FAX 910-659-1252. Ed. Allen S. Goslen. adv. circ. 600,000.
   Description: Contains information on astrology, weather, farming, household hints and jokes.

051 910.4   US   ISSN 0740-2856
BOCA RATON MAGAZINE. 1981. 6/yr. $18. J E S Publishing Corporation, 6413 Congress Ave., Ste. 100, Boca Raton, FL 33487. TEL 407-997-8683. FAX 407-997-8909. Ed. Marie B. Speed. adv. circ. 18,000. (back issues avail.)
   Description: Designed to help readers experience the magnificence of South Florida.

917 974.4   US   ISSN 0006-7989
HF1
BOSTON MAGAZINE. 1962. m. $15. Boston Magazine, Inc. (Subsidiary of: Metrocorp), 300 Massachusetts Ave., Boston, MA 02115. TEL 617-262-9700. FAX 617-262-4925. Ed. Michael Roberts. adv.; bk.rev.; film rev.; illus. circ. 121,275. (also avail. in microfilm from UMI; reprint service avail. from UMI) **Indexed:** Access (1975-), Hlth.Ind., Mag.Ind., PMR. —Faxon; UMI.

051   US   ISSN 0163-3015
BOSTON PHOENIX. 1966. w. $41.50. Phoenix Media - Communications Group, c/o Stephen M. Mindich, 126 Brookline Ave., Boston, MA 02215. TEL 617-536-5390. FAX 617-536-1463. Ed. Peter Kadzis. adv.; bk.rev.; film rev.; play rev. circ. 134,000. (tabloid format; reprint service avail. from UMI)
—UMI.
   Formerly: Boston After Dark (ISSN 0045-2602)

051   US   ISSN 0164-1441
LH1.B5
BOSTONIA. 1900. q. $15. Boston University, Bostonia Magazine, 10 Lenox St., Brookline, MA 02146. TEL 617-353-3081. FAX 617-353-6488. Keith Botsford. adv.; bk.rev.; charts; illus. circ. 185,000. (back issues avail.)

977.3   US   ISSN 0007-0149
BRIGHTON PARK LIFE. 1933. w. $60. Brighton Publishing Co., 2949 W. 43rd St., Chicago, IL 60632. TEL 312-523-3663. FAX 312-523-3983. Ed. Albert H. Silinski. adv. circ. 30,000.

974.7   US   ISSN 0007-2346
BROOKLYN HEIGHTS PRESS. 1937. w. $25. Brooklyn Journal Publications, Inc., 129 Montague St., Brooklyn, NY 11201. TEL 718-624-0536. FAX 718-875-5302. Ed. John Gardiner. adv.; bk.rev.; charts; illus. circ. 19,500.

051   US   ISSN 0300-7499
BUFFALO SPREE. 1967. q. $8. Spree Publishing Co., 4511 Harlem Rd., Box 38, Buffalo, NY 14226. TEL 716-839-3405. FAX 716-839-4384. Ed. Johanna V. Shotell. adv.; bk.rev. circ. 21,000. **Indexed:** A.I.P.P. **Document type:** consumer publication.
   Description: Covers items of local interest, and includes prose and poetry.

051   US
CACHE CITIZEN. w. free. Utah State University, Department of Communications, Box 703, Logan, UT 84321. TEL 801-750-3292. Ed. Nancy Williams. circ. 18,000 (controlled).
   Description: Covers public affairs and community news.

051   US   ISSN 0008-2031
CAMDEN COUNTY RECORD. 1928. w. $5.50. Fifth and Jersey Ave., Gloucester City, NJ 08030. TEL 609-772-0085. Ed. James H. Ricks. adv.; bk.rev.; illus. circ. 5,100. (tabloid format)

051   US   ISSN 0199-7238
CAPE COD LIFE. 1979. 6/yr. $19.75. Cape Cod Life, Inc., Box 767, Cataumet, MA 02534-0767. TEL 508-564-4466. FAX 508-564-4470. Ed. Brian F. Shortsleeve. adv. contact: Robin B. Thayer. bk.rev.; circ. 27,964 (paid); 3,694 (controlled). (back issues avail.) **Document type:** consumer publication.
   Description: Profiles of persons, institutions, and activities on the Cape, Martha's Vineyard, and Nantucket, with articles on arts, history, legends, nautical activities, planning, real estate, and the environment.

051   US   ISSN 0892-1148
CAPPER'S. 1879. fortn. $26 (effective Jul. 1993). Stauffer Communications, Inc., 1503 S.W. 42nd St., Topeka, KS 66609-1265. TEL 913-274-4300. FAX 913-274-4305. Ed. Nancy Peavler. adv. contact: Keith Chartier. illus. circ. 350,000. (also avail. in microfilm) **Indexed:** A.I.P.P. **Document type:** consumer publication.
   Formerly (until Jan. 1987): Capper's Weekly (ISSN 0008-5936)
   Description: Provides general, human interest news. Includes a homemaking section.

051   US   ISSN 0738-9604
CAREFREE ENTERPRISE; an Arizona lifestyle. 1963. m. (11/yr.). $13 (Canada $28; elsewhere $36). Box 1145, Carefree, AZ 85377. TEL 602-488-3098. Ed. Fran Barbano. adv. contact: Lynn Grant. bk.rev. circ. 3,000. (back issues avail.) **Document type:** consumer publication.

051   US
▼**CAROLINA STYLE.** 1994. m. $18; newsstand price: $3.50. Carolina Style, Inc., 3975-B Market St., Wilmington, NC 28405. TEL 919-341-3033. Ed. Anthony Policastro; Pub. Stuart Slater. adv.: B&W page $2000. circ. 100,000. **Document type:** consumer publication.

071   US   ISSN 0045-5873
CAROLINIAN. 1940. s-w. $25. Carolinian Publishing Co., 518 E. Martin St., Raleigh, NC 27601. TEL 919-834-5558. FAX 919-832-3243. Ed. P.J. Monroe. adv.; illus. circ. 10,000. **Document type:** newspaper.

CATHOLIC DIGEST. see RELIGIONS AND THEOLOGY — Roman Catholic

GENERAL INTEREST PERIODICALS — UNITED STATES

051 US ISSN 0008-8048
CATHOLIC FORESTER. 1893. bi-m. membership. Catholic Order of Foresters, 325 Shuman Blvd., Box 3012, Naperville, IL 60566-7012. TEL 708-983-4900. FAX 708-983-4057. Ed. Dorothy Deer. illus.; circ. 170,000 (controlled).

071 US
CEDAR POST; "nothing but good news". 1972. m. $12. Luke Parham, Ed. & Pub., Box 1144, Cedar Park, TX 78636-1144. TEL 512-258-8850. adv.: page $350. circ. 10,000. (tabloid format) **Document type:** newspaper.

051 US
▼**CELEBRATE! MIDWEST.** (Supplement to weekly newspapers) 1993. bi-w. Montgomery Media, Inc., 611 N. Broadway, Ste. 600, Milwaukee, WI 53202. TEL 414-233-4266. FAX 414-223-3334. adv.: B&W page $54000, color page $66000; trim 8 x 10 7/8. circ. 3,000,000.
Description: For families in the midwest. Covers health and fitness, cooking, gardening, money management, sports and lifestyle.

051 US
CENTERSTAGE. 1988. bi-m. $9.95. Parker Media Inc., 196 Trumbull St., Hartford, CT 06103-2207. TEL 203-560-2699. Ed. Kenneth Ross. circ. 70,000. **Document type:** consumer publication.
Former titles (until 1993): Metropolitan Hartford Magazine (ISSN 1067-4381); (until 1988): Hartford Monthly (ISSN 0897-7534)
Description: Performing arts magazine serving readers in Connecticut.

071.749 US
CENTRAL BUSINESS. 1988. fortn. $26. Snowden Publications Inc., Box 201, Princeton, NJ 08542. TEL 908-329-0003. FAX 908-329-0252. (Dist. by: Snowden Publications Inc., 11 Deer Park Dr., Monmouth Junction, NJ 08852) Ed. George M. Taber; Pub. Donald M. Wilson. adv. contact: Michelle McGowan. bk.rev. circ. 11,000. (tabloid format; back issues avail.) **Document type:** newspaper.
Formerly (until Sep. 1993): Business for Central New Jersey (ISSN 1042-8704)
Description: Covers the major business-related events as they occur in central New Jersey. Also provides a focus on various industries of business in the state.

051 US
CENTRAL COAST. 1988. m. $17.50. R J Nelson Enterprises, Inc., Box 552, Santa Maria, CA 93456. TEL 805-937-2087. Ed. Bob Nelson. adv.; circ. 40,000 (controlled). **Document type:** consumer publication.
Description: Presents history, lifestyles, trends and activities from Santa Barbara north to the Big Sur area near Monterey.

051 US
▼**CENTRAL NEW YORKER.** 1992. m. $2 per no. Central New Yorker Magazine, Box 850, Syracuse, NY 13210. TEL 315-443-1794. FAX 315-443-3689. adv.: B&W page $1600, color page $2000; trim 8 x 10 3/4. circ. 12,000. **Document type:** consumer publication.

051 US
CENTURY GRAPHICS. bi-m. Century Publications, Inc., 1805 S. Bellaire, Ste. 235, Denver, CO 80222. TEL 303-692-8940. **Document type:** newspaper.

051 US
CHARLESTON MAGAZINE. 1987. bi-m. $15. Charleston Magazine, Inc., Box 21770, Charleston, SC 29413. TEL 803-722-8018. FAX 803-722-8116. adv.; bk.rev. circ. 20,000.
Description: Depicts the general interests, charms and styles of the city and its tri-county area. Covers current happenings, history and local personalities.

051 US
CHARLOTTE MAGAZINE.* 1988. bi-m. $12. Charlotte Magazine, Box 11048, Charlotte, NC 28220-1048. TEL 704-552-1530. FAX 704-552-1773. Ed. Allan Maurer. adv.; bk.rev. circ. 25,000.
Description: Regional magazine, featuring local personalities, business, trends, the arts, society, fashion and sports.

071 US ISSN 0009-3394
CHESTNUT HILL LOCAL. 1958. w. $15. Chestnut Hill Community Association, 8434 Germantown Ave., Philadelphia, PA 19118. TEL 215-248-8800. FAX 215-248-8814. Ed. Marie R. Jones. adv. contact: Frank Moeschlin. bk.rev. circ. 10,000. (also avail. in microform) **Document type:** newspaper.
Description: Contains items of local interest.

051 US
CHICAGO LIFE; a resource for the professional. 1984. bi-m. $26 for 12 nos. Box 11311, Chicago, IL 60611-0311. TEL 312-528-2737. adv.; bk.rev. circ. 60,000. (back issues avail.)

071.773 US
CHICAGO STANDARD NEWS. 1984. w. $30. Standard Newspapers, 615 S. Halsted St., Chicago Heights, IL 60411. TEL 708-755-5021. FAX 708-755-5020. Ed. Lorenzo E. Martin. adv. contact: Pat Martin. bk.rev.; illus.; tr.lit. circ. 15,000. (tabloid format) **Document type:** newspaper.

071 US ISSN 0882-7729
CODEN: CSMOBF
CHRISTIAN SCIENCE MONITOR. Weekly international edition: Christian Science Monitor (World Edition) (ISSN 0896-551X) 5/wk. $159 ($79 for w. ed.) (effective 1994). Christian Science Publishing Society, One Norway St., Boston, MA 02115. TEL 617-450-2000. Ed. Richard J. Cattani. adv.; bk.rev. Indexed: Bk.Rev.Ind. (1965-), CCR, Hlth.Ind., Music Ind. **Document type:** newspaper.
●Also available online. Vendor(s): DIALOG Information Services, Inc..
—CCC.

051 US
CINCINNATI MAGAZINE. 1967. m. $14. Cincinnati Monthly Publishing Corp., 409 Broadway, Cincinnati, OH 45202-3311. Ed. Laura Pulfer. adv. circ. 21,000.
Formerly: Cincinnati Monthly.

051 US ISSN 0897-4926
CITY & COUNTRY CLUB LIFE; the social magazine for South Florida. 1984. 5/m. $15. Club Publications, 665 La Villa Dr., Miami Springs, FL 33166. TEL 305-887-1701. FAX 305-885-1923. Ed. Peta-gai Innerarity. adv.; film rev.; bibl.; circ. 26,000 (controlled). (back issues avail.)
Description: Covers the society, clubs, charity benefits, and galleries of South Florida.

051 US
CITY - COUNTY MAGAZINE. 1986. m. $10. City - County Publications, Box 517, Burlington, NC 27216. TEL 919-226-8436. FAX 919-226-8437. Ed. Kelly Potter. adv. circ. 5,000. (back issues avail.)
Description: Covers community news.

051 US
CITYVIEW. 1983. w. $50. Business Publications Corporation, The Depot at Fourth, 100 Fourth St., Des Moines, IA 50309. TEL 515-288-3336. FAX 515-288-0309. Ed. Arthur Orduna. circ. 35,000.
Formerly: Des Moines Skywalker.

301.412 370 US ISSN 0747-3826
E185.5
CLASS MAGAZINE. 1979. m. $15. R.E. John-Sandy Communications Ltd., 900 Broadway, 8th Fl., New York, NY 10003. TEL 212-677-3055. FAX 212-677-3341. (Subscr. to: Box 379, Mount Morris, IL 61054-1473k, NY 10163-0828) Ed. Constance M. Weaver. adv.; bk.rev. circ. 250,000. (back issues avail.)
Description: Focuses on a global black perspective of the Third World with a Carribean orientation.

051 US ISSN 0160-8533
F499.C6
CLEVELAND MAGAZINE. 1972. m. $18. City Magazines, Inc., Hanna Bldg., Ste. 730, 1422 Euclid Ave., Cleveland, OH 44115. TEL 216-771-2833. FAX 216-781-6318. Ed. Liz Ludlow; Pub. Lute Harmon. adv.; bk.rev.; illus. circ. 40,000. (also avail. in microform from UMI) **Indexed:** Access (1975-). **Document type:** consumer publication.
—UMI.
Formerly: Cleveland (ISSN 0340-1324)

051 US
COAST AND COUNTRY. 1984. bi-m. $12. Hastings Group, Inc., 644 Humphrey St., Ste. 43, Swampscott, MA 01907. TEL 617-592-0160. FAX 617-599-2619. Ed. Robert A. Hastings. adv. circ. 75,000.
Description: Contains articles on human and personal issues, the home, money management, health, business, dining, wine, leisure, area issues, travel and personalities.

051 US
COLORADO EXPRESSION. 1991. q. $12 to non-members. New West Publishing, Inc., 10200 E. Girard Ave., Denver, CO 80231-5500. TEL 303-751-0696. Ed. Gene Ward. adv.: B&W page $2500, color page $3000. circ. 25,000.
Description: Features Colorado arts, regional events, business and politics.

051 US
COLUMBIA METROPOLITAN. 1990. q. $10.95. 3201 Devine St., Columbia, SC 29205-1847. TEL 803-252-2327. Ed. Emily Clay. circ. 15,000.
Description: Covers Columbia's people, homes, places and events.

051 US
COLUMBUS MONTHLY. 1975. m. $16. C M Media Inc., Box 29913, Columbus, OH 43229-7513. TEL 614-888-4567. Ed. Lenore Brown. adv.; illus. circ. 38,000. **Document type:** consumer publication.

051 US
COMMUNICATOR COMMUNITY NEWS. 1982. m. $12. Gloria Greco, Ed. & Pub., Box 9090, Reno, NV 89507-9090. TEL 702-747-4400. adv.; bk.rev.; play rev.; bibl.; circ. 24,000 (controlled). (tabloid format; back issues avail.) **Document type:** newspaper.
Former titles (until Apr. 1990): Communicator (Reno) (ISSN 8756-5900); (until Dec. 1982): Good Hope News; (until Aug. 1982): Hope News.

051 US
COMMUNITY LIVING OF FLORIDA.* m. Community Associations Institute (Alexandria), Box 25037, Alexandria, VA 22313-5037. TEL 407-539-1808. Ed. Alice R. Friedman. circ. 10,000.

051 US
CONCORD AND THE NORTH; Ashland, Berlin, Bow, Colebrook, Conway, Franklin, Gilford, Gorham, Hanover, Laconia, Lancaster, Lebanon, Littleton, Meredith, Moultonborough, Plymouth, Wolfeboro. (Three other regional eds.: Hampshire East, Manchester, Nashua) 1991. m. $20. Connections Network, Inc., Network Publications, 100 Main St., Nashua, NH 03060. TEL 603-883-3150. (Subscr. to: 889 Elm St., Manchester, NH 03101. TEL 603-883-3150) Ed. Daniel Ryan.
Description: Covers people, politics, education, business and economics, food and dining, and the arts.

051 US ISSN 0163-1136
CONNECTICUT. 1971. m. $15. Communications International, 789 Reservoir Ave., Bridgeport, CT 06606. TEL 203-374-3388. FAX 203-371-6561. Ed. Charles Monagan. adv.: B&W page $5245, color page $7710; trim 8 1/4 x 10 3/4. illus. circ. 87,275. (also avail. in microform from UMI; microfilm from KTO; reprint service avail. from UMI) **Indexed:** Access (1975-).
Description: Contains items of local interest.

051 US ISSN 0300-8258
CONNECTICUT FIRESIDE. Variant title: Connecticut Fireside and Review of Books. 1972. q. $6. Albert E. Callan, Ed. & Pub., Box 5293, Hamden, CT 06518. TEL 203-248-1023. adv.; bk.rev.; film rev.; play rev.; illus. circ. 2,000.

051 US
CONNEXUS. m. $12. Box 151539, Altamonte Springs, FL 32715.

051 640 US
CORDIALITY.* 1989. q. price varies. 175 Fifth Ave., Ste. 301, New York, NY 10001. Ed. J. Joseph Finora. adv.; circ. 100,000 (controlled).
Description: Covers in-home service for 21 to 39-year-olds with information on travel, home electronics, general leisure and food; emphasis is placed on the responsible use of alcohol.

2776 GENERAL INTEREST PERIODICALS — UNITED STATES

051 US ISSN 0895-0377
COUNTRY (GREENDALE). 1987. bi-m. $16.98. Reiman Publications, Inc., 5400 S. 60th St., Greendale, WI 53129. TEL 414-423-0100. FAX 414-423-1143. (Subscr. to: Box 994, Greendale, WI 53129) Ed. Roy J. Reiman. circ. 2,100,000 (paid). **Document type:** consumer publication.

051 US ISSN 0147-4928
S521.5.A2
COUNTRY GENTLEMAN.* 1975. q. $6. Curtis Publishing Co., 1000 Waterway Blvd., Indianapolis, IA 46202-2191. Ed. Bruce Kinnaird. circ. 163,757. (also avail. in microform from UMI; reprint service avail. from UMI) **Indexed:** Access, Mag.Ind., PMR, RICS.
 Incorporates (in 1977): Country Place (ISSN 0095-5558)

051 US
COUNTRY JOURNAL (HARRISBURG); for people interested in rural country living. 1974. bi-m. $24.00. Cowles Magazines, Inc. (Subsidiary of: Cowles Media Company), 6405 Flank Dr., Box 8200, Harrisburg, PA 17105-8200. TEL 717-657-9555. FAX 717-657-9526. Ed. Peter Fossel. adv.; bk.rev.; charts; illus.; index. circ. 200,077. (also avail. in microform from UMI; reprint service avail. from UMI) **Indexed:** Gard.Lit. (1992-), Mag.Ind., MELSA, R.G. **Document type:** consumer publication.
 —UnCover.
 Formerly: Blair and Ketchum's Country Journal (ISSN 0094-0526)
 Description: Better living in rural America with building projects, gardening advice, environment and helpful how-tos.

051 US ISSN 1047-3955
COUNTRY SAMPLER. 1984. 6/yr. $19.96. Sampler Publications, Inc., 707 Kautz Rd., St. Charles, IL 60174. TEL 708-377-8000. FAX 708-377-8194. (Subscr. to: Box 352, Mt. Morris, IL 61054) adv. circ. 500,000.
 Description: Contains information about country home accessories and crafts.

051 US
COUNTRY SAMPLER'S WEST; the spirit of the frontier home. 1989. 6/yr. Sampler Publications, Inc., 707 Kautz Rd., St. Charles, IL 60174.
TEL 708-377-8000. FAX 708-377-8194. (Subscr. to: Box 423, Mt. Morris, IL 61054) adv. circ. 111,000.
 Formerly (until 1993): Southwest Sampler (ISSN 1066-7245)
 Description: Features home decorating styles from throughout the Western region of the United States, plus foods and travel ideas. Includes catalogs of decorating accessories and crafts.

640 US ISSN 8750-7595
COUNTRYSIDE AND SMALL STOCK JOURNAL. 1917. bi-m. $18. Countryside Publications, Ltd., N2601 Winter Sports Rd., Withee, WI 54498-9317. TEL 715-785-7979. FAX 715-785-7414. Ed. Jerome Belanger. adv.; bk.rev.; illus.; mkt.; index. circ. 30,000. **Indexed:** Ind.How To Do It, Mag.Ind., MELSA. **Document type:** consumer publication.
 —Faxon; UnCover; UMI.
 Former titles: Small Stock Magazine (0037-7244); Countryside (0011-0208); Which was formed by the merger of: Dairy Goat Guide and Countryside; Countryside and Small Stock Journal (0090-337X); Countryside (Waterloo) (0363-8723); Incorporates (1979-1984): Backyard Poultry (ISSN 0194-9462).

051 US
COUNTY FARE - POINTSETT REGISTER. w. $5.60. Greenville News - Piedmont Co., Box 2730, Greenville, SC 29602-2730. TEL 803-298-4100. Ed. Sharon Todd.

051 US ISSN 0195-4121
COUNTY LINES. 1977. m. $29. ValleyDel Publications, Inc., 840 E. Street Rd., Box 31, Westtown, PA 19395. TEL 215-399-1720. FAX 215-399-9738. Ed. Karen Waldauer. adv.; illus. circ. 35,000. **Document type:** consumer publication.
 Description: Lifestyle magazine for suburban Philadelphia-Wilmington area. Focuses on social events and cultural activities. Includes dining reviews.

071 US
COUNTY WIDE. 1977. w. $26. County Wide Communications, Inc., Box 497, Machias, ME 04654. Ed. Bill Reynolds; Pub. Bob Berta. adv. contact: Joyce Hartford. bk.rev.; film rev.; play rev.; charts; illus.; stat. circ. 10,800. (tabloid format; back issues avail.) **Document type:** newspaper.

051 US ISSN 1045-7011
CREATING EXCELLENCE; Vermont's journal for people in growing businesses. 1987. bi-m. $12. New World Publishing, Box 2048, S. Burlington, VT 05407. TEL 802-655-7200. FAX 802-655-7214. Ed. David Robinson. adv.; bk.rev. circ. 20,000.

051 US ISSN 0889-8685
CREATIVE LOAFING. 1972. w. $40. Eason Publications, Inc., 750 Willoughby Way, Atlanta, GA 30312-1124. FAX 404-522-1532. Ed. Deborah Eason. adv.; bk.rev.; film rev.; play rev. circ. 125,000. (tabloid format; back issues avail.) **Document type:** newspaper.
 Description: Alternative newspaper of local news and events in the Atlanta area.

051 US
DAILY NEWS DIGEST.* 1974. w. $97. Research Publications, Inc., Box 84902, Phoenix, AZ 85071-4902. TEL 602-252-4477. Eds. John Johnson, Lannon Stafford. circ. 4,000. (back issues avail.)

051 US
DE WITT DIGEST & REVIEW. 1986. 3/yr. Wilmam-Sutton House Publishers, Box 355, Seal Beach, CA 90740. Ed. G. De Witt. bk.rev. circ. 3,000. (back issues avail.)

051 US
DEAR PENELOPE. 1987. m. $17.95. Legacy Publications, Inc., 310 Cedar Ln., Teaneck, NJ 07666. TEL 201-836-9177. Ed. Joe Lewis. circ. 220,000.

071.8 US ISSN 0011-7633
DEFENSOR-CHIEFTAIN. vol.104, 1970. s-w. $28 to county residents; non-residents $38. Raljon Publishing, Inc., 200 Winkler, S.W., Box Q, Socorro, NM 87801. TEL 505-835-0520.
FAX 505-835-1837. Ed. Gwen Roath; Pub. Keith Green. adv. contact: Daniel Gains. bk.rev.; charts; illus.; tr.lit. circ. 2,907. (also avail. in microfilm) **Document type:** newspaper.

051 US ISSN 0011-779X
F161
DELAWARE TODAY. 1962. m. $18. (Delaware Today, Inc.) Suburban Publishing, Inc., Box 2087, Wlimington, DE 19899-2087. FAX 302-656-5843. Ed. Lise Monty. adv.; circ. 25,000 (paid).
 Description: News, features, profiles, and departments on the political, recreational, financial, and cultural life in the state, with classifieds, calendars of events, and restaurant listings.

071 US
DENBIGH GAZETTE.* w. Box 419, Williamsburg, VA 23187. TEL 804-872-8722. **Document type:** newspaper.

051 US
DESERT MOBILE HOME NEWS. 1955. w. Box 3386, Palm Desert, CA 92261. TEL 619-568-6633. Ed. Robert Brownell. adv.; circ. 10,000 (controlled). (tabloid format) **Document type:** newspaper.
 Description: Covers news of events in desert mobile home parks, and local activities.

051 US ISSN 0740-4921
NX504
DETAILS. 1982. m. $12 (Canada $22; elswhere $28). Details Publishing Corp. (Subsidiary of: Conde Nast Publications Inc.), 632 Broadway, New York, NY 10012. TEL 212-420-0689. FAX 212-598-0284. (Subscr. to: Box 58246, Boulder, CO 80322-8246. TEL 800-627-6367) Ed. John Leland. adv.; film rev. circ. 465,205. (back issues avail.) **Document type:** consumer publication.
 —UMI.
 Description: Covers men's interests.

051 US ISSN 0149-5976
F574.D4
DETROIT MONTHLY. 1978. m. $15. Crain Communications, Inc. (Detroit), 1400 Woodbridge Ave., Detroit, MI 48207-3187. TEL 313-446-0457. FAX 313-446-1650. (Subscr. to: 965 E. Jefferson, Detroit, MI 48207) Ed. John Barron. adv.; bk.rev.; film rev.; charts; illus. circ. 93,950. (also avail. in microfilm from UMI; back issues avail.; reprint service avail. from UMI) **Indexed:** Access (1978-), Mich.Mag.Ind.
 —CCC.
 Incorporates (1984-1987): Metropolitan Detroit (ISSN 8750-1147); Formerly (until 1986): Monthly Detroit.
 Description: Covers the Southeastern Michigan Metro area with articles about city and suburban living, politics, travel, sports, fashion, restaurants, personalities, and life styles.

051 US ISSN 1051-3434
DIABLO; the magazine of the East Bay. 1979. m. $18. Diablo Publications, 2520 Camino Diablo, Walnut Creek, CA 94596-3939. TEL 510-943-1111. FAX 510-943-1045. Eds. Joan Voight, Colleen Paretty; Pub. Steven J. Rivera. circ. 50,000 (controlled). (back issues avail.) **Document type:** consumer publication.
 Formerly: Diablo Country.
 Description: Regional lifestyle issues for residents of San Francisco East Bay counties.

051 US
DITMAS PARK WEST NEWSLETTER. 1980. q. membership. Ditmas Park West Neighborhood Association, 576 Marlborough Rd., Brooklyn, NY 11226. Ed. J. Mullikin. circ. 600. **Document type:** newsletter.
 Description: Local publication for urban homeowners. Covers crime prevention and current events.

051 US
DOOR COUNTY ALMANAK. 1982. a. $9.95. Dragonsbreath Press, 10905 Bay Shore Dr., Sister Bay, WI 54234. TEL 414-854-2742. Ed. Fred Johnson. adv.; bk.rev. circ. 4,000.
 Description: Contains items of local interest.

051 US ISSN 0012-5776
F16
DOWN EAST MAGAZINE. 1954. m. $19.95. Down East Enterprise, Inc., Box 679, Camden, ME 04843. TEL 207-594-9544. FAX 207-594-7215. Ed. Dale Kunnert. adv.; bk.rev.; illus.; cum.index every 10 yrs. circ. 75,000. **Indexed:** Access (1975-), Amer.Hist.& Life, Hist.Abstr.

051 US
DOWNTOWN; politics, poetry, philosophy, art, theatre, film, media, music and hidden agendas. no.215, 1990. w. free. Soho Arts Weekly, 151 First Ave., New York, NY 10003. TEL 212-529-2255.

051 US
DOWNTOWN MAGAZINE. Creneau Media Group, Box 3388, Houston, TX 77253. TEL 713-880-4611. FAX 713-880-4644. Ed. Cristina Adams.

051 US
DREAMIN'.* 1989. m. Hood County News, Box 879, Granbury, TX 76408. TEL 817-573-7066. Ed. Roger Enlow. adv.; circ. 10,000 (controlled).
 Description: For residents, vacationers and newcomers to Hood and Sommervell counties. Highlights the activities available in the lake country area and features a guide to lake country dream homes.

051 US
DRESDEN ENTERPRISE. 1883. w. $12 in TN; rest of U.S. $18. 117 Wilson St., Box 139, Dresden, TN 38225-0139. TEL 901-364-2234.
FAX 901-364-5774. adv. circ. 5,500.
 Description: Covers local and farm news.

071.747 US
EAST HAMPTON STAR. 1885. w. Helen S. Rattray, Ed. & Pub., 153 Main St., Box E, East Hampton, NY 11937. TEL 516-324-0002. FAX 516-324-7943. adv. contact: Gregg Robinson. bk.rev.; play rev.; illus. circ. 15,000. (broadsheet format; also avail. in microfilm; back issues avail.) **Document type:** newspaper.

GENERAL INTEREST PERIODICALS — UNITED STATES 2777

051 US
EAST SIDE MONTHLY. 1974. m. $10. Barry Fain, Ed. & Pub., 1 Park Row, Province, RI 02903. TEL 401-521-0023. FAX 401-732-3110. adv. contact: Alice Scanlon. bk.rev. circ. 14,000.
Document type: newspaper.
   Description: Focuses on art and local politics.

051 917.9
EASTSIDEWEEK. 1991. w. Sasquatch Publishing Company, Inc., 1008 Western Ave., Ste. 300, Seattle, WA 98104. TEL 206-827-5550. FAX 206-827-0952. adv. circ. 32,675. **Document type:** trade publication.
   Description: Covers the developing suburban areas east of Seattle.

051 US ISSN 0163-6650
EBERLY'S MICHIGAN JOURNAL. 1979. bi-m. $8. Michigan Journal, 115 S. Grand, Marshall, MI 49068. Ed. Carole Eberly. circ. 15,000. (back issues avail.)

808.8 US ISSN 0744-057X
ECPHORIZER; a Mensa magazine of literature and ideas. 1981. bi-m. $10 (foreign $20). Region 8 American Mensa Ltd., 240 Fernwood Way, Dixon, CA 95620-3721. TEL 916-678-2666. Ed. Dr. Rodney W. Baker. bk.rev.; circ. 400 (paid).

EMERGE; our voice in today's world. see *ETHNIC INTERESTS*

051 US ISSN 0046-1946
ENCHANTMENT. vol.22, 1972. m. $4. New Mexico Rural Electrification Cooperative Association, Inc., 614 Don Gaspar, Santa Fe, NM 87501. TEL 505-982-4671. FAX 505-982-0153. Ed. Don Begley. adv.; bk.rev.; film rev.; play rev.; abstr.; illus. circ. 102,000. (tabloid format) **Document type:** consumer publication.

051 US
ENCINITAS. 1989. bi-m. $6. Jim Baumann, Ed. & Pub., 345 First St., Ste. M, Encinitas, CA 92024. TEL 619-632-7447. adv.; circ. 6,000 (controlled).
   Description: Provides articles on the community, local people and news from the Encinitas Chamber of Commerce. Includes a calendar of events.

051 US
ENTERTAINMENT TODAY. 1967. w. $120 (foreign $170). Best Publishing Inc., 801 S. Main St., Ste. L, Burbank, CA 91506. TEL 818-566-4030. FAX 818-566-4295. Ed. Hohn Salazar. adv. contact: Joesph Connars. bk.rev.; film rev.; play rev.; abstr.; charts; illus.; stat.; tr.lit. circ. 125,000. (tabloid format; also avail. in microfilm; back issues avail.) **Document type:** newspaper.
   Description: Includes entertainment news and facts. Covers what, where, why, who and how of the entertainment world.

051 US ISSN 1049-0434
PN1993
ENTERTAINMENT WEEKLY. 1990. w. $51.48; newsstand price: $2.50. Entertainment Weekly Inc. (Subsidiary of: Time Inc.), 1675 Broadway, New York, NY 10019. TEL 212-522-5600. FAX 212-522-0074. (Subscr. to: Box 60898, Tampa, FL 33660-0898. TEL 800-828-6882) Ed. Jason McManus; Pub. Michael J. Klingensmith. adv. contact: Michael J. Kelly. bk.rev.; film rev.; charts; illus.; stat. circ. 1,000,000. (back issues avail.)
●Also available online. Vendor(s): VU/TEXT Information Services, Inc..
—UMI.
   Description: Reviews and reports on what is new and noteworthy in TV, movies, video, music, books and kids' entertainment.

051 US
ERIE & CHAUTAUQUA MAGAZINE. 1983. s-a. $10. Erie & Chautauqua Communications Corporation, 317 W. 6th St., Erie, PA 16507-1244. TEL 814-455-4772. FAX 814-455-3794. Ed. K.L. Kalvelage. adv.; bk.rev. circ. 25,000. **Document type:** consumer publication.

051 US
ESCAPE MAGAZINE. 1981. m. $12. Creative Concepts, Inc., Box 1108, St. Cloud, MN 56302. TEL 612-252-1220. adv.
   Description: Focuses on people, places and events in or near St. Cloud.

051 US
EXCLUSIVELY CONNECTICUT. m. $18. Choice Media, 315 Peck St., Box 590, New Haven, CT 06513-2933. TEL 203-782-1420. Ed. Jennifer Frey. adv. circ. 30,000.
   Formerly: New Haven County Woman.
   Description: Lifestyles publication focusing on higher education, banking issues, healthcare, retirement and local arts and entertainment.

051 US
EXCLUSIVELY YOURS MAGAZINE. 1947. m. $12. Patten Co., Inc., 161 W. Wisconsin Ave., Milwaukee, WI 53203. TEL 414-271-4270. FAX 414-271-0382. Ed. Jack Pearson. adv.

917.306 US
F A C S NEWSLETTER. 1975. m. $5 to non-members. Finnish American Club of Saima, Inc., Box 30, Fitchburg, MA 01420. TEL 508-756-9614. Ed. Tarmo Hannula. circ. 2,400. **Document type:** newsletter.

051 US ISSN 1066-6036
F A D. (Fashion Art Design) 1985. q. $19.95 for 6 issues. R.J. Garbosky Co., 3450 Third St., Ste. 2A-350, San Francisco, CA 94124. TEL 415-647-7091. FAX 415-285-2374. adv.; bk.rev. circ. 39,870. **Document type:** consumer publication.
   Description: Covers what's now and what's coming next in fashion, art design and music from San Francisco, New York, Los Angeles and the world.

F L G C NEWSLETTER. (Friends for Lesbian and Gay Concerns) see *RELIGIONS AND THEOLOGY*

051 US
FACE MAGAZINE. 1988. fortn. $30. About Face, Inc., 19 Commercial St., Portland, ME 04101-4701. TEL 207-774-9703. FAX 207-774-3233. Ed. Bennie Green. adv.; film rev. circ. 17,500. (tabloid format) **Document type:** newspaper.
   Description: Covers the various entertainment opportunities in Central and Southern Maine as well as coastal New Hampshire.

051 US
FACETS OF NEW YORK. 1987. 4/yr. (Jacob K. Javits Convention Center) NYNEX Information Technologies Company, 100 Church St., New York, NY 10007. TEL 212-513-9405. FAX 212-513-9788. Ed. Wayne J. Mitchell. adv.

071 US
FAIRFAX CONNECTION. 1987. w. free. Connection Newspaper Group, 12040 S. Lake Dr., Reston, VA 22091. TEL 703-648-9100. FAX 703-648-9143. adv.; circ. 22,050 (controlled). **Document type:** newspaper.

051 US
FAMILY LIVING. 1980. 6/yr. free. 1231 N. Tustin Ave., Anaheim, CA 92807-1603. TEL 714-632-9810. FAX 714-632-3435. Ed. Wally Hicks. adv. circ. 940,000.
   Formerly: Southern California Family Living.

051 011 US
FANATIC READER.* bi-m. $30. 1933 S.W. Sunset Blvd., Portland, OR 97201-2059. TEL 503-235-3607. Ed. Jim Burnett.

051 US
FARM PULP MAGAZINE; life in these Americas. 1990. bi-m. $10 (effective May 1993). Farm Pulp Media, 217 N.W. 70th St., Seattle, WA 98117-4845. TEL 206-782-7418. Ed. Gregory Hischak. bk.rev.; illus. circ. 275. (back issues avail.) **Document type:** consumer publication.

051 US
FINE ARTS FOLIO. q. Pacific Monthly Corp., 205 17th St., Pacific Grove, CA 93950-3326. TEL 408-375-5711. Ed. Susan Hawthorne. circ. 15,400.

051 US ISSN 0888-9600
FLORIDA LIVING. 1981. m. $17.95 (foreign $22.95). North Florida Publishing Co., Inc., 102 N.E. Tenth Ave., Ste. 6, Gainesville, FL 32601-2322. TEL 904-372-8865. Ed. John Paul Jones, Jr. adv.; bk.rev. circ. 25,000. **Document type:** consumer publication.
   Description: For Floridians and those interested in moving to Florida. Highlights information on the Florida lifestyle, food, outdoor and country life and activities, travel and vacations in Florida, history, retirement, homes and gardens and weekend activities. Includes city profiles.

071 US
FLORIDA PHOTO NEWS. 1955. w. $19.08. Florida Photo News Publishers, Inc., Box 1583-46, W. Palm Beach, FL 33402. TEL 407-833-4511. FAX 407-833-0711. Ed. Yasmin W. Cooper. circ. 2,500. **Document type:** newspaper.
   Formerly (until 1990): Photo News (ISSN 0031-854X)

071 US
FLORIDA SUN REVIEW. 1931. w. $21.50. L M H Publications, 702 18th St., Orlando, FL 32805. TEL 407-423-1156. FAX 407-849-1286. (Subscr. to: Box 2348, Orlando, FL 32802. TEL 407-423-8146) Eds. James Macon, James Madison. bk.rev. circ. 16,500. (tabloid format) **Document type:** newspaper.

051 US
FORBES F Y I. Issued with: Forbes (ISSN 0015-6914) 1990. q. free to Forbes subscribers. Forbes, Inc., 60 Fifth Ave., New York, NY 10011. TEL 212-620-0220. adv. contact: Ellen Baum. bk.rev.; film rev.; illus. **Document type:** consumer publication.
   Description: Upscale lifestyle magazine for American executives, investors and managers. Includes articles on travel, fashion, food and wine, entertainment, sports and the arts.

071 US
FORT LAUDERDALE DOWNTOWN. 1988. m. $12. Box 1596, Fort Lauderdale, FL 33302-0596. TEL 305-463-4500. FAX 305-522-3964. Ed. Helen M. Ditzler. adv. circ. 5,000. **Document type:** newspaper.
   Description: Contains news of the growing downtown. Covers finance, the arts, theatre and more.

071.7749 US ISSN 0016-0040
FRANKLIN TOWNSHIP SENTINEL. 1942. w. $13.50. Sentinel, Box 367 Delsea Dr., Franklinville, NJ 08322. FAX 609-694-0469. Ed. James R. Kinkade; Pub. James Kinkade. adv.; charts; illus. circ. 4,475. **Document type:** newspaper.

051 US ISSN 1064-2757
FREE TIME. 1987. m. $11.90 to individuals; institutions $36. Natella Vaidman, Ed. & Pub., 20 Waterside Plaza, Ste. 6F, New York, NY 10010. TEL 212-545-8900. FAX 212-213-3469. circ. 1,200 (paid). **Document type:** newsletter.
   Description: Calendar of free and low budget cultural events in Manhattan.

368 US ISSN 0279-6856
FRIENDLY EXCHANGE. 1981. q. free to qualified personnel. (Farmer's Insurance Group) Meredith Publishing Services (Subsidiary of: Meredith Corporation), 1912 Grand Ave., Des Moines, IA 50309. TEL 515-284-2008. Ed. Adele Malott. adv.: B&W page $40530, color page $63690; adv. contact: Susan Langren. circ. 5,900,000 (controlled). **Document type:** consumer publication.

051 US
FRONT ROYAL WARREN SENTINEL. w. Box 1297, Front Royal, VA 22630. TEL 703-635-4174.

051 055.1 056.1 US ISSN 0016-3724
LA GACETA; tri-lingual newspaper. (Text in English, Italian, Spanish) 1922. w. $15 in Hillsborough Co.; Florida $20; U.S. $25. La Gaceta Publishing, Inc., 3210 E. Seventh Ave., Box 5536, Tampa, FL 33675. TEL 813-248-3921. FAX 813-247-5357. Ed. Roland Manteiga. adv.; bk.rev.; film rev.; illus.; tr.lit. circ. 18,000. (also avail. in microfilm) **Document type:** newspaper.

G

GENERAL INTEREST PERIODICALS — UNITED STATES

071 US ISSN 0730-9082
GEORGETOWNER. 1954. fortn. $26. Georgetowner, Inc., 3251 Prospect St. N.W., Washington, DC 20007. TEL 202-338-4678. FAX 202-342-0751. Ed. David Roffman. adv.: B&W page $865. bk.rev.; illus. circ. 25,000. (tabloid format; also avail. in microfilm) **Document type:** newspaper.

051 US
GEORGIA JOURNAL - LIVING. 1980. q. $10. Grimes Publications, Inc., Box 27, Athens, GA 30603-0027. TEL 404-354-0463. FAX 404-354-6824. Ed. Conoly Hester. adv. contact: Ann Shepard. bk.rev.; index; circ. 14,000 (controlled). **Document type:** consumer publication.
  Formed by the merger of: Georgia Journal (ISSN 0746-5963); (1989-1991): Georgia Living (ISSN 1049-6432)

051 US
GEORGIA MAGAZINE (ATLANTA, 1945). 1945. m. $5.43. Georgia Electric Membership Corp., Box 1349, Tucker, GA 30085-1349. TEL 404-270-6950. FAX 404-270-6995. Ed. Lynn Brunson. adv. circ. 280,000.
  Formerly (until Mar. 1990): Rural Georgia.
  Description: Features Georgia's people, places and events. Covers travel, recipes, gardening, home improvement, energy conservation and rural life.

051 US
GEORGIA MAGAZINE (ATLANTA, 1990); the Japanese language business and leisure magazine. (Text in Japanese) 1990. q. free. Passport Publications, Inc., 1776 Peachtree Rd., N.W., Ste. 408 S., Atlanta, GA 30309. TEL 404-881-0407. FAX 404-881-0408. Ed. Elizabeth Rubbo; Pub. David P. Belli. adv.: B&W page $3040, color page $4650; trim 8 3/8 x 10 7/8; adv. contact: Robert Schindler. circ. 30,000 (controlled). **Document type:** consumer publication.
  Description: Covers travel, tourism and business opportunities throughout the state.

051 US ISSN 0017-0550
GIRARD HOME NEWS.* 1937. w. $55. Girard Home News, Inc., 250 W. Girard Ave., Philadelphia, PA 19123-1538. Ed. Frank Silverman. adv.; circ. 13,500 (controlled). (tabloid format)

051 US
GLOBE (BOCA RATON). 1954. w. $29.75. Globe Communications Corp. (Boca Raton), 5401 N.W. Broken Sound Blvd., Boca Raton, FL 33487. TEL 407-997-7733. (Subscr. to: Box 11, Rouses Point, NY 12979-0011) Ed. Phil Bunton. adv. circ. 1,300,000.
  Former titles: Midnight Globe; Midnight.

051 US ISSN 1071-4251
GOLD COAST. 1965. 8/yr. $15. Omnigraphics, Inc. (Ft. Lauderdale), 901 E. Las Olas Blvd., Ft. Lauderdale, FL 33301. TEL 305-764-1952. FAX 305-524-7041. Ed. Bernard McCormick. adv.: B&W page $1590, color page $1990; trim 8 3/8 x 10 7/8; adv. contact: Susan Kovarik. bk.rev.; play rev.; illus. circ. 18,000. **Document type:** consumer publication.
  Former titles (until 1992): Florida's Gold Coast; (until Nov. 1984): Gold Coast Life Magazine (ISSN 0745-4619); Gold Coast of Florida; Gold Coast Pictorial; Incorporates: Pictorial Life (ISSN 0031-9643)

051 US
GOLD COAST NEWS. 1983. m. $20. Charles Hesser & Co., Box 2115, Miami Beach, FL 33140-0115. TEL 305-674-9746. FAX 305-674-1939. Ed. Charles Hesser. bk.rev. circ. 100,000. (back issues avail.) **Document type:** newsletter.
  Description: Covers events in Southeast Florida.

051 US
GOOD LIFE (SANTA MONICA). 1929. w. $35. Independent-Journal Newspapers, 1032 Broadway, Santa Monica, CA 90401. TEL 213-393-0606. FAX 213-393-0606. Ed. Herbert S. Chase, Jr. adv.; bk.rev.; film rev.; play rev. circ. 40,100. (tabloid format)
  Formerly: Suburbia West Today.

051 US ISSN 1055-5145
GRAND RAPIDS MAGAZINE. 1964. m. $15. Gemini Publications, 549 Ottawa Ave. N.W., Grand Rapids, MI 49503-1444. TEL 616-459-4545. FAX 616-459-4800. Ed. Carole Valade Smith. adv. contact: Craig Rich. bk.rev.; illus. circ. 12,000. (back issues avail.) **Document type:** consumer publication.

051 US ISSN 0017-3673
F591
GREAT PLAINS JOURNAL. 1961. a. $15 includes Great Plains newsletter. Institute of the Great Plains, Box 68, Lawton, OK 73502. TEL 405-581-3460. Ed. Steve Wilson. adv.; bk.rev.; bibl. circ. 1,000. (tabloid format; also avail. in microform from UMI; reprint service avail. from UMI) **Indexed:** Amer.Hist.& Life, Geo.Abstr., Hist.Abstr. **Document type:** newspaper. —UnCover; UMI.

051 US
GREATER HARTFORD FAMILY MAGAZINE.* 9/yr. 17 Cherry Hill Ct., Cromwell, CT 06446-1821. TEL 203-349-7005. FAX 203-349-7032. adv. circ. 10,000.

051 US
GREATER SEATTLE INFO-GUIDE. 1979. a. (Greater Seattle Chamber of Commerce) Vernon Publications Inc., 3000 Northrup Way, Ste. 200, Bellevue, WA 98004. TEL 206-827-9900. FAX 206-822-9273. **Document type:** consumer publication.
  Description: Describes life in the region for new residents and those considering a move: what housing costs and what communities are like, including information about education, health care, shopping, dinning, and arts and entertainment.

051 US ISSN 1062-5267
GREEN LINE. 1987. m. $9. Green Line Media, Inc., Box 144, Asheville, NC 28802. TEL 704-251-1333. FAX 704-251-1311. Ed. Peter Greguttt. adv. contact: Robert Feirstein. bk.rev.; circ. 23,000 (controlled). **Document type:** newspaper.
  Description: Covers trends and events in western N. Carolina. Focuses on environmental issues, citizen action, arts, outdoors and media.

051 US
GREENWICH MAGAZINE. 1947. m. $24. Moffly Publications Inc., 39 Lewis St., Greenwich, CT 06830. TEL 203-869-0009. FAX 203-869-2549. Ed. Donna C. Moffly. adv. contact: May McDonnell. circ. 6,500. **Document type:** consumer publication.
  Description: Covers civic, social, cultural, business and political events in the lower Fairfield County area.

051 US
GRIER'S ALMANAC. 1807. a. free. Grier's Almanac Publishing Co., Box 888281, 5123 Charmant Place, Atlanta, GA 30356. TEL 404-395-6381. Ed. Brian Bachler. circ. 3,042,071.
  Description: Gardening tips and proceedures for a small town readership in the South.

051 US ISSN 0017-4289
GRIT; America's family magazine. 1882. fortn. $26.95. Stauffer Publishing Group (Subsidiary of: Stauffer Communications, Inc.), 1503 S.W. 42nd St., Topeka, KS 66609. TEL 913-274-4300. FAX 913-274-4305. Ed. Roberta Peterson. adv.; bk.rev.; illus. circ. 400,000. (tabloid format; also avail. in microfilm) **Document type:** consumer publication.
  Description: Contains features, letters, editorials, noted columnists, sketches, and humor for family reading and entertainment.

071 US
GUIDE NEWS. 1934. w. $60. Fry Communications, 800 W. Church Rd., Mechanicsburg, PA 17055. TEL 717-766-0211. FAX 717-691-5796. adv. circ. 165,391. (tabloid format) **Document type:** newspaper.
  Description: For shoppers in a four-county area in Central Pennsylvania. Covers upcoming local events, retail sales and local auctions.

051 US
GULF COAST (NAPLES).* 1987. 10/yr. $18. Gulfcoast Media Affiliates, Inc., 886 110th Ave. N., No. 5, Naples, FL 33963-1876. TEL 813-643-4232. adv. circ. 25,000.
  Description: Covers new homes and interior design, sports, arts, restaurants and food, and local history and people of Southwest Florida.

051 US ISSN 0745-0079
GULFSHORE LIFE; the lifestyle magazine of Southwest Florida. 1970. 10/yr. $19.95. Gulfshore Publishing Co., Inc., 2900 S. Horseshoe Dr., Ste. 400. Naples, FL 33942. TEL 813-643-3933. FAX 813-643-5017. Ed. Lynne Groth. adv. contact: Lisa Davis-Cox. bk.rev.; illus. circ. 20,000. **Document type:** consumer publication.

071.747 US
HAMLIN-CLARKSON HERALD. w. $35. Westside News, Inc., 1835 N. Union St., Box 106, Spencerport, NY 14559-0106. TEL 716-352-3411. FAX 716-352-4811. Ed. Evelyn Dow. adv.; illus. circ. 5,890. (tabloid format) **Document type:** newspaper.

051 US
HAMPSHIRE EAST. (Three other regional eds: Concord and the North, Manchester, Nashua) 1991. m. $20. Connections Network, Inc., Network Publications, 100 Main St., Nashua, NH 03060. TEL 603-883-3150. (Subscr. to: 889 Elm St., Manchester, NH 03101. TEL 603-883-3150)

051 US ISSN 1060-6688
E839.5
HARPOON.* 1991. bi-w. American Media of New York, Inc., 1448 Vermont St., Buffalo, NY 14213-2636.

051 US ISSN 1051-0621
HAWAIIAN EXPRESS MAGAZINE. 1989. bi-m. free. 10 Kamehameha Hwy., Wahiawa, HI 96876. TEL 808-622-2679. FAX 808-621-3329. Ed. Al Plant. adv.; bk.rev. circ. 10,000. (reprint service avail.) **Document type:** newsletter.
  Description: Community-focused articles on business, arts, and sports.

051 US
HAWAIIAN NEWSLETTER. bi-m. Kahanahou Hawaiian Foundation, Box 1639, Kealakekua, HI 96750. TEL 808-322-3901.

051 US
HELLO ORTING! NEWS. 1991. m. $10. Box 1231, Orting, WA 98360-1231. TEL 206-893-5103. FAX 206-893-5363. Ed. Pat Wilson. circ. 2,000.

317.3 US
HI CLASS LIVING. 1984. bi-m. $12.50. M N R Promotions, Inc., 111 Charlotte Pl., Englewood Cliffs, NJ 07632. TEL 201-871-2221. FAX 201-871-2223. Ed. Michael Raviv. adv.; bk.rev.; film rev.; play rev.; circ. 15,000 (controlled). **Document type:** consumer publication.
  Description: Focuses on the lifestyles and interests of N.J., Bergen County affluent residents.

051 US
HIGH TECH LIFESTYLES.* q. $2.50 per no. Business People Inc., 13033 Ridgedale Dr., Ste. 146, Minnetonka, MN 55305-1807. circ. 110,000. (tabloid format)

051 US
HOME & CONDO; southwest Florida's resource for home and garden ideas. 1980. 7/yr. $10.95. Gulfshore Publishing Co., Inc., 2900 S. Horseshoe Dr., Ste. 400, Naples, FL 33942. TEL 813-643-3933. FAX 813-643-5017. Ed. Janis Lyn Johnson. adv. contact: Lisa Davis-Cox. circ. 25,000. **Document type:** consumer publication.
  Description: For incoming home buyers and local home owners.

071.5 US
HOME TIMES NEWSPAPER. 1980. w. $25. Neighbor News, Inc, Box 16096, West Palm Beach, FL 33416. TEL 407-439-3509. Ed. Dennis Lombard; Pub. Dennis Lombard. adv.: B&W page $395. circ. 2,000 (paid); 8,000 (controlled). (tabloid format) **Document type:** newspaper.
  Formerly (until 1991): Sun and Sonlight Newspaper.
  Description: Covers national and international news, current events, polpolitics and family entertainment from a conservative perspective.

GENERAL INTEREST PERIODICALS — UNITED STATES

051 US ISSN 0441-2044
HONOLULU. (Includes: Cable Guide Supplement) 1888. m. $15 (Continental US $21). Honolulu Publishing Company, Ltd., 36 Merchant St., Honolulu, HI 96813. TEL 808-524-7400. FAX 808-531-2306. (Subscr. to: P.O. Box 80, Honolulu, HI 96810) adv.; bk.rev.; film rev.; illus. circ. 75,000. (back issues avail.) **Indexed:** Access (1976-).
—UnCover.
Former titles: Honolulu Magazine (ISSN 0018-4640); Paradise of the Pacific.
Description: City and regional magazine; includes general consumer interest about Hawaii.

051 US
HOUSE, HOME & GARDEN. 1991. m. $10. Berkeley House Enterprises, Inc., 809 Virginia Ave., Martinsburg, WV 25401. TEL 304-267-2673. Ed. Earl D. Unger. adv.; bk.rev.; circ. 15,000. **Document type:** consumer publication.

051 US
HOUSE - LIFESTYLE OF THE ISLAND.* bi-m. $15. Sheahan Publications, Inc., Box 826, Westhampton Beach, NY 11978. TEL 516-288-5400. FAX 516-288-5420. Ed. Denis Sheahan. circ. 31,500.

051 US
▼**HOUSTON PEOPLE.*** 1992. m. $18. Houston People Magazine, Inc., 9219 Katy Fwy., Ste. 273, Houston, TX 77024-1514. TEL 800-688-7001. adv. circ. 20,000.
Description: Explores the individuals and companies of the Houston area.

051 US
HOUSTON PRESS;* news and entertainment weekly. 1989. w. free. New Houston Press, Inc., 2000 W. Loop S., Ste. 1900, Houston, TX 77027-3512. TEL 713-783-7110. FAX 713-783-1320. Ed. John Ashby Wilburn. circ. 50,000.
Description: Covers politics, business, city personalities, and national entertainment.

051 US
HOUSTON TRIBUNE. m. $15. Tribune Publishing Company, 2150 W. 18th St., Ste. 213, Houston, TX 77008. TEL 713-862-9603. Ed. Terry Self. adv.: B&W page $1895; trim 10 x 12 1/4. film rev. circ. 72,500.
Formerly: Houston Heights Tribune.

051 US
HUDSON COUNTY MAGAZINE. 1991. q. $10.95. Hudson County Magazine, Inc., 111 Pavonia Ave., Jersey City, NJ 07310. TEL 201-963-4047. FAX 201-963-0762. Ed. Bart Erbach. adv.; bk.rev. circ. 50,000.
Description: Highlights lifestyle and business in Hudson County.

051 US ISSN 0191-9288
HUDSON VALLEY MAGAZINE. 1972. m. $18. Suburban Publishing Co., 297 Main Mall, Box 429, Poughkeepsie, NY 12601-3109. TEL 914-485-7844. FAX 914-485-5975. Ed. Susan Agrest; Pub. Thomas R. Martinelli. adv.; bk.rev.; illus.; cum.index: 1972-1982. circ. 27,000. **Document type:** consumer publication.
Description: Dining, theater, arts, entertainment and feature articles on the history and people of the Hudson Valley.

051 US ISSN 0899-5451
I C U C: I SEE YOU SEE. 1988. q. $20 (foreign $30). Looking Glass Publications, Box 3604, Quincy, IL 62305. Ed. Linda Ann Hughes. bk.rev.; illus. (large print edition in 18 pt.)

051 US
I V I S NEWSLETTER. 1962. s-a. International Visitors Information Service, 1623 Belmont St., N.W., Washington, DC 20009. TEL 202-939-5566. FAX 202-232-9783. Ed. Marianne H. Cruze. circ. 1,200. **Document type:** newsletter.

054.1 917 FR
ICI NEW YORK; journal de New York en francais. (Text in French) m. 160 F. Ici New York Communications SARL, 36 av. Matignon, 75008 Paris, France. (U.S. addr.: c/o John M. Taylor, 113 E. 97th St., Ste. 2-B, New York, NY 10029. TEL 212-876-8401) Ed. Jean Sebastien Stehli. adv.; illus.

917.7
ILLIANA SPIRIT. 1966. w. $45. 1492 E. Walnut, Box 250, Watseka, IL 60970. TEL 815-432-5227. FAX 815-432-5159. Ed. Steve DeVitt. adv. circ. 9,932.

051 US
▼**IN STYLE.** 1993. m. Time Inc. (Subsidiary of: Time Warner, Inc.), Time & Life Bldg., Rockefeller Center, 1271 Ave. of the Americas, New York, NY 10020-1393. Ed. Martha Nelson; Pub. Ann Jackson.

051 US
INDEPENDENT (KANSAS CITY); journal of society. 1989. w. $25. Creel Publishing, 306 E. 12th St., Ste. 1000, Kansas City, MO 64106. TEL 816-471-2800. FAX 816-474-1111. adv.: B&W page $1104, color page $1704; trim 9 1/4 x 12 1/8. circ. 7,552.
Description: Covers the social and cultural events of Kansas City.

051 US ISSN 0019-6630
INDIANA HERALD. (Supplements incl.: Black Monitor; Dawn) 1958. w. $26. 2170 N. Illinois St., Indianapolis, IN 46202. TEL 317-923-8291. FAX 317-923-8292. Ed. Mary B. Tandy. adv.; bk.rev.; illus. circ. 27,600. (tabloid format)

051 US ISSN 0195-2900
F534.I3
INDIANAPOLIS MONTHLY. 1977. 14/yr. $19.95. Emmis Publishing Corp., 950 N. Meridian St., Ste. 1200, Indianapolis, IN 46204-3908. TEL 317-237-9288. Ed. Deborah Paul. bk.rev. circ. 44,000. (back issues avail.)

051 US
▼**THE INDUSTRY (NEW YORK).*** 1992. 26/yr. $57. 455 Coleridge Rd., Rockville Centre, NY 11570-1412. Ed. Adam Moss.
Description: For the movie, music, publishing, tv, magazine, advertising, and fashion industry.

051 US ISSN 0020-1456
INLAND;* the magazine of the Middle West. 1953. q. free. Inland Steel Flat Product Co., 30 W. Monroe St., Chicago, IL 60603. TEL 312-346-0300. bk.rev.; illus.; circ. 12,000 (controlled).

051 US ISSN 0199-5073
INLAND EMPIRE. 1976. m. $13.95. Inland Empire Media Group, Inc., 3769 Tibbetts Ave., Ste. A, Riverside, CA 92506. TEL 909-682-3026. FAX 909-682-0246. adv. contact: Brenda Lorenzi. bk.rev. circ. 18,000. **Document type:** consumer publication.
Description: Covers leisure, lifestyle, business, health, dining and celebrities in and for Southern California.

051 US ISSN 1051-4880
INSIGHT ON THE NEWS. 1985. w. $39.00 (effective 1993). Washington Times Corporation, 3600 New York Ave., N.E., Washington, DC 20002. TEL 202-636-8800. FAX 202-529-2484. (Subscr. to: Box 91022, Washington, DC 20090. TEL 800-356-3588) Ed. Kirk Oberfeld. adv.; bk.rev. circ. 100,000. (also avail. in microform from UMI) **Indexed:** A.I.Abstr. **Document type:** consumer publication.
●Also available online.
Also available on CD-ROM.
—CIS; UMI. CCC.
Formerly (until 1988): Insight (Washington) (ISSN 0884-9285)

051 978.2 US
INTERCHANGE CUSTOMER NEWSLETTER. 1964. m. free. Nebraska Public Power District, Box 499, Columbus, NE 68601-0499. TEL 402-563-5811. FAX 402-563-5511. Ed. Nancy Shadel. circ. 5,000 (controlled).
Supersedes (in 1990): Spotlighting Nebraska.

051 US ISSN 0149-8932
INTERVIEW (NEW YORK). 1969. m. $20. Brant Publications, 575 Broadway, 5th Fl., New York, NY 10012. TEL 212-941-2900. Ed. Ingrid Sischy. adv. contact: Maria Triantafillou. bk.rev.; illus. circ. 137,071. (tabloid format; also avail. in microform from UMI; reprint service avail. from UMI) **Indexed:** Access (1975-), Film Lit.Ind. (1973-), Mag.Ind., PMR. **Document type:** consumer publication.
—UMI.
Formerly (until 1989): Andy Warhol's Interview (ISSN 0020-5109)

051 US ISSN 0894-7910
INVERTED-A HORN. 1985. irreg. free. Inverted-A, Inc., 401 Forrest Hill, Grande Prairie, TX 75051. TEL 214-264-0066. FAX 214-264-0066. Eds. Amnon Katz, Aya Katz. adv.; bk.rev. circ. 400. (looseleaf format)
Description: Presents articles, poetry (of classical form and flavor), short fiction and reviews dealing in freedom, justice, and honor.

051 US
IOWA CITY MAGAZINE. 1989. m. $19.30. Iowa City Magazine Publishing, Inc., Box 2672, Iowa City, IA 52244-2672. TEL 319-351-0466. FAX 319-351-0466. Ed. Christopher Green. adv.; circ. 15,000 (controlled). **Document type:** consumer publication.
Description: Combines local talent and ideas with a regional and national presentation.

051 US ISSN 0021-0722
IOWAN; Iowa's own magazine. 1952. q. $18.50. Mid-America Publishing Corporation, 108 Third St., No. 350, Des Moines, IA 50309-4733. FAX 515-282-0125. Ed. Karen Massetti-Miller. adv.; bk.rev.; illus.; index. circ. 27,000. (also avail. in microform from UMI; reprint service avail. from UMI) **Document type:** consumer publication.
—UnCover; UMI.

051 US
JABIRU TRIBE. q. $4. Box 3648, Corpus Christi, TX 78463-3648.

051 US
JACKSONVILLE MAGAZINE (JACKSONVILLE). 1985. 10/yr. $19.90. White Publishing Company, 1650 Prudential Dr., Ste. 300, Jacksonville, FL 32207-8150. TEL 904-396-8666. FAX 904-396-0926. Ed. Larry Marscheck. adv.; bk.rev. circ. 25,000. **Document type:** consumer publication.
Formerly (until 1993): Jacksonville Today (ISSN 0885-4769)
Description: Covers life-style and business topics of interest to affluent residents of northeastern Florida; also reports on fashion, health, interior design, residential real estate, and travel.

051 917.3 US
JAPAN AVENUE. 1990. bi-m. $75. Diamond Group and Avenue Inc., 145 E. 57th St., New York, NY 10022. TEL 212-758-9516. adv. circ. 50,000.
Description: For people in Japan interested in the U.S. Covers arts, business, travel, culture, architecture and fashion.

051 US ISSN 0021-5996
E185.5
JET. 1951. w. $36. Johnson Publishing Co., Inc., 820 S. Michigan Ave., Chicago, IL 60605-2190. TEL 312-322-9200. Ed. Robert Johnson. adv.; bk.rev.; film rev.; illus. circ. 850,000. (also avail. in microform from UMI; reprint service avail. from UMI) **Indexed:** Hlth.Ind., Jun.High.Mag.Abstr., Mag.Ind., PMR, PSI, TOM.
—UMI.
Description: Contains movie reviews, fashion layouts, interviews, etc.

051 US ISSN 0893-1151
LA JOLLA MAGAZINE.* 1984. bi-m. $18. La Jolla Report Publishing Co., Inc., Box 3280, La Jolla, CA 92038-3280. TEL 619-454-1923. (Subscr. to: Box 1534, La Jolla, CA 92038) Ed. P.R. Dahlberg. adv.; film rev.; play rev. circ. 18,000. (back issues avail.)
Description: Regional general interest publication covering art, travel, investing, and restaurants.

JOURNAL FRANCAIS D'AMERIQUE. see GENERAL INTEREST PERIODICALS — France

GENERAL INTEREST PERIODICALS — UNITED STATES

051 US ISSN 1050-513X
PN1992
K C T S - NINE. 1987. m. 2505 Second Ave., Ste. 602, Seattle, WA 98121-2384. TEL 206-441-8415. FAX 206-441-8325. Ed. Linda Johns. adv. circ. 150,000.
  Formerly (until 1989): K C T S Magazine.
  Description: Television program guide distributed to contributors to KCTS-9, with additional articles on arts, travel, and personalities.

051 US ISSN 0022-8435
F676
KANSAS!. 1945. q. $10. Department of Commerce and Housing, Division of Travel and Tourism, 700 S.W. Harrison, Ste. 1300, Topeka, KS 66603-3712. TEL 913-296-3479. FAX 913-296-5055. Ed. Andrea Glenn. bk.rev.; illus. circ. 53,000. (also avail. in microform from UMI) **Indexed:** GeoRef.

051 US
KANSAS CITY LIVE!. 1989. q. (Kansas City Blue Cross and Blue Shield) Warren C. Maus, Ed. & Pub., 201 E. Armour Blvd., Kansas City, MO 64111. TEL 816-968-5271. FAX 816-753-6802. adv.; bk.rev. circ. 97,000. **Document type:** consumer publication.
  Description: Lifestyle magazine for residents of Kansas City metropolitan area.

051 US ISSN 1043-853X
KENTUCKY LIVING. 1948. m. $9. Kentucky Association of Electric Cooperatives, 4515 Bishop Ln., Louisville, KY 40218. TEL 502-451-2430. FAX 502-459-3209. Ed. Gary Luhr. adv.; charts; illus. circ. 385,000.
  Formerly: Rural Kentuckian (ISSN 0036-0066)

051 US ISSN 0023-0766
KEY (PHILADELPHIA).* 1967. w. $3. Key Philadelphia, Inc., P.O. Box 03, Jenkintown, PA 19046-0003. TEL 215-473-1665. adv.
  Description: Includes items of local interest.

051 US
KEY MAGAZINE. THIS WEEK IN PITTSBURGH. 1931. w. $22. Donald B. Butler, Ed. & Pub., 1214 Fulton Bldg., 107 Sixth St., Pittsburgh, PA 15222. TEL 412-281-4490. FAX 412-281-4491. adv.; bk.rev. circ. 5,000.
  Description: Covers civic events, conventions, trade shows.

051 US
KNOW ATLANTA. 1987. q. $3.50. New South Publishing, 7840 Roswell Rd., Ste. 328, Atlanta, GA 30350-4867. TEL 404-512-0016. FAX 404-512-0405. Ed. Susan Thompson. circ. 33,000. **Document type:** trade publication.

051 US
L A WEEKLY. 1978. w. $35. Los Angeles Weekly, Inc., 2140 Hyperion Ave., Box 29905, Los Angeles, CA 90027-4708. TEL 213-667-2511. FAX 213-666-5025. Ed. Kit Rachlis. adv.
  Description: Provides regional, national and international political and arts coverage. Lists entertainment events in the L.A. area.

051 US
L.A. WEST.* 1978. m. $36. L.A. West Media Magazine, P.O. Box 3468, Rancho Santa Fe, CA 92067-3468. TEL 310-458-3376. Ed. Jan Loomis. adv.; bk.rev.; tr.lit. circ. 50,000.
  Former titles (until Apr. 1987): Previews (Santa Monica); Palisades Preview.

051 US
LADIES BIRTHDAY ALMANAC. 1890. a. free. Chattem, Inc., 1715 W. 38th St., Chattanooga, TN 37409. TEL 615-821-4571. FAX 615-821-6132. Ed. Mary Webb. adv. circ. 3,300,000.
  Description: Covers the movements of the sun and moon, the weather, household tips, holidays and stories.

051 US
LAFF-LETTER. q. membership. International Laughter Society, 16000 Glen Una Dr., Los Gatos, CA 95030. TEL 408-395-5233.
  Description: Promotes the therapeutic benefits of laughter.

051 US
LAHAINA NEWS. 1979. w. $15 in Hawaii; mainland $40. West Maui News Corporation, Box 10427, Lahaina, HI 96761. FAX 808-667-2726. Ed. William E. Worth. adv.; bk.rev. circ. 14,000. (tabloid format; back issues avail.)

051 US
LANDER'S HERALD. 1978. bi-m. $9.95. 720 Morrow Ave., Clayton, NJ 08312. Ed. Manuel Castlewitz. adv.; bk.rev. circ. 7,000. **Document type:** consumer publication.

051 US ISSN 1051-4724
LEE LIVING. 1990. 9/yr. $13.50. City Events Inc., 6719 Winkler Rd., Ste. 210, Fort Myers, FL 33919-7203. TEL 813-433-2334. FAX 813-433-3799. Ed. Meg McCarthy. circ. 14,000.
  Description: Services Lee County and includes Ft. Myers, Sanibel, Captiva, Lehigh Acres, Bonita Springs, Boca Grande and Alva, Florida.

051 US ISSN 0024-3019
AP2
LIFE (NEW YORK). 1936. m. $32.50. Time Inc. (Subsidiary of: Time Warner, Inc.), Time & Life Bldg., Rockefeller Center, 1271 Ave. of the Americas, New York, NY 10020. TEL 212-522-1212. FAX 212-522-1863. (Subscr. to: Life, Box 60001, Tampa, FL 33600-0010. TEL 800-541-1000) Ed. Ed McCarrick. adv.: color page $49500; adv. contact: Nora McAniff. circ. 1,500,000 (paid). (also avail. in microfiche from UMI; microfilm from BHP,KTO) **Indexed:** Abr.R.G., Acad.Ind., Access, Bk.Rev.Ind. (1965-1972), Chic.Per.Ind., Child.Bk.Rev.Ind. (1965-1972), Jun.High.Mag.Abstr., Mag.Ind., PMR, TOM. **Document type:** consumer publication.
  ●Also available online. Vendor(s): DIALOG Information Services, Inc., Mead Data Central, Inc..
  —Faxon; UnCover; UMI.
  Description: Chronicles the way America lives, with pictures as its vocabulary.

051 US ISSN 0047-486X
LIVING IN SOUTH CAROLINA. 1950. m. $2. South Carolina Electric Cooperative Association, 808 Knox Abbot Dr., Cayce, SC 29033. TEL 803-796-6060. FAX 803-796-6064. Ed. Larry Cribb. adv.; bk.rev.; illus.; stat.; circ. 390,000 (paid). **Document type:** consumer publication.
  Description: Contains items of statewide interest.

051 US
LONG BEACH MONTHLY. Variant title: L B Monthly. m. Champ Publishing, 215 Long Beach Blvd., No. 214, Long Beach, CA 90802. TEL 213-436-5579. FAX 213-491-5566. Ed. Tim Linden.

051 US
LONG ISLAND GOODLIVING. 1986. 10/yr. $24. Goodliving, Inc., 400 Jericho Turnpike, Ste. 115, Jericho, NY 11753. TEL 516-935-2553. FAX 516-935-2316. Ed. Marc Katz. adv. circ. 52,203.

051 US ISSN 0024-6522
LOS ANGELES; the magazine of Southern California. 1960. m. $12.95. 1888 Century Park E., Ste. 920, Los Angeles, CA 90067. TEL 310-557-7559. Ed. Lew Harris. adv.; bk.rev.; film rev.; illus. circ. 156,000. (also avail. in microform from UMI) **Indexed:** Access (1975-), Biog.Ind., Cal.Per.Ind. (1980-), Mag.Ind., PMR, R.G.
  ●Also available online. Vendor(s): Mead Data Central, Inc..
  —UMI.
  Description: Covers events in and around the Los Angeles area.

051 US ISSN 0279-6791
F366
LOUISIANA LIFE.* 1981. bi-m. $16. Louisiana Magazine Corp., 111 Veterans Memorial Blvd, No. 1810, Metairie, LA 70005-3046. TEL 800-824-6642. (Subscr. to: Neo-Data, Box 2606, Boulder, CO 80322. TEL 800-759-8370) Ed.Bd. adv.; bk.rev.; illus. circ. 32,324. **Indexed:** Access (1982-).
  Description: Covers living and working in the Bayou state of Louisiana.

051 US
LOVING ALTERNATIVES MAGAZINE. 1990. bi-m. $20. Omnific Designs West, Box 459, San Dimas, CA 91773. TEL 909-593-6110. FAX 818-915-4715. Eds. Ric Alderson, Cindy Alderson. adv.: page $140. bk.rev. circ. 8,000. (back issues avail.)
  Formerly: S S C Magazine.

510 US
M A R T A RIDER'S DIGEST. 1921. fortn. free. Metropolitan Atlanta Rapid Transit Authority, Public Information Division, 2424 Piedmont Rd. N.E., Atlanta, GA 30324-3324. TEL 404-848-5157. Ed. Judith Weisberg. adv. circ. 155,000.

051 US
MACON MAGAZINE. 1986. bi-m. $11.95. Macon Magazine, Inc., 227 Orange St., Macon, GA 31201. TEL 912-746-7779. FAX 912-743-4608. Ed. Joni W. Woolf. adv. contact: Judy Sherling. bk.rev. circ. 10,000.
  Description: Features departments and features about local and regional people, places and events.

051 US
MADISON MAGAZINE. 1958. m. $18. Madison Magazine, Inc., 625 Williamson St., Madison, WI 53703-3543. TEL 608-255-9982. FAX 608-255-9351. Ed. Doug Moe. adv.; bk.rev.; charts; illus.; tr.lit. circ. 24,000. (back issues avail.)
  Formerly (until vol.20, no.8, Aug. 1978): Madison Select (ISSN 0024-9513)

071 US
MAIN LINE TIMES. 1930. w. $31.20. Acme Newspapers, Inc., 311 E. Lancaster Ave., Ardmore, PA 19003. TEL 215-642-4300. adv. circ. 17,500. **Document type:** newspaper.
  Description: Contains items of local interest.

051 US
MAINE (DOVER-FOXCROFT); a magazine of Maine's treasures. 1977. m. $24. Country Wide Communications, Inc., 78 River St., Dover-Foxcroft, ME 04426-1321. TEL 207-564-7548. FAX 207-564-7051. Ed. Bob Berta. adv. contact: Joyce Hartford. bk.rev.; film rev.; play rev.; charts; illus.; stat. circ. 16,000. (back issues avail.) **Document type:** consumer publication.
  Description: For people who are interested in the state of Maine and its people.

051 US
MAINE MAGAZINE; the magazine of Maine's treasures. 1977. m. $28. County Wide Communications, Inc., Box 497, Machias, ME 04654. TEL 207-564-7548. Ed. Bill Reyrolds; Pub. Bob Berta. adv. contact: Joyce Hartford. bk.rev. circ. 16,000. (back issues avail.)

051 US
MANCHESTER; Auburn, Bedford, Candia, Derry, Goffstown, Hooksett, Londonderry, Mont Vernon, New Boston, Weare. (Three other regional eds.: Concord and the North, Hampshire East, Nashua) q. $20. Connections Network, Inc., Network Publications, 100 Main St., Nashua, NH 03060. TEL 603-883-3150. (Subscr. to: 889 Elm St., Manchester, NH 03101. TEL 603-883-3150) Ed. Daniel Ryan.

051 US
MANHATTAN LIVING. 1984. q. $16. 535 Fifth Ave., New York, NY 10017.

051 US
MANHATTAN MAGAZINE. 1983. q. $12. Bard Communications, Inc., 330 W. 56th St., Ste. 3G, New York, NY 10019-4241. TEL 212-265-7970. FAX 212-265-8052. Ed. Rick Bard. adv.; bk.rev. circ. 50,000. **Document type:** consumer publication.
  Formerly: Studio 54.
  Description: Presents interviews with personalities in business, the arts, fashion, and society. Includes fashion features and charity coverage.

051 US
MARBLEHEAD MAGAZINE; a seacoast journal. 1979. 3/yr. $12. Legend, Inc., Box 50, Marblehead, MA 01945. TEL 617-631-0008. FAX 617-639-2511. Ed. Bill Purdin. adv.; bk.rev. circ. 12,000. (back issues avail.)

051 US ISSN 1052-5785
MARTHA'S VINEYARD MAGAZINE. 1985. 4/yr. $15. Box 66, Edgartown, MA 02539. TEL 508-627-4311. FAX 508-627-7444. Ed. Julia Wells. adv. circ. 13,000.

GENERAL INTEREST PERIODICALS — UNITED STATES   2781

051   US   ISSN 1073-7391
▼MARY EMMERLING'S COUNTRY. 1993. bi-m. $9.98 for 4 issues. New York Times Women's Magazines, Special Interest Publications, 110 Fifth Ave., New York, NY 10011. TEL 212-463-1210. FAX 212-463-1912. adv.: B&W page $12886, color page $16460; trim 8 x 10 1/2. circ. 300,000. **Document type:** consumer publication.

051   US   ISSN 1040-7936
F176
MARYLAND MAGAZINE. 1968. q. $12.50. Maryland Magazine Inc., 2503 Davidsonville Rd., Gambrills, MD 21054. TEL 410-721-7989. FAX 410-721-7989. Ed. D. Patrick Hornberger. bk.rev.; illus.; cum.index: 1968-1989. circ. 45,000. (also avail. in microform from UMI.) **Indexed:** Access (1975-1987), Biol.Abstr. **Document type:** consumer publication.
—UnCover.
   Formerly: Maryland (ISSN 0025-4290)
   Description: Covers culture, tourism and historical activities and events in Maryland.

051   US
MAWEWI. bi-m. $10. Box 874, Mahwah, NJ 07430. Ed. Adastra West.
   Description: Covers ecology, astronomy, current events, and social trends.

051   US   ISSN 0162-282X
F444.M5
MEMPHIS. 1976. m. $15. M M Corporation, 460 Tennessee St., Box 256, Memphis, TN 38101. TEL 901-521-9000. FAX 901-521-0129. Ed. Tim Sampson. adv.; bk.rev. circ. 25,000.
   Description: Contains city and regional news and fashions.

051   US
MEMPHIS FLYER. 1989. w. $52. M M Corporation, 460 Tennessee St., Box 687, Memphis, TN 38101. TEL 901-521-9000. Ed. Dennis Freeland. adv. circ. 42,000. (back issues avail.)
   Description: Contains city and regional news, and entertainment information.

051   US
METRO MONTHLY. m. M B J Corporation, 11918 Poppleton Plaza, Omaha, NE 68144. TEL 402-330-1760. Ed. Robert G. Hoig.

051   US
METROPOLITAN BEAUMONT. 1977. 6/yr. $12. Box 3150, Beaumont, TX 77704. TEL 409-838-6581. FAX 409-833-6718. adv. circ. 4,000.

056.1   US
MIAMI MENSUAL/MIAMI MONTHLY. (Text in Spanish) 1980. m. $15.95. Quintus Communications Group Inc., 2455 S.W. 27th Ave., Ste. 200, Miami, FL 33145-3645. TEL 305-444-5678. Ed. Richard Perez-Feria. adv.; bk.rev.; film rev.; play rev.; illus. circ. 20,022. (back issues avail.) **Document type:** consumer publication.

071   US
MIAMI TODAY. 1983. w. $54. Today Enterprises, Inc., Box 1368, Miami, FL 33101. TEL 305-358-2663. Ed. Michael Lewis. adv.; bk.rev. circ. 35,000. (also avail. in microform from UMI) **Document type:** newspaper.
   Description: Serves the executive and civic leadership of South Florida with detailed reports on business, government, civic affairs, and the arts.

051   US
MICHIGAN COUNTRY LINES.* 1980. bi-m. $4. Michigan Electric Cooperative Association, 2859 Jolly Rd., Okemos, MI 48864-3547. TEL 517-484-5022. FAX 517-484-0049. Ed. Michael F. Buda. adv. circ. 163,801.
   Description: Concentrates on rural lifestyles, home energy use, family health and welfare, cooking, business development, personalities, and legislative and utility news.

051   US   ISSN 0888-1022
E169.02
MID-ATLANTIC COUNTRY MAGAZINE; the travel, leisure, lifestyle magazine of the Mid-Atlantic. 1980. m. $18. E.S.S. Ventures, Inc., 6401 Golden Triangle Dr., Ste. 120, Greenbelt, MD 20770-3202. TEL 800-777-0999. FAX 703-739-8997. (Subscr. to: Box 11207, Des Moines, IA 50340) Ed. Tim Sayles; Pub. Laurin Talley Ensslin. bk.rev.; charts; illus. circ. 1,120,855. (also avail. in microform from UMI; back issues avail.) **Document type:** consumer publication.
   Formerly (until 1986): Country Magazine (ISSN 0271-759X)

051   US   ISSN 0889-8138
F355
MIDWEST LIVING. 1986. bi-m. $16.97. Meredith Corporation, 1912 Grand Ave., Des Moines, IA 50309-3379. TEL 515-284-3000. Ed. Dan Kaercher. adv.; circ. 726,000 (paid); 22,800 (controlled). **Indexed:** Access (1988-).

051   US
MILLIONAIRE.* 1987. m. $24 (foreign $64). (Millionaire Magazine, Inc.) Douglas Lambert, Ed. & Pub., Drawer 3948, W. Palm Beach, FL 33402. (Subscr. to: Box 2903, W. Palm Beach, FL 33402-9946) adv. circ. 110,000.

051   US
MILWAUKEE MAGAZINE. 1979. m. $17. Milwaukee Magazine, Inc., 312 E. Buffalo, Milwaukee, WI 53202-5808. FAX 414-273-0016. Ed. John Fennell. adv.; bk.rev. circ. 42,000. (reprint service avail.) **Indexed:** Access (1986-). **Document type:** consumer publication.
   Description: Covers issues, people and lifestyles of southeastern Wisconsin.

051   US
MINNESOTA CALLS.* bi-m. Stolee Communications, Box 640, Duluth, MN 55801-0640. TEL 218-722-7761. FAX 218-722-8233. Ed. Kathleen James Ring.

051   US   ISSN 0739-8700
MINNESOTA MONTHLY. 1964. m. $11.95. Minnesota Monthly Publications, Inc., 15 S. Ninth St., Ste. 320, Minneapolis, MN 55402. TEL 612-371-5800. FAX 612-371-5801. Pub. Steve Fox. adv. contact: Nancy Fazendin. bk.rev. circ. 78,000. **Document type:** consumer publication.
—UnCover.
   Description: Articles, reviews, announcements, and profiles pertaining to the cultural, political, literary, and social aspects of the upper-midwest region.

051   US
MISSISSIPPI.* 1982. bi-m. $14. Downhome Publications, Inc., P.O. Box 16445, Jackson, MS 39236-6445. TEL 601-982-8418. Ed. Ann Becker. adv. circ. 25,000. (back issues avail.) **Indexed:** Access (1984-).

051   US
MISSISSIPPI COAST.* 1988. bi-m. $12. Mississippi Coast Magazine, Inc., P.O. Box 1209, Gulfport, MS 39502-1209. TEL 601-868-1182. Ed. Linda Peal White. adv. circ. 20,000.

051   US   ISSN 1047-6830
F461
MISSOURI MAGAZINE.* 1973. q. $16.95. ADmore, Inc., Box 28830, St. Louis, MO 63123-0030. TEL 800-451-0914. FAX 314-638-3880. Ed. Tony Nolan Adrignola. adv.; bk.rev.; illus. circ. 20,000. **Indexed:** Access (1975-1987).
   Formerly (until 1988): Missouri Life (ISSN 0090-760X)

051   US
MONROE DISPATCH. 1964. w. $20. Frank J. Detige, 2301 Desaird St., Monroe, LA 71201. (Subscr. to: Box 4823, Monroe, LA 71203) Ed. Irma H. Detige. adv.; bk.rev. circ. 9,500. (looseleaf format)
   Formerly (until 1975): Monroe News Leader (ISSN 0026-9840)

051   US   ISSN 0274-9955
MONTANA MAGAZINE. 1970. bi-m. $18. American and World Geographic Publishing, Inc., Box 5630, Helena, MT 59604. TEL 406-443-2842. FAX 406-443-5480. Ed. Beverly R. Magley. adv. contact: Larry Sem. bk.rev. circ. 60,000. (also avail. in microform from UMI) **Indexed:** Arts & Hum.Cit.Ind., Curr.Cont. **Document type:** consumer publication.
   Description: Informs readers on the state's people, towns, history, weather. Includes scenic color photographs.

051   US
MONTEREY BAY MAGAZINE; the Pacific's lifestyle magazine. 1984. bi-m. $12.95 (foreign $24.95). Pacific Guestlife, 205 17th St., Pacific Grove, CA 93950. TEL 408-375-5711. FAX 408-655-1004. Ed. Tom Owens. adv. contact: Sharon Bates. bk.rev. circ. 25,000.
   Former titles (until July 1991): Pacific (ISSN 1047-3610); (until 1989): Pacific Monthly.

051   US
MORRIS COUNTY. 4/yr. $10. Morris County Chamber of Commerce, 10 Park Ave., Morristown, NJ 07960. TEL 201-539-3882. FAX 201-539-3960. Ed. Kate Lilienthal. adv. circ. 10,000.

051   US
▼**MORRIS JOURNAL.** 1993. w. $20. Morris Publishing Groups, Box 1563, Cayce, SC 29033. TEL 803-256-1611. Ed. Roy Allen Morris. adv.; bk.rev. (back issues avail.) **Document type:** newsletter.

051   US   ISSN 0027-1535
AP2
MOTHER EARTH NEWS; the original country magazine. 1970-1990; resumed 1991. bi-m. $17.95. Sussex Publishers Inc., 49 E. 21st St., 11th Fl., New York, NY 10010. TEL 212-260-7210. FAX 212-260-7445. (Individual subscr. to: Box 55046, Boulder, CO 80322. TEL 800-234-8361) Ed. Owen Lipstein. adv.; bk.rev.; charts; illus.; tr.lit. circ. 350,000. (also avail. in microform from UMI) **Indexed:** Acad.Ind., Access, Consum.Ind., Gard.Lit. (1992-), Hlth.Ind., Ind.How To Do It (1978-), Mag.Ind., MELSA, New Per.Ind., PMR, R.G., TOM. **Document type:** consumer publication.
—Faxon; UnCover; UMI.

051   US
MOUNT WASHINGTON VALLEY MOUNTAIN EAR. 1976. w. $25. Mount Washington Valley Mountain Ear, Inc., Box 350, Conway, NH 03818. TEL 603-447-6336. FAX 603-447-5474. Ed. R. Stephen Eastman. circ. 15,000. **Document type:** bulletin.

071   US
MOUNTAIN TIMES. 1971. w. $49. B R D Corp., Box 183, Killington, VT 05751. TEL 802-773-6970. FAX 802-773-4482. Ed. Lisa Durstin-Madigan. circ. 310 (paid); 10,000 (controlled). (tabloid format; back issues avail.) **Document type:** newspaper.
   Description: Central Vermont's news, arts and events; includes a resort and tourist guide.

051   US   ISSN 0162-6655
MPLS.- ST. PAUL MAGAZINE. 1972. m. $18. Adams Publishing, 12 S. Sixth St., Ste. 400, Minneapolis, MN 55402. TEL 612-339-7571. Ed. Brian Anderson. adv.; bk.rev. circ. 62,000. (back issues avail.) **Indexed:** Access (1975-), Hlth.Ind., Mag.Ind.
—UMI.
   Formerly (until 1978): Mpls. (ISSN 0162-3516)

051   US   ISSN 0027-3686
MURRAY HILL NEWS. 1942. m. $12 (foreign $15). Murray Hill News Inc., 237 Madison Ave., New York, NY 10016. TEL 212-684-6728. Eds. Dorothy Frooks, Schuyler Vanderbilt. adv.; bk.rev.; film rev.; music rev.; play rev.; illus. circ. 15,000. (tabloid format)
   Description: Forum for residents and business people. Covers United Nations.

051   US
MYRTLE BEACH MAGAZINE. a. Himmelsbach Communications, Inc., 1600 S. US Hwy. 17, N. Myrtle Beach, SC 29598. TEL 803-272-8150. Ed. Gloria Marquez. circ. 20,000.

2782 GENERAL INTEREST PERIODICALS — UNITED STATES

051 US
N Y TALK. fortn. Harris Publications, Inc., 1115 Broadway, 8th Fl., New York, NY 10010. TEL 212-807-7100. Eds. C. William Poczik, Robert Seidenberg.

051 US ISSN 1074-1763
NANTUCKET MAGAZINE. 1987. q. $15.95. C.S. Lovelace, Box 779, Nantucket, MA 02554-0779. TEL 508-228-8700. FAX 508-228-9063. Ed. Hobson Woodward. adv.; bk.rev. circ. 8,000. **Document type:** consumer publication.
Formerly: Nantucket Journal (ISSN 1056-2265)
Description: Focuses on the traditions, history, environment and lifestyles of Nantucket Island.

051 US
NASHUA; Amherst, Brookline, Hollis, Hudson, Litchfield, Merrimack, Milford. (Three other regional eds.: Concord and the North, Hampshire East, Manchester) m. $20. Connections Network, Inc., Network Publications, 100 Main St., Nashua, NH 03060. TEL 603-883-3150. (Subscr. to: 889 Elm St., Manchester, NH 03101. TEL 603-883-3150)

071 US
NASSAU HERALD. 1924. w. $18. Richner Publications, Inc., 379 Central Ave, Lawrence, NY 11559. Ed. Leatrice Slote Spanierman. adv.; bk.rev. circ. 12,200. (tabloid format) **Document type:** newspaper.

370.193 US ISSN 0739-1617
NATIONAL EDUCATOR. 1969. m. $20. James H. & Lucille Townsend, Eds. & Pubs., 1051 S. Lemon St., Ste. E, Box 333, Fullerton, CA 92632. TEL 714-871-2950. adv.; bk.rev.; film rev. circ. 51,032. (tabloid format) **Document type:** newspaper.
Formerly: Educator (ISSN 0046-1555)
Description: National and international news from a conservative perspective.

051 US ISSN 1056-3482
NATIONAL ENQUIRER. 1952. w. $32.64. National Enquirer, Inc., 600 S. East Coast Ave., Lantana, FL 33464. TEL 407-586-1111. FAX 407-582-0126. Ed. Iain Calder. adv.; bk.rev. circ. 3,706,030. (tabloid format)
Description: Features unusual or sensational news items, gossip about celebrities, and human interest stories.

051 US
NATIONAL EXAMINER. w. $29.75. Globe Communications Corp. (Boca Raton), 5401 N.W. Broken Sound Blvd., Boca Raton, FL 33487. TEL 407-997-7733. (Subscr. to: Box 51, Rouses Point, NY 12979-0011. TEL 514-849-7733) Ed. Dan Dolan.
Description: Features unusual or sensational news items and gossip about celebrities.

051 US
THE NATIONAL TIMES. 1991. bi-m. $18. 318 E. 84th St., New York, NY 10028. TEL 212-861-0100. Ed. Laura Gordon. adv.: B&W page $2400; color page $3295; adv. contact: Denise Kelly. circ. 50,000. **Document type:** consumer publication.
Description: Reprints selected news articles covering a variety of subjects and political viewpoints. Sources include major U.S. newspapers, newsweeklies, political commentary and general interest magazines.

071.7 US ISSN 0028-1778
NEAR NORTH NEWS. 1956. w. $25 ($30 outside Cook County). Near North News, Inc., 222 W. Ontario St., Ste. 502, Chicago, IL 60610-3695. TEL 312-787-2677. FAX 312-787-2680. Ed. Arnie Matanky. adv.; bk.rev. circ. 7,500. (tabloid format) **Document type:** newspaper.

071 977.311 US ISSN 1069-8213
NEAR WEST GAZETTE. 1983. m. $12 (free to local residents). Near West Gazette, Inc., 1660 W. Ogden Ave., Chicago, IL 60612. TEL 312-243-4288. FAX 312-243-4270. Ed. Mark J. Valentino; Pub. Mark J. Valentino. adv. contact: Laura Sorce. film rev.; play rev.; illus.; circ. 15,000 (controlled). (tabloid format; back issues avail.) **Document type:** newspaper.
Description: Covers news and community development issues for the Near West Side, Tri-Taylor, South Loop, West Loop Gate and Heart of Chicago neighborhoods.

051 US
NEIGHBOR MAGAZINE. 9/yr. Summerhouse Press, Box 770, Challis, ID 83226. TEL 208-879-4300. Ed. Pamela Markley.

051 US ISSN 0300-8959
NEW ALASKAN. 1965. q. $7. New Alaskan Publishing Co., 8339 Snug Harbor Ln., Ketchikan, AK 99901. TEL 907-247-2490. Ed. R.W. Pickrell. adv.; bk.rev.; illus.; circ. 6,000 (controlled). (tabloid format) **Document type:** newspaper.

051 US
NEW BEDFORD MAGAZINE;* the magazine of Southeastern Massachusetts. 1981. bi-m. $10.50. New Bedford Magazine, Inc., c/o Austin, 27 Gorham Rd., No.2, Scarborough, ME 04074-8381. Ed. Dee Giles Forsythe. adv. circ. 8,000. (back issues avail.)

050 US ISSN 0160-2217
NEW BROOKLYN.* 1978. q. $6.95. Motivational Communications, Inc., 10261 Chardon Rd., Chardon, OH 44024-9725. Ed. Barry Conforte. adv.; bk.rev. circ. 25,000.
Description: Contains items of local interest.

051 US ISSN 1052-7273
AP2
NEW DIMENSIONS (GRANTS PASS);* the psychology behind the news. 1979. m. $23.97 (foreign $52). New Dimensions Publishing Company Inc., Box 811, 874 NE 7th, Grants Pass, OR 97526. Ed. David Kupelian. adv.; bk.rev.; charts; illus.; stat. circ. 85,000. (back issues avail.)
Formerly (until 1986): Iconoclast.
Description: Focuses on the real, underlying reasons behind major news events.

917.5 US
NEW DOMINION;* the magazine for and about Northern Virginia. 1974. bi-m. $20. Dominion Publishing, Inc., 210 Reinekers Ln., Alexandria, VA 22314-2823. TEL 703-527-1199. Ed. Philip Hugward. adv.; bk.rev.; circ. 40,000 (controlled).
Formerly (until 1986): Virginia Lifestyle.
Description: Articles of regional interest for northern Virginia.

051 US
NEW ENGLAND BEAT.* fortn. D.M.P. Group, c/o The Beat, 140 Harvard Ave. No. A, Boston, MA 02134-2701. TEL 617-782-7625. Ed. Michael Hill. circ. 40,000.

974.2 US ISSN 0028-5307
F31
NEW HAMPSHIRE PROFILES.* 1951. bi-m. $12.95. Isle of Shoals Publishing, Box 370, Stratham, NH 03885-0370. TEL 603-772-5252. FAX 603-778-7295. Ed. Suki Casanave. adv.; bk.rev. circ. 22,000. **Indexed:** Access (1975-1992).

051 910.03 US
NEW HAVEN LOCAL NEWS. m. $30. Publishers Press (New Haven), 230 Grand Ave., No. 173, New Haven, CT 06513. Ed. Willie Williams. **Document type:** consumer publication.

051 US ISSN 0273-270X
F131
NEW JERSEY MONTHLY. 1976. m. $24.95. M D R Publications, 55 Park Place, Box 920, Morristown, NJ 07960-0920. TEL 201-539-8230. FAX 201-538-2953. (Subscr. to: Box 1961, Marion, OH 43306-2061) Ed. Jenny DeMonte. adv.; bk.rev.; illus. circ. 91,581. **Indexed:** Access (1980-).
Incorporates (1987-1991): Garden State Home and Garden (ISSN 1044-3576); Which incorporates: New Jersey Home and Garden (ISSN 0890-3921)
Description: Features people, places, events, lifestyle, fashion, and homes and gardens in New Jersey.

051 917.403 US ISSN 0195-3192
JK3501
NEW JERSEY REPORTER. 1979. 6/yr. $40. Center for Analysis of Public Issues, 16 Vandeventer Ave., Princeton, NJ 08542. TEL 609-924-9750. FAX 609-924-0363. Ed. Neil Upmeyer. circ. 2,000.
Supersedes: N J Magazine.
Description: Articles and essays on public issues affecting the state, with regular columns covering the legislature, the governor, the courts, politics, media, and the state's relationship with the federal government.

051 US ISSN 0028-6044
HX1
NEW LEADER; a bi-weekly of news and opinion. 1927. fortn. $34. American Labor Conference on International Affairs, Inc., 275 Seventh Ave., New York, NY 10001. TEL 212-807-8240. FAX 212-727-2229. Ed. Myron Kolatch. adv.; bk.rev.; film rev.; play rev.; illus.; index. circ. 25,000. (also avail. in microform from UMI; microfilm from KTO; reprint service avail. from UMI) **Indexed:** Bk.Rev.Ind. (1965-), Child.Bk.Rev.Ind. (1965-), Film Lit.Ind. (1977-), Mag.Ind., Media Rev.Dig., Mid.East: Abstr.& Ind., P.A.I.S., PMR, R.G.
●Also available online. Vendor(s): DIALOG Information Services, Inc.
—BLDSC (6084.380000); Faxon; UnCover; UMI.

051 US
▼**NEW MEXICO ALMANAC.** 1993. a. Starlight Publishing, Inc., Box 928, Albuquerque, NM 87103. TEL 505-768-7008. FAX 505-255-7359. **Document type:** consumer publication.

051 US ISSN 0897-8174
F379.N5
NEW ORLEANS MAGAZINE. 1966. m. $17. New Orleans Publishing Group, 111 Veterans Blvd., Ste. 1810, Metairie, LA 70005. TEL 504-831-3731. FAX 504-837-2258. adv.; bk.rev. circ. 33,275. **Indexed:** Hlth.Ind., Mag.Ind. **Document type:** consumer publication.
—UMI.
Former titles (until 1987): New Orleans (ISSN 0897-8166); (until 1987): New Orleans Magazine (ISSN 0894-4555); (until 1981): New Orleans (ISSN 0192-804X); (until 1975): Metro New Orleans (ISSN 0300-7251)
Description: Explores life in New Orleans. Contains features on local issues, traditions, social trends, fashion, home and garden.

051 US
NEW SETTLER INTERVIEW. bi-m. $1 per no. Box 702, Mendocino, CA 95460. Ed. Beth Bosk.
Description: Publishes interviews with a wide range of people in Northern California such as activists, scientists, craftspeople, feminists and farmers.

051 US
NEW WORLD TIMES.* q. $10. 6900 EastSide Rd., Ukiah, CA 95482-9619. TEL 415-864-0487. Ed. Elizabeth Kehler. circ. 25,000.
Description: Provides a platform for the renaissance of the American Indian -- their cry for justice and an end to genocide.

974.7 US
NEW YORK GOOD NEWS; a journal for optimists. 1966. irreg. $10 for 5 nos. Arete Ink, 101 St. Marks Pl., New York, NY 10009. TEL 212-777-7856. Ed. Stephen Kraus. adv.; bk.rev. (also avail. in microfilm from KTO) **Document type:** consumer publication.
Formerly: Good News (New York) (ISSN 0017-2138)

071 US ISSN 1060-0167
NEW YORK GUARDIAN. 1991. m. $27. Free Press Corp., 316 Great Press Rd., Great Neck, NY 11021. TEL 718-229-8209. FAX 718-229-8134. Ed. Christopher Ruddy. circ. 15,000 (paid). **Document type:** newspaper.
Description: Covers politics, art, culture, the media and state, local and national news.

051 US
NEW YORK IMAGE.* 1984. 10/yr. $20. Zelmont Corp., c/o Paul-Felix Montez, Ed., 2720 Belden Dr., Hollywood, CA 90068-1928. adv.

051 US
NEW YORK ISSUES. 1989. m. $24. Coppola Group, 372 Central Park W., Ste. 17A, New York, NY 10025. TEL 212-678-4652. adv. circ. 30,000.
Description: Reports on the social, political, business and lifestyle aspects of New York.

GENERAL INTEREST PERIODICALS — UNITED STATES

051   US   ISSN 0028-7369
F128.1
NEW YORK MAGAZINE. 1968. w. $42. K-III Magazines, 200 Madison Ave., New York, NY 10016. TEL 212-447-4700. FAX 212-447-4778. (Subscr. to: Box 54661, Boulder, CO 80322-4661. TEL 800-678-0900) Ed. Kurt Andersen. adv.; bk.rev.; illus. circ. 415,000. (also avail. in microform from UMI; reprint service avail. from UMI) **Indexed:** Bk.Rev.Ind. (1988-), Child.Bk.Rev.Ind. (1988-), Film Lit.Ind. (1973-), Mag.Ind., Media Rev.Dig., R.G. **Document type:** consumer publication.
—Faxon; UnCover; UMI.
Incorporates (in Apr. 1980): Cue New York; Which was formerly (1932-1978): Cue (ISSN 0011-2658)
Description: Articles and reviews of theater, art and music in and around New York City, with emphasis on trends and current political events. Also contains a comprehensive guide to plays, films and other entertainment.

051   US
NEW YORK PERSPECTIVES;* the news & arts weekly of uptown Manhattan. no.140, 1992. w. $42. N Y Perspectives, Inc., 33 E. 33rd St., New York, NY 10016. TEL 212-447-0500. Ed. Bruce Shlain.

071   US
NEW YORK PRESS. 1988. w. (Wed.). $25. New York Press, Inc., 295 Lafayette St., 9th Fl., New York, NY 10012-3920. TEL 212-941-1130. FAX 212-941-7824. Ed. Russ Smith. adv.; illus. circ. 85,000. (tabloid format; also avail. in microfilm from BHP,KTO) **Document type:** newspaper.
Description: Covers the New York scene, expecially arts and cultural activities in Lower Manhattan.

072.1   US   ISSN 0362-4331
CODEN: NYTIAO
THE NEW YORK TIMES. (Supplements avail: New York Times Book Review; New York Times Magazine; Sophisticated Traveler; Fashions of the Times) 1851. d. $280 (foreign $843 by mail) (effective 1994); newsstand price: 50. New York Times Company, 229 W. 43rd St., New York, NY 10036. TEL 212-556-1234. FAX 212-556-4603. (U.S. subscr. to: Box 2047, S. Hackensack, NJ 07606. TEL 800-931-2500; Overseas subscr. to: Mail Subscriptions, Box 9564, Uniondale, NY 11555. TEL 201-343-2244. FAX 201-342-2539) Ed. Max Frankel; Pub. Arthur Ochs Sulzberger, Jr. adv.; bk.rev.; film rev.; play rev.; tele.rev.; illus.; index. Wire service(s): AP. cols./p.: 6. (broadsheet format) **Document type:** newspaper.
—UMI; CASDDS.

051   US
NEW YORK TIMES MAGAZINE (MICROFICHE EDITION). (Includes supplements) w. (delivered m.) $127.50 vesicular; silver halide $150. (New York Times Company) University Microfilms International, 300 N. Zeeb Rd., Ann Arbor, MI 48106. TEL 313-761-4700; 800-521-0600. FAX 313-761-1203. (microfiche; back issues avail.; reprint service avail. from UMI) **Indexed:** Acad.Ind., Amer.Hist.& Life, CAD CAM Abstr. (until 1993), Energy Info.Abstr. (until 1994), Environ.Abstr., Fut.Surv., Hist.Abstr., Mag.Ind., Pers.Lit., PMR, R.G.

051   US
NEW YORK UPDATE. m. $20. M MBC Publishers, 151 Alkier St., Brentwood, NY 11717-5129. TEL 516-435-8890. Ed. Cheryl Meglio. circ. 56,000.
Formerly: New York Nightlife.

071   US
NEW YORK VOICE. 1959. w. $25. New York Voice, Inc., 75-43 Parsons Blvd., Flushing, NY 11366. TEL 718-591-6600. FAX 718-591-6945. Ed. Terrence Roche. adv.; bk.rev.; film rev.; play rev.; illus.; tr.lit. circ. 90,000. (tabloid format; also avail. in microform from UMI) **Document type:** newspaper.
Formerly: Queens Voice (ISSN 0042-8051)

051   US
NEWMONTH: THE GOOD LIFE IN UPPER WISCONSIN. 1975. m. $15. Brown County Publishing Co., Box 278, Denmark, WI 54208. TEL 414-863-2154. Ed. C. Jeremy Shaw. adv.; bk.rev. circ. 15,500.

051   US
NEWPAPER.* 1978. w. $20. NewPaper Co., 21 Ogden St., Providence, RI 02906-4903. TEL 401-273-6397. Ed. Ty Davis. adv.; bk.rev. circ. 25,000. (tabloid format; also avail. in microfiche; back issues avail.)
Description: Contains items of local interest.

051   US
NEWPORT BEACH (714). 1984. bi-w. $52. Baker Communications, Inc., 901 Dover Dr., Ste. 231, Newport Beach, CA 92660. TEL 714-722-1286. FAX 714-722-6632. Ed. Donna Bunce; Pub. Seth Barer. adv. contact: Ingrid Pitrelli; circ. 50,000(controlled).
Description: Covers people, fashion, parties, and society.

051   US
NEWS FROM NOWHERE. 1989. irreg. (3-6/yr.) 2398 Parker St., Ste. 17, Berkeley, CA 94704. TEL 510-845-3749. Eds. Fay M. Blake, Morton Newman. circ. 237.
Description: Publishes articles, cartoons, satire, criticism, reviews, non-fiction, and news items.

051   US   ISSN 0737-3813
NEWSBANK (NEW CANAAN). 1970. m. (q. and a. cums.). price varies. NewsBank, Inc., 58 Pine St., New Canaan, CT 06840-5426. TEL 203-966-1100. FAX 203-966-6254. index. (paper index; articles on microfiche; CD ROM index)
Formerly: NewsBank Library.

071.4   US
NEWSGLEANER - BUSTLETON - SOMERTON EDITION. 1882. w. $25. News Gleaner Publications, Inc., 1612 Margaret St., Philadelphia, PA 19124. TEL 215-535-4270. Ed. Donald P. Brennan. adv. circ. 22,000. **Document type:** newspaper.
Former titles: Bustleton News; Bustleton-Somerton News; Bustleton-Somerton News Gleaner (ISSN 0007-7224)

071.4   US
NEWSGLEANER - FAR NORTHEAST EDITION. 1979. w. $75. News Gleaner Publications, Inc., 1612 Margaret St., Philadelphia, PA 19124. TEL 215-535-4270. Ed. Donald P. Brennan. adv. **Document type:** newspaper.
Formerly: Far Northeast News.

071.4   US
NEWSGLEANER - FRANKFORD - OXFORD CIRCLE EDITION. 1882. w. $75. News Gleaner Publications, Inc., 1612 Margaret St., Philadelphia, PA 19124. TEL 215-535-4270. Ed. Donald P. Brennan. adv. circ. 22,000. **Document type:** newspaper.
Formerly: Frankford News Gleaner (ISSN 0015-9921)
Description: Contains items of local interest.

071.4   US
NEWSGLEANER - MAYFAIR - NORTHEAST EDITION. 1939. w. $75. News Gleaner Publications, Inc., 1612 Margaret St., Philadelphia, PA 19124. TEL 215-535-4270. Ed. Donald P. Brennan. adv. circ. 22,000. **Document type:** newspaper.
Former titles: Mayfair-Northeast News; Mayfair News (ISSN 0025-617X)

320.9 051   US   ISSN 0028-9604
AP2
NEWSWEEK. Australian edition: Bulletin with Newsweek. Japanese edition: Newsweek Nihon Ban. Korean edition: Newsweek Hankuk Pan. (Demographic, Geographic (Regional and State) and International editions in English also avail.) 1933. w. $41.08 for domestic ed.; cassette tape $70.20; flexible disc free to qualified personnel. Newsweek, Inc., 444 Madison Ave., New York, NY 10022. TEL 212-350-4000. (Subscr. to: Newsweek, Box 403, Livingston, NJ 07039. TEL 800-631-1040; Flexible disc and cassette tape avail. from: American Printing House for the Blind, Inc., 1839 Frankfort Ave., Box 6389, Louisville, KY 4206-0085. TEL 502-895-2405) Ed. Richard M. Smith. adv.; B&W page $77670, color page $120835; trim 8 x 10 3/4. bk.rev.; film rev.; play rev.; index. circ. 3,100,000. (also avail. in microform from UMI,PMC; audio cassette; diskette format; reprint service avail. from UMI) **Indexed:** Abr.R.G., Acad.Ind., Bank.Lit.Ind., Biog.Ind., Biol.Dig., Bk.Rev.Ind. (1965-), CAD CAM Abstr. (until 1992), Chic.Per.Ind., Child.Bk.Rev.Ind. (1965-), CINAHL, CMI, Comput.Bus., Curr.Lit.Fam.Plan., Curr.Pack.Abstr., Environ.Abstr., Environ.Ind., Film Lit.Ind. (1973-), Fut.Surv., Hlth.Ind., Jun.High.Mag.Abstr., Mag.Ind., Media Rev.Dig., Mgmt.& Market.Abstr., Mid.East: Abstr.& Ind., Pers.Lit., PROMT, R.G., Robomat. (until 1992), Tel.Abstr., Telegen (until 1989), TOM. **Document type:** consumer publication.
● Also available online. Vendor(s): Mead Data Central, Inc..
—BLDSC (6108.789000); Faxon; UnCover; SWETS; UMI.
Description: Contains articles concerning current events.

051   US
NOB HILL GAZETTE. 1978. m. $35. Nob Hill Gazette, Inc., 5 Third St. No. 222, San Francisco, CA 94103. TEL 415-227-0190. Ed. Marsha Monroe. adv. contact: Linda Kramer. bk.rev. circ. 60,000. (tabloid format; back issues avail.) **Document type:** consumer publication.
Description: Covers high society in the San Francisco Bay Area.

051   US
NORTH BEACH NOW. 1987. m. free. 1736 Stockton St., Ste. 1, San Francisco, CA 94133. TEL 415-391-1043. FAX 415-399-8854. Ed. Joan Dahlgren. adv.; bk.rev.; film rev.; play rev.; illus.; circ. 3,500 (paid). **Document type:** newspaper.
Description: Covers the arts, neighborhood news, and life in the North Beach and South Beach sections of San Francisco.

051   US   ISSN 0885-2499
NORTH DAKOTA R E C MAGAZINE. 1954. m. $12 ($24 in Canada). North Dakota Association of Rural Electric Cooperatives, Box 727, Mandan, ND 58554-0727. TEL 701-663-6501. FAX 701-663-3745. Ed. Kent Brick. bk.rev.; illus. circ. 75,000. **Document type:** consumer publication.
Formerly: North Dakota Rural Electric Magazine (ISSN 0029-2788)
Description: Features topics related to electric power services available from rural electric cooperatives, as well as ideas for better rural living.

071.3   US   ISSN 0029-2877
NORTH LOOP NEWS. 1930. w. $35. North Loop News Corp., 1332 N. Halsted St., No. 204, Chicago, IL 60622-2632. TEL 312-787-5396. FAX 312-787-1616. Ed. Debby Madden; Pub. Anne A. Albanese. adv.; circ. 24,700 (controlled). (tabloid format; also avail. in microform) **Document type:** newspaper.

051   US   ISSN 0195-1653
NORTH SHORE (WINNETKA); serving Chicago and its northern-northwestern suburbs. 1978. m. $12. P B Communications, Inc., 874 Green Bay Rd., Winnetka, IL 60093. TEL 708-441-7892. Ed. Asher J. Birnbaum. adv.; bk.rev. circ. 55,000. (back issues avail.) **Document type:** consumer publication.
Description: Deals with North Shore area residents, and various aspects of their economic, social and cultural lifestyle.

051   US
NORTH SHORE LIFE. bi-m. Suburban Publishing Company, 10 First Ave., Box 6039, Peabody, MA 01960-4906. TEL 508-532-5880. Ed. Bob Curtin. bk.rev. circ. 30,163.

GENERAL INTEREST PERIODICALS — UNITED STATES

051 US
NORTHEAST OHIO AVENUES. 1989. m. $18 includes membership. Avenues, 2132 E. Ninth St., Ste. 310, Cleveland, OH 44115-1245. TEL 216-861-1777. FAX 216-861-1790. Ed. Brenda Lewison. adv.: B&W page $2600. circ. 49,676. **Document type:** consumer publication.
Description: Reports on the interesting people and unique lifestyle of Northeast Ohio in a manner which is positive, intelligent, informative, and useful.

051 US
NORTHERN ADVENTURES MAGAZINE; a magazine on Alaska. 1986. biennial. $12 per 6 nos. 400 Denali, Wasilla, AK 99687. FAX 907-373-3000. Ed. Lavon Barve. adv.; bk.rev. circ. 2,500.

071.749 US ISSN 1071-281X
▼**NORTHERN BUSINESS.** 1993 (Sep. 15). fortn. $26. Snowden Publications Inc., 1629 Rte. 22 E., Union, NJ 07083. TEL 908-687-5585. FAX 908-687-4066. (Dist. by: Snowden Publications Inc., 11 Deer Park Dr., Monmouth Junction, NJ 08852; Subscr. to: Box 201, Princeton, NJ 08542. TEL 908-329-0003. FAX 908-329-0252) Ed. George M. Taber; Pub. Donald M. Wilson. adv. contact: Michelle McGowan. bk.rev.; illus. (tabloid format; back issues avail.) **Document type:** newspaper.
—UMI.
Description: Covers the major business-related events as they occur in northern New Jersey. Also provides a focus on various industries of business in the state.

051 US ISSN 0271-5147
NORTHERN OHIO LIVE. 1980. m. $16. M Magazine Ltd., 11320 Juniper Rd., Cleveland, OH 44106. TEL 216-721-1800. FAX 216-721-2525. Ed. Michael von Glahn. adv. contact: Gail Kerzner. film rev.; play rev. circ. 32,000. (back issues avail.) **Document type:** consumer publication.
Description: Covers entertainment, dining out, and lifestyle. Includes a calendar of events, a guide to dining out, art and entertainment, previews and reviews, and profiles.

051 US
NOVASCOPE. 1985. 10/yr. $25 (effective 1992). Novascope, Inc., Box 283, Upperville, VA 22176. TEL 703-687-3314. FAX 703-687-4113. Eds. Joy and Mark Smith. adv.; bk.rev. circ. 15,000. (back issues avail.)
Description: Feature stories on Northern Virginia.

071.5 US
OAK LAWN REPORTER - EVERGREEN PARK REPORTER. 1960. w. $22 (effective 1994). Regional Publishing Corp., 12243 S. Harlem Ave., Palos Heights, IL 60463. TEL 708-448-6161. Ed. Ron Rehfeld; Pub. Charles Richards. adv. contact: Carol McLaughlin. circ. 17,454 (paid). **Document type:** newspaper.
Formerly: Oak Lawn Reporter.

071 US
LA OFERTA REVIEW.* (Text in English, Spanish) 1978. s-w. $35.80. 1376 N. Fourth St., San Jose, CA 95112-4713. TEL 408-729-6397. Ed. Mary Andrade. adv.: B&W page $3126.06. circ. 16,000. **Document type:** newspaper.
Description: Provides general information about Santa Clara county, and San Francisco Bay area; international and national news are also covered.

051 US ISSN 1051-2373
OH! IDAHO. 1988. q. $16. Peak Media, Inc., Box 925, Hailey, ID 83333. TEL 208-788-4500. FAX 208-788-5098. Ed. Laurie Sammis. adv. circ. 20,000.
Description: Covers the diversity of the people who live in Idaho. Stories depict Idaho artists, interesting homes, travel destinations, and profiles of the people who make up the state. Includes updates on the land and the environment.

051 US ISSN 0164-7172
F486
OHIO MAGAZINE. 1978. m. $18. 62 E. Broad St., Columbus, OH 43215. TEL 614-461-5083. FAX 614-461-5506. Ed. Ellen Stein Burbach. adv.; bk.rev. circ. 91,127. (also avail. in microfiche from UMI) **Indexed:** Access (1981-). **Document type:** consumer publication.
Description: Covers tourism and travel, lifestyle, leisure, healthcare, finance, the environment and local business.

057.85 US ISSN 1056-1595
OKAY AMERICA. (Text in Polish) 1991. m. $28 (in Poland 150000 zl.). W I R Publishing & Advertising Corp., 628 E. 14th St., New York, NY 10009. TEL 212-673-0750. FAX 212-674-8734. (Dist. in Poland by: Wydawnictwo Artystyczne i Filmowe, ul. Pulawska 61, 02-595 Warsaw, Poland) Ed. Krzysztof Klopotowski. illus. circ. 180,000.

051 US ISSN 0048-1610
OKLAHOMA RURAL NEWS. 1948. m. $2. Oklahoma Association of Electric Cooperatives, Box 54309, Oklahoma City, OK 73154-1309. TEL 405-478-1455. FAX 405-478-0246. Ed. Mary Logan; Pub. Larry Watkins. adv.: N&W page $3047, color page $3900; adv. contact: Fred Albert. circ. 230,500. (tabloid format; also avail. in microfilm) **Document type:** consumer publication.

976.6 US ISSN 0030-1892
OKLAHOMA TODAY. 1956. bi-m. $13.50. Tourism and Recreation Department, 401 Will Rogers Bldg., Box 53384, Oklahoma City, OK 73152. TEL 405-521-2496. FAX 405-521-3992. Ed. Jeanne Devlin. adv.; bk.rev.; illus.; index. circ. 43,000 (paid). **Document type:** consumer publication.
—UnCover.

051 US ISSN 1047-3068
OLD NEWS. 1989. m. (except Aug.). $15. Susquehanna Times & Magazine, Inc., 400 Stackstown Rd., Marietta, PA 17547. TEL 717-426-2212. Ed. Richard S. Bromer. circ. 25,000 (paid). (back issues avail.) **Document type:** newspaper.

051 US
ON THE TOWN. 1982. m. $12. On the Town Publications Inc., 705 Bagley Ave., S.E., Ste. 102, Grand Rapids, MI 49506-3001. TEL 616-451-0361. FAX 616-454-4666. Ed. Christopher Scapelliti. adv. circ. 35,000. **Document type:** consumer publication.
Description: Guide to arts and entertainment events in and around Western Michigan. Includes listings of restaurants, night clubs, and art galleries.

051 US
OPEN CITY. q. $20. 118 Riverside Dr., Ste. 14A, New York, NY 10024.

051 US ISSN 0279-0483
ORANGE COAST MAGAZINE. 1974. m. $19.95. Orange Coast Kommunications, 245-D Fischer Ave., No. 8, Costa Mesa, CA 92626. TEL 714-545-1900. FAX 714-545-1932. Ed. Robin Manougian; Pub. Ruth Ko. adv. contact: Linda Goldstein. bk.rev. circ. 40,000. **Indexed:** Cal.Per.Ind. (1979-). **Document type:** consumer publication.
Description: Feature articles on politics, culture, social issues, sports, literature, travel, fashion, health, fitness and dining.

051 US
OREGON COAST. 1982. bi-m. $14.95. Oregon Coast Magazine, 1870 Hwy. 126, Box 18000, Florence, OR 97439. TEL 503-997-8401. FAX 503-997-1124. adv.; tr.lit. circ. 50,000. **Document type:** consumer publication.

051 US
ORLANDO SUN REVIEW. 1977. w. $21.50. L M H Publications, Box 2348, 701 18th St., Orlando, FL 32802. circ. 16,000. (tabloid format; back issues avail.)

051 US
OUR TEXAS. q. $15 (Texas residents $10). Box 4463, Dallas, TX 75208. TEL 214-946-5315. **Document type:** consumer publication.

974.8 US ISSN 0030-7386
OVERBROOK ADVISER.* 1967. w. $3. Overbrook Press, 2039 Upland Way, Philadelphia, PA 19131. Ed. Marilyn Krantz. adv.
Description: Includes items of local interest.

051 100 US ISSN 1045-7585
P R O U T PRESS. (Progressive Utilization Theory) 1987. s-w. $200. Proutist Universal, Inc., Box 56466, Washington, DC 20040. TEL 202-829-2278. FAX 202-829-0462. Ed. D. Dhruva. adv.; bk.rev. circ. 8,250. (looseleaf format; also avail. in tabloid format; back issues avail.)
Formerly (until Aug. 1988): New Humanist.
Description: Covers events, ideas, people and organizations from the P R O U T perspective for members, supporters and the public.

051 US
P S - PUGET SOUND. bi-m. $12. Fivash Publishing Group, 2505 Second Ave., Ste. 603, Seattle, WA 98121-1426. TEL 206-441-8415.
Formerly (until 1992): Peninsula.

051 US ISSN 0199-6363
QH1
PACIFIC NORTHWEST; the travel and lifestyle magazine of the Northwest. 1966. m. $18.95. Adams Publishing of the Pacific Northwest, 701 Dexter Ave. N., Ste. 101, Seattle, WA 98109. TEL 206-284-1750. FAX 206-284-2550. Ed. Ann Naumann. adv.; bk.rev.; illus.; index. circ. 90,175. (also avail. in microform from UMI; reprint service avail. from UMI) **Indexed:** Access (1984-). **Document type:** consumer publication.
—UnCover; UMI.
Incorporates (in 1988): Oregon Magazine (ISSN 0164-9930); Which was formerly (1971-1985): Oregon Times; Search (ISSN 0191-0043); Which was formerly (until 1978): Pacific Search (ISSN 0161-7915)

071.6 US ISSN 0048-2641
PACIFIC SUN. 1963. w. (Fri.). $25. Pacific Sun Publishing Co. Inc., Box 5553, Mill Valley, CA 94942. TEL 415-383-4500. FAX 415-383-4159. Ed. Steve McNamara; Pub. Steve McNamara. adv.; bk.rev.; film rev.; play rev.; illus. circ. 34,000. (tabloid format) **Document type:** newspaper.

051 US
PALM BEACH ILLUSTRATED. (Includes: Palm Beach Social Observer) 1952. 10/yr. $40. Falcon Publishing, Inc., Box 3244, Palm Beach, FL 33480. TEL 407-659-0210. adv. circ. 12,149.
Description: Highlights events, activities, people, travel, products and services in Palm Beach.

975.9 US ISSN 0031-0417
PALM BEACH LIFE. 1906. m. $26. 265 Royal Poinciana Way, Palm Beach, FL 33480. TEL 407-655-5755. FAX 407-655-4594. Ed. Michael Gaeta. adv.; bk.rev.; illus. circ. 25,000.

051 US ISSN 1045-7259
PALM BEACH SOCIETY; the social pictorial. 1953. 30/yr (w. Nov.-Apr.; m. May-Oct.). $30. Palm Beach Society Companies, 240 Worth Ave., Palm Beach, FL 33480. TEL 407-659-5555. FAX 407-655-6209. (Subscr. to: Box 591, Palm Beach, FL 33480) Ed. James Jennings Sheeran. adv.; circ. 5,000 (paid). (back issues avail.)
Formerly: Palm Beach Social Pictorial.
Description: Covers the social, cultural, civic and sporting events of Palm Beach via photojournalism.

071.6 US ISSN 0893-3669
PARIS POST-INTELLIGENCER. 1866. d. (Mon.-Fri.). $73.50. Paris Publishing Co., Inc., 208 E. Wood St., Box 310, Paris, TN 38242. TEL 901-642-1162. FAX 901-642-1165. Ed. Michael Williams; Pub. Bill Williams. adv.: B&W page $677.25; adv. contact: Brenda Stubblefield. bk.rev.; circ. 8,185 (paid). cols./p.: 6. (also avail. in microfilm; reprint service avail.) **Document type:** newspaper.

051 US
PARK AVENUE SOCIAL REVIEW.* 1925. m. $25. Edward B. Lockwood, Inc., 435 E. 79th St., New York, NY 10021. TEL 212-249-4618. Ed. Marion L. Damroth. adv.; bk.rev. circ. 9,000.

974.7 US ISSN 0031-2126
PARK EAST. 1960. 10/yr. $7.50. Park East News, Inc., 341 E. 79th St., New York, NY 10021. TEL 212-535-5106. Ed. Hulda G. Lawrence. adv.; bk.rev.; play rev.; illus. circ. 10,000. (tabloid format; also avail. in microfiche; back issues avail.)
Description: Covers local civic, political and cultural events, with additional news on travel, shopping and dining.

GENERAL INTEREST PERIODICALS — UNITED STATES

071.9 US
PARK LABREA NEWS AND BEVERLY PRESS. 1947. w. $40. 142 S. Fairfax Ave., Los Angeles, CA 90036. TEL 213-933-5518. FAX 213-933-5812. Ed. Brian Boye. adv. circ. 13,100. **Document type:** newspaper.
Formerly: Park LaBrea News.

051 US
PEACHTREE MAGAZINE; the guide to the civilized South. 1986. m. $30. C S Publishers, Inc., 120 Interstate N. Pkwy. E., Ste. 445, Atlanta, GA 30339. TEL 404-956-1207. FAX 404-988-8972. Ed. Daniel F. DeLong. adv.; bk.rev. circ. 50,618. **Document type:** consumer publication.
Description: Features homes, fashion, food, wine, social and cultural topics.

051 US
PEACOCK NORTH WEST NEWS.* w. Peacock Publishing Co., c/o Abbott, 2702 Pisces Dr., Orlando, FL 32837-9014.

051 US
PEAK TO PEAK.* 1984. 5/yr. $8. Peak to Peak Magazine, Inc., 340 Pine Dr., Golden, CO 80403-9524. TEL 303-258-7097. Ed. John Gunn. adv. circ. 13,000.
Description: Covers the Front Range of the Colorado Rocky Mountains.

051 US
PENN LINES. 1966. m. $7.50 to non-members; members $3. Pennsylvania Rural Electric Association, Box 1266, 212 Locust St., Harrisburg, PA 17108. TEL 717-233-5704. FAX 717-234-1309. Ed. Perry A. Stambaugh. adv.; circ. 157,000 (controlled). **Document type:** consumer publication.
Description: Features energy usage, rural development, rural issues, safety, education and conservation.

051 US
PENNSYLVANIA GOOD TIMES MAGAZINE. 1990. q. $18.95. Box 325, Punxsutawney, PA 15767. TEL 800-232-2092.
Description: Leisure time guide to recreation and fun in Pennsylvania.

051 910 US ISSN 0744-4230
F146
PENNSYLVANIA MAGAZINE. 1981. bi-m. $17.90 (effective 1994). Box 576, Camp Hill, PA 17011. TEL 717-761-6620. Ed. Albert E. Holliday. adv.; bk.rev.; circ. 40,000 (paid). **Document type:** consumer publication.

051 US ISSN 0093-7673
AP2
PEOPLE WEEKLY. 1974. w. $82.68. Time Inc. (Subsidiary of: Time Warner, Inc.), Time & Life Bldg., Rockefeller Center, 1271 Ave. of the Americas, New York, NY 10020-1393. TEL 212-522-1212. (Subscr. to: Box 30603, Tampa, FL 33630-0603. TEL 800-541-1000) Ed. Landon Y. Jones Jr. adv.; illus.; circ. 3,150,000 (paid). (also avail. in microform from UMI) **Indexed:** Acad.Ind., Chic.Per.Ind., Hlth.Ind., Jun.High.Mag.Abstr., Mag.Ind., R.G., TOM. **Document type:** consumer publication.
●Also available online. Vendor(s): Mead Data Central, Inc., VU/TEXT Information Services, Inc..
—Faxon; UnCover; SWETS; UMI.
Formerly: People (New York).
Description: Articles, interviews and photographs of celebrities, newsmakers and ordinary people doing extraordinary things.

051 US
PERSONA. 1989. m. $4.95 per no. Majestic Video Publishing Inc., 10837 Washington Blvd., Culver City, CA 90232. TEL 310-838-1383. circ. 600,000. (avail. on videocassette only)

071 US ISSN 0733-6349
PHILADELPHIA CITY PAPER. 1981. w. $52. City Communications, Inc., 206 S. 13th St., Philadelphia, PA 19146. TEL 215-735-8444. Ed. David Warner; Pub. Bruce Schimmel. adv. contact: Paul Curci. bk.rev. circ. 70,000. (tabloid format; back issues avail.) **Document type:** newspaper.
Description: Covers cultural, social, political news and events in the city and nearby communities.

974.8 US ISSN 0031-7233
HC108.P5
PHILADELPHIA MAGAZINE. 1908. m. $15. (City and Regional Magazine Association) Philadelphia Magazine, Inc., 1818 Market St., Philadelphia, PA 19103. TEL 215-564-7700. FAX 215-656-3502. Ed. Eliot Kaplan. adv.; bk.rev.; illus. circ. 135,000. (also avail. in microfilm from UMI; reprint service avail. from UMI) **Indexed:** Access (1975-), Hlth.Ind., Mag.Ind., PMR. **Document type:** consumer publication.
—Faxon; UMI.
Formerly: Greater Philadelphia.
Description: Covers issues and events in and around Philadelphia.

071 US
PHILADELPHIA SUNDAY SUN. 1979. w. $36. 628 W. Rittenhouse St., Philadelphia, PA 19144. TEL 215-848-7864. FAX 215-848-7893. Pub. J. Whyatt Mondesire. adv. contact: Harriet Garrett. bk.rev.; circ. 28,000 (paid). **Document type:** newspaper.
Formerly (until 1992): Stone's Journal.

051 US ISSN 1045-1773
PHOENIX (PHOENIX). 1966. m. $14. Media America Corporation, 5555 N. Seventh Ave., B200, Phoenix, AZ 85013-1755. TEL 602-207-3750. FAX 602-207-3797. Ed. Richard Vonier. adv. circ. 48,855. (back issues avail.) **Indexed:** Access (1975-). **Document type:** consumer publication.
Former titles: Phoenix Metro (ISSN 0886-8859); Phoenix Magazine.
Description: For resident and visitors in the Phoenix metropolitan area. Covers the culture, people, problems, achievements and politics of the rapidly changing Sunbelt area. Contains reports of crucial or controversial issues confronting the community.

051 US
PHYSICIANS LIFESTYLE MAGAZINE.* (Supplement to: Physicians Financial News) 1989. m. K & K Publishing, Inc., 19 W. 34th St., Ste. 1010, New York, NY 10001-3006. TEL 212-643-0991. Ed. Emily Paulsen. adv.; bk.rev.; circ. controlled.

051 US
PINAL PIONEER.* 1989. s-m. $28.50. Arizona's Most Interesting Newspaper, 12066 W. Highway 84, Casa Grande, AZ 85222-9070. TEL 602-421-0734. Ed. Mark Acuff.
Description: Serves the Pinal County area with news, features, and current information on politics and economics.

974.8 US ISSN 0194-8431
F159.P6 CODEN: PIMAEF
PITTSBURGH; Pittsburgh's magazine of the arts and public affairs. 1969. m. $12.50 (effective 1992). Metropolitan Pittsburgh Public Broadcasting, Inc., 4802 Fifth Ave., Pittsburgh, PA 15213. TEL 412-622-1360. FAX 412-622-7066. Ed. Dianne Jacob. adv. contact: Rhonda Goldblatt. bk.rev.; illus. circ. 60,000. **Indexed:** Access (1986-).
Former titles: Pittsburgh Renaissance; Q E D Renaissance (ISSN 0048-606X)

PLUS (CHICAGO); the magazine about life and HIV. see *MEDICAL SCIENCES — Communicable Diseases*

071 US
POINTS EAST. 4/yr. free. East End Newspaper Group, 153 Main St., East Hampton, NY 11937. TEL 516-324-0002. FAX 516-324-7943. Ed. Jennifer Peltz. circ. 100,000. **Document type:** newspaper.
Formerly (until Aug. 1992): 27 East.

001.3 US
POLONIAN. (Text in English, Polish) 1960; N.S. 1990. m. $10. Polish Community Service Center, 165 11th St., San Francisco, CA 94103. TEL 415-864-6100. FAX 415-431-6450. Ed. Dalegor Wladyslaw Suchecki; Pub. Dalegor Wladyslaw Suchecki. bk.rev. circ. 1,000. **Document type:** newsletter.
Description: Serves as source of information regarding activities of the Polish community in Northern California.

051 US
POTOMAC LIFE. 1990. 10/yr. $16. C E R Publications, Box 59508, Potomac, MD 20859. TEL 301-299-5183. Ed. Claire Cooney. circ. 32,000 (controlled).
Description: For residents of Western Montgomery County, Maryland. Profiles prominent residents; includes short stories and poetry.

051 US
▼**PREVIEW MAGAZINE.** 1993. bi-m. $21.95. Network Publications, Inc., Box 3015, Littleton, CO 80161-3015. TEL 303-794-2064. FAX 303-795-8130. Ed. Edward M. Barry. adv.: B&W page $2625, color page $3125; trim 8 3/8 x 10 7/8. circ. 100,000. **Document type:** consumer publication.

051 US
▼**PRISON LIFE.*** 1992. bi-m. $19.95. 67 Wall St., No. 2411, New York, NY 10005-3101. Ed. Shan Rodgers. adv. contact: Joe Strahl.
Description: Entertainment and advocacy coverage of issues affecting prisoners.

051 US
PRIVILEGED INFORMATION. bi-w. Privileged Information, Inc., 330 W. 42nd St., New York, NY 10036. (Subscr. to: Subscription Service Center, Box 10974, Des Moines, IA 50340)

700 US
PROMENADE. 1934. s-a. $5 per no. Promenade Magazines, Inc., 20 E. 49th St., 6th Fl., New York, NY 10017. TEL 212-888-3500. FAX 212-888-3602. Ed. James M. White. adv. circ. 2,000,000.

051 US
PROSPEROUS TIMES. 1988. m. Howard Publications, 417 Fayette St., Hammond, IN 46320. TEL 219-933-3253. Ed. David Lewman. circ. 42,000 (controlled).
Description: Provides articles on local arts, entertainment, sports, business and personalities.

051 US ISSN 0889-6348
AP2
PROTEUS; a journal of ideas. 1983. s-a. $10. Shippensburg University, Shippensburg, PA 17257. TEL 717-532-1206. FAX 717-532-1253. Ed. Angelo Costanzo. bk.rev. circ. 5,000. (also avail. in microform from UMI) **Indexed:** Amer.Hist.& Life, Curr.Cont., Hist.Abstr., M.L.A., PAIS. **Document type:** academic/scholarly publication.
—BLDSC (6936.225000); Faxon; UnCover; UMI.
Description: Presents a forum for a scholarly approach to a variety of themes.
Refereed Serial

071 US
QUECHEE TIMES. 1972. q. $8 donation. Tom Lane Associates, Inc., Box 3, Quechee, VT 05059. TEL 802-295-3601. Ed. Virginia Lane. adv.; bk.rev. circ. 2,400. (tabloid format; back issues avail.) **Document type:** newspaper.

051 US
R O: THE MAGAZINE OF RIVER OAKS. m. Creneau Media Group, Box 3388, Houston, TX 77253. TEL 713-880-4611. FAX 713-880-4644. Ed. Cristina Adams. circ. 10,000.

051 US
RAIL WHISPERS. 1990. m. Whisper Publications, Inc., 1865 Palmer Ave., Ste. 202, Larchmont, NY 10538. TEL 914-833-3634. FAX 914-834-7651. Ed. John Faiella. adv.; bk.rev.; circ. 30,000 (controlled).
Description: Covers news of Fairfield County, Connecticut, and Westchester County, New York.

051 US ISSN 0164-8780
RANCH & COAST.* (Former name of issuing body: American Ranch & Coast Publishing Co., Inc.) 1964. m. $24. L.A. West Media, Inc., Box 3468, Rancho Santa Fe, CA 92067-3468. TEL 619-481-7659. FAX 619-481-6205. Ed. Kit Ladwig. adv.; bk.rev. circ. 30,000.
Description: Targeted to high income residents of San Diego County.

G

GENERAL INTEREST PERIODICALS — UNITED STATES

051 US ISSN 0034-0375
AP2
READER'S DIGEST. (Editions in 16 languages) 1922. m. $20.93 (effective 1992); large print $9.95; cassette $18; Braille free; newsstand price: $2.25. Reader's Digest Association, Inc., Pleasantville, NY 10570. TEL 914-238-1000. FAX 810-525-3449. (Subscr. for Braille, cassette, & disk editions to: American Printing House for the Blind, Inc., 1839 Frankfort Ave., Box 6389, Louisville, KY 40206-0085; Large Type ed.: Reader's Digest, Large Type Dept., Box 241, Mt. Morris IL 61054. TEL 502-895-2405) Ed. Kenneth Y. Tomlinson. adv.; illus.; index, cum.index: 1922-1981. circ. 16,250,000. (also avail. in Braille; audio cassette; microform from UMI; diskette format; large print edition in 22 pt.) **Indexed:** Abr.R.G., Acad.Ind., Chic.Per.Ind., CINAHL, Hlth.Ind., HRIS, Mag.Ind., PMR, PSI, R.G., TOM. **Document type:** consumer publication. —UnCover; SWETS; UMI.
Description: Condensed versions of articles reprinted from a variety of publications, emphasizing human interest and inspirational topics.

051 US ISSN 0275-4770
REAL TIMES. 1974. w. $10. Michael Redman, Ed. & Pub., Box 1686, Bloomington, IN 47402. TEL 812-332-3498. adv.; bk.rev.; illus. circ. 13,000. (also avail. in microform from UMI)
●Also available online.
Supersedes: Primo; Which was formerly (until 1978): Primo Times.

051 US
RENAISSANCE (SALEM).* 1988. m. 204 Lafayette St., Salem, MA 01970-4721. TEL 617-744-9799. Ed. Robert Manning. circ. 200,000.
Description: Aimed at affluent adults 50 years and older, covering fitness, travel and the arts.

976.9 US ISSN 0034-4451
RENFRO VALLEY BUGLE. 1943. m. $9. Renfro Valley Entertainment Center, Inc., 101 Main St., Renfro Valley, KY 40473. TEL 606-256-2638. FAX 606-256-2679. Ed. Kathy McCracken. adv.; illus. circ. 4,000. (tabloid format) **Document type:** newspaper.
Description: Covers news and items of local interest, with listings of upcoming events, and articles on past and present country music entertainers.

051 US ISSN 0034-5075
REPUBLICAN JOURNAL.* 1829. w. $18 to residents in-county; to residents in-state $26. Courier Publishing, Box 249, Rockland, ME 04841-0249. TEL 207-338-3333. FAX 207-338-5498. Ed. Polly Saltonstall. adv.; bk.rev.; mkt. circ. 7,820. **Document type:** newspaper.

051 US
THE REVIEW: EWING TOWNSHIP EDITION;* serving Ewing township and the entire Hopewell valley. vol.2, no.12, 1989. m. (Ewing Review, Inc.) Brian McCarthy, Ed.& Pub., 45 Harbourton Mount Airy Rd., Lambertville, NJ 08530-2902. TEL 609-737-9224.
Description: General interest publication providing news and information for the local residents.

051 US
RHODE ISLAND MONTHLY.* 1988. m. $12.95. Dan Kaplan, Ed. & Pub., 18 Imperial Place, Providence, RI 02903-4628. TEL 401-421-2552. circ. 15,000.
Description: Covers people, places and events of residents of the state; includes a calendar of events and a restaurant guide.

051 US
RHODE ISLAND REVIEW.* 1980. m. $15. Rhode Island Review, 48 Campbell Ave., East Providence, RI 02914. TEL 401-434-0489. Ed. Naomi Parker. bk.rev.; film rev.; play rev.; illus. circ. 10,000.

051 US
RICHMOND.* 1978. m. $10 (foreign $12). Target Communications, Inc., 2500 E. Parham Rd., Ste. 200, Richmond, VA 23228-2921. TEL 804-261-0034. FAX 804-261-1047. Ed. Frances Helms. adv. circ. 25,000. **Document type:** consumer publication.
Formerly (until 1993): Richmond Surroundings (ISSN 1064-1785)
Description: Represents Richmond, Henrico, Hanover, and Chesterfield counties. Focuses on people, life-styles, business, arts and entertainment, health, and politics.

051 US
RIO GRANDE SUN. 1956. w. $15. Sun Company, Inc. (Espanola), Box 790, Espanola, NM 87532. TEL 505-753-2126. Ed. Robert Trapp. adv.; bk.rev.; circ. 10,996 (paid).

051 US
ROANOKER. 1974. m. $16.95. Leisure Publishing Co. (Roanoke), Box 21535, 3424 Brambleton Ave., S.W., Roanoke, VA 24018. TEL 703-989-6138. FAX 703-989-7603. Ed. Kurt Rheinheimer. adv.; bk.rev.; illus. circ. 15,000. **Document type:** consumer publication.

051 US ISSN 0279-1447
ROBB REPORT; the magazine for the affluent lifestyle. 1976. m. $65. Robb Report, Inc., One Acton Pl., Acton, MA 01720. TEL 508-263-7749. FAX 508-263-0722. Ed. Bob Feeman; Pub. Tracy P. Rolon. adv. contact: Rick Sedler. bk.rev. circ. 48,536. (back issues avail.) **Document type:** consumer publication.
Description: Covers automobiles, lifestyles, collectibles, travel, boating, technology, recreation, investments and personality profiles.

051 US
ROCKFORD MAGAZINE. 1986. m. $17.95. Northwestern Publishing Inc. (Rockford), 331 E. State St., Rockford, IL 61104. TEL 815-961-2400. Ed. Eileen S. Townsend. adv. circ. 20,000.

051 US
ROCKLAND - BERGLAND SPOTLIGHT. m. Meadow Publications, Inc., 126 Library Lane, Mamaroneck, NY 10543-3608. TEL 914-381-4740. Ed. Susan Meadow. circ. 75,000. **Document type:** consumer publication.

051 US ISSN 0048-878X
RURAL ARKANSAS. 1946. m. $2.28. Arkansas Electric Cooperatives, Box 510, Little Rock, AR 72203. TEL 501-562-0220. Ed. Ouida H. Cox. circ. 200,000.
Description: Covers news and items of interest to residents of rural Arkansas.

051 621.393 US ISSN 1054-4801
RURAL LIVING (GLEN ALLEN). 1944. m. $4.79. Virginia, Maryland and Delaware Association of Electric Cooperatives, 4201 Dominion Blvd., Ste. 101, Glen Allen, VA 23060. TEL 804-346-3344. FAX 804-346-3448. Ed. Richard G. Johnstone, Jr. adv. circ. 250,029. **Document type:** trade publication.
Description: For members of rural electric cooperatives in Virginia and Maryland. Covers energy efficiency as well as profiles of interesting people and places in the rural areas of these states.

621.3 630 US
RURAL MONTANA. 1952. m. $6. Montana Electric Cooperatives Association, Box 1641, 501 Bay Dr., Great Falls, MT 59403. TEL 406-761-8333. FAX 406-761-8339. Ed. Mack McConnell. adv.; B&W page $868.20, color page $1068.20. bk.rev. circ. 76,000. **Document type:** consumer publication.
Formerly: Montana Rural Electric News (ISSN 0047-7974)

051 US
RURAL NETWORK ADVOCATE. 1980. m. $12. Rural Network, Inc., 6236 Borden Rd., Boscobel, WI 53805. TEL 608-375-4659. Ed. Lois Rae Fields. circ. 400. **Document type:** newsletter.
Formerly: R N Advocate.
Description: Examines issues presented by country-oriented members of the network.

051 US
RURALITE. 1954. m. $6. Ruralite Services, Inc., Box 558, Forest Grove, OR 97116. TEL 503-357-2105. FAX 503-357-8615. (Co-sponsors: Consumer-owned rural electric utilities in Oregon, Washington, Alaska, Idaho, Nevada, Wyoming, and Northern California) Ed. Curtis Condon. adv.; bk.rev. circ. 260,000. **Document type:** consumer publication.
Formerly: Northwest Ruralite (ISSN 0546-6210)

052 US ISSN 1060-2526
S F WEEKLY. 1981. w. $80. S F Weekly, 425 Brannan St., San Francisco, CA 94107. TEL 415-541-0700. FAX 415-777-1839. Ed. Andrew O'Hehir. bk.rev.; film rev.; play rev. circ. 80,000. (tabloid format; also avail. in microform from UMI; back issues avail)
Formerly: Calendar Magazine.
Description: Discusses social, political, economic and cultural issues of importance to the community.

051 US
▼**S L E NEWSWORLD.** (Second Language English) 1993. 6/yr. $9. 3010 Wilshire Blvd., Ste. 231, Los Angeles, CA 90010. **Document type:** consumer publication.
Description: Designed to help readers get comfortable with English.

051 US ISSN 1059-9665
S T L. Key Title: S T L (St. Louis, Mo.). Variant title: Art of Living in St. Louis. 1977. m. $40 membership. St. Louis Regional Educational and Public Television Commission (KETC), 6996 Millbrook Blvd., St. Louis, MO 63130. TEL 314-726-7685. FAX 314-726-0677. Ed. Gayle R. McIntosh. adv. contact: Richard Grater. circ. 51,220. **Document type:** consumer publication.
Formerly (until 1991): St. Louis Nine (ISSN 8750-877X)
Description: Features interviews and articles about life in St. Louis, focusing on the arts, local history and education, plus a public television program schedule.

810 US ISSN 0191-8796
F869.S12
SACRAMENTO MAGAZINE.* 1975. m. $24.95. Sacramento Magazine, Inc. (Subsidiary of: Micromedia Affiliates), 4471 "D" St., Sacramento, CA 95819-2840. TEL 916-446-7548. FAX 916-446-1238. Ed. Jan Haag. adv.; bk.rev. circ. 25,143.

051 US ISSN 0272-1279
ST. LOUIS. 1969. m. $19. St. Louis Magazine, Inc., Box 88908, St. Louis, MO 63188-1908. Ed. Steve Friedman. adv.; illus. circ. 28,000. (also avail. in microform from UMI; reprint service avail. from UMI)
Indexed: Access (1975-).
Formerly: St. Louisan.

051 US
SALT LAKE CITY. 1989. bi-m. $15. Utah Partners Publishing, 1270 W. 2320 South, Ste. A, Salt Lake City, UT 84119. TEL 801-975-1927. FAX 801-975-1982. Ed. Ellen Flagg. adv. circ. 17,500.
Description: Covers people, issues and cultural activities.

051 US
SALUTE; magazine for military wives. 1985. 10/yr. free to qualified personnel. Military Forces Features, Inc., 169 Lexington Ave., New York, NY 10157-0014. TEL 212-532-0660. FAX 212-779-3080. Ed. Don Hirst. adv.; bk.rev.; film rev.; software rev.; circ. 250,482 (controlled). (reprint service avail)
Description: Includes sports, music, travel, games, humor, auto care and dating for young singles in the military.

051 US
SAN ANTONIO FOCUS. m. Alamo Public Telecommunications Council, Box 9, San Antonio, TX 78291-0009. TEL 512-270-9000. Ed. Cinthya Pillot-Olive. circ. 22,000.

917.6 US ISSN 0036-3960
SAN ANTONIO MONTHLY.* 1967. m. $17 (foreign $29). Business Times Publishing Co., Inc., 9219 Katy Freeway, Ste. 273, Houston, TX 77024-1514. TEL 512-565-8801. FAX 512-656-3945. Ed. Kim Elliott. adv.; illus. circ. 15,000. (back issues avail.)
Description: Information on issues and trends of interest to Greater San Antonio.

979.4 US ISSN 0036-4045
SAN DIEGO. 1948. m. $16. San Diego Magazine Publishing Co., Box 85409, San Diego, CA 92186-5409. TEL 619-225-8953. FAX 619-222-0773. Ed. Edwin F. Self. adv.; bk.rev.; play rev.; charts; illus.; stat.; circ. 52,361 (paid). (also avail. in microform from UMI; reprint service avail. from UMI) **Indexed:** Access (1975-), Cal.Per.Ind. (1984-). **Document type:** consumer publication.
—UMI.
Description: Provides articles, criticism, photography and ideas in the fields of civic planning, art, politics, film, theater, sports, architecture and fashion in southern California and Mexico.

GENERAL INTEREST PERIODICALS — UNITED STATES

051 US
SAN DIEGO VOICE & VIEWPOINT. 1961. w. $27.06. Warren Communications, Inc., 1729 N. Euclid Ave., San Diego, CA 92105. TEL 619-266-2233. FAX 619-266-0533. Ed. John E. Warren. adv. contact: Gerri Warren. bk.rev. circ. 18,000.
Former titles: New Voice and Viewpoint; Voice News and Viewpoint.

051 US
SAN FRANCISCO BAY AREA'S 680 MAGAZINE. 1990. m. $2.50 per no. Northeast Consolidated, Box 2340, Walnut Creek, CA 94595. TEL 510-935-7673. Matthew Van Fossen. adv.: B&W page $1150, color page $2000; trim 8 1/8 x 10 7/8. circ. 18,000. **Document type:** consumer publication.
Description: Covers politics, investigative journalism, music, food, drink, sports, fitness, fashion, business, and art.

051 US ISSN 0036-4096
SAN FRANCISCO BAY GUARDIAN. (Incl. occasional Books and Writers section) 1966. w. $32. Bay Guardian Co., 520 Hampshire St., San Francisco, CA 94110. TEL 415-824-7660. Ed. Bruce B. Brugmann. adv.; bk.rev.; film rev.; play rev.; charts; illus. circ. 80,000. (tabloid format; also avail. in microfilm from UMI; reprint service avail. from UMI) **Indexed:** New Per.Ind. —UMI.

917.904 US ISSN 0274-5933
SAN FRANCISCO FOCUS; the city magazine for the San Francisco Bay Area. 1953. m. $24. K Q E D, Inc., 2601 Mariposa St., San Francisco, CA 94110. TEL 415-553-2800. Ed. Mark K. Powelson. adv.; bk.rev.; film rev.; play rev. (back issues avail.)
Description: Features on travel, food and entertainment, fashion, entrepreneurship, health, and shopping in the city, with interviews, essays, and fiction of interest to a cosmopolitan audience.

051 US
SAN GABRIEL VALLEY MAGAZINE. 1976. q. $25. Miller Books, 2908 W. Valley Blvd., Alhambra, CA 91803. TEL 818-284-7607. Ed. Joseph Miller. circ. 3,500,000.

071 US
SAN JOSE METRO. 1985. w. $76. Metro Publishing, Ltd., 550 S. First St., San Jose, CA 95113. TEL 408-298-8000. FAX 408-298-0602. Ed. Dan Pulcrano. adv. circ. 80,000. **Document type:** newspaper.
Description: Covers local news and things to do in San Jose and in the Santa Clara Valley area.

051 US ISSN 1046-3267
SANDLAPPER; the magazine of South Carolina. 1968. 4/yr. $14.95. R P W Publishing Corp., Box 1108, Lexington, SC 29071. TEL 803-359-9954. FAX 803-957-8226. Ed. Robert P. Wilkins. adv.; bk.rev.; circ. 5,000 (controlled). **Document type:** consumer publication.
Description: Covers entertainment, history, business, people, places and sports in the state of South Carolina.

051 US ISSN 0744-5199
SANTA BARBARA MAGAZINE. 1975. q. $12. Santa Barbara Magazine, Inc., 226 E. Cannon Perdido, Ste. H, Santa Barbara, CA 93101. TEL 805-965-5999. FAX 805-965-7627. Ed. Daniel Denton. adv.; bk.rev. circ. 12,000. (back issues avail.) **Indexed:** Cal.Per.Ind. (1978-).
Description: Reports on special home and lifestyles, local history, celebrity residents, the natural environment, world travel and cultural events.

051 US ISSN 1046-2708
THE SANTA FEAN MAGAZINE. 1972. m. (11/yr.). $19.35 in U.S.; Canada $45 (effective 1993). Santa Fean Magazine & Publishing Co., 1440 A St. Frances Dr., Santa Fe, NM 87501. TEL 505-983-8914. FAX 505-983-8013. Eds. Betty Bauer, Marian E. Love. adv. contact: Victor Funtanilla. illus. circ. 15,000. **Indexed:** Access (1975-). **Document type:** consumer publication.
Description: Focuses on the homes, history, personalities, arts and crafts, and events of the city. Emphasizes the arts including Native American arts and Santa Fe's internationally acclaimed opera.

051 US ISSN 0192-4265
SARASOTA MAGAZINE. 1979. m. $19.95. Clubhouse Publishing, Inc., 601 S. Ospey Ave., Sarasota, FL 34236. TEL 813-366-8225. FAX 813-365-7272. adv. circ. 13,000. **Document type:** consumer publication.
●Also available online. Vendor(s): Mead Data Central, Inc..
Description: Contains articles on local celebrities, events and issues. Features fashion, luxury homes and interior design, society, restaurants and travel.

051 US ISSN 0048-9239
AP2 CODEN: SAEPAR
SATURDAY EVENING POST. 1971. 6/yr. $13.97. (Saturday Evening Post Society) Benjamin Franklin Literary & Medical Society, Box 567, 1100 Waterway Blvd., Indianapolis, IN 46202. TEL 317-636-8881. Ed. Dr. Cory ServVaas. adv.; illus. circ. 500,000. (also avail. in microform (ISSN 0364-9733) from UMI; reprint service avail. from UMI) **Indexed:** Abr.R.G., Acad.Ind., Biog.Ind., Bk.Rev.Ind. (1974-), Child.Bk.Rev.Ind. (1974-), CINAHL, GeoRef., Hlth.Ind., Jun.High.Mag.Abstr., Mag.Ind., PMR, R.G., TOM.
●Also available online. Vendor(s): DIALOG Information Services, Inc.
—Faxon; UnCover; UMI.

051 US
SCENE (CLEVELAND). 1970. w. Northeast Scene, Inc., 1375 Euclid Ave., Ste. 312, Cleveland, OH 44115. TEL 216-241-7550. FAX 216-241-6275. adv.: B&W page $1950, color page $2225; trim 22 3/4 x 17 1/2. circ. 48,169 (controlled). **Document type:** consumer publication.

051 US ISSN 0741-0816
SCENTOURI NEWS. 1989. a. $4. Scentourri, c/o Prosperity & Profits Unlimited, Box 416, Denver, CO 80201-0416. TEL 303-575-5676. Ed. A. Doyle. circ. 3,000. (looseleaf format) **Document type:** newsletter.
Description: Contains information and tips about potpourri and fragrances.

051 US
SCOTTSDALE SCENE MAGAZINE. bi-m. $19. Lila Harnett, Pub., 4041 N. Central Ave., Ste. A100, Phoenix, AZ 85012-3331. TEL 602-277-7838. FAX 602-27-78572. Ed. Judy Harper. adv. contact: Julie Osten. circ. 30,000. **Document type:** consumer publication.

051 US
▼**SEASONS.** 1992. bi-m. Heritage Communications Corporation, 14 Hall Ave., Nyack, NY 10960. TEL 914-353-2155. FAX 914-353-0222. adv.: B&W page $13000, color page $17335; trim 8 3/8 x 10 7/8. circ. 400,000.
Description: Emphasizes home design and regional travel.

051 US
SEATTLE. 1989. 8/yr. $14.95. Adams Publishing of the Pacific Northwest, 701 Dexter Ave. N., Ste. 101, Seattle, WA 98109. TEL 206-284-1750. FAX 206-284-2550. Ed. Giselle Smith; Pub. Peggy Bilous. adv. contact: Lora Holzer. circ. 33,750 (controlled). (back issues avail.) **Document type:** consumer publication.
Former titles: Greater Seattle; (until Mar. 1992): Seattle Home and Garden.
Description: Covers contemporary life and entertaining in the greater Seattle metropolitan area. Focuses on urban issues, personalities, the arts, night life, fashion, gardening, food and wine.

051 US
SEATTLE WEEKLY. 1976. w. $19.95. Sasquatch Publishing Company, Inc., 1008 Western Ave., Ste. 300, Seattle, WA 98104. TEL 206-623-0500. FAX 206-447-4338. Ed. Knute Berger. adv.; bk.rev.; film rev.; play rev. circ. 35,961. (tabloid format; back issues avail.) **Indexed:** New Per.Ind. **Document type:** trade publication.
Former titles: Weekly: Seattle's Newsmagazine (ISSN 0279-6406); Weekly of Metropolitan Seattle.
Description: Covers current affairs, the arts, entertainment and life in Seattle.

051 US
SENIOR CAPE COD FORUM. 1990. m. $10.95. 72 Winter St., Hyannis, MA 02401. TEL 508-778-5042. FAX 508-778-5063. Ed. Marion Vuilleumier. adv. circ. 60,000. (back issues avail.) **Document type:** newspaper.

051 US
SENIOR TIMES.* 1981. m. $10. Thompson Publications, Inc., 1282 Timberlane Rd., Tallahassee, FL 32312-1765. TEL 408-289-9604. Ed. Joan Bose. adv. circ. 50,310.

057.7773 US
SENTINEL (CHICAGO). w. Sentinel Publishing Co., 150 N. Michigan, Ste. 3103, Chicago, IL 60604. TEL 312-663-1101. Ed. Jack I. Fishbein. bk.rev. circ. 45,500. **Document type:** newspaper.

051 US ISSN 1071-5185
SHEPHERD EXPRESS; Milwaukee's weekly alternative newspaper. 1982. w. $26. Alternative Publications, Inc., 1123 N. Water St., Milwaukee, WI 53202-3107. TEL 414-276-2222. FAX 1414-276-3312. Ed. Doug Hissom. adv. contact: Dane Claussen. bk.rev. circ. 50,000. (tabloid format; back issues avail.) **Document type:** newspaper.
Formerly: Milwaukee Shepherd.
Description: Forum for writers and artists that offers news, entertainment and humor and educates reading public on political and arts issues.

071.4 US
THE SHOPPER'S FRIEND; the paper with a personal touch. ne. free. 5 Bowling Green Pkwy., Ste. 5, Lakeside Shopping Center, Lake Hopatcong, NJ 07849. TEL 201-663-0441. FAX 201-663-3607. Ed. Doris Roberts. adv. cols./p.: 4; pp./issue: 16. **Document type:** newspaper.
Description: Covers leisure-time and educational opportunities in the Morris County, NJ, area.

051 US ISSN 0745-3353
SILVER CIRCLE. 1971. q. $6. Home Savings of America, 1001 Commerce Dr., Irwindale, CA 91706. Ed. Jay A. Binkly. adv.: B&W page $4954, color page $5875; trim 8 1/2 X 11. circ. 600,000 (controlled). **Document type:** consumer publication.
Description: Includes general and consumer interest on personal finance, health, travel, food, home, gardening, and hobbies.

051 US ISSN 0038-3309
SOUTH DAKOTA HIGH LINER. 1948. m. $11. South Dakota Rural Electric Association, 222 W. Pleasant Dr., Pierre, SD 57501. TEL 605-224-8823. FAX 605-224-4430. Ed. Brian J. Boyer. adv.; bk.rev. circ. 80,000. **Document type:** consumer publication.

051 917.5 US ISSN 0895-5352
F319.M6
SOUTH FLORIDA. 1921. m. $24.95 (effective 1993). Florida Media Affiliates, Inc. (Subsidiary of: Micromedia Affiliates), Box 019068, Miami, FL 33101-9068. TEL 305-445-4500. FAX 305-445-4600. (Subscr. to: Box 2051, Marion, OH 44306) Ed. Glenn Albin. adv.; bk.rev.; film rev. **Indexed:** Access (1975-).
Former titles (until 1983): Miami, the Magazine of South Florida; Miami Pictorial.
Description: Covers area arts, politics, entertainment, fashion, travel, dining and sports.

051 US ISSN 0164-1433
SOUTH JERSEY.* 1979. m. $8. South Jersey Publishing Co., 24 Westwood Terr., Millville, NJ 08332. Ed. Shirley Bailey. adv. circ. 40,000.

071.4747 US ISSN 0038-352X
SOUTH SHORE RECORD. 1953. w. $20. (Hewlett-Woodmere Public Library) South Shore Publishers, Inc., 990 Railroad Ave., Woodmere, NY 11598-0630. TEL 516-374-9200. FAX 516-374-9209. Ed. Florence B. Schwartzberg. adv. contact: Eileen Walsh. bk.rev.; film rev.; play rev.; illus. circ. 21,000. (tabloid format; also avail. in microfilm) **Document type:** newspaper.

071.773 US
SOUTH SUBURBAN STANDARD. 1979. w. $30. Standard Newspapers, 615 W. Halsted St., Chicago Heights, IL 60411. TEL 708-755-5021. FAX 708-755-5020. Ed. Lorenzo E. Martin. illus.; tr.lit. circ. 25,000. (tabloid format) **Document type:** newspaper.

051 US
SOUTHEAST GEORGIAN. 1894. w. $12.50 in Camden Co.; Georgia $17.50; elsewhere in the U.S. $25. (Southeast Georgian, Inc.) Mark Jicha, Ed. & Pub., Box 1429, Kingsland, GA 31548. TEL 912-729-5231. FAX 912-729-1589. adv. circ. 5,100. (also avail. in microform)

GENERAL INTEREST PERIODICALS — UNITED STATES

051   US
SOUTHERN CALIFORNIA MAGAZINE. 1991. bi-m. $12 (effective Jan. 1992). (I E M G Inc.) Sunwest Publishing, 3769 Tibbetts Ave., Ste. A, Riverside, CA 92506. TEL 909-682-3026. FAX 909-682-0246. Ed. Donald D. Lorenzi. adv. contact: Brenda Lorenzi. circ. 15,000. **Document type:** consumer publication.
  Description: Covers Los Angeles, Orange County and the rest of southern California from San Diego to Santa Barbara

051   US   ISSN 0038-4305
F206
SOUTHERN LIVING. 1965. m. $24 in the Southern U.S. including Washington D.C.; outside the Southern U.S. $26 (effective Jan. 1992). Southern Progress Corp. (Subsidiary of: Time, Inc. Magazine Co.), c/o H. Johnson, V.P. Circulation, 2100 Lakeshore Dr., Birmingham, AL 35209. TEL 205-877-6000. (Subscr. to: Box 830119, Birmingham, AL 35201) Ed. John Alex Floyd, Jr. adv.; illus. circ. 2,295,241. (also avail. in microfiche; microfilm; magnetic tape from UMI; reprint service avail. from UMI) **Indexed:** Bk.Rev.Ind. (1978-), Child.Bk.Rev.Ind. (1978-), Gard.Lit. (1992-), Mag.Ind., PMR, R.G.
●Also available online.
—Faxon; UnCover; UMI.

051 320   US   ISSN 0739-1714
F216.2
SOUTHERN PARTISAN. 1979. q. $18 (foreign $26). Southern Partisan Corporation, Box 11708, Columbia, SC 29211. TEL 803-254-3660. FAX 803-256-9220. (Alt addr.: 1703 Gervais St., Columbia, SC 29201.) Ed. Richard M. Quinn. adv.; bk.rev. circ. 10,000. **Document type:** consumer publication.
  Description: Features Southern history, literature and politics.

979.2   US   ISSN 0049-1659
SOUTHERN UTAH NEWS. 1930. w. $22. Southern Utah Publishing Co., Ed. Dixie Brunner, 26 N. Main, Kanab, UT 84741. TEL 801-644-2900. FAX 801-644-2926. adv.; bk.rev. circ. 1,900. (reprint service avail. from UMI)

051   US   ISSN 0038-4704
SOUTHWEST NEWS-HERALD. 1924. w. $15. Vondrak Publishing Co., 6225 S. Kedzie Ave., Chicago, IL 60629. TEL 312-476-4800. Ed. Timothy C. Hadac. adv.; bk.rev. circ. 27,604.

071   US   ISSN 0896-3363
SPECTATOR (RALEIGH); at home. 1978. w. $24. Spectator Publications, Inc., 1318 Dale St., Box 12887, Raleigh, NC 27605. TEL 919-828-7393. FAX 919-831-9217. adv.; bk.rev.; film rev.; play rev.; illus. circ. 60,000. (tabloid format) **Document type:** newspaper.
  Description: Represents an overview of The Triangle (Raleigh - Durham - Chapel Hill) lifestyle; features a calendar of events, restaurant guide, interviews, antique column, and a special pull-out section.

051   US   ISSN 0892-9459
SPECTRUM MAGAZINE (BLOOMSBURG). 1987. s-a. $5. Bloomsburg University, Mass Communication Department, Bloomsburg, PA 17815. TEL 717-389-4565. FAX 717-389-3700. Ed. Walter M. Brasch. adv. circ. 2,500.
  Description: General interest magazine for northeastern Pennsylvania.

051   US   ISSN 0745-4937
SPOTLIGHT (MAMARONECK); New York, New Jersey, Connecticut. m. $19.97. Meadow Publications, Inc., 126 Library Ln., Mamaroneck, NY 10543. TEL 914-381-4740. Ed. Susan Meadow. adv. contact: Eric Meadow.

051   US
SPRINGFIELD MAGAZINE (SPRINGFIELD, ILLINOIS). 1989. m. $19.95. J. Williams Publishing, Inc., Box 5163, Springfield, IL 62705-5163. TEL 217-585-0017. FAX 217-585-1778. Ed. Charles D. Jones; Pub. Lea J. Hudson. adv.; bk.rev. circ. 20,000. **Document type:** consumer publication.
  Description: Highlights monthly events in the Springfield area, as well as features on the people, history and local businesses of the community. For visitors, tourists and newcomers and local residents.

051   US   ISSN 0195-0894
SPRINGFIELD! MAGAZINE (SPRINGFIELD, MASSACHUSETTS). 1979. m. $16.99. Springfield Communications, Inc., 520 S. Union, Springfield, MO 65802. TEL 417-882-3966. Ed. Robert Glazier. adv.: B&W page $800; color page $1000. bk.rev. circ. 10,000. (back issues avail.) **Document type:** consumer publication.

051   US
THE SQUIRE. 1959. w. $20 (effective Jan. 1990). Squire Publishers, Inc., 3840 W. 75th St., Prairie Village, KS 66208. TEL 913-384-6397. Ed. Tom Leathers. adv.; bk.rev.; film rev.; play rev. circ. 28,500. (tabloid format; back issues avail.)
  Description: Presents general stories, commentary, news, and entertainment.

051   US   ISSN 0160-6158
STANDARD (NEW YORK). 1978. q. $1.75 per no. Banner Communications Inc., 160 Bleecker St., Ste. 10CW, New York, NY 10012. circ. 200,000.

051   US   ISSN 1052-875X
STAR (LANTANA). 1974. w. $37.44 (foreign $58.44). Enquirer - Star Group, Inc., Star Division, 600 S. East Coast Ave., Lantana, FL 33462. TEL 407-586-1111. FAX 407-582-0126. (Subscr. to: Box 10940, Des Moines, IA 50340-0940. TEL 800-888-6153) Ed. Richard Kaplan. adv.; bk.rev.; illus. circ. 3,075,526. (tabloid format) **Indexed:** Rehabil.Lit. **Document type:** newspaper.
  Formerly: National Star.
  Description: Features unusual or sensational news items, gossip about celebrities, and a weekly horoscope.

051   US
STAR-TELEGRAM CHASER; the news you want when you want it. 1983. s-w. free to employees. Fort Worth Star-Telegram, Box 1870, Fort Worth, TX 76101. TEL 817-390-7748. Ed. Karla Uecker. circ. 1,500. **Document type:** newsletter.

975.7   US   ISSN 0038-9994
F251
THE STATE (RALEIGH); down home in North Carolina. 1933. m. $18. Shaw Publishing Inc., 128 S. Tryon St., Ste. 2200, Charlotte, NC 28202. TEL 704-375-7404. Ed. Angela Terez. adv.; bk.rev.; illus.; index, cum.index: 1933-1991. circ. 21,000. (back issues avail.)
  Description: Exclusively devoted to the people, places, history and folklore of North Carolina.

051   US
STRAIGHT TALK (JUPITER); truth beyond the media coverage - facts, without fear or favor. 1970. w. $67 (foreign $114). American Way Features, 128 Lighthouse Dr., Jupiter, FL 33469. TEL 407-746-7815. (Subscr. to: 1496 Oakville Lane, Sevierville, TN 37862) Ed. Tom Anderson. bk.rev.; circ. 1,900 (paid). (back issues avail.) **Document type:** newsletter.
  Description: Analysis of government, economics, politics and world events: what it all means to you, and what you can do about it.

051   US   ISSN 1064-1629
STRATTON MAGAZINE. 1964. q. $8. Stratton Corporation, Stratton Mountain, VT 05155. TEL 802-867-0242. Ed. Marsha Norman. adv.; Lee A./Romano. circ. 20,000. (back issues avail.) **Document type:** consumer publication.
  Formerly: Stratton-Bromley Magazine.

071.747   US
SUBURBAN NEWS - BROCKPORT HOLLY EDITION. w. $35. Westside News Inc., 1835 N. Union St., Box 106, Spencerport, NY 14559-0106. TEL 716-352-3411. FAX 716-352-4811. Ed. Evelyn Dow; Pub. Keith Ryan. adv.; illus. circ. 7,355. (tabloid format) **Document type:** newspaper.

051   US
SUCCESSFUL ATTITUDES; sophisticated living in South Texas. 1982. q. $15. Successful Attitudes, Inc., 4200-A N. Bicentennial, McAllen, TX 78504. TEL 512-682-0721. Ed. Jodi Hamer. adv. circ. 4,651.
  Description: Contains items of local interest.

051   US
SUN (BOCA RATON). w. $29.75. Globe Communications Corp. (Boca Raton), 5401 N.W. Broken Sound Blvd., Boca Raton, FL 33487. TEL 407-997-7733.

051   US   ISSN 1051-2365
SUN VALLEY MAGAZINE. 1986. 2/yr. (winter and summer). $7. Wood River Publishing, Inc., 500 S. Main St., Box 1469, Ketchum, ID 83340. TEL 208-726-1246. FAX 208-726-1268. Ed. Celeste H. Earls. adv. circ. 12,500. **Document type:** consumer publication.
  Formerly: Valley Magazine (Hailey).
  Description: Contains profiles of people, places, events, and recreational activities in and around the Wood River Valley.

051   US
SUNCOAST. bi-m. 8220 S.W. 22nd St., N. Lauderdale, FL 33068. Ed. Steve Berner. bk.rev.

051   US   ISSN 0039-5404
F851
SUNSET; the magazine of Western living. (Special issues: Seven regional editions each month.) 1898. m. $21 (Canada $33; Mexico $31; elsewhere $41). Sunset Publishing Corp., 80 Willow Rd., Menlo Park, CA 94025-3691. TEL 415-321-3600. FAX 415-321-0551. (Subscr. to: Sunset Publishing, Box 56656, Boulder, CO 80322-6656) Ed. William Marken. adv.; illus.; circ. 1,428,725 (paid). (also avail. in microform from UMI; reprint service avail. from UMI) **Indexed:** Cal.Per.Ind. (1987-), Consum.Ind., Gard.Lit. (1992-), Ind.How To Do It (1977-), Mag.Ind., MELSA, PMR, R.G. **Document type:** consumer publication.
●Also available online. Vendor(s): DIALOG Information Services, Inc..
—Faxon; UnCover; UMI.
  Description: Features articles about travel, food, entertainment, homes, gardening and the environment in the thirteen western U.S. states.

071   US
SURRY SCENE. 1880. w. free. Box 608, Mt. Airy, NC 27030. TEL 919-786-4141. FAX 919-789-2816. Ed. Peter Williams. adv. contact: Bernard Flippin. circ. 25,000. (tabloid format; also avail. in microfiche) **Document type:** newspaper.
  Formerly: Times - Foothills Entertainment.
  Description: Covers civic groups, churches, family reunions and outings. Includes photos of activities in the area.

071   US
SYRACUSE NEW TIMES. 1969. w. $24.95 free. A. Zimmer Ltd., 1415 W. Genesee St., Syracuse, NY 13204. TEL 315-422-7011. FAX 315-422-1721. Ed. Mike Greenstein. adv.; bk.rev.; circ. 45,000 (controlled). (tabloid format; also avail. in microfilm) **Document type:** newspaper.
  Description: News and arts magazine for central New York State.

051   US
TALLAHASSEE MAGAZINE. 1979. bi-m. $14.98. Rowland Publishing, Box 1837, Tallahassee, FL 32302. TEL 904-878-0554. FAX 904-656-4065. Ed. A. David Fiore. adv.; bk.rev. circ. 19,000. **Document type:** consumer publication.

051   US   ISSN 1070-3845
TAMPA BAY MAGAZINE. 1986. bi-m. $12. Tampa Bay Publications, 2531 Landmark Dr., Ste. 101, Clearwater, FL 34621. TEL 813-791-4800. FAX 813-796-0527. Ed. Aaron R. Fodiman. adv.; bk.rev. circ. 35,000. **Document type:** consumer publication.
  Formerly: Tampa Bay.
  Description: Covers the lifestyle of the Greater Tampa Bay area.

051   US
TAMPA BAY METRO MAGAZINE.* 1983. m. $23.40. Florida City Magazines, Inc., 405 Reo St., Ste. 210, Tampa, FL 33609-1010. Ed. Fred Thomas. adv. circ. 25,000. (reprint service avail.)
  Formerly (until 1985): Tampa Bay Monthly.

051   US
TANGLEWOOD. m. Creneau Media Group, Box 3388, Houston, TX 77253. TEL 713-880-4611. FAX 713-880-4644. Ed. Cristina Adams. circ. 10,000.

051   US
TELLING THE STORY. 1963. m. $7. Morris Publishing Groups, Box 1563, Cayce, SC 29033. TEL 803-256-1611. Ed. Roy Allen Morris. adv.; bk.rev. (back issues avail.) **Document type:** newsletter.

GENERAL INTEREST PERIODICALS — UNITED STATES   2789

051   US
TENNESSEE MAGAZINE. 1958. m. $6 to non-members. Tennessee Electric Cooperative Association, 710 Spence Ln., Box 100912, Nashville, TN 37217. TEL 615-367-9284. Ed. Jerry L. Kirk. adv.; tr.lit. circ. 300,000.

051   US
TENNESSEE VALLEY'S HOMETOWN PRESS. 1986. 6/yr. $14.95. Hometown Press, Inc., 2007 Gallatin St., Huntsville, AL 35801. TEL 205-539-3320. FAX 205-539-3340. Ed. Mary Hindman. adv. contact: Martha Case. circ. 10,000. **Document type:** consumer publication.
  Description: Provides a positive, upbeat view of life in the new South; covers people, places, art, leisure, literature, ideas.

051   US   ISSN 0148-7736
F381
TEXAS MONTHLY. 1973. m. $18 in Texas; elsewhere $21. Texas Monthly, Inc., Box 1569, Austin, TX 78767. TEL 512-320-6900. Ed. Gregory Curtis. adv.; bk.rev.; film rev.; play rev.; illus. circ. 300,000. (also avail. in microform from UMI) **Indexed:** Access (1975-), Mag.Ind., New Per.Ind., PMR.
  —UMI.

051   US
THIS IS ALASKA.* 1968. q. $12.95. Alaska Technical Publishing Co., 8600 Hartzell Rd., Anchorage, AK 99507. TEL 907-349-7506. Ed. Frank Martone. adv. circ. 8,000.

071   US
THIS IS CHARLESTON. 1921. m. free. Community Press, Inc., Box 12110, Charleston, SC 29422. TEL 803-762-0004. FAX 803-849-0214. (Street addr.: 423 W. Coleman Blvd., Mt. Pleasant, SC 29464, TEL 803-849-1778) circ. 15,000. (tabloid format) **Document type:** newspaper.

051   US   ISSN 0040-781X
AP2   CODEN: TYMEA9
TIME; the weekly newsmagazine. 1923. w. $61.88. Time Inc. (Subsidiary of: Time Warner, Inc.), Time & Life Bldg., Rockefeller Center, 1271 Ave. of the Americas, New York, NY 10020-1393. TEL 212-522-1212. FAX 212-522-0003. (Subscr. to: Time, Box 60001, Tampa, FL 33660-0001. TEL 800-541-1000) Ed. James R. Gaines. adv.; bk.rev.; film rev.; music rev.; record rev.; illus.; index; circ. 4,335,092 (paid). (also avail. in microform from UMI) **Indexed:** Abr.R.G., Acad.Ind., Acid Rain Abstr., Acid Rain Ind., Bank.Lit.Ind., Biog.Ind., Biol.Dig., Bk.Rev.Dig., Bk.Rev.Ind. (1965-), Child.Bk.Rev.Ind. (1965-), CINAHL, Comput.Bus., Curr.Lit.Fam.Plan., Energy Info.Abstr., Film Lit.Ind. (1973-), Jun.High.Mag.Abstr., Key to Econ.Sci., Law Ofc.Info.Svc., Mag.Ind., Media Rev.Dig., Ocean.Abstr., Pers.Lit., PMR, Pollut.Abstr., PROMT, PSI, R.G., Robomat. (until 1992), So.Pac.Per.Ind., Tel.Abstr., Telegen (until 1992). **Document type:** consumer publication.
  ●Also available online. Vendor(s): Dow Jones News Retrieval, Mead Data Central, Inc., VU/TEXT Information Services, Inc..
  —BLDSC (8851.750000); Faxon; UnCover; SWETS; UMI.
  Description: Reviews the news of the week and provides in-depth analyses.

051   US
THE TIMES OF ACADIANA. w. $24. Steven May, 201 Jefferson St., Box 3528, Lafayette, LA 70501. TEL 318-237-3560. FAX 318-233-7484. Ed. Richard Baudouin, Jr. adv.; film rev. circ. 40,500. (tabloid format; back issues avail.)
  Description: Covers news, politics, business, lifestyle, arts, and entertainment.

051   US
TOLEDO METROPOLITAN. 1985. bi-m. $10. Lawrence Publications, Inc., 317 Tenth St., Toledo, OH 43624. TEL 414-244-3015. adv. circ. 27,106.
  Formerly: Metropolitan.
  Description: Highlights issues and topics in the areas of business, lifestyle, the arts, sports, entertainment and dining.

051   US
TOMORROW: MAMARONECK, HARRISON, RYE. 1983. m. $10. Marketing Tomorrow, Inc., Box 1137, New Rochelle, NY 10802-1137. TEL 914-606-4646. Ed. Glenda Palmer. bk.rev. circ. 18,000.

051   US
TOMORROW: NEW ROCHELLE, PELHAM, LARCHMONT. 1982. m. $10. Marketing Tomorrow, Inc., Box 1137, New Rochelle, NY 10802-1137. TEL 914-636-4646. Ed. Glenda Palmer. bk.rev. circ. 38,000.

051   CN
TORN SCROTUM. q. $2 per no. Box 1523, Bonaventure, Montreal, Que. H5A 1H6, Canada.

051   US   ISSN 0040-9952
AP2
TOWN AND COUNTRY. 1846. m. $24. Hearst Magazines, Town and Country, 1700 Broadway, New York, NY 10019. TEL 212-903-5000. FAX 212-765-8308. (Subscr. to: C.D.S., 1901 Bell Ave., Des Moines, IA 50315. TEL 800-289-8696) Ed. Pamela Fiori. adv.; bk.rev.; film rev.; play rev.; illus. circ. 475,000. (also avail. in microfiche from UMI; microfilm from KTO) **Indexed:** Access (1975-), Bk.Rev.Ind. (1967-), Hlth.Ind., Mag.Ind., PMR.
  —Faxon; UnCover.
  Incorporates (in Feb. 1992): Connoisseur (ISSN 0010-6275)

974.7   US   ISSN 0040-9979
TOWN & VILLAGE. 1947. w. $12. Hagedorn Communications Corp., One Madison Ave., 35th Fl., New York, NY 10010. TEL 212-679-1234. Ed. Charles G. Hagedorn. adv.; bk.rev. circ. 8,200.

051   US
TOWNSFOLK; society, sports, travel and the fine arts. 1928. m. $8. Townsfolk, 919 N. Michigan Ave., Chicago, IL 60611. TEL 312-787-6579. Ed. A.M. Adams. circ. 15,000. (back issues avail.)

051   US   ISSN 1071-3719
TRAVERSE; northern Michigan's magazine. 1981. m. $24. Prism Publications Inc., 121 S. Union St., Traverse City, MI 49684. TEL 616-941-8174. FAX 616-941-8391. Ed. Deborah Wyatt Fellows. adv. contact: Jennifer C. Szuuke. circ. 9,110 (paid). **Document type:** consumer publication.
  Formerly: Traverse, The Magazine (ISSN 0746-2735)

051   US
TRIAD STYLE. w. free. N.C. Publications, Inc., Box 20007, Greensboro, NC 27420-0007. TEL 919-373-7083. Ed. Ann Alexander. circ. 30,000.
  Formerly (until 1987): Spectator.

051   US
TRIVIA DISPATCH. 1978. m. $12. M R M Associates, Box 763, Salem, NH 03079. TEL 603-893-5123. Ed. Mardy R. Minasian. circ. 11,500.

051   US
TRUE MATCH. 1986. m. $19 membership. T M Publishing, Inc., 2609 S. Highland, Box 18000-5, Las Vegas, NV 89109. TEL 702-796-9966. FAX 702-796-5655. Ed. M.S. Bram. adv.; bk.rev. circ. 160,000.

051   US   ISSN 1062-2861
TUCSON LIFESTYLE MAGAZINE. 1982. m. $15. 7000 E. Tanque Verde, Tucson, AZ 85715-5318. TEL 602-721-2929. FAX 602-721-8665. Ed. Susan P. Giles. adv. circ. 27,000.
  Description: City magazine containing news of people, places and events in Tucson; monthly business, travel, restaurant and city guides; monthly house and garden section; and an annual health care guide.

071   US
TULSA PEOPLE. 1986. w. free. Tulsa Life, 1221 E. 33rd St., Tulsa, OK 74105. TEL 918-747-9924. FAX 918-747-9926. Ed. James F. Langdon. adv.; bk.rev. circ. 30,000. **Document type:** newspaper.

051   US   ISSN 0164-6532
F614.M6
TWIN CITIES.* 1978. m. $14.95. Dorn Communications, Inc., 15 Fifth St. S., Ste. 900, Minneapolis, MN 55402. TEL 612-835-6855. Ed. Marcia Appel. adv.

051   US
U S A MONITOR. 1940. m. $12. c/o Earnestine Cole, Box 2139, Fort Worth, TX 76113. TEL 817-654-8774. adv. contact: Kathy Burrell. bk.rev. circ. 35,000. (tabloid format) **Document type:** newspaper.
  Former titles: Fort Worth Como Monitor (ISSN 0046-466X); Fort Worth Como Weekly.

051   US
U S A WEEKEND. w. 535 Madison Ave., New York, NY 10022. TEL 212-715-2100. FAX 212-935-5576. Ed. Marcia Bullard. adv.; circ. 17,800,000 (paid). **Document type:** consumer publication.
  Description: Covers people, entertainment, travel, food, health and fitness, fashion and relationships.

051   US   ISSN 0041-5537
JK1   CODEN: XNWRAV
U S NEWS & WORLD REPORT. 1933. w. $41. U S News & World Report Inc., 2400 N St., N.W., Washington, DC 20037-1196. TEL 202-955-2000. (Subscr. to: Box 55929, Boulder, CO 80322-5929) Eds. Merl McLaughlin, Michael Ruby. adv.; charts; illus. circ. 2,351,313. (also avail. in microform from BLH,MCA,MIM) **Indexed:** Abr.R.G., Acad.Ind., BPIA, Bus.Ind., CAD CAM Abstr., CINAHL, CMI, Environ.Abstr., Environ.Ind., Hlth.Ind., HRIS, Jun.High.Mag.Abstr., Mag.Ind., Mid.East: Abstr.& Ind., P.A.I.S., Pers.Lit., PROMT, PSI, R.G., Telegen, TOM.
  ●Also available online. Vendor(s): DIALOG Information Services, Inc., Mead Data Central, Inc..
  —BLDSC (9124.757550); Faxon; UnCover; UMI.

051   US
U S 1;* Princeton's business and entertainment journal. 1984. 24/yr. $14.95. U S 1 Publishing Co., 12 Roszel Rd., No.C-205, Princeton, NJ 08540-6234. TEL 609-452-0038. FAX 609-243-0425. adv.; bk.rev. circ. 18,700. (tabloid format)

071   US
U S 1 NEWSPAPER; Princeton's business and entertainment journal. 1984. bi-w. $14.95. U S 1 Newspaper, 12 Roszel Rd., Princeton, NJ 08540. TEL 609-452-0038. FAX 609-243-0425. adv.; B&W page $895; trim 10 1/2 x 17. circ. 18,600. **Document type:** newspaper.

051   US
▼**UNION PLUS.** 1993. q. Marblehead Communications Inc., 376 Boylston St., Boston, MA 02116-3812. TEL 617-424-7700. FAX 617-437-7714. adv.; B&W page $35000, color page $43500; trim 8 x 10 7/8. circ. 2,000,000. **Document type:** consumer publication.

051   US
UNIVERSITY MESSENGER.* 1985. bi-w. (during school yr.). Oberdorf Publishing Co., 637 Market St., Lewisburg, PA 17837-1451. TEL 800-800-4047. FAX 717-529-4048. circ. 3,100.
  Former titles: University Merchant; Lewisburg Merchant.

051 700 917   US   ISSN 0889-9991
UPSTATE MAGAZINE. 1984. m. $20. Greenville Woman, Inc., 101 W. Park Ave., Greenville, SC 29601. TEL 803-232-7799. Ed. Sue Lile Inman. adv.; bk.rev. circ. 8,000. (back issues avail.)
  Formerly: Greenville Woman.
  Description: Reflects the lifestyle and the people living in Upstate South Carolina.

052   US   ISSN 0147-510X
AP2
US (NEW YORK, 1977). 1977. m. $14.97. Straight Arrow Publishers, Inc., 1290 Ave. of Americas, New York, NY 10104. TEL 212-484-1616. (Subscr. to: Box 50414, Boulder, CO 80321-0414. TEL 800-568-5576) Ed. Ian Birch. adv. contact: Paul Rothkopf. illus. (also avail. in microfilm from MCA) **Indexed:** Access (1977-).
  —UMI.

790 917   US   ISSN 0739-2311
UTAH HOLIDAY;* life in Utah. 1971. m. $15. (Utah Holiday Publishing Co.) Cumming Communications Network, Box 985, Salt Lake City, UT 84110-0985. TEL 801-532-3737. FAX 801-532-3742. Ed. Barbara Cumming. adv.; bk.rev.; film rev.; play rev. circ. 20,500. (back issues avail.)

GENERAL INTEREST PERIODICALS — UNITED STATES

051 US
VAIL MAGAZINE. 1971. q. $12. Box 368, Vail, CO 81650. TEL 303-476-6600. FAX 303-476-6152. Ed. Charles McNamara. adv. circ. 30,000.
   Description: Targeted to upper-income residents and frequent visitors who have a special interest in the Vail Valley. Includes articles on decorating second homes, real estate, shopping and upcoming events.

051 US
VAIL VALLEY MAGAZINE. 1983. 2/yr. $12 (foreign $18). Colorado West Advertising & Publishing, Box 3423, Vail, CO 81658. TEL 303-926-3969. FAX 303-926-3969. Ed. Laura Hertz. adv. circ. 100,000. (back issues avail.)
   Description: Reflective of lifestyle and activities in the Vail Valley area.

071.5 US
THE VALLEY BANNER. 1966. w. $16 (local $12). Rockingham Publishing Co., Box 126, Elkton, VA 22827. TEL 703-298-9444. FAX 703-298-2560. Ed. R.C. Murphey IV. adv.; circ. 4,750 (paid). Document type: newspaper.

051 US ISSN 8750-1430
VALLEY MAGAZINE (GRANADA HILLS). 1976. m. $15. World Communications, Inc., 16800 Devonshire St., Ste. 275, Granada Hills, CA 91344. TEL 818-368-3353. FAX 818-360-8079. Ed. Bonnie Steele. adv. circ. 24,263. Document type: consumer publication.
   Formerly: Big Valley (ISSN 0164-8799)
   Description: Serves the interests of the citizens of San Fernando, Santa Clarita, Simi, and Conejo valleys of the greater Los Angeles suburban area.

051 US ISSN 1046-0454
VALLEY MAGAZINE (SELINSGROVE).* 1989. q. $12. Meadowood Publications, Inc., P.O. Box 219, Port Trevorton, PA 17864-0219. TEL 717-374-7795. FAX 717-374-6474. Ed. Stephen A. Newton. adv.; bk.rev. circ. 30,000.
   Description: General interest publication about the Susquehanna River Valley between Lockhaven and Berwick, Pennsylvania, to the north and Havre de Grace, Maryland, to the south.

051 US ISSN 0888-0999
VALLEY TRADER.* 1980. w. $25. Oberdorf Publishing Co., 637 Market St., Lewisburg, PA 17837-1451. TEL 800-800-4047. FAX 717-529-4048. Ed. Max A. Oberdorf. adv. circ. 20,000. Document type: newspaper.
   Formerly: Susquehanna Valley.

051 US
▼**VALLEY VIEWPOINT MAGAZINE.** 1992. m. $15. Valley Viewpoint Publications, Inc., 21813 S. 158th St., Chandler, AZ 85249. TEL 602-988-2111. Ed. Patti E. Trueba. adv. circ. 10,000.
   Description: Features articles on people, places, and things; also includes interviews with celebrities, how-to's, a vet and restaurant critic column, first-person experiences, and sports.

051 US
VALLEY VOICE (BRYN MAWR). 1966. q. $3 to non-members; members free. Concerned Citizens of the Delaware Valley, Box 47, Bryn Mawr, PA 19010. TEL 610-525-1129. Ed. Harry Hyde Jr. adv.; bk.rev.; charts; illus. circ. 125. (processed; back issues avail.) Document type: newsletter.

051 US ISSN 0192-6810
VALLEY VOICE (MIDDLEBURY). w. 3 Court St., Middlebury, VT 05753. TEL 802-388-6366. Ed. Elizabeth White.

051 US
VENTURA MAGAZINE. 1989. m. Delta Publications, 2899 Agoura Rd., Ste. 185, Westlake Village, CA 91361. TEL 818-707-9154. adv. circ. 25,000.
   Description: Highlights dining, entertainment, home and garden, fashion, travel, personalities, real estate, business and lifestyles in Ventura County.

974.3 US ISSN 0042-417X
F46
VERMONT LIFE. 1946. q. $11.95. Agency of Development & Community Affairs, c/o Andrew Jackson, 61 Elm St., Montpelier, VT 05602. TEL 802-828-3241. Ed. Thomas K. Slayton. adv.; Geriame/Smart. bk.rev.; illus.; index, cum.index every 20 yrs. circ. 96,000. Indexed: Access (1975-). Document type: consumer publication.
   —UMI.
   Description: Features photography and celebrates Vermont's culture, scenery, history and seasons. Addresses the issues of growth, and preservation of Vermont's environment.

051 US ISSN 1044-940X
VERMONT MAGAZINE. 1989. bi-m. $18. David Sleeper, Ed. & Pub., Box 288, Bristol, VT 05443. TEL 802-453-3200. FAX 802-453-3940. adv. circ. 45,000.
   Description: Covers everything from fiction to political issues, and spotlights recreational facilities and activities in Vermont.

051 US ISSN 1040-6883
VICTORIA; home & garden, fashion & beauty, cooking & entertaining, crafts & collectibles. 1987. bi-m. $15.97. Hearst Magazines, Victoria, 250 W. 55th St., 11th Fl., New York, NY 10019. TEL 212-903-5190. Ed. Nancy Lindemeyer. adv. circ. 750,000. (reprint service avail. from UMI)
   Formerly (1987-1988): Good Housekeeping's Victoria.

051 US ISSN 1047-3947
VICTORIAN SAMPLER. 1983. bi-m. $19.96. Sampler Publications, Inc., 707 Kautz Rd., St. Charles, IL 60174. TEL 708-377-8000. FAX 708-377-8194. (Subscr. to: Box 344, Mt. Morris, IL 61054) adv. circ. 117,000.
   Description: Features elegant, romantic home decorating ideas, plus entertaining, cooking ideas and collectables.

051 US ISSN 0042-6180
AP2
VILLAGE VOICE. (Supplement avail: V L S (ISSN 0887-8633)) 1955. w. $47.95 (foreign $79.20). V V Publishing Corporation, 36 Cooper Sq., New York, NY 10003. TEL 212-475-3300. FAX 212-598-0629. (Subscr. to: Box 8044, Syracuse, NY 13217. TEL 800-825-0061) Ed. Jonathan Larsen; Pub. David Schneiderman. adv. contact: Kathryn V. Thornton. bk.rev.; film rev.; play rev.; illus.; circ. 156,272 (paid). (tabloid format; also avail. in microform from UMI) Indexed: Access (1975-), Bk.Rev.Ind. (1970-), Child.Bk.Rev.Ind. (1970-), Film Lit.Ind. (1973-), Media Rev.Dig., Music Ind., New Per.Ind. Document type: newspaper.
   ●Also available online. Vendor(s): Mead Data Central, Inc.
   —UMI.

974.7 US ISSN 0042-6199
AP2
VILLAGER (BRONXVILLE). 1929. m. (Oct.-Jun.). $6.50. Bronxville Women's Club, Inc., 135 Midland Ave., Bronxville, NY 10708. TEL 914-337-3252. Ed. A. Murphy. adv.; bk.rev.; charts; illus. circ. 750.

071 US ISSN 0042-6202
VILLAGER (NEW YORK). 1933. w. $21. Clean Slate Corporation, 80 Eighth Ave., New York, NY 10011. TEL 212-229-1890. FAX 212-229-2790. Ed. Thomas Butson. adv.; bk.rev.; film rev.; music rev.; play rev.; rec.rev.; illus. circ. 15,000. (tabloid format) Document type: newspaper.
   Description: Community newspaper for Greenwich Village and lower Manhattan.

051 US
VILLAGES MAGAZINE. m. Creneau Media Group, Box 3388, Houston, TX 77253. TEL 713-880-4611. FAX 713-880-4644. Ed. Elise Perrachio. circ. 10,000.

051 US ISSN 0734-6603
F221
VIRGINIA COUNTRY. 1979. q. $12. Country Publishers, 113 E. Main St., Box 798, Berryville, VA 22611. TEL 703-955-1298. Ed. Garrison Ellis. adv.; bk.rev. circ. 30,000. (back issues avail.)
   Description: Contemporary features, historical articles, short stories, and personal sketches pertaining to the culture of and recreational activities available in all rural regions of Virginia, with calendars of events, entertainment, seminars and tours.

071.4 US ISSN 0049-6480
VIRGINIA GAZETTE. 1736. s-w. $25 to local residents; out-of-state $44; senior citizens $23. Chesapeake Publishing Corp., 216 Ironbounce Rd., Williamsburg, VA 23188. TEL 804-220-1736. FAX 804-220-1665. Ed. William C. O'Donovan. adv.; bk.rev.; illus. circ. 15,500. (also avail. in microform) Document type: newspaper.

051 US
W D C PERIOD. (Washington, DC) 1984. irreg. (3-4/yr.). $2 per no. Chow Chow Productions, Box 50084, Washington, DC 20004-0084. TEL 202-462-7229. Ed. Gordon Ornelas. adv.; bk.rev.; film rev.; illus.; tr.lit. circ. 2,000. (tabloid format; back issues avail.)

975.3 US ISSN 0043-0897
F191
WASHINGTONIAN. 1965. m. $21.95 to local residents; others $34.95. Washington Magazine Inc., 1828 L St., N.W., Ste. 200, Washington, DC 20036. TEL 202-296-3600. (Subscr. to: Box 58897, Boulder CO 80322-8897) Ed. John A. Limpert. adv.; bk.rev.; play rev.; illus. circ. 157,055. (also avail. in microform from UMI; back issues avail.) Indexed: Access (1975-1991), Hlth.Ind., Mag.Ind., R.G. Document type: consumer publication.
   ●Also available online. Vendor(s): Mead Data Central, Inc.
   —UnCover; UMI.

051 US
WASHINGTON'S HILL RAG. 1976. 24/yr. Fagon Publishing Group, 224 Seventh St., S.E., No. 300, Washington, DC 20003. TEL 202-543-8300. Ed. Melissa Ashabranner. adv.; bk.rev.; circ. 20,000 (controlled).

051 US
WEEKLY RETROSPECT. 1904. w. $5. Collingswood Publishing Co., 732 Haddon Ave., Collingswood, NJ 08108. TEL 609-854-1400. Ed. Leo T. Italiano. adv.; bk.rev. circ. 5,200. (tabloid format; also avail. in microform; back issues avail.)

051 US ISSN 0199-574X
WEEKLY WORLD NEWS. w. $24.95. Weekly World News, Inc., 600 S. East Coast Ave., Lantana, FL 33464. TEL 407-586-1111. FAX 407-582-0126. Ed. Eddie Cloontz. adv. circ. 730,329. (tabloid format)
   Description: Features unusual or entertaining news items.

051 US
WEST BOCA RATON LIVING.* q. Doug Sherson, Ed. & Pub., 1121 Holland Dr., Ste. 11, Boca Raton, FL 33487-2735. TEL 407-487-4944. circ. 12,000.

051 US
WEST COAST LIFESTYLE MAGAZINE. 1984. 9/yr. W. Bill Golding, Ed. & Pub., 14148 Burbank Blvd., Spt. 7, Van Nuys, CA 91401-4943. TEL 818-780-8400. FAX 818-780-8979. film rev.; circ. 70,000 (controlled).
   Description: Features restaurants, entertainment, mini-vacations, recipes and more.

051 US
WEST HOLLYWOOD. 1989. a. West Hollywood Marketing Corporation, 9000 W. Sunset Blvd., No. 700A, West Hollywood, CA 90069-5801. TEL 213-274-7294; 800-368-6020. FAX 310-777-2577. Ed. & Dir. Mary Frost. adv. circ. 130,000. Document type: consumer publication.
   Description: Contains general-interest information on fashion, design, entertainment, and restaurants and a guide to local businesses.

051 US
WEST SIDE SPIRIT.* vol.7, no.5, 1989. w. $39. Access Press Inc., 242 W. 30th St., 5 Fl., New York, NY 10001-4903. TEL 212-594-0719. FAX 212-594-0719. Ed. Steve Bauman. circ. 90,000.

051 US
WEST UNIVERSITY MAGAZINE. m. Creneau Media Group, Box 3388, Houston, TX 77253. TEL 713-880-4611. Ed. Elise Perrachio. circ. 10,000.

051 US
▼**WESTERN ECHOES.** 1993. q. Box 60072, Nashville, TN 37206.

051 US
▼**WHAT PEOPLE ARE WEARING.** 1992. q. $1.95 per no. Enquirer - Star Group, Inc., Star Division, 600 S. East Coast Ave., Lantana, FL 33462. TEL 407-586-1111. FAX 407-582-0126. adv.; illus. circ. 750,000.
  Description: Covers celebrity fashions and related gossip, with beauty and design suggestions.

071 US
WILLAMETTE WEEK. 1974. w. $40. City of Roses Newspaper Co., Two N.W. Second, Portland, OR 97209. TEL 503-243-2122. FAX 503-243-1115. Ed. Mark L. Zusman. adv.; bk.rev. circ. 65,000. **Document type:** newspaper.
  Description: Covers news, arts, and entertainment in Oregon's largest metropolitan area.

975.6 US ISSN 0049-7649
WILMINGTON JOURNAL. 1927. w. $15. T.C. Jervay, Ed. & Pub., Box 1618, 412 S. Seventh St., Wilmington, NC 28401. TEL 919-762-5502.

051 US
WINSTON-SALEM MAGAZINE.* 1984. bi-m. $10. Forsyth Communications, Inc., Box 10921, Winston-Salem, NC 27108-0921. TEL 919-722-8706. Ed. Mary L. Rearden. adv. circ. 10,000.
  Description: Focuses on the arts, local business, consumerism, personal finance, health issues, architecture and personalities.

051 US
WISCONSIN. (Supplement to Milwaukee Journal) 1984. w. free. Milwaukee Journal, Box 661, Milwaukee, WI 53201. TEL 414-224-2341. FAX 414-224-2047. Ed. Alan Borsuk. adv. contact: Scott Stollberg. circ. 495,000. **Document type:** newspaper.
  Formerly: Insight.
  Description: Sunday newspaper magazine focusing on Wisconsin.

051 631.3 US
WISCONSIN R E C NEWS. 1940. m. $4. Wisconsin Electric Cooperative Association, Box 686, Madison, WI 53701-0686. TEL 608-273-0420. Ed. Perry Baird. adv. circ. 137,000. (tabloid format)

977.5 US ISSN 0095-4314
F576
WISCONSIN TRAILS; the magazine of life in Wisconsin. 1960. bi-m. $19.95. Wisconsin Tales & Trails, Inc., 6225 University Ave., Box 5650, Madison, WI 53705. TEL 608-231-2444. FAX 608-231-1557. Ed. Howard Mead. adv.; bk.rev.; illus. circ. 55,000. (back issues avail.) **Indexed:** Abstr.Pop.Cult., Access (1975-), Ind.Child.Mag., R.G. **Document type:** consumer publication.
  Formerly: Wisconsin Tales and Trails (ISSN 0043-6712)
  Description: Explores the history, scenery, people, places and things to do and see in Wisconsin. Includes information on dining out, places to stay, and vacation planning tips for every season of the year, along with a comprehensive calendar of events.

051 US
▼**THE WORLD ALMANAC OF THE U.S.A.** 1993. a. $8.95 (hardcover $18.95). World Almanac Books (Subsidiary of: Funk & Wagnalls), 1 International Blvd., Mahwah, NJ 07495. charts. **Document type:** consumer publication, directory.

THE WORLD ALMANAC OF U.S. POLITICS. see POLITICAL SCIENCE

051 US ISSN 0887-9346
CB428
THE WORLD & I; a chronicle of our changing era. 1986. m. $90. News World Communications, Inc. (Subsidiary of: Washington Times Corporation), 2800 New York Ave., N.E., Washington, DC 20002. TEL 202-635-4000. FAX 202-269-9353. Ed. Morton A. Kaplan. adv.; bk.rev.; index; circ. 13,550 (paid); 15,950 (controlled). **Indexed:** A.I.Abstr., Bk.Rev.Ind. (1989-), Child.Bk.Rev.Ind. (1989-), P.A.I.S.
  —BLDSC (9352.911750); UnCover.
  Description: Articles cover culture, politics, art and science. Contains fiction, nonfiction, photos, poetry.

051 US ISSN 1060-3816
THE WORLD AT LARGE. 1991. w. $65 (Canada $80). 1689 46th St., Brooklyn, New York, NY 11204. TEL 718-972-4000. FAX 718-972-9400. (Subscr. to: The World At Large Inc., P.O. Box 190330, Brooklyn, NY 11219. TEL 800-285-2743) circ. 28,400. (large print in 18 pt.) **Document type:** newspaper.
  Description: Aimed at readers, primarily seniors, with visual impairments. Contains a broad spectrum of national and worldwide news and features.

051 US ISSN 0043-8901
WORLD PROGRESS; the standard quarterly review, an alphabetically arranged quarterly covering current events. 1928. q. $7.95. Standard Educational Corporation, 200 W. Monroe St., Chicago, IL 60606. TEL 312-346-7440. Ed. Miriam Creeden. bk.rev.; play rev.; charts; illus.; index, cum.index. circ. 45,000.

051 US ISSN 0273-480X
T391
WORLD'S FAIR. 1981. q. $45 (effective Jan. 1992). World's Fair, Inc., Box 339-ABV, Corte Madera, CA 94976-0339. TEL 415-924-6035. FAX 415-924-8245. Ed. Alfred Heller. adv.; bk.rev. circ. 5,000. (back issues avail.) **Indexed:** Key to Econ.Sci. **Document type:** trade publication.
  Description: A journal of international expositions, events and festivals of the past, present and future.

051 US
X S. 1991. w. $2 per no. Gold Coast Publishing, Box 14426, Ft. Lauderdale, FL 33302. TEL 305-356-4943. FAX 305-356-4949. Ed. Stephen Wissink. adv.; bk.rev.; circ. 45,000 (controlled).

051 US ISSN 0044-0191
AP2
YANKEE. 1935. m. $22. Yankee Publishing, Inc., Box 520, Dublin, NH 03444-0520. TEL 603-563-8111. FAX 603-563-8252. Ed. Judson D. Hale, Sr. adv.; bk.rev.; illus. circ. 700,000. (also avail. in microform from IAC,UMI; reprint service avail. from UMI) **Indexed:** Access (1975-), Mag.Ind., PMR.
  —UnCover.

051 US
ZONE (TEMPE). 1990. q. $25. 119 E. 7th St., Ste. 2, Tempe, AZ 85281. Ed. Robert Sentinery. adv.; illus.

051 US ISSN 1047-451X
24 HOURS; the magazine of life past midnight. 1989. bi-m. $15 for 12 nos. Schneider Publishing Company, Box 5657, Santa Monica, CA 90409-5657. TEL 213-458-3777. FAX 213-458-3770. Ed. Timothy Schneider. adv.; bk.rev. circ. 35,000.
  Description: For people active in the late-night and early morning hours, especially those who work overnight. Includes a yellow page directory of businesses that are available on a round-the-clock basis.

051 US
516 MAGAZINE.* 1989. m. $15. 516 Publishing, Inc., Box 1310, N. Massapequa, NY 11758-0906. TEL 516-795-9143. FAX 516-795-5419. Ed. Michael Watts. circ. 45,000.
  Description: Articles on entertaining, children's activities, the arts, cinema and comedy. Includes a calendar of island-wide events and other leisure pursuits.

GENERAL INTEREST PERIODICALS — Uruguay

056.1 UY
BRECHA. 1985. w. Avda. Uruguay 844, 11100 Montevideo, Uruguay. TEL 2-916723. circ. 14,500.

079.895 UY
CAMBIO. (Supplement included: Deportes (Mon.)) 1984. d. Danelo S.A., Uruguay 769, 50000 Salto, Uruguay. TEL 598-732-5045. FAX 598-732-2579. Pub. Carlos Artia. adv. contact: Julio Aguirrezabal. illus. Wire service(s): RN. circ. 3,000 (morn. ed.); 4,500 (Sun. ed.). cols./p.: 6; pp./issue: 20. (tabloid format) **Document type:** newspaper.

056.1 UY ISSN 0009-823X
CLARIDAD. 1956. 3/wk. Urg.$200($10) Norberto Costabel, Ed. & Pub., San Jose 215, Juan Lacage, Uruguay. adv.; illus. circ. 3,500. (tabloid format)

056.1 UY
CRITICA; revista sociocultural. 1985. irreg. Ministerio de Educacion y Cultura, Calle Pando 2975, Montevideo, Uruguay. Ed. Roberto Genta Dorado.

079.895 UY
CRONICAS. 1981. d. $10 per mo. Cronicas Ltda., Colon 274, 75000 Mercedes, Soriano, Uruguay. Pub. Ricardo Nole. adv. Wire service(s): RN. circ. 4,700. cols./p.: 6; pp./issue: 16. (tabloid format; back issues avail.) **Document type:** newspaper.

056.1 UY
IMAGENES. 1977. m. $150. Fernando E. Juanico Penalva, Zapican 2577, Montevideo, Uruguay. Ed.Bd. adv.; bk.rev.; illus. circ. 5,000.

056.1 UY
NUEVA REPUBLICA. 1983. w. Talleres Graficos del Diario "El Pais", Plaza Independencia 830, Piso 8, Montevideo, Uruguay. Ed. Jose Antonio Ramirez.

056.1 UY
PROPUESTA. 1982. m. c/o Raul Gadea, Ed., Aconeagua 5177, Montevideo, Uruguay.

056.1 UY
PUEBLO ORIENTAL; revista mensual de opinion. 1976. m. Urg.$2. Editora del Uruguay, Juan Carlos Gomez 1380, Montevideo, Uruguay. Ed. Gumersindo Mercurio Giorgeta.

056.1 UY
REVISTA LO QUE IMPORTA; publicacion informativa independiente para la cuenca suroeste de la republica. 1991. m. 3500 N$ per no. Proyeccion, Centro Regional de Prensa, Av. Juan A. Lavalleja 305, Ismel Cortinas - Dept. Flores, Uruguay. TEL 0536-1611-31. Ed. Ulises Fernandez Banega. **Document type:** consumer publication.

056.1 UY
SOBRE TODO. 1991. w. 2000 N$ per no. Sobre Todo S.r.l., Colonia 1465, 11200 Montevideo, Uruguay. TEL 48-49-30. FAX 48-03-04. Ed. Ope Pasquet. (tabloid format)

079.898 UY
EL TELEGRAFO. (Supplements included: Deportes (Mon.), Quinto Dia (Fri.)) 1910. d. newsstand price: $.50. Diario El Telegrafo S.A., 18 de Julio 1027, 60000 Paysandu, Uruguay. TEL 598-722-3141. FAX 598-722-7999. Pub. Fernando Baccaro. adv. contact: Luis Provera. bk.rev.; film rev.; music rev.; play rev.; illus. Wire service(s): AFP, RN. circ. 7,500 (morn. ed.); 9,000 (Sun. ed.). cols./p.: 8; pp./issue: 12. (broadsheet format; back issues avail.) **Document type:** newspaper.

056.1 UY
UNIVERSARIO; cronicas del cambio de era. 1990. m.? 4500 N$ per no. Causa, Florida 1422, Montevideo, Uruguay. TEL 90-08-02. Ed. Mirna Arreche.

GENERAL INTEREST PERIODICALS — Venezuela

056.1 VE
BOHEMIA VENEZUELA. 1966. w. Edif. Bloque Dearmas, Final Avda. San Martin cruce con Avda. La Paz, Apdo. 575, Caracas, Venezuela. TEL 2-443-1066. Dir. Rosana Ordonez. circ. 86,270.

2792   GENERAL INTEREST PERIODICALS — VIETNAM

056.1   VE
DOMINICAL. 1970. w. Publicaciones Capriles, Torre de la Prensa, Plaza del Panteon, Apdo. 1192, Caracas, Venezuela. adv. circ. 230,250.

056.1   VE
ELITE. 1925. w. Bs.3.50 per no. Editorial Elite, Publicaciones Capriles, Torre de la Prensa, 6o, Plaza del Panteon, Apdo. Postal 2976, Caracas 101, Venezuela. TEL 2-81-4931. Dir. Asdrubal Zurita. adv.; film rev.; charts; illus. circ. 89,830.

056.1   VE   ISSN 0026-9131
AP63
MOMENTO. Issued with: Viva, 100 Anos. 1956. w. Bs.208. Editorial Momento C.A., Torre de la Prensa, Plaza del Panteon, Apdo. 2976, Caracas 101, Venezuela. TEL 2-572-0322. Ed. Armando de Armas. adv.; bk.rev.; film rev.; illus. circ. 78,520.

056.1   VE
QUE PASA?. fortn. Edif. Nuevo Central, 7o, Avda. Libertador, Chacao, Caracas, Venezuela. TEL 2-32-8603. Ed. Marysabel Paredes. circ. 50,000.
   Description: Guide to entertainment in the country.

056.1   VE
VENEZUELA GRAFICA. 1951. w. Bs.3.50 per no. Editorial Elite, Torre de la Prensa, Plaza Panteon, Apdo. Postal 2976, Caracas 101, Venezuela. TEL 2-81-4931. Ed. Miguel Angel Capriles. adv.; film rev.; charts; illus. circ. 95,870.

GENERAL INTEREST PERIODICALS — Vietnam

056.1   CU
REVISTA VIET-NAM. m. $20 in N. America; S. America $26; Europe $29; elsewhere $41. Ediciones Cubanas, Obispo No. 527, Apdo. 605, Havana, Cuba. TEL 32-5556-60.

059.959   VN
TUAN TIN TUC/NEWS WEEKLY. 1982. w. 5 Ly Thuong Kiet, Hanoi, Socialist Republic of Vietnam.

959.7   VN   ISSN 0042-5710
DS556
VIETNAM.* (Text in English) no.106, July 1966. m. 79 Ly Thuong Kiet, Hanoi, Socialist Republic of Vietnam. Ed Ngo Duc Mau.

059   VN   ISSN 0866-8140
VIETNAM COURIER. (Text in English) no.50, 1976. m. 46 Tran Hung Dao, Hanoi, Socialist Republic of Vietnam. (Subcr. to: Xunhasaba, 32 Hai Ba Trung, Hanoi, Socialist Republic of Vietnam) charts; illus.

054.1   VN
VIETNAM HEBDO. (Text in French) 1985. w. Viet-Nam News Agency, 5 Ly Thuong Kiet St., Hanoi, Socialist Republic of Vietnam. TEL 52931.

059.959   VN
VIETNAM PICTORIAL. (Editions in English, French, Khmer, Lao, Russian, Spanish, Vietnamese) 1954. m. 79 Ly Thuong Kiet, Hanoi, Socialist Republic of Vietnam. TEL 53508. Ed. Do Phuong. circ. 138,000.

051   VN
VIETNAM WEEKLY. (Text in English) 1985. w. Viet-Nam News Agency, 5 Ly Thuong Kiet St., Hanoi, Socialist Republic of Vietnam. TEL 52931.

GENERAL INTEREST PERIODICALS — West Indies

079.729   MQ   ISSN 0757-3960
ANTILLA; l'hebdo des Antilles et de la Guyane. (Text and summaries in French, Creole) 1981. w. 830 F. (effective 1991). Antilla - Production, B.P. 46, Lamentin, Martinique. TEL 19-596-75-48-68. FAX 19-596-75-58-46. (back issues avail.)
   Document type: newspaper.

051   BB
BARBADOS OFFICIAL GAZETTE. s-w. B.$120. (Ministry of External Affairs) Government Printery, Bay St., St. Michael, Barbados, W.I. **Document type:** government publication.

051   BH
BELIZE TODAY. 1971. m. free. Belize Information Service, c/o Chief Information Officer, PO Box 60, Belmopan, Belize. TEL 08-2159. FAX 501-823236. Ed. Anthony O'Ferrall. adv.; bk.rev.; illus. circ. 17,000. **Document type:** government publication.
   Formerly: New Belize.

051   US
CARIB BEAT; sounds, sights, scenes. m. Carib Comm Corp., 15 W, 39th St., New York, NY 10018. TEL 212-944-2033. Ed. Wayne A. Anderson.
   Description: Entertainment magazine of the Caribbean community.

054.1   MQ
CARIB HEBDO. 1989. w. 23 rue Yves Goussard, 97200 Fort-de-France, Martinique. Ed. Gisele de la Fargue.

079.729   BB
CARIBBEAN CONTACT. 1973. m. B.$14($15) to individuals; institutions B.$20 (US$20). (Caribbean Conference of Churches) Caribbean Contact Ltd., P.O. Box 616, Bridgetown, Barbados, W.I. TEL 809-427-2681. FAX 809-429-2075. TELEX 2335 CADEC WB. Ed. C.M. Hope. adv.; bk.rev. circ. 23,000. **Indexed:** HR Rep. **Document type:** newspaper.

052   UK   ISSN 0966-7806
▼**CARIBBEAN FOCUS.** 1992. bi-m. £60($110) Lormier J. Poultney, Ed. & Pub., P.O. Box 79, St. Albans, Hertfordshire AL1 3DA, England. TEL 0727-831381. FAX 0727-831381. **Document type:** consumer publication.
   Description: Provides data and analysis on current political and economic developments in the Caribbean region.

052   US   ISSN 1019-5076
CARIBBEAN WEEK. vol.3, no.17, 1992. w. B.$2($1.50) (Jamaica J$7.50). Caribbean Communications Inc., Lefferts Pl., River Rd., St. Michael, Barbados, W.I. TEL 809-436-1902.

051   GD
GRENADA. GOVERNMENT GAZETTE. w. Government Printing Office, St. George's, Grenada, W.I.

052   GD
GRENADA INFORMER; the fearless weekly. 1985. w. EC$190($75) Moving Target Ltd., P.O. Box 622, Market Hill, St. George's, Grenada, W.I. TEL 809-440-5762. FAX 809-440-4119. Ed. Carla R.A. Briggs. adv. circ. 6,500. (tabloid format; back issues avail.)
   Description: Covers issues of interest in Grenada and the Caribbean; and sports.

052   VB   ISSN 0257-3563
THE ISLAND SUN. 1962. w. $85. Sun Enterprises (BVI) Ltd., Main St., P.O. Box 21, Road Town - Tortola, British Virgin Islands, W.I. TEL 809-49-42476. FAX 809-494-4540. Ed. Vernon Pickering. adv.; bk.rev.; illus.; tr.lit. circ. 2,800. (tabloid format; back issues avail.)

054.1   GP
JAKATA MAGAZINE. 1977. fortn. 200 F. Aguadipress, 18 rue Conde, 97110 Pointe-a-Pitre, Guadeloupe. TEL 809-91-44-17. Ed. Frantz Succab. circ. 6,000.

052   JM
JAMAICA BEAT. no.7, 1989. bi-m. Jam.$2 per no. Newshound Publication, P.O. Box 393, Kingston 10, Jamaica, W.I. TEL 809-92-74761. (Dist. in U.S. by: PatCar Associates, Inc., 8115 Fenton St., Ste. 208, Silver Spring, MD 20910. TEL 301-587-3265) Ed. Eric McNish.
   Description: Provides news and information on sports, arts, real estate, business investment, tourism, and reggae music.

051   JM   ISSN 0021-4124
F1861
JAMAICA JOURNAL. 1967. 3/yr. J.$140($25) to individuals; institutions $30. (Institute of Jamaica) Institute of Jamaica Publications Ltd., 2A Suthermere Rd., Kingston 10, Jamaica, W.I. Ed. Leeta Hearne. adv.; bk.rev.; illus. circ. 5,000. (also avail. in microfilm from UMI; reprint service avail. from UMI) **Indexed:** Amer.Hist.& Life, Hisp.Amer.Per.Ind., Hist.Abstr. **Document type:** academic/scholarly publication.
   —BLDSC (4644.800000); UMI.

051   JM   ISSN 0021-4159
JAMAICAN WEEKLY GLEANER. 1952. w. J.$30 per no. Gleaner Company Ltd., 7 North St., P.O. Box 40, Kingston, Jamaica, W.I. TEL 809-922-3400. FAX 809-922-6223. TELEX 2319 GLEANER JA. Ed. Ken Allen. adv.; illus. circ. 30,000. (tabloid format)

052   JM
LIFESTYLE MAGAZINE. bi-m. Jam.$149($12) Creative Communications Inc. Ltd., P.O. Box 105, Kingston 10, Jamaica, W.I. TEL 809-927-4271. FAX 809-927-4996. Ed. Ashley Gambrill. illus. **Document type:** consumer publication.

054.1   GP
MAGAZINE GWADLOUPEYEN. 1981. bi-m. $30. B.P. 1286, Pointe-a-Pitre 97184, Guadeloupe. Ed. Danik Zandwonis. adv.; bk.rev. circ. 3,000.
   Formerly: Journal Guadeloupeen.

972.9   BB
THE NEW BAJAN. 1953. m. B.$60. Carib Publicity Co., Nation House, Fontabelle, Bridgetown, Barbados, W.I. FAX 809-427-6968. Ed. Glyne Murray. adv.; bk.rev.; play rev.; illus.; index. circ. 15,000.
   Former titles: Bajan; Bajan and South Caribbean (ISSN 0005-4011)

052   DQ
NEW CHRONICLE; the conscience of the nation. 1909. w. $75. Chronicle Printery Ltd., 14 Queen Mary St., P.O. Box 124, Roseau, Dominica, W.I. TEL 809-44-82121. TELEX 8625 TELAGYDO. Ed. Morris Cyrille. adv.; bk.rev. circ. 4,000. (looseleaf format)

052   US
NEW YORK CARIB NEWS; the weekly voice of the Caribbean-American community. vol.11, no.547, 1993. w. $26. Carib News Corp., 15 W. 39th St., New York, NY 10018. TEL 212-944-1991. Ed. M. Roberts. adv. contact: D. Rodney. (tabloid format) **Document type:** newspaper.

051   JM   ISSN 0039-520X
SUNDAY GLEANER. 1834. w. J.$8 per no. Gleaner Company Ltd., 7 North St., P.O. Box 40, Kingston, Jamaica, W.I. TEL 809-922-3400. FAX 809-922-6223. TELEX 2319 GLEANER JA. Ed. Ken Allen. adv.; bk.rev.; film rev.; play rev.; charts; illus.; stat.; tr.lit. circ. 96,000.

051   TR
SUNDAY GUARDIAN. 1917. w. T.T.$230 (incl. in subscr. to Trinidad Guardian). Trinidad Publishing Company Ltd., Box 122, Port-of-Spain, Trinidad & Tobago, W.I. FAX 809-625-7211. Ed. Therese Mills. adv.; bk.rev.; film rev.; play rev. circ. 78,452.

051   JM
SWING. 1968. 10/yr. 102 East St., Kingston, Jamaica, W.I. Ed. Andell Forgie. circ. 12,000.

051   TR
TRINIDAD AND TOBAGO REVIEW. 1977. m. T.T.$35($30) Trinidad & Tobago Institute of the West Indies, 24 Abercromby St., Port-of-Spain, Trinidad & Tobago, W.I. TEL 809-624-7903. Eds. Lloyd Best, Sunity Maharaj. adv.; bk.rev. circ. 5,000. (tabloid format; back issues avail.)
   Description: Reviews current affairs: economics, politics, arts, and sports of the West Indies.

079.72   TR
TRINIDAD GUARDIAN. 1917. d. T.T.$1250. Trinidad Publishing Company Ltd., Box 122, Port of Spain, Trinidad, W.I. TEL 809-623-8870. FAX 809-625-7211. Ed. Carl Jacobs. adv.; bk.rev.; film rev.; play rev. circ. 52,617. **Document type:** newspaper.

052   JM
WEEKEND STAR. 1951. w. J.$8 per no. Gleaner Company Ltd., 7 North St., P.O. Box 40, Kingston, Jamaica, W.I. TEL 809-922-3400. FAX 809-922-6223. TELEX 2319 GLEANER JA. Ed. Ken Allen. adv. circ. 95,000. (tabloid format; back issues avail.)

051   BB
WHAT'S ON IN BARBADOS. 1985. m. free. Carib Publicity Co., Nation House, Fontabelle, Bridgetown, Barbados, W.I. FAX 809-427-6968. Ed. Celine Barnard. adv. circ. 20,000.
   Supersedes (1956-1984): Barbados Tourist News; **Formerly:** Barbados News.

GENERAL INTEREST PERIODICALS — Yugoslavia

057.82   YU   ISSN 0350-6215
DUGA. fortn. 312 din.($53) Beogradski Izdavacko-Graficki Zavod, Bul. Vojvode Misica 17-III, 11001 Belgrade, Yugoslavia. TEL 650-630. FAX 011-651-841. Ed. Ilij Rapaic. illus.
   Formerly (until 1974): Adam i Eva.

057.8   YU   ISSN 0016-2027
FRONT; ilustrovani list. (Editions in Macedonian, Serbo-Croatian and Slovenian) 1944. w. 20 din.($12) (Vojnoizdavacki i Novinski Centar) Front, Ul. Svetozara Markovica 70, 11001 Belgrade, Yugoslavia. Ed. Predrag Pejcic. film rev.; illus.

057   YU   ISSN 0436-2616
GRADINA; casopis za umetnost. (Text in Serbian) 1966. m. 140 din. Gradina, Izdavacka Ustanova, Pobede 38, 18000 Nis, Serbia, Yugoslavia. Ed. Goran Stankovic. adv.; bk.rev. circ. 1,000.

057.8   YU   ISSN 0018-2869
HLAS LUDU. (Text in Slovak) 1944. w. 1000 din. (Skupstina A P Vojvodine) N I U "Hlas Ludu", Blv. 23 Oktobra 31-V, 21000 Novi Sad, Vojvodina, Yugoslavia. FAX 021-613-693. Ed. Dr. Juraj Bartos. adv. circ. 5,000. **Document type:** newspaper.

057.8   YU   ISSN 0019-0977
IBARSKE NOVOSTI; list za politicka i drustvena pitanja. 1948. w. 180 din. NIRU, Ibarske Novosti Novinsko Izdavacka i Radio Ustanova, Mire Cukulica 9, Kraljevo, Serbia, Yugoslavia. Ed. Ljiljana Djordjevic.

059.91   YU   ISSN 0019-2570
ILUSTROVANA POLITIKA. (Text in Serbo-Croatian) 1957. w. 440 din.($26) Politika, Makedonska 29, Belgrade, Yugoslavia. Ed. Miodrag Popovic.

057.8   YU   ISSN 0021-5775
JEDINSTVO. 1946. d. 600 din. (Socijalisticki Savez Radnog Naroda Kosova) Jedinstvo, Marsala Tita 49, Pristina, Kosovo, Yugoslavia. Ed. Mikola Savejeic.

949.7   YU   ISSN 0022-6033
JUGOSLAVIJA; ezemesjacnyj illustrirovanyi zurnal. (Text in Russian) 1946. bi-m. $20. Jugoslovenska Revija, Terazije 31, Belgrade, Yugoslavia. Ed. Rajko Bobot.

057.8 DR301   YU   ISSN 0022-6114
JUGOSLOVENSKI PREGLED; informativno-dokumentarne sveske. English edition: Yugoslav Survey (ISSN 0044-1341) (Text in Serbo-Croatian) 1957. q. $30. Jugoslovenski Pregled, Mose Pijade 8-I, P.O. Box 677, 11001 Belgrade, Yugoslavia. Ed. Ile Kovacevic. adv.; bk.rev. circ. 2,000.

057.8   YU   ISSN 0023-1398
KOMUNA (KIKINDA); list za drustvena i politicka pitanja. 1961. w. 156 din. Komuna, Brace Tatica 6, Kikinda, Vojvodina, Yugoslavia. Ed. Milan Kecman.
   Formerly: Kikindska Komuna.

057.8   YU   ISSN 0023-5261
KULTURNI ZIVOT. 1959. bi-m. 200 din. (Zajednica Kulturno-Prosvetnih Organizacija Jugoslavije) Kulturni Zivot, Slobodana Penezica 35, Belgrade, Yugoslavia. Ed. Radosevic Milenko. abstr.; stat. circ. 1,200.

057.8   YU   ISSN 0027-6685
AP56
N I N. (Nedeljne Informativne Novine) (Text in Serbian) 1935. w. 17664 din. N I N Politika, Makedonska 29, Belgrade, Yugoslavia. TEL 326 898. Ed. Mirko Doekic. circ. 120,000. (back issues avail.)

057.8   YU   ISSN 0027-7843
NAPRED; list za politicka i drustvena pitanja. 1946. w. 150 din. per no. (Socijalisticki Savez Radnog Naroda Opstine Valjevskog Sreza) Napred, Vojvode Misica 21, Valjevo, Yugoslavia. Ed. Stefan Ciric.

057.8   YU   ISSN 0027-7932
NARODNE NOVINE; list za drustvena i politicka pitanja. 1946. w. $22. Narodne Novine, Nis, Balkanska 2, Nis, Serbia, Yugoslavia. (Subscr. to: Kultura, P.O. Box 149, 1389 Budapest 62, Hungary) Ed. Ljubica Sokolovic. circ. 2,800.
   Description: For Yugoslavs in Hungary.

057.8   YU   ISSN 0027-8122
NASA REC. 1944? w. 180 din. (Socijalisticki Savez Leskovacke Opstine) Nasa Rec, Leskovac, Masarikov trg 7, Leskovac, Yugoslavia. Ed. Milisav Marinkovic.

057.8   YU   ISSN 0028-1980
NEDELJNE NOVINE. 1965. w. 100 din. (Socijalisticki Savez Radnog Naroda Backa Palanka) Nedeljne Novine, Trg Bratstva i Jedinstva 32, Backa Palanka, Vojvodina, Yugoslavia. Ed. Slavko Obradovic.

057.8   YU   ISSN 0028-1999
NEDELJNE NOVOSTI.* 1966. w. 50 din. per no. Borba, Trg Marksa i Engelsa 7, Belgrade, Yugoslavia. Ed. Slobodan Glumac.

057.8   YU   ISSN 0031-0662
PANCEVAC. 1952. w. 150 din. Zarka Zrenjanina 7, Pancevo, Yugoslavia. Ed. Aleksander Malusevic.

057.8   YU   ISSN 0032-1796
POBEDA. 1944. w. 100 din. Pobeda, Trg Marsala Tita 66, Krusevac, Yugoslavia. Ed. Bozidar Milosavljevic.

057.8   YU   ISSN 0032-2733
POLIMLJE; list za politicka i drustvena pitanja. 1952. w. 104 din. Polimlje, Vladimira Perica Valtera 50, Prijepolje, Yugoslavia. Ed. Milorad Vernovic.

057.8   YU   ISSN 0034-1142
REC NARODA; list za drustvena i politicka pitanja. 1944? w. Socijalisticki Savez Radnog Naroda Opstine Pozarevac, Lenjinova 4, Pozarevac, Yugoslavia. Ed. Predrag Radovanovic.

057.8 DR301   YU   ISSN 0034-6357
REVIEW; Yugoslav monthly magazine. (Editions in English, French, German, Spanish) 1963. bi-m. $20. Jugoslovenska Revija, Terazije 31, Belgrade, Yugoslavia. Ed. Rajko Bobot. **Indexed:** M.L.A.

057.8   YU   ISSN 0350-4603
RUSKE SLOVO. 1945. w. 8400 din.($60) N I U "Ruske Slovo", Bul. 23, Oktobra 31, 21000 Novi Sad, Yugoslavia. TEL 613-697. Ed. Ljubomir Ramac. adv.; bk.rev.; play rev.; bibl.; illus.; tr.lit. circ. 2,000. (back issues avail.)

057.8   YU   ISSN 0037-6884
SLOBODNA REC;* list za drustvena i politicka pitanja. 1945? w. 10 din. Socijalisticki Savez Radnog Naroda Opstine Vranje, 29 Novembra 10, Vranje, Serbia, Yugoslavia. Ed. Bora Svetkovic.

057.8   YU   ISSN 0038-1276
SOMBORSKE NOVINE. 1954. w. 2600 din. Informativni Centar Sombor, Gradska Kuca 228-23, 25000 Sombor, Yugoslavia. FAX 025-37366. Ed. Slobodan Jerkovic. adv.

057.8   YU   ISSN 0039-436X
SUBOTICKE NOVINE. 1945? w. 19 din. (Socijalisticki Savez Radnog Naroda Suboticke Opstine) N I P "Suboticke Novine", 8 Maksim Gorki St., 24000 Subotica, Yugoslavia. Ed. Josip Stipic.

057.8   YU   ISSN 0040-8204
TITOGRADSKA TRIBINA. (Text in Macdeonian) 1961. w. 104 din. Socijalisticki Savez Radnog Naroda Opstine Titograd, Novaka Miloseva 54, Titograd, Yugoslavia. Ed. Borislav Jablan.

057.8   YU
YU NOVOSTI. 1966? m. 30000 din.($18) Novinsko Izdavacka Radna Organizacija, Zmaj Jovina 21, Belgrade, Yugoslavia. FAX 637-189. TELEX 71055. Ed. Tomislav Milojevic. adv.; illus.
   Former titles: Novosti Iz Jugoslavije; Novosti (ISSN 0029-5272)

949.7 DR301   YU   ISSN 0044-1333
YUGOSLAV LIFE. (Editions in English and Russian) 1956. m. $12. Tanjug News Agency, World Service Desk, P.O. Box 439, Obilicev Venac 2, 11000 Belgrade, Yugoslavia. FAX 011-183-946. Ed. Milenko Babic. adv.; film rev.; play rev.; charts; illus. circ. 9,000.
   Description: Covers foreign affairs, home affairs, economy, culture and sports.

057.82   US
YUGOSLAV REVIEW. (Editions in English, French, German, Russian, Spanish) 1922. m. Yugoslav Illustrated Magazine, Terazije 31, Belgrade, Yugoslavia. Ed. Rajko Bobot. adv.; illus.

949.7 DR301   YU   ISSN 0044-1341
YUGOSLAV SURVEY; a record of facts and information. English translation of: Jugoslovenski Pregled (YU ISSN 0022-6114) 1960. q. $35. Jugoslovenski Pregled, Mose Pijade 8-I, P.O. Box 677, 11001 Belgrade, Yugoslavia. TEL 333-295. FAX 332-295. Ed. Ile Kovacevic. adv.; bk.rev.; charts; stat. circ. 3,000. (back issues avail.) **Indexed:** Key to Econ.Sci., Rural Recreat.Tour.Abstr., World Agri.Econ.& Rural Sociol.Abstr., World Bibl.Soc.Sec.
   —BLDSC (9421.670000); Faxon; UnCover; SWETS.

057   YU   ISSN 0514-7352
ZERI I RINISE. w. 63 din. Rilindja, Rruga Beogradi 29a, Pristina, Kosovo, Yugoslavia. Ed. Mustafa Rushiti. charts; illus.

GENERAL INTEREST PERIODICALS — Zambia

059   ZA
IMBILA. m. (11/yr.). Information Services, Box RW 50020, Lusaka, Zambia. (Subscr. to: Government Printer, Box 30136, Lusaka, Zambia)

079.68   ZA   ISSN 0020-4854
INTANDA NEWS. (Text in Tonga) 1961. m. (11/yr.). Information Services, Box RW 50020, Lusaka, Zambia. (Subscr. to: Director, Box 30136, Lusaka, Zambia) adv.; illus. circ. 7,000. **Document type:** newspaper.

050   ZA
LISELI LA ZAMBIA. m. (11/yr.). Information Services, Box RW 50020, Lusaka, Zambia. (Subscr. to: Director, Box 30136, Lusaka, Zambia)

050   ZA
LUKANGA NEWS. m. (11/yr.). Information Services, Box RW 50020, Lusaka, Zambia. (Subscr. to: Director, Box 30136, Lusaka, Zambia)

050   ZA
NGOMA NEWS. m. (11/yr.). Information Services, Box RW 50020, Lusaka, Zambia. (Subscr. to: Director, Box 30136, Lusaka, Zambia)

079.6894   ZA
SUNDAY MAIL. 1991. w. K.50 per no. Zambia Daily Mail Ltd., P.O. Box 31424, Lusaka, Zambia. **Document type:** newspaper.

079.68   ZA
SUNDAY TIMES OF ZAMBIA. 1970. w. Times Newspapers (Zambia) Ltd., P.O. Box 70069, Ndola, Zambia, Zambia. TEL 260-2-610451. FAX 260-2-614469. adv. circ. 60,970. **Document type:** newspaper.

079.68   ZA
THE TIMES OF ZAMBIA. 1966. d. K.115520 (effective 1994). Times Newspapers (Zambia) Ltd., P.O. Box 70069, Ndola, Zambia. TEL 260-2-610451. FAX 260-2-614469. adv.; illus. **Document type:** newspaper.

052 079.68   ZA   ISSN 0041-378X
TSOPANO NEWS. 1958. m. (11/yr.). Information Services, Box RW 50020, Lusaka, Zambia. (Subscr. to: Director, Box 30136, Lusaka, Zambia) adv.; illus. **Document type:** newspaper.

052   ZA
VOICE OF S O M A F C O. (Text in English) 1983. irreg. exchange basis. Solomon Mahlangu Freedom College, c/o African National Congress, P.O. Box 31791, Lusaka, Zambia. circ. 1,000.

052   ZA   ISSN 0044-1422
Z; monthly magazine in English. 1969. m. $2.88. Information Services, Box RW 50020, Lusaka, Zambia. (Subscr. to: Director, Box 30136, Lusaka, Zambia) bk.rev.; illus. circ. 10,000.

079.68   ZA
ZAMBIA DAILY MAIL. 1965. d. Zambia Daily Mail Ltd., P.O. Box 31421, Lusaka, Zambia. Ed. Emmanuel Nyirenda. circ. 40,000. (tabloid format) **Document type:** newspaper.
   Former titles (until 1970): Zambia Mail (ISSN 0044-1732); Central African Mail.

GENERAL INTEREST PERIODICALS — Zimbabwe

052   **ZA**
ZANGO/FORUM; Zambian journal of contemporary issues. 1976. 2/yr. K.6.50. University of Zambia, Box 2379, Lusaka, Zambia. Ed. Lyson P. Tembo. bk.rev. circ. 1,000. **Indexed:** Curr.Cont.Africa, Rural Ext.Educ.& Tr.Abstr.

GENERAL INTEREST PERIODICALS — Zimbabwe

052   **RH**   **ISSN 1016-3123**
DT1001
AFRICA SOUTH; the news magazine of southern Africa. 1990. m. Z.$3.50 per no. Africa South Publications, P.O. Box 7020, Harare, Zimbabwe.

079.68   **RH**
THE CHRONICLE. (Text in English) 1894. d. Z.$263.50. Zimbabwe Newspapers Ltd. (Bulawayo), P.O. Box 585, Bulawayo, Zimbabwe. TEL 65471. Ed. Stephen A. Mpofu. adv.; bk.rev. circ. 74,000. (also avail. in microfilm) **Document type:** newspaper.
    Formerly (until 1951): Bulawayo Chronicle.

079.68   **RH**
THE HERALD. (Text in English) 1891. d. Z.$263.50. Zimbabwe Newspapers Ltd., Herald House, George Silundika Ave., Second St., P.O. Box 396, Harare, Zimbabwe. TEL 263-4-795771. FAX 263-4-791311. Ed. Tommy Sithole. circ. 140,000. **Document type:** newspaper.
    Former titles (until 1978): Rhodesia Herald; Mashonaland Herald and Zambezia Times; Incorporates: Evening Standard.

052   **RH**
INDEPENDENT ZIMBABWE. a. free. Ministry of Information, Posts and Telecommunications, P.O. Box 8232, Causeway, Harare, Zimbabwe. TEL 263-4-703894. TELEX 24142 ZW. circ. 50,000. **Document type:** government publication.
    Description: Chronicle of events of the previous year.

079.68   **RH**
KWAYEDZA. w. Z.$44.20. Zimbabwe Newspapers Ltd., Herald House, George Silundika Ave., Second St., P.O. Box 396, Harare. TEL 263-4-795771. FAX 263-4-791311. Eds. P. Chidyausiku, L. Sibanda. circ. 85,000. **Document type:** newspaper.

079.9689   **RH**
MANICA POST. 1893. w. Z.$54.60 (overseas Z.$106.60). Zimbabwe Newspapers Ltd. (Mutare), 87 Herbert Chitepo St., P.O. Box 960, Mutare, Zimbabwe. TEL 263-20-61212. FAX 263-20-61149. Ed. John Gambanga. adv.; bk.rev. circ. 10,088. **Document type:** newspaper.
    Formerly: Umtali Post.

059   **RH**
MOTO. 1982. m. $20. Mambo Press, P.O. Box 779, Gweru, Zimbabwe. TEL 4886. FAX 51991. adv.; bk.rev. circ. 30,000.
    Formerly: Kristo.

052   **RH**
PARADE MAGAZINE. 1953. m. Z.$32.40. Thomson Publications Zimbabwe (Pvt) Ltd., Thomson House, P.O. Box 1683, Harare, Zimbabwe. TEL 736835. FAX 752390. TELEX 24705 ZW. Ed. Mark Chavunduka. adv.; bk.rev.; charts; illus. circ. 1,700,000. **Document type:** consumer publication.
    Formerly: Parade and Foto-Action (ISSN 0031-1618)

968.9   **RH**
DT962 .A2
SPOTLIGHT ON ZIMBABWE. (Editions in English, French, German) 1967. m. free. Ministry of Information, Posts and Telecommunications, P.O. Box 8232, Causeway, Harare, Zimbabwe. Ed. B.S.C. Chizikani. bk.rev.; charts; illus. **Document type:** government publication.
    Supersedes: Focus on Rhodesia (ISSN 0304-7628); Rhodesian Commentary (ISSN 0035-4759)

079.9689   **RH**
SUNDAY MAIL. 1935. w. Z.$49.50. Zimbabwe Newspapers Ltd., Herald House, George Silikunda Ave., 2nd St., P.O. Box 396, Harare, Zimbabwe. TEL 263-4-795771. FAX 263-4-791311. adv. circ. 140,000. **Document type:** newspaper.

079.68   **RH**
THE SUNDAY NEWS. (Text in English) 1930. w. Z.$65. Zimbabwe Newspapers Ltd. (Bulawayo), P.O. Box 585, Bulawayo, Zimbabwe. TEL 65471. Ed. Lawrence Chikuwira. **Document type:** newspaper.

079.6891   **RH**
WEEKEND GAZETTE. 1991. w. Z.$69 (Z.$99 in Africa; elsewhere Z.$114). Modus Publications, Modus House, 27 Charter Rd., P.O. Box 66070, Kopje, Harare, Zimbabwe. TEL 263-4-738722. FAX 263-4-707130. Ed. M.J. Hamilton. adv.; bk.rev.; film rev. circ. 50,000. (tabloid format) **Document type:** newspaper.

052   **RH**
WORLD VISION NEWS. vol.5, 1987. q. World Vision Zimbabwe, P.O. Box 2420, Harare, Zimbabwe. **Indexed:** P.L.E.S.A.

052   **RH**
ZIMBABWE IN BRIEF. (Text in English, French, German) 1980. a. free. Ministry of Information, Posts and Telecommunications, P.O. Box 8232, Causeway, Harare, Zimbabwe. TEL 263-4-703894. TELEX 24142 ZW. circ. 100,000. **Document type:** government publication.
    Description: Basic facts about Zimbabwe.

GENETICS

see Biology–Genetics

GEOGRAPHY

see also History; Travel and Tourism

910   **US**   **ISSN 0275-3995**
A A G NEWSLETTER. 1967. m. membership. Association of American Geographers, 1710 16th St., N.W., Washington, DC 20009-3198. TEL 202-234-1450. FAX 202-234-2744. Ed. Linda Bradshaw. circ. 6,800. (also avail. in microform from UMI) **Document type:** newsletter.
—UMI.

536.05   **US**   **ISSN 0747-9417**
TA501
A C S M BULLETIN; promoting advancement in surveying and mapping. 1950. bi-m. $75 to non-members (foreign $85). American Congress on Surveying and Mapping, 5410 Grosvenor Ln., Ste. 100, Bethesda, MD 20814. TEL 301-493-0200. FAX 301-493-8245. Ed. Lucia Chambers; Pub. John Lisack. adv.; bk.rev. circ. 10,000. (also avail. in microform from UMI; back issues avail.; reprint service avail. from UMI) **Indexed:** Bibl.Cart., GeoRef. **Document type:** bulletin.
—BLDSC (2386.545000); UnCover; SWETS; UMI. CCC.
    Formerly (until 1980): American Congress on Surveying and Mapping. Bulletin (ISSN 0097-6180)
    Description: Provides current technical and managerial information in the field of surveying, cartography and geodesy.

910   **US**
A G S NEWSLETTER. 1978. s-a. $26. American Geographical Society, 156 Fifth Ave., Ste. 600, New York, NY 10010. TEL 212-242-0214. Ed. Peter Lewis. circ. 2,000. (back issues avail.) **Document type:** newsletter.

A N A R E NEWS. (Australian National Antarctic Research Expeditions) see *SCIENCES: COMPREHENSIVE WORKS*

914   **BE**
AARDRIJKSKUNDE. (Text in Dutch; summaries in English) 1977. q. 950 BEF. Vereniging Leraars Aardrijkskunde, 42 de Croylaan, B-3001 Heverlee, Belgium. TEL 32-16-286611. Ed. Etienne van Hecke. adv.; bk.rev.; illus. circ. 1,150. **Document type:** academic/scholarly publication.
    Supersedes: Aardrijkskunde - Geographie (ISSN 0435-382X)

AARHUS UNIVERSITET. GEOLOGISK INSTITUT. GEOSKRIFTER. see *EARTH SCIENCES — Geology*

917.2 986   **GT**   **ISSN 0252-337X**
F1461
ACADEMIA DE GEOGRAFIA E HISTORIA DE GUATEMALA. ANALES. 1924. a. $20. Academia de Geografia e Historia de Guatemala, 3a Avenida 8-35, Zona 1, 01001 Guatemala City, Guatemala. TEL 23544. bk.rev.; index. circ. 1,000. (back issues avail.) **Indexed:** Anthropol.Lit. **Document type:** academic/scholarly publication.
    Description: Covers history, anthropology, ethnography, archaeology, ethno-history, geography and related sciences.

910   **US**   **ISSN 1053-0614**
F48
ACROSS THE BORDER. 1988. q. Claudette Maerz, Ed. & Pub., Box 31010, Bloomington, MN 55431.

ACTA GEODAETICA, GEOPHYSICA ET MONTANISTICA HUNGARICA. see *EARTH SCIENCES — Geophysics*

910   **FR**   **ISSN 0001-5687**
G1   **CODEN: ACGEAO**
ACTA GEOGRAPHICA. 1821. q. 250 F. (foreign 285 F.). Societe de Geographie, 184 bd. Saint-Germain, 75006 Paris, France. TEL 1-45-48-54-62. Ed. Jacqueline Beaujeu-Garnier. bk.rev.; bibl.; charts; illus.; maps. circ. 1,500. **Indexed:** Bibl.Cart., E.I., Geo.Abstr., GeoRef., Rural Recreat.Tour.Abstr., SSCI, World Agri.Econ.& Rural Sociol.Abstr.
—BLDSC (0618.960000).
    Former titles (until 1939): La Geographie; (until 1900): Bulletin de la Societe de Geographie.

551   **HU**   **ISSN 0209-9004**
ACTA GEOGRAPHICA AC GEOLOGICA ET METEOROLOGICA DEBRECINA. (Text in English, French, German, Hungarian, Russian) 1962. irreg., vol.28-29, 1991. Kossuth Lajos Tudomanyegyetem, Egyetem Ter 1, 4010 Debrecen, Hungary. Ed. Z. Borsy. **Indexed:** Geo.Abstr., GeoRef. **Document type:** monographic series.
    Formerly (until 1973): Acta Universitatis Debreceniensis. Series Geographica, Geologica et Meteorologica (ISSN 0567-7475); Which superseded in part (in 1962): Acta Universitatis Debrecensis (ISSN 0365-7817).

910   **PL**   **ISSN 0065-1249**
                           CODEN: LTWMAS
ACTA GEOGRAPHICA LODZIENSIA. (Text in English, Polish) 1947. a. price varies. Lodzkie Towarzystwo Naukowe, Ul. Piotrowska 179, 90-447 Lodz, Poland. TEL 48-42-361026. FAX 48-42-362415. TELEX 884519 PAN PL. (Dist. by: Ars Polona, Krakowskie Przedmiescie 7, Warsaw, Poland) Ed. Halina Klatkowa. **Indexed:** Geo.Abstr., GeoRef. **Document type:** academic/scholarly publication.
—BLDSC (0618.990000).

910   **BE**   **ISSN 0065-1257**
                           CODEN: AGHLAA
ACTA GEOGRAPHICA LOVANIENSIA. 1961. irreg., latest no.16. price varies. Universite Catholique de Louvain, Institut de Geographie, Batiment Mercator, 1348 Louvain-la-Neuve, Belgium. Eds. Th. Brulard, M. Goosens. circ. 250. **Indexed:** Geo.Abstr., GeoRef. **Document type:** monographic series.

ACTA HUMBOLDTIANA. see *ANTHROPOLOGY*

ACTA PHYTOGEOGRAPHICA SUECICA. see *BIOLOGY — Botany*

910   **XR**   **ISSN 0300-5402**
G58   **CODEN: AUCGBZ**
ACTA UNIVERSITATIS CAROLINAE: GEOGRAPHICA. (Text and summaries in Czech, English, French, German, Polish and Russian) 1966. s-a. 40 Kcs.($11) Universita Karlova, Prirodovedecka Fakulta, Vinicna 5, 128 44 Prague 2, Czech Republic. (Dist. by: Geographical Library, Faculty of Science, Albertov 6, 12843 Prague 2, Czech Republic) **Indexed:** Geo.Abstr., GeoRef.

GEOGRAPHY

910 370   PL   ISSN 0208-6123
ACTA UNIVERSITATIS LODZIENSIS: FOLIA GEOGRAPHICA. (Text in Polish; summaries in various languages) 1955-1974; N.S. 1982. irreg. Wydawnictwo Uniwersytetu Lodzkiego, Ul. Jaracza 34, Lodz, Poland. TEL 331671. (Dist. by: Ars Polona-Ruch, Krakowskie Przedmiescie 7, Warsaw, Poland) **Document type:** academic/scholarly publication.
  Supersedes in part: Uniwersytet Lodzki. Zeszyty Naukowe. Seria 2: Nauki Matematyczno-Przyrodnicze (ISSN 0076-0366)
  Description: Publishes the research of the staff of the University of Lodz on physical and economic geography, spatial economics and protection of the environment.

910   PL   ISSN 0208-5291
Q4   CODEN: ANCGBK
ACTA UNIVERSITATIS NICOLAI COPERNICI. GEOGRAFIA. 1963. irreg. price varies. Uniwersytet Mikolaja Kopernika, Biblioteka Uniwersytecka, Ul. Gagarina 13, 87-100 Torun, Poland. TEL 233-52. TELEX 552382. (Dist. by Osrodek Rozpowszechniania Wydwnictw Naukowych PAN, Palac Kultury i Nauki, 00-901 Warsaw, Poland) **Indexed:** Biol.Abstr., Geo.Abstr., GeoRef.

914.38   PL   ISSN 0591-2776
ACTA UNIVERSITATIS WRATISLAVIENSIS. STUDIA GEOGRAFICZNE. (Text in Polish; summaries in English or French) 1975. irreg. price varies. (Uniwersytet Wroclawski) Wydawnictwo Uniwersytetu Wroclawskiego, Pl. Uniwersytecki 9-13, 50-137 Wroclaw, Poland. (Dist. by: Ksiegarnia Uniwersytetu Wroclawskiego, Pl. Uniwersytecki 9-13, 50-137 Wroclaw, Poland) Ed. Jan Loboda. charts; illus. **Indexed:** Geo.Abstr. **Document type:** academic/scholarly publication.

910 940   SW   ISSN 0349-0564
ACTA WEXIONENSIA. SERIE 1: HISTORY & GEOGRAPHY. 1979. irreg. Hoegskolan i Vaexjoe, Box 5053, S-350 05 Vaexjoe, Sweden. circ. 600. (back issues avail.)

910   US   ISSN 0142-5889
ADVANCES IN DESERT AND ARID LAND TECHNOLOGY AND DEVELOPMENT SERIES. irreg. Harwood Academic Publishers, 820 Town Center Dr., Langhorne, PA 19047. TEL 215-750-2642. FAX 215-750-6343. (UK subscr. to: Box 90, Reading, Berkshire RG1 8JL, England. TEL 0734-560-080) Eds. A. Bishay, W.G. McGinnies. (also avail. in microform) **Document type:** monographic series.
  —BLDSC (0704.243000).
  Refereed Serial

910   NR   ISSN 0065-4698
AHMADU BELLO UNIVERSITY. DEPARTMENT OF GEOGRAPHY. OCCASIONAL PAPER. 1965. irreg. no.9, 1985. $15 (typically set in Feb.). Ahmadu Bello University, Department of Geography, Zaria, Nigeria. Ed. J.A. Ariyo. adv. circ. 350.

AINM. see *LINGUISTICS*

AKADEMIA ROLNICZA IM. HUGONA KOLLATAJA W KRAKOWIE. ZESZYTY NAUKOWE. SERIA: GEODEZJA. see *EARTH SCIENCES — Geophysics*

526.3 631.3   PL   ISSN 0209-0511
AKADEMIA ROLNICZA WE WROCLAWIU. ZESZYTY NAUKOWE. GEODEZJA I URZADZENIA ROLNE. (Subseries of: Akademia Rolnicza we Wroclawiu. Zeszyty Naukowe (ISSN 0867-7964)) (Text in Polish; summaries in English) 1980. irreg. price varies. Akademia Rolnicza we Wroclawiu, Ul. Norwida 25, 50-375 Wroclaw, Poland. FAX 22-48-49. (Subscr. to: Dzial Wydawnictw i Poligrafii Akademii Rolniczej, ul. Sopocka 23, 50-344 Wroclaw, Poland. TEL 21-12-77) circ. 270. **Document type:** academic/scholarly publication.

910.02   US   ISSN 0361-1353
F901
ALASKA GEOGRAPHIC. 1972. q. $39 (effective 1994). Alaska Geographic Society, Box 93370, Anchorage, AK 99509-3370. TEL 907-562-0164. FAX 907-562-0479. Ed. Penny Rennick. bk.rev.; charts; illus. circ. 8,000. (back issues avail.) **Indexed:** Access (1975-1988), GeoRef. **Document type:** monographic series.
  —UnCover.
  Description: Natural resources of the lands of Alaska, the Polar Rim and Pacific Rim.

ALL-ASIA GUIDE. see *TRAVEL AND TOURISM*

AMAZONIA PERUANA. see *ANTHROPOLOGY*

526.9   US
AMERICAN CONGRESS ON SURVEYING & MAPPING. PROCEEDINGS. 1942. s-a. price varies. American Congress on Surveying and Mapping, 5410 Grosvenor Ln., Ste. 100, Bethesda, MD 20814. TEL 301-493-0200. (Co-sponsor: American Society of Photogrammetry) Pub. John Lisack. abstr.; charts; illus.; stat. (back issues avail.) **Indexed:** Bibl.Cart. **Document type:** academic/scholarly publication, proceedings.

526   US   ISSN 0277-2876
TA501
AMERICAN CONGRESS ON SURVEYING AND MAPPING. TECHNICAL PAPERS. 1968. irreg. (approx. 2/yr.). American Congress on Surveying and Mapping, 5410 Grosvenor Ln., Ste. 100, Bethesda, MD 20814. TEL 301-493-0200. index. (also avail. in microfilm from UMI; reprint service avail. from UMI) **Indexed:** Bibl.Cart., GeoRef. **Document type:** monographic series.
  Formerly: American Congress on Surveying and Mapping. Proceedings of Annual Meeting (ISSN 0161-0945); Incorporates: American Congress on Surveying and Mapping. Papers from the Annual Meetings (ISSN 0065-7913)

526.982   US
AMERICAN SOCIETY FOR PHOTOGRAMMETRY AND REMOTE SENSING. TECHNICAL PAPERS FROM THE ANNUAL MEETING. a. $30 to non-members; members $20. American Society for Photogrammetry and Remote Sensing, 5410 Grosvenor Ln., Ste. 210, Bethesda, MD 20814-2160. TEL 301-493-0290. FAX 301-493-0208. index. **Indexed:** GeoRef.
  Formerly: American Society of Photogrammetry. Technical Papers from the Annual Meeting (ISSN 0277-2094)

526.982   US   ISSN 1064-2536
TA502
AMERICAN SOCIETY FOR PHOTOGRAMMETRY AND REMOTE SENSING FALL CONVENTION. TECHNICAL PAPERS. (Vol. for 1982 and 1983 published jointly with American Congress on Surveying and Mapping) a. $75 to non-members; members $45. American Society for Photogrammetry and Remote Sensing, 5410 Grosvenor Ln., Ste. 210, Bethesda, MD 20814-2160. TEL 301-493-0290. FAX 301-493-0208. **Indexed:** Bibl.Cart.
  Former titles: American Society of Photogrammetry Fall Convention. Technical Papers (ISSN 0271-4043); (until 1983): American Society of Photogrammetry Fall Convention. Proceedings (ISSN 0196-674X)

910   US   ISSN 0899-6040
AMERICAN UNIVERSITY STUDIES. SERIES 25. GEOGRAPHY. 1990. irreg. Peter Lang Publishing, Inc., 62 W. 45th St., 4th Fl., New York, NY 10036. TEL 212-302-6740. Ed. Michael Flamini. **Document type:** academic/scholarly publication.

910   MX
ANALES DE GEOGRAFIA. 1975. a. Universidad Nacional Autonoma de Mexico, Facultad de Filosofia y Letras, Villa Obregon, Ciudad Universitaria, 04510 Mexico 20, D.F., Mexico. illus.
  Formerly: Instituto de Geografia. Annales.

918.6   CK   ISSN 0120-8551
ANALISIS GEOGRAFICO. 1970. s-a. price varies. Instituto Geografico Agustin Codazzi, Subdireccion de Geografia, Carrera 30, No. 48-51, Apdo. Aereo 6721, Bogota, Colombia. TEL 244-84-13. FAX 91-364146. Ed. Victor Quintero. circ. 1,000.

910   FR   ISSN 0003-4010
              CODEN: ANGEAX
ANNALES DE GEOGRAPHIE. 1891. bi-m. 76 ECU($92) (Societe de Geographie) Armand Colin (Subsidiary of: Masson), 103 bd. St. Michel, 75240 Paris Cedex 05, France. TEL 1-46-34-19-12. FAX 1-43-26-96-38. TELEX 201 269 F. Ed. Jacqueline Beaujeu-Garnier. adv.; bk.rev.; bibl.; charts; illus. circ. 1,950. (reprint service avail. from KTO) **Indexed:** Amer.Hist.& Life (until 1993), Bibl.Cart., Curr.Cont.Africa, Geo.Abstr., GeoRef., Hist.Abstr. (until 1993), Pt.de Rep. (1979-), Rural Recreat.Tour.Abstr., SSCI, World Agri.Econ.& Rural Sociol.Abstr.
  —SWETS.

910 551   PL   ISSN 0137-1983
QE1   CODEN: ACBGA5
ANNALES UNIVERSITATIS MARIAE CURIE-SKLODOWSKA. SECTIO B. GEOGRAPHIA, GEOLOGIA, MINERALOGIA ET PETROGRAPHIA. (Text in English or Polish; summaries in English, French) 1946. a. price varies. Uniwersytet Marii Curie-Sklodowskiej, Wydawnictwo, Pl. M. Curie-Sklodowskiej 5, 20-031 Lublin, Poland. TEL 48-81-375304. FAX 48-81-336699. TELEX 0643223. Ed. Jozef Wojtanowicz. circ. 900. **Indexed:** Biol.Abstr., Chem.Abstr., Doc.Geogr., Geo.Abstr., Soils & Fert. **Document type:** academic/scholarly publication.
  —BLDSC (0956.500000).

910   IT   ISSN 0392-8713
ANNALI DI RICERCHE E STUDI DI GEOGRAFIA. (Text in Italian; summaries in English, French, German) 1944. s-a. exchange basis. Coopedit-Macerata, Casella Postale 1691, 16100 Genoa, Italy. Ed.Bd.
  Formerly (until 1947): Annali dell'Istituto di Georgrafia dell'Ateneo Genovese (ISSN 0392-8721)

910   JA
ANNALS OF HISTORICAL AND GEOGRAPHICAL STUDIES/REKISHIGAKU CHIRIGAKU NENPO. (Text in English, Japanese) 1976. a. Kyushu University, 4-2-1 Ropponmatsu, Chuo-ku, Fukuoka 810, Japan. TEL 81-92-731-8745. FAX 81-92-771-4161. **Document type:** academic/scholarly publication.

ANNALS OF REGIONAL SCIENCE; international journal of urban, regional and environmental research and policy. see *BUSINESS AND ECONOMICS*

914.4   FR   ISSN 1169-6168
▼**ANNUAIRE DE LA RECHERCHE GEOGRAPHIQUE FRANCOPHONE.** 1992. a. 150 F. Centre National de la Recherche Scientifique, Laboratoire Intergeo, 191 rue Saint-Jacques, 75005 Paris, France. TEL 46-33-74-31. FAX 43-29-65-29. **Document type:** directory.

914.4   FR
ANNUAIRE DES NOTABLES REGIONAUX. 1975. a. Editions Dany Thibaud, 52 rue Labrouste, 75015 Paris, France.

ANNUAIRE DES PAYS DE L'OCEAN INDIEN. see *SOCIAL SCIENCES: COMPREHENSIVE WORKS*

910   US
ANNUAL EDITIONS: GEOGRAPHY. 1981. a. $11.95. Dushkin Publishing Group, Inc., Sluice Dock, Guilford, CT 06437-9989. TEL 203-453-4351. FAX 203-453-6000. Ed. Gerald R. Pitzl; Pub. Lan Nielsen. illus. **Document type:** academic/scholarly publication.
  Refereed Serial

910   US
ANNUAL EDITIONS: GLOBAL ISSUES. 1985. a. $11.95. Dushkin Publishing Group, Inc., Sluice Dock, Guilford, CT 06437-9989. TEL 203-453-4351. FAX 203-453-6000. Ed. Robert M. Jackson; Pub. Lan Nielsen. illus. **Document type:** academic/scholarly publication.
  Refereed Serial

910 338 338.91   US
336
ANNUAL EDITIONS: THIRD WORLD. 1989. a. $11.95. Dushkin Publishing Group, Inc., Sluice Dock, Guilford, CT 06437-9989. TEL 203-453-4351. FAX 203-453-6000. Ed. Robert Griffiths; Pub. Lan Nielsen. **Document type:** academic/scholarly publication.
  Refereed Serial

919   NZ   ISSN 0003-5327
G845
ANTARCTIC; a news bulletin. 1956. q. NZ.$48. New Zealand Antarctic Society, Box 2110, Wellington, New Zealand. FAX 64-4-791185. Ed. R.A. Ormerod. adv.; bk.rev.; illus.; cum.index every 3 yrs. circ. 1,100. (tabloid format) **Indexed:** GeoRef.
  —UnCover. **CCC.**

919.8   AG   ISSN 0302-5691
G845   CODEN: ANTDAR
ANTARTIDA. 1971. a. Direccion Nacional del Antartico, Cerrito 1248, Buenos Aires 1010, Argentina. Ed. Juan Alberto Nadaud. charts; illus. **Indexed:** Deep Sea Res.& Oceanogr.Abstr., GeoRef.

GEOGRAPHY

910.02   US   ISSN 0066-4812
G1
ANTIPODE; a radical journal of geography. 1969. 4/yr. $39 to individuals in N. America (elsewhere $46); institutions $110.50 in N. America (elsewhere $137.50). Basil Blackwell Inc., 238 Main St., Cambridge, MA 02142. TEL 617-547-7110. FAX 617-547-0789. Eds. Joe Doherty, Richard Walker. adv.: page $350; trim 4 1/2 x 7 1/2. bk.rev. circ. 1,050. (back issues avail.; reprint service avail. from SWZ) **Indexed**: Alt.Press Ind., E.I., Geo.Abstr., Left Ind. (1986-), World Agri.Econ.& Rural Sociol.Abstr.
—BLDSC (1549.800000); Faxon; UnCover; SWETS; UMI. **CCC**.
   Description: Publishes articles on the radical analysis of spatial and environmental problems. Provides a forum for discussion on topics of vital social and political concern.

ANUARIO GEOGRAFICO DEL PERU. see HISTORY — History Of North And South America

910   UK   ISSN 0143-6228
G1
APPLIED GEOGRAPHY. 1981. q. £130 in UK and Europe; elsewhere £140. Butterworth - Heinemann (Subsidiary of: Reed International PLC), Linacre House, Jordan Hill, Oxford OX2 8DP, England. TEL 0865-310366. FAX 0865-310898. TELEX 83111 BHPOXF G. (Subscr. to: Turpin Transactions Ltd., Distribution Centre, Blackhorse Rd., Letchworth, Herts SG6 1HN, England. TEL 0462-672555) Ed. J. Hansom. illus.; index. (also avail. in microform from UMI; back issues avail.) **Indexed**: A.I.Abstr., Abstr.Rural Dev.Trop., ASCA, Energy Ind., Energy Info.Abstr., Environ.Abstr., Environ.Per.Bibl. (1985-), Field Crop Abstr., Forest Prod.Abstr., Geo.Abstr., Herb.Abstr., Irr.& Drain.Abstr., Risk Abstr., Rural Devel.Abstr., Soils & Fert., SSCI, Weed Abstr., World Agri.Econ.& Rural Sociol.Abstr. **Document type**: academic/scholarly publication.
—BLDSC (1572.590000); CIS; Faxon; UnCover; SWETS; UMI. **CCC**.
   Description: Examines man's evaluation, exploitation and management of resources. Encompasses human and physical geography, plus aspects of agriculture, ecology, planning and politics. *Refereed Serial*

910   GW   ISSN 0173-7619
APPLIED GEOGRAPHY AND DEVELOPMENT. biennial. 1973. DM.40 per no. Institute for Scientific Co-operation with Developing Countries, Landhausstr. 18, 72074 Tuebingen, Germany. FAX 07071-26753. **Indexed**: Asian-Pac.Econ.Lit., Geo.Abstr., I D A, P.A.I.S., Rice Abstr., Rural Recreat.Tour.Abstr., Soils & Fert., World Agri.Econ.& Rural Sociol.Abstr. **Document type**: academic/scholarly publication.
   Formerly (until 1980): Applied Sciences and Development (ISSN 0340-1863)

910   US   ISSN 0192-8996
G56
APPLIED GEOGRAPHY CONFERENCES. 1977. a. $20 to individuals; libraries $25; students $18. State University of New York at Binghamton, Department of Geography, Box 6000, Binghamton, NY 13902-6000. TEL 607-777-2755. Ed. John W. Frazier. charts; illus.; stat. circ. 300. (back issues avail.) **Indexed**: Geo.Abstr., World Agri.Econ.& Rural Sociol.Abstr. **Document type**: academic/scholarly publication.
—BLDSC (6396.220000).

914.3   GW   ISSN 0373-7187
CODEN: ARLKA2
ARBEITEN ZUR RHEINISCHEN LANDESKUNDE. 1950. irreg. price varies. (Universitaet Bonn, Geographisches Institut) Ferd. Duemmlers Verlag, Kaiserstr. 31-37, 53113 Bonn, Germany. (Subscr. to: Postfach 1480, 53004 Bonn, Germany) **Indexed**: GeoRef.

ARCHAEOLOGICAL SURVEY OF ISRAEL. SURVEY MAP SERIES. see ARCHAEOLOGY

ARCHIVIO BOTANICO E BIOGEOGRAFICO ITALIANO. see BIOLOGY — Botany

ARCTIC. see SCIENCES: COMPREHENSIVE WORKS

ARCTIC AND ALPINE RESEARCH. see SCIENCES: COMPREHENSIVE WORKS

ARCTIC RESEARCH OF THE UNITED STATES. see SCIENCES: COMPREHENSIVE WORKS

910   UK   ISSN 0004-0894
G7   CODEN: AREAB6
AREA. 1969. q. £50. Institute of British Geographers, 1 Kensington Gore, London SW7 2AR, England. TEL 44-71-584-6371. FAX 44-71-581-9918. circ. 2,600. **Indexed**: Avery Ind.Architt.Per., Br.Archaeol.Abstr., Curr.Adv.Ecol.Sci., Curr.Cont., E.I., Geo.Abstr., GeoRef., I D A, Mid.East: Abstr.& Ind., Rural Recreat.Tour.Abstr., SSCI, World Agri.Econ.& Rural Sociol.Abstr. **Document type**: academic/scholarly publication.
—BLDSC (1663.570000); Faxon; UnCover; SWETS.

ARGENTINE LETTER. see BUSINESS AND ECONOMICS — Economic Situation And Conditions

ASIA - PACIFIC UPLANDS; a newsletter for scientists. see EARTH SCIENCES — Oceanography

ASIAN-PACIFIC ENVIRONMENT; newsletter of the Asia Pacific people's environment network. see ENVIRONMENTAL STUDIES

910   DM
ASSOCIATION DAHOMEENE DE GEOGRAPHIE. BULLETIN DE LIAISON.* (Text in French) 1974. q. Association Dahomeene de Geographie, B.P. 526, Cotonou, Benin. Ed. S. Ako.

910   FR   ISSN 0004-5322
G11   CODEN: BAGFAO
ASSOCIATION DE GEOGRAPHES FRANCAIS. BULLETIN. (Summaries in English, French) 1925. bi-m. 390 F. Association de Geographes Francais, 191 rue St. Jacques, 75005 Paris, France. TEL 43-33-62-49. FAX 43-33-62-49. Ed. A. Metton. adv.; illus. circ. 1,000. **Indexed**: Bibl.Cart., Curr.Adv.Ecol.Sci., Curr.Tit.Ocean, Geo.Abstr., GeoRef., I D A, Rural Recreat.Tour.Abstr., World Agri.Econ.& Rural Sociol.Abstr. **Document type**: bulletin.
—BLDSC (2399.800000); SWETS.

910   US   ISSN 0004-5608
G3   CODEN: AAAGAK
ASSOCIATION OF AMERICAN GEOGRAPHERS. ANNALS. 1911. q. $70 (foreign $115.50). Basil Blackwell Inc., 238 Main St., Cambridge, MA 02142. TEL 617-547-7110. FAX 617-547-0789. Ed. Carville Earle. adv.: page $500; trim 7 x 10. bk.rev.; abstr.; bibl.; charts; maps; stat.; index. circ. 8,800. (also avail. in microform from UMI,KTO,PMC; reprint service avail. from KTO,UMI) **Indexed**: Abstr.Anthropol., Acad.Ind., Amer.Bibl.Slavic & E.Eur.Stud., Amer.Hist.& Life, Asian-Pac.Econ.Lit., Bibl.Cart., Biol.Abstr., Curr.Adv.Ecol.Sci., Deep Sea Res.& Oceanogr.Abstr., E.I., Field Crop Abstr., Geo.Abstr., GeoRef., Herb.Abstr., Hist.Abstr., Mar.Aff.Bibl., Mid.East: Abstr.& Ind., Rural Recreat.Tour.Abstr., Soc.Sci.Ind., Soils & Fert., SSCI, World Agri.Econ.& Rural Sociol.Abstr. **Document type**: academic/scholarly publication.
—BLDSC (1019.000000); Faxon; UnCover; SWETS; UMI. **CCC**.
   Description: Geography journal of record ublished in the U.S.

912   CN   ISSN 0840-9331
GA193.C3
ASSOCIATION OF CANADIAN MAP LIBRARIES AND ARCHIVES. BULLETIN. (Text in English and French) 1967. q. Can.$35 individual; institutions Can.$50. Association of Canadian Map Libraries and Archives, National Archives of Canada, Ottawa, ON K1A 0N3, Canada. TEL 613-996-7619. FAX 613-995-6575. Ed. Donald Lemon. circ. 320. **Indexed**: Bibl.Cart., So.Pac.Per.Ind.
—BLDSC (2396.833200).
   Former titles: Association of Canadian Map Libraries. Bulletin (ISSN 0318-2851); Incorporates: Association of Canadian Map Libraries. Annual Conference Proceedings (ISSN 0066-9474); Association of Canadian Map Libraries. Newsletter (ISSN 0066-9482)
   Description: Includes articles on map librarianship, map exchange, reviews and information on the activities of the Association and its members, as well as the proceedings of the annual conference and business meetings.

910   JA   ISSN 0066-958X
ASSOCIATION OF JAPANESE GEOGRAPHERS. SPECIAL PUBLICATION. (Text in English) 1966. irreg., no.4, 1980. price varies. Association of Japanese Geographers - Nippon Chiri Gakkai, c/o Japan Academic Societies Centre, 2-4-16 Yayoi, Bunkyo-ku, Tokyo 113, Japan. index. **Document type**: academic/scholarly publication.

910   US   ISSN 0066-9628
F851   CODEN: YAPGAJ
ASSOCIATION OF PACIFIC COAST GEOGRAPHERS. YEARBOOK. 1935-1942; resumed 1946. a. $15. Oregon State University Press, 101 Waldo Hall, Corvallis, OR 97331. TEL 503-737-3166. Ed. Daniel Turbeville. abstr.; bibl.; charts; illus.; cum.index. circ. 800. (also avail. in microform from UMI; back issues avail.; reprint service avail. from UMI) **Indexed**: GeoRef. **Document type**: academic/scholarly publication.
—BLDSC (9379.000000).

526.8   IT   ISSN 0044-9733
ASSOCIAZIONE ITALIANA DI CARTOGRAFIA. A I C BOLLETTINO.* no.21, 1971. q. L.2500. Associazione Italiana di Cartografia, c/o Instituto di Geografia dell'Universita, Largo San Marcellino 10, 80138 Naples, Italy. Ed.Bd. bk.rev.; bibl.; charts; illus.

910   IT   ISSN 0004-6736
G1
ATLANTE. (French edition avail.) 1965. m. L.57600. (Istituto Geografico de Agostini) Rizzoli Periodici, Via Gaspare Gozzi 5, 20129 Milan, Italy. TEL 02-700231. FAX 02-70100319. TELEX 200290. Ed. Massimo Morello. adv.; bk.rev.; abstr.; bibl.; charts; illus.; stat. circ. 90,000. **Indexed**: GeoRef.

910   HU   ISSN 0324-5268
CODEN: AGPHB5
ATTILA JOZSEF UNIVERSITY. ACTA GEOGRAPHICA. (Text in English, German and Russian) 1955. a. exchange basis. Attila Jozsef University, c/o E. Szabo, Exchange Librarian, Dugonics ter 13, P.O.B. 393, Szeged H-6701, Hungary. (Subscr. to: Kultura, Box 149, H-1389 Budapest, Hungary) Eds. Laszlo Jakucs, Gyula Krajko. charts; illus. circ. 400. **Document type**: academic/scholarly publication.
   Description: Focus on physical and economic geography, especially on problems of geomorphography, settlement geography and food production.

ATTRAVERSO IL MONDO. see TRAVEL AND TOURISM

910   AT   ISSN 0004-8089
AURORA. 1952-1979; resumed Aug. 1981. 4/yr. Aus.$25 (foreign Aus.$30). A N A R E Club Inc., 13 Doulton Rd., Blackburn, Vic. 3130, Australia. TEL 03-898-4906. (Co-sponsor: Australian National Antarctic Research Expedition) Ed. M. Kirton. adv.; bk.rev.; illus. circ. 1,500.
   Description: Articles on the history, scientific research, and politics of Antarctica.

910   AT   ISSN 0004-9182
CODEN: AUSGBD
AUSTRALIAN GEOGRAPHER. 1928. s-a. Aus.$30 (foreign Aus.$40) (typically set in Aug.). Geographical Society of New South Wales Inc., P.O. Box 602, Gladesville, N.S.W. 2111, Australia. FAX 2-817-4592. Ed. G. Aplin. adv.; bk.rev.; charts; illus.; index. circ. 1,200. (back issues avail.; reprint service avail. from KTO) **Indexed**: AESIS, Asian-Pac.Econ.Lit., Aus.P.A.I.S., Biol.Abstr., Curr.Adv.Ecol.Sci., Field Crop Abstr., Gdlns, Geo.Abstr., Herb.Abstr., Rural Devel.Abstr., Rural Recreat.Tour.Abstr., So.Pac.Per.Ind., Soils & Fert., SSCI, World Agri.Econ.& Rural Sociol.Abstr.
—BLDSC (1801.000000); Faxon; UnCover.
   Description: Focuses on environmental studies; particularly the biophysical environment and its interactions with humans.

GEOGRAPHY

910　　　　　　　AT　　ISSN 0004-9190
DU97　　　　　　　　　CODEN: AUGSBN
AUSTRALIAN GEOGRAPHICAL STUDIES. 1963. s-a. Aus.$62 (effective Apr. 1994). Institute of Australian Geographers, c/o Dept. of Geography and Oceanography, University College, ADFA, Campbell, A.C.T. 2600, Australia. FAX 61-62-6888313. Eds. M. McCaskill, R. Bourman. adv.; bk.rev.; charts; illus. circ. 1,100. **Indexed:** Aus.P.A.I.S., Bibl.Cart., Curr.Adv.Ecol.Sci., Curr.Cont., E.I., Geo.Abstr., GeoRef., Rural Recreat.Tour.Abstr., So.Pac.Per.Ind., SSCI, World Agri.Econ.& Rural Sociol.Abstr. **Document type:** academic/scholarly publication.
—BLDSC (1801.050000); Faxon; UnCover.
Description: Covers all aspects of geography in Australasia and neighbouring regions.

526　　　　　　　AT　　ISSN 0159-8910
QB301　　　　　　　　CODEN: AJGSDG
AUSTRALIAN JOURNAL OF GEODESY, PHOTOGRAMMETRY & SURVEYING. 1968. s-a. Aus.$30 to individuals; institutions Aus.$50. Institution of Surveyors, Australia Inc., 27-29 Napier Close, Deakin, A.C.T. 2600, Australia. TEL 06-282-2866. FAX 06-282-2576. Ed. W. Kearstey. bk.rev.; bibl.; charts; illus.; stat.; cum.index. circ. 300. (back issues avail.) **Indexed:** Geo.Abstr., Sci.Abstr. **Document type:** academic/scholarly publication.
—BLDSC (1808.300000).
Supersedes: Unisurv G.

910　　　　　　　US　　ISSN 0501-9966
G59
BACKGROUND NOTES ON THE COUNTRIES OF THE WORLD. irreg. $20 (foreign $25). U.S. Department of State, Bureau of Public Affairs, Office of Public Communication, 2201 C. St., N.W., Washington, DC 20520. TEL 202-783-3238. (Subscr. to: Superintendent of Documents, U.S. Government Printing Office, Box 371954, Pittsburgh, PA 15250-7954. TEL 202-783-3238. FAX 202-512-2233). **Indexed:** Ind.U.S.Gov.Per. **Document type:** government publication.
Description: Series of pamphlets on history, geography, culture, government, politics, economics and travel tips on selected countries and geographic entities of the world (except the U.S.) and on international organizations.

910　　　　　　　PL　　ISSN 0067-2807
BADANIA FIZJOGRAFICZNE NAD POLSKA ZACHODNIA. SERIA A. GEOGRAFIA FIZYCZNA. (Text in Polish; summaries in English, French or German) 1948. irreg., vol.34, 1982. price varies. Poznanskie Towarzystwo Przyjaciol Nauk, Ul. Sew. Melzynskiego 27-29, 61-725 Poznan, Poland. TEL 48-61-527-441. illus. **Indexed:** Geo.Abstr., GeoRef.

BAETICA; estudios de arte, geografia e historia. see ART

910 020 551　　　US　　ISSN 0272-8532
Z692.M3
BASE LINE. 1980. 6/yr. $15 to non-members. American Library Association, Map and Geography Round Table, 50 E. Houron St., Chicago, IL 60611. TEL 312-944-6780. (Subscr. to: Arlyn K. Sherwood, 300 S. Second, Illinois State Library, Centennial Bldg., Springfield, IL 62701) Ed. Nancy J. Butkovich. adv.; bk.rev. circ. 500. (back issues avail.) **Document type:** newsletter.
Description: Current awareness items and feature columns related to geography, cartography for map librarians.

910　　　　　　　SZ　　ISSN 0067-4486
　　　　　　　　　　　CODEN: BBGEBT
BASLER BEITRAEGE ZUR GEOGRAPHIE. (Text in German; summaries in English or French) 1968. irreg. 45 SFr. Verlag Wepf und Co., Eisengasse 5, CH-4001 Basel, Switzerland. TEL 061-2617574. FAX 061-2613597. **Document type:** monographic series.

910.02　　　　　　SZ
BASLER BEITRAEGE ZUR PHYSIOGEOGRAPHIE. 1979. irreg. 39 SFr. Verlag Wepf und Co., Eisengasse 5, CH-4001 Basel, Switzerland. TEL 061-2617574. FAX 061-2613597. **Document type:** monographic series.

910　　　　　　　SZ
BASLER FELDBUCH. 1981. irreg. 25 SFr. Verlag Wepf und Co., Eisengasse 5, CH-4001 Basel, Switzerland. TEL 061-2617574. FAX 061-2613597. **Document type:** monographic series.

526.3　　　　　　GW　　ISSN 0340-7691
BAYERISCHE KOMMISSION FUER DIE INTERNATIONALE ERDMESSUNG. VEROEFFENTLICHUNGEN. 1896. irreg., vol.53, 1993. price varies. Bayerische Kommission fuer die Internationale Erdmessung, Marstallplatz 8, 80539 Munich, Germany. TEL 089-230310. FAX 089-23031100. TELEX 5213550-YDFID. Ed.Bd. **Indexed:** Deep Sea Res.& Oceanogr.Abstr. **Document type:** academic/scholarly publication.
—BLDSC (1871.190000).
Description: Includes scientific research studies. Each volume devoted to a single subject.

BEITRAEGE ZUR HYDROLOGIE. see EARTH SCIENCES — Hydrology

910　　　　　　　GW　　ISSN 0005-9099
　　　　　　　　　　　CODEN: BDLKAH
BERICHTE ZUR DEUTSCHEN LANDESKUNDE. 1941. s-a. price varies. Zentralausschuss fuer Deutsche Landeskunde e.V., Universitaet Trier, 54286 Trier, Germany. TEL 0651-2014526. FAX 0651-2013975. (Subscr. in N. America to: Journal Fulfillment Services, 44 Hartz Way, Secaucus, NJ 07096-2491. TEL 201-348-4033. FAX 201-348-4505) adv.; bk.rev.; abstr.; bibl.; charts; index, cum.index. circ. 1,000. **Indexed:** Bibl.Cart., Geo.Abstr. **Document type:** academic/scholarly publication.
—BLDSC (1932.800000).

526.8　　　　　　IO　　ISSN 0125-9431
BERITA TOPOGRAFI.* 1965. irreg. Rps.600. Dinas Intelijen Medan dan Geografi Jawatan Topografi T.N.I.-A.D., Jalan Dr. Wahidin I-II, Jakarta, Indonesia. Ed. B. Basri.

915　　　　　　　BG
BHUGOLA SAMAYIKI. (Text in Bengali) 1974. a. Tk.10. Bangladesh National Geographical Association, c/o Dept. of Geography, Dhaka College, Dhanmondi, Dhaka 2, Bangladesh.

BIBLOS. see LITERATURE

BLAETTER FUER OBERDEUTSCHE NAMENFORSCHUNG. see LINGUISTICS

910　　　　　　　UK　　ISSN 0067-9232
BLOOMSBURY GEOGRAPHER. 1968. a. £5. University College London, Department of Geography, 26 Bedford Way, London WC1H 0AP, England. TEL 071-387-7050. FAX 071-380-7565. Ed. Ben Robertson. adv.; bk.rev. circ. 550. (back issues avail.) **Document type:** academic/scholarly publication.
Description: Student-controlled academic journal dealing with all aspects of physical and human geography.

BLUE BOOK: THE DIRECTORY OF GEOGRAPHIC, TRAVEL & DESTINATION STOCK PHOTOGRAPHY. see PHOTOGRAPHY

910　　　　　　　SZ　　ISSN 0006-548X
BODENSEE HEFTE; Zeitschrift der Euro-Region Bodensee. 1950. 10/yr. 74 SFr. (foreign 89 SFr.). Fachpresse Goldach, CH-9403 Goldach, Switzerland. TEL 071-409111. FAX 071-409511. Ed. P.E. Schaufelberger. adv.; bk.rev.; abstr.; bibl.; charts; illus.; stat.; tr.lit. circ. 10,500. **Document type:** newsletter.

BOLETIM DE GEOGRAFIA TEORETICA. see EARTH SCIENCES

910　　　　　　　BL　　ISSN 0006-6079
G1　　　　　　　　　　CODEN: BLPGAD
BOLETIM PAULISTA DE GEOGRAFIA. 1949. irreg. (2-3/yr.) $30 to individuals; institutions $45 (for 4 nos.). Associacao dos Geografos Brasileiros, Secao Regional de Sao Paulo, C.P. 64525, 05497 Sao Paulo, Brazil. Ed. Joao Evangelista de Souza Lima Neto. bk.rev.; bibl.; charts; illus. circ. 3,000. **Indexed:** Amer.Hist.& Life, Geo.Abstr., GeoRef., Hist.Abstr., I D A.
—BLDSC (2157.900000).

918.1　　　　　　BL
BOLETIM SOROCABA. 1954. m. free. Instituto Historico, Geografico e Genealogico de Sorocaba, Rua Rui Barbosa, 84, 18100 Sorocaba, SP, Brazil. FAX 55-152-33-3918. bk.rev. circ. 2,000.

910　　　　　　　GW　　ISSN 0373-0468
　　　　　　　　　　　CODEN: BGGAAH
BONNER GEOGRAPHISCHE ABHANDLUNGEN. 1948. irreg. price varies. Ferd. Duemmlers Verlag, Kaiserstr. 31-37, 53113 Bonn, Germany. TEL 0228-223031. FAX 0228-213040. (Subscr. to: Postfach 1480, 53004 Bonn, Germany) Ed.Bd. circ. 600. **Indexed:** Bibl.Cart., Forest.Abstr., Geo.Abstr., GeoRef., I D A, Rural Recreat.Tour.Abstr., Soils & Fert., World Agri.Econ.& Rural Sociol.Abstr.

BOOKS FOR YOUNG EXPLORERS SERIES. see CHILDREN AND YOUTH — For

910　　　　　　　GW　　ISSN 0524-2444
BRAUNSCHWEIGER GEOGRAPHISCHE STUDIEN. 1964. irreg. price varies. Verlag Erich Goltze GmbH und Co. KG, Hans-Boeckler-Str. 7, 37079 Goettingen, Germany. Ed. Arno Beuermann. **Indexed:** Geo.Abstr. **Document type:** academic/scholarly publication, monographic series.

910　　　　　　　GW　　ISSN 0720-9738
BREMER BEITRAEGE ZUR GEOGRAPHIE UND RAUMPLANUNG. 1978. irreg. price varies. Universitaet Bremen, Drueckschriftenlager, 28334 Bremen, Germany. **Indexed:** Geo.Abstr.

912　　　　　　　US　　ISSN 0068-1148
BRITANNICA ATLAS. (Text in English, French, German, Portuguese, and Spanish) 1969. a. $99.50. Encyclopaedia Britannica, Inc., 310 S. Michigan Ave., Chicago, IL 60604. TEL 312-347-7000. FAX 312-347-7914. TELEX 190203. Ed. William A. Cleveland. index.

910　　　　　　　CN　　ISSN 0068-1571
　　　　　　　　　　　CODEN: BCGSDC
BRITISH COLUMBIA GEOGRAPHICAL SERIES: OCCASIONAL PAPERS IN GEOGRAPHY. Title slightly varies. 1960. a. price varies. University of British Columbia, Geography Department, 1984 West Mall, Rm. 217, Vancouver, BC V6T 1Z2, Canada. TEL 604-822-3511. FAX 604-822-6150. Eds. M.J. Bovis, T.J. Barnes. circ. 400. **Document type:** monographic series.
Description: Contains monographs and occasional papers on a wide range of geographical topics, with special reference to western Canada and the Pacific Rim.

910　　　　　　　US　　ISSN 1067-456X
▼**BUSINESS GEOGRAPHICS;** geographic information in business. 1993. 6/yr. free to qualified personnel. G I S World, Inc., 155 E. Boardwalk Dr., Ste. 250, Ft. Collins, CO 80525. TEL 303-223-4848. FAX 303-223-5700. Ed. Nora Sherwood-Bryan. adv.; B&W page $3885, color page $5880; trim 8 3/8 x 10 7/8. bk.rev.; circ. 22,120 (controlled). **Document type:** trade publication.

910　　　　　　　DK　　ISSN 0007-7445
BYGD. 1970. 4/yr. DKK 135 (typically set in Jan.). Bygd-Fonden, Karl Andersensvej 37, 6710 Esbjerg V, Denmark. TEL 45-75-15-30-68. Ed. Horst Meesenburg. charts; illus. circ. 4,000.

910 301.3　　　　　UK　　ISSN 0306-6142
C A T M O G. (Concepts and Techniques in Modern Geography) 1975. irreg. (approx. 3/yr.) £3($6) per no. (varies). Environmental Publications, c/o C.D. Flack, School of Environmental Sciences, University of East Anglia, Norwich NR4 7TJ, England. TEL 0603-56161. FAX 0603-507719. (back issues avail.) **Document type:** monographic series.
—BLDSC (3399.412500).
Description: Provides graduates with guides to specific statistical techniques.

526　　　　　　　NE　　ISSN 0167-4994
GA921
CAERT-THRESOOR; tijdschrift voor de geschiedenis van kartografie in Nederland. 1982. q. fl.30 (foreign fl.50). c/o Drs. E.O. van Keulen, Rijkmuseum 'Nederlands Scheepvaart Museum', Kattenburgerplein 1, 1018 KK Amsterdam, Netherlands. Ed.Bd. adv.; bk.rev.; index. **Indexed:** E.I., Geo.Abstr.
—SWETS.

CAHIERS D'ONOMASTIQUE ARABE. see LINGUISTICS

GEOGRAPHY

910   FR   ISSN 0373-5834
CAHIERS D'OUTRE-MER; revue de geographie. (Text in French; summaries in English, Spanish) 1948. q. 30 F. (foreign 250 F.). Universite de Bordeaux III, Institut de Geographie, Domaine Universitaire, 33405 Talence, France. TEL 56-84-68-30. FAX 56-84-68-55. bk.rev.; illus.; cum.index. (reprint service avail. from SWZ) **Indexed:** Curr.Cont.Africa, Documentatieblad, E.I., Geo.Abstr., I D A, Int.Lab.Doc., P.A.I.S.For.Lang.Ind., Rural Devel.Abstr., Rural Recreat.Tour.Abstr., World Agri.Econ.& Rural Sociol.Abstr.
—BLDSC (2951.000000); Faxon.

910   CN   ISSN 0007-9766
G1
CAHIERS DE GEOGRAPHIE DU QUEBEC. (Text in English, French) N.S. 1956. 3/yr. Can.$32 to individuals (foreign Can.$35); institutions Can.$58 (foreign Can.$63). Presses de l'Universite Laval, Cite Universitaire, Sainte-Foy, PQ G1K 7P4, Canada. TEL 418-656-3132. FAX 418-656-3305. Ed. Francois Hulbert. bk.rev.; bibl.; charts; cum.index every 5 yrs. circ. 1,000. (also avail. in microform from BNQ,UMI; back issues avail.; reprint service avail. from UMI) **Indexed:** Amer.Hist.& Life, Bibl.Cart., Geo.Abstr., GeoRef., Hist.Abstr., I D A, Pt.de Rep. (1978-). **Document type:** monographic series.
—BLDSC (2948.960000); UMI.
Formerly: Universite Laval. Departement de Geographie. Travaux.

910   FR   ISSN 0526-8133
CAHIERS DES EXPLORATEURS. 1957. a. membership only. Societe des Explorateurs et des Voyageurs Francais, 184 bd. St. Germain, 75006 Paris, France.

914.402   FR   ISSN 0181-0839
CAHIERS GEOGRAPHIQUES DE ROUEN. 1973. s-a. 150 F. Association des Geographes de Haute Normandie, Universite de Haute Normandie, Faculte de Lettres et Sciences Humaines, 76821 Mont Saint Aignan Cedex, France. FAX 35-14-69-40. Ed. Yves Guermond. adv.; bk.rev.; bibl.; charts; stat. circ. 200. **Indexed:** Geo.Abstr.
—BLDSC (2948.965000).
Description: Features quantitative and theoretical geography in Europe and the geography of West African countries.

526   US
CALIFORNIA SURVEYOR. 1967. q. $25. California Land Surveying Association, Box 9098, Santa Rosa, CA 95405. Ed. Robert E. Baldwin. adv. circ. 3,327.

CALIFORNIA WEEKLY EXPLORER. see CHILDREN AND YOUTH — For

914.2   UK   ISSN 0306-9796
G1
CAMBRIA: A WELSH GEOGRAPHICAL REVIEW. 1974. a. £9. University College of Swansea, Dept. of Geography, Singleton Park, Swansea SA2 8PP, Wales. TEL 0792-205678. TELEX GB-792-205556. Ed. R.P. Walsh. adv.; bk.rev. circ. 250. **Indexed:** Br.Archaeol.Abstr., Geo.Abstr. **Document type:** academic/scholarly publication.
—BLDSC (3015.934000).

910   UK   ISSN 0068-6654
CAMBRIDGE GEOGRAPHICAL STUDIES. 1969. irreg., no.17, 1983. price varies. Cambridge University Press, Edinburgh Bldg., Shaftesbury Rd., Cambridge CB2 2RU, England. TEL 0223-312393. FAX 0223-315052. TELEX 851817256. (N. American addr.: Cambridge University Press, Journals Dept., 40 W. 20th St., New York, NY 10011. TEL 212-924-3900. FAX 212-691-3239) Ed.Bd. index. **Document type:** monographic series.

910   UK
CAMBRIDGE STUDIES IN HISTORICAL GEOGRAPHY. 1982. irreg. price varies. Cambridge University Press, Edinburgh Bldg., Shaftesbury Rd., Cambridge CB2 2RU, England. TEL 0223-312393. FAX 0223-315052. TELEX 851817256. (N. American addr.: Cambridge University Press, Journals Dept., 40 W. 20th St., New York, NY 10011. TEL 212-924-3900. FAX 212-691-3239) Ed.Bd. **Document type:** monographic series.

916.7   CM   ISSN 0301-7753
CAMEROON YEAR BOOK. (Text in English) 1973. a. 300 Fr.CFA. United Publishers, Box 200, Victoria, Cameroon. Ed. Jennie Gwellem. adv.; illus.; stat. circ. 10,000.

910   CN   ISSN 0707-3844
G4
CANADIAN ASSOCIATION OF GEOGRAPHERS. DIRECTORY. (Text in English and French) 1964. a. Can.$15 per no. Canadian Association of Geographers, Burnside Hall, McGill University, 805 Sherbrooke St. W., Montreal, PQ H3A 2K6, Canada. TEL 514-398-4946. Ed. H. Rasid. circ. 1,400. **Document type:** directory, academic/scholarly publication.
Formerly: Canadian Association of Geographers. Newsletter (ISSN 0068-8312)
Description: Directory of Canadian geography departments in universities and government, listing staff, research and recent publications.

910   CN   ISSN 0008-3658
G1   CODEN: CNGGAR
CANADIAN GEOGRAPHER/GEOGRAPHE CANADIEN. (Text in English, French) 1951. q. Can.$64.20 (foreign Can.$65). Canadian Association of Geographers, Burnside Hall, McGill University, 805 Sherbrooke St. W., Montreal, PQ H3A 2K6, Canada. TEL 514-398-4946. bk.rev.; abstr.; charts; illus.; index. circ. 2,350. (also avail. in microfiche from UMI,MML; back issues avail.) **Indexed:** Amer.Bibl.Slavic & E.Eur.Stud., Biol.Abstr., Can.Per.Ind., Chem.Abstr., CMI, Curr.Adv.Ecol.Sci., Curr.Cont., Environ.Abstr., Geo.Abstr., GeoRef., Mid.East: Abstr.& Ind., Risk Abstr., Rural Recreat.Tour.Abstr., Soc.Sci.Ind., Soils & Fert., SSCI, World Agri.Econ.& Rural Sociol.Abstr. **Document type:** academic/scholarly publication.
—BLDSC (3025.500000); Faxon; UnCover; SWETS; UMI.
Description: Broad range of geographical research in Canada.

910   CN   ISSN 0319-5228
CANOMA. (Text in English, French) 1975. s-a. free. Canadian Permanent Committee on Geographical Names, Secretariat CPCGN - Geographical Names, Room 650-615, Booth St., Ottawa, ON K1A 0E9, Canada. TEL 613-992-3892. FAX 613-943-8282. illus.; cum.index: vols.1-17; circ. 500 (controlled). (back issues avail.) **Document type:** government publication.
Description: Contains short articles pertaining to aspects of Canadian toponymy - policies and information about the CPCGN and general interest items to geographers, historians, genealogists and linguists.

910   JM   ISSN 0252-9939
F2155
CARIBBEAN GEOGRAPHY; a journal of geography for the region. 1983. s-a. $15 to individuals; institutions $30. (University of the West Indies Publishers' Association) U W I Publishers Association, P.O. Box 42, Mona, Kingston 7, Jamaica, W.I. TEL 809-977-2659. FAX 809-977-2660. Ed. David Barker. adv.; bk.rev.; abstr.; bibl.; charts; illus.; pat.; stat.; tr.lit.; cum.index. circ. 300. (back issues avail.) **Indexed:** Geo.Abstr., I D A, Rural Devel.Abstr., World Agri.Econ.& Rural Sociol.Abstr. **Document type:** academic/scholarly publication.
—UnCover.
Description: Covers geography, environment, development and culture as it relates to the Caribbean region.
Refereed Serial

526.8   UK   ISSN 0008-7041
GA101   CODEN: CGJLA8
CARTOGRAPHIC JOURNAL. 1964. s-a. £25. British Cartographic Society, Department of Surveying, The University, Newcastle NE1 7RU, England. TEL 091-222-6353. FAX 091-261-1182. TELEX 53654-UNINEW-G. Ed. D.J. Fairbairn. adv.; bk.rev.; bibl.; charts; illus.; cum.index: vols.1-15. circ. 2,000. **Indexed:** Bibl.& Ind.Geol., Bibl.Cart., Geo.Abstr., Mid.East: Abstr.& Ind. **Document type:** academic/scholarly publication.
—BLDSC (3057.600000); Faxon; UnCover; SWETS. **CCC.**
Description: Covers all aspects of cartography, mapping and spatial data display.
Refereed Serial

526   US   ISSN 1048-9053
CARTOGRAPHIC PERSPECTIVES. 1981. 3/yr. $28 to individuals; institutions $58; students $8. North American Cartographic Information Society, Box 399, Milwaukee, WI 53201. TEL 800-558-8993. FAX 414-229-3981. Ed. Sona Karentz Andrews. bibl. circ. 350. (back issues avail.) **Document type:** academic/scholarly publication.
Former titles (until 1989): Cartographic Information (ISSN 8756-3924); Map Gap.
Description: Cartographic articles and information for professionals from government, academic and private organizations.

526   CN   ISSN 0317-7173
GA101
CARTOGRAPHICA. 1971. q. $45 to individuals; institutions $95; students $30. University of Toronto Press, Journals Department, 5201 Dufferin St., Downsview, ON M3H 5T8, Canada. TEL 416-667-7781. FAX 416-667-7803. (U.S. addr.: 340 Nagel Dr., Cheektowaga, NY 14225) Ed. B.V. Gutsell. bk.rev.; abstr.; bibl.; charts; illus.; stat. circ. 1,114. (tabloid format) **Indexed:** Bibl.Cart., Comput.Abstr., Curr.Cont., Geo.Abstr., GeoRef., So.Pac.Per.Ind.
—BLDSC (3057.620000); Faxon; UnCover; SWETS; UMI. **CCC.**
Formed by the 1980 merger of: Canadian Cartographer (ISSN 0008-3127); Cartographica Monographs.

526.8   AT   ISSN 0069-0805
GA101
CARTOGRAPHY. 1954. s-a. Aus.$36. Australian Institute of Cartographers, GPO Box 1292, Canberra City, A.C.T. 2601, Australia. Ed. D. Clarke. adv.; bk.rev.; index. circ. 2,250. **Indexed:** AESIS, Bibl.Cart., Forest.Abstr., Geo.Abstr., GeoRef., Mid.East: Abstr.& Ind.
—Faxon; UnCover.

526   US   ISSN 1050-9844
GA101   CODEN: CGISES
CARTOGRAPHY AND GEOGRAPHIC INFORMATION SYSTEMS. 1974. 4/yr. $85 to non-members (foreign $95). American Congress on Surveying and Mapping, 5410 Grosvenor Ln., Ste. 100, Bethesda, MD 20814. TEL 301-493-0200. Ed. Robert McMaster. adv.; bk.rev. circ. 4,000. **Indexed:** Amer.Bibl.Slavic & E.Eur.Stud., Bibl.& Ind.Geol., Bibl.Cart., Comput.Abstr., Comput.Abstr., Curr.Cont., Geo.Abstr., SSCI.
—Faxon; UnCover; SWETS; UMI. **CCC.**
Formerly: American Cartographer (ISSN 0094-1689)
Description: Provides current information on GIS and digital mapping as well as more traditional cartographic methods.

526   IT   ISSN 1122-0902
CATALOGAZIONE DE CIMELI GEOCARTOGRAFICI. 1986. irreg., no.5, 1990. price varies. Casa Editrice Leo S. Olschki, Casella Postale 66, 50100 Florence, Italy. TEL 055-6530684. FAX 055-6530214. **Document type:** monographic series.

CATHEDRA. see HISTORY — History Of The Near East

910   CC   ISSN 0494-0911
CEHUI TONGBAO/JOURNAL OF SURVEYING. (Text in Chinese) bi-m. Cehui Chubanshe, 50, Sanlihe Lu, Beijing 100045, People's Republic of China. TEL 866568.

910   CC   ISSN 1000-8586
CEHUI YICONG. (Text in Chinese) bi-m. Cehui Chubanshe, 50, Sanlihe Lu, Beijing 100045, People's Republic of China. TEL 866568.

910   CC
CELIANG YUAN/SURVEYOR. (Text in Chinese) bi-m. Cehui Chubanshe, 50, Sanlihe Lu, Beijing 100045, People's Republic of China. TEL 866568. Ed. Lin Tianchong.

910.02 312   FR   ISSN 0223-9272
CENTRE DE GEOGRAPHIE HUMAINE ET SOCIALE. TRAVAUX. 1972. irreg. Presses Universitaires de Rennes, 2 rue du Doyen D. Leroy, 35044 Rennes Cedex, France. TEL 99-54-66-35. FAX 99-33-07-95.
Formerly: Centre Geographique d'Etude et de Recherches Rurales (ISSN 0244-5468)

CENTRE EUROPEEN D'ETUDES BOURGUIGNONNES (XIVE-XVIE S.). PUBLICATION. see HISTORY — History Of Europe

CENTRE FOR URBAN AND COMMUNITY STUDIES. BIBLIOGRAPHIC SERIES. see HOUSING AND URBAN PLANNING

526.982   CK   ISSN 0120-2499
CENTRO INTERAMERICANO DE FOTOINTERPRETACION. REVISTA. Short title: Revista C I A F. 1972. a. Col.1500. Centro Interamericano de Fotointerpretacion, Carrera 30 No. 47a-57, Apdo. Aereo 6721, Bogota, Colombia. Ed. Jonas Cirilo Leon Perez. adv.; bk.rev.; illus. circ. 1,000.
—BLDSC (7804.890000).

914.7   XR   ISSN 0375-6122
                          CODEN: ZGUCAH
CESKOSLOVENSKA AKADEMIE VED. GEOGRAFICKY USTAV, BRNO. ZPRAVY. (Text in Czech; summaries in English) 1964. 4/yr. price varies. Ceskoslovenska Akademie Ved, Geograficky Ustav, Brno, Mendlovo nam. 1, 662 82 Brno, Czech Republic. TEL 425-3160. Ed. Antonin Vaisharan. adv.; bk.rev.; charts; illus.; circ. controlled. Indexed: GeoRef.
   Description: Publishes original scientific papers devoted to geography and related sciences.

910   XR   ISSN 0231-5300
G9
CESKOSLOVENSKE GEOGRAFICKE SPOLECNOSTI. SBORNIK/CZECHOSLOVAK GEOGRAPHICAL SOCIETY. JOURNAL. (Text mainly in Czech; summaries in English, French, German) 1895. q. DM.124. (Ceskoslovenska Akademie Ved) Academia, Publishing House of the Czechoslovak Academy of Sciences, Vodickova 40, 112 29 Prague 1, Czech Republic. TEL 20-29-93. (Dist. in Western countries by: Kubon & Sagner, P.O. Box 34 01 08, 8000 Munich 34, Germany) Ed. Vaclav Kral. bk.rev.; bibl.; charts; illus.; maps. circ. 1,100. Indexed: GeoRef.
   Formerly: Ceskoslovenska Spolecnost Zemepisna. Sbornik (ISSN 0036-5254)
   Description: Original papers concerning all branches of geography, reports on geographical congresses and conferences, short items of research and contributions to geographical terminology, etc.

910   XR   ISSN 0373-7179
CESKOSLOVENSKY KRAS. 1948. a. price varies. Academia, Publishing House of the Czechoslovak Academy of Sciences, Vodickova 40, 112 29 Prague 1, Czech Republic. TEL 23-63-065. bk.rev.; bibl. circ. 500. (back issues avail.)

910.02   CE
CEYLON GEOGRAPHER. (Text in English) q. Ceylon Geographical Society, 61 Abdul Caffoo Mawatha, Colombo 3, Sri Lanka.

CHIGAKU ZASSHI/JOURNAL OF GEOGRAPHY. see EARTH SCIENCES

CHINA TRANSPORT. see TRANSPORTATION

915.1   US   ISSN 1061-9534
DS706.7
CHINESE ENVIRONMENT; a review of physical and human aspects. 1988-1991; resumed 1993. q. $200 (foreign $222). M.E. Sharpe, Inc., 80 Business Park Dr., Armonk, NY 10504. TEL 914-273-1800; 800-541-6563. FAX 914-273-2106. Eds. Shiu-hung Luk, Joseph Whitney. (back issues avail.)
—UnCover; UMI.
   Formerly (until 1990): Chinese Geography and Environment (ISSN 0896-2979)
   Description: Covers current environmental issues in China; presents original research in the areas of biophysical environment, natural resources, and urban environment; discusses new environmental concepts of interest to readers outside China; and provides information on the environmental situation in China not available elsewhere in English.

CHINESE JOURNAL OF GEOPHYSICS. see EARTH SCIENCES — Geophysics

526.8   JA
CHIZU NO TOMO/MAP AND LANDSCAPE. (Text in Japanese) 1958. m. 3000 Yen. Japan Map Association - Chizu Kyokai, Shinsen Bldg., 8-2 Shinsen-cho, Shibuya, Tokyo 150, Japan. FAX 03-3461-0244. Ed. Eizi Inoue. adv.; bk.rev.; index; circ. controlled.
   Formerly: Map's Companion (ISSN 0009-4900)

912.09   PO
CHOROGRAPHIA. 1960. irreg. Esc.600 per no. Universidade de Lisboa, Centro de Estudos Geograficos, Cidade Universitaria, 1699 Lisbon Codex, Portugal. TEL 7940218. FAX 7938690. circ. 500. **Document type:** monographic series.
   Description: Covers local studies on human and regional geography.

917.3   US   ISSN 0899-6075
CITIES OF THE UNITED STATES. (In 4 vols.) 1988. irreg. Gale Research Inc., 835 Penobscot Bldg., Detroit, MI 48226. TEL 313-961-2242. FAX 313-961-6083. Eds. Peggy Saari, Diane L. Dupuis. maps.

CITY SIERRAN; newsletter of the New York City Group of the Sierra Club. see ENVIRONMENTAL STUDIES

910   GW   ISSN 0588-3253
                          CODEN: CLGEA7
COLLOQUIUM GEOGRAPHICUM. 1952. irreg. price varies. (Geographisches Institut) Ferd. Duemmlers Verlag, Kaiserstr. 31-37, 53113 Bonn, Germany. (Subscr. to: Postfach 1480, 53004 Bonn, Germany) Indexed: GeoRef., I D A.

910   CK   ISSN 0120-5366
COLOMBIA GEOGRAFICA. 1970. s-a. price varies. Instituto Geografico Agustin Codazzi, Subdireccion de Geografia, Carrera 30, No. 48-51, Apdo. Aereo 6721, Bogota, Colombia. TEL 2-44-84-13. FAX 91-264146. TELEX 45485. Ed. Victor Julio Alvarez Q. bibl.; charts; illus. circ. 1,000. Indexed: GeoRef.
   Description: Findings of scientific geographic research dealing with Colombia.

918.606   CK   ISSN 0120-6907
F2251
COLOMBIA: SUS GENTES Y REGIONES. 1985. q. $26. Instituto Geografico Agustin Codazzi, Subdireccion de Geografia, Carrera 30, No. 48-51, Apdo. Aereo 6721, Bogota, Colombia. TEL 2-44-84-13. FAX 91-264146. TELEX 45485. Ed. Victor Julio Alvarez Q. adv.; bk.rev.; bibl.; charts; illus. circ. 5,000.
   Description: Sociological and geographical articles about Colombia.

910   IT
COMITATO DEI GEOGRAFI ITALIANI. 1975. irreg., no.5, 1980. price varies. (Commissione per la Geografia Storica delle Sedi Umane) Casa Editrice Leo S. Olschki, Casella Postale 66, 50100 Florence, Italy. TEL 055-6530684. FAX 055-6530214. **Document type:** monographic series.

910   FR   ISSN 0071-8424
G11
COMITE DES TRAVAUX HISTORIQUES ET SCIENTIFIQUES. SECTION DE GEOGRAPHIE. ACTES DU CONGRES NATIONAL DES SOCIETES SAVANTES. 1960 (congress of 1959). a. price varies. Ministere de l'Education Nationale, Comite des Travaux Historiques et Scientifiques, 1 rue d'Ulm, 75005 Paris, France. circ. 600.
—BLDSC (0675.195000).

COMMISSION ROYALE DE TOPONYMIE ET DIALECTOLOGIE. BULLETIN/KONINKLIJKE COMMISSIE VOOR TOPONYMIE EN DIALECTOLOGIE. HANDELINGEN. see LINGUISTICS

910   UK   ISSN 0069-7109
COMMONWEALTH INSTITUTE, LONDON. ANNUAL REPORT. 1926. a. £4 (free to libraries). Commonwealth Institute, Kensington High St., London W8 6NQ, England. index; circ. controlled.

918   US   ISSN 1054-3074
CONFERENCE OF LATIN AMERICANIST GEOGRAPHERS YEARBOOK. Short title: C L A G Yearbook. 1971. a. $25. Conference of Latin Americanist Geographers, c/o Institute of Latin American Studies, Sid Richardson Hall 1-325, University of Texas, TX 78712. TEL 512-471-5116. FAX 512-471-5049. adv.; bk.rev. circ. 525. (back issues avail.) Indexed: Geo.Abstr. **Document type:** academic/scholarly publication.
   Description: Scholarly journal of papers from the annual meeting of the society, which was formed to foster geographic education and research on Latin America.

CONFERENCE OF SOUTH AFRICAN SURVEYORS. PROCEEDINGS/KONFERENSIE VAN SUID-AFRIKAANSE OPMETERS. VERRIGTINGE. see ENGINEERING — Civil Engineering

CORPORATION OF BRITISH COLUMBIA LAND SURVEYORS. REPORT OF PROCEEDINGS. see ENGINEERING — Civil Engineering

917.2 980   MX   ISSN 0186-5757
EL CORREO FRONTERIZO. 1984. bi-m. free. Colegio de la Frontera Norte, Publications Department, Blvd. Abelardo L. Rodriquez No. 2925, Zona del Rio, 22320 Tijuana, Mexico. TEL 84-22-26. FAX 300050. (Orders in US: Box L, Chula Vista, CA 91912) Ed. Blas Cota Mesa. bk.rev. circ. 1,500. **Document type:** newsletter.
   Formerly: Boletin Cefnomex.
   Description: Provides information on various research projects in progress and the academic activities of COLEF. Includes lists of recent publications by COLEF and other institutions concerned with U.S.-Mexican border studies and Hispanic populations in the United States.

COSTA RICA. ARCHIVO NACIONAL. REVISTA. see HISTORY

910   SP   ISSN 0210-086X
CUADERNOS DE GEOGRAFIA. 1964. s-a. 1200 ptas. Universidad de Valencia, Facultad de Geografia e Historia, Departamento de Geografia, Apdo. 22060, 46080 Valencia, Spain. TEL 3-86-42-37. FAX 3-86-42-34. Ed. Vicente M. Rossello Verger. bk.rev. circ. 800. Indexed: Doc.Geogr., Geo.Abstr.

918.2 982   AG   ISSN 0325-8246
CUADERNOS DE GEOHISTORIA REGIONAL. 1979. irreg. Consejo Nacional de Investigaciones Cientificas y Tecnicas, Instituto de Investigaciones Geohistoricas, Av. Castelli 930, Casilla de Correo 438, 3500 Resistencia, Argentina. FAX 54-722-39983. bk.rev.; bibl.; illus.; circ. 500 (paid). **Document type:** monographic series.
   Description: Research from the institute on: population studies, colonization, agricultural activities, transportation, and communications.

910   SP   ISSN 0211-6820
CUADERNOS DE INVESTIGACION GEOGRAFICA. 1975. s-a. 1700 ptas. (foreign 2500 ptas.). Universidad de la Rioja, Servicio de Publicaciones, C. Magisterio, s-n, 26004 Logrono, Spain. TEL 34-41-231699. Ed. Jose Arnaez Vadillo. circ. 500. Indexed: Bull.Signal. **Document type:** academic/scholarly publication.
   Supersedes in part (as of 1979): Cuadernos de Investigacion: Geografia e Historia (ISSN 0210-3664)
   Description: Includes research into physical geography, especially that related either to the dynamic processes found in geomorphology or to man's transformation of his physical environment.

910   SP   ISSN 0210-5462
CUADERNOS GEOGRAFICOS. (Includes monograph supplements) (Text in Spanish; summaries in English, French) 1971. a. price varies. Universidad de Granada, Servicio de Publicaciones, Antiguo Colegio Maximo de Cartujo, Campus de Caruja, 18071 Granada, Spain. TEL 243930. Ed. Victoriano Olmedo. **Document type:** academic/scholarly publication.

910   US   ISSN 1045-7208
CURRENT TOPICS IN REMOTE SENSING. irreg., latest vol.2. Gordon and Breach Science Publishers, 820 Town Center Dr., Langhorne, PA 19047. TEL 215-750-2642. FAX 215-750-6343. (UK subscr. to: P.O. Box 90, Reading, Berkshire RG1 8JL, England. TEL 0734-560-080) Ed. C. VoFte. **Document type:** monographic series.
   Refereed Serial

910   PL   ISSN 0045-9453
G72   CODEN: CZGGA9
CZASOPISMO GEOGRAFICZNE/GEOGRAPHICAL JOURNAL. (Text in Polish; summaries in English) 1923. q. $32 (effective 1994). Polskie Towarzystwo Geograficzne, Plac Uniwersytecki 1, 50-137 Wroclaw, Poland. (Dist. by: Ars Polona, Krakowskie Przedmiescie 7, 00-068 Warsaw, Poland. TEL 48-22-267855. FAX 48-22-267855) Ed. Alfred Jahn. bk.rev.; illus. circ. 920. Indexed: Bibl.Cart., Geo.Abstr., GeoRef., I D A, World Agri.Econ.& Rural Sociol.Abstr. **Document type:** academic/scholarly publication.

GEOGRAPHY

DAMRON ROAD ATLAS. see *TRAVEL AND TOURISM*

910   DK   ISSN 0105-4856
DANMARKS LAERERHOEJSKOLE. GEOGRAFISK INSTITUT. SKRIFTER. 1978. irreg. free. Laererhoejskole, Geografisk Institut, Emdrupvej 101, DK-2400 Copenhagen, Denmark. TEL 45-39-69-66-33. FAX 45-39-66-70-10.

526.982   DK   ISSN 0105-5194
DANMARKS TEKNISKE HOEJSKOLE. INSTITUTTET FOR LANDMAALING OG FOTOGRAMMETRI. MEDDELELSE. 1941. irreg., no.13, 1990. price varies. Danmarks Tekniske Hoejskole, Instituttet for Landmaaling og Fotogrammetri, Landmaalervej 7, 2800 Lyngby, Denmark. TEL 45-2-88-48-00. FAX 45-2-42886412. TELEX 37529 DTHDIA DK. illus. circ. 300. **Indexed:** Geo.Abstr.

910   II   ISSN 0011-7269
DECCAN GEOGRAPHER. (Text in English) 1962. s-a. $40 (effective 1994). Deccan Geographical Society, Kala Basant Sahakari Grih. Sanstha, 808, Shivajinagar, Off Bhandarka Inst. Rd., Prabhat Lane-15, Pune 411 004, India. TEL 334720. (Co-sponsor: Indian Institute of Geography) Ed. B.G. Tamaskar; Pub. A.M. Deokule. adv.; bk.rev.; bibl.; charts; illus.; cum.index: every 5 yrs. circ. 1,000. **Indexed:** Mid.East: Abstr.& Ind., Rural Devel.Abstr., Rural Recreat.Tour.Abstr., World Agri.Econ.& Rural Sociol.Abstr. **Document type:** academic/scholarly publication.
Description: Promotes geographical education and research.

526   GW   ISSN 0938-846X
DEUTSCHE GEODAETISCHE KOMMISSION. JAHRESBERICHT. 1951. a. Deutsche Geodaetische Kommission, Marstallplatz 8, 80539 Munich, Germany. TEL 089-23031113. FAX 089-23031240. TELEX 5213550-DGFI-D. **Document type:** academic/scholarly publication.

526   GW   ISSN 0938-2836
DEUTSCHE GEODAETISCHE KOMMISSION. VEROEFFENTLICHUNGEN: REIHE A. THEORETISCHE GEODAESIE. (Text in English and German) 1951. irreg., vol.109, 1993. price varies. Deutsche Geodaetische Kommission, Marstallplatz 8, 80539 Munich, Germany. TEL 089-23031113. FAX 089-23031240. TELEX 5213550-DGFI-D. **Indexed:** GeoRef. **Document type:** academic/scholarly publication.
Description: Covers scientific research studies. Each volume devoted to a single subject.

526   GW   ISSN 0065-5317
QB275   CODEN: DGAGAR
DEUTSCHE GEODAETISCHE KOMMISSION. VEROEFFENTLICHUNGEN: REIHE B. ANGEWANDTE GEODAESIE. 1952. irreg., vol.297, 1992. price varies. Deutsche Geodaetische Kommission, Marstallplatz 8, 80539 Munich, Germany. TEL 089-23031113. FAX 089-23031240. TELEX 5213550-DGFI-D. **Indexed:** GeoRef. **Document type:** academic/scholarly publication.
—BLDSC (3567.925000).
Description: Devoted to scientific research studies. Each volume includes a single subject.

526   GW   ISSN 0065-5325
DEUTSCHE GEODAETISCHE KOMMISSION. VEROEFFENTLICHUNGEN: REIHE C. DISSERTATIONEN. 1952. irreg., no.399, 1993. price varies. Deutsche Geodaetische Kommission, Marstallplatz 8, 80539 Munich, Germany. TEL 089-23031113. FAX 089-23031240. TELEX 5213550-DGFI-D. **Indexed:** Geo.Abstr., GeoRef. **Document type:** academic/scholarly publication.
Description: Each volume devoted to one dissertation.

526   GW   ISSN 0065-5333
DEUTSCHE GEODAETISCHE KOMMISSION. VEROEFFENTLICHUNGEN: REIHE D. TAFELWERKE. 1956. irreg., vol.7, 1967. price varies. Deutsche Geodaetische Kommission, Marstallplatz 8, 80539 Munich, Germany. TEL 089-23031113. FAX 089-23031240. TELEX 5213550-DGFI-D. **Document type:** academic/scholarly publication, monographic series.

526   GW   ISSN 0065-5341
DEUTSCHE GEODAETISCHE KOMMISSION. VEROEFFENTLICHUNGEN: REIHE E. GESCHICHTE UND ENTWICKLUNG DER GEODAESIE. 1961. irreg., vol.24, 1986. price varies. Deutsche Geodaetische Kommission, Marstallplatz 8, 80539 Munich, Germany. TEL 089-23031113. FAX 089-23031240. TELEX 5213550-DGFI-D. **Indexed:** GeoRef. **Document type:** academic/scholarly publication, monographic series.
Description: Each volume devoted to a single subject.

DEUTSCHE OSTKUNDE; Vierteljahresschrift fuer Wissenschaft, Erziehung und Unterricht. see *HISTORY — History Of Europe*

DEUTSCHER PALAESTINA-VEREIN. ZEITSCHRIFT. see *ORIENTAL STUDIES*

910   CC
DILI/GEOGRAPHY. (Text in Chinese) q. Sichuan Sheng Dili Xuehui - Sichuan Geography Society, 9, Renmin Nanlu 4 Duan, Chengdu, Sichuan 610041, People's Republic of China. TEL 681260. Ed. Tang Bangxing.

DILI JIAOXUE/GEOGRAPHY TEACHING. see *EDUCATION — Teaching Methods And Curriculum*

910   CC   ISSN 1005-5207
DILI JIAOYU/GEOGRAPHICAL EDUCATION. (Text in Chinese) 1980. bi-m. Y1.50 per. (Sichuan Geographical Institute) Dili Jiaoyu Bianjibu, 12 Tianchen Lu, Shapingba, Chongqing, Sichuan 630047, People's Republic of China. TEL 811-961155. FAX 811-966566. (Co-sponsor: Chongqing Teachers College, Geographical Department) Ed. Zhang Chengsheng. adv. contact: Chao Xiaolu. circ. 15,000. **Document type:** academic/scholarly publication.
Description: Covers analysis of teaching materials, teaching methods and exchanges teaching experiences.

910   CC   ISSN 1000-0690
DILI KEXUE/SCIENTIA GEOGRAPHICA SINICA. English edition: Chinese Geographical Science (ISSN 1002-0063) (Text in Chinese; summaries in English) 1981. q. $56.80. (Chinese Academy of Sciences, Changchun Institute of Geography) Science Press, Marketing and Sales Department, 16 Donghuangchenggen Beijie, Beijing 100707, People's Republic of China. TEL 4010642. FAX 4012180. TELEX 210247-SPBJ-CN. adv.; bk.rev. circ. 6,000.
Description: Publishes academic papers, summaries, research reports, news of activities, and discussions related to geography, including cartography, remote sensing, telemetering, and physical and economic geography.
Refereed Serial

910   CC   ISSN 0375-5444
        CODEN: TLHPAS
DILI XUEBAO/ACTA GEOGRAPHICA SINICA. (Text in Chinese; summaries in English) 1934. bi-m. $89.40. (Zhongguo Dili Xuehui - Geographical Society of China) Science Press, Marketing and Sales Press, 16 Donghuangchenggen Beijie, Beijing 100707, People's Republic of China. TEL 4010642. FAX 4012180. TELEX 210247-SPBJ-CN. adv.; bk.rev. circ. 12,000. **Indexed:** Curr.Adv.Ecol.Sci., Geo.Abstr., GeoRef., I D A. **Document type:** academic/scholarly publication.
—BLDSC (0619.400000); UnCover.
Description: Contains theses, experimental observations and reports, theories of geographical science, studies of theories in methodology and applications. Also includes research and discussions on the history of geography, and academic activities.
Refereed Serial

910   CC   ISSN 1000-0585
DS706
DILI YANJIU/GEOGRAPHICAL RESEARCH. (Text in Chinese; summaries in English) 1982. q. $63.60. (Chinese Academy of Sciences, Institute of Geography) Science Press, Marketing and Sales Department, 16 Donghuangchenggen Beijie, Beijing 100707, People's Republic of China. TEL 4010642. FAX 4012180. TELEX 210247-SPBJ-CN. adv.; bk.rev. circ. 11,000. **Document type:** academic/scholarly publication.
—UnCover.
Description: Contains research reports and papers on theory, methodology, economic and physical regionalization, natural resource evaluation and utilization. Includes seminars, reports on academic activities, and international communications.
Refereed Serial

910   CC   ISSN 0257-019X
QE1
DILI ZHISHI/GEOGRAPHICAL KNOWLEDGE. (Text in Chinese) 1950. m. $21. (Zhongguo Dili Xuehui - Chinese Geographical Society) Science Press, Marketing and Sales Department, 16 Donghuangchenggen Beijie, Beijing 100707, People's Republic of China. TEL 4010642. FAX 4012180. TELEX 210247-SPBJ-CN. (Dist. outside China by: China International Book Trading Corp., P.O. Box 399, Beijing, P.R.C.) (Co-sponsors: Chinese Academy of Sciences, Institute of Geography) Ed. Zheng Ping. adv. circ. 200,000.
Description: Covers the geography of China and other countries. Aims to introduce geographical conditions in various countries and regions of the world, the beauty of China's mountains and rivers, and the construction of a socialist economy in China.

910   US
DIMING ZHISHI/PLACE NAMES. (Text in Chinese) bi-m. $17.60. China Books & Periodicals, Inc., 2929 24th St., San Francisco, CA 94110. TEL 415-282-2994. FAX 415-282-0994.

DIQIU WULI XUEBAO/ACTA GEOPHYSICA SINICA. see *EARTH SCIENCES — Geophysics*

912   CN   ISSN 0070-5217
DIRECTORY OF CANADIAN MAP COLLECTIONS. (Text in English and French) 1969. irreg., 6th ed. 1992. Can.$18. Association of Canadian Map Libraries and Archives, National Archives of Canada, Ottawa, ON K1A 0N3, Canada. TEL 613-996-7619. FAX 613-995-6575. Ed. Tim Ross. **Document type:** directory.
Description: Lists all major map libraries in Canada with a brief description of their holdings, names of librarians, addresses and telephone numbers, hours of operation and loan policies.

DOCUMENTOS DE GEOHISTORIA REGIONAL. see *HISTORY — History Of North And South America*

910   PL   ISSN 0012-5032
        CODEN: PGDGA4
DOKUMENTACJA GEOGRAFICZNA. 1955. bi-m. price varies. Polska Akademia Nauk, Instytut Geografii i Przestrzennego Zagospodarowania, Ul. Krakowskie Przedmiescie 30, 00-927 Warsaw, Poland. (Dist. by: ORWN PAN, Palac Kultury i Nauki, 00-901 Warsaw, Poland; And by: Ars Polona, Krakowskie Przedmiescie 7, 00-068 Warsaw, Poland) Ed. J. Grzeszczak. circ. 525. **Indexed:** Geo.Abstr. **Document type:** academic/scholarly publication.

526.9   FR   ISSN 0765-1120
DOSSIERS DE TELEDETECTION. 1985. irreg. (Centre Regional de Teledection) Presses Universitaires de Rennes, 2 rue du Doyen D. Leroy, 35044 Rennes Cedex, France. TEL 99-54-66-35. FAX 99-33-07-95.

910   UK
DRUMLIN. 1955. a. £1. University of Glasgow Geographical Society, c/o Department of Geography, University of Glasgow, Glasgow G12 8QQ, Scotland. TEL 041-339-8855. FAX 041-339-8855. Eds. Susan Mains, Eugene McCann. adv.; bk.rev. circ. 300.

910   MW   ISSN 0420-2392
G1
DZIKO; the geographical magazine. 1972. s-a. K.80. Chancellor College, Geographical Society, Box 280, Zomba, Malawi. Ed. B.E. Kamanga. adv.; charts; illus. **Indexed:** GeoRef.

| 526.8 | | KE | |

EARTH RESOURCES MAPPING IN AFRICA. (Text in English or French) 1979. q. free. Regional Centre for Services in Surveying, Mapping and Remote Sensing, Box 18118, Nairobi, Kenya. FAX 254-2-802767. TELEX 25285 KEREGS KE. Ed. Prof. Simon L.P. Ndyetabula. adv.; bk.rev. circ. 1,800. **Document type:** newsletter.
  Description: Presents cartography, GIS and remote sensing techniques.

| 916.76 | | UG | ISSN 0070-7961 |
| DT365 | | | |

EAST AFRICAN GEOGRAPHICAL REVIEW. 1963. a. $12.50. Uganda Geographical Association, Makerere University, Box 7062, Kampala, Uganda. Ed. J.B. Kabera. adv.; bk.rev. circ. 1,000. **Indexed:** Curr.Cont.Africa, Field Crop Abstr., Herb.Abstr., Rural Recreat.Tour.Abstr., World Agri.Econ.& Rural Sociol.Abstr.

| 917 | | US | ISSN 0070-8127 |
| G1 | | | |

EAST LAKES GEOGRAPHER. 1964. a. $4. (Association of American Geographers, East Lakes Division) Western Michigan University, Department of Geography, Kalamazoo, MI 49008. TEL 616-383-1839. Ed. David G. Dickason. circ. 500. (back issues avail.) **Indexed:** Geo.Abstr.
  —UnCover.

| 910 | | UK | ISSN 0012-8481 |
| DA670.M64 | | | CODEN: EMGEA2 |

EAST MIDLAND GEOGRAPHER. 1954. s-a. £8($18) University of Nottingham, Department of Geography, Nottingham NG7 2RD, England. bk.rev.; illus.; maps; index, cum.index. circ. 750-800. (also avail. in microfilm from UMI; reprint service avail. from UMI) **Indexed:** Br.Geol.Lit., Forest.Abstr., Geo.Abstr., Soils & Fert., World Agri.Econ.& Rural Sociol.Abstr.
  —BLDSC (3646.500000); UnCover; UMI.

| 910 330 | | US | ISSN 0013-0095 |
| HF1021 | | | |

ECONOMIC GEOGRAPHY. 1925. q. $35 to individuals (foreign $37); institutions $45 (foreign $47); students $20 (foreign $22) (effective 1994). Clark University, 950 Main St., Worcester, MA 01610. TEL 508-793-7311. Eds. Susan Hanson, Richard Peet. bk.rev.; charts; illus.; maps; stat.; index. circ. 2,600. (also avail. in microform from UMI,PMC; back issues avail., reprint service avail. from UMI) **Indexed:** Acad.Ind., Amer.Bibl.Slavic & E.Eur.Stud., Amer.Hist.& Life, Biol.Abstr., Bk.Rev.Ind. (1965-), BPIA, Bus.Ind., C.R.E.J., Child.Bk.Rev.Ind. (1965-), Curr.Cont., E.I., Field Crop Abstr., Geo.Abstr., Herb.Abstr., Hist.Abstr., HRIS, INIS Atomind., J.of Econ.Lit., Key to Econ.Sci., Mid.East: Abstr.& Ind., P.A.I.S., Popul.Ind., Rural Recreat.Tour.Abstr., Soc.Sci.Ind., SSCI, Tr.& Indus.Ind., World Agri.Econ.& Rural Sociol.Abstr.
  —BLDSC (3652.900000); Faxon; UnCover; SWETS; UMI.

| 910 | | US | |

ENCYCLOPEDIA OF GEOGRAPHIC INFORMATION SOURCES. (Companion to Encyclopedia of Business Information Sources) irreg. $105 for US vol.; international vol. $130. Gale Research Inc., 835 Penobscot Bldg., Detroit, MI 48226. TEL 313-961-2242. FAX 313-961-6083. TELEX 810-221-7086. Ed. Jennifer Mossman.

ENGLISH PLACE-NAME SOCIETY. see LINGUISTICS

| 910 | | UK | |

ENGLISH PLACE-NAME SOCIETY JOURNAL. 1969. £8 to non-members. English Place-Name Society, University of Nottingham, Department of English, Nottingham NG7 2RD, England. TEL 0602-515914. FAX 0602-515924. Ed. John Field. circ. 600. **Indexed:** Bibl.Ling. **Document type:** academic/scholarly publication.

ENVIRONMENT AND PLANNING A. see HOUSING AND URBAN PLANNING

| 910 | | GW | ISSN 0013-9998 |
| | | | CODEN: ERDEAM |

DIE ERDE; Zeitschrift der Gesellschaft fuer Erdkunde zu Berlin. (Supplement avail.) 1853. 4/yr. DM.125. Gesellschaft fuer Erdkunde zu Berlin, Arno-Holz-Str. 14, 12165 Berlin, Germany. TEL 030-7919001. FAX 030-7933249. Ed.Bd. adv.; bk.rev.; abstr.; bibl.; charts; illus.; maps; index. circ. 1,500. (reprint service avail. from KTO) **Indexed:** Bibl.Cart., Biol.Abstr., Curr.Cont.Africa, Geo.Abstr., GeoRef., I D A, Irr.& Drain.Abstr., Meteor.& Geoastrophys.Abstr., Rural Devel.Abstr., Rural Recreat.Tour.Abstr., Soils & Fert., World Agri.Econ.& Rural Sociol.Abstr. **Document type:** academic/scholarly publication.
  —BLDSC (3795.000000).

| 910 | | GW | ISSN 0014-0015 |
| G1 | | | CODEN: ERDKA6 |

ERDKUNDE; Archiv fuer wissenschaftliche Geographie. (Text in German; summaries in English) 1947. q. DM.82. (Universitaet Bonn, Geographisches Institut) Ferd. Duemmlers Verlag, Kaiserstr. 31-37, 53113 Bonn, Germany. (Subscr. to: Postfach 1480, 53004 Bonn, Germany) Ed. Helmut Hahn. adv.; bk.rev.; bibl.; charts; illus.; index. circ. 1,250. **Indexed:** Bibl.Cart., Curr.Cont.Africa, E.I., Geo.Abstr., GeoRef., I D A, Ind.Vet., Meteor.& Geoastrophys.Abstr., Protozool.Abstr., Rural Devel.Abstr., Rural Recreat.Tour.Abstr., Soils & Fert., World Agri.Econ.& Rural Sociol.Abstr.
  —SWETS. CCC.

| 910 | | GW | ISSN 0425-1741 |

ERDKUNDLICHES WISSEN; Schriftenfolge fuer Forschung und Praxis. (Supplement to Geographische Zeitschrift) 1952. irreg., vol.113, 1993. price varies. Franz Steiner Verlag Wiesbaden GmbH, Birkenwaldstr. 44, 70191 Stuttgart, Germany. TEL 0711-2582-0. FAX 0711-2582290. TELEX 723636-DAZ-D. (Subscr. to: Postfach 101061, 70009 Stuttgart, Germany) Ed. Gerd Kohlhepp. **Document type:** monographic series.

ERETZ-ISRAEL. ARCHAEOLOGICAL, HISTORICAL AND GEOGRAPHICAL STUDIES. see ARCHAEOLOGY

| 910 | | SP | |

ERIA; revista geografica. 1980. 3/yr. 5000 ptas. Universidad de Oviedo, Departamento de Geografia, Facultad de Geografia e Historia, 33071 Oviedo, Spain. TEL 98-5104410. FAX 98-5104488. Ed. Francisco Quiros Linares. bk.rev.; illus.; index. circ. 500. **Indexed:** Ind. SST.

| 910 | | FR | ISSN 0046-2497 |
| GF1 | | | |

L'ESPACE GEOGRAPHIQUE. (Text in French; summaries in English, French) 1972. q. in N. America (effective 1994). Doin Editeurs, 6 rue de Mezieres, 75006 Paris, France. TEL 1-45481210. FAX 1-45444331. (Subscr. in N. America to: Box 830399, Birmingham, AL 35283-0399. TEL 800-633-4931. FAX 205-995-1588) Ed. R. Brunet. adv.; bk.rev. circ. 1,000. (also avail. in microform from UMI; reprint service avail. from UMI) **Indexed:** Bibl.Cart., E.I., Geo.Abstr., I D A, Rural Recreat.Tour.Abstr., World Agri.Econ.& Rural Sociol.Abstr. **Document type:** academic/scholarly publication.
  —BLDSC (3811.320000); Faxon; SWETS; UMI. CCC.

ESPACES - POPULATIONS - SOCIETES. see POPULATION STUDIES

| 916 | | FR | ISSN 1147-3991 |

ESPACES TROPICAUX. 1971. irreg. price varies. Centre de Recherches sur les Espaces Tropicaux, Universite Michel de Montaigne, Esplanade des Antilles, 33405 Talence Cedex, France. TEL 56-84-50-50. FAX 56-84-51-28. Ed. Singaravelou. circ. 400 (controlled). **Indexed:** GeoRef., Irr.& Drain.Abstr., Rural Devel.Abstr., World Agri.Econ.& Rural Sociol.Abstr.
  Formerly (until 1990, no.63): Travaux et Documents de Geographie Tropicale (ISSN 0336-5522)

| 910 | | SP | ISSN 0014-1496 |
| G1 | | | CODEN: ESGRAF |

ESTUDIOS GEOGRAFICOS. (Text in Spanish; summaries in English, French, Spanish) 1940. q. 3300 ptas. (foreign 4950 ptas.). Consejo Superior de Investigaciones Cientificas (C.S.I.C.), Instituto de Economia y Geografia Aplicadas, Vitruvio, 8, 28006 Madrid, Spain. (And: Aplicadas, Pinar, 25, 28006 Madrid, Spain) Ed. Manuel de Teran. bk.rev.; charts; illus.; index, cum.index every 10 yrs. circ. 1,000. (also avail. in microfilm) **Indexed:** Amer.Hist.& Life, GeoRef., Hist.Abstr., I D A, Ind.SST.
  —BLDSC (3812.749000).

| 914 | | PO | |

ESTUDOS DE GEOGRAFIA DAS REGIOES TROPICAIS. 1979. irreg. Esc.600 per no. Universidade de Lisboa, Centro de Estudos Geograficos, Cidade Universitaria, 1699 Lisbon Codex, Portugal. TEL 7965469. FAX 7938690. circ. 200. **Document type:** academic/scholarly publication.

| 919 | | PO | |

ESTUDOS DE GEOGRAFIA DO MEDITERRANEO E DAS ILHAS ATLANTIDAS. (Text in French, Portuguese) 1982. irreg. Esc.200 per no. Universidade de Lisboa, Centro de Estudos Geograficos, Cidade Universitaria, 1699 Lisbon Codex, Portugal. TEL 796-5469. FAX 793-8690. circ. 200. **Document type:** academic/scholarly publication.
  Description: Covers historical and cartographic studies.

| 910.02 | | PO | |

ESTUDOS DE GEOGRAFIA FISICA. (Text in French, Portuguese) 1972. irreg., no.32, 1993. Esc.325 per no. Universidade de Lisboa, Centro de Estudos Geograficos, Cidade Universitaria, 1699 Lisbon Codex, Portugal. TEL 7940218. FAX 7938690. circ. 200. **Document type:** academic/scholarly publication.
  Description: Covers various areas in geomorphology and climatics.

| 910 914 | | PO | |

ESTUDOS DE GEOGRAFIA HUMANA E REGIONAL. (In 4 series: A - Portugal: Temas da Actualidade; B - Portugal: Estudos Gerais; C - Estudos Regionais e Locais; D - Questoes Metodologicas e Textos de Apoio ao Ensino) 1973. irreg., no.D6, 1993. Esc.1000 per no. Universidade de Lisboa, Centro de Estudos Geograficos, Cidade Universitaria, 1699 Lisbon Codex, Portugal. TEL 7940218. FAX 7938690. circ. 200. **Document type:** academic/scholarly publication.
  Description: Includes Portugal agriculture and touristic information.

| 914.6 | | PO | |

ESTUDOS DE GEOGRAFIA REGIONAL E HISTORIA. 1982. irreg., no.10, 1991. price varies. Universidade de Lisboa, Centro de Estudos Geograficos, Cidade Universitaria, 1699 Lisbon Codex, Portugal. TEL 7965469. FAX 793-8690. **Document type:** academic/scholarly publication.

| 910 | | PO | |

ESTUDOS PARA O PLANEAMENTO REGIONAL E URBANO. (Text in English, Portuguese) 1976. irreg., no.40, 1993. Esc.500. Universidade de Lisboa, Centro de Estudos Geograficos, Cidade Universitaria, 1699 Lisbon Codex, Portugal. TEL 794-0218. FAX 793-8690. circ. 200. **Document type:** academic/scholarly publication.
  Description: Covers studies in human geography, particularly demographic and economic activities and regional and urban planning studies.

ETUDES NORMANDES. see HISTORY — History Of Europe

ETUDES RURALES; revue trimestrielle d'histoire, geographie, sociologie et economie des campagnes. see SOCIOLOGY

EXPLORERS JOURNAL. see ASTRONOMY

GEOGRAPHY

526 US ISSN 1073-0613
GA102.4.E4
F G D C NEWSLETTER. 1985. irreg. free. Federal Geographic Data Committee, 590 National Center, U.S. Geological Survey, 12201 Sunrise Valley Dr., Reston, VA 22092. FAX 703-648-5755. Ed. Gary B. Chappell. circ. 3,000. **Document type:** newsletter.
Former titles (until 1993): F G D Newsletter (Federal Geographic Data) (ISSN 1055-8357); (until 1991): F D C Newsletter (Federal Digital Cartography) (ISSN 1048-5538)
Description: Provides a forum for the exchange of information on federal geographic data activities for people who work with, use, or simply are interested in geographic data.

910 FI ISSN 0015-0010
G23 CODEN: FENNAJ
FENNIA. (Text in English) 1889. s-a. FIM 250. Suomen Maantieteellinen Seura - Geografiska Saellskapet i Finland (Geographical Society of Finland), Mantieteen Laitos, PL 4 (Hallituskatu), FIN-00014 Helsingin Yliopisto, Finland. FAX 358-0-1912641. Ed. Kalevi Rikkinen. charts; illus.; index. circ. 1,000. (reprint service avail. from UMI) **Indexed:** Biol.Abstr., Chem.Abstr., Geo.Abstr., Rural Recreat.Tour.Abstr., World Agri.Econ.& Rural Sociol.Abstr. **Document type:** monographic series.
—BLDSC (3906.000000); UnCover; UMI.
Incorporates: Acta Geographica.

912 GW ISSN 0176-1633
FERNERKUNDUNG IN RAUMORDUNG UND STADTEBAU. 1952. irreg., vol.18, 1993. price varies. Bundesforschungsanstalt fuer Landeskunde und Raumordnung, Am Michaelshof 8, 53177 Bonn, Germany. TEL 0228-826-0. FAX 0228-826266. Ed. W. Strubelt. circ. 400. **Indexed:** Geo.Abstr. **Document type:** government publication.
Formerly: Landeskundliche Luftbildauswertung im Mitteileuropaeischen Raum (ISSN 0457-0715)
Description: Data analysis for land use by satellite remote sensing.

910 370 BE
FEUILLETS D'INFORMATIONS PEDAGOGIQUES. (Text in French) 5/yr. 2000 BEF membership (outside Europe 3500 BEF). Federation Belge des Professeurs de Geographie, c/o B. Andries, Av. du Sacre-Coeur 67-1, B-1090 Brussels, Belgium. TEL 32-2-4780445. **Document type:** academic/scholarly publication.

910 PO ISSN 0430-5027
FINISTERRA; revista portuguesa de geografia. (Text in English, French, Italian, Portuguese, Spanish; summaries in English, French, Portuguese) 1966. s-a. Esc.1500($15) Universidade de Lisboa, Centro de Estudos Geograficos, Cidade Universitaria, 1699 Lisbon Codex, Portugal. TEL 796-5469. FAX 796-0063. Ed.Bd. bk.rev.; bibl.; charts; illus.; stat.; cum.index: 1966-1975. circ. 1,400. **Indexed:** Geo.Abstr., GeoRef., I D A. **Document type:** academic/scholarly publication.
Description: Includes articles on various areas in geography.

FLAMENCO; boletin de informacion. see *FOLKLORE*

917.59 US ISSN 0739-0041
F311
FLORIDA GEOGRAPHER. 1967. a. $10. Florida Society of Geographers, c/o College of Liberal Arts, Florida Atlantic Univ., 2912 College Ave., Davie, FL 33314. TEL 305-476-4580. FAX 305-476-4582. Ed. Martin S. Kenzer. adv.; bk.rev. circ. 300. **Indexed:** Forest.Abstr. **Document type:** academic/scholarly publication.
Description: Publishes articles concerning the physical and human geography of the state.
Refereed Serial

910 US ISSN 0015-5004
G1 CODEN: BLOFA5
FOCUS (NEW YORK, 1950). 1950. 4/yr. $22 to individuals; institutions $30. American Geographical Society, 156 Fifth Ave., Ste. 600, New York, NY 10010-7002. TEL 212-242-0214. Ed. Hilany Lambert Hopper. illus.; maps. circ. 8,000. (also avail. in microform from UMI,MCA; reprint service avail. from UMI) **Indexed:** P.A.I.S., R.G.
—Faxon; UnCover; SWETS; UMI.
Description: Color magazine of geographical interests.

910 HU ISSN 0015-5403
DB901 CODEN: FOERAM
FOLDRAJZI ERTESITO/GEOGRAPHICAL BULLETIN. (Text in Hungarian; summaries in English, French, German and Russian) 1952. q. 400 Ft. (Magyar Tudomanyos Akademia, Foldrajztudomanyi Kutato Intezet) Akademiai Kiado, Publishing House of the Hungarian Academy of Sciences, P.O. Box 245, H-1519 Budapest, Hungary. TEL 181-2134. FAX 166-6466. TELEX 22-6228 AKNYO H. Ed. S. Marosi. bk.rev.; abstr.; bibl.; charts; illus.; stat.; index. (tabloid format) **Indexed:** Chem.Abstr., Geo.Abstr., Meteor.& Geoastrophys.Abstr.
—CCC.

910 HU ISSN 0015-5411
G9
FOLDRAJZI KOZLEMENYEK. (Text in Hungarian; summaries in English, French and German) 1873. q. $26. Magyar Foldrajzi Tarsasag, Andrassy u. 62, 1062 Budapest, Hungary. TEL 1-117-688. Eds. M. Pecsi, Gy. Miklos. bk.rev.; abstr.; bibl.; charts; illus.; stat.; index. **Indexed:** Amer.Hist.& Life, Bibl.Cart., Geo.Abstr., Hist.Abstr., Soils & Fert., Triticale Abstr., World Agri.Econ.& Rural Sociol.Abstr.

910 HU ISSN 0428-819X
FOLDRAJZI MONOGRAFIAK. (Text in Hungarian; occasional summaries in French, German or Russian) 1955. irreg. price varies. (Magyar Tudomanyos Akademia) Akademiai Kiado, Publishing House of the Hungarian Academy of Sciences, P.O. Box 245, H-1519 Budapest, Hungary. TEL 181-2134. FAX 166-6466. TELEX 22-6228 AKNYO H. **Document type:** monographic series.

910 HU ISSN 0071-6650
FOLDRAJZI TANULMANYOK. 1964. irreg., vol.22, 1992. price varies. (Magyar Tudomanyos Akademia) Akademiai Kiado, Publishing House of the Hungarian Academy of Sciences, P.O. Box 245, H-1519 Budapest, Hungary. TEL 181-2134. FAX 166-6466. TELEX 22-6228 AKNYO H.

910 PL ISSN 0071-6707
FOLIA GEOGRAPHICA. GEOGRAPHICA-OECONOMICA. (Text in Polish; summaries in English) 1968. a. price varies. (Polska Akademia Nauk, Oddzial w Krakowie, Komisja Nauk Geograficznych) Ossolineum, Publishing House of the Polish Academy of Sciences, Rynek 9, 50-106 Wroclaw, Poland. TEL 48-71-386-25. FAX 48-71-448-103. TELEX 0712771 OSS PL. Ed. B. Kortus. **Indexed:** Geo.Abstr. **Document type:** academic/scholarly publication.
—BLDSC (3970.100000).
Description: Social-geographic and economic-geographic problems of Southern Poland in comparison with problems of Poland as a whole or in foreign countries.

910 PL ISSN 0071-6715
GB235.4 CODEN: FGGPB5
FOLIA GEOGRAPHICA. GEOGRAPHICA-PHYSICA. (Text in Polish; summaries in English) 1967. a. price varies. (Polska Akademia Nauk, Oddzial w Krakowie, Komisja Nauk Geograficznych) Ossolineum, Publishing House of the Polish Academy of Sciences, Rynek 9, 50-106 Wroclaw, Poland. FAX 48-71-448-103. TELEX 0712771 OSS PL. Ed. T. Zietara. circ. 600. **Indexed:** Geo.Abstr., GeoRef. **Document type:** academic/scholarly publication.

914 DK ISSN 0071-6693
CODEN: FOGDBP
FOLIA GEOGRAPHICA DANICA. (Text in Danish and English; summaries in English and Danish) 1940. irreg. (approx. 1/yr.). price varies. Kongelige Danske Geografiske Selskab - Royal Danish Geographical Society, Oester Voldgade 10, DK-1350 Copenhagen K, Denmark. (Subscr. to: C. A. Reitzels Forlag, Noerregade 20, DK-1165 Copenhagen K, Denmark) Ed. Niels Kingo Jacobsen. abstr.; bibl.; charts; illus. (reprint service avail. from UMI) **Indexed:** Deep Sea Res.& Oceanogr.Abstr., Geo.Abstr., GeoRef. **Document type:** monographic series.

FONDAZIONE GUARASCI. BOLLETTINO MENSILE D'INFORMAZIONE. see *POLITICAL SCIENCE*

910 GW
FORSCHUNGEN ZUR DEUTSCHEN LANDESKUNDE. 1885. irreg. price varies. Zentralausschuss fuer Deutsche Landeskunde e.V., Universitaet Trier, 54286 Trier, Germany. TEL 0651-2014526. FAX 0651-2013975. **Document type:** academic/scholarly publication, monographic series.

526.982 SW ISSN 0071-8068
FOTOGRAMMETRISKA MEDDELANDEN/PHOTOGRAMMETRIC REPORTS. (Text in English, German; summaries in English) 1943. irreg. price varies. Royal Institute of Technology, Department of Geodesy and Photogrammetry - Kungl. Tekniska Hoegskolan, S-100 44 Stockholm, Sweden. TEL 46-8-7907345. FAX 46-8-7906610. Ed. Kennert Torlegaard. cum.index: 1944-69. circ. 300. **Document type:** academic/scholarly publication, monographic series.
Description: Contains papers on photogrammetry, remote sensing, geographical information systems, digital image processing, computer cartography.

914 GW ISSN 0071-8173
G13 CODEN: MFGGAD
FRAENKISCHE GEOGRAPHISCHE GESELLSCHAFT. MITTEILUNGEN. 1954. irreg. price varies. Fraenkische Geographische Gesellschaft, Kochstr. 4, 91054 Erlangen, Germany. TEL 09131-852012. Ed. Horst Kopp. adv.; bk.rev. circ. 1,000. **Indexed:** GeoRef. **Document type:** academic/scholarly publication.

910 GW ISSN 0071-9447
G1 CODEN: FGEHA4
FREIBURGER GEOGRAPHISCHE HEFTE. 1963. irreg., vol.40, 1994. price varies. Universitaet Freiburg, Institut fuer Physische Geographie, Werderring 4, 79085 Freiburg, Germany. Ed. H. Gossmann. circ. 500. **Indexed:** GeoRef. **Document type:** monographic series.
—BLDSC (4033.444000).

917 972 MX ISSN 0187-7372
E183.8.M6
FRONTERA NORTE. 1989. s-a. $25 (foreign $35). Colegio de la Frontera Norte, Publications Department, Blvd. Abelardo L. Rodriguez, 2925, Zona del Rio, 22320 Tijuana, Mexico. TEL 842226. (Orders in U.S.: Box L, Chula Vista, CA 91912) Ed. Gustavo del Castillo Vera. circ. 2,000. **Document type:** academic/scholarly publication.
Description: Provides information on problems in economy, politics, migration and ecology at the U.S.-Mexico border.

910 CC
FUJIAN DILI/FUJIAN GEOGRAPHY. (Text in Chinese) s-a. Y2. Fujian Shifan Daxue, Dili Yanjiusuo - Fujian Normal University, Institute of Geography, Shangsan Lu, Cangshan Qu, Fuzhou, Fujian 350007, People's Republic of China. TEL 541543. (Dist. overseas by: Jiangsu Publications Import & Export Corp., 56 Gao Yun Ling, Nanjing, Jiangsu, P.R.C.) (Co-sponsor: Fujian Sheng Dili Xuehui) Ed. Fu Zude.
Description: Conducts research on and exploration of Fujian and Taiwan geography.

526.3 US ISSN 1048-5104
VK562 CODEN: GPWOEN
G P S WORLD; news and applications of the Global Positioning System. 1990. 10/yr. $59 (foreign $117). Advanstar Communications, Inc., 7500 Old Oak Blvd., Cleveland, OH 44130. TEL 216-826-2839. FAX 216-891-2726. (Subscr. to: 1 E. First St., Duluth, MN 55082. TEL 800-346-0085) Ed. Glen Gibbons. circ. 32,000. (back issues avail.) **Document type:** trade publication.
—BLDSC (4206.314520); UnCover; SWETS. **CCC.**
Description: Covers new applications in GPS with regard to navigation, vehicle tracking, geodesy and surveying, military operations, and aviation.

910.02 JA ISSN 0916-3611
GAKUJUTSU KOENKAI RONBUNSHU/JAPANESE CONFERENCE OF REMOTE SENSING. PROCEEDINGS. (Text in English, Japanese) 1981. a. Nihon Rimoto Senshingu Gakkai - Remote Sensing Society of Japan, 8-16, Kanda Ogawamachi 2-chome, Chiyoda-ku, Tokyo 101, Japan. **Document type:** proceedings.

GALLIA PREHISTOIRE. SUPPLEMENT. see *ARCHAEOLOGY*

910 PO ISSN 0379-9514
GARCIA DE ORTA: SERIE DE GEOGRAFIA. 1973. 2/yr. price varies. Instituto de Investigacao Cientifica Tropical, Rua Jau 54, 1300 Lisbon, Portugal. TEL 364-5321. FAX 363-1460. (Subscr. to: Centro de Documentacao e Informacao, Rua Jau 47, 1300 Lisbon, Portugal) circ. 1,000. **Document type:** academic/scholarly publication.

GEOGRAPHY

917.1 CN ISSN 0576-1999
F1004
GAZETTEER OF CANADA/REPERTOIRE GEOGRAPHIQUE DU CANADA. (Text in English, French) 1952. irreg., latest 1990. price varies. Natural Resources Canada, Surveys, Mapping and Remote Sensing Sector, Canadian Permanent Committee on Geographical Names, 650 - 615 Booth St., Ottawa, ON K1A 0E9, Canada. (Dist. by: Canadian Government Publishing Centre, Department of Supply and Services, Hull, PQ K1A 0S9, Canada. TEL 819-956-4800. FAX 819-994-1498) maps. circ. 1,500. (also avail. in microfiche) **Document type:** government publication.
Description: Each issue details a different province or territory of Canada.

GENDER, PLACE AND CULTURE; a journal of feminist geography. see WOMEN'S STUDIES

GEO. see ENVIRONMENTAL STUDIES

910 AT ISSN 0157-1338
DU1
GEO; Australasia's geographical magazine. 1978. bi-m. Aus.$39.75 (foreign Aus.$55). Geo Productions Pty. Ltd., 2A Blakesley St., Chatswood, N.S.W. 2067, Australia. TEL 02-411-1766. FAX 02-413-2689. Ed. Michael Hohensee. adv.; bk.rev.; film rev.; charts; illus.; cum.index. circ. 65,000. (back issues avail.) **Indexed:** Pinpointer.
—BLDSC (4116.706000).
Description: Covers wildlife, flora and fauna, history, anthropology, travel, town profiles and various traditional industries.

910 GW
GEO KATALOG (YEAR). VOLUME 1. TOURISTISCHE VEROEFFENTLICHUNGEN. 1972. a. DM.190. GeoCenter Verlagsvertrieb GmbH, Neumarkterstr. 18, 81673 Munich, Germany. TEL 089-43189-0. FAX 089-43189555. adv. circ. 2,500. **Document type:** catalog.
Formerly: Geo Katalog. Band 1. Touristische Veroeffentlichungen.

913 GW
GEO SPECIAL. (Editions in English, German) 1981. bi-m. DM.76.80 (Europe DM.96; elsewhere DM.148.20). Gruner und Jahr AG & Co., Am Baumwall 11, 20459 Hamburg, Germany. TEL 040-3703-0. FAX 040-37035604. circ. 250,000. **Document type:** academic/scholarly publication.
Description: Each issue is devoted to a specific region.

910.02 GW
GEO-WISSEN. 1987. bi-m. DM.37.20 (Europe DM.37.20; elsewhere DM.73.80). Gruner und Jahr AG & Co., Am Baumwall 11, 20459 Hamburg, Germany. TEL 040-3703-0. FAX 040-37035604. circ. 250,000. **Document type:** academic/scholarly publication.

910 375 UK ISSN 0956-0629
GEOACTIVE. 1989. 3/yr. £32.50. Stanley Thornes, Ellenborough House, Wellington St., Cheltenham, Glos. GL50 1YD, England. TEL 0242-288888. FAX 0242-221914. bibl.; charts; illus. circ. 2,000. (looseleaf format)
Description: Contains case study material for teachers of geography.

910 HK ISSN 1010-6049
G70.4
GEOCARTO INTERNATIONAL; multi-disciplinary journal of remote sensing. 1986. q. $45 to individuals; institutions $75. Geocarto International Centre, G.P.O. Box 4122, Hong Kong. TEL 5464262. FAX 5593419. Ed.Bd. adv.; bk.rev. **Indexed:** Environ.Abstr., Irr.& Drain.Abstr., Soils & Fert.
—BLDSC (4116.917700); CIS; SWETS.

526 NE ISSN 0016-707X
GEODESIA. 1959. 11/yr. fl.66 (foreign fl.110) (effective 1994). Stichting Nederlands Genootschap voor Landmeetkunde, c/o Mrs C. Scherpenzeel-Vanderlei, Venkelstr. 119, 7322 KW Apeldoorn, Netherlands. TEL 31-15-781567. FAX 31-15-782348. Ed. H.J.G.L. Aalders. adv. contact: Ing. C.M. van Maris. bk.rev.; charts; illus.; tr.lit.; index. circ. 3,200. **Indexed:** Bibl.Cart.
—SWETS.
Incorporates: Nederlands Geodetisch Tijdschrift; Which superseded: Tijdschrift voor Kadaster en Landmeetkunde.

526 XR ISSN 0016-7096
GEODETICKY A KARTOGRAFICKY OBZOR. (Text in Czech; summaries in English, French, German and Russian) 1913. m. $47.40. (Cesky Urad pro Geodesii a Kartografii) Nakladatelstvi Technicke Literatury, Spalena 51, 113 02 Prague 1, Czech Republic. (Dist. by: Artia, Ve Smeckach 30, 111 27 Prague 1, Czech Republic) (Co-sponsor: Slovensky Urad pre Geodeziu a Kartografiu) Ed. Ivan Cermak. adv.; bk.rev.; abstr.; bibl.; charts; illus.; stat.; index. circ. 2,200. **Indexed:** Bibl.Cart., Geo.Abstr.

526 HU ISSN 0016-7118
TA501 CODEN: GEKGAS
GEODEZIA ES KARTOGRAFIA/GEODESY AND CARTOGRAPHY. (Text in Hungarian; table of contents in English, German, Russian) 1949. bi-m. $20 (effective 1992). (Geodeziai es Kartografiai Egyesulet) Cartographia, Box 132, 1443 Budapest, Hungary. TEL 361-163-36-39. FAX 361-163-46-39. TELEX 226218 CARTO H. bk.rev.; charts; illus. circ. 1,000. **Indexed:** Bibl.Cart., Geo.Abstr., GeoRef. **Document type:** trade publication.
Description: Covers surveying, geographical cartography and news of the trade.

GEODEZIYA I KARTOGRAFIYA. see EARTH SCIENCES — Geophysics

GEODEZJA I KARTOGRAFIA. see EARTH SCIENCES — Geophysics

GEODINAMICA ACTA. see EARTH SCIENCES — Geology

910 614.7 UK ISSN 0267-7563
GEOFILE. 1982. 3/yr. £32.50. Stanley Thornes, Ellenborough House, Wellington St., Cheltenham, Glos. GL50 1YD, England. TEL 0242-228888. FAX 0242-221914. bibl.; charts; illus.; stat.; index, cum.index. circ. 2,000. (looseleaf format)

910.02 UK ISSN 0016-7185
CODEN: GFRMA
GEOFORUM; the international multi-disciplinary journal for the rapid publication of research results and critical review articles in the physical, human and regional geosciences. (Text in English, French, German) 1970. 4/yr. £265($410) (effective 1994). Elsevier Science Ltd., Pergamon, P.O. Box 800, Kidlington, Oxford OX5 1DX, England. TEL 44-865-843000. FAX 44-865-843010. (Subscr. in U.S. and Canada to: Elsevier Science, 660 White Plains Rd., Tarrytown, NY 10591-5153. TEL 914-524-9200. FAX 914-333-2444) Ed. Judith Rees. adv.; bk.rev.; charts; illus.; stat.; index. circ. 600. (also avail. in microfilm from UMI; back issues avail.; reprint service avail. from UMI) **Indexed:** Curr.Adv.Ecol.Sci., Curr.Cont.Africa, Deep Sea Res.& Oceanogr.Abstr., E.I., Energy Info.Abstr., Environ.Abstr., Environ.Per.Bibl. (1989-), Excerp.Med., Geo.Abstr., GeoRef., I D A, Mid.East: Abstr.& Ind., Risk Abstr., Rural Devel.Abstr., SSCI. **Document type:** academic/scholarly publication.
—BLDSC (4121.450000); Faxon; UnCover; SWETS; UMI. **CCC.**
Description: Covers all aspects of the management of the human environment.
Refereed Serial

910 PL ISSN 0554-8128
GEOGRAFIA. (Text in Polish; summaries in English and German) 1957. irreg., no.56, 1993. Adam Mickiewicz University Press, Nowowiejskiego 55, 61-734 Poznan, Poland. TEL 527-380. FAX 61-525425. TELEX 413260 UAMPL. circ. 350. (also avail. in microfilm) **Indexed:** Geo.Abstr. **Document type:** academic/scholarly publication.
—BLDSC (9120.465000).
Formerly: Uniwersytet im. Adama Mickiewicza w Poznaniu. Wydzial Biologii i Nauk o Ziemi. Zeszyty Naukowe. Seria Geografia.
Description: Contains current research problems of the university's scholars in the field of geography, their Ph.D. works and monographs. Each volume contains the work of one author.

526 BL ISSN 0100-7912
GEOGRAFIA. (Text in Portuguese; summaries in English and French) 1976. s-a. $50 or exchange basis. Associacao de Geografia Teoretica, Caixa Postal 178, 13500-230 Rio Claro, SP, Brazil. FAX 55-195-249622. Ed. Antonio Christofoletti. circ. 1,200. **Indexed:** Geo.Abstr., Ref.Zh. **Document type:** academic/scholarly publication.
—BLDSC (4122.200000).

910 375 IT
GEOGRAFIA. q. Via G. Baglivi, 5, Rome, Italy. Ed. O. Baldacci.

914.5 371.3 IT ISSN 0431-1981
GEOGRAFIA NELLE SCUOLE. 1955. bi-m. L.35000 (foreign L.50000) (effective 1992). Associazione Italiana Insegnanti di Geografia, Via Tigor 22, 34124 Trieste, Italy. TEL 040-6763615. FAX 040-6763647. Ed. Gianfranco Battisti. adv.; bk.rev. circ. 7,000. **Document type:** academic/scholarly publication, bulletin.
—SWETS.
Description: Presents study and teaching methods.

910 301 BL ISSN 0533-9286
GEOGRAFIA URBANA. irreg. Universidade de Sao Paulo, Instituto de Geografia, Edificio de Geografia e Historia, Cidade Universitaria, C.P. 20.7015, 01000 Sao Paulo, Brazil.

910 PL ISSN 0137-7566
GEOGRAFIA W SZKOLE. 1948. bi-m. $10. (Ministerstwo Educacji Narodowej) Wydawnictwa Szkolne i Pedagogiczne, Pl. Dabrowskiego 8, 00-950 Warsaw, Poland. TEL 48-22-217554. (Dist. by: Ars Polona-Ruch, Krakowskie Przedmiescie 7, Warsaw, Poland) Ed. Florian Plit. bk.rev. circ. 12,844. **Indexed:** Bibl.Cart.
Description: Discusses recent developments in geography and in the methodology of teaching. Also publishes geographical notes, news of seminars and conferences on geography instruction.

900 AG
GEOGRAFICA. 1972. a., no.3, 1974. $4. Universidad Nacional del Nordeste, Instituto de Geografia, Las Heras, 727, Resistencia, Argentina. Ed.Bd. illus. circ. 1,000.

910 XO ISSN 0016-7193
CODEN: GGCAAI
GEOGRAFICKY CASOPIS/GEOGRAPHICAL REVIEW. (Text mainly in Slovak; occasionally in English; summaries in English, German) 1949. q. 100 Kcs.($18) (Slovenska Akademia Vied) Veda, Publishing House of the Slovak Academy of Sciences, Klemensova 19, 814 30 Bratislava, Slovakia. (Dist. in Western countries by: John Benjamins B.V., Amsteldijk 44, Amsterdam (Z.), Netherlands) Ed. Jozef Kvitkovic. bk.rev.; charts; illus.; index. circ. 1,000. **Indexed:** Bibl.Cart., Geo.Abstr., I D A, World Agri.Econ.& Rural Sociol.Abstr.
—BLDSC (4122.500000).

778 526.9 NE ISSN 0926-3837
GEOGRAFIE. 1967. bi-m. fl.130 (foreign fl.150) (effective 1994). Koninklijk Nederlands Aardrijkskundig Genootschap - Royal Dutch Geographical Society, P.O. Box 80123, 3508 TC Utrecht, Netherlands. TEL 31-30-532757. FAX 31-30-535523. Ed. Ben de Pater. adv.; B&W page fl.1050; 210 x 297. bk.rev.; charts; illus.; maps; index. circ. 4,300. **Indexed:** Bibl.Cart., Excerp.Med., Geo.Abstr., GeoRef., Key to Econ.Sci., So.Pac.Per.Ind. **Document type:** academic/scholarly publication.
—BLDSC (4122.900000); SWETS.
Formerly (until 1992): Geografisch Tijdschrift (ISSN 0016-7215)
Description: Covers all aspects of geography.

910 370 NE ISSN 0926-3845
▼**GEOGRAFIE EDUCATIEF.** 1992. q. fl.130 (foreign fl.140) (efffective 1994). Koninklijk Nederlands Aardrijkskundig Genootschap - Royal Dutch Geographical Society, P.O. Box 80123, 3508 TC Utrecht, Netherlands. TEL 31-30-532757. FAX 31-30-535523. Ed. Ben de Pater. adv.: B&W page fl.775; 210 x 297. bk.rev.; charts; illus.; maps; index. circ. 2,900. **Document type:** academic/scholarly publication.
Description: Journal for geography teaching.

910 LI ISSN 0072-0917
G1 CODEN: GGMEAC
GEOGRAFIJOS METRASTIS/GEOGRAPHICAL YEAR BOOK. (Text in Lithuanian; summaries in English, German and Russian) 1958. irreg. price varies. Lithuanian Academy of Sciences, Institute of Geography, Akademijos 2, 2600 Vilnius, Lithuania. TEL 35-92-45. (Co-sponsor: Geographical Society of Lithuania) Ed. Vytautas Gudelis. **Indexed:** Deep Sea Res.& Oceanogr.Abstr.

GEOGRAPHY

| 910 | DK | ISSN 0016-7223 |
| G25 | | CODEN: GGTKAV |

GEOGRAFISK TIDSSKRIFT. (Text in Danish and English) 1877. s-a. DKK 200($30) Kongelige Danske Geografiske Selskab - Royal Danish Geographical Society, Oester Voldgade 10, DK-1350 Copenhagen K, Denmark. (Subscr. to: C. A. Reitzels Forlag, Noerregade 20, DK-1165 Copenhagen K, Denmark) Ed. Niels Kingo Jacobsen. bk.rev.; abstr.; bibl.; charts; illus.; index, cum.index. (reprint service avail. from UMI) **Indexed:** Agri.Eng.Abstr., Agroforest.Abstr., Bibl.Cart., Deep Sea Res.& Oceanogr.Abstr., Geo.Abstr., Rural Recreat.Tour.Abstr., Soils & Fert., World Agri.Econ.& Rural Sociol.Abstr.
—BLDSC (4123.000000)

| 910.02 | NO | ISSN 0435-3676 |
| | | CODEN: GAPGAP |

GEOGRAFISKA ANNALER. SERIES A. PHYSICAL GEOGRAPHY. (Text in English, French, German) 4/yr. NOK 545 in the Nordic countries; elsewhere NOK 595. (Svenska Saellskapet Foer Antropologi och Geografi - Swedish Society of Anthropology and Geography) Scandinavian University Press, P.O. Box 2959 Toeyen, N-0608 Oslo, Norway. TEL 472-67-7600. FAX 472-67-7575. (U.S. addr.: Scandinavian University Press, 200 Meacham Ave., Elmont, NY 11003. TEL 516-352-7300) Ed. J.O. Mattsson. **Indexed:** Anthropol.Lit., ASTIS, Bibl.Cart., Deep Sea Res.& Oceanogr.Abstr., Forest.Abstr., Geo.Abstr., GeoRef., Meteor.& Geoastrophys.Abstr., Mid.East: Abstr.& Ind., Rural Recreat.Tour.Abstr., Soils & Fert., World Agri.Econ.& Rural Sociol.Abstr.
—BLDSC (4124.050000); Faxon; UnCover; SWETS.
Supersedes in part: Geografiska Annaler (ISSN 0016-7231)

| 907 370 | SW | ISSN 0016-724X |

GEOGRAFISKA NOTISER. 1943. 4/yr. SEK 130 in Scandinavia; elsewhere SEK 160. Geografilaerarnas Riksfoerening, Geografiska Institutionen, Solvegatan 13, S-223 62 Lund, Sweden. FAX 46-46-10-84-01. Ed. Solveig Maartensson. adv.; bk.rev.; bibl.; charts. circ. 1,200.
—BLDSC (4124.200000).
Description: Aimed at high school and university teachers.

| 910 370 | RU | ISSN 0016-7207 |
| G1 | | |

GEOGRAFIYA V SHKOLE. 1934. bi-m. $61. (Ministerstvo Obrazovaniya Rossiiskoi Federatsii) Izdatel'stvo Shkola-Press, Ul. Smolenskii bul'var, d. 4, 119034 Moscow, Russia. (Dist. in U.S. by: Victor Kamkin Inc., 4956 Boling Brook Pkwy, Rockville, MD 20852. TEL 301-881-5973) Ed. I.I. Varinova. bk.rev.; bibl.; charts; illus. circ. 109,045.

| 910 | CI | ISSN 0016-7258 |

GEOGRAFSKI GLASNIK/GEOGRAPHICAL BULLETIN. (Text in Croatian; summaries in English) 1950. a. Hrvatsko Geografsko Drustvo - Croatian Geographical Society, Marulicev trg 19, 41 000 Zagreb, Croatia. (Co-sponsor: Ministarstvo Znanosti, Tehnologije i Informatike) Ed. Miroslav Sic. circ. 1,000. **Indexed:** Art & Archaeol.Tech.Abstr., Ref.Zh. **Document type:** academic/scholarly publication.
Description: Publishes scientific papers from the field of geography and related disciplines.

| 910 | CI | ISSN 0016-7266 |

GEOGRAFSKI HORIZONT. 1955. q. Hrvatsko Geografsko Drustvo - Croatian Geographical Society, Marulicev trg 19, 41000 Zagreb, Croatia. bk.rev. circ. 6,000.

| 910 | BN | |

GEOGRAFSKI LIST. 1974. 5/yr. 10 din. Geografsko Drustvo Bosne i Hercegovine, Vojvode Putnika 66, 71000 Sarajevo, Bosnia Hercegovina. Ed. Milos Miskovic. bk.rev. circ. 35,000.

| 910 | XV | ISSN 0016-7274 |

GEOGRAFSKI OBZORNIK/GEOGRAPHIC HORIZON; revija za popularizacijo geografije. (Text in Slovenian; abstracts in English) 1954. q. $12. (Ministrstvo za Vzgojo, Izobrazevanje in Telesno Kulturo - Ministry for Education and Sport) Zveza Geografksih Drustev Slovenije - Union of the Geographical Societies of Slovenia), Askerceva 12, 61000 Ljubljana, Slovenia. FAX 38-61-159-253. Ed. Drago Perko. adv.; bk.rev. circ. 1,000.
Description: Covers geographic education.

| 910 | II | ISSN 0072-0909 |

GEOGRAPHER. (Text in English) 1926; N.S. 1948. s-a. Rs.30($15) Aligarh Muslim University, Geographical Society, Aligarh 202001, Uttar Pradesh, India. TEL 571-5661. Ed. M. Farooq Siddiqi. bk.rev. circ. 400. **Indexed:** Field Crop Abstr., Forest.Abstr., Rural Devel.Abstr.
—UnCover.

| 910 | UK | ISSN 0308-6992 |

GEOGRAPHERS; biobibliographical studies. 1977. a. price varies. (International Geographical Union, Working Group on the History of Geographical Thought) Mansell Publishing Ltd., Villiers House, 41-47 Strand, London WC2N 5JE, England. TEL 071-839-4900. FAX 071-839-1804. (Dist. in U.S. by: Cassell, PCS Data Processing Inc., 360 W. 31st St., New York, NY 10001) Ed. T.W. Freeman. index. **Document type:** academic/scholarly publication.
—BLDSC (4125.140000).
Description: Contains approximately 20 studies of individuals who have made major contributions to the development of geographical thought and to geography as scientific subject and academic discipline.

| 910 | IT | ISSN 1121-8940 |

▼**GEOGRAPHIA ANTIQUA**; rivista di geografia storica del mondo antico e di storia della geografia. 1992. a. L.60000 (effective 1993). (Universita di Perugia, Dipartimento di Scienze Storiche dell'Antichita) Giunti Gruppo Editoriale S.p.A., Via Bolognese 165, 50139 Florence, Italy. TEL 055-66791. FAX 055-6679298. Ed. Francesco Prontera.

| 910 610 | HU | ISSN 0300-807X |
| RA791 | | CODEN: GMDCB4 |

GEOGRAPHIA MEDICA; international journal on geography of health - journal international de la geographie de la sante. (Text mainly in English; occasionally in French, German; abstracts in English) 1970. a. $25 (effective 1993). (Hungarian Academy of Sciences) Hungarian Geographical Society, Medico-Geographical Section, c/o Albert Szent-Gyorgyi Med. Univ., Dept. of Public Health, Kossuth L. sgt. 35, 6724 Szeged, Hungary. TEL 36-62-311-954. TELEX 82-441 SZOTE HM. (Co-sponsor: International Geographical Union, Commission on Geography of Health and Development) Ed. Illes Desi. adv.; bk.rev.; abstr.; bibl.; charts; maps. circ. 400. **Indexed:** Biol.Abstr., Environ.Abstr., Excerp.Med., Geo.Abstr., I D A, Ind.Med. **Document type:** academic/scholarly publication.
—CIS; Faxon.
Formerly: Geographia Medica Hungarica (ISSN 0435-3730)

| 910 | PL | ISSN 0016-7282 |
| G1 | | CODEN: GGPLAE |

GEOGRAPHIA POLONICA. (Text in English and French) 1964. irreg. price varies. Polska Akademia Nauk, Instytut Geografii i Przestrzennego Zagospodarowania, Ul. Krakowskie Przedmiescie 30, 00-927 Warsaw, Poland. (Dist. by: Ars Polona, Krakowskie Przedmiescie 7, 00-068 Warsaw, Poland) Ed. Piotr Korcelli. bibl.; charts; illus. **Indexed:** Chem.Abstr., Geo.Abstr. **Document type:** academic/scholarly publication.
—BLDSC (4125.200000).

| 910 | NR | ISSN 0016-7290 |
| G58 | | |

GEOGRAPHICA. 1967. q. n.5.00. University of Ife, Geographical Society, Ile-Ife, Nigeria. Ed. Taiwo Jaiyeoba. adv.; bk.rev. **Indexed:** Amer.Hist.& Life, Hist.Abstr.

| 910 | MY | |

GEOGRAPHICA. (Text in English) 1965. a. M.$10($5) University of Malaya, Department of Geography, 59100 Kuala Lumpur, Malaysia. TEL 03-7555266. FAX 03-7573661. TELEX UNIMAL-MA-39845. Dir. R.F. Dorall. adv.; bk.rev.; bibl.; charts; illus. circ. 1,000. **Indexed:** I D A.

| 910 | SZ | ISSN 0016-7312 |
| G1 | | CODEN: GGHVA4 |

GEOGRAPHICA HELVETICA; Schweizerische Zeitschrift fuer Laender- und Voelkerkunde. (Text and title in French, German, Italian) 1946. q. 52 Fr. (Geographisch-Ethnographische Gesellschaft Zurich) Fotorotar AG, Gewebestr. 18, CH-8132 Egg/ZH, Switzerland. adv.; bk.rev.; abstr.; bibl.; charts; illus.; stat.; index. circ. 1,500. (also avail. in microfilm from UMI; reprint service avail. from UMI) **Indexed:** Bibl.Cart., Biol.Abstr., Forest.Abstr., Rural Recreat.Tour.Abstr., Soils & Fert., World Agri.Econ.& Rural Sociol.Abstr.
—BLDSC (4125.300000).

| 910 | US | ISSN 0016-7363 |
| G70 | | CODEN: GPHAA4 |

GEOGRAPHICAL ANALYSIS; an international journal of theoretical geography. 1969. q. $30 to individuals (foreign $35); libraries $75 (foreign $80) (effective July 1993). Ohio State University Press, 1070 Carmack Rd., Columbus, OH 43210. TEL 614-292-6930. FAX 614-292-2065. Ed. Emilio Casetti. adv.; bk.rev.; index. circ. 1,000. (also avail. in microform from UMI; back issues avail.; reprint service avail. from ISI,UMI) **Indexed:** Bibl.Cart., Curr.Cont., Geo.Abstr., GeoRef., Mid.East: Abstr.& Ind., Popul.Ind., Rural Devel.Abstr., Rural Recreat.Tour.Abstr., Sage Urb.Stud.Abstr., SSCI, World Agri.Econ.& Rural Sociol.Abstr. **Document type:** academic/scholarly publication.
—BLDSC (4125.440000); Faxon; UnCover; SWETS; UMI. **CCC**.
Description: Covers advances in geographical theory, model building, quantitative methods, spatial planning, and research.

| 910 | TZ | ISSN 0016-738X |
| DT440 | | |

GEOGRAPHICAL ASSOCIATION OF TANZANIA JOURNAL. 1967. s-a. membership. Geographical Association of Tanzania, P.O. Box 35049, Dar es Salaam, Tanzania. Ed. A. Armstrong. bk.rev.; charts; illus.; stat. circ. 400. (processed) **Indexed:** Geo.Abstr.

| 910 | AT | |

GEOGRAPHICAL ASSOCIATION OF WESTERN AUSTRALIA. BULLETIN. q. membership. Geographical Association of Western Australia, Box 1252, Subiaco, W.A. 6008, Australia. Ed. Chris Nedkoff. **Document type:** bulletin.

| 910 | US | ISSN 0731-3292 |
| G1 | | |

GEOGRAPHICAL BULLETIN. 1970. s-a. $4 to individuals; institutions $10. Gamma Theta Upsilon, c/o C. Nicholas Raphael, Department of Geography and Geology, Eastern Michigan University, Ypsilanti, MI 48197. TEL 313-487-1480. circ. 1,550. **Indexed:** Bibl.Cart., Geo.Abstr., Mid.East: Abstr.& Ind. **Document type:** academic/scholarly publication.
—UnCover.
Description: Scholarly research articles on the earth sciences, environment and geography, especially as they pertain to the configuration of the landscape, with news and announcements on the activities and the members of Gamma Theta Upsilon.

| 910 | II | |

GEOGRAPHICAL BULLETIN OF INDIA. (Text in English) 1977. 2/yr. Rs.30($10) Patna University, Association of Geographers, 13 Vidyapuri, P.O. Chitragupta Nagar, Patna 800 016, India. Ed.Bd. circ. 250. (back issues avail.)

GEOGRAPHICAL EDUCATION. see EDUCATION — Teaching Methods And Curriculum

| 916 | RH | |

GEOGRAPHICAL EDUCATION MAGAZINE. vol.3, 1982. 2/yr. $12 (effective 1993). Geographical Association of Zimbabwe, c/o University of Zimbabwe, Dept. of Geography, P.O. Box MP 167, Mt. Pleasant, Harare, Zimbabwe. TEL 263-4-303211. FAX 263-4-732828. TELEX 26580 UNIVZ ZW. Ed. Mrs. R.A. Heath. circ. 350. **Indexed:** P.L.E.S.A. (1989-). **Document type:** academic/scholarly publication.
Description: Discusses issues in geographical education at the secondary school level.

GEOGRAPHY

910　　　　　UK　　ISSN 0016-7398
G7　　　　　　　　CODEN: GGJOAR
GEOGRAPHICAL JOURNAL. 1893. 3/yr. £45. Royal Geographical Society, 1 Kensington Gore, London SW7 2AR, England. TEL 071-589-5466. FAX 071-584-4447. Ed. R.W. Bradnock. adv.; bk.rev.; charts; illus.; index, cum.index every 10 yrs. circ. 10,500. (also avail. in microform from BLH,UMI; reprint service avail. from UMI) **Indexed:** A.I.C.P., Acad.Ind., Amer.Hist.& Life, Asian-Pac.Econ.Lit., Bibl.Cart., Bk.Rev.Ind. (1965-), Br.Archaeol.Abstr., Br.Geol.Lit., Br.Hum.Ind., Child.Bk.Rev.Ind. (1965-), Curr.Adv.Ecol.Sci., Curr.Cont., Deep Sea Res.& Oceanogr.Abstr., E.I., Excerp.Med., Field Crop Abstr., Geo.Abstr., GeoRef., Hist.Abstr., I D A, Ind.Sci.Rev., Meteor.& Geoastrophys.Abstr., Mid.East: Abstr.& Ind., Numis.Lit., P.A.I.S., Rural Recreat.Tour.Abstr., Sci.Cit.Ind., So.Pac.Per.Ind., Soc.Sci.Ind., Soils & Fert., SSCI, World Agri.Econ.& Rural Sociol.Abstr. **Document type:** academic/scholarly publication.
● Also available on CD-ROM. Producer(s): University Microfilms International.
—BLDSC (4126.000000); Faxon; UnCover; SWETS; UMI. **CCC.**

916　　　　　RH　　ISSN 1011-5919
DT2891
GEOGRAPHICAL JOURNAL OF ZIMBABWE. vol.3, 1970. a. $10. Geographical Association of Zimbabwe, c/o University of Zimbabwe, Dept. of Geography, P.O. Box MP 167, Mt. Pleasant, Harare, Zimbabwe. TEL 263-4-303211. FAX 263-4-732828. TELEX 26580 UNIVZ ZW. Ed. L.M. Zinyama. circ. 350. **Indexed:** P.L.E.S.A. **Document type:** academic/scholarly publication.
Supersedes (with vol.18, 1987): Geographical Association of Zimbabwe. Proceedings.
Description: Covers the geography of Zimbabwe and southern Africa.

910　　　　　UK　　ISSN 0016-741X
G1　　　　　　　　CODEN: GGMAAY
GEOGRAPHICAL MAGAZINE. 1935. m. £23.50 (Europe £29.50; rest of world £35.50). (Royal Geographical Society) World Publications Ltd., B B C Enterprises, Rm. A1040, 80 Wood Ln., Woodlands, London W12 0TT, England. TEL 081-576-2000. FAX 081-576-2931. (Subscr. to: Punch Subscriptions, Stephensen House, Brunel Center, Bletchley, Milton Keyes, London MK2 2EW, England) Ed. Alexander Goldsmith. adv.; bk.rev.; illus.; maps; index. circ. 30,000. (also avail. in microform from WMP) **Indexed:** Art.Hosp.& Tour., Bibl.Cart., Br.Ceram.Abstr., Br.Geol.Lit., Br.Hum.Ind., Environ.Per.Bibl., GdIns, Geo.Abstr., I D A, Mid.East: Abstr.& Ind., P.A.I.S., Soc.Sci.Ind. **Document type:** academic/scholarly publication.
—UnCover; SWETS.

910　　　　　II　　ISSN 0072-0925
GEOGRAPHICAL OBSERVER. (Text in English and Hindi) 1965. a. $20 plus postage. Meerut College Geographical Society, c/o Department of Geography, Meerut College, Meerut 250 001, Uttar Pradesh, India. Ed. B.S. Negi. bk.rev. circ. 300. **Indexed:** Doc.Geogr., Geo.Abstr.

910　　　　　UK　　ISSN 0305-5914
　　　　　　　　　　CODEN: GPUGDM
GEOGRAPHICAL PAPERS. 1970. irreg., no.114. University of Reading, Department of Geography, Whiteknights Rd., Reading RG6 2AB, England. TEL 0734-875123. FAX 0734-755865. Eds. Sarah James, Guru Aulakh. adv. circ. 300. **Indexed:** Geo.Abstr., I D A. **Document type:** academic/scholarly publication.
—BLDSC (4126.581000).

915.502　　　　IR
GEOGRAPHICAL RESEARCH. 1984. q. Astan-i Quds Islamic Research Foundation, P.O. Box 366-91735, Meshed, Iran. TEL 63031.

910　　　　　US　　ISSN 0016-7428
G1　　　　　　　　CODEN: GEORAD
GEOGRAPHICAL REVIEW. 1916. q. $46 to individuals; institutions $65. American Geographical Society, 156 Fifth Ave., New York, NY 10010-7002. TEL 212-242-0214. Ed. Douglas R. McManis. adv.; bk.rev.; maps; illus.; index. circ. 3,000. (also avail. in microform from UMI,PMC; reprint service avail. from UMI) **Indexed:** Abstr.Anthropol., Acad.Ind., Amer.Bibl.Slavic & E.Eur.Stud., Amer.Hist.& Life, Bibl.Cart., Biol.Abstr., Bk.Rev.Ind. (1965-1977), Br.Archaeol.Abstr., Chem.Abstr., Chic.Per.Ind., Child.Bk.Rev.Ind. (1965-1977), Curr.Adv.Ecol.Sci., Curr.Cont., Deep Sea Res.& Oceanogr.Abstr., E.I., Eng.Ind., Geo.Abstr., GeoRef., Hist.Abstr., I D A, Mid.East: Abstr.& Ind., P.A.I.S., Peace Res.Abstr., Popul.Ind., Risk Abstr., Rural Recreat.Tour.Abstr., So.Pac.Per.Ind., Soc.Sci.Ind., Soils & Fert., SSCI, World Agri.Econ.& Rural Sociol.Abstr.
—BLDSC (4127.000000); Faxon; UnCover; SWETS; UMI.

910　　　　　AF　　ISSN 0016-7436
GEOGRAPHICAL REVIEW OF AFGHANISTAN.* (Text in Arabic, English and German) vol.2, 1963. Kabul University, Institute of Geography, Faculty of Letters, Kabul, Afghanistan. Ed. Gholam Jelani Arez.

910　　　　　II　　ISSN 0375-6386
GEOGRAPHICAL REVIEW OF INDIA. (Text in English) 1936. q. $60 (typically set in Jan.). Geographical Society of India, c/o Calcutta University, Geography Department, 35 Ballygunge Circular Rd., Calcutta 700 019, India. TEL 475-3681. Ed. P.K. Saha. adv.; bk.rev.; abstr.; charts; illus.; index, cum.index. circ. 1,000. (tabloid format) **Indexed:** Geo.Abstr., GeoRef., Rural Recreat.Tour.Abstr., World Agri.Econ.& Rural Sociol.Abstr. **Document type:** academic/scholarly publication.
Formerly: Calcutta Geographical Review.

910　　　　　JA　　ISSN 0016-7444
G1　　　　　　　　CODEN: CRGHAO
GEOGRAPHICAL REVIEW OF JAPAN. SERIES A/CHIRIGAKU HYORON A. (Text in Japanese; title and contents page in English) 1925. m. Association of Japanese Geographers - Nippon Chiri Gakkai, c/o Japan Academic Societies Center, 2-4-16 Yayoi, Bunkyo-ku, Tokyo 113, Japan. TEL 81-3-3815-1912. FAX 81-3-3815-1672. Ed. Eiichi Aoki. adv.; index. circ. 3,000. **Indexed:** Geo.Abstr., GeoRef. **Document type:** academic/scholarly publication.
—BLDSC (4127.200000); UnCover.
Supersedes in part: Geographical Review of Japan - Chirigaku Hyoron.

910　　　　　JA　　ISSN 0289-6001
GEOGRAPHICAL REVIEW OF JAPAN. SERIES B/CHIRIGAKU HYORON B. (Text in English) 1984. s-a. $50. Association of Japanese Geographers - Nippon Chiri Gakkai, c/o Japan Academic Societies Center, 2-4-16 Yayoi, Bunkyo-ku, Tokyo 113, Japan. TEL 81-3-3815-1912. FAX 81-3-3815-1672. (Dist. by: Business Center for Academic Societies Japan, 5-16-9 Honkomagome, Bunkyo-ku, Tokyo 113, Japan. TEL 03-5814-5811) Ed. Isao Saito. adv.; index. **Indexed:** Field Crop Abstr., GeoRef. **Document type:** academic/scholarly publication.
—BLDSC (4127.250000).
Supersedes in part: Geographical Review of Japan - Chirigaku Hyoron.
Description: Contains papers, subject review articles, and short notes that give new concepts, ideas and scope to geography.

001.6　　　　　CH
GEOGRAPHICAL SOCIETY OF CHINA. BULLETIN. 1973. a. $10. Geographical Society of China, c/o Department of Geography, National Taiwan Normal University, Taipei, Taiwan, Republic of China. FAX 02-362-2911. Ed. Chiu-Yuan Wang. adv.; abstr. circ. 1,500.

915　　　　　JA
GEOGRAPHICAL SURVEY INSTITUTE, TOKYO. BULLETIN/KOKUDO CHIRIIN HOKOKU. (Text in English) 1948. s-a. exchange basis. Kokudo Chiriin - Geographical Survey Institute, Ministry of Construction, Kitasato-1, Tsukuba-shi, Ibaraki-ken 305, Japan. **Indexed:** Geo.Abstr. **Document type:** government publication.

910　　　　　II　　ISSN 0046-5712
GEOGRAPHICAL VIEW POINT. (Text in English) 1970. s-a. Rs.10($5.) Agra Geographical Society, Raja Balwant Singh College, Department of Geography, Agra 282002, India. Ed. Madhusudan Singh. adv.; bk.rev.; charts; illus.; stat. circ. 200. **Indexed:** Geo.Abstr.
Continues: Geographical Outlook (ISSN 0433-4515)

910　　　　　GW　　ISSN 0178-7810
GEOGRAPHIE AKTUELL. 1985. bi-m. DM.72 (foreign DM.80.40). Aulis Verlag Deubner und Co. KG, Antwerpenerstr. 6-12, 50672 Cologne, Germany. TEL 0221-518051. FAX 0221-518443. Ed. Peter Schroeder. circ. 2,200. **Document type:** academic/scholarly publication.

910　　　　　FR
GEOGRAPHIE DE LA SANTE. irreg. (2-3/yr.). Universite de Montpellier (Universite Paul Valery), B.P. 5043, 34032 Montpellier Cedex 1, France. TEL 67-14-20-00. **Document type:** academic/scholarly publication.
Description: Publishes research done at the university level by geographers either in the form of excerpts, digests or research positions.

910 350　　　　BE
GEOGRAPHIE - ECOLOGIE - ENVIRONNEMENT; organisation de l'espace. (Text in French) 1977. s-a. 2000 BEF membership (outside Europe 3500 BEF). Federation Belge des Professeurs de Geographie, c/o B. Andries, Av. du Sacre-Coeur 67-1, B-1090 Brussels, Belgium. TEL 32-2-4780445. Ed. D. Belayev. circ. 1,600. (back issues avail.)

910.02　　　　　FR　　ISSN 0184-7589
GEOGRAPHIE ET RECHERCHE. 1972. q. 130 F.($22) (foreign 140 F.) (effective 1994). Association Geographie et Recherche, 11 rue Girondins, 99210 Saint Cloud, France. TEL 47-71-62-16. Dir. Jean Chardonnet. bk.rev.; index. circ. 500.

910 028.5　　　GW　　ISSN 0341-5279
GEOGRAPHIE HEUTE. 10/yr. DM.140.10. Erhard Friedrich Verlag GmbH, Im Brande 17, 30926 Seelze, Germany. TEL 0511-40004-0. (Subscr. to: Postfach 100150, 30917 Seelze, Germany) Ed. Peter Tautfest. illus. **Document type:** academic/scholarly publication.
—**CCC.**

910　　　　　GW　　ISSN 0341-8057
GEOGRAPHIE IM UNTERRICHT. 1976. 10/yr. DM.83.40. Erhard Friedrich Verlag GmbH, Im Brande 15, 30926 Seelze, Germany. (Subscr. to: Postfach 100150, 30917 Seelze, Germany) Ed.Bd. **Indexed:** Bibl.Cart.

910　　　　　CN　　ISSN 0705-7199
G1　　　　　　　　CODEN: GPHQEM
GEOGRAPHIE PHYSIQUE ET QUATERNAIRE. (Text in English and French; summaries in English and French) 1947. 3/yr. Can.$30 to individuals; institutions Can.$76. Presses de l'Universite de Montreal, C.P. 6128, Succ. A, Montreal, PQ H3C 3J7, Canada. TEL 514-343-6933. Ed. Pierre Richard. bk.rev.; abstr.; bibl.; charts; illus.; maps; stat.; index. circ. 1,000. (reprint service avail. from UMI) **Indexed:** Can.Per.Ind., Curr.Tit.Ocean, Geo.Abstr., GeoRef., Pt.de Rep. (1983-). **Document type:** academic/scholarly publication.
—BLDSC (4128.320000); UnCover; UMI.
Former titles (until vol.31, 1977): Revue de Geographie de Montreal (ISSN 0035-1148); Revue Canadienne de Geographie.

910 375　　　　GW　　ISSN 0343-7256
GEOGRAPHIE UND IHRE DIDAKTIK. 1973. q. DM.25. Hochschulverband fuer Geographie und ihre Didaktik, Institut fuer Geographie, Universitaet Hildesheim, Marienburger Platz 22, 31141 Hildesheim, Germany. TEL 05121-883183. FAX 05121-867558. Ed. G. Meier-Hilbert. adv.; bk.rev. circ. 550. (back issues avail.) **Document type:** academic/scholarly publication.
Description: Articles of interest to teachers of geography. Includes news and information from associations, events, bibliographies.

GEOGRAPHY

910 GW ISSN 0171-8649
G72
GEOGRAPHIE UND SCHULE. 1978. 6/yr. DM.72 (foreign DM.80.40). Aulis-Verlag Deubner und Co. KG, Antwerpener Str. 6-12, 50672 Cologne, Germany. TEL 0221-518051. FAX 0221-518443. TELEX 8883068-AVD. Ed.Bd. **Document type:** academic/scholarly publication.
—BLDSC (4128.322500).

914 CY
GEOGRAPHIKA CHRONIKA/GEOGRAPHICAL CHRONICLES. (Text in English or Greek) 1971. a. $10. Cyprus Geographical Association - Geographikos Homilos Kyprou, P.O. Box 3656, Nicosia, Cyprus. FAX 357-2-366123. Ed. P.A. Sophocleous. adv.; bk.rev.; illus. circ. 1,000.

910 GW ISSN 0374-9061
G13 CODEN: MGGHAN
GEOGRAPHISCHE GESELLSCHAFT IN HAMBURG. MITTEILUNGEN. irreg., vol.83, 1993. price varies. Franz Steiner Verlag Wiesbaden GmbH, Birkenwaldstr. 44, 70191 Stuttgart, Germany. TEL 0711-2582-0. FAX 0711-2582290. TELEX 723636-DAZ-D. (Subscr. to: Postfach 101061, 70009 Stuttgart, Germany) Ed. Frank Nagel. **Indexed:** Biol.Abstr., GeoRef. **Document type:** monographic series.

910 GW ISSN 0072-0941
G13 CODEN: MGGMA4
GEOGRAPHISCHE GESELLSCHAFT, MUNICH. MITTEILUNGEN. 1900. a. DM.50. Geographische Gesellschaft e.V., Muenchen, Heinrich-Vogl-Str. 7, 81479 Munich, Germany. Ed. Heinz G. Zimpel. bk.rev. circ. 700. **Indexed:** Bibl.Cart., GeoRef.

910 SZ
GEOGRAPHISCHE GESELLSCHAFT VON BERN. JAHRBUCH. (Text in French and German) 1878. irreg. (2-3/yr.) price varies. (Stadt und Universitaetsbibliothek) Geographische Gesellschaft von Bern, Muenstergasse 61, Postfach 58, CH-3000 Bern 7, Switzerland. TEL 031-3203211. FAX 031-3203299. Ed.Bd. circ. 1,100. **Document type:** bulletin.

910 GW ISSN 0723-175X
GEOGRAPHISCHE HOCHSCHULMANUSKRIPTE. 1973. irreg. price varies. Gesellschaft zur Foerderung Regionalwissenschaftlicher Erkenntnisse e.V., Sandweg 260, 26135 Oldenburg, Germany. **Indexed:** Geo.Abstr. **Document type:** academic/scholarly publication.

910 GW ISSN 0723-1679
GEOGRAPHISCHE HOCHSCHULMANUSKRIPTE. DISKUSSIONSPAPIERE. 1981. irreg. price varies. Gesellschaft zur Foerderung Regionalwissenschaftlicher Erkenntnisse e.V., Sandweg 260, 26135 Oldenburg, Germany. **Document type:** monographic series.

910 GW ISSN 0016-7460
G1 CODEN: GGRUAH
GEOGRAPHISCHE RUNDSCHAU. 1949. 11/yr. DM.117.60. Westermann Schulbuchverlag GmbH, Postfach 4938, 38039 Braunschweig, Germany. TEL 0531-708372. FAX 0531-708127. Ed. Reiner Juengst. adv.; B&W page DM.3200, color page DM.5120; trim 187 x 258. bk.rev.; abstr.; bibl.; charts; illus.; index, cum.index every 5 yrs. circ. 15,947. **Indexed:** Bibl.Cart., Curr.Cont.Africa, Excerp.Med., Geo.Abstr., I D A, P.A.I.S.For.Lang.Ind., Rural Devel.Abstr., World Agri.Econ.& Rural Sociol.Abstr. **Document type:** academic/scholarly publication.
—BLDSC (4128.420000). **CCC.**

910 GW ISSN 0016-7479
G1 CODEN: GEOZA3
GEOGRAPHISCHE ZEITSCHRIFT. (Text in English and German; summaries in English) 1905. q. DM.108 (supplements priced individually.) Franz Steiner Verlag Stuttgart GmbH, Birkenwaldstr. 44, 70191 Stuttgart, Germany. TEL 0711-2582-0. FAX 0711-2582290. TELEX 723636-DAZ-D. (Subscr. to: Postfach 101526, 70014 Stuttgart, Germany) Ed. Gerhard Sandner. adv.; bk.rev.; charts; illus.; cum.index: vols.1-50. circ. 750. (back issues avail.) **Indexed:** Bibl.Cart., Curr.Adv.Ecol.Sci., Curr.Cont.Africa, E.I., Geo.Abstr., I D A, P.A.I.S.For.Lang.Ind., Rural Devel.Abstr., Rural Recreat.Tour.Abstr., SSCI, World Agri.Econ.& Rural Sociol.Abstr. **Document type:** academic/scholarly publication.
—BLDSC (4128.480000). **CCC.**

910 GW ISSN 0072-0968
GEOGRAPHISCHES TASCHENBUCH. 1949. biennial. price varies. Franz Steiner Verlag Wiesbaden GmbH, Birkenwaldstr. 44, 70191 Stuttgart, Germany. TEL 0711-2582-0. FAX 0711-2582290. TELEX 723636-DAZ-D. (Subscr. to: Postfach 101061, 70009 Stuttgart, Germany) Eds. Eckhart Ehlers, Emil Meynen. **Indexed:** Bibl.Cart. **Document type:** directory.

910 UK ISSN 0016-7487
G73 CODEN: GGHYAD
GEOGRAPHY. 1901. q. £35.70 (effective 1993-1994). Geographical Association, 343 Fulwood Rd., Sheffield S10 3BP, England. TEL 0742-670666. FAX 0742-670688. Ed. Derek Spooner. adv.; bk.rev.; bibl.; charts; maps; stat.; index. circ. 5,500. (also avail. in microfilm) **Indexed:** Amer.Hist.& Life, Bibl.Cart., Biol.Abstr., Br.Educ.Ind., Br.Hum.Ind., Curr.Adv.Ecol.Sci., Curr.Cont.Africa, Curr.Cont., Geo.Abstr., GeoRef., Hist.Abstr., I D A, Mid.East: Abstr.& Ind., Ref.Sour., Rice Abstr., RICS, Risk Abstr., Rural Recreat.Tour.Abstr., So.Pac.Per.Ind., Soc.Sci.Ind., Soils & Fert., SSCI, World Agri.Econ.& Rural Sociol.Abstr. **Document type:** academic/scholarly publication.
—BLDSC (4129.000000); Faxon; UnCover; SWETS.

914 UK
GEOGRAPHY OF THE BRITISH ISLES SERIES. irreg. price varies. Cambridge University Press, Edinburgh Bld., Shaftesbury Rd., Cambridge CB2 2RU, England. TEL 0223-312393. FAX 0223-315052. TELEX 851817256. (N. American addr.: Cambridge University Press, Journals Dept., 40 W. 20th St., New York, NY 10011. TEL 212-924-3900. FAX 212-691-3239) Ed. A.V. Hardy. **Document type:** monographic series.

910 HU ISSN 0303-6634
GEOGRAPHY OF WORLD AGRICULTURE. (Text in English) 1972. irreg., vol.13, 1988. price varies. (Magyar Tudomanyos Akademia) Akademiai Kiado, Publishing House of the Hungarian Academy of Sciences, P.O. Box 245, H-1519 Budapest, Hungary. TEL 181-2134. FAX 166-6466. TELEX 22-6228 AKNYO H.

910 UK ISSN 0950-7035
GEOGRAPHY REVIEW. 1987. 5/yr. (Sep.-May). £19.50 (Europe £27; elsewhere £32). Philip Allan Publishers Ltd., Deddington, Oxfordshire OX15 0SE, England. TEL 0869-38652. FAX 0869-38803. Ed.Bd. adv.; bk.rev.; index. circ. 20,000. (back issues avail.)
—BLDSC (4129.370000).
Description: Oriented toward "A" level UK exam and first and second year university students.

910 370 II ISSN 0016-7517
GEOGRAPHY TEACHER.* (Text in English) 1965. bi-m. Rs.10($4) Association of Geography Teachers of India, 60 First Main Rd., R.A. Puram, Madras 600028, India. Ed. Visharda Hoon. adv.; bk.rev. circ. 775. **Indexed:** Curr.Cont.

910 AT ISSN 0156-9236
GEOGRAPHY TEACHERS ASSOCIATION OF NEW SOUTH WALES. GEOGRAPHY BULLETIN. 1969. q. Aus.$50 to individuals; institutions Aus.$65; students Aus.$20. Geography Teachers Association of New South Wales, P.O. Box 602, Gladesville, N.S.W. 2111, Australia. Ed. J.P. Harte. adv.; bk.rev.; cum.index vols.1-12 (1980), vols.13-19 (1988). circ. 1,000. (back issues avail.) **Document type:** bulletin.
Formerly: Geographical Society of New South Wales. Geography Bulletin (ISSN 0046-5704)

910.2 NE ISSN 0343-2521
HC79.E5 CODEN: GEOJDQ
GEOJOURNAL; international journal of physical, biological, social and economic geography and applications in environmental planning and ecology. (Text in English) 1977. 12/yr. fl.1746($910.50) (effective 1994). Kluwer Academic Publishers, Postbus 17, 3300 AA Dordrecht, Netherlands. TEL 31-78-334911. FAX 31-78-334254. TELEX 29245 KAPG NL. (Dist. by: Kluwer Academic Publishers Group, P.O. Box 322, 3300 AH Dordrecht, Netherlands. TEL 31-78-524400. FAX 31-78-524474; N. America dist. addr.: Box 358, Accord Sta., Hingham, MA 02018-0358. TEL 617-871-6600. FAX 617-871-6528) Ed. Wolf Tietze. adv.; bk.rev.; illus.; index. (also avail. in microform from UMI; back issues avail.; reprint service avail. from SWZ) **Indexed:** Abstr.Rural Dev.Trop., Bibl.Cart., Biol.Abstr., Curr.Adv.Ecol.Sci., Curr.Cont.Africa, Eng.Ind., Environ.Per.Bibl., Geo.Abstr., GeoRef., I D A, Meteor.& Geoastrophys.Abstr., Phys.Ber., Sci.Abstr., So.Pac.Per.Ind. **Document type:** academic/scholarly publication.
—BLDSC (4129.900000); EI; Faxon; UnCover; SWETS; UMI. **CCC.**
Refereed Serial

551 GW
GEOKATALOG. (Text in English) 1976. a. DM.450. Internationales Landkartenhaus Geo Center, Schockenriedstr. 44, 70565 Stuttgart, Germany. TEL 0711-7889340. FAX 0711-7889354. Eds. S. Bischoff, F. Grupp. circ. 1,500. **Document type:** catalog.
Former titles (until 1993): Geo Katalog. Band 2: Geowissenschaften; Geo Katalog. Band 2. International.
Description: Maps and atlases of all areas of the world.

526.982 620 CN
TA501
GEOMATICA. (Text in English, French) 1922. q. Can.$125. Canadian Institute of Geomatics, Box 5378, Sta. F, Ottawa, ON K2C 3J1, Canada. TEL 613-224-9851. FAX 613-224-9577. Ed. Neil G. Grant. adv.; bk.rev.; abstr.; charts; illus.; index. circ. 3,300. (also avail. in microfiche) **Indexed:** Bibl.Cart., Eng.Ind., Forest.Abstr., Forest Prod.Abstr., Geo.Abstr., GeoRef. **Document type:** academic/scholarly publication.
—Faxon.
Former titles: C I S M Journal A C S G (ISSN 0841-8233); Canadian Surveyor - Geometre Canadien (ISSN 0008-5103)

GEOMORPHOLOGY. see *EARTH SCIENCES — Geology*

910 US
GEOMUNDO. (Editions avail. for Chile, Colombia, Central America, Ecuador, Mexico, Peru, Puerto Rico, U.S., Venezuela) (Text in Spanish; summaries in English or Spanish) 1977. m. $28.80. Editorial America, S.A., Vanidades Continental Bldg., 6355 N.W. 36th St., Virginia Gardens, FL 33166. TEL 305-871-6400. FAX 305-871-8769. Ed. Elvira Mendoza. adv.; abstr.; charts; stat.; index. circ. 116,000. (back issues avail.)

910 551 551.4 GW ISSN 0720-454X
QH540
GEOOEKODYNAMIK. (Supplements avail.: Geooekoforum; Geooekoplus; Geooekotest) (Text in English, German; summaries in English, French, German, Italian) 1980. irreg. (2-4/yr.). price varies. (Verein fuer Erdkunde in Darmstadt e.V.) Geooekoverlag, Mainstr. 50, 64625 Bensheim, Germany. Ed. O. Seuffert. adv.; bk.rev.; index. circ. 1,000. (back issues avail.) **Indexed:** Geo.Abstr.
—BLDSC (4147.930000).

910 CN ISSN 0046-581X
GEOSCOPE. (Text in English and French) 1970. s-a. Can.$16. University of Ottawa, Department of Geography, Ottawa, ON K1N 6N5, Canada. TEL 613-564-2395. FAX 613-564-3304. bk.rev.; bibl.; charts; illus.; stat.; tr.lit.; cum.index; circ. controlled. (processed) **Indexed:** Geo.Abstr.
—BLDSC (4158.895000).

GEOSUR. see *POLITICAL SCIENCE — International Relations*

GEOGRAPHY

916 GH ISSN 0016-9536
GHANA GEOGRAPHICAL ASSOCIATION. BULLETIN.
1957. a. membership. Ghana Geographical Association, University of Ghana, Department of Geography, Legon, Accra, Ghana. Ed. John S. Nabila. adv.; bk.rev. circ. 500.

GLACIOLOGY AND QUATERNARY GEOLOGY. see *EARTH SCIENCES — Geology*

526 AT ISSN 0311-3930
GA101
GLOBE. 1974. 2/yr. Aus.$35. Australian Map Circle, P.O. Box E133, Queen Victoria Terrace A.C.T. 2600, Australia. Ed. W. Stinson. bk.rev. circ. 250. (also avail. in microfiche). Indexed: Aus.P.A.I.S., Bibl.Cart. Document type: bulletin.
—BLDSC (4195.480000).
Description: Includes selected papers from A.M.C. annual conferences and other contributed articles.

526 AU ISSN 0436-0664
GLOBUSFREUND. (Text in English, French and German) 1952. irreg. (1-3/yr.). S.280 membership. Internationale Coronelli-Gesellschaft fuer Globen- und Instrumentenkunde, Dominikanerbastei 21-23, A-1010 Vienna, Austria. TEL 01-5333285. FAX 01-5320824. Ed. Rudolf Schmidt. bk.rev.; charts; illus.; stat.; index. circ. 300. Indexed: Bibl.Cart. Document type: academic/scholarly publication.

910 GW ISSN 0341-3780
CODEN: GGABBC
GOETTINGER GEOGRAPHISCHE ABHANDLUNGEN. (Text in German; summaries in German and English) 1948. 2/yr. (Universitaet Goettingen, Geographisches Institut) Verlag Erich Goltze GmbH und Co. KG, Hans-Boeckler-Str. 7, 37079 Goettingen, Germany. Ed. Juergen Spoenemann. bk.rev. Document type: academic/scholarly publication.

917 CN
GREAT LAKES GEOGRAPHER. 1967. s-a. Can.$15. University of Western Ontario, Department of Geography, London, ON N6A 5C2, Canada. TEL 519-661-3423. FAX 519-661-3750. Eds. Stephen Boyd, Brian Ceh. bk.rev. circ. 200. Indexed: Bibl.& Ind.Geol., Geo.Abstr., Rural Recreat.Tour.Abstr., World Agri.Econ.& Rural Sociol.Abstr.
—BLDSC (6261.940000).
Formerly (until no.39, 1993): Ontario Geography (ISSN 0078-4850)

GREAT PLAINS QUARTERLY. see *HISTORY — History Of North And South America*

GROTTE D'ITALIA. see *EARTH SCIENCES — Geology*

910 US
GUIDE TO PROGRAMS IN GEOGRAPHY IN THE UNITED STATES AND CANADA - A A G MEMBERSHIP DIRECTORY (YEAR). a. $15 to members; non-members $30. Association of American Geographers, 1710 16th St., N.W., Washington, DC 20009-3198. TEL 202-234-1450. FAX 202-234-2744. Ed. Sally Meyers. (reprint service avail. from UMI) Document type: directory.
Former titles: Guide to Departments of Geography in the United States and Canada - A A G Membership Directory (Year); Guide to Departments of Geography in the United States and Canada; Guide to Graduate Departments of Geography in the United States and Canada (ISSN 0072-8497)

910 381 US
GUIDE TO SPRINGFIELD; an encyclopedia of facts and figures on the queen city of the Ozarks. 1987. a. $5. Springfield Communications, Inc., 520 S. Union, Springfield, MO 65802. TEL 417-882-3966. (Subscr. to: Box 4749, Springfield, MO 65808) Ed. R.C. Glazier. adv.; bk.rev. circ. 15,000. (back issues avail.) Document type: consumer publication.

HAGSTROM MAP AND TRAVEL NEWSLETTER. see *TRAVEL AND TOURISM*

HAKLUYT SOCIETY. EXTRA SERIES. see *HISTORY*

HAKLUYT SOCIETY. WORKS IN THE ORDINARY SERIES. SECOND SERIES. see *HISTORY*

910 GW
CODEN: GGHJA2
HANNOVERSCHE GEOGRAPHISCHE ARBEITEN. 1924. a. price varies. (Geographische Gesellschaft zu Hannover) Lit Verlag, Dieckstr. 56, 48145 Muenster, Germany. TEL 0251-23197290. Ed. Hanns J. Buchholz. circ. 800.
Formerly (until 1991): Geographische Gesellschaft zu Hannover. Jahrbuch (ISSN 0435-3838)
Description: Covers regional geography: physical, ecological and social geography.

HEIMDAL; revue d'heritage Norois. see *HISTORY — History Of Europe*

910 FR ISSN 0333-8487
HERODOTE; revue de geographie et de geopolitique. 1979. q. 240 F. Editions la Decouverte, 9 bis, rue Abel-Hovelacque, 75013 Paris, France. TEL 44-08-84-00. FAX 44-08-84-19. Ed. Yves Lacoste. bk.rev.; film rev.; bibl.
—SWETS. CCC.

700 954 II ISSN 0376-9569
DS432.N3
HIGHLANDER. (Text in English) 1973. s-a. Cultural Research and State Museum, Kohima, Nagaland, India. Ed. M. Alemchiba Ao. bibl.
Description: Explores the life, history and culture of the Nagas.

910 NP
HIMALAYAN REVIEW. (Text in English) 1968. a. Rs.40($7) Nepal Geographical Society, Tribhuvan University, Dept. of Geography, Kirtipur, Kathmandu, Nepal. Ed. Mangal S. Manandhar. adv.; bk.rev.; bibl. circ. 1,000.

910 US ISSN 0160-1725
G141
HISTORICAL GEOGRAPHY NEWSLETTER. Cover title: Historical Geography. 1971. s-a. $10 to individuals (foreign $14); institutions $12 (foreign $16). Louisiana State University, Agricultural and Medical College, Department of Geography and Anthropology, Baton Rouge, LA 70803-4105. TEL 504-388-5942. adv.: B&W page $200. bk.rev.; charts. circ. 450. Indexed: Amer.Hist.& Life (1993-), Hist.Abstr. (1993-). Document type: academic/scholarly publication.

911 UK ISSN 0143-683X
HISTORICAL GEOGRAPHY RESEARCH SERIES. 1979. 2/yr. £7.95 per no. Historical Geography Research Group, Department of Geography, Cheltenham & Gloucester College of Higher Education, St. George's Pl., Cheltenham, Glos. GL50 3PP, England. FAX 0242-532959. Ed. Charles W.J. Withers. circ. 450 (controlled). Indexed: Br.Archaeol.Abstr., Geo.Abstr. Document type: academic/scholarly publication.
—BLDSC (4316.332000).

HISTORIENS ET GEOGRAPHES. see *HISTORY*

910 US
HISTORY OF GEOGRAPHY NEWSLETTER. 1981. a. $5. Association of America Geographers, c/o Geoffrey J. Martin, Ed., Dept. of Geography, Southern Connecticut State University, New Haven, CT 06515. TEL 203-397-4355. adv. circ. 200. (back issues avail.) Document type: newsletter.
Description: Covers the history and philosophy of geography for the specialist.

910 FR ISSN 0018-439X
HOMMES ET TERRES DU NORD. 1963. q. 200 F. (foreign 400 F.). Societe de Geographie de Lille, UFR de Geographie, Bat. 2 - USTL, 59655 Villeneuve d'Ascq Cedex, France. FAX 20-43-44-41. Ed. Jean-Pierre Renard. adv.; bk.rev.; charts. circ. 800. Indexed: Forest.Abstr., Geo.Abstr.
—BLDSC (4326.300000).
Supersedes: Societe de Geographie de Lille Bulletin.
Description: Covers all aspects of geography, especially in the North of France, North-West Europe, and North America.

910 IS ISSN 0334-3774
HORIZONS; studies in geography. (Text in Hebrew; abstracts in English) 1975. q. $25. Haifa University, Department of Geography, Mount Carmel, Haifa 31905, Israel. FAX 972-4-246814. Ed. Nurit Kliot. circ. 500. Document type: academic/scholarly publication.
Refereed Serial

918.1 BL
HORIZONTE GEOGRAFICO. bi-m. Cz.$650. Audichromo Editora Ltda., Rua Guapiacu 71, 04024 Sao Paulo SP, Brazil. TEL 011-276-6999. Document type: consumer publication.

916 US ISSN 0161-4703
DT367.A2
HORN OF AFRICA; an independent journal. 1978. 4/yr. $15 to individuals; institutions $25. Horn of Africa Journal Co., Enterprise Mall Bldg., 34 Maple St., Box 803, Summit, NJ 07901. TEL 908-273-1515. Ed. Osman Sultan Ali. adv.; bk.rev. circ. 3,500. Indexed: Abstr.Mil.Bibl., Alt.Press Ind., Documentatieblad, HR Rep.

621.367 CC ISSN 1000-3312
QH541.15.R4
HUANJING YAOGAN/REMOTE SENSING OF ENVIRONMENT. (Text in Chinese; summaries in English) 1986. q. $67.60. (Chinese Geographic Society) Science Press, Marketing and Sales Department, 16 Donghuangchenggen Beijie, Beijing 100707, People's Republic of China. TEL 4010642. FAX 4012180. TELEX 210247-SPBJ-CN. adv. circ. 6,000.
—BLDSC (7356.819000).
Description: Covers remote sensing theory, computer image processing, resource and geographic information systems, instrumentation, and applications of RS technology in geography, geology, agriculture, forestry, conservation, meteorology, oceanography, construction, and surveying.
Refereed Serial

910 JA ISSN 0018-7216
HUMAN GEOGRAPHY/JIMBUN-CHIRI. (Text in Japanese; title, contents page and summaries in English) 1948. bi-m. 9500 Yen (effective 1993). Human Geographical Society of Japan - Jimbun Chiri Gakkai, Kinkichiho-Hatsumei Center, 14 Yoshida Kawara-cho, Sakyo-ku, Kyoto 606, Japan. TEL 075-751-7687. FAX 075-751-7687. Ed. K. Kobayashi. bk.rev.; bibl.; charts; illus.; index. circ. 2,100. Indexed: Geo.Abstr. Document type: academic/scholarly publication.
—UnCover.
Description: Representative journal of human geographical study in Japan based on original research on Japan and other areas of the world.

914.3 GW ISSN 0441-5302
HYDRONYMIA GERMANIAE. irreg., vol.16, 1990. price varies. (Akademie der Wissenschaften und Literatur, Mainz) Franz Steiner Verlag Wiesbaden GmbH, Birkenwaldstr. 44, 70191 Stuttgart, Germany. TEL 0711-2582-0. FAX 0711-2582290. TELEX 723636-DAZ-D. (Subscr. to: Postfach 101061, 70009 Stuttgart, Germany) Ed. Wolfgang P. Schmid. Document type: monographic series.

I C A S A L S NEWSLETTER. (International Center for Arid and Semiarid Land Studies) see *AGRICULTURE*

914 NE
I D G - BULLETIN. (Editions in English, Dutch, French, German) 1976. a. free. Information and Documentation Centre for the Geography of the Netherlands - Informatie- en Documentatie Centrum voor de Geografie van Nederland, Postbus 80115, 3508 TC Utrecht, Netherlands. TEL 31-30-531378. FAX 31-30-543260. (Co-sponsor: Ministry of Foreign Affairs) Ed. Henk Meijer. adv.; bibl.; stat. circ. 22,500 (Dutch ed. 3,000; English ed. 10,000; French ed. 4,500; German ed. 5,000). (also avail. in microfilm) Indexed: ERIC, Geo.Abstr. Document type: bulletin.
Description: Publishes articles on a geographical theme or region, notes of recent developments, addresses and other items of interest.

2808 GEOGRAPHY

910　　　　　　GW　ISSN 0018-9804
　　　　　　　　　　CODEN: IGUBDY
I G U BULLETIN/BULLETIN DE L'U G I. (Text in English or French) 1950. s-a. $20. International Geographical Union, c/o Department of Geography, University of Bonn, Meckenheimer Allee 166, 53115 Bonn, Germany. TEL 0228-739287. FAX 0228-739272. Ed. Prof. Eckart Ehlers. bk.rev. circ. 5,000. (also avail. in microform from UMI) **Indexed:** Bibl.Cart. **Document type:** bulletin.
—UMI.
　Formerly (until 1969): International Geographical Union. Newsletter (ISSN 0538-7639)
　Description: News and information of the International Geographical Union. Features reports, minutes, events.

526.982　　　　NE　ISSN 0924-2716
TA593.A2　　　　　　CODEN: IRSEE9
I S P R S JOURNAL OF PHOTOGRAMMETRY AND REMOTE SENSING. (Text in English, French, German) 1949. 6/yr. fl.416($225) (effective 1994). (International Society for Photogrammetry and Remote Sensing) Elsevier Science B.V., P.O. Box 211, 1000 AE Amsterdam, Netherlands. TEL 31-20-5803911. FAX 31-20-5803598. TELEX 18582 ESPA NL. (Subscr. in U.S. and Canada to: Elsevier Science Inc., Box 882, Madison Sq. Sta., New York, NY 10159-0882. TEL 212-989-5803. FAX 212-633-3990) Ed. J. Hothmer. adv.; bk.rev.; abstr.; bibl.; charts; illus.; index. (also avail. in microform from UMI; reprint service avail. from KTO) **Indexed:** Bibl.Cart., Bull.Signal., Curr.Adv.Ecol.Sci., Curr.Cont., Eng.Ind., Forest.Abstr., Geo.Abstr., GeoRef., Int.Aerosp.Abstr., Sci.Abstr. **Document type:** academic/scholarly publication.
—BLDSC (4583.562800); EI; Faxon; UnCover; SWETS. **CCC.**
　Formerly (until 1989): Photogrammetria (ISSN 0031-8663)
　Description: Provides a channel of communication for specialists in all countries working in the disciplines that apply photogrammetry and remote sensing.
　Refereed Serial

526　　　　　　NE　ISSN 0303-2434
TA593　　　　　　　CODEN: ITCJDP
I T C JOURNAL. (Text in English) 1973. q. fl.60 to individuals; institutions fl.80. International Institute for Aerospace Survey and Earth Sciences, P.O. Box 6, 7500 AA Enschede, Netherlands. TEL 31-53-874382. FAX 31-53-874400. TELEX 44525-ITCNL. Ed. Ann Stewart. adv.; bk.rev.; bibl.; illus.; index. circ. 6,300. **Indexed:** Bibl.Cart., Forest.Abstr., Forest Prod.Abstr., Geo.Abstr., GeoRef., I D A, Int.Aerosp.Abstr., Rural Devel.Abstr., Sci.Abstr.
—BLDSC (4588.517000); Faxon; UnCover; SWETS.
　Description: Applications of aerospace data-gathering techniques for development of natural resources.

I U G G CHRONICLE. (International Union of Geodesy and Geophysics) see *EARTH SCIENCES — Geophysics*

910　　　　　　US　ISSN 0019-2031
　　　　　　　　　　CODEN: BIGSAH
ILLINOIS GEOGRAPHICAL SOCIETY. BULLETIN. 1957; N.S. 2/yr. $20. Illinois Geographical Society, c/o Michael Sublett, 4400 Illinois State University, Normal, IL 61790-4400. TEL 309-438-7649. FAX 309-438-5310. adv.; bk.rev.; charts; illus.; maps. circ. 400. **Indexed:** Geo.Abstr. **Document type:** academic/scholarly publication, bulletin.

910　　　　　　MY　ISSN 0126-7000
DS591
ILMU ALAM. (Text in English and Malay) 1972. a. M.$10. (National University of Malaysia, Department of Geography - Universiti Kebangsaan Malyasia) Penerbit Universiti Kebangsaan Malaysia, 43600 UKM Bangi, Selangor, Malaysia. Ed. Abd. Hamid Abdullah. bk.rev. circ. 400. **Indexed:** Geo.Abstr.

910　　　　　　UK　ISSN 0308-5694
GA1
IMAGO MVNDI; a review of early cartography. (Text and summaries in English) 1935. a. $60. (International Society for the History of Cartography, PO) Imago Mundi Ltd., c/o Brian H. Dolley, 26 Lucastes Rd., Meadow Bank, Haywards Heath, W. Sussex RH16 1JW, England. Ed. E.M.J. Campbell. adv.; bk.rev.; charts; illus.; cum.index 1991 vol. 21-40. circ. 700. **Indexed:** Bibl.Cart., Geo.Abstr.
—BLDSC (4369.000000); Faxon.

910　　　　　　II　ISSN 0019-4824
DS401
INDIAN GEOGRAPHICAL JOURNAL. (Text in English) 1926. s-a. Rs.60($20) (effective 1993). Indian Geographical Society, c/o Dept. of Geography, University of Madras, Chepauk, Madras 600 005, India. TEL 91-44-568778. FAX 91-44-944444. TELEX 41-6376-UNOM-IN. Ed. S. Subbiah. adv.; bk.rev.; charts; maps; stat.; index. circ. 560. **Document type:** academic/scholarly publication.

915.4　　　　　　II
INDIAN GEOGRAPHICAL STUDIES. (Text in English) 1973. s-a. $10. Geographical Research Centre, c/o Department of Geography, Patna 800005, India. Ed. L.N. Ram. adv.; bk.rev.; bibl. circ. 500.

915.4 330.1　　II　ISSN 0970-1095
HF5475.I4
INDIAN JOURNAL OF MARKETING GEOGRAPHY. (Text in English) 1983. a. Rs.100($20) Association of Marketing Geographers of India, 19 Ka, Hirapuri Colony, University Campus, Gorakhpur 273 009, India. TEL 0551-33-0657. FAX 0551-33-3054. Ed. V.K. Shrivastava. bk.rev.; cum.index every 5 yrs. circ. 225. (back issues avail.) **Document type:** academic/scholarly publication.
　Description: Contains research on markets and marketing systems, market news, news about conferences, prospects and perspectives in marketing geography.

917.3 557　　　US　ISSN 0073-6937
INDIANA STATE UNIVERSITY. DEPARTMENT OF GEOGRAPHY AND GEOLOGY. PROFESSIONAL PAPER. Vol. 1 titled Occasional Paper. 1968. a. price varies. Indiana State University, Department of Geography and Geology, Terre Haute, IN 47809. TEL 812-237-2444. Ed. Dr. Akhtar H. Siddiqi. abstr.; bibl.; charts; maps. circ. 1,000. **Indexed:** Geo.Abstr., GeoRef.

910　　　　　　US　ISSN 0073-6953
INDIANA UNIVERSITY. DEPARTMENT OF GEOGRAPHY. GEOGRAPHIC MONOGRAPH SERIES. 1966. irreg., vol.7, 1984. Indiana University, Department of Geography, Student Bldg. 120, Bloomington, IN 47405. TEL 812-855-1153. FAX 812-855-1661. **Document type:** monographic series.

910　　　　　　US　ISSN 0073-6961
INDIANA UNIVERSITY. DEPARTMENT OF GEOGRAPHY. OCCASIONAL PUBLICATION.. 1964. irreg., vol.7, 1981. price varies. Indiana University, Department of Geography, Student Building 120, Bloomington, IN 47405. TEL 812-855-1153. FAX 812-855-1661. **Document type:** academic/scholarly publication.

910　　　　　　IO　ISSN 0024-9521
DS620
INDONESIAN JOURNAL OF GEOGRAPHY. (Text in English) 1960. s-a. $20. Gadjah Mada University, Faculty of Geography, Yogyakarta, Indonesia. TELEX 25-135-UGM-YOGYA. Ed. R. H. Bintarto. bk.rev. circ. 600. **Indexed:** E.I., Geo.Abstr., Popul.Ind. **Document type:** academic/scholarly publication.
—UnCover.

910　　　　　　CL　ISSN 0716-0364
INFORMACIONES GEOGRAFICAS. 1951. a. $5. Universidad de Chile, Faculdade de Arquitectura, Casilla 3387, Santiago, Chile. Ed. Jose Araya Vergara. circ. 1,000. **Indexed:** Geo.Abstr.
　Description: Includes original research papers dealing with methodology, physical, human & regional geography.

910　　　　　　FR　ISSN 0020-0093
G1　　　　　　　　CODEN: IFGGB4
INFORMATION GEOGRAPHIQUE; revue illustree paraissant tous les deux mois pendant la periode scolaire. (Supplement avail.) 1936. 5/yr. 48 ECU($56) Armand Colin, 103 bd. Saint-Michel, 75240 Paris Cedex 05, France. TEL 1-46-34-19-12. FAX 1-43-26-96-38. TELEX 201 269 F. Ed. J. Beaujeu-Garnier. bk.rev.; abstr.; bibl.; charts; maps; stat. circ. 2,550. (also avail. in microform from UMI) **Indexed:** Bibl.Cart., Geo.Abstr., I D A.
—BLDSC (4493.601000); SWETS; UMI. **CCC.**

INFORMATION NORTH. see *SCIENCES: COMPREHENSIVE WORKS*

INFORME DEMOGRAFICO. see *POPULATION STUDIES*

526　　　　　　GW　ISSN 0071-9196
INSTITUT FUER ANGEWANDTE GEODAESIE. MITTEILUNGEN. 1952. irreg. price varies. Institut fuer Angewandte Geodaesie, Richard-Strauss-Allee 11, 60598 Frankfurt a.M., Germany. TEL 069-6333-1. (Subscr. to: Institut fuer Angewandte Geodaesie, Aussenstelle Berlin, Stauffenbergstr. 13, 10785 Berlin, Germany) circ. 600. **Document type:** proceedings.

916.75 526.8　　ZR　ISSN 0443-3173
INSTITUT GEOGRAPHIQUE DU ZAIRE. RAPPORT ANNUEL. 1953. a. Institut Geographique du Zaire, B.P. 3086, Kinshasa, Zaire. illus.
　Continues: Institut Geographique du Congo. Rapport.

910　　　　　　UK　ISSN 0020-2754
G1　　　　　　　　CODEN: IBGTAE
INSTITUTE OF BRITISH GEOGRAPHERS. TRANSACTIONS. 1933. 4/yr. £80. Institute of British Geographers, 1 Kensington Gore, London SW7 2AR, England. TEL 44-71-584-6371. FAX 44-71-581-9918. charts; illus.; cum.index. circ. 2,800. **Indexed:** Bibl.Cart., Br.Archaeol.Abstr., Br.Geol.Lit., Curr.Adv.Ecol.Sci., Geo.Abstr., I D A, Int.Abstr.Oper.Res., Irr.& Drain.Abstr., Maize Abstr., P.A.I.S., Rural Devel.Abstr., Rural Recreat.Tour.Abstr., Soils & Fert., SSCI, Triticale Abstr., World Agri.Econ.& Rural Sociol.Abstr. **Document type:** academic/scholarly publication.
—BLDSC (8939.370000); Faxon; UnCover; SWETS.

910　　　　　　II　ISSN 0970-9851
INSTITUTE OF INDIAN GEOGRAPHERS. TRANSACTIONS. 1979. s-a. $16. Institute of Indian Geographers, c/o Department of Geography, University of Poona, Pune 411 007, India. Ed. K.R. Dikshit. bk.rev. circ. 1,000.

INSTITUTE OF MATHEMATICAL GEOGRAPHY. MONOGRAPH SERIES. see *MATHEMATICS*

INSTITUTE OF URBAN STUDIES. see *HOUSING AND URBAN PLANNING*

INSTITUTO DE INVESTIGACAO CIENTIFICA TROPICAL. CENTRO DE ESTUDOS DE HISTORIA E CARTOGRAFIA ANTIGA. STUDIA. see *HISTORY*

INSTITUTO DE INVESTIGACAO CIENTIFICA TROPICAL. CENTRO DE ESTUDOS DE HISTORIA E CARTOGRAFIA ANTIGA. SERIE SEPARATAS. see *HISTORY*

910　　　　　　PO　ISSN 0871-1747
INSTITUTO DE INVESTIGACAO CIENTIFICA TROPICAL. COMUNICACOES. SERIE DE CIENCIAS DA ENGENHARIA GEOGRAFICA. 1989. irreg. price varies. Instituto de Investigacao Cientifica Tropical, Rua Jau 54, 1300 Lisbon, Portugal. TEL 364-5321. FAX 363-1460. (Subscr. to: Centro de Documentacao e Informacao, Rua Jau 47, 1300 Lisbon, Portugal) circ. 1,000. **Document type:** monographic series.

INSTITUTO DE INVESTIGACAO CIENTIFICA TROPICAL. ESTUDOS DE HISTORIA E CARTOGRAFIA ANTIGA - MEMORIAS. see *HISTORY*

918.602　　　　CK
INSTITUTO GEOGRAFICO AGUSTIN CODAZZI. INFORME DE LABORES. ceased. a. Instituto Geografico Agustin Codazzi, Subdireccion de Geografia, Carrera 30 No. 48-51, Apdo. Aero 6721, Bogota, Colombia. illus.

INSTITUTO HISTORICO E GEOGRAFICO DE JUIZ DE FORA. see *HISTORY — History Of North And South America*

INSTITUTO HISTORICO E GEOGRAFICO DO ESPIRITO SANTO. REVISTA. see *HISTORY*

910 900　　　　MX　ISSN 0020-4188
INSTITUTO PANAMERICANO DE GEOGRAFIA E HISTORIA. BOLETIN AEREO. 1955. bi-m. free. Instituto Panamericano de Geografia e Historia, Ex-Arzobispado 29, Col. Observatorio, Deleg. Miguel Hidalgo, 11860 Mexico, D.F., Mexico. TEL 525-277-5888. FAX 525-271-6172. (Subscr. to: IPGH, Depto. de Distribucion y Ventas, Apdo. 18879, 11870 Mexico DF, Mexico) (looseleaf format) **Document type:** newsletter.

914 RM
INSTITUTUL DE SUBINGINERI ORADEA. LUCRARI STIINTIFICE: SERIA GEOGRAFIE. (Text in Rumanian, occasionally in English or French; summaries in English, French, German, or Rumanian) 1967. a. Institutul de Subingineri Oradea, Calea Armatei Rosii Nr. 5, 3700 Oradea, Rumania.
Formerly: Institutul Pedagogic Oradea. Lucrari Stiintifice: Seria Geografie; Which continued in part (in 1971): Institutul Pedagogic Oradea. Lucrari Stiintifice: Seria A and Seria B; Which was formerly (until 1969): Institutul Pedagogic Oradea. Lurari Stiintifice.

910 FR ISSN 0396-5880
INTERGEO-BULLETIN. 1966. q. 170 F. Centre National de la Recherche Scientifique, Laboratoire Intergeo, 191 rue Saint-Jacques, 75005 Paris, France. TEL 46-33-74-31. FAX 43-29-65-29. bk.rev.; index. circ. 400. (back issues avail.) Indexed: Bibl.Cart. Document type: bulletin.
Formerly: Intergeo (ISSN 0301-8768)

526 GR ISSN 0081-0312
INTERNATIONAL ASSOCIATION OF GEODESY. CENTRAL BUREAU FOR SATELLITE GEODESY. INFORMATION BULLETIN. 1966. irreg. International Association of Geodesy, Central Bureau for Satellite Geodesy, National Technical University, K. Zographou 9, Athens 624, Greece.

INTERNATIONAL ASSOCIATION OF GEODESY. COMMISSION PERMANENTE DES MAREES TERRESTRES. MAREES TERRESTRES BULLETIN D'INFORMATION. see *EARTH SCIENCES — Geophysics*

910 341 US ISSN 0502-0034
INTERNATIONAL BOUNDARY STUDY. 1961. irreg., no.175, 1985. free. U.S. Department of State, Office of the Geographer, c/o Bureau of Intelligence and Research, 2201 C St., N.W., Washington, DC 20520-6510. TEL 202-647-2021. Document type: academic/scholarly publication, government publication.

910 550 US
INTERNATIONAL GEOSCIENCE AND REMOTE SENSING SYMPOSIUM DIGEST. Short title: I G A R S S. 1981. a. price varies. (I E E E, Geoscience and Remote Sensing Society) Institute of Electrical and Electronics Engineers, Inc., 345 E. 47th St., New York, NY 10017-2394. TEL 212-705-7900. FAX 212-705-7682. (Subscr. to: 445 Hoes Lane, Box 1331, Piscataway, NJ 08855-1331)
Description: Problems and perspectives of the geoscientific disciplines on instrumentation systems, data processing techniques and sensor-target models.

INTERNATIONAL JOURNAL OF REMOTE SENSING. see *EARTH SCIENCES*

INTERNATIONAL JOURNAL OF TURKISH STUDIES. see *HISTORY — History Of The Near East*

INTERNATIONAL MAP TRADE ASSOCIATION. DIRECTORY OF SUPPLIERS. see *BUSINESS AND ECONOMICS — Trade And Industrial Directories*

INTERNATIONAL STRAITS OF THE WORLD. see *POLITICAL SCIENCE — International Relations*

526 US
INTERNATIONAL SYMPOSIUM ON AUTOMATED CARTOGRAPHY. PROCEEDINGS. biennial. $35 to non-members; members $25. American Society for Photogrammetry and Remote Sensing, 5410 Grosvenor Ln., Ste. 210, Bethesda, MD 20814-2160. TEL 301-493-0290. FAX 301-493-0208. (Co-publisher: American Congress on Surveying and Mapping)
—BLDSC (1828.120000).
Former titles: International Symposium on Computer-Assisted Cartography. Proceedings; International Symposium on Cartography and Computing. Proceedings (ISSN 0270-5133)

526 551 CN ISSN 0539-1016
INTERNATIONAL UNION OF GEODESY AND GEOPHYSICS. MONOGRAPH.* (Text in English and French) irreg. International Union of Geodesy and Geophysics, c/o Georges Balmino, Sec'y-Gen., Bureau Gravimetrique International, 18 av. Edouard Belin, 31055 Toulouse Cedex, France. Document type: monographic series.

INTERNATIONAL UNION OF GEODESY AND GEOPHYSICS. MONOGRAPH. see *GEOGRAPHY*

INTERNATIONAL UNION OF GEODESY AND GEOPHYSICS. PROCEEDINGS OF THE GENERAL ASSEMBLY. see *EARTH SCIENCES — Geophysics*

INTERNATIONALES HANDBUCH - LAENDER AKTUELL. see *POLITICAL SCIENCE — International Relations*

526.8 GW ISSN 0341-0986
GA101 CODEN: IYCTAJ
INTERNATIONALES JAHRBUCH FUER KARTOGRAPHIE. (Text in English, French, German) 1961. a. price varies. (International Cartographic Association) Universitaetsverlag Ulm GmbH, Benzstr. 12, 89079 Ulm, Germany. TEL 0731-42086. FAX 0731-42087. adv.; bk.rev.; illus. circ. 2,000. Indexed: Bibl.Cart. Document type: trade publication.
—BLDSC (4552.300000).
Description: Covers all aspects of cartography.

917.2 MX ISSN 0188-4611
F1216 CODEN: BIGFBD
INVESTIGACIONES GEOGRAFICAS. (Supplements avail.) 1969. s-a. price varies. Universidad Nacional Autonoma de Mexico, Instituto de Geografia, Ciudad Universitaria, 04510 Mexico, D.F., Mexico. TEL 622-43-37. FAX 616-21-45. Ed. Teresa Reyna Trujillo. bk.rev. circ. 1,000. Indexed: Geo.Abstr. Document type: academic/scholarly publication.
—BLDSC (2175.400000).
Formerly (until 1990): Universidad Nacional Autonoma de Mexico. Instituto de Geografia. Boletin (ISSN 0185-1977)
Description: Includes the results of research by the scholars of the Institute.

914 IE ISSN 0075-0778
DA900
IRISH GEOGRAPHY. 1944. s-a. I£30($48) Geographical Society of Ireland, Department of Geography, St. Patrick's College, Maynooth, County Kildare, Ireland. TEL 01-6285222. FAX 01-6289063. TELEX 747597. Ed. John Sweeney. bk.rev. circ. 600. Indexed: Amer.Hist.& Life, Br.Archaeol.Abstr., Br.Geol.Lit., Geo.Abstr., Hist.Abstr., Rural Recreat.Tour.Abstr., Soils & Fert., World Agri.Econ.& Rural Sociol.Abstr. Document type: academic/scholarly publication.
● Also available online.
—BLDSC (4571.500000); UnCover. **CCC.**

526.8 IS ISSN 0075-1138
ISRAEL. DEPARTMENT OF SURVEYS. GEODETIC PAPERS. (Text in Hebrew; summaries in English) 1965. irreg. price varies. Department of Surveys, P.O.B. 14171, Tel Aviv 61141, Israel. FAX 03-5610866. TELEX 34118-BX-TV-IL.

526.982 RU ISSN 0202-0726
QB280
ITOGI NAUKI I TEKHNIKI: GEODEZIYA I AEROS'EMKA. irreg., vol.27, 1989. 5.40 Rub. Vsesoyuznyi Institut Nauchno-Tekhnicheskoi Informatsii (VINITI), Baltiiskaya ul. 14, Moscow A-219, Russiaq. (Subscr. to: Mezhdunarodnaya Kniga, Dimitrova ul. 39, 113095 Moscow, Russia) Indexed: Int.Aerosp.Abstr.
—BLDSC (0047.295000).
Description: Covers geodesy and aerial photography.

910 RU ISSN 0202-7208
HC10
ITOGI NAUKI I TEKHNIKI: GEOGRAFIYA ZARUBEZHNYKH STRAN. irreg., vols.14-15, 1988. 6.60 Rub. Vsesoyuznyi Institut Nauchno-Tekhnicheskoi Informatsii (VINITI), Baltiiskaya ul. 14, Moscow A-219, Russia. (Subscr. to: Mezhdunarodnaya Kniga, Dimitrova ul. 39, 113095 Moscow, Russia)
—BLDSC (0047.195000).

526 RU ISSN 0202-7240
ITOGI NAUKI I TEKHNIKI: KARTOGRAFIYA. irreg., vol.13, 1988. 6.60 Rub. Vsesoyuznyi Institut Nauchno-Tekhnicheskoi Informatsii (VINITI), Baltiiskaya ul. 14, Moscow A-219, Russia. (Subscr. to: Mezhdunarodnaya Kniga, Dimitrova ul. 39, 113095 Moscow, Russia) Indexed: Bibl.Cart., Geo.Abstr.
—BLDSC (0088.315000).

917.29 JM ISSN 1017-4753
JAMAICAN GEOGRAPHER. 1967-1979; resumed 1981. s-a. $5 includes membership. Jamaican Geographical Society, c/o Geography Dept., University of the West Indies, Kingston 7, Jamaica, W.I. TEL 908-927-2129. Ed. David Barker. bk.rev.; bibl.; circ. 350 (controlled). Document type: newsletter.
Former titles: Jamaican Geographical Society Newsletter; Jamaica Geographical Society Proceedings; (until 1979): Jamaica Geographical Society Newsletter.

526 JA ISSN 0302-0231
JAPAN MAP CENTER NEWS/CHIZU SENTA NYUSU.* (Text in Japanese) 1972. m. 2000 Yen. Japan Map Center - Nihon Chizu Senta, 4-9-6 Aobadai, Meguto, Tokyo 153, Japan. Ed.Bd. adv.; bk.rev.; illus.

330.951 CC ISSN 1000-8462
JINGJI DILI/ECONOMIC GEOGRAPHY. (Text in Chinese) 1981. q. $24. Hunan Jingji Dili Yanjiusuo - Hunan Institute of Economic Geography, 7 Qingyuan Lu, Changsha, Hunan 410004, People's Republic of China. TEL 415-282-2994; 34716. FAX 415-282-0994. (US Dist. by: China Books and Periodicals, Inc., 2929 24th St., San Francisco, CA 94110. TEL 415-282-2994) (Co-sponsor: Zhongguo Dili Xuehui - Chinese Geographical Society)

910 UK ISSN 0140-1963
QH541.5.A74 CODEN: JAENDR
JOURNAL OF ARID ENVIRONMENTS. 1978. 8/yr. (in 2 vols.). £250 (effective 1994). Academic Press Ltd. (Subsidiary of: Harcourt Brace & Company Ltd,), 24-28 Oval Rd., London NW1 7DX, England. TEL 44-71-267-4466. FAX 44-71-482-2293. TELEX 25775-ACPRES-G. (Subscr. to: Harcourt Brace & Company Ltd., Foots Cray High St., Sidcup, Kent DA14 5HP, England. TEL 44-81-300-3322. FAX 44-81-309-0807) Ed. J.L. Cloudsley-Thompson. Indexed: Abstr.Hyg., Agroforest.Abstr., Cott.& Trop.Fibr.Abstr., Environ.Abstr., Excerp.Med., Field Crop Abstr., Forest.Abstr., GeoRef., Herb.Abstr., I D A, Ind.Sci.Rev., Irr.& Drain.Abstr., Maize Abstr., Rural Devel.Abstr., Rural Recreat.Tour.Abstr., Sci.Cit.Ind., Seed Abstr., Soils & Fert., Sorghum & Millets Abstr., Triticale Abstr., Trop.Dis.Bull., W.R.C.Inf., World Agri.Econ.& Rural Sociol.Abstr. Document type: academic/scholarly publication.
—BLDSC (4947.203000); Faxon; UnCover; SWETS. **CCC.**
Description: Introduces original scientific and technical research articles about climate, geomorphology, geology, geology, geography, botany, zoology, anthropology, sociology, and technical development in arid and desert environments, as well as reviews.

574 910 UK ISSN 0305-0270
QH84 CODEN: JBIODN
JOURNAL OF BIOGEOGRAPHY. 1974. bi-m. £297 in Europe; elsewhere £326 ($486) (effective 1994) (Subscr. includes Global Ecology & Biogeography Letters (ISSN 0962-7447) and Biodiversity Letters (ISSN 0967-9952.). Blackwell Scientific Publications Ltd., Osney Mead, Oxford OX2 0EL, England. TEL 0865-240201. FAX 0865-721205. TELEX 83355-MEDBOK-G. adv.; bk.rev.; abstr.; bibl.; illus.; index. circ. 650. (also avail. in microform from UMI; back issues avail.; reprint service avail. from ISI) Indexed: ASCA, Br.Archaeol.Abstr., Curr.Cont., Curr.Ref.Fish Res., Deep Sea Res.& Oceanogr.Abstr., Environ.Abstr., Environ.Per.Bibl. (1989-), Field Crop Abstr., Forest.Abstr., Forest Prod.Abstr., Geo.Abstr., GeoRef., Herb.Abstr., Ind.Sci.Rev., Mid.East: Abstr.& Ind., Ocean.Abstr., Rural Devel.Abstr., Sci.Cit.Ind., Seed Abstr., Sel.Water Res.Abstr., Soils & Fert., Weed Abstr., World Agri.Econ.& Rural Sociol.Abstr. Document type: academic/scholarly publication.
—BLDSC (4952.900000); Faxon; UnCover; SWETS; UMI. **CCC.**
Refereed Serial

JOURNAL OF BORDERLAND STUDIES. see *POLITICAL SCIENCE — International Relations*

2810 GEOGRAPHY

915.1   SI   ISSN 0218-1444
G1
THE JOURNAL OF CHINESE GEOGRAPHY. (Text in English) 1990. q. $37.50. (Chinese Academy of Sciences, Institute of Geography) Guoji Translation & Publishing, 6001 Beach Rd. No. 02-69, Golden Mile Tower - 0719, Singapore, Singapore. (Co-sponsor: Geographical Society of China) Ed. Bingwei Huang.
—BLDSC (4958.040000); UnCover.
Description: Covers broad areas of theoretical and applied aspects of physical - human geography, including academic findings, research results, applied theory to the national economy, and discussions of essential projects.

910 572   US
JOURNAL OF CULTURAL GEOGRAPHY. 1980. s-a. $12.50. Bowling Green State University, Popular Culture Center, Bowling Green, OH 43403. TEL 419-372-2981. Ed. Alvar W. Carlson. circ. 600. (back issues avail.) **Indexed:** Chic.Per.Ind., Geo.Abstr., I D A, M.L.A., Mid.East: Abstr.& Ind., World Agri.Econ.& Rural Sociol.Abstr.
Description: Articles on geography, anthropology, history, historic preservation and popular culture, with emphasis on the spatial aspects of cultures and cultural phenomena.

910   CH
JOURNAL OF GEOGRAPHICAL SCIENCE. (Text and summaries in Chinese or English) 1962. irreg. free. National Taiwan University, Department of Geography, National Taiwan University, Taipei, Taiwan, Republic of China. TEL 886-2-3629908. FAX 886-2-3622911. (Subscr. to: National Taiwan University Library, Serials Section, Taipei, Taiwan, Republic of China) Ed. Lan-Hung Chiang. circ. 500. **Indexed:** Geo.Abstr. **Document type:** academic/scholarly publication.
Formerly (until no.14, 1990): National Taiwan University. Department of Geography. Science Reports.

910   US   ISSN 0022-1341
G1   CODEN: JOGGA9
JOURNAL OF GEOGRAPHY. 1902. 6/yr. $60. National Council for Geographic Education, Central Office, 16A Leonard Hall, Indiana University of Pennsylvania, Indiana, PA 15705-3147. TEL 412-357-6290. adv.; bk.rev.; abstr.; bibl.; charts; illus.; stat.; index. circ. 6,700. (also avail. in microform from UMI; back issues avail.; reprint service avail. from KTO,UMI) **Indexed:** Bibl.Cart., C.I.J.E., Cont.Pg.Educ., Curr.Cont., Educ.Ind., Environ.Abstr., Geo.Abstr., GeoRef., Media Rev.Dig., Mid.East: Abstr.& Ind., Sage Urb.Stud.Abstr., SSCI. **Document type:** academic/scholarly publication.
—BLDSC (4992.000000); CIS; Faxon; UnCover; SWETS; UMI.
Description: Geographic research and teaching methods for instructors at all educational levels.

910 378   UK   ISSN 0309-8265
G72
JOURNAL OF GEOGRAPHY IN HIGHER EDUCATION. 1977. 3/yr. $98 to individuals; institutions $338 (effective 1994). Carfax Publishing Co., P.O. Box 25, Abingdon, Oxon. OX14 3UE, England. TEL 44-235-555335. FAX 44-235-553559. (U.S. subscr. to: Carfax Publishing Co., Box 2025, Dunnellon, FL 34430-2025) Ed.Bd. adv.; bk.rev (also avail. in microfiche; back issues avail.) **Indexed:** C.I.J.E., Cont.Pg.Educ., Curr.Cont., Educ.Tech.Abstr., Geo.Abstr., High.Educ.Curr.Aware.Bull., Mult.Ed.Abstr., Res.High.Educ.Abstr., Sp.Ed.Needs Abstr., SSCI, Stud.Wom.Abstr. **Document type:** academic/scholarly publication.
—BLDSC (4992.100000); Faxon; UnCover; SWETS. CCC.
Refereed Serial

911   UK   ISSN 0305-7488
G141   CODEN: JHGEDP
JOURNAL OF HISTORICAL GEOGRAPHY. 1975. q. £96 (effective 1994). Academic Press Ltd. (Subsidiary of: Harcourt Brace & Company Ltd.), 24-28 Oval Rd., London NW1 7DX, England. TEL 44-71-267-4466. FAX 44-71-482-2293. TELEX 25775-ACPRES-G. (Subscr. to: Harcourt Brace & Company Ltd., Foots Cray High St., Sidcup, Kent DA14 5HP, England. TEL 44-81-300-3322. FAX 44-81-309-0807) Ed. A.R.H. Baker. adv.; bk.rev.; charts; illus.; index. **Indexed:** Amer.Hist.& Life, Bibl.Cart., Bk.Rev.Ind. (1980-), Br.Archaeol.Abstr., Chic.Per.Ind., Child.Bk.Rev.Ind. (1980-), Curr.Cont., E.I., GeoRef., Hist.Abstr., Mid.East: Abstr.& Ind., NAA, Ref.Sour., Soc.Sci.Ind., SSCI. **Document type:** academic/scholarly publication.
—BLDSC (5000.450000); Faxon; UnCover; SWETS. CCC.
Description: Addresses all aspects of historical geography for an international and interndisciplinary readership.

JOURNAL OF RURAL STUDIES. see *SOCIOLOGY*

JOURNAL OF THE WEST; an illustrated quarterly of Western American history and Culture. see *HISTORY — History Of North And South America*

910.02   UK   ISSN 0966-6923
HE1
▼ **JOURNAL OF TRANSPORT GEOGRAPHY.** 1993. 4/yr. £92 in UK and Europe; elsewhere £96. Butterworth - Heinemann (Subsidiary of: Reed Elsevier plc), Linacre House, Jordan Hill, Oxford OX2 8DP, England. TEL 0865-310366. FAX 0865-310898. TELEX 83111 BHPOXF G. (Subscr. to: Turpin Transactions Ltd., Distribution Centre, Blackhorse Rd., Letchworth, Herts. SG6 1HN, England. TEL 0462-480947. FAX 0462-480947; N. American subscr. to: Journals Fulfillment Department, Butterworth-Heinemann, 80 Montvale Ave., Stoneham, MA 02180. TEL 617-438-8464. FAX 617-438-1479) Ed. Richard Knowles. (also avail. in microform from UMI; back issues avail.) **Document type:** academic/scholarly publication.
—BLDSC (5069.950000); UMI.
Description: Focuses on transport and spatial change.

JOURNAL OF WORLD PREHISTORY. see *ARCHAEOLOGY*

914.3   GW   ISSN 0075-4528
TX910.G4
JUGENDHERBERGS-VERZEICHNIS. 1920. a. DM.14.80. Hauptverband fuer Jugendwandern und Jugendherbergen e.V., Postfach 1455, 32704 Detmold, Germany. TEL 05231-7401-0. Ed. Bert Pichel. adv. circ. 40,000. **Document type:** directory.

910   NE   ISSN 0926-3853
K N A G NIEUWS. 1992. 10/yr. membership. Koninklijk Nederlands Aardrijkskundig Genootschap - Royal Dutch Geographical Society, P.O. Box 80123, 3508 TC Utrecht, Netherlands. TEL 31-30-532757. FAX 31-30-535523. Ed. Ben de Pater. adv.; B&W page fl.990; 210 x 297. bk.rev.; illus.; maps; circ. 4,300 (controlled). **Document type:** newsletter.
Supersedes (1977-1992): Nieuwe Geografenkrant (ISSN 0166-0926)

526.9   NO   ISSN 0047-3278
TA501
KART OG PLAN. (Text in Norwegian; abstracts in English) 1908. q. NOK 365 in the Nordic countries; elsewhere NOK 425. Scandinavian University Press, P.O. Box 2959 Toeyen, N-0608 Oslo, Norway. TEL 47-2-677600. FAX 47-2-677575. Ed. Gunnar Balle. adv.; bk.rev.; charts; illus.; index. circ. 3,300. (also avail. in microfilm from UMI; reprint service avail. from UMI) **Indexed:** Bibl.Cart., Geo.Abstr.
—BLDSC (5086.350000); EI; UMI.
Formerly: Tidsskrift for det Norske Utskiftningsvesen.

526   RU
KARTOGRAFICHESKAYA LETOPIS'. 1931. a. Izdatel'stvo Kniga, 50, Gorky St., 125047 Moscow, Russia. bibl. circ. 1,200.

526.8   GW   ISSN 0022-9164
GA101   CODEN: KANAA7
KARTOGRAPHISCHE NACHRICHTEN. 1951. bi-m. DM.60. (Deutsche Gesellschaft fuer Kartographie e.V) Kirschbaum Verlag GmbH, Siegfriedstr. 28, 53179 Bonn, Germany. TEL 0228-95453-0. FAX 0228-9545327. (Subscr. to: Postfach 210209, 53157 Bonn, Germany) adv.; bk.rev.; bibl.; charts; illus.; index. circ. 2,500. **Indexed:** Bibl.Cart., Geo.Abstr. **Document type:** academic/scholarly publication.
—CCC.

526   GW   ISSN 0936-5745
KARTOGRAPHISCHES TASCHENBUCH. 1988. biennial. DM.26. (Deutsche Gesellschaft fuer Kartographie e.V.) Kirschbaum Verlag GmbH, Siegfriedstr. 28, 53179 Bonn, Germany. TEL 0228-95453-0. FAX 0228-9545327. (Subscr. to: Postfach 210209, 53157 Bonn, Germany) Eds. Juergen Dodt, Werner Herzog. **Document type:** monographic series.

KENTUCKY EXPLORER; featuring things about Kentucky and its history. see *HISTORY — History Of North And South America*

KEVO SUBARCTIC RESEARCH INSTITUTE. REPORTS. see *BIOLOGY*

910 550 320   GW
KOBLENZER GEOGRAPHISCHES KOLLOQUIUM. 1979. a. DM.5. Geographisches Institut. Universitaet Koblenz, Rheinau 3-4, Gebaeude F10, 56075 Koblenz, Germany. FAX 0261-37524. Eds. Heinz Fischer, Richard Graafen. adv.; bk.rev.; bibl. (back issues avail.)

910   GW   ISSN 0075-6482
DD901.C71
KOELN. 1955. q. DM.6. Verkehrsamt, Unter Fettenhennen 19, 50667 Cologne, Germany. TEL 0221-2213361. FAX 0221-2213320. TELEX 8883421-TOCD. Eds. Erhard Schlieter, Marianne Esch. adv.; bk.rev. circ. 6,000. **Document type:** government publication.
—BLDSC (5103.850000).

910   NE   ISSN 0922-4939
KONINKLIJK INSTITUUT VOOR DE TROPEN. LANDENREEKS. (Text in Dutch) 1958. 7/yr. fl.115 (effective 1994). Koninklijk Instituut voor de Tropen - Royal Tropical Institute, Mauritskade 63, 1092 AD Amsterdam, Netherlands. TEL 31-20-5688272. FAX 31-20-5688286. Ed. P.H.J. van den Boorn. bibl.; maps; illus.; stat. circ. 7,000. **Indexed:** Geo.Abstr. **Document type:** monographic series.
Former titles (until 1988): Koninklijk Instituut voor de Tropen. Afdeling Plattelandsontwikkeling. Landendocumentatie (ISSN 0023-7841); Koninklijk Instituut voor de Tropen. Afdeling Agrarisch Onderzoek. Landendocumentatie.
Description: Provides background information on countries in Asia, Africa and Latin America.

909.09   NE
KONINKLIJK INSTITUUT VOOR DE TROPEN. SURVEY OF ACTIVITIES. a. Koninklijk Instituut voor de Tropen - Royal Tropical Institute, Mauritskade 63, 1092 AD Amsterdam, Netherlands. TEL 31-20-5688711. FAX 31-20-5688444. TELEX 15080 KIT NL. illus. **Document type:** corporate report.
Former titles: Koninklijk Instituut voor de Tropen. Survey; Koninklijk Instituut voor de Tropen. Annual Report.

915   KO   ISSN 0047-3596
KOREA TODAY.* m. Foreign Languages Publishing House, Pyongyang, N. Korea. Ed. Nam-Suk Hahn. charts; illus. **Indexed:** GeoRef.

KRCKI ZBORNIK. see *HISTORY — History Of Europe*

KUANGSHAN CELIANG/MINE SURVEYING. see *MINES AND MINING INDUSTRY*

910 300   DK   ISSN 0106-5866
KULTURGEOGRAFISKE HAEFTER. 1974. 3/yr. DKK 195($23) Kulturgeografike Haefter, Oestervolgade 10, 1350 Copenhagen K, Denmark. TEL 45-33-32-62-70. Ed. Joern Bech. adv. circ. 1.500. (reprint service avail. from COPYDAN DK)

910   DK   ISSN 0108-3945
KULTURGEOGRAFISKE HAEFTERS SKRIFTSERIE. 1981. irreg., no.19, 1989. DKK 120($17) Kulturgeografiske Haefter, Oestervoldgade 10, 1350 Copenhagen K, Denmark. adv. circ. 150. (reprint service avail. from COPYDAN DK)

910   DK   ISSN 0023-5245
KULTURGEOGRAFISKE SKRIFTER. (Text in Danish, English; summaries in Danish, English, German) 1936. price varies. Kongelige Danske Geografiske Selskab - Royal Danish Geographical Society, Oester Voldgade 10, DK-1350 Copenhagen K, Denmark. (Subscr. to: C. A. Reitzels Forlag, Noerregade 20, DK-1165 Copenhagen K, Denmark) Ed. Niels Kingo Jacobsen. abstr.; bibl.; charts; illus. (reprint service avail. from UMI) **Indexed:** Geo.Abstr.

910   JA   ISSN 0389-1631
KUMATOTO CHIGAKKAISHI/KUMAMOTO GEOGRAPHIC SOCIETY. JOURNAL. (Text in Japanese) 3/yr. Kumatoto Chigakkai - Kumatoto Geographical Society, Kumamoto Daigaku Kyoikugakubu Chigaku Kenkyushitsu, 2, Kurokami, Kumamoto-shi, Kumamoto-ken 860, Japan.

910   GO
LABORATOIRE DE CARTOGRAPHIE DU DEPARTMENT DE GEOGRAPHIE. RAPPORTS. irreg. Universite Omar Bongo, Laboratoire de Cartographie du Departement de Geographie, Faculte des Lettres et Sciences Humaines, B.P. 17004, Libreville, Gabon.

526.9   UK
LAND REGISTRY ANNUAL (YEAR); report by the Chief Land Registrar and Chief Executive to the Lord Chancellor on the work of HM land registry for the year. a. £6. HMSO Publications Centre, P.O. Box 276, London SW8 5DT, England. TEL 071-873-0011.
Formerly: Report on the Work of H M Land Registry for England and Wales (Year).

526   DK   ISSN 0105-4570
LANDINSPEKTOEREN. 1892. 5/yr. DKK 320. (Danske Landinspektoerforening - Association of Country Surveyors) Teknisk Forlag A-S, Skelbaekgade 4, DK-1780 Copenhagen V, Denmark. TEL 45-31-21-68-01. FAX 45-31-21-04-01. Ed. E.M. Soerensen. adv.; bk.rev.; index. circ. 2,009.

910   US   ISSN 0023-8023
G1
LANDSCAPE. 1951. 3/yr. $22 to individuals; institutions $42. Landscape, Box 7107, Berkeley, CA 94707. TEL 510-549-3233. FAX 510-843-7120. Ed. Rebecca McKee. bk.rev.; illus.; maps; index. circ. 4,000. (also avail. in microform from UMI) **Indexed:** Amer.Hist.& Life, Archit.Per.Ind., Art.Ind., Arts & Hum.Cit.Ind., Avery Ind.Archit.Per., Br.Tech.Ind., Curr.Cont., Ekist.Ind., Environ.Abstr., Environ.Per.Bibl. (1975-), Gard.Lit. (1992-), Geo.Abstr., Hist.Abstr., Mid.East: Abstr.& Ind., Rural Recreat.Tour.Abstr., Sage Urb.Stud.Abstr., Sociol.Abstr., Urb.Aff.Abstr., World Agri.Econ.& Rural Sociol.Abstr.
—BLDSC (5153.120000); CIS; Faxon; UnCover; SWETS; UMI. **CCC.**
Description: Essays, articles, photography, and graphics on cultural geography, landscape architecture and related fields, and city and regional planning from a social, historical, and contemporary perspective.

910.02   FR   ISSN 0220-0546
LETTRE D'INTERGEO. 1977. 8/yr. 80 F. Centre National de la Recherche Scientifique, Laboratoire Intergeo, 191 rue Saint Jacques, 75005 Paris, France. TEL 46-33-74-31. FAX 43-29-65-29. **Document type:** newsletter.

910   XR   ISSN 0024-2896
LIDE A ZEME/PEOPLE AND COUNTRIES. 1952. m. DM.91. (Czechoslovak Academy of Sciences) Academia, Publishing House of the Czechoslovak Academy of Sciences, Vodickova 40, 112 29 Prague 1, Czech Republic. TEL 23-63-065. Ed. L. Skokan. bk.rev.; illus.; maps. circ. 45,500. **Indexed:** Bibl.Cart.
Description: Dedicated to the popularization of geographical sciences and travel. Every issue includes a number of black-and-white photos, small maps and aerial plans from around the world.

910 550   LI
         CODEN: LTAGD5
LIETUVOS AUKSTUJU MOKYKLU MOKSLO DARBAI. GEOGRAFIJA. (Text in English and Lithuanian) 1961. a. $10. (Vilniaus Univesitetas) Leidykla Academia, A. Gostauto 12, 2600 Vilnius, Lithuania. TEL 626851. (Co-sponsor: Institute of Geography) Ed. Paulius Kavaliauskas. circ. 400. **Indexed:** Ref.Zh.
—BLDSC (0122.615800); CASDDS.
Formerly (until 1990): Lietuvos T S R Aukstuju Mokyklu Mokslo. Geografija (ISSN 0202-3288); Supersedes in part (in 1980): Lietuvos T S R Aukstuju Mokyklu Mokslo Darbai. Geografija ir Geologija (ISSN 0459-3448)

914.503   IT
LIGURIA TERRITORIO E CIVILTA. no.4, 1977. irreg. Sagep Editrice S.p.A., Piazza della Vittoria 14, 16121 Genoa, Italy. Ed. Gaspare De Fiore.

LINK (RICHMOND). see ENGINEERING — Civil Engineering

910.02   SW   ISSN 0076-146X
         CODEN: LSGPAI
LUND STUDIES IN GEOGRAPHY. SERIES A. PHYSICAL GEOGRAPHY. (Text in English, German) 1950. irreg., no.60, 1983. price varies. (Lunds Universitet, Department of Geography) Liber Forlag, S-205 10, Malmo, Sweden. index; cum.index: 1950-54, 1956-58, 1960-66. **Indexed:** GeoRef, I D A.

LUND STUDIES IN GEOGRAPHY. SERIES B. HUMAN GEOGRAPHY. see BIOLOGY

910   CN
MCGILL UNIVERSITY SAVANNA RESEARCH PROJECT - SAVANNA RESEARCH SERIES. 1964. irreg. Can.$100. McGill University, Department of Geography, 805 Sherbrooke St. West, Montreal, Que. H3A 2K6, Canada. TEL 514-392-5495. Ed. Dr. Theo L. Hills.
Formerly: Publications in Tropical Geography Savanna Research Series (ISSN 0079-7758)

910   MG   ISSN 0047-5416
DT469.M28   CODEN: MRVGA2
MADAGASCAR; REVUE DE GEOGRAPHIE. (Text in French; summaries in English, German, Malagasy, Portuguese, Spanish) 1962. s-a. FMG.3500 (foreign 12 F.) Universite de Madagascar, Laboratoire de Geographie, B.P. 907, Tananarive, Malagasy Republic. (Co-sponsors: Association de Geographes de Madagascar) Ed. Gerald Donque. bk.rev. **Indexed:** Curr.Cont.Africa, Documentatieblad, Geo.Abstr., GeoRef, I D A. **Document type:** academic/scholarly publication.

914   HU   ISSN 0076-2512
MAGYARORSZAG TAJFOLDRAJZA. 1967. irreg., vol.6, 1989. price varies. (Magyar Tudomanyos Akademia) Akademiai Kiado, Publishing House of the Hungarian Academy of Sciences, P.O. Box 245, H-1519 Budapest, Hungary. TEL 181-2134. FAX 166-6466. TELEX 22-6228 AKNYO H.

910   UG   ISSN 0075-4722
         CODEN: OMUGDL
MAKERERE UNIVERSITY. DEPARTMENT OF GEOGRAPHY. OCCASIONAL PAPER. 1967. irreg., no.71, 1977. price varies. Makerere University, Department of Geography, Box 7062, Kampala, Uganda. adv.; bk.rev. **Indexed:** GeoRef.
—CASDDS.

910   MW
MALAWIAN GEOGRAPHER. (Text in English) 1968. a. $6. Geography Teacher's Association, c/o Chancellor College, Box 280, Zomba, Malawi. Eds. Z. Kaufulu, M.B. Dolozi. adv.; bk.rev. circ. 300. **Indexed:** GeoRef, P.L.E.S.A.

910   MY   ISSN 0127-1474
G905
MALAYSIAN JOURNAL OF TROPICAL GEOGRAPHY. 1980. s-a. M.30($15) University of Malaya, Department of Geography, Kuala Lumpur 59100, Malaysia. TEL 03-7555266. FAX 03-7573661. TELEX UNIMAL-MA-39845. Ed. T.S. Bahrin. bk.rev. circ. 400. **Indexed:** Asian-Pac.Econ.Lit., Curr.Cont., Geo.Abstr., Rural Devel.Abstr., Trop.Oil Seeds Abstr., World Agri.Econ.& Rural Sociol.Abstr. **Document type:** academic/scholarly publication.
—UnCover; SWETS.

910   UK   ISSN 0260-5503
G1
THE MANCHESTER GEOGRAPHER. 1980. a. £6. Manchester Geographical Society, 385 Corn Exchange Buildings, Manchester M4 3EY, England. Ed. D.C. Gibbs. illus. circ. 250. **Indexed:** Geo.Abstr. **Document type:** academic/scholarly publication.
—BLDSC (5359.555000).

790.132 526   UK   ISSN 0140-427X
GA192
MAP COLLECTOR. 1977. q. £29 (foreign £32). Map Collector Publications Ltd., 48 High St., Tring, Herts HP23 5BH, England. TEL 0442-824977. FAX 0442-827712. Ed. Valerie G. Scott. adv.; bk.rev.; bibl.; charts; illus.; index. circ. 3,000. (back issues avail.) **Indexed:** Bibl.Cart., Geo.Abstr. **Document type:** academic/scholarly publication.
—BLDSC (5369.302000); UnCover.

526   US   ISSN 1065-6324
Z286.M3
THE MAP REPORT. 1982. m. membership. International Map Trade Association, 105 E. Court St., Box 1789, Kankakee, IL 60901. TEL 815-939-4627. FAX 815-933-8320. circ. 400. (back issues avail.) **Document type:** newsletter.
Former titles: International Map Dealers Association Newsletter; International Map Dealers Association Letter.

912 977   US   ISSN 0196-0881
GA201
MAPLINE. 1976. q. $8 (foreign $10). Newberry Library, Hermon Dunlap Smith Center for the History of Cartography, 60 W. Walton St., Chicago, IL 60610. TEL 312-943-9090. Ed. James R. Akerman. bk.rev.; bibl.; index. circ. 700. **Indexed:** Bibl.Cart., Geo.Abstr.
Description: Contains articles, notes, and announcements on the history of cartography.

526   US   ISSN 0749-3878
MAPPING SCIENCES & REMOTE SENSING. (Translation of selected papers from Russian and East European journals) 1962. 4/yr. $279 (foreign $299). V.H. Winston & Son, Inc., c/o Bellwether Publishing, Ltd., 8640 Guilford Rd., Ste. 200, Columbia, MD 21046. TEL 410-290-3870. FAX 410-290-8726. (Co-sponsors: American Congress of Surveying and Mapping; American Society of Photogrammetry) Ed. Joel Morrison. abstr.; bibl.; charts; illus.; index. circ. 300. **Indexed:** Bibl.Cart., Chem.Abstr., Forest.Abstr., GeoRef. **Document type:** academic/scholarly publication.
—BLDSC (0415.813000); Faxon; UnCover; SWETS. **CCC.**
Former titles: Geodesy, Mapping and Photogrammetry (ISSN 0361-4433); Geodesy and Aerophotography (ISSN 0016-7088)

526.3   US   ISSN 0149-0419
QB275   CODEN: MAGED9
MARINE GEODESY; an international journal of ocean surveys, mapping and sensing. 1977. q. $141. Taylor & Francis, 1900 Frost Rd., Ste. 101, Bristol, PA 19007. TEL 215-785-5800. FAX 215-785-5515. Ed. N.K. Saxena. adv.; bk.rev.; abstr.; charts; index. **Indexed:** Bibl. & Ind.Geol., Curr.Cont., Deep Sea Res.& Oceanogr.Abstr., Fluidex, Geo.Abstr., Ind.Sci.Rev., SSCI, W.R.C.Inf. **Document type:** academic/scholarly publication.
—BLDSC (5375.370000); UnCover; SWETS. **CCC.**
Description: Presents research on precise measurements within the ocean and from space to the ocean surface.
Refereed Serial

MARSCHENRAT ZUR FOERDERUNG DER FORSCHUNG IM KUESTENGEBIET DER NORDSEE. NACHRICHTEN. see SCIENCES: COMPREHENSIVE WORKS

910.02   GW   ISSN 0937-9878
MATERIAL ZUR ANGEWANDTEN GEOGRAPHIE. 1978. irreg., no.25, 1994. DM.29.80. (Deutscher Verband fuer Angewandte Geographie) Verlag Sven von Loga, Gerhard-vom-Rath-Str. 55, 50968 Cologne, Germany. TEL 0221-383680. FAX 0221-386737. Eds. A. Haberer, T. Mager. **Document type:** monographic series.

GEOGRAPHY

910   UK   ISSN 0140-7961
MATTER OF DEGREE; a guide to geography courses in the United Kingdom. 1971. a. £3. c/o Iain Bain, Nairnshire Telegraph, 10 Leopold St., Nairn, Scotland. circ. 2,000.
—BLDSC (5413.263000).
Description: Guide to UK degree courses in geography and related disciplines.

910   IE
MAYNOOTH OCCASIONAL PAPERS. 1978. irreg. price varies. St. Patrick's College, Department of Geography, Maynooth, Co. Kildare, Ireland. TEL 01-6285222. FAX 01-6289063. Ed. Dennis G. Pringle. circ. 200. (back issues avail.) **Document type:** monographic series.

914   FR   ISSN 0025-8296
D973.A1   CODEN: MERRBR
MEDITERRANEE; revue geographique des pays mediterraneens. (Text in French; occasionally in English, Italian) 1960. q. 280 F. (foreign 330 F.) Les Amis de la Revue Mediterranee, Institut de Geographie, 29 av. Robert Schuman, 13621 Aix-en-Provence, France. FAX 42-64-01-58. Ed. A. Courtot. adv.; charts. **Indexed:** Bibl.& Ind.Geol., Geo.Abstr., I D A, Rural Recreat.Tour.Abstr., World Agri.Econ.& Rural Sociol.Abstr.

910   FR   ISSN 0224-2702
MEMOIRES ET DOCUMENTS GEOGRAPHIE. a. price varies. C N R S Editions, 20-22 rue St. Amand, 75015 Paris, France. TEL 45-33-16-00. FAX 45-33-92-13. TELEX 200 356 F. adv.; bk.rev.; index; circ. 1,500. (controlled).

915.69   IS   ISSN 0081-8585
MICHKARIM BEGEOGRAFIYAH SHEL ERETZ YISRAEL/STUDIES IN THE GEOGRAPHY IN ISRAEL. (Text in Hebrew; table of contents and summaries in English) 1964. irreg., vol.14, 1993. price varies. Israel Exploration Society, P.O. Box 7041, Jerusalem 91070, Israel. TEL 972-2-257991. FAX 972-2-247772. (Co-publisher: Hebrew University of Jerusalem, Department of Geography) circ. 1,500. (back issues avail.) **Document type:** academic/scholarly publication, monographic series.
Description: Monographs from the Israel Exploration Society in collaboration with the Hebrew University of Jerusalem, Department of Geography.

910   AT   ISSN 0313-8410
MONASH PUBLICATIONS IN GEOGRAPHY. 1972. irreg., no.42, 1992. Aus.$4 (foreign Aus.$5) per no. Monash University, Department of Geography and Environmental Science, Clayton, Vic. 3168, Australia. FAX 03-565-2948. Ed. David Mercer. bibl.; illus.; index. circ. 250. **Document type:** academic/scholarly publication, monographic series.
—BLDSC (5901.592000).

MONKEYSHINES ON AMERICA. see *CHILDREN AND YOUTH — For*

MONKEYSHINES ON YOU!. see *CHILDREN AND YOUTH — For*

910   IS
MONO GEO GRAPHY; monographs series in geography. (Text in Hebrew, abstracts in English) irreg. Haifa University, Department of Geography, Mount Carmel, Haifa 31905, Israel. FAX 972-4-246814. Ed. Nurit Kliot. **Document type:** academic/scholarly publication, monographic series.
Refereed Serial

910   FR   ISSN 0047-8164
MOSELLA. 1971. q. 60 F. Universite de Metz, Centre d'Etudes Geographiques de Metz, Faculte des Lettres et Sciences Humaines, Ile du Saulcy, 57045 Metz Cedex 1, France. TEL 87-31-52-53. FAX 87-31-52-55. Ed. Francois Reitel. bk.rev.; bibl.; charts; illus.; stat. circ. 1,000. **Indexed:** Geo.Abstr.

910   RU   ISSN 0027-1381
MOSKOVSKII UNIVERSITET. VESTNIK. SERIYA 5: GEOGRAFIYA. (Text in Russian; contents page and summaries in English) 1946. bi-m. 22.80 Rub. Moskovskii Universitet, Ul. Gertsena 5-7, 103009 Moscow, Russia. (Dist. by: Mezhdunarodnaya Kniga, ul. Dimitrova 39, Moscow G-200, Russia) Ed. E.A. Deryugina. bk.rev.; bibl.; charts; illus.; index. circ. 2,175. **Indexed:** Biol.Abstr. **Document type:** academic/scholarly publication.
—CCC.

910.02   US
MOUNTAIN TRAILS. 1983. m. $10. Nandel, Inc., Box 4690, Sevierville, TN 37864. TEL 615-428-5176. Ed. Delmar Dennis. adv.; bk.rev.; circ. 1,000 (paid).

910   GW
MUENCHENER GEOGRAPHISCHE ABHANDLUNGEN. 1970. irreg. (3-4/yr.) price varies. (Universitaet Muenchen, Institut fuer Geographie) Nelles Verlag, Schleissheimer Str. 371b, 80935 Munich, Germany. circ. 600. **Indexed:** Bibl.& Ind.Geol.

910.1   GW   ISSN 0077-1902
HC281
MUENCHENER STUDIEN ZUR SOZIAL- UND WIRTSCHAFTSGEOGRAPHIE. (Text in German; summaries in English, French and Russian) 1966. irreg. price varies. (Universitaet Muenchen, Wirtschaftsgeographisches Institut) Verlag Michael Lassleben, Lange Gasse 19, 93183 Kallmuenz, Germany. **Indexed:** Rural Recreat.Tour.Abstr., World Agri.Econ.& Rural Sociol.Abstr.
—BLDSC (5983.740000).

910   GW   ISSN 0931-8747
MUENCHNER GEOWISSENSCHAFTLICHE ABHANDLUNGEN. REIHE C: GEOGRAPHIE. (Text in English, French, German) 1988. irreg. price varies. Verlag Dr. Friedrich Pfeil, Postfach 650086, 81214 Munich, Germany. TEL 089-188058. FAX 089-8341873. Ed. Friedrich H. Pfeil. circ. 700. **Document type:** monographic series.
Description: Studies all areas of geography.

MUSEUM OF ANTIQUITIES OF TEL-AVIV-YAFO. PUBLICATIONS. see *ARCHAEOLOGY*

MUSK-OX; a journal on the North. see *SCIENCES: COMPREHENSIVE WORKS*

NAAMKUNDE. see *LINGUISTICS*

526   GW   ISSN 0469-4236
QB275   CODEN: NKVEAQ
NACHRICHTEN AUS DEM KARTEN- UND VERMESSUNGSWESEN. REIHE I: ORIGINALBEITRAEGE. 1956. irreg. price varies. Institut fuer Angewandte Geodaesie, Richard-Strauss-Allee 11, 60598 Frankfurt a.M., Germany. TEL 069-6333-1. bk.rev. circ. 550. **Indexed:** Bibl.Cart., Geo.Abstr., GeoRef. **Document type:** monographic series.
Supersedes in part: Nachrichten aus dem Karten- und Vermessungswesen (ISSN 0071-920X)

526   GW   ISSN 0469-4244
QB275   CODEN: NKDDAZ
NACHRICHTEN AUS DEM KARTEN- UND VERMESSUNGSWESEN. REIHE II: UEBERSETZUNGEN. 1957. irreg. price varies. Institut fuer Angewandte Geodaesie, Richard-Strauss-Allee 11, 60598 Frankfurt a.M., Germany. TEL 069-6333-1. bk.rev. circ. 550. **Indexed:** Bibl.& Ind.Geol., Geo.Abstr. **Document type:** monographic series.
Supersedes in part: Nachrichten aus dem Karten- und Vermessungswesen (ISSN 0071-920X)

NAMENKUNDLICHE INFORMATIONEN. see *LINGUISTICS*

NAMES. see *LINGUISTICS*

NAMES SOCIETY OF SOUTHERN AFRICA. NEWSLETTER/NAAMKUNDEVERENIGING VAN SUIDER-AFRIKA. NUUSBRIEF. see *LINGUISTICS*

NAMN OCH BYGD; tidskrift foer nordisk ortnamsforskning. see *LINGUISTICS*

910   JA   ISSN 0085-7289
G845   CODEN: NSHIAO
NANKYOKU SHIRYO/ANTARCTIC RECORD. (Text in English, Japanese) 1957. 3/yr. exchange basis. National Institute of Polar Research - Kokuritsu Kyokuchi Kenkyujo, Library, 9-10, Kaga 1-chome, Itabashi-ku, Tokyo 173, Japan. TEL 03-3962-4711. FAX 03-3962-2529. TELEX 272-3515 POLRSCJ. Ed. Takao Hoshiai. charts; illus.; stat. circ. 1,000. **Indexed:** Bibl.& Ind.Geol., Biol.Abstr., Geo.Abstr., Meteor.& Geoastrophys.Abstr. **Document type:** academic/scholarly publication.
—BLDSC (1542.110000); UnCover.

910   II   ISSN 0470-0929
G1
NATIONAL GEOGRAPHER. (Text in English) 1958. s-a. $18. Allahabad Geographical Society, University of Allahabad, Department of Geography, Allahabad 211002, Uttar Pradesh, India. Ed. R.C. Tiwari. bk.rev.; illus. circ. 450. **Indexed:** Potato Abstr., Rural Devel.Abstr., Rural Recreat.Tour.Abstr., World Agri.Econ.& Rural Sociol.Abstr. **Document type:** academic/scholarly publication.

910   US   ISSN 0027-9358
G1   CODEN: NGGMAF
NATIONAL GEOGRAPHIC. 1888. m. $21 membership. National Geographic Society, 17th & M Sts., N.W., Washington, DC 20036. TEL 202-857-7000. Ed. William Graves. adv.; illus.; index, s-a. cum.index. circ. 9,700,000. (also avail. in microform from UMI,PMC; reprint service avail. from UMI) **Indexed:** A.I.C.P., Abr.R.G., Abstr.Anthropol., Acad.Ind., Amer.Bibl.Slavic & E.Eur.Stud., Anthropol.Lit., Art & Archaeol.Tech.Abstr., Bibl.& Ind.Geol., Bibl.Cart., Biol.Abstr., Biol.Dig., Br.Ceram.Abstr., CMI, Deep Sea Res.& Oceanogr.Abstr., E.I., Environ.Abstr., Gard.Lit.(1992-), Gdlns., Geo.Abstr., Ind.Child.Mag., Jun.High.Mag.Abstr., Mag.Ind., Mid.East: Abstr.& Ind., Ocean.Abstr., Pollut.Abstr., R.G., So.Pac.Per.Ind., TOM. **Document type:** consumer publication.
—BLDSC (6024.090000); Faxon; SWETS.
Description: Publishes articles on human society and culture around the world, exotic and endangered animals, modern explorations and adventures.

910   US   ISSN 0077-4618
NATIONAL GEOGRAPHIC BOOKS (SERIES). Also known as: National Geographic Society. Special Publications Series. 1966. irreg. (approx. 12-15/yr.). National Geographic Society, 17th & M Sts., N.W., Washington, DC 20036. TEL 202-857-7000. illus. **Document type:** monographic series.
Description: Covers a variety of topics in geography and related fields for a general audience, for both adults and children.

910   US   ISSN 1056-800X
QH1   CODEN: REXPE7
NATIONAL GEOGRAPHIC RESEARCH AND EXPLORATION. 1968. q. $40. National Geographic Society, 1145 17th St. N.W., Washington, DC 20036. TEL 202-857-7630. (Subscr. to: Dept. 1675, Washington, DC 20036) Ed. Anthony de Souza. **Indexed:** Anthropol.Lit., Bk.Rev.Ind. (1989-), Child.Bk.Rev.Ind. (1989-), Curr.Adv.Genetics & Molec.Biol., Environ.Abstr., GeoRef., Herb.Abstr., Ind.Vet., Soils & Fert., Triticale Abstr. **Document type:** academic/scholarly publication.
—BLDSC (7715.010000); Faxon; UnCover; SWETS.
Formerly: National Geographic Research (ISSN 8755-724X); *Supersedes (as of 1985):* National Geographic Society. Research Reports (ISSN 0077-4626)

910   II   ISSN 0027-9374
G1   CODEN: NGJIAI
NATIONAL GEOGRAPHICAL JOURNAL OF INDIA. (Text in English) 1955. q. Rs.450($100) to individuals; institutions Rs.400($125). National Geographical Society of India, Banaras Hindu University, Department of Geography, Varanasi 221005, Uttar Pradesh, India. TEL 0542-310291. FAX 91-0542-312059. TELEX 545-304-GEOG-364. Ed. Rana P.B. Singh. bk.rev.; charts; illus.; cum.index: 1955-1988. circ. 1,000. (back issues avail.) **Indexed:** Bibl.& Ind.Geol., Geo.Abstr. **Document type:** academic/scholarly publication.
Description: Publishes articles of geographical interest and includes such themes as the following: development and planning, historical and cultural geography, environmental studies, rural and urban settlements, transport, water resources, and ecological ethics and order.

333.79   UK   ISSN 0165-0203
HC55   CODEN: NRFODS
NATURAL RESOURCES FORUM. 1976. q. £140 in UK and Europe; elsewhere £140. (United Nations Centre for Natural Resources, Energy and Transport, UN) Butterworth - Heinemann (Subsidiary of: Reed International PLC), Linacre House, Jordan Hill, Oxford OX2 8DP, England. TEL 0865-310366. FAX 0865-310898. TELEX 83111 BHPOXF G. (Subscr. to: Turpin Transactions Ltd., Distribution Centre, Blackhorse Rd., Letchworth, Herts SG6 1HN, England. TEL 0462-672555) Ed. Raymond R. Knowles. (also avail. in microform from UMI) **Indexed:** Abstr.Rural Dev.Trop., AESIS, Agri.Eng.Abstr., Asian-Pac.Econ.Lit., Curr.Cont., Energy Rev., Environ.Abstr., Environ.Per.Bibl. (1977-), Excerp.Med., Geo.Abstr., I D A, Int.Lab.Doc., Petrol.Abstr., Pig News & Info., Rural Recreat.Tour.Abstr., Sci.Abstr., World Agri.Econ.& Rural Sociol.Abstr. **Document type:** academic/scholarly publication.
—BLDSC (6040.747000); CIS; Faxon; UnCover; SWETS; UMI. **CCC.**
    Description: Focuses on the development of the energy, mineral and water resources of developing countries. Examines the economic, financial, legal and technical aspects of natural resources development.
    Refereed Serial

778   NE   ISSN 0169-4839
NEDERLANDSE GEOGRAFISCHE STUDIES/NETHERLANDS GEOGRAPHICAL STUDIES. (Text mainly in Dutch, occasionally in English) 1985. irreg. (approx. 25/yr.). price varies. Koninklijk Nederlands Aardrijkskundig Genootschap - Royal Dutch Geographical Society, P.O. Box 80123, 3508 TC Utrecht, Netherlands. TEL 31-30-532757. FAX 31-30-535523. Ed. Johan G. Borchert. **Indexed:** Abstr.Rural Dev.Trop., Geo.Abstr., I D A, World Agri.Econ.& Rural Sociol.Abstr. **Document type:** monographic series.
—BLDSC (6073.792000).
    Description: Series of research reports published in cooperation with geography departments of all Dutch universities.

910.02 384   FR   ISSN 0987-6014
NETCOM. (Text in English, French) 1987. s-a. 200 F. per no. Centre National d'Etudes des Telecommunications, 38-40 rue du Gneral Leclerc, 92131 Issy-les-Moulineaux Cedex, France. TEL 45-29-54-64. FAX 45-29-01-06. (Co-sponsors: International Geographical Union, Comite National Francais de Geographie) Ed. Henri Bakis.

526 624   NE   ISSN 0165-1706
NETHERLANDS. COMMISSIE VOOR GEODESIE. PUBLICATIONS ON GEODESY. NEW SERIES. (Text usually in English) 1961. irreg. price varies. Commissie voor Geodesie - Netherlands Geodetic Commission, P.O. Box 5030, 2600 GA Delft, Netherlands. TEL 31-15-782819. FAX 31-15-782745. circ. 700. **Document type:** monographic series.
    Formerly: Netherlands. Rijkscommissie voor Geodesie. Publications on Geodesy. New Series (ISSN 0077-7625)

526.8   NZ   ISSN 1171-1337
GA101   CODEN: NZCJDK
NEW ZEALAND CARTOGRAPHY AND GEOGRAPHIC INFORMATION SYSTEMS. 1970. 2/yr. NZ.$30 (effective 1993). New Zealand Cartographic Society Inc., P.O. 12454, Thorndon, New Zealand. FAX 064-4-495-8450. bk.rev.; charts; illus.; circ. 225 (paid). **Indexed:** Bibl.& Ind.Geol., Bibl.Cart., Geo.Abstr. **Document type:** academic/scholarly publication.
—**CCC.**
    Formerly (until vol.20, no.2, 1990): New Zealand Cartographic Journal (ISSN 0110-6007)
    Description: Covers broad spectrum of cartographic, photogrammetric and GIS issues.

910   NZ   ISSN 0028-8144
G55   CODEN: NZGGAS
NEW ZEALAND GEOGRAPHER. 1945. s-a. NZ.$61 to individuals (foreign NZ.$71); institutions NZ.$145 (foreign NZ.$180) (effective 1994). New Zealand Geographical Society Inc., Dept. of Geography, Univ. of Canterbury, Private Bag 4800, Christchurch, New Zealand. FAX 03-364-2907. Ed. Richard Le Heron. adv. contact: Anne Murray. bk.rev.; charts; illus.; maps; stat.; index. cum.index: vols.1-25 (1945-1969). circ. 1,350. **Indexed:** Bibl.& Ind.Geol., Biol.Abstr., Curr.Adv.Ecol.Sci., Excerp.Med., Geo.Abstr., Mid.East: Abstr.& Ind., Rural Recreat.Tour.Abstr., So.Pac.Per.Ind., World Agri.Econ.& Rural Sociol.Abstr. **Document type:** academic/scholarly publication.
—BLDSC (6092.200000); Faxon; UnCover. **CCC.**
    Description: Contains scholarly articles, research notes, discussions and reviews.

919.31   NZ   ISSN 0078-0022
NEW ZEALAND GEOGRAPHICAL SOCIETY. MISCELLANEOUS SERIES. 1950. irreg. no.10, 1992. NZ.$30 in New Zealand; Australia & Pacific Islands NZ$35; rest of world NZ$40. New Zealand Geographical Society Inc., Dept. of Geography, Univ. of Canterbury, Private Bag 4800, Christchurch, New Zealand. FAX 03-364-2907. **Document type:** academic/scholarly publication.
—BLDSC (8379.628000). **CCC.**
    Description: Inlcudes essays reviewing past, present and future of geography in N.Z.

919.31   NZ   ISSN 0078-0030
G1   CODEN: PGECAV
NEW ZEALAND GEOGRAPHY CONFERENCE PROCEEDINGS SERIES. 1955. biennial. no.16, 1992. New Zealand Geographical Society Inc., Dept. of Geography, University of Canterbury, Private Bag, Christchurch, New Zealand. FAX 03-364-2907. circ. 950. **Indexed:** Bibl.& Ind.Geol., Excerp.Med. **Document type:** proceedings, academic/scholarly publication.
—BLDSC (3409.788200).

910   NZ   ISSN 0028-8292
G53   CODEN: NZJGA9
NEW ZEALAND JOURNAL OF GEOGRAPHY. 1946. s-a. membership; issued with subscription to New Zealand Geographer. New Zealand Geographical Society Inc., Dept. of Geography, Univ. of Canterbury, Private Bag 4800, Christchurch, New Zealand. FAX 03-642904. Ed. T.J. Hearn. bk.rev.; charts; illus.; stat. circ. 1,350. **Indexed:** Curr.Adv.Ecol.Sci., Geo.Abstr., GeoRef., Mid.East: Abstr.& Ind., Rural Recreat.Tour.Abstr., So.Pac.Per.Ind., World Agri.Econ.& Rural Sociol.Abstr. **Document type:** academic/scholarly publication.
—UnCover. **CCC.**
    Formerly: New Zealand Geographical Society. Record.
    Description: Published for students, teachers, schools, libraries and universities to promote geography especially N.Z. and South Pacific, to provide assistance to students and teachers and encourage contact and information exchange between members and geographical organizations worldwide.

910   NR   ISSN 0029-0084
DT515.A2   CODEN: NGGJA6
NIGERIAN GEOGRAPHICAL JOURNAL. (Text in English) 1957. s-a. £N5($10.50) to individuals; £N9.45 ($22.95) to libraries. Ibadan University Press, University of Ibadan, Ibadan, Nigeria. (Co-sponsors: Nigerian Geographical Association; Department of Geography) Ed. J.S. Oguntoyinbo. adv.; bk.rev.; abstr.; bibl.; charts; illus.; maps; cum.index. circ. 900. **Indexed:** Curr.Cont.Africa, Documentatieblad, Field Crop Abstr., GeoRef., Herb.Abstr. **Document type:** academic/scholarly publication.
    Formerly: Geographical Association of Nigeria. Journal (ISSN 0016-7371)

621.367   JA   ISSN 0289-7911
NIHON RIMOTO SENSHINGU GAKKAISHI/REMOTE SENSING SOCIETY OF JAPAN. JOURNAL. (Text in Japanese; summaries in English) 1981. q. 10000 Yen. Nihon Rimoto Senshingu Gakkai - Remote Sensing Society of Japan, Sankei Bldg., 8-16, Kanda Ogawa-machi 2-chome, Chiyoda-ku, Tokyo 101, Japan.
—BLDSC (4846.450000).

526.982   JA
NIHON SHASHIN SOKURYO GAKKAI. GAKUJUTSU KOENKAI HAPPYO RONBUNSHU. (Text in Japanese) s-a. 6,000 Yen. Nihon Shashin Sokuryo Gakkai - Japan Society of Photogrammetry and Remote Sensing, Dai-1 Honan Bldg., 2-8-17, Minami-Ikebukuro, Toshima-ku, Tokyo 171, Japan. FAX 81-33984-7402. **Document type:** proceedings.
    Description: Contains technical papers submitted to annual and fall conventions.

NOMINA AFRICANA. see *LINGUISTICS*

910 614.7   SP   ISSN 0213-3709
NORBA: REVISTA DE GEOGRAFIA. 1980. irreg. Universidad de Extremadura, Departamento de Geografia, Servicio de Publicaciones, Calle Pizarro, 8, 10071 Caceres, Spain. TEL 927-247650. bibl.; charts.
    Supersedes in part (in 1983): Norba (ISSN 0211-0636)
    Description: Covers natural resources, rural and urban planning, industry, population, transportation and commerce, and development studies.

NORD REFO. see *SOCIAL SCIENCES: COMPREHENSIVE WORKS*

910   FR   ISSN 0029-182X
G1   CODEN: NOROAU
NOROIS; revue geographique de l'ouest et des pays de l'atlantique nord. (Text in French; summaries in English, French, German) 1954. q. 280 F.($64) (foreign 340 F.). 95 av. du Recteur Pineau, 86022 Poitiers Cedex, France. TEL 49-45-32-39. FAX 49-45-32-39. (Co-sponsors: Universites de l'Ouest (Angers, Brest, Caen, Le Mans, Limoges, Nantes, Orleans, Poitiers, Rennes, Tours)) Ed. Jean Soumagne. bk.rev.; bibl.; charts; illus.; index. circ. 1,500. (back issues avail.) **Indexed:** Bibl.& Ind.Geol., Br.Geol.Lit., Deep Sea Res.& Oceanogr.Abstr., Forest.Abstr., Geo.Abstr., Rural Recreat.Tour.Abstr., Soils & Fert., World Agri.Econ.& Rural Sociol.Abstr. **Document type:** academic/scholarly publication.
—BLDSC (6133.500000).
    Description: Examines the human and physical geography of France, the Northern and North-Western countries of Europe, Canada and the Arctic zones.

910   NO   ISSN 0029-1951
G1   CODEN: NGGTA2
NORSK GEOGRAFISK TIDSSKRIFT/NORWEGIAN JOURNAL OF GEOGRAPHY. (Text in English) 1927. q. NOK 485 in the Nordic countries; elsewhere NOK 545. (Norwegian Geographical Society) Scandinavian University Press, P.O. Box 2959-Toeyen, N-0608 Oslo, Norway. TEL 472-67-7600. FAX 472-67-7575. (U.S. addr.: Scandinavian University Press, 200 Meacham Ave., Elmont, NY 11003. TEL 516-352-7300) Ed. Tormod Klemsdal. bk.rev.; bibl.; charts; index. circ. 800. (also avail. in microform from UMI; back issues avail.) **Indexed:** Bibl.& Ind.Geol., Curr.Adv.Ecol.Sci., Ecol.Abstr., Energy Res.Abstr., Forest.Abstr., Geo.Abstr., I D A, Rice Abstr., Rural Devel.Abstr., Rural Recreat.Tour.Abstr., World Agri.Econ.& Rural Sociol.Abstr. **Document type:** academic/scholarly publication.
—BLDSC (6139.000000); UMI. **CCC.**
    Supersedes (1889-1921): Norsk Geografisk Aarbog.

NORSK POLARINSTITUTT. AARBOK. see *EARTH SCIENCES — Geology*

NORSK POLARINSTITUTT. MEDDELELSER. see *EARTH SCIENCES — Geology*

NORSK POLARINSTITUTT. POLARHAANDBOK. see *EARTH SCIENCES — Geology*

NORSK POLARINSTITUTT. SKRIFTER. see *EARTH SCIENCES — Geology*

910   US   ISSN 0882-1968
E20
NORTH AMERICAN CULTURE. 1985. s-a. $35 to individuals; institutions $70 (effective 1994). North American Culture Society, Oklahoma State University, Department of Geography, Stillwater, OK 74078. TEL 405-744-7599. FAX 405-744-5620. Ed. Joseph Seig. illus.; circ. 115 (paid). **Document type:** academic/scholarly publication.
—UnCover.

GEOGRAPHY

910   II
NORTH EASTERN GEOGRAPHER. (Text in English) vol.10, 1978. s-a. Rs.30($10) North East India Geographical Society, c/o Department of Geography, Gauhati University, Gauhati 781014, Assam, India. TEL 88372. Ed. H.N. Sharma. adv.; bk.rev.; bibl.; charts; illus. circ. 250.
   Formerly: North East India Geographical Society. Journal.

NOUVELLE REVUE D'ONOMASTIQUE/JOURNAL OF ONOMASTIC STUDIES. see *LINGUISTICS*

NOVA SCOTIAN SURVEYOR. see *ENGINEERING — Civil Engineering*

910   GW   ISSN 0546-9112
NUERNBERGER WIRTSCHAFTS-UND SOZIALGEOGRAPHISCHE ARBEITEN. (Text in German; summaries in English) 1957. irreg., vol.45, 1992. price varies. Gesellschaft fuer Regionalforschung und angewandte Geographie e.V., Wirtschafts- und Sozialgeographisches Institut, Lange Gasse 20, 90403 Nuernberg, Germany. TEL 0911-5302321. FAX 0911-5302-658. TELEX 623274. Eds. Ernst Weigt, Wigand Ritter. circ. 700. **Document type:** monographic series.

910   JA   ISSN 0288-8726
OCHANOMIZU CHIRI/OCHANOMIZU GEOGRAPHICAL SOCIETY. ANNALS. (Text in Japanese) 1959. a. 1800 Yen($12) Ochanomizu Chiri Gakkai - Ochanomizu Geographical Society, Ochanomizu Joshi Daigaku, Chirigaku Kyoshitsu, 1-1 Otsuka 2-chome, Bunkyo-ku, Tokyo 112, Japan. TEL 03-3943-3151. index. circ. 600. (back issues avail.)

910   AU   ISSN 0029-9138
OESTERREICHISCHE GEOGRAPHISCHE GESELLSCHAFT. MITTEILUNGEN. (Text in German; summaries in English) 1857. 7/yr. S.690. Oesterreichische Geographische Gesellschaft, Karl-Schweighofer-Gasse 3, A-1070 Vienna, Austria. Ed. Martin Seger. adv.; bk.rev.; abstr.; bibl.; illus.; stat. circ. 1,500. **Indexed:** Rural Recreat.Tour.Abstr., SSCI, World Agri.Econ.& Rural Sociol.Abstr. **Document type:** academic/scholarly publication.
   Superseded: Geographische Gesellschaft in Wien. Mitteilungen.

526.982 625.72   AU
OESTERREICHISCHE ZEITSCHRIFT FUER VERMESSUNGSWESEN UND GEOINFORMATION. (Text in German; abstracts in English, German) 1903. 4/yr. S.600 (foreign S.700). Oesterreichischer Gesellschaft fuer Vermessung und Geoinformation, Schiffamtsgasse 1-3, A-1025 Vienna, Austria. TEL 0222-21176. FAX 0222-2161062. Ed.Bd. adv.; bk.rev.; bibl.; charts; illus.; index. circ. 1,200. **Indexed:** Bibl.Cart. **Document type:** academic/scholarly publication.
   Former titles (until 1994): Oesterreichische Zeitschrift fuer Vermessungswesen und Photogrammetrie; Oesterreichische Zeitschrift fuer Vermessungswesen (ISSN 0029-9650)
   Description: Covers surveying, photogrammetry and remote sensing.

917.6   US
OKLAHOMA LAKE LIVING. 1979. a. $2 per no. Oklahoma Lake Living Magazine, Box 1781, Muskogee, OK 74401. adv. circ. 50,000.

OLD CORNWALL. see *GENEALOGY AND HERALDRY*

ONOMA; bibliographical and information bulletin. see *LINGUISTICS*

400   GR
ONOMATA/REVUE ONOMASTIQUE. (Text in Greek; occasionally in English, French, German, Italian, Spanish) 1952. a. price varies. Greek Onomastic Society, Sebastopol Str. 107, 11526 Athens, Greece. TEL 69-16-287. circ. 500. (back issues avail.) **Indexed:** Bibl.Ling.
   Description: Discusses all aspects of onomastics.

910   GW   ISSN 0030-4395
ORBIS GEOGRAPHICUS; world directory of geography. (Text in English, French, German) 1952. quadrennial. price varies. (International Geographical Union) Franz Steiner Verlag Wiesbaden GmbH, Birkenwaldstr. 44, 70191 Stuttgart, Germany. TEL 0711-2582-O. FAX 0711-2582290. TELEX 723636-DAZ-D. (Subscr. to: Postfach 101061, 70009 Stuttgart, Germany) Ed. E. Ehlers. **Document type:** directory.
   —BLDSC (6277.860000).

910 614.7 016   UK
ORDNANCE SURVEY PUBLICATION NEWS. 1938. m. free. Director General of the Ordnance Survey, Romsey Rd., Maybush, Southampton SO9 4DH, England. TEL 0703-792949. FAX 0703-792962. TELEX 477843. Ed. Pete Lewis. adv. circ. 6,000. **Document type:** catalog.
   Formerly: Ordnance Survey Publication Report.

918.1   BL   ISSN 0103-3220
ORIENTACAO. 1965. a. exchange basis. Universidade de Sao Paulo, Instituto de Geografia, Departamento de Geografia, Caixa Postal 8105, 01000 Sao Paulo, SP, Brazil.

910   BG   ISSN 0030-5308
G35   CODEN: ORGGAH
ORIENTAL GEOGRAPHER. (Text in English) 1957. s-a. Tk.60($10) per no. Bangladesh Geographical Society, c/o Dept. of Geography, University of Dhaka, Dhaka 100, Bangladesh. Ed. Dr. K.B. Sajjadur Rashid. adv.; bk.rev.; bibl.; charts. circ. 1,000. **Indexed:** Bibl.& Ind.Geol., Biol.Abstr., Field Crop Abstr., Herb.Abstr., Mid.East: Abstr.& Ind.
   —UnCover.

OSTERODER ZEITUNG. see *HISTORY — History Of Europe*

910   NZ   ISSN 0030-8978
AS741
PACIFIC VIEWPOINT; specialises in the study of development, change and underdevelopment. 1960. s-a. NZ.$28 (Australia NZ.$40; elsewhere NZ$ 45($25)). (Victoria University of Wellington, Department of Geography) Victoria University Press, P.O. Box 600, Wellington, New Zealand. Eds. R.T. Lawrence, P. Morrison. adv.; bk.rev.; charts; illus.; maps. circ. 850. (also avail. in microfilm from UMI; back issues avail.) **Indexed:** Amer.Hist.& Life, Anthropol.Lit., Asian-Pac.Econ.Lit., Geo.Abstr., Hist.Abstr., I D A, Key to Econ.Sci., So.Pac.Per.Ind. **Document type:** academic/scholarly publication.
   —BLDSC (6331.700000); Faxon. **CCC**.

PELANGI; Indonesian-English bilingual magazine. see *EDUCATION — Teaching Methods And Curriculum*

910   US
PENNSYLVANIA GEOGRAPHER. 1963. s-a. $12. University of Pittsburgh at Johnstown, Department of Geography, Pennsylvania Geographical Society, Johnstown, PA 15904. TEL 814-269-2994. FAX 814-269-7255. Ed. William B. Kory. adv.; bk.rev.; charts; illus.; stat.; index. circ. 500. **Indexed:** Geo.Abstr., GeoRef. **Document type:** academic/scholarly publication.

910   US
PERSPECTIVE (INDIANA). 5/yr. (during school year). National Council for Geographic Education, Central Office, 16A Leonard Hall, Indiana University of Pennsylvania, Indiana, PA 15705-3147. TEL 412-357-6290. Ed. Joseph Bencloski.
   Description: Covers study and teaching methods.

910 301   II
PERSPECTIVES IN URBAN GEOGRAPHY. (Text in English) 1986. irreg. (approx. 7-8/yr.). price varies. Concept Publishing Company, A 15-16, Commercial Block, Mohan Garden, New Delhi 110 059, India. TEL 011-5554-042. Ed. Dr. C.S. Yadav.
   Description: Covers various sociological aspects of the study of urban populations.

910   GW   ISSN 0031-6229
G1   CODEN: PGGMA3
PETERMANNS GEOGRAPHISCHE MITTEILUNGEN. 1855. 6/yr. DM.320. Justus Perthes Verlag Gotha GmbH, Justus-Perthes-Str. 1-5, 99867 Gotha, Germany. TEL 03621-3850. FAX 03621-385103. Ed. Eberhard Benser; Pub. Christian Dornburg. bk.rev.; bibl.; charts; illus.; Bibl.& Ind.Geol. **Indexed:** Bibl.Cart., Curr.Cont., Deep Sea Res.& Oceanogr.Abstr., E.I., Excerp.Med., Meteor.& Geoastrophys.Abstr., Popul.Ind., SSCI. **Document type:** academic/scholarly publication.
   —SWETS.
   Description: Provides articles and information on all aspects of geography and cartography.

910   PH   ISSN 0031-7551
DS651
PHILIPPINE GEOGRAPHICAL JOURNAL. 1953. q. $20 to non-members. Philippine Geographical Society, P.O. Box 2116, Manila, Philippines. (Co-sponsors: Philippine National Science Society) Ed. Meliton B. Juanico. adv.; bk.rev.; bibl.; charts; illus.; maps; stat.; index, cum.index. circ. 1,000. (also avail. in microfilm from UMI; reprint service avail. from UMI) **Indexed:** Chem.Abstr., Geo.Abstr., Ind.Phil.Per. **Document type:** academic/scholarly publication.
   —Faxon; UnCover; UMI.

778   FR   ISSN 0031-8523
TR810   CODEN: POITAM
PHOTO INTERPRETATION. (Text in English, French, Spanish) 1962. 4/yr. 1072 F. (foreign 1239 F.). Editions E S K A, 27 rue Dunois, 75013 Paris, France. TEL 1-45-83-62-02. FAX 1-44-24-06-94. Ed. Fernand Verger; Pub. Serge Kebabtcheiff. illus.; index. circ. 1,000. (looseleaf format) **Indexed:** Bibl.& Ind.Geol., Forest.Abstr., Geo.Abstr., I D A, Int.Aerosp.Abstr.
   —Faxon.

526.982   US
PHOTOGRAMMETRIC COYOTE. q. free to qualified personnel; others $6. E. Coyote Enterprises, Inc., Rt. 3, Bldg. 228, Box 1119, Mineral Wells, TX 76067. TEL 817-325-0757. Ed. Marilyn O'Cuilinn. adv.; bk.rev.; circ. 10,000 (controlled).

778 526.9   US   ISSN 0099-1112
TA593.A2   CODEN: PGMEA9
PHOTOGRAMMETRIC ENGINEERING AND REMOTE SENSING. Short title: P E & R S. 1934. m. $160. American Society for Photogrammetry and Remote Sensing, 5410 Grosvenor Ln., Ste. 210, Bethesda, MD 20814-2160. TEL 301-493-0290. FAX 301-493-0208. Ed. James B. Case. adv.; bk.rev.; illus.; index, cum.index. circ. 10,500. (back issues avail.) **Indexed:** AESIS, Agri.Eng.Abstr., Bibl.Agri., Bibl.& Ind.Geol., Bibl.Cart., Chem.Abstr., Curr.Adv.Ecol.Sci., Curr.Cont., Deep Sea Res.& Oceanogr.Abstr., Energy Ind., Energy Info.Abstr., Eng.Ind., Environ.Per.Bibl. (1985-), Excerp.Med., Field Crop Abstr., Forest.Abstr., Forest Prod.Abstr., Geo.Abstr., Geotech.Abstr., Herb.Abstr., Int.Aerosp.Abstr., Irr.& Drain.Abstr., Maize Abstr., Petrol.Abstr., Potato Abstr., Sci.Abstr., Sel.Water Res.Abstr., Soils & Fert., Triticale Abstr.
   —BLDSC (6468.030000); Faxon; UnCover; SWETS; UMI. **CCC**.
   Formerly (until 1975): Photogrammetric Engineering (ISSN 0031-8671)

778 526.9   UK   ISSN 0031-868X
TA501   CODEN: PGREAY
PHOTOGRAMMETRIC RECORD. 1953. s-a. £44($88) (typically set in July). Photogrammetric Society, Department of Photogrammetry & Surveying, University College London, Gower St., London WC1E 6BT, England. TEL 071-387-7050. FAX 071-380-0453. Ed. K.B. Atkinson. adv. contact: J.E. Knipe. bk.rev.; abstr.; bibl.; charts; illus.; stat.; cum.index every 3 yrs. circ. 1,150. (reprint service avail. from ISI) **Indexed:** Bibl.& Ind.Geol., Bibl.Cart., Br.Tech.Ind., Curr.Cont., Geo.Abstr., Intl.Civil Eng.Abstr., Sci.Abstr., Soft.Abstr.Eng. **Document type:** academic/scholarly publication.
   —BLDSC (6468.100000); UnCover; SWETS.

PILIPINAS; an interdisciplinary scholarly journal of Philippine studies. see *HISTORY — History Of Asia*

PINE, THE PLOW AND THE PIONEER; histories of Three Lakes, Clearwater Lake, Gagen & Hiles areas. see *GENEALOGY AND HERALDRY*

946 301.2 574.5 SP ISSN 0373-2568
CODEN: PRNOAJ
PIRINEOS; a journal on mountain ecology. (Text in English, French, Spanish) summaries in English, French, German, Spanish) 1946. 2/yr. $35. Consejo Superior de Investigaciones Cientificas (C.S.I.C.), Instituto Pirenaico de Ecologia, Apartado 64, Jaca (Huesca), Spain. TEL 974-36-14-41. FAX 974-36-32-22. Ed. Jose Maria Garcia-Ruiz. adv.; bk.rev. circ. 1,100. **Indexed:** Bibl.& Ind.Geol., Biol.Abstr., Forest.Abstr., Geo.Abstr., Herb.Abstr., Ind.SST, Irr.& Drain.Abstr., Seed Abstr., Soils & Fert. **Document type:** academic/scholarly publication.
—BLDSC (6503.000000). **CCC.**
  Description: Papers related to the dynamics of mountain ecosystems.

919 551 US ISSN 0273-8457
G575
POLAR GEOGRAPHY AND GEOLOGY. (Translation of selected papers from Russian journals) 1977. 4/yr. $199 (foreign $230). V.H. Winston & Son, Inc., c/o Bellwether Publishing, Ltd., 8640 Guilford Rd., Ste. 200, Columbia, MD 21046. TEL 410-290-3870. FAX 410-290-8726. Ed. William Barr. charts; illus.; stat.; index. circ. 300. (back issues avail.) **Indexed:** Bibl.& Ind.Geol., Geo.Abstr., Ocean.Abstr. **Document type:** academic/scholarly publication.
—Faxon; UnCover; SWETS. **CCC.**
  Formerly (until vol.3, 1979): Polar Geography (ISSN 0148-7671)

919 UK ISSN 0032-2474
G575 CODEN: POLRAV
POLAR RECORD. 1931. q. £39($75) to individuals (overseas £57.50); institutions £62 (overseas £80.50 ($113)). (Scott Polar Research Institute) Cambridge University Press, Edinburgh Bldg., Shaftesbury Rd., Cambridge CB2 2RU, England. TEL 0223-312393. FAX 0223-315052. TELEX 851817256. (N. American addr.: Cambridge University Press, Journals Dept., 40 W. 20th St., New York, NY 10011. TEL 212-924-3900. FAX 212-691-3239) Ed. Beau Riffenburgh. adv.; bk.rev.; abstr.; bibl.; illus.; cum.index every 2 yrs. (back issues avail.) **Indexed:** Amer.Hist.& Life, Bibl.& Ind.Geol., Chem.Abstr., Curr.Adv.Ecol.Sci., Deep Sea Res.& Oceanogr.Abstr., Environ.Per.Bibl. (1991-), Geo.Abstr., Hist.Abstr., Meteor.& Geoastrophys.Abstr., Petrol.Abstr. **Document type:** academic/scholarly publication.
—BLDSC (6542.000000); Faxon; UnCover; SWETS; UMI.
  Description: Contains articles, notes and reviews on the polar and subpolar regions in archaeology, biogeography, glaciology, international law and psychology.

POLAR RESEARCH. see *SCIENCES: COMPREHENSIVE WORKS*

919 US ISSN 0032-2482
G575
POLAR TIMES. 1935. s-a. $5 (foreign $10). American Polar Society, c/o Peter J. Anderson, Ed., Byrd Polar Research Center, 125 S. Oval Mall, Columbus, OH 43210-1308. FAX 614-292-4697. TELEX 4945696 OSUPOLAR. bk.rev.; charts; illus.; maps. circ. 2,158.
—BLDSC (6542.500000).

POLARFORSCHUNG. see *EARTH SCIENCES*

POLISH ACADEMY OF SCIENCES. BULLETIN. EARTH SCIENCES. see *EARTH SCIENCES*

910 PL ISSN 0866-9708
POLISH ACADEMY OF SCIENCES. INSTITUTE OF GEOGRAPHY AND SPATIAL ORGANIZATION. CONFERENCE PAPERS. (Text in English) 1988. irreg. price varies. Polska Akademia Nauk, Instytut Geografii i Przestrzennego Zagospodarowania, Ul. Krakowskie Przemiescie 30, 00-927 Warsaw, Poland. (Dist. by: Ars Polona-Ruch, ul. Krakowskie Przedmiescie 7, Warsaw, Poland) Ed. Alicja Breymeyeyer.
—BLDSC (3409.740900).
  Formerly (until 1989): Polish Academy of Sciences. Institute of Geography and Spatial Organization. Papers from Seminars and Conferences (ISSN 0866-9694)

910 PL ISSN 0209-1585
POLISH ACADEMY OF SCIENCES. INSTITUTE OF GEOGRAPHY AND SPATIAL ORGANIZATION. GEOGRAPHICAL STUDIES. (Text in English) irreg., vol.6, 1991. price varies. Ossolineum, Publishing House of the Polish Academy of Sciences, Rynek 9, 50-106 Wroclaw, Poland. TEL 48-71-386-25. FAX 48-71-448-103. TELEX 0712771 OSS PL. (Also dist. by: ORWN PAN, Palac Kultury i Nauki, 00-901 Warsaw, Poland) Ed. R. Szczesny. **Document type:** monographic series.
  Description: Publishes original monographs and research reports as well as conference proceedings on different aspects of modern geographic research.

911 UK ISSN 0962-6298
JC319
POLITICAL GEOGRAPHY. 6/yr. £155 in UK and Europe; elsewhere £162. Butterworth - Heinemann (Subsidiary of: Reed International PLC), Linacre House, Jordan Hill, Oxford OX2 8DP, England. TEL 0865-310366. FAX 0865-310898. TELEX 83111 BHPOXF G. (Subscr. to: Turpin Transactions Ltd., Distribution Centre, Blackhorse Rd., Letchworth, Herts SG6 1HN, England. TEL 0462-672555) Ed. P.J. Taylor. bk.rev.; index. (also avail. in microform from UMI; back issues avail.) **Indexed:** A.B.C.Pol.Sci., E.I., Environ.Per.Bibl., I D A, P.A.I.S., SSCI. **Document type:** academic/scholarly publication.
—BLDSC (6543.885950); Faxon; UnCover; SWETS; UMI. **CCC.**
  Formerly (until 1992): Political Geography Quarterly (ISSN 0260-9827)
  Description: For students of political studies with an interest in the geographical or spatial aspects of their subject. Provides a central focus for developments in this subdiscipline.
  Refereed Serial

POLITICAL HANDBOOK OF THE WORLD. see *POLITICAL SCIENCE*

919 IT ISSN 0032-3667
IL POLO. (Text mainly in Italian; summaries in English) 1945. q. L.15000($18) (foreign L.20000). Istituto Geografico Polare "Silvio Zavatti", Viale Trento, Villa Vitali, 63023 Fermo, Italy. TEL 0734-226166. (Co-sponsor: Comune di Fermo) Ed. Giuliano Liberini. adv.; bk.rev.; charts; illus.
  Description: A forum that features articles on geography, traditions and culture, specifically in the Polar areas.

910 PL ISSN 0373-6547
G23 CODEN: PGPZDM
POLSKA AKADEMIA NAUK. INSTYTUT GEOGRAFII I PRZESTRZENNEGO ZAGOSPODAROWANIA. PRACE GEOGRAFICZNE. (Text in Polish; summaries in English and Russian) 1954. irreg., no.155, 1992. price varies. Ossolineum, Publishing House of the Polish Academy of Sciences, Rynek 9, 50-106 Wroclaw, Poland. TEL 48-71-386-25. FAX 48-71-448-103. TELEX 0712771 OSS PL. (Dist. by: ORWN PAN, Palac Kultury i Nauki, 00-901 Warsaw, Poland; And by: Ars Polona, Krakowskie Przedmiescie 7, 00-068 Warsaw, Poland) Ed. R. Szczesny. **Indexed:** GeoRef. **Document type:** monographic series.
—BLDSC (4128.125000).
  Formerly: Polska Akademia Nauk. Instytut Geografii. Prace Geograficzne (ISSN 0554-5749)

910 PL ISSN 0867-6836
POLSKA AKADEMIA NAUK. INSTYTUT GEOGRAFII I PRZESTRZENNEGO ZAGOSPODAROWANIA. ZESZYTY. 1991. irreg. price varies. Polska Akademia Nauk, Instytut Geografii i Przestrzennego Zagospodarowania, Ul. Krakowskie Przedmiescie 30, 00-927 Warsaw, Poland. (Dist. by: ORWN PAN, Palac Kultury i Nauki, 00-901 Warsaw, Poland) Ed. T. Kozlowska-Szczesna. **Document type:** proceedings.

526 PL ISSN 0079-3299
POLSKA AKADEMIA NAUK. ODDZIAL W KRAKOWIE. KOMISJA GORNICZO-GEODEZYJNA. PRACE: GEODEZJA. (Text in English; summaries in Polish and Russian) 1964. irreg., no.36, 1992. price varies. Ossolineum, Publishing House of the Polish Academy of Sciences, Rynek 9, 50-106 Wroclaw, Poland. TEL 48-71-386-25. FAX 48-71-448-103. TELEX 0712771 OSS PL. Ed. Jozef Jachimski. **Document type:** academic/scholarly publication.
—BLDSC (6586.550000).
  Description: Papers present results concerning geodesy, industrial and mining geodesy, photogrammetry, deformation of rock-mass, monitoring of environmental pollution and destruction.

910.02 PL ISSN 0137-2939
POLSKA AKADEMIA NAUK. ODDZIAL W KRAKOWIE. OSRODEK DOKUMENTACJI FIZJOGRAFICZNEJ. STUDIA. 1972. a. price varies. Ossolineum, Publishing House of the Polish Academy of Sciences, Rynek 9, 50-106 Wroclaw, Poland. TEL 48-71-386-25. FAX 48-71-448-103. TELEX 0712771 OSS PL. Ed. Antoni Kleczkowski. **Document type:** monographic series.
  Description: Monographs concerning different aspects of environmental research and protection.

910 PL ISSN 0324-8321
POLSKI PRZEGLAD KARTOGRAFICZNY/POLISH CARTOGRAPHICAL REVIEW. (Text in Polish; summaries in English and Russian) 1923-1935; resumed 1969. q. $25. (Polskie Towarzystwo Geograficzne) Polskie Przedsiebiorstwo Wydawnictw Kartograficznych, Ul. Solec 18-20, 00-410 Warsaw, Poland. (Dist. by: GeoCenter International, ul. Kolejowa 11-13, 01-217 Warsaw, Poland. TEL 48-22-320091. FAX 48-22-328825) bk.rev.; bibl.; illus. circ. 825. **Indexed:** Bibl.Cart.
  Description: Covers a wide range of problems in cartography: theory of cartography, design, editing, and reproduction of maps, computer assisted cartography and history of cartography.

914.7 PL ISSN 0208-4082
POMORSKIE MONOGRAFIE TOPONOMASTYCZNE. (Text in Polish; summaries in English and Russian) irreg., vol.9, 1990. price varies. (Gdanskie Towarzystwo Naukowe) Ossolineum, Publishing House of the Polish Academy of Sciences, Rynek 9, 50-106 Wroclaw, Poland. TEL 48-71-386-25. FAX 48-71-448-103. TELEX 0712771 OSS PL. (Dist. by: Ars Polona-Ruch, Krakowskie Przedmiescie 7, Warsaw, Poland) Ed. E. Breza. circ. 950. **Document type:** monographic series.

PORTUGAL - MAGAZIN. see *POLITICAL SCIENCE*

526 549 NO ISSN 0804-2233
▼**POSISJON.** 1993. fortn. NOK 350 in the Nordic countries; elsewhere NOK 425. (Norges Kartteknikse Forbund) Scandinavian University Press, P.O. Box 2959 Toeyen, N-0608 Oslo, Norway. TEL 47-22-57-54-00. FAX 47-22-57-53-53. Ed. Knut T. Pettersen. **Document type:** trade publication.
  Description: Presents articles within the field of mapping, geodata and information systems.

910 US ISSN 1060-5851
G1
POST-SOVIET GEOGRAPHY. (Includes translations) 1960. m. (Sep.-Jun.) $339 (foreign $389). V.H. Winston & Son, Inc., c/o Bellwether Publishing, Ltd., 8640 Guilford Rd., Ste. 200, Columbia, MD 21046. TEL 410-290-3870. FAX 410-290-8726. Ed. Chauncy Harris. bk.rev.; abstr.; bibl.; charts; index. circ. 650. (back issues avail.; reprint service avail. from CCC) **Indexed:** Amer.Bibl.Slavic & E.Eur.Stud., ASCA, Bibl.& Ind.Geol., Bibl.Cart., Curr.Adv.Ecol.Sci., Curr.Cont., Excerp.Med., Geo.Abstr, Meteor.& Geoastrophys.Abstr., P.A.I.S., Popul.Ind., SSCI. **Document type:** academic/scholarly publication.
—BLDSC (6559.700000); Faxon; UnCover; SWETS. **CCC.**
  Former titles (until 1992): Soviet Geography; Soviet Geography - Review and Translation (ISSN 0038-5417)

GEOGRAPHY

910   PL   ISSN 0032-6143
G1
POZNAJ SWIAT;* magazyn geograficzny. 1947. m. $8.40. Polskie Towarzystwo Geograficzne, Plac Uniwersytecki 1, 50-137 Wroclaw, Poland. (Dist. by: Ars Polona-Ruch, Krakowskie Przedmiescie 7, Warsaw, Poland) Ed. T. Lenczowski. charts; illus.; index. circ. 90,000. **Indexed:** GeoRef.

POZNANSKIE TOWARZYSTWO PRZYJACIOL NAUK. KOMISJA GEOGRAFICZNO-GEOLOGICZNA. PRACE. see *EARTH SCIENCES — Geology*

910 371.3 375   GW   ISSN 0171-5178
G72
PRAXIS GEOGRAPHIE. 1971. 11/yr. DM.120. Westermann Schulbuchverlag GmbH, Postfach 4938, 38039 Braunschweig, Germany. TEL 0531-708388. FAX 0531-708127. Ed. Barbara Steinhoff. adv.: B&W page DM.2750, color page DM.4400; trim 187 x 258. bibl.; charts; illus. circ. 14,290. **Indexed:** Bibl.Cart. **Document type:** academic/scholarly publication.
    Formerly: Geographische Rundschau. Beiheft.

910   UK   ISSN 0956-277X
PRIMARY GEOGRAPHER. 1989. q. £13 (effective 1993-1994). Geographical Association, 343 Fulwood Rd., Sheffield S10 3BP, England. TEL 0742-670666. FAX 0742-670688. Ed. Wendy Morgan. **Document type:** academic/scholarly publication.
    Description: Covers teaching topic ideas and information for the teacher of children ages 5-11.

910   US   ISSN 0033-0124
G3   CODEN: PFGGAC
PROFESSIONAL GEOGRAPHER. N.S. 1949. q. $56.50 (foreign $101.50). (Association of American Geographers) Basil Blackwell Inc., 238 Main St., Cambridge, MA 02142. TEL 617-547-7110. FAX 617-547-0789. Ed. Dennis Lord. adv.: page $450; trim 6 x 9. bk.rev.; bibl.; charts; maps; index. circ. 7,900. (also avail. in microform from UMI,KTO; reprint service avail. from UMI,KTO) **Indexed:** Agri.Eng.Abstr., Amer.Bibl.Slavic & E.Eur.Stud., Asian-Pac.Econ.Lit., Bibl.& Ind.Geol., Bibl.Cart., Curr.Adv.Ecol.Sci., Curr.Cont., Energy Ind., Energy Info.Abstr., Forest.Abstr., Geo.Abstr., High.Educ.Curr.Aware.Bull., Meteor.& Geostrophys.Abstr., Rural Devel.Abstr., Rural Recreat.Tour.Abstr., Sage Pub.Admin.Abstr., Sage Urb.Stud.Abstr., Soc.Sci.Ind., Soils & Fert., SSCI, World Agri.Econ.& Rural Sociol.Abstr.
    —BLDSC (6859.000000); Faxon; UnCover; SWETS; UMI. **CCC.**
    Description: A forum for new ideas, alternative viewpoints, and debates with emphasis on questions and problems of broad interest to geographers.

625.72   US   ISSN 0278-1425
TA501
PROFESSIONAL SURVEYOR. 1981. bi-m. $10. American Surveyors Publishing Co., 2300 Ninth St. S., Ste. 501, Arlington, VA 22204-2300. TEL 703-892-0733. FAX 703-920-3652. Ed. Nick Harrison. adv.; bk.rev.; circ. 54,725 (controlled). **Document type:** trade publication.
    Description: For readers who have a professional or personal interest in land surveying, mapping, civil engineering and directly related fields.

910   UK   ISSN 0309-1325
GF1
PROGRESS IN HUMAN GEOGRAPHY; an international review of geographical work in the social sciences and humanities. 1976. 4/yr. £60($99) to individuals; institutions £110 ($170) (effective 1994). Edward Arnold (Subsidiary of: Hodder Headline plc), Mill Rd., Dunton Green, Sevenoaks, Kent TN13 2YA, England. TEL 0732-450111. FAX 0732-461321. (Subscr. to: Turpin Distribution Services Ltd., Blackhorse Rd., Letchworth, Herts. SG6 1HN, England) adv.; bk.rev.; charts; illus.; stat.; index. (back issues avail.) **Indexed:** Br.Archaeol.Abstr., E.I., Environ.Per.Bibl. (1991-), Geo.Abstr., I D A, Sage Urb.Stud.Abstr., SSCI. **Document type:** academic/scholarly publication.
    —BLDSC (6868.437500); Faxon; UnCover; SWETS; UMI. **CCC.**
    Description: Provides an authoritative and critical appraisal of developments in this rapidly advancing field.

910.02   UK   ISSN 0309-1333
G1   CODEN: PPGEEC
PROGRESS IN PHYSICAL GEOGRAPHY; an international review of geographical work in the natural and environmental sciences. 1976. 4/yr. £60($99) to individuals; institutions £110 ($170) (effective 1994). Edward Arnold (Subsidiary of: Hodder Headline plc), Mill Rd., Dunton Green, Sevenoaks, Kent TN13 2YA, England. TEL 0732-450111. FAX 0732-461321. (Subscr. to: Turpin Distribution Services Ltd., Blackhorse Rd., Letchworth, Herts. SG6 1HN, England) adv.; bk.rev.; bibl.; charts; illus.; stat.; index. (back issues avail.) **Indexed:** Agroforest.Abstr., Curr.Tit.Ocean, Deep Sea Res.& Oceanogr.Abstr., Environ.Abstr., Environ.Per.Bibl. (1991-), Forest.Abstr., Geo.Abstr., Irr.& Drain.Abstr., Meteor.& Geostrophys.Abstr., Soils & Fert. **Document type:** academic/scholarly publication.
    —BLDSC (6873.300000); CIS; Faxon; UnCover; SWETS; UMI. **CCC.**
    Description: Aims to present the important advances in our understanding of the natural environment.

910   PL   ISSN 0033-2143
G1   CODEN: PRGGAS
PRZEGLAD GEOGRAFICZNY/GEOGRAPHICAL REVIEW. (Text in Polish; summaries in English, Russian; abstracts in Polish) 1918. q. $56. (Polska Akademia Nauk, Instytut Geografii) Wydawnictwo Naukowe P W N, Ul. Miodowa 10, 00-251 Warsaw, Poland. TEL 48-22-312737. FAX 48-22-267163. TELEX 813763 PWN PL. Ed. J. Kostrowicki. bk.rev.; charts; illus.; index. circ. 1,690. **Indexed:** Bibl.Cart., Chem.Abstr., Geo.Abstr. **Document type:** academic/scholarly publication.

QUADERNI DI TOPOGRAFIA ANTICA. see *ARCHAEOLOGY*

910   PL   ISSN 0137-477X
G1   CODEN: QGEODD
QUAESTIONES GEOGRAPHICAE. (Text in English) 1974. a., vol.15-16, 1993. price varies. Adam Mickiewicz University Press, Nowowiejskiego 55, 61-734 Poznan, Poland. TEL 527-380. FAX 61-526425. TELEX 413260 UAMPL. Ed. Stefan Kozarski. circ. 460. (also avail. in microfilm) **Indexed:** Bibl.& Ind.Geol., Geo.Abstr. **Document type:** academic/scholarly publication.
    —BLDSC (7168.116300).
    Description: Contains papers of Polish and foreign authors in the fields of geomorphology, geology, quaternary geology, soil sciences and climatology. Research results are particularly concerned with areas of Poland, Spitzbergen and other European countries.

526.92   NZ
QUANTITY SURVEYOR. q. NZ.$30. New Zealand Institute of Quantity Surveyors, P.O. Box 3635, Wellington, New Zealand. FAX 04-732918. Ed. Karl Bale. adv.; bk.rev. circ. 1,500. **Indexed:** RICS.

QUEBECENSIA. see *HISTORY*

910   UK
QUEEN MARY AND WESTFIELD COLLEGE. DEPARTMENT OF GEOGRAPHY. RESEARCH PAPERS IN GEOGRAPHY. 1974. irreg. price varies. Queen Mary and Westfield College, Department of Geography, Mile End Rd., London E1 4NS, England. FAX 071-975-5500. TELEX 893750. Ed. Geraldene Wharton. circ. 600. **Indexed:** Geo.Abstr. **Document type:** monographic series.
    —BLDSC (6219.780800).
    Former titles: Queen Mary College. Department of Geography. Research Papers in Geography; Queen Mary College. Department of Geography and Earth Science. Occasional Papers (ISSN 0951-7189); Queen Mary College. Department of Geography. Occasional Papers (ISSN 0306-2740)

910   UK
QUEEN MARY AND WESTFIELD COLLEGE. DEPARTMENT OF GEOGRAPHY. WORKING PAPERS. 1988. irreg., no.5, 1990. Queen Mary and Westfield College, Department of Geography, Mile End Rd., London E1 4NS, England. TEL 071-975-5400. **Document type:** monographic series.

RAND MCNALLY COMMERCIAL ATLAS AND MARKETING GUIDE. see *BUSINESS AND ECONOMICS — Marketing And Purchasing*

910   US
RAND MCNALLY GOODE'S WORLD ATLAS. 1922. quadrennial. $28.95. Rand McNally & Co., 8255 N. Central Park, Skokie, IL 60076. TEL 708-673-9100. (Orders to: Box 7600, Chicago, IL 60680) Ed. Edward B. Espenshade, Jr.

914.402   FR   ISSN 0396-9657
RECHERCHES GEOGRAPHIQUES A STRASBOURG. (Text in French; summaries in English, German) 1976. 3/yr. 100 F. Association Geographique d'Alsace, 3 rue de l'Argonne, 67083 Strasbourg cedex, France. Ed. Henri Nonn. circ. 350-500. **Indexed:** Bibl.Cart., Forest.Abstr., Geo.Abstr., I D A, Ref.Zh., Rural Recreat.Tour.Abstr., World Agri.Econ.& Rural Sociol.Abstr.

RECHERCHES PYRENEENNES. see *BIBLIOGRAPHIES*

526   FR   ISSN 0180-9970
RECUEIL DES CORRECTIONS DE CARTES (YEAR). 1978. a. 102 F. Service Hydrographique et Oceanographique de la Marine, 3 av. Octave Gerard, 00300 Armees, France. TEL 98-22-10-80. FAX 98-43-18-11. TELEX HYDRO 940568. (Subscr. to: EPSHOM, B.P. 426, 29275 Brest Cedex, France) **Document type:** government publication.

910   CC   ISSN 1001-5221
REDAI DILI/TROPICAL GEOGRAPHY. (Text in Chinese) q. $16.50. Guangzhou Dili Yanjiusuo - Guangzhou Institute of Geography, No. 100, Xianlie Zhonglu, Guangzhou, Guangdong 510070, People's Republic of China. TEL 775600. (Dist. in US by: China Books & Periodicals, Inc., 2929 24th St., San Francisco, CA 94110. TEL 415-282-2994) Ed. Huang Zhenyuan.
    —UnCover.

910   CN   ISSN 0228-5851
REGINA GEOGRAPHICAL STUDIES. (Each study has distinctive title) 1977. irreg., latest 1988. price varies. University of Regina, Department of Geography, Regina, Sask. S4S 0A2, Canada. TEL 306-585-4222. FAX 306-585-4815. **Indexed:** Geo.Abstr.
    —BLDSC (7336.565000).

910   SZ   ISSN 0034-3293
DQ841.J9   CODEN: RGBAAW
REGIO BASILIENSIS; Basler Zeitschrift fuer Geographie/Revue de Geographie de Bale. (Text in French and German) 1959. 3/yr. 42 SFr. Verlag Wepf und Co., Eisengasse 5, CH-4001 Basel, Switzerland. TEL 061-2617574. FAX 061-2613597. bk.rev.; bibl.; charts; illus.; index, cum.index. **Indexed:** Bibl.Cart., Bibl.& Ind.Geol. **Document type:** academic/scholarly publication.

RELIGION IN EASTERN EUROPE. see *RELIGIONS AND THEOLOGY*

526 614.7   US   ISSN 0034-4257
QE33   CODEN: RSEEA7
REMOTE SENSING OF ENVIRONMENT. 1969. 12/yr. (in 4 vols.). $995 to institutions (foreign $1070) (effective 1994). Elsevier Science Inc., 655 Ave. of the Americas, New York, NY 10010. TEL 212-989-5800. FAX 212-633-3990. TELEX 420643 AEP Ul. Ed. Marvin Bauer. adv.; bk.rev. (reprint service avail. from SWZ) **Indexed:** Agri.Eng.Abstr., Bibl.& Ind.Geol., Bibl.Cart., Biol.Abstr., Comput.Rev., Curr.Adv.Ecol.Sci., Curr.Cont., Deep Sea Res.& Oceanogr.Abstr., Energy Ind., Energy Info.Abstr., Eng.Ind., Environ.Abstr., Environ.Per.Bibl. (1974-), Excerp.Med., Field Crop Abstr., Forest.Abstr., Forest Prod.Abstr., Geo.Abstr., Herb.Abstr., INSPEC, Int.Aerosp.Abstr., Irr.& Drain.Abstr., Maize Abstr., Meteor.& Geostrophys.Abstr., Ocean.Abstr., Petrol.Abstr., Pollut.Abstr., Ref.Zh., Rice Abstr., Sci.Abstr., Sel.Water Res.Abstr., Soils & Fert., Soyabean Abstr., Triticale Abstr. **Document type:** academic/scholarly publication.
    —BLDSC (7356.820000); EI; Faxon; UnCover; SWETS. **CCC.**
    Description: Serves the remote sensing community with the publication of scientific and technical results on theory, experiments, and applications of remote sensing of earth resources and environment.
    Refereed Serial

910 550   CC   ISSN 1004-0323
REMOTE SENSING TECHNOLOGY AND APPLICATION. 1986. q. Y16. Zhongguo Kexueyuan, Lanzhou Wenxian Qingbao Zhongxin, 236 Tianshui Rd., Lanzhou, Gansu Province 730000, People's Republic of China. TEL 86-931-25317. FAX 86-931-4181667. Ed. Liu Quangen. **Document type:** academic/scholarly publication.
   Description: Introduces the latest developments and trends in remote-sensing technology, and its applications in China.

915.12   US   ISSN 1001-4179
RENMIN CHANGJIANG/PEOPLE'S YANGTZE RIVER. (Text in Chinese) m. $36. China Books & Periodicals, Inc., 2929 24th St., San Francisco, CA 94110. TEL 415-282-2994. FAX 415-282-0994.

915.11 627   CC   ISSN 1000-1379
RENMIN HUANG HE/PEOPLE'S YELLOW RIVER. (Text in Chinese) 1979. bi-m. $20.30. Shuili Bu, Huang He Shuili Weiyuanhui, 11 Jinshui Lu, Zhengzhou, Henan 450003, People's Republic of China. TEL 22971. (Dist. in US by: China Books & Periodicals, Inc., 2929 24th St., San Francisco, CA 94110. TEL 415-282-2994)

910   FR
REPERTOIRE DES GEOGRAPHES FRANCAIS. 1969. quadrennial, latest 1994. 245 F. Centre National de la Recherche Scientifique, Laboratoire Intergeo, 191 rue Saint-Jacques, 75005 Paris, France. TEL 1-43-29-79-93. FAX 1-43-29-65-29. **Document type:** directory.
   Formerly (until 1978): Annuaire des Geographes de la France et de l'Afrique Francophone (ISSN 0066-2844)

910   US
RESEARCH IN CONTEMPORARY AND APPLIED GEOGRAPHY: A DISCUSSION SERIES; a discussion series. 1977. a. $11 to individuals; libraries $16. State University of New York at Binghamton, Department of Geography, Box 6000, Binghamton, NY 13902-6000. TEL 607-777-2755. Ed. John Frazier. circ. 100. **Indexed:** Geo.Abstr. **Document type:** academic/scholarly publication.

910   AT
RESEARCH PAPERS IN GEOGRAPHY. 1975. irreg. price varies. University of Newcastle, Department of Geography, Newcastle, N.S.W. 2308, Australia. TEL 6149-215080. FAX 6149-215877. TELEX NEWUN AA 28194. Ed. Phillip O'Neill. circ. 100. **Indexed:** Geo.Abstr. **Document type:** academic/scholarly publication.

914.38   PL   ISSN 0137-1142
Q115
RESULTS OF INVESTIGATIONS OF THE POLISH SCIENTIFIC SPITSBERGEN EXPEDITIONS. (Subseries of: Acta Universitatis Wratislaviensis) 1975. irreg. price varies. (Uniwersytet Wroclawski) Wydawnictwo Uniwersyteckiego, Pl. Uniwersytecki 9-13, 50-137 Wroclaw, Poland. (Dist. by: Ksiegarnia Uniwersyteckiego, Pl. Uniwersytecki 9-13, 50-137 Wroclaw, Poland) **Document type:** academic/scholarly publication.

910   BL   ISSN 0034-723X
F2501   CODEN: RBGGA6
REVISTA BRASILEIRA DE GEOGRAFIA/BRAZILIAN GEOGRAPHIC JOURNAL. (Text in Portuguese; summaries in English) 1939. q. $120. Fundacao Instituto Brasileiro de Geografia e Estatistica, Av. Franklin Roosevelt, 166 Centro, CEP 20021-120 Rio de Janeiro, Brazil. TEL 021-284-7690. FAX 021-228-9575. TELEX 2139128. (Subscr. to: Divisao de Comercializacao e Promocao, Rua General Canbarro, 666, Bloco B 2o andar, Maracana, CEP 20271-201 Rio de Janeiro, Brazil) bibl.; charts; illus.; stat. circ. 1,000. (back issues avail.) **Indexed:** Biol.Abstr., Bull.Signal., Hisp.Amer.Per.Ind. **Document type:** government publication.

526   MX   ISSN 0080-2085
GA101   CODEN: RECAAN
REVISTA CARTOGRAFICA. (Text in English, French, Portuguese, Spanish) 1952. s-a. $34 (C. & N. America $38; S. America & Europe $43; Asia $48). Instituto Panamericano de Geografia e Historia, Ex-Arzobispado 29, Col. Observatorio, Deleg. Miguel Hidalgo, 11860 Mexico, D.F., Mexico. TEL 525-277-5888. FAX 525-271-6172. (Subscr. to: IPGH, Dpeto. de Distribucion y Ventas, Apdo. 18879, 11870 Mexico DF, Mexico) Ed. Alvaro Gonzalez F. bk.rev.; index, cum.index: nos.7-13, 16-33. **Indexed:** Bibl.& Ind.Geol. **Document type:** academic/scholarly publication.
—BLDSC (7847.400000).

914.6 910   SP   ISSN 0210-6000
REVISTA CATALANA DE GEOGRAFIA. (Text in Catalan; summaries in English and Spanish) 1978. 3/yr. 2548 ptas. Institut Cartografic de Catalunya, Carrer de Balmes 209-211, 08006 Barcelona, Spain. FAX 34-3-2188959. TELEX 98471 ICCBE. adv.; bk.rev.

910   SP   ISSN 0212-8594
REVISTA DE ESTUDIOS ANDALUCES. 1983. s-a. price varies. Universidad de Sevilla, Departamentos de Geografia, Economia Aplicada, Servicio de Publicaciones, Valparaiso 5, 41013 Seville, Spain. TEL 954-228071. FAX 954-232245.

910   SP   ISSN 0048-7708
G1
REVISTA DE GEOGRAFIA. 1967. s-a. $10. Universidad de Barcelona, Departamento de Geografia, Barcelona 7, Spain. Ed.Bd. adv.; bk.rev.; index. circ. 1,000. **Indexed:** Geo.Abstr., Ind.SST.

910   BL   ISSN 0101-9457
    CODEN: REVGD3
REVISTA DE GEOGRAFIA. (Text in Portuguese; summaries in English and Portuguese) 1982. a. $30 or exchange basis. Universidade Estadual Paulista, Av. Vicente Ferreira, 1278, Caixa Postal 603, 17515-901 Marilia SP, Brazil. TEL 0144 33-1844. FAX 0144-22-2504. TELEX 111 9016 UJME BR. Ed.Bd. adv.; bk.rev.; charts; illus.; stat. circ. 1,000. **Indexed:** Curr. Cont., Ecol.Abstr., Geo.Abstr., Geophys.Abstr., Mineral.Abstr., Ref.Zh., SSCI. **Document type:** academic/scholarly publication.

917.2   MX   ISSN 0187-6201
REVISTA DE GEOGRAFIA. irreg. Mex.$7500($2.50) Instituto Nacional de Estadistica, Geografia e Informatica, Secretaria de Programacion y Presupuesto, Prol. Heroe de Nacozari 2301 Sur, Puerta 11, Acceso, 20270 Aguascalientes Ags., Mexico. TEL 49-18-19-48. FAX 491-807-39. circ. 1,000.

914.6   SP   ISSN 0213-9480
REVISTA DE GEOGRAFIA CANARIA. 1984. a. $15 to individuals; institutions $20. Universidad de Laguna, Facultad de Geografia e Historia. Departamento de Geografia, Secretariado de Publicaciones, San Agustin, 30, 38201 La Laguna-Tenerife, Islas Canarias, Spain. TEL 922-25-81-27. adv.

910   BL
REVISTA DE GEOGRAFIA E ENSINO. 1982. 4/yr. $12. Universidade Federal de Minas Gerais, Departamento de Geografia, Campus Pampulha, Av. Antonia Carlos, 6627, CEP 31270-Belo Horizonte, Brazil. TEL 031-4415133. Dir. David Marcio Rogrigues. bk.rev. circ. 2,000.

REVISTA DOCPOP; resumos sobre populacao no Brasil. see *POPULATION STUDIES*

910   MX   ISSN 0556-6630
G1
REVISTA GEOGRAFICA. (Text in English, French, Portuguese, Spanish) 1941. s-a. $34 (C. & N. America $38; S. America & Europe $43; Asia $48). Instituto Panamericano de Geografia e Historia, Ex-Arzobispado, 29, Col. Observatorio, Deleg. Miguel Hidalgo, 11860 Mexico, D.F., Mexico. TEL 525-277-5888. FAX 525-271-6271. (Subscr. to: IPGH, Depto. de Distribucion y Ventas, Apdo. 18879, 11870 Mexico DF, Mexico) Ed. Paul Denis. bk.rev.; bibl.; charts; illus.; stat. (tabloid format; also avail. in microfiche from CIS; reprint service avail. from UMI) **Indexed:** Geo.Abstr., GeoRef., Hisp.Amer.Per.Ind., I D A, IIS, P.A.I.S.For.Lang.Ind. **Document type:** academic/scholarly publication.
—UMI.

917.2   CR   ISSN 1011-484X
REVISTA GEOGRAFICA DE AMERICA CENTRAL. (Text in Spanish; summaries in English, French, Spanish) 1974. s-a. Universidad Nacional "Campus Omar Dengo", Escuela de Ciencias Geograficas, Apdo. 86, 3000 Heredia, Costa Rica. TEL 37-28-57. Ed. Dionisio Alfaro Rodriguez. bk.rev. circ. 500.

910   CL   ISSN 0034-9577
REVISTA GEOGRAFICA DE VALPARAISO. 1967. a. $40. (Universidad Catolica de Valparaiso, Instituto de Geografia) Ediciones Universitarias de Valparaiso, Casilla 1415, Valparaiso, Chile. TEL 032-252900. FAX 032-212746. TELEX 230389 UCVAL CL. Dir. Hugo Figueroa P. charts; illus. circ. 300. **Document type:** academic/scholarly publication.

910   VE
REVISTA GEOGRAFICA VENEZOLANA. 1959. s-a. price varies. Universidad de los Andes, Instituto de Geografia y Conservacion de Recursos Naturales, Via los Chorras de Milla, Codigo Postal 5101, Merida, Venezuela. bk.rev. circ. 1,500. **Indexed:** Geo.Abstr.
   Formerly: Revista Geografica.

910   AG   ISSN 0326-0658
REVISTA PATAGONICA. 1981. q. Arg.$140000($30) (Asociacion Geografica de la Patagonia) Editorial Publicaciones Especializadas S.R.L., Maipu 459, 7th E., 1006 Buenos Aires, Argentina. TEL 322-5701. adv.; bk.rev. circ. 4,000.
   Description: Offers information on the human, historical and cultural facts of Patagonian Argentine area. Covers its resourses, natural beauties, tourist attractions.

REVISTA TIEMPO Y ESPACIO. see *HISTORY*

910   BE   ISSN 0770-0717
REVUE BELGE DE GEOGRAPHIE. 1876. irreg. (3-7/yr.). 1500 BEF to non-members (effective 1993). Societe Royale Belge de Geographie, Bld. du Triomphe, CP 246, B-1050 Brussels, Belgium. TEL 02-650-50-73. FAX 02-650-50-92. Ed. Christian Vandermotten. bk.rev.; charts; illus.; Bibl.& Ind.Geol. circ. 800. **Indexed:** Anthropol.Lit., Bibl.Cart., Geo.Abstr. **Document type:** academic/scholarly publication.
—BLDSC (7891.800000).
   Formerly: Societe Royale Belge de Geographie. Bulletin.

REVUE D'AUVERGNE. see *HISTORY — History Of Europe*

REVUE D'ECOLOGIE ALPINE. see *BIOLOGY — Botany*

910   FR   ISSN 0035-1121
DC611.A553   CODEN: RVGAAQ
REVUE DE GEOGRAPHIE ALPINE. 1913. q. 250 F. to individuals; institutions 300 F. Association Revue de Geographie Alpine, 17 rue Maurice Gignoux, 38031 Grenoble Cedex, France. TEL 76-63-59-41. FAX 76-87-82-43. Ed. Francoise Vigny. adv.; bk.rev.; charts; illus.; maps; index. circ. 1,000. **Indexed:** Bibl.& Ind.Geol., Bibl.Cart., Geo.Abstr., I D A, Rural Recreat.Tour.Abstr., World Agri.Econ.& Rural Sociol.Abstr. **Document type:** academic/scholarly publication.
—UnCover; SWETS.
   Description: Covers the geography, culture, and economy of the mountainous regions.

910   FR   ISSN 0035-113X
    CODEN: RVGLAP
REVUE DE GEOGRAPHIE DE LYON. 1925. q. 230 F.($40) (effective 1991). Association des Amis de la Revue de Geographie de Lyon, 74 rue Pasteur, 69007 Lyon, France. Ed. J. Bethemont. adv.; bk.rev.; abstr.; charts; illus.; index, cum.index: 1946-1955, 1956-1965, 1966-1974, 1975-84. circ. 850. **Indexed:** Bibl.& Ind.Geol.

910   MR   ISSN 0035-1156
DT301   CODEN: RGMCBQ
REVUE DE GEOGRAPHIE DU MAROC. (Text in French; summaries in Arabic, English and French) 1962. s-a. $48. (Association Nationale des Geographes Marocains) Librairie Internationale, Boite Postale 302, Rabat, Morocco. TEL 212-7-750183. FAX 212-7-767447. bk.rev.; abstr.; bibl.; illus.; cum.index. circ. 1,300. **Indexed:** Bibl.& Ind.Geol., Documentatieblad. **Document type:** academic/scholarly publication.

GEOGRAPHY

910 FR ISSN 0035-3213
CODEN: RGGEB2
REVUE GEOGRAPHIQUE DE L'EST. (Text in French; summaries in English, German) 1960. q. 300 F. (foreign 350 F.) Presses Universitaires de Nancy, 25 rue Baron Louis, 54001 Nancy Cedex, France. TEL 83-37-37-65. Ed.Bd. adv.; bk.rev.; index. circ. 800. (back issues avail.) **Indexed:** Bibl.& Ind.Geol., Forest.Abstr., Geo.Abstr.
—BLDSC (7917.340000).
Description: Discusses important aspects of geographical conditions impacting the history of the respective region.

914 FR ISSN 0035-3221
DC611.P98 CODEN: RGPSAK
REVUE GEOGRAPHIQUE DES PYRENEES ET DU SUD-OUEST. 1930. q. 250 F. (outside Europe 270 F.) (effective 1994). (Universite de Toulouse II (le Mirail)) Presses Universitaires du Mirail, 56 rue du Taur, 31000 Toulouse, France. TEL 61-22-58-31. FAX 61-21-84-20. Ed.Bd. bk.rev.; bibl.; charts; illus.; cum.index every 10 yrs. circ. 1,500. (back issues avail.) **Indexed:** Bibl.& Ind.Geol., Bibl.Cart., Forest.Abstr., Geo.Abstr.
—BLDSC (7917.375000).
Description: For those who wish to know geography as well as to understand the relationship between societies and their locales.

551 RM ISSN 1220-5311
QE287 CODEN: RGGGB8
REVUE ROUMAINE DE GEOGRAPHIE. (Text in English, French, German and Russian) 1957. a. $32. (Academia Romana) Editura Academiei Romane, Calea Victoriei 125, 79717 Bucharest, Rumania. (Dist. by: Rompresfilatelia, Calea Grivitei 64-66, P.O. Box 12-201, 78104 Bucharest, Rumania) Ed. Virgil Ianovici. bk.rev.; charts; illus.; index. **Indexed:** Bibl.& Ind.Geol., Bibl.Cart., Chem.Abstr., Sel.Water Res.Abstr.
Formerly (until 1990): Revue Roumaine de Geologie, Geophysique et Geographie. Geographie (ISSN 0556-8099); Which supersedes in part (in 1963): Revue de Geologie et de Geographie (ISSN 1220-1855)

910.03 TI ISSN 0330-9924
REVUE TUNISIENNE DE GEOGRAPHIE. 1978. s-a. Faculte des Lettres et Sciences Humaines de Tunis, 94 Bd. du 9 Avril, Tunis, Tunisia. Ed. A. Oueslah. **Indexed:** Documentatieblad. **Document type:** academic/scholarly publication.

621.367 JA
RIMOTO SENSHINGU SHINPOJUMU SHIRYO/PAPERS OF REMOTE SENSING SYMPOSIUM. (Text in Japanese) 1975. a. Keisoku Jido Seigyo Gakkai - Society of Instrument and Control Engineers, 35-28-303, Hongo 1-chome, Bunkyo-ku, Tokyo 113, Japan.

910 IT ISSN 0035-6697
G1
RIVISTA GEOGRAFICA ITALIANA. (Text in Italian; summaries in English) 1893. q. L.50000 (foreign L.55000) (effective 1994). (Societa di Studi Geografici di Firenze) Pacini Editore s.r.l., Via A. Gherardesca 1, 56014 Ospedaletto (Pisa), Italy. TEL 050-982439. FAX 050-983906. adv.; bk.rev.; bibl.; charts; illus.; index. (reprint service avail. from SWZ) **Indexed:** Bibl.Cart., Rural Recreat.Tour.Abstr., World Agri.Econ. & Rural Sociol.Abstr.

910 DK ISSN 0106-3545
ROSKILDE UNIVERSITETSCENTER. DEPARTMENT OF GEOGRAPHY, SOCIAL ECONOMICS AND COMPUTER SCIENCE. KOMPENDIUM. 1977. irreg. free. Roskilde Universitetscenter, Department of Geography, Social Economics and Computer Science, Postboks 260, DK-4000 Roskilde, Denmark.

910 DK ISSN 0106-2778
H67.R744
ROSKILDE UNIVERSITETSCENTER. DEPARTMENT OF GEOGRAPHY, SOCIAL ECONOMICS AND COMPUTER SCIENCE. MEDDELELSER. no.13, 1984. irreg. free. Roskilde Universitetscenter, Department of Geography, Social Economics and Computer Science, Postboks 260, 4000 Roskilde, Denmark. illus.
—BLDSC (5477.500000).

910 DK ISSN 0106-3537
ROSKILDE UNIVERSITETSCENTER. DEPARTMENT OF GEOGRAPHY, SOCIAL ECONOMICS AND COMPUTER SCIENCE. RESEARCH REPORTS. no.17, 1981. irreg. price varies. Roskilde Universitetscenter, Department of Geography, Social Economics and Computer Science, Postboks 260, DK-4000 Roskilde, Denmark.
—BLDSC (4012.159600).

910 DK ISSN 0106-5920
ROSKILDE UNIVERSITETSCENTER. DEPARTMENT OF GEOGRAPHY, SOCIAL ECONOMICS AND COMPUTER SCIENCE. WORKING PAPERS. no.24, 1981. irreg. free. Roskilde Universitetscenter, Department of Geography Social, Economics and Computer Science, Postbox 260, DK-4000 Roskilde, Denmark. illus.
—BLDSC (1587.910000).

ROTENBURGER SCHRIFTEN. see HISTORY — History Of Europe

ROYAL ASIATIC SOCIETY. MALAYSIAN BRANCH. JOURNAL. see HISTORY — History Of Asia

RURAL VIRGINIA VOICE. see AGRICULTURE

526.8 UK ISSN 0036-1984
GA101.S62
S U C BULLETIN. 1967. s-a. £20. Society of Cartographers, Middlesex University, Queensway, Enfield, Middlesex EN3 4SF, England. TEL 081-362-5355. FAX 081-805-0702. TELEX 8954762. Ed. Steve Chilton. adv.; bk.rev.; charts; illus. circ. 500. (also avail. in microform) **Indexed:** Bibl.& Ind.Geol., Bibl.Cart., Geo.Abstr., Soils & Fert. **Document type:** bulletin.

910 CN ISSN 0226-2169
LE SAGAMIEN. 1980. irreg., vol.5, 1985. Can.$4. Universite du Quebec a Chichoutimi, Laboratoires de Geographie, 555 Blvd. de l'Universite, Chicoutimi, Que. G7H 2B1, Canada. TEL 418-545-5330. FAX 418-545-5012. Ed. Prof. Majella-J. Gauthier. bk.rev. circ. 250. (also avail. in microfilm)

910 630 CN ISSN 0831-8093
SAINT MARY'S UNIVERSITY. ATLANTIC REGION GEOGRAPHICAL STUDIES. 1977. irreg. price varies. Saint Mary's University, Department of Geography, Halifax, NS B3H 3C3, Canada. TEL 902-420-5737. FAX 902-420-5561. Ed. Douglas Day. circ. 200. (back issues avail.) **Document type:** monographic series.
—BLDSC (1765.928000).
Description: Presents research on the Atlantic region of Canada.

910 550 CN ISSN 0831-8107
SAINT MARY'S UNIVERSITY. OCCASIONAL PAPERS IN GEOGRAPHY. 1977. irreg. price varies. Saint Mary's University, Department of Geography, Halifax, NS B3H 3C3, Canada. TEL 902-420-5737. FAX 902-420-5561. Ed. Hugh Millward. circ. 200. (back issues avail.) **Document type:** monographic series.

910 624 CN ISSN 0832-6266
SAINT MARY'S UNIVERSITY. STUDIES IN MARINE AND COASTAL GEOGRAPHY. (Text in English, French) 1982. a. price varies. Saint Mary's University, Department of Geography, Halifax, NS B3H 3C3, Canada. TEL 902-420-5737. FAX 902-420-5561. Ed. Peter Ricketts. circ. 200. (back issues avail.) **Document type:** proceedings.
Description: Papers presented by members of the Marine Studies and Coastal Zone Management Study Group at annual meetings of the Canadian Association of Geographers.

910 AU
SALZBURGER GEOGRAPHISCHE ARBEITEN. (Text in German; summaries in English) 1969. irreg., no.27, 1993. S.200. Universitaet Salzburg, Institut fuer Geographie, Hellbrunnerstr. 34, A-5020 Salzburg, Austria. TEL 0662-8044-5200. Ed.Bd. **Document type:** monographic series.

910 AU
SALZBURGER GEOGRAPHISCHE MATERIALIEN; Salzburger beitraege zur Geographie des Mediterraneen Raumes. (Text in German; summaries in English and Greek) 1968. irreg., no.20, 1993. S.250. Universitaet Salzburg, Institut fuer Geographie, Hellbrunnerstr. 34, A-5020 Salzburg, Austria. TEL 0662-8044-5200. Ed.Bd. circ. 350. (back issues avail.) **Document type:** monographic series.
Formerly: Salzburger Exkursionsberichte.

SANKT-PETERBURGSKII UNIVERSITET. SERIYA GEOLOGIYA I GEOGRAFIYA. see EARTH SCIENCES — Geology

SCHLERN; Zeitschrift fuer Suedtiroler Landeskunde. see ART

DER SCHULGEOGRAPH. see EDUCATION — Teaching Methods And Curriculum

910.02 378.002 US ISSN 0734-8185
SCHWENDEMAN'S DIRECTORY OF COLLEGE GEOGRAPHY OF THE UNITED STATES. 1949. a. $5. Geographical Studies and Research Center, Roark 201, Eastern Kentucky Univ., Richmond, KY 40475-3129. TEL 606-622-1418. FAX 606-622-1020. Ed. W.J. Walker. adv. circ. 400. (back issues avail.) **Document type:** directory.
Description: Lists course offerings and enrollment figures for geography in responding institutions of higher education.

910 UK
SCIENTIFIC EXPLORATION SOCIETY. NEWSLETTER. 1969. 10/yr. £3. Daily Telegraph Ltd., 135 Fleet St, London EC4P 4BS, England. Ed. Richard Snailham. circ. 250. (looseleaf format) **Document type:** newsletter.

910 UK ISSN 0036-9225
G1 CODEN: SGGMA2
SCOTTISH GEOGRAPHICAL MAGAZINE. 1885. 3/yr. $50. Royal Scottish Geographical Society, Graham Hills Bldg., 40 George St., Glasgow G1 1QE, Scotland. TEL 041-552-3330. FAX 041-552-3331. Ed. A.S. Mather. adv.; bk.rev.; bibl.; charts; illus.; maps; cum.index: 1885-1943, 1935-1965. circ. 2,500. (also avail. in microfilm from UMI; reprint service avail. from UMI) **Indexed:** Amer.Hist.& Life, ASCA, Asian-Pac.Econ.Lit., Bibl.Cart., Biol.Abstr., Br.Archaeol.Abstr., Br.Geol.Lit., Br.Hum.Ind., Curr.Adv.Ecol.Sci., Curr.Cont., Deep Sea Res.& Oceanogr.Abstr., Geo.Abstr., Hist.Abstr., I D A, Rural Devel.Abstr, Rural Recreat.Tour.Abstr., SSCI, World Agri.Econ.& Rural Sociol.Abstr. **Document type:** academic/scholarly publication.
—BLDSC (8210.000000); Faxon; UnCover; SWETS; UMI.

526.982 621.367 JA ISSN 0285-5844
SHASHIN SOKURYO TO RIMOTO SENSHINGU/PHOTOGRAMMETRY AND REMOTE SENSING. (Text in Japanese; summaries in Japanese) 1961. bi-m. 7,000 Yen. Nihon Shashin Sokuryo Gakkai - Japan Society of Photogrammetry and Remote Sensing, Dai-1 Honan Bldg., 2-8-17, Minami-Ikebukuro, Toshima-ku, Tokyo 171, Japan. FAX 81-3-3984-7402. **Indexed:** Jap.Per.Ind. **Document type:** academic/scholarly publication.

SIEBENSTERN; Vereinszeitschrift fuer Heimatpflege, Heimatkunde, Wandern und Naturschutz. see CONSERVATION

916.64 SL ISSN 0583-239X
SIERRA LEONE GEOGRAPHICAL JOURNAL. Title varies, no.1-10: Sierra Leone Geographical Association. Bulletin. 1967. a. Le.2.50($3) Sierra Leone Geographical Association, c/o Fourah Bay College Bookshop, Freetown, Sierra Leone. Ed.Bd. adv.; bk.rev.; charts.

GEOGRAPHY

910   SI   ISSN 0129-7619
G515
SINGAPORE JOURNAL OF TROPICAL GEOGRAPHY. 1980. s-a. $30. National University of Singapore, Department of Geography, Kent Ridge, Singapore 0511, Singapore. FAX 7773091. Ed. Victor R. Savage. bibl.; charts; maps; stat. circ. 660. **Indexed:** Abstr.Rural Dev.Trop., ASCA, Asian-Pac.Econ.Lit., Bibl.& Ind.Geol., Biol.Abstr., Curr.Adv.Ecol.Sci., Curr.Cont.Africa, Curr.Cont., E.I., Field Crop Abstr., Geo.Abstr., Herb.Abstr., I D A, Popul.Ind., Rural Devel.Abstr., Rural Recreat.Tour.Abstr., Soils & Fert., SSCI, World Agri.Econ.& Rural Sociol.Abstr. **Document type:** academic/scholarly publication.
—BLDSC (8285.464700); UnCover; SWETS.
Supersedes in part: Journal of Tropical Geography (ISSN 0022-5290)

970 980   US
SKYLINE (BROOKLYN); committed to a greater appreciation of the city of New York. 1989. bi-m. $19.95. Skyline of New York Publications, Inc., 857 Carroll St., Brooklyn, NY 11215. TEL 212-807-5511. Ed. William J. Lawrence. adv.; bk.rev.
Description: Deals with history of the city of New York.

SLOVAK STUDIES ASSOCIATION. NEWSLETTER. see HISTORY — History Of Europe

910   AG   ISSN 0325-2698
SOCIEDAD ARGENTINA DE ESTUDIOS GEOGRAFICOS. BOLETIN. 1931. irreg. $5 per no. Sociedad Argentina de Estudios Geograficos - GAEA, Rodriquez Pena 158, 4, 1020 Buenos Aires, Argentina. TEL 541-40-2076. bk.rev.; circ. controlled. (looseleaf format)

910   AG
SOCIEDAD ARGENTINA DE ESTUDIOS GEOGRAFICOS. CONTRIBUCIONES CIENTIFICAS. 1984. a. $15 per no. Sociedad Argentina de Estudios Geograficos - GAEA, Rodriguez Pena 158, 4, 1020 Buenos Aires, Argentina. TEL 541-402076. circ. 1,000.

SOCIEDAD DE ESTUDIOS VASCOS. CUADERNOS DE SECCION. HISTORIA Y GEOGRAFIA. see HISTORY

SOCIEDAD ECUATORIANA DE INVESTIGACIONES HISTORICAS Y GEOGRAFICAS. MEMORIA. see HISTORY — History Of North And South America

910   CK   ISSN 0037-8577
G5   CODEN: BSGCA5
SOCIEDAD GEOGRAFICA DE COLOMBIA. BOLETIN. 1903. q. Col.$30.($3.) (Sociedad Geografica de Colombia) Eduardo Acevedo Latorre, Ed. & Pub., Apdo. Nal. 2584, Bogota, Colombia. charts; illus.; index. circ. 1,000. **Indexed:** Amer.Hist.& Life, Bibl.& Ind.Geol., Hist.Abstr.

910   PE   ISSN 0037-8585
G5   CODEN: SGLBAS
SOCIEDAD GEOGRAFICA DE LIMA, PERU. BOLETIN. 1891. 9/yr. Sociedad Geografica de Lima, Apdo. 100-1176, Lima 100, Peru. bibl.; charts; illus.; index. **Indexed:** Amer.Hist.& Life, Bibl.& Ind.Geol., Hist.Abstr.

910.2   BL   ISSN 0037-8674
SOCIEDADE BRASILEIRA DE GEOGRAFIA. BOLETIM.* 1950. q. Sociedade Brasileira de Geografia, Praca da Republica, 54, 1 Andar, Rio de Janeiro-GB 20.000 ZC-14, Brazil. bk.rev.; charts.

SOCIEDADE E TERRITORIO. see SOCIOLOGY

910   IT   ISSN 0037-8755
SOCIETA GEOGRAFICA ITALIANA. BOLLETTINO. (Text in Italian; summaries in English) 1868. q. L.50000($100) (foreign L.150000) (effective Jan. 1991). Societa Geografica Italiana, Via della Navicella 12, 00184 Rome, Italy. TEL 06-7008279. FAX 06-7004677. Ed. Piergiorgio Landini. adv.; bk.rev.; abstr.; bibl.; charts; illus.; maps; index. circ. 2,000. **Indexed:** Bibl.Cart., Biol.Abstr., Geo.Abstr. **Document type:** academic/scholarly publication.

778 526 016   IT   ISSN 0392-4424
TA590
SOCIETA ITALIANA DI FOTOGRAMMETRIA E TOPOGRAFIA. BOLLETTINO. (Text in Italian; occasionally in English and French) 1951. q. L.120000 (foreign L.150000). Societa Italiana di Topografia e Fotogrammetria, Piazzale R. Morandi 2, 20121 Milan, Italy. TEL 7012-0350. FAX 70101544. (Subscr. to: Dip. I.I.A.R. Politecnico di Milano, Piazza Leonardo da Vinci 32, 20133 Milan, Italy) Ed. Carlo Monti. adv.; bk.rev.; bibl.; charts; illus.; stat. circ. 2,600. (also avail. in microfilm) **Document type:** academic/scholarly publication.

910   BE   ISSN 0037-8925
G19   CODEN: BSEGA7
SOCIETE BELGE D'ETUDES GEOGRAPHIQUES. BULLETIN/BELGISCHE VERENIGING VOOR AARDRIJKSKUNDIGE STUDIES. TIJDSCHRIFT. (Text in Dutch, English, French, German) 1931. s-a. 1000 BEF to non-members. Societe Belge d'Etudes Geographiques - Belgische Vereniging voor Aardrijkskundige Studies, De Croylaan 42, 3001 Heverlee, Belgium. TEL 32-16-286611. Ed. H. Van der Haegen. bk.rev.; bibl.; charts; illus.; maps; index, cum.index every 10 yrs. circ. 700. **Indexed:** Bibl.& Ind.Geol., E.I., Geo.Abstr., Rural Recreat.Tour.Abstr., Soils & Fert., World Agri.Econ.& Rural Sociol.Abstr. **Document type:** academic/scholarly publication, bulletin.

526.982 526.9   BE   ISSN 0771-7873
TR693.A1
SOCIETE BELGE DE PHOTOGRAMMETRIE - TELEDETECTION ET CARTOGRAPHIE. BULLETIN TRIMESTRIEL. (Text in English, Flemish, French; summaries in English, French) 1931. 4/yr. (in 2 vols., 2 nos./vol.). 450 BEF. Societe Belge de Photogrammetrie-Teledetection et Cartographie, C.A.E.-Tour Finances, Bte. 38, 50 Bd. du Jardin Botanique, B-1010 Brussels, Belgium. TEL 32-2-2103575. Ed. A. Verdin. adv.: bleed 297 x 210. bk.rev.; bibl. circ. 400. **Indexed:** Bibl.& Ind.Geol., Bibl.Cart., Geo.Abstr. **Document type:** bulletin.
Former titles (until 1985): Societe Belge de Photogrammetrie et de Teledectection. Bulletin Trimestriel; (until 1981): Societe Belge de Photogrammetrie. Bulletin Trimestriel (ISSN 0037-8917); (Until 1961): Societe Belge de Photogrammetrie. Bulletin.
Description: Covers remote sensing, map-making, and other subjects of interest to agronomists, archeologists, engineers, architects, and surveyors.
Refereed Serial

910   FR   ISSN 0081-086X
SOCIETE DES EXPLORATEURS ET DES VOYAGEURS FRANCAIS. ANNUAIRE GENERAL. 1962. irreg. membership. Societe des Explorateurs et des Voyageurs Francais, 184 bd. St. Germain, 75006 Paris, France. bk.rev. circ. 2,500. **Document type:** directory.

526.982   FR   ISSN 0244-6014
TR693   CODEN: BSFTDK
SOCIETE FRANCAISE DE PHOTOGRAMMETRIE ET DE TELEDETECTION. BULLETIN. (Text in French; summaries in English, French) 1961. q. 450 F. Societe Francaise de Photogrammetrie et de Teledetection, B.P. 68, 2 ave. Pasteur, 94160 Saint Mande, France. TEL 43-98-80-73. TELEX SMD 21-05-51 F. Ed. Guy Ducher. adv.; bk.rev.; bibl.; illus. circ. 850. **Indexed:** Bibl.& Ind.Geol., Forest.Abstr., Geo.Abstr., Int.Aerosp.Abstr., Sci.Abstr.—EI.
Formerly: Societe Francaise de Photogrammetrie. Bulletin (ISSN 0049-108X)

910   BE   ISSN 0770-7576
SOCIETE GEOGRAPHIQUE DE LIEGE. BULLETIN. (Text in French; summaries in English, French) 1965-1987; resumed. a. 800 BEF (effective 1992). Societe Geographique de Liege, 7, Place du Vingt-Aout, B-4000 Liege, Belgium. TEL 32-41-665324. FAX 32-41-665700. Ed. Emile Merenne. bk.rev.; circ. 650 (controlled). **Indexed:** Geo.Abstr. **Document type:** bulletin.
—BLDSC (2741.200000).
Supersedes: Universite de Liege. Seminaire de Geographie. Travaux; Travaux Geographigues de Liege.

914.4   FR   ISSN 0373-3297
                      CODEN: SLDGA4
SOCIETE LANGUEDOCIENNE DE GEOGRAPHIE. BULLETIN. (Text in French; summaries in French, English) 1872. 2/4yr. 180 F. (foreign 250 F.). Societe Languedocienne de Geographie, Universite Paul Valery, B.P. 5043, 34032 Montpellier Cedex, France. TEL 67-14-23-26. Ed. J.M. Miossec. adv.; bk.rev.; index. circ. 700. **Indexed:** Bibl.& Ind.Geol.
—BLDSC (2745.240000).
Description: Concerned mainly with the analysis of space, land allotment, real estate problems, leisure activities, regional imbalances and social inequalities.

910   BU   ISSN 0324-0525
SOFIISKI UNIVERSITET. GEOLOGO-GEOGRAFSKI FAKULTET. GEOGRAFIIA. GODISNIK. (Text in Bulgarian and Russian; summaries in English, French, German) 1905. irreg., vol.71, 1978. price varies. Publishing House of the Bulgarian Academy of Sciences, Acad. G. Bonchev St., Bldg. 6, 1113 Sofia, Bulgaria. circ. 550. (reprint service avail. from IRC) **Indexed:** Chem.Abstr., Geo.Abstr.

526   JA   ISSN 0038-0830
QB275
SOKUCHI GAKKAISHI/GEODETIC SOCIETY OF JAPAN. JOURNAL. (Text in English or Japanese) 1954. q. 8000 Yen (effective Apr. 1992). Geodetic Society of Japan - Nippon Sokuchi Gakkai, c/o Kokudo Chiri-in - Geographical Survey Institute, Kitazato-1, Tsukuba-shi, Ibaraki-ken 305, Japan. FAX 298-64-1802. Ed. Ryuichi Shichi. bk.rev.; charts; stat. circ. 775. **Indexed:** Bibl.& Ind.Geol., Geo.Abstr., Jap.Per.Ind. **Document type:** academic/scholarly publication.
—BLDSC (4755.800000).
Description: Contains original papers, reviews and reports on all aspects of geodesy and related subjects.

526.9   JA   ISSN 0285-7790
SOKURYO/MONTHLY SURVEYOR MAGAZINE. (Text in Japanese) 1951. m. Nippon Sokuryo Kyokai - Japanese Association of Surveyors, 3-4, Koishikawa 1-chome, Bunkyo-ku, Tokyo 112, Japan. **Indexed:** Jap.Per.Ind.

SOLSTICE: AN ELECTRONIC JOURNAL OF GEOGRAPHY AND MATHEMATICS. see MATHEMATICS

910   SA   ISSN 0378-5327
SOUTH AFRICAN GEOGRAPHER/SUID-AFRIKAANSE GEOGRAAF. (Text in Afrikaans, English; summaries in English) 1957. s-a. R.25($18) to non-members; members R.20. Society for Geography - Vereniging vir Geografie, P.O. Box 2031, Dennesig 7601, South Africa. FAX 27-21-8084336. Ed. I.J. van der Merwe. adv. contact: P.J. Eloff. bk.rev.; abstr.; charts; illus.; cum.index. circ. 1,500. **Indexed:** Geo.Abstr., Ind.S.A.Per. **Document type:** academic/scholarly publication.
—BLDSC (8337.900000).
Formerly: Journal for Geography - Tydskrif vir Aardrykskunde (ISSN 0021-8243)

910   SA   ISSN 0373-6245
G1   CODEN: SGEJAH
SOUTH AFRICAN GEOGRAPHICAL JOURNAL. (Text and summaries in Afrikaans, English) 1917. s-a. $15 to individuals, members; libraries $45 (effective 1993). South African Geographical Society, P.O. Box 128, Wits 2050, South Africa. TEL 27-11-339-1951. FAX 27-11-716-3000. TELEX 427125 SA. Ed. G.H. Pirie. adv.; bk.rev. circ. 800. (also avail. in microfiche; reprint service avail. from SWZ) **Indexed:** Bibl.& Ind.Geol, Bibl.Cart., Curr.Cont.Africa, Geo.Abstr., Ind.S.A.Per. **Document type:** academic/scholarly publication.
—BLDSC (8338.000000); Faxon.
Description: Disseminates scientific research in physical and human geography.

910 375   AT
SOUTH AUSTRALIAN GEOGRAPHER. 1960. q. Aus.$30. Geography Teachers Association of South Australia, c/o 163a Greenhill Rd., Parkside, S.A. 5063, Australia. Ed. Marie Quorn-Smith. adv.; bk.rev. circ. 400.
Former titles: S.A. Geographer Bulletin; Taminga (ISSN 0494-612X)

GEOGRAPHY

910 AT ISSN 1030-0481
G51
SOUTH AUSTRALIAN GEOGRAPHICAL JOURNAL. 1886. a. Aus.$35. Royal Geographical Society of Australasia, South Australian Branch, Box 419, Adelaide, S.A. 5001, Australia. TEL 08-207-7265. FAX 08-207-7247. Ed. Nick Harvey. bk.rev.; cum. index: vols. 1-40. circ. 450. **Indexed:** AESIS, Aus.P.A.I.S., Aus.Sci.Ind., Geo.Abstr.
—BLDSC (8348.933000).
  Formerly (until 1987): Royal Geographical Society of Australasia. South Australian Branch. Proceedings (ISSN 0085-5790)

910 AT ISSN 0811-6504
SOUTH AUSTRALIAN GEOGRAPHICAL PAPERS. 1983. irreg. Royal Geographical Society of Australasia, South Australian Branch, Box 419, Adelaide, S.A. 5001, Australia. Ed. Peter Smailes.
—BLDSC (8348.934000).

910 US ISSN 0038-366X
G1
SOUTHEASTERN GEOGRAPHER. 1961. s-a. $15 (foreign $18). Association of American Geographers, Southeastern Division, University of Georgia, Department of Geography, Athens, GA 30602. TEL 706-542-2350. FAX 706-542-2388. Ed. James O. Wheeler. adv.; bk.rev.; charts; stat. circ. 900. **Indexed:** Geo.Abstr. **Document type:** academic/scholarly publication.
—BLDSC (8352.445000); Faxon; UnCover.
  Description: Research papers on geographical topics with a focus on the American South.

910 US ISSN 0073-4950
SOUTHERN ILLINOIS UNIVERSITY, CARBONDALE. DEPARTMENT OF GEOGRAPHY. DISCUSSION PAPER. 1969. irreg., no.6, 1979. Southern Illinois University, Carbondale, Department of Geography, Carbondale, IL 62901. TEL 618-536-3375. **Document type:** academic/scholarly publication.

910 US ISSN 0073-4969
SOUTHERN ILLINOIS UNIVERSITY, CARBONDALE. OCCASIONAL PAPER SERIES IN GEOGRAPHY. 1963. irreg. price varies. Southern Illinois University, Carbondale, Department of Geography, Carbondale, IL 62901. TEL 618-536-3375. **Indexed:** Geo.Abstr. **Document type:** academic/scholarly publication.

SPECIAL LIBRARIES ASSOCIATION. GEOGRAPHY AND MAP DIVISION. BULLETIN. see *LIBRARY AND INFORMATION SCIENCES*

SPELEO. see *EARTH SCIENCES*

SPELEOLOGICAL SOCIETY OF JAPAN. JOURNAL. see *EARTH SCIENCES*

STAFFORDSHIRE STUDIES. see *HISTORY — History Of Europe*

526.3 UK ISSN 0081-4377
STAR ALMANAC FOR LAND SURVEYORS. 1951. a. price varies. (H.M. Nautical Almanac Office) H.M.S.O., P.O. Box 276, London SW8 5DT, England. **Document type:** government publication.
—CCC.

910 550 PL ISSN 0082-5549
STUDIA SOCIETATIS SCIENTIARUM TORUNENSIS. SECTIO C. GEOGRAFIA ET GEOLOGIA. (Text in Polish; summaries in English) 1953. irreg., vol.10, no.2, 1991. price varies. Towarzystwo Naukowe w Toruniu, Ul. Wysoka 16, 87-100 Torun, Poland. TEL 48-56-23941. TELEX 552388 FSBH PL. Ed. Ludmila Roszko. charts; illus. circ. 680. **Indexed:** Biol.Abstr. **Document type:** monographic series.
—BLDSC (8482.004000).

910 RM
STUDIA UNIVERSITATIS "BABES-BOLYAI". GEOGRAPHIA. (Text in English, French, German, Rumanian) 1958. s-a. exchange basis. Universitatea "Babes-Bolyai", Biblioteca Centrala Universitara, Str. Clinicilor Nr. 2, Cluj-Napoca 3400, Rumania. TEL 95-117092. FAX 95-117633. index. **Document type:** academic/scholarly publication.
  Supersedes in part (in 1990): Studia Universitatis "Babes-Bolyai". Geologia - Geographia (ISSN 0039-341X)

910 HU ISSN 0081-7961
STUDIES IN GEOGRAPHY IN HUNGARY. (Text in English) 1964. irreg., vol.26, 1992. price varies. (Magyar Tudomanyos Akademia) Akademiai Kiado, Publishing House of the Hungarian Academy of Sciences, P.O. Box 245, H-1519 Budapest, Hungary. TEL 181-2143. FAX 166-6466. TELEX 22-6228 ANKYO H.

910 RM ISSN 1220-5281
G1
STUDII SI CERCETARI DE GEOGRAFIE. (Text in Rumanian; summaries in English, French, German, Russian and Spanish) 1955. a. 55 lei($32) (Academia Romana) Editura Academiei Romane, Calea Victoriei 125, 79717 Bucharest, Rumania. (Dist. by: Rompresfilatelia, Calea Grivitei 64-66, P.O. Box 12-201, 78104 Bucharest, Rumania) Ed. V. Ianovici. bk.rev.; charts; illus.; index. circ. 900. **Indexed:** Appl.Mech.Rev., Bibl.& Ind.Geol., Chem.Abstr., Doc.Geogr., Geo.Abstr.
  Former titles (until 1990): Studii si Cercetari de Geologie, Geofizica si Geografie. Geografie (ISSN 0039-3967); **(until 1963):** Probleme de Geografie (ISSN 1013-901X)

910 GW ISSN 0343-7906
CODEN: STGPAY
STUTTGARTER GEOGRAPHISCHE STUDIEN. 1924. irreg. (1-3/yr.). price varies. Universitaet Stuttgart, Geographisches Institut, Silcherstr. 9, 70176 Stuttgart, Germany. TEL 0711-121-3760. FAX 0711-121-3759. Ed.Bd. charts; illus.; stat. circ. 500. **Indexed:** Bibl.& Ind.Geol., Geo.Abstr., I D A. **Document type:** academic/scholarly publication.
—BLDSC (8501.600000).

526.982 SR
SURINAM. CENTRAAL BUREAU LUCHTKARTERING. JAARVERSLAG. (Text in Dutch) irreg. Centraal Bureau Luchtkartering, Paramaribo, Surinam. **Document type:** government publication.

526.8 IS
SURVEY OF ISRAEL. CARTOGRAPHIC PAPERS. (Text in Hebrew; with English abstracts) 1965. irreg. price varies. Survey of Israel, P.O.B. 14171, Tel-Aviv 61141, Israel.
  Formerly: Israel. Department of Surveys. Cartographic Papers.

526.8 IS
SURVEY OF ISRAEL. PHOTOGRAMMETRIC PAPERS. (Text in Hebrew; with English Abstract) 1976. irreg. price varies. Survey of Israel, P.O.B. 14171, Tel-Aviv 61141, Israel.
  Formerly: Israel. Department of Surveys. Photogrammetric Papers.

526.9 624.72 US ISSN 1052-2905
TA501 CODEN: SLISEZ
SURVEYING AND LAND INFORMATION SYSTEMS; devoted to the advancement of the sciences of surveying and mapping. 1941. q. $85 to non-members (foreign $95). American Congress on Surveying and Mapping, 5410 Grosvenor Lane, Ste. 100, Bethesda, MD 20814. TEL 301-493-0200. Ed. Charles Schwarz. adv.; bk.rev.; index. circ. 9,000. (also avail. in microform from UMI; reprint service avail. from KTO,UMI) **Indexed:** A.S.& T.Ind., Abstr.J.Earthq.Eng., ASCA, Bibl.& Ind.Geol., Bibl.Cart., Geo.Abstr., HRIS. **Document type:** academic/scholarly publication.
—BLDSC (8551.910000); Faxon; UnCover; SWETS; UMI. **CCC.**
  Formerly: Surveying and Mapping (ISSN 0039-6273)
  Description: Offers information on theoretical and technological topics in surveying (including such fields as geodesy and hydrography) and on land information systems. Focuses on such current topics as global positioning systems and total stations.

910 SW ISSN 0081-9808
SVENSK GEOGRAFISK AARSBOK/SWEDISH GEOGRAPHICAL YEARBOOK. (Text in Swedish; summaries in English) 1925. a. SEK 100 membership. Sydsvenska Geografiska Saellskapet, Department of Geography, Lunds Universitet, Soelvegatan 13, S-223 62 Lund, Sweden. FAX 46-46-108401. (Dist. by: Gleerupska Universitetsbokhandeln, P.O. Box 172, 221 00 Lund, Sweden) Ed.Bd. bk.rev.; cum.index 1925-34, 1935-50, 1951-84. circ. 900. **Indexed:** Bibl.& Ind.Geol, Field Crop Abstr., Herb.Abstr., Hort.Abstr., I D A. **Document type:** academic/scholarly publication.
  Formerly (until 1927): Sydsvenska Geografiska Saellskapet i Lund. Aarsbok.

526.3 SW ISSN 0039-6613
SVENSK LANTMAETERITIDSKRIFT/SWEDISH LANDSURVEYING JOURNAL. (Text occasionally in English) 1908. bi-m. SEK 242. Sveriges Lantmaetarefoerening - Society of Swedish Chartered Surveyors, Box 7194, 103 88 Stockholm, Sweden. Ed. Peter Hellsten. adv.; bk.rev. circ. 2,800. **Indexed:** Bibl.Cart.

910 UK ISSN 0081-9980
SWANSEA GEOGRAPHER. 1959. a. £4. University College of Swansea, Department of Geography, Singleton Park, Swansea, Glam. SA2 8PP, Wales. FAX 0792-205556. Ed.Bd. circ. 200. **Indexed:** Geo.Abstr. **Document type:** academic/scholarly publication.
—BLDSC (8573.856000).

526 AT ISSN 0811-4684
TACTUAL MAPPING NEWSLETTER. 1983. a. free. Australian Institute of Cartographers, GPO Box H592, Perth 6001, Australia. Ed. B.E. Goodrick. circ. 200. (back issues avail.) **Document type:** newsletter.

910 370 UK ISSN 0305-8018
TEACHING GEOGRAPHY. 1975. q. £35.80 (effective 1993-1994). Geographical Association, 343 Fulwood Rd., Sheffield S10 3BP, England. TEL 0742-670666. FAX 0742-670688. Ed. David Boardman. adv.; bk.rev.; bibl.; charts; stat.; index. circ. 5,500. **Indexed:** Cont.Pg.Educ. **Document type:** academic/scholarly publication.
—BLDSC (8614.160000); Faxon; SWETS.

910 FI ISSN 0040-3741
G23 CODEN: TRRAA7
TERRA. (Text in Finnish, Swedish and occasionally English; summaries in English) 1888. q. FIM 140. Suomen Maantieteellinen Seura - Geografiska Saellskapet i Finland (Geographical Society of Finland), Maantieteen Laitos, PL 4 (Hallituskatu 11), FIN-00014 Helsingin Yliopisto, Finland. Ed. Heikki Seppa. adv.; bk.rev.; abstr.; bibl.; charts; illus.; index. circ. 1,800. (reprint service avail. from UMI) **Indexed:** Bibl.& Ind.Geol., Curr.Adv.Ecol.Sci., Geo.Abstr., I D A, Sel.Water Res.Abstr. **Document type:** academic/scholarly publication.
—UMI.

TERRA GRISCHUNA - GRAUBUENDEN; Zeitschrift fuer buendner Natur, Kultur und Freizeit. see *ENVIRONMENTAL STUDIES*

914.1 625.7 IE
THOM'S DUBLIN & COUNTY STREET DIRECTORY. 1851. a. $70. Thom's Directories Ltd., 38 Merrion Sq., Dublin 2, Ireland. TEL 767481. FAX 762620. Ed. J.L. Wootton. **Document type:** directory.

GEOGRAPHY 2821

910   NE   ISSN 0040-747X
HC10
TIJDSCHRIFT VOOR ECONOMISCHE EN SOCIALE GEOGRAFIE/NETHERLANDS JOURNAL OF ECONOMIC AND SOCIAL GEOGRAPHY. Short title: T E S G. (Text in English) 1910. 5/yr. fl.130 to individuals (foreign fl.145); institutions fl.175 (foreign fl.190) (effective 1994). Koninklijk Nederlands Aardrijkskundig Genootschap - Royal Dutch Geographical Society, P.O. Box 80123, 3508 TC Utrecht, Netherlands. TEL 31-30-532757. Ed. Jan van Weesep. adv.: B&W page fl.450; 170 x 240. bk.rev.; bibl.; charts; maps; index; circ. 1,150 (paid). (reprint service avail. from SWZ) **Indexed:** ASCA, Bibl.Cart., C.R.E.J., Curr.Cont., E.I., Excerp.Med., Forest.Abstr., Geo.Abstr., HRIS, I D A, Int.Lab.Doc., Key to Econ.Sci., P.A.I.S., Popul.Ind., Rural Devel.Abstr., Rural Recreat.Tour.Abstr., Soils & Fert., SSCI, Stud.Wom.Abstr., World Agri.Econ.& Rural Sociol.Abstr. **Document type:** academic/scholarly publication.
—BLDSC (8839.600000); UnCover; SWETS. **CCC.**
   Description: Features articles of research covering the Netherlands as well as other countries.

910   JA   ISSN 0386-8710
                      CODEN: GRTUA2
TOKYO METROPOLITAN UNIVERSITY. DEPARTMENT OF GEOGRAPHY. GEOGRAPHICAL REPORTS/TOKYO-TORITSU DAIGAKU CHIRIGAKU HOKOKU. (Text in European languages) 1966. a. price varies. Tokyo-toritsu Daigaku, Rigakubu Chirigaku Kyoshitsu - Tokyo Metropolitan University, Faculty of Science, Department of Geography, Minami Ohsawa 1-1, Hachioji-shi, Tokyo 192-03, Japan. FAX 81-0426-77-2589. Ed.Bd. bibl.; charts; illus. circ. 1,000. **Indexed:** Bibl.& Ind.Geol., Geo.Abstr., I D A, Meteor.& Geoastrophys.Abstr. **Document type:** academic/scholarly publication.
—BLDSC (4126.600000); UnCover.

TRAPANANDA. see HISTORY — History Of North And South America

526.3   RU
TSENTRAL'NYI NAUCHNO-ISSLEDOVATEL'SKII INSTITUT GEODEZII, AEROS"EMKI I KARTOGRAFII. TRUDY. vol.218, 1977. irreg. Tsentral'nyi Nauchno-Issledovatel'skii Institut Geodezii, Aeros"emki i Kartografii, Ul. Onezhskaya 26, Moscow 125413, Russia. circ. 500.

910   GW   ISSN 0564-4232
                      CODEN: TUGSBS
TUEBINGER GEOGRAPHISCHE STUDIEN. 1958. irreg. (approx. 5/yr.). price varies. Universitaet Tuebingen, Geographisches Institut, Hoelderlinstr. 12, 72074 Tuebingen, Germany. FAX 07071-295318. Ed.Bd. bibl.; charts; illus.; stat. circ. 500. **Indexed:** Bibl.& Ind.Geol. **Document type:** academic/scholarly publication.

TURUN YLIOPISTO. JULKAISUJA. SARJA A. II. BIOLOGICA - GEOGRAPHICA - GEOLOGICA. see BIOLOGY

910   GW
UEBERSEE-MUSEUM, BREMEN. VEROEFFENTLICHUNGEN. REIHE C: GEOGRAPHIE. N.S. 1977. irreg., vol.5, 1989. price varies. Uebersee-Museum, Bremen, Bahnhofsplatz 13, 28195 Bremen, Germany. **Document type:** academic/scholarly publication.
   Former titles: Deutsche Geographische Blaetter; Uebersee-Museum, Bremen. Veroeffentlichungen. Reihe C: Geographie (ISSN 0341-9258)

910   UN
UNITED NATIONS CONFERENCE ON THE STANDARDIZATION OF GEOGRAPHICAL NAMES. REPORT OF THE CONFERENCE. 1974. irreg., latest no.5. $12. (United Nations Economic and Social Council) United Nations Publications, Room DC2-0853, New York, NY 10017. TEL 212-963-8302. FAX 212-963-3489. (Or Distribution and Sales Section, Palais des Nations, CH-1211 Geneva 10, Switzerland)

526.8   UN
UNITED NATIONS REGIONAL CARTOGRAPHIC CONFERENCE FOR ASIA AND THE PACIFIC. REPORT OF THE CONFERENCE. 1955. irreg., vol.11, 1983. price varies. United Nations Publications, Room DC2-0853, New York, NY 10017. TEL 212-963-8302. FAX 212-963-3489. (Or: Distribution and Sales Section, Palais des Nations, CH-1211 Geneva 10, Switzerland) (also avail. in microfiche) **Indexed:** Bibl.& Ind.Geol.
   Formerly: United Nations Regional Cartographic Conference for Asia and the Far East. Proceedings of the Conference and Technical Papers (ISSN 0082-836X)

910   UN
UNITED NATIONS REGIONAL CARTOGRAPHIC CONFERENCE FOR THE AMERICAS. REPORT OF THE CONFERENCE. irreg. price varies. (United Nations Economic and Social Council) United Nations Publications, Room DC2-0853, New York, NY 10017. TEL 212-963-8302. FAX 212-963-3489. (Or: Distribution and Sales Section, Palais des Nations, CH-1211 Geneva 10, Switzerland)

910   US
G109
U.S. DEPARTMENT OF STATE. OFFICE OF THE GEOGRAPHER. GEOGRAPHIC AND GLOBAL ISSUES QUARTERLY. (G E Series; order ID: GN) 1964; N.S. 1986. q. $7 (foreign $8.75). U.S. Department of State, Office of the Geographer, c/o Bureau of Intelligence and Research, 2201 C St., N.W., Washington, DC 20520-6510. TEL 202-647-2021. (Subscr. to: Superintendent of Documents, U.S. Government Printing Office, Box 317954, Pittsburgh, PA 15250-7954. TEL 202-783-3238. FAX 202-512-2233) circ. 1,300. (also avail. in microfiche from CIS; reprint service avail. from CIS; back issues avail.) **Indexed:** Amer.Stat.Ind. (1985-). **Document type:** government publication, academic/scholarly publication.
—UnCover.
   Formerly: U.S. Department of State. Office of the Geographer. Geographic Notes (ISSN 0083-016X)
   Description: Contains analyses and maps and other graphics that provide a geographic perspective on such foreign policy related topics as boundary and sovereignty disputes, maritime borders, refugee issues, and transnational environmental concerns.

910   US   ISSN 0363-6828
E154
U.S. GEOLOGICAL SURVEY. BOARD ON GEOGRAPHIC NAMES. DECISIONS ON GEOGRAPHIC NAMES IN THE UNITED STATES. Key Title: Decisions on Geographic Names in the United States. 1890. a. free. U.S. Geological Survey, Board of Geographic Names, National Center 523, Reston, VA 22092. TEL 703-648-4544. FAX 703-648-5542. Ed. Roger L. Payne. circ. 1,100. **Document type:** government publication.

918.7   VE   ISSN 0076-6569
UNIVERSIDAD DE LOS ANDES. INSTITUTO DE GEOGRAFIA Y CONSERVACION DE RECURSOS NATURALES. CUADERNOS GEOGRAFICOS. 1961. irreg. price varies. Universidad de Los Andes, Instituto de Geografia y Conservacion de Recursos Naturales, Via los Chorras de Milla, Codigo Postal 5101, Merida, Venezuela. circ. 2,000.

910   SP   ISSN 0213-1781
UNIVERSIDAD DE MURCIA. PAPELES DE GEOGRAFIA. 1968. irreg., vol.16, 1990. 1000 ptas. Universidad de Murcia, Secretariado de Publicaciones e Intercambio Cientifico, Santo Cristo, 1, 30001 Murcia, Spain. TEL 968 24 92 00.
   Formerly (until 1978): Universidad de Murcia. Departamento de Geografia. Papeles.

910   MX   ISSN 0185-1322
UNIVERSIDAD NACIONAL AUTONOMA DE MEXICO. ANUARIO DE GEOGRAFIA. 1961. a. (exchange basis or donation). Universidad Nacional Autonoma de Mexico, Colegio de Geografia, Ciudad Universitaria, C.P. 04510, Mexico 20, D.F., Mexico. Eds. Raquel Guzman Villanueva, Dolores Rejon de Rejon. bk.rev. circ. 1,500. **Indexed:** Hisp.Amer.Per.Ind.
   Formerly: Universidad Nacional Autonoma de Mexico. Instituto de Geografia. Anuario de Geografia.

910   PO
UNIVERSIDADE DE LISBOA. CENTRO DE ESTUDOS GEOGRAFICOS. MEMORIAS. (Text in French, Portuguese) 1972. irreg., no.15, 1992. Esc.1000 per no. Cidade Universitaria, 1699 Lisbon Codex, Portugal. TEL 796-5469. FAX 796-0063. circ. 1,000. **Document type:** proceedings.
   Formerly: Instituto Nacional de Investigacao Cientifica, Centro de Estudios Geograficos. Memorias.
   Description: Covers thematic studies on geography.

910   BL
UNIVERSIDADE DE SAO PAULO. MUSEU PAULISTA. COLECAO. SERIE DE GEOGRAFIA. irreg. Universidade de Sao Paulo, Museu Paulista, Caixa Postal 42503, Parque da Independencia, 04263 Sao Paulo SP, Brazil.
   Supersedes in part (in 1975): Museu Paulista. Colecao (ISSN 0080-6382)

910   GW   ISSN 0720-9746
UNIVERSITAET BREMEN - SCHWERPUNKT GEOGRAPHIE. MATERIALIEN UND MANUSKRIPTE. 1979. irreg. price varies. Universitaet Bremen, Drueckschriftenlager, Postfach 330440, 28334 Bremen, Germany.

910   GW   ISSN 0563-1491
DD801.S13   CODEN: SGIAAA
UNIVERSITAET DES SAARLANDES. GEOGRAPHISCHES INSTITUT. ARBEITEN. (Text in German; summaries in English, French and Spanish) 1956. irreg., vol.40, 1993. price varies. Universitaet des Saarlandes, Fachrichtung Geographie, 66041 Saarbruecken, Germany. TEL 0681-3022954. FAX 0681-302-2364. Ed.Bd. bibl.; charts; illus. circ. 1,000. **Document type:** monographic series.

910   GW   ISSN 0723-9874
UNIVERSITAET KIEL. GEOGRAPHISCHES INSTITUT. SCHRIFTEN. 1932. irreg. price varies. Christian-Albrechts-Universitaet, Geographisches Institut, Olshausenstr. 40, 24098 Kiel, Germany. Ed.Bd. bk.rev. circ. 500. **Indexed:** Geo.Abstr. **Document type:** academic/scholarly publication, monographic series.

910.1   GW   ISSN 0077-2127
UNIVERSITAET MUENCHEN. WIRTSCHAFTSGEOGRAPHISCHES INSTITUT. "W G I"-BERICHTE ZUR REGIONALFORSCHUNG. (Text in German; summaries in English) 1970. irreg., no.14, 1974. price varies. Nelles Verlag, Schleissheimer Str. 371b, 80935 Munich, Germany.

910   FR   ISSN 0048-7163
UNIVERSITE DE REIMS. INSTITUT DE GEOGRAPHIE. TRAVAUX. (Summaries in English, French) 1970. q. 150 F. Universite de Reims, Institut de Geographie, 57 rue Pierre Taittinger, 51096 Reims, France. TEL 26-05-36-81. FAX 26-05-36-46. Ed. J.B. Domingo. adv.; bk.rev.; charts; illus.; cum.index. circ. 500. (back issues avail.) **Indexed:** Geo.Abstr.

910 550   CN   ISSN 0710-0868
UNIVERSITE DE SHERBROOKE. DEPARTMENT DE GEOGRAPHIE. BULLETIN DE RECHERCHE. (Text in French; summaries in English, French) 1972. irreg., approx. 6/yr. Can.$4 per no. Universite de Sherbrooke, Department de Geographie et Teledetection, Faculte des Lettres et Sciences Humaines, Local A4-161, Sherbrooke, Que. J1K 2R1, Canada. TEL 819-821-7210. FAX 819-821-7238. Ed. Romain Paquette. adv.; charts; illus.; stat. circ. 200. (back issues avail.) **Indexed:** Geo.Abstr.
   Description: Reports on research in various aspects of geography.

900   IV
UNIVERSITE NATIONALE DE COTE D'IVOIRE. ANNALES. SERIE G: GEOGRAPHIE. 1969. irreg., vol.8, 1979. price varies. Universite Nationale de Cote d'Ivoire, Tropical Geography Institute, B.P. 865, Abidjan 08, Ivory Coast. TEL 43-90-00. Ed.Bd. bibl.; charts; illus. **Indexed:** A.I.C.P., Geo.Abstr.
   Formerly: Universite d'Abidjan. Annales. Serie G: Geographie (ISSN 0302-0924)

GEOGRAPHY

910 — NE — ISSN 0066-1317
CODEN: PFBLA2
UNIVERSITEIT VAN AMSTERDAM. FYSISCH GEOGRAFISCH EN BODEMKUNDIG LABORATORIUM. PUBLIKATIES. (Text in English and German; summaries in Dutch, English, French and German) 1964. irreg., latest 1984. price varies. Universiteit van Amsterdam, Fysisch Geografisch en Bodemkundig Laboratorium, c/o N.G. Piersonbibliotheek, Roetersstraat 11, 1018 WB Amsterdam, Netherlands. TEL 31-20-525-4273. FAX 31-20-525-5836. **Indexed:** Bibl.& Ind.Geol., Geo.Abstr. **Document type:** academic/scholarly publication.
—BLDSC (7012.869000).

910 — NR — ISSN 0083-3975
UNIVERSITY GEOGRAPHER. 1956. a. Ibadan University Geographical Society, Ibadan, Nigeria.

910 — CN
UNIVERSITY OF ALBERTA. STUDIES IN GEOGRAPHY. MONOGRAPHS. irreg. price varies. University of Alberta, Department of Geography, Edmonton, AB T6G 2H4, Canada. TEL 403-492-4783. **Document type:** monographic series.

910 — NZ — ISSN 0112-1545
UNIVERSITY OF AUCKLAND. DEPARTMENT OF GEOGRAPHY. OCCASIONAL PUBLICATION. 1961. irreg., no.27, 1990. price varies. University of Auckland, Department of Geography, Private Bag, Auckland, New Zealand. FAX 649-33429. Ed. Dr. Warwick Neville. circ. 300.
—BLDSC (6226.602500).
Formerly: University of Auckland. Department of Geography. Occasional Papers.

910 G58 — US — ISSN 0068-6441
UNIVERSITY OF CALIFORNIA PUBLICATIONS IN GEOGRAPHY. 1913. irreg. price varies. University of California Press, 2120 Berkeley Way, Berkeley, CA 94720. TEL 510-642-4247. FAX 510-643-7127. (Orders to: California-Princeton Fulfillment Services, 1445 Lower Ferry Rd., Ewing, NJ 08618. TEL 800-999-1958. FAX 800-777-4726) Ed.Bd. (back issues avail.; reprint service avail. from JOH) **Indexed:** Deep Sea Res.& Oceanogr.Abstr. **Document type:** monographic series.
—BLDSC (9105.140000).
Description: Explores how geography affects natural ecosystems and human settlement.
Refereed Serial

910 — US — ISSN 1054-206X
UNIVERSITY OF CHICAGO. GEOGRAPHY RESEARCH PAPERS. 1948. irreg., no.233-5 1992. $12 per no. University of Chicago Press, 5801 S. Ellis Ave., Chicago, IL 60637. TEL 800-621-2736. FAX 312-660-2235. Ed.Bd. circ. 600. (also avail. in microform from UMI) **Indexed:** Geo.Abstr., I D A, Rural Devel.Abstr., World Agri.Econ.& Rural Sociol.Abstr. **Document type:** monographic series.
Formerly (until 1988): University of Chicago. Department of Geography. Research Papers (ISSN 0069-3340)
Description: Includes original research of geographical interest, encompassing human and environmental geography, including cultural, social, economic, urban, political and historical geography.
Refereed Serial

UNIVERSITY OF COLORADO. INSTITUTE OF ARCTIC AND ALPINE RESEARCH. OCCASIONAL PAPERS. see *SCIENCES: COMPREHENSIVE WORKS*

919.402 — AT — ISSN 0312-8741
UNIVERSITY OF NEW ENGLAND. DEPARTMENT OF GEOGRAPHY AND PLANNING. MONOGRAPH SERIES (NO.). irreg. price varies. University of New England, Department of Geography and Planning, Armidale, N.S.W. 2351, Australia. TEL 067-732761.

910 — AT — ISSN 0066-7714
UNIVERSITY OF NEW ENGLAND. DEPARTMENT OF GEOGRAPHY AND PLANNING. RESEARCH SERIES IN APPLIED GEOGRAPHY. 1965. irreg., no. 44, 1976. Aus.$3.50. University of New England, Department of Geography and Planning, Armidale, N.S.W. 2351, Australia. Ed. J. E. Hobbs. **Indexed:** Bibl.& Ind.Geol.

910 325 — UK — ISSN 0078-026X
UNIVERSITY OF NEWCASTLE-UPON-TYNE. DEPARTMENT OF GEOGRAPHY. RESEARCH SERIES. 1954. irreg. price varies. University of Newcastle-Upon-Tyne, Department of Geography, Newcastle-Upon-Tyne NE1 7RU, England. FAX 091-232-9259. TELEX 53654-UNINEW-G. Ed. J.D. Momsen. circ. 750. **Indexed:** Bibl.& Ind.Geol., Geo.Abstr. **Document type:** academic/scholarly publication.

910 — CN
UNIVERSITY OF OTTAWA. DEPARTMENT OF GEOGRAPHY. NOTES DE RECHERCHE - RESEARCH NOTES. (Text in English or French) 1971. irreg. price varies. University of Ottawa, Department of Geography, Ottawa, ON K1N 6N5, Canada. TEL 613-564-2395. FAX 613-564-3304. **Indexed:** Bibl.& Ind.Geol., Geo.Abstr. **Document type:** academic/scholarly publication, proceedings.
Formerly: University of Ottawa. Department of Geography and Regional Planning. Notes de Recherches - Research Notes.

910 — UK — ISSN 0305-8190
UNIVERSITY OF OXFORD. SCHOOL OF GEOGRAPHY. RESEARCH PAPERS. 1972. irreg., no.49, 1993. £4 per no. University of Oxford, School of Geography, Mansfield Rd., Oxford OX1 3TB, England. TEL 0865-271919. FAX 0865-271929. TELEX 83147-VIA-OR-G. Ed.Bd. charts. circ. 300. **Indexed:** Geo.Abstr. **Document type:** monographic series.
—BLDSC (7755.010000).

910 — PP
UNIVERSITY OF PAPUA NEW GUINEA. DEPARTMENT OF GEOGRAPHY. OCCASIONAL PAPERS IN GEOGRAPHY. 1970. irreg. (2-3/yr.). price varies. University of Papua New Guinea, Department of Geography, Box 320, University P.O., Papua New Guinea. Ed.Bd. bibl.; charts; illus. circ. 500. **Indexed:** Rural Devel.Abstr.

910 — UK
UNIVERSITY OF READING. DEPARTMENT OF GEOGRAPHY. DISCUSSION PAPER SERIES. irreg., no.18. £3. University of Reading, Department of Geography, Whiteknights Rd., Reading RG6 2AB, England. TEL 0734-875123. FAX 0734-755865. **Document type:** monographic series.

910 G1 — JA — ISSN 0082-478X
CODEN: BDGTAJ
UNIVERSITY OF TOKYO. DEPARTMENT OF GEOGRAPHY. BULLETIN. (Text mainly in English) 1969. a. available on exchange. University of Tokyo, Graduate School of Science, Department of Geography - Tokyo Daigaku Daigakuin Rigakukei Kenkyuka, c/o Faculty of Science - Library, 3-1, Hongo 7-chome, Bunkyo-ku, Tokyo 113, Japan. bibl.; charts. circ. 800. **Indexed:** Bibl.& Ind.Geol., Geo.Abstr. **Document type:** academic/scholarly publication.
—BLDSC (2480.970000).

910 — CN — ISSN 0317-9893
UNIVERSITY OF TORONTO. DEPARTMENT OF GEOGRAPHY. DISCUSSION PAPER SERIES. 1970. irreg., no.35, 1989. price varies. University of Toronto, Department of Geography, Toronto, Ont. M5S 1A1, Canada. TEL 416-978-3376. Ed. J. Britton. **Document type:** monographic series.

910.02 — JA — ISSN 0388-6174
UNIVERSITY OF TSUKUBA. INSTITUTE OF GEOSCIENCE. SCIENCE REPORTS. SECTION A: GEOGRAPHICAL SCIENCES. (Text in English) 1980. a. University of Tsukuba, Institute of Geoscience - Tsukubu Daigaku Chikyu Kagakukei, 1-1, Tennodai 1-chome, Tsukuba-shi, Ibaraki-ken 305, Japan.
—BLDSC (8153.800000).

910 — CN
UNIVERSITY OF WATERLOO. DEPARTMENT OF GEOGRAPHY. OCCASIONAL PAPERS. 1984. irreg. (1-2/yr.). price varies. University of Waterloo, Department of Geography, Waterloo, ON N2L 3G1, Canada. TEL 519-885-1211. FAX 519-746-2031. Ed. Bruce Mitchell. **Document type:** monographic series.
Description: Series includes bibliographies, field guides, regional vignettes, and specialized topics for students and researchers.

910 333.7 — CN — ISSN 0843-7378
UNIVERSITY OF WATERLOO. DEPARTMENT OF GEOGRAPHY. PUBLICATION SERIES. 1971. irreg., (approx. 2/yr.). price varies. University of Waterloo, Department of Geography, Waterloo, ON N2L 3G1, Canada. TEL 519-885-1211. FAX 519-746-2031. Ed. Bruce Mitchell. **Document type:** monographic series.
Description: Series of specialized monographs aimed at scholars, researchers, professional field workers, and university students.

910 G1 — IT — ISSN 0042-0409
CODEN: UNVSAU
L'UNIVERSO. 1920. bi-m. L.54000. Istituto Geografico Militare, Via Cesare Battisti 10, 50100 Florence, Italy. TEL 055-27751. FAX 055-282172. TELEX 575597 IGM FII. Ed. Antonio Finizio. adv.; bk.rev.; illus.; index, cum.index covering 50 yrs. circ. 6,000. **Indexed:** Bibl.& Ind.Geol., Bibl.Cart., Biol.Abstr.
Description: Covers human, historical, and physical geography.

910 — XV
UNIVERZA V LJUBLJANI. FILOZOFSKA FAKULTETA. ODDELEK ZA GEOGRAFIJO. DELA. (Text in Slovenian; summaries in English, German) 1985. irreg. $5. Univerza v Ljubljani, Filozofska Fakulteta, Oddelek za Geografijo, Askerceva 12, 61 000 Ljubljana, Slovenia. TEL 061-150-001. Ed. Mirko Pak. circ. 500. **Document type:** academic/scholarly publication.
Formerly: Univerza Edvarda Kardelja v Ljubljani. Filozofska Fakulteta. Oddelek za Geografijo. Dela (ISSN 0352-7921)

910 — XO — ISSN 0139-5076
UNIVERZITA P.J. SAFARIKA V KOSICIACH. PEDAGOGICKA FAKULTA V PRESOVE. ZBORNIK. PRIRODNE VEDY. (Text in Slovak; summaries in English, German and Russian) vol.2, 1970. s-a. exchange basis. Slovenske Pedagogicke Nakladatelstvo, Sasinkova 5, 891 12 Bratislava, Slovakia. Ed. R. Novodomec. bibl.; charts; illus. circ. 400.
Formerly: Geograficke Prace.

914.38 — PL — ISSN 0867-0102
UNIWERSYTET GDANSKI. WYDZIAL BIOLOGII, GEOGRAFII I OCEANOLOGII. ZESZYTY NAUKOWE. GEOGRAFIA. (Text in Polish; summaries in English) 1970. irreg., latest no.18. price varies. Uniwersytet Gdanski, Wydzial Biologii, Geografii i Oceanologii, c/o Biblioteka Glowna, Ul. Armii Krajowej 110, 81-824 Sopot, Poland. TEL 51-0061. TELEX 051-2247 BMOR PL. (Dist. by: Ars Polona-Ruch, Krakowskie Przedmiescie 7, Warsaw, Poland) Ed. Jerzy Szukalski. bk.rev. circ. 300. **Document type:** academic/scholarly publication.
Formerly: Uniwersytet Gdanski. Wydzial Biologii i Nauk o Ziemi. Zeszyty Naukowe. Geografia (ISSN 0208-4937)
Description: Physical geography, geomorphology, hydrology, economic geography, methodology of studies and reports on current research problems in geography departments.

910 G23 — PL — ISSN 0083-4343
UNIWERSYTET JAGIELLONSKI. ZESZYTY NAUKOWE. PRACE GEOGRAFICZNE. (Text in Polish, summaries in English) 1960. irreg. price varies. Uniwersytet Jagiellonski, Instytut Geografii, Ul. Golegia 24, 31-007 Krakow, Poland. (Dist. by: Ars Polona, Krakowskie Przedmiescie 7, 00-068 Warsaw, Poland) Ed. M. Hess. circ. 570. (also avail. in microfilm) **Indexed:** Geo.Abstr., Ref.Zh. **Document type:** academic/scholarly publication.

910 — PL — ISSN 0208-5054
UNIWERSYTET SLASKI W KATOWICACH. PRACE NAUKOWE. GEOGRAPHIA: STUDIA ET DISSERTATIONES. (Text in Polish; summaries in English and Russian) 1976. irreg. price varies. Wydawnictwo Uniwersytetu Slaskiego, Ul. Bankowa 12b, 40-007 Katowice, Poland. TEL 48-32-596-915. FAX 48-32-599-605. TELEX 0315584 USKPL. (Dist. by: CHS Ars Polona, P.O. Box 1001, 00-950 Warsaw, Poland) **Document type:** academic/scholarly publication.
Description: Covers physical geography: geomorphology, climatology, hydrology, socio-economic geography, anthropogenic impact on geographical environment.

GEOGRAPHY

910   PL   ISSN 0208-4589
G1
UNIWERSYTET WARSZAWSKI. WYDZIAL GEOGRAFII I STUDIOW REGIONALNYCH. PRACE I STUDIA GEOGRAFICZNE. (Text in Polish; summaries in English) 1979. irreg., vol.9, 1989. price varies. (Uniwersytet Warszawski, Wydzial Geografii i Studiow Regionalnych) Wydawnictwa Uniwersytetu Warszawskiego, Ul. Obozna 8, 00-032 Warsaw, Poland. (Dist. by: Ars Polona-Ruch, Krakowskie Przedmiescie 7, 00-068 Warsaw, Poland) circ. 500.
Document type: academic/scholarly publication.

910.02   PL   ISSN 0137-107X
UNIWERSYTET WROCLAWSKI. INSTYTUT GEOGRAFICZNY. PRACE. SERIA A: GEOGRAFIA FIZYCZNA. (Subseries of: Acta Universitatis Wratislaviensis) 1975. irreg. price varies. Wydawnictwo Uniwersytetu Wroclawskiego, Pl. Uniwersytecki 9-13, 50-137 Wroclaw, Poland. (Dist. by: Ksiegarnia Uniwersytetu Wroclawskiego, Pl. Uniwersytecki 9-13, 50-137 Wroclaw, Poland) Ed.Bd. **Indexed:** Bibl.& Ind.Geol.
Document type: academic/scholarly publication.

910   PL   ISSN 0137-1088
UNIWERSYTET WROCLAWSKI. INSTYTUT GEOGRAFICZNY. PRACE. SERIA B: GEOGRAFIA SPOLECZNA I EKONOMICZNA. (Subseries of: Acta Universitatis Wratislaviensis) 1975. irreg. price varies. Wydawnictwo Uniwersytetu Wroclawskiego, Pl. Uniwersytecki 9-13, 50-137 Wroclaw, Poland. (Dist. by: Ksiegarnia Uniwersytetu Wroclawskiego, Pl. Uniwersytecki 9-13, 50-137 Wroclaw, Poland) Ed.Bd. **Document type:** academic/scholarly publication.

910   BG
UPOKUL. (Text in Bengali and English) 1972. irreg. Dhaka University Geography Association, Ramna, Dhaka 2, Bangladesh. adv.; illus.

URBAN GEOGRAPHY. see *HOUSING AND URBAN PLANNING*

910   II   ISSN 0042-1618
UTTAR BHARAT BHOOGOL PATRIKA. (Text in English, Hindi) 1965. s-a. Rs.30($16) Uttar Bharat Parishad, c/o V.K. Shrivastava, Secy., Dept. of Geography, University of Gorakhpur, Gorakhpur 273 009, India. TEL 335221. Ed.Bd. bk.rev.; charts; illus.; stat.; decennial index; circ. controlled.
Former titles: Geographical Thought; Oriental Geographer.

914.8   DK   ISSN 0109-2472
VADEHAVSRAPPORT. 1982. irreg. free. Koebenhavns Universitet, Geografisk Institut, Oester Volgade 10, 1350 Copenhagen K, Denmark. Eds. Margot Jespersen, Erik Rasmussen. circ. 125.

910   GW
VERBAND DER GEOGRAPHEN AN DEUTSCHEN HOCHSCHULEN. RUNDBRIEF GEOGRAPHIE. 1974. bi-m. DM.36. Philipps Universitaet, Fachbereich Geographie, Deutschhausstr. 10, 35052 Marburg, Germany. TEL 06421-284261. FAX 06421-286727. Ed. G. Mertins. circ. 1,300.
Document type: academic/scholarly publication, newsletter.
Formerly: Zentralverband der Deutschen Geographen. Rundbrief.
Description: Information about departments of geography and geographers in German-speaking countries; announcements of congresses, symposia.

910   GW   ISSN 0083-5684
VERHANDLUNGEN DES DEUTSCHEN GEOGRAPHENTAGES. 1881. biennial. price varies. (Zentralverband der Deutschen Geographen) Franz Steiner Verlag Wiesbaden GmbH, Birkenwaldstr. 44, 70191 Stuttgart, Germany. TEL 0711-2582-0. FAX 0711-2582290. TELEX 723636-DAZ-D. (Subscr. to: Postfach 101061, 70009 Stuttgart, Germany) cum.index: 1881-1963. **Document type:** proceedings.
—BLDSC (9169.050000).

DER VERMESSUNGSINGENIEUR. see *ENGINEERING — Civil Engineering*

VERMESSUNGSWESEN UND RAUMORDNUNG (VR). see *ENGINEERING — Civil Engineering*

910   US   ISSN 0042-6512
VIRGINIA GEOGRAPHER. 1965. 2/yr. $12. Virginia Geographical Society, c/o Donald Zeigler, Ed., Old Dominion Univ., Norfolk, VA 23529-0088. FAX 804-683-3241. adv.; bk.rev.; charts; illus. circ. 400. **Document type:** academic/scholarly publication.
Description: Contains articles of interest to geographers and geography teachers in Virginia.

917.2   US   ISSN 0186-9418
F1236
VOICES OF MEXICO. 1986. q. $15. Voices of Mexico, Box 9, Mt. Shasta, CA 96067-0009. TEL 800-676-6351. Ed. Mariclaire Acosta. bk.rev.; illus.
—Faxon; UnCover.

915   RU
VOPROSY GEOGRAFII. vol.103, 1977. irreg. 1.25 Rub. per no. Izdatel'stvo Mysl', Leninskii Prospekt 15, 117011 Moscow B-71, Russia. Ed. S. Kovalev. bibl. circ. 9,800. **Indexed:** GeoRef.

VOYAGEURS OCCIDENTAUX EN EGYPTE. see *ORIENTAL STUDIES*

917   NE
VRIJE UNIVERSITEIT. CANADA. CAHIER. (Text in English) irreg., no.4, 1988. price varies. Free University Press, P.O. Box 7161, 1007 MC Amsterdam, Netherlands. (Co-sponsor: Stichting Studiegenootschap Canada) Ed.Bd.

910   RU   ISSN 0373-353X
G23
VSESOYUZNOE GEOGRAFICHESKOE OBSHCHESTVO. IZVESTIYA. (Text in Russian; contents page in English and Russian) 1865. bi-m. 25.20 Rub. (Leningradskoe Otdelenie) Izdatel'stvo Nauka, 90 Profsoyuznaya ul., 117864 Moscow, Russia. Ed. A.F. Tryoshinikov. bk.rev.; bibl.; charts; illus.; index. circ. 1,900. **Indexed:** Bibl.Cart., Biol.Abstr., GeoRef, Meteor.& Geoastrophys.Abstr.

910   AU
W S G DISCUSSION PAPERS. (Text in English) 1989. irreg. $8. Institut fuer Wirtschafts- und Sozialgeography, Augasse 2-6, A-1090 Vienna, Austria. TEL 0222-340525-836. FAX 0222-347541-885. Ed. Manfred Fischer.

WASHINGTON LETTER ON PUERTO RICO. see *POLITICAL SCIENCE*

WESTERN ASSOCIATION OF MAP LIBRARIES. INFORMATION BULLETIN. see *LIBRARY AND INFORMATION SCIENCES*

WESTERN AUSTRALIA. GEOLOGICAL SURVEY. 1: 250,000 GEOLOGICAL SERIES. EXPLANATORY NOTES. see *EARTH SCIENCES — Geology*

910   AT   ISSN 0313-8860
WESTERN GEOGRAPHER. 1972. 2/yr. Geographical Association of Western Australia, Box 1252, Subiaco, W.A. 6008, Australia. Ed. Chris Nedkoff. circ. 200. **Document type:** academic/scholarly publication.

910   CN   ISSN 0315-2022
WESTERN GEOGRAPHICAL SERIES. 1970. irreg. (1-2/yr.). price varies. University of Victoria, Department of Geography, Victoria, BC V8W 3P5, Canada. TEL 604-721-7331. FAX 604-721-6216. TELEX 049-7222. (Dist. by: Western Geographical Series, P.O. Box 3050, Victoria, BC V8W 3P5, Canada) Ed. Harold D. Foster. circ. 1,000. **Indexed:** Geo.Abstr. **Document type:** monographic series.
—BLDSC (9300.810000).
Description: Emphasizes geographical techniques, resource management, urban geography and Pacific studies.

910   UK   ISSN 0956-5353
WIDEWORLD G C S E GEOGRAPHY REVIEW. 1989. q. £13.50 (foreign £26.50). Philip Allan Publishers Ltd., Deddington, Oxfordshire OX15 0SE, England. TEL 0869-38652. FAX 0869-38803. **Document type:** academic/scholarly publication.

581   GW   ISSN 0084-0912
WISSENSCHAFTLICHE ALPENVEREINSHEFTE. 1897. irreg. Deutscher Alpenverein, Von-Kahr-Str. 2-4, 80997 Munich, Germany. (Co-sponsor: Oesterreichischer Alpenverein) **Document type:** academic/scholarly publication.

WITTGENSTEIN. see *HISTORY — History Of Europe*

526   UN   ISSN 0084-1471
GA101   CODEN: WCARB4
WORLD CARTOGRAPHY. French edition: Cartographie Mondiale (ISSN 0591-2806) 1951. irreg., latest vol.21. price varies. United Nations Publications, Rm. DC2-853, New York, NY 10017. TEL 212-963-8302. FAX 212-963-3489. (Or: Distribution and Sales Section, CH-1211 Geneva 10, Switzerland) (also avail. in microfiche) **Indexed:** Bibl.Cart.
—BLDSC (9353.040000); Faxon.

WORLD EAGLE; the monthly social studies resource. see *SOCIAL SCIENCES: COMPREHENSIVE WORKS*

WORLD LITHUANIAN ROMAN CATHOLIC DIRECTORY. see *RELIGIONS AND THEOLOGY — Roman Catholic*

WORLD MAGAZINE; the magazine of mankind. see *TRAVEL AND TOURISM*

910   327   US
WORLD NEWSMAP OF THE WEEK - HEADLINE FOCUS; world news and world geography. 1938. 30/yr. $69.95 (effective 1993-1994). Weekly Reader Corporation, 245 Long Hill Rd., Middletown, CT 06457. TEL 800-446-3355. FAX 609-786-3360. (Subscr. to: 3000 Cindel Dr., Delran, NJ 08075) Ed. Sandra Maccarone. illus.; circ. 8,859 (paid). (poster format)
Incorporates: Headline Focus; Formerly: World Newsmap of the Week (ISSN 1046-1434); Which was formerly by the merger of: World Newsmap of the Week 1 (ISSN 0270-0158); World Newsmap of the Week 2 (ISSN 0270-0166); Which were formerly: World News of the Week (ISSN 0043-874X).
Description: Highlights and explains current international news with a political, historical and geographic context. For grades 7 to 12.

910   GW   ISSN 0510-9833
G58   CODEN: WBGAA9
WUERZBURGER GEOGRAPHISCHE ARBEITEN. 1953. irreg. price varies. Universitaet Wuerzburg, Geographisches Institut, Am Hubland, 97074 Wuerzburg, Germany. TEL 0931-8885548. FAX 0931-8885544. (Co-sponsor: Geographische Gesellschaft, Wuerzburg) Ed.Bd. illus. circ. 625. (tabloid format) **Indexed:** Bibl.& Ind.Geol, Geo.Abstr. **Document type:** academic/scholarly publication, monographic series.
Supersedes: Fraenkische Studien.
Description: Presents dissertations on geography.

910   GW   ISSN 0931-8623
WUERZBURGER GEOGRAPHISCHE MANUSKRIPT. 1975. irreg. price varies. Universitaet Wuerzburg, Geographisches Institut, Am Hubland, 97074 Wuerzburg, Germany. TEL 0931-8885555. FAX 0931-8885556. **Document type:** academic/scholarly publication, monographic series.
Description: Presents working papers, diploma theses and papers on regional themes.

910   PL   ISSN 0239-796X
WYZSZA SZKOLA PEDAGOGICZNA IM. KOMISJI EDUKACJI NARODOWEJ W KRAKOWIE. ROCZNIK NUKOWO-DYDAKTYCZNY. PRACE GEOGRAFICZNE. 1958. irreg., no.8, 1991. price varies. Wydawnictwo Naukowe W S P, Ul. Karmelicka 41, 31-128 Krakow, Poland. TEL 33-78-20. (Co-sponsor: Ministerstwo Edukacji Narodowej)

XIBEI SHI-DI/HISTORICAL AND GEOGRAPHICAL REVIEW OF NORTHWEST CHINA. see *HISTORY — History Of Asia*

XUANMEI JISHU/COAL PREPARATION TECHNOLOGY. see *MINES AND MINING INDUSTRY*

GEOGRAPHY — ABSTRACTING, BIBLIOGRAPHIES, STATISTICS

621.367   CC   ISSN 1000-3177
YAOGAN XINXI/REMOTE SENSING INFORMATION. (Text in Chinese) 1986. q. $27.60. (Guojia Yaogan Zhongxin - National Remote Sensing Centre) Science Press, Marketing and Sales Department, 16 Donghuangchenggen Beijie, Beijing 100707, People's Republic of China. TEL 4010642. FAX 4012180. TELEX 210247-SPBJ-CN. (Co-sponsor: National Topographic Bureau) adv.; charts; illus. circ. 10,000.
—BLDSC (7356.820500).
   Description: Aims to promote the development and popularization of remote sensing technology in China, and to expand the field of RS applications. For general readers as well as those involved in natural resource management.

910   SW   ISSN 0044-0477
GN1   CODEN: YMERAD
YMER. 1881. a. SEK 150 membership (effective 1993). Svenska Saellskapet foer Antropologi och Geografi (SSAG), Stockholm University, Department of Physical Geography, S-106 91 Stockholm, Sweden. Ed. Lars-Erik Aase. bk.rev.; bibl.; charts; illus.; index. circ. 1,200. **Indexed:** A.I.C.P., Bibl.Cart., GeoRef.
   Formerly: Tidskrift foer Antropologi och Kulturhistoria.

910.02   CC   ISSN 1001-7852
YUNNAN DILI HUANJING YANJIU/YUNNAN GEOGRAPHIC ENVIRONMENT RESEARCH. (Text in Chinese, English) s-a. Yunnan Institute of Geography, 28 East Jiaochang Rd., Kunming, Yunnan 650223, People's Republic of China. TEL 5154021. (Dist. overseas by: China International Book Trading Corp., P.O. Box 399, Beijing, P.R. China) Ed. Guo Laixi.
—BLDSC (9421.876500).

910   ZA   ISSN 0250-8109
Z G A OCCASIONAL STUDIES. Variant title: Z G A Occasional Studies and Special Publications. 1968. irreg., no.16, 1989. price varies. Zambia Geographical Association, Box 50287, Lusaka, Zambia. Ed. R. Chanda. charts. circ. 500. (back issues avail.) **Indexed:** Geo.Abstr.

910   ZA   ISSN 0250-8117
Z G A SCHOOL SUPPLEMENT. 1973. irreg., latest 1986. $3. Zambia Geographical Association, Box 50287, Lusaka, Zambia. Ed. F. Phiri. bk.rev.; charts. circ. 400. (tabloid format)
   Description: Focuses on geography teaching in Zambian secondary schools.

526.982   GW   ISSN 0937-9800
     CODEN: BILUAE
Z P F - PHOTOGRAMMETRIE UND FERNERKUNDUNG. (Text in German; summaries in English, French and German) 1926. bi-m. DM.123 (foreign DM.134). (Deutsche Gesellschaft fuer Photogrammetrie) Herbert Wichmann Verlag GmbH, Amalienstr. 29, 76133 Karlsruhe, Germany. TEL 0721-91220-0. FAX 0721-9122020. TELEX 7825909. Ed.Bd. adv.; bk.rev.; charts; illus.; tr.lit.; index. circ. 2,000. **Indexed:** Bibl.& Ind.Geol., Bibl.Cart., Geo.Abstr., Int.Aerosp.Abstr. **Document type:** trade publication.
—CCC.
   Formerly: Bildmessung und Luftbildwesen (ISSN 0006-2421)

526.9   ZA   ISSN 0084-5078
HD990.R68
ZAMBIA. SURVEY DEPARTMENT. REPORT. a. K.200. Zambia Government Printing Department, P.O. Box 30136, Lusaka, Zambia. **Document type:** government publication.
   Description: Annual paper of the Zambian Survey Department.

910   ZA
ZAMBIA GEOGRAPHICAL ASSOCIATION. OCCASIONAL NEWSLETTER. 1977. irreg. free to members. Zambia Geographical Association, P.O. Box 50287, Lusaka, Zambia. circ. 200. (looseleaf format) **Document type:** newsletter.
   Description: News for members in Zambia: forthcoming meetings, conferences.

968.94   ZA   ISSN 0250-8133
ZAMBIA GEOGRAPHICAL ASSOCIATION. REGIONAL HANDBOOK. Cover title: Z G A Regional Handbook. irreg., no.6, 1989. Zambia Geographical Association, Box 50287, Lusaka, Zambia. illus. (back issues avail.)
   Formerly: Zambia Geographical Association. Conference Handbook.

910   ZA   ISSN 0250-5657
ZAMBIAN GEOGRAPHICAL JOURNAL. (Text and summaries in English) 1967. a. $10. Zambia Geographical Association, Box 50287, Lusaka, Zambia. Ed. R. Chanda. bk.rev.; bibl. charts. circ. 500. (back issues avail.) **Indexed:** Biol.Abstr., Curr.Cont.Africa, Geo.Abstr.
   Formerly: Z G A Magazine.

910   GW   ISSN 0044-2461
G13   CODEN: ZERDAP
ZEITSCHRIFT FUER DEN ERDKUNDEUNTERRICHT. 1949. 11/yr. DM.64.90. Paedagogischer Zeitschriftenverlag, Postfach 269, 10107 Berlin, Germany. TEL 030-20343431. FAX 030-20343432. adv.; bk.rev.; bibl.; charts; illus.; index. circ. 7,900. **Indexed:** Bibl.& Ind.Geol., Bibl.Cart., Curr.Cont.Africa. **Document type:** academic/scholarly publication.

ZEITSCHRIFT FUER GEOMORPHOLOGIE/ANNALS OF GEOMORPHOLOGY/ANNALES DE GEOMORPHOLOGIE.
see EARTH SCIENCES — Geology

910   GW
ZEITSCHRIFT FUER GEOMORPHOLOGIE, SUPPLEMENTBAENDE/ANNALS OF GEOMORPHOLOGY, SUPPLEMENT VOLUMES/ANNALES DE GEOMORPHOLOGIE, SUPPLEMENTS. (Supplement to: Zeitschrift fuer Geomorphologie) (Text in English, French and German) 1960. irreg. price varies. Gebrueder Borntraeger Verlagsbuchhandlung, Johannesstr. 3A, 70176 Stuttgart, Germany. TEL 0711-625001. FAX 0711-625005. TELEX 723363-SCHB-D. Ed. H. Bremer. adv.; bk.rev. **Indexed:** Forest.Abstr. **Document type:** academic/scholarly publication.

ZEITSCHRIFT FUER SIEBENBUERGISCHE LANDESKUNDE.
see HISTORY — History Of Europe

ZEITSCHRIFT FUER VERMESSUNGSWESEN. see ENGINEERING — Civil Engineering

910   GW   ISSN 0044-3751
HF1021
ZEITSCHRIFT FUER WIRTSCHAFTSGEOGRAPHIE. 1957. 4/yr. DM.70 to individuals; institutions DM.97. Buchenverlag, Postfach 900126, 60441 Frankfurt a.M., Germany. Ed. Dr. Karl Vorlaufer. adv.; bk.rev.; charts; illus.; index. circ. 1,000. **Indexed:** Curr.Cont.Africa, E.I., Geo.Abstr., Key to Econ.Sci., P.A.I.S.For.Lang.Ind., Rural Devel.Abstr., Rural Recreat.Tour.Abstr., World Agri.Econ.& Rural Sociol.Abstr. **Document type:** academic/scholarly publication.
—BLDSC (9492.300000).

915.1   CC
ZHONGZHOU JINGU/ZHONGZHOU TODAY & YESTERDAY. (Text in Chinese) bi-m. $16.20. Henan Sheng Difang Shizhi Bianweihui, 25, Hongqi Lu Dongduan, Zhengzhou, Henan 450003, People's Republic of China. TEL 554537. (Dist. in US by: China Books & Periodicals, Inc., 2929 24th St., San Francisco, CA 94110. TEL 415-282-2994) Ed. Chu Xiangli.

GEOGRAPHY — Abstracting, Bibliographies, Statistics

ANTARCTIC BIBLIOGRAPHY. see SCIENCES: COMPREHENSIVE WORKS — Abstracting, Bibliographies, Statistics

910 015   PL   ISSN 0523-1787
BIBLIOGRAFIA GEOGRAFII POLSKIEJ. 1956. irreg. price varies. Polska Akademia Nauk, Instytut Geografii i Przestrzennego Zagospodarowania, Ul. Krakowskie Przedmiecie 30, 00-927 Warsaw, Poland. (Dist. by: ORWN PAN, Palac Kultury i Nauki, 00-901 Warsaw, Poland) Ed. D. Gazicka.

526 016   GW   ISSN 0340-0409
Z6021
BIBLIOGRAPHIA CARTOGRAPHICA; international documentation of cartographical literature. 1957. a. DM.168. (Staatsbibliothek Preussischer Kulturbesitz) K.G. Saur Verlag KG, A Reed Reference Publishing Company, Part of the Reed Elsevier group, Ortlerstr. 8, 81373 Munich, Germany. TEL 089-76902-0. FAX 089-76902150. TELEX 5212067-SAUR-D. (Subscr. to: Postfach 701620, 81316 Munich, Germany) (Co-sponsor: Deutsche Gesellschaft fuer Kartographie e.V.) Ed. Lothar Zoegner. **Document type:** bibliography.
—BLDSC (1961.400000).
   Formerly: Bibliotheca Cartographica.
   Description: Organizes the literature under 12 broad subject categories, plus sub-categories.

551 910   US   ISSN 0197-5889
BIBLIOGRAPHIC GUIDE TO MAPS AND ATLASES.* 1979. a. $315 cloth (foreign $345). G.K. Hall & Co., c/o MacMillan Publishing Co., 866 Third Ave., 18th fl., New York, NY 10022. TEL 212-702-6789. (Orders to: MacMillan Distribution Center, 100 Front St., Box 500, Riverside, NJ 08075-7500. TEL 800-257-5755) circ. 250. (back issues avail.) **Document type:** bibliography, abstracting/indexing.
   Description: Covers books about maps.

526 011   FR   ISSN 1142-3293
Z2165
BIBLIOGRAPHIE NATIONALE FRANCAISE. ATLAS, CARTES ET PLANS. a. 410 F. (foreign 480 F.). Bibliotheque Nationale de France, 58 rue de Richelieu, 75002 Paris, France. TEL 47-03-86-10. FAX 47-03-85-86. Ed. P.-A. Berard. **Document type:** bibliography.
   Former titles (until 1991): Bibliographie de la France. Supplement 4. Atlas, Cartes et Plans (ISSN 0150-5998); (until 1977): Bibliographie de la France. 1ere Partie, Bibliographie Officielle. Supplement 4. Atlas, Cartes et Plans (ISSN 1149-6924); (until 1975): Bibliographie de la France. Supplement E. Atlas, Cartes et Plans (ISSN 1147-5982); Supersedes in part (in 1946): Bibliographie de la France (ISSN 0150-5998)

910.02   US   ISSN 1044-8349
BIBLIOGRAPHIES AND INDEXES IN GEOGRAPHY. 1989. irreg. price varies. Greenwood Press, Inc. (Subsidiary of: Greenwood Publishing Group Inc.), 88 Post Rd. W., Box 5007, Westport, CT 06881-5007. TEL 203-226-3571. FAX 203-222-1502. **Document type:** monographic series.

318 016   BL   ISSN 0406-9765
Z1677
BRAZIL. FUNDACAO INSTITUTO BRASILEIRO DE GEOGRAFIA E ESTATISTICA. BOLETIM BIBLIOGRAFICO. 1957. q. free. Fundacao Instituto Brasileiro de Geografia e Estatistica, Departamento de Documentacao e Biblioteca, Rua General Canabarro, 666 Bloco B, 20271-201 Rio de Janeiro, RJ, Brazil. FAX 021-234-6189. TELEX 21-39128. bk.rev.; abstr.; circ. 250(controlled). **Document type:** government publication, bulletin.

919.8 011   CN
Z1392.N6
CANADIAN CIRCUMPOLAR LIBRARY. BULLETIN. 1930-1991 (vol.12, no.12). m. Can.$35. Canadian Circumpolar Library, University of Alberta, B-03 Cameron, Edmonton, Alta. T6G 2J8, Canada. TEL 403-492-4409. FAX 403-492-4327. TELEX 037-2979. Ed. Robin Minion. circ. 150. (back issues avail.)
   Formerly: Boreal Institute for Northern Studies. Library Bulletin (ISSN 0225-4484)

CURRENT ANTARCTIC LITERATURE. see SCIENCES: COMPREHENSIVE WORKS — Abstracting, Bibliographies, Statistics

910 016   US   ISSN 0011-3514
Z5009
CURRENT GEOGRAPHICAL PUBLICATIONS; additions to the research catalogue of the American Geographical Society Collection of the University of Wisconsin-Milwaukee Library. 1938. m. $70. (American Geographical Society Collection) University of Wisconsin-Milwaukee Library, Current Geographical Publications, Box 399, Milwaukee, WI 53201. TEL 414-229-6282. adv.; bk.rev.; bibl.; index. circ. 1,200. (also avail. in microform from JMI; reprint service avail. from KTO,UMI) **Indexed:** Bibl.Cart., E.I., Popul.Ind. **Document type:** bibliography.
—UnCover; UMI.

910 011 FR ISSN 1157-3805
Z6001
F R A N C I S. 531: BIBLIOGRAPHIE GEOGRAPHIQUE INTERNATIONALE. 1891. q. 625 F. (outside EEC 655 F.). Centre National de la Recherche Scientifique, Institut de l'Information Scientifique et Technique, 2 allee du Parc de Brabois, 54514 Vandoeuvre-les-Nancy Cedex, France. TEL 83-50-46-00. FAX 83-50-46-50. adv. contact: Veronique Guinvarc'h. index, cum.index. (back issues avail.; reprint service avail. from KTO) **Document type:** bibliography.
●Also available online. Vendor(s): Telesystemes - Questel.
Also available on CD-ROM.
Formerly: Bibliographie Geographique Internationale (ISSN 0067-6993)

526 UK ISSN 0953-9611
GF1
GEOGRAPHICAL ABSTRACTS: HUMAN GEOGRAPHY.
(Includes: Geographical Abstracts. Annual Index) 1966. 12/yr. (plus a. cumulation). £398($615) (effective 1994). Elsevier - Geo Abstracts (Subsidiary of: Elsevier Science Ltd.), Regency House, 34 Duke St., Norwich NR3 3AP, England. TEL 44-603-626327. FAX 44-603-667934. TELEX 975247 CHACOM G. (Subscr. to: Elsevier Science Ltd., Oxford Fulfilment Centre, P.O. Box 800, Kidlington, Oxford OX5 1DX, England. TEL 44-865-843000. FAX 44-865-843010; Subscr. in U.S. and Canada to: Elsevier Science, 660 White Plains Rd., Tarrytown, NY 10591-5153. TEL 914-524-9200. FAX 914-333-2444) Eds. Patrick Hardiman, Karen Ferenczy. index. circ. 800. (back issues avail.) Indexed: Field Crop Abstr., Forest.Abstr., Forest Prod.Abstr., Herb.Abstr., Popul.Ind. **Document type:** abstracting/indexing.
●Also available online. Vendor(s): DIALOG Information Services, Inc. (File no.292), Orbit Search Service (GEOB).
—BLDSC (4125.434000). **CCC.**
Formed by the 1989 merger of: Geographical Abstracts: Economic Geography; Geographical Abstracts: Social and Historical Geography; Geographical Abstracts: Regional and Community Planning; Geographical Abstracts: Economic Geography was formerly: Geographical Abstracts C (Economic Geography) (ISSN 0268-7895), which was formerly: Geo Abstracts C (Economic Geography) (ISSN 0305-1919); Geographical Abstracts: Social and Historical Geography was formerly: Geographical Abstracts D (Social and Historical Geography) (ISSN 0268-7909), which was formerly: Geo Abstracts D (Social and Historical Geography) (ISSN 0305-1927); Geographical Abstracts: Regional and Community Planning was formerly: Geographical Abstracts F (Regional and Community Planning) (ISSN 0268-7925), which was formerly: Geo Abstracts F (Regional and Community Planning) (ISSN 0305-1945).
Description: International abstracting service for human, social and historical geographers, and planners.

910 UK ISSN 0954-0504
GB54.5 CODEN: GAPGET
GEOGRAPHICAL ABSTRACTS: PHYSICAL GEOGRAPHY.
(Includes: Geographical Abstracts. Annual Index) 1960. 12/yr. (plus a. cumulation). £550($845) (effective 1994). Elsevier - Geo Abstracts (Subsidiary of: Elsevier Science Ltd.), Regency House, 34 Duke St., Norwich NR3 3AP, England. TEL 44-603-626327. FAX 44-603-667934. TELEX 975247 CHACOM G. (Subscr. to: Elsevier Science Ltd., Oxford Fulfilment Centre, P.O. Box 800, Kidlington, Oxford OX5 1DX, England. TEL 44-865-843000. FAX 44-865-843010; Subscr. in U.S. and Canada to: Elsevier Science, 660 White Plains Rd., Tarrytown, NY 10591-5153. TEL 914-524-9200. FAX 914-333-2444) Ed.Bd. adv.; bk.rev.; index. circ. 1,000. (also avail. in magnetic tape; back issues avail.) **Indexed:** AESIS. **Document type:** abstracting/indexing.
●Also available online. Vendor(s): DIALOG Information Services, Inc. (File no.292), Orbit Search Service (GEOB).
—BLDSC (4125.437000). **CCC.**
Formed by the 1989 merger of: Geographical Abstracts: Landforms and the Quaternary; Geographical Abstracts: Sedimentology; Geographical Abstracts: Climatology and Hydrology; Geographical Abstracts: Remote Sensing Photogrammetry and Cartography.
Description: International abstracting service for physical geographers.

910 CC
GUOWAI KEJI ZILIAO MULU - CEHUIXUE/FOREIGN SCIENCE AND TECHNOLOGY LITERATURE CATALOGUE - SURVEY. (Text in Chinese) q. Quanguo Cehui Kexue Jishu Qingbaowang - National Survey Science Information Network, 16 Beitaiping Lu, Beijing 100039, People's Republic of China. TEL 8212277. Ed. Zhao Youmao.

910 II ISSN 0250-9687
I C S S R JOURNAL OF ABSTRACTS AND REVIEWS: GEOGRAPHY. (Text in English) 1975. s-a. Rs.30 to individuals; institutions Rs.50. Indian Council of Social Science Research, 35 Ferozshah Rd., New Delhi 110 001, India. TEL 381571. FAX 91-11-388037. TELEX 31-61083-ISSR-IN. Ed. Aijazuddin Ahmed. adv.; bk.rev.; index. circ. 550. (back issues avail.) **Document type:** abstracting/indexing, academic/scholarly publication.
Description: Abstracts of research published in Indian journals.

914 011 FR ISSN 0427-2218
GA66.F8 CODEN: BIIGAP
INSTITUT GEOGRAPHIQUE NATIONAL. BULLETIN D'INFORMATION. 1943. bi-m. free. Institut Geographique National, Service de la Documentation Geographique, 136 bis, rue de Grenelle, 75700 Paris, France. TEL 43-98-80-00. Eds. Jacques Schwengler, Isabelle Melot. adv.; bk.rev.; circ. controlled. **Indexed:** Bibl.Cart.
—BLDSC (2862.550000).

526 016 GR
INTERNATIONAL ASSOCIATION OF GEODESY. CENTRAL BUREAU FOR SATELLITE GEODESY. BIBLIOGRAPHY. 1965. irreg. free. International Association of Geodesy, Central Bureau for Satellite Geodesy, National Technical University, K. Zographou 9, Athens 624, Greece. **Document type:** bibliography.
Formerly: Bibliography on Satellite Geodesy and Related Subjects (ISSN 0067-7353)

910 016 UK ISSN 0262-0855
HC59.69
INTERNATIONAL DEVELOPMENT ABSTRACTS. 1982. 6/yr. (plus a. cumulation). £285($440) (effective 1994). Elsevier - Geo Abstracts (Subsidiary of: Elsevier Science Ltd.), Regency House, 34 Duke St., Norwich NR3 3AP, England. TEL 44-603-626327. FAX 44-603-667934. TELEX 975247 CHACOM G. (Subscr. to: Elsevier Science Ltd., Oxford Fulfilment Centre, P.O. Box 800, Kidlington, Oxford OX5 1DX, England. TEL 44-865-843000. FAX 44-865-843010; Subscr. in U.S. and Canada to: Elsevier Science, 660 White Plains Rd., Tarrytown, NY 10591-5153. TEL 914-524-9200. FAX 914-333-2444) Ed. M. Amos. adv.; index. circ. 500. **Document type:** abstracting/indexing.
●Also available online. Vendor(s): DIALOG Information Services, Inc. (File no.292), Orbit Search Service.
—BLDSC (4539.546000). **CCC.**
Description: International abstracting service, covering all aspects of development studies.

526.3 JA
ITTO SUIJUNTEN KENSOKU SEIKA SHUROKU. (Text in Japanese) 1954. irreg. Kokudo Chiriin, Sokuchibu - Geographical Survey Institute, Geodetic Department, Ministry of Construction, Kitasato-1, Tsukuba-shi, Ibaraki-ken 305, Japan. stat. **Document type:** government publication.
Description: Provides data on land survey results from the first bench mark.

526.3 JA
KOKYO SOKURYO NO KIROKU. 1970. a. Kokudo Chiriin - Geographical Survey Institute, Ministry of Construction, Kitasato-1, Tsukuba-shi, Ibaraki-ken 305, Japan. stat. **Document type:** government publication.
Description: Contains records of land surveys.

526 US ISSN 0734-7634
NATIONAL UNION CATALOG. CARTOGRAPHIC MATERIALS. 1983. q. $200 to N. American libraries (foreign libraries $225). (U.S. Library of Congress) Advanced Library Systems, Inc., 100 Brickstone Sq., Box 246, Andover, MA 01810-0005. TEL 508-470-0610. FAX 508-475-1072.

520 JA
NIHON TENMON GAKKAI KOEN YOKOSHU. (Text in English, Japanese) s-a. 2000 Yen. Nihon Tenmon Gakkai - Astronomical Society of Japan, Tokyo Tenmondai, 21-1, Osawa 2-chome, Mitaka-shi, Tokyo 181, Japan. abstr. **Document type:** abstracting/indexing.
Description: Abstracts from proceedings of the society.

OSAKA-FU IKKYU SUIJUN SOKURYO SEIKAHYO. see ENGINEERING — Abstracting, Bibliographies, Statistics

950 015 UN ISSN 1010-9897
PERIODICALS OF ASIA AND THE PACIFIC; a selected list of titles received and their contents. (Text in English) no.31, 1971. s-a. free or on exchange basis. Unesco, Principal Regional Office for Asia and the Pacific, P.O. Box 1425, Bangkok 10500, Thailand. FAX 391-0866. TELEX 20591 TH. bibl. circ. 850. **Document type:** abstracting/indexing.
Former titles: Periodicals of Asia and Oceania (ISSN 0251-4737); Asian Periodicals (ISSN 0044-9210)

910 016 RU ISSN 0034-2378
G1
REFERATIVNYI ZHURNAL. GEOGRAFIYA. 1956. m. 302 Rub. (320 Rub. including index). Vsesoyuznyi Institut Nauchno-Tekhnicheskoi Informatsii (VINITI), Baltiiskaya ul., 14, Moscow A-219, Russia. (Dist. by: Mezhdunarodnaya Kniga, Dimitrova Ul. 39, 113095 Moscow, Russia) **Indexed:** Bibl.Cart., Chem.Abstr. **Document type:** abstracting/indexing.

910 MX ISSN 0049-1004
SOCIEDAD MEXICANA DE GEOGRAFIA Y ESTADISTICA. BOLETIN. 1839. s-a. Sociedad Mexicana de Geografia y Estadistica, Justo Sierra No. 19, Apdo. 10739, Mexico D.F., Mexico. **Indexed:** Amer.Hist.& Life, Hist.Abstr.

910 US ISSN 0163-7347
Z6028
U.S. COPYRIGHT OFFICE. CATALOG OF COPYRIGHT ENTRIES. FOURTH SERIES. PART 6: MAPS. 1978. s-a. $5 (foreign $6.25). U.S. Library of Congress, Copyright Office, Washington, DC 20559. TEL 202-783-3238. FAX 202-512-2250. (Dist. by: Superintendent of Documents, U.S. Government Printing Office, Box 371954, Pittsburgh, PA 15250-7954. TEL 202-783-3238. FAX 202-512-2233) bibl. (microfiche).
Formerly: U.S. Copyright Office. Catalog of Copyright Entries. Third Series. Part 6. Maps and Atlases (ISSN 0041-7874)

011 910 ZA ISSN 0250-8125
Z G A BIBLIOGRAPHIC SERIES. 1974. irreg., no.4, 1982. price varies. Zambia Geographical Association, P.O. Box 50287, Lusaka, Zambia. Ed. R. Chanda. (back issues avail.) **Indexed:** Geo.Abstr. **Document type:** bibliography.

GEOGRAPHY — Computer Applications

910.285 US ISSN 1064-6108
A R C NEWS. 1987. q. Environmental Systems Research Institute, Inc., 380 New York St., Redlands, CA 92373. TEL 909-793-2853. FAX 909-793-5953. Ed. Karen Hunter. adv.: B&W page $2650. bk.rev. circ. 80,000. (back issues avail.) **Document type:** newspaper.
Description: Designed for the ESRI user community as well as others involved or interested in mapping and geographic information systems (GIS). Covers conferences, new software and hardware developments, new applications of mapping technology, and trends in GIS education.

910 UK ISSN 0926-3403
▼**G I S EUROPE.** (Geographic Information Systems) 1992. 10/yr. $80 (effective Jan. 1993). Longmans Geo Information, 307 Cambridge Science Pk., Milton Rd., Cambridge, CB44ZD, England. TEL 44-223-423020. FAX 44-223-425787. Ed. H. Dennison Parker. adv.; bk.rev. **Document type:** trade publication.
—BLDSC (4179.285000); SWETS.

GEOLOGY

910.285 US ISSN 0897-5507
G70.2
G I S WORLD. (Geographic Information Systems) 1988. 12/yr. $72 (effective Jan. 1993). G I S World Inc., 155 E. Boardwalk Dr., Ste. 250, Ft. Collins, CO 80525. TEL 303-223-4848. FAX 303-223-5700. Ed. Derry Eynon. adv.: B&W page $2948, color page $4316; trim 8 3/8 x 10 7/8. bk.rev. circ. 20,480. **Document type:** trade publication.
—BLDSC (4179.370000); UnCover; SWETS.
  Description: Contains news, technical developments, applications, features, and events relating to the field of geographic information systems.

910 US ISSN 1051-9858
G70.2
GEO INFO SYSTEMS; applications of GIS and related spatial information technologies. 1990. 10/yr. $59 (foreign $117). Advanstar Communications, Inc., 7500 Old Oak Blvd., Cleveland, OH 44130. TEL 216-826-2839. FAX 216-891-2726. (Subscr. to: 1 E. First St., Duluth, MN 55082. TEL 800-346-0085) Ed. Guy Maynard. circ. 24,511. (back issues avail.) **Document type:** trade publication.
—UnCover; SWETS. **CCC.**
  Description: Covers practical applications of geographic information systems for planning, developing and managing environments ranging from a local utility infrastructure to the North American ecosystem.

910.285 US ISSN 1057-3348
G70.2
INTERNATIONAL G I S SOURCEBOOK. (Geographic Information Systems) 1989. a. $134.95 (effective 1994). G I S World Inc., 155 E. Boardwalk, Ste. 250, Fort Collins, CO 80525. TEL 303-223-4848. FAX 303-223-5700. Ed. Gayle Rodcay. adv.; circ. 2,000 (paid). **Document type:** directory.
Formerly (until 1990): G I S Sourcebook (ISSN 1046-8412)
  Description: Contains industry directories, comparison charts for software packages, vendor profiles, articles on major application areas and the state of technology in foreign countries, and college and university course offerings.

910.285 UK ISSN 0269-3798
G70.2   CODEN: IJGSE3
INTERNATIONAL JOURNAL OF GEOGRAPHICAL INFORMATION SYSTEMS. 1987. bi-m. £83($144) to individuals; institutions £180($303). Taylor & Francis Ltd., Rankine Rd., Basingstoke, Hants RG24 8PR, England. TEL 0256-840366. FAX 0256-479438. TELEX 858540. Eds. Peter Fisher, Keith Clarke. adv.; bk.rev.; charts; illus.; index. circ. 1,150. (back issues avail.) **Indexed:** Geo.Abstr. **Document type:** academic/scholarly publication.
—BLDSC (4542.266200); Faxon; UnCover; SWETS. **CCC.**
  Description: Covers theory, research, development and applications of GIS, including associated hardware and software.
  Refereed Serial

910.285 UK
MAPPING AWARENESS AND G I S IN EUROPE; Geographic Information Systems. 1987. 10/yr. Miles Arnold Ltd., Grey Cottage, Cassington, Witney, Oxfordshire OX8 1DL, England. TEL 0865-880236. FAX 0865-883301. Ed. Peter Shand. adv.: B&W page £830, color page £1425; trim 210 x 297. circ. 8,000. **Document type:** trade publication.

GEOLOGY

see Earth Sciences–Geology

GEOPHYSICS

see Earth Sciences–Geophysics

GEOTHERMAL ENERGY

see Energy–Geothermal Energy

GERONTOLOGY AND GERIATRICS

301.435 US ISSN 1044-1123
A A R P BULLETIN. 1958. m. (11/yr.). membership. American Association of Retired Persons (Washington), 601 E St., N.W., Washington, DC 20049. TEL 202-434-2277. Ed. Elliot Carlson. adv. circ. 33,000,000. (tabloid format)
Formerly (until 1989): A A R P News Bulletin (ISSN 0001-0200)
  Description: Includes current news from the Executive Branch, Congress, courts, regulatory agencies and state legislatures. Reports on Washington activities and national trends that have a bearing on the lives of older people.

362.6 US
A A R P HIGHLIGHTS. bi-m. American Association of Retired Persons, Volunteer Chapter, 601 E St., N.W., Washington, DC 20049. TEL 202-434-3400. (Co-sponsor: Retired Teachers Association)
  Description: Reports on AARP volunteer chapter and RTA unit activities and programs.

A A R P HOUSING REPORT. (American Association of Retired Persons) see HOUSING AND URBAN PLANNING

362.6 US
A A R P - W I N. s-a. free. American Association of Retired Persons, Women's Initiative, 601 E St., N.W., Washington, DC 20049. TEL 202-434-2400. **Document type:** newsletter.
  Description: For and about the people, programs, and issues of the AARP Women's Initiative.

301.435 CN ISSN 0826-497X
A C A NEWS; the provincial newsletter for seniors. 1967. 6/yr. $10 to individuals; institutions $25. Alberta Council on Aging, 501, 10506 Jasper Ave., Edmonton, AB T5J 2W9, Canada. TEL 403-423-7781. FAX 403-425-9246. Ed. Chris Lawrence. adv.; bk.rev.; bibl.; illus. circ. 10,000. (back issues avail.) **Document type:** newsletter.
  Former titles: Alberta Council on Aging News; Horizons (ISSN 0018-4985)

362.6 378 US ISSN 0890-278X
A G H E EXCHANGE. 1975. q. $25 (foreign $30). Association for Gerontology in Higher Education, 1001 Connecticut Ave., N.W., Ste. 410, Washington, DC 20036-5504. TEL 202-429-9277. Ed. Leslie Morgan. adv. contact: Joy Lobenstine. circ. 3,500. (back issues avail.) **Document type:** newsletter.
Formerly: A G H E Newsletter.
  Description: Focuses on news of interest to gerontological educators. Sections include: Principles and Practices, Resource Briefs, Research and Training Notes, Policy Page, Research Reports, National News, Geriatric Education, Member Profiles and In and Around A G H E.

618.97 US
A M D A REPORTS. q. membership. American Medical Directors Association, 10480 Little Patuxent Pkwy., Ste. 760, Columbia, MD 21044. circ. 3,000. (tabloid format; back issues avail.; reprint service avail.)
  Description: Covers issues for medical directors of long-term care facilities.

618.97 IT ISSN 0001-5741
ACTA GERONTOLOGICA. 1950. q. L.80000. (Universita degli Studi di Pavia, Istituto Gerontologia e Geriatria) Tipografia del Libro, Via Cavallini 15, 27100 Pavia, Italy. TEL 0382-21265. FAX 29419. Ed. Pietro de Nicola. adv.; bk.rev. circ. 2,000. **Indexed:** Biol.Abstr., Chem.Abstr., Excerp.Med., Ind.Med., Nutr.Abstr., Sci.Cit.Ind.

ACTIVE AMERICAN. see PHYSICAL FITNESS AND HYGIENE

155 US ISSN 0192-4788
RC952.5   CODEN: AADADK
ACTIVITIES, ADAPTATION & AGING; the gerontological journal of activities. 1980. q. $34 to individuals; institutions $150; libraries $190. Haworth Press, Inc., 10 Alice St., Binghamton, NY 13904. TEL 607-722-5857; 800-342-9678. FAX 607-722-1424. Ed. Phyllis Foster. adv.; bk.rev.; bibl.; charts. circ. 468. (also avail. in microfiche from HAW; back issues avail.; reprint service avail. from HAW) **Indexed:** Abstr.Soc.Geront., Behav.Abstr., Biol.Abstr., Bull.Signal., Chicago Psychoanal.Lit.Ind., CLOA, Excerp.Med., Med.Care Rev., Past.Care & Couns.Abstr., PSI, Psychol.Abstr., Ref.Zh., Rehabil Lit., Soc.Work.Res.& Abstr., Sociol.Abstr. **Document type:** academic/scholarly publication.
—BLDSC (0676.470000); Faxon; UnCover; SWETS.
  Description: Provides case studies, program evaluations, research and theory for activities directors and coordinators in nursing homes and community centers, as well as other professionals concerned with the enhancement of the lifestyles of the aged.
  Refereed Serial

362.1 AT ISSN 0705-1549
ACTIVITIES DIGEST. 1979. bi-m. Aus.$50. P.O. Box 5227D, Newcastle West 2302, Australia. TEL 049-62-1069. Ed. Dean Cornish. bk.rev. (back issues avail.)
  Description: Information for staff providing recreation for aged people.

610.736 US ISSN 0885-4572
ADULT DAY CARE LETTER. 1985. m. $127. Health Resources Publishing, Brinley Professional Plaza, 3100 Hwy. 138, Box 1442, Wall Township, NJ 07719-1442. TEL 908-681-1133. FAX 908-681-0490. Ed. Robert K. Jenkins. index. (back issues avail.) **Document type:** newsletter.
—CCC.
  Description: Provides administrators and directors with current news on the services involved in running an adult day care center including social services, health care, mental health, nutrition, recreation and rehabilitation activities.

ADVANCES IN MOTOR DEVELOPMENT RESEARCH. see PHYSICAL FITNESS AND HYGIENE

362.6 DK ISSN 0904-6216
AELDRE SAGEN. 1967. 6/yr. Landsforeningen Aeldre Sagen, Vesterbrogade 97, 1620 Copenhagen V, Denmark. TEL 45-31-23-44-11. FAX 45-31-23-46-23. Ed. Jesper Haller. adv. circ. 220,000.
  Former titles (until 1988): Aktivt Otium (ISSN 0902-5960); (until 1987): Otium (ISSN 0108-5867)

612.67 US ISSN 0161-9152
   CODEN: AGEEDB
AGE. 1978. q. $35 (foreign $40). American Aging Association, 2129 Providence Ave., Chester, PA 19013. TEL 215-874-7550. FAX 215-876-7715. Ed. Dr. Arthur Balin. bk.rev.; index. circ. 400. **Indexed:** Biol.Abstr., Chem.Abstr., Curr.Adv.Biochem., Curr.Cont., Excerp.Med., Helminthol.Abstr., Ind.Sci.Rev., NRN, Protozool.Abstr., Sci.Cit.Ind. **Document type:** academic/scholarly publication.
—BLDSC (0736.070000); Faxon; UnCover; SWETS; UMI; CASDDS.
  Description: Covers the effect of age on DNA, RNA, hormones, lysosomes, mitochondria, connective tissue, catecholamines, endoplasmic reticulum, and lipid metabolism.
  Refereed Serial

GERONTOLOGY AND GERIATRICS

618.9   UK   ISSN 0002-0729
RC952   CODEN: AANGAH
AGE AND AGEING. 1972. bi-m. £90($165) (effective 1994). (British Geriatrics Society) Oxford University Press, Oxford Journals, Walton St., Oxford OX2 6DP, England. TEL 0865-56767. FAX 0865-56646. TELEX 837330-OXPRES-G. (U.S. subscr. to: Oxford University Press Inc., 2001 Evans Rd., Cary, NC 27513. TEL 919-677-0977) (Co-sponsor: British Society for Research in Ageing) Ed. J. Grimley Evans. adv.; bk.rev.; bibl.; charts; illus.; index. circ. 2,700. **Indexed:** Abstr.Health Care Manage.Stud., Abstr.Hyg., ASSIA, Bibl.Ind., Biol.Abstr., Chem.Abstr., Curr.Adv.Ecol.Sci., Curr.Cont., Dent.Ind., Excerp.Med., Ind.Med., Ind.Sci.Rev., NRN, Soc.Sci.Ind., Trop.Dis.Bull. **Document type:** academic/scholarly publication.
●Also available online. Vendor(s): BRS Online Products.
—BLDSC (0736.080000); Faxon; UnCover; SWETS; UMI; CASDDS. **CCC.**
   Description: Covers biological gerontology and geriatrics, including research on ageing and the clinical, epidemiological and psychological aspects of medicine in old age.

362.6   UK
AGE CONCERN INFORMATION CIRCULAR. 1974. m. £16. Age Concern England, Astral House, 1268 London Rd., London SW16 4ER, England. TEL 44-81-679-8000. FAX 44-81-679-6069. TELEX 24667-IMPEMP-G. Ed. Lynette Cawthra. bk.rev.; s-a. index. circ. 1,700. (back issues avail.) **Document type:** bulletin.
   Description: Covers news about legislation, policy and services affecting older persons. Reviews new books, reports and surveys and highlights forthcoming conferences

AGE DISCRIMINATION. see *POLITICAL SCIENCE — Civil Rights*

612.67   US
AGE NEWS. 1970. q. membership only. American Aging Association, 2129 Providence Ave., Chester, PA 19013. TEL 215-874-7550. FAX 215-876-7715. Ed. Dr. Sheldon Ball. **Document type:** academic/scholarly publication.
   Description: Promotes biomedical aging research.

362.6   UK
AGEING. irreg. (Board for Social Responsibility of the General Synod, Social Policy Committee) Church House Publishing, Church House, Great Smith St., London SW1P 3NZ, England. TEL 071-799-9011.

362.6   UK   ISSN 0144-686X
HQ1060
AGEING AND SOCIETY. 1981. q. £36($55) to individuals (overseas £50); institutions £67 (overseas £81 ($118)). Cambridge University Press, Edinburgh Bldg., Shaftesbury Rd., Cambridge CB2 2RU, England. TEL 0223-312393. FAX 0223-315052. TELEX 851817256. (N. American addr.: Cambridge University Press, Journals Dept., 40 W. 20th St., New York, NY 10011. TEL 212-924-3900. FAX 212-691-3239) (Co-sponsors: Centre for Policy on Ageing; British Society of Gerontology) Ed. Peter G. Coleman. adv.; bk.rev. (also avail. in microform from UMI; back issues avail.; reprint service avail. SWZ) **Indexed:** Abstr.Soc.Geront., ASCA, ASSIA, CLOA, Curr.Cont., P.A.I.S., SSCI, World Bibl.Soc.Sec. **Document type:** academic/scholarly publication.
—BLDSC (0736.225770); Faxon; UnCover; SWETS; UMI. **CCC.**
   Description: Covers human ageing all over the world: theoretical and empirical research on such issues as life-styles in later life, work and retirement, mental illness, sexuality, demography, health care and the history of old age.

618   US   ISSN 0163-5158
AGEING INTERNATIONAL. 1974. q. $20 to individuals (foreign $25); institutions $40 (foreign $45). International Federation on Ageing, 601 E St. N.W., Washington, DC 20049. TEL 202-434-2430. FAX 202-434-6494. Ed. Charlotte E. Nusberg. circ. 2,000. (back issues avail.) **Indexed:** CLOA, World Bibl.Soc.Sec. **Document type:** bulletin.
—BLDSC (0736.225800); Faxon; UnCover; SWETS.
   Description: Covers international trends, researches, policies, programs and publications about aging.

612.67   UK   ISSN 0268-1544
AGING. s-m. £110. S U B I S, 1 Northumberland Rd., Sheffield S10 2TT, England. TEL 0742-796540. FAX 0742-797066. (looseleaf format; back issues avail.) **Document type:** abstracting/indexing.
—CCC.
   Description: Current awareness service for researchers in clinical and life sciences.

362.6   US   ISSN 0273-2467
AGING (BOCA RATON). (Subseries of: S I R S Social Issues (ISSN 0740-3127)) 1976. a. price varies; a. supplement $17. Social Issues Resources Series, Box 2348, Boca Raton, FL 33427-2348. TEL 407-994-0079; 800-232-7477. FAX 407-994-4704. (looseleaf format; also avail. in microfiche; back issues avail.)
   Description: Reprints articles that explore the social, economic, and ethical issues of aging.

612.67   US   ISSN 0361-0179
AGING (NEW YORK). 1975. irreg., latest vol.39. price varies. Raven Press (Subsidiary of: Wolters Kluwer N.V.), 1185 Ave. of the Americas, New York, NY 10036. TEL 212-930-9500. FAX 212-869-3495. TELEX 640073. (reprint service avail. from UMI) **Indexed:** Biol.Abstr., Chem.Abstr., Curr.Cont., Mag.Ind., NRN, Sci.Cit.Ind. **Document type:** monographic series.
—Faxon.
Refereed Serial

618.97   NE   ISSN 0928-9917
▼**AGING AND COGNITION**; a journal of normal and dysfunctional development. (Text in English) 1994. q. fl.314($173) (effective 1994). Swets & Zeitlinger bv, Heereweg 347, 2161 CA Lisse, Netherlands. TEL 31-2521-35111. FAX 31-2521-15888. TELEX 41325. (Dist. in N. America by: Swets & Zeitlinger, 440 Creamery Way, Ste. A, Exton, PA 19341. TEL 800-447-9387. FAX 610-524-5366) Ed.Bd. **Document type:** academic/scholarly publication.
   Description: Publishes research in normal and dysfunctional aspects of cognitive development in adulthood and aging, integrating theory, method and research findings in the fields of cognitive gerontology and neuropsychology.

362.6   US
AGING ARKANSAS; it's everyone's future. 1988. m. $6. Arkansas Aging Foundation, Inc., 706 S. Pulaski St., Little Rock, AR 72201. TEL 501-376-6083. FAX 501-376-6084. Ed. Anne Howard Wasson. adv.; bk.rev.; charts; illus.; stat. circ. 42,000. (tabloid format; large print edition in 14 pt.; back issues avail.; reprint service avail.) **Document type:** newspaper.
   Description: For and about older Arkansans; focuses on health, positive retirement, consumer issues, updates on public policy and entitlement programs, activities and human interest features.
Refereed Serial

612.67   IT   ISSN 0394-9532
CODEN: AGNGET
AGING - CLINICAL AND EXPERIMENTAL RESEARCH. (Text in English) 1989. bi-m. L.80000($80) Editrice Kurtis s.r.l., Via L. Zoja, 30, 20153 Milan, Italy. TEL 02-48202740. FAX 02-48201219. Ed. G. Crepaldi. adv.; B&W page L.5150000, color page L.6500000; trim 200 x 260. **Indexed:** Curr.Cont.
—BLDSC (0736.295000).
   Description: Publishes original studies on gerontology, geriatrics and related fields.

618.97   US   ISSN 0892-8762
QR180   CODEN: AIIDE9
AGING: IMMUNOLOGY & INFECTIOUS DISEASE. q. $127 (foreign $167). Mary Ann Liebert, Inc., 1651 Third Ave., New York, NY 10128. TEL 212-289-2300. FAX 212-289-4697. Ed. Dr. G. Jeanette Thorbecke. **Indexed:** Excerp.Med. (1993-). **Document type:** academic/scholarly publication.
—BLDSC (0736.298000); SWETS.
   Description: Covers immunology and infectious diseases related to aging. Also provides a forum for basic studies on host defense mechanisms, in vivo in animals and man, in vitro, and at the molecular level.
Refereed Serial

301.435   IS
AGING IN THE JEWISH WORLD: CONTINUITY AND CHANGE. (Text in English) 1985. irreg. $22. J D C - Brookdale Institute for Gerontology and Human Development in Israel, P.O. Box 13087, Jerusalem 91130, Israel. TEL 972-2-557400. FAX 972-2-635851. circ. 500.
   Formerly (until 1992): Aging in the Jewish World (ISSN 0334-9144)

612   US   ISSN 0742-3438
AGING NETWORK NEWS. 1984. m. $55. Hansan Group Inc., Box 1223, McLean, VA 22101. TEL 703-734-3266. FAX 703-847-0573. Ed. John Hansan. adv.; bk.rev.; charts; illus. circ. 1,000. (back issues avail.) **Document type:** newsletter.
   Formerly: Aging Program Letter.

301.435   US
AGING NEWS. 1974. q. free. Office for the Aging, 2 Empire State Plaza, Albany, NY 12223. FAX 518-474-0608. Ed. R. Wendover. bk.rev.; charts; illus.; stat. circ. 35,000. **Document type:** government publication, newsletter.
   Formerly: New York (State). Office for the Aging. Newsletter; Supersedes: Cameo Newsletter (ISSN 0008-2058)

612.67   US
AGING NEWS ALERT. 1984. s-m. $207. (Community Development Services, Inc.) C D Publications, 8204 Fenton St., Silver Spring, MD 20910. TEL 301-588-6380. FAX 301-588-6385. Ed. Ken Silverstone. index. (back issues avail.) **Document type:** newsletter.
   Incorporates (1987-1992): Senior Care Professional (ISSN 1051-6913); (1989-1992): Senior Law Report (ISSN 1050-3250); Former titles: Aging Action Alert (ISSN 1050-3188); Aging Alert.
   Description: For all professionals working with the elderly. Covers news and developments in the geriatric field.

362.6   US   ISSN 0888-6830
HQ1060
AGING RESEARCH & TRAINING NEWS. 1978. s-m. $182.38 (effective Sep. 1992). Business Publishers, Inc., 951 Pershing Dr., Silver Spring, MD 20910-4464. TEL 301-587-6300. FAX 301-585-9075. Ed. Audrey Osborne. (looseleaf format) **Document type:** newsletter.
●Also available online. Vendor(s): NewsNet.
—CCC.
   Formerly (until 1987): Aging News (ISSN 0197-4017)
   Description: Provides information on current grants and contracts for aging research and training.

051   US
AGING TODAY. 1979. bi-m. $30. American Society on Aging, 833 Market St., Ste. 511, San Francisco, CA 94103-1824. TEL 415-974-9600. FAX 415-974-0300. Ed. Paul Kleyman. adv.; bk.rev. circ. 11,000. (tabloid format; back issues avail.)

612.67   NO   ISSN 0801-9991
ALDRING OG ELDRE.; gerontologisk magasin. 1984. q. NOK 375 in the Nordic countries; elsewhere NOK 435. Scandinavian University Press, P.O. Box 2959, N-0608 Oslo, Norway. TEL 472-67-7600. FAX 472-67-7575. (Dist. by: Scandinavian University Press, 200 Meacham Ave., Elmont, NY 11003. TEL 516-352-7300) Ed. Svein Olav Daatland. adv.; bk.rev. circ. 2,500.
—CCC.
   Formerly: Gerontologisk Magasin (ISSN 0800-2509)
   Description: Focuses on professional gerontological issues for those who work or have an interest in the care of older people and their position in society.

ALMSHOUSES GAZETTE. see *SOCIAL SERVICES AND WELFARE*

362.6 658   GW
▼**ALTENHEIM LEITFADEN FUER DEN EINKAUF.** 1993. a. DM.61. Baumann Fachzeitschriftenverlag, E.C.-Baumann-Str. 5, 95326 Kulmbach, Germany. Ed. Jutta Lange. adv. circ. 8,000. **Document type:** bulletin.

GERONTOLOGY AND GERIATRICS

362.6　　　　　　GW　　ISSN 0724-8849
ALTENHILFE; Beispiele, Informationen, Meinungen. 1973. m. DM.26 (monthly bibliographies included). Deutsches Zentrum fuer Altersfragen e.V., Manfred-von-Richthofen-Str. 2, 12101 Berlin, Germany. TEL 030-786071. FAX 030-7854350. index. circ. 1,500. (tabloid format; back issues avail.) **Document type:** bibliography.

ALZHEIMER DISEASE AND ASSOCIATED DISORDERS. see *MEDICAL SCIENCES — Psychiatry And Neurology*

362　　　　　　US
ALZHEIMER'S ASSOCIATION NEWSLETTER. 1981. q. free. Alzheimer's Association, Inc., 919 N. Michigan Ave., Ste. 1000, Chicago, IL 60611-1676. TEL 312-335-8700. FAX 312-335-1110. Ed. Emily Miller. bk.rev. circ. 650,000. (back issues avail.) **Document type:** newsletter.
 Formerly: A D R D A Newsletter.

362.6　　　　　　US
AMERICAN BAR ASSOCIATION. BULLETIN TO ELDER LAW SECTIONS AND BAR COMMITTEES ON THE ELDERLY. bi-m. $15. American Bar Association, Commission on Legal Problems of the Elderly, 1800 M St., N.W., Washington, DC 20036. TEL 202-331-2298. FAX 202-332-2220. **Document type:** bulletin.
 Formerly: American Bar Association. Bulletin to Bar Committees on the Elderly.

618.97　　　　　　US　　ISSN 0002-8614
　　　　　　　　　　　CODEN: JAGSAF
AMERICAN GERIATRICS SOCIETY. JOURNAL. Key Title: Journal of the American Geriatrics Society. 1900. m. $95 to individuals; institutions $160. (American Geriatrics Society) Williams & Wilkins, 428 E. Preston St., Baltimore, MD 21202. TEL 410-528-4000. FAX 410-528-4312. TELEX 420643. Ed. Dr. David H. Soloman. adv.; bk.rev.; charts; illus.; index. circ. 9,420. (also avail. in microform from UMI; reprint service avail. from UMI) **Indexed:** Abstr.Health Care Manage.Stud., Abstr.Soc.Geront., ASCA, ASSIA, Behav.Med.Abstr., Biol.Abstr., Biotech.Abstr., C.I.S. Abstr., Chem.Abstr., Curr.Adv.Ecol.Sci., Curr.Cont., Excerp.Med., Hosp.Lit.Ind., I.P.A., Ind.Med., INIS Atomind., Int.Nurs.Ind., NRN, Nutr.Abstr., Psychol.Abstr., Sci.Cit.Ind., Soc.Work Res.& Abstr., SSCI. **Document type:** academic/scholarly publication.
 ●Also available online.
 —BLDSC (4686.300000); Faxon; UnCover; SWETS; CASDDS. CCC.
 Supersedes (in 1952): American Therapeutic Society. Transactions (ISSN 0096-686X)
 Description: Contains original articles about health care for older patients for geriatricians, internists, cardiologists, gastroenterologists, and other specialists.
 Refereed Serial

618.97　　　　　　US
AMERICAN GERIATRICS SOCIETY NEWSLETTER. 1972. bi-m. membership. American Geriatrics Society, 770 Lexington Ave., Ste. 300, New York, NY 10021. TEL 212-308-1414. FAX 212-832-8646. Ed. Melissa Silvestri. adv. circ. 12,000. **Document type:** newsletter.
 Description: Covers news and activities of the society, and topical issues in geriatric medicine.

AMERICAN JOURNAL OF GERIATRIC CARDIOLOGY. see *MEDICAL SCIENCES — Cardiovascular Diseases*

618　　　　　　US　　ISSN 1064-7481
▼**AMERICAN JOURNAL OF GERIATRIC PSYCHIATRY.** 1993. q. $85 to individuals (foreign $100); institutions $135 (foreign $150). American Psychiatric Press, Inc., Journals Division, 1400 K St., N.W., Ste. 1101, Washington, DC 20005. TEL 202-682-6240. FAX 202-789-2648. (UK addr.: 17 Belgrave Sq., London SW1X 8PG, England) adv. (back issues avail.) **Indexed:** Excerp.Med. (1994-). **Document type:** academic/scholarly publication.
 —BLDSC (0824.657000); UMI.
 Description: Source of scientific and clinical information for the rapidly developing field of geriatric psychiatry.
 Refereed Serial

THE AMERICAN JOURNAL OF HOSPICE & PALLIATIVE CARE. see *SOCIAL SERVICES AND WELFARE*

051　　　　　　US　　ISSN 1055-8306
AMERICAN SENIOR. (Supplement avail.) 1991. q. $29.99. Publishing & Business Consultants, 951 S. Oxford, No. 109, Los Angeles, CA 90006. TEL 213-732-3477. FAX 213-732-9123. (Subscr. to: Box 75392, Los Angeles, CA 90075) Ed. Andeson Napoleon Atia. adv. circ. 120,000. **Document type:** consumer publication.
 Description: Covers medical breakthroughs, government programs and benefits affecting seniors and their lifestyles.

618.97　　　　　　FR　　ISSN 0990-2295
ANNEE GERONTOLOGIQUE. English edition: Facts and Research in Gerontology (ISSN 1163-0450) (Supplements avail.: Lettre Mensuelle, Newsletter) 1987. a. 65 F. Serdi, 29 rue de St. Petersbourg, 75008 Paris, France. TEL 61-75-11-28. FAX 61-75-11-28. Eds. J.L. Albarede, P. Vellas. adv. contact: Rachel Mayne. bk.rev. **Document type:** academic/scholarly publication.
 —BLDSC (1049.085000).

305.2　　　　　　US　　ISSN 0272-3808
HQ1060
ANNUAL EDITIONS: AGING. 1978. a. $11.95. Dushkin Publishing Group, Inc., Sluice Dock, Guilford, CT 06437-9989. TEL 203-453-4351. FAX 203-453-6000. Ed. Harold Cox; Pub. Lan Nielsen. illus.; index. (back issues avail.) **Indexed:** Bk.Rev.Ind. **Document type:** academic/scholarly publication.
 Formerly: Annual Editions. Focus: Aging (ISSN 0162-3621)
 Refereed Serial

362.5　　　　　　US　　ISSN 0198-8794
RC952.A1
ANNUAL REVIEW OF GERONTOLOGY & GERIATRICS. 1980. a. price varies. Springer Publishing Company, 536 Broadway, New York, NY 10012. TEL 212-431-4370. FAX 212-941-7842. Ed. M. Powell Lawton. circ. 420.
 —BLDSC (1522.565300); Faxon; UnCover.

618.97 301.435　　　　　　IE　　ISSN 0167-4943
QP86　　　　　　　CODEN: AGGEDL
ARCHIVES OF GERONTOLOGY AND GERIATRICS; an international journal integrating experimental, clinical and social studies on ageing. (Supplement avail. (ISSN 0924-7947)) 6/yr. (in 2 vols.; 3 nos./vol.). I£440($642) (effective 1994). Elsevier Science Ireland Ltd., P.O. Box 85, Limerick, Ireland. TEL 353-61-471944. FAX 353-61-472144. (Subscr. in U.S. and Canada to: Elsevier Science Inc., Box 882, Madison Sq. Sta., New York, NY 10159. TEL 212-989-5800. FAX 212-633-3990) Ed. I.Zs.-Nagy. (also avail. in microform from UMI) **Indexed:** Biol.Abstr., Chem.Abstr., CINAHL, Curr.Adv.Biochem., Curr.Adv.Cancer Res., Curr.Adv.Ecol.Sci., Curr.Cont., Excerp.Med., Ind.Med., NRN, Psychol.Abstr. **Document type:** academic/scholarly publication.
 —BLDSC (1634.401000); Faxon; UnCover; SWETS; CASDDS.
 Description: Provides a medium for the publication of papers from the fields of experimental gerontology and clinical and social geriatrics.
 Refereed Serial

159.92　　　　　　IE　　ISSN 0924-7947
RC952.A1　　　　　　CODEN: AGGSEU
ARCHIVES OF GERONTOLOGY AND GERIATRICS. SUPPLEMENT. 1989. irreg. price varies. Elsevier Science Ireland Ltd., P.O. Box 85, Limerick, Ireland. TEL 353-61-471944. FAX 353-61-472144. (Subscr. in U.S. and Canada to: Elsevier Science Inc., Box 882, Madison Sq. Sta., New York, NY 10159. TEL 212-989-5800. FAX 212-63-3990) **Document type:** academic/scholarly publication.
 —Faxon; CASDDS.
 Refereed Serial

618.97　　　　　　IT　　ISSN 1120-6888
ARGOMENTI DI GERONTOLOGIA. 1989. q. L.8100($57) (effective 1994). Masson S.p.A., Divisione Periodici, Via Statuto 2-4, 20121 Milan, Italy. TEL 02-6367-1. FAX 02-6367-211. Ed. Mario Passeri. adv.: B&W page L.3750000, color page L.6100000; trim 175 x 245. circ. 13,000. **Document type:** academic/scholarly publication.

612.67 301.435　　　　　　JA
ASU NO TOMO/FRIEND OF TOMORROW. (Text in Japanese) 1973. q. 3130 Yen. Fujin-no-Tomo Sha, 20-16, 2-chome, Nishi-Ikebukuro, Toshima-ku, Tokyo, Japan. FAX 03-3987-8958. Ed. Heishiro Kakizaki.

B I F O C A L. (Bar Associations in Focus on Aging and the Law) see *LAW*

362　　　　　　UK　　ISSN 0964-0185
BASELINE. 1975. 3/yr. £6. British Association for Service to the Elderly, 119 Hassell St., Newcastle-under-Lyme, Staffs. ST5 1AX, England. TEL 0782-661033. FAX 0782-712725. Ed. Dr. Frank Glendenning. bk.rev.; bibl. circ. 1,000. (back issues avail.)
 —BLDSC (1863.862800).
 Formerly (until 1990): Action Baseline (ISSN 0959-4459)

051　　　　　　US
THE BEACON REVIEW. 1986. bi-w. $15. Century Publications, Inc., 1805 S. Bellaire, Ste. 235, Denver, CO 80222. TEL 303-692-8940. Ed. Cathey Hix Brown. adv.; bk.rev.; film rev.; play rev.; charts; illus.; circ. 30,000 (controlled). (tabloid format; back issues avail.) **Document type:** newspaper.
 Description: Covers financial, health, entertainment, travel, legal, caregiving information and lifestyle stories for 45-65 years old.

155.67　　　　　　US　　ISSN 1049-085X
RC952.A1　　　　　　CODEN: BHAGEG
BEHAVIOR, HEALTH, AND AGING. 1990. 3/yr. $39 to individuals (foreign $44); institutions $74 (foreign $85). Springer Publishing Company, 536 Broadway, New York, NY 10012. TEL 212-431-4370. FAX 212-941-7842. Ed. Carl Eisdorfer. adv.; bk.rev. **Indexed:** Abstr.Soc.Geront., Behav.Med.Abstr., CINAHL, Excerp.Med. (1993-), Psychol.Abstr., Sociol.Abstr.
 —BLDSC (1876.700000); Faxon.
 Description: Theoretical, empirical, and clinical studies relevant to adult development and aging and the biopsychosocial aspects of health in older populations.
 Refereed Serial

301.435　　　　　　CN　　ISSN 0835-8702
LE BEL AGE. (Text in French) 1979. 10/yr. Can.$19.95($23.05) Senior Publications Inc., 5148 blvd. Saint-Laurent, Montreal, PQ H2T 1R8, Canada. TEL 514-273-9773. FAX 514-273-9034. (Subscr. to: 1100 bd. Rene Levesque, O., 24e etage, Montreal, PQ H3B 4X9, Canada) Ed. Francine Tremblay. adv.; bk.rev. circ. 111,000. (back issues avail.) **Indexed:** Can.Per.Ind., Pt.de Rep. (1989-).
 Incorporates (in 1987): Temps de Vivre (ISSN 0703-7632)

051　　　　　　US　　ISSN 1071-5851
▼**A BETTER TOMORROW**; the magazine for seniors with a future. 1992. q. $19.80. Publishing Directions, Inc., 5301 Wisconsin Ave., N.W., Ste. 620, Washington, DC 20015. TEL 202-364-8000. FAX 202-364-8910. (Subscr. to: Box 2135, Marion, OH 43305-2135. TEL 800-351-6900) Ed. Dale Hanson Bourke. adv.: B&W page $1995, color page $2695; trim 8 1/2 x 10 7/8; adv. contact: Leslie Nunn. bk.rev.; illus. circ. 100,000. **Document type:** consumer publication.

BETWEEN FRIENDS; the Beltone newsletter. see *HANDICAPPED — Hearing Impaired*

BLAETTER AUS DEM HENRIETTENSTIFT. see *HOSPITALS*

301.435 362.6　　　　　　US
BOSTON SENIORITY; serving Boston's elderly community. 1977. m. free. Mayor's Commission on Affairs of the Elderly, 174 North St., Boston, MA 02109. TEL 617-725-3716. Ed. Anthony Barnes. circ. 35,000. (tabloid format; back issues avail.)
 Description: Contains information on elderly issues and activities of the commission.

GERONTOLOGY AND GERIATRICS

612.67 312   US   ISSN 0251-6802
HQ1060
BULLETIN ON AGEING. (Text in English, French, Spanish) 1976. 3/yr. free. Department of Policy Coordination and Sustainable Development, Division for Social Policy and Development, United Nations, New York, NY 10017. TEL 212-963-3062. FAX 212-963-5959. circ. 3,000. (back issues avail.) **Indexed:** CLOA, World Bibl.Soc.Sec. **Document type:** bulletin.
—BLDSC (0736.299000).

362 301.4   US
C A P SULE (LEVITTOWN). 1980. bi-m. $25 membership. Children of Aging Parents, Woodbourne Office Campus, 1609 Woodbourne Rd., Ste. 302A, Levittown, PA 19057. TEL 215-945-6900. FAX 215-945-8720. Ed. Louise Fradkin. adv.; bk.rev. circ. 2,500. (back issues avail.) **Document type:** newsletter.
   Description: Articles geared toward those caring for the elderly, covering products, medical information, legal issues, Medicare, psychological aspects, coping skills and other caregiving help.

362.6   CN
C A R P NEWS. q. (Canadian Association of Retired Persons) Kemur Publishing Co. Ltd., 5592 Yonge St., Ste. 33, Toronto, Ont. M2N 5S2, Canada. TEL 416-229-6886. Ed. Keith Gardner. circ. 43,000.
   Description: Objective is to improve the quality of life for Canadians over 50. Discounts for travel for hostels and motels, glasses, cars, insurance plans and dental referral service are available. Informative news on legislation and financial changes as well as other items affecting people over 50.

301.435   FR   ISSN 1146-2965
C L E I R P P A. INFOS; bulletin mensuel d'informations du CLEIRPPA. 1983. m. 450 F. (foreign 545 F.) includes CLEIRPPA. Annees-Documents. Centre de Liaison, d'Etude, d'Information et de Recherche sur les Problemes des Personnes Agees, 15 rue Chateaubriand, 75008 Paris, France. TEL 42-25-78-78. FAX 42-56-48-26. Ed. Naima Segret.

301.435   FR   ISSN 0184-6531
C L E I R P P A ANNEES - DOCUMENTS; annees a venir...annees d'avenir. 1971. bi-m. 450 F. (foreign 545 F.) includes CLEIRPPA. Infos. Centre de Liaison, d'Etude, d'Information et de Recherche sur les Problemes des Personnes Agees, 15 rue Chateaubriand, 75008 Paris, France. TEL 42-25-78-78. FAX 42-56-48-26. Ed. Naima Segret. adv.; bk.rev.; abstr.; bibl.; film rev.; stat.; index. circ. 2,000. (back issues avail.)
   Formerly: Centre de Liaison, d'Etude, d'Information et de Recherche sur les Problemes des Personnes Agees. Annees Documents.

051   US
CALIFORNIA SENIOR CITIZEN. 1961. m. $5. Osmon Publications, Inc., 4805 Alta Canyada Rd., La Canada, CA 91011. TEL 818-790-0651. Ed. Carol Osmon. adv. contact: Carol Osmon. bk.rev.; illus.; stat. circ. 69,000. (tabloid format) **Indexed:** Cal.Per.Ind. (1978-). **Document type:** newspaper, consumer publication.
   Formerly: California Senior Citizen News (ISSN 0085-1531)
   Description: Lists local opportunities and services. Profiles of interesting, active seniors, legislation affecting the elderly, and travel and investments.

618.97   CN
CANADIAN JOURNAL OF GERIATRICS. 1985. 8/yr. S T A Communications, 75008 boul. St. Jean, Ste. 306, Pointe-Claire, Que. H9R 5K3, Canada. TEL 514-695-7623. FAX 514-695-8554. Ed. Paul Brand. adv. circ. 22,000.
   Formerly: Perspectives in Geriatrics.

612.67   CN   ISSN 0714-9808
CANADIAN JOURNAL ON AGING/REVUE CANADIENNE DU VIEILLISSEMENT. 1982. q. Can.$43 to individuals (foreign Can.$52); institutions Can.$58 (foreign Can.$67); students Can.$20 (foreign Can.$29). Canadian Association on Gerontology - Association Canadienne de Gerontologie, MacKinnon Bldg., Rm. 039, University of Guelph, Guelph, ON N1G 2W1, Canada. TEL 519-824-4120. FAX 519-837-9953. Ed. Francois Beland. adv.; bk.rev.; charts; stat.; circ. 2,000 (paid). (back issues avail.) **Indexed:** Abstr.Soc.Geront., Can.Per.Ind., Can.Wom.Per.Ind., CLOA, Curr.Cont., Excerp.Med., Excerp.Med., P.A.I.S., Psychol.Abstr., Soc.Work Res.& Abstr., Sociol.Abstr., SSCI. **Document type:** academic/scholarly publication.
—BLDSC (3027.920000); Faxon.
   Description: Publishes research papers in the relevant disciplines of gerontology.
   Refereed Serial

CARDIOLOGY IN THE ELDERLY. see MEDICAL SCIENCES — Cardiovascular Diseases

362   UK   ISSN 0955-4262
CARE OF THE ELDERLY; the journal for the age care team. 1989. m. (10/yr). £36 to individuals; students £20; free to qualified personnel. (Newbourne Group) Home & Law Publishing Ltd., Greater London House, Hampstead Rd., London NW1 7QQ, England. TEL 01-388-3171. FAX 01-387-9518. TELEX 269470. Ed. M. Denham.
—BLDSC (3051.549400).
   Description: Includes original papers, case reports, review articles, ABC series on aspects of age-related disease, articles reflecting specialist professional experiences and problems within the team, and reviews of drugs, equipment and patient aids.

612   US
CAREGIVER. 1980. q. $10. Duke Aging Center, Family Support Program, Duke Medical Center, Box 3600, Durham, NC 27710. TEL 919-660-7510. FAX 919-684-8569. Ed. Lisa Gwyther. bk.rev. circ. 8,000.

610.736   US
CAREGIVING. 1990. bi-m. $13.50. Creative Publishing Group, Inc., 30 Moran St., Newton, NJ 07860. TEL 201-579-5900. Ed. Wendie R. Blanchard.
   Description: For women between the ages of 40-65; includes information on private and government health care agencies, support networks, home and institutional care alternatives, finance, law, geriatrics and nutrition.

CARERS WORLD. see SOCIAL SERVICES AND WELFARE

612.67   CC
CHANG SHOU/LONGEVITY. (Text in Chinese) 1980. m. $8 per no. (effective 1994). Tianjin Kexue Jishu Chubanshe - Tianjin Science and Technology Publishing House, 130 Chifeng Dao, Tianjin 300041, People's Republic of China. TEL 022-7312720. FAX 022-732749. (Dist. in US by: China Books & Periodicals, Inc., 2929 24th St., San Francisco, CA 94110. TEL 415-282-2994) Ed. Chen Dake. adv.; bk.rev. **Document type:** consumer publication.
   Description: Covers gerontology and geriatrics. Provides advice on how to keep good health.

301.435   UK   ISSN 0262-2770
CHOICE; money, homes, health and leisure for the over 50's. 1972. m. £11.50. Choice Publications Ltd., Apex House, 5th Floor, Oundle Rd., Peterborough PE2 9NP, England. Ed. Annette Brown. adv.; illus. circ. 84,601.
   Incorporates: Life Begins at 50's; **Former titles:** Pre-Retirement Choice; Retirement Choice; Pre-Retirement Newsletter.

618.97   JA
CHUJU KAGAKU SOGO KENKYU KENKYU HOKOKU/COMPREHENSIVE STUDIES ON SCIENCE OF AGING. (Text in Japanese) 1991. a. Chuju Kagaku Shinko Zaidan - Japan Foundation for Aging and Health, 3-6, Toranomon 1-chome, Minato-ku, Tokyo 105, Japan.

618.97   JA   ISSN 0918-533X
CHUJU KAGAKU KOENKAI KIROKUSHU/LECTURES ON SCIENCE OF AGING. (Text in Japanese) 1991. irreg. Choju Kagaku Shinko Zaidan - Japan Foundation for Aging and Health, 3-6, Toranomon 1-chome, Minato-ku, Tokyo 105, Japan.

301.435 362.6   UK
CIVIL SERVICE PENSIONER. 1952. q. £6. Civil Service Pensioners Alliance, 7 The Beeches, Shaw Hill, Melksham, Wilts. SN12 8EW, England. TEL 0225-702416. Ed. Edgar Fillis. adv. contact: J.M. Butler. circ. 59,000 (controlled). (back issues avail.) **Document type:** newsletter.
   Description: Deals with the preservation of pension levels and other matters of interest to retired people.

155.67   US   ISSN 0731-7115
CLINICAL GERONTOLOGIST; the journal of aging and mental health. 1977. q. $48 to individuals; institutions $160; libraries $225. Haworth Press, Inc., 10 Alice St., Binghamton, NY 13904. TEL 607-722-5857; 800-342-9678. FAX 607-722-1424. Ed. Terry L. Brink. adv.; bk.rev.; abstr.; bibl.; index. circ. 601. (also avail. in microfiche from HAW; reprint service avail. from HAW) **Indexed:** Abstr.Health Care Manage.Stud., Abstr.Soc.Geront., Abstr.Soc.Work., Behav.Abstr., Behav.Med.Abstr., Biol.Abstr, Bull.Signal., Chicago Psychoanal.Lit.Ind., CLOA, Excerp.Med., Hosp.Abstr., Hosp.Lit.Ind., Med.Care Rev., Past.Care & Couns.Abstr., Psychol.Abstr., Ref.Zh., Rehabil.Lit., Sage Fam.Stud.Abstr., Soc.Work Res.& Abstr., Sociol.Abstr. **Document type:** academic/scholarly publication.
—BLDSC (3286.288000); Faxon; UnCover; SWETS.
   Former titles: Journal of Aged Care (ISSN 0270-3122); (until 1981): Aged Care and Services Review.
   Description: Presents material which is relevant to the needs of mental health professionals and all practitioners who deal with the aged client.
   Refereed Serial

618.97   US   ISSN 0749-0690
RC952.A1
CLINICS IN GERIATRIC MEDICINE. 1985. q. $82 to individuals (foreign $113); institutions $105 (foreign $120). W.B. Saunders Co. (Subsidiary of: Harcourt Brace & Company), Curtis Center, Independence Sq. W., Philadelphia, PA 19106-3399. TEL 215-238-7800. FAX 215-238-6445. (Subscr. to: Periodicals Fulfillment, W.B. Saunders Co., 6277 Sea Harbor Dr., 4th Fl., Orlando, FL 32891-4800. TEL 800-654-2452. FAX 800-874-6418) Ed. Leslie Kramer-Day. circ. 2,300. (also avail. in microfilm; back issues avail.) **Indexed:** Abstr.Soc.Geront., CINAHL, Excerp.Med. **Document type:** academic/scholarly publication.
—BLDSC (3286.562000); Faxon; UnCover; SWETS; UMI. **CCC.**
   Description: Each issue discusses a single aspect of the psychiatric, psychological, physical, or medical treatment of elderly patients.

353.9   US   ISSN 0090-6077
HV1468.C8
CONNECTICUT. DEPARTMENT ON AGING. REPORT TO THE GOVERNOR AND GENERAL ASSEMBLY. (Report year ends June 30) 1969. a. Department on Aging, 175 Main St., Hartford, CT 06106-1818. circ. 500 (controlled). **Document type:** government publication.

612.6   US   ISSN 0748-2760
CONTEMPORARY GERIATRIC MEDICINE. 1983. irreg. vol.3, 1988. price varies. Plenum Publishing Corp., 233 Spring St., New York, NY 10013-1578. TEL 212-620-8000. FAX 212-463-0742. TELEX 23-421139. Ed. Steven R. Gambert. (back issues avail.) **Document type:** monographic series.
—BLDSC (3425.181860).
   Refereed Serial

618.97 362.6   US   ISSN 1069-0840
▼**CONTEMPORARY GERONTOLOGY;** a journal of reviews and critical discourse. 1994. q. $36 to individuals (foreign $40); institutions $70 (foreign $79). Springer Publishing Company, 526 Broadway, New York, NY 10012-3955. TEL 212-431-4370. FAX 212-941-7842. Ed. Robert C. Atchley. bk.rev. **Document type:** academic/scholarly publication.
   Refereed Serial

301.435   US   ISSN 0732-085X
CONTRIBUTIONS TO THE STUDY OF AGING. 1982. irreg. price varies. Greenwood Press, Inc. (Subsidiary of: Greenwood Publishing Group Inc.), 88 Post Rd. W., Box 5007, Westport, CT 06881-5007. TEL 203-226-3571. FAX 203-222-1502. index. **Document type:** monographic series.
—BLDSC (3461.453300); Faxon.

GERONTOLOGY AND GERIATRICS

796 US
CORPUS CHRISTI MARINER NEWS. m.? $1 per no. Box 1960, Corpus, TX 78403. Ed. David C. Holiman. **Document type:** newsletter.
  Description: Discusses social, medical and job-related matters for people at retirement age.

301.435 US ISSN 1066-0208
COUNTRY CRIER. 1979. m. $6. Pentacle Publishing Co., 1830 US Rte. 9, Toms River, NJ 08755. TEL 908-240-3000. FAX 908-240-0002. Ed. Edward Jasin. adv. circ. 24,600. (tabloid format; back issues avail.) **Document type:** newspaper.

051 US ISSN 1072-3943
▼**CREATIVE RETIREMENT.** 1993. q. $15.80. Vacation Publications, Inc., 1502 Augusta Dr., Ste. 415, Houston, TX 77057. TEL 713-974-6903. FAX 713-974-0445. Ed. Mary Lou Abbott. adv.: B&W page $1620. circ. 35,000 (paid). **Document type:** consumer publication.
  Description: Offers advice to enable new retirees lead fuller, more satisfying lives.

DEATH STUDIES; education - counseling - care - law - ethics. see PSYCHOLOGY

DEMENTIA. see MEDICAL SCIENCES — Psychiatry And Neurology

301.435 UK
DIRECTORY FOR OLDER PEOPLE; a handbook of information & opportunities for the over-55s. 1989. biennial. $45. Harvester Wheatsheaf (Subsidiary of: Paramount Publishing International), Campus 400, Maylands Ave., Hemel Hempstead, Herts. HP2 7EZ, England. TEL 0442-881900. FAX 0442-252544. Eds. Ann Marlborough, Derek Kinrade. adv. circ. 1,400. **Document type:** directory.

362.6 338.025 US ISSN 1061-3056
HV1457
▼**DIRECTORY OF AGING RESOURCES.** 1992. a. $89. Business Publishers, Inc., 951 Pershing Dr., Silver Spring, MD 20910-4464. TEL 301-587-6300. FAX 301-585-9075. Ed. Nancy Aldrich. **Document type:** directory.
  Description: Comprehensive guide to 3,369 organizations involved in the aging fields: federal agencies, Congress, state and local agencies, international organizations, national associations, universities and corporations.

DIRECTORY OF AIDS FOR DISABLED AND ELDERLY PEOPLE. see HANDICAPPED

DIRECTORY OF FEDERAL AID FOR THE AGING. see SOCIAL SERVICES AND WELFARE

618.97 378 US
DIRECTORY OF FELLOWSHIP PROGRAMS IN GERIATRIC MEDICINE. 1980. biennial. $25 to non-members; members $18; institutions $35. American Geriatrics Society, 770 Lexington Ave., Ste. 300, New York, NY 10021. TEL 212-308-1414. FAX 212-832-8646. circ. 1,000. **Document type:** directory.
  Formerly: Directory of Geriatrics Programs for Residencies and Fellowships.
  Description: Information resource for physicians and medical students for fellowship programs in US and Canada.

362.6 610.736 US
HV1454.2.U6
DIRECTORY OF RETIREMENT FACILITIES. 1985. a. $249. H C I A Inc., 300 E. Lombard St., Baltimore, MD 21202. TEL 410-576-9600. FAX 410-783-0575. **Document type:** directory.
  Formerly: National Directory of Retirement Facilities (ISSN 1053-6825)
  Description: Lists more than 22,000 retirement facilities with contact names, addresses and telephone numbers, plus information about services and ownership.

DISTINCTIONS; financial newsletter. see BUSINESS AND ECONOMICS — Banking And Finance

362 FR ISSN 0243-0738
ECHO DE L'UNION. vol.32, 1978. m. 60 Fr. Union Nationale des Retraites et Personnes Agees (UNRPA), 50 rue Edouard Pailleron, 75019 Paris, France. TEL 16-1-42-39-21-90. Ed.Bd. adv.; bk.rev.; charts; illus.; stat.
  Former titles (until 1980): Echo; Echo des Vieux de France (ISSN 0046-1083)

051 CN
EDMONTON SENIOR. 1990. m. Can.$26.50. Alberta Business Research Ltd., 10179 105th St., Ste. 800, Edmonton, AB T5J 3N1, Canada. TEL 403-425-1185. FAX 403-421-7677. Ed. Colin Smith. adv.; bk.rev. circ. 25,000. **Document type:** newspaper.
  Description: Contains news articles and entertainment features directed at those 45 years of age and over, primarily in the Edmonton area.

EDUCATIONAL GERONTOLOGY; an international journal. see EDUCATION — Adult Education

EIJU SOGO BYOIN KIYO/EIJU GENERAL HOSPITAL. JOURNAL. see MEDICAL SCIENCES — Experimental Medicine, Laboratory Technique

301.435 970.1 US
ELDER VOICES. 1981. irreg. National Indian Council on Aging, Inc., City Centre Ste. 510 W, 6400 Uptown Blvd., N.E., Albuquerque, NM 87110. TEL 505-888-3302.
  Formerly: National Indian Council on Aging Quarterly.

612.67 US ISSN 0891-9275
ELDERLY HEALTH SERVICES LETTER. 1986. 12/yr. $127. Health Resources Publishing, Brinley Professional Plaza, 3100 Hwy. 138, Box 1442, Wall Township, NJ 07719-1442. TEL 908-681-1133. FAX 908-681-0490. Ed. Robert K. Jenkins. index. (back issues avail.)
  —CCC.
  Description: Examines range of issues, trends and projections for health services for the elderly.

362.6 EI
EUROLINK AGE BULLETIN; a European network concerned with older people and issues of ageing. (Text in Dutch, English, French; summaries in German, Italian, Spanish) 1985. 3/yr. £24. (Eurolink Age) Eurolink Age, 1268 London Rd., London SW16 4ER, England. TEL 081-679-8000. FAX 081-679-6727. (Commission of the European Communities) bk.rev. circ. 4,500. **Document type:** bulletin.

610.736 GW
EVANGELISCHE IMPULSE; Zeitschrift fuer die Arbeit mit alten Menschen. 1979. 5/yr. DM.31.90. (Deutscher Evangelischer Verband duer Altenhilfe) Lithos Verlag GmbH, Hermannstr. 5, 70178 Stuttgart, Germany. TEL 0711-627023.

EVANGELISCHER DIGEST. see RELIGIONS AND THEOLOGY

EXPERIENCE. see LAW

EXPERIMENTAL AGING RESEARCH. see PSYCHOLOGY

612.67 UK ISSN 0531-5565
QP86 CODEN: EXGEAB
EXPERIMENTAL GERONTOLOGY. 1965. 6/yr. £292($530) (effective 1994). Elsevier Science Ltd., Pergamon, P.O. Box 800, Kidlington, Oxford OX5 1DX, England. TEL 44-865-843000. FAX 44-865-843010. (Subscr. in U.S. and Canada to: Elsevier Science, 660 White Plains Rd., Tarrytown, NY 10591-5153. TEL 914-524-9200. FAX 914-333-2444) Ed. Leonard Hayflick. adv.; bk.rev. circ. 1,000. (also avail. in microfilm from UMI) Indexed: ASSIA, Biol.Abstr., Chem.Abstr., Curr.Adv.Biochem., Curr.Adv.Cell & Devel.Biol., Curr.Adv.Ecol.Sci., Curr.Cont., Excerp.Med., Helminthol.Abstr., Ind.Med., Ind.Sci.Rev., INIS Atomind., NRN, Nutr.Abstr., Sci.Cit.Ind. **Document type:** academic/scholarly publication.
  —BLDSC (3839.340000); Faxon; UnCover; SWETS; UMI; CASDDS. **CCC.**
  Description: Publishes results of research in the processes of biological aging in plants, animals and humans from the molecular level to that of the entire organism.
  Refereed Serial

612.67 FR ISSN 1167-4911
▼**FACTS AND RESEARCH IN GERONTOLOGY NEWSLETTER.** French edition: Lettre Mensuelle de l'Annee Gerontologique (ISSN 1146-0318) (Supplement to: Annee Gerontologique) (Editions in English, French, Spanish) 1992. 7/yr. 20 F. Serdi, 29 rue de St. Petersbourg, 75008 Paris, France. TEL 61-75-11-28. FAX 61-75-11-28. Ed. P. Vellas. adv.; bk.rev. circ. 45,000 (15,000 English ed., 5,000 French ed., 25,000 Spanish ed.). **Document type:** academic/scholarly publication.

301.435 US
FIFTY SOMETHING MAGAZINE. 1990. bi-m. $10.95. Media Trends Publications, 8250 Tyler Blvd., Mentor, OH 44060. TEL 216-974-9594. FAX 216-974-1004. Ed. Linda L. Lindeman. adv. contact: Kitty Kadas. circ. 25,000. **Document type:** consumer publication.
  Description: Provides information on travel, entertainment, finance, romance, health, nutrition, fitness and special events for the fifty-or-over reader. Includes feature stories on individuals, locally and nationally, and fiction.

301.435 333.33 US ISSN 0160-5739
FLORIDA RETIREMENT LIVING. 1946. 10/yr. $18 (effective 1994). Gidder House Publishing Inc., Box 161848, Altamonte Springs, FL 32716-1848. TEL 407-774-8668. FAX 407-774-1095. Ed. Dyeann Dummer. adv. contact: Dyeann Dummer. bk.rev. circ. 25,000. (back issues avail.) **Document type:** consumer publication.
  Formerly: Florida Manufactured Home Living.

301.435 US
FLORIDA SENIOR NEWS. 1986. m. $12 (typically set in Jan.). Heraty Enterprise, Inc., 621 N. Ferncreek, Orlando, FL 32803. TEL 407-896-8243. FAX 407-894-4613. Ed. Peter E. Heraty; Pub. Patrick J. McGuffin. adv.; bk.rev. circ. 35,000. (tabloid format; back issues avail.) **Document type:** newspaper.
  Description: Directed to the "over 55" age group residing in central Florida.

FOCUS: LIBRARY SERVICE TO OLDER ADULTS, PEOPLE WITH DISABILITIES. see LIBRARY AND INFORMATION SCIENCES

610.736 US ISSN 0892-7103
FOCUS ON GERIATRIC CARE AND REHABILITATION. 1987. 10/yr. $71 (foreign $85). Aspen Publishers, Inc., 200 Orchard Ridge Dr., Gaithersburg, MD 20878. TEL 301-417-7500. FAX 301-417-7550. **Document type:** newsletter.
  —UMI.

051 CN ISSN 0711-3927
FORESIGHT (RICHMOND); Canada's magazine for retirement planning. 1981. bi-m. Can.$20. Foresight Publications Inc., 12140 Horseshoe Way, Ste. 100, Richmond, BC V7A 4V5, Canada. TEL 604-272-4772. FAX 604-275-7859. Ed. Rick Delany. adv. contact: Bill Steele. bk.rev. circ. 50,000. **Document type:** consumer publication, newsletter.
  Description: Focuses on retirement issues including financial and retirement planning, health and medical issues, travel, psychological, environmental and spiritual issues, and sports.

362.6 US
FROM THE HOME & HOUSING FRONT. q. membership. North American Association of Jewish Homes & Housing for the Aging, 10830 N. Central Expwy., Ste. 150, Dallas, TX 75231-1022. TEL 214-696-9838. FAX 214-360-0753. (looseleaf format) **Document type:** newsletter.

612.67 US ISSN 0271-955X
CODEN: FROAEC
FRONTIERS IN AGING SERIES. 1980. irreg., vol.6, 1988. price varies. Human Sciences Press, Inc. (Subsidiary of: Plenum Publishing Corp.), 233 Spring St., New York, NY 10013-1578. TEL 212-620-8000. FAX 212-463-0742. Ed. Gari Lesnoff-Caravaglia. (also avail. in microform from UMI; reprint service avail. from UMI) **Document type:** monographic series.
  Refereed Serial

301.435 SZ
FUER UNS;* die schweizerische Zeitschrift fuer die zweite Lebenshaelfte. 1978. m. 25 Fr. Fuer Uns-Verlag AG, Aarauerstr. 21, CH-5600 Lenzburg, Switzerland. Ed.Bd.

GERONTOLOGY AND GERIATRICS

612.67   CN   ISSN 1188-181X
G R C NEWS. 1982. q. free. Simon Fraser University, Gerontology Research Center, 515 W. Hastings St., Vancouver, BC V6B 5K3, Canada. TEL 604-291-5062. FAX 604-291-5066. Ed. Arleen Higgs. bk.rev. circ. 900. **Document type:** newsletter.
   Formerly: G R C Information Bulletin.

301.435   US   ISSN 0738-7806
CODEN: GENREC
GENERATIONS (SAN FRANCISCO). 1976. q. $35. American Society on Aging, 833 Market St., Ste. 511, San Francisco, CA 94103-1924. TEL 415-974-9600. FAX 415-974-0300. Ed. Mary Tuckwiler Johnson. adv.; bk.rev. circ. 13,500. **Indexed:** Abstr.Anthropol., Bk.Rev.Ind. (1984-), Child.Bk.Rev.Ind. (1984-), CINAHL, Psychol.Abstr., Sage Fam.Stud.Abstr., Sociol.Abstr.
  —BLDSC (4111.755300); Faxon; UnCover.
  Description: Each issue covers a specific topic in the field of aging with emphasis on practice, research and policy.

610.736   AT
GERIACTION. 1970. q. Aus.$65. Geriaction Inc., 10-692 Pacific Hwy., Chatswood, N.S.W. 2067, Australia. FAX 02-411-6618. Ed. Raelene Allen. adv.; bk.rev. circ. 1,500. (back issues avail.)

618.97   IT   ISSN 1121-8460
▼**GERIATRIC AND MEDICAL INTELLIGENCE.** 1992. 2/yr. L.50000($50) (effective 1994). Wichtig Editore s.r.l., Via Friuli 72-74, 20135 Milan, Italy. TEL 02-5452306. FAX 02-5451843.

610.736 362.15   US
GERIATRIC CARE. 1968. m. $75 (minimum 25 sets subscr. required). Eymann Publications, Box 3577, Reno, NV 89505. TEL 702-333-6651. Ed. Ken Eymann. bk.rev. circ. 50,000. **Document type:** newsletter.
  Description: Teaching aid for nursing homes and hospitals regarding the elderly.

610.736   US
GERIATRIC CARE NEWS.* 1975. m. $89. D R S Geriatric Publishing Co., 47435 S.E. 71st St., Mercer Island, WA 98040. TEL 206-232-9689. Ed. Dr. Frances Green. circ. 1,000. (back issues avail.)
  Formerly: Geriatric and Residential Care News.
  Description: For health care professionals in the field of or related to gerontology.

618.97   US
GERIATRIC CONSULTANT. 1982. 6/yr. $19. Medical Publishing Enterprises, 15-22 Fair Lawn Ave., Fair Lawn, NJ 07410. TEL 201-796-6500. Ed. John H. Lavin. adv.; charts; illus.; index; circ. 97,500 (controlled). **Indexed:** CLOA.
  Description: For medical practitioners working with elderly clients.

618   JA
GERIATRIC MEDICINE/RONEN IGAKU. (Text in Japanese) 1957. m. 11000 Yen. Life Science Co., Ltd. - Raifu Saiensu, c/o Sudo Bldg., 1-5-2 Shibuya, Shibuya-ku, Tokyo 150, Japan. Ed.Bd. adv.

618.97   UK
GERIATRIC MEDICINE. m. £43 (foreign £59). Findlay Publications Ltd., Franks Hall, Franks Ln., Horton Kirby, Kent DA4 9LL, England. Ed. Sue Lyon. **Document type:** academic/scholarly publication.
  Formerly: Geriatrics for GPs.

GERIATRIC NEPHROLOGY AND UROLOGY. see *MEDICAL SCIENCES — Urology And Nephrology*

610.736   US   ISSN 0197-4572
RC954
GERIATRIC NURSING; American journal of care for the aging. 1980. bi-m. $29 to individuals; institutions $30. Mosby Year - Book, Inc. (Subsidiary of: Times Mirror Company), 11830 Westline Industrial Dr., St. Louis, MO 63146. TEL 800-325-4177. FAX 314-432-1380. Ed. Priscilla Ebersole. adv.; bk.rev.; charts; illus.; tr.lit.; index. circ. 16,000. (also avail. in microform from UMI; reprint service avail. from UMI) **Indexed:** CINAHL, CLOA, Curr.Adv.Ecol.Sci., Hosp.Lit.Ind., I.P.A., Ind.Med., Int.Nurs.Ind., NRN, Nurs.Abstr., Psychol.Abstr.
●Also available online.
  —BLDSC (4161.710000); Faxon; UnCover; SWETS; UMI. **CCC.**

362.6   SZ
GERIATRICA. 6/yr. Keller und Co. AG, Baselstr. 11, CH-6002 Luzern, Switzerland. TEL 041-281111. FAX 041-222253. circ. 3,000.

618.97 612.67   US   ISSN 0016-867X
RC952.A1   CODEN: GERTAZ
GERIATRICS; medicine for midlife and beyond. 1946. m. $40. Advanstar Communications, Inc., 7500 Old Oak Blvd., Cleveland, OH 44130. TEL 216-826-2839. FAX 216-891-2726. (Subscr. to: 131 W. First St., Duluth, MN 55802. TEL 800-346-0085) Ed. Alice V. Luddington. adv.; bk.rev.; abstr.; bibl.; charts; illus. circ. 55,571. (also avail. in microform) **Indexed:** Biol.Abstr., Biotech.Abstr., Chem.Abstr., CINAHL, CLOA, Curr.Adv.Ecol.Sci., Curr.Cont., Dent.Ind., Excerp.Med., Gen.Sci.Ind., Hosp.Lit.Ind., I.P.A., Ind.Med., INIS Atomind., Int.Nurs.Ind., NRN, Nutr.Abstr., Psychol.Abstr., Rev.Plant Path. **Document type:** trade publication.
  —BLDSC (4161.800000); Faxon; UnCover; SWETS. **CCC.**
Refereed Serial

618.97   IT   ISSN 0392-9663
GERIATRICS. 1984. 10/yr. L.30000. E S I Stampa Medica s.r.l., Casella Postale 42, Lgo. Volontari del Sangue 10, 20097 S. Donato, Milan, Italy. TEL 02-5274241. FAX 02-55600670. TELEX 324894. Ed. Bruno P. Pieroni. adv.; B&W page L.9000000, color page L.12000000; trim 176 x 248; adv. contact: Antonia Argentiero. bk.rev. circ. 56,000. **Indexed:** FAMLI, Ind.Sci.Rev.

618.97   GW   ISSN 0940-6131
GERIATRIE FORSCHUNG. 1991. 4/yr. DM.80. M M V Medizin Verlag, Neumarkter Str. 18, 81673 Munich, Germany. TEL 089-43189647. FAX 089-43189633. **Document type:** academic/scholarly publication.

610.736   SZ   ISSN 1011-2901
   CODEN: GTPREP
GERIATRIE FUER DIE TAEGLICHE PRAXIS. 1987. irreg. price varies. S. Karger AG, Allschwilerstr. 10, P.O. Box, CH-4009 Basel, Switzerland. TEL 061-3061111. FAX 061-3061234. Ed. W. Meier-Ruge. **Document type:** academic/scholarly publication.
  —BLDSC (4161.910300). **CCC.**

612.67   GW   ISSN 0936-7152
GERIATRIE PRAXIS. 1989. m. DM.98. M M V Medizin Verlag, Neumarkter Str. 18, 81673 Munich, Germany. TEL 089-43189-0. FAX 089-43189-633. TELEX 524631-VERVO-D. Ed. Dr. Dagmar van Thiel. adv. **Document type:** academic/scholarly publication.

612.67   SP   ISSN 0212-9744
   CODEN: GERIE5
GERIATRIKA; revista iberoamericana de geriatria y gerontologia. 1984. 10/yr. 7500 ptas.($120) (Europe 85000 ptas.). Alpe Editores, S.A., Pedro Rico, 27, 28029 Madrid, Spain. TEL 733 88 11. FAX 315-96-52. adv.; color page 150000 ptas.; 210 x 280. circ. 7,000 (controlled). **Indexed:** Excerp.Med.
  —BLDSC (4161.911000).

GERODONTOLOGY; an international journal. see *MEDICAL SCIENCES — Dentistry*

301.435   DK   ISSN 0900-114X
GERONTOLOGI OG SAMFUND; nyt om aldring, alderdom og aeldrebefolkning. 1985. q. DKK 175. Dansk Gerontologisk Selskab, c/o Victor Hansen International Boghandel, M.P. Bruunsgade 45, DK-8000 Aarhus C, Denmark. TEL 45-86-12-24-00. FAX 45-86-12-23-47. Ed. Henning Kirk. bk.rev.; illus. circ. 1,200.

301.435   US
GERONTOLOGICAL SOCIETY. MONOGRAPHS. irreg. Gerontological Society of America, 1275 K St., N.W., Ste. 350, Washington, DC 20005-4006. TEL 202-842-1275. Ed. Bettie Donley. (reprint service avail. from UMI) **Document type:** monographic series.

618.97   FR   ISSN 0016-9005
GERONTOLOGIE (YEAR). 1970. q. 330 F. (foreign 420 F.). 14 passage du Guesclin, 75015 Paris, France. TEL 47-34-64-63. FAX 47-34-64-63. adv.; bk.rev. circ. 7,500.

618.97   FR   ISSN 0990-5669
GERONTOLOGIE PRATIQUE. 1988. m. (10/yr.). 250 F. L.E.N. Medical, 48 bis, av. Kleber, 75016 Paris, France. TEL 47-55-06-06. FAX 47-55-69-41. TELEX 640 748. Ed. Dr. Cl. Gallinari.

362 618.9   US   ISSN 0016-9013
HQ1060   CODEN: GRNTA3
GERONTOLOGIST. 1960. bi-m. $55 to individuals; institutions $89. Gerontological Society of America, 1275 K St., N.W., Ste. 350, Washington, DC 20005-4006. TEL 202-842-1275. (Subscr. to: Box 5018, Washington, DC 20061-5018) Ed. Rose Gibson. adv.: B&W page $635, color page $1285. bk.rev.; bibl.; charts; illus.; index. circ. 10,373. (also avail. in microform from UMI; reprint service avail. from UMI) **Indexed:** Abstr.Health Care Manage.Stud., Abstr.Soc.Geront., Acad.Ind., ASSIA, Behav.Med.Abstr., Biol.Abstr., C.I.J.E., CERDIC, Chem.Abstr., CINAHL, Curr.Cont., Dok.Arbeitsmed., Ergon.Abstr., Excerp.Med., Hlth.Ind., Hosp.Lit.Ind., I.P.A., Ind.Med., Int.Nurs.Ind., Mid.East: Abstr.& Ind., NRN, Past.Care & Couns.Abstr., Psychol.Abstr., Risk Abstr., Sage Fam.Stud.Abstr., Sage Pub.Admin.Abstr., Sage Urb.Stud.Abstr., Soc.Sci.Ind., Soc.Work Res.& Abstr., Soc.Work Res.& Abstr., SSCI, SSCI. **Document type:** academic/scholarly publication.
●Also available online.
  —BLDSC (4162.300000); Faxon; UnCover; SWETS; UMI.
  Description: Articles by academics and gerontologists focusing on two or three topics per issue. Includes program and abstracts from the annual meeting of the Society.
Refereed Serial

618.97 612.67   SZ   ISSN 0304-324X
   CODEN: GERNDJ
GERONTOLOGY; international journal of experimental and clinical gerontology. (Text in English) 1957. bi-m. 388 SFr.($259) S. Karger AG, Allschwilerstr. 10, P.O. Box, CH-4009 Basel, Switzerland. TEL 061-3061111. FAX 061-3061234. Ed. M. Ermini. adv.; bk.rev.; index. circ. 1,250. (also avail. in microfilm) **Indexed:** Biol.Abstr., Chem.Abstr., Curr.Adv.Ecol.Sci., Dent.Ind., Excerp.Med., Helminthol.Abstr., Ind.Med., Ind.Sci.Rev., Mid.East: Abstr.& Ind., NRN, Nutr.Abstr., Psychol.Abstr., Sci.Cit.Ind. **Document type:** academic/scholarly publication.
  —BLDSC (4162.325000); Faxon; SWETS; CASDDS. **CCC.**
  Formed by the merger of (1976): Gerontologia (ISSN 0016-898X); Gerontologia Clinica (ISSN 0016-8998)

612.67 618.97   IS   ISSN 0334-2360
GERONTOLOGY. (Text in Hebrew; summaries in English) 1975. q. $90 includes Bulletin. Israel Gerontological Society, Box 1105, Ramat Gan 52111, Israel. FAX 972-3-5755010. Ed. H. Har-Paz. bk.rev. circ. 800. **Indexed:** Ind.Heb.Per. **Document type:** academic/scholarly publication.
  Description: Publishes research covering biological, medical, social science and social work aspects of gerontology.

362.605   US   ISSN 0270-1960
RC952.5
GERONTOLOGY & GERIATRICS EDUCATION. 1980. q. $38 to individuals; institutions $130; libraries $145. Haworth Press, Inc., 10 Alice St., Binghamton, NY 13904. TEL 607-722-5857; 800-342-9678. FAX 607-722-1424. Ed. Grace D. Dawson. adv.; bk.rev.; charts; illus.; stat.; index. circ. 420. (also avail. in microfiche from UMI; back issues avail.; reprint service avail. from HAW) **Indexed:** Abstr.Soc.Geront., Chicago Psychoanal.Lit.Ind., CINAHL, CLOA, Dent.Ind., Excerp.Med., Ind.Med., PSI, Psychol.Abstr., Sociol.Abstr.
  —BLDSC (4162.360000); UnCover. **CCC.**
  Description: Provides practical curriculum information for educators, trainers, and supervisors in the aging field.
Refereed Serial

GERONTOLOGY AND GERIATRICS

362.6 US
GERONTOLOGY NEWS. 1978. m. $50. Gerontological Society of America, 1275 K St., N.W., Ste. 350, Washington, DC 20005-4006. TEL 202-842-1275. (Subscr. to: Box 5018, Washington, DC 20061-5018) Ed. Linda Krogh Harootyan. circ. 7,200. (reprint service avail. from UMI) **Document type:** newsletter.
Incorporates (in 1990): Gerontology News. Grants - Fellowships - Jobs.
Description: Reports on policy issues, fellowships and grants in the field of aging.

362.6 US
GERONTOLOGY NEWS. CONFERENCE CALENDAR. (Included in Gerontology News) s-a. Gerontological Society of America, 1275 K St., N.W., Ste. 350, Washington, DC 20005-4006. TEL 202-842-1275. Ed. Linda Krogh Harootyan. circ. 6,500. (reprint service avail. from UMI) **Document type:** newsletter.

618.97 613.62 US ISSN 0279-4101
GERONTOLOGY SPECIAL INTEREST SECTION NEWSLETTER. (Consists of 9 sections: Administration and Management; Developmental Disabilities; Education; Gerontology; Mental Health; Physical Disabilities; Sensory Integration; Technology; Work Programs) vol.12, no.2, 1989. q. $15. American Occupational Therapy Association, Inc., 1383 Piccard Dr., Box 1725, Rockville, MD 20850-0822. TEL 301-948-9626. FAX 301-948-5512. **Document type:** newsletter.
Supersedes in part: American Occupational Therapy Association. Physical Disabilities Specialty Section. Newsletter (ISSN 0194-6366)

618.97 628 YU ISSN 0351-2886
GERONTOLOSKO DRUSTVO S R SRBIJE. (Text in Serbo-Croatian; summaries in English) 1973. a. 100 din.($10) Krfska 7, 11000 Belgrade, Yugoslavia. TEL 011-415766-09. Ed. Vitomir Stojakovic. circ. 500. (back issues avail.)

301.435 612.67 IS
HAGIL HECHADASH. (Text in Hebrew) 1980. q. Authority for Pensioners and Elderly, Sderot Weizmann 13, Jerusalem 91 903, Israel. TEL 02-520912. Ed. E. Gafni. circ. 4,500.
Description: Bulletin on the problems of aging in Israel.

618.97 IT ISSN 0017-0305
CODEN: GIGEAU
GIORNALE DI GERONTOLOGIA. (Supplement avail: Societa Italiana di Gerontologia e Geriatria. Bollettino) (Text in Italian; summaries in English) 1952. m. L.200000 (foreign L.280000). Societa Italiana di Gerontologia e Geriatria, Via G.C. Vanini 5, 50129 Florence, Italy. TEL 055-47-43-30. FAX 055-46-12-17. Ed. G. Crepaldi. adv.; bk.rev.; bibl.; charts; illus.; index. circ. 5,000. **Indexed:** Biol.Abstr., Chem.Abstr., Excerp.Med., Helminthol.Abstr., Ind.Med., Nutr.Abstr.
—BLDSC (4178.060000); Faxon; UMI; CASDDS.
Description: Research papers on the science of aging and the care of the aging.

051 US
GOLDEN AGE. m. $10. Senior Media Network, 2330 S. Main St., Ste. 2, Salt Lake City, UT 84115-2777. TEL 801-486-5051. FAX 801-486-5065. Ed. Miriam Murphy. adv. circ. 28,000. **Document type:** newsletter.

051 US
GOLDEN TIMES.* s-m. 80 Rockwood Pl., Rochester, NY 14610-2614. TEL 716-454-4500. FAX 716-232-7856. Ed. Carmen Viglucci. circ. 20,000.

051 US
▼**GOOD LIFE (PROVIDENCE).** 1992. m. $5. Providence Journal Bulletin, 75 Fountain St., Providence, RI 02902. TEL 401-277-7022. FAX 401-277-7804. adv.: B&W page $2603, color page $3153; trim 10 x 13. circ. 56,100. **Document type:** consumer publication.

051 UK
GOOD RETIREMENT GUIDE (YEAR). a. £14.99. Kogan Page Ltd., 120 Pentonville Rd., London N1 9JN, England. TEL 071-278-0433. FAX 071-837-6348. TELEX 263088-KOGAN-G. **Document type:** directory.

301.435 CN ISSN 0847-1126
GOOD TIMES. 1980. 10/yr. Senior Publications Inc., 5148 St. Laurent, Montreal, PQ H2T 1R8, Canada. TEL 514-273-9773. FAX 514-273-9034. Ed. Denise Crawford. adv.
Formerly (until 1989): Discovery (ISSN 0710-0957)

301.435 323.4 GW ISSN 0178-5109
GRAUER PANTHER. 1983. m. DM.25. (Senioren-Schutz-Bund "Graue Panther" e.V.) Klartext Verlag, Dickmannstr. 2-4, 45143 Essen, Germany. TEL 0201-8620631. FAX 0201-8620622. Ed. Bd. adv.; bk.rev. circ. 10,000. **Document type:** bulletin.

301.435 US ISSN 0739-2001
GRAY PANTHER NETWORK. 1972. s-a. $20 to individuals; institutions $35. Gray Panthers, 2025 Pennsylvania Ave., N.W., Ste. 821, Washington, DC 20006. Ed. d'Layne Kerr-Layton. adv.; bk.rev. circ. 12,000. (tabloid format; also avail. in microfilm) **Indexed:** Alt.Press Ind. **Document type:** newspaper.
Description: Original feature articles on health care, peace, economic and social justice to enhance the lives of all people. Also covers activities of 40 chapters in many states.

618.97 362.6 US
GREAT IDEAS FOR LONG-TERM CARE. m. Eymann Publications, Box 3577, Reno, NV 89505-3577. TEL 702-826-0795. Ed. Ken Eymann. circ. 1,000.
Formerly: Great Ideas Newsletter.

GROUP TRAVEL LEADER. see TRAVEL AND TOURISM

GROWTH, DEVELOPMENT & AGING. see MEDICAL SCIENCES

664 614.8 GW
HEIM UND PFLEGE. 1969. m. DM.72. Baumann Fachzeitschriftenverlag, E.C.-Baumann-Str. 5, 95326 Kulmbach, Germany. Ed. Frauke Albrecht. circ. 5,000. (back issues avail.) **Indexed:** Excerp.Med. **Document type:** bulletin.
Formerly: Heim und Anstalt (ISSN 0176-9243)

618.97 362.6 US
HERE'S HELP. m. Eymann Publications, Box 3577, Reno, NV 89505-3577. TEL 702-826-0795. Ed. Ken Eymann. circ. 100,000.
Formerly: Health Care Articles.

258 362.615 US
HORIZON (NEPTUNE). 1977. q. free. United Methodist Homes of New Jersey, Box 0667, Neptune, NJ 07754. TEL 201-922-9800. FAX 201-922-9375. Ed. Karen E. Hopkins. illus. circ. 18,000. **Indexed:** Mag.Ind., R.G.
Supersedes (in 1977): Methodist Homes Quarterly (ISSN 0026-1246)

HOUSING THE ELDERLY REPORT. see HOUSING AND URBAN PLANNING

I H A BULLETIN. (Independent Healthcare Association) see HOSPITALS

917.1 CN ISSN 0847-5288
INDEPENDENT SENIOR. 1990. m. Can.$15. K W Publishing Ltd., 1268 W. Pender St., Vancouver, BC V6E 2S8, Canada. TEL 604-688-2271. FAX 604-688-2038. Ed. K. Barker. adv.; bk.rev. circ. 45,000.
Formerly: Seniors' Advocate.
Description: Articles of interest for senior citizens - 55 and over.

618.97 II ISSN 0019-5219
RC952
INDIAN JOURNAL OF GERONTOLOGY; a quarterly journal devoted to research on aging. (Text in English) 1969. q. $50. (Indian Gerontological Association) Rupa books Pvt. Ltd., S-12, Shopping Complex, Tilaknagar, Jaipur 302 004, India. TEL 91-141-45753. FAX 91-141-41763. TELEX 0365-2631 KASA IN. adv.; bibl.

610 SZ ISSN 0074-1132
HQ1060 CODEN: ITGEAR
INTERDISCIPLINARY TOPICS IN GERONTOLOGY. (Text in English) 1968. irreg. (approx. 1/yr.). price varies. S. Karger AG, Allschwilerstr. 10, P.O. Box, CH-4009 Basel, Switzerland. TEL 061-3061111. FAX 061-3061234. Ed. H.P. von Hahn. (reprint service avail. from ISI) **Indexed:** Biol.Abstr., Chem.Abstr., Curr.Adv.Ecol.Sci., Curr.Cont., Ind.Med. **Document type:** academic/scholarly publication.
—BLDSC (4533.360000); Faxon; CASDDS. **CCC.**

INTERFACE (CHICAGO, 1984). see MEDICAL SCIENCES — Dentistry

301.43 612.6 US ISSN 0091-4150
HQ1060 CODEN: IJADDT
INTERNATIONAL JOURNAL OF AGING & HUMAN DEVELOPMENT. 1973. 8/yr. (in 2 vols., 4 nos./vol.). $54 to individuals; institutions $157. Baywood Publishing Co., Inc., 26 Austin Ave., Box 337, Amityville, NY 11701. TEL 516-691-1270. FAX 516-691-1770. Ed. Dr. Robert J. Kastenbaum. abstr.; charts; illus.; stat. (back issues avail.) **Indexed:** Abstr.Soc.Geront., ASSIA, Biol.Abstr., Bk.Rev.Ind. (1984-1986), C.I.J.E., Chic.Per.Ind., CLOA, Commun.Abstr., Curr.Cont., Dent.Ind., Excerp.Med., Ind.Med., Lang.& Lang.Behav.Abstr., Mid.East: Abstr.& Ind., NRN, PSI, Psychol.Abstr., Soc.Sci.Ind., Soc.Work Res.& Abstr., SSCI. **Document type:** academic/scholarly publication.
—BLDSC (4541.595000); Faxon; UnCover; SWETS.
Formerly: Aging and Human Development (ISSN 0002-0974)
Description: Includes critical reviews, trendsetting reports, case histories, and essays covering the latest research and developments in inter-generational relations, institutionalization, work, and retirement.
Refereed Serial

155.67 616.8 UK ISSN 0885-6230
RC451.4.A5 CODEN: IJGPES
INTERNATIONAL JOURNAL OF GERIATRIC PSYCHIATRY. 1986. m. $395 (effective 1994). John Wiley & Sons Ltd., Journals, Baffins Ln., Chichester, Sussex PO19 1UD, England. TEL 0243-779777. FAX 0243-775878. TELEX 86290 WIBOOK G. (Subscr. in the Americas to: John Wiley & Sons, Inc., 605 Third Ave., New York, NY 10158-0012. TEL 212-850-6000) Eds. Elaine Murphy, George Alexopoulos. circ. 586. (reprint service avail. from SWZ) **Indexed:** Curr.Cont., Excerp.Med., Psychol.Abstr. **Document type:** academic/scholarly publication.
—BLDSC (4542.266600); SWETS; UMI. **CCC.**
Description: Communicates the results of original research in the causes, treatment and care of all forms of mental disorder which affect the elderly.

INTERNATIONAL PSYCHOGERIATRICS. see MEDICAL SCIENCES — Psychiatry And Neurology

051 CN
▼**ISLAND NEWS FOR SENIORS.** 1992. m. Chapter House Publications, Main St., North Rustico, P.E.I. C0A 1X0, Canada. TEL 902-963-3102. FAX 902-963-3152. adv.: B&W page Can.$695. circ. 10,000.

301.4 IS ISSN 0047-1577
ISRAEL GERONTOLOGICAL SOCIETY. INFORMATION BULLETIN/HA-AGUDAH HA-ISRAELIT LE-GERONTOLOGYAH. YEDION. (Text in Hebrew) 1965. q. $90 includes Gerontology. Israel Gerontological Society, Box 1105, Ramat Gan 52111, Israel. FAX 972-3-5755010. Ed. H. Har-Paz. bk.rev. circ. 800. **Document type:** bulletin.

618.97 SA ISSN 1017-2572
CODEN: JARDE
J A R D - JOURNAL OF AGE RELATED DISORDERS. (Text in English) 1988. 6/yr. R.48 (foreign R.70) (effective 1994). (South African Geriatrics Society) Medical Media C C, P.O. Box 581, 1620 Kempton Park, South Africa. TEL 27-11-9756439. FAX 27-11-9702532. Ed. S.J. Louw. adv.: color page R.3850; adv. contact: Denis Middlemiss. abstr. **Indexed:** Excerp.Med. **Document type:** academic/scholarly publication.
—BLDSC (4919.997650).
Formerly (until 1989): GeriatRx (ISSN 1012-8182)
Description: Communicates results of high scientific quality in the causes, treatment and care of all forms of medical disorders in the elderly.

GERONTOLOGY AND GERIATRICS

612.67   IS
J D C - BROOKDALE INSTITUTE OF GERONTOLOGY AND HUMAN DEVELOPMENT. ANNUAL REPORT. (Text in English and Hebrew) a. free. J D C - Brookdale Institute of Gerontology and Human Development, P.O. Box 13087, Jerusalem 91130, Israel. TEL 972-2-557400. FAX 972-2-635851. **Document type:** corporate report.
    Formerly: Brookdale Institute. Annual Report.
    Description: Overview of research conducted in the past year and preview of program for coming year.

301.435   IS   ISSN 0334-9012
J D C - BROOKDALE INSTITUTE OF GERONTOLOGY AND HUMAN DEVELOPMENT. DISCUSSION PAPERS. (Text in English or Hebrew) irreg. (7-8/yr.) J D C - Brookdale Institute of Gerontology and Human Development, P.O. Box 13087, Jerusalem 91130, Israel. TEL 972-2-557400. FAX 972-2-635851.
    Formerly: Brookdale Institute of Gerontology. Discussion Papers.

301.435   IS   ISSN 0334-9101
J D C - BROOKDALE INSTITUTE OF GERONTOLOGY AND HUMAN DEVELOPMENT. INTERNATIONAL FORUM. (Text in English) irreg. J D C - Brookdale Institute of Gerontology and Human Development, P.O. Box 13087, Jerusalem 91130, Israel. TEL 972-2-557400. FAX 972-2-635851.
    Formerly: Brookdale Institute of Gerontology. International Forum.

301.435   IS   ISSN 0334-908X
J D C - BROOKDALE INSTITUTE OF GERONTOLOGY AND HUMAN DEVELOPMENT. SPECIAL SERIES. (Text in English or Hebrew) irreg. J D C - Brookdale Institute of Gerontology and Human Development, P.O. Box 13087, Jerusalem 91130, Israel. TEL 972-2-557400. FAX 972-2-635851.
    Formerly: Brookdale Institute of Gerontology. Special Series.

618.97   JA   ISSN 0915-4620
JERONTOROJI/GERONTOLOGY. (Text in Japanese) 4/yr. 1500 Yen. Medikaru Rebyusha - Medical Review Co., Ltd., 7-3, Hiranomachi 1-chome, Chuo-ku, Osaka 541, Japan.
    —BLDSC (4162.353000).

618.97   US   ISSN 1042-1882
JOHNS HOPKINS MEDICAL LETTER HEALTH AFTER 50. Variant title: Health after 50. 1989. m. $24. (Johns Hopkins Medical Institutions) Medletter Associates, 632 Broadway, New York, NY 10012. TEL 212-505-2255. FAX 212-505-5462. Pub. Rodney Friedman. circ. 400,000. **Document type:** consumer publication.
    —BLDSC (4671.583000).

612.67   US   ISSN 0898-2643
RA564.8   CODEN: JAHEEG
JOURNAL OF AGING AND HEALTH. 1989. q. $50 to individuals; institutions $120 (effective 1994). Sage Publications, Inc., 2455 Teller Rd., Thousand Oaks, CA 91320. TEL 805-499-0721. FAX 805-499-0871. (Subscr. to: Sage Publications, Inc., Box 5084, Thousand Oaks, CA 91359; Overseas subscr. to: Sage Publications, Ltd., 6 Bonhill St., London EC2A 4PU, England; Sage Publications India Pvt. Ltd., P.O. Box 4215, New Delhi 110 048, India) Ed. Kyriakos S. Markides. circ. 1,250. **Indexed:** Abstr.Soc.Geront., Behav.Med.Abstr., Psychol.Abstr. **Document type:** academic/scholarly publication.
    —BLDSC (4919.997830); UnCover; SWETS; UMI.
    Description: Provides a forum for the presentation of research and scholarly exchange dealing with social and behavioral factors related to aging and health, with emphasis on health and the quality of life.
    Refereed Serial

613.7   US   ISSN 1063-8652
QP86
▼**JOURNAL OF AGING AND PHYSICAL ACTIVITY.** 1993. q. $40 to individuals (foreign $44); institutions $90 (foreign $119); students $24 (foreign $28). Human Kinetics Publishers, Inc., Box 5076, Champaign, IL 61825-5076. TEL 217-351-5076. FAX 217-351-2674. Ed. Wojtek Chodzko-Zajko. adv. contact: Michele Watson. abstr.; bibl.; charts; stat. circ. 250. **Document type:** academic/scholarly publication.
    —BLDSC (4919.997870); UnCover. **CCC.**
    Description: Examines the relationship between physical activity and the aging process. Covers the development, implementation, and evaluation of physical activity programs for older adults.

301.435   US   ISSN 0895-9420
HV1457   CODEN: JSPOE8
JOURNAL OF AGING & SOCIAL POLICY; a journal devoted to aging & social policy. 1989. q. $36 to individuals; institutions $80; libraries $95. Haworth Press, Inc., 10 Alice St., Binghamton, NY 13904. TEL 607-722-5857; 800-342-9678. FAX 607-722-1424. Eds. Scott A. Bass, Robert Morris. adv.; bk.rev. (also avail. in microfiche from UMI; reprint service avail. from HAW) **Indexed:** Soc.Work Res.& Abstr. **Document type:** academic/scholarly publication.
    —BLDSC (4919.997880); Faxon; UnCover.
    Description: Forum for the analysis, argument, research, and advocacy of social policy as it affects the aging population.
    Refereed Serial

612.67   US   ISSN 0890-4065
HQ1060
JOURNAL OF AGING STUDIES. q. $55 to individuals (foreign $65); institutions $135 (foreign $155). J A I Press Inc., 55 Old Post Rd., No. 2, Box 1678, Greenwich, CT 06836-1678. TEL 203-661-7602. FAX 203-661-0792. (Addr. in Europe: J A I Press Ltd., The Courtyard, 28 High St., Hampton Hill, Mddx. TW12 1PD, England. TEL 44-81-943-9296. FAX 44-81-943-9317) Ed. Jaber F. Gubrium. (back issues avail.) **Indexed:** Abstr.Soc.Geront. **Document type:** academic/scholarly publication.
    —BLDSC (4919.997900); Faxon; UnCover. **CCC.**
    Description: Covers the experience of aging from the perspectives of many disciplines offering new directions in theory and research and critiques of these approaches.

618.97   US   ISSN 0733-4648
HQ1061
JOURNAL OF APPLIED GERONTOLOGY. 1982. q. $49 to individuals; institutions $134 (effective 1994). (Southern Gerontological Society) Sage Publications, Inc., 2455 Teller Rd., Thousand Oaks, CA 91320. TEL 805-499-0721. FAX 805-499-0871. (Subscr. to: Sage Publications, Inc., Box 5084, Thousand Oaks, CA 91359; Overseas subscr. to: Sage Publications, Ltd., 6 Bonhill St., London EC2A 4PU, England; Sage Publications India Pvt. Ltd., P.O. Box 4215, New Delhi 110 048, India) Ed. William J. McAuley. circ. 1,600. **Indexed:** Abstr.Soc.Geront., CLOA, Human Resour.Abstr., Psychol.Abstr., Sage Fam.Stud.Abstr., Sociol.Abstr. **Document type:** academic/scholarly publication.
    —BLDSC (4942.615000); Faxon; UMI. **CCC.**
    Description: Covers all subdisciplines of aging with conclusions, findings, or suggestions immediately applicable to the problems encountered by older persons.
    Refereed Serial

612.67 572   NE   ISSN 0169-3816
HQ1060   CODEN: JCCGEB
JOURNAL OF CROSS-CULTURAL GERONTOLOGY. 1986. 4/yr. fl.321($168) (effective 1994). Kluwer Academic Publishers, Postbus 17, 3300 AA Dordrecht, Netherlands. TEL 31-78-334911. FAX 31-78-334254. TELEX 29245 KAPG NL. (Dist. by: Kluwer Academic Publishers Group, P.O. Box 322, 3300 AH Dordrecht, Netherlands. TEL 31-78-524400. FAX 31-78-524474; N. America dist. addr.: Box 358, Accord Sta., Hingham, MA 02018-0358. TEL 617-871-6600. FAX 617-871-6528) Eds. C.M. Beall, Melvyn C. Goldstein. adv.; bk.rev.; index. (also avail. in microform from UMI; back issues avail.; reprint service avail. from SWZ) **Indexed:** Abstr.Soc.Geront., Anthropol.Lit., Biol.Abstr., CLOA, Ind.Med., Psychol.Abstr., Ref.Zh., Sage Fam.Stud.Abstr., Sociol.Abstr. **Document type:** academic/scholarly publication.
    —BLDSC (4965.660000); Faxon; UnCover; SWETS; UMI. **CCC.**
    Description: Interdisciplinary journal examining the aging process and the problems of the aged throught the world.
    Refereed Serial

JOURNAL OF CUTANEOUS AGING & COSMETIC DERMATOLOGY. see *MEDICAL SCIENCES — Dermatology And Venereology*

362.6   US   ISSN 0894-6566
HV6626.3   CODEN: JEANE2
JOURNAL OF ELDER ABUSE & NEGLECT. 1988. q. $32 to individuals; institutions $90; libraries $125. Haworth Press, Inc., 10 Alice St., Binghamton, NY 13904. TEL 607-722-5857; 800-342-9678. FAX 607-722-1424. Eds. Suzan McMurray-Anderson, Rosalie S. Wolf. adv.; bk.rev. (also avail. in microfiche from UMI; reprint service avail. from HAW) **Indexed:** Soc.Work Res.& Abstr. **Document type:** academic/scholarly publication.
    —BLDSC (4973.293000); UnCover.
    Description: Devoted to the study of causes, treatment, effects, and prevention of the mistreatment of older people. Provides a forum for the discussion of scientific investigation, program developments, policy initiatives, and personal commentary about elder abuse and neglect.
    Refereed Serial

301 910.03   US
JOURNAL OF ETHNOGERONTOLOGY. 1975. s-a. $30. National Council on Black Aging, Inc., Box 51275, Durham, NC 27717-1275. TEL 919-489-2563. Eds. Jacquelyne J. Jackson, Donald E. Ensley. bk.rev.; bibl. circ. 250. **Document type:** academic/scholarly publication.
    Former titles: Journal of Minority Aging; Minority Aging; Black Aging.
    Description: Contains research, legislative and thought-provoking materials on the current status of minorities with the psychological and sociocultural aspects of their aging.

618.97 616.5   US   ISSN 1072-8856
▼**JOURNAL OF GERIATRIC DERMATOLOGY.** 1993. 6/yr. $60 (foreign $96). Health Management Publications, Inc., 550 American Ave., King of Prussia, PA 19406. TEL 215-337-4466; 800-237-7285. FAX 215-337-0890. adv.: B&W page $1150, color page $1900; trim 8 1/8 x 11. circ. 6,902.

JOURNAL OF GERIATRIC DRUG THERAPY. see *PHARMACY AND PHARMACOLOGY*

JOURNAL OF GERIATRIC PSYCHIATRY. see *MEDICAL SCIENCES — Psychiatry And Neurology*

618.97 616.8   US   ISSN 0891-9887
JOURNAL OF GERIATRIC PSYCHIATRY AND NEUROLOGY; an interdisciplinary forum for clinicians and scientists. 1988. q. $65 to individuals (foreign $91); institutions $89 (foreign $115); students $40 (foreign $66). Decker Periodicals, One James St. S., P.O. Box 620, LCD 1, Hamilton, ON L8N 3K7. TEL 800-568-7281. FAX 416-522-7839. (U.S. addr.: Box 785 Lewiston, NY 14092-0785. TEL 800-325-4177) Ed. Michael A. Jenike. bk.rev.; illus. circ. 571. **Indexed:** Excerp.Med., Ind.Med., Psychol.Abstr.
    —BLDSC (4995.081000); UnCover; UMI. **CCC.**
    Description: For physicians who treat aging patients as well as researchers in geriatric psychiatry and neurology.

GERONTOLOGY AND GERIATRICS

610.73   US   ISSN 0098-9134
RC954
JOURNAL OF GERONTOLOGICAL NURSING. 1975. m. $34 to individuals; institutions $46. Slack, Inc., 6900 Grove Rd., Thorofare, NJ 08086. TEL 609-848-1000. FAX 609-853-5991. Ed. Edna M. Stilwell. adv.; bk.rev.; illus.; index. circ. 10,500. (also avail. in microform from UMI; reprint service avail. from UMI) **Indexed:** Abstr.Health Care Manage.Stud., CINAHL, CLOA, I.P.A., Int.Nurs.Ind., Nurs.Abstr., Psychol.Abstr.
●Also available online.
—BLDSC (4995.094000); Faxon; UnCover; SWETS; UMI. **CCC.**
Refereed Serial

301.435   US   ISSN 0163-4372
HV1451
JOURNAL OF GERONTOLOGICAL SOCIAL WORK. 1978. q. $35 to individuals; institutions $125; libraries $200. Haworth Press, Inc., 10 Alice St., Binghamton, NY 13904. TEL 607-722-5857; 800-342-9678. FAX 607-722-1424. Ed. Rose Dobrof. adv.: page $300. bk.rev. circ. 824. (also avail. in microfiche from UMI; reprint service avail. from HAW) **Indexed:** Abstr.Health Care Manage.Stud., Abstr.Soc.Geront., ASSIA, Behav.Abstr., Behav.Med.Abstr., CINAHL, CLOA, Commun.Abstr., Curr.Cont., Excerp.Med., Human Resour.Abstr., Ind.Per.Art.Relat.Law, Psychol.Abstr., Soc.Sci.Ind., Soc.Work Res.& Abstr., Sociol.Abstr., SSCI, Yrbk.Assoc.Educ.& Rehab.Blind. **Document type:** academic/scholarly publication.
—BLDSC (4995.094400); Faxon; UnCover; SWETS.
Description: Covers social work practice, theory, administration, and consultation in the field of aging.
Refereed Serial

362.6   US   ISSN 0276-3893
HD7287.9
JOURNAL OF HOUSING FOR THE ELDERLY. 1983. s-a. $40 to individuals; institutions $120; libraries $160. Haworth Press, Inc., 10 Alice St., Binghamton, NY 13904. TEL 607-722-5857; 800-342-9678. FAX 607-722-1424. Ed. Leon Pastalan. adv.; bk.rev. circ. 310. (also avail. in microfiche from UMI; reprint service avail. from HAW) **Indexed:** Archit.Per.Ind., CLOA, P.A.I.S., Psychol.Abstr., Sage Fam.Stud.Abstr., Sociol.Abstr., Urb.Aff.Abstr. **Document type:** academic/scholarly publication.
—BLDSC (5003.412000); Faxon; UnCover.
Description: Provides new research and synthesizes the cross-disciplinary efforts made in the area of residential environments for the elderly.
Refereed Serial

362.6   US   ISSN 0093-4445
RA997.A1   CODEN: JLTAD4
JOURNAL OF LONG-TERM CARE ADMINISTRATION. 1972. q. $70 to non-members (foreign $80). American College of Health Care Administrators, 325 S. Patrick St., Alexandria, VA 22314. TEL 703-549-5822. Ed. Jan Lamoglia. adv.; bk.rev.; film rev.; bibl.; charts; index. circ. 15,000. (also avail. in microform from UMI; back issues avail.) **Indexed:** Abstr.Health Care Manage.Stud., Abstr.Hosp.Manage.Stud., Abstr.Soc.Geront., Biol.Abstr., C.I.N.L., Hosp.Lit.Ind., I.P.A., Med.Care.Rev., Soc.Work Res.& Abstr. **Document type:** academic/scholarly publication.
—BLDSC (5010.560000); Faxon; UnCover; UMI. **CCC.**
Description: Publishes in-depth research, trends and developments in long-term health care administration.

JOURNAL OF LONG TERM HOME HEALTH CARE. see *HOSPITALS*

613.2   US   ISSN 0163-9366
TX361.A3   CODEN: JNELDA
JOURNAL OF NUTRITION FOR THE ELDERLY. 1980. q. $45 to individuals; institutions $90; libraries $200. Haworth Press, Inc., 10 Alice St., Binghamton, NY 13904. TEL 607-722-5857; 800-342-9678. FAX 607-722-1424. TELEX 4932599. Ed. Annette B. Natow. adv.; bk.rev.; bibl. circ. 553. (also avail. in microfiche from UMI; reprint service avail. from HAW) **Indexed:** Abstr.Soc.Geront., Biol.Abstr., Bull.Signal., Chem.Abstr., CLOA, Curr.Cont., Excerp.Med., Food Sci.& Tech.Abstr., Hosp.Lit.Ind., I.P.A., Int.Nurs.Ind., Med.Care Rev., Nutr.Abstr., Potato Abstr., Psychol.Abstr., Ref.Zh., Rehabil.Lit. **Document type:** academic/scholarly publication.
—BLDSC (5024.710000); Faxon; UnCover.
Description: Reports of dietary studies, systems and programs for providing nutritional care, and the cultural and behavioral aspects of nutrition for the elderly. Includes summaries of relevant articles in other journals.
Refereed Serial

JOURNAL OF OCULAR PHARMACOLOGY. see *MEDICAL SCIENCES — Ophthalmology And Optometry*

155.67 200   US   ISSN 1050-2289
BV4435   CODEN: JRGEES
JOURNAL OF RELIGIOUS GERONTOLOGY. 1985. q. $36 to individuals; institutions $60; libraries $125. Haworth Press, Inc., 10 Alice St., Binghamton, NY 13904. TEL 607-722-5857; 800-342-9678. FAX 607-722-1424. TELEX 4932599. Ed. William M. Clements. adv.; bk.rev. circ. 469. (also avail. in microfiche from UMI; reprint service avail. from HAW) **Indexed:** Abstr.Soc.Geront., CLOA, Past.Care & Couns.Abstr., Psychol.Abstr., Rel.& Theol.Abstr. (1984-). **Document type:** academic/scholarly publication.
—UnCover.
Formerly (until vol.7, 1990): Journal of Religion and Aging (ISSN 0738-6184)
Description: For both religious and secular professionals who work with the elderly and their families. Provides articles that cut across denominational lines and academic disciplines to present a total and current picture of the emerging field of religious gerontology.
Refereed Serial

JOURNAL OF WOMEN AND AGING. see *WOMEN'S STUDIES*

618.97 612.67
155.67   US   ISSN 0022-1422
HQ1060   CODEN: JOGEA3
JOURNALS OF GERONTOLOGY. (Consists of: Journal of Gerontology: Biological Sciences; Journal of Gerontology: Medical Sciences; Journal of Gerontology: Psychological Sciences; Journal of Gerontology: Social Sciences) 1946. bi-m. $65 to individuals; institutions $99. Gerontological Society of America, 1275 K St., N.W., Ste. 250, Washington, DC 20005-4006. TEL 202-842-1275. (Subscr. to: Box 5018, Washington, DC 20061-5018) Ed.Bd. adv.; bibl.; charts; illus. circ. 9,767. (also avail. in microform from UMI; reprint service avail. from UMI) **Indexed:** Abstr.Anthropol., Abstr.Health Care Manage.Stud., Abstr.Soc.Geront., Anim.Breed.Abstr., ASSIA, Biol.Abstr., Bk.Rev.Ind. (1984-), C.I.J.E., CERDIC, Chem.Abstr., Child.Bk.Rev.Ind. (1984-), CLOA, Curr.Adv.Ecol.Sci., Curr.Cont., Dairy Sci.Abstr., Dent.Ind., Ergon.Abstr., Excerp.Med., Helminthol.Abstr., Hosp.Lit.Ind., Ind.Med., Ind.Sci.Rev., Mid.East: Abstr.& Ind., Nutr.Abstr., P.A.I.S., Psychol.Abstr., Rehabil.Lit., Sage Fam.Stud.Abstr., Sage.Urb.Stud.Abstr., Sci.Cit.Ind., Soc.Sci.Ind., Soc.Work Res.& Abstr., SSCI. **Document type:** academic/scholarly publication.
—BLDSC (4995.095000); Faxon; UnCover; SWETS; UMI; CASDDS.
Description: Research papers on problems of aging from the viewpoint of natural and social sciences.

051   US
KEY HORIZONS. 4/yr. $5. Emmis Publishing Corp., Box 53917, Indianapolis, IN 46253. TEL 317-237-9288. Ed. Brenda Pace. adv. circ. 2,500.00.

301.435 051   US
KEYNOTES (MANHATTAN); a news magazine for older Kansans and their families. 1983. bi-m. $5 to individuals; institutions $10; senior citizens free. North Central-Flint Hills Area Agency on Aging, 437 Houston St., Manhattan, KS 66502. TEL 913-776-9294. Ed. Nelson E. Love. adv.; bk.rev. circ. 22,000. (tabloid format; also avail. in talking book) **Document type:** newspaper.
Description: Covers finance, health, nutrition and all areas of human interest.

KYORIN IGAKKAI ZASSHI/KYORIN MEDICAL SOCIETY. JOURNAL. see *MEDICAL SCIENCES*

051   US
THE LAKESIDE BANNER. m. $12 ($15 out of county). Paso Robles Newspapers, Inc., 1050 Park St., Box 427, Paso Robles, CA 93447. TEL 805-238-0330. FAX 805-238-6504. Ed. Pat Woods. adv. contact: John Echeveste. circ. 2,700. (tabloid format; back issues avail.) **Document type:** newspaper.
Formerly (until 1993): Heritage Ranch Herald.
Description: News of interest to senior citizens and resort residents.

301.435   CC
LAONIANXUE ZAZHI/JOURNAL OF GERONTOLOGY. (Text in Chinese) bi-m. Zhongguo Laonian Xuehui - Chinese Society of Gerontology, Fu 2, Dong Minzhu Dajie, Changchun, Jilin 130061, People's Republic of China. TEL 825027. (Co-sponsor: Jilin Sheng Weisheng Ting) Ed. Wu Cangping.

301.435   CC
LAOREN SHIJIE/OLD PEOPLE'S WORLD. (Text in Chinese) m. Hebei Sheng Laoling Weiyuanhui - Hebei Provincial Committee for the Aged, 20 Shiyi Lu, Shijiazhuang, Hebei 050051, People's Republic of China. TEL 32061. Ed. Hao Jincheng.

301.435   CC
LAOREN TIANDI/ELDERLY WORLD. (Text in Chinese) 1983. m. Y13.20($36.80) (Minzheng Bu) Laoren Tiandi Zazhishe, 34 Shatan Houjie, Beijing 100009, People's Republic of China. TEL 4032528. (Dist. overseas by: Guoji Shudian - China International Book Trading Corp., P.O. Box 399, Beijing, P.R.C.; US subscr. to: China Books & Periodicals, Inc., 2929 24th St., San Francisco, CA 94110. TEL 415-282-2994) Ed. Yang Ming.

LAW ENFORCEMENT VOLUNTEERS. see *CRIMINOLOGY AND LAW ENFORCEMENT*

LEARNING AND MEMORY. see *MEDICAL SCIENCES — Psychiatry And Neurology*

LEARNING & MEMORY. see *MEDICAL SCIENCES — Psychiatry And Neurology*

301.43   NE   ISSN 0165-3792
LEEFTIJD. 1963. m. fl.80.19. Nijgh Periodieken B.V., Postbus 122, 3100 AC Scheidam, Netherlands. TEL 31-10-4274100. FAX 31-10-4739911. adv.: B&W page fl.1850, color page fl.3830; trim 210 x 297; adv. contact: Bert Niewold. bk.rev. circ. 4,635. **Document type:** trade publication.
—SWETS.
Formerly (until 1977): Op Leeftijd (ISSN 0030-333X)

LEGAL ISSUES, GOVERNMENT PROGRAMS & THE ELDERLY (FLORIDA); a handbook for the advocates. see *LAW — Legal Aid*

301.435   US
LEISURE WORLD GOLDEN RAIN NEWS. 1963. w. $25. Golden Rain Foundation, Box 2338, Seal Beach, CA 90740-1338. TEL 310-430-0534. FAX 310-598-1617. Ed. David Saunders. adv.; circ. 6,708 (paid); 2,292 (controlled). **Document type:** newspaper.
Description: For the senior retirement community.

GERONTOLOGY AND GERIATRICS

362.6   US   ISSN 0146-275X
LONG-TERM CARE ADMINISTRATOR. 1967. 8/yr. $45 (foreign $55). American College of Health Care Administrators, 325 S. Patrick St., Alexandria, VA 22314. TEL 703-549-5822. Ed. Jan Lamoglia. adv.; illus. circ. 6,500. **Indexed:** CINAHL. **Document type:** newsletter.
—CCC.
    Formerly: American College of Nursing Home Administrators. Newsletter.
    Description: Features education program information, articles on key issues in long-term care administration, and news about the profession, tips, legislative updates and education calendar.

610.736   CN   ISSN 1180-2189
LONG TERM CARE MONITOR. m. Can.$107. M P L Communications Inc., 700-133 Richmond St. W., Toronto, ON M5H 3M8, Canada. TEL 416-869-1177. FAX 416-869-0456. Ed. Chris Garbutt.
    Description: Provides practical information and news about ongoing issues in the long-term care sector, for administrators of facilities.

362.6   US
LONG-TERM CARE NEWS. 1972. m. $10 to individuals; institutions $125. California Rural Legal Assistance Foundation, Public Interest Center on Long-Term Care, 2000 O St., Ste. 240, Sacramento, CA 95814. TEL 916-446-5085. FAX 916-446-3057. Ed. Thomas A. Porter. circ. 1,000. **Document type:** newsletter.
    Formerly (until 1992): Seniors in Sacramento.

051   US   ISSN 0895-8254
RA776.75   **CODEN:** LONGE2
LONGEVITY; the art and science of staying young. 1989. m. $24 (effective 1993). Longevity International, Ltd. (Subsidiary of: General Media Publishing Group), 1965 Broadway, New York, NY 10023-5965. TEL 212-496-6100. FAX 212-580-3693. (Subscr. to: Box 3226, Harlan, IA 51537-3226) Ed. Susan Millar Perry. adv. contact: Alyson Kanney. circ. 343,387. (back issues avail.) **Document type:** consumer publication.
—UMI.
    Description: Provides news and information from the frontiers of life-extension research.

052   SA
▼**LONGEVITY.** (Text in English) 1993. m. Longevity Magazine (Subsidiary of: General Media Publishing Group), P.O. Box 650663, Benmore 2010, South Africa. TEL 27-11-884-7660. FAX 27-11-884-7660. Ed. Claudia Boffard. adv. contact: Ralph Boffard. illus. **Document type:** consumer publication.

612.67   US   ISSN 0896-7032
LOOKING FORWARD. q. (Hope Heart Institute) International Health Awareness Center Inc., 350 E. Michigan Ave., Ste. 301, Kalamazoo, MI 49007-3851. TEL 616-343-0770. Ed. Carol P. Garzona. illus. (looseleaf format)
    Description: Health care news and general tips for retirees.

301.435   CN   ISSN 0831-3040
M S O S JOURNAL. 1979. m. Can.$17. Manitoba Society of Seniors, 803-294 Portage Ave., Winnipeg, MB R3C 0B9, Canada. FAX 204-943-1290. Ed. Irvin J. Kroeker. adv. contact: Ray Gislason. bk.rev. circ. 35,000. **Document type:** newspaper.
    Description: Official publication of the Manitoba Society of Seniors.

301.435   US
MCCALL'S SILVER. 1988. 6/yr. Family Circle Inc. (Subsidiary of: New York Times Company), 110 Fifth Ave., 4th Fl., New York, NY 10011. TEL 212-463-1000. FAX 212-463-1403. adv. circ. 1,000,000.
    Description: For women over 50 who desire to continue to contribute to the world around them.

610.736   US
MCKNIGHT'S LONG-TERM CARE NEWS. 1980. m. $44.95 (Canada $54.95; elsewhere $59.95). McKnight Medical Communications Co. (Subsidiary of: Medical Economics Publishing Co., Inc.), Two Northfield Plaza, Ste. 300, Northfield, IL 60093. TEL 708-441-3700. Ed. Suzanne M. Powills. adv. contact: Deborah Tobiaski. illus.; stat. circ. 41,288. (tabloid format; back issues avail.)
    Formerly (until Nov. 1989): Today's Nursing Home.

618.97 362.6   US
▼**MANAGING SENIOR CARE.** 1992. m. $150. Business Publishers, Inc., 951 Pershing Dr., Silver Spring, MD 20910-4464. TEL 301-587-6300; 800-BPI-0122. FAX 301-589-5103. **Document type:** newsletter.
    Description: Covers medical care, social services, facilities, financial management, and other aspects of senior care.

051   US
MATURE LIFESTYLES.* 1987. m. $8. Box 44327, Madison, WI 53744-4327. TEL 608-274-5200. Ed. Julia Jergensen. adv. circ. 20,000. **Document type:** newspaper.
    Description: Covers health, finance, and housing for the 50 plus age group.

301.435   US   ISSN 0742-0935
MATURE OUTLOOK; for vibrant people who enjoy life. 1983. bi-m. $9.95 to non-members; institutions $6. Meredith Publishing Co., 1912 Grand Ave., Des Moines, IA 50309-3379. TEL 800-336-6330. (Subscr. to: 6001 N. Clark St., Chicago, IL 60660) Ed. Marjorie Groves. adv.; bk.rev. circ. 1,000,000. **Document type:** consumer publication.
    Description: Covers health and fitness, food and nutrition, travel and people.

301.435   US   ISSN 0025-6021
BV4580.A1
MATURE YEARS. 1954. q. $10. (United Methodist Church, Board of Discipleship) United Methodist Publishing House, 201 Eighth Ave. S., Box 801, Nashville, TN 37202. TEL 615-749-6292. Ed. Marvin Cropsey. illus. circ. 80,000. (also avail. in microform from UMI; large print edition in 14 pt.) **Indexed:** Meth.Per.Ind. **Document type:** consumer publication.
—UMI.
    Description: Contains articles of interest to elderly persons, written from a religous perspective.

612.67   IE   ISSN 0378-5122
    CODEN: MATUDK
MATURITAS; international journal for the study of the climacteric. (Text in English) 1978. 6/yr. (in 2 vols., 3 nos./vol.). I£196($286) (effective 1994). (International Menopause Society) Elsevier Science Ireland Ltd., P.O. Box 85, Limerick, Ireland. TEL 353-61-471944. FAX 353-61-472144. (Subscr. in U.S. and Canada to: Elsevier Science Inc., Box 882, Madison Sq. Sta., New York, NY 10159. TEL 212-989-5800. FAX 212-633-3990) Eds. H. Kopera, W.H. Utian. bk.rev. (also avail. in microform from UMI; reprint service avail. from SWZ) **Indexed:** Biol.Abstr., Chem.Abstr., Curr.Adv.Ecol.Sci., Curr.Cont., Excerp.Med., Ind.Med., Ind.Sci.Rev. **Document type:** academic/scholarly publication.
—BLDSC (5413.265000); ADONIS; Faxon; UnCover; SWETS; CASDDS. **CCC.**
    Description: For gynecologists, endocrinologists, geriatricians, andrologists, sociologists, psychologists. Publishes original research on the physiological, psychological and sociological changes in function related to the climacteric in both men and women.
    Refereed Serial

301.435   CN   ISSN 0834-7948
MATURITY MAGAZINE. 1984. bi-m. Can.$12. C Y N Investments Ltd., Box 397, New Westminster, BC V3L 4Y7, Canada. TEL 604-540-7911. FAX 604-540-7912. Ed. Audrey Gill. adv.; bk.rev. circ. 175,000.
    Description: General interest for senior citizens. Includes finance, health, travel, and lifestyle.

MATURITY MARKET PERSPECTIVES. see *BUSINESS AND ECONOMICS* — *Marketing And Purchasing*

612.67   IE   ISSN 0047-6374
QP86   **CODEN:** MAGDA3
MECHANISMS OF AGEING AND DEVELOPMENT. 1972. 21/yr. (in 7 vols.; 3 nos./vol.). I£1057($1543) (effective 1994). Elsevier Science Ireland Ltd., P.O. Box 85, Limerick, Ireland. TEL 353-61-471944. FAX 353-61-472144. (Subscr. in U.S. and Canada to: Elsevier Science Inc., Box 882, Madison Sq. Sta., New York, NY 10159. TEL 212-989-5800. FAX 212-633-3990) Ed. B.L. Strehler. (also avail. in microform from UMI) **Indexed:** Anim.Breed.Abstr., Biol.Abstr., Bull.Signal., Chem.Abstr., Curr.Adv.Biochem., Curr.Adv.Cell & Devel.Biol., Curr.Adv.Ecol.Sci., Curr.Cont., Dent.Ind., Excerp.Med., Helminthol.Abstr., Ind.Med., Ind.Sci.Rev., Ind.Vet., Int.Aerosp.Abstr., Nutr.Abstr., Sci.Cit.Ind. **Document type:** academic/scholarly publication.
—BLDSC (5424.571000); Faxon; UnCover; SWETS; CASDDS. **CCC.**
    Refereed Serial

155.67 615.328
614.58   IT   ISSN 0391-4844
    CODEN: MGRCAT
MEDICINA GERIATRICA. (Text in Italian; summaries in English and Italian) 1969. bi-m. L.50000($16) (foreign L.60000). Societa Italiana Medici e Operatori Geriatrici, Via Ippolito Nievo, 16, 50129 Florence, Italy. TEL 055-474510. Ed.Bd. adv.; bk.rev.; bibl.; illus.; stat.; index. circ. 1,500. (back issues avail.) **Indexed:** Biol.Abstr. **Document type:** academic/scholarly publication.

612.67 613 155.67   US   ISSN 1061-4397
MENOPAUSE NEWS. 1991. bi-m. $24 to individuals; institutions $30 (effective 1993). Menopause News, 2074 Union St., San Francisco, CA 94123. TEL 415-567-2368. Ed. Judith Stiles Askew. bk.rev. **Document type:** newsletter.
    Description: Contains the latest medical and psychological information, as well as first-person accounts.

150 340.5   US
MENTAL CAPACITY: MEDICAL AND LEGAL ASPECTS OF THE AGING. 1977. base vol. (plus a. supplement). Shepard's - McGraw-Hill, Inc., Box 35300, Colorado Springs, CO 80935-3530. TEL 800-525-2474.
    Description: Covers the physiological and legal aspects of mental incompetence, including symptoms, causes and treatments of senility.

METROPOLITAN PENSIONER. see *SOCIAL SERVICES AND WELFARE*

MID-AMERICA SENIOR TENNIS. see *SPORTS AND GAMES* — *Ball Games*

612.67   US
MINNESOTA GERONTOLOGIST. 1977. 5/yr. $10. Minnesota Gerontological Society, 336 N. Robert St., Ste. 219, St. Paul, MN 55101. TEL 612-222-8233. Ed. Beth Wiggins. bk.rev. circ. 650. **Document type:** newsletter.
    Description: Provides information on current issues in aging to its membership; it also provides information about MGS conferences and other activities of the society.

362.6   GW   ISSN 0933-758X
HV1481.G36
MITTEILUNGEN ZUR ALTENHILFE. 1963. q. DM.20. Verband Katholischer Heime und Einrichtungen der Altenhilfe in Deutschland e.V., Karlstr. 40, 79104 Freiburg, Germany. TEL 0761-2001. circ. 2,800.

612.67   US   ISSN 0275-360X
    CODEN: MARDDR
MODERN AGING RESEARCH. 1980. irreg., vol.9, 1990. price varies. John Wiley & Sons, Inc., Journals, 605 Third Ave., New York, NY 10158. TEL 212-475-7700. Eds. Richard C. Adelman, Jay Roberts. **Indexed:** Biol.Abstr., Chem.Abstr.
●Also available online.
—CASDDS. **CCC.**
    Refereed Serial

GERONTOLOGY AND GERIATRICS

301.435   US   ISSN 0026-8046
HQ1060
MODERN MATURITY. (Avail.: Modern Maturity - N R T A Edition) 1958. bi-m. membership only. American Association of Retired Persons (Lakewood), 3200 E. Carson St., Lakewood, CA 90712.
TEL 213-496-2277. Ed. J. Henry Fenwick. adv.; bk.rev.; illus. circ. 22,200,000. (also avail. in microform from UMI) **Indexed:** Consum.Ind., Hlth.Ind., Mag.Ind., PMR, Rehabil.Lit.
—UnCover; UMI.
 Former titles (until 1960): We; Journal of Lifetime Living.
 Description: Includes articles on finance, career options, travel, health, food, personalities, current affairs and fiction of interest to persons 50 and older.

618.97   NE   ISSN 0924-7378
MODERNE GERIATRIE/GERIATRIE MODERNE. (Text in German) 1984. 9/yr. 154 SFr. P M S I Bugamor, Haak 58, 1353 AE Almere-Haven, Netherlands. TEL 31-36-5382211. FAX 31-36-5316281. Ed. Dr. W.O. Seiler. adv.; bk.rev. circ. 5,500.
 Description: Covers developments in geriatric medicine for the general practitioner.

MUSCADINE; a seniors' literary magazine. see LITERARY AND POLITICAL REVIEWS

301.4   CN
MUSKOKA SENIORS NEWS. 1989. 6/yr. Muskoka Publications Group, 34 E.P. Lee Dr., P.O. Box 1600, Bracebridge, Ont. P1L 1V6, Canada.
TEL 705-645-4463. FAX 705-645-3928. Ed. Doug Brenner. circ. 13,200.

362.6   US   ISSN 1045-9073
N C O A NETWORKS. 1971. bi-m. membership. National Council on the Aging, 409 Third St., S.W., Washington, DC 20024. TEL 202-479-1200.
FAX 202-479-0735. Ed. Louise O. Cleveland. adv.; bk.rev. circ. 8,000. (tabloid format; back issues avail.) **Document type:** newspaper.
 Formed by the 1989 merger of: Adult Day Care Quarterly & Community Care Quarterly & Older Worker News & Rural Aging Roundup & Senior Center Report & Senior Housing News & Update on Aging for the Voluntary Sector.
 Description: Highlights activities of the various units of the council, reports legislative and regulatory activity and judicial decisions affecting older persons, and explores significant developments in the field of aging.

N R T A BULLETIN. (National Retired Teachers Association) see EDUCATION

362.6 301.435   US
NATIONAL COUNCIL OF LA RAZA. ANCIANOS PROJECT NEWSLETTER. 1990. q. free. National Council of La Raza, 810 First St., N.E., Ste. 300, Washington, DC 20002-4272. TEL 202-289-1380.
FAX 202-289-8173. Ed. Cristina Lopez. **Document type:** newsletter.
 Description: Covers legislative and social issues affecting the elderly, with a focus on the Hispanic community.

NATIONAL DIRECTORY OF EDUCATIONAL PROGRAMS IN GERONTOLOGY AND GERIATRICS. see EDUCATION — Guides To Schools And Colleges

NATIONAL SENIOR CITIZENS LAW CENTER WEEKLY. see LAW

362.6   US
NETWORK NEWS (WASHINGTON, 1985). 1985. s-a. free. American Association of Retired Persons, International Activities, 601 E St., N.W., Washington, DC 20049. TEL 202-434-2402. (Co-sponsor: International Federation on Ageing) Ed. Irene Hoskins. circ. 1,500. **Document type:** newsletter.
 Description: Reports on issues and programs affecting the lives of mid-life and older women in various parts of the world. Includes reports on meetings, conferences, and network activities.

301.435   US   ISSN 1061-2157
HQ1060   CODEN: NCRLE9
NEW CHOICES FOR RETIREMENT LIVING. 1960. m. $15.97. Retirement Living Publishing Co. (Subsidiary of: Reader's Digest Association), 28 W. 23rd St., New York, NY 10010.
TEL 212-366-8800. FAX 212-336-8899. (Subscr. to: Box 2037, Marion, OH 43306-2137. TEL 800-88-6111) Ed. David Sendler; Pub. Richard Fontana, Jr. adv.; bk.rev.; illus.; index. circ. 612,000. (also avail. in microform from UMI; reprint service avail. from UMI) **Indexed:** Hlth.Ind., Mag.Ind., R.G. **Document type:** consumer publication.
—Faxon; UnCover; UMI.
 Former titles (until 1992): New Choices for the Best Years (ISSN 1041-6277); (until 1989): 50 Plus (ISSN 0163-2027); (1972-1978): Retirement Living (ISSN 0090-4910); Harvest Years (ISSN 0017-8209)
 Description: Covers such issues as leisure, travel, family, health, food and nutrition, exercise, and finance.

301.435   CN
NEW ERA. m. Fairway Group Inc., 215 Fairway Rd., Kitchener, Ont. N2G 4E5, Canada.
TEL 519-894-1630. FAX 519-894-2173. circ. 15,000.
 Description: Lifestyle articles for the over-55 set.

051   US
NEW LIFE NEWS. 1953. bi-m. Northwestern Mutual Life, 720 E. Wisconsin Ave., Milwaukee, WI 53202. TEL 414-299-1959. FAX 414-299-2463. Ed. Julianne Agnew. circ. 1,700. (back issues avail.) **Document type:** newsletter.
 Description: Informational company newsletter for Northwestern Mutual Life retirees.

301.435   CN
NEWS FOR SENIORS. 1984. m. Can.$5($15) Society for the Retired & Semi-Retired, 15 Sir Winston Churchill Sq., 100th St. & 102A Ave., Edmonton, Alta. T5J 2E5, Canada. TEL 403-489-4570. Ed. Irene Ramsell. circ. 20,000. (tabloid format; back issues avail.)

362.6   US
NORTH AMERICAN ASSOCIATION OF JEWISH HOMES & HOUSING FOR THE AGING. PERSPECTIVES. 1960. q. membership. North American Association of Jewish Homes & Housing for the Aging, 10830 N. Central Expwy., Ste. 150, Dallas, TX 75231-1022.
TEL 214-696-9838. FAX 214-360-0753. Ed. Dr. Herbert Shore. bk.rev. circ. 500. **Document type:** newsletter.
 Former titles: North American Association of Jewish Homes and Housing for the Aging. Progress Report; National Association of Jewish Homes for the Aged. Progress Report.

054.1   FR   ISSN 0029-456X
NOTRE TEMPS; journal de la retraite heureuse. 1968. m. 247 F. (outside EC 321 F.) Bayard Presse, 3 rue Bayard, 75393 Paris Cedex 08, France.
TEL 44-35-60-60. FAX 44-35-60-91. TELEX 648 094 F. (Subscr. to: B.P. 12, 99505 Paris Entreprises, France. TEL 46-30-38-00. FAX 46-30-31-67) Ed. Germaine Lacorre. adv.; bk.rev. circ. 680,000.
 Description: General interest topics for people over 55.

618.97   US
NURSING HOME MEDICINE. 10/yr. membership. American Medical Directors Association, 10480 Little Patuxent Pkwy., Ste. 760, Columbia, MD 21044. Ed. Dr. Steven Levenson. bk.rev. circ. 3,000. (back issues avail.; reprint service avail.)
 Former titles: Journal of Medical Direction; (until 1990): Annual Medical Direction.
 Description: Covers issues for long-term care.

NURSING HOME PRACTITIONER. see MEDICAL SCIENCES — Nurses And Nursing

NURSING HOMES; long term care management. see MEDICAL SCIENCES — Nurses And Nursing

610.736   UK   ISSN 0956-8115
NURSING THE ELDERLY. 1981. bi-m. £25 (foreign £50). (Royal College of Nursing) Scutari Projects Ltd., Viking House, 17-19 Peterborough Rd., Harrow-on-the-Hill, Middlesex HA1 2AX, England. TEL 081-423-1066. FAX 081-423-3867. (Subscr. to: RCN Membership Records Dept., Glynteg House, Station Terrace, Cardiff CF5 4XG, England) Ed. Linda Thomas. adv. circ. 3,000. **Document type:** trade publication.
 Former titles: Geriatric Nursing and Home Care; British Journal of Geriatric Nursing (ISSN 0262-5024)

362.15 612.67   CN
O A C A O NEWSLETTER. (Text in English, French) q. Can.$6. Older Adult Centres Association of Ontario, 1220 Sheppard Ave. E., Willowdale, Ont. M2K 2X1, Canada. TEL 416-495-4061. FAX 416-495-4310. Ed. Anita Machin. adv. circ. 350. **Document type:** newsletter.
 Description: Studies the aging process and how to enjoy it.

OGGI DOMANI ANZIANI. see SOCIAL SERVICES AND WELFARE

353.9   US
OHIO DEPARTMENT OF AGING. ANNUAL REPORT. 1973. a. Ohio Department of Aging, 50 W. Broad St., 8th Fl., Columbus, OH 43266-0501.
TEL 614-466-5500; 614-466-6191 TDD.
FAX 614-466-5741. Ed. Suzanne Kashuba. circ. 1,000. **Document type:** government publication.
 Formerly: Ohio. Commission on Aging. Annual Report (ISSN 0363-9207)

051   US
OHIO'S HERITAGE. 1968. q. free. Ohio Department of Aging, 50 W. Broad St., 8th Fl., Columbus, OH 43266-0501. TEL 614-466-5500; 614-466-6191 TDD. FAX 614-466-5741. Ed. Suzanne Kashuba. adv. contact: Pete Tamburro. **Document type:** government publication.

362.6   UK
OLD AGE: A REGISTER OF SOCIAL RESEARCH. 1955. irreg., latest Nov. 1991. Centre for Policy on Ageing, 25-31 Ironmonger Row, London EC1V 3QP, England. TEL 071-253-1787. FAX 071-490-4206. Ed. Gillian Crosby.
 Description: Describes the projects of British universities, leading hospitals, research institutes and voluntary bodies on aging.

301.435   US   ISSN 0738-9639
THE OLDER AMERICAN. 1975. q. membership. (Massachusetts Association of Older Americans) Saltus Press, 110 Arlington St., Boston, MA 02116. TEL 617-426-0804. FAX 617-426-0070. adv.; bk.rev. circ. 10,000. (tabloid format; back issues avail.) **Document type:** newspaper.
 Description: Examines issues concerning the elderly.

362.6   US
▼**OLDER AMERICANS ALMANAC.** 1993. triennial. $99.50 (effective Oct. 1993). Gale Research Inc., 835 Penobscot Bldg., Detroit, MI 48226.
TEL 313-961-2242; 800-877-4253.
FAX 313-961-6083. Ed. Ronald Manheimer.
 Description: Provides current, practical information on senior citizens in the U.S.

OLDER AMERICANS REPORT. see SOCIAL SERVICES AND WELFARE

OLDIE. see GENERAL INTEREST PERIODICALS — Great Britain

301.435   NE   ISSN 0030-3453
OPEN VENSTER; maandblad voor ouderen. 1957. m. fl.23. Boekencentrum B.V., Postbus 29, 2700 AA Zoetermeer, Netherlands. TEL 31-79-615481.
FAX 31-79-615489. Ed.Bd. adv.; bk.rev.; illus. circ. 17,000.
 Description: Social and cultural subjects for the elderly.

362.6   US
OPTIONS: NEWS FOR OLDER NEW YORKERS. 1974. q. free. Department for the Aging, 2 Lafayette St., New York, NY 10007. TEL 212-577-0846. Ed. Virginia Starke. bk.rev. circ. 30,000. **Document type:** government publication.
 Description: Information on programs and services for senior citizens in New York City.

808 US ISSN 1052-889X
PASSAGER; a journal of rememberance and discovery. 1990. q. $12 to individuals; libraries $20. c/o Kendra Kopelke, Ed., University of Baltimore, 1420 N. Charles St., Baltimore, MD 21201-5779. illus.
 Description: Publishes fiction, poetry, essays and interviews, with an emphasis on older writers.

051 CN
PENINSULA PRIME. m. Peace Arch Publications Ltd., 1335 Johnston Rd., P.O. Box 75149, White Rock, B.C. V4A 9M4, Canada. TEL 604-531-1711. FAX 604-531-7977. Ed. Miriam Sobrino. circ. 27,000.

PENNSYLVANIA. ADMINISTRATION ON AGING. STATE PLAN ON AGING. see *SOCIAL SERVICES AND WELFARE*

301.4 US ISSN 0096-2740
HQ1060
PERSPECTIVE ON AGING. 1972. q. membership. National Council on the Aging, 409 Third St., S.W., Washington, DC 20024. TEL 202-479-1200. Ed. William E. Oriol. charts; illus.; stat. circ. 8,000. **Indexed:** CLOA. **Document type:** consumer publication. —UnCover.

612.7 CN ISSN 0831-7445
PERSPECTIVES (TORONTO). 1977. q. Can.$29.50 (effective Jan. 1991). Gerontological Nursing Association, P.O. Box 368, Station "K", Toronto, ON M4P 2G7, Canada. TEL 416-884-1951. Ed. Emily McLeod. adv.; bk.rev.; index. circ. 1,800. (back issues avail.) **Indexed:** CINAHL.
 •Also available online. Vendor(s): National Library of Medicine (Perspectives - Toronto SR0051880, W1PE8705F).
 Description: Covers clinical practice, education and research in gerontological nursing.

618.97 US
PERSPECTIVES (WASHINGTON, 1985). 1985. q. free. National Eldercare Institute on Health Promotion, 601 E St., N.W., Washington, DC 20049. TEL 202-434-2200. FAX 202-434-6474. Ed. Denise Cramer. circ. 20,000. **Document type:** newsletter.
 Description: Contains updates on health issues.

618.97 US ISSN 0270-3181
RC952.A1
PHYSICAL & OCCUPATIONAL THERAPY IN GERIATRICS; current trends in geriatric rehabilitation. 1980. q. $38 to individuals; institutions $140; libraries $180. Haworth Press, Inc., 10 Alice St., Binghamton, NY 13904. TEL 607-722-5857; 800-342-9678. FAX 607-722-1424. TELEX 4932599. Ed. Ellen Dunleavey Taira. adv.; bk.rev. circ. 502. (also avail. in microfiche from UMI; back issues avail.; reprint service avail. from HAW) **Indexed:** Abstr.Soc.Geront., Biol.Abstr., Bull.Signal., CINAHL, CLOA, Excerp.Med., Int.Nurs.Ind., Med.Care Rev., P.A.I.S., Past.Care & Couns.Abstr., Psychol.Abstr., Rehabil.Lit., Soc.Work Res.& Abstr., Sociol.Abstr. **Document type:** academic/scholarly publication.
 —BLDSC (6475.277000); Faxon; UnCover; SWETS.
 Description: Provides a forum for allied health professionals to share information, clinical experience, research, and therapeutic practice in geriatrics.
 Refereed Serial

618.97 FR ISSN 0242-9772
PRACTICIENS ET 3EME AGE. 1977. 12/yr. 340 F. (foreign 500 F.). Societe d'Editions Medicales, 22-24 rue du Chateau des Rentiers, 75013 Paris, France. TEL 45-83-50-54. FAX 45-83-13-54. Ed. Colette Gallula. adv.; bibl.; illus.
 Formerly (until 1982): Medecine et Troisieme Age (ISSN 0012-1377)

301.435 052 AT ISSN 0729-5545
PRIME TIME. bi-m. Aus.$18 (foreign Aus.$29). Diverse Publishing Co. Pty. Ltd., P.O. Box 370, N. Melbourne, Vic. 3051, Australia. TEL 03-329-6040. FAX 03-328-1116. Ed. Louise Chenana. circ. 55,000.
 Description: Covers retirement planning, retirement living - health, finance, lifestyle as applied to 45 plus age group within Australia.

051 CN
PRIME TIME - LAMBTON - KENT. m. Can.$17 (foreign Can.$25). Petrolia Topic, P.O. Box 40, Petrolia, ON N0N 1P0, Canada. TEL 519-882-1770. FAX 519-882-3212. Ed. Marg Hoggard. circ. 13,000.
 Formerly: Mainly for Seniors - Lambton.

051 CN
PRIMETIME LIVING.* 1990. bi-m. PrimeTime Association, 1530K Jamacho Rd., No. 278, El Cajon, CA 92019-3754. TEL 619-278-7115. Ed. Anita McKay. circ. 110,000 (controlled).
 Description: For homeowners age 50-70 in San Diego County. Provides information on health, finance, travel, the home, retirement planning and entertainment.

155.67 FR
PSYCHO GERIATRIE. 1988. q. 350 F. (foreign 410 F.). (Societe de Psychogeriatrie de Langue Francaise) Editions Kalmann-Rose, 26 av. St-Georges, 44500 La Baule, France. Ed. Dr. Gerard le Goues. adv.; bk.rev.

155.67 150 US ISSN 0882-7974
BF724.55.A35
PSYCHOLOGY AND AGING. 1986. q. $71 to non-members (foreign $83); members $35; institutions $142 (foreign $167). American Psychological Association, 750 First St., N.E., Washington, DC 20002-4242. TEL 202-336-5500. FAX 202-336-5568. Ed. Timothy A. Salthouse. adv.; charts; illus.; index. circ. 3,600. (also avail. in microform from MIM,UMI; back issues avail.) **Indexed:** Abstr.Soc.Geront., Behav.Med.Abstr., Psychol.Abstr. **Document type:** academic/scholarly publication.
 —BLDSC (6946.535317); Faxon; UnCover; SWETS; UMI. **CCC.**
 Description: Publishes research on the psychological and behavioral aspects of aging.

QUALITY CARE ADVOCATE. see *HOSPITALS*

362.6 IT ISSN 0486-0306
RASSEGNA GERIATRICA. (Text in Italian; summaries in English) 1964. q. L.45000($70) (effective 1993). (Istituto Nazionale Riposo e Cura per Anziani) Casa Editrice Idelson, Via A. DeGasperi, 55, 80138 Naples, Italy. TEL 081-5524733. FAX 081-5518295. Ed. Luca Illuminati. **Indexed:** Excerp.Med.
 —BLDSC (7294.223000).
 Description: Contains origianl works, editorials, and scientific, medical, technical and sociological updates in the areas of gerontology and geriatrics.

612.67 618.97 BE
REJUVENATION. (Text in English) 1963. q. $100. International Gerontological Think Tank, Center for Experimental Gerontology, c/o Dr. H. le Compte, Ed., Fabiolalaan 14, B-8300 Knokke-Zoute, Belgium. (Co-sponsor: Belgische Vereniging van Geriaters) adv.; bk.rev.; bibl.; charts; illus.; stat.; tr.lit.; index. circ. 1,000. **Indexed:** Biol.Abstr., Chem.Abstr, CLOA.
 Former titles: International Association on the Artificial Prolongation of the Human Specific Lifespan. Official Journal; Acta Gerontologica et Geriatrica Belgica (ISSN 0001-575X); Acta Gerontologica Belgica.

612.67 US ISSN 0164-0275
HQ1060
RESEARCH ON AGING; a quarterly of social gerontology and adult development. 1979. q. $49 to individuals; institutions $144 (effective 1994). Sage Publications, Inc., 2455 Teller Rd., Thousand Oaks, CA 91320. TEL 805-499-0721. FAX 805-499-0871. (Subscr. to: Sage Publications, Inc., Box 5084, Thousand Oaks, CA 91359; Overseas subscr. to: Sage Publications, Ltd., 6 Bonhill St., London EC2A 4PU, England; Saga Publications India Pvt. Ltd., P.O. Box 4215, New Delhi 110 048, India) Ed. Rhonda J.V. Montgomery. adv.; bibl.; charts; stat.; index. circ. 1,400. **Indexed:** Abstr.Soc.Geront., Behav.Med.Abstr., CLOA, Curr.Cont., Excerp.Med., Lang.& Lang.Behav.Abstr., Psychol.Abstr., Sage Fam.Stud.Abstr., Soc.Work Res.& Abstr., SSCI, World Bibl.Soc.Sec. **Document type:** academic/scholarly publication.
 —BLDSC (7714.385000); Faxon; UnCover; SWETS; UMI. **CCC.**
 Description: Presents interdisciplinary research on current issues, methodological and research problems in the study of the elderly.

362.6 374 US ISSN 0892-0818
RESOURCES IN AGING; an international newsletter featuring new developments in aging. 1987. bi-m. $25. Demko Publishing, 21946 Pine Trace, Boca Raton, FL 33428. TEL 407-482-6271. Ed. David J. Demko. adv.; bk.rev.; index. (tabloid format; back issues avail.) **Document type:** newsletter.

RETIREMENT COMMUNITY BUSINESS. see *REAL ESTATE*

RETIREMENT LETTER; the money newsletter for mature people. see *BUSINESS AND ECONOMICS — Banking And Finance*

301.435 US
RETIREMENT LIFE (PORTLAND). 1973. m. $10. 10211 S.W. Barbur, No. 109A, Portland, OR 97219-5904. Ed. Scott Dalton. adv.; bk.rev.; illus. circ. 50,000.
 Formerly: Senior Citizen News.

301.435 US ISSN 0034-6179
JK791
RETIREMENT LIFE (WASHINGTON). 1954. m. $25 to non-members. National Association of Retired Federal Employees, 1533 New Hampshire Ave., N.W., Washington, DC 20036. TEL 202-234-0832. FAX 202-797-9698. Ed. Kathleen S. Delaney. adv.; bk.rev.; illus.; circ. 449,000 (paid); 1,000 (controlled). **Indexed:** Pers.Lit.
 Description: Covers legislative issues of interest to retired federal employees.

640.73 CN ISSN 0844-5982
RETIREMENT LIFESTYLE PUBLICATION; club 55. 1985. m. Can.$40 (effective Jan. 1993). (Club 55) Retirement Lifestyle Publications Inc., 12140 Horseshoe Way, Ste. 100, Richmond, BC V7A 4V5, Canada. TEL 604-275-7971. Ed. David Todd. adv. contact: Eric Buckingham. bk.rev. circ. 150,000. **Document type:** consumer publication.
 Description: Covers financial and retirement planning, health information directions, travel, psychological, environmental and spiritual issues, sports and fitness.

RETIREMENT PLACES RATED. see *HOUSING AND URBAN PLANNING*

301.435 UK
RETIREMENT WORLD. 1988. m. $15.10. Community Publishing Ltd., Unit One, City Business Park, Easton Rd., Bristol BS5, England. Ed. Tony Ferrand. circ. 110,000.
 Description: Features cooking and travel; financial, legal and medical advice.

612.67 UK ISSN 0959-2598
RC952.A1 CODEN: RCGEEB
REVIEWS IN CLINICAL GERONTOLOGY. 1991. q. £67.50($105) to individuals; institutions $120 ($205) (effective 1994). Edward Arnold, Hodder Headline plc, Sevenoaks, Kent TN13 2YA, England. TEL 0732-450111. FAX 0732-461321. (Subscr. to: Turpin Distribution Services Ltd., Blackhorse Rd., Letchworth, Herts. SG6 1HN, England) Ed. Raymond Tallis. **Indexed:** Excerp.Med. (1993-). **Document type:** academic/scholarly publication.
 —BLDSC (7788.979000). **CCC.**
 Description: Dedicated to the advancement of knowledge and clinical practice in the health care of the elderly.

612.67 301.435 SP ISSN 1130-6882
REVISTA DE GERONTOLOGIA. (Text in Spanish; summaries in English) 1991. q. 5500 ptas.($100) (students 4000 ptas.) (effective 1994). S G Editores, Casp, 79 5o, 08013 Barcelona, Spain. TEL 343-232-82-51. FAX 343-232-40-20. Ed. Ricard Vinas. adv.; bk.rev.; bibl.; charts.

618.97 SP ISSN 0214-1469
CODEN: RMGEED
REVISTA DE MEDICINA GERIATRICA. Variant title: Medicina Geriatrica. 6/yr. Saned, Apolonio Morales, 6-8, 28036 Madrid, Spain. TEL 1-403-50-14. FAX 1-457-99-18. TELEX 47331 SNED. Ed. Dr. Fernando Mantim. circ. 15,000. **Indexed:** Excerp.Med. (until 1993).

GERONTOLOGY AND GERIATRICS

612.67 618.97   SP   ISSN 0211-139X
REVISTA ESPANOLA DE GERIATRIA Y GERONTOLOGIA. 1966. bi-m. 4900 ptas.($80) (Sociedad Espanola de Geriatria) Editorial Garsi, S.A., Londres, 17, 28028 Madrid, Spain. TEL 256-08-00. FAX 361-10-07. Ed. F. Jimenez Herrero. adv.; bk.rev.; abstr.; bibl.; charts; illus.; stat. circ. 3,000. Indexed: Excerp.Med., Ind.Med.Esp.
—BLDSC (7854.002500).
 Formerly (until 1976): Revista Espanola de Gerontologia (ISSN 0034-9410)

618.97   FR
REVUE DE GERIATRIE. 1954. m. 400 F. Edimedica, 146 bd. Voltaire, 92600 Asniers, France. Ed. F. Vidal. adv.; bk.rev.; charts; illus.; index. circ. 4,200. Indexed: Biol.Abstr., Curr.Cont., Excerp.Med., Ind.Med.
 Former titles (until 1977): Revue de Gerontologie d'Expression Francaise (ISSN 0375-975X); Revue Francaise de Gerontologie (ISSN 0035-2896)

301.435   US
RHODE ISLAND SENIOR TIMES. 1991. m. $8.95. Gateway Communication Inc., 28 Jacome Way, Middletown, RI 02840. TEL 401-849-8396. adv.: B&W page $1840; trim 11 1/2 x 15. circ. 35,000. (tabloid format)

RING DES WORTES; Seelsorgebrief fuer Hoergeschaedigte, Kranke und Senioren. see RELIGIONS AND THEOLOGY — Roman Catholic

618.97 301.435   RM   ISSN 0254-2307
   CODEN: RJGGDV
ROMANIAN JOURNAL OF GERONTOLOGY AND GERIATRICS. (Text in English, French) 1980. 4/yr. $58. (National Institute of Gerontology and Geriatrics) Editura Academiei Romane, Calea Victoriei nr.125, sectorul 1, R-79717 Bucharest, Rumania. Ed. Alexandru Vrabiescu. adv.; bk.rev.; charts; stat. Indexed: Chem.Abstr., Curr.Adv.Ecol.Sci., Excerp.Med.
—CASDDS.

G

612.67   US
▼**RX REMEDY**; prescriptions for a healthy life. 1992. bi-m. $12. Rx Remedy, Inc., 120 Post Rd. W., Westport, CT 06880. TEL 203-221-4910. FAX 203-221-4913. Ed. Val Weaver. adv.: color page $26500. circ. 1,500,000 (controlled). Document type: consumer publication.
 Description: Provides health information for the over-55's.

301.435   US
S R TEXAS. (Senior Residents) 1987. m. $18. Liberty Media, Inc., 11551 Forest Central Dr., No. 305, Dallas, TX 75243. TEL 214-341-9429. FAX 214-341-9779. Ed. Frank Kelly. adv.; bk.rev. circ. 50,000. (tabloid format; back issues avail.)
 Formerly (until June 1989): S R Dallas.
 Description: Consumer publication for Texas residents over age 50. Covers lifestyles, local features, travel, financial, legislative and health issues for a mature audience.

SEARCH (YORK). see SOCIAL SERVICES AND WELFARE

301.435   GW
SECHZIG - NA UND?. 1987. bi-w. DM.30 (foreign DM.42). Sisu Steinschulte Verlag, Bismarckstr. 10, 53173 Bonn, Germany. TEL 0228-361063. FAX 0228-351130. adv.; bk.rev. circ. 75,000. (back issues avail.) Document type: consumer publication.

368.4   US   ISSN 1069-6911
SECURE RETIREMENT. 1983. 8/yr. $10. National Committee to Preserve Social Security and Medicare, 2000 K St., N.W., Ste. 800, Washington, DC 20006. TEL 202-822-9459. FAX 202-822-9459. Ed. Denise S. Fremeau; Pub. Jack McDavitt. adv. contact: Carol Havel. circ. 2,028,551. Document type: consumer publication.
 Formerly: Saving Social Security.
 Description: Covers federal agencies, congressional committees and political leaders with jurisdiction over social security, health care reform, medicare, nursing home reform and more.

SEMINARS IN ARTHRITIS & RHEUMATISM. see MEDICAL SCIENCES — Rheumatology

362.61   NE   ISSN 0168-7492
SENIOR. Variant title: Tijdschrift voor het Ouderenwerk in Nederland en Vlaenderen. 1954. s-a. fl.84.50. Uitgeverij De Tijdstroom b.v., P.O. Box 19135, 3501 DC Utrecht, Netherlands. TEL 31-30-586900. FAX 31-30-586950. Ed. Arghje de Sitter. adv.; bk.rev.; illus.; index. circ. 5,200.
—SWETS.
 Formerly (until 1980): Bejaarden (ISSN 0005-822X)
 Description: Care of the aged in the Netherlands and Belgium.

051   US
SENIOR ADVOCATE. 175. m. Mar-Len Publications, 131 Lincoln St., Worcester, MA 01605. TEL 508-752-2512. FAX 508-752-9057. Ed. Sondra Shapiro. adv.; bk.rev. circ. 100,000.
 Description: Carries national and local news, tips on health, finance, travel and entertainment for people 60 years and older.

051   US
SENIOR BEACON. 1987. m. $8. Quest Communications, Inc., 8935 N. Meridian, Ste. 106, Indianapolis, IN 46260. TEL 317-571-0101. FAX 317-571-1552. Ed. John B. Weeks. adv.; illus. circ. 30,000. (tabloid format)
 Description: Topics of interest to persons over 50 in the greater Indianapolis region.

SENIOR CITIZEN SENTINEL. see SOCIAL SERVICES AND WELFARE

051   US   ISSN 0559-4677
SENIOR CITIZENS NEWS (WASHINGTON). 1961. m. $12 (effective until 1996). National Council of Senior Citizens, Inc., 1331 F St., N.W., Washington, DC 20004-1171. TEL 202-347-8800. FAX 202-624-9595. Ed. Bette Cooper. circ. 300,000.
 Description: General interest for senior citizens, focusing on legislative issues.

301.435   US
SENIOR CITIZENS POST. 1971. q. membership. Coordinating Council for Senior Citizens, 807 S. Duke St., Durham, NC 27701. TEL 919-688-8247. FAX 919-683-3406. Ed.Bd. illus.; circ. 1,500 (controlled). Document type: newspaper.

362.6   US
SENIOR CITIZENS SERVICES. (Avail. in 4 regional vols.) 1991. biennial. $29.95. Gale Research Inc., 835 Penobscot Bldg., Detroit, MI 48266. TEL 313-961-2242. FAX 313-961-6083. Eds. Charles B. Montney, Linda S. Hubbard.
 Description: Contains descriptive listings for 57 state and 670 local area agencies on aging. Includes some 21,000 private organizations.

SENIOR CONSUMER ALERT. see CONSUMER EDUCATION AND PROTECTION

301.435   US
SENIOR EDITION. (In 3 regional eds.: Kenosha Cy., La Crosse Cy., Dodge Cy.) m. Green Isle Publishing, Box 376, Oregon, IL 61061. TEL 800-462-4827. adv. circ. 33,000. (tabloid format)

THE SENIOR GOLFER. see SPORTS AND GAMES — Ball Games

051   US
SENIOR HIGHLIGHTS. 1983. m. $18. 26801 Merit Cir., Ste. 101, Laguna Hills, CA 92653-7015. TEL 714-367-0776. FAX 714-367-1006. Ed. Lee McCamon. adv.; bk.rev. circ. 375,000. Document type: consumer publication.
 Description: Seeks to enhance the lives of people over age 50. Sections include Personal Finance, Travel, Retirement Life-Styles, Health, and Home and Garden.

155.67 301.435   US
SENIOR MAGAZINE. 1981. m. free. Senior Magazine, 3565 S. Higuera, San Luis Obispo, CA 93401. TEL 805-544-8711. FAX 805-544-4450. adv.; bk.rev. (tabloid format)
 Description: Directed to people 50 years of age or older.

162.67   US
THE SENIOR MESSENGER. 1973. m. free. City of Vancouver, Box 1995, Vancouver, WA 98668. TEL 206-696-8016. FAX 206-696-8942. Ed. Marilyn Westlake. adv.; bk.rev. circ. 12,300. (tabloid format) Document type: newspaper.
 Description: Features positive lifestyles focus for seniors, plus announcements, info and schedule for senior activities and services in Southwest Washington state.

362.6   US
SENIOR SCENE. 1978. m. $7.50 donation. (Lutheran Social Services) Council on Aging, 223 N. Yakima, Tacoma, WA 98403. TEL 206-272-2278. FAX 206-383-4055. Ed. Kari Caldwell. adv. contact: Rozelle Souza. circ. 13,500. Document type: newspaper.

362.6   US
SENIOR SPECTRUM; for the second half of your life. 1972. m. $10. 1385 S. Colorado Blvd., Ste. 218, Denver, CO 80222-3312. TEL 303-758-4040. FAX 303-758-2728. Ed. Rose Beetem. adv.; bk.rev. circ. 50,000. (tabloid format) Document type: newspaper.
 Former titles: Senior Edition U S A (ISSN 1046-0020); (until 1988): Senior Edition.
 Description: Covers national, state and local news, advice and opinions from the senior perspective, and nostalgia.

301.435 362.6   US
SENIOR SPECTRUM NEWSPAPER. 1973. 18/yr. $12. Fifty-Five Plus, Inc., Box 1030, Rancho Cordova, CA 95741-1030. TEL 916-852-6222. FAX 916-852-6397. adv. circ. 786,000. Document type: newspaper.
 Description: For active senior citizens.

SENIOR SPORTS NEWS. see SPORTS AND GAMES

301.435   US
SENIOR SPOTLITE.* 1986. m. $7.50. Senior Spotlite Newspapers, Inc., 8169 Webxter St., Arvada, CO 80003-1626. TEL 303-421-8171. FAX 303-420-7704. Ed. JoAnn Jones. adv. circ. 130,000.

917.1   CN   ISSN 0846-6238
SENIOR TIMES. m. Can.$26. Publications Newborn, 4950 Queen Mary Rd., Penthouse, Montreal, PQ H3W 1X3, Canada. TEL 514-735-0722. FAX 514-735-1492. Ed. Barbara Newborn. adv. contact: Pauline Long. Document type: newspaper.
 Description: Provides the 50 plus population with up-to-date articles on national and provincial issues, health, finance, fashion, travel and community affairs.

SENIOR TRAVEL TIPS (SAN RAFAEL). see TRAVEL AND TOURISM

051   US
SENIOR TRIBUNE.* 7/yr. Sports Publishing Services, Inc., Box 566215, Atlanta, GA 31156-6215. TEL 404-475-8088. Ed. Betty Marie. circ. 25,000.

051   US   ISSN 0741-2894
SENIOR VOICE. 1979. m. $20 (out of state $25; over 55s $15; free to low income and over 75s). Older Persons Action Group, Inc., 325 E. Third Ave., Ste. 300, Anchorage, AK 99501-2606. TEL 907-276-1059. FAX 907-278-6724. Ed. Kaylene Johnson. adv. circ. 5,500. (tabloid format) Document type: newspaper.
 Description: News and features concerning older Alaskans.

301.435 051   CN
SENIOR WORLD; Canada's national magazine for the mature reader. 1981. q. Box 128, Main Post Office, St. John, N.B., Canada. TEL 506-657-8671. Ed. Elmer T. Parlee. illus. circ. 34,000. (large type)
 Description: Provides news of interest to older Canadians from all educational and economic levels.

GERONTOLOGY AND GERIATRICS

301.435 US
SENIOR WORLD OF LOS ANGELES COUNTY. 1973. m. $30. Kendell Communications Inc., Box 1565, El Cajon, CA 92022. TEL 310-820-1125. (And: 1000 Pioneer Way, El Cajon, CA 92020) Ed. Laura Impastato. adv.; bk.rev.; circ. 150,000 (controlled). (tabloid format; back issues avail.) Document type: newspaper.
Formerly (until 1987): Senior World (ISSN 0146-2539)
Description: News, announcements, and information pertaining to the activities of older adults, with regular departments on dining, health, finance, travel, housing and lifestyle.

301.435 US
SENIOR WORLD OF ORANGE COUNTY; serving older adults in Orange County. 1984. m. $30. Kendell Communications, Inc., 1000 Pioneer Way, Box 1565, El Cajon, CA 92022. TEL 714-898-2893. Ed. Laura Impastato. adv. circ. 125,000. **Document type:** newspaper.
Description: News, announcements, and information pertaining to the activities of older adults in this California county, with regular departments on dining, health, finance, travel, housing and lifestyle.

301.435 US
SENIOR WORLD OF SAN DIEGO; serving active older adults throughout San Diego County. 1973. m. $30. Kendell Communications, Inc., 1000 Pioneer Way, Box 1565, El Cajon, CA 92022. TEL 619-593-2900. Ed. Laura Impastato. adv. circ. 100,000. **Document type:** newspaper.
Description: News, announcements, and information pertaining to the activities of older adults in this California county, with regular departments on dining, health, finance, travel, housing, lifestyle.

301.435 GW
SENIOREN ECHO; Nachrichten fuer aeltere Bonner Buerger. 1967. bi-m. Stadtverwaltung Bonn, Stadthaus, Amt 13, Berliner Platz, 53111 Bonn, Germany. TEL 0228-773462. FAX 0228-772468. Ed. Renate Hawranke. bk.rev. circ. 17,000. **Document type:** newsletter.

362.6 US
▼**SENIORITY;** magazine of New Jersey. 1993. m. $10. Elder Enterprises, Inc., 87 Woodland Rd., Short Hills, NJ 07078. TEL 201-912-8222. FAX 201-912-8670. Ed. Judith A. Matthews. adv. (tabloid format) **Document type:** consumer publication.
Description: Discusses issues that affect senior citizens in New Jersey and contains items of interest to this audience, such as specialized travel, hobbies and crafts, reminiscences, and elder care.

SENIORS CHOICE. see CLUBS

301.435 CN
SENIORS ON THE MOVE. 1991. 12/yr. Can.$24. Seniors on the Move Ltd., 24 Dunlop St. E., Barrie, Ont. L4M 1A3, Canada. TEL 705-725-0996. FAX 705-721-8548. adv.; B&W page Can.$895; trim 10 1/8 x 15 7/8. circ. 14,200.

051 CN
SENIORS TODAY. 1982. s-m. Can.$20. 232 Henderson Hwy., Winnipeg, MB R2L 1L9, Canada. TEL 204-982-4000. FAX 204-982-4001. Ed. H. McCaine-Davies. adv.; bk.rev. circ. 8,000.

051 US
SILVER YEARS NEWS. 1977. bi-m. $7. (Golden Years Council) Silver News, Box 298, Bellaire, TX 77402-0298. TEL 713-664-2266. FAX 713-664-2137. Ed. Dixie Lee Chase. adv.; B&W page $597; trim 11 3/8 x 16; adv. contact: Ben Gresham. bk.rev. circ. 10,000. (tabloid format; back issues avail.) **Document type:** newspaper.
Description: Directed to the "over-50" set in the Harris and surrounding counties.

SJOMANNADAGSBLADID. see TRANSPORTATION — Ships And Shipping

301.435 053.1 GW ISSN 0174-0350
DER SONNTAGSBRIEF. 1973. m. DM.146.40. Verlag Axel B. Trunkel, Landhausstr. 82, 70190 Stuttgart, Germany. TEL 0711-26863-0. Ed. Andrea Przyklenk. circ. 30,000. (back issues avail.)

301.435 US
SOUTHERN CALIFORNIA SENIOR LIFE. 1983. m. $20. Senior Media, Inc., 6022 W. Pico Blvd., Los Angeles, CA 90035. TEL 213-933-9228. FAX 213-933-9261. Ed. Jerry Beigel. adv.; bk.rev. circ. 160,000. **Document type:** newspaper.
Description: Covers health, travel, leisure, entertainment, financial affairs, legal matters, retirement living, housing, sports, employment, nutrition and political issues.

612.67 US ISSN 1070-6127
SOUTHWEST JOURNAL ON AGING. 1984. s-a. $50. Southwest Society on Aging, University of North Texas, Box 13438, Denton, TX 76203. TEL 817-565-2765. FAX 817-565-4370. Ed. Stan Ingman. adv. circ. 700. **Document type:** academic/scholarly publication.
Formerly (until 1993): Southwestern (Denton) (ISSN 1053-4911)

051
SOUTHWEST SENIOR. m. Vondrak Publishing Company, Inc., 6225 S. Kendzie Ave., Chicago, IL 60629-3397. TEL 312-476-4800. FAX 312-476-7811. Ed. Joe Boyle. adv.

SPORT SPECIAL - CONDITION; die Zeitschrift fuer Lauf- und Ausdauersport. see SPORTS AND GAMES

301.435 US
SUN LIFE. 1984. 10/yr. $11.95. Carolyn Publishing Co., 9192 W. Cactus, Ste. C, Peoria, AZ 85381. TEL 602-878-2210. Ed. Jerry Svendsen. adv.: B&W page $1730, color page $2270; trim 7 1/4 x 9 3/4. bk.rev. circ. 38,500.
Formerly (until 1989): Sun Cities Life.
Description: Aimed at the Northwest valley area of Phoenix, Arizona; focuses on issues of interest to the mature residents - retirees; includes local business news.

618.97 SZ ISSN 1011-3738
CODEN: TTGME6
TEACHING AND TRAINING IN GERIATRIC MEDICINE. (Text in English) 1987. irreg. price varies. S. Karger AG, Allschwilerstr. 10, P.O. Box, CH-4009 Basel, Switzerland. TEL 061-3061111. FAX 061-3061234. Ed. W. Meier-Ruge. **Document type:** academic/scholarly publication.
—BLDSC (8614.030000). CCC.

362.6 SA
THAMBODALA. irreg. free. Human Sciences Research Council, Cooperative Research Programme on Ageing, Private Bag X41, Pretoria 0001, South Africa. (Affiliate: University of Cape Town Centre for Gerontology) Ed. Dr. Monica Ferreira. **Document type:** newsletter.
Description: Publishes information on the activities of the program, as well as research findings in the field of aging.

THIS CARING BUSINESS. see SOCIAL SERVICES AND WELFARE

301.435 US
THURSTON - MASON SENIOR NEWS. 1976. m. free. Thurston County Council on Aging, 529 W. Fourth Ave., Olympia, WA 98501. TEL 206-754-2953. Ed. Rick Crawford. adv.; bk.rev. (tabloid format; back issues avail.) **Document type:** newspaper.
Description: Covers topics of interest to senior citizens such as health, travel, finance, and nutrition.

051 CN ISSN 0827-6854
TODAY'S SENIORS. 1985. m. Can.$21.95. Metroland Printing, Publishing & Distributing, 1091 Brevik Pl., Mississauga, ON L4W 3R7, Canada. TEL 416-238-0555. FAX 416-238-0026. Ed. Don Atanasoff. adv. contact: Arija LeGautt. circ. 370,000. **Document type:** consumer publication.
Formerly (until 1986): Senior - Watch Review (ISSN 0827-6862)

301.435 CN
TODAY'S TIMES. 1958. m. Can.$16. Today's Times Publications Ltd., Box 1198, Sta. A, Nanaimo, BC V9R 6E7, Canada. TEL 604-754-2387. FAX 604-754-2398. Ed. Chris Beddows. adv.; B&W & color, B&W page Can.$2059; 10 1/4 x 12 1/2. bk.rev. circ. 30,000.
Former titles: Elder Statesman (ISSN 0013-4074); Senior Citizens News; Pensioner.
Description: News and lifestyle topics aimed at people who are fifty and older.

618.97 615.82 US ISSN 0882-7524
RC952.5
TOPICS IN GERIATRIC REHABILITATION. 1985. q. $63 (foreign $76). Aspen Publishers, Inc., 200 Orchard Ridge Dr., Gaithersburg, MD 20878. TEL 301-417-7500. FAX 301-417-7550. **Indexed:** Abstr.Soc.Geront.
—BLDSC (8867.441200); Faxon; UnCover. **CCC.**

301.435 US ISSN 1066-0216
TOWNE CRIER (TOMS RIVER). 1979. m. $6. Pentacle Publishing Co., 1830 US Rte. 9, Toms River, NJ 08755. TEL 908-240-3000. FAX 908-240-0002. Ed. Edward Jasin. adv. circ. 24,950. (tabloid format; back issues avail.) **Document type:** newspaper.

TRAVEL 50 & BEYOND. see TRAVEL AND TOURISM

301.435 GW ISSN 0930-2832
TREFFPUNKT SENIOREN; Zeitschrift fuer Senioren im Lande Bremen. 1980. q. Nordwestdeutsche Verlag GmbH, Hafenstr. 142, 27576 Bremerhaven, Germany. TEL 0471-5918-0. FAX 0471-591820. circ. 50,000. **Document type:** bulletin.

301.435 368 US
UNITED RETIREMENT BULLETIN. 1975. m. $34. Babson - United Investment Advisors, Inc., 101 Prescott St., Wellesley Hills, MA 02181-3319. TEL 617-235-0900. FAX 617-267-1598. Ed. Edith Tucker. bk.rev.; index. (looseleaf format; back issues avail.)

301.435 US
VANTAGE. 1985. bi-m. $17.50. Signature Group, 200 N. Martingale Rd., Schaumburg, IL 60173. TEL 708-605-7418. adv. circ. 360,467.
Description: Focuses on the savings and discounts available to members of the Montgomery Ward Y.E.S. Discount Club.

VERMEIL; la foi au fil des ans. see RELIGIONS AND THEOLOGY — Roman Catholic

051 US ISSN 1066-1204
VILLAGE CRIER. 1979. m. $6. Pentacle Publishing Co., 1830 US Rte. 9, Toms River, NJ 08755. TEL 908-240-3000. FAX 908-240-0002. Ed. Edward Jasin. adv. circ. 26,275. (tabloid format; back issues avail.) **Document type:** newspaper.

155.67 052 US
VISIBLE; a magazine for ageful lesbians and all women. 1979. 3/yr. $12. Box 1494, Mendocino, CA 95460. TEL 707-964-2756. Ed. Vashte Doublex. adv.; bk.rev. circ. 400. (also avail. in looseleaf format; back issues avail.) **Document type:** newsletter.
Formerly: Older Women's Network.
Description: Raises women's issues on aging and ageism to network and inform, lists resources, and publishes the work of the older women.

052 US
VIVA (MOUNT VERNON).* 1988. bi-m. $9. Pulse Publications, Inc. (Mt. Vernon), 1730 Continental Pl., Mt. Vernon, WA 98273-5640. TEL 206-671-3933. adv. circ. 5,500.
Description: Covers news and issues of interest to persons over 50 years of age.

301.435 CN ISSN 0382-0068
VOICE OF UNITED SENIOR CITIZENS OF ONTARIO. 1969. m. (except July & Aug.) Can.$8. (United Senior Citizens of Ontario) Voice Association, 3303 Lakeshore Blvd. West, Etobicoke, Ont. M8V 1K5, Canada. TEL 416-252-2021. Ed. Edith M. Johnston. adv.; illus. circ. 4,000.
Formerly: United Senior Citizens of Ontario. Bulletin (ISSN 0049-5441)

301.435 US
VOICES OF EXPERIENCE. 1988. $12. Paul Casey, Pub. & Ed., 3028 Western Ave., No. 316, Seattle, WA 98121. TEL 206-448-5902. FAX 206-448-5494. adv.; bk.rev. circ. 25,000. **Document type:** newspaper.
Formerly (until Sep. 1992): Maturing.

301.435 FR ISSN 0049-6707
VOIX DU RETRAITE. 1919. m. 115 F. Societe de Presse, d'Edition et de Diffusion d'Informations Sociales, 44 Rue Vieille-Du-Temple, 75004 Paris, France. Ed. Philippe Agostini. adv.; index. circ. 25,000.

GERONTOLOGY AND GERIATRICS — ABSTRACTING, BIBLIOGRAPHIES, STATISTICS

362.6   US
VOLUNTEERS IN DIRECT ACTION. Abbreviated title: V I D A. 3/yr. American Association of Retired Persons (Washington), 601 E St., N.W., Washington, DC 20049. TEL 202-662-4842.
  Description: Covers the experiences of AARP spokespersons in carrying out the mission of AARP's Minority Affairs Initiative.

362.6   US   ISSN 0083-8438
WEST VIRGINIA. COMMISSION ON AGING. ANNUAL PROGRESS REPORT. 1961. a. free. Commission on Aging, State Capitol, Charleston, WV 25305. TEL 304-348-3317. Ed. Donna S. Hawkins. circ. 500 (controlled). **Document type:** government publication.

301.435   CN
WESTCOAST REFLECTIONS. 1990. m. Can.$27($33) Rand Communications Inc., 2604 Quadra St., Victoria, BC V8T 4E4, Canada. TEL 604-383-1149. FAX 604-388-4479. Ed. Joy Bretz; Pub. Jim Bisakowski. adv.; bk.rev. circ. 20,000. **Document type:** consumer publication.
  Description: A lifestyle magazine for those 39 and holding.

601.435   US
▼**WHERE TO RETIRE.** 1992. q. $15.80. Vacation Publications, Inc., 1502 Augusta Dr., Ste. 415, Houston, TX 77057. TEL 713-974-6903. FAX 713-974-0445. adv. circ. 50,000. **Document type:** consumer publication.
  Description: Helps retirees find the ideal setting for their new life.

WORKING AGE NEWSLETTER. see OCCUPATIONS AND CAREERS

618.97   US   ISSN 0894-2757
RC952.A1
YEAR BOOK OF GERIATRICS AND GERONTOLOGY. 1988. a. $64.95. Mosby - Year Book, Inc. (Chicago) (Subsidiary of: Times Mirror Company), 200 N. LaSalle St., Chicago, IL 60601-1080. TEL 312-726-9733. FAX 312-726-6075. TELEX 206155. Ed. Dr. John C. Beck. illus.
  ●Also available online. Vendor(s): BRS Online Products.
  —BLDSC (9412.820000).
  Description: Presents abstracts and commentary on relevant medical literature.

612.67 618.97   JA
YOKUFUKAI CHOSA KENKYU KIYO/YOKUFUKAI GERIATRIC JOURNAL. (Text in Japanese; summaries in English) 1930. a. free. Yokufukai Byoin - Yokufukai Geriatric Hospital, 1-12-1 Nishi Takaido, Suginami-ku, Tokyo 168, Japan. Indexed: Biol.Abstr., Chem.Abstr., Excerp.Med. **Document type:** academic/scholarly publication.
  —BLDSC (9420.800000).
  Formerly: Acta Gerontologica Japonica (ISSN 0001-5768)

612.67 618.97   GW   ISSN 0044-281X
RC952   CODEN: ZGERAG
ZEITSCHRIFT FUER GERONTOLOGIE. (Text in German; summaries in English) 1968. bi-m. DM.290. (Deutsche Gesellschaft fuer Gerontologie) Dr. Dietrich Steinkopff Verlag, Saalbaustr. 12, 64283 Darmstadt, Germany. TEL 06151-26538. FAX 06151-20849. (Subscr. to: Postfach 111442, 64229 Darmstadt, Germany) (Co-sponsors: Schweizerische Gesellschaft fuer Gerontologie; Oesterreichische Gesellschaft fuer Geriatrie) Ed.Bd. adv.; bk.rev.; illus.; index. circ. 1,000. (reprint service avail. from UMI) Indexed: Biol.Abstr., Chem.Abstr., Curr.Cont., Dent.Ind., Excerp.Med., Ger.J.Psych., Ind.Med., Nutr.Abstr., Psychol.Abstr., Sci.Cit.Ind., SSCI. **Document type:** academic/scholarly publication.
  —BLDSC (9462.740000); Faxon; SWETS; UMI; CASDDS. **CCC.**
  Incorporates: Aktuelle Gerontologie (ISSN 0300-5704)

155.67   SZ   ISSN 1011-6877
ZEITSCHRIFT FUER GERONTOPSYCHOLOGIE UND PSYCHIATRIE. (Text in English and German) 1988. q. 96 SFr. Verlag Hans Huber, Laenggasstr. 76, CH-3000 Bern 9, Switzerland. TEL 031-3004500. FAX 031-3004590. Ed. Wolf Oswald. adv. circ. 500. (back issues avail.) **Document type:** academic/scholarly publication.

301.435   CC
ZHONGGUO LAONIAN/ELDERLY CHINESE. (Text in Chinese) m. $37.70. (Zhongguo Laonian Wenti Quanguo Weiyuanhui - National Committee on China's Elderly Problems) Zhongguo Laonian Zazhishe, 10 Hepingli Qiqu (Seventh Dist.), Beijing 100013, People's Republic of China. (Dist. in US by: China Books & Periodicals, Inc., 2929 24th St., San Francisco, CA 94110. TEL 415-282-2994) Ed. Zhao Yan.

301.435   US
ZHONGGUO LAONIAN BAO/CHINA'S ELDERLY DAILY. (Text in Chinese) w. $51. China Books & Periodicals, Inc., 2929 24th St., San Francisco, CA 94110. TEL 415-282-2994. FAX 415-282-0994. **Document type:** newspaper.

618.97   CC   ISSN 0254-9026
ZHONGHUA LAONIAN YIXUE ZAZHI/CHINESE JOURNAL OF GERIATRICS. (Text in Chinese) q. $2.50 per no. Zhonghua Yixuehui - Chinese Society of Medical Sciences, Beijing Yiyuan (Beijing Hospital), Dongdan, Beijing 100730, People's Republic of China. TEL 5126611. Ed. Wang Xinde.
  —BLDSC (3180.345000).

052
39 PLUS; for those of us who are no longer kids. 1988. m. $6 (effective 1994). Westchester Publications, 66 Flint St., Asheville, NC 28801. TEL 704-251-5881. Ed. David George. adv.; bk.rev.; circ. 60,000 (paid). (tabloid format; back issues avail.) **Document type:** consumer publication.
  Formerly: Carolina Senior Citizen.
  Description: Profiles mature adults and reports on diverse subjects that pertain to their interests. Includes crossword puzzles, cartoons, restaurant reviews and recipes.

301.435   CN
40 PLUS. 1991. m. Can.$35.40. Trustar Ltd., 10000 Lajeunesse St., Ste. 200, Montreal, PQ H3L 2E1, Canada. TEL 514-383-3400. FAX 514-383-1766. Ed. Louise Pilon. adv.; color page Can.$1800; trim 8 1/8 x 10 7/8. circ. 39,000 (paid); 600 (controlled).

301.435   IT
50 E PIU. 1979. m. L.5000. Via del Melangolo, 26, 00186 Rome, Italy. TEL 06-6867618. Ed. Paolo Bartoli. adv. circ. 300,000.

301.435   US
50 PLUS LIFESTYLES. 1984. m. $14. Box 230, Hartland, WI 53029-0230. TEL 414-367-5303. FAX 414-367-9517. Ed. E.J. McLoone; Pub. Thomas E. Slattery. adv.; bk.rev. circ. 40,000. (tabloid format)
  Formerly: Senior Citizens News and Views.

GERONTOLOGY AND GERIATRICS — Abstracting, Bibliographies, Statistics

612.67 016   US   ISSN 1047-4862
ABSTRACTS IN SOCIAL GERONTOLOGY: CURRENT LITERATURE ON AGING. 1957. q. $70 to individuals; institutions $145 (effective 1994). (National Council on Aging) Sage Publications, Inc., 2455 Teller Rd., Thousand Oaks, CA 91320. TEL 805-499-0721. (Subscr. to: Sage Publications, Inc., Box 5084, Thousand Oaks, CA 91359; Overseas subscr. to: Sage Publications, Ltd., 6 Bonhill St., London EC2A 4PU, England; Sage Publications India Pvt. Ltd., P.O. Box 4215, New Delhi 110 048, England) Ed. Julie L. Moore. index. circ. 8,300. **Document type:** abstracting/indexing, government publication.
  —UMI.
  Formerly (until 1990): Current Literature on Aging (ISSN 0011-3662)
  Description: Provides abstracts and bibliographies of major articles, books, reports, and other materials on all aspects of gerontology, including demography, economics, family relations, government policy, and health.

301.435   US   ISSN 0743-7560
BIBLIOGRAPHIES AND INDEXES IN GERONTOLOGY. 1985. irreg. price varies. Greenwood Press, Inc. (Subsidiary of: Greenwood Publishing Group Inc.), 88 Post Rd. W., Box 5007, Westport, CT 06881-5007. TEL 203-226-3571. FAX 203-222-1502. **Document type:** monographic series, bibliography.
  —BLDSC (1993.097370).

618.97 016   NE   ISSN 0014-424X
  CODEN: GERGB
EXCERPTA MEDICA. SECTION 20: GERONTOLOGY AND GERIATRICS. 1958. 8/yr. fl.1079($583) (effective 1994). Excerpta Medica (Subsidiary of: Elsevier Science B.V.), P.O. Box 548, 1000 AM Amsterdam, Netherlands. TEL 31-20-5803911. FAX 31-20-5803222. TELEX 18582 ESPA NL. (Dist. by: Elsevier Science Ireland Ltd., P.O. Box 85, Limerick, Ireland. TEL 353-61-471944. FAX 353-61-472144; Subscr. in U.S. and Canada to: Elsevier Science Inc., Box 882, Madison Sq. Sta., New York, NY 10159. TEL 212-989-5800. FAX 212-633-3990) adv.; index, cum.index. **Document type:** abstracting/indexing.
  ●Also available online. Vendor(s): BRS Online Products, DIMDI, Data-Star, DIALOG Information Services, Inc., JICST.
  Also available on CD-ROM. Producer(s): SilverPlatter Information, Inc.
  —BLDSC (3835.834000). **CCC.**
  Description: Covers all clinical aspects of aging and experimental work on the aging process. Mental and emotional problems in the elderly and social and organizational aspects of health care for the aged are also included.

362.6   US
GERIATRIC DIRECTORY OF GERIATRIC PUBLICATIONS. *
1979. a. $69. D R S Geriatric Publishing Co., 7435 S.E. 71st St., Mercer Island, WA 98040. TEL 206-232-9689. Ed. Frances Greer. bk.rev. **Document type:** bibliography.
  Formerly: Geriatric Guide to Pertinent Publications (ISSN 0745-5070)
  Description: For all health care professionals caring for the elderly. Covers 1,800 books, journals and newsletters.

GERIATRIC LENGTH OF STAY BY DIAGNOSIS AND OPERATION, UNITED STATES. see HOSPITALS — Abstracting, Bibliographies, Statistics

612.67 016   US
GERONTOLOGICAL ABSTRACTS. * vol.5, 1978. bi-m. $90 to individuals; institutions $130. University Information Services, Inc., 5212 School of Dentistry, University of Michigan, Ann Arbor, MI 48109-1078. TEL 313-764-1555. Ed. Seong S. Han. **Document type:** abstracting/indexing.

646.79 286   US   ISSN 0162-427X
MATURE LIVING. 1977. m. $13.30. Southern Baptist Convention, Sunday School Board, 127 Ninth Ave., N., Nashville, TN 37234. TEL 800-458-2772.
  Description: Deals with issues of those over 50 from a Protestant perspective.

MENOPAUSE NEWS. see GERONTOLOGY AND GERIATRICS

362.6   UK   ISSN 0140-2447
NEW LITERATURE ON OLD AGE. 1977. 6/yr. £18. Centre for Policy on Ageing, 25-31 Ironmonger Row, London EC1V 3QP, England. TEL 071-253-1787. FAX 071-490-4206. (Subscr. to: Bailey Management Services, 127 Sandgate Rd., Folkestone, Kent CT20 2BL, England) Ed. Gillian Crosby. **Document type:** bibliography.
  —BLDSC (6084.465000).
  Description: Details on new books, government reports and periodical articles. Includes courses and conferences section.

155.67   UK   ISSN 0267-0348
SELECTED BIBLIOGRAPHIES ON AGEING. 1984. irreg. Centre for Policy on Ageing, 25-31 Ironmonger Row, London EC1V 3QP, England. TEL 071-253-1787. FAX 071-490-4206. Ed. Gillian Crosby. **Document type:** bibliography.

051   US
STATISTICAL HANDBOOK ON AGING AMERICANS. a. Oryx Press, 4041 N. Central Ave., Ste. 700, Phoenix, AZ 85012-3397. TEL 800-279-6799. FAX 800-279-4663. Ed. Renee Schick. charts.

612.67 360   GW   ISSN 0721-1872
ZEITSCHRIFTENBIBLIOGRAPHIE GERONTOLOGIE. 1977. a. DM.8. Deutsches Zentrum fuer Altersfragen e.V., Manfred-von-Richthofen-Str. 2, 12101 Berlin, Germany. TEL 030-7866071. FAX 030-7854350. Ed.Bd. circ. 1,500. (back issues avail.) **Document type:** bibliography.

GIFTWARE AND TOYS

688   SP   ISSN 0211-7959
ARTE REGALO. 1972. 6/yr. 9500 ptas.($96) (effective 1992). Publica S.A., Ecuador, 75, entlo., 08029 Barcelona, Spain. TEL 93-321-50-46. FAX 93-322-19-72. Ed. Carlos Romagosa. adv.; illus. circ. 5,000.

ARTEREGALO; rivista bimestrale della cristalleria, ceramica, articoli da regalo e di qualita per la casa. see CERAMICS, GLASS AND POTTERY

688 643.6   US   ISSN 0254-1157
ASIAN SOURCES GIFTS & HOME PRODUCTS. 1982. m. $60. Asian Sources Trade Journals, c/o Wordright Enterprises Inc., 1020 Church St., Evanston, IL 60201. TEL 708-475-1900. FAX 708-475-2794. (Subscr. in Asia to: ASIMAG Ltd., P.O. Box 12367, Hong Kong) circ. 24,700.

AUSTRALIAN DOLL DIGEST; the magazine for the doll collector. see HOBBIES

688   AT   ISSN 0312-5327
AUSTRALIAN GIFTGUIDE MAGAZINE. 1975. q. Aus.$55 (effective Aug. 1992). Australian GiftGuide Productions Pty. Ltd., P.O. Box 606, Rozelle, N.S.W. 2039, Australia. TEL 02-818-4111. FAX 02-818-4738. Ed. Vicki Jarvis. adv.: Color page Aus.$1850; trim 295 x 206; adv. contact: Simon Grover. bk.rev.; circ. 4,100 (paid). Document type: trade publication.
    Description: Trade publication for the giftware, china, and glass retailing industry.

AUSTRALIAN HARDWARE JOURNAL. see BUILDING AND CONSTRUCTION — Hardware

658.72 790.13   UK
B T H A BUYERS GUIDE. 1954. a. British Toy & Hobby Association, 80 Camberwell Rd., London, SE5 OEG, England. Ed. Gordon Webb. adv.

338   US
▼**BA PAPYRUS**. 1992. irreg. (2-4/yr.). membership. African Greeting Card Collective, Box 90485, Washington, DC 20090-0485. TEL 202-269-0064. Ed. Aziza Gibson-Hunter. adv. Document type: newsletter.
    Description: Serves as a link between African American greeting card, gift manufacturers and retailers.

BEAR FACTS REVIEW; the magazine for teddy collectors. see HOBBIES

658.8   US   ISSN 0747-069X
BEST REPORT;* exploring the world of quality. 1981. q. $18. Wilton Communications, Inc., 314 W. 56th St., A, No. 1C, New York, NY 10019-4208. TEL 212-983-4320. FAX 212-370-1879. Ed. Peter Filichia. adv. circ. 93,000.
    Description: Information on high-quality consumer goods and services, with emphasis on unusual, one-of-a-kind, customized products.

BETTER HOMES AND GARDENS GUIDE TO CHILDREN'S PRODUCTS. see CHILDREN AND YOUTH — About

BLUE BOOK DOLLS AND VALUES. see HOBBIES

688.72   UK
BRITISH TOYS & HOBBIES BRIEFING. 1954. m. £150. British Toy & Hobby Association, 80 Camberwell Rd., London SE5 OEG, England. Ed. G.A. Webb. adv.; illus.; tr.lit. circ. 750.
    Former titles (until 1984): British Toys and Hobbies (ISSN 0308-6712); British Toys (ISSN 0007-1897)

C L. (CartoLibraio) see BUSINESS AND ECONOMICS — Office Equipment And Services

CANADIAN COLLECTIBLES RETAILER. see ART

CANADIAN JEWELLERY & GIFTWARE DIRECTORY. see BUSINESS AND ECONOMICS — Trade And Industrial Directories

658.72   US
CATALOG CONNECTION. 1988. biennial. $7.50. 490 Three Corners Rd., Box 1427, Guilford, CT 06437. TEL 203-453-9701. Ed. Holly Pasiuk. circ. 1,500.
    Description: Lists catalogs by subject.

658   US
CHICAGO MARKET. 1956. s-a. (Chicago Giftware Association) Bolger Publications Inc., 3301 Como Ave., S.E., Minneapolis, MN 55414. TEL 612-645-6311. FAX 612-645-1750. Ed. Dick Powell. adv.; circ. 26,000 (controlled).

679   US
CHRISTIAN FAMILY CATALOG. Variant title: Abbey Press Christian Family Catalog. 1963. 11/yr. $1. Abbey Press, 52 Hill Dr., St. Meinrad, IN 47577. TEL 812-357-8011. circ. 23,000. Document type: catalog.
    Description: Lists merchandise for home and family having inspirational messages from the Judaeo-Christian tradition.

COLLECTIBLES CANADA. see ART

658   US
COLUMBUS MARKET. 1990. s-a. (Columbus Giftware Association) Bolger Publications Inc., 3301 Como Ave. S.E., Minneapolis, MN 55414. TEL 612-645-6311. FAX 612-645-1750. adv.; circ. 16,000 (controlled).

688   CN
COUNTRY CANADA. a. Bluestone House Inc., 12 Mill St. S., Port Hope, ON L1A 3S5, Canada. TEL 905-885-2449. FAX 905-885-5355. Ed. J.E. Rumgay. circ. 40,000. Document type: consumer publication.

DECOR; the magazine of fine interior accessories. see INTERIOR DESIGN AND DECORATION — Furniture And House Furnishings

688   GW   ISSN 0940-8703
DEDICA. 4/yr. Dr. Harnisch Verlags GmbH, Blumenstr. 15, 90402 Nuernberg, Germany. TEL 0911-203658. FAX 0911-204579. Ed. Hans Riedel. adv.: B&W page DM.5620, color page DM.7570; trim 190 x 270. circ. 15,000. Document type: trade publication.

DOLL READER. see HOBBIES

FASHION ACCESSORIES. see JEWELRY, CLOCKS AND WATCHES

FRAMING AND ART. see ART

688   US   ISSN 0894-4113
G R. (Gift Reporter) m. $36 (free to qualified personnel). G L M Publications (Subsidiary of: George Little Management, Inc.), 2 Park Ave., Ste. 1100, New York, NY 10016. TEL 212-686-6070. (Subscr. to: Box 482, Winchester, MA 01890) adv.; circ. controlled.
    Description: Covers gifts ideas for everyone. Includes calendar of events.

GADGET. see INSTRUMENTS

GEMENGDE BRANCHE (1978); vakblad voor de handel in huishoudelijke en luxe artikelen, glas, porselein, aardewerk en kunstnijverheidsartikelen. see CERAMICS, GLASS AND POTTERY

658.8   IT
GIFT. (Text in English, Italian) 1979. 3/yr. free to qualified personnel. Via Trieste 53, 50139 Florence, Italy. TEL 055-477-841. FAX 055-480-110. TELEX 580242 FGM I. Ed. Marco Tullio Vezzani. adv. contact: Rosanna Poletto. circ. 16,000. Document type: consumer publication, trade publication.

688   US   ISSN 0072-4505
T2
GIFT AND DECORATIVE ACCESSORIES BUYERS DIRECTORY. 1917. a. incl. in subscr. to Gifts and Decorative Accessories. Geyer-McAllister Publications, Inc., 51 Madison Ave., New York, NY 10010. TEL 212-689-4411. Ed. Phyllis Sweed. adv. circ. 34,702. Document type: directory.

688 676.282   US   ISSN 0896-4092
HD9773.A1
GIFT & STATIONERY BUSINESS. 1962. m. $39. Miller Freeman Inc. (New York) (Subsidiary of: United Newspapers Group), 1515 Broadway, New York, NY 10036. TEL 212-869-1300. Ed. Maria Sagurton. adv.; bk.rev.; illus.; stat. circ. 34,476. (also avail. in microform from UMI) Document type: trade publication.
—UMI. CCC.
    Former titles (until 1987): Giftware Business (ISSN 0199-4069); (until 1979): Gifts and Tableware (ISSN 0163-2175); (until 1978): Gift and Tableware Reporter (ISSN 0016-9846); Incorporates: Gift and Tableware Reporter. Gift Guide (ISSN 0148-9437).
    Description: For retailers of gifts, stationery and accessories providing news, product, trend and merchandising information.

688   US   ISSN 0016-9889
HD9999.G49
GIFTS & DECORATIVE ACCESSORIES; the international business magazine of gifts, tabletop, gourmet, home accessories, greeting card and social stationery. 1917. m. $37 (foreign $85). Geyer-McAllister Publications, Inc., 51 Madison Ave., New York, NY 10010. TEL 212-689-4411. Ed. Phyllis Sweed. adv.; bk.rev.; charts; illus.; stat. circ. 33,000. (reprint service avail. from ISI,UMI) Indexed: Key to Econ.Sci., Tr.& Indus.Ind. Document type: trade publication.
●Also available online. Vendor(s): DIALOG Information Services, Inc.
—UnCover. CCC.
    Former titles: Gift; Art Buyer.

688   CN   ISSN 0700-9380
GIFTS & TABLEWARES. (Includes annual Trade Directory) 1976. 7/yr. Can.$38.52($47) (foreign $73). Southam Magazine Group, 1450 Don Mills Rd., Don Mills, ON M3B 2X7, Canada. TEL 416-445-6641. FAX 416-442-2213. Ed. Dawn Dickinson. adv. contact: Brenda Bishop. circ. 10,500.
    Description: Serves the retail gift trade as well as wholesalers, exporters and importers.

658.8   UK   ISSN 0262-5946
GIFTS INTERNATIONAL. 1908. m. £42 (foreign £52). Timothy Benn Publishing, 244-249 Temple Chambers, Temple Ave., London EC4Y ODT, England. TEL 071-583-3030. Ed. Alison Jarman. adv. Document type: trade publication.
    Formerly: Gifts (ISSN 0308-7646)
    Description: Covers all aspects of the gift industry for professional buyers.

645   US   ISSN 0193-2551
GIFTWARE NEWS; the international magazine for gifts, china and glass, stationery and home accessories. 1976. 12/yr. $32. Giftware News, Box 5398, Deptford, NJ 08096. TEL 609-227-0798. (Subscr. to: Talcott Corporation, 20 N. Wacker St., Ste. 3230, Chicago, IL 60606. TEL 312-664-4040) Ed. Anthony Demasi. adv.; bk.rev.; charts; illus.; stat.; tr.lit.; circ. 42,400 (controlled). (tabloid format; back issues avail.) Document type: trade publication.
    Description: Trade magazine for buyers active in the gift and importing industry.

688   IT   ISSN 0017-0054
GIOCATTOLI. 1955. 12/yr. L.12.000. Associazione Nazionale Fabbricanti Giocattoli, Via Bianca di Savoia 6, 20122 Milan, Italy. adv.; bk.rev.; illus. circ. 5,000.

688.72   IT
IL GIORNALE DEI GIOCATTOLI; bimestrale di informazione degli operatori dei sectore. 1963. bi-m. L.110000. Pubbliemme International s.r.l., Via Caracciolo 77, 20155 Milan, Italy. TEL 02-33100954. FAX 02-313864. Dir. Massimo Martini. adv.; illus. circ. 9,900. Document type: trade publication.

GIORNALE IN CARTOLERIA. see BUSINESS AND ECONOMICS — Office Equipment And Services

741.6 658.8   US
GREETINGS. 1960. m. $15. Mackay Publishing Corp., 309 Fifth Ave., New York, NY 10016. TEL 212-679-6777. FAX 212-679-6374. Ed. Milton J. Kristt. adv. contact: Alan Szydlowski. tr.lit. circ. 7,300. Document type: trade publication.
    Formerly: Greeting Card Magazine (ISSN 0017-4106)

2842 GIFTWARE AND TOYS

688　　　　　　　FR　ISSN 0997-2676
GUIDE DU CADEAU ET DES ARTS DE LA TABLE. 1957. a. 290 F. (foreign 249.22 F.). Pierre Johanet et ses Fils, 7, av. Franklin Roosevelt, 75008 Paris, France. TEL 43-59-61-29. FAX 42-25-59-47. **Document type:** directory.
　　Former titles (until 1984): Guide du Specialiste en Articles de Cadeau (ISSN 0752-9295); (until 1980): Guide du Cadeau (ISSN 0396-4299); (until 1976): Guide du Specialiste en Articles de Cadeau (ISSN 0396-4450)

HOME ACCENTS TODAY; the merchandising and fashion news magazine of the home accent industry. see *INTERIOR DESIGN AND DECORATION*

687 688　　　　HK　ISSN 0018-4586
HONG KONG ENTERPRISE. (Text in English) 1967. m. $400 (free to qualified personnel). Hong Kong Trade Development Council, 36-39th Fl., Office Tower, Convention Plaza, 1 Harbour Rd., Wanchai, Hong Kong. TEL 584-4333. FAX 824-0249. Ed. Saul Lockhart. adv.; illus.; stat. circ. 65,000. **Indexed:** Key to Econ.Sci.
　　Supersedes: Hong Kong Trade Bulletin.

688　　　　　　　HK
HONG KONG GIFTS, PREMIUMS & STATIONERY. (Text in English) 1986. s-a. $40 (free to qualified personnel). Hong Kong Trade Development Council, 36-39th Fl., Office Tower, Convention Plaza, 1 Harbour Rd., Wanchai, Hong Kong. TEL 584-4333. FAX 824-0249. Ed. Saul Lockhart. circ. 30,000.
　　Formerly: Hong Kong Gifts and Premiums (ISSN 1021-8890)

HONG KONG HOUSEHOLD. see *BUILDING AND CONSTRUCTION — Hardware*

658.8　　　　　　HK
HONG KONG TOYS. (Text in English) 1969. s-a. $80 free to qualified personnel. Hong Kong Trade Development Council, 36-39th Fl., Office Tower, Convention Plaza, 1 Harbour Rd., Wanchai, Hong Kong. TEL 584-4333. FAX 824-0249. Ed. Saul Lockhart. adv.; illus.; stat.; circ. 35,000 (controlled).

688.72　　　　　　IT
ITALIAN TOYS; journal of Italian toys production and trade. (Text in English) 1979. s-a. free to qualified personnel. Etas s.r.l., Via Mecenate 89-91, 20138 Milan, Italy. Ed. Aldo Rotta. adv. circ. 7,000.

658.8　　　　　　　IT
ITALY EXPORT. 4/yr. Via Govone 56, 20155 Milan, Italy. TEL 2-34-91-113. Ed. Giuseppe Binetti. circ. 10,000.

688　　　　　　CN　ISSN 0713-4118
JEUX ET JOUETS. (Text in French) 1981-19?? a. Can.$7.95. Services Documentaires Multimedia Inc., 75 Port-Royal E., No. 300, Montreal, Que. H3L 3T1, Canada. TEL 514-382-0895. FAX 514-384-9139. circ. 1,500. (back issues avail.)
　　Formerly: Choix Jeunesse: Jeux et Jouets.

688　　　　　　　FR
JEUX ET JOUETS MAGAZINE. 10/yr. 22-24 rue du President Wilson, 92532 Levallois-Perret Cedex, France. TEL 47-39-34-81. FAX 47-39-34-79. Ed. L. Andre. circ. 5,000.

688　　　　FR　ISSN 0075-4056
JOUETS ET JEUX. (Text in French; summaries in English, German, Italian, Spanish) 1950. a. 287 F. C E P P Publications, 1 Place d'Estienne d'Orves, 75009 Paris, France. TEL 42-80-67-62. FAX 42-82-99-30. Ed. Martine Clavel. adv. circ. 8,500.

688.72　　　　　　AG
JUGUETES. 1945. s-a. Arg.$15000($15) Camara Argentina de la Industria del Juguete, Cochabamba 4067, 1252 Buenos Aires, Argentina. TEL 54-1-922-1537. FAX 54-1-923-6658. Ed. Carlos Alberto Montini. adv.; bk.rev circ. 1,500. (back issues avail.)

688.7　　　　　SP　ISSN 0022-6157
JUGUETES Y JUEGOS DE ESPANA; revista espanola de juguetes, juegos y sus derivados para el mercado nacional y extranjero. (Supplement avail.: Express) 1961. bi-m. 6000 ptas.($82) (foreign 9800 ptas.) (effective 1994). (Asociacion Espanola de Fabricantes de Juguetes) Ediciones Just, S.A., San German, 5, 08004 Barcelona, Spain. TEL 93-325-32-87. FAX 93-424-44-60. Ed. Fernando Cortes. adv.; charts; illus.; mkt.; pat. circ. 5,000. **Document type:** trade publication.
　　Description: Covers news in the toy industry.

688.7　　　　　　SP
JUGUETES Y JUEGOS DE ESPANA EXPRESS. (Supplement to: Juguetes y Juegos de Espana) 4/yr. free with subscr. to Juguetes y Juegos de Espana. Ediciones Just, S.A., San German 5, 08004 Barcelona, Spain. TEL 93-325-32-87. FAX 93-424-44-60. Dir. Fernando Cortes. circ. 6,000. **Document type:** trade publication.

JUNGE FAMILIE. see *MEDICAL SCIENCES — Pediatrics*

KINDER; das Journal des Kindergartens. see *CHILDREN AND YOUTH — About*

688.72　　　　　　FR
LUDORAMA. 1977. 5/yr. Jouet Expansion, 73 rue Henri Barbusse, 92110 Clichy, Paris, France. Ed. Christian Sainderichin. adv.

MAGAZINE PREMIERE. see *CERAMICS, GLASS AND POTTERY*

658.72 643 640　　　US
NATIONWIDE DIRECTORY OF GIFT, HOUSEWARES & HOME TEXTILE BUYERS. a. $157. Salesman's Guide, A Reed Reference Publishing Company, Part of the Reed Elsevier group, 121 Chanlon Rd., New Providence, NJ 07974. TEL 908-464-6800. FAX 908-665-3560. TELEX 138 755. (Subscr. to: Order Dept., Box 31, New Providence, NJ 07974-9903. TEL 800-521-8110) **Document type:** directory, trade publication.
　　Formerly: Nationwide Directory of Gift and Housewares Buyers.
　　Description: Lists 14,000 buyers and executives for 6,500 stores carrying giftware and home furnishings.

658　　　　　　　JA
NIKKEI GIFTS/NIKKEI GIFUTO. (Text in Japanese) 1989. m. 16800 Yen. Nikkei Business Publications, Inc. (Subsidiary of: Nihon Keizai Shimbun, Inc.), 2-7-6 Hirakawa-cho, Chiyoda-ku, Tokyo 102, Japan. TEL 03-5210-8502. FAX 03-5210-8119. Ed. Hiroshi Nagai. adv. contact: Atsuo Hiruta. circ. 14,514. **Document type:** trade publication.
　　Description: For store and shop management. Provides practical information on the Japanese gift business, including trends, best-selling items, wrapping, buying, store management, and distribution.

688　　　　　FR　ISSN 0220-3928
OFFRIR INTERNATIONAL; revue des industries d'art. 1954. q. 390 F. Pierre Johanet et ses Fils, 7 Av. Franklin-D.-Roosevelt, 75008 Paris, France. TEL 43-59-08-91. FAX 42-25-59-47. adv.; illus. circ. 6,500.
　　Former titles: Revue des Industries d'Art - Offrir; Offrir (ISSN 0035-2101)

051　　　　　　　US
PARTY SOURCE. 1991. q. Miller Freeman Inc. (New York) (Subsidiary of: United Newspapers Group), 1515 Broadway, New York, NY 10036. TEL 212-869-1300. FAX 212-302-6273. Ed. Maria Sagurtan. circ. 11,000.

688.72　　　　US　ISSN 0032-1567
TS2301.T7
PLAYTHINGS; for today's merchandisers of toys, hobbies and crafts. 1903. m. $24. Geyer-McAllister Publications, Inc., 51 Madison Ave., New York, NY 10010. TEL 212-689-4411. Ed. Frank Reysen, Jr. adv.; illus.; mkt.; tr.lit. circ. 15,000. (reprint service avail. from ISI,UMI) **Indexed:** Bus.Ind., PROMT, Tr.& Indus.Ind. **Document type:** trade publication.
　　●Also available online. Vendor(s): DIALOG Information Services, Inc.
　　—UnCover. **CCC.**
　　Description: Covers the major toy and hobby categories, industry news and new products.

PLAYTHINGS DIRECTORY. see *BUSINESS AND ECONOMICS — Trade And Industrial Directories*

PRESENT; international trade magazine for giftware and trendy goods. see *ARTS AND HANDICRAFTS*

688　　　　　UK　ISSN 0958-5133
PROFITABLE GIFTS; for retailers, producers and distributors of gift products. 1989. m. $42.50. International Thomson Business Publishing, Greater London House, Hampstead Rd., London NW1 7SD, England. TEL 01-387-6611. Ed. Peter Arnott-Job. circ. 12,000.

688　　　　　UK　ISSN 0266-7703
PROFITABLE GREETINGS. 1982. 10/yr. $42.50. International Thomson Business Publishing, Greater London House, Hampstead Rd., London NW1 7QZ, England. TEL 01-387-6611. Ed. Janice Randall. circ. 11,037.

745.592　　　　GW　ISSN 0722-2408
PUPPEN UND SPIELZEUG; internationales Sammlermagazin. 1976. 8/yr. DM.80. Verlagshaus Wohlfarth, Postfach 101461, 47014 Duisburg, Germany. TEL 0203-305270. FAX 0203-337765. Ed. Ulrike Asche-Zeit. adv.: B&W page DM.1350, color page DM.2700; trim 178 x 259. bk.rev. circ. 7,200. **Document type:** consumer publication.
　　Description: Covers doll and toy collecting.

688　　　　　　　GW
▼**PUPPENKUNST UND HANDWERK.** 1992. q. DM.40. Verlagshaus Wohlfarth, Postfach 101461, 47014 Duisburg, Germany. TEL 0203-305270. FAX 0203-337765. Ed. Petra Daniels. adv.: B&W page DM.1450. circ. 6,000. **Document type:** consumer publication.

658.8　　　　　　　IT
REGALO D'AFFARI. 6/yr. Via S. Simpliciano 4, 20121 Milan, Italy. TEL 2-86-23-27. FAX 2-863-856. Ed. Mario Mancini.

688　　　　　FR　ISSN 0035-2594
REVUE DU JOUET. 1948. 10/yr. 330 F. (foreign 495 F.). Editions Ampere, Groupe C.E.P.P., 25, rue Dagorno, 75012 Paris, France. TEL 43-47-30-20. FAX 43-47-30-80. Ed. C. Chapelon. adv.; bk.rev. circ. 6,000. **Document type:** trade publication.
　　—CCC.
　　Description: Professional journal providing information on toys exports, imports, sales, and new products in France.

688　　　　　BE　ISSN 0021-6232
REVUE INTERNATIONALE DES JEUX ET JOUETS/INTERNATIONAL TIJDSCHRIFT VOOR SPEL EN SPEELGOED. Cover title: Jeux et Jouets. Cover title: Spel en Speelgoed. 1960. q. 2000 BEF. Hayez S.A., Rue Fin 4, 1080 Brussels, Belgium. Ed. Geert Degrande. adv.; bk.rev. circ. 5,000. **Document type:** trade publication.

658 739.27　　　　US
SAN FRANCISCO GIFTCENTER AND JEWELRYMART BUYER'S GUIDE. 1985. s-a. (San Francisco Giftcenter and JewelryMart) Bolger Publications Inc., 3301 Como Ave., S.E., Minneapolis, MN 55414. TEL 612-645-6311. FAX 612-645-1750. adv.; circ. 20,000 (controlled).

SMALL WORLD; the magazine of nursery furniture, wheel goods, toys and accessories. see *INTERIOR DESIGN AND DECORATION — Furniture And House Furnishings*

645 910　　　　　　US
SOUVENIR. 1987. 6/yr. $18. 20 N. Wacker Dr., Ste. 3230, Chicago, IL 60606-3102. TEL 312-664-4040. adv. circ. 18,643. **Document type:** trade publication.
　　Description: Trade information for buyers active in the souvenir and tourist industry.

688　　　　　US　ISSN 0038-4968
SOUVENIRS AND NOVELTIES; for the souvenir, novelty, post card and gift field. 1962. 7/yr. $25 for 2 yrs. Kane Communications, Inc., 7000 Terminal Square, Ste. 210, Upper Darby, PA 19082. TEL 610-734-2420. Ed. Sandy Meskow. adv.; index. circ. 29,000.

GIFTWARE AND TOYS

688.72 — NE
SPEELGOED & HOBBY. 1975. fl.190. Stichting Vakbladen Gemengde en Gespecialiseerde Branches, Postbus 7105, 2701 AC Zoetermeer, Netherlands. FAX 079-514811. circ. 4,000. **Indexed:** Key to Econ.Sci. **Document type:** trade publication.

688 — GW — ISSN 0038-7525
DAS SPIELZEUG. (Text in English and German) 1910. m. DM.116 (foreign DM.120). (Verband der Deutschen Spielwarenindustrie) Meisenbach GmbH, Hainstr. 18, 96047 Bamberg, Germany. TEL 0951-861-135. FAX 0951-861-158. (Subscr. to: Postfach 2069, 96011 Bamberg, Germany) (Co-sponsors: Arbeitsgemeinschaft Spielzeug e.V.; Deutsches Spielzeug Institut e.V.; Gesamtverband des Deutschen Spielwaren - Gross- und Aussenhandels e.V.) Ed. A.G. Kropfeld. adv.: B&W page DM.3920, color page DM.6507.20; trim 260 x 184; adv. contact: Hilde Haas. circ. 8,239. **Indexed:** Key to Econ.Sci. **Document type:** trade publication.

658.8 688 — GW
SPIELZEUG-MARKT; Hobby, Modellbau, Basteln. 1966. m. DM.97.50. Goeller Verlag GmbH, Hauptstr. 4, 76534 Baden-Baden, Germany. TEL 07221-71011-3. FAX 07221-75758. TELEX 781244. Ed. Juergen Doerk. adv. circ. 6,300.
 Incorporates: Spielzeug Markt-Scale; Which was formerly: Scale.

SPORTS & LEISURE RETAILER. see *SPORTS AND GAMES*

SPOTLIGHT; journal for the books, gifts, greeting cards, office products, stationery and toy trades of N.Z. see *PUBLISHING AND BOOK TRADE*

688 — SW — ISSN 0039-6621
SVENSK LEKSAKSREVY. 1958. 7/yr. SEK 175. Sveriges Leksakshandlares Riksfoerbund, Kungsgatan 19, S-105 61 Stockholm, Sweden. TEL 08-21-70-95. FAX 08-10-24-23. Ed. Per Sparre. adv.: B&W page SEK 4300, color page SEK 1700. bk.rev.; illus.; mkt.; stat.; tr.lit. circ. 1,450. **Document type:** trade publication.

TABLE ET CADEAU. see *INTERIOR DESIGN AND DECORATION — Furniture And House Furnishings*

028.5 — CH
TAIWAN TOY BUYER'S GUIDE. (Text in English) a. $30. Trade Winds, Inc., No. 7, Lane 75, Yungkang St., Taipei, Taiwan 10602, Republic of China. TEL 02-393-2718. FAX 02-396-4022. TELEX 24177-FCTRADE.
 Description: Examines Taiwan-made products for export.

TODAY'S HOSPITAL GIFT SHOP BUSINESS. see *BUSINESS AND ECONOMICS — Marketing And Purchasing*

TOY AND DECORATION FAIR DIRECTORY. see *BUSINESS AND ECONOMICS — Trade And Industrial Directories*

658.8 — AT — ISSN 1035-9176
TOY & HOBBY RETAILER. 1990. m. Aus.$35 (foreign Aus.$90) (effective Jul. 1993). Yaffa Publishing Group, 17-21 Bellevue St., Surry Hills, N.S.W. 2010, Australia. TEL 02-281-2333. FAX 020-281-2750. (Subscr. addr.: G.P.O. Box 606, Sydney, N.S.W. 2001, Australia) Ed. Genevieve Meegan. adv.: B&W page Aus.$1240, color page Aus.$1880; trim 297 x 210. circ. 3,617. **Document type:** trade publication.
 Description: Covers developments, trends, latest products, etc. in the toy and hobby industry. For manufacturers, wholesalers and retailers.

688 790.023 — US — ISSN 0041-011X
HD9993.T69
TOY & HOBBY WORLD.* (Includes s-a insert: Electronics for Kids of all Ages, Electronic Games Today) 1962. m. $60. Toy & Hobby World (Subsidiary of: V S D Communications), 41 Madison Ave., New York, NY 10010-2202. TEL 212-594-4237. Ed. Larry Carlat. adv.; illus.; tr.lit. circ. 18,173.

688 790.023 — US
TOY & HOBBY WORLD LATIN AMERICA.* (Text in Spanish) m. Toy & Hobby World (Subsidiary of: V S D Communications), 41 Madison Ave., New York, NY 10010-2202. TEL 212-594-4237. (And: Calle 20640, Caracas 1020-A, Venezuela)

638.72 — US
TOY BOOK.* 1985. m. $36 (foreign $200). Adventure Publishing, 150 Broadway, Ste. 500, New York, NY 10036-5503. TEL 212-575-4510. Ed. Stephan Weitzman. circ. 14,341. (tabloid format)

688.72 — US
▼**TOY COLLECTOR AND PRICE GUIDE**. 1992. bi-m. $16.95. Krause Publications, Inc., 700 E. State St., Iola, WI 54990-0001. TEL 715-445-2214. FAX 715-445-4087. Ed. Roger Case. circ. 77,066.
 Formerly: Toys and Prices (ISSN 1063-3618)

688.72 — US — ISSN 0894-5055
TS2301.T7
TOY FARMER. 1978. m. $17.95. Toy Farmer Publications, Inc., HC 2, Box 5, LaMoure, ND 58458. TEL 800-533-8293. FAX 701-883-5208. Ed. Claire Scheibe. adv. circ. 27,400.
 Description: Features articles on collectors and manufacturers, restoring and customizing, and market trends.

688.72 — CN
TOY REPORT. 1952. a. Can.$8.95. Canadian Toy Testing Council, 22 Hamilton Ave. W., Ottawa, ON K1Y 1B6, Canada. TEL 613-729-7101. FAX 613-729-7185. circ. 40,000. (back issues avail.)

TOY SHOP. see *HOBBIES*

688.72 658.8 — UK — ISSN 0041-0136
TOY TRADER. 1908. m. £61. Turret Group Plc., Turret House, 171 High St., Rickmansworth, Herts WD3 1SN, England. TEL 0923-777000. FAX 0923-771297. Ed. David Coombs. adv.; bk.rev.; illus. **Document type:** trade publication.

688.72 — UK
TOY TRADER. 1964. m. £48 (foreign £58). Turrett Group Plc., Turrett House, 171 High St., Rickmansworth, Herts WD3 1SN, England. TEL 0923-777000. FAX 0923-771297. Ed. Dave Coombs. adv. contact: Ray McWilliam. bk.rev.; illus. circ. 5,100. **Document type:** trade publication.
 Former titles: Toys International and Toy Buyer (ISSN 0260-4760); (until 1987): Toys International and the Retailer; Superseded (as of Oct. 1980): Toys International (ISSN 0041-0195)

TOY TRADER DAILY NEWS (EARLS COURT). see *BUSINESS AND ECONOMICS — Domestic Commerce*

TOY TRADER DAILY NEWS (HARROGATE). see *BUSINESS AND ECONOMICS — Domestic Commerce*

688.72 — US — ISSN 1051-2187
TOY TRUCKER AND CONTRACTOR. 1983. m. $17.95. Toy Farmer Publications, Inc., HC 2, Box 5, La Moure, ND 58458. TEL 800-533-8293. FAX 701-883-5208. Ed. Claire Scheibe. adv. circ. 5,100.
 Description: Concentrates on toy trucks and other collectibles, including banks, fire engines and Tonka trucks. Covers construction equipment news, truck news and new items on the market.

688.72 — US
▼**TOYBOX MAGAZINE**; for the collector of childhood treasures. 1992. q. $3.95 per no. Long Publications, Inc., 8393 E. Holly Rd., Holly, MI 48442. TEL 313-634-9675. FAX 313-634-0301.
 Description: Features farm toys, dolls, teddy bears, model trains.

688 790.13 — CN — ISSN 0381-9930
TOYS & GAMES. 1973. bi-m. Can.$34.24($70) Laurentian Media Inc., 501 Oakdale Rd., Downsview, ON M3N 1W7, Canada. TEL 613-475-3217; 800-565-8148. FAX 416-746-1421. Ed. Lynne Winston. illus. circ. 7,300.

688.72 658.8 — UK
TOYS AND GAMES: THE INTERNATIONAL MARKET. a. £1375($2750) Euromonitor, 87-88 Turnmill St., London EC1M 5QU, England. TEL 071-251-8024. FAX 071-608-3149. (Addr. in N. America: Euromonitor International, 111 W. Washington St., Ste. 920, Chicago, IL 60602. TEL 312-541-8024. FAX 312-541-1567) (looseleaf format) **Document type:** trade publication.
 ●Also available online. Vendor(s): Data-Star, DIALOG Information Services, Inc.
 Description: Analyzes the market for toys and games in France, Germany, Italy, Spain, the U.K., the U.S., and Japan.

TRADEWINDS. see *SPORTS AND GAMES — Outdoor Life*

658.8 — US
TRIM-A-TREE BUSINESS.* 1979. a. V S D Communications, 8451 Glenwood Rd., Ste. A, Raleigh, NC 27612-7311. TEL 919-781-8990. adv. circ. 17,200.
 Description: Focuses on the retailing of lights, artificial trees, ornaments, decorations, giftwrap and greeting cards.

688.72 745.1 — US — ISSN 1044-1344
U S TOY COLLECTOR MAGAZINE. 1985. m. $18. Gordon Rice, Box 4244, Missoula, MT 59806-4244. TEL 406-549-3175. adv. (back issues avail.)
 Description: Contains articles about the history of vintage toy cars.

688.72 — IT — ISSN 0391-7290
V G VENDOGIOCATTOLI; giochi, giocattoli, hobby, modellistica. 1978. m. L.52000. Etas s.r.l., Via Mecenate 89-91, 20138 Milan, Italy. Ed. Aldo Rotta. adv.: B&W page L.2110000, color page L.3475000; trim 210 x 297. bk.rev. circ. 8,500.

688 658.9 — GW
WERBEARTIKEL DIREKT; adviser for the use of business gifts, promotions and incentives. 1970. 4/yr. Vogel Verlag und Druck KG, Max-Planck-Str. 7-9, 97082 Wuerzburg, Germany. TEL 0931-4182145. FAX 0931-4182640. (Subscr. to: Vogel Verlag, 97064 Wuerzburg, Germany; Dist. in U.S. by: Vogel Europublishing, Inc., 20092 Gibbs Dr., Sonora, CA 95370. TEL 209-533-3555. FAX 209-533-9555) adv.: B&W page DM.4500. bk.rev.; abstr.; illus.; tr.lit.; circ. 20,000 (controlled). **Document type:** trade publication.
 —CCC.
 Former titles (until 1994): Industrie Promotion; Werbeartikel - Berater (ISSN 0341-5600); Werbegeschenk - Berater (ISSN 0043-2709)

658 —
WESTERN SHOW NEWS. 1989. s-a. (Western Exhibitors, Inc.) Bolger Publications Inc., 3301 Como Ave., S.E., Minneapolis, MN 55414. TEL 612-645-6311. FAX 612-645-1750. adv.; circ. 24,000 (controlled).

745.5 — US
WOMAN'S DAY BEST IDEAS FOR CHRISTMAS. a. $2.50. Hachette Magazines, Inc., Woman's Day Special Publications, 1633 Broadway, 45th Fl., New York, NY 10019. TEL 212-767-6000. Ed. Linda Whitmarsh. adv.; charts; illus.; tr.lit. (back issues avail.)
 Formerly: Woman's Day Gifts You Can Make for Christmas (ISSN 0092-3850)

WORLD GIFT REVIEW MONTHLY NEWSLETTER. see *BUSINESS AND ECONOMICS — Marketing And Purchasing*

XIANDAI SHENGHUO YONGPIN/MODERN DAILY NECESSITIES. see *CONSUMER EDUCATION AND PROTECTION*

658.72 — US
6100 BUILDING GIFT MARKET NEWS. 1991. s-a. Bolger Publications Inc., 3301 Como Ave., S.E., Minneapolis, MN 55414. TEL 612-645-6311. adv. circ. 150,000. **Document type:** trade publication.
 Description: Reports on events at the 6100 Building of the Seattle-Northwest Market Gift Show for buyers and retailers of giftware, tableware, stationery, decorative accessories and related products.

GROCERY TRADE

see Food and Food Industries—Grocery Trade

GUIDES TO SCHOOLS AND COLLEGES

see Education—Guides to Schools and Colleges

HANDICAPPED

see also Handicapped—Computer Applications; Handicapped—Hearing Impaired; Handicapped—Physically Impaired; Handicapped—Visually Impaired; Education—Special Education and Rehabilitation; Social Services and Welfare

362.1 616.8   BE   ISSN 0777-4761
A B P CONTACT/B V V CONTACT. (Text in Flemish, French) 1938. q. 250 BEF. Association Belge des Paralyses - Belgische Vereniging voor Verlamden, 61-63 rue des Champs Elysees, B-1050 Brussels, Belgium. TEL 32-2-648-64-33.
FAX 32-2-647-56-70. Ed. Paul Hofman. adv.; bk.rev.; illus. circ. 4,000. **Document type:** bulletin.
Former titles (until 1990): A B P Magazine (ISSN 0777-4753); A B P - Association Belge des Paralyses. Bulletin (ISSN 0001-0553)
Description: Articles concerning activities of the association and information for disabled persons.

362.4   AT   ISSN 0729-8463
A C R O D NEWSLETTER. 1981. m. Aus.$65 (foreign Aus.$75). (Australian Council for Rehabilitation of Disabled) A C R O D Ltd., P.O. Box 60, Curtin, A.C.T. 2605, Australia. TEL 062-824333.
FAX 062-813488. Ed. Kerin Cox. adv.; bk.rev. circ. 1,700. (back issues avail.) **Document type:** newsletter.

A D A COMPLIANCE MANUAL FOR EMPLOYERS. (Americans with Disabilities Act) see BUSINESS AND ECONOMICS — Labor And Industrial Relations

362.4 347   US
▼**A D A FASTSEARCH**; Americans with Disabilities Act reference guide. 1992. a. (plus irreg. updates). $98. D M S A Corporation, FastSearch Corporation, 1000 Shelard Pkwy., Ste. 200, Minneapolis, MN 55426. TEL 612-595-0244; 800-232-4590.
FAX 612-595-0229. Ed. Alan Rosenauer. circ. 2,200. (diskette format)

362.4 385   US   ISSN 1067-4713
A D A POLICY & LAW. (Americans with Disabilities Act) m. Buraff Publications (Subsidiary of: Millin Publications, Inc.), 1350 Connecticut Ave., N.W., Ste. 1000, Washington, DC 20036.
TEL 800-333-1291. FAX 202-862-0999. **Document type:** newsletter.
—CCC.
Description: Reports and analysis of litigation brought under the Americans with Disabilities Act as well as regulatory developments and policy guidelines.

362.4   CN
ABILITIES; Canada's lifestyle magazine for people with disabilities. q. Can.$12. Box 527, Sta. P, Toronto, ON M5S 2T1, Canada. TEL 416-588-8431.
FAX 416-588-4695. (also avail. in audio cassette) **Description:** Covers sports, travel, health, the arts, new technology, services, opportunities.

500   AT   ISSN 1038-2860
ACCESS (MELBOURNE). q. Aus.$30 to individuals; institutions Aus.$50 (effective 1993). Arts Access Society, Inc., 109-111 Sturt St., S. Melbourne, Vic. 3205, Australia. TEL 03-699-8299.
FAX 03-685-5112. bk.rev. **Document type:** newsletter.
Description: Reports on events, activities, research and opportunities in the arts for people with disabilities and people disadvantaged by social conditions.

362.4   US
ACCOMMODATING DISABILITIES. 1991. 2 base vol. (plus bi-m. updates). $270. Commerce Clearing House, Inc., 4025 W. Peterson Ave., Chicago, IL 60646. TEL 312-583-8500.

362.4   US
ACCREDITATION COUNCIL ON SERVICES FOR PEOPLE WITH DISABILITIES. UPDATE ON QUALITY. 1980. 3/yr. Accreditation Council on Services for People with Disabilities, 8100 Professional Pl., Ste. 204, Landover, MD 20785. TEL 301-459-3191.
FAX 301-577-0703. Ed. Tina Companella. circ. 5,000.

THE ADVOCATE (ALBANY). see SOCIAL SERVICES AND WELFARE

362.4   TS
AFAQ/HORIZONS. (Text in Arabic) 1988. irreg. Center for the Supervision of the Handicapped, P.O. Box 216-809, Abu Dhabi, United Arab Emirates.
TEL 668512. Ed. Amira al-Shibani. circ. 1,000.
Description: Covers topics concerning the handicapped.

362.4   SW   ISSN 1103-8063
ALLT OM HJAELPMEDEL. 1946. 6/yr. SEK 165. Handikappinstitutet - Swedish Handicap Institute, P.O. Box 510, S-162 15 Vaellingby, Sweden.
TEL 08-620-1700. FAX 08-739-2152. TELEX 11926. Ed. Anne-Marie Nenzell. adv.; bk.rev.; charts; illus.; stat.; circ. controlled. (also avail. in audio cassette) **Indexed:** Excerp.Med.
Formerly (until vol.6, 1992): Information om Rehabilitering (ISSN 0020-0174)
Description: Covers issues concerning technical aids for the handicapped in Sweden.

362.3   BE   ISSN 0002-7022
AMENTIA; la voix des parents. (Text in Dutch, French) 1963. q. 750 BEF. Association Nationale d'Aide aux Handicapes Mentaux, 66 rue de la Limite, B-1030 Brussels, Belgium. TEL 32-2-2198800.
FAX 32-2-2199061. Ed. Th. Kempeneers-Foulon. adv.; bk.rev.; bibl.; illus. circ. 8,000.
Description: Covers all aspects of mental retardation.

AMERICANS WITH DISABILITIES ACT TECHNICAL ASSISTANCE MANUAL: TITLE I. see SOCIAL SERVICES AND WELFARE

AMERICANS WITH DISABILITIES ACT TECHNICAL ASSISTANCE MANUAL: TITLE II. see SOCIAL SERVICES AND WELFARE

AMERICANS WITH DISABILITIES ACT TECHNICAL ASSISTANCE MANUAL: TITLE III. see SOCIAL SERVICES AND WELFARE

362.4 347   US   ISSN 1071-7382
▼**AMERICANS WITH DISABILITIES ACT UPDATE.** 1992. m. $75. Nyper Publications, Box 370, Latham, NY 12112-0370. TEL 518-786-1654.
FAX 518-456-8582. Ed. Harvey Randall. bk.rev.; index. circ. 600. **Document type:** newsletter.

371.92   US   ISSN 0749-1425
LC4631   CODEN: JPSHEF
ASSOCIATION FOR PERSONS WITH SEVERE HANDICAPS. JOURNAL. Key Title: Journal of the Association for Persons with Severe Handicaps. 1975. q. $85 to individuals; parents $45; students $35; family (group rate) $90. The Association for Persons with Severe Handicaps (TASH), 11201 Greenwood Ave. N., Seattle, WA 98133. TEL 206-361-8870.
FAX 206-361-9208. Ed. James Halle. adv.; bk.rev.; index. circ. 8,500. (also avail. in microform from UMI; reprint service avail. from UMI; back issues avail.) **Indexed:** C.I.J.E., Educ.Ind., Except.Child.Educ.Abstr., Psychol.Abstr.
—BLDSC (4705.078000); Faxon; UnCover; UMI.
Former titles (until 1983): Association for the Severely Handicapped. Journal (JASH) (ISSN 0274-9483); (until vol.5, no.1): A A E S P H Review (American Association for the Education of the Severely-Profoundly Handicapped) (ISSN 0147-4375)

362.4   US
ASSOCIATION FOR PERSONS WITH SEVERE HANDICAPS. NEWSLETTER. m. The Association for Persons with Severe Handicaps (TASH), 11201 Greenwood Ave. N., Seattle, WA 98133. TEL 206-361-8870.
FAX 206-361-9208. (reprint service avail. from UMI) **Document type:** newsletter.

617.087 615.82   AT   ISSN 0813-4537
AUSTRALIAN DISABILITY REVIEW. 1977. q. (Disability Advisory Council of Australia) Australian Government Publishing Service, G.P.O. Box 84, Canberra, A.C.T. 2601, Australia. TEL 61-6-295-4612.
FAX 61-295-4500. (Subscr. to: Disability Advisory Council of Australia, G.P.O. Box 9848, Canberra, A.C.T. 2601, Australia) Ed. L.H. Costello. bk.rev.; bibl.; illus.; stat.; cum.index. circ. 1,500. **Document type:** government publication.
—BLDSC (1798.482000). CCC.
Former titles (until 1984): Australian Rehabilitation Review (ISSN 0728-490X); (until 1981): National Rehabilitation Digest (ISSN 0314-111X)

B N A'S AMERICANS WITH DISABILITIES ACT MANUAL NEWSLETTER. see LAW — Legal Aid

362.4 371.9   GW   ISSN 0170-902X
DAS BAND. 1970. bi-m. DM.18. Bundesverband fuer Koerper- und Mehrfachbehinderte e.V., Brehmstr. 5-7, 40239 Duesseldorf, Germany.
TEL 0211-626651. FAX 0211-613972. Ed. Rudi Tarneden. adv.; bk.rev.; play rev.; abstr.; illus.; tr.lit. circ. 21,000. **Document type:** newsletter.

BEHINDERTENPAEDAGOGIK; Vierteljahresschrift fuer Behindertenpaedagogik in Praxis, Forschung und Lehre und Integration Behinderter. see EDUCATION — Special Education And Rehabilitation

C D R REPORTS. (Council for Disability Rights) see POLITICAL SCIENCE — Civil Rights

362.4   US
C S D NEWSLETTER. 1978. q. membership. Coalition on Sexuality and Disability, Inc., 122 E. 23rd St., New York, NY 10010. TEL 212-242-3900. Ed. Pamela Boyle. bk.rev. circ. 300. (tabloid format)

CANADIAN REHABILITATION COUNCIL. ANNUAL REPORT/CONSEIL CANADIEN DE READAPTATION. RAPPORT ANNUEL. see EDUCATION — Special Education And Rehabilitation

371.42   US
HV3018
CAREERS & THE DISABLED. 1986. 3/yr. $10. Equal Opportunity Publications, Inc., 150 Motor Pkwy. No. 420, Hauppauge, NY 11788. TEL 516-261-8899.
FAX 516-261-8935. Ed. James Schneider. adv. circ. 11,674.
Formerly: Careers and the Handicapped (ISSN 0891-5202)

CARERS WORLD. see SOCIAL SERVICES AND WELFARE

CHILD & ADOLESCENT MENTAL HEALTH CARE. see MEDICAL SCIENCES — Psychiatry And Neurology

362.4   US   ISSN 1063-0023
HV1553
▼**COMPLETE DIRECTORY FOR PEOPLE WITH DISABILITIES.** 1992. a. $135. Grey House Publishing, Pocket Knife Sq., Lakeville, CT 06039. TEL 203-435-0868; 800-562-2139.
FAX 203-435-0867. Ed. Leslie Mackenzie. (also avail. in magnetic tape; diskette format; back issues avail.) **Document type:** directory.
Description: Lists associations, magazines, newsletters, support groups, vocational and educational programs, rehabilitation facilities, sports opportunities and more.

362.4   US
CONNECTOR. 1973. q. contribution. Minnesota State Council on Disability, 121 E. Seventh Pl., Ste. 145, St. Paul, MN 55101. TEL 612-296-6785.
FAX 612-296-5935. Ed. Tom Brick. circ. 8,000.

D P H D NEWSLETTER. (Division for Physical & Health Disabilities) see HANDICAPPED — Physically Impaired

DIALOGUE (SALEM); the magazine for the visually impaired. see HANDICAPPED — Visually Impaired

DIKTA. see LIBRARY AND INFORMATION SCIENCES

HANDICAPPED

362.4 UK ISSN 0309-4413
DIRECTORY FOR DISABLED PEOPLE. 1977. irreg., 7th ed., Nov. 1994. $35.95. (Royal Association for Disability and Rehabilitation (RADAR)) Harvester Wheatsheaf (Subsidiary of: Paramount Publishing International), Campus 400, Maylands Ave., Hemel Hempstead, Herts. HP2 7EZ, England. TEL 0442-881900. FAX 0442-252544. TELEX 82445. Eds. Ann Darnbrough, Derek Kinrade. circ. 2,500. (back issues avail.) **Document type:** directory. —BLDSC (3593.412000).
Description: Contains information and lists opportunities for disabled and handicapped people.

362.4 612.67 UK
DIRECTORY OF AIDS FOR DISABLED AND ELDERLY PEOPLE. 1986. irreg. $43.50. Harvester Wheatsheaf (Subsidiary of: Paramount Publishing International), Campus 400, Maylands Ave., Hemel Hempstead, Herts. HP2 7EZ, England. TEL 0442-881900. FAX 0442-252544. circ. 2,500. **Document type:** directory.
Description: A wide-ranging directory of useful equipment helpful to disabled people and others with difficulties in daily living.

DIRECTORY OF COLLEGE FACILITIES AND SERVICES FOR PEOPLE WITH DISABILITIES. see EDUCATION — Guides To Schools And Colleges

DIRECTORY OF FEDERAL AID FOR THE HANDICAPPED. see SOCIAL SERVICES AND WELFARE

362.4 371.9 US
HV1553
DIRECTORY OF GRANTS FOR ORGANIZATIONS SERVING PEOPLE WITH DISABILITIES; a guide to sources of funding in the United States for handicapped programs & services. 1978. biennial, 8th ed., 1993. $47.50. Research Grant Guides, Box 1214, Loxahatchee, FL 33470. TEL 407-795-6129. Ed. Richard M. Eckstein. bk.rev. **Document type:** directory.
Formerly: Handicapped Funding Directory (ISSN 0733-4753)
Description: Lists funding sources for programs and services for the disabled and provides extensive profiles on foundations, corporations, government agencies and associations. Includes essays on grantsmanship to help guide the reader through the intricate process of securing a grant.

362.4 US
DIRECTORY OF INFORMATION RESOURCES FOR THE HANDICAPPED. irreg. Ready Reference Press, Box 5169, Santa Monica, CA 90405. **Document type:** directory.

DISABILITIES IN THE WORKPLACE ALERT. see LAW — Legal Aid

362.4 US
DISABILITIES STUDIES QUARTERLY. 1982. q. $30 to individuals; institutions $40. Brandeis University, Department of Sociology, Waltham, MA 02254. TEL 617-736-2644. FAX 617-736-2653. Ed. Irving K. Zola. bk.rev. circ. 1,200.
Description: A digest for and by those concerned with policy and research aspects of disability.

DISABILITY ADVOCATES BULLETIN. see LAW

617.087 615.8 UK ISSN 0963-8288
CODEN: DREHET
DISABILITY AND REHABILITATION. (Text in English) 1979. q. £82($138) Taylor & Francis Ltd., Rankine Road, Basingstoke, Hants RG24 8PR, England. TEL 0256-840366. FAX 0256-479438. TELEX 858540. Ed. D. Mueller. adv.; bk.rev. circ. 1,000. **Indexed:** Excerp.Med., Ind.Med. **Document type:** academic/scholarly publication.
—BLDSC (3595.420300); Faxon; UnCover; SWETS. CCC.
Former titles (until 1991): International Disability Studies (ISSN 0259-9147); (until 1987): International Rehabilitation Medicine (ISSN 0379-0797)
Refereed Serial

DISABILITY AND REHABILITATION SERIES. see EDUCATION — Special Education And Rehabilitation

DISABILITY COMPLIANCE BULLETIN. see LAW

362.41 US
DISABILITY ISSUES. 1980. m. donation. Information Center for Individuals with Disabilities, 27-43 Wormwood St., Boston, MA 02210-1606. TEL 617-727-5540; 800-462-5015. FAX 617-345-5318. Ed. Linda Hillyer. adv.: half page $225. bk.rev. circ. 4,500. (also avail. in magnetic tape; large print edition in 16 pt.) **Document type:** newsletter.
Description: Information for persons with disabilities, their family, friends, and service providers.

362.4 340 US ISSN 1063-2506
▼**DISABILITY LAW COMPLIANCE REPORT.** 1992. m. $136.50 (foreign $183.50). Warren Gorham Lamont, One Penn Plaza, New York, NY 10119. TEL 212-971-5000. FAX 212-971-5240. (Subscr. to: The Park Square Bldg., 31 St. James Ave., Boston, MA 02116-4112. TEL 800-950-1207) Ed. Gary S. Marx. index. (looseleaf format; back issues avail.) **Document type:** newsletter.
—CCC.
Description: Analyzes recent court interpretations of the Americans with Disabilities Act.

362.4 331 323.4 US
HV1553
DISABILITY RAG & RESOURCE. 1980. bi-m. $17.50 to individuals; institutions $35; foreign $42 (effective Jan. 1993). Advocado Press, Box 145, Louisville, KY 40201. TEL 502-459-5343. Ed. Barrett Shaw. adv.; bk.rev. circ. 5,000. (also avail. in audio cassette; Braille; diskette format; back issues avail., large print edition in 14 pt.) **Indexed:** Alt.Press Ind.
Formerly: Disability Rag (ISSN 0749-8586)
Description: Attempts to discern the causes of the discrimination, devaluation and disenfranchisement suffered by disabled people at the hands of the nondisabled majority, and publishes material to commmunicate the true nature of relationship between American society and its disabled members.

362.4 US ISSN 1070-7220
▼**DISABILITY RESOURCES MONTHLY.** 1993. m. $25 (Canada $30; elsewhere $35). Disability Resources, 4 Glatter Ln., Centereach, NY 11720-1032. TEL 516-585-0290. Ed. Julie Klauber. index. **Document type:** newsletter.
Description: Features short topical articles and news items about books, pamphlets, periodicals, videotapes, computer software, organizations and other resources for and about people with disabilities.

DISABLED OUTDOORS MAGAZINE. see SPORTS AND GAMES — Outdoor Life

DIVISION ON VISUAL HANDICAPS QUARTERLY. see HANDICAPPED — Visually Impaired

DOWN SYNDROME NEWS. see MEDICAL SCIENCES — Psychiatry And Neurology

EARLY CHILDHOOD REPORTER. see LAW

EDUCATION DAILY; the American educator's independent, daily news service. see EDUCATION

616.858 300 CN ISSN 0829-8815
ENTOURAGE. (Text in English, French) 1958. q. Can.$18 (foreign Can.$20). (Canadian Association for the Community Living) Roeher Institute, Kinsmen Bldg., York University, 4700 Keele St., Toronto, ON M3J 1P3, Canada. TEL 416-661-9611. FAX 416-661-5701. Ed. Laura Code. adv.; bk.rev. circ. 4,000. **Indexed:** C.I.J.E., Can.Educ.Ind., Can.Per.Ind., Except.Child.Educ.Abstr., Psychol.Abstr., Sp.Ed.Needs Abstr. **Document type:** consumer publication.
—BLDSC (3790.527000).
Incorporates (in Jun. 1988): Information Exchange Bulletin; **Former titles (until 1986):** Revue Canadienne de la Deficience Mentale - Canadian Journal on Mental Retardation; Deficience Mentale - Mental Retardation (ISSN 0011-7668)
Description: Explores the issues affecting people who have been labelled mentally handicapped, their families and the advocates working for them. Keeps readers up-to-date on new developments in the disability movement across Canada and around the world.

362.4 SZ
FAIRE FACE. (Text in French, German) m. Laenggassstr. 68D, CH-3012 Bern, Switzerland. TEL 031-238344. Ed. Ernst Gerber. circ. 3,300.

362.4 US
FIRST WHOLE REHAB CATALOG; a comprehensive guide to products and services for the physically disadvantaged. irreg. $16.95. Betterway Publications, Box 219, Crozet, VA 22932. TEL 804-823-5661. FAX 804-823-2047. Ed. Hilary W. Swinson. **Document type:** catalog.
Description: Lists US and foreign products and services for the physically challenged. Includes company name, address, and phone number. Covers home management, personal care, access, communication, mobility, transport, health and fitness, recreation, and education.

362.4 US
FOCUS (WASHINGTON, 1978). 1978. q. free. National Council on Disability, 800 Independence Ave. S.W., Ste. 814, Washington, DC 20591. TEL 202-267-3846. FAX 202-453-4240. (also avail. in audio cassette; large print edition in 14 pt.)
Description: Focuses on council news and upcoming events.

FOCUS: LIBRARY SERVICE TO OLDER ADULTS, PEOPLE WITH DISABILITIES. see LIBRARY AND INFORMATION SCIENCES

362.4 SZ
FREUNDE DER MILCHSUPPE. 6/yr. Postfach 205, CH-4025 Basel, Switzerland. TEL 061-2718410. Ed. Christiane Muschter. circ. 7,200.

362.4 790.13 CN
HABILETES LOISIRS. 1983. q. free. Association Quebecoise de Loisir pour Personnes Handicapees, 4545 Pierre de Coubertin, Box 1000, Sta. M, Montreal, Que. H1V 3R2, Canada. TEL 514-252-3144. FAX 514-252-3164. Ed.Bd. adv. circ. 3,000. (also avail. in record; magnetic tape; back issues avail.)
Description: Hobbies for handicapped people.

362.4 DK ISSN 0106-3197
HANDICAP IDRAET. 1979. m. (11/yr.) DKK 100. Dansk Handicap Idraets Forbund, Idraettens Hus, 2600 Glostrup, Denmark. Ed. Steffen Andersen. adv. circ. 10,000.
Formerly: Handicap Information.

362.4 NO
HANDICAP IDRETT. bi-m. (Norges Handicapidrettsforbund) Per Sletholt og Co., Postboks 57, Tveita, Oslo 6, Norway. adv.

362.4 US ISSN 0896-131X
HANDICAP NEWS. 1984. m. $12.50 (foreign $35). Phyllis Burns, Ed. & Pub., 3060 E. Bridge, Ste. 342, Brighton, CO 80601-2724. adv.; bk.rev. circ. 400.

362.4 DK ISSN 0904-8081
HANDICAP - NYT. 1925. 8/yr. DKK 128. Dansk Handicap Forbund - National Association of Disabled in Denmark, Hans Knudsens Plads 1A, 2100 Copenhagen OE, Denmark. TEL 45-31-29-35-55. FAX 45-31-29-39-48. Ed. Keld Sogaard. adv. circ. 18,000.
Formerly: Vanfoerebladet (ISSN 0042-2541)
Description: Cultural, political and social activities and aims of the handicapped.

362.4 331 US ISSN 0194-7818
HANDICAPPED REQUIREMENTS HANDBOOK. 1978. base vol. (plus m. updates) $196 or $35 per chapter. Thompson Publishing Group, 1725 K St., N.W., Ste. 200, Washington, DC 20006. TEL 800-677-6739. FAX 202-296-1091. Ed. Donald Montuori. bk.rev.
—CCC.

362.4 BE ISSN 0779-3367
HANDISCOOP. (Text in Dutch) 1945. 10/yr. 470 BEF (effective 1994). Katholieke Vereniging Gehandicapten, Vormingsbeweging v.z.w., Arthur Goemaerelei 66, B-2018 Antwerp, Belgium. TEL 32-3-2162990. FAX 32-3-2481442. Eds. Lief Vanbael, Luc Vantolhuyzen. adv.; bk.rev. circ. 35,000. (also avail. in video cassette)
Formerly (until 1993): K V G Blad (ISSN 0779-3359)
Description: Covers issues relating to social services for the disabled and their integration into society.

HEARING CONCERN. see HANDICAPPED — Hearing Impaired

HANDICAPPED

790.13 362.4   US   ISSN 1042-4334
I H N NEWS. 1984. q. free. International Handicapper's Net, Box 55, Bostwick, GA 30623. TEL 503-488-2691. Ed. Jack Olsen. adv. circ. 400. (looseleaf format; also avail. in magnetic tape)
   Description: News, information, sources of interest to disabled, with emphasis on disabled amateur radio operators (hams).

I R V SERIES IN REHABILITATION RESEARCH. see *EDUCATION — Special Education And Rehabilitation*

362.4   US   ISSN 1071-4901
ILLUSTRATED DIRECTORY OF DISABILITY PRODUCTS. 1989. a. $15.95 to individuals; institutions $24.95. Trio Publications, Inc., 3600 W. Timber Ct., Lawrence, KS 66049-2149. TEL 913-749-1453. FAX 913-749-0867. adv.; illus.; circ. 5,000 (paid).
   Document type: directory, consumer publication.
   Formerly: Illustrated Directory of Handicap Products.
   Description: Guide to products for the disabled.

362.4   AT   ISSN 0815-2276
INDEPENDENT LIVING. 1984. q. Aus.$22 (foreign Aus.$34)(effective Sep. 1991). (Independent Living Centre NSW Inc.) Rala Information Service Pty. Ltd., 203-205 Darling St., Bamain, N.S.W. 2041, Australia. TEL 02-555-1944. FAX 02-555-1496. (Subscr. addr.: P.O. Box 706, Ryde, N.S.W. 2112, Australia) Ed. Charlotte Smedley. adv.; bk.rev.; cum.index: 1984-1990. circ. 1,500.
   Description: Information on equipment, audio-visual resources and organizations for people with disabilities, caregivers, health professionals, builders and architects.

INDIVIDUALS WITH DISABILITIES EDUCATION LAW REPORTER. see *EDUCATION — Special Education And Rehabilitation*

INTERNATIONAL JOURNAL OF DISABILITY, DEVELOPMENT AND EDUCATION; the Australian journal on the education of handicapped children. see *EDUCATION — Special Education And Rehabilitation*

617.09 371.9   UK   ISSN 0342-5282
RM695   CODEN: IJRRDK
INTERNATIONAL JOURNAL OF REHABILITATION RESEARCH. (Text in English, French and German; summaries in English, French, German and Spanish) 1977. q. £65 to institutions in EC nations (North America $110; elsewhere £70). (Rehabilitation International, US) Chapman & Hall, 2-6 Boundary Row, London SE1, England. TEL 071-865-0066. FAX 071-522-9623. TELEX 290164-CHAPMAG. (Dist. by: International Thomson Publishing Services, Ltd., N. Way, Andover, Hants. SP10 5BE, England. TEL 0264-342919; US addr.: Chapman & Hall, Journals Promotion Department, One Penn Plaza, 41st Fl., New York, NY 10019. TEL 212-244-3336. FAX 212-564-1505) Ed. Paul Cornes. adv.; bk.rev.; charts. circ. 750. **Indexed:** Biol.Abstr., C.I.J.E.; Child Devel.Abstr., Crim.Just.Abstr., Ergon.Abstr., Excerp.Med., Ind.Med., Lang.& Lang.Behav.Abstr., Psychol.Abstr., Rehabil.Lit., SSCI, Yrbk.Assoc.Educ.& Rehab.Blind. **Document type:** academic/scholarly publication.
—BLDSC (4542.526000); ADONIS; EI; Faxon; UnCover; SWETS.
   Description: Provides an interdisciplinary forum for research into disability and handicaps people in both industrial and developing nations experience.
Refereed Serial

362.4 617.087   US   ISSN 8756-8160
KF480.A15   CODEN: ILAME3
ISSUES IN LAW AND MEDICINE. 1985. q. $69 (effective 1993). National Legal Center for the Medically Dependent and Disabled, Inc., Box 1586, Terre Haute, IN 47808-1586. TEL 812-232-0103. (Co-sponsors: Horatio R. Storer Foundation, Inc.; American Academy of Medical Ethics, Inc.) Ed. James Bopp, Jr. bk.rev. circ. 5,000. (back issues avail.) **Indexed:** C.L.I., Curr.Cont., Hlth.Ind., Hosp.Lit.Ind., Ind.Med., Int.Nurs.Ind., L.R.I., Leg.Per., Psychol.Abstr. **Document type:** academic/scholarly publication.
● Also available online. Vendor(s): National Library of Medicine, West Services, Inc.
—BLDSC (4584.302000); Faxon; UnCover.
   Description: Provides technical and informational assistance to attorneys, health care professionals, educators and administrators concerned with severley disabled persons of all ages who may be subjected to discrimination in the delivery of medical care.
Refereed Serial

362.3   US   ISSN 1056-263X
HV1551   CODEN: JDPDE6
JOURNAL OF DEVELOPMENTAL AND PHYSICAL DISABILITIES. 1988. q. $140 (foreign $165) (effective 1994). Plenum Publishing Corp., 233 Spring St., New York, NY 10013-1578. TEL 212-620-8000. FAX 212-463-0742. TELEX 23-421139. Eds. V.B. Van Hasselt, M. Hersen. adv.; bk.rev.; bibl.; charts; illus.; index. (also avail. in microfilm from JSC; back issues avail.) **Indexed:** Psychol.Abstr. **Document type:** academic/scholarly publication.
—BLDSC (4969.290200); UnCover; UMI. **CCC**.
   Formerly (until 1992): Journal of the Multihandicapped Person (ISSN 0892-7561)
   Description: Reports the latest developments, methodologies and technologies for professionals in all fields working with disabled persons, including comprehensive coverage of original research and clinical reports involving persons with multiple handicaps.
Refereed Serial

362.4 340   US   ISSN 1044-2073
HV1551
JOURNAL OF DISABILITY POLICY STUDIES. 1990. s-a. $14 to individuals; institutions $22. University of Arkansas, Department of Rehabilitation Education and Research, 346 N. West Ave., Fayetteville, AR 72701. TEL 501-575-3656. FAX 501-575-3253. Ed. Kay Fletcher Schriner. adv.; bk.rev. circ. 500. (back issues avail.) **Document type:** academic/scholarly publication.
   Description: Publishes research, discussion and review articles, and brief reports pertaining to both macro- and micro-policy issues affecting people with disabilities.

JOURNAL OF RELIGION IN DISABILITY & REHABILITATION; innovations in ministry for independent living. see *RELIGIONS AND THEOLOGY*

362.4 808 700   US   ISSN 0748-8742
PS153.P48
KALEIDOSCOPE (AKRON); international magazine of literature, fine arts and disability. 1979. s-a. $9 to individuals in the U.S.; Canada $14; elsewhere $17; institutions in U.S. $14; Canada $19; elsewhere $22. (United Disability Services) Kaleidoscope Press (Akron), 326 Locust St., Akron, OH 44302. TEL 216-762-9755. FAX 216-762-0912. Ed. Darshan Perusek. bk.rev. circ. 2,000. (also avail. in audio cassette; back issues avail.) **Document type:** consumer publication.
—UnCover.
   Description: Addresses the experience of disability through literature and the fine arts.

362.4   AT   ISSN 1034-8883
LINK DISABILITY JOURNAL. 1980. bi-m. Aus.$22.50 (foreign Aus.$30). Disabled Peoples' International, South Australian Branch, G.P.O. Box 909, Adelaide. S.A. 5001, Australia. TEL 61-8-277-0700. FAX 61-8-277-5465. Ed. Jeff Heath. adv.; bk.rev. circ. 4,500. (also avail. in talking book; back issues avail.) **Document type:** consumer publication.
   Description: Examines all issues relevant to disability, from the perspective of the disabled and their families.

362.41 020   AT   ISSN 0158-5460
LINK-UP. 1980. bi-m. free. National Library of Australia, Community Liaison Section, Canberra, A.C.T. 2600, Australia. TEL 06-262-1207. FAX 06-273-4493. TELEX 062-62100. Ed. Virginia Rowland. bk.rev. circ. 1,200. (also avail. in audio cassette) **Indexed:** Aus.Educ.Ind., Aus.P.A.I.S., LISA. **Document type:** newsletter.
—BLDSC (5221.473500).
   Description: National Library newsletter concerned with the provision of library services for people with disabilities in Australia and overseas.

362.4   UK
LONDON DISABILITY NEWS. m. £7. Greater London Association of Disabled People, 336 Brixton Rd., London SW9 7AA, England. TEL 071-274-0107. FAX 071-274-7840. Ed. Nick Lewis. adv. circ. 3,000. (tabloid format) **Document type:** newsletter.
   Formerly (until 1989): G L A D Newsletter.
   Description: For disabled people and those who work with them.

362.4   UK   ISSN 0047-5475
MAGIC CARPET. 1948. q. £8 single; joint £12. Disabled Drivers' Association, Registered Office, The Hall, Ashwellthorpe, N. Norwich NR16 1EX, England. Ed. Michael Elmore. adv.; bk.rev.; illus. circ. 17,000. **Document type:** newsletter.
   Description: Concerned with the welfare of disabled people and encourages greater independence through mobility.

362.4   US   ISSN 0278-8225
HV3023.C3
MAINSTREAM (SAN DIEGO); magazine of the able-disabled. 1975. 10/yr. $24 (foreign $44.50). Exploding Myths, Inc., 2973 Beech St., San Diego, CA 92102. Ed. Cyndi Jones. adv.; bk.rev.; illus. circ. 18,200. **Indexed:** Comput.Lit.Ind., Hlth.Ind., Rehabil.Lit. **Document type:** consumer publication.
—UnCover.
   Description: Attempts to serve the interests of active, disabled consumers by examining the current thought and politics directly affecting them. Looks at the marketing devices used by manufacturers to facilitate their independent lifestyle.

362.4   TS
AL-MANAAL/HOPE. (Text in Arabic) 1980. m. Human Services Office, P.O. Box 5696, Sharjah, United Arab Emirates. TEL 353072. Ed. Gamila M. al-Qasimi. circ. 2,000.
   Description: Publishes research and articles on assistance to the handicapped in the U.A.E.

MEALEY'S LITIGATION REPORT: AMERICANS WITH DISABILITIES ACT. see *LAW — Judicial Systems*

362   FR
MIEUX-VIVRE CHEZ LES AVEUGLES ET LES GRANDS INFIRMES. 1974. q. 20 F. Confederation de Defense des Handicapes et Retraites, 13 rue Blaise-Pascal, 78800 Houilles, France. Ed. Claude Jacade. adv. circ. 2,000.
   Former titles: Mieux-Vivre; Entre Deux Mondes.

362.4   US   ISSN 1056-7240
MOVING FORWARD;* the national newspaper for the disabled. 1984. bi-m. $11.50. Aziz Unlimited, 1123 W. 210th St., Torrance, CA 90502-1627. TEL 310-603-9923. FAX 310-603-9932. Eds. Paul and Agena Aziz. adv.; bk.rev. circ. 25,000. (tabloid format; also avail. in talking book)
   Former titles (until Mar. 1991): Challenged American (ISSN 0892-290X); (until 1987): Moving Forward.
   Description: National coverage of events, topics, and activities, dealing with and about people with disabilities, their family, and the people they work with like doctors, therapists and councilors. Coverage and review of products and services related to disabilities.

N A R H A NEWS. (North American Riding for the Handicapped Association, Inc.) see *SPORTS AND GAMES — Horses And Horsemanship*

362.4 352.7   US
NATIONAL HOUSING DIRECTORY FOR PEOPLE WITH DISABILITIES. every 5 yrs. $29.95 for 3 state chapters; each additional $12. Grey House Publishing, Pocket Knife Sq., Lakeville, CT 06039. TEL 203-435-0868; 800-562-2139. FAX 203-435-0867. **Document type:** directory.
  Description: Lists 900 state and federal agencies, 6500 referral agencies, 3700 large institutional and intensive care facilities, 7500 group homes, 3200 independent living centers, and 10,000 contact names.

362.4   US
NATIONAL INFORMATION CENTER FOR CHILDREN AND YOUTH WITH DISABILITIES. NEWS DIGEST. 1985. 3/yr. free. National Information Center for Children and Youth with Disabilities (NICHCY), Box 1492, Washington, DC 20013. TEL 202-416-0300. (Co-sponsor: U.S. Department of Education) Ed. Lisa Kupper. circ. 70,000. (also avail. in microfiche from EDR; back issues avail.) **Document type:** newsletter.
  Formerly: National Information Center for Children and Youth with Handicaps. News Digest.
  Description: Focuses on a specific topic related to disabilities in each issue.

362   US
NATIONAL INFORMATION CENTER FOR CHILDREN AND YOUTH WITH DISABILITIES. PARENT'S GUIDE. 1986. a. National Information Center for Children and Youth with Disabilities (NICHCY), Box 1492, Washington, DC 20013. TEL 202-416-0300. (Co-sponsor: U.S. Department of Education) Ed. Lisa Kupper. circ. 20,000. **Document type:** government publication.
  Formerly: National Information Center for Children and Youth with Handicaps. Parent's Guide.
  Description: Provides information on issues assocaited with parenting a child with special needs.

371.9 020   US
NATIONAL INFORMATION CENTER FOR CHILDREN AND YOUTH WITH DISABILITIES. TRANSITION SUMMARY. 1985. a. free. National Information Center for Children and Youth with Disabilities (NICHCY), Box 1492, Washington, DC 20013. TEL 202-416-0300. (Co-sponsor: U.S. Department of Education) Ed. Lisa Kupper. circ. 70,000. (back issues avail.) **Document type:** newsletter.
  Formerly: National Information Center for Children and Youth with Handicaps. Transition Summary.
  Description: Discusses specific aspects of youth with disabilities making the transition from school to the adult world.

362.41 371   JA   ISSN 0285-1350
NATIONAL REHABILITATION CENTER FOR THE DISABLED. RESEARCH BULLETIN. (Text in English, Japanese) 1980. a. free. National Rehabilitation Center for the Disabled, 4-1 Namiki, Tokorozawa, Saitama-ken, Japan. TEL 81-429-95-3100. FAX 81-429-95-3102. Ed. S. Yamauchi. circ. 500.

NATIONAL WHEELCHAIR BASKETBALL ASSOCIATION. DIRECTORY. see SPORTS AND GAMES — Ball Games

NATIONAL WHEELCHAIR BASKETBALL ASSOCIATION. NEWSLETTER. see SPORTS AND GAMES — Ball Games

NEW YORK (STATE). OFFICE OF ADVOCATE FOR THE DISABLED. ANNUAL REPORT. see SOCIAL SERVICES AND WELFARE

362.4 027.663   US   ISSN 0883-5845
NEWS ABOUT LIBRARY SERVICES FOR THE BLIND AND PHYSICALLY HANDICAPPED. 1975. q. free. South Carolina State Library, 1500 Senate St., Box 11469, Columbia, SC 29211. TEL 803-737-9970. Ed. Naomi Bradey. circ. 7,200 (controlled). (processed) **Document type:** newsletter.

370.196
OVER THE RAINBOW. 1982. q. $10. Mobility International U S A, Box 3551, Eugene, OR 97440. TEL 503-343-1284. FAX 503-343-6812. Ed. Sharon Brown. adv.; bk.rev. circ. 1,000. (back issues avail.) **Document type:** newsletter.
  Description: Provides information on the latest opportunities concerning travel and international exchange programs, and provides information on scholarships, specialized tours and new publications. Provides details on MIUSA's community service programs and educational tours, and upcoming international conferences.

362.4 613.7 371.9   US   ISSN 8756-5811
PALAESTRA; the forum of sport, physical education and recreation for the disabled. 1984. q. $18 to individuals; institutions and libraries $24. (United States Olympic Committee on Sports for the Disabled) Challenge Publications, Ltd., Circulation Department, 1948 Riverview Dr., Macomb, IL 61455-1277. TEL 309-833-1902. Ed. David P. Beaver. adv.; bk.rev. circ. 6,000. (back issues avail.) **Indexed:** Hlth.Ind., Phys.Ed.Ind., Sports Per.Ind., Sportsearch (1984-).
—BLDSC (6345.214200); Faxon; UnCover.
  Description: Provides technical, "how-to" articles and practical research on recreation and physical education activities for individuals with a disability. Covers national and international sports events and looks at equipment and facility modification.

371.9 616.837   CN   ISSN 0048-2935
PARAGRAPHIC. 1957. q. membership. Canadian Paraplegic Association, British Columbia Division, 780 S.W. Marine Dr., Vancouver, B.C. V6P 5Y7, Canada. TEL 604-324-3611. Ed. M. Hoy. adv.; bk.rev. circ. 2,000.

362.4   US
PARENT NEWS. vol.15, no.3, 1992. q. free. Center for Persons with Disabilities, Outreach, Development & Dissemination Division, Department of Special Education, Utah State University, Logan, UT 84322-6845. TEL 801-750-1991. FAX 801-750-2044. Ed. Amy Santos. circ. 1,400. **Document type:** consumer publication, trade publication.
  Description: Designed for parents and professionals.

PHYSICAL DISABILITIES - EDUCATION & RELATED SERVICES. see HANDICAPPED — Physically Impaired

362.3   US   ISSN 0279-411X
PHYSICAL DISABILITIES SPECIAL INTEREST SECTION NEWSLETTER. (Consists of 9 sections: Administration and Management; Developmental Disabilities; Education; Gerontology; Mental Health; Physical Disabilities; Sensory Integration; Technology; Work Programs) q. American Occupational Therapy Association, Inc., 1383 Piccard Dr., Box 1725, Rockville, MD 20850-0822. TEL 301-948-9626. FAX 301-948-5512. **Document type:** newsletter.
  Supersedes in part: American Occupational Therapy Association. Physical Disabilities Specialty Section. Newsletter (ISSN 0194-6366)

362.4   RU   ISSN 0869-477X
PREODOLENIE. (Supplement avail.: Blue Carriage) (Text in Russian) 1991. bi-m. 100 Rub. Russian Information Agency Novosti, Zubovskii blvd. 4, 103786 Moscow GSP, K-21, Russia. TEL 2015159. FAX 2302170. TELEX 411323. Ed. Tatiana Kalinichev. adv.: B&W page $200, color page $600; adv. contact: Konstantin Bobrov. illus. circ. 10,000.
  Description: Covers various aspects of life for disabled people.

PREVENTING SCHOOL FAILURE; for special class teachers and parents of the handicapped. see EDUCATION — Special Education And Rehabilitation

362.4 617.087   UK   ISSN 0954-237X
R A D A R BULLETIN. m. (11/yr.). £12 (foreign £14.50). Royal Association for Disability and Rehabilitation, 25 Mortimer St., London W1N 8AB, England. TEL 071-637-5400. FAX 071-637-1827. Ed. Celia Mayfield. circ. 2,000. **Document type:** bulletin.
  Formerly: Royal Association for Disability and Rehabilitation.

362.4   US
REACHING OUT. 1977. bi-m. $15 to families; professionals $25. Cornelia de Lange Syndrome Foundation, Inc., 60 Dyer Ave., Collinsville, CT 06022. TEL 800-223-8355. FAX 203-693-8355. Ed. Elaine Evan. circ. 3,500. **Document type:** newsletter.
  Description: Provides articles of general interest (medical and educational) to families and professionals caring for a child with CdLS; includes a medical column by doctors and letters from parents; source of current information on this syndrome.

362.4 790   US
RECREATION - ACCESS IN THE '90'S. 1991. bi-m. $35 to non-members; members $25. National Recreation and Park Association, 3101 Park Center Dr., Alexandria, VA 22302. TEL 703-820-4940. FAX 703-671-6772. (Co-sponsor: Challenges Unlimited, Inc.) Eds. Rikki S. Epstein, Christina Cullinan.
  Description: Presents information about disability awareness; product assessments; construction evaluations; issues pertaining to the accessibility of park and recreation facilities; programs for the handicapped.

REHABILITACION: PREVENCION Y INTEGRACION. see MEDICAL SCIENCES — Physical Medicine And Rehabilitation

362.4 616.8   US   ISSN 0034-3552
HD7255.A2   CODEN: RECBAQ
REHABILITATION COUNSELING BULLETIN. 1957. 4/yr. $18. (American Rehabilitation Counseling Association) American Counseling Association, 5999 Stevenson Ave., Alexandria, VA 22304-3300. TEL 703-823-9800. FAX 703-823-0252. Ed. Randall M. Parker. adv.; charts; stat.; index. circ. 4,100. (also avail. in microform from UMI; reprint service avail. from UMI) **Indexed:** Abstr.Soc.Work, C.I.J.E., Curr.Cont., Psychol.Abstr., Rehabil.Lit., Sage Pub.Admin.Abstr., Soc.Work Res.& Abstr., SSCI.
—BLDSC (7350.230000); Faxon; UnCover; SWETS; UMI. **CCC.**
  Description: Discusses psychological and social aspects of disability, psychiatric rehabilitation, developmental disabilities, career development and job placement of persons with special needs.

362.4   US   ISSN 0361-4166
HV1553   CODEN: RHGZA
REHABILITATION GAZETTE; international journal of independent living by and for persons with a disability. 1958. s-a. $12 to individuals (foreign $14); health professionals and institutions $20 (foreign $22). Gazette International Networking Institute, 5100 Oakland Ave., Ste. 206, St. Louis, MO 63110-1406. TEL 314-534-0475. Ed. Joan Headley. adv.; abstr.; illus. circ. 7,000. (back issues avail.) **Indexed:** Except.Child.Educ.Abstr., Excerp.Med. **Document type:** newsletter.
—UnCover.
  Formerly: Toomey J Gazette (ISSN 0495-8667)
  Description: News, features, and profiles pertaining to persons with disabilities, focusing on technologies for assuming independent living and pursuing careers and social opportunities.

362.4   SA   ISSN 0034-3501
REHABILITATION IN SOUTH AFRICA/REHABILITASIE IN SUID-AFRIKA. (Text and summaries in Afrikaans, English) 1957. q. free. Department of Manpower - Departement van Mannekrag, Private Bag X117, Pretoria 0001, South Africa. Ed. E. Jeffery. bk.rev.; illus.; stat. circ. 7,000. **Indexed:** CINAHL, Excerp.Med., Ind.S.A.Per. **Document type:** government publication, newsletter.
—BLDSC (7350.320000).
  Description: Aims to disseminate information on rehabilitation, to illustrate the integration of the handicapped as an additional source of manpower, to remove prejudice against them, and to promote their employment.

REPORT ON ALCOHOL, DRUGS, AND DISABILITY. see DRUG ABUSE AND ALCOHOLISM

REPORT ON DISABILITY PROGRAMS. see SOCIAL SERVICES AND WELFARE

RESOURCE DIRECTORY OF SCIENTISTS AND ENGINEERS WITH DISABILITIES. see BIOGRAPHY

RYOIKU/REHABILITATION. see EDUCATION — Special Education And Rehabilitation

S.C. DISABLED AMERICAN VETERANS JOURNAL. see MILITARY

SANYUEFENG/SPRING BREEZES. see COMMUNICATIONS

362.4   SZ
SCHWEIZERISCHE INVALIDEN ZEITUNG. 6/yr. Schweizerischer Invaliden Verband, Froburgstr. 4, CH-4601 Olten, Switzerland. TEL 062-321262. FAX 062-323105. Ed. H. Steiger. circ. 20,000.

HANDICAPPED — ABSTRACTING, BIBLIOGRAPHIES, STATISTICS

SEXUALITY AND DISABILITY; a journal devoted to the study of sex in psychological and medical aspects of sexuality in rehabilitation and community settings. see *MEDICAL SCIENCES*

SPECIAL EDUCATION REPORT; the independent bi-weekly news service on legislation, programs and funding for special education. see *EDUCATION — Special Education And Rehabilitation*

362.4   US
SPINAL NETWORK; the total resource for the wheelchair community. 1988. irreg., 2nd ed. 1993. $41.95 (wire-ring binding $43.95). Spinal Network, Box 4162, Boulder, CO 80306. TEL 800-338-5412.

362.4 617.087   US   ISSN 1065-2124
RD594.3.S69
SPINAL NETWORK'S NEW MOBILITY; total resource magazine for the disability community. 1989. bi-m. $18 (effective 1992). Spinal Network, Box 4162, Boulder, CO 80306. TEL 303-449-5412. FAX 303-449-5187. Ed. Barry Corbet. adv. contact: Kathleen Carrigan. illus.
    Formerly (until 1992): Spinal Network Extra (ISSN 1058-3483)
    Description: Fosters a sense of community among the disabled, and reports medical and technical news of interest to families and health-care workers.

SZKOŁA SPECJALNA. see *EDUCATION — Special Education And Rehabilitation*

362.4 371.9   US
TEAM OF ADVOCATES FOR SPECIAL KIDS NEWSLETTER. 1984. bi-m. $25. Team of Advocates for Special Kids (TASK), 100 Cerritos Ave., Anaheim, CA 92805. TEL 714-533-8275. FAX 714-533-2533. Ed. Melinda Harrington. adv.; bk.rev. circ. 600. **Document type:** newsletter.
    Description: Provides information on educational, medical, and support services for parents of children with disabilities.

617.087 615.82   US   ISSN 1053-5926
HD9995.P54
TEAM REHAB REPORT. 1990. 9/yr. $24 (free to rehab professionals). Miramar Publishing Co., Box 3640, Culver City, CA 90231-3640. TEL 310-337-9717. FAX 310-337-1041. Ed. Andria Segedy. adv.; bk.rev.; tr.lit.; circ. 12,000 (controlled). (reprint service avail.)
    Description: Covers rehabilitation technology as it relates to the needs of people who are permanently disabled.

362.4 620   AT   ISSN 0725-2919
TECHNICAL AID TO THE DISABLED JOURNAL. 1981. q. Aus. $30. Technical Aid to the Disabled, P.O. Box 108, Ryde, N.S.W. 2112, Australia. TEL 02-809-2022. FAX 02-809-7670. Ed. P.M. Manning. adv.; bk.rev.; illus.; stat. circ. 5,000. (back issues avail.)
    Description: Reports the application of innovative technology towards improving the quality of life of persons with disabilities.

371.9   US   ISSN 1055-4181
HV1551
TECHNOLOGY AND DISABILITY. 1991. q. $60 to individuals (foreign $75); institutions $95 (foreign $110). Butterworth - Heinemann, Part of the Reed Elsevier group, 313 Washington St., Newton, MA 02158. TEL 617-928-2500; 800-366-2665. FAX 617-928-2610. TELEX 880052. Eds. Joseph Lane, William C. Mann. (back issues avail.) **Document type:** academic/scholarly publication.
    —BLDSC (8758.612000); UMI. **CCC.**
    Description: Deals with the application of rehabilitative and assistive technology for persons with disabilities.

362.4 384   SW   ISSN 1102-7967
▼**TECHNOLOGY, COMMUNICATION AND DISABILITY/TEKNIK, KOMMUNIKATION OCH HANDIKAPP.** (Text in English, Swedish) 1992. irreg. free. Stockholm University, Department of Education, S-106 91 Stockholm, Sweden. TEL 46-8-16-31-47. FAX 46-8-15-83-54. Eds. Jane Brodin, Magnus Magnusson. circ. 350. (also avail. in magnetic tape) **Document type:** academic/scholarly publication, monographic series.
    Description: Covers reports on research in telecommunication and disability.

TOKYO METROPOLITAN REHABILITATION CENTER FOR THE PHYSICALLY AND MENTALLY HANDICAPPED. BULLETIN. see *MEDICAL SCIENCES — Physical Medicine And Rehabilitation*

617.8   JA   ISSN 0917-5601
UNDO SHOGAI/MOVEMENT DISORDER AND DISABILITY. (Text in Japanese; summaries in English, Japanese) 1991. s-a. Undo Shogai Kenkyukai - Society of Movement Disorder and Disability, Jichi Ika Daigaku Iryo Senta Shinkei Naika, 1-847, Tenumacho, Omiya-shi, Saitama-ken 330, Japan.

VOICE. see *MEDICAL SCIENCES*

362.4 616.836   US   ISSN 0738-8012
WORD FROM WASHINGTON. 1969. bi-m. $25 to disabled individuals; others $55. United Cerebral Palsy Associations, Inc., Governmental Activities Office, 1522 K St., N.W., No. 1112, Washington, DC 20005-1202. TEL 202-842-1266. FAX 202-842-3519. Ed. Christopher Button. bk.rev.; illus. circ. 8,000. Indexed: Except.Child Educ.Abstr., Rehabil.Lit. **Document type:** newsletter.

362.4   GW
Z B - ZEITSCHRIFT: BEHINDERTE IM BERUF. 4/yr. DM.6 membership. (Arbeitsgemeinschaft der Deutschen Hauptfuersorgestellen) Universum Verlagsanstalt GmbH KG, Roesslerstr. 7, 65193 Wiesbaden, Germany. TEL 0611-58020. FAX 0611-3989625. Eds. Michael Fritton, Sabine Wolf. circ. 300,000 (paid). **Document type:** bulletin.

362.4   CC   ISSN 1003-1081
ZHONGGUO CANJIREN/DISABILITY IN CHINA. (Text in Chinese) m. Y10.80. (Zhongguo Canjiren Fuli Lianhehui - China Disabled Persons' Federation) Disability in China, Inc., A-8 Huixin Li, Anwai, Chaoyang-qu, Beijing 100101, People's Republic of China. TEL 4227849. (Dist. by: Bureau pf Industrial and Commercial Administration, Chaoyang-qu, Beijing, P.R. China; Dist. in US by: China Books and Periodicals, Inc., 2929 24th St., San Francisco, CA 94110. TEL 415-282-2994) Ed. Zhao Xiaoqian.
    Description: Introduces laws and policies concerning people with disabilities. Contains rehabilitation and special education information.

HANDICAPPED — Abstracting, Bibliographies, Statistics

BIBLIOGRAFIA ERITYISRYHMIEN LIIKUNNAN TUTKIMUKSESTA/BIBLIOGRAPHY ON RESEARCH IN PHYSICAL EDUCATION AND SPORT FOR THE HANDICAPPED. see *EDUCATION — Abstracting, Bibliographies, Statistics*

371.911   US   ISSN 0277-5247
Z5346.Z9
BRAILLE BOOKS (LARGE PRINT EDITION). 1966. biennial. free to qualified individuals. U.S. Library of Congress, National Library Service for the Blind and Physically Handicapped, Washington, DC 20542. TEL 202-707-5100. FAX 202-707-0712. bk.rev.; index. (also avail. in Braille; large print in 14 pt.) **Document type:** catalog, government publication.
    Formerly: Press Braille, Adult (ISSN 0079-502X)

BRITISH INSTITUTE OF LEARNING DISABILITIES. CURRENT AWARENESS SERVICE. see *EDUCATION — Abstracting, Bibliographies, Statistics*

027.663 020   US   ISSN 0363-9029
Z5347
CASSETTE BOOKS. 1977. a. free to qualified individuals. U.S. Library of Congress, National Library Service for the Blind and Physically Handicapped, Washington, DC 20542. TEL 202-707-5100. FAX 202-707-0712. bk.rev.; index. (also avail. in diskette format; large print edition in 14 pt.) **Document type:** catalog, government publication.

011   US   ISSN 0000-1120
Z5348
COMPLETE DIRECTORY OF LARGE PRINT BOOKS AND SERIALS. 1970. a. $149.95. R.R. Bowker, A Reed Reference Publishing Company, Part of the Reed Elsevier group, 121 Chanlon Rd., New Providence, NJ 07974. TEL 908-464-6800. FAX 908-655-3502. TELEX 138 755. (Subscr. to: Order Dept, Box 31, New Providence, NJ 07974-9903. TEL 800-521-8110) (also avail. in magnetic tape; microfiche) **Document type:** bibliography, directory.
    ●Also available online.
    Also available on CD-ROM. Producer(s): Bowker - Reed Reference Electronic Publishing.
    —CCC.
    Formerly (until 1988): Large Type Books in Print (ISSN 0163-3198)
    Description: Provides finding and ordering information on large-print books, magazines and newspapers. Books are indexed by author, subject and title.

371.911   US   ISSN 0093-2825
Z5346.A2
FOR YOUNGER READERS, BRAILLE AND TALKING BOOKS (LARGE PRINT EDITION). 1967. biennial. free to qualified individuals. U.S. Library of Congress, National Library Service for the Blind and Physically Handicapped, Washington, DC 20542. TEL 202-707-5100. FAX 202-707-0712. bk.rev.; index. (also avail. in diskette format; large print in 14 pt.) **Document type:** catalog, bibliography, government publication.

027.663   US   ISSN 0889-6518
Z5346
MAGAZINES IN SPECIAL MEDIA (LARGE-PRINT EDITION). biennial. free. U.S. Library of Congress, National Library Service for the Blind and Physically Handicapped, Washington, DC 20542. TEL 202-707-5100. FAX 202-707-0712. (also avail. in Braille; diskette format; large print in 16 pt.) **Document type:** directory, government publication.
    Incorporates (1978-198?): Magazines (Washington) (ISSN 0161-2689)
    Description: Lists periodicals available in special media to blind and physically handicapped persons throughout the country.

362   MW
MALAWI. NATIONAL STATISTICAL OFFICE. SURVEY OF HANDICAPPED PERSONS. 1983. irreg. K.10. National Statistical Office, P.O. Box 333, Zomba, Malawi. **Document type:** government publication.

027.663 016 780   US   ISSN 0145-3173
MUSIC & MUSICIANS: BRAILLE SCORES CATALOG - CHORAL (LARGE-PRINT EDITION). irreg. free to qualified personnel. U.S. Library of Congress, National Library Service for the Blind and Physically Handicapped, Music Section, Washington, DC 20542. TEL 202-707-5100. FAX 202-707-0712. (also avail. in Braille; large print in 14 pt.) **Document type:** catalog, government publication.

780   US   ISSN 0145-3165
ML136.U52
MUSIC & MUSICIANS: BRAILLE SCORES CATALOG - INSTRUMENTAL (LARGE-PRINT EDITION). irreg. free to qualified personnel. U.S. Library of Congress, National Library Service for the Blind and Physically Handicapped, Music Section, Washington, DC 20542. TEL 202-707-5100. FAX 202-707-0712. (also avail. in Braille; large print in 14 pt.) **Document type:** catalog, bibliography, government publication.

027.663 016 780   US   ISSN 0145-3149
ML136.U52
MUSIC & MUSICIANS: BRAILLE SCORES CATALOG - ORGAN (LARGE-PRINT EDITION). irreg. free to qualified personnel. U.S. Library of Congress, National Library Service for the Blind and Physically Handicapped, Music Section, Washington, DC 20542. TEL 202-707-5100. FAX 202-707-0712. (also avail. in Braille; large print in 14 pt.) **Document type:** catalog, bibliography, government publication.

027.663 016 780   US   ISSN 0145-3130
MUSIC & MUSICIANS: BRAILLE SCORES CATALOG - PIANO (LARGE-PRINT EDITION). irreg. free to qualified personnel. U.S. Library of Congress, National Library Service for the Blind and Physically Handicapped, Music Section, Washington, DC 20542. TEL 202-707-5100. FAX 202-707-0712. (also avail. in Braille; large print in 14 pt.) **Document type:** catalog, government publication.

027.663 016 780   US
MUSIC & MUSICIANS: BRAILLE SCORES CATALOG - VOCAL. PART I: CLASSICAL (LARGE-PRINT EDITION). irreg. free to qualified personnel. U.S. Library of Congress, National Library Service for the Blind and Physically Handicapped, Music Section, Washington, DC 20542. TEL 202-707-5100. FAX 202-707-0712. (also avail. in Braille; large print in 14 pt.) **Document type:** catalog, government publication.
 Supersedes in part: Music and Musicians: Braille Scores Catalog - Vocal (Large-Print Edition); Which was formerly: Music and Musicians: Braille Scores Catalog - Voice (ISSN 0145-3157)

027.663 016 780   US
MUSIC & MUSICIANS: BRAILLE SCORES CATALOG - VOCAL. PART II: POPULAR (LARGE-PRINT EDITION). irreg. free to qualified personnel. U.S. Library of Congress, National Library Service for the Blind and Physically Handicapped, Washington, DC 20542. TEL 202-707-5100. FAX 202-707-0712. (also avail. in Braille; large print in 14 pt.) **Document type:** catalog, government publication.
 Supersedes in part: Music and Musicians: Braille Scores Catalog - Vocal (Large-Print Edition); Which was formerly: Music and Musicians: Braille Scores Catalog - Voice (ISSN 0145-3157)

027.663 016 780   US   ISSN 0145-2525
ML156.2
MUSIC & MUSICIANS: INSTRUCTIONAL CASSETTE RECORDINGS CATALOG (LARGE-PRINT EDITION). irreg. free to qualified personnel. U.S. Library of Congress, National Library Service for the Blind and Physically Handicapped, Music Section, Washington, DC 20542. TEL 202-707-5100. FAX 202-707-0712. (also avail. in audio cassette; large print in 14 pt.) **Document type:** catalog, government publication.

027.663 016 780   US   ISSN 0145-2517
ML156.2
MUSIC & MUSICIANS: INSTRUCTIONAL DISC RECORDINGS CATALOG (LARGE-PRINT EDITION). irreg. free to qualified personnel. U.S. Library of Congress, National Library Service for the Blind and Physically Handicapped, Music Section, Washington, DC 20542. TEL 202-707-5100. FAX 202-707-0712. (also avail. in record; large print in 14 pt.) **Document type:** catalog, government publication.

027.663 016 780   US
MUSIC & MUSICIANS: LARGE-PRINT SCORES AND BOOKS CATALOG (LARGE-PRINT EDITION). 1977. irreg. free to qualified personnel. U.S. Library of Congress, National Library Service for the Blind and Physically Handicapped, Music Section, Washington, DC 20542. TEL 202-707-5100. (large print in 14 pt.)
 Formerly: Music and Musicians: Large Print Scores and Books Catalog for the Blind and Physically Handicapped (ISSN 0363-8472)

027.663   AT   ISSN 1032-8149
NATIONAL UNION CATALOGUE OF LIBRARY MATERIALS FOR PEOPLE WITH DISABILITIES. Short title: N U C: D. 1981. 4/yr. Aus.$110. National Library of Australia, Publications Section, Cultural and Educational Services Division, Canberra, A.C.T. 2600, Australia. TEL 06-262-1365. FAX 06-273-4493. circ. 150. (reprint service avail. from ISI,UMI) **Document type:** bibliography.
 Formerly: National Union Catalogue of Library Materials for the Handicapped (ISSN 0159-060X)
 Description: Lists audio and Braille monographs, audio, Braille and large print serials, book and tape kits produced for people with disabilities and captioned films and videos held in Australian libraries.

027.6 016 362.4   US   ISSN 0484-1506
RECORDING FOR THE BLIND. CATALOG OF RECORDED BOOKS. 1960. irreg. $14. Recording for the Blind, Inc., 20 Roszel Rd., Princeton, NJ 08540. TEL 609-452-0606. FAX 609-987-8116. Ed. John Kelly. circ. 15,000. **Document type:** catalog.

027.6 362.4   US
RECORDING FOR THE BLIND. QUARTERLY DISK CATALOG. Abbreviated title: Q D C. 4/yr. $16. Recording for the Blind, Inc., 20 Roszel Rd., Princeton, NJ 08540. TEL 609-452-0606. FAX 609-987-8116. (diskette format) **Document type:** catalog.
 Description: Complete descriptive listing of books available on computer disk and recent additions to the audiocassette library, in IBM or Apple - Macintosh format.

027.6 362.4   US
RECORDING FOR THE BLIND. QUARTERLY RECORDED CATALOG. Abbreviated title: Q R C. 4/yr. $16. Recording for the Blind, Inc., 20 Roszel Rd., Princeton, NJ 08540. TEL 609-452-0606. FAX 609-987-8116. (audio cassette; also avail. in diskette format) **Document type:** catalog.
 Description: Contains annotated listings of audiocassette and electronic text titles recently added to Recording for the Blind's library.

371.9 362.42   GW
STATISTISCHE NACHRICHTEN BILDUNGS- UND SOZIALEINRICHTUNGEN FUER HOERGESCHAEDIGTE IN DER BUNDESREPUBLIK DEUTSCHLAND. 1930. triennial. DM.35. (Berufsverband Deutscher Hoergeschaedigtenpaedagogen) Julius Groos Verlag, Hertzstr. 6, 69126 Heidelberg, Germany. TEL 06221-303621. FAX 06221-301993. Ed.Bd. **Document type:** academic/scholarly publication.
 Formerly: Statistische Nachrichten ueber Bildungs- und Sozialeinrichtungen fuer Hoergeschaedigte im Deutschsprachigen Raum.

HANDICAPPED — Computer Applications

371.94 362.4   US   ISSN 0163-5727
HV1569.5   CODEN: SGNWD2
S I G C A P H NEWSLETTER. q. $22. Association for Computing Machinery, Special Interest Group on Computers and the Physically Handicapped, 1515 Broadway, 17th Fl., New York, NY 10036. TEL 212-869-7440. FAX 212-302-5826. Ed. Carl Friedlander. bk.rev. (also avail. in Braille) **Indexed:** Sci.Abstr. **Document type:** newsletter.
 —UnCover.

HANDICAPPED — Hearing Impaired

371.912   CN   ISSN 0382-7976
HV2350
A C E H I JOURNAL/ASSOCIATION CANADIENNE DES EDUCATEURS DES DEFICIENTS AUDITIFS. REVUE. 1974. 3/yr. Can.$25 to individuals; institutions Can.$40. (Association of Canadian Educators of the Hearing Impaired) University of Alberta, Publication Services, 4-116 Education North, Edmonton, AB T6G 2G5, Canada. TEL 403-492-4204. FAX 403-492-0390. Ed. M. Rodda. adv.; bk.rev.; index. circ. 600. (back issues avail.) **Indexed:** C.I.J.E., DSH Abstr., ERIC, Sp.Ed.Needs Abstr.
 —BLDSC (0573.850000).
 Formerly: Canadian Teacher of the Deaf (ISSN 0045-5431)

617.8   US
A D A R A NEWSLETTER. 1970. q. $43 (foreign $60) membership. (American Deafness & Rehabilitation Association) A D A R A, Box 251554, Little Rock, AR 72225. TEL 501-868-8850. Ed. Nancy M. Long. adv. circ. 1,100. **Document type:** newsletter.
 Description: Issues pertaining to rehabilitation and service for the deaf.

617.8 616.855   US   ISSN 0001-2475
RC423.A1
A S H A. 1959. m. $60 to individuals (foreign $90); institutions $90 (foreign $110). American Speech - Language - Hearing Association, 10801 Rockville Pike, Rockville, MD 20852. TEL 301-897-5700. FAX 301-571-0457. Ed. Frederick T. Spahr. adv.; bk.rev.; illus. circ. 73,000. (also avail. in microfiche from UMI; back issues avail.; reprint service from UMI) **Indexed:** Biol.Abstr., Child Devel.Abstr., Educ.Ind., Except.Child.Educ.Abstr., Ind.Med., Noise Pollut.Publ.Abstr., Psychol.Abstr., Rehabil.Lit. **Document type:** bulletin.
 —BLDSC (1742.020000); Faxon; UnCover; SWETS; UMI. **CCC.**
 Description: Pertains to the professional and administrative activities of speech, language and hearing professions.

617.8 616.855   US   ISSN 0066-071X
A S H A MONOGRAPHS. 1950. irreg., no.29, 1993. American Speech - Language - Hearing Association, 10801 Rockville Pike, Rockville, MD 20852. TEL 301-897-5700. FAX 301-571-0457. Ed. James C. Hardy. **Indexed:** DSH Abstr., Ind.Med., Psychol.Abstr. **Document type:** monographic series.
 —BLDSC (1742.030000); UnCover.

362.4 617.8   AT   ISSN 0816-2220
ABILITIES. 4/yr. Royal N S W Institute for Deaf and Blind Children, Deaf & Blind Children's Centre, 361-365 North Rocks Rd., N. Rocks, N.S.W. 2151, Australia. TEL 02-871-1233. circ. 120,000.

ACADEMY OF REHABILITATIVE AUDIOLOGY. JOURNAL. see MEDICAL SCIENCES — Otorhinolaryngology

362.42   AG
AD VERBUM. 1969. q. free. Confederacion Argentina de Sordomudos, Av. Pedro Medrano 1352, Buenos Aires, Argentina. (Co-sponsor: Federacion Mondial de Sordos) Eds. Alvaro Daniel de Tomaso, Teodoro Manzanedo. adv.; bk.rev.; bibl.; illus.; stat.; circ. 5,000 (controlled).

ALERT (RENTON). see PETS

371.912   II
ALL INDIA INSTITUTE OF SPEECH AND HEARING. JOURNAL. (Text in English) 1970. a. Rs.50($8) All India Institute of Speech and Hearing, Manasagangothri, Mysore 570 006, India. TEL 304449. Ed. S. Nikam. circ. 200. **Document type:** academic/scholarly publication.

371.912   US   ISSN 0002-726X
HV2510   CODEN: ANDFAL
AMERICAN ANNALS OF THE DEAF. (Annual reference issue avail.) 1847. 5/yr. $50 (Canada $55; elsewhere $65). Convention of American Instructors of the Deaf, KDES, PAS-6, 800 Florida Ave., N.E., Washington, DC 20002. TEL 202-651-5340. FAX 202-651-5708. (Co-sponsor: Conference of Educational Administrators Serving the Deaf) Ed. Dr. Donald Moores. adv.; bk.rev.; bibl.; charts; illus.; stat.; index. circ. 3,900. (also avail. in microfilm from UMI; back issues avail.; reprint service avail. from UMI) **Indexed:** Bibl.Ind., Biol.Abstr., C.I.J.E., Child Devel.Abstr., Curr.Cont., Educ.Admin.Abstr., Educ.Ind., Except.Child.Educ.Abstr., Excerp.Med., Ind.Med., Lang.& Lang.Behav.Abstr., Mult.Ed.Abstr., P.A.I.S., Psychol.Abstr., Rehabil.Lit., Sp.Ed.Needs Abstr., SSCI. **Document type:** trade publication, academic/scholarly publication.
 —BLDSC (0810.150000); Faxon; UnCover; SWETS; UMI. **CCC.**
 Formerly: American Annals of the Deaf and Dumb (ISSN 0093-1284)
 Description: For teachers, administrators, and researchers in the field of deaf education.
 Refereed Serial

371.912   US   ISSN 0899-9228
HV2350
AMERICAN DEAFNESS & REHABILITATION ASSOCIATION. JOURNAL. 1967. q. $43 (foreign $60) membership. (American Deafness & Rehabilitation Association) A D A R A, Box 251554, Little Rock, AR 72225. TEL 501-868-8850. Ed. Gerard Walter. adv.; bk.rev. circ. 1,000. (back issues avail.) **Indexed:** Curr.Cont., Except.Child.Educ.Abstr., Lang.& Lang.Behav.Abstr., Psychol.Abstr., Rehabil.Lit., SSCI.
 —BLDSC (4686.050000); Faxon; UnCover.
 Formerly: Journal of Rehabilitation of the Deaf (ISSN 0022-4170)
 Description: Deals with research findings (pragmatic application) program descriptions and articles on deafness and the disciplines of rehabilitation, social services, mental health, and other related areas.

617.8   US   ISSN 1059-0889
RF286
AMERICAN JOURNAL OF AUDIOLOGY; a journal of clinical practice. 1991. 3/yr. $20 to individuals (foreign $32); institutions $32 (foreign $44); members $15. American Speech - Language - Hearing Association, 10801 Rockville Pike, Rockville, MD 20852. TEL 301-897-5700. FAX 301-571-0457. **Document type:** trade publication.
 —BLDSC (0821.800000). **CCC.**
 Description: Addresses all aspects of clinical practice in audiology.

HANDICAPPED — HEARING IMPAIRED

362.42 US ISSN 1058-0360
RC423.A1
AMERICAN JOURNAL OF SPEECH - LANGUAGE PATHOLOGY; a journal of clinical practice. 1991. 3/yr. $20 to individuals (foreign $32); institutions $32 (foreign $44); members $15. American Speech - Language - Hearing Association, 10801 Rockville Pike, Rockville, MD 20852. TEL 301-897-5700. FAX 301-571-0457. adv. circ. 70,865. Document type: academic/scholarly publication.
—BLDSC (0838.350000).
   Description: Addresses all aspects of clinical practice in speech language pathology.

362.42 US
AMERICAN SOCIETY FOR DEAF CHILDREN. PRESIDENT'S UPDATE. q. $25 membership. American Society for Deaf Children, E. Tenth and Tahlequah St., Sulphur, OK 73086-3099. TEL 800-942-2732. Document type: newsletter.

362.42 US
AMERICAN SPEECH - LANGUAGE - HEARING ASSOCIATION. DIRECTORY. biennial. price varies. American Speech - Language - Hearing Association, 10801 Rockville Pike, Rockville, MD 20852. TEL 301-897-5700. FAX 301-571-0457. Document type: directory.
   Formerly: A S H A Directory (ISSN 0569-8561)

362.42 612.85 US
AMERICAN SPEECH - LANGUAGE - HEARING ASSOCIATION REPORTS. 1972. irreg., no.20, 1990. American Speech - Language - Hearing Association, 10801 Rockville Pike, Rockville, MD 20852. TEL 301-897-5700. FAX 301-571-0457. Ed. David P. Kuehn. Indexed: Biol.Abstr., Educ.Ind., Psychol.Abstr. Document type: monographic series.
   Formerly: A S H A Reports (ISSN 0569-8553)

362.42 CN
ATLANTIC SILENT NEWS. 1979. q. Can.$2. Coordinating Council on Deafness of Nova Scotia, 1657 Barrington, Roy Bldg., Ste. 101, Halifax, N.S. B3J 2A1, Canada. TEL 902-423-3667. (Co-sponsors: Society of Deaf and Hard of Hearing Nova Scotians; Ecumenical Ministry of the Deaf) illus. circ. 50.
   Former titles: Coordination Council on Deafness of Nova Scotia. News & Access (Halifax) (ISSN 0227-1435); Coordinating Council on Deafness of Nova Scotia. Newsletter (ISSN 0227-1427)

617.89 US ISSN 0004-7473
AUDECIBEL. 1952. q. $25 (foreign $35). International Hearing Society, 20361 Middlebelt, Livonia, MI 48152. TEL 313-478-2610. FAX 313-478-4520. Ed. Lois M. White. adv.; bk.rev.; charts; illus.; index. circ. 21,000. (also avail. in microform from UMI; reprint service avail. from UMI) Indexed: Except.Child.Educ.Abstr. Document type: trade publication.
—BLDSC (1787.700000); Faxon; UnCover; UMI.
   Description: Provides technical and business information to help hearing instrument professionals serve hearing impaired people.

362.42 FR
AUDIO JOURNAL. 1966. q. 80 F. (foreign 100 F.). Association pour l'Information des Troubles de l'Audition, de la Parole et du Language, 18 rue Rene Baschet, 93220 Gagny, France. TEL 43-81-40-57. Ed. Pierre Rosset. adv.; illus. circ. 15,000.

362.42 UK ISSN 0004-8054
AURAL NEWS. 1946. q. £0.50. Middlesex & Surrey League for the Hard of Hearing, 11 Josephs Rd., Guilford, Surrey GU1 DN1, England. Ed. J.W. Penycate. adv.; bk.rev.; film rev.; charts; illus.; stat. circ. 2,000. (also avail. in microform)

617.89 SW ISSN 0045-0030
AURIS; tidskrift for hoerselskadade. 1921. 8/yr. SEK 190 (effective 1994). Hoerselskadades Riksfoerbund (HRF), Skoeldungagatan 7, P.O. Box 5615, 114 86 Stockholm, Sweden. FAX 08-203367. Ed. Kerstin Loevgren. adv.; charts; illus.; tr.lit. circ. 38,000. (also avail. in audio cassette)
   Former titles (until 1949): Meddelanden fraan Hoerselfraemjandet; (until vol.4, 1947): Meddelanden fraan Svenska Foereningen foer Doevas Vael.

371.912 AT ISSN 0005-0334
AUSTRALIAN TEACHER OF THE DEAF.* 1956. a. Aus.$15. Australian Association of Teachers of the Deaf, Cornwall St., Annerley, Qld. 4103, Australia. Ed. Cathy Byrnes. adv.; bk.rev.; stat.; cum.index. circ. 500. Indexed: Aus.Educ.Ind., Cont.Pg.Educ., DSH Abstr.
—BLDSC (1822.550000).

362.42 SZ
AUX ECOUTES. 1924. 6/yr. 30 SFr. Case Postale 55, CH-2103 Noiraigue, Switzerland. TEL 038-633001. Ed. Lilia Pellet. adv. circ. 1,500.

362.42 SZ
B S S V MONATSBLATT. m. Leonhardstr. 45, CH-4051 Basel, Switzerland. TEL 061-7411444. Ed. Rudolf Kuhn. circ. 12,000.

371.9 IS
BAT KOL. 1986. s-a. Shema Parents' Association of Deaf & Hard of Hearing Children, Pelitei Hasefer 30, Tel Aviv 67894, Israel. TEL 972-3-5715656. FAX 972-3-5712017. Ed. Zevulun Gooreni. adv.; bk.rev.

362.42 US
BETWEEN FRIENDS; the Beltone newsletter. vol.7, 1972. bi-m. free to qualified personnel. Beltone Corp., 4201 W. Victoria St., Chicago, IL 60646. TEL 312-583-3600. FAX 312-583-1955. Ed. Renee Rockoff. adv. contact: Joyce Sherry. charts; illus. circ. 180,000. Document type: newsletter.
   Formerly (until 1980): Hearing News Digest.

371.92 UK
BRITISH ASSOCIATION OF TEACHERS OF THE DEAF. JOURNAL. 1902. 5/yr. £23.50 (effective 1994). British Association of Teachers of the Deaf, 41 The Orchard, Leven, N. Humberside HU17 5QA, England. TEL 0964-544243. (Subscr. to: c/o G.F.E. Clark, 2 Gaters Gardens, Sandford, Crediton, Devon EX17 4LU, England) Ed. I.G. Tucker. adv.; bk.rev.; charts; index. circ. 2,100. Indexed: Cont.Pg.Educ., Curr.Cont., High.Educ.Curr.Aware.Bull., Lang.& Lang.Behav.Abstr., Sp.Ed.Needs Abstr., SSCI. Document type: academic/scholarly publication.
—BLDSC (4712.980000); UnCover.
   Formerly: Teacher of the Deaf (ISSN 0040-0459)
   Description: Directed to professionals working with the hearing-impaired children and adolescents. Refereed Serial

362.42 UK ISSN 0007-0602
BRITISH DEAF NEWS. 1955. m. £8 (overseas £26). British Deaf Association, 38 Victoria Place, Carlisle, England. FAX 0228-48844. Ed. Irene Hall. adv.; bk.rev.; illus.; cum.index every 12 nos. circ. 6,400. Indexed: ASSIA.
   Description: Contains features and articles on many topics of interest to the deaf public. Provides in-depth interviews with well-known deaf personalities, and occasional historical features.

617.8 UK ISSN 0300-5364
QP460 CODEN: BJAYAC
BRITISH JOURNAL OF AUDIOLOGY. 1967. 6/yr. £102. (Royal National Institute for the Deaf) W.B. Saunders Co. Ltd. (Subsidiary of: Harcourt Brace & Company Ltd.), 24-28 Oval Rd., London NW1 7DX, England. TEL 44-71-267-4466. FAX 44-71-482-2293. TELEX 25775-ACPRES-G. (Subscr. to: Harcourt Brace & Company Ltd., Foots Cray High St., Sidcup, Kent DA14 5HP, England. TEL 44-81-300-3322. FAX 44-81-309-0807; US, Canada, Mexican subscr. to: W.B. Saunders Co., Journal Subscription Fulfillment, 6277 Sea Harbor Dr., 4th Fl., Orlando, FL 32887-4800. TEL 800-654-2452. FAX 800-874-6418) (Co-sponsor: British Society of Audiology) Ed. M. Lutman. adv.; bk.rev.; abstr.; index. (also avail. in microform from UMI; back issues avail.; reprint service avail. from UMI) Indexed: ASSIA, Biol.Abstr., Curr.Cont., Eng.Ind., Excerp.Med., Lang.& Lang.Behav.Abstr., NBA, Noise Pollut.Publ.Abstr. Document type: academic/scholarly publication.
—BLDSC (2306.500000); Faxon; UnCover; SWETS. CCC.
   Formerly: Sound (ISSN 0038-1799)
   Description: Examines the fundamental psychophysical and physiological aspects of hearing and hearing loss for the specialist and technologist; covers a broad spectrum of topics within the field of audiological studies.

DAS BRUDERHAUS. see EDUCATION — Special Education And Rehabilitation

155.4512 US ISSN 0885-7962
C O D A NEWSLETTER. 1983. q. $15. Children of Deaf Adults, Box 30715, Santa Barbara, CA 93130. TEL 805-682-0997. bk.rev. circ. 500. (back issues avail.) Document type: newsletter.

617.89 FR ISSN 0980-3483
CAHIERS DE L'AUDITION. 1961. q. 360 F. (Syndicat National Unifie des Audioprothesistes) Galatee, s.a.r.l., 5 av. Joffre, 92380 Garches, France. TEL 61-21-10-38. FAX 62-27-29-31. Ed. F. Degove. adv.; bk.rev. Document type: newspaper.
   Formerly: Audioprothesiste Francais.

371.912 CN ISSN 0008-2805
CANADIAN (BELLEVILLE). 1892. 4/yr. free. Sir James Whitney School, 350 Dundas St. W., Belleville, Ont. K8P 1B2, Canada. TEL 613-962-5361. Ed. G.J. Gervis. illus. circ. 644.

636.7 US
CANINE LISTENER. 1977. q. Dog for the Deaf, Inc., 10175 Wheeler Rd., Central Point, OR 97502. TEL 503-826-9220. FAX 503-826-6696. Ed. Robin Dickson. circ. 28,000. (tabloid format) Document type: newsletter.

CAPTION. see COMMUNICATIONS — Television And Cable

CATALOG OF CAPTIONED FILMS FOR THE DEAF. see MOTION PICTURES

362.42 296 US
CONGREGATION NEWS. 1961. m. $10 (foreign $15). Temple Beth Solomon of the Deaf, 13580 Osborne St., Arleta, CA 91331. TEL 818-899-2202. FAX 818-899-2202. (Alt. tel. for the hearing impaired: 818-896-6721) circ. 429. (tabloid format; also avail. in microfilm from JPC) Document type: bulletin.
   Description: Religion, Jewish education, recreation and workshops for the Jewish deaf.

362.4 US
CONNECTICUT. COMMISSION ON THE DEAF AND HEARING-IMPAIRED. ANNUAL REPORT. (Included in Connecticut Administrative Reports) 1974. a. free. Department of Human Resources, Commission on the Deaf and Hearing-Impaired, 141 N. Main St., W. Hartford, CT 06107. TEL 203-566-7414. Ed. Richard B. Schreiber. circ. 5,000. Document type: government publication.
   Formerly: Connecticut. Commission to Study and Investigate the Problems of Deaf and Hearing-Impaired Persons. Annual Report (ISSN 0094-727X)

362.42 IE ISSN 0332-2491
CONTACT; voice of the Irish deaf. 1979. bi-m. $20. 37 Offaly Rd., Cabra, Dublin 7, Ireland. TEL 01-8680202. FAX 01-8388131. Ed. Stan Foran. circ. 900. (back issues avail.) Document type: bulletin.

617.8 616.2 US ISSN 1060-2496
CONTACT (BUFFALO). 1985. q. $15. Cochlear Implant Club International, Box 464, Buffalo, NY 14223-0464. Ed. Lawrence Orloff. circ. 1,500.
   Description: Publishes articles covering cochlear implant medical advances, assistive learning devices.

COURAGE NEWS. see EDUCATION — Special Education And Rehabilitation

371.912 US ISSN 1041-6196
CUED SPEECH CENTER LINES. 1984. irreg. (1-4/yr.). $20 (foreign $25). Cued Speech Center, Inc., 1615B Oberlin Rd., Box 31345, Raleigh, NC 27622. TEL 919-828-1218. Ed. Mary Elsie Daisey. bk.rev. circ. 3,000. (back issues avail.)
   Description: For families, professionals and others; regarding uses of Cued Speech with deaf, hard-of-hearing and hearing individuals.

371.912 US ISSN 1059-8243
CUED SPEECH JOURNAL. Short title: C S Journal. 1985. a. $10 to non-members. National Cued Speech Association, Box 31345, Raleigh, NC 27622-1345. TEL 919-828-1218. FAX 919-828-1862. Ed. Carol J. Boggs. adv. circ. 500. (back issues avail.) Document type: academic/scholarly publication.
   Formerly: Cued Speech Annual (ISSN 1041-6226)
   Description: Discusses professional use of and research on Cued Speech, a system of communication for people with hearing, speech and language needs.

HANDICAPPED — HEARING IMPAIRED

362.42   US
D C A R A NEWS.* (10/yr.). membership (free to qualified personnel). Deaf Counseling Advocacy and Referral Agency, 22289 Pearce St., Hayward, CA 94541-3915. FAX 510-895-5108. Ed. Lisa Allphin. adv.; bk.rev. circ. 20,000.
  Description: Information on events, people and issues affecting the deaf community. Supports cultural and social pride, self-determination, and the civil rights of deaf people.

284   US   ISSN 0744-9100
DAILY DEVOTIONS FOR THE DEAF. 1980. q. free. Deaf Missions, Rural Rte. 2, Box 26, Council Bluffs, IA 51503. TEL 712-322-5493. Ed. Karan Riley. adv.; illus. circ. 19,500. (large print edition in 14 pt.)
  Description: Thematic devotion geared to hearing-impaired and deaf people.

362   US   ISSN 0011-720X
HV2350
DEAF AMERICAN; a national magazine. 1948. a. $20. National Association of the Deaf, 814 Thayer Ave., Silver Spring, MD 20910-4500. TEL 301-587-1788; 301-587-1789 TDD. FAX 301-587-1791. Ed. Mervin Garretson. adv.; bk.rev.; charts; illus.; index. circ. 6,600. (also avail. in microfilm from UMI) **Indexed:** Except.Child.Educ.Abstr., Pers.Lit.
  —Faxon; UnCover; UMI.

DEAF - BLIND WEEKLY NEWS & NEWS SUMMARY. see *HANDICAPPED — Visually Impaired*

371.912   US
DEAF CENTER NEWS.* vol.9, 1989. m. Lutheran Social Services, Deaf Center Services, 750 Kelly Dr., York, PA 17404-2433. TEL 717-848-6238.
  Description: Provides news and information for the deaf community and their hearing friends.

362.42   US
DEAF SAN DIEGO. 1987-1990; resumed 1992. m. free. Deaf Community Services of San Diego, Inc., 3788 Park Blvd., San Diego, CA 92103. TEL 619-497-2811. FAX 619-692-4486. Ed. J. Kay Vincent. adv. contact: Mike Eisele. bk.rev. circ. 3,000. **Document type:** newsletter.
  Formerly (until 1990): Deaf Community Services Magazine of San Diego.
  Description: Focuses on community services for the deaf and hard-of-hearing in the San Diego area. Includes information on club activities.

371.89   GW
DEUTSCHE GEHOERLOSEN-ZEITUNG. m. DM.48. (Deutsche Gehoerlosen-Bund) Gehoerlosen-Verlag Essen GmbH, Adolfstr. 3, 45130 Essen, Germany. TEL 0201-774660. adv.; bk.rev. circ. 9,000.
  Description: Introduces sports programs, social services and welfare for deaf communities worldwide.

371.912   DK   ISSN 0105-7723
DOEVES JUL. 1957. a. DKK 20. Danske Doeves Landsforbund, Fensmarkgade 1, P.O. Box 704, DK-2200 Copenhagen N, Denmark. TEL 45-35-36-52-00. FAX 45-35-36-01-55. Ed. Eva Kistrup. adv. contact: Gurli Andersen. bk.rev.

371.9 420   NO   ISSN 0332-6942
DOEVES TIDSSKRIFT. 1920. w. NOK 350 in Norway; other Nordic countries NOK 380; elsewhere NOK 400. Doeves Forlag AS, Postboks 3171, N-5029 Bergen, Norway. TEL 47-5-200747. FAX 47-5-200559. Ed. Ingeborg Skaten. adv.; bk.rev. circ. 3,200.
  —CCC.
  Formerly: Tegn og Tale.
  Description: Information about and for deaf people, their families and those working with the deaf; sign language, interpretation. News from the Norwegian Deaf Association and news from schools for the deaf.

DOTS AND TAPS; Canada's national magazine for the deaf-blind. see *HANDICAPPED — Visually Impaired*

371.912   IT
EDUCAZIONE DEI SORDOMUTI. bi-m. Via Tommaso Pendola 30, 53100 Siena, Italy. Ed. Giovanni Bonuccelli.

362   IT   ISSN 0013-2195
EFFETA; pubblicazione mensile dell'opera Gualandi. 1907. m. L.20000($40) Istituto Gualandi per Sordomuti, Via Nosadella 49, 40123 Bologna, Italy. TEL 051-330-552. Ed.Bd. adv.; bk.rev.; illus. circ. 2,500. **Indexed:** Lang.& Lang.Behav.Abstr.

362.42   US
ENDEAVOUR (SULPHUR). 1967. q. $30 membership. American Society for Deaf Children, E. Tenth and Tahlequah St., Sulphur, OK 73086-3099. TEL 800-942-2732. Ed. Barbara Aschenbrenner. adv. (tabloid format) **Document type:** newsletter.
  Description: Covers equipment for the deaf, activities of affiliates, and news pertinent to current concerns of the Society and families with deaf children.

362.42   SP
FARO DEL SILENCIO; la revista de todos los sordos Espanoles. 1977. bi-m. 3300 ptas.($42) Spanish National Confederation of the Deaf, Alcala, 160, 28028 Madrid, Spain. TEL 356-5776. FAX 355-4336. adv.; bk.rev. circ. 2,000. (back issues avail.)
  Description: Covers the association's activities and information related to deafness, including education, health and interpreting.

617.8   SP
FIAPAS. 1987. 6/yr. 2500 ptas. (foreign 5000 ptas.). Federacion Espanola de Asociaciones de Padres y Amigos de los Sordos, Nunez de Balboa 3, 28001 Madrid, Spain. TEL 1-576-51-49. FAX 1-576-57-46. Ed. Carmen Danvila. adv.; bk.rev. circ. 12,000.

371.912   US   ISSN 0015-4288
HV1796
FLORIDA SCHOOL HERALD. 1891. 6/yr. $6. Florida School for the Deaf and the Blind, St. Augustine, FL 32084. TEL 904-823-4000. Ed. Mary Jane Dillon. abstr.; illus. circ. 1,550. **Document type:** newsletter.
  Description: Highlights education of the deaf and blind.

362.428   AT
FOUR CORNERS. 1949. q. Aus.$3. Western Australia Deaf Society, 16 Brentham St., Leederville, WA 6007, Australia. TEL 619-443-2677. FAX 619-444-3592. Ed. Glen Prideaux. adv.; bk.rev. circ. 460. (back issues avail.) **Document type:** newsletter.
  Description: General interest and local social activities.

362.42   US   ISSN 0739-9243
FRAT. 1904. bi-m. $8. National Fraternal Society of the Deaf, 1300 W. Northwest Hwy., Mt. Prospect, IL 60056. TEL 708-392-9282. FAX 708-392-9298. Ed. Robert R. Anderson. adv. circ. 7,500. (back issues avail.) **Document type:** newspaper.
  Description: Articles on life insurance and the deaf, with news from the divisions.

371.912   US   ISSN 0739-7453
G L A D NEWS. 1968. q. $15. Greater Los Angeles Council on Deafness, Inc., 616 S. Westmoreland Ave., Los Angeles, CA 90005. TEL 213-383-2220. FAX 213-383-3808. Ed. Marge Klugman. adv. circ. 3,000. (back issues avail.)

GALLAUDET ALUMNI NEWSLETTER. see *COLLEGE AND ALUMNI*

371.912 378   US   ISSN 0016-4089
HV2561
GALLAUDET TODAY. 1970. q. $10 (foreign $12). Gallaudet University, Department of Publications and Production, 800 Florida Ave., N.E., Washington, DC 20002-3695. TEL 202-651-5671. FAX 202-651-5670. Ed. Vickie Walter. bk.rev.; illus.; index. circ. 14,000. **Indexed:** Rehabil.Lit. **Document type:** academic/scholarly publication.
  Formerly: Gallaudet Bulletin.
  Description: Discusses issues concerning deafness.

371.912   XR   ISSN 0323-0732
GONG. (Text in Czech and Slovak) 1972. m. 30 Kcs. (Czechoslovak Association of Handicapped) Vydavatelstvi Nase Vojsko, Vladislavova 26, Prague 1, Czech Republic. (Subscr. to: Gong, Sokolovska 63, Karlin, 18600 Prague 8, Czech Republic) Ed. Oldrich Jendrulek. adv.; bk.rev. circ. 7,600.
  Description: Explores deaf education and technical aids for the deaf in Czechoslovakia.

GUIDE TO GRADUATE EDUCATION IN SPEECH - LANGUAGE PATHOLOGY AND AUDIOLOGY. see *EDUCATION — Guides To Schools And Colleges*

371.912 614.8   US
GUILDER. 1916. q. donation. Boston Guild for the Hard of Hearing, 283 Commonwealth Ave., Boston, MA 02115. TEL 617-267-4730. FAX 617-267-9422. Ed. Donna E. Holt. adv. circ. 1,300. (tabloid format; back issues avail.) **Document type:** newsletter.
  Description: Presents information of interest to hard-of-hearing people; includes Guild activities.

617.89   II   ISSN 0971-0949
HEARING AID JOURNAL. (Text in English) 1977. q. Rs.500($50) Dr. Narendra Kumar, Ed. & Pub., P.O. Box 2812, New Delhi 110 060, India. adv.; bk.rev. circ. 1,200. **Indexed:** Psychol.Abstr.
  Description: For audiologists, speech pathologists and hearing aid dealers.

362.42 362.9   UK
HEARING CONCERN. q. £5. Hearing Concern, 7-11 Armstrong Rd., London W3 7JL, England. TEL 081-743-1110. FAX 081-742-9043. Ed. Jackie Mitchell. adv. contact: Jackie Mitchell. bk.rev. circ. 6,000. (back issues avail.) **Document type:** consumer publication, newsletter.
  Formerly: Hark.
  Description: Covers issues relating to hearing-impaired persons and professionals involved with them.

371.912   US
HEARING HEALTH; the voice on hearing issues. 1984. 6/yr. $14 (foreign $25). Voice International Publishing, Inc., 723 Upper N. Broadway, Ste. 522, Corpus Christi, TX 78401. TEL 512-884-8388. FAX 512-884-3314. (Subscr. to: Box 2663, Corpus Christi, TX 78403; Alt. addr.: Box 2663, Corpus Christi, TX 78403) Ed. Paula Bartone-Bonillas. adv. contact: Dave Bakker. bk.rev.; illus.; tr.lit. circ. 20,000. (back issues avail.) **Document type:** consumer publication.
  Formerly (until 1992): Voice (ISSN 0888-2517)
  Description: Entertains and educates hearing and hearing-impaired people nationwide on the issue of hearing loss.

617.89   US   ISSN 0092-4466
RF310
HEARING INSTRUMENTS. 1951. m. $35. Advanstar Communications, Inc., 7500 Old Oak Blvd., Cleveland, OH 44130. TEL 216-826-2839. FAX 216-891-2726. (Subscr. to: 131 W. First St., Duluth, MN 55802. TEL 800-346-0085) Ed. Karen S. Cranmer-Brisk. adv.; illus. circ. 19,046. **Document type:** trade publication.
  —BLDSC (4275.285000); UnCover. CCC.
  Formerly: Hearing Dealer (ISSN 0017-9205)
  Description: Covers research, hearing evaluation, hearing aid selection and fitting, technological developments, noise protection and control.

362.4   US   ISSN 0360-9278
HV2350
HEARING REHABILITATION QUARTERLY 1975. q. $25. New York League for the Hard of Hearing, 71 W. 23rd St., New York, NY 10010-4162. TEL 212-741-7650. FAX 212-255-4413. Ed. John McKendry. adv.; bk.rev. circ. 2,500. **Indexed:** DSH Abstr., Except.Child.Educ.Abstr., Psychol.Abstr., Rehabil.Lit.
  Former titles (1960-1975): Highlights (ISSN 0360-9286); New York League for the Hard of Hearing. Quarterly Bulletin.

371.92   US
HEARING RESEARCH DEVELOPMENTS. vol.5, 1974. bi-m. membership. C H E A R, Inc., National Foundation for Children's Hearing, Education and Research, 928 McLean Ave., Yonkers, NY 10704. TEL 914-237-2676. Eds. Norman H. Kessler, Zita Rohn. adv.; bk.rev. circ. 3,500.

362.42   DK   ISSN 0018-4934
HOERELSEN. 1913. 10/yr. DKK 150. Landsforeningen for Bedre Hoerelse - Danish Association for Better Hearing, Mariendalsvej 27, DK-2000 Frederiksberg, Denmark. TEL DK-38 88 16 44. FAX 45-31-86-51-28. adv.; bk.rev.; charts; illus.; index. circ. 18,000.
  Formerly: Tidsskrift for Tunghoere.

HANDICAPPED — HEARING IMPAIRED

371.912 GW ISSN 0018-3121
HOERGESCHAEDIGTE KINDER. 1964. q. DM.19.80. (Deutsche Gesellschaft zur Foerderung der Hoer-Sprach-Geschaedigten e.V.) Verlag Hoergeschaedigte Kinder GmbH, Bernadottestr. 126, 22605 Hamburg, Germany. TEL 040-8807031. FAX 040-8806793. Ed. Dr. H. Feuchte. adv.; bk.rev.; bibl.; illus.; stat.; index. circ. 4,500. **Document type:** academic/scholarly publication.

371.912 GW ISSN 0342-4898
HOERGESCHAEDIGTEN-PAEDAGOGIK. 1946. 6/yr. DM.49. (Berufsverband Deutscher Hoergeschaedigtenpaedagogen) Julius Groos Verlag, Hertzstr. 6, 69126 Heidelberg, Germany. TEL 06221-303621. FAX 06221-301993. Ed. M. Breitinger. adv.; bk.rev.; bibl.; illus.; index. circ. 2,100. (reprint service avail. from UMI) **Document type:** academic/scholarly publication.
—CCC.
Formerly: Neue Blaetter fuer Taubstummenbildung (ISSN 0028-310X)
Description: For educators of the deaf and hard-of-hearing.

371.912 AU ISSN 0255-0326
I F H O H JOURNAL. (Text in English) 1980. 3/yr. DM.25 for 2 yrs. International Federation of the Hard of Hearing, Radegunderstr. 10, 8045 Graz, Austria. TEL 43-316-671327. FAX 43-316-681093. Ed. Dr. Mark Ross. adv.; bk.rev. circ. 750.
Description: News of the Federation and about the field of hearing loss.

371.912 US ISSN 0745-1539
ILLINOIS ADVANCE. 1870. 4/yr. free. Illinois School for the Deaf, 125 Webster Ave., Jacksonville, IL 62650. TEL 217-479-4241. Ed. Carole Hack. illus. circ. 2,000. **Indexed:** Rehabil.Lit.
Description: Serves as a learning project for students in the business education and printing classes, and as a means of communicating the school's affairs to family, friends, alumni, staff, and to sister schools in the U.S. and abroad.

362.42 BE
INFO-SOURDS JOURNAL. (Text in French) 1984. 3/yr. 300 BEF. Federation Francophone des Associations de Sourds de Belgique, 32 rue Capronnier, B-1030 Brussels, Belgium. TEL 02-2452363. (Subscr. to: 38 rue Saxe-Cobourg, 1030 Bruxelles, Belgium) Ed. Martine Fraiture. adv. circ. 450. (back issues avail.)
Description: Presents news and facts of interest to the hard of hearing in Belgium. Includes calender of events and puzzles.

362.42 384.6 US
INTERNATIONAL DIRECTORY FOR T T Y USERS (YEAR). 1968. a. $15 to individuals; institutions $30. Telecommunications for the Deaf, Inc., 8719 Colesville Rd., Ste. 300, Silver Spring, MD 20910. TEL 301-589-3786. FAX 301-589-3797. Ed. Alfred Sonnenstrahl. adv.; bk.rev. circ. 14,000. (back issues avail.) **Document type:** directory.
Formerly: International Telephone Directory of T D D Users (ISSN 0160-7472)
Description: Telephone directory of business, organizations, residential numbers that can be accessed via TTY (telecommunication device for the deaf).

371.912 JA
JAPANESE DEAF NEWS; silent press for the deaf. 1948. m. 3000 Yen($30) Japanese Federation of the Deaf, c/o S.K. Bldg., Ste. 130, Yamabuki-cho, Shinjuku-ku, Tokyo, Japan. TEL 03-3268-8847. (Subscr. to: c/o Seni-Kaiken, Muromachi-dori, Imadegawa Sagaru, Kamigyo-ku, Kyoto, Japan. TEL 075-441-6079. FAX 075-441-6147) Ed. Kikuji Nakanishi. adv. circ. 20,000. (tabloid format; back issues avail.) **Document type:** newspaper.
Formerly: Japan Hearing - Handicap News Paper.

362.42 US ISSN 0022-4685
RC423 CODEN: JSPHAH
JOURNAL OF SPEECH AND HEARING RESEARCH. 1958. bi-m. $60 to individuals (foreign $82); institutions $114 (foreign $136); members $30. American Speech - Language - Hearing Association, 10801 Rockville Pike, Rockville, MD 20852. TEL 301-897-5700. FAX 301-571-0457. bibl.; charts; illus. circ. 73,000. (also avail. in microform from UMI; reprint service avail. from UMI) **Indexed:** ASSIA, Bibl.Dev.Med.& Child Neur., Biol.Abstr., C.I.J.E., Chem.Abstr., Curr.Cont., Dent.Ind., Educ.Ind., Except.Child.Educ.Abstr., Excerp.Med., Ind.Med., Lang.& Lang.Behav.Abstr., M.L.A., NBA, Noise Pollut.Publ.Abstr., Psychol.Abstr., Rehabil.Lit., Sci.Abstr, Sp.Ed.Needs Abstr., SSCI. **Document type:** academic/scholarly publication.
—BLDSC (5066.150000); Faxon; UnCover; SWETS; UMI. **CCC.**
Description: Includes papers pertaining to the process and disorder of hearing, language, and speech, and to the diagnosis and treatment of these disorders.

371.912 US
KA KULI O'HAWAI'I. 1970. bi-m. $7.50. Aloha State Association of Deaf, c/o Waikiki Community Center, 310 Paoakalani Ave., Rm. 201-A, Honolulu, HI 96815. TEL 808-926-8203. FAX 808-924-9664. Ed. Francine Kenyon. circ. 325. (back issues avail.) **Document type:** newsletter.
Formerly: H A N D S (Hawaiian Aloha Needs Deaf Spirit).
Description: Community and educational news on the deaf.

362.42 FI ISSN 0023-5741
KUULOVIESTI/HEARING NEWS. (Text in Finnish; summary in English and Swedish) 1934. 8/yr. Fmk.150. Kuulonhuoltoliitto - Finnish Federation of the Hard of Hearing, Iikantie 4, 00400 Helsinki, Finland. FAX 5803770. Ed. Seppo Matinvesi. adv.; bk.rev. circ. 13,500.

LANGUAGE, SPEECH AND HEARING SERVICES IN SCHOOLS. see EDUCATION — Special Education And Rehabilitation

617.89 US
LISTENER. 1954. bi-m. free. Hear Center, 301 E. Del Mar Blvd., Pasadena, CA 91101. TEL 818-796-2016. Ed. Beverly Biber. bk.rev.; film rev.; illus.; stat. circ. 5,000. (looseleaf format) **Document type:** newsletter.
Description: Information and data for the hearing and speech impaired.

317.912 IS
MABAT SHELANU. (Text in English and Hebrew) q. World Organization of Jewish Deaf, Helen Keller House, P.O. Box 9001, Tel Aviv 61090, Israel. TEL (03)303355.

371.912 SZ
LES MAINS DU C R A L. 1981. 10/yr. 30 Fr. (foreign 40 Fr.). Centre de Rencontres d'Accueil et de Loisirs, 2b, Chemin de Vincy, CH-1202 Geneva, Switzerland. TEL 022-7343274. FAX 022-7349631. Ed.Bd. adv.; bk.rev. circ. 850. (back issues avail.)
Description: General information for the deaf in Geneva and surrounding area.

371.912 CN ISSN 0704-0652
MARITIMER. 1963. q. free. (Atlantic Provinces Special Education Authority Resource Centre for the Hearing Impaired) Atlantic Technological Vocational Centre, Box 308, Amherst, NS B4H 3Z6, Canada. TEL 902-667-3808. FAX 902-667-0893. Ed. Phyllis A. Cameron. bk.rev. circ. 1,500. **Document type:** newsletter.
Formerly: New Scotian (ISSN 0028-6672)
Description: Newsletter on the center's programs for the hearing-impaired.

371.912 US
MILL NECK MANOR BULLETIN. 1951. q. free. Mill Neck Foundation, Frost Mill Rd., Box 100, Mill Neck, NY 11765. TEL 516-922-4100. FAX 516-922-3759. (Subscr. to: Mill Neck Manor Lutheran School for the Deaf, Box 12, Frost Mill Rd., Mill Neck, NY 11765) Ed. Henry O. Bjorlie. circ. 76,000 (controlled).
Description: Covers education for the deaf.

371.912 US
MISSOURI RECORD. 1879. 5/yr. free. Missouri School for the Deaf, 505 E. 5th St., Fulton, MO 65251-1799. TEL 314-592-4000. FAX 314-592-2570. Ed. Peter H. Ripley. circ. 1,029. (also avail. in microfilm)
Description: Dedicated to parents of deaf children, alumni of the Missouri School for the Deaf and professionals in the education of the deaf.

MOON RAINBOW. see HANDICAPPED — Visually Impaired

362.42 US ISSN 0887-0004
N D BANNER. 1891. 3/yr. $2. North Dakota School for the Deaf, 1401 College Dr., Devils Lake, ND 58301. TEL 701-662-5031. FAX 701-662-6605. Ed. Barbara J. Duncan. circ. 600. **Document type:** academic/scholarly publication.

637
N H C A PROFESSIONAL SERVICE ORGANIZATION DIRECTORY. 1974. a. free. National Hearing Conservation Association, 431 E. Locust St., Ste. 202, Des Moines, IA 50309-1999. TEL 515-243-1558. FAX 515-243-2049. circ. 700. **Document type:** directory.
Description: Lists professional service organizations which provide hearing conservation services to industry.

362.42 US
NATIONAL CONGRESS OF JEWISH DEAF. QUARTERLY. 1958. q. $15. National Congress of Jewish Deaf, Temple Beth Solomon of the Deaf, 13580 Osborne St., Arleta, CA 91331. Ed. Jushua Mandelsohn. adv.; bk.rev.; film rev.; play rev. circ. 1,000.
Description: News, Judaism topics and reports keeping members abreast of new developments in the deaf world.

155.4512 UK
NATIONAL DEAF CHILDREN'S SOCIETY. ANNUAL REPORT. 1948. a. free. National Deaf Children's Society, 45 Hereford Rd., London W2 5AH, England. TEL 071-229-9272. FAX 071-243-0195. Ed. Mark Askarika. adv. circ. 2,000. **Document type:** corporate report.
Formerly: National Deaf Children's Society. Yearbook and Annual Accounts.
Description: Report of the Society's activities for the previous year.

371.912 UK
NATIONAL DEAF CHILDREN'S SOCIETY. DIRECTORY. a. £5. National Deaf Children's Society, 45 Hereford Rd., London W2 5AH, England. TEL 071-229-9272. FAX 071-243-0195. **Document type:** directory.
Description: Lists deaf schools in the UK, manufacturers of equipment for deaf children and addresses of local social services.

362.42 384
NATIONAL DIRECTORY OF T T Y NUMBERS. a. $15. Telecommunications for the Deaf, Inc., 8719 Colesville Rd., Ste. 300, Silver Spring, MD 20910. TEL 301-589-3786. FAX 301-589-3786. adv. contact: Anne Edwards. circ. 20,000. **Document type:** directory.
Description: Lists T T Y numbers for business and residential subscribers throughout the U.S. and Canada.

NEW JERSEY SPEECH AND HEARING ASSOCIATION. JOURNAL. see MEDICAL SCIENCES

371 US ISSN 0896-6478
HV2561
NEW MEXICO PROGRESS. 1909. bi-m. free. New Mexico School for the Deaf, 1060 Cerrillos Rd., Santa Fe, NM 87503. TEL 505-827-6747. Ed. Lester D. Graham. illus. circ. 900. **Document type:** newsletter.
Description: News and activities of the School. Recognizes outstanding students.

HANDICAPPED — HEARING IMPAIRED

362.42   US
NORCAL CENTER ON DEAFNESS NEWSLINE. 1978. q. $15. NorCal Center on Deafness, 2848 Arden Way, Ste. 210, Sacramento, CA 95825-1373. TEL 916-973-8448. FAX 916-973-0633. Eds. Dawn Ramos, Ron Reeberg. adv.; bk.rev. circ. 1,200. (also avail. in Braille)
    Former titles: NorCal Community Forum; Deaf Community News; Deaf Community Newsletter.
    Description: Covers deaf awareness, community news and items of interest to the deaf and hearing-impaired communities, including community events.

371.912   SW   ISSN 0029-1471
NORDISK TIDSKRIFT FOER DOEVUNDERVISNINGEN. Short title: N T D. (Text in Danish, Norwegian, Swedish) 1899. 4/yr. SEK 200 (effective 1991). Nordisk Tidskrift foer Doevundervisningen AB, c/o A. Fraendh, Graenv. 35 B, 135 52 Tyresoe, Sweden. TEL 046-142016. Ed. Karin Gustafsson. adv.; bk.rev.; abstr.; charts; illus.; stat.; index. circ. 1,200. **Document type:** trade publication.
    Former titles (until 1957): Nordisk Tidskrift foer Doefstumskolan (ISSN 0347-7991); (until 1956): Tidskrift foer Doefstumskolan.

371.92   US   ISSN 1041-6234
ON CUE. 1984. bi-m. membership. National Cued Speech Association, Box 31345, Raleigh, NC 27622-1345. TEL 919-828-1218. FAX 919-828-1862. Ed. Marianne Flanagan. adv. circ. 350. (back issues avail.) **Document type:** newsletter.
    Description: Information for professionals and families regarding the use of Cued Speech, a system of communication for people with hearing, speech and language needs.

362.42 419   CN
ONTARIO DEAF LIFE. q. Can.$25 to individuals; institutions Can.$50. Ontario Association of the Deaf, 271 Spadina Rd., 3rd Fl., Toronto, ON M5R 2V3, Canada. TEL 416-925-5258. FAX 416-964-2066. Ed. Laura Hardman. adv. circ. 350. (back issues avail.)
    Formerly: Ontario Association of the Deaf News.
    Description: Serves to protect the rights of the deaf and preserve the North American sign language.

371.912   US
OREGON OUTLOOK. 1910. 6/yr. $1.50. (Department of Education) Oregon School for the Deaf, c/o Alan Yankus, 999 Locust St. N.E., Salem, OR 97303-5254. TEL 503-378-3825. FAX 503-373-7879. Ed.Bd. adv.; circ. 500 (paid).

362.42   IS   ISSN 0792-0814
OUR REVIEW/MABAT SHELANV. (Text in English, Hebrew) no.92, 1969. m? free. Association of the Deaf in Israel, Helen Keller Center, P.O. Box 9001, Tel Aviv 61090, Israel. TEL 03-303355. FAX 03-396419. Ed. Hava Savir. adv.; illus. circ. 2,000.
    Former titles: Demama Shelanv (ISSN 0333-9319); Demana (ISSN 0011-8176)

OUR WAY. see RELIGIONS AND THEOLOGY — Judaic

R E S N A NEWS. see EDUCATION — Special Education And Rehabilitation

REEDUCATION ORTHOPHONIQUE. see MEDICAL SCIENCES — Otorhinolaryngology

371.912   US
REGISTRY OF INTERPRETERS FOR THE DEAF. NATIONAL CONVENTION PROCEEDINGS. 1978. biennial. $19.95. (Registry of Interpreters for the Deaf, Inc.) R I D Publications, 8719 Colesville Rd., No. 310, Silver Spring, MD 20910-3919. TEL 301-608-0050. circ. 6,000. **Document type:** proceedings.
    Description: Papers presented at convention, covering a diverse selection of interpreter-related issues and concerns.

371.912   GW
RELIGIONSUNTERRICHT UND KONFIRMANDENUNTERRICHT FUER GEHOERLOSE UND SCHWERHOERIGE; ein Informationsdienst. 1976. s-a. free. Arbeitsgemeinschaft fuer Evangelische Schwerhoerigenseelsorge (AFESS) e.V., Krokusstr. 1, 48527 Nordhorn, Germany. TEL 05921-703-12. Ed. Dietfried Gewalt. bk.rev. circ. 450. **Document type:** bulletin.
    Description: Geared to teachers and ministers of the deaf.

362.42   YU   ISSN 0027-8076
REVIJA (BELGRADE). 1948. bi-m. 24 din.($6) Savez Gluvih i Nagluvih Jugoslavije - Federation of the Deaf of Yugoslavia, Svetog Save 16-18, Belgrade, Yugoslavia. Ed. Aleksandar Zoric. adv.; bk.rev. circ. 5,000.
    Formerly (until 1977): Nas Glas.

RING DES WORTES; Seelsorgebrief fuer Hoergeschaedigte, Kranke und Senioren. see RELIGIONS AND THEOLOGY — Roman Catholic

362.4   US   ISSN 0883-1688
S H H H JOURNAL; a journal about hearing loss. 1980. bi-m. $20 to individuals; libraries $50; organizations $100. Self Help for Hard of Hearing People, Inc., 7910 Woodmont Ave., Ste. 1200, Bethesda, MD 20814. TEL 301-657-2248. Ed. Barbara G. Harris. adv.; bk.rev. circ. 47,000. (back issues avail.)
    Description: Contains information about hearing loss, assistance, technology, and coping techniques.

SCANDINAVIAN AUDIOLOGY. see MEDICAL SCIENCES — Otorhinolaryngology

371.912 360   UK   ISSN 0968-5529
SEE HEAR! 1984. m. £11 to individuals; institutions £15. Royal National Institute for Deaf People, 105 Gower St., London WC1E 6AH, England. TEL 01-387-8033. FAX 01-388-2346. Ed. Stephen Iuffe. adv.; bk.rev.; film rev.; play rev. circ. 10,500. (back issues avail.) **Document type:** consumer publication.
    Formerly: Soundbarrier.
    Description: General interest news and features for deaf individuals and related professionals.

362.42   IT
SETTIMANA DEL SORDO; organo di informazione dei minorati dell'udito e della parola. 1954. bi-m. L.20000. Ente Nazionale Sordomuti, Via Gregorio VII, 120, 00165 Rome, Italy. TEL 6377041. Ed. Armando Giuranna. bk.rev.; index. circ. 40,000. (tabloid format)
    Formerly: Settimana del Sordomuto (ISSN 0037-2919)
    Description: Includes articles on activities for the deaf, how victims can cope with this handicap and how others can help and live with its victims.

371.912   US
SIGHTS AND SOUNDS. 1981. q. free. Alabama Institute for Deaf & Blind, Box 698, Talladega, AL 35160. TEL 205-761-3206. FAX 205-761-3247. Ed. Lynne Hanner. circ. 10,000. (also avail. in audio cassette; Braille) **Document type:** consumer publication.
    Description: Gives educators, parents, and friends a better understanding of the institute.

SIGNPOST. see LINGUISTICS

371.912   US   ISSN 0037-5187
SILENT ADVOCATE. 1916. q. free. St. Rita School for the Deaf, 1720 Glendale-Milford Rd., Cincinnati, OH 45215. TEL 513-771-7600. FAX 513-771-7607. Ed. Kelly J. Deters. illus.; circ. 25,000 (controlled). **Document type:** newsletter.
    Description: News about students and school activities of interest to parents, alumni and supporters.

362.42   SA   ISSN 0037-5195
SILENT MESSENGER/STILLE BOODSKAPPER. (Text in Afrikaans, English) m. donation. South African National Council for the Deaf, Private Bag X4, Westhoven 2142, South Africa. TEL 27-11-4821610. FAX 27-11-7265873. Ed. H.A. Opperman. adv.; illus. circ. 3,500.
    Description: Articles and news snippets on deafness, deaf people, as well as information on new technological developments.

155.451   US   ISSN 0049-0490
SILENT NEWS. 1969. m. $18. Silent News, Inc., Box 23330, Rochester, NY 14692-3330. FAX 716-334-0962. Ed. Tom Willard; Pub. Julins Wiggins. adv. contact: Steven Wiggins. bk.rev. circ. 10,000. (back issues avail.) **Document type:** newspaper.

SONDERSCHULE. see EDUCATION

649.13   US
SOUNDS OF LEXINGTON. 1945. m. (11/yr.). $3. Lexington School for the Deaf, Parents Association, 26-26 75th St., Jackson Heights, NY 11370. Ed. Diane Rosen. bk.rev. circ. 500. (processed; also avail. in cards)
    Formerly: Lexington School for the Deaf. Parents' Newsletter. (ISSN 0031-1928)

362.42   SA
SOUTH AFRICAN NATIONAL COUNCIL FOR THE DEAF. SERVICE INFORMATION BOOKLET. 1955. biennial. R.7.50. South African National Council for the Deaf, Private Bag X4, Westhoven 2142, South Africa. TEL 27-11-4821610. FAX 27-11-7265873. Ed. H.A. Opperman. circ. 4,000.
    Supersedes (in 1994): South African National Council for the Deaf. Annual Diary.

617.89   US
SPECTRUM (DES MOINES). 1974. q. free. National Hearing Conservation Association, 431 E. Locust St., Ste. 202, Des Moines, IA 50309-1999. TEL 515-243-1558. FAX 515-243-2049. Ed. Martha Layne. adv.; bk.rev. circ. 700. (looseleaf format; back issues avail.) **Document type:** newsletter.
    Former titles (until 1988): Hearing Conservation News; (until 1987): National Hearing Conservation Association Newsletter.
    Description: Provides up-to-date information on technology, research and practices of hearing conservation; and reports on the continually evolving legal and regulatory activities at state and federal levels which impact hearing conservation practice.

SPEECH COMMUNICATION. see LINGUISTICS

371.912   UK   ISSN 0049-2906
TALK. 1956. q. £10 (foreign £20). National Deaf Childrens Society, 45 Hereford Rd., London W2 5AH, England. TEL 071-229-9272. FAX 071-243-0195. Ed. Kate Appleton. adv.; bk.rev.; film rev. circ. 14,000. (processed) **Indexed:** ASSIA. **Document type:** consumer publication.
    Description: For parents of deaf children. Contains news items, feature articles, and informational reports on the life-style and social integration of deaf children.

TEACHING ENGLISH TO DEAF AND SECOND LANGUAGE STUDENTS. see EDUCATION — Special Education And Rehabilitation

TINNITUS TODAY. (American Tinnitus Association) see MEDICAL SCIENCES — Otorhinolaryngology

TOPICS IN LANGUAGE DISORDERS. see EDUCATION — Special Education And Rehabilitation

155.4512 790.1   US
U S TEAM SPOTLIGHT.* 1987. q. $5. American Athletic Association of the Deaf, c/o East Bay Counseling Advocacy, 22289 Pearce St., Hayward, CA 94541-3915. TEL 415-895-2430. FAX 415-895-5108. Eds. Jack Levesque, Donalda Ammons. circ. 5,000.
    Description: Focuses on deaf athletes.

371.912   NE   ISSN 0156-5677
VAN HOREN ZEGGEN. 1960. q. fl.30 (foreign $25). Vereniging ter Bevordering van het Onderwijs aan Doven in Nederland (VEDON), Postbus 36117, 1020 MC Amsterdam, Netherlands. TEL 31-5908-12335. (Co-sponsor: Nederlandse Vereniging tot Bevordering van het Onderwijs aan Slechthorende Kinderen en Kinderen met Spraak- en Taalmoeilijkheden (VeBOSS)) Ed. B.G. Hofman. bk.rev. circ. 1,500.

HANDICAPPED — PHYSICALLY IMPAIRED

617.7   CN   ISSN 0227-6755
VIBRATIONS. 1974. q. membership. Canadian Hearing Society, 271 Spadina Rd., Toronto, ON M5R 2V3, Canada. TEL 416-964-9595. FAX 416-964-2066. Ed. Liz Brady. adv.: B&W page Can.$900; 8 5/8 x 11 1/8. bk.rev. circ. 10,000. **Document type:** newsletter.
  Description: Provides practical and useful information to aid in the understanding of and coping with hearing loss.

371.912   US
VIEWS (SILVER SPRING). 1967. m. $24. (Registry of Interpreters for the Deaf, Inc.) R I D Publications, 8719 Colesville Rd., No. 310, Silver Spring, MD 20910-3919. TEL 301-608-0050. circ. 4,000. (back issues avail.)
  Formerly: Interpreter Views.
  Description: Contains information on interpreting issues, local, national and international interpreting news, reports on the testing system and RID committee actions, employment opportunities.

362.42   IT
VOICE OF SILENCE NEWSLETTER. (Text in English, French) 1957. q. membership. World Federation of the Deaf, 120 via Gregoria VII, Rome 00165, Italy. Ed. Dr. Cesare Magarotto. adv.; bk.rev.; circ. 500 (controlled). (tabloid format) **Document type:** newsletter.
  Formerly: Voix du Silence (ISSN 0042-8388).
  Description: Social rehabilitation of the deaf.

371.912   US   ISSN 0042-8639
HV2350   CODEN: VOLRAT
VOLTA REVIEW. 1899. 5/yr. $42. Alexander Graham Bell Association for the Deaf, Inc., 3417 Volta Place, N.W., Washington, DC 20007. TEL 202-337-5220. Ed. David F. Conway. adv.; bk.rev.; charts; illus.; tr.lit.; index. circ. 5,700. (also avail. in microform from UMI; reprint service avail. from UMI) **Indexed:** ASSIA, C.I.J.E., Child Devel.Abstr., Curr.Cont., Educ.Ind., Except.Child.Educ.Abstr., Lang.& Lang.Behav.Abstr., Psychol.Abstr., SSCI, Yrbk.Assoc.Educ.& Rehab.Blind. **Document type:** academic/scholarly publication.
  —BLDSC (9254.400000); Faxon; UnCover; SWETS; UMI. **CCC**.
  Description: Promotion and knowledge of deaf oralism, speech-therapy, mainstream education of the deaf.

371.912   617.8   US
VOLTA VOICES. 1976. 6/yr. $40 includes membership. Alexander Graham Bell Association for the Deaf, Inc., 3417 Volta Pl., N.W., Washington, DC 20007. TEL 202-337-5220. FAX 202-337-8314. Ed. K. Brooke Rigler. adv. circ. 5,700. **Indexed:** Rehabil.Lit.
  —BLDSC (6108.741000).
  Formed by the 1994 merger of (1976-1993): Newsounds (ISSN 0147-4057); (1982-1993): Our Kids Magazine.
  Description: Contains articles on the latest technological advances in the field of hearing impairment, inspirational stories, creative writings, children's educational issues and government action.

371.912   NE   ISSN 0042-9139
VRIEND. 1906. 5/yr. fl.15. Instituut voor Doven - Institute for the Deaf, Theeresstraat 42, 5271 GD St. Michielsgestel, Netherlands. TEL 31-4105-88111. FAX 31-4105-12157. TELEX 50868 INSDO NL. Ed. Toine Schakenraad-Hilker. bk.rev.; illus. circ. 2,800.

362.42   CN
W I D H H NEWS. 1967. q. Can.$15 membership. Western Institute for the Deaf & Hard of Hearing, 2125 W. 7th Ave., Vancouver, BC V6K 1X9, Canada. TEL 604-736-7391. FAX 604-736-4381. Ed. Caroline Tanner. adv. circ. 1,050. **Document type:** newsletter.
  Formerly: W I D News (ISSN 0049-7436).

371.912   NE
WOORD EN GEBAAR. m. fl.40($30) Stichting Nederlandse Dovenraad - Dutch Council of the Deaf, P.O. Box 19, 3500 AA Utrecht, Netherlands. TEL 030-316487. FAX 030-315317. Ed. Aukje Bijlsma. adv. circ. 2,000. (back issues avail.)
  Description: Examines the world of the deaf, from sign-language, education and sports, to participation in the workforce.

371.912   US   ISSN 0199-8293
WORLD AROUND YOU. (Teacher's ed. avail.) bi-m. (during school yr.). $7 (foreign $12). Gallaudet University, Outreach Services KDES, PAS-6, 800 Florida Ave., N.E., Washington, DC 20002-3695. TEL 202-651-5340. FAX 202-651-5708. Ed. Cathryn Carroll. circ. 6,500. (back issues avail.)
  Description: News magazine for hearing impaired teens.

371.912   US
WORLD AROUND YOU. TEACHER'S EDITION. bi-m. $10 (foreign $15). Gallaudet University, Outreach Services KDES, PAS-6, 800 Florida Ave., N.E., Washington, DC 20002-3695. TEL 202-651-5340. FAX 202-651-5780.
  Description: Teaching materials for use with hearing impaired teenagers.

362   IT   ISSN 0510-8292
WORLD CONGRESS OF THE W F D. PROCEEDINGS. 1951. quadrennial, 1983, Palermo. World Federation of the Deaf, c/o C. Magarotto, Secretary, Via Gregorio VII N. 120, 00165 Rome, Italy. **Document type:** proceedings.
  Formerly: World Congress of the Deaf. Lectures and Papers (ISSN 0084-1625)

HANDICAPPED — Physically Impaired

362.4   US   ISSN 0001-4508
ACCENT ON LIVING. 1956. q. $10. Cheever Publishing, Inc., Box 700, Bloomington, IL 61702. TEL 309-378-2961. FAX 309-378-4420. Ed. Betty Garee. adv.; bk.rev.; tr.lit. circ. 20,000. (also avail. in microform from UMI; reprint service avail. from UMI) **Indexed:** CHNI, Hlth.Ind., Rehabil.Lit. **Document type:** consumer publication.
  •Also available online. Vendor(s): DIALOG Information Services, Inc. (File no.149).
  —BLDSC (0570.812000); UnCover; UMI.
  Description: General interest for physically handicapped people.

362.4   US   ISSN 0272-2461
HV3011
ACCENT ON LIVING BUYER'S GUIDE. 1977. biennial. $12. Cheever Publishing, Inc., Box 700, Bloomington, IL 61702. TEL 309-378-2961. FAX 309-378-4420. Ed. Betty Garee. adv. circ. 20,000. (back issues avail.) **Document type:** directory.

ADDRESS LIST, REGIONAL AND SUBREGIONAL LIBRARIES FOR THE BLIND AND PHYSICALLY HANDICAPPED. see HANDICAPPED — Visually Impaired

362.4   747   US
▼**AN APPROACH TO BARRIER FREE DESIGN.** 1993. q. $12.95. A Positive Approach Inc., Box 910, Millville, NJ 08332. TEL 609-451-4777. FAX 609-451-6678. adv.: B&W page $1283, color page $1883; trim 8 1/2 x 11. bk.rev. circ. 200,000.
  Description: Promotes awareness and understanding of the requirements of wheelchair users and victims of stroke or arthritis. For architects, designers, builders, hospital personnel and others responsible for making environments convenient, functional and efficient.

ASSOCIATION OF CHILDREN'S PROSTHETIC-ORTHOTIC CLINICS. JOURNAL. see MEDICAL SCIENCES

BREAKING NEW GROUND; cultivating independence for farmers and ranchers with disabilities. see AGRICULTURE — Agricultural Equipment

362.4   US   ISSN 0007-8808
C O P H BULLETIN. 1960. q. $2. National Congress of Organizations of the Physically Handicapped, Inc., 6106 N. 30th St., Arlington, VA 22207. Ed. Rose A. Wilson. adv.; bk.rev.; illus. circ. 2,500. (tabloid format) **Indexed:** Rehabil.Lit.

362.4   CN   ISSN 0045-4001
CALIPER. 1945. q. Can.$10 to individuals; institutions Can.$13. Canadian Paraplegic Association, National Office, 1500 Don Mills Rd., Ste. 201, Don Mills, ON M3B 3K4, Canada. TEL 416-391-0203. FAX 416-391-2144. Ed. Howard Barrie. adv.; bk.rev.; film rev. circ. 5,000.

362.4   US
CAN-DO.* 1987. bi-m. $9. Can-Do, 6737 Morella Ave., N. Hollywood, CA 91606. Ed. Bill Baugh. illus.

362.4   CN   ISSN 0068-9424
CANADIAN PARAPLEGIC ASSOCIATION. ANNUAL REPORT. 1946. a. free. Canadian Paraplegic Association, National Office, 1500 Don Mills Rd., Ste. 201, Don Mills, ON M3B 3K4, Canada. TEL 416-391-0203. FAX 416-391-2144. circ. 5,000. **Document type:** corporate report.

362.4   UK   ISSN 0009-3297
CHESHIRE SMILE. 1954. q. free. Leonard Cheshire Foundation, Arnold House, 66 The Ridgeway, Enfield, Middx EN2 8JA, England. TEL 081-367-3544. Ed. Kay Christiansen. adv.: page £140. bk.rev.; illus.; circ. 7,450 (controlled). **Indexed:** Rehabil.Lit. **Document type:** newsletter.
  Description: News about the foundation's homes for the disabled worldwide, home care services in the U.K., and general articles about disability.

D A V MAGAZINE. (Disabled American Veterans) see MILITARY

362.4   371.9   US
D P H D NEWSLETTER. 1980. q. membership only. Council for Exceptional Children, Division for Physical & Health Disabilities, 1920 Association Dr., Reston, VA 22091-1589. TEL 703-620-3660. FAX 703-264-9494. Ed. Steve Castle. adv. circ. 2,200. **Document type:** newsletter.
  Description: Provides information on the division and its activities. Includes news about education for the physically handicapped child.

301   UK   ISSN 0968-7599
HV1551   CODEN: DHSOEG
DISABILITY & SOCIETY. 1986. q. $69 to individuals; institutions $228 (effective 1994). Carfax Publishing Co., P.O. Box 25, Abingdon, Oxon. OX14 3UE, England. TEL 44-235-555335. FAX 44-235-553559. (U.S. subscr. to: Carfax Publishing Co., Box 2025, Dunnellon, FL 32630) Ed. Len Barton. adv.; bk.rev.; illus.; stat.; index, cum.index. (also avail. in microfiche) **Indexed:** ASSIA, Curr.Adv.Ecol.Sci., Mult.Ed.Abstr., Psychol.Abstr., Sp.Ed.Needs Abstr., Stud.Wom.Abstr. **Document type:** academic/scholarly publication.
  —BLDSC (3595.421000); UnCover. **CCC**.
  Formerly (until 1993): Disability, Handicap and Society (ISSN 0267-4645)
  Refereed Serial

362.4   UK
DISABILITY NOW. 1953. m. £10 to individuals; institutions £15. The Spastics Society, 12 Park Crescent, London W1N 4EQ, England. TEL 071-383-4575. FAX 071-436-4582. Ed. Mary Wilkinson. adv. contact: Richard Gresham. bk.rev. circ. 23,000. **Indexed:** Rehabil.Lit., Sp.Ed.Needs Abstr. **Document type:** consumer publication.
  Formerly (until 1984): Spastics News (ISSN 0049-1810)
  Description: Topical news, information items, features, announcements and events of interest to disabled people, their parents, enablers and professionals.

DISABLED DRIVER. see TRANSPORTATION — Automobiles

362.4   616.836   US
FAMILY SUPPORT BULLETIN. q. free. United Cerebral Palsy Associations, Inc., Governmental Activities Office, 1522 K St., N.W., No. 1112, Washington, DC 20005-1202. TEL 202-842-1266. FAX 202-842-3519. **Document type:** bulletin.
  Description: Directed to families affected by cerebral palsy and other similar disabilities, consumers, care providers and advocates. Provides local and national information updates on trends in family support.

362.4   UK
GROOMS NEWS. 1979. s-a. free. John Grooms Association for Disabled People, 10 Gloucester Dr., Finsbury Park, London N4 2LP, England. TEL 081-802-7272. FAX 081-809-1754. adv. circ. 40,000. **Document type:** newsletter.
  Formerly: John Grooms Newsletter.

HANDICAPPED — VISUALLY IMPAIRED

362.4   JA   ISSN 0017-6605
HAGEMI/ENCOURAGEMENT; a journal for the guidance of the parents with crippled children. (Text in Japanese) 1955. bi-m. 3100 Yen. Japanese Society for Disabled Children - Nihon Shitai Fujiyuji Kyokai, 1-7, 1-chome, Komone, Itabashi-ku, Tokyo 173, Japan. Ed.Bd. adv.; bk.rev.; charts; illus.; stat. circ. 10,000.
Description: Medical and educational facts for parents and rehabilitation workers involved with the disabled.

617.087   UK
IN FOCUS. bi-m. free. Muscular Dystrophy Group of Great Britain and Northern Ireland, 7-11 Prescott Pl., London SW4 6BS, England. TEL 071-720-8055. FAX 071-498-0670. Ed. Alex Duncan. circ. 8,000. **Document type:** newsletter.

ITINERARY (BAYONNE); the magazine for travelers with physical disabilities. see *TRAVEL AND TOURISM*

LIBRARY RESOURCES FOR THE BLIND AND PHYSICALLY HANDICAPPED (PRINT EDITION). see *LIBRARY AND INFORMATION SCIENCES*

362.4   US   ISSN 1071-5657
MOUTH; the voice of disability rights. 1990. bi-m. $32 to individuals; institutions $48. Free Hand Press, Inc., 61 Brighton St., Rochester, NY 14607. FAX 716-442-2916. Ed. Lucy Gwin. bk.rev.; circ. 4,500 (paid). (also avail. in audio cassette; large print edition) **Document type:** consumer publication.

617.087   UK
MUSCULAR DYSTROPHY GROUP OF GREAT BRITAIN AND NORTHERN IRELAND. ANNUAL REVIEW. a. free. Muscular Dystrophy Group of Great Britain and Northern Ireland, 7-11 Prescott Pl., London SW4 6BS, England. TEL 071-720-8055. FAX 071-498-0670. **Document type:** corporate report.

362.4   SZ
PARACONTACT. (Text in French, German) q. Kantonstr. 40, CH-6207 Nottwil, Switzerland. circ. 11,000. **Document type:** newsletter.

616.087 362.4   US   ISSN 0031-1766
PARAPLEGIA NEWS. 1946. m. $15 (foreign $22). (Paralyzed Veterans of America, Inc.) P V A Publications, 2111 E. Highland Ave., Ste. 180, Phoenix, AZ 85016-4702. TEL 602-224-0500. FAX 602-224-0507. Ed. Cliff Crase. adv.; bk.rev.; illus. circ. 27,000. **Indexed:** Hlth.Ind., Rehabil.Lit., Sportsearch (1983-). **Document type:** consumer publication.
—UnCover.

362.4   SZ
PARAPLEGIE. (Text in French, German, Italian) q. Schweizer Paraplegiker-Stiftung, St.-Alban-Vorstadt 110, CH-4052 Basel, Switzerland. TEL 061-2814828. FAX 061-2814228. Ed. Guido Zaech. circ. 900,000. **Document type:** bulletin.

617.087   GW   ISSN 0723-5070
PARAPLEGIKER; das Nachrichtenmagazin der Querschnittgelaehmten. q. DM.28. Verlag fuer Medizin Dr. Ewald Fischer GmbH, Fritz-Frey-Str. 21, 69121 Heidelberg, Germany. TEL 06221-4062-0. Ed. Peter Mand. **Document type:** academic/scholarly publication.
—CCC.

362.4 371.9   US
PHYSICAL DISABILITIES - EDUCATION & RELATED SERVICES. 1978. s-a. membership only. Council for Exceptional Children, Division for Physical & Health Disabilities, 1920 Association Dr., Reston, VA 22091. TEL 703-620-3660. FAX 703-264-9494. Ed. Dr. Richard Sobsey. adv.; bk.rev. circ. 2,100.
Formerly: D P H Journal.
Description: Provides educational and support services for physically handicapped individuals.

362.4 371.9   US   ISSN 0891-8791
A POSITIVE APPROACH; a national magazine for the physically challenged. 1986. q. $15. A Positive Approach, Inc., Box 910, Millville, NJ 08332. TEL 609-451-4777. FAX 609-451-6678. Ed. Patricia Johnson. adv.; bk.rev. circ. 200,000.
Description: Features profiles and articles on endurance, training and motivation used in rehabilitation centers and hospitals throughout the nation. Covers a range of topics from arthritis to neuromuscular disorders, and encourages driving, education and employment for the physically challenged reader.

PRAXIS DER PSYCHOMOTORIK. see *PHYSICAL FITNESS AND HYGIENE*

340.5
RIGHTS OF PHYSICALLY HANDICAPPED PERSONS. 1984. base vol. (plus a. suppl.). $95. Shepard's - McGraw-Hill, Inc., Box 35300, Colorado Springs, CO 80935-3530. TEL 800-525-2474.
Description: Outlines both substantive and procedural provisions of federal laws and offers suggestions for remedial actions that can be pursued on behalf of handicapped clients.

S I G C A P H NEWSLETTER. (Special Interest Group on Computers and the Physically Handicapped) see *HANDICAPPED — Computer Applications*

617.087   UK
SEARCH (LONDON, 1957). 1957. 2/yr. free. Muscular Dystrophy Group of Great Britain and Northern Ireland, 7-11 Prescott Pl., London SW4 6BS, England. TEL 071-720-8055. FAX 071-498-0670. Ed. Alex Duncan. adv.; bk.rev. circ. 13,000 (controlled). **Indexed:** Rehabil.Lit. **Document type:** newsletter.
Formerly (until 1987): Muscular Dystrophy Journal (ISSN 0027-3740)

617.087
SPINAL CORD INJURY LIFE. 1972. q. $30 (foreign $50). National Spinal Cord Injury Association, 600 W. Cummings Pk., No. 2000, Woburn, MA 01801-6343. TEL 617-935-2722. Ed. Pamela Majors. adv.; bk.rev.; film rev. (back issues avail.) **Indexed:** Rehabil.Lit. **Document type:** newsletter.
Formerly (until July 1985): Paraplegia Life.
Description: Covers legislation, medical and research issues. Includes editorials, stories and news of interest to those who have sustained spinal cord injuries.

362.4   US   ISSN 0161-6706
GV709.3
SPORTS 'N SPOKES. 1975. bi-m. $12 (foreign $16). (Paralyzed Veterans of America, Inc.) P V A Publications, 2111 E. Highland Ave., Ste. 180, Phoenix, AZ 85016-4702. TEL 602-224-0500. FAX 602-224-0507. Ed. Cliff Crase. adv.; bk.rev. circ. 14,000. (back issues avail.) **Indexed:** Phys.Ed.Ind., Sports Per.Ind., Sportsearch (1978-). **Document type:** consumer publication.
—Faxon; UnCover.
Description: Covers wheelchair sports and recreation.

UPDATE (WASHINGTON). see *HANDICAPPED — Visually Impaired*

362.4   UK
W H. 1959. bi-m. £7. Wider Horizons, Ghyll Cottage, Ings, Kendal, Cumbria LA8 9PU, England. TEL 0539-821274. (Subscr. to: A.B. Fletcher, "Westbrook", Back Lane, Malvern, Worcs WR14 2HJ, England) Ed. Anne M. Dobson. bk.rev. circ. 570. (also avail. in talking book; back issues avail.) **Document type:** newsletter.
Description: Promotes wider interests, friendship through correspondence, and creative writing for physically handicapped and housebound people.

HANDICAPPED — Visually Impaired

362.41   US
A E R REPORT. 1984. bi-m. membership. Association for Education and Rehabilitation of the Blind and Visually Impaired (AER), 206 N. Washington St., Alexandria, VA 22314. TEL 703-548-1884. Ed. Lynn Abbott. circ. controlled.
Former titles: American Association of Workers for the Blind with Association for Education of the Visually Handicapped. Alliance News; (until 1983): American Association of Workers for the Blind. News and Views (ISSN 0002-7510)

362.41   US   ISSN 1067-5833
HV1790
A F B DIRECTORY OF SERVICES FOR BLIND AND VISUALLY IMPAIRED PERSONS IN THE UNITED STATES AND CANADA. biennial. $75. American Foundation for the Blind, Inc., 15 W. 16th St., New York, NY 10011. TEL 212-620-2000. FAX 212-620-2105. bibl. **Document type:** directory.
Former titles: A F B Directory of Services for Blind and Visually Impaired Persons in the United States (ISSN 0899-2533); A F B Directory of Agencies Serving the Visually Handicapped in the U S (ISSN 0732-1341)
Description: Lists and describes more than 3000 local, state, regional, and national services that help blind and visually impaired persons of all ages participate fully in the mainstream. All listings include organization name, address, telephone, contact person, and program description.

362.4
A F B NEWS. 1966. 4/yr. free. American Foundation for the Blind, Inc., 15 W. 16th St., New York, NY 10011. TEL 212-620-2000. FAX 212-620-2105. Ed. Liz Greco. adv. circ. 15,000. (tabloid format; back issues avail.; reprint service avail. from UMI) **Indexed:** Rehabil.Lit. **Document type:** newsletter.
Former titles: American Foundation for the Blind News; American Foundation for the Blind Newsletter (ISSN 0002-855X)
Description: For general readership about blindness and visual impairment, featuring people, programs, services, and activities.

362.41   US   ISSN 0195-363X
A L L-O-GRAMS. 1977. bi-m. Affiliated Leadership League of and for the Blind of America, 1101 17th St., N.W., Ste. 803, Washington, DC 20036-4704. TEL 202-775-8261. Ed. James H. Johnson. circ. 7,500.

A O. (Aktuele Onderwerpen) see *GENERAL INTEREST PERIODICALS — Netherlands*

686.2   US
A P H SLATE. s-a. free. American Printing House for the Blind, Inc., 1839 Frankfort Ave., Box 6085, Louisville, KY 40206-0085. TEL 502-895-2405. FAX 502-895-1509. (also avail. in Braille; large print edition in 14 pt.) **Document type:** newsletter.
Description: Contains articles about new products and new processes and APH.

A S. MAANDBLAD AKTIVITEITENSEKTOR; informatieblad voor bezigheidstherapie - aktiviteitenbegeleiding. see *SOCIAL SERVICES AND WELFARE*

ABILITIES. see *HANDICAPPED — Hearing Impaired*

026 020   US
ADDRESS LIST, REGIONAL AND SUBREGIONAL LIBRARIES FOR THE BLIND AND PHYSICALLY HANDICAPPED. 1971. s-a. free. U.S. Library of Congress, National Library Service for the Blind and Physically Handicapped, Washington, DC 20542. TEL 202-707-5100. FAX 202-707-0712. **Document type:** directory, government publication.

ADULT QUARTERLY. see *RELIGIONS AND THEOLOGY — Protestant*

362   UK
ADVOCATE. 1899. irreg. £4. National League of the Blind and Disabled, 2 Tenterden Rd., London N17 8BE, England. Ed. M.A. Barrett. adv.; bk.rev.; abstr.; stat. circ. 2,000. **Document type:** newsletter.
Formerly: Blind Advocate (ISSN 0006-4807)

362.41   US
AID & APPLIANCES REVIEW. Abbreviated title: A A R. ceased 1984; resumed 1992. irreg. Carroll Center for the Blind, 770 Center St., Newton, MA 02158. TEL 617-969-6200.

362.41   US   ISSN 0065-8359
AMERICAN FOUNDATION FOR THE BLIND. ANNUAL REPORT. 1923. a. free. American Foundation for the Blind, Inc., 15 W. 16th St., New York, NY 10011. TEL 212-620-2000. FAX 212-620-2105. **Document type:** corporate report.
Description: Highlights of the year's programs, services, publications, products, and personalities.

HANDICAPPED — VISUALLY IMPAIRED

371.9 US
AMERICAN PRINTING HOUSE FOR THE BLIND. DEPARTMENT OF EDUCATIONAL AND TECHNICAL RESEARCH. REPORT OF RESEARCH AND DEVELOPMENT ACTIVITIES. 1958. a. free. American Printing House for the Blind, Department of Educational and Technical Research, Box 6085, Louisville, KY 40206-0085. TEL 502-895-2405. FAX 502-895-2405. Ed. June E. Morris. circ. 1,000.
Former titles: American Printing House for the Blind. Department of Educational Research. Report of Research and Development Activities; American Printing House for the Blind. Department of Educational Research. Annual Report. (ISSN 0065-9800)

362.61 US ISSN 0005-3430
B V A BULLETIN. 1946. 6/yr. free. Blinded Veterans Association, National Board of Directors, 477 H St. N.W., Washington, DC 20001. TEL 202-371-8880. FAX 202-371-8258. Ed. Chris Bentley. illus.; stat. circ. 21,200. (also avail. in audio cassette; large print edition in 14 pt.) **Document type:** newsletter.
Description: Covers legislation, employment, aids and appliances, and association activities.

362 IE ISSN 0006-4815
BLIND CITIZEN. 1923. bi-m. National Council for the Blind of Ireland, P V Doyle House, Whitworth Rd., Drumcondra, Dublin 9. Ireland. TEL 01-307033. FAX 01-307787. Ed. Patrick Lyons. adv.; bk.rev. circ. 200. (also avail. in Braille)

371.911 GW ISSN 0176-7836
BLIND - SEHBEHINDERT; Zeitschrift fuer das Sehgeschaedigten-Bildungswesen. 1881. q. DM.30. Verein zur Foerderung der Blindenbildung e.V., c/o Bernd Hamann, Kronaeckerstr. 13, 71155 Altdorf, Germany. adv.; bk.rev.; abstr.; index. circ. 1,200.
Former titles: Zeitschrift fuer das Blinden- und Sehbehindertenbildungswesen (ISSN 0006-4858); Blindenfreund.

362.41 II ISSN 0006-4823
BLIND WELFARE. (Text in English) 1959. 3/yr. Rs.30 (Asia & Africa $15; Europe $20; U.S. & Canada $25). National Association for the Blind, 11 Khan Abdul Gaffar Khan Rd., Worli Seaface, Bombay 400 025, India. TEL 4936930. Ed. Subhash A. Datrange. adv.; bk.rev.; illus. circ. 1,000. (tabloid format)

361.42 052 SA
BLINDABA; braille magazine for black youth. (Text in English) 1989. m. free. South African National Council for the Blind, P.O. Box 11149, Brooklyn, Pretoria 0011, South Africa. TEL 012-346-1171. FAX 012-346-1177. circ. 900. **Document type:** consumer publication.

362.4 614.59 GW
DER BLINDENHELFER.* 1960. q. DM.7.80. Bund der Blindenfreunde e.V., Humboldtstr. 86, D-8500 Nuremberg, Germany. Ed. Erich Lohka. bk.rev. circ. 5,000.

371.911 DK ISSN 0901-4306
BLINDES JUL.* 1937. a. DKK 15. Dansk Blindesamfund, Moellebrovej 9, 9320 Klotterholm, Denmark. Ed. J. Kildegaard Hansen.

369.4 US
BOYS' LIFE (BRAILLE EDITION). Inkprint edition (ISSN 0006-8608) m. free to qualified personnel. Boy Scouts of America, Box 152079, Irving, TX 75015-2079. TEL 214-580-2000. Ed. Scott Stuckey. adv.; bk.rev.; film rev.; rec.rev.; illus.; tr.lit. circ. 500. **Indexed:** Ind.How To Do It (1963-).

027.663 US ISSN 0006-873X
Z5346.Z9
BRAILLE BOOK REVIEW (LARGE PRINT EDITION). 1932. bi-m. free to qualified individuals. U.S. Library of Congress, National Library Service for the Blind and Physically Handicapped, Washington, DC 20542. TEL 202-707-5100. FAX 202-707-0712. Ed. Ruth Nieland. bk.rev.; index. circ. 32,000. (also avail. in Braille; large print in 14 pt.; back issues avail.) **Document type:** bibliography, government publication.
Description: News of developments and activities in library services for blind and physically handicapped individuals and announcements of braille books and magazines recently added to the N.L.S. collection.

BRAILLE BOOKS (LARGE PRINT EDITION). see HANDICAPPED — Abstracting, Bibliographies, Statistics

794.1 UK ISSN 0006-8756
BRAILLE CHESS MAGAZINE. 1934. q. £0.77 per no. Royal National Institute for the Blind, Bakewell Rd., Orton Southgate, Peterborough, Cambridgeshire PE2 0XU, England. TEL 0733-370777. FAX 0733-317555. Ed. Hans Cohn. index. circ. 113. (Braille) **Document type:** consumer publication.

071 UK ISSN 0006-8764
BRAILLE DIGEST. 1940. m. £3.35. Royal National Institute for the Blind, Bakewell Rd., Orton Southgate, Peterborough, Cambridgeshire PE2 0XU, England. TEL 0733-370777. FAX 0733-317555. Ed. Ann Lee. circ. 645.
Formerly: Selections from World Digest of Current Fact and Comment.

284 US
BRAILLE EVANGELISM BULLETIN. 1956. q. donation. Lutheran Braille Evangelism Association, 1740 Eugene St., White Bear, MN 55110. TEL 612-426-0469. (Subscr. to: 1740 Eugene St., White Bear Lake, MN 55110) Ed. Rev. Dennis A. Hawkinson. circ. 1,000. (back issues avail.)
Description: Information on available religious material for the blind.

051 US ISSN 0006-8772
BRAILLE FORUM. 1962. m. free. American Council of the Blind, 1155 15th St. N.W., Ste. 720, Washington, DC 20005. TEL 202-467-5081. FAX 202-467-5085. Ed. Nolan Crabb. bk.rev. circ. 20,000. (also avail. in diskette format; Braille; large print edition in 16 pt.) **Indexed:** Yrbk.Assoc.Educ.& Rehab.Blind. **Document type:** newsletter.
●Also available online.
—UnCover.
Description: News and articles for council members.

615.8 UK ISSN 0006-8780
BRAILLE JOURNAL OF PHYSIOTHERAPY. 1947. m. free. Royal National Institute for the Blind, Bakewell Rd., Orton Southgate, Peterborough, Cambridgeshire PE2 0XU, England. TEL 0733-370777. FAX 0733-317555. circ. 126. (Braille) **Document type:** academic/scholarly publication.

070 JA
BRAILLE MAINICHI WEEKLY.* 1922. w. 350 Yen per no. Mainichi Newspapers, Osaka, Braille Mainichi Section, 2-36-Dojima, Kita-ku, Osaka, Japan. TEL 06-3348-8826. FAX 06-3348-8966. TELEX 22324. Ed. Katsuke Makita. adv. circ. 12,000. (Braille)
Formerly: Braille Mainichi (ISSN 0006-8799)

071 US ISSN 0006-8810
BRAILLE MIRROR; a current topic magazine. 1926. 10/yr. free to blind U.S. citizens. Braille Institute of America, Inc., 741 N. Vermont Ave., Los Angeles, CA 90029. TEL 213-663-1111. Ed. Douglas Menville. circ. 2,053. (Braille)
Description: For Braille grade II readers.

362.41 US ISSN 0006-8829
BRAILLE MONITOR (INKPRINT EDITION). 1956. m. $25 to non-members. National Federation of the Blind, 1800 Johnson St., Baltimore, MD 21230. TEL 410-659-9314. FAX 410-685-5653. Ed. Mrs. Barbara Pierce. bk.rev.; illus.; index. circ. 30,000. (also avail. in Braille; talking book; audio cassette; back issues avail.)
●Also available online.
—UnCover.
Description: Covers blindness and matters affecting the blind from the blind person's point of view. Includes social concerns, legal cases, reports on action by the NFB on current legislative issues, news of aids and appliances, how-to information, and features on blind persons.

781.24 780 UK ISSN 0006-8837
BRAILLE MUSIC MAGAZINE. 1910. m. £8. Royal National Institute for the Blind, Bakewell Rd., Orton Southgate, Peterborough, Cambridgeshire PE2 0XU, England. TEL 0733-370777. FAX 0733-317555. Ed. Roger Firman. adv. contact: Charlotte Cohen. circ. 425. (Braille) **Document type:** consumer publication.
Formerly: Braille Musical Magazine.
Description: Contains topical information of interest to blind musicians, teachers, students and music lovers.

072 UK ISSN 0006-8853
BRAILLE NEWS SUMMARY. 1947. w. free. Royal National Institute for the Blind, Bakewell Rd., Orton Southgate, Peterborough, Cambridgeshire PE2 0XU, England. TEL 0733-370777. FAX 0733-317555. Ed. Jo Solomon. circ. 1,004.

791.4 UK ISSN 0006-887X
BRAILLE RADIO TIMES. 1927. w. £0.29 per no. Royal National Institute for the Blind, Bakewell Rd., Orton Southgate, Peterborough, Cambridgeshire PE2 0XU, England. TEL 0733-370777. FAX 0733-317555. circ. 1,992. (Braille) **Document type:** consumer publication.

500 600 UK ISSN 0006-8896
BRAILLE SCIENCE JOURNAL; a record of scientific progress. 1936. m. £6. Scottish Braille Press, Craigmillar Park, Edinburgh EH16 5NB, Scotland. TEL 031-662-4445. FAX 031-622-1968. Ed. P. Duncan. adv. circ. 300. **Document type:** academic/scholarly publication.

790 362.4 UK ISSN 0006-890X
BRAILLE SPORTING RECORD. 1950. w. £8. Scottish Braille Press, Craigmillar Park, Edinburgh EH16 5NB, Scotland. TEL 031-662-4445. FAX 031-662-1968. Ed. J.H. Adams. adv. circ. 800. **Document type:** bulletin.

212.5 US ISSN 0006-8918
BRAILLE STAR THEOSOPHIST. 1926. q. free. (Theosophical Society) Theosophical Book Association for the Blind, Inc., 54 Krotona Hill, Ojai, CA 93023. TEL 805-646-2121. Ed. Dennis Gottschalk. circ. 2,000.

371.911 US
BRAILLE TECHNICAL TABLES BANK CATALOG. 1979. irreg. National Braille Association, Inc., 3 Townline Cir., Rochester, NY 14623. TEL 716-427-8260. circ. controlled. **Document type:** catalog.
Description: Lists braille standard technical tables for sale.

052 384.55 UK
BRAILLE TELEVISION TIMES. 1984. w. £0.29 per no. Royal National Institute for the Blind, Bakewell Rd., Orton Southgate, Peterborough, Cambridgeshire PE2 0XU, England. TEL 0733-370777. FAX 0733-317555. circ. 2,065. (Braille) **Document type:** consumer publication.

052 SA
BRAILLORAMA. (Text in Afrikaans, English) 1968. m. free. South Africa Blind Workers Organisation, P.O. Box 45129, Mayfair 2108, South Africa. TEL 839-1793. Ed. E. J.J. Kruger. bk.rev. circ. 354.

052 SA
BRAILLORETTE. SUPPLEMENT. bi-m. South Africa Blind Workers Organisation, P.O. Box 45129, Mayfair 2108, South Africa. TEL 839-1793. FAX 839-1795.

371.911 UK ISSN 0264-6196
HV1571
BRITISH JOURNAL OF VISUAL IMPAIRMENT. 1979. 3/yr. £25. South Regional Association for the Blind, 55 Eton Ave., London NW3 3ET, England. TEL 071-722-9703. (Co-sponsor: Association for the Education and Welfare of the Visually Handicapped) Eds. Monique Raffray, Michael Tobin. adv.; bk.rev.; illus.; index. circ. 1,500. (also avail. in Braille; audio cassette) **Indexed:** Mult.Ed.Abstr., Sp.Ed.Needs Abstr., Yrbk.Assoc.Educ.& Rehab.Blind. **Document type:** academic/scholarly publication.
—BLDSC (2326.400000); UnCover.
Formerly (until vol.4, 1983): Insight (London, 1979); Which superseded (in 1979): Teacher of the Blind (ISSN 0040-0440)
Description: Provides a focus for scholarship in the field of work with visually impaired people. Articles cover aspects of health, welfare, education and employment insofar as they are affected by a visual disability.

DAS BRUDERHAUS. see EDUCATION — Special Education And Rehabilitation

371.9 GW
DAS BUERO. bi-m. DM.100.10. Deutsche Blindenstudienanstalt e.V., Postfach 1160, 35001 Marburg, Germany. TEL 06421-606-0. Ed. Gerhard Freunscht. circ. 330. (also avail. in Braille) **Document type:** bulletin.

HANDICAPPED — VISUALLY IMPAIRED

371.911 GW
BUEROJOURNAL. bi-m. DM.36. Deutscher Blindenverband e.V., Bismarckallee 30, 53173 Bonn, Germany. TEL 0228-354037. FAX 0228-357719. (audio cassette) **Document type:** bulletin.

027.663 AG ISSN 0007-6015
BURBUJAS. 1968. m. free. Biblioteca Argentina para Ciegos, Lezica 3909, Buenos Aires, Argentina. (also avail. in Braille)

630 360 US
C B M I FAMILY MAGAZINE. 1990. q. donation. Christian Blind Mission International Inc., Box 19000, Greenville, SC 29602-9000. TEL 803-239-0065. FAX 803-239-0069. Eds. Beth Jost, Dave McComiskey.
Description: For Christians serving the blind and handicapped in developing nations.

362 CN
CANADIAN NATIONAL INSTITUTE FOR THE BLIND. NATIONAL ANNUAL REVIEW. (Text in English, French) 1919. a. Canadian National Institute for the Blind, National Office - Institut National Canadien pour les Aveugles, 1931 Bayview Ave., Toronto, Ont. M4G 4C8, Canada. TEL 416-480-7580. circ. 1,500.
Former titles: Canadian National Institute for the Blind. National Annual Report (ISSN 0826-838X); Canadian National Institute for the Blind. National Report (ISSN 0068-9378); Canadian National Institute for the Blind. Annual Report (ISSN 1191-4882)

CATHOLIC REVIEW (NEW YORK). see RELIGIONS AND THEOLOGY — Roman Catholic

362 ISSN 0009-1529
CHANNELS OF BLESSING. 1893. bi-m. £0.29 per no. for Braille ed.; Moon ed. free. Royal National Institute for the Blind, Bakewell Rd., Orton Southgate, Peterborough, Cambridgeshire PE2 0XU, England. TEL 0733-370777. FAX 0733-317555. circ. 229. (Braille; also avail. in Moon Embossed Type)
Document type: bulletin.

051 284 US
CHRISTIAN MAGNIFIER. 1955. m. $6. Lutheran Braille Evangelism Association, 1740 Eugene St., St. Paul, MN 55110. TEL 612-426-0469. Ed. Rev. Dennis Hawkinson. (audio cassette; large print edition in 18 pt.)

260 US ISSN 0009-5575
CHRISTIAN RECORD; for adult blind. 1899. m. free. Christian Record Services, 4444 S. 52nd St., Lincoln, NE 68516. TEL 402-488-0981. Ed. R.J. Kaiser. circ. 6,400. (also avail. in Braille)

260 US ISSN 0009-5583
CHRISTIAN RECORD TALKING MAGAZINE. 1955. bi-m. free. Christian Record Services, 4444 S. 52nd St., Lincoln, NE 68516. TEL 402-488-0981. Ed. R.J. Kaiser. circ. 22,300. (also avail. in talking book)

289.5 252 US ISSN 0145-7166
CHRISTIAN SCIENCE BIBLE LESSONS (BRAILLE EDITION). m. $2.50. (First Church of Christ, Scientist) Christian Science Publishing Society, Box 11341, Des Moines, IA 50350-1341. TEL 800-456-4851.

200 US
CHRISTIAN TALKING MAGAZINE. bi-m. free. Christian Mission for the Blind, 5354 Boy Scout Rd., Indianapolis, IN 46226. TEL 317-549-2386. circ. 457. (audio cassette)
Description: Compilation of sermons, music, interviews, poetry, and other features.

200 US
CHURCH OF SCOTLAND BRAILLE MAGAZINE. 1934. m. £0.30. (Church of Scotland, Publications Department) Scottish Braille Press, Craigmillar Park, Edinburgh EH16 5NB, Scotland. TEL 031-662-4445. FAX 031-662-1968. Ed. Gloria Rintoul. circ. 150. **Document type:** bulletin.

362.41 UK
COME GARDENING. (Text in Moon Embossed Type) 1973. q. free. Royal National Institute for the Blind, Bakewell Rd., Orton Southgate, Peterborough, Cambridgeshire PE2 0XU, England. TEL 0733-370777. FAX 0733-317555. c rc. 73. **Document type:** consumer publication.
Formerly: Gardener (Reigate).

COMPLETE DIRECTORY OF LARGE PRINT BOOKS AND SERIALS. see HANDICAPPED — Abstracting, Bibliographies, Statistics

371.911 370 US
COMPUTER ACCESS FOR THE BLIND IN EDUCATION AND EMPLOYMENT; project cable resource manual. 1984. a. $20. Carroll Center for the Blind, 770 Centre St., Newton, MA 02158. TEL 617-969-6200. Ed. Dina Rosenbaum. circ. 150. (looseleaf format; also avail. in magnetic tape; back issues avail.)
Description: Curriculum for teaching computer technology to the blind and visually impaired.

CONNECTIVE ISSUES. see MEDICAL SCIENCES — Cardiovascular Diseases

362.41 IT ISSN 0010-9169
CORRIERE DEI CIECHI. 1946. w. L.15000. Unione Italiana dei Ciechi, Via Borgognona 38, Rome, Italy. TEL 396-69940750. FAX 396-6786815. Dir. Tommaso Daniele. adv.; bk.rev.; illus. circ. 16,000. **Document type:** newsletter.
Description: Deals with subjects concerning life and social problems of visually impaired in Italy.

DAILY WORD. see RELIGIONS AND THEOLOGY

054.1 028.5 FR
DANS LE VENT. m. 74 F. Association pour les Aveugles, 106 rue de la Pompe, 75016 Paris, France. (also avail. in Braille)
Description: Aimed at adolescents aged 12-18.

051 US
DEAF - BLIND WEEKLY NEWS & NEWS SUMMARY. fortn. free to qualified personnel. Xavier Society for the Blind, 154 E. 23rd St., New York, NY 10010. TEL 212-473-7800. FAX 212-473-7801. Ed. Jeanette Scott. circ. 300. (also avail. in Braille; large print edition in 20 pt.)
Formerly: Deaf - Blind News Summary.
Description: World news written for the beginning reader; especially of religious interest.

371.911 US ISSN 1069-6857
DIALOGUE (SALEM); the magazine for the visually impaired. 1961. q. $25. Blindskills, Inc., Box 5181, Salem, OR 97304. TEL 503-581-4224. Ed. Carol McCarl. bk.rev. circ. 5,000. (also avail. in Braille (ISSN 1069-6865); audio cassette (ISSN 1069-6873); large print edition in 18 pt.) **Document type:** consumer publication.
Description: Includes articles, fiction, and poetry by blind writers; reports on current legislation, new products, and services; home and gardening hints; information about vocational, recreation, and travel opportunities.

052 UK ISSN 0012-236X
DIANE. (Text in Moon Embossed Type) 1960. m. free. Royal National Institute for the Blind, Bakewell Rd., Orton Southgate, Peterborough, Cambridgeshire PE2 0XU, England. TEL 0733-370777. FAX 0733-317555. Ed. Charlotte Cohen. circ. 218.

362.4 SA
DIENSGIDS VIR GESIGSGESTREMDE SUID-AFRIKANERS. (Editions in Afrikaans and English) 1985. biennial. R.25. South African National Council for the Blind, P.O. Box 11149, Brooklyn, Pretoria 0011, South Africa. TEL 012-346-1171. FAX 012-346-1177. circ. 250. **Document type:** directory.
Former titles (until 1990): Directory of Services for Visually Handicapped South Africans; Directory of Services Available to Visually Handicapped South Africans.

362.4 371.9 US
DIVISION ON VISUAL HANDICAPS QUARTERLY. 1956. q. membership only. Council for Exceptional Children, Division for the Visually Handicapped, 1920 Association Dr., Reston, VA 22091. TEL 703-620-3660. FAX 703-264-9494. Ed. Bob Brasher. adv. circ. 1,200.
Formerly: D V H Quarterly.
Description: Provides information on current developments concerning educating visually handicapped children.

052 CN ISSN 0012-5679
DOTS AND TAPS; Canada's national magazine for the deaf-blind. 1952. 4/yr. free. Canadian National Institute for the Blind, Ontario Division, 1929 Bayview Ave., Toronto, Ont. M4G 3E8, Canada. TEL 416-480-7417. FAX 416-480-7699. Ed. K.G. Wadman. circ. 310 (controlled). (also avail. in Braille)

051 US
ENSIGN TALKING BOOK. 1976. m. $10 suggested donation. Church of Jesus Christ of Latter-day Saints, 50 E. North Temple, 24th Fl., Salt Lake City, UT 84150. TEL 801-240-2477. circ. 3,000. (audio cassette)

499.992 899.992 FR ISSN 0014-0600
ESPERANTA LIGILO. (Text in Esperanto) 1904. 10/yr. fl.25. Ligo Internacia de Blindaj Esperantistoj, 20 Av. de Saint Exupery, 69100 Villeurbanne, France. Ed. Prof. Raymond Gonin. bk.rev. (Braille)

362.41 FR ISSN 0046-2586
ET LA LUMIERE FUT. 1943. m. (11/yr.). 97 F. Association pour les Aveugles, 106 rue de la Pompe, 75016 Paris, France. (also avail. in Braille)

808.068 US
EXPECTATIONS. 1948. a. free. Braille Institute of America, Inc., 741 N. Vermont Ave., Los Angeles, CA 90029. TEL 213-663-1111. Ed. Douglas Menville. illus.; circ. 3,000 (controlled). (Braille)
Description: For grades 3-6; Braille grade II.

054.1 028.5 FR
FEE CLAUDINE. bi-m. (with alt. bi-m supplement). 65 F. Association pour les Aveugles, 106 rue de la Pompe, 75016 Paris, France. (also avail. in Braille)

FIGHTING BLINDNESS NEWS. see MEDICAL SCIENCES — Ophthalmology And Optometry

371.911 UK
FIZZ. 1913. w. £0.19 per no. Royal National Institute for the Blind, Bakewell Rd., Orton Southgate, Peterborough, Cambridgeshire PE2 0XU, England. TEL 0733-370777. FAX 0733-317555. Ed. Sharon O'Keefe. circ. 186. (Braille)
Formerly: Royal National Institute for the Blind. School Magazine (ISSN 0048-8712)

052 200 UK
FLASH. bi-m. free. Torch Trust for the Blind, Torch House, Hallaton, Market Harborough, Leics. LE16 8UJ, England. TEL 0858-89301. FAX 0858-89371. (Braille; also avail. in audio cassette; large print) **Document type:** bulletin.
Description: Forum magazine for younger blind teenagers.

FLORIDA SCHOOL HERALD. see HANDICAPPED — Hearing Impaired

FOR YOUNGER READERS, BRAILLE AND TALKING BOOKS (LARGE PRINT EDITION). see HANDICAPPED — Abstracting, Bibliographies, Statistics

362.41 US ISSN 0883-3419
FUTURE REFLECTIONS. 1981. q. $15 to non-members; members $8. National Federation of the Blind, 1800 Johnson St., Baltimore, MD 21230. TEL 410-659-9314. FAX 410-685-5653. Ed. Barbara A. Cheadle. bk.rev.; film rev.; illus. circ. 10,000. (also avail. in audio cassette; back issues avail.) **Document type:** consumer publication.
Description: Provides practical guidance in the day-to-day aspects of raising blind children of all ages.

362.41 GW ISSN 0016-5859
DIE GEGENWART; Magazin fuer Blinde, Sehbehinderte und ihre Freunde. 1912. 11/yr. DM.55 for printed ed.; Braille, floppy disk and cassette eds. DM.60. Deutscher Blindenverband e.V., Bismarckallee 30, 53173 Bonn, Germany. TEL 0228-354037. FAX 0228-357719. Ed. Dr. Thomas Nicolai. adv.; bk.rev. circ. 4,720 (1,750 printed ed., 1,130 cassette ed., 1,840 Braille ed.). (also avail. in Braille; audio cassette; diskette format) **Document type:** bulletin.
Incorporates: Blindenselbsthilfe (ISSN 0172-0163); Which was formerly (until 1974): Blindenwelt (ISSN 0006-4866)

GLAD TIDINGS OF GOOD THINGS. see RELIGIONS AND THEOLOGY — Other Denominations And Sects

HANDICAPPED — VISUALLY IMPAIRED

240 US ISSN 0017-2359
GOSPEL MESSENGER. vol.19, 1966. m. free to the blind. Gospel Association for the Blind, Inc., Box 62, Del Ray Beach, FL 33447. TEL 407-274-9700. Ed. Rev. Robert Rathbun. circ. 1,600. (audio cassette)

GUIDE DOG NEWS. see *PETS*

GUIDE LINES (YORKTOWN HEIGHTS). see *PETS*

371.91 US
H K N C - T A C NEWS. s-a. free. Helen Keller National Center, Technical Assistance Center, 111 Middleneck Rd., Sands Point, NY 11050. TEL 516-944-8900. FAX 516-944-8751. Ed. Theresa Carr. (also avail. in Braille; large print edition in 24 pt.; back issues avail.) **Document type:** newsletter.
  Description: Topics relating to services for people who are deaf-blind, especially young adults.

027.663 AG ISSN 0017-6478
HACIA LA LUZ. 1927. m. free. Biblioteca Argentina para Ciegos, Lezica 3909, Buenos Aires, Argentina. (Braille)

371.911 GW
DIE HANDARBEITSBEILAGE. 4/yr. DM.11 for Braille ed.; cassette DM.25. Deutscher Blindenverband e.V., Bismarckallee 30, 53173 Bonn, Germany. TEL 0228-354037. FAX 0228-357719. (also avail. in Braille; audio cassette) **Document type:** bulletin.

647.96 GW
HILDESHEIMER BLINDENMISSION. q. Hildesheimer Blindenmission e.V., Helmerstr. 6, 31134 Hildesheim, Germany. TEL 05121-32044. FAX 05121-39911. **Document type:** newsletter.

011 GW
HOERBUCHVERZEICHNIS. a. DM.6. Zentralbuecherei fuer Blinde, Gustav-Adolf-Str. 7, 04105 Leipzig, Germany. TELEX 70976. bibl. (also avail. in Braille)

362.41 UK
HOME HELP. 1958. w. £8. Scottish Braille Press, Craigmillar Park, Edinburgh EH16 5NB, Scotland. TEL 031-662-4445. FAX 031-662-1968. Ed. Gloria Rintoul. (also avail. in Braille) **Document type:** bulletin.

371.911 GW
HORUS; Beitraege zur Integration Sehgeschaedigter. vol.37, 1975. q. DM.128. Deutsche Blindenstudienanstalt e.V., Postfach 1160, 35001 Marburg, Germany. TEL 06421-606-0. Ed.Bd. adv.; bk.rev.; illus. circ. 4,000. **Document type:** academic/scholarly publication.
  Description: For and about the blind and sight-impaired: education, integration, conference information.

I C E V H EDUCATOR. (International Council for Education of the Visually Handicapped) see *EDUCATION — Special Education And Rehabilitation*

I C U C: I SEE YOU SEE. see *GENERAL INTEREST PERIODICALS — United States*

I G E NEWS. (International Guiding Eyes) see *PETS*

362 US
ILLINOIS BRAILLE MESSENGER (BRAILLE EDITION). 1930. q. $5. Illinois Council of the Blind, Box 1336, Springfield, IL 62705. Ed. Clyde Forth. abstr.; tr.lit. circ. 2,000 (combined). (Braille)
  Description: Disseminates material submitted by agencies, organizations and individuals to inform, encourage, and inspire the visually impaired people of Illinois.

362 US ISSN 0019-1906
ILLINOIS BRAILLE MESSENGER (INKPRINT EDITION). 1930. q. $5. Illinois Council of the Blind, Box 1336, Springfield, IL 62705. Ed. Clyde Forth. abstr.; tr.lit. circ. 2,000 (combined). (also avail. in Braille)

362.41 SA
IMFAMA (BRAILLE EDITION). (Text in Afrikaans, English) 1962. bi-m. R.30 contribution (effective 1993). South African National Council for the Blind, P.O. Box 11149, Brooklyn, Pretoria 0011, South Africa. TEL 012-346-1171. FAX 012-346-1177. Ed. William Rowland. circ. 631. (Braille; also avail. in audio cassette; also avail. in print) **Document type:** academic/scholarly publication.

362.41 SA ISSN 0019-2724
IMFAMA (INKPRINT EDITION). (Text in Afrikaans, English) 1961. bi-m. R.30 contribution (effective 1993). South African National Council for the Blind, P.O. Box 11149, Brooklyn, Pretoria 0011, South Africa. TEL 012-346-1171. FAX 012-346-1177. Ed. William Rowland. adv.; illus. circ. 1,224. (also avail. in Braille; magnetic tape) **Document type:** academic/scholarly publication.

362.41 SA
IMFAMA (TAPE EDITION). (Text in Afrikaans, English) 1961. bi-m. R.15. South African National Council for the Blind, P.O. Box 11149, Brooklyn, Pretoria 0011, South Africa. TEL 012-346-1171. FAX 012-346-1177. Ed. William Rowland. circ. 362. (magnetic tape; also avail. in Braille) **Document type:** academic/scholarly publication.

362.41 US
IN FOCUS (MOUNTAIN VIEW). q. free (typically set in Jan.). TeleSensory, Inc., 455 N. Bernardo Ave., Box 7455, Mountain View, CA 94043. TEL 415-960-0920. FAX 415-969-9064. Ed. Kathy Guleff. circ. 60,000. (back issues avail.) **Document type:** newsletter.
  Former titles: Focus on Technology; (until 1989) R E News.
  Description: Offers technological aids serving the low vision and blind community.

051 028.5 US
IN FOCUS (NEW YORK). 1972. irreg. (1-2/yr.). free. National Association for Visually Handicapped, 22 W. 21st St., 6th Fl., New York, NY 10010. TEL 212-889-3141. Ed. Lorraine H. Marchi. circ. 10,000. (only avail. in large print in 18 pt.) **Document type:** newsletter.
  Description: Stories by and for children. Information for parents and educators.

027.663 362.4 US
IN TOUCH (AUSTIN). Spanish edition: Avisos. 1982. q. free. Texas State Library, Talking Book Program, Box 12927, Austin, TX 78711. Ed. Renulfo Ramirez. circ. 8,000. (looseleaf format; also avail. in Braille; Spanish ed. avail. on audio cassette; large print edition in 14 pt.) **Document type:** newsletter.

362.41 UK
IN TOUCH (REIGATE). (Text in Moon Embossed Type) 1984. q. free. Royal National Institute for the Blind, Bakewell Rd., Orton Southgate, Peterborough, Cambridgeshire PE2 0XU, England. TEL 0733-370777. FAX 0733-317555. circ. 91.

052 CN
IN TOUCH (TORONTO). 1975. q. avail. on request. John Milton Society for the Blind in Canada, 40 St. Clair Ave., E., Ste. 202, Toronto, ON M4T 1M9, Canada. TEL 416-960-3953. circ. 125. (Braille) **Document type:** consumer publication.

371.911 US
INSIGHT (NEW YORK, 1978). 1978. s-a. free. Helen Keller International Incorporated, 90 Washington St., New York, NY 10006. TEL 212-943-0890. FAX 212-943-1220. TELEX 668152. Ed. John M. Palmer. circ. 3,000. **Document type:** newsletter.
  Formerly (until 1987): H K I Report.

052 CN ISSN 0315-5757
INSIGHT (TORONTO). 1973. bi-m. avail. on request. John Milton Society for the Blind in Canada, 40 St. Clair Ave., E. Ste. 202, Toronto, ON M4T 1M9, Canada. TEL 416-960-3953. circ. 3,200. **Document type:** newspaper.

INSIGHT (WASHINGTON, 1990). see *MEDICAL SCIENCES — Ophthalmology And Optometry*

052 CN
INSOUND. 1974. q. avail. on request. John Milton Society for the Blind in Canada, 40 St. Clair Ave. E., Ste. 202, Toronto, ON M4T 1M9, Canada. TEL 416-960-3953. circ. 350. (audio cassette)

371.911 371.9 617.7 GW
JAHRBUCH FUER BLINDENFREUNDE. a. DM.5. Deutscher Blindenverband e.V., Bismarckallee 30, 53173 Bonn, Germany. TEL 0228-354037. FAX 0228-357719. Ed.Bd. circ. 40,000. (back issues avail.) **Document type:** corporate report.

362.41 US
JEWISH BRAILLE INSTITUTE OF AMERICA. DIRECTORY OF SERVICES. a. Jewish Braille Institute of America, Inc., 110 E. 30th St., New York, NY 10016. TEL 212-889-2525. FAX 212-689-3692. **Document type:** directory.
  Description: Directory that describes Jewish Braille Institute programs, activities and services.

296 US ISSN 0021-6321
JEWISH BRAILLE REVIEW. 1931. m. free to the blind. Jewish Braille Institute of America, Inc., 110 E. 30th St., New York, NY 10016. TEL 212-889-2525. Ed. Dr. Jacob Freid. bk.rev.; bibl. circ. 2,300.
  Description: Covers articles, stories and poetry from all sources of Judaic content for blind Jewish readers or non-Jewish blind readers interested in Judaica.

647.9654 US
JEWISH GUILD FOR THE BLIND. NEWSLETTER. 1960. q. free. Jewish Guild for the Blind, 15 W. 65th St., New York, NY 10023. TEL 212-769-6200. FAX 212-769-6237. Ed. Peter C. Williamson. circ. 19,000. **Document type:** newsletter.
  Formerly: Jewish Guild of the Blind. Guild News.
  Description: Covers events, programs and people at the guild and its affiliate organizations.

362 AU ISSN 0021-7174
JOHANN WILHELM KLEIN; literarische Zeitschrift fuer Blinde. 1904. m. S.470. Bundes-Blindenerziehungsinstitut, Wittelsbachstr. 5, A-1020 Vienna, Austria. Ed. Eva Papsttig. bk.rev.; bibl.; charts. circ. 180. (tabloid format) **Document type:** bulletin.

JOHN MILTON ADULT LESSONS QUARTERLY. see *RELIGIONS AND THEOLOGY*

200 US
JOHN MILTON MAGAZINE. (Supplements avail.: Motto Calendar, World Day of Prayer Service, World Community Day Service, May Fellowship Day Service) 1935. m. free. John Milton Society for the Blind. Rm. 455, 475 Riverside Dr., New York, NY 10115. TEL 212-870-3335. Eds. Pam Toplisky, Darcy Quigley. bk.rev. circ. 10,050 (Braille ed. 2,850; large print ed. 7,200). (also avail. in Braille; large print edition in 24 pt.) **Document type:** newsletter.
  Description: Contains stories, poetry, informative, educational and devotional reading material from over 50 religious periodicals.

015 US
JOHN MILTON TALKING BOOK MAGAZINE. 1952. bi-m. free. John Milton Society for the Blind, Rm. 455, 475 Riverside Dr., New York, NY 10115. TEL 212-870-3335. Eds. Pam Toplisky, Darcy Quigley. circ. 1,850. (audio cassette) **Document type:** newsletter.
  Formerly: John Milton Talking Book (ISSN 0021-7220)
  Description: Includes three hours of sacred music, poetry, stories, historical and biographical material, and devotional and informative articles.

371.911 US
JOTTINGS. 1950. m. free. Gospel Association for the Blind, Inc., Box 62, Delray Beach, FL 33447. TEL 407-274-9700. Ed. Bea Montanus. circ. 15,000.

HANDICAPPED — VISUALLY IMPAIRED

362.41 US ISSN 0145-482X
HV1571
JOURNAL OF VISUAL IMPAIRMENT & BLINDNESS. 1907. bi-m. $75. American Foundation for the Blind, Inc., 15 W. 16th St., New York, NY 10011. TEL 212-620-2000. FAX 212-620-2105. (Subscr. to: 49 Sheridan Ave., Albany, NY 12210. TEL 518-436-9686. FAX 518-436-7433) Ed. Mary Ellen Mulholland. adv. contact: Karen McVeigh. bk.rev. circ. 3,200. (also avail. in microform from UMI; audio cassette; Braille; reprint service avail. from UMI) **Indexed:** Abstr.Soc.Work., Adol.Ment.Hlth.Abstr., C.I.J.E., Curr.Cont., Educ.Ind., Except.Child Educ.Abstr, Excerp.Med., Lang.& Lang.Behav.Abstr., Psychol.Abstr., Rehabil.Lit., Soc.Work Res.& Abstr., Sp.Ed.Needs Abstr., SSCI, Yrbk.Assoc.Educ.& Rehab.Blind. **Document type:** academic/scholarly publication.
—BLDSC (5072.495000); Faxon; UnCover; SWETS; UMI.
Formerly (until 1977): New Outlook for the Blind (ISSN 0028-6435); **Incorporates** (1962-1977): A F B Research Bulletin (ISSN 0065-8367)
Description: Interdisciplinary journal of record on blindness and visual impairment that serves as a forum for the exchange of ideas, airing of controversies, and discussion of issues.
Refereed Serial

KEIRAKU SHINRYO. see *ALTERNATIVE MEDICINE*

052 KE
KENYA SOCIETY FOR THE BLIND. ANNUAL REPORT AND ACCOUNTS. (English) 1957. a. free. Kenya Society for the Blind, P.O. Box 46656, Nairobi, Kenya. TEL 254-2-501657. circ. 2,000 (controlled). **Document type:** corporate report.

362.41 GW ISSN 0023-463X
HV1571
DER KRIEGSBLINDE; Zeitschrift fuer Verstaendnis und Verstaendigung. 1950. m. DM.26. Bund der Kriegsblinden Deutschlands e.V., Schumannstr. 35, 53113 Bonn, Germany. Ed. Alfred Lauster. adv.; illus.

371.911 US ISSN 0023-8414
LANTERN. 1931. 2/yr. free. Perkins School for the Blind, 175 N. Beacon St., Watertown, MA 02172-9982. TEL 617-924-3434. FAX 617-926-2027. TELEX 910 240 9886. Ed. Jennifer T. Brewster. bk.rev. circ. 50,345 (345 Braille ed., 50,000 inkprint ed.). (also avail. in Braille) **Indexed:** Except.Child.Educ.Abstr. **Document type:** newsletter.

617.7 616.21 AT
LANTERN LIGHT; news and views from clubs, committees and auxiliaries. 1986. q. free. Royal N S W Institut for Deaf and Blind Children, Deaf and Blind Children's Centre, 361-365 North Rocks Rd., North Rocks, N.S.W. 2151, Australia. FAX 02-871-2196. Ed. Tom Sweeney. circ. 1,400. (back issues avail.) **Document type:** newsletter.

054.1 840 FR
LIAISON. (Includes two supplements) bi-m. 78 F. Association pour les Aveugles, 106 rue de la Pompe, 75016 Paris, France. (also avail. in Braille)

LIBRARY RESOURCES FOR THE BLIND AND PHYSICALLY HANDICAPPED (PRINT EDITION). see *LIBRARY AND INFORMATION SCIENCES*

LIFEGLOW. see *RELIGIONS AND THEOLOGY*

051 US
LIFEPRINTS. 1983. 4/yr. $20. Blindskills, Inc., Box 5181, Salem, OR 97304. TEL 503-581-4224. Ed. Carol McCarl. circ. 500. (also avail. in Braille; audio cassette; large print edition in 18 pt.) **Document type:** consumer publication.
Description: Covers careers, sports, and leisure.

630 360 US
LIGHT (WHEATON). 1978. bi-m. free. Christian Blind Mission International Inc., Box 19000, Greenville, SC 29602-9000. TEL 803-239-0065. FAX 803-239-0069. stat.; circ. 38,000 (controlled). (looseleaf format)
Description: Overview of the medical rehabilitational and spirtual activities of CBM co-workers in over 98 developing countries.

371.911 US
LIGHT: ANNUAL REPORT. 1929. a. Braille Institute of America, Inc., 741 N. Vermont Ave., Los Angeles, CA 90029. TEL 213-663-1111. Ed. Paul J. Porrelli. charts; illus.; stat. circ. 66,000.

362.41 UK ISSN 0024-3361
LIGHT OF THE MOON. (Text in Moon Embossed Type) 1939. m. free. Royal National Institute for the Blind, Bakewell Rd., Orton Southgate, Peterborough, Cambridgeshire PE2 0XU, England. TEL 0733-370777. FAX 0733-317555. Ed. Jim Cummings. circ. 200.

362.41 US ISSN 0792-0873
LIKUTIM; a journal of visual impairment and blindness. (Text in Hebrew) 1981. s-a. free. Jewish Braille Institute of America, Inc., 110 E. 30th St., New York, NY 10016. TEL 212-889-2525. Ed. Joanne Jahr. circ. 1,000. (also avail. in talking book; back issues avail.)
Description: Covers information on blindness and visual impairment distributed in Israel for Israeli blind persons.

362 FR ISSN 0024-6727
LOUIS BRAILLE. 1882. m. 97 F. Association Valentin Hauy pour le Bien des Aveugles, 5 rue Duroc, 75343 Paris Cedex 07, France. Pub. Louis Ciccone. circ. 1,800. (Braille)

380 US
LUTHERAN DIGEST (LARGE PRINT EDITION). 1990. q. free. (Lutheran Church - Missouri Synod) Lutheran Library for the Blind, 1333 S. Kirkwook Rd., St. Louis, MO 63122. TEL 800-433-3954. Ed. Rev. R. Rynerson. (also avail. in Braille; large print in 14 pt.)
Description: Includes inspirational stories and features.

284 284 US ISSN 0024-7480
LUTHERAN MESSENGER FOR THE BLIND. 1927. m. free. Lutheran Church - Missouri Synod, Board for Mission Services, 1333 S. Kirkwood Rd., St. Louis, MO 63122. TEL 314-965-9000. Ed. Rev. David Andrus. bk.rev. circ. 900. (Braille; also avail. in audio cassette)
Description: Includes Christian devotionals, Bible studies, poetry and short stories.

LUTHERAN WITNESS (LARGE PRINT EDITION). see *RELIGIONS AND THEOLOGY — Protestant*

362 FR ISSN 0024-7685
LUX VERA. 1929. bi-m. 22 F. per no. Association la Croisade des Aveugles, 15 rue Mayet, 75006 Paris, France. Ed. Jacques Dard. illus. circ. 6,500.

052 UK ISSN 0024-9351
MADAM. 1937. m. £8.50. Scottish Braille Press, Craigmillar Park, Edinburgh EH16 5NB, Scotland. TEL 031-662-4445. FAX 031-662-1968. Ed. Gloria Rintoul. adv. circ. 750. (also avail. in Braille) **Document type:** bulletin.

362.4 CC ISSN 1003-1103
MANGREN YUEKAN/THE BLIND MONTHLY. (Text in Chinese) m. (Zhongguo Canjiren Fuli Lianhehui) Disability in China, Inc., A-8 Huixin Li, Anwai, Chaoyang-qu, Beijing 100101, People's Republic of China. TEL 4227840. (Dist. in US by: China Books & Periodicals, Inc., 2929 24th St., San Francisco, CA 94110. TEL 415-228-2994) Ed. Yang Zhongchen.
Description: General interest magazine for the blind.

371.9 GW
MARBURGER BEITRAEGE ZUR INTEGRATION SEHGESCHAEDIGTER. bi-m. DM.85. Deutsche Blindenstudienanstalt e.V., Postfach 1160, 35001 Marburg, Germany. TEL 06421-606-0. (Co-sponsor: Deutscher Verein Blinder und Sehbehinderter in Studium und Beruf) adv.; bk.rev. circ. 800. (also avail. in Braille) **Document type:** bulletin.
Formerly: Marburger Beitraege zum Blindenbildungswesen.

371.9 GW
MARBURGER BUECHERLISTEN. bi-m. free. Deutsche Blindenstudienanstalt e.V., Postfach 1160, 35001 Marburg, Germany. TEL 06421-606-0. adv.; bk.rev. circ. 2,500. (also avail. in Braille) **Document type:** bibliography.

051 362 US ISSN 0025-5955
MATILDA ZIEGLER MAGAZINE FOR THE BLIND. 1907. 12/yr. free. Matilda Ziegler Publishing Co. for the Blind, Inc., 20 W. 17th St., New York, NY 10011. Ed. Michael Mellor. bk.rev. circ. 10,000. (Braille; audio cassette)

MICRO MATERIALS UPDATE. see *COMPUTERS — Personal Computers*

362.41 UK ISSN 0027-0911
MOON MAGAZINE. (Text in Moon Embossed Type) 1906. m. free. Royal National Institute for the Blind, Bakewell Rd., Orton Southgate, Peterborough, Cambridgeshire PE2 0XU, England. TEL 0733-370777. FAX 0733-317555. Ed. Charlotte Cohen. circ. 450.

362.41 UK
MOON MESSENGER. (Text in Moon Embossed Type) 1939. m. free. Royal National Institute for the Blind, Bakewell Rd., Orton Southgate, Peterborough, Cambridgeshire PE2 0XU, England. TEL 0733-370777. FAX 0733-317555. circ. 155.

052 UK
MOON NEWSPAPER. w. free. Royal National Institute for the Blind, Bakewell Rd., Orton Southgate, Peterborough, Cambridgeshire PE2 0XU, England. TEL 0733-370777. FAX 0733-317555. Ed. Jim Cummings.

362.41 UK ISSN 0047-8083
MOON RAINBOW. (Text in Moon Embossed Type) 1934. q. free. Royal National Institute for the Blind, Moon Branch, P.O. Box 173, Peterborough PE2 0WS, England. TEL 0733-370777. circ. 94.

MUSIC & MUSICIANS: BRAILLE SCORES CATALOG - CHORAL (LARGE-PRINT EDITION). see *HANDICAPPED — Abstracting, Bibliographies, Statistics*

MUSIC & MUSICIANS: BRAILLE SCORES CATALOG - INSTRUMENTAL (LARGE-PRINT EDITION). see *HANDICAPPED — Abstracting, Bibliographies, Statistics*

MUSIC & MUSICIANS: BRAILLE SCORES CATALOG - ORGAN (LARGE-PRINT EDITION). see *HANDICAPPED — Abstracting, Bibliographies, Statistics*

MUSIC & MUSICIANS: BRAILLE SCORES CATALOG - PIANO (LARGE-PRINT EDITION). see *HANDICAPPED — Abstracting, Bibliographies, Statistics*

MUSIC & MUSICIANS: BRAILLE SCORES CATALOG - VOCAL. PART I: CLASSICAL (LARGE-PRINT EDITION). see *HANDICAPPED — Abstracting, Bibliographies, Statistics*

MUSIC & MUSICIANS: BRAILLE SCORES CATALOG - VOCAL. PART II: POPULAR (LARGE-PRINT EDITION). see *HANDICAPPED — Abstracting, Bibliographies, Statistics*

MUSIC & MUSICIANS: INSTRUCTIONAL CASSETTE RECORDINGS CATALOG (LARGE-PRINT EDITION). see *HANDICAPPED — Abstracting, Bibliographies, Statistics*

MUSIC & MUSICIANS: INSTRUCTIONAL DISC RECORDINGS CATALOG (LARGE-PRINT EDITION). see *HANDICAPPED — Abstracting, Bibliographies, Statistics*

MUSIC & MUSICIANS: LARGE-PRINT SCORES AND BOOKS CATALOG (LARGE-PRINT EDITION). see *HANDICAPPED — Abstracting, Bibliographies, Statistics*

HANDICAPPED — VISUALLY IMPAIRED

780 US ISSN 0364-7501
ML1
MUSICAL MAINSTREAM (LARGE-PRINT EDITION). 1942. q. free to qualified personnel. U.S. Library of Congress, National Library Service for the Blind and Physically Handicapped, Music Section, Washington, DC 20542. TEL 202-707-5100. FAX 202-707-0712. circ. 300. (also avail. in Braille; diskette format; large print in 14 pt.) **Document type:** government publication.
—UnCover.
Former titles (until Dec. 1976): New Braille Musician (ISSN 0006-8845); Braille Musician.
Description: Contains selected articles from music magazines.

284 US
MY DEVOTIONS (LARGE PRINT EDITION). m. free. Lutheran Library for the Blind, 1333 S. Kirkwood Ave., St. Louis, MO 63122. TEL 800-433-3954. (also avail. in Braille; large print in 22 pt.)
Description: For ages 8-13.

371.91 US
NAT - CENT NEWS. 3/yr. $10. Helen Keller National Center for Deaf-Blind Youths and Adults, 111 Middleneck Rd., Sands Point, NY 11050. TEL 516-944-8900. FAX 516-944-7302. Ed. Robert J. Smithdas. circ. 3,700. (also avail. in Braille; large print edition in 24 pt.)
Description: Contains articles on legislation, services, aids, devices, human interest, and problems related to deaf-blindness.

647.9654 II
NATIONAL ASSOCIATION FOR THE BLIND, INDIA. ANNUAL REPORT. (Text in English) 1959. a. free. National Association for the Blind, India, 11 Khan Abdul Gaffar Khan Road, Worli Seaface, Bombay 400025, India. TEL 4936930. FAX 49325399. Ed. Subhash A. Datrange. stat. circ. 1,000.

371.911 US
NATIONAL ASSOCIATION FOR VISUALLY HANDICAPPED. ANNUAL BULLETIN. 1964. a. free. National Association for Visually Handicapped, 22 W. 21st St., 6th Fl., New York, NY 10010. TEL 212-889-3141. Ed. Lorraine H. Marchi. circ. 16,000. (back issues avail.) **Document type:** bulletin.
Description: Covers progress and new programs of the association.

362.4 US ISSN 0550-5666
HV1788
NATIONAL BRAILLE ASSOCIATION. BULLETIN. Key Title: Bulletin of the National Braille Association, Inc. 1946. 4/yr. $30 (foreign $40). National Braille Association, Inc., 3 Townline Cir., Rochester, NY 14623. TEL 716-427-8260. circ. 2,000. (also avail. in Braille; audio cassette) **Indexed:** ERIC, Yrbk.Assoc.Educ.& Rehab.Blind. **Document type:** newsletter.
Formerly: National Braille Club. Bulletin (ISSN 0097-6512)
Description: Series of articles called "Sharpen Your Skills", a thorough summary of technical advice to keep transcribers and narrators up-to-date.

371.911 US
NATIONAL BRAILLE ASSOCIATION. GENERAL INTEREST CATALOG. irreg. National Braille Association, Inc., 3 Townline Cir., Rochester, NY 14623. TEL 716-427-8260. circ. controlled. (also avail. in audio cassette) **Document type:** catalog.
Description: Lists recreational and vocational braille books for sale.

371.911 780 US
ML136.U5
NATIONAL BRAILLE ASSOCIATION. MUSIC CATALOG. 1975. irreg. (approx. every 3 yrs.). National Braille Association, Inc., 3 Townline Cir., Rochester, NY 14623. TEL 716-427-8260. circ. controlled. (also avail. in audio cassette) **Document type:** catalog.
Description: Lists braille music for sale.

371.911 US
NATIONAL BRAILLE ASSOCIATION. TEXTBOOK CATALOG. irreg. (approx. every 3 yrs.). National Braille Association, Inc., 3 Townline Cir., Rochester, NY 14623. TEL 716-427-8260. circ. controlled. (also avail. in audio cassette) **Document type:** catalog.
Description: Lists college level and adult braille books for sale.

052 UK ISSN 0047-8768
NATIONAL BRAILLE MAIL. 1906. s-w. £5.75. Royal National Institute for the Blind, Bakewell Rd., Orton Southgate, Peterborough, Cambridgeshire PE2 0XU, England. TEL 0733-370777. FAX 0733-317555. circ. 276.

362.41 US
NATIONAL BRAILLE PRESS RELEASE. 1991. 2/yr. free. National Braille Press, Inc., 88 St. Stephen St., Boston, MA 02115. TEL 617-266-6160. FAX 617-437-0456. Ed.Sarah Ellis. **Document type:** newsletter.
Description: Newsletter covering new releases from the Press in print and in Braille.

362.41 780 US
NATIONAL LIBRARY SERVICE. CIRCULAR SERIES (LARGE-PRINT). irreg., latest no.19, 1993. free to qualified individuals. U.S. Library of Congress, National Library Service for the Blind and Physically Handicapped, Washington, DC 20542. TEL 202-707-5100. FAX 202-707-0712. (also avail. in Braille; large print in 18 pts.) **Document type:** monographic series, government publication.

NATIONAL SOCIETY TO PREVENT BLINDNESS. ANNUAL REPORT. see *PUBLIC HEALTH AND SAFETY*

NATIONAL SOCIETY TO PREVENT BLINDNESS. MEMBER NEWS. see *PUBLIC HEALTH AND SAFETY*

362.41 UK
NEW BEACON (BRAILLE EDITION); the journal of blind welfare. 1951. m. £1.10. Royal National Institute for the Blind, Bakewell Rd., Orton Southgate, Peterborough, Cambridgeshire PE2 0XU, England. TEL 0733-370777. FAX 0733-317555. Ed. Ann Lee. adv.; charts; index. circ. 1,262. **Indexed:** ASSIA, Yrbk.Assoc.Educ.& Rehab.Blind.

362.41 UK ISSN 0028-4270
NEW BEACON (INKPRINT EDITION); the journal of blind welfare. 1917. m. £1.10 per no. Royal National Institute for the Blind, Bakewell Rd., Orton Southgate, Peterborough, Cambridgeshire PE2 0XU, England. TEL 0733-370777. FAX 0733-317555. Ed. Ann Lee. adv.; bk.rev.; charts; index. circ. 2,044. (also avail. in Braille) **Indexed:** ASSIA, Except.Child.Educ.Abstr., Sp.Ed.Needs Abstr.
—BLDSC (6082.190000).

071 US ISSN 0028-7814
NEW YORK TIMES LARGE TYPE WEEKLY. 1967. w. $58 (foreign $74). New York Times Company, 229 W. 43rd St., New York, NY 10036. TEL 212-556-1734. (Subscr. to: Box 9564, Uniondale, NY 11555-9948. TEL 800-631-2580) Ed. Dee Wedemeyer. bk.rev. (record; large print in 18 pt.)
Description: Highlights from the New York Times, including a crossword puzzle.

NOORUS. see *CHILDREN AND YOUTH — For*

054.1 FR
NOTRE REVUE. m. (except Aug. & Sep. combined). 67 F. Association pour les Aveugles, 106 rue de la Pompe, 75016 Paris, France. (also avail. in Braille)

362.41 UK ISSN 0048-1106
NUGGETS. m. St. Dunstan's for Men and Women Blinded in the Services, P.O. Box 4XB, 12-14 Harcourt St., London W1A 4XB, England. TEL 071-723-5021. Ed. Kay Lord. circ. 210. (Braille) **Document type:** abstracting/indexing.

362.41 AU ISSN 0029-9723
OESTERREICHISCHER BLINDENVERBAND. MITTEILUNGEN. vol.23, 1970. bi-m. Oesterreichischer Blindenverband, Mariahilfer Guertel 4, A-1060 Vienna, Austria. Ed. Matthias F. Bleier.

371.911 US ISSN 0740-218X
ON THE BEAM. 1982. 3/yr. $15. Lowe's Syndrome Association, Inc., 222 Lincoln St., W. Lafayette, IN 47906. TEL 317-743-3634. Ed. Jane Gallery. bk.rev. circ. 300. (back issues avail.) **Document type:** newsletter.
Description: Medical and educational articles about Lowe's syndrome, letters from parents and news.

301.412 US ISSN 0030-6959
OUR SPECIAL; magazine devoted to matters of interest to blind women. 1930. 6/yr. free to the blind. National Braille Press, Inc., 88 St. Stephen St., Boston, MA 02115. TEL 617-266-6160. FAX 617-437-0456. Ed. Jeanne Neale. bk.rev. circ. 2,559. (Braille)

617.712 UK ISSN 0048-4083
PHYSIOTHERAPISTS' QUARTERLY. 1950. q. £0.48 per no. Royal National Institute for the Blind, Bakewell Rd., Orton Southgate, Peterborough, Cambridgeshire PE2 0XU, England. TEL 0733-370777. FAX 0733-317555. circ. 105. (Braille)

786 UK ISSN 0048-4105
PIANO-TUNERS QUARTERLY. 1954. q. £0.38 per no. Royal National Institute for the Blind, Bakewell Rd., Orton Southgate, Peterborough, Cambridgeshire PE2 0XU, England. TEL 0733-370777. FAX 0733-317555. Ed. Christopher Bridgman. circ. 111. (Braille)

PILOT DOGS. see *PETS*

362.41 UK ISSN 0048-4881
PORTLAND MAGAZINE. 1960. m. £4. Royal National Institute for the Blind, Bakewell Rd., Orton Southgate, Peterborough, Cambridgeshire PE2 0XU, England. TEL 0733-370777. FAX 0733-317555. Ed. Donald Bell. circ. 309. (Braille)

362.61 UK ISSN 0033-0566
PROGRESS. 1881. m. £0.38 per issue. Royal National Institute for the Blind, Bakewell Rd., Orton Southgate, Peterborough, Cambridgeshire PE2 0XU, England. TEL 0733-370777. FAX 0733-317555. Ed. Jim Cummings. adv.; bk.rev. circ. 747. (Braille)
—BLDSC (6865.200000).

371.911 GW
PULSSCHLAG. bi-m. DM.24. Deutscher Blindenverband e.V., Bismarckallee 30, 53173 Bonn, Germany. TEL 0228-354037. FAX 0228-357719. (audio cassette) **Document type:** bulletin.

R E S N A NEWS. see *EDUCATION — Special Education And Rehabilitation*

362 US
R F B ISSUES. 3/yr. free. Recording for the Blind, Inc., 20 Roszel Rd., Princeton, NJ 08540. TEL 609-452-0606. Ed. Elizabeth Callahan. circ. 10,000. (back issues avail.) **Document type:** newsletter.
Formerly: Recording for the Blind News.
Description: Covers news and information about the organization's activities.

362 UK
RAINBOW (PETERBOROUGH). 1932. q. Royal National Institute for the Blind, Bakewell Rd., Orton Southgate, Peterborough, Cambridgeshire PE2 0XU, England. TEL 0733-370777. FAX 0733-317555. (Co-sponsor: National Deaf-Blind Helpers' League) circ. 339. (Braille; also avail. in Moon Embossed Type)
Formerly: Braille Rainbow (ISSN 0006-8888)

371.394 US ISSN 0890-0019
RAISED DOT COMPUTING NEWSLETTER. 1984. q. $18 for large print; cassette $20; diskette $24. Raised Dot Computing Inc., 408 S. Baldwin, Madison, WI 53703. TEL 608-257-9595. FAX 608-255-1800. bk.rev. circ. 250. (also avail. in audio cassette; diskette format; large print edition in 13 pt.) **Document type:** newsletter.
Description: Brief articles about the use of small computers for the blind; topics include low-cost braille devices, voice synthesis, paperless braille, use of computers by transcribers, and braille translation.

053.1 GW
READER'S DIGEST - DAS BESTE (GERMAN BRAILLE EDITION). m. DM.174.90. (Deutsche Blindenstudienanstalt) Verlag das Beste GmbH, Augustenstr. 1, Postfach 106020, 7000 Stuttgart 10, Germany. Ed. Renate Wriedt. circ. 530.
Formerly: Beste aus Reader's Digest (German Braille Edition).

RECORDING FOR THE BLIND. CATALOG OF RECORDED BOOKS. see *HANDICAPPED — Abstracting, Bibliographies, Statistics*

HANDICAPPED — VISUALLY IMPAIRED

RECORDING FOR THE BLIND. QUARTERLY DISK CATALOG. see *HANDICAPPED — Abstracting, Bibliographies, Statistics*

RECORDING FOR THE BLIND. QUARTERLY RECORDED CATALOG. see *HANDICAPPED — Abstracting, Bibliographies, Statistics*

362   US
RECORDING FOR THE BLIND ANNUAL REPORT. 1951. a. Recording for the Blind, Inc., 20 Roszel Rd., Princeton, NJ 08540. TEL 609-452-0606. FAX 609-987-8116. Ed. Elizabeth Callahan. circ. 10,000. (back issues avail.) **Document type:** corporate report.
    Description: Provides news, information and financial reports of the organization.

371.911   US   ISSN 0899-1510
HV1571
REVIEW (WASHINGTON); rehabilitation and education for blindness and visual impairment. 1951. q. $27 to individuals; institutions $53. (Helen Dwight Reid Educational Foundation) Heldref Publications, 1319 Eighteenth St., N.W., Washington, DC 20036-1802. TEL 202-296-6267. FAX 202-296-5149. (Co-sponsor: Association for the Education and Rehabilitation of the Blind and Visually Impaired) Ed. Helen Strang. adv. contact: Raymond Rollo. bk.rev.; bibl.; index. circ. 3,600. (also avail. in microform; reprint service avail.) Indexed: C.I.J.E., Cont.Pg.Educ., Curr.Cont., Educ.Ind., ERIC, Except.Child.Educ.Abstr., Psychol.Abstr., Rehabil.Lit., SSCI, Yrbk.Assoc.Educ.& Rehab.Blind. **Document type:** academic/scholarly publication.
—BLDSC (7300.261500); Faxon; UnCover; SWETS; UMI. CCC.
    Former titles: Education of the Visually Handicapped (ISSN 0013-1458); International Journal for the Education of the Blind.
    Description: Reports on useful practises, research findings, experiments, professional experiences and controversial issues. For all persons concerned with education and rehabilitation of children, youth and adults who have visual impairments including those who are multihandicapped and or deaf-blind.
    Refereed Serial

371.911   GW
RITA. bi-m. DM.36. Deutscher Blindenverband e.V., Bismarckallee 30, 53173 Bonn, Germany. TEL 0228-354037. FAX 0228-357719. (also avail. in Braille; audio cassette) **Document type:** bulletin.

362.41   IT
RIVISTA DI OFTALMOLOGIA SOCIALE. 1977. q. L.30000. Agenzia Internazionale per la Prevenzione della Cecita, Sezione Italiana - International Agency for the Prevention of Blindness, Italian Section, Via Borgognona 38, 00187 Rome, Italy. TEL 6-68-40-750. FAX 6-67-86-815. adv. circ. 5,000.

028.5   UK   ISSN 0048-8666
ROUNDABOUT. 1964. q. £0.14 per no. Royal National Institute for the Blind, Bakewell Rd., Orton Southgate, Peterborough, Cambridgeshire PE2 0XU, England. TEL 0733-370777. FAX 0733-317555. Ed. Jim Cummings. circ. 87. (Braille)
    Description: For ages 7-11.

362   UK   ISSN 0080-4479
ROYAL NATIONAL INSTITUTE FOR THE BLIND. INFORMATION LEAFLETS. irreg. free. Royal National Institute for the Blind, Bakewell Rd., Orton Southgate, Peterborough, Cambridgeshire PE2 0XU, England. TEL 0733-370777. FAX 0733-317555.

340   UK   ISSN 0023-9291
ROYAL NATIONAL INSTITUTE FOR THE BLIND. LAW NOTES. EXTRACTS. 1949. m. £0.58 per no. Royal National Institute for the Blind, Bakewell Rd., Orton Southgate, Peterborough, Cambridgeshire PE2 0XU, England. TEL 0733-370777. FAX 0733-317555. circ. 61. (Braille)

052   SA
S A B W O NEWS. m. South Africa Blind Workers Organisation, P.O. Box 45129, Mayfair 2108, South Africa. TEL 839-1793. FAX 839-1795.

362.41   SA
S A N C B NEWS. Afrikaans Edition: S A N R B Nuus. (Text in English) 1982. s-a. free. South African National Council for the Blind, P.O. Box 11149, Brooklyn, Pretoria 0011, South Africa. TEL 012-346-1171. FAX 012-346-1177. Ed. William Rowland. circ. 45,000. **Document type:** newsletter.

362.61   UK
ST. DUNSTAN'S ANNUAL REVIEW. 1916. a. free. St. Dunstan's for Men and Women Blinded in the Services, P.O. Box 4XB, 12-14 Harcourt St., London W1A 4XB, England. TEL 071-723-5021. Ed. Raymond Hazan. illus.; circ. controlled. **Document type:** corporate report.
    Formerly: St. Dunstan's Annual Report.

362.61   UK   ISSN 0036-2808
ST. DUNSTAN'S REVIEW. 1915. bi-m. £12. St. Dunstan's for Men and Women Blinded in the Services, P.O. Box 4XB, 12-14 Harcourt St., London W1A 4XB, England. TEL 071-723-5021. Ed. Raymond Hazan. bk.rev.; illus. circ. 2,500. **Document type:** newsletter.

362 647.965   US
ST. JOSEPH'S MESSENGER AND ADVOCATE OF THE BLIND. 1898. q. $5. St. Joseph Home, Sisters of St. Joseph of Peace, 541 Pavonia Ave., Jersey City, NJ 07306. TEL 201-798-4141. (Subscr. to: Box 228, Jersey City, NJ 07303) Ed. Sr. Ursula Maphet. illus. circ. 20,000. **Document type:** newsletter.
    Formerly: Orphan's Messenger and Advocate of the Blind (ISSN 0030-5774)
    Description: Presents religious inspirational articles for blind people.

052   UK
SEARCHLIGHT (HALLATON). q. free. Trust for the Blind, Torch House, Hallaton, Market Harbourough, Leics. LE16 8UJ, England. TEL 0858-89301. FAX 0858-89371. (Braille; also avail. in audio cassette) **Document type:** bulletin.

051   US
SEEING CLEARLY. irreg. (1-2/yr.). free. National Association for Visually Handicapped, 22 W. 21st St., 6th Fl., New York, NY 10010. TEL 212-889-3141. circ. 15,000. (large print in 18 pt.) **Document type:** newsletter.
    Description: Contains, stories, poems and ideas for partially seeing adults and information on new items for them.

362.41   US
THE SEEING EYE ANNUAL REPORT. 1939. a. free. The Seeing Eye, Inc., Box 375, Morristown, NJ 07963-0375. TEL 201-539-4425. FAX 201-539-0922. Ed. Carol Lippert Gray. illus. circ. 25,000. **Document type:** corporate report.

636.088   US   ISSN 0037-0819
THE SEEING EYE. 1935. q. free. The Seeing Eye, Inc., Box 375, Morristown, NJ 07963-0375. TEL 201-539-4425. FAX 201-539-0922. Ed. Carol Lippert Gray. illus. circ. 25,000.

SIBLING INFORMATION NETWORK NEWSLETTER. see *CHILDREN AND YOUTH — About*

SIGHTS AND SOUNDS. see *HANDICAPPED — Hearing Impaired*

808.81   US
SLATE & STYLE. 1983. q. $6 in all formats (effective 1994). National Federation of the Blind, Writers Division, 2704 Beach Dr., Merrick, NY 11566. TEL 516-868-8718. FAX 516-868-9076. Ed. Loraine E. Stayer. bk.rev.; circ. 200. circ. 200 (paid). (also avail. in Braille; audio cassette; large print edition in 14 pt.) **Document type:** newsletter.
    Description: Publishes poetry, nonfiction, short stories and articles of interest to blind writers and readers; discusses resources available to assist blind writers.

621.3 370.196   US
SMITH - KETTLEWELL TECHNICAL FILE; a biannual technical journal for the blind and visually impaired. 1980. bi-a. $18 for braille; talking book $14; diskette $16 (for 2 yrs.). Smith - Kettlewell Eye Research Institute, 2232 Webster St., San Francisco, CA 94115. TEL 415-561-1619. (Co-sponsor: National Institute of Disability & Rehabilitation) Ed. Bill Gerrey. circ. 300. (also avail. in Braille; diskette format; talking book; back issues avail.)

SONDERSCHULE. see *EDUCATION*

362   UK
SOUNDINGS. 1960. m. £0.29 per no. Royal National Institute for the Blind, Bakewell Rd., Orton Southgate, Peterborough, Cambridgeshire PE2 0XU, England. TEL 0733-370777. FAX 0733-317555. Ed. Charlotte Cohen. circ. 243. (Braille)
    Formerly: Tape Record (ISSN 0039-9531)

362.41   SA
SOUTH AFRICAN NATIONAL COUNCIL FOR THE BLIND. BIENNIAL REPORT. (Editions in Afrikaans, English) 1932. biennial. South African National Council for the Blind, P.O. Box 11149, Brooklyn, Pretoria 0011, South Africa. TEL 012-346-1171. FAX 012-346-1177. circ. 1,500. (also avail. in Braille) **Document type:** corporate report.

052 283   UK
SPARK. m. free. Torch Trust for the Blind, Torch House, Hallaton, Market Harborough, Leics. LE16 8UJ, England. TEL 0858-89301. FAX 0858-89371. (also avail. in audio cassette; large print) **Document type:** bulletin.
    Description: For blind children 7-11 years old.

052   UK
▼**SPECTRUM (EDINBURGH)**; the lifestyle magazine for today. 1992. m. £6. Scottish Braille Press, Craigmillar Park, Edinburgh EH16 5NB, Scotland. TEL 031-662-4445. FAX 031-662-1968. (also avail. in Braille) **Document type:** consumer publication.
    Description: Reports on lifestyle issues with regard to health, fitness, and diet.

362   US
SPIRIT OF SERVICE. 1985. s-a. free. Seva Foundation, 8 N. San Pedro Rd., San Rafael, CA 94903-4007. TEL 415-492-1829. FAX 415-492-8705. (Co-sponsor: Seva Service Society) Ed. Mirabai Bush. bk.rev. circ. 30,000. (tabloid format) **Document type:** catalog.
    Description: News on service work of the Nepal Blindness Program, Aravind Eye Hospital, development projects in Guatemala and Mexico, and community service projects in the U.S. and Canada.

051 284   US
SPIRITUAL LIGHT. 1970. bi-m. free. Christian Mission for the Blind, 5354 Boy Scout Rd., Indianapolis, IN 46226. TEL 317-549-2386. Ed. Kathy Harless. circ. 450 (200 large print ed.; 250 cassette). (also avail. in audio cassette; large print edition in 24 pt.)
    Description: Includes articles relating to self help, personal growth, motivation, as well as poems and personal testimonies.

STRENGTH FOR THE DAY. see *RELIGIONS AND THEOLOGY — Protestant*

371.911   US   ISSN 0039-2677
STUDENT (LINCOLN). 1926. m. free. Christian Record Services, 4444 S. 52nd St., Lincoln, NE 68516. TEL 402-488-0981. Ed. R.J. Kaiser. circ. 6,300 (combined). (also avail. in record; Braille)

362 070   US
SYNDICATED COLUMNISTS WEEKLY. 1984. w. $20.80. National Braille Press, Inc., 88 St. Stephen St., Boston, MA 02115. TEL 617-266-6160. FAX 617-437-0456. Ed. Diane Croft. bk.rev. (Braille)
    Description: Presents syndicated columnists from major U.S. newspapers.

001.6 621.381   US
TACTIC. 1985 Braille ed.; 1990 Large Print ed. q. $20. (Clovernook Center Opportunities for the Blind) Clovernook Printing House, 7000 Hamilton Ave., Cincinnati, OH 45231. TEL 513-321-2232. Ed. Deborah Kendrick. adv. contact: Mike Walsh. (also avail. in Braille; large print edition in 16 pt.) **Document type:** consumer publication.
    Description: Computer technology for visually impaired persons; readers forum and practical information submitted by hardware and software users.

HARDWARE

028 US ISSN 0039-9183
HV1708
TALKING BOOK TOPICS (LARGE-PRINT EDITION). 1935. bi-m. free to qualified personnel. U.S. Library of Congress, National Library Service for the Blind and Physically Handicapped, Washington, DC 20542. TEL 202-707-5100. FAX 202-707-0712. Ed. George Thuronyi. bk.rev. circ. 350,000. (also avail. in diskette format; large print in 14 pt.; back issues avail.) **Indexed:** Rehabil.Lit. **Document type:** newsletter, government publication.
   Description: Contains news of developments and activities in library services and announcements of recorded books and magazines recently added to the N.L.S. collection.

TALKING BOOKS IN THE PUBLIC LIBRARY SYSTEMS OF METROPOLITAN TORONTO. see *LIBRARY AND INFORMATION SCIENCES*

362.31 US ISSN 0896-8586
TECHNOLOGY UPDATE (PALO ALTO); the bi-monthly consumer's guide to technology for blind and visually impaired persons. 1987. bi-m. $37 to individuals (foreign $57); institutions $47 (foreign $67); blind, visually impaired $30 (foreign $47). Sensory Access Foundation, 385 Sherman Ave., Ste. 2, Palo Alto, CA 94306. TEL 415-329-0430. FAX 415-323-1062. Ed. Margaret Kahn. adv.; bk.rev.; software rev. (also avail. in diskette format; large print edition in 18 pt.) **Document type:** consumer publication.

TEEN TIME (LARGE PRINT EDITION). see *CHILDREN AND YOUTH — For*

052 UK
▼**TEMPO.** 1992. m. £6. Scottish Braille Press, Craigmillar Park, Edinburgh EH16 5NB, Scotland. TEL 031-662-4445. FAX 031-662-1968. (also avail. in Braille) **Document type:** consumer publication.

200 UK ISSN 0049-3651
THEOLOGICAL TIMES. 1950. q. £0.67 per no. Royal National Institute for the Blind, Bakewell Rd., Orton Southgate, Peterborough, Cambridgeshire PE2 0XU, England. TEL 0733-370777. FAX 0733-317555. Ed. Rev. J.C. Cockerton. circ. 86. (Braille)

052 UK
THE TORCH (HALLATON). bi-m. free. Torch Trust for the Blind, Torch House, Hallaton, Market Harborough, Leics. LE16 8UJ, England. TEL 0858-89301. FAX 0858-89371. (Braille; also avail. in audio cassette; large print) **Document type:** bulletin.
   Description: Appeals to blind family members of all ages.

052 UK
TORCH FAMILY NEWS. q. free. Torch Trust for the Blind, Torch House, Hallaton, Market Harborough, Leics. LE16 8UJ, England. TEL 0858-89301. FAX 0858-89371. (Braille; also avail. in audio cassette) **Document type:** bulletin.

052 UK
TORCH TIMES. q. £1. Torch Trust for the Blind, Torch House, Hallaton, Market Harbourogh, Leics. LE16 8UJ, England. TEL 0858-89301. FAX 0858-89371. (Braille; also avail. in audio cassette) **Document type:** bulletin.

379.11 US ISSN 0040-9928
TOWERS. 1947. q. free. Overbrook School for the Blind, 6333 Malvern Ave., Philadelphia, PA 19151. TEL 215-877-0313. charts; illus. circ. 7,500.

284 US ISSN 0041-0357
TRACT MESSENGER. 1953. m. free. Lutheran Braille Evangelism Association, 1740 Eugene St., St. Paul, MN 55110. TEL 612-426-0469. Ed. Rev. Dennis A. Hawkinson. circ. 500. (Braille)

369.4 UK ISSN 0049-4615
TREFOIL TRAIL; a journal for blind guides. 1958. m. (except Aug.). free. Royal National Institute for the Blind, Bakewell Rd., Orton Southgate, Peterborough, Cambridgeshire PE2 0XU, England. TEL 0733-370777. FAX 0733-317555. circ. 160. (Braille)

U S A B A AGENDA. (United States Association for Blind Athletes) see *SPORTS AND GAMES*

362.61 FR
UNION DES AVEUGLES DE GUERRE. BULLETIN BIMESTRIEL. 1921. bi-m. free to qualified personnel. Union des Aveugles de Guerre, 49 rue Blanche, 75009 Paris, France. TEL 48-74-56-18. FAX 45-26-24-34. Ed. Pierre Guillernet. **Document type:** bulletin.
   Formerly: Union des Aveugles de Guerre. Bulletin Mensuel (ISSN 0041-6843)

027.663 362 020 US ISSN 1046-1663
HV1783
U.S. LIBRARY OF CONGRESS. NATIONAL LIBRARY SERVICE FOR THE BLIND AND PHYSICALLY HANDICAPPED. NEWS. 1958. q. free. U.S. Library of Congress, National Library Service for the Blind and Physically Handicapped, Washington, DC 20542. TEL 202-707-5100. FAX 202-707-0712. Ed. Vicki Fitzpatrick. circ. 30,000. (also avail. in Braille) **Document type:** newsletter, government publication.
   Former titles: U.S. Library of Congress. National Library for the Blind and Physically Handicapped. News (ISSN 0160-9211); D B P H News.

053 AU ISSN 0042-0492
UNSER SCHAFFEN; Monatsschrift fuer das Blindenwesen. 1956. m. S.150. Hilfsgemeinschaft der Blinden und Sehschwachen Oesterreichs, Treustr. 9, A-1200 Vienna, Austria. TEL 01-330354516. FAX 01-330354511. Ed. Sonja Cernyl. adv.; bk.rev. circ. 22,000. (talking book) **Document type:** corporate report.

371.9 GW
UNTER UNS; Zeitschrift fuer Frauen und Maedchen. m. DM.110. Deutsche Blindenstudienanstalt e.V., Postfach 1160, 35001 Marburg, Germany. TEL 06421-606-0. adv.; bk.rev. circ. 360. (also avail. in Braille) **Document type:** consumer publication.

026 020 US ISSN 0160-9203
HV1783
UPDATE (WASHINGTON). 1977. q. free. U.S. Library of Congress, National Library Service for the Blind and Physically Handicapped, Washington, DC 20542. TEL 202-707-5100. FAX 202-707-0712. Ed. Freddie Peaco. circ. 8,000. (also avail. in Braille; large print edition in 14 pt.) **Indexed:** Rehabil.Lit. **Document type:** newsletter, government publication.
   Description: Covers volunteer activities in library service to blind and physically handicapped persons.

UPPER ROOM; daily devotional guide, interdenominational, international. see *RELIGIONS AND THEOLOGY — Protestant*

362 FR ISSN 1163-1317
VALENTIN HAUY. 1947. q. 110 F. Association Valentin Hauy pour le Bien des Aveugles, 5 rue Duroc, 75343 Paris Cedex 07, France. TEL 44-49-27-27. FAX 44-49-27-10. TELEX AVH 200 995 F. Pub. Louis Ciccone. adv.

371.911 GW
VEREINSMITTEILUNGEN. 1946. bi-m. Schleswig - Holsteinischer Blindenverein e.V., Memelstr. 4, 23554 Luebeck, Germany. TEL 0451-40349. FAX 0451-407530. circ. 1,600. (also avail. in audio cassette)

371.911 US
VISION RESOURCE LIST. a. free. Vision Foundation, Inc., 818 Mt. Auburn St., Watertown, MA 02172. TEL 617-926-4232. Ed. Fran Weisse. circ. 2,000. (also avail. in audio cassette; large print edition in 16 pt.)
   Description: Provides resources for inividuals who are blind or visually impaired.

371.911 US
VISION RESOURCE UPDATE. 1988. bi-m. membership. Vision Foundation, Inc., 818 Mt. Auburn St., Watertown, MA 02172. TEL 617-926-4232. Ed. Fran Weisse. bk.rev. (also avail. in audio cassette; large-print edition in 16 pt.)
   Description: Provides information and resources for blind and visually impaired individuals.

VISIONARY. see *MEDICAL SCIENCES — Ophthalmology And Optometry*

362.41 616.46 US ISSN 1041-8490
VOICE OF THE DIABETIC; a support and information network. 1986. q. free. National Federation of the Blind, Diabetics Division, 811 Cherry St., Ste. 309, Columbia, MO 65201. TEL 314-875-8911. Ed. Ed Bryant. adv.; bk.rev. circ. 29,000. (also avail. in audio cassette) **Document type:** consumer publication.
   Description: Contains personal stories and practical guidance by blind diabetics, medical news, a resource column, and a recipe corner.

027.663 US ISSN 0193-113X
HV1790
VOLUNTEERS WHO PRODUCE BOOKS; braille, tape, and large print. 1963. biennial. free to qualified individuals. U.S. Library of Congress, National Library Service for the Blind and Physically Handicapped, Washington, DC 20542. TEL 202-707-5100. FAX 202-707-0712. (also avail. in Braille; large-print edition in 14 pt.) **Document type:** directory, government publication.

362.41 SZ
DER WEG. French edition: Clin d'Oeil. 1914. 6/yr. 30 SFr. Schweizer Blinden- und Sehbehindertenverband, Maulbeerstr. 14, CH-3011 Bern, Switzerland. TEL 031-3811811. FAX 031-3810228. circ. 10,000. (also avail. in audio cassette; Braille) **Document type:** corporate report.

WELTWEITEN CHRISTLICHEN BEHINDERTENDIAKONTE. BERICHTE. see *RELIGIONS AND THEOLOGY*

371.911 GW
WIR FUEHRHUNDHALTER. bi-m. DM.18. Deutscher Blindenverband e.V., Bismarckallee 30, 53173 Bonn, Germany. TEL 0228-354037. FAX 0228-357719. (audio cassette) **Document type:** bulletin.

THE WORLD AT LARGE. see *GENERAL INTEREST PERIODICALS — United States*

028.5 280 US
YOUNG & ALIVE (LARGE PRINT EDITION). 1954. q. free to qualified personnel. Christian Record Services, 4444 S. 52nd St., Lincoln, NE 68516. TEL 402-488-0981. Ed. Richard Kaiser. circ. 31,800. (also avail. in Braille; large print in 22 pt.)
   Formerly: Youth Happiness (ISSN 0044-121X)
   Description: Interdenominational articles for young adults.

HARDWARE

see *Building and Construction–Hardware*

HARDWARE (COMPUTER)

see *Computers–Hardware*

HEARING IMPAIRED

see *Handicapped–Hearing Impaired*

HEAT

see *Physics–Heat*

HEATING, PLUMBING AND REFRIGERATION

697 BE
A B C/B J V. (Annuaire Belge de Chauffage et Climatisation) (Text in Flemish and French) 1970. a. 800 BEF. Editions Coppieters S.P.R.L., 393 Bd. de Smet de Naeyer, Bte 5, B-1090 Brussels, Belgium. TEL 02-478-40-98. FAX 02-478-35-02. adv.; bk.rev. circ. 4,000.

HEATING, PLUMBING AND REFRIGERATION

697 US
A C C A NEWS. 1967. 10/yr. membership. Air Conditioning Contractors of America, 1712 New Hampshire Ave., N.W., Washington, DC 20009. TEL 202-483-9370. FAX 202-234-4721. Ed. Simone Guthery. circ. 3,300.
  Description: Informs members of association and industry news and how it will affect them in their daily business operations.

A H A M MAJOR APPLIANCE FACTORY SHIPMENT REPORT. (Association of Home Appliance Manufacturers) see *INTERIOR DESIGN AND DECORATION — Furniture And House Furnishings*

A H A M MAJOR APPLIANCE INDUSTRY FACTS BOOK (YEAR). (Association of Home Appliance Manufacturers) see *INTERIOR DESIGN AND DECORATION — Furniture And House Furnishings*

697 621.56 FR ISSN 0001-2122
T2 CODEN: APAVBZ
A.P.A.V.E. REVUE TECHNIQUE; revue technique du groupement des associations de proprietaires d'appareils a vapeur et electriques. 1920. q. 304 F. (outside EC 359 F.). S A D A V E, 191 rue Vaugirard, 75015 Paris, France. TEL 45-66-99-44. FAX 45-67-90-47. TELEX 206476 F. Ed. Maurice Ribonet. adv.; bk.rev.; charts; illus. circ. 12,797. **Indexed:** C.I.S.Abstr., INIS Atomind.
—CASDDS.

621.56 US
A R W COUNTERLINE;* published quarterly for counter & inside salespeople of A R W Wholesalers. q. Air-Conditioning & Refrigeration Wholesalers, 10251 W. Sample Rd., Ste. B, Coral Springs, FL 33065-3939. Ed. Charles Willits.

621.56 338 US
A R W SUPPLIER.* q. Air-Conditioning & Refrigeration Wholesalers, 10251 W. Sample Rd., Ste. B, Coral Springs, FL 33065-3939. Ed. N.F. Aramino.

621.56 330 US
A R W WHOLESALER.* bi-m. Air-Conditioning & Refrigeration Wholesalers, 10251 W. Sample Rd., Ste. B, Coral Springs, FL 33065-3939. Ed. N.F. Aramino.

A S A MEMBERSHIP DIRECTORY. (American Supply Association) see *BUSINESS AND ECONOMICS — Trade And Industrial Directories*

696 US ISSN 1070-1125
A S A NEWS. bi-m. American Supply Association, 222 Merchandise Mart Pl., Ste. 1360, Chicago, IL 60654. TEL 312-464-0090. FAX 312-464-0091. adv.; circ. 15,000 (controlled). **Document type:** newsletter.
  Description: Contains news for plumbing, heating, cooling and piping wholesale distributors in the United States.

697 US ISSN 1041-2344
TH7015
A S H R A E HANDBOOK. (In 4 vols.: Fundamentals; Refrigeration Systems - Applications; Equipment; HVAC Systems - Applications) 1922. a. $119. American Society of Heating, Refrigerating and Air-Conditioning Engineers, Inc., 1791 Tullie Circle, N.E., Atlanta, GA 30329. TEL 404-636-8400. FAX 404-321-5478. index. circ. 60,000. **Indexed:** Eng.Ind.
—CCC.
  Former titles: A S H R A E Handbook and Product Specification File; A S H R A E Handbook and Product Directory (ISSN 0066-0620); A S H R A E Handbook of Fundamentals; Supersedes in part: A S H R A E Guide and Data Book. Fundamentals and Equipment.

697 621.56 US ISSN 0001-2491
CODEN: ASHRAA
A S H R A E JOURNAL; heating, refrigeration, air-conditioning, ventilation. 1914. m. $49 to non-members. American Society of Heating, Refrigerating and Air-Conditioning Engineers, Inc., 1791 Tullie Circle, N.E., Atlanta, GA 30329. TEL 404-636-8400. FAX 404-321-5478. Ed. William R. Coker. adv.; bk.rev.; abstr.; bibl.; charts; illus.; tr.lit.; index. circ. 60,000. (also avail. in microform (ISSN 0364-9962) from UMI; reprint service avail. from UMI) **Indexed:** A.I.Abstr., A.S.& T.Ind., Abstr.Health Care Manage.Stud., Appl.Mech.Rev., C.I.S. Abstr., Chem.Abstr., Corros.Abstr., Curr.Cont., Energy Info.Abstr., Eng.Ind., Environ.Abstr., Excerp.Med., Fluidex, Fuel & Energy Abstr., Gas Abstr., INIS Atomind., Int.Build.Serv.Abstr., ISMEC.
—BLDSC (1742.091000); CIS; EI; Faxon; UnCover; SWETS; UMI; CASDDS. **CCC.**
  Refereed Serial

A S H R A E TECHNICAL DATA BULLETIN. (American Society of Heating, Refrigerating and Air-Conditioning Engineers, Inc.) see *ENGINEERING — Mechanical Engineering*

697 621.56 US ISSN 0001-2505
TH7201 CODEN: ASHTAG
A S H R A E TRANSACTIONS. 1895. s-a. $170 per vol. to non-members. American Society of Heating, Refrigerating and Air-Conditioning Engineers, Inc., 1791 Tullie Circle, N.E., Atlanta, GA 30329. TEL 404-636-8400. FAX 404-321-5478. Ed. Mildred Geshwiler. charts; illus.; index. circ. 1,000. (also avail. in microform from UMI; reprint service avail.) **Indexed:** Agri.Eng.Abstr., Chem.Abstr., Eng.Ind., Food Sci.& Tech.Abstr., Fuel & Energy Abstr., Gas Abstr., INIS Atomind.
—BLDSC (8896.300000); EI; Faxon; SWETS; UMI; CASDDS. **CCC.**

AIR CONDITIONING & HEATING SERVICE & REPAIR - DOMESTIC CARS, LIGHT TRUCKS & VANS. see *TRANSPORTATION — Automobiles*

AIR CONDITIONING & HEATING SERVICE & REPAIR - IMPORTED CARS & TRUCKS. see *TRANSPORTATION — Automobiles*

697 US ISSN 0002-2276
TP497.A1
AIR CONDITIONING, HEATING & REFRIGERATION NEWS. (Includes annual directory, and statistical summary issue) 1926. w. $72 (foreign $80). Business News Publishing Company, 755 W. Big Beaver Rd., Ste. 1000, Troy, MI 48084. TEL 313-362-3700. FAX 313-362-0317. (Subscr. to: Box 2600, Troy, MI 48007) Ed. Wayne Johnson. adv.; bk.rev.; illus.; pat.; stat.; tr.lit.; index. circ. 35,724. (also avail. in microform from UMI; microfiche from CIS; reprint service avail. from UMI) **Indexed:** B.P.I., Bus.Ind., Fuel & Energy Abstr., Gas Abstr., Hlth.Ind., PROMT, SRI, Tr.& Indus.Ind. **Document type:** newspaper, trade publication.
  ●Also available online. Vendor(s): BRS Online Products (TSAP), DIALOG Information Services, Inc. (File no.648), Dow Jones News Retrieval.
—SWETS; UMI.
  Description: Reaches decision-makers who are contractors, wholesalers, manufacturers and others allied to the field. Includes news and features on all air conditioning and heating.

697 UK ISSN 0143-6643
AIR INFILTRATION REVIEW. 1979. q. free. International Energy Agency, Air Infiltration and Ventilation Centre, Barclay's Venture Centre, Sir William Lyon's Rd., Coventry CVL 7EZ, England. Ed. J. Blacknell. bk.rev.; bibl. circ. 3,500. (back issues avail.) **Document type:** trade publication.
—BLDSC (0776.250000).

ANTIQUE STOVE ASSOCIATION. YEARBOOK. see *ANTIQUES*

696 AT ISSN 0817-6337
AUSTRALIAN PLUMBING INDUSTRY; official publication for business within the greater plumbing industry. 1949. bi-m. Aus.$60 for 2 yrs. Master Plumbers & Mechanical Services Association of Victoria, 525 King St., West Melbourne, Vic 3003, Australia. TEL 03-329-9622. FAX 03-329-5060. Ed. Ray W. Herbert. adv.: B&W page Aus.$1058, color page Aus.$2365; trim 297 x 210; adv. contact: Larissa Herbert. circ. 6,500. **Document type:** trade publication.
  Formerly (until 1986): Master Plumbers and Mechanical Services Bulletin.

621.56 697 AT ISSN 0005-0148
AUSTRALIAN REFRIGERATION, AIR CONDITIONING AND HEATING. 1963. m. Aus.$90 (foreign Aus.$235) (effective Jul. 1993). (Australian Institute of Refrigeration, Air Conditioning and Heating, Inc.) Yaffa Publishing Group, 17-21 Bellevue St., Surry Hills, N.S.W. 2010, Australia. TEL 02-281-2333. FAX 02-281-2750. Ed. John Bremner. adv.: B&W page Aus.$1570, color page Aus.$2320; trim 297 x 210. bk.rev.; charts; illus.; index. circ. 2,969. **Indexed:** Chem.Abstr., Food Sci.& Tech.Abstr., Int.Build.Serv.Abstr. **Document type:** trade publication.
—EI.
  Description: For all areas of engineering and management within the air conditioning and heating industry.

343 US ISSN 1055-6680
KF5709
B O C A NATIONAL PLUMBING CODE. triennial. $36. Building Officials and Code Administrators International, 4051 W. Flossmoor Rd., Country Club Hills, IL 60478-5795. illus.
  Formerly: B O C A Basic Plumbing Code (ISSN 0098-1702)

697 UK ISSN 0309-8435
B S R I A ANNUAL REPORT. a. Building Services Research and Information Association, Old Bracknell Ln. W., Bracknell, Berks. RG12 7AH, England. TEL 0344-426511. FAX 0344-487575. **Document type:** corporate report.
  Formerly: Heating and Ventilating Research Association Annual Report (ISSN 0305-599X)

697 UK ISSN 0305-5973
B S R I A APPLICATION GUIDES. 1959. irreg. price varies. Building Services Research and Information Association, Old Bracknell Ln. West, Bracknell, Berks. RG12 7AH, England. TEL 0344-426511. FAX 0344-487575. bk.rev. circ. 1,500. **Document type:** monographic series.
  Formerly: Heating and Ventilating Research Association. Laboratory Reports.

697 UK ISSN 0309-0248
B S R I A TECHNICAL NOTES. 1959. irreg. price varies. Building Services Research and Information Association, Old Bracknell Ln. W., Bracknell, Berks. RG12 7AH, England. TEL 0344-426511. FAX 0344-487575. **Document type:** monographic series.
  Formerly: Heating and Ventilating Research Association. Technical Notes.

BLU E ROSSO. see *INTERIOR DESIGN AND DECORATION*

697 690 UK ISSN 0951-9270
BUILDING SERVICES JOURNAL. 1933. m. £60 (overseas £82) (effective 1994). Builder Group plc, Builder House, 1 Millharbour, London E14 9RA, England. TEL 071-537-2222. FAX 071-537-2007. (Subscr. to: The Builder Group, Freepost, CN 2792, Bromley BR2 9BR, England. TEL 081-402-8486) Ed. Roderic Bunn. adv.; bk.rev.; charts; illus.; index, cum.index. circ. 18,500. (reprint service avail. from UMI) **Indexed:** BMT, Br.Tech.Ind., Build.Manage.Abstr., C.I.S. Abstr., Chem.Abstr., Eng.Ind., Excerp.Med., Fuel & Energy Abstr., Gas Abstr., Int.Build.Serv.Abstr., Int'l.Civil Eng.Abstr., RICS, Sci.Abstr., Soft.Abstr.Eng., Therm.Abstr. **Document type:** trade publication.
—BLDSC (2365.620000); SWETS.
  Formerly (until 1985): Chartered Institution of Building Services. Journal (ISSN 0142-3630); Which was formed by the 1978 merger of: Lignt and Lighting and Environmental Design (ISSN 0307-5192); Building Services Engineer (ISSN 0301-6536); Which was formerly (until 1971): I.H.V.E. Journal (ISSN 0018-9847)

HEATING, PLUMBING AND REFRIGERATION

696   UK
BUSINESS RATIO REPORT. PROCESS PLANT; an industry sector analysis. a. I C C Business Ratios Ltd. (Subsidiary of: I C C Information Group Ltd.), Field House, 72 Oldfield Rd., Hampton, Middlesex TW12 2HQ, England. TEL 081-783-0922. FAX 081-783-1940.
—BLDSC (6849.990400).
   Formerly (until 1989): Business Ratio Report. The Process Plant Industry (ISSN 0261-944X)

697 696   FR   ISSN 0750-1552
C.F.P. CHAUD - FROID - PLOMBERIE. 1947. m. 902 F. Editions Parisiennes, 4 rue Charles Divry, 75014 Paris, France. FAX 33-1-45-41-02-30. Ed. Christian Auger. adv.; bk.rev.; abstr.; charts; illus.; tr.lit.; index. circ. 13,500. **Indexed:** Int.Build.Serv.Abstr.
   Formerly: Chaud - Froid - Plomberie (ISSN 0009-2010); Incorporating: Gas - Mazout - Electricite.

697   IT   ISSN 0008-1760
CALORE. 1929. m. L.12000. Associazione Nazionale per il Controllo della Combustione, Via Urbana 167, 00184 Rome, Italy. Ed. Agostino Pavan. adv.; abstr.; charts; illus. stat. **Indexed:** C.I.S. Abstr., Chem.Abstr.

CANADIAN BENEFITS ADMINISTRATION MANUAL. see *INSURANCE*

697   US
▼**CAROLINA H V A C NEWS**. 1992. m. $10. Holco Communications Inc., Box 80727, Conyers, GA 30208-0727. TEL 404-483-4860. FAX 404-483-2447. circ. 7,000. (tabloid format) **Document type:** trade publication.
   Description: Contains wholesale and manufacturing news and local distributor news for dealers and contractors-installers of central heating and cooling equipment; residential, light commercial and industrial.

697   FR   ISSN 0153-999X
CATALOGUE NATIONAL DU GENIE CLIMATIQUE-CHAUFFAGE ET CONDITIONNEMENT D'AIR/NATIONAL CATALOGUE OF HEATING AND AIR CONDITIONING/NAZIONALE KATALOG DER HEIZUNG UND KLIMATISIERUNG. 1952. a. 212 F. C E P P Publications, 1 pl. d'Estienne-d'Orves, 75009 Paris, France. TEL 42-80-67-62. FAX 42-82-99-30. Ed. Martine Clavel. adv. circ. 12,000. **Document type:** trade publication.
   Former titles (until 1973): Catalogue National du Chauffage et du Conditionnement d'Air; (until 1966): Annuaire-Guide du Chauffage et du Conditionnement d'Air.
   Description: Listings of products, trade organizations - the entire French market of heating and air conditioning.

697   AT   ISSN 1033-1808
CELSIUS. 1972. m. Aus.$60. Racca-Celsius Management, 104 Parramatta Rd., Homebush, N.S.W. 2140, Australia. TEL 02-764-3404. FAX 02-764-2697. Ed. Phillip Ross. bk.rev. circ. 2,500. (back issues avail.) **Document type:** trade publication.
   Description: Publishes articles of interest to contractors, installers, and engineers of heating ventilation, air conditioning and refrigeration equipment.

697   BE
CHALEUR ET CLIMATS. (Text in Flemish and French) 1935. m. (10/yr.) 1900 BEF (foreign 2300 BEF). (Union Belges des Installateurs en Chauffage Central, Ventilation et Climitisation) Editions Coppieters S.P.R.L., 393 Bd. de Smet de Naeyer, Bte 5, B-1090 Brussels, Belgium. TEL 02-478-40-98. FAX 02-478-35-02. (Co-sponsors: Association des Techniciens et Ingenieurs de ces Branches; Association Belge des Bruleurs Automatiques) adv.; bk.rev. circ. 5,000. **Document type:** trade publication.
   Former titles: E T B - T U G; (until 1976): Installateur; (1956-1975): Chaleur et Climat.

697   FR
CHAUFFAGE MAGAZINE. 4/yr. 61 bd. Bessieres, 75017 Paris, France. TEL 46-27-03-57. FAX 42-29-18-68. TELEX 642 934. Ed. Georges Benyai'ch. circ. 135,000.

697 621.56   FR   ISSN 0009-2029
TH7201
CHAUFFAGE - VENTILATION - CONDITIONNEMENT. 1910. 10/yr. 480 F. (foreign 730 F.). (Association des Ingenieurs de Climatique, Ventilation et Froid) P Y C Edition, B.P. 105, 5, av. de Verdun, 94208 Ivry sur Seine Cedex, France. TEL 1-49-60-86-36. FAX 1-46-72-41-85. Ed. Claudie Cabourdin. adv.; bk.rev.; charts; illus. circ. 4,555. **Indexed:** C.I.S.Abstr., Int.Build.Serv.Abstr. **Document type:** trade publication.
—CCC.

621.56   PL   ISSN 0009-4919
                                               CODEN: CLDCAK
CHLODNICTWO. (Text in Polish; summaries in English, French, Polish and Russian) 1966. m. $71.50. Wydawnictwo Czasopism i Ksiazek Technicznych SIGMA - NOT, Ul. Ratuszowa 11, P.O. Box 1004, 00-950 Warsaw, Poland. TEL 48-22-180918. FAX 48-22-192187. TELEX 814550 SIGMA PL. (Dist. by: SIGMA NOT Ltd., Ul. Bartycka 20, 00-716 Warsaw, Poland) Ed.Bd. adv.; bk.rev.; abstr.; charts; illus.; pat.; index; circ. 1,050 (controlled). **Indexed:** Chem.Abstr., Food Sci.& Tech.Abstr., Nutr.Abstr.
—BLDSC (3181.486100); CASDDS.

697 621.56   GW   ISSN 0009-8914
CLIMA COMMERCE INTERNATIONAL. Abbreviated title: C C I. 1967. 14/yr. DM.198. Promotor Verlags- und Forderungsgesellschaft mbH, Hardtstr. 26, 76185 Karlsruhe, Germany. TEL 0721-559020. FAX 0721-590525. Ed. Guenther Keller. adv.; bk.rev.; charts; illus.; pat.; stat. circ. 6,000. **Indexed:** INIS Atomind., Int.Build.Serv.Abstr. **Document type:** trade publication.
   Description: Gives air conditioning installation and repair techniques.

697   UK
COLD STORAGE & DISTRIBUTION FEDERATION. DIRECTORY. a. £30 (effective through end of 1993). Cold Storage & Distribution Federation, Downmill Rd., Bracknell, Berks. RG12 1GH, England. TEL 44-344-869533. FAX 44-344-869527. circ. 1,000. **Document type:** directory.
   Formerly (until 1991): National Cold Storage Federation. Directory.
   Description: Provides a guide for persons or companies offering temperature controlled services to the food industry.

697   UK
COMFORT ENGINEERING. q. £10. (Institute of Domestic Heating & Environmental Engineers) E. Eric Farrow, Ed. & Pub., 37A High Rd., Benfleet, Essex, England. adv.; bk.rev.; charts; illus.; tr.lit. circ. 5,000.
   Formerly (until 1980): Domestic Heating Engineer (ISSN 0046-0540)

COMPRESSOR NEWS AND PATENTS. see *MACHINERY*

697   IT
CONDIZIONAMENTO DELL'ARIA, RISCALDAMENTO, REFRIGERAZIONE. 1956. m. L.91000($151) Editoriale P E G SpA, Via Fratelli Bressan 2, 20126 Milan, Italy. TEL 02-25-79-841. FAX 02-25-52-779. TELEX 323088 PEGMOS I. Ed. Mara Portoso. adv.: B&W page L.1700000, color page L.2720000; trim 185 x 260. bk.rev.; charts; illus.; tr.lit. circ. 4,300. **Document type:** trade publication.
—BLDSC (3405.900000).
   Formerly: Condizionamento dell'Aria (ISSN 0373-7772)
   Description: Covers technical information and topical data addressed to planners, technicians, entrepreneurs of heating, ventilation, air-conditioning and their components.

CONSTRUIRE. see *BUILDING AND CONSTRUCTION*

697   US   ISSN 0279-4071
TP490
CONTRACTING BUSINESS; the magazine of mechanical systems & design - build contracting. 1944. m. $55 (free to qualified personnel). Penton Publishing (Subsidiary of: Pittway Company), 1100 Superior Ave., Cleveland, OH 44114-2543. TEL 216-696-7000. FAX 216-696-8765. (Subscr. to: Box 95759, Cleveland, OH 44101) Ed. James Wheeler. adv.; circ. 52,600 (controlled). (also avail. in microfilm; reprint service avail. from UMI) **Document type:** trade publication.
—UMI. **CCC**.
   Formerly: Airconditioning and Refrigeration Business (ISSN 0002-2640)
   Description: Articles cover new marketing opportunities, design, service and maintenance of heating, ventilating, air conditioning and refrigeration systems.

696   FR   ISSN 1157-545X
COUVERTURE PLOMBERIE; technique et documentation. 1956. q. 330 F. Union Nationale des Chambres Syndicales de Couverture et de Plomberie de France, 9 rue de la Perouse, 75784 Paris Cedex 16, France. TEL 40-69-53-07. FAX 47-23-02-84. TELEX 611 975 F FEDBAT. (Co-sponsor: Societe pour le Developpement des Installations Sanitaires et du Confort Menager (SODECOME)) adv.; charts; stat.; tr.lit.; index. circ. 9,000.
   Former titles (until 1991): Informations Couverture Plomberie (ISSN 1157-5514); (until 1971): Revue de la Couverture Plomberie.

697   DK   ISSN 0902-5456
DANSK V V S. Variant title: Dansk Varme Ventilation Sanitet. 1949. m. DKK 315. Danish National Federation of Master Plumbers, Heating and Ventilation installation Contractors - Dansk V V S Installatoer Forening, 75 Hoejnaesvej, 2610 Roedovre, Denmark. FAX 36-720244. Ed. Lotte Keinicke. adv. circ. 3,900.
   Former titles: V V S Installatoeren (ISSN 0106-8881); Blikkenslager- Roer- og Sanitets Mesteren (ISSN 0006-4793)

697   US
DIRECTORY OF CERTIFIED DEHUMIDIFIERS. s-a. $0.25 per no. Association of Home Appliance Manufacturers, 20 N. Wacker Dr., Chicago, IL 60606. TEL 312-984-5800. FAX 312-984-5823. **Document type:** directory.
   Description: Lists all brands and models certified. Gives the AHAM-certified water removal capacity in pints per 24 hours for each model. Also includes a dehumidification selection guide to help consumer determine the capacity needed.

697   US
DIRECTORY OF CERTIFIED HUMIDIFIERS. s-a. $0.25 per no. Association of Home Appliance Manufacturers, 20 N. Wacker Dr., Chicago, IL 60606. TEL 312-984-5800. FAX 312-984-5823. **Document type:** directory.
   Description: Lists all brands and models certified. Gives AHAM-certified water output capacity in gallons per 24 hours for each model. Also includes a humidification selection guide to help the consumer determine the capacity needed.

621.56   US
DIRECTORY OF CERTIFIED REFRIGERATORS AND FREEZERS. s-a. $1 per no. Association of Home Appliance Manufacturers, 20 N. Wacker Dr., Chicago, IL 60606. TEL 312-984-5800. FAX 312-984-5823. **Document type:** directory.
   Description: Lists all brands and models of certified refrigerators, combination refrigerator-freezers and freezers. Gives the AHAM-certified ratings in cubic feet volume, both total and separate for the fresh food and freezers sections, and square feet of shelf area.

697   US
DIRECTORY OF CERTIFIED ROOM AIR CONDITIONERS. s-a. $1 per no. Association of Home Appliance Manufacturers, 20 N. Wacker Dr., Chicago, IL 60606. TEL 312-984-5800. FAX 312-984-5823. **Document type:** directory.
   Description: Lists all brands and models certified both residential and built-in models. The certified Btu/hr cooling capacity and amps rating are given for each model along with the Energy Efficiency Rating (based on Department of Energy test procedures) and the operating voltage.

HEATING, PLUMBING AND REFRIGERATION

696 US
DIRECTORY OF LISTED PLUMBING PRODUCTS. m. $97.50. International Association of Plumbing & Mechanical Officials, 20001 Walnut Dr., S., Walnut, CA 91789-2825. TEL 909-595-8449. FAX 909-594-3690. circ. 2,500. **Document type:** trade publication.
   Former titles: Directory of Plumbing Research Recommendations; International Association of Plumbing and Mechanical Officials. Directory of Research Recommendations.

696 US
DIRECTORY OF LISTED PLUMBING PRODUCTS FOR MANUFACTURED HOUSING AND RECREATIONAL VEHICLES; trailer research directory. bi-m. $80. International Association of Plumbing & Mechanical Officials, 20001 Walnut Dr., S., Walnut, CA 91789. TEL 909-595-8449. FAX 909-594-3690. circ. 300.
   Former titles: Directory of Listed Plumbing Products for Mobile Homes and Recreational Vehicles; Directory of Research Recommendations for Mobile Homes and Recreational Vehicles; Directory of Research Recommendations for Manufactured Housing - Recreation Vehicles.
   Description: Directory of plumbing products for manufactured housing and recreational vehicles.

697 US ISSN 0898-1213
DISTRIBUTOR; the leading voice in wholesaling. 1983. m. free. Palmer Publishing Co., 651 W. Washington St., Ste. 300, Chicago, IL 60661. TEL 312-993-0929. FAX 312-993-0960. Ed. Mary Dolan. adv. circ. 17,500. **Document type:** trade publication.

697 US ISSN 0885-6621
DISTRICT HEATING AND COOLING. 1910. q. $40 (outside N. America $75). International District Heating & Cooling Association, 1101 Connecticut Ave. N.W., Ste. 700, Washington, DC 20036. TEL 202-429-5111. Ed. John F. Kattner. adv. contact: Tammie Jackson. illus.; tr.lit.; index. circ. 3,500. **Indexed:** Chem.Abstr., Eng.Ind., Fuel & Energy Abstr., Gas Abstr., Int.Build.Serv.Abstr. **Document type:** trade publication.
   Formerly: District Heating (ISSN 0012-401X)

697 GW ISSN 0933-6540
DISTRICT HEATING INTERNATIONAL/FERNWAERME INTERNATIONAL/CHAUFFAGE URBAIN INTERNATIONAL. (Text in English and German) 1971. m. DM.214. (Arbeitsgemeinschaft Fernwaerme e.V.) Verlags- und Wirtschaftsgesellschaft der Elektrizitaetswerke mBH, Stresemannallee 30, 60596 Frankfurt a.M., Germany. TEL 069-6304-311. FAX 069-6304359. TELEX 411284-VDEW. Ed. G. Andreas. adv. **Indexed:** INIS Atomind., Sci.Abstr. **Document type:** trade publication.
   —BLDSC (3604.249000); EI; SWETS. **CCC.**
   Formerly (until 1987): Fernwaerme International - District Heating (ISSN 0340-3572)

696 US
DUCTILE IRON PIPE NEWS. a. Ductile Iron Pipe Research Association, 245 Riverchase Pkwy E., Ste O, Birmingham, AL 35244. TEL 205-988-9870.

697 GW ISSN 0340-3513
ELEKTROWAERME INTERNATIONAL. PART A: ELEKTROWAERME IM TECHNISCHEN AUSBAU. Variant title: Elektrowaerme und Technischer Ausbau. Short title: E T A. 1931. 4/yr. DM.125 (combined subscr. Parts A & B DM.230). Vulkan-Verlag GmbH, Postfach 103962, 45039 Essen, Germany. TEL 0201-82002-0. FAX 0201-82002-40. Ed.Bd. adv.; bk.rev.; abstr.; bibl.; charts; pat.; tr.lit.; index. **Indexed:** Chem.Abstr., Eng.Ind., Excerp.Med., INIS Atomind., Met.Abstr., Sci.Abstr., World Alum.Abstr. **Document type:** trade publication.
   —SWETS. **CCC.**
   Supersedes in part: Elektrowaerme International (ISSN 0020-9147); Which was formerly: International Zeitschrift fuer Elektrowaerme.

621 US ISSN 0891-9976
TH7121 CODEN: ENSYEV
ENGINEERED SYSTEMS; serving the heating, ventilating, air conditioning and refrigerating engineering community. 1985. 12/yr. $39 (foreign $51). Business News Publishing Co.mpany, 755 W. Big Beaver Rd., Ste. 1000, Troy, MI 48084. TEL 810-362-3700. FAX 810-362-0317. (Subscr. to: Box 7016, Troy, MI 48007) Ed. Anne M. Hayner. adv.; tr.lit. circ. 57,518. (reprint service avail. from UMI) **Document type:** trade publication.
   —EI; UMI.
   Description: Covers HVACR design, specification, installation, service in commercial, industrial and institutional buildings.

697 BE ISSN 0777-6357
L'ENTREPRISE. Dutch edition: Onderneming (ISSN 0777-6349) (Text in French) 1950. m. 2200 BEF. Editions "Distrigraph" s.p.r.l., 50 Av. Alexandre Bertrand, B-1190 Brussels, Belgium. TEL 32-2-343-9347. FAX 32-2-344-33-69. adv.; bk.rev.; tr.lit. circ. 12,000 (6,000 Dutch ed., 6,000 French ed.). **Document type:** trade publication.
   Supersedes: Entreprise (1947) (ISSN 0013-905X)

697 US
FACT. 1988. bi-m. membership. (Florida Air Conditioning Contractors Association) Jafic Assoc. Management, Inc., Box 180458, Casselberry, FL 32718-0458. TEL 407-260-2212. FAX 407-260-5732. Ed. Cheryl DeFilippo. adv. circ. 500. (back issues avail.)
   Description: Covers business and industry, education and building codes.

697 DK ISSN 0106-6234
FJERNVARMEN. (Text in Danish; summaries in English) 1960. bi-m. DKK 375. Danske Fjernvarmevaerkers Forening - Danish District Heating Association, Galgebjergvej 44, 6000 Kolding, Denmark. FAX 75-528962. adv. circ. 2,200.

696 US ISSN 0046-4112
FLORIDA CONTRACTOR; plumbing-heating-cooling. 1941. m. $20. Florida Association of Plumbing, Heating, Cooling Contractors, Box 13089, Tallahassee, FL 32317. TEL 904-878-3134. Ed. Marian Smith. adv.; bk.rev. circ. 2,900.
   Former titles: Florida Plumbing and Heating Contractor; Florida Master Plumber.

FLORIDA FORUM. see *BUILDING AND CONSTRUCTION*

621.56 IT ISSN 0016-0296
  CODEN: FREDAZ
IL FREDDO. 1947. bi-m. L.47000($76) (Unione Frigorifera Italiana) Editoriale P E G SpA, Via Fratelli Bressan 2, 20126 Milan, Italy. TEL 02-25-79-841. FAX 02-25-52-779. TELEX 323088 PEGMOS I. Ed. Giancarlo Meani. adv.: B&W page L.1320000, color page L.2112000; trim 210 x 297. bk.rev.; charts; illus.; stat.; tr.lit. circ. 2,250. **Indexed:** Agri.Eng.Abstr., Chem.Abstr., Food Sci.& Tech.Abstr., Hort.Abstr., Sci.Abstr.
   —CASDDS.
   Description: Covers technical and plant installation problems, related to industrial refrigerated warehouses.

697 SP
FRIO, CALOR Y AIRE ACONDICIONADO. m. $100. Vifeca, S.L., Antonio Rodriquez Villa, 3, Bajo B-1, 28002 Madrid, Spain. TEL 562-86-83. FAX 411-29-22. (back issues avail.)

697 US
FUEL OIL & OIL HEAT. m. Industry Publications, Inc., 389 Passaic Ave., Fairfield, NJ 07004-2015. TEL 201-227-5151. FAX 201-227-9219. Ed. Paul Geiger. circ. 13,280.

697 720 GW ISSN 0016-3406
G A. (Gas und Architektur); Internationale Zeitschrift ueber Verwendungsmoeglichkeiten von Gas im Bauwesen. (Text in German, Italian, Spanish) 1963. 4/yr. DM.32. Karl Kraemer Verlag, Schulze-Delitzsch-Str. 15, 70565 Stuttgart, Germany. TEL 0711-78496-0.
FAX 0711-7849620. Ed. Karl Horst Kraemer. adv.; bk.rev.; charts; illus. circ. 16,100. **Document type:** trade publication.

GAS, WASSER, WAERME. see *PETROLEUM AND GAS*

697 GW ISSN 0020-9384
  CODEN: GWINAT
GASWAERME INTERNATIONAL; Zeitschrift fuer industrielle und gewerbliche Gasanwendung. (Summaries in English, French and German) 1952. m. DM.285. (Gaswaerme Institut Essen) Vulkan-Verlag GmbH, Postfach 103962, 45039 Essen, Germany. TEL 0201-82002-0. FAX 0201-82002-40. Ed.Bd. adv.; bk.rev.; charts; illus.; pat.; tr.lit.; index. circ. 4,000. (also avail. in microform from UMI; reprint service avail. from UMI) **Indexed:** C.I.S. Abstr., Chem.Abstr., Eng.Ind., Excerp.Med., Fuel & Energy Abstr., Gas Abstr., INIS Atomind., ISMEC. **Document type:** trade publication.
   —SWETS; CASDDS. **CCC.**
   Formerly: Internationale Zeitschrift fuer Gaswaerme.

697 NE ISSN 0926-6062
GAWALO - V K L JOURNAAL; vaktijdschrift voor installatietechniek. 1946. m. fl.109 (effective 1994). Wegener Tijl Tijdschriften Groep B.V., Postbus 9943, 1006 AP Amsterdam, Netherlands. TEL 31-20-5182828. FAX 31-20-5182843. Ed. W. Gielissen; Pub. H. de Roog. adv.; bk.rev.; charts; illus.; mkt.; pat.; stat. circ. 6,600. **Indexed:** Excerp.Med., Key to Econ.Sci. **Document type:** trade publication.
   Former titles (until 1987): De Schouw (ISSN 0036-6927); Installateursinfo (ISSN 0921-5298)
   Description: Independent magazine for the installation branch in the gas, water, plumbing, heating, cooling and air conditioning sectors. Covers technical developments, new equipment and systems, and market developments.

GAZ, WODA I TECHNIKA SANITARNA. see *ENGINEERING — Hydraulic Engineering*

697 FR
GUIDE PRATIQUE DE L'ENTREPRENEUR - CHAUFFAGE. 6/yr. Editions S E R I P, 40 rue Guy-Moquet, 94501 Champigny Cedex, France. TEL 48-81-91-91. FAX 48-81-81-77. Ed. Michael Gruny. circ. 15,000.
   Description: Covers heating, plumbing, roofing, sanitation.

696 GW
GUSSROHR - TECHNIK. 1966. a. Fachgemeinschaft Gusseiserne Rohre, Konrad-Adenauer-Ufer 33, 50668 Cologne, Germany. TEL 0221-125064. FAX 0221-124564. circ. 30,000. **Document type:** trade publication.
   Formerly: Informationen fuer das Gas- und Wasserfach.
   Description: Presents information on the design, performance and practical applications of ductile cast iron tubes for gas, water and sewage pipelines.

697 UK
H & V NEWS. 1956. w. £95($102) E M A P Maclaren Ltd., 19 Scarbrook Rd., Croydon, Surrey CR9 1QH, England. TEL 081-688 7788. FAX 081-760-0473. Ed. J. McDavid. adv.; bk.rev.; charts; tr.lit. circ. 22,093. (also avail. in microform from UMI) **Indexed:** Fluidex.
   Former titles: Heating and Ventilating News (ISSN 0017-9388); Heating and Ventilating Equipment News.
   Description: Articles for the heating and ventilating trade.

697 GW
  CODEN: HLHZAS
H L H, HEIZUNG, LUEFTUNG, KLIMA, HAUSTECHNIK. 1949. m. DM.310($107.50) (Verein Deutscher Ingenieure, Gesellschaft Technische Gebaeudeausruestung) V D I Verlag Gmbh, Heinrichstr. 24, 40239 Duesseldorf, Germany. TEL 0211-6188-0. FAX 0211-6188-112. TELEX 8587743. (Subscr. to: Postfach 101054, 40001 Duesseldorf, Germany) Ed. D. Volk. adv.; bk.rev.; abstr.; bibl.; charts; illus.; pat.; tr.mk.; index. circ. 5,500. **Indexed:** C.I.S. Abstr., Eng.Ind., Excerp.Med., Fluidex, INIS Atomind., Int.Build.Serv.Abstr., Sci.Abstr. **Document type:** trade publication.
   —BLDSC (4319.200000); EI; SWETS; CASDDS. **CCC.**
   Former titles: H L H, Zeitschrift fuer Heizung, Lueftung, Klimatechnik, Haustechnik (ISSN 0017-9906); Heizung, Lueftung, Haustechnik.

HEATING, PLUMBING AND REFRIGERATION

697 **CN**
H R A I NEWS. 1969. bi-m. membership. Heating, Refrigerating and Air Conditioning Institute of Canada, 5045 Orbitor Dr., Bldg. 11, Ste. 300, Mississauga, ON L4W 4Y4, Canada. TEL 905-602-4700. FAX 905-602-1197. circ. 1,200.
  Formerly: Environment.

697 **SZ**
HAUS TECH; Fachzeitschrift fuer Energie und Gebaeudekomfort, Klimatechnik, Lueftung, Isolierung und Heizung. 1962. 10/yr. 76 SFr. (foreign 110 SFr.). (Schweizerischer Verein fuer Kaeltetechnik) S H Z Fachverlag AG, Alte Landstr. 43, CH-8700 Kuesnacht, Switzerland. TEL 01-9108022. FAX 01-9105155. adv.; bk.rev.; charts; illus. circ. 11,000. Indexed: Chem.Abstr., Excerp.Med., Food Sci.& Tech.Abstr., Key to Econ.Sci. Document type: trade publication.
  Formerly: Kaelte- und Klima Rundschau (ISSN 0022-751X)
  Description: Trade news about home heating, refrigeration and other home technologies.

697 **GW** **ISSN 0344-2330**
HAUSTECHNISCHE RUNDSCHAU. 1901. m. DM.110. Krammer Verlag, Hermannstr. 3, 40233 Duesseldorf, Germany. TEL 0211-67972-0. FAX 0211-6797231. TELEX 8586639-KRVG-D. Ed. Bernd Genath. adv.: color page DM.2500; trim 185 x 257; adv. contact: Heinz Martin. bk.rev.; pat.; index. circ. 6,000. Indexed: Excerp.Med.

696 697 **US**
HEARTLAND RETAILER. 1973. m. $10. Podany Printing Co., 10310 Ellison Circle, Omaha, NE 68134. TEL 402-496-0717. FAX 402-496-0678. Ed. Eugene Podany. adv.; bk.rev.; circ. 14,500 (controlled). (tabloid format; back issues avail.) Document type: trade publication.
  Formerly: Nebraska - Iowa Retailer.
  Description: Carries news of new products in the home goods industry to dealers.

HEAT TRANSFER - FLUID FLOW DATA BOOKS. see ENGINEERING — Mechanical Engineering

697 **UK** **ISSN 0307-7950**
TJ275 **CODEN: HACJBF**
HEATING AND AIR CONDITIONING JOURNAL. 1931. m. £50. Maclean Hunter Ltd., Maclean Hunter House, Chalk Lane, Cockfosters Rd., Barnet, Herts EN4 OBU, England. TEL 081-242-3000. FAX 081-242-3185. TELEX 299072-MACHUN-G. Ed. Paul Haddlesey. adv.; bk.rev.; charts; illus.; tr.lit. circ. 17,519. (also avail. in microform from UMI; reprint service avail. from UMI) Indexed: Br.Ceram.Abstr., Br.Tech.Ind., Eng.Ind., Fluidex, Fuel & Energy Abstr., Gas Abstr., Int.Build.Serv.Abstr., Intl.Civil Eng.Abstr., ISMEC, Met.Abstr., Sci.Abstr., Soft.Abstr.Eng., World Alum.Abstr. Document type: trade publication.
  —BLDSC (4237.430000); SWETS; UMI.
  Formerly: Steam and Heating Engineer (ISSN 0039-0836)

697 **UK** **ISSN 0265-7899**
HEATING & PLUMBING MONTHLY INC. VENTILATION. 1984. 10/yr. £45. Industrial Trade Journals Ltd., Stakes House, Quebec Sq., Westerham, Kent TN16 1TD, England. TEL 0959-564212. FAX 0959-562325. Ed. Barbara Field. circ. 31,796. Indexed: Br.Tech.Ind. Document type: trade publication.

697 **UK**
HEATING AND VENTILATING ENGINEER. 1927. bi-m. £68. Turret Group Plc., Turret House, 171 High St., Rickmansworth, Herts WD3 1SN, England. TEL 0923-777000. FAX 0923-771297. Ed. Norman Sheperd. adv.; bk.rev.; charts; illus.; pat.; tr.lit.; index. circ. 5,800. Indexed: Br.Tech.Ind., C.I.S. Abstr., Eng.Ind., Excerp.Med., Int.Build.Serv.Abstr., Intl.Civil Eng.Abstr., Sci.Abstr., Soft.Abstr.Eng. Document type: trade publication.
  —BLDSC (4237.164000).
  Formerly: Heating and Ventilating Engineer and Journal of Air Conditioning (ISSN 0017-937X)

697 **UK** **ISSN 0017-9396**
TH7201
HEATING AND VENTILATING REVIEW. 1960. m. £35 (foreign £44). Faversham House Group, Faversham House, 111 St. James's Rd., Croydon, Surrey CR9 2TH, England. TEL 081-684-4082. FAX 081-684-9729. Ed. F.W. Burton. adv.; bk.rev.; illus.; circ. 23,282 (controlled). Document type: trade publication.

696 **US** **ISSN 0017-940X**
TH7201 **CODEN: HPAOAM**
HEATING - PIPING - AIR CONDITIONING; the magazine of mechanical systems engineering. 1929. m. $50 (free to qualified personnel). Penton Publishing (Subsidiary of: Pittway Company), 1100 Superior Ave., Cleveland, OH 44114-2543. TEL 216-969-7000. FAX 216-696-8765. (Subscr. to: Box 95759, Cleveland, OH 44101) Ed. Robert T. Korte. adv.; bk.rev.; charts; illus.; pat.; tr.lit.; circ. 52,000 (controlled). (also avail. in microform from UMI; reprint service avail. from UMI) Indexed: A.S.& T.Ind., Abstr.Health Care Manage.Stud., Appl.Mech.Rev., BMT, Chem.Abstr., Eng.Ind., Excerp.Med., Fuel & Energy Abstr., Gas Abstr., Ind.Sci.Rev., INIS Atomind., Int.Build.Serv.Abstr., ISMEC, PROMT, Sh.& Vib.Dig. Document type: trade publication.
  —BLDSC (4280.000000); Faxon; UnCover; SWETS; UMI. **CCC.**
  Description: Serves the engineered systems market in the areas of building construction, renovation, and retrofit. Publishes current articles about HVAC-R systems, piping and plumbing systems, control, and cogeneration.

696 **CN** **ISSN 0017-9418**
HEATING, PLUMBING, AIR CONDITIONING. 1923. 7/yr. Can.$29.96 (US Can.$43, elsewhere Can.$65). Cowgate Communications Inc., 1370 Don Mills Rd., Ste. 300, Don Mills, ON M3B 3N7, Canada. TEL 416-759-2500. FAX 416-759-6979. Ed. Bruce Cole; Pub. Bruce Meacock. adv. contact: Bill James. charts; illus.; stat.; tr.lit. circ. 16,237. Indexed: Can.B.P.I. Document type: trade publication.
  Formerly: Automatic Heating, Plumbing, Air Conditioning; Incorporating: Environment Systems and Industries (ISSN 0705-9272)
  Description: Keeps the industry informed about the market, products and technology, government regulations and other pertinent information.

696 **CN** **ISSN 0382-6996**
HEATING, PLUMBING, AIR CONDITIONING BUYERS' GUIDE. 1923. a. Can.$32.10($30) Cowgate Communications Inc., 1370 Don Mills Rd., Ste. 300, Don Mills, ON M3B 3N7, Canada. TEL 416-759-2500. FAX 416-759-6979. Ed. Bruce Cole; Pub. Bruce Meacock. adv. circ. 14,893. Document type: trade publication.

697 **UK** **ISSN 0265-4571**
HEATING, VENTILATING & PLUMBING. 1979. m. (11/yr.) £36 (foreign £44). B & M Publications (London) Ltd., Box 13, Hereford House, Bridle Path, Croydon, Surrey CR9 4NL, England. TEL 081-680-4200. FAX 081-681-5049. Ed. Sara Wharton. adv.: B&W page £1550, color page £2000; trim 210 x 297. tr.lit. circ. 31,609. Document type: trade publication.
  Formerly: Heating and Ventilating Products.

697 **SZ**
HEIZUNG KLIMA. m. (11/yr.). 75 Fr. Verlag Aargauer Tagblatt AG, Bahnhofstrasse 39-43, 5001 Aarau, Switzerland. adv.

697 **AU**
HEIZUNG - LUEFTUNG - KLIMATECHNIK. 9/yr. Technopress Fachzeitschriften Verlagsgesellschaft mbH, Iglaseegasse 21-23, Postfach 176, A-1191 Vienna, Austria. TEL 01-322551. FAX 01-327427. Ed. Wolfgang Kadrnoska. circ. 13,500. Document type: trade publication.

697 **SZ**
HEIZUNG UND LUEFTUNG/CHAUFFAGE ET VENTILATION; Magazin gebaeudetechnik - revue technique du batiment. (Text in French and German) 1934. q. 45 SFr. (foreign 110 SFr.). Verband Schweizerischer Heizungs- und Lueftungsfirmen (VSHL), Olgastr. 6, Postfach, CH-8024 Zurich 1, Switzerland. TEL 01-251-95-69. FAX 01-252-92-31. (Co-sponsor: Association Suisse des Entreprises de Chauffage et de Ventilation (ASCV)) adv.; bk.rev.; charts; illus.; tr.lit. circ. 3,500. Indexed: C.I.S. Abstr., Chem.Abstr., Dairy Sci.Abstr. Document type: trade publication.
  Formerly: Schweizerische Blatter fuer Heizung und Lueftung - Revue Suisse du Chauffage et de la Ventilation (ISSN 0036-7559)

HOME AUTOMATION NEWS. see ELECTRONICS

HUTOIPAR. see FOOD AND FOOD INDUSTRIES

697 **GW**
I K Z - HAUSTECHNIK; Fachzeitschrift fuer Sanitaer-, Heizung-, Klimatechnik. 1872. s-m. DM.160. (Zentralverband fuer Sanitaer-, Heizung- und Klimatechnik) Verlag A. Strobel KG, Postfach 5654, 59806 Arnsberg, Germany. TEL 02931-8900-0. FAX 02931-890048. Ed. Ekkehard Strobel. adv.; bk.rev.; bibl.; charts; illus. circ. 25,000. Document type: trade publication.
  Formerly: I K Z (ISSN 0018-9936)
  Description: Trade journal for planning and executing experts in the fields of sanitation, heating, ventilation and air conditioning.

697 **US**
ICE NEWS. bi-m. $25. Packaged Ice Association, 4101 Lake Boone Trail, Ste. 201, Raleigh, NC 27607-6518. TEL 919-787-5181. FAX 919-787-4916. adv. circ. 350. Document type: trade publication.
  Description: For manufacturers and distributors of packaged ice, and manufacturers of ice-making equipment and supplies.

696 **US** **ISSN 0019-2112**
ILLINOIS MASTER PLUMBER MAGAZINE. 1916. m. $9 (effective 1992). Illinois Association of Plumbing - Heating - Cooling Contractors, 821 S. Grand Ave. West, Springfield, IL 62704. TEL 217-522-7219. FAX 217-522-4315. Ed. Dorothy Sharpe-Clem. adv.: B&W page $325, color page $550; trim 8 1/2 x 11. circ. 1,868. Document type: trade publication.

IMPACT PUMP NEWS AND PATENTS. see MACHINERY

IMPIANTISTICA ITALIANA. see MACHINERY

696 697 **US**
INDIANA CONTRACTOR. 1957. bi-m. $10. Indiana Association of Plumbing - Heating - Cooling Contractors, Inc., Box 40963, Indianapolis, IN 46240. TEL 317-575-9292. FAX 317-575-9378. Ed. Melissa Bloom. adv.; charts; illus.; mkt.; stat.; circ. 5,100 (controlled). Document type: trade publication.
  Formerly: Indiana Plumbing - Heating - Cooling Contractor (ISSN 0019-6703)

697 **US** **ISSN 0446-0138**
INDOOR COMFORT NEWS. 1955. m. $12. Institute of Heating & Air Conditioning Industries, 606 N. Larchmont Blvd., Ste. 4A, Los Angeles, CA 90004. TEL 213-467-1158. FAX 213-461-2588. Ed. Michelle Miller. adv. contact: Melissa Austin. circ. 23,000. Document type: trade publication.
  Description: Provides topical industry news and information on products and equipment for heating and air conditioning engineers and contractors in the western states.

697 331.8 **US** **ISSN 0569-4043**
TH7392.M6
INDUSTRIAL VENTILATION; A MANUAL OF RECOMMENDED PRACTICE.* 1951. biennial, 21st ed., 1992. $45 (Canada $54; Mexico $63). American Conference of Governmental Industrial Hygienists, Inc., 1330 Kemper Meadow Dr., Ste. 600, Cincinnati, OH 45240-1634. TEL 513-661-7881. circ. 25,000.
  —BLDSC (4462.880000).

HEATING, PLUMBING AND REFRIGERATION

697   SP   ISSN 0214-4034
INSTALACIONES Y TECNICAS DEL CONFORT. 10/yr. Santisima Trinidad 6, 5o, 28010 Madrid, Spain. TEL 1-448-61-26. FAX 1-446-80-69. Ed. D.V. Redondo Polo. circ. 6,000.

697   SP   ISSN 0210-4091
INSTALADOR. 1967. 11/yr. Navaleno 9, Residencial el Bosque de Chamarti, 28033 Madrid, Spain. TEL 1-302-81-46. FAX 1-766-16-64. circ. 7,000.

697 696   FR   ISSN 0399-9874
L'INSTALLATEUR; chauffage, genie climatique, plomberie, sanitaire, couverture-isolation, electricite appliquee. 1947. 9/yr. $136 (typically set in Jan.). E S I Publications, Villa Laromiguiere, 75005 Paris, France. TEL 1-40-46-62-00. FAX 1-40-46-62-01. Ed. Guillaume d'Eon. adv.; charts; illus.; pat.; stat.; tr.lit.; tr.mk. circ. 8,000. **Document type:** trade publication.

696   SZ
INSTALLATEUR. m. (11/yr.). 91 SFr. A T Zeitschriftenverlag, Bahnhofstr. 39-43, CH-5001 Aarau, Switzerland. TEL 064-266161. FAX 064-266213. adv. **Document type:** trade publication.

696   SZ
INSTALLATEUR SANITAIRE. (Text in French) bi-m. 49.50 SFr. A T Zeitschriftenverlag, Bahnhofstr. 39-43, CH-5001 Aarau, Switzerland. TEL 064-266161. FAX 064-266213. adv. **Document type:** trade publication.

697   NE   ISSN 0020-2096
INSTALLATIE; vakblad voor de gehele installatiebranche. 1962. m. fl.139.50. Audet Tijdschriften bv (Subsidiary of: C. Misset B.V.), Postbus 9000, 6800 DA Arnhem, Netherlands. TEL 31-85-209911. FAX 31-85-233007. Ed. H. Nijen Twilhaar. adv.; B&W page fl.2582, color page fl.5107; trim 210 x 297; adv. contact: Cor van Nek. bk.rev.; charts; illus.; stat.; index. circ. 6,940. **Indexed:** Excerp.Med., Key To Econ.Sci. **Document type:** trade publication.
—SWETS.
Description: Describes the latest developments in products and installation of gas, water, sanitation as well as heating and cooling systems.

697   AU
INSTALLATION IM SPIEGEL. q. Dynamis Werbe- und Verlagsgesellschaft mbH, Heinestr. 3, A-1020 Vienna, Austria. TEL 01-2143344. FAX 01-2167929. Ed. Johannes Vater. circ. 5,700.

697   IT   ISSN 0020-2118
L'INSTALLATORE ITALIANO; la rivista mensile degli impianti tecnici. 1950. m. L.94000($158) Editoriale P E G SpA, Via Fratelli Bressan 2, 20126 Milan, Italy. TEL 02-25-79-841. FAX 02-25-52-779. TELEX 323088 PEGMOS I. Ed. Franco Adami. adv.; B&W page L.2300000, color page L.3680000; trim 210 x 297. bk.rev.; abstr.; charts; illus.; index. circ. 8,265. **Indexed:** C.I.S.Abstr., Int.Build.Serv.Abstr. **Document type:** trade publication.
—BLDSC (4518.730000).
Description: Covers technical installations in the field of heating, air conditioning, plumbing, sanitary installations, electricity, telephony, security and industrial refrigeration.

697   IT
INSTALLATORE TECNICO. 12/yr. National Federation of Italian Artisans and Craftsmen, Viale Certosa 238, 20156 Milan, Italy. TEL 2-30-85-141. FAX 2-30-88-503. Ed. Franco Pigozzi. circ. 35,000.

621.56   FR   ISSN 0020-6970
TP490
INSTITUT INTERNATIONAL DU FROID. BULLETIN/INTERNATIONAL INSTITUTE OF REFRIGERATION. BULLETIN. (Text in English, French) 1910. bi-m. 590 F. Institut International du Froid - International Institute of Refrigeration, 177 bd. Malesherbes, 75017 Paris, France. FAX 47-63-17-98. TELEX 643269 ININFRI. adv.; bk.rev.; charts; illus.; index. circ. 3,000. **Indexed:** BMT, Fluidex, Food Sci.& Tech.Abstr., INIS Atomind., Sci.Abstr.
Description: Features articles and documents on cryophysics and cryogenics, thermodymanics, refrigerating machinery, preservation and treatment of foodstuffs, the cold chain, air conditioning, heat pumps, energy recovery, cryobiology, economics, education and regulations. Presents research, announcements and news. Lists available computer programs.

621.56   FR   ISSN 0074-6541
INSTITUT INTERNATIONAL DU FROID. COMPTES RENDUS DE REUNIONS DE COMMISSIONS/INTERNATIONAL INSTITUTE OF REFRIGERATION. PROCEEDINGS OF COMMISION MEETINGS. (Text and summaries in English, French) 1952. irreg. price varies. Institut International du Froid - International Institute of Refrigeration, 177 bd. Malesherbes, 75017 Paris, France. FAX 47-63-17-98. TELEX 643269 ININFRI. circ. 2,000. **Document type:** proceedings.
Description: Presents reports given at meetings along with accompanying discussions.

621.56   UK
INSTITUTE OF REFRIGERATION. PROCEEDINGS. 1899. a. £22. Institute of Refrigeration, Kelvin House, 76 Mill Ln., Carshalton, Surrey SM5 2JR, England. TEL 081-647-7033. FAX 081-773-0165. circ. 2,500. **Document type:** proceedings.

INSULATION CONTRACTORS MONTHLY. see *BUILDING AND CONSTRUCTION*

697   NE   ISSN 0921-5492
INTECH; maandblad voor de installatiebranche. 1981. 11/yr. fl.140 (effective 1992). (Vereniging van Nederlandse Installatiebedrijven) S E V I, Postbus 7272, 2701 AG Zoetermeer, Netherlands. TEL 31-79-214402. FAX 31-79-210702. Ed. W. Keyzer-Broers. adv. contact: R. Steltman. bk.rev. circ. 5,000. **Document type:** trade publication.
—SWETS.
Formerly (until 1987): Installatietechniek (ISSN 0921-5484)

697   UK   ISSN 0955-8896
INTERFACE (BRACKNELL). q. Building Services Research and Information Association, Old Bracknell Ln. W., Bracknell, Berks. RG12 7AH, England. TEL 0344-426511. FAX 0344-487575. **Document type:** trade publication.

621.56   US
TP372.2
INTERNATIONAL DIRECTORY OF PUBLIC REFRIGERATED WAREHOUSES. 1930. a. $150 (free to qualified personnel). International Association of Refrigerated Warehouses, 7315 Wisconsin Ave., Ste. 1200N, Bethesda, MD 20814. TEL 301-652-5674. FAX 301-652-7269. Dir. J. William Hudson. adv. circ. 6,000. **Document type:** directory.
Formerly: Directory of Public Refrigerated Warehouses. (ISSN 0070-6167)

697   US   ISSN 0074-4638
TH7201   CODEN: IDHOAI
INTERNATIONAL DISTRICT HEATING ASSOCIATION. PROCEEDINGS. 1909. a. $150 to non-members; members $75. International District Heating Association, 1101 Connecticut Ave., Ste. 700, Washington, DC 20036. TEL 202-429-5111. FAX 202-429-5113. adv. contact: Tanya Vetter. circ. 500. **Indexed:** Therm.Abstr. **Document type:** proceedings.
—CASDDS.

621.56   UK   ISSN 0140-7007
TP490   CODEN: IJRFDI
INTERNATIONAL JOURNAL OF REFRIGERATION. (Text in English or French) 1978. bi-m. £160. (International Institute of Refrigeration, FR) Butterworth - Heinemann (Subsidiary of: Reed International PLC), Linacre House, Jordan Hill, Oxford OX2 8DP, England. TEL 0865-310366. FAX 0865-310898. TELEX 83111 BHPOXF G. (Subscr. addr.: Turpin Transactions Ltd., Distribution Centre, Blackhorse Rd., Letchworth, Herts SG6 1HN, England. TEL 0462-672555) adv.; bk.rev.; abstr.; bibl.; illus.; index. (also avail. in microform from UMI; back issues avail.) **Indexed:** Agri.Eng.Abstr., Chem.Abstr., Energy Info.Abstr., Excerpt.Med., Food Sci.& Tech.Abstr., Foul.Prev.Res.Dig., Hort.Abstr., Int.Build.Serv.Abstr. **Document type:** academic/scholarly publication.
—BLDSC (4542.525500); SWETS; UMI; CASDDS. **CCC.**
Description: Research and industrial news in refrigeration, air conditioning and associated fields. *Refereed Serial*

697   RU   ISSN 0202-8190
ITOGI NAUKI I TEKHNIKI: KOTEL'NYE USTANOVKI I VODOPODGOTOVKA. irreg. 3.20 Rub. Vsesoyuznyi Institut Nauchno-Tekhnicheskoi Informatsii (VINTI), Ul. Usievicha 20-A, 125219 Moscow A-129, Russian. (Subscr. to: Mezhdunarodnaya Kniga, Moscow 121200, Russian)

621.56   JA   ISSN 0910-0040
TP490   CODEN: NRKRET
JAPANESE ASSOCIATION OF REFRIGERATION. TRANSACTIONS/NIHON REITO KYOKAI RONBUNSHU. (Text in Japanese; summaries in English) 1984. 3/yr. 3500 Yen per no. Japanese Association of Refrigeration, 8 San'ei-cho, Shinjuku-ku, Tokyo 160, Japan. Ed. S. Mori. adv. circ. 1,500. **Indexed:** Sci.Abstr. **Document type:** academic/scholarly publication.
—BLDSC (8975.112000); CASDDS.

697   FR   ISSN 1146-1470
JOURNAL C C I. 1990. 11/yr. 450 F. (foreign 680 F.). Promotor France, B.P. 205, 75524 Paris Cedex 11, France. TEL 48-07-14-40. FAX 48-07-14-43. Ed. Jan Meyer. circ. 5,000. **Document type:** newspaper.
Description: Covers heating, ventilation, air-conditioning, refrigeration.

JOURNAL OF THERMAL INSULATION AND BUILDING ENVELOPES. see *ENGINEERING*

697   GW   ISSN 0945-0459
TH7687.A1   CODEN: KKHEDS
K I - LUFT- UND KAELTETECHNIK. (Klima und Kaelteingenieur) 1973. m. DM.232 (foreign DM.262). Verlag C.F. Mueller GmbH, Amalienstr. 29, 76133 Karlsruhe, Germany. TEL 0721-91220-0. FAX 0721-9122020. Ed. Fritz Steimle. adv.; bk.rev.; charts; illus.; tr.lit. circ. 4,000. **Indexed:** Appl.Mech.Rev., Chem.Abstr., Eng.Ind., Excerp.Med., Fluidex, Food Sci.& Tech.Abstr., INIS Atomind., Int.Build.Serv.Abstr. **Document type:** trade publication.
—BLDSC (5099.275700); SWETS; CASDDS. **CCC.**
Formed by the merger of (1965-1994): Luft- und Kaeltetechnik (ISSN 0024-7251); (1979-1944): K I - Klima, Kaelte, Heizung (ISSN 0172-1984); Which was formerly: Klima- Kaelteingenieur (ISSN 0340-398X); Which was formed by the merger of: Kaelte Klima Praktiker (ISSN 0022-7528); Kaeltetechnik Klimatisierung (ISSN 0047-3073)

697   GW   ISSN 0343-2246
TP490   CODEN: KAKLDS
K K - DIE KAELTE UND KLIMATECHNIK. 1947. m. DM.198.60 (foreign DM.229.60). A.W. Gentner Verlag, Forststr. 131, 70193 Stuttgart, Germany. TEL 0711-63672-0. FAX 0711-6367211. Ed. Peter Weissenborn. adv.; bk.rev.; bibl.; charts; illus.; mkt.; pat.; tr.mk.; index. circ. 5,750. **Indexed:** Chem.Abstr., Food Sci.& Tech.Abstr., INIS Atomind. **Document type:** trade publication.
—SWETS; CASDDS. **CCC.**
Formerly: Kaelte (ISSN 0022-7501)

697   GW   ISSN 0931-3117
K UND L MAGAZIN; offizielle Fachzeitschrift fuer den Kachelofen und Luftheizungsbau. bi-m. DM.81 (foreign DM.104.70). A.W. Gentner Verlag, Forststr. 131, 70193 Stuttgart, Germany. TEL 0711-63672-0. FAX 0711-6367211. Ed. Otto Lieberwirth. circ. 3,100. **Document type:** trade publication.

HEATING, PLUMBING AND REFRIGERATION

697   GW   ISSN 0722-4605
KAELTE KLIMA AKTUELL. 1981. bi-m. DM.70 (foreign DM.85). S W I Bahmann GmbH, Heslacher Wand 28, 70199 Stuttgart, Germany. TEL 0711-602490. FAX 0711-6402226. Ed. Georg Bahmann. circ. 3,800. **Document type:** trade publication.

697   US
KENTUCKY INDEX. 1950. m. free. Kentucky Association of Plumbing - Heating - Cooling Contractors, Inc., 1501 Durrett Ln., Louisville, KY 40213-1826. TEL 502-451-5577. FAX 502-451-5551. Ed. Linda Griffey. adv.; illus.; tr.lit. circ. 2,500.
    Kentucky Plumbing and Heating Index.

KHIMIYA TVERDOGO TOPLIVA. see *ENGINEERING — Chemical Engineering*

621.56   RU   ISSN 0023-124X
CODEN: KHTEAU
KHOLODIL'NAYA TEKHNIKA. (Text in Russian; contents page in English) 1923. 6/yr. $97. (Rosmyasomolgtorg) Izdatel'stvo Kolos, Sadovaya-Spasskaya 18, 107807 Moscow, Russia. TEL 207-23-96. FAX 207-28-70. (Co-sponsor: Interkholod) Ed. L.D. Akimova. adv.: page $1500; adv. contact: Z.D. Mishina. bk.rev.; charts; illus.; index. **Indexed:** Agri.Eng.Abstr., Chem.Abstr., Dairy Sci.Abstr., Food Sci.& Tech.Abstr., Hort.Abstr., Int.Build.Serv.Abstr., Nutr.Abstr., Packag.Sci.Tech. —BLDSC (0396.000000); CASDDS.

697   NE   ISSN 0165-5523
CODEN: KOEKEQ
KLIMAATBEHEERSING; tijdschrift voor verwarming, luchtbehandeling en milieuverzorging. 1971. m. fl.92.50. Keesing Noordervliet B.V., De Molen 82-86, 3995 AX Houten, Netherlands. TEL 31-3403-58585. FAX 31-3403-58500. Ed. F. Stouthart. adv. contact: J. van 't Hoofd. bk.rev.; charts; illus. circ. 2,431. **Indexed:** Int.Build.Serv.Abstr. **Document type:** trade publication.
—SWETS.
    Description: For professionals in the climate control field, including facilities maintenance and production engineers.

621.56 697   US
KOLDFAX. 1953. m. membership. Air-Conditioning and Refrigeration Institute, 4301 Fairfax Dr., Ste. 425, Arlington, VA 22203-1627. TEL 703-524-8800. FAX 703-528-3816. Ed. Nancy St. Jean. circ. controlled. (tabloid format) **Document type:** newsletter.

697 662   NE   ISSN 0925-6318
KOUDE MAGAZINE. 1965. m. fl.86. Keesing Noordervliet B.V., De Molen 82-86, 3995 AX Houten, Netherlands. TEL 31-3403-58585. FAX 31-3403-58500. Ed. F. Stouthart. adv. contact: J. van 't Hoofd. circ. 3,050. **Indexed:** Chem.Abstr., Dairy Sci.Abstr., Excerp.Med., Key to Econ.Sci. **Document type:** trade publication.
—SWETS.
    Formerly (until 1990): Koude Klimaat (ISSN 0923-6554); Which supersedes in part (in 1989): Koeltechniek, Klimaatregeling (ISSN 0165-5477); Which was formerly (until 1973): Koeltechniek (ISSN 0368-6361)
    Description: For management personnel in the field of refrigeration and climate engineering.

KUKI CHOWA EISEI KOGAKU/HEATING, AIR-CONDITIONING AND SANITARY ENGINEERING. see *PUBLIC HEALTH AND SAFETY*

621.56   NO   ISSN 0801-7093
KULDE; tidsskrift for kuldebransjen. 1984. 6/yr. NOK 240. Skarland Press A-S, P.O. Box 5042 Maj., 0301 Oslo 3, Norway. TEL 47-22-60-13-90. FAX 47-22-69-36-50. Ed. Halvor Roestad. circ. 6,032 (controlled). **Document type:** trade publication.
    Description: Discusses technological advances and trends within the field of the cooling and refrigeration industry. Addresses environmental matters and the industry's economic policies.

697   US
LENNOX NEWS. 1946. q. free to qualified personnel. Lennox International Inc., Office of Government and Public Relations, Box 799900, Dallas, TX 75379-9900. TEL 214-497-5258. FAX 214-497-5292. Ed. Rhonda R. Hewitt. circ. 15,000 (controlled). (tabloid format) back issues avail.) **Document type:** newsletter.
    Description: For independent Lennox dealers and secondary audiences.

697   SP
M A B - H R & C ESPANA. 4/yr. Manso 37 bis 1o, 1aB, 08015 Barcelona, Spain. TEL 3-418-47-42.
    Description: Covers heating, cooling and air conditioning.

697   SP   ISSN 0210-184X
M I. (Montajes e Instalaciones); revista mensual de arquitectura e ingenieria de las instalaciones. 1971. m. (11/yr.). 10000 ptas.($164) (effective 1993). Editorial Alcion, S.A., Triana 51-53, 28016 Madrid, Spain. TEL 341-457-64-00. FAX 341-457-39-45. TELEX 49236 QUIMI E. Ed. R. Madrid. adv.; bk.rev.; abstr.; bibl.; charts; illus.; index. circ. 4,500. **Indexed:** Ind.SST.

697   SP
MADERA Y CARBON. 4/yr. Costa Rica 13, 4o A-2, 28016 Madrid, Spain. TEL 2505885. FAX 345-93-13.

696 697   US
MARYLAND P H C C NEWS & VIEWS. 1926. m. free. Maryland Plumbing-Heating-Cooling Contractors, Inc., 10176 Baltimore National Pike, Ste. 205, Ellicott City, MD 21042. FAX 301-461-5977. Ed. Diane P. Kastner. adv. circ. 2,300.
    Formerly: Maryland Master Plumber.

696   AT   ISSN 0025-5068
MASTER PLUMBER OF SOUTH AUSTRALIA.* 1955. m. Master Plumbers & Mechanical Services Association, 219 Henley Rd., Torrensville, S.A. 5031, Australia. Ed. R.J. Hollis. adv.; illus.; stat.; circ. 550 (controlled).

621.56 697   CN   ISSN 1183-9015
MECHANICAL BUYER AND SPECIFIER - H V A C - REFRIGERATION. 1991. m. Can.$24.95($30) Nytek Publishing Inc., 452 Attwell Dr., Ste. 100, Etobicoke, ON M9W 5C3, Canada. TEL 416-798-3181. FAX 416-798-2526. Ed. Ron Shuker. adv. circ. 7,982. **Document type:** trade publication.
    Description: Covers forced-air heating, ventilation, air conditioning, refrigeration and related technical, market, product and application information.

696   CN   ISSN 1183-9007
MECHANICAL BUYER AND SPECIFIER - PLUMBING, PIPING AND HEATING. 1991. m. Can.$24.95($30) Nytek Publishing, Inc., 452 Attwell Dr., Ste. 100, Etobicoke, ON M9W 5C3, Canada. TEL 416-798-3181. FAX 416-798-2526. Ed. Ron Shuker. adv. circ. 13,020. **Document type:** trade publication.
    Description: Covers plumbing, piping, hydronic heating, DHW heating, fire sprinkler and related technical, market, management, product, and application information.

696   US
MICHIGAN MASTER PLUMBER & MECHANICAL CONTRACTOR; a monthly magazine for Michigan's plumbing, heating, cooling industry. 1952. m. free. Michigan Plumbing & Mechanical Contractors Association, 400 N. Walnut St., Lansing, MI 48933-1125. TEL 517-694-8171. FAX 517-694-0980. Ed. Cindy Hall-Maher. adv. circ. 3,000. **Document type:** trade publication.
    Formerly: Michigan Master Plumber.

697   US
▼**MID-ATLANTIC H V A C NEWS.** 1993. m. $10. Holco Communications Inc., Box 80727, Stone Mountain, GA 30208-0727. TEL 404-483-4860. FAX 404-483-2447. circ. 2,500. (tabloid format) **Document type:** trade publication.
    Formerly: Virginia H V A C News.
    Description: Provides wholesale and manufacturing news and local distributor news for dealers and contractors-installers of central heating and cooling equipment; residential, light commercial and industrial.

696   US
MINNESOTA P - H - C CONTRACTOR. 1948. m. $9. (Minnesota Association of Plumbing - Heating - Cooling Contractors Inc.) Minnesota Master Plumber Publishing Co., Inc., c/o Donald E. Sullivan, Ed., 8085 Wayzata Blvd., no. 109, Minneapolis, MN 55426-1456. TEL 612-546-4448. FAX 612-546-4507. adv.; charts; stat.; illus.; bibl.; circ. 2,500 (controlled). **Document type:** trade publication.
    Description: Presents news and information relating to the plumbing, heating, and cooling industry.

696   AT   ISSN 0819-1824
N.S.W. MASTER PLUMBER. (New South Wales) 1923. bi-m. Aus.$30. Master Plumbers and Mechanical Contractors Association of New South Wales, P.O. Box 65, Haberfield, N.S.W. 2045, Australia. TEL 02-797-7055. FAX 02-799-5841. Ed. Richard Rolls. adv. contact: Richard Rolls. bk.rev.; illus.; tr.lit.; circ. 1,600 (controlled). **Document type:** trade publication.
    Formerly (until 1986): Master Plumber (ISSN 0025-5041)

NATIONAL CHIMNEY SWEEP GUILD. NEWSLINK. see *FIRE PREVENTION*

696   US
NEW ENGLAND PROGRESS. 1938. m. free. 5 The Mountain Rd., Framingham, MA 01701-8803. TEL 508-879-6799. FAX 508-879-3044. Ed. Carolyn Davis. adv. contact: Bernadette Masur. circ. 3,000. **Document type:** trade publication.

696   NZ   ISSN 0028-8594
NEW ZEALAND PLUMBING REVIEW; heating and ventilation. 1963. m. NZ.$8. (Modern Productions Ltd.) Akron Consolidated Ltd., Box 51-182, Auckland 6, New Zealand. Ed. L. Soffe. adv.; bk.rev.; illus.; circ. 1,250 (controlled).
—CCC.

697 621.56   JA   ISSN 0029-036X
NIHON REITO REIBO SHINBUN/JAPAN REFRIGERATION AND AIR CONDITIONING NEWS. (Text in Japanese) 1955. w. 15000 Yen. 2-11-7 Tsukiji, Chuo-ku, Tokyo 104, Japan. TEL 03-3543-4911. FAX 03-3543-4653. Ed. Tadashi Okuma. adv.; bk.rev.; tr.lit. circ. 28,000. (also avail. in microform) **Document type:** bulletin.

697   NO   ISSN 0029-2265
NORSK V V S. 1957. 16/yr. NOK 395. (Norsk V.V.S. Energy- og Miljoeteknisk Forening - Norwegian Society of Heating, Air-Conditioning and Sanitary Engineers) Skarland Press A-S, Postboks 5042, Maj 0301 Oslo 3, Norway. TEL 47-22-60-13-90. FAX 47-22-69-36-50. Ed. Arne S. Rognar Nielsen. adv.; bk.rev.; illus.; stat.; index; circ. 5,000 (controlled). **Indexed:** Int.Build.Serv.Abstr.

696 697   US   ISSN 0739-3830
NORTH CAROLINA PLUMBING - HEATING - COOLING FORUM. 1942. m. $14. North Carolina Association of Plumbing - Heating - Cooling Contractors, Inc., 413 Glenwood Ave., Raleigh, NC 27603. TEL 919-833-0372. FAX 919-833-0921. Ed. Tom Elkins. adv.; bk.rev.; pat.; stat.; tr.lit.; circ. 4,000 (controlled). **Document type:** trade publication.

621.56   UK
NUSLECA. 1955. q. £2. Nusleca Publications, Shripney Works, Bognor Regis, W. Sussex PO22 9NQ, England. FAX 0243-868052. Ed. Jane Rackham. adv.; circ. 5,000 (controlled).

697   AU   ISSN 0029-9227
DER OESTERREICHISCHE INSTALLATEUR. 1948. m. S.772. (Bundesinnung und Landesinnungen der Sanitaer- und Heizungsinstallateure Oesterreichs) Bohmann Druck und Verlag GmbH & Co. KG, Leberstr. 122, A-1110 Vienna, Austria. TEL 0222-74095-0. FAX 0222-74095-183. TELEX 132312. adv.; charts; illus.; pat.; stat. circ. 10,000. **Document type:** trade publication.

697   AU   ISSN 0029-9235
OESTERREICHISCHE INSTALLATEURZEITUNG.* 1967. bi-m. S.48. Verlag Piletzky, Nikolsdorfer Gasse 7, 1050 Vienna, Austria. Ed. Heinrich Piletzky. adv.; charts; illus.; stat.; circ. 4,600 (controlled).

696 352   US   ISSN 0192-5784
OFFICIAL (LOS ANGELES). 1958. bi-m. $27 to non-members (free to members). International Association of Plumbing and Mechanical Officials, 20001 Walnut Dr. S., Walnut, CA 91789. TEL 909-595-8449. FAX 909-594-3690. Ed. Kenneth S. Kochmann. adv. circ. 5,000.

696   CN   ISSN 0048-1823
ONTARIO PLUMBING INSPECTORS ASSOCIATION. BULLETIN.* 1942. bi-m. membership. Ontario Plumbing Inspectors Association, Gregory Rd., R.R. No. 3, St. Catharines, Ont. L2R 6P9, Canada. Ed. Jack Vanderaa. illus. circ. 900. (processed)

HEATING, PLUMBING AND REFRIGERATION

696 US
OREGON CONTRACTOR PIPELINE. m. Oregon State Association of Plumbing Heating Cooling Contractors, 8755 S.W. Citizens Dr., No.202, Wilsonville, OR 97070-8405. TEL 503-682-7165. FAX 503-682-8009. Ed. Linda Lindsten. circ. 1,500.

696 US ISSN 0048-2781
PALMETTO PIPER. 1953. m. free. Mechanical Contractors Association of South Carolina, 1504 Morninghill Dr., Box 384, Columbia, SC 29202. TEL 803-772-7834. Ed. William J. Burton. adv.; tr.lit. circ. 2,800. (tabloid format)

697 ISSN 0031-4412
PENNSYLVANIA CONTRACTOR; plumbing - heating - cooling. 1949. 6/yr. $4. Pennsylvania Association of Plumbing - Heating - Cooling Contractors, Inc., 4015 Jonestown Rd., Harrisburg, PA 17109. TEL 717-541-9109. FAX 717-541-9823. Ed. Meg Irish. adv.; charts; illus.; tr.lit. circ. 4,500. (tabloid format) **Document type:** trade publication.

696 697
PIPELINE (OREGON CITY).* 1948. m. $3. Jon David Agency, White, Box 448, Welches, OR 97067-0448. Ed. Linda Lindsten. adv.; illus.; stat.; tr.lit. circ. 1,400.
  Formerly: Oregon Plumbing - Heating - Cooling Contractor.

PIPELINES. see *LABOR UNIONS*

696 SW ISSN 0345-9438
PLAATSLAGERI; tidningen om plaat foer byggebranschen. 1909. m. (11/yr.). SEK 190 (effective 1991). Plaatslageriernas Riksfoerbund, P.O. Box 5471, 114 84 Stockholm, Sweden. Ed. Lars Klefelt. adv. circ. 2,100.
  Former titles (until 1969): Svensk Bleck- och Plaatslageritidning; (until 1931): Tidning foer Sveriges Bleck- och Plaatslageriidkare.

696 CN ISSN 0032-1591
PLOMBERIE CHAUFFAGE ET CLIMATISATION. (Includes Buyers Guide) 1936. q. Can.$20 (US Can.$25; elsewhere Can.$30). Southam Business and Communications Group Inc. (Subsidiary of: Southam Business Publications), 3300 Cote Vertu, St.-Laurent, Que. HR4 2B7, Canada. TEL 514-339-1399. FAX 514-339-1396. TELEX 058-24168. Ed. Luc Masson. adv.: B&W page Can.$1585; trim 8 1/8 x 10 7/8; adv. contact: Claude Dagenais. illus.; tr.lit. circ. 5,682. (tabloid format) **Document type:** trade publication.
  Formerly: Entrepreneur en Plomberie-Chauffage (ISSN 0013-9033)

696 US
PLUMB. bi-m. Georgia Association of Plumbing, Heating and Cooling Contractors, 3338 Gwinnett Plantation Way, Duluth, GA 30136-4647. TEL 404-458-4414. FAX 404-457-3893. Ed. Dianne Olson. circ. 5,000.

696 UK
PLUMB AND HEAT. 1953. m. £6. S.P. Technical Publications Ltd., 2 Walker Street, Edinburgh, EH3 7LB, Scotland. Ed. W. Todd-Soutar. adv.; bk.rev.; charts; illus.; tr.lit. circ. 1,850.
  Former titles: Plumbing and Heating; British Plumbing and Heating (ISSN 0308-0862); Scottish and Northern Ireland Plumbing and Heating; Scottish Plumbing and Heating Monthly (ISSN 0036-9365); Scottish Master Plumber and Domestic Heating Engineer.

696 US ISSN 0085-4905
PLUMBERS FRIEND. 1951. q. Utah Plumbing, Heating, Cooling Contractors, 669 South Second E. St., Salt Lake City, UT 84111. TEL 801-364-7768. FAX 801-531-7725. Ed. Avard W. Booth. adv.; bk.rev.; bibl.; tr.lit.; circ. controlled.

694 AT ISSN 0728-0408
PLUMBERS' NEWS. 1960. q. Electrical, Electronic, Plumbing & Allied Workers Union of Australia, Plumbing Division, 48 Victoria St., Carlton South, Australia. FAX 061-03-6637516. Ed. J. Rutherford. adv. circ. 31,000. **Document type:** trade publication.

696 UK ISSN 0032-1656
PLUMBING. 1970. bi-m. £30. Institute of Plumbing, 64 Station Ln., Hornchurch, Essex RM12 6NB, England. TEL 0708-472791. FAX 0708-448987. Ed. Pamela Robinson. adv.; bk.rev.; illus. circ. 15,000. **Indexed:** Build.Manage.Abstr., Cadscan, Int.Build.Serv.Abstr., Lead Abstr., Zincscan. **Document type:** trade publication.
  —BLDSC (6540.700000).
  Formerly: Registered Plumbers Association. Journal.

697 696 UK
PLUMBING AND HEATING NEWS. 1963. m. £24 (foreign £30). Peterson Publications Ltd., Peterson House, Northbank, Berryhill Industrial Estate, Droitwich, Worcs. WR9 9BL, England. TEL 0905-795564. FAX 0905-795905. Ed. Derek Johnson. adv.; charts; illus. circ. 31,336. (tabloid format) **Indexed:** Cadscan, Lead Abstr., Zincscan. **Document type:** trade publication.
  Former titles: Plumbing and Heating Equipment News (ISSN 0308-373X); Plumbing Equipment News and Heating Engineer (ISSN 0032-1672)

696 US ISSN 8750-6041
PLUMBING & MECHANICAL. 1983. m. $50 (foreign $62). Business News Publishing Company, 755 W. Big Beaver Rd., Ste. 1000, Troy, MI 48084. TEL 313-362-3700. FAX 313-362-0317. (Subscr. to: Box 2600, Troy, MI 48007) Ed. Jim Olsztynski. adv. circ. 32,000. **Document type:** trade publication.
  —CCC.
  Description: Provides plumbing - hydronics - piping and mechanical contractors with the latest technologies, induster news and product coverage. Features include troubleshooting tips, business management strategies and a hydronics forum.

PLUMBING AND MECHANICAL DIRECTORY. see
BUSINESS AND ECONOMICS — Trade And Industrial Directories

696 US ISSN 0192-1711
TH6101 CODEN: PLENDY
PLUMBING ENGINEER. 1973. 10/yr. $50. (American Society of Plumbing Engineers) T M B Publishing, 1884 Techny Ct., Northbrook, IL 60062. TEL 708-564-1127. FAX 708-564-1264. Ed. Tom Brown. adv.; circ. 23,000 (controlled). (also avail. in microform from UMI; reprint service avail. from UMI) **Indexed:** Eng.Ind., Int.Build.Serv.Abstr., W.R.C.Inf.
  —BLDSC (6540.570000); Faxon.
  Description: Technical journal serving engineers and specification writers in plumbing, piping and related activities.

696 US
PROCESS PLANT LAYOUT AND PIPING DESIGN.* base vol. (plus a. update). $195. c o Daniel Lundeen (Subsidiary of: Sroufe, Zameeki, Payne & Lundeen), 1700 W. Loop South, Houston, TX 77027-3008. TEL 212-971-5000. FAX 617-423-2026. (Subscr. to: 210 South St., Boston, MA 02111-9990. TEL 800-950-1218) Ed. Ed Bausbacher. (looseleaf format)
  Description: Comprehensive reference for engineering practitioners who are responsible for or who need to have a command of process plant layouts and piping design.

PROFESSIONAL BUILDER; small builders and contractors business magazine. see *BUILDING AND CONSTRUCTION — Carpentry And Woodwork*

696 AT ISSN 0048-637X
QUEENSLAND MASTER PLUMBER. 1960. m. Aus.$65. Master Plumbers Association of Queensland, P.O. Box 408, Fortitude Valley, Queensland 4006, Australia. TEL 617 252 1266. FAX 617-257-1910. Ed. T. Lyon. adv. circ. 1,100. **Document type:** trade publication.

697 GW ISSN 0033-6769
R A S. (Rohr-Armatur-Sanitaer-Heizung); Wirtschaftsjournal fuer Sanitaer und Heizung. 1944. m. DM.72 (foreign DM.78). Krammer Verlag, Hermannstr. 3, 40233 Duesseldorf, Germany. TEL 0211-67972-0. FAX 0211-6797231. TELEX 8586639-KRVG-D. Ed. Siegfried Heil. adv.: color page DM.3960; trim 185 x 257; adv. contact: Heinz Martin. bk.rev.; charts; illus.; stat.; pat.; tr.lit.; index. circ. 12,000. **Indexed:** Key to Econ.Sci. **Document type:** trade publication.
  Description: Covers the latest developments affecting the bathroom fixtures and plumbing industries, including marketing and economic aspects.

697 FR
R P F. 1947. fortn., 22/yr. 650 F. (foreign 935 F.). P Y C Edition, B.P. 105, 5, av. de Verdun, 94280 Ivry sur Seine Cedex, France. TEL 1-49-60-86-36. FAX 1-46-72-41-85. Ed. Pierre Mitev. adv.; bk.rev.; bibl.; illus. circ. 6,064. **Indexed:** Chem.Abstr., Dairy Sci.Abstr., Eng.Ind., Food Sci.& Tech.Abstr. **Document type:** trade publication.
  —El. CCC.
  Former titles: Journal R P F (ISSN 0337-2693); Revue Pratique du Froid et du Conditionnement d'Air (ISSN 0370-6699) & Revue Pratique du Froid (ISSN 0035-3868)
  Description: Air conditioning installation and maintenance.

696 697 US ISSN 0048-7066
REEVES JOURNAL; plumbing, heating & cooling. 1920. m. $36 (foreign $48). Business News Publishing Company, 755 W. Big Beaver Rd., Ste. 1000, Troy, MI 48084. TEL 313-362-3700. FAX 313-362-0317. (Subscr. to: Box 7001, Troy, MI 48007) Eds. Larry Dill. adv.; bk.rev. circ. 20,238. (also avail. in microfilm; reprint service avail. from UMI) **Document type:** trade publication.
  —El.
  Description: Serves plumbing contractors, wholesalers, manufacturers and maintenance personnel in 14 western states.

621.56 SP
REFRIGERACION - FRIAL. 4/yr. Navaleno 9, Residencial el Bosque de Charmartin, 28033 Madrid, Spain. TEL 1-303-81-46. FAX 1-766-16-64. circ. 3,000.

621.56 JA ISSN 0034-3714
CODEN: RITOA8
REFRIGERATION/REITO. (Text in Japanese; summaries in English) 1926. m. 16800 Yen. Japanese Association of Refrigeration - Nihon Reito Kyokai, 8 San'ei-cho, Shinjuku-ku, Tokyo 160, Japan. Ed. S. Mori. adv.; bk.rev.; index. circ. 10,000. **Indexed:** Chem.Abstr., Food Sci.& Tech.Abstr., Sci.Abstr. **Document type:** academic/scholarly publication.
  —CASDDS.
  Incorporates (in 1984): Techniques of Refrigeration and Air Conditioning; **Formerly:** Refrigeration and Air Conditioning Technology (ISSN 0034-3722)

621.56 US ISSN 0034-3137
REFRIGERATION. 1906. m. $21. John W. Yopp Publications, Inc., Box 1147, Beaufort, SC 29901. TEL 800-849-9677. Ed. John W. Yopp. adv.; illus. circ. 3,000.

621.56 697 UK ISSN 0263-5739
REFRIGERATION AND AIR CONDITIONING. 1898. m. £34.50. E M A P Response Publishing Ltd., Wentworth House, Wentworth St., Peterborough PE1 1DS, England. TEL 0733-63100. FAX 0733-62656. Ed. Andrew Bailey. adv.; bk.rev.; abstr.; charts; illus.; pat.; tr.lit.; tr.mk.; index. circ. 6,022. (also avail. in microform from UMI; reprint service avail. from UMI) **Indexed:** Agri.Eng.Abstr., BMT, Br.Tech.Ind., Chem.Abstr., Dairy Sci.Abstr., Eng.Ind., Int.Build.Serv.Abstr., Sci.Abstr. **Document type:** trade publication.
  —BLDSC (7335.150000); UnCover; SWETS. **CCC.**
  Former Title: Refrigeration Air Conditioning and Heat Recovery (ISSN 0026-8364); Modern Refrigeration and Air Conditioning.
  Description: For the heating and cooling trades.

HEATING, PLUMBING AND REFRIGERATION

697 621.56   UK   ISSN 0305-0777
REFRIGERATION AND AIR CONDITIONING YEAR BOOK. 1898. a. price varies. E M A P Response Publishing Ltd., Wentworth House, Wentworth St., Peterborough PE1 1DS, England. FAX 0733-63100. TELEX 0733-62656. Ed. Terry O'Gorman. adv.: B&W page £770, color page £1480; trim 297 x 210. bk.rev.; index. (also avail. in microfilm) **Document type:** directory.
—CCC.
Formerly: Refrigeration and Air Conditioning Directory (ISSN 0080-0503)
Description: Provides listings of plants and equipment supplers, specialist services and training services, ect.

697   US
REFRIGERATION NEWS. q. National Commercial Refrigeration Sales Association, 1900 Arch St., Philadelphia, PA 19103. TEL 215-564-3484.

621.56   US   ISSN 0148-382X
REFRIGERATION SERVICE AND CONTRACTING. Abbreviated title: R.S.C. 1933. m. $36 (foreign $48). Business News Publishing Company, 755 W. Big Beaver Rd., Ste. 1000, Troy, MI 48084. TEL 313-362-3700. FAX 313-362-0317. (Subscr. to: Box 7021, Troy, MI 48007) Ed. Peter Powell. adv.; charts; illus.; tr.lit.; index. circ. 40,167. (also avail. in microfilm from UMI; reprint service avail. from UMI) **Document type:** trade publication.
—Faxon; UMI.
Description: Hands-on service information for HVACR professionals.

697   NE
REGELVISIE. 1983. q. free. Honeywell B.V., Marketing Division, Postbus 12683, 1100 AR Amsterdam, Netherlands. Ed. A.C. Moser. circ. 5,000. **Document type:** bulletin.

697   JA   ISSN 0386-1538
REITO TO KUCHO/JAPAN REFRIGERATION AND AIRCONDITIONING INDUSTRY ASSOCIATION. JOURNAL. (Text in Japanese) 1959. m. 6500 Yen. Nihon Reito Kucho Kogyokai - Japan Refrigeration and Airconditioning Industry Association, 5-8, Shiba Koen 3-chome, Minato-ku, Tokyo 102, Japan.

697   SP
REVISTA TECNICO-CIENTIFICA CLIMA INTERIOR, CONFORT Y CONTROL DE AMBIENTE. 11/yr. Gascuena 21, 28022 Madrid, Spain. TEL 1-747-80-00. FAX 1-747-90-56. circ. 7,000.

696   NO   ISSN 0048-8526
ROERFAG. 1936. m. NOK 395. (Norske Roerleggerbedrifters Landsforening - Norwegian Plumbers Federation) Skarland Press A-S, Postboks 5042, Maj 0301 Oslo, Norway. TEL 47-22-60-13-90. FAX 47-22-69-36-50. Ed. Grete Utengen. adv.; illus.; pat.; stat.; index; circ. 4,210 (controlled).
Formerly: Roerfagskrift.

621.56 697   SA
S A REFRIGERATION AND AIRCONDITIONING. (Text in English) 1985. bi-m. R.35. (South African Institute of Refrigeration and Airconditioning) Phase Four (Pty) Ltd., P.O. Box 784279, Sandton 2146, South Africa. TEL 011-444-4566. FAX 011-444-7888. Ed. Caroline Edwards. circ. 3,000. (back issues avail.)
Description: Serves as a shop window for the air conditioning and refrigeration industries through technical and educational articles, project features, and industry news.

697   GW   ISSN 0342-8206
S B Z-MONTEUR; Berufsmagazin fuer den jungen Handwerker. 1955. m. DM.85.80 (foreign DM.101). A.W. Gentner Verlag, Forststr. 131, 70193 Stuttgart, Germany. TEL 0711-63672-0. FAX 0711-63672-11. Ed. E.W. Streidt. circ. 6,700. **Document type:** trade publication.

697 628   GW   ISSN 0342-8184
S B Z - SANITAER, HEIZUNGS- UND KLIMATECHNIK. 1946. fortn. DM.219.60 (foreign DM.292.80). (Zentralverband Sanitaer-, Heizungs- und Klimatechnik) A.W. Gentner Verlag, Forststr. 131, 70193 Stuttgart, Germany. TEL 0711-63672-0. FAX 0211-6797231. Eds. E.F. Reisch, D. Schlattmann. adv.; bk.rev.; charts; illus.; pat.; tr.lit.; index. circ. 20,500. **Indexed:** Int.Build.Serv.Abstr. **Document type:** trade publication.
Former titles: S B Z - Sanitaer-Technik, Heizungs-, und Lueftungsbau (ISSN 0036-1070); Sanitaer-Installation.

340   GW   ISSN 0344-8789
S I INFORMATIONEN; Sanitaer, Heizung, Klima. 1975. 11/yr. DM.145 (free to qualified personnel). A T Fachverlag GmbH, Postfach 500180, 70331 Stuttgart, Germany. TEL 0711-952951-0. FAX 0711-952951-99. Ed. R. Hinden. adv.; bk.rev.; charts; illus. circ. 27,000. **Document type:** trade publication.

S M A C N A CONVENTION DAILY. (Sheet Metal & Air Conditioning Contractors of North America) see *BUILDING AND CONSTRUCTION*

697 628   GW   ISSN 0344-9122
SANITAER UND HEIZUNGS REPORT. Short title: S und H Report. 9/yr. DM.31.50 (foreign DM.34.20). Krammer Verlag, Hermannstr. 3, 40233 Duesseldorf, Germany. TEL 0211-67972-0. FAX 0211-6797231. TELEX 8586639-KRVG-D. Ed. Thomas Burska-Erler. adv.: color page DM.6380; trim 185 x 257; adv. contact: Heinz Martin. bk.rev. circ. 25,000.
Description: Trade publication for the bath and plumbing industry. Information on new technology, latest trends and design, marketing, and new products.

697 628   GW   ISSN 0036-4401 TD3
SANITAER- UND HEIZUNGSTECHNIK. 1911. m. DM.78 (foreign DM.84). Krammer Verlag, Hermannstr. 3, 40233 Duesseldorf, Germany. TEL 0211-67972-0. FAX 0211-6797231. Ed. Bernd Genath. adv.: color page DM.5170; trim 185 x 257; adv. contact: Heinz Martin. bk.rev.; charts; illus.; pat.; tr.lit.; tr.mk. circ. 23,000. **Indexed:** Int.Build.Serv.Abstr.
—SWETS.
Description: Trade publication for the heating and plumbing industry. Features the latest news, developments and research in technology, solar energy and new products. Includes positions available.

696   BE
SANITAIRE - COUVERTURE/SANITAIR - DAKWERK. bi-m. Union des Entreprises du Sanitaire et de la Couverture a Bruxelles - Unie der Aanemers van het Sanitair- en Dakbedrijt te Brussel, Rue Lieutenant Liedel 27, B-1070 Brussels, Belgium. TEL 5230789.

SANTECHNIKA IR HIDRAULIKA/SANITARY ENGINEERING AND HYDRAULICS. see *ENGINEERING — Hydraulic Engineering*

621.56   DK   ISSN 0284-0758
SCAN REF; Scandinavian refrigeration energy food. (Text in Danish, English, Norwegian, Swedish) 1972. bi-m. price varies. Scandinavian Trade Magazines ApS, Industrivej 9, DK-4160 Herlufmagle, Denmark. TEL 45-53-75-23-63. FAX 45-53-75-24-29. (Subscr. to: Nordic Subscription Service, Rokhoej 6,DK-8520 Lystrup, Denmark) Ed. Jens Peder Tornvig. adv.; bk.rev.; illus.; index. circ. 3,740. (reprint service avail.) **Indexed:** Appl.Mech.Rev., Dairy Sci.Abstr., Food Sci.& Tech.Abstr., Fuel & Energy Abstr., Hort.Abstr. **Document type:** trade publication.
—BLDSC (8087.706500).
Incorporating: Kjoleteknikk og Fryserinaering (ISSN 0023-1991); Kulde (ISSN 0023-5059); Kylteknisk Tidskrift (ISSN 0023-5970) Which was formerly: Scandinavian Refrigeration (ISSN 0048-9301)
Description: Presents information about technical research and development in the refrigeration industry in the Nordic countries and business news about companies and products in the industry worldwide.

696   SZ
SCHWEIZERISCHE SPENGLERMEISTER- UND INSTALLATEUR-ZEITUNG/JOURNAL SUISSE DES MAITRES FERBLANTIERS ET APPAREILLEURS. (Text in German, French and Italian) 1900. 24/yr. 68 SFr. to members; non-members 108 SFr. Schweizerische Spenglermeister- und Installateur-Verband, Auf der Mauer 11, Postfach 6340, CH-8023 Zurich, Switzerland. TEL 01-2517400. FAX 01-2513228. Ed. Jean Haag. adv.: B&W page 1410 SFr., color page 2755 SFr.; trim 185 x 265. bk.rev. circ. 5,050. **Indexed:** C.I.S. Abstr. **Document type:** trade publication.

697   US   ISSN 0193-2128
SERVICE REPORTER; the magazine that works for contractors and in-plant engineers. 1968. m. $12. Palmer Publishing Co., 651 W. Washington, Ste. 300, Chicago, IL 60661. TEL 312-993-0929. FAX 312-993-0960. Ed. Ed Schwenn. adv.; charts; illus.; stat.; tr.lit. circ. 45,000. (tabloid format) **Document type:** trade publication.

697   US   ISSN 0737-2205
SNEWS; the chimney sweep news. 1979. m. (10/yr.). $68 (foreign $85). Jay Hensley, Ed. & Pub., Box 98, Wilmore, KY 40390. TEL 606-986-8001. FAX 606-858-4043. adv. contact: Tim Hensley. bk.rev. circ. 800. (back issues avail.) **Document type:** trade publication.
Description: Provides information on the maintenance of chimneys, safe practices in woodburning, fireplace and chimney renovation, and safety in the workplace for chimney sweeps. Also contains business tips, feature stories on individuals, and news about masonry heaters and stone masons.

697   US   ISSN 0037-7457
SNIPS. 1932. m. $12. Snips Magazine, Inc., 1949 Cornell Ave., Melrose Park, IL 60160. TEL 708-544-3870. FAX 708-544-3884. Ed. Nick Carter. adv.; bk.rev.; circ. 29,000 (controlled). **Document type:** trade publication.

697   UK   ISSN 0038-1055
SOLID FUEL. 1972. m. £30. Harper Trade Journals Ltd, Harling House, 47-51 Great Suffolk St., London SE1 0BS, England. TEL 071-261-1604. FAX 071-633-0281. Ed. Jonathan Brind. adv.; bk.rev.; illus.; stat.; tr.lit. circ. 6,000. **Document type:** trade publication.

SOUTHERN BUILDING CODE CONGRESS. STANDARD PLUMBING CODE. see *BUILDING AND CONSTRUCTION*

696 697   US   ISSN 0038-4461
SOUTHERN PLUMBING, HEATING, COOLING. 1945. m. $10. Southern Trade Publications Co., Box 18343, Greensboro, NC 27419. TEL 919-454-3516. Ed. Emmet Atkins, Jr. adv.; bk.rev.; illus. circ. 9,000. **Document type:** trade publication.

697   UK
THE SPECIFIER'S GUIDE TO HEATING, VENTILATING, AIR CONDITIONING, AND REFRIGERATION. 1968. a. £37.95. E M A P Maclaren Ltd., Maclaren House, Scarbrook Rd., Croydon CR9 1QH, England. TEL 081-688--7788. FAX 081-688-9300. (Subscr. to: HUCA Publications Dept., Old Mansion House, Eamont Bridge, Penrith, Cubria CA10 2BX, England) (Co-sponsors: H E V A C Association) Ed. Jack McDavid, Terry O'Gorman. adv. circ. 5,000.
Former titles: Heating, Ventilating and Air Conditioning Year Book (ISSN 0306-3585); Heating and Ventilating Year Book (ISSN 0073-1552)
Description: Lists manufacturers, suppliers and H V A C contractors for specifiers of heating, ventilation, air conditioning and refrigeration equipment and services.

697   GW   ISSN 0038-898X
STADT- UND GEBAEUDETECHNIK;* Fachzeitschrift fuer Heizung, Lueftung, Waerme, Sanitaertechnik, Rohrleitungsbau und Isoliertechnik. 1947. m. DM.55.20. (VEB Kombinat Technische Gebaeudeausruestung, Institut) Verlag fuer Bauwesen, Am Friedrichshain 22, 10407 Berlin, Germany. Ed. Sigrid Narulin. abstr.; charts; illus.; index. **Indexed:** Int.Build.Serv.Abstr.

STOVE PARTS NEEDED. see *ANTIQUES*

HEATING, PLUMBING AND REFRIGERATION

696 666   IT
SUPPLIERS SANITARY - TABLEWARE BOOK. 1989. a. L.16000. Gruppo Editoriale Faenza Editrice S.p.A., Via Pier. de Crescenzi, 44, 48018 Faenza RA, Italy. TEL 0546-663488. FAX 0546-660440. TELEX 550287 EDITFA I. Ed. Franco Rossi. adv. circ. 8,000. (back issues avail.)

697   US   ISSN 0039-5935
TH6101
SUPPLY HOUSE TIMES. 1958. 12/yr. $65 (Canada $100; Mexico $90; elsewhere $120). Cahners Publishing Company (Des Plaines), Division of Reed Elsevier Inc., 1350 E. Touhy Ave., Box 5080, Des Plaines, IL 60017-5080. TEL 708-635-8800. FAX 708-390-2690. (Subscr. to: 44 Cook St., Denver, CO 80206. TEL 800-662-7776) Ed. John O'Reilly. adv.; illus. circ. 29,305. **Document type:** trade publication.
—UMI. **CCC.**
   Description: Serves the wholesaler distribution segments of the plumbing, heating, air conditioning, and industrial piping markets.

SWEEPING. see *FIRE PREVENTION*

697   GW   ISSN 0341-2032
T A B. (Technik am Bau); technische Gebaeude ausruestung/Heizung-Kaelte-Elektro-Klima-Lueftung. 1970. m. DM.168. Bertelsmann Fachzeitschriften GmbH, Postfach 120, 33111 Guetersloh, Germany. TEL 05241-802332. FAX 05241-73055. Ed. Burkhard Froehlich. adv.: B&W page DM.6120, color page DM.9050; trim 270 x 186. index. circ. 9,915. **Document type:** trade publication.
   Description: Covers technical building equipment in the heating, air-conditioning, ventilation, electricity and sanitation areas.

697   IT   ISSN 0393-9723
T I S IL CORRIERE TERMOIDROSANITARIO; mensile di rescaldamento, idrosanitaria, accessori bagno. 1986. m. (11/yr.). L.19000($50) Editoriale P E G SpA, Via Fratelli Bressan 2, 20126 Milan, Italy. TEL 02-25-79-841. FAX 02-25-52-779. TELEX 323088 PEGMOS I. Ed. Franco Adami. adv. circ. 20,500.
   Description: Covers technical, practical and informative matters related to industrial production in plumbing and in the sanitary field.

621.56   AG
TECNICA DEL FRIO. 1952. m. $100. Editora Tecnica Integral s.r.l., Av. Corrientes 2763, 2nd fl., of. 9 y 10, 1046 Buenos Aires, Argentina. TEL 541-962-6100. FAX 963-8655. (Co-sponsors: Argentine Chamber of Refrigeration and Air Conditioning Industries; Argentine Association of Refrigeration) Ed. Beatriz Liberatore. adv.; bk.rev.; abstr.; charts; illus.; stat.; index. circ. 5,000. **Document type:** trade publication.
   Former titles: Tecnica del Frio y del Calor (ISSN 0326-9035); (until 1985): Tecnica del Frio (ISSN 0040-1730)

696 613.7   SP
TERMALISMO - BALNEARIOS. 1991. 52/yr. (Asociacion Nacional de Estaciones Termales) Editorial J.S. Publicaciones Especiales, Santa Susana 55, 5o 1 y 2, 28033 Madrid, Spain. TEL 1-7633401. Ed. Jaime Sanchez Villar. adv.: B&W page 90000 ptas., color page 120000 ptas.; trim 258 x 185. circ. 20,000 (controlled).

697   IT   ISSN 0040-3725
TJ260.A1   CODEN: TERMAK
TERMOTECNICA. 1947. m. L.60000. (Associazione Termotecnica Italiana) Editrice B.I.A.S. s.a.s., Viale Premuda 2, 20129 Milan, Italy. Eds. Cesare Codegone, Gino Morandi. adv.; bk.rev.; illus.; index. **Indexed:** Appl.Mech.Rev., Chem.Abstr., Chem.Eng.Abstr., Eng.Ind., Excerp.Med., Fluidex, Int.Build.Serv.Abstr., T.C.E.A.
—BLDSC (8793.980000); EI; CASDDS.

621.56 699   US
TEXAS JOURNAL. 1935. bi-m. $15. Associated Plumbing, Heating and Cooling Contractors of Texas, Inc., 2201 North Lamar, Ste. 100, Austin, TX 78705. TEL 512-472-7422. FAX 512-452-6566. Ed. Richard Blackmon. adv. contact: Richard Blackmon. bk.rev.; tr.lit. circ. 25,000. **Document type:** trade publication.
   Description: For professionals in the heating, plumbing, and refrigeration industry.

697   RU   ISSN 0040-9472
    CODEN: TORPAV
TORFYANAYA PROMYSHLENNOST. 1924. m. 20.40 Rub. (Gosudarstvennyi Nauchno-tekhnicheskii Komitet pri Sovete Ministrov) Izdatel'stvo Nedra, Pl. Belorusskogo Vokzala, 3, 125047 Moscow, Russia. TEL 250-52-55. Ed. S.H. Solopov. bibl.; charts; illus. circ. 5,140. **Indexed:** Chem.Abstr., Gas Abstr., GeoRef.
—CASDDS.

696   US
UNIFORM PLUMBING CODE. triennial. $49.90 to non-members; members $38.95. International Association of Plumbing and Mechanical Officials, 20001 Walnut Dr. S., Walnut, CA 91789. TEL 909-595-8449. FAX 909-594-3690.
   Former titles: U P C Plumbing Code.

697   DK   ISSN 0042-1944
V V S. (Varme Ventilation Sanitet) 1965. 15/yr. DKK 375. Teknisk Forlag A-S, Skelbaekgade 4, DK-1780 Copenhagen V, Denmark. TEL 45-31-21-68-01. FAX 45-31-21-04-01. Ed. Poul W. Udengaard. adv.: B&W page DKK 9360, color page DKK 14610; trim 265 x 185. bk.rev.; charts; illus.; tr.lit.; index; circ. 4,876 (controlled). **Indexed:** C.I.S.Abstr.
   Description: Covers the special problems of the heating, ventilation and sanitation trade and provides information on technical developments in the heating, ventilation and sanitary field.

697   SW   ISSN 0346-4644
V V S - FORUM. 1931. m. SEK 190 (effective 1993). Roerfirmornas Riksfoerbund - Swedish Association of Plumbing, Heating, Ventilation Contractors, P.O. Box 17537, 118 91 Stockholm, Sweden. TEL 46-8-616-04-00. FAX 46-8-669-12-04. Aake Askensten. adv.: B&W page SEK 13850, color page SEK 20400; trim 185 x 262; adv. contact: Aake Askensten. bk.rev.; charts; illus.; mkt.; index. circ. 16,100. **Document type:** trade publication.
   Formed by the 1972 merger of: Roermokaren; Roerinstallatoeren.
   Description: Focuses on the heating, ventilating, plumbing, sanitary and refrigeration trades, including insulation, energy-saving, environmental and allied subjects.

628   DK   ISSN 0042-2770
VARME OG SANITETS NYT. 1966. 13/yr. DKK 170. Christtreu, Strandlodsvei 48, DK-2300 Copenhagen S, Denmark. TEL 32-844848. FAX 31-582055. Ed. B. Remby. adv.; bk.rev.; charts; illus.; circ. 12,456 (controlled).

697   DK   ISSN 0107-9379
VARME OG SANITETS NYT. LEVERANDOERREGISTER. 1976. a. free to libraries. Christtreu, Strandlodsvei 48, DK-2300 Copenhagen S, Denmark. TEL 32-844848. FAX 31-582055. Ed. B. Remby. illus. circ. 12,456.

697   NE   ISSN 0042-451X
VERWARMING EN VENTILATIE. 1942. m. fl.120. Vereniging van Nederlandse Installatiebedrijven (VNI), Postbus 7272, 2701 AG Zoetermeer, Netherlands. Ed. E.J. Wagenaar. adv.; bk.rev.; abstr.; bibl.; charts; tr.mk.; index; circ. 4,000 (controlled). **Indexed:** Chem.Abstr., Ergonom.Abstr., Int.Build.Serv.Abstr., Key to Econ.Sci.
—SWETS.

696   US
VIRGINIA P H C IMAGE. Cover title: Image. 1934. m. free. Virginia Association of Plumbing - Heating - Cooling Contractors, 2103 Lake Ave., Richmond, VA 23230. TEL 804-288-2080. FAX 804-282-1620. Ed. James B. Muncy, Jr. adv.: B&W page $445; trim 8 1/2 x 11. illus.; tr.lit.; circ. 4,400 (controlled). (processed) **Document type:** trade publication.
   Description: Contains association news and alerts members to coming events.

697   GW
W K S B; Zeitschrift fuer Waermeschutz, Kaelteschutz, Schallschutz, Brandschutz. 1975. s-a. DM.32. Gruenzweig & Hartmann AG, Buergermeister-Gruenzweig-Str. 1, 67059 Ludwigshaven, Germany. FAX 0621-4701-392. bk.rev. circ. 5,000. (back issues avail.) **Document type:** trade publication.

697   GW   ISSN 0720-3438
TH7201   CODEN: WTECDW
WAERMETECHNIK; internationales Fachorgan fuer Feuerungs- und Haustechnik. 1955. m. DM.157.80 (foreign DM.181.80). (Bundesverband Energie-Umwelt-Feuerungen e.V.) A.W. Gentner Verlag, Forststr. 131, 70193 Stuttgart, Germany. TEL 0711-63672-0. FAX 0711-6367211. Ed. W-R. Pfundtner. adv.; bk.rev.; bibl.; charts; illus.; mkt.; pat.; index. circ. 7,475. **Indexed:** Chem.Abstr., Int.Build.Serv.Abstr. **Document type:** trade publication.
—CASDDS. **CCC.**
   Formerly: Oel- und Gasfeuerung (ISSN 0029-8662)

696   UK
WATER FITTINGS AND MATERIALS DIRECTORY. 2/yr. £60. Richard Joseph Publishers Ltd., Unit 2, Monks Walk, Farnham, Surrey GU9 8HT, England. TEL 0252-734347. FAX 0252-734307. **Document type:** directory.
   Description: Reference directory for those involved in the purchase and use of materials and water fittings in the UK.

697   US
WESTERN H V A C R NEWS.* (Heating, Ventilating, Air Conditioning and Refrigeration) 1981. m. $12. 4215 N. Figueroa St., Los Angeles, CA 90065-3011. TEL 213-225-8035. Ed. Sam Jaffe. circ. 16,713. (tabloid format) **Document type:** newspaper, trade publication.

696 697   US   ISSN 0032-1680
HD9999.P6868
WHOLESALER. 1946. m. $75. Delta Communications Inc. (Subsidiary of: Cahners Publishing Company), Division of Reed Elsevier Inc., 455 N. Cityfront Plaza Dr., 24th Fl., Chicago, IL 60611. TEL 312-222-2000. FAX 312-222-2026. Ed. Mary Ann Falkman. adv.; bk.rev.; illus. circ. 25,024. (tabloid format) **Document type:** trade publication.
—**CCC.**
   Formerly: Plumbing - Heating - Air Conditioning Wholesaler.

696   US
WISCONSIN P-H-C CONTRACTOR. 1979. 4/yr. free. Target Communications Corp., 7626 W. Donges Bay Rd., Box 188, Meguon, WI 53092. TEL 414-242-3990. Ed. Glenn Helgeland. adv.; circ. 6,000 (controlled).
   Formerly: Wisconsin Master Plumber (ISSN 0199-1639)
   Description: For plumbing, heating and cooling contractors, with an emphasis on business management.

697   XR   ISSN 0044-1988
ZDRAVOTNI TECHNIKA A VZDUCHOTECHNIKA/SANITARY AND AIR TECHNICS. (Text in Czech or Slovak; summaries in English, French, German, Russian) 1958. bi-m. DM.124. (Czechoslovak Academy of Sciences) Academia, Publishing House of the Czechoslovak Academy of Sciences, Vodickova 40, 112 29 Prague 1, Czech Republic. (Dist. in Western countries by: Kubon & Sagner, P.O. Box 34 01 08, 8000 Munich 34, Germany) Ed. L. Oppl. bk.rev.; illus.; index. circ. 2,825. **Indexed:** C.I.S. Abstr., Chem.Abstr., Int.Build.Serv.Abstr.
   Description: Original articles and essays on heating, ventilation, air conditioning, dust reduction techniques, gas cleaning, drying, sanitary and industrial plumbing, noise and vibration and lighting.

621.56   IT
ZERO SOTTO ZERO. bi-m. L.35000 (foreign L.100000) (effective 1994). Tecniche Nuove S.p.A., Via Ciro Menotti 14, 20129 Milan, Italy. TEL 02-75701. FAX 02-7610351. TELEX 334647 TECH I. adv.: B&W page L.1150000, color page L.1840000; trim 185 x 266. circ. 3,000.

HEATING, PLUMBING AND REFRIGERATION — Abstracting, Bibliographies, Statistics

969 US
A C C A QUALITY CONTRACTOR'S CATALOG OF MATERIALS, PRODUCTS AND SERVICES. 1968. a. Air Conditioning Contractors of America, 1712 new Hampshire Ave., N.W., Washington, DC 20009. TEL 202-483-9370. FAX 202-234-4721. Ed. Elaine W. Smith. circ. 3,300.
  Formerly: A C C A Catalog of Technical Materials and Business Management Aids.
  Description: Lists technical manuals and business management books, videos and other products for heating, ventilating and air conditioning contractors.

696 US ISSN 1045-6198
AMERICAN SUPPLY ASSOCIATION. OPERATING PERFORMANCE REPORT. a. $150 to non-members; members $45. American Supply Association, 222 Merchandise Mart Pl., Ste. 1360, Chicago, IL 60654. TEL 312-464-0090. FAX 312-464-0091. **Document type:** trade publication.

697 UK ISSN 0308-6224
B S R I A STATISTICS BULLETIN. vol. 6, 1981. 4/yr. £155 to non-members in Europe; £165 elsewhere (free to members). Building Services Research and Information Association, Old Bracknell Ln. W., Bracknell, Berks. RG12 7AH, England. TEL 0344-426511. FAX 0344-487575. Ed. G. Samuelsson-Brown. charts; stat. (back issues avail.) **Indexed:** Copper Abstr. **Document type:** bulletin.

697 016 UK ISSN 0140-4237
TH7201
INTERNATIONAL BUILDING SERVICES ABSTRACTS. 1966. bi-m. £98 to non-members worldwide; members £50. Building Services Research and Information Association, Old Bracknell Ln. W., Bracknell, Berks. RG12 7AH, England. TEL 0344-426511. FAX 0344-487575. Ed. M. McCarthy. index. circ. 300. **Indexed:** Agri.Eng.Abstr., Build.Manage.Abstr., Copper Abstr. **Document type:** abstracting/indexing.
  ●Also available online.
  —BLDSC (4537.660000).
  Former titles (until 1978): Thermal Abstracts (ISSN 0305-6007); H.V.R.A. Library Bulletin.
  Description: Contains a survey of world literature on the mechanical and technical services of buildings, including heating, ventilation, air-conditioning, sanitation, lighting, and communications. Provides a current awareness of services and reference sources for designers, contractors, manufacturers, and building operators.

696 US ISSN 1042-3850
TH6235
MEANS PLUMBING COST DATA. 1989. a. $79.95. R.S. Means Company, Inc., 100 Construction Plaza, Box 800, Kingston, MA 02364-0800. TEL 617-585-7880. FAX 617-585-7466.

621.9 016 RU ISSN 0370-8098
REFERATIVNYI ZHURNAL. KHIMICHESKOE, NEFTEPERERABATYVAYUSCHCHEE I POLIMERNOE MASHINOSTROENIE. 1962. m. 60 Rub. (64 Rub. including index). Vsesoyuznyi Institut Nauchno-Tekhnicheskoi Informatsii (VINITI), Baltiiskaya ul., 14, Moscow A-219, Russia. (Subscr. to: Mezhdunarodnaya Kniga, Dimitrova ul. 39, 113095 Moscow, Russia) **Indexed:** Chem.Abstr. **Document type:** abstracting/indexing.
  Formerly: Referativnyi Zhurnal. Khimicheskoe i Kholodil'noe Mashinostroenie (ISSN 0034-2416)

HEMATOLOGY

see Medical Sciences–Hematology

HIGHER EDUCATION

see Education–Higher Education

HINDUISM

see Religions and Theology–Hindu

HISTORY

see also History–Computer Applications; History–History of Africa; History–History of Asia; History–History of Australasia and Other Areas; History–History of Europe; History–History of North and South America; History–History of the Near East; Anthropology; Archaeology; Folklore;
also specific subjects

A.A.M.U.C. FOOTLOCKER. (Association of American Military Uniform Collectors) see *MILITARY*

900 CN ISSN 0709-4604
A C A BULLETIN. 1975. bi-m. membership. Association of Canadian Archivists, P.O. Box 2596, Sta. "D", Ottawa, ON K1P 5W6, Canada. TEL 613-443-0251. Ed. Ian Moir. circ. 850. **Document type:** academic/scholarly publication, bulletin.
  Description: News about archives and archivists in Canada and overseas; news about the Association.

A M S STUDIES IN CULTURAL HISTORY. see *HUMANITIES: COMPREHENSIVE WORKS*

900 US ISSN 0270-6253
A M S STUDIES IN SOCIAL HISTORY. 1976. irreg., no.12, 1993. price varies. A M S Press, Inc., 56 E. 13th St., New York, NY 10003. TEL 212-777-4700. FAX 212-995-5413. (back issues avail.)
  Description: Monographs, reference works and bibliographies on topics such as religion, education and the women's movement.

A M S STUDIES IN THE EIGHTEENTH CENTURY. see *LITERATURE*

A M S STUDIES IN THE EMBLEM. see *GENEALOGY AND HERALDRY*

900 800 US ISSN 0270-6261
A M S STUDIES IN THE MIDDLE AGES. 1978. irreg., no.24, 1994. price varies. A M S Press, Inc., 56 E. 13th St., New York, NY 10003. TEL 212-777-4700. FAX 212-995-5413. (back issues avail.) **Indexed:** M.L.A.
  —BLDSC (0859.554000).
  Description: Monographs, reference works and bibliographies on the history and literature of medieval Europe.

900 US
A S E C S NEWS CIRCULAR. 1969. q. $10. American Society for Eighteenth-Century Studies, c/o Jeffrey Smitten, Exec. Sec., Utah State University, USU CC108, Logan, UT 84322-3730. TEL 801-797-4065. circ. 1,900. (back issues avail.)

930 US ISSN 0898-4212
E457.1
ABRAHAM LINCOLN ASSOCIATION. JOURNAL. 1979. 2/yr. $25 (foreign $30). University of Illinois Press, 1325 S. Oak St., Champaign, IL 61820. TEL 217-333-0950. FAX 217-244-8082. Ed. Thomas F. Schwartz. adv.: B&W page $160; adv. contact: Cat Warren. circ. 650. (also avail. in microform from UMI) **Indexed:** Amer.Hist.& Life, Hist.Abstr. **Document type:** academic/scholarly publication.
  —UMI. **CCC.**
  Formerly (until vol.8): Abraham Lincoln Association. Papers (ISSN 0195-914X)
  Refereed Serial

987 AG ISSN 0325-0482
ACADEMIA NACIONAL DE LA HISTORIA. BOLETIN. 1912. irreg., no.61, 1988. Academia Nacional de la Historia, Balcarce 139, 1064 Buenos Aires, Argentina. TEL 541-331-5147. FAX 541-331-4633. (Subscr. to: Libreria Platero S.R.L., Talcahuano 485, C.P. 1013 Buenos Aires, Argentina) bk.rev.; index. circ. 3,000. **Indexed:** Amer.Hist.& Life, Hist.Abstr. **Document type:** bulletin.
  Formerly (until 1938): Junta de Historia y Numismatica Americana. Boletin.

943.91 HU ISSN 0001-5849
DB901
ACADEMIA SCIENTIARUM HUNGARICA. ACTA HISTORICA. (Text in English, French, German, Russian) 1951. q. $80 (effective 1992). (Magyar Tudomanyos Akademia) Akademiai Kiado, Publishing House of the Hungarian Academy of Sciences, P.O. Box 245, H-1519 Budapest, Hungary. TEL 181-2134. FAX 166-6466. TELEX 22-6228 AKNYO H. Ed. Zsigmond Pal Pach. adv.; bk.rev.; bibl.; index. **Indexed:** Biol.Abstr., Curr.Cont.
  —SWETS. **CCC.**
  Description: Publishes studies on medieval, modern and contemporary universal and Hungarian history.

900 CH
ACADEMIA SINICA. INSTITUTE OF MODERN HISTORY. BULLETIN/CHUNG YANG YEN CHIU YUAN. CHIN TAI SHIH YEN CHIU SO CH'I K'AN. (Text in Chinese) 1969. a. $3. Academia Sinica, Institute of Modern History - Chung Yang Yen Chiu Yuan Chin Tai Shih Yen Chiu So, Nankang, Taipei Hsien, Taiwan 11529, Republic of China. TEL Lu Pao-ch'ien. bk.rev. circ. 1,500. **Indexed:** Amer.Hist.& Life, Hist.Abstr.

ACADEMIE DES INSCRIPTIONS ET BELLES-LETTRES. ETUDES ET COMMENTAIRES. see *LINGUISTICS*

ACADEMIE ROYALE DES SCIENCES D'OUTRE MER. CLASSE DES SCIENCES MORALES ET POLITIQUES. MEMOIRES IN 8/KONINKLIJKE ACADEMIE VOOR OVERZEESE WETENSCHAPPEN. KLASSE DER MORELE EN POLITIEKE WETENSCHAPPEN. VERHANDELINGEN IN 8. see *HUMANITIES: COMPREHENSIVE WORKS*

900 IT ISSN 0391-8181
ACCADEMIA NAZIONALE DEI LINCEI. ATTI. CLASSE DI SCIENZE MORALI, STORICHE E FILOLOGICHE. RENDICONTI. (Text in English, French, German, Italian and Spanish) 1847. 4/yr. L.70000 (foreign L.80000). Accademia Nazionale dei Lincei, Via della Lungara 10, 00165 Rome, Italy. TEL 06-683-88-31. Ed. Cesare Franco Golisano. circ. 850. **Indexed:** Bibl.Ling.
  Formerly (until 1946): Accademia d'Italia. Atti. Classe di Scienze Morali, Storiche e Filologiche. Rendiconti.

ACME. see *LITERATURE*

ACROSS THE BORDER. see *GEOGRAPHY*

ACTA REGIAE SOCIETATITIS HUMANIORUM LITTERATUM LUNDENSIS. see *ARCHAEOLOGY*

900 AU
ACTA STUDENTICA. 1970. q. $10. Oesterreichischer Verein fuer Studentengeschichte, Tuersgasse 21, A-1130 Vienna, Austria. Ed. Peter Krause. adv.; bk.rev. circ. 700. **Document type:** academic/scholarly publication.

900 370   PL   ISSN 0208-6050
D1
ACTA UNIVERSITATIS LODZIENSIS: FOLIA HISTORICA.
(Text in Polish; summaries in various languages)
1955-1974; N.S. 1980. irreg. Wydawnictwo
Uniwersytetu Lodzkiego, Ul. Jaracza 34, Lodz,
Poland. TEL 331671. (Dist. by: Ars Polona-Ruch,
Krakowskie Przedmiescie 7, Warsaw, Poland)
Document type: academic/scholarly publication.
—BLDSC (0585.207000).
   Supersedes in part: Uniwersytet Lodzki. Zeszyty
Naukowe. Seria 1: Nauki Humanistyczno-Spoleczne
(ISSN 0076-0358)
   Description: Presents studies of universal and
Polish history from history of Byzantium to modern
history.

900   PL   ISSN 0524-4498
ACTA UNIVERSITATIS WRATISLAVIENSIS. HISTORIA.
(Text in Polish, occasionally in German; summaries
in English or German) irreg. price varies.
(Uniwersytet Wroclawski) Wydawnictwo Uniwersytetu
Wroclawskiego, Pl. Uniwersytecki 9-13, 50-137
Wroclaw, Poland. TEL 44-10-06. (Dist. by:
Ksiegarnia Uniwersytetu Wroclawskiego, Pl.
Uniwersytecki 9-13, 50-137 Wroclaw, Poland) Ed.
Leszek Wiatrowski. circ. 300. **Document type:**
academic/scholarly publication.

900 378   PL   ISSN 0866-9279
**ACTA UNIVERSITATIS WRATISLAVIENSIS. STUDIA I
MATERIALY Z DZIEJOW UNIWERSYTETU
WROCLAWSKIEGO.** 1989. irreg. price varies.
(Uniwersytet Wroclawski) Wydawnictwo Uniwersytetu
Wroclawskiego, Pl. Uniwersytecki 9-13, 50-137
Wroclaw, Poland. TEL 44-10-06. (Dist. by:
Ksiegarnia Uniwersytetu Wroclawskiego, Pl.
Uniwersytecki 9-13, 50-137 Wroclaw, Poland)
Document type: academic/scholarly publication.

AEROMILITARIA; Air-Britain military aviation historical
journal. see MILITARY

AEROPLANE MONTHLY. see AERONAUTICS AND SPACE
FLIGHT

AEVUM; rassegna di scienze storiche, linguistiche e
filologiche. see LINGUISTICS

960   US   ISSN 1074-1836
▼**AFRICAN PROFILES INTERNATIONAL.** 1992. bi-m.
171 W. 73rd St., Gr. Fl., New York, NY 10023.
TEL 212-877-5444. Ed. F. Alayande.
   Formerly (until 1993): Profiles International.

960 950   BL   ISSN 0002-0591
AFRO-ASIA. (Text in Portuguese; summaries in English
and French) 1965. irreg. $3 exchange. Universidade
Federal da Bahia, Centro de Estudos Afro-Orientais,
C.P. 1163, 40000 Salvador, Bahia, Brazil. Ed.
Leovigildo Filgueiras. bk.rev.; bibl.; charts; illus. circ.
1,000. **Indexed:** Amer.Hist.& Life, Hist.Abstr.
Document type: academic/scholarly publication.

AGE OF JOHNSON; a scholarly annual. see LITERATURE

AGRICULTURAL HISTORY. see AGRICULTURE

AIR POWER HISTORY. see AERONAUTICS AND SPACE
FLIGHT

**AKADEMIE DER WISSENSCHAFTEN IN GOETTINGEN.
NACHRICHTEN 1. PHILOLOGISCH-HISTORISCHE
KLASSE.** see LINGUISTICS

900 100 340   AJ
**AKADEMIYA NAUK AZERBAIJANA. IZVESTIYA. SERIYA
ISTORIYA, FILOSOFIYA I PRAVO.** 1967. q. 15 Rub.
Izdatel'stvo Elm, Ul. Narimanova, 37, 370073 Baku,
Azerbaijan. bk.rev.; index.
   Formerly: Akademiya Nauk Azerbaidzhanskoi
S.S.R. Izvestiya. Seriya Istoriya, Filosofiya i Pravo
(ISSN 0002-3116)

ALABAMA BAPTIST HISTORIAN. see RELIGIONS AND
THEOLOGY — Protestant

DAS ALTERTUM. see CLASSICAL STUDIES

AMERICAN BAPTIST QUARTERLY; a Baptist journal of
history, theology and ministry. see RELIGIONS AND
THEOLOGY — Protestant

AMERICAN BENEDICTINE REVIEW. see RELIGIONS AND
THEOLOGY — Roman Catholic

**AMERICAN CATHOLIC HISTORICAL SOCIETY OF
PHILADELPHIA. RECORDS.** see RELIGIONS AND
THEOLOGY — Roman Catholic

900   US   ISSN 0065-8561
E172
AMERICAN HISTORICAL ASSOCIATION. ANNUAL REPORT.
a. American Historical Association, 400 A St., S.E.,
Washington, DC 20003-3889. TEL 202-544-2422.
FAX 202-544-8307. (also avail. in microform from
PMC,UMI; reprint service avail. from UMI) **Document
type:** corporate report.
—UMI.

973   US   ISSN 0002-8762
E171
AMERICAN HISTORICAL REVIEW. 1895. 5/yr. $48.
American Historical Association, 400 A St., S.E.,
Washington, DC 20003-3889. TEL 202-544-2422.
FAX 202-544-8307. Ed. David Ransel. adv.; bk.rev.;
bibl.; index, cum.index. circ. 23,000. (also avail. in
microform from KTO,MIM,PMC,UMI; reprint service
avail. from KTO,UMI) **Indexed:** Acad.Ind.,
Amer.Bibl.Slavic & E.Eur.Stud., Amer.Hist.& Life, Arts
& Hum.Cit.Ind., Bk.Rev.Dig., Bk.Rev.Ind. (1965-),
Chic.Per.Ind., Child.Bk.Rev.Ind. (1965-), Curr.Cont.
Hist.Abstr., Hum.Ind., J.of Econ.Lit., Mag.Ind.,
Mid.East: Abstr.& Ind., Mult.Ed.Abstr., Peace
Res.Abstr., R.G., Rel.Ind.One, RILA, Sage
Urb.Stud.Abstr., SSCI, Stud.Wom.Abstr. **Document
type:** academic/scholarly publication.
—BLDSC (0818.500000); Faxon; UnCover; SWETS;
UMI.
   Description: Scholarly reviews and articles in all
fields of history.
   Refereed Serial

AMERICAN JEWISH ARCHIVES; devoted to the
preservation and study of the American Jewish
experience. see ETHNIC INTERESTS

938   US   ISSN 0362-8914
DE1
AMERICAN JOURNAL OF ANCIENT HISTORY. (Text in
English, French or German) 1976. 2/yr. $16
(foreign $18.75). Robinson Hall, Harvard University,
Cambridge, MA 02138. TEL 617-495-2545.
FAX 617-496-3425. Ed. E. Badian. adv.; circ. 600.
circ. 600 (paid). **Indexed:** Mid.East: Abstr.& Ind.
Document type: academic/scholarly publication.
—BLDSC (0821.030000); UnCover; SWETS.
   Description: Covers ancient Greek and Roman
history and related areas.

AMERICAN JOURNAL OF LEGAL HISTORY. see LAW

AMERICAN PHILOSOPHICAL SOCIETY. MEMOIRS. see
SCIENCES: COMPREHENSIVE WORKS

900 001.3   US   ISSN 0003-049X
Q11   CODEN: PAPCAA
AMERICAN PHILOSOPHICAL SOCIETY. PROCEEDINGS.
1838. q. $27 (foreign $35) per no. American
Philosophical Society, 104 S. Fifth St., Philadelphia,
PA 19106. TEL 215-440-3400. Ed. Herman H.
Goldstine. illus.; index, cum.index: vols.1-100
(1838-1957), vols.101-125 (1958-1981)(in 3
vols.). circ. 1,400. (also avail. in microform from
MIM,UMI; reprint service avail. from ISI,KTO,UMI)
Indexed: A.B.C.Pol.Sci., Amer.Bibl.Slavic &
E.Eur.Stud., Amer.Hist.& Life, Arts & Hum.Cit.Ind.,
Biol.Abstr., Chem.Abstr., Curr.Cont., Deep Sea Res.&
Oceanogr.Abstr., Geo.Abstr., GeoRef., Hist.Abstr.,
Lang.& Lang.Behav.Abstr., P.A.I.S., Risk Abstr., SSCI.
Document type: proceedings.
—BLDSC (6630.500000); Faxon; UnCover; SWETS;
UMI; CASDDS.

AMERICAN PHILOSOPHICAL SOCIETY. TRANSACTIONS.
see SCIENCES: COMPREHENSIVE WORKS

**AMERICAN PRESBYTERIANS: JOURNAL OF
PRESBYTERIAN HISTORY.** see RELIGIONS AND
THEOLOGY — Protestant

**AMERICAN UNIVERSITY STUDIES. SERIES 7. THEOLOGY
AND RELIGION.** see RELIGIONS AND THEOLOGY

900   US   ISSN 0740-0462
                       CODEN: AUSHEJ
AMERICAN UNIVERSITY STUDIES. SERIES 9. HISTORY.
1984. irreg. Peter Lang Publishing, Inc., 62 W. 45th
St., 4th Fl., New York, NY 10036.
TEL 212-302-6740. Ed. Kathryn Earle. **Document
type:** academic/scholarly publication.

LES AMIS DE CURNONSKY. see FOLKLORE

ANALECTA BOLLANDIANA; revue critique
d'hagiographie. see RELIGIONS AND THEOLOGY

ANALECTA CISTERCIENSIA. see RELIGIONS AND
THEOLOGY — Roman Catholic

ANALECTA ORDINIS CARMELITARUM. see RELIGIONS
AND THEOLOGY — Roman Catholic

ANCIENS PAYS ET ASSEMBLEES D'ETATS. see
POLITICAL SCIENCE

ANCIENT GREEK CITIES REPORT. see HOUSING AND
URBAN PLANNING

375 940   AT
ANCIENT HISTORY; RESOURCES FOR TEACHERS. 1971.
3/yr. Aus.$28.50 (foreign Aus.$30). Macquarie
Ancient History Association, School of History,
Philosophy and Politics, North Ryde, N.S.W. 2109,
Australia. TEL 02-850-8852. FAX 02-850-8892.
Ed. Boyo Ockinga. adv.; bk.rev.; bibl.; charts. circ.
300. (back issues avail.) **Document type:**
academic/scholarly publication.
   Formerly: Ancient Society; Resources for Teachers
(ISSN 0310-5814)
   Description: For secondary school teachers: new
developments in ancient history and archaeology.

930   BE   ISSN 0066-1619
ANCIENT SOCIETY; journal of ancient history of the
Greek, Hellenistic and Roman world. (Text in Dutch,
English, French, German, Italian) 1970. a.
3000 BEF (effective 1994). (Katholieke Universiteit
Leuven) Editions Peeters s.p.r.l., Bondgenotenlaan
153, B-3000 Louvain, Belgium.
TEL 32-16-235170. FAX 32-16-228500. Eds. H.
Verdin, P. Van Dessel. index. circ. 500. (back issues
avail.) **Indexed:** Br.Archaeol.Abstr., Numis.Lit.
Document type: academic/scholarly publication.
—BLDSC (0900.326000).

THE ANCIENT TIMES. see MUSIC

930 913   US   ISSN 0160-9645
DE1
ANCIENT WORLD; a scholarly journal for the.study of
antiquity. 1978. s-a. $25 to individuals; institutions
$30. Ares Publishers, Inc., 7406 N. Sheridan Rd.,
Chicago, IL 60626. TEL 312-743-1405.
FAX 312-743-0657. Ed. Martin C.J. Miller. adv.;
bk.rev. circ. 1,200. **Indexed:** Arts & Hum.Cit.Ind.,
Curr.Cont., Hist.Abstr., Mid.East: Abstr.& Ind., Old Test.Abstr.
—BLDSC (0900.326300); Faxon; UnCover.

ANGLO-AMERICAN FORUM. see LITERATURE

ANNALES DU MIDI; revue de la France Meridionale. see
ARCHAEOLOGY

900   PL   ISSN 0239-4251
D1
**ANNALES UNIVERSITATIS MARIAE CURIE-SKLODOWSKA.
SECTIO F. HISTORIA.** (Text in English, French or
Polish; summaries in English, French, German)
1946. a. price varies. Uniwersytet Marii
Curie-Sklodowskiej, Wydawnictwo, Pl. M.
Curie-Sklodowskiej 5, 20-031 Lublin, Poland.
TEL 48-81-375304. FAX 48-81-336699. TELEX
0643223. Ed. Wieslaw Sladkowski. circ. 550.
Indexed: Amer.Hist.& Life, Hist.Abstr. **Document type:**
academic/scholarly publication.
—BLDSC (0962.130000).
   Formerly (until 1983): Annales Universitatis Mariae
Curie-Sklodowska. Sectio F. Humaniora (ISSN
0137-2033)

900   US   ISSN 0735-0392
ANNUAL EDITIONS: WESTERN CIVILIZATION. (Vol. I:
Pre-History Through the Reformation; Vol. II:
Early-Modern History Through the 20th Century)
1981. a. (in 2 vols.). $11.95 per vol. Dushkin
Publishing Group, Inc., Sluice Dock, Guilford, CT
06437-9989. TEL 203-453-4351.
FAX 203-453-6000. Ed. William Hughes; Pub. Lan
Nielsen. illus. **Document type:** academic/scholarly
publication.
   Refereed Serial

2874 HISTORY

909   US   ISSN 1054-2779
D1
ANNUAL EDITIONS: WORLD HISTORY. (Vol.I: Pre-history to 1500; Vol.II: 1500 to 20th Century) 1989. a. $11.95 per vol. Dushkin Publishing Group, Inc., Sluice Dock, Guilford, CT 06437-9989. TEL 203-453-4351; 800-243-6532. FAX 203-453-6000. Ed. David McComb; Pub. Lan Nielsen. illus. **Document type:** academic/scholarly publication.
   Refereed Serial

909 938.9   US   ISSN 0885-2316
ANNUAL THIRD WORLD CONFERENCE PROCEEDINGS. 1980. a. $45. Third World Conference Foundation, Box 53110, Chicago, IL 60653. TEL 312-241-6688. Ed. Roger K. Oden. **Document type:** proceedings.
   Description: Interdisciplinary focus on problems and issues in the Third World and diaspora communities from an interregional and cultural perspective.

ANNUARIUM HISTORIAE CONCILIORUM; Internationale Zeitschrift fuer Konziliengeschichtsforschung. see *RELIGIONS AND THEOLOGY*

913 100 400   IT   ISSN 0066-4766
ANTICHITA CLASSICA E CRISTIANA. 1965. irreg., latest no.30. price varies. Paideia Editrice, Via Corsica 130, 25125 Brescia, Italy. TEL 030-222094. FAX 030-223269. **Document type:** monographic series.

930   GW   ISSN 0066-4839
ANTIQUITAS. REIHE 1. ABHANDLUNGEN ZUR ALTEN GESCHICHTE. (Text in English, French, German and Italian) 1955. irreg., no.43, 1993. price varies. Dr. Rudolf Habelt GmbH, Am Buchenhang 1, 53115 Bonn, Germany. TEL 0228-232016. FAX 0228-232017. Ed.Bd. **Document type:** monographic series.

930   GW   ISSN 0066-4847
ANTIQUITAS. REIHE 2. ABHANDLUNGEN AUS DEM GEBIETE DER VOR- UND FRUEHGESCHICHTE. 1955. irreg., no.12, 1982. price varies. Dr. Rudolf Habelt GmbH, Am Buchenhang 1, 53115 Bonn, Germany. TEL 0228-232016. FAX 0228-232017. Ed.Bd. **Document type:** monographic series.

930 913   GW   ISSN 0066-4855
ANTIQUITAS. REIHE 3. ABHANDLUNGEN ZUR VOR- UND FRUEHGESCHICHTE, ZUR KLASSISCHEN UND PROVINZIAL-ROEMISCHEN ARCHAEOLOGIE UND ZUR GESCHICHTE DES ALTERTUMS. (Text in German and French) 1960. irreg., no.32, 1992. price varies. Dr. Rudolf Habelt GmbH, Am Buchenhang 1, 53115 Bonn, Germany. TEL 0228-232016. FAX 0228-232017. Ed.Bd. **Document type:** monographic series.

930   GW   ISSN 0066-4863
ANTIQUITAS. REIHE 4. BEITRAEGE ZUR HISTORIA-AUGUSTA-FORSCHUNG. (Text in German, English, French, Italian) 1963. irreg., vol.21, 1991. price varies. Dr. Rudolf Habelt GmbH, Am Buchenhang 1, 53115 Bonn, Germany. TEL 0228-232016. FAX 0228-232017. Ed. A. Alfoeldi. **Document type:** monographic series.

930   GW
ANTIQUITAS. REIHE 4, SERIE 2. BIBLIOGRAPHIEN. 1985. irreg., vol.4, 1987. price varies. Dr. Rudolf Habelt GmbH, Am Buchenhang 1, 53115 Bonn, Germany. TEL 0228-232016. FAX 0228-232017. **Document type:** monographic series.

930   GW
ANTIQUITAS. REIHE 4, SERIE 3. KOMMENTARE. 1991. irreg. Dr. Rudolf Habelt GmbH, Am Buchenhang 1, 53115 Bonn, Germany. TEL 0228-232016. FAX 0228-232017. **Document type:** monographic series.

909   SP
DP160.9
ANUARIO DE HISTORIA CONTEMPORANEA. 1974. a. price varies. Universidad de Granada, Servicio de Publicaciones, Antiguo Colegio Maximo, Campus de Cartuja, 18071 Granada, Spain. TEL 243980. Ed. Cristina Vines Millet.
   Formerly: Anuario de Historia Moderna y Contemporanea (ISSN 0210-9603)

ANZEIGER FUER DIE ALTERTUMSWISSENSCHAFT. see *CLASSICAL STUDIES*

AQUINAS JOURNAL. see *RELIGIONS AND THEOLOGY — Roman Catholic*

ARCHAEOLOGIE OESTERREICHS. see *ARCHAEOLOGY*

900   GW   ISSN 0003-9233
CB3
ARCHIV FUER KULTURGESCHICHTE. 1903. 2/yr. DM.68. Boehlau Verlag GmbH, Theodor-Heuss-Str. 76, 51149 Cologne, Germany. TEL 02203-307021. FAX 02203-307349. Ed. Egon Boshof. bk.rev.; illus. circ. 1,000. (reprint service avail. from KTO) **Indexed:** Amer.Hist.& Life, Hist.Abstr., M.L.A. **Document type:** academic/scholarly publication.
—SWETS. CCC.

913 931   GW   ISSN 0066-6459
PA3339
ARCHIV FUER PAPYRUSFORSCHUNG UND VERWANDTE GEBIETE. 1901. a. DM.168. B.G. Teubner Verlagsgesellschaft mbH, Johannisgasse 16, 04103 Leipzig, Germany. TEL 216860. Ed.Bd. adv.; bk.rev. **Document type:** academic/scholarly publication.
   Description: Results of the deciphering and interpretation of papyrus sources.

ARCHIV FUER SCHLESISCHE KIRCHENGESCHICHTE. see *RELIGIONS AND THEOLOGY*

001.3 300   US
ARCHIVAL ISSUES. 1976. s-a. $16 to individuals; institutions $36. Midwest Archives Conference, University of Minnesota, Immigration History Research Center, 826 Berry St., St. Paul, MN 55114. Ed. Joel Wurl. adv.; bk.rev. circ. 1,100. (also avail. in microfilm; back issues avail.; reprint service avail. from UMI) **Indexed:** Amer.Hist.& Life, Hist.Abstr., Inform.Sci.Abstr., Lib.Lit., LISA.
   Formerly: Midwestern Archivist.

900   GW   ISSN 0003-9497
D111
ARCHIVALISCHE ZEITSCHRIFT. 1950. a. price varies. (Hauptstaatsarchiv) Boehlau Verlag GmbH, Theodor-Heuss-Str. 76, 51149 Cologne, Germany. TEL 02203-307021. FAX 02203-307349. bk.rev. circ. 700. (reprint service avail. from KTO) **Indexed:** Amer.Hist.& Life, Hist.Abstr. **Document type:** academic/scholarly publication.

025.17   GW   ISSN 0003-9500
CD9
DER ARCHIVAR; Mitteilungsblatt fuer deutsches Archivwesen. 1947. q. DM.42. (Nordrhein-Westfaelischen Hauptstaatsarchiv) Verlag Franz Schmitt, Kaiserstr. 99-101, 53721 Siegburg, Germany. TEL 02241-64030. FAX 02241-53891. Ed. Peter Dohms. adv. contact: Ingeborg Welde. bk.rev.; bibl.; charts; illus.; index. circ. 2,000. (back issues avail.) **Indexed:** Amer.Hist.& Life, Bibl.Cart., Hist.Abstr., P.A.I.S.For.Lang.Ind. **Document type:** government publication.

ARCHIVES. see *LIBRARY AND INFORMATION SCIENCES*

900   IT
▼**ARCHIVIO STORICO DEL SANNIO.** 1992. s-a. L.52000 to individuals; institutions L.72000; foreign L.85000 (effective 1993). Edizioni Scientifiche Italiane S.p.A., Via Chiatamone 7, 80121 Naples, Italy. TEL 081-7645768. FAX 081-7646477.

ARCHIVIUM HISTORICUM CARMELITANUM. see *RELIGIONS AND THEOLOGY — Roman Catholic*

ARCHIVMITTEILUNGEN; Zeitschrift fuer Theorie und Praxis des Archivwesens. see *LIBRARY AND INFORMATION SCIENCES*

ARCHIVUM FRANCISCANUM HISTORICUM. see *RELIGIONS AND THEOLOGY — Roman Catholic*

900 913   RU
ARKHEOGRAFICHESKII EZHEGODNIK. 1957. a. Izdatel'stvo Nauka, 90 Profsoyuznaya ul., 117864 Moscow, Russia. TEL 234-50-84. Ed. S.O. Shmidt. bibl.; index. circ. 1,500.

948.5 026   DK   ISSN 0004-203X
ARKIV; tidsskrift for arkivforskning. 1966. s-a. DKK 86. Rigsarkivet - National Record Office, Rigsdagsgaarden 9, 1218 Copenhagen K, Denmark. TEL 33-923310. Ed. Jan Kanstrup. bk.rev.; bibl.; illus. circ. 600. **Indexed:** Amer.Hist.& Life, Hist.Abstr.
   Description: Articles on the theory and practice of records management in public archives including the history of public archives in Denmark.

ARKIV, SAMHAELLE OCH FORSKNING. see *LIBRARY AND INFORMATION SCIENCES*

ASPRENAS; rivista di scienze teologiche. see *RELIGIONS AND THEOLOGY — Roman Catholic*

969   RE
ASSOCIATION HISTORIQUE INTERNATIONALE DE L'OCEAN INDIEN. BULLETIN DE LIAISON ET D'INFORMATION. (Text in English, French) 1981. a. Association Historique Internationale de l'Ocean Indien, c/o Archives Departementales de la Reunion, B.P. 289, 97490 Sainte Clotilde, Reunion. **Indexed:** P.L.E.S.A. (1988-). **Document type:** bulletin.

ASSOCIATION INTERNATIONALE D'ETUDES PATRISTIQUES. BULLETIN D'INFORMATION ET DE LIAISON. see *RELIGIONS AND THEOLOGY*

914.6   SP
ASTURIENSIA MEDIEVALIA. (Subseries of Dept's Publicaciones) 1972. a. 2500 ptas.($30) per no. Universidad de Oviedo, Departamento de Historia Medieval, Avenida del Cristo, s-n, 33006, Oviedo, Spain. illus.

ATENEO VENETO; rivista di scienze, lettere ed arti. see *SCIENCES: COMPREHENSIVE WORKS*

AUDACITY; the magazine of business experience. see *BUSINESS AND ECONOMICS*

AUGUSTAN SOCIETY OMNIBUS; an international journal of history, genealogy & heraldry. see *GENEALOGY AND HERALDRY*

901   US   ISSN 0067-0588
F536
AUGUSTANA HISTORICAL SOCIETY, ROCK ISLAND, ILLINOIS. PUBLICATIONS. 1930. irreg., no.39, 1988. price varies. Augustana Historical Society, c/o Augustana College Library, Rock Island, IL 61201. TEL 309-794-7266. bk.rev. circ. 1,000. (reprint service avail. from UMI) **Document type:** monographic series.

AUSTRALIAN DEFENCE FORCE JOURNAL; journal of Australian profession of arms. see *MILITARY*

990   AT   ISSN 1031-461X
DU80
AUSTRALIAN HISTORICAL STUDIES. 1940. s-a. Aus.$36($45) (effective 1994). University of Melbourne, Department of History, Parkville, Vic. 3052, Australia. TEL 03-344-5963. FAX 03-344-7894. Ed. J. Rickard. adv.; bk.rev.; bibl.; circ. 1,500 (controlled). (back issues avail.) **Indexed:** Amer.Hist.& Life, Arts & Hum.Cit.Ind., Aus.P.A.I.S., Br.Hum.Ind., Curr.Cont., Gdlns., Hist.Abstr., So.Pac.Per.Ind. **Document type:** academic/scholarly publication.
—Faxon; UnCover.
   Former titles (until Jan. 1988): Historical Studies (ISSN 0018-2559); Historical Studies: Australia and New Zealand.
   Description: Includes articles and reviews on Australian history.

AUSTRALIAN RAILWAY HISTORICAL SOCIETY. BULLETIN. see *TRANSPORTATION — Railroads*

AVALON TO CAMELOT; issued quarterly on matters Arthurian. see *LITERATURE*

AYRSHIRE MONOGRAPHS. see *ARCHAEOLOGY*

B E F A R. PUBLICATION. (Bibliotheque des Ecoles Francaises d'Athenes et de Rome) see *ARCHAEOLOGY*

BAPTIST HISTORY AND HERITAGE. see *RELIGIONS AND THEOLOGY — Protestant*

BAPTIST QUARTERLY. see *RELIGIONS AND THEOLOGY — Protestant*

ULRICH'S INTERNATIONAL PERIODICALS DIRECTORY 1994-95

900　　　　　　SZ
BASLER BEITRAEGE ZUR GESCHICHTSWISSENSCHAFT. 1938. irreg. price varies. Helbing und Lichtenhahn Verlag AG, Freie Str. 84, CH-4051 Basel, Switzerland. TEL 064-268626. FAX 064-245780. (Subscr. to: Sauerlaender AG, Postfach, CH-5001 Aarau, Switzerland) **Document type:** monographic series.

BAUERNHAEUSER AUS MITTELEUROPA; Aufmasse und Publikationen von Gerhard Eitzen. see ARCHITECTURE

900　　　　　　GW
BAYERISCHE AKADEMIE DER WISSENSCHAFTEN. HISTORISCHE KOMMISSION. SCHRIFTENREIHE. 1957. irreg. Vandenhoeck und Ruprecht, Robert-Bosch-Breite 6, 37079 Goettingen, Germany. TEL 0551-6959-0. FAX 0551-695917. (Subscr. to: 37070 Goettingen, Germany) **Document type:** monographic series.

BEHIND THE HEADLINES. see POLITICAL SCIENCE — International Relations

930　　　　　　GW
BEITRAEGE ZUM DENKMALSCHUTZ FRANKFURT AM MAIN. 1989. irreg., no.8, 1994. price varies. (Denkmalamt der Stadt Frankfurt am Main) Dr. Rudolf Habelt GmbH, Am Buchenhang 1, 53115 Bonn, Germany. TEL 0228-232016. FAX 0228-232017. **Document type:** monographic series.

BEITRAEGE ZUR GESCHICHTE DER ARBEITERBEWEGUNG. see POLITICAL SCIENCE

BEITRAEGE ZUR NATIONALSOZIALISTISCHEN GESUNDHEITS- UND SOZIALPOLITIK. see MEDICAL SCIENCES

940　　　　　　GW
BEITRAEGE ZUR SOZIAL- UND WIRTSCHAFTSGESCHICHTE. 1970. a. price varies. Universitaetsbuchhandlung Muehlau, Holtenauer Str. 116, 24105 Kiel, Germany. TEL 0431-8009-0. Ed. Wilhelm Koppe. **Document type:** academic/scholarly publication.

901　　　　　　GW　　ISSN 0723-3299
BEITRAEGE ZUR ZEITGESCHICHTE. 1980. irreg. Colloquium Verlag, Luetzowstr. 105, 10785 Berlin, Germany. Eds. Peter Haungs, Eckhard Jesse. circ. 5,000.

BELARUSKAYA CARKVA. see RELIGIONS AND THEOLOGY — Eastern Orthodox

902　　　　　　GW　　ISSN 0934-4470
BERICHT DER BAYERISCHEN BODENDENKMALPFLEGE. 1960. a. price varies. (Bayerisches Landesamt fuer Denkmalpflege) Dr. Rudolf Habelt GmbH, Am Buchenhang 1, 53115 Bonn, Germany. TEL 0228-232016. FAX 0228-232017.
Formerly (until 1992): Jahresbericht der Bayerischen Bodendenkmalpflege (ISSN 0075-2835)

900　　　　　　AU
BEZIRKSHAUPTMANNSCHAFT AMSTETTEN. HEIMATKUNDLICHE BEILAGE ZUM AMSTBLATT. 1972. irreg. Bezirkshauptmannschaft Amstetten, Preinsbacherstr. 11, 3302 Amstetten, Austria.

900　　　　　　AU
BEZIRKSHAUPTMANNSCHAFT MELK. HEIMATKUNDLICHE BEILAGE ZUM AMTSBLATT. 1975. irreg. Bezirkshauptmannschaft Melk, Abt-Karl-Str. 23, 3390 Melk, Austria.

900　　　　　　AU
BEZIRKSHAUPTMANNSCHAFT TULLN. HEIMATKUNDLICHES BEIBLATT ZUM AMTSBLATT. 1974. irreg. Bezirkshauptmannschaft Tulln, Hauptplatz 33, 3430 Tulln, Austria.

BIBBIA E ORIENTE; rivista per la conoscenza della Bibbia. see RELIGIONS AND THEOLOGY

BIBLIOTECA DE MENENDEZ PELAYO. BOLETIN. see LITERATURE

900　　　　　　SW
BIBLIOTECA HISTORICA LUNDENSIS. (Text in Swedish; summaries in English or German) 1955. irreg. price varies. A W I International AB, P.O. Box 4627, S-116 91 Stockholm, Sweden. TEL 641-640-8800. FAX 468-641-1180. Eds. Birgitta Oden, Goeran Rystad.

BIBLIOTEKA POLONIJNA/POLONIA LIBRARY. see POLITICAL SCIENCE

900　　　　　　SW　　ISSN 0519-9700
BIBLIOTHECA HISTORICA LUNDENSIS. (Text in English and Swedish) 1955. irreg. price varies. Lund University Press, P.O. Box 141, S-22100 Lund, Sweden. TEL 46 46 31 20 00. FAX 46-46-30-53-38. Ed.Bd. **Document type:** academic/scholarly publication.

BIBLIOTHECA HISTORICO-ECCLESIASTICA LUNDENSIS. see RELIGIONS AND THEOLOGY — Protestant

930　　　　　　GW　　ISSN 0067-8201
BIBLIOTHEK DER KLASSISCHEN ALTERTUMSWISSENSCHAFTEN. NEUE FOLGE. 1963. irreg. price varies. Universitaetsverlag C. Winter Heidelberg GmbH, Hans-Bunte-Str. 18, 69123 Heidelberg, Germany. **Document type:** monographic series.

909 016　　　GW　　ISSN 0081-900X
BIBLIOTHEK FUER ZEITGESCHICHTE, STUTTGART. SCHRIFTEN.* 1962. irreg. price varies. Bernard und Graefe Verlag, Karl-Mand-Str. 2, Postfach 2060, 5400 Koblenz, Germany.

900　　　　　　SZ　　ISSN 0006-1980
BIBLIOTHEQUE DE L'ECOLE DES CHARTES; revue d'erudition. 1838. 2/yr. 120 SFr. (Societe de l'Ecole des Chartes) Librairie Droz S.A., 11, rue Massot, CH-1211 Geneva 12, Switzerland. TEL 022-3466666. FAX 022-3472391. bk.rev.; bibl.; index, cum.index. (also avail. in microfilm from BHP; reprint service avail. from SCH) **Indexed:** Bibl.Ling. **Document type:** academic/scholarly publication.
—BLDSC (2020.340000). **CCC.**

900　　　　　　FR　　ISSN 0520-0601
BIBLIOTHEQUE HISTORIQUE. 1976. irreg. Editions Payot, 106 bd Saint-Germain, 75006 Paris, France. TEL 33-1-43297410. FAX 33-1-43256845. **Document type:** monographic series.

BIBLOS. see LITERATURE

949　　　　　　BE　　ISSN 0006-2286
BIJDRAGEN TOT DE GESCHIEDENIS; inzonderheid van het aloude hertogdom Brabant. 1902. s-a. 550 BEF (foreign 650 BEF). Universitaire Faculteiten Sint Ignatius te Antwerpen, Prinsstraat 13, 2000 Antwerp, Belgium. TEL 03-220-42-92. FAX 03-220-44-20. Ed. A. Thijs. adv.; bk.rev.; index. circ. 400.

900　　　　　　BE
BIJDRAGEN TOT DE GESCHIEDENIS DER STAD DEINZE EN VAN HET LAND AAN LEIE EN SCHELDE. (Text in Dutch) 1934. a. 500 BEF. Kunst en Oudheidkundige Kring-Deinze, Ten Bosse 11, 9800 Deize, Belgium. FAX 32-9-3862453. circ. 350.

943.6　　　AU　　ISSN 0006-4459
DB681
BLAETTER FUER HEIMATKUNDE. 1923. q. S.160. Historischer Verein fuer Steiermark, Hamerlinggasse 3, A-8010 Graz, Austria. Ed. Guenter Cerwinka. bk.rev.; charts; illus.; index, cum.index. circ. 1,400. **Indexed:** Amer.Hist.& Life, Hist.Abstr. **Document type:** academic/scholarly publication.

900　　　　　　UY
BOLETIN HISTORICO DEL EJERCITO. 1929. irreg., no. 287-290, 1993. $6. Estado Mayor del Ejercito, Departamento de Estudios Historicos, Garibaldi 2313, Montevideo, Uruguay. TEL 20-71-18. FAX 23-66-00. bk.rev. circ. 500. **Indexed:** Amer.Hist.& Life, Hist.Abstr.
Former titles: Estado Mayor General del Ejercito. Boletin Historico (ISSN 0797-1958); (until 1935): Estado Mayor del Ejercito. Boletin de Informaciones (ISSN 0797-4345)

900 800 011 320　　US　　ISSN 0891-9607
BORGO REFERENCE GUIDES. 1981. irreg., no.6, 1993 (approx. 5/yr.). price varies. Borgo Press, Box 2845, San Bernardino, CA 92406. TEL 909-884-5813. FAX 909-888-4942. Ed. Michael Burgess.
Formerly: Borgo Reference Library (ISSN 0270-3653)
Description: Modern reference books on topics of current interest.

DER BOTE AUS DEM WEHRGESCHICHTLICHEN MUSEUM. see MILITARY

BRANDSCHUTZ; Deutsche Feuerwehr-Zeitung. see FIRE PREVENTION

BRETAGNE REELLE; tribune libre-la voix du pays gallo. see POLITICAL SCIENCE

BRILL'S SERIES IN JEWISH STUDIES. see RELIGIONS AND THEOLOGY — Judaic

BULLETIN OF MEDIEVAL CANON LAW. NEW SERIES. see LAW

979　　　　　　US
BUNCHGRASS HISTORIAN. 1973. 3/yr. $10. Whitman County Historical Society, Box 67, Colfax, WA 99111. (Subscr. to: Box 67, Colfax, WA 99111) Ed. Lawrence R. Stark. bk.rev. circ. 800. **Document type:** consumer publication.
Description: Covers the local history of Whitman County, Washington.

BYZANTINISCHE ZEITSCHRIFT. see ORIENTAL STUDIES

CAHIERS D'ARCHEOLOGIE ET D'HISTOIRE DU BERRY. see ARCHAEOLOGY

700　　　　　　FR　　ISSN 0008-008X
D1
CAHIERS D'HISTOIRE (LYON). 1956. q. 160 F. Comite Historique du Centre-Est, 86 rue Pasteur, 69007 Lyon, France. Ed. M. Garrier. adv.; bk.rev.; index. circ. 700. (also avail. in microform) **Indexed:** Amer.Hist.& Life, Arts & Hum.Cit.Ind., Curr.Cont., Hist.Abstr., RADAR. **Document type:** academic/scholarly publication.
—BLDSC (2948.975000); SWETS.

900 800 709　　FR　　ISSN 0007-9731
CB3
CAHIERS DE CIVILISATION MEDIEVALE. 1958. q. 390 F. (foreign 430 F.) (effective 1993). Universite de Poitiers, Centre d'Etudes Superieures de Civilisation Medievale, Hotel Berthelot, 24 rue de la Chaine, 86022 Poitiers, France. TEL 49-41-03-86. Eds. Pierre Bec, Robert Favreau. adv.; bk.rev.; bibl.; illus.; index. (back issues avail.) **Indexed:** Arts & Hum.Cit.Ind., Bibl.Ling., Br.Archaeol.Abstr., CERDIC, Curr.Cont., M.L.A., Numis.Lit., RILA.
—Faxon; SWETS.

900 800 709　　FR　　ISSN 0068-5011
CAHIERS DE CIVILISATION MEDIEVALE. SUPPLEMENT. 1958. q. 390 F. (foreign 430 F.). Universite de Poitiers, Centre d'Etudes Superieures de Civilisation Medievale, 24 rue de la Chaine, 86022 Poitiers, France. adv.; bk.rev.; cum.index.

900 323.4　　FR　　ISSN 0182-2705
CAHIERS DE L'AVENIR DE LA BRETAGNE. 1975. a. 150 F.($30) 21, place Duguesclin, 22000 Saint-Brieuc, Brittany, France. Ed. Yann Fouere. bk.rev. circ. 2,500. **Document type:** academic/scholarly publication.
Description: Studies history of Brittany and its position, directions, regions, minorities and nationalities in Europe

CAHIERS DE L'UNIVERSITE DE PERPIGNAN. see LITERATURE

944 913　　FR　　ISSN 0008-025X
CAHIERS HAUT-MARNAIS; revue d'histoire, de lettres et d'art. 1946. q. 120 F. (foreign 135 F.). Amis des Cahiers Haut-Marnais, B.P. 565, 52012 Chaumont Cedex, France. TEL 25-03-33-54. Ed. Lionel Gallois. bk.rev.; illus.; cum.index: 1946-1980. circ. 1,200.
Description: Presents the heritage, geography, economy and sociology of the Haut-Marnais region.

HISTORY

900 913   FR   ISSN 0399-1415
CAHIERS LEOPOLD DELISLE. 1947. s-a. 135 F. (typically set in Jan.). Societe Parisienne d'Histoire et d'Archeologie Normandes, 26 rue 8 Mai 1945, 94450 Limeil-Brevannes, France. Ed. M. Nortier. circ. 450. **Document type:** bulletin.

909 800   US   ISSN 1050-7086
D1
CALLIOPE (PETERBOROUGH); world history for young people. 1981. 5/yr. $17.95 (foreign $23.95). Cobblestone Publishing, Inc., 7 School St., Peterborough, NH 03458. TEL 603-924-7209. FAX 603-924-7380. Eds. Rosalie F. Baker, Charles Baker. illus.; cum.index: 1990-1992. circ. 9,000. (back issues avail.) **Indexed:** Ind.Child.Mag. —UnCover.
   Supersedes (in Sep. 1990): Classical Calliope (ISSN 0271-1966)
   Description: Designed to interest youth (ages 9-15) in world history. Each issue devoted to a single theme suitable for classroom use as well.

909   UK   ISSN 0084-8336
CAMBRIDGE STUDIES IN EARLY MODERN HISTORY. 1970. irreg. price varies. Cambridge University Press, Edinburgh Bldg., Shaftesbury Rd., Cambridge CB2 2RU, England. TEL 0223-312393. FAX 0223-315052. TELEX 851817256. (N. American addr.: Cambridge University Press, Journals Dept., 40 W. 20th St., New York, NY 10011. TEL 212-924-3900. FAX 212-691-3239) Ed.Bd. **Document type:** monographic series.

CAMBRIDGE UNIVERSITY LIBRARY. HISTORICAL BIBLIOGRAPHY SERIES. see *BIBLIOGRAPHIES*

013 900   CN
CANADA. REGISTER OF POST GRADUATE DISSERTATIONS IN PROGRESS IN HISTORY AND RELATED SUBJECTS. 1966. a. Can.$10. Canadian Historical Association, 395 Wellington St., Ottawa, ON K1A 0N3, Canada. TEL 613-233-7885. Ed. P. Aubin. circ. 800. **Document type:** directory.
   Formerly: Canada. Public Archives. Register of Post Graduate Dissertations in Progress in History and Related Subjects (ISSN 0068-8088)

CANADA & THE WORLD; the magazine for students of current events. see *SOCIAL SCIENCES: COMPREHENSIVE WORKS*

CANADIAN CATHOLIC HISTORICAL STUDIES. see *RELIGIONS AND THEOLOGY — Roman Catholic*

CANADIAN CHURCH HISTORICAL SOCIETY JOURNAL. see *RELIGIONS AND THEOLOGY*

971   CN
F1001
CANADIAN HISTORICAL ASSOCIATION. BULLETIN. (Text in English, French) 1974. q. membership. Canadian Historical Association, 395 Wellington St., Ottawa, ON K1A 0N3, Canada. TEL 613-233-7885. Eds. E. Munn, N. St-Onge. circ. 2,500. **Document type:** bulletin.
   Formerly: Canadian Historical Association. Newsletter (ISSN 0382-4764)

971   CN   ISSN 0847-4478
F1001
CANADIAN HISTORICAL ASSOCIATION. JOURNAL; a selection from the papers presented at the annual meeting. (Text in English, French) 1923. a. $10. Canadian Historical Association, 395 Wellington St., Ottawa, ON K1A 0N3, Canada. TEL 613-233-7885. Eds. S. Harris, D. Marshall. cum.index: 1922-1959. circ. 3,000. **Indexed:** Can.Per.Ind.; CMI.
   Formerly (until 1989): Canadian Historical Association. Historical Papers (ISSN 0068-8878)

971   CN   ISSN 0008-3755
F1001
CANADIAN HISTORICAL REVIEW. (Text in English, French) 1920. q. $37 to individuals; institutions $63; students $26. University of Toronto Press, Journals Department, 5201 Dufferin St., Downsview, ON M3H 5T8, Canada. TEL 416-667-7781. FAX 416-667-7803. (U.S. addr.: 340 Nagel Dr., Cheektowaga, NY 14225) Eds. J.R. Miller, Susan Houston. adv.; bk.rev.; bibl.; index. circ. 2,580. (also avail. in microform from JAI,MIM,UMI,PMC; reprint service avail. from UMI) **Indexed:** Abstr.Anthropol., Amer.Bibl.Slavic & E.Eur.Stud., Amer.Hist.& Life, Arts & Hum.Cit.Ind., Bk.Rev.Ind. (1986-), Can.Per.Ind., Can.Wom.Per.Ind., Child.Bk.Rev.Ind. (1986-), CMI, Curr.Cont., Hist.Abstr., Hum.Ind., Mag.Ind., SSCI.
   —BLDSC (3027.350000); Faxon; UnCover; SWETS; UMI. **CCC.**

900   CN   ISSN 0008-4107
D1
CANADIAN JOURNAL OF HISTORY/ANNALES CANADIENNES D'HISTOIRE. 1966. 3/yr. Can.$24 to individuals; institutions Can.$28; students Can.$23. University of Saskatchewan, Saskatoon, SK S7N 0W0, Canada. TEL 306-966-5792. FAX 306-966-5852. Ed.Bd. adv.; bk.rev. circ. 700. (also avail. in microform from UMI; reprint service avail. from UMI) **Indexed:** Amer.Bibl.Slavic & E.Eur.Stud., Amer.Hist.& Life, Arts & Hum.Cit.Ind., Can.Wom.Per.Ind., Curr.Cont., Hist.Abstr., Hum.Ind., M.L.A, Mid.East: Abstr.& Ind.
   —BLDSC (3031.630000); Faxon; UnCover; UMI.
   Description: Includes history of all periods and all countries except Canada.
   Refereed Serial

970 320 001.3   CN   ISSN 0317-7904
JC311
CANADIAN REVIEW OF STUDIES IN NATIONALISM. (Text in English, French, German) 1973. a. $13. Canadian Review of Studies in Nationalism, Inc., c/o University of Prince Edward Island, Charlottetown, PE C1A 4P3, Canada. TEL 902-566-0527. FAX 902-628-4323. Ed. Thomas Spira. adv.; bk.rev.; bibl. circ. 650. **Indexed:** A.B.C.Pol.Sci., Amer.Bibl.Slavic & E.Eur.Stud., Amer.Hist.& Life, Hist.Abstr., Lang.& Lang.Behav.Abstr., P.A.I.S., Peace Res.Abstr.
   —Faxon; UnCover.

CANADIAN SOCIAL STUDIES. see *EDUCATION — Teaching Methods And Curriculum*

900   CN
CANADIAN WAR MUSEUM. HISTORICAL PUBLICATIONS.* (Text in English and French) 1968. irreg., no.16, 1981. price varies. Canada War Museum, 330 Sussex Dr., Ottawa, Ont. K1A 0M8, Canada.

CARMELUS; commentarii ab Instituto Carmelitano editi. see *RELIGIONS AND THEOLOGY — Roman Catholic*

CASA DE VELASQUEZ, MADRID. MELANGES/CASA DE VELASQUEZ, MADRID. MISCELLANIES. see *ART*

940 949   YU   ISSN 0590-9597
                                   CODEN: CSUPER
CASOPIS ZA SUVREMENU POVIJEST/MAGAZINE OF CONTEMPORARY HISTORY. 1969. 3/yr. 450 din.($11.50) Institut za Suvremenu Povijest, Opaticka 10, 41000 Zagreb, Croatia, Yugoslavia. TEL 41-425-982. FAX 41-428-199. Ed. Ivan Jelic. adv.; bk.rev. **Indexed:** Amer.Hist.& Life (1992-), Hist.Abstr. (1992-).

CATALOGO DANTE. see *LITERATURE*

CATHOLIC HISTORICAL REVIEW. see *RELIGIONS AND THEOLOGY — Roman Catholic*

270 026   US
CENTER FOR REFORMATION RESEARCH. NEWSLETTER. 1968. 4/yr. free. Center for Reformation Research, 6477 San Bonita Ave., St. Louis, MO 63105. TEL 314-727-6655. Ed. William Maltby. circ. 3,000. (also avail. in microform from UMI; reprint service avail. from UMI) **Document type:** newsletter.
   Formerly: Foundation for Reformation Research. Newsletter (ISSN 0015-895X)

900   US   ISSN 0069-1461
CENTERS OF CIVILIZATION SERIES. 1958. irreg. price varies. University of Oklahoma Press, 1005 Asp Ave., Norman, OK 73019. TEL 405-325-5111. FAX 405-325-4000. **Indexed:** M.L.A.

CENTRE DE RECHERCHE D'HISTOIRE ET CIVILISATION DE BYZANCE. TRAVAUX ET MEMOIRES. see *HISTORY — History Of Europe*

CENTRO DI CULTURA E STORIA AMALFITANA. RASSEGNA. see *ART*

900   IT
CENTRO DI RICERCA E DI STUDIO SUL MOVIMENTO DEI DISCIPLINATI. QUADERNI. 1965. irreg., no.21, 1981. Centro di Documentazione sul Movimento dei Disciplinati, Casella Postale 73, Perugia 06100, Italy. Ed. Ugolini Nicolini. adv.; bk.rev.; bibl.; illus.
   Formerly: Centro di Documentazione sul Movimento dei Disciplinati. Quaderni (ISSN 0009-0026)

CERCLE D'ETUDES NUMISMATIQUES. BULLETIN. see *NUMISMATICS*

CERCLE ERNEST RENAN. CAHIERS. see *RELIGIONS AND THEOLOGY*

900   UK   ISSN 0069-2263
CEREDIGION. (Text in English and Welsh; summaries in Welsh) 1950. a. £7. Ceredigion Antiquarian Society, Skomer, Llanbadarn Rd., Aberystwyth, Dyfed SY23 3QW, Wales. TEL 44-970-627066. FAX 44-970-626717. Ed. Geraint H. Jenkins. bk.rev. circ. 800. **Indexed:** Br.Archaeol.Abstr., Br.Hum.Ind. **Document type:** academic/scholarly publication, proceedings.
   —BLDSC (3120.039000).

900   CN   ISSN 0069-2646
CHAMPLAIN SOCIETY, TORONTO. REPORT.* 1906. a. membership. Champlain Society, Box 592, Station "R", Toronto, Ont. M4G 4E1, Canada. TEL 416-487-2693.

978   US   ISSN 0162-217X
CHARLES REDD MONOGRAPHS IN WESTERN HISTORY. 1972. irreg. (1-2/yr.). price varies. (Charles Redd Center for Western Studies) Signature Books, 564 W. 400 North, Salt Lake City, UT 84116. TEL 801-531-1483. FAX 801-531-1488. Ed.Bd. circ. 2,000. **Document type:** monographic series.
   —CCC.
   Description: Looks at all aspects of the American West experience through the eyes of various disciplines.

500 610   US   ISSN 0073-2745
CHICAGO HISTORY OF SCIENCE AND MEDICINE. 1971. irreg., vol.4, 1981. price varies. University of Chicago Press, 5801 S. Ellis Ave., Chicago, IL 60637. TEL 312-702-7899. Ed. Allen G. Debus. (reprint service avail. from UMI,ISI)
   Refereed Serial

951   US   ISSN 0009-4633
CHINESE STUDIES IN HISTORY; a journal of translations. 1967. q. $315 (foreign $347). M.E. Sharpe, Inc., 80 Business Park Dr., Armonk, NY 10504. TEL 914-273-1800. FAX 914-273-2106. Ed. Li Yu-ning. adv.; index. (back issues avail.) **Indexed:** Amer.Hist.& Life, Curr.Cont., Hist.Abstr.
   —BLDSC (3181.118000); Faxon; UnCover; SWETS; UMI.
   Formerly: Chinese Studies in History and Philosophy.
   Refereed Serial

CHIROPRACTIC HISTORY. see *MEDICAL SCIENCES — Chiropractic, Homeopathy, Osteopathy*

CHRISTIAN HISTORY MAGAZINE. see *RELIGIONS AND THEOLOGY*

CHURCH OF ENGLAND HISTORICAL SOCIETY (DIOCESE OF SYDNEY). JOURNAL. see *RELIGIONS AND THEOLOGY — Protestant*

CIVILIAN-BASED DEFENSE. see *POLITICAL SCIENCE — International Relations*

900 309   US
CIVILIZATION AND SOCIETY: STUDIES IN SOCIAL, ECONOMIC AND CULTURAL HISTORY. irreg., latest 1987. D.C. Heath & Company, 125 Spring St., Lexington, MA 02173. TEL 617-862-6650.

CLAIRLIEU: TIJDSCHRIFT GEWIJD AAN DE GESCHIEDENIS DER KRUISHEREN. see *RELIGIONS AND THEOLOGY*

CLASSICAL ASSOCIATION. PROCEEDINGS. see *LITERATURE*

900   IT
CLIO. q. L.80000 to individuals; institutions L.100000; foreign L.116000 (effective 1993). Edizioni Scientifiche Italiane S.p.A., Via Chiatamone, 7, 80121 Naples, Italy. TEL 081-7645768. FAX 081-7646477. Ed. Carlo Ghisalberti. circ. 1,000.

800 900   US
CLIO (FORT WAYNE); a journal of literature, history, and the philosophy of history. 1971. 4/yr. $14 to individuals; institutions $36. Indiana University, 2101 Coliseum Blvd. E., Fort Wayne, IN 46805. TEL 219-481-6753. FAX 219-481-6880. (Co-sponsor: Purdue University) Ed. Henry Kozicki. adv.; bk.rev.; cum.index every 2 yrs. circ. 800. (also avail. in microform from UMI) **Indexed:** Abstr.Engl.Stud., Amer.Hist.& Life, Bk.Rev.Ind. (1980-), Can.Rev.Comp.Lit., Child.Bk.Rev.Ind. (1980-), Curr.Cont., Hist.Abstr., Hum.Ind., Lang.& Lang.Behav.Abstr., M.L.A., Phil.Ind., Sociol.Abstr.

900   US
CLIO (PROVIDENCE); a journal of history. ceased Spring 1991. s-a. $5 free. c/o Undergraduate Council of Students, Box 1930, Brown University, Providence, RI 02912. TEL 401-863-6309. Ed. Erich P. Horn. circ. 1,000. **Indexed:** Abstr.Engl.Stud., Hum.Ind.

900   SP ISSN 0077-2054
COLECCION MUNDO ANTIGUO. 1962. irreg., no.7, 1987. price varies. (Universidad de Navarra, Departamento de Historia Antigua) Ediciones Universidad de Navarra, S.A., Apdo. 396, 31080 Pamplona, Spain. TEL 94 825 6850.

COLLECTANEA BIBLIOGRAPHICA CARMELITANA. see *BIBLIOGRAPHIES*

COMITATUS; a journal of Medieval and Renaissance studies. see *LITERATURE*

987   BE ISSN 0001-415X
COMMISSION ROYALE D'HISTOIRE. BULLETIN. (Text in Dutch, French) 1834. q. 1000 BEF. Commission Royale d'Histoire, Palais des Academies, 1 rue Ducale, 1000 Brussels, Belgium. (Subscr. to: Librarie Alain Ferraton, 162 Chaussee de Charleroi, 1060 Brussels, Belgium) Ed.Bd. charts; illus.; index, cum.index. circ. 550. **Indexed:** Amer.Hist.& Life, Hist.Abstr. **Document type:** bulletin.

930 340   BE
COMMISSION ROYALE DES ANCIENNES LOIS ET ORDONNANCES DE BELGIQUE. BULLETIN/KONINKLIJKE COMMISSIE VOOR DE UITGAVE DER OUDE WETTEN EN VERORDENINGEN VAN BELGIE. HANDELINGEN. (Editions in Flemish and French) 1848. irreg., vol.31, 1986. Commission Royale des Anciennes Lois et Ordonnances de Belgique - Koninklijke Commissie voor de Uitgave van de Oude Wetten en Verordeningen van Belgie, Ministere de la Justice, Place Poelaert, 1000 Brussels, Belgium. Ed. P.H. Godding. circ. 500.
Formerly: Commission des Anciennes Lois et Ordonnances de Belgique. Proces-Verbaux.

993   NZ ISSN 0045-7620
COMMONWEALTH AND COLONIAL HISTORY NEWSLETTER. 1969. s-a. NZ.$10. University of Canterbury, Department of History, Private Bag, Christchurch, New Zealand. FAX 03-364-2003. Ed. Luke Trainor. bk.rev.; bibl. circ. 150. **Document type:** newsletter.
—CCC.
Description: New research in history.

COMPARATIVE STUDIES IN SOCIETY AND HISTORY; an international quarterly. see *SOCIOLOGY*

COMTE DE JETTE BULLETIN/GRAAFSCHAP JETTE BULLETIN. see *ARCHAEOLOGY*

CONCORDIA HISTORICAL INSTITUTE QUARTERLY. see *RELIGIONS AND THEOLOGY — Protestant*

900   FR
CONFLUENTS. no.2, 1976. irreg. Societe d'Edition les Belles Lettres, 95 Bd. Raspail, 75006 Paris, France. illus. **Indexed:** M.L.A.

944 700   FR
CONNAISSANCE DE L'EURE. 1971. q. 120 F. Societe Libre de l'Eure, 2 rue de Verdun, 27025 Evreux, France. TEL 32-31-50-85. Ed. Jacques Auboin. bk.rev.; illus. circ. 1,000. (back issues avail.)
Description: Covers the history, culture, arts and publications from Eure.

977   IT
CONSPIRACY DIGEST; evidence-theory-speculation. 1976. q. $25. A-albionic Research, Box 20273, Ferndale, MI 48220. Ed. Lloyd Miller. adv.; bk.rev.; bibl. circ. 2,000. (looseleaf format; back issues avail.)
Description: Conspiracy scholarship; inquiry into non-pluralistic theories of society.

900 800   IT
CONTEMPORANEA; studi e testi. irreg., latest no.9. price varies. Angelo Longo Editore, Via Paolo Costa 33, P.O. Box 431, 48100 Ravenna, Italy. TEL 0544-217026. circ. 2,000. **Document type:** monographic series.

900   US ISSN 0277-1446
D1
CONTINUITY; a journal of history. 1980. s-a. $12. Young America's Foundation, F.M. Kirby Freedom Center, 110 Elden St., Herndon, VA 22070. TEL 703-318-9608. FAX 703-318-9122. Ed. Burton W. Folsom, Jr. adv.; bk.rev. circ. 700. (back issues avail.) **Indexed:** Amer.Hist.& Life, Hist.Abstr. **Document type:** academic/scholarly publication.
Description: Covers general history, thematic issues, including conservatism and history and the state of historiography.

CONTRIBUTIONS TO THE HISTORY OF LABOR AND SOCIETY. see *LABOR UNIONS*

909 917.306 US ISSN 0885-9159
CONTRIBUTIONS TO THE STUDY OF WORLD HISTORY. irreg. Greenwood Press, Inc. (Subsidiary of: Greenwood Publishing Group Inc.), 88 Post Rd. W., Box 5007, Westport, CT 06881-5007. TEL 203-226-3571. FAX 203-222-1502.
—BLDSC (3461.460500).

900   IT
CONTROSTORIA. 1989. bi-m. L.36000. Istituto per lo Studio della Storia Contemporanea d'Italia, Via Appia Antica 249B, 00178 Rome, Italy. TEL 06-7180406. FAX 06-7188001. Ed. Emilio Cavaterra. adv.

CORPUS VITREARUM MEDII AEVI. see *ART*

976 069.5   US
CORRAL DUST. 1977. q. $30. Panhandle-Plains Historical Society, Box 967, W.T.A.M.U., Canyon, TX 79016. TEL 806-656-2244. FAX 806-656-2250. Ed. Linda J. Moreland. circ. 1,000. (looseleaf format; back issues avail.) **Document type:** newsletter.

CORRIERE UNESCO. see *ANTHROPOLOGY*

972.86   CR ISSN 0034-9003
F1541
COSTA RICA. ARCHIVO NACIONAL. REVISTA. 1936. irreg., vol.52, 1988. $20. Archivo Nacional, Apartado 10217, San Jose, Costa Rica. TEL 34-75-69. FAX 34-73-12. Ed. Virginia Chacon Arias. charts; illus.; index. circ. 1,000.
Description: Contains articles on archivism and history topics.

974   US
COUNTY CIRCULAR. q. free. Heritage Commission, Morris County Courthouse, Morristown, NJ 07963-0900. TEL 201-829-8117.
Description: Informs readers on Morris County's past and announces forthcoming cultural events.

CRITICAL REVIEW. see *LITERATURE*

051   US
CRYPTIC SCHOLAR. 1991. s-a. $15. Northern Michigan University, Department of English, Marquette, MI 49855. Ed. Don J. McDermott.

CURRENT HISTORY; the monthly magazine of world affairs. see *POLITICAL SCIENCE*

CUYAHOGA REVIEW. see *LITERATURE*

900 320   US ISSN 0882-7095
D D R STUDIEN/EAST GERMAN STUDIES. (Text in English, German) irreg., vol.2, 1987. Peter Lang Publishing, Inc., 62 W. 45th St., 4th Fl., New York, NY 10036. TEL 212-302-6740. Ed. Richard Zipser. **Document type:** academic/scholarly publication.
—BLDSC (3646.449000).

900   GW ISSN 0011-5908
DAMALS; das aktuelle Geschichtsmagazin. 1969. m. DM.96.60 (foreign DM.102.60). Deutsche Verlags-Anstalt GmbH, Postfach 106012, 70049 Stuttgart, Germany. TEL 0711-2631-0. FAX 0711-2623685. Ed. Brigitte Roethlein. adv.: B&W page DM.3060, color page DM.4900; trim 175 x 245. bk.rev.; charts; illus.; index. circ. 50,000. **Document type:** academic/scholarly publication.

DANCE: CURRENT SELECTED RESEARCH. see *DANCE*

900   IS ISSN 0333-5151
DAPIM LICHEKER TIKUFAT HASHOAH. (Text in Hebrew) 1979. a. IS.16. University of Haifa, Institute for Research of the Holocaust Period, Hacarmel, Haifa 31999, Israel. TEL 972-4-348683. FAX 972-4-342101. Ed.Bd. bk.rev. circ. 1,000.

900   NE
DAT WAS DE TOESTAND IN DE WERELD. 1973. a. B.V. Uitgeversmaatschappij Bonaventura, Box 152, Amsterdam, Netherlands. illus.
Supersedes: Toestand in de Wereld.

943   GW ISSN 0012-1223
DEUTSCHES ARCHIV FUER ERFORSCHUNG DES MITTELALTERS. 1937. 2/yr. price varies. Boehlau Verlag GmbH, Theodor-Heuss-Str. 76, 51149 Cologne, Germany. TEL 02203-307021. FAX 02203-307349. Eds. Horst Fuhrmann, Hans Martin Schaller. adv.; bk.rev.; illus.; index. circ. 900. **Indexed:** Bibl.Cart., Bibl.Ling., M.L.A. **Document type:** academic/scholarly publication.
—BLDSC (3576.277800); SWETS. CCC.

900   AG ISSN 0012-1665
DEVENIR HISTORICO.* 1970. q. Correa 2957, Buenos Aires, Argentina. Ed. Jose Raed. bk.rev.; abstr.

930   FR
DIALOGUES D'HISTOIRE ANCIENNE. (Subseries of: Besancon, France. Universite. Annales Litteraires) 1969. a. price varies. (Universite de Besancon, Centre de Recherches d'Histoire Ancienne) Societe d'Edition les Belles Lettres, 95 Boulevard Raspail, 75006 Paris, France.

909   PK ISSN 0070-4873
DIGEST OF WORLD EVENTS. (Text in English) 1957. a. Rs.3.25. Modern Book Depot, Sialkot Cantt, Pakistan. Ed. Qayyum Wazirabadi. circ. 1,000.

DIMENSIONS: A JOURNAL OF HOLOCAUST STUDIES. see *ETHNIC INTERESTS*

900   IT
DIPARTIMENTO DI DISCIPLINE STORICHE. PUBBLICAZIONE. 1991. irreg., no.2, 1991. price varies. Liguori Editore s.r.l., Via Mezzocannone 19, 80134 Naples, Italy. TEL 081-5527139. **Document type:** monographic series.

900 327   US ISSN 0145-2096
E183.7
DIPLOMATIC HISTORY. 1977. q. $30 to individuals; institutions $50; students $10 (foreign $60). (Society for Historians of American Foreign Relations) Scholarly Resources, Inc., 104 Greenhill Ave., Wilmington, DE 19805. TEL 302-654-7713. FAX 302-654-3871. (Subscr. to: SHAFR Business Office, Department of History, Wright State University, Dayton, OH 45434) Ed. Michael Hogan. adv.: Full page $250. bk.rev. circ. 1,750. (back issues avail.) **Indexed:** Amer.Bibl.Slavic & E.Eur.Stud., Amer.Hist.& Life, Arts & Hum.Cit.Ind., Hist.Abstr., Mid.East: Abstr.& Ind. **Document type:** academic/scholarly publication.
—BLDSC (3589.355000); Faxon; UnCover; SWETS.
Description: Takes a scholarly look at the history of American diplomacy and foreign affairs, from the colonial period through the Vietnam era.
Refereed Serial

HISTORY

900   US
DIRECTORY OF AFFILIATED SOCIETIES (YEAR). a., latest 1994. $10 to non-members; members $7. American Historical Association, 400 A St., S.E., Washington, DC 20003-3889. TEL 202-544-2422. FAX 202-544-8307. Ed. Sharon Tune. **Document type:** directory.
    Description: Provides current information on the officers, activities, and publications of the 98 specialized historical societies that are officially recognized as affiliates of AHA.

900   US
DIRECTORY OF FEDERAL HISTORICAL PROGRAMS AND ACTIVITIES. irreg., latest 1990. $10 to non-members; members $7. American Historical Association, 400 A St., S.E., Washington, DC 20003-3889. TEL 202-544-2422. FAX 202-544-8307. (Co-publishers: Society for History in the Federal Government; National Coordinating Committee for the Promotion of History) Document type: directory.
    Description: Lists over 250 programs and agencies, with a program description, contacts, and a roster of current personnel for each. Over 1,500 public historians, archivists, and librarians in government offices are indexed.

920.72   US   ISSN 1048-4418
D14
DIRECTORY OF WOMEN HISTORIANS. 1975. irreg., latest 1988. $10 to non-members; members $7. American Historical Association, 400 A St., S.E., Washington, DC 20003-3889. TEL 202-544-2422. FAX 202-544-8307. **Document type:** directory.
    Description: Over 1,300 women historians are listed with work address, specializations, rank, and number of articles and books published.

900 711.5   US   ISSN 0300-7316
DISCOVERY (RICHMOND). 1969. a. membership. Association for the Preservation of Virginia Antiquities, 2300 E. Grace St., Richmond, VA 23223-7152. TEL 804-648-1889. Ed. Catherine A. Long. illus. circ. 4,500.

943   GW   ISSN 0012-4125
DITHMARSCHEN; Zeitschrift fuer Landeskunde und Heimatpflege. N.S. 1969. q. DM.16. (Verein fuer Dithmarscher Landeskunde) Westholsteinische Verlagsanstalt Boyens und Co., Am Wulf-Isebrand-Platz, 25746 Heide, Germany. TEL 0481-691-0. Ed.Bd. adv.; bk.rev.; charts; illus.; index. circ. 1,300.
    Formerly: Verein fuer Dithmarscher Landeskunde.

920   US
THE DOBIE CONNECTION. 1984. s-a. $2 per no. Dobie Clan of North America, 20001 Ridge Rd., North Royalton, OH 44133. TEL 216-237-6657. Ed. George N. Dobie II. circ. 250. (back issues avail.)

901   US
DOCUMENTARY REFERENCE COLLECTIONS. 1971. irreg. price varies. Greenwood Press, Inc. (Subsidiary of: Greenwood Publishing Group Inc.), 88 Post Rd. W., Box 5007, Westport, CT 06881-5007. TEL 203-226-3571. FAX 203-222-1502.

900   US   ISSN 0749-4831
DOCUMENTS IN IMPERIAL HISTORY. 1985. irreg. price varies. Greenwood Press, Inc. (Subsidiary of: Greenwood Publishing Group Inc.), 88 Post Rd. W., Box 5007, Westport, CT 06881-5007. TEL 203-226-3571. FAX 203-222-1502.
—BLDSC (3609.095000).

900   US
DOCUMENTS OF MODERN HISTORY. irreg. price varies. St. Martin's Press, 175 Fifth Ave., New York, NY 10010.

DRESS. see *CLOTHING TRADE — Fashions*

900   GW
DRITTE WELT MATERIALIEN. 1973. s-a. DM.30. Informationszentrum Dritte Welt Hannover, Postfach 1129, 37189 Katlenburg, Germany. TEL 05552-322. FAX 05552-396. Ed. Martin Weskott. circ. 500. Document type: newsletter.

900   US   ISSN 0070-7562
DUMBARTON OAKS TEXTS. (English translation of original Greek) 1968. irreg. price varies. (Dumbarton Oaks Center for Byzantine Studies) J.J. Augustin, Inc., Locust Valley, NY 11560. TEL 506-676-1510.

DURHAM UNIVERSITY JOURNAL. see *LITERATURE*

943.8   PL   ISSN 0419-8824
DZIEJE NAJNOWSZE; kwartalnik poswiecony historii XX wieku. (Text in Polish; summaries in English) 1969. q. $54. Polska Akademia Nauk, Instytut Historii, Rynek Starego Miasta 29-31, 00-272 Warsaw, Poland. (Dist. by: Ars Polona-Ruch, Krakowskie Przedmiescie 7, Warsaw, Poland) Ed. Cz. Madajczyk.
    Description: Polish and general history of the 20th century.

E L H. (English Literary History) see *LITERATURE*

ECOLE FRANCAISE DE ROME. COLLECTION. see *ARCHAEOLOGY*

930   AT   ISSN 0085-0187
EDUBBA; studies ancient history. 1967. a. price varies. University of Sydney, Department of History, Sydney, N.S.W. 2006, Australia. (Co-sponsor: Ancient History Society) Ed.Bd. bk.rev. circ. 500.

EDUCATIONAL ADMINISTRATION AND HISTORY MONOGRAPHS. see *EDUCATION — School Organization And Administration*

EIGHTEENTH CENTURY: A CURRENT BIBLIOGRAPHY. see *BIBLIOGRAPHIES*

900 800   US   ISSN 0013-2586
NX452
EIGHTEENTH-CENTURY STUDIES. 1967. q. $52. American Society for Eighteenth-Century Studies, c/o Jeffrey Smitten, Exec. Sec., USU CC108, Utah State Univ., Logan, UT 84322-3730. TEL 801-797-4065. Ed.Bd. adv.; bk.rev.; illus. circ. 3,000. **Indexed:** Abstr.Engl.Stud., Amer.Hist.& Life, Arts & Hum.Cit.Ind., Bk.Rev.Ind. (1987-), Child.Bk.Rev.Ind. (1987-), Curr.Cont., Hist.Abstr., Hum.Ind., Ind.Bk.Rev.Hum., M.L.A., RILA. **Document type:** academic/scholarly publication.
—BLDSC (3665.250000); Faxon; UnCover; SWETS.
    Description: Addresses English and American literature, classics, drama, history, religion, philosophy, music, science and political science.

EIRE - IRELAND; a journal of Irish studies. see *HUMANITIES: COMPREHENSIVE WORKS*

ENGINEERS AND ENGINES MAGAZINE. see *TRANSPORTATION — Railroads*

909   GW
ENGLISCH AMERIKANISCHE STUDIEN; Zeitschrift fuer Unterricht, Wissenschaft und Politik. (Text in English and German) 1979. 4/yr. Redaktion "East", Herrn Dieter Keiner, Postfach 2565, 48012 Muenster, Germany. **Indexed:** Lang.Teach.& Ling.Abstr.

900 320   UK   ISSN 0262-7612
DA485
ENLIGHTENMENT AND DISSENT. 1982. a. £8.50 to individuals (overseas £9 ($17)); institutions £17.40 ($32). c/o Prof. D.O. Thomas, 31 N. Parade, University College of Wales, Aberystwyth, Dyfed SY23 2JN, Wales. TEL 0970-623808. Eds. Martin Fitzpatrick, D.O. Thomas. adv.; bk.rev. circ. 250. **Indexed:** Rel.& Theol.Abstr. (1989-).
    Formerly: Price-Priestley Newsletter.

900   AG
ENTREPASADOS; revista de historia. 1991. s-a. Arevalo 2240, 1425 Buenos Aires, Argentina. Dir. Juan Suriano.

EPHEMERIDES THEOLOGICAE LOVANIENSES; revue de theologie et de droit canon de Louvain/Leuvens tijdschrift voor theologie en kerkelijk recht/Louvain journal of theological and canonical studies. see *RELIGIONS AND THEOLOGY — Roman Catholic*

900   GW   ISSN 0071-0989
EPIGRAPHISCHE STUDIEN. 1967. irreg., vol.15, 1993. Rheinland Verlag GmbH, Abtei Brauweiler, Postfach 2140, 50250 Pulheim, Germany. TEL 02234-8051. FAX 02234-82503. (Dist. by: Dr. Rudolf Habelt GmbH, Am Buchenhang 1, 53115 Bonn, Germany. TEL 0228-232016. FAX 0228-232017) **Indexed:** Br.Archaeol.Abstr. **Document type:** monographic series.

EPOCHE; journal of the history of religions at U.C.L.A. see *RELIGIONS AND THEOLOGY*

ERBA D'ARNO. see *LITERATURE*

ERBA D'ARNO. QUADERNI; supplemento a Erba d'Arno. see *LITERATURE*

900 011 581 551   GW
ERLANGER BAUSTEINE ZUR FRAENKISCHEN HEIMATFORSCHUNG. 1954. a. DM.30 membership. Heimat- und Geschichtsverein Erlangen e.V., Marktplatz 1, 91054 Erlangen, Germany. Ed.Bd. bk.rev. (back issues avail.)

900   HU   ISSN 0071-1233
ERTEKEZESEK A TORTENETI TUDOMANYOK KOREBOL. 1857. irreg., vol.115, 1992. price varies. (Magyar Tudomanyos Akademia) Akademiai Kiado, Publishing House of the Hungarian Academy of Sciences, P.O. Box 245, H-1519 Budapest, Hungary. TEL 181-2134. FAX 166-6466. TELEX 22-6228 AKNYO H.

900   US   ISSN 0071-1411
ESSAYS IN HISTORY. 1954. a. $5. University of Virginia, Corcoran Department of History, Charlottesville, VA 22903. TEL 804-924-4784. Ed. Frank Edgar Grizzard, Jr. cum.index: vols.1-20. circ. 250. (reprint service avail. from UMI) **Document type:** academic/scholarly publication.
—UMI.

ESSAYS IN PUBLIC WORKS HISTORY. see *PUBLIC ADMINISTRATION*

ESTUDIOS PUBLICOS. see *BUSINESS AND ECONOMICS — Economic Situation And Conditions*

ESTUDOS ITALIANOS EM PORTUGAL. see *ART*

ETHNOHISTORY; a quarterly journal relating to the past of culture and societies in all areas of the world, emphasizing the use of documentary and field materials and historiographic and anthropological approaches. see *ANTHROPOLOGY*

900   HU   ISSN 0071-2108
ETUDES HISTORIQUES. (Text in English, French, German, Russian) 1960. quinquennial. (Magyar Tudomanyos Akademia) Akademiai Kiado, Publishing House of the Hungarian Academy of Sciences, P.O. Box 245, H-1519 Budapest, Hungary. TEL 181-2134. FAX 166-6466. TELEX 22-6228 AKNYO H. **Indexed:** Amer.Hist.& Life, Hist.Abstr.
    Supersedes: International Congress of Historical Sciences. Proceedings.

ETUDES INTERNATIONALES. see *POLITICAL SCIENCE — International Relations*

ETUDES RURALES; revue trimestrielle d'histoire, geographie, sociologie et economie des campagnes. see *SOCIOLOGY*

EX LIBRIS (PORTSMOUTH). see *PUBLISHING AND BOOK TRADE*

900 330   US   ISSN 0014-6641
FACTS ON FILE WORLD NEWS DIGEST WITH INDEX. 1940. w. $605. Facts on File, Inc., 460 Park Ave. S., New York, NY 10016. TEL 212-683-2244. Ed. Steve Orlofsky. cum.index: 1946-1985. circ. 8,900. (looseleaf format; also avail. in microfiche; magnetic tape; back issues avail.)
● Also available online. Vendor(s): DIALOG Information Services, Inc. (File no.264); Mead Data Central, Inc.
Also available on CD-ROM.
—SWETS.

FACULTES DE DROIT ET DE LA SCIENCE JURIDIQUE. REVUE D'HISTOIRE. see *LAW*

930 914   IT
LA FENICE. 1983. irreg., no.8, 1987. price varies. (Universita di Venezia, Dipartimento di Scienze Storico-Archeologiche e Orientalistiche) L'Erma di Bretschneider, Via Cassiodoro 19, 00193 Rome, Italy. TEL 06-687-41-27. FAX 06-687-41-29. Ed. Gustavo Traversari.

FERRUM; Nachrichten aus der Eisenbibliothek. see *METALLURGY*

900 200 US ISSN 0884-5379
FIDES ET HISTORIA. 1968. 3/yr. $15. Conference on Faith and History, c/o Richard V. Pierard, Dept. of History, Indiana State University, Terre Haute, IN 47809. TEL 812-232-2707. Ed. Frank C. Roberts. adv.; bk.rev. circ. 850. (also avail. in microform from UMI; back issues avail.) **Indexed:** Amer.Hist.& Life, CERDIC, Chr.Per.Ind., Hist.Abstr., Old Test.Abstr., Rel.& Theol.Abstr. (1971-), Rel.Ind.One. **Document type:** academic/scholarly publication.
—UMI.
Description: Publishes scholarly articles dealing with questions that relate to the interaction between Christian faith and historical developments.
Refereed Serial

FILM & HISTORY. see *MOTION PICTURES*

FILM HISTORY; an international journal. see *MOTION PICTURES*

025 946.9 PO ISSN 0373-8531
FILMOTECA ULTRAMARINA PORTUGUESA. BOLETIM. 1954. irreg. price varies. Instituto de Investigacao Cientifica Tropical, Centro de Estudos de Historia Cartografia Antiga, Rua Jau 54, 1300 Lisbon, Portugal. TEL 364-5321. FAX 363-1460. (Subscr. to: Centro de Documentacao e Informacao, Rua Jau 47, 1300 Lisbon, Portugal) bibl. circ. 1,000. **Document type:** academic/scholarly publication.
Description: Contains documents microfilmed from other archives related to the ancient Portuguese colonies.

930 PL ISSN 0015-1815
FILOMATA. 1929. bi-m. (Ministerstwo Edukacji Narodowej) Wydawnictwo Naukowe P W N, Ul. Miodowa 10, 00-251 Warsaw, Poland. TEL 48-22-312738. FAX 48-22-267163. TELEX 813763 PWN PL. Ed. Jozef Korpanty. bk.rev.; illus.; index. circ 1,260.

FILOSOFIA POLITICA. see *POLITICAL SCIENCE*

900 790.13 920 US ISSN 0882-3715
FINEST HOUR. (Supplement avail.: Churchill Handbook) 1968. q. $25. International Churchill Society, 1847 Stonewood Dr., Baton Rouge, CA 70816. TEL 603-746-4433. FAX 603-746-4260. Ed. Richard M. Langworth. adv.; bk.rev.; index. circ. 2,000. **Document type:** bibliography.
Description: Contains biographical, bibliographical, historical articles and columns on the life and times of Sir Winston Churchill.

FLAG BULLETIN. see *GENEALOGY AND HERALDRY*

FLORIDA MUSEUM NATURAL HISTORY. BULLETIN. BIOLOGICAL SCIENCES. see *BIOLOGY*

320 SA
FOCUS ON POLITICS. irreg., no.2, 1976. price varies. University of the Orange Free State, Institute for Contemporary History - Universiteit van die Oranje-Vrystaat, Instituut vir Eietydse Geskiedenis, P.O. Box 2320, Bloemfontein 9300, South Africa. FAX 27-51-473416. Ed.Bd.

900 IT ISSN 0392-0003
FONDAZIONE BASSO. ANNALI.* 1975. a. Fondazione Basso, Via della Dogana Vecchia 5, 00186 Rome, Italy. Ed. Alberto Caracciolo. circ. 700.

321.07 IT
▼**FORME DELL'UTOPIA.** (Text in English, French, Italian) 1992. irreg. price varies. (Universita di Bologna, Centro Interdipartimentale di Ricerca sull'Utopia) Angelo Longo Editore, Via Paolo Costa 33, 48100 Ravenna, Italy. TEL 0544-217026. Ed. Vita Fortunati. circ. 3,000. **Document type:** monographic series.
Description: Contains studies on the history of utopia.

943.6 AU
FORSCHUNGEN UND BEITRAEGE ZUR WIENER STADTGESCHICHTE. 1978. irreg. (2-3/yr.) price varies. Verein fuer Geschichte der Stadt Wien, Rathaus, A-1082 Vienna, Austria. TEL 4000-84815. Ed. Felix Czeike. circ. 2,100.

930 GW ISSN 0071-7665
HT857
FORSCHUNGEN ZUR ANTIKEN SKLAVEREI. 1967. irreg., vol.24, 1991. price varies. (Akademie der Wissenschaften und der Literatur, Mainz, Kommission fuer Geschichte des Altertums) Franz Steiner Verlag Wiesbaden GmbH, Birkenwaldstr. 44, 70191 Stuttgart, Germany. TEL 0711-2582-0. FAX 0711-2582290. TELEX 723636-DAZ-D. (Subscr. to: Postfach 101061, 70009 Stuttgart, Germany) Eds. Joseph Vogt, Heinz Bellen. **Document type:** monographic series.

FORTITUDINE; newsletter of the Marine Corps historical program. see *MILITARY*

DER FREIWILLIGE. see *MILITARY*

930 GW
FREUNDE DER BAYERISCHEN VOR- UND FRUEHGESCHICHTE. MITTEILUNGEN. 1976. irreg. (3-4/yr.). membership. Freunde der Bayerischen Vor- und Fruehgeschichte e.V., Von-der-Tann-Str. 2, 80539 Munich, Germany. TEL 089-28627225. FAX 089-28627304. circ. 600. **Document type:** newsletter.

FUTURES RESEARCH QUARTERLY. see *SCIENCES: COMPREHENSIVE WORKS*

909 GW ISSN 0173-539X
G - GESCHICHTE MIT PFIFF. 1979. m. DM.63.60. Johann Michael Sailer Verlag GmbH, Aeusserer-Laufer-Platz 22, 90403 Nuernberg, Germany. Ed. Franz Metzger. adv.; bk.rev.; charts; illus. circ. 40,000. (back issues avail.) **Document type:** bulletin.
—CCC.
Incorporates (1979-1991): Journal Geschichte; Which was formerly: Journal fuer Geschichte (ISSN 0171-953X)
Description: Monthly views of world history in single topic issues.

909 II ISSN 0016-4437
DS481.G3
GANDHI MARG. (Text in Hindi) 1957-1976; resumed 1979. m. $20. Gandhi Peace Foundation, 221-223 Deen Dayal Upadhyaya Marg, New Delhi 110002, India. Ed.Bd. adv.; bk.rev.; index. circ. 1,100. (also avail. in microfilm from UMI; reprint service avail. from UMI) **Indexed:** Amer.Hist.& Life, Hist.Abstr., M.L.A.

GANITA BHARATI. see *MATHEMATICS*

969.8 MF ISSN 1143-9300
GAZETTE DES ILES DE LA MER DES INDES. (Text in French) 1986. irreg. $30 for 10 nos. La Sentinelle Ltee, 3 rue Brown Sequard, Port Louis, Mauritius. TEL 212-1826. FAX 208-8174. Ed. Yvan Martial. **Indexed:** P.L.E.S.A.
Description: Covers the history of Mauritius and other Indian Ocean islands.

900 UK ISSN 0953-5233
GENDER AND HISTORY. 1989. 3/yr. £21($42.50) to individuals; institutions £60($95). Basil Blackwell Ltd., 108 Cowley Rd., Oxford OX4 1JF, England. TEL 0865-791100. FAX 0865-791347. TELEX 837022 OXBOOK G. Ed. Leonore Davidoff. **Indexed:** Mult.Ed.Abstr., Wom.Stud.Abstr. (1990-).
—BLDSC (4096.401350); Faxon; SWETS. **CCC.**
Description: Addresses the ways in which societies have been shaped by studying the history of gender relations, men and masculinity, and women and femininity.

GENEALOGICAL SOCIETIES & HISTORICAL SOCIETIES IN THE UNITED STATES. see *GENEALOGY AND HERALDRY*

900 296 US
GENERATION AFTER. 1980. q. $5 to non-members. T G A, Inc. (The Generation After), 2205 E. 29th St., Brooklyn, New York, NY 11229. TEL 718-743-6640. Ed. John Ranz. bk.rev. circ. 600.

900 GW
GESCHICHTE (ESSEN); historisches Magazin. 1974. 6/yr. DM.56. (Historiographisches Institut GmbH (Solothurn)) Stamm-Werbung GmbH und Co., Dinnendahlstr. 16, 45136 Essen, Germany. Ed. Helmut von Frisching. adv.; bibl.; charts; illus. circ. 67,000.

GESCHICHTE BETRIFFT UNS. see *EDUCATION*

900 GW ISSN 0016-9056
D1
GESCHICHTE IN WISSENSCHAFT UND UNTERRICHT. 1950. m. DM.144. (Verband der Geschichtslehrer Deutschlands) Erhard Friedrich Verlag GmbH, Im Brande 17, 30926 Seelze, Germany. TEL 0511-40004-0. (Subscr. to: Postfach 100150, 30917 Seelze, Germany) Ed.Bd. adv.; bk.rev.; bibl.; cum.index. circ. 6,000. **Indexed:** Amer.Hist.& Life, Hist.Abstr. **Document type:** academic/scholarly publication.
—SWETS. **CCC.**

900 SA
GISTER EN VANDAG/YESTERDAY AND TODAY. (Text in Afrikaans and English) 1981. 2/yr. R.25 (effective 1993). South African Society for History Teaching, c/o P.H. Kapp, Ed., P.O. Box 7209, Stellenbosch 7600, South Africa. TEL 27-21-8082179. FAX 27-21-8034336. bk.rev.; charts; illus. circ. 5,000. **Document type:** academic/scholarly publication.
Supersedes (1956-1981): Historia Junior (ISSN 0439-2116)

930 GW ISSN 0344-385X
GOETTINGER MISZELLEN. 1972. bi-m. DM.8 per no. Universitaet Goettingen, Seminar fuer Agyptologie und Koptologie, Bibliothek, Prinzenstr. 21, 37073 Goettingen, Germany. bk.rev. **Indexed:** Bibl.Ling. **Document type:** academic/scholarly publication.

900 US
GRANTS, FELLOWSHIPS, AND PRIZES OF INTEREST TO HISTORIANS (YEAR). a. $10 to non-members; members $8. American Historical Association, 400 A St., S.E., Washington, DC 20003-3889. TEL 202-544-2422. FAX 202-544-8307. **Document type:** directory.
Description: Provides information on over 400 history-oriented sources of humanities grants, fellowships, prizes, internships, and awards from the undergraduate to senior postdoctorial level.

900 UK ISSN 0533-9685
GREAT BRITAIN. ROYAL COMMISSION ON HISTORICAL MANUSCRIPTS. SECRETARY'S REPORT TO THE COMMISSIONERS. 1968. a. price varies. H.M.S.O., P.O. Box 276, London SW8 5DT, England. **Document type:** government publication.
—CCC.

900 990 387 AT ISSN 0156-8698
VK15
THE GREAT CIRCLE. 1979. s-a. Aus.$30 to individuals; institutions Aus.$40. Australian Association of Maritime History, c/o G.R. Henning, Ed., Dept. of Economic History, University of New England, Armidale, N.S.W. 2351, Australia. FAX 067-73-3596. (Subscr. to: Peter Ridgway, 19 Connaught St., Forrestfield, W.A. 6058, Australia. TEL 09-222-7548) adv.; bk.rev.; cum.index: 1979-1984. circ. 450. (back issues avail.) **Indexed:** Amer.Hist.& Life, Hist.Abstr. **Document type:** academic/scholarly publication.

909 031 US ISSN 0072-7288
AY59
GREAT IDEAS TODAY. 1961. a. $29.95. Encyclopaedia Britannica, Inc., 310 S. Michigan Ave, Chicago, IL 60604. TEL 312-347-7000. FAX 312-347-7914. TELEX 190203. Ed. John Van Doren.

GREEK ORTHODOX THEOLOGICAL REVIEW. see *RELIGIONS AND THEOLOGY — Eastern Orthodox*

355 FR ISSN 0984-2292
GUERRES MONDIALES ET CONFLITS CONTEMPORAINS. 1950. q. 520 F. (foreign 585 F.). Presses Universitaires de France, Departement des Revues, 14 Avenue du Bois-de-l'Epine, B.P.90, 91003 Evry Cedex, France. TEL 1-60-77-82-05. FAX 1-60-79-20-45. TELEX PUF 600 474 F. Ed. Guy Pedroncini. bibl.; charts. (also avail. in microform from UMI; reprint service avail. from KTO) **Indexed:** Amer.Hist.& Life, Arts & Hum.Cit.Ind., Curr.Cont., Hist.Abstr.
—CCC.
Formerly (until no. 125): Revues d'Histoire de la Deuxieme Guerre Mondiale (ISSN 0035-2314)
Description: Presents opposing points of view from critics and historians on World War II and conflicts up to the present day.

HISTORY

965
F296
US ISSN 0892-9025
GULF COAST HISTORICAL REVIEW. 1985. 2/yr. $14. University of South Alabama, History Department, Humanities 344, Mobile, AL 36688. TEL 205-460-6210. FAX 205-460-6750. Ed. Michael V. Thomason. adv.; bk.rev. circ. 500. **Document type:** academic/scholarly publication.
 Description: Articles on the history of the Gulf Coast for a general audience.

GUTENBERG - GESELLSCHAFT. KLEINE DRUCKE. see *PRINTING*

930 GW ISSN 0072-9175
HABELTS DISSERTATIONSDRUCKE. REIHE ALTE GESCHICHTE. 1963. irreg., no.38, 1993. price varies. Dr. Rudolf Habelt GmbH, Am Buchenhang 1, 53115 Bonn, Germany. TEL 0228-232016. FAX 0228-232017. Ed.Bd. **Document type:** monographic series.

930 GW ISSN 0072-9213
HABELTS DISSERTATIONSDRUCKE. REIHE MITTELALTERLICHE GESCHICHTE. 1965. irreg., no.2, 1981. price varies. Dr. Rudolf Habelt GmbH, Am Buchenhang 1, 53115 Bonn, Germany. TEL 0228-232016. FAX 0228-232017.

HADTORTENELMI KOZLEMENYEK. see *MILITARY*

900 UK ISSN 0951-6158
HAKLUYT SOCIETY. EXTRA SERIES. 1903. irreg., vol. 45, 1993. price varies. Hakluyt Society, c/o British Library, Great Russell St., London WC1B 3DG, England. TEL 0986-86359. FAX 0986-868181. illus, maps. (also avail. in microfiche; reprint service avail. from KTO) **Document type:** monographic series.
 Description: Scholarly editions of accounts of travels and expeditions of geographical and ethnographic significance, with commentary.

900 UK ISSN 0072-9396
HAKLUYT SOCIETY. WORKS IN THE ORDINARY SERIES. SECOND SERIES. Key Title: Works Issued by the Hakluyt Society. 1847; N.S. 1899. 2/yr. £18($40) membership. Hakluyt Society, c/o British Library, Great Russell St., London WC1B 3DG, England. TEL 0986-86359. FAX 0986-868181. index. circ. 2,400. (also avail. in microform from CIS; reprint service avail. from KTO) **Document type:** monographic series.
 Description: Publishes scholarly editions of important historical documents recording voyages, travels, navigations and other geographical and ethnographic subjects, with annotations, additional illustrations and commentary.

900 US ISSN 0073-0521
HARVARD HISTORICAL MONOGRAPHS. 1932. irreg., no.74, 1987. price varies. (Harvard University, Department of History) Harvard University Press, 79 Garden St., Cambridge, MA 02138. TEL 617-495-2600. FAX 617-495-5898. **Document type:** monographic series.
 Refereed Serial

900 US ISSN 0073-053X
HARVARD HISTORICAL STUDIES. 1886. irreg., no.111, 1992. price varies. (Harvard University, Department of History) Harvard University Press, 79 Garden St., Cambridge, MA 02138. TEL 617-495-2600. FAX 617-495-5898. **Document type:** monographic series.
 —BLDSC (4267.160000).
 Refereed Serial

HARVEST BOOK SERIES. see *SOCIOLOGY*

930 GW ISSN 0930-1208
HEIDELBERGER ALTHISTORISCHE BEITRAEGE UND EPIGRAPHISCHE STUDIEN. irreg., vol.15, 1994. price varies. Franz Steiner Verlag Wiesbaden GmbH, Birkenwaldstr. 44, 70191 Stuttgart, Germany. TEL 0711-2582-0. FAX 0711-2582290. TELEX 723636-DAZ-D. (Subscr. to: Postfach 101061, 70009 Stuttgart, Germany) Ed. Geza Alfoeldy. **Document type:** monographic series.

900 GW
HEIMATBUCH DES KREISES VIERSEN. 1950. a. DM.12. Kreisverwaltung Viersen, Kulturamt, Thomasstr. 20, 47906 Kempen, Germany. circ. 15,000. (back issues avail.) **Document type:** bulletin.

949.35 LU ISSN 0018-0270
HEMECHT; Zeitschrift fuer Luxemburger Geschichte/revue d'histoire luxembourgeoise. (Text in French, German) 1895. q. 800 Fr. Éditions Saint Paul, S.A., 2 rue Christophe Plantin, L-2988 Luxembourg, Luxembourg. TEL 49-93-501. Ed. Paul Margue. bk.rev.; bibl.; illus.; index. circ. 2,500. **Indexed:** Br.Archaeol.Abstr., Numis.Lit.
 —SWETS.

HER OWN WORDS; women's history & literature media. see *WOMEN'S STUDIES*

930 NE ISSN 0165-8158
HERMENEUS; Tijdschrift voor de Antieke Cultuur. 1929. 5/yr. fl.95. (Nederlands Klassiek Verbond) Uitgeverij de Doelenpers, Ramen 36, 1811 LC Alkmaar, Netherlands. TEL 31-72-152222.
 —SWETS.

HESPERIS - TAMUDA. see *ORIENTAL STUDIES*

900 UK ISSN 0958-3637
HINDSIGHT G C S E MODERN HISTORY REVIEW. 1990. 3/yr. £13.50 (foreign £22). Philip Allan Publishers Ltd., Deddington, Oxfordshire OX15 OSE, England. TEL 0869-38652. FAX 0869-38803.

HISPANIA SACRA. see *RELIGIONS AND THEOLOGY*

909
D1
FR ISSN 0182-2411
HISTOIRE. (Text in French; summaries in English) 1978. m. 310 F. Societe d'Editions Scientifiques, 57 rue de Seine, 75280 Paris Cedex 06, France. TEL 43-54-32-84. FAX 46-34-75-08. Ed. Stephane Khemis. adv.; bk.rev.; charts; illus.; index. circ. 59,000. (reprint service avail. from ISI) **Indexed:** Amer.Hist.& Life (until 1991), Arts & Hum.Cit.Ind., Curr.Cont., Hist.Abstr. (until 1991), Pt.de Rep. (1981-).
 —BLDSC (4316.006050); SWETS. **CCC.**

090 SZ ISSN 0073-2419
HISTOIRE ET CIVILISATION DU LIVRE. 1966. irreg., no.21, 1992. price varies. (Ecole Pratique des Hautes Etudes, Centre de Recherches d'Histoire et de Philologie, FR) Librairie Droz S.A., 11, rue Massot, CH-1211 Geneva 12, Switzerland. TEL 022-33466666. FAX 022-3472391. circ. 1,000. **Document type:** monographic series.
 —**CCC.**

HISTOIRE ET MAQUETTISME. see *HOBBIES*

900
HN1
CN ISSN 0018-2257
HISTOIRE SOCIALE/SOCIAL HISTORY. (Text in English, French) 1968. 2/yr. Can.$25 to individuals; institutions Can.$37.50; students Can.$20. University of Ottawa, Department of History, 155 Seraphin Marion St., Ottawa, ON K1N 6N5, Canada. TEL 613-564-3417. FAX 613-564-9599. Eds. Chad Gaffield, Gordon Darroch. adv.: B&W page Can.$350. bk.rev.; abstr.; bibl. circ. 650. (back issues avail.) **Indexed:** Amer.Bibl.Slavic & E.Eur.Stud.; Amer.Hist.& Life, Arts & Hum.Cit.Ind., Curr.Cont., Hist.Abstr., Mid.East: Abstr.& Ind., Pt.de Rep. (1979-), SSCI, Stud.Wom.Abstr. **Document type:** academic/scholarly publication.
 —BLDSC (8318.094900); UnCover.
 Description: Publishes studies pertaining to various types of social phenomena, whether cultural, political, economic or demographic, without methodological, temporal or geographic restrictions.

900 FR ISSN 0018-2281
HISTORIA.* 1946. m. 249 F. (foreign 291 F.). Librairie Jules Tallandier, 61 rue de la Tombe Issoire, 75677 Paris Cedex 14, France. TEL 43-20-14-33. TELEX 210 311. adv.; bk.rev.; illus. circ. 320,000. **Indexed:** Amer.Hist.& Life, Hist.Abstr., Mid.East: Abstr.& Ind., Pt.de Rep. (1979-).
 —BLDSC (4316.035000).

900 GW ISSN 0018-2311
D51
HISTORIA; Zeitschrift fuer Alte Geschichte/revue d'histoire ancienne/journal of ancient history/rivista di storia antica. (Text in English, French, German and Italian) 1952. q. DM.198 (supplements priced individually). Franz Steiner Verlag Stuttgart GmbH, Birkenwaldstr. 44, 70191 Stuttgart, Germany. TEL 0711-2582-0. FAX 0711-2582290. TELEX 723636-DAZ-D. (Subscr. to: Postfach 101061, 70009 Stuttgart, Germany) Ed.Bd. adv.; index. circ. 1,200. (back issues avail.) **Indexed:** Bibl.Ling., Curr.Cont. **Document type:** academic/scholarly publication.
 —Faxon; UnCover; SWETS. **CCC.**

968 SA ISSN 0018-229X
HISTORIA. (Text and summaries in Afrikaans, English) 1956. 2/yr. R.25 (effective 1993). Historical Association of South Africa - Historiese Genootskap van Suid-Afrika, Department of History & Cultural History, University of Pretoria, Pretoria 0002, South Africa. TEL 27-12-420-2323. FAX 27-12-432-185. Ed. O.J.O. Ferreira. adv. contact: J.E.H. Grobler. bk.rev.; bibl.; illus. circ. 600. **Indexed:** Amer.Hist.& Life, Hist.Abstr., Ind.S.A.Per. **Document type:** academic/scholarly publication.

900 BL ISSN 0101-9074
CODEN: HISPDZ
HISTORIA. (Text in Portuguese; summaries in English, Portuguese) 1982. a. $30 or exchange basis. Universidade Estadual Paulista, Av. Vicente Ferreira, 1278, Caixa Postal 603, 17515-901 Marilia SP, Brazil. TEL 0144-33-1844. FAX 0144-22-2504. TELEX 111 9016 UJME BR. (And: Caixa Postal 335, 19800 Assis, SP, Brazil) bk.rev.; charts. circ. 1,000. **Indexed:** Amer.Hist.& Life, Hist.Abstr. **Document type:** academic/scholarly publication.
 Formed by the 1982 merger of: Anais de Historia (ISSN 0100-2139); Estudos Historicos.
 Description: Contains original articles on the history of the Americas and Europe, with emphasis on Brazil, Portugal and the Caribbean.

900 GW ISSN 0341-0056
HISTORIA. EINZELSCHRIFTEN. (Supplement to Historia) (Text in English, French, and German) irreg., vol.84, 1993. price varies. Franz Steiner Verlag Wiesbaden GmbH, Birkenwaldstr. 44, 70191 Stuttgart, Germany. TEL 0711-2582-0. FAX 0711-2582290. TELEX 723636-DAZ-D. (Subscr. to: Postfach 101061, 70009 Stuttgart, Germany) Ed.Bd. **Document type:** monographic series.

900 SP
HISTORIA 16. 1976. m. Informacion y Revistas, S.A., Hermanos Garcia Noblejas 41, 6o, 28037 Madrid, Spain. TEL 91-4072700. FAX 91-4075850. Dir. Jose David Solar. circ. 28,000.

900 BL ISSN 0103-409X
HISTORIA E PERSPECTIVAS. s-a. Universidade Federal de Uberlandia, Curso de Historia, Av. Universitaria s/n Bloco H sala 28, Campus Santa Monica, 38400 Uberlandia MG, Brazil. TEL 034-235-2888. **Document type:** academic/scholarly publication.
 Formerly (until 1987): Universidade Federal de Uberlandia. Curso de Historia. Boletim da Coordenacao.

HISTORIA HOSPITALIUM. see *HOSPITALS*

909 SP
HISTORIA UNIVERSAL. 1979. irreg., no.14, 1984. 5570 ptas. (Universidad de Navarra, Facultad de Filosofia y Letras) Ediciones Universidad de Navarra, S.A., Apdo. 396, 31080 Pamplona, Spain. TEL 94 825 6850.

900 SP ISSN 0018-2354
D1
HISTORIA Y VIDA. 1968. m. 4632 ptas.($51) (effective 1993). Tallers 62 y 64, 08001 Barcelona, Spain. TEL 93-3010404. FAX 93-3010532. Ed. Josep Tomas Cabot. adv.; bk.rev.; abstr.; illus.; index. circ. 25,000. (tabloid format; back issues avail.) **Indexed:** Amer.Hist.& Life (until 1992), Hist.Abstr. (until 1992). **Document type:** consumer publication.

900   FI   ISSN 0018-2362
HISTORIALLINEN AIKAKAUSKIRJA. 1903. q. FIM 160. Suomen Historiallinen Seura - Finnish Historical Society, Arkadiankatu 16 B 28, 00100 Helsinki 10, Finland. TEL 90-440-369. FAX 90-441-468. (Co-sponsor: Historian Ystavain Liitto) Ed. Ohto Manninen. adv.; bk.rev.; bibl.; index, cum.index (1903-1980). circ. 2,100. **Indexed:** Amer.Hist.& Life, Hist.Abstr.

900   FI   ISSN 0359-3223
HISTORIALLINEN KIRJASTO. 1929. irreg., no.21, 1988. Historian Ystavain Liitto - Society of the Friends of History, Add. Kaupinkatu 22 A 5, 33500 Tampere, Finland.

900   UK   ISSN 0265-1076
HISTORIAN. 1983. 4/yr. membership. Historical Association, 59a Kennington Park Rd., London SE11 4JH, England. TEL 071-735-3901. Ed. C.J. Wrigley. circ. 9,000. **Document type:** academic/scholarly publication.
—BLDSC (4316.074400); Faxon.

900   US   ISSN 0018-2370
D1
THE HISTORIAN (TEMPE); a journal of history. 1938. q. $22.50 to non-members; members $20 (effective 1993). Phi Alpha Theta International Honor Society in History, c/o Roger Adelson, Ed., History Dept., Arizona State Univ., Tempe, AZ 85287-2501. TEL 602-965-8364. FAX 602-965-0310. (Alt. addr.: c/o D.B. Hoffman, 2333 Liberty St., Allentown, PA 18104. TEL 215-433-4140) adv.; bk.rev.; cum.index every 5 vols. circ. 15,500. (also avail. in microform from UMI; reprint service avail. from UMI) **Indexed:** Amer.Hist.& Life & Hum.Cit.Ind., Bk.Rev.Ind. (1980-), Br.Archaeol.Abstr., Child.Bk.Rev.Ind. (1980-), Curr.Cont., Hist.Abstr., Hum.Ind., Mag.Ind., Mid.East:Abstr.& Ind. **Document type:** academic/scholarly publication.
—BLDSC (4316.074000); Faxon; UnCover; UMI.

900   FI   ISSN 0439-2183
HISTORIAN AITTA. 1929. irreg., latest no.21, 1989. Historian Ystavain Liitto - Society of the Friends of History, Add. Kaupinkatu 22 A 5, 33500 Tampere, Finland. **Indexed:** Amer.Hist.& Life, Hist.Abstr. **Document type:** monographic series.

972   MX
HISTORIAS. 1982. s-a. $35. Instituto Nacional de Antropologia e Historia, Direccion de Estudios Historicos, Apdo. Postal 5-119, CP 11850, Mexico, D.F., Mexico. TEL 553 80 52. Ed. Carlos Aguinre. adv. circ. 3,000.

HISTORIC WORLD LEADERS. see *POLITICAL SCIENCE*

900   IT   ISSN 0018-2427
HISTORICA; rivista trimestrale di cultura. 1948. q. L.45000($10) Historica Rivista di Cultura, Via Domenico Muratori 25, Reggio Calabria, Italy. Ed. Domenico de Giorgio. adv.; bk.rev.; abstr.; bibl.; illus.; index. circ. 2,000. **Indexed:** Amer.Hist.& Life, Arts & Hum.Cit.Ind., Hist.Abstr.
—BLDSC (4316.094000).

HISTORICA. see *MILITARY*

900   UK
HISTORICAL ASSOCIATION, LONDON. GENERAL SERIES. irreg. Historical Association, 59a Kennington Park Rd., London SE11 4JH, England. TEL 071-735-3901. (reprint service avail.) **Indexed:** Br.Archaeol.Abstr. **Document type:** academic/scholarly publication.

900   UK   ISSN 0018-246X
D1
HISTORICAL JOURNAL. 1958. q. £50($75) to individuals (overseas £70); institutions £89 (overseas £109 ($174)). (Cambridge Historical Society) Cambridge University Press, Edinburgh Bldg., Shaftesbury Rd., Cambridge CB2 2RU, England. TEL 0223-312393. FAX 0223-315052. TELEX 851817256. (N. American addr.: Cambridge University Press, Journals Dept., 40 W. 20th St., New York, NY 10010. TEL 212-924-3900. FAX 212-691-3239) Eds. J. Steinberg, J.S. Morrill. adv.; bk.rev.; index. (also avail. in microform from UMI; back issues avail.; reprint service avail. from SWZ) **Indexed:** Amer.Hist.& Life, Br.Hum.Ind., Curr.Cont., Hist.Abstr., Hum.Ind., Rel.Ind.One, SSCI. **Document type:** academic/scholarly publication.
—BLDSC (4316.360000); Faxon; UnCover; SWETS; UMI. **CCC.**
Description: Covers all aspects of European and world history since the 15th century.

900 791.43 384   UK   ISSN 0143-9685
PN1993.5.A1
HISTORICAL JOURNAL OF FILM, RADIO AND TELEVISION. 1980. 4/yr. $112 to individuals; institutions $298 (effective 1994). (International Association for Media and History) Carfax Publishing Co., P.O. Box 25, Abingdon, Oxon. OX14 3UE, England. TEL 44-235-555335. FAX 44-235-553559. (U.S. subscr. to: Carfax Publishing Co., Box 2025, Dunnellon, FL 34430-2025) Ed. David Culbert. bk.rev.; index. circ. 900. (also avail. in microfiche; back issues avail.) **Indexed:** Amer.Hist.& Life, Arts & Hum.Cit.Ind., Curr.Cont., Educ.Tech.Abstr., Film Lit.Ind. (1981-), Hist.Abstr., Intl.Ind.Film Per., Intl.Ind.TV, Media Rev.Dig., Mult.Ed.Abstr., Stud.Wom.Abstr. **Document type:** academic/scholarly publication.
—BLDSC (4316.395000); Faxon; UnCover; SWETS. **CCC.**
Refereed Serial

HISTORICAL MESSENGER. see *RELIGIONS AND THEOLOGY — Protestant*

900 310   US   ISSN 0161-5440
H1
HISTORICAL METHODS. 1967. q. $37 to individuals; institutions $79. (University of Illinois at Chicago Circle, Department of History) Heldref Publications, 1319 Eighteenth St., N.W., Washington, DC 20036-1802. TEL 202-296-6267. FAX 202-296-5149. (Co-sponsor: Helen Dwight Reid Educational Foundation) Ed. Barbara Kahn. adv. contact: Raymond Rallo. bk.rev.; charts; stat. circ. 650. (processed; also avail. in microform; reprint service avail.) **Indexed:** Amer.Bibl.Slavic & E.Eur.Stud., Amer.Hist.& Life, Arts & Hum.Cit.Ind., Curr.Cont., Excerp.Med., Hist.Abstr., Popul.Ind., SSCI. **Document type:** academic/scholarly publication.
—BLDSC (4316.490500); Faxon; UnCover; SWETS; UMI. **CCC.**
Formerly (until 1977): Historical Methods Newsletter (ISSN 0018-2494)
Refereed Serial

900   US   ISSN 0315-7997
D1   CODEN: HIREEW
HISTORICAL REFLECTIONS/REFLEXIONS HISTORIQUES. 1974. 3/yr. $25 to individuals; institutions $44. Alfred University, Division of Human Studies, Kanakadea Hall, Alfred, NY 14802. Ed. Stuart Campbell. circ. 350. (back issues avail.) **Indexed:** Abstr.Pop.Cult., Amer.Hist.& Life, Arts & Hum.Cit.Ind., Curr.Cont., Hist.Abstr. **Document type:** academic/scholarly publication.
—BLDSC (4316.710000); UnCover.
Description: Covers all fields of intellectual-cultural history and the histories of religion and mentalities.

900   UK   ISSN 0950-3471
D1
HISTORICAL RESEARCH. (Supplement avail.) (Text mainly in English, occasionally French; documents in original languages) 1923. 3/yr. £30($65) (University of London, Institute of Historical Research) Basil Blackwell Ltd., 108 Cowley Rd., Oxford OX4 1JF, England. TEL 0865-791100. FAX 0865-791347. TELEX 837022-OXBOOK-G. Ed. F.M.L. Thompson. adv.; bibl. circ. 1,400. (reprint service avail. from UMI) **Indexed:** Br.Hum.Ind., Curr.Cont.
—BLDSC (4316.800000); Faxon; UnCover; SWETS; UMI. **CCC.**
Formerly: University of London. Institute of Historical Research. Bulletin (ISSN 0020-2894)

900   UK   ISSN 0268-6716
Z6201
HISTORICAL RESEARCH FOR HIGHER DEGREES IN THE UNITED KINGDOM. PART 1: THESES COMPLETED. 1967. a. £3. University of London, Institute of Historical Research, Senate House, London WC1E 7HU, England. TEL 071-636-0272. FAX 071-436-2183. Ed. Joyce M. Horn. index. circ. 750. **Document type:** academic/scholarly publication.
Formerly: Historical Research for University Degrees in the United Kingdom. Part 1: Theses Completed (ISSN 0308-7417)
Description: Lists and classifies completed theses on historical topics with details of author, supervisor and university.

900   UK   ISSN 0268-6724
Z6201
HISTORICAL RESEARCH FOR HIGHER DEGREES IN THE UNITED KINGDOM. PART 2: THESES IN PROGRESS. 1967. a. £6. University of London, Institute of Historical Research, Senate House, London WC1E 7HU, England. TEL 071-636-0272. FAX 071-436-2183. Ed. Joyce M. Horn. index. circ. 750. **Document type:** academic/scholarly publication.
Formerly: Historical Research for University Degrees in the United Kingdom. Part 2: Theses in Progress (ISSN 0308-7425)
Description: Lists and classifies all known theses in progress on historical topics.

966.7 966.81   GH   ISSN 0073-2648
HISTORICAL SOCIETY OF GHANA. TRANSACTIONS. 1952-19??; resumed 1993. s-a. $15 to individuals; institutions $20. Historical Society of Ghana, c/o Albert van Dantzig, Dept. of History, University of Ghana, P.O. Box 14, Legon, Ghana. Ed. G. Austin. bk.rev. circ. 1,000. (also avail. in microform from UMI) **Indexed:** Curr.Cont.Africa, Curr.Cont.

966.9   NR   ISSN 0018-2540
DT515.A2
HISTORICAL SOCIETY OF NIGERIA. JOURNAL. 1956. s-a. $60 (typically set in Jan.). Impact Publishers Ltd., Hycone - Serials Supplier International, P.O. Box 9739, University of Ibadan, Ibadan, Nigeria. Ed. A.E. Ekoko. adv.; bk.rev. circ. 10,000. **Indexed:** A.I.C.P., Amer.Hist.& Life, Anthropol.Lit., Curr.Cont.Africa, Documentatieblad, Hist.Abstr. **Document type:** academic/scholarly publication.
—SWETS. **CCC.**

HISTORICAL STUDIES IN IRISH SCIENCE AND TECHNOLOGY. see *SCIENCES: COMPREHENSIVE WORKS*

900   XO   ISSN 0018-2575
DB661
HISTORICKY CASOPIS/HISTORICAL JOURNAL. (Text in Slovak; summaries in English, French, German, Russian) 1953. bi-m. 120 Kcs.($21) (Slovenska Akademia Vied, Historicky Ustav) Veda, Publishing House of the Slovak Academy of Sciences, Klemensova 19, 814 30 Bratislava, Slovakia. (Dist. in Western countries by: John Benjamins B.V., Amsteldijk 44, Amsterdam (Z.), Netherlands) Ed. Samuel Cambel. bk.rev.; bibl.; charts; illus.; index, cum.index: 1953-1968. circ. 1,400. **Indexed:** Amer.Hist.& Life, Arts & Hum.Cit.Ind., CERDIC, Curr.Cont., Hist.Abstr.
Description: Deals with the problems of Czechoslovak history with a special view to the history of Slovakia. Special attention is given to economic history and to the history of class struggles.

900   DK   ISSN 0046-7561
HISTORIE. 1866. s-a. DKK 250 (subscr. includes Nyt fra Historien). (Jysk Selskab for Historie) Aarhus University Press, Aarhus University, DK-8000 Aarhus C., Denmark. TEL 45-86-19-70-33. FAX 45-86-19-84-33. Ed. Joergen Fink. bk.rev. circ. 1,300. **Indexed:** Amer.Hist.& Life, Hist.Abstr., NAA.
—SWETS.

HISTORIE A VOJENSTVI. see *MILITARY*

907   DK
HISTORIE OG SAMTIDSORIENTERING. irreg., 5-8/yr. Dansk Historielaererforening, Noerrebakken 26, 2820 Gentofte, Denmark. Ed. Heino Doeygaard. adv. circ. 3,800.

HISTORY

907   FR   ISSN 0046-757X
HISTORIENS ET GEOGRAPHES. 1910. 4/yr. 360 F. (foreign 425 F.). Association des Professeurs d'Histoire et de Geographie de l'Enseignement Public, B.P. 49, 75060 Paris Cedex 02, France. Ed. Daniel-Jean Jay. adv.; bk.rev.; bibl. circ. 11,000. **Indexed:** Amer.Hist.& Life, Hist.Abstr.
—BLDSC (4317.240000).

HISTORIOGRAPHIA LINGUISTICA; international journal for the history of the language sciences. see *LINGUISTICS*

900 320   GW   ISSN 0018-2605
DAS HISTORISCH-POLITISCHE BUCH; Ein Wegweiser durch das Schrifttum. 1953. bi-m. DM.298. Muster-Schmidt Verlag, Brauweg 36a, 37073 Goettingen, Germany. TEL 0551-71741. FAX 0551-7702774. TELEX 96704-GOFAFI. Ed. Dr. Salewski. adv.; bk.rev.; bibl. index. circ. 1,000. **Document type:** academic/scholarly publication.
—CCC.

900 320   GW   ISSN 0943-691X
▼**HISTORISCH-POLITISCHE MITTEILUNGEN;** Archiv fuer Christlich-Demokratische Politik. 1993. a. DM.38. Boehlau Verlag GmbH, Theodor-Heuss-Str. 76, 51149 Cologne, Germany. TEL 02203-307021. FAX 02203-307021. Eds. Guenter Buchstab, Hans-Otto Kleinmann. **Document type:** academic/scholarly publication.

943   GW   ISSN 0942-8704
▼**HISTORISCHE ANTHROPOLOGIE;** Kultur - Gesellschaft - Alltag. 1993. 3/yr. DM.78. Boehlau Verlag GmbH, Theodor-Heuss-Str. 76, 51149 Cologne, Germany. TEL 02203-307021. FAX 02203-307349. Ed. Richard van Duelmen. **Document type:** academic/scholarly publication.

900   GW   ISSN 0440-9558
HISTORISCHE FORSCHUNGEN. (Text in English, French, and German) irreg., vol.18, 1993. price varies. (Akademie der Wissenschaften und der Literatur, Mainz, Historische Kommission) Jan Thorbecke Verlag GmbH und Co., Postfach 546, 72482 Sigmaringen, Germany. TEL 07571-728-100. FAX 07571-728-280. Ed.Bd. **Document type:** monographic series.

930   GW   ISSN 0930-6404
HISTORISCHE GRUNDWISSENSCHAFTEN IN EINZELDARSTELLUNGEN. irreg., vol.2, 1986. Franz Steiner Verlag Wiesbaden GmbH, Birkenwaldstr. 44, 70191 Stuttgart, Germany. TEL 0711-2582-0. FAX 0711-2582290. TELEX 723636-DAZ-D. (Subscr. to: Postfach 101061, 70009 Stuttgart, Germany) Eds. Thomas Frenz, Peter-Johannes Schuler. **Document type:** monographic series.

900   GW   ISSN 0067-5857
HISTORISCHE KOMMISSION ZU BERLIN. EINZELVEROEFFENTLICHUNGEN. 1968. irreg. price varies. Colloquium Verlag, Luetzowstr. 105, 10785 Berlin, Germany. circ. 1,000. **Document type:** monographic series.

900 DD1   GW   ISSN 0936-5796
HISTORISCHE MITTEILUNGEN. (Text in English and German) 1988. s-a. DM.58. (Vereinigung fuer Geschichte im Oeffentlichen Leben e.V.) Franz Steiner Verlag Stuttgart GmbH, Birkenwaldstr. 44, 70191 Stuttgart, Germany. TEL 0711-2582-0. FAX 0711-2582290. TELEX 723636-DAZ-D. (Subscr. to: Postfach 101061, 70009 Stuttgart, Germany) (Co-sponsor: Ranke Gesellschaft) Eds. Michael Salewski, Juergen Elvert. **Document type:** academic/scholarly publication.

900   GW   ISSN 0939-5385
HISTORISCHE MITTEILUNGEN. BEIHEFTE. irreg., vol.7, 1994. (Vereinigung fuer Geschichte im oeffentlichen Leben e.V.) Franz Steiner Verlag Wiesbaden GmbH, Birkenwaldstr. 44, 70191 Stuttgart, Germany. TEL 0711-2582-0. FAX 0711-2582-290. (Subscr. to: Postfach 101061, 70009 Stuttgart, Germany) (Co-sponsor: Ranke Gesellschaft) Eds. Michael Salewski, Juergen Elvert. **Document type:** academic/scholarly publication.

907   GW   ISSN 0723-3264
HISTORISCHE UND PAEDAGOGISCHE STUDIEN. 1971. irreg. price varies. Colloquium Verlag, Luetzowstr. 105, 10785 Berlin, Germany. Eds. Otto Buesch, Gerd Heinrich. circ. 1,000.

900 D1   GW   ISSN 0018-2613
HISTORISCHE ZEITSCHRIFT. 1859. bi-m. DM.418. R. Oldenbourg Verlag GmbH, Rosenheimerstr. 145, 81671 Munich, Germany. TEL 089-45051-0. FAX 089-45051207. (Subscr. to: Postfach 801360, 81613 Munich, Germany) Ed. Lothar Gall. adv.; bk.rev.; bibl.; index. circ. 2,800. (also avail. in microfilm from UMI; back issues avail.; reprint service avail. from GMC,UMI,SCH) **Indexed:** Amer.Hist.& Life, Arts & Hum.Cit.Ind., Bibl.Cart., Curr.Cont., Hist.Abstr., SSCI. **Document type:** academic/scholarly publication.
—BLDSC (4317.430000); Faxon; SWETS. **CCC**.
Description: Scholarly publication with articles covering all periods of European history. Includes large section devoted to reviews of recently published works on European history.

900 D1   GW   ISSN 0018-2621
HISTORISCHES JAHRBUCH. 1880. s-a. DM.128. (Goerres-Gesellschaft) Karl Alber GmbH, Hermann-Herder-Str. 4, 79104 Freiburg, Germany. Ed. Johannes Spoerl. bk.rev.; abstr. circ. 1,000. (reprint service avail. from SCH) **Indexed:** Amer.Hist.& Life, Arts & Hum.Cit.Ind., Curr.Cont., Hist.Abstr.
—BLDSC (4317.460000); SWETS. **CCC**.

900 D1   UK   ISSN 0018-2648
HISTORY. 1912. 3/yr. £35($65) (Historical Association) Basil Blackwell Ltd., 108 Cowley Rd., Oxford OX4 1JF, England. TEL 0865-791100. (Subscr. addr.: c/o Marston Book Services, P.O. Box 87, Oxford OX2 0DT, England) Ed. W.A. Speck. adv.; bk.rev.; bibl.; index, cum.index. circ. 5,300. (also avail. in microform from MIM,UMI; back issues avail.; reprint service avail. from UMI) **Indexed:** Amer.Hist.& Life, Arts & Hum.Cit.Ind., Br.Archaeol.Abstr., Br.Educ.Ind., Br.Hum.Ind., Curr.Cont., Hist.Abstr., Hum.Ind., Mid.East: Abstr.& Ind., So.Pac.Per.Ind., SSCI.
—BLDSC (4317.710000); Faxon; UnCover; SWETS; UMI. **CCC**.

900   US   ISSN 1058-174X
HISTORY. (Subseries of: S I R S Global Perspectives (ISSN 1058-1731)) 1991. a. $80. Social Issues Resources Series, Box 2348, Boca Raton, FL 33427-2348. TEL 407-994-0079; 800-232-7477. FAX 407-994-4704. (looseleaf format; also avail. in microfiche; back issues avail.) **Description:** Reprints 70 selected articles covering important events and personalities of the past 500 years.

HISTORY AND ANTHROPOLOGY. see *ANTHROPOLOGY*

410   US
HISTORY AND APPLIED LINGUISTICS. irreg. Peter Lang Publishing, Inc., 62 W. 45th St., 4th Fl., New York, NY 10036. TEL 212-302-6740. FAX 212-302-7574. Ed. Maria E. Stoffers. **Document type:** academic/scholarly publication.

901 D16.8   US   ISSN 0935-560X
HISTORY & MEMORY; studies in representation of the past. 1989. 2/yr. $15 to individuals; institutions $30. (Tel Aviv University, Eva and Marc Besen Institute for the Study of Historical Consciousness, IS) Indiana University Press, 601 N. Morton St., Bloomington, IN 47404. Ed. Saul Friedlander.
—UnCover.

900 600 T14.7   US   ISSN 0734-1512   CODEN: HITEE8
HISTORY AND TECHNOLOGY. 8/yr. (in 2 vols., 4 nos./vol.). 64 ECU per vol. (effective 1993). Harwood Academic Publishers, 820 Town Center Dr., Langhorne, PA 19047. TEL 215-750-2642. FAX 215-750-6343. (UK subscr. to: P.O. Box 90, Reading, Berkshire RG1 8JL, England. TEL 0734-560-080) Ed. Pietro Redondi. adv. (also avail. in microform) **Indexed:** Art & Archaeol.Tech.Abstr.
—BLDSC (4317.840000); Faxon; UnCover. **CCC**.
Refereed Serial

901 D1   US   ISSN 0018-2656
HISTORY AND THEORY; studies in the philosophy of history. 1960. 4/yr. $25 to individuals; institutions $40. Wesleyan University, Wesleyan Sta., Middletown, CT 06459. TEL 203-347-9411. FAX 203-343-3934. Ed. Brian C. Fay. adv.; bk.rev.; charts; index, cum.index: vols. 1-5, 6-10, 11-15, 16-20, 21-25, 26-30. circ. 2,100. (also avail. in microform from UMI; reprint service avail. from UMI) **Indexed:** Amer.Hist.& Life, Arts & Hum.Cit.Ind., Bk.Rev.Ind. (1977-), Child.Bk.Rev.Ind. (1977-), Curr.Cont., Hist.Abstr., Hum.Ind., Lang.& Lang.Behav.Abstr., Phil.Ind., SSCI. **Document type:** academic/scholarly publication.
—BLDSC (4317.850000); Faxon; UnCover; SWETS; UMI.
Description: Publishes articles and essays in the critical philosophy of history, speculative philosophy of history, historiography, historical methodology, and related topics in other disciplines.

HISTORY OF EDUCATION SOCIETY BULLETIN. see *EDUCATION*

HISTORY OF NURSING JOURNAL. see *MEDICAL SCIENCES — Nurses And Nursing*

HISTORY OF POLITICAL THOUGHT. see *POLITICAL SCIENCE*

HISTORY OF RELIGIONS; an international journal for comparative historical studies. see *RELIGIONS AND THEOLOGY*

900 Z6205   US   ISSN 0361-2759
HISTORY: REVIEWS OF NEW BOOKS. 1972. q. $43.50 to individuals (foreign $53.50); institutions $83 (foreign $97). (Helen Dwight Reid Educational Foundation) Heldref Publications, 1319 Eighteenth St., N.W., Washington, DC 20036-1802. TEL 202-296-6267. FAX 202-296-5149. Ed. John Neikirk. adv. contact: Raymond Rallo. bk.rev.; bibl. circ. 700. (also avail. in microform; back issues avail.; reprint service avail.) **Indexed:** Amer.Bibl.Slavic & E.Eur.Stud., Amer.Hist.& Life, Arts & Hum.Cit.Ind., Biog.Ind., Bk.Rev.Ind. (1975-), Chic.Per.Ind., Child.Bk.Rev.Ind. (1975-), Curr.Cont., Hist.Abstr., Mid.East: Abstr.& Ind., Per.Islam. (1991-). **Document type:** academic/scholarly publication.
—Faxon; UnCover; UMI.
Description: Provides informative evaluations of books one to twelve months after their publication.
Refereed Serial

907 370 D1   US   ISSN 0018-2745
HISTORY TEACHER. 1967. q. $22 to individuals; institutions $28. Society for History Education, Inc., California State University, 1250 Bellflower Blvd., Long Beach, CA 90840. TEL 310-985-1653. FAX 310-985-5431. Ed. Edward A. Gosselin. adv.; bk.rev. circ. 2,000. (also avail. in microfilm from UMI; back issues avail.; reprint service avail. from UMI) **Indexed:** Amer.Hist.& Life, C.I.J.E., Educ.Ind., Hist.Abstr., M.M.R.I. **Document type:** academic/scholarly publication.
—BLDSC (4318.540000); Faxon; UnCover; SWETS; UMI.
Description: Presents study and teaching methods.

HISTORY TEACHERS ASSOCIATION OF NEW SOUTH WALES. NEWSLETTER. see *EDUCATION — Teaching Methods And Curriculum*

907   UK
HISTORY TEACHING REVIEW YEARBOOK. (Supplements avail.: History Teaching Review Bulletin (3/yr.); Resources Review Supplement (2/yr.)) 1969. a. £7 to non-members. Scottish Association of Teachers of History, 7 Dunnottar Dr., Stenhousemuir, Larbert, Stirlingshire FK5 4TE, Scotland. (Subscr. to: S. Naismith, George Heriots School, Edinburgh, Scotland) Ed. Andrew Hunt. adv.; bk.rev. circ. 400. (back issues avail.)
Formerly: History Teaching Review.

900　　　　　　　UK　　ISSN 0018-2753
D1
HISTORY TODAY. 1951. m. $52. History Today Ltd., 20 Compton St., London W1V 5PE, England. Ed. Gordon Marsden. adv.; bk.rev.; illus.; index. circ. 35,000. (microform; reprint service avail. from UMI) **Indexed:** Acad.Ind., Amer.Hist.& Life, Arts & Hum.Cit.Ind., Bk.Rev.Ind. (1965-), Br.Archaeol.Abstr., Br.Hum.Ind., Child.Bk.Rev.Ind. (1965-), Curr.Cont., Gdlns., Hist.Abstr., Hum.Ind., Mag.Ind., Mid.East: Abstr.& Ind., Numis.Lit., Peace Res.Abstr., PMR, R.G., So.Pac.Per.Ind., TOM.
—BLDSC (4318.580000); Faxon; UnCover; SWETS; UMI.

900　　　　　　　UK　　ISSN 0309-2984
D1
HISTORY WORKSHOP; a journal of socialist historians. 1975. s-a. £34($63) (effective 1994). (History Workshop) Oxford University Press, Oxford Journals, Walton St., Oxford OX2 6DP, England. TEL 0865-56767. FAX 0865-56646. TELEX 837330-OXPRES-G. (U.S. subscr. to: Oxford University Press Inc., 2001 Evans Rd., Cary, NC 27513. TEL 919-677-0977) Ed.Bd. adv. contact: Jane Parker. bk.rev.; bibl. circ. 1,450. (back issues avail.) **Indexed:** Alt.Press Ind., Amer.Hist.& Life, Arts & Hum.Cit.Ind., Curr.Cont., E.I., Hist.Abstr., Lang.& Lang.Behav.Abstr., Left Ind. (1985-), Mid.East: Abstr.& Ind., SSCI. **Document type:** academic/scholarly publication.
—BLDSC (4318.640000); Faxon; UnCover; SWETS; UMI. **CCC.**
Description: Covers fundamental elements of social life today and in the past - work and material culture, class relations and politics, sex divisions, marriage, family, school and home, language, culture and ideology, oppression and resistance from the socialist and feminist perspectives.

HOLSTON PASTFINDER. see *GENEALOGY AND HERALDRY*

900　　　　　　　FR　　ISSN 0073-3202
HOMMES ET LA TERRE. 1956. irreg., no.21, 1992. price varies. Editions de l' Ecole des Hautes Etudes en Sciences Sociales, 131 bd. St-Michel, 75005 Paris, France. TEL 43-54-47-15. FAX 43-54-80-73. (Dist. by: Centre Interinstitutionnel pour la Diffusion de Publications en Sciences Humaines, 131 bd. St-Michel, 75005 Paris, France.)

HUNTINGTON LIBRARY QUARTERLY; studies in English and American literature, history, and art. see *LITERATURE*

HUTSULIYA. see *ETHNIC INTERESTS*

907 371.3　　　　　NE
I A M H I S T NEWSLETTER. q. International Association of Audio-Visual Media in Historical Research and Education, c/o Miriam Prenger, Ed., Stichting Film Wetenskap, Zeeburgerkade 8, 1019 HA Amsterdam. TEL 31-20-6659086. FAX 31-20-6652966. **Document type:** newsletter.

I P A BULLETIN. (International Psychohistorical Association) see *PSYCHOLOGY*

900　　　　　　　GW
ILLUSTRIERTE HISTORISCHE HEFTE. 1976. irreg. DM.7. (Zentralinstitut fuer Geschichte der Akademie der Wissenschaften der DDR) VEB Deutscher Verlag der Wissenschaften, Postfach 1216, 1080 Berlin, Germany.

IMMIGRATION HISTORY NEWSLETTER. see *POPULATION STUDIES*

909 355　　　　　UK　　ISSN 0951-3094
IMPERIAL WAR MUSEUM REVIEW. 1986. a. £9.50. Imperial War Museum, Lambeth Road, London SE1 6HZ, England. Ed. Suzanne Bardgett. illus. circ. 2,000. (back issues avail.)
—BLDSC (4371.411150).

INCITE INFORMATION; inquiry and commentary. see *JOURNALISM*

INDIAN JOURNAL OF HISTORY OF SCIENCE. see *SCIENCES: COMPREHENSIVE WORKS*

900　　　　　　　FR　　ISSN 0046-9351
D1
INFORMATION HISTORIQUE. 1938. 5/yr. 48 ECU($56) Armand Colin, 103 bd. Saint-Michel, 75240 Paris Cedex 05, France. TEL 1-46-34-19-12. FAX 1-43-26-96-38. TELEX 201 269 F. Ed. L. Trenard. bk.rev.; bibl.; illus.; index. (also avail. in microform from UMI) **Indexed:** Amer.Hist.& Life, Hist.Abstr.
—BLDSC (4493.607000); SWETS; UMI. **CCC.**

INNES REVIEW. see *RELIGIONS AND THEOLOGY — Roman Catholic*

900 700 100 300　　SP　　ISSN 0211-8998
INSTITUCION FERNAN-GONZALEZ. BOLETIN. 1844. s-a. 1500 ptas. Institucion Fernan Gonzalez, Palacio del Espolon, 14, 09003 Burgos, Spain. bk.rev. (reprint service avail. from UMI) **Indexed:** Amer.Hist.& Life, Hist.Abstr. **Document type:** bulletin.

INSTITUT ARCHEOLOGIQUE DU LUXEMBOURG. BULLETINS; archeologie-art-histoire-folklore. see *ARCHAEOLOGY*

900　　　　　　　GW　　ISSN 0170-365X
INSTITUT FUER EUROPAEISCHE GESCHICHTE, MAINZ. VEROEFFENTLICHUNGEN. ABTEILUNG UNIVERSALGESCHICHTE. BEIHEFTE. (Text in English, French, and German) irreg., vol.31, 1989. price varies. Verlag Philipp Von Zabern, Welschnonnengasse 13A, 55116 Mainz, Germany. TEL 06131-232217. FAX 06131-223710. Ed. K.O. von Aretin. **Document type:** monographic series.

900 200　　　　　　GW
INSTITUT FUER EUROPAEISCHE GESCHICHTE, MAINZ. VEROEFFENTLICHUNGEN. ABTEILUNG UNIVERSALGESCHICHTE UND ABTEILUNG FUER ABENDLAENDISCHE RELIGIONSGESCHICHTE. (Text in English, French, and German) irreg., vol.140, 1989. price varies. Verlag Philipp Von Zabern, Welschnonnengasse 13A, 5516 Mainz, Germany. TEL 06131-232217. FAX 06131-223710. Ed. P. Manns. **Document type:** monographic series.
Formerly: Institut fuer Europaeische Geschichte, Mainz. Veroeffentlichungen. Abteilung Universitaetsgeschichte und Abteilung fuer Abendlaendische Religionsphilosophie (ISSN 0537-7919)

900 200　　　　　　GW
INSTITUT FUER EUROPAEISCHE GESCHICHTE, MAINZ. VORTRAEGE. ABTEILUNG UNIVERSALGESCHICHTE UND ABTEILUNG FUER ABENDLAENDISCHE RELIGIONSGESCHICHTE. (Text in English, French, and German) irreg., vol.83, 1988. price varies. Verlag Philipp von Zabern, Welschnonnengasse 13A, 55116 Mainz, Germany. TEL 06131-232217. FAX 06131-223710. Ed. P. Manns. **Document type:** monographic series.
Formerly: Institut fuer Europaeische Geschichte, Mainz. Vortraege. Abteilung Universalgeschichte und Abteilung fuer Abendlaendische Religionsphilosophie (ISSN 0537-7927)

940.27　　　　　　FR　　ISSN 0020-2371
INSTITUT NAPOLEON. REVUE.* 1933. s-a. 170 F. (foreign 202 F.). Editions Tallandier, 18 rue Neuve-des-Boulets, 75011 Paris, France. TEL 320-14-33. Ed. Jean Tulard. bk.rev.; illus.; index. circ. 100,000. (also avail. in microform) **Indexed:** Amer.Hist.& Life, Hist.Abstr.
—BLDSC (7879.280000).
Description: Devoted to studies, research, chronicles and bibliographies on Napoleon.

930　　　　　　PO　　ISSN 0870-0028
JV4201
INSTITUTO DE INVESTIGACAO CIENTIFICA TROPICAL. CENTRO DE ESTUDOS DE HISTORIA E CARTOGRAFIA ANTIGA. STUDIA. 1958. irreg. price varies. Instituto de Investigacao Cientifica Tropical, Centro de Estudos de Historia e Cartografia Antiga, Rua Jau 54, 1300 Lisbon, Portugal. TEL 364-5321. FAX 363-1460. (Subscr. to: Centro de Documentacao e Informacao, Rua Jau 47, 1300 Lisbon, Portugal) circ. 1,000. **Indexed:** Documentatieblad. **Document type:** academic/scholarly publication.
Formerly: Junta de Investigacaoes Cientificas do Ultramar. Centro de Estudos de Historia e Cartografia Antiga. Studia.

930　　　　　　PO　　ISSN 0870-6735
DP538
INSTITUTO DE INVESTIGACAO CIENTIFICA TROPICAL. CENTRO DE ESTUDOS DE HISTORIA E CARTOGRAFIA ANTIGA. SERIE SEPARATAS. 1961. irreg. price varies. Instituto de Investigacao Cientifica Tropical, Centro de Estudos de Historia e Cartografia Antiga, Rua Jau 54, 1300 Lisbon, Portugal. TEL 364-5321. FAX 363-1460. (Subscr. to: Centro de Documentacao e Informacao, Rua Jau 47, 1300 Lisbon, Portugal) circ. 1,500. **Document type:** monographic series.
Description: Covers ancient history and cartography.

900 300　　　　　PO　　ISSN 0871-1771
INSTITUTO DE INVESTIGACAO CIENTIFICA TROPICAL. COMUNICACOES. SERIE DE CIENCIAS HISTORICAS, ECONOMICAS E SOCIOLOGICAS. irreg. Instituto de Investigacao Cientifica Tropical, Rua Jau, 54, 1300 Lisbon, Portugal. TEL 364-5321. FAX 363-1460. (Subscr. to: Centro de Documentacao e Informacao, Rua Jau 47, 1300 Lisbon, Portugal) circ. 1,000. **Document type:** monographic series.

946.9　　　　　　PO　　ISSN 0870-015X
INSTITUTO DE INVESTIGACAO CIENTIFICA TROPICAL. ESTUDOS DE HISTORIA E CARTOGRAFIA ANTIGA - MEMORIAS. 1963. irreg. price varies. Instituto de Investigacao Cientifica Tropical, Centro de Estudos de Historia e Cartografia Antiga, Rua Jau 54, 1300 Lisbon, Portugal. TEL 364-5321. FAX 363-1460. (Subscr. to: Centro de Documentacao e Informacao, Rua Jau 47, 1300 Lisbon, Portugal) circ. 1,000. **Document type:** monographic series.
Formerly: Estudos de Cartografia Antiga.
Description: Covers history and ancient cartography.

900　　　　　　AG　　ISSN 0327-5574
INSTITUTO DE INVESTIGACIONES HISTORICAS JUAN MANUEL DE ROSAS. REVISTA. 1939. q. Instituto de Investigaciones Historicas Juan Manuel de Rosas, Hipolito Yrigoyen 788, 1o piso, 1086 Buenos Aires, Argentina. TEL 38-5635.

900 910　　　　　BL
INSTITUTO HISTORICO E GEOGRAFICO DO ESPIRITO SANTO. REVISTA. (Text in Portuguese) 1917. a. $3. Instituto Historico e Geografico do Espirito Santo, Avenida Republica, 374, Vitoria, Espirito Santo, Brazil. bk.rev. circ. 1,000. (back issues avail.)

940　　　　　　RM
INSTITUTUL DE SUBINGINERI ORADEA. LUCRARI STIINTIFICE: SERIA ISTORIE. (Text in Rumanian, occasionally in English or French; summaries in English, French, German or Rumanian) a. Institutul de Subingineri Oradea, Calea Armatei Rosii Nr. 5, 3700 Oradea, Rumania.
Formerly: Institutul Pedagogic Oradea. Lucrari Stiintifice: Seria Istorie; Which continues in part (in 1973): Institutul Pedagogic Oradea. Lucrari Stiintifice: Seria Istorie, Stiinte Sociale, Pedagogie; Which superseded (in 1971): Institutul Pedagogic Oradea. Lucrari Stiintifice: Seria A and Seria B; Which was formerly (until 1969): Institutul Pedagogic Oradea. Lucrari Stiintifice.

900　　　　　　FR　　ISSN 0020-5613
INTERMEDIAIRE DES CHERCHEURS ET CURIEUX; de questions et responses historiques, litteraires, artistiques et sur toutes autres curiosites. 1864. m. 685 F. Residence Orsay, Parly 2, 8 Square Surcouf, 78150 Le Chesnay, France. TEL 47-07-54-90. (Subscr. to: 28 rue Geofroy Saint-Hilaire, 75005 Paris, France) Ed. Patrice de Clinchamps. adv.; bk.rev.; charts. circ. 2,000. (also avail. in microfiche from BHP)

900　　　　　　US　　ISSN 1047-3408
D16.14
INTERNATIONAL ANNUAL OF ORAL HISTORY. 1980. a. $59.50 to institutions. Greenwood Press, Inc. (Subsidiary of: Greenwood Publishing Group), 88 Post Rd. W., Box 5007, Westport, CT 06881-9990. TEL 203-226-6967. Ed. Ronald Grele. adv.; bk.rev.; index. circ. 400. (also avail. in microform from UMI; reprint service avail. from UMI) **Indexed:** Amer.Bibl.Slavic & E.Eur.Stud., Amer.Hist.& Life, Arts & Hum.Cit.Ind., C.I.J.E., Curr.Cont., Hist.Abstr., Stud.Wom.Abstr.
—BLDSC (4535.880000); UMI.
Formerly (until 1989): International Journal of Oral History (ISSN 0195-6787)

HISTORY

900   FR   ISSN 0074-2783
INTERNATIONAL COMMITTEE FOR HISTORICAL SCIENCE. BULLETIN D'INFORMATION. 1953. irreg., no.11, 1980. International Committee for Historical Science, c/o Michel Francois, Sec. Gen, 270 Bd. Raspail, 75014 Paris, France. (Subscr. to: Jean-Charles Biaudet, la Folie, CH 1605 Chexbres, Switzerland)

INTERNATIONAL CONFERENCE OF ORIENTALISTS IN JAPAN. TRANSACTIONS. see *ORIENTAL STUDIES*

900   CN   ISSN 0707-5332
D1
INTERNATIONAL HISTORY REVIEW. 1979. q. $30 to individuals; institutions $89. Simon Fraser University, Burnaby, BC V5A 1S6, Canada. TEL 604-291-3561. FAX 604-291-3429. Ed. Edward Ingram. adv.; bk.rev.; bibl.; index. circ. 800. (back issues avail.) **Indexed:** Amer.Bibl.Slavic & E.Eur.Stud., Amer.Hist.& Life, Arts & Hum.Cit.Ind., Can.Per.Ind., Curr.Cont., Hist.Abstr., Mid.East: Abstr.& Ind., So.Pac.Per.Ind. **Document type:** academic/scholarly publication.
—BLDSC (4540.724200); Faxon; UnCover; SWETS. **CCC.**
   Description: Examines relations between all states throughout history.

INTERNATIONAL JOURNAL OF THE HISTORY OF SPORT. see *SPORTS AND GAMES*

INTERNATIONAL LABOR AND WORKING CLASS HISTORY. see *BUSINESS AND ECONOMICS — Labor And Industrial Relations*

300 900   UK   ISSN 0020-8590
INTERNATIONAL REVIEW OF SOCIAL HISTORY. (Text in Dutch, English, French, German) 1937. 3/yr. (plus supplement). £33($49) to individuals (overseas £45.50); institutions £52 (overseas £64.50 ($89)). (Internationaal Intsituut voor Sociale Geschiedenis) Cambridge University Press, Edinburgh Bldg., Shaftesbury Rd., Cambridge CB2 2RU, England. TEL 0223-312393. FAX 0223-315052. TELEX 851817256. (N. American addr.: Cambridge University Press, Journals Dept., 40 W. 20th St., New York, NY 10011. TEL 212-924-3900. FAX 212-691-3239) Ed. Marcel van der Linden. adv.; bk.rev.; bibl.; index. (also avail. in microform from UMI; back issues avail.) **Indexed:** Amer.Hist.& Life, Arts & Hum.Cit.Ind., Curr.Cont., Hist.Abstr., Mid.East: Abstr.& Ind., Soc.Sci.Ind., SSCI. **Document type:** academic/scholarly publication.
—BLDSC (4547.740000); Faxon; UnCover; SWETS; UMI.
   Formerly (until 1956): International Institute for Social History. Bulletin (ISSN 0921-254X)
   Description: Covers a very wide variety of social history issues.

900   GW
INTERNATIONALES HANDBUCH - ZEITARCHIV; Chronik-Dokumente-Uebersichten. 1913. w. DM.89.10 per quarter. Munzinger-Archiv GmbH, Hans-Zuericher-Weg 7, 88274 Ravensburg, Germany. TEL 0751-31916. FAX 0751-17261. Ed. Ludwig Munzinger. circ. 400. **Document type:** newsletter.
   Formerly: Zeit- und Kulturarchiv (ISSN 0044-2097)

INTERVENTI CLASSENSI. see *ART*

IRISH SWORD. see *MILITARY*

ISIS; international review devoted to the history of science and its cultural influences. see *SCIENCES: COMPREHENSIVE WORKS*

DER ISLAM; Zeitschrift fuer Geschichte und Kultur des Islamischen Orients. see *ORIENTAL STUDIES*

942 500.9   UI
ISLE OF MAN NATURAL HISTORY AND ANTIQUARIAN SOCIETY. PROCEEDINGS. 1888. biennial. £6.50. Isle of Man Natural History and Antiquarian Society, c/o Manx Museum, Douglas, Isle of Man, U.K. Ed. Joyce Warham. index, cum.index. circ. 300. **Indexed:** Br.Archaeol.Abstr. **Document type:** academic/scholarly publication.
   Description: Papers on all Manx studies: archaeology, history, folk-life, Manx language, geology, meteorology and natural history.

900   IT   ISSN 0578-9931
ISTITUTO ITALIANO PER GLI STUDI STORICI. ANNALI. 1968. a. Societa Editrice Il Mulino, Strada Maggiore 37, 40125 Bologna, Italy. TEL 051-256011. FAX 051-256034. circ. 600. (back issues avail.)

900   BU   ISSN 0323-9748
DR51
ISTORICHESKI PREGLED. (Text in Bulgarian; contents page in French) 1945. 8/yr. 1.10 lv. per no. (Bulgarska Akademiia na Naukite, Institut za Istoriia) Publishing House of the Bulgarian Academy of Sciences, Acad. G. Bonchev St., Bldg. 6, 1113 Sofia, Bulgaria. (Dist. by: Hemus, 6, Rouski Blvd., 1000 Sofia, Bulgaria) Ed. V. Khadzhinikolov. bk.rev.; bibl.; index. circ. 3,120. (reprint service avail. from IRC) **Indexed:** Amer.Hist.& Life, Hist.Abstr.
—BLDSC (0087.845000).

900   RU
ISTORICHESKIE ZAPISKI. vol.97, 1976. irreg. price varies. (Akademiya Nauk S.S.S.R., Institut Istorii S.S.S.R.) Izdatel'stvo Nauka, 90 Profsoyuznaya ul., 117864 Moscow, Russia. TEL 234-05-84. (Dist. by: Mezhdunarodnaya Kniga, ul. Dimitrova D.39, 113095 Moscow, Russia) Ed. A.M. Samsonov. circ. 2,050. (reprint service avail. from KTO) **Indexed:** Amer.Hist.& Life, Hist.Abstr.

900   RM   ISSN 0075-1626
ISTORIE SI CIVILIZATIE. 1970. irreg., vol.9, 1978. (Academia Romana) Editura Academiei Romane, Calea Victoriei 125, 79717 Bucharest, Rumania. (Subscr. to: Artexim, Str. Piata Presei Libere 1, P.O. Box 33-16, 70055 Bucharest, Rumania)

900   YU   ISSN 0021-2644
DR301
ISTORIJSKI GLASNIK. (Text in Serbo-Croatian) 1948. s-a. 60 din.($8) Drustvo Istoricara SR Srbije, Cika Ljubina 18-20, Belgrade, Yugoslavia. Ed. Bogumil Hrabak. **Indexed:** Amer.Hist.& Life (until 1988), Hist.Abstr. (until 1988).

900   YU   ISSN 0021-2652
ISTORIJSKI ZAPISI. (Text in Serbo-Croatian; title page and introduction also in French) 1947. q. 499 din. Istorijski Institut SR Crne Gore, Titograd, P.O. Box 96, 81000 Titograd, Yugoslavia. TEL 081-41-624. (Co-sponsor: Drustvo Istoricara Crne Gore) Ed. Jovan Bojovis. circ. 1,200. **Indexed:** Amer.Hist.& Life, Hist.Abstr.
   Formerly: Zapisi: Casopis za Nuku i Knjizevnost.

900   KR   ISSN 0135-2202
D410
ISTORYCHNI DOSLIDZHENNYA. ISTORIYA ZARUBIZHNYKH KRAYIN; respublikanskyj mizhvidomchyj zbirnik naukovykh prac. (Text in Ukrainian; summaries in Russian) 1974. a. (Akademiya Nauk Ukrainy, Institut Istorii) Vidavnitstvo Naukova Dumka, Vul. Tereshchenkivska 3, 252601 Kiev, Ukraine. TEL 044-244-4068. FAX 044-244-7060. (Dist. by: Mezhdunarodnaya Kniga, B. Yakimanka 39, 117049 Moscow, Russia) Ed. Yu.Yu. Kondufor.
—BLDSC (0087.857000).

900   KR   ISSN 0135-2210
DK508.A3
ISTORYCHNI DOSLIDZHENNYA. VITCHYZNYANA ISTORIYA; respublikanskyj mizhvidomchyj zbirnyk naukovykh prac. (Text in Ukrainian; summaries in Russian) 1974. a. (Akademiya Nauk Ukrainy, Institut Istorii) Vidavnitstvo Naukova Dumka, Vul. Tereshchenkivska 3, 252601 Kiev, Ukraine. TEL 044-224-4068. (Dist. by: Mezhdunarodnaya Kniga, B. Yakimanka 39, 117049 Moscow, Russia) Ed. Yu.Yu. Kondufor.
—BLDSC (0087.856000).

909   NE   ISSN 0165-1153
ITINERARIO. (Text in English) 1975. 3/yr. $40 to individuals; institutions $50 (effective 1992). Institute for the History of European Expansion, Postbus 9515, 2300 RA Leiden, Netherlands. Ed.Bd. adv.; bk.rev.; cum.index: 1975-1986. circ. 1,000. (also avail. in microfiche from IDC; back issues avail.) **Indexed:** Documentatieblad, E.I. **Document type:** bulletin.
—BLDSC (4588.656000); Faxon; UnCover; SWETS.
   Formerly: Centre for the History of European Expansion. Newsletter.

ITINERARIUM; revista quadrimestral de cultura. see *RELIGIONS AND THEOLOGY — Roman Catholic*

929.5   GW   ISSN 0937-3624
JC599.G3
JAHRBUCH ZUR LIBERALISMUS FORSCHUNG. 1989. a. Nomos Verlagsgesellschaft mbH und Co. KG, Waldseestr. 3-5, 76530 Baden-Baden, Germany. TEL 07221-21040. FAX 07221-210427. (Subscr. to: Postfach 610, 76484 Baden-Baden, Germany) **Document type:** academic/scholarly publication.

900   US   ISSN 0075-3874
JOHNS HOPKINS SYMPOSIA IN COMPARATIVE HISTORY. 1970. irreg. price varies. Johns Hopkins University Press, 701 W. 40th St., Ste. 275, Baltimore, MD 21211. TEL 410-516-6900. FAX 410-516-6998. (reprint service avail. from UMI)

900 320   US   ISSN 0075-3904
H31
JOHNS HOPKINS UNIVERSITY STUDIES IN HISTORICAL AND POLITICAL SCIENCE. 1882. irreg. price varies. Johns Hopkins University Press, 701 W. 40th St., Ste. 275, Baltimore, MD 21211. TEL 410-516-6900. FAX 410-516-6998. (also avail. in microform from UMI; reprint service avail. from UMI) **Document type:** academic/scholarly publication.
—UMI. **CCC.**

JOHNSONIAN NEWS LETTER. see *LITERATURE*

JOURNAL FOR CONTEMPORARY HISTORY/JOERNAAL VIR EIETYDSE GESKIEDENIS. see *POLITICAL SCIENCE — International Relations*

JOURNAL FUER DRUCKGESCHICHTE/JOURNAL D'HISTOIRE DE L'IMPRIMERIE/JOURNAL OF PRINTING HISTORY. see *PRINTING*

930   US
JOURNAL OF ANCIENT AND MEDIEVAL STUDIES. 1982. a. $25. Octavian Society, Box 386, Torrance, CA 90507. TEL 213-326-8603. Ed. Sir Rodney Hartwell. adv.; bk.rev. circ. 200. (looseleaf format)
   Formerly: Societas Gaius Julius Caesar Octavianus. Newsletter.

JOURNAL OF ART HISTORY/BIJUTSU SHI. see *ART*

900   UK   ISSN 0022-0094
D410   CODEN: JCHID7
JOURNAL OF CONTEMPORARY HISTORY. 1966. q. £32 to individuals; institutions £82. Sage Publications Ltd., 6 Bonhill St., London EC2A 4PU, England. TEL 071-374-0645. FAX 071-374-8741. Eds. Walter Laqueur, George L. Mosse. adv.: color page £220; trim 177 x 101; adv. contact: Bernie Folan. abstr.; index. (also avail. in microform from UMI; reprint service avail. from UMI) **Indexed:** A.B.C.Pol.Sci., Abstr.Pop.Cult., Amer.Hist.& Life, Arts & Hum.Cit.Ind., Br.Hum.Ind., Curr.Cont.Africa, Curr.Cont., Hist.Abstr., Hum.Ind., Mid.East: Abstr.& Ind., Sage Pub.Admin.Abstr., Sage Urb.Stud.Abstr., SSCI. **Document type:** academic/scholarly publication.
—BLDSC (4965.230000); Faxon; UnCover; SWETS; UMI.
   Description: International forum for the discussion of critical aspects of twentieth century European history.
   Refereed Serial

JOURNAL OF ECCLESIASTICAL HISTORY. see *RELIGIONS AND THEOLOGY*

JOURNAL OF EDUCATIONAL ADMINISTRATION AND HISTORY. see *EDUCATION — School Organization And Administration*

900   II   ISSN 0022-1562
DS401
JOURNAL OF HISTORICAL RESEARCH. (Text in English) 1958. s-a. $10. Ranchi University, Department of History, Ranchi 1, Bihar 834008, India. (Co-sponsor: Historical and Archaeological Society) Ed. A.P. Sharma. bk.rev.; charts. **Indexed:** Arts & Hum.Cit.Ind., Curr.Cont. **Document type:** academic/scholarly publication.

900   US   ISSN 0195-6752
D1
JOURNAL OF HISTORICAL REVIEW. 1980. 6/yr. $40 (foreign $50). Institute for Historical Review, Box 2739, Newport Beach, CA 92659. Ed. Mark Weber. adv.; bk.rev.; index, cum.index: 1980-1993 in vol.13, no.6, 1993; circ. 5,800 (paid). (back issues avail.) **Document type:** academic/scholarly publication.
     Incorporates: I H R Newsletter.
     Description: Emphasis on 20th century European and US history, especially Second World War and Holocaust Revisionism.

JOURNAL OF HISTOTECHNOLOGY. see *TECHNOLOGY: COMPREHENSIVE WORKS*

900   UK   ISSN 0308-6534
DA10
JOURNAL OF IMPERIAL AND COMMONWEALTH HISTORY. 1972. 3/yr. £32($48) to individuals; institutions £85 ($135). Frank Cass & Co. Ltd., Gainsborough House, 11 Gainsborough Rd., London E11 1RS, England. TEL 081-530-4226. FAX 081-530-7795. Eds. Peter Burroughs, A.J. Stockwell. adv.: B&W page £185; adv. contact: Anne Kidson. bk.rev.; index. (also avail. in microfilm from UMI; back issues avail.) **Indexed:** Amer.Hist.& Life, Arts & Hum.Cit.Ind., Br.Hum.Ind., Curr.Cont., Hist.Abstr. **Document type:** academic/scholarly publication.
     —BLDSC (5005.050000); UnCover; SWETS; UMI.
     Description: Covers the history of the British Empire and Commonwealth as well as comparative European colonial experiences.

900   US   ISSN 0022-1953
D1
JOURNAL OF INTERDISCIPLINARY HISTORY. 1969. q. $34 to individuals (foreign $48); institutions $90 (foreign $104); students $25 (foreign $39). M I T Press, 55 Hayward St., Cambridge, MA 02142. TEL 617-253-2889. FAX 617-258-6779. TELEX 921473. E-mail: mit.edu. (Editorial addr.: c/o Managing Ed., Lafayette College, 316 Markle Hall, Easton, PA 18042-1768) Eds. Robert I. Rotberg, Theodore K. Rabb. adv.; bk.rev.; index. circ. 1,680. (also avail. in microform from MIM,UMI; back issues avail.; reprint service avail. from SCH,UMI) **Indexed:** A.B.C.Pol.Sci., Acad.Ind., Amer.Bibl.Slavic & E.Eur.Stud., Amer.Hist.& Life, Arts & Hum.Cit.Ind., Bk.Rev.Ind. (1981-), Child.Bk.Rev.Ind. (1981-), Curr.Bk.Rev.Cit., Curr.Cont., Hist.Abstr., Hum.Ind., Lang.& Lang.Behav.Abstr., Mid.East: Abstr.& Ind., Popul.Ind., RILA, Sage Urb.Stud.Abstr., Sociol.Abstr., SSCI, Stud.Wom.Abstr.
     —BLDSC (5007.547000); Faxon; UnCover; SWETS; UMI. **CCC.**
     Description: Historical research spanning all geographical areas related to work in applied fields such as economics and demographics.

JOURNAL OF LEGAL HISTORY. see *LAW*

JOURNAL OF MEDIEVAL AND RENAISSANCE STUDIES. see *HUMANITIES: COMPREHENSIVE WORKS*

900   US   ISSN 0022-2801
D1
JOURNAL OF MODERN HISTORY. 1929. q. $31 to individuals; institutions $65; students $24. University of Chicago Press, Journals Division, 5720 S. Woodlawn Ave., Chicago, IL 60637. TEL 312-753-3347. FAX 312-753-0811. TELEX 25-4603. (Subscr. to: Box 37005, Chicago, IL 60637) Eds. John Boyer, Julius Kirshner. adv.; bk.rev.; bibl.; index. circ. 4,000. (also avail. in microform from UMI,PMC; back issues avail.; reprint service avail. from UMI,ISI) **Indexed:** Acad.Ind., Amer.Bibl.Slavic & E.Eur.Stud., Amer.Hist.& Life, Arts & Hum.Cit.Ind., Bk.Rev.Ind. (1965-), Child.Bk.Rev.Ind. (1965-), Curr.Cont., Hist.Abstr., Hum.Ind., Mid.East: Abstr.& Ind., Peace Res.Abstr., SSCI. **Document type:** academic/scholarly publication.
     —BLDSC (5020.680000); Faxon; UnCover; SWETS; UMI. **CCC.**
     Description: Covers the history of the European continent since the Renaissance; studies intellectual, political, and cultural history of events and movements in specific countries as well as broader questions.
     Refereed Serial

JOURNAL OF NEGRO HISTORY. see *ETHNIC INTERESTS*

JOURNAL OF NORTHERN LUZON; a semi-annual research forum. see *SOCIOLOGY*

974   US   ISSN 0898-0306
H96   CODEN: JPHIEV
JOURNAL OF POLICY HISTORY. 1989. q. $20 to individuals (foreign $27); institutions $30 (foreign $35). Pennsylvania State University Press, Barbara Bldg., Ste. C, 820 N. University Dr., University Park, PA 16802-1003. TEL 814-865-1327. FAX 814-863-1408. Ed. Donald T. Critchlow. (also avail. in microform from UMI; reprint service avail. from UMI) **Indexed:** Amer.Hist.& Life, Hist.Abstr., Sage.Pub.Admin.Abstr., Sociol.Abstr. **Document type:** academic/scholarly publication.
     —Faxon; UnCover. **CCC.**
     Refereed Serial

JOURNAL OF PSYCHOHISTORY. see *PSYCHOLOGY*

JOURNAL OF RELIGIOUS HISTORY. see *RELIGIONS AND THEOLOGY*

JOURNAL OF SOCIAL HISTORY. see *SOCIOLOGY*

JOURNAL OF SPELEAN HISTORY. see *EARTH SCIENCES — Geology*

JOURNAL OF THE HISTORY OF BIOLOGY. see *BIOLOGY*

JOURNAL OF THE HISTORY OF IDEAS; a quarterly devoted to cultural and intellectual history. see *HUMANITIES: COMPREHENSIVE WORKS*

JOURNAL OF THE HISTORY OF MEDICINE AND ALLIED SCIENCES. see *MEDICAL SCIENCES*

JOURNAL OF THE HISTORY OF PHILOSOPHY. see *PHILOSOPHY*

JOURNAL OF THE HISTORY OF THE BEHAVIORAL SCIENCES. see *PSYCHOLOGY*

907   US   ISSN 8755-3449
JOURNAL OF THIRD WORLD STUDIES. 1984. s-a. $45. Association of Third World Studies, Inc., Box 1232, Americus, GA 31709. TEL 912-924-8287. Ed. Harold Isaacs. adv.; bk.rev. circ. 700. (back issues avail.) **Indexed:** Amer.Hist.& Life, Hist.Abstr. **Document type:** academic/scholarly publication.
     Description: An interdisciplinary scholarly periodical focusing on Third World problems and issues.

JOURNAL OF TRANSPORT HISTORY. see *TRANSPORTATION*

900   US   ISSN 0096-1442
HT111
JOURNAL OF URBAN HISTORY. 1974. q. $48 to individuals; institutions $151 (effective 1994). Sage Publications, Inc., 2455 Teller Rd., Thousand Oaks, CA 91320. TEL 805-499-0721. FAX 805-499-0871. (Subscr. to: Sage Publications, Inc., Box 5084, Thousand Oaks, CA 91359; Overseas subscr. to: Sage Publications, Ltd., 6 Bonhill St., London EC2A 4PU, England; Sage Publications India Pvt. Ltd., P.O. Box 4215, New Delhi 110 048, India) Ed. David Goldfield. adv.; bk.rev.; bibl.; charts; illus.; stat.; index. circ. 1,350. (back issues avail.) **Indexed:** A.B.C.Pol.Sci., Amer.Bibl.Slavic & E.Eur.Stud., Amer.Hist.& Life, Arts & Hum.Cit.Ind., Avery Ind.Archit.Per., Bibl.Cart., Bk.Rev.Ind. (1980-), Child.Bk.Rev.Ind. (1980-), Curr.Cont., Geo.Abstr., Hist.Abstr., Hum.Ind., Lang.& Lang.Behav.Abstr., Mid.East: Abstr.& Ind., Sage Pub.Admin.Abstr., Sociol.Abstr., SSCI. **Document type:** academic/scholarly publication.
     —BLDSC (5071.557000); Faxon; UnCover; SWETS; UMI. **CCC.**
     Description: Studies the history of cities and urban societies thoughout the world in all periods of human history.

976   US   ISSN 1049-5932
JOURNAL OF WILKINSON COUNTY HISTORY. 1990. irreg., vol.3, 1992. price varies. Woodville Civic Club, Box 1055, Woodville, MS 39669.
TEL 601-888-3998.

JOURNAL OF WOMEN'S HISTORY. see *WOMEN'S STUDIES*

HISTORY   2885

909   US   ISSN 1045-6007
D1   CODEN: JWHIEC
JOURNAL OF WORLD HISTORY. 1990. s-a. $25 to individuals; institutions $35 (foreign $40). (World History Association) University of Hawaii Press, Journals Department, 2840 Kolowalu St., Honolulu, HI 96822. TEL 808-956-8833.
FAX 808-988-6052. (Individual subscr. to: c/o Prof. Richard Rosen, Exec. Dir., Department of History and Politics, Drexel University, Philadelphia, PA 19104) Ed. Jerry H. Bentley. adv.; bk.rev.; index. circ. 1,565. (back issues avail.; reprint service avail. from UMI) **Document type:** academic/scholarly publication.
     —BLDSC (5072.675000); Faxon; UnCover; UMI.
     Description: Devoted to historical analysis from a global point of view.
     Refereed Serial

940 949   YU
JUGOSLOVENSKI ISTORIJSKI CASOPIS. 1962. q. 60 din. Savez Drustava Istoricara Jugoslavije, Karnedzijeva 2, Box 545, Belgrade, Yugoslavia. **Indexed:** Amer.Hist.& Life (until 1986), Hist.Abstr. (until 1986).

KAERNTNER MUSEUMSSCHRIFTEN. see *MUSEUMS AND ART GALLERIES*

900 491   PL
KATOLICKI UNIWERSYTET LUBELSKI. WYDZIAL HISTORYCZNO-FILOLOGICZNY. ROZPRAWY. (Text in Polish; summaries in German) 1947. irreg. price varies. Katolicki Uniwersytet Lubelski, Towarzystwo Naukowe, Ul. Gliniana 21, 20-616 Lublin, Poland. index. circ. 450.

720   US   ISSN 0883-0061
VK1000
KEEPER'S LOG. 1984. q. membership. United States Lighthouse Society, 244 Kearny St., 5th Fl., San Francisco, CA 94108. TEL 415-362-7255. Ed. Wayne Wheeler. adv.; bk.rev.; video rev.; circ. 6,000 (paid). (back issues avail.)
     Description: Educates, informs, and entertains those interested in America's lighthouses, past and present.

930   US   ISSN 0899-3564
KEEPING ANCIENT ROME ALIVE. 1987. 6/yr. $5. 27824 Hummingbird Ct., Hayward, CA 94545-4042. TEL 415-784-0761. Ed. Martin E. Morrison. adv. circ. 150.
     Description: Devoted to ancient Rome and its influence as seen through archeology, culture, history, mythology, numismatics, religion, language, and literature.

900   SA   ISSN 0023-2084
DT766
KLEIO. (Text in Afrikaans, English) 1969. a. R.7.98 (overseas $6) (effective 1994). University of South Africa, Department of History, P.O. Box 392, Pretoria 0001, South Africa. FAX 27-12-429-2533. TELEX 350068 SA. Ed. L.J. Twyman. adv.; bk.rev.; bibl.; illus.; cum.index: vols.1-4 in vol.6, no.2, 1974. circ. 3,100. (also avail. in microfilm; back issues avail.) **Indexed:** Amer.Hist.& Life, Hist.Abstr., Ind.S.A.Per. **Document type:** academic/scholarly publication.

940   NE   ISSN 0165-6449
KLEIO. 1959. 10/yr. fl.90 (Europe fl.120; elsewhere fl.130) (effective 1994). Vereniging van Docenten in Geschiedenis en Staatsinrichting in Nederland, Omloop West 9, 3402 XM IJsselstein, Netherlands. TEL 31-3408-83576. Ed. Mrs. T. Bogaerts-Stoopman. adv.; bk.rev. circ. 2,500. **Indexed:** Amer.Hist.& Life (until 1992), Hist.Abstr. (until 1992). **Document type:** academic/scholarly publication.
     Description: Covers history and the teaching history.

KLIO; Beitraege zur Alten Geschichte. see *CLASSICAL STUDIES*

KNJIZEVNA KRITIKA; casopis za umetnicku, istorijsku i filosofsku kritiku. see *LITERATURE*

KOKALOS. see *ARCHAEOLOGY*

900   II
KOODAL HISTORICAL SERIES. (Text in English) irreg. Koodal Publishers, 217-A South Masi St., Madurai 625001, Tamil Nadu, India. Ed. N. Subrahmanian. bibl.

HISTORY

KRISIS; beitraege zur kritik der warengesellschaft. see POLITICAL SCIENCE

900　　　　　　　GW
KRITISCHE STUDIEN ZUR GESCHICHTSWISSENSCHAFT. 1972. irreg. price varies. Vandenhoeck und Ruprecht, Robert-Bosch-Str. 6, 37079 Goettingen, Germany. TEL 0551-6959-0. FAX 0551-695917. (Subscr. to: 37070 Goettingen, Germany) **Document type:** monographic series.

300 900　　　　GW
KULTUR UND GESELLSCHAFT; Neue historische Forschungen. 1976. irreg. price varies. Friedrich Frommann Verlag Guenther Holzboog, Koenig-Karl-Str. 27, 70372 Stuttgart, Germany. TEL 0711-9559690. FAX 0711-9559691. Ed. R. van Duelmen. **bibl. Document type:** monographic series.

900 790.13 310　　AU
KULTUR- UND STADTNACHRICHTEN AUS WEITRA. 1965. q. Stadtgemeinde Weitra, Rathaus, A-3970 Weitra, Austria. TEL 02856-2378. FAX 02856-3148. Ed. Hans Klestorfer. **adv.; bk.rev.** circ. 1,500. **Document type:** government publication, newsletter.
Description: Covers municipal affairs, rules and regulations, municipal budget and expenditures. Includes list of cultural events and exhibitions, population statistics, and personals.

900　　　　CI　　ISSN 0351-0557
KULTURNA BASTINA. (Text in Croatian) 1973. a. $5. Drustvo Prijatelja Kulturne Bastine Split, Titova Obala 23, 58000 Split, Croatia. TEL 058 583-999. (Co-sponsor: Samoupravna Interesna Zajednica u Oblasti Kulture Opcine Split) circ. 800. (back issues avail.)
Description: Covers history, culture, the arts, and archeology.

KUNSTHISTORISCHES INSTITUT IN FLORENZ. MITTEILUNGEN. see ART

KWARTALNIK HISTORII PRASY POLSKIEJ. see JOURNALISM

943.8　　　　PL　　ISSN 0023-592X
DK4600.066
KWARTALNIK OPOLSKI. (Text in Polish; summaries in English) 1955. q. $10. (Polska Akademia Nauk) Opolskie Towarzystwo Przyjaciol Nauk, Ul. Zamkowa 2, 45-016 Opole, Poland. (Dist. by: Ars Polona-Ruch, Krakowskie Przedmiescie 7, Warsaw, Poland) bk.rev.; charts; illus.; index, cum.index every 5 yrs. circ. 1,000. **Indexed:** Bibl.Ling.

296 943　　　US　　ISSN 0023-625X
DS135.G3
L B I NEWS. 1960. s-a. membership. Leo Baeck Institute, 129 E. 73rd St., New York, NY 10021. TEL 212-744-6400. Ed. Gabrielle Bamberger. illus. circ. 3,500. (tabloid format)

L H R T NEWSLETTER. (Library History Round Table) see LIBRARY AND INFORMATION SCIENCES

350 100 800　　NE　　ISSN 0304-0003
AS243
L I A S: SOURCES AND DOCUMENTS RELATING TO THE EARLY MODERN HISTORY OF IDEAS.. (Text in English, French, German) 1974. s-a. fl.80($40) (Stichting L I A S) A P A, Postbus 122, 3600 AC Maarssen, Netherlands. TEL 31-30-436166. FAX 31-30-420250. Eds. J.A.H. Bots, J. Roegiers. adv.; bk.rev.; bibl. circ. 500. (back issues avail.) **Indexed:** Arts & Hum.Cit.Ind., Curr.Cont. **Document type:** academic/scholarly publication.
—BLDSC (5186.250000); Faxon.

LABOUR HISTORY; a journal of labour and social history. see BUSINESS AND ECONOMICS — Labor And Industrial Relations

LABOUR HISTORY REVIEW. see BUSINESS AND ECONOMICS — Labor And Industrial Relations

LABYRINTHOS. see ART

900　　　　US　　ISSN 0075-7772
LAMAR LECTURE SERIES. 1958. a. price varies. (Eugenia Dorothy Blount Lamar Lectures at Mercer University, Macon, Georgia) University of Georgia Press, 330 Research Dr., Athens, GA 30602-4901. TEL 706-369-6130. FAX 706-369-6131. (reprint service avail. from UMI) **Document type:** monographic series.

LANDESMUSEUM FUER KAERNTEN. BUCHREIHE. see MUSEUMS AND ART GALLERIES

930　　　　GW　　ISSN 0232-5446
LANDESMUSEUM FUER VORGESCHICHTE, DRESDEN. KLEINE SCHRIFTEN. 1980. irreg., vol.5, 1986. price varies. (Landesmuseum fuer Vorgeschichte) VEB Deutscher Verlag der Wissenschaften, Postfach 1216, Berlin, Germany. **Document type:** monographic series.

LANTERNINO; bimestrale di storia della medicina e medicina sociale. see MEDICAL SCIENCES

900　　　　　IT
LATOMISTICA. (Text in English and Italian) irreg., latest no.4. price varies. Angelo Longo Editore, Via Paolo Costa 33, P.O. Box 431, 48100 Ravenna, Italy. TEL 0544-217026. Ed. Giordano Gamberini. circ. 2,000. **Document type:** monographic series.

LECCIONES DE HISTORIA JURIDICA. see LAW

946　　　　　US　　ISSN 1046-1671
LECTURE SERIES WORKING PAPERS. 1988. irreg. University of Maryland, Dept. of Spanish and Portuguese, 2215 Jimenez Hall, College Park, MD 20742.

LEEDS PHILOSOPHICAL AND LITERARY SOCIETY. PROCEEDINGS. LITERARY AND HISTORICAL SECTION. see LITERATURE

900　　　　UK
LEICESTER - NOTTINGHAM STUDIES IN ANCIENT SOCIETY. 1991. irreg. Routledge, 11 New Fetter Ln., London EC4P 4EE, England. TEL 071-583-9855. FAX 071-583-4519. TELEX 263398-ROUT-G. **Document type:** academic/scholarly publication.

942 929　　　UK　　ISSN 0024-0664
LEICESTERSHIRE HISTORIAN. 1967. a. £5. Leicestershire Local History Council, c/o Mr. P.G. Lindley, 42 Priesthills Rd., Hinckley, Leics. LE10 1AJ, England. Ed. J. Goodacre. bk.rev.; bibl. circ. 500. **Indexed:** Br.Archaeol.Abstr., Br.Hum.Ind. **Document type:** academic/scholarly publication.

296 943　　　GW　　ISSN 0024-0915
DS135.G3
LEO BAECK INSTITUT. BULLETIN. (Text in German) 1957. 3/yr. DM.38. Verlag Anton Hain Meisenheim GmbH, Savignystr. 61, 60325 Frankfurt a.M., Germany. FAX 069-747822. Ed.Bd. adv.; index, cum.index: vol.1-12. circ. 2,500. **Indexed:** Amer.Hist.& Life, Hist.Abstr., M.L.A.

900　　　　UK　　ISSN 0075-8744
DS135.G3
LEO BAECK INSTITUTE. YEAR BOOK. 1956. a. £27. Secker & Warburg, Michelin House, 81 Fulham Rd., London SW3 6RB, England. TEL 071-581-9393. FAX 071-589-8421. TELEX 920191. (Dist. in U.S. by: Leo Baeck Institute, 129 E. 73rd St., New York, NY 10021) Ed. Max Eilenberg. bibl.; index, cum.index: vols.1-35, pub. in 1993. circ. 2,700. **Indexed:** Amer.Bibl.Slavic & E.Eur.Stud., Amer.Hist.& Life., Hist.Abstr. **Document type:** academic/scholarly publication.
—BLDSC (9388.990000).

LEOBENER GRUENE HEFTE. NEUE FOLGE. see MINES AND MINING INDUSTRY

LETTRES ET CULTURES DE LANGUES FRANCAISES. see LITERATURE

900 020　　　HU　　ISSN 0024-1512
LEVELTARI KOZLEMENYEK/ARCHIVAL PUBLICATIONS. (Text in Hungarian; summaries in English) 1923. s-a. $19. Magyar Orszagos Leveltar, Becsi Kapu ter 2-4, 1014 Budapest, Hungary. TEL 1-565-811. (Dist. by: Akademiai Kiado, P.O. Box 245, 1519 Budapest, Hungary) Ed. Janos Lakos. adv.; bk.rev.; illus.; index. **Indexed:** Amer.Hist.& Life, Hist.Abstr., Numis.Lit. **Document type:** academic/scholarly publication.

296 943　　　US
LIBRARY & ARCHIVES NEWS. 1975. s-a. free to qualified personnel. Leo Baeck Institute, 129 E. 73rd St., New York, NY 10021. TEL 212-744-6400. Ed. Gabrielle Bamberger. circ. 2,500.
Description: Describes German-Jewish history.

LIBRARY HISTORY. see LIBRARY AND INFORMATION SCIENCES

LINGUARUM MINORUM DOCUMENTA HISTORIOGRAPHICA. see LINGUISTICS

907 371.3　　　CC　　ISSN 0457-6241
LISHI JIAOXUE/HISTORY TEACHING. (Text in Chinese; table of contents in English) m. Y15($52.20) Tianjin Lishi Jiaoxue She, 251, Machang Dao, Hexi Qu, Tianjin 300074, People's Republic of China. TEL 318434. (Dist. outside China by: China International Book Trading Corp., P.O. Box 2820, Beijing, P.R.C.; Dist. in US by: China Books & Periodicals, Inc., 2929 24th St., San Francisco, CA 94110. TEL 415-282-2994) Ed. Wu Tingqin. bk.rev.
—UnCover.
Description: Contains articles on historical research as well as on the teaching of history, including textbooks and educational methods.

907 371.3　　　CC
LISHI JIAOXUE WENTI. (Text in Chinese) bi-m. Y8.10. Huadong Shifan Daxue, Lishi Xi - East China Normal University, Department of History, 3663 Zhongshan Beilu, Shanghai 200063, People's Republic of China. TEL 2577577.
Description: Covers problems in the teaching of history.

907　　　　CC　　ISSN 0459-1909
LISHI YANJIU/HISTORICAL RESEARCH. (Text in Chinese) 1954. bi-m. $60. Shehui Kexue Zazhishe, A-158 Gulou Xidajie, Beijing 100720, People's Republic of China. TEL 441531.

LITHIQUES. see ARCHITECTURE

LITTERAE NUMISMATICAE VINDOBONENSES. see NUMISMATICS

900　　　　US
LIVING HISTORY ASSOCIATION QUARTERLY. 1987. q. (Living History Association, Inc.) Historical Supply Co., Box 578, Wilmington, VT 05363-0578. Ed. Stephen DelSignore. **Document type:** academic/scholarly publication.

900　　　　SZ
LIVRET DE LA QUATRIEME SECTION, ECOLE PRATIQUE HAUTES ETUDES. 1880. irreg., no.3, 1987. price varies. Librairie Droz S.A., 11 rue Massot, CH-1211 Geneva 12, Switzerland. TEL 022-3466666. FAX 022-3472391. **Indexed:** Numis.Lit. **Document type:** monographic series.
Formerly (until 1979): Ecole Pratique des Hautes Etudes. Quatrieme Section. Historiques et Philologiques. Annuaire (ISSN 0078-964X)

LONGITUDE; tidskrift fraan de sju haven/magazine of the seven seas. see TRANSPORTATION — Ships And Shipping

900 800　　　CN
CB411
LUMEN. (Text in English and French) 1982. a. $29.95. (Canadian Society for Eighteenth Century Studies) Academic Printing & Publishing, P.O. Box 4218, S. Edmonton, AB T6E 4T2, Canada. TEL 403-435-5898. FAX 403-435-5852. Ed. R.J. Merrett. circ. 300.
—BLDSC (5358.010300).
Formerly (until 1992): Man and Nature (ISSN 0824-3298)

LUND STUDIES IN ART HISTORY. see ART

900　　　　SW　　ISSN 0076-1494
LUND STUDIES IN INTERNATIONAL HISTORY. (Text in English and German) 1970. irreg. price varies. (University of Lund) Lund University Press, P.O. Box 141, S-221 00 Lund, Sweden. TEL 46-46-312000. FAX 46-46-305338. TELEX 33345. Ed.Bd. index. circ. 850. **Document type:** academic/scholarly publication.

909 CN ISSN 0226-7586
F1022
MCGILL UNIVERSITY. REGISTER. (Text in English and French) 1980. s-a. Can.$5($5) McGill University, Arts & Science Undergraduate Society, 3480 McTavish St., Montreal, Que., Canada. TEL 514-392-4311. Ed. Anne MacLennan. bk.rev.; index.

900 II ISSN 0464-5030
MAHARAJA SAYAJIRAO UNIVERSITY OF BARODA. DEPARTMENT OF HISTORY SERIES. 1958. irreg. price varies. Maharaja Sayajirao University of Baroda, Department of History, Baroda 390002, Gujarat, India. Ed. Satish C. Misra. circ. 500.

900 GW
▼**MAJESTAS;** Rulership - Souverainete - Herrschertum. 1993. irreg. DM.58. Boehlau Verlag GmbH, Theodor-Heuss-Str. 76, 51149 Cologne, Germany. TEL 02203-307021. FAX 02203-307349. Ed.Bd. **Document type:** monographic series.

900 US
MAKING OF THE TWENTIETH CENTURY. irreg. St. Martin's Press, 175 Fifth Ave., New York, NY 10010.

909 UK ISSN 0025-3359
VK1
MARINER'S MIRROR. 1911. q. $40 to individuals; institutions $55. Society for Nautical Research, Department of History, University of Exeter, Devon, England. FAX 0392-264377. Ed. Michael Duffy. adv.; bk.rev.; illus.; index, cum.index. circ. 2,200. (reprint service avail. from KTO) **Indexed:** Amer.Hist.& Life, Br.Archaeol.Abstr., Br.Hum.Ind., Curr.Cont., Hist.Abstr., Mid.East: Abstr.& Ind., Numis.Lit., So.Pac.Per.Ind. **Document type:** academic/scholarly publication.
—BLDSC (5381.000000); Faxon; UnCover; SWETS.

MARK. see LITERARY AND POLITICAL REVIEWS

MARTYRS' SHRINE MESSAGE. see RELIGIONS AND THEOLOGY — Roman Catholic

900 US ISSN 0025-424X
E171
MARYLAND HISTORIAN. 1970. s-a. $10 to individuals; institutions $15. University of Maryland, Department of History, College Park, MD 20742. TEL 301-405-4331. Ed. Kevin Murphy. adv.; bk.rev.; bibl.; stat. circ. 200. (also avail. in microform from UMI; reprint service avail. from UMI) **Indexed:** Amer.Hist.& Life, Arts & Hum.Cit.Ind., Chic.Per.Ind., Curr.Cont., Hist.Abstr.
—UMI.
Refereed Serial

900 CN ISSN 1183-1073
F1021
MATERIAL HISTORY REVIEW/REVUE D'HISTOIRE DE LA CULTURE MATERIELLE. (Text in English and French) 1977. s-a. Can.$18 to individuals; institutions Can.$30. National Museum of Science and Technology - Musee National des Sciences et de la Technologie, Box 9724, Sta. T, Ottawa, ON K1G 5A3, Canada. TEL 613-990-7529. FAX 613-990-3635. Ed. Robin Inglis. adv. contact: Bob Jeckells. bk.rev.; illus. circ. 500. (back issues avail.) **Indexed:** Amer.Hist.& Life, Hist.Abstr. **Document type:** academic/scholarly publication.
Formerly (until 1991): Material History Bulletin - Bulletin d'Histoire de la Culture Materielle (ISSN 0703-489X)
Description: Presents the material history of Canada through feature articles, research reports, exhibit reviews, conference reports and notes and comments.
Refereed Serial

900 PL ISSN 0079-4481
MATERIALY HISTORYCZNO-METODYCZNE. 1966. irreg. price varies. Politechnika Poznanska, Pl. Curie Sklodowskiej 5, Poznan, Poland. **Document type:** academic/scholarly publication.
Formerly: Politechnika Poznanska. Materialy Historyczno-Metodyczne. Studia Filozoficzne.
Description: History of Politechnika Poznanska.

900 US ISSN 0897-3954
AG5
A MATTER OF FACT: STATEMENTS CONTAINING STATISTICS ON CURRENT SOCIAL, ECONOMIC AND POLITICAL ISSUES. Key Title: A Matter of Fact. 1984. s-a. $91.50 (effective 1994). Pierian Press, Box 1808, Ann Arbor, MI 48106. TEL 313-434-5530. FAX 313-434-6409. Ed. C. Edward Wall. **Document type:** abstracting/indexing.
●Also available online.
Also available on CD-ROM. Producer(s): SilverPlatter Information, Inc.
Formerly: Matter of Fact: A Digest of Current Facts, with Citations to Sources.

937 GW ISSN 0927-1759
MAVORS. ROMAN ARMY RESEARCHES. irreg., vol.10, 1993. Franz Steiner Verlag Wiesbaden GmbH, Birkenwaldstr. 44, 70191 Stuttgart, Germany. TEL 0711-2582-0. FAX 0711-2582-290. TELEX 723636-DAZ-D. (Subscr. to: Postfach 101061, 70009 Stuttgart, Germany) Ed. M.P. Speidel. **Document type:** academic/scholarly publication.
—BLDSC (5413.279930).

900 GW
MAX-PLANCK-INSTITUT FUER GESCHICHTE. VEROEFFENTLICHUNGEN. 1958. irreg. price varies. (Max-Planck-Institut fuer Geschichte) Vandenhoeck & Ruprecht, Robert-Bosch-Breite 6, 37079 Goettingen, Germany. Ed.Bd. (back issues avail.) **Document type:** proceedings.

MEANDER; miesiecznik poswiecony kulturze swiata starozytnego. see CLASSICAL STUDIES

976 US ISSN 0890-7595
MEDALLION. 1963. bi-m. $7. Texas Historical Commission, Box 12276, Austin, TX 78711. TEL 512-463-6100. FAX 512-463-4960. Ed. Roni Morales. bk.rev. circ. 2,000. (back issues avail.) **Document type:** newsletter.
Description: Gives news about historic preservation in Texas.

MEDIEVAL AND EARLY MODERN MYSTICISM. see RELIGIONS AND THEOLOGY

940.1 950 NE ISSN 0928-5520
▼**THE MEDIEVAL MEDITERRANEAN;** peoples, economies and cultures 400-1453. 1993. irreg., vol.3, 1993. price varies. E.J. Brill, P.O. Box 9000, 2300 PA Leiden, Netherlands. TEL 31-71-312624. FAX 31-71-312532. TELEX 39296 BRILL NL. (In N. America, E.J. Brill, 24 Hudson St., Kinderhook, NY 12106. TEL 800-962-4406. FAX 518-758-1959) Ed.Bd. illus. (back issues avail.) **Document type:** monographic series.
Description: Publishes studies relating to all aspects of the medieval Mediterranean world, including discussions of specific areas, cities, and ideas, as well as investigations of broader issues crossing linguistic, political and cultural boundaries.
Refereed Serial

MEDIZINHISTORISCHES JOURNAL. see MEDICAL SCIENCES

900 SP ISSN 0210-2943
MEMORIAS DE HISTORIA ANTIGUA. 1978. a. 2800 ptas. Universidad de Oviedo, Instituto de Historia Antigua, Facultad de Geografia e Historia, Oviedo, Spain. (Subscr. to: Servicio de Publicaciones, Un. de Oviedo, Calle Arias de Velasco s-n, 30005 Oviedo, Spain) Ed. Narciso Santos Yanguas. circ. 500.

900 200 IT ISSN 1121-9343
MEMORIE DOMENICANE. 1884; N.S. 1970. a. price varies. Centro Riviste della Provincia Romana dei Frati Predicatori, Piazza S. Domenico 1, 51100 Pistoia, Italy. Ed. Eugenio Marino. bk.rev.; bibl. circ. 400. (tabloid format) **Indexed:** CERDIC, RILA.

940 GW ISSN 0340-8140
MENDELSSOHN STUDIEN; Beitraege zur neueren deutschen Kultur- und Wirtschaftsgeschichte. (Text in English and German) 1972. irreg., vol.8, 1993. price varies. (Mendelssohn-Gesellschaft e.V.) Duncker und Humblot GmbH, Postfach 410329, 12113 Berlin, Germany. TEL 030-7900060. FAX 030-79000361. Eds. Cecile Lowenthal-Hensel, Rudolf Elvers. **Indexed:** RILM. **Document type:** monographic series.

900 150 NZ ISSN 0111-8854
AP7.5
MENTALITIES/MENTALITES. (Text in English and French) 1982. 2/yr. $40 to individuals; institutions $60. Outrigger Publishers Ltd., P.O. Box 1198, Hamilton, New Zealand. Ed.Bd. adv.; bk.rev.
—CCC.

900 BU
METODOLOGICHESKI I ISTORIOGRAFSKI PROBLEMI NA ISTORICHESKATA NAUKA. (Text in Bulgarian; summaries in English, French, German and Russian) 1973. irreg. 4.31 lv. (Bulgarska Akademiia na Naukite, Institut za Istoriia) Publishing House of the Bulgarian Academy of Sciences, Acad. G. Bonchev St., Bldg. 6, 1113 Sofia, Bulgaria. (Dist. by: Hemus, 6, Rouski Blvd., 1000 Sofia, Bulgaria) circ. 570. (reprint service avail. from IRC)

900 IS ISSN 0334-0740
METOV TIBERIA. 1983. irreg. Bar Ilan University, Faculty for Israel History, Center for Research on Tiberias, Ramat Gan, Israel.

MIDDLE EASTERN STUDIES. see POLITICAL SCIENCE

MILITAERGESCHICHTE. see MILITARY

MILITAERGESCHICHTLICHE MITTEILUNGEN. see MILITARY

MILITARY COLLECTOR & HISTORIAN. see ANTIQUES

MILITARY HISTORICAL SOCIETY. BULLETIN. see MILITARY

MILITARY HISTORY JOURNAL/KRYGSHISTORIESE TYDSKRIF. see MILITARY

951 CC
MINGUO CHUNQIU. (Text in Chinese) bi-m. Jiangsu Guji Chubanshe - Jiangsu Classic Literature Publishers, 165 Zhongyang Lu, Nanjing, Jiangsu 210009, People's Republic of China. TEL 631836. Ed. Gao Jiyan.

MINIATURE WARGAMES. see MILITARY

MISCELLANEA FRANCESCANA; rivista trimestrale di scienze teologiche e di studi francescani. see RELIGIONS AND THEOLOGY — Roman Catholic

900 022 GW ISSN 0540-4746
MITTEILUNGEN FUER DIE ARCHIVPFLEGE IN BAYERN. 1955. irreg., vol.31, 1989. price varies. Generaldirektion der Staatlichen Archive Bayerns, Postfach 221152, 80501 Munich, Germany. TEL 089-28638482. FAX 089-28638615. (Subscr. to: Verlag Michael Lassleben, Lange Gasse 19, 93183 Kallmunz, Germany) Ed. Bodo Uhl. (back issues avail.) **Document type:** government publication.

909 UK ISSN 0956-0726
MODERN HISTORY REVIEW. 1989. q. £16.50 (foreign £26.50). Philip Allan Publishers Ltd., Deddington, Oxfordshire OX15 0SE, England. TEL 0869-38652. FAX 0869-38803. (back issues avail.)

MONUMENTA CHARTAE PAPYRACEAE HISTORIAM ILLUSTRANTIA/COLLECTION OF WORKS AND DOCUMENTS ILLUSTRATING THE HISTORY OF PAPER. see PAPER AND PULP

MONUMENTA NIPPONICA; studies in Japanese culture. see ORIENTAL STUDIES

947 RU ISSN 0130-0083
DK1
MOSKOVSKII UNIVERSITET. VESTNIK. SERIYA 9: ISTORIYA. (Text in Russian; contents page in English) 1946. bi-m. 13.50 Rub. Moskovskii Universitet, Ul. Gertsena 5-7, 103009 Moscow, Russia. (Dist. by: Mezhdunarodnaya Kniga, ul. Dimitrova 39, Moscow G-200, Russia) bk.rev.; bibl.; index. circ. 1,600. **Indexed:** Amer.Hist.& Life, Hist.Abstr., Numis.Lit.
Formerly: Moskovskii Universitet. Vestnik. Seriya Istoricheskie Nauki (ISSN 0027-139X)

790.1 US ISSN 1073-5151
MOVES. bi-m. $23 (foreign $30). Decision Games, Box 4049, Lancaster, CA 93539-4049. TEL 805-722-2088. Ed. Scott Jackson; Pub. Chirstopher R. Cummins. circ. 4,000.
Description: Review and analysis of historical board games, including variants and player tips.

HISTORY

930   GW   ISSN 0077-2003
MUENSTERSCHE BEITRAEGE ZUR VOR- UND FRUEHGESCHICHTE. 1964. irreg. price varies. (Universitaet Muenster) Verlag August Lax, Postfach 10 08 65, 31108 Hildesheim, Germany. Eds. K Tackenberg, K.J. Narr.
    Formerly: Muenstersche Beitraege zur Vorgeschichtsforschung.

913 069   GW   ISSN 0079-4376
MUSEUM FUER UR- UND FRUEHGESCHICHTE DER BEZIRKE POTSDAM, FRANKFURT - ODER UND COTTBUS. VEROEFFENTLICHUNGEN. 1962. a. price varies. (Museum fuer Ur- und Fruehgeschichte, Potsdam) VEB Deutscher Verlag der Wissenschaften, Postfach 1216, 1080 Berlin, Germany. Ed. Bernhard Gramsch. **Indexed:** A.I.C.P.

MUSEUM NEWS. see *MUSEUMS AND ART GALLERIES*

NAMIBIA SCIENTIFIC SOCIETY. NEWSLETTER. see *SCIENCES: COMPREHENSIVE WORKS*

NARODNI MUZEUM V PRAZE. CASOPIS: RADA HISTORICKA. see *MUSEUMS AND ART GALLERIES*

900   XR   ISSN 0036-5335
NARODNI MUZEUM V PRAZE. SBORNIK. RADA A: HISTORIE/ACTA MUSEI NATIONALIS PRAGAE. SERIES A: HISTORIA. (Text mainly in Czech; summaries in English, French, German, Russian) 1937. q. 20 Kcs.($21.20) Narodni Muzeum, Historicke Muzeum, Vaclavske nam. 68, 115 79 Prague 1, Czech Republic. (Dist. by: Artia, Ve Smeckach 30, 111 27 Prague 1, Czech Republic) Ed. Karel Sklenar. adv.; illus.; index, cum.index. **Indexed:** Hist.Abstr., Numis.Lit.
    Formerly: Narodni Muzeum v Praze. Sbornik: Historie.

NARODNI TECHNICKE MUZEUM. ROZPRAVY. see *TECHNOLOGY: COMPREHENSIVE WORKS*

900   US
NATIONAL HISTORIC COMMUNAL SOCIETIES ASSOCIATION. NEWSLETTER. 4/yr. University of Southern Indiana, School of Liberal Arts, History Department, Center for Communal Studies, Evansville, IN 47712. TEL 812-464-1719. FAX 812-464-1960.

900   CN   ISSN 0316-1900
NATIONAL MUSEUM OF MAN. MERCURY SERIES. HISTORY DIVISION. PAPERS/MUSEE NATIONAL DE L'HOMME. COLLECTION MERCURE. DIVISION DE L'HISTOIRE. DOSSIERS.* (Text in English or French) 1972. irreg., latest no.41. free. National Museum of Man, History Division, c/o Canadian Museum of Civilization, 100 Laurier St., Hull, PQ J8X 4H2, Canada.

NEGRO HISTORY BULLETIN. see *ETHNIC INTERESTS*

NETHERLANDS. RIJKSMUSEUM AMSTERDAM. BULLETIN. see *ART*

943   GW
NEUZEIT IM AUFBAU; Darstellung und Dokumentation. 1977. irreg. price varies. Friedrich Frommann Verlag Guenther Holzboog, Koenig-Karl-Str. 27, 70372 Stuttgart, Germany. TEL 0711-9559690. FAX 0711-9559691. Ed.Bd. **Document type:** monographic series.

900   US
NEW PERSPECTIVES IN HISTORY.* irreg. price varies. Houghton Mifflin Co., 222 Berkeley St., Boston, MA 02116-3764. TEL 617-725-5000. FAX 617-227-5409.

NEW SOCIETY OF LETTERS AT LUND. PUBLICATIONS. see *ART*

300   US   ISSN 0190-1990
NEW YORK TIMES CURRENT EVENTS EDITION. 1979. m. $280. (New York Times Company) University Microfilms International, 300 N. Zeeb Rd., Ann Arbor, MI 48106. TEL 313-761-4700; 800-521-0600. FAX 313-761-2003. s-a. cum.index.

975   US
NEWARK HISTORICAL SOCIETY NEWSLETTER. 1982. q. $10. Newark Historical Society, Box 711, Newark, DE 19715. TEL 302-453-0966. circ. 500. (tabloid format; back issues avail.)
    Description: Studies the history of Newark.

NEWCOMEN SOCIETY FOR THE STUDY OF THE HISTORY OF ENGINEERING AND TECHNOLOGY. TRANSACTIONS. see *ENGINEERING*

NEWSCOPE - ELEMENTARY EDITION; weekly news summary and teaching quiz. see *EDUCATION — Teaching Methods And Curriculum*

NEWSCOPE - HIGH SCHOOL-COLLEGE EDITION; a weekly news summary and teaching quiz. see *EDUCATION — Teaching Methods And Curriculum*

NEWSCOPE - MIDDLE-INTERMEDIATE-JUNIOR HIGH SCHOOL EDITION; a weekly news summary and teaching quiz. see *EDUCATION — Teaching Methods And Curriculum*

900   GW
NIEDERSAECHSISCHE ARCHIVVERWALTUNG. VEROEFFENTLICHUNGEN. 1953. irreg. Vandenhoeck und Ruprecht, Robert-Bosch-Breite 6, 37079 Goettingen, Germany. TEL 0551-6959-0. FAX 0551-695917. (Subscr. to: 37070 Goettingen, Germany) **Document type:** monographic series.

NIEUWE NEDERLANDSE BIJDRAGEN TOT DE GESCHIEDENIS DER GENEESKUNDE EN DER NATUURWETENSCHAPPEN. see *MEDICAL SCIENCES*

900   GW   ISSN 0934-8913
GV573
NIKEPHOROS; Zeitschrift fuer Sport und Kultur im Altertum. 1988. a. DM.98. Weidmannsche Verlagsbuchhandlung GmbH, Hagentorwall 7, 31134 Hildesheim, Germany. TEL 05121-15010. FAX 05121-150150. TELEX 927454-OLMS-D. (Dist. by: Hy Cohen Literary Agency Ltd., 111 W. 57th St., New York, NY 10019) Ed.Bd. circ. 600. **Document type:** academic/scholarly publication. —CCC.
    Description: Contains interdisciplinary research of sports and its cultural environment throughout ancient history.

NINETEENTH-CENTURY STUDIES. see *LITERATURE*

900   SP   ISSN 0213-375X
NORBA: REVISTA DE HISTORIA. 1980. irreg., no.10, 1990. Universidad de Extremadura, Facultad de Filosofia y Letras, Servicio de Publicaciones, C. Pizzaro 8, 10071 Caceres, Spain. TEL 24-76-50. bibl.; charts; illus.; maps.
    Supersedes in part (in 1983): Norba (ISSN 0211-0636)
    Description: Covers prehistory to contemporary history.

NORDISK TIDSKRIFT FOR VETENSKAP, KONST OCH INDUSTRI. see *LITERARY AND POLITICAL REVIEWS*

900   NO   ISSN 0029-2311
AS283
NORSKE VIDENSKAPS-AKADEMI. HISTORISK-FILOSOFISK KLASSE. AVHANDLINGER. (Text in several languages) 1925. irreg. price varies. Drammensveien 78, N-0271 Oslo 2, Norway. TEL 472-444296. FAX 472-562656. bibl. circ. 775.

NORTHWESTERNER. see *TRANSPORTATION — Railroads*

900   US   ISSN 8750-8923
E169
NOSTALGIA (MILWAUKEE). 6/yr. $14.95. R A SA RA Corporation, 9401 W. Beloit Rd., Ste. 311, Milwaukee, WI 53227. Ed. Valerie Mindel.

NOTEBOOK/CUADERNO; a literary journal. see *LITERATURE*

NOTICIARIO DE HISTORIA AGRARIA. see *AGRICULTURE*

LES NOUVEAUX CAHIERS. see *RELIGIONS AND THEOLOGY — Judaic*

909   RU   ISSN 0029-5124
NOVAYA I NOVEISHAYA ISTORIYA. (Text in Russian; summaries in English) 1957. bi-m. $101. (Rossiiskaya Akademiya Nauk, Institut Vseobshchei Istorii) Izdatel'stvo Nauka, 90 Profsoyuznaya ul., 117864 Moscow, Russia. TEL 095-336-0266. FAX 095-420-2220. (Dist. by: Mezhdunarodnaja Kniga, B. Yakimanka 39, 117049 Moscow, Russia; Dist. in U.S. by: Victor Kamkin Inc., 4956 Boiling Brook Pkwy., Rockville, MD 20852. TEL 301-881-5973. FAX 301-881-1637) Ed. S.L. Tihvinskii. bk.rev.; bibl.; illus.; index. circ. 16,000. **Indexed:** Amer.Hist.& Life, Hist.Abstr.

NUCLEAR RESISTER; a chronicle of hope. see *POLITICAL SCIENCE*

NUMEN; international review for the history of religions. see *RELIGIONS AND THEOLOGY*

NUMEN SUPPLEMENTS; studies in the history of religions. see *RELIGIONS AND THEOLOGY*

900   GW   ISSN 0078-2742
NUNTIATURBERICHTE AUS DEUTSCHLAND NEBST ERGAENZENDEN AKTENSTUECKEN. (Text in German and Latin) 1959. irreg. price varies. (Deutsches Historisches Institut in Rom, IT) Max Niemeyer Verlag, Postfach 2140, 72011 Tuebingen, Germany. TEL 07071-98940. FAX 07071-989450. (back issues avail.) **Document type:** monographic series.
    Description: Editions of the reports of the papal nuncios in the Middle Ages.

945   IT   ISSN 0029-6236
D1
NUOVA RIVISTA STORICA. 1917. 3/yr. L.118000 (foreign L.145000) (effective 1992). Societa Editrice Dante Alighieri, Via Timavo. 3-5, 00195 Rome, Italy. TEL 06-383491. FAX 06-312538. Ed. Alberto Boscolo. bk.rev.; bibl.; index, cum.index: 1917-1966. **Indexed:** Amer.Hist.& Life, Arts & Hum.Cit.Ind., Curr.Cont., Hist.Abstr., M.L.A. —BLDSC (6184.910000).

NUOVA TRADOTTA. see *MILITARY*

NUOVA UNIVERSALE STUDIUM. see *LITERATURE*

900   DK   ISSN 0029-6848
Z1007
NYT FRA HISTORIEN. 1949. s-a. DKK 140. (Jysk Selskab for Historie) Aarhus University Press, Aarhus University, DK-8000 Aarhus C, Denmark. TEL 45-86-19-70-33. FAX 45-86-19-84-33. Ed. Joergen Fink. adv.; bk.rev.; index. circ. 1,400. —SWETS.

900   KR
             CODEN: NITPAZ
OCHERKI PO ISTORII ESTESTVOZNANIYA I TEKHNIKI; respublikanskii mezhvedomstvennyi sbornik nauchnykh trudov. 1962. s-a. (Akademiya Nauk Ukrainy, Tsentr Issledovanii Nauchno-Tekhnicheskogo Potentsiala i Istorii Nauki (C.I.N.P.I.N.T.)) Vidavnitstvo Naukova Dumka, Vul. Tereshchenkivska 3, 252601 Kiev, Ukraine. (Dist. by: Mezhdunarodnaya Kniga, B. Yakimanka 39, 117049 Moscow, Russia) Ed. Yu.A. Khramov. —BLDSC (0119.156000); CASDDS.
    Formerly (until 1987): Naryzy z Istoriyi Pryrodoznavstva i Tekhniky (ISSN 0320-0647)

OESTERREICH IN GESCHICHTE UND LITERATUR MIT GEOGRAPHIE. see *LITERATURE*

OPUSCULUM; kirja- ja oppihistoriallinen aikakauskirja. Bok- och laerdomshistorisk tidskrift. see *PUBLISHING AND BOOK TRADE*

900   US
ORAL HISTORY ASSOCIATION. ANNUAL REPORT AND MEMBERSHIP DIRECTORY. a. $50 to libraries (includes all publications). Oral History Association, 1093 Broxton Ave., No. 720, Los Angeles, CA 90024. TEL 213-825-0597. **Document type:** corporate report, directory.

900 US ISSN 0474-3253
ORAL HISTORY ASSOCIATION. NEWSLETTER. Key Title: Newsletter - Oral History Association. 1967. q. $50 to libraries (includes all publications). Oral History Association, 1093 Broxton Ave., No. 720, Los Angeles, CA 90024. TEL 213-825-0597. illus.; circ. 1,400 (controlled). (back issues avail.) **Document type:** newsletter.
—BLDSC (6108.127000).

900 US ISSN 0094-0798
D16
ORAL HISTORY REVIEW. 1966. s-a. $50 to libraries (includes all publications). Oral History Association, 1093 Broxton Ave., No. 720, Los Angeles, CA 90024. TEL 213-825-0597. Ed. Michael Frisch. adv.; bk.rev.; film rev.; bibl. circ. 1,900. (back issues avail.) **Indexed:** Amer.Bibl.Slavic & E.Eur.Stud., Amer.Hist.& Life, Anthropol.Lit., Hist.Abstr., Hum.Ind. **Document type:** academic/scholarly publication.
—BLDSC (6277.520000); Faxon; UnCover; UMI.
Formerly (until 1972): National Colloquium on Oral History. Proceedings (ISSN 0077-3832)

ORAL HISTORY SERIES. see HISTORY — History Of North And South America

900 US ISSN 0882-228X
D16.3
ORGANIZATION OF AMERICAN HISTORIANS MAGAZINE OF HISTORY. 1985. q. $25 to individuals; institutions $30; members $20. Organization of American Historians, 112 N. Bryan St., Bloomington, IN 47408. TEL 812-855-7311. adv.; bk.rev.; film rev.; bibl.; charts; illus.; stat. circ. 4,000. (also avail. in microform from UMI; reprint service avail. from UMI)
—BLDSC (5333.250000); UnCover; SWETS; UMI.

ORVOSTORTENETI KOZLEMENYEK/COMMUNICATIONS DE HISTORIA ARTIS MEDICINAE. see MEDICAL SCIENCES

OSIRIS (CHICAGO); a research journal devoted to the history of science and its cultural influences. see SCIENCES: COMPREHENSIVE WORKS

PACIFIC CURRENTS. see MUSEUMS AND ART GALLERIES

PACIFIC RAIL NEWS; your Western news source. see TRANSPORTATION — Railroads

PACIFIC STUDIES; an interdisciplinary journal devoted to the study of the Pacific--its islands and adjacent countries. see SOCIAL SCIENCES: COMPREHENSIVE WORKS

PAKIN. see LITERATURE

954.9 PK ISSN 0030-9796
DS376
PAKISTAN HISTORICAL SOCIETY. JOURNAL. (Text in English, Urdu) 1953. q. Rs.220($45) (effective 1994). Pakistan Historical Society, 30 Dr. Moinul Hag Rd., New Karachi Housing Society, Karachi 75400, Pakistan. TEL 92-21-4557847. Ed. Ansar Zahid Khan. bk.rev.; bibl.; illus. circ. 2,000. (back issues avail.) **Document type:** academic/scholarly publication.
—SWETS.

930 IT
PAPYROLOGICA FLORENTINA. 1976. irreg, vol.24, 1993. price varies. Edizioni Gonnelli, Via Ricasoli, 14r, 50122 Florence, Italy. TEL 055-216835. FAX 055-2396812. Ed. Rosario Pintaudi. illus. **Document type:** monographic series.

900 GW ISSN 0933-498X
PAPYROLOGISCHE TEXTE UND ABHANDLUNGEN. 1968. irreg., no.41, 1993. price varies. Dr. Rudolf Habelt GmbH, Am Buchenhang 1, 53115 Bonn, Germany. TEL 0228-232016. FAX 0228-232017. Ed.Bd. **Document type:** monographic series.

390 913 AT
PAPYROLOGY AND HISTORICAL PERSPECTIVES. 1989. irreg., latest 1991. price varies. Ancient History Documentary Research Centre, Macquarie University, N.S.W. 2109, Australia. TEL 02-805-7512. FAX 02-805-8892. TELEX AA 122377 MACUNI. Ed.Bd. **Document type:** academic/scholarly publication.
Description: Covers studies of Greek papyri.

PARDES. see RELIGIONS AND THEOLOGY — Judaic

PARERGON. see LITERATURE

900 UK ISSN 0264-2824
JN500
PARLIAMENTARY HISTORY. 1982. 3/yr. £27.50($52.50) (Parliamentary History Yearbook Trust) Edinburgh University Press, 22 George Sq., Edinburgh EH8 9LF, Scotland. TEL 031-650-4218. FAX 031-662-0053. Ed. Clyve Jones. adv. contact: Kathryn Maclean. bk.rev.; index. circ. 500. (also avail. in microform from AMP) **Document type:** academic/scholarly publication.
—BLDSC (6406.847200); UMI. CCC.
Description: Publishes research articles and papers on all aspects of parliamentary history (including the Scottish and Irish Parliaments) from the Middle Ages to the twentieth century, covering parliamentary management, political structure, elections and the electorate, architecture and representative art.
Refereed Serial

900 UK ISSN 0260-6755
JF501
PARLIAMENTS, ESTATES & REPRESENTATION/PARLEMENTS, ETATS & REPRESENTATION. (Text in English, French or German) 1981. s-a. £65($122.50) (International Commission for the History of Representative and Parliamentary Institutions) Pageant Publishing, 5 Turners Wood, London NW11 6TD, England. TEL 081-455-3703. FAX 081-209-0726. (Dist. by: Baileys Management Services, 127 Sandgate Rd., Folkestone, Kent CT20 2BL, England) Ed. A.A. Thompson. adv.; bk.rev.; index. circ. 500. **Indexed:** Curr.Cont. **Document type:** academic/scholarly publication.
—BLDSC (6406.870500); SWETS. CCC.
Description: All aspects of the history of parliamentary and representative institutions in all countries covering all periods.

THE PASSING SHOW. see THEATER

900 UK ISSN 0031-2746
D1
PAST AND PRESENT: A JOURNAL OF HISTORICAL STUDIES. 1952. 4/yr. £54($125) (effective 1994). (Past and Present Society) Oxford University Press, Oxford Journals, Walton St., Oxford OX2 6DP, England. TEL 0865-56767. FAX 0865-56646. TELEX 837330-OXPRES-G. (U.S. subscr. to: Oxford University Press Inc., 2001 Evans Rd., Cary, NC 27513. TEL 919-677-0977) Eds. Paul Slack, Joanna Innes. adv. contact: Jane Parker. bk.rev.; charts; illus.; cum.index. circ. 3,650. **Indexed:** Amer.Hist.& Life, Br.Archaeol.Abstr., Br.Hum.Ind., Curr.Cont., Hist.Abstr., Hum.Ind., SSCI. **Document type:** academic/scholarly publication.
—BLDSC (6409.200000); Faxon; UnCover; SWETS; UMI. CCC.

940 AG ISSN 0325-2280
B5
PATRISTICA ET MEDIAEVALIA. 1975. a. $12. Universidad de Buenos Aires, Centro de Estudios de Filosofia Medieval, 25 de Mayo 217, Piso 2, 1002 Buenos Aires, Argentina. (Co-sponsor: Consejo Nacional de Investigaciones Cienficas y Tecnicas (CONICET)) Ed. Carlos Francisco Bertelloni. adv.; bk.rev. circ. 1,000. (back issues avail.) **Document type:** academic/scholarly publication.
Description: Covers research and various studies in the field of patristic and medieval philosophy.

974 US
F72.E7
PEABODY ESSEX MUSEUM COLLECTIONS. 1859. q. $25 (foreign $30) (effective 1994). Peabody Essex Museum, East India Sq., Salem, MA 01970. TEL 508-744-3390. FAX 508-744-0036. Ed. William T. La Moy. adv.; bk.rev.; index, cum.index through 1969. circ. 1,100. (also avail. in microform from UMI; reprint service avail. from UMI; back issues avail.) **Indexed:** Amer.Hist.& Life, Arts & Hum.Cit.Ind., Biol.Abstr., Curr.Cont., Hist.Abstr. **Document type:** academic/scholarly publication.
—Faxon; UnCover.
Formerly (until Oct. 1993): Essex Institute Historical Collections (ISSN 0014-0953)
Description: Highlights and promotes all facets of the Museum's international holdings in arts and culture.

PENSIERO POLITICO; rivista di storia delle idee politiche e sociali. see POLITICAL SCIENCE

905 US ISSN 1041-066X
D1
PEOPLE IN WORLD HISTORY. 1989. biennial. A B C - Clio, 130 Cremona Dr., Box 1911, Santa Barbara, CA 93116. TEL 805-968-1911. FAX 805-685-9685. Ed. Susan K. Kinnell. adv. contact: Laura Wilson. **Document type:** directory.

900 GW
PERIPLUS; Jahrbuch fuer aussereuropaeische Geschichte. 1991. a. Lit Verlag, Dieckstr. 56, 48145 Muenster, Germany. TEL 0251-235091. **Document type:** academic/scholarly publication.

973 US
PERSPECTIVES (WASHINGTON, 1962). 1962. m. membership. American Historical Association, 400 A St., S.E., Washington, DC 20003-3889. TEL 202-544-2422. FAX 202-544-8307. Ed. Robert Townsend. adv. circ. 18,000. (also avail. in microfilm from UMI) **Indexed:** Amer.Hist.& Life, Hist.Abstr., Rehabil.Lit. **Document type:** newsletter.
—BLDSC (6428.137180).
Former titles: A.H.A. Perspectives (ISSN 0745-0516); (until 1982): A.H.A. Newsletter (ISSN 0001-138X)
Description: News of the American Historical Association's activities.

900 BL ISSN 0553-8491
PESQUISAS: PUBLICACOES DE HISTORIA. (Numbering continues those of articles published in Pesquisas) no.12, 1960. irreg. price varies or exchange basis. (Universidade do Vale do Rio dos Sinos, Instituto Anchietano de Pesquisas) Unisinos, Av. Unisinos, 950, 93010 Sao Leopoldo RS, Brazil. TEL 051-5926333. FAX 0512-921035. TELEX 524076. **Indexed:** Amer.Hist.& Life, Hist.Abstr. **Document type:** academic/scholarly publication.
Supersedes in part: Pesquisas.

900 GR
PETALON; sylloge historikou hylikou peri tes nesou Androu. 1977. biennial. $10. D.I. Polemis, Ed. & Pub., Apatouria, Andros, Greece.

PHILOLOGUS; Zeitschrift fuer klassische Philologie. see CLASSICAL STUDIES

PHOTOGRAPHIC CANADIANA. see PHOTOGRAPHY

900 UK ISSN 0266-5433
PLANNING PERSPECTIVES; an international journal of history, planning and the environment. 1986. 4/yr. £145 (foreign £155). E. & F.N. Spon, 2-6 Boundary Row, London SE1 8HN, England. TEL 071-865-0066. FAX 071-522-9623. (U.S. addr.: Chapman & Hall, One Penn Plaza, 41st Fl., New York, NY 10119. TEL 212-564-1060. FAX 212-564-1505) Eds. G. Cherry, A. Sutcliffe. **Document type:** academic/scholarly publication.
—BLDSC (6509.252300); UnCover; SWETS; UMI. CCC.
Description: Historical studies of all aspects of planning with the emphasis on the industrial era.

900 327 PL ISSN 0860-5882
POLISH-ANGLOSAXON STUDIES. 1987. biennial. $11. Adam Mickiewicz University, Department of Polish-AngloSaxon Cultural Relations, Niepodleglosci 4, 61874 Poznan, Poland. TEL 52-8820. FAX 52-3103. Ed. Wojciech Liponski. adv. circ. 1,000. **Document type:** academic/scholarly publication.
Description: Covers relations of Poland with English speaking countries. Features academic level articles specializing in history and international relations.

900 PL ISSN 0239-7927
POLSKA AKADEMIA NAUK. ODDZIAL W KRAKOWIE. KOMISJA HISTORYCZNA. MATERIALY. (Text in Latin and Polish) 1958. irreg., no.31, 1989. price varies. Ossolineum, Publishing House of the Polish Academy of Sciences, Rynek 9, 50-106 Wroclaw, Poland. TEL 48-71-386-25. FAX 48-71-448-103. TELEX 0712771 OSS PL. Ed. Helena Madurowicz-Urbanska. **Document type:** monographic series, academic/scholarly publication.
Formerly (until no.29, 1984): Polska Akademia Nauk. Oddzial w Krakowie. Komisja Nauk Historycznych. Materialy.

HISTORY

800 900 PL ISSN 0079-337X
POLSKA AKADEMIA NAUK. ODDZIAL W KRAKOWIE. KOMISJA HISTORYCZNOLITERACKA. ROCZNIK. (Text in Polish; summaries in English, French, German, Russian) 1963. a. price varies. Ossolineum, Publishing House of the Polish Academy of Sciences, Rynek 9, 50-106 Wroclaw, Poland. TEL 48-71-386-25. FAX 48-71-448-103. TELEX 0172771 OSS PL. Ed. Stanislaw Burkot. circ. 580. **Document type:** academic/scholarly publication.
  Description: Papers on history of literature and theatre as well as comparative studies on Polish and foreign literature.

POMMERN; Kunst - Geschichte - Volkstum. see *ART*

900 SW ISSN 1102-0822
POPULAER HISTORIA. 1991. bi-m. SEK 250 in Sweden; other Nordic countries SEK 280; elsewhere SEK 290. Historiska Media, P.O. Box 935, S-220 09 Lund, Sweden. (Subscr. to: PROGEK, P.O. Box 31003, S-400 32 Goeteborg, Sweden. TEL 46-31-24-34-25)

PORTUGAL - MAGAZIN. see *POLITICAL SCIENCE*

900 CI ISSN 0032-5171
PORUKA BORCA. 1966. 7/yr. 15 din. Savez Udruzenja Borca Narodno Oslobodilackog Rata, Opcinski Odbori Dalmacije, Ban Mladenova 9-II, Split, Croatia. Ed. Ivan Kuljis.

900 CI ISSN 0351-9767
POVIJESNI PRILOZI/HISTORICAL CONTRIBUTIONS. (Text in Croatian; summaries in Croatian and English) 1982. a. Institut za Suvremenu Povijest - Institute for Contemporary History, Opaticka 10, 41000 Zagreb, Croatia.
  Refereed Serial

PRAXIS GESCHICHTE. see *EDUCATION — Teaching Methods And Curriculum*

907 RU ISSN 0132-0696
D16.2
PREPODAVANIE ISTORII V SHKOLE. 1934. bi-m. 9 Rub. (effective 1992). Smolensky bulv., 4, 119034 Moscow, Russia. TEL 261-6932. Ed. A.P. Prokhorov. adv.; bk.rev.; bibl.; illus.; index. cum.index: 1951-1955. circ. 135,000. **Indexed:** Amer.Hist.& Life, Hist.Abstr.
  Description: Publishes articles on history, philosophy, sociology as well as on the methodology of history teaching and social studies.

PREPUBLICATIONS. see *LINGUISTICS*

PRIMEVAL SCULPTURE. see *ANTHROPOLOGY*

PRINCETON SERIES IN CULTURE - POWER - HISTORY. see *HUMANITIES: COMPREHENSIVE WORKS*

PRINCETON STUDIES IN INTERNATIONAL HISTORY AND POLITICS. see *POLITICAL SCIENCE*

PROBLEMS OF THE CONTEMPORARY WORLD/PROBLEMES DU MONDE CONTEMPORAIN/PROBLEMAS DEL MUNDO CONTEMPORANEO. see *SOCIAL SCIENCES: COMPREHENSIVE WORKS*

PROJECT; ruling class conspiracy analysis for investors & political activists. see *POLITICAL SCIENCE*

900 BL
PROJECTO HISTORIA. irreg. price varies. Editora da Pontificia Universidade Catolica de Sao Paulo, Rua Monte Alegre, 984, 05014 Sao Paulo, SP, Brazil. TEL 62-0280. **Document type:** academic/scholarly publication.

900 IT
PROMETEO (MILAN); trimestrale di scienze e storia. 1983. q. L.48000 (foreign L.45600). Arnoldo Mondadori Editore S.p.A., Casella Postale 3968, 20101 Milan, Italy. TEL 3199345. Ed. Andreina Vanni. circ. 7,000.

930 800 NZ ISSN 0110-487X
PRUDENTIA. 1969. s-a. NZ.$25 (effective 1994). University of Auckland, Department of Classic and Ancient History, Attn: Dr. T.C. Gilmour, Private Bag, Auckland, New Zealand. TEL 3737-999. FAX 3732-878. Ed. Philip Rousseau. adv.; bk.rev.; circ. 200 (paid). (back issues avail.) **Document type:** academic/scholarly publication.
  —Faxon. **CCC.**
  Description: Devoted to thought, history and literature of the ancient world.
  Refereed Serial

900 PL ISSN 0033-2186
DK4010
PRZEGLAD HISTORYCZNY. (Text in Polish; summaries in French and Russian) 1905. q. $17. (Towarzystwo Milosnikow Historii w Warszawie) Polska Oficyna Wydawnicza B G W, Al. Jerozolimskie 91, 02-001 Warsaw, Poland. (Dist. by: Ars Polona- Ruch, Krakowskie Przedmiescie 7, Warsaw, Poland) Ed. Stefan Kieniewicz. bk.rev. circ. 2,500. (also avail. in microfiche from IDC) **Indexed:** Amer.Hist.& Life, Hist.Abstr., Numis.Lit. **Document type:** academic/scholarly publication.
  —SWETS.

900 US ISSN 0272-3433
HN1
THE PUBLIC HISTORIAN; a journal of public history. 1978. q. $37 to individuals (foreign $42); institutions $53 (foreign $58); students $17 (foreign $22) (effective 1994). (National Council on Public History) University of California Press, Journals Division, 2120 Berkeley Way, Berkeley, CA 94720. TEL 510-643-7154. FAX 510-642-9917. Ed. Otis Graham, Jr. adv.; bk.rev.; illus.; index. circ. 1,250. (also avail. in microform from UMI; back issues avail.) **Indexed:** Amer.Hist.& Life, Arts & Hum.Cit.Ind., Bk.Rev.Ind., Curr.Cont., Hist.Abstr., Mid.East: Abstr.& Ind., Soc.Sci.Ind. **Document type:** academic/scholarly publication.
  —BLDSC (6966.900000); Faxon; UnCover; UMI. **CCC.**
  Description: Covers research on public history and policy, museum exhibits, and historic preservation.
  Refereed Serial

PUBLIKATIONEN ZU WISSENSCHAFTLICHEN FILMEN. SEKTION GESCHICHTE, PUBLIZISTIK. see *MOTION PICTURES*

900 UY ISSN 0079-8061
PUPILA: LIBROS DE NUESTRO TIEMPO.* irreg. Editorial Arca, Colonia 1263, Montevideo, Uruguay.

QUADERNI FIORENTINI PER LA STORIA DEL PENSIERO GIURIDICO MODERNO. see *LAW*

900 IT ISSN 0301-6307
QUADERNI STORICI. 1966. 3/yr. L.120000. Societa Editrice Il Mulino, Strada Maggiore, 37, 40125 Bologna, Italy. TEL 051-256011. FAX 051-256034. Ed. Alberto Caracciolo. adv.; index. circ. 2,500. (back issues avail.) **Indexed:** Amer.Hist.& Life, Arts & Hum.Cit.Ind., Curr.Cont., Hist.Abstr.
  —SWETS.
  Formerly: Quaderni Storici delle Marche.

900 II ISSN 0033-5800
D1
QUARTERLY REVIEW OF HISTORICAL STUDIES. (Text in English) 1961. q. Rs.60($10) Institute of Historical Studies, 35, Theatre Road, Shakespeare Sarani, Calcutta 700 017, India. TEL 44-5326. Ed. N.R. Roy. adv.; bk.rev. circ. 900. **Indexed:** Amer.Hist.& Life, Arts & Hum.Cit.Ind., Curr.Cont., Hist.Abstr. **Document type:** academic/scholarly publication.
  —BLDSC (7207.200000).
  Description: Contains research data of interest to those in the academic fields of history.

900 910.02 CN ISSN 0226-210X
QUEBECENSIA. (Text in French) 1980. 5/yr. Can.$40 membership. Societe Historique de Quebec Inc., 43 de la Fabrique, Quebec, PQ G1R 5M1, Canada. Ed. Jacques Boutet. bk.rev.; bibl.; cum.index: 1980-1986. circ. 600. (back issues avail.) **Indexed:** RADAR. **Document type:** bulletin.
  Description: Keeps members of the Societe Historique de Quebec informed of lectures, publications, tours and members' public achievements.

900 GW ISSN 0079-9068
D5
QUELLEN UND FORSCHUNGEN AUS ITALIENISCHEN ARCHIVEN UND BIBLIOTHEKEN. (Text in German, Greek, Italian, Latin) a. price varies. (Deutsches Historisches Institut in Rom, IT) Max Niemeyer Verlag, Postfach 2140, 72011 Tuebingen, Germany. TEL 07071-98940. FAX 07071-989450. (back issues avail.) **Indexed:** Amer.Hist.& Life, Hist.Abstr. **Document type:** academic/scholarly publication.
  Description: Essays on Italian, German and Italian-German History, especially the Middle Ages.

900 UK ISSN 0163-6545
HX1
RADICAL HISTORY REVIEW. 1973. 3/yr. £19($25) to individuals (overseas £32); institutions £35 (overseas £48 ($50)). (Mid-Atlantic Radical Historians Organization) Cambridge University Press, Edinburgh Bldg., Shaftesbury Rd., Cambridge CB2 2RU, England. TEL 0223-312393. FAX 0223-315052. TELEX 851817256. (N. American addr.: Cambridge University Press, Journals Dept., 40 W. 20th St., New York, NY 10011. TEL 212-924-3900. FAX 212-691-3239) Ed. D. Walkowitz. adv.; bk.rev.; film rev.; bibl.; illus. circ. 1,800. (also avail. in microfilm; back issues avail.; reprint service avail. from ISI) **Indexed:** Alt.Press Ind., Amer.Hist.& Life, Arts & Hum.Cit.Ind., Bk.Rev.Ind., Curr.Cont., Film Lit.Ind. (1989-), Hist.Abstr., Left Ind. (1982-), New Per.Ind., SSCI. **Document type:** academic/scholarly publication.
  —BLDSC (7228.092700); Faxon; UnCover; SWETS.
  Description: Takes a critical look at the past, scrutinizing conventional historical interpretations.

RAILROAD HISTORY. see *TRANSPORTATION — Railroads*

RAILWAY DIGEST. see *TRANSPORTATION — Railroads*

900 US
READINGS IN WESTERN CIVILIZATION. 1986. irreg. price varies. University of Chicago Press, 5801 S. Ellis Ave., Chicago, IL 60637. TEL 312-702-7899. (Subscr. to: 11030 Langley Ave., Chicago, IL 60628) Eds. John W. Boyer, Julius Kirshner.
  Refereed Serial

900 SP ISSN 0034-0626
DP1.A16
REAL ACADEMIA DE LA HISTORIA. BOLETIN. 1877. q. 3600 ptas.($50.50) (effective Jan. 1991). Real Academia de la Historia, Calle de Leon 21, 28014 Madrid, Spain. illus.; index. circ. 750. (also avail. in microfilm from BHP; reprint service avail. from KTO) **Indexed:** Amer.Hist.& Life, Curr.Cont., Hist.Abstr., Numis.Lit.
  —SWETS.

REAL SOCIEDAD ARQUEOLOGICA. BOLETIN ARQUEOLOGICO. see *ARCHAEOLOGY*

900 FR ISSN 0249-5619
RECHERCHES D'HISTOIRE ET DE SCIENCES SOCIALES/STUDIES IN HISTORY AND THE SOCIAL SCIENCES. 1980. irreg., latest no.54, 1992. Editions de l' Ecole des Hautes Etudes en Sciences Sociales, 131 bd. St-Michel, 75005 Paris, France. TEL 43-54-47-15. FAX 43-54-80-73. (Dist. by: Centre Interinstitutionnel pour la Diffusion de Publications en Sciences Humaines, 131 bd. St-Michel, 75005 Paris, France)

RECHTSHISTORISCH INSTITUUT LEIDEN. SERIES 1. see *LAW*

900 US ISSN 0080-0287
RECORDS OF CIVILIZATION. SOURCES AND STUDIES. 1915. irreg., latest no.96. price varies. Columbia University Press, 562 W. 113th St., New York, NY 10025. TEL 212-678-6777.

900 US ISSN 1054-9110
REFERENCE GUIDES TO ARCHIVAL AND MANUSCRIPT SOURCES IN WORLD HISTORY. 1991. irreg. price varies. Greenwood Press, Inc. (Subsidiary of: Greenwood Publishing Group Inc.), 88 Post Rd. W., Box 5007, Westport, CT 06881-5007. TEL 203-226-3571. FAX 203-222-1502. **Document type:** monographic series.

900		US
REFERENCE GUIDES TO STATE HISTORY AND RESEARCH. 1982. irreg. price varies. Greenwood Press, Inc. (Subsidiary of: Greenwood Publishing Group Inc.), 88 Post Rd. W., Box 5007, Westport, CT 06881-5007. TEL 203-226-3571. FAX 203-222-1502.

REISEN UND LEBEN. see TRAVEL AND TOURISM

900		JA
REKISHI TO JINBUTSU/HISTORY AND PERSONALITIES. (Text in Japanese) 1971. m. 8750 Yen. Chuokoron-Sha, Inc., 2-8-7 Kyobashi, Chuo-ku, Tokyo 104, Japan. Ed. Keiichi Yokoyama. adv.

REMINISCE. see FOLKLORE

RENAISSANCE QUARTERLY. see LITERATURE

900		UK	ISSN 0269-1213
CB361			
RENAISSANCE STUDIES. 1987. q. £58($108) (effective 1994). (Society for Renaissance Studies) Oxford University Press, Oxford Journals, Walton St., Oxford OX2 6DP, England. TEL 0865-56767. FAX 0865-56646. TELEX 837330-OXPRES-G. (U.S. subscr. to: Oxford University Press Inc., 2001 Evans Rd., Cary, NC 27513. TEL 919-677-0977) Ed. Gordon Campbell. adv. contact: Jane Parker. bk.rev. circ. 700. **Document type:** academic/scholarly publication.
—BLDSC (7356.866500); Faxon; UnCover; SWETS; UMI. **CCC.**
Description: Multi-disciplinary papers covering all aspects of Renaissance history and culture.

900		CK
REVISTA DE HISTORIA. 1977. irreg. Libreria y Editorial America Latina, Avda Caracas 55-16, Apdo. Aereo 53613, Bogota 2, Colombia. **Indexed:** Amer.Hist.& Life, Hist.Abstr.

900 913		CU	ISSN 0138-8207
F1751			
REVISTA DE HISTORIA. (Text in Spanish; summaries in English, Spanish) 1986. q. exchange basis. Comite Provincial del Partido Comunista de Cuba, Seccion de Investigaciones Historicas, Ave. 20 Aniversario y Plaza de la Revolucion, Holguin, Cuba. TEL 462013. TELEX 21136. circ. 3,000 (controlled).
Description: Covers local history from the native tribes to the present. Includes archaeology, culture, and analysis on the teaching of history.

901 330.1		PO	ISSN 0870-6077
REVISTA DE HISTORIA ECONOMICA E SOCIAL. 1978. 3/yr. Esc.250($29) Livraria Sa da Costa Editora, Praca Luis de Camoes, 22-4, 1294 Lisbon, Portugal. TEL 3607215. TELEX 15574 SACOST. Dir. Vitorino Magalhaes Godinho. bk.rev. **Indexed:** Amer.Hist.& Life (until 1989), Hist.Abstr. (until 1989).

901 330.1		PO
REVISTA DE HISTORIA ECONOMICA E SOCIAL. CADERNOS. 1981. irreg., latest no.11-12. price varies. Livraria Sa da Costa Editora, Praca Luis de Camoes, 22-4o, 1294 Lisbon, Portugal. TEL 3607215. TELEX 15574 SACOST.

900 910		CL	ISSN 0716-9671
REVISTA TIEMPO Y ESPACIO. (Text in Enlgish and Spanish) 1990. a. $5. Universidad del Bio-Bio, Departamento de Historia y Geografia, Casilla 447, Chillan, Chile. TEL 223514. FAX 214417. Ed. Didima Olave Farias. **Document type:** academic/scholarly publication.
Description: Publishes papers by domestic and international researchers, alternating the subjects of geography and history each year.

949.3		BE	ISSN 0035-0869
REVUE BELGE D'HISTOIRE CONTEMPORAINE/BELGISCH TIJDSCHRIFT VOOR NIEUWSTE GESCHIEDENIS. (Text in Dutch and French; summaries in Dutch, English, French) 1969. s-a. 1200 BEF (foreign 1400 BEF). Jan Dhondt Foundation v.z.w., Blandijnberg 2, B-9000 Ghent, Belgium. TEL 32-9-2644003. FAX 32-9-2644189. Ed. R. van Eenoo. adv.; bk.rev.; bibl.; index. circ. 500. **Document type:** academic/scholarly publication.
—BLDSC (7891.900000).

900 400		BE	ISSN 0035-0818
P2			
REVUE BELGE DE PHILOLOGIE ET D'HISTOIRE. (Text and title in Dutch, French and other European languages) 1922. q. 2250 Fr. Societe pour le Progres des Etudes Philologiques et Historiques, Bibliotheque Royale, 4 Bd. l'Empereur, B-1000 Brussels, Belgium. Ed. J.M. Duvosquel. adv.; bk.rev.; bibl.; index. circ. 1,000. **Indexed:** Amer.Hist.& Life, Arts & Hum.Cit.Ind., Bibl.Ling., Curr.Cont., Hist.Abstr., M.L.A., Numis.Lit.
—Faxon; UnCover; SWETS.

REVUE D'EGYPTOLOGIE. see ARCHAEOLOGY

320 900		FR	ISSN 0035-2365
JX3			
REVUE D'HISTOIRE DIPLOMATIQUE. 1887. q. 310 F. (Societe d'Histoire et d'Histoire Diplomatique) Editions A. Pedone, 13 rue Soufflot, 75005 Paris, France. FAX 1-46-34-07-60. Eds. M. Vaise, G.H. Souton. adv.; bk.rev.; index, cum.index: 1887-1964. circ. 900. (also avail. in microfilm from BHP; reprint service avail. from KTO) **Indexed:** Amer.Hist.& Life, Arts & Hum.Cit.Ind., Curr.Cont., Hist.Abstr.
—Faxon; SWETS. **CCC.**

900		CN	ISSN 0381-8454
F1054.S3			
REVUE D'HISTOIRE DU BAS-SAINT-LAURENT. (Text in French) 1973. s-a. Can.$20 to individuals; institutions Can.$35. Societe d'Histoire Regionale du Bas-Saint-Laurent, c/o Pierre Collins, 300 des Ursulines, Rimouski, PQ G5L 3A1, Canada. TEL 418-724-1986. Ed.Bd. adv.; bk.rev.; index. circ. 300. (back issues avail.) **Document type:** academic/scholarly publication.
Description: Relates the history of the lower St. Laurence Region.

REVUE D'HISTOIRE ET DE PHILOSOPHIE RELIGIEUSES. see RELIGIONS AND THEOLOGY

REVUE D'HISTOIRE LITTERAIRE DE LA FRANCE. see LITERATURE

900		FR	ISSN 0048-8003
D1			
REVUE D'HISTOIRE MODERNE ET CONTEMPORAINE. 1950. q. 535 F. Societe d'Histoire Moderne et Contemporaine, 39 rue Saint-Ferdinand, 75017 Paris, France. Ed. Pierre Milza. bk.rev.; illus. (also avail. in microfilm from UMI; reprint service avail. from SWZ) **Indexed:** Amer.Hist.& Life, Arts & Hum.Cit.Ind., Curr.Cont., Geo.Abstr., Hist.Abstr., Pt.de Rep. (1979-).
—BLDSC (7919.500000); Faxon; SWETS.

REVUE DE L'ART. see ART

REVUE DE L'HISTOIRE DES RELIGIONS. see RELIGIONS AND THEOLOGY

REVUE DES ETUDES JUIVES. see RELIGIONS AND THEOLOGY — Judaic

REVUE DES SCIENCES RELIGIEUSES. see RELIGIONS AND THEOLOGY — Roman Catholic

900		FR	ISSN 0300-9513
REVUE FRANCAISE D'HISTOIRE D'OUTRE-MER; explorations, colonisations, independences. (Text and summaries in English, French) 1913. q. 350 F. (foreign 375 F.). Societe d'Histoire d'Outre Mer, 9 rue Robert de Flers, 75015 Paris, France. Ed. Charles-Robert Ageron. adv.; bk.rev. circ. 1,200. (also avail. in microfiche from BHP) **Indexed:** Amer.Hist.& Life, Arts & Hum.Cit.Ind., Curr.Cont.Africa, Curr.Cont., Documentatieblad, Hist.Abstr. **Document type:** academic/scholarly publication.
—Faxon; SWETS.

REVUE FRANCAISE D'HISTOIRE DU LIVRE. see LIBRARY AND INFORMATION SCIENCES

900		FR	ISSN 0035-3264
D1			
REVUE HISTORIQUE. 1876. q. 460 F. (foreign 555 F.). Presses Universitaires de France, Departement des Revues, 14 av. du Bois-de-l'Epine, B.P.90, 91003 Evry Cedex, France. TEL 1-60-77-82-05. FAX 1-60-79-20-45. TELEX PUF 600 474 F. Ed.Bd. bk.rev.; bibl.; index. (also avail. in microform from UMI; reprint service avail. from KTO,UMI) **Indexed:** Amer.Hist.& Life, Arts & Hum.Cit.Ind., Curr.Cont., Hist.Abstr., Numis.Lit., Pt.de Rep. (1979-).
—Faxon; SWETS. **CCC.**
Description: For those who wish to keep up-to-date with the rapid progress of historical research.

REVUE HISTORIQUE ARDENNAISE. see ARCHAEOLOGY

REVUE HISTORIQUE DE DROIT FRANCAIS ET ETRANGER. see LAW

REVUE HISTORIQUE DES ARMEES. see MILITARY

REWRITING INDIAN AND WORLD HISTORY. see HISTORY — History Of Asia

RHODE ISLAND JEWISH HISTORICAL NOTES. see ETHNIC INTERESTS

900		IT	ISSN 1120-9526
RICERCHE DI STORIA POLITICA. 1988. a. (Centro Ricerche di Storia Politica) Societa Editrice Il Mulino, Strada Maggiore 37, 40125 Bologna, Italy. TEL 051-256011. FAX 051-256034. Ed. Paolo Pombeni. circ. 900. (back issues avail.)

900		IT	ISSN 0392-162X
RICERCHE STORICHE (NAPLES). 1971. 3/yr. L.72000 to individuals; institutions L.95000; foreign L.126000 (effective 1993). Edizioni Scientifiche Italiane S.p.A., Via Chiatamone, 7, 80121 Naples, Italy. TEL 081-7645768. FAX 081-7646477. Ed. Ivan Tognarini. bibl.; cum.index. circ. 700. (back issues avail.)
Formerly: Archivio Piombinese di Studi Storici.

907		US
RICHARD B. RUSSELL LECTURE SERIES. 1983. a. price varies. University of Georgia Press, 330 Research Dr., Athens, GA 30602-4901. TEL 706-369-6130. FAX 706-369-6131. **Document type:** monographic series.

900		IT
RIVISTA DI STORIA CONTEMPORANEA. 1972. q. (foreign L.61000) (effective 1994). Editore Loescher, Via Vittorio Amedeo II, 18, 10121 Turin, Italy. TEL 011-5624622. FAX 011-5625822. **Indexed:** P.A.I.S.For.Lang.Ind., P.A.I.S.

RIVISTA DI STORIA E LETTERATURA RELIGIOSA. see RELIGIONS AND THEOLOGY

RIVISTA DI STORIA E LETTERATURA RELIGIOSA. BIBLIOTECA. TESTI E DOCUMENTI. see RELIGIONS AND THEOLOGY

900		IT	ISSN 0035-7065
RIVISTA STORICA DEL MEZZOGIORNO. 1966. q. L.50000. (Societa Storica di Terra d'Otranto) Edizioni del Lavoro s.r.l., Via G.B. Martini 6, 00198 Rome, Italy. Dir. Pier Fausto Palumbo. adv.; bk.rev.; bibl.; illus.; index, cum.index. (also avail. in microform)

930		IT	ISSN 0300-340X
RIVISTA STORICA DELL'ANTICHITA. (Text in English, French, German, Italian) 1971. s-a. L.80000. Patron Editore, Via Badini 12, 40050 Quarto Inferiore (Bologna), Italy. Eds. Ida Calbi, Giancarlo Susini. illus.
—BLDSC (7993.015000).

900		US
ROCKEFELLER ARCHIVE CENTER. NEWSLETTER. 1982. a. free. Rockefeller University, Rockefeller Archive Center, Pocantico Hills, 15 Dayton Ave., N. Tarrytown, NY 10591-1598. TEL 914-631-4505. FAX 914-631-6017. Eds. Kenneth W. Rose, Erwin Levold. circ. 14,000. **Document type:** newsletter.

HISTORY

900   US
ROCKEFELLER UNIVERSITY. ROCKEFELLER ARCHIVE CENTER. RESEARCH REPORTS. Cover title: Research Reports from the Rockefeller Archive Center. (Supplement to: Rockefeller University. Rockefeller Archive Center. Newsletter) 1990. a. free. Rockefeller University, Rockefeller Archive Center, 15 Dayton Ave., Pocantico Hills, N. Tarrytown, NY 10591-1598. TEL 914-631-4505. FAX 914-631-6017. Eds. Erwin Levold, Kenneth Rose. **Document type:** newsletter.
    Description: Publishes short research reports by scholars who have completed work with research grants from the Rockefeller Archive Center.

900 069   GW   ISSN 0076-275X
ROEMISCH-GERMANISCHES ZENTRALMUSEUM, MAINZ. KATALOGE VOR- UND FRUEHGESCHICHTLICHER ALTERTUEMER. 1909. irreg., no.25, 1991. price varies. Dr. Rudolf Habelt GmbH, Am Buchenhang 1, 53115 Bonn, Germany. TEL 0228-232016. FAX 0228-232017. **Document type:** monographic series.

ROGUE DIGGER. see *GENEALOGY AND HERALDRY*

900   AT   ISSN 0085-5804
ROYAL HISTORICAL SOCIETY OF QUEENSLAND. JOURNAL. 1914. q. Aus.$35 (includes Bulletin). Royal Historical Society of Queensland, P.O. Box 12057, Elizabeth St., Qld. 4002, Australia. Ed. John D. Kerr. bk.rev. circ. 650. **Indexed:** Aus.P.A.I.S., So.Pac.Per.Ind.
    Description: Contains papers and articles on Queensland history.

994   AT   ISSN 0035-8916
ROYAL HISTORICAL SOCIETY OF QUEENSLAND BULLETIN. no.267, 1969. m. Aus.$35 (includes Journal). Royal Historical Society of Queensland, P.O. Box 12057, Elizabeth St., Qld. 4002, Australia. bk.rev.
    Description: Abstracts of papers given at Royal Historical Society of Queensland functions along with news of Society activities.

ROYAL SOCIETY OF TASMANIA, HOBART. PAPERS AND PROCEEDINGS. see *SCIENCES: COMPREHENSIVE WORKS*

900   AT   ISSN 0557-4242
ROYAL WESTERN AUSTRALIAN HISTORICAL SOCIETY. NEWSLETTER. 1962. 10/yr. Aus.$50. Royal Western Australian Historical Society, Stirling House, 49 Broadway, Nedlands, W.A. 6009, Australia. bk.rev. circ. 1,000. **Indexed:** Aus. P.A.I.S. **Document type:** newsletter.
    Description: Contains news about meetings and functions held at the society during the year, as well as news of affiliated societies, and council meetings.

RUSKIN COLLEGE, OXFORD. LIBRARY. OCCASIONAL PUBLICATION. see *BUSINESS AND ECONOMICS — Labor And Industrial Relations*

900   US   ISSN 1061-1983
D1
RUSSIAN STUDIES IN HISTORY; a journal of translations. 1962. q. $315 (foreign $347). M.E. Sharpe, Inc., 80 Business Park Dr., Armonk, NY 10504. TEL 914-273-1800. FAX 914-273-2106. Ed. Donald Raleigh. adv.; index. (back issues avail.) **Indexed:** Amer.Hist.& Life, Curr.Cont., Hist.Abstr., Mid.East: Abstr.& Ind.
    —BLDSC (8052.930500); Faxon; UnCover; SWETS; UMI.
    Formerly: Soviet Studies in History (ISSN 0038-5867)
    Refereed Serial

900   KN
RYOKSAGWAHAK/HISTORICAL SCIENCE. (Text in Korean) q. Academy of Social Sciences, Pyongyang, N. Korea.

974   US
S P N E A NEWS. 3/yr. $35 membership; students $25. Society for the Preservation of N E Antiquities, 141 Cambridge St., Boston, MA 02114. TEL 617-227-3956. FAX 617-227-3956. Ed. Nancy Curtis. circ. 6,000. (back issues avail.)
    Description: News on the preservation efforts of the Society.

930   GW   ISSN 0080-5181
SAARBRUECKER BEITRAEGE ZUR ALTERTUMSKUNDE. 1964. irreg., no.58, 1993. price varies. Dr. Rudolf Habelt GmbH, Am Buchenhang 1, 53115 Bonn, Germany. TEL 0228-232016. FAX 0228-232017. Ed.Bd. **Indexed:** Br.Archaeol.Abstr. **Document type:** monographic series.

900 913 700   IT
SABAZIA. 1982. s-a. L.9000 (effective 1993). Societa Savonese di Storia Patria, C.P. 358, Piazza della Maddalena 14, 17100 Savona SV, Italy. TEL 19-811960. adv. circ. 600. (back issues avail.) **Document type:** bulletin.
    Description: Focuses on actual cultural problems of interest to the local area.

SABRETACHE. see *MILITARY*

SAECHSISCHE AKADEMIE DER WISSENSCHAFTEN, LEIPZIG. PHILOLOGISCH-HISTORISCHE KLASSE. ABHANDLUNGEN. see *LINGUISTICS*

SAECHSISCHE AKADEMIE DER WISSENSCHAFTEN, LEIPZIG. PHILOLOGISCH-HISTORISCHE KLASSE. SITZUNGSBERICHTE. see *LINGUISTICS*

930 001.3   GW   ISSN 0343-2009
SAECULA SPIRITALIA. (Text in English, French, German, Italian, Latin) 1979. irreg., vol.28, 1994. price varies. Verlag Valentin Koerner GmbH, Postfach 304, 76482 Baden-Baden, Germany. TEL 07221-22423. FAX 07221-38697. Ed. Dieter Wuttke. **Document type:** monographic series.
    Description: Interdisciplinary research in medieval and early modern studies.

900   GW   ISSN 0080-5319
D2
SAECULUM; Jahrbuch fuer Universalgeschichte. 1950. a. DM.68. Karl Alber GmbH, Hermann-Herder-Str. 4, 79104 Freiburg, Germany. Ed. Oskar Koehler. (reprint service avail. from SCH) **Indexed:** Amer.Hist.& Life, Arts & Hum.Cit.Ind., Curr.Cont., Hist.Abstr.
    —BLDSC (8062.970000); Faxon; SWETS. **CCC.**

930   IT
SAGGI DI STORIA ANTICA. 1990. irreg., no.4, 1992. price varies. L'Erma di Bretschneider, Via Cassiodoro 19, 00193 Rome, Italy. TEL 06-687-41-27. FAX 06-687-41-29. Dirs. A. Giardina, A. Fraschetti.

900   BE
SAINT HUBERT D'ARDENNE; cahiers d'histoire. (Text in French) 1977. a. 1750 Fr. per no. Cercle d'Histoire et d'Archeologie Terre et Abbaye de Saint Hubert, Palais Abbatial, B-6900 Saint Hubert, Belgium.

SALZBURGER BEITRAEGE ZUR PARACELSUSFORSCHUNG. see *PHILOSOPHY*

900 800   BE
SAMBRE ET HEURE. 1984. q. Centre d'Histoire et d'art de la Thudinie, 6, rue M. des Ombiaux, CH-6530 Thuin, Belgium.

900 400 800   RU   ISSN 1019-8962
AS262.L463 subser.
SANKT-PETERBURGSKII UNIVERSITET. VESTNIK. SERIYA 2: ISTORIYA, YAZYKOZNANIE, LITERATUROVEDENIE. (Text in Russian; contents page and summaries in English) 1946. q. 18.60 Rub. Sankt-Peterburgskii Universitet, Universitetskaya Nab., 7-9, St. Petersburg V-164, Russia. (Subscr. to: Mezhdunarodnaya Kniga, ul. Dimitrova 39, Moscow G-200, Russia) Ed. N.I. Sokolov. bk.rev.; index. circ. 1,840. **Indexed:** Amer.Hist.& Life, Hist.Abstr., Lang.& Lang.Behav.Abstr.
    —BLDSC (0032.758000).
    Formerly (until 1992): Leningradskii Universitet. Vestnik. Seriya 2: Istoriya, Yazyk i Literatura (ISSN 0024-0842)

SBORNIK ARCHIVNICH PRACI. see *LIBRARY AND INFORMATION SCIENCES*

900   SW   ISSN 0036-5483
DL1
SCANDIA; tidskrift foer historisk forskning. (Text in Danish, English, Norwegian, Swedish) 1928. s-a. SEK 110 (effective 1994). Scandia Foundation, University of Lund, Department of History, P.O. Box 2074, S-220 02 Lund, Sweden. TEL 46-46-10-70-60. FAX 46-46-10-42-07. (Co-sponsors: Charles X Gustaf's Fund; Swedish Council for Research in the Humanities and the Social Sciences) Eds. Lars Edgren, Jasmine Aimag. circ. 680. **Indexed:** Amer.Hist.& Life, Hist.Abstr. **Document type:** academic/scholarly publication.
    —SWETS.
    Description: Presents articles in the field of history, mainly Swedish and Scandinavian.

SCANDINAVIAN - CANADIAN STUDIES/ETUDES SCANDINAVES AU CANADA. see *LITERATURE*

900   NO   ISSN 0346-8755
DL1
SCANDINAVIAN JOURNAL OF HISTORY. (Text in English) 1976. 4/yr. NOK 725 in the Nordic countries; elsewhere NOK 775. (Historical Associations of Denmark, Finland, Norway and Sweden) Scandinavian University Press, P.O. Box 2959 Toeyen, N-0608 Oslo, Norway. TEL 47206707600. FAX 472-67-7575. (U.S. addr.: Scandinavian University Press, 200 Meacham Ave., Elmont, NY 11003. TEL 516-352-7300) Ed. Helge Pharo. **Indexed:** Amer.Hist.& life, Arts & Hum.Cit.Ind., Curr.Cont., Hist.Abstr. **Document type:** academic/scholarly publication.
    —SWETS.
    Incorporates: Excerpta Historica Nordica (ISSN 0085-0365)
    Description: Presents articles on Scandinavian history and review essays surveying themes in recent Scandinavian historical research.

SCHLERN; Zeitschrift fuer Suedtiroler Landeskunde. see *ART*

900 930   GW   ISSN 0138-3361
SCHRIFTEN ZUR UR- UND FRUEHGESCHICHTE. 1953. irreg., vol.45, 1993. price varies. Akademie Verlag GmbH, Muehlenstr. 33-34, 13187 Berlin, Germany. TEL 030-47889348. FAX 030-47889357. **Document type:** monographic series, academic/scholarly publication.
    Supersedes: Akademie der Wissenschaften, Berlin. Sektion fuer Vor- und Fruehgeschichte. Schriften (ISSN 0065-5198)

900 320   US
SCHULER LECTURES IN HISTORY AND POLITICAL SCIENCE. irreg. price varies. Johns Hopkins University Press, 701 W. 40th St., Ste. 275, Baltimore, MD 21211. TEL 410-516-6900. FAX 410-516-6998. (reprint service avail. from UMI)

949.4   SZ   ISSN 0036-7834
D1
SCHWEIZERISCHE ZEITSCHRIFT FUER GESCHICHTE/REVUE SUISSE D'HISTOIRE/RIVISTA STORICA SVIZZERA. (Text in French, German) 1921. q. 90 SFr. (Allgemeine Geschichtforschende Gesellschaft der Schweiz) Schwabe und Co. AG, Steinentorstr. 13, CH-4010 Basel, Switzerland. TEL 061-2725523. FAX 061-2725573. Eds. G. Kreis, F. Python. adv.; bk.rev.; bibl.; charts; index. circ. 2,050. (back issues avail.) **Indexed:** Amer.Hist.& Life, Arts & Hum.Cit.Ind., Bibl.Cart., Curr.Cont., Hist.Abstr. **Document type:** academic/scholarly publication.
    —BLDSC (7953.364500); Faxon; SWETS. **CCC.**

HISTORY

941   UK   ISSN 0036-9241
DA750
SCOTTISH HISTORICAL REVIEW. 1903. s-a. £15($30) Edinburgh University Press, 22 George Sq., Edinburgh EH8 9LF, Scotland. TEL 031-650-4218. FAX 031-662-0053. Eds. Alexander Grant, Stuart J. Borwn. adv. contact: Kathryn MacLean. bk.rev.; index. circ. 900. (also avail. in microfilm from UMI; microfiche from IDC; reprint service avail. from KTO) **Indexed:** Amer.Hist.& Life, Arts & Hum.Cit.Ind., Br.Archaeol.Abstr., Br.Hum.Ind., Curr.Cont., Hist.Abstr., Numis.Lit. **Document type:** academic/scholarly publication.
—BLDSC (8210.150000); Faxon; UnCover; SWETS; UMI. **CCC.**
    Description: Covers all periods of Scottish history from the early to the modern; encourages a variety of historical approaches.
    Refereed Serial

SCOTTISH INDUSTRIAL HISTORY. see *TECHNOLOGY: COMPREHENSIVE WORKS*

SEA HERITAGE NEWS. see *SPORTS AND GAMES — Boats And Boating*

SEKAI/WORLD. see *POLITICAL SCIENCE*

SELDEN SOCIETY, LONDON. HANDBOOK: PUBLICATIONS, LIST OF MEMBERS AND RULES. see *LAW*

SELDEN SOCIETY, LONDON. LECTURES. see *LAW*

SELDEN SOCIETY, LONDON. MAIN (ANNUAL) SERIES. see *LAW*

SELDEN SOCIETY, LONDON. SUPPLEMENTARY SERIES. see *LAW*

900 320   AT
SENNACHIE.* 1963. q. Aus.$1.50. Clanalder Press, Havelock, Vic. 3465, Australia. Ed. John J. Alderson. bk.rev.; bibl. circ. 500.

THE SEVENTEENTH CENTURY. see *LITERATURE*

SEVENTEENTH - CENTURY NEWS. see *LITERATURE*

SHANGHAI DANG'AN GONGZUO/SHANGHAI ARCHIVAL WORK. see *LIBRARY AND INFORMATION SCIENCES*

909   CC
SHIJIE LISHI/WORLD HISTORY. (Text in Chinese) bi-m. Y14.40($40.50) 1, Dongchang Hutong, Wangfujing Dajie, Beijing 100006, People's Republic of China. (Dist. in US by: China Books & Periodicals, Inc., 2929 24th St., San Francisco, CA 94110. TEL 415-282-2994) bk.rev. **Document type:** academic/scholarly publication.
    Description: Covers the theory and methods of historiography.

909   CC
SHIJIE YANJIU DONGTAI. (Text in Chinese) m. Y14.40. 1, Dongchang Hutong, Wangfujing Dajie, Beijing 100006, People's Republic of China. (Dist. outside China by: China International Book Trading Corp., P.O. Box 2399, Beijing, P.R.C.) bk.rev.

900 029.7   US
SHIXUE JIKAN/COLLECTION OF HISTORICAL MATERIALS. (Text in Chinese) q. $18. China Books & Periodicals, Inc., 2929 24th St., San Francisco, CA 94110. TEL 415-282-2994. FAX 415-282-0994.

900   CC
SHIXUE YANJIU/HISTORY STUDIES. (Text in Chinese) q. Beijing Shifan Daxue, Shixue Yanjiusuo - Beijing Normal University, Institute of History, Beitanpingzhuang, Beijing 100875, People's Republic of China. TEL 2012288. Ed. Bai Shouyi.

900   CC   ISSN 0583-0214
SHIXUE YUEKAN/JOURNAL OF HISTORICAL SCIENCE. (Text in Chinese; table of contents in English) 1951. bi-m. Y7.20($41.90) Henan Daxue - Henan University, Building No. 6, Henan Daxue, Kaifeng, Henan 475001, People's Republic of China. (Dist. outside China by: China International Book Trading Corp., P.O. Box 399, Beijing, P.R.C.; Dist. in US by: China Books & Periodicals, Inc., 2929 24th St., San Francisco, CA 94110) (Co-sponsor: Henan Sheng Lishi Xuehui) Ed. Jin Dexing. charts. **Document type:** academic/scholarly publication.
—UnCover.
    Formerly: Xin Shixue Tongxun

907.2   US
SHIXUESHI YANJIU/JOURNAL OF HISTORIOGRAPHY. (Text in Chinese) q. $22.25. China Books & Periodicals, Inc., 2929 24th St., San Francisco, CA 94110. TEL 415-282-2994. FAX 415-282-0994.

SIKELIKA. SERIE ARCHEOLOGICA. see *ARCHAEOLOGY*

930 913   IT   ISSN 0392-0917
SIKELIKA. SERIE STORICA. 1958. irreg., vol.7, 1981. price varies. (Centro Siciliano di Studi Storico-Archeologici "Biagio Pace") Giorgio Bretschneider, Via Crecenzo 43, 00193 Rome, Italy. (back issues avail.)

SIMIOLUS; Netherlands quarterly for the history of art. see *ART*

943.8   PL   ISSN 0037-7511
SLASKI KWARTALNIK HISTORYCZNY "SOBOTKA". (Text in Polish; summaries in German) 1946. q. $40. (Wroclawskie Towarzystwo Milosnikow Historii) Ossolineum, Publishing House of the Polish Academy of Sciences, Rynek 9, 50-106 Wroclaw, Poland. TEL 48-71-386-25. FAX 48-72-448-103. TELEX 0712771 OSS PL. Ed. A. Galos. bk.rev.; charts; stat.; index. circ. 750. **Indexed:** Amer.Hist.& Life, Hist.Abstr., Numis.Lit. **Document type:** academic/scholarly publication.
    Description: Contains studies and sources to the history and culture of Silesia from the past to the present days.

SLAVE AND POST-SLAVE SOCIETIES AND CULTURES. see *SOCIOLOGY*

SLAVERY & ABOLITION; a journal of slave and post-slave studies. see *SOCIOLOGY*

SLAVIC REVIEW. see *SOCIAL SCIENCES: COMPREHENSIVE WORKS*

SLEZSKY SBORNIK/ACTA SILESIACA; ctvrtletnik pro vedy o spolecnosti. see *SOCIOLOGY*

SLOVANSKY PREHLED/SLAVONIC REVIEW. see *POLITICAL SCIENCE*

900   US   ISSN 0081-0193
SMITH COLLEGE STUDIES IN HISTORY. 1915. irreg., vol.51, 1988. price varies. Smith College, History Department, Wright Hall, Northampton, MA 01063-0001. TEL 413-585-3702. (reprint service avail. from UMI) **Document type:** academic/scholarly publication.

900 600   US   ISSN 0081-0258
SMITHSONIAN STUDIES IN HISTORY AND TECHNOLOGY. 1969. irreg., no.51, 1991. free. Smithsonian Institution Press, 470 L'Enfant Plaza, Ste. 7100, Washington, DC 20560. TEL 202-287-3738. FAX 202-287-3637. Ed. Don Fisher. circ. 1,400. (reprint service avail. from UMI) **Document type:** monographic series.

900 910   SP   ISSN 0212-6397
DP302.B41
SOCIEDAD DE ESTUDIOS VASCOS. CUADERNOS DE SECCION. HISTORIA Y GEOGRAFIA. 1983. irreg., no.3, 1984. Eusko Ikaskuntza, Legazpi, 10-1, 20004 Donostia-San Sebastian, Spain. TEL 425 111.

900   IT
SOCIETA E STORIA. 1978. 4/yr. L.98000 (foreign L.130000) (effective 1993). Franco Angeli Editore, Viale Monza 106, 20127 Milan, Italy. TEL 02-28-27-651. Ed.Bd.

900   IT   ISSN 0085-6231
SOCIETA STORICA VALTELLINESE. BOLLETTINO. 1921. a. L.35000 foreign membership. Societa Storica Valtellinese, Villa Quadrio, Via Quattro Novembre, 20, 23100 Sondrio, Italy. Ed. Laura Meli Bassi. bk.rev. circ. 1,500. **Document type:** bulletin, academic/scholarly publication.

SOCIETE D'EMULATION DU BOURBONNAIS. BULLETIN; lettres, sciences et arts. see *ARCHAEOLOGY*

SOCIETE D'HISTOIRE ET D'ARCHAEOLOGIE DE GENEVE. BULLETIN. see *ARCHAEOLOGY*

900   FR
SOCIETE D'HISTOIRE MODERNE ET CONTEMPORAINE. ANNUAIRE. 1957. irreg., latest 1988. $10. 47 bd. Bessieres, 75017 Paris, France.
    Formerly: Societe d'Histoire Moderne. Annuaire (ISSN 0081-0975)

900   FR   ISSN 0991-1367
SOCIETE D'HISTOIRE MODERNE ET CONTEMPORAINE. BULLETIN. (Supplement to: Revue d'Histoire Moderne et Contemporaine) 1901. q. 385 F. Secretaire General, Guy Boquet, 47 bd. Bessieres, 75017 Paris, France. Dir. E. Du Reau. bk.rev.; abstr.; bibl. **Indexed:** Amer.Hist.& Life, Hist.Abstr. **Document type:** bulletin.
    Formerly: Societe d'Histoire Moderne. Bulletin.

526.8   SZ   ISSN 0078-9518
SOCIETE DE L'ECOLE DES CHARTES. MEMOIRES ET DOCUMENTS. 1896. irreg., no.38, 1993. price varies. Librairie Droz S.A., 11, rue Massot, CH-1211 Geneva 12, Switzerland. TEL 022-3466666. FAX 022-3472391. circ. 1,000. **Document type:** monographic series.

930   FR   ISSN 0294-5495
SOCIETE SPELEOLOGIQUE ET PREHISTORIQUE DE BORDEAUX. MEMOIRE. 1949. irreg. 50 F. Societe Speleologique et Prehistorique de Bordeaux, Hotel des Societes Savantes, 1 place Bardinaux, Bordeaux, France. Pub. Jean-Michel Lesbats. illus. circ. 500. **Document type:** bulletin.

SOCIETY FOR ARMY HISTORICAL RESEARCH. JOURNAL. see *MILITARY*

SOCIETY FOR HISTORICAL ARCHAEOLOGY NEWSLETTER. see *ARCHAEOLOGY*

SOCIETY OF ARCHITECTURAL HISTORIANS. JOURNAL. see *ARCHITECTURE*

SOCIETY OF ARCHITECTURAL HISTORIANS. NEWSLETTER. see *ARCHITECTURE*

SOCIETY OF ARCHIVISTS. JOURNAL. see *LIBRARY AND INFORMATION SCIENCES*

900   BU   ISSN 0204-4005
SOFIISKI UNIVERSITET. ISTORICHESKI FAKULTET. GODISHNIK/UNIVERSITE DE SOFIA. FACULTE D'HISTOIRE. ANNUAIRE. (Text in Bulgarian) irreg., vol.71, 1977. 4.93 lv. Sofiiski Universitet, Istoricheski Fakultet, Sofia, Bulgaria. Ed.Bd. circ. 550. **Indexed:** Amer.Hist.& Life, Hist.Abstr.

SOUTH STAFFORDSHIRE ARCHAEOLOGICAL AND HISTORICAL SOCIETY. TRANSACTIONS. see *ARCHAEOLOGY*

SOUTH EAST ASIAN MONOGRAPH SERIES. see *POLITICAL SCIENCE*

900 301.42   US
SOUTHERN ASSOCIATION FOR WOMEN HISTORIANS. NEWSLETTER. 1970. 3/yr. membership. Southern Association for Women Historians, c/o Old Main 525, University of Arkansas, Fayetteville, AR 72701. TEL 501-575-4801. FAX 501-575-2642. Ed. Suzanne Maberry. adv.; bk.rev. circ. 500. **Document type:** newsletter.
    Description: Provides news about and for members. Includes calls for papers and employment opportunities.

900   FR
SOUVENIR FRANCAIS. 1920. q. free. 9 rue Clichy, 75009 Paris, France. circ. 30,000.
    Description: Offers perspectives on the history of France.

900   NE   ISSN 0038-7487
D1
SPIEGEL HISTORIAEL; maandblad voor geschiedenis en archeologie. 1966. m. (11/yr.) fl.79.50. Unieboek, Postbus 97, 3990 DB Houten, Netherlands. (Subscr. to: C. de Boer Jr., N.V., Box 1918, Hilversum, Netherlands) Ed. F.K.M. Anzion. adv.; bk.rev.; charts; illus.; index. circ. 8,500. **Indexed:** Amer.Hist.& Life, Br.Archaeol.Abstr., E.I., Hist.Abstr.
—SWETS.

SPORTING TRADITION. see *SPORTS AND GAMES*

HISTORY

954.93   **CE**   ISSN 0009-0832
SRI LANKA JOURNAL OF HISTORICAL AND SOCIAL STUDIES. (Text in English) 1958. s-a. Rs.30($7) University of Peradeniya, Department of History, University Park, Peradeniya, Sri Lanka. Ed. K.M. De Silva. adv.; bk.rev.; bibl.; charts; illus.; cum.index. circ. 1,000. **Indexed:** Amer.Hist.& Life, Hist.Abstr.

DER STAAT; Zeitschrift fuer Staatslehre, Oeffentliches Recht und Verfassungsgeschichte. see *POLITICAL SCIENCE*

900   **CN**
STATE AND ECONOMIC LIFE SERIES. 1979. irreg. price varies. University of Toronto Press, 5201 Dufferin St., Downsview, ON M3H 5T8, Canada. TEL 416-667-7791. FAX 416-667-7832. (U.S. addr.: 340 Nagel Dr., Cheektowaga, NY 41225) Eds. Mel Watkins, Leo Panitch.

907   **US**   ISSN 0361-7491
CB351
STATE UNIVERSITY OF NEW YORK AT BINGHAMTON. CENTER FOR MEDIEVAL AND EARLY RENAISSANCE STUDIES. ACTA. 1974. a. $15. Binghampton University, Box 6000, Binghampton, NY 13902-6000. TEL 607-777-2130. (Avail. from: S U N Y Press, c/o C U P Services, Box 6525, Ithaca, NY 14851) Ed. Paul Szarmach; Pub. R.S. Oggins. circ. 300. (back issues avail.; reprint service avail. from ISI) **Indexed:** M.L.A., RILA. **Document type:** proceedings.
    Description: Summarizes papers presented at the S.U.N.Y. Conference on Medieval and Renaissance Studies

901 320   **US**   ISSN 0270-5338
STOKVIS STUDIES IN HISTORICAL CHRONOLOGY & THOUGHT. 1982. irreg., no.14, 1993 (approx. 3/yr.). price varies. Borgo Press, Box 2845, San Bernardino, CA 92406. TEL 909-884-5813. FAX 909-888-4942. **Document type:** academic/scholarly publication.
—BLDSC (8465.854000).
    Description: Includes scholarly monographs in history, chronology, current affairs, and political science.

900   **IT**   ISSN 0039-1875
D410
STORIA CONTEMPORANEA. (Text in Italian; summaries in English) 1970. bi-m. L.150000. Societa Editrice Il Mulino, Strada Maggiore, 37, 40125 Bologna, Italy. Ed. Renzo De Felice. adv.; bk.rev.; index. circ. 2,500. (tabloid format; back issues avail.) **Indexed:** Amer.Hist.& Life, Arts & Hum.Cit.Ind., Hist.Abstr.
—BLDSC (8466.430000).

900   **IT**   ISSN 0039-1913
STORIA ILLUSTRATA; mensile di storia, geografia archeologia. 1957. m. L.95400. Arnoldo Mondadori Editore S.p.A., Casella Postale 1833, 20101 Milan, Italy. Ed. Gabriele Bacchi. adv.; illus. circ. 105,701.

945   **IT**
STRADA MAESTRA; quaderni della biblioteca comunale "Giulio Cesare Croce" di San Giovanni in Persiceto. 1968. s-a. L.30000 (effective 1993). (Comune di San Giovanni in Persiceto) Edizioni Aspasia, Piazza Garibaldi 19, 40017 San Giovanni in Persiceto, Italy. TEL 051-827017. FAX 051-825028. Ed. Mario Gandini. bk.rev.; circ. 500 (controlled). (back issues avail.) **Document type:** academic/scholarly publication.
    Description: Publishes studies of history, biography and bibliography concerning the west side of the region of Bologna.

STRATEGY AND TACTICS; the magazine of conflict simulation. see *MILITARY*

STUDI GENUENSI. see *ARCHAEOLOGY*

945   **IT**   ISSN 0039-2995
STUDI ROMANI. 1953. q. L.70000. Istituto Nazionale di Studi Romani, Piazza dei Cavalieri di Malta 2, 00153 Rome, Italy. Dir. Gaetano Miarelli Mariani. bk.rev.; bibl.; charts; illus.; index. **Indexed:** Amer.Hist.& Life, Arts & Hum.Cit.Ind., Curr.Cont., Hist.Abstr., M.L.A.
—Faxon.

901   **IT**   ISSN 0392-7326
STUDI SETTECENTESCHI. 1981. s-a. L.55000. Bibliopolis, Via Arangio Ruiz 83, 80122 Naples, Italy. TEL (081) 664606. Ed.Bd. **Indexed:** RILA.
    Description: Collects articles and essays devoted to the philosophy and literature of the Enlightenment.

900   **IT**   ISSN 0039-3037
DG401
STUDI STORICI/HISTORICAL STUDIES. 1959. q. L.60000 (foreign L.90000) (effective 1994). (Istituto Gramsci Roma) Edizioni Dedalo s.r.l., Casella Postale 362, 70100 Bari, Italy. TEL 080-5311413. FAX 080-5311414. TELEX EDIRIU I 625292. (Edit. addr.: Istituto Gramsci, Via del Conservatorio 55, 00186 Rome, Italy. TEL 06-6833756. FAX 06-6877736) Ed. Francesco Barbagallo. adv.; bk.rev.; bibl.; charts; index, cum.index. circ. 20,000. **Indexed:** Amer.Hist.& Life, Arts & Hum.Cit.Ind., Curr.Cont., Hist.Abstr.
—BLDSC (8481.920000); Faxon; SWETS.

STUDIA AMSTELODAMENSIA AD EPIGRAPHICAM, IUS ANTIQUUM ET PAPYROLOGICAM PERTINENTIA. see *ARCHAEOLOGY*

STUDIA COPERNICANA - BRILL SERIES. see *ASTRONOMY*

900 340   **VC**
STUDIA ET DOCUMENTA HISTORIAE ET IURIS. 1935. a. $135. Pontificia Universita Lateranense, Pontificio Istituto Utriusque Iuris, Piazza S. Giovanni in Laterano 4, 00120 Vatican City (Rome), State of the Vatican City. Ed. Gabrio Lombardi. bk.rev.; bibl.; index. (tabloid format)

900   **HU**   ISSN 0076-2458
STUDIA HISTORICA ACADEMIAE SCIENTIARUM HUNGARICAE. (Text in English, French, German, Russian) 1951. irreg., vol.192, 1991. price varies. (Magyar Tudomanyos Akademia) Akademiai Kiado, Publishing House of the Hungarian Academy of Sciences, P.O. Box 245, H-1519 Budapest, Hungary. TEL 181-2134. FAX 166-6466. TELEX 22-6228 AKNYO H. **Document type:** academic/scholarly publication.

900   **PL**   ISSN 0137-3587
STUDIA MARITIMA. (Text in English, French, German) 1979. irreg. price varies. (Polska Akademia Nauk, Komitet Nauk Historycznych) Ossolineum, Publishing House of the Polish Academy of Sciences, 50-106 Wroclaw, Poland. TEL 48-71-386-25. FAX 48-71-448-103. TELEX 0712771 OSS PL. Ed. E. Cieslak. **Document type:** academic/scholarly publication.
    Description: Devoted to maritime history from Middle Ages to the present time.

STUDIA MONASTICA; commentarium ad rem monasticam historice investigandam. see *RELIGIONS AND THEOLOGY*

STUDIA SILENSIA. see *RELIGIONS AND THEOLOGY*

STUDIA SLAVICA ACADEMIAE SCIENTIARUM HUNGARICAE. see *LINGUISTICS*

900   **RM**   ISSN 0039-3428
STUDIA UNIVERSITATIS "BABES-BOLYAI". HISTORIA. (Text in English, French, German, Italian, Rumanian) 1956. s-a. exchange basis. Universitatea Babes-Bolyai, Biblioteca Centrala Universitara, Str. Clinicilor Nr. 2, Cluj-Napoca 3400, Rumania. TEL 95-117092. FAX 95-117633. bk.rev.; charts; illus.; index. **Indexed:** Numis.Lit. **Document type:** academic/scholarly publication.

900   **GW**   ISSN 0081-7309
STUDIEN ZUR GESCHICHTE DES NEUNZEHNTEN JAHRHUNDERTS. irreg. price varies. R. Oldenbourg Verlag GmbH, Rosenheimerstr. 145, 81671 Munich, Germany. TEL 089-45051-0. FAX 089-45051207. (Subscr. to: Postfach 801360, 81613 Munich, Germany) **Document type:** monographic series.

900   **GW**   ISSN 0178-8310
STUDIEN ZUR MODERNEN GESCHICHTE. irreg., vol.47, 1994. price varies. Franz Steiner Verlag Wiesbaden GmbH, Birkenwaldstr. 44, 70191 Stuttgart, Germany. TEL 0711-2582-0. FAX 0711-2582290. TELEX 723636-DAZ-D. (Subscr. to: Postfach 101061, 70009 Stuttgart, Germany) Ed.Bd. **Document type:** monographic series.

STUDIES IN ANCIENT MEDICINE. see *MEDICAL SCIENCES*

572 900   **US**   ISSN 1055-2464
STUDIES IN ANTHROPOLOGY AND HISTORY. irreg. Harwood Academic Publishers, 820 Town Center Dr., Langhorne, PA 19047. TEL 215-750-2642. FAX 215-750-6343. (UK subscr. to: Box 90, Reading, Berkshire RG1 8JL, England. TEL 0734-560-080) Ed. N. Thomas. (also avail. in microform) **Document type:** academic/scholarly publication.
Refereed Serial

STUDIES IN EIGHTEENTH CENTURY CULTURE. see *HUMANITIES: COMPREHENSIVE WORKS*

900   **US**   ISSN 1046-526X
▼**STUDIES IN HISTORIOGRAPHY.** 1990. irreg. price varies. Greenwood Press, Inc. (Subsidiary of: Greenwood Publishing Group Inc.), 88 Post Rd. W., Box 5007, Westport, CT 06881-5007. TEL 203-226-3571. FAX 203-222-1502. **Document type:** monographic series.

907   **II**   ISSN 0258-1698
DS401
STUDIES IN HISTORY (SAHIBABAD).* 1979-1982. s-a. Rs.75($18) Vikas Publishing House Pvt. Ltd, 576 Masjid Rd., Jangpura, New Delhi 110 014, India. TEL 11-624605. TELEX 31592252. (Dist. by: UBS Publishers' Distributors Ltd., 5 Ansari Rd., New Delhi 11002, India) Ed.Bd. bk.rev.
—UnCover; UMI.

900 700   **US**   ISSN 0743-2879
STUDIES IN HISTORY AND CULTURE. 1985. irreg. Peter Lang Publishing, Inc., 62 W. 45th St., 4th Fl., New York, NY 10036. TEL 212-302-6740. Ed. Norman Cantor. **Document type:** academic/scholarly publication.
    Description: Focuses on works in cultural and intellectual history.

900 320   **US**   ISSN 0228-6939
STUDIES IN HISTORY AND POLITICS/ETUDES D'HISTOIRE ET DE POLITIQUE. (Text in English, French) a. $29.95 to individuals; institutions $29.95. Edwin Mellen Press, 415 Ridge St., Box 450, Lewiston, NY 14092. TEL 716-754-2788. FAX 716-754-4056. Eds. Andrew F. Johnson, Karl Schweizer.
    Description: Includes articles and research notes on special themes of current historical or political interest.

STUDIES IN INTELLIGENCE. see *POLITICAL SCIENCE — International Relations*

STUDIES IN JUDAICA & THE HOLOCAUST. see *ETHNIC INTERESTS*

STUDIES IN MEDIEVAL AND RENAISSANCE TEACHING. see *LITERATURE*

900 800   **US**   ISSN 0085-6878
CB351
STUDIES IN MEDIEVAL CULTURE. 1964. irreg., no.31, 1992. $33 (effective 1993). Medieval Institute Publications, Western Michigan University, Kalamazoo, MI 49008. TEL 616-387-8755. FAX 616-387-8750. charts; illus.; stat. circ. 1,000. (tabloid format) **Indexed:** M.L.A., Rel.Ind.Two.
—BLDSC (8491.107500).
    Description: Essays examine a particular topic or interdisciplinary approach to a single subject. Largely drawn from the International Congress on Medieval Studies.

STUDIES IN POPULAR CULTURE. see *SOCIOLOGY*

677.09   **NE**   ISSN 0924-7696
▼**STUDIES IN TEXTILE AND COSTUME HISTORY.** 1992. irreg., vol.2, 1993. price varies. E.J. Brill, P.O. Box 9000, 2300 PA Leiden, Netherlands. TEL 31-71-312624. FAX 31-71-317532. TELEX 39296 BRILL NL. (In N. America: E.J. Brill, 24 Hudson St., Kinderhook, NY 12106. TEL 800-962-4406. FAX 518-758-1959) Ed. Gillian Vogelsang-Eastwood. (back issues avail.) **Document type:** monographic series.
Refereed Serial

HISTORY

900   UK
STUDIES IN THE EARLY HISTORY OF BRITAIN. 1960. irreg. Leicester University Press, Fielding Johnson Bldg., University of Leicester, University Rd., Leicester LE1 7RH, England. TEL 0533-523333. Ed. Nicholas Brooks. **Document type:** academic/scholarly publication.
    Formerly: Studies in Early English History (ISSN 0081-7821)

STUDIES IN THE HISTORY AND INTERPRETATION OF MUSIC. see *MUSIC*

STUDIES IN THE HISTORY OF PHILOSOPHY. see *PHILOSOPHY*

900   956.94 296   UK   ISSN 0334-1771
DS149.A1
STUDIES IN ZIONISM; a journal of Israel studies. (Text in English) 1980. 3/yr. £24($34) to individuals; institutions £60 ($90). (Tel Aviv University, Institute for Zionist Research, IS) Frank Cass & Co. Ltd., Gainsborough House, 11 Gainsborough Rd., London E11 1RS, England. TEL 081-530-4226. FAX 081-530-7795. Eds. Ronald Zweig, Michael Oren. adv.: B&W page £185; adv. contact: Anne Kidson. bk.rev.; index. (also avail. in microfiche; back issues avail.) **Indexed:** Amer.Hist.& Life, Hist.Abstr., Ind.Jew.Per., Rel.& Theol.Abstr. (1988-), Zion.Lit. **Document type:** academic/scholarly publication.
—Faxon; UnCover. **CCC.**
    Supersedes (in 1982): Zionism: Studies in the History of the Zionist Movement and of the Jews in Palestine - Ha-Tsiyonut (ISSN 0084-5523)
    Description: Covers Zionism and the State of Israel's social, political, and intellectual history.

STUDII SI CERCETARI DE ISTORIA ARTEI. SERIA ARTA PLASTICA. see *ART*

900   AA   ISSN 0563-5799
DR901
STUDIME HISTORIKE/ETUDES HISTORIQUES. (Text in Albanian; summaries in French) q. $924. Academie des Sciences de la RPSA, Institut d'Histoire, Tirana, Albania. **Indexed:** Bibl.Ling.

SURMACH. see *MILITARY*

SVENSKA LITTERATURSAELLSKAPET I FINLAND. SKRIFTER. see *LITERATURE — Poetry*

949.4 973   US
E184.S9
SWISS - AMERICAN HISTORICAL SOCIETY. REVIEW. 1965. 3/yr. $25 membership. Swiss - American Historical Society, c/o Erdmann Schmocker, 6440 N. Bosworth Ave., Chicago, IL 60626. TEL 312-262-8336. Ed. Leo Schelbert. bk.rev.; bibl. circ. 375. (processed) **Indexed:** Amer.Hist.& Life, Hist.Abstr. **Document type:** academic/scholarly publication.
    Formerly: Swiss-American Historical Society. Newsletter (ISSN 0036-0740)

870   BE
SYMBOLAE. SERIES A. 1976. irreg., vol.16, 1988. Leuven University Press, Krakenstraat 3, B-3000 Louvain, Belgium. TEL 32-16-284175. FAX 32-16-284176. **Document type:** academic/scholarly publication, monographic series.

870   BE
SYMBOLAE. SERIES B. (Text in Dutch) 1982. irreg., vol.11, 1993. price varies. Leuven University Press, Krakenstraat 3, B-3000 Leuven, Belgium. TEL 32-16-284175. FAX 32-16-284176. Ed.Bd. **Document type:** academic/scholarly publication, monographic series.

900   HU   ISSN 0039-8098
DB901
SZAZADOK/CENTURIES. (Text in Hungarian; summaries in French and Russian) 1867. bi-m. $29. Magyar Tortenelmi Tarsulat, Uri u 51-53, 1014 Budapest, Hungary. Eds. Gy. Ember, F. Mucsi. adv.; bk.rev.; illus.; index. **Indexed:** Amer.Hist.& Life, Hist.Abstr.

900   TZ   ISSN 0039-9507
DT447
TANZANIA ZAMANI; a journal of historical research and writing. 2/yr. $10. Historical Association of Tanzania, Box 35050, Department of History, University of Dar es Salaam, Dar es Salaam, Tanzania. Ed. N.N. Luanda. bk.rev.; bibl. circ. 600.

900   GW   ISSN 0082-1950
TASCHENBUCH GESCHICHTE. 1969. irreg. price varies. VEB Deutscher Verlag der Wissenschaften, Postfach 1216, 1080 Berlin, Germany.

TEACHING HISTORY. see *EDUCATION — Teaching Methods And Curriculum*

TEACHING HISTORY. see *EDUCATION — Teaching Methods And Curriculum*

TEACHING HISTORY: A JOURNAL OF METHODS. see *EDUCATION — Teaching Methods And Curriculum*

TEACHING OF HISTORY. see *EDUCATION — Teaching Methods And Curriculum*

TECHNOLOGY AND CULTURE; devoted to the study of the development of technology and its relations with society and culture. see *TECHNOLOGY: COMPREHENSIVE WORKS*

900   US   ISSN 0082-2884
G2
TERRAE INCOGNITAE; the journal for the history of discoveries. 1969. a. $20 (foreign $25). Society for the History of Discoveries, c/o The Hermon Dunlap Smith Center for the History of Cartography, The Newberry Library, 60 W. Walton St., Chicago, IL 60610. TEL 312-943-9090. Ed. David Buisseret. adv.; bk.rev.; bibl.; charts; illus.; cum.index. circ. 1,000. (back issues avail.) **Indexed:** Amer.Hist.& Life, Geo.Abstr., Hist.Abstr. **Document type:** academic/scholarly publication.
—Faxon.

TESTIMONIA SICILIAE ANTIQUA. see *ARCHAEOLOGY*

930   US   ISSN 0082-3759
TEXTS FROM CUNEIFORM SOURCES. 1966. irreg. price varies. J. J. Augustin, Inc., Locust Valley, NY 11560. TEL 516-676-1510. Ed. A. Leo Oppenheimer. index.
    Description: Up-to-date editions of Akkadian, Sumerian, Hittite and other sources written in Cuneiform.

TEXTUS ET STUDIA HISTORICA CARMELITANA. see *RELIGIONS AND THEOLOGY — Roman Catholic*

930   IT   ISSN 0082-4097
THESAURISMATA. (Text in Greek and other languages; summaries in Italian) 1962. a. L.70000($40) Istituto Ellenico di Studi Bizantini e Post-Bizantini, Castello 3412, 30122 Venice, Italy. FAX 003941-5238248. circ. 1,050. **Indexed:** M.L.A., RILA. **Document type:** bulletin.

900   UK   ISSN 0082-4232
DA670.Y59
THORESBY SOCIETY, LEEDS, ENGLAND. PUBLICATIONS. 1891. a. £12.50. Thoresby Society, Claremont, 23 Clarendon Rd., Leeds LS2 9NZ, England. TEL 0532-457910. Eds. R. Stephens, J.W. Kirby. circ. 530. (back issues avail.) **Indexed:** Br.Archaeol.Abstr., Br.Hum.Ind. **Document type:** academic/scholarly publication.
—BLDSC (7113.707000).

THUERINGER FEUERWEHRZEITSCHRIFT. see *FIRE PREVENTION*

900   NE   ISSN 0040-7518
D1
TIJDSCHRIFT VOOR GESCHIEDENIS. 1886. 4/yr. fl.112.50 (students fl.77.50). WoltersgroepGroningen b.v. (Subsidiary of: Wolters Kluwer N.V.), Postbus 58, 9700 MB Groningen, Netherlands. TEL 31-50-226922. FAX 31-50-264866. Ed.Bd. adv.; bk.rev.; abstr.; bibl.; illus.; index, cum.index every 10 yrs. circ. 3,300. **Indexed:** Amer.Hist.& Life, Arts & Hum.Cit.Ind., Curr.Cont., E.I., Hist.Abstr. **Document type:** academic/scholarly publication.
—UnCover; SWETS.

TIJDSCHRIFT VOOR RECHTSGESCHIEDENIS/REVUE D'HISTOIRE DU DROIT/LEGAL HISTORY REVIEW. see *LAW*

TITANIC COMMUTATOR. see *TRANSPORTATION — Ships And Shipping*

TOOLS AND TILLAGE; a journal on the history of the implements of cultivation and other agricultural processes. see *AGRICULTURE*

900   HU   ISSN 0040-9634
TORTENELMI SZEMLE/HISTORICAL REVIEW. (Text in Hungarian; summaries in French and Russian) 1958. q. $27.50. Magyar Tudomanyos Akademia, Tortenettudomanyi Intezet, Uri u, 53, 1014 Budapest, Hungary. Ed. F. Szakaly. bk.rev.; illus.; index. **Indexed:** Amer.Hist.& Life, Hist.Abstr.

TOWARZYSTWO NAUKOWE W TORUNIU. FONTES. see *HISTORY — History Of Europe*

900   PL   ISSN 0082-5522
TOWARZYSTWO NAUKOWE W TORUNIU. ROCZNIKI. (Text in Polish; summaries in English, French, German) 1878. 3/yr. price varies. Towarzystwo Naukowe w Toruniu, Ul. Wysoka 16, 87-100 Torun, Poland. TEL 48-56-23941. TELEX 552388 FSBH PL. Ed. Antoni Czacharowski. circ. 400. **Document type:** monographic series.

TRACTRIX; yearbook for the history of science, medicine, technology, and mathematics. see *SCIENCES: COMPREHENSIVE WORKS*

TRAINMASTER. see *TRANSPORTATION — Railroads*

960   KE   ISSN 0251-0391
DT1
TRANSAFRICAN JOURNAL OF HISTORY. (Text in English) 1971-1974; resumed 1976. a. KShs.200($34) P.O. Box 10622, Nairobi, Kenya. TEL 254-2-331135. (Co-sponsors: Kenya Literature Bureau; University of Nairobi, Department of History) Ed. Gideon S. Were. adv.; bk.rev.; bibl. circ. 200. **Indexed:** Amer.Hist.& Life, Arts & Hum.Cit.Ind., Curr.Cont.Africa, Documentatieblad, Hist.Abstr., P.L.E.S.A. **Document type:** academic/scholarly publication.

900   GW   ISSN 0941-0597
TRANSATLANTISCHE HISTORISCHE STUDIEN. irreg., vol.2, 1993. (Deutsches Historisches Institut Washington) Franz Steiner Verlag Wiesbaden GmbH, Birkenwaldstr. 44, 70191 Stuttgart, Germany. TEL 0711-2582-0. FAX 0711-2582-290. TELEX 723636-DAZ-D. (Subscr. to: Postfach 101061, 70009 Stuttgart, Germany) Eds. Norbert Finzsch, Hartmut Lehmann. **Document type:** academic/scholarly publication.

TRANSPORT HISTORY. see *TRANSPORTATION*

900   SZ   ISSN 0082-6073
TRAVAUX D'HISTOIRE ETHICO-POLITIQUE. 1963. irreg., no.53, 1993. price varies. Librairie Droz S.A., 11, rue Massot, CH-1211 Geneva 12, Switzerland. TEL 022-3466666. FAX 022-3472391. Ed. Alain Dufour. circ. 800. **Document type:** monographic series.
—CCC.
    Description: Disseminates political ethics.

TREASURES. see *MEDICAL SCIENCES*

TRENI. see *TRANSPORTATION — Railroads*

900   GW
TUDUV-STUDIE. REIHE GESCHICHTSWISSENSCHAFTEN. 1986. irreg. price varies. Tuduv Verlagsgesellschaft mbH, Gabelsbergerstrasse 15, 8000 Munich 2, Germany.

901   US   ISSN 0276-864X
D1
U C L A HISTORICAL JOURNAL. 1980. a. $10 to individuals; institutions $12 (effective Oct. 1993). University of California, Los Angeles, Graduate Students Association, Dept. of History, Los Angeles, CA 90024. TEL 213-825-4601. Ed. Jo Ann Woodsum. adv.; bk.rev. circ. 800. **Indexed:** Amer.Hist.& Life, Hist.Abstr. **Document type:** academic/scholarly publication.
—BLDSC (9079.631000); UnCover.

900   US
U S L HISTORY SERIES. 1970. s-a. price varies. University of Southwestern Louisiana, Center for Louisiana Studies, Box 40831, Lafayette, LA 70504. TEL 318-231-6027. Ed. Glenn R. Conrad.

HISTORY

973 952 327   US
E183.8.J3
U S - THIRD WORLD POLICY PERSPECTIVES. irreg. (2-3/yr). $24.95 cloth; paper $15.95. Transaction Publishers, Transaction Periodicals Consortium, Department 3092, Rutgers University, New Brunswick, NJ 08903. TEL 908-932-2280. FAX 908-932-3138. Ed. Sheldon Annis. **Document type:** academic/scholarly publication.
   Formerly: U S - Japan Relations (ISSN 0748-2809)
   Description: Offers a variety of perspectives on different facets of a single policy theme.

THE UKRAINIAN QUARTERLY; a journal of Ukranian and international affairs. see *POLITICAL SCIENCE*

900   US   ISSN 0041-6061
DK508.A2
UKRAINS'KYI ISTORYK/UKRAINIAN HISTORIAN; zhurnal ukrainskoho istorychnoho towarystwa. (Text in English, Ukrainian) 1963. q. $35 to individuals; institutions $40. Ukrainian Historical Association, Box 312, Kent, OH 44240. (In Europe subscr. to: Ukrainian Historian, Postfach 37 02 48, 8000 Munich 37, Germany) Ed. L. Wynar. adv.; bk.rev.; abstr.; bibl.; index. **Indexed:** Amer.Bibl.Slavic & E.Eur.Stud., Amer.Hist.& Life, Hist.Abstr.

900   US   ISSN 0083-1611
U.S. LIBRARY OF CONGRESS. MANUSCRIPT DIVISION. REGISTERS OF PAPERS. 1958. irreg. free to libraries. U.S. Library of Congress, Washington, DC 20540. TEL 202-707-5383. circ. 500. **Document type:** bibliography, government publication.

720   US
UNITED STATES LIGHTHOUSE SOCIETY. BULLETIN. Issued with: Keeper's Log (ISSN 0883-0061) q. membership. United States Lighthouse Society, 244 Kearny St., 5th Fl., San Francisco, CA 94108. TEL 715-362-7255. circ. 6,000 (paid). **Document type:** bulletin.
   Description: Details the society's projects around the nation.

UNIVERS HISTORIQUE. see *SCIENCES: COMPREHENSIVE WORKS*

UNIVERSIDAD INTERAMERICANA DE PUERTO RICO. RECINTO DE SAN GERMAN. REVISTA DE CIENCIAS SOCIALES E HISTORIA. ANALES. see *SOCIAL SCIENCES: COMPREHENSIVE WORKS*

900   BL
UNIVERSIDADE DO PARANA. SETOR DE CIENCIAS HUMANAS, LETRAS E ARTES. DEPARTAMENTO DE HISTORIA. BOLETIM. Title varies: Historia Moderna e Contemporanea. 1962. irreg., no.29, 1984. exchange basis. Universidade Federal do Parana, Setor de Ciencias Humanas, Letras e Artes, Departamento de Historia, Rua General Carneiro, 460-6 andar, 80.060 Curitiba, Parana, Brazil. charts; illus.; stat. circ. 500.
   Formerly: Universidade do Parana. Departamento de Historia. Boletim (ISSN 0070-1815)

930   IT
UNIVERSITA DEGLI STUDI DI BARI. CENTRO STUDI BIZANTINI. CORSI DI STUDI. 1976. irreg., no.5, 1991. price varies. L'Erma di Bretschneider, Via Cassiodoro 19, 00193 Rome, Italy. TEL 06-687-41-27. FAX 06-687-41-29.
   Description: Course symposia in Byzantine studies.

909   IT   ISSN 0068-4805
UNIVERSITA DEGLI STUDI DI CAGLIARI. ISTITUTO DI STORIA MEDIOEVALE. PUBLICAZIONI. 1961. irreg., no.25, 1977. price varies. Casa Editrice Dott. Antonio Milani, Via Jappelli 5, 35100 Padua, Italy. TEL 049-656677. FAX 049-8752900. circ. 800.

930   IT
UNIVERSITA DEGLI STUDI DI GENOVA. FONDAZIONE NOBILE AGOSTINO POGGI (PUBBLICAZIONE). 1940. irreg., no.14, 1979. Casa Editrice Dott. A. Giuffre, Via Busto Arsizio 40, 20151 Milan, Italy. TEL 02-38000905. FAX 02-38009581.
   Description: Covers the Roman empire.

UNIVERSITA DEGLI STUDI DI MACERATA. FACOLTA DI LETTERE E FILOSOFIA. ANNALI. see *ARCHAEOLOGY*

900   IT   ISSN 0078-7744
UNIVERSITA DEGLI STUDI DI PADOVA. ISTITUTO DI STORIA ANTICA. PUBBLICAZIONI. 1953. irreg., no.16, 1989. price varies. L'Erma di Bretschneider, Via Cassiodoro, 19, 00193 Rome, Italy. TEL 06-687-41-27. FAX 06-687-41-29.

900 300   IT
UNIVERSITA DI NAPOLI. FACOLTA DI LETTERE E FILOSOFIA. ANNALI. 1950. a. exchange basis only. Universita di Napoli, Facolta di Lettere e Filosofia, Via Porta Di Massa 1, 80133 Naples, Italy. TEL 5518963. (Subscr. to: D'Auria Editore, Calata Trinita Maggiore 52, 80134 Naples, Italy) Ed. Marcello Gigante. circ. 600. **Indexed:** Bibl.Ling.

090 950   GW   ISSN 0072-4491
UNIVERSITAETSBIBLIOTHEK GIESSEN. KURZBERICHTE AUS DEN PAPYRUS-SAMMLUNGEN. (Text in various languages) 1956. irreg. price varies. Universitaetsbibliothek Giessen, Otto-Behaghel-Str. 8, 35394 Giessen, Germany. TEL 0641-702-2330. FAX 0641-46406. circ. 500. **Document type:** academic/scholarly publication.
   Description: Results of research on the papyrus collections of the University library.

900   RM   ISSN 0041-9125
DR201
UNIVERSITATEA "AL. I. CUZA" DIN IASI. ANALELE STIINTIFICE. SECTIUNEA 3A: ISTORIE. (Text in English, French, German, Italian, Rumanian or Russian) 1955. a. 35 lei. Universitatea "Al. I. Cuza" din Iasi, Calea M. Eminescu 11, Jassy, Rumania. (Subscr. to: ILEXIM, Str. 13 Decembrie Nr. 3, P.O. Box 136-137, Bucharest, Rumania) Ed. J. Toderascu. bk.rev.; abstr.; charts; illus. circ. 300.
   Description: Romanian and world history, origin and continuity of the Romanian people, union and sovereignty in Romanian history.

UNIVERSITE CATHOLIQUE DE LOUVAIN. FACULTE DE PHILOSOPHIE ET LETTRES. TRAVAUX. see *HUMANITIES: COMPREHENSIVE WORKS*

900 800 709   FR   ISSN 0079-256X
UNIVERSITE DE POITIERS. CENTRE D'ETUDES SUPERIEURES DE CIVILISATION MEDIEVALE. PUBLICATIONS. 1958. q. 370 F. (foreign 410 F.). Universite de Poitiers, Centre d'Etudes Superieures de Civilisation Medievale, 24 rue de la Chaine, 86022 Poitiers, France.

900   CN
UNIVERSITE LAVAL. LES CAHIERS D'HISTOIRE. 1959. irreg. Presses de l'Universite Laval, Quebec, PQ G1K 7R4, Canada. TEL 418-656-5106. FAX 418-656-2600. **Document type:** monographic series.
   Formerly: Universite Laval. Institut d'Histoire. Cahiers (ISSN 0079-8398)

900   US   ISSN 0068-6239
UNIVERSITY OF CALIFORNIA AT LOS ANGELES. CENTER FOR MEDIEVAL AND RENAISSANCE STUDIES. CONTRIBUTIONS. no.10, 1979. irreg., no.11, 1984. price varies. University of California Press, 2120 Berkeley Way, Berkeley, CA 94720. TEL 415-642-4247. FAX 415-643-7127. (Orders to: California-Princeton Fulfillment Services, 1445 Lower Ferry Rd., Ewing, NJ 08618. TEL 800-777-4726. FAX 800-999-1958) (back issues avail.)
   Refereed Serial

900   US   ISSN 0068-6220
UNIVERSITY OF CALIFORNIA AT LOS ANGELES. CENTER FOR MEDIEVAL AND RENAISSANCE STUDIES. PUBLICATIONS. no.6, 1973. irreg., no.24, 1991. price varies. University of California Press, 2120 Berkeley Way, Berkeley, CA 94720. TEL 415-642-4247. FAX 415-643-7127. (Orders to: California-Princeton Fulfillment Services, 1445 Lower Ferry Rd., Ewing, NJ 08618. TEL 800-777-4726. FAX 800-999-1958) (back issues avail.) **Document type:** monographic series.
   Refereed Serial

909   CN
UNIVERSITY OF OTTAWA. MEDIEVAL TEXTS AND STUDIES/UNIVERSITE D'OTTAWA. PUBLICATIONS MEDIEVALES. (Text in English and French) 1973. irreg. University of Ottawa Press, 542 King Edward, Ottawa, ON K1N 6N5, Canada. TEL 613-564-2270. FAX 613-564-9284. Ed. Pierre Kunstmann. **Document type:** academic/scholarly publication.
   Description: Studies and texts in English and French mediaeval literature.

940   UK   ISSN 0306-1108
UNIVERSITY OF SUSSEX. CENTRE FOR CONTINUING EDUCATION. OCCASIONAL PAPER. 1975. irreg., no.31, 1991. price varies. University of Sussex, Centre for Continuing Education, Falmer, Brighton, Sussex BN1 9RG, England. TEL 0273-678025. FAX 0273-678466. Ed. Fred Gray. circ. 1,000. **Indexed:** Geo.Abstr. **Document type:** monographic series.
   Description: Contains aspects of local history and social studies; designed to aid tutors and adult students, and often being the result of research done by adult classes.

UNIVERSITY OF WARWICK LIBRARY. OCCASIONAL PUBLICATIONS.. see *LIBRARY AND INFORMATION SCIENCES*

900 800   US   ISSN 0749-4149
UNIVERSITY STUDIES IN MEDIEVAL AND RENAISSANCE LITERATURE. (Text in English and other West European language.) 1988. irreg. Peter Lang Publishing, Inc., 62 W. 45th St., 4th Fl., New York, NY 10036. TEL 212-302-6740. Ed. Richard A. Katz. **Document type:** academic/scholarly publication. —BLDSC (9118.234000).

900   XO   ISSN 0083-4122
UNIVERZITA KOMENSKEHO. FILOZOFICKA FAKULTA. ZBORNIK: HISTORICA. (Text in Slovak; summaries in German and Russian) 1958. irreg. exchange basis. Univerzita Komenskeho, Filozoficka Fakulta, c/o Ustredna Kniznica Filozofickej Fakulty, Gondova 2, 818 01 Bratislava, Slovakia. Ed. Jan Hucko. bk.rev. circ. 700. **Document type:** academic/scholarly publication.
   Incorporates: Univerzita Komenskeho. Ustav Marxismu-Leninizmu. Zbornik: Dejiny Robotnickeho Hnutia (ISSN 0139-5599)

UNIWERSYTET GDANSKI. WYDZIAL HUMANISTYCZNY. ZESZYTY NAUKOWE. PRACE HISTORYCZNO-LITERACKIE. see *LITERATURE*

UNSER NEUSTADT. see *CONSERVATION*

900   GW
UNSERE ARCHIVE. 1974. s-a. free. Landesarchivverwaltung Rheinland-Pfalz, Karmeliterstr. 1-3, 56068 Koblenz, Germany. TEL 0261-33068. FAX 0261-33086. bk.rev. (back issues avail.) **Document type:** government publication.

VACARE DEO. see *RELIGIONS AND THEOLOGY — Roman Catholic*

VERDI. see *MUSIC*

VEREENIGING NEDERLANDSCH HISTORISCH SCHEEPVAART MUSEUM TE AMSTERDAM. JAARBOEK. see *TRANSPORTATION — Ships And Shipping*

900   NE
VEREENIGING TOT UITGAAF DER BRONNEN VAN HET OUD-VADERLANDSE RECHT. WERKEN. a. 1968. price varies. Walburg Pers BV, Postbus 4159, 7200 BD Zutphen, Netherlands. TEL 31-5750-10522. FAX 31-5750-41025. **Document type:** monographic series.

VERKEHRSGESCHICHTLICHE BLAETTER. see *TRANSPORTATION — Railroads*

HISTORY

900   RU   ISSN 0321-0391
VESTNIK DREVNEI ISTORII/JOURNAL OF ANCIENT HISTORY. (Text in Russian; contents page in English and Russian) 1937. q. $103. (Rossiiskaya Akademiya Nauk, Institut Vseobshchei Istorii) Izdatel'stvo Nauka, 90 Profsoyuznaya ul., 117864 Moscow, Russia. TEL 095-336-0266. FAX 095-420-2220. (Dist. by: Mezhdunarodnaya Kniga, B. Yakimanka 39, 117049 Moscow, Russia; Dist. in U.S. by: Victor Kamkin Inc., 4956 Boiling Brook Pkwy., Rockville, MD 20852. TEL 301-881-5973. FAX 301-881-1637) Ed. Z.V. Udal'tsova. bk.rev.; charts; illus.; index, cum.index every 5 yrs.: 1966-1970. circ. 3,910. **Indexed:** Anthropol.Lit., Bibl.Ling., Numis.Lit. **Document type:** academic/scholarly publication.

900   US   ISSN 0083-5897
CB3
VIATOR; Medieval and Renaissance studies. (Contributions in English and other major modern languages) 1970. a. $56 (foreign $61) (effective 1994). (University of California at Los Angeles, Center for Medieval and Renaissance Studies) University of California Press, Journals Division, 2120 Berkeley Way, Berkeley, CA 94720. TEL 510-643-7154. FAX 510-642-9917. Eds. Mary Rouse, Simon Varey. illus. circ. 400. (also avail. in microform from UMI; back issues avail.) **Indexed:** Amer.Bibl.Slavic & E.Eur.Stud., Amer.Hist.& Life, Br.Archaeol.Abstr., Geo.Abstr., Hist.Abstr., M.L.A., RILA. **Document type:** academic/scholarly publication.
—BLDSC (9232.230000); Faxon; UnCover; UMI. **CCC.**
    Description: Covers the entire medieval period, from late antiquity through the Renaissance.
    Refereed Serial

VICHIANA. see *LINGUISTICS*

900 940   AT   ISSN 1030-7710
VICTORIAN HISTORICAL JOURNAL. 1911. 2/yr. Aus.$50. Royal Historical Society of Victoria, Inc., Royal Mint, 280 William St., Melbourne, Vic. 3000, Australia. TEL 03-670-1219. Ed. Andrew Lemon. adv.; bk.rev. circ. 1,400. (back issues avail.) **Indexed:** Amer.Hist.& Life, Hist.Abstr. **Document type:** academic/scholarly publication.
    Formerly (until 1987): Royal Historical Society of Victoria. Journal (ISSN 0813-1295)
    Description: Studies history of Victoria.

VIERTELJAHRSCHRIFT FUER SOZIAL- UND WIRTSCHAFTSGESCHICHTE. see *SOCIAL SCIENCES: COMPREHENSIVE WORKS*

VIERTELJAHRSCHRIFT FUER SOZIAL- UND WIRTSCHAFTSGESCHICHTE. BEIHEFTE. see *SOCIAL SCIENCES: COMPREHENSIVE WORKS*

900   GW   ISSN 0042-5702
D410
VIERTELJAHRSHEFTE FUER ZEITGESCHICHTE. (Supplement: Bibliographie zur Zeitgeschichte) 1953. q. DM.69.60. (Institut fuer Zeitgeschichte) R. Oldenbourg Verlag GmbH, Rosenheimerstr. 145, 81671 Munich, Germany. TEL 089-4112-0. FAX 089-4112207. (Subscr. to: Postfach 801360, 81613 Munich, Germany) adv.; bibl.; index. circ. 4,700. **Indexed:** Amer.Hist.& Life, Curr.Cont., E.I., Hist.Abstr., P.A.I.S.For.Lang.Ind. **Document type:** academic/scholarly publication.
—BLDSC (9235.900000); Faxon; SWETS. **CCC.**
    Description: Contains essays on contemporary German history since World War II. Covers political, as well as industrial, technological, social and economic history.

900   HU   ISSN 0083-6265
VILAGTORTENET. 1964. q. $18. Magyar Tudomanyos Akademia, Nador u. 7, 1054 Budapest, Hungary. (Subscr. to: Kultura, Box 149, H-1389 Budapest, Hungary) Ed.Bd. bk.rev.; abstr.; bibl. circ. 1,600. **Indexed:** Amer.Hist.& Life, Hist.Abstr.

180   NE   ISSN 0042-7543
B1
VIVARIUM; an international journal for the philosophy and intellectual life of the Middle Ages and Renaissance. 1963. 2/yr. fl.72($41.25) to individuals; institutions fl.108(61.75) (effective 1994). E. J. Brill, P.O. Box 9000, 2300 PA Leiden, Netherlands. TEL 31-71-312624. FAX 31-71-317532. TELEX 39296 BRILL NL. (In N. America: E.J. Brill, 24 Hudson St., Kinderhook, NY 12106. TEL 800-962-4406. FAX 518-758-1959) Ed.Bd. (reprint service avail. from SWZ) **Indexed:** Arts & Hum.Cit.Ind., Bibl.Ling., Curr.Cont., M.L.A., Mid.East: Abstr.& Ind., Phil.Ind. **Document type:** academic/scholarly publication.
—Faxon; UnCover; SWETS. **CCC.**
    Description: Publishes extended examinations of fundamental philosophical problems and of the history of ideas, studies on manuscript tradition and the history of texts.
    Refereed Serial

900 800 325 398   IT
VOCE DI FIUME. 1966. m. free. Libero Comune di Fiume in Esilio, Riviera Ruzzante, 4, 35123 Padua, Italy. Dir. Mario Dassovich. bk.rev. circ. 9,200. (back issues avail.)

VOENNO-ISTORICHESKII ZHURNAL. see *MILITARY*

900   GW
VOLKSLEBEN; Deutsche Zeitschrift fuer Geschichte. 1909. 4/yr. DM.48. Verlag Peter Wegener, Bonner Talweg 18, 53015 Bonn, Germany. adv.; bk.rev.; charts; illus. circ. 1,100. (also avail. in microform) **Indexed:** Anthropol.Lit.
    Formerly: Mannus (ISSN 0025-2360)

900   RU   ISSN 0042-8779
VOPROSY ISTORII. (Text in Russian; contents page in English, French, Russian and Spanish; summaries in English) 1926. m. $121. (Rossiiskaya Akademiya Nauk, Otdelenie Istorii) Izdatel'stvo Pressa, Ul. Pravdy, 24, Moscow 125047, Russia. (Dist. by: Mezhdunarodnaya Kniga, ul. Dimitrova 39, Moscow G-200, Russia; Dist. in U.S. by: Victor Kamkin Inc., 4956 Boiling Brook Pkwy, Rockville, MD 20852. TEL 301-881-5973) Ed. V.G. Trukhanovskii. bk.rev.; abstr.; bibl.; index. (also avail. in microform) **Indexed:** Amer.Hist.& Life, Arts & Hum.Cit.Ind., Curr.Cont., Curr.Dig.Sov.Press, Hist.Abstr., Lang.& Lang.Behav.Abstr., Numis.Lit.
—BLDSC (0042.730000). **CCC.**

W W I AERO; the journal of the early aeroplane (1900-1918). (World War I Aeroplanes, Inc.) see *AERONAUTICS AND SPACE FLIGHT*

900 970 355   AT   ISSN 0729-2473
HM36.5
WAR AND SOCIETY. 1983. s-a. Aus.$22. University of New South Wales, Department of History, University College, Australian Defence Force Academy, Campbell, A.C.T. 2600, Australia. TEL 61-6-268-8879. FAX 61-6-268-8879. Ed. Jeffrey Grey. adv. circ. 500. (back issues avail.) **Indexed:** Amer.Hist.& Life, Hist.Abstr. **Document type:** academic/scholarly publication.
—BLDSC (9261.759000).
    Description: Covers war and its impact on society.

942   UK   ISSN 0043-2431
DA700
WELSH HISTORY REVIEW. (Text in English) 1960. s-a. £10. (Board of Celtic Studies) University of Wales Press, 6 Gwennyth St., Cathays, Cardiff CF2 4YD, Wales. TEL 0222-231919. FAX 0222-230908. Ed. Kenneth O. Morgan. adv.; bk.rev.; bibl.; charts; maps; index, cum.index. circ. 500. (also avail. in microfilm from UMI; reprint service avail. from UMI) **Indexed:** Amer.Hist.& Life, Arts & Hum.Cit.Ind., Br.Archaeol.Abstr., Br.Hum.Ind., Curr.Cont., Geo.Abstr., Hist.Abstr., M.L.A. **Document type:** academic/scholarly publication.
    Description: Publishes articles on topics in the history of Wales.

930   GW   ISSN 0340-6229
DIE WELT DES ORIENTS; wissenschaftliche Beitraege zur Kunde des Morgenlandes. 1947. irreg. Vandenhoeck und Ruprecht, Robert-Bosch-Breite 6, 37079 Goettingen, Germany. TEL 0551-6959-26. FAX 0551-695917. (Subscr. to: 37070 Goettingen, Germany) Eds. Wolfgang Roellig, Wolfram von Soden. adv.; bk.rev. **Indexed:** Bibl.Ling. **Document type:** monographic series.

WESLEY HISTORICAL SOCIETY. PROCEEDINGS. see *RELIGIONS AND THEOLOGY — Protestant*

WHISTLE STOP; Harry S. Truman Library Institute newsletter. see *LIBRARY AND INFORMATION SCIENCES*

900 301.412   US
WHOM NEWSLETTER. 1972. q. $15. Women Historians of the Midwest, 550 Rice St., No. 101, St. Paul, MN 55103-2116. Ed. Patricia Harpole. bk.rev. circ. 230. (back issues avail.) **Document type:** newsletter.

900   PL   ISSN 0511-9162
D16.4.P6
WIADOMOSCI HISTORYCZNE. 1957. bi-m. $18. (Ministerstwo Edukacji Narodowej) Wydawnictwa Szkolne i Pedagogiczne, Pl. Dabrowskiego 8, 00-950 Warsaw, Poland. TEL 44-22-265451. (Dist. by: Ars Polona-Ruch, Krakowskie Przedmiescie 7, Warsaw, Poland) Ed. Jerzy Centkowski. circ. 6,000. **Indexed:** Amer.Hist.& Life, Hist.Abstr.
    Description: Focuses on the teaching history, its influence on students, and on methods of awakening students' historical interest.

900 913 700   US
WILBOUR MONOGRAPHS. 1968. irreg., no.7, 1974. Brooklyn Museum, Department of Egyptian and Classical Art, The Gallery Shop, Eastern Pkwy., Brooklyn, NY 11238. TEL 718-638-5000. circ. 1,000. **Document type:** monographic series.

WOCHENSCHAU FUER POLITISCHE ERZIEHUNG, SOZIAL- UND GEMEINSCHAFTSKUNDE. AUSGABE FUER SEKUNDARSTUFE I. see *SOCIAL SCIENCES: COMPREHENSIVE WORKS*

WOCHENSCHAU FUER POLITISCHE ERZIEHUNG, SOZIAL- UND GEMEINSCHAFTSKUNDE. AUSGABE FUER SEKUNDARSTUFE II. see *SOCIAL SCIENCES: COMPREHENSIVE WORKS*

WOJSKOWY PRZEGLAD HISTORYCZNY. see *MILITARY*

900 020 800 011   GW   ISSN 0931-4032
WOLFENBUETTELER BIBLIOTHEKS - INFORMATIONEN. 1976. q. free. Herzog - August - Bibliothek, Lessingplatz 1, 38304 Wolfenbuttel, Germany. FAX 05331-808173. Ed. Oswald Schoenberg. adv. circ. 10,000. (back issues avail.) **Document type:** academic/scholarly publication.

900   GW
WOLFENBUETTELER STUDIEN ZUR AUFKLAERUNG. SCHRIFTENREIHE. 1974. irreg. price varies. Max Niemeyer Verlag, Postfach 2140, 72011 Tuebingen, Germany. TEL 07071-98940. FAX 07071-989450. **Indexed:** M.L.A. **Document type:** monographic series.

WOMAN IN HISTORY. see *WOMEN'S INTERESTS*

WORLD WAR II REVIEW. see *MILITARY*

951   CC   ISSN 1000-6176
WUTAISHAN YANJIU/MOUNTAIN WUTAI RESEARCHES. (Text in Chinese) 1985. bi-m. $2 per no. Wutaishan Yanjiuhui, 38, Bingzhou Nanlu, Taiyuan, Shanxi 030006, People's Republic of China. TEL 7075841. Ed. Liu Guangweng; Pub. Cui Zhengsen. bibl.
    Refereed Serial

900   PL   ISSN 0137-5873
WYZSZA SZKOLA PEDAGOGICZNA IM. KOMISJI EDUKACJI NARODOWEJ W KRAKOWIE. ROCZNIK NAUKOWO-DYDAKTYCZNY. PRACE HISTORYCZNE. 1962. irreg., no.15, 1989. price varies. Wydawnictwo Naukowe W S P, Ul. Karmelicka 41, 31-128 Krakow, Poland. TEL 33-78-20. (Co-sponsor: Ministerstwo Edukacji Narodowej)

XIN WENXUE SHILIAO/HISTORICAL MATERIALS OF NEW LITERATURE. see *LITERATURE*

900   US   ISSN 0084-3350
YALE HISTORICAL PUBLICATIONS. 1914. irreg. price varies. Yale University Press, Box 209040, New Haven, CT 06520. TEL 203-432-0940. **Document type:** academic/scholarly publication.

HISTORY — ABSTRACTING, BIBLIOGRAPHIES, STATISTICS

900   UN   ISSN 0084-4322
JX1977
YOUR UNITED NATIONS; official guidebook. 1952. irreg., latest 1987. $6.95. United Nations Publications, Room DC2-853, New York, NY 10017. TEL 212-963-8302. FAX 212-963-3489. (Or: Distribution and Sales Section, CH-1211 Geneva 10, Switzerland) (also avail. in microfiche)

900   PL   ISSN 0044-1791
DD491.P71
ZAPISKI HISTORYCZNE; poswiecone historii pomorza i krajow Baltyckich. (Text in Polish; summaries in English, German, Russian) 1908. q. $60. Towarzystwo Naukowe w Toruniu, Ul. Wysoka 16, 81-100 Torun, Poland. TEL 48-56-23941. TELEX 552388 FSBH PL. Ed. Marian Biskup. bk.rev.; index. circ. 500. **Indexed**: Amer.Hist.& Life, Hist.Abstr. **Document type**: academic/scholarly publication.

ZEICHEN. see *RELIGIONS AND THEOLOGY — Protestant*

900   AU
ZEITGESCHICHTE. 1973. 6/yr. S.350. (Verein zur Wissenschaftlichen Aufarbeitung der Zeitgeschichte) J & V Edition Wien - Dachs Verlag GmbH, Rainergasse 38, A-1050 Vienna, Austria. TEL 01-5458210. FAX 01-545821027. Ed. Erika Weinzierl. adv.: B&W page S.6000; trim 130 x 195. bk.rev. circ. 700. **Indexed**: Amer.Hist.& Life, Arts & Hum.Cit.Ind., Curr.Cont., Hist.Abstr., SSCI. **Document type**: academic/scholarly publication.
Description: Publishes research on contemporary history.

943   GW   ISSN 0044-2364
DD801.B31
ZEITSCHRIFT FUER BAYERISCHE LANDESGESCHICHTE. 1928. 3/yr. DM.96. (Bayerische Akademie der Wissenschaften, Kommission fuer Bayerische Landesgeschichte) C.H. Beck'sche Verlagsbuchhandlung, Wilhelmstr. 9, 80801 Munich, Germany. TEL 089-38189-338. FAX 089-38189-398. TELEX 5215085-BECK-D. (Co-sponsor: Gesellschaft fuer Fraenkische Geschichte, Schwaebische Forschungsgemeinschaft) Ed. A. Kraus. adv.; bk.rev.; cum.index.: 1938-1957. circ. 650. (reprint service avail. from SCH) **Indexed**: Bibl.Cart. **Document type**: academic/scholarly publication.
—SWETS.

ZEITSCHRIFT FUER KUNSTGESCHICHTE. see *ART*

ZEPHYRUS. see *ARCHAEOLOGY*

900   FR   ISSN 0044-4391
DK401
ZESZYTY HISTORYCZNE. (Text in Polish) 1962. q. 330 F.($64) Institut Litteraire, 91 Ave. de Poissy, Le Mesnil-le-Roi, 78600 Maisons Laffitte, France. TEL 1-39-62-19-04. FAX 33-1-39-62-57-52. Ed. Jerzy Giedroyc. bk.rev. circ. 2,500. **Indexed**: Amer.Hist.& Life, Hist.Abstr.

ZHONGGONG DANGSHI/HISTORY OF THE CHINESE COMMUNIST PARTY. see *POLITICAL SCIENCE*

ZHONGGUO NONG-SHI/AGRICULTURAL HISTORY OF CHINA. see *AGRICULTURE*

900   IS
ZIMANIM; quarterly of history. q. Tel Aviv University, School of History, Ramat Aviv, Tel Aviv, Israel. Ed. Shlomo Ben-Ami.

ZION; a quarterly for research in Jewish history. see *ETHNIC INTERESTS*

900   CC
ZIRAN YU REN/NATURE AND MAN. (Text in Chinese) 1979. bi-m. Shanghai Ziran Bowuguan - Shanghai Natural History Museum, 260 Yan'an Donglu, Shanghai 200002, People's Republic of China. TEL 3213548. Eds. Rao Zhonghua, Wang Yijiong. adv. circ. 50,000. **Document type**: consumer publication.

901   GW   ISSN 0514-8294
ZUR POLITIK UND ZEITGESCHICHTE. 1961. irreg. price varies. (Landeszentrale fuer Politische Bildung, Berlin) Colloquium Verlag, Luetzowstr. 105, 10785 Berlin, Germany. circ. 3,000.

---

900   SP   ISSN 1130-3948
XX SIGLOS. 1990. 5/yr. 3000 ptas. (foreign 4000 ptas.). Centro de Estudios Teologicos "San Damasco", San Buenaventura, 9, 28005 Madrid, Spain. TEL 91-365-24-04. Ed. Juan M. Laboa. bk.rev. circ. 2,000. (back issues avail.)

39 - 45 MAGAZINE. see *MILITARY*

HISTORY — Abstracting, Bibliographies, Statistics

947 016   UK
A B R E E S. (Abstracts Russian and East European Series) (Former name of issuing body: British Association for Slavonic and East European Studies) 1970. 3/yr. $699. (A B R E E S Ltd.) Pergamon Journals, St. Andrews House, Roupell St., London SE1 8SS, England. Ed. Ray Hutchings. adv.; abstr.; bibl.; index. circ. 200. (also avail. in microfiche) **Indexed**: Curr.Cont., PROMT. **Document type**: abstracting/indexing.
●Also available on CD-ROM.
—CCC.
Formerly (until 1993): A B S E E S (Abstracts Soviet and East European Series) (ISSN 0044-5622); Incorporates: C R E E S Soviet Press Abstracts; Soviet Studies. Information Supplement (ISSN 0584-567X)
Description: Contains economic and business information covering Eastern Europe & Russia abstracted from newspapers and periodicals.

956   BE   ISSN 0240-8910
ABSTRACTA IRANICA. (Supplement to: Studia Iranica (0772-7852)) 1978. a. 1800 BEF (effective 1994). (Institut Francais de Recherche en Iran, IR) Editions Peeters s.p.r.l., Bondgenotenlaan 153, B-3000 Louvain, Belgium. TEL 32-16-235170. FAX 32-16-228500. Ed. Y. Richard. adv.; bk.rev.; index. circ. 800. (back issues avail.) **Document type**: abstracting/indexing, academic/scholarly publication.
—BLDSC (0570.244000).
Description: Bibliographical journal of Iranian studies.

016   US   ISSN 0749-2308
AFRICAN SPECIAL BIBLIOGRAPHIC SERIES. 1985. irreg. price varies. Greenwood Press, Inc. (Subsidiary of: Greenwood Publishing Group Inc.), 88 Post Rd. W., Box 5007, Westport, CT 06881-5007. TEL 203-226-3571. FAX 203-222-1502. **Document type**: bibliography.
—BLDSC (0733.980500).
Supersedes: African Bibliographic Center, Washington D.C. Special Bibliographic Series (ISSN 0065-3934)

970 011   US
AMERICA: HISTORY AND LIFE. ANNUAL INDEX. a. A B C-Clio, 130 Cremona, Box 1911, Santa Barbara, CA 93116-1911. TEL 805-968-1911. FAX 805-685-9685. Ed. Peter S. Quimby; Pub. Heather Cameron. adv. contact: Laura Wilson. **Document type**: abstracting/indexing.
●Also available on CD-ROM.
Description: Covers all aspects of US and Canadian history, culture, and current affairs from prehistoric times to the present. Cumulative subject, author, title, and reviewer indexing for all abstracts and citations in the volume.

---

970 011   US
Z1236
AMERICA: HISTORY AND LIFE. ARTICLE ABSTRACTS AND CITATIONS OF REVIEWS AND DISSERTATIONS COVERING THE UNITED STATES AND CANADA. 1964. 5/yr. (including a. index). price varies. A B C-Clio, 130 Cremona, Box 1911, Santa Barbara, CA 93116-1911. TEL 805-968-1911. FAX 805-685-9685. Ed. Peter S. Quimby; Pub. Heather Cameron. adv. contact: Laura Wilson. index. **Document type**: abstracting/indexing.
●Also available online. Vendor(s): DIALOG Information Services, Inc. (File no.38).
Also available on CD-ROM.
Former titles: America: History and Life. Part A: Article Abstracts and Citation (ISSN 0002-7065); America: History and Life. Part B: Index to Book Reviews (ISSN 0097-6172); America: History and Life. Part C: American History Bibliography (ISSN 0363-1249); America: History and Life. Part D: Annual Index (ISSN 0362-0883)
Description: Includes citations and abstracts to history, social science and humanities literature on all aspects of US and Canadian history, culture, and current affairs from prehistoric times to the present.

016 940   US   ISSN 0094-3770
Z2483
AMERICAN BIBLIOGRAPHY OF SLAVIC AND EAST EUROPEAN STUDIES. 1956. a. $43 to non-members (foreign $44); members $28 (foreign $29). American Association for the Advancement of Slavic Studies, Jordan Quad - Acacia Bldg., Stanford University, Stanford, CA 94305-4130. TEL 415-723-9668. bibl. **Document type**: bibliography.
—BLDSC (0810.791000).
Formerly: American Bibliography of Russian and East European Studies.

973 015   US
AMERICAN HERITAGE CUMULATIVE INDEX. irreg., latest 1990 (indexes 1954-1989). American Heritage (Subsidiary of: Forbes, Inc.), 60 Fifth Ave., New York, NY 10011. TEL 212-206-5500. FAX 212-620-2332. **Document type**: abstracting/indexing.
Formerly: American Heritage Index.

011   US
AMERICAN HISTORY; a bibliographic review. 1985. a. $59.50. Greenwood Press, Inc. (Subsidiary of: Greenwood Publishing Group Inc.), 88 Post Rd. W., Box 5007, Westport, CT 06881-5007. TEL 203-226-3571. FAX 203-221-1502. Ed. Carol Bondhus Fitzgerald. **Document type**: bibliography.

011 962   NE   ISSN 0165-9111
ANNUAL EGYPTOLOGICAL BIBLIOGRAPHY/BIBLIOGRAPHIE EGYPTOLOGIQUE ANNUELLE/JAEHRLICHE AEGYPTOLOGISCHE BIBLIOGRAPHIE. Short title: A E B. (Text in English, French, German) 1947. a., latest 1991 (for the year 1986). fl.100. (International Association of Egyptologists) Nederlands Instituut voor het Nabije Oosten, Witte Singel 24, P.O. Box 9515, 2300 RA Leiden, Netherlands. (Co-sponsor: Instituut voor Egyptologie) Ed. L.M.J. Zonhoven. bk.rev.; index. circ. 500. (back issues avail.) **Document type**: bibliography.

950 016   UN   ISSN 0497-9400
Z3008.E2
ASIAN BIBLIOGRAPHY. 1952. s-a. exchange basis only. United Nations Economic and Social Commission for Asia and the Pacific (ESCAP), Library, Rajadamnern Ave., Bangkok 10200, Thailand. **Document type**: bibliography.
—BLDSC (1742.400000).

979   US
ASSOCIATION OF CARIBBEAN STUDIES. ABSTRACTS. (Text in English, French, Spanish) a. $50 to individuals; institutions $200. Association of Caribbean Studies, Box 22202, Lexington, KY 40522-2202. TEL 606-257-6966. FAX 606-258-1072. Ed. O.R. Dathorne. circ. 1,000. **Document type**: abstracting/indexing.
Description: Abstracts of the most recent annual conference of the association.

HISTORY — ABSTRACTING, BIBLIOGRAPHIES, STATISTICS

949.5   GR   ISSN 1105-5901
BALKAN BIBLIOGRAPHY/BALKANIKE BIBLIOGRAFIA.
(Has supplement: Balkanike Bibliografia. Parartema (ISSN 1105-591X)) 1973. irreg. $30. Institute for Balkan Studies, 31 Ave. Megalou Alexandrou, 546 41 Thessaloniki, Greece. TEL 30-31-832143. FAX 30-31-831429. **Document type:** bibliography.

011   MX   ISSN 0185-1578
BIBLIOGRAFIA HISTORICA MEXICANA. 1967. irreg., latest no.18. $25 (effective 1993). (Centro de Estudios Historicos) Colegio de Mexico, A.C., Departamento de Publicaciones, Camino al Ajusco 20, C.P. 01000 Mexico D.F., Mexico. TEL 6455955. FAX 6450454. TELEX 1777585 COLME. circ. 1,500. (back issues avail.; reprint service avail. from SWZ) **Document type:** bibliography.

016 943.8   PL   ISSN 0067-6721
BIBLIOGRAFIA HISTORII POLSKIEJ. 1962. irreg., latest 1988. (Polska Akademia Nauk, Instytut Historii) Ossolineum, Publishing House of the Polish Academy of Sciences, Rynek 9, 50-106 Wroclaw, Poland. TEL 48-71-386-25. FAX 48-71-448-103. TELEX 0712771 OSS PL. (Dist. by: Ars Polona-Ruch, Krakowskie Przedmiescie 7, Warsaw, Poland) Ed. W. Bienkowski. circ. 1,500. **Document type:** bibliography.

970 016   US   ISSN 0147-6491
Z1236
BIBLIOGRAPHIC GUIDE TO NORTH AMERICAN HISTORY.* a. $300 cloth (foreign $330). G.K. Hall & Co., c/o MacMillan Publishing Co., 866 Third Ave., 18th fl., New York, NY 10022. TEL 212-702-6789. (Orders to: MacMillan Distribution Center, 100 Front St., Box 500, Riverside, NJ 08075-7500. TEL 800-257-5755) **Document type:** bibliography, abstracting/indexing.
Description: Covers all aspects of U.S. and Canadian history.

960 016   FR
BIBLIOGRAPHIE ANALYTIQUE DE L'AFRIQUE ANTIQUE. 1969. irreg. Edition-Diffusion De Boccard, 11 rue de Medicis, 75006 Paris, France. (U.S. subscr. to: Institute for the Arts, Rice University, Box 1892, Houston TX 77001) Eds. Jehan Desanges, Serge Lancel. **Document type:** bibliography.

944   FR   ISSN 0067-6918
Z2176
BIBLIOGRAPHIE ANNUELLE DE L'HISTOIRE DE FRANCE. 1955. a. price varies. (Centre National de la Recherche Scientifique) C N R S Editions, 20-22 rue St. Amand, 75015 Paris, France. TEL 45-33-16-00. FAX 45-33-92-13. TELEX 200 356 F. adv.; bk.rev.; index; circ. 1,500 (controlled). **Document type:** bibliography.
—BLDSC (1975.770000).

940.1   BE   ISSN 0778-9777
BIBLIOGRAPHIE ANNUELLE DU MOYEN AGE TARDIF; auteurs et textes latins, vers 1250-1500. 1991. a. 1850 BEF (effective 1994). (Centre National de Recherche Scientifique, Institut de Recherche et d'Histoire des Textes, FR) N.V. Brepols, Steenweg op Tielen 68, 2300 Turnhout, Belgium. TEL 32-14-415463. FAX 32-14-428919. **Document type:** bibliography.

949.35 016   LU   ISSN 0067-7043
BIBLIOGRAPHIE D'HISTOIRE LUXEMBOURGEOISE. 1964. a. 200 Fr. Bibliotheque Nationale, 37 Boulevard F.D. Roosevelt, L-2450 Luxembourg, Luxembourg. TEL 22-62-55. FAX 475672. circ. 500. **Document type:** bibliography.
Description: Lists publications concerning the history of the Grand-Duchy of Luxembourg and the territories of the former Duchy of Luxembourg.

949.4   SZ   ISSN 0250-5673
BIBLIOGRAPHIE DER BERNER GESCHICHTE/BIBLIOGRAPHIE DE L'HISTOIRE BERNOISE. (Text in French, German) 1975. a. 15 SFr. Burgerbibliothek Bern - Bibliotheque de la Bourgeoisie de Berne, Muenstergasse 63, CH-3000 Bern 7, Switzerland. Ed.Bd. circ. 1,500. **Document type:** bibliography.

BIBLIOGRAPHIE GESCHICHTE DER TECHNIK. see TECHNOLOGY: COMPREHENSIVE WORKS — Abstracting, Bibliographies, Statistics

960   US   ISSN 0742-6925
BIBLIOGRAPHIES AND INDEXES IN AFRO-AMERICAN AND AFRICAN STUDIES. 1984. irreg. price varies. Greenwood Press, Inc. (Subsidiary of: Greenwood Publishing Group Inc.), 88 Post Rd. W., Box 5007, Westport, CT 06881-5007. TEL 203-226-3571. FAX 203-222-1502.

970   US   ISSN 0742-6828
BIBLIOGRAPHIES AND INDEXES IN AMERICAN HISTORY. 1984. irreg. price varies. Greenwood Press, Inc. (Subsidiary of: Greenwood Publishing Group Inc.), 88 Post Rd. W., Box 5007, Westport, CT 06881-5007. TEL 203-226-3571. FAX 203-222-1502. **Document type:** bibliography.

980 300   US   ISSN 1054-9102
BIBLIOGRAPHIES AND INDEXES IN LATIN AMERICAN AND CARIBBEAN STUDIES. 1991. irreg. price varies. Greenwood Press, Inc. (Subsidiary of: Greenwood Publishing Group Inc.), 88 Post Rd. W., Box 5007, Westport, CT 06881-5007. TEL 203-226-3571. FAX 203-222-1502. **Document type:** bibliography, monographic series.

900   US   ISSN 0742-6852
BIBLIOGRAPHIES AND INDEXES IN WORLD HISTORY. 1984. irreg. price varies. Greenwood Press, Inc. (Subsidiary of: Greenwood Publishing Group Inc.), 88 Post Rd. W., Box 5007, Westport, CT 06881-5007. TEL 203-226-3571. FAX 203-222-1502. **Document type:** bibliography.
—BLDSC (1993.097590).

BIBLIOGRAPHIES OF THE PRESIDENTS OF THE UNITED STATES. see POLITICAL SCIENCE — Abstracting, Bibliographies, Statistics

BIBLIOGRAPHIES OF WORLD LEADERS. see POLITICAL SCIENCE — Abstracting, Bibliographies, Statistics

950 016   US   ISSN 0067-7159
Z3001
BIBLIOGRAPHY OF ASIAN STUDIES. 1954. a. $70. Association for Asian Studies, Inc., 1 Lane Hall, University of Michigan, Ann Arbor, MI 48109. TEL 313-665-2490. FAX 313-665-3801. Ed. Wayne Surdom. circ. 3,000. (also avail. in microform from UMI; back issues avail.; reprint service avail. from UMI) **Indexed:** A.I.C.P., E.I. **Document type:** bibliography.
—UMI.
Description: Bibliography of articles on Asia in Western languages published during a given year.

948 448   DK   ISSN 0067-7213
Z2556
BIBLIOGRAPHY OF OLD NORSE-ICELANDIC STUDIES. (Text in several languages) 1964. a. price varies. Kongelige Bibliotek, 8 Christians Brygge, DK-1219 Copenhagen K, Denmark. Ed. Hans Bekker-Nielsen. circ. 600. **Document type:** academic/scholarly publication, bibliography.

016 028.1   NE   ISSN 0006-1913
Z3001
BIBLIOTHECA ORIENTALIS. (Text in English, French, German) 1943. bi-m. fl.225. Nederlands Instituut voor het Nabije Oosten - Netherlands Institute for the Near East, Witte Singel 24, P.O. Box 9515, 2300 RA Leiden, Netherlands. Ed. J. de Roos. bk.rev.; index. circ. 800. (back issues avail.) **Indexed:** Bibl.Ling., Mid.East: Abstr.& Ind., Numis.Lit., Old Test.Abstr. **Document type:** academic/scholarly publication, bibliography.
—SWETS.
Description: Contains reviews and bibliographical data on books published on the ancient and modern Near East.

900 016   GW   ISSN 0081-8992
BIBLIOTHEK FUER ZEITGESCHICHTE, STUTTGART. JAHRESBIBLIOGRAPHIE; Neue Folge der Buecherschau der Weltkriegsbuecherei. 1961. irreg. price varies. (Bibliothek fuer Zeitgeschichte, Stuttgart) Bernard und Graefe Verlag, Karl-Mand-Str. 2, Postfach 2060, 56070 Koblenz, Germany. TEL 0261-80706-0. TELEX 862662-SPS-D. **Document type:** bibliography.

015 918.9   NQ
BOLETIN NICARAGUENSE DE BIBLIOGRAFIA Y DOCUMENTACION.* 1974. bi-m. free. Ministerio de Comercio Exterior (MICE), Apdo. 2412, Managua, Nicaragua. Ed. Ramon Cabrales. bibl.; illus. circ. 1,500. **Document type:** bibliography, government publication.

BOOKS ABOUT SINGAPORE. see TRAVEL AND TOURISM — Abstracting, Bibliographies, Statistics

BOOKS AND ARTICLES ON ORIENTAL SUBJECTS PUBLISHED IN JAPAN. see ORIENTAL STUDIES — Abstracting, Bibliographies, Statistics

BOOKS IN POLISH OR RELATING TO POLAND. see PUBLISHING AND BOOK TRADE — Abstracting, Bibliographies, Statistics

892.7 011   BE   ISSN 0778-6727
BULLETIN D'ARABE CHRETIEN. BIBLIOGRAPHIE DES AUTEURS ARABES CHRETIENS. Key Title: B A C Bulletin d'Arabe Chretien. (Text in French) vol.6, 1990. a. 420 BEF (effective 1994). (Association Internationale d'Etudes Arabes Chretiennes) Editions Peeters s.p.r.l., Bondgenotenlaan 153, B-3000 Louvain, Belgium. TEL 32-16-235170. FAX 32-16-228500. Ed.Bd. bk.rev. (back issues avail.) **Document type:** academic/scholarly publication, bibliography.

CARMELUS; commentarii ab Instituto Carmelitano editi. see RELIGIONS AND THEOLOGY — Roman Catholic

940 001.3   US
CLIO BIBLIOGRAPHY SERIES. 1972. irreg., vol.151, 1992. A B C-Clio, 130 Cremona, Box 1191, Santa Barbara, CA 93116-1911. TEL 805-968-1911. FAX 805-685-9685. **Document type:** bibliography.

900   US
COMPUBIBS. 1984. irreg. price varies. Vantage Information Consultants, Inc., 3516 Castlegate E., Wynd., Lexington, KY 40502-7701. Ed. Charlotte L. Levy. abstr. (back issues avail.)

948.9   DK   ISSN 0901-5507
Z2576
DANSK HISTORISK BIBLIOGRAFI. 1967. irreg. DKK 226.30. Dansk Historisk Faellesraad, Landsarkivet, Box 661, Jagtvej 10, DK 2200 Copenhagen N, Denmark. Dir. Grethe Ilsoee. **Document type:** bibliography.
Formerly (until 1986): Dansk Historisk Aarsbibliografi (ISSN 0107-0436)

960 016   II   ISSN 0418-582X
DOCUMENTATION LIST: AFRICA. (Text in English, French) 1962. a. $40. University of Delhi, Department of African Studies, Delhi 110 007, India. TEL 7257725. Ed. R.P. Sood. subject index. circ. 300.

016 940   FR   ISSN 0151-0827
DOCUMENTS; revue des questions allemandes. 1945. 5/yr. 220 F. (foreign 240 F.) (Bureau International de Liaison et de Documentation) Documents, 50 rue de Laborde, 75008 Paris, France. Ed. Joseph Rovan. adv.; bk.rev. **Indexed:** Amer.Hist.& Life, Hist.Abstr.
—SWETS.
Description: Provides a forum for the discussion and examination of German life.

E I. (Excerpta Indonesica) see ANTHROPOLOGY — Abstracting, Bibliographies, Statistics

967   TZ   ISSN 0856-0455
Z3516
EAST AFRICANA ACCESSIONS BULLETIN. (Text in English) 1973. s-a. $5 (typically set in July). University of Dar es Salaam, Library, Box 35092, Dar es Salaam, Tanzania. TEL 49192. FAX 051-48409. TELEX 41327 UNISCIE; 41561 UNIVIPTZ. Ed. G.K. Puja. circ. 200.
Formerly: New Accessions to East Africana.
Description: Information for researchers on East Africa.

EAST EUROPE IN GERMAN BOOKS; a bulletin listing new books on East Europe published in the German language. see TRAVEL AND TOURISM — Abstracting, Bibliographies, Statistics

942 015   UK   ISSN 0029-2885
EAST MIDLANDS BIBLIOGRAPHY. 1963. q. £8. Library Association, East Midlands Branch, c/o Mrs. V. Langworthy, Ed., Singing Hill, Alderwasley, Derbyshire, England. bibl.; index, cum.index every 5 yrs. circ. 120. **Indexed:** World Text.Abstr. **Document type:** bibliography.
—BLDSC (3646.510000).
Formerly: North Midland Bibliography.

HISTORY — ABSTRACTING, BIBLIOGRAPHIES, STATISTICS

940 IT
ESTRATTI DAGLI STUDI MEDIEVALI. 1977. irreg., no.13, 1987. price varies. Centro Italiano di Studi sull'Alto Medioevo, Palazzo Ancaiani, 06049 Spoleto, Italy. TEL 0743-220418. FAX 0743-223507. **Document type:** monographic series.

963 ET
ETHIOPIAN MANUSCRIPTS MICROFILM LIBRARY. BULLETIN. 1974. q. $2. Ethiopian Manuscript Microfilm Library, P.O. 30274, Addis Ababa, Ethiopia. adv.; bibl. circ. 500.

950 016 FR ISSN 0140-492X
Z2483
EUROPEAN BIBLIOGRAPHY OF SOVIET, EAST EUROPEAN AND SLAVONIC STUDIES/BIBLIOGRAPHIE EUROPEENE DES TRAVAUX SUR L'URSS ET L'EUROPE DE L'EST/EUROPAISCHE BIBLIOGRAPHIE DER SOWJET- UND OESTEUROPASTUDIEN. (Text in English, French and German) 1975. a. 420 F. (Ecole des Hautes Etudes en Sciences Sociales) Institut d'Etude Slaves, 9 rue Michelet, 75006 Paris, France. Ed. Monique Armand. bk.rev. circ. 550. **Document type:** bibliography.
—BLDSC (3829.489200).
Supersedes: Soviet, East European and Slavonic Studies in Western Europe.

900 FR ISSN 1157-3724
Z7405.H6
F R A N C I S. 522: HISTOIRE DES SCIENCES ET DE TECHNIQUES. (Text in English, French, Spanish) 1947. q. 465 F. (outside EEC 490 F.). Centre National de la Recherche Scientifique, Institut de l'Information Scientifique et Technique, 2 allee du Parc de Brabois, 54514 Vandoeuvre-les-Nancy Cedex, France. TEL 83-50-46-00. FAX 83-50-46-50. adv. contact: Veronique Guinvarc'h. cum.index. **Document type:** bibliography.
•Also available online. Vendor(s): European Space Agency, Telesystemes - Questel.
Also available on CD-ROM.
Formerly: Bulletin Signaletique. Part 522: Histoire des Sciences et des Techniques (ISSN 0007-5574)

F R A N C I S. 525: PREHISTOIRE ET PROTOHISTOIRE. see ARCHAEOLOGY — Abstracting, Bibliographies, Statistics

940 016 GW ISSN 0067-5881
FREIE UNIVERSITAET BERLIN. OSTEUROPA-INSTITUT. BIBLIOGRAPHISCHE MITTEILUNGEN. 1959. irreg., vol.26, 1989. price varies. (Freie Universitaet Berlin, Osteuropa Institut) Harrassowitz Verlag, Taunustr. 14, 65183 Wiesbaden, Germany. TEL 0611-530-0. FAX 0611-530570. TELEX 4186135. (Subscr. to: Postfach 2929, 65019 Wiesbaden, Germany) **Document type:** bibliography.

FRENCH 17; an annual descriptive bibliography of French seventeenth century studies. see LITERATURE — Abstracting, Bibliographies, Statistics

900 011 GW ISSN 0940-9483
GESCHICHTE - ZEITGESCHEHEN - POLITIK. (Text in English, French, German) 1956. s-a. DM.27.80. Buchwerbung in Berlin GmbH, Luetzowstr. 105-106, 10785 Berlin, Germany. circ. 3,500. **Document type:** abstracting/indexing.
Description: Bibliography on the subject of history.

942 UK
GREATER LONDON LOCAL HISTORY DIRECTORY AND BIBLIOGRAPHY. 1988. triennial. £15. Peter Marcan Publications, P.O. Box 3158, London SE1 4RA, England. circ. 500. **Document type:** bibliography, directory.
Description: Borough by borough guide to local history organizations and their recent publications, including public library authorities.

090 994 016 AT ISSN 0725-9107
GUIDE TO COLLECTIONS OF MANUSCRIPTS RELATING TO AUSTRALIA; a selective union list. 1964. irreg., latest 1992. Aus.$10. National Library of Australia, Publications Section, Cultural and Educational Services Division, Canberra, A.C.T. 2600, Australia. TEL 06-262-1365. FAX 06-273-4493. circ. 300. (looseleaf format; reprint service avail from ISI,UMI) **Document type:** bibliography.
Formerly: Guide to Manuscripts Relating to Australia.

980 US ISSN 0072-9833
Z1605
HANDBOOK OF LATIN AMERICAN STUDIES: A SELECTED AND ANNOTATED GUIDE TO RECENT PUBLICATIONS. (Beginning with no.36, even-numbered vols. cover humanities, odd-numbered vols. cover social sciences) 1935. a. price varies. (U.S. Library of Congress, Hispanic Division) University of Texas Press, Box 7819, Austin, TX 78713. TEL 512-471-4278. Ed. Dolores Moyano Martin. bk.rev. circ. 1,500. **Document type:** abstracting/indexing.
•Also available on CD-ROM. Producer(s): NISC (Latin American Studies - Vol.1).

HESSISCHES STAATSARCHIV DARMSTADT. MITTEILUNGEN. see HISTORY — History Of Europe

980 US ISSN 0361-5502
Z1605
HISPANIC AMERICAN PERIODICALS INDEX. 1978. a. $375. (University of California at Los Angeles, Latin American Studies Center) Latin American Studies Center Publications, University of California at Los Angeles, 10353 Bunche Hall, Los Angeles, CA 90024. TEL 310-825-0810. FAX 310-206-2634. Ed. Barbara G. Valk. **Document type:** abstracting/indexing.
•Also available on CD-ROM. Producer(s): NISC (Latin American Studies - Vol.1).
Description: Includes current periodical articles about Latin America, the Caribbean, and Hispanics in the U.S.

900 016 US ISSN 0363-2717
D299
HISTORICAL ABSTRACTS. PART A: MODERN HISTORY ABSTRACTS, 1450-1914. 1955. 4/yr. (including a. index). price varies. A B C-Clio, 130 Cremona, Box 1911, Santa Barbara, CA 93116-1911. TEL 805-968-1911. FAX 805-685-9685. Ed. Roger W. Davis; Pub. Heather Cameron. adv. contact: Laura Wilson. index, cum.index every 5 yrs. **Document type:** abstracting/indexing.
•Also available online. Vendor(s): DIALOG Information Services, Inc. (File no.39).
Also available on CD-ROM.
—BLDSC (4316.103000).
Superseded in part: Historical Abstracts (ISSN 0018-2435)
Description: Covers the history of the world 1450-1914 except for the US and Canada. Includes citations and abstracts to the literature published worldwide.

900 016 US ISSN 0363-2725
D299
HISTORICAL ABSTRACTS. PART B: TWENTIETH CENTURY ABSTRACTS, 1914 TO THE PRESENT. 1955. 4/yr. (including a. index). price varies. A B C-Clio, 130 Cremona, Box 1911, Santa Barbara, CA 93116-1911. TEL 805-968-1911. FAX 805-685-9685. Ed. Roger W. Davis; Pub. Heather Cameron. adv. contact: Laura Wilson. index, cum.index every 5 yrs. **Document type:** abstracting/indexing.
•Also available online. Vendor(s): DIALOG Information Services, Inc. (File no.39).
Also available on CD-ROM.
—BLDSC (4316.104000).
Supersedes in part: Historical Abstracts (ISSN 0018-2435)
Description: Covers the history of the world 1914 to the present except for the US and Canada. Includes citations and abstracts of the literature published worldwide.

900 016 US ISSN 0363-2725
HISTORICAL ABSTRACTS. PART B: TWENTIETH CENTURY ABSTRACTS. 1914 TO THE PRESENT. ANNUAL INDEX. a. A B C-Clio, 130 Cremona, Box 1911, Santa Barbara, CA 93116-1911. TEL 805-968-1911. FAX 805-685-9685. Ed. Roger W. Davis; Pub. Heather Cameron. adv. contact: Laura Wilson. **Document type:** abstracting/indexing.
•Also available online. Vendor(s): DIALOG Information Services, Inc. (File no.39).
Also available on CD-ROM.
Description: Covers the history of the world 1914 to the present except for the US and Canada. Cumulative subject, author, title, and reviewer indexing for all abstracts and citations published in the volume.

HISTORIOGRAFIA Y BIBLIOGRAFIA AMERICANISTA. see HISTORY — History Of North And South America

900 GW ISSN 0933-5420
Z6201
HISTORISCHE BIBLIOGRAPHIE. 1987. a. DM.88 (hardcover DM.98). R. Oldenbourg Verlag, Rosenheimer Str. 145, 81671 Munich, Germany. TEL 089-45051-0. FAX 089-45051207. (Subscr. to: Postfach 801360, 81613 Munich, Germany) Ed. Horst Moeller. circ. 1,200. **Document type:** bibliography.
Description: Bibliography of books and articles on history.

960 016 ZA
HISTORY IN ZAMBIA.* 1970. a., latest no.12, 1980. $5. Historical Association of Zambia, c/o University of Zambia, Box 31338, Lusaka, Zambia. Eds. Kusum Datta, Martin Kaniki. adv.; bk.rev.; bibl. circ. 350.

980 SW ISSN 0046-8444
IBERO-AMERICANA; Nordic journal of Latin American studies/revista nordica de estudios Latinoamericanos. (Text in English, Spanish) 1960-1970; resumed 1971. s-a. $15 to individuals; institutions $20. Institute of Latin American Studies, University of Stockholm, S-106 91 Stockholm, Sweden. TEL 46-8-16-28-82. FAX 46-8-15-65-82.

954 016 II
INDIA AND WORLD AFFAIRS: AN ANNUAL BIBLIOGRAPHY.* (Part 1: India's Foreign Policy and Relations with Other Countries of the World; Part 2: Indian Opinions on World Events) (Text in English) 1958. a. (Jawaharlal Nehru University, School of International Studies) Vikas Publishing House Pvt. Ltd., 576 Masjid Rd., Jangpura, New Dehli 110 014, India. TEL 11-624605. TELEX 31592252. **Document type:** bibliography.

900 SP ISSN 1130-099X
Z6205
INDICE ESPANOL DE HUMANIDADES. SERIES B: HISTORICAL SCIENCES. 1978. a. 10000 ptas. or exchange basis (effective 1993). Centro de Informacion y Documentacion Cientifica (Cindoc), Pinar 25, 3, 28006 Madrid, Spain. TEL 1-5635482. FAX 1-5632644. **Document type:** bibliography.
•Also available online.
Also available on CD-ROM.
Supersedes in part (in 1989): Indice Espanol de Humanidades (ISSN 0210-8488)

946 980 016 SP ISSN 0537-3522
Z2696
INDICE HISTORICO ESPANOL. 1953. 2/yr. $110 (effective 1993). Universidad de Barcelona, Facultad de Geografia e Historia, Centro de Estudios Historicos Internacionales, C. Brusi 61, 08006 Barcelona, Spain. TEL 200-43-89. Ed. Rosa Ortega. adv.; bk.rev.; index. circ. 1,100. (reprint service avail. from KTO) **Document type:** bibliography.
—BLDSC (4432.960000).
Formerly: Bibliografia Historica de Espana e Hispanoamerica (ISSN 0006-1026)

INSTITUTE OF SOUTHEAST ASIAN STUDIES. LIBRARY. ACCESSIONS LIST. see ORIENTAL STUDIES — Abstracting, Bibliographies, Statistics

900 GW ISSN 0074-2015
Z6205
INTERNATIONAL BIBLIOGRAPHY OF HISTORICAL SCIENCES. (Text in English and French) 1947. a. DM.228. (International Committee of Historical Sciences) K.G. Saur Verlag KG, A Reed Reference Publishing Company, Part of the Reed Elsevier group, Ortlerstr. 8, 81373 Munich, Germany. TEL 089-76902-0. FAX 089-76902150. TELEX 5212067. (Subscr. to: Postfach 701620, 81316 Munich, Germany) Eds. Jean Glenisson, Michel Keul. (reprint service avail. from KTO) **Document type:** bibliography.
Description: Selective, descriptive bibliography organized according to a methodological and chronological scheme developed by the Committee.

HISTORY — ABSTRACTING, BIBLIOGRAPHIES, STATISTICS

900 016   UK   ISSN 0020-7950
Z6203
INTERNATIONAL MEDIEVAL BIBLIOGRAPHY. 1967. 2/yr. $157.35 to individuals (cloth $172); institutions $277.50 (cloth $303.50). International Medieval Bibliography, School of History, University of Leeds, Leeds LS2 9JT, England. TEL 44-532-333614. FAX 44-532-333616. Ed. Simon Forde. adv.; subject and author indexes. circ. 650. (back issues avail.) **Indexed:** Br.Archaeol.Abstr. **Document type:** bibliography.
Formerly: International Medieval Bibliography. Annual Subject Guide.
Description: Lists more than 5000 articles each issue on every aspect of the European Middle Ages (c.450-1500). Covers periodicals, festschriften, conference proceedings and essay collections. Receives material from more than 50 contributors in 18 countries.

900   RU
ISTORIYA: OTECHESTVENNYA LITERATURA; referativnyi zhurnal. 1973. q. $44. Rossiiskaya Akademiya Nauk, Institut Nauchnoi Informatsii po Obshchestvennym Naukam, Ul. Krasikova 28-21, 117418 Moscow V-418, Russia. Ed. J.I. Korablev.
Formerly: Obshchestvennye Nauki v S.S.S.R. Istoriya (ISSN 0202-2079)

900   RU
ISTORIYA: ZARUBEZHNAYA LITERATURA; referativnyi zhurnal. 1973. q. $32. Rossiiskaya Akademiya Nauk, Institut Nauchnoi Informatsii po Obshchestvennym Naukam, Ul. Krasikova 28-21, 117418 Moscow V-418, Russia. Ed. M.M. Narinskii.
Formerly: Obshchestvennye Nauki za Rubezhom. Istoriya (ISSN 0135-5856)

JOINT ACQUISITIONS LIST OF AFRICANA. see ANTHROPOLOGY — Abstracting, Bibliographies, Statistics

952 011   JA   ISSN 0289-6265
JOURNAL OF HISTORICAL STUDIES. ANNUAL ENGLISH ABSTRACTS. Key Title: Rekishigaku Kenkyu. (Text in English) 1984. a. Historical Science Society of Japan - Rekishigaku Kenkyukai, Seika Bldg., 2, Kanda Jimbo-cho 2 Chome, Chiyoda-ku, Tokyo 101, Japan. **Document type:** abstracting/indexing.

959.802   NE
KONINKLIJK INSTITUUT VOOR DE TROPEN. KLEIN REPERTORIUM. irreg. Koninklijk Instituut voor de Tropen, Centrale Bibliotheek - Royal Tropical Institute, Mauritskade 63, 1092 AD Amsterdam, Netherlands. TEL 31-20-5688272. FAX 31-20-5688286. TELEX 15080 KIT NL. index. **Document type:** bibliography.
Description: Bibliography of Dutch language literature on the history of the former East Indies.

016 980   UK   ISSN 0956-9006
LATIN AMERICAN STUDIES IN THE UNIVERSITIES AND POLYTECHNICS OF THE UNITED KINGDOM. 1967. irreg. £4.50. University of London, Institute of Latin American Studies, 31 Tavistock Sq., London WC1H 9HA, England. TEL 071-387-5671. Ed. A. Bell. **Document type:** academic/scholarly publication.
—BLDSC (5160.167000).
Formerly (until 1988): Latin American Studies in the Universities of the United Kingdom (ISSN 0085-2694)

952   UK   ISSN 0269-2317
Z2016
LOCAL STUDIES INDEX. 1981. 3/yr. £21 (foreign £25). Blackthorn Publications, 2 Denmark St., Gateshead, Tyne & Wear NE8 1NQ, England. TEL 091-478-6637. Ed. M. Maddison. cum.index: 1981-1985, 1986-1990. (back issues avail.) **Document type:** abstracting/indexing.
Description: Covers all subjects of interest to students of places in England and Wales.

015   MY   ISSN 0126-5210
MALAYSIAN NATIONAL BIBLIOGRAPHY/BIBLIOGRAFI NEGARA MALAYSIA. (Text in Bahasa Malaysia, Chinese, English, Tamil) 1967. q. (plus a. cum. until 1983). M.$160 (foreign M.$200). National Library of Malaysia, 323 Jalan Tun Razak, 50572 Kuala Lumpur, Malaysia. TEL 03-2943483. FAX 03-2927899. (Subscr. to: University of Malaya Cooperative Bookshop Ltd, Library Bldg., University of Malaya, 59100 Kuala Lumpur, Malaysia) Ed. Nafisah Ahmad. circ. 180. **Document type:** bibliography.
—BLDSC (1947.880000).

940   IT
MEDIOEVO LATINO. 1978. a. L.230000 for paperback; hard cover L.240000. (Societa Internazionale per lo Studio del Medioevo Latino) Centro Italiano di Studi sull'Alto Medioevo, Palazzo Ancaiani, 06049 Spoleto, Italy. TEL 0743-220418. FAX 0743-223507. Ed. Claudio Leonardi. **Document type:** academic/scholarly publication.
Description: Covers European culture from the Sixth Century to the Thirteenth.

940 016   UK   ISSN 0077-0280
MONARCHIST BOOK REVIEW; an annotated list of new and reprinted books dealing with various aspects of monarchy. 1968. a. 30p.($0.75) Monarchist Press Association, 7 Sutherland Rd., West Ealing, London W13 0DX, England. Ed. James Page. circ. 600. **Document type:** bibliography.

016   US
NEW MEXICO. STATE RECORDS CENTER & ARCHIVES. ANNUAL PUBLICATIONS LIST. 1969. irreg. State Records Center and Archives, State Rules and Publications Division, 404 Montezuma, Santa Fe, NM 87503. TEL 505-827-8860. FAX 505-827-7331. Ed. Vickie J. Ortiz. circ. 30 (controlled). (only avail. on microfiche) **Document type:** government publication, bibliography.
Supersedes in part: New Mexico. State Records Center and Archives. Publications and Rules Filed; **Formerly:** New Mexico. State Records Center and Archives. Publications Filed (ISSN 0090-0931)
Description: List of titles of the publications filed by New Mexico State Agencies during that calendar year.

NORTHERN TITLES: K W I C INDEX. (Key Word in Context) see POLITICAL SCIENCE — Abstracting, Bibliographies, Statistics

900 572 011   RU
NOVAYA LITERATURA PO SOTSIAL'NYM I GUMANITARNYM NAUKAM. ISTORIYA - ARKHEOLOGIYA - ETNOGRAFIYA. 1992. m. $120. Rossiiskaya Akademiya Nauk, Institut Nauchnoi Informatsii po Obshchestvennym Naukam, Ul. Krasikova 28-21, 117418 Moscow V-418, Russia. Ed. V.N. Babenko.
—BLDSC (0087.859000).
Formed by the merger of (1947-1992): Novaya Inostrannaya Literatura po Obshchestvennym Naukam. Istoriya - Arkheologiya - Etnografiya (ISSN 0134-2827); (1947-1992): Novaya Sovetskaya Literatura po Obshchestvennym Naukam. Istoriya - Arkheologiya - Etnografiya (ISSN 0134-2746)

930 016   IT   ISSN 0392-0925
NOVITA BIBLIOGRAFICHE: ANTICHITA GRECA E ROMANA. (Text in English, German and Italian) 1974. s-a. Giorgio Bretschneider, Via Crescenzo 43, 00193 Rome, Italy. adv.; bk.rev. **Document type:** bibliography.

970 929 011   US
PERIODICAL SOURCE INDEX. 1987. a. $45. Allen County Public Library Foundation, Genealogy Department, Box 2270, Fort Wayne, IN 46801. TEL 219-424-7241. FAX 219-422-9688. Ed. Michael B. Clegg. **Document type:** abstracting/indexing.
Description: An index to articles drawn from nearly 3,200 local history and genealogy publications. Includes article title, magazine code, volume, number and date.

319 993.1   NZ   ISSN 0079-2411
HA3032
POCKET DIGEST OF NEW ZEALAND STATISTICS. 1927. a. NZ.$14.95. Department of Statistics, P.O. Box 2922, Wellington, New Zealand. circ. 9,700. **Document type:** government publication.

940   PL   ISSN 0860-0732
POLSKA AKADEMIA NAUK. ODDZIAL W KRAKOWIE. KOMISJA HISTORYCZNA. PRACE. (Text in Polish; summaries in English, French or Russian) 1958. irreg., no.52, 1988. price varies. Ossolineum, Publishing House of the Polish Academy of Sciences, Rynek 9, 50-106 Wroclaw, Poland. TEL 48-71-386-25. FAX 48-71-448-103. TELEX 0712771 OSS PL. Ed. Helena Madurowicz-Urbanska. bibl. **Document type:** monographic series.
Formerly (until vol.46, 1985): Polska Akademia Nauk. Oddzial w Krakowie. Komisja Nauk Historycznych. Prace (ISSN 0079-3388)
Description: Covers publications and source books concerning Polish and world history.

900   US   ISSN 0885-7555
REFERENCE GUIDES TO ARCHIVES AND MANUSCRIPT COLLECTIONS ON IMMIGRANT CULTURE. 1986. irreg. price varies. Greenwood Press, Inc. (Subsidiary of: Greenwood Publishing Group Inc.), 88 Post Rd. W., Box 5007, Westport, CT 06881-5007. TEL 203-226-3571. FAX 203-222-1502. **Document type:** bibliography.

951 016   FR   ISSN 0080-2484
REVUE BIBLIOGRAPHIQUE DE SINOLOGIE. (Text in Chinese, French) 1955; N.S. 1984. a. price varies. Editions de l' Ecole des Hautes Etudes en Sciences Sociales, 131 bd. St-Michel, 75005 Paris, France. TEL 43-54-47-15. FAX 43-54-80-73. (Dist. by: Centre Interinstitutionnel pour la Diffusion de Publications en Sciences Humaines, 131 bd. St-Michel, 75005 Paris, France) Eds. Michel Cartier, Danielle Elliseeff. adv.; bk.rev. circ. 400. **Document type:** abstracting/indexing.
Description: Aims at providing a quick survey of the most recent trends in Chinese studies. Each volume offers a number of abstracts of books and articles selected from various periodicals in different fields, from archaeology to history of science and technology.

942 015   UK   ISSN 0308-4558
Z2016
ROYAL HISTORICAL SOCIETY. ANNUAL BIBLIOGRAPHY OF BRITISH AND IRISH HISTORY. (Text in English, French, German, Italian, Russian, Spanish) 1976. a. £35. Oxford University Press, Oxford Journals, Walton St., Oxford OX2 6DP, England. TEL 0865-56767. FAX 0865-56646. TELEX 837330-OXPRES-G. (U.S. subscr. to: Oxford University Press Inc., 2001 Evans Rd., Cary, NC 27513. TEL 919-677-0977) Eds. Barbara English, J.J.N. Palmer. circ. 2,000. **Document type:** academic/scholarly publication, bibliography.
—BLDSC (1075.718000).
Incorporates (in 1975): Writings on British History (ISSN 0084-2753)
Description: Covers the history of England, Scotland, Wales and Ireland.

SCHARNHORST AUSLESE. see MILITARY — Abstracting, Bibliographies, Statistics

948.9   DK   ISSN 0105-9475
SELECT BIBLIOGRAPHY OF DANISH WORKS ON THE HISTORY OF TOWNS PUBLISHED. (Forms also part of: Byhistoriske Hjaelpemidler) (Text in various languages) 1973. irreg. varies. Dansk Komite for Byhistorie, c/o Thomas Riis, 101B C.F. Richs Vej, 2000 Frederiksberg, Denmark. TEL 31-873677. FAX 33-14-06-08. Ed.Bd. circ. 120. **Document type:** bibliography.

959 016   SI   ISSN 0129-315X
SINGAPORE NATIONAL BIBLIOGRAPHY. (Text in Chinese, English, Malay, Tamil) 1967. q. (plus a. cum.). price varies. National Library, Stamford Rd., Singapore 0617, Singapore. TEL 3323606. FAX 3371470. Ed. Chang Soh Choo. circ. 270. **Document type:** bibliography.

200 016   US
SIXTEENTH CENTURY BIBLIOGRAPHY. 1975. irreg., vol.29, 1991. price varies. Center for Reformation Research, 6477 San Bonita Ave., St. Louis, MO 63105. TEL 314-727-6655. Ed. William Maltby. circ. 300. (also avail. in microfilm from UMI; reprint service avail. from UMI) **Indexed:** Amer.Hist.& Life, CERDIC, Hist.Abstr. **Document type:** bibliography, bulletin.
Formerly: Foundation for Reformation Research. Bulletin of the Library (ISSN 0015-8941)

011 960   SA
SOUTH AFRICA. OFFICE OF THE DIRECTOR OF ARCHIVES AND THE STATE HERALD. ANNUAL REPORT/SOUTH AFRICA. KANTOOR VAN DIE DIREKTEUR VAN ARGIEWE EN DIE STAATSHERALDIKUS. JAARVERSLAG. 1965. a. Office of the Director of Archives, State Archives Service, Private Bag X236, 24 Hamilton Street, Arcadia, Pretoria 0001, South Africa. bibl. circ. 150.
Formerly: South Africa. Office of the Director of Archives. Annual Report of the Director of Archives - South Africa. Kantoor van die Direkteur van Argiewe. Jaarverslag van die Direkteur van Argiewe.

HISTORY — Computer Applications

968 312   SA   ISSN 0302-0681
DT751
SOUTH AFRICA. OFFICIAL YEARBOOK OF THE REPUBLIC OF SOUTH AFRICA. 1979. a. Chris van Lensburg Publications, P.O. Box 29159, Melville, 2109 Johannesburg, South Africa. Ed. Elize Keyter.

318   US   ISSN 0081-4687
HA935
STATISTICAL ABSTRACT OF LATIN AMERICA. 1956. a. price varies. University of California, Los Angeles, Latin American Center, Los Angeles, CA 90024. TEL 213-825-6634. Ed. James W. Wilkie. abstr.; stat. (also avail. in microfiche from CIS) **Indexed:** SRI. **Document type:** abstracting/indexing.
    Description: Includes the latest data available on the 20 major Latin American republics; statistics gathered from nearly 150 sources.

947.1   FI   ISSN 0081-9417
SUOMEN HISTORIALLINEN SEURA. KASIKIRJOJA. (Text in Finnish) 1925. irreg., no.14, 1993. price varies. Suomen Historiallinen Seura - Finnish Historical Society, Arkadiankatu 16 B 28, 00100 Helsinki 10, Finland. FAX 441-468. circ. 200.
    Description: Includes Finnish historical bibliographies from the year 1544 on.

SWEDEN. STATISTISKA CENTRALBYRAAN. STATISTISKA MEDDELANDEN. SERIE BE, BEFOLKNING OCH LEVNADSFOERHAALANDEN. see *POPULATION STUDIES — Abstracting, Bibliographies, Statistics*

012 943   GW   ISSN 0232-3907
THURINGEN-BIBLIOGRAPHIE: REGIONALBIBLIOGRAPHIE. 1969. a. DM.30. Thueringer Universitaets- und Landesbibliothek Jena, Fuerstengraben 6, 07743 Jena, Germany. TEL 03641-632235. FAX 03641-632369. Ed. Konrad Marwinski. **Document type:** bibliography.

940 016   CN   ISSN 0082-5042
TORONTO MEDIEVAL BIBLIOGRAPHIES. 1967. irreg. price varies. (University of Toronto, Centre for Medieval Studies) University of Toronto Press, 5201 Dufferin St., Downsview, ON M3H 5T8, Canada. TEL 416-667-7791. FAX 416-667-7832. (U.S. addr.: 340 Nagel Drive, Cheektowaga, NY 14225) Ed. J. Leyerle. **Document type:** bibliography.
—BLDSC (8868.767000).

HISTORY — Computer Applications

956   US   ISSN 0742-2334
COMPUTER AIDED RESEARCH IN NEAR EASTERN STUDIES. Short title: C A R N E S. (Subseries of: Cybernetica Mesopotamia) 1983. irreg. price varies. (International Institute of Mesopotamian Area Studies) Undena Publications, Box 97, Malibu, CA 90265. TEL 805-746-5870. FAX 805-746-2728. (Dist. by: Crescent Academic Services, 29528 Madera Ave., Shafter, CA 93263) Eds. G. Buccellati, O. Rouault.

956   US   ISSN 0742-1427
DATA SETS: CUNEIFORM TEXTS; electronic data processing of Mesopotamian materials, philological and artifactual. 1979. irreg., latest no.3. price varies. (International Institute of Mesopotamian Area Studies) Undena Publications, Box 97, Malibu, CA 90265. TEL 805-746-5870. FAX 805-746-2728. (Dist. by: Crescent Academic Services, 29528 Madera Ave., Shafter, CA 93263) (back issues avail.)

907.2   UK
D16.12H59
HISTORY AND COMPUTING (MANCHESTER). vol.3, 1990. irreg. (Association for History and Computing) Manchester University Press, Oxford Rd., Manchester M13 9PL, England. TEL 061-273-5539. FAX 061-274-3346. TELEX 666517-UNIMAN. Ed.Bd. **Document type:** monographic series.

900   FR   ISSN 0223-3843
MEDIEVISTE ET L'ORDINATEUR. 1979. 2/yr. free. Institut de Recherche et d'Histoire des Textes (IRHT), 40 Av. d'Iena, 75116 Paris, France. Ed.Bd. bk.rev. (back issues avail.) **Document type:** bulletin.
—BLDSC (5534.267350).
    Description: Aims to define the role of information technology in the treatment of medieval sources.

HISTORY — History Of Africa

968   SX
A.D.K. INFORMATIONS/A.D.K. INFORMATIONEN. (Text in English, French and German) 1975. q. R.10. Afrikaans-Duitse Kultuurunie (SWA), P.O. Box 2185, 9100 Windhoek, Namibia. Ed. Erno Gauerke. circ. 207,000 (combined eds.).
    Description: Development in South Africa and Namibia.

A S C NEWSLETTER (EAST LANSING). (African Studies Center) see *ETHNIC INTERESTS*

960   IT   ISSN 0001-9747
DT1
AFRICA; rivista trimestrale di studi e documentazione. (Text and summaries in English, French and Italian) 1946. q. L.40000. Istituto Italo-Africano, Via Ulisse Aldrovandi 16, 00197 Rome, Italy. Ed. Teobaldo Filesi. adv.; bk.rev.; illus.; bibl. (also avail. in microfiche from BHP; reprint service avail. from KTO) **Indexed:** Amer.Hist.& Life, Bibl.Ling., Curr.Cont.Africa, Documentatieblad, Int.Lab.Doc., M.L.A., P.A.I.S.For.Lang.Ind., Rural Devel.Abstr. **Document type:** academic/scholarly publication.
—BLDSC (0732.150000).

960 301 572   BL   ISSN 0100-8153
AFRICA. (Text in English, French, Portuguese, Spanish) 1978. a. $14. Universidade de Sao Paulo, Centro de Estudos Africanos, Faculdade de Filosofia, Letras, Ciencias Humanas, Caixa Postal 8105, Cidade Universitaria, 05508-900 Sao Paulo, Brazil. TEL 11-210-9416. FAX 11-211-6281. TELEX 11-80902 RUSPAULO. Ed. Fernando A.A. Mourao. adv.; bk.rev.; charts; illus.; stat. circ. 1,500. (back issues avail.) **Document type:** academic/scholarly publication.
    Description: Presents results of research on Africa and Afro-Brazil conducted both in Brazil and outside the country. Covers history, sociology, law, literature, philosophy and social anthropology and politics.

968   UK   ISSN 0001-9720
PL8000
AFRICA (EDINBURGH). 1928. q. £58 to individuals (foreign £55); institutions £105 (foreign £112). (International African Institute) Edinburgh University Press, 22 George Sq., Edinburgh EH8 9LF, Scotland. TEL 031-650-4218. FAX 031-662-0053. Ed. M. Last. adv. contact: Kathryn MacLean. bk.rev.; illus.; bibl.; index. circ. 1,250. (back issues avail.) **Indexed:** Anthropol.Lit., Documentatieblad, Mult.Ed.Abstr., Rural Devel.Abstr., Stud.Wom.Abstr. **Document type:** academic/scholarly publication.
—BLDSC (0732.100000); Faxon; UnCover; SWETS; UMI. **CCC.**
    Description: Devoted to the study of African societies and cultures.
    Refereed Serial

330 960   US   ISSN 0065-3845
DT1
AFRICA CONTEMPORARY RECORD. ANNUAL SURVEY AND DOCUMENTS. 1968. a. $375. Holmes & Meier Publishers, Inc., 160 Broadway E. Wing, New York, NY 10038. TEL 212-374-0100. FAX 212-374-1313. (U.K. addr.: Book Representation & Distribution, Ltd., 244 A London Rd., Hadleigh, Essex SS7 2DE, England. TEL 702-552912. FAX 702-556095) Eds. Colin Legum, Marion E. Doro. adv. circ. 3,000. (back issues avail.) **Indexed:** Curr.Cont.Africa, Documentatieblad.
—BLDSC (0732.154000).

960   SA   ISSN 0256-2804
HC501
AFRICA INSIGHT. 1971. 4/yr. R.50($50) Africa Institute of South Africa, P.O. Box 630, Pretoria 0001, South Africa. Ed. Richard Cornwell. adv.; bk.rev.; illus.; index. circ. 5,000. (also avail. in microfilm from UMI; reprint service avail. from UMI) **Indexed:** Curr.Cont.Africa, Documentatieblad, I D A, Ind.S.A.Per., Mid.East: Abstr.& Ind., Rural Devel.Abstr., Rural Recreat.Tour.Abstr., World Agri.Econ.& Rural Sociol.Abstr.
—BLDSC (0732.159500); UnCover.
    Formerly: South African Journal of African Affairs (ISSN 0085-638X)

960   SA
AFRICA INSTITUTE. RESEARCH COMMUNICATION. 1964-1985; resumed. irreg., no.53, 1990. price varies. Africa Institute of South Africa, P.O. Box 630, Pretoria 0001, South Africa. (reprint service avail. from UMI) **Document type:** monographic series.
    Formerly (until no.53, 1990): Africa Institute. Communications (ISSN 0065-3861)

960   FR
AFRICA INTERNATIONAL.* 1959. m. 200 F.($42) (foreign 300 F.) Marie-Roger Biloa, Ed.& Pub., 33 rue du Faubourg St-Antoine, 75011 Paris, France. TEL 47-63-96-35. FAX 46-22-11-34. TELEX 651 525. adv.; bk.rev.; mkt. circ. 65,000. **Indexed:** CERDIC, Rural Recreat.Tour.Abstr., World Agri.Econ.& Rural Sociol.Abstr.
    Formerly: Africa (ISSN 0001-9755)

AFRICA LETTER. see *POLITICAL SCIENCE*

960   BE   ISSN 0001-9879
DT641
AFRICA TERVUREN. (Text in Dutch, English, and French) 1955. q. 550 BEF (foreign 650 BEF) (effective 1993). Musee Royal de l'Afrique Centrale - Koninklijk Museum voor Midden-Afrika, 13 Steenweg Op Leuven, B-3080 Tervuren, Belgium. TEL 32-2-7675401. FAX 32-2-7670242. (Co-sponsor: Amis du Musee Royal de l'Afrique Centrale - Vrienden van het Koninklijk Museum voor Midden-Afrika) bk.rev.; charts; illus.; index. circ. 500. (back issues avail.) **Indexed:** Anthropol.Lit., Bibl.Ling., Documentatieblad, M.L.A. **Document type:** academic/scholarly publication.
—BLDSC (0732.189500).
    Formerly (until 1960): Congo Tervuren.

AFRICAN ARCHAEOLOGICAL REVIEW. see *ARCHAEOLOGY*

960.05   NR
AFRICAN CRUSADER; international journal for social, political and economic emancipation. 1978. m. Pacific Printers Ltd., 38 Commercial Ave., Yaba, Lagos, Nigeria.

960   US
AFRICAN DOCUMENTS SERIES. 1969. irreg., no.5, 1984. price varies. Boston University, African Studies Center, 270 Bay State Rd., Boston, MA 02215. TEL 617-353-3673. FAX 617-353-4975. TELEX 9103501947 BUASC. (back issues avail.)

960   US
AFRICAN HISTORICAL DICTIONARIES. 1974. irreg., no.49, 1992. price varies. Scarecrow Press, Inc., 52 Liberty Street, Box 4167, Metuchen, NJ 08840. TEL 800-537-7107. Ed. J. Woronoff.

960   US   ISSN 0149-0796
DT30.5
AFRICAN INDEX. 1978. s-m. $165. Vision, Inc., 310 Madison Ave., No. 1412, New York, NY 10017-6000. Ed. Helen Kitchen. bk.rev. (looseleaf format) **Document type:** abstracting/indexing.

AFRICAN OCCASIONAL PAPERS SERIES. see *ANTHROPOLOGY*

AFRICAN RESEARCH STUDIES. see *SOCIAL SCIENCES: COMPREHENSIVE WORKS*

AFRICAN RURAL AND URBAN STUDIES. see *ETHNIC INTERESTS*

960.05   GH
AFRICAN STUDIES JOURNAL. 1975. s-a. University of Cape Coast, Department of Educational Foundations, Faculty of Education, Cape Coast, Ghana.

960   UK   ISSN 0065-406X
AFRICAN STUDIES SERIES. 1971. irreg., no.78, 1993. price varies. Cambridge University Press, Edinburgh Bldg., Shaftesbury Rd., Cambridge CB2 2RU, England. TEL 0223-312393. FAX 0223-315052. TELEX 851817256. (N. American addr.: Cambridge University Press, Journals Dept., 40 W. 20th St., New York, NY 10011. TEL 212-924-3900. FAX 212-691-3239) Ed. John Lansdale. **Indexed:** A.B.C.Pol.Sci., Rural Devel.Abstr. **Document type:** monographic series.
—BLDSC (0734.900000).

AFRICANA IN THE LIBRARY OF THE SCANDINAVIAN INSTITUTE OF AFRICAN STUDIES. see *BIBLIOGRAPHIES*

HISTORY — HISTORY OF AFRICA

AFRICANA JOURNAL; a bibliographic library journal and review annual. see *BIBLIOGRAPHIES*

960   GW   ISSN 0174-5603
AFRICANA MARBURGENSIA. (Text in English, French and German) 1968. s-a. exchange basis. Universitaet Marburg, Am Plan 3, 35037 Marburg, Germany. Eds. Hans-Juergen Greschat, H.-H. Muenkner. adv.; bk.rev. circ. 500. **Indexed:** Bibl.Ling., CERDIC, Curr.Cont.Africa, Documentatieblad, M.L.A. **Document type:** academic/scholarly publication.
—BLDSC (0735.174000).
Description: African studies: religious, social, economic and legal aspects.

968   SA   ISSN 0379-6574
AFRICANA SOCIETY OF PRETORIA. JOURNAL. (Text in Afrikaans and English) 1975. irreg. R.15. Africana Society of Pretoria, P.O. Box 3239, Pretoria 116, South Africa. TEL 27-12-4292839. Ed. M. Willmer. adv.; bk.rev.; bibl.; illus. circ. 250. (back issues avail.) **Indexed:** Ind.S.A.Per.

968.005   SA
AFRICANA SOCIETY OF PRETORIA. YEARBOOK/AFRICANA VERENIGING VAN PRETORIA. JAARBOEK. (Text in Afrikaans and English) 1975. a. R.50 to institutions. Africana Society of Pretoria, P.O. Box 3239, Pretoria 0001, South Africa. TEL 27-12-4292839. Ed. M. Willmer. adv.; bk.rev. circ. 250.

960   BE   ISSN 0772-084X
AFRIKA FOCUS. (Text in Dutch, English, French) 1985. q. 600 BEF to individuals (in Netherlands fl.35; elsewhere 750 BEF); institutions 2000 BEF (in Netherlands fl.100; elsewhere 2150 BEF) (effective 1994). (Afrika Vereiniging van de Rijksuniversiteit Gent) Afrika Brug v.z.w., Coupure Links 653, B-9000 Gent, Belgium. TEL 32-9-2646089. (In Netherlands: Afrika Focus P.A. Dhr. Gilbert Braspenning, Zijlsingel 55, 2315 KG Leiden, Netherlands) Ed.Bd. bk.rev.; bibl. **Indexed:** Documentatieblad, Per.Islam. (1992-). **Document type:** academic/scholarly publication.
Description: Provides a forum for the multidisciplinary study of Africa.

960   US   ISSN 0741-2592
DT1
AFRIQUE HISTOIRE. 1982. q. $16. Box 88622, Indianapolis, IN 46208. TEL 317-687-1525. Ed. Amadou Koly Niang. adv.; illus. circ. 2,500.
Description: Covers a wide variety of topics, from African history to related matters from anthropology, art, and sociology.

AFRO-ASIA. see *HISTORY*

950 960   UA   ISSN 0065-4191
AFRO-ASIAN PEOPLES' CONFERENCE. PROCEEDINGS. (Text in Arabic, English and French) 1957. irreg., 5th, 1972, Cairo. Afro-Asian Peoples' Solidarity Organization, 89 Abdel Aziz al- Saoud St., Manial, Cairo, Egypt.

950 960   UA   ISSN 0078-6233
AFRO-ASIAN PEOPLES' SOLIDARITY ORGANIZATION. COUNCIL DOCUMENTS OF THE SESSION. (Subseries of Afro-Asian Publications) irreg, 13th, 1981, Dem. Rep. of Yemen. Afro- Asian Peoples' Solidarity Organization, 89, Abdel Aziz al Saoud St., Manial, Cairo, Egypt.

961   UA   ISSN 0515-6327
AFRO-ASIAN PUBLICATIONS. irreg. Afro-Asian Peoples' Solidarity Organization, 89 Abdel Aziz al Saoud, 89 Abdel Aziz al-Saoud St., Cairo, Egypt.

966.9   NR
AHMADU BELLO UNIVERSITY. NORTHERN HISTORY RESEARCH SCHEME. INTERIM REPORT. 1966. irreg., latest 1981. £N3. (Ahmadu Bello University, Department of History) A.B.U. Press Ltd., Zaria, Nigeria. TEL 069-50054. circ. 2,000.
Formerly: Ahmadu Bello University. Northern History Research Scheme. Papers (ISSN 0065-4760)

AKKADICA. see *ARCHAEOLOGY*

966.901   NR   ISSN 0189-2207
DT515.9.B597
ANNALS OF BORNO. 1983. a. $90 (hardcover ed. $135). University of Maiduguri Press, P.M.B. 1069, Maiduguri, Nigeria. Ed. C.C. Aguolu. adv.; bk.rev. circ. 1,200. (back issues avail.) **Indexed:** Bibl.Ling., Documentatieblad. **Document type:** academic/scholarly publication.
Description: Carries research articles, research notes, research in progress; lists master's theses and doctoral dissertations awarded by the University of Maiduguri. Presents studies on the north-eastern part of Nigeria, including the Chad basin, the point of contact between Nigeria, Chad, Cameroon and Niger, i.e., unrestricted coverage, with a regional focus.

968   NE   ISSN 0924-2791
ANTI-APARTHEIDSKRANT. bi-m. $10. Anti-Apartheids Beweging Nederland, Lauriergracht 116, Amsterdam, Netherlands. FAX 20-6237335. adv.
Formerly (until 1989): Zuidelijk Afrika News.

960 913   FR   ISSN 0066-4871
DT191
ANTIQUITES AFRICAINES. 1967. a. price varies. (Centre National de la Recherche Scientifique) C N R S Editions, 20-22 rue St. Amand, 75015 Paris, France. TEL 45-33-16-00. FAX 45-33-92-13. TELEX 200 356 F. adv.; bk.rev.; index. circ. 1,500. **Indexed:** Numis.Lit.
—BLDSC (1550.600000).

960   MZ   ISSN 0302-1629
ANUARIO DO ESTADO DE MOCAMBIQUE; informacoes oficias, comerciais, geograficas e historicas. irreg. A.W. Bayly & Ca., Lda., Av. 25 de Setembro 195-197, C.P. 185, Maputo, Mozambique.
Formerly: Anuario da Provincia de Mocambique (ISSN 0570-4022)

ARAB HISTORICAL REVIEW FOR OTTOMAN STUDIES. see *HISTORY — History Of The Near East*

960   GW
ARBEITSKREIS DER DEUTSCHEN AFRIKA-FORSCHUNGS- UND DOKUMENTATIONSSTELLEN. RUNDBRIEF. 1967. a. free. I F O Institut fuer Wirtschaftsforschung, Poschingerstr. 5, 81679 Munich, Germany. TEL 089-9224-0.
Description: Yearly documentation of African studies in Germany.

ARCHIV ORIENTALNI/ORIENTAL ARCHIVES; quarterly journal of African, Asian and Latin-American studies. see *ORIENTAL STUDIES*

967.3   AO   ISSN 0004-2781
DT611
ARQUIVOS DE ANGOLA. 1933. q. Instituto de Investigacao Cientifica de Angola, Departamento de Documentacao e Informacao, C.P. 3244, Luanda, Angola. bk.rev.; bibl.; illus. (microform) **Indexed:** Amer.Hist.& Life, Hist.Abstr.

ASIAN AND AFRICAN STUDIES. see *HISTORY — History Of Asia*

ASIAN AND AFRICAN STUDIES. see *ORIENTAL STUDIES*

ASIEN, AFRIKA, LATEINAMERIKA/ASIA, AFRICA, LATINAMERICA. see *HISTORY — History Of Asia*

ASSOCIATION OF HISTORY TEACHERS IN NIGERIA. see *EDUCATION — Teaching Methods And Curriculum*

966   SG
ASSOCIATION SENEGALAISE POUR L'ETUDE DU QUATERNAIRE AFRICAIN. BULLETIN DE LIAISON. (Text in English, French) 1964. q. membership. Association Senegalaise pour l'Etude du Quaternaire Africain, Laboratoire de Geologie, Faculte des Sciences, Dakar-Fann, Senegal. bk.rev.; index, cum.index. circ. 700. **Indexed:** Biol.Abstr., GeoRef.
Formerly: Association Senegalaise pour l'Etude du Quaternaire de l'Ouest African. Bulletin de Liaison (ISSN 0044-9725)

AU COEUR DE L'AFRIQUE. see *RELIGIONS AND THEOLOGY*

916.1 297   FR   ISSN 0764-7573
AWAL. 1985. a. 130 F. to individuals (foreign 150 F.); institutions 200 F. (foreign 220 F.). (Centre d'Etudes et de Recherches Amazigh) Editions de la Maison des Sciences de l'Homme, 54 bd. Raspail, 75270 Paris. TEL 49-54-20-44. FAX 45-48-83-53. TELEX MSH 203 104 F. (Subscr. to: CERAM, 4 rue de Chevreuse, 75006 Paris. TEL 46-33-04-34)

967 913   KE   ISSN 0067-270X
DT365.3
AZANIA. 1966. a. $30. British Institute in Eastern Africa, P.O. Box 30710, Nairobi, Kenya. Ed. J.E.G. Sutton. bk.rev. (back issues avail.) **Indexed:** Anthropol.Lit., Bibl.Ling., Documentatieblad, P.L.E.S.A. **Document type:** academic/scholarly publication.
—BLDSC (1841.470000); UnCover.
Description: Contains articles and notes on later prehistory and archaeology and precolonial history of eastern Africa.

962   GW   ISSN 0170-3218
BEITRAEGE ZUR AEGYPTISCHEN BAUFORSCHUNG UND ALTERTUMSKUNDE. (Text in French and German) 1932. irreg., vol.12, 1971. price varies. (Schweizerisches Institut fuer Aegyptische Bauforschung und Altertumskunde in Kairo) Franz Steiner Verlag Wiesbaden GmbH, Birkenwaldstr. 44, 70191 Stuttgart, Germany. TEL 0711-2582-0. FAX 0711-2582290. TELEX 723636-DAZ-D. (Subscr. to: Postfach 101061, 70009 Stuttgart, Germany) **Document type:** monographic series.

960   SZ   ISSN 0171-1660
BEITRAEGE ZUR AFRIKAKUNDE. 1978. irreg. price varies. Basler Afrika Bibliographien, Postfach 2037, CH-4001 Basel, Switzerland. TEL 061-2713345. FAX 061-2713155. circ. 300. **Document type:** monographic series.

960   SA
BETWEEN THE CHAINS. (Text in Afrikaans and English) 1978. a. R.25 includes membership. Johannesburg Historical Foundation - Johannesburgse Historiese Stigting, P.O. Box 87739, Houghton 2041, South Africa. TEL 27-11-646-4179. Ed. C.D. Saul. bk.rev.; illus. circ. 500. **Indexed:** Ind.S.A.Per.
Formerly: Johannesburg Historical Foundation. Journal (ISSN 0250-1163)
Description: Contains items of local interest.

960   AO   ISSN 0067-9631
BOLETIM OFICIAL DE ANGOLA.* (Text in Portuguese) 1845. d. Imprensa Nacional, UEE, C.P. 1306, Luanda, Angola. Ed. A. Duarte de Almeida e Carmo.

BOSTON UNIVERSITY PAPERS ON AFRICA. see *SOCIAL SCIENCES: COMPREHENSIVE WORKS*

968.1   BS   ISSN 0525-5090
DT790
BOTSWANA NOTES AND RECORDS. 1969. a. P.50 (rest of southern Africa P.55; elsewhere £15 or $25). Botswana Society, National Museum and Art Gallery, Independence Ave., P.O. Box 71, Gaborone, Botswana. TEL 00267-351500. FAX 00267-359321. Ed. Doreen Nteta. adv.; bk.rev. circ. 1,000. (back issues avail.) **Indexed:** A.I.C.P., Amer.Hist.& Life, Anthropol.Lit., Documentatieblad, Field Crop Abstr., Herb.Abstr., Hist.Abstr., Ind.S.A.Per., Key Word Ind.Wildl.Res., M.L.A., P.L.E.S.A., Rural Devel.Abstr., Rural Recreat.Tour.Abstr., World Agri.Econ.& Rural Sociol.Abstr. **Document type:** academic/scholarly publication.

968   BS
BOTSWANA SOCIETY. SYMPOSIUM PROCEEDINGS. irreg. price varies. Botswana Society, National Museum & Art Gallery, Indepandence Ave., P.O. Box 71, Gaborone, Botswana. TEL 00267-351500. FAX 00267-359321. (back issues avail.) **Document type:** proceedings.

967.6   KE   ISSN 0068-2152
BRITISH INSTITUTE IN EASTERN AFRICA. ANNUAL REPORT. 1962. a. membership. British Institute in Eastern Africa, P.O. Box 30710, Nairobi, Kenya. **Document type:** corporate report.
Formerly: British Institute of History and Archaeology in East Africa. Report.
Description: Annual report of institute activities and accounts issued to members.

HISTORY — HISTORY OF AFRICA

960   KE
BRITISH INSTITUTE IN EASTERN AFRICA. MEMOIRS. 1966. irreg., no.11, 1989. price varies. British Institute in Eastern Africa, PO Box 30710, Nairobi, Kenya. bk.rev. **Indexed:** Anthropol.Lit. **Document type:** monographic series.
    Description: Monographs and edited volumes on archaeology and precolonial history in eastern Africa.

960   SG
C O D E S R I A BULLETIN. (Text in English, French) q. free. Council for the Development of Economic and Social Research in Africa (CODESRIA), B.P. 3304, Dakar, Senegal. TELEX 61339 CODES SG. Ed. Tade Akin Aina. **Indexed:** Documentatieblad. **Document type:** bulletin.
    Formerly: Africana Newsletter.

968   UK
C S A S OCCASIONAL PAPERS. 1986. irreg. £1 per vol. University of York, Centre for Southern African Studies, Heslington, York YO1 5DD, England. Eds. Anne V. Akeroyd, Landeg White.

960   BE   ISSN 1021-9994
DT1
CAHIERS AFRICAINS/AFRIKA STUDIES. (Text mainly in French; occasionally in English, Flemish) 1971. 6/yr. 2500 BEF (foreign 2800 BEF). Institut Africain, Centre d'Etudes et de Documentation Africaines, 65 Rue Belliard, B-1040 Brussels, Belgium. TEL 32-2-2307562. FAX 32-2-2307605. Ed. Edwine Simons; Pub. Gauthier de Villers. bibl. circ. 300. **Document type:** academic/scholarly publication, monographic series.
    Former titles (until 1993): Cahiers du C E D A F (ISSN 0250-1619); Centre d'Etudes et de Documentation Africaines. Cahiers (ISSN 0008-9753)
    Description: Publishes monographs about the political and economic situation in Africa, with particular emphasis on Zaire, Rwanda and Burundi.

CAHIERS D'ETUDES AFRICAINES. see ANTHROPOLOGY

960 320   TI
CARTHAGE; Tunisian quarterly review. 1972. q. $4. Universite de Tunis, Centre d'Etudes et de Recherches Economiques et Sociales, 23 rue d'Espagne, Tunis, Tunisia. Ed. Mohamed Ben Smail. adv.; charts; illus.

960   UK   ISSN 0069-0899
CASS LIBRARY OF AFRICAN STUDIES. GENERAL STUDIES. 1962. irreg, no.137, 1973. price varies. Frank Cass & Co. Ltd., Gainsborough House, 11 Gainsborough Rd., London E11 1RS, England. TEL 081-530-4226. FAX 081-530-7795. (Dist. in U.S. by: ISBS, 5804 N.E. Hassalo St., Portland, OR 97213-3644) **Document type:** academic/scholarly publication.

960 916   UK   ISSN 0069-0902
CASS LIBRARY OF AFRICAN STUDIES. RESEARCHES AND TRAVELS. 1968. irreg., no.25, 1973. price varies. Frank Cass & Co. Ltd., Gainsborough House, 11 Gainsborough Rd., London E11 1RS, England. TEL 081-530-4226. FAX 081-530-7795. (Dist. in U.S. by: ISBS, 5804 N.E. Hassalo St., Portland, OR 97213-3644) **Document type:** academic/scholarly publication.

960 916   UK   ISSN 0069-0910
CASS LIBRARY OF AFRICAN STUDIES. SOUTH AFRICAN STUDIES. 1968. irreg., no.6, 1970. price varies. Frank Cass & Co. Ltd., Gainsborough House, 11 Gainsborough Rd., London E11 1RS, England. TEL 081-530-4226. FAX 081-530-7795. (Dist. in U.S. by: ISBS, 5804 N.E. Hassalo St., Portland, OR 97213-3644) **Document type:** academic/scholarly publication.

960 916   UK   ISSN 0069-0929
CASS LIBRARY OF AFRICAN STUDIES. TRAVELS AND NARRATIVES. 1964. irreg., no.40, 1968. price varies. Frank Cass & Co. Ltd., Gainsborough House, 11 Gainsborough Rd., London E11 1RS, England. TEL 081-530-4226. FAX 081-530-7795. (Dist. in U.S. by: ISBS, 5804 N.E. Hassalo St., Portland, OR 97213-3644) **Document type:** academic/scholarly publication.

CENTRE D'ETUDES ETHNOLOGIQUES. PUBLICATIONS. SERIE 2: MEMOIRES ET MONOGRAPHIES. see ANTHROPOLOGY

CENTRE D'ETUDES ETHNOLOGIQUES BANDUNDU. PUBLICATIONS. see ANTHROPOLOGY

CENTRE OF ARABIC DOCUMENTATION. RESEARCH BULLETIN. see LINGUISTICS

968   SA   ISSN 0379-4695
CHRISTIAAN DE WET ANNALE. (Text in Afrikaans) 1972. s-a. price varies. Suid-Afrikaanse Akademie vir Wetenskap en Kuns, P.O. Box 538, Pretoria 0001, South Africa. TEL 27-12-285082. FAX 27-12-285091. bibl.; charts; illus. circ. 5,000. **Document type:** academic/scholarly publication.

968   SA
COELACANTH. (Text in Afrikaans, English) 1963. s-a. R.7. Border Historical Society, c/o East London Museum, P.O. Box 11021, Southernwood 5213, South Africa. TEL 0431-22623. Ed. G.N. Vernon. adv.; bk.rev.; cum.index: 1963-1982. circ. 300. (back issues avail.) **Document type:** academic/scholarly publication.

960   AO
COLECCAO N'GOLA. a. price varies. Livrangol Editores, Ave. dos Restauradores 21-1, Luanda, Angola. illus.

960   TZ   ISSN 0069-9330
CONTEMPORARY AFRICAN MONOGRAPHS.* 1965. irreg. (East African Institute of Social and Cultural Affairs) East African Publishing House, PO Box 3209, Dores Salaam, Tanzania. circ. 3,000.

968   SA   ISSN 0379-9867
DT751
CONTREE; journal for South African urban and regional history/tydskrif vir Suid-Afrikaanse stedelike en streekgeskiedenis. (Text in Afrikaans, English) 1977. 2/yr. R.15 (effective 1993). Rand Afrikaans University, Department of History, P.O. Box 524, Auckland Park 2006, South Africa. TEL 27-11-4892001. FAX 27-11-4892797. Ed. H.J. van Aswegen. adv.; bk.rev.; abstr.; index, cum.index. circ. 500. **Indexed:** Amer.Hist.& Life, Hist.Abstr., Ind.S.A.Per. **Document type:** academic/scholarly publication.

960 361   US   ISSN 0069-9624
CONTRIBUTIONS IN AFRO-AMERICAN AND AFRICAN STUDIES. 1970. irreg., no.155, 1992. price varies. Greenwood Press, Inc. (Subsidiary of: Greenwood Publishing Group Inc.), 88 Post Rd. W., Box 5007, Westport, CT 06881-5007. TEL 203-226-3571. FAX 203-222-1502. Eds. John W. Blassingame, Henry Louis Gates, Jr. **Indexed:** Rel.Ind.Two.
—BLDSC (3458.150000).

960   RH   ISSN 0250-2992
DT2871
COOKEIA. (Text in English) irreg. National Museums and Monuments, P.O. Box 8540, Causeway, Harare, Zimbabwe. circ. 350. **Indexed:** Anthropol.Lit.
—BLDSC (3463.810000).

960   SG
COTE D'IVOIRE EN CHIFFRES. a. 10000 Fr.CFA. Societe Africaine d'Edition, 16 bis, rue de Thiong, Dakar, Senegal. (And 32 rue de l'Echiquier, Paris, France)

CULTURES AU ZAIRE ET EN AFRIQUE. see SOCIAL SCIENCES: COMPREHENSIVE WORKS

960   SW   ISSN 0280-2171
CURRENT AFRICAN ISSUES. 1981. irreg. SEK 45 per no. Nordiska Afrikainstitutet - Scandinavian Institute of African Studies, Box 1703, S-751 47 Uppsala, Sweden. TEL 018-155480. FAX 018-695629. circ. 1,500.
—BLDSC (3494.088000).

CURRENT CONTENTS AFRICA. see ABSTRACTING AND INDEXING SERVICES

960   SO   ISSN 0045-9542
DALKA;* monthly of current affairs. 1967. m. Sh.15. P.O. Box 388, Mogadishu, Somalia. Ed. Yousuf Jama Ali Duhul. adv.; illus.

DICTIONNAIRE DE BIOGRAPHIE MAURICIENNE/DICTIONARY OF MAURITIAN BIOGRAPHY. see BIOGRAPHY

DISCUSSION PAPERS IN THE AFRICAN HUMANITIES. see HUMANITIES: COMPREHENSIVE WORKS

960   TZ   ISSN 0012-8309
DT421
EAST AFRICA JOURNAL.* 1964. m. East African Publishing House, POB 3209, Dores Salaam, Tanzania. TEL 724711. Ed. B.A. Ogot. adv.; bk.rev.; charts; illus.; stat. circ. 3,000. (tabloid format; also avail. in microform from UMI; reprint service avail. from UMI) **Indexed:** New Test.Abstr.
    Description: Contains political, economic, social, and cultural material.

960   GH   ISSN 0013-712X
ENCYCLOPAEDIA AFRICANA. INFORMATION REPORT. 1962. irreg., no.18, 1979. free. Encyclopaedia Africana Project, Box 2797, Accra, Ghana.

ENCYCLOPEDIE BERBERE. see RELIGIONS AND THEOLOGY — Islamic

967.5   BE   ISSN 0772-6112
ENQUETES ET DOCUMENTS D'HISTOIRE AFRICAINE. 1975. irreg., approx. 2/yr. 1000 BEF per no. Universite Catholique de Louvain, Centre d'Histoire de l'Afrique, 1 Place Blaise Pascal, B-1348 Louvain-la-Neuve, Belgium. FAX 32-10-47-25-79. (Dist. by: Libraire Transatlantique, 126 Chaussee de Wavre, 1050 Brussels, Belgium) Ed. J.L. Vellut. adv. circ. 300. **Document type:** academic/scholarly publication.

960   EA
ETHIOPIAN JOURNAL OF AFRICAN STUDIES. (Text in English) 1981. s-a. Eth.$12($23) Asmara University, Institute of African Studies, P.O. Box 1220, Asmara, Eritrea. TEL 04-113600. FAX 42091. Ed. Amanuel Sahle. adv.; bk.rev. circ. 500. (back issues avail.) **Indexed:** P.L.E.S.A. **Document type:** academic/scholarly publication.

960   FR
ETHIOPIQUES. no.17, May, 1979. 100 F. Editions du Seuil, 27 rue Jacob, 75261 Paris Cedex 6, France. **Indexed:** Curr.Cont.Africa.

966.8   DM   ISSN 0014-2018
ETUDES DAHOMEENNES. 1963. q. 1000 Fr.CFA. Institut de Recherches Appliquees du Dahomey, B.P.6, Porto-Novo, Benin. **Indexed:** A.I.C.P., Amer.Hist.& Life, Hist.Abstr.

372   RW
ETUDES RWANDAISES. (Text in French) 1966. 4/yr. $41. Universite Nationale du Rwanda, Rectorat, B.P. 56, Butare, Rwanda. TEL 30302. TELEX 605. Ed.Bd. bk.rev. circ. 1,000.
    Formed by the 1986 merger of: Recontres; Etudes Rwandaises; Which was formerly: Informateur (ISSN 0019-9885)
    Description: Covers pure and applied science, literature and human sciences.

ETUDES SENEGALAISES. see SOCIOLOGY

EVANGELIKALE MISSIOLOGIE. see RELIGIONS AND THEOLOGY — Protestant

FASETTE/FACETS/FACETTEN. see EDUCATION

969   RE   ISSN 0224-1404
FONDATION POUR LA RECHERCHE ET LE DEVELOPPEMENT DANS L'OCEAN INDIEN. DOCUMENTS ET RECHERCHES. 1975. irreg. 118 Fr.CFA. Fondation pour la Recherche et le Developpement dans l'Ocean Indien, Bibliotheque Departementale, Rue Roland Garros, St. Denis, Reunion.

HERITAGE; the African quarterly of arts and letters. see ETHNIC INTERESTS

960   RH
HERITAGE OF ZIMBABWE. 1981. a. £13($20) to individuals; institutions £20($30) (effective 1993). History Society of Zimbabwe, P.O. Box 8268, Causeway, Harare, Zimbabwe. TEL 263-4-39175. Ed. Michael J. Kimberley. adv.; bk.rev.; bibl.; charts; illus.; index, cum.index: 1956-1973. circ. 1,000. **Indexed:** Amer.Hist.& Life, Documentatieblad, Hist.Abstr., Ind.S.A.Per. **Document type:** academic/scholarly publication.
    Supersedes (1956-1980): Rhodesiana (ISSN 0556-9605)
    Description: Contains articles on the prehistory and history of Zimbabwe and neighboring territories.

HISTORY — HISTORY OF AFRICA

960   TZ   ISSN 0440-9264
HISTORICAL ASSOCIATION OF TANZANIA. PAPERS.* irreg. East African Publishing House, POB 3209, Dores Salaam, off Lusaka Rd., Tanzania. bibl.

960   RH
HISTORICAL ASSOCIATION OF ZIMBABWE. LOCAL SERIES PAMPHLETS. 1959. a. Historical Association of Zimbabwe, c/o Z.I.P., P.O. Box 2054, Harare, Zimbabwe.
    Formerly: Central Africa Historical Association. Local Series Pamphlets (ISSN 0577-036X)

960   US   ISSN 0361-5413
DT19
HISTORY IN AFRICA; an annual journal of method. 1974. a. $40 to institutions (foreign $42). African Studies Association, Credit Union Bldg., Emory University, Atlanta, GA 30322. TEL 404-329-6410. Ed. David Henige. bk.rev.; bibl. circ. 450. **Indexed:** A.I.C.P., Amer.Hist.& Life, Arts & Hum.Cit.Ind., Bibl.Ling., Curr.Cont.Africa, Curr.Cont., Documentatieblad, Hist.Abstr. **Document type:** academic/scholarly publication.
    —BLDSC (4317.750000); Faxon; UnCover.

960   MW
HISTORY IN MALAWI. 1971. irreg. price varies. Chancellor College, Department of History, PO Box 280, Zomba, Malawi. bk.rev.; bibl. circ. 6,200. (processed; back issues avail.)

I C A INFORMATION. (African Cultural Institute) see FOLKLORE

960.05   NR
IFE AFRICAN STUDIES. 1974. s-a. $3.80. University of Ife, Institute of African Studies, Ile-Ife, Nigeria. illus.; bibl. **Indexed:** A.I.C.P.

960   NR
IFE JOURNAL OF HISTORY. 1963. s-a. $60 (U.K. £40) (effective 1992). J A D Publishers Ltd., P.O. Box 72320, Victoria Island, Lagos, Nigeria. Ed. Sola Akinrinade.
    Supersedes (in 1992): African Historian (ISSN 0568-1332)

960   NR
DT515.A2
IKORO. 1971. irreg., vol.6, no.1, 1981. University of Nigeria, Institute of African Studies, Nsukka, Nigeria. FAX 234-42-770644. TELEX 51496 ULIONS NIG. Ed. Ifeoma Ekejiuba. bk.rev.; bibl. (back issues avail.) **Document type:** academic/scholarly publication, bulletin.
    Formerly: Ikorok (ISSN 0046-8592)

IND-AFRICANA: COLLECTED RESEARCH PAPERS ON AFRICA. see SOCIAL SCIENCES: COMPREHENSIVE WORKS

AL-INSAF. see HISTORY — History Of The Near East

962 961   FR   ISSN 0153-5021
INSTITUT DE PAPYROLOGIE ET D'EGYPTOLOGIE DE LILLE. CAHIERS DE RECHERCHE. 1973. a. 190 F. Universite de Lille III, Institut de Papyrologie et d'Egyptologie, Rue du Barreau, B.P. 143, 59653 Villeneuve d'Ascq Cedex, France. TEL 20-33-61-12. FAX 20-33-63-06. Ed. Dominique Valbelle. illus. **Indexed:** Bibl.Ling. **Document type:** academic/scholarly publication.

960   SG   ISSN 0070-2617
INSTITUT FONDAMENTAL D'AFRIQUE NOIRE. CATALOGUES ET DOCUMENTS. 1947. irreg., no.22, 1972. price varies. Institut Fondamental d'Afrique Noire - Cheikh Anat Diop, Boite Postale 206, Dakar, Senegal.

960   SG   ISSN 0070-2625
INSTITUT FONDAMENTAL D'AFRIQUE NOIRE. INITIATIONS ET ETUDES AFRICAINES. Short title: Initiations et Etudes Africaines. 1955. irreg., no.35, 1989. price varies. Institut Fondamental d'Afrique Noire - Cheikh Anta Diop, Boite Postale 206, Dakar, Senegal.

960   UK   ISSN 0951-1377
INTERNATIONAL AFRICAN LIBRARY. 1986. irreg. price varies. (International African Institute) Manchester University Press, Oxford Rd., Manchester M13 9PL, England. TEL 061-273-5539. FAX 061-274-3346. Eds. J.D.Y. Peel, D. Parkin. **Document type:** monographic series.
    —BLDSC (4535.646100).

963   ET   ISSN 0074-2945
INTERNATIONAL CONFERENCE OF ETHIOPIAN STUDIES. PROCEEDINGS. (Text in Amharic, English, French, Italian) irreg., vol.8, 1984. Addis Ababa University, Institute of Ethiopian Studies, P.O. Box 1176, Addis Ababa, Ethiopia. **Document type:** proceedings.

960   US   ISSN 0361-7882
DT1
INTERNATIONAL JOURNAL OF AFRICAN HISTORICAL STUDIES. (Text in English, French) 1968. q. $35 to individuals; institutions $98. Boston University, African Studies Center, 270 Bay State Rd., Boston, MA 02215. TEL 617-353-3673. FAX 617-353-4975. TELEX 9103501947 BUASC. Ed. Norman R. Bennett. adv.; bk.rev.; charts; index. circ. 700. (back issues avail.) **Indexed:** Amer.Hist.& Life, Bibl.Ling., Curr.Cont., Documentatieblad, Hist.Abstr., Hum.Ind., SSCI. **Document type:** academic/scholarly publication.
    —BLDSC (4541.580000); Faxon; UnCover; SWETS.
    Formerly: African Historical Studies (ISSN 0001-9992)
    Description: Covers all aspects of African history, from the stone age to the present.

960   BE
INVENTAIRE DES ARCHIVES HISTORIQUES/INVENTARIS VAN HET HISTORISCH ARCHIEF. 1961. irreg., no.7, 1977. price varies. Musee Royal de l'Afrique Centrale - Koninklijk Museum voor Midden-Afrika, 13 Steenweg op Leuven, B-3080 Tervuren, Belgium. TEL 32-2-7675401. FAX 32-2-7670242. illus. (back issues avail.)

961 297   FR   ISSN 0984-7685
BP64.A4
ISLAM ET SOCIETES AU SUD DU SAHARA. a. price varies. Editions de la Maison des Sciences de l'Homme, 54 bvd. Raspail, 75270 Paris Cedex 06, France. TEL 49-54-20-44. FAX 45-48-83-53. TELEX MSH 203 104 F. (Dist. by: C.I.D., 131 bvd. St-Michel, 75005 Paris, France. TEL 43-54-47-15) (Co-sponsors: Programme Islam, Universite de Paris VII) Ed. Jean Louis Triaud. **Indexed:** Documentatieblad. **Document type:** academic/scholarly publication.
    Description: Forum for the exchange of ideas among scholars interested in sub-Saharan African Islam.

960 052   US
JAMES S. COLEMAN MEMORIAL PAPERS SERIES. irreg. $6 per no. University of California at Los Angeles, James S. Coleman African Studies Center, 405 Hilgard Ave., 10244 Buche Hall, Los Angeles, CA 90024-1310. TEL 310-825-3779. FAX 310-206-2250. (back issues avail.) **Document type:** monographic series.
    Description: Discusses topics in education in Africa.

JOURNAL OF AFRICAN CIVILIZATIONS. see ANTHROPOLOGY

960   UK   ISSN 0021-8537
DT1
JOURNAL OF AFRICAN HISTORY. (Text in English and French) 1960. 3/yr. £33($57) to individuals (overseas £46); institutions £61 (overseas £74 ($111)). Cambridge University Press, Edinburgh Bldg., Shaftesbury Rd., Cambridge CB2 2RU, England. TEL 0223-312393. FAX 0223-315052. TELEX 851817256. (N. American addr.: Cambridge University Press, Journals Dept., 40 W. 20th St., New York, NY 10011. TEL 212-924-3900. FAX 212-691-3239) Ed.Bd. adv.; bk.rev.; bibl.; charts; illus.; index. (also avail. in microform from UMI; back issues avail.; reprint service avail. from SWZ) **Indexed:** A.I.C.P., Acad.Ind., Amer.Hist.& Life, Anthropol.Lit., Arts & Hum.Cit.Ind., Bibl.Ling., Br.Hum.Ind., Curr.Cont.Africa, Curr.Cont., Documentatieblad, Hist.Abstr., Hum.Ind., Mid.East: Abstr.& Ind., Numis.Lit., Ref.Sour., Rel.Ind.One, SSCI. **Document type:** academic/scholarly publication.
    —BLDSC (4919.990000); Faxon; UnCover; SWETS; UMI. **CCC.**
    Description: Covers history of Africa to about 1960. Includes original research on African history.

960   JA   ISSN 0065-4140
JOURNAL OF AFRICAN STUDIES/AFURIKA KENKYU. 1964. irreg. 600 Yen. Japan Association of Africanists - Nihon Afrika Gakkai, c/o University of Tokyo, Dept. of Geography, Hongo, Bunkyo-ku, Tokyo 113, Japan. Ed. Shoji Hasegawa.

967   KE   ISSN 0251-0405
JOURNAL OF EASTERN AFRICAN RESEARCH & DEVELOPMENT. 1971-1976; resumed 1979. a. KShs.200($34) (effective 1994). P.O. Box 10622, Nairobi, Kenya. TEL 254-2-331135. Gideon S. Were. adv.; bk.rev. circ. 200. **Indexed:** Curr.Cont.Africa, Documentatieblad, I D A, Int.Lab.Doc., P.L.E.S.A., Rural Devel.Abstr. **Document type:** academic/scholarly publication.
    —BLDSC (4971.550000).

963 300   ET   ISSN 0022-0922
JOURNAL OF ETHIOPIAN STUDIES. (Text in Amharic, English, French, Italian) 1963. s-a. $16 per no. Addis Ababa University, Institute of Ethiopian Studies, P.O. Box 1176, Addis Ababa, Ethiopia. charts; stat. circ. 1,000. (back issues avail.) **Indexed:** A.I.C.P., Amer.Hist.& Life, Anthropol.Lit., Bibl.Ling., Documentatieblad, Hist.Abstr., Numis.Lit. **Document type:** academic/scholarly publication.
    —UnCover.
    Description: Social sciences and humanities as applied to Ethiopia and the Horn of Africa.

969   MF   ISSN 1013-0152
JOURNAL OF MAURITIAN STUDIES. (Text in English, French) 1986. 2/yr. Rs.80($6) Mahatma Gandhi Institute, Moka, Mauritius. TEL 464-8022. FAX 230-464-8265. bk.rev. (back issues avail.) **Indexed:** P.L.E.S.A. **Document type:** academic/scholarly publication.

968.4   SA   ISSN 0259-0123
JOURNAL OF NATAL AND ZULU HISTORY. (Text and summaries in English) 1979. a. R.30 to individuals; institutions R.40 (effective 1993). University of Natal, Department of History, King George V Ave., Durban 4001, South Africa. TEL 27-31-2602620. FAX 27-31-2602621. TELEX 621231 SA. Eds. M.G. Spencer, Y. Seleti. bk.rev. circ. 100. **Indexed:** Amer.Hist.& Life, Documentatieblad, Hist.Abstr. **Document type:** academic/scholarly publication.

JOURNAL OF THE THIRD WORLD SPECTRUM. see ORIENTAL STUDIES

KANO STUDIES; journal of Saharan and Sudanic research. see SOCIOLOGY

960   KE
KENYA. MINISTRY OF INFORMATION AND BROADCASTING. ANNUAL REPORT. 1963. a. Ministry of Information and Broadcasting, PO Box 30025, Nairobi, Kenya. (Orders to: Government Printing and Stationery Department, PO Box 30128, Nairobi, Kenya)
    Former titles: Kenya. Ministry of Information, Broadcasting and Tourism. Annual Report; Kenya. Ministry of Information. Annual Report (ISSN 0075-5885)

967.6   KE
KENYA NATIONAL ACADEMY FOR ADVANCEMENT OF ARTS AND SCIENCES. RESEARCH INFORMATION CIRCULARS. 1968. a., no. 9, 1978. EAs.40($5) Kenya National Academy for Advancement of Arts and Sciences, PO Box 47288, Nairobi, Kenya.
    Formerly: East African Research Information Centre. E A R I C Information Circular (ISSN 0070-8011)

967.62 500.9   KE
KENYA PAST AND PRESENT. 1971. a. $40. Kenya Museum Society, c/o Kenya National Museums, P.O. Box 40658, Nairobi, Kenya. adv.; illus. circ. 2,000. **Indexed:** Curr.Cont.Africa.

960   KE
DT433.5.A2
KENYA UHURU FACTBOOK. 1973. a. $30. Newspread International, POB 46854, Nairobi, Kenya. FAX 245-2-333448. TELEX 22143. Ed. Kul Bhushan. adv.; bk.rev. circ. 5,000.
    Formerly: Kenya Uhuru Yearbook (ISSN 0378-2158)
    Description: Examines Kenyan history, economics, finance, current affairs, and tourism.

HISTORY — HISTORY OF AFRICA

960   NE   ISSN 0046-3116
DT36
KOMITEE ZUIDELIJK AFRIKA. FACTS AND REPORTS; press cuttings on Southern Africa. Key Title: Facts and Reports - Holland Committee on Southern Africa. (Text mainly in English; occasionally in French) 1971. fortn. fl.135 to individuals; institutions fl.190 (effective 1993). Komitee Zuidelijk Afrika - Holland Committee on Southern Africa, O.Z. Achterburgwal 173, 1012 DJ Amsterdam, Netherlands. TEL 31-20-6270801. FAX 31-20-6270441. Ed. Rian van den Wyngaard. s-a. index. circ. 1,800. **Document type:** bulletin.
—SWETS.

960 929   SA   ISSN 0259-0190
DT1701
KRONOS; journal of Cape history. (Text in Afrikaans, English) 1979. a. $5 (effective 1994). University of the Western Cape, Institute for Historical Research, Private Bag X17, Bellville 7530, South Africa. TEL 27-21-9592616. FAX 27-21-9593178. Eds. Colin Bundy, Henry C. Bredekamp. adv.; bk.rev. circ. 600. (back issues avail.) **Document type:** academic/scholarly publication.
    Description: Forum for the scholarly presentation and discussion of original research relating primarily to Cape history, from pre-colonial times to the present.
    Refereed Serial

LIBYA ANTIQUA/LIBIYA AL-QADIMAT. see *HISTORY — History Of The Near East*

LIBYAN STUDIES. see *ARCHAEOLOGY*

960   ZR
LIKUNDOLI. ARCHIVES ET DOCUMENTS. vol.11, 1988. irreg. Universite de Lubumbashi, Centre d'Etudes et de Recherches Documentaires sur l'Afrique Centrale, B.P. 1825, Lubumbashi, Zaire. **Indexed:** P.L.E.S.A. **Document type:** academic/scholarly publication.

960   ZR
LIKUNDOLI. ENQUETE D'HISTORIE ZAIROISE. vol.9, no.1, 1989. irreg. Universite de Lubumbashi, Centre d'Etudes et de Recherches Documentaires sur l'Afrique Centrale, B.P. 1825, Lubumbashi, Zaire. **Indexed:** P.L.E.S.A. **Document type:** academic/scholarly publication.

960   ZR
LIKUNDOLI, HISTOIRE ET DEVENIR. vol.7, no.2, 1989. irreg. Universite de Lubumbashi, Centre d'Etudes et de Recherches Documentaires sur l'Afrique Centrale, B.P. 1825, Lubumbashi, Zaire. **Indexed:** P.L.E.S.A. **Document type:** academic/scholarly publication.

960 069.9   ZA
LIVINGSTONE MUSEUM. RESEARCH NOTES. 2/yr. K.1. National Museums Board, Livingstone Museum, PO Box 60498, Livingstone, Zambia. **Indexed:** Anthropol.Lit.
    Formerly: Zambia. National Museums Board. Occasional Paper Series.

968   SA   ISSN 0024-6417
LOOKING BACK/KYKIES IN DIE VERLEDE. (Text in English; occasionally in Afrikaans) 1960. 2/yr. R.6 per no. Historical Society of Port Elizabeth - Historiese Vereniging van Port Elizabeth, P.O. Box 12070, Centrahil, Port Elizabeth 6006, South Africa. TEL 041-55-2073. Ed.Bd. adv.; bk.rev.; illus.; index, cum.index: vols. 1-12, 13-22. circ. 500. **Indexed:** Ind.S.A.Per. **Document type:** academic/scholarly publication.

969   MF
M G I MAGAZINE. a. Mahatma Gandhi Institute, Moka, Mauritius.

960 320   UK   ISSN 0309-457X
DT181
THE MAGHREB REVIEW; a quarterly journal on all aspects of North African and Islamic studies from AD 600 to the present day. 1976. q. £130($230) (effective 1992). 45 Burton St., London WC1H 9AL, England. TEL 071-388-1840. Ed. Mohamed Ben-Madani. adv.; bk.rev. circ. 10,000. **Indexed:** Curr.Cont.Africa, Documentatieblad, Geo.Abstr., I D A, Ind.Islam. **Document type:** academic/scholarly publication.
—BLDSC (5334.760000); UnCover; SWETS.

MAJALLAT AL-BUHUTH AL-TA'RIKHIYYAH. see *HISTORY — History Of The Near East*

962.4 915.6   SJ
MAJALLAT AL-DIRASAT AL-SUDANIYYA. (Text in Arabic) 1988. s-a. $13. (School of African and Asian Studies - Mahad al-Dirasat al-Ifriqiyya wal-Asiawiyya) Khartoum University Press, P.O. Box 321, Khartoum, Sudan. TEL 80558. TELEX 22738 KUP SD.

968.97   MW
MALAWI HANDBOOK. 1969. a. K.10.800. Department of Information and Tourism, P.O. Box 494, Blantyre, Malawi. Ed. Anthony Chamveka. adv.; bk.rev.; illus. circ. 5,000.
    Former titles: Malawi. Department of Information. Year in Review; Malawi Yearbook (ISSN 0076-3012)
    Description: Sourcebook of information about Malawi, its people and institutions.

MATATU; journal for African culture and society. see *LITERATURE*

960   US
MONOGRAPHS IN INTERNATIONAL STUDIES: AFRICA SERIES. 1968. irreg. price varies. Ohio University, Center for International Studies, Burson House, 56 E. Union St., Athens, OH 45701. TEL 614-593-1155. (Subscr. to: Ohio University Press, Scott Quad., Athens, OH 45701) Ed. James L. Cobban. bibl.; charts; illus. circ. 500. (back issues avail.; reprint service avail. from UMI) **Indexed:** M.L.A., SSCI. **Document type:** monographic series.
    Formerly: Papers in International Studies: Africa Series (ISSN 0078-9100)

960   BE   ISSN 0773-5006
MUSEE ROYAL DE L'AFRIQUE CENTRALE. ANNALES - SCIENCES HISTORIQUES. SERIE IN 8/KONINKLIJK MUSEUM VOOR MIDDEN-AFRIKA. ANNALEN - HISTORISCHE WETENSCHAPPEN. REEKS IN 8. 1964. irreg., vol.18, 1992. Musee Royal de l'Afrique Centrale - Koninklijk Museum voor Midden-Afrika, 13 Steenweg op Leuven, B-3080 Tervuren, Belgium. TEL 32-2-7675401. FAX 32-2-7670242. charts; illus. (back issues avail.) **Document type:** monographic series.

MUSEUM FUER VOELKERKUNDE, BERLIN. VEROEFFENTLICHUNGEN. NEUE FOLGE. ABTEILUNG: AFRIKA. see *ANTHROPOLOGY*

N A; the magazine for the cross-culturally aware. (Network Africa) see *HUMANITIES: COMPREHENSIVE WORKS*

968 572   SX   ISSN 0259-2010
DT711
NAMIBIANA. (Text in Afrikaans, English, German) 1979. irreg., no.11, 1987. price varies. Namibia Scientific Society, Ethno-Historical Study Group, 110 Leutwein St., P.O. Box 67, Windhoek 9000, Namibia. TEL 061-225372. Ed. K.F.R. Budack. circ. 1,500. (back issues avail.) **Indexed:** Anthropol.Lit.

960   SA   ISSN 0085-3674
NATALIA. 1971. a. R.22 (effective 1993). Natal Society, P.O. Box 415, Pietermaritzburg 3200, Natal, South Africa. TEL 27-331-452383. FAX 27-331-940095. Ed. G.A. Dominy. adv.; bk.rev.; bibl.; illus. circ. 500 (paid). **Indexed:** Ind.S.A.Per. **Document type:** academic/scholarly publication.
—BLDSC (6015.660000).
    Description: Covers the history, geography, environment and current problems of Natal and Zululand.

NATIONAL ARCHIVES OF ZAMBIA. ANNUAL REPORT. see *LIBRARY AND INFORMATION SCIENCES*

960 350   ZA
NATIONAL ARCHIVES OF ZAMBIA. CALENDARS OF THE DISTRICT NOTEBOOKS. (Issued in 4 vols.: Copperbelt, Luapula, Northern, Western Provinces) irreg. K.500. National Archives, P.O. Box RW 50010, Ridgeway, Lusaka, Zambia. Ed. P.M. Mukula. **Document type:** government publication.

960   ZA
NATIONAL ARCHIVES OF ZAMBIA. INFORMATION. 1981. irreg. K.500. National Archives, P.O. Box RW 50010, Ridgeway, Lusaka, Zambia. Ed. P.M. Mukula. **Document type:** government publication.

960   ZA
NATIONAL ARCHIVES OF ZAMBIA. NATIONAL ARCHIVES OCCASIONAL PAPER. no.2, 1973. irreg. K.800. National Archives, P.O. Box RW 50010, Ridgeway, Lusaka, Zambia. Ed. Robin Palmer. bibl. circ. 500. **Document type:** government publication.

968   NE   ISSN 0077-6416
NEDERLANDS-ZUIDAFRIKAANSE VERENIGING. JAARVERSLAG. 1882. a. fl.40 membership. Nederlands-Zuidafrikaanse Vereniging, Keizersgracht 141, 1015 CK Amsterdam, Netherlands. TEL 31-20-6249318. FAX 31-20-6382596. bk.rev. circ. 1,000.

NORTHEAST AFRICAN MONOGRAPH SERIES. see *ETHNIC INTERESTS*

NORTHEAST AFRICAN STUDIES. see *ETHNIC INTERESTS*

O A U ECHO. (Organization of African Unity) see *POLITICAL SCIENCE — International Relations*

960   NR   ISSN 0029-8522
DT515.A2
ODU; a journal of West African studies. 1964; N.S. 1969. s-a. $8 per no. Obafemi Awolowo University, Ile-Ife, Nigeria. Ed. Biodun Adediran. adv.; bk.rev.; charts; illus. circ. 1,000. **Indexed:** A.I.C.P., Amer.Hist.& Life, Hist.Abstr., M.L.A.

960 383   GH   ISSN 0072-9825
OFFICIAL HANDBOOK OF GHANA.* Title varies slightly: Handbook of Ghana. a. Information Services Department, P.O. Box 745, Accra, Ghana. **Document type:** government publication.

967   MG
OMALY SY ANIO/HIER ET AUJOURD'HUI. (Text in French; summaries in English and Malagasy) 1975. s-a. Universite de Madagascar, Departement d'Histoire, B.P. 907, Antananarivo, Malagasy Republic. **Indexed:** Documentatieblad.

960   KE
P A F MAGAZINE. 1977. q. EAs.35($5) (Pan African Festival) Complex Ltd., Box 20011, Cargen House, 4th Floor, Harambee Ave., Nairobi, Kenya. Ed. P.G. Mundia. circ. 25,000.

962   GW
PAPYRUS; aegyptologisches Info. s-a. DM.4 per no. Fachschaft Orientalistische Faecher, Schlaunstr. 2, 48143 Muenster, Germany. Ed. Magnus Reisinger. circ. 500. **Document type:** newsletter.

960 301.2   TZ
PEOPLES OF EAST AFRICA.* irreg. East African Publishing House, POB 3209, Dar es Salaam, Tanzania. bibl.; illus.

PERSPECTIVES ON SOUTHERN AFRICA. see *POLITICAL SCIENCE*

968.2   SA
PRETORIANA. 1948. 2/yr. Old Pretoria Society - Genootskap Oud-Pretoria, P.O. Box 4063, Pretoria 0001, South Africa. TEL 27-12-464886. FAX 27-12-346-2669. **Document type:** academic/scholarly publication.
    Description: Publishes studies in the local history of Pretoria.

PULA; Botswana journal of African studies. see *POLITICAL SCIENCE — International Relations*

962   GW   ISSN 0481-0023
QUELLEN ZUR GESCHICHTE DES ISLAMISCHEN AEGYPTENS. 1978. irreg., vol.3, 1986. price varies. (Deutsches Archaeologisches Institut, Cairo, UA) Franz Steiner Verlag Wiesbaden GmbH, Birkenwaldstr. 44, 70191 Stuttgart, Germany. TEL 0711-2582-0. FAX 0711-2582290. TELEX 723636-DAZD. (Subscr. to: Postfach 101061, 70009 Stuttgart, Germany)

960   IT
RASSEGNA DI STUDI ETIOPICI. vol.13, 1954. a. $60. (Istituto per l'Oriente) Herder Editrice e Libreria s.r.l., Piazza Montecitorio, 120, 00186 Rome, Italy. TEL 67-94-628. FAX 678-47-51. Ed. L. Ricci. **Indexed:** Bibl.Ling., Documentatieblad. **Document type:** academic/scholarly publication.

HISTORY — HISTORY OF AFRICA

960 953   BE
REMARQUES ARABO-AFRICAINES. 1959. m. 700 Fr. Societe International de Presse, d'Edition et de Diffusion S.P.R.L., Avenue Albert 208, B-1180 Brussels, Belgium. Ed. Jean Wolf.
    Supersedes: Remarques Africaines (ISSN 0034-4192)

962 300   AG   ISSN 0327-3822
DT57
REVISTA DE ESTUDIOS DE EGIPTOLOGIA. 1990. a. Consejo Nacional de Investigaciones Cientificas y Tecnicas, Programa de Estudios de Egiptologia, Biblioteca Rosenvasser, Academia Argentina de Letras, Sanchez de Bustamente 2663, 1425 Buenos Aires, Argentina. TEL 054-1-802-3814. FAX 054-1-313-4818. Dir. Perla Fuscaldo.

960   PO   ISSN 0871-2344
REVISTA INTERNACIONAL DE ESTUDOS AFRICANOS. 1984. 2/yr. price varies. Instituto de Investigacao Cientifica Tropical, Centro de Estudos Africanos e Asiaticos, Rua Jau, 54, 1300 Lisbon, Portugal. TEL 364-5321. FAX 363-1460. (Subscr. to: Centro de Documentacao e Informacao, Rua Jau 47, 1300 Lisbon, Portugal) circ. 1,500. **Indexed:** Bibl.Ling., Documentatieblad. **Document type:** academic/scholarly publication.

REVUE C E L F A N - C E L F A N REVIEW. see *LITERATURE*

960   AE   ISSN 0556-7343
REVUE D'HISTOIRE ET DE CIVILISATION DU MAGHREB. (Text in Arabic and French) irreg. (3-4/yr.). Societe Historique Algerienne, c/o Universite d'Alger, Faculte des Lettres, 2 rue Didouche Mourad, Algiers, Algeria. (Dist. in US by: African Imprint Library Service, Box 350, West Falmouth, MA 02574. TEL 508-540-5378) Ed. M. Kaddache.

960   TI   ISSN 0330-8987
REVUE D'HISTOIRE MAGHREBINE/NORTH AFRICAN HISTORICAL REVIEW. (Text in Arabic, English, French) 1974. 4/yr. $200. Centre d'Etudes et de Recherches Ottomanes Morisques de Documentation et d'Information (CEROMDI), B.P. 50, Cite des Andalous, 1110 Zaghouan, Tunisia. TEL 216-2-676446. FAX 216-2-676710. Ed. Abdeljelil Temimi. bk.rev.; bibl. **Indexed:** Amer.Hist.& Life (until 1990), Curr.Cont.Africa, Documentatieblad, Hist.Abstr. (until 1990). **Document type:** academic/scholarly publication.
    Description: Covers the modern and contemporary history of the Maghreb and its relations with the East, Africa, Europe, Middle East and particularly the Ottoman Empire.

960   US
S A I S STUDIES ON AFRICA. 1984. irreg. price varies. Praeger Publishers (Subsidiary of: Greenwood Publishing Group Inc.), 88 Post Rd. W., Box 5007, Westport, CT 06881-5007. TEL 203-226-3571. FAX 203-222-1502. **Document type:** monographic series.

964   GW   ISSN 0177-0969
SAHARA INFO. 1980. bi-m. DM.20. Gesellschaft der Freunde des Sahrauischen Volkes e.V., Bambergerstr. 34, 28215 Bremen, Germany. TEL 0421-354671. bk.rev. circ. 1,400. (back issues avail.)

960   SW   ISSN 0080-6714
DT1
SCANDINAVIAN INSTITUTE OF AFRICAN STUDIES. RESEARCH REPORT. (Text in English) 1967. irreg. price varies. Nordiska Afrikainstitutet - Scandinavian Institute of African Studies, PO Box 1703, S-751 47 Uppsala, Sweden. TEL 018-155480. FAX 018-695629. circ. 1,200. **Indexed:** Cott.& Trop.Fibr.Abstr., Geo.Abstr., I D A, Rural Devel.Abstr., Rural Recreat.Tour.Abstr., World Agri.Econ.& Rural Sociol.Abstr.
    —BLDSC (7766.030000).

960   SW   ISSN 0281-0018
SCANDINAVIAN INSTITUTE OF AFRICAN STUDIES. SEMINAR PROCEEDINGS. 1964. irreg. price varies. Nordiska Afrikainstitutet - Scandinavian Institute of African Studies, PO Box 1703, S-751 47 Uppsala, Sweden. TEL 018-155480. FAX 018-695629. circ. 1,500. **Indexed:** Rural Devel.Abstr. **Document type:** proceedings.
    —BLDSC (8239.424300).
    Formerly: Scandinavian Institute of African Studies. Annual Seminar Proceedings (ISSN 0080-6706)

960   SW   ISSN 1100-6749
DT19.8
SCANDINAVIAN INSTIUTE OF AFRICAN STUDIES. ANNUAL REPORT. (Text in English) 1963. a. free. Nordiska Afrikainstitutet - Scandinavian Institute of African Studies, P.O. Box 1703, S-751 47 Uppsala, Sweden. TEL 018-155480. FAX 018-695629. circ. 2,000. (back issues avail.)
    —BLDSC (1432.019000).
    Formerly (until 1987): Scandinavian Institute of African Studies. Newsletter (ISSN 0549-6330)

960   SG
SENEGAL EN CHIFFRES. a. 12500 Fr.CFA. Societe Africaine d'Edition, B.P. 1877, Dakar, Senegal. (And 32 rue de l'Echiquier, Paris, France)

AL-SHAHID. see *HISTORY — History Of The Near East*

960   US   ISSN 1062-0109
▼**SIERRA LEONE REVIEW;** a journal of policy studies and culture. 1992. q. $28. Sierra Leone Institute for Policy Studies, Box 65231, Washington, DC 20035. Ed. Sorie Musa.
    Description: Provides a forum to advance policy, ideas and views on Sierra Leone; offers features on education, economic trends, culture, and the arts.

968   SA   ISSN 0037-5470
SIMON'S TOWN HISTORICAL SOCIETY BULLETIN. 1960. s-a. R.15 membership (effective 1993). Simon's Town Historical Society, P.O. Box 56, Simon's Town 7995, South Africa. Ed. G.B Read. bk.rev.; abstr.; bibl.; charts; illus. circ. 800. (processed) **Indexed:** Ind.S.A.Per. **Document type:** bulletin.

SOCIAAL-HISTORISCHE STUDIEN. see *SOCIAL SCIENCES: COMPREHENSIVE WORKS*

SOCIAL DYNAMICS. see *SOCIAL SCIENCES: COMPREHENSIVE WORKS*

SOUTH AFRICAN BIOGRAPHICAL AND HISTORICAL STUDIES. see *BIOGRAPHY*

960   SA   ISSN 0258-2473
SOUTH AFRICAN HISTORICAL JOURNAL/SUID-AFRIKAANSE HISTORIESE JOERNAAL. (Text in Afrikaans and English; summaries in English) 1969. s-a. R.50 ($20)(£12) to non-members (effective 1994). South African Historical Society - Suid-Afrikaanse Historiese Vereniging, c/o University of South Africa, Department of History, P.O. Box 392, Pretoria 0001, South Africa. TEL 27-12-4296272. FAX 27-12-4293221. Ed. J.T. Du Bruyn. adv.: B&W page R.300; adv. contact: Karen Harris. bk.rev.; bibl.; index. circ. 800. **Indexed:** Amer.Hist.& Life, Arts & Hum.Cit.Ind., Curr.Cont.Africa, Hist.Abstr., Ind.S.A.Per. **Document type:** academic/scholarly publication.
    Description: Devoted to articles on southern African history based on original research, historiographical articles, critical reviews, and review articles.

SOUTHERN AFRICA MONTHLY REGIONAL BULLETIN. see *POLITICAL SCIENCE*

SOUTHSCAN; a bulletin of southern African affairs. see *POLITICAL SCIENCE*

960   IT
STUDI MAGREBINI. 1966. a. $60. (Istituto Universitario Orientale) Herder Editrice e Libreria s.r.l., Piazza Montecitorio, 120, 00186 Rome, Italy. TEL 67-94-628. FAX 678-47-51. Ed. C. Sarnelli Cerqua. **Indexed:** Amer.Hist.& Life (1990-), Bibl.Ling., Hist.Abstr. (1990-). **Document type:** academic/scholarly publication.

STUDIA AFRICANA. see *ETHNIC INTERESTS*

STUDIEN ZUR ALTAEGYPTISCHEN KULTUR. BEIHEFTE. see *CLASSICAL STUDIES*

301   US   ISSN 0890-4847
STUDIES IN AFRICAN AND AFRO-AMERICAN CULTURE. irreg. Peter Lang Publishing, Inc., 62 W. 45th St., 4th Fl., New York, NY 10036. TEL 212-302-6740. FAX 212-302-7574. Ed. James L. Hill. **Document type:** academic/scholarly publication.

968.7   SA   ISSN 0259-1944
STUDIES IN THE HISTORY OF CAPE TOWN. (Text in English) 1979. irreg., vol.6, 1988. price varies. University of Cape Town, Centre for African Studies, Private Bag, Rondebosch 7700, South Africa. TEL 27-21-650-2308. Ed. C.C. Saunders. circ. 280. **Document type:** monographic series.

STUDIES IN ZAMBIAN SOCIETY. see *SOCIOLOGY*

968   SA   ISSN 1010-9226
DT1706.C37
SUID-AFRIKAANSE KULTUURHISTORIESE MUSEUM. ANNALE/SOUTH AFRICAN CULTURAL HISTORY MUSEUM. ANNALS. (Text in Afrikaans, English) 1987. irreg. R.6 per no. Suid-Afrikaanse Kultuurhistoriese Museum - South African Cultural History Museum, P.O. Box 645, Cape Town 8000, South Africa. TEL 27-21-4618280. FAX 27-21-4619592. Ed.Bd. circ. 500. **Document type:** academic/scholarly publication.

968 301.2   SA   ISSN 0258-7157
SUID-AFRIKAANSE KULTUURHISTORIESE MUSEUM. BULLETIN/SOUTH AFRICAN CULTURAL HISTORY MUSEUM. BULLETIN. (Text in Afrikaans, English) 1980. a. R.7. Suid-Afrikaanse Kultuurhistoriese Museum - South African Cultural History Museum, P.O. Box 645, Cape Town 8000, South Africa. TEL 27-21-4619592. Ed.Bd. adv.; bk.rev. circ. 500. **Indexed:** Ind.S.A.Per. **Document type:** bulletin.

968.3   SQ
SWAZILAND NATIONAL TRUST COMMISSION. ANNUAL REPORT. 1983. irreg., latest 1991. free. Swaziland National Museum, P.O. Box 100, Lobamba, Swaziland. Ed. S. Sukati. illus. circ. 1,000.
    Former titles: Swaziland National Museum. Yearbook; Swaziland National Centre. Yearbook.

SYRACUSE UNIVERSITY. FOREIGN AND COMPARATIVE STUDIES. AFRICAN SERIES. see *SOCIAL SCIENCES: COMPREHENSIVE WORKS*

969.1   MG
TANTARA. 1973. a. FMG.2500. Societe d'Histoire de Madagascar, B.P. 3384, Antananarivo, Malagasy Republic.

960   TZ
TANZANIAN STUDIES. irreg. Tanzania Publishing House, PO Box 2138, Dar es Salaam, Tanzania.

968   SA
TOPOSCOPE. (Text in English) 1970. a. $0.90. Lower Albany Historical Society, 24 Colgate St., Port Alfred 6170, South Africa. Ed. A.S. Basson. bk.rev. circ. 250.

960   LB
TORCH.* no.9, 1976. irreg. Torch Services, PO Box 1394, Monrovia, Liberia. Ed. Bill Frank Enoanyi. adv.; illus.

960   KE
TRANSAFRICA HISTORICAL PAPERS. 960. irreg. Transafrica Publishers Ltd., PO Box 42990, Nairobi, Kenya.

960   US
TUESDAY BULLETIN. w. Michigan State University, African Studies Center, 100 International Center, East Lansing, MI 48824-1035. Ed. David S. Wiley. circ. 1,700. (looseleaf format; back issues avail.) **Document type:** bulletin.
    Description: Features Africa-related seminars, programs, lectures, career opportunities, classes and publications.

960   GW   ISSN 0344-4317
UEBERSEE-MUSEUM, BREMEN. VEROEFFENTLICHUNGEN. REIHE F: BREMER AFRIKA-ARCHIV. Short title: B A A. 1977. irreg., vol.25, 1988. price varies. Uebersee-Museum, Bremen, Bahnhofsplatz 13, 28195 Bremen, Germany. **Document type:** academic/scholarly publication.

967.61   UG   ISSN 0041-574X
DT434.U2
UGANDA JOURNAL. 1934. irreg. S.500($20) membership. Uganda Society, PO Box 4980, Kampala, Uganda. Ed.Bd. adv.; bk.rev.; bibl.; index. circ. 450. **Indexed:** A.I.C.P., Biol.Abstr.

HISTORY — HISTORY OF ASIA

960   US
UNESCO GENERAL HISTORY OF AFRICA. 1980. irreg., vol.8, 1993. price varies. (Unesco) University of California Press, 2120 Berkeley Way, Berkeley, CA 94720. TEL 510-777-4726. FAX 510-643-7127. (Orders to: California-Princeton Fulfillment Services, 1445 Lower Ferry Rd., Ewing, NJ 08618. TEL 800-777-4726. FAX 800-999-1958) (back issues avail.) **Document type:** monographic series.
   Description: Covers the entire history and prehistory of Africa.
Refereed Serial

960   UK   ISSN 0001-3196
DT19.95.A3
UNIVERSITY OF ABERDEEN. AFRICAN STUDIES GROUP. BULLETIN. 1967. irreg. (1-2/yr.). exchange basis. University of Aberdeen, African Studies Group, Kings College, Aberdeen AB9 2UB, Scotland. TEL 0224-272534. TELEX 73458-UNIABN-G. Ed. J.C. Stone. bk.rev. circ. 350. (processed) **Document type:** academic/scholarly publication, bulletin.
—BLDSC (2366.900000).

960 052   US
UNIVERSITY OF CALIFORNIA AT LOS ANGELES. JAMES S. COLEMAN AFRICAN STUDIES CENTER. NEWSLETTER. 1972. s-a. free. University of California at Los Angeles, James S. Coleman African Studies Center, 405 Hilgard Ave., 10244 Buche Hall, Los Angeles, CA 90024-1310. TEL 310-825-3779. FAX 310-206-2250. Ed. Muadi Mukenge. illus. circ. 1,200. **Document type:** newsletter.
   Formerly (until May 1989): African Studies Center Newsletter.
   Description: Presents current events and activities of the African Center.

960 052   US
UNIVERSITY OF CALIFORNIA AT LOS ANGELES. JAMES S. COLEMAN AFRICAN STUDIES CENTER. OCCASIONAL PAPERS SERIES. irreg. $5 per no. University of California at Los Angeles, James S. Coleman African Studies Center, 405 Hilgard Ave., 10244 Buche Hall, Los Angeles, CA 90024-1310. TEL 310-825-3779. FAX 310-206-2250. **Document type:** monographic series.
   Description: Discusses cultural and educational issues affecting Africans and African-Americans.

968.7   SA
UNIVERSITY OF CAPE TOWN. CENTRE FOR AFRICAN STUDIES. COMMUNICATIONS. 1979. irreg., no.24, 1993. price varies. University of Cape Town, Centre for African Studies, Private Bag, Rondebosch 7700, South Africa. TEL 27-21-650-2308. (back issues avail.) **Document type:** academic/scholarly publication.

UNIVERSITY OF LONDON. SCHOOL OF ORIENTAL AND AFRICAN STUDIES. BULLETIN. see *HUMANITIES: COMPREHENSIVE WORKS*

960 330.9   KE   ISSN 1015-6704
UNIVERSITY OF NAIROBI. INSTITUTE FOR DEVELOPMENT STUDIES. WORKING PAPER. irreg., no.491, 1993. University of Nairobi, Institute for Development Studies, P.O. Box 30197, Nairobi, Kenya. TEL 254-2-334244. FAX 254-2-336885. TELEX 22095. Ed. Mr. Kibisu-Kabatesi. **Indexed:** Rural Devel.Abstr., Rural Recreat.Tour.Abstr., World Agri.Econ.& Rural Sociol.Abstr. **Document type:** monographic series.
—BLDSC (9349.530000).

968   SA
UNIVERSITY OF THE ORANGE FREE STATE. INSTITUTE FOR CONTEMPORARY HISTORY. ANNUAL REPORT. a. University of the Orange Free State, Institute for Contemporary History - Universiteit van die Oranje-Vrystaat, Instituut vir Eietydse Geskiedenis, P.O. Box 2320, Bloemfontein 9300, South Africa. FAX 27-51-473416.

960   SA
UNIVERSITY OF THE WITWATERSRAND. AFRICAN STUDIES INSTITUTE. SEMINAR PAPERS. 1979. irreg., (10-12/yr.). R30. University of Witwatersrand, African Studies Institute, Wits 2050, South Africa. FAX 403-1926. circ. 90. **Document type:** academic/scholarly publication.

968   UK
UNIVERSITY OF YORK. CENTRE FOR SOUTHERN AFRICAN STUDIES. COLLECTED PAPERS. 1974. irreg., vol.5, 1980. £1 per vol. University of York, Centre for Southern African Studies, Heslington, York YO1 5DD, England. Eds. Anne V. Akeroyd, Christopher R. Hill.

VASANT. see *ORIENTAL STUDIES*

VOSTOK; Afro-Aziatskie obshchestva - istoria i sovremennost' see *ORIENTAL STUDIES*

AL-WATHA'IQ WAL-MAKHTUTAT. see *HISTORY — History Of The Near East*

916.605   NR   ISSN 0083-8144
DT471
WEST AFRICA ANNUAL. (Text in English) 1963. bi-a. $65 (typically set in Jan.). John West Publications Ltd., John West House, Plot 2, Block A, Acme Rd. OGBA, P.M.B. 21001, Ikeja, Lagos, Nigeria. TEL 961910. TELEX 26446 WESPAL NG. Ed. L.K. Jakende. adv.; bk.rev. circ. 5,000.

WORKING PAPERS IN AFRICAN STUDIES. see *SOCIAL SCIENCES: COMPREHENSIVE WORKS*

960   US   ISSN 0084-2281
DT1
WORLD TODAY SERIES: AFRICA. 1966. a. $8.50. Stryker-Post Publications, P.O. Drawer 1200, Harpers Ferry, WV 25425. TEL 800-995-1400. FAX 304-535-6513. Ed. Pierre Etienne Dostert. circ. 12,500. **Document type:** academic/scholarly publication.
   Description: Contains valuable insight into current economic and social problems of the continent.

YORUBA. see *LINGUISTICS*

960   ZA   ISSN 0084-4810
ZAMBIA. INFORMATION SERVICES. ANNUAL REPORT.* 1964. a. Information Services, PO Box RW 50090, Lusaka, Zambia. (Orders to: Director, Box 30136, Lusaka, Zambia)

968.94   ZA   ISSN 0084-5124
ZAMBIAN PAPERS. 1938. a. price varies. University of Zambia, PO Box 32379, Lusaka, Zambia. Ed.Bd. circ. 1,000.
   Supersedes: Rhodes-Livingstone Papers.
   Description: Monographs in social research in Africa.

968.9 069   RH   ISSN 0301-4347
CD2433
ZIMBABWE. NATIONAL ARCHIVES. ANNUAL REPORT. 1971. a. free. National Archives, Private Bag 7729, Causeway, Harare, Zimbabwe. circ. 350. **Document type:** government publication.

968.9 069   RH   ISSN 0035-4716
ZIMBABWE. NATIONAL ARCHIVES. OCCASIONAL PAPERS. 1963. irreg. Z.$0.75. National Archives, Private Bag 7729, Causeway, Harare, Zimbabwe. circ. 750. **Document type:** government publication, monographic series.
   Formerly: Southern Rhodesia. National Archives. Occasional Papers.

960   RH   ISSN 0250-3018
DT962.3
ZIMBABWEA. (Text in English) irreg. National Museums and Monuments, P.O. Box 8540, Causeway, Harare, Zimbabwe. circ. 350. **Indexed:** Anthropol.Lit.

968   RH
ZIMBABWEAN HISTORY. (Text in English) 1970. a. $8 to individuals; institutions $12. Historical Association of Zimbabwe, c/o Z.I.P., P.O. Box 2054, Harare, Zimbabwe. Ed. R.D. Roberts. bibl. circ. 1,000. **Indexed:** Amer.Hist.& Life, Curr.Cont.Africa, Hist.Abstr., Ind.S.A.Per. **Document type:** academic/scholarly publication.
   Former titles: Rhodesian History (ISSN 1015-8588); Journal of Rhodesian History (ISSN 0075-434X)

HISTORY — History Of Asia

see also Oriental Studies

950   US   ISSN 0748-5476
A M S ASIAN STUDIES. 1976. irreg., no.3, 1987. price varies. (Abrahams Magazine Service) A M S Press, Inc., 56 E. 13th St., New York, NY 10003. TEL 212-777-4700. FAX 212-995-5413. (back issues avail.) **Document type:** monographic series.
   Description: Series of monographs and reference works dealing with various aspects of Asian culture and history.

959   AT
A P S E C S NEWSLETTER. 1971. s-a. Aus.$10.50 to institutions and members; students Aus.$3.50. Australasian and Pacific Society for Eighteenth-Century Studies, Gippsland Institute of Advanced Education, Switchback Rd., Churchill, Vic. 3842, Australia. TEL 051-220-200. FAX 051-222-876. Ed. Bryan Coleborne. bk.rev. circ. 120.
   Formerly: A P S E C S Eighteenth-Century News (ISSN 0812-9428)

A S A I H L SEMINAR REPORTS. (Association of Southeast Asian Institutions of Higher Learning) see *EDUCATION — Higher Education*

400 410 951   CH   ISSN 1012-4195
AS455.T2575
ACADEMIA SINICA. INSTITUTE OF HISTORY AND PHILOLOGY. BULLETIN. (Text in Chinese and English) 1928. 4/yr. $30 per no. (effective 1991). Academia Sinica, Institute of History and Philology, Nankang, Taipei, Taiwan 115, Republic of China. TEL 886-2-782-9555. FAX 886-2-7868834. Ed. Kuan Tung-Kuei. bk.rev. circ. 1,500. **Indexed:** Amer.Hist.& Life, Bibl.Ling., Hist.Abstr., Lang.& Lang.Behav.Abstr. **Document type:** academic/scholarly publication, bulletin.

958.1   AF   ISSN 0001-9682
DS350
AFGHANISTAN. (Text in English and French) 1946. q. $8. Afghanistan Academy of Sciences, Sher Alikhan St., Kabul, Afghanistan. Ed. Ms. Maliha F. Zafer. bk.rev.; bibl.; illus.; index, cum.index. circ. 1,000. **Indexed:** Amer.Hist.& Life, Hist.Abstr. **Document type:** academic/scholarly publication.

954   US   ISSN 0889-2148
AFGHANISTAN FORUM. 1972. bi-m. $25 to individuals (foreign $25); institutions $35 (foreign $45). Afghanistan Forum, Inc., 201 E. 71st St., Apt. 2K, New York, NY 10021. TEL 212-861-4272. Ed. Mary Ann Siegfried. bk.rev. circ. 250. **Document type:** newsletter.
   Formerly (until 1982): Afghanistan Council Newsletter.
   Description: Contains a chronology of events, including items from the Kabul government, articles from national and international publications, notices of conferences, exhibitions and lectures, information on organizations and projects concerned with Afghanistan.

958.1   AF   ISSN 0304-6133
JQ1761.A1
AFGHANISTAN REPUBLIC ANNUAL. (Text in English) a. Ministry of Information and Culture, Kabul, Afghanistan. illus.

AFRO-ASIAN PEOPLES' CONFERENCE. PROCEEDINGS. see *HISTORY — History Of Africa*

AFRO-ASIAN PEOPLES' SOLIDARITY ORGANIZATION. COUNCIL. DOCUMENTS OF THE SESSION. see *HISTORY — History Of Africa*

958.6   TA
AKADEMIYA NAUK TAJIKISTANA. IZVESTIYA. OTDELENIE OBSHCHESTVENNYKH NAUK. (Text in Russian and Tadzhik) 1952. 4/yr. 12.40 Rub. Akademiya Nauk Tajikistana, Pr. Rudaki 33, 734025 Dushanbe, Tajikistan. **Indexed:** A.I.C.P. **Document type:** academic/scholarly publication.
   Formerly (until 1992): Akademiya Nauk Tadzhikskoi S.S.R. Izvestiya. Otdelenie Obshchestvennykh Nauk (ISSN 0321-1738)

HISTORY — HISTORY OF ASIA

959 II ISSN 0065-6259
ALIGARH MUSLIM UNIVERSITY, ALIGARH, INDIA. DEPARTMENT OF HISTORY. PUBLICATION.* (Text in English) 1963. irreg. price varies. Aligarh Muslim University, Department of History, Aligarh 202002, Uttar Pradesh, India.

954 GW ISSN 0170-3242
ALT- UND NEU-INDISCHE STUDIEN. irreg., vol.45, 1993. price varies. (Universitaet Hamburg, Seminar fuer Kultur und Geschichte Indiens) Franz Steiner Verlag Wiesbaden GmbH, Birkenwaldstr. 44, 70191 Stuttgart, Germany. TEL 0711-2582-0. FAX 0711-2582290. TELEX 723636-DAZ-D. (Subscr. to: Postfach 101061, 70009 Stuttgart, Germany) Ed.Bd. Indexed: Rel.Ind.Two. Document type: monographic series.

950 US ISSN 0737-6650
DS701
AMERICAN ASIAN REVIEW. 1984. q. $15. St. John's University, Institute of Asian Studies, Jamaica, NY 11439. Ed. John Watt. bk.rev. circ. 500. Indexed: E.I.
—Faxon; UnCover.

954 US
AMERICAN INSTITUTE OF INDIAN STUDIES. BIENNIAL REPORT. biennial. American Institute of Indian Studies, Foster Hall, University of Chicago, Chicago, IL 60637. TEL 312-947-1000.
Formerly: A I I S Annual Report (ISSN 0360-3687)

996.1 913 NE ISSN 0066-1554
ANATOLICA; annuaire internationale pour les civilisations de l'Asie anterieure. 1967. a. fl.110 (effective 1991). Nederlands Instituut voor het Nabije Oosten - Netherlands Institute for the Near East, Witte Singel 24, P.O. Box 9515, 2300 RA Leiden, Netherlands. (Co-sponsor: Institut Historique et Archeologique Neerlandais a Istanbul, TU) Ed.Bd. bk.rev. circ. 500. (back issues avail.) Indexed: Anthropol.Lit., Bibl.Ling., M.L.A. Document type: academic/scholarly publication.

930 NE ISSN 0929-077X
▼**ANCIENT CIVILIZATIONS FROM SCYTHIA TO SIBERIA;** an international journal for the comparative study of ancient civilizations. (Text in English) 1994. 3/yr. fl.120($68.75) to individuals; institutions fl.190($108.75) (effective 1994). E.J. Brill, Postbus 9000, 2300 PA Leiden, Netherlands. TEL 31-71-312624. FAX 31-71-317532. TELEX 39296 BRILL NL. (In N. America: E.J. Brill, 24 Hudson St., Kinderhook, NY 12106. TEL 800-962-4406. FAX 518-758-1959) Ed.Bd. bk.rev.; abstr.; bibl.; illus.; index. Document type: academic/scholarly publication.
Previously announced as: Journal of Ancient Civilizations.
Description: Publishes comparative studies of the civilizations of the ancient world, with particular emphasis on the intercultural history, archaeology, art and material culture relating to the Black Sea area, the Caucasus, Aisa Minor, Siberia and Central Asia.
Refereed Serial

954 II
ANDHRA HISTORICAL RESEARCH SOCIETY. JOURNAL. (Text in English) 1926. a. Department of Archaeology and Museums, Hyderabad 500001, Andhra Pradesh, India. (Or: Publications Bureau, Directorate of Government Printing, Chanchalguda, Hyderabad, India) Indexed: Numis.Lit.

954 II ISSN 0570-0655
ANDHRA PRADESH. (Text in Telegu) 1956-1985; resumed 1990. m. Rs.24. Department of Information and Public Relations, Hyderabad 500001, Andhra Pradesh, India. illus. circ. 25,300.

ANDHRA PRADESH, INDIA. DEPARTMENT OF ARCHAEOLOGY AND MUSEUMS. EPIGRAPHY SERIES. see ARCHAEOLOGY

ANDHRA PRADESH, INDIA. DEPARTMENT OF ARCHAEOLOGY AND MUSEUMS. MUSEUM SERIES. see NUMISMATICS

909.0492 NO ISSN 0801-2067
DS37.6.A2
ARABY. NORDIC STUDIES ON THE ARAB AND ISLAMIC WORLD.* 1982. q. free. University of Oslo, Department of Semitic Studies, Oslo, Norway. (Co-sponsor: Nordic Institute of Asian Studies) Ed. Haakon Stang. bk.rev. circ. 1,000.
Formerly (until 1986): Arab Studies in Scandinavia (ISSN 0108-1586)

ARCHIPELAGO. see TRAVEL AND TOURISM

ARCHIV ORIENTALNI/ORIENTAL ARCHIVES; quarterly journal of African, Asian and Latin-American studies. see ORIENTAL STUDIES

ARIZONA STATE UNIVERSITY. CENTER FOR ASIAN STUDIES. MONOGRAPH SERIES. see ORIENTAL STUDIES

958.1 AF ISSN 0004-4164
ARYANA. (Text in Dari and Pashtu) 1943. q. $6. Afghanistan Academy of Sciences, Sher Alikhan St., Kabul, Afghanistan. Ed. Abd al-Hadi Hand. adv.; bk.rev.; bibl.; charts; illus.; cum.index. circ. 1,000. Indexed: Numis.Lit.

950 US
ASIA FOUNDATION. ANNUAL REPORT. 1968. a. free. Asia Foundation, Box 193223, San Francisco, CA 94119-3223. TEL 415-982-4640. FAX 415-392-8863. TELEX 278726 ASIA UR. Ed. Jim Mullins. illus. circ. 10,000. Document type: corporate report.
Former titles: Asia Foundation. President's Review and Annual Report (ISSN 0732-3085); Asia Foundation. President's Review (ISSN 0587-3606)

950 US
ASIA FOUNDATION NEWS. 1987. q. free. Asia Foundation, Box 193223, San Francisco, CA 94119-3223. TEL 415-982-4640. FAX 415-392-8863. TELEX 27826 ASIA UR. Ed. Jim Mullins. circ. 4,000. Document type: newsletter.
Formerly: Asia Foundation Quarterly.

950.06 US ISSN 0098-1214
DS1
THE ASIA SOCIETY. ANNUAL REPORT. Key Title: Annual Report - The Asia Society. a. Asia Society, 725 Park Ave., New York, NY 10021. TEL 212-288-6400. FAX 212-517-8315. TELEX 224953 ASIA UR. illus.

950 960 IS ISSN 0066-8281
DS1
ASIAN AND AFRICAN STUDIES. 1965. 3/yr. $40 to individuals; institutions $60. Haifa University, Gustav Heinemann Institute of Middle Eastern Studies, Haifa 31999, Israel. TEL 972-4-240654. Ed. Gabriel R. Warburg. Indexed: Amer.Hist.& Life, Bibl.Ling., Curr.Cont.Africa, Hist.Abstr., M.L.A., Mid.East: Abstr.& Ind., Per.Islam. (1991-). Document type: academic/scholarly publication.
—BLDSC (1742.291000); Faxon; UnCover; UMI. CCC.
Description: Explores the economic, political and social histories of the Middle East, Africa and Asia.

ASIAN AND AFRICAN STUDIES. see ORIENTAL STUDIES

950 320 XR
ASIAN AND PACIFIC BULLETIN/BULLETIN D'ASIE.* (Text in English, French) ceased. 10/yr. free. International Union of Students, c/o Jirina Vrabkova, Pravizska 25, 110 01 Prague 1, Czech Republic.
Formerly: Asian Bulletin (ISSN 0862-0628)

ASIAN BULLETIN. see POLITICAL SCIENCE

950 JA ISSN 0454-2150
ASIAN CULTURAL STUDIES. (Text in English or Japanese) 1960. irreg. 2000 Yen($15) per no. International Christian University, Institute of Asian Cultural Studies - Kokusai Kirisutokyo Daigaku, 3-10-2 Osawa, Mitaka, Tokyo 181, Japan. Ed. Masayoshi Uozumi. bk.rev.; illus. circ. 1,000.

951 CH ISSN 0571-2939
ASIAN PEOPLES' ANTI-COMMUNIST LEAGUE. CHARTS ABOUT CHINESE COMMUNISTS ON THE MAINLAND. 1955. irreg. Rs.3. World Anti-Communist League, Asian People's Anti-Communist League - China Chapter, 1 Tsingtao East Rd., Taipei, Taiwan, Republic of China.

ASIAN PROFILE. see ORIENTAL STUDIES

ASIAN STUDIES ASSOCIATION OF AUSTRALIA. CONFERENCE PAPERS. see ORIENTAL STUDIES

950 CN
ASIAN STUDIES MONOGRAPHS SERIES. 1981. irreg. price varies. University of British Columbia Press, 6344 Memorial Rd., Vancouver, BC V6T 1Z2, Canada. TEL 604-822-3259. FAX 604-822-6083. Document type: monographic series.
Description: Devoted to the study of Asian history, politics and society.

950 AT ISSN 1035-7823
DS32.9.A8
ASIAN STUDIES REVIEW. 1975. 3/yr. Aus.$50($42) (foreign Aus.$52.50). Asian Studies Association of Australia, c/o Mr. Leon Comber, Monash Asia Institute, Monash University, Clayton, Vic. 3168, Australia. TEL 61-3-565-5481. FAX 61-3-565-5370. Ed. Joan Grant. adv. contact: Leon Comber. bk.rev.; bibl. circ. 800. Indexed: E.I. Document type: academic/scholarly publication.
—UnCover.
Former titles (until vol.13-3, 1990): Asian Studies Association of Australia. Review (ISSN 0314-7533); Asian Studies Association of Australia. Newsletter.

ASIAWEEK; the Asian news weekly. see GENERAL INTEREST PERIODICALS — Hong Kong

950 960 960 US ISSN 0323-3790
ASIEN, AFRIKA, LATEINAMERIKA/ASIA, AFRICA, LATINAMERICA. 1973. bi-m. 47 ECU (effective 1993). (Zentraler Rat fuer Asien-, Afrika- und Lateinamerikawissenschaften) Harwood Academic Publishers, 820 Town Center Dr., Langhorne, PA 19047. TEL 215-750-2642. FAX 215-750-6343. (UK subscr. to: P.O. Box 90, Reading, Berkshire RG1 8JL, England. TEL 0734-560-080) Ed. G. Barthel. charts; illus.; index. Indexed: Bibl.Ling., Curr.Cont.Africa, P.A.I.S.For.Lang.Ind., Rural Recreat.Tour.Abstr., World Agri.Econ.& Rural Sociol.Abstr.
—CCC.

950 US
ASSOCIATION FOR ASIAN STUDIES. MONOGRAPHS, OCCASIONAL PAPERS AND REFERENCE SERIES. 1951. irreg. price varies. Association for Asian Studies, Inc., University of Michigan, 1 Lane Hall, Ann Arbor, MI 48109. TEL 313-665-2490. FAX 313-665-3801. Ed.Bd. (back issues avail.) Document type: monographic series.
Formerly: Association for Asian Studies. Enduring Scholarship. Reference Series.

954.9 BG
BANGLADESH ITIHAS SAMITI. JOURNAL/ITIHASA SAMITI PATRIKA. (Text in Bengali or English) no.2, 1973. a. Tk.15. Bangladesh Itihas Samiti, c/o Dept. of History, University of Dhaka, Dhaka 2, Bangladesh. Ed. M. Delwar Hussai. bk.rev. circ. 1,000.

BEIHEFTE ZUR WIENER ZEITSCHRIFT FUER DIE KUNDE DES MORGENLANDES. see ORIENTAL STUDIES

BEITRAEGE ZUR JAPANOLOGIE. see ORIENTAL STUDIES

950 GW ISSN 0170-3137
BEITRAEGE ZUR SUEDASIENFORSCHUNG. 1974. irreg., vol.156, 1993. price varies. (Universitaet Heidelberg, Suedasien-Institut) Franz Steiner Verlag Wiesbaden GmbH, Birkenwaldstr. 44, 70191 Stuttgart, Germany. TEL 0711-2582-0. FAX 0711-2582290. TELEX 723636-DAZ-D. (Subscr. to: Postfach 101061, 70009 Stuttgart, Germany) Indexed: I D A. Document type: monographic series.

954 II ISSN 0005-8807
DS486.C2
BENGAL: PAST AND PRESENT. (Text in English) 1907. 3/yr. Rs.20($8) Calcutta Historical Society, 7 Ballygunge Circular Rd., Calcutta 700 019, West Bengal, India. Ed. Dr. Narendra K. Sinha. bk.rev.; index. Indexed: Amer.Hist.& Life (1993-), Hist.Abstr. (1993-).
—UnCover.

954 II
BHARATI RESEARCH INSTITUTE. JOURNAL. (Text in English) 1979. q. Rs.60. Bharati Research Institute, Bharati Bhuwan, 151 Imali Bazar, Indore-452004, India.

BOCHUMER JAHRBUCH ZUR OSTASIENFORSCHUNG. see ORIENTAL STUDIES

HISTORY — HISTORY OF ASIA

951.5 — II — ISSN 0525-1516
BULLETIN OF TIBETOLOGY. 1964. 3/yr. $50. Sikkim Research Institute of Tibetology and Other Studies, Gangtok 737 101, Sikkim, India. Ed.Bd. **Indexed:** Amer.Hist.& Life, Hist.Abstr.

C I I L. FOLKLORE SERIES. (Central Institute of Indian Languages) see FOLKLORE

954 — II — ISSN 0254-9794
CALCUTTA HISTORICAL JOURNAL. (Text in English) 1975. 2/yr. Rs.50 (foreign £10 or $20). (University of Calcutta, Department of History) Sri Pradip Kumar Ghosh, 48 Hazra Rd., Calcutta 700 019, India. (Subscr. to: c/o Pro-Vice-Chancellor, Calcutta University, College St., Calcutta 700 073, India) Ed. Binay Bhusan Chaduri. adv.; bk.rev.; bibl. circ. 1,000.
 Description: Covers the historical aspects of Indian economics, labor relations, political movements, as well as recent trends in research and historical writings.

954 — UK — ISSN 0575-6863
CAMBRIDGE SOUTH ASIAN STUDIES. 1966. irreg., no.37, 1987. price varies. Cambridge University Press, Edinburgh Bldg., Shaftesbury Rd., Cambridge CB2 2RU, England. TEL 0223-312393. FAX 0223-315052. TELEX 851817256. (N. American addr.: Cambridge University Press, Journals Dept., 40 W. 20th St., New York, NY 10011. TEL 212-924-3900. FAX 212-691-3239) Ed.Bd. **Document type:** monographic series.

951 — UK
CAMBRIDGE STUDIES IN CHINESE HISTORY, LITERATURE AND INSTITUTIONS. 1970. irreg. price varies. Cambridge University Press, Edinburgh Bldg., Shaftesbury Rd., Cambridge CB2 2RU, England. TEL 0223-312393. FAX 0223-315052. TELEX 851817256. (N. American addr.: Cambridge University Press, Journals Dept., 50 W. 20th St., New York, NY 10011. TEL 212-924-3900. FAX 212-691-3239) Eds. P. Hanan, D. Twitchett. **Document type:** monographic series.

950 930 — UK — ISSN 0068-6891
CAMBRIDGE UNIVERSITY. ORIENTAL PUBLICATIONS. 1956. irreg., no.36, 1986. price varies. (Cambridge University, Faculty of Oriental Languages) Cambridge University Press, Edinburgh Bldg., Shaftesbury Rd., Cambridge CB2 2RU, England. TEL 0223-312393. FAX 0223-315052. TELEX 851817256. (N. American addr.: Cambridge University Press, Journals Dept., 40 W. 20th St., New York, NY 10011. TEL 212-924-3900. FAX 212-691-3239) index. **Document type:** monographic series.
 —BLDSC (9106.195000).

954 — II
CARITAS INDIA BULLETIN. (Text in English) 1971. q. Caritas India, C.B.C.I. Centre, Ashok Place, New Delhi 110001, India. Ed. R.V. Robinson. bk.rev. circ. 2,000.
 Formerly: Seva Vani.

959 — US
CENTER FOR SOUTHEAST ASIA STUDIES. NEWSLETTER. s-a. University of California, Berkeley, Center for Southeast Asia Studies, 2223 Fulton, Rm. 617, Berkeley, CA 94720. TEL 510-642-3609. FAX 510-643-7062. circ. 1,600. **Document type:** newsletter.

951 327 — US — ISSN 0893-2301
DS327
CENTRAL AND INNER ASIAN STUDIES. 1987. a. $13 to individuals; institutions $17. c/o Morris Rossabi, Ed., 175 Riverside Dr., New York, NY 10024. TEL 212-362-3526. adv.; bk.rev. circ. 125. (back issues avail.)
 Description: Covers history, art, literature, and political and economic conditions of Chinese, Russian, and Soviet Central Asia.

950 — UK — ISSN 0967-8689
CENTRAL ASIA AND THE CAUCASUS IN WORLD AFFAIRS. w. £400($860) (overseas £430). A F I Ltd., P.O. Box 35, Hastings, E. Sussex TN34 2UX, England. TEL 44-424-442741. FAX 44-424-442913. (Subscr. to: Kingsgate Business Centre, 12-50 Kingsgate Rd., Kingston-upon-Thames, Surrey KT2 5AA, England. TEL 44-81-547-2411; And: VNIIOENG, 14 Nametkin St., 117420 Moscow, Russia. TEL 7-095-332-0037) Ed. Stuart Christie. **Document type:** newsletter.
 Description: Covers various historical topics of the central Asian nations of the Commonwealth of Independent States

951 — US
CENTRAL ASIA BOOK SERIES. 1986. irreg. price varies. Duke University Press, 6697 College Station, Durham, NC 27708. TEL 919-687-3600. FAX 919-688-4574. Ed. Edward Allworth.

CENTRAL ASIA BRIEF. see POLITICAL SCIENCE

CENTRAL ASIAN SURVEY. see POLITICAL SCIENCE

959 — UK — ISSN 0269-1760
CENTRE FOR SOUTH-EAST ASIAN STUDIES. BIBLIOGRAPHY AND LITERATURE SERIES. 1986. irreg., latest no. 11. price varies. Centre for South-East Asian Studies, University of Hull, Cottingham Rd., Hull HU6 7RX, England. FAX 0482-465758. TELEX 592592-KHMAIL-G-HULIB 375. Ed. V.T. King. (back issues avail.) **Document type:** bibliography.
 —BLDSC (2002.080000).

959 — UK — ISSN 0269-1779
CENTRE FOR SOUTH-EAST ASIAN STUDIES. OCCASIONAL PAPERS. 1980. irreg. (approx. 2/yr.); latest no. 24. price varies. Centre for South-East Asian Studies, University of Hull, Cottingham Rd., Hull HU6 7RX, England. FAX 0482-465758. TELEX 592592-KHMAIL-G-HULIB 375. Ed. V.T. King. circ. 300. (looseleaf format; back issues avail.) **Document type:** monographic series.
 —BLDSC (6223.150000).

954.91 — PK
CENTRE FOR THE STUDY OF THE CIVILIZATIONS OF CENTRAL ASIA. PUBLICATIONS. (Text in English) 1973. irreg., vol.13, 1992. price varies. Quaid-i-Azam University, Centre for the Study of the Civilizations of Central Asia, Islamabad 45320, Pakistan. Ed. Dr. Ahmad Hasan Dani. (back issues avail.) **Document type:** monographic series.
 Description: Publishes research studies on the history, culture, sciences and archaeology of Pakistan and the Central Asian regions.

950 — MX — ISSN 0066-8249
CENTRO DE ESTUDIOS ORIENTALES. ANUARIO. 1968. a. price varies. Universidad Nacional Autonoma de Mexico, Facultad de Filosofia y Letras, Ciudad Universitaria, Mexico 20, D.F., Mexico. Ed. Lothar Knauth.

958 — CE — ISSN 0577-4691
CEYLON HISTORICAL JOURNAL.* (Text in English) 1951. irreg. Tisara Prakaskayo Ltd, 137 Dutugemunu St., Dehiwala, Sri Lanka.

959.802 — NE
CHANGING ECONOMY IN INDONESIA. 1975. irreg. (approx. a.). Koninklijk Instituut voor de Tropen - Royal Tropical Institute, Mauritskade 63, 1092 AD Amsterdam, Netherlands. TEL 31-20-5688272. FAX 31-20-5688286. TELEX 15080 KIT NL. **Document type:** academic/scholarly publication.
 Description: Statistical analysis of Indonesian economic history through 1940.

CHINA FACTS AND FIGURES ANNUAL. see POLITICAL SCIENCE

951 — CH
CHINA FORUM. (Text in Chinese, English) 1974. s-a. NT.$180($9) China Forum Incorporation, 7 Linsen N. Rd., Taipei, Taiwan, Republic of China. Ed. Tsao Poi. bk.rev.; bibl. circ. 2,500.

951 — US — ISSN 0069-3693
CHINA RESEARCH MONOGRAPHS. 1967. irreg., vol.40, 1992. price varies. University of California at Berkeley, Institute of East Asian Studies, 2223 Fulton St., Berkeley, CA 94720. TEL 510-643-6325. FAX 510-643-7062. (reprint service avail. from UMI) **Document type:** monographic series, academic/scholarly publication.
 Description: Contains in-depth scholarly studies of topics relating to the history and culture of China. *Refereed Serial*

951 355 — US — ISSN 1017-8716
UA835
CHINA'S MILITARY: P L A IN (YEAR). irreg., latest 1992-1993. price varies. (Chinese Council of Advanced Policy Studies) Westview Press, 5500 Central Ave., Boulder, CO 80301. TEL 303-444-3541. FAX 303-449-3356. Ed. Richard H. Yang. **Document type:** academic/scholarly publication.
 Formerly: S C P S Yearbook on P L A Affairs.
 Description: Covers the activities of the People's Liberation Army in the Chinese mainland.

CHINESE HISTORICAL SOCIETY OF AMERICA. BULLETIN. see ETHNIC INTERESTS

CHINESE SCIENCE. see SCIENCES: COMPREHENSIVE WORKS

951 — IT — ISSN 0529-7451
CINA. (Includes: Supplements) 1956. irreg., vol.24, 1993. $40. (Istituto Italiano per il Medio ed Estremo Oriente) Herder Editrice e Libreria s.r.l., Piazza Montecitorio 120, 00186 Rome, Italy. TEL 67-94-628. FAX 678-47-51. TELEX 621427-NATEL. Ed. Lionello Lanciotti. **Document type:** academic/scholarly publication.

950 — IT — ISSN 0069-4312
CIVILTA ASIATICHE. 1960. irreg., vol.5, 1963. price varies. (Fondazione Giorgio Cini, Centro di Cultura e Civilta) Casa Editrice Leo S. Olschki, 50100 Florence, Italy. TEL 055-6530684. FAX 055-6530214. circ. 500. **Document type:** monographic series.

COLUMBIA UNIVERSITY. EAST ASIAN INSTITUTE. STUDIES. see ORIENTAL STUDIES

COMMITTEE ON EAST ASIAN LIBRARIES DIRECTORY. see LIBRARY AND INFORMATION SCIENCES

COMPARATIVE STUDIES IN OVERSEAS HISTORY. see HISTORY — History Of Europe

959 — US
CONTEMPORARY CHINA PAPERS. 1971. irreg. price varies. M.E. Sharpe, Inc., 80 Business Park Dr., Armonk, New York, NY 10504. TEL 914-273-1800. FAX 914-273-2106. Ed. Jonathan Unger. **Document type:** monographic series.

CONTEMPORARY SOUTHEAST ASIA; a quarterly journal of international and strategic affairs. see POLITICAL SCIENCE

951 — HK — ISSN 0069-9535
CONTINENTAL RESEARCH SERIES. (Text in English) 1970. irreg. Continental Research Institute, G.P.O. Box 5699, Hong Kong, Hong Kong.

956 — NP
CONTRIBUTIONS TO NEPALESE STUDIES. (Text in English, Nepalese) 1973. 2/yr. $20. Tribhuvan University, Research Centre for Nepal and Asian Studies, Kirtipur, Nepal. Ed. Prayag Raj Sharma. bk.rev. circ. 900. **Indexed:** Anthropol.Lit., I D A, Rural Devel.Abstr., Rural Ext.Educ.& Tr.Abstr., World Agri.Econ.& Rural Sociol.Abstr. **Document type:** academic/scholarly publication.

954 — US — ISSN 0741-2037
DS520
CROSSROADS (DEKALB); an interdisciplinary journal of Southeast Asian studies. 1983. 2/yr. $20. Northern Illinois University, Center for Southeast Asian Studies, DeKalb, IL 60115. TEL 815-753-1771. FAX 815-753-1832. Ed. Grant A. Olson. adv. circ. 500. **Document type:** academic/scholarly publication.
 —UnCover.

HISTORY — HISTORY OF ASIA

951   CC
DAJIANG NANBEI/SOUTH & NORTH OF THE YANGTSE RIVER. (Text in Chinese) m. $39.50. Dajiang Nanbei Zazhishe, 41 Caoxi Beilu, Shanghai 200030, People's Republic of China. TEL 4379849. (Dist. in US by: China Books & Periodicals, Inc., 2929 24th St., San Francisco, CA 94110. TEL 415-282-2994)

DANG'ANXUE TONGXUN/ARCHIVES SCIENCE BULLETIN. see *LIBRARY AND INFORMATION SCIENCES*

959.9   PH   ISSN 0115-6276
DS651
DE LA SALLE UNIVERSITY. DEPARTMENT OF HISTORY AND AREA STUDIES. ANUARYO - ANNALES; journal of history and area studies. (Text in English) 1983. a. P.30($4.40) De La Salle University Press, 2401 Taft Ave., Manila, Philippines. TEL 2-59-48-32. FAX 632-521-9094. adv.; bk.rev. circ. 300.
Document type: academic/scholarly publication.
—UnCover.
Description: Publishes scholarly articles reflecting significant quantitative or qualitative research. Includes speeches, research reports, and "state of the art" papers.

DECCAN COLLEGE. POSTGRADUATE & RESEARCH INSTITUTE. BULLETIN. see *SOCIAL SCIENCES: COMPREHENSIVE WORKS*

DHANIRAM BHALLA GRANTHAMALA. see *ORIENTAL STUDIES*

951   US   ISSN 0362-5028
DS701
EARLY CHINA. 1975. a. $30 includes Early China News. (Society for the Study of Early China) University of California, Berkeley, Institute of East Asian Studies, 2223 Fulton St., Berkeley, CA 94720. TEL 510-643-6325. FAX 510-643-7062. Ed. Edward L. Shaughnessy. adv.; bk.rev.; abstr.; bibl.; charts; illus.; circ. 250 (controlled). **Indexed:** Arts & Hum.Cit.Ind., Curr.Cont. **Document type:** academic/scholarly publication.
—UnCover.
Formerly: Society for the Study of Pre-Han China. Newsletter (ISSN 0361-9613)

951   US   ISSN 1048-2520
DS715
EARLY CHINA NEWS. 1988. a. $30 includes Early China. (Society for the Study of Early China) University of California, Berkeley, Institute of East Asian Studies, 2223 Fulton St., Berkeley, CA 94720. TEL 510-643-6325. FAX 510-643-7062.

EAST. see *GENERAL INTEREST PERIODICALS — Japan*

EAST ASIAN HISTORICAL MONOGRAPHS. see *ORIENTAL STUDIES*

950   AT   ISSN 1036-6008
DS511
EAST ASIAN HISTORY. 1970. s-a. $45. Australian National University, Division of Pacific and Asian History, Canberra, A.C.T. 0200, Australia. FAX 06-257-1893. TELEX AA62694 SOPAC. Ed. Geremie Barme. adv.; charts. circ. 400. (reprint service avail. from ISI) **Indexed:** Amer.Hist.& Life, Arts & Hum.Cit.Ind., Aus.P.A.I.S., Curr.Cont., Hist.Abstr., Mid.East: Abstr.& Ind. **Document type:** academic/scholarly publication.
—BLDSC (3645.936000); UnCover.
Formerly (until 1991): Papers on Far Eastern History (ISSN 0048-2870)
Description: Covers history of China, Japan and Korea.

950   US
EAST ASIAN SOCIAL SCIENCE MONOGRAPHS. irreg. price varies. Oxford University Press, 200 Madison Ave., New York, NY 10016. TEL 212-679-7300.

ENLIGHTENMENT BOOK CLUB. see *PHILOSOPHY*

ERETZ-ISRAEL. ARCHAEOLOGICAL, HISTORICAL AND GEOGRAPHICAL STUDIES. see *ARCHAEOLOGY*

959   NE
EUROPEAN NEWSLETTER OF SOUTHEAST ASIAN STUDIES. 1991. 2/yr. fl.30. K I T L V Press, P.O. Box 9515, 2500 RA Leiden, Netherlands. TEL 31-71-272372. FAX 31-71-272638. Ed. C. van Dijk. **Document type:** newsletter.
Description: Facilitates communication among European scholars working in the field of Southeast Asian studies. Covers recent and future activities, meetings, research projects and conferences, as well as announcements of institutional research activities and staff changes.

EVANGELIKALE MISSIOLOGIE. see *RELIGIONS AND THEOLOGY — Protestant*

951   CC
FUJIAN WENSHI ZILIAO/FUJIAN CULTURAL AND HISTORICAL RECORDS. (Text in Chinese) 1962. irreg. Y2 per no. Fujiansheng Zhengxie Wenshi Ziliao Weiyuanhui, Zhengxie Dalou, Wusi Lu, Fuzhou, Fujian 350001, People's Republic of China. TEL 0591-552337. FAX 0591-527020. (Dist. overseas by: Jiangsu Publications Import & Export Corp., 56 Gao Yun Ling, Nanjing, Jiangsu, P.R.C.) Ed. Wu Xiubing.
Description: Carries oral accounts of contemporary and modern historical events.

950   II   ISSN 0072-0348
GAZETEER OF INDIA. (4 volume series; vol 1: Land and People, vol.2: History and Culture, vol.3: Economic Structure and Activities, vol 4: Administration and Public Welfare) (Text in English) 1965. irreg. price varies per vol. Ministry of Information & Broadcasting, Publications Division, Patiala House, Tilak Marg, New Delhi 110001, India. (Subscr. in U.S. to: M-S Inter Culture Association, Thompson, CT 06277) Ed. P.N. Chopra. circ. 5,000 (per vol.).
Document type: government publication.

GAZI HUSREVBEGOVA BIBLIOTEKA. ANALI. see *ORIENTAL STUDIES*

951   IT
GIAPPONE. 1963. a. $30. Istituto Italiano per il Medio ed Estremo Oriente, Via Merulana 248, 00185 Rome, Italy. TEL 6794628. FAX 6784751. TELEX 621427 NATEL. (Subscriptions to: Herclev Editrice e Libreria, Piazza Montecitorio 120, 00186 Rome, Italy) Ed. Adolfo Tamburello.

GLORY OF INDIA; quarterly on Indology. see *ORIENTAL STUDIES*

GOETTINGER ORIENTFORSCHUNGEN. REIHE I: SYRIACA. see *ORIENTAL STUDIES*

GOETTINGER ORIENTFORSCHUNGEN. REIHE IV: AEGYPTEN. see *ORIENTAL STUDIES*

954.9   PK
GRASSROOTS. (Text in English) 1977. s-a. Rs.15. University of Sind, Pakistan Studies Centre, Jamshoro, Hyderabad 6, Pakistan. (also avail. in microfilm from UMI; reprint service avail. from UMI)

GREATER VANCOUVER JAPANESE CANADIAN CITIZENS ASSOCIATION. BULLETIN; a monthly publication containing news and articles of interest to Japanese Canadians. see *ETHNIC INTERESTS*

951   CC   ISSN 1000-8705
GUIZHOU WENSHI CONGKAN/GUIZHOU HISTORICAL STUDIES. (Text in Chinese) q. $16.50. Guizhou Sheng Wenshi Yanjiuguan, No. 175, Beijie, Guiyang, Guizhou 550001, People's Republic of China. TEL 623306. (Dist. in US by: China Books & Periodicals, Inc., 2929 24th St., San Francisco, CA 94110. TEL 415-282-2994) Ed. Zhao Rong.

GUJI ZHENGLI YANJIU XUEKAN. see *LIBRARY AND INFORMATION SCIENCES*

HANDBUCH DER ORIENTALISTIK. 2. ABTEILUNG. INDIEN. see *ORIENTAL STUDIES*

HANDBUCH DER ORIENTALISTIK. 3. ABTEILUNG. INDONESIEN, MALAYSIA UND DIE PHILIPPINEN. see *ORIENTAL STUDIES*

HANDBUCH DER ORIENTALISTIK. 4. ABTEILUNG. CHINA. see *ORIENTAL STUDIES*

HANDBUCH DER ORIENTALISTIK. 5. ABTEILUNG. JAPAN. see *ORIENTAL STUDIES*

951   US
HARVARD CONTEMPORARY CHINA SERIES. 1985. irreg., no.8, 1991. price varies. (Harvard University, Council on East Asian Studies) Harvard University Press, 79 Garden St., Cambridge, MA 02138. index.
Document type: academic/scholarly publication.

950   US   ISSN 0073-0483
HARVARD EAST ASIAN MONOGRAPHS. irreg., no.160, 1993. price varies. Harvard University, Council on East Asian Studies, Cambridge, MA 02138. (Dist. by: Harvard University Press, 79 Garden St., Cambridge, MA 02138) **Indexed:** M.L.A. **Document type:** academic/scholarly publication.
—BLDSC (4265.887000).

950   US   ISSN 0073-0491
HARVARD EAST ASIAN SERIES. (Title varies nos.1-10, 1959-61 Harvard East Asian Studies) 1959. irreg., vol.153, 1990. price varies. (Harvard University, East Asian Research Center) Harvard University Press, 79 Garden St., Cambridge, MA 02138. TEL 617-495-2600. FAX 617-495-5898. **Document type:** academic/scholarly publication.
Refereed Serial

959   US
HARVARD STUDIES IN AMERICAN - EAST ASIAN RELATIONS. 1972. irreg., no.11, 1986. price varies. Harvard University, Council on East Asian Studies, Cambridge, MA 02138. (Dist. by: Harvard University Press, 79 Garden St., Cambridge, MA 02138)

951   US   ISSN 0073-084X
HARVARD - YENCHING INSTITUTE. MONOGRAPH SERIES. irreg., vol.36, 1993. price varies. Harvard University, Council on East Asian Studies, Cambridge, MA 02138. (Dist. by: Harvard University Press, 79 Garden St., Cambridge, MA 02138) **Document type:** monographic series, academic/scholarly publication.

951   US   ISSN 0073-0858
HARVARD - YENCHING INSTITUTE. STUDIES. 1950. irreg., no.29, 1972. price varies. Harvard University Press, 79 Garden St., Cambridge, MA 02138. TEL 617-495-2600. FAX 617-495-5898. **Document type:** monographic series, academic/scholarly publication.
Refereed Serial

HERITAGE. see *ART*

HIGHLANDER. see *GEOGRAPHY*

900   JA   ISSN 0018-2478
HISTORICAL JOURNAL OF JAPAN/SHIGAKU ZASSHI. (Text in Japanese; title and summaries in English) 1889. m. 11000 Yen for members. Nihon Shigaku-kai - Historical Society of Japan, University of Tokyo, 3-1 Hongo 7-chome, Bunkyo-ku, Tokyo 113, Japan. Ed. T. Yamamoto. adv.; bk.rev.; index. circ. 4,000. **Indexed:** Amer.Hist.& Life, Hist.Abstr. **Document type:** academic/scholarly publication.
—UnCover.

954   930.1   II   ISSN 0970-3314
THE HISTORICAL REVIEW. s-a. Rs.25 per no. Indian Institute of Oriental Studies and Research, 155A Sarat Ghosh Garden Rd., Calcutta 700031, India. Ed.Bd. (back issues avail.)
—BLDSC (4316.819800).
Description: Covers the subjects of history and archaeology.

354.9   PK
HISTORICAL STUDIES (PAKISTAN) SERIES. 1976. irreg. price varies. National Commission on Historical and Cultural Research, Islamabad, Pakistan. **Document type:** government publication.

HOKKAIDO KAITAKU KINENKAN KENKYU NENPO/HISTORICAL MUSEUM OF HOKKAIDO. ANNUAL REPORT. see *MUSEUMS AND ART GALLERIES*

951   HK
HONG KONG: A REVIEW OF (YEAR). a. Information Services Department, Publications Sales Office, 1 Battery Path, Central, Hong Kong. TEL 84288011. FAX 537-1543. Ed. David Roberts.

954   II   ISSN 0376-9682
DS401
I C H R NEWSLETTER. (Text in English) q. Indian Council of Historical Research, 35 Ferozeshah Rd., New Delhi 110001, India.

HISTORY — HISTORY OF ASIA

952 300   SI   ISSN 0218-5474
▼**I S E A S SERIES ON JAPAN AND THE ASIA-PACIFIC.** (Text in English) 1993. irreg. price varies. Institute of Southeast Asian Studies, Heng Mui Keng Terrace, Pasir Panjang Rd., Singapore 0511, Singapore. TEL 778-0955. FAX 778-1735. TELEX RS 37068 ISEAS. (Subscr. in U.S. to: Ashgate, Old Post Rd., Brookfield, VT 05036. TEL 802-276-3162) **Document type:** monographic series, academic/scholarly publication.
   Description: Contains studies on Japan, Southeast Asia, and countries within the Pacific. Focuses on the current political and economic issues.

IMPRESSIONS (NEW YORK). see *ART*

INDIA ABROAD. see *ETHNIC INTERESTS*

INDIAN ARCHIVES. see *LIBRARY AND INFORMATION SCIENCES*

INDIAN CHURCH HISTORY REVIEW. see *RELIGIONS AND THEOLOGY*

954   II   ISSN 0304-7032
DS401
INDIAN COUNCIL OF HISTORICAL RESEARCH. ANNUAL REPORT. Key Title: Annual Report - Indian Council of Historical Research. (Text in English) 1972. a. Indian Council of Historical Research, 35 Ferozeshah Rd., New Delhi 110001, India.

INDIAN ECONOMIC AND SOCIAL HISTORY REVIEW. see *SOCIAL SCIENCES: COMPREHENSIVE WORKS*

954.005   II   ISSN 0376-9836
DS401
INDIAN HISTORICAL REVIEW.* 1974. s-a. Rs.50($14) (Indian Council of Historical Research) Vikas Publishing House Pvt. Ltd., 576 Masjid Rd., Jangpura, New Dehli 110 014, India. TEL 11-624605. TELEX 31592252. (Dist. by: UBS Publishers' Distributors Ltd., 5 Ansari Rd., New Delhi 110002, India) **Indexed:** Amer.Hist.& Life, Hist.Abstr.

954   II
INDIAN HISTORY AND CULTURE. SERIES. 1984. irreg. Bahri Publications, 997-A, Street No. 9, P.O. Box 4453, Gobindpuri, Kalkaji, New Delhi 110 019, India. TEL 644-5710. FAX 91-11-64601796. Ed. Ujjal Singh Bahri. **Document type:** monographic series.
   Description: Discusses recent research into ancient, medieval and modern studies of Indian history and culture.

950   II   ISSN 0378-2964
INDIAN HORIZONS. 1952. q. Rs.100($40) Indian Council for Cultural Relations, Azad Bhavan, Indraprastha Estate, New Delhi 110002, India. TEL 3319309. TELEX 31-61860. Ed. Amit Dasgupta; Pub. Shri Niranjan Desai. bk.rev.; bibl. circ. 1,900. (also avail. in microform from UMI; reprint service avail. from UMI) **Indexed:** Amer.Hist.& Life, Arts & Hum.Cit.Ind., Curr.Cont., Hist.Abstr., M.L.A.
   —Faxon; UnCover; UMI.
   Formerly: Indo-Asian Culture (ISSN 0019-7203)

INDIAN YEARBOOK OF INTERNATIONAL AFFAIRS. see *POLITICAL SCIENCE — International Relations*

900   II   ISSN 0019-7211
AP8
INDO-BRITISH REVIEW; a journal of history. (Text in English) 1968. q. Rs.500($50) (effective 1993). Indo-British Historical Society, Sinai, 21 Rajaram Mehta Ave., Nelson Rd., Madras 600 029, India. TEL 044-422404. Ed. George T. Verghese. adv.; bk.rev.; bibl.; illus. circ. 500. (back issues avail.) **Indexed:** Amer.Hist.& Life, Hist.Abstr. **Document type:** academic/scholarly publication.
   —BLDSC (4437.584000).
   Description: Promotes the study of Indian history with an emphasis on the Indo-British relationship which has spanned over three centuries. Includes questions of contemporary history from an academic perspective.

959 300   SI   ISSN 0218-608X
▼**INDOCHINA UNIT SERIES.** (Text in English) 1993. irreg. price varies. Institute of Southeast Asian Studies, Heng Mui Keng Terrace, Pasir Panjang Rd., Singapore 0511, Singapore. TEL 778-0955. FAX 778-1735. TELEX RS 37068 ISEAS. (Subscr. in U.S. to: Ashgate, Old Post Rd., Brookfield, VT 05036. TEL 802-276-3162) **Document type:** monographic series, academic/scholarly publication.
   Description: Contains studies on current issues and the development of Vietnam, Cambodia and Laos.

INDONESIAN STUDIES. see *POLITICAL SCIENCE — International Relations*

915.95   MY   ISSN 0126-6195
INFORMATION MALAYSIA. 1963. a. M.$15. Berita Publishing, 22 Jalan Liku, 59100 Kuala Lumpur, Malaysia. (Dist. in U.S. by: International Publications Service, 303 Park Ave. S., New York, NY 10010)
   Incorporating: Malaysia Year Book (ISSN 0076-339X)

950   KO
INQUIRY INTO THE FUTURE. (Text in English or Korean) 1970. a. $5. Korean Society for Future Studies, Graduate School of Environmental Studies, Rm. 13-211, Seoul National University, Seoul 151, S. Korea. Ed. An-Jae Kim. bk.rev. circ. 200.

959   SI
INSTITUTE OF SOUTHEAST ASIAN STUDIES. ANNUAL REPORT. (Text in English) 1969. a. free. Institute of Southeast Asian Studies, Heng Mui Keng Terrace, Pasir Panjang, Singapore 0511, Singapore. TEL 7780955. FAX 7781735. TELEX RS 37068 ISEAS. **Document type:** corporate report.
   Description: Report of research activities of the Institute of Southeast Asian Studies.

959   SI
INSTITUTE OF SOUTHEAST ASIAN STUDIES. CURRENT ISSUES SEMINAR SERIES. (Text in English) 1973. irreg., no. 12, 1981. price varies. Institute of Southeast Asian Studies, Heng Mui Keng Terrace, Pasir Panjang, Singapore 0511, Singapore. TEL 7780955. FAX 7781735. TELEX RS 37068 ISEAS. (Subscr. in U.S. to: Ashgate, Old Post Rd., Brookfield, VT 05036. TEL 802-276-3162) **Document type:** academic/scholarly publication.

959   SI
INSTITUTE OF SOUTHEAST ASIAN STUDIES. LOCAL HISTORY AND MEMOIRS. (Text in English) 1973. irreg., no.8, 1992. price varies. Institute of Southeast Asian Studies, Heng Mui Keng Terrace, Pasir Panjang, Singapore 0511, Singapore. TEL 7780955. FAX 7781735. TELEX RS 37068 ISEAS. (Subscr. in U.S. to: Ashgate, Old Post Rd., Brookfield, VT 05036. TEL 802-276-3162) **Document type:** academic/scholarly publication.
   Formerly (until 1982): Institute of Southeast Asian Studies. Oral History Programmes.
   Description: Local and oral history of Southeast Asia.

954   II   ISSN 0074-123X
INTERNATIONAL ACADEMY OF INDIAN CULTURE. SATAPITAKA SERIES. (Text in English) 1957. a. price varies. International Academy of Indian Culture, J-22 Hauzkhas Enclave, New Delhi 110 016, India. TEL 665494. Ed. Lokesh Chandra. circ. 100.
   Supersedes: International Academy of Indian Culture. Report.

915.19   KO   ISSN 0303-3007
DS901
INTERNATIONAL JOURNAL OF KOREAN STUDIES. (Text in English) 1973. s-a. $5. (Korean Studies Institute) Yonsei University Press, Yonsei University, 134 Sinchon-Dong, Seodaemoon-Ku, Seoul 120, S. Korea.

952   IT   ISSN 0080-3928
ISTITUTO GIAPPONESE DI CULTURA, ROME. NOTIZIARIO.. 1965. a. free. (Kokusai Koryu Kikin) Istituto Giapponese di Cultura in Roma, Via Antonio Gramsci 74, 00197 Roma, Italy. TEL 06-3224794. FAX 06-3222165. circ. 2,500. **Document type:** bulletin.

954   II   ISSN 0970-812X
ITIHAS; journal of the Andhra Pradesh archives. (Text in English, Telugu, Urdu) 1973. s-a. Rs.130. Commissioner of State Archives and Research Institute, Tarnaka, Hyderabad 500 007, Andhra Pradesh, India. TEL 868373. Ed. H. Rajendra Prasad. adv.; bk.rev.; illus. circ. 200. **Indexed:** Amer.Hist.& Life, Hist.Abstr.
   Description: Promotes the study of history, art, and culture. Includes latest research topics.

954.9   BG
JAHANE NAO. (Text in Bengali) w. Tk.0.60 per no. Oriental Press, 13 Karkunbari Lane, Dhaka 1, Bangladesh.
   Description: Povides political news and views.

952   JA
JAPAN ECHO. (Text in English) 1974. 5/yr. $120. Intercontinental Marketing Corp., I.P.O. Box 5056, Tokyo 100-30, Japan. **Indexed:** A.I.Abstr.

959   MY
JEBAT. (Text in English and Malay) 1971. a. M.10($15) (National University of Malaysia, Historical Society - Universiti Kebangsaan Malaysia) Penerbit Universiti Kebangsaan Malaysia, 43600 UKM Bangi, Selangor, Malaysia. TEL 603-825-0001. FAX 603-825-6484. Ed.Bd. bk.rev.; bibl.; illus. circ. 2,000. **Indexed:** E.I.

954   II   ISSN 0377-743X
DS423
JIJNASA; journal of the history of ideas and culture. (Text in English) 1974. 2/yr. University of Rajasthan, Department of History and Indian Culture, Gandhi Nagar, Jaipur 302004, India. Ed. M.S. Jain.

951   CC   ISSN 1001-6708
JINDAI SHI YANJIU/STUDIES ON MODERN CHINESE HISTORY. (Text in Chinese) bi-m. Y15($41.90) (Zhongguo Shehui Kexueyuan, Jindai Shi Yanjiusuo - Chinese Academy of Social Sciences, Institute of Modern History) Jindai Shi Janjiu Zazhishe, Faxingzu, 1 Dongchang Hutong, Wangfujing Dajie, Beijing 100006, People's Republic of China. TEL 555131. (Dist. outside China by: China International Book Trading Corp., P.O. Box 399, Beijing, P.R.C.; Dist. in US by: China Books & Periodicals, Inc., 2929 24th St., San Francisco, CA 94110. TEL 415-282-2994) Ed. Xia Liangcai. bk.rev.
   Description: Contains studies on modern Chinese history.

959 956   US   ISSN 1058-3947
DS518.8
▼**JOURNAL OF AMERICAN - EAST ASIAN RELATIONS.** 1992. q. $60. Imprint Publications, 100 E. Ohio St., Ste. 630, Chicago, IL 60611. Ed. Michael A. Barnhat.
   —UnCover; SWETS.

954   II   ISSN 0075-4110
JOURNAL OF ANCIENT INDIAN HISTORY. 1967. a. Rs.30($6) University of Calcutta, Centre of Advanced Study in Ancient Indian History and Culture, 51-2 Hazra Rd., Calcutta 19, India. Ed. D.C. Sircar. **Indexed:** Numis.Lit.

950   GW   ISSN 0021-910X
DS1
JOURNAL OF ASIAN HISTORY. (Text and summaries in English, French, German) 1967. 2/yr. DM.128. Harrassowitz Verlag, Taunusstr. 14, 65183 Wiesbaden, Germany. TEL 0611-530-0. FAX 0611-530560. (Subscr. to: Postfach 2929, 65019 Wiesbaden, Germany) Ed. Denis Sinor. adv.; bk.rev.; abstr.; charts; illus.; index. circ. 600. (tabloid format; also avail. in microfilm from UMI; back issues avail.; reprint service avail. from UMI) **Indexed:** Amer.Hist.& Life, Arts & Hum.Cit.Ind., Curr.Cont., E.I., Hist.Abstr., Hum.Ind., Numis.Lit, SSCI. **Document type:** academic/scholarly publication.
   —BLDSC (4947.240000); Faxon; UnCover; SWETS; UMI. **CCC.**

JOURNAL OF CENTRAL ASIA. see *ARCHAEOLOGY*

951   CH   ISSN 0022-1228
JOURNAL OF FUKIEN HISTORY.* 1968. q. NT.$40($1) Fukien Humanities Society, 22, Lane 113, Hsia-men St. (Amoy St.), Taipei, Taiwan, Republic of China. Eds. Li Han-Ching, Chen Han-Kuang. adv.; bk.rev.; abstr.; bibl.; illus. circ. 5,000.
   Description: Includes items of local interest.

959.9   PH   ISSN 0115-2297
JOURNAL OF HISTORY. 1950. irreg., no.31, 1987. $7. (Philippine National Historical Society) Philippine Social Science Council, Central Subscription Service, P.O. Box 655, Greenhills, Metro Manila 3113, Philippines. Ed. Marcelino A. Foronda. circ. 200. **Indexed:** Ind.Phil.Per.

954   II   ISSN 0022-1775
DS401
JOURNAL OF INDIAN HISTORY. 1921. 3/yr. Rs.55. University of Kerala, Department of History, Trivandrum, Kerala, India. Ed. M.J. Koshy. bk.rev.; illus.; index. **Indexed:** Amer.Hist.& Life, Curr.Cont., Hist.Abstr., Numis.Lit.

JOURNAL OF JAPANESE STUDIES. see *ORIENTAL STUDIES*

954   II   ISSN 0377-0443
DS485.K4
JOURNAL OF KERALA STUDIES. 1974. q. University of Kerala, Department of History, Trivandrum, Kerala, India. Ed. M.J. Koshy. bk.rev.

959   US   ISSN 0738-7997
DS501
JOURNAL OF NORTHEAST ASIAN STUDIES. 1982. q. $42 to individuals (foreign $66); institutions $84 (foreign $108). (George Washington University, Institute for Sino-Soviet Studies) Transaction Publishers, Transaction Periodicals Consortium, Department 3092, Rutgers University, New Brunswick, NJ 08903. TEL 908-932-2280. FAX 908-932-3138. Eds. Young C. Kim, Gaston J. Sigur. adv. circ. 800. (reprint service avail.) **Indexed:** Amer.Hist.& Life, Asian-Pac.Econ.Lit., Hist.Abstr., I D A, Int.Bibl.Soc.Sci., Int.Polit.Sci.Abstr., P.A.I.S. **Document type:** academic/scholarly publication.
—BLDSC (5022.844700); Faxon; UnCover; SWETS. **CCC.**
   Description: Provides analyses of social, political, economic, and military developments in post-World War II northeast Asia.

JOURNAL OF POLITICAL SCIENCE. see *POLITICAL SCIENCE*

JOURNAL OF SOUTH ASIAN AND MIDDLE EASTERN STUDIES. see *HISTORY — History Of The Near East*

950   SI   ISSN 0022-4634
DS501
JOURNAL OF SOUTHEAST ASIAN STUDIES. 1970. s-a. S.$44($27) (National University of Singapore, History Department) Singapore University Press, Yusof Ishak House, National University of Singapore, 10 Kent Ridge Crescent, Singapore 0511, Singapore. TEL 7761148. FAX 7740652. Ed. Ng Chin Keong. adv.; bk.rev. circ. 1,200. **Indexed:** A.B.C.Pol.Sci., Abstr.Anthropol., Acad.Ind., Amer.Hist.& Life, Arts & Hum.Cit.Ind., Asian-Pac.Econ.Lit., Bibl.Ling., Curr.Cont., E.I., Hist.Abstr., Hum.Ind., Rural Recreat.Tour.Abstr., SSCI, World Agri.Econ.& Rural Sociol.Abstr. **Document type:** academic/scholarly publication.
—BLDSC (5066.008000); Faxon; UnCover; SWETS. **Supersedes:** Journal of Southeast Asian History.

954 320 301 398   NP   ISSN 0377-7499
KAILASH; journal of Himalayan studies. (Text in English or Hindi) 1973. q. $18. Ratna Pustak Bhandar, Bhotahitiy, Kathmandu, Nepal. Ed. John K. Locke. bk.rev.; bibl.; illus. circ. 1,000. **Indexed:** Anthropol.Lit.

950 913   GW   ISSN 0075-532X
KEILSCHRIFTURKUNDEN AUS BOGHAZKOEI. 1953. irreg., no.60, 1990. price varies. Akademie Verlag GmbH, Muehlenstr. 33-34, 13187 Berlin, Germany. TEL 030-47889348. FAX 030-47889357. **Indexed:** Bibl.Ling. **Document type:** monographic series.

954   II
KERALA ARCHIVES BULLETIN. 1974. q. free. Directorate of State Archives, State Archives Dept., Trivandrum 695 003, Kerala, India. TEL 433759. Ed.Bd. bk.rev. circ. 500. **Document type:** bulletin.
   Formerly (until 1989): Kerala Archives Newsletter.
   Description: Intended to bring to light unpublished materials of historical interest in the possession of the Kerala State Archives.

KHOSANA. see *SOCIOLOGY*

950 490   HU   ISSN 0075-6911
KOROSI CSOMA KISKONYVTAR. 1966. irreg., vol.21, 1993. price varies. (Magyar Tudomanyos Akademia) Akademiai Kiado, Publishing House of the Hungarian Academy of Sciences, P.O. Box 245, H-1519 Budapest, Hungary. TEL 181-2134. FAX 166-6466. TELEX 22-6228 AKNYO H. **Document type:** academic/scholarly publication.

930 950   FR   ISSN 0221-5896
KTEMA; civilisations de l'Orient, de la Grece et de Rome Antiques. 1976. a. 395 F. Universite de Strasbourg II, Groupe de Recherche d'Histoire Romaine, Association pour l'Etude et la Civilisation Romaine (AECR), B.P. 4, 67043 Strasbourg Cedex, France. Eds. Edmond Frezouls, Edmond Levy. adv. **Document type:** academic/scholarly publication.

951   US   ISSN 0884-3236
DS754
LATE IMPERIAL CHINA. (Text in English) 1975. s-a. $15 to individuals (foreign $20); institutions $25 (foreign $35). University of Southern California, Department of History, Los Angeles, CA 90089-0034. TEL 213-740-1668. FAX 213-740-6999. Eds. Charlotte Furth, James Lee. bibl.; illus. circ. 500. **Document type:** academic/scholarly publication.
—Faxon. **CCC.**
   Formerly (until 1984): Ch'ing-shih Wen-t'i (ISSN 0577-9235).
   Description: Covers all aspects of Chinese history, literature, society, economics, politics, philosophy, religion, and art during the Ming and Qing Dynasties, from the 14th to the early 20th century.

951   CC
LISHI DAGUANYUAN. (Text in Chinese) 1985. m. $2 per.no. Zhongshan Daxue, Lishi Xi - Zhongshan University, History Department, Xingang Lu, Guangzhou, Guangdong 510275, People's Republic of China. TEL 4446300. TELEX 44604 ZSUFO. Ed. Cai Hongsheng. bk.rev. circ. 55,000.
   Description: Covers all aspects of Chinese history.

029 900   CC
LISHI DANG'AN/HISTORICAL ARCHIVES. (Text in Chinese; table of contents in English) q. Y5.60($19.50) (First Historical Archives of China) Historical Archives Magazine House, Palace Museum inside Xihuamen, Beijing 100031, People's Republic of China. FAX 3096489. (Dist. outside China by: China International Book Trading Corp., P.O. Box 399, Beijing, P.R.C.; Dist. in US by: China Books & Periodicals, Inc., 2929 24th St., San Francisco, CA 94110. TEL 415-282-2994) Ed. Xu Yipu.
   Description: Publishes papers on historical research.

954   II   ISSN 0076-2571
MAHRATTA. (Text in English) 1881. a. Kesari-Mahratta Trust Publication, The Kesari and the Mahratta Office, 568 Narayan, Poona 2, India. Ed. J.S. Tilak.

915.95   MY   ISSN 0301-7095
DS591
MALAYSIA IN BRIEF. (Text in English) irreg. Ministry of Foreign Affairs - Kementerian Luar Negeri, Jalan Wisma Putra, Kuala Lumpur, Malaysia. illus. circ. 60,000.

959.5   MY   ISSN 0126-6098
MALAYSIA OFFICIAL YEAR BOOK. (Text in English and Malay) a. Information Services Malaysia, Angkasapuri, Kuala Lumpur, Malaysia. TEL 03-2985542. FAX 03-230733. TELEX MA-731651. Ed. Foong Bee Leng. circ. 6,000. **Document type:** government publication.
   Description: Reports on the administration and national economy of Malaysia. Gives a factual account of the progress of national institutions, both government and quasi-government, and shows the role played by the government in the life of the community.

329.9   MY   ISSN 0542-397X
DS595.2.C5
MALAYSIAN CHINESE ASSOCIATION. ANNUAL REPORT. (Text in English) 1963. a. free. Malaysian Chinese Association, Wisma MCA, 8th Fl., 163 Jalan Ampang, Peti Surat 10626, Kuala Lumpur, Malaysia. TEL 2618044. FAX 2619772. TELEX 33278 MCAH.

MARGA. see *SOCIAL SCIENCES: COMPREHENSIVE WORKS*

959.7   BE
MESSAGE D'EXTREME-ORIENT. 1971. irreg., no.2, 1977. Librairie-Editions Thanh-Long, 34 rue Dekens, B-1040 Brussels, Belgium. **Document type:** monographic series.

951   US
MICHIGAN MONOGRAPHS IN CHINESE STUDIES. 1968. irreg. (3-4/yr.), no.61, 1989. University of Michigan, Center for Chinese Studies, 104 Lane Hall, Ann Arbor, MI 48109. TEL 313-764-1817. (back issues avail.)
—BLDSC (5755.515000).
   Incorporating (1970-1979, no.6): Michigan Abstracts of Chinese and Japanese Works on Chinese History (ISSN 0076-7808); Former titles: Michigan Papers in Chinese Studies (ISSN 0076-8065); University of Michigan. Center for Chinese Studies. Occasional Papers.

959   US
MICHIGAN PAPERS ON SOUTH AND SOUTHEAST ASIA. 1970. irreg., no.41, 1993. price varies. University of Michigan, Center for South and Southeast Asian Studies, 130 Lane Hall, Ann Arbor, MI 48109-1290. TEL 313-763-5790. Ed. M. Mayer. adv.; bk.rev. **Indexed:** Anthropol.Lit., Rural Devel.Abstr.

950   US   ISSN 0076-812X
MICHIGAN STATE UNIVERSITY. ASIAN STUDIES CENTER. OCCASIONAL PAPERS: EAST ASIA SERIES. 1969. irreg., no.10, 1990. Michigan State University, Asian Studies Center, 109 International Center, E. Lansing, MI 48824. TEL 517-353-1680. (also avail. in microform from UMI; reprint service avail. from UMI) **Document type:** monographic series.

950   US   ISSN 0076-8138
MICHIGAN STATE UNIVERSITY. ASIAN STUDIES CENTER. OCCASIONAL PAPERS: SOUTH ASIA SERIES. 1965. irreg., no.39, 1991. Michigan State University, Asian Studies Center, 109 International Center, E. Lansing, MI 48824. TEL 517-353-1680. **Document type:** monographic series.
—UMI.

MINDANAO ART & CULTURE. see *FOLKLORE*

025.171 951.04   CC   ISSN 1000-4491
DS773.89
MINGUO DANG'AN/ARCHIVES OF THE REPUBLIC OF CHINA. (Text and summaries in Chinese; table of contents in English) 1985. q. Y8($24) (Zhongguo Di-2 Lishi Dang'anguan) Minguo Dang'an Zazhi She, 309 Zhongshan Donglu, Nanjing, Jiangsu 210016, People's Republic of China. TEL 401261. (Dist. outside China by: China International Book Trading Corp., P.O. Box 399, Beijing, P.R.C.; Dist. in US by: China Books & Periodicals, Inc., 2929 24th St., San Francisco, CA 94110. TEL 415-282-2994) Ed. Chen Xingtang. bibl.
—UnCover.
   Description: Covers the Republican period of China's history (1911-1949).

951   US   ISSN 0097-7004
DS701
MODERN CHINA; an international quarterly of history and social science. 1975. q. $54 to individuals; institutions $152 (effective 1994). Sage Publications, Inc., 2455 Teller Rd., Thousand Oaks, CA 91320. TEL 805-499-0721. FAX 805-499-0871. (Subscr. to: Sage Publications, Inc., Box 5084, Thousand Oaks, CA 91359; Overseas subscr. to: Sage Publications, Ltd., 6 Bonhill St., London EC2A 4PU, England; Sage Publications India Pvt. Ltd., P.O. Box 4215, New Delhi 110 048, India) Ed. Philip C.C. Huang. adv.; bk.rev.; bibl.; charts; illus.; index. circ. 1,250. (back issues avail.) **Indexed:** A.B.C.Pol.Sci., Amer.Hist.& Life, Asian-Pac.Econ.Lit., Curr.Cont., Hist.Abstr., I D A, Int.Lab.Doc., Mid.East: Abstr.& Ind., P.A.I.S., Sage Fam.Stud.Abstr., Sage Urb.Stud.Abstr., SSCI. **Document type:** academic/scholarly publication.
—BLDSC (5886.005000); Faxon; UnCover; SWETS; UMI. **CCC.**
   Description: Encourages interdisciplinary scholarship and dialogue on China's ongoing revolution.

956   US   ISSN 0077-0027
MODERN MIDDLE EAST SERIES. 1970. irreg., no.4, 1979. Columbia University Press, 562 W. 113th St., New York, NY 10025. TEL 212-678-6777.

HISTORY — HISTORY OF ASIA

959   AT   ISSN 0729-3623
MONASH UNIVERSITY. CENTRE OF SOUTHEAST ASIAN STUDIES. ANNUAL INDONESIAN LECTURE SERIES. Key Title: Annual Indonesian Lecture Series. 1977. a. Monash University, Centre of Southeast Asian Studies, Clayton, Vic. 3168, Australia. FAX 61-3-565-4007. Ed. David P. Chandler.

959 320   AT   ISSN 0727-6680
MONASH UNIVERSITY. CENTRE OF SOUTHEAST ASIAN STUDIES. MONASH PAPERS ON SOUTHEAST ASIA. Key Title: Monash Papers on Southeast Asia. 1972. irreg. price varies. Monash University, Centre of Southeast Asian Studies, Clayton, Vic. 3168, Australia. FAX 61-3-565-4007. Ed. David P. Chandler. circ. 300. **Document type:** monographic series.
—BLDSC (5901.591700).

959   AT   ISSN 0314-6804
MONASH UNIVERSITY. CENTRE OF SOUTHEAST ASIAN STUDIES. WORKING PAPERS. 1974. irreg. price varies. Monash University, Centre of Southeast Asian Studies, Clayton, Vic. 3168, Australia. FAX 61-3-565-4007. Ed. David P. Chandler. **Document type:** monographic series.

951   US   ISSN 0077-0396
DS798
MONGOLIA SOCIETY. OCCASIONAL PAPERS. 1964. irreg., no.15, 1990. price varies. Mongolia Society, Inc., 322 Goodbody Hall, Indiana University, Bloomington, IN 47405-2401. TEL 812-855-4078. FAX 812-855-7500. Ed. John R. Krveger. circ. 400.

950   US
MONGOLIA SOCIETY. SPECIAL PAPERS. (Text in Mongolian) 1964. irreg., no.12, 1993. price varies. Mongolia Society, Inc., 321-322 Goodbody Hall, Indiana University, Bloomington, IN 47405-2401. TEL 812-855-4078. FAX 812-855-7500. Ed. John Krveger.

951   US   ISSN 0894-6523
DS798.A2
MONGOLIA SOCIETY NEWSLETTER. NEW SERIES. 1950; N.S. 1985. irreg., no.14, 1993. Mongolia Society, Inc., 322 Goodbody Hall, Indiana University, Bloomington, IN 47405-2401. TEL 812-855-4078. FAX 812-855-7500. Ed. Ruth I. Meserve.
Description: Travel accounts, cultural news and other information relating to Mongolia and activities of members of the Mongolia Society.

959   US
MONOGRAPHS IN INTERNATIONAL STUDIES: SOUTHEAST ASIA SERIES. 1968. irreg. price varies. Ohio University, Center for International Studies, Burson House, 56 E. Union St., Athens, OH 45701. TEL 614-593-1155. (Subscr. to: Ohio University Press, Scott Quad., Athens, OH 45701) Ed. James L. Cobban. bibl.; charts; illus. circ. 700. (back issues avail.; reprint service avail. from UMI) **Indexed:** Anthropol.Lit., M.L.A., SSCI. **Document type:** monographic series.
Formerly: Papers in International Studies: Southeast Asia Series (ISSN 0078-9119)

MONUMENTA SERICA MONOGRAPH SERIES. see ORIENTAL STUDIES

MYTHIC SOCIETY. QUARTERLY JOURNAL. see FOLKLORE

025.17   MY   ISSN 0076-3381
NATIONAL ARCHIVES OF MALAYSIA. ANNUAL REPORT/ARKIB NEGARA MALAYSIA. LAPORAN TAHUNAN. (Text in English and Malay) 1963. a. M.$8 (effective 1990). National Archives, Jalan Duta, Kuala Lumpur 50568, Malaysia. TEL 2562688. FAX 255-5679. circ. 1,000.
Supersedes: Malaya (Federation) Public Records Office and National Archives. Report.
Description: Provides information to the public on the activities of the National Archives.

951 709   CH
NATIONAL INSTITUTE FOR COMPILATION AND TRANSLATION. COLLECTED PAPERS ON HISTORY OF CHINA. irreg. National Institute for Compilation and Translation, Committee for Compilation and Examination of the Series of Chinese Classics, Taipei, Taiwan, Republic of China. FAX 02-362-9256.

NEUINDISCHE STUDIEN. see LINGUISTICS

949   US   ISSN 0199-9796
Z3001
NEW BOOKS ON ASIA ANNOUNCED FOR PUBLICATION IN THE SOVIET UNION. a. University of Illinois at Urbana-Champaign, Center for Asian Studies, 1208 W. California, Urbana, IL 61801. TEL 217-333-1000. **Document type:** bibliography.

NEWSLETTER EAST ASIAN ART & ARCHEOLOGY. see ART

950   II   ISSN 0078-0855
NITYANAND UNIVERSAL SERIES. (Text in Hindi and Sanskrit) 1960. irreg., vol.11, 1976. price varies. Vishveshvaranand Vedic Research Institute, P.O. Sadhu Ashram, Hoshiarpur 146021, Punjab, India. Ed. S. Bhaskaran Nair. **Document type:** monographic series.

959   US
NORTHERN ILLINOIS UNIVERSITY. CENTER FOR SOUTHEAST ASIAN STUDIES. OCCASIONAL PAPERS SERIES. 1974. irreg., no.16, 1992. price varies. Northern Illinois University, Center for Southeast Asian Studies, DeKalb, IL 60115. TEL 815-753-1771. FAX 815-753-1832. Ed. Grant A. Olson. circ. 450. **Indexed:** Anthropol.Lit. **Document type:** academic/scholarly publication, monographic series.

959   US   ISSN 0073-4934
NORTHERN ILLINOIS UNIVERSITY. CENTER FOR SOUTHEAST ASIAN STUDIES. SPECIAL REPORT SERIES. 1969. irreg., no.27, 1992. price varies. Northern Illinois University, Center for Southeast Asian Studies, De Kalb, IL 60115. TEL 815-753-1771. FAX 815-753-1832. Ed. Grant A. Olson. adv. circ. 450. **Document type:** academic/scholarly publication, monographic series.
—BLDSC (8386.800000).

OCCASIONAL PAPERS - REPRINT SERIES IN CONTEMPORARY ASIAN STUDIES. see LAW

ORIENS. see ORIENTAL STUDIES

ORIENTAL INSTITUTE NUBIAN EXPEDITION. see ARCHAEOLOGY

950   JA   ISSN 0082-562X
AS552
ORIENTAL LIBRARY. RESEARCH DEPARTMENT. MEMOIRS/ZAIDAN HOJIN TOYO BUNKO. (Text in English) 1926. a. 6000 Yen. Oriental Library - Toyo Bunko, 2-28-21 Honkomagome, Bunkyo-ku, Tokyo 113, Japan. TEL 03-3942-0121. FAX 03-3942-0258. Ed. Shiba Yoshinobu. circ. 550. **Indexed:** A.I.C.P. **Document type:** academic/scholarly publication.
—UnCover.

ORIENTAL NOTES AND STUDIES. see HISTORY — History Of The Near East

PACIFIC AFFAIRS; an international review of Asia and the Pacific. see POLITICAL SCIENCE

954.7   PK   ISSN 0078-8171
PAKISTAN HISTORICAL SOCIETY. MEMOIR. (Text in English) 1953. a. Rs.100. Pakistan Historical Society, New Karachi Housing Society, 30 Dr. Moinul Haq Rd., Karachi 75400, Pakistan. TEL 92-21-4557847. adv. circ. 1,000. (back issues avail.) **Document type:** monographic series.
—Faxon.

954.7   PK   ISSN 0078-818X
PAKISTAN HISTORICAL SOCIETY. PROCEEDINGS OF THE PAKISTAN HISTORY CONFERENCE. (Text in English) 1953. a. Rs.160($30) Pakistan Historical Society, New Karachi Housing Society, 30 Dr. Moinul Haq Rd., Karachi 75400, Pakistan. TEL 92-21-4557847. adv.; bk.rev. circ. 1,000. (back issues avail.) **Document type:** proceedings.

954.9   UK
PAKISTAN STUDIES. 1981. q. £12. London Centre for Pakistan Studies, 5-A Bathurst St., London W2 2SD, England. Ed. Muazzam Ali. adv. circ. 2,000.

954   II   ISSN 0031-0786
DS485.P2
PANJAB PAST AND PRESENT. (Text in English) 1967. s-a. Rs.20. Punjabi University, Department of Punjab Historical Studies, Patiala 147 002, Punjab, India. TEL 822161. Ed. S. Parm Bakhshish Singh. adv.; bk.rev.; bibl.; charts; illus.; stat.; cum.index every 5 yrs. circ. 500.

PELANGI; Indonesian-English bilingual magazine. see EDUCATION — Teaching Methods And Curriculum

930   BE   ISSN 0079-0893
DS251
PERSICA. (Text in English, French and German) 1963. irreg., vol.14, 1990. 2000 BEF. (Genootschap Nederland - Iran - Societe Neerlando - Iranienne) Editions Peeters s.p.r.l., Bondgenotenlaan 153, B-3000 Louvain, Belgium. TEL 32-16-235170. FAX 32-16-228500. adv.; bk.rev.; bibl. circ. 350. (back issues avail.) **Indexed:** Bibl.Ling. **Document type:** monographic series.
Description: Critical discussion of the history of Iranian civilizations and the Central Asian regions.

950 327   PH   ISSN 0115-5555
PHILIPPINES CHINESE HISTORICAL ASSOCIATION. ANNALS. (Text in English) vol.5, 1975. a. P.25($6) Philippine Chinese Historical Association, Box 3131, Manila, Philippines. Ed. Gideon Hsu. bibl.

959.9 915.06   US   ISSN 0889-5244
DS651
PILIPINAS; an interdisciplinary scholarly journal of Philippine studies. 1980. s-a. $16 to individuals; students $10; institutions $40 (foreign $45). Association for Asian Studies, Southeast Asia Council, Philippine Studies Group, c/o James Eder, Man. Ed., Department of Anthropology, Arizona State University, Tempe, AZ 85287-2402. TEL 602-965-4232. (Subscr. to: c/o Connie Cox Bodner, Rochester Museum and Science Center, 657 East Ave., Box 1480, Rochester, NY 14603-1480. TEL 716-271-4320) adv.; bk.rev. circ. 250. **Indexed:** HR Rep. **Document type:** academic/scholarly publication.
Formerly (until 1983): Filipinas.
Description: Devoted exclusively to scholarly writing on the Philippines. Contains articles on Philippine literature, the arts, history, the social sciences and the natural sciences.

PUNJAB UNIVERSITY INDOLOGICAL SERIES. see ORIENTAL STUDIES

954 915   II   ISSN 0970-1923
PURABHILEKH - PURATATVA/ARCHIVES - ARCHAEOLOGY. (Text in English, Marathi, Portuguese) 1983. s-a. price varies. Directorate of Archives, Archaeology and Museum, Rua de Ourem, Panaji-Goa 403 001, India. TEL 46692. Ed. P.P. Shirodkar. adv.; bk.rev. circ. 500. (back issues avail.) **Document type:** academic/scholarly publication.
Description: Examines research in archives, archaeology, history, museum, and related subjects with special reference to Goa and the former Portuguese colonies.

PURUSHARTHA. see SOCIAL SCIENCES: COMPREHENSIVE WORKS

951.03   US
QINGSHI YANJIU/STUDIES ON HISTORY - QING DYNASTY. (Text in Chinese) q. $29. China Books & Periodicals, Inc., 2929 24th St., San Francisco, CA 94110. TEL 415-282-2994. FAX 415-282-0994.
Formerly: Qingshi Yanjiu Tongxun.

R I M A: REVIEW OF INDONESIAN AND MALAYSIAN AFFAIRS; a semi-annual survey of political, economic, social and cultural aspects of Indonesia and Malaysia. see POLITICAL SCIENCE — International Relations

954   II   ISSN 0079-9572
RAJASTHAN YEAR BOOK AND WHO'S WHO. (Text in English) 1962. a. Rs.60. Samriddhi Publications, C-5 Bapunagar, Jaipur 302 015, India. Ed. Milap Chand Dandia. adv. circ. 2,000.

954   NP   ISSN 0034-348X
REGMI RESEARCH SERIES. (Text in English) 1969. m. Rs.300($20) Regmi Research (Pvt) Ltd., Lazimpat, Kathmandu, Nepal. TEL 4-11927. Ed. Mahesh C. Regmi. bk.rev.; index.
Description: Materials on the history of Nepal's law, government, society, politics and economics.

RENMIN/PEOPLE. see BIOGRAPHY

HISTORY — HISTORY OF ASIA

951 320 US
REPUBLICAN CHINA. 1975. s-a. $9. University of Illinois, Center for East Asian and Pacific Studies, 1208 W. California, 201, Urbana, IL 61801. TEL 217-333-4850. Ed. Herman Mast III. bk.rev.; bibl. circ. 300. Indexed: Amer.Hist.& Life, Hist.Abstr. **Document type:** academic/scholarly publication.
Formerly (until 1983): Chinese Republican Studies Newsletter.

954.9 PK ISSN 0034-5431
DS376
RESEARCH SOCIETY OF PAKISTAN. JOURNAL. (Text in English and Urdu) 1964. q. Rs.40($8) Research Society of Pakistan, University of the Punjab, Old Campus, Lahore, Pakistan. TEL 92-42-322542. Ed. A. Shakoor Ahsan. bk.rev. circ. 500. **Document type:** academic/scholarly publication.

954 II
REWRITING INDIAN AND WORLD HISTORY. (Text in English) 1965. a. $5. Institute for Rewriting Indian History, Plot No. 10, Goodwill Society, Aundh, Pune 411 007, India. TEL 0212-338449. Ed. P.N. Oak. adv.; bk.rev. circ. 2,000. **Document type:** academic/scholarly publication.
Formerly (until 1987): Institute for Rewriting Indian History. Annual Report and General Meeting Invitation.

915.903 959 MY ISSN 0304-2251
ROYAL ASIATIC SOCIETY. MALAYSIAN BRANCH. JOURNAL. (Text and summaries in English) 1878-1941, resumed 1946. s-a. M.30 to individuals (foreign $20); institutions M.$50 (foreign $40). Malaysian Branch of the Royal Asiatic Society, 130M. Jalan Thamby Abdullah, Off Jaln Tun Sambanthan (Brickfields), 50470 Kuala Lumpur, Malaysia. TEL 03-2748345. Ed. Tan Sri Dato' Mubin Sheppard. adv.; bk.rev.; cum.index: 1878-1963 in 1970, supplement in 1975. circ. 1,000. (also avail. in microfiche from IDC; back issues avail.; reprint service avail. from SCH) Indexed: A.I.C.P., Amer.Hist.& Life, Anthropol.Lit., Bibl.Ling., Biol.Abstr., Hist.Abstr. **Document type:** academic/scholarly publication, monographic series.
—SWETS.

950 GW ISSN 0340-6687
RUHR-UNIVERSITAET BOCHUM. OSTASIEN INSTITUT. VEROEFFENTLICHUNGEN. irreg., vol.40, 1993. price varies. Harrassowitz Verlag, Taunusstr. 14, 65183 Wiesbaden, Germany. TEL 0611-530-0. FAX 0611-530570. TELEX 4186135. (Subscr. to: Postfach 2929, 65019 Wiesbaden, Germany) Ed. Rudolf Herzer. **Document type:** monographic series.

958 II ISSN 0080-6137
SANTAKUTI VEDIC RESEARCH SERIES. (Text in English and Sanskrit) 1935. irreg., no.24, 1972. price varies. Vishveshvaranand Vedic Research Institute, P.O. Sadhu Ashram, Hoshiarpur 146021, Punjab, India. Ed. Vishva Bandhu. **Document type:** monographic series.

SAPTAHIKA THIKANA. see *POLITICAL SCIENCE*

950 II ISSN 0080-6471
SARVADANAND UNIVERSAL SERIES. (Text in English, Hindi and Sanskrit) 1950. irreg., vol.67, 1976. price varies. Vishveshvaranand Vedic Research Institute, P.O. Sadhu Ashram, Hoshiarpur 146021, Punjab, India. Ed. S. Bhaskaran Nair. **Document type:** monographic series.

950 US
SCHOOL OF INTERNATIONAL STUDIES. PUBLICATIONS ON ASIA. Title varies: Studies on Asia. 1952. irreg., no.41, 1987. price varies. (University of Washington, School of International Studies) University of Washington Press, Box 50096, Seattle, WA 98105. TEL 206-543-4050. **Document type:** monographic series.
Formerly: Publications on Asia (ISSN 0079-7782)
Refereed Serial

954 890 II ISSN 0254-0215
SERIES IN SIKH HISTORY AND CULTURE. 1979. irreg, no.8, 1992. price varies. Bahri Publications, 997-A, Street No. 9, P.O. Box 4453, Gobindpuri, Kalkaji, New Delhi 110 019, India. TEL 91-11-644-5710. FAX 91-11-641-0092. Ed. Ujjal Singh Bahri. **Document type:** monographic series.
Description: Studies of the political, religious and social history of the Sikhs and Sikhism as a world religion.

951 CC
SHANXI DIFANG ZHI. (Text in Chinese) bi-m. Shanxi Sheng Difang Zhi Xuehui, 3, Dongji Huying, Taiyuan, Shanxi 030009, People's Republic of China. TEL 440917. Ed. Yin Shiming.

SHREYE; international research quarterly. see *ORIENTAL STUDIES*

951 029 CC ISSN 1001-5264
SICHUAN DANG'AN/SICHUAN ARCHIVES. (Text in Chinese) 1983. q. Y1.60 per no. Sichuan Dang'an Ju - Sichuan Archives Bureau, 191 Huapaifang Jie, Chengdu, Sichuan 610031, People's Republic of China. TEL 669866. (Co-sponsor: Sichuan Archives Society) Ed. Wang Chenghu. adv. contact: Chen Wei. bk.rev. **Document type:** academic/scholarly publication, directory.

SIND JOURNAL OF POLITICAL SCIENCE AND MODERN HISTORY; an international publication. see *POLITICAL SCIENCE*

SINDH QUARTERLY. see *SOCIAL SCIENCES: COMPREHENSIVE WORKS*

959.5 SI ISSN 0217-7773
HC445.8.A1
SINGAPORE FACTS AND PICTURES. (Text in English) 1961. a. S.$3 (foreign S.$5). Ministry of Information and the Arts, Publicity Division, PSA Buiding, 30th Fl., 460 Alexandra Rd., Singapore 0511, Singapore. TEL 021-2799825. FAX 2799860. TELEX RS 22428 MITA SI. Ed. Ng Poey Siong. circ. 22,000. **Document type:** government publication.

951 NE ISSN 0169-9563
DS701
SINICA LEIDENSIA. 1938. irreg., vol.29, 1993. price varies. E.J. Brill, P.O. Box 9000, 2300 PA Leiden, Netherlands. TEL 31-71-312624. FAX 31-71-317532. TELEX 39296 BRILL NL. (In N. America: E.J. Brill, 24 Hudson St., Kinderhook, NY 12106. TEL 800-962-4406. FAX 518-758-1959) **Document type:** monographic series, academic/scholarly publication.
Description: Scholarly monographs on topics in Chinese history, culture, society and religion.
Refereed Serial

950 US ISSN 1041-8830
SINO - JAPANESE. 1988. s-a. $15. University of California, Santa Barbara, History Department, Santa Barbara, CA 93106. TEL 805-893-4065. FAX 805-893-8018. Ed. Joshua A. Fogel. adv.; bk.rev.; bibl. circ. 120. (back issues avail.)
Formerly: Sino - Japanese Studies Newsletter.
Description: Presents an academic forum for specialists in Chinese and Japanese studies.
Refereed Serial

950 410 800 US
SINO-PLATONIC PAPERS. 1986. irreg. price varies. University of Pennsylvania, Department of Oriental Studies, Philadelphia, PA 19104-6305. TEL 215-898-8432. (Alt. addr.: c/o V. Mair, Box 254, Swarthmore, PA 19081) Ed. Victor H. Mair. bk.rev. circ. 400. (back issues avail.) **Document type:** monographic series.
Description: Discusses the unconvnconventional or controversial nature of language, literature, and script.

SINOLOGICA COLONIENSIA; Ostasiatische Beitraege der Universitaet zu Koeln. see *ORIENTAL STUDIES*

SOCIETY FOR THE STUDY OF STATE GOVERNMENTS. JOURNAL. see *PUBLIC ADMINISTRATION*

954 301 US ISSN 0732-3867
DS335
SOUTH ASIA BULLETIN. 1981. s-a. $40. c/o Dept. of History, Duke University, Durham, NC 27708-0719. TEL 919-684-5439. FAX 919-286-1589. Eds. Sucheta Mazumdar, Vasant Kaiwar. adv.; bk.rev. circ. 700. Indexed: Alt.Press Ind., HR Rep., I D A, IBZ, Int.Bibl.Soc.Sci., Lang.& Lang.Behav.Abstr., P.A.I.S., Sociol.Abstr. **Document type:** academic/scholarly publication.
—UnCover.
Description: Examines the politics, economics, societies and cultures of southern Asia in depth and encourages cooperative studies of this region and the Middle East and Africa.

954 572 301 AT ISSN 0085-6401
DS331
SOUTH ASIA: JOURNAL OF SOUTH ASIAN STUDIES. 1971. 3/yr. $60 (effective 1994). South Asian Studies Association, c/o Department of History, University of New England, Armidale, N.S.W. 2351, Australia. TEL 067-732479. FAX 067-733520. TELEX 166050. Ed. H.V. Brasted. adv.; bk.rev. circ. 450. (also avail. in diskette format; back issues avail.) Indexed: Aus.P.A.I.S. **Document type:** academic/scholarly publication.
—UnCover.

954 US
SOUTH ASIA NEWS. 1970. 2/yr. free. University of Pennsylvania, South Asia Regional Studies Center, 820 Williams Hall, Philadelphia, PA 19104. TEL 215-898-7475. Ed. Clare Wilkinson Weber. bk.rev.; bibl. circ. 1,400.
Formerly: Society for South India Studies. Newsletter (ISSN 0145-7861)

SOUTH ASIAN STUDIES. see *ORIENTAL STUDIES*

954 UK ISSN 0266-6030
SOUTH ASIAN STUDIES. 1978. a. £20($35) to individuals; institutions £25($50). Society for South Asian Studies, c/o British Academy, 20-21 Cornwall Terrace, London NW1 4QP, England. TEL 0223-870494. FAX 0223-61125. Ed. B. Allchin. adv.; bk.rev. circ. 400. Indexed: Bibl.Ling., Geo.Abstr., I D A, Numis.Lit. **Document type:** academic/scholarly publication.
—UnCover.
Formerly (until 1985): Afghan Studies (ISSN 0265-4822)

954 PK
SOUTH ASIAN STUDIES. 1984. s-a. Rs.55($25) Centre for South Asian Studies, University of the Punjab, Quaid-i-Azam Campus, Lahore 54590, Pakistan. TEL 92-42-5864014. FAX 92-42-5867206. Ed. Rafique Ahmad. bk.rev. **Document type:** academic/scholarly publication.
Description: Publishes articles, chronologies of important events, and bibliographies pertaining to South Asia.

991 SI ISSN 0081-2889
SOUTH SEAS SOCIETY. JOURNAL. (Text in Chinese and English) 1940. s-a. $20. South Seas Society, P.O. Box 709, Singapore 9014, Singapore. Ed. Gwee Yee Hean. bk.rev. circ. 1,000. (reprint service avail. from SWZ)

991 SI ISSN 0081-2897
SOUTH SEAS SOCIETY. MONOGRAPH. (Text in Chinese and English) 1959. irreg., no.33, 1990. price varies. South Seas Society, P.O. Box 709, Singapore 9014, Singapore. Ed. Gwee Yee Hean. circ. 1,000. **Document type:** monographic series.

959 MY ISSN 0129-511X
SOUTHEAST ASIA MICROFILMS NEWSLETTER. (Text in English) 1972. s-a. $12. Southeast Asian Regional Branch, International Council on Archives, c/o National Archives of Malaysia, 50568 Jalan Duta, Kuala Lumpur, Malaysia. FAX 03-2555679. bk.rev.; bibl. (processed)

950 MY ISSN 0085-6509
CD2001
SOUTHEAST ASIAN ARCHIVES. (Text in English) 1968. a. M.15. Southeast Asian Regional Branch, International Council on Archives, c/o National Archives of Malaysia, 50568 Jalan Duta, Kuala Lumpur, Malaysia. Ed. Shamsi Rih Sharifl. adv.; bk.rev. Indexed: Amer.Hist.& Life, E.I., Hist.Abstr.

959 SI
SOUTHEAST ASIAN PERSPECTIVE SERIES. (Text in English) 1973. irreg., no.4, 1978. price varies. Institute of Southeast Asian Studies, Heng Mui Keng Terrace, Pasir Panjang, Singapore 0511, Singapore. TEL 7780955. FAX 7781735. TELEX RS 37068 ISEAS. **Document type:** academic/scholarly publication.

959 II ISSN 0257-7364
SOUTH EAST ASIAN REVIEW. Variant title: S E A R. (Text in English) 1976. s-a. Rs.200($30) Centre for South East Asian Studies, Dhanesh Bhawan Compound, Shahmir Takiya, Gaya 823001, Bihar, India. Ed. Sachchidanad Sahai. adv.; bk.rev. circ. 500. **Document type:** academic/scholarly publication.

HISTORY — HISTORY OF ASIA

950 490 II ISSN 0081-3907
SRI VENKATESWARA UNIVERSITY. ORIENTAL JOURNAL. (Text in English, Hindi, Sanskrit, Tamil and Telugu) 1958. a. (issued in 2 pts.). Rs.15. Sri Venkateswara University, Oriental Research Institute, Tirupati 517502, District Chittoor, India. TEL 91-8574-24166. FAX 91-8574-24111. Ed. M. Srimannarayana Murti. bk.rev.; cum.index: vols.1-29 (1958-1986). circ. 375. **Document type:** academic/scholarly publication, monographic series.
Description: Contains articles on language and literature of Sanskrit and Telugu, Indian philosophy, comparative religions, ancient Indian history, art, architecture, and ancient Indian sciences.

STUDI CLASSICI E ORIENTALI. see *CLASSICAL STUDIES*

956 410 GW ISSN 0341-4191
DS423
STUDIEN ZUR INDOLOGIE UND IRANISTIK. (Text in English, French and German) 1975. a. DM.30. Dr. Inge Wezler Verlag fuer Orientalistische Fachpublikationen, Bernhard-Ihnen-Str. 18, 21465 Reinbek, Germany. Ed.Bd. circ. 225. **Indexed:** Bibl.Ling.

954 US ISSN 0257-6430
STUDIES IN HISTORY (NEWBURY PARK). 1979; N.S. 1985. 2/yr. $33 to individuals; institutions $65 (effective 1994). (Jawaharlal Nehru University, Centre for Historical Studies, II) Sage Publications, Inc., 2455 Teller Rd., Thousand Oaks, CA 91320. TEL 805-499-0721. FAX 805-499-0871. (Subscr. to: Sage Publications, Inc., Box 5084, Thousand Oaks 91359; Overseas subscr. to: Sage Publications, Ltd., 6 Bonhill, St., London EC2A 4PU, England; Sage Publications Pvt. Ltd., P.O. Box 4215, New Delhi 110 048, India) Ed. S. Gopal. **Indexed:** Amer.Hist.& Life, Hist.Abstr. **Document type:** academic/scholarly publication.
Description: Reflects the expansion and diversification that has taken place in historical research in India recently.

STUDIES IN ORIENTAL CULTURE. see *ORIENTAL STUDIES*

954 II
STUDIES IN RAJPUT HISTORY AND CULTURE SERIES. 1976. irreg. Rs.70. Bharatiya Publishing House, 42-43 U. B. Jawahar Nagar, Delhi 110007, India. TEL 236080. bibl. circ. 1,100. **Document type:** academic/scholarly publication.

STUDIES OF CLASSICAL INDIA. see *PHILOSOPHY*

951 US
STUDIES ON CHINA. vol.2, 1984. irreg., vol.18, 1993. price varies. University of California Press, 2120 Berkeley Way, Berkeley, CA 94720. TEL 510-642-4247. FAX 510-643-7127. (Orders to: California-Princeton Fulfillment Services, 1445 Lower Ferry Rd., Ewing, NJ 08618. TEL 800-777-4726. FAX 800-999-1958) (back issues avail.) **Document type:** monographic series.
Description: Covers the history, politics, art, and culture of China.
Refereed Serial

STUDIES ON SOUTHEAST ASIA. see *ORIENTAL STUDIES*

SUI YUAN WEN HSIEN. see *ETHNIC INTERESTS*

954 II
SULTAN. (Text in English, Kannada, Urdu) 1983. a. Rs.257($5) Tipu Sultan Research Institute & Museum Gumbaz-Ganjam, Srirangapatne 571438, Karnataka, India. Ed. Mahmood Husine. illus. circ. 5,000.

SURYA INDIA. see *GENERAL INTEREST PERIODICALS — India*

900 PK
SWARBICA JOURNAL. (Text in English) 1978. a. Rs.15. National Archives, Director General of Archives, Administrative Block Area, Block 'N', Pakistan Secretariat, Islamabad, Pakistan.

951.249 CH
T'AI-WAN WEN HSIEN/REPORTS ON HISTORIOGRAPHICAL STUDIES OF TAIWAN. (Text in Chinese; table of contents in English) q. NT.$200 per no. Historical Research Commission of Taiwan Province, 8th Fl., Kang Ming Bldg., Li Ming Hsin-Tsun, Nan T'un District, Taichung, Taiwan, Republic of China. Ed. Liu Ning-yen. charts; illus.
Description: Contains papers and reports on the history of Taiwan.

TAIWAN COMMUNIQUE. see *POLITICAL SCIENCE — Civil Rights*

954 II
TAMIL CIVILIZATION. (Text in English) 1983. q. Rs.50($10) Tamil University, Thanjavur 613 001, Tamil Nadu, India.

954 700 410 II
TAMIL KALAI; research journal on Tamilology. (Text in Tamil) 1983. q. Rs.50($10) Tamil University, Thanjavur 613 001, Tamil, Nadu, India.

TIBET SOCIETY JOURNAL. see *ORIENTAL STUDIES*

T'OUNG PAO; revue internationale de sinologie. see *ORIENTAL STUDIES*

T'OUNG PAO. MONOGRAPHIES. see *ORIENTAL STUDIES*

951 CC ISSN 1002-7971
DS734.7
TRENDS IN THE STUDY OF CHINESE HISTORY/ZHONGGUOSHI DONGTAI. (Text in Chinese) 1979. q.? Zhongguo Shehui Kexueyuan, Lishi Yanjiusuo - Chinese Adademy of Social Sciences, Institute of History, 6 Ritan Lu, Beijing 100020, People's Republic of China. TEL 5063337. (Dist. overseas by: China International Book Trading Corp., P.O. Box 399, Beijing, P.R. China; Dist. in U.S. by: China Books & Periodicals, Inc., 2929 24th St., San Francisco, CA 94110) circ. 4,100. **Document type:** academic/scholarly publication.
Description: Covers current trends in research on Chinese history.

TRIVENI; a literary and cultural quarterly. see *LITERATURE*

952 US
TWENTIETH CENTURY JAPAN: THE EMERGENCE OF A WORLD POWER. 1990. irreg., vol.2, 1992. price varies. University of California Press, 2120 Berkeley Way, Berkeley, CA 94720. TEL 510-642-4247. FAX 510-643-7127. (Orders to: California-Princeton Fulfillment Services, 1445 Lower Ferry Rd., Ewing, NJ 08618. TEL 800-777-4726. FAX 800-999-1958) (back issues avail.) **Document type:** monographic series.
Description: Discusses Japan's emergence from a defeated nation after World War II to a major economic power in the global marketplace.
Refereed Serial

UNIVERSITAET ZU KOELN. KUNSTHISTORISCHES INSTITUT. ABTEILUNG ASIEN. PUBLIKATIONEN. see *ART*

950 BE ISSN 0076-1265
UNIVERSITE CATHOLIQUE DE LOUVAIN. INSTITUT ORIENTALISTE. PUBLICATIONS. Short title: P.I.O.L. Variant title: Publications de l'Institute Orientaliste de Louvain. (Supplement to: Le Museon) 1970. irreg., vol.54, 1991. price varies. Editions Peeters s.p.r.l., Bondgenotenlaan 153, B-3000 Louvain, Belgium. TEL 32-16-235170. FAX 32-16-228500. adv. **Indexed:** Rel.Ind.Two. **Document type:** monographic series.
Supersedes (1932-1968): Bibliotheque du Museon.
Description: Covers topics in Near Eastern Christian history and relevant historical sources.

954 II ISSN 0068-5380
UNIVERSITY OF CALCUTTA. CENTRE OF ADVANCED STUDY IN ANCIENT INDIAN HISTORY AND CULTURE. LECTURES. 1965. irreg. price varies. University of Calcutta, Centre of Advanced Study in Ancient Indian History and Culture, 51-2 Hazra Rd., Calcutta 19, W. Bengal, India.

954 II ISSN 0068-5399
UNIVERSITY OF CALCUTTA. CENTRE OF ADVANCED STUDY IN ANCIENT INDIAN HISTORY AND CULTURE. PROCEEDINGS OF SEMINARS. vol.2, 1966. irreg., vol.11, 1973. price varies. University of Calcutta, Centre of Advanced Study in Ancient Indian History and Culture, 51-2 Hazra Rd., Calcutta 19, W. Bengal, India. **Document type:** proceedings.

950 US ISSN 0068-600X
UNIVERSITY OF CALIFORNIA. CENTER FOR SOUTH AND SOUTHEAST ASIA STUDIES. OCCASIONAL PAPERS. 1969. irreg., no.11, 1973. University Press of America, 4720 Boston Way, Ste. A, Lanham, MD 20706. TEL 301-459-3366. **Document type:** monographic series.

950 US ISSN 0068-6018
UNIVERSITY OF CALIFORNIA. CENTER FOR SOUTH AND SOUTHEAST ASIA STUDIES. RESEARCH MONOGRAPH SERIES. 1970. irreg., latest no.28, 1985. University Press of America, 4720 Boston Way, Ste. A, Lanham, MD 20706. TEL 301-459-3366. bibl.; index. **Document type:** monographic series.

951 US
UNIVERSITY OF CALIFORNIA AT BERKELEY. CENTER FOR CHINESE STUDIES. SERIES. (Text in English) 1967. irreg., no.31, 1990. price varies. (Center for Chinese Studies) University of California Press, 2120 Berkeley Way, Berkeley, CA 94720. TEL 510-642-4247. FAX 510-643-7127. (Orders to: California-Princeton Fulfillment Services, 1445 Lower Ferry Rd., Ewing, NJ 08618. TEL 800-642-4247. FAX 800-999-1958) (back issues avail.) **Document type:** academic/scholarly publication, monographic series.
Description: Publishes papers on the history, culture, philosophy and politics of China.
Refereed Serial

956 US ISSN 0068-6514
UNIVERSITY OF CALIFORNIA PUBLICATIONS. NEAR EASTERN STUDIES. vol.18, 1982. irreg., latest 1990. price varies. University of California Press, 2120 Berkeley Way, Berkeley, CA 94720. TEL 510-642-4247. FAX 510-643-7127. (Orders to: California-Princeton Fulfillment Services, 1445 Lower Ferry Rd., Ewing, NJ 08618. TEL 800-777-4726. FAX 800-999-1958) Ed.Bd. (back issues avail.) **Document type:** monographic series.
Description: Publishes research in the study of the culture, life, literature, and history of the Near East.
Refereed Serial

950 100 US ISSN 0070-8070
UNIVERSITY OF KANSAS. CENTER FOR EAST ASIAN STUDIES. INTERNATIONAL STUDIES: EAST ASIAN SERIES. REFERENCE SERIES. 1967. irreg., no.12, 1975. price varies. University of Kansas, Center for East Asian Studies, 105 Lippincott Hall, Lawrence, KS 66045. TEL 913-864-3849. FAX 913-864-5034. **Document type:** academic/scholarly publication.

950 100 US ISSN 0070-8062
UNIVERSITY OF KANSAS. CENTER FOR EAST ASIAN STUDIES. INTERNATIONAL STUDIES: EAST ASIAN SERIES. RESEARCH SERIES. 1967. irreg., no.12, 1988. price varies. University of Kansas, Center for East Asian Studies, 105 Lippincott Hall, Lawrence, KS 66044. TEL 913-864-3849. FAX 913-864-5034. **Document type:** academic/scholarly publication.

950 II ISSN 0076-2229
UNIVERSITY OF MADRAS. HISTORICAL SERIES.* 1919. irreg. University of Madras, Chepauk, Triplicane, Madras 600005, Tamil Nadu, India. **Document type:** academic/scholarly publication.

950 SI ISSN 0217-913X
DS1
UNIVERSITY OF SINGAPORE. HISTORY SOCIETY. JOURNAL. 1963. a. S.$3. National University of Singapore, History Department, History Society, Kent Ridge, Singapore 0511, Singapore. TEL 772-3839. Ed. Boey Swee Siang. adv.; cum.index; circ. 500 (controlled). **Indexed:** Amer.Hist.& Life, Hist.Abstr.

950 PH ISSN 0079-9238
UNIVERSITY OF THE PHILIPPINES. ASIAN CENTER. MONOGRAPH SERIES. (Text in English) 1965. irreg. price varies. University of the Philippines, Asian Center, Diliman, Quezon City 1101, Philippines. TELEX 2231 UPDIL PU. circ. 500. **Document type:** monographic series.

HISTORY — HISTORY OF AUSTRALASIA AND OTHER AREAS

950 PK ISSN 0079-8029
UNIVERSITY OF THE PUNJAB. ARABIC AND PERSIAN SOCIETY. JOURNAL.* a. (Text in Arabic, English or Persian) a. University of the Punjab, Arabic and Persian Society, Lahore, Pakistan. **Document type:** academic/scholarly publication.

954 II
UTTARAKHANDA BHARATI. (Text in Hindi) 1973. q. Rs.10. Uttarakhanda Sevanidhi, 2 Badri Niwas, Nainitala, India. illus.
Description: Covers the culture and history of Northern India.

950 947 RU ISSN 0868-7196
VATAN. (Editions in Crimean-Tatar, Russian) 1990. m. Vatan, Ul. Sovetskaya 11-4, 334871 Primorskii, Krymskaya Obl., Russia. Ed. Refik Muzafarov. circ. 1,000.

959.7 VN ISSN 0085-7823
DS556
VIETNAMESE STUDIES. French edition: Etudes Vietnamiennes (ISSN 0531-206X) 1964. q. $24 (effective 1994). G I O I Publishers - Foreign Languages Publishing House, 46 Tran Hung Dao, Hanoi, Socialist Republic of Vietnam. TEL 84-4-253841. FAX 84-4-262996. Ed. Mai Ly Quang. illus. **Document type:** academic/scholarly publication.

VISHVA VICHARAMALA. see ORIENTAL STUDIES

954 II ISSN 0083-6613
VISHVESHVARANAND INDOLOGICAL PAPER SERIES. (Text in English, Hindi and Sanskrit) 1950. irreg., no.325, 1977. price varies. Vishveshvaranand Vedic Research Institute, P.O. Sadhu Ashram, Hoshiarpur 146021, Punjab, India. Ed. S. Bhaskaran Nair.

VISHVESHVARANAND INDOLOGICAL SERIES. see LINGUISTICS

VISHVESHVARANAND VEDIC RESEARCH INSTITUTE. RESEARCH AND GENERAL PUBLICATIONS. see ORIENTAL STUDIES

954 NP
VOICE OF HISTORY.* (Text in English or Nepali) 1975. a. Rs.10.50. (Tribhuvan University History Association) Tribhuvan University, Tribhuvan University, P.O. Box 3757, Kirtipur, Nepal. Ed. K.B. Thape. adv.; bk.rev.; bibl.

956.1 330 950 NE ISSN 0075-2118
VOORAZIATISCH-EGYPTISCH GENOOTSCHAP "EX ORIENTE LUX". JAARBERICHT; annuaire de la Societe Orientale Neerlandaise "Ex Oriente Lux". Short title: Jaarbericht "Ex Oriente Lux". 1933. biennial. fl.60($30) Vooraziatisch-Egyptisch Genootschap "Ex Oriente Lux" - Societe Orientale Neerlandaise "Ex Oriente Lux", Postbus 9515, 2300 RA Leiden, Netherlands. Ed. K.R. Veenhof. circ. 800. **Indexed:** Bibl.Ling.

935 330 950 NE
VOORAZIATISCH-EGYPTISCH GENOOTSCHAP "EX ORIENTE LUX". MEDEDELINGEN EN VERHANDELINGEN. (Text in Dutch, English, French and German) no.5, 1943. irreg. price varies. Vooraziatisch-Egyptisch Genootschap "Ex Oriente Lux", Postbus 9515, 2300 RA Leiden, Netherlands. Ed. K.R. Veenhof.
Formerly: Mededelingen "Ex Oriente Lux" (ISSN 0081-1211)

VOSTOK; Afro-Aziatskie obshchestva - istoria i sovremennost' see ORIENTAL STUDIES

WENWU TIANDI. see ARCHAEOLOGY

WIENER ZEITSCHRIFT FUER DIE KUNDE SUEDASIENS UND ARCHIV FUER INDISCHE PHILOSPHIE. see PHILOSOPHY

951 US ISSN 0084-053X
WISCONSIN CHINA SERIES. (Text in Chinese and English) 1966. irreg., latest no.3. $3. University of Wisconsin-Madison, Department of East Asian Languages and Literature, 1212 Van Hise Hall, Madison, WI 53706. TEL 608-262-2291. Ed. Tse-tsung Chow.

950 980 US
WORLD TODAY SERIES: EAST ASIA AND THE WESTERN PACIFIC. 1968. a. $8.50. Stryker-Post Publications, P.O. Drawer 1200, Harpers Ferry, WV 25425. TEL 800-995-1400. FAX 304-535-6513. Ed. Patrick M. Mayerchak. circ. 12,500. **Document type:** academic/scholarly publication.
Formerly: World Today Series: Far East and Southwest Pacific (ISSN 0084-229X)
Description: Contains valuable insights into economic developments of the past year, particularly in Japan.

950 US ISSN 0084-2311
DS44
WORLD TODAY SERIES: MIDDLE EAST AND SOUTH ASIA. 1967. a. $8.50. Stryker-Post Publications, P.O. Drawer 1200, Harpers Ferry, WV 25425. TEL 800-995-1400. FAX 304-535-6513. Ed. Malcolm B. Russell. circ. 12,500. **Document type:** academic/scholarly publication.
—Faxon.
Description: Covers Israeli-Arab relations and the latest developments in the Persian Gulf.

951 915.1 CC ISSN 1000-4076
DS793.N6
XIBEI SHI-DI/HISTORICAL AND GEOGRAPHICAL REVIEW OF NORTHWEST CHINA. (Text in Chinese; occasionally in Japanese and English) 1980-1989; resumed 1990. q. $32 (effective 1994). Lanzhou Daxue, Sichou zhi Lu Wenhua Kaifa Jingying Zhongxin - Lanzhou University, Cultural Development & Trading Centre of "Silk Road", Lanzhou, Gansu 730000, People's Republic of China. TEL 25500. FAX 485076. (Dist. outside China by: China International Book Trading Corporation, P.O. Box 399, Beijing, P.R.C.; Dist. in US by: China Books & Periodicals, Inc., 2929 24th St., San Francisco, CA 94110. TEL 415-282-2994) Eds. Yang Jianxin, Ma Manli. adv. contact: Sun Zhenyu. bk.rev.; charts; illus. circ. 2,200. (back issues avail.; reprint service avail.) **Document type:** academic/scholarly publication.
Description: Covers studies of Dunhuang documents, the Juyan Han Bamboo Strips, minorities, the Silk Road, and religions of the Northwest China.

951 301 CC
XIN WENHUA SHILIAO/HISTORICAL RECORDS OF THE NEW CULTURE. (Text in Chinese) bi-m. Wenhua-bu, Dangshi Ziliao Zhengji Weiyuanhui, 2, Shatan Beijie, Beijing 100722, People's Republic of China. TEL 4012255. Ed. Xu Hanru.

YAZHOU ZHOUKAN. see GENERAL INTEREST PERIODICALS — Hong Kong

951 CC ISSN 1001-0238
YINDU XUEKAN/YINDU JOURNAL. (Text in Chinese) 1980. q. $14. Anyang Shifan Gaodeng Zhuanke Xuexiao, Anyang, Henan 455000, People's Republic of China. TEL 422928. FAX 424520. (Dist. in U.S. by: China Books & Periodicals, Inc., 2929 24th St., San Francisco, CA 94110. TEL 415-282-2994) Ed. Bingyao Zhao. circ. 1,266. **Document type:** academic/scholarly publication.

950 GW ISSN 0514-857X
DS785.A1
ZENTRALASIATISCHE STUDIEN. 1967. a. DM.148. (Seminar fuer Sprach- und Kulturwissenschaft Zentralasiens) Harrassowitz Verlag, Taunusstr. 14, 65183 Wiesbaden, Germany. TEL 0611-530-0. FAX 0611-530570. TELEX 4186135. (Subscr. to: Postfach 2929, 65019 Wiesbaden, Germany) Eds. Walther Heissig, Michael Weiers. adv.; bk.rev. circ. 380. (back issues avail.) **Indexed:** Bibl.Ling. **Document type:** academic/scholarly publication.

ZHONG GONG DANGSHI YANJIU/JOURNAL OF CHINESE COMMUNIST PARTY HISTORY. see POLITICAL SCIENCE

951 300 CC ISSN 1000-422X
ZHONGGUO SHEHUI JINGJISHI YANJIU/JOURNAL OF CHINESE SOCIAL AND ECONOMIC HISTORY. (Text in Chinese; table of contents in English) 1982. q. Y6 (foreign $16.50). Xiamen Daxue, Lishi Yanjiusuo - Xiamen University, Research Institute of History, Xiamen, Fujian 361005, People's Republic of China. TEL 27377. (Dist. outside China by: China International Book Trading Corp., P.O. Box 399, Beijing, P.R.C.; Dist. in US by: China Books & Periodicals, Inc., 2929 24th St., San Francisco, CA 94110. TEL 415-282-2994) Ed. Yang Guozhen. bk.rev.; charts; stat.

ZHONGGUO WENWU BAO/CHINA'S CULTURAL RELICS NEWS. see ARCHAEOLOGY

951 CC ISSN 1001-2672
ZHONGGUO XIANDAI SHI/CHINESE CONTEMPORARY HISTORY. (Subseries of: Fuyin Baokan Ziliao) (Text in Chinese) m. Y58.80. Zhongguo Renmin Daxue, Shubao Ziliao Zhongxin - China People's University, Book & Newspaper Information Center, P.O. Box 1122, 3 Zhang Zizhong Lu, Beijing 100007, People's Republic of China. TEL 441792. **Indexed:** Amer.Hist.& Life (until 1992), Hist.Abstr. (until 1992).
Description: Contains reprints of papers and articles on modern Chinese history.

951 CC ISSN 1002-7963
ZHONGGUOSHI YANJIU/STUDY OF CHINESE HISTORY. (Text in Chinese; table of contents in English) 1979. q. Y9.20($26.40) Zhongguo Shehui Kexueyuan, Lishi Yanjiusuo - Chinese Academy of Social Sciences, Institute of History, 6 Ritan Lu, Beijing 100020, People's Republic of China. TEL 5063337. (Dist. outside China by: China International Book Trading Corp., P.O. Box 399, Beijing, P.R.C.; Dist. in US by: China Books & Periodicals, Inc., 2929 24th St., San Francisco, CA 94110. TEL 415-282-2994) Ed. Li Zude. circ. 5,500. **Document type:** academic/scholarly publication.
—UnCover.
Description: Publishes research on Chinese history.

ZHONGNAN MINZU XUEYUAN XUEBAO (SHEHUI KEXUE BAN)/SOUTH-CENTRAL COLLEGE FOR NATIONALITIES. JOURNAL (SOCIAL SCIENCE EDITION). see SOCIAL SCIENCES: COMPREHENSIVE WORKS

ZHONGYUAN WENWU/RELICS OF CENTRAL CHINA. see ARCHAEOLOGY

HISTORY — History Of Australasia And Other Areas

ABORIGINAL HISTORY. see ANTHROPOLOGY

990 929 AT ISSN 0813-6645
ALBURY & DISTRICT HISTORICAL SOCIETY. BULLETIN. 1961. 11/yr. Aus.$15. Albury & District Historical Society Inc., P.O. Box 822, Albury, N.S.W. 2640, Australia. TEL 060-25-3687. Ed. Janice Lynch. circ. 200. (looseleaf format) **Document type:** bulletin.

994 AT ISSN 0084-6732
ARMIDALE AND DISTRICT HISTORICAL SOCIETY. JOURNAL AND PROCEEDINGS. 1961. a. $17.506. Armidale and District Historical Society, c/o Secretary, P.O. Box 692, Armidale, N.S.W. 2350, Australia. Ed.Bd. bk.rev. circ. 400. **Indexed:** Amer.Hist.& Life, Hist.Abstr.

990 NZ ISSN 0111-7653
AUCKLAND-WAIKATO HISTORICAL JOURNAL. 1962. s-a. NZ.$12. Auckland Historical Society Inc., 14 Ayr St., Parnell, Auckland 1, New Zealand. TEL 377-8915. Ed. John P. Webster. adv.; bk.rev. circ. 1,200. (back issues avail.)
—CCC.

994 AT ISSN 0082-2116
HA3111
AUSTRALIA. BUREAU OF STATISTICS. TASMANIAN OFFICE. TASMANIAN YEAR BOOK. 1967. a. Aus.$31. Australian Bureau of Statistics, Tasmanian Office, G.P.O. Box 66A, Hobart, Tas. 7001, Australia. index. circ. 2,700. **Document type:** government publication.
Description: Provides information on history, environment, government, public finance, demography, agriculture, forestry, mining, fishery, manufaturing, energy, trade, transport, tourism, education and construction, etc.

994 330 AT ISSN 0083-8772
HA3153
AUSTRALIA. BUREAU OF STATISTICS. WESTERN AUSTRALIAN OFFICE. WESTERN AUSTRALIAN YEARBOOK. Variant title: Official Year Book of Western Australia. 1957. a. Aus.$26.50. Australian Bureau of Statistics, Western Australian Office, 30 Terrace Rd., E. Perth, W.A. 6004, Australia. circ. 312. **Document type:** government publication.
Description: Provides a general reference for Western Australia in terms of its geography, climate and geology, plant and animal life and the activities and social patterns of its people in relation to this environment.

HISTORY — HISTORY OF AUSTRALASIA AND OTHER AREAS

994 AT ISSN 0084-7259
AUSTRALIAN CATHOLIC HISTORICAL SOCIETY. JOURNAL. 1954. a. Aus.$10. Australian Catholic Historical Society, P.O. Box A621, Sydney South, N.S.W. 2000, Australia. Ed. T. Kearney. adv.; bk.rev. circ. 300. **Indexed:** Amer.Hist.& Life, Aus.P.A.I.S., Hist.Abstr.

990 200 AT
AUSTRALIAN CHURCHES OF CHRIST HISTORICAL SOCIETY. DIGEST. 1960. q. Aus.$3 (effective 1994). Australian Churches of Christ Historical Society, c/o Robert Clymer, Secy., P.O. Box 629, Mulgrave North, Vic. 3170, Australia. TEL 03 701-1887. Ed. G. Chapman. circ. 3,000.
Description: Offers information about the history of Churches of Christ in Australia.

990 AT ISSN 0728-8433
AUSTRALIAN CULTURAL HISTORY. 1982. a. Aus.$13. Deakin University, Faculty of Humanities, Geelong, Vic. 3217, Australia. FAX 02-313-7525. Ed. David Walker. circ. 1,000. (back issues avail.) **Indexed:** Amer.Hist.& Life, Aus.P.A.I.S., Hist.Abstr.
Description: Aims to stimulate critical, scholarly inquiry into the history of culture in Australia. Addresses the general reader as well as scholars, teachers and students.

994 378 AT ISSN 0312-6986
AUSTRALIAN HISTORICAL ASSOCIATION. BULLETIN. 1974. 3/yr. Aus.$30 to individuals; institutions $40; students $10. Australian Historical Association, c/o Dr. David Blaazer, Dept. of History, Faculty of Arts, Australian National University, G.P.O. Box 4, Canberra, A.C.T. 2601, Australia. TEL 06-2494083. FAX 06-2494789. adv.; bibl. circ. 500. **Document type:** bulletin.
Description: Contains articles of professional and academic interest by the AHA.

AUSTRALIAN JOURNAL OF POLITICS AND HISTORY. see *POLITICAL SCIENCE*

917.106 UK ISSN 0954-0954
AUSTRALIAN STUDIES. 1988. a. £15 (foreign £18). University of Stirling, Department of English Studies, Stirling FK9 4LA, Scotland. TEL 0786-467496. FAX 0786-451335. (Co-sponsor: British Australian Studies Association) Ed. Martin Gray. **Document type:** academic/scholarly publication.

AVIATION HISTORICAL SOCIETY OF NEW ZEALAND. JOURNAL. see *AERONAUTICS AND SPACE FLIGHT*

994 NE ISSN 0067-7876
BIBLIOTHECA AUSTRALIANA; eighty-nine volumes of personal accounts of adventurous exploration. (Text mainly in English) 1967. irreg., vol.76, 1976. price varies. Nico Israel Publishing Co., Keizersgracht 489, 1017 DM Amsterdam, Netherlands. TEL 020-6222255. FAX 020-6382666. abstr.; bibl.; charts; illus.; stat. circ. 500.
Description: Discusses the largest division of the hydrosphere lying between Asia and Australia and North and South America.

999 CL ISSN 0716-0763
G890.C45
BOLETIN ANTARTICO CHILENO. 1981. s-a. exchange basis. Instituto Antartico Chileno, Luis Thayer Ojeda 814, Casilla 16521, Correo 9, Santiago, Chile. FAX 2320440. TELEX 346261 IMACH CK. **Document type:** bulletin.
Supersedes (1965-1981): Instituto Antartico Chileno. Boletin (ISSN 0073-9863)

BRANDYWINE DOCUMENTS ON THE HISTORY OF BOOKS & PRINTING. see *PRINTING*

BRANDYWINE KEEPSAKE. see *PRINTING*

994 AT
BRIGHTON NEWSLETTER. 1963. 3/yr. Aus.$6. Brighton Historical Society, PO Box 50, North Brighton, Vic. 3186, Australia. Ed. Rosalind Landells. bk.rev.; bibl.; index. circ. 400. (looseleaf format) **Document type:** newsletter.
Formerly: Brighton Historical Society. Newsletter (ISSN 0007-0130)

994 AT ISSN 0310-1584
CABBAGES AND KINGS. 1973. a. membership only. University of South Australia, Department of History and Australian Studies, 15 Lorne Ave., Magill, S.A. 5072, Australia. Ed. Elizabeth Milburn. circ. 50. **Document type:** academic/scholarly publication.

994 AT ISSN 0313-5977
DU145
CANBERRA HISTORICAL JOURNAL. 1955. s-a. Aus.$12 plus postage. Canberra & District Historical Society Inc., P.O. Box 970, Civic Square, A.C.T. 2608, Australia. TEL 06-248-8401. FAX 06-249-6700. Ed. Patricia Clarke. adv.; bk.rev. circ. 650. **Indexed:** Aus.P.A.I.S. **Document type:** academic/scholarly publication.
Formerly: Canberra and District Historical Society. Journal (ISSN 0045-5601)

COLLECTION OF AUSTRALIAN STAMPS. see *PHILATELY*

990 990 AT
COMMUNITY HISTORY. 1979. 4/yr. Aus.$18. State History Centre, Old Parliament House, North Terrace, Adelaide, S.A. 5000. TEL 08-207-1077. FAX 08-207-1088. Ed. Brian Samuels. adv. circ. 800. (back issues avail.)
Supersedes (in 1991): Local Museum (ISSN 0157-6127)

DESPATCH. see *MILITARY*

994 AT ISSN 0080-4738
EARLY DAYS. 1926. a. Aus.$20. Royal Western Australian Historical Society, 49 Broadway, Nedlands, W.A. 6009, Australia. TEL 09-386-3841. FAX 09-386-3309. circ. 1,000. **Indexed:** Aus.P.A.I.S.
Formerly: Royal Western Australian Historical Society. Journal and Proceedings.
Description: Reprints of research papers on the history of Western Australia and related topics.

990 320 AT ISSN 0726-7215
FLINDERS JOURNAL OF HISTORY AND POLITICS. 1969. irreg. Aus.$8 (students Aus.$6). Flinders University of South Australia, History and Politics Society, School of Social Sciences, c/o D. Jarvis, Ed., Politics Dept., Bedford Park, S.A. 5042, Australia. FAX 08-276-8213. TELEX AA 89624. Ed.Bd. adv.; bk.rev. circ. 400. **Indexed:** Amer.Hist.& Life, Aus.P.A.I.S., Hist.Abstr.

959.9 JA
FORUM FOR THE SURVEY OF RECORDS CONCERNING THE JAPANESE OCCUPATION OF THE PHILIPPINES. NEWSLETTER. (Text in Japanese) irreg., no.5, 1991. Forum for the Survey of Records Concerning the Japanese Occupation of the Philippines, c/o Shinzo Hayase, History Program, College of Liberal Arts, Kagoshima University, Kagoshima City, Kagosh Prefecture 890, Japan.
Description: Reports on aspects of WWII era history of the Philippines and research conducted in archives and document repositories.

THE GREAT CIRCLE. see *HISTORY*

990 US
HAWAIIAN HISTORICAL SOCIETY. ANNUAL REPORT. 1893. a. membership only. Hawaiian Historical Society, 560 Kawaiahao St., Honolulu, HI 96813. TEL 808-537-6271. (reprint service avail. from KTO) **Indexed:** Amer.Hist.& Life, Hist.Abstr. **Document type:** corporate report.

990 US ISSN 0440-5145
DU1
HAWAIIAN JOURNAL OF HISTORY; devoted to the history of Hawaii, Polynesia and the Pacific area. 1967. a. $15. Hawaiian Historical Society, 560 Kawaiahao St., Honolulu, HI 96813. TEL 808-537-6271. illus.; circ. 2,000. (controlled). **Indexed:** Amer.Hist.& Life, Hist.Abstr., So.Pac.Per.Ind. **Document type:** academic/scholarly publication.

990 NZ ISSN 0439-2345
HISTORICAL NEWS. 1960. s-a. NZ.$6. University of Canterbury, History Department, Private Bag, Christchurch 1, New Zealand. TEL 03-366-7001. FAX 03-364-2003. adv.; bk.rev. circ. 525. (back issues avail.) **Document type:** academic/scholarly publication.
—CCC.
Description: News to keep school teachers informed about modern historical scholarship.

993 NZ ISSN 0018-2516
HISTORICAL REVIEW; Bay of Plenty journal of history. 1952. s-a. NZ.$27. Whakatane & District Historical Society, P.O. Box 203, Whakatane, New Zealand. bk.rev.; charts; maps. circ. 900. **Document type:** academic/scholarly publication.
—CCC

994 720 AT ISSN 0312-9640
HISTORICAL SOCIETY OF SOUTH AUSTRALIA. JOURNAL. 1973. a. Aus.$12. Historical Society of South Australia, Inc., 122 Kintore Ave., Adelaide, S.A. 5000, Australia. TEL 08-297-9844. Ed. John Playford. circ. 500. (back issues avail.) **Document type:** academic/scholarly publication.
Description: Historical facts of people and buildings involved in forming South Australia.

994 720 AT
HISTORICAL SOCIETY OF SOUTH AUSTRALIA NEWSLETTER. 1974. bi-m. Aus.$12. Historical Society of South Australia, Inc., Institute Bldg., 122 Kintore Ave., Adelaide, S.A. 5000, Australia. TEL 08-297-9844. Ed. I. Harmstorf. circ. 500. (back issues avail.) **Document type:** academic/scholarly publication.
Description: Presents historical facts of the people and buildings involved in shaping South Australia.

HOCKEN LECTURE. see *ANTHROPOLOGY*

990 GU
▼**I S L A: A JOURNAL OF MICRONESIAN STUDIES.** (Irreg. supplements avail.) 1992. s-a. $25 to individuals; institutions and libraries $25. (University of Guam, Graduate School and Research) University of Guam Press, UOG Station, Mangilao, Guam 96923. TEL 671-734-9401. FAX 617-734-3676. Ed. Robert A. Underwood. bk.rev.; maps. **Indexed:** Amer.Hist.& Life (1993-), Hist.Abstr. (1993-).
Description: Publishes original research, policy analyses, and analytical essays on the social sciences, history, business and economics, and education of Micronesia.
Refereed Serial

991.4 PH ISSN 0019-2538
ILOCOS REVIEW. (Text in English) 1969. a. P.100($10) S.V.D. Colleges and Schools of Northern Suzon, Divine Word College, Bangued, Abra 2800, Philippines. TEL 752-83-72. Ed. A.E. Alagao. bk.rev.; bibl.; charts; illus.; index. circ. 300. **Indexed:** Ind.Phil.Per.
Description: Dedicated to the preservaion and promotion of Ilocano and Northern Luzon culture, history, literature, language and local theology.

INDIAN OCEAN CENTRE FOR PEACE STUDIES. BRIEFING PAPERS. see *POLITICAL SCIENCE*

INDIAN OCEAN CENTRE FOR PEACE STUDIES. OCCASIONAL PAPERS AND MONOGRAPHS. see *POLITICAL SCIENCE*

INDIAN OCEAN REVIEW. see *POLITICAL SCIENCE*

994 720 AT
▼**INSIGHTS INTO SOUTH AUSTRALIAN HISTORY.** 1992. irreg., vol.2, 1994. Aus.$12. Historical Society of South Australia Inc., Institute Bldg., 122 Kintore Ave., Adelaide, S.A. 5000, Australia. TEL 08-297-9844. Ed. I.A. Harmstorf. **Document type:** monographic series.

994 AT ISSN 0021-0013
INVESTIGATOR. 1966. q. Aus.$8. Geelong Historical Society, 23 Cook St., Newtown, Geelong, Vic. 3220, Australia. Ed. Ian Wynd. bk.rev.; index. circ. 700.

917.106 AT ISSN 0314-769X
JOURNAL OF AUSTRALIAN STUDIES. 1977. s-a. Aus.$36.50 to institutions (foreign Aus.$39.50). La Trobe University Press, Bundoora, Vic. 3083, Australia. Ed. B. Bessant. bk.rev. circ. 1,000. **Indexed:** Aus.P.A.I.S.

900 AT ISSN 0022-3344
DU1
JOURNAL OF PACIFIC HISTORY. 1966. 3/yr. Aus.$30($35) Journal of Pacific History Inc., c/o Research School of Pacific Studies, Australian National Univ., Canberra, A.C.T. 0200, Australia. FAX 06-249-5525. Eds. Deryck Scarr, Alan Ward. adv.; bk.rev.; bibl.; circ. 800 (paid). (back issues avail.) **Indexed:** A.I.C.P., Abstr.Anthropol., Amer.Hist.& Life, Arts & Hum.Cit.Ind., Aus.P.A.I.S., Curr.Cont., E.I., Hist.Abstr., Hum.Ind., So.Pac.Per.Ind., SSCI. **Document type:** academic/scholarly publication.
—BLDSC (5027.750000); Faxon; UnCover; SWETS.

JOURNAL OF THE AUSTRALIAN WAR MEMORIAL. see *MILITARY*

HISTORY — HISTORY OF AUSTRALASIA AND OTHER AREAS

KONINKLIJK INSTITUUT VOOR DE TROPEN. KLEIN REPERTORIUM. see *HISTORY — Abstracting, Bibliographies, Statistics*

990   AT   ISSN 0155-4840
LEICHHARDT HISTORICAL JOURNAL; Annandale, Balmain, Glebe, Leichhardt, Lilyfield, Rozelle. 1971. a. Aus.$15. 9 The Avenue, Balmain E., N.S.W. 2041, Australia. TEL 02-810-8560. FAX 02-555-9277. Ed. P.L. Reynolds. bk.rev.; charts; illus.; stat.; index, cum.index: 1971-1993. circ. 300. **Document type:** academic/scholarly publication.

990   AT   ISSN 0811-1197
MAFFRA & DISTRICT HISTORICAL SOCIETY. BULLETIN. 1972. q. Aus.$8 (effective 1994). Maffra & District Historical Society Inc., P.O. Box 321, Maffra, Vic. 3860, Australia. TEL 051-472-680. Ed. Jeremy Hales. cum.index. circ. 275. (back issues avail.) **Document type:** bulletin.
    Description: Covers family histories, industrial and social changes, and notable events relevant to Central Gippsland, Victoria, especially Maffra and Avon Shires.

990   AT   ISSN 0814-5296
MANSFIELD HISTORICAL SOCIETY'S MAGAZINE. 1983. irreg. Aus.$5. Mansfield Historical Society, Inc., P.O. Box 309, Mansfield, Vic. 3722, Australia. Ed. Mark Klingsporn. adv.; bk.rev.; illus. circ. 400. (back issues avail.)

994   AT   ISSN 0076-6232
D1
MELBOURNE HISTORICAL JOURNAL. 1961-1986; resumed 1990. a. Aus.$16. Melbourne University Historical Society, Dept. of History, University of Melbourne, Parkville, Vic. 3052, Australia. TEL 61-3-344-4000. FAX 61-3-344-7894. Ed. Adina Hamilton. adv. contact: Elizabeth Freeman. bk.rev. circ. 500. **Indexed:** Amer.Hist.& Life, Hist.Abstr. **Document type:** academic/scholarly publication.
—BLDSC (5536.814500).

MUSEUM FUER VOELKERKUNDE, BERLIN. VEROEFFENTLICHUNGEN. NEUE FOLGE. ABTEILUNG: SUEDSEE. see *ANTHROPOLOGY*

MUSEUM OF VICTORIA. MEMOIRS - ANTHROPOLOGY AND HISTORY. see *ANTHROPOLOGY*

NATIONAL TRUST OF AUSTRALIA (NEW SOUTH WALES) NATIONAL TRUST QUARTERLY. see *CONSERVATION*

994   AT
NATIONAL TRUST OF AUSTRALIA (W.A.) ANNUAL REPORT. 1958. a. free to members. National Trust of Australia (W.A.), 4 Havelock St., West Perth, W.A. 6005, Australia. TEL 09-321-6088. FAX 09-324-1571. adv.; bk.rev. circ. 2,000. **Document type:** corporate report.

993   NZ   ISSN 0114-9172
DU400
NEW ZEALAND HISTORIC PLACES. 1983. bi-m. NZ.$40($60) New Zealand Historic Places Trust, P.O. Box 512, Christchurch, New Zealand. FAX 64-04-4990669. Ed. John Wilson. adv. contact: T. Reeves. bk.rev.; illus.; cum.index. circ. 19,000. (back issues avail.) **Indexed:** Anthropol.Lit. **Document type:** consumer publication.
—CCC.
    Formerly (until 1990): Historic Places in New Zealand (ISSN 0112-0743)

993   NZ   ISSN 0028-8322
DU420
NEW ZEALAND JOURNAL OF HISTORY. 1967. 2/yr. NZ.$35. University of Auckland, Department of History, Private Bag 92019, Auckland, New Zealand. FAX 64-9-3737438. Eds. J. Binney, K. Sorrenson. adv.; bk.rev.; illus.; cum.index. circ. 800. **Indexed:** Amer.Hist.& Life, Arts & Hum.Cit.Ind., Aus.P.A.I.S., Br.Hum.Ind., Curr.Cont., E.I., Hist.Abstr., Ind.N.Z.Per., So.Pac.Per.Ind.
—BLDSC (6094.530000); Faxon. **CCC.**

919.31   NZ   ISSN 0078-0170
DU400
NEW ZEALAND OFFICIAL YEAR-BOOK. 1892. a. NZ.$59.95 (effective 1992). Department of Statistics, P.O. Box 2922, Wellington, New Zealand. TEL 044-954-600. FAX 044-729-135. Ed. J. Evans. circ. 10,000.

994.42   AT   ISSN 0078-0243
DU180.N56   CODEN: NHMODR
NEWCASTLE HISTORY MONOGRAPHS. 1966. irreg., no.13, 1989. price varies. Newcastle Region Public Library, P.O. Box 489, Newcastle N.S.W. 2300, Australia. FAX 049-296568. Ed.Bd. circ. 1,000. (back issues avail.)

NOTES & FURPHIES. see *LITERATURE*

990   AT   ISSN 0311-1016
NURUNGI. 1971. bi-m. Aus.$2.00. Concord Historical Society, 3 Flavelle St., Concord, N.S.W. 2137, Australia. FAX 02-744-8528. Ed. Keith Elliot. circ. 100.

993   NZ   ISSN 0472-6480
OHINEMURI; regional history journal. 1964. a. NZ.$5. Paeroa and District Historical Society, c/o Mrs M. Townshend, Hon. Treas., 16 Taylor's Ave., Paeroa, New Zealand. Ed. Gary Staples. illus. circ. 450.

993   NZ   ISSN 0110-4896
ONSLOW HISTORIAN. 1971. q. price varies. Onslow Historical Society Inc., P.O. Box 29-005, Ngaio, Wellington 6004, New Zealand. TEL 64-4-479-6896. FAX 64-4-479-6540. Ed.Bd. charts; illus.; circ. 260 (paid). **Document type:** academic/scholarly publication.
—CCC.

995   PP
ORAL HISTORY. (Text in English) 1973. q. K.6. National Research Institute, P.O. Box 5854, Boroko, NCD, Papua New Guinea. TEL 675-26-0300. FAX 675-26-0312. Ed. Andrew Strathern. adv.; bk.rev.; charts; index. circ. 1,000. **Indexed:** Abstr.Anthropol., Anthropol.Lit.

990   AT   ISSN 0158-7366
ORAL HISTORY ASSOCIATION OF AUSTRALIA. JOURNAL. 1979. a. Aus.$35 (typically set in July). Oral History Association of Australia, Institute Bldg., 122 Kintore Ave., Adelaide, S.A. 5000, Australia. TEL 08-278-4045. bk.rev. circ. 700. (back issues avail.)
    Description: Contains articles and reports about work-in-progress and the methodology of oral history in Australia.

990   AT   ISSN 0078-7523
PACIFIC ISLANDS YEAR BOOK. 1930. irreg., 16th ed., 1989. Aus.$45. Pacific Publications (Australia) Pty. Ltd., G.P.O. Box 4245, Sydney, N.S.W. 2001, Australia. adv.
—BLDSC (6329.860000).
    Formerly: Pacific Islands Year Book and Who's Who.

PACIFIC SOCIETY. JOURNAL/TAIHEIYO GAKKAI SHI. see *ANTHROPOLOGY*

994   AT   ISSN 0085-4670
PAPERS ON THE HISTORY OF BOURKE. 1966. irreg., vol.12, 1992. price varies. Bourke Historical Society, P.O. Box 180, Bourke, N.S.W. 2840, Australia. TEL 068-722-429. Ed. W.J. Cameron. bk.rev.; cum.index: vols.1-4. circ. 200. **Document type:** academic/scholarly publication.

959.9   US
PHILIPPINE STUDIES NEWSLETTER. vol.20, 1992. 3/yr. $8 to individuals; institutions $10. Philippine Studies Group, University of Hawaii at Manoa, Center for Philippine Studies, 1890 East-West Rd., Moore Hall 415, Honolulu, HI 96822. (Subscr. to: C.C. Bodner, Rochester Museum & Science Center, 657 East Ave., Rochester, NY 14603-1480) (Affiliate: Southeast Asia Council, Association for Asian Studies) Ed. Alice W. Mak. abstr.; bibl. (back issues avail.) **Document type:** newsletter.
    Description: News of group activities, academic opportunities and projects, recent publications, and other items relating to the Philippines.

959.9   US
PHILIPPINE STUDIES OCCASIONAL PAPER. irreg., no.10, 1992. University of Hawaii at Manoa, Center for Philippine Studies, 1890 East-West Rd., Moore Hall 415, Honolulu, HI 96822. **Document type:** monographic series.

990   AT
THE PUSH: A JOURNAL OF EARLY AUSTRALIAN SOCIAL HISTORY. 1978. a. Aus.$10. University of New England, Department of History, Armidale, N.S.W. 2351, Australia. TEL 067-732067. Ed. A. Atkinson.
    Formerly: Push from the Bush (ISSN 0155-8633)

990   AT   ISSN 0157-5740
R.H.S.V. HISTORY NEWS. 1979. m. (10/yr.). Aus.$15. Royal Historical Society of Victoria, Inc., Royal Mint, 280 William St., Melbourne, Vic. 3000, Australia. TEL 03-6701219. FAX 03-670-1241. Ed. Leonie Foster. bk.rev. circ. 1,650. (back issues avail.) **Document type:** newsletter.
    Description: Covers events, seminars, books of local history societies in Victoria; includes proceedings of the society.

990   AT
ROYAL AUSTRALIAN HISTORICAL SOCIETY. HISTORY MAGAZINE. bi-m. Royal Australian Historical Society, 133 Macquarie St., Sydney, N.S.W. 2000, Australia. Ed. P. Parker. circ. 3,000. (back issues avail.)
    Formerly: Royal Australian Historical Society. Newsletter (ISSN 0813-815X)

994   AT   ISSN 0035-8762
DU80
ROYAL AUSTRALIAN HISTORICAL SOCIETY. JOURNAL. 1901. 2/yr. Aus.$75. Royal Australian Historical Society, History House, 133 Macquarie St., Sydney, N.S.W. 2000, Australia. Ed.Bd. adv.; bk.rev.; bibl.; charts; illus.; index. circ. 3,000. **Indexed:** Amer.Hist.& Life, Arts & Hum.Cit.Ind., Aus.P.A.I.S., Br.Hum.Ind., Curr.Cont., Hist.Abstr.
—Faxon; UnCover.

990 929   AT
ROYAL AUSTRALIAN HISTORICAL SOCIETY. TECHNICAL INFORMATION SERVICE. 1986. bi-m. Aus.$18 to members; non-members Aus.$25. Royal Australian Historical Society, History House, 133 Macquarie St., Sydney, N.S.W. 2000, Australia. TEL 02-278001. Ed. Mari Metzke. circ. 500. (back issues avail.)
    Description: Provides practical advice on local history research, geneaological research and museum management and education.

990 333.7   NZ   ISSN 0111-7343
RUSSELL REVIEW. 1977. a. NZ.$10($5) Russell Review Partnership, P.O. Box 103, Russell, New Zealand. TEL 09-4037-431. Ed. Eva B. Brown. adv.; bk.rev. circ. 750. (back issues avail.)
    Description: Local history of Russel and the Bay of Islands. Includes local news, events and current issues.

994   AT   ISSN 0048-8879
RYDE RECORDER. vol.22, 1988. bi-m. Aus.$12. Ryde District Historical Society, Inc., Willandra, 770 Victoria Rd., Ryde, N.S.W. 2112, Australia. TEL 02-809-1531. Ed. Mrs. J.M. Dawson. bk.rev. circ. 100. (processed) **Document type:** newsletter.

990   NL
SOCIETE D'ETUDES HISTORIQUES DE LA NOUVELLE-CALEDONIE. BULLETIN. 1969. q. $70. Societe d'Etudes Historiques de la Nouvelle-Caledonie, B.P. 63, Noumea, New Caledonia. Ed. Bernard Brou. adv.; bk.rev.; illus. circ. 850. **Indexed:** So.Pac.Per.Ind.

990   NZ   ISSN 0110-4926
STOCKADE. 1973. a. NZ.$8 free to members. Karori Historical Society, P.O. Box 17196, Wellington, New Zealand. TEL 04-476-4342. bk.rev. circ. 200. (back issues avail.)
    Description: Promotes the study of New Zealand history, with particular reference to that part of Wellington known as Karori.

STUDIES IN MELANESIAN ANTHROPOLOGY. see *ANTHROPOLOGY*

900   AT   ISSN 0039-9809
DU80
TASMANIAN HISTORICAL RESEARCH ASSOCIATION. PAPERS AND PROCEEDINGS. 1951. q. Aus.$25 (foreign Aus.$35). Tasmanian Historical Research Association, Inc., P.O. Box 441, Sandy Bay, Tas. 7005, Australia. Eds. N. Hugh Campbell, D.S. Dilger. bk.rev.; bibl.; charts; illus.; index. circ. 450. **Indexed:** Amer.Hist.& Life, Aus.P.A.I.S., Hist.Abstr. **Document type:** proceedings.
—Faxon.
    Description: Covers original research of Australian history, with emphasis on Tasmania.

HISTORY — HISTORY OF EUROPE

990   AT
TORRENS VALLEY HISTORICAL JOURNAL. 1977. s-a. Aus.$12. Torrens Valley & District Historical Society, P.O. Box 126, Gumeracha, S.A. 5233, Australia. Ed. Alan R. Phillips. adv.; bk.rev.; cum.index. circ. 70. (back issues avail.)

990 020   NZ   ISSN 0110-1625
TURNBULL LIBRARY RECORD. 1940. s-a. $20 to non-members. Alexander Turnbull Library Endowment Trust, Alexander Turnbull Library, P.O. Box 12-349, Wellington, New Zealand. FAX 4743-063. Ed. Margaret Calder. bibl. circ. 1,300. (also avail. in microfilm) **Indexed:** Ind.N.Z.Per. **Document type:** academic/scholarly publication. —UnCover. **CCC.**

990   GW   ISSN 0342-6610
UEBERSEE-MUSEUM, BREMEN. VEROEFFENTLICHUNGEN. REIHE G: BREMER SUEDPAZIFIK-ARCHIV. 1977. irreg., vol.3, 1988. price varies. Uebersee-Museum, Bremen, Bahnhofsplatz 13, 28195 Bremen, Germany. **Document type:** academic/scholarly publication.

994   NZ   ISSN 0067-0480
UNIVERSITY OF AUCKLAND HISTORICAL SOCIETY. ANNUAL. 1967. a. NZ.$3. University of Auckland, Department of History, Private Bag 92019, Auckland, New Zealand. FAX 64-9-3737438.

990   AT   ISSN 0310-4729
UNIVERSITY OF SYDNEY. ARCHIVES RECORD. 1973. 2/yr. free. University of Sydney, Archives, Sydney, N.S.W. 2006, Australia. Ed. Kenneth E. Smith. circ. 400.

VICTORIAN BAR NEWS. see LAW

994   AT   ISSN 0085-7858
WAGGA WAGGA AND DISTRICT HISTORICAL SOCIETY. JOURNAL. 1968. irreg. $8 per no. Wagga Wagga & District Historical Society, P.O. Box 90, Wagga Wagga, N.S.W. 2650, Australia. Ed. Alan Ives. adv.; bk.rev. circ. 1,000.

994   PP   ISSN 0085-7866
WAIGANI SEMINAR. PAPERS. 1969. irreg. price varies. University of Papua New Guinea, P.O. Box 320, University, Papua New Guinea. charts; illus.; index. circ. 1,000.

993   NZ   ISSN 0110-4004
WHAKATANE & DISTRICT HISTORICAL SOCIETY. MONOGRAPHS. 1977. irreg., latest 24. Whakatane & District Historical Society, P.O. Box 203, Whakatane, New Zealand. circ. 400. **Document type:** monographic series.

HISTORY — History Of Europe

see also Classical Studies

940   US   ISSN 0162-976X
A A B S NEWSLETTER. 1976. q. $25 to institutions (effective 1994). Association for the Advancement of Baltic Studies, 111 Knob Hill Rd., Hackettstown, NJ 07840. TEL 908-852-5258. FAX 908-852-3233. Ed. Inara Punga. (back issues avail.)

948 630   NE   ISSN 0511-0726
S12
A A G BIJDRAGEN. (Text in Dutch; summaries in English) 1958. irreg. exchange basis. Landbouwuniversiteit Wageningen, Vakgroep Agrarische Geschiedenis - Agricultural University, Wageningen, Department of Rural History, Hollandseweg 1, 6706 KN Wageningen, Netherlands. TEL 31-8370-84027. Ed. J. Bieleman. circ. 1,100 (controlled). **Indexed:** Amer.Hist.& Life, Hist.Abstr. **Document type:** academic/scholarly publication.
   Description: Contains articles on rural history.

A B R E E S. (Abstracts Russian and East European Series) see HISTORY — Abstracting, Bibliographies, Statistics

946   UK   ISSN 0955-4270
A C I S. 1987. s-a. £20. Association for Contemporary Iberian Studies, c/o Michael Newton, Newcastle Polytechnic, Lipman Bldg., Sandyford Rd., Newcastle NE12 8ST, England. TEL 0494-464535. FAX 0494-24392. Ed. Francisco Ariza.
—BLDSC (0578.561400).

942 820   US
A C I S NEWSLETTER. 3/yr. $14. American Conference for Irish Studies, Marquette University, English Dept., Milwaukee, WI 53233. TEL 414-288-3480. FAX 414-288-3300. Eds. Michael Patric Gillespie, Thomas Hachey. circ. 1,600. **Document type:** newsletter.
   Description: Information relating to the activities of the American Conference for Irish Studies.

943   GW   ISSN 0065-0137
AACHENER GESCHICHTSVEREIN. ZEITSCHRIFT. 1879. a. membership. Aachener Geschichtsverein e.V., Fischmarkt 3, 52062 Aachen, Germany. Ed. Herbert Lepper. bk.rev.; index. circ. 1,500. **Document type:** bulletin.

948   FI
AALANDSK ODLING. 1938. a. Aalands Folkminnesforbund, Aalands Museum, Ohbergsvagen 1, 22100 Mariehamn, Finland. cum.index: 1938-64.

940   BE
AAN DE SCHREVE; driemaandelijks heemkundig tijdschrift voor Poperinge en Omstreken. 1971. 4/yr. 400 Fr. Kring voor Heemkunde voor Poperinge en Omiggende Gemeenten, Korte Werf 3, 8970 Poperinge, Belgium. Ed. Willy Tillie. adv.

AARBOG FOR ARBEJDERBEVAEGELSENS HISTORIE. see BUSINESS AND ECONOMICS — Labor And Industrial Relations

948   DK   ISSN 0106-2220
AARBOG FOR SVENDBORG & OMEGNS MUSEUM. (Summaries in English and occasionally in German) 1979. a. DKK 100. Museumforeningen for Svendborg og Omegns Museum, Grubbemoellevej 13, 5700 Svendborg, Denmark. TEL 62-210261. Ed. Henrik M. Jansen. bk.rev.; illus. circ. 1,300.
   Description: Report on museum activities in the past year. Includes articles on prehistory, medieval archaeology, and maritime history.

948.1   NO   ISSN 0572-4562
AARBOK FOR HADELAND. 1968. a. NOK 125. Aarbok for Hadeland, 2770 Jaren, Norway. TEL 47-613-34012. bk.rev.; bibl.; illus. circ. 2,500.
—CCC.

948.1   NO   ISSN 0587-4076
AARBOK FOR TELEMARK. 1955. a. NOK 90. Telemark Maallag, 3841 Flatdal, Norway. TEL 47-350-52-253. FAX 47-35--52-253. Ed. Dag Aanderaa. adv.
—CCC.

948 709   DK
AARET FORTALT I BILLEDER. 1942. a. DKK 59.75. Carlsen Forlag A-S, Krogshoejvej 32, DK-2880 Bagsvaerd, Denmark. TEL 45-44-44-32-33. FAX 45-44-44-36-33. Ed. Peter Marslew.

AARHUS STIFTS AARBOEGER. see RELIGIONS AND THEOLOGY — Protestant

947   DK   ISSN 0105-4112
AARHUS UNIVERSITET. SLAVISK INSTITUT. ARBEJDSPAPIRER. 1976. irreg. price varies. Aarhus Universitet, Slavisk Institut, Ny Munkegade 116, DK-8000 Aarhus C, Denmark. TEL 45-89-42-35-00. FAX 45-86-19-21-55. circ. 100. **Document type:** academic/scholarly publication.
   Description: Presents papers on Slavic languages and the history and culture of Slavic speaking peoples.

940   FI   ISSN 0355-1644
AARNI. 1886. irreg. Kuopion Isaenmaallinen Seura, Kauppakatu 23, 70100 Kuopio 10, Finland. **Document type:** academic/scholarly publication.

948.9   DK   ISSN 0108-2787
AARSSKRIFT FOR SOTTRUP SOGN. 1982. a. membership. Lokalhistorisk Forening for Sottrup Sogn, c/o Ellen Moeller, Legbjergvej 9, V.Sottrup, 6400 Soenderborg, Denmark. illus. circ. 650.

942   UK
ABERTAY HISTORICAL SOCIETY. SERIES OF MONOGRAPHS; dealing with Dundee and Tayside history. 1953. a. price varies. Abertay Historical Society, Archive & Record Centre, c/o Publications Secretary, 21 City Sq., Dundee DD1 3BY, Scotland. FAX 44-382-203302. bk.rev. circ. 4,000. **Document type:** monographic series.

330 940   GW   ISSN 0065-0358
ABHANDLUNGEN ZUR HANDELS- UND SOZIALGESCHICHTE. 1958. irreg., vol.29, 1994. price varies. (Hansische Arbeitsgemeinschaft) Verlag Hermann Boehlaus Nachfolger, Meyerstr. 50a, 99403 Weimar, Germany. TEL 03643-202071. **Document type:** monographic series.

940   PO
ACADEMIA PORTUGUESA DA HISTORIA. ANAIS. 1940. a. price varies. Academia Portuguesa da Historia, Palacio da Rosa, Largo da Rosa 5, Lisbon 1100, Portugal. circ. 550. **Indexed:** Amer.Hist.& Life, Hist.Abstr.

940   FR
ACADEMIE D'HISTOIRE, PARIS. CAHIERS. 1970. q. Academie d'Histoire, Paris, 23, rue Louis-le-Grand, 75002 Paris, France. Ed. Jean Savant. bibl.

940   IT
ACADEMIE DE FRANCE A ROME. CORRESPONDANCE DES DIRECTEURS. NOUVELLE SERIE. (Text in French) 1979. a. price varies. Edizioni dell' Elefante, Piazza de Caprettari 70, 00186 Rome, Italy. Ed. Georges Brunel. circ. 1,000. **Document type:** academic/scholarly publication.

ACADEMIE ROYALE DE MARINE DE BELGIQUE. COMMUNICATIONS/KONINKLIJKE BELGISCHE MARINE ACADEMIE. MEDEDELINGEN. see TRANSPORTATION — Ships And Shipping

ACADEMIE ROYALE DES SCIENCES D'OUTRE-MER. BULLETIN DES SEANCES/KONINKLIJKE ACADEMIE VOOR OVERZEESE WETENSCHAPPEN. MEDEDELINGEN DER ZITTINGEN. see SCIENCES: COMPREHENSIVE WORKS

937.5   IT   ISSN 0065-0730
ACCADEMIA ETRUSCA DI CORTONA. ANNUARIO. 1934. a. price varies. Casa Editrice Leo S. Olschki, Casella Postale 66, 50100 Florence, Italy. TEL 055-6530684. FAX 055-6530214. circ. 500. **Document type:** academic/scholarly publication.

949.2   NE
DE ACHTTIENDE EEUW. DOCUMENTATIEBLAD WERKGROEP 18E EEUW. (Text in Dutch, English, French) 1968. 2/yr. fl.37.50 to individuals; institutions fl.53. Werkgroep 18e Eeuw, Institute for the History of Science, Nieuwe Gracht 187, 3512 LM Utrecht, Netherlands. TEL 31-30-538283. FAX 31-30-536313. E-mail: L.C.PALM@FYS.RUU.NL. Ed. L.C. Palm. adv.; bk.rev.; circ. 450 (paid). **Document type:** academic/scholarly publication.
—SWETS.
   Formerly (until vol.25, 1993): Documentatieblad Werkgroep 18e Eeuw (ISSN 0166-6304)
   Description: Publishes articles on the cultural history of the 18th century from an interdisciplinary perspective.

940   GW   ISSN 0722-740X
DAS ACHTZEHNTE JAHRHUNDERT. 1976. s-a. DM.46. (Gesellschaft fuer die Erforschung des Achtzehnten Jahrhunderts) Dr. Wolfram Hitzeroth Verlag, Franz-Tuczek-Weg 1, 35039 Marburg, Germany. TEL 06421-409261. FAX 06421-409199. circ. 1,100.
—SWETS.

943.6   AU   ISSN 1015-406X
DAS ACHTZEHNTE JAHRHUNDERT UND OESTERREICH. irreg., vol.6, 1991. varies. Verband der Wissenschaftlichen Gesellschaften Oesterreichs, Lindengasse 37, A-1070 Vienna, Austria. TEL 932166.

940   GW   ISSN 0567-7289
DK511.B25
ACTA BALTICA. 1961. a. DM.49.50. Institutum Balticum, Albertus-Magnus-Kolleg, Bischof-Kaller-Str. 3, 61462 Koenigstein, Germany. TEL 06174-299123. FAX 06174-299114. Ed. Ernst Benz. bk.rev.; index. circ. 600. **Indexed:** Amer.Hist.& Life, Hist.Abstr., M.L.A. **Document type:** academic/scholarly publication.

947 301   PL   ISSN 0065-1044
DK511.B25
ACTA BALTICO - SLAVICA. (Text mainly in Polish; summaries in English and German) a. price varies. Polska Akademia Nauk, Instytut Slowianoznawstwa, Palac Kultury i Nauki, P.O. Box 24, 00-901 Warsaw, Poland. (Dist. by: Ars Polona-Ruch, Krakowskie Przedmiescie 7, Warsaw, Poland) Ed. Jan Safarewicz. **Indexed:** A.I.C.P., Bibl.Ling., M.L.A., Numis.Lit. **Document type:** academic/scholarly publication.
   Description: Deals with the Slavonic-Baltic contacts in the field of linguistics, material culture and history.

940   NE   ISSN 0169-7293
ACTA COLLEGII HISTORIAE URBANAE. 1967. irreg., vol.4, 1992. price varies. E.J. Brill, P.O. Box 9000, 2300 PA Leiden, Netherlands. TEL 31-71-312624. FAX 31-71-317532. TELEX 39296 BRILL NL. (In N. America: E.J. Brill, 24 Hudson St., Kinderhook, NY 12106. TEL 800-962-4406. FAX 518-758-1959) **Document type:** monographic series, academic/scholarly publication.
   Description: Texts and chronologies illustrating the constitutional and administrative history of European towns through the middle of the thirteenth century.

940   XR   ISSN 0231-5955
ACTA COMENIANA. ARCHIV PRO BADANI O ZIVOTE A DILE JANA AMOSE KOMENSKEHO. (Text in English, French, German and Russian) 1910. irreg. (Czechoslovak Academy of Sciences) Academia, Publishing House of the Czechoslovak Academy of Sciences, Vodickova 40, 112 29 Prague 1, Czech Republic. (Dist. in Western countries by: Verlag Werner Dausien, Postfach 1355, D-6450 Hanau-Main, Germany) Ed. Marta Beckova. circ. 700. **Indexed:** Amer.Hist.& Life, Bibl.Ling., Hist.Abstr.
—BLDSC (0611.652000).
   Formerly: Archiv pro Badani o Zivote a Dile Jana Amose Komenskeho.

940 550   XR   ISSN 0231-6005
ACTA HISTORIAE RERUM NATURALIUM NEC NON TECHNICARUM. (Text in English, French, German and Russian) 1965. irreg. exchange basis only. Ceskoslovenska Akademie Ved, Ustav Teorie a Dejin Vedy, Jilska 1, 110 00 Prague 1, Czech Republic. Ed. Jan Janko. **Indexed:** Bull.Signal., Math.R.
   Description: Comprehensive coverage of history and technology.

ACTA HISTORICA ET ARCHAEOLOGICA MEDIAEVALIA. see ARCHAEOLOGY

949.7   CI
ACTA HISTORICA NOVA. (Text in Italian and Serbo-Croatian; occasionally in Slovene) 1981. irreg. $8. Centro di Ricerche Storiche, Piazza Matteotti 13, 52210 Rovigno-Rovinj, Croatia. TEL 052 811-133. index. circ. 2,000. (back issues avail.)

940   PL   ISSN 0137-3064
ACTA MEDIAEVALIA. (Text in Latin or Polish; summaries in French) 1973. irreg. price varies. Katolicki Uniwersytet Lubelski, Towarzystwo Naukowe, Ul. Gliniana 21, 20-616 Lublin, Poland.

394.8   IT
ACTA NUNTIATURAE POLONAE. (Text in original language; comments in Latin) irreg. L.70000($50) Institutum Historicum Polonicum Romae - Polish Historical Institute in Rome, Via Virginio Orsini 19, 00192 Rome, Italy. TEL 06-3211646. (Subscr. to: Herder Editrice e Libreria, Piazza Montecitorio 120, 00186 Rome, Italy; U.K. subscr. to: Orbis Ltd., Kenway Rd. 66, London SW5, England)

940   GW   ISSN 0065-146X
ACTA PACIS WESTPHALICAE. 1962. irreg. price varies. (Rheinisch-Westfaelische Akademie der Wissenschaften) Aschendorffsche Verlagsbuchhandlung, Soesterstr. 13, 48155 Muenster, Germany. TEL 0251-690-0. FAX 0251-690143. (Co-sponsor: Vereinigung zur Erforschung der Neueren Geschichte e.V.) Ed. Konrad Repgen. **Document type:** academic/scholarly publication.

943.8   PL   ISSN 0001-6829
DK401
ACTA POLONIAE HISTORICA. (Text in English, French, German) 1958. s-a. $58. Polska Akademia Nauk, Instytut Historii - Polish Academy of Sciences, Institute of History, Rynek Starego Miasta 29-31, 00-272 Warsaw, Poland. TEL 48-22-313642. (Dist. by: Ars Polona-Ruch, Krakowskie Przedmiescie 7, Warsaw, Poland; Or subscr. to: Scientific Publishers "SEMPER", ul. Bednarska 2-4, Warsaw, Poland) Ed. Maria Bogucka. bk.rev.; bibl.; charts. circ. 500. **Indexed:** Amer.Hist.& Life, Arts & Hum.Cit.Ind., Curr.Cont., Hist.Abstr., Hist.Abstr.
—BLDSC (0658.800000); SWETS.
   Description: Polish historical thought, Polish and European culture.

943.7   XR   ISSN 0323-0562
ACTA UNIVERSITATIS CAROLINAE. HISTORIA UNIVERSITATIS CAROLINAS PRAGENSIS. 1960. 2/yr. Universita Karlova, Ovocny Trh 5, Prague 1, Czech Republic. bk.rev. **Document type:** academic/scholarly publication.

943.8   HU   ISSN 0418-4556
DB903.5
ACTA UNIVERSITATIS DEBRECENIENSIS DE LUDOVICO KOSSUTH NOMINATAE. SERIES HISTORICA. (Text in Hungarian; summaries in English and Russian) 1962. irreg., vol.19, 1986. Kossuth Lajos Tudomanyegyetem, Magyar Toerteneti Tanszek, Egyetem Ter 1, 4010 Debrecen, Hungary. bibl. **Document type:** academic/scholarly publication.
—BLDSC (0585.050000).
   Formerly (until 1962): Debreceni Kossuth Lajos Tudomanyegyetem Tortenelmi Intezetenek Evkonyve (ISSN 0324-5101).

943.8   PL   ISSN 0137-5830
DK401
ACTA UNIVERSITATIS NICOLAI COPERNICI. HISTORIA. 1965. irreg. price varies. Uniwersytet Mikolaja Kopernika, Biblioteka Uniwersytecka, Ul. Gagarina 13, 87-100 Torun, Poland. TEL 233-52. TELEX 552382. (Dist. by: Osrodek Rozpowszechniania Wydanictw Naukowych PAN, Palac Kultury i Nauki, 00-901 Warsaw, Poland) **Document type:** academic/scholarly publication.
   Formerly: Uniwersytet Mikolaja Kopernika, Torun. Nauki Humanistyczno-Spoleczne. Historia (ISSN 0083-4491)

940 980   HU   ISSN 0324-6965
ACTA UNIVERSITATIS SZEGEDIENSIS DE ATTILA JOZSEF NOMINATAE. ACTA HISTORICA. (Text in Hungarian and Spanish) 1957. irreg. (2-3/yr). exchange basis. Attila Jozsef University, c/o E. Szabo, Exchange Librarian, Dugonics ter 13, P.O.B. 393, 6701 Szeged, Hungary. (Subscr. to: Kultura, Box 149, 1389 Budapest, Hungary) Ed.Bd. circ. 400. **Indexed:** Amer.Hist.& Life, Hist.Abstr. **Document type:** academic/scholarly publication.
   Incorporating: Studia Latino-Americana (ISSN 0231-2255)
   Description: Hungarian history from pre-conquest times to the present age. Spanish American history of colonial and modern times.

940.53 320   PL   ISSN 0137-1126
DK4404
ACTA UNIVERSITATIS WRATISLAVIENSIS. STUDIA NAD FASZYZMEM I ZBRODNIAMI HITLEROWSKIMI. (Text and summaries in English, French, German, Polish) 1974. irreg. (Uniwersytet Wroclawski, Wydzial Prawa) Wydawnictwo Uniwersytetu Wroclawskiego, Pl. Uniwersytecki 9-13, 50-137 Wroclaw, Poland. TEL 44-10-06. (Dist. by: Ksiegarnia Uniwersytetu Wroclawskiego, Pl. Uniwersytecki 9-13, 50-137 Wroclaw, Poland) Ed. Karol Jonca. circ. 400. (tabloid format) **Document type:** academic/scholarly publication.

948.5   SW   ISSN 0065-1702
ACTA VISBYENSIA; Visby-symposiet foer historiska vetenskaper. (Text in English and German) 1965. irreg., VIII, 1989. SEK 86($6) Gotlands Fornsal, Mellangatan 19, S-62156 Visby, Sweden. TEL 04-98-247010. FAX 04-98-248325. (Co-sponsor: Swedish Council for Research in the Humanities and Social Sciences) Ed. Sven-Olof Lindquist. circ. 1,500. **Document type:** academic/scholarly publication.

ACTA WEXIONENSIA. SERIE 1: HISTORY & GEOGRAPHY. see GEOGRAPHY

900   IT   ISSN 0391-9994
ACTUM LUCE; rivista di studi lucchesi. (Text in English and Italian) 1972. 2/yr. L.50000. Istituto Storico Lucchese, Cortile Carrara 12, Casella Postale 314, 55100 Lucca, Italy. Dir. Antonio Romiti.

AD FONTES. see LITERATURE

948.9 328.09   DK   ISSN 0065-3667
AELDRE DANSKE TINGBOEGER.* 1954. irreg. price varies. Landbohistorisk Selskab, P.B. 401, DK-5220 Odense SOe, Denmark.

380 332   FR   ISSN 0065-3799
AFFAIRES ET GENS D'AFFAIRES. 1952. irreg., no.36, 1973. price varies. Editions de l' Ecole des Hautes Etudes en Sciences Sociales, 131 bd. Saint Michel, 75005 Paris, France. TEL 43-54-47-15. FAX 43-54-80-73. (Dist. by: Centre Interinstitutionnel pour la Diffusion de Publications en Sciences Humaines, 131 bd. St-Michel, 75005 Paris, France.)

AFTER THE BATTLE. see MILITARY

940   US   ISSN 1045-4497
THE AGE OF REVOLUTION AND ROMANTICISM: INTERDISCIPLINARY STUDIES. irreg. Peter Lang Publishing, Inc., 62 W. 45th St., 4th Fl., New York, NY 10036. TEL 212-302-6740. FAX 212-302-7574. Ed. Gita May. **Document type:** academic/scholarly publication.
   Description: Promotes studies concerned with a crucial period in European cultural, political, and literary history: Enlightenment, Revolution and Romanticism.

AGRIKULTURA. see AGRICULTURE

AISLING; the new voice of Druidry. see RELIGIONS AND THEOLOGY — Other Denominations And Sects

AKADEMIA ATHENON. KENTRON EREVNES TIS HELLENIKIS LAOGRAPHIAS. EPETERIS. see FOLKLORE

949.5
AKADEMIA ATHENON. PRAGMATEIAI. (Text in English, French, German and Greek) 1935. irreg. Akademia Athenon, Odos Panepistemiou 28, Athens 143, Greece. cum.index: vols.1-20, 1969.

949.5
AKADEMIA ATHENON. PRAKTIKA. 1926. a. Akademia Athenon, Odos Panepistemiou 28, Athens 143, Greece. cum.index: vols.1-30 (1926-1955), vols.31-45 (1956-1969). **Indexed:** Math.R.

949   BN   ISSN 0350-0020
AKADEMIJA NAUKA I UMJETNOSTI BOSNE I HERCEGOVINE. CENTAR ZA BALKANOLOSKA ISPITIVANJA. GODISNJAK. vol.3, 1965. a. price varies. Akademija Nauka i Umjetnosti Bosne i Hercegovine, Centar za Balkanoloska Ispitivanja, Ul. 6 Novembra br.7, p.p.01-54, 7100 Sarajevo, Bosnia Hercegovina. Ed. Borivoj Covic. circ. 600. **Indexed:** M.L.A.

949 891 491   BN
AKADEMIJA NAUKA I UMJETNOSTI BOSNE I HERCEGOVINE. ODJELJENJE DRUSTVENIH NAUKA. DJELA. 1954. irreg. price varies. Akademija Nauka i Umjetnosti Bosne i Hercegovine, Odjeljenje Drustvenih Nauka, Ul. 6 Novembra br. 7, P.O. Box 01-54, 7100 Sarajevo, Bosnia Hercegovina. circ. 600.
   Formerly: Akademija Nauka i Umjetnosti Bosne i Hercegovine. Odjeljenje Istorijsko Filoloskih Nauka. Djela.

AKADEMISKA DZIVE/ACADEMIC LIFE. see ETHNIC INTERESTS

940   US   ISSN 0095-1390
DA20
ALBION; a quarterly journal concerned with British studies. 1969. q. $45 to individuals; institutions $70 (foreign $80). (North American Conference on British Studies) Appalachian State University, Department of History, Boone, NC 28608. TEL 704-262-6004. FAX 704-262-2592. Ed. Michael J. Moore. adv.; bk.rev.; index. circ. 1,500. (also avail. in microform from UMI,KTO) **Indexed:** Amer.Hist.& Life, Arts & Hum.Cit.Ind., Hist.Abstr. **Document type:** academic/scholarly publication.
—BLDSC (0786.603000); Faxon; UnCover; UMI.

HISTORY — HISTORY OF EUROPE

943   **GW**   ISSN 0516-5644
DD772.2
ALEMANNISCHES JAHRBUCH. 1951. irreg., latest 1993. Konkordia Verlag GmbH, Eisenbahnstr. 31, 77815 Buehl, Germany. TEL 07223-988964. FAX 07223-988945. Indexed: M.L.A. Document type: academic/scholarly publication.
—BLDSC (0786.830000).

949   **NE**
ALKMAARSE HISTORISCHE REEKS. 1977. a. fl.29.50. Walburg Pers BV, Postbus 4159, 7200 BD Zutphen, Netherlands. TEL 31-5750-10522. FAX 31-5750-41025. Ed. E.H. Cordfunke. illus. Document type: monographic series.

948 913   **DK**   ISSN 0108-9846
ALLE TIDERS ODSHERRED. 1968. a. price varies. Odsherreds Museum, Kirkestraede 12, DK-4500 Nykoebing Sjaelland, Denmark. TEL 53-41-33-25. Ed. Kirsten Strandgaard. adv. circ. 1,000. Document type: academic/scholarly publication.
Formerly (until 1984): Ting og Sager fra Odsherred.

940   **GW**
ALLENSBACHER ALMANACH. 1950. a. DM.3. Allensbacher Arbeitsgemeinschaft e.V., Kappelerbergstr. 29, 78476 Allensbach, Germany. Ed. Stefan Egenhofer. bk.rev.; illus.

948.9   **DK**   ISSN 0108-7142
ALLESOE, BROBY, NAESBY LOKALARKIV. 1982. a. DKK 40 membership. Naesby Skole, Skolevej 9, 5270 Odense N, Denmark. TEL 45-66-18-01-00.

340   **GW**   ISSN 0178-6199
ALLGAEUER GESCHICHTSFREUND. 1888. a. DM.20. Heimatverein Kempten (Allgaeu), Braut- und Bahrweg 14, 87435 Kempten, Germany. Ed. Wolfgang Haberl. bk.rev.; illus.; index. circ. 1,200.

943   **GW**
ALSTERVEREIN JAHRBUCH. 1901. a. membership. Alsterverein Vereinigung fuer Heimatkunde und Heimatpflege, Basaltweg 72, 22395 Hamburg, Germany. TEL 040-6020948. Ed. Ernst Reusch. adv.; bk.rev. circ. 700. Document type: academic/scholarly publication.

943   **GW**   ISSN 0174-8726
ALT-OFFENBACH. 1979. irreg. DM.6. Offenbacher Geschichtsverein, Herrnstr. 61, 63065 Offenbach a.M., Germany. Ed. Alfred Kurt. circ. 600.

949.5 913   **GR**
AMALTHEIA. 1970. 4/yr. Historike Laographike Hetaireia Nomou Lasithiou, Odos N. Plastera 14, Hagios Nikolaos, Crete, Greece. bk.rev.; cum.index.

AMERICAN FRIENDS OF LAFAYETTE. GAZETTE. see
HISTORY — History Of North And South America

AMERICAN HISTORICAL SOCIETY OF GERMANS FROM RUSSIA. JOURNAL. see ETHNIC INTERESTS

AMERICAN PORTUGUESE SOCIETY. JOURNAL. see TRAVEL AND TOURISM

943.9 020   **US**   ISSN 1054-4607
▼**AMERIKAI MAGYAR LEVELESTAR/HUNGARIAN ARCHIVES OF AMERICA.** (Text in Hungarian) 1992. irreg. Eurolingua, Box 101, Bloomington, IN 47402-0101. TEL 812-332-8918.

AMIS DU CHATEAU DE PAU. BULLETIN. see ART

943   **GW**   ISSN 0003-1992
AMPERLAND; heimatkundliche Vierteljahresschrift fuer die Kreise Dachau, Freising und Fuerstenfeldbruck. 1965. q. DM.30. Grosse Kreisstadt Dachau, Konrad-Adenauer-Str. 4, 85221 Dachau, Germany. TEL 08131-84568. Ed. Dr. Gerhard Hanke. adv.; bk.rev.; illus.; index, cum.index every 2 yrs. circ. 1,400. (back issues avail.) Document type: newsletter.
Description: Contains articles on local history and culture. Includes readers' comments.

AMSTERDAMER BEITRAEGE ZUR AELTEREN GERMANISTIK. see LITERATURE

AMSTERDAMER BEITRAEGE ZUR NEUEREN GERMANISTIK. see LITERATURE

949.5   **GR**
ANAGNOSTIKA HETAIREIA KERKYRAS. DELTION. 1964. a. Dr.500. Anagnostika Hetaireia Kerkyras, Corfu, Greece. bibl. circ. 600.
Formerly: Deltion Pneumatikes kai Kallitechnikes Drasteriotetos.

ANALECTA CARTUSIANA; review for Carthusian history and spirituality. see RELIGIONS AND THEOLOGY

940   **BE**   ISSN 0517-6735
ANALECTA PRAEMONSTRATENSIA. (Text in Dutch, English, French, German, Latin) 1925. 2/yr. 1500 BEF. Praemonstratensia V.z.w., Abdij van Averbode, Abdijstraat 1, B-3271 Averbode, Belgium. bk.rev.; cum.index: 1925-1967. Indexed: CERDIC. Document type: academic/scholarly publication.
—SWETS.

930   **IT**   ISSN 0066-1392
ANALECTA ROMANA INSTITUTI DANICI. (Text in English, French, German, Italian) 1960. irreg., no.20, 1990. price varies. (Accademia di Danimarca, Roma) L'Erma di Bretschneider, Via Cassiodoro 19, 00193 Rome, Italy. TEL 06-687-41-27. FAX 06-687-41-29. (back issues avail.) Indexed: Avery Ind.Archit.Per., RILA.

930   **IT**   ISSN 0066-1406
ANALECTA ROMANA INSTITUTI DANICI. SUPPLEMENTUM. (Text in English, French, German, Italian) 1960. irreg., no.19, 1990. price varies. (Accademia di Danimarca, Roma) L'Erma di Bretschneider, Via Cassiodoro 19, 00193 Rome, Italy. TEL 06-687-41-27. FAX 06-687-41-29. (back issues avail.) Indexed: Avery Ind.Archit.Per.

ANCIENT HISTORY; RESOURCES FOR TEACHERS. see HISTORY

948   **IC**
ANDVARI; nyr flokkur. 1874. a. Bokautgafa Menningarsjods og Thjodvinafelagsins, Skalholtsstigur 7, Reykjavik, Iceland. TEL 354-91-62-18-22. cum.index: 1874-1975.

940   **UK**   ISSN 0144-5863
ANGLO-CATALAN SOCIETY. OCCASIONAL PUBLICATIONS. 1980. irreg. £4.50 to members; non-members £6.50. Anglo-Catalan Society, c/o Dr. Alan Yates, Ed., Department of Hispanic Studies, University of Sheffield, Sheffield S10 2TN, England. FAX 44-742-768496. TELEX 547216-UGSHEF-G. circ. 800. Document type: academic/scholarly publication.

940   **US**   ISSN 0261-9857
DA195
ANGLO-NORMAN STUDIES. 1980. a. price varies. Boydell & Brewer, Inc., Box 41026, Rochester, NY 14604. TEL 716-275-0419. FAX 716-271-8778. Document type: proceedings.
Formerly: Battle Conference on Anglo-Norman Studies III.

942   **UK**   ISSN 0263-6751
DA152.2
ANGLO-SAXON ENGLAND. 1972. a. £46($65) to individuals (overseas £73.50); institutions £61 (overseas £69.50 ($99)). International Society for Anglo-Saxonists, Edinburgh Bldg., Shaftesbury Rd., Cambridge CB2 2RU, England. TEL 0223-312393. FAX 0223-315052. TELEX 851817256. (N. American addr.: Cambridge University Press, 40 W. 20th St., New York, NY 10011. TEL 212-924-3900. FAX 212-691-3239) Ed.Bd. adv (also avail. in microform from UMI; back issues avail.) Indexed: Arts & Hum.Cit.Ind., Bibl.Ling., Br.Archaeol.Abstr., M.L.A., Rel.Ind.Two, RILA. Document type: academic/scholarly publication.
—BLDSC (0902.878000); Faxon; UMI. **CCC.**
Description: Contains articles on Anglo-Saxon history and culture: linguistic, textual, paleographic, religious, intellectual, historical, archaeological and artistic.

944   **FR**   ISSN 0003-3901
ANNALES DE BOURGOGNE; revue historique trimestrielle. 1929. q. 140 F. (foreign 200 F.). Societe des Annales de Bourgogne, 36 rue Chabot Charny, 21000 Dijon, France. (Co-sponsors: Centre d'Etudes Historiques de l'Universte de Dijon; Centre Nationale de la Recherche Scientifique) Ed. Jean Richard. adv.; bk.rev.; bibl.; index, cum.index. circ. 700. Indexed: Amer.Hist.& Life, Bull.Signal., Hist.Abstr. Document type: bibliography, bulletin.
—SWETS.

944 301   **FR**   ISSN 0365-2017
DC603.1
ANNALES DE L'EST. (Includes yearly bibliography on Lorraine history) 1887. q. 260 F. (foreign 320 F.). Presses Universitaires de Nancy, 25 rue Baron Louis, 54001 Nancy Cedex, France. TEL 83-37-37-65. Ed. Jean M. Bonnet. adv.; bk.rev.; bibl. circ. 800. (back issues avail.) Indexed: Amer.Hist.& Life, Hist.Abstr.
—BLDSC (0972.500000); SWETS.
Description: Devoted to the history of eastern France.

944   **FR**   ISSN 0003-4134
DC611.N841
ANNALES DE NORMANDIE; revue d'etudes regionales. 1951. 5/yr. 180 F. to individuals; institutions 200 F.; students 110 F. Comite des Annales de Normandie, Logis des Gouverneurs, Chateau, 14000 Caen, France. TEL 31-86-06-24. FAX 31-85-27-94. Ed. Jean-Jacques Bertaux. bk.rev.; charts; illus. circ. 1,000. Indexed: Amer.Hist.& Life, Br.Archaeol.Abstr., Hist.Abstr., Numis.Lit. Document type: academic/scholarly publication.
—BLDSC (0989.800000); Faxon; SWETS.

944.4   **FR**   ISSN 0003-4436
DC139
ANNALES HISTORIQUES DE LA REVOLUTION FRANCAISE. 1908. q. 280 F. Societe des Etudes Robespierristes, Universite de Paris I, 17 rue de la Sorbonne, 75231 Paris Cedex 05, France. Ed. M. Bertand. adv.; bk.rev.; charts; index, cum.index every 20 yrs. circ. 1,200. (reprint service avail. from SCH) Indexed: Amer.Hist.& Life, Arts & Hum.Cit.Ind., Curr.Cont., Hist.Abstr. Document type: academic/scholarly publication.
—BLDSC (0979.850000); Faxon; UnCover; SWETS.

943.8   **PL**   ISSN 0066-2224
DD491.S4
ANNALES SILESIAE. (Text in English, French, German and Polish) 1960. a. price varies. (Wroclawskie Towarzystwo Naukowe) Ossolineum, Publishing House of the Polish Academy of Sciences, Rynek 9, 50-106 Wroclaw, Poland. FAX 48-71-448-103. TELEX 0712771 OSS PL. Ed. J. Kolbuszewski. Document type: academic/scholarly publication.
Description: Devoted to the development of sciences and culture of Wroclaw and Lower Silesia region in the past and in the present days.

940   **UK**
ANNALS OF THE LOTHIAN FOUNDATION. 1991. a. £10 to individuals; institutions £15. Lothian Foundation, 1 Whitehall Pl., London SW1A 2DA, England. Document type: bulletin.

940 914.4   **DK**
ANNUAIRE SOUVENIR NORMAND. (Text in English and French; summaries in Danish) 1979. biennial. DKK 50. Dansk-normannisk Selskab, Kultorvet 2, Postbox 85, DK-1003 Copenhagen K, Denmark. TEL 45-33-13-94-18. Ed. Folmer Wisti. adv.; bk.rev.; illus. circ. 1,000.
Formerly: Souvenir Normand (ISSN 0106-5017)

ANTIQUITE TARDIVE; revue internationale d'histoire et d'archeologie. see ARCHAEOLOGY

946   **SP**   ISSN 0066-5061
ANUARIO DE ESTUDIOS MEDIEVALES. (Text in Romance languages; summaries in English and French) 1964. a. 7500 ptas. (foreign 11000 ptas.). Consejo Superior de Investigaciones Cientificas (C.S.I.C.), Institucion "Mila I. Fontanals", Calle Vitruvio, 8, 28006 Madrid, Spain. TEL 93-4423489. FAX 93-4427424. Ed. Maria Teresa Ferrer. adv.; bk.rev.; index. circ. 1,000. Indexed: Amer.Hist.& Life, Hist.Abstr. Document type: academic/scholarly publication.
Description: Studies history, politics, sociology, economics, religion, art, institutions and thought of the middle ages, with an emphasis on Spain.

ANUARIO DE HISTORIA DEL DERECHO ESPANOL. see LAW

943 709   GW   ISSN 0934-5191
ANZEIGER DES GERMANISCHEN NATIONALMUSEUMS UND BERICHTE AUS DEM FORSCHUNGSINSTITUT FUER REALIENKUNDE. 1832. a. DM.65. Germanisches Nationalmuseum, Nuernberg, Postfach 119580, 90105 Nuernberg, Germany. TEL 0911-1331-0. FAX 0911-1331-200. circ. 600. (back issues avail.) **Indexed:** Artbibl.Mod., RILA. **Document type:** academic/scholarly publication.
—BLDSC (1566.930000).
Formerly (until 1987): Anzeiger des Germanischen Nationalmuseums (ISSN 0341-8383)

949 398   BE   ISSN 0776-202X
APPELTJES VAN HET MEETJESLAND. (Text in Dutch) 1950. a. 600 BEF (Europe 700 BEF; elsewhere 750 BEF). Heemkundig Genootschap van het Meetjesland, Gentstraat 13, B-9971 Kaprijke (Lembeke), Belgium. TEL 091-772-854. bk.rev. circ. 550.

949   RM   ISSN 1013-428X
APULUM. At head of title: Acta Musei Apulensis. (Text in English, French, German, Italian, Rumanian; summaries in English, French, German, Italian) 1939. a. Muzeul de Istorie si Arheologie Alba Julia, Str. Mihai Vieazul nr. 12-14, Alba Julia, Rumania. illus. **Indexed:** Anthropol.Lit., Numis.Lit.
Former titles (until 1962): Studii si Comunicari, Arheologie, Istorie, Etnografie (ISSN 1013-4271); (until 1958): Apulum (ISSN 1013-4263)

943 296   GW   ISSN 0341-8340
DS135.G3
ARBEITSINFORMATIONEN UEBER STUDIENPROJEKTE AUF DEM GEBIET DER GESCHICHTE DES DEUTSCHEN JUDENTUMS UND DES ANTISEMITISMUS. 1963. every three yrs. DM.10. Germania Judaica, Koelner Bibliothek zur Geschichte des Deutschen Judentums, Josef-Haubrich-Hof 1, 50676 Cologne, Germany. TEL 0221-232349. Ed. Annette Haller. circ. 1,500. **Document type:** academic/scholarly publication. **Description:** International survey of current research on German-Jewish history.

ARBETARHISTORIA. see *LABOR UNIONS*

942 914.2   UK   ISSN 0261-3417
ARCHAEOLOGIA AELIANA. a. £15.65. Society of Antiquaries of Newcastle upon Tyne, The Black Gate, Castle Garth, Newcastle upon Tyne NE1 1RQ, England. circ. 700. **Document type:** academic/scholarly publication.
—BLDSC (1594.570000).
Description: Articles on history and archaeology of northeastern England.

943   GW   ISSN 0341-1222
ARCHAEOLOGISCHE AUSGRABUNGEN; in Baden-Wuerttemberg. 1974. a. (Gesellschaft fuer Vor- und Fruehgeschichte in Wuerttemberg und Hohenzollern) Konrad Theiss Verlag GmbH und Co., Villastr. 11, 70190 Stuttgart, Germany. TEL 0711-26861-01. FAX 0711-26861-27. Ed. D. Planck. **Indexed:** Anthropol.Lit., Br.Archaeol.Abstr. **Document type:** academic/scholarly publication.

940   PL   ISSN 0066-6041
CD1740
ARCHEION. (Text in Polish; summaries in English, French and Russian) 1927. irreg., vol.90, 1992. price varies. (Naczelna Dyrekcja Archiwow Panstwowych) Wydawnictwo Naukowe P W N, Ul. Miodowa 10, 00-251 Warsaw, Poland. Ed. Boleslaw Woszczynski. cum.index: vols.1-50 in 1969. circ. 820. (also avail. in microfiche from IDC) **Indexed:** Amer.Hist.& Life, Hist.Abstr. **Document type:** academic/scholarly publication.

949.5   GR
ARCHEION EKKLESIASTIKOU KAI KANONIKOU DIKAIOU. 1946. 3/yr. I.M. Petritakes, Odos Ionos 5, Athens 101, Greece. bk.rev.; cum.index: 1946-1955. **Indexed:** CERDIC.

949.5 913   GR   ISSN 1010-3724
ARCHEION EUVOIKON MELETON. 1936. irreg. Dr.3500. Hetaireia Euvoikon Spoudon, Odos Harilaou Trikoupi 60, 106 80 Athens, Greece. TEL 3629504. bk.rev.; bibl.; cum.index: vols.1-27 in 1988. circ. 2,000. **Indexed:** Amer.Hist.& Life, Hist.Abstr., M.L.A. **Document type:** bulletin.

949.5 913   GR
ARCHEION THESSALIKON MELETON. 1972. irreg. Hetaireia Thessalikon Ereunon, Odos Lasonos 73, 38221 Volos, Greece. bibl.

ARCHEOLOGICKE VYSKUMY A NALEZY NA SLOVENSKU. see *ARCHAEOLOGY*

944   FR   ISSN 0181-0197
ARCHISTRA: ARCHIVES - HISTOIRE - TRADITIONS; journal d'informations sur l'histoire de la France meridionale. (In 2 editions: France Meridionale; Toulouse et pays Tolosan) 1972. bi-m. 200 F. c/o Ed. Pierre Salies, 42 rue Capus, 31400 Toulouse, France. TEL 61-52-75-80. bk.rev.; illus. **Indexed:** Amer.Hist.& Life, Hist.Abstr.

943   GW   ISSN 0587-5277
HN19
ARCHIV DER DEUTSCHEN JUGENDBEWEGUNG. JAHRBUCH. 1969. a. Archiv der Deutschen Jugendbewegung, Burg Ludwigstein, 37214 Witzenhausen, Germany. Ed. Winfried Mogge. bk.rev.; illus. circ. 2,000.

940   GW   ISSN 0066-6297
ARCHIV FUER DIPLOMATIK, SCHRIFTGESCHICHTE, SIEGEL- UND WAPPENKUNDE. 1955. a. price varies. Boehlau Verlag GmbH, Theodor-Heuss-Str. 76, 51149 Cologne, Germany. TEL 02203-307021. FAX 02203-307349. Ed. W. Heinemeyer. **Document type:** academic/scholarly publication.

943   GW   ISSN 0341-8324
ARCHIV FUER FRANKFURTS GESCHICHTE UND KUNST. 1837. irreg. (Frankurter Verein fuer Geschichte und Landeskunde) Buechhaendler Vereinigung, Gr. Hirschgraben 17-21, 60311 Frankfurt, Germany. Ed. W. Kloetzer.

943   GW   ISSN 0066-6335
ARCHIV FUER GESCHICHTE VON OBERFRANKEN. 1827. a. price varies. Historischer Verein fuer Oberfranken, Ludwigstr. 21, Neues Schloss, 95444 Bayreuth, Germany. bk.rev. circ. 800.

943   GW   ISSN 0066-636X
ARCHIV FUER HESSISCHE GESCHICHTE UND ALTERTUMSKUNDE. 1835. a. DM.50 for members. Historischer Verein fuer Hessen, Staatsarchiv, Schloss, 64283 Darmstadt, Germany. bk.rev. circ. 900. **Document type:** academic/scholarly publication. **Description:** Focuses on the regional history of Hessen (medieval, modern and contemporary).

940   GW   ISSN 0066-6505
HN1
ARCHIV FUER SOZIALGESCHICHTE. 1960. a. DM.188. (Friedrich-Ebert Stiftung) Verlag J.H.W. Dietz Nachf. GmbH, In der Raste 2, 53129 Bonn, Germany. TEL 0228-238083. FAX 0228-234104. (Co-sponsor: Institut fuer Sozialgeschichte) bk.rev. circ. 1,500. **Indexed:** Amer.Hist.& Life, Hist.Abstr. **Document type:** academic/scholarly publication.

900   AU   ISSN 0003-9462
ARCHIV FUER VATERLAENDISCHE GESCHICHTE UND TOPOGRAPHIE. 1849. irreg. price varies. Geschichtsverein fuer Kaernten, Museumgasse 2, A-9020 Klagenfurt, Austria. TEL 0463-536-30573. Ed. Alfred Ogris. bk.rev. **Document type:** monographic series.

900 020   UK   ISSN 0003-9535
CD1
ARCHIVES; journal of the British Records Association. 1949. s-a. £18 to individuals (foreign $30); institutions £38 (foreign $60). British Records Association, 18 Padbury Court, London E2 7EH, England. TEL 071-729-1415. adv.; bk.rev.; bibl.; illus.; cum.index every 2 yrs. circ. 1,300. (back issues avail.) **Indexed:** Amer.Hist.& Life, Arts & Hum.Cit.Ind., Br.Archaeol.Abstr., Br.Hum.Ind., Curr.Cont., Hist.Abstr., Lib.Lit., Lib.Sci.Abstr., LISA, Mid.East: Abstr.& Ind. **Document type:** academic/scholarly publication.
—BLDSC (1625.687500); Faxon; UnCover; SWETS.

020 949   BE   ISSN 0003-9748
CD1670
ARCHIVES ET BIBLIOTHEQUES DE BELGIQUE/ARCHIEF- EN BIBLIOTHEEKWEZEN IN BELGIE. (Includes irregular special issues) (Text in Dutch, English, French, German, Italian, Latin, Spanish) 1923. irreg. (2-4/yr.). 1050 BEF($35) (Association des Archivistes et Bibliothecaires - Vereniging van Archivarissen en Bibliothecarissen) Archives et Bibliotheques de Belgique a.s.b.l., Rue de Ruysbroeck, 2-6, B-1000 Brussels, Belgium. FAX 32-2-5137681. Ed.Bd. adv.; bk.rev.; bibl.; charts; illus.; index, cum.index: vols.1-25. **Indexed:** Amer.Hist.& Life, Hist.Abstr., Lib.Lit., Lib.Sci.Abstr. **Document type:** academic/scholarly publication, monographic series.
Former titles (until 1963): Archives, Bibliotheques et Musees de Belgique; (until 1928): Archives et Bibliotheques de Belgique.

945   IT   ISSN 0390-1297
ARCHIVIO SARDO DEL MOVIMENTO OPERAIO CONTADINO E ANTONOMISTICO.* 1973. q. L.7000. Universita degli Studi di Cagliari, Facolta di Magistero, Istituto di Studi Storici, 09100 Cagliari, Italy. Ed. Girolamo Sotgiu. bibl.; charts; illus.

945   IT
ARCHIVIO STORICO BERGAMASCO; rassegna semestre di storia e cultura. (Text in Italian; summaries in English and German) 1981. s-a. $25. Pierluigi Lubrina Editore, Viale Vittorio Emanuele, 19, 24100 Bergamo, Italy. Ed. Pierluigi Lubrina. adv.; bk.rev.; cum.index. circ. 700.

945   IT   ISSN 0391-7770
ARCHIVIO STORICO ITALIANO. (Text in English, French, German and Italian) 1842. q. L.75000 (foreign L.95000) (effective 1994). (Deputazione Toscana di Storia Patria) Casa Editrice Leo S. Olschki, Casella Postale 66, 50100 Florence, Italy. TEL 055-6530684. FAX 055-6530214. Ed. Emilio Cristiani. adv.; bk.rev.; index, cum.index: 1842-1941, 1942-1967. circ. 1,500. (reprint service avail. from SCH) **Indexed:** Amer.Hist.& Life, Arts & Hum.Cit.Ind., Curr.Cont., Hist.Abstr., M.L.A. **Document type:** academic/scholarly publication.
—BLDSC (1648.160000); SWETS.

945   IT   ISSN 0066-6718
ARCHIVIO STORICO ITALIANO. BIBLIOTECA. 1949. irreg., vol.27, 1992. price varies. Casa Editrice Leo S. Olschki, Casella Postale 66, 50100 Florence, Italy. TEL 055-6530684. FAX 055-6530214. circ. 1,000. **Document type:** academic/scholarly publication.

945   IT   ISSN 0004-0347
ARCHIVIO STORICO LODIGIANO. 1881. a. L.30000 (effective 1993). Comune di Lodi, Societa Storica Lodigiana, Via Fissiraga, 17, 20075 Lodi (Milan), Italy. TEL 0371-424128. FAX 0371-420814. Ed. Luigi Samarati. bk.rev.; index. circ. 500.

945   IT   ISSN 0004-0355
ARCHIVIO STORICO PER LA CALABRIA E LA LUCANIA.* 1931. q. L.5000. Palazzo Taverna, Monte Giordano 36, Rome, Italy. Dir. Ernesto Pontieri. adv.; bk.rev.; bibl.; charts; illus.; index, cum.index: 1931-1960. circ. 400.

900   IT   ISSN 0004-0363
ARCHIVIO STORICO PER LA SICILIA ORIENTALE. 1904. q. L.12000. Societa di Storia Patria per la Sicilia Orientale, Piazza Stesicoro 29, 95124 Catania, Italy. Dir. Giuseppe Giarrizzo. bk.rev.; bibl.; index. circ. 600. (also avail. in microfilm from BHP) **Indexed:** Numis.Lit.

945   IT
ARCHIVIO STORICO PER LE PROVINCE PARMENSI. 1892. a. L.40800. Deputazione Storia Patria, Borgo Schizzati, 3, 43100 Parma, Italy. Ed. Marco Pellegri. **Document type:** monographic series.

945   IT   ISSN 0391-2337
ARCHIVIO STORICO SARDO. (Text in Italian, Spanish) 1905. a. L.40000 (effective 1990). (Deputazione di Storia Patria per la Sardegna) Libreria Dessi, Largo Cavallotti 17, 07100 Sassari, Italy. TEL 079-231673.

HISTORY — HISTORY OF EUROPE

945   IT   ISSN 0044-8737
ARCHIVIO STORICO SIRACUSANO. 1955. a. L.20000. Societa Siracusana di Storia Patria, Villa Reimann, Via Necropoli Grotticelle, 14, 96100 Siracusa, Italy. TEL 0931-411939. FAX 0931-411989. bk.rev.; bibl.; illus.; index, cum.index: 1955-1964, 1965-1976. circ. 400. (tabloid format) **Document type:** academic/scholarly publication.

945   SZ   ISSN 0004-0371
ARCHIVIO STORICO TICINESE. 1960. q. 80 Fr. Edizioni Casagrande SA, Casella Postale 1291, CH-6500 Bellinzona, Switzerland. illus.; cum.index. circ. 1,000.

914.5   IT   ISSN 1120-4184
ARCHIVIO TRENTINO DI STORIA CONTEMPORANEA. MUSEO DEL RISORGIMENTO E DELLA LOTTA PER LA LIBERTA. BOLLETTINO. 1950. 3/yr. L.9000 per no. Museo Trentino del Risorgimento e della Lotta per la Liberta, Trento Castello Buon Consiglio, Via Bernardo Clesio 3, 38100 Trentino, Italy. TEL 0461-230482. FAX 0461-237418. bk.rev. circ. 900. **Document type:** academic/scholarly publication.
     Formerly (until 1990): Museo Trentino del Risorgimento e della Lotta per la Liberta. Bollettino (ISSN 0027-3961)

941.5   IE   ISSN 0044-8745
ARCHIVIUM HIBERNICUM; Irish historical records. 1912. a. £10. Catholic Record Society of Ireland, c/o St. Patrick's College, Maynooth, Co. Kildare, Ireland. TEL 01-6285222. FAX 01-6289063. Ed. Colm Lennon. index. circ. 400. **Indexed:** Amer.Hist.& Life, Hist.Abstr. **Document type:** academic/scholarly publication.

980   SP   ISSN 0004-0452
BX3601
ARCHIVO IBERO-AMERICANO; revista de estudios historicos. (Text in Portuguese and Spanish) 1914. q. 2290 ptas.($55) (effective 1992). Franciscanos Espanoles, Joaquin Costa 36, 28002 Madrid, Spain. Dir. Antolin Abad. bk.rev.; bibl.; index. circ. 550. **Indexed:** Amer.Hist.& Life, Hisp.Amer.Per.Ind., Hist.Abstr.

946   SP   ISSN 0004-0630
ARCHIVOS LEONESES; estudios y documentacion de los reinos hispano-occidentales. 1947. s-a. 5000 ptas.($150) Centro de Estudios e Investigacion San Isidoro, Plaza de Regla, 6, 24003 Leon, Spain. TEL 987-25-79-21. Ed. Jose M. Fernandez Caton. bk.rev.; bibl.; index, cum.index: 1947-1977. (also avail. in microform)

940   IT   ISSN 0391-7320
ARCHIVUM FRATRUM PRAEDICATORUM. (Text in English, French, German and Italian) 1931. a. price varies. Istituto Storico Domenicano, Largo Angelicum 1, 00153 Rome, Italy. TEL 06-5743575. FAX 06-67-90-407. (Subscr. to: Piazza Pietro d'Illiria 1, 00153 Rome, Italy) Ed. Raymond Bertheaux.
     Description: Covers history of the Dominican Order.

ARCHIVUM HISTORICUM SOCIETATIS IESU. see *RELIGIONS AND THEOLOGY — Roman Catholic*

943.7 330   XR   ISSN 0231-7486
ARCHIVUM TREBONENSE. 1971. irreg. Statni Oblastni Archiv v Treboni, 379 01 Treboni, Czech Republic.

027.83   PL   ISSN 0518-3766
ARCHIWA, BIBLIOTEKI I MUZEA KOSCIELNE/ARCHIVA, BIBLIOTHECAE ET MUSEA ECCLESIASTICA. (Text in Polish; summaries in English, German) 1959. s-a. price varies. Katolicki Uniwersytet Lubelski, Biblioteka, Ul. Chopina 29-7, 20-023 Lublin, Poland. TEL 48-81-22810. Ed. Stanislaw Librowski. index. circ. 1,000.

025.17   PL   ISSN 0004-0711
ARCHIWISTA; biuletyn Stowarzyszenia Archiwistow Polskich. 1965. q. $5. Stowarzyszenie Archiwistow Polskich - Polish Archivists Association, Ul. Dluga 6, P.O. Box 1005, 00-950 Warsaw, Poland. (Dist. by: Ars Polona-Ruch, Krakowskie Przedmiescie 7, Warsaw, Poland) Ed. Mieczyslaw Motas. adv.; bk.rev.; bibl. circ. 1,200. (processed)

949.7 069   XV   ISSN 0570-8869
ARGO. 1892. 4/yr. $3. Narodni Muzej v Ljubljani in Skuposnot Muzejev Slovenije, Narodni Muzej, Presernova Ul. 20, P.O. Box 529-X, 61000 Ljubljana, Slovenia. FAX 061-221-882. bk.rev. **Indexed:** Numis.Lit.

949.7   YU   ISSN 0351-2819
ARHEOGRAFSKI PRILOZI. (Text in Serbo-Croatian) 1979. irreg., no.12, 1990. $5 per no. Narodna Bibioteka Srbije, Arheografsko Odeljenje, Skerliceva 1, 11000 Belgrade, Yugoslavia. TEL 451-242. FAX 011-452-952. TELEX 12208 NB SRB YU. Ed. Milomir Petrovic.

949.8 571   RM   ISSN 0066-7358
ARHEOLOGIA MOLDOVEI/ARCHEOLOGIE DE LA MOLDAVIE. (Text in Rumanian; summaries in French) 1961. irreg., vol.10, 1985. (Institutul de Arheologie) Editura Academiei Romane, Calea Victoriei 125, 79717 Bucharest, Rumania. (Subscr. to: Artexim, Export-Import Presa, Piata Presei Libere nr. 1, P.O. Box 33-16, 70055 Bucharest, Rumania) **Indexed:** A.I.C.P., Numis.Lit.
     —BLDSC (1664.445000).

949.7   CI   ISSN 0353-4960
ARHIV HRVATSKE. BILTEN/ARCHIVES OF CROATIA. BULLETIN. (Text in Croatian) 1989. m. price varies. Arhiv Hrvatske, Marulicev trg. 21, 41001 Zagreb, Croatia. TEL 445-609. FAX 446-325. Ed. Josip Kolanovic. adv.

949   YU   ISSN 0350-2856
CD15
ARHIVIST. (Text in Serbo-Croatian, Slovenian; summaries in English, French, Italian, Russian) 1951. s-a. 5000 din. Savez Arhivskih Radnika Jugoslavije, Karnedzijeva 2, Belgrade, Yugoslavia. TEL 650-755. (Co-sponsor: Savez Drustava Arhivskih Radnika Jugoslavije i Arhiva u Jugoslaviji) Ed. Bogdan Lekic. bibl. **Indexed:** Amer.Hist.& Life, Hist.Abstr.

949   CI   ISSN 0570-9008
CD1187.C8
ARHIVSKI VJESNIK. (Text in Croatian; summaries in English, French, German, Italian) 1899. a. price varies. Arhiv Hrvatske, Marulicev trg 21, 41001 Zagreb, Croatia. TEL 445-609. FAX 446-325. Ed. Josip Kolanovic. bk.rev.; illus. circ. 700. **Indexed:** Amer.Hist.& Life, Hist.Abstr.
     Description: Covers history of Croatia.

948   DK   ISSN 0108-3589
ARILDS LOKALTIDENDE. 1982. irreg. DKK 70 (typically set in Apr.). Dragsholm Lokalhistoriske Forening, Dragsholm Bibliotek, Storegade 16, P.O. Box 61, DK-4550 Asnaes, Denmark. TEL 53-45-07-52. FAX 53-45-03-35. Ed. Bent Kjaersgaard. adv.; illus. circ. 400.

949.5   GR
ARISTOTELES. 1957. 6/yr. Dr.150. Philekpaideftikos Syllogos Florines tou Aristotele, Periodikon Aristoteles, Florina, Greece. bk.rev.; bibl. circ. 1,800.

949.5   GR
ARISTOTELION PANEPISTEMION THESSALONIKES. PHILOSOPHIKE SCHOLE. EPISTEMONIKE EPETERIS. (Text in English, French, German and Greek) 1927. a. Dr.1000. Aristotelion Panepistemion Thessaloniki, Philosophike Schole - Aristotle University of Thessaloniki, School of Philosophy, University Campus, Salonika, Greece. Ed. Christos Theodoridis. illus. **Indexed:** M.L.A.

ARISTOTELION PANEPISTEMION THESSALONIKES. THEOLOGIKE SCHOLE. EPISTEMONIKE EPETERIS. see *RELIGIONS AND THEOLOGY*

947 026   KR
ARKHIVY UKRAINY. 1946. 6/yr. Golovne Arkhivne Upravlinnia pry Radi Ministriv U.S.S.R., Solom'ians'ka 24, 252601 Kiev 110, Ukraine. bk.rev.; index. (also avail. in microfiche from IDC) **Indexed:** Numis.Lit.
     Formerly (until 1965): Arkhivne Upravlinnia pry Radi Ministriv U.R.S.R. Naukovo-Informatsiinyi Biuleten.

ARKIV FOR STUDIER I ARBETARROERELSENS HISTORIA. see *BUSINESS AND ECONOMICS — Labor And Industrial Relations*

ARMAMENTARIA. see *MILITARY*

940   BE
ARMARIUM CODICUM INSIGNIUM. 1980. irreg., vol.4, 1988. N.V. Brepols, Steenweg op Tielen 68, 2300 Turnhout, Belgium. TEL 32-14-41-54-63. FAX 32-14-42-89-19. Ed.Bd. **Document type:** monographic series.
     Description: Publishes facsimiles of important manuscripts of Christian inspiration from the Graeco-Roman world, with scholarly commentary.

940   PO
ARMAS E TROFEUS; revista de historia, heraldica, genealogia e arte. 1959. irreg. (approx. 1/yr.). Esc.1000 per no. (Instituto Portugues de Heraldica) Livraria Ferin, Rua Nova de Almada 70, 1200 Lisbon, Portugal. Ed. Manuel A. Norton. bk.rev.; bibl.; charts; illus. circ. 500.

947   US
ARMENIAN TEXTS AND STUDIES. irreg. (University of Pennsylvania) Scholars Press, Box 15399, Atlanta, GA 30333-0399. TEL 404-727-2320. FAX 404-727-2348. Ed. Michael E. Stone. **Document type:** monographic series.
     Description: Monographs on Armenian literature and civilizations.

ARMSTRONG NEWS. see *ETHNIC INTERESTS*

ARS SUECICA. see *ART*

ARTHURIAN STUDIES. see *LITERATURE*

948   FI   ISSN 0358-3414
ARX TAVASTICA. 1967. irreg. FIM 30 per no. Haemeelinna-seura, Haemmeenlinnan Maakunta-Arkisto, Arvi Kariston Katu 2A, 13100 Hameenlinna, Finland. TEL 358-17-533-801. FAX 358-17-533-810. Ed. Seppo Myllyniemi. bk.rev. circ. 500. **Document type:** academic/scholarly publication.

940   II   ISSN 0378-7516
D1
ASIAN JOURNAL OF EUROPEAN STUDIES. 3/yr. $36. K.K. Roy (Private) Ltd., 55 Gariahat Rd., P.O. Box 10210, Calcutta 700 019, India. Ed. Kuldip Kumar Roy.
     —BLDSC (1742.490000).

948.9   DK   ISSN 0109-4718
ASK; tidsskrift for dansk folkekultur. 1984. q. DKK 40 per no. Dansk Folkekultur, Hoerhaven 5, DK-2750 Ballerup, Denmark. TEL 45-44-97-79-52. FAX 45-44-77-27-18. Ed. Joergen O. Bjerregaard. adv.; bk.rev.; illus. circ. 600.

940   RM   ISSN 0004-5551
DR1
ASSOCIATION INTERNATIONALE D'ETUDES DU SUD-EST EUROPEEN. BULLETIN. (Text in English, French, Rumanian) 1963. s-a. $40. International Association of South-East European Studies, 47, Chaussee Kiseleff, 71268 Bucharest 2, Rumania. Ed. Virgil Candea. bk.rev.; charts; illus.; stat. **Indexed:** Amer.Hist.& Life (until 1987), Hist.Abstr. (until 1987), Numis.Lit.

ASSOCIATION OF COLLEGE AND RESEARCH LIBRARIES. SLAVIC AND EASTERN EUROPEAN SECTION NEWSLETTER. see *LIBRARY AND INFORMATION SCIENCES*

940   SZ   ISSN 0571-6322
ASSOCIATION OF INSTITUTES FOR EUROPEAN STUDIES. ANNUAIRE.* 1957. a. Association of Institutes for European Studies, European Cultural Centre, 122 rue de Lausanne, Geneva, Switzerland.

378 940   SZ   ISSN 0571-6330
ASSOCIATION OF INSTITUTES FOR EUROPEAN STUDIES. YEAR-BOOK.* a. Association of Institutes for European Studies, European Cultural Centre, 122 rue de Lausanne, Geneva, Switzerland.

949.5   GR
TA ATHENAIKA. 1955. 3/yr. Syllogos ton Athinaion, Odos Kydathinaion 20, Athens 119, Greece. bk.rev.; bibl.; cum.index. **Indexed:** M.L.A.

949.5   GR
ATHENS. ETHNIKON KAI KAPODISTRIAKON PANEPISTEMION. PHILOSOPHIKE SCHOLE. EPISTEMONIKE EPETERIS. (Text in English, French, German, Greek and Italian) 1935. a. Panepistemion Athenon, Philosophike Schole, Odos Panepistemiou, 143 Athens, Greece. illus.

944 FR
ATLAS DE LA REVOLUTION FRANCAISE. 1987. irreg., no.6, 1992. Editions de l' Ecole des Hautes Etudes en Sciences Sociales, 131 bd. St-Michel, 75005 Paris, France. TEL 43-54-47-15. FAX 43-54-80-73. (Dist. by: Centre Interinstitutionnel pour la Diffusion de Publications en Sciences Humaines, 131 bd. St-Michel, 75005 Paris, France)

940 FR ISSN 0765-0817
ATLAS HISTORIQUE DES VILLES DE FRANCE. irreg. price varies. C N R S Editions, 20-22 rue St. Amand, 75015 Paris, France. TEL 45-33-16-00. FAX 45-33-92-13. TELEX 200 356 F. adv.; bk.rev.; index; circ. 1,500 (controlled).

940 GW ISSN 0178-7128
B2621
AUFKLAERUNG; interdisziplinare Halbjahresschrift zur Erforschung des 18. Jahrhunderts und seiner Wirkungsgeschichte. 1986. s-a. DM.96. Felix Meiner Verlag GmbH, Richardstr. 47, 22081 Hamburg, Germany. TEL 040-294870. FAX 040-2993614. Ed.Bd. adv.; bk.rev. **Document type:** academic/scholarly publication.
—SWETS.

943 GW ISSN 1013-1442
D299
AUFKLAERUNG - VORMAERZ - REVOLUTION. 1981. a. (Demokratische Bewegung in Mitteleuropa) Peter Lang GmbH Europaeischer Verlag der Wissenschaften, Eschborner Landstr. 42-50, 60489 Frankfurt a.M., Germany. TEL 069-7807050. FAX 069-785893. Ed. Helmut Reinalter. **Document type:** academic/scholarly publication.
Description: Examines democratic movements in central Europe from 1770-1850.

943.6 AU
AUFRISSE; Zeitschrift fuer politische Bildung. 1980. 4/yr. Verlag fuer Gesellschaftskritik, Rathausstr. 18, 1010 Vienna, Austria.

943 GW
AUS DER WEHRHEIMER GESCHICHTE. 1978. a. DM.3. Geschichts- und Heimatverein Wehrheim, Usingerstr. 2, 61273 Wehrheim, Germany. TEL 06081-5561. Ed. Helmut Michel. circ. 300. (back issues avail.)
Description: All aspects of the history of the village of Wehrheim.

943.6 US ISSN 0067-2378
DB1
AUSTRIAN HISTORY YEARBOOK. 1965. a. University of Minnesota, Center for Austrian Studies, 314 Social Science Bldg., Minneapolis, MN 55455. TEL 612-624-9811. FAX 612-626-2242. (Co-sponsor: Conference Group for Central European History) Ed. William E. Wright. bk.rev. circ. 950. **Indexed:** Amer.Hist.& Life, Hist.Abstr.
—UnCover.
Supersedes: Austrian History Newsletter.

943.6 US
AUSTRIAN STUDIES NEWSLETTER. q. University of Minnesota, Center for Austrian Studies, 314 Social Science Bldg., Minneapolis, MN 55455. TEL 612-624-9811. FAX 612-626-2242. **Document type:** newsletter.

946 SP
L'AVENC. (Supplement avail. bi-m.: Plecs d'Historia Local) (Text in Catalan) m. 4500 ptas. (Europe 5500 ptas.; elsewhere 6250 ptas.). L' Avenc, S.A., Consell de Cent, 278 1o-2a, 08007 Barcelona, Spain. TEL 93-488-34-82. FAX 93-317-08-93. Dir. Daniel Fernandez. adv. contact: Nadala Fernandez. circ. 8,500.
Description: Covers the past history of Catalonia, comparing it to other peoples' experience, moving towards more contemporary and universal themes.

940 UK
AXBRIDGE ARCHAEOLOGICAL AND LOCAL HISTORY SOCIETY. JOURNAL. 1970. irreg. £5 to non-members. Axbridge Archaeological and Local History Society, King John's Hunting Lodge Museum, The Square, Axbridge, Somerset, England. Ed. Jane Panter. illus. circ. 50. **Document type:** academic/scholarly publication.

947 AJ
AZERBAIDJAN. GOSUDARSTVENNYI UNIVERSITET. NAUCHNYE TRUDY. SERIYA ISTORICHESKIKH I FILOSOFSKIKH NAUK. (Text in Azerbaijani and Russian) 1979. 8/yr. Azerbaidzhanskii Gosudarstvennyi Universitet, Ul. Patrisy Lumumby 23, 370122 Baku, Azerbajan.
Formerly: Azerbaidjan. Gosudarstvennyi Universitet. Uchenye Zapiski. Seriya Istoricheskikh i Filosofiskikh Nauk.

940 PL ISSN 0067-2793
BADANIA Z DZIEJOW SPOLECZNYCH I GOSPODARCZYCH. (Text in Polish; summaries in English, French or German) irreg., vol.58, 1981. price varies. Poznanskie Towarzystwo Przyjaciol Nauk, Ul. Sew. Mielzynskiego 27-29, 61-725 Poznan, Poland. TEL 48-61-527-441.

940 GW
BADISCHE BIOGRAPHIEN NEUE FOLGE. 1981. irreg. price varies. Kommission fuer Geschichtliche Landeskunde in Baden-Wuerttemberg, Eugenstr. 7, 70182 Stuttgart, Germany. circ. 1,000. **Document type:** bulletin.
Description: Short biographies of persons who died after 1910 and are connected to ancient Bade.

943 GW ISSN 0522-0033
DER BAER VON BERLIN. 1951. irreg. DM.38. Westkreuz Druckerei und Verlag, Toepchiner Weg 198-200, 12309 Berlin, Germany. TEL 030-7452047. FAX 030-7453066. **Document type:** academic/scholarly publication.

BAETICA; estudios de arte, geografia e historia. see *ART*

949 YU
BALCANICA. vol.5, 1974. a. Srpska Akademija Nauka i Umetnosti, Koordinacioni Medjuakademski Odbor za Balkanologiju, Belgrade, Yugoslavia. (Co-sponsor: Srpska Akademija Nauka i Umetnosti. Balkanoloski Institut) Ed. Mehmed Begovic. bk.rev. circ. 20. **Indexed:** M.L.A.

949.6 GR ISSN 0005-4313
DR1
BALKAN STUDIES. (Text in English, French, German, Italian) 1960. s-a. Dr.4000($40) Institute for Balkan Studies, 31A Ave. Megalou Alexandrou, 546 41 Thessaloniki, Greece. TEL 30-31-832143. FAX 30-31-831429. Ed. B. Kondis. bk.rev.; abstr.; illus.; index. circ. 2,000. (back issues avail.; reprint service avail. from SWZ) **Indexed:** Amer.Bibl.Slavic & E.Eur.Stud., Amer.Hist.& Life, Arts & Hum.Cit.Ind., Bibl.Ling., Curr.Cont., Hist.Abstr., M.L.A., Numis.Lit. **Document type:** academic/scholarly publication.
—BLDSC (1860.700000); UnCover.
Description: Contains historical, international, political, economic, liguistic, and folkloric information about the Balkan area.

949.5 GR ISSN 1105-0136
BALKANIKA SYMMEIKTA. 1981. a. Dr.2,000($9) Institute for Balkan Studies, 31A Ave. Megalou Alexandrou, 546 41 Thessaloniki, Greece. TEL 30-31-832143. FAX 30-31-831429. **Document type:** academic/scholarly publication.

949.6 RU
BALKANSKIE ISSLEDOVANIYA. 1974. irreg. price varies. (Akademiya Nauk S.S.S.R., Institut Slavyanovedeniya i Balkanistiki) Izdatel'stvo Nauka, 90 Profsoyuznaya ul., 117864 Moscow, Russia. TEL 234-05-84. (Dist. by: Mezhdunarodnaya Kniga, ul. Dimistrova D.39, 113095 Moscow, Russia) Ed. G.L. Arsh. circ. 1,700.

947.4 929 GW ISSN 0005-4534
DK511.B25
BALTISCHE HEFTE. 1954. a. DM.14.80. Harro V. Hirschheydt, Postfach 281769, 3000 Hannover-Doehren, Germany. adv.; bk.rev.; bibl.; illus.; index. circ. 1,100. **Indexed:** Amer.Hist.& Life, Hist.Abstr., M.L.A.

940 GW ISSN 0067-3099
DD491.P5
BALTISCHE STUDIEN. 1835. a. DM.30. (Gesellschaft fuer Pommersche Geschichte, Altertumskunde und Kunst) N.G. Elwert Verlag, Reitgasse 7-9, 35037 Marburg, Germany. Ed.Bd. bk.rev. circ. 1,000. **Document type:** academic/scholarly publication.

947 AI
BANBER HAYASTANI ARKHIVNERI/VESTNIK ARKHIVOV ARMENII. (Text in Armenian and Russian) 1960. 3/yr. Arkhivnoe Upravlenie pri Sovete Ministrov Armenskoi S.S.R., Ul. Rachiia Kochara 5, Yerevan 33, Armenia. bibl.; cum.index every 2 yrs.

940 SZ ISSN 0067-4540
DQ361
BASLER ZEITSCHRIFT FUER GESCHICHTE UND ALTERTUMSKUNDE. (Text in French and German) 1902. a. 75 SFr. Historische und Antiquarische Gesellschaft zu Basel, Universitaetsbibliothek, Schoenbeinstr. 18-20, CH-4056 Basel. Eds. Josef Zwicker, Martin Steinmann. circ. 1,200. **Document type:** academic/scholarly publication.

940 GW ISSN 0942-606X
DAS BAYERISCHE INN-OBERLAND. 1902. a. DM.36. Historischer Verein Rosenheim, Stadtarchiv Rosenheim, Max-Bram-Platz 2a, 83022 Rosenheim, Germany.

940 GW ISSN 0341-3918
BAYERISCHE VORGESCHICHTSBLAETTER. (Text in English, French, German) 1921. a. DM.80. (Bayerische Akademie der Wissenschaften, Kommission fuer Bayerische Landesgeschichte) C.H. Beck'sche Verlagsbuchhandlung, Wilhelmstr. 9, 80801 Munich, Germany. TEL 089-38189-338. FAX 089-38189-398. TELEX 5215085-BECK-D. (Co-sponsor: Bayerisches Landesamt fuer Denkmalpflege) Ed. H.J. Kellner. bk.rev.; bibl.; illus. circ. 600. **Indexed:** Anthropol.Lit., Numis.Lit. **Document type:** academic/scholarly publication.

943 GW ISSN 0405-0851
BAYERWALD; Zeitschrift des Bayerischen Waldvereins fuer Heimat und Volkstum. Naturschutz, Landschaftspflege und Wandern. 1903. 4/yr. Kultur-und Presseausschuss des Bayerischen Waldvereins, Angerstr. 34, 8372 Zweisel, Germany.

BEAKEN. see *LINGUISTICS*

942 UK ISSN 0067-4826
DA670.B29
BEDFORDSHIRE HISTORICAL RECORD SOCIETY. PUBLICATIONS. 1913. a. £8 to individuals; institutions £12. Bedfordshire Historical Record Society, County Record Office, County Hall, Bedford MK42 9AP, England. TEL 0234 228833. Ed. C.J. Pickford. circ. 500. (also avail. in microfiche) **Indexed:** Br.Archaeol.Abstr., Br.Hum.Ind.

942 UK ISSN 0005-7592
BEDFORDSHIRE MAGAZINE; a miscellany and review of Bedfordshire life and history. 1947. q. £15.60 for 2 years. White Crescent Press Ltd., Crescent Rd., Luton, Bedfordshire LU2 0AG, England. TEL 0582-23122. FAX 0582-23126. Ed. Betty Chambers. adv.; bk.rev.; charts; illus.; cum.index every 2 yrs. circ. 2,000. **Indexed:** Br.Archaeol.Abstr., Br.Hum.Ind. **Document type:** academic/scholarly publication.
—BLDSC (1872.817000).

DIE BEIDEN TUERME; Niederaltaicher Rundbrief. see *RELIGIONS AND THEOLOGY*

943 GW
BEITRAEGE ZUR GESCHICHTE DER CAROLO-WILHELMINA. 1973. irreg. Braunschweigischer Hochschulbund, Schleinitzstr. 17, 38106 Braunschweig, Germany. Ed. Karl Gerke.

274.3 GW ISSN 0408-8344
BEITRAEGE ZUR GESCHICHTE DER REICHSKIRCHE IN DER NEUZEIT. irreg., vol.14, 1994. price varies. Franz Steiner Verlag Wiesbaden GmbH, Birkenwaldstr. 44, 70191 Stuttgart, Germany. TEL 0711-2582-0. FAX 0711-2582290. TELEX 723636-DAZ-D. (Subscr. to: Postfach 101061, 70009 Stuttgart, Germany) Ed. Rudolf Reinhardt. **Document type:** monograph series.

943.08 GW ISSN 0408-8379
LF2955
BEITRAEGE ZUR GESCHICHTE DER UNIVERSITAET MAINZ. irreg., vol. 16, 1992. price varies. (Universitaet Mainz) Franz Steiner Verlag Wiesbaden GmbH, Birkenwaldstr. 44, 70191 Stuttgart, Germany. TEL 0711-2582-0. FAX 0711-2582290. TELEX 723636-DAZ-D. (Subscr. to: Postfach 101061, 70009 Stuttgart, Germany) Ed.Bd. **Document type:** monograph series.

HISTORY — HISTORY OF EUROPE

943   GW   ISSN 0078-2785
BEITRAEGE ZUR GESCHICHTE UND KULTUR DER STADT NUERNBERG. (Sub-series: Nuernberg-Bibliographie) 1959. irreg., vol. 23, 1988. price varies. Stadtbibliothek Nuernberg, Egidienplatz 23, 90317 Nuernberg, Germany. Ed. G. Thomann. **Document type:** bibliography.

940   GW   ISSN 0343-2785
BEITRAEGE ZUR HEIMATKUNDE DER STADT SCHWELM UND IHRER UMGEBUNG. 1951. a. price varies. Verein fuer Heimatkunde Schwelm, Haus Martfeld, 58332 Schwelm, Germany. Ed. Luetz Koch. **Document type:** bulletin.

940   GW   ISSN 0522-6848
BEITRAEGE ZUR KOLONIAL UND UEBERSEEGESCHICHTE. irreg., vol.57, 1993. price varies. Franz Steiner Verlag Wiesbaden GmbH, Birkenwaldstr. 44, 70191 Stuttgart, Germany. TEL 0711-2582-0. FAX 0711-2582290. TELEX 723636-DAZ-D. (Subscr. to: Postfach 101061, 70009 Stuttgart, Germany) Eds. Rudolf von Albertini, Eberhard Schmitt. **Document type:** monographic series.

943   GW   ISSN 0408-8492
BEITRAEGE ZUR LANDESKUNDE; regelmaessige Beilage zum Staatsanzeiger fuer Baden-Wuerttemberg. 1962. bi-m. DM.15. Staatsanzeiger Baden-Wuerttemberg GmbH, Postfach 104363, 70038 Stuttgart, Germany. FAX 0711-6660119. Ed.Bd. bk.rev. circ. 18,000. (back issues avail.) **Document type:** academic/scholarly publication.
Description: History of the south-west part of Germany.

943   GW   ISSN 0067-5164
BEITRAEGE ZUR OBERPFALZFORSCHUNG. 1965. irreg. price varies. Verlag Michael Lassleben, Lange Gasse 19, 93183 Kallmuenz, Germany. Ed. Heinz K. Rademacher. **Document type:** monographic series.

943   GW   ISSN 0405-2161
BEITRAEGE ZUR SCHLESWIGER STADTGESCHICHTE. 1956. a. DM.30. Gesellschaft fuer Schlesiwger Stadtgeschichte, Staedtisches Museum, Friedrichstr. 7-11, 24837 Schleswig, Germany. TEL 04621-814280. FAX 04621-814400. Eds. Holger Ruedel, Reimer Pohl. circ. 1,000. **Document type:** academic/scholarly publication.

943   GW   ISSN 0175-6303
BEITRAEGE ZUR SOZIALGESCHICHTE BREMEN. 1979. 2/yr. DM.19.80. Edition Temmen, Hohenlohestr. 21, 28209 Bremen, Germany. TEL 0421-344280. FAX 0421-348094. **Document type:** academic/scholarly publication.

943   GW
BEITRAEGE ZUR SUEDOSTEUROPA-FORSCHUNG. irreg. (Arbeitskreis Suedosteuropa-Forschung) Slavica Verlag Dr. Anton Kovac, Elisabethstr. 22, 80796 Munich, Germany. TEL 089-2725612. FAX 089-2716594. **Document type:** monographic series.

940   GW   ISSN 0723-5453
BEITRAEGE ZUR WIRTSCHAFTS UND SOZIALGESCHICHTE. irreg., vol.56, 1994. price varies. Franz Steiner Verlag Wiesbaden GmbH, Birkenwaldstr. 44, 70191 Stuttgart, Germany. TEL 0711-2582-0. FAX 0711-2582290. TELEX 723636-DAZ-D. (Subscr. to: Postfach 101061, 70009 Stuttgart, Germany) Ed.Bd. **Document type:** monographic series.

943.6   AU
BEITRAEGE ZUR ZEITGESCHICHTE OBEROESTERREICHS. 1974. irreg. Oberoesterreichisches Landesarchiv, Anzengruberstr. 19, A-4020 Linz, Austria. TEL 0732-6555230. FAX 0732-655523-4619. **Document type:** monographic series.

943.9   HU   ISSN 0522-7232
BEKESI ELET. 1966. 4/yr. $15.50. Tudomanyos Ismeretterjeszto Tarsulat Bekes Megyei Szervezete, Bekes Megyei Tanacs V.B. Muvelodesugyi Osztalya, Istvan Kiraly Ter 8, 5601 Bekesccaba, Hungary. Ed. Krupa Andras. adv.; bk.rev.; bibl. circ. 1,500.

947   BW   ISSN 0321-0359
BELARUSKI DZIARZHAUNY UNIVERSITET. VESNIK. SERYIA 3; HISTORIYA, FILOSOFIYA, NAVUKOVY KAMUNISM, EKANOMIKA, PRAVA/BELORUSSKII GOSUDARSTVENNYI UNIVERSITET. VESTNIK. SERIYA 3; ISTORIYA, FILOSOFIYA, NAUCHNYI KOMMUNIZM, EKONOMIKA, PRAVO. (Text in Belorussian and Russian) 1969. 3/yr. Belorusskii Gosudarstvennyi Universitet, Fakul'tet Zhurnalistiki, Universitetskii Gorodok, Minsk 80, Belarus. bk.rev.
—BLDSC (0026.410000).
Formerly: Belaruski Dziarzhauny Universitet. Vesnik. Seryia; Historyia, Filasofia, Ekanomika, Prava.

947 917.306   US   ISSN 0510-3746
DK507.A2
BELARUSKI INSTYTUT NAVUKII MASTATSTVA. ZAPISY/BELARUSAN INSTITUTE OF ARTS AND SCIENCES. ANNALS. (Text in Belarusan; summaries in English) 1952. a. $30. (Belarusan Institute of Arts and Sciences, Inc.) Byelorussian Press, 230 Springfield Ave., Rutherford, NJ 07070. TEL 201-933-6807. FAX 201-438-4565. Eds. Vitaut Kipel, Thomas E. Bird. adv.; bk.rev.; bibl.; illus.; stat. circ. 1,000. (also avail. in microfilm; back issues avail.) **Document type:** academic/scholarly publication.

940   IT   ISSN 0392-0356
BENEDICTINA. (Text in Italian; occasionally in English, French) 1947. s-a. L.55000 (foreign L.65000). Benedictina Editrice, Via Ostiense, 186, 00146 Rome, Italy. TEL 06-541-0341. FAX 06-5403381. Ed. Luigi Crippa. bk.rev.; index, cum.index. circ. 1,000. (back issues avail.) **Document type:** academic/scholarly publication.
—BLDSC (1891.340000).

943   GW   ISSN 0067-5792
BERGISCHER GESCHICHTSVEREIN. ZEITSCHRIFT. 1863. irreg. DM.18. Bergischer Geschichtsverein e. V., Friedrich-Engels-Allee 89-91, 5600 Wuppertal 2, Germany. Eds. Wolfgang Koellmann, Juergen Reulecke. bk.rev. circ. 3,000.
—BLDSC (9441.750000); SWETS.

948.5   SW   ISSN 1100-7087
BERGLAGSARKIV; aarsbok foer historia och kulturhistoria i Bergslagen. 1989. a. SEK 100 to individuals; institutions SEK 750. Foereningen Bergslagsarkiv, c/o Bode Janzon, Vaermlandsarkiv, P.O. Box 475, S-651 11 Karlstad, Sweden. TEL 46-54-15-22-80. FAX 46-54-18-90-77. Ed. Ivan Bratt.

945 800 700   IT   ISSN 0005-8955
DG975.B48
BERGOMUM; studi di letteratura, storia ed arte. 1907. q. L.30000 (foreign L.50000). Civica Biblioteca A. Mai, Piazza Vecchia 15, Bergamo, Italy. FAX 035-240655. TELEX 399430-31. Ed. Gianni Barachetti. adv.; bk.rev.; bibl.; charts; illus.; index, cum.index: 1907-1980. circ. 500. **Indexed:** Amer.Hist.& Life, Hist.Abstr., M.L.A.

949.50 930   GW   ISSN 0067-6055
BERLINER BYZANTINISTISCHE ARBEITEN. (Text mainly in German; occasionally in Greek) 1956. irreg., no.59, 1993. price varies. Akademie Verlag GmbH, Muehlenstr. 33-34, 13187 Berlin, Germany. TEL 030-47889348. FAX 030-47889357. **Indexed:** M.L.A. **Document type:** monographic series.

943   GW   ISSN 0067-611X
BERLINISCHE REMINISZENZEN. 1963. irreg., no.68, 1993. price varies. Haude und Spenersche Verlagsbuchhandlung GmbH, Potsdamer Str. 199, 10783 Berlin, Germany. TEL 030-2165061. FAX 030-2165064. **Document type:** monographic series.

949.4   SZ
BERNER HEIMATBUECHER. 1941. irreg., vol.142, 1992. price varies. Paul Haupt AG, Falkenplatz 14, CH-3001 Bern, Switzerland. TEL 031-3012345. FAX 031-3014669. **Document type:** monographic series.

949.4   SZ   ISSN 0005-9420
DQ401
BERNER ZEITSCHRIFT FUER GESCHICHTE UND HEIMATKUNDE. 1939. q. 50 SFr. Historischer Verein des Kantons Bern, Stadt- und Universitaetsbibliothek Bern, Muenstergasse 61, CH-3000 Bern 7, Switzerland. TEL 031-225519. adv.; bk.rev.; illus.; index, cum.index: 1939-1965. circ. 1,400. **Document type:** academic/scholarly publication.

943.8   PL   ISSN 0860-4096
DK4600.B52
BIALOSTOCCZYZNA. q. Bialostockie Towarzystwo Naukowe, Ul. M.C. Sklodowskiej 2, 15-097 Bialystok, Poland. Ed. Henryk Majecki. **Indexed:** Bibl.Ling.

943.8   PL   ISSN 0067-6470
BIALOSTOCKIE TOWARZYSTWO NAUKOWE. PRACE. 1963. irreg. 400 Zl. Bialostockie Towarzystwo Naukowe. Dom Technika, Ul. M.C. Sklodowskiej 2, 15-097 Bialystok, Poland. (Dist. by Ars Polona-Ruch, Krakowskie Przedmiescie 7, Warsaw, Poland) bk.rev.

BIBLE RESEARCHER. see *RELIGIONS AND THEOLOGY*

BIBLIOGRAFSKI VJESNIK. see *LIBRARY AND INFORMATION SCIENCES*

BIBLIOGRAPHIA HISTORIAE RERUM RUSTICARUM INTERNATIONALIS/INTERNATIONAL BIBLIOGRAPHY OF AGRICULTURAL HISTORY. see *AGRICULTURE*

940 015.47   US   ISSN 0162-5322
Z2483
BIBLIOGRAPHIC GUIDE TO SOVIET AND EUROPEAN STUDIES. (Text in Bulgarian, Czech, English, Latvian, Polish, Russian, Slovak and Ukrainian) 1978. a. $600 (foreign $660). G.K. Hall & Co., c/o MacMillan Publishing Co., 866 Third Ave., 18th fl., New York, NY 10022. TEL 212-702-6789. (Orders to: MacMillan Distribution Center, 100 Front St., Box 500, Riverside, NJ 08075-7500. TEL 800-257-5755) **Document type:** bibliography, abstracting/indexing.
Description: Covers all materials published in East European countries, or in the Soviet Union.

BIBLIOGRAPHIE ANNUELLE DU MOYEN AGE TARDIF; auteurs et textes latins, vers 1250-1500. see *HISTORY — Abstracting, Bibliographies, Statistics*

BIBLIOGRAPHIE LUXEMBOURGEOISE. see *BIBLIOGRAPHIES*

943 331   GW   ISSN 0343-4117
Z7164.L1
BIBLIOGRAPHIE ZUR GESCHICHTE DER DEUTSCHEN ARBEITERBEWEGUNG. (Text in English, French and German) 1976. a. DM.72. Verlag J.H.W. Dietz Nachf. GmbH, In der Raste 2, 53129 Bonn, Germany. TEL 0228-238083. FAX 0228-234104. Ed. Wolfgang Budde-Roth. **Document type:** bibliography.
—CCC.

943.6   AU
BIBLIOGRAPHIE ZUR GESCHICHTE OBEROESTERREICHS. 1929. irreg. Oberoesterreichisches Landesarchiv, Anzengruberstr. 19, A-4020 Linz, Austria. TEL 0732-6555230. FAX 0732-655523-4619. **Document type:** monographic series.

BIBLIOLOGIA; elementa ad librorum studia pertinentia. see *PUBLISHING AND BOOK TRADE*

949.5 686.2   GR
BIBLIOPHILIA. 1976. 4/yr. $20. Kostas H. Spanos, Ed. & Pub., Vivliopoleion ton Vivliophilon, Odos Mavromichale 7, Athens, Greece. TEL 3614332. adv.; bk.rev.; illus. circ. 9,000.

940   IT
BIBLIOTECA DI MEDIOEVO LATINO. 1990. irreg., no.7, 1991. price varies. (Societa Internazionale per lo Studio del Medioevo Latino) Centro Italiano di Studi sull'Alto Medioevo, Palazzo Ancaiani, 06049 Spoleto, Italy. TEL 0743-220418. FAX 0743-223507. **Document type:** monographic series.

HISTORY — HISTORY OF EUROPE

945 IT ISSN 0067-7442
BIBLIOTECA DI STORIA TOSCANA MODERNA E CONTEMPORANEA. STUDI E DOCUMENTI. 1965. irreg., vol.39, 1993. price varies. (Unione Regionale delle Provincie Toscane, Florence) Casa Editrice Leo S. Olschki, Casella Postale 66, 50100 Florence, Italy. TEL 055-6530684. FAX 055-6530214. circ. 1,000. **Document type:** monographic series.

940 IT ISSN 0523-3437
BIBLIOTECA DI STUDI MEDIEVALI. 1966. irreg., no.15, 1989. price varies. Centro Italiano di Studi sull'Alto Medioevo, Palazzo Ancaiani, 06049 Spoleto, Italy. TEL 0743-220418. FAX 0743-223507. **Document type:** monographic series.

949.8 RM ISSN 0067-7493
BIBLIOTECA ISTORICA. 1957. irreg., vol.71, 1988. (Academia Romana, Institutul de Istorie "N. Iorga") Editura Academiei Romane, Calea Victoriei 125, 9717 Bucharest, Rumania. (Subscr. to: Artexim, Export-Import Presa, Str. Piata Presei Libere nr.1, P.O. Box 33-16, 70055 Bucharest, Rumania)

945 940.27 IT
BIBLIOTECA NAPOLETANA DI STORIA E ARTE. 1976. irreg. price varies. Congedo Editore, Galatina, Italy. Dir. Franco Strazzullo.

945 IT ISSN 0392-0550
BIBLIOTECA STATALE E LIBRERIA CIVICA DI CREMONA. ANNALI. 1948. a. price varies. Biblioteca Statale e Libreria Civica di Cremona, Via Ugolani Dati 4, Cremona, Italy. Ed. Goffredo Dotti. circ. 1,780.

945
BIBLIOTECA STORICA TOSCANA. SERIE I. 1923. irreg., no.29, 1993. price varies. (Deputazione Toscana di Storia Patria) Casa Editrice Leo S. Olschki, Casella Postale 66, 50100 Florence, Italy. TEL 055-6530684. FAX 055-6530214. circ. 1,000. **Document type:** academic/scholarly publication.
Supersedes in part (in 1977): Biblioteca Storica Toscana (ISSN 0391-819X)

945
BIBLIOTECA STORICA TOSCANA. SERIE II. 1923. irreg., vol.23, 1991. price varies. (Società Toscana della Storia del Risorgimento) Casa Editrice Leo S. Olschki, Casella Postale 66, 50100 Florence, Italy. TEL 055-6530684. FAX 055-6530214. **Document type:** academic/scholarly publication.
Supersedes in part (in 1977): Biblioteca Storica Toscana (ISSN 0391-819X)

BIBLIOTEKA KRAKOWSKA. see *ART*

949.8 RM ISSN 0067-799X
BIBLIOTHECA HISTORICA ROMANIAE. MONOGRAPHIES. (Text in English, French, German, Russian) 1963. irreg., vol.24, 1988. (Academia Romana) Editura Academiei Romane, Calea Victoriei 125, 79717 Bucharest, Rumania. (Subscr. to: Artexim, Export-Import Presa, Str. Piata Presei Libere nr.1, P.O. Box 33-16, 70055 Bucharest, Rumania) Eds. St. Pascu, St. Stefanescu. **Document type:** monographic series.

949.8 RM ISSN 0067-7981
BIBLIOTHECA HISTORICA ROMANIAE. STUDIES. (Text in English, French, German, Russian) 1963. irreg., vol.71, 1988. (Academia Romana) Editura Academiei Romane, Calea Victoriei 125, 79717 Bucharest, Rumania. (Subscr. to: Artexim, Export-Import Presa, Str. Piata Presei Libere nr.1, P.O. Box 33-16, 70055 Bucharest, Rumania) Eds. St. Pascu, St. Stefanescu.

940 PL ISSN 0067-8031
BIBLIOTHECA LATINA MEDII ET RECENTIORIS AEVI. (Text in Latin) 1960. irreg., vol.24, 1989. price varies. (Polska Akademia Nauk, Komitet Nauk o Kulturze Antycznej) Ossolineum, Publishing House of the Polish Academy of Sciences, Rynek 9, 50-106 Wroclaw, Poland. TEL 48-71-386-25. FAX 48-71-448-103. TELEX 0712771 OSS PL. Ed. M. Cytowska. **Document type:** monographic series.

270.3 BE
BIBLIOTHECA VICTORINA; subsidia ad historiam canonicorum regularium investigandam. (Text in French) 1991. irreg., vol.4, 1993. price varies. N.V. Brepols, Steenweg op Tielen 68, 2300 Turnhout, Belgium. TEL 32-14-402500. FAX 32-14-428919. (back issues avail.) **Document type:** monographic series, proceedings.

909 SZ ISSN 0006-1999
CB361
BIBLIOTHEQUE D'HUMANISME ET RENAISSANCE; travaux et documents. (Text in English, French, German and Italian) 1941. 3/yr. 100 SFr.($70) (Association d'Humanisme et Renaissance) Librarie Droz S.A., 11 rue Massot, CH-1211 Geneva 12, Switzerland. TEL 022-3466666. FAX 022-472391. bk.rev.; illus. circ. 800. (reprint service avail. from SWZ) **Indexed:** Amer.Hist.& Life, Arts & Hum.Cit.Ind., Curr.Cont., Hist.Abstr., M.L.A. **Document type:** academic/scholarly publication.
—Faxon; SWETS. CCC.
Description: Presents research on the 15th and 16th centuries.

940 SZ ISSN 0067-8406
DQ721
BIBLIOTHEQUE HISTORIQUE VAUDOISE. 1940. irreg., no.19, 1988. price varies. Petit-Chene 18, 1002 Lausanne, Switzerland. Ed. Colin Martin. cum.index. **Indexed:** Numis.Lit.

948 069 SZ ISSN 1011-8268
BIBLIOTHEQUES ET MUSEES. 1948. a. free. Affaires Culturelles, c/o Bibliotheque Publique et Universitaire, 3 place Numa-Droz, CH-2000 Neuchatel, Switzerland. **Document type:** bulletin.
Superseded (in 1962): Bibliotheques et Musees de la Ville de Neuchatel (ISSN 1011-825X)

944 US
BICENTENNIAL REFLECTIONS ON THE FRENCH REVOLUTION. 1989. irreg. Duke University Press, 6697 College Station, Durham, NC 27708. TEL 919-684-2173. FAX 919-684-8644. Eds. Keith M. Baker, Stephen L. Kaplen.

948 NE ISSN 0165-0505
DJ1
BIJDRAGEN EN MEDEDELINGEN BETREFFENDE DE GESCHIEDENIS DER NEDERLANDEN. vol.97, 1982. 4/yr. fl.90. Nederlands Historisch Genootschap, Postbus 90406, 2509 LK The Hague, Netherlands. TEL 31-70-3140363. Ed.Bd. bk.rev. **Indexed:** Amer.Hist.& Life, E.I., Hist.Abstr. **Document type:** academic/scholarly publication, bibliography.
—SWETS.
Description: Covers various aspects of Dutch history, such as political, philosophical and religious. Includes announcements of events and exhibitions.

949.2 NE ISSN 0067-8554
BIJDRAGEN TOT DE GESCHIEDENIS VAN ARNHEM. 1966. irreg., no.5, 1981. price varies. Gemeentearchief - Arnhem Municipal Archives, Westervoortsedijk 2, 6827 AS Arnhem, Netherlands. circ. 1,000.

944 700 800 FR ISSN 0398-9453
BIZA NEIRA (BISE NOIRE); sur l'Auvergne et la civilisation Auvergnate. (Text in Auvergnat, French) 1974. q. 150 F. Cercle Terre d'Auvergne, 11 rue des Saulees, 63400 Chamalieres, France. TEL 73-61-32-16. Ed. P. Bonnaud. bk.rev.; bibl.; illus.

948.6 SW ISSN 0523-7157
BJAEREBYGDEN. 1931. a. SEK 85 (effective 1990). Bjaere Haerads Hembygdsfoerening, c/o G. Nilsson, Foervaltarev. 11, S-269 00 Baastad, Sweden.

948.9 DK ISSN 0107-072X
BJERG-POSTEN. MEDLEMSBLAD. 1977. a. DKK 40 to members. Lokalhistorisk Forening i Frejlev-Noerholm- Soenderholm Sogne, Nibevej 476, DK-9240 Nibe, Denmark. Ed. Arne Fristrup. illus. circ. 400.

942 UK ISSN 0006-4335
DA670.B55
THE BLACKCOUNTRYMAN. 1968. q. free to members (overseas £10). Black Country Society, 32 Lawnswood Ave., Stourbridge, W. Midlands DY8 5LP, England. TEL 44-384-295606. (Subscr. to: R. Julian, 97 Stream Rd., Kingswinford, W. Midlands DY6 9NP, England) Ed. Stan Hill. adv.; bk.rev.; illus. circ. 3,000. **Indexed:** Br.Hum.Ind.
Description: Contains articles on local history, personalities past and present, reviews books on the locality, and some poetry and art by lay people of the Black Country subregion of England.

943 GW ISSN 0006-4408
BLAETTER FUER DEUTSCHE LANDESGESCHICHTE. 1852. a. DM.135. Gesamtverein der Deutschen Geschichts- und Altertumsvereine, c/o Landeshauptarchiv Koblenz, Karmeliterstr. 1-3, 56068 Koblenz, Germany. TEL 0261-33068. FAX 0261-33086. Ed. H.-G. Borck. bk.rev. circ. 1,000. **Indexed:** Amer.Hist.& Life, Bibl.Cart., Hist.Abstr., Numis.Lit. **Document type:** academic/scholarly publication.
—SWETS.

BLAETTER FUER WUERTTEMBERGISCHE KIRCHENGESCHICHTE. see *RELIGIONS AND THEOLOGY*

948.6 SW ISSN 0348-9639
BLEKINGEBOKEN; aarsbok foer Blekinge Laens Hembygdsfoerbund och Blekinge Laens museum. 1923. a. SEK 75 (effective 1993). Blekinge Laens Hembyggdsfoerbunds Foerlag, P.O. Box 111, S-371 22 Karlskrona, Sweden. TEL 46-455-80120. FAX 46-455-13168. circ. 2,090.

948 DK ISSN 0107-6094
BLICHEREGNENS MUSEUMSFORENING. AARSSKRIFT. 1980. a. DKK 50. Blicheregnens Museumsforening, Blichersvej 30, Thorning, 8620 Kjellerup, Denmark. Eds. Anton Lauritzen, Gudmund Lund. illus.

BOARD OF CELTIC STUDIES. BULLETIN. see *LITERATURE*

940 GW ISSN 0523-8587
DB193
BOHEMIA: ZEITSCHRIFT FUER GESCHICHTE UND KULTUR DER BOHEMISCHEN LAENDER. 1960. s-a. DM.76. (Collegium Carolinum) R. Oldenbourg Verlag GmbH, Rosenheimerstr. 145, 81671 Munich, Germany. TEL 089-45051-0. FAX 089-45051207. (Subscr. to: Postfach 801360, 81613 Munich, Germany) Eds. Ferdinand Seibt, Hans Lemberg. **Indexed:** Amer.Hist.& Life, Hist.Abstr. **Document type:** academic/scholarly publication.
—SWETS. CCC.
Supersedes: Verein fuer Geschichte der Deutschen in den Sudetenlaendern. Jahrbuch; Formerly: Collegium Carolinum. Bohemia-Jahrbuch.

948.6 SW ISSN 0348-937X
BOHUSLAEN; aarsbok. 1960. a. SEK 60 (effective 1990). Bohuslaens Museum, P.O. Box 33, S-451 12 Uddevalla, Sweden.

940 700 IT
BOLLETTINO LIGUSTICO PER LA STORIA E LA CULTURA REGIONALE. vol.24, 1972. q. Società Ligure di Storia Patria, Viale Villa Gloria 1-3, 16128 Genoa, Italy. Ed. Teofilo Ossian de Negri. bk.rev.; abstr.; bibl.; charts; illus.

945
BOLLETTINO STORICO-BIBLIOGRAFICO SUBALPINO. 1896. s-a. L.65000 (foreign L.75000) (effective 1994). Deputazione Subalpina di Storia Patria, Via Principe Amedeo 5, 10123 Turin, Italy. TEL 011-537226. circ. 600.

949.4 SZ ISSN 0006-6869
DQ1
BOLLETTINO STORICO DELLA SVIZZERA ITALIANA. 1879. 4/yr. 75 Fr. Arti Grafiche A. Salvoni e Co., S.A., Conto Postale 65-79, Bellinzona, Switzerland. Ed. Dr. Giuseppe Martinola. bibl.; illus. circ. 400. (also avail. in microfilm from UMI; reprint service avail. from UMI) **Indexed:** Amer.Hist.& Life, Hist.Abstr.

945 IT ISSN 0006-6591
BOLLETTINO STORICO PIACENTINO. 1906. 2/yr. L.30000 (foreign L.60000). Tip Le Co., Via S. Salotti 39-41, 29100 Piacenza, Italy. TEL 0523-380102. FAX 0523-380520. (Dist. outside Italy by: Labardi Book Service, Via XX Settembre 40, 50129 Florence, Italy) bk.rev.; abstr.; bibl. circ. 750. **Document type:** academic/scholarly publication, bulletin.

945 IT
BOLLETTINO STORICO PISANO. vol.59, 1990. a. L.50000 (foreign L.60000) (effective 1992). Pacini Editore s.r.l., Via A. Gherardesca 1, 56014 Ospedaletto (Pisa), Italy. TEL 050-982439. FAX 050-983906. Ed. O. Banti.

HISTORY — HISTORY OF EUROPE

943 GW ISSN 0068-0052
DD901.B6
BONNER GESCHICHTSBLAETTER. 1937. a. DM.50. Bonner Heimat- und Geschichtsverein, Berliner Platz 2, 53111 Bonn, Germany. TEL 0228-773707. FAX 0228-772400. (Co-sponsor: Stadtarchiv Bonn) Ed. Manfred van Rey. circ. 1,500. **Document type:** bulletin.

943 GW ISSN 0067-9976
DD491.R4
BONNER JAHRBUECHER; des Rheinischen Landesmuseums in Bonn. 1842. a., vol.190, 1990. DM.180. Boehlau Verlag GmbH, Theodor-Heuss-Str. 76, 51149 Cologne, Germany. TEL 02203-307021. FAX 02203-307349. cum.index. (reprint service avail. from KTO) **Document type:** academic/scholarly publication.
—BLDSC (2247.687000).

942 UK ISSN 0142-7660
BONNY MOOR HEN. 1978. a. £3($6) Weardale Field Study Society, c/o L. Gooch, 12 Melbourne Place, Wolsingham, Co. Durham DL13 3EH, England. TEL 527747. charts; illus. circ. 300.

948 DK ISSN 0084-7976
BORNHOLMSKE SAMLINGER. 1906. irreg. DKK 135. Bornholms Historiske Samfund, Stenbrudsvej 5 A, DK 3730 Nexo, Denmark. Ed. Olaf Hansen. bk.rev. circ. 600. **Indexed:** Numis.Lit.

942 UK ISSN 0084-7984
BOROUGH OF TWICKENHAM LOCAL HISTORY SOCIETY. PAPERS. 1965. irreg. price varies. Twickenham Local History Society, 72 Heathfield South, Twickenham, Middlesex TW2 7SS, England. TEL 081-892-8943. Ed. D.H. Simpson. circ. 1,000. **Document type:** monographic series.
Description: Covers the history of Twickenham, Teddington, Hampton and Whitton.

943.9 HU ISSN 0520-626X
BORSODI SZEMLE. 1955. 4/yr. 266 Ft.($15) Borsod Megyei Lapkiado Vallalat, Bajcsy-Zsilinsky 14, 3530 Miskolc, Hungary. Ed. Kun Laszlo. bk.rev.; cum.index: 1956-67. circ. 600. **Indexed:** World Agri.Econ.& Rural Sociol.Abstr.

940 UK ISSN 0524-0913
BORTHWICK INSTITUTE OF HISTORICAL RESEARCH. BORTHWICK PAPERS. 1952. s-a. £3.50. (University of York) St. Anthony's Press, St. Anthony's Hall, York YO1 2PW, England. TEL 0904-642315. Ed. W.J. Sheils. adv.; bk.rev.; bibl. circ. 350. **Document type:** academic/scholarly publication.
—BLDSC (2251.750000).
Description: Concerned with the history of Yorkshire and the ecclesiastical history of the North of England.

914.221 UK ISSN 0520-6790
DA670.B66
BOURNE SOCIETY LOCAL HISTORY RECORDS. 1962. a. £2. Bourne Society, c/o 17 Manor Ave., Caterham, Surrey CR3 6AP, England. Ed. T.J. Boyle. adv.; bibl.; charts; illus.; index. circ. 4,000. **Indexed:** Br.Archaeol.Abstr.

946.9 PO ISSN 0006-8640
BRACARA AUGUSTA; revista cultural de regionalismo e historia. 1949. irreg. price varies. (Camara Municipal de Braga) Livraria Cruz, Rua D. Diogo de Sousa 129-133, Braga, Portugal. Ed.Bd. bibl.; illus.; index.

943 700 GW
BRAUNSCHWEIGISCHE HEIMAT; Zeitschrift fuer Natur- u. Heimatpflege, Landes- u. Volkskunde, Geschichte, Kunst u. Kultur Ostfalens. 1913. s-a. DM.36. Braunschweigischer Landesverein fuer Heimatschutz, Burgplatz 1, 38100 Braunschweig, Germany. TEL 0531-474-2602. Ed.Bd. adv.; bk.rev. circ. 32. (back issues avail.)

943 GW ISSN 0068-0745
BRAUNSCHWEIGISCHES JAHRBUCH. 1902. a. DM.32. Braunschweigischer Geschichtsverein e.V., Schriftleitung, Forstweg 2, 3340 Wolfenbuettel, Germany. Ed. H.R. Jarck. circ. 1,300. **Indexed:** Bibl.Cart.

941 IE ISSN 0068-0877
BREIFNE; journal of Cumann Seanchais Bhreifne. (Text in English and Irish Gaelic) 1958. a. I£10. Breifne Historical Society, Cana House, Cavan, Co. Cavan, Ireland. TEL 049-61094. Ed. Daniel Gallogly. bk.rev. circ. 800. **Document type:** academic/scholarly publication.

940 GW ISSN 0341-9622
DD901.B71
BREMISCHES JAHRBUCH. 1863. a. price varies. Staatsarchiv Bremen, Am Staatsarchiv 1, 28203 Bremen, Germany. TEL 0421-3616217. FAX 0421-36110247. (Co-sponsor: Historische Gesellschaft Bremen) Ed. Andreas Roepcke. bk.rev.; illus. circ. 1,500. **Indexed:** Bibl.Cart. **Document type:** academic/scholarly publication.

949 NE
BRIEVEN VAN PAULUS; geschied- en heemkundige artikelen en berichten. 1975. 5/yr. fl.25. Heemkundekring Paulus van Daesdonck, Postbus 89, 4850 AB Ulvenhout, Netherlands. Ed. C.J.M. Leijten. bk.rev. circ. 750.

BRISTOL AND GLOUCESTERSHIRE ARCHAEOLOGICAL SOCIETY, BRISTOL, ENGLAND. TRANSACTIONS. see ARCHAEOLOGY

942 UK ISSN 0068-1075
DA630
BRITAIN: AN OFFICIAL HANDBOOK. a. $31. Central Office of Information, Reference and Translations Divisions, Hercules Rd., London SE1 7DU, England. (Orders to: Government Bookshop, 49 High Holborn, London WC1V 6HB, England; Dist. in U.S. by Unipub, 4611-F Assembly Dr., Lanham, MD 20706-4391 Lanham, MD 20706) illus.
—BLDSC (2286.040000). CCC.
Description: Describes many features in the life of the country, including the workings of the Government and other major institutions.

940 NE ISSN 0066-1821
BRITAIN AND THE NETHERLANDS. 1960. a. price varies. Walburg Pers BV, Postbus 4159, 7200 BD Zutphen, Netherlands. TEL 31-5750-10522. FAX 31-5750-41025.
—BLDSC (2286.047000).

940 UK ISSN 0068-113X
DA145
BRITANNIA. 1970. a. £25($50) to individuals; institutions £30($60). Society for the Promotion of Roman Studies, 31-34 Gordon Sq., London WC1H 0PP, England. TEL 071-387-8157. Ed. M.G. Fulford. adv.; bk.rev. circ. 1,500. (back issues avail.) **Indexed:** Bibl.Ling., Numis.Lit. **Document type:** academic/scholarly publication.
—BLDSC (2286.300000).
Description: Articles on all aspects of Romano-British studies; includes survey of Romano-British excavations.

942 942 UK
BRITISH ACADEMY. PROCEEDINGS. 1903. a. Oxford University Press, Oxford Journals, Walton St., Oxford OX2 6DP, England. TEL 0865-56767. FAX 0865-267773. TELEX 837330-OXPRES-G. (U.S. subscr. to: Oxford University Press Inc., 2001 Evans Rd., Cary, NC 27513. TEL 919-677-0977) cum.index: vols.1-63. (reprint service avail. from KTO) **Indexed:** Amer.Hist.& Life, Bibl.Ling., Br.Archaeol.Abstr., Br.Hum.Ind., Hist.Abstr., RILA. **Document type:** academic/scholarly publication.

942 US ISSN 0195-2633
BRITISH HERITAGE. 1974. bi-m. $30. Cowles Magazines, Inc. (Subsidiary of: Cowles Media Company), 17112 Flank Dr., Box 8200, Harrisburg, PA 17105-8200. TEL 717-657-9555. FAX 717-657-9526. (Subscr. to: Box 1066. Mt. Morris, IL 61054) Ed. Gail Huganir. adv.; bk.rev.; bibl.; illus.; cum.index: 1974-1979. circ. 100,195. (also avail. in microform from UMI; reprint service avail. from UMI) **Indexed:** Amer.Hist.& Life (until 1991), Hist.Abstr. (until 1991). **Document type:** consumer publication.
—BLDSC (2301.310000); UnCover; UMI.
Incorporates: British History Illustrated.

943 370 UK ISSN 0966-095X
▼**BRITISH JOURNAL OF HOLOCAUST EDUCATION.** 1992. 2/yr. £20($30) to individuals; institutions £36 ($55). Frank Cass & Co. Ltd., Gainsborough House, 11 Gainsborough Rd., London E11 1RS, England. TEL 081-530-4226. FAX 081-530-7795. Ed. John P. Fox. adv.: B&W page £185; adv. contact: Anne Kidson. bk.rev.; index. (back issues avail.) **Indexed:** Amer.Hist.& Life (1992-), Hist.Abstr. (1992- **Document type:** academic/scholarly publication.
—BLDSC (2309.440000).
Description: Provides a forum for informed debate on a range of historical, educational, philosophical, religious and sociological issues concerned with the teaching and research of the Holocaust in the UK.

BRITISH SCHOOL AT ATHENS. ANNUAL. see GENERAL INTEREST PERIODICALS — Greece

BRITISH SCHOOL AT ROME. PAPERS. ARCHAEOLOGY, HISTORY, HISTORY OF ART. see ARCHAEOLOGY

BRYGGAN. see POPULATION STUDIES

948 FI ISSN 0302-2447
DL30
BUDKAVLEN. (Text in English, Swedish; summaries in German) 1922. a. FIM 60. Aabo Akademi, Institutet foer Folklivsforskning, Budkavlen, 20500 Aabo 50, Finland. TEL 358-21-654396. Ed. Nils Storaa. bk.rev.; cum.index 1922-55. circ. 300. **Indexed:** Anthropol.Lit. **Document type:** academic/scholarly publication.

949.77 BU ISSN 0204-8906
BULGARIAN HISTORICAL REVIEW/REVUE BULGARE D'HISTOIRE. (Text in English, French, German; summaries in Russian) 1973. q. 2.70 lv. per issue. (Bulgarska Akademiia na Naukite) Publishing House of the Bulgarian Academy of Sciences, Acad. G. Bonchev St., Bldg. 6, 1113 Sofia, Bulgaria. (Dist. by: Hemus, 6, Rouski Blvd., 1000 Sofia, Bulgaria) Ed. D. Kosev. adv.; bk.rev.; abstr.; bibl.; illus.; index. circ. 670. (also avail. in microfilm; reprint service avail. from IRC) **Indexed:** Amer.Hist.& Life, Arts & Hum.Cit.Ind., Curr.Cont., Hist.Abstr.
—BLDSC (2366.682000); UnCover.

949 BU ISSN 0323-9985
BULGARSKA AKADEMIIA NA NAUKITE. INSTITUT ZA ISTORIIA. IZVESTIIA. Title varies slightly. (Text in Bulgarian; summaries in various languages) 1951. irreg. 2.41 lv. Publishing House of the Bulgarian Academy of Sciences, Acad. G. Bonchev St., Bldg. 6, 1113 Sofia, Bulgaria. (Dist. by: Hemus, 6, Rouski Blvd., 1000 Sofia, Bulgaria) Ed. D. Kosev. circ. 778. (reprint service avail. from IRC)

947 320 BU ISSN 0861-444X
AP58.B8
BULGARSKI DNEVNIK/BULGARIAN DIARY.* 1976. w. Blvd. Vitosha 18, 1080 Sofia, Bulgaria. TEL 2-881221. (Dist. by: Hemus Foreign Trade Co., 6 Ruski Blvd., 1000 Sofia, Bulgaria) Ed. Dimitur Ezekiev. illus. circ. 60,000.
Formerly (until 1991): Otechestvo (ISSN 0204-4056)

BULGARSKI ZHURNALIST/BULGARIAN JOURNALIST. see JOURNALISM

944 FR ISSN 0766-4516
BULLETIN D'HISTOIRE DE LA REVOLUTION FRANCAISE. 1961. biennial. price varies. Ministere de l'Education Nationale, Commission d'Histoire de la Revolution Francaise, 1 rue d'Ulm, 75005 Paris, France. TEL 49-55-23-64. FAX 49-55-23-84. bk.rev.; cum.index. circ. 650. **Indexed:** Amer.Hist.& Life, Hist.Abstr. **Document type:** bulletin.
Formerly: Bulletin d'Histoire Economique et Sociale de la Revolution Francaise (ISSN 0068-4058)

900 FR ISSN 0007-4640
PQ6001
BULLETIN HISPANIQUE. (Text in French and Spanish) 1899. s-a. (Universite Bordeaux III, Institut Hispaniques) Editions Biere, 18-22 rue du Peugue, 33000 Bordeaux, France. bk.rev.; abstr.; bibl.; charts; illus.; s-a. index, cum.index: vols.1-60 (1899-1958), vols.61-70 (1959-1968). circ. 1,500. (reprint service avail. from SWZ) **Indexed:** Amer.Hist.& Life, Arts & Hum.Cit.Ind., Bibl.Ling., Curr.Cont., Hisp.Amer.Per.Ind., Hist.Abstr., M.L.A.
—SWETS.

HISTORY — HISTORY OF EUROPE

944 500   FR   ISSN 0007-4659
BULLETIN HISTORIQUE ET SCIENTIFIQUE DE L'AUVERGNE. 1881. q. membership. Academie des Sciences, Belles-Lettres et Arts de Clermont-Ferrand, 19 rue Bardoux, 63000 Clermont-Ferrand (Puy-de-Dome), France. illus.; index.

945 709   IT   ISSN 0007-5795
BULLETTINO STORICO EMPOLESE. 1957. s-a. L.30000 to members (effective 1991). Associazione Turistica Pro-Empoli (ATPE), Piazza Farinata degli Uberti 8-9, 50053 Empoli, Italy. TEL 0571-76-115. Ed. Dott. Alessandro Masoni. adv.; bk.rev. circ. 700.

945   IT   ISSN 0007-5809
BULLETTINO STORICO PISTOIESE. 1899; 3rd series 1966. s-a. L.30000($18) Societa Pistoiese di Storia Patria, Vicolo della Sapienza, 12, 51100 Pistoia, Italy. Ed. Elena Vannucchi. bk.rev.; abstr.; index, cum.index. **Document type:** bulletin.

940   GW   ISSN 0007-6201
BURGEN UND SCHLOESSER. 1960. 3/yr. DM.40. Deutsche Burgenvereinigung e.V., Marksburg, 56338 Braubach, Germany. TEL 02627-536. FAX 02627-8866. Ed. Hartmut Hofrichter. adv.; bk.rev.; abstr.; bibl.; charts; illus.; cum.index. circ. 3,500. (tabloid format) **Indexed:** NAA, RILA. **Document type:** academic/scholarly publication.
—BLDSC (2931.610000).

940   AU   ISSN 0007-621X
BURGENLAENDISCHE FORSCHUNGEN. 1947. irreg. Amt der Burgenlaendischen Landesregierung, Landesarchiv und Landesbibliothek, Freiheitsplatz 1, A-7001 Eisenstadt, Austria. bk.rev. circ. 1,000. **Document type:** monographic series.

500.9   AU   ISSN 0007-6236
BURGENLAENDISCHE HEIMATBLAETTER. 1932. q. S.120. Amt der Burgenlaendischen Landesregierung, Landesarchiv und Landesbibliothek, Freiheitsplatz 1, A-7001 Eisenstadt, Austria. bk.rev.; abstr.; bibl.; index. circ. 1,200. **Indexed:** Amer.Hist.& Life, Hist.Abstr. **Document type:** academic/scholarly publication.

BUZETSKI ZBORNIK. see *ARCHAEOLOGY*

943.8   PL   ISSN 0068-4589
BYDGOSKIE TOWARZYSTWO NAUKOWE. WYDZIAL NAUK HUMANISTYCZNYCH. PRACE. SERIA C (HISTORIA I ARCEOLOGIA). 1963. irreg. price varies. Bydgoskie Towarzystwo Naukowe, Jezuicka 4, Bydgoszcz, Poland. (Dist. by Ars Polona-Ruch, Krakowskie Przedmiescie 7, Warsaw, Poland)

942   UK   ISSN 0262-5342
BYGONE KENT; a monthly journal on all aspects of Kent local history. 1979. m. £26. Meresborough Books, 17 Station Rd., Rainham, Kent ME8 7RS, England. TEL 0634-388812. Ed. P. O'Driscoll. adv.; bk.rev. circ. 2,000. **Document type:** newsletter.

948 914   DK   ISSN 0105-6433
BYHORNET; nyt fra Egnsmuseet i Pederstrup. 1972. a. DKK 20. Ballerup Historiske Forening, Egnsmuseet Lindbjerggaard, Pederstrupvej 51, Pederstrup, DK-2750 Ballerup, Denmark. TEL 44 97 11 13. FAX 44-97-27-18. Ed. Jorgen O. Bjerregaard. circ. 400. **Document type:** academic/scholarly publication.

948.1   NO   ISSN 0007-7631
BYMINNER. 1955. q. NOK 150 (effective Jan 1992). Oslo Bymuseum, Frognervn. 67, Oslo 2, Norway. TEL 47-22-43-06-45. FAX 47-22-43-48-01. Ed. Jorunn Sanstoel. adv.; illus. circ. 3,000. **Indexed:** Numis.Lit.
—CCC.

940 880   AT   ISSN 0725-3079
BYZANTINA AUSTRALIENSIA. 1981. irreg., approx. biennial. price varies. Australian Association for Byzantine Studies, University of Sydney, Department of Modern Greek, Sydney, N.S.W. 2006, Australia. TEL 01-692-3658. FAX 02-692-3543. **Document type:** academic/scholarly publication.
—BLDSC (2941.902500).
Description: Translations of texts and related studies on all aspects of the Byzantine Empire.

949   NE   ISSN 0525-4507
BYZANTINA NEERLANDICA. 1969. irreg., vol.11, 1990. price varies. E.J. Brill, P.O. Box 9000, 2300 PA Leiden, Netherlands. TEL 31-71-312624. FAX 31-71-317532. TELEX 39296 BRILL NL. (In N. America: E.J. Brill, 24 Hudson St., Kinderhook, NY 12106. TEL 800-962-4406. FAX 518-758-1959) Ed.Bd. (back issues avail.) **Document type:** monographic series.
Refereed Serial

949.5   UK   ISSN 0307-0131
DF541
BYZANTINE AND MODERN GREEK STUDIES. (Text in English; quotations in Greek) 1975. a. £25($55) to individuals; institutions £40 ($85). c/o Prof. Anthony Bryer, Centre for Byzantine, Ottoman and Modern Greek Studies, University of Birmingham, P.O. Box 363, Birmingham B15 2TT, England. TEL 021-414-5775. FAX 021-414-3656. Ed. J.F. Haldon. adv. circ. 300. **Indexed:** Amer.Bibl.Slavic & E.Eur.Stud, Amer.Hist.& Life, Bibl.Ling., Curr.Cont., Hist.Abstr., M.L.A. **Document type:** academic/scholarly publication.
—BLDSC (2941.950000); Faxon.
Description: Welcomes research, criticism, contributions on theory and method in the form of articles, critical studies and short notes.

949.5   SP   ISSN 0167-5346
BYZANTINISCHE FORSCHUNGEN. (Text in French, English and German) 1966. irreg. A.M. Hakkert, Calle Alfambra, 26, 35010 Las Plamas de Gran Canaria, Spain. TEL 28277550. (Dist. by: J.C. Gieben, Nieuwe Herengracht 35, 1011 RM Amsterdam, Netherlands. TEL 31-20-6275170. FAX 31-20-6275170; Dist. in N. America by: John Benjamins Publishing Co., 821 Bethlehem Pike, Philadelphia, PA 19118. TEL 215-836-1200. FAX 215-836-1204) **Indexed:** Numis.Lit. **Document type:** monographic series.

947   BU   ISSN 0068-4686
BYZANTINOBULGARICA. (Text in English, French, German and Russian) 1962. irreg., no.2, 1966. (Bulgarska Akademiya na Naukite) Publishing House of the Bulgarian Academy of Sciences, Ul. Akad. G. Bonchev, Bldg. 6, 1113 Sofia, Bulgaria. (reprint service avail. from IRC) **Indexed:** Numis.Lit., RILA.

940   BE
C I V I C I M A. 1988. irreg., vol.6, 1993. price varies. (Comite International du Vocabulaire des Institutions et de la Communication Intellectuelles au Moyen Age) N.V. Brepols, Steenweg op Tielen 68, 2300 Turnhout, Belgium. TEL 32-14-402500. FAX 32-14-428919. Ed. O. Weijers. (back issues avail.) **Document type:** proceedings.
Description: Studies issues relating to the intellectual life of Europe in the Middle Ages.

949.3   BE   ISSN 0007-9626
DH802.A2
CAHIERS BRUXELLOIS; revue d'histoire urbaine. 1956. q. 550 Fr. c/o Mina Martens, 25, rue Felix Delhasse, 1060 Brussels, Belgium. Ed. Mina Martens. bk.rev.; charts; illus. circ. 500.

943.9   FR   ISSN 1149-6525
CAHIERS D'ETUDES HONGROISES. (Text in French; summaries in Hungarian) 1989. a. 90 F. Centre Interuniversitaire d'Etudes Hongroises, 1 rue Censier, 75005 Paris, France. TEL 45-87-41-83. FAX 43-37-10-01. (Co-sponsor: Institut Hongrois de Paris) Ed. Gyorgy Tverdota. adv. contact: Monique Raynaud. bk.rev. adv. 400. **Indexed:** Bibl.Ling. **Document type:** academic/scholarly publication.
Description: Offers articles, chronicles and book reviews focusing on Hungarian culture, society and history, or on French-Hungarian bilateral relations.

CAHIERS DE L'EMIGRATION RUSSE. see *LITERATURE*

944   FR   ISSN 0007-9898
CAHIERS DE L'IROISE. 1954. q. 160 F. Societe d'Etudes de Brest et du Leon, Rue des Archives, 29200 Brest, France. adv.; bk.rev.; charts; illus.; index. circ. 1,500. (back issues avail.) **Document type:** academic/scholarly publication.
Description: Devoted to local history and heritage, Breton culture and art.

940   FR   ISSN 0395-9317
CAHIERS DE LA MEDITERRANEE. 1970. s-a. 120 F. Centre de la Mediterranee Moderne et Contemporaine, U.E.R. Lettres, B.P. 369, 98 Blvd. E. Herriot, 06007 Nice, France. bk.rev. (back issues avail.)

940   FR   ISSN 1147-3797
CAHIERS DU LEOPARD D'OR. 1989. irreg. Editions le Leopard d'Or, 8 rue du Couedic, 75014 Paris, France.

947   FR   ISSN 0008-0160
DK1
CAHIERS DU MONDE RUSSE ET SOVIETIQUE. 1960. q. 270 F. to individuals; institutions 400 F. (foreign 460 F.). Editions de l' Ecole des Hautes Etudes en Sciences Sociales, 131 bd. St. Michel, 75005 Paris, France. (Dist. by: Gauthier-Villars, Centrale des Revues, 11 rue Gossin, 92543 Montrouge Cedex, France. TEL 1-46-56-52-66) Ed.Bd. adv.; bk.rev.; bibl.; index. circ. 1,000. **Indexed:** Amer.Hist.& Life, Arts & Hum.Cit.Ind., Curr.Cont., Excerp.Med., Hist.Abstr., M.L.A., SSCI.
—Faxon; UnCover; SWETS.

944 930.1   FR   ISSN 0763-9945
CAHIERS DU VITREZAIS. 1971. q. 120 F. (foreign 150 F.). Amis du Vitrezais, Maison de Pays, 33920 Saint Savin, France. Ed. Johel Coutura.

942   FR   ISSN 0184-7678
PR1
CAHIERS ELISABETHAINS; late medieval and renaissance English studies. (Text in English, French) 1972. s-a. 140 F. (foreign 180 F.). Universite de Montpellier (Universite Paul Valery), Centre d'Etudes et de Recherches Elisabethaines, B.P. 5043, 34032 Montpellier Cedex 1, France. TEL 67-14-22-00. FAX 67-14-22-00. Ed. Jean-Marie Maguin. adv.; bk.rev.; play rev.; charts; stat.; cum.index every 10 issues. circ. 500. (back issues avail.) **Indexed:** Arts & Hum.Cit.Ind., Curr.Cont., M.L.A. **Document type:** academic/scholarly publication.
—BLDSC (2948.862800); UnCover; SWETS.
Description: Features articles, notes and reviews on all aspects of the English Renaissance.

914.4   FR   ISSN 0758-6760
CAHIERS LORRAINS. 1920. q. 240 F. (typically set in Nov.). Societe d'Histoire et d'Archeologie de la Lorraine, Archives Departementales de la Moselle, 1 allee du Chateau, 57070 Saint Julien les Metz, France. TEL 87-76-26-26. (Affiliate: Academie Nationale de Metz) adv.; bk.rev.; bibl.; illus.
Supersedes (in 1980): Societe d'Histoire et d'Archeologie de la Lorraine. Annuaire.

949   NE   ISSN 0168-8367
CAHIERS SOCIALE GESCHIEDENIS. 1982. irreg. price varies. Kluwer Academic Publishers, Postbus 17, 3300 AA Dordrecht, Netherlands. TEL 31-78-334911. FAX 31-78-334254. TELEX 29245 KAPG NL. (Dist. by: Kluwer Academic Publishers Group, P.O. Box 322, 3300 AH Dordrecht, Netherlands. TEL 31-78-524400. FAX 31-78-524474; N. America dist. addr.: Box 358, Accord Sta., Hingham, MA 02018-0358. TEL 617-871-6600. FAX 617-871-6528) **Document type:** monographic series.
Refereed Serial

942   UK   ISSN 0008-0535
CAKE AND COCKHORSE. 1959. 3/yr. £5 (with a record volume £8) (typically set in Jan.). Banbury Historical Society, Banbury Museum, 8 Horsefair, Banubry, Oxfordshire OX16 0AA, England. TEL 0295-259855. Ed. D.A. Hitchcox. bk.rev.; bibl.; index. circ. 400. **Indexed:** Br.Archaeol.Abstr. **Document type:** academic/scholarly publication.
Description: Local history publication covering the history and archaeology of Banbury and the surrounding villages.

CALABRIA NOBILISSIMA. see *ART*

CALENDAR OF HISTORY EVENTS. see *HISTORY — History Of North And South America*

HISTORY — HISTORY OF EUROPE

942 800 410   UK
CAMBRIAN MEDIEVAL CELTIC STUDIES. 1981. 2/yr. £10 to individuals; institutions £14. (Old College, Department of Welsh) C M C S Publications, Department of Welsh, King St., Aberystwyth SY23 2AX, Wales. Ed. Patrick Sims-Williams. adv.; bk.rev. (back issues avail.) **Indexed:** Arts & Hum.Cit.Ind., Bibl.Ling., Br.Archaeol.Abstr., Curr.Cont., M.L.A. **Document type:** academic/scholarly publication.
—Faxon; UnCover.
  Formerly (until 1993): Cambridge Medieval Celtic Studies (ISSN 0260-5600)
  Description: Covers Medieval Celtic language, literature, history, and archaeology of Ireland, Scotland, Wales, and Brittany from A.D. 400 to 1500.

942 913   UK   ISSN 0309-3603
CC23
CAMBRIDGE ANTIQUARIAN SOCIETY. PROCEEDINGS. 1840. a. £10 to individuals; institutions £15. Cambridge Antiquarian Society, Museum of Archaeology and Anthropology, Downing St., Cambridge CB2 3DZ, England. FAX 0223-333503. Ed. A.S. Bendall. bk.rev.; cum.index. circ. 700. **Indexed:** Br.Archaeol.Abstr., Br.Hum.Ind., Numis.Lit., RILA. **Document type:** proceedings.
  Formerly: Cambridge Antiquarian Communications.
  Description: Contains local history, archaeology, and excavation reports for Cambridge and Cambridgeshire.

942   UK   ISSN 0950-6314
CAMBRIDGE STUDIES IN MEDIEVAL LIFE AND THOUGHT; fourth series. 1920; N.S. 1967. irreg., no.6, 1987. price varies. Cambridge University Press, Edinburgh Bldg., Shaftesbury Rd., Cambridge CB2 2RU, England. TEL 0223-312393. FAX 0223-315052. TELEX 851817256. (N. American addr.: Cambridge University Press, Journals Dept., 40 W. 20th St., New York, NY 100011. TEL 212-924-3900. FAX 212-691-3239) Ed. J.C. Holt. index. **Indexed:** M.L.A. **Document type:** monographic series.
—BLDSC (3015.995000).
  Supersedes: Cambridge Studies in Medieval Life and Thought: Third Series (ISSN 0068-6786)

942   UK   ISSN 0960-1163
DA20
CAMDEN FIFTH SERIES. Key Title: Camden Series. 1838; 4th series 1964; 5th series 1993. a. membership. Royal Historical Society, University College London, Gower St., London WC1E 6BT, England. TEL 071-387-7532. **Document type:** academic/scholarly publication.
  Supersedes (in 1993): Camden Fourth Series (ISSN 0068-6905)

940   UK   ISSN 0305-4756
CAMDEN HISTORY REVIEW. 1973. irreg., no.15, 1988. £3 per no. Camden History Society, Swiss Cottage Library, Avenue Rd., London NW3, England. Ed. John Gage. bk.rev.; bibl.; cum.index. circ. 2,000. **Indexed:** Br.Tech.Ind.
—BLDSC (3016.033000).
  Description: Regional English history.

945   IT
CAMPANIA DOCUMENTI. 1974. bi-m. L.8000. (Istituto di Studi Carlo Pisacane di Napoli) Societa Editrice Napoletana s.r.l., Corso Umberto I 34, 80138 Naples, Italy. Ed. G. Buonpane.

940 200   IT   ISSN 0392-1352
CAMPANIA SACRA; rivista di storia sociale e religiosa del Mezzogiorno. 1970. s-a. L.65000($45) (effective 1994). (Facolta Teologica dell'Italia Meridionale, Sezione "S. Tommaso d'Aquino") Edizioni Dehoniane Roma, Viale Colli Aminei, 2, 80131 Naples, Italy. TEL 081-7413166. FAX 081-7413041. Ed. Domenico Ambrasi. circ. 1,000. **Document type:** academic/scholarly publication.

945   IT
CAMPUS MAIOR; rivista di studi camaioresi. a. L.30000 membership. Istituto Storico Lucchese, Sezione di Camaiore, Biblioteca Comunale Michele Rosi, Via Vittorio Emanuele 101, 55041 Camaiore, Italy. Ed. Andrea Roncoli.

940   FR   ISSN 1167-6817
CAMPUS STELLAE. 1991. a. (Secretaire General du Conseil de l'Europe) Editions Klincksieck, 11 rue de Lille, 75007 Paris, France. Ed. Denise Pericard-Mea.

CANADIAN JOURNAL OF ITALIAN STUDIES. see LITERATURE

CANADIAN JOURNAL OF NETHERLANDIC STUDIES/REVUE CANADIENNE D'ETUDES NEERLANDAISES. see LITERATURE

CANADIAN PAPERS IN RURAL HISTORY. see HISTORY — History Of North And South America

943   GW
CANAL - VEREIN. MITTEILUNGEN. 1981. a. DM.25. Canal-Verein e.V., c/o Dr. Fuersen und Kaminski, Rendsburgerstr. 30, 24768 Rendsburg, Germany. TEL 04331-61065. FAX 04331-63311. Eds. E.J. Fuersen, C. Mueller-Boysen. adv. circ. 900. **Document type:** academic/scholarly publication.
  Description: History of canals in Schleswig-Holstein and other areas of Germany.

943.6   AU   ISSN 0008-6606
DB281
CARINTHIA 1; Zeitschrift fuer geschichtliche Landeskunde von Kaernten. 1811. a. S.300. Geschichtsverein fuer Kaernten, Museumgasse 2, A-9020 Klagenfurt, Austria. TEL 0463-536-30573. Ed. Alfred Ogris. bk.rev.; charts; illus.; stat.; index, cum.index. circ. 3,000. **Indexed:** Amer.Hist.& Life, Hist.Abstr. **Document type:** bulletin.

CARPATHO-RUSYN AMERICAN. see ETHNIC INTERESTS

945   IT   ISSN 0394-4344
CARTEGGI UMANISTICI. 1984. irreg., no.5. 1991. price varies. (Istituto Nazionale di Studi sul Rinascimento) Casa Editrice Leo S. Olschki, Casella Postale 66, 50100 Florence, Italy. TEL 055-6530684. FAX 055-6530214. **Document type:** monographic series.

943.7 320   XR   ISSN 0323-052X
DB541
CASOPIS MATICE MORAVSKE. 1869. s-a. Matice Moravska, Gorkeho 14, 602 00 Brno, Czech Republic. (Dist. by: Artia, Ve Smeckach 30, 111 27 Prague 1, Czech Republic) Ed. Jan Janak. bk.rev.; cum.index: vols.1-50, 1929; vols.51-60, 1937; vols. 61-100, 1983. circ. 520. **Indexed:** Amer.Hist.& Life, Bibl.Ling., CERDIC, Hist.Abstr.

CASOPIS ZA SUVREMENU POVIJEST/MAGAZINE OF CONTEMPORARY HISTORY. see HISTORY

949.7   XV   ISSN 0590-5966
DR381.S6
CASOPIS ZA ZGODOVINO IN NARODOPISJE. 1904; N.S. 1965. 2/yr. 840 SLT. Univerza v Mariboru, Zalozba Obzorja, Partizanska 5, 62001 Maribor, Slovenia. TEL 38-62-25681. Ed. Vladimir Bracic. bk.rev.; illus.; cum.index: 1924-1940. circ. 600. **Indexed:** Amer.Hist. & Life, Hist.Abstr.

940.54 355   UK
CASS SERIES ON THE SOVIET STUDY OF WAR. 1991. irreg., vol. 2, 1991. Frank Cass & Co. Ltd., Gainsborough House, 11 Gainsborough Rd., London E11 1RS, England. TEL 081-530-4226. FAX 081-530-7795. (In U.S.: c/o International Specialized Book Services, Inc., 5804 N.E. Hassalo St., Portland, OR 97213-3644) Ed. David M. Glantz. **Document type:** monographic series.

946   CR
CATALUNYA AYER Y HOY. 1988. bi-m. $8. Editorial Papiro, Calle 15, No. 635, San Jose, Costa Rica.

942   IE   ISSN 0332-4117
CATHAIR NA MART. 1981. a. $10. Westport Historical Society, c/o Carrowholly Lodge, Westport, Co. Mayo, Ireland. Ed. Sheila Mulloy. adv.; illus. circ. 1,000. **Document type:** academic/scholarly publication.
—BLDSC (3092.984000).

CELTIC KNOT. see GENEALOGY AND HERALDRY

945   IT   ISSN 0392-1409
CENACOLO (TARANTO); rivista di lettere, storia e arte. 1971. a. L.25000. (Societa di Storia Patria per la Puglia, Sezione di Taranto) Mandese Editore s.r.l., Viale Liguria 82, 74100 Taranto, Italy. TEL 099-374174. (Edit. addr.: c/o Archivio di Stato, Via Di Palma 4, 74100 Taranto, Italy) Ed. Giovanni Massagli.

940   US
CENTER FOR EUROPEAN STUDIES WORKING PAPER SERIES. irreg. (approx. 8/yr.) $4 (foreign $5) per no. Harvard University, Minda de Gunzburg Center for European Studies, 27 Kirkland St., Cambridge, MA 02138-2043. TEL 617-495-4303. FAX 617-495-8509. Ed. Peter A. Hall. **Document type:** monographic series, academic/scholarly publication.

943   US   ISSN 0008-9389
D901
CENTRAL EUROPEAN HISTORY. 1968. q. $36 to individuals; institutions $58. (American Historical Association, Conference Group for Central European History) Humanities Press, 165 First Ave., Atlantic Highlands, NJ 07716. TEL 908-872-1441. FAX 908-872-0717. Ed. Kenneth Barkin. adv.; bk.rev.; bibl.; charts; stat.; index. circ. 1,800. (back issues avail.) **Indexed:** Amer.Bibl.Slavic & E.Eur.Stud., Amer.Hist.& Life, Arts & Hum.Cit.Ind., Bk.Rev.Ind. (1975-), Child.Bk.Rev.Ind. (1975-), Curr.Cont., Hist.Abstr., Hum.Ind., SSCI. **Document type:** academic/scholarly publication.
—BLDSC (3106.138000); Faxon; UnCover; SWETS.
  Description: Covers the comparative history, film history, social history of art, theory and methodology of Germany and Austria, as well as the area historically included in the Holy Roman Empire.

940   BE   ISSN 0076-1192
CENTRE BELGE D'HISTOIRE RURALE. PUBLICATIONS/BELGISCH CENTRUM VOOR LANDELIJKE GESCHIEDENIS. PUBLIKATIES. (Text in Dutch, French, English, German) 1963. irreg., no.98, 1991. price varies. Centre Belge d'Histoire Rurale, 1 Place Blaise Pascal, 1348 Louvain-La-Neuve, Belgium. circ. 500.

944 320   FR   ISSN 0244-9404
CENTRE D'HISTOIRE CONTEMPORAINE DU LANGUEDOC-ROUSSILLON. BULLETIN. 2/yr. Universite de Montpellier (Universite Paul Valery), Centre d'Histoire Contemporaine du Languedoc-Mediterraneen et du Rousillon, B.P. 5043, 34032 Montpellier Cedex 1, France. TEL 67-14-20-00.

920   BE
CENTRE D'HISTOIRE ET D'ART DE LA THUDINIE. PUBLICATIONS. 1977. irreg. (1-2/yr.). 300 Fr. Centre d'Histoire et d'Art de la Thudinie, 6, rue M. des Ombiaux, CH-6530 Thuin, Belgium. illus.

940 956   FR
CENTRE DE RECHERCHE D'HISTOIRE ET CIVILISATION DE BYZANCE. TRAVAUX ET MEMOIRES. irreg. (Centre de Recherche d'Histoire et Civilisation de Byzance) Edition-Diffusion De Boccard, 11 rue de Medicis, 75006 Paris, France. **Document type:** monographic series.

940.27   BE   ISSN 0775-6046
D731
CENTRE DE RECHERCHES ET D'ETUDES HISTORIQUES DE LA SECONDE GUERRE MONDIALE. CAHIERS/NAVORSINGS- EN STUDIECENTRUM VOOR DE GESCHIEDENIS VAN DE TWEEDE WERELDOORLOG. BIJDRAGEN. (Text in Dutch, French) 1969. a. 750 BEF. Centre de Recherches et d'Etudes Historiques de la Seconde Guerre Mondiale - Navorsings- en Studiecentrum voor de Geschiedenis van de Tweede Wereldoorlog, Residence Palace, Rue de la Loi, 155 - B2, B-1040 Brussels, Belgium. TEL 32-2-2874811. FAX 32-2-2874710. Ed.Bd. bk.rev.; bibl.; illus. circ. 1,000. **Indexed:** Amer.Hist.& Life, Hist.Abstr. **Document type:** academic/scholarly publication.
  Former titles (until 1985): Cahiers d'Histoire de la Seconde Guerre Mondiale - Bijdragen tot de Geschiedenis van de Tweede Wereldoorlog (ISSN 0771-6435); (until 1970): Cahiers d'Histoire de la Deuxieme Guerre Mondiale - Bijdragen tot de Geshiedenis van de Tweede Wereldoorlog (ISSN 0779-2069)

940   BE   ISSN 0069-1895
CENTRE EUROPEEN D'ETUDES BOURGUIGNONNES (XIVE-XVIE S.). PUBLICATION. (Text in English, French, German, Italian) 1959. a. 20 Fr. Centre Europeen d'Etudes Bourguignonnes, Facultes Universitaires Saint-Louis, Bd. du Jardin Botanique 43, B-1000 Brussels, Belgium. Ed. J.M. Cauchies. cum.index: 1959-1985.
  Description: Examines historical studies of the Burgonets (14th-16th centuries).

CENTRE INTERNATIONAL DE DOCUMENTATION OCCITANE. SERIE BIBLIOGRAPHIQUE. see BIBLIOGRAPHIES

944   FR   ISSN 0398-3765
CENTRE INTERNATIONAL DE DOCUMENTATION OCCITANE. SERIE ETUDES. 1978. irreg. price varies. Centre International de Documentation Occitane, B.P. 4202, 34544 Beziers Cedex, France.

943   BE   ISSN 0577-179X
CENTRE INTERUNIVERSITAIRE D'HISTOIRE CONTEMPORAINE. CAHIERS/INTERUNIVERSITAIR CENTRUM VOOR HEDENDAAGSE GESCHIEDENIS. MEDEDELINGEN. (Text in Dutch, French) irreg., no.103, 1992. Editions Nauwelaerts S.A., Rue de l'Eglise St. Suplice 19, B-1320 Beauvechain, Belgium. TEL 32-10-866737. FAX 32-2-751408. Ed.Bd. bk.rev.; bibl. **Document type:** monographic series.

944   FR
HC278.L9
CENTRE PIERRE LEON D'HISTOIRE ECONOMIQUE ET SOCIALE. BULLETIN. 1969. q. 120 F. Centre Pierre Leon d'Histoire Economique et Sociale, c/o Maurice Garden, Ed., 14, Av. Berthelot, 69363 Lyon Cedex 07, France. TEL 72-72-64-01. bk.rev.; charts. circ. 1,000. **Document type:** bulletin.
    Formerly: Centre d'Histoire Economique et Sociale de la Region Lyonnaise. Bulletin (ISSN 0249-5902)

949.7   CI
CENTRO DE RICERCHE STORICHE, ROVIGNO. LA RICERCA. 1991. irreg. $3. Centro de Ricerche Storiche, Piazza Matteotti 13, 52210 Rovigno-Rovinj, Croatia. TEL 052-811-133. FAX 052-811-121. Text in Italian. (looseleaf format)

949.7   CI   ISSN 0352-1427
CENTRO DI RICERCHE STORICHE, ROVIGNO. ATTI. (Text in Italian; summaries in Croatian, Slovenian) 1970. a. $35. Centro di Ricerche Storiche, Piazza Matteotti 13, 52210 Rovigno-Rovinj, Croatia. TEL 052 811-133. index. (looseleaf format)

949.7   CI   ISSN 0353-3301
CENTRO DI RICERCHE STORICHE, ROVIGNO. COLLANA DEGLI ATTI. (Text in Italian; summaries in Croatian, Slovenian) 1977. irreg. price varies. Centro di Ricerche Storiche, Piazza Matteotti 13, 52210 Rovigno-Rovinj, Croatia. TEL 052-811-133. index. (looseleaf format)

949.7   CI
CENTRO DI RICERCHE STORICHE, ROVIGNO. DOCUMENTI. (Text in Italian; summaries in Croatian, Slovenian) 1972. irreg. $17. Centro di Ricerche Storiche, Piazza Matteotti 13, 52210 Rovigno-Rovinj, Croatia. TEL 052-811-133. FAX 052-811-121. index. (looseleaf format)

949.7   CI   ISSN 0353-3271
CENTRO DI RICERCHE STORICHE, ROVIGNO. ETNIA. (Text in Italian; summaries in Croatian, Slovenian) 1990. a. 350 din.($30) Centro di Ricerche Storiche, Piazza Matteotti 13, 52210 Rovigno-Rovinj, Croatia. TEL 052-811-133. FAX 052-811-121. index. (looseleaf format)

949.7   CI
CENTRO DI RICERCHE STORICHE, ROVIGNO. FONTI. (Text in Italian; summaries in Croatian and Slovenian) 1983. irreg. $20. Centro di Ricerche Storiche, Piazza Matteotti 13, 52210 Rovigno-Rovinj, Croatia. TEL 052-811-133. FAX 052-811-121. index. (looseleaf format)

949.7   CI   ISSN 0353-328X
CENTRO DI RICERCHE STORICHE, ROVIGNO. MONOGRAFIE. (Text in Italian; summaries in Croatian, Slovenian) 1971. irreg. price varies. Centro di Ricerche Storiche, Piazza Matteotti 13, 52210 Rovigno-Rovinj, Croatia. TEL 052-811-133. index. (looseleaf format)

949.7   CI   ISSN 0350-6746
CENTRO DI RICERCHE STORICHE, ROVIGNO. QUADERNI. (Text in Italian; summaries in Croatian, Slovenian) 1971. irreg. $35. Centro di Ricerche Storiche, Piazza Matteotti 13, 52210 Rovigno-Rovinj, Croatia. TEL 052 811-133. index. (looseleaf format)

949.7   CI   ISSN 0353-474X
CENTRO DI RICERCHE STORICHE, ROVIGNO. RICERCHE SOCIALI. (Text in Italian; summaries in Croatian, Slovenian) 1989. irreg. $9. Centro di Ricerche Storiche, Piazza Matteotti 13, 52210 Rovigno-Rovinj, Croatia. TEL 052-811-133. FAX 052-811-121. index. (looseleaf format)

940   IT
CENTRO ITALIANO DI STUDI SULL'ALTO MEDIOEVO. SETTIMANE DI STUDIO. ATTI. 1954. a. price varies. Centro Italiano di Studi sull'Alto Medioevo, Palazzo Ancaiani, 06049 Spoleto, Italy. TEL 0743-220418. FAX 0743-223507. **Document type:** academic/scholarly publication.

949.3   BE
CERCLE D'HISTOIRE ET D'ARCHEOLOGIE DE SAINT-GHISLAIN ET DE LA REGION. ANALES. a. Cercle d'Histoire et d'Archeologie de Saint-Ghislain et de la Region, Saint-Ghislain, Belgium. adv.
    Supersedes: Cercle d'Histoire et d'Archeologie de Saint-Ghislain et de la Region. Miettes d'Histoire.

944   FR
CERCLE FUSTEC DE COULANGES. DOCUMENTS. s-a. 5 F. per no. Cercle Fustec de Coulanges, 4 Avenue de Louvois, 92 Chaille, France. Ed. J.C. Choisnard.

949 913   BE
CERCLE HISTORIQUE ET FOLKLORIQUE DE BRAINE-LE-CHATEAU DE TUBIZE ET DES REGIONS VOISINES. ANNALES. 1972. a. Entente Culturelle Taille d'Aulme, Musee de la Porte, Ave. Bel-air 46, 1440 Braine le Chateau, Belgium.

949 724   BE
CERCLE HUTOIS DES SCIENCES ET BEAUX-ARTS. ANNALES. 1875. a. Cercle Hutois des Sciences et Beaux-Arts, Ancien Couvent des Freres Mineurs, Rue Vankeerberghen 20, 5200 Huy, Belgium.

943.7   XR   ISSN 0232-0266
CESKOSLOVENSKA AKADEMIE VED. USTAV PRO JAZYK CESKY. ONOMASTICKY ZPRAVODAJ. Key Title: Onomasticky Zpravodaj C S A V. (Text in Czech, German, Polish, Russian, Slovak) 1960. a. Ceskoslovenska Akademie Ved, Ustav pro Jazyk Cesky, Krakovska 10, 110 00 Prague 1, Czech Republic. TEL 264301. Ed. M. Knappova. bk.rev. circ. 350. **Indexed:** Bibl.Ling.
    Formerly (until 1983): Zpravodaj Mistopisne Komise C S A V (ISSN 0231-6358)

943.7   XR
CESKOSLOVENSKO-SOVETSKE VZTAHY. 1972. a. Universita Karlova, Filosoficka Fakulta, Nam. Krasnoarmejcu 1, 116 38 Prague 1, Czech Republic. (Dist. by: Artia, Ve Smeckach 30, 111 27 Prague 1, Czech Republic)

900   XR   ISSN 0045-6187
DB191
CESKOSLOVENSKY CASOPIS HISTORICKY/CZECHOSLOVAK HISTORICAL JOURNAL. (Text in Czech or Slovak; summaries in English, French, German, Russian) 1953. bi-m. DM.158. (Czechoslovak Academy of Sciences, Institute of Czechoslovak and World History) Academia, Publishing House of the Czechoslovak Academy of Sciences, Vodickova 40, 112 29 Prague 1, Czech Republic. TEL 221-413. (Dist. in Western countries by: Kubon & Sagner, P.O. Box 34 01 08, 8000 Munich, Germany) Ed. Oldrich Riha. bk.rev. circ. 2,000. **Indexed:** Amer.Hist.& Life, CERDIC, Hist.Abstr., Numis.Lit.
    Description: Deals with Czech, Slovak and world history.

942   UK   ISSN 0141-8696
CHESHIRE HISTORY. 1978. s-a. £7 to individuals; institutions £9 (effective 1994). Cheshire Community Council, 96 Lower Bridge St., Chester, Cheshire CH1 1RU, England. TEL 44-244-322602. FAX 44-244-315389. (Ed. addr.: Langdale, Pulford Lane, Dodleston, Chester CH4 9NN, England) Ed. D. Nuttall. bk.rev.; illus. circ. 300. **Document type:** academic/scholarly publication.
    Description: Historical interests in the old and new county of Cheshire.

942   UK   ISSN 0080-0880
CHETHAM SOCIETY PUBLICATIONS - REMAINS, HISTORICAL AND LITERARY, CONNECTED WITH THE PALATINE COUNTIES OF LANCASTER AND CHESTER. 1843. a. £10 to individuals; institutions £15. (Chetham Society) Carnegie Publishing Ltd., 18 Maynard St., Preston, Lancs PR2 2AL, England. TEL 0772-881246. FAX 0772-881442. (also avail. in microfiche from IDC) **Document type:** academic/scholarly publication.

900 320 301   AU   ISSN 0254-4334
CHRISTLICHE DEMOKRATIE; Vierteljahresschrift fuer Zeitgeschichte, Sozial-, Kultur- und Wirtschaftsgeschichte. 1983. q. S.300. Karl v. Vogelsang-Institut zur Erforschung der Geschichte der Christlichen Demokratie in Oesterreich, Tivoligasse 73, A-1120 Vienna, Austria. Ed. Anneliese Weber-Hawel. adv.; bk.rev. circ. 500. (back issues avail.)
    Description: Christian Democratic Party publication devoted to Austria and politics.

940   US   ISSN 0009-5931
CHRONICA.* 1967. a. $10. Medieval Association of the Pacific, c/o Scott Waugh, Department of History, University of California, 405 Hilgard Ave., Los Angeles, CA 90024. TEL 310-825-4601. circ. 350.

946   SP
CHRONICA NOVA; revista de historia moderna. 1968. irreg., no.16, 1988. price varies. Universidad de Granada, Servicio de Publicaciones, Antiguo Colegio Maximo, Campus de Cartuja, 18071 Granada, Spain. TEL 243930. Ed. Manuel Barrios Aguilero.

949.5   GR
CHRONIKA TES CHALKIDIKES. 1961. 2/yr. Historike kai Laographike Hetaireia Chalkidikes, Odos Pringipos Nikolaou 10, Salonika, Greece.

CIRENCESTER EXCAVATIONS. see ARCHAEOLOGY

CIRPLAN. see RELIGIONS AND THEOLOGY — Protestant

CITTANOVA; mensile indipendente per Nocera, il suo agro e un po piu oltre. see ARCHAEOLOGY

944 300   FR   ISSN 0069-4290
CIVILISATIONS ET SOCIETES. 1965. irreg., no.86, 1992. price varies. Editions de l' Ecole des Hautes Etudes en Sciences Sociales, 131 bd. St-Michel, 75005 Paris, France. TEL 43-54-47-15. FAX 43-54-80-73. (Dist. by: Centre Interinstitutionnel pour la Diffusion de Publications en Sciences Humaines, 131 bd. St-Michel, 75005 Paris, France)

CIVILTA VENEZIANA. FONTI E TESTI. SERIE PRIMA: FONTI E TESTI PER LA STORIA DELL'ARTE VENETA. see ART

945   IT   ISSN 0069-4347
CIVILTA VENEZIANA. FONTI E TESTI. SERIE TERZA. 1962. irreg., no.4, 1982. price varies. (Fondazione Giorgio Cini) Casa Editrice Leo S. Olschki, Casella Postale 66, 50100 Florence, Italy. TEL 055-6530684. FAX 055-6530214. circ. 500. **Document type:** monographic series.

945   IT   ISSN 0069-4371
CIVILTA VENEZIANA. SAGGI. 1955. irreg., vol.40, 1993. price varies. (Fondazione Giorgio Cini) Casa Editrice Leo S. Olschki, Casella Postale 66, 50100 Florence, Italy. TEL 055-6530684. FAX 055-6530214. circ. 1,000. **Document type:** monographic series.

945   IT   ISSN 0069-438X
CIVILTA VENEZIANA. STUDI. 1953. irreg., vol.44, 1993. price varies. (Fondazione Giorgio Cini) Casa Editrice Leo S. Olschki, Casella Postale 66, 50100 Florence, Italy. TEL 055-6530684. FAX 055-6530214. circ. 1,000. **Document type:** monographic series.

CLAN ROSS NEWSLETTER. see ETHNIC INTERESTS

CLASSICS OF BRITISH HISTORICAL LITERATURE. see LITERATURE

949   PO   ISSN 0870-4104
CLIO (LISBON). (Text in French and Portuguese) 1979. a. price varies. Universidade de Lisboa, Centro de Historia, Cidade Universitaria, 1699 Lisbon Codex, Portugal. (Co-sponsor: Instituto Nacional de Investigacao Cientifica) bk.rev. circ. 1,000.

2932 HISTORY — HISTORY OF EUROPE

942 029   IE
CLOGHER RECORD. 1953. a. £7($15) membership. Clogher Historical Society, c/o Theo McMahon, Ed., 6 Tully, Monaghan, Co. Monaghan, N. Ireland. bk.rev.; index. circ. 900. (back issues avail.)
   Description: Deals with the history of Clogher diocese.

942   UK   ISSN 0260-0250
DA740.C6
CLWYD HISTORIAN. (Text in English and Welsh) 1977. 2/yr. £2.50. Clwyd Local History Council, Clwyd Record Office, 46 Clwyd St., Ruthin, Clwyd, Wales. TEL 0824-703077. FAX 0824-705180. (Co-sponsor: Clwyd Voluntary Services Council) Eds. R.K. Matthias, Derrick Pratt. bk.rev.; index. circ. 400. **Document type:** academic/scholarly publication.
   Description: Consists of a collection of articles and writings on the history of Clwyd, a county in northeastern Wales.

940   GW   ISSN 0084-8808
DD801.A201
COBURGER LANDESSTIFTUNG. JAHRBUCH. 1956. a. DM.40. Coburger Landesstiftung, Schloss Ehrenburg, 96450 Coburg, Germany. TEL 09561-95055. Ed. Alfred Geibig. bk.rev.; bibl.; illus.; index. circ. 600. (back issues avail.) **Indexed:** Numis.Lit., RILA.
—BLDSC (4619.300000).
   Description: History, history of art, geography and natural history restricted to the local area around Coburg.

940   PO
COLECCAO ARQUIVOS. no. 4, 1982. irreg. Assirio e Alvim, Cooperativa Editora e Livreira, SCARL, Rua Passos Manuel, 67-B, 1100 Lisbon, Portugal. Ed. Manuel Herminio Monteiro. circ. 3,000.

946   SP
COLECCION ARAGON. no.10, 1977. irreg., no.77, 1991. 660 ptas. Mira Editores, S.A., C. Hermanos Gimeno Vizarra, 19-21, 50007 Zaragoza, Spain. TEL 25-02-46. FAX 27-55-34.
   Description: Studies the culture of the region of Aragon, Spain.

940   SP
COLECCION CORRESPONDENCIA DIPLOMATICA DE LOS NUNCIOS EN ESPANA. 1976. irreg., no.2, 1982. price varies. (Universidad de Navarra, Facultad de Filosofia y Letras) Ediciones Universidad de Navarra, S.A., Apdo. 396, 31080 Pamplona, Spain. TEL 94 825 6850.

946   SP   ISSN 0069-5106
COLECCION HISTORICA. 1958. irreg., no.46, 1990. price varies. (Universidad de Navarra, Facultad de Filosofia y Letras) Ediciones Universidad de Navarra, S.A., Apdo. 396, 31080 Pamplona, Spain. TEL 94 825 6850.

940   IT   ISSN 0391-3279
COLLANA DI STORIA MODERNA E CONTEMPORANEA. 1978. irreg., no.15, 1992. price varies. Liguori Editore s.r.l., Via Mezzocannone 19, 80134 Naples, Italy. TEL 081-5527139. Ed. Aurelio Lepre. **Document type:** monographic series.

940 551.46   BE   ISSN 0775-3322
COLLECTANEA MARITIMA. (Text in Dutch, occasionally summaries in English) 1984. irreg., vol.5, 1991. price varies. Koninklijke Academie voor Wetenschappen, Letteren en Schone Kunsten van Belgie, 1 Hertogsstraat, B-1000 Brussels, Belgium, (Dist. by: N.V. Brepols, Steenweg op Tielen 68, 2300 Turnhout, Belgium. TEL 32-14-415463. FAX 32-14-428919) abstr.; bibl.; maps. (back issues avail.) **Document type:** monographic series.
   Description: Publishes papers and documents on topics relating to maritime history and related hydrographical and navigational studies.

940   GW   ISSN 0530-9794
COLLEGIUM CAROLINUM. VEROEFFENTLICHUNGEN. vol.30, 1977. irreg. price varies. R. Oldenbourg Verlag GmbH, Rosenheimerstr. 145, 81671 Munich, Germany. TEL 089-45051-0. FAX 089-45051207. (Subscr. to: Postfach 801360, 81613 Munich, Germany) **Document type:** monographic series.

947   US
COLUMBIA UNIVERSITY. HARRIMAN INSTITUTE. STUDIES. 1953. irreg., latest 1991. price varies. Columbia University, Harriman Institute, 420 W. 118th St., New York, NY 10027. TEL 212-854-4623. **Document type:** monographic series, academic/scholarly publication.
   Supersedes: Columbia University. Russian Institute. Studies (ISSN 0588-5477)
   Description: Scholarly monographs on topics in Russian language, culture and history.

943 947   US
COLUMBIA UNIVERSITY. INSTITUTE ON EAST CENTRAL EUROPE. EAST CENTRAL EUROPEAN STUDIES. irreg., latest 1968. price varies. Columbia University Press, 562 W. 113th St., New York, NY 10025. TEL 212-678-6777.

945   IT
COLUMBUS 92; mensile di informazione culturali e studi sull'epoca colombiana e le manifestazioni per il cinquecentenario del 1992. 1985. m. L.60000 in Italy; Europe L.72000; elsewhere L.84000 (effective Dec. 1990). (Columbus 92 S.p.A.) Edizioni Colombo s.r.l., Via Serra 6b, 16122 Genoa, Italy. TEL 010-532073. FAX 010-543197. Ed. Mario Bottaro. adv.

944   FR
COMITE DES TRAVAUX HISTORIQUES ET SCIENTIFIQUES. SECTION DE PHILOLOGIE ET HISTOIRE. ACTES DU CONGRES NATIONAL DES SOCIETES SAVANTES. 1970. a. price varies. Comite des Travaux Historiques et Scientifiques, 1 rue d'Ulm, 75005 Paris, France. TEL 49-55-23-64.

940   BE   ISSN 0572-9327
COMITE INTERNATIONAL DE DACHAU. BULLETIN. 1960. irreg. International Dachau Committee - Comite International de Dachau, Rue des Ortolans 95, B-1170 Brussels, Belgium. TEL 32-2-6726664.
   Document type: bulletin.

940   NE   ISSN 0922-9744
COMPARATIVE STUDIES IN OVERSEAS HISTORY. (Text in English) 1978. irreg., vol.8, 1989. price varies. (Leiden Centre for the History of European Expansion) E.J. Brill, P.O. Box 9000, 2300 PA Leiden, Netherlands. TEL 31-71-312624. FAX 31-71-317532. TELEX 39296 BRILL NL. (In N. America: E.J. Brill, 24 Hudson St., Kinderhook, NY 12106. TEL 800-962-4406. FAX 518-758-1959) Ed. H.L. Wesseling. **Document type:** monographic series.

942 913   UK   ISSN 0144-8439
CONDUIT. 1980. s-a. membership. Cambridge Antiquarian Society, Norris Museum, St. Ives, Huntingdon, Cambs. PE17 4BX, England. TEL 0480-65101. (Co-sponsor: Cambridge Local History Society) Ed. R.I. Burn-Murdock. adv.; bk.rev. circ. 600.

CONFERENCE ON EDITORIAL PROBLEMS: UNIVERSITY OF TORONTO. see LITERATURE

940   IT
CONGRESSO INTERNAZIONALE DI STUDI DULL'ALTO MEDIOEVO. ATTI. 1951. irreg., no.13, 1992. price varies. Centro Italiano di Studi sull'Alto Medioevo, Palazzo Ancaiani, Piazza della Liberta 12, 06049 Spoleto (PG), Italy. TEL 0743-220485. FAX 0743-223507. **Document type:** proceedings.

949.3   BE   ISSN 0010-602X
CONNAITRE LA WALLONIE/TO KNOW WALLONY. Alternate title: Institut Jules Destree. Collection: Connaitre la Wallonie. 1960. irreg., latest no.22. price varies. Institut Jules Destree, Rue du Chateau 3, 6100 Mont-sur-Marchienne Charleroi, Belgium.

940 011 300   US
D299
CONSORTIUM ON REVOLUTIONARY EUROPE. SELECTED PAPERS. (Text in English, French) 1972. a. $15 (effective 1994). Consortium on Revolutionary Europe, c/o Dr. Martha Turner Keber, Secy.-Treas., Box 9561, Savannah, GA 31412. TEL 912-234-0917. illus. circ. 250. (back issues avail.) **Indexed:** Amer.Hist.& Life, Hist.Abstr. **Document type:** academic/scholarly publication.
   Formerly (until 1994): Consortium on Revolutionary Europe. Proceedings (ISSN 0093-2574)
   Description: Paperbound collection of papers presented by scholars of the period 1750-1850 in European history at the Consortium's annual meeting.

948   DK   ISSN 0105-7669
CONTACT WITH DENMARK. French edition: Contact avec le Danemark (ISSN 0105-7677); German edition: Kontakt mit Daenemark (ISSN 0105-7634); Flemish edition: Kontakt met Denemarken (ISSN 0105-7642); Italian edition: Contatti con la Danimarca (ISSN 0106-0287) (Text in English) 1970. irreg. DKK 30. Danish Cultural Institute, 2 Kultorvet, DK-1175 Copenhagen K, Denmark. FAX 45-33-15-10-91. illus.

CONTEMPORARY APPROACHES TO IBSEN. see LITERATURE

940   UK   ISSN 0960-7773
D1050
▼**CONTEMPORARY EUROPEAN HISTORY.** 1992. 3/yr. £22($42) to individuals (overseas £38); institutions £44 (overseas £55 ($71)). Cambridge University Press, Edinburgh Bldg., Shaftesbury Rd., Cambridge CB2 2RU, England. TEL 0223-312393. FAX 0223-315052. TELEX 851817256. (N. American addr.: Cambridge University Press, Journals Dept., 40 W. 20th St., New York, NY 10011. TEL 212-924-3900. FAX 212-691-3239) Eds. Kathleen Burk, Dick Geary. adv.; bk.rev.; abstr. (back issues avail.) **Document type:** academic/scholarly publication.
—BLDSC (3425.181770); UnCover.
   Description: Covers European history - both Eastern and Western Europe, including the U.K., from 1918 to the present.

500   UK   ISSN 0951-9297
CONTEMPORARY FRANCE; a review of interdisciplinary studies. 1987. a. £35. Pinter Publishers Ltd., 25 Floral St., London WC2E 9DS, England. TEL 071-240-9233. FAX 071-379-5553. Ed. Jolyon Howorth. bibl.; index. circ. 900. **Document type:** bulletin.
—BLDSC (3425.181820).
   Description: An interdisciplinary view of key changes in France over the past year.

944   US   ISSN 0147-9156
DC33.9
CONTEMPORARY FRENCH CIVILIZATION. (Text in English and French) 1976. s-a. $15 to individuals (foreign $19); institutions $30 (foreign $34). Montana State University, Department of Modern Languages, Bozeman, MT 59717. TEL 406-994-6447. FAX 406-994-2893. Ed. Douglas J. Daniels. adv.; bk.rev.; bibl. circ. 1,100. (also avail. in microfiche; reprint service avail. from GMC,UMI) **Indexed:** Amer.Hist.& Life, Arts & Hum.Cit.Ind., C.I.J.E., Curr.Cont., ERIC, Hist.Abstr., So.Pac.Per.Ind. **Document type:** academic/scholarly publication.
—BLDSC (3425.181830); Faxon; UnCover; UMI.

CONTEMPORARY GERMAN STUDIES: OCCASIONAL PAPERS. see LITERATURE

940 320   UK   ISSN 0950-9224
CONTEMPORARY RECORD; the journal of contemporary British history. 1987. 3/yr. £25($45) to individuals; institutions £60 ($95). Frank Cass & Co. Ltd., Gainsborough House, 11 Gainsborough Rd., London E11 1RS, England. TEL 081-530-4226. FAX 081-530-7795. Ed.Bd. adv.; B&W page £185; adv. contact: Anne Kidson. bk.rev.; index. (back issues avail.) **Indexed:** Amer.Hist.& Life, Br.Hum.Ind., Hist.Abstr. **Document type:** academic/scholarly publication.
—BLDSC (3425.278000).
   Description: Covers academic research on British history since the Second World War.

HISTORY — HISTORY OF EUROPE

946   SP   ISSN 0213-5477
CONTRASTES: REVISTA DE HISTORIA MODERNA. 1955. a. 1300 ptas. Universidad de Murcia, Secretariado de Publicaciones e Intercambio Cientifico, Santo Cristo, 1, 30001 Murcia, Spain. TEL 968-239450.
   Supersedes in part (in 1985): Univerisdad de Murcia. Filosofia y Letras. Anales (ISSN 0463-9863)

940   SP
CONVERSACIONES INTERNACIONALES DE HISTORIA. 1985. irreg., no.4, 1989. price varies. (Universidad de Navarra, Facultad de Filosofia y Letras) Ediciones Universidad de Navarra, S.A., Apdo. 396, 31080 Pamplona, Spain. TEL 94 825 6850.

CORK HISTORICAL AND ARCHAEOLOGICAL SOCIETY. JOURNAL. see *ARCHAEOLOGY*

942   UK   ISSN 0045-8570
CORNISH NATION. (Text mainly in English; occasionaly in Cornish) 1969. q. £1.50. Mebyon Kernow Publications - Cornish National Movement, Trewirgie Hill, Redruth, Cornwall, England. Eds. Pedyr Prior, Julyan Holmes. adv.; bk.rev. circ. 2,000. (tabloid format)

CORPUS DES ASTRONOMES BYZANTINS. see *ASTRONOMY*

940   FR
CORPUS DES LUTHISTES FRANCAIS. a. price varies. C N R S Editions, 20-22 rue St. Amand, 75015 Paris, France. TEL 45-33-16-00. FAX 45-33-92-13. TELEX 200 356 F. adv.; bk.rev.; index; circ. 1,500 (controlled).

940   FR
CORPUS VITREARUM. biennial. price varies. C N R S Editions, 20-22 rue St. Amand, 75015 Paris, France. TEL 45-33-16-00. FAX 45-33-92-13. TELEX 200 356 F. adv.; bk.rev.; index; circ. 1,500 (controlled).

CORPUS VITREARUM MEDII AEVI. see *ART*

945   IT   ISSN 1122-5130
COSCIENZA STORICA; rivista di studi per una nuova tradizione. 1991. 3/yr. L.100000 (foreign L.130000) (effective 1993). Centro di Studi Storici Umanistici e Sociali per la Calabria, Casella Postale 27, 87010 Lungro (CS), Italy. TEL 0981-947555. (Subscr. to: C. Marco Editore, Via Camicia Rossa 12, 87010 Lungro (CS), Italy) Ed. Constantino Marco. adv.; bk.rev. **Document type:** academic/scholarly publication.

COSTUME. see *CLOTHING TRADE — Fashions*

270 940   UK   ISSN 0070-1394
COURTENAY LIBRARY OF REFORMATION CLASSICS. 1963. irreg. price varies. Sutton Courtenay Press, c/o Appleford, Abingdon, Oxford OX14 4PB, England. Ed. G.E. Duffield.
   Description: Major reformation texts and scholarly introductions for specialist use.

230 940   UK
COURTENAY REFORMATION FACSIMILES. 1973. irreg. price varies. Sutton Courtenay Press, c/o Appleford, Abingdon, Oxford OX14 4PB, England. Ed. G.E. Duffield.
   Formerly: Courtenay Facsimiles.
   Description: Rare texts of the reformation with scholarly comments.

230 940   UK   ISSN 0070-1408
COURTENAY STUDIES IN REFORMATION THEOLOGY. 1966. irreg. price varies. Sutton Courtenay Press, c/o Appleford, Abingdon, Oxford OX14 4PB, England. Ed. G.E. Duffield.
   Description: Studies of major figures of the reformation.

940   BE
CREDIT COMMUNAL DE BELGIQUE. ACTES DES COLLOQUES INTERNATIONAUX. COLLECTION HISTOIRE. SERIES IN 8. 1964. biennial. Credit Communal de Belgique, 44 bd. Pacheco, B-1000 Brussels, Belgium. **Document type:** proceedings.

CRETAN STUDIES. see *ARCHAEOLOGY*

CRITICA PENALE. see *LAW*

940   UK   ISSN 0307-5583
CROMWELLIANA. 1969. a. £10 uK membership. Cromwell Association, c/o Dr. Peter Gaunt, Ed., Chester College, Cheyney Rd., Chester CH1 4BJ, England. FAX 44-244-373379. bk.rev. circ. 550.
Document type: academic/scholarly publication.
   Description: Concentrates on Oliver Cromwell and Parliamentarians in the English Civil War and Interregnum, 1642-1660. Includes popular and academic articles, reviews, and bibliographies.

CRYSTAL PALACE FOUNDATION NEWS. see *ARCHITECTURE*

940   SP
CUADERNOS DE ESTUDIOS MEDIEVALES. (Text in French and Spanish; summaries in English and French) 1973. a. price varies. Universidad de Granada, Departamento de Historia Medieval, Servicio de Publicaciones, Antiguo Colegio Maximo, Campus de Cartuja, 18071 Granada, Spain. TEL 243930. Ed. Cristobal Torres. index. circ. 875. **Indexed:** Amer.Hist.& Life, Hist.Abstr.

946   SP   ISSN 0214-4670
CUADERNOS DE INVESTIGACION HISTORICA. BROCAR. 1975. a. 1600 ptas. (foreign 1900 ptas.). Universidad de la Rioja, Servicio de Publicaciones, C. Magisterio, s-n, 26004 Logrono, Spain. TEL 34-41-231699. circ. 750. **Indexed:** Amer.Hist.& Life, Hist.Abstr. **Document type:** academic/scholarly publication.
   Formerly (until 1985): Cuadernos de Investigacion Historia (ISSN 0211-6839); Which supersedes in part (in 1979): Cuadernos de Investigacion: Geografia e Historia (ISSN 0210-3664)
   Description: Includes pieces of historical work, research on pre-history and history down to contemporary times. Discusses the dynamics of technological, as well as economic and social evolution.

940   SP
CUADERNOS DE TRABAJO DE HISTORIA. 1973. irreg., no.8, 1978. price varies. (Universidad de Navarra, Departamento de Historia Medieval) Ediciones Universidad de Navarra, S.A., Apdo. 396, 31080 Pamplona, Spain. TEL 94 825 6850.

946   SP
CUADERNOS SIMANCAS DE INVESTIGACIONES HISTORICAS: MONOGRAFIAS. irreg., latest 1984. price varies. Universidad de Valladolid, Secretariado de Publicaciones, C. Juan Mambrilla, 14, 47003 Valladolid, Spain. TEL 983-423000. FAX 34-83-290300. TELEX 26357. **Document type:** monographic series.

940 100   PO   ISSN 0870-4546
CULTURA, HISTORIA Y FILOSOFIA. 1982. a. Esc.650. (Instituto Nacional de Investigacao Cientifica, Centro de Linguistica) Universidade de Coimbra, Centro de Estudos Clasicos y Humanisticos, Faculdade de Letras, Coimbra, Portugal. Ed. Jose S. da Silva Diaz. bk.rev.

945   IT
CULTURA SARDA.* 1975. irreg. Libreria Dessi, Largo Cavallotti 17, 07100 Sassari, Italy.

CULTURES ET SOCIETES DE L'EST. see *SOCIOLOGY*

949   NE
CULTUUR HISTORISCH JAARBOEK VOOR FLEVOLAND. 1991. a. fl.29.50. Walburg Pers BV, Postbus 4159, 7200 BD Zutphen, Netherlands. TEL 31-5750-10522. FAX 31-5750-41025. (Co-sponsor: Social Historisch Centrum voor Flevoland)

940   PL   ISSN 0070-2471
CZASOPISMO PRAWNO-HISTORYCZNE. (Text in Polish; summaries in French) 1948. irreg., vol.36, 1984. price varies. Polska Akademia Nauk, Instytut Historii, Komisja Historii Panstwa i Prawa, Rynek Starego Miasta 29-31, 00-272 Warsaw, Poland. (Dist. by: Ars Polona, Krakowskie Przedmiescie 7, 00-068 Warsaw, Poland) Ed. Henryk Olszewski. bk.rev.; bibl.; charts. circ. 370. **Indexed:** Amer.Hist.& Life, Hist.Abstr.

940   US   ISSN 1056-005X
D1
CZECHOSLOVAK AND CENTRAL EUROPEAN JOURNAL.* Abbreviated title: C C E J. 1982. 2/yr. $20 to non-members; members $10. Czechoslovak Society of Arts and Sciences - Spolecnost pro Vedy a Umeni, 245 E. 63rd St., New York, NY 10021-7453. Ed. Paul I. Transky. circ. 250. (tabloid format; back issues avail.) **Indexed:** Amer.Hist.& Life (until 1994), Hist.Abstr. (until 1994).
—UnCover.
   Formerly (until 1989): Kosmas (ISSN 0731-5430)
   Description: Devoted to research in the humanities and social sciences, especially Czech and Slovak-related topics.

CZECHOSLOVAK HISTORY NEWSLETTER. see *ETHNIC INTERESTS*

D I Z SCHRIFTEN. (Dokumentations und Informations Zentrum Emslandlager) see *MILITARY*

943   GW   ISSN 0934-361X
DACHAU REVIEW; history of Nazi concentration camps: studies, reports, documents. German edition: Dachauer Hefte (ISSN 0257-9472) (Text in English) 1988. irreg. DM.25($16) Verlag Dachauer Hefte, Alte Roemerstr. 75, 85221 Dachau, Germany. TEL 08131-1741. FAX 08131-26967. Eds. Wolfgang Benz, Barbara Distel. adv. circ. 5,000.
Document type: academic/scholarly publication.

943   GW   ISSN 0257-9472
D805.G3
DACHAUER HEFTE; Studien und Dokumente zur Geschichte der Nationalsozialistischen Konzentrationslager. English edition: Dachau Review (ISSN 0934-361X) 1985. a. DM.19.80. Verlag Dachauer Hefte, Alte Roemerstr. 75, 85221 Dachau, Germany. TEL 08131-1741. FAX 08131-26967. Eds. Wolfgang Benz, Barbara Distel. circ. 5,000. **Document type:** academic/scholarly publication.

948.7   SW   ISSN 0348-3762
DALARNAS HEMBYGDSBOK. 1931. a. SEK 100 (effective 1990). (Dalarnas Fornminnes- och Hembygdsfoerbund) Dalarnas Museum, Falun, P.O. Box 22, S-791 21 Falun, Sweden.

948 330   DK
DANSK INDUSTRI EFTER 1870. irreg. DKK 158.40. Odense University Press, Campusvej 55, DK-5230 Odense M, Denmark. TEL 66-157999. FAX 66-158126.

948   DK   ISSN 0106-4622
DANSK UDSYN. 1921. 4/yr. DKK 190. Askov Hoejskole, Dansk Udsyns Kontor, Askov, DK-6600 Vejen, Denmark. Ed. H.C. Hansen. bk.rev. circ. 500. **Indexed:** M.L.A.

948.9   DK   ISSN 0070-2846
AP42
DANSKE MAGAZIN. (In 8 series; series 1-6 out of print) 1745. a. DKK 150. Kobenhavns Universitet, Historisk Institut, Njalsgade 102, 2300 Copenhagen K, Denmark. Ed. Esben Albrectsen. index. circ. 300. **Indexed:** Amer.Hist.& Life, Hist.Abstr.

948   DK   ISSN 0106-4525
DANSKE STUDIER. (Subseries of: Universitets-Jubilaets Danske Samfunds Skriftserie (ISSN 0105-449X)) 1904. a. Akademisk Forlag, Store Kannikestraede 8, P.O. Box 54, 1002 Copenhagen, Denmark. **Indexed:** Bibl.Ling., M.L.A.
   Formerly: Dania.

943   GW
DARMSTAEDTER ARCHIVSCHRIFTEN. 1975. irreg., no.8, 1992. price varies. Historischer Verein fuer Hessen, Staatsarchiv, Schloss, 64283 Darmstadt, Germany. (Co-sponsors: Hessisches Staatsarchiv; Stadtarchiv Darmstadt) **Document type:** monographic series.
   Description: Instructs researchers on state holdings, biographical directories.

HISTORY — HISTORY OF EUROPE

940 NE ISSN 0169-7994
DAVIS MEDIEVAL TEXTS AND STUDIES. 1978. irreg., vol.9, 1994. price varies. E.J. Brill, P.O. Box 9000, 2300 PA Leiden, Netherlands. TEL 31-71-312624. FAX 31-71-317532. TELEX 39296 BRILL NL. (In N. America: E.J. Brill, 24 Hudson St., Kinderhook, NY 12106. TEL 800-962-4406. FAX 518-758-1959) Ed. D. Silvia. (back issues avail.) Document type: monographic series.
   Description: Scholarly contributions on medieval literature and history.

945 IT ISSN 0300-4422
DEPUTAZIONE DI STORIA PATRIA PER L'UMBRIA. BOLLETTINO. (Supplement avail. irreg.: Appendici al Bollettino) 1895. a. L.40000 (effective 1992). Deputazione di Storia Patria per l'Umbria, Palazzo della Penna, Via Podiani 11, C.P. 130, 06100 Perugia, Italy. TEL 075-5727057. Ed. Giovanni Antonelli. bk.rev.; bibl. circ. 500. Indexed: Amer.Hist.& Life, Hist.Abstr., RILA.

945 700 IT ISSN 0418-7296
DEPUTAZIONE DI STORIA PATRIA PER LE ANTICHE PROVINCIE MODENESI. ATTI E MEMORIE. 1862. a. L.40000. Deputazione di Storia Patria per le Antiche Provincie Modenesi, Via Pomposa 1, 41100 Modena, Italy. TEL 059-241104. Ed. Giordano Bertuzzi. bk.rev. circ. 800. (back issues avail.) Indexed: Amer.Hist.& Life, Hist.Abstr., M.L.A., Numis.Lit. Document type: academic/scholarly publication, monographic series.

940.53 SZ
DERNIERE GUERRE OU L'HISTOIRE CONTROVERSEE DE LA DEUXIEME GUERRE MONDIALE. 1972. 52/yr. Kister, Quai Wilson 33, 1200 Geneva, Switzerland.

943 430 GW ISSN 0070-3893
DEUTSCH-SLAWISCHE FORSCHUNGEN ZUR NAMENKUNDE UND SIEDLUNGSGESCHICHTE. irreg., vol.37, 1992. price varies. (Saechsische Akademie der Wissenschaften, Leipzig) Akademie Verlag GmbH, Muehlenstr. 33-34, 13187 Berlin, Germany. TEL 030-47889348. FAX 030-47889357. Indexed: M.L.A. Document type: monographic series.

943 GW
DEUTSCHE ANNALEN. 1972. a. DM.34.80. Druffel-Verlag, Assenbucher Str. 28, 82335 Berg, Germany. FAX 08151-51856. Ed. Gert Sudholt. illus. circ. 11,500.

943 GW ISSN 0070-4016
DEUTSCHE GAUE; Zeitschrift fuer Heimatforschung, Landes- und Volkskunde. 1899. irreg. (Wilhelm Heinrich Riehl-Doktor Christian Frank-Gedaechtnisstiftung, Kaufbeuren) Verlag Deutsche Gaue, 87600 Kaufbeuren, Germany. —BLDSC (3567.882000).

940 GW ISSN 0075-286X
DEUTSCHE GESCHICHTE. JAHRESBERICHTE. 1952. a. price varies. Akademie Verlag GmbH, Muehlenstr. 33-34, 13187 Berlin, Germany. TEL 030-47889348. FAX 030-47889357. Document type: bibliography.

943 GW ISSN 0170-3080
DEUTSCHE HANDELSAKTEN DES MITTELALTERS UND DER NEUZEIT. irreg., vol.17, 1988. price varies. (Bayerische Akademie der Wissenschaften, Historische Kommission) Franz Steiner Verlag Wiesbaden GmbH, Birkenwaldstr. 44, 70191 Stuttgart, Germany. TEL 0711-2582-0. FAX 0711-2582290. TELEX 723636-DAZ-D. (Subscr. to: Postfach 101061, 70009 Stuttgart, Germany) Ed.Bd. Document type: monographic series.

DER DEUTSCHE HUGENOTT. see RELIGIONS AND THEOLOGY — Protestant

940 800 910 370 GW ISSN 0415-6102
DEUTSCHE OSTKUNDE; Vierteljahresschrift fuer Wissenschaft, Erziehung und Unterricht. 1954. q. DM.15($10) Druckhaus Waiblingen, Siemensstr. 11, 71257 Waiblingen, Germany. Ed.Bd. adv.; bk.rev. circ. 11,000. (back issues avail.)

DEUTSCHE TRACHTENZEITUNG. see FOLKLORE

940 270 GW ISSN 0344-2934
BX9458.G3
DEUTSCHER HUGENOTTEN-VEREIN E.V. GESCHICHTSBLAETTER. 1890. irreg. price varies. Deutscher Hugenotten-Verein e.V., Hafenplatz 9a, 34385 Bad Karlshafen, Germany. TEL 05672-1433. Ed. Jochen Desel. circ. 1,000. Document type: monographic series.

DEUTSCHES SCHIFFAHRTSARCHIV. see TRANSPORTATION — Ships And Shipping

914.3 GW ISSN 0340-5710
DEUTSCHLAND IN GESCHICHTE UND GEGENWART; Vierteljahres-Zeitschrift fuer Kultur, Geschichte und Politik. 1951. q. DM.45. (Institut fuer Deutsche Nachkriegsgeschichte) Grabert Verlag GmbH, Am Apfelberg 18, 72076 Tuebingen, Germany. TEL 07071-68011. FAX 07071-68014. Ed. Wigbert Grabert. adv.; bk.rev. Document type: academic/scholarly publication.
   Formerly: Deutsche Nation in Geschichte und Gegenwart.

942 UK ISSN 0012-1681
DEVON AND CORNWALL NOTES AND QUERIES; a journal devoted to the local history, archaeology, biography and antiquities of the Counties of Devon and Cornwall. 1900. 2/yr. $15. Devon and Cornwall Notes and Queries Publishing Co., c/o Mrs. M. Rowe, Ed., 21 Clyst Valley Rd., Clyst St. Mary, Nr. Exeter, Devon, England. adv.; bk.rev.; illus.; index. circ. 400. Indexed: Br.Archaeol.Abstr., Br.Hum.Ind. Document type: academic/scholarly publication.

942 UK
DEVON AND CORNWALL RECORD SOCIETY. NEW SERIES. a. £13 to individuals; libraries £12. Devon and Cornwall Record Society, 7 Cathedral Close, Exeter, EX1 1EZ, England. TEL 0392-74727. Ed.Bd. (back issues avail.) Document type: academic/scholarly publication.
   Description: Contains original historical research on the two counties.

940 UK ISSN 0305-8549
DEVON HISTORIAN. 1970. 2/yr. membership. Devon History Society, c/o Devon & Exeter Institution, 7 The Close, Exeter EX1 1EZ, England. Ed. Helen Harris. adv.; bk.rev. circ. 500. Indexed: Br.Archaeol.Abstr. Document type: academic/scholarly publication.
—BLDSC (3579.107000).

DIALOGOS; Hellenic studies review. see CLASSICAL STUDIES

940 IT
DIMENSIONI E PROBLEMI DELLA RICERCA STORICA. 1988. s-a. L.50000 (foreign L.70000) (effective 1993). (Universita di Roma La Sapienza, Dipartimento di Studi Storici dal Medioevo all'Eta Contemporanea) Franco Angeli Editore, Viale Monza 106, Casella Postale 17175, 20100 Milan, Italy. TEL 02-2895762. Ed. Francesco Pitocco. Indexed: Amer.Hist.& Life (1988-), Hist.Abstr. (1988-).

DIPLOMACY & STATECRAFT. see POLITICAL SCIENCE — International Relations

949.8 RM ISSN 0070-6825
DOCUMENTA ROMANIAE HISTORICA. SERIE A: LA MOLDAVIE. 1969. irreg., vol.3, 1980. Editura Academiei Romane, Calea Victoriei 125, 79717 Bucharest, Rumania. (Subscr. to: Artexim, Export-Import Presa, Piata Presci Libere nr.1, P.O. Box 33-16, 70055 Bucharest, Rumania)

949.8 RM ISSN 0070-6833
DOCUMENTA ROMANIAE HISTORICA. SERIE B: LA VALACHIE. 1966. irreg., vol.7, 1988. Editura Academiei Romane, Calea Victoriei 125, 79717 Bucharest, Rumania. (Dist. by: Artexim, Str. Piata Presei Libere 1, P.O. Box 33-16, 70055 Bucharest, Rumania)

945 IT
DOCUMENTI DELL'ARCIERE. 1976. q. L.8000. Edizioni l'Arciere Cuneo, Cuneo, Italy. Dir. Miche Berra.

945 IT
DOCUMENTI DI STORIA ITALIANA. 1867, N.S. 1952. irreg., no.5, 1993. price varies. (Deputazione di Storia Patria per la Toscana) Casa Editrice Leo S. Olschki, Casella Postale 66, 50100 Florence, Italy. TEL 055-6530684. FAX 055-6530214. (also avail. in microfiche from BHP) Document type: monographic series.

946 SP
DOCUMENTOS DE REINADO DE FERNANDO VII. 1965. irreg., no.8, 1972. price varies. (Universidad de Navarra, Facultad de Filosofia y Letras) Ediciones Universidad de Navarra, S.A., Apdo. 396, 31080 Pamplona, Spain. TEL 94 825 6850.

900 500 BE
DOCUMENTS HISTORIQUES DES SCIENCES. (Editions in Flemish, French) 1966. irreg. Comite Belge d'Histoire des Sciences, Koninklyke Bibliotheek, Keizerslaan 4, B-1000 Brussels, Belgium.

943.6 AU
DOEBLINGER MUSEUMSBLAETTER. 1964. irreg. S.50. Museumsverein Doebling, Doeblinger Haupstr. 96, 1190 Vienna, Austria. circ. 1,000.
   Formerly: Doeblinger Heimatmuseum.

948.9 DK
DOEVEHISTORISK TIDSSKRIFT. 1984. s-a. membership. Doevehistorisk Selskab, Kastelvej 58, 2100 Copenhagen OE, Denmark. Ed. Jan William Rasmussen. illus.
   Formerly: Doeveforsorgens Historiske Selskab (ISSN 0109-5021)

940 AU
DOKUMENTATIONSARCHIV DES OESTERREICHISCHEN WIDERSTANDES. MITTEILUNGEN. 1972. bi-m. free. Dokumentationsarchiv des Oesterreichischen Widerstandes, Wipplingerstr. 8, A-1010 Vienna, Austria. FAX 01-5343699771. Ed. Christa Mehany-Mitterrutzner. bk.rev. circ. 5,500. Document type: academic/scholarly publication.

DOKUMENTE ZUR DEUTSCHLANDPOLITIK. see POLITICAL SCIENCE

DOKUMENTE ZUR DEUTSCHLANDPOLITIK. BEIHEFTE. see POLITICAL SCIENCE

949.2 286 NE ISSN 0167-0441
DOOPSGEZINDE BIJDRAGEN. 1975. a. fl.37.50. Doopsgezinde Historische Kring, Singel 452, 1017 AW Amsterdam, Netherlands. FAX 31-20-6278919. (Subscr. to: Doopsgezinde Bijdragen, H. Smit, Elpermeer 27, 1025 AA Amsterdam, Netherlands. TEL 31-20-6369330) Ed. Sjouke Voolstra. bk.rev.; bibl.; illus. circ. 700. Indexed: CERDIC. Document type: academic/scholarly publication.
   Description: Covers the history of Mennonitism and Anabaptism and related fields.

942 UK ISSN 0046-0621
DORSET; the county magazine. 1968. 12/yr. £19. John Newth, Ed. & Pub., Trinity Lane, Wareham, Dorset BH20 4LN, England. adv.; bk.rev.; illus. circ. 6,000.
   Description: Articles on all historical and cultural aspects of Dorset.

DREVNEISHIE GOSUDARSTVA NA TERRITORII S.S.S.R/ANCIENT STATES IN THE TERRITORY OF THE U.S.S.R.; materialy i issledovaniya. see ARCHAEOLOGY

941 IE ISSN 0012-6861
DUBLIN HISTORICAL RECORD. 1938. 2/yr. £10. Old Dublin Society, City Assembly House, 58 S. William St., Dublin 2, Ireland. Ed. P.F. Byrne. adv.; bk.rev. circ. 850. Indexed: Br.Archaeol.Abstr.
—Faxon.

949 497 CI ISSN 0419-7925
DUBROVACKI HORIZONTI. 1970. a. 90 din. Drustvo Dubrovcana i Prijatelja Dubrovacke Starine, Szabova 21-III ulaz, Zagreb, Croatia. Ed. Josip Lucic. circ. 1,800.

HISTORY — HISTORY OF EUROPE

941.5　　　　　　US
DUCAS. 1972. bi-m. membership. Irish American Cultural Institute, 2115 Summit Ave., No. 5026, St. Paul, MN 55105-1096. TEL 612-962-6040. FAX 612-962-6043. Ed. James Rogers. adv.; bk.rev.; film rev.; play rev.; illus. circ. 10,000. **Document type:** newsletter.
　Description: Explores the cultural heritage of Irish Americans and serves as the Cultural Institute's membership newsletter.

943　　　　　　GW　ISSN 0342-0019
DUESSELDORFER JAHRBUCH. 1886. irreg., vol.64, 1993. Droste Verlag GmbH, 40196 Duesseldorf, Germany. TEL 0211-5052604. FAX 0211-5052603. bk.rev. **Document type:** bulletin.
　Formerly (until 1912): Beitraege zur Geschichte des Niederrheins. Jahrbuch des Duesseldorfer Geschichtsvereins.

DUGNAD; tidskrift for etnologi. see ANTHROPOLOGY

943　　　　　　GW　ISSN 0343-3277
DUISBURGER JOURNAL; Beitraege und Nachrichten aus dem kulturellen Leben, Stadtgeschichte, Veranstaltungskalender, Wegweiser. 1977. m. H. Oppenberg Verlag, Kardinal-Galen-Str. 6, 47051 Duisburg, Germany. TEL 0203-335083. Ed. Werner Francke. circ. 6,000.

940　　　　　　US
DUKE MONOGRAPHS IN MEDIEVAL AND RENAISSANCE STUDIES. 1979. irreg. Duke University Press, 6697 College Station, Durham, NC 27708. TEL 919-687-3600. FAX 919-688-4574.

DURHAM ARCHAEOLOGICAL JOURNAL. see ARCHAEOLOGY

DUTCH ARCHAEOLOGICAL AND HISTORICAL SOCIETY. STUDIES. see ARCHAEOLOGY

943.8　　　　　　PL　ISSN 0419-8816
DZIEJE LUBLINA. 1965. irreg. price varies. Wydawnictwo Lubelskie, Okopowa 7, 20-022 Lublin, Poland. TEL 48-81-27344.

943.8　　　　　　PL　ISSN 0070-7791
DZIEJE POLSKIEJ GRANICY ZACHODNIEJ. 1961. irreg. Instytut Zachodni, Stary Rynek 78-79, 61-772 Poznan, Poland. circ. 20,000. **Document type:** monographic series.

940　　　　　　UK　ISSN 0963-9462
D111
▼**EARLY MEDIEVAL EUROPE.** 1992. 2/yr. £26($49) to individuals; institutions £42($78). Longman Group UK Ltd., Longman House, Burnt Mill, Harlow, Essex CM20 2JE, England. TEL 0279-426721. FAX 0279-431059. Ed.Bd. adv.; bk.rev. (back issues avail.) **Document type:** academic/scholarly publication.
　—BLDSC (3642.988700); UnCover.

EAST EUROPEAN POLITICS & SOCIETIES. see POLITICAL SCIENCE

942　　　　　　UK　ISSN 0070-8208
DA670.Y59
EAST YORKSHIRE LOCAL HISTORY SERIES. 1952. irreg. £8 per no. to non-member individuals (overseas £10); included in membership. East Yorkshire Local History Society, Beverley Library, Champney Rd., Beverley, N. Humberside HU17 9BQ, England. TEL 0482-864108. FAX 0482-881084. bk.rev. circ. 400. **Document type:** monographic series.

942　　　　　　UK
EAST YORKSHIRE LOCAL HISTORY SOCIETY. BULLETIN. 2/yr. membership. East Yorkshire Local History Society, Beverley Library, Champney Rd., Beverley, N. Humberside HU17 9BQ, England. TEL 0482-864108. FAX 0482-881084. circ. 420 (controlled). **Document type:** bulletin.

943　　　　　　GW
EBERBACHER GESCHICHTSBLATT. 1901. a. DM.12. Stadtverwaltung Eberbach, Postfach 1134, 69401 Eberbach, Germany. TEL 06271-87-1. Ed. Helmut Joho. bk.rev. circ. 1,500. **Document type:** monographic series.

940　　　　　　FR
ECOLE FRANCAISE DE ROME. MELANGES: MOYEN AGES, TEMPS MODERNE. (In two vols.) a. Edition-Diffusion De Boccard, 11 rue de Medicis, 75006 Paris, France. **Indexed:** Amer.Hist.& Life, Hist.Abstr., Numis.Lit.

940 869　　　　　　FR
ECOLE PRATIQUE DES HAUTES ETUDES. CENTRE DE RECHERCHES SUR LE PORTUGAL DE LA RENAISSANCE. SERIES TEXTES. (Text in French) 1979. irreg. price varies. (Ecole Pratique des Hautes Etudes, Centre de Recherches sur le Portugal de la Renaissance) Librarie Touzot, 38 rue Saint Sulpice, 75278 Paris Cedex 06, France.

914.9　　　　　　NE　ISSN 0925-1669
HC321
ECONOMIC AND SOCIAL HISTORY IN THE NETHERLANDS. (Text in English) 1989. a. $35 (effective 1992). Vereniging Het Nederlandsch Economisch-Historisch Archief, Cruquiusweg 31, 1019 AT Amsterdam, Netherlands. TEL 31-20-6685866. FAX 31-20-6654181. adv. **Indexed:** Amer.Hist.& Life, Hist.Abstr. **Document type:** academic/scholarly publication.
　Description: Covers the economic and social history of the Netherlands and former colonies.

ECONOMISCH- EN SOCIAAL-HISTORISCH JAARBOEK. see BUSINESS AND ECONOMICS — Economic Systems And Theories, Economic History

949.5　　　　　　GR
EDESSAIKA CHRONIKA. 1972. 3/yr. Philoproodos Syllogos Edesses Megas Alexandros, Odos Agiou Demetriou 7, Edessa, Greece. bk.rev.

940 370.09　　　　　　NE　ISSN 0926-6070
EDUCATION AND SOCIETY IN THE MIDDLE AGES AND THE RENAISSANCE. 1991. irreg., vol.3, 1994. price varies. E.J. Brill, P.O. Box 9000, 2300 PA Leiden, Netherlands. TEL 31-71-312624. FAX 31-71-312624. TELEX 39296 BRILL NL. (In N. America: E.J. Brill, 24 Hudson St., Kinderhook, NY 12106. TEL 800-962-4406. FAX 518-758-1959) (back issues avail.) **Document type:** monographic series.
　Refereed Serial

948.9　　　　　　DK　ISSN 0109-0194
EGNSHISTORISK FORENING I GRUNDSOE. AARSSKRIFT. 1972. a. DKK 50. Egnshistorisk Forening i Grundsoe, Moellevej 24, 4040 Jyllinge, Denmark. illus.

974 301　　　　　　US　ISSN 0098-2601
HN1
EIGHTEENTH CENTURY LIFE. 1974. 3/yr. $19 to individuals (foreign $23.60); institutions $37 (foreign $44.60). (College of William and Mary, Department of English) Johns Hopkins University Press, Journals Publishing Division, 2715 N. Charles St., Baltimore, MD 21218. TEL 410-516-6987. FAX 410-516-6968. Ed. Robert P. Maccubbin. adv.; bk.rev.; bibl.; illus.; stat. circ. 757. (back issues avail.) **Indexed:** Amer.Hist.& Life, Arts & Hum.Cit.Ind., Curr.Cont., Hist.Abstr., LCR, M.L.A. **Document type:** academic/scholarly publication.
　—BLDSC (3665.230000); Faxon; UnCover. CCC.
　Description: Interdisciplinary journal of eighteenth-century studies.

810 900　　　　　　US　ISSN 0193-5380
DA506.B9
EIGHTEENTH CENTURY: THEORY AND INTERPRETATION. 1959. 3/yr. $19 to individuals; institutions $33. Texas Tech University Press, Box 41037, Lubbock, TX 79409-1037. TEL 806-742-2982; 800-832-4042. FAX 806-742-2979. Ed. Bruce Clarke. adv.; bk.rev.; bibl.; illus.; cum.index every 5 yrs. circ. 522. **Indexed:** Abstr.Engl.Stud., Amer.Hist.& Life, Amer.Hum.Ind., Arts & Hum.Cit.Ind., Curr.Cont., Hist.Abstr., M.L.A. **Document type:** academic/scholarly publication.
　—BLDSC (3665.215000); Faxon.
　Formerly (until vol.20, 1979): Studies in Burke and His Time (ISSN 0039-3584)

943　　　　　　GW　ISSN 0723-0877
EINHORN-JAHRBUCH. 1974. a. DM.26. Einhorn Verlag GmbH, Sebaldstr. 9-11, 73525 Schwaebisch-Gmuend, Germany. Ed. Eduard Dietenberger. circ. 2,500. **Document type:** bulletin.

947 913　　　　　　NE　ISSN 0046-1628
EIRENE; studia graeca et latina. (Not published in 1979 and 1991) (Text in English, French, German, Latin and Russian) 1960. a., vol.28, 1992. fl.152($92) (Czech Academy of Sciences, Institute for Greek, Latin and Roman Studies, XR) John Benjamins Publishing Co., Amsteldijk 44, P.O. Box 75577, 1070 AN Amsterdam, Netherlands. TEL 31-20-6738156. FAX 31-20-6792956. (In N. America: 821 Bethlehem Pike, Philadelphia, PA 19118. TEL 215-836-1200. FAX 215-836-1204) Ed. J. Janda. (back issues avail.) **Indexed:** Bibl.Ling., Bull.Signal. **Document type:** academic/scholarly publication.
　Description: Provides a source of information on Greek and Latin studies published in Eastern European countries.
　Refereed Serial

EKAINA; revue d'etudes basques. see CLASSICAL STUDIES

943　　　　　　GW　ISSN 0933-7334
ELBINGER NACHRICHTEN. 1951. m. DM.45.60. Landsmannschaft Westpreussen e.V., Norberstr. 29, 48151 Muenster, Germany. TEL 0251-523424. FAX 0251-533830. Ed. Hans Juergen Schuch. illus.

943.8　　　　　　IT　ISSN 0070-9972
DK402
ELEMENTA AD FONTIUM EDITIONES; unpublished sources to mediaeval and modern European history, 14th-17th centuries. (Text in original language; comments in Latin) 1960. irreg., vol.76, 1992. L.30000($22) Institutum Historicum Polonicum Romae - Polish Historical Institute in Rome, Via Virginio Orsini 19, 00192 Rome, Italy. TEL 06-3211646. (Subscr. to: Herder Editrice e Libreria, Piazza Montecitorio 120, 00186 Rome, Italy) cum.index.

949.5 327　　　　　　CY
ELEUTHERE KYTHREA. 1978. 4/yr. £C3($7) Somateion Eleuthere Kythrea, Nicosia, Cyprus. TEL 357-2-472000. adv. circ. 1,000. **Document type:** corporate report.
　Description: Examines the issues relating to areas controlled by Turkish troops.

942　　　　　　US　ISSN 0085-0225
ELIZABETHAN CLUB SERIES. 1960. irreg., no.7, 1982. price varies. Yale University Press, Box 209040, New Haven, CT 06520. TEL 203-432-0940.

940　　　　　　US　ISSN 1066-7059
▼**THE ELIZABETHAN REVIEW.** 1993. s-a. $30 to individuals; institutions $45; foreign $55. 123-60 83rd Ave., Kew Gardens, NY 11415. TEL 718-575-9656. Ed. Gary B. Goldstein. adv.: page $150. bk.rev.; circ. 100 (paid); 900 (controlled). **Document type:** academic/scholarly publication.
　Description: Endeavors to integrate the disparate efforts of scholars of the Elizabethan Era (1558-1603) within a multidisciplinary framework, providing a more rounded perspective of the period.

ELLINIKA; philological, historical and folkloric review. see CLASSICAL STUDIES

940 700 800　　　　　　US　ISSN 0885-968X
CR1
EMBLEMATICA; an interdisciplinary journal for emblem studies. 1986. s-a. $55. A M S Press, Inc., 56 E. 13th St., New York, NY 10003. TEL 212-777-4700. FAX 212-995-5413. Ed.Bd. bk.rev. (back issues avail.)
　—SWETS.
　Description: Interdisciplinary journal for emblem studies; contains essays and review articles.

942　　　　　　US　ISSN 0071-058X
ENGLISH HISTORICAL DOCUMENTS. irreg., vol.12, 1977. price varies. Oxford University Press, 200 Madison Ave., New York, NY 10016. TEL 212-679-7300. Ed. David C. Douglas.

HISTORY — HISTORY OF EUROPE

942 UK ISSN 0013-8266
DA20
ENGLISH HISTORICAL REVIEW. 1886. 4/yr. £61($114) (foreign £67). Longman Group UK Ltd., Longman House, Burnt Mill, Harlow, Essex CM20 2JE, England. TEL 0279-426721. FAX 0279-431059. Eds. P.H. Williams, R.J.W. Evans. adv.; bk.rev.; index, cum.index: vols. 71-100, 1986. (also avail. in microfilm from UMI,PMC; reprint service avail. from UMI,SCH; back issues avail.) **Indexed:** Acad.Ind., Amer.Hist.& Life, Arts & Hum.Cit.Ind., Bk.Rev.Ind. (1965-), Br.Archaeol.Abstr., Br.Hum.Ind., Child.Bk.Rev.Ind. (1965-), Curr.Cont., Hist.Abstr., Hum.Ind., Mid.East: Abstr.& Ind., Rel.Ind.One. **Document type:** academic/scholarly publication.
—BLDSC (3774.700000); Faxon; UnCover; SWETS; UMI. **CCC.**

942 US ISSN 0071-0628
ENGLISH MONARCHS SERIES. 1964. irreg., vol.10, 1993. price varies. University of California Press, 2120 Berkeley Way, Berkeley, CA 94720. TEL 510-642-4247. FAX 510-643-7127. (Orders to: California-Princeton Fulfillment Services, 1445 Lower Ferry Rd., Ewing, NJ 08618. TEL 800-777-4726. FAX 800-999-1958) (back issues avail.) **Document type:** monographic series.
Description: Covers the reigns of various English kings and queens.
Refereed Serial

940 US ISSN 1043-576X
THE ENLIGHTENMENT: GERMAN AND INTERDISCIPLINARY STUDIES. irreg. Peter Lang Publishing, Inc., 62 W. 45th St., 4th Fl., New York, NY 10036. TEL 212-302-6740. FAX 212-302-7574. Ed. Charlotte M. Craig. **Document type:** academic/scholarly publication.

ENVOI; a review journal of medieval literature. *see* LITERATURE

943 GW ISSN 0174-6545
EPIGRAPHICA ANATOLICA; Zeitschrift fuer Epigraphik und historische Geographie Anatoliens. 1983. irreg., no.21, 1993. price varies. Dr. Rudolf Habelt GmbH, Am Buchenhang 1, 53115 Bonn, Germany. TEL 0228-232016. FAX 0228-232017. Ed.Bd. **Indexed:** Anthropol.Lit., Bibl.Ling. **Document type:** monographic series.

949.5 GR ISSN 0021-0765
EPIROTIKI ESTIA. 1952. 12/yr. $45. M. Geografou 53, GR-45333 Ioannina, Greece. Ed. Demosthenes Kokkinos. adv.; bk.rev.; bibl. circ. 5,000. **Indexed:** Amer.Hist. & Life, Hist.Abstr., M.L.A.

ERASMUS OF ROTTERDAM SOCIETY YEARBOOK. *see* PHILOSOPHY

943 GW
ERDINGER LAND. 1977. irreg. Kreisverein Erding, Alois-Schiessl-Platz 2, 85435 Erding, Germany. circ. 1,000. (back issues avail.) **Document type:** newsletter.

948 DK
ERHVERVSHISTORISK AARBOG (YEAR). 1949. a. DKK 198. Erhvervsarkivet, Vester Alle 12, DK-8000 Aarhus C, Denmark. TEL 45-86-12-85-33. FAX 45-86-12-85-60. bk.rev.; cum.index: 1949-58, 1959-68, 1969-80. circ. 400. **Indexed:** Amer.Hist.& Life, Hist.Abstr.

ESSEX JOURNAL; a review of Essex archaeology and local history. *see* ARCHAEOLOGY

ESTRATTI DAGLI STUDI MEDIEVALI. *see* HISTORY — *Abstracting, Bibliographies, Statistics*

946 SP ISSN 0014-150X
ESTUDIOS HISTORICOS SOBRE SAN SEBASTIAN. BOLETIN. (Text mainly in Spanish; occasionally in English, French, German) 1969. q.? 120 ptas. Real Sociedad Vascongada de los Amigos del Pais, Po. Ramon Ma. de Lili, 6-4o, Izqda., Apdo. 992, 20002 San Sebastian, Spain. TEL 28-55-77.

949.6 BU ISSN 0014-1976
ETUDES BALKANIQUES. (Text in English, French, German and Russian) 1965. q. 3 lv. per no. (Bulgarska Akademiia na Naukite, Institut za Balkanistika) Publishing House of the Bulgarian Academy of Sciences, Acad. G. Bonchev St., Bldg. 6, 1113 Sofia, Bulgaria. (Dist. by: Hemus, 6, Rouski Blvd., 1000 Sofia, Bulgaria) Ed. Nikolai Todorov. bk.rev.; bibl. circ. 910. (also avail. in microform from UMI; reprint service avail. from IRC,UMI) **Indexed:** Amer.Hist.& Life, Bibl.Ling., Curr.Cont., Hist.Abstr., Numis.Lit.
—UMI.

ETUDES DE PHILOLOGIE ET D'HISTOIRE. *see* LITERATURE

947 BU ISSN 0525-0846
ETUDES HISTORIQUES. (Text in English, French, German and Russian) 1960. irreg. (Bulgarska Akademiya na Naukite) Publishing House of the Bulgarian Academy of Sciences, Ul. Akad. G. Bonchev, Bldg. 6, 1113 Sofia, Bulgaria. (Dist. by: Hemus Foreign Trade Co., 6 Ruski Blvd., 1000 Sofia, Bulgaria) (reprint service avail. from IRC) **Document type:** academic/scholarly publication.

941.5 800 FR ISSN 0183-973X
DA925
ETUDES IRLANDAISES; revue bilingue d'histoire, civilisation et litterature irlandaises. (Text and summaries in English, French) 1972. 2/yr. 180 F. (effective 1991). Universite de Lille III, B.P. 20, 59262 Sainghin en Melantois, France. (Subscr. to: Centre de Gestion de Revues, B.P. 149, 59653 Villeneuve d'Ascq Cedex, France) Ed.Bd. adv.; bk.rev.; bibl. circ. 400. (back issues avail.) **Indexed:** Arts & Hum.Cit.Ind., Curr.Cont., M.L.A.
—BLDSC (3820.723000); UnCover.
Description: Each issue features Irish writings, literary studies, and studies in Irish history and civilization.

940.27 FR ISSN 1156-9778
ETUDES NAPOLEONIENNES. 1969. a. 200 F. (foreign 220 F.). Societe de Sauvegarde du Chateau Imperial de Pont-de-Briques, 12 rue Pasteur, 92300 Levallois, France. TEL 47-37-06-65. FAX 47-93-04-05. Ed. Fernand Beaucour. bk.rev.
Formerly (until 1981): Societe de Sauvegarde du Chateau Imperial de Pont-de-Briques. Bulletin (ISSN 0765-1813)
Description: Studies the history of the Napoleonic periods, from the French Revolution to the Second Empire, particularly the history of Napoleon I, his epoch, the Bonaparte and the Chateau de Pont-de-Briques, the Camp de Boulogne and the events and places about it.

944 330 914 FR ISSN 0014-2158
ETUDES NORMANDES. 1951. q. 200 F. Association d'Etudes Normandes, Universite de Rouen, 7 rue Thomas Becket, 76130 Mont St. Aignan, France. FAX 35-14-69-40. Ed. J. Pierre Chaline. bk.rev. circ. 1,200. **Indexed:** Geo.Abstr.

944 FR
ETUDES SAVOISIENNES. no.2, 1975. irreg. 100 F. University de Savoie, Institut d'Etudes Savoisiennes, Departement d'Histoire, B.P. 143, 73000 Chambery, France. (Co-sponsor: Societe Savoisiene d'Histoire et d'Archeologie) Dir. Jacques Lovie. bibl.; illus.

944 FR ISSN 0249-1664
ETUDES SUR L'HERAULT. 1982. a. 200 F. Association Etudes sur l'Heraut, B.P. 1266, 2, Av. de Castelnau, 34011 Montpellier Cedex, France. Dirs. Jean Nougaret, Jean-Claude Richard. adv.; bk.rev.; bibl.; illus.
Former titles: Etudes sur Pezenas et l'Herault (ISSN 0183-7591); Etudes sur Pezena et Sa Region.

ETUDES SUR LE JUDAISME MEDIEVAL. *see* RELIGIONS AND THEOLOGY — *Judaic*

ETUDES SUR LES MONDES HISPANOPHONES. *see* LITERATURE

900 US
EURASIAN STUDIES YEARBOOK. (Text in English, French, German, Russian) 1921. a. $74. Eurolingua, Box 101, Bloomington, IN 47402-0101. TEL 812-332-8918. Eds. Gyula Decsy, A.E.J. Bodrogligeti. adv.; bk.rev.; charts; illus. circ. 450. **Indexed:** Bibl.Ling., Lang.& Lang.Behav.Abstr., M.L.A.
Former titles (until vol. 65, 1993): Ural-Altaische Jahrbuecher (ISSN 0042-0786); *(Until vol. 24, 1944):* Ungarische Jahrbuecher.
Description: Covers language, history, literature and folklore of the people of Northern Eurasia.

940 GW ISSN 0932-0520
EUROPA. 1985. q. DM.28. (Nationaleuropaeisches Jugendwerk e.V.) Satzbuero Thomas, Postfach 1616, 50380 Wesseling, Germany. TEL 02236-49999. FAX 02236-49722. adv.; bk.rev. circ. 3,500.

940 IT
EUROPA MEDITERRANEA. 1986. irreg., no.7, 1991. price varies. (Gruppo Interuniversitario per la Storia dell' Europa Mediterranea) Liguori Editore s.r.l., Via Mezzocannone, 19, 80134 Naples, Italy. TEL 081-5527139. Ed. Bd. **Document type:** monographic series.

940 NE
EUROPE IN THE MIDDLE AGES; selected studies. (Text in English) 1977. irreg., vol.17, 1980. price varies. Elsevier Science B.V., Books Division, P.O. Box 211, 1000 AE Amsterdam, Netherlands. TEL 31-20-5803911. FAX 31-20-5803705. TELEX 18582 ESPA NL. (Subscr. in U.S. and Canada to: Elsevier Science Inc., Box 882, Madison Sq. Sta., New York, NY10159. TEL 212-989-5800) Ed. Richard Vaughan. (back issues avail.) **Document type:** monographic series.
Refereed Serial

940 UK ISSN 0265-6914
D1 CODEN: EHIQEH
EUROPEAN HISTORY QUARTERLY. 1971. q. £32 to individuals; institutions £80. Sage Publications Ltd., 6 Bonhill St., London EC2A 4PU, England. TEL 071-374-0645. FAX 071-374-8741. Ed. R.M. Blinkhorn. adv.: color page £190; trim 177 x 101; adv. contact: Bernie Folan. bk.rev.; charts; illus.; index. **Indexed:** A.B.C.Pol.Sci., Amer.Hist.& Life, Arts & Hum.Cit.Ind., Curr.Cont., Hist.Abstr., Hum.Ind., Mid.East: Abstr.& Ind., SSCI. **Document type:** academic/scholarly publication.
—BLDSC (3829.717650); Faxon; UnCover; SWETS.
Formerly (until Jan. 1984): European Studies Review (ISSN 0014-3111)
Description: Focuses on European history since the later middle ages, and on historical aspects of social and political thought.
Refereed Serial

940 UK ISSN 1350-7486
▼**EUROPEAN REVIEW OF HISTORY/REVUE EUROPEENE D'HISTOIRE.** 1994. s-a. $36 to individuals; institutions $92 (effective 1994). Carfax Publishing Co., P.O. Box 25, Abingdon, Oxon. OX14 3UE, England. TEL 44-235-553559. FAX 44-235-553559. (N. American subscr. to: Carfax Publishing Co., Box 2025, Dunellon, FL 34430-2025) Ed. Justin Champion. adv.; bk.rev.; index. (also avail. in microfiche) **Document type:** academic/scholarly publication.

940 800 DK ISSN 0906-0308
D16.5.A2
EUROPEAN STUDIES. (Text in Danish, English, French, German, Spanish) 1990. irreg. price varies. Aalborg University, European Research Unit, Fibigerstraede 2, P.O. Box 159, DK-9220, Aalborg Oe, Denmark. TEL 45-98-15-85-22. FAX 45-98-15-69-50. (Co-sponsors: Department of Languages and Intercultural Studies; Department of Development and Planning) Ed. Ernst-Ullrich Pinkert. **Document type:** monographic series.
Description: Focuses on the history, literature, and social studies of modern Europe.

940 913 200   US   ISSN 0820-6244
EUROPEAN STUDIES JOURNAL. 1984. s-a. $20 to individuals (foreign $25); libraries $30 (foreign $35). University of Northern Iowa, Department of Modern Languages, Cedar Falls, IA 50614-0504. TEL 319-273-2749. FAX 319-273-2921. Ed. Reinhold K. Bubser. bk.rev.; charts; illus.; stat. circ. 200. **Document type:** academic/scholarly publication.
   Description: Critical analysis of present and past major influences on European political and intellectual history, predominantly English.

EUROPEAN STUDIES NEWSLETTER. see *SOCIAL SCIENCES: COMPREHENSIVE WORKS*

940   IT   ISSN 1121-1628
▼**EUTOPIA;** commentarii novi de antiquitatibus totius europae. 1992. s-a. 28 ECU($38) (L.50000) (effective 1993). (Associazione Culturale Roma Europa) Edizioni Quasar, Via IV Novembre 152, 00187 Rome, Italy. TEL 06-679522. FAX 06-6795612. Ed. Adriano La Regina.

EVANGELICAL MAGAZINE OF WALES. see *RELIGIONS AND THEOLOGY* — *Protestant*

EXPLORATIONS IN RENAISSANCE CULTURE. see *HUMANITIES: COMPREHENSIVE WORKS*

948   DK   ISSN 0106-8822
FAABORG-AARBOGEN. Cover title: Faaborg-Bogen. vol.5, 1979. a. DKK 70. (Faaborg Lokalhistorisk Selskab) Edvard Andersen, Oesterbro 42, DK-5600 Faaborg, Denmark. TEL 45-62-61-18-13. (Co-sponsor: Byhistorisk Vennekreds) Ed. Edvard Andersen. illus.
   Formerly: Arkiver: Folkemindesamlinger og Museer i Faaborg Kommune.

948   DK   ISSN 0106-3324
FABRIK OG BOLIG. 1975. 2/yr. DKK 100. Koebenhavns Stadsarkiv, Raadhuset, DK-1599 Copenhagen V, Denmark. Ed. Torben Ejlersen. bk.rev. **Indexed:** RILA.

FAGUO YANJIU/ETUDES FRANCAISES. see *SOCIAL SCIENCES: COMPREHENSIVE WORKS*

942   UK   ISSN 0309-8559
CS1
FAMILY HISTORY NEWS AND DIGEST. 1977. 2/yr. £4($11) (foreign £4.40). Federation of Family History Societies, c/o Patricia Berner, 15 Dover Close, Hill Head, Fareham, Hants. PO14 3SU, England. (U.K. subscr. to: Mr. J.B. Rowlands, 18 Marine Terrace, Aberystwyth, Dyfed SY23 2AZ, Wales) bk.rev. circ. 4,000. **Document type:** academic/scholarly publication.

948   FI   ISSN 0356-5629
DK445
FARAVID. 1977. a. $16. Pohjois-Suomen Historiallinen Yhdistys, Oulun Yliopisto, Historian Laitos, Postilokero 191, 90101 Oulu, Finland. Ed. Kyoesti Julku. circ. 700. **Indexed:** NAA.

940   PL   ISSN 0071-4038
FASCICULI HISTORICI. (Text in English, French, German and Russian) 1968. irreg., vol.14, 1986. price varies. (Uniwersytet Warszawski, Instytut Historyczny) Wydawnictwa Uniwersytetu Warszawskiego, Ul. Obozna 8, 00-032 Warsaw, Poland. (Dist. by: Ars Polona-Ruch, Krakowskie Przedmiescie 7, 00-068 Warsaw, Poland) circ. 300. **Indexed:** Amer.Hist.& Life, Hist.Abstr.

942   UK   ISSN 0014-892X
FAVERSHAM PAPERS. 1964. 2/yr. membership. Faversham Society, Fleur-de-Lis Heritage Centre, 13 Preston St., Faversham, Kent ME13 8NS, England. TEL 0795-534542. Ed. Arthur Percival. charts; illus. circ. 500. (processed) **Document type:** monographic series.
   Description: Monographs about aspects of the town and district, past and present.

940 398 913   BE
FEDERATION ARCHEOLOGIQUE ET HISTORIQUE DE BELGIQUE. ANNALES/FEDERATIE VAN NEDERLANDSTALIGE VERENIDENIS VOOR OUDHUIDKUNDE EN GESCHIEDENIS VAN BELGIE. JAARBOEKEN. (Text in Dutch and French) 1886. irreg. 1500 Fr. Federatie van Nederlandstalige Verenigingen voor Oudheidkunde en Geschiedenis van Belgie, Leopoldlei 34, 2070 Antwerp, Belgium. adv.

FIGURA. NOVA SERIES; Uppsala studies in the history of art. see *ART*

949   BE   ISSN 0069-5386
FIGURES DE WALLONIE. Alternate title: Institut Jules Destree. Collection: Figures de Wallonie. irreg., no. 19. price varies. Institut Jules Destree, Rue du Chateau 3, 6100 Mont sur Marchienne Charleroi, Belgium.

947.1   FI   ISSN 0356-827X
FINLAND; books and publications in politics, political history and international relations. (Text in English) 1965. a. $1. University of Turku, Department of Political History, SF-20500 Turku 50, Finland. FAX 358-21-633-6585. bk.rev. circ. 3,000.

942 914.2   UK   ISSN 0140-8429
FLINTSHIRE HISTORICAL SOCIETY. PUBLICATIONS, JOURNAL AND RECORD SERIES. 1911. biennial. £5. Flintshire Historical Society, 50 Hafod Park, Mold, Clwyd CH7 1QW, Wales. Ed. J. Gwynn Williams. bk.rev. circ. 750. **Indexed:** Br.Archaeol.Abstr. **Document type:** academic/scholarly publication.
—BLDSC (4754.160000).

947 300   US
FLORIDA STATE UNIVERSITY. CENTER FOR YUGOSLAV-AMERICAN STUDIES, RESEARCH, AND EXCHANGES. PROCEEDINGS AND REPORTS OF SEMINARS AND RESEARCH. 1967. a. $12. Florida State University, Center for Yugoslav-American Studies, Research, and Exchanges, 930 W. Park Ave., Tallahassee, FL 32306. TEL 904-644-7828. Ed. George Macesich. adv.; bk.rev. circ. 650. **Indexed:** Amer.Bibl.Slavic & E.Eur.Stud.
   Formerly: Florida State University. Slavic Papers (ISSN 0430-7291)

940   HU   ISSN 0133-6622
FOLIA HISTORICA. 1972. a. exchange basis. Magyar Nemzeti Muzeum, Muzeum-krt. 14-16, 1370 Budapest 8, Hungary. TEL 134-400. Eds. Fodor Istvan, Haider Edit. illus. circ. 700. **Indexed:** Art & Archaeol.Tech.Abstr.

943.7   XR   ISSN 0231-7494
DB2000
FOLIA HISTORICA BOHEMICA. (Text in Czech, English, German, Russian) 1979. irreg. (1-2/yr.). exchange basis only. Ceska Akademie Ved, Hisotricky Ustav, Vysehradska 49, 128 26 Prague 2, Czech Republic. TEL 00422-350054. Ed. Jaroslav Panek. bk.rev.; bibl. **Document type:** academic/scholarly publication.
   Description: History of Bohemia and Europe in 16th - 18th century.

FOLIA PRAEHISTORICA POSNANIENSIA. see *ARCHAEOLOGY*

948.9   DK   ISSN 0109-8365
FOLK FORTAELLER. 1978. a. DKK 50. (Boldrup Museumsforening) Hans F. Jensen, Bredgade 50, DK-9610 Noerager, Denmark. illus.
   Description: Local history from a small farming community in Northern Jutland, Denmark.

948.9   DK   ISSN 0109-2766
FOLK OG LIV PAA ROENDEEGNEN-DENGANG. 1979. biennial. DKK 112. Si-Mi Tryk, Ravneej 5, 8410 Roende, Denmark. TEL 45-86-37-19-82. Ed. Vilfred Friborg Hansen. adv.; illus. circ. 900. **Indexed:** Amer.Hist.& Life, Hist.Abstr.

948.9   DK   ISSN 0900-002X
FOLK OG MINDER FRA KOEBENHAVN. 1984. a. DKK 70. Dansk Bladsforlag A-S, Fredensborg, Denmark. (Subscr. to: Danske Boghaendlers Kommissionsanstalt, Siljangade 6, 2300 Copenhagen S, Denmark)

948   DK   ISSN 0105-9610
FOLK OG MINDER FRA NORDSJAELLAND. vol.31, 1976. a. DKK 55. Dansk Bladforlag ApS, Hellerupvej 78, 2900 Hellerup, Denmark.
   Formerly (until 1976): Jul i Nordsjaelland.

948   SW   ISSN 0349-6279
FOLKETS HISTORIA. 1973. 4/yr. SEK 120. Riksfoereningen for Folkets Historia, Renstiernasgata 25, S-116 31 Stockholm, Sweden. TEL 08-640-58-72. Ed. Carl-Magnus Wendt. adv.; bk.rev.; illus.; bibl. circ. 1,600. **Indexed:** NAA. **Document type:** academic/scholarly publication.
   Formerly (until 1980): Arkivet foer Folkets Historia. Meddelanden (ISSN 0345-7605)

940.53   BE   ISSN 0772-652X
DS135.B4
FONDATION AUSCHWITZ. BULLETIN. 1984. q. 1200 BEF to individuals; institutions 2200 BEF. Fondation Auschwitz, 65, rue des Tanneurs, 1000 Bruxelles, Belgium. TEL 32-2-512-79-98. FAX 32-2-512-58-84. bk.rev. circ. 2,500.
   Description: Publishes research, studies and inquiries about the history and the memory of Nazi crimes and genocides.

FONTES ARCHAEOLOGICI POSNANIENSES/ANNALES MUSEI ARCHAEOLOGICI POSNANIENSIS. see *ARCHAEOLOGY*

943   AU   ISSN 0071-6871
FONTES RERUM AUSTRIACARUM. REIHE 1. SCRIPTORES. (Text in German and Latin) 1855. irreg. price varies. (Oesterreichische Akademie der Wissenschaften, Historische Kommission) Verlag der Oesterreichischen Akademie der Wissenschaften, Dr. Ignaz-Seipel-Platz 2, A-1010 Vienna, Austria. FAX 0222-5139541.

943   AU   ISSN 0071-688X
FONTES RERUM AUSTRIACARUM. REIHE 2. DIPLOMATARIA ET ACTA. (Text in German and Latin) 1849. irreg. price varies. (Oesterreichische Akademie der Wissenschaften, Historische Kommission) Verlag der Oesterreichischen Akademie der Wissenschaften, Dr. Ignaz-Seipel-Platz 2, A-1010 Vienna, Austria. FAX 0222-5139541.

943 340   AU   ISSN 0071-6898
FONTES RERUM AUSTRIACARUM. REIHE 3. FONTES JURIS. (Text in German and Latin) 1953. irreg., vol.12, 1993. price varies. Boehlau Verlag GmbH & Co.KG., Sachsenplatz 4-6, Postfach 87, A-1201 Vienna, Austria. TEL 0222-3302427-0. FAX 0222-3302432. TELEX 114-506-SPRIW-A. Ed. Werner Ogris. **Document type:** monographic series.

945   IT
FONTI DI STORIA TOSCANA. 1969. irreg., no.6, 1992. price varies. (Accademia Toscana de Scienze e Lettere La Colombaria) Casa Editrice Leo S. Olschki, Casella Postale 66, 50100 Florence, Italy. TEL 055-6530684. FAX 055-6530214. **Document type:** monographic series.

FONTI E STUDI PER LA STORIA DI BOLOGNA E DELLE PROVINCE EMILIANE E ROMAGNOLE. see *ART*

945   IT
FONTI ORALI; studi e ricerche. 1981. s-a. free. Istituto A. Gramsci, Via Vanchiglia 3 bis, 10124 Turin, Italy. TEL 11 8395402. circ. 1,000.

945   IT
FONTI PER LA STORIA DELL'UMBRIA. 1966. irreg., no.20, 1992. price varies. Deputazione di Storia Patria per l'Umbria, Palazzo della Penna, Via Podiani 11, C.P. 130, 06100 Perugia, Italy. TEL 075-5727057. **Document type:** monographic series.

945   IT   ISSN 0071-6901
FONTI SUI COMUNI RURALI TOSCANI. 1962. irreg., no.9, 1984. price varies. (Deputazione di Storia Patria, Florence) Casa Editrice Leo S. Olschki, Casella Postale 66, 50100 Florence, Italy. TEL 055-6530684. FAX 055-6530214. Ed. Arnaldo D'Addario. circ. 1,000. **Document type:** monographic series.

948.1   NO   ISSN 0071-7436
FORENINGEN TIL NORSKE FORTIDSMINNESMERKERS BEVARING. AARBOK. (Text in English, Norwegian) 1845. a. NOK 175. Foreningen til Norske Fortidsminnesmerkers Bevaring, Dronningensgt. 11, N-0152 Oslo, Norway. TEL 47-22-422-732. adv.; bk.rev. **Indexed:** NAA. **Document type:** academic/scholarly publication.
—CCC.

943.9   HU   ISSN 0133-056X
PH3001
FORRAS. m. $23. Bacs-Kiskun Megyei Lapkiado Vallalat, Szabadsag ter 1a, H-6001 Kecskemet, Hungary. bk.rev.; illus.

940   GW
FORSCHUNGEN UND QUELLEN ZUR ZEITGESCHICHTE. irreg., vol.25. DM.68. (Konrad-Adenauer-Stiftung) Droste Verlag GmbH, 40196 Duesseldorf, Germany. TEL 0211-5052604. FAX 0211-5052603. **Document type:** monographic series.

HISTORY — HISTORY OF EUROPE

FORSCHUNGEN ZU OSTEUROPA. see *POLITICAL SCIENCE — International Relations*

943 GW ISSN 0934-1234
FORSCHUNGEN ZUR BRANDENBURGISCHEN UND PREUSSISCHEN GESCHICHTE. 1991. q. DM.74. Duncker und Humblot GmbH, Postfach 410329, 12113 Berlin, Germany. TEL 030-7900060. FAX 030-79000631. Ed. J. Kunisch. **Document type:** academic/scholarly publication.

943.6 AU ISSN 0429-1565
FORSCHUNGEN ZUR GESCHICHTE OBEROESTERREICHS. 1950. irreg. price varies. Oberoesterreichisches Landesarchiv, Anzengruberstr. 19, A-4020 Linz, Austria. TEL 0732-6555230. FAX 0732-655523-4619. Eds. Siegfried Haider, Georg Heilingsetzer. circ. 500. (back issues avail.) **Indexed:** M.L.A. **Document type:** monographic series.

940 GW ISSN 0071-7673
FORSCHUNGEN ZUR MITTELALTERLICHEN GESCHICHTE. 1956. irreg., vol.35, 1992. price varies. Verlag Hermann Boehlaus Nachfolger, Meyerstr. 50a, 99403 Weimar, Germany. TEL 03643-202071. **Document type:** monographic series.

FORSCHUNGSBERICHTE ZUR UR- UND FRUEHGESCHICHTE. see *ARCHAEOLOGY*

943 GW ISSN 0179-6356
FORSCHUNGSSTELLE OSTMITTELEUROPA AN DER UNIVERSITAET DORTMUND. STUDIEN. 1986. irreg., vol.15, 1993. Harrassowitz Verlag, Taunusstr. 14, 65183 Wiesbaden, Germany. TEL 0611-530-0. FAX 0611-530-570. (Subscr. to: Postfach 2929, 65019 Wiesbaden, Germany) Ed. Johannes Hoffmann. **Document type:** monographic series.

FORT; the international journal of fortification and military architecture. see *MILITARY*

940 DK ISSN 0106-4797
FORTID OG NUTID. 1914. q. DKK 185. Dansk Historisk Faellesraad, Landsarkivet, P.O. Box 661, Jagtvej 10, DK-2200 Copenhagen N, Denmark. Dir. Grethe Ilsoee. bk.rev.; bibl.; charts; illus. circ. 1,400. **Indexed:** Amer.Hist.& Life, Anthropol.Lit., Hist.Abstr., NAA, Numis.Lit.

948.1 NO ISSN 0332-7205
FORTIDSVERN. 1975. q. NOK 135. Foreningen til Norske Fortidsminnesmerkers Bevaring, Dronningensgt. 11, N-0152 Oslo, Norway. TEL 47-22-422-732. **Document type:** academic/scholarly publication.
—CCC.

948 DK ISSN 0085-0845
FRA ALS OG SUNDEVED. 1928. a. DKK 95. Historisk Samfund for Als og Sundeved, Soenderborg Slot, DK-6400 Soenderborg, Denmark. Curator Inge Adriansen. illus. circ. 1,500.
Description: Contains items of local interest: local ethnology and culture, architecture and art.

948 DK ISSN 0107-2757
FRA BJERRINGBRO KOMMUNE. 1980. biennial. DKK 40. Bjerringbro Kommunes Lokalhistoriske Arkiv, EKSP. Bjerringbro Bibliotek, Realskolevej 12, 8850 Bjerringbro, Denmark. illus. circ. 350.

948 DK ISSN 0107-9301
FRA HIMMERLAND OG KJAER HERRED. 1912. a. DKK 95. Historisk Samfund for Himmerland og Kjaer Herred, Birke Alle 8, 9200 Aalborg SV, Denmark. TEL 98-181476. Ed. Gunnar H. Rebstrup. circ. 1,000.

948 DK ISSN 0107-878X
FRA HOLBAECK AMT: HISTORISKE AARBOEGER. 1907. a. DKK 80($13) Historisk Samfund for Holbaek Amt, Museet for Holbaek og Omegn, Klosterstraede 14-16, 4300 Holbaek, Denmark. Ed. Peter Korsgaard. adv.; bk.rev.; charts; illus. circ. 500. **Indexed:** NAA.
Description: Contains items of local interest.

948.9 DK ISSN 0107-895X
FRA KVANGAARD TIL HUMLEKULE. 1971. a. membership. Havebrugshistorisk Selskab, Rolighedsvej 23, DK-1958 Frederiksberg, Denmark. FAX 43-710414. Ed. Johan Lange. bk.rev.; illus.

948 DK ISSN 0046-4864
FRA RIBE AMT. 1903. a. DKK 100 (typically set in Apr.). Historisk Samfund for Ribe Amt, Faurskovvej 9, Lindknud, DK-6650 Broerup, Denmark. TEL 45-75-38-80-31. Ed. Hans Joergen L. Larsen. index every 3 yrs. circ. 1,200. **Indexed:** NAA.
Description: Contains items of local historical interest in the county of Ribe.

948 DK ISSN 0085-0853
FRA VIBORG AMT. AARBOG. 1929. a. DKK 85. Historisk Samfund for Viborg Amt, Landsarkivet, 8800 Viborg, Denmark. FAX 6-621788. Ed. Paul G. Oerberg. adv.; bk.rev. **Indexed:** NAA.
Description: Covers local history events.

948.7 SW ISSN 0429-2820
FRAAN GAESTRIKLAND. 1889. a. SEK 40 membership (effective 1990). Gaestriklands Kulturhistoriska Foerening, c/o G. Severin, Svang. 8 G, S-803 46 Gaevle, Sweden.
Formerly (until 1930): Meddelanden af Gestrikslands Kulturhistoriska Foerening.

948.6 SW ISSN 0349-9278
FRAAN GUTABYGD; aarsskrift foer den gotlaendska hembygdsroerelsen. 1979. a. SEK 165 (effective 1991). Gotlands Hembygdsfoerbund, Cramergatan 5, S-621 81 Visby, Sweden. Ed. Laila Press.

948.5 SW ISSN 0283-7994
FRAAN RANSBERG OCH KIRKEFALLA; aarsskrift. 1949-1975; resumed 1985. a. SEK 40 (effective 1990). (Ransbergs Hembygdsfoerening) Fraan Ransberg och Kirkefalla, Tibro Museum, Borgarg. 27, S-543 00 Tibro, Sweden.
Formerly (until 1975): Tibrobygden.

940 FR ISSN 0071-8440
DC33
FRANCE. COMITE DES TRAVAUX HISTORIQUES ET SCIENTIFIQUES. SECTION D'HISTOIRE MODERNE ET CONTEMPORAINE. ACTES DU CONGRES NATIONAL DES SOCIETES SAVANTES. 1951. a. price varies. Ministere de l'Education Nationale, Comite des Travaux Historiques et Scientifiques, 1 rue d'Ulm, 75005 Paris, France. cum.index: 1950-1960. circ. 650.
—BLDSC (0675.195500).

944 FR
FRANCE. COMMISSION DEPARTEMENTALE D'HISTOIRE ET D'ARCHEOLOGIE. MEMOIRES.. 1889. irreg., no.30, 1993. price varies. Commission Departementale d'Histoire et d'Archeologie, Archives Departementales, 1 rue du 19 mars 1962, 62000 Dainville, France.
Formerly: France. Commission Departementale des Monuments Historiques du Pas-de-Calais. Memoires.

943 GW ISSN 0015-9905
FRANKENLAND; Zeitschrift fuer Fraenkische Landeskunde und Kulturpflege. 1949; N.S. 1954. m. membership. Frankenbund - Vereinigung fuer Fraenkische Landeskunde und Kulturpflaege e.V., Hofstr. 3, 8700 Wuerzburg, Germany. Ed. Ulrike Schoemig. bk.rev.; abstr.; bibl.; illus.; index. circ. 4,400.

940 GW
FRANKFURTER ALTHISTORISCHE STUDIEN. 1968. irreg. price varies. (Universitaet Frankfurt, Seminar fuer Alte Geschichte) Verlag Michael Lassleben, Lange Gasse 19, 93183 Kallmuenz, Germany. Eds. Jochen Bleicken, Helga Gesche. **Document type:** monographic series.

940 GW ISSN 0170-3226
FRANKFURTER HISTORISCHE ABHANDLUNGEN. (Text in English and German) irreg., vol.35, 1993. price varies. Franz Steiner Verlag Wiesbaden GmbH, Birkenwaldstr. 44, 70191 Stuttgart, Germany. TEL 0711-2582-0. FAX 0711-2582290. TELEX 723636-DAZ-D. (Subscr. to: Postfach 101061, 70009 Stuttgart, Germany) Ed.Bd. **Document type:** monographic series.

943 200 GW
FRANKFURTER KIRCHLICHES JAHRBUCH. 1967. a. Evangelischer Gemeindeverband Frankfurt am Main, 6000 Frankfurt, Germany. illus.

944 DK ISSN 0900-2995
FRANKRIG INFORMATION. NYHEDSBREV. 1985. 8/yr. DKK 275. Frankrig Information, Postboks 260, 4000 Roskilde, Denmark. TEL 46-757711. FAX 45-46-75-44-10. Ed. Joergen Sand. bk.rev. circ. 800. **Document type:** newsletter.

948 DK ISSN 0108-8777
FREDERIKSBERG GENNEM TIDERNE. biennial. DKK 30. Historisk-Topografisk Selskab for Frederiksberg, Solbjergvej 25, DK-2000 Copenhagen F, Denmark.

FREIE UNIVERSITAET BERLIN. OSTEUROPA-INSTITUT. BERICHTE. see *HUMANITIES: COMPREHENSIVE WORKS*

947 GW ISSN 0067-5903
DR1
FREIE UNIVERSITAET BERLIN. OSTEUROPA-INSTITUT. HISTORISCHE VEROEFFENTLICHUNGEN; Forschungen zur Osteuropaeischen Geschichte. 1954. irreg., vol.49, 1993. price varies. Harrassowitz Verlag, Taunusstr. 14, 65183 Wiesbaden, Germany. TEL 0611-530-0. FAX 0611-530570. TELEX 4186135. (Subscr. to: Postfach 2929, 65019 Wiesbaden, Germany) Ed. H.T. Torke. **Indexed:** Amer.Hist.& Life, Hist.Abstr. **Document type:** monographic series.

944 US ISSN 0362-7055
JV1803
FRENCH COLONIAL HISTORICAL SOCIETY. PROCEEDINGS OF THE MEETING. (Text in English and French) 1976. irreg., 10th, 1985. University Press of America, 4720 Boston Way, Ste. A, Lanham, MD 20706. TEL 301-459-3366. Ed. James J. Cooke. circ. 300. **Document type:** proceedings.

944 UK ISSN 0957-1558
DC415 CODEN: FCUSEP
FRENCH CULTURAL STUDIES. 1990. 3/yr. £44 (U.S. & Japan $95; elsewhere £47). Alpha Academic (Subsidiary of: Richard Sadler Ltd.), Halfpenny Furze, Mill Ln., Chalfont St. Giles, Bucks. HP8 4NR, England. TEL 0494-872509. (back issues avail.) **Document type:** academic/scholarly publication.
—BLDSC (4034.218000); UnCover; SWETS.
Description: Designed to encourage and give a forum to the full range of research being conducted on all aspects of modern French culture. Emphasis is given to such areas as television, cinema, the press, visual arts, and popular culture.

944 US ISSN 0016-1071
DC1
FRENCH HISTORICAL STUDIES. (Text in English and French) 1958. s-a. $20 to individuals (foreign $24); institutions $30 (foreign $34). Duke University Press, Box 90660, Durham, NC 27708-0660. TEL 919-687-3600. FAX 919-688-4574. Eds. James Farr, John Certreni. adv.; cum.index. circ. 1,200. (reprint service avail. from KTO) **Indexed:** Amer.Hist.& Life, Arts & Hum.Cit.Ind., Curr.Cont., Hist.Abstr., Hum.Ind., Mid.East: Abstr.& Ind. **Document type:** academic/scholarly publication.
—BLDSC (4034.300000); Faxon; UnCover; SWETS; UMI.
Description: Covers all aspects of French history from the middle ages to the present.

944 UK ISSN 0269-1191
FRENCH HISTORY. 1987. q. £58($108) (effective 1994). Oxford University Press, Oxford Journals, Walton St., Oxford OX2 6DP, England. TEL 0865-56767. FAX 0865-56646. TELEX 837330-OXPRES-G. (U.S. subscr. to: Oxford University Press Inc., 2001 Evans Rd., Cary, NC 27513. TEL 919-677-0977) Ed. R.J. Bonney. adv. contact: Jane Parker. bk.rev. circ. 700. **Document type:** academic/scholarly publication.
—BLDSC (4034.310000); Faxon; UnCover; SWETS; UMI. **CCC.**
Description: Covers French history from Francia to the Fifth Republic, including historically oriented articles from other disciplines.

FRENCH POLITICS & SOCIETY. see *POLITICAL SCIENCE*

FRENCH STUDIES; a quarterly review. see *LITERATURE*

FRENCH STUDIES BULLETIN. see *LITERATURE*

HISTORY — HISTORY OF EUROPE

940 GW ISSN 0071-9706
D121
FRUEHMITTELALTERLICHE STUDIEN; Jahrbuch. 1967. a. price varies. (Universitaet Muenster, Institut fuer Fruehmittelalterforschung) Walter de Gruyter und Co., Genthiner Str. 13, 10785 Berlin, Germany. TEL 030-26005-0. FAX 030-26005251. TELEX 184027. (U.S. addr.: Walter de Gruyter, Inc., 200 Saw Mill Rd., Hawthorne, N.Y. 10532) Eds. H. Keller, J. Wollasch. adv.; bk.rev. **Indexed**: Avery Ind.Archit.Per., Bibl.Ling., Br.Archaeol.Abstr., RILA. **Document type**: academic/scholarly publication.
—SWETS.

940 GW
▼**FRUEHNEUZEIT INFO.** 1992. s-a. DM.78. (Institut fuer die Erforschung der Fruehen Neuzeit) Peter Lang GmbH Europaeischer Verlag der Wissenschaften, Eschborner Landstr. 42-50, 60489 Frankfurt a.M., Germany. TEL 069-7807050. FAX 069-785893. Ed.Bd. adv.: B&W page DM.900; trim 170 x 230. circ. 900. **Document type**: academic/scholarly publication.

943 GW ISSN 0016-2612
FULDAER GESCHICHTSBLAETTER. 1902. a. DM.25. Fuldaer Geschichtsverein, Stadtschloss, 6400 Fulda, Germany. Ed. Otto Berge. bk.rev.; illus.; tr.lit.; index. circ. 1,000.

948 DK ISSN 0107-8399
FYENS STIFTSBOG. 1969. a. DKK 65. Fyens Stifts Landemode, Stiftsoevrighedens Kontor, Klaregade 17, 5000 Odense, Denmark. TEL 45-66-12-53-02. Ed. Poul Erik Andersen. illus. circ. 2,400. (also avail. in diskette format) **Indexed**: NAA.

948 DK ISSN 0085-0918
FYNSKE AARBOEGER. 1939. a. DKK 90. Historisk Samfund for Fyns Stift, c/o H. H. Jacobsen, Ed., Hyrdinden 5, 5270 Odense N, Denmark. bk.rev.

948 913 DK ISSN 0427-7945
FYNSKE MINDER. 1951. a. DKK 90. Odense Bys Museer - City of Odense Museums, Jernbanegade 13, 5000 Odense C, Denmark. FAX 65-918900. Ed. Joergen Ganshorn. cum.index: 1951-1976. circ. 3,000. **Indexed**: Br.Archaeol.Abstr., NAA.

G I P. (Germansk Instituts Publikationer) see LINGUISTICS

G.W. LEIBNIZ: SAEMTLICHE SCHRIFTEN UND BRIEFE. see PHILOSOPHY

948 DK ISSN 0108-3791
GAMLE LOEJT. 1978. a. DKK 110. Loejt Sogns Lokalhistoriske Forening, Noerregade 8, 6200 Aabenraa, Denmark. TEL 45-74-61-75-19. Ed. Jens Bruun. bk.rev.; illus. circ. 600. **Document type**: academic/scholarly publication.
Description: History of Loejt parish.

943.6 AU
GARSER KULTURBRIEF. 1968. 6/yr. Marktgemeinde Gars-Kamp, 3571 Gars-Kamp, Austria.

948.1 NO
GAULDALSMINNE; arbok for bygdehistorie og folkeminne. 1926. irregg. NOK 30. Gauldal Historielag, c/o Jens Haukdal, 7450 Soknedal, Norway. Ed. Eirik Karstad. adv.; bk.rev.

914.03 913 PO
GAYA. 1983. a. price varies. Gabinete de Historia e Arqueologia de Vila Nova de Gaia, Solar dos Condes de Resende-Canelas, 4405 Valadares, Portugal. TEL 398468. (Dist. by: Biblioteca Publica Municipal de V.N. de Gaia, Rua de Angola, 4400 V.N. de Gaia, Portugal) circ. 1,000.

944 FR ISSN 0016-5522
GAZETTE DES ARCHIVES. 1933. q. 250 F. Association des Archivistes Francais, 60 rue des Francs-Bourgeois, 75141 Paris Cedex 03, France. TEL 40-27-60-00. Ed. Gerard Moyse. adv.; bk.rev. circ. 1,500. **Indexed**: Amer.Hist.& Life, Hist.Abstr.
—BLDSC (4092.970000).

943.8 PL
GDANSKI ROCZNIK KULTURALNY. 1965. irreg., vol.12, 1988. 4000 Zl. per no. Gdanskie Towarzystwo Przyjaciol Sztuki, Chlebnicka 2, 80-830 Gdansk, Poland. TEL 31-25-35.
Formerly: Rocznik Kulturalny Ziemi Gdanskiej (ISSN 0435-1568)
Description: A yearly review of cultural events in Gdansk area. Includes articles and essays on history and history of culture.

943.8 913 PL ISSN 0072-0410
GDANSKIE TOWARZYSTWO NAUKOWE. WYDZIAL 1 - NAUK SPOLECZNYCH I HUMANISTYCZNYCH. KOMISJA ARCHEOLOGICZNA. PRACE. (Text in Polish; summaries in English and German) 1959. irreg., no.9, 1983. price varies. (Komisja Archeologiczna) Ossolineum, Publishing House of the Polish Academy of Sciences, Rynek 9, 50-106 Wroclaw, Poland. TEL 48-71-386-25. FAX 48-71-448-103. TELEX 0712771 OSS PL. Ed. Jadwiga Kaminska. charts; illus. circ. 500. **Document type**: monographic series.
Description: Monographic papers devoted to the archaeology of Gdansk in the early Middle Ages.

943.8 PL ISSN 0433-230X
GDANSKIE TOWARZYSTWO NAUKOWE. WYDZIAL 1 - NAUK SPOLECZNYCH I HUMANISTYCZNYCH. SERIA MONOGRAFII. 1959. irreg., no.91, 1991. price varies. Ossolineum, Publishing House of the Polish Academy of Sciences, Rynek 9, 50-106 Wroclaw, Poland. TEL 48-71-386-25. FAX 48-71-448-103. TELEX 0712771 OSS PL. Ed. Edmund Cieslak. bibl.; illus. circ. 1,500. **Document type**: monographic series.
Description: Studies and materials related to the history of Gdansk.

943.8 PL ISSN 0072-0429
GDANSKIE TOWARZYSTWO NAUKOWE. WYDZIAL 1 - NAUK SPOLECZNYCH I HUMANISTYCZNYCH. SERIA POPULARNONAUKOWA "POMORZE GDANSKIE". 1965. irreg., no.18, 1988. price varies. Ossolineum, Publishing House of the Polish Academy of Sciences, Rynek 9, 50-106 Wroclaw, Poland. TEL 48-71-386-25. FAX 48-71-448-103. TELEX 0712771 OSS PL. Ed. J. Borzyszkowski. circ. 740. **Document type**: monographic series.
Description: General interest publications devoted to the history and culture of Gdansk and Pomerania.

943.8 PL ISSN 0072-0437
GDANSKIE TOWARZYSTWO NAUKOWE. WYDZIAL 1 - NAUK SPOLECZNYCH I HUMANISTYCZNYCH. SERIA ZRODEL. irreg., no.11, 1984. Ossolineum, Publishing House of the Polish Academy of Sciences, Rynek 9, 50-106 Wroclaw, Poland. TEL 48-71-386-25. FAX 48-71-448-103. TELEX 0712771 OSS PL. Ed. Z. Binerowski. circ. 600. **Document type**: monographic series.
Description: Sources for the history and culture of Pomerania.

943 GW
GEDENKSTAETTEN RUNDBRIEF. 1983. bi-m. DM.40. Stiftung Topographie des Terrors Gedenkstaettenreferat, Budapesterstr. 44, 10787 Berlin, Germany. Ed. Thomas Lutz. circ. 350. **Document type**: newsletter.
Description: Reports on the work of memorial museums for the victims of Nazi terrorism.

GEDENKTAGE DES MITTELDEUTSCHEN RAUMES. see BIOGRAPHY

GEISTLICHE LITERATUR DER BAROCKZEIT. see LITERATURE

913 NE
GELDERS ERFGOED.* 1957. 6/yr. fl.25. Stichting Gelders Oudheidkundig Contact, Oude Wand 31-33, 7201 LJ Zutphen, Netherlands. Ed. F.W.J. Scholten. adv.; bk.rev.; charts; illus. circ. 1,500.
Formerly (until 1992): Gelders Oudheidkundig Contactbericht (ISSN 0016-6014)

940 NE
GELDERSE HISTORISCHE REEKS. 1971. a. price varies. Walburg Pers BV, Postbus 4159, 7200 BD Zutphen, Netherlands. TEL 31-5750-10522. FAX 31-5750-41025. (Co-sponsor: Stichting Gelderse Historische Reeks) **Document type**: monographic series.

943 UK ISSN 0266-3554
GERMAN HISTORY. 1984. 3/yr. £45($86) (effective 1994). Oxford University Press, Oxford Journals, Walton St., Oxford OX2 6DP, England. TEL 0865-56767. FAX 0865-56646. TELEX 837330-OXPRES-G. (U.S. subscr. to: Oxford University Press Inc., 2001 Evans Rd., Cary, NC 27513. TEL 919-677-0977) Eds. Mary Fulbrook, Jill Stephenson. adv. contact: Jane Parker. bk.rev. circ. 700. (also avail. in microfiche) **Document type**: academic/scholarly publication.
—BLDSC (4162.113900); Faxon; SWETS; UMI. CCC.
Description: History of Germany and other German-speaking areas.

943 US ISSN 0899-9899
GERMAN LIFE AND CIVILIZATION. irreg. Peter Lang Publishing, Inc., 62 W. 45th St., 4th Fl., New York, NY 10036. TEL 212-302-6740. FAX 212-302-7574. Ed. Jost Hermand. **Document type**: academic/scholarly publication.
Description: Provides contributions to a critical understanding of Central European cultural history from medieval times to the present.

GERMAN POLITICS & SOCIETY. see POLITICAL SCIENCE

940 830 US ISSN 0149-7952
DD1
GERMAN STUDIES REVIEW. (Text in English and German) 1978. 3/yr. $25 (Canada $27; elsewhere $30) (effective 1994). German Studies Association, c/o Prof. Gerald R. Kleinfeld, Ed., Arizona State University, Tempe, AZ 85287-4205. TEL 602-965-4839. FAX 602-965-8989. adv.; bk.rev. circ. 1,700. (back issues avail.) **Indexed**: Amer.Bibl.Slavic & E.Eur.Stud., Amer.Hist.& Life, Arts & Hum.Cit.Ind., Bibl.Ling., Curr.Cont., Hist.Abstr., M.L.A.
—BLDSC (4162.157400); Faxon; UnCover.

943 GW ISSN 0720-3659
GESCHICHTE IN KOELN. 1978. s-a. DM.30. Janus Verlagsgesellschaft, Simon-Meister-Str. 42, 50733 Cologne, Germany. TEL 0221-723432. FAX 0221-737884. Ed. Bernd Frick. adv.; bk.rev. circ. 800. **Document type**: academic/scholarly publication.

943 230 GW ISSN 0343-4648
GESCHICHTE, POLITIK UND IHRE DIDAKTIK. 1973. s-a. DM.36. (Verband der Geschichtslehrer Deutschlands) Verlag Ferdinand Schoeningh GmbH, Postfach 2540, 33055 Paderborn, Germany. TEL 05251-127665. FAX 05251-127860. (Co-sponsors: Landesbaende Hessen, Niedersachesen, Nordrhein-Westfalen, Schleswig-Holstein) Ed. Paul Leidinger. adv.; bk.rev. circ. 5,000. **Document type**: academic/scholarly publication.
—BLDSC (4162.520100). CCC.

GESCHICHTE UND GESELLSCHAFT; Zeitschrift fuer Historische Sozialwissenschaft. see SOCIAL SCIENCES: COMPREHENSIVE WORKS

943 GW ISSN 0072-4203
GESCHICHTLICHE LANDESKUNDE. 1964. irreg., vol.41, 1994. price varies. (Universitaet Mainz, Institut fuer Geschichtliche Landeskunde) Franz Steiner Verlag Wiesbaden GmbH, Birkenwaldstr. 44, 70191 Stuttgart, Germany. TEL 0711-2582-0. FAX 0711-2582290. TELEX 723636-DAZ-D. (Subscr. to: Postfach 101061, 70009 Stuttgart, Germany) Ed. Alois Gerlich. (back issues avail.) **Document type**: monographic series.

943 949 BE
GESCHICHTLICHES EUPEN. (Text in German) 1839. a. Eupener Geschichts- und Museumsverein, Obere Ibern 12, 4700 Eupen, Belgium.

943 GW ISSN 0723-2098
GESCHICHTSBLAETTER DES KREISES COESFELD. 1976. a. DM.13. Arbeitskreis fuer Geschichte und Archivwesen e.V., Friedrich-Ebert-Str. 7, 48653 Coesfeld, Germany. Ed. Willy Schmitz. circ. 800. (back issues avail.)

HISTORY — HISTORY OF EUROPE

943 398   GW   ISSN 0342-0965
GESCHICHTSBLAETTER FUER WALDECK. 1901. a. DM.20. Waldeckischer Geschichtsverein e.V. Arolsen, Schlossstr. 24, 34454 Arolsen, Germany. TEL 05691-6652. Ed.Bd. bk.rev.; cum.index. circ. 1,300.
    Description: Articles on regional history and culture, including genealogy and heraldry.

940   BE   ISSN 0591-1133
GESCHIED- EN OUDHEIDKUNDIGE KRING VAN RONSE EN HET TENEMENT VAN INDE. ANNALEN/CERCLE HISTORIQUE ET ARCHEOLOGIQUE DE RENAIX ET DU TENEMENT D'INDE. ANNALES. (Editions in Flemish, French) 1948. a. 600 BEF (effective 1994). Geschied- en Oudheidkundige Kring van Ronse en Het Tenement van Inde, Cercle Historique et Archeologique de Renaix et du Tenement d'Inde, Glorieuxlaan 17, 9600 Ronse, Belgium. bk.rev. circ. 400. **Document type:** academic/scholarly publication.

940   BE   ISSN 0774-5435
GESCHIED- EN OUDHEIDKUNDIGE KRING VOOR LEUVEN EN OMGEVING. JAARBOEK. (Text in Dutch) 1961. a. 750 BEF (effective 1993). (Geschied- en Oudheidkundige Kring voor Leuven en Omgeving) Editions Peeters s.p.r.l., Bondgenotenlaan 153, B-3000 Louvain, Belgium. TEL 32-16-235170. FAX 32-16-228500. bk.rev. (back issues avail.) **Document type:** academic/scholarly publication.
    Formerly (until 1975): Geschied- en Oudheidkundige Kring voor Leuven en Omgeving. Mededelingen (ISSN 0774-5427)

949   NE
GESCHIEDENIS VAN HET ZUIDEN VAN NEDERLAND. 1964. irreg. 4-5/yr. fl.110. Stichting Zuidelijk Historisch Contact, Warandelaan 2, 5037 GC Tilburg, Netherlands. Ed. H.F.J.M. van der Eerenbeemt. circ. 1,200. **Document type:** monographic series.

943.6 284   AU
GESELLSCHAFT FUER DIE GESCHICHTE DES PROTESTANTISMUS IN OESTERREICH. JAHRBUCH. 1880. a. DM.38. Gesellschaft fuer die Geschichte des Protestantismus in Oesterreich, Severin-Schreiber-Gasse 3, A-1180 Vienna, Austria. TEL 0222-4791523. Eds. Gustav Reingrabner, Karl Schwarz. bk.rev. circ. 30. **Indexed:** Amer.Hist.& Life, Hist.Abstr. **Document type:** bulletin.

943.6   AU
GESELLSCHAFT FUER NATUR UND HEIMATKUNDE. HEIMATKUNDLICHE MITTEILUNGEN. 1968. 12/yr. Gesellschaft fuer Natur und Heimatkunde, Thalheimergasse 1-7-3-3, 1166 Vienna, Austria.

943 284   GW   ISSN 0072-4238
GESELLSCHAFT FUER NIEDERSAECHSISCHE KIRCHENGESCHICHTE. JAHRBUCH. 1896. a. DM.25. (Gesellschaft fuer Niedersaechsische Kirchengeschichte) Buchdruckerei Willi Rihn, 4733 Blomberg, Germany. Ed. Inge Mager. bk.rev. circ. 250. **Document type:** academic/scholarly publication.

943.6   AU
GESELLSCHAFT FUER SALZBURGER LANDESKUNDE. MITTEILUNGEN. 1861. a. Gesellschaft fuer Salzburger Landeskunde, Landesarchiv Michael-Pacher-Str. 40, A-5020 Salzburg, Austria. **Document type:** proceedings.

943   GW   ISSN 0072-4254
GESELLSCHAFT FUER SCHLESWIG-HOLSTEINISCHE GESCHICHTE. ZEITSCHRIFT. 1870. a. DM.50. Wachholtz Verlag GmbH, Rungestr. 4, 24537 Neumuenster, Germany. TEL 04321-906270. FAX 04321-906275. cum.index: 1933-1975. circ. 2,000. **Indexed:** Bibl.Cart., Numis.Lit. **Document type:** academic/scholarly publication.

GESELLSCHAFT FUER VERGLEICHENDE KUNSTFORSCHUNG IN WIEN. MITTEILUNGEN. see MUSEUMS AND ART GALLERIES

GESTA. see ART

948.9   DK   ISSN 0109-6656
GILLELEJE MUSEUM. 1979. irreg. price varies. Gilleleje Museum, Rostgaardsvej 2, DK-3250 Gilleleje, Denmark. Ed. Soeren Frandsen. illus. circ. 100.
    Description: Features articles, in popular form, on the local prehistory and local cultural history of the area, with particular emphasis on the coastal fishing during the last three centuries.

945 913   IT   ISSN 0017-050X
GIORNALE STORICO DELLA LUNIGIANA E DEL TERRITORIO LUCENSE. 1950. a. L.40000. Istituto Internazionale di Studi Liguri - International Institute of Ligurian Studies, Via Romana, 39, 18012 Bordighera, Italy. bk.rev.; illus.; cum.index every 5 yrs. circ. 1,000. **Document type:** academic/scholarly publication.
    Formerly (until 1960): Giornale Storico della Lunigiana.
    Description: Covers history of the Lunigian areas.

949   BN   ISSN 0436-046X
GLASNIK ARHIVA I DRUSTVA ARHIVSKIH RADNIKA BOSNE I HERCEGOVINE. 1961. a. price varies. Drustvo Arhivskih Radnika Bosne i Hercegovine, Bitt Save Kovacevica 6, 71000 Sarajevo, Bosnia Hercegovina. TEL 071-213-657. Ed. Matko Kovacevic. bk.rev. circ. 500. (also avail. in microfilm)

940.53 323.4   GW
DIE GLOCKE VOM ETTERSBERG. 1958. q. $5. Lagergemeinschaft Buchenwald, Wolf, Hamburgerstr. 39, 63073 Offenbach, Germany. TEL 069-895639. circ. 1,200.
    Description: Studies war, fascism and democracy, and the history of the Nazi concentration camp at Buchenwald.

GLOSSAE; revista de historia del derecho europeo. see LAW

942   UK   ISSN 0260-5139
GLOUCESTERSHIRE LOCAL HISTORY NEWSLETTER. 1979. a. free with Gloucestershire History. Gloucestershire Rural Community Council, Community House, 15 College Green, Gloucestershire GL1 2LZ, England. Ed. E. Bourne. bk.rev. circ. 550. **Document type:** newsletter.

942   UK
GLOUCESTERSHIRE RECORD SERIES. 1988. a. £18 to individuals; institutions £23.50. Bristol and Gloucestershire Archaeological Society, 22 Beaumont Rd., Gloucester GL2 OEJ, England. TEL 045-302610. Ed. D.J.H. Smith. circ. 350. **Document type:** monographic series.
    Description: Provides original sources for local history research in Gloucestershire.

943   GW   ISSN 0436-1024
GODESBERGER HEIMATBLAETTER. 1963. a. DM.20. Verein fuer Heimatpflege und Heimatgeschichte, Bad Godesberg e.V., Eschenweg 2, 53177 Bonn, Germany. TEL 0228-325185. Ed. Herbert Strack. bk.rev. circ. 1,400. **Document type:** proceedings.
    Description: Local history of Bad Godesberg and surroundings.

947   BU   ISSN 0204-4048
GODISHNIK NA MUZEITE OT SEVERNA BULGARIIA. 1975. irreg. Knigoizdatelstvo G. Bakalov, 9th of September Sq., 6 Varna, Bulgaria. TEL 2-12-96. (Dist. by: Historical Museum, 2 Nikola Picolo, 5000 V. Turnovo, Bulgaria) Ed. Todorka Draganova. circ. 630.

943   GW   ISSN 0072-4882
DD901.G55
GOETTINGER JAHRBUCH.* 1952. a. price varies. (Geschichtsverein fuer Goettingen und Umgebung) Reise Verlag, Kurmainzer Weg 22, 37083 Goettingen, Germany. Ed. W. Roehrbein.

943.6   SW
GRAEZER BEITRAEGE; Zeitschrift fuer klassische Altertumswissenschaft. (Text in English, French, German and Italian) 1973. a. S.890($80) (Universitaet Graz, Institut fuer Klassische Philologie) Verlag Ferdinand Berger und Soehne GmbH, Wiener Str. 21-23, A-3580 Horn, Austria. TEL 02982-2317-0. **Document type:** academic/scholarly publication.

940   FR   ISSN 0072-5404
GRANDES FIGURES DE LA CHARITE.* 1970. irreg. price varies. Editions S.O.S., 106 rue du Bac, 75007 Paris, France.

943   GW   ISSN 0343-1258
GRATIA; Bamberger Schriften zur Renaissanceforschung. 1979. irreg. vol.24, 1993. Harrassowitz Verlag, Taunusstr. 14, 65183 Wiesbaden, Germany. TEL 0611-530-0. FAX 0611-530-570. TELEX 4186135. (Subscr. to: Postfach 2929, 65019 Wiesbaden, Germany) Ed. Dieter Wuttke. **Document type:** monographic series.

942 571   UK
GREAT BRITAIN. ROYAL COMMISSION ON ANCIENT AND HISTORICAL MONUMENTS IN WALES. INTERIM REPORT. 1909. irreg. price varies. (Royal Commission on Ancient and Historical Monuments in Wales) H.M.S.O., P.O. Box 276, London SW8 5DT, England. **Document type:** government publication.
    Formerly: Great Britain. Royal Commission on the Ancient and Historical Monuments and Constructions in Wales and Monmouthshire. Interim Report (ISSN 0072-7075)

GREAT BRITAIN. ROYAL COMMISSION ON THE HISTORICAL MONUMENTS OF ENGLAND. NEWSLETTER. see ARCHAEOLOGY

940 809   CN   ISSN 1183-1286
GREEK INDEX PROJECT SERIES. 1989. irreg., vol.3, 1990. Pontifical Institute of Mediaeval Studies, 59 Queen's Park Cres. E., Toronto, ON M5S 2C4, Canada. TEL 416-926-7144. FAX 416-926-7258. (Dist. outside N. America and UK by: N.V. Brepols, Steenweg op Tielen 68, 2300 Turnhout, Belgium. TEL 32-14-415463. FAX 32-14-428919) (back issues avail.) **Document type:** monographic series.

942   UK
GREENWICH HISTORICAL SOCIETY. JOURNAL. 1991? q.? Greenwich Historical Society, c/o A.W.H. Pearsall, Ed., 71 Parkside, London SE10, England.

949.5 281.9   GR   ISSN 1011-3010
BX610
GREGORIOS O PALAMAS. 1917. 5/yr. $50. Metropolis Thessalonikes, P.O. Box 10335, Salonika, Greece. FAX 031-230-722. Ed. Rev. Demetrios Vakaros. bk.rev.; bibl. circ. 1,000. **Indexed:** CERDIC, M.L.A.

949.2   NE   ISSN 0169-2801
D1
GRONIEK; Groningen historisch tijdschrift. 1967. q. fl.47.50 to individuals; students fl. 35. University of Groningen, Department of History, Oude Kijk in 't Jatstraat 26, 9712 EK Groningen, Netherlands. TEL 31-50-636020. FAX 31-50-637253. Ed.Bd. adv.; bk.rev. circ. 1,000.
—SWETS.
    Formerly: Groniek. Onafhankelijk Gronings Historisch Studentenblad.
    Description: Discusses a variety of topics such as time, geography and genius from an historical perspective.

945   IT
GUIDA. 1978. m. (11/yr.). free. Libreria Guida, Via Port'Alba 20-23, 80134 Naples, Italy. TEL 081-446377. FAX 081-451883. circ. 20,000.

942   UK
GUILD OF FREEMEN OF THE CITY OF LONDON. 1908. a. £16 to non-members. P.O. Box 153, 40A Ludgate Hill, London EC4M 7DE, England. TEL 01-223 7638. adv. circ. 3,000. **Indexed:** P.A.I.S.
    Description: A history of the Guild of Freeman of the city of London from 1908 to 1980.

GUMBINNER HEIMATBRIEF. see FOLKLORE

948   DK
HADERSLEV STIFTSBOG. 1946. a. (Haderslev Stiftsfond) J.D. Nielsens Forlag, 6100 Haderslev, Denmark.
    Formerly: Haderslav Stifts Arbog.

948.6   SW   ISSN 0440-0585
HAELSINGERUNOR; en hembygdsbok. 1947. a. SEK 120 (effective 1990). Helsinglands Hembygdskrets, Snarboele 3494, S-826 94 Norrala, Sweden. TEL 0270-35128. Ed. Sigvard Bodin.

HAGIOGRAPHICA; rivista di agiografia e biografia. see RELIGIONS AND THEOLOGY — Roman Catholic

948.6   SW   ISSN 0347-4364
HALLAND; aarsbok foer kulturhistoria och hembygdsvaard i Hallands laen. (Supplement avail.: Halland i Litteraturen (ISSN 0347-4372)) (Text in Swedish; summaries in English) 1961. a. SEK 50 (effective 1990). Stiftelsen HallandsLaensmuseer, Halmstad och Varberg, TEL 46-35-10-94-80. FAX 46-35-18-60-67. (Dist by: Museet i Halmstad, Tollsg., S-302 31 Halmstad, Sweden) Ed. Bjoern Petersen. circ. 1,250. **Document type:** academic/scholarly publication, bibliography.

943.1   GW
HAMBURGISCHE GESCHICHTS- UND HEIMATBLAETTER. 1877. s-a. DM.6. Verein fuer Hamburgische Geschichte, ABC-Str. 19, 20354 Hamburg, Germany. Ed. Renate Hauschild-Thiessen. bk.rev. circ. 1,700.

948   FI
HAMEENLINNA - WANAJA.* 1951. a. Hameenlinna Seura Wanaja Seura, Lukiokatu 21 B 24, 13200 Hameenlinna, Finland. cum.index: 1951-70.
    Formerly: Hameenlinna.

948   FI
HAMEENMAA. 1928. irreg. (Hameen Heimoliitto) Karisto Oy, Paroistentie 2, 13600 Hameenlinna, Finland. Ed. Kanerva Unto. cum.index: 1928-59 in vol. 11, 1962. circ. 1,500.

HAMPSHIRE FIELD CLUB AND ARCHAEOLOGICAL SOCIETY PROCEEDINGS. see ARCHAEOLOGY

943   GW   ISSN 0342-1104
HANNOVERSCHE GESCHICHTSBLAETTER. 1947. s-a. price varies. Verlag Hahnsche Buchhandlung, Postfach 2460, 30024 Hannover, Germany. TEL 0511-322294. FAX 0511-363698. bibl.; illus. circ. 1,500. **Indexed:** Bibl.Cart. **Document type:** academic/scholarly publication.

940   GW   ISSN 0073-0327
HANSISCHE GESCHICHTSBLAETTER. 1882. a. price varies. (Hansischer Geschichtsverein) Boehlau Verlag GmbH, Theodor-Heuss-Str. 76, 51149 Cologne, Germany. TEL 02203-307021. FAX 02203-307349. Eds. Klaus Friedland, Volker Henn. **Indexed:** Bibl.Cart. **Document type:** academic/scholarly publication.

948   DK   ISSN 0046-6840
HARDSYSSELS AARBOG. 1907; N.S. 1967. a. DKK 160 to non-members; members DKK 125. Historisk Samfund for Ringkoebing Amt, c/o Erik Noergaard, Holsterbro Bibliotek, Kirkestraede 11, DK-7500 Holsterbro, Denmark. TEL 97-42-33-99. Ed. Esben Graugaard. bibl.; illus.; index, cum.index: 1907-1966, 1967-1986. circ. 1,900. **Indexed:** NAA.
    Description: Contains items of local historical interest in the county of Ringkoebing.

HARVARD CELTIC COLLOQUIUM. PROCEEDINGS. see LINGUISTICS

917.306 947   US   ISSN 0363-5570
DK508.A2
HARVARD UKRAINIAN STUDIES. 1977. s-a. fl.63($28) to individuals; institutions fl.70($28); foreign $32. Harvard University, Ukrainian Research Institute, 1583 Massachusetts Ave., Cambridge, MA 02138. TEL 617-495-4243. FAX 617-495-8097. Ed.Bd. adv.; bk.rev.; bibl.; index. circ. 412. (back issues avail.) **Indexed:** Amer.Bibl.Slavic & E.Eur.Stud., Bibl.Ling., M.L.A. **Document type:** academic/scholarly publication.
    —BLDSC (4270.750000); UnCover.
    Description: Serves as an international forum for current research in Ukrainian studies, cultivating an interdisciplinary approach.

947   US   ISSN 0073-0831
HARVARD UNIVERSITY. RUSSIAN RESEARCH CENTER. STUDIES. (Text in English; one vol. in Russian) 1950. irreg., no.85, 1991. price varies. Harvard University Press, 79 Garden St., Cambridge, MA 02138. TEL 617-495-2600. FAX 617-495-5898. **Document type:** monographic series.
    Refereed Serial

943   GW   ISSN 0073-0882
HARZ - ZEITSCHRIFT. 1868; N.S. 1948. a. DM.30. Harzverein fuer Geschichte und Altertumskunde, c/o Braunschweigisches Landesmuseum, Burgplatz 1, 38100 Braunschweig, Germany. FAX 0531-4842607. (Affiliate: Braunschweigisches Landesmuseum) Ed. Christof Roemer. bk.rev. **Document type:** academic/scholarly publication.
    —BLDSC (4271.200000).

HASKALA; wissenschaftliche Abhandlungen. see ETHNIC INTERESTS

941 929   UK   ISSN 0309-5118
DA690.S16
HATCHER REVIEW. 1976. s-a. £5($12.50) Hatcher Review Trust, King Alfred's College, Winchester SO22 4NR, England. TEL 0962-842280. FAX 0962-841515. Ed. M. Doughty. bk.rev.; illus.; index. circ. 500.
    Description: Local journal reflecting the history and literature of Mid-Wessex, Dorset, Wiltshire, and Hampshire.

940   SZ   ISSN 0073-0955
HAUTES ETUDES MEDIEVALES ET MODERNES. 1964. irreg., no.71, 1992. price varies. (Ecole Pratique des Hautes Etudes, Centre de Recherches d'Histoire et de Philologie, FR) Librairie Droz S.A., 11, rue Massot, CH-1211 Geneva 12, Switzerland. TEL 022-3466666. FAX 022-3472391. circ. 1,000. **Document type:** monographic series.
    —CCC.

949 914.2   BE
HEEMKRING OKEGEM. ANNALEN. (Text in Flemish) 1975. a. $10. Heemkring Okegem, Idevoordelaan 27, 9400 Ninove-Okegem, Belgium. **Document type:** monographic series.

949 914.9   BE
HEEMKRING OKEGEM. MEDEDELINGEN. (Text in Flemish) a. Heemkring Okegem, Idevoordelaan 27, 9400 Ninove-Okegem, Belgium. **Document type:** monographic series.

943   GW   ISSN 0017-9701
                CODEN: HEIMEH
DIE HEIMAT. 1891. m. DM.60. (Verein zur Pflege der Natur- und Landeskunde in Schleswig-Holstein und Hamburg) Wachholtz Verlag GmbH, Rungestr. 4, 24537 Neumuenster, Germany. TEL 04321-906270. FAX 04321-906275. bk.rev.; charts; illus.; index, cum.index: 1947-1985. circ. 1,700. **Document type:** bulletin.

943
HEIMAT AM INN. 1972. a. Rudolf Vierlinger, Ed. & Pub., Jakob-Weindler Str. 4, 84359 Simbach Inn, Germany. circ. 1,200.

943.6   AU
HEIMAT IM WEINLAND; heimatkundliches Beiblatt zum Amtsblatt der Bezirkshauptmannschaft Mistelbach. 1950. irreg. Bezirkhauptmannschaft Mistelbach, Hauptplatz 4-5, 2130 Mistelbach, Austria. cum.index: 1960-69.
    Formerly: Heimatkundliches Beiblatt (ISSN 0462-9086)

943   GW   ISSN 0017-9752
HEIMAT - ZEITUNG ROEMERSTAEDTER LAENDCHEN; und angrenzende Gemeinden. 1947. bi-m. DM.18. Heimatkreis Roemerstadt-Altxater e.V., Schwalbengraben 82, 35576 Wetzlar-Dalheim, Germany. TEL 06441-51445. adv.; illus.

943   GW   ISSN 0935-364X
HEIMATBLAETTLE; eine Schwenninger Monatsschrift fuer Heimat und Volkstum. 1953. m. DM.40. (Schwenninger Heimatverein e.V.) S W A N O-Verlag, Buerkstr. 18, 78054 VS-Schwenningen, Germany. TEL 07720-31662. bk.rev circ. 3,000. (back issues avail.)

945   GW
HEIMATBOGEN DER GEMEINDE SCHNELLDORF. 1969. q. DM.12. Gemeinde Schnelldorf, Rothenburger Str. 13, 91625 Schnelldorf, Germany. TEL 07950-622. circ. 600.

943 398   GW
HEIMATBRIEF DER STADT GERMERSHEIM. 1960. a. DM.7. Stadtverwaltung Germersheim, Stadthaus Kolpingplatz 3, 76726 Germersheim, Germany. FAX 07274-540. circ. 1,150.

947.5   GW   ISSN 0440-6230
HEIMATGRUSS. 1956. a. DM.8. Landsmannschaft der Deutschen aus Litauen, c/o Manfred Franzkeit, In den Wiesen 3, 27259 Wehrbleck, Germany. TEL 04274-527. Ed. Alfred Franzkeit. circ. 2,000. **Document type:** bulletin.

943.6   AU
HEIMATKUNDE, KULTURPFLEGE, STADTGESCHICHTE; kulturbeilage zum Amtsblatt der Stadt Klosterneuburg. 1968. irreg. Arbeitskreis zur Foerderung der Heimatkunde in Klosterneuburg, Rathausplatz 1, 3400 Klosterneuburg, Austria.

943.6   AU
HEIMATKUNDLICHE NACHRICHTEN. 1970. irreg. free. Heimatmuseum Traiskirchen, Stadtgemeinde Traiskirchen, 2514 Traiskirchen, Austria. Ed. Franz Schlogl. bk.rev. circ. 200.

943   GW
HEIMATKUNDLICHES JAHRBUCH FUER DEN KREIS SEGEBERG. 1955. a. DM.23.80. (Heimatverein des Kreises Segeberg) Verlag C.H. Waeser GmbH, Hamburgerstr. 26, 23795 Bad Segeberg, Germany. TEL 04551-904-0. FAX 04551-904-64. bk.rev.; bibl.; illus. circ. 1,200. **Document type:** academic/scholarly publication.

948   SZ
HEIMATLEBEN. (Text in French and German) 1928. 3/yr. 21 SFr. Schweizerische Trachtenvereinigung - Federation Nationale de Costumes Suisses, Postfach, Muehlegasse 15, CH-3400 Burgdorf, Switzerland. TEL 034-222239. FAX 034-232253. illus. circ. 23,000. **Indexed:** Text.Tech.Dig.
    Formerly (until 1936): Schweizertracht.

943.6   AU   ISSN 0017-9809
DAS HEIMATMUSEUM ALSERGRUND. 1960. q. free. Museumsverein Alsergrund, Waehringer Str. 43, A-1090 Vienna, Austria. Ed. Ing. Alfred Wolf. adv.; bk.rev.; illus. circ. 1,000. (processed)

943   GW   ISSN 0177-2899
HEIMATSTIMMEN AUS DEM KREIS OLPE. 1948. q. DM.16($10) Kreisheimatbund Olpe e.V., Kurfuerst-Heinrich-Str. 34, 57462 Olpe, Germany. TEL 02761-81658. FAX 02761-81600. Ed. Guenther Becker. bk.rev.; a. index. circ. 1,800. (back issues avail.) **Document type:** academic/scholarly publication.

944 914.4 572   FR   ISSN 0336-030X
HEIMDAL; revue d'heritage Norois. 1971. q. price varies. Editions Heimdal, Chateau de Damigny, 14400 Bayeux, France. Ed. Georges Bernage. adv.; bibl.; charts; illus. (back issues avail.)
    Description: French Normandy region.

948.1   NO   ISSN 0017-9841
DL401
HEIMEN. 1922. q. NOK 230($34) (new price typically set in Oct.). Landslaget for Lokalhistorie, Historisk Institutt, N-7055 Dragvoll, Norway. TEL 47-73-59-64-33. FAX 47-73-59-64-41. Ed.Bd. bk.rev.; illus.; maps; index. circ. 1,200. **Indexed:** Amer.Hist.& Life (until 1991), Hist.Abstr. (until 1991), NAA. **Document type:** academic/scholarly publication.
    —CCC.
    Description: Details local Norwegian history.

943   US   ISSN 1062-3582
PT2354
HERDER YEARBOOK. (Text in English, French, German) 1992. a. (International Herder Society) Camden House, Inc., Drawer 2025, Columbia, SC 29202. Ed.Bd.

948.9   DK   ISSN 0108-9692
HEREFORD; avlsjournal. vol.11, no.4, 1981. q. membership. Hereforforeningen for Danmark, c/o Knud Erichsen, Kammergaardsvej 30, DK-7760 Hurup, Denmark. illus.
    Formerly: Herefordbladet (ISSN 0106-5114)

943   GW
HERFORDER JAHRBUCH; BEITRAEGE ZUR GESCHICHTE DER STADT DES KREISES UND DES STIFTES HERFORD. 1960. irreg. DM.29.80. (Herforder Verein fuer Heimatkunde) Maximilian-Verlag, Steintorwall 17, 32052 Herford, Germany. TEL 5221-59910. FAX 5221-599149.
    —BLDSC (4300.027000).
    Formerly: Herforder Jahrbuch; Beitraege zur Geschichte der Stadt und des Stiftes Herford (ISSN 0073-196X)

942   UK   ISSN 0260-4957
HERITAGE. 1980. 2/yr. £3. Wesley Historical Society, East Midlands Branch, c/o Rev. S.Y. Richardson, Ed., 22 Garton Rd., Loughborough, Leics. LE11 2DY, England. adv.; bk.rev.; illus. circ. 85. **Document type:** bulletin.

948.9   DK   ISSN 0108-8017
HERNING - BOGEN. 1982. a. DKK 100. Historisk Forening for Herning Kommune, Wenche Aamodt, Holmparken 58II, DK-7400 Herning, Denmark. adv.; illus. circ. 800.

HISTORY — HISTORY OF EUROPE

943 331.88 GW
HESSISCHE BEITRAEGE ZUR GESCHICHTE DER ARBEITERBEWEGUNG. irreg. price varies. Historischer Verein fuer Hessen, Staatsarchiv, Schloss, 64283 Darmstadt, Germany. **Document type:** monographic series.
  Description: Details the history of the workers' movement in Hessen since the mid-nineteenth century.

943 GW ISSN 0073-2001
DD801.H5
HESSISCHES JAHRBUCH FUER LANDESGESCHICHTE. 1951. a. price varies. Hessisches Landesamt fuer Geschichtliche Landeskunde, Wilhelm-Roepke-Str. 6C, 35039 Marburg, Germany. bk.rev. **Indexed:** Bibl.Cart., Numis.Lit, RILA.

943 GW
HESSISCHES STAATSARCHIV DARMSTADT. MITTEILUNGEN. 1971. s-a. Hessisches Staatsarchiv Darmstadt, Karolinenplatz 3, 64289 Darmstadt, Germany. TEL 06151-165900. FAX 06151-165901. **Document type:** government publication.

943 GW
HESSISCHES STAATSARCHIV DARMSTADT. REPERTORIEN. 1971. irreg. price varies. Hessisches Staatsarchiv Darmstadt, Schloss, 6100 Darmstadt, Germany. TEL 06151-125753. FAX 06151-126497. Ed.Bd. circ. 250.

943.9 HU ISSN 0133-7564
HEVESI SZEMLE. 1973. 4/yr. 96 Ft. Heves Megyei Lapkiado Vallalat, Beloiannisz U. 1-3, 3300 Eger, Hungary. TEL 13-644 3300. Ed. Istvan Pecsi. adv.; bk.rev.; illus. circ. 2,500.

940 913 398 400 GR ISSN 1105-0225
HIAKA KHRONIKA. (Text in English, Greek; summaries in English, French, Italian) 1911. a. Dr.1500($20) S. Fassoulakis, Ed. & Pub., 47 Righa Pheraiou St., 161 22 Kaisariani, Greece. TEL 77-56-834. bk.rev.; bibl.; charts; illus. circ. 1,000. (back issues avail.) **Indexed:** M.L.A.

949.7 YU
HID. (Text in Hungarian) 1934. m. Forum Lap-es Konyvkiado Vallalat, Vojvoda Misic U. 1, 21000 Novi Sad, Vojvodina, Yugoslavia. bk.rev.; illus. **Indexed:** Int.Bibl.Soc.Sci.

948.9 913.489 DK ISSN 0105-8118
HIKUIN. (Text in Danish, Norwegian, Swedish) 1974. a. price varies. Forlaget Hikuin, Moesgaard, DK-8270 Hoejbjerg, Denmark. Ed. Jens Vellev. **Indexed:** Anthropol.Lit., NAA.
  Description: Publishes articles on archaeology, art history and cultural history.

946 SP ISSN 0018-2141
DP1
HISPANIA; revista espanola de historia. 1940. 3/yr. 5000 ptas. (foreign 7500 ptas.)(effective 1991). Centro de Estudios Historicos, Duque de Medinaceli, 6, 28014 Madrid, Spain. FAX 585-6197. (Dist. by: Consejo Superior de Investigaciones Cientificas, Vitrubio 8, 28006 Madrid, Spain) Dir. Manuel Espadas Birgos. bk.rev.; bibl.; index, cum.index. circ. 1,100. **Indexed:** Amer.Hist.& Life, Arts & Hum.Cit.Ind., Curr.Cont., Hist.Abstr.
—Faxon; SWETS

946 SP ISSN 1130-0515
HISPANIA ANTIQUA; revista de historia antigua. 1971. irreg., vol.17, 1993. 3500 ptas. Universidad de Valladolid, Secretariado de Publicaciones, C. Juan Mambrilla, 14, 47003 Valladolid, Spain. TEL 983-423000. FAX 34-83-290300. TELEX 26357. **Document type:** monographic series, academic/scholarly publication.

940 320 SZ
HISPO. (Text in French) 1983. s-a. 20 SFr.($12) Association d'Histoire et de Science Politique de Berne, 96 Eichholzstr., CH-3084 Wabern-Bern, Switzerland. charts; illus. circ. 600. (back issues avail.)

944 FR ISSN 0046-7510
HISTOIRE EN SAVOIE; revue de culture et d'information historique. 1856. q. 270 F. (foreign 290 F.). Societe Savoisienne d'Histoire et d'Archeologie, Square de Lannoy de Bissy, 73000 Chambery, France. TEL 79-69-43-33. adv.; bk.rev.; bibl.; illus. circ. 2,000.

HISTOIRE ET DEFENSE. see MILITARY

944 FR ISSN 0766-1827
HISTOIRE ET SES REPRESENTATIONS. 1984. irreg., no.3, 1992. price varies. Editions de l' Ecole des Hautes Etudes en Sciences Sociales, 131 bd. St-Michel, 75005 Paris, France. TEL 43-54-47-15. FAX 43-54-80-73. (Dist. by: Centre Interinstitutionnel pour la Diffusion de Publications de Sciences Humaines, 131 bd. St-Michel, 75005 Paris, France)

945 IT
HISTORIA. 1957. m. L.62400. Industrie Grafiche Cino del Duca S.p.A., Via Borgogna 5, 20122 Milan, Italy. Ed. Carla Bordignon. adv. circ. 50,000.

943.9 HU ISSN 0139-2409
DB901
HISTORIA (BUDAPEST). 1979. m. $28. Foundation Historia, Uri u. 53, 1014 Budapest I, Hungary. Ed. Ferenc Glatz. bk.rev.; illus. circ. 330,000.

HISTORIA ARCHAEOLOGICA. see ARCHAEOLOGY

946 SP
HISTORIA DE ESPANA EN EL MUNDO MODERNO. ESTUDIOS.* irreg., no.2, 1981. Consejo Superior de Investigaciones Cientificas (C.S.I.C.), Escuela de Historica, Serrano 117, 28006 Madrid, Spain.

946 SP
HISTORIA GRAFICA DE CATALUNYA DIA A DIA. 1978. a. Edicions 62, S.A., Provenca 278, 08008 Barcelona, Spain. TEL 216-00-62. Dir. Ramon Bastardes.

947.1 FI ISSN 0073-2540
DK445
HISTORIALLINEN ARKISTO. (Text in Finnish or Swedish; summaries in English or German) 1866. irreg., no.103, 1993. FIM 95. Suomen Historiallinen Seura - Finnish Historical Society, Arkadiankatu 16 B 28, 00100 Helsinki 10, Finland. FAX 441-468. cum.index: nos. 1-50, 1886-1944. circ. 700. **Indexed:** Amer.Hist.& Life, Hist.Abstr.
  Description: Includes articles on Finnish and Scandinavian history.

947.1 FI ISSN 0073-2559
DL1002
HISTORIALLISIA TUTKIMUKSIA. (Text in Finnish or Swedish; summaries in English or German) 1920. irreg., no.176, 1993. FIM 120. Suomen Historiallinen Seura - Finnish Historical Society, Arkadiankatu 16 B 28, 00100 Helsinki 10, Finland. FAX 441-468. circ. 300. **Document type:** monographic series.
  Description: Historical monograph series.

942 UK
HISTORIC HOUSES, CASTLES AND GARDENS IN GREAT BRITAIN AND IRELAND. 1952. a. £7.80. Reed Information Services (Subsidiary of: Reed Elsevier group), Windsor Court, E. Grinstead House, E. Grinstead, W. Sussex RH19 1XA, England. TEL 0342-326972. FAX 0342-335612. TELEX 95127 INFSER G. Ed. Deborah Valentine. adv. circ. 30,000. **Indexed:** Avery Ind.Archit.Per.
  Formerly: Historic Houses, Castles and Gardens (ISSN 0073-2567)
  Description: Directed to visitors and travelers of historic properties and gardens in the United Kingdom.

942 UK ISSN 0140-332X
DA670.L19
HISTORIC SOCIETY OF LANCASHIRE AND CHESHIRE. TRANSACTIONS. 1848. a. membership. Historic Society of Lancashire and Cheshire, c/o Department of History, Manchester University, Manchester M13 9PL, England. (Subscr. to: Hon. Mem. Sec. J. E. Hollinshead, Liverpool Institute of Higher Education, Stand Park Rd., Liverpool L16 9JD, England) Eds. C.B. Phillips, C. P. Lewis. bk.rev.; charts; illus.; index, cum.index. circ. 500. (also avail. in microfiche) **Indexed:** Br.Archaeol.Abstr., Br.Hum.Ind., Geo.Abstr. **Document type:** academic/scholarly publication.
Refereed Serial

943.7 XR ISSN 0440-9205
HISTORICA. (Text in English, French, German and Russian) 1959. irreg. price varies. (Czechoslovak Academy of Sciences) Academia, Publishing House of the Czechoslovak Academy of Sciences, Vodickova 40, 112 29 Prague 1, Czech Republic. (Dist. by: Artia, Ve Smeckach 30, 111 27 Prague 1, Czech Republic) bk.rev. **Indexed:** Amer.Hist.& Life (until 1991), Arts & Hum.Cit.Ind., Hist.Abstr. (until 1991).

HISTORICA CARPATICA. see POLITICAL SCIENCE

940 301 GW ISSN 0172-6404
HM1
HISTORICAL SOCIAL RESEARCH/HISTORISCHE SOZIALFORSCHUNG. (Text in English, German; summaries in English) 1976. q. DM.40 to individuals; institutions DM.60. Zentrum fuer Historische Sozialforschung, Bachemerstr. 40, 50931 Cologne, Germany. TEL 0221-4769434. FAX 0221-4769455. Ed.Bd. adv.; bk.rev. circ. 1,000. **Indexed:** Amer.Hist.& Life, Hist.Abstr., Int.Polit.Sci.Abstr., Sociol.Abstr. **Document type:** academic/scholarly publication.
—BLDSC (4316.845000).

HISTORICAL SOCIETY OF THE CHURCH IN WALES. JOURNAL. see RELIGIONS AND THEOLOGY — Protestant

HISTORICAL SOCIETY OF THE PRESBYTERIAN CHURCH OF WALES. JOURNAL. see RELIGIONS AND THEOLOGY — Protestant

943.7 XR ISSN 0323-0937
HISTORICKA DEMOGRAFIE. (Text in Czech; summaries in English, French, German, Russian) 1967. irreg. $10. Ceska Akademie Ved, Sociologicky Ustav - Academy of Sciences of the Czech Republic, Institute of Sociology, Jilska 1, 110 00 Prague 1, Czech Republic. TEL 422-24-220256. FAX 422-24-220278. Ed. Pavla Horska. bk.rev.; bibl. circ. 300. **Document type:** academic/scholarly publication.
  Description: Demographics in the history of Europe.

943.7 XR ISSN 0323-0988
HISTORICKA GEOGRAFIE. (Text in Czech, English, German, Russian) 1968. irreg. exchange basis only. Ceska Akademie Ved, Historicky Ustav, Vysehradska 49, 128 26 Prague 2, Czech Republic. Ed. Zdenek Bohac. bk.rev.; bibl. **Indexed:** Bibl.Ling. **Document type:** academic/scholarly publication.
—BLDSC (4317.140000).
  Description: The historical geography of Europe.

943.7 XO ISSN 0440-9515
DB661
HISTORICKE STUDIE. (Text in Slovak; summaries in German and Russian) irreg., vol.22, 1977. fl.35 per no. (Slovenska Akademia Vied, Historicky Ustav) Veda, Publishing House of the Slovak Academy of Sciences, Klemensova 19, 814 30 Bratislava, Slovakia. (Dist. in Western countries by: John Benjamins B.V., Amsteldijk 44, Amsterdam (Z.), Netherlands) **Indexed:** Amer.Hist.& Life, Hist.Abstr.

949.8 340 CI ISSN 0353-9520
HISTORIJSKI ARHIV RIJEKA. VJESNIK. (Text in Serbo-Croatian; summaries in English, German, Italian) 1953. a. $10 (set in Oct. 1991). Historijski Arhiv Rijeka, Park Vladimira Nazora 2, 51000 Rijeka, Croatia. TEL 38-51-515533. (Co-sponsor: Republicki S I Z Znanosti) Ed. Jadranka Koloper-Bakrac. bk.rev. circ. 1,000. (back issues avail.)
  Formerly (until May, 1990): Historijski Arhiv u Rijeci i Pazinu. Vjesnik (ISSN 0351-0891)
  Description: Publishes original papers and archival materials on economic, legal and national history of the regions of Rijeka, Istria, Venezia Giulia, Trieste and Krain.

949 NE
HISTORISCH JAARBOEK VLAARDINGEN. 1977. a. $17. (Historische Vereniging Vlaardingen) Uitgeverij De Draak, Vlaardingen, Netherlands. Ed.Bd. circ. 1,200.
  Supersedes: Historische Vereniging Vlaardingen. Tijdschrift.

943 GW
HISTORISCHE STUDIEN. irreg., vol.441, 1986. price varies. Matthiesen Verlag GmbH, Postfach 1480, 25804 Husum, Germany. FAX 04841-61397. (reprint service avail. from KTO) **Document type:** monographic series.

HISTORY — HISTORY OF EUROPE

943 GW ISSN 0073-2680
DD801.B5
HISTORISCHER VEREIN DER PFALZ. MITTEILUNGEN. 1870. a. price varies. Historischer Verein der Pfalz, Domplatz 4, 67346 Speyer, Germany. Ed. Joachim Kermann.

949.4 SZ
HISTORISCHER VEREIN DES KANTONS BERN. ARCHIV. 1848. a. price varies. Historischer Verein des Kantons Bern, Stadt- und Universitaetsbibliothek, Muenstergasse 61, CH-3000 Bern 7, Switzerland. TEL 031-225519. charts; illus.; cum.index: vols.1-38, vols.39-55. circ. 1,750. **Document type:** academic/scholarly publication.

940 SZ
HISTORISCHER VEREIN DES KANTONS ST. GALLEN. NEUJAHRSBLATT. 1861. a. price varies. Verlagsgemeinschaft St. Gallen in Kommission, Vadianstr. 8, CH-9001 St. Gallen, Switzerland. TEL 071-221661. FAX 071-221688. Ed.Bd. adv.; bibl.; illus. circ. 300.

943 GW ISSN 0073-2699
HISTORISCHER VEREIN DILLINGEN AN DER DONAU. JAHRBUCH. 1888. a. price varies. Historischer Verein Dillingen an der Donau, Kardinal-Waldburg-Str. 51, 89407 Dillingen, Germany. Ed. Rudolf Poppa. bk.rev. circ. 1,000. **Document type:** academic/scholarly publication.

943 GW ISSN 0936-5869
HISTORISCHER VEREIN EICHSTAETT. SAMMELBLATT. 1887. a. DM.30. Historischer Verein Eichstaett e.V., Schimmelleite 14, 85071 Eichstaett, Germany. TEL 08421-20331. FAX 08421-20283. (Subscr. to: Universitaetsbibliothek Eichstaett, Universitaetsallee 1, 85071 Eichstaett, Germany) Ed. Klaus W. Littger. bk.rev.; charts; illus.; index. circ. 1,000. (back issues avail.) **Document type:** academic/scholarly publication.
Description: History, arts and news about the Eichstaett area in Bavaria.

943 914 LH
HISTORISCHER VEREIN FUER DAS FUERSTENTUM LIECHTENSTEIN. JAHRBUCH. 1901. a. 52.50 Fr. Historischer Verein fuer das Fuerstentum Liechtenstein, Postfach 626, FL-9495 Triesen, Liechtenstein. cum.index: 1901-1986. **Indexed:** Amer.Hist.& Life, Hist.Abstr. **Document type:** academic/scholarly publication.

943 GW
HISTORISCHER VEREIN FUER NIEDERBAYERN. VERHANDLUNGEN. 1834. biennial. DM.35. Historischer Verein fuer Niederbayern, Altstadt 79, 84028 Landshut, Germany. TEL 0871-881218. bk.rev. **Document type:** academic/scholarly publication, monographic series.

943.6 AU
HISTORISCHER VEREIN FUER STEIERMARK. ZEITSCHRIFT. 1909. a. S.240. Historischer Verein fuer Steiermark, Hamerlinggasse 3, 8010 Graz, Austria. Ed.Bd. bk.rev. circ. 1,400. **Indexed:** Amer.Hist.& Life, Hist.Abstr. **Document type:** academic/scholarly publication.

943.6 AU ISSN 0440-9728
HISTORISCHES JAHRBUCH DER STADT GRAZ. 1968. a. S.300. Stadt Graz, Stadtarchiv, Hans-Sachs-Gasse 1, A-8010 Graz, Austria. Eds. Helfried Valentinitsch, Friedrich Bouvier. bk.rev. circ. 1,000. **Document type:** government publication.

943.6 AU ISSN 0440-9736
HISTORISCHES JAHRBUCH DER STADT LINZ. 1935. a. S.360. Archiv der Stadt Linz, Neues Rathaus, Hauptstr. 1-5, A-4041 Linz, Austria. FAX 0732-237465. TELEX 232-3732411-MALIA. Eds. Fritz Mayrhofer, Walter Schuster. bk.rev.; cum.index. circ. 500. **Indexed:** Amer.Hist.& Life, Bibl.Cart., Hist.Abstr. **Document type:** government publication.

940 GW
HISTORISCHES MAGAZIN-GESCHICHTE. 1974. bi-m. (Historiographisches Institut) Archiv Verlag GmbH, Postfach 3221, 38022 Braunschweig, Germany. TEL 0531-8091-01. FAX 0531-17318. circ. 12,000. (back issues avail.) **Document type:** academic/scholarly publication.

948.9 DK ISSN 0109-2138
HISTORISK AARBOG FOR FELSTED SOGN. 1983. a. DKK 100. (Historisk Forening for Felsted) H C J Staugaard, Ed. & Pub., Hellinghoejvej 6, Tumboel, 6200 Abenraa, Denmark. circ. 300.

948 DK ISSN 0107-721X
HISTORISK AARBOG FOR SKIVE OG OMEGN. 1909. a. DKK 80. Historisk Samfund for Skive og Omegn, Lyngbakken 13, Thise, DK 7870 Roslev, Denmark. Ed. Steen Soerensen. bk.rev. circ. 2,000. **Indexed:** Amer.Hist.& Life, Hist.Abstr.

948 DK ISSN 0108-4100
HISTORISK AARBOG FRA RANDERS AMT. 1907. bi-a. DKK 130 (typically set in September). Randers Amts Historiske Samfund, Slyngborggade 21, DK-8900 Randers, Denmark. TEL 45-86-43-02-11. Ed.Bd. adv.; illus. circ. 1,450. **Indexed:** NAA, Numis.Lit.
Description: Articles on subjects from the local and cultural history of Randers County from prehistoric to present time.

948 DK ISSN 0904-6267
HISTORISK AARBOG FOR THY OG VESTER HANHERRED. 1906. a. DKK 120 to non-members; members DKK 90. Historisk Samfund for Thy og Vester Hanherred, Rosenvaenget 21, DK-7752 Snedsted, Denmark. Ed.Bd. circ. 1,200.
Former titles (until 1988): Historisk Arbog for Thy, Mors og Vester Hanherred (ISSN 0107-9395); Historisk Arbog for Thy og Mors; Which supersedes: Historisk Arbog for Thisted Amt.
Description: Covers historical events, buildings, local people and news from the museums and local historical collections.

948 DK
HISTORISK AARBOG FRA ROSKILDE AMT. 1910. a. Historisk Samfund for Roskilde Amt, Baldersvej 22, 4000 Roskilde, Denmark. cum.index: 1910-1968. **Indexed:** NAA.

948.9 DK ISSN 0109-0674
HISTORISK ARKIV FOR BROERUP OG OMEGN. AARSSKRIFT. 1974. biennial. DKK 30. Historisk Arkiv for Broerup og Omegn, Broerup Bibliotek, Stadionvej 6, DK-6650 Broerup, Denmark. illus. circ. 250.

948 DK ISSN 0108-6804
HISTORISK FORENING FOR VAERLOESE KOMMUNE. ARSSKRIFT. 1949. a. DKK 40 (typically set in Feb.). Historisk Forening for Vaerloese Kommune, Skovgards Alle 37, 3500 Vaerloese, Denmark. TEL 42-480070. circ. 1,200.

HISTORISK FORENING FOR VISHERRED, BOV MUSEUM. see MUSEUMS AND ART GALLERIES

948.9 DK ISSN 0109-2944
HISTORISK SAMFUND FOR HOEJE-TAASTRUP KOMMUNE. MEDDELELSER. 1980. q. membership. Historisk Samfund for Hoeje-Taastrup Kommune, c/o Joergen Hegner Christiansen, Lindevej 28 A, 2630 Taastrup, Denmark. Ed. Joergen Hegner Christiansen. bk.rev.; illus. circ. 200. **Document type:** newsletter.

948 DK ISSN 0107-6868
HISTORISK SAMFUND FOR PRAESTO AMT. AARBOG. 1912. a. DKK 100. Verner Lundgaard Jacobsen, Ed.& Pub., Nygade 27, DK-4640 Fakse, Denmark. bk.rev.; illus. circ. 1,000. **Indexed:** NAA.

948 DK ISSN 0109-9264
HISTORISK SAMFUND FOR SOENDERJYLLAND. SKRIFTER. 1939. irreg. Historisk Samfund for Soenderjylland, Haderslevvej 45, 6200 Aabenraa, Denmark. **Document type:** monographic series.

948 DK
HISTORISK SAMFUND FOR SORO AMT. AARBOG. 1912. a. DKK 90. Historisk Samfund for Soro Amt, Suserupvej 55, Broby, DK-4180 Soroe, Denmark. Ed. Ole G. Nielsen. bk.rev.; cum.index: 1912-1978. circ. 800.

948 SW ISSN 0345-469X
DL601
HISTORISK TIDSKRIFT. (Text in Swedish; summaries in English) 1881. 4/yr. SEK 210 (typically set in Jan.). Svenska Historiska Foreningen, P.O.Box 5405, 114 84 Stockholm, Sweden. TEL 08-783-2502. FAX 08-7832515. Ed. Lars Magnusson. bk.rev. circ. 2,200. **Indexed:** Amer.Hist.& Life, Curr.Cont., Hist.Abstr., M.L.A., Numis.Lit.
—SWETS.

947.1 FI ISSN 0046-7596
DK445
HISTORISK TIDSKRIFT FOER FINLAND. (Text in Swedish) 1916. q. FIM 95. Historiska Foereningen, Berggatan 6 A 4, SF-00100 Helsinki 10, Finland. Ed. Max Engman. adv.; bk.rev.; bibl.; index. circ. 1,000. **Indexed:** Amer.Hist.& Life, Hist.Abstr., NAA.
—SWETS.

948 NO ISSN 0018-263X
HISTORISK TIDSSKRIFT; scholarly journal on Norwegian and European history. (Text in Norwegian; summaries in English) 1870. q. NOK 515 in the Nordic countries; elsewhere NOK 570. (Norwegian Historical Association) Scandinavian University Press, P.O. Box 2959 Toeyen, N-0608 Oslo, Norway. TEL 472-67-7600. FAX 472-67-7575. (U.S. addr.: Scandinavian University Press, 200 Meacham Ave., Elmont, NY 11003. TEL 516-352-7300) Ed.Bd. adv.; bk.rev.; index. circ. 1,500. **Indexed:** Amer.Hist.& Life, Arts & Hum.Cit.Ind., Curr.Cont., Hist.Abstr. **Document type:** academic/scholarly publication.
—CCC.
Description: Serves as a forum for Norwegian historians.

948 DK ISSN 0106-4991
HISTORISK TIDSSKRIFT. 1840. s-a. Danske Historiske Forening, Institut for Historie, Njalsgade 102, Tr. 15, DK-2300 Copenhagen S, Denmark. TEL 45-31-54-22-11. **Indexed:** Amer.Hist.& Life, Arts & Hum.Cit.Ind., Hist.Abstr.
—Faxon; SWETS.
Formerly (until 1958): Nyt Historisk Tidsskrift.

948 DK ISSN 0903-2738
DL291.G56
HISTORISK-TOPOGRAFISK SELSKAB FOR GLADSAXE KOMMUNE. AARBOG. * 1968. a. Historisk-Topografisk Selskab for Gladsaxe Kommune, Til Jernbanen 20, 2880 Bagsvaerd, Denmark.
Formerly (until 1986): Historisk-Topografisk Selskab for Gladsaxe Kommune. Aarsskrift (ISSN 0440-9809).

948 FI ISSN 0356-1496
HISTORISKA SAMFUNDET I ABO. SKRIFTER UTGIVNA. (Text in Swedish) 1942. irreg. Historiska Samfundet i Abo, Abo Akademi, 20500 Abo, Finland. circ. 600.

940 DK
HISTORISKE MEDDELELSER OM KOEBENHAVN. 1907. a. DKK 110. Koebenhavns Stadsarkiv, Raadhuset, DK-1599 Copenhagen V, Denmark. FAX 45-33-15-92-12. Ed. Helle Linde. bk.rev.; bibl.; illus.; cum.index every 4 yrs. circ. 1,450. (back issues avail.) **Indexed:** Amer.Hist.& Life, Hist.Abstr. **Document type:** academic/scholarly publication.

940 340 UK
HISTORY AND LAW SERIES. 1929. irreg. price varies. (Board of Celtic Studies) University of Wales Press, 6 Gwennyth St., Cathays, Cardiff CF2 4YD, Wales. TEL 0222-231919. FAX 0222-230908. Ed. Glanmor Williams. **Document type:** academic/scholarly publication.
Description: Aims to make source documents more readily available.

940 IR ISSN 0791-8224
▼**HISTORY IRELAND.** 1993. 4/yr. I£12 (Europe I£16; rest of world $30). History Ireland Ltd., P.O. Box 695, Dublin 8, Ireland. TEL 01-4535730. Eds. Hiram Morgan, Tommy Graham. circ. 5,000. **Indexed:** Amer.Hist.& Life (1993-), Hist.Abstr. (1993-). **Document type:** academic/scholarly publication.

HISTORY — HISTORY OF EUROPE

940   UK   ISSN 0191-6599
D1
HISTORY OF EUROPEAN IDEAS. 1980. 12/yr. (in 2 vols., 6 nos. per vol.). £390($600) (effective 1994). (International Society for the Study of European Ideas) Elsevier Science Ltd., Pergamon, P.O. Box 800, Kidlington, Oxford OX5 1DX, England. TEL 44-865-843000. FAX 44-865-843010. (Subscr. in U.S. and Canada to: Elsevier Science, 660 White Plains Rd., Tarrytown, NY 10591-5153. TEL 914-524-9200. FAX 914-333-2444) (Co-sponsor: European Cultural Foundation) Ed. Ezra Talmor, Sascha Talmor. adv.; bk.rev. (also avail. in microfilm from UMI; back issues avail.; reprint service avail. from UMI) **Indexed:** Amer.Hist.& Life, Arts & Hum.Cit.Ind., ASSIA, Curr.Cont., Hist.Abstr., Lang.& Lang.Behav.Abstr., Phil.Ind., Sociol.Abstr. **Document type:** academic/scholarly publication.
—BLDSC (4318.138000); Faxon; UnCover; SWETS; UMI. **CCC.**
   Description: Multidisciplinary journal covering the study of history of the cultural exchange between European nations, the influence of this exchange on the formation of European ideas and emergence of the idea of Europe.
   Refereed Serial

HISTORY OF UNIVERSITIES. see *EDUCATION — Higher Education*

940   PL   ISSN 0073-277X
HISTORYKA; STUDIA METODOLOGICZNE. (Text in Polish; summaries in English, French) 1967. a. price varies. (Polska Akademia Nauk, Oddzial w Krakowie, Komisja Nauk Historycznych) Ossolineum, Publishing House of the Polish Academy of Sciences, Rynek 9, 50-106 Wroclaw, Poland. TEL 48-71-386-25. FAX 48-71-488-103. TELEX 0712771 OSS PL. Ed. Celina Bobinska. bk.rev. (reprint service avail.) **Document type:** academic/scholarly publication.
   Description: Theory and methodology of history, particularly of the historical processes. Also covers the history of historiography.

943   GW   ISSN 0938-4731
HOCHTAUNUSBLAETTER. 1973. irreg. DM.10. Geschichtsverein Hochtaunus e.V., Hauptstr. 20, 61389 Schmitten, Germany. TEL 06082-582. Ed. Beatrice Traeger. circ. 1,000. (back issues avail.) **Document type:** bulletin.

948.9   DK   ISSN 0900-2596
HOEJE-TASTRUP KOMMUNES LOKALHISTORISKE ARKIV. AARSKRIFT. 1983. a. DKK 50. Hoeje-Taastrup Kommunes Lokalhistoriske Arkiv, Blaakildegaard Skolevej 54, 2630 Taastrup, Denmark. TEL 42 52 58 03. illus. circ. 800.

943   GW   ISSN 0018-3253
HOHENZOLLERISCHE HEIMAT. 1951. q. DM.11. Hohenzollerischer Geschichtsverein, Karlstr. 3, 72488 Sigmaringen, Germany. TEL 07571-101558. Ed. Herbert Burkarth. adv.; bk.rev.; illus. circ. 700. **Document type:** academic/scholarly publication.

940.53   US   ISSN 8756-6583
D810.J4
HOLOCAUST AND GENOCIDE STUDIES; an international journal. 1986. 3/yr. $39 to individuals; institutions $148 (effective 1994). (United States Holocaust Museum) Oxford University Press, Journals, 200 Madison Ave., New York, NY 10016. TEL 212-679-7300. FAX 212-689-5312. TELEX 6859654. (Subscr. to: Oxford Journals Fulfillment, 2001 Evans Rd., Cary, NC 25713. TEL 919-677-0977. FAX 919-677-1714) (Co-sponsor: United States Holocaust Memorial Council) Eds. Yehuda Bauer, Hubert G. Locke. bk.rev.; bibl. circ. 580. **Document type:** academic/scholarly publication.
—BLDSC (4322.413800); UnCover; SWETS; UMI. **CCC.**
   Description: Interdisciplinary essays and reviews integrating history, literature, economics, anthropology, political science, religious studies and sociology to address moral, social, technological and political issues of the Holocaust and its consequences, including the application of these studies to other genocides.
   Refereed Serial

943 323   US   ISSN 0738-0739
D804.3
HOLOCAUST STUDIES ANNUAL. 1984. a. price varies. Penkevill Publishing Company, Box 212, Greenwood, FL 32443. TEL 904-569-2811. Eds. Sanford Pinsker, Jack Fischel. circ. 250.
—UnCover.

948   DK   ISSN 0107-6752
HOLSTEBRO MUSEUM. AARSSKRIFT. 1969. a. DKK 175. Holstebro Museum, Museumsvej 2, P.O Box 1240, DK-7500 Holstebro, Denmark. TEL 45-97-422933. FAX 45-97-428109. Ed. Torben Skov. **Indexed:** NAA.

943.9   HU   ISSN 0324-7627
HONISMERET. 1972. 6/yr. $12. (Hazafias Nepfront Honismereti Bizottsaga) Lapkiado Vallalat, Lenin krt. 9-10, Budapest, Hungary. TEL 222-408. Ed. Peter Halasz. bk.rev.; illus.
   Formerly (until 1975): Honismereti Hirado.

942   UK   ISSN 0955-8071
HORNSEY HISTORICAL SOCIETY. BULLETIN; a north London history review. 1973. a. £3 (free to members). Hornsey Historical Society, The Old Schoolhouse, 136 Tottenham Ln., Hornsey, London N8 7EL, England. TEL 081-348-8429. adv.; bk.rev. circ. 700. (back issues avail.) **Document type:** bulletin.
—BLDSC (2555.321500).
   Description: Contains articles on reminiscences or original research on northern London.

HOROS. see *ARCHAEOLOGY*

943.7   XR   ISSN 0231-7540
HOSPODARSKE DEJINY/ECONOMIC HISTORY. (Text in Czech, English, German, Russian, Slovak) 1978. 2/yr. exchange basis only. Ceska Akademie Ved, Historicky Ustav, Vysehradska 49, 128 26 Prague 2, Czech Republic. Ed. Jan Hajek. bk.rev.; bibl. **Document type:** academic/scholarly publication.
   Description: Economic history of Europe.

940 398   BE
HOUTLAND. (Text in Flemish) 1959. a. 350 Fr. Heemkundige Kring Houtland, Kwaplasstraat 74, B-8820 Torhout, Belgium.

949.7   CI
HRVATSKA AKADEMIJA ZNANOSTI I UMJETNOSTI. ZAVOD ZA POVIJESNE ZNANOSTI. RADOVI. 1954. a. $10. Hrvatska Akademija Znanosti i Umjetnosti, Zavod za Povijesne Znanosti, Obala Kneza Trpimira 8, 57000 Zadar, Croatia. TEL 057-443-094. **Indexed:** Amer.Hist.& Life (1993-), Hist.Abstr. (1993-).
   Former titles: Jugoslavenska Akademija Znanosti i Umjetnosti. Zavod za Povijesne Znanosti. Radovi (ISSN 0351-6709); (until 1978): Centar Jugoslavenske Akademije Znanosti i Umjetnosti u Zadru. Radovi (ISSN 0350-1299); (until 1973): Institut Jugoslavenske Akademije Znanosti i Umjetnosti. Radovi (ISSN 0449-3672)

940 929   UK
BX9450
HUGUENOT SOCIETY OF GREAT BRITAIN AND IRELAND. PROCEEDINGS. 1885. a. £15. Huguenot Society of Great Britain and Ireland, c/o Huguenot Library, University College, Gower St., London WC1E 6BT, England. TEL 01-380-7094. Ed. Randolph Vigne. bk.rev.; illus.; cum.index. **Indexed:** Amer.Hist.& Life, Hist.Abstr.
—BLDSC (6708.350000).
   Formerly: Huguenot Society of London. Proceedings (ISSN 0309-8346)

900 929   UK
HUGUENOT SOCIETY OF GREAT BRITAIN AND IRELAND. QUARTO SERIES. 1885. irreg. (2-4/yr.). Huguenot Society of Great Britain and Ireland, c/o Huguenot Library, University College, Gower St., London WC1E 6BT, England. TEL 01-380-7094. Ed. Randolph Vigne.
   Formerly: Huguenot Society of London. Quarto Series (ISSN 0309-8354)

940   US   ISSN 0742-115X
HUMANA CIVILITAS; sources and studies relating to the Middle Ages and the Renaissance. 1976. irreg., latest no.9. price varies. Peter Lang Publishing, Inc., 62 W. 45th St., 4th Fl., New York, NY 10036. TEL 212-302-6740. FAX 212-302-7574. Ed.Bd. (back issues avail.) **Document type:** academic/scholarly publication.

943.7   XR
HUSITSKY TABOR. 1978. a. 190 Kcs. (effective 1992). Husitske Muzeum, 390 01 Tabor, Czech Republic. TEL 0361-22242. (Dist. by: Artia, Ve Smeckach 30, 111 27 Prague 1, Czech Republic) Ed. Milos Drda. bk.rev. circ. 70.

948.9   DK   ISSN 0902-3046
HVIDOVRE LOKALHISTORIE. 1983. q. membership. Hvidovre Lokalhistoriske Selskab, Hvidovrevej 280, 2650 Hvidovre, Denmark. Ed. Lisbeth Magnussen. bk.rev.; illus. circ. 300. **Document type:** academic/scholarly publication.
   Formerly (until 1987): Lokalhistorisk Orientering Hvidovre (ISSN 0109-0747)

945   MM
HYPHEN; journal of melitensia and the humanities. (Text in English, French, Italian, Maltese) 1977. q. $12. Arts Lyceum, Msida, Malta. Ed. L.J. Scerri. adv. circ. 1,000. (back issues avail.)

I W K. (Internationale Wissenschaftliche Korrespondenz zur Geschichte der Deutschen Arbeiterbewegung) see *LABOR UNIONS*

IBERIAN STUDIES. see *SOCIAL SCIENCES: COMPREHENSIVE WORKS*

940   US   ISSN 1056-5000
IBERICA. irreg. Peter Lang Publishing, Inc., 62 W. 45th St., 4th Fl., New York, NY 10036. TEL 212-302-6740. FAX 212-302-7574. Ed. A. Robert Lauer. **Document type:** academic/scholarly publication.

940   US
ILLINOIS MEDIEVAL MONOGRAPH SERIES. irreg. University of Illinois Press, 1325 S. Oak St., Champaign, IL 61820. TEL 217-333-0950. FAX 217-244-8082. **Document type:** monographic series.
   Refereed Serial

IMAFRONTE. see *ART*

945   IT   ISSN 0393-8638
L'IMPEGNO; rivista di storia contemporanea. 1981. 3/yr. L.18000 (foreign L.28000. Istituto per la Storia della Resistenza (Borgosesia), Via Sesone, 10, Borgosesia, Italy. TEL 0163-21564. Ed. Piero Ambrosio. adv.; bk.rev. circ. 1,000.
   Description: Covers political, economic, social and cultural aspects of the regions of Vercellese, Biellese and Valsesia.

945   IT   ISSN 0019-3488
DG819
INCONTRI MERIDIONALI; rivista di storia e cultura. (Text in English, Italian) 1962. 3/yr. L.50000 (foreign L.75000) (effective 1991). (Istituto di Storia Medioevale e Moderna, Facolta di Lettere e Filosofia) Rubbettino Editore, Viale dei Pini, 8, 88049 Soveria Mannelli, Italy. FAX 0968-662035. Ed. Saverio di Bella. circ. 3,000. (back issues avail.)

946   SP
INSTITUCION PRINCIPE DE VIANA. COLECCION HISTORIA. no.3, 1974. irreg., latest no.73. price varies. Gobierno de Navarra, Fondo de Publicaciones, Navas de Tolosa, 21, 31002 Pamplona, Spain. TEL 10-71-21. FAX 22-76-73. **Document type:** monographic series.

940   CN   ISSN 0384-8825
INSTITUT D'ETUDES MEDIEVALES. PUBLICATIONS. Key Title: Publications de l'Institut d'Etudes Medievales. (Text in French) 1950. irreg., vol.24, 1989. price varies. (Universite de Montreal, Institut d'Etudes Medievales) Pontifical Institute of Mediaeval Studies, 59 Queen's Park Crescent E., Toronto, ON M5S 2C4, Canada. TEL 416-926-7194. FAX 416-926-7258. (Dist. outside N. America and the U.K. by: N.V. Brepols, Steenweg op Tielen 68, 2300 Turnhout, Belgium. TEL 32-14-402500. FAX 32-14-428919) **Document type:** monographic series.

943   FR   ISSN 0079-0001
INSTITUT D'ETUDES SLAVES, PARIS. COLLECTION HISTORIQUE. 1920. irreg., vol.34, 1992. price varies. Institut d'Etudes Slaves, 9 rue Michelet, 75006 Paris, France. **Document type:** academic/scholarly publication, monographic series.
—BLDSC (3310.573000).

INSTITUT D'ETUDES SLAVES, PARIS. TRAVAUX. see *LITERATURE*

940   AU   ISSN 0073-8484
DB1
**INSTITUT FUER OESTERREICHISCHE
GESCHICHTSFORSCHUNG. MITTEILUNGEN.** (Text in English, French and German) 1880. s-a. (often double issues). price varies. (Universitaet Wien, Institut fuer Oesterreichische Geschichtsforschung) Verlag fuer Geschichte und Politik, Neulinggasse 26, A-1030 Vienna, Germany. adv.; bk.rev.; bibl.; illus.; index. circ. 800. (reprint service avail. from SWZ) **Indexed:** Amer.Hist.& Life, Hist.Abstr.
—SWETS.

949   BE   ISSN 0073-8522
INSTITUT HISTORIQUE BELGE DE ROME. BIBLIOTHEQUE. 1949. irreg., latest vol.30. price varies. (Institut Historique Belge de Rome - Belgische Historisch Instituut te Rome) N.V. Brepols, Steenweg op Tielen 68, 2300 Turnhout, Belgium. TEL 32-14-41-54-63. FAX 32-14-42-89-19. TELEX 34 182. **Document type:** monographic series.

949   BE   ISSN 0073-8530
D1
INSTITUT HISTORIQUE BELGE DE ROME. BULLETIN. (Text in French or Italian) 1919. a., vol.62, 1992. 1050 BEF (effective 1994). (Institut Historique Belge de Rome - Belgisch Historisch Instituut te Rome) N.V. Brepols, Steenweg op Tielen 68, 2300 Turnhout, Belgium. TEL 32-14-41-54-63. FAX 32-14-42-89-19. TELEX 34 182. circ. controlled. (back issues avail.) **Indexed:** Amer.Hist.& Life, Hist.Abstr., RILA. **Document type:** academic/scholarly publication, bulletin.
Description: Articles on Belgian and Italian history, art history and archaeology.

949   BE   ISSN 0073-8557
INSTITUT JULES DESTREE. ETUDES ET DOCUMENTS. Alternate title: Institut Jules Destree. Collection: Etudes et Documents. irreg., no. 21. price varies. Institut Jules Destree, Rue du Chateau 3, 6100 Mont-sur-Marchienne Charleroi, Belgium.

949   XN   ISSN 0583-4961
INSTITUT ZA NACIONALNA ISTORIJA, SKOPJE. GLASNIK/INSTITUT OF NATIONAL HISTORY, SKOPJE. REVIEW. 1957. 3/yr. $10. Institut za Nacionalna Istorija, Skopje, Gligor Prlicev br. 3, 91000 Skopje, Macedonia. Ed. Krste Misirkov. bk.rev.; illus. circ. 1,000.
—BLDSC (0050.205000).

INSTITUT ZUR ERFORSCHUNG DER EUROPAEISCHEN ARBEITERBEWEGUNG. MITTEILUNGSBLATT. see *LABOR UNIONS*

945   GR   ISSN 0073-862X
INSTITUTE FOR BALKAN STUDIES. PUBLICATIONS/IDRYMA MELETON CHERSONESOU AIMOU. EKDOSEIS. (Text in English, French, German, Greek) 1953. irreg., no.254, 1993. price varies. Institute for Balkan Studies, 31A Ave. Megalou Alexandrou, 546 41 Thessaloniki, Greece. TEL 30-31-832143. FAX 30-31-831429. **Document type:** monographic series.

946.19   SP   ISSN 0020-384X
DP302.A78
INSTITUTO DE ESTUDIOS ASTURIANOS. BOLETIN. 1947. 3/yr. 2000 ptas. Instituto de Estudios Asturianos, Plaza Porlier 5, Oviedo, Spain. bk.rev.; charts; illus.; index. circ. 1,000. **Indexed:** Amer.Hist.& Life, Hist.Abstr., M.L.A.

940   SP   ISSN 0561-3590
INSTITUTO DE ESTUDIOS GIENNENSES. BOLETIN. vol.15, 1969. q. $26. Instituto de Estudios Giennenses, c/o Palacio Provincial, Jaen, Spain. Ed. Jose Chamorro Lozano. bibl. **Indexed:** Amer.Hist.& Life, Hist.Abstr. **Document type:** bulletin.

946.73   SP   ISSN 0534-3364
INSTITUTO DE ESTUDIOS TARRACONENSES RAMON BERENGUER IV. PUBLICACION. 1952. irreg. Instituto de Estudios Tarraconenses Ramon Berenguer IV, Diputacion Provincial de Tarragona, Calle Santa Ana 8, Tarragona, Spain. bibl.; illus.

INSTITUTUL DE ARHEOLOGIE - CLUJ-NAPOCA. ANUARUL. see *ARCHAEOLOGY*

INSTITUTUL DE ISTORIE "A.D. XENOPOL". ANUARUL. see *ARCHAEOLOGY*

940   IT
INSTITUTUM ROMANUM FINLANDIAE. ACTA. 1963. irreg., vol.12, 1991. price varies. Bardi Editore, Salita de'Cresenzi, 16, 00186 Rome, Italy. FAX 06-6878576.
Incorporates (1981-1989, vol.4): Institutum Romanum Finlandiae. Opuscola.

940   NE   ISSN 0927-1864
INSTITUUT PIERRE BAYLE. STUDIES. Variant title: S I B. (Text in Dutch, English, French) 1973. irreg., vol.23, 1994. price varies. A P A, Postbus 122, 3600 AC Maarssen, Netherlands. TEL 31-30-436166. FAX 31-30-420250. Ed. Hans Bots. (back issues avail.) **Document type:** monographic series.
Former titles (until 1988): Instituut voor Intellectuele Betrekkingen tussen de Westeuropese Landen in de Nieuwe Tijd. Studies (ISSN 0927-1856); (until 1987): Instituut voor Intellectuele Betrekkingen tussen de Westeuropese Landen in de Moderne Tijd. Studies (ISSN 0927-1848); (until 1986): Instituut voor Intellectuele Betrekkingen tussen de Westeuropese Landen in de Zeventiende Eeuw. Studies (ISSN 0921-3937).
Description: Publishes critical editions and scholarly studies relating to the intellectual history of Western Europe, with particular emphasis on international scholarly contacts and scholars of the 17th and 18th centuries.

943.8 914   PL   ISSN 0137-5253
INSTYTUT BALTYCKI GDANSK. KOMUNIKATY. 1964. 2/yr. Instytut Baltycki, Ul. Tkacka 11-13, 80-958 Gdansk, skr. 358, Poland. bk.rev.

940   PL   ISSN 0239-7846
INSTYTUT ZACHODNI. STUDIUM NIEMCOZNAWCZE. (Text in Polish; summaries in English or Russian) 1946. irreg., vol.65, 1993. price varies. Instytut Zachodni, Stary Rynek 78-79, 61-772 Poznan, Poland. circ. 1,750. **Document type:** monographic series.

949.5   GR   ISSN 0571-5857
INTERNATIONAL ASSOCIATION FOR BYZANTINE STUDIES. BULLETIN D'INFORMATION ET DE COORDINATION. 1964. irreg. International Association for Byzantine Studies, c/o D. A. Zakythinos, Pres., Rue Sissini 31, Athens 612, Greece. Ed. Helene Ahrweiler. circ. 1,000.

949.5   GR   ISSN 0074-3542
INTERNATIONAL CONGRESS FOR BYZANTINE STUDIES. ACTS/CONGRES INTERNATIONAL DES ETUDES BYZANTINES. ACTES.* (Published in host country) irreg., 1971, 14th, Bucharest. International Association for Byzantine Studies, Rue Sissimi 31, Athens 612, Greece. (reprint service avail. from KTO)

INTERNATIONAL DOCUMENTATION ON MACEDONIA. see *POLITICAL SCIENCE — Civil Rights*

INTERNATIONAL HAJJI BABA SOCIETY. NEWSLETTER. see *TEXTILE INDUSTRIES AND FABRICS*

INTERNATIONAL JOSEPH MARTIN KRAUS-GESELLSCHAFT. MITTEILUNGEN. see *MUSIC*

940   CN   ISSN 0319-1095
INTERUNIVERSITY CENTRE FOR EUROPEAN STUDIES. BULLETIN. (Text in English and French) 1973. m. Can.$10. Interuniversity Centre for European Studies, P.O. Box 8892, Montreal, Que. H3C 3P3, Canada. TEL 514-282-6193. bk.rev.; bibl. circ. 800.

940   CN
INTERUNIVERSITY CENTRE FOR EUROPEAN STUDIES. INTERNATIONAL COLLOQUIUM PROCEEDINGS. 1974. irreg. Can.$8.50. Interuniversity Centre for European Studies, Box 8892, Montreal, Que. H3C 3P3, Canada. TEL 514-282-6193. **Document type:** proceedings.

940   CN
INTERUNIVERSITY CENTRE FOR EUROPEAN STUDIES. RESEARCH REPORT. 1980. irreg. Can.$2.50. Interuniversity Centre for European Studies, P.O. Box 8892, Montreal, Que. H3C 3P3, Canada. TEL 514-282-6193.

946   SP   ISSN 0210-9425
INVESTIGACIONES HISTORICAS. 1979. irreg., vol.14, 1994. 3000 ptas. Universidad de Valladolid, Secretariado de Publicaciones, C. Juan Mambrilla, 14, 47003 Valladolid, Spain. TEL 983-423000. FAX 34-83-290300. TELEX 26357. circ. 500. **Document type:** monographic series, academic/scholarly publication.
Description: Covers modern and contemporary history.

IRISH ANCESTOR. see *GENEALOGY AND HERALDRY*

941   IE   ISSN 0332-4893
IRISH ECONOMIC AND SOCIAL HISTORY. 1974. a. $17. Economic and Social History Society of Ireland, History Department, University College, Belfield, Dublin 4, Ireland. TEL 0353-17068376. FAX 0353-12837022. (Subscr. to: Dublin Diocesan Library, Clonliffe Rd., Dublin 3, Ireland. TEL 0353-18741680) Eds. Mary Daly, Frank Geary. adv.; bk.rev.; abstr.; bibl.; stat. circ. 550. (back issues avail.) **Indexed:** Amer.Hist.& Life, Hist.Abstr. **Document type:** academic/scholarly publication.
—BLDSC (4571.320000); Faxon.

941   IE   ISSN 0332-3633
IRISH HISTORY WORKSHOP/SAOTHARLANN STAIRE EIREANN. 1981. irreg. Irish History Workshop Co-op, 127 Bothar na Tra, Baile Atha Cliath, Dublin, Ireland. Ed.Bd. illus.

941 947   IE   ISSN 0260-2067
DJK1
IRISH SLAVONIC STUDIES. (Special issue (no.5, 1984): Irish-Russian Contacts) 1980. a. I£5 to individuals; institutions I£8. Irish Slavists' Association, Department of Russian, Trinity College, Dublin 2, Ireland. TEL 01-6772941. FAX 01-6770546. Ed. Ronald Hill. adv.; bk.rev. circ. 250. **Indexed:** M.L.A. **Document type:** academic/scholarly publication.
—BLDSC (4574.745000).
Description: Articles on language, history, society, politics and literature of all East European countries.

942   US   ISSN 1043-5743
IRISH STUDIES. irreg. Peter Lang Publishing, Inc., 62 W. 45th St., 4th Fl., New York, NY 10036. TEL 212-302-6740. FAX 212-302-7574. Ed. Robert Mahony. **Document type:** academic/scholarly publication.
—BLDSC (4574.816000).
Description: Includes scholarly monographs and collections of essays on aspects of Irish history, politics, sociology, business and management, and of literature whether in Irish or English.

941 052   UK   ISSN 0260-8154
IRISH STUDIES IN BRITAIN. 1981. s-a. $4. Addison Press, 14 Tremaine Close, London SE4 1YF, England. Ed. Jonathan Moorp. adv.; bk.rev. circ. 2,000. (back issues avail.)
—BLDSC (4574.820000).

949.12 914   IC   ISSN 0256-8462
DL301
HID ISLENZKA FORNLEIFAFELAG. ARBOK. (Text in Icelandic; summaries in English) 1881. a. ISK 2700 (effective 1992). National Museum of Iceland, Archeological Society of Iceland, P.O.Box 1489, 101 Reykjavik, Iceland. TEL 1-28988. FAX 354-1-28967. Ed. Mjoell Snaesdottir. bk.rev. circ. 750.
Description: Publishes studies in archaeology, cultural history, ethnology and art in Iceland.

930 949.5   IT   ISSN 0075-1502
ISTITUTO ELLENICO DI STUDI BIZANTINI E POSTBIZANTINI, VENICE. BIBLIOTECA. 1962. a. price varies. Istituto Ellenico di Studi Bizantini e Post-Bizantini, Castello 3412, 30122 Venice, Italy. FAX 003941-5238248. circ. 1,500. **Document type:** monographic series.

945 001.3 300 IT   ISSN 0080-391X
DS834.95
ISTITUTO GIAPPONESE DI CULTURA IN ROMA. ANNUARIO. (Text in Italian) 1963. a. free. (Kokusai Koryu Kikin) Istituto Giapponese di Cultura in Roma, Via Antonio Gramsci 74, 00197 Roma, Italy. TEL 06-3224794. FAX 06-3222165. circ. 1,000. (back issues avail.) **Document type:** academic/scholarly publication.

HISTORY — HISTORY OF EUROPE

945 800   IT
ISTITUTO NAZIONALE DI STUDI SUL RINASCIMENTO. ATTI DI CONVEGNI. 1940. irreg., no.19, 1993. price varies. Casa Editrice Leo S. Olschki, Casella Postale 66, 50100 Florence, Italy. TEL 055-6530684. FAX 055-6530214. **Document type:** monographic series.

945 800   IT   ISSN 0394-4409
ISTITUTO NAZIONALE DI STUDI SUL RINASCIMENTO. STUDI E TESTI. 1970. irreg., no.33, 1993. price varies. Casa Editrice Leo S. Olschki, Casella Postale 66, 50100 Florence, Italy. TEL 055-6530684. FAX 055-6530214. **Document type:** monographic series.

945   IT
ISTITUTO NAZIONALE PER LA STORIA DEL MOVIMENTO DI LIBERAZIONE IN ITALIA. NOTIZIE E DOCUMENTI. (Text in Italian; summaries in English) 1978-1983; N.S. 1987. a. Istituto Nazionale per la Storia del Movimento di Liberazione in Italia, Piazza del Duomo, 14, 20122 Milan, Italy. TEL 02-86463233. FAX 72003826. Ed. Massimo Legnani. **Document type:** bulletin.

ISTITUTO SICILIANO DI STUDI BIZANTINI E NEOELLENICI. MONUMENTI. see *ART*

949.5   IT   ISSN 0075-1545
ISTITUTO SICILIANO DI STUDI BIZANTINI E NEOELLENICI. QUADERNI. 1965. irreg., no.12, 1984. price varies. Istituto Siciliano di Studi Bizantini e Neoellenici, Via Noto, 34, 90141 Palermo, Italy. TEL 091-625-9541.

949.5 880   IT   ISSN 0075-1553
ISTITUTO SICILIANO DI STUDI BIZANTINI E NEOELLENICI. TESTI E MONUMENTI. TESTI. 1954. irreg., no.13, 1979. price varies. Istituto Siciliano di Studi Bizantini e Neoellenici, Via Noto, 34, 90141 Palermo, Italy. TEL 091-625-9541.

940   IT   ISSN 0391-8211
N15
ISTITUTO STORICO ARTISTICO ORVIETANO. BOLLETTINO. 1945. a. L.30000 (free to institutions). Istituto Storico Artistico Orvietano, Piazza Febei N.1, 05018 Orvieto, Italy. (Dist. by: Viella s.r.l. Libreria Editrice, 32 Via delle Aepi, 00198 Rome, Italy) Ed. Lucio Riccetti. adv.; bk.rev.; illus.; circ. controlled.
   Description: Features articles on the history of Orvieto

940   IT   ISSN 0392-0011
ISTITUTO STORICO ITALO-GERMANICO IN TRENTO. ANNALI/ITALIENISCH-DEUTSCHEN HISTORISCHEN INSTITUTS IN TRENTO. JAHRBUCH. (Text in German, Italian; summaries in Italian) 1975. a. (Istituto Storico Italo-Germanico) Editrice Il Mulino, Strada Maggiore, 37, 40125 Bologna, Italy. TEL 051-256011. FAX 051-256034. Eds. Pierangelo Schiera, Paolo Prodi. circ. 800. (back issues avail.)

907 947   RU
ISTOCHNIKOVEDENIE OTECHESTVENNOI ISTORII. 1973. irreg. price varies. (Akademiya Nauk S.S.S.R., Institut Istorii S.S.S.R.) Izdatel'stvo Nauka, 90 Profsoyuznaya ul., 117864 Moscow, Russia. TEL 234-05-84. (Dist. by: Mezhdunarodnaya Kniga, ul. Dimitrova D.39, 113095 Moscow, Russia) Ed. N.I. Pavlenko. bibl. (also avail. in microfiche from IDC)

940 949   XN
ISTORIJA. 1968. s-a. 30 din. Sojuz na Istoriskite Drustva na SR Makedonija, Boris Kidric 66, 91000 Skopje, Macedonia. Ed. Aleksander Apostolov. **Indexed:** Amer.Hist.& Life, Hist.Abstr.

947   RU
ISTORIYA I ISTORIKI. a. price varies. Izdatel'stvo Nauka, 90 Profsoyuznaya ul., 117864 Moscow, Russia. TEL 234-05-84. (Dist. by: Mezhdunarodnaya Kniga, ul. Dimitrova D.39, 113095 Moscow, Russia) Ed. M.V. Nechkina. circ. 3,200.

940 945   IT   ISSN 0392-3568
DG572
ITALIA CONTEMPORANEA. (Supplement avail: Notizie e Documenti) (Text in Italian, summaries in English) 1949. q. L.60000 (foreign $50). Istituto Nazionale per la Storia del Movimento di Liberazione in Italia, Piazza del Duomo 14, 20122 Milan, Italy. TEL 02-86463233. FAX 72003826. Ed. Massimo Legnani. adv. contact: Paolo Ferrari. bk.rev.; bibl.; index, cum.index: 1949-1965. circ. 1,000. **Indexed:** Amer.Hist.& Life, Hist.Abstr. **Document type:** academic/scholarly publication.
   Formerly: Movimento di Liberazione in Italia (ISSN 0027-2809)

945   US   ISSN 0894-1793
                CODEN: ITJAEY
ITALIAN JOURNAL. 1987. 5/yr. $36 (foreign $56). Italian Academy Foundation, Inc., 278 Clinton Ave., Dobbs Ferry, NY 10522. TEL 914-693-5329. FAX 914-693-7399. Ed. Victor Tesoro. adv.; bk.rev.; index; circ. 25,000 (controlled). (back issues avail.) **Document type:** academic/scholarly publication.
   —Faxon; UnCover.
   Description: Digest of Italian affairs and heritage including politics, economy and finance, social issues, art and literature, commerce, and cultural history.

945   IT   ISSN 1122-0821
ITALIAN MEDIEVAL AND RENAISSANCE STUDIES. 1989. irreg., no.4, 1992. price varies. Casa Editrice Leo S. Olschki, Casella Postale 66, 50100 Florence, Italy. TEL 055-6530684. FAX 055-6530214. (Co-publisher: University of Western Australia Press, AT) **Document type:** monographic series.

ITALIAN POLITICS; a review. see *BUSINESS AND ECONOMICS*

945 850   UK   ISSN 0261-4340
ITALIANIST. (Text in English and Italian) 1981. a. £5.50($12) Nova Graphics Ltd., 22-25 Bartholomew Sq., London EC1, England. (Subscr. to: Dept. of Italian Studies, University of Reading, Whiteknights, Reading, Berks. RG6 2AA, England) Eds. Z.G. Baranski, B.K. Jones. bk.rev. (back issues avail.) **Indexed:** M.L.A.
   —BLDSC (4588.377000).

ITALICA. see *ARCHAEOLOGY*

ITALIENISCHE STUDIEN. see *LITERATURE*

940   SZ
ITINERA. 1985. irreg., no.15. 1993. 35 SFr. (Allgemeine Geschichtforschende Gesellschaft der Schweiz) Schwabe und Co. AG, Steinentorstr. 13, CH-4010 Basel, Switzerland. TEL 061-2725523. FAX 061-2725573. **Document type:** monographic series.

940   BU
IZSLEDOVANIIA PO BULGARSKA ISTORIIA. Title varies slightly. 1976. irreg. 5 lv. per issue. (Bulgarska Akademiia na Naukite, Institut za Istoriia) Publishing House of the Bulgarian Academy of Sciences, Acad. G. Boncev St., Bldg. 6, 1113 Sofia, Bulgaria. circ. 2,000. (reprint service avail. from IRC)

947   BU
IZSLEDOVANIYA ZA ISTORIIATA NA BULGARSKIYA NAROD. 1970. irreg. (Bulgarska Akademiya na Naukite) Publishing House of the Bulgarian Academy of Sciences, Ul. Akad. G. Bonchev, 1113 Sofia, Bulgaria. (Dist. by: Hemus Foreign Trade Co., 6 Ruski Blvd., 1000 Sofia, Bulgaria) (reprint service avail. from IRC)

947 329.9   BU   ISSN 0323-9780
CD1950
IZVESTIYA NA DARZHAVNITE ARKHIVI. 1957. 2/yr. 57 Fr. (Ministerski Suvet, Tsentraino Upravienie na Arkhivete) Foreign Trade Co. "Hemus", 7 Levsky St., 1000 Sofia, Bulgaria. TELEX 22267 HEMKIK.
   —BLDSC (0084.645000).

IZVESTIYA NA MUZEITE OT IUGOIZTOCHNA BULGARIYA. see *ARCHAEOLOGY*

IZVESTIYA NA MUZEITE OT IUZHNA BULGARIYA. see *ARCHAEOLOGY*

948   NE
JAARBOEK ACHTERHOEK EN LIEMERS. 1980. a. fl.25. Walburg Pers BV, Postbus 4159, 7200 BD Zutphen, Netherlands. TEL 31-5750-10522. FAX 31-5750-41025. **Document type:** academic/scholarly publication.

942   UK
JACOBETE. 1967. 3/yr. membership only. 1745 Association, c/o Barbara Fairweather, Ed., Invercoe House, Glencoe, Argyll, Scotland. bk.rev. circ. 325.
   Formerly: 1745 Association and National Military History Society. Quarterly Notes.

943   GW   ISSN 0075-2436
JAHRBUCH DES BALTISCHEN DEUTSCHTUMS. 1952. a. DM.25. Carl Schirren Gesellschaft, Am Berge 35, 21335 Lueneburg, Germany. TEL 04131-36788. Ed. Gabriele von Mickwitz. adv.; bk.rev. circ. 1,000. **Document type:** bulletin.

943   GW   ISSN 0932-822X
JAHRBUCH DES SCHWALM-EDER-KREISES (YEAR). 1975. a. DM.6. Kreisausschuss des Schwalm-Eder-Kreises, Parkstr. 6, 34576 Homberg, Germany. FAX 05681-71-438. adv.; index. circ. 15,000.

943   GW   ISSN 0448-150X
JAHRBUCH FUER DEN KREIS PINNEBERG. 1967. a. DM.26. (Heimatverband fuer den Kreis Pinneberg) A. Beig Verlag, Damm 9-15, 25421 Pinneberg, Germany. TEL 04101-20510. FAX 04101-206165. TELEX 02189146-BEIG-D. Ed. Dieter Beig. bk.rev.; bibl. illus. circ. 1,300. **Document type:** bulletin.

943   GW
JAHRBUCH FUER DIE GESCHICHTE MITTEL- UND OSTDEUTSCHLANDS. 1952. a. price varies. (Historische Kommission zur Berlin) Colloquium Verlag, Luetzowstr. 105, 10785 Berlin, Germany. Ed. Felix Escher. bk.rev.; bibl.; index. circ. 650. **Indexed:** Amer.Hist.& Life (until 1991), Hist.Abstr. (until 1991).

943 312   GW   ISSN 0446-3943
DD801.B465
JAHRBUCH FUER FRAENKISCHE LANDESFORSCHUNG. (Text in English, French, German; summaries in English) 1935. a. DM.50. Universitaet Erlangen-Nuernberg, Zentralinstitut fuer Fraenkische Landeskunde und Allgemeine Regionalforschung, Kochstr. 4, 91054 Erlangen, Germany. TEL 09131-852367. Ed. Alfred Wendehorst. adv.; cum.index. circ. 700. **Indexed:** M.L.A. **Document type:** academic/scholarly publication.

940   GW
▼**JAHRBUCH FUER HISTORISCHE FRIEDENSFORSCHUNG.** 1992. irreg., no.1, 1992. (Arbeitskreis Historische Friedensbildung) Lit Verlag, Dieckstr. 56, 48145 Muenster, Germany. TEL 0251-40022. **Document type:** monographic series.

940   GW   ISSN 0085-2341
DD280
JAHRBUCH FUER REGIONALGESCHICHTE. 1965. a. price varies. (Saechsische Akademie der Wissenschaften, Leipzig, Historische Kommission) Verlag Hermann Boehlaus Nachfolger, Meyerstr. 50a, 99403 Weimar, Germany. TEL 03643-202071. bk.rev. **Document type:** academic/scholarly publication.

940   GW   ISSN 0170-2025
JAHRBUCH FUER WESTDEUTSCHE LANDESGESCHICHTE. 1975. a. price varies. Landesarchivverwaltung Rheinland-Pfalz, Karmeliterstr. 1-3, 56068 Koblenz, Germany. TEL 0261-33068. FAX 0261-33086. Ed.Bd. **Indexed:** Bibl.Cart. **Document type:** government publication.

943   GW
JAHRBUCH FUER WESTFAELISCHE KIRCHENGESCHICHTE. 1899. a. DM.30. Verein fuer Westfaelische Kirchengeschichte e.V., Altstaedter Kirchplatz 5, 33602 Bielefeld, Germany. TEL 0521-594-296. Eds. Ernst Brinkmann, Bernd Hey. adv.; bk.rev. **Document type:** academic/scholarly publication.

HISTORY — HISTORY OF EUROPE

943.6   AU
JAHRBUCH FUER ZEITGESCHICHTE. 1978. a. S.315. Geyer-Edition Wien-Salzburg, Seilergasse 3, A-1010 Vienna, Austria. TEL 0222-512-2896. **Document type:** bulletin.

943   GW
JAHRBUCH LANDKREIS KASSEL. 1973. a. DM.10. Kreisausschuss des Landkreises Kassel, Humboldtstr. 24, 34112 Kassel, Germany. TEL 0561-1003472. FAX 0561-779964. Ed. Helmut Burmeister. adv.; bk.rev. circ. 7,000. (back issues avail.) **Document type:** academic/scholarly publication.

940   GW   ISSN 0021-4019
D1
JAHRBUECHER FUER GESCHICHTE OSTEUROPAS. (Text in English, German) N.S. 1953. q. DM.188. (Osteuropa-Institut, Munich) Franz Steiner Verlag Stuttgart GmbH, Birkenwaldstr. 44, 70191 Stuttgart, Germany. TEL 0711-2582-0. FAX 0711-2582290. TELEX 723636-DAZ-D. (Subscr. to: Postfach 101526, 70014 Stuttgart, Germany) Ed. Edgar Hoesch. adv.; bk.rev.; bibl.; illus.; cum.index: 1953-1972 (vols. 1-20). circ. 750. (back issues avail.) **Indexed:** Amer.Hist.& Life, Curr.Cont., Hist.Abstr. **Document type:** academic/scholarly publication.
—BLDSC (4631.475000); Faxon; UnCover; SWETS. **CCC.**

940   GW   ISSN 0075-2932
JAHRESSCHRIFT FUER MITTELDEUTSCHE VORGESCHICHTE. 1964. a. price varies. VEB Deutscher Verlag der Wissenschaften, Postfach 1216, 1080 Berlin, Germany. Ed. H. Behrens. **Indexed:** A.I.C.P., Anthropol.Lit.

JAKOBUS-STUDIEN. see *RELIGIONS AND THEOLOGY — Roman Catholic*

948   FI
JATULI. 1949. irreg. FIM 40. Kemin Kotiseutuyhdistys Jatuli, Kemin Museo, Meripuisto, Kemi, Finland. Ed. Pauli Sutela. cum.index: 1949-92 in vol.22.

940   XR
JEDNOTA KLASICKYCH FILOLOGU PRAGUE. ZPRAVY. (Text in Czech, Greek, Latin and Slovak) 1959. 4/yr. 35 Kcs. Jednota Klasickych Filologu, Lazarska 8, 120 00 Prague 2, Czech Republic. TEL 204-668. Ed. J. Burian. bk.rev. **Indexed:** Bibl.Ling. **Description:** Articles and reviews about classical antiquity and Latin literature of the middle ages.

940 296   UK   ISSN 0306-7998
DS135.E5
JEWISH HISTORICAL SOCIETY OF ENGLAND. ANNUAL REPORT AND ACCOUNTS FOR THE SESSION. 1893. a. membership. Jewish Historical Society of England, 33 Seymour Pl., London W1H 5AP, England. TEL 071-723-4404. **Document type:** corporate report.
Formerly: Jewish Historical Society of England. Report and Balance Sheet.

940 296   UK
JEWISH HISTORICAL SOCIETY OF ENGLAND. BULLETIN. 1982. a. membership. Jewish Historical Society of England, 33 Seymour Pl., London W1H 5AP, England. TEL 071-723-4404. **Document type:** bulletin.

940 296   UK
JEWISH HISTORICAL STUDIES. TRANSACTIONS. 1893. biennial. membership. Jewish Historical Society of England, 33 Seymour Pl., London W1H 5AP, England. TEL 071-723-4404. **Document type:** bulletin.
Formerly: Jewish Historical Society of England. Transactions.

JEWS AND JEWISH TOPICS IN THE SOVIET UNION AND EASTERN EUROPE. see *POLITICAL SCIENCE — Civil Rights*

943.7 320   XR
JIHOCESKY SBORNIK HISTORICKY. 1928. 4/yr. (Jihoceske Muzeum Ceske Budejovice) Artia, Ve Smeckach 30, 111 27 Prague 1, Czech Republic. FAX 42-2-231-5106. TELEX 121065 ARTA C.

943.7   XR   ISSN 0449-0436
JIZNI MORAVA. 1965. a. (Teps Praha) Blok, Rosseveltova 4, 657 00 Bron, Czech Republic. (Dist. by: Artia, Ve Smeckach 30, 111 27 Prague 1, Czech Republic) bk.rev.; bibl.; cum.index: vols.1-10, 1975.

948   FI   ISSN 1236-4215
JOUKO. 1910. irreg., latest vol.9, 1992. FIM 60. Pohjois-Pohjalainen Osakunta, Toolonkatu 3A, 00100 Helsinki 10, Finland.

947   US   ISSN 0162-9778
DK511.B25
JOURNAL OF BALTIC STUDIES. (Text in English and German) 1970. q. $60 to institutions (effective 1994). Association for the Advancement of Baltic Studies, 111 Knob Hill Rd., Hackettstown, NJ 07840. TEL 908-852-5258. FAX 908-852-3233. Ed. William Urban. adv.; bk.rev.; charts; illus.; stat. circ. 1,300. (also avail. in microform from UMI; back issues avail.; reprint service avail. from UMI) **Indexed:** Amer.Bibl.Slavic & E.Eur.Stud., Amer.Hist.& Life, Arts & Hum.Cit.Ind., Bibl.Ling., Curr.Cont., Hist.Abstr., M.L.A., NAA, Numis.Lit., RILA.
—BLDSC (4951.105000); Faxon; UMI.

942   US   ISSN 0021-9371
DA20
JOURNAL OF BRITISH STUDIES. 1961. q. $43 to individuals; institutions $70. (North American Conference on British Studies) University of Chicago Press, Journals Division, 5720 S. Woodlawn Ave., Chicago, IL 60637. TEL 312-753-3347. FAX 312-753-0811. TELEX 25-4603. (Subscr. to: Box 37005, Chicago, IL 60637) Ed. Cynthia Herrup. adv.; bk.rev.; index. circ. 1,000. (also avail. in microform from UMI; reprint service avail. from UMI) **Indexed:** Amer.Hist.& Life, Arts & Hum.Cit.Ind., Br.Archaeol.Abstr., Curr.Cont., Hist.Abstr., Hum.Ind., M.L.A., Mid.East: Abstr.& Ind. **Document type:** academic/scholarly publication.
—BLDSC (4954.520000); Faxon; UnCover; SWETS; UMI. **CCC.**
Description: Covers various aspects of British history.
Refereed Serial

949.7   US   ISSN 0075-4218
DB361
JOURNAL OF CROATIAN STUDIES; annual review. 1960. a. $20 to individuals; institutions $30. Croatian Academy of America, Inc., Box 1767, Grand Central Sta., New York, NY 10163-1767. Eds. Jerome Jareb, Karlo Mirth. bk.rev. circ. 1,000. **Indexed:** Amer.Hist.& Life, Hist.Abstr., M.L.A., P.A.I.S.
Description: Contains critical articles pertinent to Croatian history and culture in the fields of literature, fine arts and music, sociology, history, economics, government and law, philology, philosophy, creative translations of standard Croatian short stories and poems, unpublished documents of historical and cultural significance.

940   UK   ISSN 0047-2441
D1   CODEN: JEUSEF
JOURNAL OF EUROPEAN STUDIES. (Text mainly in English; occasionally in French and German) 1971. 4/yr. £60 (U.S. & Japan $124; elsewhere £62). Alpha Academic (Subsidiary of: Richard Sadler Ltd.), Halfpenny Furze, Mill Ln., Chalfont St. Giles, Bucks. HP8 4NR, England. TEL 0494-872509. Ed. J.E. Flower. adv.; bk.rev.; bibl.; charts; index. circ. 550. (also avail. in microform from UMI; back issues avail.; reprint service avail. from UMI) **Indexed:** Amer.Hist.& Life, Arts & Hum.Cit.Ind., Can.Rev.Comp.Lit., Curr.Cont., Hist.Abstr., Hum.Ind., M.L.A., RILA, SSCI. **Document type:** academic/scholarly publication.
—BLDSC (4979.610000); Faxon; UnCover; SWETS; UMI. **CCC.**
Description: Covers European literature and ideas from the Renaissance to the present.

940 913 200   PK   ISSN 0258-9680
D1
JOURNAL OF EUROPEAN STUDIES. (Text in English) 1985. s-a. Rs.50($2) University of Karachi, Area Study Centre for Europe, University Rd., Karachi 32, Pakistan. TEL 92-21-479001. Ed. A.A. Kadeer. bk.rev. circ. 500. **Indexed:** Amer.Hist.& Life, Hist.Abstr., Int.Polit.Sci.Abstr. **Document type:** academic/scholarly publication.
Description: Publishes articles relating to all aspects of the contemporary societies of Europe, ranging from archaeology, art and civilizations, to economic and political strategy and technology transfer.

940   MM   ISSN 0075-4285
DG987
JOURNAL OF MALTESE STUDIES. (Text in English, French, Italian, Maltese) 1961. irreg. price varies. University of Malta, Faculty of Arts, Msida, Malta. TEL 356-336451. FAX 356-336450. TELEX 407 HIEDUC MW. Ed. Oliver Friggieri. bk.rev. circ. 500. **Indexed:** A.I.C.P., Bibl.Ling. **Document type:** academic/scholarly publication.
Description: Publishes articles on Maltese language and literature.

949.2   NE   ISSN 0304-4181
D111
JOURNAL OF MEDIEVAL HISTORY. (Text in English; summaries in French, German) 1975. 4/yr. fl.396($214) (effective 1994). Elsevier Science B.V., P.O. Box 211, 1000 AE Amsterdam, Netherlands. TEL 31-20-5803911. FAX 31-20-5803598. TELEX 18582 ESPA NL. (Subscr. in U.S. and Canada to: Elsevier Science Inc., Box 882, Madison Sq. Sta., New York, NY 10159. TEL 212-989-5800. FAX 212-633-3990) Ed. David Abulafia. bk.rev.; bibl. (also avail. in microform from UMI) **Indexed:** Arts & Hum.Cit.Ind., Br.Archaeol.Abstr., CERDIC, Curr.Cont., Mid.East: Abstr.& Ind., RILA. **Document type:** academic/scholarly publication.
—BLDSC (5017.570000); Faxon; UnCover; SWETS. **CCC.**
Description: Covers the history of Europe in the Middle Ages.
Refereed Serial

JOURNAL OF MEDIEVAL LATIN. see *LINGUISTICS*

JOURNAL OF MEDITERRANEAN STUDIES; history, culture and society in the Mediterranean world. see *HUMANITIES: COMPREHENSIVE WORKS*

949.5 949   US   ISSN 0738-1727
DF741
JOURNAL OF MODERN GREEK STUDIES. (Text in English; excerpts in Greek) s-a. $20 to individuals (foreign $24.10); institutions $45 (foreign $49.10). (Modern Greek Studies Association) Johns Hopkins University Press, Journals Publishing Division, 2715 N. Charles St., Baltimore, MD 21218. TEL 410-516-6987. FAX 410-516-6967. Ed. Peter Bien. adv.; bk.rev. circ. 604. (back issues avail.) **Indexed:** Curr.Cont., M.L.A.
—BLDSC (5020.670000); Faxon. **CCC.**
Description: Focuses exclusively on contemporary Greece, including critical analyses of Greek social, cultural, and political affairs.

JOURNAL OF MODERN HELLENISM. see *ETHNIC INTERESTS*

940 300   UK   ISSN 0265-7325
JOURNAL OF REGIONAL AND LOCAL STUDIES. 1980. s-a. £14. c/o Univeristy of Humberside, Inglemire Ave., Hull HU6 7LU, England. FAX 0482-449624. TELEX 592717-HUMCOL-G. Ed. Philip Swan. adv.; bk.rev. circ. 300. (back issues avail.) **Document type:** academic/scholarly publication.
—BLDSC (5048.670000).
Formerly (until 1983): Journal of Local Studies (ISSN 0144-4077)

JOURNAL OF SLAVIC MILITARY STUDIES. see *MILITARY*

948.9   DK   ISSN 0906-1614
DL101
JOURNALEN. LOKAL- OG KULTURHISTORISK TIDSSKRIFT. 1972. 4/yr. DKK 110. Dansk Lokalhistorisk Forening, Vester Tvaervej 16, DK-8900 Randers, Denmark. Ed. Henning Ringgaard Laudidsen. adv.; bk.rev.; bibl. circ. 2,100. **Document type:** bulletin.
Supersedes (in 1991): Lokalhistorisk Journal (ISSN 0106-5351)

HISTORY — HISTORY OF EUROPE

JUGENDBUECHER ZUM THEMA; Drittes Reich. see CHILDREN AND YOUTH — For

947   CI   ISSN 0449-3648
DB879.R2
JUGOSLAVENSKA AKADEMIJA ZNANOSTI I UMJETNOSTI. HISTORIJSKI INSTITUT, DUBROVNIK. ANALI. (Text in Croatian; summaries in English, French or other languages) 1952. a. $5. Jugoslavenska Akademija Znanosti i Umjetnosti, Historijski Institut, Lapadska Obala 6, Dubrovnik, Croatia. Ed.Bd. illus.

JUGOSLOVENSKI ISTORIJSKI CASOPIS. see HISTORY

948   DK   ISSN 0107-5446
JUL I FREDERIKSSUND. 1979. a. DKK 19. Thorsgaard, Tvaerstraede 5, 3600 Frederikssund, Denmark. adv.; illus. circ. 6,000.

948   DK   ISSN 0108-2965
JUL I LEJRE. 1981. a. DKK 10. Lejre-Posten, Munkedammen 5, 4320 Lejre, Denmark. illus.

943   GW   ISSN 0171-9386
JUNGES FORUM. 1964. bi-m. DM.15($5) Verlag Deutsch-Europaischer Studien GmbH, Postfach 111927, 20419 Hamburg, Germany. Ed. Heinz-Dieter Hansen. adv.; bk.rev. circ. 1,000. (back issues avail.)

948 913   DK   ISSN 0107-2854
JYSK ARKAEOLOGISK SELSKABS. SKRIFTER/JUTLAND ARCHAEOLOGICAL SOCIETY. PUBLICATIONS. 1951. a. Jysk Arkaeologisk Selskab - Jutland Archeological Society, 8270 Hoejbjerg, Denmark. (Dist. By: Aarhus University Press, Aarhus University, DK-8000 Aarhus, Denmark) Ed. Poul Kjaerum. circ. 1,000. Indexed: Anthropol.Lit.
—BLDSC (5078.350000).

948   DK   ISSN 0109-9280
DEN JYSKE HISTORIKER. 1969. q. DKK 230. (Aarhus Universitet, Historisk Institut) Aarhus University Press, Aarhus University, DK-8000 Arhus C, Denmark. TEL 45-86-19-70-33. FAX 45-86-19-84-33. Ed. Thorsten Borrig Olesen. adv.; bk.rev. circ. 1,000. **Indexed:** Amer.Hist.& Life (1993-), Hist.Abstr. (1993-).

949.7 200   CI   ISSN 0453-0578
KACIC. (Text in Croatian; summaries in English, French, German, Italian, Latin and occasionally in Albanian, Portuguese, Slovenian, Spanish) 1967. a. DM.30. Franjevacka Provincija Presvetoga Otkupitelja, Trg. G. Bulata 3, 5800 Split, Croatia. adv.; bk.rev. circ. 900. (also avail. in microform)

948   FI
KAIKUJA HAMEESTA. 1872. irreg. Hamalais-Osakunta, Kampinkatu 4-6 D, 00100 Helsinki 10, Finland.

949 355   US
KAISERZEIT. 1973. 3/yr. $15 in U.S.; Europe $20; Australia $25. Imperial German Military Collector's Association, 82 Atlantic St., Keyport, NJ 07735. TEL 908-739-1799. Ed. Eric Johansson. bk.rev. circ. 400. (back issues avail.) **Document type:** academic/scholarly publication.

948.6   SW   ISSN 0451-2715
KALMAR LAEN; aarsbok for kulturhistoria och hembygdsvaard. 1898. a. SEK 100 (effective 1993). Kalmar Laens Muuseum, TEL 46-480-56300. FAX 46-480-56307. (Dist. by: Kalmar Laens Museum, P.O. Box 104, S-391 21 Kalmar, Sweden) (Co-sponsor: Kalmars Laens Fornminnesfoerbund) Ed. Gunnel Forsberg Warringer. **Document type:** monographic series.

940   AU
KAMPTAL-STUDIEN. irreg. Verein der Freunde des Kamptals, Wienerstr. 409, A-3571 Gars am Kamp, Austria. Ed. Friedrich Polleross. **Document type:** monographic series.

948   FI   ISSN 0782-8764
KARJALA. 1910. irreg. Karjalainen Osakunta, Liisankatu 17 B, 00170 Helsinki 17, Finland. circ. 1,000.

948   FI   ISSN 0783-6864
KARLEBYNEJDEN. (Text in Swedish) 1970. irreg. $1 per no. Karlebynejdens Bygde- och Slaktforskare, SF-68410 Nedervetil, Finland. Ed. Jan-Erik Nygren. circ. 350.

KARLSBADER ZEITUNG. see ETHNIC INTERESTS

943   GW
KARPATEN JAHRBUCH. 1950. a. DM.19. Arbeitsgemeinschaft der Karpatendeutschen aus der Slowakei, Schlossstr. 92, 70176 Stuttgart, Germany. TEL 0711-626262. FAX 0711-625576. Ed. Theo Deters. adv. circ. 3,200. **Document type:** newsletter.
Description: Historical and cultural topics preserving the heritage of Germans who lived in Slovakia until 1945.

948   FI
KAUKOMIELI. 1876. irreg. price varies. Wiipurilainen Osakunta, Liisankatu 17 B, 00170 Helsinki 17, Finland. adv. circ. 1,000.

948   FI   ISSN 0786-8456
KELLON - HAUKIPUTAAN KOTISEUTUJULKAISU. 1961. irreg. Kellon-Haukiputaan Kotiseutuyhdistys, Oiva Kurkela, 90830 Haukipudas, Finland.

941   US   ISSN 0192-1207
CB206
KELTICA; the Inter-Celtic journal. 1980. a. $5.95. Society of Inter-Celtic Arts and Culture, 96 Marguerite Ave., Waltham, MA 02154. TEL 617-899-2204. Ed. Kevin Dixon Gilligan. adv.; bk.rev. circ. 2,500. (back issues avail.)

949   BE
KEN UW DORP EN UW FAMILIE: TIJDSCHRIFT VAN DE HEEMKUNDIGE KRING. (Text in Flemish) 1966. a. Heemkundige Kring, Kasteeldreef 17, Lede, Belgium.

KENTAVR. see POLITICAL SCIENCE

949   YU
KEPES IFJUSAG. (Text in Hungarian) 1945. w. $51. Forum, Novi Sad, Vojvode Misica 1, Novi Sad, Vojvodina, Yugoslavia. illus.

940   IS
KESHEV; studies and sources. (Text in Hebrew; summaries in English) 1986. q. $6. Bar-Ilan University, Institute of Holocaust Research, Ramat Gan 52100, Israel. Ed. Judith Tydor Baumel. bk.rev.; circ. 1,000 (controlled).

948   FI   ISSN 0355-1393
Z2520
KESKI-SUOMI. (Text in Finnish; summaries in English) 1935. irreg., vol.19, 1992. FIM 80. Keski-Suomen Museo, P.O. Box 634, 40101 Jyvaskyla, Finland. TEL 941-624-919. FAX 941-624-933. Ed. Janne Vilkuna. adv. contact: Ritva Palviainen. circ. 1,500. **Document type:** academic/scholarly publication.

947   RU
KHABAROVSKII GOSUDARSTVENNYI PEDAGOGICHESKII INSTITUT. VOPROSY ISTORII DAL'NEGO VOSTOKA. 1972. irreg. Khabarovskii Gosudarstvennyi Pedagogicheskii Institut, Khabarovsk, Russia.

940 200   GW   ISSN 0932-9951
BR140
KIRCHLICHE ZEITGESCHICHTE; Internationale Halbjahresschrift fuer Theologie und Geschichtswissenschaft. (Text in English, German) 1988. s-a. DM.86. Vandenhoeck und Ruprecht, Robert-Bosch-Breite 6, 37079 Goettingen, Germany. TEL 0551-6959-26. FAX 0551-695917. (Subscr. to: 37070 Goettingen, Germany) Ed. Gerhard Besier. adv.; bk.rev.; bibl. circ. 500. (back issues avail.) **Document type:** academic/scholarly publication.
Description: Studies history and church history in Europe and North America in the 20th century.

940   GW
KLEINE HEFTE ZUR STADTGESCHICHTE. irreg., vol.10, 1993. DM.19.80. (Archiv der Hansestadt Luebeck) Schmidt-Roemhild Verlag, Mengstr. 16, 23552 Luebeck, Germany. TEL 0451-1605-0. FAX 0451-1605253. **Document type:** monographic series.

KNIGA ISSLEDOVANIYA. see PUBLISHING AND BOOK TRADE

948.9   DK   ISSN 0525-6844
KOEBENHAVNS UNIVERSITET. HISTORISK INSTITUT. SKRIFTER. Key Title: Skrifter Udgivet af Det Historiske Institut ved Koebenhavns Universitet. 1957. irreg., no. 5, 1975. Koebenhavns Universitet, Historisk Institut, Bispetorvet 3, DK-1167 Copenhagen K, Denmark. (Co-sponsor: Danske Historiske Forening)

948   DK   ISSN 0105-9254
KOEBSTADMUSEET DEN GAMLE BY. 1928. a. DKK 250. DK-8000 Aarhus C, Denmark. TEL 86-12-31-88. FAX 86-76-06-87. Eds. Erik Kjersgaard, Henrik Nyrop-Christensen. cum.index: 1927-1972. circ. 4,500.

940 309 330   GW
KOELNER VORTRAEGE ZUR SOZIAL- UND WIRTSCHAFTSGESCHICHTE. 1969. irreg., no.37, 1983. price varies. Universitaet zu Koeln, Forschungsinstitut fuer Sozial- und Wirtschaftsgeschichte, Unter Sachsenhausen 10-26, 50667 Cologne, Germany. Ed. Friedrich-Wilhelm Henning.

948   DK   ISSN 0901-8077
KOLDING BOGEN. 1970. a. DKK 75. Kulturudvalget i Kolding, DK-6000 Kolding, Denmark. FAX 45-75-52-00-14. Ed. Birgitte Dedenroth-Schou. bk.rev.; cum.index: 1970-1986. circ. 1,500. **Document type:** academic/scholarly publication.
Description: Features articles on the history of the city of Kolding in Denmark.

943.7   XR
KOMISE PRO DEJINY ZAVODU V C S S R. ZPRAVODAJ. 1962. irreg. Komise pro Dejiny Zavodu v C S S R, Ustredni Skola Revolucniho Odboroveho Hnuti Antonina, Francouzska 4, 120 00 Prague, Czech Republic. bk.rev.
Formerly: Komise pro Dejiny Zavodu v C S S R. Zpravy.

943   GW   ISSN 0067-2831
KOMMISSION FUER GESCHICHTLICHE LANDESKUNDE IN BADEN-WUERTTEMBERG. VEROEFFENTLICHUNGEN. REIHE A. QUELLEN. 1958. irreg. price varies. Kommission fuer Geschichtliche Landeskunde in Baden-Wuerttemberg, Eugenstr. 7, 70182 Stuttgart, Germany. circ. 800. **Document type:** monographic series.
Description: Publication of historical sources from the archives in Southwest Germany.

943   GW   ISSN 0521-9884
KOMMISSION FUER GESCHICHTLICHE LANDESKUNDE IN BADEN-WUERTTEMBERG. VEROEFFENTLICHUNGEN. REIHE B: FORSCHUNGEN. 1958. irreg. price varies. Kommission fuer Geschichtliche Landeskunde in Baden-Wuerttemberg, Eugenstr. 7, 70182 Stuttgart, Germany. circ. 800. **Document type:** academic/scholarly publication, monographic series.
Description: Academic dissertations and monographs about the history of southwest Germany.

943.6   AU
KOMMISSION FUER NEUERE GESCHICHTE OESTERREICHS. VEROEFFENTLICHUNGEN. 1924. irreg., vol.83, 1992. price varies. Boehlau Verlag GmbH & Co.KG., Sachsenplatz 4-6, Postfach 87, A-1201 Vienna, Austria. TEL 0222-3302427-0. FAX 0222-3302432. TELEX 114-506-SPRIW-A. Ed. Gerald Stourzh. (back issues avail.; reprint service avail. from KTO) **Document type:** monographic series.

943.8   PL   ISSN 0023-3196
KOMUNIKATY MAZURSKO-WARMINSKIE; czasopismo poswiecone przeszlosci ziem Polski polnocno-wschodniej. (Text in Polish; summaries in German) 1946. q. $13. Polskie Towarzystwo Historyczne, Instytut Mazurski, Partyzantow 87, 10-402 Olsztyn, Poland. TEL 48 89 276618. (Dist. by: Ars Polona-Ruch, Krakowskie Przedmiescie 7, Warsaw, Poland) (Co-sponsor: Osrodek Badan Naukowych im. Wojciecha Ketrzynskiego) Ed.Bd. bk.rev.; bibl.; index. circ. 750. (also avail. in microfiche) **Indexed:** Amer.Hist.& Life, Hist.Abstr., Numis.Lit.
—BLDSC (5105.880000).

HISTORY — HISTORY OF EUROPE

949 BE
KONINKLIJKE GESCHIED- EN OUDHEIDKUNDIGE KRING VAN KORTRIJK. HANDELINGEN/CERCLE ROYAL HISTORIQUE ET ARCHEOLOGIQUE DE COURTRAI. MEMOIRES. (Text in Flemish and French) 1903. a. Koninkijke Gescheid- en Oudheidkundige Kring van Kortrijke - Cercle Royal Historique et Archeologique de Courtrai, Aalbeeksesteenweg 84, 8500 Kortrijk, Belgium. bk.rev.; illus. **Indexed:** Numis.Lit.

949 913 BE
KONINKLIJKE KRING VOOR OUDHEIDKUNDE LETTEREN EN KUNST VAN MECHELEN. HANDELINGEN. (Text in Flemish) 1889. a. 600 BEF. Koninklijke Kring voor Oudheidkunde Letteren en Kunst van Mechelen, Hof van Habsburg G. de Stassartstraat 145, B-2800 Mechelen, Belgium. **Document type:** academic/scholarly publication.
 Description: Discusses the history and history of art of Mechelen (Malines).

KONINKLIJKE NEDERLANDSE OUDHEIDKUNDIGE BOND. BULLETIN. see *ARCHAEOLOGY*

947 330 BU ISSN 0861-2994
DR93.45
KONTAKTI. (Text in Bulgarian and English) 1945. q. 62 Fr. (Slavianski Komitet v Bulgariia) Foreign Trade Co. "Hemus", 7 Levsky St., 1000 Sofia, Bulgaria. TELEX 22267 HEMKIK.
 Formerly (until 1990): Rodoliubie (ISSN 0205-194X)

948 FI
KOTISEUTUKUVAUKSIA LOUNAIS-HAEMEESTAE. 1925. irreg. Lounais-Haemeen Kotiseutu-ja Museoyhdistys, Wahreninkatu, SF-30100 Forssa, Finland. cum.index: 1925-1964.

949.7 890 CI
KRCKI ZBORNIK. (Text in Croatian; summaries in English, French, German, Italian) 1970. irreg. price varies. Povijesno Drustvo Otoka Krka, Vlade Bagata 7, Krk, Croatia. Ed. Petar Strcic. (back issues avail.)

940 970 GW ISSN 0943-1160
▼**KREFELDER HEFTE ZUR DEUTSCH-AMERIKANISCHEN GESCHICHTE.** 1993. irreg., vol.1, 1993. Franz Steiner Verlag Wiesbaden GmbH, Birkenwaldstr. 44, 70191 Stuttgart, Germany. TEL 0711-2582-0. FAX 0711-2582290. TELEX 723636-DAZ-D. (Subscr. to: Postfach 101061, 70009 Stuttgart, Germany) **Document type:** academic/scholarly publication, monographic series.

948 DK ISSN 0107-6701
KREJL; localhistorisk tidsskrift for Loegstoer og omegn. 1981. q. DKK 55. N.H. Lindhard, Eksp. Balles Boghandel, Oesterbrogade, 9670 Loegstoer, Denmark. TEL 45-98-67-15-66. Ed. N.H. Lindhard. illus. circ. 750.

940 GW ISSN 0935-9060
PN56.W3
KRIEG UND LITERATUR/WAR AND LITERATURE; internationale Beitraege zur Erforschung der Kriegs- und Antikriegsliteratur. (Text in English, German) 1989. s-a. DM.55 (typically set in Jan.). H.Th. Wenner Verlag, Hegerstr. 2-3, 49074 Osnabrueck, Germany. TEL 49-541-3310366. FAX 49-541-3310339. Ed.Bd. bk.rev.; bibl.
 —SWETS.

948 DK ISSN 0454-5230
KRIGSHISTORISK TIDSSKRIFT. 1965. 3/yr. DKK 125. Militaere Laeseselskab Rendsborg, Kastellet 60, DK-2100 Copenhagen Oe, Denmark. Ed. J.C. Andreassen. circ. 650.

940 914 770 XV ISSN 0023-4923
DR381.S6
KRONIKA; casopis za Slovensko krajevno zgodovino. 1953. 3/yr. $5. Zgodovinsko Drustvo za Slovenijo, Askerceva 12, Ljubljana, Slovenia. TEL 061-218-886. Ed. Masa Zvanut. adv.; bk.rev.; record rev.; charts; illus.; index. circ. 1,000. **Indexed:** Amer.Hist.& Life, Hist.Abstr.

948.5 SW ISSN 0083-6796
KUNGLIGA VITTERHETS HISTORIE OCH ANTIKVITETS AKADEMIEN. AARSBOK. 1926. a. SEK 150. Kungliga Vitterhets Historie och Antikvitets Akademien - Royal Academy of Letters, History and Antiquities, P.O. Box 5622, S-114 86 Stockholm, Sweden. (Dist. by: Almqvist & Wiksell International, P.O. Box 4627, S-116 91 Stockholm, Sweden) **Indexed:** Bibl.Ling., Br.Archaeol.Abstr.

948.5 SW ISSN 0083-6761
KUNGLIGA VITTERHETS HISTORIE OCH ANTIKVITETS AKADEMIEN. HANDLINGAR. ANTIKVARISKA SERIEN/ROYAL ACADEMY OF LETTERS, HISTORY AND ANTIQUITIES. PROCEEDINGS. ANTIQUARIAN SERIES. (Text in English, French, German and Swedish) 1954. irreg., no.38, 1992. price varies. Kungliga Vitterhets Historie och Antikvitets Akademien, P.O. Box 4627, S-11691 Stockholm, Sweden. (Dist. by: Almqvist & Wiksell International, P.O. Box 4627, S-116 91 Stockholm, Sweden)

940 SW ISSN 0083-6788
KUNGLIGA VITTERHETS HISTORIE OCH ANTIKVITETS AKADEMIEN. HANDLINGAR. HISTORISKA SERIEN/ROYAL ACADEMY OF LETTERS, HISTORY AND ANTIQUITIES. PROCEEDINGS. HISTORICAL SERIES. (Text in German and Swedish; summaries in English and French) 1957. irreg., no. 21, 1979. price varies. Kungliga Vitterhets Historie och Antikvitets Akademien, P.O. Box 5622, S-114 86 Stockholm, Sweden. (Dist. by: Almqvist & Wiksell International, P.O. Box 4627, S-11691 Stockholm, Sweden) index.

940 SW ISSN 0083-6753
KUNGLIGA VITTERHETS HISTORIE OCH ANTIKVITETS AKADEMIEN. HISTORISKT ARKIV. (Text in English, French, German or Swedish) 1954. irreg., no.18, 1986. price varies. Kungliga Vitterhets Historie och Antikvitets Akademien - Royal Academy of Letters, History and Antiquities, P.O. Box 5622, S-114 86 Stockholm, Sweden. (Dist. by: Almqvist & Wiksell International, P.O. Box 4627, S-11691 Stockholm, Sweden) index.

KUNST UND ARCHITEKTUR IN DER SCHWEIZ/ART ET ARCHITECTURE EN SUISSE/ARTE E ARCHITETTURA IN SVIZZERA. see *ARCHITECTURE*

946 GW ISSN 0452-9081
DD901.T8
KURTRIERISCHES JAHRBUCH. (Includes supplement) 1961. a. DM.29.50. Kurtrierishes Jahrbuch e.V., Weberbach 25, 54290 Trier, Germany. TEL 0651-718-2430. FAX 0651-718-3432. Ed. Gunther Franz. adv.; bk.rev. circ. 1,200. (back issues avail.) **Document type:** academic/scholarly publication.

943.8 331 PL ISSN 0860-9357
HD6735.7
KWARTALNIK HISTORII I TEORII RUCHU ZAWODOWEGO. 1962. q. 350 Zl. per no. (Centrum Studiow Zwiazkow Zawodowych, Zaklad Historii i Teorii Ruchu Zawodowego) Instytut Wydawniczy Zwiazkow Zawodowych, Ul. Spasowskiego 1-3, 00-950 Warsaw, Poland. TEL 48-22-279011. Ed.Bd. adv.; bk.rev. circ. 3,000. **Indexed:** Amer.Hist.& Life, Hist.Abstr.
 Former titles (until 1989): Kwartalnik Historii Ruchu Zawodowego (ISSN 0454-7330); (until 1966): Centralna Rada Zwiazkow Zawodowych w Polsce. Biuro Historyczne. Biuletyn (ISSN 0528-4252)

600 913 PL ISSN 0023-5881
DK401
KWARTALNIK HISTORII KULTURY MATERIALNEJ. (Text in Polish; summaries in English, French, German) 1953. q. $40. Polska Akademia Nauk, Instytut Archeologii i Etnologii, Al. Solidarnosci (d-Swierczewskiego) 105, 00-140 Warsaw, Poland. TEL 48-22-202881. FAX 48-22-240100. (Dist. by: Ars Polona-Ruch, Krakowskie Przedmiescie 7, 00-068 Warsaw, Poland) Ed. A. Klonder. bk.rev.; abstr.; charts; illus.; index, cum.index every 10 yrs. circ. 940. **Indexed:** Amer.Hist.& Life, Hist.Abstr., Numis.Lit. **Document type:** academic/scholarly publication.

900 PL ISSN 0023-5903
D1
KWARTALNIK HISTORYCZNY. (Text in Polish; summaries in English, French, German and Russian) 1887. q. $48. (Polska Akademia Nauk, Instytut Historii) Wydawnictwo Naukowe P W N, Ul. Miodowa 10, 00-251 Warsaw, Poland. Ed. J. Michalski. bk.rev.; bibl.; charts; index. circ. 3,540. (also avail. in microfiche from IDC) **Indexed:** Amer.Hist.& Life, Hist.Abstr. **Document type:** academic/scholarly publication.
 —BLDSC (5134.771000).

949.5 CY
KYPRIAKOS LOGOS. 1969. 6/yr. Petros Stylianou, Odos Kimonos 10, Egome, Nicosia, Cyprus. adv.; bk.rev. circ. 2,000. **Indexed:** Amer.Hist. & Life, Hist.Abstr.

948.9 DK ISSN 0108-7711
L A N A NYT. 1982. q. membership. Lokalhistoriske Arkiver i Nordjyllands Amt, c/o Lokalhistorisk Arkiv for Aalborg Kommune, Arkivstraede 1, P.O. Box 1353, DK-9100 Aalborg, Denmark. TEL 45-98-12-85-77. FAX 45-98-10-22-48. Ed. Jens Topholm. illus.; circ. 800 (controlled).
 Description: News from and about archives of local history in Northern Jutland.

949.5 GR
LAKONIKA. 1964. 5/yr. $25. Lacedaemonian's Association of Attika, 43, Pan. Tsaldari St., Athens 105 53, Greece. TEL 30 03 32 41848. Ed. Venizelos Leontaritis. adv.; bk.rev. circ. 1,300.
 Description: Aspects of the history and culture of Sparta and generally of Laconia throughout the centuries.

941 UK
LANCASHIRE AND CHESHIRE ANTIQUARIAN SOCIETY. NEWSLETTER. 1977. irreg. membership. Lancashire and Cheshire Antiquarian Society, 59 Malmesbury Rd., Cheadle Hulme, Cheadle, Cheshire SK8 7QL, England. Ed M. Garratt. bk.rev. circ. 300. **Document type:** newsletter.

943 929 GW
LAND AN DER MIESA. 1949. m. DM.36. Heimatkreis Mies-Pilsen e.V., Postfach 127, 91542 Dinkelsbuhl, Germany. TEL 09851-90245. adv.; bk.rev.; cum.index. circ. 3,450. **Document type:** academic/scholarly publication.
 Description: History of western part of Bohemia. Information about displaced people of former Kreis Mies and Pilsen.

948.9 630 DK
LANDBOHISTORISK TIDSSKRIFT; bol og by. 1956; N.S. 1977. 2/yr. DKK 140. Landbohistorisk Selskab, P.B. 401, DK-5220 Odense Soe, Denmark. Eds. Torben Groengaard Jeppesen, Erland Porsmose.
 Formerly: Bol og By (ISSN 0067-9550)

943.6 AU
LANDESKUNDE VON NIEDEROESTERREICH. JAHRBUCH; neue Folge. 1865. irreg., vol.53, 1987. Verein fuer Landeskunde von Niederoesterreich, Herrengasse 11, 1014 Vienna, Austria. **Indexed:** Amer.Hist.& Life (until 1990), Hist.Abstr. (until 1990).
 Description: Covers history and geography of Lower Austria.

943 GW ISSN 0458-6905
LANDESKUNDLICHE VIERTELJAHRSBLAETTER. 1955. q. DM.20. Arbeitsgemeinschaft fuer Landesgeschichte und Volkskunde des Trierer Raumes, Stadt Archiv, Weberbach 25, 54290 Trier, Germany. TEL 0651-7182439. FAX 0651-7182432. Ed. Reiner Nolden. bk.rev. circ. 1,800. **Document type:** academic/scholarly publication.
 —BLDSC (5151.500000).

LANDESMUSEUM FUER VORGESCHICHTE, DRESDEN. VEROEFFENTLICHUNGEN. see *MUSEUMS AND ART GALLERIES*

LANDESMUSEUM FUER VORGESCHICHTE, HALLE. VEROEFFENTLICHUNGEN. see *MUSEUMS AND ART GALLERIES*

943 GW ISSN 0174-4631
LANDKREISES BIRKENFELD. HEIMATKALENDER; beitraege zur geschichte und gegenwart des landes an der oberen nahe. 1956. a. DM.9.50. Landkreis Birkenfeld, Schlossalee 11, 55765 Birkenfeld, Germany. TEL 06782-15220. FAX 06782-15490. circ. 10,000. (back issues avail.)

940 720 UK ISSN 0143-3768
GF101
LANDSCAPE HISTORY. 1979. a. £15 to non-members. Society for Landscape Studies, 91 Oakfield Rd., Selly Park, Birmingham B29 7HL, England. TEL 021-472-4253. Ed. Della Hooke. adv.; bk.rev.; charts; illus. circ. 424. **Indexed:** Br.Archaeol.Abstr., Geo.Abstr. **Document type:** academic/scholarly publication.
 —BLDSC (5153.146000).

HISTORY — HISTORY OF EUROPE

943   GW
LANDSCHAFTSVERBAND RHEINLAND. ARCHIVBERATUNGSSTELLE RHEINLAND. ARCHIVHEFTE. 1929. irreg., no.26, 1993. (Landschaftsverband Rheinland, Archivberatungsstelle Rheinland) Rheinland Verlag GmbH, Abtei Brauweiler, Postfach 2140, 50250 Pulheim, Germany. TEL 02234-8051. FAX 02234-82503. (Dist. by: Dr. Rudolf Habelt GmbH, Am Buchenhang 1, 53115 Bonn, Germany. TEL 0228-232016. FAX 0228-232017) **Document type:** monographic series.

943   GW
LANDSCHAFTSVERBAND RHEINLAND. BEITRAEGE ZUR INDUSTRIE- UND SOZIALGESCHICHTE. 1989. irreg., no.4, 1993. Rheinland Verlag GmbH, Abtei Brauweiler, Postfach 2140, 50250 Pulheim, Germany. TEL 02234-8051. FAX 02234-82503. (Dist. by: Dr. Rudolf Habelt GmbH, Am Buchenhang 1, 53115 Bonn, Germany. TEL 0228-232016. FAX 0228-232017) **Document type:** monographic series.

943   GW
LANDSCHAFTSVERBAND RHEINLAND. DOKUMENTE UND DARSTELLUNGEN ZUR GESCHICHTE DER RHEINISCHEN PROVINZIALVERWALTUNG. 1987. irreg., no.8, 1993. Rheinland Verlag GmbH, Abtei Brauweiler, Postfach 2140, 50250 Pulheim, Germany. TEL 02234-8051. FAX 02234-82503. (Dist. by: Dr. Rudolf Habelt GmbH, Am Buchenhang 1, 53115 Bonn, Germany. TEL 0228-232016. FAX 0228-232017) **Document type:** monographic series.

948.9   DK   ISSN 0109-0178
LANGAA; lokalhistorisk aarbog. 1972. a. DKK 40 to members; non-members DKK 50. Langaa Lokalhistoriske Forening, Bredgade 6, DK-8870 Langaa, Denmark. Ed. Ejlev Hintze. illus.

949.5 945   CI   ISSN 0350-414X
LATINA ET GRAECA. 1974. 2/yr. $6. Vjesnikova Press Agencija, Avenija Bratstva i Jedinstva 4, 41000 Zagreb, Croatia. Ed. Zlatko Seselj. bk.rev.

945   IT
LATIUM. a. L.25000. Istituto di Storia e di Arte del Lazio Meridionale, Centro di Anagni, Palazzo Bonifacio VIII, I-03012 Anagni, Italy. Dir. Gioacchino Giammaria.

LAZIO IERI E OGGI; rivista mensile di cultura, arte, turismo. see *TRAVEL AND TOURISM*

LE MARCHE ARCHEOLOGIA, STORIA, TERRITORIO. see *ARCHAEOLOGY*

943.6   AU
LEBENSBILDER ZUR GESCHICHTE OBEROESTERREICHS. 1981. irreg. Oberoesterreichisches Landesarchiv, Anzengruberstr. 19, A-4020 Linz, Austria. TEL 0732-6555230. FAX 0732-655523-4619. **Document type:** monographic series.

948.9   DK   ISSN 0905-8834
LEDOEJE-SMOERUM HISTORISK FORENING OG ARKIV - AARSSKRIFT. 1979. 3/yr. membership. Ledoeje-Smoerum Historisk Forening og Arkiv, Smoerum Bygade 35, DK-2765 Smoerum, Denmark. illus. circ. 300.
    Formerly (until 1989): Ledoeje-Smoerum Historisk Forening og Arkiv (ISSN 0109-0712)

LEICESTERSHIRE ARCHAEOLOGICAL AND HISTORICAL SOCIETY. TRANSACTIONS. see *ARCHAEOLOGY*

943   GW
LEIPZIG AUS VERGANGENHEIT UND GEGENWART; Beitraege zur Stadtgeschichte. 1963. irreg. Museum fuer Geschichte der Stadt Leipzig, Markt 1, 04109 Leipzig, Germany.
    Former titles (until 1981): Geschichte der Stadt Leipzig. Jahrbuch; (until 1974): Arbeitsberichte zur Geschichte der Stadt Leipzig.

944   FR   ISSN 0024-0761
LEMOUZI; revue franco-limousine. 1893. q. 210 F. (foreign 260F.)(effective Jan. 1991). Societe Historique du Bas-Limousin, c/o Robert Joudoux, Ed., 13 Place Municipale, 19000 Tulle, France. adv.; bk.rev.; abstr.; bibl.; charts; illus.; index. circ. 4,000.

709   BE
LEODIUM. (Text in French) 1902. s-a. 350 Fr. Societe d'Art et d'Histoire du Diocese de Liege, Rue Bonne Fortune 6, 4000 Liege, Belgium. bibl.; cum.index: 1902-1963. circ. 400.

949   PO   ISSN 0870-6182
LER HISTORIA. (Text in English, French, Portuguese, Spanish) 1983. 3/yr. Esc.4620 (Europe $40; elsewhere $60). I S C T E, Av. das Forcas Armadas, 1600 Lisbon, Portugal. Dir. Miriam Halpern Pereira. adv.; bk.rev. circ. 2,000. **Document type:** academic/scholarly publication.
    Description: Promotes the results of historical research and the dialogue between the different branches of the social sciences.

943   GW   ISSN 0522-5078
DD491.L3
LETOPIS. REIHE B. GESCHICHTE; Jahresschrift des Instituts fuer Sorbische Volksforschung. 1953. a. (Institut fuer Sorbische Volksforschung in Bautzen) Domowina Verlag GmbH, Tuchmacher-Str. 27, 02625 Bautzen, Germany. cum.index, 1974. **Document type:** academic/scholarly publication.

943   GW   ISSN 0522-5086
DD491.L3
LETOPIS. REIHE C. VOLKSKUNDE. 1958. a. (Institut fuer Sorbische Volksforschung in Bautzen) Domowina Verlag GmbH, Tuchmacher-Str. 27, 02625 Bautzen, Germany. **Document type:** academic/scholarly publication.

943.9   HU   ISSN 0457-6047
CD1170
LEVELTARI SZEMLE. (Text in Hungarian; contents page in English, French, German, Russian) 1951. 4/yr. 280 Ft. (effective 1994). Muvelodesi es Kozoktatasi Miniszterium Leveltari Osztalya, Uri u. 54-56, 1014 Budapest, Hungary. TEL 1-156-0939. (Subscr. to: Hirlapelofizetesi es Lapellatasi Iroda, Lehel ut 10-A, 1900 Budapest, Hungary. TEL 1-149-9463) Ed. Sudar Kornelia. adv.; bk.rev. circ. 1,100. **Indexed:** Amer.Hist.& Life, Hist.Abstr. **Document type:** academic/scholarly publication.

947   UK   ISSN 0267-7105
LIBERTARIAN ALLIANCE. HISTORICAL NOTES. 1985. irreg. £10($20) Libertarian Alliance, 25 Chapter Chambers, Esterbrooke St., London SW1P 4NN, England. TEL 071-821-5502. FAX 071-834-2031. Ed.Bd. adv.; bk.rev.; film rev.; bibl. circ. 1,000. (back issues avail.) **Document type:** monographic series.

LIBRARY & ARCHIVES NEWS. see *HISTORY*

943.64   LH
LIECHTENSTEIN - PRINCIPALITY IN THE HEART OF EUROPE. French edition: Liechtenstein - Principaute au Coeur de l'Europe. German edition: Liechtenstein - Fuerstentum im Herzen Europas. Italian edition: Liechtenstein - Un Principato nel Cuore dell'Europa. (Text in English) 1988. irreg. Presse- und Informationsamt, Government Palace, FL-9490 Vaduz, Liechtenstein. TEL 075-2366720. FAX 075-2366460. TELEX 889290-REPI-FL. illus. circ. 30,000. **Document type:** government publication.
    Description: Presents the history, geography, government, economic and political situation of Liechtenstein.

947   US   ISSN 0091-4347
DK511.L2
LIETUVIU TAUTOS PRAEITIS/LITHUANIAN HISTORICAL REVIEW. (Text in English, French, German and Lithuanian) 1959. a. price varies. Lithuanian Research and Studies Center, Inc., 5620 S. Claremont Ave., Chicago, IL 60636. TEL 312-434-4545. FAX 312-434-9363. Ed. John A. Rackauskas. bk.rev. circ. 1,000. **Indexed:** Amer.Hist.& Life (until 1993), Hist.Abstr. (until 1993).

940   UK   ISSN 0459-4487
DA670.L69
LINCOLNSHIRE HISTORY AND ARCHAEOLOGY. 1966. a. £16 membership. Society for Lincolnshire History & Archaeology, Jew's Court, Steep Hill, Lincoln LN2 1LS, England. TEL 0522-521337. Ed.Bd. bk.rev. circ. 700. **Indexed:** Br.Archaeol.Abstr., Br.Hum.Ind., Numis.Lit. **Document type:** academic/scholarly publication.
    —BLDSC (5220.430000).

LINCOLNSHIRE METHODIST HISTORY SOCIETY. JOURNAL. see *RELIGIONS AND THEOLOGY — Protestant*

942   UK   ISSN 0960-9555
LINCOLNSHIRE PAST AND PRESENT. 1974. q. membership. Society for Lincolnshire History and Archaeology, Jew's Court, Steep Hill, Lincoln LN2 1LS, England. TEL 0522-521337. circ. 700. **Document type:** academic/scholarly publication.
    Formerly (until 1989): Society for Lincolnshire History and Archaeology. Newsletter (ISSN 0308-2741)

949   NE   ISSN 0168-7107
LINSCHOTEN-VEREENIGING. WERKEN. 1909. irreg. price varies. Walburg Pers BV, Postbus 4159, 7200 BD Zutphen, Netherlands. TEL 31-5750-10522. FAX 31-5750-41025. (back issues avail.) **Document type:** monographic series.

943   GW   ISSN 0342-0876
LIPPISCHE MITTEILUNGEN AUS GESCHICHTE UND LANDESKUNDE. 1902. a. DM.50. Naturwissenschaftliche und Historische Verein F.D. Land Lippe, Willi-Hofmann-Str. 2, 32756 Detmold, Germany. FAX 05231-766114. bk.rev. circ. 1,250. **Document type:** bulletin.

LITERATURE & HISTORY. see *LITERATURE*

943.7   XR   ISSN 0075-9988
LITOMERICKO; vlastivedny sbornik. 1964. a. 15 Kcs. Okresni Vlastivedne Muzeum, Mirove nam. 171, 412 01 Litomerice, Czech Republic. Ed. Eva Stibrova.

947   PL   ISSN 0860-0066
LITUANO-SLAVICA POSNANIENSIA; studia historica. (Text in Polish; summaries in English and German) 1985. biennial. price varies. (Adam Mickiewicz University, Institute of History) Adam Mickiewicz University Press, Nowowiejskiego 55, 61-734 Poznan, Poland. TEL 527-380. Ed. Jerzy Ochmanski. bk.rev. circ. 1,000. **Document type:** academic/scholarly publication.
    Description: Covers history and culture of Lithuania.

940.53   IS   ISSN 0334-9470
LO NISHKACH. 1985. a. free. Second Generation For Perpetuation of Greek Jewish Holocaust, 68 Levinsky St., Tel Aviv 66855, Israel. TEL 972-3-381930. Ed. Shmuel Sasson. bk.rev. **Document type:** bulletin.
    Description: Discusses issues relating to the holocaust.

942   UK   ISSN 0024-5585
THE LOCAL HISTORIAN. 1952. q. £22 (effective 1994). British Association for Local History, Shopwyke Manor Barn, Chichester, W. Sussex PO20 6BG, England. TEL 0243-787639. Ed. Margaret Bonney. adv.; bk.rev.; charts; illus.; index. circ. 2,500. (back issues avail.) **Indexed:** Amer.Hist.& Life, Br.Archaeol.Abstr., Br.Hum.Ind., Geo.Abstr., Hist.Abstr. **Document type:** consumer publication, academic/scholarly publication.
    —BLDSC (5290.040200).
    Formerly: Amateur Historian.
    Description: Contains a wide variety of topics of interest to local historians and general readers.

941   UK   ISSN 0266-2698
LOCAL HISTORY MAGAZINE. 1984. bi-m. £12 (foreign £18). Local History Press, 3 Devonshire Promenade, Nottingham NG7 2DS, England. TEL 0602-700369. Eds. Susan and Robert Howard. adv.; bk.rev. circ. 1,500. **Document type:** academic/scholarly publication.
    Description: News items and scholarly articles on the practical and administrative aspects of local history, as well as historical analysis and narrative with lists of publications, conferences, and seminars, and information requests from readers.

942   UK   ISSN 0969-3521
LOCAL HISTORY NEWS. q. membership. British Association for Local History, Shopwyke Manor Barn, Chichester, W. Sussex PO20 6BG, England. TEL 0243-787639. **Document type:** newsletter.
    Description: Supplies news of local societies, record offices, libraries, museums, and issues of concern to local historians.

948.9   DK   ISSN 0106-0430
LOEGUMKLOSTER-STUDIER. 1978. irreg. DKK 100. Historisk Forening for Loegumkloster Kommune, Museet Holmen Loegumkloster, DK-6240 Loegumkloster, Denmark. circ. 500.

HISTORY — HISTORY OF EUROPE

948.9   DK   ISSN 0109-002X
LOKALHISTORIE: HADSUND KOMMUNE. 1982. 10/yr. DKK 98. Jysk Lokalhistorisk Forlag, Jyllandsgade 43B, 9520 Skoerping, Denmark. illus.

948.9   DK   ISSN 0109-6699
LOKALHISTORISK ARKIV, AALESTRUP. AARSSKRIFT. 1983. biennial. DKK 100. Lokalhistorisk Arkiv, Aalestrup, c/o Bogcentret, Jernbanegade 6, DK-9620 Aalestrup, Denmark. Ed. Poul Gade. illus. circ. 600.

948.9   DK   ISSN 0900-3126
LOKALHISTORISK ARKIV FOR FREDERICIA OG OMEGN. AARSSKRIFT. 1984. a. DKK 35. Lokalhistorisk Arkiv for Fredericia og Omegn, Frederik den III's Vej 6, 7000 Fredericia, Denmark. TEL 45-75-93-23-90. FAX 45-93-23-90. adv.; illus. circ. 300.
  Description: Short historical articles about the city of Fredericia; combines an annual report on the Local Historical Archive of Fredericia.

948.9   DK   ISSN 0109-8551
LOKALHISTORISK ARKIV, ROEDBY. AARSSKRIFT. (Text in Danish) 1980. a. DKK 35. Lokalhistorisk Arkiv, Roedby, Kirkealle 1, 4970 Roedby, Denmark. TEL 54-60-15-31. Ed. Hans Ivar Bentsen. bk.rev. circ. 300.

948.9   DK   ISSN 0109-2162
LOKALHISTORISK ARKIV STUBBEKOEBING. AARSSKRIFT. 1983. a. DKK 20. Lokalhistorisk Arkiv Stubbekoebing, Stubbekoebing Bibliotek, Dosseringen 3, 4850 Stubbekoebing, Denmark. bk.rev.; illus.

948.9   DK   ISSN 0109-2839
LOKALHISTORISK FORENING FOR HOERUP SOGN. AARSSKRIFT. 1983. a. DKK 30. Lokalhistorisk Forening for Hoerup Sogn, c/o Chresten Wolff, Osterbakken 11, Hoeruphav, 6470 Sydals, Denmark. illus. circ. 600.

948   DK   ISSN 0106-9748
LOKALHISTORISK FORENING FOR SEJLFLOD KOMMUNE. no.4, 1981. irreg. price varies. Lokalhistorisk Forening for Sejlflod Kommune, Sekretariat, Gl. Egensevej 31 A, Mou, 9280 Storvorde, Denmark. illus.

948   DK   ISSN 0109-4017
LOKALHISTORISK FORENING FOR SOENDERHALD KOMMUNE. AARSSKRIFT. 1977. a. DKK 50. Lokalhistorisk Forening for Soenderhald Kommune, c/o Helga Soerensen, Aarslev, 8900 Randers, Denmark. Ed.Bd.

948   NO   ISSN 0802-8931
LOKALHISTORISK MAGASIN. 1990. q. NOK 50($8.50) (new price typically set in Oct.). Landslaget for Lokalhistorie, Historisk Institutt, N-7055 Dragvoll, Norway. TEL 73-59-64-33. FAX 73-59-64-41. (Subscr. to: Hoerdalands Fylkesarkiv, Kulturetaten, N-5020 Bergen, Norway) Eds. Egil Nysaeter, Hermund Kleppa. bk.rev.; illus. circ. 750. **Document type:** newsletter.
  Description: Provides information on local history and local archives.

948   DK   ISSN 0107-8798
LOLLAND-FALSTERS HISTORISKE SAMFUND. AARBOG. 1913. a. DKK 120 to non-members; members DKK 90. Lolland-Falsters Historiske Samfund, Arne Heyn, Hamborgskovvej 32, 4800 Nykoebing F, Denmark. TEL 54 86 10 29. Ed. Arne Heyn. adv.; bk.rev.; illus. circ. 1,000. **Indexed:** Chem.Abstr.

948   DK   ISSN 0109-2731
LOLLAND-FALSTERS STIFTSMUSEUM. AARSSKRIFT. Variant title: Lolland-Falsters Kunstmuseum. Aarsskrift. 1940. a. DKK 75. Lolland-Falsters Stiftsmuseum, Museumsgade 1, 4930 Maribo, Denmark. TEL 53-881101. (Co-sponsor: Lolland-Falsters Kunstmuseum) Ed. Thomas W. Larsen. circ. 1,000. **Indexed:** NAA.
  Formerly (until 1983): Lolland-Falsters Stiftsmuseums Aarsskrift (ISSN 0542-6820)

942   UK   ISSN 0305-8034
DA688
LONDON JOURNAL. 1975. 2/yr. £15($30) to institutions; individuals £30($60). London Journal Trust, c/o Museum of London, London Wall, London EC2Y 5HN, England. TEL 071-600-3699. FAX 071-600-1058. Ed. Patricia Garside. bk.rev. circ. 370. **Indexed:** Amer.Hist.& Life, Hist.Abstr. **Document type:** bulletin.
—BLDSC (5293.660000); UnCover; SWETS.
  Description: A review of metropolitan society both past and present.

942   UK   ISSN 0085-2848
LONDON RECORD SOCIETY. PUBLICATIONS. 1965. a. price varies. London Record Society, c/o Institute of Historical Research, Senate House, London WC1E 7HU, England. TEL 081-636-0272. FAX 081-436-2183. Ed. V. Harding. circ. 390. (back issues avail.) **Document type:** academic/scholarly publication.
—BLDSC (5294.090000).

948   FI
LOUNAIS-HAEMEEN KOTISEUTU JA MUSEOYHDISTYS. VUOSIKIRJA. 1924. a. Lounais-Haemeen Kotiseutu ja Museoyhdistys, Wahreninkatu, SF-30100 Forssa, Finland. cum.index: 1924-61 in vol.31, 1962-71 in vol.40, 1972-81 in vol.50, 1982-1992 in vol.61.

945 355   IT
LUCIANO MANARA. 1921. bi-m. L.10000. Bersaglieri Club, Via Burigozzo 4, 20122 Milan, Italy. TEL 583-083-44. Ed. Lauro Enzo. circ. 2,000.

943   GW   ISSN 0179-1842
DD801.W99
LUDWIGSBURGER GESCHICHTSBLAETTER. 1900. a. DM.29.80. Historischer Verein fuer Stadt und Kreis Ludwigsburg e.V., Stadtarchiv Ludwigsburg, Kaiserstr. 14, 71636 Ludwigsburg, Germany. TEL 07141-910412. FAX 07141-910342. Ed. Wolfgang Schmierer. bk.rev. circ. 1,000. **Document type:** monographic series.
  Description: Covers history of the Ludwigsburg area.

940   PO   ISSN 0076-1508
BR910
LUSITANIA SACRA. 1956. a. $35. Universidade Catolica Portuguesa, Centro de Estudos de Historia Religiosa, Palma de Cima, 1600 Lisbon, Portugal. FAX 351-1-727-02-56. TELEX 65094 UNICAP P. Ed. Paulo Lonres. bk.rev. **Indexed:** Amer.Hist.& Life, Hist.Abstr. **Document type:** monographic series.

940   PL   ISSN 0076-1516
LUSTRACJE DOBR KROLEWSKICH XVI-XVIII WIEKU. 1959. irreg. latest 1992. price varies. (Polska Akademia Nauk, Instytut Historii) Wydawnictwo Naukowe P W N, Miodowa 10, 00-251 Warsaw, Poland. Ed. Leonid Zytkowicz.

948.9   DK   ISSN 0107-1238
LYBOEN. 1979. a. DKK 20. Lokalhistorisk Forening for Lyoe, Redaktionen, Nygade 6, 6760 Ribe, Denmark. illus.

948   DK   ISSN 0107-7848
LYNGBY-BOGEN. 1933. a. DKK 100.
(Historisk-Topografisk Selskab for Lyngby-Taarbaek Kommune) Byhistorisk Samling, Lyngby Hovedgade 2, 2800 Lyngby, Denmark. TEL 45-42-88-43-83. FAX 45-45-88-86-27. Ed. Jeppe Toensberg. illus. circ. 1,800. **Document type:** monographic series.
  Description: Focuses on the local history of Lyngby-Tarbaek, earlier Denmark's oldest industrial district, now a suburb of Copenhagen and a popular recreation area.

943.9 200   CN
M E T E M - INTERNATIONAL SOCIETY OF TORONTO FOR HUNGARIAN CHURCH HISTORY. NEWSLETTER/M E T E M. HIREK. (Text in English, Hungarian) 1991. q. free to members. M E T E M - International Society of Toronto for Hungarian Church History, Regis College, 15 St. Mary St., Toronto, ON M4Y 2R5, Canada. TEL 416-922-2476. FAX 416-922-2898. Ed. Sandor Kostya. adv.; circ. controlled. (back issues avail.) **Document type:** newsletter.
  Formerly: International Society of Toronto for Hungarian Church History. Newsletter (ISSN 1183-6350)

948   DK   ISSN 0107-9328
M I V: MUSEERNE I VIBORG AMT. 1971. a. DKK 110. Museumsraadet for Viborg Amt, c/o Fur Museum, DK-7884 Fur, Denmark. FAX 86-27-23-78. (Subscr. to: Jens Vellev, Hikuin, Moesgaard, DK-8270 Hoejbjerg, Denmark) Ed. Jens Vellev. illus. circ. 1,000. (back issues avail.) **Indexed:** NAA.

940   NE   ISSN 1380-4170
DE MAASGOUW. 1879. 4/yr. fl.60 includes Jaarboek. Limburgs Geschied- en Oudheidkundig Genootschap, Postbus 83, 6200 AB Maastricht, Netherlands. FAX 31-43-218572. **Document type:** academic/scholarly publication.

943   GW   ISSN 0024-9661
DER MAERKER; Landeskundliche Zeitschrift fuer den Bereich der ehemaligen Grafschaft Mark und den Maerkischen Kreis. 1951. q. DM.24. Maerkischer Kreis, Postfach 1453, 58744 Altena, Germany. Ed. R.D. Kohl. adv.; bk.rev.; cum.index. circ. 1,500. **Indexed:** Numis.Lit. **Document type:** bulletin.

943.9 200   CN   ISSN 0865-5227
BR869.5
MAGYAR EGYHAZTORTENETI VAZLATOK/ESSAYS IN CHURCH HISTORY IN HUNGARY. 1989. 4/yr. (in 2 vols., 2 nos./vol.). Can.$20 to individuals; institutions Can.$30. M E T E M - International Society of Toronto for Hungarian Church History, Regis College, 15 St. Mary St., Toronto, ON M4Y 2R5, Canada. TEL 416-922-2476. FAX 416-922-2898. Ed. Tibor Horvath. bk.rev. (back issues avail.) **Document type:** academic/scholarly publication.
  Description: Features articles dealing with the history of over 6000 parishes, numerous institutions, persons, Church activities, monuments, writings, documents, sources related to the Church in Hungarian linguistic communitites.
  Refereed Serial

943   HU   ISSN 0076-2407
MAGYAR KOZLONY; official gazette. irreg. $99.50. (Minisztertanacs) Lapkiado Vallalat, Lenin korut 9-11, 1073 Budapest, Hungary. TEL 222-408. (Distr. by: Kultura, Box 149, 1389 Budapest, Hungary) Ed. Elemer Kiss. circ. 90,000. (also avail. in microfilm from KTO)

MAGYAR MEZOGAZDASAGI MUZEUM KOZLEMENYEI/HUNGARIAN AGRICULTURAL MUSEUM. PROCEEDINGS. see *AGRICULTURE*

943.9   AG   ISSN 0300-3817
MAGYAR TORTENELMI SZEMLE/HUNGARIAN HISTORICAL REVIEW/REVISTA HISTORICA HUNGARA. (Text in various languages) 1969. q. $15. Eugenio Matias Feher, Espana 635, Castelar. Prov., Buenos Aires, Argentina. bk.rev.; bibl.; illus.; index. circ. 800.

MAGYARORSZAG MUEMLEKI TOPOGRAFIAJA. see *ART*

948 913   NO   ISSN 0333-0974
MAIHAUGEN. 1931. a. NOK 170. (Maihaugen) Sandvigske Samlinger, 2600 Lillehammer, Norway. TEL 47-612-88900. FAX 47-612-53-959. Ed. Anders Ole Hauglid. **Document type:** academic/scholarly publication.
  Formerly (until 1949): Sandvigske Samlinger. Aarbok.

943 709   GW   ISSN 0076-2725
DD801.B49
MAINFRAENKISCHES JAHRBUCH FUER GESCHICHTE UND KUNST. 1949. a. DM.80. Freunde Mainfraenkischer Kunst und Geschichte e.V., Hofstr. 11, 8700 Wuerzburg, Germany. Ed. Dr. Ernst G. Krenig. bk.rev. circ. 900. **Indexed:** Numis.Lit., RILA. **Document type:** bulletin.

MAINZER ZEITSCHRIFT; Mittelrheinisches Jahrbuch fuer Archaeologie, Geschichte und Kunst. see *ART*

949.5 398 913 400   GR   ISSN 0076-289X
MAKEDONIKA. (Text and summaries in English, French, German, Greek) 1940. a. Dr.3000($16) Society for Macedonian Studies, Ethnikis Amymis 4, 546 21 Thessaloniki, Greece. TEL 30-31-268710. FAX 30-31-271501. Ed.Bd. bk.rev. **Indexed:** Amer.Hist.& Life, Hist.Abstr. **Document type:** academic/scholarly publication.
  Description: Contains articles that promote research in the archaeology, folklore, history, and linguistics of Macedonia, Greece.

2952 HISTORY — HISTORY OF EUROPE

947   GW
MARBURGER ABHANDLUNGEN ZUR GESCHICHTE UND KULTUR OSTEUROPAS. 1958. irreg., vol.27, 1988. DM.65. Wilhelm Schmitz Verlag, Staufenbergerweg 22, 35457 Lollar, Germany. TEL 06406-2324. **Document type:** monographic series.

945   IT
MARCHE CONTEMPORANEE. 1984. s-a. (Centro Regionale per la Storia del Movimento Cattolico e la Resistenza nelle Marche) Istituto Internazionale di Studi Piceni, Piazza Matteotti, 60047 Sassoferrato (AN), Italy. TEL 0732-9465. Eds. Gianfranco Brocanelli, Stefano Trojani.
    Description: Contains historical, religious, and social research and studies on the Resistance movement.

945   IT
MARCO POLO. (Text in English, Italian) m. L.50000 (foreign L.100000) (effective 1994). Marsilio Editori S.p.A., Marittimo - Fabbricato 205, 30135 Venice, Italy. TEL 041-5227822. FAX 041-5238352.
    Description: Covers the culture of the city of Venice.

920   FR   ISSN 0025-2891
MARECHAL. 1959. q. 25 F. Association pour Defendre la Memoire du Marechal Petain, 6 rue Marengo, 75001 Paris, France. Ed. Rene Minguet.

945   GW
MARIENBURGER ZEITUNG. 1950. m. DM.28.80 (foreign DM.33.60). Landsmannschaft Westpreussen e.V., Norbertstr. 29, 48151 Muenster, Germany. TEL 0251-523424. FAX 0251-533830.

948   DK   ISSN 0106-5122
MARINEHISTORISK TIDSSKRIFT. 1967. 4/yr. DKK 55. Orlogsmuseet, Overgaden oven Vandet 58, DK-1415 Copenhagen K, Denmark. FAX 45-31-54-29-80. Ed. J.H. Barfod. bk.rev. circ. 2,500.

948   DK   ISSN 0105-0826
MARK OG MONTRE; aarbog for kunst og kulturhistoriske museer. 1965. a. DKK 50. Ribe Amts Museumsraad, Noerregade 25, DK-6700 Esbjerg, Denmark. TEL 45-75-12-78-11. FAX 45-75-13-59-49. Ed.Bd. illus. **Indexed:** NAA.
    Formerly: Fra Esbjerg Museums Virke.
    Description: Publishes material from the art and historical museums in Ribe Amt on museum research projects, excavations, collections, exhibitions, education, etc.

943   GW
DAS MARKGRAEFLERLAND. 1929. s-a. DM.30. Geschichtsverein Markgraeflerland e.V., Talmatten 3, 79639 Grenzach-Wyhlen, Germany. TEL 07624-5898. bk.rev. circ. 14,000.
    Description: Local history and news.

MARTYRDOM AND RESISTANCE. see *ETHNIC INTERESTS*

943 947   XR
MASARYKOVA UNIVERSITA. FILOZOFICKA FAKULTA. SBORNIK PRACI. C: RADA HISTORICKA. 1954. irreg. (approx. a.). price varies. Masarykova Universita, Filozoficka Fakulta, A. Novaka 1, 660 88 Brno, Czech Republic. FAX 41-211241. bk.rev. **Document type:** proceedings.
    Formerly: Universita J.E. Purkyne. Filozoficka Fakulta. Sbornik Praci. C: Rada Historicka (ISSN 0231-7710)
    Description: Articles in the fields of general and Czechoslovak history, auxiliary historical sciences, the philosophy of history and the history of Central, South-East and Eastern Europe.

MASARYKOVA UNIVERSITA. FILOZOFICKA FAKULTA. SBORNIK PRACI. E: RADA ARCHEOLOGICKO-KLASICKA. see *ARCHAEOLOGY*

MASSUA. see *ETHNIC INTERESTS*

945   SZ   ISSN 0088-7714
MATERIALI E DOCUMENTI TICINESI. q. 64 Fr. Edizioni Casagrande SA, Casella Postale 1291, CH-6500 Bellinzona, Switzerland.

940   AU
MATERIALIEN ZUR WIRTSCHAFTS- UND SOZIALGESCHICHTE. 1978. irreg. Verlag fuer Geschichte und Politik, Neulinggasse 26, A-1030 Vienna, Austria. Ed.Bd. **Document type:** monographic series.

940   PL   ISSN 0076-5236
MATERIALY ZACHODNIO-POMORSKIE. (Text in Polish; summaries in English, French and German) 1957. a. price varies. Muzeum Narodowe, Szczecin, Staromlynska 27, 70-561 Szczecin, Poland. TEL 335-066. FAX 347-894. (Dist. by: Ars Polona-Ruch, Krakowskie Przedmiescie 7, Warsaw, Poland) Ed. Wladyslaw Filipowiak. bk.rev. circ. 700. **Indexed:** Numis.Lit. **Document type:** monographic series.
    Description: Covers history of Pomeranian region.

944 320   FR   ISSN 0769-3206
D410
MATERIAUX POUR L'HISTOIRE DE NOTRE TEMPS. 1985. q. 210 F. (foreign 280 F.). Association des Amis de la BDIC et du Musee, 6 allee de l'Universite, 92001 Nanterre Cedex, France. Dir. Rene Girault. illus.; index. circ. 500. (back issues avail.)
    Description: Presents studies, documents and testimonies about twentieth century history.

948   DK   ISSN 0076-5864
MEDIAEVAL SCANDINAVIA; a journal devoted to the study of mediaeval civilization in Scandinavia and Iceland. (Text in English and German) 1968. irreg. price varies. Odense University Press, Campusvej 55, DK-5230 Odense M, Denmark. TEL 66-157999. FAX 66-158126. Ed. Hans Bekker-Nielsen. (back issues avail.) **Indexed:** Bibl.Ling., M.L.A.
    —BLDSC (5525.278000).

948   DK   ISSN 0106-102X
MEDIAEVAL SCANDINAVIA SUPPLEMENTS. (Text in English) 1980. irreg. price varies. Odense University Press, Campusvej 55, DK-5230 Odense M, Denmark. TEL 66-157999. FAX 66-158126. Ed. Hans Bekker-Nielsen.
    —BLDSC (5525.278100).

MEDIAEVAL SOURCES IN TRANSLATION. see *LITERATURE*

940   CN   ISSN 0076-5872
MEDIAEVAL STUDIES. (Text in English; occasionally in French, German, Latin and other languages) 1939. a. $55 (2000 BEF) (effective 1994). Pontifical Institute of Mediaeval Studies, 59 Queen's Park Crescent E., Toronto, ON M5S 2C4, Canada. TEL 416-926-7144. FAX 416-926-7258. (Dist. outside N. America and UK by: N.V. Brepols, Steenweg op Tielen 68, 2300 Turnhout, Belgium. TEL 32-14-415463. FAX 32-14-428919) Ed. James Farge. cum.index: vols.1-25, supplement index: vols.26-30, vols.31-40. circ. 1,100. (back issues avail.) **Indexed:** Amer.Bibl.Slavic & E.Eur.Stud., Arts & Hum.Cit.Ind., Cath.Ind., Curr.Cont., M.L.A., M.L.A., Phil.Ind., RILA. **Document type:** academic/scholarly publication.
    —UnCover; SWETS. **CCC.**

940   US   ISSN 0361-946X
CB351
MEDIAEVALIA. 1975. a. $25. State University of New York at Binghamton, Center for Medieval and Early Renaissance Studies, Binghamton, NY 13902-6000. TEL 607-777-2730. FAX 607-777-2408. Ed. Paul E. Szarmach. circ. 400. (reprint service avail. from ISI) **Indexed:** Curr.Cont., M.L.A., RILA.
    —BLDSC (5525.285000); SWETS.

940   BE
MEDIAEVALIA LOVANIENSIA. SERIES I. (Text in Dutch, English, French, German) 1972. irreg., vol.22, 1992. price varies. (Katholieke Universiteit te Leuven, Instituut voor Middeleeuwse Studies) Leuven University Press, Krakenstraat 3, B-3000 Leuven, Belgium. TEL 32-16-284175. FAX 32-16-284176. **Document type:** academic/scholarly publication.

940   GW   ISSN 0934-7453
MEDIAEVISTIK; Internationale Zeitschrift fuer Interdisziplinaere Mittelalterforschung. a. DM.98. Peter Lang GmbH Europaeischer Verlag der Wissenschaften, Eschborner Landstr. 42-50, 60489 Frankfurt a.M., Germany. TEL 069-7807050. FAX 069-785893. Ed. Peter Dinzelbacher. adv.: B&W page DM.500; trim 121 x 190. **Document type:** academic/scholarly publication.

940   US
MEDIEVAL ACADEMY BOOKS. 1928. irreg., no.100, 1992. Medieval Academy of America, 1430 Massachusetts Ave., Cambridge, MA 02138. TEL 617-491-1622. (reprint service avail.)
    Formerly: Mediaeval Academy of America. Publications (ISSN 0076-583X)

940   CN
MEDIEVAL ACADEMY REPRINTS FOR TEACHING. 1978. irreg., no. 29, 1993. price varies. (Medieval Academy of America) University of Toronto Press, 5201 Dufferin St., Downsview, ON M3H 5T8, Canada. TEL 416-667-7791. FAX 416-667-7832. (U.S. Address: 340 Nagel Dr., Cheektowaga, NY 14225) **Document type:** academic/scholarly publication.

MEDIEVAL AND RENAISSANCE AUTHORS. see *LITERATURE*

940   NE   ISSN 0925-7683
MEDIEVAL AND RENAISSANCE AUTHORS AND TEXTS. 1991. irreg. price varies. E.J. Brill, P.O. Box 9000, 2300 PA Leiden, Netherlands. TEL 31-71-312624. FAX 31-71-317532. TELEX 39296 BRILL NL. (In N. America: E.J. Brill, 24 Hudson St., Kinderhook, NY 12106. TEL 800-962-4406. FAX 518-758-1959) **Document type:** monographic series.
    Refereed Serial

940   NE   ISSN 0169-9105
MEDIEVAL AND RENAISSANCE TEXTS. 1981. irreg., vol.5, 1991. price varies. E.J. Brill, P.O. Box 9000, 2300 PA Leiden, Netherlands. TEL 31-71-312624. FAX 31-71-317532. TELEX 39296 BRILL NL. (In N. America: E.J. Brill, 24 Hudson St., Kinderhook, NY 12106. TEL 800-962-4406. FAX 518-758-1959) Eds. Douglas Gray, Nicholas Mann. **Document type:** monographic series.
    Refereed Serial

MEDIEVAL ARCHAEOLOGY. see *ARCHAEOLOGY*

946   NE   ISSN 0076-6100
MEDIEVAL IBERIAN PENINSULA; texts and studies. 1961. irreg., no.8, 1993. price varies. E.J. Brill, P.O. Box 9000, 2300 PA Leiden, Netherlands. TEL 31-71-312624. FAX 31-71-317532. TELEX 39296 BRILL NL. (In N. America: E.J. Brill, 24 Hudson St., Kinderhook, NY 12106. TEL 800-962-4406. FAX 518-758-1959) (back issues avail.) **Document type:** monographic series.
    Description: Covers the medieval history and culture of Spain, with particular emphasis on Islamic history and relations between medieval Christians and Muslims.
    Refereed Serial

940   US   ISSN 0198-9405
D115
MEDIEVAL PROSOPOGRAPHY. 1980. s-a. $20. Medieval Institute Publications, Western Michigan University, Kalamazoo, MI 49008. TEL 616-387-8755. FAX 616-387-8750. Ed.Bd. circ. 200. (back issues avail.)
    —BLDSC (5534.266100); UnCover.
    Description: Scholarly essays employing the prosopographic approach to the study of Medieval Europe. Includes announcements, bibliographies and reviews of relevant scholarship.

940 800 700   US   ISSN 0076-6127
D111
MEDIEVALIA ET HUMANISTICA; studies in medieval and renaissance culture. 1943. a. $47.50. (Modern Language Association) Medieval and Renaissance Society, Box 13348, North Texas Station, Denton, TX 76203. TEL 817-565-2168. FAX 817-565-4919. Ed. Paul Maurice Clogan. bk.rev.; cum.index. circ. 2,000. (also avail. in microfiche; back issues avail.) **Indexed:** M.L.A., RILA. **Document type:** academic/scholarly publication.
    —BLDSC (5534.267000).
    Description: Publishes scholarly articles on all aspects of medieval and renaissance culture: history, literature, art, music, science, law, economics, and philosophy.

940   IT
MEDIOEVO E RINASCIMENTO. 1986; N.S. 1990. a. L.100000. (Universita di Firenze, Dipartimento di Studi sul Medioevo e il Rinascimento) Centro Italiano di Studi sull'Alto Medioevo, Palazzo Ancaiani, 06049 Spoleto, Italy. TEL 0743-220418. FAX 0743-223507. **Document type:** academic/scholarly publication.

HISTORY — HISTORY OF EUROPE

MEDIOEVO LATINO. see *HISTORY — Abstracting, Bibliographies, Statistics*

940   IT
MEDIOEVO - TRADUZIONI. 1991. irreg., no.4, 1993. Centro Italiano di Studi sull'Alto Medioevo, Palazzo Ancaiani, 06049 Spoleto, Italy. TEL 0743-220418. FAX 0743-223507. Ed. Ovidio Capitani. **Document type:** monographic series.

943   GW   ISSN 0539-2896
DD901.M522
MEMMINGER GESCHICHTSBLAETTER. 1912. a. DM.15. Heimatpflege Memmingen, Ulmer Str. 19, 87700 Memmingen, Germany. TEL 08331-850-136. FAX 08331-5433. Ed. Uli Braun. bk.rev.; cum.index. circ. 1,500. (back issues avail.)
Description: History of Memmingen city and area.

945   IT
MEMOIRES ET DOCUMENTS SUR ROME ET L'ITALIE MERIDIONALE. (Text in French) 1980, N.S. 1984. irreg., no.3, 1988. price varies. (Institut Francais de Naples, Bibliotheque) L'Erma di Bretschneider, Via Cassiodoro 19, 00193 Rome, Italy. TEL 06-687-41-27. FAX 06-687-41-29.

MEMORIA DEL TEMPO; studi e testi medievali e rinascimentali. see *LITERATURE*

945   IT
▼**MEMORIA STORICA.** 1992. q.? Centro di Studi Storici Terni, Via degli Artieri 13, 05100 Terni, Italy. TEL 0744-417308. Ed. Vincenzo Pirro.

MENNONITISCHE GESCHICHTSBLAETTER. see *RELIGIONS AND THEOLOGY — Protestant*

970   US   ISSN 0543-5056
Z733
MERCHANT EXPLORER. 1961. a. $15 membership. Associates of the James Ford Bell Library, 472 Wilson Library, University of Minnesota, Minneapolis, MN 55455. TEL 612-624-1528. FAX 612-626-9353. Ed. Carol Urness. bk.rev.; bibl. circ. 500. **Document type:** monographic series.
Description: Contains listing of acquisitions with commentary on some items.

940 330   BU   ISSN 0324-1092
MEZHDUNARODNI OTNOSHENIYA. 1972. 4/yr. (Institut za Vunshna Politika Ivan Bashev) Institut za Mezhdunarodni Otnosheniia i Sotsialisticheska Intergratsiia, 7 Noemuri 1, Sofia, Bulgaria. (Dist. by: Hemus Foreign Trade Co., 6 Ruski Blvd., 1000 Sofia, Bulgaria.) **Indexed:** BSL Econ.

940 500   BE
▼**MICROLOGUS**; natura, scienza e societa medievali - nature, science and medieval societies. (Text in French, Italian) 1993. a. 1800 BEF. (Societa Internazionale per lo Studio del Medioevo Latina, IT) N.V. Brepols, Steenweg op Tielen 68, 2300 Turnhout, Belgium. TEL 32-14-402500. FAX 32-14-428919. TELEX 32806. **Document type:** academic/scholarly publication.
Description: Publishes interdisciplinary contributions on the history of science in medieval times, the medieval philosophy of nature and the relationship of nature and medieval society.

940   US
MIDDLE AGES. 1897. irreg., latest 1993. University of Pennsylvania Press, Brockley Hall, 31th Fl., 418 Service Dr., Philadelphia, PA 19104. TEL 215-898-6261. Ed. Edward M. Peters. **Document type:** monographic series.
Supersedes: Translations and Reprints from the Original Sources of European History (ISSN 0082-593X)

942   UK   ISSN 0047-729X
DA670.M64
MIDLAND HISTORY. 1971. a. £20. University of Birmingham, School of History, Edgbaston, Birmingham B15 2TT, England. TEL 021-414-5759. Ed. R.P. Cust. adv.; bk.rev. circ. 500. **Indexed:** Amer.Hist.& Life, Br.Archaeol.Abstr., Br.Hum.Ind., Hist.Abstr. **Document type:** academic/scholarly publication.
—BLDSC (5761.416000); SWETS.
Description: Covers all aspects of history relating to the Midland region in England.

MIGRACIJSKE TEME/MIGRATION THEMES; casopis za istrazivanje migracija i narodnosti. see *SOCIOLOGY*

948.5 355   SW   ISSN 0283-8400
MILITAERHISTORISK TIDSKRIFT. (Includes Krigsvetenskapsakademiens Handlingar och Tidskrift) (Text in Swedish; summaries in English) 1954. a. SEK 125 incl. supplement. Kungliga Militaerhoegskolan, Militaerhistoriska Avdelningen - Royal Armed Forces Staff College, P.O. Box 27805, S-115 93 Stockholm, Sweden. FAX 46-8-7889499. (Subscr. to: Kungl. Krigsakademiens Handlingar och Tidskrift, Oestermalmsgatan 87, S107 87 Stockholm, Sweden (FAX 46-8-788 99 11)) Eds. Col. B. Hugemark, K.R. Boehme. circ. 2,000. **Indexed:** Amer.Hist.& Life, Hist.Abstr.
Formerly (until 1979): Aktuellt och Historiskt (ISSN 0065-5619)

943   GW   ISSN 0340-188X
MINDENER GESCHICHTSVEREIN. MITTEILUNGEN. 1923. a. DM.16. Mindener Geschichtsverein, Tonhallenstr. 7, 32423 Minden, Germany. TEL 0571-89475. FAX 0571-89479. Ed. Hans Nordsiek. circ. 1,100. (back issues avail.) **Document type:** bulletin.

943.7   XR
MINULOSTI ROKYCANSKA.* 1967. irreg. Zapadoceske Nakladatelstvi, Palackeho Nam. 2, 301-16 Plzen, Czech Republic. (Dist. by: Artia, Ve Smeckach 30, 111 27 Prague 1, Czech Republic.) cum.index: vols.1-11, 1967-1972.

943.7   XR   ISSN 0544-3830
MINULOSTI ZAPADOCESKEHO KRAJE.* 1962. irreg. (Archiv Mesta Plzne) Zapadoceske Nakladatelstvi, Palackeho Nam. 2, 301-16 Plzen, Czech Republic. (Dist. by: Artia, Ve Smeckach 30, 111 27 Prague 1, Czech Republic) bk.rev.; bibl.

946   SP
MISCELLANIA DE TEXTOS MEDIEVALS. At head of title: Institucion Mila y Fontanals. (Text in Catalan, French, English, Italian, Portuguese, Spanish) 1972. irreg., vol.6, 1992. price varies. Institucion Mila y Fontanals, Departamento de Estudios Medievales, C. Egipciacas 15, 08001 Barcelona, Spain. TEL 93-442-3489. FAX 93-442-7424. adv.; bk.rev.; bibl. circ. 1,000.
Formerly: Miscelanea de Textos Medievales (ISSN 0213-2257)
Description: Devoted to the publication of documents, texts, and chronicles of the Middle Ages.

949.5 809   GW   ISSN 0076-9347
MISCELLANEA BYZANTINA MONACENSIA. 1965. irreg. price varies. Universitaet Muenchen, Institut fuer Byzantinistik und Neugriechische Philologie, Geschwister Scholl Platz 1, 80539 Munich, Germany. Eds. Hans-Georg Beck, Armin Hohlweg. index. **Document type:** monographic series.

945   IT   ISSN 0026-5888
MISCELLANEA STORICA DELLA VALDELSA. 1893. q. L.30000. Societa Storica della Valdelsa, Via Tilli 27, 50051 - Castelfiorentino, Florence, Italy. adv.; bk.rev. circ. 700.

943.6   AU
MISTELBACH IN VERGANGENHEIT UND GEGENWART; heimatkundliche Beilage zu den Mitteilungen der Stadtgemeinde. 1961. a. Stadtgemeinde Mistelbach, Hauptplatz 6, 2130 Mistelbach, Austria. circ. 4,500.

940   NE   ISSN 0076-9754
MITTELLATEINISCHE STUDIEN UND TEXTE. 1965. irreg., vol.18, 1990. price varies. E.J. Brill, P.O. Box 9000, 2300 PA Leiden, Netherlands. TEL 31-71-312624. FAX 31-71-317532. TELEX 39296 BRILL NL. (In N. America: E.J. Brill, 24 Hudson St., Kinderhook, NY 12106. TEL 800-962-4406. FAX 518-758-1959) Ed. P.G. Schmidt. **Document type:** monographic series.
Refereed Serial

940   GW   ISSN 0076-9762
PA2802
MITTELLATEINISCHES JAHRBUCH. 1964. a. DM.98. Anton Hiersemann Verlag, Rosenbergstr. 113, 70193 Stuttgart, Germany. TEL 0711-638265. FAX 0711-6369010. (Subscr. to: Postfach 140155, 70071 Stuttgart, Germany) Ed. Fritz Wagner. circ. 600. **Indexed:** Bibl.Ling., M.L.A. **Document type:** academic/scholarly publication.

949.5 913   GR
MNEMOSYNE. (Text in English, French, Greek) 1967. a. Dr.4000($25) Hetairia Historikon Spoudon epi tou Neoterou Hellenismou, 16 Dervenion St., 106 80 Athens, Greece. Ed. T. Gritsopoulos. bk.rev. circ. 1,000. (back issues avail.)
Description: Covers Greek history.

944 054   UK   ISSN 0267-761X
MODERN AND CONTEMPORARY FRANCE. 1980. q. £20 (foreign £22) to individuals; institutions £35 (foreign £39). (Association for the Study of Modern & Contemporary France) Longman Group UK Ltd., Longman House, Burnt Mill, Harlow, Essex CM20 2JE, England. TEL 0279-426721. FAX 0279-431059. Ed.Bd. adv.; bk.rev.; index. circ. 500. (back issues avail.) **Document type:** academic/scholarly publication.
—BLDSC (5883.605000).
Description: Geared to teachers of French and French studies in secondary and higher education.

949   US   ISSN 0147-0779
DF755.82.U6
MODERN GREEK SOCIETY: A SOCIAL SCIENCE NEWSLETTER. 1973. s-a. $15 to individuals; institutions $20 (effective 1993). Modern Greek Society, Box 9411, Providence, RI 02940-9411. TEL 401-274-2397. (Co-sponsor: Rhode Island College) Eds. Nikiforos P. Diamandouros, Peter S. Allen. bk.rev.; bibl. circ. 600. (back issues avail.) **Indexed:** Amer.Bibl.Slavic & E.Eur.Stud. **Document type:** newsletter.
Formerly: Modern Greek Society: A Newsletter.
Description: Provides bibliographic references to publications on Greece in the social sciences.

410 930   US   ISSN 0047-7702
MODERN GREEK STUDIES ASSOCIATION BULLETIN. 1969. s-a. $40 to individuals; institutions $50. Modern Greek Studies Association, Box 1826, New Haven, CT 06508. TEL 203-397-4189. FAX 203-397-4691. Ed. John O. Iatrides. adv.; bk.rev.; bibl.; charts; illus. circ. 600. **Document type:** bulletin.
Description: Covers modern Greek studies.

948.5   DK   ISSN 0106-4479
MOELDRUP KOMMUNES LOKALHISTORISKE ARKIV. AARSSKRIFT. 1978. biennial. DKK 80. Lokalhistorisk Udvalg-Moeldrup, Noerregade 15, 9632 Moeldrup, Denmark. TEL 86-69-12-00. FAX 86-69-21-84. illus. circ. 600.

MOELLEN. see *AGRICULTURE — Feed, Flour And Grain*

948.9   DK   ISSN 0106-1917
MOELPOSEN. 1978. a. DKK 20. Spoettrup Lokalhistoriske Arkiv, Spoettrup Bibliotek, Aalbaekevej 18, Lihme, 7861 Balling, Denmark. illus.

946   SP
MOLL MONOGRAFIES D'HISTORIA LOCAL. (Text in Catalan) irreg. 2000 ptas. Editorial Moll, Apdo. 142, 07080 Palma de Mallorca, Spain. TEL 971-72-41-76. FAX 971-72-62-52. **Document type:** monographic series.

948.95   DK   ISSN 0900-8764
MOLSBIBLIOTEKETS LOKALHISTORISKE ARKIV.* 1984. a. DKK 35. Molsbiblioteket. Lokalhistorisk Arkiv, Knebel, Denmark. Ed. Niels Berthelsen.

942   UK   ISSN 0077-0299
MONARCHIST PRESS ASSOCIATION. HISTORICAL SERIES. 1964. irreg. Monarchist Press Association, 7 Sutherland Rd., West Ealing, London, W13 0DX, England. circ. 3,000.

MONOGRAFIE SLAWISTYCZNE. see *LITERATURE*

943   GW   ISSN 0026-9832
MONOGRAPHIEN ZUR GESCHICHTE DES MITTELALTERS. 1970. irreg., vol.37, 1993. price varies. Anton Hiersemann Verlag, Rosenbergstr. 113, 70193 Stuttgart, Germany. TEL 0711-638265. FAX 0711-6369010. (Subscr. to: Postfach 140155, 70071 Stuttgart, Germany) Ed. Friedrich Prinz. **Document type:** monographic series.

HISTORY — HISTORY OF EUROPE

949.2 839.31　　UK
MONOGRAPHS IN MODERN DUTCH STUDIES. 1980. irreg. University of Hull Press, Hull HU6 7RX, England. TEL 0482-46311. FAX 0482-465936. TELEX 592592-KHMAIL-G FAO HULIB 375. Ed. P.A. Holmes. **Document type:** monographic series.
—BLDSC (6224.785000).
　Formerly: Occasional Papers in Modern Dutch Studies (ISSN 0144-3070)

942　　UK　　ISSN 0951-8916
MONOGRAPHS IN REGIONAL AND LOCAL HISTORY. 1987. irreg. price varies. University of Hull Press, Hull HU6 7RX, England. TEL 0482-46311. FAX 0482-465936. TELEX 592592-KHMAIL-G FAO HULIB 375. Ed. P.A. Holmes. **Document type:** monographic series.
—BLDSC (5915.974500).

943.6　　AU　　ISSN 0027-0148
DB761
MONTFORT; Vierteljahresschrift fuer Geschichte und Gegenwart Voralbergs. 1947. q. S.700. (Landesregierung) Vorarlberger Verlagsanstalt, Schwefel 81, A-6850 Dornbirn, Austria. Ed. Karl-Heinz Burmeister. bk.rev.; charts; illus.; stat.; index. circ. 1,000. **Indexed:** Amer.Hist.& Life, Hist.Abstr. **Document type:** government publication.
　Description: Contains regional news.

943.7 914　　XR　　ISSN 0323-0570
MORAVSKE ZEMSKE MUZEUM. CASOPIS. VEDY SPOLECENSKE/ACTA MUSEI MORAVIAE - SCIENTIAE SOCIALES. (Supplement avail.: Acta Musei Moraviae. Supplementum: Folia Numismatica (ISSN 0862-1195)) (Text in Czech, English, German; summaries in English, German) 1901. a. $69. Moravske Zemske Muzeum, Zelny trh 5, 659 37 Brno, Czech Republic. TEL 42-5-22241. FAX 42-5-25279. Eds. Z. Mechurova, M. Oliva. bk.rev. **Indexed:** Bull.Signal., Numis.Lit. **Document type:** academic/scholarly publication.
—BLDSC (0582.310000).

207　　FR　　ISSN 0047-8105
PR2322
MOREANA; time trieth truth. (Text in English, French) 1963. q. 250 F.($50) to individuals; institutions 325 F.($65). (Amici Thomae Mori) Moreana Publications, B.P. 808, 49008 Angers Cedex 01, France. TEL 41-87-19-32. FAX 41-88-74-42. Ed. Germain Marc'hadour. adv.; bk.rev.; film rev.; play rev.; abstr.; illus.; cum.index: vols.1-20 (1963-1983). circ. 800. **Indexed:** Abstr.Engl.Stud., Amer.Hist.& Life, Arts & Hum.Cit.Ind., Curr.Cont., Hist.Abstr., M.L.A.
—Faxon; UnCover; SWETS.
　Description: Aims to provide a forum for research and discussion about Thomas More and the world of humanism.

940　　UK　　ISSN 0959-4655
MORGANNWG. 1957. a. £7.50 to non-members; members £6. Glamorgan History Society, c/o Dr. J.R. Alban, 27 Glanmor Park Rd., Sketty, Swansea SA2 0QG, Wales. TEL 0792-302126. FAX 0792-467432. Eds. J.R. Alban, B.L. James. bk.rev.; illus. circ. 500. **Indexed:** Br.Archaeol.Abstr. **Document type:** academic/scholarly publication.

947 359　　RU　　ISSN 0134-9236
　　　　　　　CODEN: MORSAV
MORSKOI SBORNIK. 1848. m. 22.20 Rub. Izdatel'stvo Krasnaya Zvezda, Chaplygina 15, 103175 Moscow K-175, Russia. Ed. G. Agafonov. bk.rev.; index. circ. 2,500. **Indexed:** Amer.Hist.& Life, Hist.Abstr.
—BLDSC (0117.950000).

943.8　　PL　　ISSN 0580-0943
MOWIA WIEKI; magazyn historyczny. 1958. m. Oficyna Wydawnicza "Mowia Wieki" Spolka z o.o., Ul. Lwowska 15, 00-660 Warsaw, Poland. TEL 48-22-297252. Ed. Stefan Meller. bk.rev. **Indexed:** Numis.Lit.

909　　BE　　ISSN 0027-2841
D111
LE MOYEN AGE. (Text in French) 1888. q. 2800 BEF (Europe 3150 BEF; elsewhere 3200 BEF) (effective 1994). De Boeck Universite, Fond Jean-Paques 4, B-1348 Louvain-la-Neuve, Belgium. TEL 32-10-482509. FAX 32-10-482519. Eds. A. Joris, P. Toubert. adv.; bk.rev.; bibl.; illus.; index. circ. 1,000. (also avail. in microfilm from UMI) **Indexed:** Amer.Hist.& Life (until 1990), Arts & Hum.Cit.Ind., Bibl.Ling., Curr.Cont., Hist.Abstr. (until 1990), M.L.A. **Document type:** academic/scholarly publication.
—BLDSC (5980.450000); Faxon; SWETS.

943　　GW　　ISSN 0723-7286
DAS MUEHLRAD; Beitraege zur Geschichte des Inn- und Isenguas. 1951. a. DM.13. Heimatbund Mueldorf e.V., Margeritenstr. 7, 84453 Mueldorf, Germany. TEL 08631-4647. Ed. Josef Steinbichler. circ. 2,000. (back issues avail.) **Document type:** bulletin.
　Description: Local history of Muehldorf.

MUENCHENER BEITRAEGE ZUR MEDIAEVISTIK UND RENAISSANCE-FORSCHUNG. see CLASSICAL STUDIES

943　　GW　　ISSN 0170-8929
DR1
MUENCHNER ZEITSCHRIFT FUER BALKANKUNDE. 1978. a. DM.138. Slavica Verlag Dr. Anton Kovac, Elisabethstr. 22, 80796 Munich, Germany. TEL 089-2725612. FAX 089-2716594. Ed. Peter Bartl. bk.rev. **Indexed:** Bibl.Ling. **Document type:** academic/scholarly publication.

MUENSTERSCHE BEITRAEGE ZUR ANTIKEN HANDELSGESCHICHTE. see CLASSICAL STUDIES

949.12　　IC
MULATHING. 1966. a. ISK 1800. Heradsnefnd Mulasyslna, P.O. Box 141, IS-700 Egilsstadir, Iceland. TEL 354-97-1-14-17. Ed. Armann Halldorsson.
　Description: Devoted to the local history of East Iceland.

MULOT'SCHEN FAMILIENVERBAND. ZEITSCHRIFT; genealogische Mitteilungen fuer Hugenotten- und Waldensernachkommen. see GENEALOGY AND HERALDRY

943.6　　AU
MUSEALVEREIN WELS. JAHRBUCH. 1954. a. S.250. Musealverein Wels, A-4600 Wels, Austria. TEL 07242-483-255. Ed. Kurt Holter. circ. 800.

949.3　　BE　　ISSN 0776-1414
MUSEES ROYAUX D'ART ET D'HISTOIRE. BULLETIN/KONINKLIJKE MUSEA VOOR KUNST EN GESCHIEDENIS. BULLETIN. 1901. 2/yr. 700 BEF. Editions Peeters s.p.r.l., Bondgenotenlaan 153, B-3000 Louvain, Belgium. TEL 32-16-235170. FAX 32-16-228500. Ed.Bd. (back issues avail.) **Indexed:** Anthropol.Lit. **Document type:** academic/scholarly publication, bulletin.
　Former titles (until **1928**): Musees Royaux du Cinquantenaire. Bulletin (ISSN 0776-1406); (until 1911): Musees Royaux des Arts Decoratifs et Industriels. Bulletin (ISSN 0776-1392)

945　　IT　　ISSN 0523-9478
MUSEO RISORGIMENTO. BOLLETTINO. 1956. a. L.15000. Museo Risorgimento, Via dei Musei, 8, Bologna, Italy. TEL 051-225583. bk.rev. **Document type:** bulletin.
　Description: Articles on Italian history of the eighteenth century focusing on problems of unification.

235　　SP　　ISSN 0212-9248
MUSEU ARXIU DE SANTA MARIA. FULLS. (Text in Catalan) 1978. q. 1.650 ptas. Museu Arxiu de Santa Maria, Carrer Beata Maria 3, 08301 Mataro, Catalonia, Spain. bk.rev.; illus.; index.

943.8　　PL　　ISSN 0068-4651
MUZEUM GORNOSLASKIE W BYTOMIU. ROCZNIK. SERIA HISTORIA. 1963. irreg. $15. Muzeum Gornoslaskie, Pl. Sobieskiego 2, 41-902 Bytom, Poland. TEL 81-34-01. **Document type:** proceedings.

949.8　　RM
MUZEUM MILITAR CENTRAL ROMANIA. STUDII SI MATERIALE DE MUZEOGRAFIE SI ISTORIE MILITARA. 1968. a. 50 lei. Muzeum Militar Central Romania, Str. Stefan Furtuna n.125-127, sector 1, 76111 Bucharest, Rumania. circ. 1,000.

943.7　　XO
MUZEUM UKRAJINSKEJ KULTURY VO SVIDNIKU. VEDECKY ZBORNIK. (Text in Slovak and Ukrainian) 1965. irreg. Slovenske Pedagogicke Nakladatelstvo, Sasinkova 5, 891 12 Bratislava, Slovakia. (Dist. by: Slovart, Gottwaldovo Nam. 6, 805 32 Bratislava, Slovakia) bk.rev.; bibl.

N W S S NEWS. (Network of Women in Slavic Studies) see LINGUISTICS

943　　GW　　ISSN 0721-9733
NACHRICHTEN AUS DEN STAATLICHEN ARCHIVEN BAYERNS. 1971. s.a. Generaldirektion der Staatlichen Archive Bayerns, Postfach 221152, 80501 Munich, Germany. TEL 089-28638482. FAX 089-28638615. circ. 2,500. (back issues avail.) **Document type:** government publication.

940.27　　UK　　ISSN 0027-7827
NAPOLEON. 1970. s.a. free. Napoleonic Society, 157 Vicarage Rd., London E10 5DU, England. TEL 081-539-3876. Ed. Ronald King. bk.rev.; illus. **Document type:** academic/scholarly publication.
　Description: French history 1789-1945.

940 920　　US
NAPOLEONIC SOCIETY OF AMERICA. MEMBER'S BULLETIN. 1983. q. $36. Napoleonic Society of America, 1115 Ponce de Leon Blvd., Clearwater, FL 34616. TEL 813-586-1779. FAX 813-581-2578. Ed. Robert M. Snibbe. adv.; bk.rev.; circ. 2,200 (paid). **Document type:** bulletin, newsletter.

948　　FI　　ISSN 0355-9106
DK465.H5
NARINKKA. (Text in English, Finnish and Swedish) 1976. a. price varies. Helsingin Kaupunginmuseo - Helsinki City Museum, Dagmarinkatu 6, 00100 Helsinki 10, Finland. TEL 358-0-1693437. FAX 358-0-490324. Ed. Leena Arkio-Laine. **Indexed:** Artbibl.Mod.

943　　GW　　ISSN 0077-2887
DD491.H6
NASSAUISCHE ANNALEN. 1812. a. DM.72. Verein fuer Nassauische Altertumskunde und Geschichtsforschung e.V., Mosbacher Str. 55, 65187 Wiesbaden, Germany. TEL 0611-881-0. FAX 0611-881145. Ed. Hans-Joachim Haebel. adv.; bk.rev. circ. 2,200. **Document type:** academic/scholarly publication.

949.7　　CI　　ISSN 0350-6541
NASTAVA POVIJESTI. 1967. 4/yr. $8. Skolska Knjiga, Masarykova 28, 41000 Zagreb, Croatia. bk.rev.; illus.; bibl.
　Supersedes: Historijski Pregled.

943.8 282　　PL　　ISSN 0137-3218
BX1564
NASZA PRZESZLOSC. 1946. 2/yr. 3000 Zl. (typically set in May and Dec.). Instytut Wydawniczy "Nasza Przeszlosc", Ul. Strzelnica 6, 30-215 Krakow, Poland. TEL 48-12-378913. Ed. Jan Dukala. bk.rev.; cum.index: 1946-1988. circ. 1,000. **Indexed:** Amer.Hist.& Life, CERDIC, Hist.Abstr. **Document type:** academic/scholarly publication.

NATSIONALEN VOENNOISTORICHESKI MUZEI, SOFIA. IZVESTIYA. see MILITARY

947　　US
NAUKOVE TOVARYSTVO IMENI SHEVCHENKA. BIBLIOTEKA UKRAINOZNAVSTVA/LIBRARY OF UKRAINIAN STUDIES. (Text in English and Ukrainian) 1949. irreg. price varies. Shevchenko Scientific Society, 63 Fourth Ave., New York, NY 10003.

025.17　　NE　　ISSN 0028-2049
CD1690
NEDERLANDS ARCHIEVENBLAD. 1892. q. fl.140. (Vereniging van Archivarissen in Nederland - Dutch Association of Archivists) B.V. Erven B. van der Kamp, St. Jansstraat 1-3, 9712 JM Groningen, Netherlands. adv.; bk.rev.; bibl.; index. circ. 1,000. (also avail. in microfiche) **Indexed:** Amer.Hist.& Life, Hist.Abstr.
—SWETS.

949.2 914 NE ISSN 0169-6572
NEDERLANDS INSTITUUT TE ROME. MEDEDELINGEN.
(Text in Dutch and English) 1921. a.
Staatsuitgeverij, Chr. Plantijnstr. 2, 2500 EA The
Hague, Netherlands. cum.index: 1939-1959.
Indexed: Avery Ind.Archit.Per., RILA. **Document type:**
academic/scholarly publication.
Formerly (until 1971): Nederlands Historisch
Institute Rome. Mededelingen (ISSN 0921-9013)

949.2 NE ISSN 0166-3801
NEDERLANDSE HISTORIEN. 1967. 6/yr. Gerberasingel
94, Berkel en Rodenrijs, Netherlands.

948 NE ISSN 0920-4032
NEDERLANDSE HISTORISCHE BRONNEN. 1979. irreg.
price varies. Nederlands Historisch Genootschap -
Dutch Historical Association, Postbus 90406,
2509 LK The Hague, Netherlands.
TEL 31-70-3140363. **Document type:** monographic
series.

949.2 NE
NEGENTIENDE EEUW. 1977. 4/yr. fl.40. Maatschappij
der Nederlandse Letterkunde,
Universiteitsbibliotheek, Postbus 9501, 2300 RA
Leiden, Netherlands. Ed.Bd. bk.rev.; bibl.

943 GW
**NEISSER HEIMATBLATT FUER DEN STADT- UND
LANDKREIS NEISSE.** 1948. q. DM.28. Neisser Kultur-
und Heimatbund e.V., Gelber Stern 21, 31137
Hildesheim, Germany. (Subscr. to: Joseph Herrmann,
Heidlaender Weg 6, 49201 Dissen, Germany) circ.
4,000. **Document type:** bulletin.

940 NE ISSN 0066-1287
**NETHERLANDS. RIJKSINSTITUUT VOOR
OORLOGSDOCUMENTATIE. DOCUMENTEN.** 1967.
irreg. Rijksinstituut voor Oorlogsdocumentatie -
Netherlands Institute for War Documentation,
Herengracht 474, 1017 CA Amsterdam,
Netherlands. FAX 31-20-6278208.

949 NE
**NETHERLANDS. RIJKSINSTITUUT VOOR
OORLOGSDOCUMENTATIE. PROGRESS REPORT.**
1953. irreg. free. Rijksinstituut voor
Oorlogsdocumentatie - Netherlands State Institute
for War Documentation, Herengracht 474, 1017 CA
Amsterdam, Netherlands. FAX 31-20-6278208.
circ. 300.

943 GW ISSN 0939-2904
DD801.J861
NEUE BEITRAEGE ZUR JUELICHER GESCHICHTE. 1990.
a. DM.25. Joseph Kuhl Gesellschaft fuer die
Geschichte der Stadt Juelich, Kommstr. 11, 52428
Juelich, Germany. Ed. Guenter Bers. adv.; bk.rev.
Document type: academic/scholarly publication.

943 GW
NEUE NETTELSTEDTER BLAETTER; fuer Ortsgeschichte.
1984. s-a. DM.8 (foreign DM.10). Uhlenweg 5,
21279 Appel, Germany. TEL 04165-6673. Ed.
Hanna Wilde. circ. 1,000.
Description: History of local affairs in Westfalian
villages from the 16th century to the present.

943.8 GW
**DIE NEUE ODER ZEITUNG - CROSSENER
HEIMATGRUESSE;** Sommerfelder Nachrichten. 1949.
bi-m. DM.24 (Europe DM.30; rest of world DM.36).
Verlag H.U. Wein, August-Woehler-Str. 4, 29614
Soltau, Germany. TEL 05191-3326. Ed.
Hanns-Ulrich Wein. adv.; bk.rev. circ. 3,800.
Document type: newspaper.

943 GW
**NEUES TRIERISCHES JAHRBUCH FUER HEIMATPFLEGE
UND HEIMATGESCHICHTE.** 1961. a. DM.9.50. Verein
Trierisch e.V., Loewenbrueckener Str. 23, 54290
Trier, Germany. Ed. Claus Zander.
Formerly: Neues Trierisches Jahrbuch (ISSN
0077-7765)

943 GW
NEUNHOFER LAND; Forschungen und Arbeitsberichte
der Freunde des Neunhofer Landes. 1975. a. DM.8.
Gesellschaft des Frankenbundes e.V., Freunde des
Neunhofer Landes, Im Lohe 7, 91207 Lauf,
Germany. TEL 09126-8669. circ. 400.
Description: History of the region of Nuenhof in
Bavaria.

943 GW ISSN 0077-7862
**NEUSSER JAHRBUCH FUER KUNST,
KULTURGESCHICHTE UND HEIMATKUNDE.** 1956. a.
DM.15. Clemens-Sels-Museum, Am Obertor, 41460
Neuss, Germany. TEL 02131-904130.
FAX 02131-902472. TELEX 8517775-SKNE-D. Ed.
Max Tauch. bk.rev. circ. 1,000. **Document type:**
bulletin.

944 840 US
**NEW YORK UNIVERSITY STUDIES IN FRENCH CULTURE
AND CIVILIZATION.** 1987. irreg., latest 1992. price
varies. New York University Press, 70 Washington
Square So., New York, NY 10012.
TEL 212-998-2575. FAX 212-995-3833. TELEX
235128 NYU UR. Ed. Nicholas Wahl. **Document type:**
monographic series.

**NEWSLETTER OF THE INTERNATIONAL STUDY OF
ORGANIZED PERSECUTION OF CHILDREN.** see
CHILDREN AND YOUTH — About

NICOLAUS. STUDI STORICI. see *RELIGIONS AND
THEOLOGY* — Roman Catholic

940 GW
NIEDERSACHSISCHES JAHRBUCH. 1924. a. DM.52.80.
(Historische Kommission fuer Niedersachsen und
Bremen) Verlag Hahnsche Buchhandlung, Postfach
2460, 30024 Hannover, Germany.
TEL 0511-322294. FAX 0511-363698. circ.
1,660. **Indexed:** Amer.Hist.& Life (until 1988),
Hist.Abstr. (until 1988). **Document type:**
academic/scholarly publication.
Formerly: Niedersaechsisches Jahrbuch fuer
Landesgeschichte (ISSN 0078-0561)

948.8 US ISSN 0272-0280
DK401
NIEPODLEGLOSC/INDEPENDENCE; czasopismo
poswiecone najnowszym dziejom Polski. (Text in
Polish) 1948. a. $15. Pilsudski Institute of America,
180 Second Ave., New York, NY 10003-5778.
TEL 212-505-9077. Ed. Janusz Cisek. bk.rev. circ.
600. **Document type:** academic/scholarly publication.
Description: Examines the history of modern
Poland since 1863.

948 DK ISSN 0106-6145
**NOERRE-ALSLEV KOMMUNE. LOKALHISTORISK ARKIV.
AARSSKRIFT.** 1979. a. DKK 54.75. Noerre-Alslev
Kommune, Lokalhistorisk Arkiv, Eksp. Schleyer,
Egelevgade 26, 4840 Noerre-Alslev, Denmark. illus.

940 NE
NOORDBRABANTS HISTORISCH JAARBOEK. 1984. a.
fl.29.50. Stichting Brabantse Regionale
Geschiedbeoefening, P.O. Box 1104, 5200 BD
's-Hertogenbosch, Netherlands. TEL 31-73-146193.

948.5 SW ISSN 0345-8601
NORD-SVERIGE. 1919. w. SEK 160 (effective 1991).
Nord-Sverige, P.O. Box 210, S-881-01 Sollefteaa,
Sweden.

943 GW ISSN 0078-1037
DD491.S622
NORDELBINGEN; Beitraege zur Kunst- und
Kulturgeschichte. a. price varies. (Gesellschaft fuer
Schleswig-Holsteinische Geschichte)
Westholsteinische Verlagsanstalt Boyens und Co.,
Am Wulf-Isebrand-Platz, Postfach 1880, 25746
Heide, Germany. TEL 0481-691-0. Ed.Bd. **Indexed:**
M.L.A., RILA.

949.2 GW ISSN 0078-1045
DD491.S695
NORDFRIESISCHES JAHRBUCH. 1965. a. price varies.
Nordfriisk Instituut, Suederstr. 30, 25821
Bredstedt, Germany. TEL 04671-2081.
FAX 04671-1333. Ed.Bd. bk.rev. circ. 950. **Indexed:**
Bibl.Ling., M.L.A. **Document type:** academic/scholarly
publication.

948 SW ISSN 0546-2851
CD1760
NORDISK ARKIVNYT. (Text in Danish, Norwegian,
Swedish) 1956. 4/yr. SEK 100 (foreign SEK 130).
Riksarkivet - Swedish National Archives, Box 12541,
S-102 29 Stockholm, Sweden. FAX 08-737-63-50.
Ed. Kerstin Abukhanfusa. bk.rev. circ. 1,500.
Document type: newsletter.
Description: Contains articles and news on archives
in Denmark, Finland, Iceland, Norway and Sweden.

947 NO ISSN 0801-7220
NORDISK OESTFORUM; samfunn og kultur i Rusland og
Oest-Europa. (Text in Danish, Norwegian, Swedish)
1979. q. NOK 310 in the Nordic countries;
elsewhere NOK 350. Scandinavian University Press,
P.O. Box 2959 Toeyen, N-0608 Oslo, Norway.
TEL 47-22-57-54-00. FAX 47-22-57-53-53. Ed.Bd.
Formed by the 1987 merger of: Bulletin foer
Statsstudier i Norden (ISSN 0349-3709); Forum
Oest (ISSN 0800-4951); Which was formerly:
Forum for Sovjet- og Oest-Europa Studier. Bulletin
(ISSN 0801-1915)
Description: Focuses on culture and society in
Eastern Europe, including Russia and other states
within the former Soviet Union.

943 GW
NORDLAUENBURGISCHE CHRONIK; altes und neues aus
nordlauenburgischen Gemeinden und altluebischen
Doerfern im Sueden der Hansestadt. 1982. 5/yr.
DM.1. Pfeil Verlag, Moehlenbarghaus, Dorfstr. 28,
23847 Sierksrade, Germany. TEL 04501-585. Ed.
Ulla Duering.

943 GW
DK4600.033
**NORDOST-ARCHIV. ZEITSCHRIFT FUER
REGIONALGESCHICHTE.** 1968. s-a. DM.60. Institut
Nordostdeutsches Kulturwerk, Conventstr. 1, 21335
Lueneburg, Germany. TEL 04131-37097.
FAX 04131-391143. Ed. Eckhard Matthes. adv.;
bk.rev.; bibl.; illus.; index. circ. 500. (tabloid format)
Indexed: Amer.Hist.& Life (1992-), Hist.Abstr.
(1992-).
Formerly (until 1991): Nordost-Archiv. Zeitschrift
fuer Kulturgeschichte und Landeskunde (ISSN
0029-1595)
Description: Presents information on the history
and development of the northeastern region of
Central Europe.

948 DK ISSN 0107-9336
NORDSLESVIGSKE MUSEER. 1974. a. DKK 85.
Museumsrad for Soenderjyllands Amt, Soenderborg
Slot, 6400 Soenderborg, Denmark. circ. 1,000.
Indexed: NAA.

942 UK ISSN 0078-1169
NORFOLK RECORD SOCIETY. PUBLICATIONS. 1931. a.
£10 to individuals; institutions £12. Norfolk Record
Society, 17 Christchurch Rd., Norwich NR2 2AE,
England. TEL 0603-53004. Ed.Bd. circ. 300.
Indexed: Br.Hum.Ind. **Document type:** directory.

359 NO ISSN 0801-423X
NORSK SJOEFARTSMUSEUM. AARSBERETNING. (Text in
Norwegian; summaries in English) 1965. a.
NOK 150. Norsk Sjoefartsmuseum - Norwegian
Maritime Museum, Bygdoeynesveien 37, 0286 Oslo
2, Norway. TEL 472-22438340.
FAX 472-22562037. Ed. Baard Kolltveit. adv.; illus.;
cum.index. circ. 2,000. **Indexed:** NAA.
Description: Presents articles on maritime history.

948 NO ISSN 0549-6896
NORSK SKOGBRUKSMUSEUM. AARBOK. (Text in
Norwegian; summaries in English) 1958. biennial.
NOK 175. Norsk Skogbruksmuseum, Elverum,
Norway. TEL 47-62-41-02-99.
FAX 47-62-41-30-15. Ed. Tore Fossum. bk.rev. circ.
2,500.

914.2 UK ISSN 0140-9131
NORTHAMPTONSHIRE PAST AND PRESENT. 1948. a.
£11.50 to individuals; institutions £17.50.
Northamptonshire Record Society, Wootton Hall
Park, Northampton NN4 9BQ, England.
TEL 0604-762297. Ed.Bd. adv.; bk.rev.; illus.;
cum.index every 5 or 6 yrs. circ. 2,000. **Indexed:**
Br.Archaeol.Abstr., Br.Hum.Ind., RILA. **Document type:**
newsletter.

NORTHEIMER JAHRBUCH. see *ARCHAEOLOGY*

942 UK ISSN 0078-172X
DA20
NORTHERN HISTORY; a review of the history of the
North of England and the Borders. 1966. a.
£15($28) University of Leeds, School of History,
Leeds LS2 9JT, England. FAX 0532-342759. Ed.
G.C.F. Forster. bk.rev. circ. 800. **Indexed:**
Amer.Hist.& Life, Arts & Hum.Cit.Ind.,
Br.Archaeol.Abstr., Br.Hum.Ind., Curr.Cont.,
Hist.Abstr. **Document type:** academic/scholarly
publication.
—BLDSC (6151.004000); Faxon.

HISTORY — HISTORY OF EUROPE

941 UK ISSN 0306-5278
DA750
NORTHERN SCOTLAND. 1972. a. £7. University of Aberdeen, Centre for Scottish Studies, Old Brewery, King's College, Old Aberdeen AB9 2UB, Scotland. TEL 0224-272203. FAX 0224-487048. TELEX 73458-UNIABM-G. Ed. Peter Payne. bk.rev. circ. 400. **Indexed:** Amer.Hist.& Life, Br.Archaeol.Abstr., Hist.Abstr. **Document type:** academic/scholarly publication.
—BLDSC (6151.200000).
Description: Devoted to historical, geographical, economical, and environmental studies relating to the North of Scotland. Includes report and surveys of archives in Northern Scotland.

NORTH WESTERN EUROPEAN LANGUAGE EVOLUTION. see *LINGUISTICS*

943.9 HU ISSN 0238-4043
NOTARIUS; a zalai honismereti mozgalom folyoirata. 1987. s-a. price varies. (Zala Megyei Onkormanyzati Kozgyules Hivatala) Zala Megyei Leveltar, Szechenyi ter 3, 8901 Zalaegerszeg, Hungary. TEL 92-12794. (Co-sponsor: Degre Alajos Honismereti Alapitvany) Ed. Endre Gyimesi. adv.; bk.rev.; abstr.; bibl.; charts; illus. circ. 1,000. (back issues avail.)
Description: Learned journal of the local historical movement of Zala county.

943.8 PL ISSN 0029-389X
NOTATKI PLOCKIE; pismo regionalne Mazowsza Plockiego. 1956. q. $7. Towarzystwo Naukowe Plockie, Plac Narutowicza 8, 09-402 Plock, Poland. (Dist. by: Ars Polona-Ruch, Krakowskie Przedmiescie 7, Warsaw, Poland) Ed. Wieslaw Konski. bk.rev. circ. 2,030. (also avail. in microfilm) **Indexed:** Numis.Lit.

900 BE ISSN 0048-0924
NOTRE COMTE/ONS GRAAFSCHAP. (Text in Dutch and French) 1971. q. 400 BEF. Cercle d'Histoire, d'Archeologie et de Folklore du Comte de Jette et des Environs, 35 Avenue de Brouckere, B-1080 Brussels, Belgium. adv.; bk.rev.; illus. **Document type:** academic/scholarly publication.

936 US
NOTRE DAME CONFERENCES IN MEDIEVAL STUDIES. 1990. irreg., vol.4, 1994. price varies. University of Notre Dame Press, Notre Dame, South Bend, IN 46656. TEL 219-631-6346. FAX 219-631-8148. (Orders to: Box 635, South Bend, IN 46624) **Document type:** academic/scholarly publication.

NOTTINGHAM FRENCH STUDIES. see *LITERATURE*

940 UK ISSN 0078-2122
PN661
NOTTINGHAM MEDIEVAL STUDIES. 1957. a. £12($20) University of Nottingham, History Department, Nottingham NG7 2RD, England. FAX 0602-515948. TELEX 37346-UNINOT-G. Ed. Michael Jones. bk.rev. circ. 500. **Indexed:** Abstr.Engl.Stud., Br.Archaeol.Abstr., Br.Hum.Ind., M.L.A. **Document type:** academic/scholarly publication.
—Faxon; UnCover.
Description: Interdisciplinary journal for medieval studies from the fall of Rome to the Reformation.

942.5 UK ISSN 0308-6348
NOTTINGHAMSHIRE HISTORIAN. 1968. 2/yr. £4 to non-members. Nottinghamshire Local History Association, Bromley House, Angel Row, Nottingham, England. Ed. Sheila Cooke. bk.rev. circ. 800. **Document type:** academic/scholarly publication.
Former titles: Historian; Nottinghamshire Local History Council. Newsletter.

940.27 FR
NOUVEAUX CAHIERS DU SECOND EMPIRE. (Text in English, French) 1967. m. 50 F. Association les Amis de Napoleon 3rd, 1 avenue Gambetta, 94160 Saint Mande, France. Ed. D. Lambert. adv.; bk.rev.; illus. circ. 1,500. (processed) **Indexed:** Amer.Hist.& Life, Hist.Abstr.
Formerly: Amis de Napoleon 3rd. Bulletin Interne (ISSN 0003-1828)

944 FR ISSN 0029-4799
NOUVELLE REVUE FRANC-COMTOISE. 1946. q. 100 F. (foreign 120 F.). c/o Dir. B. Chazelle, Ed., 13 rue Pasteur, 39102 Dole Cedex, France. adv.; bk.rev.; bibl.; charts; illus.; index.
Description: Covers all aspects of French history.

949.4 SZ
NOUVELLE REVUE NEUCHATELOISE. 1957. q. 25 Fr. Case Postale 1827, CH-2002 Neuchatel, Switzerland. Ed.Bd. adv.; bk.rev.; illus. circ. 2,000.
Formerly: Revue Neuchateloise (ISSN 0035-3779)

943 GW ISSN 0078-2653
NUERNBERGER FORSCHUNGEN. irreg. price varies. Verein fuer Geschichte der Stadt Nuernberg, Egidienplatz 23, 90403 Nuernberg, Germany. circ. 850. **Document type:** monographic series.
Description: Studies history of Nuernberg.

949.2 NE ISSN 0029-5949
NUMAGA; tijdschrift gewijd aan heden en verleden van Nijmegen en omgeving. 1954. q. fl.35. Vereniging Numaga, P.O. Box 1359, 6501 BJ Nijmegen, Netherlands. Ed. H.J. Hendriks. adv.; bk.rev.; abstr.; bibl.; illus.; index; circ. 1,300. (controlled)

NUMISMATICKY SBORNIK. see *NUMISMATICS*

NUOVO BULLETTINO ARCHEOLOGICO SARDO. see *ARCHAEOLOGY*

940 IT ISSN 0391-6049
NUOVO MEDIOEVO. 1976. irreg., no.38, 1993. price varies. Liguori Editore s.r.l., Via Mezzocannone 19, 80134 Naples, Italy. TEL 081-5527139. Ed. Massimo Oldoni. **Document type:** monographic series.

949.7 YU ISSN 0350-9400
OBELEZJA. 1971. 6/yr. Nip Jedinstvo, Marsala Tita 33, 38000 Pristina, Kosovo, Yugoslavia. bk.rev.

943.6 AU ISSN 0029-7550
DB151
OBEROESTERREICHISCHE HEIMATBLAETTER. 1947. q. S.190. Institut fuer Volkskultur, Spittelwiese 4, A-4020 Linz, Austria. TEL 0732-2720-0. Eds. Alexander Jalkotzy, Dietmar Assmann. bk.rev.; abstr.; charts; illus.; cum.index. circ. 1,500. **Document type:** government publication.

943.6 913 AU
OBEROESTERREICHISCHER MUSEALVEREIN. JAHRBUCH. 1840. a. S.270. Oberoesterreichischer Musealverein, Gesellschaft fuer Landeskunde, Landstr. 31, A-4010 Linz, Austria. Eds. Georg Heilingsetzer, Dr. Schwanzar. adv.; bk.rev. circ. 1,000. **Indexed:** Amer.Hist.& Life, Bibl.& Ind.Geol., Br.Archaeol.Abstr., Hist.Abstr.

943.6 AU ISSN 0572-192X
DB153
OBEROESTERREICHISCHES LANDESARCHIV. MITTEILUNGEN. 1950. a. Oberoesterreichisches Landesarchiv, Anzengruberstr. 19, A-4020 Linz, Austria. TEL 0732-6555230. FAX 0732-655523-4619. Eds. Siegfried Maider, Georg Heilingsetzer. bk.rev.; illus. **Indexed:** Amer.Hist.& Life, Hist.Abstr. **Document type:** bulletin.

943 GW
OBERPFALZ; Heimatszeitschrift fuer den ehemaligen Bayerischen Nordgau. 1907. bi-m. DM.32. Verlag Michael Lassleben, Lange Gasse 19, 93183 Kallmuenz, Germany. Ed. Erich Lassleben. circ. 2,000.
Description: Local history of the Oberpfalz area.

943.7 320 XR
OBLASTNI MUZEUM JIHOVYCHODNI MORAVY. ACTA MUSEALIA. 1956. irreg. Oblastni Muzeum Jihovychodni Moravy, Soudni 1, 762 57 Zlin, Czech Republic. (Dist. by: Artia, Ve Smeckach 30, 111 27 Prague 1, Czech Republic) Ed. Petr Starosta. bibl. circ. 600.
Former titles (until 1991): Oblastni Muzeum v Gottwaldove. Zpravy; (1962-1966): Oblastni Muzeum Jihovychodni Moravy v Gottwaldove. Zpravy.

949.4 SZ
OBWALDNER GESCHICHTSBLAETTER. 1901. irreg. price varies. Historisch-Antiquarischer Verein Obwalden, CH-6060 Sarnen, Switzerland. illus. circ. 400.

942 UK ISSN 0078-303X
OCCASIONAL PAPERS IN ENGLISH LOCAL HISTORY. 1969. irreg., 4th series. price varies. Leicester University Press, Fielding Johnson Bldg., University of Leicester, University Rd., Leicester LE1 7RH, England. TEL 0533-523333. Eds. H. Fox, C. Phythian-Adams. **Document type:** monographic series.

OCCASIONAL PAPERS IN GERMAN STUDIES. see *LITERATURE*

900 300 DK ISSN 0078-3307
ODENSE UNIVERSITY STUDIES IN HISTORY AND SOCIAL SCIENCES. (Text in Danish and English; summaries in English) 1970. irreg. (vol.169, 1993). price varies. Odense University Press, Campusvej 55, DK-5230 Odense M, Denmark. TEL 66-157999. FAX 66-158126. (back issues avail.)

947 PL ISSN 0029-8514
ODRODZENIE I REFORMACJA W POLSCE. (Text in Polish; summaries in English) 1956. a. price varies. (Polska Akademia Nauk, Instytut Historii) Ossolineum, Publishing House of the Polish Academy of Sciences, Rynek 9, 50-106 Wroclaw, Poland. TEL 48-71-386-25. FAX 48-71-448-103. TELEX 0712771 OSS PL. Ed. J. Tazbir. **Document type:** academic/scholarly publication.
Description: Dissertations on philosophical and social-political problems of the Polish Renaissance and Reformation.

949.7 YU ISSN 0350-6584
ODZIVI. 1972. 4/yr. $2. Zajednica za Kulturu Opstine Bijelo Polje, Postanski Fah 69, 84000 Bijelo Polje, Montenegro, Yugoslavia. TEL 084-22-208. Ed. Ljubislav Milicevic. adv.; bk.rev.

943.6 AU
OESTERREICH ARCHIV. 1959. irreg. price varies. (Institut fuer Oesterreichkunde) Verlag fuer Geschichte und Politik, Neulinggasse 26, A-1030 Vienna, Austria. Ed. Erich Zoellner. **Document type:** monographic series.

943.6 AU
OESTERREICHISCHE AKADEMIE DER WISSENSCHAFTEN. ARCHIV FUER OESTERREICHISCHE GESCHICHTE. 1848. irreg. price varies. (Oesterreichische Akademie der Wissenschaften, Historische Kommission) Verlag der Oesterreichischen Akademie der Wissenschaften, Dr. Ignaz-Seipel-Platz 2, A-1010 Vienna, Austria. FAX 0222-5139541. (also avail. in microform from BHP)

940 930 AU
OESTERREICHISCHE AKADEMIE DER WISSENSCHAFTEN. KOMMISSION FUER DIE TABULA IMPERII BYZANTINI. VEROEFFENTLICHUNGEN. (Subseries of: Oesterreichische Akademie der Wissenschaften. Philosophisch-Historische Klasse. Denkschriften) 1973. irreg. Verlag der Oesterreichischen Akademie der Wissenschaften, Dr. Ignaz-Seipel-Platz 2, A-1010 Vienna, Austria. FAX 0222-5139541. bibl.; illus. **Document type:** monographic series.

940 100 AU ISSN 0378-8652
AS142
OESTERREICHISCHE AKADEMIE DER WISSENSCHAFTEN. PHILOSOPHISCH-HISTORISCHE KLASSE. ANZEIGER. 1864. a. price varies. Verlag der Oesterreichischen Akademie der Wissenschaften, Dr. Ignaz-Seipel-Platz 2, A-1010 Vienna, Austria. FAX 0222-5139541. **Indexed:** Amer.Hist.& Life, Bibl.Ling., Hist.Abstr., M.L.A.

940 AU
OESTERREICHISCHE AKADEMIE DER WISSENSCHAFTEN. PHILOSOPHISCH-HISTORISCHE KLASSE. SITZUNGSBERICHTE. 1848. irreg. price varies. Verlag der Oesterreichischen Akademie der Wissenschaften, Dr. Ignaz-Seipel-Platz 2, A-1010 Vienna, Austria. FAX 0222-5139541. charts. **Indexed:** Bibl.Ling.

940 AU ISSN 0065-5376
GN700
OESTERREICHISCHE AKADEMIE DER WISSENSCHAFTEN. PRAEHISTORISCHE KOMMISSION. MITTEILUNGEN. 1887. irreg. price varies. Verlag der Oesterreichischen Akademie der Wissenschaften, Dr. Ignaz-Seipel-Platz 2, A-1010 Vienna, Austria. FAX 0222-5139541. **Indexed:** A.I.C.P.

HISTORY — HISTORY OF EUROPE

949.5   AU   ISSN 0378-8660
DF501
OESTERREICHISCHE BYZANTINISTIK. JAHRBUCH. (Text in English, French, German, ancient and modern Greek and Latin) 1951. a. price varies. (Oesterreichische Akademie der Wissenschaften, Kommission fuer Byzantinistik) Verlag der Oesterreichischen Akademie der Wissenschaften, Dr. Ignaz-Seipel-Platz 2, A-1010 Vienna, Austria. FAX 0222-5139541. Ed. Herbert Hunger. bk.rev. **Indexed:** M.L.A., RILA.
  Formerly: Oesterreichische Byzantinische Gesellschaft Jahrbuch.

943.6   AU
OESTERREICHISCHEN GESELLSCHAFT ZUR ERFORSCHUNG DES 18. JAHRHUNDERTS. BEIHEFTE ZUM JAHRBUCH. irreg., no.2, 1990. varies. Verband der Wissenschaftlichen Gesellschaften Oesterreichs, Lindengasse 37, A-1070 Vienna, Austria. TEL 932166.

940   AU
OESTERREICHISCHES KULTURINSTITUT, ROM. ABTEILUNG FUER HISTORISCHE STUDIEN. PUBLIKATIONEN I. ABTEILUNG: ABHANDLUNGEN. (Text in English, French and German) 1954. irreg. price varies. Verlag der Oesterreichischen Akademie der Wissenschaften, Dr. Ignaz-Seipel-Platz 2, A-1010 Vienna, Austria. FAX 0222-5139541.

940   AU
OESTERREICHISCHES KULTURINSTITUT, ROM. ABTEILUNG FUER HISTORISCHE STUDIEN. PUBLIKATIONEN II. ABTEILUNG: QUELLEN. 1968. irreg. price varies. Verlag der Oesterreichischen Akademie der Wissenschaften, Dr. Ignaz-Seipel-Platz 2, A-1010 Vienna, Austria. FAX 0222-5139541.

940   AU   ISSN 0078-3439
OESTERREICHISCHES OST- UND SUEDOSTEUROPA INSTITUT. SCHRIFTENREIHE. 1967. irreg., vol.21, 1992. price varies. Verlag fuer Geschichte und Politik, Neulinggasse 26, A-1030 Vienna, Austria. Eds. Arnold Suppan, K. Mack. **Document type:** monographic series.

940 020   AU   ISSN 0067-2297
OESTERREICHISCHES STAATSARCHIV. MITTEILUNGEN. (Supplements avail.) (Text in English, French, German and Italian) 1948. a. price varies. Verlag Ferdinand Berger und Soehne GmbH, Wienerstr. 21-23, A-3580 Horn, Austria. TEL 02982-2317-0. Eds. Gerhard Rill, Christiane Thomas. bk.rev.; bibl.; illus.; cum.index every 25 yrs.; circ. 500 (controlled). **Indexed:** Amer.Hist.& Life, Hist.Abstr. **Document type:** government publication.

940   GW   ISSN 0078-3714
OFFA-JAHRBUCH; VOR- UND FRUEHGESCHICHTE. a. Wachholtz Verlag GmbH, Rungestr. 4, 24537 Neumuenster, Germany. TEL 04321-906270. FAX 04321-906275. circ. 500. **Document type:** bulletin.

943   GW   ISSN 0471-122X
OFFENBACHER GESCHICHTSBLAETTER. irreg. Offenbacher Geschichtsverein, Herrnstr. 61, 63065 Offenbach a.M., Germany. illus.

900   FR   ISSN 0030-0691
D70
OGAM; tradition Celtique. (Supplement: Celticum) (Text in English and French; summaries in English or German) vol.14, 1962. q. 115 F.($2) Societe des Amis de la Tradition Celtique, B.P. 574, 35007 Rennes, France. Ed. Christian J. Guyonvarc'h. bk.rev.; bibl.; charts; illus.; index. circ. 1,800. **Indexed:** M.L.A., Numis.Lit.

943.7 912   XR
OKRESNI MUZEUM V BLANSKU. SBORNIK. 1969. a. 21 Kcs. Okresni Muzeum v Blansku, Blansko, Czech Republic. (Dist. by: Artia, Ve Smeckach 30, 111 27 Prague 1, Czech Republic) bk.rev.
  Formerly: Okresni Vlastivedneho Muzeum v Blansku. Sbornik.
  Description: Covers history, archaeology and speleology of Central Europe.

941   IE   ISSN 0475-1388
OLD ATHLONE SOCIETY JOURNAL. 1969. irreg. (approx. biennial). I£6 to non-members. Old Athlone Society, c/o Gearoid O'Brien, Ed., 52 Roslevin Lawn, Athlone, Ireland. adv.; charts; illus. circ. 750. **Document type:** bulletin.

OLD CORNWALL. see GENEALOGY AND HERALDRY

940   FR   ISSN 0078-4591
OMBRES DE L'HISTOIRE.* 1969. irreg. price varies. R. Laffont, 6 Place Saint-Sulpice, Paris 6e, France.

ON THE MAKING OF EUROPE. see PHILOSOPHY

OORLOGSDOCUMENTATIE '40-'45. see MILITARY

944   FR
OR DU RHINE.* 1977. irreg. Editions Copernic, 21 rue Cassette, 75006 Paris, France. Ed. Alain de Benoist.

942 572   UK   ISSN 0143-0955
D16.14
ORAL HISTORY. 1971. 2/yr. £12 to individuals; institutions £18. University of Essex, Department of Sociology, Oral History Society, Wivenhoe Park, Colchester CO4 3SQ, England. TEL 0206-873-333. FAX 0206-873-410. (Subscr. to: Oral History, BKT Subscription Services, Lansdowne Mews, 196 High St., Tonbridge, Kent TN9 1EF, England. TEL 0732-770823. FAX 0732-361708) adv.; bk.rev. circ. 1,000. **Indexed:** Amer.Hist.& Life, Hist.Abstr. **Document type:** academic/scholarly publication. —BLDSC (6277.510000); UnCover; SWETS.

943   GW   ISSN 0342-1503
ORTENAU. 1910. a. DM.40. Historischer Verein fuer Mittelbaden e.V., Postfach 1569, 77602 Offenburg, Germany. TEL 0781-24168. **Document type:** academic/scholarly publication.

943.6
ORTSCHRONIKEN. 1973. irreg. (2-3/yr.). price varies. Tiroler Landesarchiv, Herrengasse 1, A-6010 Innsbruck, Austria. **Document type:** monographic series.
  Formerly: Tiroler Ortschroniken.
  Description: Historical chronicles about Tyrolean villages.

943   GW   ISSN 0474-8158
OSNABRUECKER MITTEILUNGEN; Mitteilungen des Vereins fuer Geschichte und Landeskunde von Osnabrueck. 1848. a. DM.50. Verein fuer Geschichte und Landeskunde von Osnabrueck, Schlossstr. 29, 49074 Osnabrueck, Germany. TEL 0541-28577. Ed. Dr. Gerd Steinwascher. bk.rev.circ. 1,250. (back issues avail.) **Document type:** bulletin.

943   GW   ISSN 0078-6845
OSTBAIRISCHE GRENZMARKEN. 1957. a. DM.45 (members DM.35). Universitaet Passau, Institut fuer Ostbairische Heimatforschung, Schustergasse 19-21, 94030 Passau, Germany. TEL 0851-509640. FAX 0851-509622. Ed. August Leidl. bk.rev. circ. 750. **Indexed:** RILA. **Document type:** academic/scholarly publication.

948   FI   ISSN 0473-8063
OSTERBOTTEN. (Text in Swedish) 1953. a. FIM 100. Svensk-Osterbottniska Samfundet, Hovraettsesplanaden 16 A, 65100 Vasa, Finland. Ed. Kurt Jern. circ. 500.
  Formerly (until 1964): Osterbottnisk Arsbok.

943   GW   ISSN 0030-638X
OSTERODER ZEITUNG. 1834. s-a. DM.5 per no. Kreisgemeinschaft Osterode Ostpreussen, c/o G. Biell, Ed., Kuestrinerstr. 8, 25421 Pinneberg, Germany. bk.rev.; charts; illus.; stat.; index. circ. 5,800. **Document type:** newsletter.

943   GW   ISSN 0078-687X
OSTEUROPA INSTITUT, MUNICH. VEROEFFENTLICHUNGEN. REIHE GESCHICHTE. 1953. irreg., vol.63, 1993. Harrassowitz Verlag, Taunusstr. 14, 65183 Wiesbaden, Germany. TEL 0611-530-0. FAX 0611-530570. TELEX 4186135. (Subscr. to: Postfach 2929, 65019 Wiesbaden, Germany) Ed. E. Hoesch. **Document type:** monographic series.

943.7   XR   ISSN 0232-0967
OSTRAVA.* 1963. irreg. (Archiv Mesta Ostravy) Nakladatelstvi Profil, c/o Artia, Ve Smeckach 30, 111 27 Prague 1, Czech Republic. bk.rev.; bibl

947   RU
OTECHESTVENNAYA ISTORIYA. (Text in Russian; contents page in English) 1957. bi-m. $68. (Rossiiskaya Akademiya Nauk, Institut Istorii) Izdatel'stvo Nauka, 90 Profsoyuznaya ul., 117864 Moscow, Russia. (Dist. by: Mezhdunarodnaya Kniga, ul. Dimitrova D.39, 113095 Moscow, Russia; Dist. in U.S. by: Victor Kamkin Inc., 4956 Boiling Brook Pkwy, Rockville, MD 20852. TEL 301-881-5973) Ed. I.D. Koval'chenko. bk.rev.; bibl.; stat.; index. circ. 9,500. **Indexed:** Amer.Hist.& Life, Arts & Hum.Cit.Ind., Curr.Cont., Curr.Dig.Sov.Press, Hist.Abstr., Lang.& Lang.Behav.Abstr., Numis.Lit.
  Formerly (until 1992): Istoriya S.S.S.R. (ISSN 0131-3150)

025.17   RU   ISSN 0869-4427
CD1710
OTECHESTVENNYE ARCHIVY. (Text in Russian; contents page in French) 1959. bi-m. $50. Glavnoe Arkhivnoe Upravlenie, B. Pirogovskaya 17, Moscow G-435, Russia. TEL 246-03-00. Ed. S.I. Kuzmin. adv.; bk.rev.; illus.; index. circ. 5,000. (also avail. in microfiche from IDC) **Indexed:** Amer.Hist.& Life, Hist.Abstr., Numis.Lit.
  Formerly: Sovetskie Arkhivy (ISSN 0038-5166); Supersedes (in 1966): Voprosy Arkhivovedeniya.

949.2   NE   ISSN 0030-6738
OUD UTRECHT. MAANDBLAD. 1926. m. fl.47 to individuals; non-profit institutions fl.80; commercial organizations fl.100. Vereniging Oud Utrecht - Old Utrecht Society, Alex. Numankade 199, 3572 KW Utrecht, Netherlands. TEL 31-30-736611. FAX 31-30-711814. adv.; bk.rev. circ. 1,900. **Indexed:** Curr.Cont. **Document type:** academic/scholarly publication.

940   US
OXFORD HISTORICAL MONOGRAPHS. irreg. price varies. Oxford University Press, 200 Madison Ave., New York, NY 10016. TEL 212-679-7300. Ed.Bd. **Document type:** monographic series.

949.7 890   UK   ISSN 0078-7256
PG2025
OXFORD SLAVONIC PAPERS. a. price varies. Oxford University Press, Oxford Journals, Walton St., Oxford OX2 6DP, England. TEL 0865-56767. FAX 0865-56646. TELEX 837330-OXPRES-G. (U.S. subscr. to: Oxford University Press Inc., 2001 Evans Rd., Cary, NC 27513. TEL 919-677-0977) Ed.Bd. (also avail. in microform from UMI) **Indexed:** Amer.Hist.& Life, Bibl.Ling., Br.Hum.Ind., Hist.Abstr., M.L.A. **Document type:** academic/scholarly publication.

942   UK   ISSN 0260-7565
OXFORDSHIRE LOCAL HISTORY. 1980. 2/yr. £5. Oxfordshire Local History Association, 19 Templars Close, Wheatley, Oxford OX33 1PA, England. Ed. John Brooks. adv.; bk.rev.; circ. 300 (controlled). **Document type:** academic/scholarly publication.
  Description: Reviews ongoing research in the history of Oxfordshire.

941   UK
OXFORDSHIRE RECORD SOCIETY. 1919. irreg. £8($16) Bodleian Library, Oxford OX1 3BG, England. circ. 350. **Document type:** monographic series.

OXONIENSIA. see ARCHAEOLOGY

940   IT   ISSN 0394-5359
PADANIA; storia cultura istituzioni. 1987. 2/yr. L.48000 (Europe L.55000; elsewhere L.80000) (effective 1993). (Istituto Storia Contemporanea, Movimento Operaio e Contadino, Ferrara) Rosenberg & Sellier, Via Andrea Doria, 14, 10123 Turin, Italy. TEL 011-561-39-07. FAX 011-532188. Ed. Angelo Varni. adv.; bk.rev. circ. 600. (back issues avail.)
  Description: Covers history, culture, and institutions of the Padana region of northern Italy.

940 282   GW   ISSN 0340-7993
PAEPSTE UND PAPSTTUM. (Text in English, German and Italian) 1971. irreg., vol.27, 1994. Anton Hiersemann Verlag, Rosenbergstr. 113, 70193 Stuttgart, Germany. TEL 0711-638265. FAX 0711-6369010. (Subscr. to: Postfach 140155, 70071 Stuttgart, Germany) **Document type:** academic/scholarly publication, monographic series.

HISTORY — HISTORY OF EUROPE

947　　　　　　BU　ISSN 0204-4021
PALAEOBULGARICA. (Text in Bulgarian, English, French, German and Russian) 1977. q. 156 lv.($55) to US subscribers. Bulgarska Akademiia na Naukite, 15 Noemvri St. 1, 1040 Sofia, Bulgaria. bk.rev. (reprint service avail. from IRC) **Indexed:** Bibl.Ling. **Document type:** academic/scholarly publication.
—BLDSC (0168.091000).

943.8 329.9　　　PL　ISSN 0137-3234
CT1230
PAMIETNIKARSTWO POLSKIE. 1971. 2/yr. (Panstwowe Wydawnictwo Naukowe Oddzial w Lodzi) Ars Polona-Ruch, Krakowskie Przedmiescie 7, 00-068 Warsaw, Poland. bk.rev.; bibl. **Indexed:** Potato Abstr.

947 915　　　　KR
PAM'IYATKY UKRAINY. (Text in Ukrainian) 1969. 4/yr. 2.40 Rub. Ukrains'ke Tovarystvo Okhorony Pamiatok Istorii ta Kul'tury, 8-1 Borichiv Tik St., Kiev 70, Ukraine. Ed. Anatoly Syrykov. adv.; bk.rev. circ. 80,000.
Formerly (until 1989): Pam'iyatnyky Ukrainy.

947 720　　　　RU　ISSN 0207-2203
PAMYATNIKI OTECHESTVA. (Text in Russian; summaries in English) 1980. q. $20. (Vserossiiskoye Obshchestvo Okhrany Pamyatnikov - All-Russian Society for Conservation of Monuments and Memorial Buildings) Izdatel'stvo Pamyatniki Otechestva, 103009 Tverskoi bul. 16, 103009 Moscow, Russia. TEL 7-095-2915584. FAX 7-095-2912424. Ed. Sergei Razgonoff. adv.: page $1000; adv. contact: Olga Babanova. illus. circ. 50,000.
Description: Publishes articles on Russian history, architecture and art.

943.6　　　　AU　ISSN 0250-1562
PANNONIA; Magazin fuer Europaeische Zusammenarbeit. 1973. m. S.140. Edition Roetzer GmbH, Mattersburger Str. 25, A-7000 Eisenstadt, Austria. TEL 02682-62494. adv.; bk.rev. circ. 4,000. **Document type:** bulletin.

940 929　　　　UK
PANORAMA. 1956. a. 40p.($2) Thurrock Local History Society, Thurrock Museums Dept., Orsett Rd., Grays, Essex RM17 5DX, England. Ed. Randal Bingley. circ. 400. **Indexed:** Br.Archaeol.Abstr.

940　　　　CN　ISSN 0228-8605
PAPERS IN MEDIAEVAL STUDIES. 1981. irreg., vol.13, 1991. price varies. Pontifical Institute of Mediaeval Studies, 59 Queen's Park Crescent E., Toronto, ON M5S 2C4, Canada. TEL 416-926-7144. FAX 416-926-7258. (Dist. outside N. America and UK by: N.V. Brepols, Steenweg op Tielen 68, 2300 Turnhout, Belgium. TEL 32-14-415463. FAX 32-14-428919) (back issues avail.) **Document type:** monographic series.
—BLDSC (6396.960050).

943　　　　GW　ISSN 0078-9410
PAPYROLOGICA COLONIENSIA. 1964. irreg. price varies. (Rheinisch-Westfaelische Akademie der Wissenschaften) Westdeutscher Verlag GmbH, Postfach 300944, 51338 Leverkusen, Germany. TEL 0611-1602-25. FAX 0611-160229. **Document type:** monographic series.

940　　　　IT　ISSN 1121-5542
PARALLELI. 1991. bi-m. L.57000 (foreign L.90000). Editoriale Domus, Via A. Grandi 5-7, 20089 Rozzano (MI), Italy. TEL 06-824721. FAX 02-3498293. Ed. Claudio Serra.

945 914　　　　IT
PARMA NELL'ARTE. 1969. s-a. L.7000. Comitato Parmense per l'Arte, Via Cavestro 14, 43100 Parma, Italy. Ed.Bd. adv.; bk.rev.
Supersedes (1951-1966): Parma per l'Arte.

PARNASSOS; an annual literary journal. see *HUMANITIES: COMPREHENSIVE WORKS*

940　　　　FR
PAROISSES ET COMMUNES DE FRANCE. a. price varies. C N R S Editions, 20-22 rue St. Amand, 75015 Paris, France. TEL 45-33-16-00. FAX 45-33-92-13. TELEX 200 356 F. adv.; bk.rev.; index; circ. 1,500 (controlled).

947 915　　　　AI　ISSN 0130-6812
DS161
PATMA-BANASIRAKAN ANDES/ISTORIKO-FILOLOGICHESKII ZHURNAL. (Text in Armenian and Russian) 1958. 4/yr. 17.60 Rub. Akademiya Nauk Armenii, Pr. Marshala Bagramayana, 24, 375019 Erevan, Armenia. TEL 52-45-80. TELEX 243344. bk.rev.; index, cum.index: 1958-1967. (also avail. in microfiche from IDC) **Indexed:** Amer.Hist.& Life, Bibl.Ling., Hist.Abstr., M.L.A., Numis.Lit.

940 200　　　　US　ISSN 0737-738X
PATRISTIC AND BYZANTINE REVIEW. (Text in English, French; summaries in English, Greek, Italian) 1982. q. $50. American Institute for Patristic and Byzantine Studies, RR 1, Minuet Lane, Box 353-A, Kingston, NY 12401. TEL 914-336-8797. Ed. Constantine Tsirpanlis. adv.; bk.rev.; index. circ. 1,500. (back issues avail.) **Indexed:** Rel.& Theol.Abstr. (1989-), Rel.Ind.One.
—BLDSC (6412.975800).

944　　　　FR　ISSN 0031-3386
PAYS BAS-NORMAND. 1908. q. 250 F. (effective 1994). Pays Bas-Normand, Societe d'Art et d'Histoire, B.P. 232, 61103 Flers Cedex, France. TEL 33-64-33-87. Ed. Yves Letortu. bk.rev.; bibl.; illus.; index, cum.index. circ. 1,800.
Description: Focuses on the wooded regions of Orne and Normandy.

944　　　　FR　ISSN 0031-3394
PAYS LORRAIN. 1904. q. 200 F. Societe d'Archeologie Lorraine, Palais Ducal, Grande-Rue 64, Nancy, France. TEL 8332-1874. FAX 83-37-99-15. (Co-sponsor: Musee Historique Lorrain) Ed. P. Sadoul. adv.; bk.rev.; bibl.; illus.; index. circ. 1,700. **Indexed:** RILA.
Description: Presents the archeology, arts, history, geography, literature, sciences and folklore of the province.

970　　　　US　ISSN 0149-1547
HD101
PEASANT STUDIES. 1972. q. $25 to individuals; institutions $30. University of Utah, Department of History, Salt Lake City, UT 84112. TEL 801-581-6121. Ed. Anand A. Yang. adv.; bk.rev.; bibl. circ. 1,200. **Indexed:** A.I.C.P., Abstr.Anthropol., Amer.Hist.& Life, Anthropol.Lit., Asian-Pac.Econ.Lit., ASSIA, E.I., Hist.Abstr., Lang.& Lang.Behav.Abstr., Mid.East: Abstr.& Ind., Rural Devel.Abstr., Rural Recreat.Tour.Abstr., World Agri.Econ.& Rural Sociol.Abstr.
—BLDSC (6413.930000); Faxon; UnCover.
Formerly: Peasant Studies Newsletter.

948　　　　FI
PEDERSORE. (Text in Swedish) 1909. a. Jakobstads Tidning, P.O. Box 22, 68600 Jakobstad, Finland. FAX 967-18277. cum.index 1909-48.

942　　　　UK
PEMBROKESHIRE HISTORICAL SOCIETY. JOURNAL. 1985. a. £5. Pembrokeshire Historical Society, Eastham, Dolau Dwrbach, Fishguard, Dyfed SA65 9RN, Wales. TEL 0348-873316. Ed. R. Turvey. bk.rev.; illus. circ. 400. (back issues avail.) **Document type:** proceedings.

943.6　　　　AU
PENZINGER MUSEUMSBLAETTER. 1963. 4/yr. Museumsverein Penzing, Penzingerstr. 59, 1140 Vienna, Austria.

949.7　　　　YU　ISSN 0553-6979
PEPARIMI. 1946. 6/yr. N G B G Rilindija, Rruga Beogradi 29-a, 38000 Pristina, Yugoslavia. bk.rev.

940 410　　　　IE　ISSN 0332-1592
CB351
PERITIA. (Text in English, French and German) 1982. a. $30. (Medieval Academy of Ireland, IE) N.V. Brepols, Steenweg op Tielen 68, 2300 Turnhout, Belgium. TEL 32-14-402500. FAX 32-14-428919. TELEX 34182. (Editorial addr.: c/o Department of Irish History, University College, Cork, Ireland. TEL 353-21-276871) Ed. Donnchadh O. Corrain. adv.; bk.rev. circ. 900. (back issues avail.) **Indexed:** Bibl.Ling., Br.Archaeol.Abstr., M.L.A. **Document type:** academic/scholarly publication.
—BLDSC (6426.457500).

943　　　　GW　ISSN 0031-6679
DD801.P422
PFAELZER HEIMAT; Zeitschrift fuer pfaelzische Landeskunde. 1950. q. DM.36. Pfaelzische Gesellschaft zur Foerderung der Wissenschaften in Speyer, Gr. Pfaffengasse 7, 67346 Speyer, Germany. Ed. Rudolf Fendler. bk.rev.; charts; illus.; index. circ. 6,000. **Indexed:** Biol.Abstr., Numis.Lit. **Document type:** bulletin.
—BLDSC (6437.500000).

941　　　　UK　ISSN 0966-1115
PICTISH ARTS SOCIETY JOURNAL. 3/yr. Pictish Arts Society, 27 George Sq., Edinburgh EH8 9LD, Scotland. Ed. Niall Robertson. **Document type:** bulletin.
Formerly (until 1992): Pictish Arts Society Newsletter.

PIERS PLOWMAN STUDIES. see *LITERATURE*

945 850　　　　IT　ISSN 1122-1399
PIETRA SERENA; ricerca storica e creativita letteraria. (Supplement avail.: Quaderni di Pietra Serena (ISSN 1122-1402)) 1989. q. L.30000 (effective 1994). (Associazione Culturale Pietraserena) Nova Graficas N.C. - Masso delle Fate Edizioni, Via Cavalcanti 9-A, 50058 Signa (FI), Italy. TEL 055-8734414. FAX 055-875713. Ed. Walter Nesti. adv.: page L.350000. bk.rev. circ. 1,000.

947　　　　US
PITTSBURGH SERIES IN RUSSIAN & EAST EUROPEAN STUDIES. 1977. irreg. University of Pittsburgh Press, 127 N. Bellefield Ave., Pittsburgh, PA 15260. TEL 800-666-2211. FAX 412-624-7380. Ed. Jonathan Harris. **Document type:** monographic series.

940　　　　US
▼**THE PLANTAGENET CONNECTION.** 1993. s-a. $24 ($24 Canada; foreign $30). Heliotrope Communications, Box 1401, Arvada, CO 80001. illus. circ. 1,900.

940　　　　IT　ISSN 0394-4883
PLUTEUS. a. L.30000. Edizioni dell' Orso, Via Piacenza 66, 15100 Alessandria, Italy. Ed. Alessandro Vitale-Brovarone. bk.rev. circ. 750.

947　　　　GW
POIKILA BYZANTINA. 1981. irreg., vol.12, 1993. (Freie Universitaet Berlin, Byzantinisch-Neugriechisches Seminar) Dr. Rudolf Habelt GmbH, Am Buchenhang 1, 53115 Bonn, Germany. TEL 0228-232016. FAX 0228-232017. **Document type:** monographic series.

943.8 369.4　　　PL　ISSN 0551-2050
POKOLENIA. 1959. 4/yr. Mlodziezowa Agencja Wydawnicza, Al. Stanow Zjednoczonych 53, Warsaw, Poland. (Dist. by: Centrala Kolportazu Prasy i Wydawnictw, Ul. Towarowa 28, 00-958 Warsaw, Poland) bk.rev.; cum.index 1959-1963.
Formerly (until 1962): Komisja Historyczna Przy Komitecie Centralnym Zwiazku Mlodziezy Socjalistycznej. Biuletyn.

POLEN UND WIR; Zeitschrift fuer Deutsch-Polnische Verstaendigung. see *POLITICAL SCIENCE — International Relations*

943.8　　　　PL　ISSN 0208-7359
POLISH HISTORICAL LIBRARY. ANTHOLOGIES. MONOGRAPHS. OPERA MINORA. (Text in English, French) irreg., vol.8, 1991. price varies. (Polish Historical Society) Ossolineum, Publishing House of the Polish Academy of Sciences, Rynek 9, 50-106 Wroclaw, Poland. TEL 48-71-386-25. FAX 48-71-448-103. TELEX 0712771 OSS PL. (Dist. by: Ars Polona, Krakowskie Przedmiescie 7, 00-068 Warsaw, Poland) Ed. Marian Biskup. **Document type:** monographic series.
—BLDSC (6543.663000).
Description: Studies different aspects of Polish history - politics, culture and social life.

POLITICAL HISTORY OF RUSSIA. see *POLITICAL SCIENCE — International Relations*

POLSKA AKADEMIA NAUK. INSTYTUT HISTORII NAUKI, OSWIATY I TECHNIKI. ANALECTA. see *SOCIAL SCIENCES: COMPREHENSIVE WORKS*

HISTORY — HISTORY OF EUROPE

943.8 947   PL   ISSN 0137-3544
POLSKA AKADEMIA NAUK. INSTYTUT KRAJOW SOCJALISTYCZNYCH. BIULETYN INFORMACYJNY. 1966. q. free. Polska Akademia Nauk, Instytut Krajow Socjalistycznych, Palac Kultury i Nauki, Pok. 1706, 00-901 Warsaw, Poland. TEL 48 22 20-09-34. Ed. Wojciech Materski. bk.rev. circ. 400.

POLSKA AKADEMIA NAUK. INSTYTUT SLOWIANOZNAWSTWA. PRACE SLAWISTYCZNE. see *LINGUISTICS*

943.8   PL   ISSN 0208-4090
POLSKA MYSL POLITYCZNA XIX I XX WIEKU. (Text in Polish; summaries in English) irreg., latest vol.6, 1988. price varies. (Polish Academy of Sciences, Historical Sciences Committee) Ossolineum, Publishing House of the Polish Academy of Sciences, Rynek 9, 50-106 Wroclaw, Poland. TEL 48-71-386-25. FAX 48-71-448-103. TELEX 0712771 OSS PL. Ed. Wojciech Wrzesinski.
Document type: monographic series.
Description: Presentation of papers analyzing Polish political ideas in the 19th and 20th centuries.

DIE POMMERSCHEN LEUTE. see *ETHNIC INTERESTS*

949.5   GR
PONTIAKE HESTIA. 1950; N.S. 1975. 4/yr. $20. Somateion Panagia Soumela, Odos Metropoleos 15, Salonika, Greece.

940   CN   ISSN 0082-5328
PONTIFICAL INSTITUTE OF MEDIAEVAL STUDIES. STUDIES AND TEXTS. 1955. irreg., vol.115, 1993. price varies. Pontifical Institute of Mediaeval Studies, 59 Queen's Park Crescent E., Toronto, ON M5S 2C4, Canada. TEL 416-926-7144. FAX 416-926-7258. (Dist. outside N. America and UK by: N.V. Brepols, Steenweg op Tielen 68, 2300 Turnhout, Belgium. TEL 32-14-415463. FAX 32-14-428919) circ. 600. (back issues avail.)
Indexed: M.L.A. **Document type:** monographic series.

947   BU   ISSN 0554-7040
POREDITSA BALKANI. Title slightly varies. 1966. irreg. (Bulgarska Akademiya na Naukite) Publishing House of the Bulgarian Academy of Sciences, Ul. Akad. G. Bonchev, Bldg. 6, 1113 Sofia, Bulgaria. (Subscr. to: Hemus Foreign Trade Co., 6 Ruski Blvd., 1000 Sofia, Bulgaria) (reprint service avail. from IRC)

940   UK   ISSN 0554-7598
PORTSMOUTH PAPERS. 1967. 3/yr. price varies. Portsmouth City Records Office, 3 Museum Rd., Portsmouth PO1 2LE, England. TEL 0705-829765. FAX 0705-874079. Ed.Bd. bibl.; illus. circ. 4,000.
Document type: monographic series.
Description: Research articles on the history, politics, economy, culture, architecture, industrial development, geography, personages, and civic evolution of this city in southern England.

946.9   PO
PORTUGALIAE HISTORICA.* irreg. Universidade de Lisboa, Instituto Historico Infante Dom Henrique, Alameda da Universidade, 1699 Lisbon, Portugal.

940   GW   ISSN 0079-421X
DP501
PORTUGIESISCHE FORSCHUNGEN DER GOERRESGESELLSCHAFT. REIHE 1: AUFSAETZE ZUR PORTUGIESISCHEN KULTURGESCHICHTE. 1960. irreg. price varies. (Goerres-Gesellschaft) Aschendorffsche Verlagsbuchhandlung, Soesterstr. 13, 48155 Muenster, Germany. TEL 0251-690-0. FAX 0251-690405. Ed. Hans Flasche. **Indexed:** Bibl.Ling., M.L.A. **Document type:** monographic series.

940   GW   ISSN 0079-4228
PORTUGIESISCHE FORSCHUNGEN DER GOERRESGESELLSCHAFT. REIHE 2: MONOGRAPHIEN. 1961. irreg. price varies. (Goerres-Gesellschaft) Aschendorffsche Verlagsbuchhandlung, Soesterstr. 13, 48155 Muenster, Germany. TEL 0251-690-0. FAX 0251-690143. Ed. Hans Flasche. **Document type:** monographic series.

942   UK   ISSN 0261-8818
POYNTON LOCAL HISTORY SOCIETY NEWSLETTER. 1980. irreg. £1 per issue. Poynton Local History Society, 33 Beech Crescent, Poynton, Stockport, Cheshire SK12 1AW, England. Ed. Gillian Kendall. bk.rev.; charts. circ. 200. **Document type:** newsletter.

POZADINA. see *MILITARY*

940   PL   ISSN 0079-4651
POZNANSKIE TOWARZYSTWO PRZYJACIOL NAUK. KOMISJA HISTORYCZNA. PRACE. (Text in Polish; summaries in French, German) vol.29, 1976. irreg., vol.37, 1983. price varies. Poznanskie Towarzystwo Przyjaciol Nauk, Komisja Historyczna, Ul. Mielzynskiego 27-29, 61-725 Poznan, Poland. Ed. W.R. Rzepka. bibl.; charts; illus. circ. 750.

743.7   XR   ISSN 0232-0118
PRACE Z DEJIN PRIRODNICH VED. (Text in Czech, Slovak) 1969. irreg. avail. on exchange basis only. Ceskoslovenska Akademie Ved, Ustav Teorie a Dejin Vedy, Jilska 1, 110 00 Prague 1, Czech Republic. Ed. Jan Janko. bk.rev.; bibl.
Description: Covers natural science history in Europe.

945   IT   ISSN 0032-6925
PRATO - STORIA ED ARTE. 1960. s-a. L.15000 (foreign L.20000). Azienda di Promozione Turistica di Prato, Via Luigi Muzzi 51, 50047 Prato, Italy. FAX 607925. Dir. Mario Bellandi. bk.rev.; play rev.; bibl.; charts; illus.; stat. **Indexed:** RILA.

943.7 913   XR   ISSN 0555-0238
PRAZSKY SBORNIK HISTORICKY. 1962. a. price varies. (Archiv Hlavniho Mesta Prahy) Panorama, Halkova 1, 120 72 Prague 2, Czech Republic. (Dist. by: Artia, Ve Smeckach 30, 111 27 Prague 1, Czech Republic) Ed. Frantisek Holec. bk.rev.; bibl. circ. 1,500. **Indexed:** Numis.Lit. **Document type:** academic/scholarly publication.
Description: Essays and articles providing a variety of perspectives on the history of Prague.

945   IT   ISSN 1121-7499
PRESENTE E LA STORIA. 1972. s-a. L.30000. Istituto Storico della Resistenza in Cuneo e Provincia, Via Massimo d'Azeglio 2, 12100 Cuneo, Italy. TEL 0171-445289. Ed. Michele Calandri. adv.; bk.rev.; cum.index: 1972-1985, 1986-1991. circ. 2,000. (back issues avail.) **Document type:** academic/scholarly publication.
Formerly (until 1992): Istituto Storico della Resistenza in Cuneo e Provincia. Notiziario (ISSN 1120-0634)
Description: Contains contemporary local history connected with national and general history.

948 301.16   DK   ISSN 0106-6579
PRESSENS AARBOG. (Text in Danish, Norwegian and Swedish) 1963. a. (Dansk Pressehistorisk Selskab) C.A. Reitzels Boghandel, Noerregade 20, 1165 Copenhagen, Denmark.

943   GW   ISSN 0032-7972
PREUSSENLAND. 1963. irreg. (2-4/yr.). DM.12. N.G. Elwert Verlag, Reitgasse 7-9, 35037 Marburg, Germany. bk.rev. circ. 500. **Document type:** academic/scholarly publication.
—CCC.

PRILOZI/CONTRIBUTIONS. see *ARCHAEOLOGY*

PRILOZI ZA KNJIZEVNOST, JEZIK, ISTORIJU I FOLKLOR. see *LINGUISTICS*

949.5   US
PRINCETON MODERN GREEK STUDIES. irreg. Princeton University Press, 41 William St., Princeton, NJ 08540. TEL 609-258-4900. FAX 609-258-6305. **Document type:** monographic series.

946   SP   ISSN 0032-8472
PRINCIPE DE VIANA. (Annual supplement avail. since 1981: Suplemento de Ciencias) 1940. 3/yr. 2700 ptas. Gobierno de Navarra, Fondo de Publicaciones, Navas de Tolosa, 21, 31002 Pamplona, Spain. TEL 10-71-21. FAX 22-76-73. bk.rev.; bibl.; illus.; index.

949.7   XV   ISSN 0353-0329
PRISPEVKI ZA NOVEJSO ZGODOVINO. 1960. 2/yr. $20 (typically set in Jan.). Institut za Novejso Zgodovino, Trg Osvoboditve 1, 61000 Ljubljana, Slovenia. TEL 061-217-521. (Co-sponsor: Republiski Sekretariat za Raziskovalno Dejavnost in Tehnologijo) adv.; bk.rev.; bibl. circ. 600. **Indexed:** Amer.Hist.& Life, Hist.Abstr.
Formerly (until 1986): Prispevki za Zgodovino Delavskega Gibanja (ISSN 0555-1838)

PRO AUSTRIA ROMANA. see *ARCHAEOLOGY*

PROBLEMI SJEVERNOG JADRANA. see *ANTHROPOLOGY*

947 329.9   RU
PROBLEMY DAL'NEGO VOSTOKA/FAR EASTERN AFFAIRS. (Text in English, Japanese, Russian and Spanish) 1972. q. Institut Dal'nego Vostoka, Ul. Krasikova, 27, 117218 Moscow, V-218, Russia. bk.rev.
Indexed: Amer.Hist.& Life (until 1989), Asian-Pac.Econ.Lit., Curr.Dig.Sov.Press, Hist.Abstr. (until 1989).

947   KR   ISSN 0203-9494
PROBLEMY SLOV'IYANOZNAVSTVA. 1970. 2/yr. Izdatel'stvo Vysshaya Shkola, L'vovskoe Otdelenie, Ul. Universitetskaya 1, 290000 Lvov, Ukraine.
Indexed: Bibl.Ling.
Formerly (until 1975): Ukrains'ke Slov'ianoznavstvo.

943   US
PROGRAM ON CENTRAL AND EASTERN EUROPE WORKING PAPER SERIES. irreg. $4 per no. (foreign $5). Harvard University, Minda de Gunzburg Center for European Studies, 27 Kirkland St., Cambridge, MA 02138-2043. TEL 617-495-4303. FAX 617-495-8509. Ed. Grzegorz Ekiert. **Document type:** monographic series, academic/scholarly publication.
Description: Stimulates scholarly discussion in the field of Eastern European studies and provides a forum for the dissemination of works in progress.

943 327   GW
IHR PROGRAMM. 1975. 12/yr. DM.77. I K C Presse, Mendelssohnstr. 10, 45966 Gladbeck, Germany. TEL 02043-51832. Ed. G. Schmalbrock. adv.; bk.rev. circ. 5,500. (back issues avail.) **Document type:** academic/scholarly publication.

PROLOGUE (WASHINGTON); quarterly of the National Archives. see *HISTORY — History Of North And South America*

944   FR   ISSN 0033-1856
DC611.P951
PROVENCE HISTORIQUE. 1950. q. 180 F. (foreign 210 F.). Federation Historique de Provence, 66 B rue Saint-Sebastien, 13259 Marseille Cedex 6, France. TEL 91-57-32-12. FAX 91-57-36-49. Ed. Noel Coulet. bk.rev.; bibl.; illus.; index. circ. 1,200.
Document type: academic/scholarly publication.
—BLDSC (6937.450000).

944   FR   ISSN 0033-1880
LA PROVINCE DU MAINE. 1893. q. 280 F. Societe Historique de la Province du Maine, 26 rue des Chanoines, 72000 Le Mans, Sarthe, France. adv.; bk.rev.; bibl.; charts; illus.; index, cum.index. circ. 700.
Description: Studies the history of the province.

940   GW
PROVINZIALINSTITUT FUER WESTFAELISCHE LANDES- UND VOLKSFORSCHUNG DES LANDSCHAFTSVERBANDES WESTFALEN-LIPPE. VEROEFFENTLICHUNGEN. 1937. irreg. price varies. Verlag Ferdinand Schoeningh GmbH, Postfach 2540, 33055 Paderborn, Germany. TEL 05251-127665. FAX 05251-127860. Eds. Alfred Hartlieb von Wallthor, Karl-Heinz Kirchhoff. **Document type:** proceedings.
Formerly: Provinzialinstitut fuer Westfaelische Landes- und Volkforschung. Veroeffentlichungen (ISSN 0171-3736)

PRUMYSLOVE OBLASTI. see *BUSINESS AND ECONOMICS — Labor And Industrial Relations*

947   PL   ISSN 0137-303X
PRZEGLAD POLONIJNY. (Text in Polish; summaries in English) 1975. q. $40. (Polska Akademia Nauk, Komitet Badania Problemow Polonii) Ossolineum, Publishing House of the Polish Academy of Sciences, Rynek 9, 50-106 Wroclaw, Poland. TEL 48-71-386-25. FAX 48-71-448-103. TELEX 0712771 OSS PL. Ed. H. Kubiak. circ. 2,800.
Indexed: Amer.Bibl.Slavic & E.Eur.Stud, Bibl.Ling.
Document type: academic/scholarly publication.
—BLDSC (6944.570000).
Description: Studies and materials concerning Polish emigration patterns and ethnic Polish emigrants in different countries of the world.

PRZEGLAD ZACHODNI. see *POLITICAL SCIENCE — International Relations*

PUBBLICAZIONI DI VERIFICHE. see *PHILOSOPHY*

HISTORY — HISTORY OF EUROPE

943 GW ISSN 0171-3426
PULHEIMER BEITRAEGE ZUR GESCHICHTE UND HEIMATKUNDE. 1977. a. DM.20. Verein fuer Geschichte und Heimatkunde e.V., Adamistr. 9, 50259 Pulheim-Brauweiler, Germany. TEL 02234-82567. illus. circ. 1,800. **Document type:** academic/scholarly publication.
  Description: History of the area of Koeln and the Rhineland region.

930 930.1 IT
PUTEOLI; studi di storia antica. (Text in English, French, German and Italian) 1977. a. price varies. Azienda Autonoma di Cura, Soggiorno e Turismo, Via Campi Flegrei (S.S. Domiziana), 3, 80078 Pozzuoli (NA), Italy. Ed. Giuseppe Camodeca. bk.rev. circ. 1,000. (back issues avail.)

944 FR ISSN 0033-474X
PYRENEES. no.9, Jan.-Mar., 1952. q. 150 F. to non-members. Musee Pyreneen du Chateau-Fort de Lourdes, Societe des Amis du Musee, c/o Louis Anglade, B.P. 204, 64002 Pau Cedex, France. Ed. A.J. Dussert. adv.; bk.rev.; illus. circ. 2,400.

947 KR
PYTANNYA ISTORII S R S R. 1965. 2/yr. Izdatel'stvo Vysshaya Shkola, Khar'kovskoe Otdelenie, Ul. Universitetskaya 16, 310003 Kharkov, Ukraine. illus.
  —BLDSC (0042.803000).
  Formerly (until 1973): Pytannia Istorii Narodiv S R S R (ISSN 0320-8931)

945 850 IT
QUADERNI DEL CARDELLO. 1990. a. L.30000 (typically set in Oct.). (Ente "Casa di Oriani" Biblioteca di Storia Contemporanea) Angelo Longo Editore, Via Paolo Costa 33, P.O. Box 431, 48100 Ravenna, Italy. TEL 0544-217026. FAX 0544-217554. circ. 1,000. **Document type:** monographic series.
  Description: Publishes studies on Italian culture, history and literature in the 19th century.

945 IT
QUADERNI DELL'ATLANTE LESSICALE TOSCANO. 1983. irreg., vol.8, 1993. price varies. Casa Editrice Leo S. Olschki, Casella Postale 66, 50100 Florence, Italy. TEL 055-6530684. FAX 055-6530214. **Indexed:** Bibl.Ling. **Document type:** monographic series.

945 IT
QUADERNI DI CULTURA MATERIALE. 1977. irreg., latest vol.3. L'Erma di Bretschneider, Via Cassiodoro 19, 00193 Rome, Italy. TEL 06-687-41-27. FAX 06-687-41-29. Ed. Andrea Carandini.

940 IT
QUADERNI DI CULTURA MEDIOLATINA. 1991. irreg., no.9, 1993. price varies. (Fondazione Ezio Franceschini) Centro Italiano di Studi sull'Alto Medioevo, Palazzo Ancaiani, 06049 Spoleto, Italy. TEL 0743-220418. FAX 0743-223507. Ed. Claudio Leonardi. **Document type:** monographic series.

945 850 IT ISSN 1122-1402
▼**QUADERNI DI PIETRA SERENA.** (Supplement to: Pietra Serena (ISSN 1122-1399) 1992. q. (Associazione Culturale Pietra Serena) Nova Graficas N.C. - Masso delle Fate Edizioni, Via Cavalcanti 9-A, 50058 Signa (FI), Italy. TEL 055-8734414. FAX 055-875713. **Document type:** monographic series.

945 300 IT ISSN 0066-2283
QUADERNI INTERNAZIONALI DI STORIA ECONOMICA E SOCIALE/INTERNATIONAL JOURNAL OF ECONOMIC AND SOCIAL HISTORY/CAHIERS INTERNATIONAUX D'HISTOIRE ECONOMIQUE ET SOCIALE. (Text in English, French, German, Italian, Spanish) 1960. a. 80 Fr. Istituto Italiano per la Storia dei Movimenti Sociali e delle Structure Sociali, Via G. B. Ruoppolo 69, Naples, Italy. (And Librairie Droz, 11, rue Massot, CH-1211 Geneva 12, Switzerland.) Ed. Domenico Demarco. adv.; bk.rev. (back issues avail.) **Indexed:** Amer.Hist.& Life, Hist.Abstr.
  Formerly: Annali di Storia Economica e Sociale.

945 IT ISSN 0392-1875
QUADERNI MEDIEVALI. 1976. s-a. L.30000 (foreign L.45000) (effective 1994). Edizioni Dedalo s.r.l., Casella Postale 362, 70100 Bari, Italy. TEL 080-5311413. FAX 080-5311414. (Edit. addr.: Via Che Guevara 37D, 70124 Bari, Italy. TEL 080-5510445) Dir. Giosue Musca. circ. 4,000.
  Description: Promotes the image of the middle ages to the modern mass audience.

945 IT
QUADERNI SARDI DI STORIA. 1980. irreg., no.5, 1986. L.15000. Libreria Dessi, Largo Cavallotti 17, 07100 Sassari, Italy. TEL 079-231673. Ed.Bd. **Indexed:** P.A.I.S.For.Lang.Ind.

QUADERNS D'HISTORIA TARRACONENSE. see ARCHAEOLOGY

945 IT ISSN 0393-6082
QUALESTORIA. 1973. 3/yr. L.40000 (foreign L.70000) (effective 1993). Istituto Regionale per la Storia del Movimento di Liberazione nel Friuli - Venezia Giulia, Salita di Gretta 38, 34136 Trieste, Italy. TEL 040-44004. Ed. Giovanni Miccoli.
  Formerly (until 1977): Istituto Regional per la Storia del Movimento di Liberazione nel Friuli Venezia Giulia. Bollettino (ISSN 0393-6031)

949.4 SZ ISSN 0079-9076
QUELLEN UND FORSCHUNGEN ZUR BASLER GESCHICHTE. 1966. irreg., no.14, 1992. price varies. (Staatsarchiv) Friedrich Reinhardt Verlag, Missionsstr. 36, CH-4012 Basel, Switzerland. Ed. Josef Zwicker. circ. 500.

940 GW ISSN 0170-3595
QUELLEN UND STUDIEN ZUR GESCHICHTE DES OESTLICHEN EUROPA. irreg., vol.39, 1993. price varies. (Arbeitskreis der Osteuropahistoriker an den Hochschulen des Landes Nordrhein-Westfalen) Franz Steiner Verlag Wiesbaden GmbH, Birkenwaldstr. 44, 70191 Stuttgart, Germany. TEL 0711-2582-0. FAX 0711-2582290. TELEX 723636-DAZ-D. (Subscr. to: Postfach 101061, 70009 Stuttgart, Germany) Ed. Helmut Altrichter. **Document type:** monographic series.

940 GW ISSN 0079-9114
QUELLEN UND STUDIEN ZUR GESCHICHTE OSTEUROPAS. 1958. irreg., vol.31, 1993. price varies. Akademie Verlag GmbH, Muehlenstr. 33-34, 13187 Berlin, Germany. TEL 030-47889348. FAX 030-47889357. Eds. Eduard Winter, Heinz Lemke. **Document type:** monographic series.
  Description: Monographs on the history of Eastern European states and their relations with Germany.

940 AU
QUELLEN ZUR GESCHICHTE DES 19. UND 20. JAHRHUNDERTS. (Text in English and German) 1977. irreg. Wolfgang Neugebauer Verlag GmbH, Kalvariengurtel 62, A-8020 Graz, Austria. TEL 05522-74770. (Subscr. to: Kreuzgasse 6, A-6800 Feldkirch, Austria) Ed. Fritz Fellner. (back issues avail.) **Document type:** monographic series.

943.6 AU
QUELLEN ZUR GESCHICHTE OBEROESTERREICHS. 1987. irreg. Oberoesterreichisches Landesarchiv, Anzengruberstr. 19, A-4020 Linz, Austria. TEL 0732-6555230. FAX 0732-655523-4619. **Document type:** monographic series.

944 FR ISSN 0335-3958
QUERCY RECHERCHE. 1974. bi-m. 45 F. Association Quercy Recherche, B.P. 123, 46005 Cahors, France. TEL 65-22-58-63. Ed. Jean-Luc Obereiner. adv.; bk.rev.; bibl.; illus.

940 PL
QUESTIONES MEDII AEVI. (Text in English, French, German) 1977. irreg., vol.3, 1986. price varies. (Uniwersytet Warszawski, Instytut Historyczny) Wydawnictwa Uniwersytetu Warszawskiego, Ul. Obozna 8, 00-032 Warsaw, Poland. (Dist. by: Ars Polona, Krakowskie Przedmiescie 7, 00-068 Warsaw, Poland) Ed. Henryk Samsonowicz. circ. 500.

943 GW ISSN 0342-2860
RAD UND SPARREN. 1975. s-a. DM.8. Historischer Verein Rhein-Main-Taunus e.V., Fischbacherstr. 29, 65779 Kelkheim, Germany. (Subscr. to: Verlag Dr. Waldemar Kramer, Postfach 600445, 60344 Frankfurt a.M., Germany) adv.; bk.rev. circ. 1,000. **Document type:** academic/scholarly publication.

942 UK ISSN 0306-848X
RADNORSHIRE SOCIETY. TRANSACTIONS. 1931. a. £5 to individuals; institutions £6. Radnorshire Society, c/o Coleg Powys, Llandrindod Wells, Powys LD1 5ES, Wales. bk.rev.; index: 1956-1980. circ. 500. **Indexed:** Br.Archaeol.Abstr., Br.Hum.Ind. **Document type:** academic/scholarly publication.
  —BLDSC (8994.450000).

948 DK ISSN 0106-9616
RAETHINGE-POSTEN. 1978. a. membership. Ringe Museumsforening, Ringe Museum, 5750 Ringe, Denmark. (Co-sponsor: Ringe Lokalhistoriske Forening) illus.

RAMBAM. see ETHNIC INTERESTS

941.1 US
RAMPANT LION. 1964. 11/yr. $15 to individuals; families $15. Scottish Historic and Research Society of the Delaware Valley, 102 St. Pauls Rd., Ardmore, PA 19003-2811. TEL 610-649-4144. Ed. Blair C. Stonier. adv.; bk.rev. circ. 400. (looseleaf format; back issues avail.) **Document type:** newsletter.
  Description: Discusses all subjects related to Scotland and the isles.

945 IT ISSN 0037-2781
RASSEGNA DEGLI ARCHIVI DI STATO. 1955. q. L.125000 (effective 1993). (Ufficio Centrale Beni Archivistici) Ministero per i Beni Culturali e Ambientali, Via Gaeta, 8A, 00185 Rome, Italy. FAX 4742177. TELEX 623278. (Subscr.to: Libreria dello Stato, Piazza Verdi 10, 00198 Rome, Italy. TEL 85081) Ed. Salvatore Mastruzzi. adv.; bk.rev. circ. 2,500. **Indexed:** Amer.Hist.& Life (until 1987), Hist.Abstr. (until 1987).
  Description: Covers studies on Italian history, institutions, history of archives. Includes inventories of archival resources and information on Italian archives.

945 IT ISSN 0033-9873
DG552.A15
RASSEGNA STORICA DEL RISORGIMENTO. (Text in English, French, Italian, Spanish) 1914 q. (foreign L.60000). Istituto per la Storia del Risorgimento Italiano, Vittoriano, Piazza Venezia, 00186 Rome, Italy. TEL 06-6793526. Ed. Emilia Morelli. bk.rev.; bibl.; index, cum.index: 1914-1963. circ. 3,000. **Indexed:** Amer.Hist.& Life, Arts & Hum.Cit.Ind., Curr.Cont., Hist.Abstr., M.L.A. **Document type:** academic/scholarly publication.
  —SWETS.

945 IT ISSN 0033-9881
RASSEGNA STORICA TOSCANA. 1955. s-a. L.60000 (foreign L.76000) (effective 1994). (Societa Toscana per la Storia del Risorgimento) Casa Editrice Leo S. Olschki, Casella Postale 66, 50100 Florence, Italy. TEL 055-6530684. FAX 055-6530214. Ed. Clementina Rotondi. adv.; bk.rev.; index. **Indexed:** Amer.Hist.& Life, Arts & Hum.Cit.Ind., Hist.Abstr. **Document type:** academic/scholarly publication.

948 FI
RAUTULAISTEN LEHTI. 1968. 6/yr. Rautulaisten Pitajaseura, Kiukkulantie 12, 50600 Mikkeli 60, Finland.

352.7 FR
RECHERCHES REGIONALES (ALPES MARITIME ET CONTREE LIMITROPHE). 1961. q. 80 F. Archives Departementales des Alpes-Maritimes, Centre Administratif Departemental, 06036 Nice Cedex, France. TEL 93-18-61-71. FAX 93-18-60-46. Ed. Jean-Bernard Lacroix. bk.rev.; bibl.; charts; illus.
  Former titles: Recherche Regionales (Cote d'Azur et Contree Limitrophe); Centre de Documentation des Archives des Alpes-Maritimes. Recherches Regionales.

HISTORY — HISTORY OF EUROPE

940   FR
RECHERCHES SUR LA RENAISSANCE (PARIS). (Text in French) 1975. a. price varies. (Universite de Paris-Sorbonne, Institute de Recherches sur les Civilisations de l'Occident Moderne) Librarie Touzot, 38 rue Saint Sulpice, 75278 Paris Cedex 06, France.

943   GW   ISSN 0179-2938
RECHTSRHEINISCHES KOELN; Jahrbuch fuer Geschichte und Landeskunde. 1975. a. price varies. Geschichts und Heimatverein Rechtsrheinisches Koeln, Friedrich-Ebert-Ufer 64-70, 51143 Cologne, Germany. Eds. Gebhard Aders, Wilhelm Becker. adv.; bk.rev. circ. 2,000. **Document type:** newsletter.

942   UK   ISSN 0034-1738
RECORDS OF HUNTINGDONSHIRE. 1965. a. £2.35 per no. Huntingdonshire Local History Society, 7 Post St., Godmanchester, Huntingdon, Cambs. PE18 8BA, England. Ed. J. Hadley. bk.rev.; abstr.; charts; illus. circ. 350. **Indexed:** Br.Archaeol.Abstr. **Document type:** academic/scholarly publication.
—BLDSC (7325.704000).

940 282   UK   ISSN 0034-1932
BX1491.A1
RECUSANT HISTORY. 1957. 2/yr. £15($30) Catholic Record Society, c/o Secretary L. Gooch, 12 Melbourne Place, Wolsingham, Co. Durham DL13 3EH, England. Ed.Bd. adv.; index, cum.index every 2 yrs. circ. 800. (back issues avail.) **Indexed:** Amer.Hist.& Life, Br.Hum.Ind., CERDIC, Hist.Abstr.
—BLDSC (7331.155000); Faxon; UnCover; SWETS.

945   IT   ISSN 0393-8034
REGGIO STORIA. 1978. q. L.18000 (foreign L.30000) (effective 1992). (Societa Reggiana di Studi Storici) Edizioni Ediarte, Viale Umberto I 17-A, 42100 Reggio Emilia, Italy. Ed. Gino Badini. adv.; bk.rev. circ. 3,300. (also avail. in microform)

943   GW
REGIONALMUSEUM XANTEN. FUEHRER UND SCHRIFTEN. 1975. irreg., no.37, 1994. (Regionalmuseum Xanten) Rheinland Verlag GmbH, Abtei Brauweiler, Postfach 2140, 50250 Pulheim, Germany. TEL 02234-8051. FAX 02234-82503. (Dist. by: Dr. Rudolf Habelt GmbH, Am Buchenhang 1, 53115 Bonn, Germany. TEL 0228-232016. FAX 0228-232017) **Document type:** monographic series.

943.7   XR
REGIONALNI MUZEUM V TEPLICICH. ZPRAVY A STUDIE. 1965. a. price varies. Regionalni muzeum v Teplicich, Zamecke Nam 14, 415 01 Teplice, Czech Republic. TEL 0417-250-85.
Former titles (until 1991): Krajske Muzeum v Teplicich. Zpravy a Studie (ISSN 0231-7648); Oblastni Vlastivedne Muzeum v Teplicish. Zpravy a Studie.

940   US   ISSN 0897-7836
RENAISSANCE AND BAROQUE: STUDIES AND TEXTS. irreg. Peter Lang Publishing, Inc., 62 W. 45th St., 4th Fl., New York, NY 10036. TEL 212-302-6740. FAX 212-302-7574. Ed. Eckhard Berstein. **Document type:** academic/scholarly publication.

RENAISSANCE AND REFORMATION/RENAISSANCE ET REFORME. see *LITERATURE*

943   GW
RENDSBURGER JAHRBUCH. 1951. a. DM.40. Kreisverein fuer das Museum in Rendsburg, Arsenalstr. 2-10, 24768 Rendsburg, Germany. TEL 04331-206632. circ. 1,400.

940   FR   ISSN 0080-1151
REPERTOIRE INTERNATIONAL DES MEDIEVISTES. 1965. irreg. 350 F.($28.80) Centre d'Etudes Superieures de Civilisation Medievale, Hotel Berthelot, 24, rue de la Chaine, 86000 Poitiers, France. adv.; bk.rev.; cum.index.

940   GW   ISSN 0724-9578
REPERTORIEN ZUR ERFORSCHUNG DER FREUHEN NEUZEIT. 1977. irreg., vol.13, 1993. price varies. Harrassowitz Verlag, Taunusstr. 14, 65183 Wiesbaden, Germany. TEL 0611-530-0. FAX 0611-530570. TELEX 4186135. (Subscr. to: Postfach 2929, 65019 Wiesbaden, Germany) Ed.Bd. **Document type:** monographic series.

949.2   NE
RESPUBLICA LITERARIA NEERLANDICA. irreg., vol.8, 1993. price varies. Van Gorcum en Co. B.V., P.O. Box 43, 9400 AA Assen, Netherlands. TEL 31-5920-46846. FAX 31-5920-72064. **Document type:** monographic series.

RESTORATION & EIGHTEENTH CENTURY THEATRE RESEARCH. see *THEATER*

942   UK   ISSN 0261-5061
RETROSPECT. 1980. a. £1.50 (effective 1993). Burnley and District Historical Society, c/o Central Library, Burnley, Lancs., England. TEL 44-37115. Ed. Roger Frost. adv.; bk.rev. circ. 150. **Document type:** academic/scholarly publication.
Description: Articles on local history.

940   SW   ISSN 0348-9078
REVISIONIST HISTORY. (Text in Arabic, English, French, German, Japanese, Polish, Russian, Swedish and Spanish; summaries in English) 1980. irreg. SEK 150($20) European Human Rights, Marknadsvagen 289, S-183 34 Taby, Sweden. TEL 08-768-1398. Ed. Ditlieb Felderer. bk.rev. circ. 5,000. (back issues avail.) **Document type:** newsletter.

949.8 025   RM   ISSN 0034-7043
CD15.R8
REVISTA ARHIVELOR. 1924. q. 100 lei($28) Arhivele Statului, Directia Generala, Bd. Gheorghe Gheorghiu-Dej 29, Bucharest, Rumania. (Dist. by: Rompresfilatelia, Sectorul Export-Import Presa, P.O. Box 12-201, Calea Grivitei 64-66, Bucharest, Rumania) Ed. Mioara Tudorica. adv.; bk.rev. circ. 7,000. (also avail. in microfiche from IDC) **Indexed:** Amer.Hist.& Life, Hist.Abstr.

946 860   SP   ISSN 0214-834X
REVISTA AWRAQ. (Text in Arabic, English, French, and Spanish; summaries in English) 1978. a. 2120 ptas.($40) Instituto de Cooperacion con el Mundo Arabe, Paseo de Juan XXIII, 5, 28040 Madrid, Spain. FAX 5-35-33-98. bk.rev.; bibl.; charts; illus. circ. 2,000. (back issues avail.)
Former titles (until 1988): Awraq Yadida (ISSN 0213-6635); (until 1983): Awraq (ISSN 0210-0045)

946.9   PO   ISSN 0034-8295
REVISTA DE GUIMARAES. 1884. a. Esc.800($25) (typically set in Jan.). Sociedade Martins Sarmento, Rua de Paio Galvao, 4800 Guimaraes, Portugal. TEL 053-415969. bk.rev.; bibl.; charts; illus.; index. circ. 1,000. **Indexed:** Amer.Hist.& Life, Br.Archaeol.Abstr., Hist.Abstr.

946   SP   ISSN 0212-4416
DP203
REVISTA DE HISTORIA CONTEMPORANEA. 1982. a. price varies. Universidad de Sevilla, Departamento de Historia de Espana Moderna y Contemporanea, Servicio de Publicaciones, Valparaiso 5, 41013 Seville, Spain. TEL 954-231958. FAX 954-232245.

946   SP   ISSN 0213-9472
REVISTA DE HISTORIA DE CANARIAS. Key Title: Revista de Historia Canarias. 1924-1986 (no.175); resumed 1992. a. $20 to individuals; institutions $30. Universidad de la Laguna, Facultad de Geografia e Historia, Secretariado de Publicaciones, Edif. Central, 38071 La Laguna-Tenerife, Islas Canarias, Spain. TEL 922-25-81-27. adv. **Indexed:** Amer.Hist.& Life, Hist.Abstr.
Formerly (until 1956): Revista de Historia (ISSN 0213-9464)
Description: Devoted to the art, history and geography of the Canary Islands.

945   SP   ISSN 0044-5517
D1
REVISTA DE HISTORIA JERONIMO ZURITA. 1966. a., latest no.61-2, 1992. 1500 ptas. Institucion "Fernando el Catolico", Plaza de Espana, 2, 50004 Zaragoza, Spain. TEL 976-28-88-78. FAX 976-28-88-69. bk.rev.; charts; illus.; index, cum.index.

947   MV   ISSN 0236-3100
DK509.1
REVISTA DE ISTORIE A MOLDOVEI/MOLDAVSKII ISTORICHESKII ZHURNAL. (Text in Rumanian, Russian) 1951. 4/yr. 4.80 Rub. Academia de Stiinte a Republica Moldova, Bd. Stefan cel Mare, 1, Kishinev 277001, Moldava. bk.rev. circ. 5,300. **Indexed:** Amer.Hist.& Life (1993-), Hist.Abstr. (1993-).
—BLDSC (7862.148000).
Supersedes in part (in 1990): Akademiya Nauk Moldavskoi S.S.R. Izvestiya. Seriya Obshchestvennykh Nauk (ISSN 0321-1681)
Description: Devoted to the problems of the history of the Moldavian people.

946 020   SP   ISSN 0211-3945
REVISTA DE LIBRERIA ANTIQUARIA. vol.6, 1985. s-a. 500 ptas. Paletes, 4, 08034 Barcelona, Spain. Ed. Roser Lopez Reynals.

REVISTA DEL V CENTENARIO DEL DESCUBRIMIENTO Y DE LA EVANGELIZACION DE AMERICA. see *HISTORY* — History Of North And South America

REVISTA ESTUDIOS; revista trimestral publicada por los frailes de la orden de la merced. see *RELIGIONS AND THEOLOGY*

940   RM   ISSN 0567-6304
D1
REVISTA ISTORICA. Title varies: Studii. Revista Istorica. (Text in Rumanian; summaries in French) 1947. 12/yr. 180 lei($68) (Institutul de Istorie N. Iorga) Editura Academiei Romane, Calea Victoriei 125, 79717 Bucharest, Rumania. (Dist. by: Rompresfilatelia, Calea Grivitei 64-66, P.O. Box 12-201, 78104 Bucharest, Rumania) Ed. Serban Papacostea. bk.rev.; bibl. circ. 1,150. **Indexed:** Amer.Hist.& Life, Hist.Abstr.
Formerly (until 1990): Revista de Istorie (ISSN 0251-3099)

947   UK   ISSN 0954-6545
DK265
REVOLUTIONARY RUSSIA; journal of the Study Group on the Russian Revolution. 1988. 2/yr. £26($40) to individuals; institutions £60 ($95). Frank Cass & Co. Ltd., Gainsborough House, 11 Gainsborough Rd., London E11 1RS, England. TEL 081-530-4226. FAX 081-530-7795. Ed. John Slatter. adv.: B&W page £185; adv. contact: Anne Kidson. bk.rev.; index. (back issues avail.) **Document type:** academic/scholarly publication.
—BLDSC (7874.350310); Faxon; UnCover.
Description: Offers interdisciplinary academic approach on the history of Russia in the revolutionary period.

944   FR   ISSN 0556-7335
REVUE ANNUELLE D'HISTOIRE DU QUATORZIEME ARRONDISSEMENT DE PARIS. 1955. a. 35 F. Societe Historique du Quatorzieme Arrondissement de Paris, 2 place Ferdinand Brunot, 75675 Paris Cedex 14, France. Ed. G. N. Perroy. adv.; illus.

REVUE BELGE DE NUMISMATIQUE ET DE SIGILLOGRAPHIE. see *NUMISMATICS*

944   FR   ISSN 0035-1008
DC611.A94   CODEN: RVUAUM
REVUE D'AUVERGNE. 1884. q. 200 F. Societe des Amis de l'Universite de Clermont, 3 av. Vercingetorix, 6300 Clermont-Ferrand, France. Ed. Henri Peuchot. bk.rev.; bibl.; charts; illus.; index, cum.index 1884-1972; 1973-1982. circ. 900. (back issues avail.) **Indexed:** Amer.Hist.& Life, GeoRef., Hist.Abstr.

REVUE D'HISTOIRE DES TEXTES. see *LITERATURE*

944   FR   ISSN 0035-1059
REVUE DE COMMINGES. 1885. q. 180 F. Societe des Etudes de Comminges, 5 rue de la Republique, B.P. 15, 31801 Saint Gaudens Cedex, France. bk.rev.; bibl.; illus.; index. circ. 1,200.

944   FR   ISSN 0035-1288
REVUE DE L'AGENAIS. 1874. q. 270 F. membership. Societe Academique d'Agen, B.P. 268, 47007 Agen Cedex, France. TEL 53-47-18-04. Ed. Jean Cubelier; Pub. Georges de Sevin. bk.rev.; illus.; maps. circ. 2,800. **Document type:** academic/scholarly publication, monographic series.

HISTORY — HISTORY OF EUROPE

944   FR
REVUE DE LA SAINTONGE ET DE L'AUNIS. 1975. a. 90 F. Societe d'Archeologie et d'Histoire de la Charente Maritime, 9, rue Mauny, 17100 Saintes, France. TEL 46-74-67-75.

947.922   BE   ISSN 0991-8086
REVUE DES ETUDES GEORGIENNES ET CAUCASIENNES. (Text in English, French, German, Italian) 1948. a. 1500 BEF (effective 1994). Editions Peeters s.p.r.l., Bondgenotenlaan 153, B-3000 Louvain, Belgium. TEL 32-16-235170. FAX 32-16-228500. Ed.Bd. adv.; bk.rev. (back issues avail.) **Indexed:** A.I.C.P., Bibl.Ling. **Document type:** academic/scholarly publication.
Formerly (until 1985): Bedi Kartlisa (ISSN 0373-1537)
Description: Multidisciplinary articles on the history, archaeology, ethnology, arts, and oral and written literature of Georgia and the Caucasus region.
Refereed Serial

944 913   FR   ISSN 0035-2624
DC1
REVUE DU NORD. 1910. 5/yr. 365 F. to individuals (foreign 415 F.); institutions 465 F. (foreign 515 F.). Universite de Lille III, B.P. 149, 59653 Villeneuve d'Ascq Cedex, France. TEL 20-05-18-79. FAX 20-33-63-61. Dir. Y.M. Hilaire. bk.rev.; bibl.; charts; illus.; map, cum.index: 1910-1950, 1951-1960, 1961-1970, 1971-1980, 1981-1990. circ. 1,700. (also avail. in microfiche; reprint service avail. from SWZ) **Indexed:** Amer.Hist.& Life, Arts & Hum.Cit.Ind., Br.Archaeol.Abstr., Curr.Cont., Hist.Abstr.
—UnCover; SWETS.

940   FR   ISSN 1250-3312
REVUE DU SOUVENIR VENDEEN.* no.106, 1974. bi-m. 15 F. B.P. 204-44 rue du Paradis, 49306 Cholet, France. adv.; bk.rev.; bibl.; illus.
Formerly: Souvenir Vendeen (ISSN 1250-3304)

949.4   SZ
REVUE DU VIEUX GENEVE. 1921. a. 19 SFr. Promoedition SA, 2 rue Bovy-Lysberg, Case postale 5615, CH-1211 Geneve 11, Switzerland. TEL 022-3215466. FAX 022-3219862. Ed. Bernard Lescaze. adv.; bibl.; charts; illus. circ. 3,000. **Document type:** academic/scholarly publication.
Formerly: Almanach du Vieux Geneve.

943   FR
▼**REVUE GERMANIQUE INTERNATIONALE.** 1993. s-a. Presses Universitaires de France, Departement des Revues, 14 av. du Bois-de-l'Epine, 91003 Evry Cedex, France. TEL 60-77-82-05. FAX 60-79-20-45. TELEX PUF 600 474 F. Eds. Jacques le Rider, Michel Espagne. **Document type:** academic/scholarly publication.
Description: Studies the cultural history of Germany.

944   FR
REVUE HISTORIQUE DE BORDEAUX ET DU DEPARTEMENT DE LA GIRONDE. N.S. 1952. a. 150 F. Archives Municipales, 71 rue du Loup, 33000 Bordeaux, France. Ed. Jean Paul Avisseau. bk.rev. circ. 450. (back issues avail. (1908-1945))

REVUE HISTORIQUE ET ARCHEOLOGIQUE DU MAINE. see *ARCHAEOLOGY*

REVUE HISTORIQUE VAUDOISE. see *ARCHAEOLOGY*

REVUE INTERNATIONALE DES DROITS DE L'ANTIQUITE. see *LAW*

949.8   RM
REVUE ROUMAINE D'HISTOIRE. vol.19, 1980. 4/yr. 160 lei($56) (Academia Romana) Editura Academiei Romane, Calea Victoriei 125, 79717 Bucharest, Rumania. (Dist. by: Rompresfilatelia, Calea Grivitei 64-66, P.O. Box 12-201, 78104 Bucharest, Rumania) **Indexed:** Arts & Hum.Cit.Ind., Bibl.Ling., Numis.Lit.

943 398 572   GW   ISSN 0556-8218
RHEINISCH-WESTFAELISCHE ZEITSCHRIFT FUER VOLKSKUNDE. 1954. a. DM.38. Volkskundliche Abteilung Institut fuer Geschichtliche Landeskunde der Rheinlande, Universitaet Bonn, Am Hofgarten 22, 53113 Bonn, Germany. TEL 0228-737618. FAX 0228-737562. Ed.Bd. bk.rev. **Document type:** academic/scholarly publication.

943   GW
RHEINISCHE FREILICHTMUSEUM - LANDESMUSEUM FUER VOLKSKUNDE KOMMERN. FUEHRER UND SCHRIFTEN. 1966. irreg., no.50, 1993. (Rheinische Freilichtmuseum - Landesmuseum fuer Volkskunde Kommern) Rheinland Verlag GmbH, Abtei Brauweiler, Postfach 2140, 50250 Pulheim, Germany. TEL 02234-8051. FAX 02234-82503. (Dist. by: Dr. Rudolf Habelt GmbH, Am Buchenhang 1, 53115 Bonn, Germany. TEL 0228-232016. FAX 0228-232017) **Document type:** monographic series.

943 398   GW   ISSN 0342-1805
RHEINISCHE HEIMATPFLEGE. 4/yr. (Verband Rheinischer Heimatmuseen) Rheinland Verlag GmbH, Abtei Brauweiler, Postfach 2140, 50250 Pulheim, Germany. TEL 02234-8051. FAX 02234-82503. (Subscr. to: Dr. Rudolf Habelt GmbH, Am Buchenhang 1, 53115 Bonn, Germany. TEL 0228-232016. FAX 0228-232017) **Document type:** academic/scholarly publication.

943   GW   ISSN 0035-4473
DD491.R4
RHEINISCHE VIERTELJAHRSBLAETTER. 1931. q. DM.56. (Universitaet Bonn, Institut fuer Geschichtliche Landeskunde der Rheinlande) Bouvier Verlag, Am Hof 28, 53113 Bonn, Germany. TEL 0228-7290141. FAX 0228-7290179. bk.rev. (reprint service avail. from UMI) **Indexed:** Amer.Hist.& Life, Bibl.Cart., Bibl.Ling., Hist.Abstr., M.L.A., Numis.Lit. **Document type:** academic/scholarly publication.

948   DK   ISSN 0108-0806
RIBE STIFTSBOG. 1970. a. DKK 35. Stiftsoevrigheds-og Bispekontoret, Korsbroedregade 7, 6760 Ribe, Denmark.
Formerly: Ribe Stift.

942.04   UK   ISSN 0048-8267
DA260
RICARDIAN. 1961. q. £9. Richard 3rd Society, 17 Enfield Cloisters, Fanshaw St., London N1 6LD, England. Ed. Anne F. Sutton. adv.; bk.rev.; illus.; cum.index: 1961-1973, 1974-1978, 1979-1984, 1985-1990. circ. 4,400. **Indexed:** Amer.Hist.& Life, Hist.Abstr. **Document type:** academic/scholarly publication.
—BLDSC (7963.794500).

942   US
RICARDIAN REGISTER. 1950. q. $30. Richard III Society, Inc., 4934 S. Galvez, New Orleans, LA 70125. TEL 504-897-9673. FAX 504-897-0125. TELEX 784011. Ed. Carole Rike. adv.; bk.rev. circ. 800. (back issues avail.) **Document type:** newsletter.
Description: Covers English Medieval history.

RICERCHE PER LA STORIA RELIGIOSA DI ROMA. see *RELIGIONS AND THEOLOGY*

945   IT   ISSN 0035-5070
RICERCHE STORICHE (REGGIO EMILIA); rivista di storia della Resistenza Reggiana e della societa contemporanea. 1967. 3/yr. L.10000($12) (foreign L.15000). Istituto per la Storia della Resistenza Reggio Emilia, Via Dante 11, Reggio Emilia, Italy. Ed.Bd. bk.rev.; bibl.; illus. circ. 1,000.

945   IT
RIETI. 1973. bi-m. L.6000. Associazione Culturale della Provincia di Rieti, Via Roma, 36, Rieti, Italy. illus.

940   NE   ISSN 0066-1295
RIJKSINSTITUUT VOOR OORLOGSDOCUMENTATIE. MONOGRAFIEEN. irreg. price varies. Kluwer Academic Publishers, Postbus 17, 3300 AA Dordrecht, Netherlands. TEL 31-78-334911. FAX 31-78-334254. TELEX 29245 KAPG NL. (Dist. by: Kluwer Academic Publishers Group, P.O. Box 322, 3300 AH Dordrecht, Netherlands. TEL 31-78-524400; N. Amer.ica dist. addr.: Box 358, Accord Sta., Hingham, MA 02018-0358. TEL 617-871-6600) **Document type:** monographic series.
Refereed Serial

RINASCIMENTO. see *HUMANITIES: COMPREHENSIVE WORKS*

948   DK
RINGKOEBING AARBOG. 1926. a. A. Rasmussens Bogtrykkeri, 6950 Ringkoebing, Denmark. FAX 45-97-324056. Eds. S.A. Jacobsen, Helle Rasmussen.

945   IT   ISSN 0035-5607
DG552.A15
RISORGIMENTO. 1949. 3/yr. L.25000 (foreign L.40000). Comune di Milano, "Amici del Museo del Risorgimento", Via Borgonuovo 23, 20121 Milan, Italy. TEL 02-8693549. FAX 02-72001483. Ed. Roberto Guerri. adv.; bk.rev.; index. circ. 400. **Indexed:** Amer.Hist.& Life, Arts & Hum.Cit.Ind., Curr.Cont., Hist.Abstr.
Description: Forum on 19th and 20th century Italian and European history.

945 055   IT   ISSN 0393-4624
RIVISTA DALMATICA. 1899. q. L.30000 (foreign L.35000) (effective Jan. 1991). Associazione Nazionale Dalmata, Archivio Dalmato della Societa Dante Alighieri, Piazza di Firenze, 27, 00186 Rome, Italy. TEL 06-6873686. Ed. Nicolo Luxardo de Franchi. adv.; bk.rev. circ. 750. **Indexed:** M.L.A.
Description: Covers the history, literature, arts, folklore and traditions of Dalmatia.

945   IT
RIVISTA DI ARCHEOLOGIA, STORIA E COSTUME. 1973. 4/yr. L.30000 membership (effective 1991). Istituto Storico Lucchese, Cortile Francesco Carrara 12, Casella Postale 315, 55100 Lucca, Italy. TEL 0583-55290. Ed. Guglielmo Lera.

945   SZ
RIVISTA DI BELLINZONA. m. 39.50 Fr. Edizion Casagrande SA, Casella Postale 1291, CH-6500 Bellinzona, Switzerland.

RIVISTA DI STORIA DELLA CHIESA IN ITALIA. see *RELIGIONS AND THEOLOGY*

945   IT   ISSN 0035-6603
RIVISTA DI STUDI LIGURI/REVUE D'ETUDES LIGURES. (Text in English, French, Italian, Spanish) 1934. q. L.60000. Istituto Internazionale di Studi Liguri - International Institute of Ligurian Studies, Via Romana, 39, 18012 Bordighera, Italy. bibl.; illus.; index, cum.index: vols.1-20 (1934-1954), vols.21-40 (1955-1974). circ. 1,000. **Indexed:** A.I.C.P., Anthropol.Lit., Br.Archaeol.Abstr., Numis.Lit. **Document type:** academic/scholarly publication.
—BLDSC (7993.140000).
Description: Covers research and scholarly study on prehistory, protohistory and classical archaeology in Liguria (a northwestern coastal region of Italy).

940.27   IT   ISSN 0035-6913
DC197
RIVISTA ITALIANA DI STUDI NAPOLEONICI. (Text in French and Italian) 1962. s-a. L.38000($38) (Centro Nazionale di Studi Napoleonici e di Storia dell'Elba) Giardini Editori e Stampatori, Via Santa Bibbiana 28, 56100 Pisa, Italy. TEL 050-502531. Dir. Mario Bigotti. bk.rev.; abstr.; bibl.; charts; illus.; stat. (also avail. in microform) **Indexed:** Amer.Hist.& Life, Hist.Abstr.
Description: Covers English and French history of the Napoleonic Era.

945 055   IT   ISSN 0393-022X
RIVISTA STORICA CALABRESE. N.S. 1986. s-a. L.30000. Deputazione di Storia Patria per la Calabria, Piazza G. De. Nava, 26, 89100 Reggio Calabria, Italy. TEL 0965-21949. Dir. Maria Mariotti.

945   IT   ISSN 0035-7073
DG401
RIVISTA STORICA ITALIANA. 1884. 3/yr. L.132000 to individuals; institutions L.165000; foreign L.230000 (effective 1993). Edizioni Scientifiche Italiane S.p.A., Via Chiatamone 7, 80121 Naples, Italy. TEL 081-7645768. FAX 081-7646477. Ed. Franco Venturi. adv.; bk.rev.; charts; illus.; index. circ. 1,600. **Indexed:** Amer.Hist.& Life, Arts & Hum.Cit.Ind., Curr.Cont., Hist.Abstr., M.L.A.
—SWETS.

940 800   US   ISSN 0195-8453
CB351
ROCKY MOUNTAIN MEDIEVAL AND RENAISSANCE ASSOCIATION. JOURNAL. 1980. a. $15. Rocky Mountain Medieval and Renaissance Association, c/o Steven A. Epstein, Sec.-Treas., Department of History, University of Colorado at Boulder, Boulder, CO 80309-0234. Ed. John S. Tanner. adv.; bk.rev.; illus. circ. 200. (back issues avail.) **Indexed:** Amer.Hist.& Life, Hist.Abstr., M.L.A.
—BLDSC (4848.840000); UnCover.

943.8 PL ISSN 0080-3421
ROCZNIK BIALOSTOCKI. (Text in Polish; summaries in English and Russian) 1961. irreg., vol.18, 1993. price varies. (Muzeum Okregowe w Bialymstoku) Wydawnictwo Naukowe P W N, Miodowa 10, 00-251 Warsaw, Poland. illus. Indexed: A.I.C.P., Anthropol.Lit., Numis.Lit.

943.8 PL ISSN 0080-3464
ROCZNIK GRUDZIADZKI. 1960. irreg., vol. 9, 1994. price varies. Polskie Towarzystwo Historyczne, Oddzial w Grudziadzu, Ul. Legionow 2, 86-300 Grudziadz, Poland. adv.; bk.rev. Document type: bibliography.
 Description: Covers the history of the city of Grudziadz.

943.8 PL ISSN 0080-3480
ROCZNIK JELENIOGORSKI. 1963. a. price varies. Towarzystwo Przyjaciol Ziemi Jeleniogorskiej - Society of Friends of the Jelenia Gora Region, Ul. Bartka Zwyciezcy 1, P.O. Box 183, 58-500 Jelenia Gora, Poland. (Dist. by: Ars Polona-Ruch, Krakowskie Przedmiescie 7, Warsaw, Poland) Ed. Stanislaw Lejde. Indexed: Numis.Lit.
 Description: Papers on political, social, economical and cultural phenomena in Jelenia Gora region.

940 PL ISSN 0137-3501
ROCZNIK KALISKI. 1968. a. price varies. Polskie Towarzystwo Historyczne, Oddzial w Kaliszu) Wydawnictwo Poznanskie, Ul. Fredry 8, 61-701 Poznan, Poland. TEL 061-531901. (Co-sponsor: Muzeum Okregowe Ziemi Kaliskiej in Kalisz) Ed. Andrzej Nowak. bk.rev.; illus. circ. 1,000.

940 PL ISSN 0080-3499
ROCZNIK KRAKOWSKI. 1898. irreg., vol.54, 1988. price varies. Towarzystwo Milosnikow Historii i Zabytkow Krakowa, Ul. Sw. Jana 12, 31-018 Krakow, Poland. (Dist. by: Ars Polona-Ruch, Krakowskie Przedmiescie 7, Warsaw, Poland) Ed. J.M. Malecki. circ. 600. Indexed: Numis.Lit.
 Description: Papers on the history, monuments and relics of Cracow.

943.8 PL ISSN 0080-3510
DK511.L7
ROCZNIK LUBELSKI. (Text in Polish; summaries in French, Russian) 1959. a. price varies. (Polskie Towarzystwo Historyczne, Oddzial w Lublinie - Polish Historical Society) Wydawnictwo Lubelskie, Okopowa 7, 20-022 Lublin, Poland. TEL 48-81-27344. (Dist. by: Ars Polona-Ruch, Krakowskie Przedmiescie 7, Warsaw, Poland) Ed. Kazimierz Myslinski. circ. 500.

943.8 PL ISSN 0080-3537
ROCZNIK OLSZTYNSKI. (Text in Polish; summaries in German and Russian) 1958. a. 100000 Zl. Muzeum Warmii i Mazur, Ul. Zamkowa 2, 10-074 Olsztyn, Poland. TEL 279596. (Dist. by Ars Polona-Ruch, Krakowskie Przedmiescie 7, Warsaw, Poland) Ed. Janusz Cyganski. bk.rev. Indexed: A.I.C.P.

ROCZNIK SADECKI. see FOLKLORE

947 PL
ROCZNIK ZIEMI KLODZKIEJ. a., latest 1984 (for the years 1974-78). price varies. Towarzystwo Milosnikow Ziemi Klodzkiej - Society of Friends of the Klodzko Region, Pl. Jagielly 1, 57-300 Klodzko, Poland. (Dist. by: Ars Polona-Ruch, Krakowskie Przedmiescie 7, Warsaw, Poland)
 Description: Covers topics related to the Klodzko region.

940 PL ISSN 0080-3634
HC337.P7
ROCZNIKI DZIEJOW SPOLECZNYCH I GOSPODARCZYCH/ANNALES D'HISTOIRE SOCIALE ET ECONOMIQUES. (Text in Polish; summaries in French) 1931. irreg., vol.44, 1983. price varies. Poznanskie Towarzystwo Przyjaciol Nauk, Ul. Mielzynskiego 27-29, 61-725 Poznan, Poland. (Dist. by: Ars Polona, Krakowskie Przedmiescie 7, 00-068 Warsaw, Poland) Ed. Wladyslaw Rusinski. bk.rev.; bibl.; charts; cum.index: vols.1-40. circ. 430. (also avail. in microfiche from IDC; reprint service avail. from SCH) Indexed: Amer.Hist.& Life, Hist.Abstr.

900 069 GW ISSN 0076-2741
CC27
ROEMISCH-GERMANISCHES ZENTRALMUSEUM, MAINZ. JAHRBUCH. 1954. a. DM.96. Dr. Rudolf Habelt GmbH, Am Buchenhang 1, 53115 Bonn, Germany. TEL 0228-232016. FAX 0228-232017. bk.rev. Document type: corporate report.

937 GW ISSN 0171-1474
ROEMISCH-GERMANISCHES ZENTRALMUSEUM, MAINZ. MONOGRAPHIEN. 1975. irreg., no.34, 1993. price varies. Dr. Rudolf Habelt GmbH, Am Buchenhang 1, 53115 Bonn, Germany. TEL 0228-232016. FAX 0228-232017. Document type: monographic series.

940 AU ISSN 0080-3790
ROEMISCHE HISTORISCHE MITTEILUNGEN. 1958. a. price varies. (Oesterreichisches Kulturinstitut, Rome, IT) Verlag der Oesterreichischen Akademie der Wissenschaften, Dr. Ignaz-Seipel-Platz 2, A-1010 Vienna, Austria. FAX 0222-5139541. Indexed: Amer.Hist.& Life, Hist.Abstr.

945 IT ISSN 1122-0244
▼ROMA MODERNA E CONTEMPORANEA; rivista interdisciplinare di storia. 1993. 3/yr. L.80000 (foreign L.110000) (effective 1993). (Universita di Roma La Sapienza, Dipartimento di Studi Geoeconomici Statistici Storici per l'Analisi Regionale) Archivio Guido Izzi s.r.l., Via Ottorino Lazzarini 19, 00136 Rome, Italy. TEL 06-383193. FAX 06-3722231. (Subscr. to: Licosa S.p.A., Via Duca di Calabria 1-1, 50125 Florence, Italy. TEL 055-645415. FAX 055-641257) Ed. Giuseppe Talamo.

ROMANIA; revue consacree a l'etude des langues et des litteratures romanes. see LINGUISTICS

949.8 US ISSN 0098-6054
DR201
ROMANIAN SOURCES.* 1975. s-a. $5 to individuals; students $3. 3110 Gaewood Ct., Alliance, OH 44601-4821. TEL 412-782-1563. bk.rev.; bibl.; charts; illus. circ. 475. Indexed: Amer.Bibl.Slavic & E.Eur.Stud., Amer.Hist.& Life, Hist.Abstr.
 —BLDSC (8019.760000).

ROMANTIZM V RUSSKOI I SOVETSKOI LITERATURE. see LITERATURE

940 UK ISSN 0306-1140
ROMFORD RECORD. no.4, 1971. a. 25p. Romford and District Historical Society, c/o Central Library, Romford, Essex, England. Ed. Brian D. Evans. charts; illus.

937 930.1 SW ISSN 0349-5590
ROMHORISONT. 1981. s-a. SEK 150 (membership). Foereningen Svenska Rominstitutets Vaenner, Kungl. Slottet, S-111 30 Stockholm, Sweden. (Co-sponsor: Svenska Institutet i Rom)

947 RU
ROSSIISKAYA AKADEMIYA NAUK. SIBIRSKOE OTDELENIE. IZVESTIYA. SERIYA OBSHCHESTVENNYKH NAUK. 1963. 3/yr. Rossiiskaya Akademiya Nauk, Sibirskoe Otdelenie, Pr. Akademika Lavrenteva 17, 630090 Novosibirsk, Russia. TEL 234-05-84. bk.rev.; illus. Indexed: Amer.Hist.& Life, Hist.Abstr.
 Formerly: Akademiya Nauk S.S.S.R. Sibirskoe Otdelenie. Izvestiya. Seriya Obshchestvennykh Nauk (ISSN 0130-1748)

943 910 581 GW
ROTENBURGER SCHRIFTEN. 1953. s-a. DM.25. Heimatbund Rotenburg - Wuemme e.V., Postfach 1480, 27356 Rotenburg, Germany. TEL 04261-83767. Ed. Guenter Petschel. bk.rev.; cum.index: 1953-1991. circ. 2,000. (back issues avail.) Document type: academic/scholarly publication.
 Description: Concerns history, geography and regional ethnology of northern regions of Germany.

943 GW ISSN 0722-7531
BX1534.A1
ROTTENBURGER JAHRBUCH FUER KIRCHENGESCHICHTE. 1982. a. price varies. (Geschichtsverein der Dioezese Rottenburg-Stuttgart) Jan Thorbecke Verlag GmbH und Co., Postfach 546, 72482 Sigmaringen, Germany. TEL 07571-728-100. FAX 07571-728-280. TELEX 732534. bk.rev. (back issues avail.) Document type: academic/scholarly publication.

HISTORY — HISTORY OF EUROPE 2963

948.95 DK ISSN 0106-5327
ROUGSOE LOKALHISTORISKE FORENING. AARSSKRIFT. 1979. a. membership. Rougsoe Lokalhistoriske Forening, P.O. Box 15, DK-8961 Allingaabro, Denmark. illus.

942 UK ISSN 0080-4398
ROYAL HISTORICAL SOCIETY. GUIDES AND HANDBOOKS. (Supplementary Series) 1938; N.S. 1974. irreg. membership. Royal Historical Society, University College London, Gower St., London WC1E 6BT, England. TEL 071-387-7532. Document type: monographic series.
 —BLDSC (8030.250000).

942 UK ISSN 0080-4401
DA20
ROYAL HISTORICAL SOCIETY. TRANSACTIONS. SIXTH SERIES. 1872. a. membership. Royal Historical Society, University College London, Gower St., London WC1E 6BT, England. TEL 071-387-7532. (also avail. in microform from PMC; reprint service avail. from KTO) Indexed: Amer.Hist.& Life, Br.Archaeol.Abstr., Br.Hum.Ind., Geo.Abstr., Hist.Abstr. Document type: academic/scholarly publication.
 —BLDSC (8998.100000); UnCover.

940 US ISSN 0269-2244
ROYAL HISTORICAL SOCIETY STUDIES IN HISTORY. 1977. irreg., latest no.68. Boydell & Brewer Inc., Box 41026, Rochester, NY 14604. TEL 716-275-0419. FAX 716-271-8778.

ROYAL IRISH ACADEMY. PROCEEDINGS. SECTION C: ARCHAEOLOGY, CELTIC STUDIES, HISTORY, LINGUISTICS AND LITERATURE. see ARCHAEOLOGY

ROYAL SOCIETY OF ANTIQUARIES OF IRELAND. JOURNAL. see ARCHAEOLOGY

943 GW
RUND UM DEN ALHEIMER. 1979. a. DM.13.50. Geschichtsverein Rotenburg, Andersenstr. 9, 36199 Rotenburg, Germany. TEL 06623-1200.

940 UK ISSN 0956-7933
HN8 CODEN: RUHIEI
RURAL HISTORY; economy, society, culture. 1990. s-a. £22($39) to individuals (overseas £31); institutions £41 (overseas £50 ($69)). Cambridge University Press, Edinburgh Bldg., Shaftesbury Rd., Cambridge CB2 2RU, England. TEL 0223-312393. FAX 0223-315052. TELEX 851817256. (N. American addr.: Cambridge University Press, Journals Dept., 40 W. 20th St., New York, NY 10011. TEL 212-924-3900. FAX 212-691-3239) Ed.Bd. adv. (back issues avail.) Indexed: Amer.Hist.& Life, Hist.Abstr. Document type: academic/scholarly publication.
 —BLDSC (8052.466500); UnCover; UMI.
 Description: Covers all aspects of the study of rural society

947 IT
RUSSIA. (Text in English, French, Russian) s-a. L.50000 (effective 1994). Marsilio Editori S.p.A., Marittima - Fabbricato 205, 30135 Venice, Italy. TEL 041-5227822. FAX 041-5238352.
 Description: Covers the history of Russian civilization.

947 GW ISSN 0721-9431
RUSSIA MEDIAEVALIS. (Text in English, German, Russian) 1973. irreg. price varies. Wilhelm Fink Verlag, Ohmstr. 5, 80802 Munich, Germany. TEL 089-348017. FAX 089-341378. Ed.Bd. Indexed: Bibl.Ling.

RUSSIAN ARCHIVAL SERIES. see ETHNIC INTERESTS

HISTORY — HISTORY OF EUROPE

947 US ISSN 0036-0341
DK1
THE RUSSIAN REVIEW; an American quarterly devoted to Russia past and present. 1941. q. $28 to individuals (foreign $33); institutions $46 (foreign $51). Ohio State University Press, 1070 Carmack Rd., Columbus, OH 43210. TEL 617-292-6930. FAX 617-292-2065. Ed. Allan Wildman. adv.; bk.rev.; charts; illus.; index, cum.index vols.1-30, 1941-1971. circ. 1,700. (also avail. in microfilm from UMI; back issues avail.; reprint service avail. from ISI,UMI) Indexed: Abstr.Mil.Bibl., Acad.Ind., Amer.Bibl.Slavic & E.Eur.Stud., Amer.Hist.& Life, Arts & Hum.Cit.Ind., Bk.Rev.Ind. (1990-), Child.Bk.Rev.Ind. (1990-), Curr.Cont., Hist.Abstr., Hum.Ind., Ind.Bk.Rev.Hum., M.L.A., P.A.I.S., Peace Res.Abstr., RILA. **Document type:** academic/scholarly publication.
●Also available online. Vendor(s): Information Access Co.
—BLDSC (8052.820000); Faxon; UnCover; SWETS.
Description: Publishes articles and reviews of interest to Russian specialists in all disciplines, including history, literature, social sciences, art, and other humanistic studies.

947 NE ISSN 0080-4916
RUSSIAN SERIES ON SOCIAL HISTORY. 1970. irreg. price varies. (International Institute for Social History) Kluwer Academic Publishers, Postbus 17, 3300 AA Dordrecht, Netherlands. TEL 31-78-334911. FAX 31-78-334254. TELEX 29245 KAPG NL. (Dist. by: Kluwer Academic Publishers Group, P.O. Box 322, 3300 AH Dordrecht, Netherlands. TEL 31-78-524400; N.America dist. addr.: P.O. Box 358, Accord Sta., Hingham, MA 02018-0358. TEL 617-871-6600) Ed. Boris Sapir. **Document type:** monographic series.
Refereed Serial

RUSSKOE VOZROZHDENIE; nezavisimyi russkii pravoslavnyi natsional'nyi zhurnal. see *RELIGIONS AND THEOLOGY — Eastern Orthodox*

RUSSLAND UND WIR; ein Forum. see *POLITICAL SCIENCE — International Relations*

942 UK ISSN 0260-3322
DA670.R89
RUTLAND RECORD. 1980. a. £5.50 to individuals; institutions £7.50. Rutland Local History & Record Society, Rutland County Museum, Catmose St., Oakham, Rutland LE15 6HW, England. TEL 0572-723654. Ed. C. Firmin. adv.; bk.rev. circ. 600. Indexed: Geo.Abstr. **Document type:** academic/scholarly publication.
—BLDSC (8053.474000).
Description: Articles on the history of Rutland and historical method.

940 GW ISSN 0942-7392
▼**SAARBRUECKER STUDIEN UND MATERIALEN ZU ALTERTUMSKUNDE**. 1992. irreg. price varies. Dr. Rudolf Habelt GmbH, Am Buchenhang 1, 53115 Bonn, Germany. TEL 0228-232016. FAX 0228-232017. Eds. Jan Lichardus, Frauke Stein. **Document type:** monographic series.

943 GW ISSN 0486-8234
SAECHSISCHE HEIMATBLAETTER. 1954. 6/yr. DM.36. Kulturbund e.V., Landesverband Sachsen, Goetheallee 37, 01309 Dresden, Germany. bk.rev (reprint service avail.)
—BLDSC (8062.700000).

SAFN TIL SOEGU ISLANDS OG ISLENSKRA BOKMENNTA. see *LITERATURE*

SAGA OCH SED. see *FOLKLORE*

943 GW ISSN 0036-2573
SAGAN-SPROTTAUER HEIMATBRIEFE; offizielles Organ und Monatschrift fuer den Kreis Sprottau. 1949. m. DM.24. C.J. Laumanns, Kolpingstr. 5, 59555 Lippstadt, Germany. adv.; illus.

949.12 IC ISSN 0258-3755
SAGNIR; timarit um soeguleg efni. 1980. a. ISK 1500($23) (effective 1993). Sagnir, P.O. Box 7182, Arnagardi v. Sudurgoetu, IS-127 Reykjavik, Iceland. TEL 354-1-812719. FAX 354-1-694410. Ed. Thora Thorvalds. circ. 1,600. (back issues avail.) **Document type:** academic/scholarly publication.
Description: Deals with the history of Iceland from the Middle Ages to the present. Each issue addresses a specific historical theme or aspect.

900 NO ISSN 0036-2859
ST. HALLVARD. 1915. 4/yr. NOK 240. Selskabet for Oslo Byes Vel, Grev Wedels Plass 1, 0151 Oslo 1, Norway. TEL 02-477440. FAX 02-333697. Ed. Jan Sigurd Oestberg. adv.; bk.rev.; illus.; maps; index. circ. 5,500.

947 915 GS ISSN 0132-6058
SAK'ART'VELOS S.S.R. MEC'NIEREBAT'A AKADEMIIS MAC'NE. ISTORIIS ARK'EOLOGIIS, ET'NOGRAP'IISA DA XELOVNEBIS ISTORIIS SERIA. 1971. 4/yr. Akademiya Nauk Gruzinskoi S.S.R., Ul. Kutuzova 19, 380060 Tbilisi, Georgia.

947 SZ ISSN 0254-1521
SAMISDAT; Stimmen aus den "anderen Russland". 1972. irreg. price varies. Kuratorium Geistige Freiheit, Postfach 1227, 3601 Thun, Switzerland. Ed. Udo Robe. circ. 2,000.
Supersedes: Russischer Samisdat (ISSN 0253-2158)

SAMMLUNG DENKWUERDIGER REISEN. see *TRAVEL AND TOURISM*

945 700 IT ISSN 0391-8718
DG975.S265
SAMNIUM. (Text in Italian) 1928. q. L.20000. Alfredo Zazo, Ed. & Pub., c/o Biblioteca Provinciale, Corso Garibaldi, 47, 82100 Benevento, Italy.

943.6 AU
SANCTA CRUX; Zeitschrift des Zisterzienserstiftes und der Philosophisch-Theologischen Hochschule. 1933. irreg. price varies. Stift Heiligenkreuz, A-2532 Heiligenkreuz, Austria. TEL 02258-2282. Ed. P. Gerhard Hradil. bk.rev. circ. 1,000.

945 700 IT ISSN 0391-7819
SANTO; rivista antoniana di storia dottrina arte. (Text in English, French, Italian) 1961. 3/yr. L.50000($45) (effective 1993). Centro Studi Antoniani, Basilica del Santo, Piazza del Santo 11, 35123 Padua, Italy. TEL 049-663944. Ed. Luciano Bertazzo. bk.rev.; abstr.; index. circ. 450. (back issues avail.)

SAVOIA. see *POLITICAL SCIENCE*

943.7 XR ISSN 0231-6307
SBORNIK PRACI VYCHODOCESKYCH ARCHIVU. 1970. irreg. (Statni Obastni Archiv v Zamrsku) Nakladatelstvi Kruh, Dlouha 108, 500 21 Hradec Kralove, Czech Republic. (Dist. by: Artia, Ve Smeckach 30, 111 27 Prague 1, Czech Republic)

943.7 XR ISSN 0487-5648
SBORNIK VLASTIVEDNYCH PRACI Z PODBLANICKA. 1957. a. (Okresni Muzeum, Benesov) Statni Zemedelske Nakladatelstvi, Vaclavske Nam. 47, 113 78 Prague 1, Czech Republic. TEL 62 59 51. (Dist. by: Artia, Ve Smeckach 30, 111 27 Prague 1, Czech Republic) cum.index: vol.1-15, 1957-1974.

948 DK
SCANDINAVIAN ATLAS OF HISTORIC TOWNS. irreg. price varies. Odense University Press, Campusvej 55, DK-5230 Odense M, Denmark. TEL 66-157999. FAX 66-158126.

945 IT ISSN 0392-5404
D111
SCHEDE MEDIEVALI. 1981. s-a. L.55000 (foreign L.70000) (effective 1994). Officina di Studi Medievali, Via del Parlamento, 32, 90133 Palermo, Italy. TEL 091-6161333. FAX 091-333121. adv.; bk.rev. **Document type:** academic/scholarly publication, bibliography.
Description: Lists about 100 newly published books in the field of medieval studies in each issue. Lists conventions, seminars and meetings. Publishes research works and conference papers.

943 GW
SCHLESIERBUNDES NUERNBERG. RUNDBRIEF. 1947. m. DM.20($14.30) Schlesierbundes Nuernberg e.V., Pillenreutherstr. 158, 90458 Nuernberg, Germany. TEL 049-9175-352. Ed. Guenter Piosecny. (looseleaf format; back issues avail.)

943 GW ISSN 0937-7247
DD801.S6331
SCHLESWIG-HOLSTEIN. 1949. m. DM.48. (Schleswig-Holsteinischer Heimatbund) Husum Druck- und Verlagsgesellschaft mbH, Postfach 1480, 25804 Husum, Germany. TEL 04841-6081. FAX 04841-61397. Ed. J. Paulsen Jr. adv.; bk.rev.; charts; illus.; index. circ. 5,000. **Document type:** academic/scholarly publication.

943 GW
SCHLESWIG-HOLSTEIN-KALENDER. 1938. a. DM.24.80. Wachholtz Verlag GmbH, Rungestr. 4, 24537 Neumuenster, Germany. TEL 04321-906270. FAX 04321-906275. circ. 4,000. (back issues avail.) **Document type:** bulletin.

943 GW
SCHNELLERTSBERICHT. 1976. a. DM.5. Forschungsgemeinschaft Schnellerts, Talstr. 8, 61203 Reichelsheim, Germany. TEL 06164-2116. circ. 1,000. (tabloid format; back issues avail.)

943 GW ISSN 0177-4492
SCHOENERE HEIMAT. 1903. 4/yr. DM.32. Bayerischer Landesverein fuer Heimatpflege e.V., Ludwigstr. 23, 80539 Munich, Germany. FAX 089-282434. bk.rev. **Document type:** academic/scholarly publication.
—BLDSC (8092.544900).

940 US ISSN 1059-9185
D219
SCHOLARS OF EARLY MODERN STUDIES. 1966. a. $25. Sixteenth Century Journal Publishers, Inc., Northeast Missouri State University, LB 115, Kirksville, MO 63501. TEL 816-785-4665. (Co-sponsors: Society for Reformation Research; Sixteenth Century Studies Conference) Ed. R.V. Schnucker. adv. circ. 2,200. (back issues avail.) **Document type:** newsletter.
Formerly: Historians of Early Modern Europe (ISSN 0883-3559); **Incorporates:** American Society for Reformation Research. Newsletter.

940 GW ISSN 0340-6490
SCHRIFTEN ZUR GEISTESGESCHICHTE DES OESTLICHEN EUROPA. 1967. irreg., vol.19, 1991. price varies. Harrassowitz Verlag, Taunusstr. 14, 65183 Wiesbaden, Germany. TEL 0611-530-0. FAX 0611-530570. TELEX 4186135. (Subscr. to: Postfach 2929, 65019 Wiesbaden, Germany) Ed.Bd. **Document type:** monographic series.

943 GW
SCHWAEBISCHER HEIMATKALENDER. 1884. a. W. Kohlhammer GmbH (Stuttgart), Hessbruhlstr. 69, 70549 Stuttgart, Germany. TEL 0711-7863-232. FAX 0711-7863263. Ed. Heinz Schramm. circ. 20,000. (back issues avail.) **Document type:** bulletin.

943 GW
SCHWAELMER JAHRBUCH. 1970. a. DM.18. Schwaelmer Heimatbund e.V., Paradeplatz 1, 34613 Schwalmstadt-Ziegenhain, Germany. TEL 06691-3893. Ed. Gerhard Stuebing. bk.rev.; index. circ. 2,700.

943 GW ISSN 0944-4505
DER SCHWARZWALD. 1894. 4/yr. DM.10. Schwarzwaldverein e.V., Bismarckallee 2a, 79098 Freiburg, Germany. TEL 0761-22794. FAX 0761-286640. Ed. Karlheinz Scherfling. adv.; bk.rev. circ. 60,000. **Document type:** academic/scholarly publication.

949.4 SZ
SCHWEIZER HEIMATBUECHER. 1941. irreg., vol.190, 1991. price varies. Paul Haupt AG, Falkenplatz 14, CH-3001 Bern, Switzerland. TEL 031-3012345. FAX 031-3014669. **Document type:** monographic series.

943 SZ ISSN 0080-7273
SCHWEIZERISCHE BEITRAEGE ZUR ALTERTUMSWISSENSCHAFT. (Text in French, German) 1942. irreg., no.23, 1992. price varies. Friedrich Reinhardt Verlag, Missionsstr. 36, CH-4012 Basel, Switzerland. (Dist. by: Albert J. Phiebig Books, Box 352, White Plains, NY 10602) Ed. Christoph Schaeublin. circ. 1,000.

HISTORY — HISTORY OF EUROPE

930   SZ   ISSN 0252-1881
GN841
SCHWEIZERISCHE GESELLSCHAFT FUER UR- UND FRUEHGESCHICHTE. JAHRBUCH. (Text in French, German, Italian) 1908. a. 150 SFr. Petersgraben 9-11, CH-4001 Basel, Switzerland. TEL 061-2613078. bk.rev.; index. **Indexed:** A.I.C.P., Br.Archaeol.Abstr., Numis.Lit. **Document type:** academic/scholarly publication.

945   IT   ISSN 1122-3693
SCIENZA E STORIA. 1983. s-a. L.70000 (foreign L.100000). Centro Internazionale di Storia dello Spazio e del Tempo, Via Roma 100, 35020 Brugine (PD), Italy. TEL 049-5806768.
   Formerly (until 1986): Centro Internazionale A. Beltrame di Storia dello Spazio e del Tempo. Bollettino (ISSN 1122-3685)

SCOTTISH CHURCH HISTORY SOCIETY. RECORDS. see *RELIGIONS AND THEOLOGY*

SCOTTISH LABOUR HISTORY SOCIETY. JOURNAL. see *BUSINESS AND ECONOMICS — Labor And Industrial Relations*

SCOTTISH SLAVONIC REVIEW. see *LITERATURE*

941 301   UK   ISSN 0036-9411
AS121
SCOTTISH STUDIES. (Text in English; occasionally in Gaelic, Scots) 1957. a. £10($25) University of Edinburgh, School of Scottish Studies, 27 George Square, Edinburgh EH8 9LD, Scotland. TEL 031-650-3060. Ed. A. Fenton. bk.rev.; illus. circ. 800. (also avail. in microform from SWZ; reprint service avail. from SWZ) **Indexed:** A.I.C.P., Amer.Hist.& Life, Arts & Hum.Cit.Ind., Br.Archaeol.Abstr., Br.Hum.Ind., Curr.Cont., Hist.Abstr., Ind.Bk.Rev.Hum., M.L.A. **Document type:** academic/scholarly publication.
   —BLDSC (8211.250000); Faxon; SWETS.
   Description: Articles and notes on Scottish social, cultural and intellectual history with particular reference to oral tradition.

941   CN   ISSN 0703-1580
SCOTTISH TRADITION. 1968. a. Can.$20. Canadian Association for Scottish Studies, Department of History, University of Guelph, Guelph, ON N1G 2W1, Canada. TEL 519-824-4120. Ed. Scott McLean. bk.rev. circ. 250. **Document type:** academic/scholarly publication.
   Incorporates: Colloquium on Scottish Studies. Proceedings (ISSN 0069-5823)

948   FI   ISSN 0358-710X
D1
SCRIPTA HISTORICA. (Text in English, Finnish, German and Swedish) 1967. irreg. FIM 80. Oulun Historiaseura, PL 31, 90101 Oulu, Finland. TEL 981-3117-066. circ. 500. **Indexed:** Amer.Hist.& Life, Hist.Abstr.

940 970   JA
SEIYOSHIGAKU/STUDIES IN WESTERN HISTORY. (Text in Japanese; summaries in English, French, German) 1948. q. 2920 Yen. Japanese Society of Western History, Osaka University, Faculty of Letters, 1-1 Machikaneyama-cho, Toyonaka-Shi 560, Japan. TEL 06-844-1151. bk.rev. circ. 950.

940   NE   ISSN 0921-0717
SELECTED WORKS OF JUAN LUIS VIVES. 1987. irreg., vol. 5, 1991. price varies. E.J. Brill, P.O. Box 9000, 2300 PA Leiden, Netherlands. TEL 31-71-312624. FAX 31-71-317532. TELEX 39296 BRILL NL. (In N. America: E.J. Brill, 24 Hudson St., Kinderhook, NY 12106. TEL 800-962-4406. FAX 518-758-1959) Ed. C. Matheussen. (back issues avail.) **Document type:** monographic series.

940 709   PL
SEMINARIA NIEDZICKIE/NIEDZICA SEMINARS. (Text in English, French, German) 1981. biennial. price varies. Miedzynarodowe Centrum Kultury - International Cultural Center, Rynek Glowny 25, Krakow, Poland. (Dist. by: Ars-Polona, Krakowskie Przedmiescie 7, Warsaw, Poland) (Co-sponsor: Stowarzyszenie Historykow Sztuki; Muzeum Narodowe w Krakowie) Ed. Ewa Sniezynska-Stolot. circ. 600.

SEVENTEENTH CENTURY FRENCH STUDIES. see *LITERATURE*

943.7 320   XR   ISSN 0231-6323
SEVERNI MORAVA. (Text in Czech; summaries in English, German) 1957. 2/yr. 20 Kcs. Okresni Vlastivedne Muzeum v Sumperku, 787 34 Sumperk, Czech Republic. TEL 0649-4070. (Dist. by: Artia, Ve Smeckach 30, 111 27 Prague 1, Czech Republic) Ed. Milos Melzer. bk.rev. circ. 1,500.

947   RU   ISSN 0321-3056
H8.R9
SEVERO-KAVKAZSKII NAUCHNYI TSENTR VYSSHEI SHKOLY. OBSHCHESTVENNYE NAUKI. IZVESTIYA/NORTH-CAUCASUS SCIENTIFIC CENTER OF HIGH SCHOOL. SOCIAL SCIENCE. NEWS. 1973. 4/yr. 6.60 Rub. Rostovskii Universitet, Ul. Pushkinskaia 160, 344 700 Rostov-na-Donu, Russia. TEL 8-8630654131. TELEX 123520 NAUKA. bk.rev.; bibl.; index. circ. 1,300. **Indexed:** Int.Bibl.Soc.Sci.

940.1   BE   ISSN 0896-1638
CB351
SEWANEE MEDIAEVAL STUDIES. (Text in English) vol.5, 1990. a. 600 BEF. (University of the South, Sewanee Mediaeval Colloquium, US) Editions Peeters s.p.r.l., Bondgenotenlaan 153, B-3000 Louvain, Belgium. TEL 32-16-235170. FAX 32-16-228500. Eds. E.B. King, S.J. Ridyard. (back issues avail.) **Document type:** academic/scholarly publication.

SICILIA. see *FOLKLORE*

943.6   AU
SIMMERINGER MUSEUMSBLAETTER. 1977. irreg. Bezirksmuseum Simmering, Enkplatz 2, 1110 Vienna, Austria.

940   NE
SIR THOMAS BROWNE INSTITUTE. PUBLICATIONS. NEW SERIES. (Text in English) 1962; N.S. 1982. irreg., vol.12, 1991. E.J. Brill, P.O Box 9000, 2300 PA Leiden, Netherlands. TEL 31-71-312624. FAX 31-71-317532. TELEX 39296 BRILL NL. (N. America dist. addr.: E.J. Brill, 24 Hudson St., Kinderhook, NY 12106. TEL 800-962-4406. FAX 518-758-1959) (Co-publisher: Leiden University Press) (back issues avail.) **Document type:** monographic series.
   Supersedes: Sir Thomas Browne Institute. Publications. General Series; Sir Thomas Browne Institute. Publications. Special Series.
   Description: Scholarly treatment of Anglo-Dutch cultural relations, with a focus on the 17th and 18th centuries.
   Refereed Serial

900   US   ISSN 0361-0160
D219
SIXTEENTH CENTURY JOURNAL; an interdisciplinary journal for Renaissance and Reformation students and scholars. 1970. q. $45 to individuals; institutions $45. (Sixteenth Century Studies Conference) Sixteenth Century Journal Publishers, Inc., Northeast Missouri State University, LB 115, Kirksville, MO 63501. TEL 816-785-4665. Eds. Robert Kingdon, Robert V. Schnucker. adv.; bk.rev.; illus.; bibl.; index. circ. 2,400. (also avail. in microform; back issues avail.) **Indexed:** Amer.Bibl.Slavic & E.Eur.Stud., Amer.Hist.& Life, Arts & Hum.Cit.Ind., CERDIC, Curr.Cont., Hist.Abstr., M.L.A., Ref.Sour., Rel.& Theol.Abstr. (1974-), Rel.Per., RILA. **Document type:** academic/scholarly publication.
   —BLDSC (8294.718000); Faxon; UnCover; SWETS. CCC.
   Formerly (until vol.2): Sixteenth Century Essays and Studies.

940   NO   ISSN 0080-9888
SJOEFARTSHISTORISK AARBOK/NORWEGIAN YEARBOOK OF MARITIME HISTORY. (Text in English, Norwegian; summaries in English) 1965. a. NOK 90 to non-members; members NOK 75. Bergens Sjoefartsmuseum - Bergen Maritime Museum, P.O. Box 2736, Moehlenpris, 5026 Bergen, Norway. TEL 47-532-7980. FAX 32-91-37. Ed.Bd. adv. circ. 1,100. **Indexed:** A.B.C.Pol.Sci., Amer.Hist.& Life, Hist.Abstr. **Document type:** academic/scholarly publication.

948   DK   ISSN 0108-397X
SKAEPPEN; aarsskrift for Herrested Sogn. 1982. a. DKK 20. Herrested Sogns Lokalhistoriske Arbejdsgruppe, c/o Poul Erik Steffansen, Odensevej 59, Herrested, 5853 Oerbaek, Denmark. illus. circ. 100.

948 913   DK   ISSN 0560-1894
SKALK; nyt om gammelt. 1957. 6/yr. DKK 140 (typically set in Feb.). Tidsskriftet Skalk, Jelshoejvaenget 29, DK-8270 Hojbjerg, Denmark. TEL 45-86-27-37-11. FAX 45-86-27-30-46. Eds. Harald Andersen, Christian Adamsen. adv.; bk.rev. circ. 50,000. **Indexed:** Anthropol.Lit., NAA.
   Description: Articles on Danish cultural history, ranging from the earliest times through 1900.

948   DK   ISSN 0903-3424
SKANDERBORG MUSEUM. AARBOG. no.14, 1982. a. DKK 80. Skanderborg Museum, Adelgade 5, DK-8660 Skanderborg, Denmark. TEL 45-86-52-24-99. (Co-sponsor: Museumsforeningen for Skanderborg og Omegn) Ed.Bd. illus. circ. 500. (back issues avail.) **Document type:** academic/scholarly publication.
   Former titles: Skanderborg Museum. Aarsskrift (ISSN 0108-0342); Skvaet.

SKIRNIR; timarit Hins Islenska Bokmenntafelags. see *LITERATURE*

948   DK   ISSN 0106-2697
SKIVE-EGNENS JUL. 1978. a. DKK 55. Lokalhistorisk Forlag-Skiveegnen, Lyngbakken 13, Sdr. Thise, 7870 Roslev, Denmark. Ed. E. Steen Soerensen. adv.; bk.rev.; illus. circ. 3,000. **Indexed:** Amer.Hist.& Life, Hist.Abstr.
   Formerly: Jul i Skive.

948   FI
SKOLHISTORISKT ARKIV; uppsatser och urkunder. (Text in Swedish) 1952. irreg. FIM 60. Svenska Skolhistoriska Foereningen i Finland r.f., c/o Jarl Stormbon, Krukmakarvaagen 2A6, 01600 Vanda S-F, Helsingfors, Finland.

948   NO   ISSN 0802-0434
SKRIFTER - LANDSLAGET FOR LOKALHISTORIE. 1965. irreg., vol.6, 1986. Landslaget for Lokalhistorie, Historisk Institutt, Universitetet i Trondheim, N-7055 Dragvoell, Norway. TEL 47-73-59-64-33. FAX 47-73-59-64-41. **Document type:** monographic series.
   Formerly (until 1980): Skrifter fra Landslaget for Bygde- og Byhistorie (ISSN 0458-7073)
   Description: Provides information on local history

948   FI   ISSN 0783-1803
SLAEKT OCH HAEVD (TERJAERV). (Text in Swedish) 1961. irreg. membership only. Terjaerv Hembygdsfoerening, c/o Bernard Sjoelind, Kortjaervivagen 609, FIN-68700 Terjaerv, Finland. TEL 968-8676539.
   Description: Focuses on the history and present of Terjaerv, its inhabitants and their ancestors.

SLAEKTHISTORISKT FORUM. see *GENEALOGY AND HERALDRY*

SLAVONIC AND EAST EUROPEAN REVIEW. see *LITERATURE*

948   GW
SLESVIGLAND. (Text in Danish and German) 1980. bi-m. DM.10. Slesvigland Verlag, Schiffbruecke 42, 24939 Flensburg, Germany. TEL 0461-56782. FAX 0461-582503. **Document type:** bulletin.

943.7   XR   ISSN 0323-0678
AM101
SLEZSKE MUZEUM. CASOPIS. SERIE B. VEDY HISTORICKE. 1951. 3/yr. Slezske Muzeum, Tyrsova 1, 746 46 Opava, Czech Republic. (Dist. by: Artia, Ve Smeckach 30, 111 27 Prague 1, Czech Republic) bk.rev. **Indexed:** Numis.Lit.

572 943.7   XO   ISSN 0081-0061
SLOVACI V ZAHRANICI. (Text in Slovak; summaries in English) 1971. a. price varies. Matica Slovenska, Ul. Mudronova 26, 036 52 Martin, Slovakia. TEL 42-842-38706. FAX 42-842-32454. bk.rev. **Indexed:** A.I.C.P.

947 914.7   US
SLOVAK STUDIES ASSOCIATION. NEWSLETTER. 1977. s-a. $5 to individuals; institutions $10. Slovak Studies Association, Dept. of Political Science, Lincoln Hall 361, 702 S. Wright St., Urbana, IL 61801. (Subscr. to: c/o Prof. Susan Mikula, 5455 N. Sheridan Rd., Chicago, IL 60640) Ed. Carol S. Leff. bibl. circ. 150. (back issues avail.)

HISTORY — HISTORY OF EUROPE

947   XR   ISSN 0081-007X
D147
SLOVANSKE HISTORICKE STUDIE. (Text in Czech; summaries in English, French, German, Russian) 1955. irreg., vol.16, 1989. price varies. (Czechoslovak Academy of Sciences) Academia, Publishing House of the Czechoslovak Academy of Sciences, Vodickova 40, 112 29 Prague 1, Czech Republic. **Indexed:** Amer.Hist.& Life, Hist.Abstr.

947   XO   ISSN 0583-564X
DR37
SLOVANSKE STUDIE. vol.17, 1976. irreg. fl.45. (Slovenska Akademia Vied, Ustav Historickych Vied) Veda, Publishing House of the Slovak Academy of Sciences, Klemensova 19, 814 30 Bratislava, Slovakia. (Dist. in Western countries by: John Benjamins B.V., Amsteldijk 44, Amsterdam (Z.), Netherlands) **Indexed:** Amer.Hist.& Life, Hist.Abstr.

940 410   US   ISSN 0193-1075
DR1352
SLOVENE STUDIES. (Text in English; summaries in Slovene) 1979. s-a. $20. Society for Slovene Studies, c/o Slavic Dept., BH502, Indiana University, Bloomington, IN 47405. (Subscr. to: c/o T. Pogacar, Bowling Green State University, Bowling Green, OH 43403) Ed. Tom M.S. Priestly. bk.rev.; bibl.; charts; illus.; stat. circ. 300. (back issues avail.) **Indexed:** Amer.Bibl.Slavic & E.Eur.Stud., Amer.Hist.& Life, Bibl.Ling., Hist.Abstr., M.L.A. **Document type:** academic/scholarly publication.
—Faxon.
Supersedes (1973-1978): Papers in Slovene Studies (ISSN 0360-179X); Society for Slovene Studies Newsletter (ISSN 0145-6830)
Description: Covers topics relating to Slovenia or Slovenes in diaspora.

943.7 329.9   XO   ISSN 0231-6722
SLOVENSKA ARCHIVISTIKA. 1966. 2/yr. 18 Kcs. per issue. Ministerstva Vnutra SR, Odbor Archivnictva, Krizkova 7, 811 04 Bratislava, Slovakia. FAX 7-494530. (Subscr. to: Slovart, Dept. of Journals, Slobody 6, 817 64 Bratislava, Slovakia) Ed. Peter Kartous. circ. 800.

949.7   XV   ISSN 0351-2908
GN301
SLOVENSKO ETNOLOSKO DRUSTVO. GLASNIK. 1956. 4/yr. $20. Slovensko Etnolosko Drustvo - Slovene Ethnological Society, Askerceva 12, 61000 Ljubljana, Slovenia. TEL 332-611. bk.rev.; bibl. circ. 700. **Indexed:** Anthropol.Lit.
Supersedes (in 1958): Slovenska Akademija Znanosti in Umetnosti v Ljubljana. Institut za Slovensko Narodopisje. Glasilo.

941.608   UK
SOCIAL ATTITUDES IN NORTHERN IRELAND. 1991. irreg. Blackstaff Press Limited, 3 Galway Park, Dundonald, Belfast BT16 0AN, N. Ireland.

940   UK   ISSN 0969-4331
HX21
▼**SOCIALIST HISTORY.** 1993. 3/yr. £15 to individuals; institutions £20. Pluto Publishing Ltd., 345 Archway Rd., London N6 5AA, England. TEL 081-348-2724. FAX 081-349-9133. Ed. Willie Thompson. **Document type:** academic/scholarly publication.

940   SP   ISSN 0210-1475
DP302.C55
SOCIEDAD CASTELLONENSE DE CULTURA. BOLETIN. 1920. q. 2000 ptas. (foreign 3000 ptas.) Sociedad Castellonense de Cultura, Plaza de la Hierba (Casa Abadia), Apdo. de Correos 16, Castellon de la Plana, Spain. Ed. E. Diaz Manleca. bk.rev.; bibl.; index. circ. 1,000. **Indexed:** Amer.Hist.& Life, Hist.Abstr. **Document type:** bulletin.

945   IT   ISSN 0081-0681
SOCIETA DI STUDI ROMAGNOLI. GUIDA. 1967. irreg., no.5, 1983. L.5000. Societa di Studi Romagnoli, c/o Biblioteca Malatestiana, 47023 Cesena, Italy. circ. controlled.

945   IT   ISSN 0037-8739
SOCIETA DI STUDI VALDESI. BOLLETTINO. (Text in English, French, Italian; summaries in English) 1884. s-a. L.40000 (foreign L.60000) to institutions; members L.40000 (foreign L.50000) (effective 1994). Societa di Studi Valdesi, Via Charles Beckwith, 3, 10066 Torre Pellice, Italy. TEL 0121-932179. FAX 0121-932566. bk.rev. circ. 800. **Indexed:** Amer.Hist.& Life, Hist.Abstr., Rel.Ind.One. **Document type:** academic/scholarly publication, bulletin.

945 914   IT   ISSN 0392-033X
SOCIETA SAVONESE DI STORIA PATRIA. ATTI E MEMORIE. (Text in French, Italian, Latin) 1888. a. L.45000 (effective 1993). Societa Savonese di Storia Patria, C.P. 358, Piazza della Maddalena 14, 17100 Savona (SV), Italy. TEL 19-811960. bk.rev.; index. circ. 700. (back issues avail.) **Document type:** academic/scholarly publication.
Description: Local history, both recent and medieval, and archaeology and art.

948   FI   ISSN 0783-5876
Q60   CODEN: ASSVED
SOCIETAS SCIENTIARUM FENNICA. ARSBOK VUOSIKIRJA SERIES A. (Text in Finnish, Swedish) 1923. a. price varies. Societas Scientiarum Fennica - Finnish Society of Sciences and Letters, Mariankatu 5, FIN-00170 Helsinki, Finland. TEL 358-0-633-005. FAX 358-0-661-065. Ed. Johan Chydenius. circ. 700. (reprint service avail.) **Indexed:** Biol.Abstr., GeoRef.
—BLDSC (1714.100000).
Supersedes in part (in 1984): Societas Scientiarum Fennica. Arsbok Vuosikirja (ISSN 0371-2885); Which supersedes in part: Suomen Tiedeseura. Arsbok-vuosikiria.

948   FI   ISSN 0783-5892
SOCIETAS SCIENTIARUM FENNICA. ARSBOK VUOSIKIRJA SERIES B. SPHINX. (Text in Finnish, Swedish) 1923. a. price varies. Societas Scientiarum Fennica - Finnish Society of Sciences and Letters, Mariankatu 5, FIN-00170 Helsinki, Finland. TEL 358-0-663-005. FAX 358-0-661-065. Ed. Johan Chydenius. circ. 700.
—BLDSC (8413.612380).
Supersedes in part (in 1984): Societas Scientiarum Fennica. Arsbok Vuosikirja (ISSN 0371-2885); Which supersedes in part: Suomen Tiedeseura. Arsbok-vuosikiria.

SOCIETE ARCHEOLOGIQUE DE TOURAINE. MEMOIRES. see ARCHAEOLOGY

SOCIETE ARCHEOLOGIQUE, HISTORIQUE, LITTERAIRE & SCIENTIFIQUE DU GERS. BULLETIN. see ARCHAEOLOGY

SOCIETE D'ARCHEOLOGIE, D'HISTOIRE ET DE FOLKLORE DE NIVELLES ET DU BRABANT WALLON. ANNALES. see ARCHAEOLOGY

SOCIETE D'ART ET D'HISTOIRE DU DIOCESE DE LIEGE. BULLETIN. see ART

944   FR
SOCIETE D'EMULATION DE MONTBELIARD. BULLETIN ET MEMOIRES. 1852. a. 150 F. Societe d'Emulation de Montbeliard, Musee Beurnier-Rossel, 8 place Saint-Martin, 25200 Montbeliard, France. Ed.Bd. circ. 700.
Formerly: Societe d'Emulation de Montbeliard. Memoires.

944   FR   ISSN 0081-0819
SOCIETE D'EMULATION HISTORIQUE ET LITTERAIRE D'ABBEVILLE. BULLETIN. 1888. a. 170 F.($10) Societe d'Emulation Historique et Litteraire d'Abbeville, Maison des Associations, 8 place du General de Gaulle, 80100 Abbeville, France. bk.rev.; cum.index every 4-5 yrs. circ. 400.

944   FR   ISSN 0081-0940
SOCIETE D'HISTOIRE DE FRANCE. ANNUAIRE. 1834. a. price varies. Editions Klincksieck, 11 rue de Lille, 75005 Paris, France. Ed. Michel Francois.

SOCIETE D'HISTOIRE ET D'ARCHEOLOGIE. MEMOIRES ET DOCUMENTS. SERIE IN 4. see ARCHAEOLOGY

SOCIETE D'HISTOIRE ET D'ARCHEOLOGIE. MEMOIRES ET DOCUMENTS. SERIE IN 8. see ARCHAEOLOGY

SOCIETE D'HISTOIRE ET D'ARCHEOLOGIE DE LA GOELE. BULLETIN D'INFORMATION. see ARCHAEOLOGY

SOCIETE D'HISTOIRE ET D'ARCHEOLOGIE DE VICHY ET DES ENVIRONS. BULLETIN. see ARCHAEOLOGY

913 913   FR   ISSN 0037-9190
SOCIETE DES ANTIQUAIRES DE L'OUEST. BULLETIN. 1834. q. 220 F. Societe des Antiquaires de l'Ouest, Rue Paul Guillon, B.P. 179, 86004 Poitiers Cedex, France. bk.rev.; index every 2 yrs. cum.index. circ. 1,000.

944   FR
SOCIETE DES ANTIQUAIRES DE L'OUEST. MEMOIRES. 1834. irreg. price varies. Societe des Antiquaires de l'Ouest, Rue Paul Guillon, B.P. 179, 86004 Poitiers Cedex, France.

SOCIETE DES ANTIQUAIRES DE PICARDIE. MEMOIRES. see ARCHAEOLOGY

SOCIETE DES ANTIQUAIRES DE PICARDIE. QUARTERLY BULLETIN. see ARCHAEOLOGY

944 914   FR   ISSN 0989-9200
SOCIETE DES SCIENCES HISTORIQUES ET NATURELLES DE SEMUR EN AUXOIS ET DES FOUILLES D'ALESIA. BULLETIN. 1864. s-a. 80 F. Societe des Sciences Historiques et Naturelles de Semur en Auxois et des Fouilles d'Alesia, 21140 Semur en Auxois, France. TEL 80-30-54-60. Ed. Benoist d'Anthenay. circ. 500.
Former titles: Tour de l'Orle d'Or (ISSN 0240-5407); Societe des Sciences Historiques et Naturelles de Semur en Auxois. Bulletin.
Description: Articles on various excavations, archeological discoveries, and their historical implications.

940.2   FR   ISSN 0988-9639
SOCIETE FRANCAISE D'ETUDE DU DIX-HUITIEME SIECLE. BULLETIN. 1971. q. 800 F. (foreign 100 F.). Societe Francaise d'Etude du Dix-Huitieme Siecle, Universite de Paris IV, 75005 Paris, France. Ed. Lucette Perol. adv.; bk.rev.; bibl. circ. 1,700. **Document type:** bulletin.

942 913   UI   ISSN 0144-1973
LA SOCIETE GUERNESIAISE. REPORT AND TRANSACTIONS. (Text in English) 1882. a. £10 membership. Societe Guernesiaise, Candie Gardens, St. Peter Port, Guernsey GY1 1UG, Channel Islands. TEL 0481-725093. FAX 0481-66217. Ed. C. David. bk.rev.; bibl.; illus.; index. circ. 1,350. **Indexed:** Br.Archaeol.Abstr. **Document type:** corporate report.
Description: Explores the history and natural history of Guernsey.

944   FR
SOCIETE HISTORIQUE DE VILLIERS SUR MARNE ET DE LA BRIE FRANCAISE. REVUE.* 1968. a. 10 F. Centre Culturel du Belvedere, 94350 Villiers S-Marne, France.

949.2   NE   ISSN 0167-6652
SOCIETE HISTORIQUE ET ARCHEOLOGIQUE DANS LE LIMBOURG. PUBLICATIONS/LIMBURGS GESCHIED- EN OUDHEIDKUNDIG GENOOTSCHAP. JAARBOEK. (Text in Dutch) 1864. a. fl.60 includes De Maasgouw. Limburgs Geschied- en Oudheidkundig Genootschap, Postbus 83, 6200 AB Maastricht, Netherlands. FAX 31-43-218572. bk.rev. circ. 3,000. **Indexed:** Amer.Hist.& Life (until 1984), Hist.Abstr. (until 1984). **Document type:** academic/scholarly publication.
—SWETS.

944   FR
SOCIETE HISTORIQUE ET ARCHEOLOGIQUE DE PONTOISE, DU VAL D'OISE ET DU VEXIN. MEMOIRES. irreg. Societe Historique et Archeologique de Pontoise, du Val d'Oise et du Vexin, 43 rue de la Roche, Pontoise, France. illus.

944   FR   ISSN 0037-9425
DC611.P441
SOCIETE HISTORIQUE ET ARCHEOLOGIQUE DU PERIGORD. BULLETIN. (Supplement avail.) 1874. 4/yr. 230 F. Societe Historique et Archeologique du Perigord, 18 rue du Plantier, 24000 Perigueux, France. Ed. J. Lagrange. bk.rev.; charts; illus.; index, cum.index vols.1-95 (1874-1984). circ. 1,000. (also avail. in microfilm from UMI) **Document type:** bulletin.

HISTORY — HISTORY OF EUROPE

944   FR
SOCIETE PHILOMATIQUE VOSGIENNE. BULLETIN. 1875. a. 150 F. Societe Philomatique Vosgienne, Bibliotheque Municipale, Rue St.-Charles, 88100 Saint-Die-des-Vosges, France. Ed. Albert Ronsin. adv.; bk.rev. circ. 650. **Document type:** bulletin.
    Description: Covers history, art, natural sciences, genealogy, ethnology.

947   US
SOCIETY AND CULTURE IN EAST-CENTRAL EUROPE. 1985. irreg., no.8, 1991. price varies. University of California Press, 2120 Berkeley Way, Berkeley, CA 94720. TEL 510-643-7127. FAX 510-643-7127. (Orders to: California-Princeton Fulfillment Services, 1445 Lower Ferry Rd., Ewing, NJ 08618. TEL 800-777-4726. FAX 800-999-1958) Eds. Irena Grudzinska, Jan T. Gross. (back issues avail.) **Document type:** monographic series.
    Description: Publishes translations of Polish and other East European scholarship on cultural and political history.
    Refereed Serial

945   US   ISSN 0081-1424
SOCIETY FOR ITALIAN HISTORICAL STUDIES. NEWSLETTER. 1963. a. free to members. Boston College, Society for Italian Historical Studies, Dept. of History, Chestnut Hill, MA 02167. TEL 617-969-0100. FAX 617-552-3814. Ed. Alan Reinerman. circ. 350. **Document type:** newsletter.

940   UK   ISSN 0306-4859
SOCIETY FOR LINCOLNSHIRE HISTORY AND ARCHAEOLOGY. ANNUAL REPORT AND STATEMENT OF ACCOUNTS. a. membership. Society for Lincolnshire History & Archaeology, Jew's Court, Steep Hill, Lincoln LN2 1LS, England. TEL 0522-521337. circ. 700. **Document type:** corporate report.

SOCIETY FOR RENAISSANCE STUDIES. BULLETIN. see *LITERATURE*

947 407   US
SOCIETY FOR SLOVENE STUDIES. DOCUMENTATION SERIES. 1975. irreg. price varies. Society for Slovene Studies, c/o Slavic Dept., BH502, Indiana University, Bloomington, IN 47405. Ed. Rado L. Lencek. index. circ. 350. **Document type:** academic/scholarly publication.

946   US   ISSN 0739-182X
SOCIETY FOR SPANISH AND PORTUGUESE HISTORICAL STUDIES. BULLETIN. (Text in Catalan, English, Portuguese, Spanish) 1969. 3/yr. $20 to members in N. America; elsewhere $25; institutions $25. Society for Spanish and Portuguese Historical Studies, c/o Paul Freedman, General Sec., History Department, Vanderbilt University, Nashville, TN 37235. TEL 615-322-2575. FAX 615-343-8028. Eds. Benjamine Taggie, Dan Crews. adv.; bk.rev.; bibl.; index. circ. 400. (also avail. in microfiche; microfilm; back issues avail.) **Document type:** academic/scholarly publication.
    Formerly (until vol.4, 1977): Society for Spanish and Portuguese Historical Studies. Newsletter.

942   UK   ISSN 0265-1785
SOCIETY OF ANTIQUARIES OF NEWCASTLE UPON TYNE. MONOGRAPH SERIES. 1979. irreg. price varies. Society of Antiquaries of Newcastle upon Tyne, The Black Gate, Castle Garth, Newcastle upon Tyne NE1 1RQ, England. Ed. John Philipson. bk.rev. **Document type:** monographic series.

942   UK
SOCIETY OF ANTIQUARIES OF NEWCASTLE UPON TYNE. RECORD SERIES. 1968. irreg. price varies. Society of Antiquaries of Newcastle upon Tyne, The Black Gate, Castle Garth, Newcastle upon Tyne NE1 1RQ, England. Ed. John Philipson. bk.rev. **Document type:** monographic series.

942 913   UK   ISSN 0263-3191
SOCIETY OF ANTIQUARIES OF SCOTLAND. MONOGRAPH SERIES. 1982. irreg. price varies. Society of Antiquaries of Scotland, Royal Museum of Scotland, Queen St., Edinburgh EH2 1JD, Scotland. Ed. Mrs. A. Shepherd. Indexed: Br.Archaeol.Abstr. **Document type:** monographic series.
    —BLDSC (5917.106000).
    Description: Covers major archeaological excavations in Scotland.

942   UK   ISSN 0081-1564
SOCIETY OF ANTIQUARIES OF SCOTLAND. PROCEEDINGS. 1851. a. £18 to non-members. Society of Antiquaries of Scotland, Royal Museum of Scotland, Queen St., Edinburgh EH2 1JD, Scotland. index. circ. 3,300. **Indexed:** A.I.C.P., Anthropol.Lit., Avery Ind.Archit.Per., Numis.Lit., RILA. **Document type:** proceedings.
    —BLDSC (6811.689000); UMI.
    Description: Studies in Scottish archeaology and history.

SOCIETY OF ARCHITECTURAL HISTORIANS OF GREAT BRITAIN NEWSLETTER. see *ARCHITECTURE*

480 938   CY   ISSN 0081-1580
SOCIETY OF CYPRIOT STUDIES. BULLETIN/KYPRIAKAI SPOUDAI. (Text in Greek and other languages) 1937. a. £C10($23) Society of Cypriot Studies, Box 1436, Nicosia, Cyprus. Ed. George Ioannides. bk.rev. circ. 500. **Indexed:** Amer.Hist.& Life, Hist.Abstr., M.L.A.

948   DK   ISSN 0085-6339
SOELLEROEDBOGEN. 1942. a. DKK 100. Historisk-Topografisk Selskab for Soelleroed Kommune, Byhistorisk Arkiv, Gl. Holtegaard, Attemosevej 170, 2840 Holte, Denmark. TEL 45-42-80-01-69. FAX 45-42-80-15-60. Eds. Niels Peter Stilling, Jens Johansen. illus. circ. 1,600.
    Description: Contains essays on local history

948.9   DK   ISSN 0049-125X
SOENDERJYSK MAANEDSSKRIFT. 1924. m. DKK 130. Historisk Samfund for Soenderjylland, Haderslevvej 45, 6200 Aabenraa, Denmark. adv.; bk.rev.; bibl.; charts; illus.; stat.; cum.index. circ. 2,100. **Indexed:** Numis.Lit.
    Description: Covers local interests.

948   DK   ISSN 0106-4452
SOENDERJYSKE AARBOEGER. 1889. a. Historisk Samfund for Soenderjylland, Haderslevvej 45, 6200 Aabenraa, Denmark. cum.index: 1889-1988.

948.5   SW   ISSN 0349-0297
SOERMLANDSBYGDEN. 1932. a. SEK 125 (effective 1990). Soedermanlands Hembygdsfoerbund, P.O. Box 138, S-611 23, Nykoeping, Sweden. TEL 0155-28-43-00. FAX 0155-21-74-77. Ed. Ingegerd Wachtmeister. adv.; bk.rev. circ. 6,000. **Document type:** monographic series.

940   GW
SOESTER BEITRAEGE. 1949. irreg. price varies. Verein fuer Geschichte und Heimatpflege Soest e.V., Stadtarchiv, Postfach 2252, 59491 Soest, Germany. bibl. **Document type:** monographic series.

940   GW   ISSN 0176-3946
DD491.W512
SOESTER ZEITSCHRIFT. 1881. a. DM.30. Verein fuer Geschichte und Heimatpflege Soest e.V., Stadtarchiv, Postfach 2252, 59491 Soest, Germany. **Document type:** bulletin.

940   BU   ISSN 0081-184X
SOFIISKI UNIVERSITET. FILOSOFSKI FAKULTET. GODISNIK/UNIVERSITE DE SOFIA. FACULTE DE PHILOSOPHIE. ANNUAIRE. (Text in Bulgarian; summaries in various languages) vol.67, 1973. irreg. price varies. Publishing House of the Bulgarian Academy of Sciences, Acad. G. Bonchev St., Bldg. 6, 1113 Sofia, Bulgaria. circ. 555. (reprint service avail. from IRC)
    Supersedes: Sofiiski Universitet. Filosofski-Istoriceski Fakultet. Godisnik.

947 320   BU   ISSN 0324-0037
SOFIYA. 1958. m. 62 Fr. (Sofiiski Gradski Naroden Suvet) Foreign Trade Co. "Hemus", 7 Levsky St., 1000 Sofia, Bulgaria. TELEX 22267 HEMKIK. Ed. Stefan Prodev.

942   UK   ISSN 0049-1306
SOMERSET AND DORSET NOTES AND QUERIES. 1888. 2/yr. £5($15) c/o Michael McGarvie, Marston House, Marston Bigot, Frome, Somerset BA11 5DU, England. TEL 0373-451001. Eds. D.M.M. Shorrocks, G.J. Davies. adv.; bk.rev.; charts; illus.; index. circ. 500. **Document type:** academic/scholarly publication.
    Description: Covers local history, archaeology, folklore, genealogy and heraldry, and history of Europe.

943.9   HU   ISSN 0133-0748
SOPRONI SZEMLE. 1937. 4/yr. $15.50. Gyor-Sopron Megyei Lapkiado Vallalat, P.O. Box 28, 9002 Gyor, Hungary. Ed. Mollay Karoly. illus.; bibl. circ. 1,000. **Indexed:** Numis.Lit.

SOTAHISTORIALLINEN AIKAKAUSKIRJA. see *MILITARY*

940   FR   ISSN 0398-3811
SOURCES D'HISTOIRE MEDIEVALE. 1965. a. price varies. (Centre National de la Recherche Scientifique, Institut de Recherche et d'Histoire des Textes) C N R S Editions, 20-22 rue St. Amand, 75005 Paris, France. TEL 45-33-16-00. FAX 45-33-92-13. TELEX 200 356 F. (Dist. outside France by: N.V. Brepols, Steenweg op Tielen 68, 2300 Turnhout, Belgium. TEL 32-14-402500. FAX 32-14-428919) adv.; bk.rev.; index; circ. 1,250 (controlled). (back issues avail.) **Document type:** monographic series.

944   FR   ISSN 0248-5516
SOURCES ET TRAVAUX D'HISTOIRE HAUT-PYRENEENNE. 1980. irreg. 70 Fr. Association Guillaume Mauran, Archives Departementales des Hautes-Pyrenees, Rue des Ursulines, 65000 Tarbes, France.

940   UK   ISSN 0142-4688
DA20
SOUTHERN HISTORY. 1979. a. £12.50 to institutions; individuals £10. Southern History Society, c/o R.A.E. Wells, Ed., School of Historical and Critical Studies, University of Brighton, Grand Parade, Brighton BN2 2JY, England. TEL 0273-643111. FAX 0273-679179. adv.; bk.rev. circ. 450. (also avail. in microfiche) **Indexed:** Amer.Hist.& Life, Br.Archaeol.Abstr., Hist.Abstr. **Document type:** academic/scholarly publication.
    —BLDSC (8354.140000).
    Description: Contains articles on all aspects of the history of the southern counties of England from pre-historical times to the present.

947   RU
SOVETSKOE SLAVIANOVEDENIE. 1965. 6/yr. 27.60 Rub. Izdatel'stvo Nauka, 90 Profsoyuznaya ul., 117864 Moscow, Russia. (Subscr. to: Trubnikovskii Per. 30-A, Moscow , G-69, Russia) bibl.; index. **Indexed:** Amer.Hist.& Life, Bibl.Ling., Hist.Abstr., Int.Bibl.Soc.Sci.

940 100   NE   ISSN 0561-2551
SOVIETICA. PUBLICATIONS AND MONOGRAPHS. 1959. irreg., vol.56, 1991. price varies. (Universite de Fribourg, Institute of East-European Studies, SZ) Kluwer Academic Publishers, Postbus 17, 3300 AA Dordrecht, Netherlands. TEL 31-78-334911. FAX 31-78-334254. TELEX 29245 KAPG NL. (Dist. by: Kluwer Academic Publishers Group, P.O. Box 322, 3300 AH Dordrecht, Netherlands. TEL 31-78-524400. FAX 31-78-524474; N. America dist. addr.: Box 358, Accord Sta., Hingham, MA 0218-0358. TEL 617-871-6600. FAX 617-871-6528) Ed.Bd. **Document type:** monographic series.
    Formed by the merger of: Sovietica. Publication (ISSN 0081-3206); Sovietica. Monographs (ISSN 0081-3192)
    Refereed Serial

947   BW   ISSN 0236-1019
SPADCYNA. (Text in Byelorussian; summary in English) 1970. bi-m. Storozhovskaya 5, 220029 Minsk, Belarus. TEL 0172-342650. FAX 0172-395869. Ed. K. Tarasau. bk.rev. circ. 10,000.
    —BLDSC (0166.302200).
    Formerly (until 1989): Pomniki Histor'ii Kul'tury Belarusi (ISSN 0131-2669)

946   IT   ISSN 1121-7480
▼**SPAGNA CONTEMPORANEA.** 1992. s-a. L.45000 (foreign L.60000) (effective 1992). (Instituto si Studi Storici "Gaetano Salvemini") Edizioni dell' Orso, Via Piacenza 66, 15100 Alessandria, Italy. TEL 0131-252349. Eds. Claudio Venza, Alfonso Botti. bk.rev.; bibl.
    Description: Covers contemporary Spanish history and its connections with Italy.

946   GW   ISSN 0342-1058
SPANISCHE FORSCHUNGEN DER GOERRESGESELLSCHAFT. REIHE 1: GESAMMELTE AUFSAETZE ZUR KULTURGESCHICHTE SPANIENS. 1928. irreg. price varies. (Goerres-Gesellschaft) Aschendorffsche Verlagsbuchhandlung, Soesterstr. 13, 48155 Muenster, Germany. TEL 0251-690-0. FAX 0251-690143. Ed. Odilo Engels. **Document type:** monographic series.

HISTORY — HISTORY OF EUROPE

946   GW   ISSN 0081-3494
SPANISCHE FORSCHUNGEN DER GOERRESGESELLSCHAFT. REIHE 2: MONOGRAPHIEN. 1931. irreg. price varies. (Goerres-Gesellschaft) Aschendorffsche Verlagsbuchhandlung, Soesterstr. 13, 48155 Muenster, Germany. TEL 0251-690-0. FAX 0251-690143. Ed. Odilo Engels. **Document type:** monographic series.

909.07   US   ISSN 0038-7134
PN661
SPECULUM; a journal of Medieval studies. 1926. q. $70 to non-members in N. America (foreign non-members $80). Medieval Academy of America, 1430 Massachusetts Ave., Cambridge, MA 02138. TEL 617-491-1622. Ed. Luke Wenger. adv.; bk.rev.; bibl.; index. circ. 6,200. (also avail. in microform from MIM,UMI; back issues avail.; reprint service avail.) **Indexed:** Abstr.Engl.Stud., Acad.Ind., Amer.Bibl.Slavic & E.Eur.Stud., Art Ind., Bibl.Ling., Bk.Rev.Ind. (1965-), Br.Archaeol.Abstr., Can.Rev.Comp.Lit., Child.Bk.Rev.Ind. (1965-), Curr.Cont., Hum.Ind., Ind.Bk.Rev.Hum., Ind.Vet., Numis.Lit., Ref.Sour., Rel.Ind.One, RILA, Vet.Bull.
—BLDSC (8411.178000); Faxon; UnCover; SWETS; UMI.

909.07   US
SPECULUM ANNIVERSARY MONOGRAPHS. 1977. irreg., no.15, 1989. price varies. Medieval Academy of America, 1430 Massachusetts Ave., Cambridge, MA 02138. TEL 617-491-1622.

949.2   NE   ISSN 0169-8931
SPECULUM HISTORIALE. (Text in English) 1965. irreg., vol.13, 1993. price varies. Van Gorcum en Co. B.V., P.O. Box 43, 6400 AA Assen, Netherlands. TEL 31-5920-46846. FAX 31-5920-72064. **Document type:** monographic series.

940 296   IS   ISSN 0333-9378
SPIEGEL LECTURES IN EUROPEAN JEWISH HISTORY. 1982. irreg. $5 per no. Tel Aviv University, School of Jewish Studies, Ramat Aviv, Tel Aviv, Israel. Ed. Lloyd P. Gartner. circ. 1,500. **Document type:** academic/scholarly publication.

949.7   YU   ISSN 0350-4778
SPONE. 1969. 2/yr. Centar za Informativnu Djelatnost, Novice Cerovica 30, 81400 Niksic, Montenegro, Yugoslavia. (Co-sponsor: O.S.I.Z. Kulture i Naucnih Djelatnosti) circ. 1,000.

943   GW   ISSN 0933-8799
SPUREN SUCHEN. 1988. a. DM.3. Koerber Stiftung, Kampchaussee 10, 21033 Hamburg, Germany. TEL 040-72502439. FAX 040-72503798. adv.; bk.rev. circ. 125,000. (back issues avail.) **Document type:** academic/scholarly publication.

SRPSKI ETNOGRAFSKI ZBORNIK. NASELJA I POREKLO STANOVNISTVA. see *ANTHROPOLOGY*

SRPSKI ETNOGRAFSKI ZBORNIK. RASPRAVE I GRADJA. see *ANTHROPOLOGY*

SRPSKI ETNOGRAFSKI ZBORNIK. SRPSKE NARODNE UMOTVORINE. see *ANTHROPOLOGY*

SRPSKI ETNOGRAFSKI ZBORNIK. ZIVOT I OBICAJI NARODNI. see *ANTHROPOLOGY*

943   GW
STAATLICHEN DENKMALPFLEGE IM SAARLAND. BERICHT. 1923. biennial. Staatliches Konservatoramt, Schlossplatz 16, 66119 Saarbruecken, Germany. TEL 0681-503-1.

943   GW   ISSN 0930-8946
STADER JAHRBUCH; Stader Archiv Neue Folge. 1862. a. DM.35. Stader Geschichts- und Heimatverein, Rathaus, 21682 Stade, Germany. TEL 04141-401-200. Ed. Bernd Kappelhoff. **Document type:** bulletin.

943.6   AU
STADTARCHIV KREMS. MITTEILUNGEN. 1961. irreg. price varies. Kulturamt der Stadt Krems, Koernermarkt 13, 3500 Krems an der Donau, Austria. Ed. Harry Kuehnel. bk.rev. circ. 400.

914.3   GW   ISSN 0936-3483
STADTARCHIV SANKT AUGUSTIN. BEITRAEGE ZUR STADTGESCHICHTE. irreg. Stadtarchiv Sankt Augustin, Markt 1, 53757 Sankt Augustin, Germany. TEL 02241-243224.

913   UK   ISSN 0950-1630
CODEN: STSTE8
STAFFORDSHIRE STUDIES. 1988. a. £7.50($18) University of Keele, Centre for Local History, Keele, Staffordshire ST5 5BG, England. TEL 0782-621111. FAX 0782-583195. Ed. J.R. Studd. adv. contact: A. Seaton. circ. 350. **Indexed:** Br.Archaeol.Abstr., Br.Hum.Ind., Geo.Abstr., Numis.Lit. **Document type:** academic/scholarly publication.
—BLDSC (8426.427000).
   Formerly: North Staffordshire Journal of Field Studies (ISSN 0078-1649)

940.3 355   UK   ISSN 0261-6548
STAND TO!. 1981. 3/yr. £14 membership. Western Front Association, P.O. Box 1914, Reading, Berkshire RG4 7YP, England. Ed. R.W. Butcher. adv.; bk.rev.; illus. circ. 3,900. (back issues avail.) **Document type:** academic/scholarly publication.

STANFORD FRENCH REVIEW. see *LITERATURE*

940   NE
HET STARING INSTITUUT. WERKEN. 1980. a. price varies. Walburg Pers BV, Postbus 4159, 7200 BD Zutphen, Netherlands. TEL 31-5750-10522. FAX 31-5750-41025. (Co-sponsor: Het Staring Instituut) **Document type:** monographic series.

949.5   CY
STASINOS. (Text in English, Greek) 1963. irreg. Syndesmos Hellenon Philologon Kyprou Stasinos, Stasinos, Pankyprion Oikonomikon Lykeion, Nicosia, Cyprus.

943.7   XR   ISSN 0862-2507
STATNI OBLASTNI ARCHIV V OPAVE. SBORNIK. 1969. every 5 yrs. Statni Archiv v Opava, Archivni Sprava, Snemovni 1, 746 22 Opava, Czech Republic. bk.rev.; illus.
   Formerly (until 1982): Statni Archiv v Opave. Sbornik (ISSN 0231-6250)

943.7 913   XR
STATNI OKRESNI ARCHIV V OLOMOUCI. ROCENKA. 1974. a. Okresni Archiv v Olomouci, Krizkovskeho 2, Olomouc, Czech Republic. TEL 42-68-5223607. (Dist. by: Artia, Ve Smeckach 30, 111 27 Prague 1, Czech Republic) Ed. Vladimir Spacil. circ. 700.
   Formerly (until 1993): Okresni Archiv v Olomouci. Vyrocni Zprava (ISSN 0862-2833)

943.6   AU   ISSN 0434-3883
STEIERMAERKISCHES LANDESARCHIV. MITTEILUNGEN. 1951. a. Steiermaerkisches Landesarchiv, Buergergasse 2-A, A-8010 Graz, Austria. TEL 0316-8772361. circ. 2,275. **Indexed:** Amer.Hist.& Life, Hist.Abstr. **Document type:** proceedings.

949.2 340   NE
STICHTING TOT UITGAAF DER BRONNEN VAN HET OUD-VADERLAANDSE RECHT. 2 SERIES: WERKEN, VERSLAGEN EN MEDEDELINGEN. (Issued in two parts) 1885. irreg., latest vol.17. fl.35. (Juridisch Instituut) Walburg Pers BV, Postbus 4159, 7200 BD Zutphen, Netherlands. TEL 31-5750-10522. FAX 31-5750-41025. Ed. F.C.J. Ketelaar. circ. 500. **Indexed:** Amer.Hist.& Life, Hist.Abstr. **Document type:** monographic series.
   Formerly: Vereniging tot Uitgave der Bronnen van het oud Vaderlandsche Recht. Verslagen en Mededelingen.

940   NE
STICHTSE HISTORISCHE REEKS. 1975. a. price varies. (Stichting Stichtse Historische Reeks) Walburg Pers BV, Postbus 4159, 7200 BD Zutphen, Netherlands. TEL 31-5750-10522. FAX 31-5750-41025. **Document type:** monographic series.

060   GW   ISSN 0342-0124
AM51.B4
STIFTUNG PREUSSISCHE KULTURBESITZ. JAHRBUCH. 1962. a. price varies. Gebr. Mann Verlag GmbH, Lindenstr. 76, 10969 Berlin, Germany. TEL 030-2591-3589. FAX 030-2591-3537. (Subscr. to: 10888 Berlin, Germany) (reprint service avail.) **Indexed:** Avery Ind.Archit.Per. **Document type:** academic/scholarly publication.

STILLE SCHAR. see *RELIGIONS AND THEOLOGY — Roman Catholic*

941   UK   ISSN 0957-3771
STOCKPORT HERITAGE MAGAZINE; Cheshire heritage past and present. 1987. q. £8 (foreign £12). Stockport Heritage Publications, 12 Devon Close, Stockport, Cheshire SK5 8DD, England. TEL 061-427-7035. Ed. Steve Cliffe. adv.: B&W page £500, color page £700; adv. contact: Jean Cliffe. bk.rev. circ. 6,000. (back issues avail.) **Document type:** consumer publication.

945   IT   ISSN 0392-8926
STORIA DELLA STORIOGRAFIA/HISTORY OF HISTORIOGRAPHY/HISTOIRE DE L'HISTORIOGRAPHIE/GESCHICHTE DER GESCHICHTSSCHREIBUNG. (Text in English, French, German, Italian) 1982. s-a. L.70000 (foreign L.80000) (effective 1994). Editoriale Jaca Book s.p.a., Via Gioberti 7, 20123 Milan, Italy. TEL 02-4982341. FAX 02-48193361. TELEX 324267 JACATE I. (Subscr. to: Via Rovani 7, 20123 Milan, Italy) Ed. Bianca Valota. bk.rev. circ. 1,000. (back issues avail.)
—UnCover; SWETS.

945   IT
STORIA E CIVILTA. 1985. q. L.50000. (Centro di Studi sulla Civilta Comunale) Edizioni del Lavoro s.r.l., G.B. Martini, 6, I-00198 Rome, Italy.

STORIA E LETTERATURA. see *LITERATURE*

945   IT
▼**STORIA E MEMORIA.** 1992. s-a. L.30000 (foreign L.50000). Istituto Storico della Resistenza in Liguria, Via Garibaldi 14, 16124 Genoa, Italy. Ed. Guido Arato.

945   IT   ISSN 1120-4206
HN418.M37
STORIA E PROBLEMI CONTEMPORANEI. 1981. s-a. L.37000 (foreign L.65000) (effective 1994). Istituto Regionale per la Storia del Movimento di Liberazione nelle Marche, Via Villafranca 1, 60122 Ancona, Italy. (Dist. by: Edizioni Quattroventi S.n.c., Cas. Post. 156, Urbino, Italy) Ed. Massimo Papini.
   Formerly (until 1987): Quaderni di Resistenza Marche (ISSN 0393-6430)

945   IT
STORIA E SOCIETA. 1976. irreg. (Istituto di Storia Contemporanea del Movimento Operaio e Contadino di Ferrera) Ricardo F. Levi Editore S.p.A., 1085-2 via Vaciglio, 41010 Modena, Italy. **Document type:** monographic series.

945   IT
STORIA IN LOMBARDIA. 1982. 3/yr. L.69000 (foreign L.90000) (effective 1993). (Istituto Lombardo per la Storia del Movimento di Liberazione) Franco Angeli Editore, Viale Monza, 106, Casella Postale 17175, 20100 Milan, Italy. TEL 02-2895762.

945   IT
STORIA, LETTERATURA E ARTE NEL MEZZOGIORNO. 1974. irreg., no.5, 1976. L.5000. T D C Telediffusione Cattolica, Piazza S. Eframo Vecchio 21, 80137 Naples, Italy. TEL 081-751-94-03. FAX 081-751-93-74. Ed. Fiorenzo F. Mastroianni. **Document type:** monographic series.

945   IT
STORIADENTRO; rivista di studi su Conegliano e il Coneglianese. 1977. biennial. Comune, Piazza Beccaria-Biblioteca Civica, 31015 Conegliano, Italy. TEL 0438 35041.

945 700   IT
STUDI BITONTINI. 3/yr. Centro Ricerche di Storia e Arte Bitontina, Viale Giovanni XXIII, 129, 70032 Bitonto, Italy. Ed. Felice Moretti.

STUDI E RICERCHE SULL'ORIENTE CRISTIANO. see *RELIGIONS AND THEOLOGY*

940   IT
STUDI ETRUSCHI. 1927. a. price varies. Giorgio Bretschneider, Via Crescenzio 43, 00193 Rome, Italy. Eds. M. Pallottino, A. Neppi Modona. index. **Indexed:** Bibl.Ling.

STUDI LUNIGIANESI. see *ETHNIC INTERESTS*

940   IT
STUDI MEDIEVALI. 1904-1913; N.S. 1923-1927; N.S. 1928-1942; N.S. 1960. s-a. L.180000 (effective 1993). Centro Italiano di Studi sull'Alto Medioevo, Palazzo Ancaiani, 06049 Spoleto, Italy. TEL 0743-220418. FAX 0743-223507. Ed. Claudio Leonardi. cum.index: 1960-1979 (vols.1-20), 1980-1989 (vols.21-30). **Indexed:** Arts & Hum.Cit.Ind., Bibl.Ling., M.L.A. **Document type:** academic/scholarly publication.

945   IT
STUDI PIACENTINI. s-a. L.25000 to non-members. Istituto Storico della Resistenza e dell'Eta Contemporanea, Palazzo Farnese, 29100 Piacenza, Italy. Ed. Angelo Del Boca.

945   IT   ISSN 0081-6205
STUDI ROMAGNOLI. 1950. a. L.30000. Societa di Studi Romagnoli, c/o Biblioteca Malatestiana, 47023 Cesena, Italy. **Indexed:** Numis.Lit., RILA.

945   IT   ISSN 0081-6213
STUDI ROMAGNOLI. ESTRATTI DI SEZIONE. 1951. irreg. price varies. Societa di Studi Romagnoli, c/o Biblioteca Malatestiana, 47023 Cesena, Italy.

945   IT   ISSN 0081-6221
STUDI ROMAGNOLI. QUADERNI. 1962. irreg., no.15, 1993. price varies. Societa di Studi Romagnoli, c/o Biblioteca Malatestiana, 47023 Cesena, Italy.

945   IT   ISSN 0039-3002
STUDI SALENTINI. 1956. q. L.50000. (Centro di Studi Salentini) Edizioni del Lavoro s.r.l., Via G.B. Martini 6, 00198 Rome, Italy. Ed. Dir. Prof. Pier Fausto Palumbo. adv.; bk.rev.; bibl.; illus. (also avail. in microform)

STUDI SENESI. see *LAW*

945   IT
STUDI STORICI MERIDIONALI. 1981. q. L.41000. Capone Editore s.r.l., Via Caprarica 35, 73020 Cavallino (LE), Italy. TEL 0832-611877. FAX 0832-612618. Ed. Tommaso Pedio. adv.

947   BU
STUDIA BALCANICA. (Text in English, French, German, Russian) irreg., no.3, 1970. price varies. Publishing House of the Bulgarian Academy of Sciences, Acad. G. Boncev St., Bldg. 6, 1113 Sofia, Bulgaria. (reprint service avail. from IRC)

STUDIA CAUCASICA. see *LINGUISTICS*

STUDIA CELTICA. see *LINGUISTICS*

940   XR   ISSN 0323-2220
LB475.C6
STUDIA COMENIANA ET HISTORICA. (Text in Czech, English, German, Polish, Russian, Slovak) 1971. 2/yr. 60 Kc. Muzeum J.A. Komenskeho - Museum of J.A. Comenius, Premysla Otakara II, 36, 688 12 Uhersky Brod, Czech Republic. TEL 0042-0633-2288. FAX 0042-0633-4078. Ed. Libuse Velcovska. bk.rev. circ. 400. **Indexed:** Amer.Hist.& Life, Bibl.Ling., Hist.Abstr. **Document type:** academic/scholarly publication.
    Description: Presents history of the 16th, 17th and 18th centuries in Europe and the regional history and ethnography of the Moravian-Slovakian borderland.

STUDIA HIBERNICA. see *LINGUISTICS*

947.1   FI   ISSN 0081-6493
D1
STUDIA HISTORICA. (Text in English, French or German) 1959. irreg., no.45, 1993. Fmk.140. Suomen Historiallinen Seura - Finnish Historical Society, Arkadiankatu 16 B 28, 00100 Helsinki 10, Finland. FAX 441-468. circ. 350. **Document type:** monographic series.
    Description: Monographs on topics in Finnish and world history.

945   IT   ISSN 0081-6507
STUDIA HISTORICA. 1964. irreg., no.127, 1981. price varies. L'Erma di Bretschneider, Via Cassiodoro, 19, 00193 Rome, Italy. TEL 06-687-41-27. FAX 06-687-41-29.

946   SP   ISSN 0213-2052
STUDIA HISTORICA. HISTORIA ANTIGUA. 1983. a. 1200 ptas. Ediciones Universidad de Salamanca, Apdo. 325, 37080 Salamanca, Spain. TEL 923-26-14-54. Dir. Maria Jose Hidalgo de Vega. **Document type:** academic/scholarly publication.
    Description: Contains studies on ancient Roman and Spanish history.

946   SP   ISSN 0213-2087
STUDIA HISTORICA. HISTORIA CONTEMPORANEA. 1983. a. 1200 ptas. Ediciones Universidad de Salamanca, Apdo. 325, 37080 Salamanca, Spain. TEL 923-26-14-54. Dir. Esther Martinez Quinteiro. **Indexed:** Amer.Hist.& Life (1992-), Hist.Abstr. (1992-). **Document type:** academic/scholarly publication.
    Description: Contains studies on contemporary Spanish history.

946   SP   ISSN 0213-2060
DP99
STUDIA HISTORICA. HISTORIA MEDIEVAL. 1983. a. 1200 ptas. Ediciones Universidad de Salamanca, Apdo. 325, 37080 Salamanca, Spain. TEL 923-26-14-54. Dir. Jose Maria Minguez Fernandez. **Document type:** academic/scholarly publication.
    Description: Contains studies on medieval Spanish history.

946   SP   ISSN 0213-2079
STUDIA HISTORICA. HISTORIA MODERNA. 1983. a. 1200 ptas. Ediciones Universidad de Salamanca, Apdo. 325, 37080 Salamanca, Spain. TEL 923-26-14-54. Dir. Manuel Fernandez Alvarez. **Indexed:** Amer.Hist.& Life (1992-), Hist.Abstr. (1992-). **Document type:** academic/scholarly publication.
    Description: Contains studies on modern Spanish history.

947.1   FI   ISSN 0081-6523
STUDIA HISTORICA JYVASKYLAENSIA. (Text in English, Finnish, French, German, Swedish; summaries in English, German) 1962. irreg. price varies. Jyvaskylan Yliopisto - University of Jyvaskyla, Library, PL 35, 40100 Jyvaskyla 10, Finland. TEL 941-601-371. FAX 603-371. TELEX 28219 JYK SF. Eds. Erkki Lehtinen, Jorma Ahvenainen. circ. 450. **Document type:** monographic series.

940   FI   ISSN 0356-8199
STUDIA HISTORICA SEPTENTRIONALIA. (Text in English) 1978. a. FIM 90($14) Pohjois-Suomen Historiallinen Yhdistys, Oulun Yliopisto, Historian Laitos - Historical Association of Northern Finland, Postilokero 191, 90101 Oulu, Finland. Ed. Kyoesti Julku.

918 930   PL   ISSN 0301-6420
STUDIA HISTORICA SLAVO-GERMANICA. (Text in German and Polish; summaries in German) 1973. irreg., vol.17, 1992. price varies. Adam Mickiewicz University Press, Nowowiejskiego 55, 61-734 Poznan, Poland. TEL 527-380. FAX 61-526425. TELEX 413260 UAMPL. Ed. Antoni Czubinski. bk.rev.; bibl. circ. 360. **Document type:** academic/scholarly publication.
—BLDSC (8482.846000).
    Description: Papers and articles written by Polish and foreign authors. Contains research results and opinions in the field of history, political education, and literature.

943.7   XO
STUDIA HISTORICA SLOVACA. (Text in English, French, German, Russian) 1963. a. Veda, Publishing House of the Slovak Academy of Sciences, Klemensova 19, 814 30 Bratislava, Slovakia. (Dist. by: Slovart, Nam. Slobody 6, 817 64 Bratislava, Slovakia) bk.rev. **Indexed:** Amer.Hist.& Life, Hist.Abstr.

940   SW   ISSN 0081-6531
STUDIA HISTORICA UPSALIENSIA. (Subseries of Acta Universitatis Upsala) (Text in English, French, German, Norwegian, Swedish; summaries in English, French, German) 1960. irreg. price varies. (Uppsala Universitet, Historiska Institutionen) A W I International AB, P.O. Box 4627, S-116 91 Stockholm, Sweden. TEL 468-640-8800. FAX 468-641-1180. Ed.Bd. index.

900   PL   ISSN 0025-1429
DK511.M24
STUDIA HISTORYCZNE. (Text in Polish; summaries in English) 1956. q. $50. (Polska Akademia Nauk, Oddzial w Krakowie, Komisja Nauk Historycznych) Ossolineum, Publishing House of the Polish Academy of Sciences, Rynek 9, 50-106 Wroclaw, Poland. TEL 48-71-386-25. FAX 48-71-448-103. TELEX 0712771 OSS PL. Ed. J. Buszko. bk.rev.; index. **Indexed:** Amer.Hist.& Life, Hist.Abstr. **Document type:** academic/scholarly publication.
—BLDSC (8482.855000).
    Formerly: Malopolskie Studia Historyczne.

940 270   NE   ISSN 0324-7880
STUDIA HUMANITATIS. 1973. irreg., vol.5, 1982. price varies. E.J. Brill, P.O. Box 9000, 2300 PA Leiden, Netherlands. TEL 31-71-312624. FAX 31-71-317532. TELEX 39296 BRILL NL. (In N. America: E.J. Brill, 24 Hudson St., Kinderhook, NY 12106. TEL 800-962-4406. FAX 518-758-1959) **Document type:** monographic series.
Refereed Serial

943.8   PL   ISSN 0081-654X
STUDIA I MATERIALY DO DZIEJOW WIELKOPOLSKI I POMORZA. 1955. irreg., vol.18, 1991. price varies. (Polskie Towarzystwo Historyczne, Oddzial w Poznaniu) Wydawnictwo Naukowe P W N, Ul. Miodowa 10, 00-251 Warsaw, Poland. (Dist. by: Ars Polona, Krakowskie Przedmiescie 7, 00-068 Warsaw, Poland) Ed. Jerzy Topolski. bk.rev.; illus. circ. 300.

STUDIA I MATERIALY DO HISTORII WOJSKOWOSCI. see *MILITARY*

943.8   PL   ISSN 0137-4354
STUDIA KIELECKIE. 4/yr. 15000 Zl. (effective 1993). Kieleckie Towarzystwo Naukowe, Ul. Zamkowa 5, 25-009 Kielce, Poland. TEL 454-53. bk.rev. circ. 200. **Document type:** bulletin.
—BLDSC (8482.957200).
    Formerly (until 1971): Kieleckie Towarzystwo Naukowe. Kwartalnik.

943.8   PL   ISSN 0860-7249
STUDIA LOMZYNSKIE. 1989. irreg., vol.4, 1993. price varies. (Lomzynskie Towarzystwo Naukowe im. Wagow) Wydawnictwo Naukowe P W N - Polish Scientific Publishers P W N Ltd., Ul. Miodowa 10, 00-251 Warsaw, Poland. TEL 48-22-260207. FAX 48-22-267163. (Dist. by: Ars Polona, Krakowskie Przedmiescie 7, 00-251 Warsaw, Poland)

946   SP   ISSN 1132-130X
B765.L84
STUDIA LULLIANA. (Text in Catalan, English, French, German, Spanish) 1957. 2/yr. 1800 ptas. (Schola Lullistica of Mallorca) Editorial Moll, Apdo. 142, 07080 Palma de Mallorca, Spain. TEL 72 41 76. FAX 726252. Eds. S. Trias Mercant, A. Bonner. adv.; bk.rev.; bibl.; illus.; cum.index: 1957-1983. circ. 1,500. **Document type:** academic/scholarly publication.
—Faxon.
    Formerly (until 1990): Estudios Lulianos (ISSN 0425-3752)
    Description: Presents modern studies on the Mallorcan medieval philosopher, missionary, novelist and mystic, Ramon Llull (1232-1316). Discusses his philosophical, literary and historical background.

914.38   PL   ISSN 0081-6752
STUDIA NAD ZAGADNIENIAMI GOSPODARCZYMI I SPOLECZNYMI ZIEM ZACHODNICH. 1960. irreg. price varies. Instytut Zachodni, Stary Rynek 78-79, 61-772 Poznan, Poland.

949.7   XV   ISSN 0585-5543
STUDIA SLOVENICA. 1958. irreg., no.17, 1991. Studia Slovenica, P.O. Box 28, 61210 Ljubljana, Slovenia. (Dist. by: Studia Slovenica, 13209 Hathaway Dr., Silver Spring, MD 20906-3730, U.S.A.) Ed. John A. Arnez. **Document type:** monographic series.

949.7   XV   ISSN 0081-6922
STUDIA SLOVENICA. SPECIAL SERIES. 1966. irreg., no.6, 1994. Studia Slovenica, P.O. Box 28, 61210 Ljubljana, Slovenia. (Dist. by: Studia Slovenica, 13209 Hathaway Dr., Silver Spring, MD 20906-3730, U.S.A.) Ed. John A. Arnez. **Document type:** monographic series.

HISTORY — HISTORY OF EUROPE

947 **PL** ISSN 0081-7082
D410
STUDIA Z DZIEJOW Z S R R I EUROPY SRODKOWEJ. (Text in Polish; summaries in English, Russian) 1966. a. price varies. (Polska Akademia Nauk, Instytut Historii) Ossolineum, Publishing House of the Polish Academy of Sciences, Rynek 9, 50-106 Wroclaw, Poland. TEL 48-71-386-25. FAX 48-71-448-103. TELEX 0712771 OSS PL. Ed. P. Lossowski. bk.rev. circ. 700. **Document type:** academic/scholarly publication.
  Description: Studies in the history of the Soviet Union and Central Europe.

943.8 **PL** ISSN 0081-7147
STUDIA ZRODLOZNAWCZE. (Text in Polish; summaries in English, French, German, Polish) 1957. irreg., vol.34, 1993. price varies. Polska Akademia Nauk, Instytut Historii, Rynek Starego Miasta 29-31, 00-272 Warsaw, Poland. TEL 48-22-313642. (Dist. by: Ars Polona, Krakowskie Przedmiescie, 00-068 Warsaw, Poland) Ed.Bd. bk.rev.; illus. circ. 440. **Indexed:** Numis.Lit.
  Description: Comments on primary sources, mediaeval and modern; auxiliary sciences of history; history of historical sciences.

943.7 **XR** ISSN 0585-5691
STUDIE O RUKOPISECH. (Text in Czech, German, Latin) 1962. a. Ceskoslovenska Akademie Ved, Ustredni Archiv, Karlova 2, Prague 1, Czech Republic. TEL 265765. FAX 2358941. bibl.; circ. 400 (controlled). **Indexed:** CERDIC.

STUDIE Z DEJIN HORNICTVI. see *MINES AND MINING INDUSTRY*

940 **AU**
STUDIEN UND QUELLEN ZUR OESTERREICHISCHEN ZEITGESCHICHTE. 1978. irreg. (Wissenschaftliche Kommission zur Erforschung der Geschichte der Republik Oesterreich) Verlag fuer Geschichte und Politik, Neulinggasse 26, A-1030 Vienna, Austria. Eds. Rudolf Neck, Isabella Ackerl. **Document type:** monographic series.

940 **GW** ISSN 0938-6432
STUDIEN UND TEXTE. 1991. irreg., vol.5. (Monumenta Germaniae Historica) Verlag Hahnsche Buchhandlung, Postfach 2460, 30024 Hannover, Germany. TEL 0511-322294. FAX 0511-363698. circ. 1,200. **Document type:** academic/scholarly publication.

STUDIEN UND TEXTE ZUR GEISTESGESCHICHTE DES MITTELALTERS. see *PHILOSOPHY*

940 **GW** ISSN 0081-7252
STUDIEN ZUR EUROPAEISCHEN GESCHICHTE. 1955. irreg. price varies. Colloquium Verlag, Luetzowstr. 105, 10785 Berlin, Germany. circ. 1,000.

940 **GW** ISSN 0944-954X
STUDIEN ZUR GESCHICHTE DES ALLTAGS. irreg., vol.10, 1991. Franz Steiner Verlag Wiesbaden GmbH, Birkenwaldstr. 44, 70191 Stuttgart, Germany. TEL 0711-2582-0. FAX 0711-2582290. TELEX 723636-DAZ-D. (Subscr. to: Postfach 101061, 70009 Stuttgart, Germany) Eds. H.J. Teuteberg, P. Borscheid. **Document type:** monographic series.

STUDIEN ZUR PROBLEMGESCHICHTE DER ANTIKEN UND MITTELALTERLICHEN PHILOSOPHIE. see *PHILOSOPHY*

943 **GW** ISSN 0938-8672
STUDIENKREIS ZUR ERFORSCHUNG UND VERMITTLUNG DER GESCHICHTE DES DEUTSCHEN WIDERSTANDS 1933-1945. INFORMATIONEN. 1976. 2/yr. DM.18. Studienkreis zur Erforschung und Vermittlung der Geschichte des Deutschen Widerstands, Rosserstr. 9, 60323 Frankfurt a.M., Germany. TEL 069-721575. bk.rev. **Document type:** newsletter.

942 **UK** ISSN 0585-6515
STUDIES IN ANGLESEY HISTORY. 1966. irreg. (approx. biennial). price varies. Anglesey Antiquarian Society and Field Club, c/o Hon. Secretary, 1 Fronheulog, Tregarth, Bangor, Gwynedd, Wales. Ed. Helen Ramage. bk.rev. **Document type:** monographic series.

940 **US** ISSN 0950-3412
STUDIES IN ANGLO-SAXON HISTORY. 1990. irreg., latest no.6. Boydell & Brewer Inc., Box 41026, Rochester, NY 14604. TEL 716-275-0419. FAX 716-271-8778.
  —BLDSC (8489.457950).

940 **US**
STUDIES IN BRITISH HISTORY. 1986. irreg., latest no.33. $39.95 per no. Edwin Mellen Press, 415 Ridge St., Box 450, Lewiston, NY 14092. TEL 716-754-2788. FAX 716-754-4056. **Document type:** monographic series.

943 **US** ISSN 1043-5786
STUDIES IN EUROPEAN THOUGHT. irreg. Peter Lang Publishing, Inc., 62 W. 45th St., 4th Fl., New York, NY 10036. TEL 212-302-6740. FAX 212-302-7574. Ed. E. Allen McCormick. **Document type:** academic/scholarly publication.
  Description: Covers comparative and interdisciplinary topics from the early eighteenth century to the present.

STUDIES IN GERMAN THOUGHT AND HISTORY. see *ETHNIC INTERESTS*

942 **UK**
STUDIES IN LOCAL AND REGIONAL HISTORY. irreg. University of Nottingham, Department of Adult Education, Education Bldg., University Park, Nottingham NG7 2RD, England. TEL 0602-484848. FAX 0602-420825. TELEX 37346-UNINOT-G.

940.1 **US** ISSN 0081-8224
D119
STUDIES IN MEDIEVAL AND RENAISSANCE HISTORY. (Text in English, French) 1963; N.S. 1978. a. $49.50. A M S Press, Inc., 56 E. 13th St., New York, NY 10003. TEL 212-777-4700. FAX 212-995-5413. Eds. J.A.S. Evans, R.W. Unger. index. (back issues avail.)
  —BLDSC (8491.107000).
  Description: Annual collection of longer research articles on topics in European history from the Middle Ages through the Renaissance.

940 **US** ISSN 0893-6897
STUDIES IN MODERN EUROPEAN HISTORY. irreg. Peter Lang Publishing, Inc., 62 W. 45th St., 4th Fl., New York, NY 10036. TEL 212-302-6740. FAX 212-302-7574. Ed. Frank J. Coppa. **Document type:** academic/scholarly publication.
  Description: Focuses on aspects of the political, social, economic, cultural and religious history of Europe from the Renaissance to the present. Emphasis is placed on the state of Western Europe especially Great Britain, France, Italy and Germany.

940 **US** ISSN 0098-275X
D1
STUDIES IN MODERN EUROPEAN HISTORY AND CULTURE. 1975-1977 (vol.3); resumed 1989. a. $16. Institute for the Study of Nineteenth Century Europe, 188 Lawton Rd., Riverside, IL 60546. Ed. E.T. Wilke. bk.rev. circ. 500. (also avail. in microform from UMI; reprint service avail. from UMI) **Indexed:** Amer.Hist.& Life, Hist.Abstr.

940 **UK**
STUDIES IN RUSSIAN AND EAST EUROPEAN HISTORY. irreg. price varies. (University of London, School of Slavonic and East European Studies) Macmillan Press Ltd., Houndmills, Basingstoke, Hants RG2 2XS, England. TEL 0256-29242. FAX 0256-28339. **Document type:** academic/scholarly publication.

949.2 **NE** ISSN 0923-8956
STUDIES IN THE HISTORY OF LEIDEN UNIVERSITY. (Text in English) 1983. irreg., vol.6, 1989. price varies. E.J. Brill, P.O. Box 9000, 2300 PA Leiden, Netherlands. TEL 31-71-312624. FAX 31-71-317532. TELEX 39296 BRILL NL. (In N. America: E.J. Brill, 24 Hudson St., Kinderhook, NY 12106. TEL 800-962-4406. FAX 518-758-1959) (back issues avail.) **Document type:** monographic series.
  Supersedes (in 1989): Studies over de Geschiedenis van de Leidse Universiteit (ISSN 0169-8362)
  Refereed Serial

940 **UK** ISSN 0141-030X
STUDIES IN WELSH HISTORY. 1977. irreg. price varies. (Board of Celtic Studies) University of Wales Press, 6 Gwennyth St., Cathays, Cardiff CF2 4YD, Wales. TEL 0222-231919. FAX 0222-230908. Ed.Bd. **Document type:** academic/scholarly publication, monographic series.
  —BLDSC (8491.880000).
  Description: Monographs that will make the conclusions of recent research more widely available.

940.53 **US** ISSN 1054-3120
STUDIES ON THE SHOAH. irreg. price varies. Peter Lang Publishing, Inc., 62 W. 45th St., 4th Fl., New York, NY 10036. TEL 212-302-6740. Ed. Asher Cohen. **Document type:** academic/scholarly publication.

STUDIES ON VOLTAIRE AND THE EIGHTEENTH CENTURY. see *LITERATURE*

949 **RM** ISSN 0585-749X
DR201
STUDII SI ARTICOLE DE ISTORIE. 1972. a. 1000 lei (effective 1994). Societatea de Stiinte Istorice din Romania, Bdul. Republicii 13, 70031 Bucharest, Rumania. TEL 40-1-613-13-29. Ed. Gheorghe Smarandache; Pub. Nichita Adanilaie. bk.rev. circ. 500. **Indexed:** Amer.Hist.& Life, Hist.Abstr. **Document type:** bulletin.

940 **RM** ISSN 0567-6312
DR203
STUDII SI MATERIALE DE ISTORIE MEDIE. (Text in Rumanian; summaries in English, French, German, Russian) 1956. irreg., vol.10, 1983. (Academia Romana, Institutul de Istorie "N. Iorga") Editura Academiei Romane, Calea Victoriei 125, 79717 Bucharest, Rumania. (Subscr. to: Artexim, Export-Import Presa, Str. Piata Presei Libere nr.1, P.O. Box 33-16, 70055 Bucharest, Rumania) adv.; bk.rev. circ. 800. **Indexed:** Amer.Hist.& Life, Hist.Abstr., Numis.Lit.

940 **RM** ISSN 0567-6320
DR242
STUDII SI MATERIALE DE ISTORIE MODERNA. (Text in Rumanian; summaries in French) 1970. irreg., vol.7, 1983. (Academia Romana, Institutul de Istorie "N. Iorga") Editura Academiei Romane, Calea Victoriei 125, 79717 Bucharest, Rumania. (Subscr. to: Artexim, Export-Import Presa, Str. Piata Presei Libere nr.1, P.O. Box 33-16, 70055 Bucharest, Rumania) Eds. N. Adaniloaie, D. Berindei. adv.; bk.rev. **Indexed:** Amer.Hist.& Life, Hist.Abstr.

947 890 **UK**
STUDY GROUP ON EIGHTEENTH-CENTURY RUSSIA. NEWSLETTER. 1973. a. £7.50 to individuals; institutions £12. Study Group on Eighteenth-Century Russia, c/o Prof. A.G. Cross, Ed., Department of Slavonic Studies, University of Cambridge, Sidgwick Ave., Cambridge CB3 9DA, England. bk.rev.; bibl. circ. 200. **Document type:** newsletter.

943.8 069 **PL** ISSN 0137-5377
STUTTHOF MUZEUM. ZESZYTY. (Text in Polish; summaries in German) irreg. price varies. Ossolineum, Publishing House of the Polish Academy of Sciences, Rynek 9, 50-106 Wroclaw, Poland. TEL 48-71-386-25. FAX 48-71-448-103. Ed. Donald Steyer. **Document type:** academic/scholarly publication.
  Description: Reports on the scientific and expositional activity of the Martyrology Museum and contributions to research of history of the struggle against the Nazis from Gdansk Pomerania.

940 **CN** ISSN 0316-0769
SUBSIDIA MEDIAEVALIA. 1972. irreg., vol.20, 1992. price varies. Pontifical Institute of Mediaeval Studies, 59 Queen's Park Crescent E., Toronto, ON M5S 2C4, Canada. TEL 416-926-7144. FAX 416-926-7258. (Dist. outside N. America and UK by: N.V. Brepols, Steenweg op Tielen 68, 2300 Turnhout, Belgium. TEL 32-14-415463. FAX 32-14-428919) circ. 600. (back issues avail.) **Document type:** monographic series.

943 **US** ISSN 0585-8364
SUCASNIST.* (Text in Ukrainian) 1961. 12/yr. $60. Prolog Research and Publishing Corporation, 140-142 Second Ave., Ste. 401, New York, NY 10003-8383. Ed. Taras Hunczak. adv.; bk.rev. circ. 2,500. **Indexed:** Amer.Hist.& Life.

943 **GW**
SUEDMAEHRISCHE LANDSCHAFT; Heimatskunde des politischen Berzirkes Znaim. 1970. a. DM.12($7) c/o Thomas Berger, Ed., Eberleweg 7, 75179 Pforzheim, Germany. TEL 07231-43200. bk.rev. circ. 300. **Document type:** academic/scholarly publication.
  Description: History of South Moravia until 1945.

HISTORY — HISTORY OF EUROPE

943.7   GW   ISSN 0081-9077
SUEDOST-FORSCHUNGEN; Internationale Zeitschrift fuer Geschichte, Kultur und Landeskunde Suedosteuropas. (Text in English, French, German) 1936. a. DM.136. (Suedost-Institut) R. Oldenbourg Verlag, 81671 Munich, Germany. TEL 089-45051-0. FAX 089-45051207. (Subscr. to: Postfach 801360, 81613 Munich, Germany) Eds. Edgar Hoesch, Karl Nehring. bk.rev. **Indexed:** Amer.Hist.& Life, Hist.Abstr., M.L.A., Numis.Lit. **Document type:** academic/scholarly publication.
—SWETS.

940   GW
SUEDOSTDEUTSCHE HISTORISCHE KOMMISSION. BUCHREIHE. 1958. irreg. price varies. R. Oldenbourg Verlag GmbH, Rosenheimerstr. 145, 81671 Munich, Germany. TEL 089-45051-0. FAX 089-45051207. (Subscr. to: Postfach 801360, 81613 Munich, Germany) Ed. Adam Wandruzska. **Document type:** monographic series.

943   GW   ISSN 0562-5297
SUEDOSTDEUTSCHE VIERTELJAHRESBLAETTER. 1952. 4/yr. DM.36. (Suedostdeutschen Kulturwerks) Verlag Suedostdeutsches Kulturwerk, Leo-Graetz-Str. 1, 81379 Munich, Germany. TEL 089-78344. FAX 089-7851190. Ed. Johann Adam Stupp. bk.rev. circ. 2,000.
Formerly (until 1957): Suedostdeutsche Heimatblaetter.

940 398   GW   ISSN 0081-9085
DR27.G4
SUEDOSTDEUTSCHES ARCHIV. 1958. irreg. DM.60. (Suedostdeutsche Historische Kommission) R. Oldenbourg Verlag GmbH, Rosenheimerstr. 145, 81671 Munich, Germany. TEL 089-45051-0. FAX 089-45051207. (Subscr. to: Postfach 801360, 81613 Munich, Germany) Eds. Adam Wandruszka, Felix v. Schroeder. **Indexed:** Amer.Hist.& Life, Hist.Abstr., Numis.Lit. **Document type:** monographic series.

943 831 700   GW
SUEDOSTDEUTSCHES KULTURWERK. VEROEFFENTLICHUNGEN. REIHE A: KULTUR UND DICHTUNG. 1953. irreg. price varies. Verlag Suedostdeutsches Kulturwerk, Leo-Graetz-Str. 1, 8000 Munich 70, Germany. TEL 089-783744. FAX 089-7851190.
Formerly: Suedostdeutsches Kulturwerk, Munich. Schriftenreihen. Reihe A: Kultur und Dichtung (ISSN 0081-9107)
Description: Contains art monographs, poems and shorter lyric prose.

943 830   GW
SUEDOSTDEUTSCHES KULTURWERK. VEROEFFENTLICHUNGEN. REIHE B: WISSENSCHAFTLICHE ARBEITEN. 1954. irreg. price varies. Verlag Suedostdeutsches Kulturwerk, Leo-Graetz-Str. 1, 8000 Munich 70, Germany. TEL 089-7837440. FAX 089-7851190.
Formerly: Suedostdeutsches Kulturwerk, Munich. Schriftenreihen. Reihe B: Wissenschaftliche Arbeiten (ISSN 0081-9115)
Description: Monographs in history, cultural history, arts and letters.

940 800   GW
SUEDOSTDEUTSCHES KULTURWERK. VEROEFFENTLICHUNGEN. REIHE C: ERINNERUNGEN UND QUELLEN. 1958. irreg. price varies. Verlag Suedostdeutsches Kulturwerk, Leo-Graetz-Str. 1, 81379 Munich, Germany. TEL 089-7837440. FAX 089-7851190.
Formerly: Suedostdeutsches Kulturwerk, Munich. Schriftenreihen. Reihe C. Erinnerungen und Quellen (ISSN 0081-9123)
Description: Publishes memoirs and other historical source materials.

943 800   GW
SUEDOSTDEUTSCHES KULTURWERK. VEROEFFENTLICHUNGEN. REIHE D: KLEINE SUEDOSTREIHE. 1957. irreg. price varies. Verlag Suedostdeutsches Kulturwerk, Leo-Graetz-Str. 1, 8000 Munich 70, Germany. TEL 089-783744. FAX 089-7851190.
Formerly: Suedostdeutsches Kulturwerk, Munich. Kleine Suedostreihe (ISSN 0081-9093)
Description: Monographs on literary personalities and special topics regarding South-East Europe.

940   GW   ISSN 0081-914X
HC244
SUEDOSTEUROPA - JAHRBUCH. 1957. a., vol.24, 1993. price varies. Suedosteuropa-Gesellschaft e.V., Widenmayerstr. 49, 80538 Munich, Germany. TEL 089-2285291. FAX 089-2289469. **Indexed:** RILA. **Document type:** academic/scholarly publication.

940   GW   ISSN 0340-174X
DR1
SUEDOSTEUROPA - MITTEILUNGEN. 1960. q. DM.40. Suedosteuropa-Gesellschaft e.V., Widenmayerstr. 49, 80538 Munich, Germany. TEL 089-2285291. FAX 089-2289469. Ed. Hansjoerg Brey. bk.rev.; abstr.; bibl. circ. 1,500. **Document type:** bulletin.
Formerly: Suedost-Gesellschaft. Mitteilungen (ISSN 0039-4572)

940   GW   ISSN 0081-9166
SUEDOSTEUROPA - STUDIEN. 1962. irreg., no.53, 1994. price varies. Suedosteuropa-Gesellschaft e.V., Widenmayerstr. 49, 80538 Munich, Germany. TEL 089-2285291. FAX 089-2289469. **Document type:** monographic series.

SUEDOSTEUROPAEISCHE ARBEITEN. no.13, 1937. irreg. price varies. (Suedost-Institut) R. Oldenbourg Verlag GmbH, Rosenheimerstr. 145, 81671 Munich, Germany. TEL 089-45051-0. FAX 089-45051207. (Subscr. to: Postfach 801360, 81613 Munich, Germany) Ed. M. Bernath. **Document type:** monographic series.

943   GW   ISSN 0940-4325
DER SUELCHGAU. 1957. a. DM.30. Suelchgauer Altertums Verein, Postfach 29, 72101 Rottenburg, Germany. TEL 07472-165351. FAX 07472-165369. circ. 800. (back issues avail.) **Document type:** academic/scholarly publication.

SUFFOLK INSTITUTE OF ARCHAEOLOGY AND HISTORY. PROCEEDINGS. see *ARCHAEOLOGY*

948 929   FI   ISSN 0357-9492
SUKUVIESTI. 1949. 7/yr. Sukuyhteisojen Tuki, Westendintie 91 B 8, 02160 Espoo 16, Finland.
Formerly (until 1978): Vartiaisten Viesti.

SULUR. see *FOLKLORE*

947.1   FI   ISSN 0081-9425
SUOMEN HISTORIAN LAEHTEITAE/SOURCE MATERIAL OF FINNISH HISTORY. (Text in Finnish or Swedish) 1936. irreg., no.9, 1985. price varies. Suomen Historiallinen Seura - Finnish Historical Society, Arkadiankatu 16 B 28, 00100 Helsinki 10, Finland. FAX 441-468. circ. 200.
Description: Includes historical sources.

948   FI   ISSN 0357-1068
SVENSKA FOLKSKOLANS VAENNERS KALENDER. (Text in Swedish) 1886. a. FIM 60. Svenska Folkskolans Vaenner, Annegatan 12, 00120 Helsinki 12, Finland. TEL 358-0-645-115. FAX 358-0-611-979. adv. circ. 12,000.

948.5   SW
SVENSKA HISTORISKA FOERENINGEN. SKRIFTER. irreg. price varies. A W I International AB, P.O. Box 4627, S-116 91 Stockholm, Sweden. TEL 468-640-8800. FAX 468-41-1180.

948.9   DK   ISSN 0900-2103
SYDTHY AARBOG. 1984. a. DKK 90 (typically set in Oct.). Egnshistorisk Forening for Sydthy, c/o Elly Mardal, Ez., Burhoejgaardvej 2, Boddum, 7760 Hurup, Denmark. circ. 1,300.
Description: Presents the findings and results of research activities and events of the Egnshistorisk Forening for Sydthy.

SYMBOLA ET EMBLEMATA. see *ART*

943.9   US   ISSN 1057-1140
DB919.2.S94
SZEKELY NEP. (Text in Hungarian) irreg. Box 10069, Rochester, NY 14610.

948   FI
TAMMERKOSKI. 1938. 10/yr. FIM 110. Tampere Seura, Kauppakatu 1, 33200 Tampere 20, Finland. Ed. Arvi Laakso. adv. circ. 5,000.

TARBIZ; a quarterly for Jewish studies. see *RELIGIONS AND THEOLOGY* — *Judaic*

956   TU   ISSN 1015-1818
TARIH DERGISI. 1949. a. Istanbul Universitesi, Edebiyat Fakultesi - University of Istanbul, Faculty of Letters, Beyazit, Istanbul, Turkey. TEL 520-7540. Ed.Bd. circ. 1,000. **Indexed:** Amer.Hist.& Life (until 1980), Hist.Abstr. (until 1980).

945   IT   ISSN 0393-5949
DG445
I TATTI STUDIES; essays in the Renaissance. 1985. a. L.85000 (effective 1994). (Harvard University Center for Italian Renaissance Studies, Florence) Casa Editrice Leo S. Olschki, Casella Postale 66, 50100 Florence, Italy. TEL 055-6530684. FAX 055-6530214. **Document type:** academic/scholarly publication.

TEATRO E STORIA. see *THEATER*

943.8   UK   ISSN 0085-4956
TEKI HISTORYCZNE. (Text in Polish; summaries in English) 1947. irreg., vol.20, 1993. £10. Polish Historical Society in Great Britain, 20 Princes Gate, London SW7 1QA, England. bk.rev. circ. 500. **Document type:** academic/scholarly publication, monographic series.

943   GW   ISSN 0932-8408
DD4
TEL AVIVER JAHRBUCH FUER DEUTSCHE GESCHICHTE. 1972. a. DM.58. (Universitaet Tel Aviv, Institut fuer Deutsche Geschichte) Bleicher Verlag GmbH, Postfach 100123, 70839 Gerlingen, Germany. TEL 07156-4308-0. Ed. Frank Stern. bk.rev. circ. 800. **Indexed:** Amer.Hist.& Life, Hist.Abstr. **Document type:** academic/scholarly publication.

948   FI
TELJAN TANHUVILTA. 1964. irreg. Kokemaki-Seura, Esko Pertola, 32800 Kokemaki, Finland.

946   SP
TEMAS DE HISTORIA Y POLITICA CONTEMPORANEAS. 1977. irreg. Ediciones 62, S.A., Provenca 278, 08008 Barcelona, Spain. TEL 487-00-62.

945   IT
TERRA D'ESTE; rivista di storia e cultura. 1991. s-a. L.45000 (foreign L.60000). Gabinetto di Lettura di Este, Piazza Maggiore n. 12, 35042 Este (PD), Italy. TEL 0429-2301. Dir. Giuseppe Toffanin.

940.53   NE   ISSN 0924-8803
TERUGBLIK 40-45. 1963. 10/yr. fl.50. Documentatiegroep 40-45, Spechtenkamp 170, 3607 KJ Maarssenbroek, Netherlands. TEL 31-3465-71340. adv.; bk.rev. circ. 1,800.
Former titles (until 1988): Terugblik (ISSN 0920-3958); (until 1985): Documentatiegroep 40-45. Maandorgaan (ISSN 0165-7224)
Description: Covers the history of World War II.

943.7   XR   ISSN 0139-7605
TESINSKO. 1957. 4/yr. (Okresni Vlastivedne Muzeum v Ceskem Tesine) Artia, Ve Smeckach 30, 111 27 Prague 1, Czech Republic. FAX 42-2-231-5206. TELEX 121-65 ARTA C. bk.rev.; bibl.; cum.index: 1959-1973.

940   BE
TEXTES, ETUDES, CONGRES. (Text in French) 1977. irreg., vol.14, 1993. price varies. (Universite Catholique de Louvain, Institut d'Etudes Medievales) N.V. Brepols, Steenweg op Tielen 68, 2300 Turnhout, Belgium. TEL 32-14-402500. FAX 32-14-428919. (back issues avail.) **Document type:** monographic series, proceedings.

THAT WAS YUGOSLAVIA. see *POLITICAL SCIENCE*

948   DK   ISSN 0107-2676
THEMATA. 1980. irreg. free. Aarhus Universitet, Institut for Oldtids-og Middelalderforskning, Bygn. 323, 800 Aarhus C, Denmark. Ed. Soeren Soerensen. bk.rev. circ. 1,000.

THEOLOGIE DER GEGENWART. see *RELIGIONS AND THEOLOGY*

THIRD REICH STUDY GROUP BULLETIN. see *PHILATELY*

THOROTON SOCIETY OF NOTTINGHAMSHIRE. TRANSACTIONS. see *ARCHAEOLOGY*

2972   HISTORY — HISTORY OF EUROPE

948   DK   ISSN 0902-6592
THORSLUNDE ISHOEJ LOKALHISTORISKE FORENING.*
1976. irreg. (2-3/yr.). Thorslunde Ishoej
Lokalhistoriske Forening, Lille Bygade 6, DK-2635
Ishoej, Denmark. illus.
 Former titles (until 1986): Lokalhistorien for
Torslunde Ishoej og Tranegilde (ISSN 0108-3244);
(until 1982): Thorslunde Ishoej Lokalhistoriske
Forening (ISSN 0108-3805)

949.8 914 572   RM
THRACO-DACICA. s-a. $44. (Thracology Institute)
Editura Academiei Romane, Calea Victoriei nr.125,
sectorul 1, R-79717 Bucharest, Rumania. Ed.
Dumitru Berciu.

947   RM
TIBISCUS. SERIA ISTORIE. (Text in Rumanian;
summaries in German) a. Muzeul Banatului, Piata
Huniade Nr. 1, Timisoara, Rumania.

948   FI   ISSN 0358-8882
TIEDE JA ASE. 1933. a. FIM 100. Suomen
Sotatieteellinen Seura r.y., Sotatieteen Laitos, Box
266, 00171 Helsinki 17, Finland. Ed. Anssi
Vuorenmaa. circ. 1,250. **Document type:**
academic/scholarly publication, monograph series.

943 327   GW
DER TIROLER; Zeitung fuer ein einiges und freies Tirol.
1980. q. DM.10($5) Arbeitsgemeinschaft zur
Herausgabe des "Tiroler", Beilengrieser Str. 61,
90403 Nuremberg, Germany. (Subscr. to: Postfach
210 143, D-8500 Nuremberg, Germany) adv.;
bk.rev. circ. 50,000. (looseleaf format; back issues
avail.)
 Description: Political publication advocating
complete freedom of southern Tirol from Italian
annexation.

943.6   AU
TIROLER GESCHICHTSQUELLEN. 1976. irreg. (1-2/yr.).
price varies. Tiroler Landesarchiv, Herrengasse,
A-6010 Innsbruck, Austria. **Document type:**
monograph series.
 Description: Summaries of documents of the
archives of Tyrolean towns, villages, churches and
families.

943.6   AU   ISSN 1013-8919
TIROLER HEIMAT; Jahrbuch fuer Geschichte und
Volkskunde. 1921. a. price varies.
Universitaetsverlag Wagner, Andreas-Hofer-Str. 13,
Postfach 165, A-6010 Innsbruck, Austria.
TEL 0512-587721. FAX 0512-582209. Eds. Josef
Riedmann, Fridolin Doerrer. bk.rev. circ. 500.
Indexed: Amer.Hist.& Life, Hist.Abstr. **Document type:**
academic/scholarly publication.

943.6   AU   ISSN 0040-8115
TIROLER HEIMATBLAETTER. 1923. q. S.240. (Verband
fuer Heimatschutz und Heimatpflege in Tirol)
Verlagsanstalt Tyrolia Innsbruck, Exlgasse 20,
A-6020 Innsbruck, Austria. TEL 0512-5948977.
FAX 0512-5948988. Ed. Ellen Hastaba. adv.;
bk.rev.; illus. circ. 1,300. **Indexed:** Amer.Hist.& Life,
Hist.Abstr. **Document type:** bulletin.

943.6   AU
TIROLER LANDESARCHIV. VEROEFFENTLICHUNGEN.
1972. irreg. price varies. Tiroler Landesarchiv,
Herrengasse 1, A-6010 Innsbruck, Austria.
Document type: monograph series.
 Description: Monographs on the history of Tyrol.

943.9   HU   ISSN 0133-1167
AP82
TISZATAJ. 1947. m. $7 (effective 1993). (Csongrad
Megyei Lapkiado Vallalat) Kultura, P.O. Box 149,
1389 Budapest, Hungary. TEL 361-180-31-94.
FAX 361-180-33-06. TELEX 20-2855 KULT H. Ed.
Voros Laszlo. bk.rev.; illus.; cum.index: 1947-1972.
Indexed: Int.Bibl.Soc.Sci.

949.7   YU
TOKOVI. 1971. 4/yr. Udruzenje Naucnih Kulturnih i
Javnih Radnika Polimija, Postanski Fah 6, Ivangrad,
Montenegro, Yugoslavia. bk.rev.

946   SP
TOLEDANOS. ANALES. no.4, 1976. irreg. Instituto
Provincial de Investigaciones y Estudios Toledanos,
Plaza de la Merced, 4, 45002 Toledo, Spain. TEL 22
52 00.

948 930.1   SW   ISSN 0495-8772
TOR; tidskrift foer nordisk fornkunskap. 1948. biennial.
SEK 125 (effective 1990). Societas Archaeologica
Upsaliensis, Gustavianum, S-753 10 Uppsala,
Sweden.

948   FI
TORNIONLAAKSON VUOSIKIRJA. 1963. a. FIM 80.
Tornionlaakson Kotiseututoimikunta, Vesaisenkatu 4
B, 95400 Tornio, Finland. TEL 358-698-40219.
circ. 1,000.
 Description: Covers the history and natural history
of the Tornio river valley.

TORONTO MEDAEVAL LATIN TEXTS. see LITERATURE

943.9   HU   ISSN 1217-4602
TORTENETI TANULMANYOK. (Text in Hungarian;
summaries in English and Russian) 1992. irreg.
Kossuth Lajos Tudomanyegyetem, Egyetemes
Torteneti Tanszek, Egyetem Ter 1, 4010 Debrecen,
Hungary. Ed. Orosz Istvan. bibl. **Document type:**
academic/scholarly publication.
 Formed by the merger of (1967-1988): Magyar
Torteneti Tanulmanyok (ISSN 0324-5454);
(1966-1990): Egyetemes Torteneti Tanulmanyok
(ISSN 0324-5152)

948   FI
TOTTO. 1952. irreg. Kotiseutuyhdistys Rovaniemen
Totto, Ylikyla, 96100 Rovaniemi 10, Finland.
cum.index 1952-1968.

940   PL   ISSN 0082-5506
TOWARZYSTWO NAUKOWE W TORUNIU. FONTES. Short
title: Fontes. (Text in Polish; summaries in English,
German) 1897. irreg., vol.75, 1992. price varies.
Towarzystwo Naukowe w Toruniu, Ul. Wysoka 16,
87-100 Torun, Poland. TEL 48-56-23941. TELEX
552388 FSBH PL. Ed. Zenon Nowak. circ. 400.
Document type: monograph series.

940   US   ISSN 0362-1529
D111
TRADITIO; studies in ancient and medieval history,
thought, and religion. 1943. a. $52. Fordham
University Press, University Box L, Bronx, NY
10458-5172. TEL 718-817-4780.
FAX 718-817-4785. circ. 900. (also avail. in
microform from UMI; back issues avail.; reprint
service avail. from UMI) **Indexed:** Arts & Hum.Cit.Ind.,
CERDIC, Curr.Cont., M.L.A., New Test.Abstr.,
Rel.Ind.One.
—UnCover; SWETS; UMI. **CCC.**

943   GW
**TRADITIONSVERBANDE EHEMALIGER SCHUTZ- UND
UEBERSEETRUPPEN. MITTEILUNGSBLATT.** 1956. a.
Traditionsverbande Ehemaliger Schutz- und
Ueberseetruppen e.V., Alte Waiblingerstr. 32,
71336 Waiblingen, Germany. TEL 07151-83492.
Ed. Werner Haupt. **Document type:** proceedings.

TRAJECTA; tijdschrift voor de geshiedenis van het
katholiek leven in de Nederlanden. see RELIGIONS
AND THEOLOGY — Roman Catholic

940.08 840   SZ
TRANSEUROPEENNES. 1978. q. 95 SFr. Centre
Europeen de la Culture - European Cultural Centre,
Villa Moynier, 120B rue de Lausanne, CH-1202
Geneva, Switzerland. Ed. G. Glasson-Deschaumes.
adv.; bk.rev.; bibl.; illus. circ. 2,500. **Indexed:** ELLIS.
Document type: academic/scholarly publication.
 Formerly (until 1993): Cadmos; Which supersedes
(1953-1978): Centre Europeen de la Culture.
Bulletin.

301 947   RM   ISSN 0255-0539
TRANSILVANIA. 1868. q. $40 in Europe; elsewhere
$50 (effective 1993). Str. Dr. Ion Ratiu nr.2, 2400
Sibiu, Rumania. Ed. Ion Mircea. adv.; bk.rev.; circ.
4,000 (controlled).
 Description: Presents issues on themes of the
theology and philosophy of culture. Interested in
humanism.

940 800 900   SZ   ISSN 0082-6081
TRAVAUX D'HUMANISME ET RENAISSANCE. (Text in
French; occasionally in English) no.4, 1953. irreg.,
no.278, 1993. price varies. Librairie Droz S.A., 11,
rue Massot, CH-1211 Geneva 12, Switzerland.
TEL 022-3466666. FAX 022-3472391. circ. 800.
Document type: monograph series.
—**CCC.**
 Description: Explores the renaissance in France
from a literary perspective.

943   GW
TROISDORFER JAHRESHEFT. 1971. a. DM.15.
Stadtdirektor, Postfach, 53827 Troisdorf, Germany.
TEL 02241-482227. FAX 02241-482202. circ.
3,000. **Document type:** government publication.
 Description: Local history and news of Troisdorf.

947   GW
TUEBINGER MITTEL- UND OSTEUROPASTUDIEN. irreg.,
vol.5, 1993. DM.68. Francke Verlag GmbH,
Postfach 2560, 72015 Tuebingen, Germany.
TEL 07071-78091. FAX 07071-75288. Ed. Gerd
Meyer. **Document type:** monograph series.

948   FI   ISSN 0085-7440
TURUN HISTORIALLINEN ARKISTO. Variant title: Turun
Historiallisen Yhdistyksen Julkaisuja. 1924. a. price
varies. Turun Historiallinen Yhdistys, Turun Yliopisto,
SF-20500 Turku 50, Finland.
TEL 358-21-633-53-65. FAX 358-21-633-65-85.
Ed. Timo Soikkanen. circ. 600. **Indexed:** Amer.Hist.&
Life, Hist.Abstr. **Document type:** academic/scholarly
publication, monograph series.

940   UK   ISSN 0955-2359
DA566
TWENTIETH CENTURY BRITISH HISTORY. 1990. 3/yr.
£43($82) (effective 1994). Oxford University Press,
Oxford Journals, Walton St., Oxford OX2 6DP,
England, Oxford OX8 1JJ, England.
TEL 0865-56767. FAX 0865-56646. TELEX
837330-OXPRES-G. (U.S. subscr. to: Oxford
University Press Inc., 2001 Evans Rd., Cary, NC
27513. TEL 919-677-0977) Eds. Ross McKibbin,
John Rowett. adv. contact: Jane Parker. bk.rev.;
index. circ. 600. **Document type:** academic/scholarly
publication.
—BLDSC (9076.828000); UMI. **CCC.**

940   BE   ISSN 0775-3381
TYPOLOGIE DES SOURCES DU MOYEN AGE OCCIDENTAL.
1972. irreg., vol.65, 1992. (Universite Catholique
de Louvain, Institut d'Etudes Medievales) N.V.
Brepols, Steenweg op Tielen 68, 2300 Turnhout,
Belgium. TEL 32-14-41-54-63.
FAX 32-14-42-89-19. Ed.Bd. (back issues avail.)
Document type: monograph series.

948.9 839.8   DK   ISSN 0109-2804
U J D S - STUDIER. 1984. a. price varies.
(Universitets-Jubilaeets Danske Samfundsstudier)
Museum Tusculanum Press, University of
Copenhagen, Njalsgade 92, DK-2300 Copenhagen
S, Denmark. TEL 45-35-32-91-09.
FAX 45-35-32-91-13. (Dist. in U.S. and Canada by:
Paul & Co, c/o P C S Data Processing, Inc., 360 W.
31st St., New York, NY 10001. TEL
212-564-3730. FAX 212-971-7200) Eds.
Flemming Lundgreen, Iver Kjaer. **Document type:**
academic/scholarly publication.
 Description: Covers Danish language, literature and
folklore.

943.7 373.246   XR
UCITELSKE VZDELANI. irreg. Ustav pro Ucitelske
Vzdelani Universita Karlova, Ovocny Trh. 5, 116 36
Prague 1, Czech Republic. charts; illus. **Indexed:**
Amer.Hist.& Life, Hist.Abstr.

943   GW   ISSN 0342-2364
ULM UND OBERSCHWABEN; Zeitschrift fuer Geschichte
und Kunst. 1843. a. (Verein fuer Kunst und
Altertum in Ulm und Oberschwaben und Stadt Ulm)
W. Kohlhammer GmbH, Hessbruehlstr. 69, 70565
Stuttgart, Germany. TEL 0711-7863-1. Ed. H.E.
Specker. bk.rev. (back issues avail.) **Document type:**
bulletin.

ULSTER EDITIONS AND MONOGRAPHS. see LITERATURE

945   IT
L'ULTIMA CROCIATA; periodico mensile della solidarieta
nazionale. 1950. m. L.30000 (foreign L.40000)
(effective Jan. 1992). Associazione Nazionale
Famiglie Caduti e Dispersi R.S.I., Via Cavalieri 53,
47037 Rimini, Italy. TEL 0541-50584. Ed.
Gianfrancesco Tassani. bk.rev. circ. 4,300.

944 398   FR   ISSN 1159-0769
UNE VILLE, UN PAYS. a. 300 F. Geste Editions, Maison
des Ruralies, B.P. 1, 79230 Vouille, France.
TEL 49-75-67-71. Ed. Jean-Louis Neveu. illus.
Document type: monograph series.
 Description: Monographies of a town and its
surroundings.

UNITARIAN HISTORICAL SOCIETY, LONDON. TRANSACTIONS. see *RELIGIONS AND THEOLOGY — Protestant*

943 282   GW
UNITAS FRATRUM. 1977. s-a. DM.40. (Verein fuer Geschichte und Gegenwartsfragen der Bruedergemeine) Friedrich Wittig Verlag, In der Masch 6, 22453 Hamburg, Germany. TEL 040-5535019. FAX 040-5531266. circ. 500. (back issues avail.) **Document type:** academic/scholarly publication.

944   FR   ISSN 0768-4258
UNIVERS DE LA FRANCE ET DES PAYS FRANCOPHONES. vol.44, 1979. irreg. Editions Edouard Privat, 14 rue des Arts, B.P. 828, 31080 Toulouse Cedex, France. Dirs. Bartolome Bennassar, Jean Sentou.

946   SP
UNIVERSIDAD DE LA LAGUNA. COLECCION ESTUDIOS DE HISTORIA. no.2, 1976. irreg. Universidad de la Laguna, Secretariado de Publicaciones, San Agustin, 30, 38201 La Laguna-Tenerife, Islas Canarias, Spain. TEL 922-25-81-27.

946   SP   ISSN 0212-6559
UNIVERSIDAD DE MURCIA. ANALES DE HISTORIA CONTEMPORANEA. 1982. a. 1500 ptas. Universidad de Murcia, Secretariado de Publicaciones e Intercambio Cientifico, Santo Cristo, 1, 30001 Murcia, Spain. TEL 968-239450.

946 913   SP
UNIVERSIDAD DE MURCIA. ANALES DE PREHISTORIA Y ARQUEOLOGIA. 1985. a. 1500 ptas. Universidad de Murcia, Secretariado de Publicaciones e Intercambio Cientifico, Santo Cristo, 1, 30001 Murcia, Spain. TEL 968 24 92 00. Ed. D. Pedro Lillo Carpio.

946   SP   ISSN 0210-4903
DP302.M8
UNIVERSIDAD DE MURCIA. MISCELANEA MEDIEVAL MURCIANA. 1973. irreg., vol.13, 1986. 2000 ptas. Universidad de Murcia, Secretariado de Publicaciones e Intercambio Cientifico, Santo Cristo, 1, 30001 Murcia, Spain. TEL 968-239450.

940
UNIVERSIDAD DE NAVARRA. DOCUMENTOS MEDIEVALES. 1965. irreg., no.2, 1965. price varies. (Departamento de Historia Medieval) Ediciones Universidad de Navarra, S.A., Apdo. 396, 31080 Pamplona, Spain. TEL 94 825 6850.

900   IT
UNIVERSITA DEGLI STUDI DI GENOVA. ISTITUTO DI MEDIEVISTICA. COLLANA. STORICA DI FONTI E STUDI. (Text in English, French, German, Italian, Portuguese, Spanish) 1958. irreg. price varies. Universita degli Studi di Genova, Istituto di Medievistica, Via Lomellini 8, 16124 Genoa, Italy. (Dist. by: Libreria Bozzi, via Cairoli 2, Genoa, Italy) Ed. Geo Pistarino. circ. 400.
Formerly: Universita degli Studi di Genova. Istituto di Paleografia e Storia Medievale. Collana. Storica di Fonti e Studi (ISSN 0072-0860)

945   IT   ISSN 0078-771X
UNIVERSITA DEGLI STUDI DI PADOVA. CENTRO PER LA STORIA DELLA TRADIZIONE ARISTOTELICA NEL VENETO. SAGGI E TESTI. 1961. irreg., no.24, 1992. price varies. Editrice Antenore, Via G. Rusca 15, 35100 Padua, Italy.

490 144   IT
UNIVERSITA DI PERUGIA. CENTRO PER IL COLLEGAMENTO DEGLI STUDI MEDIEVALI E UMANISTICI. BIBLIOTECA. 1989. irreg., no.12, 1993. price varies. Centro Italiano di Studi sull'Alto Medioevo, Palazzo Ancaiani, 06049 Spoleto, Italy. TEL 0743-220418. FAX 0743-223507. Eds. Claudio Leonardi, Enrico Menesto. **Document type:** monographic series.

490 144   IT
UNIVERSITA DI PERUGIA. CENTRO PER IL COLLEGAMENTO DEGLI STUDI MEDIEVALI E UMANISTICI. QUADERNI. 1977? irreg., no.31, 1993. price varies. Centro Italiano di Studi sull'Alto Medioevo, Palazzo Ancaiani, 06049 Spoleto, Italy. TEL 0743-220418. FAX 0743-223507.

943.7 320   XR   ISSN 0567-8293
AS141
UNIVERSITA KARLOVA. ACTA UNIVERSITATIS CAROLINAE. PHILOSOPHICA ET HISTORICA. (Text in Czech, English) 1954. 5/yr. Universita Karlova, Ovocny Trh 5, Prague 1, Czech Republic. (Dist. by: Artia, Ve Smeckach 30, 111 27 Prague 1, Czech Republic) **Indexed:** Amer.Hist.& Life, Hist.Abstr.

943.7   XR   ISSN 0556-1183
UNIVERSITA KARLOVA. PEDAGOGICKY FAKULTA. SBORNIK. HISTORIE. (Text in Czech, German and Russian) 1966. a. Universita Karlova, Pedagogicky Fakulta, Ovocny trh 5, Prague 1, Czech Republic. (Dist. by: Artia, Ve Smeckach 30, 111 27 Prague 1, Czech Republic) **Indexed:** Amer.Hist.& Life, Hist.Abstr.

UNIVERSITATEA BUCURESTI. ANALELE. FILOZOFIE. ISTORIE. DREPT. see *PHILOSOPHY*

940   FR   ISSN 0065-5007
UNIVERSITE D'AIX-MARSEILLE I. INSTITUT D'HISTOIRE DES PAYS D'OUTRE-MER. ETUDES ET DOCUMENTS. 1970. irreg. 25 F. Universite d'Aix-Marseille I, Institut d'Histoire des Pays d'Outre-Mer, 29 Avenue Robert Schuman, 13621 Aix-en-Provence, France. circ. 250. (also avail. in microform)

940   DK   ISSN 0591-0358
PA1009
UNIVERSITE DE COPENHAGUE. INSTITUT DU MOYEN-AGE GREC ET LATIN. CAHIERS. (Text in English, French, German, Greek, Latin) 1969. a. price varies. Kobenhavns Universitet, Institut for Graesk og Latin - Copenhagen University. Institute of Greek and Latin, Njalsgade 90, DK-2300 Copenhagen S, Denmark. (Dist. by: Erik Paludan - International Boghandel, Fiolstraede 10, DK-1171 Copenhagen, Denmark) Ed. Sten Ebbesen. circ. 500. (back issues avail.) **Indexed:** Bibl.Ling. **Document type:** academic/scholarly publication.
Description: Text editions and papers in medieval studies, especially on grammar, logic and Byzantine music.

949.4   SZ
UNIVERSITE DE FRIBOURG. HISTORISCHE SCHRIFTEN. 1976. irreg. Universitaetsverlag, Perolles 42, CH-1700 Fribourg, Switzerland. TEL 037-864311. FAX 037-864300. **Document type:** monographic series.

940   SZ   ISSN 0072-0836
UNIVERSITE DE GENEVE. SECTION D'HISTOIRE. DOCUMENTS. 1966. irreg., no.14, 1985. price varies. Librairie Droz S.A., 11, rue Massot, CH-1211 Geneva 12, Switzerland. TEL 022-3466666. FAX 022-3472391. circ. 800. **Document type:** monographic series.
—CCC.

944   FR   ISSN 0983-2424
DC603.1
UNIVERSITE DE NANTES. CENTRE DE RECHERCHES SUR L'HISTOIRE DU MONDE ATLANTIQUE. ENQUETES ET DOCUMENTS. 1971. a. price varies. (Universite de Nantes, Centre de Recherches sur l'Histoire du Monde Atlantique) Ouest Editions, 1 rue de la Noe, 44071 Nantes Cedex 03, France. TEL 40-14-36-36. FAX 40-14-34-34. Ed. Y.-H. Nouailmat; Pub. Yves Suaudeau. bk.rev.; illus.; stat. **Document type:** academic/scholarly publication.
Formerly: Universite de Nantes. Centre de Recherches sur l'Histoire de la France Atlantique. Enquetes et Documents (ISSN 0395-3203)

949.3   BE
UNIVERSITE LIBRE DE BRUXELLES. GROUPE D'ETUDE DU DIX-HUITIEME SIECLE. ETUDES SUR LE DIX-HUITIEME SIECLE. 1974. a. Editions de l'Universite de Bruxelles, Av. Paul Heger 26 - C.P. 163, B-1050 Brussels, Belgium. TEL 32-2-6503799. FAX 32-2-6503794. TELEX 23069 UNILIB BRUX. **Document type:** monographic series.

940   BE
UNIVERSITE LIBRE DE BRUXELLES. INSTITUT POUR L'ETUDE DE LA RENAISSANCE ET DE L'HUMANISME. COLLOQUES. 1963. irreg., no.9, 1991. Universite Libre de Bruxelles, Institut pour l'Etude de la Renaissance et de l'Humanisme, C.P. 240, Bd. de la Plaine 2, 1050 Brussels, Belgium.

UNIVERSITETETS OLDSAKSAMLING. AARBOK. see *ARCHAEOLOGY*

947   US
UNIVERSITY OF CALIFORNIA, BERKELEY. CENTER FOR SLAVIC & EAST EUROPEAN STUDIES. NEWSLETTER. 1982. q. University of California, Berkeley, Center for Slavic & East European Studies, 361 Stephens Hall, Berkeley, CA 94720. TEL 510-642-3230. FAX 510-643-5045. Ed. Anne F. Hawkins. circ. 2,500. **Document type:** newsletter.

940 800   US   ISSN 0888-3882
UNIVERSITY OF CINCINNATI STUDIES IN HISTORICAL AND CONTEMPORARY EUROPE. (Text in English and other West European languages.) 1988. irreg., vol.2, 1988. Peter Lang Publishing, Inc., 62 W. 45th St., 4th Fl., New York, NY 10036. TEL 212-302-6740. Ed. Otis C. Mitchell. **Document type:** academic/scholarly publication.

UNIVERSITY OF NEVADA. BASQUE STUDIES PROGRAM NEWSLETTER. see *ETHNIC INTERESTS*

940   UK   ISSN 0141-0008
UNIVERSITY OF NOTTINGHAM. DEPARTMENT OF ADULT EDUCATION. BULLETIN OF LOCAL HISTORY, EAST MIDLANDS REGION. 1966. a. price varies. University of Nottingham, Department of Adult Education, Publications Unit, Education Bldg., University Park, Nottingham NG7 2RD, England. TEL 0602-484848. FAX 0602-420825. TELEX 37346-UNINOT-G. Ed. Mark Dale. adv.; bk.rev.; bibl.; cum.index. circ. 300.

943.7   XO   ISSN 0139-5548
UNIVERZITA KOMENSKEHO. PEDAGOGICKE FAKULTA V TRNAVE. ZBORNIK. SPOLOCENSKE VEDY. HISTORIA. 1968. irreg. Univerzita Komenskeho, Pedagogicke Fakulta v Trnave, c/o Study and Information Center, Safarikova nam. 6, 818 06 Bratislava, Slovakia. (Dist. by: Slovart, Gottwaldovo Nam. 6, 805 32, Bratislava, Slovakia)
Formerly: Univerzita Komenskeho v Bratislave so Sidlom v Trnva. Pedagogicka Fakulta. Zbornik.

943.8   PL   ISSN 0137-5814
UNIWERSYTET GDANSKI. WYDZIAL HUMANISTYCZNY. ZESZYTY NAUKOWE. HISTORIA. (Text in Polish; summaries in English, Russian) 1965. irreg., latest no.19. price varies. Uniwersytet Gdanski, Wydzial Humanistyczny, c/o Biblioteka Glowna, Ul. Armii Krajowej 110, 81-824 Sopot, Poland. TEL 51-0061. TELEX 051-2247 BMOR PL. (Dist. by: Ars Polona-Ruch, Krakowskie Przedmiescie 7, 00-680 Warsaw, Poland) circ. 250. **Document type:** academic/scholarly publication.
Formerly (until 1971): Wyzsza Szkola Pedagogiczna. Gdanskie Zeszyty Humanistyczne. Historia (ISSN 0072-0461)
Description: Studies on Polish and general history from ancient to modern times.

943.8   PL   ISSN 0083-4351
DK4010
UNIWERSYTET JAGIELLONSKI. ZESZYTY NAUKOWE. PRACE HISTORYCZNE. (Text in English, French, German, Russian) 1955. irreg., no.643, 1984. price varies. Uniwersytet Jagiellonski, Ul. Golegia 24, 31-007 Krakow, Poland. (Dist. by: Ars Polona, Krakowskie Przedmiescie 7, 00-068 Warsaw, Poland) Ed. St. Cynarski. circ. 690. **Document type:** academic/scholarly publication.

943   GW
UNSER NIEDERLAND; Blaetter fuer die Heimatvertriebenen aus den Bezirken Hainspach, Rumburg, Schluckenau, Warnsdorf. 1948. m. DM.89($53.60) (Bund der Niederlaender e.V.) Niederland-Verlag, Winnender Str. 20, 71522 Backnang, Germany. TEL 07191-62027. FAX 07191-85931. Ed. Helmut Michel. adv.; bk.rev. circ. 4,500. (back issues avail.) **Document type:** academic/scholarly publication.

943   GW   ISSN 0343-5113
UNSER OBERSCHLESIEN; Hindenburger Heimatbrief. 1951. s-m. DM.88. Verlag Chmielorz GmbH, Wilhelmstr. 42, 65183 Wiesbaden, Germany. TEL 06121-39671. Ed. J. Huth.

943.6   AU   ISSN 0502-6938
UNSERE HEIMAT (VIENNA). 4/yr. Verein fuer Landeskunde von Niederoesterreich, Herrengasse 11, 1014 Vienna, Austria. bk.rev. **Indexed:** Amer.Hist.& Life, Hist.Abstr., Numis.Lit.
Description: Covers history, archaeology, zoology, botany, geography, and art history. Includes association news.

HISTORY — HISTORY OF EUROPE

948   SZ
UNSERE HEIMAT (WOHLEN). 1927. a. Historische Gesellschaft Freiamt, CH-5610 Wohlen, Switzerland.

940   GW   ISSN 0933-3428
UNTERHALTUNG FUER FRIEDRICHSTADT UND DIE ANGRAENZENDE GEGEND. 1799. irreg. Gesellschaft fuer Friedrichstaedter Stadtgeschichte, Schleswigerstr. 13, 25840 Friedrichstadt, Germany. **Document type:** bulletin.

940 300   UK   ISSN 0963-9268
HT101
URBAN HISTORY. 1974. s-a. £25($41) to individuals (overseas £36); institutions £45 (overseas £56 ($72)). Cambridge University Press, Edinburgh Bldg., Shaftesbury Rd., Cambridge CB2 2RU, England. TEL 0223-312393. FAX 0223-312-315052. TELEX 851817256. (N. American addr.: Cambridge University Press, Journals Dept., 40 W. 20th St., New York, NY 10011. TEL 212-924-3900. FAX 212-691-3239) Ed. Richard Rodger. adv.; bk.rev.; bibl. (back issues avail.) **Indexed:** Amer.Hist.& Life, Br.Archaeol.Abstr., Br.Tech.Ind., Geo.Abstr., Hist.Abstr. **Document type:** academic/scholarly publication.
—BLDSC (9123.389000); UnCover; SWETS. CCC.
Formerly: Urban History Yearbook (ISSN 0306-0845)
Description: Covers all aspects of urban history; contains a detailed bibliography.

948.6   SW   ISSN 0349-036X
VAERMLAND FOERR OCH NU. 1905. a. SEK 160 (effective 1989). (Stiftelsen Vaermlands Museum) Vaermlands Museum, P.O. Box335, S-651 08 Karlstad, Sweden.

948.8   SW   ISSN 0346-4938
VAESTERBOTTEN. 1920. q. SEK 110 (effective 1994). (Vaesterbottens Laens Hembygdsfoerbund) Vaesterbottens Museum, P.O. Box 6083, S-90603, Umeaa, Sweden. TEL 46-90-11-86-35. FAX 46-90-11-90-00. Ed. Britta M. Lundgren. **Document type:** academic/scholarly publication.

948.5   SW
VAESTERBOTTENS NORRA FORNMINNESFOERENING. SKELLEFTEA MUSEUM. MEDDELANDE. no.37, 1975. irreg. SEK 18.50. Vaesterbottens Norra Fornminnesfoerening, Skelleftea Museum, Skelleftea, Sweden. Eds. Peter Gustafsson, Stig-Henrik Viklund. illus.

VAESTERGOETLANDS FORNMINNESFOERENINGS TIDSKRIFT. see ARCHAEOLOGY

948.   SW   ISSN 0346-4954
VAESTGOETABYGDEN; tidskrift foer hembygdsarbete, natur- och kulturminnesvaard. 1946. bi-m. SEK 60 (effective 1990). Vaestgoetlands Hembygdsfoerbund, c/o M. Kjellberg, Forsg. 1, S-465 00 Nossebro, Sweden.

940   NO   ISSN 0800-0999
VALDRES HISTORIELAG. AARBOK. 1916. a. price varies. Valdres Historielag, Box 55-2901 Fagernes, Norway. Ed.Bd. bk.rev.; bibl.; illus. circ. 2,500.

949.7   XV   ISSN 0350-9494
VARSTVO SPOMENIKOV/MONUMENT CONSERVATION. 1948. a. $10. Zavod Republike Slovenije za Varstvo Naravne in Kulturne Dediscine, Plecnikov Trg 2, P.O. Box 176, 61 001 Ljubljana, Slovenia. Ed. Jerneja Batic. cum.index: 1948-1975; 1976-1987. circ. 850.

943.9   HU   ISSN 0505-0332
VASI SZEMLE. 1958. 4/yr. $13. Vas Megye Kulturajaert Alapityany, Karoli Gaspar Ter. 2-4, 9700 Szombathely, Hungary. TEL 94-329-718. Ed. Jozsef Gal. bk.rev.; illus.; bibl. circ. 500. **Indexed:** Geo.Abstr., Numis.Lit., World Agri.Econ.& Rural Sociol.Abstr.
Formerly: Dunantuli Szemle.

VATAN. see HISTORY — History Of Asia

948   DK   ISSN 0108-2906
VEJBY-TIBIRKE AARBOG.* 1967. a. Vejby-Tibirke Selskabet, Vejby-Tibirke, Denmark. cum.index: 1967-1979.

948   DK   ISSN 0108-514X
VEJLE AMTS AARBOG. 1905. a. DKK 75. Vejle Amts Historiske Samfund, Vejle Kulturhistoriske Museum, Flegborg 18, 7100 Vejle, Denmark. Ed. K.E. Reddersen. **Indexed:** NAA.

947 320   BU   ISSN 0324-0967
VEKOVE. 1972. 6/yr. 52 Fr. (Nauki i Izkustvo) Foreign Trade Co. "Hemus", 7 Levsky St., 1000 Sofia, Bulgaria. TELEX 22267 HEMKIK. bk.rev.; illus.; bibl.; index. **Indexed:** Anthropol.Lit., Bull.Signal., Numis.Lit.

948   DK   ISSN 0085-7645
VENDSYSSEL AARBOG. 1915. a. DKK 40($5) (Historisk Samfund for Vendsyssel) Joergen Joergensen, Ed. & Pub., Jensensvej 14, DK-9493 Saltum, Denmark. circ. 3,500.
Formerly: Vendsysselske Aarboeger.

948.9   DK   ISSN 0108-867X
VENDSYSSEL HISTORISKE MUSEUM. 1981. a. DKK 10. Vendsyssel Historiske Museum, Museumsgade 2, DK-9800 Hjoerring, Denmark. TEL 08-920677. illus. circ. 1,000.

948   DK   ISSN 0105-2608
VENDSYSSEL NU OG DA. 1977. a. DKK 116. Vendsyssel Historiske Museum, Museumsgade 2, DK-9800 Hjoerring, Denmark. TEL 08-92-06-77. illus. circ. 1,000.

945   IT
VENETICA; rivista di storia delle Venezie. 1984. s-a. L.60000 (foreign L.120000). Aldo Francisci Editore, Via Puccini, 27, I-35031 Abano Terme, Italy. Dir. Giulio Antonio Gallo.

335 331.88   IT   ISSN 1121-0680
HX7
VENTESIMO SECOLO; rivista di storia contemporanea. 1955. 3/yr. L.50000 (Europe L.80000; elsewhere L.100000) (effective 1992). Centro Ligure de Storia Sociale, Piazza Campetto 8a, 16123 Genoa, Italy. TEL 010-297408. Ed.Bd. adv.; bk.rev.; bibl.; illus.; index. circ. 1,000. **Indexed:** Amer.Hist.& Life, Hist.Abstr.
Former titles (until 1990): Movimento Operaio e Socialista (ISSN 0027-2817); (until 1962): Movimento Operaio e Socialista in Liguria.
Description: Covers historical studies done on the working class in Italy and Europe, also studies the national and international movement of the working class.

943.1 352   GW
VEREIN FUER DIE GESCHICHTE BERLINS. MITTEILUNGEN.* 1904. w. DM.24. Verein fuer die Geschichte Berlins, Kuftsteinerstr. 2, 10825 Berlin, Germany. Ed. H.G. Schulze-Berndt. bk.rev.; bibl. **Indexed:** Bibl.Cart.

943   GW   ISSN 0083-5579
VEREIN FUER GESCHICHTE DER STADT NUERNBERG. MITTEILUNGEN. 1879. a. DM.55. Verein fuer Geschichte der Stadt Nuernberg, Egidienplatz 23, 90403 Nuernberg, Germany. TEL 0911-162770. Ed.Bd. bk.rev. circ. 1,200. (back issues avail.) **Document type:** bulletin.

943.6   AU
VEREIN FUER GESCHICHTE DER STADT WIEN. JAHRBUCH. 1939. a. price varies. Verein fuer Geschichte der Stadt Wien, Rathaus, A-1082 Vienna, Austria. TEL 4000-84815. Eds. Ferdinand Opll, Karl Fischer. adv. circ. 1,700. (back issues avail.) **Indexed:** Amer.Hist.& Life, Hist.Abstr.

943   AU   ISSN 0342-2070
VEREIN FUER GESCHICHTE DES BODENSEES UND SEINER UMGEBUNG. SCHRIFTEN. 1869. a. DM.30. Verein fuer Geschichte des Bodensees und seiner Umgebung, Fluherstr. 4, A-6901 Bregenz, Austria. TEL 05574-5114410. FAX 05574-5114453. Ed. Ulrich Leiner. bibl. circ. 1,500. (back issues avail.) **Document type:** bulletin.

943   GW   ISSN 0083-5587
VEREIN FUER HAMBURGISCHE GESCHICHTE. ZEITSCHRIFT. 1841. a. DM.40. Verein fuer Hamburgische Geschichte, ABC-Str. 19, 20354 Hamburg, Germany. Ed. Hans-Dieter Loose. adv.; bk.rev.; cum.index. circ. 1,650.
—BLDSC (9445.080000).

943   GW   ISSN 0341-6992
VEREIN FUER HEIMATKUNDE IM LANDKREIS BIRKENFELD UND DER HEIMATFREUNDE OBERSTEIN. MITTEILUNGEN. 1927. a. Verein fuer Heimatkunde im Landkreis Birkenfeld unde der Heimatfreunde Oberstein e.V., Postfach 301240, 55760 Birkenfeld, Germany. TEL 06782-15220. Ed. Wolfgang Muenchen. cum.index 1927-1976. circ. 750. (back issues avail.)
Description: Covers the history of the area surrounding Birkenfeld.

943   GW   ISSN 0083-5609
VEREIN FUER LUEBECKISCHE GESCHICHTE UND ALTERTUMSKUNDE. ZEITSCHRIFT. 1920. a. Schmidt-Roemhild Verlag, Mengstr. 16, 23552 Luebeck, Germany. TEL 0451-1605-0. FAX 0451-1605281. (Co-sponsor: Archiv de Hansestadt Lubeck) Ed. A. Grassmann. bk.rev. **Document type:** bulletin.

943   GW
VEREIN FUER NIEDERSAECHSISCHES VOLKSTUM E.V. BREMEN. MITTEILUNGEN. 1904. q. membership. Verein fuer Niedersaechsisches Volkstum e.V., Bremer Heimatbund, Erlenstr. 76, 28199 Bremen, Germany. TEL 0421-504216. Eds. Karl Dillschneider, Wilhelm Klocke. adv.; bk.rev. circ. 1,000. (back issues avail.) **Document type:** corporate report.

VEROEFFENTLICHUNGEN ZUR KULTUR UND GESELLSCHAFT IM OESTLICHEN EUROPA. see POLITICAL SCIENCE — International Relations

VEROEFFENTLICHUNGEN ZUR VERFASSUNGSGESCHICHTE VON BADEN-WUERTTEMBERG SEIT 1945. see LAW

948.9   DK   ISSN 0108-6391
VESTFYNSK HJEMSTAVN. 1931. a. DKK 80. Vestfyns Hjemstavnsgaard, Klaregade 23, Gummerup, DK-5620 Glamsbjerg, Denmark. TEL 45-64-72-16-00. Ed. Ellen Christensen-Dalsgaard. illus. circ. 1,200.

947 057.1   US   ISSN 1055-2278
E184.R9
VESTNIK (BALTIMORE). (Text in Russian) 1991. bi-w. $48. Vestnik Information Agency, 6100 Park Heights Ave., Baltimore, MD 21215. TEL 410-358-0900. FAX 410-358-3867. adv.; bk.rev.

949.7   XV   ISSN 0350-7130
VESTNIK KOROSKIH PARTIZANOV. 1967. 4/yr. $4. Osrednji Odbor Koroskih Partizanov, Titova Cesta 131, 61000 Ljubljana, Slovenia. Ed. Boris Jesih. adv.; bk.rev. circ. 1,000.

948   DK   ISSN 0107-8925
VIBORG STIFTS AARBOG. 1972. a. free. Viborg Stiftsoevrighed, Sct. Mogensgade 35, DK-8800 Viborg, Denmark. Ed. Poul Nielsen. illus. circ. 3,800. **Document type:** government publication.

VICTORIAN HISTORICAL JOURNAL. see HISTORY

VIENNA CIRCLE COLLECTION. see BIOGRAPHY

VIERTE INTERNATIONALE; Zeitschrift fuer internationalen Marxismus. see POLITICAL SCIENCE

944 914   FR   ISSN 0988-1808
VIEUX MARLY. 1932. a. 50 F. Societe Archeologique, Historique et Artistique de Marly-le-Roi, 4 Place de la Vierge, 78160 Marly-le-Roi, France. Ed.Bd. circ. 500.

948   DK
THE VIKING COLLECTION. (Text in English) 1983. irreg. price varies. Odense University Press, Campusvej 55, DK-5230 Odense M, Denmark. TEL 66-157999. FAX 66-158126.

948   UK   ISSN 0305-9219
VIKING SOCIETY FOR NORTHERN RESEARCH. SAGA BOOK. 1892. a. £10. Viking Society for Northern Research, c/o Dept. of Scandinavian Studies, University College, London WC1E 6BT, England. TEL 071-380-7176. Ed. Anthony Faulkes. bk.rev. circ. 650 (controlled). **Indexed:** Br.Archaeol.Abstr. **Document type:** academic/scholarly publication.
—BLDSC (8069.206000).

HISTORY — HISTORY OF EUROPE

940   FR   ISSN 0294-1759
D410
VINGTIEME SIECLE: REVUE D'HISTOIRE. (Text in French, summaries in English) 1984. 4/yr. 265 F. to individuals (foreign 305 F.); institutions 385 F. (foreign 450 F.); students 215 F. Presses de la Fondation Nationale des Sciences Politiques, 44 rue du Four, 75006 Paris, France. TEL 44-39-39-60. FAX 1-45-48-04-41. Ed. Jean-Pierre Rioux. adv.; bk.rev. circ. 2,500.
—BLDSC (9236.866000); Faxon; SWETS. **CCC.**

VINGRAD GOSPODNJI; list za duhovnu kulturu. see RELIGIONS AND THEOLOGY — Eastern Orthodox

VINTAGE ROADSCENE. see TRANSPORTATION — Roads And Traffic

943.7 320   XR
VLASTIVEDNE MUZEUM V OLOMOUCI. ZPRAVY. 1951. 6/yr. 25 Kcs. Vlastivedne Muzeum, Nam Republiky 5-6, 771 73 Olomouc, Czech Republic. (Dist. by: Artia, Ve Smeckach 30, 111 27 Prague 1, Czech Republic) Ed. Vlastimil Tlustak. circ. 800.
    Former titles: Krajske Vlastivedne Muzeum v Olomouci. Zprava (ISSN 0139-617X); Krajske Vlastivedne Strediska v Olomouci. Zpravy; Studijni a Lidovychovne Ustav Kraje Olomoucke. Zpravy.

947.3 320   XO
VLASTIVEDNY CASOPIS PAMIATKY A MUZEA. (Text in Czech or Slovak; summaries in German, Russian) 1952. 4/yr. $41. Obzor, Ceskoslovenskej Armady 35, 815 85 Bratislava, Slovakia. (Dist. by: Slovart, Gottwaldovo Nam 6, 805 32 Bratislava, Slovakia) bk.rev.

943.7   XR   ISSN 0139-9462
VLASTIVEDNY SBORNIK OKRESU NOVY JICIN. 1967. 2/yr. 16 Kcs. Vlastivedny Ustav v Novem Jicine, Ul. 28, rijna 12, 741 11 Novy Jicin, Czech Republic. bk.rev.; cum.index: vols.11-20, 1979. circ. 1,200.
    Description: Covers history, archaeology, zoology, ecology, botany, fine arts, and culture of Novy Jicin district.

943.7   XR   ISSN 0231-5165
VLASTIVEDNY SBORNIK PODBRDSKA. 1966. irreg. price varies. Okresni Museum a Okresni Archiv Pribram, Dlouha 142, 261 01 Pribram, Czech Republic. Ed. Stanislav Polak. circ. 1,000.

943.7 914   XR   ISSN 0323-2581
VLASTIVEDNY VESTNIK MORAVSKY. 1946. 3/yr. (Muzejni a Vlastivedna Spolecnost) Artia, Ve Smeckach 30, 111 27 Prague 1, Czech Republic. FAX 42-2-231-5206. TELEX 121065 ARTA C. cum.index: 1946-1955. Indexed: Bibl.Ling.
—BLDSC (9246.030000).

947 355   BU   ISSN 0204-4080
VOENNO ISTORICHESKI SBORNIK. 1927. 6/yr. 76 Fr. (Ministerstvo na Narodnata Otbrana, Generalen Shtab) Foreign Trade Co. "Hemus", 7 Levsky St., 1000 Sofia, Bulgaria. TELEX 22267 HEMKIK. bk.rev.
—BLDSC (0041.300000).

323.1   FR   ISSN 0042-8396
VOIX ET VISAGES. no.121, 1969. bi-m. 50 F. Association Nationale des Anciennes Deportees et Internees de la Resistance, 241 bd. Saint-Germain, 75007 Paris, France. TEL 45-51-34-14. Ed. G. Anthonioz. bk.rev.; charts; illus. Document type: bulletin.

VOLKSKUNDE IN NIEDERSACHSEN. see FOLKLORE

VOLKSKUNDIG BULLETIN; tijdschrift voor Nederlandse cultuurwetenschap. see ANTHROPOLOGY

VOPROSY ISTORII ESTESTVOZNANYA I TEKHNIKI. see SCIENCES: COMPREHENSIVE WORKS

943.6   AU   ISSN 1011-8748
VORARLBERGER LANDESMUSEUMSVEREIN. JAHRBUCH. 1859. a. S.300. Vorarlberger Landesmuseumsverein, Kornmarkt, Bregenz, Austria. TEL 05574-46050. Ed.Bd. bk.rev. circ. 1,500. Document type: bulletin.

948 493.2   NE   ISSN 0923-6279
VRIJE FRIES. (Text in Dutch and Frisian) 1839. a. Fryske Akademy, Doelestrijtte 8, 8911 DX Ljouwert-Leeuwarden, Netherlands.
TEL 31-58-131414. FAX 31-58-131409.
    (Co-sponsor: Fries Genootschap)

940 920   RU
VSPOMOGATEL'NYE ISTORICHESKIE DISTSIPLINY. 1968. a. Izdatel'stvo Nauka, 90 Profsoyuznaya ul., 117864 Moscow, Russia. TEL 234-05-84. Ed. V.A. Shishkin. circ. 2,000. (also avail. in microfiche from IDC)

948.9   DK   ISSN 0108-691X
VULKANEN: REN L A V A. 1982. irreg., 2-3/yr. DKK 50. Lokalhistoriske Arkiver i Vestsjaellands Amt, c/o Gitte Strange Hansen, Malivej 12, DK-4200 Slagelse, Denmark. Ed. Charlotte S.H. Jensen. circ. 250.

VYZKUMY V CECHACH. see ARCHAEOLOGY

940   UK
WAKEFIELD COURT ROLLS SERIES. 1976. irreg. £5. Yorkshire Archaeological Society, 23 Clarendon Rd., Leeds LS2 9NZ, England. TEL 0532-457910. Ed. M. Fraser. circ. 200. Document type: monographic series.

943   GW
WALDECKISCHER LANDESKALENDER. 1727. a. DM.8. Wilhelm Bing Verlag, Lengefelderstr. 6, 34497 Korbach, Germany. TEL 05631-33376. FAX 05631-560069. Eds. Ursula Wolkers, Wilhelm Bing. adv. circ. 9,000. Document type: bulletin.

943.6   AU
WALDVIERTEL. 6/yr. Waldviertier Heimatbund, Obere Landstr. 12, Krems, Austria.

943   GW   ISSN 0723-7553
WARTTURM. 1981. q. DM.24 membership. Verein Bezirksmuseum e.V. Buchen, Kellereistr. 25-29, 74722 Buchen, Germany. TEL 06281-8898. Eds. Helmut Brosch, Rainer und Gerlinde Trunk. bk.rev. circ. 1,422. Document type: academic/scholarly publication.

940   UK   ISSN 0307-5281
WATFORD AND DISTRICT INDUSTRIAL HISTORY SOCIETY. JOURNAL. 1971. irreg. £1.50. Watford and District Industrial History Society, c/o R.P. Gregory, Dimmocks Ln., Sarrat, Rickmansworth, Herts. WD3 6AP, England. TEL 0923-269452. Ed. R.P. Gregory. bk.rev.; charts; illus. circ. 100. Document type: bulletin.
    Formerly: Watford and District Industrial History Society Bulletin.

949.3   BE   ISSN 0043-1567
WAVRIENSIA. 1952. 6/yr. 500 BEF($15) membership. Cercle Historique et Archeologique de Wavre, Rue de l'Ermitage, 23, 1300 Wavre, Belgium.
TEL 32-10-244377. bk.rev.; illus.; cum.index: vols.1-51 (1952-1992) in vol.52, no.1. circ. 700. Indexed: Numis.Lit. Document type: bulletin.
    Description: Covers the archaeology and local history of Wavre and the surrounding district.

943   GW   ISSN 0173-7007
WEILHEIMER HEIMATBLAETTER. 1979. a. DM.10. Heimat- und Museumsverein Weilheim i. Ob. und Umgebung, Stainharstr. 12, 82362 Weilheim, Germany. bk.rev. circ. 600. (back issues avail.)

WEIMAR AND NOW: GERMAN CULTURAL CRITICISM. see LITERATURE

WELCOME TO SALISBURY DISTRICT. see TRAVEL AND TOURISM

941.2 370   UK
WELSH HISTORIAN/HANESYDD CYMREIG. (Text in English, Welsh) 1984. 2/yr. £10 membership. Association of History Teachers in Wales, c/o Grahame Nelmes, King Henry VIII School, Old Hereford Rd., Abergavenny, Gwent NP7 6EP, Wales. TEL 44-873-852701. FAX 44-873-850430. Ed. Rob Philips. adv.; bk.rev.; charts; illus.; tr.lit. circ. 500. (back issues avail.) Document type: academic/scholarly publication.
    Description: Assists all levels of history teaching in Wales. Joins the efforts of primary, secondary, college, and university teachers with archivists, museums, and historical publishers.

943 330   GW
WELTWIRTSCHAFTSLAGE AM JAHRESWECHSEL. 1958. a. DM.5. (Bundesministerium fuer Wirtschaft) Bundesstelle fuer Aussenhadelsinformation, Blaubach 13, 50676 Cologne, Germany.
TEL (0221)2057-1.
    Formerly: Weltwirtschaft am Jahreswechsel (ISSN 0433-7603)

940   UK
WEMBLEY HISTORY SOCIETY JOURNAL. vol.3, 1972. s-a. £0.30 per no. Wembley History Society, 25 Forty Ave., Wembley, Middlesex HA9 8JL, England. Ed. A.H. Murgatroyd. bk.rev.; index. circ. 100. (processed)
    Description: Covers local interests.

949   NE
WERKGROEP ELITES. BULLETIN. 1978. a. free. Werkgroep Elites, Rijksuniversiteit Leiden, Doelensteeg 16, 2311 VL Leiden, Netherlands. circ. 250. Document type: bulletin.

WESLEY HISTORICAL SOCIETY. LANCASHIRE AND CHESHIRE BRANCH. JOURNAL. see RELIGIONS AND THEOLOGY — Protestant

944   US   ISSN 0099-0329
DC1
WESTERN SOCIETY FOR FRENCH HISTORY. PROCEEDINGS OF THE ANNUAL MEETING. Key Title: Proceedings of the Annual Meeting of the Western Society for French History. 1974. a. $25 to individuals; institutions $35. Western Society for French History, c/o Dept. of History, University of California, Riverside, CA 92521. Ed. Norman Ravitch. adv. circ. 500. Indexed: Amer.Hist.& Life, Hist.Abstr., M.L.A. Document type: proceedings, academic/scholarly publication.
—BLDSC (6841.976200); UnCover.

943   GW   ISSN 0083-9027
DD491.W4
WESTFAELISCHE FORSCHUNGEN. a. price varies. (Westfaelisches Institut fuer Regionalgeschichte) Aschendorffsche Verlagsbuchhandlung, Soesterstr. 13, 48155 Muenster, Germany. TEL 0251-690-0. FAX 0251-690143. Ed. K. H. Kirchhoff. bk.rev. Indexed: Bibl.Cart. Document type: academic/scholarly publication.

WESTFALIA SACRA; Quellen und Forschungen zur Kirchengeschichte Westfalens. see RELIGIONS AND THEOLOGY

943   GW   ISSN 0511-8484
DD491.O8
WESTPREUSSEN - JAHRBUCH. 1950. a. DM.28. (Landsmannschaft Westpreussen e.V.) Westpreussen-Verlag Muenster, Norbertstr. 29, 48151 Muenster, Germany. TEL 0251-523424. FAX 0251-533830. Ed. Hans-Juergen Schuch. adv.; bibl.; illus.; stat. circ. 2,000.
●Also available online.

943   GW   ISSN 0508-6213
WETTERAUER GESCHICHTSBLAETTER; Beitraege zur Geschichte und Landeskunde. 1909. a. Friedberger Geschichtsverein e.V., Augustinergasse 8, 61169 Friedberg, Germany. TEL 06031-88218. FAX 06031-18396. Ed. Michael Keller. bk.rev.; index. circ. 700. (back issues avail.) Document type: monographic series.
—BLDSC (9309.201000).
    Formerly (until 1950): Friedberger Geschichtsblaetter.

WIADOMOSCI ARCHEOLOGICZNE/BULLETIN ARCHEOLOGIQUE POLONAIS. see ARCHAEOLOGY

943   AU
WIENER BEITRAEGE ZUR GESCHICHTE DER NEUZEIT. 1974. irreg. price varies. Verlag fuer Geschichte und Politik, Neulinggasse 26, A-1030 Vienna, Austria. Ed.Bd. Indexed: Amer.Hist.& Life, Hist.Abstr. Document type: monographic series.

943.6   AU   ISSN 0043-5317
DB841
WIENER GESCHICHTSBLAETTER. 1946. q. S.240 or membership. Verein fuer Geschichte der Stadt Wien, Rathaus, A-1082 Vienna, Austria. TEL 4000-84815. Ed. Felix Czeike. adv.; bk.rev.; bibl.; illus.; cum.index. circ. 1,800. Indexed: Amer.Hist.& Life, Hist.Abstr.

WILHELM FURTWAENGLER SOCIETY OF AMERICA. NEWSLETTER. see MUSIC

HISTORY — HISTORY OF EUROPE

949.2   NE
WINKLER PRINS ENCYCLOPEDISCH JAARBOEK. 1970. a. fl.67.50. Uitgeversmaatschappij Elsevier Boeken, Jan van Galenstraat 335, 1061 AZ Amsterdam, Netherlands. Ed. J.N.M Brugge. illus. circ. 50,000.
Former titles (until 1976): Het Jaar in Woord en Beeld; (until 1972): Winkler Prins Jaarboek.

WIR SELBST; Zeitschrift fuer nationale Identitaet. see *POLITICAL SCIENCE*

940   AU
WISSENSCHAFTLICHE KOMMISSION ZUR ERFORSCHUNG DER GESCHICHTE DER REPUBLIK OESTERREICH. VEROEFFENTLICHUNGEN. 1973. irreg. price varies. Verlag fuer Geschichte und Politik, Neulinggasse 26, A-1030 Vienna, Austria. Eds. R. Neck, Isabella Ackerl. **Document type:** monographic series.
Formerly: Wissenschaftliche Kommission des Theodor-Koerner-Stiftungsfonds und des Leopold-Kunschak-Preises zur Erforschung der Oesterreichischen Geschichte der Jahre 1918 bis 1938. Veroeffentlichungen.

973   GW   ISSN 0043-7093
WITTGENSTEIN. 1956. q. DM.30. Wittgensteiner Heimatverein e.V, Puderbacher Weg 18a, 57334 Bad Laasphe, Germany. TEL 02752-6606. Eds. Eberhard Bauer, Eckhard Linke. bk.rev.; charts; illus.; index, cum.index. circ. 1,150. **Document type:** academic/scholarly publication.

940   UK
THE WOKINGHAM HISTORIAN. m. Wokingham Society, Local History Group, c/o Rosemary Lea, 52 Valley Crescent, Wokingham RG11 1NP, England. TEL 0734-781147. Ed. Roger Hosking. **Document type:** academic/scholarly publication.

943   GW   ISSN 0937-5724
WOLFENBUETTLER MITTELALTER STUDIEN. 1991. irreg., vol.5, 1992. Harrassowitz Verlag, Taunusstr. 14, 65183 Wiesbaden, Germany. TEL 0611-530-0. FAX 0611-530-570. TELEX 4186135. (Subscr. to: Postfach 2929, 65019 Wiesbaden, Germany) **Document type:** monographic series.

940   GW   ISSN 0342-4340
WOLFENBUETTELER RENAISSANCE MITTEILUNGEN. (Text in English, German) 1977. 3/yr. DM.84. (Wolfenbuetteler Arbeitskreis fuer Renaissanceforschung) Harrassowitz Verlag, Taunusstr. 14, 65183 Wiesbaden, Germany. TEL 0611-530-0. FAX 0611-530-570. TELEX 4186135. (Subscr. to: Postfach 2929, 65019 Wiesbaden, Germany) Ed. A. Buck. circ. 500. **Document type:** academic/scholarly publication.
—SWETS. **CCC.**

940   GW   ISSN 0724-956X
WOLFENBUETTLER ABHANDLUNGEN ZUR RENAISSANCEFORSCHUNG. 1981. irreg., vol.13, 1992. price varies. (Herzog August Bibliothek Wolfenbuettel) Harrassowitz Verlag, Taunusstr. 14, 65183 Wiesbaden, Germany. TEL 0611-530-0. FAX 0611-530570. TELEX 4186135. (Subscr. to: Postfach 2929, 65019 Wiesbaden, Germany) Ed. August Buck. **Document type:** monographic series.

940   GW   ISSN 0724-472X
WOLFENBUETTLER ARBEITEN ZUR BAROCKFORSCHUNG. 1973. irreg., vol.23, 1993. price varies. (Herzog August Bibliothek Wolfenbuettel) Harrassowitz Verlag, Taunusstr. 14, 65183 Wiesbaden, Germany. TEL 0611-530-0. FAX 0611-530570. TELEX 4186135. (Subscr. to: Postfach 2929, 65019 Wiesbaden, Germany) Ed. Martin Bircher. **Document type:** monographic series.

940   GW   ISSN 0724-9594
WOLFENBUETTLER FORSCHUNGEN. 1977. irreg., vol.57, 1993. Harrassowitz Verlag, Taunusstr. 14, 65183 Wiesbaden, Germany. TEL 0611-530-0. FAX 0611-530570. TELEX 4186135. (Subscr. to: Postfach 2929, 65019 Wiesbaden, Germany) Ed.Bd. **Document type:** monographic series.

WOMEN'S HISTORY REVIEW. see *WOMEN'S STUDIES*

WORCESTERSHIRE RECUSANT. see *RELIGIONS AND THEOLOGY* — Roman Catholic

940   US   ISSN 1062-3574
DK1
WORLD TODAY SERIES: RUSSIA, EURASIAN STATES, AND EASTERN EUROPE. 1970. a. $10.50. Stryker-Post Publications, P.O. Drawer 1200, Harpers Ferry, WV 25425. TEL 800-995-1400. FAX 304-535-6513. Ed. M. Wesley Shoemaker. **Document type:** academic/scholarly publication.
Formerly: World Today Series: Soviet Union and Eastern Europe (ISSN 0090-3868)
Description: Emphasis on current political and military affairs.

940   US   ISSN 0084-2338
D901
WORLD TODAY SERIES: WESTERN EUROPE. 1982. a. $16.50. Stryker-Post Publications, P.O. Drawer 1200, Harpers Ferry, WV 25425. TEL 800-995-1400. FAX 304-535-6513. Ed. Wayne C. Thompson. **Document type:** academic/scholarly publication.
—Faxon.
Description: Analyzes the geography, history, current affairs, economic and social problems, and prospects of Western European nations.

943   GW   ISSN 0084-2613
DER WORMSGAU; Wissenschaftliche Zeitschrift der Stadt Worms und des Altertumsvereins Worms. (Supplement avail.: Beiheft) 1926. irreg. DM.45. Stadtarchiv im Raschi-Haus, Hintere Judengasse 6, 67547 Worms, Germany. TEL 06241-853-347. FAX 06241-853-558. Dir. Fritz Reuter. bk.rev. **Document type:** academic/scholarly publication.

943   GW   ISSN 0084-3067
WUERTTEMBERGISCH FRANKEN. 1847. a. DM.40. Historischer Verein fuer Wuerttembergisch Franken, A. Rothmund, Muenzstr. 1, 74523 Schwaebisch Hall, Germany. FAX 0791-755362. TELEX 74844. Ed.Bd. bk.rev. circ. 1,500.

943   GW
WUERZBURGER DIOEZESANGESCHICHTSBLAETTER. 1933. a. DM.20. Wuerzburger Dioezesangeschichtsverein, Domerschulstrasse, 8700 Wuerzburg 1, Germany. Ed. Klaus Wittstadt. bk.rev.; charts; illus. circ. 800. (tabloid format) **Indexed:** CERDIC.
Description: Deals with the history of the Diocese of Wuerzburg.

940   PL   ISSN 0078-5393
DK4010
WYZSZA SZKOLA PEDAGOGICZNA, OPOLE. ZESZYTY NAUKOWE. SERIA A. HISTORIA. (Text in Polish; summaries in English, German, Russian) 1960. irreg., vol.29, 1993. price varies; available on exchange. Wyzsza Szkola Pedagogiczna, Opole, Oleska 48, 45-951 Opole, Poland. TEL 48-77-383-87. (Dist. by: Ars Polona-Ruch, Krakowskie Przedmiescie 7, Warsaw, Poland) **Document type:** academic/scholarly publication.
—BLDSC (9512.478974).

YEARBOOK OF ROMANIAN STUDIES. see *LITERATURE*

942   UK   ISSN 0084-4047
JN248
YEARBOOK OF THE COMMONWEALTH. a. price varies. H.M.S.O., P.O. Box 276, London SW8 5DT, England. (reprint service avail. from UMI) **Document type:** government publication.
Supersedes (in 1969): Great Britain. Commonwealth Office. Yearbook.

940   UK
YORKSHIRE ARCHAEOLOGICAL SOCIETY RECORD SERIES. 1885. a. £12. Yorkshire Archaeological Society, Claremont, 23 Clarendon Rd., Leeds LS2 9NZ, England. TEL 0532-457910. Ed. S. Thomas. index. circ. 350. **Document type:** academic/scholarly publication.

Z DEJIN HUTNICTVI. see *METALLURGY*

943.7   XO
Z DEJIN VIED A TECHNIKY NA SLOVENSKU. 1962. irreg. Veda, Publishing House of the Slovak Academy of Sciences, Klemensova 19, 814 30 Bratislava, Slovakia. (Dist. by: Slovart, Nam. Slobody 6, 817 64 Bratislava, Slovakia) bk.rev.; bibl.

943.9   HU   ISSN 0133-5499
DB975.Z3
ZALAI GYUJTEMENY; kozlemenyek zala megye kozgyujtemenyeinek kutatasaibol. (Text in Hungarian; summaries in English and German) 1974. s-a. price varies. (Zala Megyei Onkormanyzati Kozgyules Hivatala) Zala Megyei Leveltar, Szechenyi ter 3, 8901 Zalaegerszeg, Hungary. TEL 92-12794. Ed. Endre Gyimesi. abstr.; bibl.; charts; illus. circ. 3,000. (back issues avail.)
Description: Contains learned treatises by researchers of archives, museums, and libraries of Zala county.

943.7   XO
ZAPADNE SLOVENSKO. (Text in Czech or Slovak; table of contents in German, Russian) 1973. a. Obzor, Ceskoslovenskej Armady 29, 893 36 Bratislava, Slovakia. (Dist. by: Slovart, Gottwaldovo Nam. 6, 805 32 Bratislava, Slovakia)

943.72   PL   ISSN 0044-183X
ZARANIE SLASKIE. 1907. q. $7. Slaski Instytut Naukowy, Ul. Graniczna 32, 40-956 Katowice, Poland. (Dist. by: Ars Polona-Ruch, Krakowskie Przedmiescie 7, Warsaw, Poland) Ed. Henryk Rechowicz.
Description: Covers Silesian early history.

949.7   CI   ISSN 0351-2142
ZAVOD ZA HRVATSKU POVIJEST. RADOVI. (Text in Croatian; summaries in English, French, German, Italian, Russian) 1971. a. $10. Zavod za Hrvatsku Povijest, Filozofski Fakultet, Krcka 1, 41000 Zagreb, Croatia. TEL 041 519-044. Ed. Josip Lucic. adv.; bk.rev. circ. 600. (back issues avail.)

947   YU
ZBORNIK ZA ISTORIJU. (Text in Serbian) vol.10, 1974. s-a. Matica Srpska, Odeljenje za Drustvene Nauke, Matice Srpske 1, Novi Sad, Vojvodina, Yugoslavia. Ed. Slavko Gavrilovic. **Indexed:** A.I.C.P., Amer.Hist.& Life, Hist.Abstr.

949.7   YU   ISSN 0084-5191
ZBORNIK ZA ISTORIJU, JEZIK I KNJIZEVNOST SRPSKOG NARODA. FONTES RERUM SLAVORUM MERIDIONALIUM. (Text in Serbo-Croatian; summaries in English, French, German or Russian) 1932. irreg. price varies. Srpska Akademija Nauka i Umetnosti, Knez Mihailova 35, 11001 Belgrade, Serbia, Yugoslavia. FAX 38-11-182-825. TELEX 72593 SANU YU. (Dist. by: Prosveta, Terazije 16, Belgrade, Serbia, Yugoslavia) circ. 1,000.

949.7   YU   ISSN 0084-5213
ZBORNIK ZA ISTORIJU, JEZIK I KNJIZEVNOST SRPSKOG NARODA. SPOMENICI NA TUDJIM JEZICIMA. 1904. irreg. price varies. Srpska Akademija Nauka i Umetnosti, Knez Mihailova 35, 11001 Belgrade, Serbia, Yugoslavia. FAX 38-11-182-825. TELEX 72593 SANU YU. (Dist. by: Prosveta, Terazije 16, Belgrade, Serbia, Yugoslavia) circ. 1,000.

947 891   GW   ISSN 0044-2356
DR1
ZEITSCHRIFT FUER BALKANOLOGIE. (Text in English, French, German, Italian) 1962. s-a. DM.98. Harrassowitz Verlag, Taunusstr. 14, 65183 Wiesbaden, Germany. TEL 0611-530-0. FAX 0611-530570. TELEX 4186135. (Subscr. to: Postfach 2929, 65019 Wiesbaden, Germany) Ed.Bd. adv.; bk.rev. circ. 380. (back issues avail.) **Indexed:** Bibl.Ling., M.L.A. **Document type:** academic/scholarly publication.
—SWETS. **CCC.**

943   GW   ISSN 0044-2607
ZEITSCHRIFT FUER DIE GESCHICHTE DES OBERRHEINS. 1850. a. DM.79. (Kommission fuer geschichtliche Landeskunde, Stuttgart) W. Kohlhammer GmbH, Hessbruehlstr. 69, 70565 Stuttgart, Germany. TEL 0711-7863-1. bk.rev. circ. 800. **Indexed:** Numis.Lit. **Document type:** academic/scholarly publication.
—SWETS.
Description: Articles and reviews about ancient Bade and neighboring countries.

943   GW   ISSN 0342-3344
ZEITSCHRIFT FUER DIE GESCHICHTE UND ALTERTUMSKUNDE ERMLANDS. (Text in German; summaries in English and Polish) 1856. a. DM.40. Historischer Verein fuer Ermland e.V., Ermlandweg 22, 48159 Muenster, Germany. TEL 02507-1070. bk.rev. circ. 750. (back issues avail.)

| 940 | GW | ISSN 0340-0174 |

D1
ZEITSCHRIFT FUER HISTORISCHE FORSCHUNG; vierteljahresschrift zur erforschung des spaetmittelalters und der fruehen neuzeit. (Supplements avail.) 1974. q. DM.148. Duncker und Humblot GmbH, Postfach 410329, 12113 Berlin, Germany. TEL 030-7900060. FAX 030-79000631. Ed. Johannes Kunisch. bk.rev.; bibl. Indexed: Arts & Hum.Cit.Ind., Bibl.Cart., Curr.Cont. **Document type:** academic/scholarly publication.
—SWETS. **CCC.**

| 943 | GW | ISSN 0514-8561 |

DD491.H81
ZEITSCHRIFT FUER HOHENZOLLERISCHE GESCHICHTE. 1964. a. DM.30. Hohenzollerischer Geschichtsverein, Karlstr. 3, 72488 Sigmaringen, Germany. TEL 07571-101558. FAX 07571-101552. Ed.Bd. bk.rev.; bibl.; illus.; index. circ. 1,000. (back issues avail.) **Document type:** academic/scholarly publication.

| 940 | GW | ISSN 0044-3239 |

DR1
ZEITSCHRIFT FUER OSTFORSCHUNG; Laender und Voelker im oestlichen Mitteleuropa. (Text in German; summaries in English) 1952. 4/yr. DM.114. Herder Institut e.V., Gisonenweg 5-7, 35037 Marburg, Germany. TEL 06421-184-0. FAX 06421-184139. Ed.Bd. bk.rev.; bibl.; charts; cum.index: 1952-1961, 1962-1971, 1972-1981. circ. 750. Indexed: Amer.Hist.& Life, Bibl.Cart., Hist.Abstr. **Document type:** academic/scholarly publication.
—Faxon.

| 947 910 | GW | ISSN 0344-3418 |

DR279.92.G4
ZEITSCHRIFT FUER SIEBENBUERGISCHE LANDESKUNDE. 1878; N.S. 1978. s-a. DM.42 to non-members; members DM.30. Arbeitskreis fuer Siebenbuergische Landeskunde e.V., Schloss Horneck, 74831 Gundelsheim, Germany. FAX 06269-8397. Eds. Konrad Guendisch, Harald Roth. bk.rev. circ. 850. **Document type:** academic/scholarly publication.
—CCC.

| 943 | GW | ISSN 0044-3786 |

DD801.W6
ZEITSCHRIFT FUER WUERTTEMBERGISCHE LANDESGESCHICHTE. 1937. a. DM.79. (Kommission fuer geschichtliche Landeskunde in Baden-Wuerttemberg) W. Kohlhammer GmbH, Hessbruehlstr. 69, 70565 Stuttgart, Germany. TEL 0711-7863-1. bk.rev.; bibl.; index. circ. 1,300. Indexed: Amer.Hist.& Life, Bibl.Cart., Hist.Abstr. **Document type:** academic/scholarly publication.
Description: Articles and reviews about ancient Wuerttemberg and neighboring countries.

ZEMEDELSKE MUZEUM. VEDECKE PRACE/MUSEUM OF AGRICULTURE. SCIENTIFICAL WORKS. see *AGRICULTURE*

| 943 | YU | |

ZENTAI FUZETEK. (Text in Hungarian) 1960. irreg. 25 din.($3) Udruzenje Prijatelja Muzeja i Arhiva "Dudas Gyula", 24400 Senta, Yugoslavia. (Dist. by: Forum NIP, Vojvode Misica 1, 21000 Novi Sad, Yugoslavia) Ed. Janos Szloboda. circ. 650.

| 943.8 913 | PL | ISSN 0514-3446 |

ZESZYTY GLIWICKIE. 1963. biennial. price varies. Towarzystwo Przyjaciol Gliwic, Rynek 23, 44-100 Gliwice, Poland. TEL 31-49-84. Ed. Wlodzimierz Blaszczyk. circ. 1,000. (back issues avail.)

| 940 914 | XV | ISSN 0350-5774 |

ZGODOVINSKI CASOPIS. istoriceskij zurnal. (Text in Slovenian; summaries in English, German, Italian) 1947. 4/yr. $12. Zveza Zgodovinskih Drustev Slovenije, Askerceva 12, 61000 Ljubljana, Slovenia. TEL 61-150-001. FAX 38-061-159-337. Ed. Vasilij Melik. adv.; bk.rev.; bibl. circ. 2,000. Indexed: Amer.Hist.& Life, Hist.Abstr.
—BLDSC (9512.658500).
Description: Covers the history of Slovenian people and Slovenia with Middle European countries.

| 943.8 | PL | ISSN 0084-5507 |

ZIEMIE ZACHODNIE. STUDIA I MATERIALY. (Text in Polish; summaries in English, Russian) 1957. irreg. price varies. Instytut Zachodni, Stary Rynek 78-79, 61-772 Poznan, Poland. circ. 2,000.

| 943.8 | PL | ISSN 0084-568X |

ZRODLA DO DZIEJOW BYDGOSZCZY. 1963. irreg. price varies. Bydgoskie Towarzystwo Naukowe, Jezuicka 4, Bydgoszcz, Poland. (Dist. by: Ars Polona-Ruch, Krakowskie Przedmiescie 7, Warsaw, Poland)

| 949.4 | SZ | ISSN 0084-5809 |

ZUR LAGE DER SCHWEIZ; Beitraege zu einem Rueckblick. 1962. a. 10 Fr. Schweizerische Arbeitsgemeinschaft fuer Demokratie, Postfach 387, 8034 Zurich, Switzerland. Ed.Bd.
Description: Covers the political, economic and cultural year in Switzerland.

ZWISCHEN EIDER UND WIEDAU; Heimatkalender fuer Nordfriesland. see *FOLKLORE*

| 940 | NE | |

ZWISCHEN HAUSMANNSTURM UND WALBECKER WARTE. (Text in German) vol.17, 1976. irreg. price varies. Europese Bibliotheek, Waalkade 34, Postbus 49, 5300 AA Zaltbommel, Netherlands. Ed. R. Schaper. **Document type:** monographic series.

ZYDOWSKI INSTYTUT HISTORYCZNY W POLSCE. BIULETYN. see *ETHNIC INTERESTS*

| 940.53 | BE | |

30 - 50. BERICHTENBLAD. French edition: 30 - 50. Bulletin de Nouvelles. (Text in Dutch) 1969. s-a. free. Centre de Recherches et d'Etudes Historiques de la Seconde Guerre Mondiale - Navorsings- en Studiecentrum voor de Geschiedenis van de Tweede Wereldoorlog, Residence Palace, Rue de la Loi, 155 - B2, 1040 Brussels, Belgium. TEL 32-2-2874811. FAX 32-2-2874710. bk.rev. **Document type:** newsletter.
Formerly (until 1992): Navorsings- en Studiecentrum voor de Geschiedenis van de Tweede Wereldoorlog. Mededelingen (ISSN 0772-1196)
Description: Covers Belgian history from 1930 to 1950.

| 940.53 | BE | |

30 - 50. BULLETIN DE NOUVELLES. Dutch edition: 30-50. Berichtenblad. (Text in French) 1969. s-a. free. Centre de Recherches et d'Etudes Historiques de la Seconde Guerre Mondiale - Navorsings- en Studiecentrum voor de Geschiedenis van de Tweede Wereldoorlog, Residence Palace, Rue de la Loi, 155 - B2, 1040 Brussels, Belgium. TEL 32-2-2874811. FAX 32-2-2874710. bk.rev. circ. 5,000. Indexed: Amer.Hist.& Life, Hist.Abstr. **Document type:** newsletter.
Formerly (until 1992): Centre de Recherches et d'Etudes Historiques de la Seconde Guerre Mondiale. Bulletin (ISSN 0772-120X)
Description: Covers Belgian history from 1930 to 1950.

| 940 1066 | DK | ISSN 0106-0627 |

; tidsskrift for historisk forskning. Variant title: Tusind og Seksogtres. 1971. bi-m. DKK 95. Tusind og seksogtres, c/o Svend Honore, Njalsgade 102, DK-2300 Copenhagen S, Denmark. Ed. Svend Honore. adv.; bk.rev.; bibl.; index. circ. 800.
—SWETS.
Formerly: Tidsskrift for Historisk Forskning.

HISTORY — History Of North And South America

A A M U C FOOTLOCKER. (Association of American Military Uniforms Collectors) see *HOBBIES*

| 011 | US | ISSN 0892-4600 |

A B H BULLETIN. 1978. s-a. $10 includes membership. Association for the Bibliography of History, c/o Reference Department, Georgia State University Library, 100 Decatur St., Atlanta, GA 30303. TEL 404-651-2422. Eds. Carol Jones, Elizabeth Cooksey. (back issues avail.) **Document type:** newsletter.

A I H P NOTES. (American Institute of the History of Pharmacy) see *PHARMACY AND PHARMACOLOGY*

| 973 | AT | ISSN 0705-7113 |

E169.1
A J A S: AUSTRALASIAN JOURNAL OF AMERICAN STUDIES. 1979. 2/yr. Aus.$35 (typically set in July in even years). Australian and New Zealand American Studies Association, c/o School of History, University of New South Wales, P.O. Box 1, Kensington, N.S.W. 2033, Australia. FAX 62-02-6972344. Ed. I. Tyrrel. adv.; bk.rev.; circ. 700 (paid). Indexed: Amer.Hist.& Life, Hist.Abstr. **Document type:** academic/scholarly publication.
—Faxon; UnCover.
Former titles: A.N.Z.A.S.A. Bulletin; A.N.Z.A.S.A. Newsletter.

A N Q: A QUARTERLY JOURNAL OF SHORT ARTICLES, NOTES AND REVIEWS. see *LITERATURE*

| 979.8 | US | |

A P U PRESS ALASKANA BOOK SERIES. 1963. irreg., no.46, 1992. price varies. (Alaska Pacific University) Alaska Pacific University Press, Anchorage, AK 99508. TEL 907-564-8304. FAX 907-562-4276. index. circ. 3,000. Indexed: Amer.Hist.& Life, Hist.Abstr.
Former titles: A P U Press Alaskana Series; A M U Press Alaskana Series (Alaska Methodist University) (ISSN 0002-4554); (until 1972): Alaska Review.
Description: Covers Alaska's statehood and the pledges that were made to Alaskans.

| 975 | US | ISSN 0890-2518 |

A P V A NEWSLETTER. 1983. 3/yr. membership. Association for the Preservation of Virginia Antiquities, 2300 E. Grace St., Richmond, VA 23223-7152. TEL 804-684-1889. Ed. Catherine A. Long. circ. 4,500. **Document type:** newsletter.

| 900 | EC | ISSN 1010-3848 |

F3731
A R N A H I S. (Archivo Nacional de Historia) vol.13, 1973. s-a. Casa de la Cultura Ecuatoriana, Avda. 6 de Diciembre 332, Apdo. 67, Quito, Ecuador. bibl. Indexed: Amer.Hist.& Life, Hist.Abstr.

| 970 | US | ISSN 0742-9290 |

A S A NEWSLETTER. 1977. q. membership. American Studies Association, 2101 S. Campus Surge Bldg., University of Maryland, College Park, MD 20742. TEL 301-405-1364. Ed. John F. Stephens. adv. circ. 3,750. (looseleaf format) **Document type:** newsletter.

A S L H NEWSLETTER. (American Society for Legal History) see *LAW*

ACADEMIA DE GEOGRAFIA E HISTORIA DE GUATEMALA. ANALES. see *GEOGRAPHY*

| 989.5 | VE | |

ACADEMIA DE HISTORIA DEL TACHIRA. BOLETIN. 1943. irreg. exchange basis. Academia de Historia del Tachira, Carrera 4, No. 13-68, San Cristobal, Tachira, Venezuela. Ed. Raul Mendez-Moncada. circ. 1,000.
Formerly: Centro de Historia del Tachira. Boletin (ISSN 0411-5023)

| 972.9 | DR | ISSN 0567-5871 |

ACADEMIA DOMINICANA DE LA HISTORIA. PUBLICACIONES. 1955. irreg., vol.57, 1980. price varies. (Academia Dominicana de la Historia) Editora Taller, Isabel la Catolica 309, Apdo. de Correos 2190, Z-1, Santo Domingo, Dominican Republic. **Document type:** monographic series.

| 972 | MX | ISSN 0188-7416 |

ACADEMIA MEXICANA DE LA HISTORIA. MEMORIAS. 1952. a. $25 (effective 1994). Academia Mexicana de la Historia, Plaza de Carlos Pacheco 21, 06170 Mexico, D.F., Mexico. TEL 52-5521-9653. FAX 52-5-645-0464. Ed. Josefina Zoraida Vazquez. circ. 750. **Document type:** academic/scholarly publication.

| 987 | AG | ISSN 0539-242X |

F2801
ACADEMIA NACIONAL DE LA HISTORIA. INVESTIGACIONES Y ENSAYOS. 1966. irreg., no.42, 1991. Academia Nacional de la Historia, Balcarce 139, 1064 Buenos Aires, Argentina. TEL 541-331-5147. FAX 541-331-4633. (Subscr. to: Libreria Platero S.R.L., Talcahuano 485, C.P. 1013 Buenos Aires, Argentina) **Document type:** academic/scholarly publication.

HISTORY — HISTORY OF NORTH AND SOUTH AMERICA

982 AG ISSN 0567-6029
F2961
ACADEMIA PROVINCIAL DE LA HISTORIA. BOLETIN.* no.6, 1971. a. Academia Provincial de la Historia, Avda. Jose I de la Roza, San Juan, Argentina. Ed.Bd. bk.rev.; bibl.

970 CN ISSN 0044-5851
F1035.8
ACADIENSIS: JOURNAL OF THE HISTORY OF THE ATLANTIC REGION. (Text in English, French) 1971. s-a. Can.$21 to individuals; institutions Can.$27.50 (foreign $30). University of New Brunswick, Department of History, Fredericton, NB E3B 5A3, Canada. TEL 506-453-4978. FAX 506-453-4599. TELEX 014-46202. Ed. David Frank. bk.rev.; bibl.; cum.index. circ. 900. **Indexed:** Amer.Hist.& Life, Arts & Hum.Cit.Ind., Can.Per.Ind., CMI, Curr.Cont., Hist.Abstr. **Document type:** academic/scholarly publication.
—Faxon. **CCC.**

900 BL ISSN 0102-700X
ACERVO. 1970. m. free. Arquivo Nacional, Rua Azeredo Coutinho 77, CEP 20230 Rio de Janeiro, Brazil. Dir. Raul Lima. bk.rev.; illus.; circ. 2,000 (controlled).
Supersedes (in 1986): M A N (Mensario de Arquivo Nacional) (ISSN 0045-2726)

ACTA UNIVERSITATIS SZEGEDIENSIS DE ATTILA JOZSEF NOMINATAE. ACTA HISTORICA. see *HISTORY — History Of Europe*

980 CL ISSN 0716-8098
ACTAS COLOMBINAS. 1990. q. Universidad de La Serena, Departamento de Artes, Letras y Ciencias Sociales, Casilla 554, IV Region, La Serena, Chile. FAX 211775. Dir. Roberto Paez C. bibl. **Document type:** academic/scholarly publication.

986 EC
ACTAS DEL CABILDO COLONIAL DE GUAYAQUIL. 1972. irreg. Archivo Historico del Guayas, Casilla 1333, Guayaquil, Ecuador.

977 US
ADAMS COUNTY TRUMPETER. 3/yr. $5 includes membership. Adams County, Indiana, Historical Society, Box 262, Decatur, IN 46733. (looseleaf format)

AFRICAN-AMERICAN SITES & INSIGHTS; a guide to places to go and people to know. see *TRAVEL AND TOURISM*

AFRO-AMERICAN HISTORICAL AND GENEALOGICAL SOCIETY. JOURNAL. see *GENEALOGY AND HERALDRY*

AFRO-AMERICAN HISTORICAL AND GENEALOGICAL SOCIETY. NEWSLETTER. see *GENEALOGY AND HERALDRY*

AFRO-AMERICANS IN NEW YORK LIFE AND HISTORY. see *ETHNIC INTERESTS*

056 AG ISSN 0002-2039
AHIJUNA.* 1967. m. $6. Ediciones Nuestro Tiempo, Rivadavia 1255, Buenos Aires, Argentina. bk.rev.; play rev.; bibl.

976 US ISSN 0887-493X
F326
ALABAMA HERITAGE. 1986. q. $16.95. University of Alabama, College of Arts and Sciences, Center for Southern History and Culture, Box 870342, Tuscaloosa, AL 35487. TEL 205-348-7467. FAX 205-348-7473. Ed. Suzanne Wolfe. adv.; circ. 15,000 (paid).
Description: Covers the history and culture of Alabama and the South.

976.1 US ISSN 0002-4341
F321
ALABAMA REVIEW; a journal of Alabama history. 1948. q. $25. (Alabama Historical Association) University of Alabama Press, Box 870380, Tuscaloosa, AL 35487-0380. TEL 205-348-5180. FAX 205348-9201. Ed. Sarah W. Wiggins. bk.rev.; charts; index, cum.index every 10 yrs. circ. 1,700. (also avail. in microform from UMI) **Indexed:** Amer.Hist.& Life, CERDIC, Hist.Abstr., Ind.Bk.Rev.Hum., M.L.A. **Document type:** academic/scholarly publication.
—Faxon; UnCover; UMI. **CCC.**

979 572 US ISSN 0890-6149
F904
ALASKA HISTORY. 1984. s-a. $10. Alaska Historical Society, Box 100299, Anchorage, AK 99510-0299. TEL 907-276-1596. FAX 907-762-2628. Ed. James H. Ducker. adv.; bk.rev.; bibl.; illus. circ. 700. (back issues avail.) **Indexed:** Amer.Hist.& Life, Hist.Abstr. **Document type:** academic/scholarly publication.

974 700 US
ALBANY INSTITUTE OF HISTORY & ART. ANNUAL REPORT. Albany Institute of History & Art, 125 Washington Ave., Albany, NY 12210.

971 CN ISSN 0316-1552
F1075 CODEN: ALHIE6
ALBERTA HISTORY. (Text and summaries in English) 1953. q. Can.$20 to non-members. Historical Society of Alberta, 95 Holmwood Ave., N.W., Calgary, AB T2K 2G7, Canada. TEL 403-261-3662. (Subscr. to: Box 4035, Sta. C, Calgary, AB T2T 5M9, Canada) Ed. Hugh A. Dempsey. bk.rev.; charts; illus.; cum.index. circ. 1,600. (also avail. in microform from UMI; back issues avail.) **Indexed:** Amer.Hist.& Life, Can.Per.Ind., CMI, Curr.Cont., Hist.Abstr.
—UnCover; UMI.
Formerly (until 1975): Alberta Historical Review (ISSN 0002-4783)

977 US
ALLEN COUNTY HISTORICAL SOCIETY. NEWSLETTER. 1983. bi-m. $10 includes Allen County Reporter. Allen County Historical Society, Allen County Museum, 620 W. Market St., Lima, OH 45801. TEL 419-222-9426. Ed. Raymond F. Schuck. **Document type:** newsletter.

970 US
ALLEN COUNTY REPORTER. 1943. 3/yr. $10 includes Allen County Historical Society Newsletter. Allen County Historical Society, 620 W. Market St., Lima, OH 45801. TEL 419-222-9426. Eds. Anna B. Selfridge, Mrs. Lee A. Williams, Jr. bibl. circ. 650.

918.5 PE
ALMANAQUE DEL PERU.* 1973. a. Selecciones Tauro S.A., Jr. Huancavelica 421, Of. 402, Lima, Peru. TEL 321762. FAX 321762. TELEX 44002. illus.; stat.

AMERASIA JOURNAL. see *SOCIOLOGY*

AMERICAN ANTIQUARIAN SOCIETY. NEWS-LETTER. see *LIBRARY AND INFORMATION SCIENCES*

AMERICAN ANTIQUARIAN SOCIETY. PROCEEDINGS. see *LIBRARY AND INFORMATION SCIENCES*

973 US ISSN 0360-9081
CD3020
AMERICAN ARCHIVIST. 1938. q. $75 (overseas $90). Society of American Archivists, 600 S. Federal, Ste. 504, Chicago, IL 60605. FAX 312-347-1452. Ed. Richard J. Cox. adv.; bk.rev.; bibl.; charts; illus.; index, cum.index: 1938-67. circ. 4,300. (also avail. in microform from PMC) **Indexed:** Amer.Bibl.Slavic & E.Eur.Stud., Amer.Hist.& Life, Art & Archaeol.Tech.Abstr., Arts & Hum.Cit.Ind., Bk.Rev.Ind. (1965-), CERDIC, Child.Bk.Rev.Ind. (1965-), Curr.Cont., Hist.Abstr., Lib.Lit., Lib.Sci.Abstr., LISA, Mid.East: Abstr.& Ind., P.A.I.S., Ref.Sour., Resour.Ctr.Ind., SSCI. **Document type:** academic/scholarly publication.
—BLDSC (0810.390000); Faxon; UnCover; SWETS; UMI.
Description: Provides essays on archival theory and practice in North America, as well as the international scene.

AMERICAN ART JOURNAL. see *ART*

AMERICAN CANALS. see *TRANSPORTATION — Ships And Shipping*

910 917 US ISSN 0065-8219
AMERICAN EXPLORATION AND TRAVEL. 1937. irreg. price varies. University of Oklahoma Press, 1005 Asp Ave., Norman, OK 73019. TEL 405-325-5111. FAX 405-325-4000. **Indexed:** M.L.A.

AMERICAN FOREIGN POLICY LIBRARY. see *POLITICAL SCIENCE — International Relations*

974 US
AMERICAN FRIENDS OF LAFAYETTE. GAZETTE. 1932. irreg. $20. American Friends of Lafayette, Skillman Library, Lafayette College, Easton, PA 18042. TEL 215-250-5161. FAX 215-252-0370. Ed. Leonard Panaggio. bk.rev. circ. 500. (tabloid format; back issues avail.) **Document type:** newsletter.
Description: Historical research about the Marquis de Lafayette and the AFL.
Refereed Serial

973 US ISSN 0002-8738
E171
AMERICAN HERITAGE. 1954. 8/yr. $29 (leather bound $54) (effective 1993). (Society of American Historians) American Heritage (Subsidiary of: Forbes, Inc.), 60 Fifth Ave., New York, NY 10011. TEL 212-206-5500. FAX 212-620-2332. (Subscr. to: Box 5020, Harlan, IA 50315. TEL 800-777-1222) Ed. Richard Snow. illus.; cum.index: 1954-1989. circ. 300,000. (also avail. in microform from UMI,MCA,MCE; talking book) **Indexed:** Abr.R.G., Acad.Ind., Amer.Hist.& Life, Arts & Hum.Cit.Ind., Bk.Rev.Ind. (1965-), Child.Bk.Rev.Ind. (1965-), Curr.Cont., Hist.Abstr., Jun.High.Mag.Abstr., M.L.A., Mag.Ind., PMR, R.G. **Document type:** consumer publication.
●Also available online. Vendor(s): DIALOG Information Services, Inc.
—BLDSC (0817.700000); Faxon; UnCover; SWETS; UMI. **CCC.**

AMERICAN HERITAGE CUMULATIVE INDEX. see *HISTORY — Abstracting, Bibliographies, Statistics*

AMERICAN HERITAGE OF INVENTION & TECHNOLOGY. see *TECHNOLOGY: COMPREHENSIVE WORKS*

973 US ISSN 0002-8770
E171
AMERICAN HISTORY ILLUSTRATED. 1966. bi-m. $21. Cowles Magazines, Inc. (Subsidiary of: Cowles Media Company), 6405 Flank Dr., Box 8200, Harrisburg, PA 17105-8200. TEL 717-657-9555. FAX 717-657-9526. Ed. Ed Holm. adv.; bk.rev.; illus.; index. circ. 140,864. (also avail. in microform from UMI; reprint service avail. from UMI) **Indexed:** Amer.Hist.& Life, Arts & Hum.Cit.Ind., Curr.Cont., Hist.Abstr., Jun.High.Mag.Abstr., Mag.Ind., PMR, R.G., TOM.
—Faxon; UnCover; UMI.
Description: A magazine of cultural, social, political, and military history for a general audience.

AMERICAN INDIAN BASKETRY AND OTHER NATIVE ARTS. see *ARTS AND HANDICRAFTS*

975 340 US ISSN 0145-7993
KF8201.A3
AMERICAN INDIAN JOURNAL.* 1975. q. $50. Institute for the Development of Indian Law, 2501 N. Blackwelder, Oklahoma City, OK 73106. TEL 703-938-7822. Ed. Lynn Kickingbird. bk.rev.; illus.; charts. circ. 750. (also avail. in microform from UMI,WSH; back issues avail.; reprint service avail. from WSH) **Indexed:** Amer.Hist.& Life, C.I.J.E., C.L.I., Cont.Pg.Educ., Hist.Abstr., L.R.I.
Formed by the merger of: Institute for the Development of Indian Law. Education Journal (ISSN 0090-0958); Institute for the Development of Indian Law. Legislative Review; Which was formerly: Indian Legal Information Development Service Legislative Review (ISSN 0300-7677)

AMERICAN INDIAN QUARTERLY. see *ANTHROPOLOGY*

AMERICAN INDIAN STUDIES. see *ETHNIC INTERESTS*

970 US ISSN 0065-8936
AMERICAN JEWISH COMMUNAL HISTORY. 1954. irreg., no.5, 1969. price varies. American Jewish Historical Society, 2 Thornton Rd., Waltham, MA 02154. TEL 617-891-8110. FAX 617-899-9208. index. circ. 1,000. **Document type:** monographic series.

AMERICAN JEWISH HISTORY. see *ETHNIC INTERESTS*

970 US ISSN 0882-5351
AMERICAN MAGAZINE AND HISTORICAL CHRONICLE. 1943 (suspended 1989-1994). s-a. membership. (Clements Library Associates) University of Michigan, William L. Clements Library of American History, Ann Arbor, MI 48109. TEL 313-764-2347. Eds. John Dann, John Harriman. circ. 900. (back issues avail.)
Supersedes (in 1984): Quarto (Ann Arbor)

HISTORY — HISTORY OF NORTH AND SOUTH AMERICA

973 387 US ISSN 0003-0155
V1
AMERICAN NEPTUNE; a quarterly journal of maritime history & arts. 1941. q. $32 (foreign $35) (effective 1994). Peabody Museum of Salem, East India Sq., Salem, MA 01970-3783. TEL 508-745-1876. FAX 508-744-6776. Ed. Timothy J. Runyan; Pub. Donald S. Marshall. adv. contact: Geraldine M. Ayers. bk.rev.; bibl.; charts; illus.; maps; cum.index every 5 yrs. circ. 1,000. (also avail. in microfilm from UMI.) **Indexed:** Amer.Hist.& Life, Arts & Hum.Cit.Ind., Curr.Cont., Hist.Abstr. **Document type:** academic/scholarly publication.
—BLDSC (0847.000000); Faxon; UnCover; SWETS; UMI.
Description: Covers all aspects of international maritime history, shipping and seafaring, including technical, nautical and marine history research, scientific navigation, sea lore, marine arts, biography and marine museums.

970 US ISSN 0193-6859
AMERICAN POPULAR CULTURE. 1980. irreg. price varies. Greenwood Press, Inc. (Subsidiary of: Greenwood Publishing Group Inc.), 88 Post Rd. W., Box 5007, Westport, CT 06881-5007. TEL 203-226-3571. FAX 203-222-1502. Ed. M. Thomas Inge.

973 US
AMERICAN PROBLEMS STUDIES.* irreg. price varies. Holt, Rinehart and Winston, Inc., c/o Harcourt Brace Jovanovich, Orlando, FL 32887. TEL 407-345-2500.

AMERICAN REVIEW. see *POLITICAL SCIENCE*

970 980 US
AMERICAN SOCIAL EXPERIENCE. 1985. irreg. price varies. New York University Press, 70 Washington Square S., New York, NY 10012. TEL 212-998-2575. FAX 212-995-3833. TELEX 235128 NYU UR. Ed. James Kirby Martin. **Document type:** monographic series.

971 DK ISSN 0044-8060
E11
AMERICAN STUDIES IN SCANDINAVIA. (Text in English) 1968. s-a. $29. University of Copenhagen, Department of English, Njalsgade 84, DK-2300 Copenhagen S, Denmark. TEL 45-31-54-22-11. Ed. Niels Thorsen. adv.; bk.rev.; bibl. circ. 400. (also avail. in microform from UMI.) **Indexed:** Amer.Hist.& Life, Amer.Hist.& Life, Arts & Hum.Cit.Ind., Curr.Cont., Hist.Abstr.

AMERICAN STUDIES INTERNATIONAL. see *HUMANITIES: COMPREHENSIVE WORKS*

973 II ISSN 0066-0795
AMERICAN STUDIES RESEARCH CENTRE. NEWSLETTER. Variant title: A S R C Newsletter. (Text in English) 1964. s-a. membership. American Studies Research Centre, Osmania University Campus, Hyderabad 500007, India. TEL 091-040-868608. FAX 091-040-818114. Ed. David E. Harrell. circ. 5,000. **Document type:** newsletter.

910.2 US ISSN 0066-0884
AMERICAN TRAIL SERIES. irreg. Arthur H. Clark Co., Box 14707, Spokane, WA 99214. index. **Document type:** monographic series.

980 970 US ISSN 0895-0490
AMERICAN UNIVERSITY STUDIES. SERIES 22. LATIN AMERICAN STUDIES. (Text in English and other West European languages.) 1988. irreg. Peter Lang Publishing, Inc., 62 W. 45th St., 4th Fl., New York, NY 10036. TEL 212-302-6740. Ed. Michael Flamini. **Document type:** academic/scholarly publication.

AMERICAN VISIONS; the magazine of Afro-American culture. see *ETHNIC INTERESTS*

970.1 US ISSN 0066-121X
AMERICANS BEFORE COLUMBUS. 1969. bi-m. membership. National Indian Youth Council, 318 Elm St., S.E., Albuquerque, NM 87102-3614. Ed. Sherry Robinson. bk.rev. circ. 40,000.

970 390 US ISSN 0003-1615
E11
THE AMERICAS; a quarterly review of Inter-American cultural history. 1944. q. $30 to individuals; institutions $55 (effective 1993). (Catholic University of America) Academy of American Franciscan History, 1712 Euclid Ave., Berkeley, CA 94709. TEL 510-843-4803. Ed. Vincent Peloso. bk.rev.; index, cum.index: vols. 1-20, 21-47. circ. 1,000. **Indexed:** Acad.Ind., Amer.Hist.& Life, Bk.Rev.Ind. (1965-), Chic.Per.Ind., Child.Bk.Rev.Ind. (1965-), Curr.Cont., Hisp.Amer.Per.Ind., Hist.Abstr., Hum.Ind., Mag.Ind., Soc.Sci.Ind., SSCI. **Document type:** academic/scholarly publication.
—Faxon.
Description: Publishes articles and review articles in the area of Inter-American cultural history.

970 355 US ISSN 1046-2899
AMERICA'S CIVIL WAR. 6/yr. $16.95 (foreign $22.95). Empire Press, 602 S. King St., Ste. 300, Leesburg, VA 22075. TEL 703-771-9400. FAX 703-777-4627. (Subscr. to: Box 383, Mt. Morris, IL 61054-7947, TEL 815-734-1115) Ed. Roy Morris, Jr. circ. 76,000.
—UMI.
Description: Relives the passion and policy - from the soldiers' daily lives to strategy sessions inside commanders' tents.

973 GW ISSN 0340-2827
E169.1
AMERIKASTUDIEN/AMERICAN STUDIES. 1955. q. DM.128. (Deutsche Gesellschaft fuer Amerikastudien) Verlag Ferdinand Schoeningh GmbH, Postfach 2540, 33055 Paderborn, Germany. TEL 05251-127-5. FAX 05251-127860. Ed. Gerhard Hoffmann. adv.; bk.rev.; cum.index. circ. 1,000. **Indexed:** Abstr.Engl.Stud., Amer.Hist.& Life, Arts & Hum.Cit.Ind., Bibl.Ling., Curr.Cont., Hist.Abstr., M.L.A. **Document type:** academic/scholarly publication.
—BLDSC (0857.658000). CCC.
Formerly (until 1973): Jahrbuch fuer Amerikastudien (ISSN 0075-2533)

971 CN
▼**AMERIQUE FRANCAISE/FRENCH AMERICA.** 1993. irreg. price varies. University of Ottawa Press, 542 King Edward, Ottawa, ON K1N 6N5, Canada. TEL 613-564-2270. Ed. Andre Lapierre.
Description: Interdisciplinary publication that aims at promoting the "fait francais."

980 910.09 340 MX
AMISTAD. (Text in English) 1942. m. $20. American Society of Mexico, A.C., Apdo. 555, Mexico 06000, D.F., Mexico. TEL 592-1800. FAX 525-566-3957. Ed. Jane Brown. adv. circ. 6,000.
Formerly: American Society of Mexico. Bulletin.

974 US ISSN 0894-9492
AMITYVILLE HISTORICAL SOCIETY DISPATCH. 1970. q. $5 to individuals; institutions $20. Amityville Historical Society, Box 764, Amityville, NY 11701. TEL 516-598-1486. Ed. Seth Purdy, Jr. circ. 500 (controlled). **Document type:** newsletter.
Formerly: Amityville Historical Society Newsletter.

ANCHOR WATCH. see *MILITARY*

940 UK ISSN 0956-5361
CODEN: ANMSE7
ANCIENT MESOAMERICA. 1990. s-a. £32($48) to individuals (£58.50); institutions £63 (overseas 73.50 ($95)). (Society for American Archaeology) Cambridge University Press, Edinburgh Bldg., Shaftesbury Rd., Cambridge CB2 2RU, England. TEL 0223-312393. FAX 0223-315052. TELEX 851817256. (N. American addr.: Cambridge University Press, 40 W. 20th St., New York, NY 10011. TEL 212-924-3900. FAX 212-691-3239) (Co-sponsor: Midwestern Conference on Mesoamerican Archaeology and Ethnohistory) Eds. William R. Fowler, Jr., Stephen D. Houston. adv. (back issues avail.) **Document type:** academic/scholarly publication.
—Faxon; UnCover; SWETS; UMI.
Description: International forum for the method, theory, substance and interpretation of Mesoamerican archaeology, art history and ethnohistory, chiefly concerned with the Precolumbian period.

977.7 US ISSN 0003-4827
F616
ANNALS OF IOWA. 1863. q. $20. State Historical Society of Iowa, 402 Iowa Ave., Iowa City, IA 52240. TEL 319-335-3916. FAX 319-335-3924. Ed. Marvin Bergman. bk.rev.; illus.; index. circ. 1,000. (also avail. in microfilm from UMI; reprint service avail. from UMI) **Indexed:** Amer.Hist.& Life, Hist.Abstr., R.G. **Document type:** academic/scholarly publication.
—BLDSC (1041.370000); Faxon; UnCover; UMI. CCC.

970 020 US ISSN 0160-8460
E171
ANNOTATION. 1973. 3/yr. free. National Historical Publications and Records Commission, National Archives Bldg., Washington, DC 20408. TEL 202-501-5600. Ed. Gerald George. circ. 4,000. **Document type:** government publication, newsletter.
Description: Announces publications, records grants, promulgates commission policies, and provides other information about developments in documentary preservation and publication.

917.3 US ISSN 0090-4511
E171
ANNUAL EDITIONS: AMERICAN HISTORY. (Vol. I: Pre-Colonial Through Reconstruction; Vol. II: Reconstruction Through the Present) 1972. a. (in 2 vols.). $11.95 per vol. Dushkin Publishing Group, Inc., Sluice Dock, Guilford, CT 06437-9989. TEL 203-453-4351. FAX 203-453-6000. Ed. Robert James Maddox; Pub. Lan Nielsen. illus. **Document type:** academic/scholarly publication.
Formerly: Readings in American History.
Refereed Serial

974 US
ANTIQUARIAN (PLATTSBURGH). 1984. a. $25 membership to institutions (includes North Country Notes). Clinton County Historical Association, 48 Court St., Plattsburgh, NY 12901. TEL 518-561-0340. Ed. Allan Everest. **Document type:** academic/scholarly publication.
Description: Articles on Clinton County history.

970 918.5 PE ISSN 0066-5223
ANUARIO GEOGRAFICO DEL PERU. 1962. a. price varies. Sociedad Geografica de Lima, Apdo. 100-1176, Lima 100, Peru.

982 020.6 AG ISSN 0326-842X
CD3680
ANUARIO INTERAMERICANO DE ARCHIVOS. 1974. a. $8. Centro Interamericano de Desarrollo de Archivos, Avd. Hipolito Irigoye 174, 5000 Cordoba, Argentina. Ed. Aurelio Tanodi. adv.; bk.rev.; bibl.; index. circ. 700,273. **Indexed:** Amer.Hist.& Life, Hisp.Amer.Per.Ind., Hist.Abstr.
Formerly (until 1982): Boletin Interamericano de Archivos (ISSN 0325-3899)

309.1 974 US ISSN 0090-3779
F216.2
APPALACHIAN JOURNAL; a regional studies review. 1972. q. $18 (effective Jan. 1991). Appalachian State University, Boone, NC 28608. TEL 704-262-4072. Ed. Jerry W. Williamson. bk.rev.; illus. circ. 1,000. **Indexed:** Abstr.Engl.Stud., Amer.Hist.& Life, Arts & Hum.Cit.Ind., Hist.Abstr., M.L.A.
—BLDSC (1569.250000); Faxon.
Description: Multidisciplinary research, scholarship, criticism, and interpretation of the Appalachian region, its past and its present.

977 US
ARCHAEOLOGICAL COMPLETION REPORT SERIES. 1977. irreg. (approx. a.). price varies. Mackinac Island State Park Commission, Box 30028, Lansing, MI 48909. TEL 906-847-3328. bibl.; illus. circ. 500. **Document type:** monographic series.
Description: Scholarly archeological reports.

HISTORY — HISTORY OF NORTH AND SOUTH AMERICA

971   CN   ISSN 0318-6954
CD3620
ARCHIVARIA. (Text in English; occasionally in French) 1975. s-a. Can.$35 to individuals; institutions Can.$45. Association of Canadian Archivists, P.O. Box 2596, Sta. "D", Ottawa, ON K1P 5W6, Canada. TEL 613-443-0251. Ed. Jay Atherton. bk.rev.; bibl.; charts; illus. circ. 1,300. (back issues avail.) **Indexed:** Amer.Hist.& Life, Art & Archaeol.Tech.Abstr., Can.Per.Ind., CMI, Hist.Abstr., LISA, Mid.East: Abstr.& Ind. **Document type:** academic/scholarly publication.
—BLDSC (1625.686000); Faxon; UnCover.
    Supersedes: Canadian Archivist (ISSN 0068-824X)

970   CN   ISSN 0705-2855
CD3623
ARCHIVIST. (Text in English, French) 1973. q. free. National Archives of Canada, 344 Wellington St., Ottawa, Ont. K1A 0N3, Canada. TEL 613-996-1538. FAX 613-943-1374. Eds. Joy McDonell, Marcel Larocque. circ. 17,500. (back issues avail.)
    Description: Collections and activities at the Archives, news about preserving historical documents.

984   BO
ARCHIVO DE LA PAZ. BOLETIN. 1976. irreg. Bs.3($1) Universidad Mayor de San Andres, Archivo de la Paz, Ave. 6 de Agosto 2080, La Paz, Bolivia. TEL 359602. circ. 300.

ARCHIVO HISTORICO ALBERTO Y FERNANDO VALVERDE. REVISTA. see *LIBRARY AND INFORMATION SCIENCES*

987   VE   ISSN 0004-0444
ARCHIVO HISTORICO DE MIRAFLORES. BOLETIN. 1959. bi-m. free. Ministerio de la Secretaria de la Presidencia, Galeria Sur, Plaza Bicentenario, Palacio de Miraflores, Caracas, Venezuela. Dir. Nora Bustamante. illus. circ. 6,500.
    Description: Covers contemporary history of Venezuela.

986.6   EC
ARCHIVO HISTORICO DEL GUAYAS. COLECCION MONOGRAFICA. 1972. irreg. Archivo Historico del Guayas, Casilla 1333, Guayaquil, Ecuador.

986   EC
ARCHIVO HISTORICO DEL GUAYAS. REVISTA. 1972. s-a. S/300($18) Archivo Historico del Guayas, Casilla 1333, Guayaquil, Ecuador. Ed. Julio Estrada Ycaza. adv.; bibl.; illus.

917.2 572   MX
ARCHIVO HISTORICO DIOCESANO DE SAN CRISTOBAL DE LAS CASAS. BOLETIN. 1981. irreg., vol.4, 1990. $50. Instituto de Asesoria Antropologica para la Region Maya, Archivo Historico Diocesano, Apdo. Postal 6, San Cristobal de las Casas, 29200 Chiapas, Mexico. Ed. Angelica Inda. circ. 500. **Document type:** bulletin.
    Description: Features transcriptions of documents found in the archives of the diocese of San Cristobal that are of historical interest to the region. Includes introductions and brief commentaries.

985 398   PE
ARCHIVOS DE HISTORIA ANDINA. irreg., no.1013, 1990. price varies. Centro de Estudios Regionales Andinos "Bartolome de Las Casas", Apdo. 477, Cusco, Peru. TEL 084-236494. FAX 084-238255.

972   MX   ISSN 0004-055X
ARCHIVOS DE HISTORIA POTOSINA. 1969. q. Mex.$80($6) (Academia de Historia Potosina) Universidad Autonoma de San Luis Potosi, Biblioteca Publica, Av Damian Carmona 130, San Luis Potosi S.L.P., Mexico. Ed. Lic. Rafael Montejano y Aguinaga. bk.rev.; bibl.

ARCHIVOS DE LA BIBLIOTECA NACIONAL. see *LIBRARY AND INFORMATION SCIENCES*

ARGENTINA. DEPARTAMENTO DE ESTUDIOS HISTORICOS NAVALES. SERIE E: DOCUMENTOS. see *MILITARY*

355 982   AG   ISSN 0066-7293
ARGENTINA. SECRETARIA DE GUERRA. DIRECCION DE ESTUDIOS HISTORICOS. BOLETIN BIBLIOGRAFICO.★ 1967. irreg. $350. Secretaria de Guerra, Comando en Jefe del Ejercito, Azopardo 250 Planta Baja, Buenos Aires, Argentina.

ARGONAUTA. see *TRANSPORTATION — Ships And Shipping*

ARIZONA COAST. see *TRAVEL AND TOURISM*

979.1   US
ARIZONA HISTORICAL SOCIETY. HISTORICAL MONOGRAPHS. 1973. irreg., no.79 1993. price varies. Arizona Historical Society, Publications Division, 949 E. Second St., Tucson, AZ 85719. TEL 602-628-5774. **Document type:** monographic series.

970   US
ARIZONA HISTORICAL SOCIETY. MUSEUM MONOGRAPH SERIES. 1964. irreg., no.7, 1976. price varies. Arizona Historical Society, Publications Division, 949 E. Second St., Tucson, AZ 85719. TEL 602-628-5774. Ed.Bd. bibl.; charts; illus. **Document type:** monographic series.

918   US
ARIZONA STATE UNIVERSITY. CENTER FOR LATIN AMERICAN STUDIES. MONOGRAPH. 1975. irreg., latest 1992. price varies. Arizona State University, Center for Latin American Studies, Tempe, AZ 85287-2401. TEL 602-965-5127. FAX 602-965-6679. TELEX 1561058 ASU UT. **Document type:** monographic series.

918   US
ARIZONA STATE UNIVERSITY. CENTER FOR LATIN AMERICAN STUDIES. SPECIAL STUDIES. no.19, 1980. irreg., no.27, 1991. price varies. Arizona State University, Center for Latin American Studies, Tempe, AZ 85287-2401. TEL 602-965-5127. FAX 602-965-6679. TELEX 1561058 ASU UT. **Document type:** monographic series.

976.7   US   ISSN 0004-1823
F406
ARKANSAS HISTORICAL QUARTERLY. 1942. q. $16. Arkansas Historical Association, University of Arkansas, Department of History, Old Main 416, Fayetteville, AR 72701. TEL 501-575-5884. FAX 501-575-2642. Ed. Jeannie M. Whayne. adv.: Page $100. bk.rev.; illus.; index, cum.index: vols.1-35 in 1981. circ. 1,600. (also avail. in microform from UMI; magnetic tape; reprint service avail. from KTO) **Indexed:** Amer.Hist.& Life, Arts & Hum.Cit.Ind., Curr.Cont., Hist.Abstr. **Document type:** academic/scholarly publication.
●Also available online.
Also available on CD-ROM.
—BLDSC (1671.200000); UnCover; UMI.
    Description: Economic, political, and cultural history of Arkansas from pre-history to comtemporary issues in original scholarly research.

973.05   US
ARKANSAS TECH UNIVERSITY. DEPARTMENT OF HISTORY. OCCASIONAL PAPERS. 1970. irreg., vol.6, 1984. $1. Arkansas Tech University, Department of History, Russellville, AR 72801. TEL 501-968-0389. Ed. B.B. McCool. bk.rev. circ. 100.

975.5   US   ISSN 0066-7684
F232.A4
ARLINGTON HISTORICAL MAGAZINE. 1957. a. membership. Arlington Historical Society, Inc., Box 402, Arlington, VA 22210. Ed. Phyllis W. Johnson. index, cum.index 1957-present. circ. 650. **Indexed:** Amer.Hist.& Life, Geo.Abstr., Hist.Abstr., Va.Hist.Abstr.
    Description: Covers a variety of subjects relating to the history of Arlington county - geography, cemeteries, communities, genealogies, transportation, and public works.

970   US
▼**ARMCHAIR HISTORIAN.** 1993. bi-m. $29. Box 25038, Chicago, IL 60625. Ed. Elias Crim.

974   ISSN 0884-4747
ARTILLERYMAN. 1978. q. $18 (foreign $24). Cutter & Locke Incorporated, Rt. 1, Box 36, Tunbridge, VT 05077. TEL 802-889-3500. FAX 802-889-5627. Ed. C. Peter Jorgensen. adv.; bk.rev. circ. 2,300.
    Formerly (until 1985): Muzzleloading Artilleryman (ISSN 0195-038X)
    Description: Directed to collectors and shooters; covers 18th- and 19th-century artillery, as well as safety, history, preservation, technical aspects, and travel.

ASIEN, AFRIKA, LATEINAMERIKA/ASIA, AFRICA, LATINAMERICA. see *HISTORY — History Of Asia*

982 020.6   AG
ASOCIACION ARCHIVISTICA ARGENTINA BOLETIN.★ 1971. 3/yr. Asociacion Archivistica Argentina, Av. Cordoba 1556, Buenos Aires, Argentina. Ed. Arelio Tanodi. bk.rev.; bibl.

975.8   US   ISSN 0896-3975
F294.A8
ATLANTA HISTORY; a journal of Georgia and the South. 1927. q. $20. Atlanta Historical Society, Inc., 130 West Places Ferry Rd., Atlanta, GA 30305-1366. TEL 404-814-4000. FAX 404-814-4186. Ed. Elizabeth Tucker. adv. contact: Elizabeth Tucker. bk.rev.; charts; illus.; index, cum.index: 1927-1993; circ. 6,000 (paid). (back issues avail.) **Indexed:** Amer.Hist.& Life, Hist.Abstr. **Document type:** academic/scholarly publication.
    Former titles (until 1987): Atlanta Historical Journal (ISSN 0162-5721); (until 1977): Atlanta Historical Bulletin (ISSN 0145-1405)
    Description: Features original scholarly research on the politics, culture, peoples, personalities, history, arts, and architecture of Atlanta, Georgia, and the South.
    Refereed Serial

974 929   US
ATLANTIC COUNTY HISTORICAL SOCIETY YEARBOOK. 1947. a. $11. Atlantic County Historical Society, 907 Shore Rd., Box 301, Somers Point, NJ 08244. TEL 609-927-5218. Ed. Robert Nigro. cum.index 1948-1983. circ. 650. (back issues avail.)
    Description: Historical and genealogical information on Atlantic County and its families.

976   US   ISSN 0571-8236
ATTAKAPAS GAZETTE. 1966. q. $10. (Attakapas Historical Association) University of Southwestern Louisiana, Center for Louisiana Studies, Box 43010, USL, Lafayette, LA 70504. TEL 318-231-6027. Ed. Gertrude Taylor. bk.rev.; index. circ. 600. (back issues avail.) **Indexed:** Amer.Hist.& Life, Hist.Abstr.

971.4   CN   ISSN 0836-3102
AU PAYS DE MATANE. (Text in French) 1965. s-a. Can.$8. Societe d'Histoire et Genealogie de Matane, 145 Soucy, Matane, PQ G4W 2E1, Canada. Dir. Robert Fournier. adv.; bk.rev.; charts; illus. circ. 1,000. **Indexed:** Pt.de Rep.
    Formerly: Histoire au Pays de Matane (ISSN 0046-7499)

975   US   ISSN 0571-8899
AUGUSTA HISTORICAL BULLETIN. 1965. s-a. $10 membership. (Augusta County Historical Society) Mid-Valley Press, Box 686, Staunton, VA 24402-0686. TEL 703-886-1479. Ed. Katherine G. Bushman. circ. 450. **Document type:** academic/scholarly publication.

979   US
AUTOGRAPH COLLECTOR'S MAGAZINE. 1986. 10/yr. $25 (Canada and Mexico $30; elsewhere $35). Box 55328, Stockton, CA 95205. TEL 209-473-0570. Ed. Joe Kraus. adv.; bk.rev. circ. 5,000. (back issues avail.)
    Description: Covers autographs, letters and historical documents of personalities in all fields for hobbyists and investors of all ages.

AVIATION. see *AERONAUTICS AND SPACE FLIGHT*

976 640   US
BACKWOODSMAN. 1980. 6/yr. $14. Backwoodsman Press, c/o Charlie Richie, Ed., Box 627, Westcliffe, CO 81252. adv.; bk.rev. circ. 10,000. **Document type:** consumer publication.

975   US   ISSN 1052-0996
BALTIMORE - ANNAPOLIS (YEAR); a comprehensive directory of the area's major institutions and the people who run them. 1987. s-a. $55. Columbia Books Inc., 1212 New York Ave., N.W., Ste. 330, Washington, DC 20005. TEL 202-898-0662. Ed. John Russell. index. circ. 1,600. **Document type:** directory.
    Description: Compilation of over 2,200 public and private institutions of influence in the economic and political "capitals" of Maryland, categorized by such subjects as government, business, cultural and education institutions, medicine and health, the bar, and community affairs. Includes combined alphabetical index of organizations and individuals.

HISTORY — HISTORY OF NORTH AND SOUTH AMERICA

975 US
BALTIMORE COUNTY MUSTER. 1987. bi-m. $15 membership. Sons of the American Revolution, Maryland Society, Colonel Nicholas Ruxton Moore Chapter, 10605 Lakespring Way, Hunt Valley, MD 21030-2818. TEL 410-628-2490. Ed. Willis C. Tull, Jr. circ. 200 (controlled). (looseleaf format) **Document type:** newsletter.
   Description: Chapter news, calendar of events, profiles of members, historical notes, editorials, kudos, quotations and reading lists.

BAMPTON LECTURES IN AMERICA. see *RELIGIONS AND THEOLOGY*

972.9 BB ISSN 0005-5891
F2041
BARBADOS MUSEUM AND HISTORICAL SOCIETY. JOURNAL. 1933. a. $20. Barbados Museum and Historical Society, St. Ann's Garrison, Barbados, W.I. TEL 809-427-0201. FAX 809-429-5946. Ed. Anthony Philips. bk.rev. circ. 1,000. **Indexed:** Amer.Hist.& Life, Hist.Abstr. **Document type:** academic/scholarly publication.

BARTON COUNTY GENEALOGICAL SOCIETY. QUARTERLY. see *GENEALOGY AND HERALDRY*

BASEBALL QUARTERLY REVIEWS; the ideal baseball research journal. see *SPORTS AND GAMES — Ball Games*

BATTLE CALL. see *MILITARY*

976 US
BEDFORD HISTORICAL QUARTERLY. 1975. q. $12.50. Bedford County Historical Society, 250 Riverbend Rd., Shelbyville, TN 37160-7217. Ed. Richard Poplin. circ. 187. **Document type:** bulletin.

979.2 US ISSN 0883-8380
BEEHIVE HISTORY. 1975. a. $2.50. State Historical Society, 300 Rio Grande, Salt Lake City, UT 84101. TEL 801-533-3500. Ed. Miriam B. Murphy. circ. 3,300. **Document type:** academic/scholarly publication.
   —UnCover.

971 GW
BEITRAEGE ZUR KANADISTIK. irreg., latest vol.4. DM.32. (Gesellschaft fuer Kanada-Studien) A V - Verlag Franz Fischer, Schroeckstr. 8, 86152 Augsburg, Germany. TEL 0821-158083. FAX 0821-155518. **Document type:** monographic series.

BELCHER BULLETIN. see *GENEALOGY AND HERALDRY*

972.82 BH ISSN 0250-6831
F1441
BELIZEAN STUDIES; a journal of social research and thought. 1973. 3/yr. B.$15 $25 in America; elsewhere $30 (effective 1992). St. John's College, Belize Institute for Social Research (BISRA), Box 548, Belize City, Belize. TEL 3-3732. FAX 501-2-32752. Ed. Herman J. Byrd. bk.rev.; illus. circ. 500. (back issues avail.) **Indexed:** Amer.Hist.& Life, Anthropol.Lit., Hist.Abstr. **Document type:** academic/scholarly publication.
   Formerly: National Studies (ISSN 0303-8688)
   Description: Publishes original articles on contemporary Belizean affairs, history, politics, economics, and culture.

977 929 398 US ISSN 1063-9241
BEND OF THE RIVER; the magazine of the historic Maumee Valley. 1972. m. $9 to individuals; senior citizens $8.50. 143 W. Third, Box 39, Perrysburg, OH 43552. TEL 419-874-7534. FAX 419-874-1466. Ed. R. Lee Raizk. adv.; bk.rev. circ. 4,000.
   Description: Regional magazine dealing with nostalgia and local history.

977 020 US
BENTLEY HISTORICAL LIBRARY. 1967. a. free. University of Michigan, Bentley Historical Library, 1150 Beal Ave., Ann Arbor, MI 48109-2113. TEL 313-764-3482. Ed. W.K. Wallach. circ. 800.
   Formerly: Michigan Gazette.
   Description: Covers the history of Michigan and the activities of the Bentley Historical Library.

976 US
BEREA COLLEGE APPALACHIAN CENTER NEWSLETTER. 1972. q. $4. Berea College, Appalachian Center, CPO 2336, Berea, KY 40404. TEL 606-986-9341. Eds. Loyal Jones, Thomas Parrish. bk.rev. circ. 1,800. **Document type:** newsletter.

974 US ISSN 0749-9108
BETHEL COURIER. 1976. q. $10 includes membership. Bethel Historical Society, Inc., 14 Broad St., Box 12, Bethel, ME 04217. TEL 316-283-2500. FAX 207-824-2908. Ed. Stanley Russell Howe. bk.rev. circ. 1,000. (looseleaf format; back issues avail.) **Indexed:** Amer.Hist.& Life, Hist.Abstr.
   Description: Explores local history.

974 US ISSN 0894-8917
BETWEEN THE LAKES NEWSLETTER. 1975. q. $5. Interlaken Historical Society, Interlaken, NY 14847. TEL 607-532-4430. Ed. Maurice L. Patterson. circ. 200. **Document type:** newsletter.

986.6 EC
BIBLIOTECA AZUAYA. a. Consejo Provincial del Azuay, Departamento de Cultura, Cuenca, Ecuador.

985 398 PE
BIBLIOTECA DE LA TRADICION ORAL ANDINA. irreg., no.2011, 1988. Centro de Estudios Regionales Andinos "Bartolome de Las Casas", Apdo. 477, Cusco, Peru. TEL 084-236494. FAX 084-238255.

987 VE
BIBLIOTECA DE TEMAS Y AUTORES DE ANZOATEGUI. no.4, 1980. irreg. Ediciones de la Presidencia de la Republica, Ministry of the Secretariat of the Presidency, Palacio de Miraflores, Caracas, Venezuela.

972.9 GP
BIBLIOTHEQUE D'HISTOIRE ANTILLAISE. 1972. irreg. Societe d'Histoire de la Guadeloupe, Basse-Terre, Guadeloupe.

BIBLIOTHEQUE DE LA REVUE D'HISTOIRE ECCLESIASTIQUE. see *RELIGIONS AND THEOLOGY*

977 960 US ISSN 1058-4900
E185.93.I4
BLACK HISTORY NEWS & NOTES. 1979. q. $20 membership. Indiana Historical Society, 315 W. Ohio St., Indianapolis, IN 46202. TEL 317-232-1879. FAX 317-233-3109. Ed. Wilma L. Gibbs. illus. circ. 800. **Document type:** newsletter.
   Description: Highlights the library's Black History Program.

977 US
BLOOMING GROVE COURIER. 1972. irreg. membership. Historic Blooming Grove Historical Society, c/o C. Anne Wellman, Pres., 1000 Nickels Rd., Monona, WI 53716. TEL 608-222-9001. Ed. Jeannette L. Mundstock. circ. 125.

981 BL ISSN 0006-5218
BLUMENAU EM CADERNOS. 1957. m. Cr.$25($3.50) Fundacao Casa Dr. Blumenau, Alameda Duque de Caixas 64, Caixa Postal 425, 89015 Blumenau, Santa Catarina, Brazil. TEL 22-1711. Ed. Jose Goncalves. stat.

986 CK ISSN 0006-6303
F2251
BOLETIN DE HISTORIA Y ANTIGUEDADES. 1902. m. Col.$8000($50) Academia Colombiana de Historia, Calle 10, No. 8-95, Apdo. Aereo 14428, Bogota, D.E., Colombia. Eds. Pilar Moreno de Angel, Ricardo Ortiz McCormick. adv.; index, cum.index. circ. 1,200. (back issues avail.) **Indexed:** Amer.Hist.& Life, Hisp.Amer.Per.Ind., Hist.Abstr.

BOLSILIBROS. see *LITERATURE*

BORDER ISSUES AND PUBLIC POLICY. RESEARCH PAPERS. see *POLITICAL SCIENCE*

BORDER PERSPECTIVES. RESEARCH PAPERS. see *POLITICAL SCIENCE*

917.3 US ISSN 0092-4571
E169.1.
BORDER STATES. 1973. a. $5. American Studies Association, Kentucky-Tennessee Chapter, c/o Michael Dunne, Sarah Howell, Eds., Department of English, Middle Tennessee State University, Murfreesboro, TN 37132. TEL 615-898-2649. circ. 200. **Document type:** academic/scholarly publication.
   Description: Covers the history and culture of Kentucky and Tennessee.

970 CN ISSN 0068-0524
BOUNDARY HISTORICAL SOCIETY. REPORT. 1958. irreg., latest no.12. Can.$12.95. Boundary Historical Society, Box 580, Grand Forks, BC V0H 1H0, Canada. TEL 604-422-3283.

791.8 US
BRAND BOOK. 1968. irreg. (every 3-4 yrs.). $39. Westerners, San Diego Corral, Box 87307, San Diego, CA 92138-7307. **Indexed:** A.I.C.P.

978 970 US ISSN 0006-9078
BRANDING IRON. 1946. q. $25. The Branding Iron, 731 Fairview Ave., No. 10, Arcadia, CA 91007. TEL 818-447-3002. Ed. Siegfried Demke. bk.rev.; bibl.; illus.; index; circ. 400 (controlled).

981 BL
BRASIL DIA-A-DIA. 1988. biennial. price varies. Victor Civita, Rua Geraldo Flausino Gomes, 61, 11 andar, 04575 Sao Paulo, Brazil. Ed. Bias Arrudao. charts; illus. circ. 60,000.
   Description: Covers Brazil's history from 1930 to date. Chronological accounts of the main facts in areas such as politics, foreign relations, economy, energy, transportation, religion, science, culture and education.

973 BL
BRAZIL. ARQUIVO NACIONAL. SERIE DE PUBLICACOES. Continues its Publicacoes. irreg. Arquivo Nacional, Praca da Republica 26, Rio de Janeiro, R.J., Brazil. illus.

BRIDGE (SALEM). see *ETHNIC INTERESTS*

975 US ISSN 1052-4681
A BRIEF RELATION. 1979. q. $20. Friends of Historic St. Mary's City, Box 24, St. Mary's City, MD 20686. TEL 301-862-0990. FAX 301-862-0968. Ed. Karin B. Stanford. adv.; bk.rev. circ. 900. **Document type:** newsletter.
   Former titles: Historic St. Mary's City Newsletter; St. Marie's City Newsletter; Our Town We Call St. Maries.
   Description: News on the activities, exhibits, programs, staffing of and visitations to this national historic landmark in Maryland, which is an outdoor museum of history, archaeology, and natural history.

BRITISH ASSOCIATION FOR CANADIAN STUDIES. NEWSLETTER. see *SOCIOLOGY*

971 CN ISSN 1195-8294
BRITISH COLUMBIA HISTORICAL NEWS. 1968. q. Can.$12 (foreign Can.$17). British Columbia Historical Federation, P.O. Box 5254, Sta. B, Victoria, BC V8R 6N4, Canada. TEL 604-422-3594. FAX 604-426-4440. Ed. Naomi Miller. bk.rev.; cum.index every 5 yrs. circ. 1,250. (also avail. in microfiche; reprint service avail. from MML) **Indexed:** CMI. **Document type:** academic/scholarly publication.
   Description: British Columbian history: articles ranging from scholarly to anecdotal.

BRITISH JOURNAL OF CANADIAN STUDIES. see *SOCIOLOGY*

971 CN ISSN 0381-6206
BROME COUNTY HISTORICAL SOCIETY. PUBLICATION. Key Title: Publication - Brome County Historical Society. 1937. irreg. price varies. Brome County Historical Society, P.O. Box 690, Knowlton, PQ J0E 1V0, Canada. TEL 514-243-6782. illus.

HISTORY — HISTORY OF NORTH AND SOUTH AMERICA

974.7 US ISSN 0007-2249
BRONX COUNTY HISTORICAL SOCIETY JOURNAL. 1964. s-a. $20. Bronx County Historical Society, 3309 Bainbridge Ave., Bronx, NY 10467. TEL 212-881-8900. Ed. Gary Hermalyn. adv.; bk.rev.; bibl.; illus.; index. circ. 2,500. (also avail. in microform from UMI) **Indexed:** Amer.Hist.& Life, Hist.Abstr. **Document type:** academic/scholarly publication, monographic series.
—UMI.
Description: Publishes work on the history and heritage of the people of New York City.

974
BROOKSIDE COLUMNS. irreg. Saratoga County Historical Society, c/o Saratoga County Museum, Brookside, Bolston Spa, NY 12020.
Description: Describes the activities of the Saratoga County Historical Society.

974 US
BROOME COUNTY HISTORICAL SOCIETY NEWSLETTER. 1939. 3/yr. $20. Broome County Historical Society, 30 Front St., Binghamton, NY 13905. TEL 607-772-0660. Ed. F. Marie Scott. bk.rev. circ. 800. (back issues avail.) **Document type:** newsletter.
Description: Intended for the general reader, covering the history of Broome County, New York.

975 US
BROWN THRASHER BOOKS. 1980. 4/yr. price varies. University of Georgia Press, 330 Research Dr., Athens, GA 30602-4901. TEL 706-369-6130. FAX 706-369-6131. **Document type:** monographic series.

971 CN ISSN 0084-8115
BRUCE COUNTY HISTORICAL SOCIETY. YEAR BOOK. 1967. a. Can.$8. Bruce County Historical Society, Box 1900, Port Elgin, Ont. N0H 2L0, Canada. TEL 519-797-5361. Ed. Isobelle Underwood. adv.; illus. circ. 1,000.
Supersedes: Bruce County Historical Notes (ISSN 0045-3250)
Description: Consists of articles and illustrations describing events in the county's past and present; also includes memoirs and family histories.

BUCKS COUNTY GENEALOGICAL SOCIETY. NEWSLETTER. see *GENEALOGY AND HERALDRY*

982 AG ISSN 0524-9864
BUENOS AIRES (PROVINCE). ARCHIVO HISTORICO. PUBLICACIONES. SEXTA SERIE. 1951. irreg. Ministerio de Educacion, Archivo Historico, La Plata, Argentina.

974 387 639.2 US
BULLETIN FROM JOHNNY CAKE HILL. 1974. q. $15. Old Dartmouth Historical Society, New Bedford Whaling Museum, 18 Johnny Cake Hill, New Bedford, MA 02740. TEL 508-997-0046. FAX 508-997-0018. Ed. Anthony M. Zane. bk.rev.; bibl.; illus. circ. 2,000. **Indexed:** Amer.Hist.& Life, Hist.Abstr. **Document type:** bulletin.

BULLETIN OF LATIN AMERICAN RESEARCH. see *SOCIAL SCIENCES: COMPREHENSIVE WORKS*

970
BURLINGTON STORY. 1971. s-a. free. (City of Burlington Common Council) Henry H. Bisbee, Ed. & Pub., 216 High St., Burlington, NJ 08016. TEL 609-386-0733. circ. 5,000.

C C W H P - C G W H NEWSLETTER. (Coordinating Committee on Women in the Historical Profession - Conference Group on Women's History) see *WOMEN'S STUDIES*

973 US
C H I DISPATCH. 1979. m. $20 membership. Confederate Historical Institute, Box 7388, Little Rock, AR 72217. Ed. Jerry L. Russell. circ. 600. **Document type:** newsletter.
Description: Features the history of the Confederate States of America, and contemporary events relevant to that history.

C S A NEWS. (Costume Society of America) see *CLOTHING TRADE — Fashions*

979 US
LAS CALAVERAS. 1952. q. $10 membership. Calaveras County Historical Society, 30 Main St., Box 721, San Andreas, CA 95249. TEL 209-754-1058. Ed. George Hoeper, Jr. illus. circ. 850. **Indexed:** Amer.Hist.& Life, Hist.Abstr.
Description: Covers all aspects of Calaveras County history: families, events, ranches and prominent people.

974 942 US
CALENDAR OF HISTORY EVENTS. 1987. 4/yr. $10. New Hampshire Committee for the Promotion of History, c/o Brian Nelson Burford, Ed., Box 192, Antrim, NH 03440-0192. TEL 603-588-2920. circ. 150.
Description: Listing of local, New Hampshire, and New England history events.

979.4 US ISSN 0575-5751
CALIFORNIA HISTORIAN. 1954. q. $15 (effective Sep. 1993). Conference of California Historical Societies, University of Pacific, Stockton, CA 95211-0001. TEL 209-946-2169. FAX 209-946-2406. Ed. Mary Otis Ave. adv. contact: Art Almeida. bk.rev. circ. 17,000. (back issues avail.) **Document type:** academic/scholarly publication.

979.4 US ISSN 0162-2897
F856
CALIFORNIA HISTORY (SAN FRANCISCO). 1922. q. $40 (foreign $50). California Historical Society, 2099 Pacific Ave., San Francisco, CA 94109. TEL 415-567-1848. FAX 415-567-2394. Ed. Richard J. Orsi. adv.; bk.rev.; charts; illus.; index, cum.index: 1922-1961; 1962-1975. circ. 5,000. (also avail. in microform; back issues avail.) **Indexed:** Abstr.Engl.Stud., Amer.Hist.& Life, Arts & Hum.Cit.Ind., Cal.Per.Ind. (1978-), Curr.Cont., Hist.Abstr., Risk Abstr.
—BLDSC (3014.160000); Faxon; UnCover.
Former titles: California Historical Quarterly (ISSN 0097-6059); California Historical Society Quarterly (ISSN 0008-1175)

CALIFORNIA STATE LIBRARY FOUNDATION BULLETIN. see *LIBRARY AND INFORMATION SCIENCES*

CALIFORNIA WEEKLY EXPLORER. see *CHILDREN AND YOUTH — For*

CALUMET. see *ETHNIC INTERESTS*

800 974 US
CALVIN COOLIDGE MEMORIAL FOUNDATION NEWSLETTER. 1967. irreg. free. Calvin Coolidge Memorial Foundation, Inc., Box 97, Plymouth, VT 05056. TEL 802-672-3389. Ed. Cynthia D. Bittinger. circ. 750. **Document type:** newsletter.
Formerly: Plymouth Notch Newsletter.
Description: News announcements and activities of the Foundation.

980 UK ISSN 0068-6689
CAMBRIDGE LATIN AMERICAN STUDIES. 1967. irreg., no.59, 1986. price varies. Cambridge University Press, Edinburgh Bldg., Shaftesbury Rd., Cambridge CB2 2RU, England. TEL 0223-312393. FAX 0223-315052. TELEX 851817256. (N. American addr.: Cambridge University Press, Journals Dept., 40 W. 20th St., New York, NY 10011. TEL 212-924-3900. FAX 212-691-3239) Ed. S. Collier. **Document type:** monographic series.

971 CN ISSN 0315-1433
F1001
CANADIAN ANNUAL REVIEW OF POLITICS AND PUBLIC AFFAIRS. 1961. a. price varies. University of Toronto Press, 5201 Dufferin St., Downsview, ON M3H 5T8, Canada. TEL 416-667-7791. FAX 416-667-7832. (U.S. address: 340 Nagel Drive, Cheektowaga, NY 14225) Ed. David Leyton Brown. index. (also avail. in microfilm from BHP)
Formerly: Canadian Annual Review (ISSN 0068-8215)

971 CN
CANADIAN CIRCUMPOLAR LIBRARY. OCCASIONAL PUBLICATIONS SERIES. 1964. irreg. price varies. Canadian Circumpolar Library, University of Alberta, Edmonton, Alta. T6G 2E9, Canada. TEL 403-492-4512. **Indexed:** GeoRef.
—BLDSC (6226.602000).
Former titles: Boreal Institute for Northern Studies. Occasional Publications; Boreal Institute, Edmonton. Occasional Publications (ISSN 0068-0303)

971 CN
G575
CANADIAN CIRCUMPOLAR LIBRARY. REPORT OF ACTIVITIES. 1963. a. free. Canadian Circumpolar Library, University of Alberta, Edmonton, Alta. T6G 2E9, Canada. TEL 403-492-4512. **Indexed:** Biol.Abstr.
Former titles: Boreal Institute for Northern Studies. Report of Activities (ISSN 0820-988X); Boreal Institute, Edmonton. Report of Activities (ISSN 0316-7828); Boreal Institute, Edmonton. Annual Report (ISSN 0068-0281)

971 CN ISSN 0068-886X
CANADIAN HISTORICAL ASSOCIATION. HISTORICAL BOOKLETS - BROCHURES HISTORIQUES. (Text in English, French) 1953. irreg. Can.$3 per issue. Canadian Historical Association, 395 Wellington St., Ottawa, ON K1A 0N3, Canada. TEL 613-233-7885. Ed. T. Cook. circ. 4,000.
—CCC.

CANADIAN JEWISH HISTORICAL SOCIETY JOURNAL. see *ETHNIC INTERESTS*

CANADIAN MARITIME BIBLIOGRAPHY. see *TRANSPORTATION — Abstracting, Bibliographies, Statistics*

971.006 CN ISSN 0383-6894
F1021
CANADIAN ORAL HISTORY ASSOCIATION. JOURNAL. (Text in English and French) 1976. a. Can.$15 to individuals; institutions Can.$25. Canadian Oral History Association, Box 2064, Sta. "D", Ottawa, ON K1P 5W3, Canada. TEL 613-996-6996. FAX 613-995-6575. Ed. James Morrison. bk.rev. circ. 300. **Indexed:** Amer.Hist.& Life, Can.Wom.Per.Ind., Hist.Abstr., M.L.A. **Document type:** academic/scholarly publication.

970 630 CN
CANADIAN PAPERS IN RURAL HISTORY. 1978. biennial. $39.50. Langdale Press, RR1, Gananoque, ON K7G 2V3, Canada. FAX 613-382-7059. Ed. D.H. Akenson. circ. 1,000. (back issues avail.) **Indexed:** Amer.Hist.& Life, Geo.Abstr., Hist.Abstr., M.L.A.

CANADIAN QUAKER HISTORY JOURNAL. see *RELIGIONS AND THEOLOGY — Other Denominations And Sects*

970 810 CN ISSN 0007-7720
CANADIAN REVIEW OF AMERICAN STUDIES. 1969. 3/yr. Can.$40. (Canadian Association for American Studies, Social Science Centre) University of Calgary Press, 2500 University Dr., N.W., Calgary, AB T2N 1N4, Canada. Ed.Bd. adv.; bk.rev. circ. 500. **Indexed:** Abstr.Engl.Stud., Abstr.Pop.Cult., Amer.Hist.& Life, Amer.Hum.Ind., Arts & Hum.Cit.Ind., Curr.Cont., Hist.Abstr., Ind.Bk.Rev.Hum., M.L.A., SSCI.
—BLDSC (3044.630000); Faxon; UnCover. **CCC.**
Formerly (until 1970): C A A S Bulletin.

971 CN ISSN 0829-5026
F1060.A1
CANADIAN WEST. 1969. q. Can.$15 (foreign US$13). Sunfire Publications Ltd, P.O. Box 3399, Langley, BC V3A 4R7, Canada. TEL 604-534-9378. Ed. Garnet Basque. adv.; bk.rev.; charts; illus.; stat.; index; circ. 9,000. (paid). (also avail. in microfilm from MML; back issues avail.) **Indexed:** Can.Per.Ind.
—UnCover.
Former titles: History of the Canadian West; (until 1985): Canada West (ISSN 0590-7853)
Description: Devoted to the life and times of early pioneer history in B.C., Alberta and the Yukon, with the emphasis on B.C..

CANADIANA GERMANICA; a journal of German-Canadian Studies. see *ETHNIC INTERESTS*

977 386 US ISSN 0890-7137
CANAL SOCIETY OF OHIO. NEWSLETTER. 1973. q. membership. Canal Society of Ohio, 1890 Gallo Dr., Powell, OH 43065. TEL 614-766-2854. (Subscr. to: Corresponding Secretary, 550 Copley Rd., Akron, OH 44320) Ed. Scott Bieszczad. circ. 400. (tabloid format) **Document type:** newsletter.
Description: Current information and events regarding Ohio's canals.

CANAL TIMES. see *TRANSPORTATION — Ships And Shipping*

HISTORY — HISTORY OF NORTH AND SOUTH AMERICA

971 CN ISSN 0829-7983
CAP-AUX-DIAMANTS; revue d'histoire du Quebec. 1985. 4/yr. Can.$25 to individuals; institutions Can.$32. Editions Cap-aux-Diamants Inc., C.P. 609, Haute Ville, PQ G1R 4S2, Canada. TEL 418-656-5040. FAX 418-656-7282. Ed. Yves Beauregard. adv. contact: Jacques Belanger. bk.rev. circ. 7,000. **Indexed:** Pt.de Rep. (1987-).

971 398 917.106 CN ISSN 0319-4639
F1039.C2
CAPE BRETON'S MAGAZINE; devoted to history, natural history & future of Cape Breton Island. (Text in English, French, Gaelic) 1972. 3/yr. Can.$17($25) for 4 issues. Ronald Caplan, Ed. & Pub., Wreck Cove, Cape Breton, NS B0C 1H0, Canada. TEL 902-539-3817. FAX 902-539-9117. adv.; bk.rev. circ. 7,500. (also avail. in microform from MML; back issues avail.) **Indexed:** CMI.

974 US
CAPONIER. 1981. q. $10. Fort Hamilton Historical Society, Brooklyn, NY 11252. bk.rev. circ. 500.
 Description: Covers the military history of New York City.

946 980 FR ISSN 0008-0152
F1401
CARAVELLE; cahiers du monde hispanique et luso-bresilien. (Text in French, Portuguese and Spanish) 1963. s-a. 200 F. (effective 1994). (Universite de Toulouse II (le Mirail)) Presses Universitaires du Mirail, 56 rue du Taur, 31000 Toulouse, France. TEL 61-22-58-31. FAX 61-21-84-20. Ed. Georges Baudot. adv.; bk.rev.; abstr. circ. 1,000. (back issues avail.) **Indexed:** Amer.Hist.& Life, Hist.Abstr., M.L.A. **Document type:** academic/scholarly publication.
—Faxon; SWETS.
 Description: Presents critiques, research results, interviews with authors and unedited texts in the area of Latin-American humanities.

027.5 GP ISSN 0396-2679
CARIBBEAN ARCHIVES/ARCHIVES ANTILLAISES/ARCHIVOS DEL CARIBE. (Text in English, French or Spanish) 1973. s-a. $5. Caribbean Archives Association, B.P. 74, Basse-Terre, Guadeloupe, W.I. Ed. J.P. Hervieu. bk.rev. circ. 300.

972.9 PR ISSN 0069-0511
CARIBBEAN MONOGRAPH SERIES. 1964. irreg., no.15, 1980. price varies. Universidad de Puerto Rico, Institute of Caribbean Studies, Box BM, Rio Piedras, PR 00931. Ed. Sybil Farrell Lewis. adv.; bk.rev. circ. 1,020.
 Incorporates: Universidad de Puerto Rico. Institute of Caribbean Studies. Special Studies (ISSN 0079-788X)

972.9 PR
CARIBBEAN OCCASIONAL SERIES. irreg., latest no.4. Universidad de Puerto Rico, Institute of Caribbean Studies, Box BM, Rio Piedras, PR 00931.

979 US ISSN 1053-9700
F2130
CARIBBEAN PERSPECTIVES. 1991. irreg., latest 1992. Transaction Publishers, Transaction Periodicals Consortium, Department 3092, Rutgers University, New Brunswick, NJ 08903. (back issues avail.)

972.9 574 VI
CARIBBEAN RESEARCH INSTITUTE. REPORT. 1965. irreg., latest 10th anniv. issue, 1975. free. Caribbean Research Institute, University of the Virgin Islands, St. Thomas, VI 00801. Ed. Clara Wimbro Mitchell Lewis. circ. 750.
 Formerly: Caribbean Islands Research Institute. Annual Report (ISSN 0069-0503)

979 US ISSN 0275-5793
CARIBBEAN STUDIES (NEW YORK). 1981. irreg., latest vol.7. Gordon & Breach Science Publishers, 820 Town Center Dr., Langhorne, PA 19047. TEL 215-750-2642. FAX 215-750-6343. (UK subscr. to: P.O. Box 90, Reading, Berkshire RG1 8JL, England. TEL 0734-560-080) Eds. Roberta M. Delson, Louk Box. **Document type:** monographic series.
—BLDSC (3053.129500).
 Refereed Serial

975 US ISSN 0576-808X
F251
CAROLINA COMMENTS. 1952. bi-m. $8 (free to subscribers of North Carolina Historical Review). Division of Archives and History, 109 E. Jones St., Raleigh, NC 27601-2807. TEL 919-733-7442. Ed. Robert M. Topkins. illus.; index. circ. 1,800. (also avail. in microfilm from UMI; back issues avail.; reprint service avail. from UMI) **Indexed:** Amer.Hist.& Life, Hist.Abstr.
—UMI.
 Description: News of historical activities throughout the state and of the programs of the North Carolina Division of Archives and History.

975 US
CAROLOGUE; a bulletin of South Carolina history. 1985. 4/yr. membership. South Carolina Historical Society, Fireproof Bldg., 100 Meeting St., Charleston, SC 29401-2299. TEL 803-723-3225. Ed. Stephen Hoffius. adv.; bk.rev. **Document type:** bulletin.

970 US
CARROLL COUNTY HISTORY JOURNAL. 1952. 4/yr. $25 includes membership. Carroll County Historical Society, 210 E. Main St., Westminster, MD 21157. TEL 301-848-6494. Dir. Joseph M. Getty. bk.rev.; bibl. circ. 1,000.
 Formerly: Historical Society of Carroll County Newsletter.
 Description: Promotes the preservation of Carroll County's heritage.

918.6 020.6 CK
CARTA DE ARCHIVO. 1972. q. Asociacion Colombiana de Archivistas, Capitulo de Cundinamarca, Aptado. Aereo 49701, Bogota, Colombia. bk.rev.; bibl.

974 US
CASTLE LIGHT. 1968. q. $7 to libraries; members free. Passaic County Historical Society, Lambert Castle, 3 Valley Rd., Paterson, NJ 07503. TEL 201-881-2761. FAX 201-881-2672. Ed. Kate Gordon. circ. 1,000. (back issues avail.) **Document type:** newsletter.
 Formerly (until vol.24): Castle Lite.
 Description: Covers local history topics and genealogy.

973 US
THE CAVALRY JOURNAL. 1976. q. $20 membership. U S Cavalry Association, P.O. Box 2325, Ft. Riley, KS 66442. TEL 915-784-5797. FAX 913-784-5797. Ed. Patricia S. Bright. bk.rev.; circ. 3,000 (paid). (looseleaf format; back issues avail.) **Document type:** newsletter.
 Formerly: Crossed Sabers Newsletter.

974 US
CENTRE COUNTY HERITAGE. 1956-1958; resumed 1967. s-a. $8. Centre County Historical Society, 1001 E. College Ave., State College, PA 16801. TEL 814-234-4779. Ed. W. Douglas MacNeal. circ. 600. (back issues avail.) **Indexed:** Amer.Hist.& Life, Hist.Abstr.

CENTRE DE GENEALOGIE ET D'HISTOIRE DES ILES D'AMERIQUE. see *GENEALOGY AND HERALDRY*

972 917.2 PR
CENTRO DE ESTUDIOS AVANZADOS DE PUERTO RICO Y EL CARIBE. REVISTA. 1985. s-a. $6 per no. Centro de Estudios Avanzados de Puerto Rico y el Caribe, Box S-4467, San Juan, PR 00902-4467. TEL 809-723-4481. Ed. Ricardo E. Alegua. bk.rev. circ. 2,000. (back issues avail.) **Document type:** academic/scholarly publication.

972.91 CU
CENTRO DE ESTUDIOS MARTIANOS. ANUARIO. 1978. a. Centro de Estudios Martianos, Calzada 807, Esquina A 4, El Vedado, Havana 4, Cuba. bk.rev.; bibl.
 Supersedes (1969-1977, no.7): Anuario Martiano (ISSN 0066-524X)

987 VE ISSN 0008-9990
CENTRO DE HISTORIA DEL ESTADO FALCON. BOLETIN. vol.13, 1965. free. Centro de Historia del Estado Falcon, Coro, Venezuela. Ed.Bd. **Indexed:** Amer.Hist.& Life, Hist.Abstr.

977 US
CHADBURN. q. $35 membership. Great Lakes Historical Society, 480 Main St., Vermillion, OH 44089-1099. TEL 216-967-3467. FAX 216-967-1519. Ed. Rita Summers. **Document type:** newsletter.

977 770 US
CHAMPAIGN COUNTY HISTORICAL ARCHIVES HISTORICAL PUBLICATIONS SERIES. 1977. irreg., no.11, 1988. price varies. Urbana Free Library, 201 S. Race St., Urbana, IL 61801-3283. TEL 217-367-4025. FAX 217-367-4061. Ed. Frederick A. Schlipf. (back issues avail.)
 Formerly: Historical Reprint Series.
 Description: Original publications and reprints of scarce books and maps pertaining to the history and people of Champaign County and east-central Illinois.

971 CN ISSN 0316-6724
CHARLOTTES. 1971. irreg. price varies. Queen Charlotte Islands Museum Society, Second Beach Skidegate, Queen Charlotte, B.C. V0T 1S0, Canada. TEL 604-559-4643. Eds. T. & N. Gessler. circ. 2,500.

971 CN ISSN 0319-1249
CHATEAUGUAY VALLEY HISTORICAL SOCIETY ANNUAL JOURNAL/JOURNAL ANNUEL DE LA SOCIETE HISTORIQUE DE LA VALLEE DE LA CHATEAUGUAY. a. Can.$12. Chateauguay Valley Historical Society, P.O. Box 61, Howick, PQ J0S 1G0, Canada. Ed. Robert McGee. illus. circ. 1,000. (back issues avail.)

CHEMICAL HERITAGE. see *CHEMISTRY*

974 US
CHEMUNG HISTORICAL JOURNAL. 1955. q. $8. Chemung County Historical Society, 415 E. Water St., Elmira, NY 14901. TEL 607-734-4167. Ed. Thomas E. Byrne. adv.; cum.index: 1955-1982. circ. 1,100. (back issues avail.) **Indexed:** Amer.Hist.& Life, Hist.Abstr.

CHESAPEAKE AND OHIO HISTORICAL MAGAZINE. see *TRANSPORTATION — Railroads*

970 US ISSN 0272-8540
F548.1   CODEN: CHHIEY
CHICAGO HISTORY. 1945. 3/yr. $30 to individuals; students $25. Chicago Historical Society, 1601 N. Clark St., Chicago, IL 60614. TEL 312-642-4600. FAX 312-266-2077. Ed. Claudia L. Wood. bk.rev.; index. circ. 8,500. (also avail. in microfilm from UMI; reprint service avail. from UMI) **Indexed:** Amer.Hist.& Life, Hist.Abstr.
—UnCover; UMI.

970 US ISSN 0069-3278
CHICAGO HISTORY OF AMERICAN CIVILIZATION. 1956. irreg., latest 1983. price varies. University of Chicago Press, 5801 S. Ellis Ave., Chicago, IL 60637. TEL 312-702-7899. (Subscr. to: 11030 Langley Ave., Chicago IL 60628) Ed. Daniel J. Boorstin. adv.; bk.rev. (reprint service avail. from UMI,ISI)
 Refereed Serial

CHICKASAW TIMES PAST. see *GENEALOGY AND HERALDRY*

CHINESE HISTORIAN. see *ORIENTAL STUDIES*

CHINESE HISTORICAL SOCIETY OF AMERICA. BULLETIN. see *ETHNIC INTERESTS*

977 US ISSN 0440-9426
F561
CHRONICLE (ANN ARBOR). 1964. s-a. $25. Historical Society of Michigan, 2117 Washtenaw Ave., Ann Arbor, MI 48104. TEL 313-769-1828. Ed. Thomas L. Jones. adv.; bk.rev.; bibl.; illus. circ. 4,000. (back issues avail.) **Indexed:** Amer.Hist.& Life, Hist.Abstr., Mich.Mag.Ind.
 Formerly: H S M Bulletin.

976.6 US ISSN 0009-6024
F691
CHRONICLES OF OKLAHOMA. 1921. q. $15 to individuals; institutions $25 (includes Mistletoe Leaves). Oklahoma Historical Society, Historical Bldg., 2100 N. Lincoln, Oklahoma City, OK 73105. TEL 405-521-2491. FAX 405-525-3272. Ed. Bob L. Blackburn. bk.rev.; bibl.; charts; illus.; index, cum.index. circ. 6,300. (also avail. in microfilm) **Indexed:** Amer.Hist.& Life, Hist.Abstr. **Document type:** academic/scholarly publication.
—UnCover.
 Description: Topics include narrative history, biographies, historiography, archeology and anthropology in Oklahoma.

HISTORY — HISTORY OF NORTH AND SOUTH AMERICA

975 US
CHRONICLES OF ST. MARY'S. 1953. m. membership. St. Mary's County Historical Society, Box 212, Leonardtown, MD 20650. TEL 301-475-2467. Ed. Regina Combs Hammett. bk.rev.; index. circ. 800. (back issues avail.)

982 330.1 AG
CICLOS; en la historia, la economia y la sociedad. 1991. s-a. Instituto de Investigaciones de Historia Economica y Social, Fac. de Ciencias Economicas (UBA), Av. Cordoba 2122, 2o piso, 1120 Buenos Aires, Argentina. (Subscr. to: Casilla de Correo 147, Suc. 53 B, 1453 Buenos Aires, Argentina) Ed. Mario Rapoport.

976 059 US ISSN 0898-0330
CIRCUIT RIDER (FRANKFORT). 1978. q. $9.50. Historical Confederation of Kentucky, Box H, Frankfort, KY 40602-2108. TEL 502-564-3016. FAX 502-564-4701. Ed. Charles Roger Stapleton. circ. 400. (tabloid format; back issues avail.) **Document type:** newsletter.
   Description: Details events in historic interpretation and management among history minded groups in Kentucky and surrounding states. Each issue contains a technical insert on a specific topic of interest to readers.

CIVIL WAR. see *MILITARY*

973.7 US ISSN 0009-8078
E461
CIVIL WAR HISTORY; a journal of the Middle Period. 1955. q. $18 to individuals; institutions $28. (Kent State University, Department of History) Kent State University Press, Kent, OH 44242-0021. TEL 216-672-7913. Ed. John T. Hubbell. adv.; bk.rev. circ. 1,600. (also avail. in microform from MIM,UMI; reprint service avail. from UMI) **Indexed:** Amer.Hist.& Life, Arts & Hum.Cit.Ind., Curr.Cont., Hist.Abstr., Hum.Ind.
   —Faxon; UnCover; SWETS; UMI. **CCC.**
   Description: Examines the war, its causes and the aftermath.

974 US ISSN 1053-1181
CIVIL WAR NEWS; for people with an active interest in the Civil War today. 1974. 11/yr. $24 (foreign $35). Cutter & Locke Incorporated, Rt. 1, Box 36, Tunbridge, VT 05077. TEL 802-889-3500. FAX 802-889-5627. Ed. C. Peter Jorgensen. adv.; bk.rev. circ. 8,000. (tabloid format; back issues avail.)
   Former titles: Civil War Book Exchange and Collector's Newspaper; Civil War Book Exchange.

973.7 US ISSN 0009-8086
CIVIL WAR ROUND TABLE DIGEST. 1968. m. $12.50. Civil War Round Table Associates, Box 7388, Little Rock, AR 72217. TEL 501-225-3996. FAX 501-225-5167. Ed. J.L. Russell. tr.lit. circ. 1,400. **Document type:** newsletter.

973.7 US ISSN 0009-8094
E461
CIVIL WAR TIMES ILLUSTRATED; a magazine for persons interested in American History, particularly in the Civil War period. 1959. 6/yr. $21. Cowles Magazines, Inc. (Subsidiary of: Cowles Media Company), 6405 Flank Dr., Box 8200, Harrisburg, PA 17105-8200. TEL 717-657-9555. FAX 717-657-9526. Ed. John E. Stanchak. adv.; bk.rev.; illus.; maps; index. circ. 174,054. (also avail. in microfiche; reprint service avail. from UMI) **Indexed:** Amer.Hist.& Life, Hist.Abstr. **Document type:** consumer publication.
   —Faxon; UnCover; UMI.

970.1 US ISSN 0069-4304
CIVILIZATION OF THE AMERICAN INDIAN. 1932. irreg. price varies. University of Oklahoma Press, 1005 Asp Ave., Norman, OK 73019. TEL 405-325-5111. FAX 405-325-4000.

977 US
CLARK COUNTY HISTORICAL SOCIETY. NEWSLETTER. 1971. q. membership. Clark County Historical Society, Box 2157, Springfield, OH 45501-2157. Ed. Floyd A. Barmann. bk.rev. circ. 631. **Document type:** newsletter.

917.97 US ISSN 0090-449X
F897.C6
CLARK COUNTY HISTORY. 1960. a. $6.50. Fort Vancouver Historical Society, Box 1834, Vancouver, WA 98668. TEL 206-695-4681. bibl.; cum.index for 33 yrs. in vol.33, 1992. circ. 1,000. **Document type:** academic/scholarly publication.
   Description: Portrays the history of the first and oldest county of the state, which is known as the "Cradle of Pacific Northwest History".

CLASSICAL BULLETIN. see *CLASSICAL STUDIES*

CLASSICAL JOURNAL. see *CLASSICAL STUDIES*

974 US ISSN 0197-2871
CLINTON HISTORICAL SOCIETY. NEWSLETTER. 1963. irreg. membership. Clinton Historical Society, Inc., Box 42, Clinton, NY 13323. Ed. Philip E. Munson. circ. 300. **Document type:** newsletter.

COAS: NEW MEXICO ARCHAEOLOGY AND HISTORY. see *ARCHAEOLOGY*

COBBLESTONE; the history magazine for young people. see *CHILDREN AND YOUTH — For*

976 US
COFFEE COUNTY HISTORICAL SOCIETY QUARTERLY. q. $10. Coffee County Historical Society, Box 524, Manchester, TN 37355. Ed. Betty Anderson Bridgewater. index.

COLE CHRONICLE; a genealogical journal for family historians. see *GENEALOGY AND HERALDRY*

981 BL
COLECAO DE ESTUDOS HISTORICOS. 1978. irreg. Fundacao Casa de Rui Barbosa, Rua Sao Clemente 134, Botafogo 22260, Rio de Janeiro, RJ, Brazil. FAX 5371114. Dir. Agnello Uchoa Bittencourt.

981 BL
COLECAO TEMAS BRASILEIROS. no.13, 1972. irreg. Conquista, Av. 28 de Setembro 174, Rio de Janeiro GB, Brazil. Dir. Arthur C. Ferreira Reis. illus.

COLECCION ESTUDIOS LATINOAMERICANOS. see *LITERATURE*

987 VE ISSN 0069-5084
COLECCION "FOROS Y SEMINARIOS." SERIE FOROS. 1965. irreg., no.5, 1968. Universidad Central de Venezuela, Direccion de Cultura, Biblioteca Piso 10, Cuidad Universitaria, Caracas, Venezuela.

987 VE ISSN 0069-5092
COLECCION "FOROS Y SEMINARIOS." SERIE SEMINARIOS. 1964. irreg., no.2, 1966. Universidad Central de Venezuela, Direccion de Cultura, Biblioteca, Piso 10, Ciudad Universitaria, Caracas, Venezuela.

989.2 PY
COLECCION HISTORIA. 1982. irreg. El Lector, 25 de Mayo y Antequera, Asuncion, Paraguay.

COLLECTORS CLUB PHILATELIST. see *PHILATELY*

970 US ISSN 1063-5769
F1412
▼**COLONIAL LATIN AMERICAN HISTORICAL REVIEW.** (Text in English, Spanish) 1992. q. $30 to individuals; institutions $35 (foreign $40). Spanish Colonial Research Center, Zimmerman Library, University of New Mexico, Albuquerque, NM 87131. TEL 505-766-8743. FAX 505-277-4603. Ed. Joseph P. Sanchez. adv.; bk.rev. circ. 1,200. (back issues avail.) **Indexed:** Amer.Hist.& Life, Curr.Cont., Hisp.Amer.Per.Ind., Hist.Abstr. **Document type:** academic/scholarly publication.
   Description: Publishes original research articles dealing with the Spanish colonial era in the Americas (1492-1821).
   Refereed Serial

974 US
COLONIAL SOCIETY OF MASSACHUSETTS. PUBLICATIONS. (Transactions and Collections) 1895. irreg., vol.65, 1993. $35. Colonial Society of Massachusetts, 87 Mount Vernon St., Boston, MA 02108. TEL 617-227-2782. Ed. John W. Tyler. circ. 500. (also avail. in microfilm from BHP) **Document type:** proceedings.

975 US ISSN 1064-2501
COLONIAL WILLIAMSBURG. 1978. q. $3.50 per no. Colonial Williamsburg Foundation, Box 1776, Williamsburg, VA 23187-1776. TEL 804-220-7284. FAX 804-220-7970. Ed. Wayne Barrett. adv.: B&W page $3615, color page $4460; trim 8 1/4 x 10 7/8. circ. 70,000. **Document type:** consumer publication.
   Formerly (until 1984): Colonial Williamsburg Today (ISSN 8755-6278)

COLONIAL WILLIAMSBURG ARCHAEOLOGICAL SERIES. see *ARCHAEOLOGY*

COLORADO EXPRESS. see *TRAVEL AND TOURISM*

978.8 US ISSN 0272-9377
F771
COLORADO HERITAGE. 1981. q. $30. Colorado Historical Society, 1300 Broadway, Denver, CO 80203. TEL 303-866-5786. Ed. Clark Secrest. bk.rev.; illus. circ. 7,500. (back issues avail.) **Indexed:** Amer.Hist.& Life, Hist.Abstr.
   —BLDSC (3321.310000); UnCover.
   Formerly (until 1981): Colorado Magazine (ISSN 0010-1648)

978.8 US ISSN 0895-0083
COLORADO HISTORY NEWS. 1981. m. $30. Colorado Historical Society, 1300 Broadway, Denver, CO 80203. TEL 303-866-5786. Ed. Peg Ekstrand. illus. circ. 10,000.
   Former titles: Colorado Heritage News (ISSN 0272-8907); (until 1981): Mountain and Plain History Notes (ISSN 0047-8261)

978.8 US ISSN 0010-1702
COLORADO PROSPECTOR; Colorado history from early day newspapers. 1969. q. $8. Alan J. Kania, Box 623, Parker, CO 80134-0623. TEL 303-841-0609. adv.; bk.rev. circ. 4,000. (tabloid format; also avail. in microform; back issues avail.) **Document type:** newspaper.
   Description: Presents Colorado's past through reprints of original newspaper accounts and vintage photographs.

979 US ISSN 0892-3094
COLUMBIA (TACOMA); the magazine of Northwest history. 1987. q. membership. Washington State Historical Society, 315 Stadium Way, Tacoma, WA 98403. TEL 206-593-2830. FAX 206-597-4186. Ed. David Nicandri. adv. contact: Christina Orange. bk.rev.; bibl.; illus. circ. 3,000. (back issues avail.) **Indexed:** Amer.Hist.& Life (1993-), Hist.Abstr. (1993-). **Document type:** academic/scholarly publication.
   Description: Focuses on Washington State history but also covers area that was originally the Oregon Country. Contains biographical sketches and local history pieces.

977.5 US ISSN 0196-1306
COLUMNS (MADISON). 1980. bi-m. membership. State Historical Society of Wisconsin, 816 State St., Madison, WI 53706. TEL 608-264-6463. Ed. John D. Holzheuter. illus. circ. 6,000. **Document type:** newsletter.
   Supersedes (1954-1979): Wisconsin Then and Now (ISSN 0043-6739)

COME - ALL - YE; a review journal. see *FOLKLORE*

CONCHO RIVER REVIEW. see *LITERATURE*

974 US
CONCORD REVIEW. 1988. q. $35. Box 476, Canton, MA 02021. Ed. Will Fitzhugh.
   Description: For American high school students; includes work from about a dozen young people.

970 US
CONFEDERATE VETERAN. 1984. bi-m. $13. Sons of Confederate Veterans, Box 710287, Houston, TX 77271-0287. TEL 713-778-0074. Ed. James N. Vogler. adv.; circ. 20,000 (paid). (also avail. in diskette format; back issues avail.)
   ●Also available on CD-ROM.
   Description: Contains articles on the South during the Civil War and association news.

HISTORY — HISTORY OF NORTH AND SOUTH AMERICA

980   US   ISSN 0010-5570
CONFERENCE ON LATIN AMERICAN HISTORY NEWSLETTER. 1949. s-a. $20. Institute for Latin American Studies, Auburn University, Auburn, AL 36849-5236. TEL 205-844-4161. FAX 205-844-2378. adv. circ. 800. **Document type:** newsletter.

CONGRESS AND THE PRESIDENCY. see *POLITICAL SCIENCE*

974 700   US   ISSN 0885-4831
F91
CONNECTICUT HISTORICAL SOCIETY. BULLETIN. 1935. s-a. $20. Connecticut Historical Society, 1 Elizabeth St., Hartford, CT 06105. TEL 203-236-5621. FAX 203-236-2664. Ed. Everett C. Wilkie, Jr. adv.; bk.rev.; charts; illus.; cum.index: every 5 yrs. circ. 850. **Document type:** academic/scholarly publication.
—BLDSC (2458.800000); UnCover.
Description: Scholarly articles relating to Connecticut and early New England.

974   US   ISSN 0734-8916
CONNECTICUT HISTORICAL SOCIETY. NOTES & NEWS. 1966. 3/yr. membership. Connecticut Historical Society, 1 Elizabeth St., Hartford, CT 06105. TEL 203-236-5621. FAX 203-236-2664. Ed. Diana Ross McCain. circ. 3,000. **Document type:** newsletter.
Description: Articles on events, exhibitions and activities of the Connecticut Historical Society.

970   US   ISSN 0069-9357
CONTEMPORARY AMERICAN HISTORY SERIES. 1969. irreg., no.10, 1977. Columbia University Press, 562 W. 113th St., New York, NY 10025. TEL 212-678-6777. Ed. William E. Leuchtenburg.

971   CN   ISSN 0714-9476
CONTINUITE. 1982. q. Can.$23.11($32) (Conseil des Monuments et Sites du Quebec) Editions Continuite Inc., 82 Grande Allee O., Quebec, PQ G1R 2G6, Canada. TEL 418-647-6483. FAX 418-647-4525. Ed. Micheline Peche. adv.; bk.rev. **Indexed:** Pt.de Rep. (1987-).
Description: Dedicated to historic preservation. Also focuses on Quebec heritage and architectural history.

CONTRIBUTIONS IN AFRO-AMERICAN AND AFRICAN STUDIES. see *HISTORY — History Of Africa*

973   US   ISSN 0084-9219
CONTRIBUTIONS IN AMERICAN HISTORY. 1970. irreg., no.147, 1992. price varies. Greenwood Press, Inc. (Subsidiary of: Greenwood Publishing Group Inc.), 88 Post Rd. W., Box 5007, Westport, CT 06881-5007. TEL 203-226-3571. FAX 203-222-1502. Ed. Jon L. Wakelyn.
—BLDSC (3458.205000).

973   US   ISSN 0084-9227
CONTRIBUTIONS IN AMERICAN STUDIES. 1969. irreg., no.102, 1992. price varies. Greenwood Press, Inc. (Subsidiary of: Greenwood Publishing Group Inc.), 88 Post Rd. W., Box 5007, Westport, CT 06881-5007. TEL 203-226-3571. FAX 203-222-1502. Ed. Robert H. Walker.
—BLDSC (3458.208000).

970   US   ISSN 0163-3813
CONTRIBUTIONS IN COMPARATIVE COLONIAL STUDIES. 1979. irreg. price varies. Greenwood Press, Inc. (Subsidiary of: Greenwood Publishing Group Inc.), 88 Post Rd. W., Box 5007, Westport, CT 06881-5007. TEL 203-226-3571. FAX 203-222-1502.
—BLDSC (3458.294000).

980 300   US   ISSN 1054-6790
CONTRIBUTIONS IN LATIN AMERICAN STUDIES. 1991. irreg. price varies. Greenwood Press, Inc. (Subsidiary of: Greenwood Publishing Group Inc.), 88 Post Rd. W., Box 5007, Westport, CT 06881-5007. TEL 203-226-3571. FAX 203-222-1502. **Document type:** monographic series.

978   US   ISSN 0270-5699
CORNERSTONE (LINCOLN). 1977. q. free. Nebraska State Historical Society, State Historic Preservation Office, 1500 R St., Box 82854, Lincoln, NE 68501. TEL 402-471-4767. FAX 402-471-3100. Ed. L. Robert Puschendorf. circ. 7,500. **Document type:** newsletter.
Description: Covers the activities of the office, and reports on historic preservation in Nebraska.

980   SP   ISSN 0589-8056
CORPUS HISPANORUM DE PACE. 1963. irreg., no.27, 1988. price varies. Consejo Superior de Investigaciones Cientificas (C.S.I.C.), Instituto Francisco de Vitoria, Vitruvio, 8, 28006 Madrid, Spain.
Description: Contains criticism and historical interpretation of Spain's occupation of the Americas and domination of the native tribes.

EL CORREO FRONTERIZO. see *GEOGRAPHY*

977   US
COTEAU HERITAGE. 1987. s-a. membership. (Pipestone County Historical Society) Pipestone Publishing Co., Box 277, Pipestone, MN 56164. TEL 507-825-3333. (Co-sponsor: Pipestone County Museum) Ed. David Rambow. circ. 1,500. (back issues avail.) **Document type:** academic/scholarly publication.
Description: Covers the history of Pipestone County.

970   US   ISSN 0010-9967
COUNCIL ON AMERICA'S MILITARY PAST. PERIODICAL. 1967. q. $35 membership (incl. Headquarters Heliogram). Council on America's Military Past, U.S.A., Inc., Box 1151, Ft. Myer, VA 22211. TEL 202-479-2258. Ed. Logan Osterad Orf. adv.; illus.; cum.index. circ. 1,400.
Formerly: Council on Abandoned Military Posts. Periodical.
Description: Covers the background, aims and projects of American military history and historic preservation.

974   US   ISSN 0011-071X
COVERED BRIDGE TOPICS. 1943. q. membership only. National Society for the Preservation of Covered Bridges, Inc., c/o Mrs. Christine Ellsworth, Corr.Sec., 44 Cleveland Ave., Worcester, MA 01603. TEL 617-268-7502. Ed. Joseph Conwill. adv.; bk.rev.; charts; illus.; tr.lit.; cum.index. circ. 1,000.
Description: Presents information on covered bridges, and preservation.

979.4   US   ISSN 0574-3680
F868.S49
COVERED WAGON. 1943. a. $12.50. Shasta Historical Society, Box 990277, Redding, CA 96099-0277. TEL 916-225-4155. Ed. Madge R. Walsh. adv.; illus.; index, cum.index 1943-1989. circ. 600. (back issues avail.)
Description: Contains articles about Shasta County history or related topics, perosnal recollections or original research, and pioneer family histories.

974   US
COW NECK PENINSULA HISTORICAL JOURNAL. 1965. a. membership only. Cow Neck Peninsula Historical Society, 336 Port Washington Blvd., Port Washington, NY 11050. TEL 516-365-9074. Ed. Catherine E. Sandy. illus.; cum.index 1965-1980. circ. 500.

COWBOY ARTISTS OF AMERICA NEWSLETTER. see *MUSEUMS AND ART GALLERIES*

970   US
CRESCENT CITY SUTLER CATALOG. s-a. Crescent City Sutler Inc., 17810 N. Hwy. 57, Evansville, IN 47711.

CRUISER. see *FORESTS AND FORESTRY*

CUADERNOS DE GEOHISTORIA REGIONAL. see *GEOGRAPHY*

983   CL   ISSN 0716-1832
CUADERNOS DE HISTORIA. 1981. a. $15. Universidad de Chile, Faculdad de Filosofia y Humanidades, Departamento de Ciencias Historicas, Santiago, Chile. FAX 2731919. Ed. Rolando Mellafe. bk.rev. circ. 1,000. **Indexed:** Amer.Hist.& Life, Hist.Abstr.

200   PE   ISSN 1012-2737
CUADERNOS PARA LA HISTORIA DE LA EVANGELIZACION EN AMERICA LATINA. 1986. irreg., latest no.8007. S/4000($20) to individuals (foreign $25); institutions $25 (foreign $30). Centro de Estudios Regionales Andinos "Bartolome de las Casas", Centro Las Casas, Apto. 477, Cuzco, Peru. TEL 084-233472. FAX 084-238255. Ed.Bd. adv.; bk.rev.; bibl.; charts; stat. circ. 600. (back issues avail.) **Indexed:** Bk.Rev.Ind.
Description: Covers the history of evangelization in Latin America.

972.91064   DK   ISSN 0900-8365
CUBA-BLADET. 1975. q. DKK 30 to individuals; institutions DKK 56. Dansk-Cubansk Forening, 11-13 Cort Adelerg. 1, Copenhagen, Denmark. Ed.Bd. bk.rev.; bibl.; illus.

CUICUILCO. see *ANTHROPOLOGY*

975 976   US   ISSN 1051-371X
F209
CULTURAL PERSPECTIVES ON THE AMERICAN SOUTH. 1981. irreg., vol.5, 1991. Gordon & Breach Science Publishers, 820 Town Center Dr., Langhorne, PA 19047. TEL 215-750-2642. FAX 215-750-6343. (UK subscr. to: P.O. Box 90, Reading, Berkshire RG1 8JL, England. TEL 0734-560-080) Ed. Charles Reagan Wilson. **Document type:** monographic series.
—BLDSC (6428.137840).
Formerly (until vol.4): Perspectives on the American South (ISSN 0275-584X)
Refereed Serial

979   US
CURRY COUNTY ECHOES. 1974. m. $7.50 includes membership. Curry County Historical Society, 920 S. Ellensburg Ave., Gold Beach, OR 97444. TEL 503-247-6113. Eds. Marguerite Metzgus, Lola Gardner. circ. 400. (looseleaf format) **Document type:** bulletin.
Description: Covers the history of Curry County, its families, and events.

CYPRESS BASIN GENEALOGICAL AND HISTORICAL SOCIETY REPORTER. see *GENEALOGY AND HERALDRY*

DALLAS QUARTERLY. see *GENEALOGY AND HERALDRY*

973 369.135   US   ISSN 0011-7013
DAUGHTERS OF THE AMERICAN REVOLUTION MAGAZINE. 1892. m. (except July & Aug.) $12. National Society of the Daughters of the American Revolution, 1776 D St., N.W., Washington, DC 20006. TEL 202-879-3286. FAX 202-879-3252. Ed. Mary Rose Hall. adv.; charts; illus.; index. circ. 50,000. (also avail. in microfilm from UMI; reprint service avail. from UMI) **Indexed:** Amer.Hist.& Life, Geneal.Per.Ind., Hist.Abstr.
—Faxon; UnCover; UMI.
Former titles (until 1946): National Historical Monthly Magazine; (until 1937): American Monthly Magazine.

978 929   US
DAWSON COUNTY HISTORICAL & GENEALOGICAL NEWSLETTER. 1989. q. $5. Sylvia Mickelson, Ed. & Pub., 1477 Hwy. 200S, Glendive, MT 59330-9402. **Document type:** newsletter.

975   US
DELAWARE DOCUMENTATION. 1977. a. free. Bureau of Archives and Records Management, Division of Historical and Cultural Affairs, Hall of Records, Dover, DE 19901. TEL 302-739-5318. FAX 302-739-6710. Ed. James R. Frazier. circ. 600. (also avail. in microfiche) **Document type:** bibliography.

975.1   US   ISSN 0011-7765
F161
DELAWARE HISTORY. 1946. s-a. $15 to non-members. Historical Society of Delaware, 505 Market St., Wilmington, DE 19801. TEL 302-655-7161. FAX 302-655-7844. Ed. John Munroe. bibl.; index. circ. 1,500. (reprint service avail. from KTO) **Indexed:** Amer.Hist.& Life, Hist.Abstr. **Document type:** academic/scholarly publication.
—Faxon; UnCover; SWETS.
Description: Articles about all aspects of the history of Delaware.

978   US
DICKINSON COUNTY HERITAGE CENTER. GAZETTE. 1970. q. $10. Dickinson County Heritage Center, 412 S. Campbell St., Abilene, KS 67410-2905. TEL 913-263-2681. Ed. Jeff Sheets. bk.rev.; circ. 600 (controlled). (looseleaf format) **Document type:** newsletter.
Formerly: Dickinson County Historical Society. Gazette.

979   US
DIGGIN'S. 1957. q. $15. Butte County Historical Society, Box 2195, Oroville, CA 95965. Ed. Roberta R. Hammon. bk.rev.; charts; illus.; index, cum.index. circ. 750.
Description: Contains items of local interest.

HISTORY — HISTORY OF NORTH AND SOUTH AMERICA

983   CL   ISSN 0716-1484
DIMENSION HISTORICA DE CHILE. 1984. a. $7. (Universidad Metropolitana de Ciencias de la Educacion, Departamento de Historia y Geografia) Ediciones Hoja, Av. Jose Pedro Alessandri 774, Santiago, Chile. FAX 498495. Ed. Patricia Arancibia Clavel. bk.rev. circ. 500.

918.2   AG
DINAMIS. 1968. m. Arg.$10 per no. Sindicato Luz y Fuerza Capital, Defensa 453, 9 Piso, Buenos Aires, Argentina. TEL 331-0591. adv.; bk.rev.; illus. circ. 49,000.

918   US
DIRECTORY OF A S U LATIN AMERICANISTS. 1972. a. free. Arizona State University, Center for Latin American Studies, Tempe, AZ 85287-2401. TEL 602-965-5127. FAX 602-965-6679. TELEX 1561058 ASU UT. Ed. K. Lynn Stoner. **Document type:** directory.
    Formerly: Directory of Latin Americanists (ISSN 0091-3235)

973   US   ISSN 1045-456X
E172
DIRECTORY OF HISTORICAL ORGANIZATIONS IN THE UNITED STATES AND CANADA. every 4 yrs. $79.95. American Association for State and Local History, 530 Church St., Ste. 600, Nashville, TN 37219-2325. TEL 615-255-2971. adv. **Document type:** directory.
● Also available online.
    Formerly: Directory of Historical Societies and Agencies in the United States and Canada (ISSN 0070-5659)

DIRECTORY OF HISTORY DEPARTMENTS AND ORGANIZATIONS (YEAR); colleges, universities, and research institutions in the United States and Canada. see EDUCATION — Guides To Schools And Colleges

977   US
DISCOVER MID-AMERICA. 1971. m. $18. Discovery Publications, Inc., 400 Grand Ave., Kansas City, MO 64106. TEL 800-899-9730. FAX 816-474-1427. Ed. Kenneth C. Weyand. adv. circ. 60,000.
    Former titles: Discover K C; Discover (Kansas City); Discover North.
    Description: Guide to unique shops in the Midwest, with articles pertaining to local history, antiques and collectibles, plus events calendars.

THE DISPATCH (MIDLAND); American airpower a proud heritage. see AERONAUTICS AND SPACE FLIGHT

977   US
DISPATCH NEWS. 1968. q. membership. (Association of Illinois Museums & Historical Societies) Illinois State Historical Society, Old State Capitol, Springfield, IL 62701-1507. TEL 217-524-7080. circ. 650 (controlled). (back issues avail.) **Document type:** academic/scholarly publication.
    Formerly: Dispatch - Congress News; Which was formed by the merger of: Dispatch (Springfield) (ISSN 0419-4187) & Congress News; Which was formerly: C I H S M News; Historically Speaking.

975   US
DOCTORAL DISSERTATIONS IN HISTORY. a. $10 to non-members; members $7. American Historical Association, 400 A St., S.E., Washington, DC 20003-3889. TEL 202-544-2422. FAX 202-544-8307. Ed. Wendi Maloney. **Document type:** academic/scholarly publication.
    Description: Update of history dissertations in progress at all Ph.D-granting institutions in North America.

DOCUMENTARY EDITING. see HUMANITIES: COMPREHENSIVE WORKS

970 980   AG   ISSN 0325-9404
DOCUMENTOS DE GEOHISTORIA REGIONAL. 1980. irreg. Consejo Nacional de Investigaciones Cientificas y Tecnicas, Instituto de Investigaciones Geohistoricas, Casilla de Correo 438, 3500 Resistencia, Argentina. FAX 54-722-39983.
Document type: bibliography.
    Description: Lists works that contribute to the field of geohistory in the northeast region of Argentina.

970   JA   ISSN 0420-0918
E171
DOSHISHA AMERICAN STUDIES. (Text in English, Japanese; summaries in English) 1963. a. 1000 Yen. Doshisha University, Center for American Studies, Karasuma Imadegawa, Kamigyo-ku, Kyoto 602, Japan. FAX 075-251-3091. Ed.Bd. bk.rev.; index. circ. 750. **Indexed:** Jap.Per.Ind.

973.7   US   ISSN 1059-9851
DR. SAMUEL MUDD NEWSLETTER. 1990. q. free. 3428 Hess St., Philadelphia, PA 19136. TEL 215-333-0605. Ed. George McNamara. adv. circ. 725. (back issues avail.) **Document type:** newsletter.
    Description: Provides news of the ongoing effort to overturn the conspiracy charge against Dr. Samuel Mudd relating to the assassination of Abraham Lincoln. Includes factual information and suggestions for action.

DUBLIN SEMINAR FOR NEW ENGLAND FOLKLIFE. ANNUAL PROCEEDINGS. see FOLKLORE

974   US   ISSN 0418-1379
F72.M5
DUKES COUNTY INTELLIGENCER. 1958. q. $25 membership. Dukes County Historical Society, Box 827, Edgartown, MA 02539. TEL 508-627-4441. Ed. Arthur R. Railton. bk.rev.; charts; illus. circ. 1,400. **Indexed:** Amer.Hist.& Life, Hist.Abstr. **Document type:** academic/scholarly publication.
    Description: Focuses on the history of Martha's Vineyard and the Elizabeth Islands.

974   US   ISSN 0739-8565
DUTCHESS COUNTY HISTORICAL SOCIETY. YEARBOOK. 1915. a. $25. Dutchess County Historical Society, Box 88, Poughkeepsie, NY 12602. adv.; bk.rev.; bibl.; charts; illus.; index, cum.index: 1976-1980. circ. 650. (back issues avail.) **Indexed:** Amer.Hist & Life, Hist.Abstr.
● Also available online. Vendor(s): DIALOG Information Services, Inc.

EAGLE (NAUGATUCK). see ETHNIC INTERESTS

970   US   ISSN 0070-8089
EAST CAROLINA UNIVERSITY PUBLICATIONS IN HISTORY. 1964. irreg., vol.6, 1985. $19.95 for cloth; paper $9.95. East Carolina University, Department of History, Greenville, NC 27858-4353. TEL 919-757-6587. Ed. Fred D. Ragan. circ. 500.
    Formerly: East Carolina College Publications in History.

975.9   US
EAST - FLORIDA GAZETTE. 1977. q. $5. St. Augustine Historical Society, 271 Charlotte St., St. Augustine, FL 32084. TEL 904-824-2872. Ed. Jean Parker Waterbury. illus. circ. 700. **Document type:** newsletter.
    Description: Discusses the history of St. Augustine and other eastern Florida sites.

976   US
EAST TEXAS HISTORICAL JOURNAL. 1963. s-a. $15. East Texas Historical Association, Box 6223, SFA Sta., Nacogdoches, TX 75962. TEL 409-568-2407. FAX 409-568-2190. Ed. Archie P. McDonald. adv.; bk.rev. circ. 650. (back issues avail.) **Indexed:** Amer.Hist.& Life, Hist.Abstr. **Document type:** academic/scholarly publication.

977.1   US   ISSN 0012-933X
F486
ECHOES. 1928. m. membership only. Ohio Historical Society, 1982 Velma Ave., Columbus, OH 43211-2497. TEL 614-297-2332. Ed. Corinne Colbert. circ. 14,000. (also avail. in microform from UMI; reprint service avail. from UMI) **Indexed:** Amer.Hist.& Life, Hist.Abstr. **Document type:** newsletter.
—UMI.
    Formerly: Museum Echoes.

972   MX   ISSN 0422-2555
ECO. 1960. 3/yr. Instituto Jaliciense de Antropologia e Historia, Biblioteca "Lic. Jose Parres Arias", Calle de Escorza No. 130, Guadalajara, Mexico. illus.

ECONOMICS CLASSICS - OLD AND RARE BOOKS ON ECONOMICS. see BUSINESS AND ECONOMICS — Economic Systems And Theories, Economic History

977   US   ISSN 0883-3532
EDITING HISTORY. 1985. s-a. $25. (Conference of Historical Journals) Sixteenth Century Publishers, NMSU LB 115, Kirksville, MO 63501. TEL 816-785-4665. FAX 816-785-4181. Ed. R.V. Schnucker. bk.rev.; index. circ. 1,000 (paid). (back issues avail.) **Document type:** academic/scholarly publication.
    Description: Aimed at editors of history journals. Topics include circulation control, copy editing, production techniques, plagiarism and copyrights, and permissions.

977   US
EDWARDS COUNTY HISTORICAL SOCIETY. QUARTERLY. 1980. q. $7. Edwards County Historical Society, Box 205, Albion, IL 62806. Ed. Terry L. Harper. bk.rev. circ. 400.
    Formerly: Edwards County Historical Society.

ES ELBEDRITSCH; All die Nei-ichkeete unn Schtofft vun Deitsche Wege. see ETHNIC INTERESTS

977   US
ELK EYE. q. Morgan County Historical Society, 142 E. Main St., McConnelville, OH 43756.

974   US
ELK HORN. 1965. 3/yr. $5. Elk County Historical Society, Box 361, Ridgway, PA 15853. TEL 814-776-1032. Ed. Iva A. Fay. circ. 500. (tabloid format; back issues avail.) **Indexed:** Amer.Hist.& Life, Hist.Abstr.
    Description: Contains items of local interest.

ELKINS EAGLE; a genealogical research journal for family historians. see GENEALOGY AND HERALDRY

976   US
ELM FORK ECHOES. 1973. a. $4.33 per no. Peters Colony Historical Society of Dallas County, Texas, Box 110846, Carrollton, TX 75011. Ed.Bd. circ. 500.

970 800 591 150   US   ISSN 0424-9399
EMPORIA STATE RESEARCH STUDIES. irreg. $3 per issue. (Emporia State University) Emporia State University Press, 1200 Commercial, Emporia, KS 66801-5087. TEL 316-341-5208. FAX 316-341-5997. index. circ. 2,000. (back issues avail.) **Indexed:** M.L.A. **Document type:** academic/scholarly publication.
—Faxon; UnCover.

970   US
ENCYCLOPEDIC DICTIONARY OF AMERICAN HISTORY. irreg., 4th ed., 1991. $13.95 for softcover; hardcover $17.95. Dushkin Publishing Group, Inc., Sluice Dock, Guilford, CT 06437-9989. TEL 203-453-4351. FAX 203-453-6000. Ed. John Mark Faragher; Pub. Lan Nielsen. illus.

ENFOPRENSA. see POLITICAL SCIENCE

974   US
ENQUIRER NEWSLETTER. q. membership. Friends for Long Island's Heritage, 1864 Muttontown Rd., Syosset, NY 11791. TEL 516-571-7600. FAX 516-571-7623. **Document type:** newsletter.
    Description: Contains local history of Long Island.

ENTRAIDE GENEALOGIQUE. see GENEALOGY AND HERALDRY

ENVIRONMENTAL HISTORY REVIEW. see ENVIRONMENTAL STUDIES

EQUIPMENT ECHOES. see BUILDING AND CONSTRUCTION

975.9   US   ISSN 0014-0376
F319.S2
EL ESCRIBANO; St. Augustine journal of history. 1959. a. $10 to institutions and libraries. St. Augustine Historical Society, 271 Charlotte St., St. Augustine, FL 32084. TEL 904-824-2872. Ed. Jacqueline K. Fretwell. bk.rev.; charts; illus.; cum.index: 1959-1984. circ. 700. (back issues avail.) **Indexed:** Amer.Hist.& Life, Hist.Abstr. **Document type:** academic/scholarly publication.
    Description: Focuses on over four centuries of northeast Florida history.

HISTORY — HISTORY OF NORTH AND SOUTH AMERICA

978   US   ISSN 0899-0409
ESSAYS AND MONOGRAPHS IN COLORADO HISTORY. 1982. 3/yr. $38. Colorado Historical Society, 1300 Broadway, Denver, CO 80203. TEL 303-866-5786. Ed. David N. Wetzel. bk.rev. circ. 1,500. (back issues avail.)
—BLDSC (3811.671600); UnCover.
Formerly (until 1983): Colorado Historical Society. Monograph Series (ISSN 0731-2474)

970.1   MX   ISSN 0185-2574
ESTUDIOS DE CULTURA MAYA. (Text in English and Spanish) 1960. irreg. price varies. Universidad Nacional Autonoma de Mexico, Centro de Estudios Mayas, Instituto de Investigaciones Filologicas, Ciudad Universitaria, 04510 Mexico, D.F., Mexico. bk.rev. circ. 1,500. **Indexed:** A.I.C.P., Anthropol.Lit., Hisp.Amer.Per.Ind., M.L.A.

972   MX   ISSN 0014-147X
ESTUDIOS DE HISTORIA MODERNA Y CONTEMPORANEA DE MEXICO. 1965. a. price varies. Universidad Nacional Autonoma de Mexico, Instituto de Investigaciones Historicas, Delegacion Coyoacan, Ciudad Universitaria, 04510 Mexico, D.F., Mexico. Ed.Bd. bk.rev.; bibl.; illus.; index. circ. 2,000. **Indexed:** Amer.Hist.& Life, Hisp.Amer.Per.Ind., Hist.Abstr.

972   MX   ISSN 0185-2523
F1231
ESTUDIOS DE HISTORIA NOVOHISPANA. 1947. a. price varies. Universidad Nacional Autonoma de Mexico, Instituto de Investigaciones Historicas, Delegacion Coyoacan, Ciudad Universitaria, 04510 Mexico, D.F., Mexico. **Indexed:** Amer.Hist.& Life, Hist.Abstr.
Formerly: Universidad Nacional Autonoma de Mexico. Instituto de Investigaciones Historicas. Serie de Historia Novohispana (ISSN 0076-7379)

986.6 572   EC
ESTUDIOS ETNOHISTORICOS DEL ECUADOR. 1976. irreg. Casa de la Cultura Ecuatoriana, Nucleo de Guayas, Quito, Ecuador.

985   PE   ISSN 1019-4533
ESTUDIOS HISTORICOS. 1972. irreg, no.13, 1992. price varies. (Instituto de Estudios Peruanos) I E P Ediciones, Horacio Urteaga 694, Lima 11, Peru. TEL 323070. FAX 324981. (also avail. in microfiche; back issues avail.)

980   PL   ISSN 0137-3080
F1401
ESTUDIOS LATINOAMERICANOS. (Text in Portuguese and Spanish) a. price varies. (Polska Akademia Nauk, Instytut Historii) Ossolineum, Publishing House of the Polish Academy of Sciences, Rynek 9, 50-106 Wroclaw, Poland. TEL 48-71-386-25. FAX 48-71-448-103. TELEX 0712771 OSS PL. Ed. Ryszard Stemplowski. **Indexed:** Hisp.Amer.Per.Ind. **Document type:** academic/scholarly publication.
Description: Studies on history and culture of the countries in Latin America.

972 572   MX
ESTUDIOS MICHOACANOS. 1986. biennial. Mex.$48. Colegio de Michoacan, Martinez de Navarrete 505, Esq. Avda. del Arbol, 59690 Zamora, Michoacan, Mexico. TEL 91-351-263-81. FAX 91-351-553-07. Ed. Heron Perez Martinez. bk.rev. circ. 2,000. **Document type:** academic/scholarly publication.
Description: Covers the anthropology, history, economics of this Mexican people.

981   BL   ISSN 0103-2186
ESTUDOS HISTORICOS. (Text in Portuguese; summaries in English, French) 1988. s-a. $40 (effective 1994). (Associacao de Pesquisa e Documentacao Historica) Fundacao Getulio Vargas, C.P. 9052, 22272-970 Rio de Janeiro, RJ, Brazil. FAX 021-551-7801. TELEX 21-36811. Ed.Bd. circ. 1,000. **Indexed:** Hisp.Amer.Per.Ind.
Description: Analyzes Brazilian history in relation to the major social science fields.

EVANGELICAL & REFORMED HISTORICAL SOCIETY NEWSLETTER. see *RELIGIONS AND THEOLOGY*

EVANGELIKALE MISSIOLOGIE. see *RELIGIONS AND THEOLOGY — Protestant*

980   RU
EVROPA I AMERIKA. (Editions in Russian and Spanish) 1969. m. (Spanish ed. q.) 24 Rub.($33.60) (Spanish ed. $6.60). Rossiiskaya Akademiya Nauk, Institut Latinskoi Ameriki, Kropotkinskii per., 24, 119034 Moscow, Russia. TEL 201-54-84. (Dist. by: Mezhdunarodnaya Kniga, ul. Dimitrova D.39, 113095 Moscow, Russia) Ed. Yurii Korolev. bk.rev.; bibl.; illus.; stat. **Indexed:** Curr.Dig.Sov.Press.
—BLDSC (0095.600000).
Formerly (until 1991): Latinskaya Amerika (ISSN 0044-748X)

974 330   US   ISSN 0196-0040
GV1623
FACTS ON FILE. YEARBOOK. 1941. a. $95. Facts on File, Inc., 460 Park Ave. S., New York, NY 10016. TEL 212-683-2244. 5-year cum.index. (back issues avail.)

FAMILY HISTORY CAPERS. see *GENEALOGY AND HERALDRY*

976   US   ISSN 0430-1188
F417.F3
FAULKNER FACTS AND FIDDLINGS. 1959. q. $10 membership. Faulkner County Historical Society, Box 731, Conway, AR 72032. Ed. Robert W. Meriwether. bk.rev.; charts. circ. 350. (back issues avail.)

975   US   ISSN 0736-8151
THE FEDERALIST. 1980. q. $22 includes membership. Society for History in the Federal Government, Box 14139, Washington, DC 20044. TEL 703-351-2621. Ed. Kevin Ruffner. adv.; bk.rev. circ. 400. **Document type:** academic/scholarly publication, newsletter.
Description: Covers historical issues and activities of the federal government.

974   US
FEDERATION ROUNDTABLE. q. Federation of Historical Services, Box 331, Kinderhook, NY 12106. TEL 518-758-7684. Ed. Ruth Winnie Roberts.

976   US   ISSN 0015-1874
F446
FILSON CLUB HISTORY QUARTERLY. 1926. q. $24 to non-members. Filson Club, Inc., 1310 S. Third St., Louisville, KY 40208-2306. TEL 502-635-5083. FAX 502-635-5086. Ed. Nelson L. Dawson. adv.; bk.rev.; bibl.; index. circ. 3,400. (also avail. in microform from UMI; reprint service avail. from UMI) **Indexed:** Amer.Hist.& Life, Hist.Abstr. **Document type:** academic/scholarly publication.
—Faxon; UnCover; UMI.
Description: Covers history of Kentucky, with some attention to surrounding Southern states.

FLASH POINT. see *CERAMICS, GLASS AND POTTERY*

976   US   ISSN 0428-5573
FLASHBACK. 1951. q. $10 membership. Washington County (Arkansas) Historical Society, Inc., 118 E. Dickson St., Fayetteville, AR 72701-5612. TEL 501-521-2970. Ed. Thomas E. Jordan. bk.rev.; bibl.; illus. circ. 1,000. **Document type:** academic/scholarly publication.

FLINTLOCK & POWDERHORN. see *GENEALOGY AND HERALDRY*

FLORIDA GENEALOGIST. see *GENEALOGY AND HERALDRY*

975.9   US   ISSN 0015-4113
F306
FLORIDA HISTORICAL QUARTERLY. 1908. q. $25 individual membership; libraries $35. (University of Florida (Gainesville)) Florida Historical Society, Univ. of S. Florida, 4202 E. Fowler Ave., Tampa, FL 33620. TEL 904-392-8188. Ed. George E. Pozzetta. bk.rev.; bibl.; illus.; index, cum.index: vols.1-35, 36-53, 54-66. circ. 2,500. (also avail. in microfilm) **Indexed:** Amer.Hist.& Life, Hist.Abstr.
—Faxon; UnCover.
Description: Covers the history of Florida and the southern U.S. and the Caribbean.

980   US   ISSN 1046-3690
FLORIDA INTERNATIONAL UNIVERSITY. LATIN AMERICAN AND CARIBBEAN CENTER, OCCASIONAL PAPERS SERIES. 1982. irreg. $4. Florida International University, Latin American and Caribbean Center, Miami, FL 33199. TEL 305-348-2894. FAX 305-348-3593. Eds. Richard Tardanico, A. Douglas Kincaid.
Description: Presents lists of scholarly papers on economic, political, educational, cultural, and historical research focusing on countries represented by this center.

982   AG   ISSN 0325-8238
HC171
FOLIA HISTORICA DEL NORDESTE. 1974. irreg. $12. Consejo Nacional de Investigaciones Cientificas y Tecnicas, Instituto de Investigaciones Geohistoricas, Casilla de Correo 438, 3500 Resistencia, Argentina. TEL 54-722-39983. (Co-sponsor: Universidad Nacional del Nordeste, Instituto de Historia) Ed. Ernesto J.A. Maeder. bk.rev. circ. 500. **Document type:** academic/scholarly publication.
Description: Publishes articles, notes, documents, bibliographies and reviews about Northeast Argentina.

FOOTHILLS INQUIRER. see *GENEALOGY AND HERALDRY*

977   US   ISSN 0891-2653
FOR THE RECORD (SPRINGFIELD). 1975. 2/yr. free. Illinois State Archives, Office of the Secretary of State, Archives Bldg., Springfield, IL 62756. TEL 217-782-3674. FAX 217-784-3930. illus. circ. 3,206. **Document type:** government publication, newsletter.
Description: Information on the holdings and activities of the State Archives.

THE FORMER PRESIDENTS QUARTERLY; a focus on our current retired presidents of the United States. see *POLITICAL SCIENCE*

978.9   US   ISSN 0071-7754
FORT BURGWIN RESEARCH CENTER. PUBLICATIONS. 1961. irreg. price varies. Fort Burgwin Research Center, Inc., Southern Methodist University, Dallas, TX 75275. bk.rev. circ. 1,000. **Indexed:** GeoRef.

FORT CONCHO GUIDON. see *MUSEUMS AND ART GALLERIES*

979   US   ISSN 0736-4261
F419.F7
FORT SMITH HISTORICAL SOCIETY. JOURNAL. 1977. s-a. $15 membership. Fort Smith Historical Society, Inc., c/o Ft. Smith Public Library, 61 S. 8th St., Ft. Smith, AR 72901. TEL 501-783-1237. FAX 501-782-8571. Ed. Amelia Martin. bk.rev. circ. 600.
Description: Covers the history, genealogy and primary records of Fort Smith area. Contains abstracts from 100 year old newspapers.

FORT TICONDEROGA MUSEUM. BULLETIN. see *MILITARY*

975   US
FOUNDATIONS OF AMERICA SERIES. 1986. irreg., no.4, 1988. price varies. Colonial Williamsburg Foundation, Box 1776, Williamsburg, VA 23187-1776. TEL 804-220-7349.

979   US   ISSN 0739-8158
FRAM: THE JOURNAL OF POLAR STUDIES. 1984. s-a? $50. Polaris Publications, Box 8089, Bangor, ME 04401. Ed. Stephen Carter Jackson. adv.; bk.rev.; illus.
—CCC.

971 973   CN   ISSN 1183-2487
FRANCOPHONIES D'AMERIQUE. 1991. a. Can.$20. University of Ottawa Press, 542 King Edward, Ottawa, ON K1N 6N5, Canada. TEL 613-564-2270. Ed. Jules Tessier.
Description: Studies and articles on French-Canadian and Louisiana literary history and culture.

976.8   US   ISSN 0046-4961
FRANKLIN COUNTY HISTORICAL REVIEW. 1969. s-a. $15. Franklin County (Tennessee) Historical Society, Box 130, Winchester, TN 37398. Ed. J.R. Brock. index, cum.index: vols.1-5. circ. 730. (processed) **Indexed:** Amer.Hist.& Life, Hist.Abstr.

HISTORY — HISTORY OF NORTH AND SOUTH AMERICA

979 US
FRANKLIN FLYER; key to Franklin County history. 1968. q. $15 to individuals; libraries $7.50. Franklin County Historical Society, 305 N. Fourth, Pasco, WA 99301. TEL 509-547-3714. Ed. Mary Jane Lewis. bk.rev. circ. 900. (back issues avail.) **Indexed:** Amer.Hist.& Life, Hist.Abstr.

970 GW
FREIE UNIVERSITAET BERLIN. JOHN F. KENNEDY-INSTITUT FUER NORDAMERIKA STUDIEN. MATERIALIEN. (Text in English and German) 1972. irreg., no.31, 1993. price varies. Freie Universitaet Berlin, John F. Kennedy-Institut fuer Nordamerika Studien, Lansstr. 7-9, 14195 Berlin, Germany. TEL 030-8382703. FAX 030-8382882. bibl. circ. 400. **Document type:** monographic series.

970 840 CN ISSN 0069-1771
FRENCH - CANADIAN CIVILIZATION RESEARCH CENTER. CAHIERS/CENTRE DE RECHERCHE EN CIVILISATION CANADIENNE - FRANCAISE. CAHIERS. 1968. irreg. price varies. University of Ottawa Press, 542 King Edward, Ottawa, ON K1N 6N5, Canada. TEL 613-564-2270. FAX 613-564-9284. Ed. Yolande Grise.
 Formerly: Centre de Recherche en Litterature Canadienne - Francaise. Cahiers.
 Description: French-Canadian culture and literary history.

FRIENDS OF FINANCIAL HISTORY. see *BUSINESS AND ECONOMICS — Banking And Finance*

FRONTERA NORTE. see *GEOGRAPHY*

FRONTIER MILITARY SERIES. see *MILITARY*

985 PE ISSN 1019-4487
FUENTES E INVESTIGACIONES PARA LA HISTORIA DEL PERU. 1966. irreg., no.9, 1992. price varies. (Instituto de Estudios Peruanos) I E P Ediciones, Horacio Urteaga 694, Lima 11, Peru. TEL 323070. FAX 324981. (back issues avail.)

970.1 MX ISSN 0071-9773
FUENTES INDIGENAS DE LA CULTURA NAHUATL. (Title varies: Fuentes Indigenas de la Cultura Nahuatl. Textos de los Informantes de Sahagun) 1958. irreg., no.7, 1969. price varies. Universidad Nacional Autonoma de Mexico, Instituto de Investigaciones Historicas, Deleg. Coyoacan, Ciudad Universitaria, 04510 Mexico D.F., Mexico. Ed.Bd. circ. 3,000. **Document type:** monographic series.
 Description: Translations from Classic Nahuatl language texts.

572 301.2 MX
FUENTES PARA EL ESTUDIO DE LA CULTURA MAYA. 1983. irreg. Universidad Nacional Autonoma de Mexico, Centro de Estudios Mayas, Instituto de Investigaciones Filologicas, Ciudad Universitaria, 04510 Mexico, D.F., Mexico. (Subscr. to: Departamento de Publicaciones, Instituto de Investigaciones, Filologicas, Circuito Mario de la Cueva, Cd. Universitaria, 04510 Mexico, D.F., Mexico) Ed. Mercedes de la Garza. circ. 3,000.

976.3 US
FULTON COUNTY (ILLINOIS) HISTORICAL & GENEALOGICAL SOCIETY NEWSLETTER. 1969. q. $12. Fulton County Historical & Genealogical Society, c/o Curtis W. Strode, Ed., R.R. No.2, Box 12, Marietta, IL 61459. TEL 309-926-7411. bk.rev.; illus.; cum.index. circ. 350. (processed) **Document type:** newsletter.
 Formerly: Fulton County (Illinois) Historical Society Newsletter (ISSN 0046-5275)

FULTON COUNTY IMAGES. see *GENEALOGY AND HERALDRY*

981 BL
FUNDACAO JOAQUIM NABUCO. SERIE REPUBLICA. 1989. irreg., no.16, 1993. Editora Massangana, Rua Dois Irmaos, 15, Apipucos, 52071-440 Recife, Brazil. TEL 081-268-4611. FAX 081-268-9600.

970 US ISSN 0090-4368
F281
G H S FOOT-NOTES. 1972. q. membership. Georgia Historical Society, 501 Whitaker St., Savannah, GA 31499. TEL 912-651-2125. Ed. Carey Shellman. bibl. circ. 2,500.

980 DK
GACELA - GAZELA. REVISTA DE ESTUDIOS LATINOAMERICANOS. (Text in English, Portuguese, Spanish; occasionally translations into Danish) 1985. irreg. (1-2/yr.). DKK 80 per no. in Europe; elsewhere $20. Aarhus Universitet, Center for Latinamerikastudier, Niels Juelsgade 84, DK-8200 Aarhus N, Denmark. TEL 45-89-42-18-81. FAX 45-86-16-38-61. (Co-sponsor: Selskabet Danmark-Latinamerika) Ed. Svend Lindhardtsen. adv.; bk.rev.; illus. circ. 600. **Document type:** academic/scholarly publication.
 Formerly (until 1992): Gacela - Gazela. Tidsskrift for Latinamerikastudier (ISSN 0901-036X)
 Description: Covers history, anthropology, social science, and cultural studies of Latin America.

971 CN ISSN 0227-1370
F1054.G2
GASPESIE. (Text in English, French) 1963. q. Can.$15($18) Societe Historique de la Gaspesie, 80, bd. Gaspe, Box 680, Gaspe, Que. G0C 1R0, Canada. TEL 418-368-5710. Ed. Jean-Marie Fallu. adv.; bk.rev.; illus. circ. 1,500. **Indexed:** Pt.de Rep., RADAR.
 Former titles (until 1979): Revue d'Histoire et de Traditions Populaires de la Gaspesie; Revue d'Histoire de la Gaspesie (ISSN 0035-2322)

976 US
GATEWAY (MIDDLESBORO). 1982. 3/yr. $10 membership. Bell County Historical Society, Inc., Box 1344, Middlesboro, KY 40965. TEL 606-248-5304. Ed. Allan E. Green. bk.rev. circ. 130. **Document type:** newsletter.

977 US ISSN 0198-9375
F466
GATEWAY HERITAGE. 1980. q. $20. Missouri Historical Society, Jefferson Memorial Bldg., Forest Park, St. Louis, MO 63112. TEL 314-746-4557. FAX 314-746-4548. Ed. Martha Kohl. bk.rev.; illus. circ. 6,000. (also avail. in microfilm from UMI; reprint service avail. from UMI) **Indexed:** Amer.Hist.& Life, Hist.Abstr.
 —UnCover; UMI.
 Formerly: Missouri Historical Society. Bulletin (ISSN 0026-6590)
 Description: Features articles on the history of Missouri and the development of the West.

GENEALOGY BULLETIN. see *GENEALOGY AND HERALDRY*

975 355 US
GEORGE C. MARSHALL FOUNDATION. TOPICS. 1968. q. free. George C. Marshall Foundation, V M I Parade, Box 1600, Lexington, VA 24450. TEL 703-463-7103. FAX 703-464-5229. Ed. Joellen K. Bland. circ. 9,500. (back issues avail.) **Document type:** academic/scholarly publication, newsletter.

975.8 US ISSN 0016-8297
F281
GEORGIA HISTORICAL QUARTERLY. 1917. q. $30 (foreign $33). Georgia Historical Society, 501 Whitaker St., Savannah, GA 31499. TEL 912-651-2125. Ed. John Inscoe. bk.rev.; index, cum.index: vols.1-60 (1917-1976). circ. 2,500. (also avail. in microform from MIM,UMI,PMC; reprint service avail. from UMI) **Indexed:** Amer.Hist.& Life, Hist.Abstr.
 —BLDSC (4158.405000); Faxon; UnCover; UMI.

GERMAN-CANADIAN YEARBOOK/DEUTSCHKANADISCHES JAHRBUCH. see *ETHNIC INTERESTS*

970 US
GETTYSBURG. 1989. s-a. $28. Morningside House Inc., 260 Oak St., Dayton, OH 45010. TEL 800-648-9710. FAX 513-461-4260. Ed. Bob Younger. adv. circ. 12,500. **Document type:** academic/scholarly publication.
 Description: Scholarly approach to the study of the Gettysburg historical site.

977 US ISSN 1053-4946
F532.G4
GIBSON COUNTY LINES. 1988. m. $10 membership. Gibson County Historical Society, Box 516, Princeton, IN 47670. TEL 812-782-3641. **Document type:** newsletter.
 Description: Contains updates of society activities, local history articles, reprints of early news items and county records.

973 700 US ISSN 1070-7808
E151
THE GILCREASE JOURNAL. 1958. q. $45 membership in Oklahoma; elsewhere $35. Thomas Gilcrease Museum Association, 1400 Gilcrease Museum Rd., Tulsa, OK 74127. TEL 918-596-2700. FAX 918-596-2770. Ed. Carol Haralson. bk.rev.; bibl.; illus. circ. 4,200. **Indexed:** Amer.Hist.& Life, Hist.Abstr.
 —UnCover.
 Former titles (until vol.14, no.2 1993): Gilcrease Magazine of American History and Art (ISSN 0730-5036); American Scene (ISSN 0003-0929)
 Description: Contains articles about American history and art with an emphasis on items in the Gilcrease collection.

976 US
GILES COUNTY HISTORICAL SOCIETY BULLETIN.* 1974. q. $5. Giles County Historical Society, 429 W. Jefferson St., Pulaski, TN 38478. Ed. Margaret Butler.

970 US ISSN 0431-915X
GLADES STAR. 1941. q. membership. Garrett County Historical Society, c/o Bradley A. Stewart, Ed., 32 S. Second St., Oakland, MD 21550. bk.rev.; bibl.; index. circ. 600.

913 CN ISSN 0710-3697
GLENBOW. 1968-1974; 1981. q. Can.$15 (foreign Can.$17). Glenbow Museum, 130 Ninth Ave. S.E., Calgary, AB T2G 0P3, Canada. TEL 403-264-8300. FAX 403-265-9769. Ed. Donna Livingstone. adv.; charts; illus. circ. 8,000.
 Formerly (until 1976): Glenbow Newsletter (ISSN 0017-1174)
 Description: Presents historical articles, features on exhibitions, interviews, photo essays, and a calendar of events of the Museum, whose focus is on western Canadian art and history.

970.1 CN ISSN 0072-467X
GLENBOW - ALBERTA INSTITUTE. OCCASIONAL PAPERS. 1966. irreg. Glenbow - Alberta Institute, 130-9th Ave. S.E., Calgary, AB T2G 0P3, Canada. TEL 403-268-4100. adv.; illus.; circ. 5,000 (paid).
 Formerly: Glenbow Foundation. Occasional Paper (ISSN 0700-6365)

975.5 US ISSN 0099-0159
F241
GOLDENSEAL; West Virginia traditional life. 1975. q. $15 (effective Sep. 1991). Division of Culture and History, Cultural Center, 1900 Kanawha Blvd. E., Charleston, WV 25305-0300. TEL 304-558-0220. FAX 304-558-2779. Ed. Ken Sullivan. bk.rev.; illus. circ. 32,000. **Indexed:** Amer.Hist.& Life (1993-), Hist.Abstr. (1993-). **Document type:** government publication.
 Description: Contains information on West Virginia folklife and tradition.

977 US ISSN 0278-0208
F621
GOLDFINCH. 1980. q. $10. State Historical Society of Iowa, 402 Iowa Ave., Iowa City, IA 52240. TEL 319-335-3916. FAX 319-335-3924. Ed. D.G. Ohrn. illus. circ. 2,000.
 —CCC.
 Description: Iowa regional history for young people ages 9-13.

971 CN ISSN 0316-2702
GRAND MANAN HISTORIAN. 1934. a. Can.$3. Grand Manan Historical Society, c/o Secretary, Grand Manan, N.B. EOG 1L0, Canada. Ed. L. Keith Ingersoll. circ. 300.

977 US
GRAND RIVER VALLEY HISTORY. 1980. a. $10 (effective 1993). Grand Rapids Historical Society, c/o Public Library, Grand Rapids, MI 49503. TEL 616-456-3629. FAX 616-456-3602. Ed. Gordon L. Olson. adv.; bk.rev. circ. 1,000. **Indexed:** Mag.Ind.
 Formerly (until 1992): Grand River Valley Review (ISSN 0739-084X)
 Description: Addresses the personalities and history of West Michigan.

HISTORY — HISTORY OF NORTH AND SOUTH AMERICA

970 US ISSN 0148-771X
GRASS ROOTS PERSPECTIVES ON AMERICAN HISTORY. 1978. irreg. price varies. Greenwood Press, Inc. (Subsidiary of: Greenwood Publishing Group Inc.), 88 Post Rd. W., Box 5007, Westport, CT 06881-5007. TEL 203-226-3571. FAX 203-222-1502. Ed. David Thelen.
—BLDSC (4213.350000).

GRASSY KNOLL GAZETTE. see *CRIMINOLOGY AND LAW ENFORCEMENT*

975 255 US ISSN 1071-670X
GREAT BATTLES. bi-m. $16.95 (foreign $22.95). Empire Press, 602 S. King St., Ste. 300, Leesburg, VA 22075. TEL 703-771-9400. FAX 703-777-4627. (Subscr. to: Box 417, Mt. Morris, IL 61054-8021)
Formerly (until 1993): Military History Magazine Presents Great Battles (ISSN 1060-9490)

910 US ISSN 0275-7664
F591
GREAT PLAINS QUARTERLY. 1981. q. $20 to individuals; institutions $25. University of Nebraska, Lincoln, Center for Great Plains Studies, 1214 Oldfather Hall, Lincoln, NE 68588-0313. TEL 402-472-6058. FAX 402-472-1123. Ed. Frances W. Kaye. adv.; bk.rev.; bibl.; charts; illus.; index. circ. 1,000. (also avail. in microform) Indexed: Amer.Hist.& Life, Arts & Hum.Cit.Ind., Curr.Cont., Geo.Abstr., Hist.Abstr., I D A, M.L.A. Document type: academic/scholarly publication.
—BLDSC (4214.564000); Faxon; UnCover; UMI.
Description: Scholarly, interdisciplinary journal publishing articles on the geography, history, literature, anthropology, ethnology, folklore, fine arts, sociology, political science, economics, and agriculture of the Great Plains region.
Refereed Serial

978 970.1 US ISSN 0072-7342
GREAT WEST AND INDIAN SERIES. 1945. irreg. price varies. Westernlore Press, Box 35305, Tucson, AZ 85740. TEL 602-297-5491. FAX 602-624-9951. Ed. Lynn R. Bailey.

976 US
GREATER NEW ORLEANS ARCHIVISTS NEWSLETTER. q. $5. Greater New Orleans Archivists Association, c/o New Orleans Notarial Archives, Civil District Court Bldg., 421 Loyola Ave., New Orleans, LA 70112. TEL 504-568-8577. Ed. Sally K. Reeves. circ. 50. Document type: newsletter.
Description: Covers new additions, grant activities, and document preservation; staff activities and meetings.

975 929 US ISSN 1064-0711
GREENBRIER HISTORICAL SOCIETY. JOURNAL. 1963. a. $15 to non-members. Greenbrier Historical Society, 101 Church St., Lewisburg, WV 24901. TEL 304-645-3398. circ. 600. Document type: academic/scholarly publication.
Description: Publishes articles on the Greenbrier Valley area of West Virginia, historic events, people and culture.

974 US ISSN 0894-8135
GREENE COUNTY HISTORICAL JOURNAL. 1977. q. $10. Greene County Historical Society, Inc., Coxsackie, NY 12051. Ed. Robert A. D'Agostino. cum.index every 5 yrs. circ. 1,100.
Description: Publishes research articles concerning people, places and events in the history of Greene County, New York.

974 US
GREENE HILLS OF HOME. 1984. q. $12 (effective 1993). Greene Township Historical Society, Box 186, Greentown, PA 18426. TEL 717-676-3509. Ed. Peggy Bancroft. circ. 350. (back issues avail.)
Description: Covers history of Greene Township, Pike County, Pennsylvania, and surrounding areas.

974 US
GRIST MILL. 1965. q. $5. Saratoga County Historical Society, c/o Saratoga County Museum, Brookside, Ballston Spa, NY 12020. circ. 600.
Description: Devoted to the local history of Saratoga County.

946.9 PO ISSN 0871-7478
GUIMARAES. ARQUIVO MUNICIPAL "ALFREDO PIMENTA." BOLETIM DE TRABALHOS HISTORICOS. 1933. a. Esc.1300 (foreign Esc.2500). Arquivo Municipal "Alfredo Pimenta", Largo Conego Jose Maria Gomes, 4800 Guimaraes, Portugal. TEL 053-515123. Dir. Isabel Maria Roeha e Sousa. circ. 500. Document type: academic/scholarly publication.
Description: Covers historical studies and archivism.

973 US
GULF COAST CONFERENCE PROCEEDINGS. 1970. irreg. $10 paperbound; cloth edition $15. University of South Alabama, History Department, Humanities 344, Mobile, AL 36688. TEL 205-460-6210. FAX 205-460-6750. (Co-sponsor: Gulf Coast History and Humanities Conference) (back issues avail.) Document type: academic/scholarly publication.

917.306 970 US ISSN 0017-6834
F130.D9
DE HALVE MAEN. 1922. q. $28.50 (foreign $32.50). Holland Society of New York, 122 E. 58th St., New York, NY 10022. Ed. David William Voorhees. bk.rev.; illus. circ. 1,500. (back issues avail.) Indexed: Amer.Hist.& Life, Hist.Abstr.
Description: Features articles by scholars concerned with the Nieuw Netherland Colony as well as genealogy relating to families arriving in the Colony prior to 1675.

976 US ISSN 8755-6073
F443.H3
HARDIN COUNTY HISTORICAL QUARTERLY. 1982. q. $12. Hardin County Historical Society, Box 1012, Savannah, TN 38372. Ed. Ronney R. Brewington. bk.rev. circ. 350.
Description: Provides genealogical and historical information, and articles with emphasis on the 1800's time period in the Hardin County, Tennessee area.

976 US
HART COUNTY HISTORICAL SOCIETY QUARTERLY. 1969. q. $8. Hart County Historical Society, Box 606, Munfordville, KY 42765. TEL 502-524-0101. Ed. Nadine G. Hawkins. cum.index: 1969-1981. circ. 400. Document type: bulletin.

918 US
HASTINGS HISTORIAN. 1971. q. $10. Hastings Historical Society, 41 Washington Ave., Hastings-on-Hudson, NY 10706. TEL 914-478-2249. Ed. Mary L. Allison. circ. 1,200. (tabloid format)
Description: Articles on events, people, and buildings in Hastings' past.

900 US ISSN 0364-5924
E682
HAYES HISTORICAL JOURNAL; a journal of the Gilded Age. 1976. q. $20 to individuals; libraries $40. Hayes Presidential Center, Spiegel Grove, Fremont, OH 43420-2796. TEL 419-332-2081. Ed. Bruce Bowlus. bk.rev.; index. circ. 600. Indexed: Amer.Hist.& Life, Hist.Abstr.
—BLDSC (4274.260000).

970 US
HEADQUARTERS HELIOGRAM; military history - historic preservation. 1967. m. membership. Council on America's Military Past, U.S.A., Inc., Box 1151, Ft. Myer, VA 22211. TEL 202-479-2258. Ed. Herbert M. Hart. adv.; illus.; cum.index. (tabloid format)
Description: News on current legislation and activities pertaining to the history and historic preservation of military landmarks, machinery, museums, and sites, with news on archives and research in the field.

976 US
HEMPSTEAD COUNTY HISTORICAL SOCIETY. JOURNAL. 1977. irreg. $7. Hempstead County Historical Society, Box 1257, Hope, AR 71801. TEL 202-785-2047. Ed. Mary Nell Turner. circ. 300.
Formerly: Hempstead County Historical Society (Publication).

HENRY COUNTY HISTORICALOG. see *GENEALOGY AND HERALDRY*

970 US ISSN 0883-1513
HERITAGE (COOPERSTOWN). 1984. q. $10. New York State Historical Association, Lake Rd., Box 800, Cooperstown, NY 13326. TEL 607-547-2533. Ed. Paul S. D'Ambrosio. illus. circ. 6,500. Indexed: Amer.Hist.& Life (1993-), Hist.Abstr. (1993-).
—UnCover.
Supersedes: Yorker; Which was formerly (until 1975): Yorker Annual; (until 1974): Yorker News (ISSN 0044-0574)

900 US ISSN 8756-5242
F292.G9
HERITAGE (LAWRENCEVILLE). 1968. q. $10 to individuals; families $15; corporate $50; lifetime $250. Gwinnett Historical Society, Inc., Box 261, Lawrenceville, GA 30246. TEL 404-822-5174. Ed. Anna Carroll. bk.rev. circ. 700. Document type: newsletter.
Former titles (until 1986): Gwinnett Historical Society. Quarterly; Gwinnett Historical Society. Newsletter.
Description: Covers topics such as historic preservation, genealogical information, activities of the society and books published by GHS.

973.794 US
HERITAGE AND HISTORY. 1977. m. Ventura County Historical Society, Ventura County Museum of History & Art, 100 E. Main St., Ventura, CA 93001. TEL 805-653-0323. Ed. Charles Nelson Johnson. Document type: newsletter.

979 US
HERITAGE NEWSLETTER. 1973. bi-m. membership. Foundation for San Francisco's Architectural Heritage, 2007 Franklin St., San Francisco, CA 94109. TEL 415-441-3000. FAX 415-441-3015. Ed. Donald Andreini. adv.; bk.rev.; illus. circ. 4,000. (tabloid format) Indexed: AESIS.
Description: Covers San Francisco architectural history and current preservation issues.

977.3 US ISSN 0018-0718
HERITAGE OF VERMILION COUNTY. 1964. q. membership. Vermilion County Museum Society, 116 N. Gilbert St., Danville, IL 61832. TEL 217-442-2922. Eds. Donald & Susan Richter. adv.; illus. circ. 1,100. Indexed: Amer.Hist.& Life, Hist.Abstr.

974 US
HERKIMER COUNTY HISTORICAL SOCIETY. 1976. a. Herkimer County Historical Society, 400 N. Main St., Herkimer, NY 13350. TEL 315-866-6413.

900 US ISSN 0018-2168
F1401
HISPANIC AMERICAN HISTORICAL REVIEW. Variant title: H A H R. 1921. q. $40 to individuals (foreign $48); institutions $88 (foreign $96); students $20 (foreign $28). (American Historical Association, Conference on Latin American Studies) Duke University Press, Box 90660, Durham, NC 27708-0660. TEL 919-687-3600. FAX 919-688-4574. Ed. Mark Szuchmanl. adv.; bk.rev.; index, cum.index. circ. 2,400. (also avail. in microform from MIM,UMI,PMC; reprint service avail. from ISI,UMI,KTO) Indexed: Acad.Ind., Amer.Hist.& Life, Arts & Hum.Cit.Ind., Bk.Rev.Ind. (1975-), Chic.Per.Ind., Child.Bk.Rev.Ind. (1975-), Curr.Cont., Hisp.Amer.Per.Ind., Hist.Abstr., Hum.Ind., Numis.Lit., Ref.Sour. Document type: academic/scholarly publication.
—BLDSC (4315.770000); Faxon; UnCover; SWETS; UMI.
Refereed Serial

983 CL ISSN 0073-2435
F3051
HISTORIA. 1961. a. $30 (effective 1993). Pontificia Universidad Catolica de Chile, Instituto de Historia, Av. Diagonal Oriente 3300, Santiago, Chile. TEL 2744741. FAX 2225515. Ed.Bd. adv.; bk.rev.; abstr.; bibl. circ. 700. Indexed: Amer.Hist.& Life, Hisp.Amer.Per.Ind., Hist.Abstr.
Description: Journal of Chilean and Latin American history. Includes research articles and documents covering Chilean historiographical production.

982 056 AG ISSN 0326-1352
F2801
HISTORIA. 1981. q. Arg.$500000($60) Ediciones A P, Tte. Gral. Peron 1515-10A, 1037 Buenos Aires, Argentina. TEL 45-5347. adv.; bk.rev. circ. 3,000. Indexed: Amer.Hist.& Life, Hist.Abstr.

HISTORY — HISTORY OF NORTH AND SOUTH AMERICA

980   PE   ISSN 1019-4541
HISTORIA ANDINA. 1973. irreg., no.20, 1993. price varies. (Instituto de Estudios Peruanos) I E P Ediciones, Horacio Urteaga 694, Lima 11, Peru. TEL 323070. FAX 324981.

972   MX   ISSN 0185-0172
F1201
HISTORIA MEXICANA. 1951. 4/yr. Mex.$76($32) to individuals (foreign $42); institutions $50 (foreign $60) (effective 1993). Colegio de Mexico, A.C., Departamento de Publicaciones, Camino al Ajusco 20, 01000 Mexico D.F., Mexico. TEL 645 5955. FAX 6450464. TELEX 1777585 COLME. Ed.Bd. adv.; bk.rev.; bibl.; charts. circ. 1,500. (back issues avail.; reprint service avail. from SWZ) **Indexed:** Amer.Hist.& Life, Arts & Hum.Cit.Ind., Chic.Per.Ind., Curr.Cont., Hisp.Amer.Per.Ind., Hist.Abstr. —Faxon; SWETS.

989.7   PY
HISTORIA MILITAR DEL PARAGUAY. 1985. a. Academia de Historia Militar del Paraguay, Avda. Eusebio Ayala 3386, Asuncion, Paraguay.

981   BL   ISSN 0100-6932
HISTORIA: QUESTOES E DEBATES. 1980. s-a. Associacao Paranaense de Historia, Caixa Postal 1538, 80000 Curitiba PR, Brazil. Ed. Sergio Odilon Nadalin. **Document type:** academic/scholarly publication.

985   PE   ISSN 0073-2486
HISTORIA Y CULTURA. 1965. a. $10. Museo Nacional de Historia, Plaza Bolivar, Pueblo Libre, Apdo. 1992, Lima, Peru. Ed. Amalia Castelli. bk.rev. circ. 1,000. **Indexed:** Amer.Hist.& Life, Hisp.Amer.Per.Ind., Hist.Abstr.

984   BO
HISTORIA Y CULTURA. no.4, 1981. s-a. $24. Sociedad Boliviana de Historia, Apdo. 7146, La Paz, Bolivia. Ed. Alberto Crespo. adv.; bk.rev. circ. 1,000.

HISTORIAN'S DIGEST. see *RELIGIONS AND THEOLOGY*

974   US
HISTORIC BETHLEHEM. NEWSLETTER. 1977. irreg. membership. Historic Bethlehem Inc., 459 Old York Rd., Bethlehem, PA 18018. TEL 215-691-5300. Ed. Ralph G. Schwarz. illus. circ. 1,500.

970 980   US   ISSN 0892-080X
E839.5
HISTORIC DOCUMENTS. 1972. a. $112. Congressional Quarterly Inc., 1414 22nd St., N.W., Washington, DC 20037. TEL 202-887-8500. bibl.
Description: Preserves for research important documents relating to major events of the previous year, preceded by a brief introduction. Includes topic and key-word index.

977   US
HISTORIC GENEALOGICAL MAGAZINE.* 1982. s-a. $20. Joan C. Bohm, Ed. & Pub., 1240 Vineland Rd., Ste. 57, Winter Garden, FL 34787-4339. TEL 317-654-6446. adv.; bk.rev.; index. circ. 150.
Formerly (until 1990): Clinton County, Indiana Roots.

971   CN   ISSN 0709-5562
F1059.5.G9
HISTORIC GUELPH; the royal city. 1977. a. Can.$5.50 to non-members. Guelph Historical Society, P.O. Box 1502, Guelph, ON N1H 6N9, Canada. TEL 519-822-6741. Eds. Ruth and Eber Pollard. circ. 700. (back issues avail.) **Document type:** academic/scholarly publication.
Description: Studies the history of Guelph and Wellington County.

979 720   US
HISTORIC HAWAII MAGAZINE. 1975. bi-m. $35. Historic Hawaii Foundation, P.O. Box 1658, Honolulu, HI 96806. TEL 808-537-9564. FAX 808-526-3989. Ed. Dion-Magrit Coschigano. adv.; bk.rev.; charts; illus.; cum.index: 1975-84; 1985-89. circ. 4,000. (also avail. in microform; back issues avail.)
Formerly: Historic Hawaii News.

HISTORIC HOUSE NEWS. see *CONSERVATION*

978 720   US
HISTORIC KANSAS CITY FOUNDATION GAZETTE. 1976. q. $20. Historic Kansas City Foundation, 712 Broadway, Ste. 404, Kansas City, MO 64105-2271. TEL 816-471-3391. Ed. Leslie Bayer. adv.; bk.rev.; illus.; cum.index: 1976-1983. circ. 1,600. (back issues avail.)
Formerly: Historic Kansas City News.
Description: Dedicated to Kansas City's architectural, cultural and historic environment.

979.4   US   ISSN 0018-2397
HISTORIC KERN. 1949. q. $3.50. Kern County Historical Society, Box 141, Bakersfield, CA 93302. Ed. John Ludeke. bk.rev.; illus. circ. 450. (processed) **Document type:** academic/scholarly publication.
Description: Historical notes and vignettes on Kern County (Bakersfield), California.

977.5   US   ISSN 0361-574X
F589.M1
HISTORIC MADISON. JOURNAL. Key Title: Journal of Historic Madison, Inc. of Wisconsin. 1975. a. $5 (effective 1991). Historic Madison, Inc., of Wisconsin, Box 2721, Madison, WI 53701-2721. Ed. Michael Knight. bk.rev.; illus. circ. 500. **Document type:** academic/scholarly publication.
Description: Scholarly journal on the history of Madison, Wisconsin.

974   US   ISSN 0439-2248
F72.N2
HISTORIC NANTUCKET. 1953. q. $25 membership. Nantucket Historical Association, Box 1016, Nantucket, MA 02554. TEL 508-228-1894. FAX 508-558-5618. Ed. Douglas K. Burch. bk.rev.; illus.; cum.index: circ. 2,875 (controlled). **Indexed:** Amer.Hist.& Life, Hist.Abstr. **Document type:** consumer publication.
Description: Publishes original research, accounts, reminiscences, historic logs, letters and photographs pertaining to Nantucket history.

HISTORIC NEW ORLEANS COLLECTION. MANUSCRIPTS DIVISION UPDATE. 1981. a. free. Historic New Orleans Collection, 533 Royal St., New Orleans, LA 70130-2179. TEL 504-523-4662. circ. 1,000. (back issues avail.) **Document type:** newsletter.

976   US
HISTORIC NEW ORLEANS COLLECTION QUARTERLY. 1983. q. free. Kemper and Leila Williams Foundation, Historic New Orleans Collection, 533 Royal St., New Orleans, LA 70130. TEL 504-523-4662. FAX 504-522-2890. Ed. Louise C. Hoffman. circ. 5,200. **Document type:** newsletter.
Formerly: Historic New Orleans Collection Newsletter (ISSN 0886-2109)
Description: Contains information about activities and holdings of the Historic New Orleans Collection and articles about local history.

975 720   US
HISTORIC PALM BEACH COUNTY PRESERVATION BOARD NEWSLETTER.* 1986. q. Historic Palm Beach County Preservation Board, Box 1221, Delray Beach, FL 33447-1221. TEL 407-395-6771. Ed. John P. Johnson. illus. circ. 1,000. (back issues avail.) **Document type:** newsletter.
Description: Covers current events throughout Palm Beach county, historic preservation projects, illustrations and photographs of historic sites.

970 398   US
HISTORIC SCHAEFFERSTOWN RECORD. 1967. q. $15. Historic Schaefferstown, Inc., c/o C. Richard Beam, Ed., 406 Spring Dr., Millersville, PA 17551. TEL 717-949-2244. bk.rev. circ. 250.
Formerly: Schaefferstown Bulletin.

HISTORIC TRAVELER; a newsletter about travel to America's architectural and historical landmarks. see *ARCHITECTURE*

985   PE   ISSN 0376-4052
F3401
HISTORICA. Variant title: Revista Historica. 1977. s-a. $12. Pontificia Universidad Catolica del Peru, Departamento de Humanidades, Fondo Editorial, Apdo. 1761, Lima 100, Peru. TEL 626390. FAX 5114-611785. Ed. Franklin Pease. bk.rev. circ. 500. **Indexed:** Amer.Hist.& Life, Arts & Hum.Cit.Ind., Hist.Abstr.

974   US   ISSN 0886-5272
HISTORICAL FOOTNOTES (STONINGTON). 1962. q. $10 membership. Stonington Historical Society, Box 103, Stonington, CT 06378. TEL 203-535-1131. Eds. Victor Boatwright. adv. contact: Robert Vested. illus. circ. 800. **Indexed:** Amer.Hist.& Life, Hist.Abstr.
Description: Contains articles, sketches, and data about the history of the people, buildings, genealogy, and activities in Stonington, Connecticut.

973   US   ISSN 0276-8313
E171
HISTORICAL JOURNAL OF MASSACHUSETTS. 1972. s-a. $7. Westfield State College, Institute for Massachusetts Studies, Westfield, MA 01086. TEL 413-572-5344. FAX 413-562-3613. Ed. Martin Kaufman. adv.; bk.rev.; illus.; index. circ. 1,250. (also avail. in microform from UMI; back issues avail.) **Indexed:** Amer.Hist.& Life, Hist.Abstr. **Document type:** academic/scholarly publication. —BLDSC (4316.398000); Faxon; UnCover; UMI.
Formerly: Historical Journal of Western Massachusetts (ISSN 0163-3929)
Description: Contains articles and reviews on state and local history.

974.2   US   ISSN 0018-2508
F31
HISTORICAL NEW HAMPSHIRE. 1944. q. $30 membership (effective 1992). New Hampshire Historical Society, 30 Park St., Concord, NH 03301. TEL 603-225-3381. adv.; bk.rev.; bibl.; charts; illus.; cum.index: vols.1-25, 1944-1970. circ. 2,800. (reprint service avail. from KTO) **Indexed:** Amer.Hist.& Life, Hist.Abstr. **Document type:** academic/scholarly publication. —UnCover.
Description: Encourages research in New Hampshire history and brings fresh historical material to the public.

974.8   US   ISSN 0018-2524
F157.B3
HISTORICAL REVIEW OF BERKS COUNTY. 1935. q. $12 per vol. to non-members. Historical Society of Berks County, 940 Centre Ave., Reading, PA 19601. TEL 215-375-4375. Ed. James C. Flippin. adv.; bk.rev.; illus.; index. circ. 2,200. (also avail. in microfilm) **Indexed:** Amer.Hist.& Life, Hist.Abstr.

974.9   US   ISSN 0018-2532
HISTORICAL SOCIETY OF HADDONFIELD. BULLETIN. 1958. 4/yr. membership. Historical Society of Haddonfield, 343 King's Hwy. E., Haddonfield, NJ 08033. TEL 609-429-7375. circ. 450. **Document type:** newsletter, bulletin.
Description: Contains items of local interest.

977   US   ISSN 0160-8541
HISTORICAL SOCIETY OF MICHIGAN NEWSLETTER. 1977. bi-m. $25. Historical Society of Michigan, 2117 Washtenaw Ave., Ann Arbor, MI 48104. TEL 313-769-1828. FAX 313-769-4267. Ed. Thomas L. Jones. circ. 4,000. (back issues avail.) **Document type:** newsletter.
Description: Provides news of events sponsored by the Society, news briefs from other organizations, calendar of events, conference programs.

974   US
HISTORICAL SOCIETY OF MONTGOMERY COUNTY. BULLETIN. 1935. 2/yr. $15. Historical Society of Montgomery County, 1654 DeKalb St., Norristown, PA 19401. TEL 215-272-0297. index. circ. 1,000. (back issues avail.)

974   US
HISTORICAL SOCIETY OF ROCKLAND COUNTY NEWS. q. Historical Society of Rockland County, 20 Zukor Rd., Box 495, New City, NY 10956.

977 929   US
HISTORICAL TIME CAPSULES OF MONROE COUNTY. 1975. 4/yr. $5 membership; family membership $7. Monroe County Historical Society, Box 422, Sparta, WI 54656-0422. TEL 608-269-8680. Ed. Jim Schlosser. bk.rev. circ. 240. (looseleaf format) **Document type:** newsletter.

HISTORY — HISTORY OF NORTH AND SOUTH AMERICA

977.1 US
HISTORICALOG. 1950. q. $20 membership. Warren County Historical Society (Lebanon), Box 223, Lebanon, OH 45036. TEL 513-932-1817. Ed. Patricia George. circ. 600. **Document type:** academic/scholarly publication.
Description: Focuses on the activities and accomplishments of the Warren County Historical Society and features articles pertaining to the history of Warren County and the genealogy of county residents.

970 980 SP
HISTORIOGRAFIA Y BIBLIOGRAFIA AMERICANISTA. s-a. 2000 ptas. (foreign 3000 ptas.). Consejo Superior de Investigaciones Cientificas (C.S.I.C.), C. Vitruvio, 8, 28006 Madrid, Spain. TEL 261-28-33. FAX 262-96-34.

970 US ISSN 0363-7492
E172
HISTORY NEWS; the magazine for historical agency and museum professionals and volunteers. 1940. bi-m. $50 to individuals; institutions $75; libraries $55. American Association for State and Local History, 530 Church St., Ste. 600, Nashville, TN 37219-2325. TEL 615-255-2971. Ed. Lu Anne Sneddon. adv.; bk.rev.; film rev.; illus.; stat.; tr.lit.; index. circ. 7,000. (also avail. in microfiche from UMI; back issues avail., reprint service avail. from UMI) **Indexed:** Amer.Hist.& Life, Art & Archaeol.Tech.Abstr., Hist.Abstr. **Document type:** trade publication.
—BLDSC (4318.381000); Faxon; UnCover; UMI.

970 US
HISTORY NEWS DISPATCH. m. membership includes "History News". American Association for State and Local History, 530 Church St., Ste. 600, Nashville, TN 37219-2325. TEL 615-255-2971. Ed. Lu Anne Sneddon. **Document type:** newsletter.

972 US
HISTORY OF THE AZTEC CLUB OF 1847; Military Society of the Mexican War. 1880. a. membership. Aztec Club, c/o John C. Hunt, 5225 Westpath Way, Bethesda, MD 20816. circ. 125.

975 US
HORN & WHISTLE. 1982. bi-m. $21 (foreign $30). Air Horn and Steam Whistle Enthusiasts, c/o Richard J. Weisenberger, Pub., 160 Woodcreek, Paducah, KY 42001. Eds. Bill Williamson, Lin Chapman. circ. 175. (back issues avail.) **Document type:** consumer publication.
Description: Covers the history, development, preservation, and technical advancement of horns and whistles currently used in the marine, industry, railroad service. Includes general signaling and warning applications, with emphasis on safety.

976 US ISSN 0272-4030
F394.H857
HOUSTON REVIEW: HISTORY AND CULTURE OF THE GULF COAST. 1979. 3/yr. $7.50 to individuals; institutions $12. (Houston Library Board) Houston Metropolitan Research Center, Houston Public Library, 500 McKinney, Houston, TX 77002. TEL 713-247-1661. Ed. Louis J. Marchiafava. bk.rev. circ. 700. (back issues avail.) **Indexed:** Amer.Hist.& Life, Hist.Abstr.

989.5 UY
HOY ES HISTORIA. 1983. bi-m. $38. Editorial Raices, Casilla de Correo, No.6311, Montevideo, Uruguay.
Description: Covers the history of Uruguay and Latin America.

970 929 CN ISSN 0441-6910
F1035.H76
HUGUENOT TRAILS. 1968. q. $30 (effective 1992). Huguenot Society of Canada, 10 Adelaide East, Toronto, ON M5C 1J3, Canada. TEL 416-361-1685. Ed. Sally Lomas. bk.rev. circ. 300.

986.1 CK
HUILA. 1956. q. $8. Academia Hilense de Historia, Gobernacion del Huila, Neiva, Colombia. Ed. Jaime Guzman y Cia. circ. 1,000.

976 US
HUMPHREYS COUNTY HISTORICAL SOCIETY. PUBLICATION. 1978. irreg. c/o Mrs. John H. Whitfield, 105 1-2 Carroll Ave., Waverly, TN 37185.

HUNTERDON HISTORICAL NEWSLETTER. see *GENEALOGY AND HERALDRY*

976 US ISSN 1048-3152
F334.H9
HUNTSVILLE HISTORICAL REVIEW. 1971. q. $10. Huntsville-Madison County Historical Society, Box 666, Huntsville, AL 35804. Ed.Bd. bk.rev.; bibl.; illus. circ. 200.
Description: Provides items of local interest.

980 US ISSN 0046-8401
I S L A. (Regional sections also avail. separately) 1970. m. $640. Information Services on Latin America, 464 19th St., Oakland, CA 94612. TEL 510-835-0678. FAX 510-835-3017. Ed. Cary Barclay. bk.rev.; illus.; s-a. index. circ. 250. (looseleaf format; also avail. in microfilm; back issues avail.)
Description: Provides a selection of articles drawn from nine major English-language newspapers, covering political, economic and social developments in Latin America.

980 860 460 XR
IBERO-AMERICANA PRAGENSIA. 1966. a. $30. Universita Karlova, Centro de Estudios Ibero-Americanos, Nam. J. Palacha 2, 116 38 Prague 1, Czech Republic. Ed. Simona Binkova. bk.rev. circ. 700. **Document type:** academic/scholarly publication.

972 700 800 GW ISSN 0340-3068
F1401
IBERO-AMERIKANISCHES ARCHIV. (Text in English, German, Portuguese, Spanish) 1975. q. DM.90($58) (Ibero-Amerikanisches Institut, Berlin) Vervuert Verlag GmbH, Wielandstr. 40, 60318 Frankfurt a.M., Germany. TEL 069-599615. FAX 069-5978743. Ed.Bd. bk.rev.; bibl. circ. 500. **Indexed:** Anthropol.Lit., Hisp.Amer.Per.Ind. **Document type:** academic/scholarly publication.
—CCC.

979.6 US ISSN 0019-1264
F741
IDAHO YESTERDAYS. 1957. q. $15. Idaho State Historical Society, 450 N. Fourth St., Boise, ID 83702. TEL 208-334-3428. FAX 208-334-3198. Ed. Judith Austin. bk.rev.; charts; illus. circ. 1,200. **Indexed:** Abstr.Anthropol., Amer.Hist.& Life, Hist.Abstr.
—BLDSC (4362.303000); Faxon; UnCover.
Description: State and regional journal with focus on Idaho and Pacific Northwest.
Refereed Serial

973 II ISSN 0301-9101
E169.1
IDEAS; Indian doctoral engagements in American studies. (Text in English) 1971. a. membership. American Studies Research Centre, Osmania University Campus, Hyderabad 500007, India. Ed. Joseph L. Plakkoottam. abstr. circ. 3,000.

ILLIANA GENEALOGIST. see *GENEALOGY AND HERALDRY*

ILLINOIS. NATURAL HISTORY SURVEY. REPORTS. see *CONSERVATION*

ILLINOIS. STATE MUSEUM. SCIENTIFIC PAPERS SERIES. see *SCIENCES: COMPREHENSIVE WORKS*

977.3 US ISSN 0748-8149
F536
ILLINOIS HISTORICAL JOURNAL. 1908. 4/yr. $25 to individuals; institutions $20. Illinois Historic Preservation Agency, Old State Capitol, Springfield, IL 62701. TEL 217-782-4836. Ed. Evelyn Taylor. bk.rev.; illus.; index, cum.index: vols.1-60, vols. 61-82. circ. 2,900. (also avail. in microfilm from UMI; back issues avail.; reprint service avail. from UMI) **Indexed:** Amer.Hist.& Life, Hist.Abstr., M.L.A. **Document type:** academic/scholarly publication.
—Faxon; UnCover; UMI.
Formerly (until vol.77, no.3, 1984): Illinois State Historical Society. Journal (ISSN 0019-2287)

977.3 028.5 US ISSN 0019-2058
ILLINOIS HISTORY; a magazine for young people. 1947. 3/yr. $3 to individuals; free to history teachers in Illinois. Illinois Historic Preservation Agency, Old State Capitol, Springfield, IL 62701. TEL 217-785-6916. Ed. Keith A. Sculle. charts; illus.; index, cum.index. circ. 6,500. (back issues avail.) **Indexed:** Ind.Child.Mag. **Document type:** newsletter.

973 US ISSN 0743-7617
IMAGE FILE. 1984. q. $20 to individuals; institutions $30. Curt Teich Postcard Archives, Lake County Museum, Lakewood Forest Preserve, Wauconda, IL 60084. TEL 708-526-8638. FAX 708-526-1545. Ed. Katherine H. Smith. bk.rev. circ. 1,400. **Document type:** newsletter.
Formerly (until vol.5, no.3, 1989): Postcard Journal.
Description: Provides a forum for discussion of North American twentieth century culture, with emphasis on mass distribution formats of visual information, such as postcards and stereographs.

IMPRINT (BROOKLYN HEIGHTS). see *ART*

970 US
INDEPENDENCE COUNTY CHRONICLE. 1959. s-a. $10. Independence County Historical Society, Box 2036, Batesville, AR 72501. TEL 501-793-5126. FAX 501-793-9268. Ed. A.C. McGinnis. bk.rev. circ. 500.

975.7 US ISSN 0046-8843
INDEPENDENT REPUBLIC QUARTERLY. 1967. q. $20. Horry County Historical Society, Box 2025, Conway, SC 29526. charts; illus.; cum.index. circ. 400.
Description: Contains items of local historical interest.

INDIAN - ARTIFACT MAGAZINE. see *ARCHAEOLOGY*

970 980 II
INDIAN ASSOCIATION OF AMERICAN STUDIES. PAPERS. no.9, 1973. a. Indian Association of American Studies, c/o Dwijendra Tripathi, Indian Institute of Management, Vastrapur, Ahmedabad 380015, India. bibl.
Formerly: Indian Congress of American History. Papers.

810 II ISSN 0019-5030
E169.12
INDIAN JOURNAL OF AMERICAN STUDIES. (Text in English) 1971. s-a. Rs.50($5) to members; non-members Rs.100 (foreign $10); institutions Rs.200 (foreign $20). American Studies Research Centre, Osmania University Campus, Hyderabad 500007 (A.P.), India. Ed. M. Glen Johnson. adv.: page Rs.1000. bk.rev.; abstr.; bibl. circ. 1,000. **Indexed:** Amer.Hist.& Life, Hist.Abstr., M.L.A. **Document type:** academic/scholarly publication.
—BLDSC (4410.140000); UnCover.
Description: Covers the history, political system and government, economics, law, institutions, literature and cultures of the United States.

INDIANA; contributions to ethnology and linguistics, archaeology and physical anthropology of Indian America. see *ANTHROPOLOGY*

977.2 US ISSN 0019-655X
INDIANA COVERED BRIDGE SOCIETY. NEWSLETTER. 1964. q. $3. Indiana Covered Bridge Society, 725 Sanders St., Indianapolis, IN 46302. Ed. George E. Gould. adv.; bk.rev.; illus.; cum.index every 7 yrs. circ. 500. **Document type:** newsletter.

977 US ISSN 1071-3301
INDIANA HISTORIAN. 8/yr. $7.50. Indiana Historical Bureau, 140 N. Senate Ave., Indianapolis, IN 46204. TEL 317-232-2537. FAX 317-232-3728. Ed. Pamela J. Bennett. circ. 3,700 (paid). **Document type:** monographic series.
Formerly: Indiana Junior Historian.
Description: Provides resources and models for the study of local history to encourage Indiana's citizens of all ages to become engaged with the history of their communities and the state of Indiana.

973 US ISSN 0073-6880
INDIANA HISTORICAL COLLECTIONS. 1916. irreg. price varies. Indiana Historical Bureau, 408 State Library and Historical Bldg., 140 N. Senate Ave., Indianapolis, IN 46204. TEL 317-232-2537. FAX 317-232-3728. bk.rev.; index. circ. 600. **Document type:** monographic series, government publication.

973 US ISSN 0073-6902
F521
INDIANA HISTORICAL SOCIETY. PUBLICATIONS. 1897. irreg., vol.27, no.1, 1984. $20 membership. Indiana Historical Society, 315 W. Ohio St., Indianapolis, IN 46202. TEL 317-232-1882. FAX 317-233-3109. circ. 9,500. **Document type:** monographic series.
Description: Publishes historical studies of Indiana and its people.

HISTORY — HISTORY OF NORTH AND SOUTH AMERICA

977 US ISSN 1047-708X
INDIANA HISTORICAL SOCIETY NEWS. 1978. bi-m. $20 membership. Indiana Historical Society, 315 W. Ohio St., Indianapolis, IN 46202. TEL 317-232-1882. FAX 317-233-3109. Ed. J. Kent Calder. circ. 9,500 (controlled). **Document type:** newsletter.
 Supersedes (in 1986): Indiana Historical Society Newsletter.
 Description: Informs members about society activities, conferences, acquisitions, publications and programs.

977.2 US ISSN 0019-6649
F521
INDIANA HISTORY BULLETIN. 1923. q. $5. Indiana Historical Bureau, 408 State Library and Historical Bldg., 140 N. Senate Ave., Rm. 408, Indianapolis, IN 46204-2298. TEL 317-232-2537. FAX 317-232-3728. Ed. Virginia L. Terpening. bibl.; illus.; index. circ. 2,800. **Indexed:** Amer.Hist.& Life, Hist.Abstr.
 Description: Promotes the mission and programs of the IHB and serves as a communication vehicle among Indiana organizations and individuals in order to promote the value of state and local history.

977
INDIANA HISTORY RESOURCE SERIES. 1980. irreg. price varies. Indiana Historical Bureau, 408 State Library and Historical Bldg., 140 N. Senate Ave., Indianapolis, IN 46204. TEL 317-232-2537. index. circ. 600. **Document type:** monographic series, government publication.

977 US ISSN 0019-6673
F521
INDIANA MAGAZINE OF HISTORY. 1905. q. $10. Indiana University, Department of History, Ballantine Hall 742, Bloomington, IN 47405. TEL 812-855-4139. (Co-sponsor: Indiana Historical Society) Ed. Richard Blackett. adv.; bk.rev.; charts; illus. circ. 11,000. (also avail. in microfilm; reprint service avail. from KTO) **Indexed:** Amer.Hist.& Life, Bk.Rev.Ind., Hist.Abstr.
 —Faxon; UnCover.

980 PE
INEDITA. 1973. irreg. Universidad Nacional de San Agustin, Direccion Universitaria de Investigacion, Apdo. 23, Arequipa, Peru. Ed. Alejandro Malaga Medina.

977 US ISSN 0020-1537
F551
INLAND SEAS. 1945. q. $35 to individuals; senior citizens $22. Great Lakes Historical Society, 480 Main St., Vermilion, OH 44089. TEL 216-967-3467. FAX 216-967-1519. Ed. William D. Ellis. bk.rev.; charts; illus.; stat.; index. circ. 3,200. **Indexed:** Amer.Hist.& Life, Hist.Abstr., Mich.Mag.Ind. **Document type:** academic/scholarly publication.
 —Faxon.

INSTITUT DES HAUTES ETUDES DE L'AMERIQUE LATINE. COLLECTION DES TRAVAUX ET MEMOIRES. see HUMANITIES: COMPREHENSIVE WORKS

973 290 US ISSN 0020-2843
INSTITUTE OF EARLY AMERICAN HISTORY AND CULTURE. NEWS LETTER. 1952. irreg. free to individual subscribers of William & Mary Quarterly. Institute of Early American History & Culture, Box 8781, Williamsburg, VA 23187. TEL 804-221-1110. Ed. Michael McGiffert. circ. 2,000. **Document type:** newsletter.
 Description: Reports news of the institute and professional developments in early studies including conferences, opportunities for study and scholarly publications and prizes.

946 AG ISSN 0020-3637
INSTITUTO AMERICANO DE ESTUDIOS VASCOS. BOLETIN. 1950. q. Arg.$100000($13) Editorial Vasca Ekin s.r.l., Av. Belgrano 1144, 1092 Buenos Aires, Argentina. TEL 37-1529. (Co-sponsor: Fundacion Juan de Garay) Dir. Andres Ma. de Irujo. adv.; bk.rev.; bibl.; charts. circ. 1,000. **Indexed:** Amer.Hist.& Life, Hist.Abstr.

355 981 BL ISSN 0020-3890
INSTITUTO DE GEOGRAFIA E HISTORIA MILITAR DO BRASIL. REVISTA.* 1941. s-a. free. Instituto de Geografia e Historia Militar do Brazil, Ministerio do Exercito, Praca Duque de Caxias, Rio de Janeiro, Brazil. Ed. Dir. Adalardo Fiatho. illus.
 Description: Covers military history.

980 574 CL ISSN 0716-6478
F3186 CODEN: APSOE5
INSTITUTO DE LA PATAGONIA. ANALES. CIENCIAS SOCIALES. (Text in Spanish; summaries in English) 1970. a. Esc.3500($15) Universidad de Magallanes, Instituto de la Patagonia, Casilla de Correo 113-D, Punta Arenas, Magallanes, Chile. TEL 56-61-212913. FAX 56-61-212973. TELEX 380004 UMAG-CK. Ed. Mateo Martinic. adv.; bk.rev.; bibl.; charts; illus. circ. 500. **Document type:** academic/scholarly publication.
 Supersedes in part (vol.25, 1984): Instituto de la Patagonia. Anales (ISSN 0085-1922)
 Description: Publishes original papers by researchers of the institute in the area of social sciences referring to Patagonia, Tierra del Fuego, Antarctica, adjacent islands and the southeastern Pacific Ocean.
 Refereed Serial

980 BL ISSN 0101-4366
INSTITUTO HISTORICO E GEOGRAFICO BRASILEIRO. REVISTA. 1839. q. $10 per no. Instituto Historico e Geografico Brasileiro, Av. Augusto Severo, 8-10o, 20021 Rio de Janeiro, Brazil. FAX 021-252-4430. Ed. Carlos Wehrs. bk.rev. circ. 1,000. (tabloid format; reprint service avail. from KTO) **Indexed:** Amer.Hist.& Life, Hisp.Amer.Per.Ind., Hist.Abstr.
 Formerly: Instituto Historico, Geografico e Ethnografico do Brasil. Revista Trimensal (ISSN 0102-9053)

981 BL ISSN 0020-4218
INSTITUTO HISTORICO E GEOGRAFICO DE JUIZ DE FORA. vol.4, 1969. q. $1. Instituto Historico e Geografico de Juiz de Fora, Caixa Postal 438, Juiz de Fora, Minas Gerais, Brazil. Ed.Bd. bibl. circ. 1,000.

INSTITUTO PANAMERICANO DE GEOGRAFIA E HISTORIA. BOLETIN AEREO. see GEOGRAPHY

980 300 US ISSN 0074-0918
INTER-AMERICAN ECONOMIC AND SOCIAL COUNCIL. FINAL REPORT OF THE ANNUAL MEETING AT THE MINISTERIAL LEVEL. (Text in English, French, Portuguese and Spanish) 1962. a. $2. Organization of American States, 1889 F St., N.W., Washington, DC 20006. TEL 703-941-1617. circ. 2,000.

INTERNATIONAL JOURNAL OF MARITIME HISTORY. see TRANSPORTATION — Ships And Shipping

998 398 CN ISSN 0020-9872
E99.E7
INUKTITUT. (Text in English, French and Inuktitut) 1959. irreg. Can.$30 for 4 nos. Inuit Tapirisat of Canada, 170 Laurier Ave. W., Ste. 510, Ottawa, ON K1P 5V5, Canada. TEL 613-238-8181. FAX 613-234-1991. Ed. John Bennett. illus. circ. 6,600. (also avail. in microfilm from UMI) **Indexed:** CMI.
 —UnCover.
 Description: Cultural magazine for Canadian Inuit.

977 US
IOWA HISTORIAN. 1947. bi-m. membership. State Historical Society of Iowa, 402 Iowa Ave., Iowa City, IA 52240. TEL 319-335-3916. FAX 319-335-3924. Ed. Steven Blaski. bibl.; illus. circ. 5,000. **Document type:** newsletter.
 Formerly (until 1985): State Historical Society of Iowa. News for Members.

IROQUOIS STALKER. see GENEALOGY AND HERALDRY

971 CN ISSN 0384-8175
F1048
ISLAND MAGAZINE. 1976. s-a. Can.$8($10) (foreign Can.$12). Prince Edward Island Museum and Heritage Foundation, 2 Kent St., Charlottetown, PE C1A 1M6, Canada. TEL 902-982-9127. FAX 902-368-5544. Ed. G. Edward MacDonald. bk.rev.; illus. circ. 2,000. **Document type:** academic/scholarly publication.
 Description: Devoted to the human and natural heritage of Prince Edward Island.

ITAWAMBA SETTLERS. see GENEALOGY AND HERALDRY

976 US
JACKSON COUNTY CHRONICLES. 1976. 4/yr. $10. Jackson County, Alabama Historical Association, Rt. 4, Box 250, Scottsboro, AL 35768. Ed. Ann B. Chambless. bk.rev. circ. 600.

980 GW ISSN 0075-2673
F1401
JAHRBUCH FUER GESCHICHTE VON STAAT, WIRTSCHAFT UND GESELLSCHAFT LATEINAMERIKAS. 1964. a. DM.118. Boehlau Verlag GmbH, Theodor-Heuss-Str. 76, 51149 Cologne, Germany. TEL 02203-307021. FAX 02203-307349. Ed.Bd. **Indexed:** Amer.Hist.& Life, Hisp.Amer.Per.Ind., Hist.Abstr. **Document type:** academic/scholarly publication.

989 JM
JAMAICAN HISTORICAL REVIEW. 1946. irreg. (approx. a.). $15. Jamaican Historical Society, c/o Institute of Jamaica, 12-16 East St., Kingston, Jamaica, W.I. TEL 809-968-7280. FAX 809-926-2217. Ed. Carl Campbell. adv.; bk.rev.; illus.; circ. 1,000 (controlled). (back issues avail.) **Indexed:** Amer.Hist.& Life, Hist.Abstr.

JASPER COUNTY MISSOURI JOURNAL. see GENEALOGY AND HERALDRY

JAZZLETTER. see MUSIC

974.9 370 US
JERSEY JOURNEYS. 7/yr. $65. New Jersey Historical Society, 230 Broadway, Newark, NJ 07104. TEL 201-483-3939.

975 US ISSN 8755-3805
JOHANNES SCHWALM HISTORICAL ASSOCIATION. JOURNAL. 1977. a. price varies. Johannes Schwalm Historical Association, 800 F Westbury Pl., 4807 Old Spartanburg Rd., Taylors, SC 29687. TEL 803-292-5982. (Subscr. to: Box 99, Pennsauken, NJ 08110) Ed. R. Carl Barth. circ. 600. (back issues avail.) **Document type:** academic/scholarly publication.
 Description: Covers the Hessian participation in the revolutionary war.

980 US
JOHNS HOPKINS STUDIES IN ATLANTIC HISTORY AND CULTURE. 1977. irreg. price varies. Johns Hopkins University Press, 701 W. 40th St., Ste. 275, Baltimore, MD 21211. TEL 410-516-6900. FAX 410-516-6998. Ed.Bd. (reprint service avail. from UMI)

974 398 US
JONES COUNTY HISTORICAL REVIEW.* 1973. q. $8. Jones County Historical Society, 301 N. Chestnut, Monticello, IA 52310. Ed. C.L. Norlin. bibl.; stat. circ. 500.

JOURNAL OF AFRO-LATIN AMERICAN STUDIES AND LITERATURES. see HUMANITIES: COMPREHENSIVE WORKS

JOURNAL OF AMERICAN ETHNIC HISTORY. see ETHNIC INTERESTS

973 US ISSN 0021-8723
E171
JOURNAL OF AMERICAN HISTORY. 1914. q. membership. Indiana University, 1125 E. Atwater, Bloomington, IN 47408. TEL 812-855-2816. FAX 812-855-9939. Ed. David Thelen. adv.; bk.rev.; index, cum.index every 50 yrs. circ. 12,000. (also avail. in microform from MIM,UMI,PMC; reprint service avail. from UMI,KTO) **Indexed:** Acad.Ind., Amer.Bibl.Slavic & E.Eur.Stud., Amer.Hist.& Life, Arts & Hum.Cit.Ind., Bk.Rev.Dig., Bk.Rev.Ind. (1965-), Chic.Per.Ind., Child.Bk.Rev.Ind. (1965-) Curr.Cont., Hist.Abstr., Hum.Ind., Lang.& Lang.Behav.Abstr., M.L.A., Mag.Ind., Mid.East: Abstr.& Ind., Ref.Sour., SSCI.
 —BLDSC (4927.280000); Faxon; UnCover; SWETS; UMI.
 Formerly (until 1964): Mississippi Valley Historical Review.

HISTORY — HISTORY OF NORTH AND SOUTH AMERICA

973   UK   ISSN 0021-8758
JOURNAL OF AMERICAN STUDIES. 3/yr. £59($104) to institutions £59 (overseas £71 ($104)). (British Association for American Studies) Cambridge University Press, Edinburgh Bldg., Shaftesbury Rd., Cambridge CB2 2RU, England. TEL 0223-312393. FAX 0223-315052. TELEX 851817256. (N. American addr.: Cambridge University Press, Journals Dept., 40 W. 20th St., New York, NY 10011. TEL 212-924-3900. FAX 212-691-3236) (Co-sponsor: European Association for American Studies) Ed. Michael Heale. adv.; bk.rev.; bibl.; index. (also avail. in microform from UMI; back issues avail.; reprint service avail. from SWZ,UMI) **Indexed:** Abstr.Engl.Stud., Amer.Hist.& Life, Bk.Rev.Ind. (1980-), Br.Hum.Ind., Child.Bk.Rev.Ind. (1980-), Curr.Cont., Film Lit.Ind. (1973-), Geo.Abstr., Hist.Abstr., Hum.Ind., M.L.A., Mid.East: Abstr.& Ind., Ref.Sour. **Document type:** academic/scholarly publication.
—BLDSC (4927.400000); Faxon; UnCover; SWETS; UMI.
Formerly (until 1967): British Association for American Studies. Bulletin (ISSN 0524-5001)
Description: Covers American literature, history, institutions, politics, economics, film, popular culture, and geography and related subjects.

979.1   US   ISSN 0021-9053
F806
JOURNAL OF ARIZONA HISTORY. 1960. q. $25. Arizona Historical Society, Publications Division, 949 E. Second St., Tucson, AZ 85719. TEL 602-628-5774. Ed. Bruce J. Dinges. bk.rev.; illus.; index. circ. 4,100. (also avail. in microform from JAI,MIM) **Indexed:** Amer.Hist.& Life, Chic.Per.Ind., Hist.Abstr. **Document type:** academic/scholarly publication.
—UnCover; UMI.
Formerly: Arizoniana.
Description: Contains items of local interest.

972.9   BB   ISSN 0047-2263
F2155
JOURNAL OF CARIBBEAN HISTORY. 1970. s-a. $18 per vol. University of the West Indies, Department of History, P.O. Box 64, Bridgetown, Barbados, W.I. TEL 809-425-1310. FAX 809-425-1327. Ed.Bd. bk.rev. circ. 500. **Indexed:** Amer.Hist.& Life, Hist.Abstr.

JOURNAL OF CARIBBEAN STUDIES. see *ETHNIC INTERESTS*

970.004 917.306   US   ISSN 0146-2962
E99.C5
JOURNAL OF CHEROKEE STUDIES. 1976. q. Museum of the Cherokee Indian, Box 1599, Cherokee, NC 28719. TEL 704-497-3481. (Co-sponsor: Cherokee Historical Association) Ed.Bd. **Indexed:** Anthropol.Lit.

970   US   ISSN 1058-2126
F442.1
JOURNAL OF EAST TENNESSEE HISTORY. 1929. a. $15 or membership. East Tennessee Historical Society, 500 W. Church Ave., Knoxville, TN 37902-2505. TEL 615-544-7532. Ed. R.B. Rosenburg. circ. 2,000. **Indexed:** Amer.Hist.& Life, Hist.Abstr. **Document type:** academic/scholarly publication.
Formerly: East Tennessee Historical Society's Publications (ISSN 0361-6193)

970   US   ISSN 0090-1938
F159.E7
JOURNAL OF ERIE STUDIES. 1972. s-a. $10. Erie County Historical Society, 417 State St., Erie, PA 16501. TEL 814-454-1813. Ed. Carl Lechner. bk.rev.; bibl. circ. 950. **Document type:** academic/scholarly publication.
Description: Interdisciplinary publication examining the culture of northwestern Pennsylvania, and those sections of Ohio, New York, and Ontario bordering on Lake Erie.

980   UK   ISSN 0022-216X
F1401
JOURNAL OF LATIN AMERICAN STUDIES. 1969. 3/yr. £31($56) to individuals (overseas £43); institutions £59 (overseas £71 ($124)). (Society for Latin American Studies) Cambridge University Press, Edinburgh Bldg., Shaftesbury Rd., Cambridge CB2 2RU, England. TEL 0223-312393. FAX 0223-315052. TELEX 851817256. (N. American addr.: Journals Dept., Cambridge University Press, 40 W. 20th St., New York, NY 10011. TEL 800-431-1580. FAX 212-691-3239) Eds. Victor Bulmer-Thomas, Laurence Whitehead. adv.; bk.rev.; abstr.; bibl.; charts; index. (also avail. in microform from UMI; back issues avail.; reprint service avail. from SWZ) **Indexed:** A.B.C.Pol.Sci., Amer.Hist.& Life, Anthropol.Lit., Arts & Hum.Cit.Ind., CERDIC, Chic.Per.Ind., Curr.Cont., Hisp.Amer.Per.Ind., Hist.Abstr., I D A, Int.Polit.Sci.Abstr., Lang.& Lang.Behav.Abstr., Ref.Sour., Soc.Sci.Ind., SSCI. **Document type:** academic/scholarly publication.
—BLDSC (5010.110000); Faxon; UnCover; SWETS; UMI. CCC.
Description: Focuses on the anthropology, geography, history, economics, international relations, politics and sociology of Latin America.

JOURNAL OF MILITARY HISTORY. see *MILITARY*

976.2   US   ISSN 0022-2771
F336
JOURNAL OF MISSISSIPPI HISTORY. 1939. q. $15. Mississippi Historical Society, Box 571, Jackson, MS 39205. TEL 601-359-6850. FAX 601-359-6905. (Co-sponsor: Mississippi Department of Archives and History) Ed. Elbert R. Hilliard. bk.rev.; bibl.; charts; illus.; index, cum.index: 1939-1982. circ. 1,825. (also avail. in microform from UMI; back issues avail.; reprint service avail. from UMI) **Indexed:** Amer.Hist.& Life, Hist.Abstr. **Document type:** academic/scholarly publication.
—UnCover; UMI.
Description: Focuses on the history and culture of the lower Mississippi Valley. Includes archaeology, political history and social history.

975   US   ISSN 0094-8039
F334.M85
JOURNAL OF MUSCLE SHOALS HISTORY. 1973. irreg. (latest 1993, vol.13). $9. Tennessee Valley Historical Society, Box 149, Sheffield, AL 35660. TEL 205-381-2298. Ed. Richard C. Sheridan. illus.; index. circ. 1,000. (back issues avail.) **Document type:** academic/scholarly publication.
Refereed Serial

979.4   US   ISSN 0022-4383
F868.S15
JOURNAL OF SAN DIEGO HISTORY. 1955. q. $40. San Diego Historical Society, Box 81825, San Diego, CA 92138. TEL 619-232-6203. FAX 619-232-6297. Ed. Richard W. Crawford. adv.; bk.rev.; index. circ. 3,500. (also avail. in microform from UMI; reprint service avail. from UMI) **Indexed:** Amer.Hist.& Life, Cal.Per.Ind. (1985-), Hist.Abstr. **Document type:** academic/scholarly publication.
—UMI.
Former titles: Times Gone By; San Diego Historical Society Quarterly.

976   US   ISSN 0022-4642
F206
JOURNAL OF SOUTHERN HISTORY. 1935. q. $25 to individuals; institutions $35. Southern Historical Association, Rice University, Box 1892, Houston, TX 77251. TEL 713-527-3069. FAX 713-285-5207. (Subscr. to: c/o William F. Holmes, Sec.-Treas., Department of History, University of Georgia, Athens, GA 30602) Ed. John B. Boles. adv. contact: Patricia Burgess. bk.rev.; bibl.; index, cum.index: vols.1-20, 21-30, 31-40; circ. 5,000 (paid). (also avail. in microform; reprint service avail. from UMI) **Indexed:** Acad.Ind., Amer.Hist.& Life, Arts & Hum.Cit.Ind., Biog.Ind., Bk.Rev.Ind. (1973-), Chic.Per.Ind., Child.Bk.Rev.Ind. (1973-), Curr.Cont., Hist.Abstr., Hum.Ind., Ref.Sour., SSCI. **Document type:** academic/scholarly publication.
—Faxon; UnCover; SWETS; UMI.
Description: Contains well-documented articles on all areas of southern history. Includes reviews of scholarly literature.

975   US   ISSN 0739-1943
F286
JOURNAL OF SOUTHWEST GEORGIA HISTORY. 1983. a. $20. Thronateeska Heritage Center, 100 Roosevelt Ave., Albany, GA 31701. TEL 912-430-4870. FAX 912-430-4830. (Alternative addr.: Albany State College, Albany, GA 31705) Ed. Lee W. Formwalt. adv.; bk.rev. circ. 400. **Indexed:** Amer.Hist.& Life, Hist.Abstr. **Document type:** academic/scholarly publication.
Description: Invites discussion about documents relating to the social, political, economic, and cultural history of south Georgia.
Refereed Serial

975   US   ISSN 0276-7449
F217.A3
JOURNAL OF THE ALLEGHENIES. 1963. a. $10. Council of the Alleghenies Inc., Box 514, Frostburg, MD 21532. Ed. Anthony E. Crosby, Jr. bk.rev.; cum.index: 1963-1984. circ. 200. (back issues avail.)
Description: Devoted to preserving and sharing the traditions, folklore, history, human values and natural resources of the mountain peoples of the Alleghenies (primarily of northern West Virginia, Western Maryland, Western Pennsylvania).

970   US   ISSN 0275-1275
E164
JOURNAL OF THE EARLY REPUBLIC. 1981. q. price varies. Society for Historians of the Early American Republic, Purdue University, Department of History, W. Lafayette, IN 46901. TEL 317-274-7247. FAX 317-274-2374. Ed. Ralph D. Gray. adv.; bk.rev.; bibl.; illus.; index. circ. 1,300. (also avail. in microfilm from UMI; back issues avail.; reprint service avail. from UMI) **Indexed:** Amer.Hist.& Life, Hist.Abstr. **Document type:** academic/scholarly publication.
—BLDSC (4970.720000); Faxon; UnCover; UMI.
Description: Studies the history and culture of the United States from 1789-1850.

973.3   US   ISSN 1069-9201
▼**JOURNAL OF THE FOUNDING ERA.** 1994. q. $16 (effectve 1994). Witness Publications, Box 8053, Falls Church, VA 22041-8053. Ed. William Rogers. adv.; bk.rev. (back issues avail.) **Document type:** newsletter.
Description: Covers the political, diplomatic, social and economic history of America during the period 1754-1824.

973.7   US
JOURNAL OF THE LINCOLN ASSASSINATION. 3/yr. $10. Autograph Press, c/o Fred Hatch, Box 241579, Los Angeles, CA 90024-1579. TEL 310-673-1908. adv. circ. 100. (back issues avail.) **Document type:** academic/scholarly publication.
Description: Provides information about assossination of Lincoln. Each issue contains two articles, one original and one reprint.

979 572   US   ISSN 0894-8410
F806
JOURNAL OF THE SOUTHWEST. 1959. 4/yr. $18 to individuals (foreign $21); institutions $24 (foreign $27). University of Arizona, 1052 N. Highland, Tucson, AZ 85721. TEL 602-621-2484. Ed. Joseph C. Wilder. adv.; bk.rev.; illus.; index, cum.index: 1959-1963. circ. 1,200. (also avail. in microform from UMI) **Indexed:** Amer.Hist.& Life, Arts & Hum.Cit.Ind., Chic.Per.Ind., Curr.Cont., Hist.Abstr. **Document type:** academic/scholarly publication.
—BLDSC (5066.055000); Faxon; UnCover; UMI.
Formerly: Arizona and the West (ISSN 0004-1408)

973.05 328.5   US   ISSN 1069-918X
▼**JOURNAL OF THE U S SENATE.** 1994. q. $24 (effective 1994). Witness Publications, Box 8053, Falls Church, VA 22041-8053. bk.rev. (back issues avail.) **Document type:** newsletter.
Description: Studies the history of the US Senate and its place in American history.

HISTORY — HISTORY OF NORTH AND SOUTH AMERICA

978 US ISSN 0022-5169
F591 CODEN: JNLWA7
JOURNAL OF THE WEST; an illustrated quarterly of Western American history and Culture. 1962. q. $38 to individuals; institutions $48: (foreign $56). Journal of the West, Inc., 1531 Yuma, Box 1009, Manhattan, KS 66502-4228. TEL 913-539-1888. Ed. Robin Higham. adv.; bk.rev.; charts; illus.; index. circ. 4,500. (reprint service avail. from KTO) **Indexed:** Acad.Ind., Amer.Hist.& Life, Arts & Hum.Cit.Ind., Chic.Per.Ind., Curr.Cont., GeoRef, Hist.Abstr., Hum.Ind., Ref.Sour. **Document type:** academic/scholarly publication, consumer publication.
—BLDSC (5072.560000); Faxon; UnCover.
Description: Devoted to Western history and culture.

▼ **973 305.896** US ISSN 1069-9198
JOURNAL OF TWENTIETH CENTURY AFRICAN AMERICAN ACTIVISM. 1993. q. $12. Witness Publications, Box 8053, Falls Church, VA 22041-8053. Ed. Randolph Clark. adv.; bk.rev. (back issues avail.) **Document type:** newsletter.
Description: Covers African American activism since 1885, and discusses activism in the context of African American history and in the wider context of American history.

980 AG ISSN 0076-6380
F2911
JUNTA DE ESTUDIOS HISTORICOS DE MENDOZA. REVISTA. 1934. irreg. $30. Junta de Estudios Historicos de Mendoza, Calle Montevideo 544, 5500 Mendoza, Argentina. TEL 241092. Ed. Edmundo Correas. bk.rev.; illus. circ. 1,150. **Indexed:** Amer.Hist.& Life, Hist.Abstr.

K W M NEWSLETTER. (Kendall Whaling Museum) see MUSEUMS AND ART GALLERIES

978.1 US ISSN 0149-9114
F681
KANSAS HISTORY; a journal of the Central Plains. 1978. q. $25 to non-members. Kansas State Historical Society, Center for Histortial Research, 120 W. Tenth, Topeka, KS 66612. TEL 913-296-3251. FAX 913-296-1005. Ed. Virgil W. Dean. bk.rev.; bibl.; charts; illus.; index. circ. 3,800. (also avail. in microform from UMI) **Indexed:** Amer.Hist.& Life, GeoRef, Hist.Abstr. **Document type:** academic/scholarly publication.
—UnCover; UMI.
Supersedes (1931-1977): Kansas Historical Quarterly (ISSN 0022-8621); Historical Society Mirror.
Description: Contains scholarly articles, edited documents, and other materials that contribute to an understanding of the history and cultural heritage of Kansas and the Central Plains.

973 US
KELSO COURIER. 1967. m. (Sep.-May). $10 includes membership. Brimfield Memorial House Association, 4158 State Rt. 43, Kent, OH 44240. Ed. Terri Lea Ulrich. circ. 305. (back issues avail.) **Document type:** newsletter.
Description: Includes items of local history.

KENTUCKY. ADJUTANT-GENERAL'S OFFICE. REPORT. see MILITARY

KENTUCKY ANCESTORS. see GENEALOGY AND HERALDRY

976 US
KENTUCKY ARCHIVIST. 1978. s-a. $6. Kentucky Council on Archives, c/o Jeffrey Duff, Treas., Kentucky Dept. of Libraries and Archives, 300 Coffee Tree Rd., Frankfort, KY 40601. TEL 502-745-6263. (Subscr. to: Kentucky Department for Libraries and Archives, Public Records Division, Box 537, Frankfort, KY 40602-0537) Ed. Jonathan Jeffrey. circ. 120. **Document type:** newsletter.
Description: Shares information to its members about their archival and manuscript repositories.

973.7 US ISSN 0023-0146
KENTUCKY CIVIL WAR ROUND TABLE. BULLETIN. 1957. 5/yr. $15 membership. Kentucky Civil War Round Table, c/o James C. Klotter, P.O. Box H, Frankfort, KY 40602. FAX 502-564-4701. Ed. Nicky Hughes. bk.rev. circ. 650. **Document type:** newsletter.

976.9 910 US ISSN 0890-8362
KENTUCKY EXPLORER; featuring things about Kentucky and its history. 1986. m. $15. 1792 Hayes Valley Rd., Box 227, Jackson, KY 41339. TEL 606-666-5060. Ed. Charles Hayes, Jr. illus. circ. 11,000. (back issues avail.)

976 US
KENTUCKY HERITAGE. 1961. 2/yr. membership. Kentucky Junior Historical Society, Box H, Frankfort, KY 40602-2108. TEL 502-564-2662. Eds. Ann B. Bevins, Susan Lyons Hughes. circ. 3,700.

976 US
KENTUCKY HISTORICAL SOCIETY. BULLETIN. 1975. q. $35. Kentucky Historical Society, Old State Capitol, Box H, Frankfort, KY 40602-2108. TEL 502-564-3016. FAX 502-564-4701. Ed. Thomas H. Appleton, Jr. bk.rev. circ. 4,800. (back issues avail.)
Description: Presents news of historical interest to the community of the state of Kentucky.

976.9 US ISSN 0023-0243
F446
KENTUCKY HISTORICAL SOCIETY. REGISTER. 1903. q. $35. Kentucky Historical Society, Old State Capitol, Box H, Frankfort, KY 40602-2108. TEL 502-564-3016. FAX 502-564-4701. Ed. Thomas H. Appleton, Jr. bk.rev.; index. circ. 4,300. (also avail. in audio cassette; back issues avail.) **Indexed:** Amer.Hist.& Life, Geneal.Per.Ind., Hist.Abstr., Hum.Ind., R.G., Soc.Sci.Ind.
—BLDSC (7337.020000); UnCover.
Description: Covers all fields of Kentucky history, as well as Southern and American history.

KIRCHLICHE ZEITGESCHICHTE; Internationale Halbjahresschrift fuer Theologie und Geschichtswissenschaft. see HISTORY — History Of Europe

KIVA. see ARCHAEOLOGY

KREFELDER HEFTE ZUR DEUTSCH-AMERIKANISCHEN GESCHICHTE. see HISTORY — History Of Europe

L A S A FORUM. (Latin American Studies Association) see SOCIAL SCIENCES: COMPREHENSIVE WORKS

LABOUR/TRAVAIL; journal of Canadian labour studies - revue d'etudes ouvrieres canadiennes. see BUSINESS AND ECONOMICS — Labor And Industrial Relations

LADING MEIZHOU YANJIU/LATIN AMERICAN STUDIES. see SOCIAL SCIENCES: COMPREHENSIVE WORKS

978 US
LAKE CHELAN HISTORY NOTES. 1973. irreg. (approx. a.). $3.50 per no. Lake Chelan Historical Society, Box 1948, Chelan, WA 98816. TEL 509-682-5644. Ed. Hobbie Morehead. circ. 500.

977 US
LAKE COUNTY HERITAGE. 1990. a. $5. Lake County Historical Society, 8610 King Memorial Rd., Mentor, OH 44060. TEL 216-255-8979.
Description: Focuses on the history, culture and heritage of the county and of the region of the Western Reserve in Northern Ohio.

977 US ISSN 0890-3050
LAKE SUPERIOR MAGAZINE. 1979. bi-m. $21. Lake Superior Port Cities, Inc., 325 Lake Ave. S., Duluth, MN 55802. TEL 218-722-5002. FAX 218-722-4096. Ed. Paul L. Hayden. adv.; bk.rev.; index. circ. 20,000. (back issues avail.) **Document type:** consumer publication.
Formerly: Lake Superior Port Cities (ISSN 0199-7173)
Description: Covers history, travel, tourism and photography in the Lake Superior area.

974.8 US ISSN 0023-7477
F157.L2
LANCASTER COUNTY HISTORICAL SOCIETY. JOURNAL. 1896. irreg. membership. Lancaster County Historical Society, 230 N. President Ave., Lancaster, PA 17603-3125. TEL 717-392-4633. FAX 717-293-2738. Ed. John W.W. Loose. bk.rev.; charts; illus.; index, cum.index published separately. circ. 2,600. **Indexed:** Amer.Hist.& Life, Hist.Abstr.
—Faxon.
Description: Lancaster county history, biography and genealogy.

977 US ISSN 0458-6972
SB469
LANDMARK (NEW BERLIN). 1958. q. $2 per no. Waukesha County Historical Society, Inc., 20245 W. National Ave., New Berlin, WI 53146. TEL 414-679-0162. Ed. Libbie Nolan. bibl.; illus. circ. 1,000. **Indexed:** Rehabil.Lit.

974 720 US
LANDMARKS OBSERVER. 1970. s-a. $25. Greater Portland Landmarks, Inc., 165 State St., Portland, ME 04101. TEL 207-774-5561. Ed. Linda J. Murnik. adv.; bk.rev.; illus. circ. 7,000. (tabloid format; back issues avail.) **Indexed:** Amer.Hist.& Life, Avery Ind.Archit.Per., Hist.Abstr. **Document type:** newspaper.
Description: Covers historic preservation in the greater Portland area.

978 929 US ISSN 1062-8886
THE LAST LEAF. q.? Sylvia Michelson, Ed. & Pub., 1477 Hwy. 200S, Glendive, MT 59330-9402.

979 398 US
LATAH LEGACY. 1980. s-a. $10. Latah County Historical Society, 327 East Second, Moscow, ID 83843. TEL 208-882-1004. Ed. Steven Lyons. bk.rev. circ. 540.

LATIN AMERICA - CHICAGO. see ETHNIC INTERESTS

980 US
LATIN AMERICAN HISTORICAL DICTIONARIES SERIES. 1967. irreg., latest no.22. price varies. Scarecrow Press, Inc., 52 Liberty St., Box 4167, Metuchen, NJ 08840. TEL 800-537-7107. Ed. Lawrence Hallewell.

977 296 US ISSN 0738-1379
LATIN AMERICAN JEWISH STUDIES NEWSLETTER. 1980. 2/yr. $20 to individuals; institutions $30. Latin American Jewish Studies Association, 2104 Georgetown Blvd., Ann Arbor, MI 48105. TEL 313-996-2880. Ed. Judith Laikin Elkin. adv.; bk.rev.; bibl. circ. 500. (looseleaf format; back issues avail) **Document type:** academic/scholarly publication, newsletter.
Description: Presents professional news, current bibliography and special field reports.

980 US
LATIN AMERICAN LITERATURE AND CULTURE. 1989. irreg., vol.10, 1993. price varies. University of California Press, 2120 Berkeley Way, Berkeley, CA 94720. TEL 510-642-4247. FAX 510-643-7127. (Orders to: California-Princeton Fulfillment Services, 1445 Lower Ferry Rd., Ewing, NJ 08618. TEL 800-777-4726. FAX 800-999-1958) (back issues avail.) **Document type:** monographic series.
Description: Examines the literary heritage of South America and offers selected writings in translation.
Refereed Serial

972 DK ISSN 0906-6292
LATINAMERIKABLADET MANANA. 1981. 4/yr. DKK 70 to individuals; institutions DKK 130. Foreningen Latinamerikabladet Manana, c/o Kulturhuset Cikaden, Griffenfeldsgade 35, DK-2200 Copenhagen N. TEL 35 37 18 88. FAX 35-37-19-80. Ed. Erik Zinglersen. bk.rev.; illus. circ. 3,000. (back issues avail.)
Former titles (until Nov. 1991): M A Nyt (ISSN 0904-6089); (until 1988): Mellemamerika Nyt (ISSN 0900-7156); (until 1985): El Salvador Nyt (ISSN 0108-6510)

LAUREL MESSENGER. see GENEALOGY AND HERALDRY

LAW AND HISTORY REVIEW. see LAW

974 US
LEGACY (HERKIMER); annals of Herkimer County. q. $11 to non-members; members $9. Herkimer County Historical Society, 400 North Main St., Herkimer, NY 13350. TEL 315-866-6413. Ed. Jane Dieffenbacher. circ. 625.
Description: Contains popular articles about the New York county's history.

HISTORY — HISTORY OF NORTH AND SOUTH AMERICA

974.7   US
LEHIGH COUNTY HISTORICAL SOCIETY. PROCEEDINGS. 1906. biennial. $15. Lehigh County Historical Society, Old Court House, Hamilton at 5th, Allentown, PA 18101. TEL 610-435-4664. FAX 610-435-9812. Ed. Mahlon H. Hellerich. cum.index. circ. 1,500. (back issues avail.) **Document type:** proceedings.
    Description: Information on local history and architecture.

971   CN   ISSN 0838-7249
LETHBRIDGE HISTORICAL SOCIETY NEWLETTER. 1967. bi-m. Can.$8.50. Lethbridge Historical Society, P.O. Box 974, Lethbridge, Alta. T1J 4A2, Canada. bk.rev.; bibl. circ. 300. (back issues avail.) **Document type:** newsletter.
    Formerly: Historical Society of Alberta Newsletter (ISSN 0382-9812)
    Description: Covers items of local interest.

974.7   US   ISSN 0895-500X
LEWIS COUNTY HISTORICAL SOCIETY JOURNAL. 1967. a. $3 to non-members. Lewis County Historical Society, High St., Box 277, Lyons Falls, NY 13368. TEL 315-348-8089. Ed. Vivian Smith. bk.rev. circ. 700. (back issues avail.)
    Description: Covers local history.

LIBRARIES & CULTURE. see *LIBRARY AND INFORMATION SCIENCES*

974 020   US   ISSN 0734-3698
Z733.L734
LIBRARY COMPANY OF PHILADELPHIA. OCCASIONAL MISCELLANY. 1977. irreg. (2-3/yr.). free. Library Company of Philadelphia, 1314 Locust St., Philadelphia, PA 19107. TEL 215-546-3181. FAX 215-546-5167. Ed. John C. Van Horne. circ. 2,000. (back issues avail.) **Document type:** newsletter.

LINCOLN COUNTY TENNESSEE PIONEERS. see *GENEALOGY AND HERALDRY*

973   US   ISSN 0024-3671
E457
LINCOLN HERALD; magazine of Lincoln and the Civil War. 1901. q. $20. Lincoln Memorial University, Abraham Lincoln Museum, Harrogate, TN 37752. TEL 615-869-3611. Ed. Thomas R. Turner. adv.; bk.rev.; illus.; index, cum.index. circ. 1,173. (also avail. in microform from UMI; back issues avail.) **Indexed:** Amer.Hist.& Life, Hist.Abstr.
    —UnCover; UMI.
    Formerly (until 1938): Mountain Herald.
    Description: Covers research in the field of Lincolniana and the Civil War and the promotion of Lincoln ideals in American education.

979 355   US
LINCOLN MEMORIAL ASSOCIATION NEWSLETTER. 1971. q. $10. Lincoln Memorial Association, 125 W. Vine St., Redlands, CA 92373. TEL 909-798-7566. Eds. Don McCue, Christie Hammond. bk.rev.; bibl.; illus. circ. 250. (looseleaf format; back issues avail.) **Document type:** newsletter.
    Description: Lists events and contains research pertaining to recent acquisitions of the association, which is dedicated to increasing understanding of Abraham Lincoln and the Civil War.

974   US
LIVING HISTORIAN. 1987. q. (Living History Association, Inc.) Historical Supply Co., Box 578, Wilmington, VT 05363-0578. Ed. James Dassatti.

976.4   US   ISSN 0361-3577
F392.P17
LOBLOLLY.* 1973. q. $5. Loblolly Inc., Box 189, Gary, TX 75643. Ed. Annette Davis. adv.; bk.rev.; illus. circ. 1,500.

976   US   ISSN 0898-8056
LOCUS (DENTON); an historical journal of regional perspectives on national topics. 1988. 2/yr. $8 to individuals; institutions $12; foreign $20. University of North Texas Press, Journals Division, Box 13856, Denton, TX 76203. TEL 817-565-2142. Eds. Randolph B. Campbell, Donald E. Chipman. adv.; bk.rev. circ. 300.

974.7   US   ISSN 0024-628X
F127.L8
LONG ISLAND FORUM. 1938. q. $20 for 2 yrs. to non-members; members $8. Friends for Long Island's Heritage, 1864 Muttontown Rd., Syosset, NY 11791. TEL 516-571-7600. FAX 516-571-7623. (Or: 55 Cold Spring Hills Rd., Huntington, NY 11743) Ed. Richard F. Welch. adv.; bk.rev.; charts; illus.; index. circ. 3,000. (also avail. in microform from UMI) **Indexed:** Amer.Hist.& Life, Hist.Abstr.
    —UMI.
    Description: Explores the island's unique environment; interprets the history of its communities, people, industries, social customs and natural surroundings.

973   US   ISSN 0898-7084
LONG ISLAND HISTORICAL JOURNAL. 1988. s-a. $15. SUNY at Stony Brook, Department of History, Stony Brook, NY 11794-4348. TEL 516-632-7500. FAX 516-632-7367. Ed. Roger Wunderlich. adv.; bk.rev. circ. 800. (back issues avail.) **Indexed:** Amer.Hist.& Life, Hist.Abstr. **Document type:** academic/scholarly publication, abstracting/indexing.
    Description: Covers social, political, economic, and cultural history of Long Island.

LOUISIANA ARCHIVES AND MANUSCRIPTS ASSOCIATION. NEWSLETTER. see *LIBRARY AND INFORMATION SCIENCES*

976.3   US   ISSN 0024-6816
F366
LOUISIANA HISTORY. 1960. q. $25. Louisiana Historical Association, Box 42808, Lafayette, LA 70504. TEL 318-231-6871. Ed. Carl A. Brasseux. adv. contact: Glenn R. Conrad. bk.rev.; bibl.; illus.; index, cum.index. circ. 1,400. (back issues avail.) **Indexed:** Amer.Hist.& Life, Hist.Abstr.
    —BLDSC (5296.080000); Faxon; UnCover.
    Description: Historical review of Louisiana with the French and Spanish in the lower Mississippi Valley.

976.3   US
LOUISIANA HISTORY QUARTERLY NEWSLETTER. q. $25. Louisiana Historical Association, Box 42808, Lafayette, LA 70504. TEL 318-231-6871. Ed. Glenn Conrad.

970   US
LOWER CAPE FEAR HISTORICAL SOCIETY. BULLETIN. 1957. 3/yr. membership. Lower Cape Fear Historical Society, Box 813, Wilmington, NC 28402. TEL 919-762-0492. Ed. Susan T. Block. bk.rev. circ. 800. **Document type:** bulletin.
    Formerly (until 1989): Lower Cape Fear Historical Society. Journal.
    Description: Covers regional history.

973   US
LOYAL LEGION HISTORICAL JOURNAL. q. $10. Military Order of the Loyal Legion of the U S, Memorial Fund, 1805 Pine St., Philadelphia, PA 19103. TEL 414-263-3200. FAX 414-227-4152. Ed. Thomas P. Curtis. bk.rev.; illus. circ. 1,200. (tabloid format) **Document type:** academic/scholarly publication.
    Description: Includes articles on the Civil War and life of Lincoln, as well as MOLLUS and DOLLUS news.

929   CN   ISSN 0047-5149
F1058
LOYALIST GAZETTE. 1963. s-a. Can.$12.50 (outside US and Canada US$15). United Empire Loyalists' Association of Canada, Dominion Office, The George Brown House, 50 Baldwin St., Toronto, ON M5T 1L4, Canada. TEL 416-591-1783. FAX 416-591-1783. Ed. D.K. Dorward. bk.rev.; illus.; cum.index: 1963-1990. circ. 3,500. (also avail. in microfiche from UMI) **Indexed:** Amer.Hist.& Life, Hist.Abstr.
    Description: Contains information on UEL's activities, historical articles and reports from Association branches in Canada.

LUTHER FAMILY NEWSLETTER; devoted to the interest of the descendants of Captain John Luther, Mass. Bay Colony 1630. see *GENEALOGY AND HERALDRY*

LUTHERAN HISTORICAL CONFERENCE. ESSAYS AND REPORTS. see *RELIGIONS AND THEOLOGY — Protestant*

970   US   ISSN 0887-543X
LYCOMING COUNTY HISTORICAL SOCIETY JOURNAL. 1955. a. $25 membership. Lycoming County Historical Society, 858 W. Fourth St., Williamsport, PA 17701. TEL 717-326-3326. adv.; circ. 1,200 (controlled). (back issues avail.)
    Description: Covers history and folklore relevant to north-central Pennsylvania. Includes articles detailing information from 10,000 BC to present day.

980   US
M A L A S FORUM. 1962. q. $10 to members; institutions $10. Midwest Association for Latin American Studies, c/o Robin Montgomery, 1017 Claremont, Weatherford, OK 73096. Ed. Jack W. Hopkins. adv.; bk.rev.; bibl. circ. 1,000. (processed)
    Former titles (until Oct. 1989): M A L A S Noticias; M A L A S Newsletter.
    Description: Association newsletter, featuring articles, thought pieces and news of forthcoming events.

M H Q: THE QUARTERLY JOURNAL OF MILITARY HISTORY. see *MILITARY*

974.4   US   ISSN 0024-8185
F61
M H S MISCELLANY. N. 1955. 4/yr. free. Massachusetts Historical Society, 1154 Boylston St., Boston, MA 02215. TEL 617-536-1608. FAX 617-859-0074. Ed. Conrad E. Wright. circ. 3,500. **Document type:** newsletter.
    Description: Newsletter of society activities. Includes articles on historical topics relating to society's holdings.

MCNEESE REVIEW. see *LITERATURE*

974   US
MADISON COUNTY HERITAGE. 1977. a. $3. Madison County Historical Society, 435 Main St., Box 415, Oneida, NY 13421. TEL 315-363-4136. Ed.Bd. bk.rev.; cum.index every 5 yrs. circ. 500.
    Description: Publishes articles on New York State persons, industries, and events of historical interest.

970   GW   ISSN 0170-2513
F596
MAGAZIN FUER AMERIKANISTIK; Zeitschrift fuer Amerikanische Geschichte. 1977. q. DM.28. Verlag fuer Amerikanistik, Rebbelstieg 37, Postfach 1332, 2270 Wyk, Germany. TEL 04681-3112. FAX 04681-3258. Ed. Dietmar Kuegler. adv.; bk.rev. circ. 2,000.
    Description: Covers the history of North American Indians, and westward expansion of European settlers.

975   US   ISSN 0076-2342
F232
MAGAZINE OF ALBEMARLE COUNTY HISTORY. 1940. a. $4.50 to libraries. Albemarle County Historical Society, Publications Committee, 200 Second St., N.E., Charlottesville, VA 22902. TEL 804-296-1492. Ed. Dorothy Twohig. bk.rev.; cum.index: vols. 1-20 (1940-1962). circ. 900. (back issues avail.) **Indexed:** Amer.Hist.& Life, Hist.Abstr. **Document type:** academic/scholarly publication.
    Description: Contains articles and edited primary source materials relating to the history of the county, which was important in the early settlement of central Virginia and home to Thomas Jefferson and other distinguished Americans.

974   US
MAIL CALL; the most stirring newsletter for Civil War enthusiasts. 1990. bi-m. $24.95. Box 5031, S. Hackensack, NJ 07606. Ed. Anna Pansini; Pub. Chris Jackson. adv.; bk.rev. circ. 500. **Document type:** newsletter.
    Description: Presents excerpts from letters, journals and memoirs written by soldiers and their families during the Civil War era.

974   US   ISSN 0163-1152
F19
MAINE HISTORICAL SOCIETY QUARTERLY. 1961. q. $30. Maine Historical Society, 485 Congress St., Portland, ME 04101. TEL 207-744-1822. Ed. Richard W. Judd. adv.; bk.rev. circ. 2,000. **Indexed:** Amer.Hist.& Life, Hist.Abstr. **Document type:** academic/scholarly publication.
    —BLDSC (5352.294000); UnCover.
    Formerly (until 1977): Maine Historical Society. Newsletter (ISSN 0464-5820)

HISTORY — HISTORY OF NORTH AND SOUTH AMERICA

971   CN   ISSN 0226-5036
MANITOBA HISTORICAL SOCIETY. NEWSLETTER. 1969. 6/yr. membership. Manitoba Historical Society, 470-167 Lombard Ave., Winnipeg, MB R3B 0T6, Canada. TEL 204-947-0559. circ. 900. (back issues avail.) **Document type:** newsletter.
  Description: Covers information of interest to members regarding programs, field trips, dinners, and events.

971   CN   ISSN 0226-5044
MANITOBA HISTORY. 1980. s-a. Can.$18.50 (Can.$20.50 to USA; elsewhere Can.$22.50). Manitoba Historical Society, 470-167 Lombard Ave., Winnipeg, MB R3B 0T6, Canada. TEL 204-947-0559. Eds. Morris Mott, Bob Coutts. bk.rev.; film rev.; play rev.; illus. circ. 1,000. (back issues avail.) **Indexed:** Amer.Hist.& Life, CMI, Hist.Abstr.

971   CN   ISSN 0076-3896
MANITOBA RECORD SOCIETY. PUBLICATIONS. (Text in English; occasionally French) 1965. a. Can.$30. Manitoba Record Society, Fletcher Argue Bldg., Rm. 401, University of Manitoba, Winnipeg, MB R3T 2N2, Canada. FAX 204-275-5781. Ed. Debra Lindsay. circ. 1,000.

973   US
MANITOWOC COUNTY HISTORICAL SOCIETY. OCCUPATIONAL MONOGRAPHS. 1967. a. $12. Manitowoc County Historical Society, Box 574, Manitowoc, WI 54221-0574. TEL 414-684-4445. circ. 1,000. **Document type:** monographic series.
  Description: Concerns local history.

MAPLINE. see GEOGRAPHY

986.6 572   EC
MARKA INSTITUTO DE HISTORIA Y ANTROPOLOGIA ANDINA. MEMORIA. 1990. a. $15. Marka Instituto de Historia y Antropologia Andina, Av. 12 de Octubre 959 y Roca, Casilla 17-03-262, Quito, Ecuador. TEL 503640. Ed. Cristobal Landazuri N. adv.; bk.rev.

976   US
MARSHALL COUNTY HISTORICAL QUARTERLY. 1970. q. $10. Marshall County, Tennessee, Historical Society, c/o Mrs. Knox Bigham, 224 Third Ave. N., Lewisburg, TN 37091. Ed. Foster Nicholas. bk.rev. circ. 310.

MARTIN LUTHER KING, JR. MEMORIAL STUDIES IN RELIGION, CULTURE AND SOCIAL DEVELOPMENT. see RELIGIONS AND THEOLOGY

975.2   US   ISSN 0025-4258
F176   CODEN: MDHMDP
MARYLAND HISTORICAL MAGAZINE. 1906. q. $20 (foreign $35). Maryland Historical Society, 201 W. Monument St., Baltimore, MD 21201. TEL 410-685-3750. Ed. Robert J. Brugger. adv.; bk.rev.; charts; illus.; index. circ. 5,300. (also avail. in microform from KTO,MIM,WWS; reprint service avail.) **Indexed:** Amer.Hist.& Life, Geneal.Per.Ind., Hist.Abstr. **Document type:** academic/scholarly publication.
  —Faxon; UnCover; CASDDS.
  Incorporates: Maryland Magazine of Genealogy (ISSN 0191-6505)

975.2   US
MARYLAND HISTORICAL SOCIETY. NEWS AND NOTES. 1943; N.S. 1972. bi-m. $4. Maryland Historical Society, 201 W. Monument St., Baltimore, MD 21201. TEL 410-685-3750. Ed. Paula Dozier. illus. circ. 6,000. **Document type:** newsletter.
  Formerly: Maryland History Notes (ISSN 0025-4266)
  Description: Features exhibitions and information on seminars, events and general activities of the museum and library.

970   US   ISSN 0076-4981
F61
MASSACHUSETTS HISTORICAL SOCIETY. PROCEEDINGS. 1859. a. $30. Massachusetts Historical Society, 1154 Boylston St., Boston, MA 02215. TEL 617-536-1608. FAX 617-859-0074. (Dist. by: Northeastern University Press, Box 6525, Ithaca, NY 14851) Ed. Conrad E. Wright. circ. 750. **Indexed:** Abstr.Engl.Stud., Amer.Hist.& Life, Arts & Hum.Cit.Ind., Curr.Cont., Hist.Abstr. **Document type:** proceedings.
  —BLDSC (6755.600000); UnCover.
  Description: Scholarly historical articles and proceedings of society meetings.

973   US   ISSN 0883-3680
E179.5
MATERIAL CULTURE. 1968. 3/yr. $20. Pioneer America Society, c/o Dr. Charles F. Calkins, Department of Geography, Carroll College, Waukesha, WI 53186. (Subscr. to: Frank Ainsley, Department of Earth Sciences, University of North Carolina at Wilmington, Wilmington, NC 28403-3297) Ed. William D. Walters. adv.; bk.rev.; charts; illus.; index. circ. 700. (also avail. in microform from UMI; reprint service avail. from UMI) **Indexed:** Amer.Hist.& Life, Avery Ind.Archit.Per., Geo.Abstr., Hist.Abstr., M.L.A.
  —Faxon.
  Formerly (until 1984): Pioneer America (ISSN 0032-0005)

MATTANAWCOOK OBSERVER; a magazine of local history and genealogy of Lincoln, Penobscot County, Maine and the surrounding towns. see GENEALOGY AND HERALDRY

MAYFLOWER QUARTERLY; a journal of family history in colonial New England. see GENEALOGY AND HERALDRY

978   US
MEADE COUNTY HISTORIAN. 1974. a. Meade County Historical Society, c/o Ora Fletcher, Pres., Box 336, Meade, KS 67864. TEL 316-873-2359. Ed. W.P. Bunyan. circ. 1,500. (looseleaf format)

MEETING GROUND. see ETHNIC INTERESTS

981   BL
MEMORIA E HISTORIA. irreg., no.2, 1982. Livraria Editora Ciencias Humanas, Rua 7 de Abril, 264 Subsolo B-Sala 5, Sao Paulo, Brazil.

979.4   US   ISSN 0025-9268
MENDOCINO COUNTY HISTORICAL SOCIETY. NEWSLETTER. 1962. 4/yr. $7.50 individual membership. Mendocino County Historical Society, 603 W. Perkins St., Ukiah, CA 95482. TEL 707-462-6969. adv.; bk.rev.; abstr. circ. 800. (looseleaf format) **Document type:** newsletter.
  Description: Covers Mendocino County history, its people, places and events.

MENNONITE FAMILY HISTORY. see GENEALOGY AND HERALDRY

MENNONITE HISTORICAL BULLETIN. see RELIGIONS AND THEOLOGY — Other Denominations And Sects

974   US
MERCER COUNTY HERITAGE. q. Mercer County Historical Society, 119 S. Pitt St., Mercer, PA 16137. Ed. Robert Olson.
  Formerly: Mercer County Historical Society Newsletter.

972 320   CR
MESOAMERICA. 1982. m. $39.50 to individuals; institutions $70; students and seniors $28.50. Institute for Central American Studies, Apdo. 300, 1002 San Jose, Costa Rica. TEL 27-9928. FAX 506-24-8910. Ed. Linda Holland. bk.rev. circ. 1,000. (back issues avail.) **Indexed:** HR Rep.
  Description: Provides news and analysis of Central America.

MEXICAN STUDIES/ESTUDIOS MEXICANOS. see HUMANITIES: COMPREHENSIVE WORKS

972   MX   ISSN 0185-1926
F1203
MEXICO. ARCHIVO GENERAL DE LA NACION. BOLETIN.* 1977. q. Mex.$360($24) Archivo General de la Nacion, Apdo. Postal 1999, 06010 Mexico, D.F., Mexico. adv.; bibl.; illus.; index. circ. 1,500. (back issues avail.) **Indexed:** Amer.Hist.& Life, Hist.Abstr.
  —BLDSC (2160.150000).

MIAMI MEANDERINGS. see GENEALOGY AND HERALDRY

977   US   ISSN 0439-237X
MICHIGAN HISTORICAL REVIEW (MT. PLEASANT). 1957. s-a. $12.50 (foreign $15). Clarke Historical Library, Central Michigan University, Mt. Pleasant, MI 48859. TEL 517-774-6567. FAX 517-774-4499. (Co-sponsor: Historical Society of Michigan) Ed. Carol Devens. adv.: B&W page $175; adv. contact: Carol Riddle. bk.rev.; illus. circ. 4,800. **Indexed:** Amer.Hist.& Life, Arts & Hum.Cit.Ind., Curr.Cont., Environ.Abstr., Hist.Abstr., Mich.Mag.Ind. **Document type:** academic/scholarly publication.
  —BLDSC (5755.126000).
  Formerly (until vol.12, no.1, 1986): Great Lakes Review (ISSN 0360-1846)
  Description: Articles related to Michigan's political, economic, social and cultural history.
  Refereed Serial

977.4   US
MICHIGAN HISTORY MAGAZINE. 1917. bi-m. $12.95. Department of State, Bureau of History, 717 W. Allegan, Lansing, MI 48918-1805. TEL 517-373-3703. FAX 517-373-0851. (Co-sponsor: Michigan Historical Commission) Ed. Roger L. Rosentreter. bk.rev.; charts; illus.; index, cum.index. circ. 37,500. (also avail. in microform from UMI,PMC; reprint service avail. from UMI,KTO) **Indexed:** Amer.Hist.& Life, Hist.Abstr., Mich.Mag.Ind. **Document type:** consumer publication.
  —UnCover; UMI.
  Formerly: Michigan History (ISSN 0026-2196)
  Description: Examines every facet of Michigan's varied past.

980   US   ISSN 0076-8189
MICHIGAN STATE UNIVERSITY. LATIN AMERICAN STUDIES CENTER. MONOGRAPH SERIES. irreg. price varies. Michigan State University, Latin American Studies Center, 206 International Center, E. Lansing, MI 48824. TEL 517-353-1690. (reprint service avail. from UMI) **Document type:** monographic series.

980   US   ISSN 0076-8200
MICHIGAN STATE UNIVERSITY. LATIN AMERICAN STUDIES CENTER. RESEARCH REPORTS. 1968. irreg. price varies. Michigan State University, Latin American Studies Center, 206 International Center, E. Lansing, MI 48824. TEL 517-353-1690. (reprint service avail. from UMI)

970   US   ISSN 0026-2927
MID-AMERICA (CHICAGO); an historical review. 1918. 3/yr. $15 (foreign $16) (effective 1994). Loyola University of Chicago, Department of History, 6525 Sheridan Rd., Chicago, IL 60626. TEL 708-508-2230. Ed. William J. Galush. adv.; charts; illus.; index. circ. 600. (also avail. in microfilm from UMI; reprint service avail. from UMI) **Indexed:** Abstr.Engl.Stud., Amer.Hist.& Life, Bk.Rev.Ind. (1980-), Cath.Ind., Child.Bk.Rev.Ind. (1980-), Hist.Abstr., Hum.Ind. **Document type:** academic/scholarly publication.
  —BLDSC (5761.313000); UnCover; UMI.
  Refereed Serial

976   US
MIDDLE TENNESSEE CROSSROADS.* 1981. 3/yr. $10. 6435 Audaily Covington Rd., College Grove, TN 37046.

977   US
MIDDLETON AREA HISTORICAL SOCIETY. NEWSLETTER. no.17, 1977. q. membership. Middleton Area Historical Society, 7426 Hubbard Ave., Middleton, WI 53562. Ed. Sylvia Dennis. **Document type:** newsletter.

975   US   ISSN 0540-0694
MILFORD HISTORICAL SOCIETY NEWSLETTER. 1963. s-a. membership. Milford Historical Society, Box 352, Milford, DE 19963. TEL 302-422-3702. Ed. David W. Kenton. circ. 300. **Document type:** newsletter.

HISTORY — HISTORY OF NORTH AND SOUTH AMERICA

975 355 US ISSN 0889-7328
D25
MILITARY HISTORY. 1984. bi-m. $19.95 (foreign $25.95). Empire Press, 602 S. King St., Ste. 300, Leesburg, VA 22075. TEL 703-771-9400. FAX 703-777-4627. (Subscr. to: Box 417, Mt. Morris, IL 61054-8021. TEL 800-435-9610) Ed. C. Brian Kelley. adv.; bk.rev. circ. 200,000.
  Description: Brings land, naval and air battles to life - from ancient history to modern times. Features include personality profiles, espionage, weaponry, historic travel and interviews.

976 355 US ISSN 1071-2011
F381
MILITARY HISTORY OF THE WEST. 1961. 2/yr. $8 to individuals; institutions $12; foreign $20. University of North Texas Press, Journals Division, Box 13856, Denton, TX 76203. TEL 817-565-2142. Eds. Richard Lowe, Ronald Marcello. adv.; bk.rev.; bibl.; charts; illus.; index. circ. 500. **Indexed:** Amer.Hist.& Life, Hist.Abstr.
  —UnCover.
  Former titles (until 1993): Military History of the Southwest (ISSN 0898-8064); (until 1989): Mitary History of Texas and the Southwest (ISSN 0047-7389); (until 1971): Texas Military History.
  Description: Deals with military affairs in the southwestern United States.

974 US
MILTON CHRONICLES. 1955. q. membership. Historical Society of Battle Creek, Kimball House Museum, 196 Capital Ave., N.E., Battle Creek, MI 49017. TEL 616-965-2613. FAX 616-966-2495. Ed. Diane Beckley. circ. 500. **Indexed:** HR Rep. **Document type:** newsletter.
  Formerly (until 1991): Up-To-Date (ISSN 0502-7179)

977.5 US ISSN 0163-7622
F587.M6
MILWAUKEE HISTORY. 1978. q. $25 membership. Milwaukee County Historical Society., 910 N. Third St., Milwaukee, WI 53203. TEL 414-273-8288. Eds. Ralph M. Aderman, Kathleen M. O'Hara. illus. circ. 1,100. **Indexed:** Amer.Hist.& Life, Hist.Abstr.
  Formerly: Milwaukee County Historical Society. Historical Messenger (ISSN 0361-1671)

973 AT ISSN 0310-3471
MINIE NEWS. 1972. 12/yr. $25 (effective 1993). American Civil War Round Table of Australia, c/o Barry Crompton, 14 Sunlight Cres., E. Brighton, Vic. 3187, Australia. TEL 061-3-592-4968. Eds. Barry J. Crompton, Stuart P. Duff. adv.; bk.rev. circ. 100. **Indexed:** Aus.P.A.I.S. **Document type:** newsletter.

977.6 US ISSN 0026-5497
F601
MINNESOTA HISTORY. 1915. q. $15. Minnesota Historical Society, 345 Kellogg Blvd, W., St. Paul, MN 55102-1906. TEL 612-297-4462. Ed. Anne R. Kaplan. bk.rev.; illus.; cum.index vols.1-40. circ. 10,000. (also avail. in microform from MIM,UMI; back issues avail.) **Indexed:** Amer.Hist.& Life, Hist.Abstr.
  —UnCover; UMI. CCC.
  Description: Articles and documents on all phases of Minnesota's history.

973 US
MINNESOTA HISTORY SOCIETY. MEMBER NEWS. 1959. m. membership. Minnesota Historical Society, 345 Kellogg Blvd., W., St. Paul, MN 55102-1906. TEL 612-296-6126. Ed. Brenda Kramer. **Document type:** newsletter.
  Formerly (until 1992): Minnesota History News (ISSN 0544-358X)
  Description: Covers news and events of the Society.

974 255 US ISSN 0738-7237
MIRROR (LANCASTER). 1969. bi-m. membership. Lancaster Mennonite Historical Society, 2215 Mill Stream Rd., Lancaster, PA 17602-1499. TEL 717-393-9745. Ed. Carolyn C. Wenger. illus. circ. 9,300. **Document type:** newsletter.
  Description: Newsletter on the collections, activities of, and individuals involved with the society.

MISSIQUOI HISTORICAL SOCIETY REPORTS. see GENEALOGY AND HERALDRY

700 976 720 US
MISSISSIPPI HISTORY NEWSLETTER. 1959. m. free. Department of Archives and History, Box 571, Jackson, MS 39205. TEL 601-359-6850. FAX 601-359-6905. Ed. Chrissy Wilson. circ. 7,000. (looseleaf format; back issues avail.) **Document type:** newsletter.
  Description: Events and books relating to Mississippi history, art and literature.

977.8 US ISSN 0026-6582
F461
MISSOURI HISTORICAL REVIEW. 1906. q. $10. State Historical Society of Missouri, 1020 Lowry St., Columbia, MO 65201. TEL 314-882-7083. FAX 314-884-4950. Ed. James W. Goodrich. bk.rev.; bibl.; illus.; maps; index, cum.index: 1906-1931, 1931-1951, 1951-1976. circ. 8,000. (also avail. in microform from UMI; back issues avail.; reprint service avail. from UMI) **Indexed:** Amer.Hist.& Life, Hist.Abstr. **Document type:** academic/scholarly publication.
  —UnCover; UMI.
  Description: Contains articles and documents pertaining to the history of Missouri, its role in the exploration and settlement of the West, and its contributions to the nation's heritage.

908 US
MISTLETOE LEAVES. 1893. m. $15 to individuals; institutions $25 (includes Chronicles of Oklahoma). Oklahoma Historical Society, Historical Bldg., 2100 N. Lincoln, Oklahoma City, OK 73105. TEL 405-521-2491. FAX 405-525-3272. Ed. Bob L. Blackburn. circ. 6,450. (tabloid format) **Document type:** newsletter.

MODERN POSTAL HISTORY JOURNAL. see COMMUNICATIONS — Postal Affairs

MONKEYSHINES ON AMERICA. see CHILDREN AND YOUTH — For

MONKEYSHINES ON YOU!. see CHILDREN AND YOUTH — For

970 980 US
MONOGRAPHS IN INTERNATIONAL STUDIES: LATIN AMERICA SERIES. 1977. irreg. price varies. Ohio University, Center for International Studies, Burson House, 56 E. Union St., Athens, OH 45701. TEL 614-593-1155. (Subscr. to: Ohio University Press, Scott Quad., Athens, OH 45701) Ed. James L. Cobban. bibl.; charts; illus. circ. 500. (back issues avail.; reprint service avail. from UMI) **Indexed:** SSCI. **Document type:** monographic series.
  —BLDSC (6396.928300).
  Formerly: Papers in International Studies: Latin American Series (ISSN 0149-4880)

978.6 US ISSN 0026-9891
F726
MONTANA; the magazine of western history. 1951. q. $20. Montana Historical Society, 225 N. Roberts St., Box 201201, Helena, MT 59620-1201. TEL 406-444-4708. FAX 406-444-2696. Ed. Charles E. Rankin. adv.; bk.rev.; bibl.; illus.; index, cum.index: 1951-1990; circ. 10,000. (controlled). (also avail. in microfilm from UMI; back issues avail.; reprint service avail. from UMI) **Indexed:** Amer.Hist.& Life, Arts & Hum.Cit.Ind., Curr.Cont., Hist.Abstr.
  —UnCover; UMI.
  Description: Presents an interpretive approach to major developments in western history.

978.6 US ISSN 0047-7958
MONTANA POST. 1963. q. membership. Montana Historical Society, Box 201201, 225 N. Roberts St., Helena, MT 59620-1201. TEL 406-444-4708. FAX 406-444-2696. Ed. Marilyn Grant. adv.; illus. circ. 9,000. **Document type:** newsletter.
  Description: Contains news of the Society and announcements of interest to subscribers to Montana magazine.

MONUMENTA AMERICANA. see ARCHAEOLOGY

978 US ISSN 0146-8855
MOUNTAIN DIGGINGS. 1971. a. $3. Lake County Civic Center Association, Inc. (LCCCA), Box 962, Leadville, CO 80461. TEL 719-486-1878. Ed. Victoria Camp. circ. 400.
  Description: Covers the collection and preservation of local history.

979.6 US
MOUNTAIN LIGHT. 1958. q. membership. Idaho State Historical Society, 450 N. Fourth St., Boise, ID 83709. TEL 208-334-3428. FAX 208-334-3198. (Subscr. to: 210 Main St., Boise, ID 83709) Ed. Judith Austin. circ. 2,100.
  Description: Covers state and local historical and preservation activities.

MOUNTAIN TRAILS. see GEOGRAPHY

976 US
MT. JULIET - WEST WILSON HISTORICAL SOCIETY. CHRONICLE. 1979. q. $5. Mt. Juliet - West Wilson Historical Society, Box 337, Mt. Juliet, TN 37122. Ed. Mamie Worrell. bk.rev. circ. 100.

976 US ISSN 1054-1039
F457.M9
MUHLENBERG COUNTY HERITAGE. 1978. q. Muhlenberg County Heritage, Central City Public Library, Broad St., Central City, KY 42330.

MUSEUM NOTES (SPOKANE). see MUSEUMS AND ART GALLERIES

MUSEUM OF AFRICAN-AMERICAN HISTORY. NEWSLETTER. see ETHNIC INTERESTS

978 US ISSN 0027-4135
HD9944.U44
MUSEUM OF THE FUR TRADE QUARTERLY. 1965. q. $6. Museum of the Fur Trade, HC-74, Box 18, Chadron, NE 69337. TEL 308-432-3843. Ed. Charles E. Hanson Jr. bk.rev.; abstr.; illus.; cum.index; circ. 2,600 (controlled). **Indexed:** Amer.Hist.& Life, Hist.Abstr. **Document type:** academic/scholarly publication.
  —UnCover.
  Description: Devoted to original scholarly articles on the materials and methods of the North American fur trade.

980 860 UY ISSN 0077-2844
NARRATIVA LATINOAMERICANA.* irreg. Editorial Arca, Colonia 1263, Montevideo, Uruguay.

NATIONAL RAILWAY BULLETIN. see TRANSPORTATION — Railroads

974 US
NATIONAL SOCIETY FOR THE PRESERVATION OF COVERED BRIDGES NEWSLETTER. q. membership. National Society for the Preservation of Covered Bridges, Inc., c/o Mrs. Christine Ellsworth, Corr.Sec., 44 Cleveland Ave., Worcester, MA 01603. TEL 603-623-8406. Ed. Richard Roy. circ. 693. **Document type:** newsletter.

NATIONAL SOCIETY OF UNITED STATES DAUGHTERS OF 1812. NEWSLETTER. see GENEALOGY AND HERALDRY

978 US ISSN 0890-068X
NATIONAL TOMBSTONE EPITAPH; the historical journal of the old West. 1975. m. $12.50. Tombstone Epitaph Corp., Box 1880, Tombstone, AZ 85638. TEL 602-457-2211. Ed. Wallace E. Clayton. adv.; bk.rev.; charts; illus.; tr.lit. circ. 8,600. (tabloid format; back issues avail.)
  Formerly: Tombstone Epitaph National Edition.

NAVAL HISTORY. see MILITARY

978.2 US ISSN 0028-1859
F661
NEBRASKA HISTORY. 1918. q. membership. Nebraska State Historical Society, 1500 R St., Box 82554, Lincoln, NE 68501. TEL 402-471-3270. Ed. James E. Potter. bk.rev.; illus.; maps; index, cum.index: 1918-1958, 1959-1979. circ. 4,500. (also avail. in microfilm from UMI,BHP; back issues avail.; reprint service avail. from UMI) **Indexed:** Amer.Hist.& Life, Hist.Abstr.
  —BLDSC (6068.210000); UnCover; UMI.

970 US ISSN 0199-9664
F661
NEBRASKA STATE HISTORICAL SOCIETY. HISTORICAL NEWSLETTER. 1947. m. membership. Nebraska State Historical Society, 1500 R St., Box 82554, Lincoln, NE 68501. TEL 402-471-3270. Ed. Robert Selzer. illus. circ. 4,500. (looseleaf format) **Document type:** newsletter.

HISTORY — HISTORY OF NORTH AND SOUTH AMERICA

979.3   US   ISSN 0047-9462
F836
NEVADA HISTORICAL SOCIETY QUARTERLY. 1957. q. $25. Nevada Historical Society, 1650 N. Virginia St., Reno, NV 89503. TEL 702-688-1190. Ed. William D. Rowley. adv.; bk.rev.; illus.; index. circ. 1,650. (processed; also avail. in microfilm from UMI; reprint service avail. from UMI) **Indexed:** Amer.Hist.& Life, CERDIC, Hist.Abstr.
—UnCover; UMI.
Description: Scholarly and popular history of Nevada and the West.

971   CN
NEW BRUSWICK HISTORICAL SOCIETY NEWSLETTER. q. membership. New Brunswick Historical Society, 120 Union St., St. John, N.B. E2L 1A3, Canada. Ed. Willard F. Merritt. **Document type:** newsletter.

974   US   ISSN 0734-2802
NEW CANAAN HISTORICAL SOCIETY ANNUAL. 1943. a. price varies. New Canaan Historical Society, 13 Oenoke Ridge, New Canaan, CT 06840. TEL 203-966-1776. circ. 1,000. (back issues avail.) **Document type:** academic/scholarly publication.

NEW ENGLAND HISTORICAL AND GENEALOGICAL REGISTER. see *GENEALOGY AND HERALDRY*

974   US
H1
NEW ENGLAND JOURNAL OF HISTORY. 1943. 3/yr. $15. New England History Teachers Association, Home Office, Bentley College, Waltham, MA 02254. Ed. James Weland. adv.; bk.rev. circ. 800. (also avail. in microfilm from UMI; reprint service avail. from UMI) **Indexed:** Amer.Hist.& Life, C.I.J.E., Hist.Abstr. **Document type:** academic/scholarly publication.
Former titles: New England Social Studies Bulletin (ISSN 0028-4912); N E H T A Newsletter (ISSN 0085-3933)
Description: Presents study and teaching methods.

NEW ENGLAND QUARTERLY; a historical review of New England life and letters. see *LITERATURE*

NEW GLEANINGS. see *MUSEUMS AND ART GALLERIES*

974   US
NEW HAMPSHIRE COMMITTEE FOR THE PROMOTION OF HISTORY. BULLETIN. 1980. a. $10. University of New Hampshire, New Hampshire Committee for the Promotion of History, Horton Social Science Center, Durham, NH 03824. Ed.Bd. adv. circ. 2,500.
Formerly: New Hampshire Committee for the Promotion of History. Newsletter.
Description: Historical articles and information on events and activities of the committee.

974.2   US
NEW HAMPSHIRE HISTORICAL SOCIETY NEWSLETTER. 1963. q. membership. New Hampshire Historical Society, 30 Park St., Concord, NH 03301. TEL 603-225-3381. **Document type:** newsletter.

974   US   ISSN 0548-4987
F91
NEW HAVEN COLONY HISTORICAL SOCIETY. JOURNAL. 1952. 2/yr. $15. New Haven Colony Historical Society, 114 Whitney Ave., New Haven, CT 06510. Ed. Lawrence Kenney. circ. 1,200.
Description: Covers historical and genealogical matters relating to the early settlement and subsequent history of New Haven, Connecticut and the surrounding area.

974.9   US   ISSN 0047-9772
NEW JERSEY HISTORICAL COMMISSION NEWSLETTER. 1970. m. (10/yr.). $10 (effective 1994). (Department of State) New Jersey Historical Commission, CN-305, Trenton, NJ 08625-0305. TEL 609-292-6062. FAX 609-633-8168. Ed. Lee R. Parks. bk.rev.; bibl.; illus. circ. 1,000. (back issues avail.) **Document type:** newsletter.

974.9   US   ISSN 0028-5757
F131
NEW JERSEY HISTORY; a magazine of New Jersey history. 1845. q. $15 to individuals; institutions $30. New Jersey Historical Society, 230 Broadway, Newark, NJ 07104. TEL 201-483-3939. Ed. Mark Edward Lender. adv.; bk.rev.; charts; illus.; index. circ. 3,000. (also avail. in microfilm from UMI,BHP; back issues avail.; reprint service avail. from UMI,KTO) **Indexed:** Amer.Hist.& Life, Hist.Abstr.
—UnCover; UMI.
Formerly: New Jersey Historical Society. Proceedings.

974.9   US   ISSN 0028-582X
NEW JERSEY MESSENGER. 1958. 6/yr. $25 membership. New Jersey Historical Society, 230 Broadway, Newark, NJ 07104. Ed. Robert B. Burnett.

978.9   US   ISSN 0028-6206
F791
NEW MEXICO HISTORICAL REVIEW. 1926. q. $24 to individuals; institutions $28. University of New Mexico, Mesa Vista 1013, Albuquerque, NM 87131. TEL 505-277-5839. FAX 505-277-6023. Ed. Robert Himmerich y Valencia. adv.; bk.rev.; bibl.; illus.; index, cum.index: v.1-15 (1926-1940), v.16-30 (1941-1955), v.31-45 (1956-1970), v.46-60 (1971-1985). circ. 1,300. (also avail. in microform from UMI,BHP; reprint service avail. from UMI) **Indexed:** A.I.C.P., Amer.Hist.& Life, Arts & Hum.Cit.Ind., Chic.Per.Ind., Curr.Cont., Hist.Abstr. **Document type:** academic/scholarly publication.
—Faxon; UnCover; UMI.

976   US
NEW PERSPECTIVES ON THE SOUTH. 1979. irreg., latest 1990. price varies. University Press of Kentucky, 663 S. Limestone St., Lexington, KY 40508-4008. TEL 606-257-2951. FAX 606-257-2984. Ed. Charles P. Roland. (reprint service avail. from UMI)

975   US   ISSN 0548-6599
NEW RIVER NEWS. 1962. q. $10. Fort Lauderdale Historical Society, Box 14043, Fort Lauderdale, FL 33302. TEL 305-463-4431. bk.rev.; bibl. circ. 750.
Description: Presents news, informational articles, historical vignettes, and publications pertaining to Fort Lauderdale, Florida. Includes news on the members and activities of the city's historical society.

975   US
NEW SOUTH CAROLINA STATE GAZETTE. 1968. s-a. Department of Archives and History, 1430 Senate St., Box 11669, Capitol Sta., Columbia, SC 29211. TEL 803-734-8577. Ed. Judith M. Brimelow. bibl.; illus.; circ. 7,800 (paid).

975.4   US   ISSN 0887-4743
NEW WEST VIRGINIA HILLBILLY. 1957. m. $25. Leader Publishing Co. Inc., Box 430, Richwood, WV 26261. adv.; bk.rev.; bibl.; illus. circ. 5,000.
Formerly (until 1985): West Virginia Hillbilly (ISSN 0043-3241)

NEW YORK (CITY). MUSEUM OF THE CITY OF NEW YORK. ANNUAL REPORT. see *MUSEUMS AND ART GALLERIES*

974.7   US   ISSN 0146-437X
F116
NEW YORK HISTORY. 1919. q. $20. New York State Historical Association, Lake Rd., Box 800, Cooperstown, NY 13326. TEL 607-547-2508. Ed. Wendell Tripp. bk.rev.; illus.; index, cum.index every 10 yrs.: vols.1-66, 1919-1985 (in 6 vols.). circ. 2,850. (also avail. in microfilm from UMI) **Indexed:** Amer.Hist.& Life, Arts & Hum.Cit.Ind., Curr.Cont., Hist.Abstr., M.L.A. **Document type:** academic/scholarly publication.
—Faxon; UnCover; UMI.
Description: Articles relating to all aspects of the history of New York State.

NEW YORK STATE ARCHAEOLOGICAL ASSOCIATION. BULLETIN. see *ARCHAEOLOGY*

975   US
NEWBERRY COUNTY HISTORICAL SOCIETY. BULLETIN. 1970. s-a. $5. Newberry County Historical Society, c/o Prof. M. Foster Farley, Ed., Box 364, Newberry, SC 29108. circ. 200.

974.5   US   ISSN 0028-8918
F89.N5
NEWPORT HISTORY. 1912. q. $25 includes membership. Newport Historical Society, 82 Touro St., Newport, RI 02840. TEL 401-846-0813. FAX 401-846-1853. Ed. Ronald M. Potvin. bk.rev.; illus. circ. 1,300. (also avail. in microform from UMI; back issues avail.; reprint service avail. from UMI) **Indexed:** Amer.Hist.& Life, Hist.Abstr. **Document type:** academic/scholarly publication.
—UMI.
Description: Covers local and statewide history and culture.

NEWS FROM NATIVE CALIFORNIA. see *ETHNIC INTERESTS*

974 720   US
NEWSBRIEFS (PORTLAND). s-a. $25 membership. Greater Portland Landmarks, Inc., 165 State St., Portland, ME 04101. TEL 207-774-5561. **Document type:** newsletter.

970   US
NEWSLINE (KNOXVILLE). 1955. q. free with subscr. to Publications or Tennessee Ancestors. East Tennessee Historical Society, 500 W. Church, Knoxville, TN 37902-2505. TEL 615-544-5732. Ed. Cherel B. Henderson. bibl. circ. 1,200. **Indexed:** Amer.Hist.& Life, Hist.Abstr. **Document type:** newsletter.
Incorporates: Echoes from the East Tennessee Historical Society (ISSN 0422-2482); **Formerly:** Echoes.

NICARAGUA UPDATE. see *POLITICAL SCIENCE*

974 745.1   US
NINETEENTH CENTURY (WESTFIELD). 1986. q. membership. (Victorian Society in America) Foursquare Enterprises Inc., Box 2516, Westfield, NJ 07090. TEL 201-789-9219. FAX 201-789-3375. Ed. Richard O. Aichele. adv.; bk.rev. circ. 5,000.
Formerly (until Jan. 1990): Classic America.

977 387   US
NOR'EASTER (DULUTH). 1976. bi-m. $15. Lake Superior Marine Museum Association, Box 177, Duluth, MN 55802. TEL 218-727-2497. FAX 218-720-5270. Ed. Charles Patrick Labadie. bk.rev.; illus. circ. 600. (tabloid format; back issues avail.) **Document type:** newsletter.
Description: Articles on the historical and contemporary events affecting maritime commerce in the Upper Great Lakes, focusing especially on Lake Superior.

982   AG
NORTE. 1975 (third series). irreg. Consejo Provincial de Difusion Cultural, Departamento de Literatura, San Miguel de Tucuman, Argentina.

NORTH AMERICAN CULTURE. see *GEOGRAPHY*

NORTH AMERICAN REVIEW. see *LITERARY AND POLITICAL REVIEWS*

387.5   US
NORTH AMERICAN SOCIETY FOR OCEANIC HISTORY. NEWSLETTER. 1977. 3/yr. $15. North American Society for Oceanic History, Inc., c/o Program in Maritime History, East Carolina University, Greenville, NC 27858-4353. TEL 919-757-6097. Ed. Carl E. Swanson. bk.rev. circ. 250. **Document type:** newsletter.
Supersedes: North American Society for Oceanic History. Proceedings (ISSN 0198-7194)
Description: Offers short, informative articles for a college-level audience, covering recent scholarship, meetings and other items about maritime history.

NORTH AMERICAN SOCIETY FOR SPORT HISTORY. NEWSLETTER. see *SPORTS AND GAMES*

NORTH AMERICAN SOCIETY FOR SPORT HISTORY. PROCEEDINGS. see *SPORTS AND GAMES*

HISTORY — HISTORY OF NORTH AND SOUTH AMERICA

975.6 US ISSN 0029-2494
F251
NORTH CAROLINA HISTORICAL REVIEW. 1924. q. $30 includes Carolina Comments. Division of Archives and History, 109 E. Jones St., Raleigh, NC 27601-2807. TEL 919-733-7442. Eds. Jeffrey J. Crow, Kathleen B. Wyche. bk.rev.; illus.; maps; index, cum.index: 1924-1983. circ. 1,800. (also avail. in microfilm from UMI; back issues avail.; reprint service avail. from UMI) Indexed: Amer.Hist.& Life, Hist.Abstr., M.L.A.
—Faxon; UnCover; UMI.
Description: Contains documented articles on North Carolina and Southern history.

976 US
NORTH CAROLINA PRESERVATION. 1971. m. $30. Historic Preservation Foundation of North Carolina, Box 27644, Raleigh, NC 27611. TEL 919-832-3652. FAX 919-832-1651. Ed. J. Myrick Howard. adv.; bk.rev. circ. 3,200. **Document type:** newsletter.
Description: Covers historical preservation activities in North Carolina, especially those of the Historic Preservation Foundation, as well as listing historic properties for sale throughout the state.

974 US
NORTH CASTLE HISTORY. 1974. a. $5 (effective 1992). North Castle Historical Society, 440 Bedford Rd., Armonk, NY 10504. TEL 914-273-4510. Ed. Barbara S. Massi. bibl.; charts; illus. circ. 700. (back issues avail.) **Document type:** academic/scholarly publication.

974 US
NORTH COUNTRY NOTES. 1960. m. membership. Clinton County Historical Association, 48 Court St., Plattsburgh, NY 12901. TEL 518-561-0340. Ed. Helen Allan. circ. 450. (looseleaf format; back issues avail.) **Document type:** newsletter.
Description: News and views for members of the Clinton County Historical Association.

978.4 US ISSN 0029-2710
F631
NORTH DAKOTA HISTORY; journal of the Northern Plains. 1926. q. $30. State Historical Society of North Dakota, North Dakota Heritage Center, Bismarck, ND 58505. TEL 701-224-2799. FAX 701-224-3710. Ed. Janet Daley Lysengen. bk.rev.; illus. circ. 2,000. (also avail. in microform from UMI; reprint service avail. from UMI) **Indexed:** Amer.Hist.& Life, Biol.Abstr., Hist.Abstr. **Document type:** academic/scholarly publication.
—Faxon; UnCover; UMI.
Description: Contains items about the history and culture of North Dakota and the northern Great Plains.

381 US
NORTH DAKOTA HORIZONS. 1971. q. $15. Greater North Dakota Association, Box 2639, Bismark, ND 58502-2639. TEL 701-222-0929. FAX 701-222-1611. Ed. Lyle Halvorson. bk.rev. circ. 19,000. (back issues avail.) **Document type:** consumer publication.

NORTH GEORGIA JOURNAL. see *TRAVEL AND TOURISM*

974.9 US ISSN 0029-2850
F134
NORTH JERSEY HIGHLANDER. 1959. a. $6. North Jersey Highlands Historical Society, Box 248, Ringwood, NJ 07456. Ed. Ralph Colfax. bk.rev.; illus.; index. circ. 250. (reprint service avail. from UMI) **Indexed:** Amer.Hist.& Life, Hist.Abstr.

976 US ISSN 0739-005X
F369.N67a
NORTH LOUISIANA HISTORICAL ASSOCIATION. JOURNAL. 1952. 3/yr. $10. North Louisiana Historical Association, Box 6701, Shreveport, LA 71136. TEL 318-797-5337. Ed. Alan S. Thompson. bk.rev.; index; circ. 500 (controlled). (back issues avail.) **Indexed:** Amer.Hist.& Life, Hist.Abstr. **Document type:** academic/scholarly publication.

974 US ISSN 1053-0010
NORTH SOUTH TRADER'S CIVIL WAR; for Civil War collectors, relic hunters and historians. 1974. bi-m. $25 (foreign $30). Drawer 631, Orange, VA 22960. TEL 703-672-4845. Ed. Nancy Dearing Rossbacher. adv.; B&W page $370; trim 7 x 9 1/2. bk.rev.; film rev.; illus. circ. 5,000. **Document type:** consumer publication.
Formerly (until 1987): North South Trader.

976 929 US ISSN 1060-5568
F340
NORTHEAST MISSISSIPPI HISTORICAL AND GENEALOGICAL SOCIETY QUARTERLY. 1980. q. $15. Northeast Mississippi Historical and Genealogical Society, Box 434, Tupelo, MS 38802-0434. Ed. Martis D. Ramage, Jr. bk.rev.; circ. 350 (paid).

979 US ISSN 0160-9602
F841
NORTHEASTERN NEVADA HISTORICAL SOCIETY QUARTERLY. 1970. q. $10 (foreign $20). Northeastern Nevada Historical Society, Northeastern Nevada Museum, 1515 Idaho St., Elko, NV 89801. TEL 702-738-3418. Ed. Shawn Hall. bk.rev.; index. circ. 1,300. **Indexed:** Amer.Hist.& Life, Hist.Abstr. **Document type:** academic/scholarly publication.
Description: Contains historical items of local interest.

979 US ISSN 0272-1570
F851
NORTHWEST DISCOVERY; the journal of northwest history and natural history. 1980. irreg., vol.3, 1982. $15 for 4 nos. Northwest Press, 1439 E. Prospect St., Seattle, WA 98112. Ed. Harry M. Majors. **Indexed:** GeoRef.

NORTHWEST GEORGIA HISTORICAL & GENEALOGICAL QUARTERLY. see *GENEALOGY AND HERALDRY*

973 US ISSN 0078-1789
NORTHWEST HISTORICAL SERIES. 1923. irreg. price varies. Arthur H. Clark Co., Box 14707, Spokane, WA 99214. index. **Document type:** monographic series.

977.1 US ISSN 0029-3407
NORTHWEST OHIO QUARTERLY. 1929. q. $25. Maumee Valley Historical Society, c/o David Curtis Skaggs, Ed., Department of History, Bowling Green State University, Bowling Green, OH 43403. TEL 419-372-2030. (Subscr. to: Secretary, Maumee Valley Historical Society, 1031 River Rd., Maumee, OH 43537) adv.; bk.rev.; illus. circ. 500. **Indexed:** Amer.Hist.& Life, Hist.Abstr., M.L.A., Mich.Mag.Ind. **Document type:** academic/scholarly publication.
Description: Covers archaeological, architectural, intellectual, cultural, political and social history of Toledo and Northwest Ohio, and of the Old Northwest and Great Lakes regions.

900 325 US ISSN 0078-1967
NORWEGIAN-AMERICAN HISTORICAL ASSOCIATION. NEWSLETTER. 1934. irreg. free. Norwegian-American Historical Association, St. Olaf College, Northfield, MN 55057. TEL 507-663-3221. Ed. Lloyd Hustvedt. circ. 1,700. **Document type:** newsletter.

948 973 US ISSN 0085-4352
NORWEGIAN-AMERICAN HISTORICAL ASSOCIATION. TOPICAL STUDIES. 1971. irreg., vol.4, 1988. price varies. Norwegian-American Historical Association, St. Olaf College, Northfield, MN 55057. TEL 507-646-3221. Ed. Odd S. Lovoll. circ. 1,700. (reprint service avail. from UMI) **Document type:** monographic series.

900 US ISSN 0078-1975
NORWEGIAN-AMERICAN HISTORICAL ASSOCIATION. TRAVEL AND DESCRIPTION SERIES. 1926. irreg., vol.11, 1990. price varies. Norwegian-American Historical Association, St. Olaf College, Northfield, MN 55057. TEL 506-646-3221. Ed. Odd S. Lovoll. circ. 1,700. (reprint service avail. from UMI) **Document type:** academic/scholarly publication, monographic series.

900 US ISSN 0078-1983
E184.S2
NORWEGIAN-AMERICAN STUDIES. 1926. irreg., vol.33, 1992. $15. Norwegian-American Historical Association, St. Olaf College, Northfield, MN 55057. TEL 507-646-3221. Ed. Odd S. Lovoll. circ. 1,900. (also avail. in microform from UMI; reprint service avail. from UMI) **Indexed:** Amer.Hist.& Life, Hist.Abstr., M.L.A. **Document type:** academic/scholarly publication.
Formerly: Norwegian-American Studies and Records.

979 011 US ISSN 0886-7151
NOTICIAS DEL PUERTO DE MONTEREY. (Text mainly in English, some Spanish) 1957. q. $10. Monterey History and Art Association Ltd., 5 Custom House Plaza, Monterey, CA 93940. TEL 408-372-2608. FAX 408-655-3054. Ed.Bd. bibl.; illus.; index; circ. 1,800 (controlled).
Description: Features articles on Monterey history.

971 CN ISSN 0227-4752
F1036
NOVA SCOTIA HISTORICAL REVIEW. 1971. s-a. Can.$20($20) Public Archives of Nova Scotia, 6016 University Ave., Halifax, NS B3H 1W4, Canada. TEL 902-424-6085. FAX 902-424-0628. Ed. Barry Cahill. adv.; bk.rev. circ. 600. (also avail. in microform from UMI; reprint service avail. from UMI) **Document type:** academic/scholarly publication.
Formerly (until 1980): Nova Scotia Historical Quarterly (ISSN 0300-3728)

983 UK ISSN 0261-2909
NUEVA HISTORIA; revista de historia de Chile. (Text in Spanish) 1981. q. £8. (World University Service) Asociacion de Historiadores Chilenos (UK), c/o Institute of Latin American Studies, 31 Tavistock Sq., London WC1H 9HA, England. Ed. Leonardo Leon-Solis. adv.; bk.rev. circ. 300. **Indexed:** Amer.Hist.& Life (until 1985), Hist.Abstr. (until 1985).

973 US ISSN 1059-1125
E172
O A H NEWSLETTER. 1973. 4/yr. membership. Organization of American Historians, 112 N. Bryan St., Bloomington, IN 47408. TEL 812-855-7311. circ. 13,000. (also avail. in microform from UMI; reprint service avail. from UMI) **Document type:** newsletter.
—SWETS.
Formerly (until 1981): Organization of American Historians. Newsletter (ISSN 0196-3341)

980 US ISSN 0078-6403
F1402.A4
O A S. GENERAL SECRETARIAT. ANNUAL REPORT. 1960. a. $20. Organization of American States, General Secretariat, Department of Publications, 1889 F St., N.W., Washington, DC 20006. TEL 703-941-1617. (also avail. in microfiche from CIS) **Indexed:** IIS.

O I W COMMUNIQUE. (Order of the Indian Wars) see *MILITARY*

OCULI. see *ART*

971 800 CN
▼**OEUVRES ET AUTEURS.** 1994. irreg. price varies. University of Ottawa Press, 542 King Edward, Ottawa, ON K1N 6N5, Canada. TEL 613-564-2270. Ed. Robert Major. **Document type:** monographic series.
Description: Monographs of Quebecois and French-Canadian authors.

974 US
OFFICE FOR METROPOLITAN HISTORY. PLANS FILED. 1991. w. $520 (effective 1992). Office for Metropolitan History, 246 W. 80th St., New York, NY 10024. TEL 212-799-0520. FAX 212-799-0542. circ. 38.
Supersedes (in 1991): Office for Metropolitan History. Research and Remarks on Current Topics.

978.9 US ISSN 0732-3093
JK8030
OFFICIAL NEW MEXICO BLUE BOOK. 1882. biennial. free. Secretary of State, Executive Legislative Bldg., Santa Fe, NM 87503. TEL 505-827-3600. FAX 505-827-3634. Ed. Stephanie Gonzales. bibl.; charts; illus.; stat. circ. 3,000. **Document type:** government publication.
Former titles: New Mexico Blue Book (ISSN 0196-3929); Historical Blue Book of New Mexico.
Description: Covers the history and culture of New Mexico, including its different branches of government.

3000 HISTORY — HISTORY OF NORTH AND SOUTH AMERICA

977.1 US ISSN 0030-0934
F486
OHIO HISTORY. 1887. 2/yr. $15 to non-members; institutions $25; members $5. Ohio Historical Society, 1982 Velma Ave., Columbus, OH 43211. TEL 614-297-2332. Ed. Robert Daugherty. bk.rev.; bibl.; illus.; index. circ. 3,500. (also avail. in microform from UMI,PMC; microfiche from BHP; reprint service avail. from UMI) **Indexed:** Amer.Hist.& Life, Hist.Abstr. **Document type:** academic/scholarly publication.
—UMI.

977 US
OHIO SOUTHLAND. 1989. q. $9. Stephen Kelley, Ed. & Pub., Box 208, Seaman, OH 45679-0001. adv. circ. 1,020.
   Description: Focuses on the Appalachian heritage of Adams, Brown, Clermont and Highland counties in Ohio. Covers the area's history, natural history, archaeology and geneaology.

971 CN ISSN 0830-0739
OKANAGAN HISTORY; report. 1926. a. Can.$14.95. Okanagan Historical Society, P.O. Box 313, Vernon, BC V1T 6M3, Canada. Ed. Robert Cowan. bk.rev. circ. 1,500. (back issues avail.)
   Formerly (until 1984): Okangan Historical Society. Report (ISSN 0317-0691)

OKLAHOMA BAPTIST CHRONICLE. see *RELIGIONS AND THEOLOGY — Protestant*

917.66 US ISSN 0091-1054
F702.P74
OKLAHOMA PONTOTOC COUNTY QUARTERLY. Variant title: Pontotoc County Quarterly. 1969. q. $15. Pontotoc County Historical and Genealogical Society, 221 W. 16th St., Ada, OK 74820-7603. Ed. Patricia Smith. adv.; bk.rev. circ. 225.

OLD ABE'S NEWS. see *AGRICULTURE — Agricultural Equipment*

977 US ISSN 0196-7045
OLD FORT NEWS. 1936. s-a. $25. Allen County - Ft. Wayne Historical Society, 302 E. Berry St., Ft. Wayne, IN 46802. TEL 219-426-2882. Ed. Walter Font. circ. 1,500. **Document type:** academic/scholarly publication.
   Description: Covers history of northeast Indiana.

976 721 US ISSN 0276-3338
TJ859
OLD MILL NEWS. 1972. 4/yr. $12.50. Society for Preservation of Old Mills, 604 Ensley Dr., Rt. 29, Knoxville, TN 37920. Ed. Michael LaForest. adv.; bk.rev. circ. 2,000. **Indexed:** Avery Ind.Archit.Per. **Document type:** academic/scholarly publication.

977 US ISSN 0360-5531
F351
OLD NORTHWEST. 1975. q. $10 to individuals; institutions $15. Miami University, 302 Bachelor Hall, Oxford, OH 45056. TEL 513-529-5253. Ed. Robert R. Kettler. bk.rev. circ. 550. (also avail. in microform from UMI; back issues avail.; reprint service avail. from UMI) **Indexed:** Abstr.Engl.Stud., Amer.Hist.& Life (until 1992), Hist.Abstr. (until 1992), Hum.Ind., M.L.A., Mich.Mag.Ind.
—UMI. **CCC.**

974 US ISSN 0485-6724
F74.S93
OLD STURBRIDGE VISITOR. 1960. q. $25. (Friends of Old Sturbridge Village) Old Sturbridge Inc., Sturbridge, MA 01566. TEL 508-347-3362. FAX 508-347-9012. Ed. Holly Izard. circ. 11,300. **Indexed:** Amer.Hist.& Life, Hist.Abstr.
   Formerly: Rural Visitor.
   Description: Covers the history of everyday life in rural new England from the 1790s to the 1840s.

978 979 US ISSN 0030-2058
F591
OLD WEST. 1964. q. $7.95. Western Publications, 205 W. Seventh St., Ste. 202, Box 2107, Stillwater, OK 74076-2107. TEL 405-743-3373. FAX 405-743-3374. Ed. John Joerschke. illus. circ. 29,000. (back issues avail.)

974 US
OLD YORK ROAD HISTORICAL SOCIETY BULLETIN. 1937. a. membership. Old York Road Historical Society, c/o Jenkintown Library, York and Vista Rds., Jenkintown, PA 19046. TEL 215-884-0593. Ed. Suzanne M. Hilton. cum.index: 1937-1985; circ. 265 (controlled).
   Description: Covers the history of southeastern Montgomery County, PA.

900 US
ONIOTA. 1966. q. $20 includes membership. Oneida County Historical Society, 1608 Genessee St., Utica, NY 13502-5425. TEL 315-735-3642. FAX 315-732-0806. Ed. Douglas M. Preston. bk.rev. circ. 900. (looseleaf format; back issues avail.) **Document type:** newsletter.
   Description: Reports the Society's activities and other events of interest to members, and includes articles, excerpts from documents, notices of publications.

971 CN ISSN 0714-6736
ONTARIO HISTORICAL SOCIETY. BULLETIN. Key Title: O H S Bulletin. 1968. bi-m. membership. Ontario Historical Society, 34 Parkview Ave., Willowdale, ON M2N 3Y2, Canada. TEL 416-226-9011. FAX 416-226-2740. Ed. Meribeth Clow. adv. contact: Meribeth Clow. circ. 3,000. (tabloid format) **Document type:** newsletter.
   Formerly (until 1978): Ontario Historical Society. Local Societies Committee. Bulletin (ISSN 0078-4869)
   Description: Contains upcoming and current events, news and issues concerning Ontario's heritage community.

971 CN
ONTARIO HISTORICAL STUDIES SERIES. 1977. irreg. (Ministry of Citizenship and Culture) University of Toronto Press, 5201 Dufferin St., Downsview, ON M3H 5T8, Canada. TEL 416-667-7791. FAX 416-667-7832. (U.S. addr.: 340 Nagel Dr., Cheektowaga, NY 14225) Ed.Bd. **Document type:** academic/scholarly publication.

971.3 CN ISSN 0030-2953
F1056
ONTARIO HISTORY. 1899. q. Can.$42.80 (US $45; elsewhere $50). Ontario Historical Society, 5151 Yonge St., Willowdale, ON M2N 5P5, Canada. TEL 416-226-9011. FAX 416-226-2740. Ed. Jean Burnet. adv.; Page Can.$150; adv. contact: Jean Burnet. circ. 1,200. (reprint service avail. from KTO) **Indexed:** Amer.Hist.& Life, Can.Per.Ind., CMI, Hist.Abstr. **Document type:** academic/scholarly publication.

350 US
ORAL HISTORY SERIES. 1980. a. $20. Public Works Historical Society, 106 W. 11th St., Ste. 1800, Kansas City, MO 64105-1806. TEL 816-472-6100. FAX 816-472-1610. **Document type:** monographic series.
   Description: Interviews with prominent individuals in public works.

979.5 US ISSN 0030-4727
F871
OREGON HISTORICAL QUARTERLY. 1900. q. $25. Oregon Historical Society, 1200 S.W. Park Ave., Portland, OR 97205. TEL 503-222-1741. FAX 503-221-2035. Ed. Rick Harmon. bk.rev.; bibl.; charts; illus.; cum.index: 1900-1980. circ. 8,500. (also avail. in microform from PMC; back issues avail.; reprint service avail. from ISI) **Indexed:** Amer.Bibl.Slavic & E.Eur.Stud., Amer.Hist.& Life, Arts & Hum.Cit.Ind., Curr.Cont., GeoRef., Hist.Abstr. **Document type:** academic/scholarly publication.
—BLDSC (6281.420000); UnCover.
   Description: Popular historical publication containing research and essays on the history and culture of the Pacific Northwest, particularly the state of Oregon.

970 US ISSN 1063-6943
F871
OREGON HISTORY. 1958. q. membership. Oregon Historical Society, 1200 S.W. Park Ave., Portland, OR 97205. TEL 503-222-1741. FAX 503-221-2035. Ed. Lori McEldowney. illus. circ. 11,000.
   Formerly (until 1992): Oregon Historical Society. News (ISSN 0474-4535)
   Description: Covers events, activities and programs of the society, as well as other historical societies and museums throughout the state, and publishes articles of historical interest.

980 016 US ISSN 0078-642X
ORGANIZATION OF AMERICAN STATES. OFFICIAL RECORDS. INDICE Y LISTA GENERAL. Spanish edition: Documentos Oficiales de la Organizacion de los Estados Americanos: Lista General Indice Analitico (ISSN 0078-6365) (Editions also in French and Portuguese) 1960. a. price varies. Organization of American States, General Secretariat, Department of Publications, 1889 F St., N.W., Washington, DC 20006. TEL 703-941-1617. circ. 2,000.

980 341.8 US ISSN 0078-6438
ORGANIZATION OF AMERICAN STATES. PERMANENT COUNCIL. DECISIONS TAKEN AT MEETINGS (CUMULATED EDITION). (Text in English and Spanish) 1951. a. price varies. Organization of American States, 1889 F St., N.W., Washington, DC 20006. TEL 703-941-1617. circ. 1,000.

OUR STORIES. see *HOMOSEXUALITY*

OUTBOUND. see *AERONAUTICS AND SPACE FLIGHT*

OUTDOOR INDIANA; experiencing Indiana's valuable natural resources. see *CONSERVATION*

979 US ISSN 0738-1093
F593
OVERLAND JOURNAL. 1983. q. $30. Oregon-California Trails Association, Box 1019, Independence, MO 64051-0519. TEL 816-252-2276. Ed. Lois Daniel. adv.; bk.rev.; circ. 2,350 (paid).
—UnCover.
   Description: Articles related to Westward trans-Mississippi migration: Oregon-California Trail, Santa Fe Trail and Pony Express, Mormon Trail, and the Southern Trail to California.

977.8 US ISSN 0030-7750
OZARKER.* 1964. m. $2. Shannon County Historical Society, c/o Dr. Robert Jacquot Lee, Ed., 2403 Pebble Beach Cove, Austin, TX 78747. TEL 510-835-4890. adv.; bk.rev.; illus. circ. 800. (tabloid format) **Indexed:** Amer.Hist.& Life, Hist.Abstr.
   Formerly: Shannon County Historical Review.

P S (WYNANTSKILL); a quarterly journal of postal history. see *COMMUNICATIONS — Postal Affairs*

979 US ISSN 0030-8684
F851
PACIFIC HISTORICAL REVIEW. 1932. q. $23 to individuals (foreign $28); institutions $45 (foreign $50); students $15 (foreign $20) (effective 1994). (American Historical Association, Pacific Coast Branch) University of California Press, Journals Division, 2120 Berkeley Way, Berkeley, CA 94720. TEL 510-643-7154. FAX 510-642-9917. Ed. Norris C. Hundley. adv.; bk.rev.; index. circ. 1,700. (also avail. in microform from UMI; back issues avail.; reprint service avail. from UMI) **Indexed:** Acad.Ind., Amer.Bibl.Slavic & E.Eur.Stud., Amer.Hist.& Life, Arts & Hum.Cit.Ind., Bk.Rev.Ind. (1965-), Cal.Per.Ind. (1987-), Chic.Per.Ind., Child.Bk.Rev.Ind. (1965-), Curr.Cont., Hist.Abstr., Hum.Ind., Mid.East: Abstr.& Ind., Ref.Sour., SSCI. **Document type:** academic/scholarly publication.
—BLDSC (6329.450000); Faxon; UnCover; SWETS; UMI. **CCC.**
   Description: Focuses on the history of U.S. expansionism to the Pacific and beyond.
   Refereed Serial

979 US
PACIFIC ISLANDS MONOGRAPH SERIES. 1983. irreg., no.5, 1988. (University of Hawaii, Center for Pacific Islands Studies) University of Hawaii Press, 2840 Kolowalu St., Honolulu, HI 96822. TEL 808-956-8255. FAX 808-988-6052. TELEX 6712668. **Document type:** monographic series.
   Description: Presents works in the humanities and social sciences that focus on the insular Pacific.
   Refereed Serial

HISTORY — HISTORY OF NORTH AND SOUTH AMERICA

971   CN   ISSN 0847-0529
PACIFIC MARITIME STUDIES SERIES. 1980. irreg. price varies. University of British Columbia Press, 6344 Memorial Rd., Vancouver, BC V6T 1Z2, Canada. TEL 604-822-3259. FAX 604-822-6083. **Document type:** monographic series.
—BLDSC (9104.313500).
    Description: Deals with naval history and related Pacific maritime subjects.

979   US
PACIFIC NORTHWEST FORUM. 1975. 2/yr. $8. Eastern Washington University, Department of History, MS 27, Cheney, WA 99004. TEL 509-359-7951. Ed. J. William T. Youngs. bk.rev.; film rev.; illus. circ. 500. **Indexed:** Amer.Hist.& Life (1992-), Hist.Abstr. (1992-). **Document type:** academic/scholarly publication.
    Formerly: Historian's Bicentennial Newsletter.
    Description: Contains articles on the history, literature and environment of the Northwest.

979   US   ISSN 0030-8803
F886
PACIFIC NORTHWEST QUARTERLY. 1906. q. $22 (foreign $28). University of Washington, 4045 Brooklyn Ave., N.E., JA-15, Seattle, WA 98105. TEL 206-543-2992. Ed. John M. Findlay. bk.rev.; illus. circ. 1,200. **Indexed:** Amer.Bibl.Slavic & E.Eur.Stud, Amer.Hist.& Life, Arts & Hum.Cit.Ind., Chic.Per.Ind., Curr.Cont., Hist.Abstr. **Document type:** academic/scholarly publication.
—Faxon; UnCover.
    Formerly (until 1936): Washington Historical Quarterly.
    Description: Scholarly history of Washington, Oregon, Idaho, British Columbia, Alaska and western Montana.

979   US   ISSN 0030-882X
F852
PACIFIC NORTHWESTERNER. 1957. q. $10. Westerners, Spokane Corral, Box 14707, Spokane, WA 99210-1717. TEL 509-928-9540. Ed. Robert Clark. bk.rev.; circ. 600 (paid). **Indexed:** Amer.Hist.& Life, Hist.Abstr. **Document type:** monographic series.
—UnCover.
    Description: Authentic history of the American West.

978   US   ISSN 0031-0158
F791
EL PALACIO; magazine of the museum of New Mexico. 1913. 2/yr. $18. Museum of New Mexico Foundation, Box 2065, Santa Fe, NM 87504-2065. TEL 505-827-6451. FAX 505-827-6427. adv.; bk.rev.; bibl.; charts; illus.; index. circ. 8,000. (also avail. in microfiche from BHP; back issues avail.) **Indexed:** A.I.C.P., Amer.Hist.& Life, Anthropol.Lit., Artbibl.Mod., Chic.Per.Ind., Hist.Abstr., M.L.A.
—UnCover.
    Description: Contains articles on Southwestern history, fine art, anthropology and folk art.

977.7   US   ISSN 0031-0360
F616
PALIMPSEST. 1920. q. $15. State Historical Society of Iowa, 402 Iowa Ave., Iowa City, IA 52240. TEL 319-335-3916. FAX 319-335-3924. Ed. Ginalie Swaim. illus.; index. circ. 3,300. **Indexed:** Amer.Hist.& Life, Hist.Abstr., M.L.A. **Document type:** academic/scholarly publication.
—Faxon; UnCover. **CCC.**
    Description: Examines the history of Iowa.

976   US   ISSN 0148-7795
F381
PANHANDLE-PLAINS HISTORICAL REVIEW. 1928. a. $10 to non-members; members free. Panhandle-Plains Historical Society, Box 967, W.T.A.M.U., Canyon, TX 79016. TEL 806-656-2244. FAX 806-656-2250. Ed. Frederick W. Rathjen. index. circ. 1,200. (back issues avail.) **Indexed:** Amer.Hist.& Life, Hist.Abstr. **Document type:** academic/scholarly publication.

973   US
PAPERS OF ROBERT MORRIS, 1781-1784. 1973. irreg. price varies. University of Pittsburgh Press, 127 North Bellefield Ave., Pittsburgh, PA 15260. TEL 800-666-2211. FAX 412-624-7380. **Document type:** academic/scholarly publication.

976.4   US   ISSN 0031-2738
F786
PASSWORD. 1956. q. $25. El Paso County Historical Society, c/o L. Collingwood, Ed., 207 Maricopa Dr., El Paso, TX 79912-4401. TEL 915-858-1928. (Subscr. to: Box 28, El Paso, TX 79940) bk.rev.; illus.; index, cum.index: 1956-1970, 1971-1980, 1981-1993. circ. 1,000. **Indexed:** Amer.Hist.& Life, Hist.Abstr.
—UnCover.
    Description: Covers regional history of West Texas, Arizona, and New Mexico.

977   US   ISSN 0895-0857
PAST, PRESENT, AND FUTURE. 1979. bi-m. $25. La Crosse County Historical Society, Inc., Box 1272, La Crosse, WI 54602-1272. TEL 608-782-1980. Ed. James Arneson. circ. 800. **Document type:** newsletter.
    Description: Focuses on the history of the upper Mississippi River Valley from prehistoric times to the present. Concentrates mainly on the western Wisconsin area.

976   US   ISSN 8755-4747
F443.U6
PATHWAYS (MAYNARDVILLE); history and genealogical journal. 1982. q. $15 (typically set in Jan.). Union County Historical Society, Box 95, Maynardville, TN 37807. Ed. William G. Tharpe. bk.rev. circ. 500. **Document type:** academic/scholarly publication.
    Description: Focuses on history and genealogy relating to Union County and east Tennessee.

975   US
PEA RIVER TRAILS. 1975. q. $15. Pea River Historical and Genealogical Society, Box 628, Enterprise, AL 36331. TEL 205-393-2901. Ed. Clayton Metcalf. adv.; bk.rev. circ. 325.

975 635   US   ISSN 0895-786X
PEELINGS (WASHINGTON).* 1975. bi-m. $20. Potato Museum, 4 Tumbleweed St., N.W., Albuquerque, NM 87120-1823. TEL 202-544-1558. Ed. Meredith Hughes. circ. 350. (looseleaf format; back issues avail.)

PENNSYLVANIA. HISTORICAL AND MUSEUM COMMISSION. ANTHROPOLOGICAL SERIES. see ANTHROPOLOGY

974.8 390   US   ISSN 0031-4498
F146
PENNSYLVANIA FOLKLIFE. 1949. 3/yr. $15. Pennsylvania Folklife Society, Box 92, Collegeville, PA 19426. TEL 215-489-4111. Ed. Nancy K. Gaugler. illus.; cum.index: vols.1-35. (back issues avail.) **Indexed:** Amer.Hist.& Life, Hist.Abstr.
—Faxon; UnCover.

PENNSYLVANIA GERMAN SOCIETY. ANNUAL VOLUME SERIES. see ETHNIC INTERESTS

917.4   US   ISSN 0270-7500
PENNSYLVANIA HERITAGE. 1974. q. $15 (effective 1993). Historical and Museum Commission, William Penn Memorial Museum and Archives Bldg., Box 1026, Harrisburg, PA 17108-1026. TEL 717-787-7522. Ed. Michael J. O'Malley, III. charts; illus. circ. 10,000. **Indexed:** Amer.Hist.& Life, Hist.Abstr.
—Faxon.

974.8   US   ISSN 0031-4528
F146
PENNSYLVANIA HISTORY. 1933. q. $20 to individuals; institutions $30. Pennsylvania Historical Association, Dept. of History, Gettysburg College, Gettysburg, PA 17325. Ed. Michael Birkner. adv.; bk.rev.; illus.; index. circ. 850. (also avail. in microfilm from UMI; reprint service avail. from UMI) **Indexed:** Amer.Hist.& Life, Hist.Abstr.
—Faxon; UnCover; UMI.

974.8   US   ISSN 0031-4587
F146
PENNSYLVANIA MAGAZINE OF HISTORY AND BIOGRAPHY. 1877. q. $40 to individuals (foreign $35); institutions $35 (foreign $45). Historical Society of Pennsylvania, 1300 Locust St., Philadelphia, PA 19107. TEL 215-732-6201. FAX 215-732-2680. Ed. Ian M.G. Guimby. adv.; bk.rev.; cum.index: vols.1-75, 1877-1951; circ. 3,200 (paid). (also avail. in microform from MIM,UMI; back issues avail.; reprint service avail. from UMI) **Indexed:** Amer.Hist.& Life, Arts & Hum.Cit.Ind., Curr.Cont., Hist.Abstr., M.L.A. **Document type:** academic/scholarly publication.
—BLDSC (6421.730000); Faxon; UnCover; UMI.
    Description: Regional history journal: articles and reviews on aspects of American history and life from settlement to present.

PENNSYLVANIA MENNONITE HERITAGE. see GENEALOGY AND HERALDRY

975   US
PENSACOLA HISTORY ILLUSTRATED. 1983. s-a. $25 membership. Pensacola Historical Society, Inc., Old Christ Church, 405 S. Adams St., Seville Sq., Pensacola, FL 32501. TEL 904-433-1559. Ed. Virginia Parks. bk.rev. circ. 1,000. **Document type:** academic/scholarly publication.
    Description: Information on the history and culture of the Greater Pensacola area and its environs.

973   US   ISSN 0093-707X
F596
PERSIMMON HILL. 1970. q. $20. National Cowboy Hall of Fame and Western Heritage Center, 1700 N.E. 63rd St., Oklahoma City, OK 73111. TEL 405-478-2250. FAX 405-478-4714. Ed. M.J. Van Deventer. bk.rev.; illus.; circ. 1,000 (paid). (back issues avail.) **Document type:** academic/scholarly publication.
—UnCover.
    Description: Features historical and contemporary articles on notable persons connected with pioneering the American West, Western art, rodeo, coboys, Western flora and fauna and other phenomena of the West of today and yesterday.

971   CN   ISSN 0380-6642
PETERBOROUGH HISTORICAL SOCIETY BULLETIN. 1968. 9/yr. Can.$15 membership. Peterborough Historical Society, 270 Brock St., Peterborough, ON K2H 2P9, Canada. TEL 705-743-9710. Ed. Florence Maynes. bk.rev. circ. 350. (looseleaf format) **Document type:** bulletin.

974   US
PETTAQUAMSCUTT REPORTER. vol.13, 1977. q. membership. Pettaquamscutt Historical Society, 2636 Kinstown Rd., Kingston, RI 02881. TEL 401-783-1328. Ed. Shirley Barrett. circ. 300.

PHILATELION. see PHILATELY

976   US   ISSN 1046-4204
F417.P45
PHILLIPS COUNTY HISTORICAL REVIEW. 1962. s-a. (combines two issues in one). $10. Phillips County Historical Quarterly, 623 Pecan St., Helena, AR 72342. TEL 501-338-3271. Ed. Ivey S. Gladin. circ. 350.
    Formerly: Phillips County Historical Quarterly (ISSN 8755-5913)

977   US
PICKAWAY QUARTERLY. 1961. q. membership. Pickaway County Historical Society, 162 W. Union St., Circleville, OH 43113. Ed. Steve Jones. bk.rev.; illus.; index, cum.index: 1961-1985. circ. 800. (reprint service avail. from UMI,ISI)

979   US
PIONEER (SAN FRANCISCO). a. Society of California Pioneers, Pioneer Hall-Civic Center, 456 McAllister St., San Francisco, CA 94102. Ed. J. Roger Jobson.

973 398   US
PIONEER AMERICA SOCIETY. NEWSLETTER. s-a. $20. (Pioneer America Society) University of Akron, Department of Geography, Akron, OH 44325. TEL 919-395-3000. (Subscr. to: Frank Ainsley, Department of Geography, University of North Carolina at Wilmington, Wilmington, NC 28403) Ed. Abigail Beyer. adv.; bk.rev.; abstr.; illus.; stat.; index.

HISTORY — HISTORY OF NORTH AND SOUTH AMERICA

973 398   US   ISSN 0884-3309
E179.5
PIONEER AMERICA SOCIETY TRANSACTIONS. Short title: P.A.S.T. 1977. a. $20. (Pioneer America Society) University of Akron, Department of Geography, Akron, OH 44325. TEL 919-395-3000. (Subscr. to: c/o Frank Ainsley, Department of Geogrpaphy, University of North Carolina at Wilmington, Wilmington NC 28403) Ed. William Walter. adv.; bk.rev.; abstr.; illus.; stat.; index. (back issues avail.) **Document type:** academic/scholarly publication.

971   CN   ISSN 0847-0537
PIONEERS OF BRITISH COLUMBIA. 1975. irreg. price varies. University of British Columbia Press, 303-6344 Memorial Rd., Vancouver, BC V6T 1Z2, Canada. TEL 604-822-3259. FAX 604-822-6083. Ed.Bd. **Document type:** monographic series.
    Former titles: Recollections of the Pioneers of British Columbia; British Columbia Historical Documents Series.
    Description: Important documents on the colonial and early provincial history of British Columbia.

977   US
PIPESTONE COUNTY HISTORICAL SOCIETY NEWS. irreg. membership. (Pipestone County Historical Society) Pipestone Publishing Co., 113 South Hiawatha Ave., Pipestone, MN 56164. TEL 507-825-3333. Ed. Dave Raybar. illus. **Document type:** newsletter.

974.8   US   ISSN 1069-4706
F146
PITTSBURGH HISTORY; a magazine of the city and its region. 1918. q. $30 to libraries (foreign $35). Historical Society of Western Pennsylvania, 4338 Bigelow Blvd., Pittsburgh, PA 15213. TEL 412-338-6009. FAX 412-338-9163. Ed. Paul Roberts. adv.; bk.rev.; charts; illus.; index, cum.index: vols. 1-43 (1918-1960), vols. 44-53 (1961-1970). circ. 2,900. (also avail. in microform from UMI) **Indexed:** Amer.Hist.& Life, Hist.Abstr. **Document type:** academic/scholarly publication, consumer publication.
  —Faxon; UnCover; UMI.
    Formerly (until vol.71): Western Pennsylvania Historical Magazine (ISSN 0043-4035)
    Description: Publishes articles on the history of Pittsburgh, rural and suburban Western Pennsylvania and bordering parts of Ohio, and West Virginia. Includes articles about topics in other regions that have a significant impact on, or shared similarities with this region.

978   US
PLAINS TALK. 1963. q. free to subscribers to North Dakota History. State Historical Society of North Dakota, North Dakota Heritage Center, Bismarck, ND 58505. TEL 701-224-2799. Ed. Janet Daley Lysengen. circ. 1,800. **Document type:** newsletter.

PLATTE COUNTY HISTORICAL AND GENEALOGICAL SOCIETY BULLETIN. see *GENEALOGY AND HERALDRY*

976 929   US   ISSN 0898-5197
F392.C2
PLUM CREEK ALMANAC. 1983. s-a. $15. Genealogical and Historical Society of Caldwell County, 215 S. Pecan Ave., Luling, TX 78648. TEL 210-875-9466. FAX 210-875-2038. Ed. Mary Wanda Harp. adv.; bk.rev. circ. 500. **Document type:** newsletter.

POLYPHONY. see *ETHNIC INTERESTS*

986.1   CK   ISSN 0032-4388
POPAYAN. 1907. 2/yr. $2 per no. Universidad del Cauca, Academia de Historia del Cauca, Apdo. Aereo 878, Popayan, Colombia. Ed. Ricardo L. Rodriguez Arce. adv.; charts; illus. circ. 500.

970   US   ISSN 0193-6891
POPULAR CULTURE BIO-BIBLIOGRAPHIES. 1982. irreg. price varies. Greenwood Press, Inc. (Subsidiary of: Greenwood Publishing Group Inc.), 88 Post Rd. W., Box 5007, Westport, CT 06881-5007. TEL 203-226-3571. FAX 203-222-1502. Ed. M. Thomas Inge.

974   US   ISSN 0895-0865
POTTER COUNTY HISTORICAL SOCIETY. QUARTERLY BULLETIN. 1966. q. $5. Potter County Historical Society, 308 N. Main St., Coudersport, PA 16915. TEL 814-274-8124. Ed. Robert K. Currin. circ. 340. **Indexed:** Amer.Hist.& Life, Hist.Abstr. **Document type:** bulletin.
    Description: Articles about Potter County history.

977 929   US
POWESHIEK COUNTY, IOWA SEARCHER. 1978. q. $10 includes membership. Poweshiek Historical and Genealogical Society, Box 280, Montezuma, IA 50171. TEL 515-623-3322. Ed. Ferne Norris. circ. 150.

917.8   US   ISSN 0092-8313
PRAIRIE SCOUT. 1973. irreg., latest vol.5. $15. Westerners, Kansas Corral, Box 531, Abilene, KS 67410. Ed. Leo E. Oliva. illus. circ. 250.

978   US
PRESERVATION NEW MEXICO. 1984. q. free. Office of Cultural Affairs, 228 E. Palace Ave., Santa Fe, NM 87503. TEL 505-827-6320. adv.; bk.rev. circ. 2,000. (back issues avail.)
    Description: Focuses on architecture, archaeology and historic preservation programs, activities and publications related to New Mexico and the American southwest.

PRESERVATION PERSPECTIVE. see *ARCHITECTURE*

975   US   ISSN 1051-0192
PRESERVATION PROGRESS (CROWNSVILLE). 1973. q. free. Maryland Historical & Cultural Publications-DHCD, 100 Community Place, Crownsville, MD 21032-2023. TEL 410-514-7624. FAX 410-987-4071. Ed. Millie Riley. bk.rev. circ. 3,000.
    Formerly (until Nov. 1985): S W A P: Some Words About Preservation.
    Description: Profiles the cultural conservation and historical, architectural, and archaeological resource management and preservation education activities of the state of Maryland.

977 910.09   US   ISSN 8755-8939
790.132
PRESIDENTS' JOURNAL. 1985. q. $12. Cottontail Publications, 79 Drakes Ridge, Bennington, IN 47011. TEL 812-427-3914. Ed. Ellyn Kern. bk.rev.; illus.; index. (looseleaf format; back issues avail.) **Document type:** newsletter.
    Description: Covers homes, history, and collectibles related to presidential lore.

THE PRIMARY SOURCE. see *LIBRARY AND INFORMATION SCIENCES*

974   US
PRINCETON HISTORY. 1971. a. $5. Historical Society of Princeton, 158 Nassau St., Princeton, NJ 08542. TEL 609-921-6748. Ed. Gloria B. Halpern. bk.rev. circ. 1,300. **Indexed:** Amer.Hist.& Life, Hist.Abstr. **Document type:** academic/scholarly publication.

974   US
PRINCETON RECOLLECTOR. 1975. 5/yr. $9. Princeton History Project, 158 Nassau St., Princeton, NJ 08540. TEL 609-921-8330. Ed.Bd. adv. circ. 2,000.
    Formerly: Princeton Recollection.

980   FR   ISSN 0765-1333
D411
PROBLEMES D'AMERIQUE LATINE. (Subseries of: Notes et Etudes Documentaires) 1973. q. 240 F. (Europe 290 F., elsewhere 370 F.). (Centre d'Etudes et de Documentation sur l'Amerique Latine) Documentation Francaise, 29-31 Quai Voltaire, 75340 Paris Cedex 07, France. TEL 1-40-15-70-00. FAX 40-15-72-30. TELEX 215 666 DOCFRAN. (Subscr. to: 124 rue Henri Barbusse, 93308 Aubervilliers Cedex, France. TEL 48-39-56-00. FAX 48-39-56-01) circ. 5,000. (also avail. in microfiche from DFR) **Indexed:** Amer.Hist.& Life, Hist.Abstr., Int.Lab.Doc. **Document type:** government publication.

986.6   EC
PROCESOS; revista ecuatoriana de historia. 1991. s-a. Corporacion Editora Nacional, Roca 230 y Tamayo, Apdo. Postal 17-12-00886, Quito, Ecuador. TEL 554358. FAX 566340. Dir. Enrique Ayala Mora.

PROFMEX SPECIAL PAPERS SERIES. see *POLITICAL SCIENCE*

973   US   ISSN 0033-1031
CD3020
PROLOGUE (WASHINGTON); quarterly of the National Archives. 1969. q. $12. U.S. National Archives and Records Administration, Trust Fund Board, Seventh St. and Pennsylvania Ave., N.W., Washington, DC 20408. TEL 202-724-0087. FAX 202-219-1250. Ed. Henry J. Gwiazda II. bibl.; charts; illus.; index. circ. 4,000. (also avail. in microfilm; back issues avail.; reprint service avail. from KTO) **Indexed:** Amer.Hist.& Life, Bibl.Cart., Hist.Abstr., Hum.Ind., Ind.U.S.Gov.Per. **Document type:** academic/scholarly publication, government publication.
  —BLDSC (6924.980000); Faxon; UnCover; SWETS; UMI.

390 973   UK   ISSN 0361-2333
E169.1
PROSPECTS; an annual of American cultural studies. 1975. a. £26($43) to individuals (overseas £37); institutions £48 (overseas £59 ($77)). Cambridge University Press, The Edinburgh Bldg., Shaftesbury Rd., Cambridge CB2 2RU, England. TEL 0223-312393. FAX 0223-315052. TELEX 851817256. (N. American addr.: Cambridge University Press, Journals Dept., 40 W. 20th St., New York, NY 10011. TEL 212-924-3900. FAX 212-691-3239) Ed. Jack Salzman. adv. (back issues avail.) **Indexed:** Mid.East: Abstr.& Ind. **Document type:** academic/scholarly publication.
  —UMI. CCC.
    Description: Presents works of criticism and scholarship that explore the essential nature of American civilization.

900   US   ISSN 0739-4241
PROVENANCE. 1972. s-a. $20. Society of Georgia Archivists, Box 80631, Athens, GA 30608. TEL 706-542-7123. FAX 706-542-6522. adv.; bk.rev. circ. 400. (also avail. in microform) **Indexed:** Amer.Hist.& Life, Hist.Abstr.
    Formerly: Georgia Archive (ISSN 0095-6201)
    Description: Covers issues concerning the theory and practice of archival management.

974   US   ISSN 0891-2610
PUBLIC HISTORY NEWS. 1980. q. $37 to individuals; libraries and institutions $53; students $17. National Council on Public History, 327 Cavanaugh Hall, Indiana University - Purdue University at Indianapolis, 425 University Blvd., Indianapolis, IN 46202-5140. TEL 317-274-2716. FAX 317-274-2347. Ed. Elizabeth B. Monroe. bibl. circ. 1,700. **Document type:** newsletter.
    Description: Contains news and features on public history activities, NCPH news, job advertisements, legislative reports and listings of fellowships, meetings, publications and awards.

970   US
PUBLIC WORKS HISTORICAL SOCIETY NEWSLETTER. q. Public Works Historical Society, 106 W. 11th St., Ste. 1800, Kansas City, MO 64105-1806. TEL 816-472-6100. FAX 816-472-1610. Ed. Howard Rosen. **Indexed:** Amer.Hist.& Life, Hist.Abstr. **Document type:** newsletter.

973   US   ISSN 0085-5227
PUBLICATIONS IN THE AMERICAN WEST. 1969. irreg., vol.30, 1992. price varies. University of Utah Press, Salt Lake City, UT 84112. TEL 801-581-6771. **Document type:** monographic series.

982   AG
PUCARA; la historia nacional. m. Arg.$8000 per no. Marcos Paz 904, 4000 San Miguel de Tucuman, Argentina. TEL 081-217912. Dir. Arturo Arroyo.

970   US
PUTNAM COUNTY HERITAGE. 1978. q. $5. Putnam County Historical Society, 201 E. Main St., Box 264, Kalida, OH 45853. TEL 419-532-3008. Ed. Edward A. Rieman. circ. 550. **Document type:** newsletter.

QUAPAW QUARTER CHRONICLE. see *ARCHITECTURE*

QUARTERDECK. see *MUSEUMS AND ART GALLERIES*

QUEBEC STUDIES. see *LITERATURE*

HISTORY — HISTORY OF NORTH AND SOUTH AMERICA

977 US ISSN 0746-3472
F486
QUEEN CITY HERITAGE. 1943. q. $20. Cincinnati Historical Society, The Museum Center, Cincinnati Union Terminal, 1301 Western Ave., Cincinnati, OH 45203-1129. TEL 513-287-7058. FAX 513-287-7095. Ed. Dottie Lewis. illus.; index. circ. 11,000. (back issues avail.) **Indexed:** Amer.Hist.& Life, Hist.Abstr.
Former titles: Cincinnati Historical Society Bulletin (ISSN 0194-2883); Historical and Philosophical Society of Ohio. Bulletin.
Description: Covers Cincinnati and its surrounding region, and the old Northwest Territory as it pertains to Ohio and the Ohio River.

970 980 GW ISSN 0079-9157
QUELLENWERKE ZUR ALTEN GESCHICHTE AMERIKAS. irreg., vol.13, 1981. price varies. (Ibero-Amerikanisches Institut Preussischer Kulturbesitz Berlin) Gebr. Mann Verlag GmbH, Lindenstr. 76, 10969 Berlin, Germany. TEL 030-2591-3589. FAX 030-2591-3537. (Subscr. to: 10888 Berlin, Germany) Ed. Gerdt Kutscher. (reprint service avail.) **Document type:** monographic series.

QUIPU; revista latinoamericana de historia de las ciencias y la tecnologia. see SCIENCES: COMPREHENSIVE WORKS

980 EC
QUITUMBE. 1971. a. S/1,000($3) or on exchange basis. Pontificia Universidad Catolica del Ecuador, Departamento de Historia y Geografia, Avda. 12 de Octubre 1076 y Carrion, Apdo. 2184, Quito, Ecuador. FAX 237-165. Eds. Juan F. Regalado, Guillermo Bustos L. adv.; bk.rev. circ. 1,000.
Description: Contains articles mostly on Ecuador's history, by the faculty and students at PUCE's history department.

QUOTE...UNQUOTE; a public information service. see RELIGIONS AND THEOLOGY — Roman Catholic

974 US
RADICAL HISTORIANS NEWSLETTER. 1969. 2/yr. $3 (foreign $6). Mid-Atlantic Radical Historians Organization, Box 632, N. Cambridge, MA 02140. Ed.Bd. circ. 1,300. **Document type:** newsletter.

974 US
RADNOR HISTORICAL SOCIETY. BULLETIN. 1950. a. $3. Radnor Historical Society, 113 W. Beech Tree Ln., Wayne, PA 19087. TEL 610-688-2668. Ed. Patricia J. Henry. adv.: B&W page $75; adv. contact: George Walker. circ. 300. (back issues avail.) **Indexed:** Amer.Hist.& Life, Hist.Abstr. **Document type:** bulletin.
Description: Covers topics relating to the local history of Radnor and the surrounding area.

977 US ISSN 1055-3827
D11.5
READ MORE ABOUT IT - BOOK OF DAYS. 1987. a. $98. Pierian Press, Box 1808, Ann Arbor, MI 48106. TEL 313-434-5530. FAX 313-434-6409. Ed. C. Edward Wall.
Formerly: Book of Days (ISSN 0891-0146)
Description: An encyclopedia of information sources on historical figures and events, keyed to calendar dates.

980 970 US ISSN 0899-2371
RECENT AMERICAN HISTORY. 1988. irreg. Peter Lang Publishing, Inc., 62 W. 45th St., 4th Fl., New York, NY 10036. TEL 212-302-6740. Ed. Kenneth E. Hendrickson, Jr. **Document type:** academic/scholarly publication.
—BLDSC (7303.999000).
Description: Includes topics from the late nineteenth and twentieth centuries. Focuses on biographical and monographic studies at the local, state and regional levels which have implications for issues of national importance.

981 BL
RECIFE, BRAZIL. SECRETARIA DE EDUCACAO E CULTURA. ARQUIVOS. irreg. Secretaria de Educacao e Cultura, Recife, Pernambuco, Brazil.

977 US
RED RIVER VALLEY HERITAGE PRESS. 1976. bi-m. $25. Red River Valley Heritage Society, Box 157, Moorhead, MN 56561-0157. TEL 218-233-5604. (Co-sponsor: Heritage Hjemkomst Interpretative Center) Ed. Pauline Marcil. adv.; bk.rev.; illus. circ. 8,000. (tabloid format) **Indexed:** Amer.Hist.& Life, Hist.Abstr.
Formerly (until 1980): Red River Valley Historian.
Description: Covers topics relating to the history of the Red River valley, and news of activities at the Center.

971 CN ISSN 1187-6484
REGROUPEMENT DES CHERCHEURS-RES EN HISTOIRE DES TRAVAILLEURS ET TRAVAILLEUSES DU QUEBEC. BULLETIN. 1972. 3/yr. Can.$14 to individuals; institutions Can.$20. (Universite du Quebec a Montreal, Regroupement des Chercheurs-res en Histoire des Travailleurs et Travailleuses du Quebec) Universite de Montreal, Departement d'Histoire, C.P. 8888 Succ. A., Montreal, PQ H3C 3P8, Canada. TEL 514-987-7813. FAX 514-343-2483. (Subscr. to: C.P. 8888 Succ. A, Montreal, PQ H3C 3P8, Canada. TEL 514-987-7813) Ed. Bernard Dansereau. adv.; cum.index. circ. 100. (looseleaf format; back issues avail.) **Indexed:** Pt.de Rep. (1983-). **Document type:** newsletter, bulletin.

972 309 MX ISSN 0185-3929
F1201
RELACIONES; estudios de historia y sociedad. 1980. q. Mex.$48000($48) (typically set in Nov.). Colegio de Michoacan A.C., Martinez de Navarette, No. 505, 59690 Zamora, Michoacan, Mexico. TEL 351-26381. FAX 351-55307. Ed. Eugenia M. de Williams. adv.; bk.rev.; bibl.; index. circ. 1,000. (also avail. in microfilm; back issues avail.)
Description: Covers research in agricultural, anthropological, socioeconomic and cultural history, especially with a regional focus on Mexican history and society.

974.9 US ISSN 0034-3897
RELICS. 1955. q. $10. Pascack Historical Society, Box 285, Park Ridge, NJ 07656. TEL 201-573-0307. Ed. Katharine Randall. bk.rev.; illus.; index. circ. 375. (processed)
Description: Articles and original material on local history.

978 US ISSN 1064-2730
RENTON HISTORICAL SOCIETY NEWSLETTER. 1970. q. $8. Renton Historical Society, 235 Mill Ave. S., Renton, WA 98055. TEL 206-255-2330. Ed. Ethel Telban. adv.; bk.rev.; illus. circ. 1,000. (looseleaf format) **Document type:** newsletter.

948 BO
REPORTAJES: DOCUMENTOS PARA LA HISTORIA.* 1970. s-m. Bol.$2. Edificio Almarez 50, Casilla Postal 382, La Paz, Bolivia. illus.

977 917
REPORTS IN MACKINAC HISTORY AND ARCHAEOLOGY. 1972. irreg. (approx. a.). price varies. Mackinac Island State Park Commission, Box 30028, Lansing, MI 48909. TEL 906-847-3328. Ed. David A. Armour. bibl.; illus. **Document type:** monographic series.

RESEARCH ON LATIN AMERICA IN THE HUMANITIES AND SOCIAL SCIENCES IN THE UNIVERSITIES AND POLYTECHNICS OF THE UNITED KINGDOM. see BIBLIOGRAPHIES

970 US ISSN 0048-7511
Z1236
REVIEWS IN AMERICAN HISTORY. 1973. q. $23 to individuals (foreign $31.25); institutions $63 (foreign $71.25). Johns Hopkins University Press, Journals Publishing Division, 701 W. 40th St., Ste. 275, Baltimore, MD 21211. TEL 301-338-6987. FAX 301-338-6998. Ed. Stanley I. Kutler. adv.; bk.rev.; index. circ. 4,000. (also avail. in microform from UMI; back issues avail.; reprint service avail. from UMI) **Indexed:** Amer.Bibl.Slavic & E.Eur.Stud., Amer.Hist.& Life, Arts & Hum.Cit.Ind., Bk.Rev.Ind. (1975-), Child.Bk.Rev.Ind. (1975-), Curr.Cont., Hist.Abstr.
—BLDSC (7786.910000); Faxon; UnCover; SWETS. CCC.
Description: Presents more than twenty comparative and interpretive essays analyzing recent research published in all specialties of American history, including economics, military history, women in history, law, political philosophy, and religion.

981 378 BL
REVISTA BRASILEIRA DE HISTORIA. 1981. 2/yr. Cr.$6000($60) Associacao Nacional dos Professores Universitarios de Historia, Caixa Postal 8.105, 01000 Sao Paulo, SP, Brazil. Ed. Marco Zero. adv.; bk.rev. circ. 2,000. **Indexed:** Amer.Hist.& Life, Hist.Abstr.

980 CL ISSN 0080-2093
REVISTA CHILENA DE HISTORIA Y GEOGRAFIA. 1911. a. $37 for 2 yrs. Sociedad Chilena de Historia y Geografia, Londres 65, Casilla 1386, Santiago, Chile. TEL 6382489. Ed. Norma Figueroa. bk.rev.; cum.index. circ. 1,000. (also avail. in microfilm from BHP,KTO) **Indexed:** Amer.Hist.& Life, Hisp.Amer.Per.Ind., Hist.Abstr.
Description: Publishes articles and conference proceedings written by members, on subjects such as history, geography, numismatics, genealogy and folklore.

986.1 US
REVISTA DE ESTUDIOS COLOMBIANOS. (Text occasionally in English and Spanish) irreg. $10 to individuals; institutions $12. Association of North American Colombianists - Asociacion de Colombianistas Norteamericanos, Department of Foreign Languages, University of West Virginia, Morgantown, VA 26506. (Co-sponsors: Washington University; Editorial Plaza y Janes) Ed. Raymond L. Williams.

900 BL ISSN 0034-8309
D1
REVISTA DE HISTORIA. 1950. s-a. $10. Universidade de Sao Paulo, Faculdade de Filosofia, Letras e Ciencias Humanas, Departamento de Historia, C.P. 8105, CEP 05508, Sao Paulo, Brazil. TEL 011-813-3222. bk.rev.; cum.index. circ. 3,000. **Indexed:** M.L.A.

990 CR ISSN 1012-9790
F1541
REVISTA DE HISTORIA. 1975. s-a. $20. (Universidad Nacional, Escuela de Historia) Editorial de la Universidad de Costa Rica, Apartado 75-2060, Ciudad Universitaria Rodrigo Facio, 2050 San Pedro de Montes de Oca, San Jose, Costa Rica. TEL 506-25-3133. FAX 506-24-9367. TELEX UNICORI 2544. Ed.Bd. bk.rev.; bibl.; charts; stat. circ. 1,000. (back issues avail.) **Indexed:** Amer.Hist.& Life, Hist.Abstr. **Document type:** academic/scholarly publication.
—BLDSC (7858.392000).

983 CL ISSN 0716-9108
REVISTA DE HISTORIA. 1991. a. $10. Universidad de Concepcion, Departamento de Ciencias Historicas y Sociales, Edmundo Larenas 240, Barrio Univ., Casilla 82-C, Correo 3, Concepcion, Chile. FAX 259108. Dir. Guido Donoso Nunez. **Document type:** academic/scholarly publication.

970 980 MX ISSN 0034-8325
F1401
REVISTA DE HISTORIA DE AMERICA. (Text in English, French, Portuguese and Spanish) 1938. s-a. $38 (C. & N. America $42; S. America & Europe $47; Asia $52). Instituto Panamericano de Geografia e Historia, Ex-Arzobispado 29, Col. Observatorio, Deleg. Miguel Hidalgo, 11860 Mexico, D.F., Mexico. TEL 525-277-5888. FAX 525-271-6271. (Subscr. to: IPGH, Dpeto. de Distribucion y Ventas, Apdo. 18879, 11870 Mexico D.F., Mexico) Ed. Jorge Salvador Lara. adv.; bk.rev.; bibl.; illus.; cum.index: 1938-1962, 1963-1969, 1970-1972, 1973-1978. circ. 1,500. (also avail. in microform from UMI; reprint service avail. from UMI) **Indexed:** Amer.Hist.& Life, Arts & Hum.Cit.Ind., Curr.Cont., Hisp.Amer.Per.Ind., Hist.Abstr. **Document type:** academic/scholarly publication.
—Faxon; UMI.

986.6 EC ISSN 0556-5987
REVISTA DE HISTORIA DE LAS IDEAS. 1959. irreg. Instituto Panamericano de Geografia e Historia, Casa de la Cultura Ecuatoriana, Quito, Ecuador. **Indexed:** Hisp.Amer.Per.Ind. (until 1993).

982 AG ISSN 0556-5995
REVISTA DE HISTORIA DE ROSARIO. 1963. a. Arg.$18($5) Sociedad de Historia de Rosario, 1 de Mayo 1082, 2000 Rosario, Argentina. TEL 47225. Ed. Wladimir C. Mikielievich. adv.; bk.rev. circ. 1,100.

HISTORY — HISTORY OF NORTH AND SOUTH AMERICA

900   SP   ISSN 0034-8341
F1401
REVISTA DE INDIAS. 1940. 3/yr. 5000 ptas. (foreign 7500 ptas.). Consejo Superior de Investigaciones Cientificas (C.S.I.C.), Instituto G. Fernandez de Oviedo, Vitruvio, 8, 28006 Madrid, Spain. Ed. Francisco De Solano. bk.rev.; charts; illus.; maps; index, cum.index. circ. 1,500. (back issues avail.) **Indexed:** A.I.C.P., Amer.Hist.& Life, Arts & Hum.Cit.Ind., Curr.Cont., Hisp.Amer.Per.Ind., Hist.Abstr.
—SWETS.

980 940   AG   ISSN 0327-6511
REVISTA DEL V CENTENARIO DEL DESCUBRIMIENTO Y DE LA EVANGELIZACION DE AMERICA. 1991. a. $40 (effective 1993). Universidad del Salvador, Facultad de Historia y Letras, Rodriguez Pena 770, 2o piso, 1020 Buenos Aires, Argentina. TEL 42-1381. FAX 42-0631. **Document type:** academic/scholarly publication.
  Description: Focuses on Hispanic and Latin American themes in the humanities. Analyzes Latin American culture with special emphasis on their classical and Spanish heritage.

REVISTA DOMINICANA DE ANTROPOLOGIA E HISTORIA. see ANTHROPOLOGY

989   UY
REVISTA HISTORICA. vol.67, 1973. a. Museo Historico Nacional, Casa Rivera, Rincon 437, Montevideo, Uruguay. Ed.Bd. **Indexed:** Hisp.Amer.Per.Ind.

972 700   CR
REVISTA NACIONAL DE CULTURA. 1988. q. Universidad Estatal a Distancia, Apdo. 474-2050, San Pedro Montes de Oca, San Jose, Costa Rica.

986.2   PN
REVISTA PATRIMONIO HISTORICO. 1977. q.? Instituto Nacional de Cultura, Apdo. 662, Panama 1, Panama. TEL 62-3497. Ed. Marcela Camargo.

REVISTA 13 GRAFICO. see GENERAL INTEREST PERIODICALS — Guatemala

971   CN   ISSN 0035-2357
F1001
REVUE D'HISTOIRE DE L'AMERIQUE FRANCAISE. (Text in French) 1947. q. Can.$50($54) Institut d'Histoire de l'Amerique Francaise, 261 Avenue Bloomfield, Montreal, PQ H2V 3R6, Canada. TEL 514-278-2232. FAX 514-271-6369. Ed. Jacques Rouillard. adv.; bk.rev.; index, cum.index every 10 yrs. circ. 1,300. (also avail. in microform from UMI; reprint service avail. from UMI) **Indexed:** Amer.Hist.& Life, Arts & Hum.Cit.Ind., Can.Per.Ind., Curr.Cont., Hist.Abstr., M.L.A., Periodex, Pt.de Rep. (1979-), SSCI.
—Faxon; UMI.

REVUE D'HISTOIRE ECCLESIASTIQUE. see RELIGIONS AND THEOLOGY

974.5   US   ISSN 0035-4619
F76
RHODE ISLAND HISTORY. 1942. q. $20 to non-member libraries and institutions (effective 1993). Rhode Island Historical Society, 110 Benevolent St., Providence, RI 02906. TEL 401-331-8575. FAX 401-351-0127. Ed. Albert T. Klyberg. adv.; bk.rev.; illus.; cum.index vols.1-5, 6-15, 16-25. circ. 2,700. (also avail. in microform from UMI) **Indexed:** Amer.Hist.& Life, Hist.Abstr.
—Faxon; UnCover; UMI.

975.5   US   ISSN 0276-6515
F234.R557
RICHMOND QUARTERLY. 1978. q. $16. Richmond Literature and History Quarterly, Inc., 2405 Vollmer Rd., Richmond, VA 23229. TEL 804-285-8899. Ed. Julia Killian. circ. 275.
  Description: Publishes fiction, poetry, and historical articles relating to the Richmond area.

970   US
RIDING LINE. q. Texas State Historical Association, 2.306 Sid Richardson Hall, University Station, Austin, TX 78712. TEL 512-471-1525. FAX 512-471-1551. adv. contact: page $250. **Document type:** newsletter.
  Description: Informs members of association activities and programs and contains items of interest on the news in the studies of Texas regional history.

RIPLEY P. BULLEN MONOGRAPHS IN ANTHROPOLOGY AND HISTORY. see ARCHAEOLOGY

RITCHIE COUNTY HISTORICAL SOCIETY NEWSLETTER. see GENEALOGY AND HERALDRY

975.5   US   ISSN 0278-2936
F262.R5
ROANOKE VALLEY HISTORICAL SOCIETY JOURNAL. 1964. a. $6 to non-members; members free. Roanoke Valley Historical Society, Box 1904, Roanoke, VA 24008. TEL 703-342-5770. Ed. George Kegley. illus. circ. 800. (back issues avail.) **Document type:** academic/scholarly publication.
  Formerly: Roanoke Historical Society. Journal (ISSN 0035-7359)

ROBESON COUNTY REGISTER. see GENEALOGY AND HERALDRY

974.7   US   ISSN 0035-7413
F129.R7
ROCHESTER HISTORY. 1939. q. $6. (Office of the City Historian) Rochester Public Library, 115 South Ave., Rochester, NY 14604. TEL 716-428-7340. FAX 716-428-7313. Ed. Ruth Rosenberg-Naparsteck. circ. 1,000. (also avail. in microfilm from UMI; reprint service avail. from UMI) **Indexed:** Amer.Hist.& Life, Hist.Abstr.
—Faxon; UMI.

ROCHESTER MUSEUM AND SCIENCE CENTER. RESEARCH DIVISION. RESEARCH RECORDS. see ARCHAEOLOGY

970   US   ISSN 0080-3383
F232.R68
ROCKBRIDGE HISTORICAL SOCIETY, LEXINGTON, VIRGINIA. PROCEEDINGS. 1941. irreg., vol.10, 1990. $32. Rockbridge Historical Society, c/o Larry I. Bland, Ed., 502 Pickett St., Lexington, VA 24450. cum.index: vols.1-10 in vol.10. circ. 750. **Document type:** proceedings.
  Description: Covers aspects of the history and life of the county, western Virginia and famous former residents.

ROUGE. see GENEALOGY AND HERALDRY

THE ROUNDUP MAGAZINE. see JOURNALISM

974.3   US   ISSN 0748-2493
F59.R9
RUTLAND HISTORICAL SOCIETY QUARTERLY. 1970. q. $10 membership. Rutland Historical Society, 96 Center St., Rutland, VT 05701-4023. TEL 802-775-2006. Ed. Mrs. Jean L. Ross. bk.rev.; illus.; cum.index. circ. 600. **Indexed:** Amer.Hist.& Life, Hist.Abstr. **Document type:** academic/scholarly publication.
  Formerly: Rutland Historical Society Newsletter (ISSN 0048-8852)
  Description: Covers the past and present history of the town of Rutland, Vermont, and the adjacent towns of Proctor and West Rutland.

980   US   ISSN 0081-2951
F1408
S E C O L A S ANNALS. 1970. a. $12 to individuals; institutions $20. Southeastern Council on Latin American Studies, L.B. 8054, Georgia Southern University, Statesboro, GA 30460. TEL 912-681-5586. Ed. T. Ray Shurbutt. circ. 500. (also avail. in microfilm from UMI; back issues avail.) **Indexed:** Amer.Hist.& Life, Hist.Abstr., M.L.A., P.A.I.S. **Document type:** academic/scholarly publication.
—BLDSC (8216.120000).

970   US   ISSN 0584-5025
S M R C NEWSLETTER. 1967. q. $10. Southwestern Mission Research Center, Inc., Arizona State Museum, University of Arizona, Tucson, AZ 85721. TEL 602-621-4898. FAX 602-621-2976. Ed. Thomas E. Sheridan. bk.rev.; bibl. circ. 750. **Document type:** academic/scholarly publication, bulletin, bibliography.
  Description: Publishes news and a bibliography concerning scholarship and activities related to northern New Spain (Spanish Borderlands).

S P N E A'S HISTORIC HOUSES IN NEW ENGLAND. (Society for the Preservation of New England Antiquities) see ARCHITECTURE

S S G H S NEWSLETTER. (South Suburban Genealogical and Historical Society) see GENEALOGY AND HERALDRY

973   RU   ISSN 0321-2068
E838
S.SH.A.; politika, ekonomika, ideologiya. 1970. m. 19.20 Rub. Izdatel'stvo Nauka, 90 Profsoyuznaya ul., 117864 Moscow, Russia. TEL 234-05-84. bk.rev.; stat.; illus.; index. **Indexed:** Curr.Dig.Sov.Press, Int.Bibl.Soc.Sci., Int.Polit.Sci.Abstr. —BLDSC (0175.600000).

977   US
SAGINAW COUNTY HISTORIAN. q. $32. Historical Society of Saginaw County, Box 390, Saginaw, MI 48606. **Indexed:** Mich.Mag.Ind.

971   CN   ISSN 0581-295X
SAGUENAYENSIA. 1959. q. Can.$25($30) Societe Historique du Saguenay, C.P. 456, 930 rue Jacques-Cartier est, Chicoutimi, PQ G7H 5C8, Canada. TEL 418-549-2805. Ed. Roland Belanger. adv.; bk.rev.; charts; illus.; cum.index: 1959-1982, 1983-1988. circ. 1,200. **Indexed:** Amer.Hist.& Life, Hist.Abstr., Pt.de Rep.

970   US
ST. JOSEPH VALLEY RECORD. 1967. 2/yr. $30. Northern Indiana Historical Society, 808 W. Washington, S. Bend, IN 46601. TEL 219-284-9664. FAX 219-235-9059. Ed.Bd. bk.rev.; bibl.; illus.; circ. 2,500. (controlled). **Document type:** academic/scholarly publication.
  Formerly (until 1992): Old Courthouse News.

974   US   ISSN 0558-1931
ST. LAWRENCE COUNTY HISTORICAL ASSOCIATION. QUARTERLY. 1956. q. $25. St. Lawrence County Historical Association, Box 8, Canton, NY 13617. TEL 315-386-8133. FAX 315-386-8133. Eds. Cornel Reinhart, Mark Petersen. adv.; cum.index: 1956-1987. circ. 1,150. **Indexed:** Amer.Hist.& Life, Hist.Abstr. **Document type:** academic/scholarly publication.
  Description: Covers the history of St. Lawrence County and its people.

974.9   US   ISSN 0036-3383
SALEM COUNTY HISTORICAL SOCIETY NEWSLETTER. 1959. q. $.15 per sheet. Salem County Historical Society, 79-83 Market St., Salem, NJ 08079. TEL 609-935-5004. Ed. Patricia Wright Blakely. bk.rev. circ. 1,000. (processed)

978   US
SALVO. 1967. a. (plus q. supplement). $20 membership (effective Apr. 1991). Fort Point and Presidio Historical Association, Box 29163, Presidio of San Francisco, CA 94129. TEL 415-921-8193. Ed. M.B. Halsey, Jr. charts, illus.; circ. 900 (controlled). (back issues avail.) **Indexed:** Amer.Hist.& Life, Hist.Abstr.
  Formerly (until May 1990): Fort Point Salvo.

978.8   US   ISSN 0036-4215
SAN LUIS VALLEY HISTORIAN. 1969. q. $12 membership. San Luis Valley Historical Society, Inc., Box 982, Alamosa, CO 81101. Ed. Frances McCullough. bk.rev.; bibl.; charts; illus. circ. 500. (processed) **Document type:** academic/scholarly publication.
  Description: Presents historical research papers and first-person historical accounts.

978   US
SANTA ANA MOUNTAIN SERIES. 1977. irreg. price varies. California Classics, Box 291, Trabuco Canyon, CA 92678. Ed. Jim Sleeper. circ. 5,000. **Document type:** monographic series.
  Description: Historical vignettes and rare photographs tracing the evolution of the silent movie industry in this California county from 1903 to the first talkie in 1930, with notes of plots, players, and reviews and an index to subjects in text and notes.

SANTA CLARA COUNTY CONNECTIONS. see GENEALOGY AND HERALDRY

981   BL   ISSN 0034-9216
SAO PAULO (CITY) ARQUIVO MUNICIPAL. REVISTA. 1934-1984; resumed 1987 (no. 197). irreg. free. Arquivo Municipal, Divisao de Arquivo Historico, Rua da Consolacao 1024, Sao Paulo, Brazil. illus.; circ. 1,000 (controlled).

HISTORY — HISTORY OF NORTH AND SOUTH AMERICA

971   CN   ISSN 0036-4908
F1071
SASKATCHEWAN HISTORY. 1948. 2/yr. Can.$15. Saskatchewan Archives Board, Murray Building, Univ. of Saskatchewan, Saskatoon, SK S7N 0W0, Canada. TEL 306-933-8326. FAX 306-933-7305. Ed. J. Champ. bk.rev.; illus.; index. circ. 700. **Indexed:** Amer.Hist.& Life, Can.Per.Ind., CMI, Hist.Abstr. **Document type:** academic/scholarly publication.
—BLDSC (8076.536000).
  Description: Offers previously unpublished history, news of historical-archival affairs for the province of Saskatchewan.
Refereed Serial

973   US   ISSN 0361-8528
SCHOHARIE COUNTY HISTORICAL REVIEW. 1937. s-a. $12.50 (senior citizens and students $10) (membership) (index $3). Schoharie County Historical Society, Stone Ft. Museum Complex, North Main St., Schoharie, NY 12157. TEL 518-295-7192. Ed. Edward A. Hagan. bk.rev.; illus.; cum.index. circ. 1,200. **Indexed:** Amer.Hist.& Life, Hist.Abstr. **Document type:** academic/scholarly publication.
  Former titles (1948-1950): County Historical Review; (until 1946): Schoharie County Historical Society. Quarterly Bulletin; (until 1941): Yo-Sko-Ha-Ro Quarterly.
  Description: Examines the history and Schoharie County, Catskills, and Leatherstocking Region of New York.

974.7   US
SCHUYLER COUNTY HISTORICAL SOCIETY. JOURNAL. 1964. q. $15. Schuyler County Historical Society, Gray Brick Museum, Montour Falls, NY 14865. TEL 607-535-9741. Ed. Barbara Bell. bibl.; illus.; index. circ. 400.
  Description: Publishes short articles on the county's history. Covers the society's activities and programs.

973   US
SCHUYLERITE. 1972. q. $10 (typically set in Nov.). Schuyler Jail Museum and Genealogical Association, 200 S. Congress, Rushville, IL 62681. Ed. Lavina Walton. circ. 260. (back issues avail.)

SEA CHEST. see *TRANSPORTATION — Ships And Shipping*

970 980   US   ISSN 0743-6246
SEAPORT: NEW YORK'S HISTORY MAGAZINE. 1967. q. $35. South Street Seaport Museum, 207 Front St., New York, NY 10038. TEL 212-669-9400. FAX 212-732-5168. Ed. Madeline Rogers. adv. contact: Ann Wells. bk.rev.; illus.; cum.index. circ. 21,000. (tabloid format) **Indexed:** Avery Ind.Archit.Per.
  Former titles: Seaport Magazine; (until vol.12, Oct. 1978): South Street Reporter (ISSN 0038-3538)

SEIYOSHIGAKU/STUDIES IN WESTERN HISTORY. see *HISTORY — History Of Europe*

SEMINAR ON THE ACQUISITION OF LATIN AMERICAN LIBRARY MATERIALS. PAPERS. see *LIBRARY AND INFORMATION SCIENCES*

350   US
SENATE HISTORY. 1978. a. free. U.S. Senate, Historical Office, Office of the Secretary, Washington, DC 20510. TEL 202-224-6900. FAX 202-224-5329. Ed. Richard A. Baker. circ. 3,500. **Document type:** newsletter.

976   US
SENTINEL (FRANKLIN). 1974. q. $25 membership. Heritage Foundation of Franklin & Williamson County, Box 723, Franklin, TN 37064. TEL 615-790-0378. Dir. Mary Evins. circ. 900. **Document type:** newsletter.

981 320   BL
SERIE NOVAS PERSPECTIVAS. irreg., no.2, 1982. price varies. Editora Mercado Aberto, Rua Santos Dumont, 1186, C.P. 1432, 90000 Porto Alegre, RS, Brazil.

970   US
THE SETTLER. 1952. q. $10. Bradford County Historical Society, 21 Main St., Towanda, PA 18848. TEL 717-265-2240. Ed. Pat Parsons. circ. 800. **Indexed:** Amer.Hist.& Life, Hist.Abstr.

SEVENTEENTH CENTURY REVIEW. see *CLUBS*

979   US   ISSN 0889-0277
SHAW HISTORICAL LIBRARY. JOURNAL. 1986. a. $10. (Oregon Tech Foundation) Oregon Institute of Technology, Shaw Historical Library, Klamath Falls, OR 97601. TEL 503-885-1775. FAX 503-885-1777. Ed. Leonard Freiser. circ. 500. **Indexed:** Amer.Hist.& Life, Hist.Abstr.
—UnCover.
  Description: Presents articles relating to the High Desert Area and the "Land of Lakes", including portions of Southern Oregon, Northern Nevada, and Northern California.

SHILOH MUSEUM. NEWSLETTER. see *MUSEUMS AND ART GALLERIES*

979.4   US   ISSN 0583-4449
SISKIYOU PIONEER AND YEARBOOK. 1946. a. $15 includes monthly newsletter: Nuggets. Siskiyou County Historical Society, 910 S. Main St., Yreka, CA 96097. TEL 916-842-3836. adv.; charts; illus. circ. 1,500. **Indexed:** Amer.Hist.& Life, Hist.Abstr.

SKYLINE (BROOKLYN); committed to a greater appreciation of the city of New York. see *GEOGRAPHY*

979   US
SNAKE RIVER ECHOES. 1971. bi-a. $10 to individuals. Upper Snake River Valley Historical Society, Box 244, Rexburg, ID 83440. TEL 208-356-9101. Ed. Ralph W. Thompson. bk.rev.; illus.; cum.index in vol.10; circ. 650 (paid). (back issues avail.) **Indexed:** Amer.Hist.& Life, Hist.Abstr. **Document type:** academic/scholarly publication.
  Formerly: Upper Snake River Valley Historical Quarterly.

SOCIAL HISTORY OF ALCOHOL REVIEW. see *BEVERAGES*

971   CN   ISSN 0085-6207
SOCIAL HISTORY OF CANADA. 1971. irreg. price varies. University of Toronto Press, 5201 Dufferin St., Downsview, ON M3H 5T8, Canada. TEL 416-667-7791. FAX 416-667-7832. (U.S. address: 340 Nagel Drive, Cheektowaga, NY 14225) Eds. Craig Heron, Franca Iacouetta. **Document type:** academic/scholarly publication.

972.9   JM
SOCIAL HISTORY PROJECT NEWSLETTER. 1980. 2/yr. J.$10($5) to individuals; students J.$5. University of the West Indies, Department of History, Mona, Kingston 7, Jamaica, W.I. TEL 809-927-1922. FAX 809-927-1640. TELEX 2123. Ed. Linnette Vassell. adv.; bk.rev. circ. 150.

920   VE   ISSN 0037-8402
SOCIEDAD BOLIVARIANA DE VENEZUELA. REVISTA. 1939. q. free. Sociedad Bolivariana de Venezuela, Apdo. 874, Caracas, Venezuela. Ed.Bd. circ. 2,000. **Indexed:** Amer.Hist.& Life, Hist.Abstr.

972   MX
SOCIEDAD CHIHUAHUENSE DE ESTUDIOS HISTORICOS. BOLETIN.* vol.13, 1974. q. Sociedad Chihuahuense de Estudios Historicos, Calle 2A, Num. 600, Despachos 103 Y 109, Chihuahua, Chih, Mexico. Ed.Bd. illus.

986.6 918.66   EC
SOCIEDAD ECUATORIANA DE INVESTIGACIONES HISTORICAS Y GEOGRAFICAS. MEMORIA. a. Sociedad Ecuatoriana de Investigaciones Historicas y Geograficas, c/o Isla Seymur 391, Quito, Ecuador. Ed. P. Julian G. Bravo S.J. circ. 1,000.

SOCIEDAD GEOLOGICA DEL PERU. BOLETIN. see *EARTH SCIENCES — Geology*

SOCIEDAD LATINOAMERICANA DE HISTORIA DE LA CIENCIA Y LA TECNOLOGIA. BOLETIN INFORMATIVO. see *SCIENCES: COMPREHENSIVE WORKS*

985   PE
SOCIEDAD PERUANA DE HISTORIA. SERIE: ACTOS ACADEMICOS. irreg. Universidad Nacional Mayor de San Marcos, Lima, Peru.

972   GP   ISSN 0583-8266
F2066
SOCIETE D'HISTOIRE DE LA GUADELOUPE. BULLETIN. 1964. q. 120 F.($20) Societe d'Histoire de la Guadeloupe, Archives Departementales, Box 74, Basse-Terre, Guadeloupe. Ed. John Paul Hervieu. bk.rev.; bibl.; illus. circ. 1,000. (back issues avail.)

900   CN   ISSN 0049-1098
SOCIETE HISTORIQUE ACADIENNE. CAHIERS. (Text in French) 1960. 4/yr. Can.$25 (foreign Can.$30) (effective 1992). Societe Historique Acadienne, C.P. 632, Moncton, NB E1C 8M7, Canada. TEL 506-386-6536. Ed. Robert Pichette. bk.rev. circ. 450. (back issues avail.) **Document type:** academic/scholarly publication, bibliography.

971 929 069   CN   ISSN 0384-0158
SOCIETE HISTORIQUE DE SAINT-BONIFACE. BULLETIN. 1914. q. Can.$25. Societe Historique de Saint-Boniface, C.P. 125, St. Boniface, MB R2H 3B4, Canada. TEL 204-233-4888. FAX 204-237-3240. circ. 250. **Document type:** bulletin.
  Description: Aims to promote and preserve the heritage of francophone Manitoba.

970
SOCIETE HISTORIQUE DU MADAWASKA. REVUE. (Text in French) 1971. q. Can.$4 per no. Societe Historique du Madawaska, C.P. 474, Edmundston, N.B., Canada. bk.rev.; bibl. circ. 500.
  Former titles: Brayon (ISSN 0226-6156); Societe Historique du Madawaska.

970   CN   ISSN 0381-9388
SOCIETE HISTORIQUE NICOLAS DENYS. REVUE D'HISTOIRE. (Text in French) 1970. 3/yr. Can.$15 to individuals; institutions Can.$20. Societe Historique Nicolas Denys, Centre Universitaire, Shippagan, NB E0B 2P0, Canada. Ed. Jacinthe Lessard. adv.; bk.rev.; bibl.; illus.; circ. 800 (controlled).

SOCIETE SUISSE DES AMERICANISTES. BULLETIN/SCHWEIZERISCHE AMERIKANISTEN-GESELLSCHAFT. BULLETIN. see *ANTHROPOLOGY*

970 355
SOCIETY OF COLONIAL WARS. BULLETIN. 1934. s-a. membership. Society of Colonial Wars, 122 E. 58th St., New York, NY 10022. TEL 212-755-7082. Ed. Sutherland McColley. bibl. circ. 750. **Document type:** bulletin.

SOL. see *HUMANITIES: COMPREHENSIVE WORKS*

974   US
SOLANO HISTORIAN. 1985. s-a. $4 per no. to non-members. Solano County Historical Society, Box 922, Vallejo, CA 94590. Ed. Matthew Fountain. circ. 400. (back issues avail.)

SONS AND DAUGHTERS OF THE SODDIES. REPORTS; sod houses and dugouts in North America. see *GENEALOGY AND HERALDRY*

973 369.13   US   ISSN 0161-0511
E202.3
SONS OF THE AMERICAN REVOLUTION MAGAZINE. Variant title: S A R Magazine. 1906. q. $10. National Society of the Sons of the American Revolution, 1000 S. Fourth St., Louisville, KY 40203. TEL 502-589-1776. Ed. Winston C. Williams. adv.: B&W page $1025, color page $1815; trim 8 1/2 x 11. bk.rev.; illus.; circ. 2,500 (paid). **Document type:** consumer publication.
—UnCover.
  Description: Covers SAR activities and related historical, patriotic and educational matters.

977   US   ISSN 0888-4072
SOUNDINGS (MILWAUKEE). 1959. q. $25 membership. Wisconsin Marine Historical Society, 814 W. Wisconsin Ave., Milwaukee, WI 53233. TEL 414-286-3074. FAX 414-286-2137. Ed. Gene C. Harrison. bk.rev.; illus. circ. 500. **Indexed:** Amer.Hist.& Life, Hist.Abstr. **Document type:** newsletter.
  Description: Promotes interest in discovering, collecting, recording and preserving material relating to Great Lakes marine history with particular emphasis on commerce and industry of the Great Lakes and the St. Lawrence Seaway.

SOURCES OF MUSIC AND THEIR INTERPRETATION, DUKE STUDIES IN MUSIC. see *MUSIC*

975   US
SOUTH CAROLINA. DEPARTMENT OF ARCHIVES AND HISTORY. ANNUAL REPORT. 1906. a. free. Department of Archives and History, 1430 Senate St., Box 11669, Capitol Sta., Columbia, SC 29211. TEL 803-734-8577. circ. 300.

HISTORY — HISTORY OF NORTH AND SOUTH AMERICA

975　　　　　　US　ISSN 0361-6207
F266
SOUTH CAROLINA HISTORICAL ASSOCIATION. PROCEEDINGS. Key Title: Proceedings of the South Carolina Historical Association. 1932. a. $15. South Carolina Historical Association, USCA History Dept., 171 University Pkwy., Aiken, SC 29801. TEL 803-641-3223. Ed. William S. Brockington, Jr., adv.; index; circ. 300 (paid). (also avail. in microform from UMI; some back issues avail.; reprint service avail. from UMI) **Indexed:** Amer.Hist.& Life, Hist.Abstr. **Document type:** proceedings.
—UMI.

975.7　　　　　US　ISSN 0038-3082
F266
SOUTH CAROLINA HISTORICAL MAGAZINE. 1900. q. $40 to individuals (foreign $50); institutions $50 (foreign $60) (includes Carologue newsletter). South Carolina Historical Society, Fireproof Bldg., 100 Meeting St., Charleston, SC 29401-2299. TEL 803-723-3225. Ed. Stephen Hoffius. bk.rev.; index, cum.index: vols.1-81, subj.index: 1900-1980 vols.1-81. circ. 5,500. (processed; also avail. in microform from UMI; reprint service avail. from UMI) **Indexed:** Amer.Hist.& Life, Hist.Abstr. **Document type:** academic/scholarly publication.
—Faxon; UnCover; UMI.

978　　　　　　US　ISSN 1061-4427
SOUTH DAKOTA HALL OF FAME. 1975. q. $27.50 to individuals; institutions $50 (membership). South Dakota Hall of Fame, Box 180, Chamberlain, SD 57525-0180. TEL 605-734-4216. Ed. Travis Vilovec. bk.rev.; circ. 1,000 (paid).
Formerly: South Dakota Heritage (ISSN 0898-2074)
Description: Focuses on the people, places, and events in South Dakota.

978　　　　　　US　ISSN 0361-8676
F646
SOUTH DAKOTA HISTORY. 1970. q. $20 (foreign $30). South Dakota State Historical Society, 900 Governors Dr., Pierre, SD 57501-2217. TEL 605-773-3458. Ed. Nancy Tystad Koupal. bk.rev.; charts; illus.; index. circ. 2,300. (also avail. in microform from UMI; back issues avail.; reprint service avail. from UMI) **Indexed:** Amer.Hist.& Life, Hist.Abstr. **Document type:** academic/scholarly publication.
—BLDSC (8350.700000); UnCover; UMI.
Description: Designed for professional historians and lay readers interested in western and Great Plains history.

975　　　　　　US
SOUTH FLORIDA HISTORY MAGAZINE. 1973. q. $35 includes Tequesta. Historical Association of Southern Florida, 101 W. Flagler St., Miami, FL 33130. TEL 305-854-3289. Ed. Natalie Brown. bk.rev. circ. 3,800.
Formerly (until 1989): Historical Association of Southern Florida. Update.

974　　　　　　US　ISSN 0489-9563
SOUTH OF THE MOUNTAINS. 1957. q. $10 to institutions. Historical Society of Rockland County, 20 Zukor Rd., Box 495, New City, NY 10956. TEL 914-634-9629. Ed. Marianne B. Leese. bk.rev.; cum.index: 1957-1981. circ. 1,700. (back issues avail.) **Document type:** academic/scholarly publication.
Description: Articles on Rockland County, NY history.

977　　　　　　US
SOUTH WOOD COUNTY HISTORICAL CORPORATION. NEWSLETTER. 1962. irreg. free. South Wood County Historical Corporation, 540 Third St. So., Wisconsin Rapids, WI 54494. TEL 715-423-1580. Ed. J. Marshall Buehler. circ. 250.

980　　　　　　US　ISSN 0049-1527
SOUTH EASTERN LATIN AMERICANIST. 1956. q. $12 to individuals; institutions $20. Converse College, South Eastern Council on Latin American Studies, c/o Rafael E. Hernandez, Ed., Spartanburg, SC 29302-0006. FAX 803-596-9158. adv.; bk.rev.; bibl. circ. 400. (also avail. in microfilm from UMI; reprint service avail. from UMI) **Document type:** academic/scholarly publication.
—UMI.

979.4　　　　　US　ISSN 0038-3929
SOUTHERN CALIFORNIA QUARTERLY. 1884. q. membership. Historical Society of Southern California, 200 East Ave., No. 43, Los Angeles, CA 90031. TEL 213-222-0546. Ed. Dr. Doyce B. Nunis, Jr. bk.rev.; bibl.; illus.; index, cum.index: 1884-1957; 1958-1976; circ. 1,000 (paid). **Indexed:** Amer.Hist.& Life, Cal.Per.Ind. (1988-), Chic.Per.Ind., Hist.Abstr. **Document type:** academic/scholarly publication.
—Faxon; UnCover.
Description: Devoted to the history of California, with special focus on Southern California.

973　　　　　　US　ISSN 1068-8218
▼**SOUTHERN CULTURES.** 1993. q. $24 to individuals (foreign $32); institutions $32 (foreign $40). Duke University Press, Box 90660, Durham, NC 27708-0660. TEL 919-687-3600. FAX 919-688-4574. Eds. John Shelton Reed, Harry L. Watson. **Indexed:** Amer.Hist.& Life (1993-), Hist.Abstr. (1993-). **Document type:** academic/scholarly publication.

289.609　　　　US　ISSN 0743-7439
BX7648.N8
SOUTHERN FRIEND. 1979. s-a. $15. North Carolina Friends Historical Society, Box 8502, Greensboro, NC 27419-0502. TEL 919-316-2264. FAX 919-316-2950. Ed. Herbert Poole. bk.rev. circ. 405. **Indexed:** Amer.Hist.& Life, Hist.Abstr.
—UnCover.
Description: Covers Quaker history, with particular emphasis on the Southeastern U.S.

973　　　　　　US　ISSN 0038-478X
F381
SOUTHWESTERN HISTORICAL QUARTERLY. 1897. q. $25. Texas State Historical Association, Richardson Hall 2-306, University Station, Austin, TX 78712. TEL 512-471-1525. FAX 512-471-1551. Ed. Ron Tyler. adv.; bk.rev.; bibl.; illus.; index, circ. 3,150. (also avail. in microform from UMI; back issues avail.) **Indexed:** Abstr.Anthropol., Amer.Hist.& Life, Arts & Hum.Cit.Ind., Chic.Per.Ind., Curr.Cont., Hist.Abstr., SSCI. **Document type:** academic/scholarly publication.
—Faxon; UnCover; SWETS; UMI.
Description: Scholarly research on the history of Texas and the Southwest.

SOUTHWESTERN LORE. see ARCHAEOLOGY

973　　　　　　US　ISSN 0081-315X
SOUTHWESTERN STUDIES. MONOGRAPHS. 1963. irreg. (3-4/yr.). $10. (University of Texas at El Paso) Texas Western Press, University of Texas at El Paso, El Paso, TX 79968-0633. TEL 915-747-5688. circ. 2,000. (also avail. in microform from UMI) **Indexed:** SSCI. **Document type:** academic/scholarly publication.

929　　　　　　US　ISSN 0038-4984
SOU'WESTER (SOUTH BEND). 1966. q. $85 (effective 1994). Pacific County Historical Society, Box P, South Bend, WA 98586. TEL 206-875-5224. Eds. Ruth McCausland, Joan Mann. charts; illus.; circ. 750 (paid). **Document type:** academic/scholarly publication.

975　　　　　　US
SPANISH RIVER PAPERS.* 1973. 3/yr. membership only. Boca Raton Historical Society, Inc., 71 N. Federal Hwy., Boca Raton, FL 33432-3919. Ed. D.W. Curl. circ. 1,200. (back issues avail.) **Document type:** academic/scholarly publication.

SPECTRUM (ST. PAUL). see POPULATION STUDIES

971　　　　　　CN
STANSTEAD HISTORICAL SOCIETY. JOURNAL. 1965. biennial. Can.$15. Stanstead County Historical Society, Box 268, Stanstead, Que. J0B 3E0, Canada. TEL 819-876-7322. Ed. Denis A. Chenette. illus. circ. 600.
Formerly: Stanstead County Historical Society. Journal (ISSN 0081-4369)

STATE AND NATIONAL REGISTERS OF HISTORIC PLACES. see TRAVEL AND TOURISM

974.7　　　　　US　ISSN 0039-0232
F127.S7
STATEN ISLAND HISTORIAN. 1938; N.S. 1983. q. $9. Staten Island Historical Society, 441 Clarke Ave., Staten Island, NY 10306. TEL 718-351-1617. Ed. John B. Woodall. bk.rev.; illus.; cum.index. circ. 800.

971　　　　　　CN
STEAM AND STONE. (Text in English and French) 1977. 4/yr. free. Rideau Waterway Co-ordinating Association, 1 Jasper, Smiths Falls, Ont. K7A 4B5, Canada. TEL 613-283-5810. Ed. Allison King. adv.; illus. circ. 5,000. (tabloid format)
Formerly: Of Steam and Stone (ISSN 0707-1027)

978　　　　　　US
STEILACOOM HISTORICAL MUSEUM QUARTERLY. 1972. q. $10. Steilacoom Historical Museum Association, Box 88016, Steilacoom, WA 98388. FAX 206-584-4133. Eds. Joan Curtis, Bette Bradley. bk.rev.; illus. circ. 450.
Description: Articles and photographs of historical significance to Steilacoom and the Puget Sound area. Includes information on the Museum's activities.

974　　　　　　US　ISSN 0562-0031
STEPPING STONES. 1955. 3/yr. $1.25 per no. to non-members. Warren County Historical Society, 210 Fourth Ave., Box 427, Warren, PA 16365. TEL 814-723-1795. Ed. Chase Putnam. cum.index: 1955-1971, 1971-1976, 1977-1981, 1982-1986, 1987-1991. circ. 1,100. (tabloid format; back issues avail.) **Indexed:** Amer.Hist.& Life, Hist.Abstr.

976　　　　　　US
STONE COUNTY HISTORICAL SOCIETY NEWSLETTER. 1972. s-a. price varies. Stone County Historical Society, Box 284, Mountain View, AR 72560.

STORIES FROM THE HILLS. see LITERATURE

970　　　　　　US
STREAM OF HISTORY. 1963. q. $4. Jackson County Historical Society, c/o James Logan Morgan, Ed., 314 Vine St., Newport, AR 72112. bk.rev.; bibl.; illus. circ. 400.

STUDIES IN AFRICAN AND AFRO-AMERICAN CULTURE. see HISTORY — History Of Africa

976　　　　　　US
SULLIVAN COUNTY HISTORICAL SOCIETY NEWSLETTER. 1977. 5/yr. $10. Sullivan County Historical Society, Box 60, Blountville, TN 37617. TEL 615-538-4593. Ed. Floyd Weymouth. bk.rev. circ. 300.

973　　　　　　US　ISSN 0730-028X
E184.S23
SWEDISH-AMERICAN HISTORICAL QUARTERLY. 1950. 4/yr. $25. Swedish-American Historical Society, 5125 N. Spaulding Ave., Chicago, IL 60625. TEL 312-583-5722. Ed. Raymond Jarvi. adv.; bk.rev.; index. circ. 1,250. (also avail. in microform from UMI; reprint service avail. from UMI) **Indexed:** Amer.Hist.& Life, Hist.Abstr., M.L.A. **Document type:** academic/scholarly publication.
—UMI.
Formerly (until 1982): Swedish Pioneer Historical Quarterly (ISSN 0039-7326)
Description: Contains articles, bibliography and news items concerning the history of Swedish emigration and Swedes in North America.

979　　　　　　US　ISSN 0732-0523
TABLE ROCK SENTINEL. 1973. bi-m. $30 membership. Southern Oregon Historical Society, 106 N. Central Ave., Medford, OR 97501-5926. TEL 503-773-6536. FAX 503-776-7994. Ed. Robert C. Kenneth. bk.rev.; cum.index: 1980-1988. circ. 4,000. **Document type:** academic/scholarly publication, newsletter.
Formerly: Southern Oregon Historical Society. Newsletter.
Description: Discusses the cultural history of the American Pacific Northwest, featuring stories ranging from prehistory to modern times.

970　　　　　　US
TAKING SIDES: CLASHING VIEWS ON CONTROVERSIAL ISSUES IN AMERICAN HISTORY. (In 2 vols.) irreg., 4th ed., 1991. $12.95 per vol. Dushkin Publishing Group, Inc., Sluice Dock, Guilford, CT 06437-9989. TEL 203-453-4351. FAX 203-453-6000. Eds. Larry Madaras, James M. SoRelle; Pub. Ian Nielsen. illus. **Document type:** academic/scholarly publication.

979　　　　　　US
TALES OF THE PARADISE RIDGE. 1960. s-a. $9. Paradise Fact and Folklore, Inc., Box 1696, Paradise, CA 95967. TEL 916-873-6110. Ed. Lois McDonald. circ. 500. (back issues avail.) **Indexed:** Amer.Hist.& Life, Hist.Abstr.

HISTORY — HISTORY OF NORTH AND SOUTH AMERICA

976 US ISSN 0896-3630
F332.T14
TALLADEGA COUNTY HISTORICAL ASSOCIATION. NEWSLETTER. 1972. m. $10. Talladega County Historical Association, 106 Broome St., Talladega, AL 35160. FAX 205-362-2219. Ed. Vern Scott. bk.rev. circ. 435. **Document type:** newsletter.

975 US ISSN 0272-1406
F319.T2
TAMPA BAY HISTORY. 1979. s-a. $15. University of South Florida, College of Social and Behavioral Sciences, Dept. of History, Tampa, FL 33620. TEL 813-974-2807. FAX 813-974-6228. Ed. Robert P. Ingalls. bk.rev. circ. 900. (back issues avail.) **Indexed:** Amer.Hist.& Life, Hist.Abstr.

975 US ISSN 0496-8913
TAR HEEL JUNIOR HISTORIAN. 1961. 2/yr. $4. Division of Archives and History, 109 E. Jones St., Raleigh, NC 27601-2807. TEL 919-715-0200. FAX 919-733-8655. Ed. Lea Marshall. illus. circ. 8,000. (also avail. in magnetic tape; back issues avail.; reprint service avail from UMI)

TAREAS. see *SOCIAL SCIENCES: COMPREHENSIVE WORKS*

TATE TRAILS. see *GENEALOGY AND HERALDRY*

TEACHING FOR CHANGE. see *EDUCATION*

976 US ISSN 0040-2702
VK23.7
TELESCOPE (DETROIT). (Supplements avail.) 1952. 6/yr. $30 membership. Great Lakes Maritime Institute, Dossin Great Lakes Museum, Belle Isle, Detroit, MI 48207. TEL 313-267-6440. Ed. Kathy McGraw. illus.; index. circ. 1,400. (processed) **Indexed:** Mich.Mag.Ind.
Description: Covers Great Lakes history.

301 SP
TEMAS AMERICANISTAS. irreg., latest no.9. 320 ptas. (foreign 802 ptas.). Universidad de Sevilla, Departamento de Historia de America, Servicio de Publicaciones, Valparaiso 5, 41013 Seville, Spain. TEL 954-231958. FAX 954-232245.

976.8 US ISSN 0040-3261
F431
TENNESSEE HISTORICAL QUARTERLY. 1942. q. $25 to individuals; institutions $35. Tennessee Historical Society, War Memorial Bldg., Nashville, TN 37243. TEL 615-741-8934. Ed. Van West. adv.; bk.rev.; illus.; index, cum.index: vols.1-45 (1942-1986). circ. 3,000. (also avail. in microform from UMI,PMC) **Indexed:** Amer.Hist.& Life, Hist.Abstr., M.L.A.
—UnCover; UMI.

975.9 US ISSN 0363-3705
F306
TEQUESTA. 1941. a. $35 includes South Florida History Magazine. Historical Association of Southern Florida, 101 W. Flagler St., Miami, FL 33130. TEL 305-375-1492. Ed. Arva Moore Parks. bk.rev.; bibl. circ. 3,800. **Indexed:** Amer.Hist.& Life, Hist.Abstr.

TERRA. see *MUSEUMS AND ART GALLERIES*

976.4 US
TEXAS ALMANAC AND STATE INDUSTRIAL GUIDE. Cover title: Texas Almanac. 1857. biennial. $16.95 hardbound; paperbound $10.95. Dallas Morning News, Box 655237, Dallas, TX 75265. TEL 214-977-8261. (Dist. by: Andrews & McMeel, 4900 Main St., Kansas City, MO 64112. TEL 800-642-6480. FAX 816-932-6706) Ed. Mike Kingston. adv.; charts; illus.; stat.; index. circ. 50,000. (also avail. in microform) **Indexed:** SRI.

976.4 US ISSN 0022-6602
F381
TEXAS HISTORIAN. 1941. 4/yr. $6. Texas State Historical Association, Richardson Hall 2-306, University Sta., Austin, TX 78712. TEL 512-471-1525. FAX 512-471-1551. Ed. Ron Tyler. illus. circ. 2,500. (back issues avail.) **Indexed:** Amer.Hist.& Life, Hist.Abstr. **Document type:** academic/scholarly publication.
Formerly: Junior Historian.

THEM DAYS. see *FOLKLORE*

THEODORE ROOSEVELT ASSOCIATION JOURNAL. see *BIOGRAPHY*

975 US
THREE RIVERS CHRONICLE. 1981. q. membership. Box 218, Hemingway, SC 29554. Ed. William Chandler.

975 US
THRONATEESKA HERITAGE CENTER. NEWSLETTER. q. $20 membership. Thronateeska Heritage Center, 100 Roosevelt Ave., Albany, GA 31701. Ed. Donna Heidenreich. adv.
Formerly: Heritage Express.

970 CN ISSN 0082-4283
THUNDER BAY HISTORICAL MUSEUM SOCIETY. PAPERS AND RECORDS. 1908. a. Can.$6.85 (typically set in Nov.). Thunder Bay Historical Museum Society, 219 S. May St., Thunder Bay, ON P7E 1B5, Canada. TEL 807-623-0801. FAX 807-622-6880. Ed. Thorold J. Tronrud. circ. 750.
Description: Articles pertaining to the history of Northwestern Ontario.

987 VE
TIEMPO Y ESPACIO. 1984. 2/yr. Bs.60($6) Instituto Universitario Pedagogico de Caracas, Centro de Investigaciones Historicas, Departamento de Geografia, Av. Jose Antonio Paez, El Paraiso, Caracas 1021, Venezuela. Ed. Tarcila Briceno de Bermudez. bk.rev. circ. 1,000. (back issues avail.)

976 US ISSN 8755-9854
TIPPAH COUNTY HISTORICAL AND GENEALOGICAL SOCIETY. NEWS AND JOURNAL. 1975. q. $12 (effective Jan. 1992). Tippah County Historical and Genealogical Society, 308 N. Commerce St., Ripley, MS 38663. TEL 601-837-7773. Ed. Tim Childers. circ. 200. **Document type:** newsletter.
—UnCover.

971 CN
TORONTO HISTORICAL BOARD. ANNUAL REPORT. 1975. a. Toronto Historical Board, Marine Museum, Exhibition Place, Toronto, Ont. M6K 3C3, Canada. TEL 416-392-6827. FAX 416-392-6834. illus. circ. 600.
Formerly: Toronto Historical Board. Year Book (ISSN 0226-7209)
Description: Provides a brief description of the organization's key accomplishments over the past year and introduces some of the challenges for the future.

977 387 US ISSN 0890-7129
TOWPATHS. 1963. q. $18. Canal Society of Ohio, 1890 Gallo Dr., Powell, OH 43065. TEL 614-766-2854. (Subscr. to: Corresponding Secretary, 550 Copley Rd., Akron, OH 44320) circ. 400. (back issues avail.)
Description: Articles, maps, photos on the history of canals in Ohio.

973 SP
TRABAJOS MONOGRAFICOS SOBRE LA INDEPENDENCIA DE NORTEAMERICA. 1977. irreg. Ministerio de Asuntos Exteriores, Direccion General de Relaciones Culturales, Madrid, Spain.

TRACES (GLASGOW). see *GENEALOGY AND HERALDRY*

977 US ISSN 1040-788X
TRACES OF INDIANA AND MIDWESTERN HISTORY. 1989. q. $20 membership. Indiana Historical Society, 315 W. Ohio, Indianapolis, IN 46202. TEL 317-232-1882. FAX 317-233-3109. Ed. J. Kent Calder. adv.; circ. 9,500 (controlled). **Document type:** academic/scholarly publication.
—UnCover.
Description: For current and former Indiana residents and their descendants. Focuses on topics of general historical interest.
Refereed Serial

TRAIL BREAKERS. see *GENEALOGY AND HERALDRY*

980 910 551 CL
TRAPANANDA. 1978. a. $5. Co-Austral y Chile Futuro, Coyhaique, Chile. Ed. Antonio Horvath Kiss. circ. 3,000.

978 US ISSN 0041-3615
AP2
TRUE WEST. 1953. m. $19.95. Western Publications, 205 W. 7th St., Ste. 202, Box 2107, Stillwater, OK 74076-2107. TEL 405-743-3373. FAX 405-743-3374. Ed. John Joerschke. adv.; bk.rev.; illus.; cum.index: 1953-1979. circ. 29,000. (back issues avail.)
—UnCover.
Incorporates (1923-1981): Frontier Times (ISSN 0016-2124)

981 BL
TUDO E HISTORIA. 1981. irreg., latest no.105. Editora Brasiliense, S.A., 01416 Rua da Consolacao 2697, Sao Paulo, Brazil. Ed. Caio Graco Prado. circ. 5,000.

974 398 US
TURKEY TRACKS. 1965. q. $10 membership. New Providence Historical Society, Municipal Center, 360 Elkwood Ave., New Providence, NJ 07974. Ed. Jacqueline Gorton. bk.rev. circ. 125. **Document type:** newsletter.
Description: Covers the history of New Providence and the surrounding area.

980 US
U C L A LATIN AMERICAN CENTER. SPECIAL STUDIES SERIES. 1980. irreg. University of California, Los Angeles, Latin American Center, 405 Hilgard Ave., Los Angeles, CA 90024. TEL 213-825-6634. Ed. Ludwig Lauerhass, Jr.
Description: Includes conference proceedings, working papers, document collections, student research essays, and other papers.

974 US
ULSTER COUNTY GAZETTE. 1963. q. membership. Ulster County Historical Society, Box 3752, Kingston, NY 12401. TEL 914-338-5614. Ed. Lynn Mulvaney. bk.rev. circ. 300. (looseleaf format) **Document type:** newsletter.

979.5 US ISSN 0041-6339
UMPQUA TRAPPER. 1965. q. $10. Douglas County Historical Society, 733 W. Ballf St., Roseburg, OR 97470. Ed.Bd. bk.rev.; illus.; cum.index: 1965-1975. circ. 300.
Description: Articles and illustrations concerning the history of Douglas County, Oregon.

UNITED DAUGHTERS OF THE CONFEDERACY MAGAZINE. see *CLUBS*

989.5 UY
UNIVERSIDAD DE LA REPUBLICA. FACULTAD DE HUMANIDADES Y CIENCIAS. REVISTA. SERIE HISTORIA. irreg. exchange basis. Universidad de la Republica, Facultad de Humanidades y Ciencias, Seccion Revista, Tristan Narvaja 1674, Montevideo, Uruguay. Dir. Beatriz Martinez Osorio.
Supersedes in part: Universidad de la Republica. Facultad de Humanidades y Ciencias. Revista.

970.1 MX ISSN 0076-7166
UNIVERSIDAD NACIONAL AUTONOMA DE MEXICO. CENTRO DE ESTUDIOS MAYAS. CUADERNOS. 1969. irreg. price varies. Universidad Nacional Autonoma de Mexico, Centro de Estudios Mayas, Instituto de Investigaciones Filologicas, Ciudad Universitaria, 04510 Mexico, D.F., Mexico. (Subscr. to: Departamento de Publicaciones, Instituto de Investigaciones Filologicas, Circuito Mario de la Cueva, Cd. Universitaria, 04510 Mexico, D.F., Mexico) Ed. Mercedes de la Garza. bk.rev. circ. 2,000. **Indexed:** M.L.A.

972 MX ISSN 0076-7271
UNIVERSIDAD NACIONAL AUTONOMA DE MEXICO. INSTITUTO DE INVESTIGACIONES HISTORICAS. CUADERNOS SERIE DOCUMENTAL. 1963. irreg., no.6, 1968. price varies. Universidad Nacional Autonoma de Mexico, Instituto de Investigaciones Historicas, Departamento de Distribucion de Libros Universitarias, Deleg. Coyoacan, C. Univer., 04510 Mexico D.F., Mexico. **Document type:** monographic series.

972 MX ISSN 0076-7301
UNIVERSIDAD NACIONAL AUTONOMA DE MEXICO. INSTITUTO DE INVESTIGACIONES HISTORICAS. SERIE BIBLIOGRAFICA. 1948. irreg., no.5, 1969. price varies. Universidad Nacional Autonoma de Mexico, Instituto de Investigaciones Historicas, Departamento de Distribucion de Libros Universitarias, Ciudad Univ., Del. Coyoacan, 04510 Mexico, D.F., Mexico. **Document type:** monographic series.

HISTORY — HISTORY OF NORTH AND SOUTH AMERICA

972   MX   ISSN 0076-731X
UNIVERSIDAD NACIONAL AUTONOMA DE MEXICO. INSTITUTO DE INVESTIGACIONES HISTORICAS. SERIE DOCUMENTAL. 1947. irreg., no.11, 1974. price varies. Universidad Nacional Autonoma de Mexico, Instituto de Investigaciones Historicas, Departamento de Distribucion de Libros Universitarias, Insurgentes sur 299, 04511 Mexico, D.F., Mexico. **Document type:** monographic series.

972   MX   ISSN 0076-7328
UNIVERSIDAD NACIONAL AUTONOMA DE MEXICO. INSTITUTO DE INVESTIGACIONES HISTORICAS. SERIE DE CULTURAS MESOAMERICANAS. 1967. irreg., no.2, 1968. price varies. Universidad Nacional Autonoma de Mexico, Instituto de Investigaciones Historicas, Departamento de Distribucion de Libros Universitarias, Insurgentes sur 299, 04511 Mexico, D.F., Mexico. **Document type:** monographic series.

972   MX   ISSN 0071-1675
F1219
UNIVERSIDAD NACIONAL AUTONOMA DE MEXICO. INSTITUTO DE INVESTIGACIONES HISTORICAS. SERIE DE CULTURA NAHUATL. ESTUDIOS DE CULTURA NAHUATL. 1959. a. price varies. Universidad Nacional Autonoma de Mexico, Instituto de Investigaciones Historicas, Villa Obregon, Ciudad Universitaria, 004510 Mexico, D.F., Mexico. **Indexed:** A.I.C.P., Amer.Hist.& Life, Anthropol.Lit., Hist.Abstr., M.L.A. **Document type:** monographic series.

972   MX   ISSN 0076-7212
UNIVERSIDAD NACIONAL AUTONOMA DE MEXICO. INSTITUTO DE INVESTIGACIONES HISTORICAS. SERIE DE CULTURA NAHUATL. FUENTES. 1958. irreg., no.7, 1969. price varies. Universidad Nacional Autonoma de Mexico, Instituto de Investigaciones Historicas, Departamento de Distribucion de Libros Universitarias, Insurgentes sur 299, 04511 Mexico, D.F., Mexico. **Document type:** monographic series.

972   MX   ISSN 0076-7344
UNIVERSIDAD NACIONAL AUTONOMA DE MEXICO. INSTITUTO DE INVESTIGACIONES HISTORICAS. SERIE DE CULTURA NAHUATL. MONOGRAFIAS. 1959. irreg., no.19, 1975. price varies. Universidad Nacional Autonoma de Mexico, Instituto de Investigaciones Historicas, Departamento de Distribucion de Libros Universitarias, Insurgentes sur 299, 04511 Mexico, D.F., Mexico. **Document type:** monographic series.

972   MX   ISSN 0076-7352
UNIVERSIDAD NACIONAL AUTONOMA DE MEXICO. INSTITUTO DE INVESTIGACIONES HISTORICAS. SERIE DE HISTORIA GENERAL. 1949. irreg., no.8, 1972. Universidad Nacional Autonoma de Mexico, Instituto de Investigaciones Historicas, Departamento de Distribucion de Libros Universitarias, Insurgentes sur 299, 04511 Mexico, D.F., Mexico. **Document type:** monographic series.

972   MX   ISSN 0076-7387
UNIVERSIDAD NACIONAL AUTONOMA DE MEXICO. INSTITUTO DE INVESTIGACIONES HISTORICAS. SERIE DE HISTORIADORES Y CRONISTAS. 1967. irreg., no.6, 1977. price varies. Universidad Nacional Autonoma de Mexico, Instituto de Investigaciones Historicas, Departamento de Distribucion de Libros Universitarias, Insurgentes sur 299, 04511 Mexico, D.F., Mexico. **Document type:** monographic series.

980   AG
UNIVERSIDAD NACIONAL DE TUCUMAN. DEPARTAMENTO DE HISTORIA. REVISTA. 1991. s-a. Universidad Nacional de Tucuman, Departamento de Historia, Avda. Benjamin Araoz 800, S.M. de Tucuman, Argentina. **Document type:** academic/scholarly publication.

985   PE
UNIVERSIDAD NACIONAL FEDERICO VILLAREAL. DEPARTAMENTO DE CIENCIAS HISTORICO SOCIALES. PUBLICACIONES. 1976. irreg. Universidad Nacional Federico Villareal, Departamento de Ciencias Historico Sociales, Colmena 412, Lima, Peru.

981   BL
UNIVERSIDADE DE SAO PAULO. DEPARTAMENTO DE HISTORIA. BOLETIM. 1977; N.S. irreg., latest no.18. Universidade de Sao Paulo, Departamento de Historia, Caixa Postal 8.105, Sao Paulo, Brazil. Dir. Myriam Ellis. bibl.

980.2   BL   ISSN 0080-6374
UNIVERSIDADE DE SAO PAULO. MUSEU PAULISTA. ANAIS. (Text in Portuguese; summaries in English) 1922. a. Universidade de Sao Paulo, Museu Paulista, C.P. 42503, 04263 Sao Paulo, Brazil. **Indexed:** Anthropol.Lit.

708   BL
UNIVERSIDADE DE SAO PAULO. MUSEU PAULISTA. COLECAO. SERIE DE HISTORIA. 1963. irreg. Universidade de Sao Paulo, Museu Paulista, C.P. 42503, Parque da Independencia, 04263 Sao Paulo, Brazil. Ed. Setembrino Petri.
  Supersedes in part (in 1975): Museu Paulista. Colecao (ISSN 0080-6382)

980   US   ISSN 0075-8132
UNIVERSITY OF CALIFORNIA AT LOS ANGELES. LATIN AMERICAN CENTER. LATIN AMERICAN STUDIES SERIES. 1965. irreg., no.49, 1980. price varies. (University of California at Los Angeles, Latin American Studies Center) Latin American Studies Center Publications, University of California at Los Angeles, 10353 Bunche Hall, Los Angeles, CA 90024-1447. Ed.Bd. **Document type:** monographic series.
  Description: Devoted to theoretical studies and interdisciplinary research in the social sciences, humanities, professional fields and the fine arts.
Refereed Serial

980   US   ISSN 0068-6263
UNIVERSITY OF CALIFORNIA, LOS ANGELES. LATIN AMERICAN CENTER. REFERENCE SERIES. 1962. irreg., latest vol.12. price varies. University of California, Los Angeles, Latin American Center, 405 Hilgard Ave., Los Angeles, CA 90024. TEL 213-825-6634. Ed. Ludwig Lauerhass, Jr.
  Description: Listing of bibliographies, dictionaries, handbooks, guides, directories designed to facilitate research by the nonspecialist and the Latin Americanist alike.

980   UK   ISSN 0076-0846
UNIVERSITY OF LONDON. INSTITUTE OF LATIN AMERICAN STUDIES. MONOGRAPHS. 1969. irreg., no. 14, 1988. Athlone Press Ltd., 1 Park Dr., London NW11 7 SQ, England. TEL 081-458-0888. FAX 081-201-8115. (Dist. in U.S. by: 165 1st Ave., Athlone Press, Atlantic Highlands, NJ 07781. TEL 908-872-1441)
  Description: Monographs on aspects of Latin American history, society and culture.

980   UK   ISSN 0957-7947
UNIVERSITY OF LONDON. INSTITUTE OF LATIN AMERICAN STUDIES. RESEARCH PAPERS. irreg. (2-3/yr.). University of London, Institute of Latin American Studies, 31 Tavistock Sq., London WC1H 9HA, England. TEL 071-387-5671. **Document type:** academic/scholarly publication.
  —BLDSC (7755.008835).
  Former titles: University of London. Institute of Latin American Studies. Occasional Papers (ISSN 0953-6825); University of London. Institute of Latin American Studies. Working Papers (ISSN 0142-1875)
  Description: Discusses the fields of humanities and social sciences in Latin American countries.

UNIVERSITY OF MISSOURI MONOGRAPHS IN ANTHROPOLOGY. see *ANTHROPOLOGY*

980   US   ISSN 0084-0831
UNIVERSITY OF WISCONSIN-MILWAUKEE. CENTER FOR LATIN AMERICA. DISCUSSION PAPER SERIES. 1968. irreg., no.87, 1992. $4 per no. University of Wisconsin-Milwaukee, Center for Latin America, Milwaukee, WI 53201. TEL 414-229-4401. **Document type:** monographic series.

980   US   ISSN 0084-084X
UNIVERSITY OF WISCONSIN-MILWAUKEE. CENTER FOR LATIN AMERICA. ESSAY SERIES. 1968. irreg., no.8, 1980. price varies. University of Wisconsin-Milwaukee, Center for Latin America, Milwaukee, WI 53201. TEL 414-229-4401. **Document type:** monographic series.

301.36   CN   ISSN 0703-0428
HT127
URBAN HISTORY REVIEW/REVUE D'HISTOIRE URBAINE. 1954. 2/yr. Can.$35 to individuals; institutions Can.$40. City of Toronto Archives, 36 Bessemer, Unit 3, Concord, ON L4K 3C9, Canada. TEL 905-669-5373. FAX 905-669-1927. Ed. Richard Harris. adv.; bk.rev.; cum.index. circ. 600. **Indexed:** Amer.Hist.& Life, Arts & Hum.Cit.Ind., ASSIA, Can.Per.Ind., CMI, Curr.Cont., E.I., Geo.Abstr., Hist.Abstr., Sage Pub.Admin.Abstr., Sage Urb.Stud.Abstr. **Document type:** academic/scholarly publication.
  —Faxon; UnCover.
  Formerly (until 1975): Urban History Group Newsletter; **Incorporates (1975-1985):** Urbanism Past and Present (ISSN 0160-2780)

979   US   ISSN 0887-3771
UTAH CENTENNIAL SERIES. 1985. irreg., latest vol.6. price varies. University of Utah Press, Salt Lake City, UT 84112. TEL 801-581-6771. Ed. Charles S. Peterson.

979.2   US   ISSN 0042-143X
F821
UTAH HISTORICAL QUARTERLY. 1928. q. $20. State Historical Society, 300 Rio Grande, Salt Lake City, UT 84101. TEL 801-533-3500. FAX 801-533-3503. Ed. Stanford J. Layton. bk.rev.; bibl.; charts; illus.; index. circ. 3,300. (also avail. in microfiche) **Indexed:** Amer.Hist.& Life, Hist.Abstr. **Document type:** academic/scholarly publication.
  —Faxon; UnCover.

979.2   US   ISSN 0042-1529
UTAH STATE HISTORICAL SOCIETY NEWSLETTER. 1950. bi-m. membership. State Historical Society, 300 Rio Grande, Salt Lake City, UT 84101. TEL 801-533-5755. Ed. Stanford J. Layton. circ. 3,300. (tabloid format) **Document type:** newsletter.

974.8   US   ISSN 0734-5712
F159.V18
VALLEY FORGE JOURNAL; a record of patriotism and American culture. 1982. s-a. $10. Valley Forge Historical Society, 250 Wyncote Rd., Jenkintown, PA 19481. TEL 215-783-0535. Ed. Lawrence Curry. adv.; bk.rev.; illus. circ. 1,200. **Indexed:** Amer.Hist.& Life, Hist.Abstr.
  —Faxon.
  Supersedes (1943-1982): Picket Post (ISSN 0031-9619)

974   US   ISSN 1056-4853
VALLEY GAZETTE. 1972. m. $14. Gazette Publications, Inc., 102 W. Water St., Lansford, PA 18232. TEL 717-645-4692. adv.; bk.rev. circ. 1,800. (tabloid format; back issues avail.)
  Description: Covers local history, coal mining, reminiscences, vintage photographs, and feature articles.

974   US   ISSN 0740-4727
VALLEY JOURNAL. 1983. q. Neva Barrick, Pub., Box 112, Plainfield, PA 17081. Ed. Edward L. Rosenberry.

976 929   US
VALOR. 1971. s-a. $5. (Hood's Texas Brigade Association) Confederate Research Center, Box 619, Hillsboro, TX 76645. TEL 817-582-2555. Ed. B.D. Patterson. circ. 900. (looseleaf format) **Document type:** newsletter.
  Description: Provides news to association members; includes stories about the war.

976   US
VAN BUREN COUNTY HISTORICAL SOCIETY NEWSLETTER. 1981. q. $10 membership. Van Buren County Historical Society, Spencer, TN 38585. Ed. Landon D. Medley. circ. 110.

987   VE   ISSN 0042-3378
CD4260
VENEZUELA. ARCHIVO GENERAL DE LA NACION. BOLETIN. 1923. s-a. exchange basis. Archivo General de la Nacion, Santa Capilla a Carmelitas 15, Avenida Urdaneta, Caracas 1010, Venezuela. Ed. Mario Briceno Perozo. bk.rev.; bibl. **Indexed:** Amer.Hist.& Life, Hist.Abstr.

987   VE
VENEZUELA. CONGRESO DE LA REPUBLICA. ARCHIVO HISTORICO. BOLETIN. 1978. q. Congreso de la Republica, Archivo Historico, Caracas, Venezuela.

HISTORY — HISTORY OF NORTH AND SOUTH AMERICA

979.4 US ISSN 0042-3491
F868.V5
VENTURA COUNTY HISTORICAL SOCIETY QUARTERLY. 1955. q. $35. Ventura County Historical Society, Ventura County Museum of History & Art, 100 E. Main St., Ventura, CA 93001. TEL 805-653-0323. Ed. Charles Nelson Johnson. cum.index: vols.1-30. circ. 1,900. (back issues avail.) **Indexed:** Amer.Hist.& Life, Hist.Abstr.

VERA LEX; historical & philosophical study of natural law and right. see *PHILOSOPHY*

974.3 US ISSN 0042-4161
F46
VERMONT HISTORY. 1930. q. membership. Vermont Historical Society, Pavilion Bldg., 109 State St., Montpelier, VT 05609-0901. TEL 802-828-2291. Ed. Neil Stout. bk.rev.; index, cum.index: vols.1-10, 11-20, 21-45, 46-55. circ. 2,600. (back issues avail.) **Indexed:** Amer.Hist.& Life, Hist.Abstr., I.N.E.P. **Document type:** academic/scholarly publication.
—UnCover.
Description: Scholarly research on Vermont history.

974 US ISSN 0364-3387
VERMONT HISTORY NEWS. 1949. bi-m. membership. Vermont Historical Society, 109 State St., Pavilion Bldg., Montpelier, VT 05609-0901. TEL 802-828-2291. Ed. Michael Sherman. circ. 2,600. (back issues avail.) **Indexed:** Amer.Hist.& Life, Hist.Abstr. **Document type:** academic/scholarly publication, newsletter.
—UnCover.
Formerly: Vermont Historical Society News and Notes.
Description: Covers news and activities of the Society. Includes occasional feature articles on Vermont history.

972.9 VI
VIRGIN ISLANDS (U.S.) DIVISION OF LIBRARIES, MUSEUMS AND ARCHAEOLOGICAL SERVICES. OCCASIONAL PAPER SERIES. 1977. irreg. $5 per no. Division of Libraries, Museums and Archaeological Services, Department of Conservation and Cultural Affairs, 23 Dronningens Gade, St. Thomas, VI 00802. circ. 500.
Formerly: Virgin Islands (U.S.) Bureau of Libraries, Museums and Archaeological Services. Occasional Paper Series.

975.5 US ISSN 0042-6474
F221
VIRGINIA CAVALCADE. 1951. q. $6. Virginia State Library and Archives, 11th St. at Capitol Sq., Richmond, VA 23219-3491. TEL 804-786-2312. FAX 804-371-6909. Ed. Edward D.C. Campbell, Jr. charts; illus.; index. circ. 8,500. (also avail. in microform from UMI; reprint service avail. from UMI) **Indexed:** Access (1978-), Amer.Hist.& Life, Hist.Abstr. **Document type:** government publication.
—UMI.

975.5 US ISSN 0083-6389
VIRGINIA HISTORICAL SOCIETY. DOCUMENTS. 1961-1984; resumed 1990. irreg. price varies. Virginia Historical Society, Box 7311, Richmond, VA 23221. TEL 804-358-4901. FAX 804-355-2399. Ed. Sara B. Bearss. **Document type:** academic/scholarly publication.
Description: Edited and annotated documents relating to the history of Virginia.

975.5 US
F221
VIRGINIA HISTORICAL SOCIETY. HISTORY NOTES. 1960. q. free to subscribers of Virginia Magazine of History and Biography. Virginia Historical Society, Box 7311, Richmond, VA 23221. TEL 804-358-4901. Ed. Nelson D. Lankford. illus. circ. 5,100. (reprint service avail. from UMI) **Indexed:** Amer.Hist.& Life, Hist.Abstr. **Document type:** academic/scholarly publication.
—UnCover.
Formerly: Virginia Historical Society. Occasional Bulletin (ISSN 0042-6555)
Description: Covers acquisitions, collections, and activities of the society.

975 US
VIRGINIA INDEPENDENT;* a chronicle of the Constitution's bicentenary in Virginia. 1986. q. Virginia Commission on the Bicentennial of the United States Constitution, 207 Minor Hall, University of Virginia, Charlottesville, VA 22903. TEL 804-924-0948. Ed. Tracy K. Warren. bk.rev.; illus. circ. 10,000.

975.5 US ISSN 0042-6636
F221
VIRGINIA MAGAZINE OF HISTORY AND BIOGRAPHY. 1893. q. $35. Virginia Historical Society, Box 7311, Richmond, VA 23221. TEL 804-358-4901. FAX 804-355-2399. Ed. Nelson D. Lankford. adv.; bk.rev.; illus.; index. circ. 5,100. (also avail. in microform from UMI,PMC; reprint service avail. from KTO,UMI) **Indexed:** Amer.Hist.& Life, Arts & Hum.Cit.Ind., Curr.Cont., Hist.Abstr. **Document type:** academic/scholarly publication.
—BLDSC (9239.600000); Faxon; UnCover; SWETS; UMI.
Description: Covers Virginia history and related fields.

LA VOIX DES PRAIRIES. see *GENEALOGY AND HERALDRY*

980 320 US
WAGNER LATIN AMERICAN NEWSLETTER. 1977. fortn. $28. Wagner and Associates, 6405 E. Prairie St., Cottonwood, MN 56229. Ed. W.F. Wagner. circ. 200.

973 US ISSN 0083-7121
WALTER LYNWOOD FLEMING LECTURES IN SOUTHERN HISTORY. 1937. irreg. price varies. Louisiana State University Press, Box 25053, Baton Rouge, LA 70894-5053. TEL 504-388-6666. **Document type:** academic/scholarly publication.

WAR AND SOCIETY. see *HISTORY*

977 US
WARREN COUNTY REFLECTIONS. 1976. q. $5. Warren County (Indiana) Historical Society, Box 176, Williamsport, IN 47993. Ed. Jane Rasmussen. bk.rev. circ. 1,000.

979.5 US ISSN 1042-9719
F194
WASHINGTON HISTORY. 1987. s-a. $28. Historical Society of Washington, D.C., 1307 New Hampshire N.W., Washington, DC 20036-1507. TEL 202-785-2478. FAX 202-331-1979. Ed. Howard Gillette, Jr. adv.: B&W page $350. bk.rev. circ. 3,000. **Indexed:** Amer.Hist.& Life, Hist.Abstr. **Document type:** academic/scholarly publication.
Formerly (until vol.52, 1989): Columbia Historical Society. Record.
Description: Focuses on the history of the nation's capital and the Washington DC metropolitan area. Serves scholars and the general public.
Refereed Serial

971 CN ISSN 0315-503X
WATERLOO HISTORICAL SOCIETY. ANNUAL VOLUME. 1913. a. $15 to non-members. Waterloo Historical Society, 85 Queen St. N., Kitchener, ON N2H 2H1, Canada. FAX 519-570-1360. Ed.Bd. circ. 600.
Formerly: Waterloo Historical Society. Report (ISSN 0083-7733)

978 US ISSN 0275-6706
WE PROCEEDED ON; trans-Mississippi-west-exploration. 1974. q. $20. Lewis and Clark Trail Heritage Foundation, Inc., Box 3434, Great Falls, MT 59403. TEL 406-453-2826. Ed. Martin L. Erickson. bk.rev.; charts; illus.; circ. 1,500 (controlled). (back issues avail.) **Indexed:** Amer.Hist.& Life, Hist.Abstr.

970 929 US ISSN 1041-4037
WEST COAST STUDIES. 1985. 2/yr. price varies. Borgo Press (Subsidiary of: Sidewinder Press), Box 2845, San Bernardino, CA 92406. TEL 909-884-5813. FAX 909-888-4942. Ed. Allan Adrian.
Formerly (until 1989): San Bernardino County Studies (ISSN 0748-0784)
Description: Monographs, directories, and indexes dealing with the largest county in the United States, including San Bernardino-Riverside-Ontario-Redlands area, and the Mojave Desert.

976 US ISSN 0361-6215
F442.3
WEST TENNESSEE HISTORICAL SOCIETY. PAPERS. 1947. a. $15. West Tennessee Historical Society Inc., Box 111046, Memphis, TN 38111-1046. TEL 901-767-3757. (Affiliate: Tennessee Historical Commission) Ed. Edwin G. Frank. adv.; bk.rev.; bibl.; illus. circ. 600. **Indexed:** Amer.Hist.& Life, Hist.Abstr.

976 US
WEST TEXAS HISTORICAL ASSOCIATION YEARBOOK. 1924. a. $15. Rupert Richardson Press, Box 152-Hardin-Simmons University, Abilene, TX 79698. TEL 915-670-1239. FAX 915-677-8351. Eds. B.W. Aston, Ken Jacobs. bk.rev. circ. 350. (also avail. in microform; back issues avail.) **Indexed:** Amer.Hist.& Life, Hist.Abstr. **Document type:** academic/scholarly publication.
Description: Contains articles and book reviews relating to West Texas.

975.4 US ISSN 0043-325X
F236
WEST VIRGINIA HISTORY. 1939. a. $12. Department of Education and the Arts, Archives and History, Cultural Center, 1900 Kanawha Blvd., E., Charleston, WV 25305-0300. TEL 304-558-0230. Ed. Fredrick H. Armstrong. bk.rev.; bibl.; illus. circ. 1,000. (reprint service avail. from KTO) **Indexed:** Amer.Hist.& Life, Hist.Abstr. **Document type:** government publication, academic/scholarly publication.
—UnCover.
Description: Covers state history, biography, bibliography, and genealogy, as well as Appalachian cultural, social, political, economic, and military history.

974.7 US ISSN 0049-7266
WESTCHESTER HISTORIAN. 1925. q. $25. Westchester County Historical Society, 2199 Saw Mill River Rd., Elmsford, NY 10523. TEL 914-592-4323. Ed.Bd. adv.; bk.rev.; charts; illus.; index, cum.index: vols. 1-65. circ. 1,000. (back issues avail.) **Document type:** academic/scholarly publication.
—Faxon.
Description: Articles concerning all aspects of Westchester County history, including all its towns.

978 US ISSN 0083-887X
WESTERN FRONTIER LIBRARY. 1953. irreg. price varies. University of Oklahoma Press, 1005 Asp Ave., Norman, OK 73019. TEL 405-325-5111. FAX 405-325-4000. **Indexed:** M.L.A.

973 US ISSN 0083-8888
WESTERN FRONTIERSMEN SERIES. 1937. irreg. price varies. Arthur H. Clark Co., Box 14707, Spokane, WA 99214. index. **Document type:** monographic series.

973 US ISSN 0043-3810
F591
WESTERN HISTORICAL QUARTERLY. 1969. q. $30 to individual members; libraries $40. Western History Association, Utah State University, Main 321C, Logan, UT 84322-0740. TEL 801-750-1301. FAX 801-750-3899. Ed. Clyde A. Milner II. adv.; bk.rev.; bibl.; index. circ. 3,000. **Indexed:** Air Un.Lib.Ind., Amer.Bibl.Slavic & E.Eur.Stud., Amer.Hist.& Life, Arts & Hum.Cit.Ind., Bk.Rev.Ind. (1981-), Chic.Per.Ind., Child.Bk.Rev.Ind. (1981-), Curr.Cont., Hist.Abstr., Hum.Ind. **Document type:** academic/scholarly publication.
—BLDSC (9300.817000); Faxon; UnCover; SWETS.
Description: Presents original articles dealing with the American West such as the westward movement from the Atlantic to the Pacific, 20th Century regional studies, the Spanish borderlands, and developments in Western Canada, Northern Mexico, Alaska, and Hawaii.

WESTERN KENTUCKY JOURNAL. see *GENEALOGY AND HERALDRY*

WESTERN LEGAL HISTORY. see *LAW*

978 GW
WESTERN MAGAZIN; Zeitschrift fuer Western Historik. 1972. irreg. K.F. Bender Verlag, Bessunger Str. 47, 64285 Darmstadt, Germany.

3010 HISTORY — HISTORY OF NORTH AND SOUTH AMERICA

973 US ISSN 0882-3154
F486
WESTERN RESERVE HISTORICAL SOCIETY NEWS. 1946. q. $30 includes membership. Western Reserve Historical Society, Public Relations Dept., 10825 East Blvd., Cleveland, OH 44106. TEL 216-721-5722. FAX 216-721-0645. bk.rev. circ. 7,300. **Document type:** newsletter.
  Formerly: Western Reserve Historical Society, Cleveland. Publications (ISSN 0083-8985)

979 US ISSN 0083-9019
WESTERNLORE GHOST TOWN SERIES. 1963. irreg. price varies. Westernlore Press, Box 35305, Tucson, AZ 85740. TEL 602-297-5491. FAX 602-624-9951. Ed. Lynn R. Bailey.

971 CN ISSN 0382-0831
WESTMORLAND HISTORICAL SOCIETY. NEWSLETTER. 1965. 3/yr. Can.$10 membership. Westmorland Historical Society, R.R. No. 1, College Bridge, NB E0A 1L0, Canada. Ed. Edith Gillcash. bk.rev. circ. 200. **Document type:** newsletter.

977 US
WESTWARD. 1948. s-a. membership. St. Louis Westerners, 9 Shaw Place, St. Louis, MO 63110. TEL 314-621-2656. Ed. Robert L. Nicolay. circ. 200.

976.7 US ISSN 0043-4906
F417.W4
WHITE COUNTY HERITAGE. 1963. a. $10. White County Historical Society, Box 537, Searcy, AR 72143. TEL 501-268-8726. Ed. Cloie Presley. bk.rev. circ. 90. (processed; back issues avail. ($12 per vol.)) **Document type:** academic/scholarly publication.
  ●Also available online.
  Description: Covers the history and culture of White County.

977 US ISSN 0510-372X
F472.W5
WHITE RIVER VALLEY HISTORICAL QUARTERLY. 1961. q. $14 membership. White River Valley Historical Society, Box 555, Point Lookout, MO 65726. TEL 314-751-2212. FAX 417-538-4388. stat. circ. 200. (back issues avail.)
  Description: Information on the Valley's historical and genealogical heritage.

973 320 US
WILBUR S. SHEPPERSON SERIES IN HISTORY AND HUMANITIES. 1960. irreg. price varies. (University of Nevada, Departments of History and Political Science) University of Nevada Press, c/o Sandy Crooms, Reno, NV 89557-0076. TEL 702-784-6573. Ed. Jerome Edwards. circ. 1,300.
  Formerly: Nevada Studies in History and Political Science (ISSN 0077-7935)

975 US
WILD APPLE PRESS. 1976. q. $5. Friendship Landmark Society, West Main St., Friendship, NY 14739. Eds. John Maxson, Jennifer Wildman. illus.

WILD WEST. see *MILITARY*

973 390 US ISSN 0043-5597
F221
WILLIAM AND MARY QUARTERLY; a magazine of early American history and culture. 1892. q. $25 to individuals; students $12.50; institutions $30. Institute of Early American History and Culture, Box 8781, Williamsburg, VA 23187. TEL 804-221-1110. (Co-sponsors: College of William and Mary; Colonial Williamsburg Foundation) Ed. Michael McGiffert. bk.rev.; illus.; index, cum.index: vols.1-15, 16-30, 31-45. circ. 3,700. (also avail. in microform from JSC,KTO,UMI,PMC; reprint service avail. from KTO,UMI) **Indexed:** Abstr.Engl.Stud., Acad.Ind., Amer.Hist.& Life, Arts & Hum.Cit.Ind., Bk.Rev.Ind. (1965-), CERDIC, Child.Bk.Rev.Ind. (1965-), Curr.Cont., Hist.Abstr., Hum.Ind., Ind.Bk.Rev.Hum., M.L.A., Rel.& Theol.Abstr. (1991-).
  —BLDSC (9318.910000); Faxon; UnCover; SWETS; UMI.
  Description: Contains articles, notes, documents, and symposia reviews.

WILLIAMSBURG DECORATIVE ARTS SERIES. see *ART*

976 US
WILLIAMSON COUNTY HISTORICAL SOCIETY PUBLICATION. 1970. a. membership. Williamson County Historical Society, Box 71, Franklin, TN 37064. circ. 250.
  Formerly: Williamson County Historical Society Newsletter.
  Description: Contains articles written by society members pertaining to the county's history, geography and culture.

974 US
WILSON MUSEUM BULLETIN. 1963. 3/yr. $5 (free to libraries and schools). Castine Scientific Society, c/o Wilson Museum, Box 196, Castine, ME 04421-0196. TEL 207-326-8753. Ed. Norman Doudiet. circ. 700. **Indexed:** Amer.Hist.& Life, Hist.Abstr. **Document type:** bulletin.
  Description: Covers local history and museum activities.

970 970.1 US
WIND RIVER RENDEZVOUS. 1971. q. $10. St. Stephens Indian Mission Foundation, Box 306, St. Stephens, WY 82524. FAX 307-856-6797. Ed. Ronald L. Mamot. illus. circ. 39,000.

977.5 US ISSN 0043-6534
F576
WISCONSIN MAGAZINE OF HISTORY. 1917. q. $25. State Historical Society of Wisconsin, 816 State St., Madison, WI 53706. TEL 608-264-6400. Ed. Paul H. Hass. bk.rev.; bibl.; illus.; index, cum.index every 10 yrs. circ. 7,000. (also avail. in microform from MIM,UMI; reprint service avail. from KTO,UMI) **Indexed:** Amer.Bibl.Slavic & E.Eur.Stud., Amer.Hist.& Life, Hist.Abstr., Ind.Lit.Amer.Indian, M.L.A. **Document type:** academic/scholarly publication.
  —UnCover.
  Description: Publishes scholarly articles on the history of Wisconsin and the upper Midwest.

977 US ISSN 0276-4156
WISCONSIN PRESERVATION. 1977. bi-m. free. State Historical Society of Wisconsin, 816 State St., Madison, WI 53706. TEL 608-264-6501. Ed. Larry A. Reed. circ. 4,000. **Document type:** newsletter.
  Formerly: Wisconsin Preservation: National Register of Historic Places in Wisconsin. Newsletter.

977 917.704 US
WISCONSIN WEST MAGAZINE. 1900. bi-m. $14. Modern Communications, Inc., 2645 Harlem St., Ste. 1C, Eau Claire, WI 54701-4506. TEL 715-835-3800. Ed. Wayne D. Turnquist. adv. (back issues avail.)
  Description: Contains local folklore, history, and travel news.

WOMEN'S HISTORY NETWORK NEWS. see *WOMEN'S STUDIES*

WOMEN'S HISTORY RESOURCE CATALOG. see *WOMEN'S STUDIES*

WOODROW WILSON BIRTHPLACE NEWSLETTER. see *MUSEUMS AND ART GALLERIES*

974 US
WORLD GUIDE TO COVERED BRIDGES. 1959. irreg., latest 1989. $8. National Society for the Preservation of Covered Bridges, Inc., c/o Mrs. Christine Ellsworth, Corr.Sec., 44 Cleveland Ave., Worcester, MA 01603. TEL 508-756-4516. Ed. Bill Helsel. **Document type:** directory.
  Description: Lists authentic covered bridges throughout the world.

WORLD OF WINNERS; a current and historical perspective on awards and their winners. see *BIOGRAPHY*

971 US ISSN 0883-8135
F1001
WORLD TODAY SERIES: CANADA. 1985. a. $8.50. Stryker-Post Publications, P.O. Drawer 1200, Harpers Ferry, WV 25425. TEL 800-995-1400. FAX 304-535-6513. Ed. Wayne C. Thompson. **Document type:** academic/scholarly publication.
  Description: Contains valuable insight into the "Quiet Revolution" and US-Canada economic relations.

980 US ISSN 0092-4148
F1401
WORLD TODAY SERIES: LATIN AMERICA. 1967. a. $8.50. Stryker-Post Publications, P.O. Drawer 1200, Harpers Ferry, WV 25425. TEL 800-995-1400. FAX 304-535-6513. Ed. Pierre Etienne Dostert. circ. 15,000. **Document type:** academic/scholarly publication.
  Description: Centers on the economic problems of South America, as well as the current tensions in Central America.

975 355 US ISSN 0898-4204
WORLD WAR II. 1986. bi-m. $16.95 (foreign $22.95). Empire Press, 602 S. King St., Ste. 300, Leesburg, VA 22075. TEL 703-771-9400. FAX 703-777-4627. (Subscr. to: Box 375, Mt. Morris, IL 61054-7963. TEL 815-734-1115) Ed. C. Brian Kelly. adv.; bk.rev. circ. 227,000.
  —UnCover; UMI.
  Description: Articles look at the fighting men, the tactics, the weapons, the little-known incidents and unusual facts behind the major engagements.

975.8 920 US ISSN 0084-2621
WORMSLOE FOUNDATION. PUBLICATIONS. 1955. irreg., no.18, 1988. price varies. University of Georgia Press, 330 Research Dr., Athens, GA 30602-4901. TEL 706-369-6130. FAX 706-369-6131. (reprint service avail. from UMI) **Document type:** monographic series.

979 US ISSN 0512-4077
WRANGLER. 1968. 4/yr. $12. Westerners, San Diego Corral, Box 87307, San Diego, CA 92138-7307. TEL 619-442-8360. Ed. Bob Michaelis. bk.rev. circ. 230.

978.7 US
F756
WYOMING ANNALS. 1923. q. $9 individual membership; institutions $12. Wyoming Department of Commerce, Division of Parks & Cultural Resources, Barrett Bldg., Cheyenne, WY 82002. TEL 307-777-7019. FAX 307-777-6005. Ed. Mark Junge. bk.rev.; charts; illus.; index. circ. 2,000. **Indexed:** Amer.Hist.& Life, Hist.Abstr. **Document type:** government publication.
  —UnCover.
  Formerly: Annals of Wyoming (ISSN 0003-4991)

978.7 US ISSN 0043-972X
WYOMING HISTORY NEWS. 1953. 10/yr. $9 membership. Wyoming State Historical Society, Cheyenne, WY 82002. TEL 307-777-7015. Ed. Loren Jost. circ. 1,950. **Document type:** newsletter.
  Formerly: History News.

978 US ISSN 0084-3563
YALE WESTERN AMERICANA SERIES. 1962. irreg., latest 1992. price varies. Yale University Press, Box 209040, New Haven, CT 06520. TEL 203-432-0940.

YAXKIN. see *ANTHROPOLOGY*

YELLOWED PAGES. see *GENEALOGY AND HERALDRY*

976 US
YESTERDAY AND TODAY IN LAWRENCE COUNTY. 1978. s-a. $5 membership. Lawrence County Historical Society, c/o Mary L. Bailey, Box 431, Lawrenceburg, TN 38464. TEL 615-762-2249. FAX 615-762-2240. Ed. Virginia F. Lindsey. circ. 250.

974 US ISSN 1058-059X
YESTERDAY TODAY IN NEW JERSEY. 1991. bi-m. $6. C & S Publications, Inc., Box 374, Jersey City, NJ 07303-0374. TEL 201-332-2598. FAX 201-413-0023. Ed. Gary Burke. adv. contact: Charlene Burke. circ. 60,000.
  Description: Exploration of historic sites in New Jersey; lists current activities; walking tours and stories on New Jersey communities and how they evolved.

974.7 929 US ISSN 0044-037X
F116
YESTERYEARS; a quarterly magazine for the appreciation and study of New York State history and genealogy. 1956. q. $9. Malcolm O. Goodelle, Ed.& Pub., 3 Seymour St., Auburn, NY 13021. TEL 315-253-4058. adv.; bk.rev.; abstr.; bibl.; charts; illus.; stat. circ. 500. (also avail. in microform from UMI; reprint service avail. from UMI)
  —UMI.

971   CN   ISSN 0513-2711
YORK PIONEER. 1952. a. Can.$13 to non-members (foreign US$13). York Pioneer and Historical Society, P.O. Box 45026, Mid-Yonge PO, 2482 Yonge St., Toronto, ON M4P 3E3, Canada. TEL 416-481-8648. Ed. Jeanine C. Avigdor. circ. 600.
  Description: Contains short articles on the history of Toronto and the area.

971.9   CN
YUKON READER; recording the spirit and the times of the Far Northwest. 1989. m. $24. World Yukon Publications Ltd., Box 4306, Whitehorse, Yukon Y1A 3T3, Canada. TEL 403-668-2355. FAX 403-668-7953. Ed. Sam Holloway. adv. circ. 7,000.
  Description: Covers the history and people of the Yukon.

971   GW   ISSN 0944-7008
F1001
ZEITSCHRIFT FUER KANADA-STUDIEN. (Text in English, French, German) 1981. s-a. DM.50. (Gesellschaft fuer Kanada-Studien) A V - Verlag Franz Fischer, Schroeckstr. 8, 86152 Augsburg, Germany. TEL 0821-158083. FAX 0821-155518. Ed. Udo Kempf. circ. 850. (back issues avail.) **Indexed:** Amer.Hist.& Life, Hist.Abstr. Document type: academic/scholarly publication.
  Formerly: Gesellschaft fuer Kanada-Studien. Zeitschrift (ISSN 0722-849X)

946.3   AU   ISSN 0049-8645
ZEITSCHRIFT FUER LATEINAMERIKA WIEN. (Summaries in Spanish) 1971. 2/yr. S.180($10) Oesterreichisches Lateinamerika Institut, Schmerlingplatz 8, A-1010 Vienna, Austria. TEL 0222-5233315. Ed. Gerhard Drekonja. adv.; bk.rev. circ. 500. **Document type:** academic/scholarly publication.
  —BLDSC (9468.870000).

HISTORY — History Of The Near East

956   NE   ISSN 0378-4215
ACTA IRANICA; encyclopedie permanente des etudes iraniennes. (Consists of 2 sub-series: Hommages et Opera Minora; Textes et Memoires) 1974. irreg., vol.29, 1990. price varies. E.J. Brill, P.O. Box 9000, 2300 PA Leiden, Netherlands. TEL 31-71-312624. FAX 31-71-317532. TELEX 39296 BRILL NL. (In N. America: E.J. Brill, 24 Hudson St., Kinderhook, NY 12106. TEL 800-962-4406. FAX 518-758-1959) (back issues avail.) **Indexed:** Bibl.Ling. **Document type:** monographic series.
  Description: Scholarly studies of topics in the art, archaeology, ancient history and linguistics of the Iranian region.
  Refereed Serial

930 913 722   US
AEGYPTOLOGISCHE FORSCHUNGEN. irreg., vol.1-25, 1973. price varies. J.J. Augustin, Inc., Locust Valley, NY 11560. TEL 516-676-1510.

956   US   ISSN 0732-6505
AIDS AND RESEARCH TOOLS IN ANCIENT NEAR EASTERN STUDIES. Short title: ARTANES. 1977. irreg., no.5, 1990. price varies. (International Institute of Mesopotamian Area Studies) Undena Publications, Box 97, Malibu, CA 90265. TEL 805-746-5870. FAX 805-746-2728. (Dist. by: Crescent Academic Services, 29528 Madera Ave., Shafter, CA 93263) Ed. Giorgio Buccellati. bibl.; charts; illus. (back issues avail.)

956   US
AIDS AND RESEARCH TOOLS IN MIDDLE EASTERN STUDIES. Abbreviated title: A R T M E S. 1983. irreg. price varies. Undena Publications, Box 97, Malibu, CA 90265. TEL 805-746-5870. FAX 805-746-2728. (Dist. by: Crescent Academic Services, 29528 Madera Ave., Shafter, CA 93263) charts; illus.; index.

965   AE
ALGERIE ACTUALITE; hebdomadaire national politique - economique. (Text in French) 1965. w. Moujahid, 2 rue Jacques Cartier, 16000 Algiers, Algeria. TEL 2-63-54-20. TELEX 66475. (Dist. in US by: African Imprint Library Services, Box 350, West Falmouth, MA 02574. TEL 508-540-5378) Ed. Kamel BelKacem. adv.; illus.; tr.lit. circ. 250,000.

930   GW   ISSN 0232-8461
ALTORIENTALISCHE FORSCHUNGEN. (Subseries of: Schriften zur Geschichte und Kultur des Alten Orients) (Text in English, German) 1974. 2/yr. DM.198 (foreign DM.205). Akademie Verlag GmbH, Muehlenstr. 33-34, 13187 Berlin, Germany. TEL 030-47889348. FAX 030-47889357. (U.S. subscr. to: VCH Publishers Inc., 303 N.W. 12th Ave., Deerfield Beach, FL 33442-1788) Ed. V. Haas. bibl.; illus. **Indexed:** Bibl.Ling. Document type: academic/scholarly publication.

AMERICAN ACADEMY FOR JEWISH RESEARCH. MONOGRAPH SERIES. see *RELIGIONS AND THEOLOGY — Judaic*

AMERICAN ACADEMY FOR JEWISH RESEARCH. PROCEEDINGS OF THE A A J R. see *RELIGIONS AND THEOLOGY — Judaic*

AMERICAN ACADEMY FOR JEWISH RESEARCH. TEXT AND STUDIES SERIES. see *RELIGIONS AND THEOLOGY — Judaic*

956   US
AMERICAN INSTITUTE FOR THE STUDY OF MIDDLE EASTERN CIVILIZATION. JOURNAL. 1980. q. $20 to individuals; institutions $25. American Institute for the Study of Middle Eastern Civilization, 125 Onslow Pl., Kew Gardens, NY 11415. TEL 718-441-6989. Ed. J.D. Kreindler.

950   US   ISSN 0066-0035
DS101
AMERICAN SCHOOLS OF ORIENTAL RESEARCH. ANNUAL. irreg., latest 1980-81. (American Schools of Oriental Research) Scholars Press, Box 15399, Atlanta, GA 30333-0399. TEL 404-727-2320. FAX 404-727-2348. Ed. William G. Dever. (also avail. in microform from UMI) **Indexed:** A.I.C.P., Anthropol.Lit.
  —UMI.

AMERICAN SCHOOLS OF ORIENTAL RESEARCH. BULLETIN. see *ORIENTAL STUDIES*

ANCIENT HISTORY; RESOURCES FOR TEACHERS. see *HISTORY*

956   US
ANCIENT NEAR EASTERN TEXTS AND STUDIES. 1986. irreg., latest no.11. $39.95 per no. Edwin Mellen Press, 415 Ridge St., Box 450, Lewiston, NY 14092. TEL 716-754-2788. FAX 716-754-4056. **Document type:** monographic series.

956   SP   ISSN 0212-159X
ANDALUCIA ISLAMICA. TEXTOS Y ESTUDIOS. 1980. a. 2120 ptas. Universidad de Granada, Facultad de Filosofia y Letras, Departamento de Historia del Islam, Campus Universitario de Cartuja, Granada, Spain. Ed. J. Bosch-Vila. adv.; bk.rev. circ. 1,000.

955.3   SU
AL-ARAB. 1967. bi-m. 200 SRI. P.O. Box 137, Riyadh 11411, Saudi Arabia. TEL 966-1-4621223. Ed. Hamad al-Jasser. adv.; bk.rev.; cum.index: 1967-1990. circ. 6,000.
  Description: Specialized journal concered with the history and geography of the Arabian peninsula.

956 808 330   US   ISSN 0890-1341
ARAB BOOK WORLD. 1981. q. $48. Inter-Crescent Publishing Co., Inc., 12021 Nieta Dr., Garden Grove, CA 92640. TEL 714-537-1000. Ed. J. Younis. bk.rev. circ. 600. (back issues avail.)
  —BLDSC (1583.224120).

956   US
ARAB DIGEST. 1973. m. $25. Gulf Publishing Ltd., G.P.O. Box 2754, New York, NY 10116. Ed. James Nazer. adv.; bk.rev.; illus. circ. 25,000.

956 961   TI   ISSN 0330-8081
DS62.4
ARAB HISTORICAL REVIEW FOR OTTOMAN STUDIES. (Text in Arabic, English, French) 1990. 2/yr. $160. Centre d'Etudes et de Recherches Ottomanes Morisques de Documentation et d'Information (CEROMDI), B.P. 50, Cite des Andalous, 1110 Zaghouan, Tunisia. TEL 216-2-676446. FAX 216-2-676710. Ed. Abdeljelil Temimi. **Indexed:** Amer.Hist.& Life (until 1990), Hist.Abstr. (until 1990). Document type: academic/scholarly publication.
  Description: Covers the history of the Arab countries during the Ottoman period.

956   NE   ISSN 0925-2908
ARAB HISTORY AND CIVILIZATION; studies and texts. 1991. irreg., vol.3, 1993. price varies. E.J. Brill, P.O. Box 9000, 2300 PA Leiden, Netherlands. TEL 31-71-312624. FAX 31-71-317532. TELEX 39296 BRILL NL. (In N. America: E.J. Brill, 24 Hudson St., Kinderhook, NY 12106. TEL 800-962-4406. FAX 518-758-1959) **Document type:** monographic series.

953 956 320   NE
ARAB STRUGGLE. (Text in Arabic, English) suspended 1982; resumed 1985. q. free. International Union of Students, 211 Lann Van Meerdervoort, The Hague, Netherlands.
  Formerly: Arab Bulletin.

ARAB WORLD ALMANAC. see *EDUCATION — Teaching Methods And Curriculum*

956   UK
ARABIA PAST & PRESENT SERIES. 1972. irreg. (approx. 1/yr.), latest vol.23. price varies. Oleander Press, 17 Stansgate Ave., Cambridge CB2 2QZ, England. (U.S. address: 80 Eighth Ave., Ste. 303, New York, N.Y. 10011) Ed. Philip Ward. circ. 1,500. **Document type:** academic/scholarly publication.

953.57   TS
ARABIAN GULF RESEARCH REVIEW. q. Cultural Foundation, Center for Documentation and Research, P.O. Box 2380, Abu Dhabi, United Arab Emirates. TEL 215300. FAX 336059. TELEX 2214 CULCEN EM. Ed. Muhammad Morsi Abdullah.

953 320   UK   ISSN 0305-036X
DS201
ARABIAN STUDIES. 1974. irreg. price varies. (Cambridge University, Middle East Centre) Cambridge University Press, Edinburgh Bldg. Shaftesbury Rd., Cambridge CB2 2RU, England. TEL 0223-312393. FAX 0223-315052. TELEX 851817256. (N. American addr.: Cambridge University Press, Journals Dept., 40 W. 20th St., New York, NY 10011. TEL 212-924-3900. FAX 212-691-3239) Eds. R.B. Serjeant, R.L. Bidwell. bk.rev.; bibl.; charts. **Document type:** academic/scholarly publication.

956   AU   ISSN 0066-6440
PJ5
ARCHIV FUER ORIENTFORSCHUNG; internationale Zeitschrift fuer die Wissenschaft vom Vorderen Orient. irreg., vol.36, 1989. price varies. Universitaet Wien, Institut fuer Orientforschung, Universitaetsstr. 7, A-1010 Vienna, Austria. (reprint service avail. from SCH) **Indexed:** Bibl.Ling. Document type: academic/scholarly publication.
  —BLDSC (1621.585000).

956 297   GW   ISSN 0378-2808
ARCHIVUM OTTOMANICUM. (Text in English, French, German) 1969. a. DM.148. Harrassowitz Verlag, Taunusstr. 14, 65183 Wiesbaden, Germany. TEL 0611-530-0. FAX 0611-530570. TELEX 4186135. (Subscr. to: Postfach 2929, 65019 Wiesbaden, Germany) Ed.Bd. bk.rev. circ. 350. (back issues avail.) **Indexed:** Amer.Hist.& Life, Bibl.Ling., Hist.Abstr. Document type: academic/scholarly publication.

956   US   ISSN 0145-6334
ASSUR. (Subseries of: Monographic Journals of the Near East) 1974. irreg., vol.4, no.3. price varies. (International Institute of Mesopotamian Area Studies) Undena Publications, Box 97, Malibu, CA 90265. TEL 805-746-5870. FAX 805-746-2728. (Dist. by: Crescent Academic Services, 29528 Madera Ave., Shafter, CA 93263) Ed. Dr. Claudio Saporetti. bibl.; charts; illus. (back issues avail.) **Indexed:** M.L.A., Old Test.Abstr.
  —BLDSC (1746.772500).

BABYLON; Beitraege zur Juedischen Gegenwart. see *RELIGIONS AND THEOLOGY — Judaic*

320   BA
AL-BAHRAIN. (Text in Arabic) 1959. w. Ministry of Information, P.O. Box 26005, Isa Town, Bahrain. TEL 683986. FAX 685114. TELEX 8399. Ed. Hamad al-Mannai. circ. 3,000.
  Formerly: Bahrain News - Akhbar al-Bahrain (ISSN 0408-2133)

HISTORY — HISTORY OF THE NEAR EAST

026 296   BA
BAHRAIN TODAY MAGAZINE/BAHRAIN AL-YAUM. (Text in English) w. 2400 din. Ministry of Information, Box 253, Manama, Bahrain. Ed. Ammad S. Kamal.

956 890 400 100   IT
BAZMAVEP. (Text in Armenian, English, French, Italian; summaries in Armenian and French) 1843. s-a. L.27000($25) Academia Armena Sancti Lazari, Isola di San Lazzaro, 30126 Venice, Italy. Ed. Boghoslevon Zekiyan. bk.rev. (back issues avail.) **Indexed:** Bibl.Ling., MLA.

BEER-SHEVA. see *RELIGIONS AND THEOLOGY — Judaic*

BEIRUT REVIEW. see *POLITICAL SCIENCE — International Relations*

950   GW   ISSN 0067-4931
BEIRUTER TEXTE UND STUDIEN. (Text in Arabic and German) 1964. irreg., vol.56, 1994. price varies. (Deutsche Morgenlaendische Gesellschaft Beirut, Orient-Institut, LE) Franz Steiner Verlag Wiesbaden GmbH, Birkenwaldstr. 44, 70191 Stuttgart, Germany. TEL 0711-2582-0. FAX 0711-2582290. TELEX 723636-DAZ-D. (Subscr. to: Postfach 101061, 70009 Stuttgart, Germany) **Document type:** monographic series.

BIBLIOTHECA AEGYPTIACA. see *ARCHAEOLOGY*

956   US   ISSN 0732-6440
BIBLIOTHECA MESOPOTAMICA. 1975. irreg., latest no.24, 1991. price varies. (International Institute of Mesopotamian Area Studies) Undena Publications, Box 97, Malibu, CA 90265. TEL 805-746-5870. FAX 805-746-2878. (Dist. by: Crescent Academic Services, 29528 Madera Ave., Shafter, CA 93262) Ed. Giorgio Buccellati. bibl.; charts; illus. (back issues avail.)

BIBLIOTHECA ORIENTALIS. see *HISTORY — Abstracting, Bibliographies, Statistics*

956   UK
BRITISH JOURNAL OF MIDDLE EASTERN STUDIES. 1974. s-a. £20 (U.S. $40; elsewhere £22). (University of Durham, Centre for Middle Eastern & Islamic Studies) Brismes, South End Hse., South Rd., Durham DH1 3TG, England. TEL 091-374-3035. FAX 091-374-2830. Ed. P.G. Starkey. adv.; bk.rev. circ. 1,000. **Indexed:** A.I.C.P., Amer.Hist.& Life (1993-), Bibl.Ling., Hist.Abstr. (1993-), I D A, Mid.East: Abstr.& Ind., Per.Islam. (1991-). **Document type:** academic/scholarly publication. —UnCover; SWETS.
    Formerly (until 1991): British Society for Middle Eastern Studies. Bulletin (ISSN 0305-6139)
    Description: Promotes the study of Middle Eastern cultural region in the UK.

BULLETIN DES ETUDES KARAITES. see *RELIGIONS AND THEOLOGY — Judaic*

956   US   ISSN 0742-1141
BYZANTINA KAI METABYZANTINA. 1978. irreg., no.4, 1986. price varies. Undena Publications, Box 97, Malibu, CA 90265. TEL 805-746-5870. FAX 805-746-2728. (Dist. by: Crescent Academic Services, 29528 Madera Ave., Shafter, CA 93263) Ed. Spiros Vyronis, Jr. (back issues avail.)

939 956   DK   ISSN 0902-5499
C N I PUBLICATIONS. (Text in English, German) s-a. (Carsten Niebuhr Institute) Museum Tusculanum Press, University of Copenhagen, Njalsgade 92, DK-2300 Copenhagen S, Denmark. TEL 45-35-32-91-09. FAX 45-35-32-91-13. (Dist. in U.S. and Canada by: Paul & Co., c/o P C S Data Processing, Inc., 360 W. 31st St., New York, NY 10001. TEL 212-564-3730. FAX 212-971-7200) Ed. Paul John Frandsen. illus. **Document type:** academic/scholarly publication.
    Description: Covers all aspects of life and culture in the ancient Near and Middle East as well as North Africa.

956.94   IS   ISSN 0334-4657
CATHEDRA. (Text in Hebrew; abstracts in English) 1971. q. $45 (effective Fall 1993). Yad Izhak Ben-Zvi, P.O. Box 7660, Jerusalem 91076, Israel. TEL 972-2-637268. FAX 972-2-638310. bk.rev. circ. 2,500. **Indexed:** Amer.Hist.& Life, Hist.Abstr., Ind.Artic.Jew.Stud., Ind.Heb.Per. **Document type:** academic/scholarly publication.

026 296   IS
CENTRAL ARCHIVES FOR THE HISTORY OF THE JEWISH PEOPLE NEWSLETTER/ARKHIYON HA-MERKAZI LE-TOLDOT HA-AM HA-YEHUDI. YEDIOT. 1961. a. $5. Central Archives for the History of the Jewish People, Hebrew University Campus, Sprinzak Bldg., Box 1149, 91010 Jerusalem, Israel. Eds. Daniel J. Cohen, Aryeh Segall. illus. circ. 1,200.

CENTRE DE RECHERCHE D'HISTOIRE ET CIVILISATION DE BYZANCE. TRAVAUX ET MEMOIRES. see *HISTORY — History Of Europe*

CHRONIQUE D'EGYPTE. see *ORIENTAL STUDIES*

COMPUTER AIDED RESEARCH IN NEAR EASTERN STUDIES. see *HISTORY — Computer Applications*

DATA SETS: CUNEIFORM TEXTS; electronic data processing of Mesopotamian materials, philological and artifactual. see *HISTORY — Computer Applications*

956   GW   ISSN 0342-118X
DS41
DEUTSCHE ORIENT-GESELLSCHAFT. MITTEILUNGEN. (Text and summaries in English, French, German) 1898. a. DM.80 to members; non-members DM.105. Deutsche Orient-Gesellschaft e.V., Altorientalisches Seminar, Bitterstr. 8-12, 14195 Berlin, Germany. TEL 030-8383347. FAX 030-8314252. Ed. Reinhard Dittmann. circ. 900. (back issues avail.) **Indexed:** Bibl.Ling., M.L.A. **Document type:** academic/scholarly publication.
    Description: Preliminary reports on excavations in the Near East, with emphasis on philology and archaeology.

936   NE   ISSN 0169-7943
DOCUMENTA ET MONUMENTA ORIENTIS ANTIQUI. 1947. irreg., vol.20, 1983. price varies. E.J. Brill, P.O. Box 9000, 2300 PA Leiden, Netherlands. TEL 31-71-312624. FAX 31-71-317532. TELEX 39296 BRILL NL. (In N. America: E.J. Brill, 24 Hudson St., Kinderhook, NY 12106. TEL 800-962-4406. FAX 518-758-1959) Ed. J. Sasson. illus. (back issues avail.) **Document type:** monographic series.
Refereed Serial

EASTERN ART REPORT. see *ART*

932   NE   ISSN 0927-0043
EGYPTOLOGISCHE UITGAVEN/EGYPTOLOGICAL EDITIONS. 1982. irreg., vol.7, 1991. price varies. Nederlands Instituut voor het Nabije Oosten - Netherlands Institute for the Near East, Witte Singel 24, P.O. Box 9515, 2300 RA Leiden, Netherlands. Ed.Bd. **Document type:** monographic series.

ETUDES SUR LE JUDAISME MEDIEVAL. see *RELIGIONS AND THEOLOGY — Judaic*

FARHANG-E IRAN ZAMIN. see *ORIENTAL STUDIES*

FIHRIST; index to Arabic periodical literature. see *BIBLIOGRAPHIES*

956   FR   ISSN 0533-0866
FRANCE - PAYS ARABES. 1968. m. 150 F. (foreign 200 F.). 12-14 rue Augereau, 75007 Paris, France. TEL 45-55-27-52. FAX 45-51-27-26. Ed. Lucien Bitterlin. adv.; bk.rev.; film rev. circ. 37,500.

956   NE
GESCHICHTE DES ARABISCHEN SCHRIFTTUMS. 1967. irreg., vol.9, 1984. price varies. E.J. Brill, P.O. Box 9000, 2300 PA Leiden, Netherlands. TEL 31-71-312624. FAX 31-71-317532. TELEX 39296 BRILL NL. (In N. America: E.J. Brill, 24 Hudson St., Kinderhook, NY 12106. TEL 800-962-4406. FAX 518-758-1959) Ed. Fuat Sezgin. **Document type:** monographic series.
    Description: Covers the history of Arabic literature until circa 430 AH (11th century CE), covering Qur'an, poetry, medicine and the sciences, lexicography and grammatical writings.

350   UK   ISSN 0340-6369
GIORGIO LEVI DELLA VIDA CONFERENCES. REPORTS OF THE CONFERENCE.. 1970. biennial. price varies. Cambridge University Press, Edinburgh Bldg., Shaftesbury Rd., Cambridge DB2 2RU, England. TEL 0223-312393. FAX 0223-315052. TELEX 8151817256. (N. American addr.: Cambridge University Press. Journals Dept., 40 W. 20th St., New York, NY 10011. TEL 212-924-3900. FAX 212-691-3239) (Co-sponsor: University of California, Los Angeles) (back issues avail.) **Document type:** proceedings.

956   US
GULF HANDBOOK; a guide to the eight Persian Gulf countries. 1977. irreg. $15.95. Garrett Park Press, Box 190F. Garrett Park, MD 20896. TEL 301-946-2553. Eds. Peter Kilner, Jonathan Wallace. illus.

932   GW   ISSN 0170-2769
HABELTS DISSERTATIONSDRUCKE. REIHE AEGYPTOLOGIE. 1976. irreg., no.5, 1985. price varies. Dr. Rudolf Habelt GmbH, Am Buchenhang 1, 53115 Bonn, Germany. TEL 0228-232016. FAX 0228-232017. **Document type:** monographic series.

HANDBUCH DER ORIENTALISTIK. see *ORIENTAL STUDIES*

HANDBUCH DER ORIENTALISTIK. 1. ABTEILUNG. DER NAHE UND DER MITTLERE OSTEN. see *ORIENTAL STUDIES*

956.01   US   ISSN 0073-0459
HARVARD ARMENIAN TEXTS AND STUDIES. 1965. irreg., no.8, 1989. price varies. Harvard University Press, 79 Garden St., Cambridge, MA 02138. TEL 617-495-2600. FAX 617-495-5898. Ed. Avedis K. Sanjian.
Refereed Serial

955   US
HARVARD IRANIAN SERIES. 1973. irreg, no.5, 1988. price varies. Harvard University Press, 79 Garden St., Cambridge, MA 02138. TEL 617-495-2600. FAX 617-495-5898.

956   US
HARVARD MIDDLE EASTERN MONOGRAPHS. 1958. irreg., vol.28, 1994. price varies. Harvard University, Center for Middle Eastern Studies, 1737 Cambridge St., Cambridge, MA 02138. TEL 617-495-4232. FAX 617-496-8584. E-mail: mideast@husc4.harvard.edu. **Document type:** monographic series, academic/scholarly publication.
    Formerly: Harvard Middle Eastern Studies (ISSN 0073-0580)
    Description: Features volumes on the contemporary and medieval Middle East.

950   SZ   ISSN 0073-0947
HAUTES ETUDES ISLAMIQUES ET ORIENTALES D'HISTOIRE COMPAREE. 1970. irreg, no.8, 1978. price varies. (Ecole Pratique des Hautes Etudes, Centre de Recherches d'Histoire et de Philologie, FR) Librairie Droz S.A., 11, rue Massot, CH-1211 Geneva 12, Switzerland. TEL 022-3466666. FAX 022-3472391. Ed. Jean Aubin. circ. 500. **Document type:** monographic series.
—CCC.

HOLY LAND; illustrated quarterly of the Franciscan custody of the holy land. see *RELIGIONS AND THEOLOGY — Roman Catholic*

HOLY PLACES OF PALESTINE. see *RELIGIONS AND THEOLOGY*

956.12   LY
AL-INSAF. a. Libyan Studies Center, P.O. Box 5070, Sidi Munaider, Tripoli, Libya. TEL 33996. FAX 31616. TELEX 20424. **Document type:** academic/scholarly publication.

950   BE   ISSN 0575-1330
PJ9
INSTITUT DOMINICAIN D'ETUDES ORIENTALES DU CAIRE. MELANGES. vol.19, 1989. a. 3000 BEF (effective 1994). Editions Peeters s.pr.l., Bondgenotenlaan 153, B-3000 Louvain, Belgium. TEL 32-16-235170. FAX 32-16-228500. bk.rev.; index. (back issues avail.) **Indexed:** Bibl.Ling., Per.Islam. (1991-). **Document type:** academic/scholarly publication.

HISTORY — HISTORY OF THE NEAR EAST

956   NE   ISSN 0073-8549
INSTITUT HISTORIQUE ET ARCHEOLOGIQUE NEERLANDAIS DE STAMBOUL. PUBLICATIONS. (Text in English, French, German) 1956. irreg., vol.69, 1992. price varies. (Institut Historique et Archeologique Neerlandais de Stamboul, TU - Nederlands Historisch-Archaeologisch Instituut te Istanbul) Nederlands Instituut voor Het Nabije Oosten, Witte Singel 24, P.O. Box 9515, 2300 RA Leiden, Netherlands. Ed.Bd. Document type: monographic series.
    Description: Scholarly monographs on archaeological, historical, and linguistic topics pertaining to the Near East.

956.94   LE
INSTITUTE FOR PALESTINE STUDIES. ISRAELI KNESSET SERIES. (Text in Arabic) 1971. irreg. price varies. Institute for Palestine Studies, Box 11-7164, Beirut, Lebanon. TEL 868387. FAX 814193. TELEX 23317 MADAF LE. (U.S. subscr. to: Box 25301, Georgetown Sta., Washington, DC 20007. TEL 202-342-3990. FAX 202-342-3927) Document type: monographic series.

956.94   LE   ISSN 0073-8816
INSTITUTE FOR PALESTINE STUDIES. MONOGRAPH SERIES. (Text mainly in Arabic; occasionally in English or French) 1966. irreg. price varies. Institute for Palestine Studies, P.O. Box 11-7164, Beirut, Lebanon. TEL 868387. FAX 814193. TELEX 23317 MADAF LE. (U.S. subscr. to: Box 25301, Georgetown Sta., Washington, DC 20007. TEL 202-342-3990. FAX 202-342-3927) Document type: monographic series.

956.94   LE
INSTITUTE FOR PALESTINE STUDIES. ZIONIST CONGRESS SERIES. (Text in Arabic) 1971. irreg. price varies. Institute for Palestine Studies, P.O. Box 11-7164, Beirut, Lebanon. TEL 868387. FAX 814193. TELEX 23317 MADAF LE. (U.S. subscr. to: Box 25301, Georgetown Sta., Washington, DC 20007. TEL 202-342-3990. FAX 202-342-3927) Document type: monographic series.

956   UK   ISSN 0266-6952
BP52.5
INSTITUTE OF MUSLIM MINORITY AFFAIRS. JOURNAL. (Text and summaries in English) 1979. s-a. £15($23) to individuals; institutions £30 ($45). Institute of Muslim Minority Affairs, 46 Goodge St., London W1P 1FJ, England. TEL 636-6740. FAX 632-4194. TELEX 66601327. Ed. Syed Z. Abedin. adv.; bk.rev.; circ. 5,000 (controlled). (back issues avail.) **Indexed:** Amer.Hist.& Life, ASSIA, Documentatieblad, Hist.Abstr., HR Rep., Int.Lab.Doc., Refug.Abstr., Rel.Ind.One, Sociol.Abstr., SOPODA.
●Also available online. Vendor(s): BRS Online Products, DIALOG Information Services, Inc.
—BLDSC (4777.760000); UnCover.
    Description: Devoted to the social, economic and political affairs of the Muslim minority.

INTERNATIONAL ASSOCIATION FOR BYZANTINE STUDIES. BULLETIN D'INFORMATION ET DE COORDINATION. see HISTORY — History Of Europe

INTERNATIONAL CONGRESS FOR BYZANTINE STUDIES. ACTS/CONGRES INTERNATIONAL DES ETUDES BYZANTINES. ACTES. see HISTORY — History Of Europe

059.927   US   ISSN 0740-5375
INTERNATIONAL JOURNAL OF ISLAMIC AND ARABIC STUDIES. 1984. 2/yr. $20 to individuals; institutions $30; students $15. International Institute of Islamic and Arabic Studies, Box 6165, Bloomington, IN 47407. TEL 812-339-6180. Ed. Salman H. Al-Ani. adv.; bk.rev. circ. 1,200. (back issues avail.) **Indexed:** Bibl.Ling., Per.Islam. Document type: academic/scholarly publication.

956   US   ISSN 0272-7919
DR401
INTERNATIONAL JOURNAL OF TURKISH STUDIES. 1979. irreg., latest vol.5, nos.1&2. $21 to individuals; institutions $27. University of Wisconsin, 4255 Humanities Bldg., Madison, WI 53706. TEL 608-263-1825. FAX 608-262-2150. Ed. Kemal H. Karpat. adv.; bk.rev. circ. 700. (back issues avail.) **Indexed:** Amer.Bibl.Slavic & E.Eur.Stud. Document type: academic/scholarly publication.
—BLDSC (4542.696500); UnCover.

956   US   ISSN 0742-1133
INVITED LECTURES ON THE MIDDLE EAST AT THE UNIVERSITY OF TEXAS AT AUSTIN. 1976. irreg., no.4, 1980. (University of Texas, Austin) Undena Publications, Box 97, Malibu, CA 90265. TEL 805-746-5870. FAX 805-746-2728. (Dist. by: Crescent Academic Services, 29528 Madera Ave., Shafter, CA 93263) Ed. D. Schmandt-Besserat. (back issues avail.)

955   UK   ISSN 0578-6967
DS251
IRAN. (Text in English) 1963. a. £30($60) British Institute of Persian Studies, c/o British Academy, 20-21 Cornwall Terrace, London NW1 4QP, England. TEL 44-71-920-0823. (Back issues avail. from: Publications Secretary, 42 Thomas More House, Barbican, London EC2Y 8BT, England) Ed. Vesta Curtis. circ. 600. (back issues avail.) **Indexed:** A.I.C.P., Anthropol.Lit., Avery Ind.Archit.Per., Bibl.Ling. Document type: academic/scholarly publication.
—BLDSC (4567.522400); SWETS.
    Description: Discusses political, social and cultural issues related to Iran.

958   IR
▼**IRAN AND CENTRAL ASIA.** (Text in Farsi, summaries in English) 1993. a. Mu'assasah-i Mutala'at va tahqiqat-i Farhangi, Mo'assaseh Bldg., 64 St., Seyyed Jamal-eddin Ave., Tehran 14374, Iran. TEL 98-21-688037. FAX 98-21-686317. Ed. Vahab Vali. circ. 1,500. Document type: academic/scholarly publication.
    Description: Publishes studies in the history, civilization, geography and culture of Iran and Central Asia.

955   US
IRAN NAMEH; a Persian journal of Iranian studies. 1982. 4/yr. $35 to individuals; institutions $65; students $20. Foundation for Iranian Studies, 4343 Montgomery Ave., Ste. 200, Bethesda, MD 20814. TEL 301-657-1990. FAX 301-657-4381. Ed. Hormoz Hekmat. adv.; bk.rev. circ. 1,000. **Indexed:** Mid.East: Abstr. & Ind. Document type: academic/scholarly publication.

955   IR
IRANSHENASI; a journal of Iranian studies. (Text in Persian) 1991. m. IRl.500 per no. Iranshenasi Magazine, c/o Bank Tejarat, S. Hafez Ave., P.O. Box 11365-8761, Tehran, Iran.
    Description: Historical, social and cultural studies of Iran.

956.7   II   ISSN 0047-1429
IRAQ NEWS BULLETIN. (Text in English) 1972. q. Embassy of the Republic of Iraq, Press Section, 33 Golf Links, New Delhi, India. charts; illus.

ISLAMIC ART AND ARCHITECTURE. see ART

ISRAELI FOREIGN AFFAIRS; an independent research report on Israel's diplomatic and military activities around the world. see POLITICAL SCIENCE — International Relations

956.1   GW   ISSN 0418-9701
DS401
ISTANBULER MITTEILUNGEN. BEIHEFTE. 1966. irreg. price varies. (Deutsches Archaeologisches Institut, Abteilung Istanbul) Ernst Wasmuth Verlag GmbH, Fuerststr. 133, 72072 Tuebingen, Germany. TEL 07071-33658. FAX 07071-35776. circ. 600. Document type: academic/scholarly publication.

ISTITUTO ELLENICO DI STUDI BIZANTINI E POSTBIZANTINI, VENICE. BIBLIOTECA. see HISTORY — History Of Europe

JEWISH QUARTERLY REVIEW. see RELIGIONS AND THEOLOGY — Judaic

JORDANIAN NATIONAL BIBLIOGRAPHY; annual register of book production in Jordan. see BIBLIOGRAPHIES

JOURNAL OF ASIAN HISTORY. see HISTORY — History Of Asia

281.7 932.023   BE   ISSN 1016-5584
JOURNAL OF COPTIC STUDIES. 1990. a. 1500 BEF (effective 1993). (International Association for Coptic Studies) Editions Peeters s.p.r.l., Bondgenotenlaan 153, B-3000 Louvain, Belgium. TEL 32-16-235170. FAX 32-16-228500. Ed.Bd. bk.rev. (back issues avail.) Document type: academic/scholarly publication.
—BLDSC (4965.325000).
    Description: Publishes articles on all apects of pre-modern Coptic society, including literature, history, archaeology, art, religion, linguistics and related subjects.

JOURNAL OF MEDITERRANEAN STUDIES; history, culture and society in the Mediterranean world. see HUMANITIES: COMPREHENSIVE WORKS

956.94   US   ISSN 0377-919X
DS119.7
JOURNAL OF PALESTINE STUDIES; a quarterly on Palestinian affairs and the Arab-Israeli conflict. (Supplement to: A J M E News) (Text in English) 1971. q. $30 to individuals (foreign $36); institutions $46 (foreign $52); students $19 (foreign $25) (effective 1994). (Institute for Palestine Studies) University of California Press, Journals Division, 2120 Berkeley Way, Berkeley, CA 94720. TEL 510-643-7154. FAX 510-642-9917. (Co-sponsor: Kuwait University) Eds. Hisham Sharabi, Philip Maltar. adv.; bk.rev.; bibl.; cum.index: 1971-1981. circ. 4,500. (also avail. in microform from UMI; back issues avail.; reprint service avail. from UMI) **Indexed:** A.B.C.Pol.Sci., Alt.Press Ind., Amer.Hist.& Life, Curr.Cont., Hist.Abstr., Int.Polit.Sci.Abstr., Mid.East: Abstr.& Ind., P.A.I.S., Polit.Sci.Abstr., Refug.Abstr., Sociol.Abstr., SSCI, SSCI. Document type: academic/scholarly publication.
—BLDSC (5028.200000); Faxon; UnCover; SWETS; UMI. CCC.
    Description: Devoted exclusively to Palestinian affairs and the Arab-Israeli conflict.
    Refereed Serial

JOURNAL OF SEMITIC STUDIES. see LINGUISTICS

950   US   ISSN 0149-1784
DS41
JOURNAL OF SOUTH ASIAN AND MIDDLE EASTERN STUDIES. 1977. q. $20 to individuals; institutions $25; foreign $30. Pakistan American Foundation, c/o Dr. Hafeez Malik, Ed., 421 SAC, Villanova University, Villanova, PA 19085. TEL 215-519-4738. FAX 215-519-6419. adv.; bk.rev.; charts; illus.; stat. circ. 7,500. (reprint service avail. from SCH) **Indexed:** Amer.Bibl.Slavic & E.Eur.Stud., Curr.Cont.M.E., I D A, Per.Islam., Rural Devel.Abstr. Document type: academic/scholarly publication.
—BLDSC (5066.002500); Faxon; UnCover; SWETS.
    Description: Provides analysis of political, economic and social developments in the modern Islamic and non-Islamic societies in South Asia, the Middle East and North Africa.

950   NE   ISSN 0022-4995
HC411
JOURNAL OF THE ECONOMIC AND SOCIAL HISTORY OF THE ORIENT/JOURNAL D'HISTOIRE ECONOMIQUE ET SOCIALE DE L'ORIENT. (Text in English, French and German) 1957. 4/yr. fl.110($63) to individuals; institutions fl.155($88.75) (effective 1994). E.J. Brill, P.O. Box 9000, 2300 PA Leiden, Netherlands. TEL 31-71-312624. FAX 31-71-317532. TELEX 39296 BRILL NL. (In N. America: E.J. Brill, 24 Hudson St., Kinderhook, NY 12106. TEL 800-962-4406. FAX 518-758-1959) Ed. H.T. Zurndorfer. adv.; bk.rev.; charts; index. (also avail. in microform from SWZ; reprint service avail. from SWZ) **Indexed:** Amer.Hist.& Life, E.I., Hist.Abstr., Mid.East: Abstr.& Ind., Numis.Lit. Document type: academic/scholarly publication.
—BLDSC (4972.600000); Faxon; UnCover; SWETS. CCC.
    Description: Specialized studies furthering the knowledge of the economic and social history of Asia and North Africa from the earliest times to the beginning of the 19th century.
    Refereed Serial

HISTORY — HISTORY OF THE NEAR EAST

956   KU   ISSN 0254-4288
JOURNAL OF THE GULF AND ARABIAN PENINSULA STUDIES/MAJALLAT DIRASAT AL-KHALIJ WAL-JAZIRAH AL-ARABIYAH. 1975. q. $18 to individuals; institutions $43 (effective 1994). University of Kuwait, P.O. Box 17073, Al-Khaldiah 72451, Kuwait. TEL 965-4816807. FAX 965-4814295. Ed. Dr. Maimona K. Al-Sabah. adv.; bk.rev. **Indexed:** Lang.& Lang.Behav.Abstr., Potato Abstr., Rural Ext.Educ.& Tr.Abstr., World Agri.Econ.& Rural Sociol.Abstr. **Document type:** academic/scholarly publication, bibliography.
    Description: Publishes papers addressing Gulf and Arabian Peninsula affairs, from economic, social and political perspectives.
    Refereed Serial

956.1   US   ISSN 0743-0019
JOURNAL OF TURKISH STUDIES/TURKLUK BILGISI ARASTIRMALARI. 1977. a. $200. Harvard University, Near Eastern Languages and Civilizations, Box 1447, Duxbury, MA 02331. TEL 617-585-8796. Eds. Sinasi Tekin, Gonul A. Tekin. bk.rev. (back issues avail.) **Indexed:** Bibl.Ling.

956 297   US   ISSN 0888-9007
DS41
JUSUR; the U C L A journal of Middle Eastern studies. 1985. a. $8 to individuals; institutions $16; students $4 (effective 1994). University of California, Los Angeles, Von Grunebaum Center for Near Eastern Studies, 10286 Bunche Hall, Los Angeles, CA 90024. TEL 213-825-1181. Ed. Sandy De Gris. adv. contact: Robert Bond. bk.rev.; film rev. circ. 130. (also avail. in microfilm; back issues avail.) **Indexed:** Amer.Hist.& Life, Hist.Abstr. **Document type:** academic/scholarly publication.
—Faxon.

KATIB AL-FILASTINI. see *POLITICAL SCIENCE — International Relations*

956   IQ
AL-KHALIJ AL-ARABI/ARAB GULF; an academic journal dealing with affairs of the Arab Gulf and Arabic Peninsula. (Text in Arabic, English and French; summaries in Arabic and English) 1973. a. $30. University of Basrah, Centre for Arab Gulf Studies, Basrah, Iraq. Ed. Qahtan S. Al Nasseri. bk.rev. circ. 2,000. (also avail. in microfilm) **Indexed:** Biol.Abstr., Deep Sea Res.& Oceanogr.Abstr.

KING FAISAL CENTER FOR RESEARCH AND ISLAMIC STUDIES. NEWSLETTER. see *RELIGIONS AND THEOLOGY — Islamic*

KOINONIA; the Princeton Theological Seminary graduate forum. see *RELIGIONS AND THEOLOGY — Protestant*

LEBANON REPORT. see *POLITICAL SCIENCE — International Relations*

956.12   LY   ISSN 0459-2980
LIBYA ANTIQUA/LIBIYA AL-QADIMAT. (Text in Arabic and various European languages) 1964. a. General People's Committee for Education, Department of Antiquities, National Archives, As-Sarai al-Hamra, Tripoli, Libya. Dir. Abdullah Shaibub.

LUQMAN. see *RELIGIONS AND THEOLOGY — Islamic*

M A A S JOURNAL OF ISLAMIC SCIENCE. (Muslim Association for the Advancement of Science) see *ORIENTAL STUDIES*

M A A S NEWSLETTER. (Muslim Association for the Advancement of Science) see *ORIENTAL STUDIES*

MAJALLAH-I BASTANSHINASI VA TARIKH/IRANIAN JOURNAL OF ARCHAEOLOGY AND HISTORY. see *ARCHAEOLOGY*

955   IR
MAJALLA-I TAHQIQAT-I TARIKHI/JOURNAL OF HISTORICAL RESEARCH. (Text in Farsi, summaries in English) 1989. 4/yr. $25 (effective 1993). Mu'assasah-i Mutala'at va Tahqiqat-i Farhangi - Cultural Studies and Research Institute, Mo'asseseh Bldg., 64 St., Seyyed Jamal-eddin Ave., Teheran 14374, Iran. TEL 98-21-688037. FAX 98-21-686317. Ed. Azar M. Faridani. bk.rev. circ. 2,000. **Document type:** academic/scholarly publication.
    Description: Publishes studies on various aspects of Iranian history, including social, cultural, economic and other topics.

956.12   LY
MAJALLAT AL-BUHUTH AL-TA'RIKHIYYAH. s-a. Libyan Studies Center, P.O. Box 5070, Sidi Munaider, Tripoli, Libya. TEL 33996. FAX 31616. TELEX 20424. **Document type:** academic/scholarly publication.

956.94   LE
MAJALLAT AL-DIRASAT AL-FILASTINIYYA/JOURNAL OF PALESTINE STUDIES. (Text in Arabic) 1990. q. $40 to individuals; institutions $60. Institute for Palestine Studies, P.O. Box 11-7164, Beirut, Lebanon. TEL 868387. FAX 814193. TELEX 23317 MADAF LE. (U.S. subscr. to: Box 25301, Georgetown Sta., Washington, DC 20007. TEL 202-342-3990. FAX 202-342-3927) Ed. Ahmad Khalidi. **Document type:** academic/scholarly publication.
    Description: Provides an international forum for scholars of Palestinian affairs and the Arab-Israeli conflict.

MAJALLAT AL-DIRASAT AL-SUDANIYYA. see *HISTORY — History Of Africa*

950   BE   ISSN 0920-0401
MANUSCRIPTS OF THE MIDDLE EAST; journal devoted to the study of handwritten materials of the Middle East. (Text in English) vol.4, 1989. a. 2500 BEF. Editions Peeters s.p.r.l., Bondgenotenlaan 153, B-3000 Louvain, Belgium. TEL 32-16-235170. FAX 32-16-228500. Eds. Jan Just Witkam, A. Gacek. adv.; bk.rev. (back issues avail.) **Indexed:** Bibl.Ling. **Document type:** academic/scholarly publication.
—BLDSC (5367.288800).

956   UK   ISSN 0950-3110
DS36.85
AL-MASAQ; studia arabo-islamica mediterranea. (Text in English, French) 1988. a. £6($12) to individuals; institutions ?8($16). University of Leeds, School of History, Leeds LS2 9JT, England. TEL 0532-333614. FAX 0532-342759. TELEX 554673-UNILDS-G. (Dist. in U.S. and Canada by: Medieval Institute Publications, University of Western Michigan, Kalamazoo, MI 49008-3899) Ed. Dionisius A. Agius. adv.; bk.rev.; bibl. circ. 500. (also avail. in microfilm; back issues avail.) **Indexed:** Bibl.Ling. **Document type:** academic/scholarly publication.
    Description: Devoted to the study of all aspects of the Arabo-Islamic medieval Mediterranean studies.

943   GW   ISSN 0344-449X
MATERIALIA TURCICA. 1975. irreg. price varies. (Ruhr-Universitaet, Bochum, Sprachwissenschaftliches Institut, Lektorat fuer Tuerksprachen) Universitaetsverlag Dr. N. Brockmeyer, Querenburger Hoehe 281, 44801 Bochum, Germany. TEL 0234-706978. Ed. Hermann Vary. bk.rev. **Indexed:** Bibl.Ling.

MATERIALS AND STUDIES FOR KASSITE HISTORY. see *ORIENTAL STUDIES*

956.94   IS
ME'ASEF; studies in the history and problems of the Israeli labor movement. a. Documentation and Research of Hashamer Hatzair, Givat Haviva 37 850, Israel. Ed. Haim Kahana.

THE MEDIEVAL MEDITERRANEAN; peoples, economies and cultures 400-1453. see *HISTORY*

956   UK   ISSN 0951-8967
MEDITERRANEAN HISTORICAL REVIEW. 1986. 2/yr. £25($45) to individuals; institutions £60 ($95). Frank Cass & Co. Ltd., Gainsborough House, 11 Gainsborough Rd., London E11 1RS, England. TEL 081-530 4226. FAX 081-530-7795. Eds. Benjamin Arbel, Alisa Ginio Meyuhas. adv.: B&W page £185; adv. contact: Anne Kidson. bk.rev.; index. (also avail. in microfilm from UMI; back issues avail.) **Indexed:** Amer.Hist.& Life, Geo.Abstr., Hist.Abstr. **Document type:** academic/scholarly publication.
—BLDSC (5534.734000); UnCover; SWETS.
    Description: Provides an international forum for the discussion of topics on the ancient, medieval, and modern history of the Mediterranean basin.

956.94   IS
MERKAZ HARIBAZ; sephardi synagogues in the Jewish quarter of the old city - Jerusalem. 1965. q. Council of the Sephardi and Oriental Communities, P.O. Box 10, 12a Haavatzelet St., Jerusalem 91000, Israel. Ed. Yehezkel Soffer. circ. 2,500.
    Former titles (until 1989): Sephardi Heritage; Challenge; Which superseded (in 1976): Israel's Oriental Problems (ISSN 0021-2350)

956   US   ISSN 0163-5476
DS62.8
MIDDLE EAST CONTEMPORARY SURVEY. 1978. a. $89.95. (Tel Aviv University, Moshe Dayan Center for Middle Eastern and African Studies, IS) Westview Press, 5500 Central Ave., Boulder, CO 80301. TEL 303-444-3541. FAX 303-449-3356. Ed. Ami Ayalon. bibl.; charts; maps; index. circ. 800. (back issues avail.) **Document type:** academic/scholarly publication.
    Description: Presents portrait of the region's political, social, and economic developments, drawn from hundreds of newspapers, periodicals, news agencies, and broadcast sources.

MIDDLE EAST INSIGHT. see *POLITICAL SCIENCE — International Relations*

956   IS   ISSN 0076-8529
MIDDLE EAST RECORD. 1960. irreg., vol.5, 1977. (Tel-Aviv University, Shiloah Center for Middle Eastern and African Studies) Keter Publishing House Ltd., P.O. Box 7145, Jerusalem, Israel.

956   US   ISSN 0899-2851
DS42
MIDDLE EAST REPORT. 1971. 6/yr. $25 to individuals (foreign $43); institutions $50 (foreign $68). Middle East Research & Information Project, 1500 Massachusetts Ave., N.W., Ste. 119, Washington, DC 20005. TEL 202-223-3677. FAX 202-223-3604. Ed. Joe Stork. adv.; bk.rev.; film rev.; bibl.; charts; illus.; stat.; index, cum.index. circ. 6,200. (also avail. in microform from UMI; back issues avail.) **Indexed:** Alt.Press Ind., HR Rep., I D A, Ind.Islam., Int.Polit.Sci.Abstr., Left Ind. (1982-), Mid.East: Abstr.& Ind., P.A.I.S., Sociol.Abstr. **Document type:** academic/scholarly publication.
—Faxon; UnCover; SWETS.
    Formerly: M E R I P Reports (ISSN 0047-7265); *Incorporates:* Pakistan Report (ISSN 0315-7725)
    Description: Focuses on politics and society in the contemporary Middle East. Examines key events and controversial issues in the region.

MIDDLE EAST STUDIES ASSOCIATION BULLETIN. see *SOCIAL SCIENCES: COMPREHENSIVE WORKS*

956 320   US   ISSN 0888-2460
MIDEAST MONITOR.* q. $10 (foreign $13). Association of Arab-American University Graduates, Inc., Box 408, Normal, IL 61761-0408. TEL 617-484-5483. Ed. Janice Terry. circ. 5,000.

MISHKAT. see *RELIGIONS AND THEOLOGY — Islamic*

MONOGRAPHIES REINE ELISABETH. see *ARCHAEOLOGY*

900   US   ISSN 0732-6491
MONOGRAPHS ON THE ANCIENT NEAR EAST. 1974. irreg., vol.2, no.3. price varies. (International Institute of Mesopotamian Area Studies) Undena Publications, Box 97, Malibu, CA 90265. (Dist. by: Crescent Academic Services, 29528 Madera Ave., Shafter, CA 93263) Eds. Dr. Giorgio Buccellati, M. Kelly-Buccellati. bibl.; charts; illus. (back issues avail.)

MONUMENTA AEGYPTIACA. see *ARCHAEOLOGY*

MUENCHNER ZEITSCHRIFT FUER BALKANKUNDE. see *HISTORY — History Of Europe*

MUQARNAS; an annual on Islamic art and architecture. see *ART*

MUQARNAS, SUPPLEMENTS. see *ART*

LE MUSEON; revue d'etudes orientales. see *ORIENTAL STUDIES*

NEAR EAST ARCHAEOLOGICAL SOCIETY BULLETIN. see *ARCHAEOLOGY*

NETHERLANDS INSTITUTE OF ARCHAEOLOGY AND ARABIC STUDIES IN CAIRO. PUBLICATIONS. see *ARCHAEOLOGY*

HISTORY — HISTORY OF THE NEAR EAST

956 II
NEW ARAB. (Text in English) 1974. m. Rs.5($10) League of Arab States Mission, 62 Golf Links, New Delhi 110003, India. Ed. Ibrahim Shukrallah. bk.rev.; illus. circ. 20,000.

NEW YORK UNIVERSITY. STUDIES IN NEAR EASTERN CIVILIZATION. see *ORIENTAL STUDIES*

956 DK
NORDISK MELLEMOESTEN INSTITUT. BULLETIN/NORDIC MIDDLE EAST INSTITUTE. BULLETIN. 1974. q. DKK 30($7.50) Editions Nordiques, P.O. Box 1521, DK-8220 Brabrand, Denmark. Ed. Robin Albertsen. bk.rev.; bibl.

956 US ISSN 0732-6475
OCCASIONAL PAPERS ON THE NEAR EAST. (Sub-series of: Monographic Journals of the Near East) 1979. irreg., vol.2, no.2. price varies. (International Institute of Mesopotamian Area Studies) Undena Publications, Box 97, Malibu, CA 90265. TEL 805-746-5870. FAX 805-746-2728. (Dist. by: Crescent Academic Services, 29528 Madera Ave., Shafter, CA 93263) Ed. Dr. Giorgio Buccellati. bibl.; charts; illus. (back issues avail.) **Indexed:** Old Test.Abstr.
—BLDSC (6224.851000).

956 AU
OESTERREICHISCHE AKADEMIE DER WISSENSCHAFTEN. IRANISCHE KOMMISSION. VEROEFFENTLICHUNGEN. (Subseries of: Oesterreichische Akademie der Wissenschaften. Philosophisch-Historische Klasse. Sitzungsberichte) 1973. irreg. Verlag der Oesterreichischen Akademie der Wissenschaften, Dr. Ignaz-Seipel-Platz 2, A-1010 Vienna, Austria. FAX 0222-5139541.

956 GW ISSN 0342-4839
OESTERREICHISCHEN KULTURINSTITUTS KAIRO. ARCHAEOLOGISCH-HISTORISCHE ABTEILUNG. SCHRIFTEN. 1969. irreg., vol.3, 1982. price varies. Harrassowitz Verlag, Taunusstr. 14, 65183 Wiesbaden, Germany. TEL 0611-530-0. FAX 0611-530570. TELEX 4186135. (Subscr. to: Postfach 2929, 65019 Wiesbaden, Germany) **Document type:** monographic series.

ORIENS. see *ORIENTAL STUDIES*

956 IS ISSN 0078-6543
ORIENTAL NOTES AND STUDIES. 1949. irreg. price varies. Israel Oriental Society, Hebrew University, Jerusalem 91905, Israel. Ed. Jacob M. Landau. bk.rev. circ. 1,500. **Document type:** monographic series.

ORIENTALIA. see *ORIENTAL STUDIES*

932 NE ISSN 0169-9458
ORIENTALIA MONSPELIENSIA. 1979. irreg. price varies. (Universite de Montpellier (Universite Paul Valery), Institut d'Egyptologie, FR) E.J. Brill, P.O. Box 9000, 2300 PA Leiden, Netherlands. TEL 31-71-312624. FAX 31-71-317532. TELEX 39296 BRILL NL. (In N. America: E.J. Brill, 24 Hudson St., Kinderhook, NY 12106. TEL 800-962-4406. FAX 518-758-1959) **Document type:** monographic series.

ORIENTATIONS. see *ORIENTAL STUDIES*

956 330.9 NE
▼**THE OTTOMAN EMPIRE AND ITS HERITAGE: POLITICS, SOCIETY AND ECONOMY**. 1994. irreg. price varies. E.J. Brill, P.O. Box 9000, 2300 PA Leiden, Netherlands. TEL 31-71-312624. FAX 31-71-317532. (In N. America: E.J. Brill, 24 Hudson St., Kinderhook, NY 12106. TEL 800-962-4406. FAX 518-758-1959) **Document type:** academic/scholarly publication, monographic series.
   Refereed Serial

PALAESTINA ANTIQUA. see *ARCHAEOLOGY*

PALESTINE EXPLORATION QUARTERLY. see *ARCHAEOLOGY*

956.94 IS ISSN 0334-4088
PE'AMIM; studies in Oriental Jewry. (Text in Hebrew; summaries in English) 1979. q. IS.72($40) Ben Zvi Institute for the Study of Jewish Communities in the East, P.O. Box 7504, Jerusalem 91076, Israel. TEL 972-2-639204. FAX 972-2-638310. Ed. Itzhak Bezalel. bk.rev.; abstr.; charts; illus. circ. 2,000. (back issues avail.) **Indexed:** Ind.Heb.Per. **Document type:** academic/scholarly publication.

956 US ISSN 1065-9382
PRINCETON PAPERS IN NEAR EAST STUDIES. 1992. irreg., no.2, 1993. $15. Darwin Press, Inc., Box 2202, Princeton, NJ 08543. TEL 609-737-1349. Eds. Charles Issawi, Bernard Lewis. adv. **Indexed:** Amer.Hist.& Life (1992-), Hist.Abstr. (1992-). **Document type:** academic/scholarly publication.

956 US
PRINCETON STUDIES ON THE NEAR EAST. irreg. price varies. Princeton University Press, 41 William St., Princeton, NJ 08540. TEL 609-258-4900. FAX 609-258-6305. **Document type:** monographic series.

QUADERNI DE "LA TERRA SANTA". see *RELIGIONS AND THEOLOGY*

930.533 BE ISSN 1015-4523
RAYDAN; journal of ancient Yemeni antiquities and epigraphy. 1978. irreg., vol.6, 1989. 1500 BEF. (Yemeni Centre for Cultural and Archaeological Research, YE) Editions Peeters s.p.r.l., Bondgenotenlaan 153, B-3000 Louvain, Belgium. TEL 32-16-235170. FAX 32-16-228500. Ed.Bd. bk.rev. (back issues avail.) **Indexed:** Bibl.Ling. **Document type:** academic/scholarly publication.

READINGS IN GLASS HISTORY. see *ARCHAEOLOGY*

REGIONAL CULTURAL INSTITUTE. JOURNAL. see *BUSINESS AND ECONOMICS — International Development And Assistance*

REMARQUES ARABO-AFRICAINES. see *HISTORY — History Of Africa*

REVUE C E L F A N - C E L F A N REVIEW. see *LITERATURE*

956.62 BE ISSN 0080-2549
REVUE DES ETUDES ARMENIENNES NOUVELLE SERIE. 1920; N.S. vol.21, 1988. a. 3000 BEF (effective 1994). Editions Peeters s.p.r.l., Bondgenotenlaan 153, B-3000 Louvain, Belgium. TEL 32-16-235170. FAX 32-16-228500. Eds. N.G. Garsoian, J.-P. Mahe. adv.; bk.rev.; index. (also avail. in microfiche from IDC; back issues avail.) **Indexed:** Bibl.Ling. **Document type:** academic/scholarly publication.
—BLDSC (7900.152500).
   Description: Publishes original works relating to Armenia and Armenian culture from prehistory through the 18th century, in the following disciplines: humanities, history, philology and linguistics, literature and the fine arts.

956 FR ISSN 0766-5598
REVUE DES ETUDES BYZANTINES. (Text and summaries in English, French, German) 1943. a. 350 F. Association de l'Institut Francais d'Etudes Byzantines, 14 rue Seguier, 75006 Paris, France. adv.; bk.rev. circ. 600. (back issues avail.)

956 TU ISSN 0578-9761
SARKIYAT MECMUASI. 1956. irreg. TL.34. Istanbul University, Sarkiyat Enstitusu, Istanbul, Turkey. bk.rev. circ. 1,500.

956 913 572 CN
SCRIPTA MEDITERRANEA.* (Text in English, French and German) 1980. a. Can.$18($18) to non-members. (Society for Mediterranean Studies) Benben Publications, Box 308 New College, University of Toronto, Toronto, Ont. M5S 1A1, Canada. TEL 416-274-4380. Ed. Anthony Percival. bk.rev.; bibl. circ. 250.
   Description: Studies all aspects of Mediterranean culture and civilization, past and present.

915.3 296 SP ISSN 0037-0894
DS101
SEFARAD; revista de estudios Hebraicos, Sefardies y de Oriente Proximo. (Text in English, French, German, Hebrew, Italian and Spanish) 1940. q. 4000 ptas. (foreign 6000 ptas.). Consejo Superior de Investigaciones Cientificas (C.S.I.C.), Instituto de Filologia, Vitrubio, 8, 28006 Madrid, Spain. Ed. Francisco Cantera y Burgos. bk.rev.; abstr.; bibl.; charts; illus.; index, cum.index every 15 yrs. circ. 800. (reprint service avail. from SCH) **Indexed:** Amer.Hist.& Life, Bibl.Ling., Hist.Abstr., M.L.A., New Test.Abstr., Numis.Lit., Old Test.Abstr.
—BLDSC (8218.490000); Faxon.
   Description: Studies the text of the Hebrew Bible and its ancient versions and cultures; the history and culture of Jews in Spain; the language, literature, history and culture of the Sephardim; and the Hebrew and Aramaic languages.

SEMINAR FOR ARABIAN STUDIES. PROCEEDINGS. see *POLITICAL SCIENCE — International Relations*

930 956.9 DK ISSN 0105-7618
SFINX. 1977. 4/yr. DKK 152. Orbis Terrarum, Institut Belysning av Middelhavsomraadets Kulturelle Arv, Aarhus Univ., 8000 Aarhus, Denmark. TEL 86-136711. FAX 86-19-16-99. Ed. Erik Hallager. adv.; bk.rev. circ. 8,500.

956.12 LY
AL-SHAHID. a. Libyan Studies Center, P.O. Box 5070, Sidi Munaider, Tripoli, Libya. TEL 33996. FAX 31616. TELEX 20424. **Document type:** academic/scholarly publication.

955 IR
SHIRAZ UNIVERSITY. ASIAN INSTITUTE. BULLETIN. (Text in various languages) 1975. q. Rs.500. Shiraz University, Asian Institute, Naranjestan Museum, P.O.B. 71365-977, Shiraz, Iran. Ed. Ali Hasuri. adv.; bk.rev.
   Formerly: Pahlavi University. Asian Institute. Bulletin.

956 NE ISSN 0085-6193
SOCIAL, ECONOMIC AND POLITICAL STUDIES OF THE MIDDLE EAST. 1971. irreg., vol.48, 1994. price varies. E.J. Brill, P.O. Box 9000, 2300 PA Leiden, Netherlands. TEL 31-71-312624. FAX 31-71-317532. TELEX 39296 BRILL NL. (In N. America: E.J. Brill, 24 Hudson St., Kinderhook, NY 12106. TEL 800-962-4406. FAX 518-758-1959) Ed. C.A.O. van Nieuwenhuijze. (back issues avail.) **Document type:** monographic series.
   Description: Scholarly studies of economic, political, social, religious and historical issues affecting the Middle East, with particular emphasis on development related concerns, the role of women in Islamic societies, recent political history and law in Middle Eastern countries.
   Refereed Serial

956 US ISSN 0732-6424
SOURCES FROM THE ANCIENT NEAR EAST. Abbreviated title: S A N E. 1974. irreg., vol.2, no.3. price varies. (International Institute of Mesopotamian Area Studies) Undena Publications, Box 97, Malibu, CA 90265. TEL 805-746-5870. FAX 805-746-2728. (Dist. by: Crescent Academic Publishers, 29528 Madera Ave., Shafter, CA 93263) Eds. G. Buccellati, M. Kelly-Buccellati. (back issues avail.) **Indexed:** Old Test.Abstr.
—BLDSC (8330.587000).

STUDI CLASSICI E ORIENTALI. see *CLASSICAL STUDIES*

STUDI EBLAITI. see *ARCHAEOLOGY*

STUDIA ORIENTALIA CHRISTIANA. COLLECTANEA. see *RELIGIONS AND THEOLOGY*

STUDIA ORIENTALIA CHRISTIANA. MONOGRAPHIAE. see *RELIGIONS AND THEOLOGY*

STUDIES IN ANCIENT ORIENTAL CIVILIZATION. see *ORIENTAL STUDIES*

STUDIES IN ARABIC LITERATURE. see *LITERATURE*

950 960 US
STUDIES IN MIDDLE EASTERN HISTORY. 1974. irreg., no.9, 1987. price varies. Bibliotheca Islamica, Inc., Box 14474, University Sta., Minneapolis, MN 55414. **Document type:** monographic series.

3016 HOBBIES

956 US ISSN 0742-1168
STUDIES IN NEAR EASTERN CULTURE AND SOCIETY. Abbreviated title: SNECS. 1977. irreg., no.7, 1986. price varies. Scholars Press, Box 15399, Atlanta, GA 30333-3099. TEL 404-727-2320. FAX 404-727-2348. (Co-sponsor: University of California at Los Angeles) Ed.Bd. (back issues avail.) **Document type:** monographic series.

930 NE ISSN 0169-9024
STUDIES IN THE HISTORY OF THE ANCIENT NEAR EAST. 1982. irreg., vol.4, 1994. price varies. E.J. Brill, P.O. Box 9000, 2300 PA Leiden, Netherlands. TEL 31-71-312624. FAX 31-71-317532. TELEX 39296 BRILL NL. (In N. America: E.J. Brill, 24 Hudson St., Kinderhook, NY 12106. TEL 800-962-4406. FAX 518-758-1959) (back issues avail.) **Document type:** monographic series.
Description: Scholarly studies on historical and archaeological topics pertaining to the ancient Near East.

STUDIUM BIBLICUM FRANCISCANUM. COLLECTIO MAIOR. see *ARCHAEOLOGY*

STUDIUM BIBLICUM FRANCISCANUM. COLLECTIO MINOR. see *ARCHAEOLOGY*

STUDIUM BIBLICUM FRANCISCANUM. LIBER ANNUUS. see *ARCHAEOLOGY*

STUDIUM BIBLICUM FRANCISCANUM. MUSEUM. see *ARCHAEOLOGY*

956 SJ
SUDAN NOTES AND RECORDS. (Text in English) 1918. a. Box 555, Khartoum, Sudan. Ed. Yusuf Fadl Hasan. adv.; bk.rev. circ. 2,000. (back issues avail.; reprint service avail. from KTO) **Indexed:** A.I.C.P., Anthropol.Lit., Bibl.Ling., Biol.Abstr., Documentatieblad, GeoRef.

956 SJ ISSN 0378-8059
DT154.1
SUDANOW. (Text in English) 1976. m. $50. Ministry of Culture and Information, Box 2651, Khartoum, Sudan. (Subscr. to: Subscriptions Office, Sudanow, P.O. Box 2651, Khartoum, Sudan) Ed. Fath El Rahman Mahgoub. adv.; bk.rev.; illus. circ. 4,000. **Indexed:** Refug.Abstr.

956 US ISSN 0732-6483
SYRO-MESOPOTAMIAN STUDIES. (Subseries of: Monographic Journals of the Near East) 1974. irreg., vol.5, no.1. price varies. (International Institute of Mesopotamian Area Studies) Undena Publications, Box 97, Malibu, CA 90265. TEL 805-746-5870. FAX 805-746-2728. (Dist. by: Crescent Academic Services, 29528 Madera Ave., Shafter, CA 93263) Ed. Dr. Giorgio Buccellati. bibl.; charts; illus. (back issues avail.) **Indexed:** Old Test.Abstr.

TARBIZ; a quarterly for Jewish studies. see *RELIGIONS AND THEOLOGY — Judaic*

956 US ISSN 1059-1222
DS41
TARIH. 1990. s-a. University of Pennsylvania, Center for Judaic Studies, 420 Walnut St., Philadelphia, PA 19106. TEL 215-238-1291. FAX 215-238-1540. Ed. Bonnie Blankenship. **Document type:** academic/scholarly publication.

TERRA SANTA. see *RELIGIONS AND THEOLOGY*

956 TU ISSN 0041-4247
TURK TARIH KURUMU. BELGELER. 1964. a. price varies. Turkish Historical Society, Ankara, Turkey. illus. circ. 1,000.

956 TU ISSN 0041-4255
DR401
TURK TARIH KURUMU. BELLETEN. (Text in English, French, German and Turkish) 1937. 3/yr. $52. Turkish Historical Society, Ankara, Turkey. bk.rev.; bibl.; charts; illus.; cum.index: no. 1-100, 101-140. circ. 1,500. **Indexed:** Anthropol.Lit., Bibl.Ling.

956.1 US ISSN 0275-6048
TURKISH STUDIES ASSOCIATION BULLETIN. 1976. s-a. $25. Turkish Studies Association, c/o Madeline Zilfi, Ed., History Dept., University of Maryland, College Park, MD 20742. TEL 301-405-4303. FAX 301-314-9399. (Subscr. to: History Dept., University of Arizona, Tucson, AZ 85721) adv.; bk.rev.; abstr.; cum.index: 1984-1988. circ. 260. (back issues avail.) **Document type:** academic/scholarly publication, bulletin. —UnCover.
Description: Covers all subjects dealing with Ottoman and Turkish studies.

956 TU ISSN 0085-7432
TURKIYAT MECMUASI. 1925. irreg. price varies. Istanbul University, Institute of Turcology - Istanbul Universitesi, Turkiyat Enstitusu, Ayniyat, Istanbul, Turkey. Ed. M. Kaplan. circ. 1,000.

913.39 AG ISSN 0325-1209
DS56
UNIVERSIDAD DE BUENOS AIRES. INSTITUTO DE HISTORIA ANTIGUA ORIENTAL. REVISTA. 1972. a. Universidad de Buenos Aires, Instituto de Historia Antigua Oriental, 25 de Mayo 217, Buenos Aires, Argentina. bk.rev.; bibl.; illus. circ. 800.

913 AG
UNIVERSIDAD DE BUENOS AIRES. INSTITUTO DE HISTORIA ANTIGUO ORIENTAL. COLECCION ESTUDIOS. irreg., no.8, 1978. Universidad de Buenos Aires, Instituto de Historia Antigua Oriental, 25 de Mayo 217, 3 Piso, Buenos Aires, Argentina.

UNIVERSITE DES SCIENCES HUMAINES DE STRASBOURG. CENTRE DE RECHERCHE SUR LE PROCHE ORIENT ET LA GRECE ANTIQUES. TRAVAUX. see *CLASSICAL STUDIES*

UNIVERSITY OF CHICAGO ORIENTAL INSTITUTE. PUBLICATIONS. see *ORIENTAL STUDIES*

UNIVERSITY OF LONDON. SCHOOL OF ORIENTAL AND AFRICAN STUDIES. BULLETIN. see *HUMANITIES: COMPREHENSIVE WORKS*

955 IR
UNIVERSITY OF TEHERAN. FACULTY OF LETTERS AND HUMANITIES. BULLETIN OF IRANIAN STUDIES/DANESHGAH-E TEHRAN. DANESHKADE-YE ADABIYAT VA 'OLUM-E ENSANI. MAJALLE-YE IRANSHENASI. Short title: Bulletin of Iranian Studies. (Text in Farsi) 1963. irreg. price varies. University of Teheran, Faculty of Letters and Humanities, Enghelab Ave., Teheran, Iran. TELEX 13944. Ed. Fereydun Badre'I.

913 915 IT
VICINO ORIENTE. 1978. a. $60. (Universita di Roma "La Sapienza") Herder Editrice e Libreria s.r.l., Piazza Montecitorio 120, 00186 Rome, Italy. TEL 67-94-628. FAX 678-47-51. TELEX 621427 NATEL. Ed. Mario Liverani. **Indexed:** Bibl.Ling. **Document type:** academic/scholarly publication.

953.57 059.927 TS
WAQA'I DAWLAT AL-IMARAT/EMIRATES EVENTS. (Text in Arabic) 1979. a. exchange basis. Cultural Foundation, Centre for Documentation and Research, P.O. Box 2380, Abu Dhabi, United Arab Emirates. TEL 212900. FAX 541595. TELEX 22414 CULCEN EM. circ. 2,000.

956.9 TS
AL-WATHA'IQ AL-FILASTINIYYAH/PALESTINIAN DOCUMENTS. (Text in Arabic) vol.6, 1970. a. Cultural Foundation, Centre for Documentation and Research, P.O. Box 2380, Abu Dhabi, United Arab Emirates. TEL 212900. FAX 541595. TELEX 22414 CULCEN EM. circ. 1,000 (controlled).
Description: Publishes reports and studies on Palestinian issues.

953.57 TS
WATHA'IQ DAWLAT AL-IMARAT/EMIRATES DOCUMENTS. (Text in Arabic) 1979. a. exchange basis. Cultural Foundation, Centre for Documentation and Research, P.O. Box 2380, Abu Dhabi, United Arab Emirates. TEL 212900. FAX 541595. TELEX 22414 CULCEN EM. index. circ. 2,000.
Description: Publishes government documents, speeches by rulers and cabinet ministers, and reports from the ministries.

956.12 LY
AL-WATHA'IQ WAL-MAKHTUTAT. a. Libyan Studies Center, P.O. Box 5070, Sidi Munaider, Tripoli, Libya. TEL 33996. FAX 31616. TELEX 20424. **Document type:** academic/scholarly publication.

956 BA
AL-WATHIQA. 1982. 2/yr. $8 per no. Historical Documentation Centre, Heir Apparent's Office, P.O. Box 28882, Manama, Bahrain. TEL 664854. FAX 651050. Ed. Shaikh Abdullah bin Khalid al-Khalifa. **Document type:** government publication, academic/scholarly publication.
Description: Covers topics relating to the history of Bahrain.

956 IR
WISDOM OF PERSIA. 1971. irreg., no.38, 1986. McGill University, Teheran Branch, Institute of Islamic Studies, Box 13-145-133, Teheran, Iran. Ed. Mehdi Mohaghegh.

956 US
YALE EGYPTOLOGICAL STUDIES. no.3, 1989. irreg. Yale University, Department of Near Eastern Languages and Civilizations, Yale Egyptological Seminar, New Haven, CT 06520. Ed. William Kelly Simpson. **Document type:** monographic series.

956 US ISSN 0084-3385
YALE NEAR EASTERN RESEARCHES. 1967. irreg., no.10, 1989. price varies. Yale University Press, Box 209040, New Haven, CT 06520. TEL 203-432-0940. Ed. William W. Hallo. **Document type:** monographic series.
—BLDSC (9370.270000).

935 US
YALE ORIENTAL SERIES. BABYLONIAN TEXTS. 1915. irreg., vol.18, 1991. Yale University Press, Box 209040, New Haven, CT 06520. TEL 203-432-0940. Ed. William W. Hallo.

ZEITSCHRIFT FUER BALKANOLOGIE. see *HISTORY — History Of Europe*

ZEITSCHRIFT FUER TUERKEISTUDIEN. see *ORIENTAL STUDIES*

HOBBIES

see also Antiques; Needlework; Numismatics; Philately; Sports and Games

355 973 US
A A M U C FOOTLOCKER. 1977. q. $15 (foreign $20). Association of American Military Uniforms Collectors, Box 1876, Elyvia, OH 44036. TEL 216-365-5321. Ed. Gil Sanow. circ. 300. (back issues avail.) **Document type:** newsletter.
Description: Presents articles on collection, preservation and studies of US military uniforms.

793.8 GW
A B C OF MAGIC SETS. 1980. q. DM.20($20) Moylandstr. 23, 47804 Krefeld, Germany. TEL 02151-711670. FAX 02151-712225. Ed. Wittus Witt. index. circ. 80. (back issues avail.)

A C F BULLETIN. (American Checker Federation) see *SPORTS AND GAMES*

A F A S QUARTERLY. (Automotive Fine Arts Society) see *ART*

790.13 US
A L P C A NEWSLETTER. 1954. bi-m. $20 (foreign $32). Automobile License Plate Collectors Association, c/o Gary Brent Kincade, Box 77, Horner, WV 26372. TEL 304-842-3773. Ed. Paul M. Maginnity. adv. circ. 2,620. (back issues avail.) **Document type:** newsletter.

625.19 AT ISSN 0045-0715
A M R A JOURNAL. 1951. bi-m. membership. Australian Model Railway Association, Box 46, Nunawading, Vic. 3131, Australia. Ed. Rex Little. adv.; bk.rev.; index. circ. 800.

HOBBIES 3017

790.13 GW ISSN 0721-7021
A M T. (Auto Modell und Technik) m. DM.72 (foreign DM.82.20). Verlag fuer Technik und Handwerk GmbH, Robert-Bosch-Str. 4, 76532 Baden-Baden, Germany. TEL 07221-5087-0. FAX 07221-508752. Ed. Heiner Martin. **Document type:** consumer publication.

793 US
A S M I C NEWSLETTER. 1976. bi-m. membership only. American Society of Military Insignia Collectors, Inc. (ASMIC), c/o Donal J. Sexton, Pres., 400 Flamingo Circle, Greeneville, TN 37743. (Subscr. to: George Duell, 526 Lafayette Ave., Palmerton, PA 18071) Ed. J.F. Greene, Jr. tr.lit. rep. 3,000. **Document type:** newsletter.
  Description: Provides information for membership and members advertisements of insignia available for trade or sale.

629.133 IT ISSN 0393-9626
AEREI MODELLISMO; mensile di attualita e tecnica modellistica. 1980. m. (11/yr.). L.50000. Delta Editrice s.n.c., Borgo Regale 21-5, Casella Postale 409, 43100 Parma, Italy. Ed. Corrado Barbieri. adv.; illus.

629.133 JA
AERO FAN/KOKU FAN. (Text in English, Japanese) 1951. m. $7. Bunrin-do Co. Ltd., 2-3-16 Kabuki-cho, Shinjuku-ku, Tokyo, Japan. Ed. Ichiro Mitsui. adv.; bk.rev.; charts; illus. circ. 100,000.

629.133 UK ISSN 0001-9232
TL770.A1
AERO MODELLER. 1935. m. £25.20. Argus Specialist Publications Ltd., Argus House, Boundary Way, Hemel Hempstead, Herts. HP2 7ST, England. TEL 0442-66551. FAX 0442-66998. (Subscr. to: Argus Subscription Services, Queensway House, 2 Queensway, Redhill, Surrey, England. TEL 0737-768611) Ed. John Stroud. adv.; charts; illus. circ. 70,172. **Indexed:** Ind.How To Do It (1979-). **Document type:** consumer publication.
  Description: Covers the building and flying of model airplanes.

629.133 355 US ISSN 0147-7668
TL501
AEROPHILE. 1972. s-a. $15. Aerophile, Inc., 4014 Belle Grove, San Antonio, TX 78230. TEL 512-696-4435. Ed. James Wogstad. adv.; bk.rev.; illus. circ. 12,000.
  Formerly (until vol.3, 1976): Replica in Scale.
  Description: Details various aspects of aviation.

AIR FAN; mensuel de l'aeronautique militaire. see *MILITARY*

AIR INTERNATIONAL. see *AERONAUTICS AND SPACE FLIGHT*

AIR SONIC. see *AERONAUTICS AND SPACE FLIGHT*

790.13 AT
AIRBORNE MAGAZINE; comprehensive coverage of Australian and New Zealand radio control modelling sports. 1971. bi-m. Aus.$24. Ropomod Production Pty. Ltd., 11, 67-75 Garden Dr., Tullamarine, Vic. 3043, Australia. Ed. M. Buckmaster. adv.; bk.rev. circ. 12,500.

AIRBRUSH ACTION. see *ART*

AK EXPRESS; Internationalen Fachzeitschrift fuer Ansichtskarten-, Heimat-, Modir-, und Forschungssammler. see *FOLKLORE*

639.34 SW ISSN 0002-3922
AKVARIET. 1927. 10/yr. SEK 268. (Sveriges Akvariefoereningars Riksfoerbund) Tidskriften Akvariet, P.O. Box 22020, S-400 72 Goeteborg 22, Sweden. TEL 46-31-42-88-04. FAX 46-31-42-88-04. Ed. Kjell Nilsson. adv.; bk.rev.; illus.; index. circ. 5,000.

793.8 II
ALL INDIA MAGIC CIRCLE BULLETIN. 1961. m. Rs.12($2) (Society of Indian Magicians) All India Magic Circle, 276-1 Rash Behary Ave., Ballyganj, Calcutta 700019, India. Ed. Madhab Choudhuri. adv.; bk.rev.; illus. circ. 5,000.

ALLELOGRAPHIA WORLDWIDE; publication for international correspondence-hobby exchange personal acquaintance. see *CLUBS*

655.19 SW ISSN 0002-6190
ALLT OM HOBBY. 1966. 8/yr. SEK 265($44) Allt om Hobby AB, P.O. Box 90133, S-120 21 Stockholm, Sweden. TEL 08-999333. FAX 08-998866. Ed. Freddy Stenbom. adv.; bk.rev.; charts; illus. circ. 30,000. **Document type:** consumer publication.

AMERICAN BOOK COLLECTOR. see *PUBLISHING AND BOOK TRADE*

AMERICAN COUNTRY COLLECTIBLES. see *INTERIOR DESIGN AND DECORATION — Furniture And House Furnishings*

AMERICAN GUNSMITH. see *SPORTS AND GAMES — Outdoor Life*

799 US ISSN 0145-4250
TS537
AMERICAN HANDGUNNER. 1976. bi-m. $16.95. Publishers Development Corp., 591 Camino de la Reina, Ste. 200, San Diego, CA 92108. TEL 619-297-8520. FAX 619-297-5353. TELEX 695-478. Ed. Cameron Hopkins. circ. 163,000. (back issues avail.)
—SWETS.

AMERICAN HANDGUNNER BOOK OF COMBAT. see *SPORTS AND GAMES*

AMERICAN HANDGUNNER BOOK OF THE 10MM. see *SPORTS AND GAMES*

620 US
▼**AMERICAN MODELER**; the newspaper of scale modeling. 1992. 6/yr. $14.95. Box 1446, Raleigh, NC 27602. TEL 919-779-3232. Ed. Robert Thamason. adv.: B&W page $658. circ. 5,000.

790.132 760 US ISSN 0275-1569
Z993S
AMERICAN SOCIETY OF BOOKPLATE COLLECTORS AND DESIGNERS. YEAR BOOK. 1922. irreg., approx. a. $35. American Society of Bookplate Collectors and Designers, 605 N. Stoneman Ave., No. F, Alhambra, CA 91801. TEL 213-283-1936. Ed. Audrey Spencer Arellanes. bk.rev.; bibl.; illus.; cum.index: 1922-1950, 1951-1972. circ. 200.

AMERICAN WINE SOCIETY. BULLETIN. see *BEVERAGES*

AMERICAN WOODTURNER. see *BUILDING AND CONSTRUCTION — Carpentry And Woodwork*

790.13 FR ISSN 0752-7055
ANNUAIRE INTERNATIONAL DES COLLECTIONNEURS. 1973. biennial. Editions Dany Thibaud, 52 rue Labrouste, 75015 Paris, France.

ANTIEK & CURIOSA; verzamelhobby. see *ANTIQUES*

790.132 US
ANTIQUE LABEL COLLECTOR MAGAZINE.* 1986. 4/yr. $25. D.W. King & Associates, Publishers, Box 412, Rapid City, SD 57709-0412. Ed. David King. adv.; illus. circ. 3,000. (back issues avail.)
  Description: For persons interested in the collection, preservation and history of N. American labels of all types.

790.13 US ISSN 0742-0420
ANTIQUE TOY WORLD. 1971. m. $25. Antique Toy World, Box 34509, Chicago, IL 60634. Ed. Dale Kelley. adv.; illus.

ANTIQUES & COLLECTING MAGAZINE. see *ANTIQUES*

639.34 FR ISSN 0151-6981
AQUARAMA. 1966. q. 108 F.($25) Societe d'Organisation Publicitaire Industrielle et Commerciale, 3 rue St. Pierre Lejeune, 67000 Strasbourg, France. Ed. Jacques Puymartin. adv. circ. 70,000.
—BLDSC (1581.866280).

AQUARIUM; maandblad voor aquarium-, terrarium- en insektenkunde. see *FISH AND FISHERIES*

629.221 FR ISSN 0182-0230
ARGUS DE LA MINIATURE; officiel de l'automobile miniature. 1978. 10/yr. 690 F. (effective 1993). S A F A M, S.a.r.l., B.P. 40, 78230 Le Pecq, France. FAX 39-76-96-36. Ed. F. Flament. adv. circ. 10,000.

629 US ISSN 0195-5632
ARMY MOTORS. 1976. q. membership. Military Vehicle Preservation Association, Box 520378, Independence, MO 64052-0378. TEL 816-737-5111. FAX 816-737-5423. Ed. Reg Hodgson. adv. contact: Kay M. Willard. bk.rev. circ. 5,500. **Document type:** academic/scholarly publication.
  Description: Concerned with issues dealing with the acquisition, restoration and preservation of military vehicles.

ARROWHEAD. see *SPORTS AND GAMES*

ART AND CRAFTS CATALYST. see *ARTS AND HANDICRAFTS*

AUSTRALIAN CLAY TARGET SHOOTING NEWS. see *SPORTS AND GAMES*

736.2 688.72 AT
AUSTRALIAN DOLL DIGEST; the magazine for the doll collector. 1985. bi-m. Aus.$33($59) Doll Digest Publications, Locked Bag, Mass Vale, N.S.W. 2577, Australia. TEL 048-681-338. FAX 048-691-438. Ed. Mrs. J. Brooks. bk.rev. (back issues avail.) **Document type:** consumer publication.
  Description: For collectors and makers of dolls, teddy bears and antique juvenilia.

625.19 AT
AUSTRALIAN MODEL RAILWAY MAGAZINE. 1963. bi-m. Aus.$32. Southern Cross Model Railway Association, P.O. Box 345, Matroville, N.S.W. 2036, Australia. TEL 02-311-2036. FAX 02-661-4323. Ed. Bob Gallagher. adv.; bk.rev. circ. 10,000. **Indexed:** Pinpointer.
  Formerly (until 1977): Australian Model Railroad Magazine (ISSN 0045-009X)

790.13 FR
AUTO 8; le magazine de la voiture radiocommandee. (Text in French) 11/yr. 240 F. (foreign 285 F.). Editions Lariviere, 15-17 Quai de l'Oise, 75166 Paris Cedex 19, France. TEL 1-40-34-22-07. FAX 1-40-35-84-41. TELEX 211 678 F. Ed. Jose Rosas. adv.

AVALON HILL GENERAL. see *MILITARY*

AVIATION NEWS. see *AERONAUTICS AND SPACE FLIGHT*

B T H A BUYERS GUIDE. (British Toy & Hobby Association) see *GIFTWARE AND TOYS*

790.13 US
▼**BABY BOOMER COLLECTIBLES**. 1993. m. $18.95. Add Inc., 600 Industrial Dr., Waupaca, WI 54981.

796.3 US
BALLSTREET NEWS; the consolidated baseball card pocket price guide. 1991. m $49.95. Ballstreet, Inc., 7200 Montgomery N.E. Ste. 356, Albuquerque, NM 87109. TEL 505-343-1215. FAX 505-343-1218. adv.: B&W page $1250; trim 4 x 6 3/8. circ. 25,000. **Document type:** consumer publication.
  Formerly: Ballstreet Journal.
  Description: Lists prices of sports cards. Contains articles and stats on ten athletes in each issue.

795.4 US ISSN 0744-4540
BARR'S POST CARD NEWS. 1974. w. $29 (Canada $39; elsewhere $150). Barr Enterprises, 70 S. Sixth St., Box 310, Lansing, IA 52151. TEL 800-397-0145. FAX 319-538-4038. Ed. Bill E. Cote. adv.; bk.rev. circ. 5,500. **Document type:** trade publication.
  Description: Deltiology newspaper (the collecting of picture post cards) with national and international distribution.

796.357 US ISSN 1074-0341
▼**BASEBALL ROOKIE RUN DOWN (YEAR)**; a unique rookie card - subset card guide. 1993. a. $6.95 (effective 1994). Pop Fly Publishing, Box 22863, Lincoln, NE 68502. TEL 402-474-0255. Ed Michael P. Towey. **Document type:** consumer publication.
  Description: Provides baseball fans and card collectors with an index of baseball rookie cards issued in the preceding year, along with performance statistics.

3018 HOBBIES

790.132 US ISSN 1044-775X
BASICALLY BUCKLES. 1980. bi-m. $17.95. Toy Farmer Publications, Inc., HC 2, Box 5, LaMoure, ND 58458. TEL 800-533-8293. FAX 701-883-5208. Ed. Claire Scheibe. adv. circ. 1,317.
 Description: For collectors of belt buckles, watch fobs, key rings, and related collectibles.

745.5 US
BASKETMAKER MAGAZINE.* 1983. q. $16. M K S Publications, In., Box 85340, Westland, MI 48185-0340. Ed. Sue Kurginski. bk.rev.

790.13 GW
BASTEL-BOUTIQUE. q. Verlag Guenter Kyi, Hermann-Loens-Str. 4, 67304 Eisenberg, Germany. TEL 06351-6065. FAX 06351-2679. Ed. Guenter Kyi. adv. contact: Anne Weber. circ. 45,000. **Document type:** consumer publication.

BEAD FORUM. see *ARCHAEOLOGY*

BEADS. see *ANTHROPOLOGY*

736.2 688.72 AT
▼**BEAR FACTS REVIEW;** the magazine for teddy collectors. 1992. 2/yr. Aus.$12.50($18.50) Doll Digest Publications, Locked Bag, Moss Vale, N.S.W. 2577, Australia. TEL 048-681-338. FAX 048-691-438. Ed. Mrs. J. Books. bk.rev. (back issues avail.) **Document type:** consumer publication.
 Description: For collectors and makers of teddy bears.

795.4 796.357 US ISSN 0886-0599
BECKETT BASEBALL CARD MONTHLY. 1984. m. $19.95. Beckett Publications, 15850 Dallas Parkway, Dallas, TX 75248. TEL 214-991-6657. FAX 214-991-8930. (Subscr. to: Box 1915, Marion, OH 43305-1915) Ed. James Beckett. adv. circ. 800,000. (back issues avail.) **Document type:** consumer publication.
 Description: Baseball card and sports memorabilia collecting.

795.4 796.323 US ISSN 1055-8179
BECKETT BASKETBALL MONTHLY. m. $19.95. Beckett Publications, 4887 Alpha Rd., Ste. 200, Dallas, TX 75244. TEL 214-991-6657. FAX 214-991-8930. (Subscr. to: Box 1915, Marion, OH 43305-1915) **Document type:** consumer publication.

795.4 790.1 US ISSN 1060-2801
BECKETT FOCUS ON FUTURE STARS. m. $19.95. Beckett Publications, 4887 Alpha Rd., Ste. 200, Dallas, TX 75244. TEL 214-991-6657. FAX 214-991-8930. (Subscr. to: Box 1915, Marion, OH 43305-1915) Ed. James Beckett. **Document type:** consumer publication.

795.4 796.332 US ISSN 1055-2294
BECKETT FOOTBALL CARD MONTHLY. 1989. m. $19.95. Beckett Publications, 4887 Alpha Rd., Ste. 200, Dallas, TX 75244. TEL 214-991-6657. FAX 214-991-8930. (Subscr. to: Box 1915, Marion, OH 43305-1915) Ed. Fred Reed. **Document type:** consumer publication.
 Formerly (until 1990): Beckett Fotball Card Magazine (ISSN 1053-1521)

795.4 796 US ISSN 1058-5958
BECKETT HOCKEY MONTHLY. m. $19.95. Beckett Publications, 4887 Alpha Rd., Ste. 200, Dallas, TX 75244. TEL 214-991-6657. FAX 214-991-8930. (Subscr. to: Box 1915, Marion, OH 43305-1915) **Document type:** consumer publication.

663.4 US
BEER CAN COLLECTORS NEWS REPORT. 1971. bi-m. $27 includes membership. Beer Can Collectors of America, 747 Merus Ct., Fenton, MO 63026-2092. TEL 314-343-6486. Ed. Marcia Butterbaugh. adv.; bk.rev.; circ. 400 (controlled). (back issues avail.) **Document type:** consumer publication.

790.132 UK ISSN 0306-7912
BEERMAT MAGAZINE. 1960. m. £8.50. British Beer-mat Collectors Society (BBCS), c/o John F. Feenan, Hon. Sec., 30 Carters Orchard, Quedgeley, Glos. GL2 6WB, England. TEL 0452-721643. Ed. John Richards. adv.; bk.rev.; illus.; circ. 500 (controlled). (processed) **Document type:** newsletter.
 Former titles: Coasters; Beermat (ISSN 0045-1657)

790.13 JA
BEST MOTORING. (Text in Japanese) 1981. m. Kodansha Ltd., 12-21 Otowa 2-chome, Bunkyo-ku, Tokyo 112, Japan. TEL 03-3945-9685. FAX 03-3945-9591. TELEX J34509 KODANSHA. Ed. Hisashi Niimi. circ. 80,000. **Document type:** consumer publication.
 Formerly (until 1987): Best Bike.
 Description: For motorcycle enthusiasts.

BETTER HOMES AND GARDENS CHRISTMAS IDEAS. see *HOME ECONOMICS*

790.132 US ISSN 0894-4911
BILL NELSON NEWSLETTER; pin and button newsletter. 1985. m. $20 (foreign $30). Nelson Newsletter Publishing Corp., Box 41630, Tucson, AZ 85717-1630. TEL 602-629-0868. FAX 602-629-0387. Ed. Bill Nelson. circ. 87,000. (back issues avail.) **Document type:** newsletter.
 Formerly: Olympic Collectors Newsletter.
 Description: Features news, ads and tips for pin collectors.

BLACK & DECKER BUILD IT. see *HOW-TO AND DO-IT-YOURSELF*

790.13 US ISSN 0744-6179
TS380
BLADE MAGAZINE. 1973. 8/yr. $17.99 (foreign $35). American Blade Inc., 6237 Vance Rd., Ste. 1, Chattanooga, TN 37421. TEL 615-894-0339. FAX 615-892-7254. (Subscr. to: Box 22007, Chattanooga, TN 37422) Ed. Steve Shackleford. adv.; bk.rev.; illus.; index. circ. 80,000. (back issues avail.) **Document type:** bulletin.
 Formerly: American Blade (ISSN 0097-8949)

790.13 US
BLUE BOOK DOLLS AND VALUES. a. $17.95. Hobby House Press, 1 Corporate Dr., Grantsville, MD 21536. TEL 301-895-3792. Ed. Jan Foulke; Pub. Gary R. Ruddell.

625.19 UK ISSN 0520-3015
BLUEBELL NEWS. 1959. q. membership. (Bluebell Railway Preservation Society) Bluebell Railway Operating Ltd., Sheffield Park Station, Nr. Uckfield, East Sussex TN22 3QL, England. TEL 082572-3777. Ed. K. Marx. adv.; bk.rev. circ. 5,500.
 Description: News briefs, profiles, historical sketches, and photography on the operation of the railway and on the members and activities of the Society, with appraisals of locomotives, carriages, wagons and announcements of special events.

790.023 US ISSN 0006-7229
BOOK COLLECTING WORLD. 1961. 48/yr. $165. Celmer & Twente Associates, 913 W. Cullom Ave., Chicago, IL 60613-8179. Ed. Ernest V. Celmer. bk.rev.; tr.lit. circ. 5,500. (also avail. in microfiche; reprint service avail. from UMI)

790.13 US ISSN 0045-2521
BOOKPLATES IN THE NEWS. 1970. q. $25. American Society of Bookplate Collectors and Designers, 605 N. Stoneman Ave., No. F, Alhambra, CA 91801. TEL 213-283-1936. Ed. Audrey Spencer Arellanes. bk.rev.; index. circ. 200. (also avail. in microform from UMI; reprint service avail. from UMI)
 Description: Covers bookplate collecting.

623.820 US
BOTTLE SHIPWRIGHT. 1983. q. $18. Ships in Bottles Association of America, c/o Ray Handwerker, Ed., 5075 Freeport Dr., Springhill, FL 34606. TEL 619-435-3555. (Subscr. to: Don Hubbard, Box 180550, Coronado, CA 92178) adv.; bk.rev. circ. 350. (back issues avail.) **Document type:** newsletter.
 Description: Covers the art of building ship models and other objects in bottles.

790.13
BRANDSTAND; viewing the world of cigarette collecting. 1976. bi-m. $5. Cigarette Pack Collectors Association, 61 Searle St., Georgetown, MA 01833. TEL 617-352-7377. Ed. Richard Elliott. circ. 350. (back issues avail.) **Document type:** newsletter.
 Former titles: Smoke Signals; Cigarette Pack Collectors News.
 Description: Covers the hobby of collecting obsolete cigarette brand packaging and advertising.

790.13 UK ISSN 0306-7947
BRITISH MODEL SOLDIER SOCIETY. BULLETIN. 1935. q. £12 (effective Jan. 1992). British Model Soldier Society, 52 Broadway Ave., Hasbury, Halesowen, England. TEL 021-503-0237. Ed. S.G. Westwood. adv. contact: P. Hamilton. bk.rev.; illus. circ. 1,000. **Document type:** bulletin.

BRITISH TOYS & HOBBIES BRIEFING. see *GIFTWARE AND TOYS*

BROWNIE ANNUAL. see *CHILDREN AND YOUTH — For*

799.202 GW ISSN 0007-3067
DER BUECHSENMACHER. 1914. m. DM.89. Lothar Haus Druck und Verlag, Hainstr. 50, 63526 Erlensee, Germany. adv.; bk.rev.; illus. circ. 5,200. **Document type:** consumer publication.

BULLETIN DU BIBLIOPHILE (PARIS, 1965). see *PUBLISHING AND BOOK TRADE*

790.13 GW
BURDA FASCHINGSHEFT. a. Verlag Aenne Burda, Am Kestendamm 2, 77652 Offenburg, Germany. TEL 0781-8402. Ed. Beate Mannes. circ. 205,000.

790.13 GW
BURDA GROSSES BASTELHEFT. a. Verlag Aenne Burda, Am Kestendamm 2, 77652 Offenburg, Germany. TEL 0781-8402. Ed. Margret Seewald. circ. 180,000.

790.13 GW
BURDA GROSSES WEIHNACHTSHEFT. a. Verlag Aenne Burda, Am Kestendamm 2, 77652 Offenburg, Germany. TEL 0781-8402. Eds. Elisabeth Klapper-Hund, Veronika Seufert-Beege. circ. 280,000.

790.13 367 UK
CALLIGRAPHER. 1984. bi-m. £3.25. (International Friendship League (British Section)) I F L Pen Friend Service U.K., P.O. Box 117, Leicester LE3 6EE, England. Ed. M. Weston. bk.rev. (back issues avail.) **Document type:** newsletter.
 Description: Explores pen friendship and the hobby of writing to pen friends in Britain and Ireland.

355 US
CAMPAIGN;* journal of strategy gaming. 1970. bi-m. $12. Lowry Enterprises, 644 E. Fallbrook St., Fallbrook, CA 92028-3440. Ed. Don Lowry. adv.; bk.rev.; bibl.; charts; illus. circ. 2,200. **Indexed:** BPIA.
 Former titles (until 1977): Panzerfaust and Campaign; (until 1975): Panzerfaust.

625.19 CN ISSN 1181-7909
CANADIAN RAILWAY MODELLER. 1990. 6/yr. Can.$24($30) 1453 Henderson Hwy., 28103-1453 Henderson Hwy., Winnipeg, MB R2G 4E9, Canada. TEL 204-668-0168. FAX 204-668-0168. Ed. Morgan Turney. adv.; bk.rev.; video rev. circ. 3,800. (back issues avail.)

795.4 790.1 CN
CANADIAN SPORTSCARD COLLECTOR. 1990. m. Can.$22.95 (in US Can.$26.95; elsewhere Can.$38.95). Trajan Publishing Corp., 103 Lakeshore Rd., Ste. 202, St. Catharines, ON L2N 2T6, Canada. TEL 905-646-7744. FAX 905-646-0995. Ed. Jeffrey Morris. adv. contact: Mario Bacek. circ. 12,377 (paid); 327 (controlled).

790.13 US
THE CANE COLLECTOR'S CHRONICLE. 1990. q. $35. Cane Collector's Chronicle, 15 Second St., N.E., Washington, DC 20002-7301. TEL 202-544-1366. FAX 202-544-1372. adv. circ. 160. **Document type:** newsletter.
 Description: For antique walking stick collectors.

683.4 AT ISSN 0045-5695
CAPS AND FLINTS. 1966. q. Aus.$0.40 per no. Antique & Historical Arms Collectors Guild of Victoria, P.O. Box 27, S. Blackburn, Vic. 3130, Australia. TEL 03-583-9551. Ed. Ray A. Hellier. adv.; bk.rev. circ. 1,700.

ULRICH'S INTERNATIONAL PERIODICALS DIRECTORY 1994-95

HOBBIES

790.132 US
▼**CARD COLLECTOR'S PRICE GUIDE.** 1992. m. $29.95. Century Publishing Co., 990 Grove St., Evanston, IL 60201-4370. TEL 708-491-6440. (Subscr. to: Box 443, Mt. Morris, IL 61054-0443. TEL 800-877-5893) Ed. Douglas Kale. adv.; illus. **Document type:** consumer publication.
Description: Comprehensive coverage of non-sports cards for collectors, including entertainment, TV, history, music cards.

795.4 796.357 US ISSN 1062-2977
CARD NEWS & PRICE GUIDE. 1981. bi-w. $26.95. Krause Publications, Inc., 700 E. State St., Iola, WI 54990. TEL 715-445-2214. FAX 715-445-4087. TELEX 55 6461 KRAUSE PUB UD. Ed. Scott Kelnhofer. adv. circ. 81,000. (also avail. in microform from UMI.)
Formerly: Baseball Card News (ISSN 0746-7966)
Description: Contains updates on new collectibles for baseball, football, hockey, basketball, and other card sets. Provides in-depth spotlights on baseball players and new card sets. Contains buy and sell ads for all types of sports collectibles.

790.13 UK ISSN 0956-5124
CARD TIMES. 1986. m. £20. Magpie Publications, 70 Winifred Ln., Aughton, Ormskirk, Lancs. L39 5DL, England. TEL 0695-423470. Ed. David Stuckey. circ. 2,500. (back issues avail.) **Document type:** consumer publication.

745.1 US ISSN 0008-6916
CARRIAGE JOURNAL. 1963. q. $45 includes membership. Carriage Association of America, Inc., Rd. 1, Box 115, Salem, NJ 08079. TEL 609-935-1616. FAX 609-358-6138. Ed. Jill Ryder. adv.; bk.rev.; abstr.; bibl.; illus. circ. 3,200. Indexed: Sportsearch. **Document type:** trade publication, newsletter.
Description: Provides information on the collecting, restoring and showing of horse drawn vehicles.

737 FR ISSN 0183-8490
CARTES POSTALES ET COLLECTIONS. 1977. bi-m. Paul Noel Armand, B.P. 15, 95220 Herblay, France. adv.; bk.rev. circ. 12,000.
Formerly (until no.56, 1977): Collections et Monnaies (ISSN 0339-0608)

795.4 IT
LA CARTOLINA. 1981-1986; resumed 1987. bi-m. L.45000 (Europe L.60000; U.S. L.70000). Edizione La Cartolina, Via Barrili 35, 00152 Rome, Italy. TEL 06-5815164. FAX 06-5897240. Ed. Furio Arrasich. circ. 2,000.

790.023 UK ISSN 0008-7076
CARTOPHILIC NOTES & NEWS. 1965. bi-m. £11. Cartophilic Society of Great Britain Ltd., c/o K. Fox, 116 Hillview Road, Ensbury Park, Bournemouth, Dorset BH10 5BJ, England. Ed. Alan Harris. adv.; bk.rev.; illus.; cum.index covering 2 yrs. circ. 960.
Description: Devoted to propagating, enhancing and preserving the hobby of cigarette and trade card collecting.

790.132 FR ISSN 0224-7232
CASSE-TETE MAGAZINE. bi-m. 103 F. Publications Guy Hachette, La Petite Motte Senille, 86100 Chatellerault, France.
—CCC.

CAST POLYMER CONNECTION. see BUSINESS AND ECONOMICS — Small Business

793 FR ISSN 0243-1327
CASUS BELLI. 1980. 6/yr. 175 F. (foreign 206 F.) (effective 1992). Excelsior Publications, 1 rue du Colonel Pierre Avia, 75503 Paris Cedex 15, France. TEL 46-48-48-48. FAX 46-48-48-09. TELEX 631 994 F. Ed. Didier Guiserix. adv. contact: Gilles de Keranflech. circ. 37,000.

790.132 US
CAT COLLECTORS. Running title: Cat Talk. 1982. bi-m. $18 (Canada $22; elsewhere $25). Cat Collectors, 33161 Wendy Dr., Sterling Hts., MI 48310. TEL 313-264-0285. Ed. Marilyn Dipboye. adv.; bk.rev.; index. circ. 1,000. **Document type:** catalog, newsletter.
Description: News, articles, and illustrations on antique and new cat collectibles, artists and craftspersons. Includes book reviews, museum holdings, and catalog shopping advice.

CERAMICS (FRESNO). see ARTS AND HANDICRAFTS

790.13 665.5 US ISSN 1042-7341
"CHECK THE OIL!" MAGAZINE; the publication devoted exclusively to Petroliana. 1983. bi-m. $16 (Canada $25; overseas $30) (effective Jan. 1993). (International Petroliana Collectors' Association) Three Fifty Six, Inc., Box 937, Powel, OH 43065-0937. TEL 614-848-5038. Ed. Jerry Keyser. adv.; bk.rev.; circ. 4,000. (paid). (back issues avail.) **Document type:** consumer publication.
Description: Aimed at those interested in the history and collectibles of the petroleum and gas industry.

799.202 FR ISSN 0009-6679
CIBLES. 1967. 12/yr. 390 F. Editions Crepin-Leblond et Cie, 14, rue du Patronage Laique, 52003 Chaumont Cedex, France. TEL 25-03-65-42. FAX 25-32-67-87. adv.; bk.rev.; charts; illus.; tr.lit. circ. 40,000.

745.592 GW ISSN 0931-1556
CIESLIK'S PUPPENMAGAZIN. 1987. q. DM.74($70) Marianne Cieslik Verlag, Theodor-Heuss-Str. 185, 52428 Juelich, Germany. TEL 02461-51222. FAX 02461-52772. Ed. Juergen Cieslik. adv.; bk.rev.; illus. circ. 8,500. (back issues avail.) **Document type:** consumer publication.

790.023 UK ISSN 0009-6822
CIGARETTE CARD NEWS AND TRADE CARD CHRONICLE. 1933. m. £22($40) London Cigarette Card Co. Ltd., Sutton Rd., Somerton, Somerset TA11 6QP, England. TEL 0458-73452. Ed. F.C. Doggett. adv.; bk.rev.; abstr.; illus. circ. 1,500. **Document type:** consumer publication.
Description: Descriptions of current stocks of issues and articles on special issues, with a list of reference books.

790.13 UK ISSN 0950-3315
CLASSIC BOAT. 1987. m. £35.40($90) Boating Publications Ltd., Link House, Dingwall Ave., Croydon, Surrey CR9 2TA, England. TEL 081-686-2599. FAX 081-781-6535. (Subscr. to: Classic Boat Subscr., 1st Fl., Stephenson House, Brunel Centre, Milton Keynes, Bucks. MK2 2EW, England) Ed. Robin Gates. adv.; bk.rev.; illus.; index; circ. 17,043 (paid). (back issues avail.) **Document type:** consumer publication.
Description: Covers restorations of classic boats, traditional boat building, boat design, maritime art, and yacht regattas.

790.13 US
CLASSIC RANGES; parts, services, restoration, sales. q. $3.50 per issue. c/o Macy's Texas Stove Works, 5515 Almeda Rd., Houston, TX 77004. TEL 713-521-0934. FAX 713-521-0889. **Document type:** newsletter.
Description: Newsletter for Classic owners and buyers.

625.19 US ISSN 0895-0997
CLASSIC TOY TRAINS. 1987. bi-m. $19.95 (foreign $26). Kalmbach Publishing Co., Box 1612, Waukesha, WI 53187-1612. TEL 414-796-8776. FAX 414-796-0126. Ed. Richard Christianson. circ. 44,500.
Description: For toy train collectors and operators. Each issue recalls and reports on trains built by Lionel, American Flyer, Ives, LGB, and a variety of other manufacturers.

790.13 FR
COGITO. bi-m. 36 F. Publications Guy Hachette, La Petite Motte Senille, 86100 Chatellerault, France.

793 US
COIN SLOT (WHEAT RIDGE). 1974. q. $36. Hoflin Publishing Ltd., 4401 Zephyr St., Wheat Ridge, CO 80033-3299. TEL 303-467-0089. FAX 303-420-1076. Ed. Cynthia L. Kerstiens. adv.; bk.rev. circ. 1,200.

070 790.132 US
COLLECTIBLE NEWSPAPERS. 1984. q. $18 (Europe $28). Newspaper Collectors Society of America, Box 19134, Lansing, MI 48901. TEL 517-887-1255. Ed. Rick Brown. adv.; B&W page $90. index; circ. 400 (paid). (looseleaf format; back issues avail.)
Description: Covers topics relating to newspaper collecting.

790.13 US
▼**COLLECTING TOYS.** 1993. bi-m. Kalmbach Publishing Co., Box 1612, Waukesha, WI 53187-1612. TEL 414-796-8776. FAX 414-796-0126. Ed. Jim Bunte. adv.; illus. **Document type:** consumer publication.
Description: For hobbyists and collectors of new and antique toys.

790.13 FR ISSN 0588-2583
COLLECTIONNEUR FRANCAIS. 1965. m. 200 F. 10 rue du Pont Louis Philippe, 75004 Paris, France. Ed. Andre Escaro. adv.; illus. Indexed: Numis.Lit.

790.132 332.6 SA
COLLECTOR AND INVESTOR. m. R.10 to non-members. (Collector's Club R. S. A.) Management and Promotional Services, Box 6191, Johannesburg 2000, South Africa. Ed. Phillip Prim. adv.

790.13 US ISSN 0733-2130
AM201
COLLECTOR EDITIONS. 1973. bi-m. $19.97. Collector Communications Corp., 170 Fifth Ave., New York, NY 10010. TEL 212-989-8700. FAX 212-645-8976. (Subscr. to: Box 1941, Marion, OH 43305) Ed. Joan M. Pursley; Pub. Robert C. Rowe. adv. contact: Diane G. Kane. bk.rev.; charts; illus. circ. 100,000. (also avail. in microform from UMI) **Document type:** consumer publication.
—UMI.
Former titles (until 1981): Collector Editions Quarterly (ISSN 0199-929X); (until 1977): Acquire.

790.13 AT ISSN 1036-6997
COLLECTORS DIRECTORY; for everyone interested in collecting. 1990. q. Aus.$10($20) Sr. & J. Coleman, Ed. & Pub., P.O. Box 1357, Penrith, N.S.W. 2751, Australia. TEL 047-392652. adv.; bk.rev.; illus. circ. 200. (back issues avail.) **Document type:** directory.
Description: Contains contacts by phone or address. Provides a service to buy, sell, swap, or chat with others interested in anything old, interesting, antique or collectible

790.12 UK
COLLECTORS MART. 1980. q. £9.52 (Ireland and rest of Europe £10.88; Elsewhere £12.20). Kollectarama, Parkgate House, 27 High St., Hampton Hill, Mddx. TW12 1NB, England. TEL 081-941-4512. FAX 801-941-8630. Ed. John Pitman. adv.; B&W page £250; adv. contact: Anne Morrell. bk.rev.; illus. circ. 3,000. **Document type:** consumer publication.
Formerly: New Collecting Lines; Incorporates: Finders Keepers (Wellingborough) (ISSN 0260-5236)
Description: Covers trade ephemera and advertising marterial, including bottles, enamel signs, hand bills, and figures, of interest to collectors. Announces trade fairs and auctions.

790.132 IT
▼**COLTELLI, CHE PASSIONE!.** 1992. q. L.24000. Casella Postale 519, 20101 Milan, Italy. TEL 02-48-40-28-57. Ed. Y. Gagueche. adv. **Document type:** consumer publication.
Description: Devoted to all types of knives: sporting, custom, industrial, collectible.

790.132 US
▼**COMIC BOOK COLLECTOR.** 1993. m. Century Publishing Co., 990 Grove St., Evanston, IL 60201-4370. TEL 708-491-6440. (Subscr. to: Box 443, Mt. Morris, IL 61054-0443. TEL 800-877-5893) Ed. Doug Kale. **Document type:** consumer publication.
Description: Covers comic book collecting, with prices from 1938 to present.

808.836 US ISSN 1053-8704
COMIC BUYERS GUIDE PRICE GUIDE. 1990. 6/yr. $14.95. Krause Publications, Inc., 700 E. State St., Iola, WI 54990-0001. TEL 715-445-2214. FAX 715-445-4087. TELEX 556461 KRAUSE PUB UD. Eds. Don Thompson, Maggie Thompson. circ. 61,824.
Description: Gives current prices for over 25,000 comic books. grading information, historical perspectives and buying-selling trends.

3020 HOBBIES

808.836 US ISSN 0745-4570
COMICS BUYERS GUIDE. 1971. w. $34.95. Krause Publications, Inc., 700 E. State St., Iola, WI 54990. TEL 715-445-2214. FAX 715-445-4087. TELEX 556461 KRAUSE PUB UD. Eds. Don Thompson, Maggie Thompson. circ. 21,471. (tabloid format; also avail. in microform from UMI.)
  Description: Directed to comics fans, collectors and the comics industry. Contains articles and news about comics from the past and the present and the people who write, draw and publish them.

790.13 US
COMPETITION (HARRISBURG).* 1989. a. $16.95. Commonwealth Communications Services, Inc., 5067 Ritter Rd., Mechanicsburg, PA 17055-6921. TEL 717-234-5091. FAX 717-234-1359. Ed. Cathy Hart. adv. circ. 5,000.

745.592 US ISSN 1052-486X
NK4894.U6
CONTEMPORARY DOLL MAGAZINE. 1990. bi-m. $19.90 (foreign $37.90). Scott Advertising & Publishing Co., 30595 Eight Mile Rd., Livonia, MI 48152-1798. TEL 810-477-6650. FAX 810-477-6795. Ed. Barbara Campbell. circ. 43,000. **Document type:** consumer publication.
  Description: Covers contemporary dolls of all types, including artists' dolls, one-of-a-kind dolls and limited editions; also includes advice for collectors and profiles of artists and manufacturers here and abroad.

790.13 US ISSN 0195-9735
CONTEST HOTLINE.* 1977. m. $12. Nationwide Shopper, Box 3197, Burbank, CA 91508-3197. Ed. Jerry Haws. (tabloid format)

790.13 US
CONTEST NEWS-LETTER.* 1975. m. $15.97. Contest Partners, Box 25227, Arlington, VA 22202-9227. (Subscr. to: Box 58637, Boulder, CO 80322-8637) Eds. Deni Hamilton, Les Whiteley. circ. 550,000.
  Description: For people who enter sweepstakes as a hobby.

625.19 US
CONTINENTAL MODELLER. 1979. m. £26.40. Peco Publications and Publicity Ltd., Beer, Seaton, Devon EX12 3NA, England. Ed. Andrew Burnham.

CRAFT AND NEEDLEWORK AGE. see ARTS AND HANDICRAFTS

CURRENT BLACKJACK NEWS. see SPORTS AND GAMES

DATA EXTRACT. see COMMUNICATIONS — Television And Cable

790.13 US
DECALCOMANIA. 1982. 10/yr. $11. DecaloMania Club, Box 126, Lincroft, NJ 07738. TEL 908-591-2522. FAX 908-576-4429. Ed. Phil Bytheway. adv. contact: Paul Richards. bk.rev. circ. 100. **Document type:** newsletter.
  Description: Covers the collection of radio paraphernalia and promotional items such as stickers and "airchecks".

745.5 JA
DECORATIVE DESIGN. (Text in Japanese) 1982. q. 8800 Yen. Gakken Co., Ltd., 40-5, 4 chome, Kamiikedai, Ohta-ku, Tokyo 145, Japan. Ed. Jiro Takeuchi.

790.13 US ISSN 1055-0364
SK335
DECOY MAGAZINE. 1980. bi-m. $30 (Canada $35, elsewhere $60) (effective 1993). Joe Engers, Ed. & Pub., Box 277, Burtonsville, MD 20866. TEL 301-890-0262. adv.; B&W page $450, color page $685; trim 8 1/2 x 11. bk.rev. circ. 3,000.
  Description: Serves the needs and interests of decoy collectors worldwide. Contains auction coverage, calendar, and general articles on decoys.

790.13 GW
DEUTSCHER KLEINTIER ZUCHTER: AUSGABE GEFLUGEL. bi-m. DM.105.60. Oertel & Spoerer, Burgstr. 1-7, 72764 Reutlingen, Germany. TEL 07121-302555. FAX 07121-302512. index. circ. 12,000. (back issues avail.) **Document type:** consumer publication.

790.13 GW
DEUTSCHER KLEINTIER ZUCHTER: AUSGABE GEMISCHTE. bi-m. DM.105.60. Oertel & Spoerer, Burgstr. 1-7, 72764 Reutlingen, Germany. TEL 07121-302555. FAX 07121-302512. index. circ. 5,300. (back issues avail.) **Document type:** consumer publication.

790.13 GW
DEUTSCHER KLEINTIER ZUCHTER: AUSGABE KANINCHEN. s-a. DM.105.60. Oertel & Spoerer, Burgstr. 1-7, 72764 Reutlingen, Germany. TEL 07121-302555. FAX 07121-302512. index. circ. 18,000. (back issues avail.) **Document type:** consumer publication.

739 GW ISSN 0012-138X
DEUTSCHES WAFFEN-JOURNAL. 1965. m. DM.97.10 (foreign DM.118.20). Journal Verlag Schwend GmbH, Schmollerstr. 31, 74523 Schwaebisch Hall, Germany. TEL 0791-404-500. FAX 0791-404111. Eds. Gerhard Wirnsberger, Klaus Schinmeyer. adv.; bk.rev.; illus.; tr.mk.; index. circ. 72,000. **Document type:** consumer publication.

799.202 IT ISSN 0012-2351
DIANA ARMI. 1967. m. L.76000 (foreign L.102000). Editoriale Olimpia S.p.A., Viale Milton 7, 50129 Florence, Italy. TEL 055-473843. FAX 055-499195. TELEX 573084 EDOL I. Dir. Emanuele Marciano. adv.; illus. circ. 45,000.

DIME NOVEL ROUND-UP; devoted to the collecting, preservation and literature of the old time dime and nickel novels, libraries and popular story papers. see PUBLISHING AND BOOK TRADE

DIVER MAGAZINE. see SPORTS AND GAMES

790.13 US ISSN 0363-7972
TT175
DOLL CASTLE NEWS; the doll collector's magazine. 1961. 6/yr. $13.95. Castle Press Publications, Inc., Box 247, Washington, NJ 07882. TEL 201-689-7042. Ed. Edwina Mueller. adv.; bk.rev.; charts; illus. circ. 8,000.

745.592 US
DOLL COLLECTOR'S PRICE GUIDE. q. $12.97. House of White Birches Publishing, 306 E. Parr Rd., Berne, IN 46711. TEL 219-589-8741. FAX 219-589-8093. Ed. Cary Raesner. **Document type:** consumer publication.

790.13 US ISSN 1050-4796
DOLL DESIGNS. 1984. bi-m. $14.95. House of White Birches Publishing, 306 E. Parr Rd., Berne, IN 46711. TEL 219-589-8741. Ed. Cary Raesner. adv.; bk.rev. circ. 19,190. (back issues avail.) Indexed: Ind.How To Do It (1990-). **Document type:** consumer publication.
  Formerly: National Doll World Omnibook (ISSN 0199-1043)
  Description: Contains restoration ideas and techniques, patterns, features and other items of interest to toy crafters.

745.592 US ISSN 1069-7896
DOLL LIFE. 1991. q. $15.97. All American Crafts, Inc., 243 Newton-Sparta Rd., Newton, NJ 07860-2848. TEL 201-383-8080. Ed. Michele Epstein. adv. contact: Barbara Smith. **Document type:** consumer publication.
  Description: Focuses on collecting and making dolls.

790.13 US ISSN 0744-0901
DOLL READER. 1972. 9/yr. $26.95. Cowles Magazines, Inc., 6405 Flank Dr., Box 8200, Harrisburg, PA 17105-8200. TEL 717-540-8192. FAX 717-657-9526. Ed. Carolyn B. Cook. adv.; bk.rev.; bibl.; illus.; tr.lit. circ. 135,000. **Document type:** consumer publication.

790.13 US ISSN 1066-4726
DOLL WORLD. 1977. bi-m. $17.77. House of White Birches Publishing, 306 E. Parr Rd., Berne, IN 46711. TEL 219-589-8741. Ed. Cary Raesner. adv.; bk.rev.; illus. circ. 49,109. (back issues avail.)
  Former titles: International Doll World (ISSN 1050-3994); National Doll World (ISSN 0147-4685)
  Description: Covers doll identification, history, patterns, books and other items of interest to the collector.

745.592 US ISSN 0885-2707
TT175
DOLLMAKING. 1986. q. $14.95. Joe Jones Publishing, Inc., 121 N. Main St., Box 337, Iola, WI 54945. TEL 715-445-5000. FAX 715-445-4053. Ed. Pune Dracker. **Document type:** consumer publication.

790.132 US ISSN 0733-2238
NK4893
DOLLS; the collector's magazine. 1982. 10/yr. $29.95. Collector Communications Corp., 170 Fifth Ave., New York, NY 10010. TEL 212-989-8700. (Subscr. to: Box 1972, Marion, OH 43305) Ed. Joan M. Pursley. adv.; bk.rev. circ. 114,000.

790.13 UK ISSN 0961-0928
DOLLS HOUSE WORLD. 1990. bi-m. £21($42) (rest of Europe £29; elsewhere £35). Ashdown Publishing Ltd., Shelly House, 104 High St., Steyning, W. Sussex BN4 3RD, England. TEL 0903-815622. FAX 0903-815599. Ed. Richard Jennings. adv.; bk.rev.; index. circ. 15,000. (back issues avail.) **Document type:** consumer publication.

790.13 US ISSN 0279-6848
DRAGON MAGAZINE. 1976. m. $30. T S R Inc., Box 111, Lake Geneva, WI 53147. TEL 414-248-3625. (Subscr. to: Box 72089, Chicago, IL 60678) Ed. Roger E. Moore. adv.; bk.rev. circ. 80,000. (back issues avail.) **Document type:** consumer publication.

790.13 791.43 US ISSN 0887-2155
DUCKBURG TIMES. 1977. irreg. $12. 3010 Wilshire Blvd., No.362, Los Angeles, CA 90010-1146. TEL 213-388-2364. Ed. Dana Gabbard. adv.; bk.rev. circ. 1,400.
  Description: Devoted to Disney and Carl Barks.

DX MONITOR. see COMMUNICATIONS — Radio

DX REPORTER. see COMMUNICATIONS — Radio

E A A. TECHNICAL COUNSELOR NEWSLETTER. (Experimental Aircraft Association, Inc.) see AERONAUTICS AND SPACE FLIGHT

790.13 US
EDGES. 1981. q. $12.95. (American Blade Collectors Association) American Blade, Inc., 6237 Vance Rd., Ste. 1, Chattanooga, TN 37421. TEL 615-899-0339. FAX 615-892-7254. (Subscr. to: Box 22007, Chattanooga, TN 37422) Ed. Steve Shackleford. adv.; bk.rev.; illus. circ. 18,000. (back issues avail.) **Document type:** bulletin.

EGGCUP COLLECTORS' CORNER. see ANTIQUES

625.19 SZ ISSN 0013-2764
EISENBAHN-AMATEUR; Schweizerische Zeitschrift fuer Eisenbahn- und Modellbaufreunde. 1947. m. 80 Fr. Schweizerischer Verband Eisenbahn Amateur, Postfach 1257, 8058 Zuerich, Switzerland. adv.; bk.rev.; abstr.; bibl.; illus.; stat.; index. circ. 16,000. (tabloid format)
  Description: Publication for railroad hobbyists, featuring new, old, and renovated cars, railroad news, and model railroad cars. Includes reports and list of events, activities and new publications.

625.19 GW ISSN 0170-5288
EISENBAHN-KURIER; Modell und Vorbild. 1966. m. DM.148.80 (foreign DM.152.40). E K Verlag GmbH, Postfach 5560, 79022 Freiburg, Germany. TEL 0761-703100. FAX 0761-7031050. adv.; bk.rev. circ. 49,500. **Document type:** trade publication.
  —SWETS.

EISENBAHN MODELLBAHN MAGAZIN. see TRANSPORTATION — Railroads

ELETTRONICA 2000 MISTER KIT. see ELECTRONICS

ENFANTS S'AMUSENT. see CHILDREN AND YOUTH — For

745.5 UK
ENGINEERING IN MINIATURE. 1979. m. £16.80. T E E Publishing, The Fosse, Fosse Way, Radford Semele, Leamington Spa CV31 1XN, England. TEL 0926-614101. FAX 0926-614293. Ed. C.L. Deith. adv.; bk.rev. circ. 20,000. (back issues avail.) **Document type:** consumer publication.

ESTES EDUCATOR NEWS. see EDUCATION — Teaching Methods And Curriculum

EXTRA 2200 SOUTH; locomotive news magazine. see TRANSPORTATION — Railroads

629.133 GW ISSN 0015-458X
F M T. (Flug- und Modell-Technik) 1945. m. DM.96 (foreign DM.104.40). Verlag fuer Technik und Handwerk GmbH, Robert-Bosch-Str. 4, 76532 Baden-Baden, Germany. TEL 07221-5087-0. FAX 07221-508752. Ed. Michal Sip. adv.; bk.rev.; bibl.; charts; illus.; tr.lit.; circ. 43,000 (controlled). **Document type**: consumer publication.

736.2 AT ISSN 1035-0977
FACET TALK. 1981. bi-m. Aus.$25 (foreign Aus.$35). Australian Facetors' Guild, P.O. Box 47, Sandgate, Qld. 4017, Australia. TEL 61-7-269-2904. FAX 61-7-864-3985. Ed. John Broadfoot. adv.; bk.rev. circ. 1,100. **Document type**: newsletter.
Description: Covers gemstone faceting, gemology, geology, and faceting competitions.

790.13
FAI DA TE. 1973. m. L.96000. Edifai, Via Leonardo da Vinci, 9, 20012 Cuggiono (MI), Italy. Ed. Andrea Sganzerla. adv. circ. 80,000.
Description: A do-it-yourself magazine.

790.13 IT
FAI DA TE MOTOVERDE. 1977. m. L.10500. Edifai, Via Leonardo Da Vinci, 9, 20012 Cuggiono (MI), Italy. Ed. Dino Bellomi. adv. circ. 45,000.

790.13 338 US
FAMILIES TOGETHER PEN PALS. 1988. bi-m. $10 (foreign $17) (effective July 1993). F T Marketing, 224 Cherry Creek Rd., Marquette, MI 49855. Ed. Beverly Qualheim. adv.; bk.rev. circ. 90. **Document type**: newsletter.
Formerly: Families Together Newsletter.
Description: Features home-based or cottage industries, crafts, and reviews for families who are penpal writers. Includes penpal listings, recipes, and traders.

790.13 US ISSN 1046-9125
FANTASY BASEBALL. 1990. q. $9.95. Krause Publications, Inc., 700 E. State St., Iola, WI 54990. TEL 715-445-2214. FAX 715-445-4087. TELEX 55 6461 KRAUSE PUB UD. Ed. Greg Ambrosius. circ. 110,134.
Description: Guide to fantasy baseball leagues. Provides information on best picks for drafting players, including statistics from the previous year. Each major-league player is ranked. Batting averages, pitching ratios and player interviews. New products are reviewed and advertised.

790.13 IT
FAR DA SE. 1975. m. L.83000. Edizioni Fardase, Casella Postale 100, 15066 Gavi (Al.), Italy. Ed. Massimo Casolaro. adv. circ. 120,000.
Description: A do-it-yourself magazine.

790.13 IT
FAR DA SE ALMANACCO. 1977. a. L.9500. Edizioni Fardase, Casella Postale 100, 15066 Gavi (Al.), Italy. Ed. Massimo Casolaro.
Description: Catalog for do-it-yourself purchases and materials.

790 TT154 US ISSN 0277-979X
FINESCALE MODELER. 1982. 8/yr. $19.95 (foreign $26). Kalmbach Publishing Co., Box 1612, Waukesha, WI 53187. TEL 414-796-8776. FAX 414-796-0126. Ed. Bob Hayden. adv.; bk.rev.; charts; illus.; index. circ. 82,000. (back issues avail.)
Description: Presents the hobby of scale modeling - building accurate, realistic models of aircraft, ships, cars, trucks, military vehicles, and miniature figures. Emphasis on how-to-do-it techniques and challenging modeling projects.

FINEST HOUR. see HISTORY

FIRE WORLD. see FIRE PREVENTION

FISH CULTURIST. see FISH AND FISHERIES

FLAG & BANNER. see GENEALOGY AND HERALDRY

780 US ISSN 0149-7499
FLORAL UNDERAWL & GAZETTE TIMES. 1977. m. $20. Kxe6s Verein Chess Society, Box 2066, Chapel Hill, NC 27514. Ed. Steven Leslie-Buntin. adv.; bk.rev.; film rev.; play rev.; bibl.; charts; illus.; pat.; stat.; tr.lit.; index. circ. 2,000. (back issues avail.)

THE FLOWER ARRANGER. see ARTS AND HANDICRAFTS

FLUGZEUG; Aktuell-Historie-Modell. see AERONAUTICS AND SPACE FLIGHT

629.133 US ISSN 0015-4849
FLYING MODELS; the model builder's how-to-do-it magazine. 1927. m. $23. Carstens Publications, Inc., Box 700, Newton, NJ 07860. TEL 201-383-3355. FAX 201-383-4064. Ed. Robin Hunt. adv.; charts; illus. circ. 35,000. (back issues avail.)
—UnCover.
Description: Provides news and information on model airplanes, cars, boats, and sport flying.

FORD ENTHUSIAST MAGAZINE. see TRANSPORTATION — Automobiles

790 GW
FREIZEIT REVUE. 1970. w. $120. Burda Verlag GmbH, Postfach 1230, 77602 Offenburg, Germany. TEL 089-9250-0. FAX 089-92503519. (U.S. dist.: GLP International, 153 S. Dean St., Englewood, NJ 07631. TEL 201-871-1010. FAX 201-871-0870) Ed. Lothar Strobach. adv.; illus. circ. 1,092,300. **Document type**: consumer publication.

790.13 II ISSN 0046-5100
FRIEND INTERNATIONAL. (Text in English) 1970. Rs.3($3) International Penpals Pool, Sundar Mahal, R.No. 43, Subhash Rd., Marine Dr., Bombay 20, India. Ed. Bhojan Krishnan. bk.rev.; film rev. circ. 1,000.

790.13 US ISSN 1068-946X
FRIENDSHIP EXPRESS. 1988. bi-m. $15. Penpals at Large, Box 167492, Irving, TX 75062. Ed. Karie Rochelle Koutz. adv. circ. 5,000. **Document type**: newsletter.
Description: Contains hundreds of listings of US and international pen pals. Promotes peace through world friendship.

790.13 US ISSN 1041-1852
FRONT STRIKER BULLETIN. 1986. q. $17.50. American Matchcover Collecting Club, Box 18481, Asheville, NC 28814-0481. TEL 704-254-4487. FAX 704-254-1066. Ed. Bill Retskin. adv.; bk.rev. circ. 750. (back issues avail.) **Document type**: bulletin.
Description: Covers the history and current status of the matchbook industry as well as the matchcover collecting hobby.

GAMES INTERNATIONAL. see SPORTS AND GAMES

625.19 US ISSN 0747-0622
GARDEN RAILWAYS. 1984. bi-m. $21 (foreign $28). Box 61461, Denver, CO 80206. TEL 303-733-4779. Ed. Marc Horovitz. adv. contact: Marc Horovitz. bk.rev.; illus. circ. 14,000. **Document type**: consumer publication.
Description: Discusses how to integrate large-scale model railroading into an outdoor environment; covers gardening and landscaping concerns, how to build and maintain the track and rolling stock, with product reviews and profiles of enthusiasts and their railways.

GAS ENGINE MAGAZINE. see ENGINEERING — Mechanical Engineering

790.13 FR ISSN 0767-869X
GAZETTE DES ARMES. 1970. m. (11/yr.). 345 F. Editions Elysees, 122, av. des Champs-Elysees, 75008 Paris, France. TEL 43-59-27-71. FAX 45-61-18-29. Ed. Arty Tackian. adv.; bk.rev. circ. 45,000.
Former titiles: Gazette des Armes & Poudre Noire.

GREAT WESTERN ECHO. see TRANSPORTATION — Railroads

790.13 UK
GUN & ACCESSORIES MART. 1984. m. £13.20 (foreign £39). Aceville Publications Ltd., 89 East Hill, Colchester, Essex CO1 2QN, England. TEL 0206-871139. FAX 0206-871537. Ed. Matthew Tudor. circ. 30,000.
Description: Covers modern and antique weapons.

799.202 700 US ISSN 0017-5617
GUN REPORT; dedicated to the interests of gun enthusiasts everywhere. 1955. m. $29.95. World Wide Gun Report, Inc., Box 38, Aledo, IL 61231-0038. TEL 309-582-5311. FAX 309-582-5555. Ed. Kenneth W. Liggett. adv. contact: Kathy Jackson. bk.rev.; index, cum.index: 1955-1979. circ. 5,000. **Document type**: trade publication.

799.202 790.023 CN ISSN 0017-5625
GUN TALK. 1960. q. Can.$10 to non-members. Saskatchewan Gun Collectors Association, Box 1334, Regina, Sask. S4P 3B8, Canada. Ed. Morley Bogues. adv.; charts; illus.; stat. circ. 250. (processed)

GUNS & AMMO. see SPORTS AND GAMES — Outdoor Life

799.202 790.023 UK ISSN 0017-5692
GUNS REVIEW. 1960. m. £18 (foreign £21). Ravenhill Publishing Co. Ltd., Standard House, Bonhill St., London EC2A 4DA, England. TEL 071-628-4741. FAX 071-638-8497. TELEX 888602-MONEWS-G. Ed. Colin Greenwood. adv.; bk.rev.; charts; illus.; mkt.; tr.lit.; index. circ. 19,728. **Document type**: consumer publication.

H A C TECHLINE. (Historical Aircraft Corporation) see AERONAUTICS AND SPACE FLIGHT

HABILETES LOISIRS. see HANDICAPPED

799.202 790.023 US ISSN 0017-7393
HANDLOADER; the journal of ammunition reloading. 1966. bi-m. $19. Wolfe Publishing Co., 6471 Airpark Dr., Prescott, AZ 86301. TEL 602-645-7810; 800-899-7810. FAX 602-778-5124. Ed. Dave Scovill. adv.; bk.rev.; charts; illus.; mkt.; tr.lit.; index, cum.index. circ. 36,000.

HANDS ON GUIDE. see ARTS AND HANDICRAFTS

HERO ILLUSTRATED. see PUBLISHING AND BOOK TRADE

790.13 US
▼**HEROES OF THE GAME.** 1993. bi-m. $24. Blue Book Publishers, Inc., 7807 Girard Ave., Ste. 200, La Jolla, CA 92037. TEL 619-454-7939. Ed. Richard Levin. adv.; B&W page $1195. circ. 10,000 (paid). **Document type**: consumer publication.

629 335 FR
HISTOIRE ET MAQUETTISME. bi-m. 32 F. per no. Editions Heimdal, Chateau de Damigny, 14400 Bayeux, France. (back issues avail.)
Description: Looks at military models.

HOB-NOB. see LITERATURE

790.023 NE ISSN 0929-4805
HOBBY BULLETIN. 1948. m. fl.69. Muiderkring B.V., Hogeweyselaan 227, 1382 JL Weesp, Netherlands. TEL 31-2940-15210. FAX 31-2940-12782. Ed. H.B. Stuurman. adv.; bk.rev.; charts; illus. circ. 20,000.
Former titles (until 1993): H B Modelbouw Magazine (ISSN 0922-2170); (until 1988): H B Modelbouw en Techniek (ISSN 0169-1465); (until 1984): H B Model en Techniek (ISSN 0165-5949); (until 1978): Hobby Bulletin (ISSN 0018-2931)

HOBBY - BUSINESS WORLD. see BUSINESS AND ECONOMICS — Public Finance, Taxation

790.13 TT159 US ISSN 0744-1738
HOBBY MERCHANDISER. 1982. m. $20. Hobby Publications, Inc., 225 Gordons Corner Plaza, Box 420, Manalapan, NJ 07726. TEL 908-446-4900. FAX 908-446-5488. Ed. Andrew Hecht. adv. circ. 9,000. **Document type**: trade publication.

HOBBIES

790.2 746 US
HOBBY MERCHANDISER ANNUAL TRADE DIRECTORY. a. $30. Hobby Publications, Inc., 225 Gordons Corner Plaza, Box 420, Manalapan, NJ 07726. TEL 908-446-4900. FAX 908-446-5488. Ed. Andrew Hecht. circ. 10,000. **Document type:** directory.
   Former titles: Hobby Publications Annual Trade Directory; Craft and Needlework Age - World of Miniatures Annual Trade Directory; Craft, Model and Hobby Industry Annual Trade Directory; Annual Basic Hobby Industry Trade Directory (ISSN 0066-3778)

790.13 US ISSN 1045-0602
GV1201.5
HOBBYIST SOURCEBOOK. irreg. $49.95. Gale Research Inc., 835 Penobscot Bldg., Detroit, MI 48226. TEL 800-347-GALE. FAX 313-961-6083. TELEX 810-221-7086. Ed. Denise M. Allard. stat.
   Description: Guides hobbyists to primary sources of information for 43 hobbies. Entries are sorted by hobby, with a general introduction for each. Also includes information on record setters, famous names, start-up costs, facts and statistics, and trends.

HOBO TIMES. see TRANSPORTATION — Railroads

HOFKLATSCH; Magazin fuer Schueler. see EDUCATION — Higher Education

790.13 UK ISSN 0143-554X
HOME MINIATURIST. 1979. bi-m. £14.50($21) (in Europe £21; Australia £23). 22 Churchway, Haddenham, Aylesbury, Bucks. HP17 8AA, England. TEL 0844-291419. Ed. Silvia Rowbottom. adv.; bk.rev. circ. 4,000.
   Description: Covers doll houses and miniatures.

HOME SHOP MACHINIST; dedicated to precision metalworking. see MACHINERY

790.13 385 UK
HORSE BRASS. 1976. s-a. £18. National Horse Brass Society, 69 West Chiltern, Woodcote, Reading RG8 OSG, England. Ed. G.R. Hawthorne. adv.; bk.rev.; circ. 500 (controlled). **Document type:** consumer publication.

625.19 US
HOTBOX; the magazine of model railroaders. 1963. m. $18. Teen Association of Model Railroaders, 1800 E. 38th St., Oakland, CA 94602. TEL 510-482-2993. Ed. John Reichel. adv.; bk.rev.; circ. 100 (paid). **Document type:** consumer publication.

625.19 GW ISSN 0941-3480
HP 1 MODELLBAHN. 1981. q. DM.36 (foreign DM.42). (Freundeskreis Europaeischer Modellbahner e.V.) Willy Kosak Verlagsgesellschaft mbH, Burgstr. 17, 91284 Neuhaus a.d. Pegnitz, Germany. TEL 09156-1040. FAX 09156-1017. Ed.Bd. adv.; bk.rev. circ. 4,800. (back issues avail.)

I H N NEWS. (International Handicapper's Net) see HANDICAPPED

790.13 UK
I.P.M.S. (UK) MAGAZINE. 1963. bi-m. £15 (foreign £20). International Plastic Modellers Society (UK), The Gate Inn, Milton Rd., Hoyland, Barnsley, S. Yorks. S74 9AU, England. TEL 0226-742328. Ed. Neil Robinson. adv.; bk.rev.; illus. circ. 2,500. **Document type:** consumer publication.
   Formerly: I.P.M.S. Magazine.
   Description: Helps its members attain skill and enjoyment out of the hobby of plastic kit construction, to review kit releases, and provide modeling, color scheme, and markings articles.

790.132 US
THE ILLUSTRATOR COLLECTORS NEWS. 1983. bi-m. $17. Spectrum of Rainbows, Box 1958, Seqium, WA 98382. TEL 206-683-2559. Ed. Denis C. Jackson. adv.: Full page $64 ($32 to subscribers). bk.rev. circ. 1,000. **Document type:** consumer publication.
   Description: For collectors of old paper items, magazines, pinups, and illustrated art items.

IN SACHEN SPIEL UND FEIER. see THEATER

INDIANA COVERED BRIDGE SOCIETY. NEWSLETTER. see HISTORY — History Of North And South America

391.45 US ISSN 0894-7902
INNER CIRCLE LETTER. 1986. m. membership only. Nelson Newsletter Publishing Corp., Box 41630, Tucson, AZ 85717-1630. TEL 602-629-0434; 800-368-8434. FAX 602-629-0387. circ. controlled. **Document type:** newsletter.
   Description: Covers pin collecting.

790.13 FR ISSN 0181-9445
INTELLECT. bi-m. 85 F. Publications Guy- Hachette, La Petite Motte Senille, 86100 Chatellerault, France. —CCC.

INTERNATIONAL BOND & SHARE SOCIETY JOURNAL. see ANTIQUES

790.023 US ISSN 0020-7039
INTERNATIONAL JOURNAL; the news and views paper for the hobbyist. 1966. q. $60. Levine Publications, Box 9090, Trenton, NJ 08650. Ed. D.M.R. Levine. adv.; bk.rev.; charts; illus.; mkt.; tr.lit. circ. 3,013. (tabloid format)

790.13 IS ISSN 0792-318X
ISRAELI MAP COLLECTORS SOCIETY. JOURNAL. (Text in English) 1986. irreg. (1-2/yr.). IS.25($25) Israeli Map Collectors Society, 4 Brenner St., Jerusalem 92103, Israel. TEL 972-2-611687. Ed. Eva Wajntraub. adv.; bk.rev.; circ. 200 (paid); 100 (controlled).
   Description: Publishes articles relating to old maps and prints of the Holy Land.

790.13 US ISSN 0887-7688
JACKPOTUNITIES. 1978. bi-m. $8.99. Jackpotunities, Inc., Box 393, Centuck Sta., Yonkers, NY 10710. TEL 914-337-4114. Ed. Shirley Liss. adv. circ. 5,000. (tabloid format; back issues avail.) **Document type:** newsletter.
   Description: Sweepstakes guide.

790 US ISSN 0010-7646
PL2653
JAYBEE.* 1962. m. $9. J.B. Printing, c/o Claudine Moffatt, Ed., 901 Brookvale Terr., Manchester, MO 63021. adv.; illus. circ. 10,000.
   Incorporates: Contest Magazine.

549 US ISSN 0274-8193
QE351
JEWELRY MAKING, GEMS AND MINERALS; gems, gem cutting, minerals, silverwork, geology. 1937. m. $12. Gemac Corporation, c/o Jewelers Bench, Box 226, Cortaro, AZ 85652-0226. Ed. Jack R. Cox. adv.; bk.rev.; charts; illus. circ. 38,000. (also avail. in microform from UMI) **Indexed:** Chem.Abstr., Gen.Sci.Ind., GeoRef., Ind.How To Do It.
   Formerly: Gems and Minerals (ISSN 0016-6278); Incorporates: Mineralogist; Which was formerly (until 1964): Oregon Mineralogist.

793.8 US
JUGGLER'S WORLD MAGAZINE. 1949. q. $30. International Jugglers Association, c/o Bill Giduz, Ed., Box 443, Davidson, NC 28036. TEL 704-892-1296. FAX 704-892-2499. (Subscr. to: Richard Dingman, Box 218, Montage, MA 01351) adv.; bk.rev.; bibl.; illus. circ. 3,500. (processed; also avail. in microfiche)
   Formerly: International Jugglers Association Newsletter (ISSN 0300-8053)
   Description: Features articles about jugglers and juggling with how-to information for those who want to learn juggling tricks.

790.13 SP ISSN 0214-7122
JUGUETECNICA; revista de modelismo, RC, maquetas y hobbys. 1989. m. 4800 ptas.($90) (foreign 9000 ptas.). Novofer S.A., San German, 5, 08004 Barcelona, Spain. TEL 93-325-32-87. FAX 93-424-44-60. Dir. Fernando Cortes. adv.; charts; illus. circ. 10,000.
   Description: Provides information on model-making, kits and hobbies.

480 US ISSN 1053-6884
JUKEBOX COLLECTOR. 1977. m. $30. Jukebox Collector, 2545 S.E. 60th Ct., Des Moines, IA 50317-5099. TEL 515-265-8324. Ed. Barb Botts. adv. contact: Rick Botts. bk.rev. circ. 3,500. **Document type:** consumer publication.
   Formerly: Jukebox Collector Newsletter (ISSN 0882-4908)

790.13 GW
KIT. 11/yr. DM.80 (foreign DM.90). Kit Verlag GmbH, Burgschmietstr. 34, 90419 Nuernberg, Germany. TEL 0911-331222. FAX 0911-333448. Ed. Inka Deul. adv. contact: Norbert Deul. circ. 51,000. **Document type:** consumer publication.

796.77 US ISSN 1072-7981
KIT CAR. 1982. bi-m. $15.95. Petersen Publishing Co., 6420 Wilshire Blvd., Los Angeles, CA 90048. TEL 213-782-2000. Ed. Steve Temple. adv.; illus. circ. 80,000. (also avail. in microfiche from UMI) **Document type:** consumer publication.
   Former titles (until Sep. 1993): Specialty Car (ISSN 1068-2627); Petersen's Kit Car (ISSN 0883-5705)

KITPLANES. see AERONAUTICS AND SPACE FLIGHT

790.13 US ISSN 0277-0725
TS380
KNIVES (YEAR). 1981. a. price varies. D B I Books, Inc., 4092 Commercial Ave., Northfolk, IL 60062. Ed. Ken Warner.

790.13 US
KNIVES ILLUSTRATED. q. $3.50 per no. McMullen Publishing, 2145 W. La Palma Ave., Anaheim, CA 92801. TEL 714-635-9040.

629.133 JA ISSN 0450-6669
KOKU JOHO/AIREVIEW. (Text in Japanese) 1951. m. $175 (effective 1993). Kantosha Co. Ltd., 601 Kojun Bldg., 8-7, 6-chome, Ginza, Chuo-ku, Tokyo 104, Japan. TEL 03-3572-3421. FAX 03-3572-3425. Ed. M. Majima. adv.; bk.rev.; illus. circ. 50,000. **Indexed:** JTA.

748.8 US
KOVELS' BOTTLE PRICE LIST. a. $10.95. Crown Publishers, Inc., 201 E. 50th St., New York, NY 10022. TEL 212-254-1600. Eds. Ralph Kovel, Terry Kovel.
   Formerly: Kovel's Complete Bottle Price List.

KULTUR- UND STADTNACHRICHTEN AUS WEITRA. see HISTORY

790.132 SZ
KURIOSUM; Magazin fuer den Hobbysammler. 1990. q. 12 SFr. Emmentaler Druck AG, Dorfstr. 5, CH-3550 Langnau, Switzerland. circ. 14,000.

549 US ISSN 0023-8457
NK7300 CODEN: LAJOA6
LAPIDARY JOURNAL. 1947. m. $24. Lapidary Journal, Inc., c/o Cindi Willcox, Circ. Dir., 60 Chestnut Ave., Ste. 201, Devon, PA 19333. TEL 215-293-1112. FAX 215-293-1717. Ed. Merle White. adv.; bk.rev.; bibl.; charts; illus.; index. circ. 42,000. **Indexed:** AESIS, Art & Archaeol.Tech.Abstr., Chem.Abstr., GeoRef., Ind.How To Do It (1978-), Mag.Ind. **Document type:** consumer publication. —Faxon; UnCover; SWETS.
   Description: Discusses gemology, jewelry making, earth sciences, minerology, and paleontology.

790.13 US
LAUGH-MAKERS; variety arts for family entertainment. 1981. bi-m. $24 (foreign $30) (effective Feb. 1994). Fun Technicians, Inc., Box 160, Syracuse, NY 13215-0160. TEL 315-492-4523. Ed. Cathy Gibbons. adv.; bk.rev. circ. 3,500. (back issues avail.) **Document type:** trade publication.
   Description: Features and informational articles on professional entertainment for kidshow and family audiences, including: magic, clowning, ventriloquism, comedy props, puppetry, balloon sculpture, storytelling, business-promotion, and convention listings.

LEGENDS SPORTS MEMORABILIA. see SPORTS AND GAMES

790.13 US
LEISURE ARTS. bi-m. Box 420126, Palm Coast, FL 32142. TEL 800-829-9157. FAX 904-445-2728. Ed. Anne Van Wagner Young.

LEISURE MANAGEMENT. see LEISURE AND RECREATION

LETTERS; letters from Abraham Lincoln. see ARTS AND HANDICRAFTS

HOBBIES

790.023 US ISSN 0024-4023
GV1541
LINKING RING. 1923. m. membership. International Brotherhood of Magicians, c/o Philip R. Willmarth, Exec.Ed., 348 S. Wishire La., Arlington Heights, IL 60004. TEL 708-577-7337. FAX 708-577-7337. adv.; bk.rev.; illus.; index; circ. 13,000 (controlled). **Document type:** trade publication.

385 US ISSN 0364-5177
TJ630
LIVE STEAM. 1966. bi-m. $31. Village Press, Inc., 2779 Aero Park Dr., Box 629, Traverse City, MI 49685. TEL 616-946-3712. FAX 616-946-3289. Ed. Joe D. Rice. adv.; bk.rev.; illus.; stat.; index. circ. 11,223. (also avail. in microform from UMI) **Document type:** consumer publication.
—UMI.
 Formerly: Live Steam Magazine (ISSN 0300-7804)
 Description: Features articles on locomotive, marine, automotive, traction, and stationary steam engines, with club news, shopping advice, and working-model plans for the hobbyist.

625.19 FR ISSN 0024-5739
LOCO-REVUE; pour les modelistes et amateurs de chemins de fer. 1937. m. (except Aug.) 325 F. (effective Jan. 1993). Editions Loco-Revue s.a.r.l., B.P. 104, Le Sablen, 56401 Auray Cedex, France. TEL 97-24-01-65. FAX 97-56-55-89. Ed. Christian Fournereau. adv.: B&W page 5000 F., color page 7900 F.; trim 190 x 265. bk.rev.; illus.; index. circ. 20,000. (back issues avail.) **Document type:** consumer publication.
 Description: Discusses railroad models.

623.820 GW ISSN 0175-7601
DAS LOGBUCH. 1964. q. DM.80. Arbeitskreis Historischer Schiffbau e.V., Wildschwanbrook 49a, 22145 Hamburg, Germany. TEL 040-6782489. Ed. Horst Menzel. adv.; bk.rev. circ. 1,000. **Document type:** bulletin.
—BLDSC (5292.305800).

625.19 385 DK ISSN 0108-9307
LOKOMOTIVET; tidsskrift om jernbaner i virkeligched og model. 1983. q. DKK 220. P.O. Box 477, DK-4700 Naestved, Denmark. adv.; bk.rev.; illus. circ. 1,500.
 Description: Devoted to Danish railroads and model-railroads.

398 US ISSN 0195-2692
G521
LOST TREASURE; the treasure hunter's guide to adventure & fortune. 1966. m. $17.92. Lost Treasure, Inc., Box 1589, Grove, OK 74344. TEL 918-786-2182. FAX 918-786-2192. Ed. Grace Michael. adv.; bk.rev.; charts; illus.; stat.; tr.lit. circ. 40,000. **Indexed:** GeoRef.
 Formerly: Treasure World (ISSN 0041-3607)

790.13 GW ISSN 0722-9879
M B Z - MODELLBAHNZEITSCHRIFT. bi-m. DM.52 (foreign DM.60). Verlag Berthold Weber, Erbsengasse 5, 65451 Kelsterbach, Germany. TEL 06107-4311. FAX 06107-61771. Ed. Berthold Weber. circ. 38,000. **Document type:** consumer publication.

793.8 US ISSN 0047-5300
M U M.* (Magic, Unity, Might) 1911. m. membership. Society of American Magicians, Box 510260, St. Louis, MO 63151. Ed. David R. Goodsell. adv.; bk.rev.; illus.; tr.lit.; index. circ. 6,000.

M - U - M. see *COMPUTERS*

625.19 GW ISSN 0024-9688
MAERKLIN-MAGAZIN; Zeitschrift fuer grosse und kleine Modell-Eisenbahner. 1965. 6/yr. DM.52.80. Modellbahnen-Welt Verlags GmbH, Postfach 940, 73009 Goeppingen, Germany. FAX 07161-608-550. Ed. Michael Echterbecker. adv.; bk.rev.; charts; illus.; index. circ. 65,000. **Document type:** consumer publication.

793.8 US ISSN 1062-2845
GV1541
MAGIC; an independent magazine for magicians. 1991. m. $30. Stan Allen and Associates, 7380 S. Eastern Ave., Ste. 124-179, Las Vegas, NV 89123. TEL 702-361-4200. FAX 702-361-1877. Ed. Stan Allen. adv.; bk.rev. circ. 6,500. (back issues avail.) **Document type:** bulletin.

793.8 US ISSN 0024-9904
MAGIC CAULDRON. 1964. q. $2. F. William Kuethe, Jr., Ed. & Pub., 700 Glenview Ave., S.W., Glen Burnie, MD 21061. TEL 301-766-3842. bk.rev.; cum.index every 4 yrs. circ. 130.

793.8 UK
MAGIC CIRCULAR. 1906. m. membership. Magic Circle, 5 Folkington Corner, Woodside Park, Finchley, London N12 7BH, England. TEL 081-445-7607. Ed. Alan Snowden. adv.; bk.rev.; play rev.; bibl.; illus.; index. (back issues avail.) **Document type:** newsletter.

793.8 GW ISSN 0940-5852
"MAGISCHE" WELT; Zeitschrift fuer angewandte Tricktechnik und Wahrnehmungstaeuschung. 1952. q. DM.40.65 (foreign DM.43.60). Verlag W. Geissler-Werry, In den Benden 13, 52355 Dueren, Germany. TEL 02421-51667. Ed. W. Geissler-Werry. adv.: B&W page DM.221.60. bk.rev.; circ. 1,600. **Document type:** consumer publication.

625.19 US ISSN 0199-5421
TF197
MAINLINE MODELER. 1980. m. $29.75. Hundman Publishing Co., Inc., 5115 Monticello Dr., Edmonds, WA 98020. Ed. Robert L. Hundman. adv.; bk.rev. circ. 14,000.

MAN AT ARMS; the magazine of arms collecting-investing. see *ANTIQUES*

629.221 790.023 IT ISSN 0025-2387
MANOVELLA; e route a raggi. 1961. m. (10/yr.) L.90000($110) (Europe L.110000; US $125). (Automotoclub Storico Italiano) Giorgio Nada Editore s.r.l., Via Claudio Treves, 15-17, 20090 Vimodrone (Milan), Italy. TEL 02-27301126. FAX 02-27301454. Ed. Giorgio Nada. adv. contact: Aldo Ghirardi. bk.rev.; bibl.; illus. circ. 30,000. (tabloid format)
 Description: Covers historic cars and motorcycles.

090 US ISSN 0025-262X
Z41.A2
MANUSCRIPTS. 1948. q. $25 membership to individuals; institutions $30 (includes Manuscript Society News). Manuscript Society, 350 N. Niagara St., Burbank, CA 91505. Ed. David R. Chesnutt. adv.; illus.; mkt.; tr.lit.; cum.index: vols.1-28, 29-40. circ. 1,600. (also avail. in microfilm from KTO) reprint service avail. from KTO) **Indexed:** Amer.Hist.& Life, Amer.Hum.Ind., Hist.Abstr., M.L.A., Mid.East: Abstr.& Ind.
—Faxon; UnCover.
 Description: For collectors, dealers, libraries, archivists, scholars and others with interest in original manuscripts.

625.19 SP ISSN 1132-2063
▼**MAQUETREN.** 1992. m. 5500 ptas. Editorial Resistor, S.A., C. Maudes 15, entlo. C, 28003 Madrid, Spain. TEL 91-534-29-67. FAX 91-534-47-51. adv.: B&W page 100000 ptas., color page 150000 ptas.; trim 180 x 215; adv. contact: Maria Martin. circ. 13,000. **Document type:** consumer publication.
 Description: Contains news, features, articles and reviews on model trains.

790.13 US
MARBLE MART NEWSLETTER. 1978. q. $10. Marble Collectors Unlimited, Box 206, Northboro, MA 01532. TEL 508-393-2923. Ed. Beverly Brule. adv. circ. 800. **Document type:** newsletter.

MARGARETOLOGIST. see *JEWELRY, CLOCKS AND WATCHES*

623.820 UK ISSN 0268-3326
MARINE MODELLING. 1985. m. £20 (Europe £28; rest or world £38). Traplet Publications Ltd., Traplet House, Severn Dr., Upton-upon-Severn, Worcestershire WR8 OJL, England. TEL 0684-594505. FAX 0684-594586. (Dist. by: Comag Magazine Marketing, Tavistock Rd., W. Drayton, Middx. UB7 7QE, England. TEL 0895-444055. FAX 0895-445255; Subscr. in U.S. to: Box 167, Florham Park, NJ 07932) Ed. Chris Jackson. adv. contact: Jane Stephenson. index. (back issues avail.) **Document type:** consumer publication.
 Description: Provides information on all aspects of boat modelling.

790.023 UK ISSN 0025-3944
MARQUETARIAN. 1952. q. £12. Marquetry Society, 63 Church Ln., Sproughton, Ipswich, Suffolk IP8 3AY, England. Ed. Ernie Ives. adv.; bk.rev. circ. 1,100. **Document type:** consumer publication.
 Description: Examines practical marquetry, informs about exhibitions, and contains book and product reviews.

MARVEL AGE. see *CHILDREN AND YOUTH — For*

MECANICA POPULAR. see *TECHNOLOGY: COMPREHENSIVE WORKS*

790.023 FR ISSN 0025-6625
MEDAILLES. 1938. s-a. membership. Federation Internationale de Medaille, 6 place Saint Germain des Pres, 75006 Paris, France. bk.rev.; bibl.; illus.

790.13 UK ISSN 0958-4986
MEDAL NEWS. 1982. 10/yr. £24 (foreign £28.50). Token Publishing Ltd., 105 High St., Honiton, Devon EX14 8PE, England. TEL 0404-45414. FAX 0404-45313. Ed. Diana Birch. bk.rev. circ. 3,000. (back issues avail.) **Document type:** newsletter.

MEN'S CLUB. see *CLOTHING TRADE — Fashions*

790.13 FR ISSN 0396-4914
MES PREMIERES GRILLES. bi-m. 73 F. Publications Guy-Hachette, La Petite Motte Senille, 86100 Chatellerault, France.
—CCC.

795.4 US
METRO NEWS; continuing the correspondence begun long ago. 1946. bi-m. $10 includes membership. Metropolitan Post Card Collectors Club, 67-00 192nd St., Flushing, NY 11365. TEL 718-454-0582. Ed. Leah Schnall. adv. circ. 600. **Document type:** newsletter.

629.222 US
MILE POST. 1971. bi-m. $25. Milestone Car Society Inc., 22832 Buena Vista Rd., Rockbridge, OH 43149. Ed. Thomas D. Behnke. adv.; bk.rev.; bibl.; illus. circ. 2,000.
 Description: Aimed at antique automobile collectors.

355 US ISSN 1055-5919
U790
MILITARY ADVISOR; the publication for international military hobbyists and historians. 1990. q. $20 (foreign $25). R. James Bender Publishing, Box 23456, San Jose, CA 95153. TEL 408-225-5777. FAX 408-225-4739. Ed. Roger James Bender. circ. 2,500.
 Description: Covers rare to common collectibles (military) plus their historical significance. Concentrates on German-American WW I to present.

MILITARY HOBBIES. see *MILITARY*

790.1 UK ISSN 0967-7062
▼**MILITARY IN SCALE.** 1992. m. £20. Traplet Publications Ltd., Traplet House, Severn Dr., Upton-upon-Severn, Worcestershire WR8 OJL, England. TEL 0684-594505. FAX 0684-594586. (Dist. by: Comag Magazine Marketing, Tavistock Rd., W. Drayton, Middx. UB7 7QE, England. TEL 0895-444055. FAX 0895-445255; Subscr. in U.S. to: Box 167, Florham Park, NJ 07932. TEL 201-383-4064) Ed. Ian Young. adv. contact: Jane Stephenson. bk.rev.; index. (back issues avail.) **Document type:** consumer publication.

745.5 UK ISSN 0026-4083
MILITARY MODELLING. 1971. m. £22.80. Argus Specialist Publications Ltd., Argus House, Boundary Way, Hemel Hempstead, Herts. HP2 7ST, England. TEL 0442-876661. (Subscr. to: Argus Subscription Services, Queensway House, 2 Queensway, Redhill, Surrey, England. TEL 0767-786111; U.S. subscr. to: c/o Joseph J. Daleida, 4314 W. 238th St., Torrence, CA 90505) Ed. Ken Jones. adv.; bk.rev.; film rev.; charts; illus.; index. **Document type:** consumer publication.
 Description: Contains articles of interest to modellers of military figures and armor, wargamers, and general military enthusiasts.

HOBBIES

736.2 US ISSN 0885-4327
MINERAL NEWS; the mineral collector's newsletter. 1985. m. $15 (foreign $19). L.R. Ream Publishing, Box 2043, Coeur d'Alene, ID 83816-2043. TEL 208-667-0453. Ed. Lanny R. Ream. adv.; bk.rev. circ. 900. (looseleaf format; back issues avail.) **Document type:** newsletter.
 Description: Details localities, new minerals, mineral shows and symposiums.

549 US ISSN 0026-4628
QE351 CODEN: MRECA7
MINERALOGICAL RECORD. 1970. bi-m. $39 to individuals; institutions $60. Mineralogical Record, Inc., 4631 Paseo Tubutama, Tucson, AZ 85740. FAX 602-544-0815. Ed. Wendell E. Wilson. adv.; bk.rev.; bibl.; charts; illus.; cum.index. circ. 7,400. (also avail. in microfilm from UMI; reprint service avail. from UMI) **Indexed:** AESIS, Chem.Abstr., Gen.Sci.Ind., GeoRef., Ind.Sci.Rev., Mineral.Abstr. —BLDSC (5788.500000); Faxon; UnCover; SWETS; UMI; CASDDS.
 Description: For advanced mineral collectors and specimen-oriented mineralogists and curators. Contains technical and non-technical articles.

790.132 US
MINI LICENSE PLATE & KEYCHAIN TAG COLLECTOR'S NEWSLETTER. q. $10. Edward H. Miles, Ed. & Pub., 888 8th Ave., New York, NY 10019. TEL 212-765-2660. circ. 150. **Document type:** newsletter.

625.19 GW ISSN 0723-3841
MINIATURBAHNEN M I B A. 1948. m. (plus special toy fair issue). DM.127.80 (foreign DM.135.90). M I B A - Verlag Werner Walter Weinstoetter GmbH und Co., Senefelderstr. 11, 90409 Nuernberg, Germany. TEL 0911-51965-0. FAX 0911-5196540. Ed. Werner Walter Weinstoetter. adv.; bk.rev. circ. 35,000. **Document type:** consumer publication.
 —CCC.
 Formerly: Miniaturbahnen (ISSN 0047-7478)

790.023 US ISSN 0026-5128
MINIATURE BOOK NEWS. 1965-1982; resumed. q. $10 (overseas $13). Julian I. Edison, Ed. & Pub., 16 Dromara Rd., St. Louis, MO 63124. illus.; tr.lit. (back issues avail.)

790.132 US ISSN 0199-9184
MINIATURE COLLECTOR. 1976. bi-m. $17.95. Scott Publishing Company (Livonia), 30595 W. Eight Mile Rd., Livonia, MI 48152-1798. TEL 810-477-6650. FAX 810-477-6795. Ed. Marguerite Winter; Pub. Ruth Keesen. adv. contact: Tom Grimes. bk.rev.; circ. 39,000 (paid). **Document type:** consumer publication.

745.592 US
MINIATURE GAZETTE. 1972. q. $25 membership (foreign $30). National Association of Miniature Enthusiasts, Box 69, Carmel, IN 46032. TEL 317-571-8094. FAX 317-571-8105. Ed. Kathy Schoup. adv. circ. 12,000.
 Description: Covers dollhouse and scale miniature accessories, including show, workshop, and convention information.

790 US
MINIATURES CATALOG; for hobbyists and collectors. 1978. a. $16.95. Kalmbach Miniatures Inc., 21027 Crossroads Circle, Box 1612, Waukesha, WI 53187. TEL 414-796-8776. FAX 414-796-0126. Ed. Geraldine Willems. adv.; bk.rev.; illus.; tr.lit. circ. 10,000. **Document type:** catalog.

MODEL A NEWS. see TRANSPORTATION — Automobiles

629.133 US ISSN 0026-7295
TL770
MODEL AIRPLANE NEWS. 1929. m. $27.95. Air Age Publishing, Rt. 7, 251 Danbury Rd., Wilton, CT 06897. TEL 203-834-2900. FAX 203-762-9803. (Subscr. to: Box 428, Mt. Morris, IL 61054. TEL 800-837-0323) Ed. Tom Atwood. adv.; bk.rev.; charts; illus.; circ. 90,000 (paid). (processed; also avail. in microfilm from UMI) **Indexed:** Consum.Ind., Mag.Ind. **Document type:** consumer publication. —UMI.

629.1 UK
MODEL & ACCESSORIES MART. m. £13.20 (foreign £38). Aceville Publications Ltd., 89 East Hill, Colchester, Essex CO1 2QN, England. TEL 0206-871450. FAX 0206-871537. Ed. David Bridle. adv.

790.3 UK
MODEL & COLLECTORS MART MAGAZINE. 1986. m. £17($35.50) (effective Feb. 1994). Aceville Publications Ltd., Castle House, 97 High St., Colchester, Essex CO1 1TH, England. TEL 0206-540621. FAX 0206-564214. (Dist. by: United Magazine Distributors, Castle House, 37-45 Paul St., London EC2A 4PB, England. TEL 0206-563363) Ed. Meredith Pfeffer. adv. contact: Sharonn Armin. bk.rev. circ. 21,000. (back issues avail.) **Document type:** consumer publication.
 Description: Contains news and topical features on model cars, aircraft, science fiction subjects, ships and military railways and on model-building tools.

790.13 US
MODEL AND TOY COLLECTOR; collectible models, toys and various other memorabilia from the 50's through today. 1986. q. $20. Cap'n Penny Productions, Inc., 137 Casterton Ave., Akron, OH 44303. TEL 216-836-0668. FAX 216-869-8668. Ed. Joanne M. Bruegman; Pub. William R. Bruegman, Ill. bk.rev.; illus.; tr.lit. circ. 5,000. (back issues avail.) **Document type:** consumer publication.
 Formerly: Model Figure Collector.
 Description: Discusses collectible toys and nostalgia items from the baby boom era.

629.133 US ISSN 0744-5059
MODEL AVIATION. 1975. m. $18 to individuals (foreign $38); schools $10. Academy of Model Aeronautics, 5151 E. Memorial Dr., Muncie, IN 47302. TEL 317-288-4899. Ed. Jim Haught. adv.; illus.; index. circ. 170,000. **Document type:** academic/scholarly publication.

629.133 CN ISSN 0317-7831
MODEL AVIATION CANADA. 1971. bi-m. Can.$12($18) Model Aeronautics Association of Canada, 5100 S. Service Rd., Unit 9, Burlington, ON L7L 6A5, Canada. TEL 416-632-9808. FAX 416-632-3304. Ed. Peter Perry. adv.; bk.rev. circ. 12,000.
 Description: For avid modellers and association members who build and fly radio controlled airplanes, gliders, model cars and boats.

MODEL BOATS. see SPORTS AND GAMES — Boats And Boating

629.133 US ISSN 0194-7079
TL770.A1
MODEL BUILDER. 1971. m. $25. Gallant Models, Inc., 34249 Camino Capistrano, Capistrano Beach, CA 92624-1156. TEL 714-496-5411. FAX 714-496-5427. Ed. Mark Thiffault. adv.; bk.rev. circ. 107,000. **Document type:** consumer publication.

790.13 UK ISSN 0951-6840
MODEL COLLECTOR. 1987. m. £32.50. Link House Magazines Ltd., Link House, Dingwall Ave., Croydon, Surrey CR9 2TA, England. TEL 081-686-2599. FAX 081-760-0973. (Subscr. to: C P G, 120-126 Lavender Ave., Mitcham, Surrey CR4 3HP, England) Ed. Richard West. adv.; bk.rev.; index. circ. 22,218. (back issues avail.) **Document type:** consumer publication.

745.5 UK ISSN 0026-7325
MODEL ENGINEER. 1898. fortn. £36. Argus Specialist Publications Ltd., Argus House, Boundary Way, Hemel Hempstead, Herts. HP2 7ST, England. TEL 0442-66551. FAX 0442-66998. (Subscr. to: Argus Subscription Services, Queensway House, 2 Queensway, Redhill, Surrey. England. TEL 0737-768611) Ed. Ted Joliffe. adv.; bk.rev.; charts; illus.; index. **Indexed:** Pinpointer. **Document type:** consumer publication.
 Description: Covers every aspect of building and collecting working models.

790.13 US ISSN 0959-6909
MODEL ENGINEERS' WORKSHOP. bi-m. Argus Specialist Publications Ltd., Argus House, Boundary Way, Hemel Hempstead, Herts. HP2 7ST, England. TEL 0442-66551. FAX 0442-66998. (Subscr. to: Argus Subscription Services, Queensway House, 2 Queensway, Redhill, Surrey. England. TEL 0737-768611) **Document type:** consumer publication.
 Formerly (until 1990): World of Model Engineering (ISSN 0958-8078)
 Description: Helps amateur machinists get the best from their tools and equipment.

629.133 UK ISSN 0953-7880
MODEL HELICOPTER WORLD. 1988. m. £32 (Europe £42; rest of world £48). Traplet Publications Ltd., Traplet House, Severn Dr., Upton-upon-Severn, Worcestershire WR8 0JL, England. TEL 0684-594505. FAX 0684-504586. (Dist. by: Comag Magazine Marketing, Tavistock Rd., W. Drayton, Middx. UB7 7QE, England. TEL 0895-444055. FAX 0895-445255; Subscr. in U.S. to: Box 167, Florham Park, NJ 07932) Ed. Jon Tanner. adv. contact: Jane Stephenson. index. (back issues avail.) **Document type:** consumer publication.

745.5 UK
MODEL HOBBY TRADER. 1977. 6/yr. free to retailers. Model & Allied Publications Ltd., Wolsey House, Wolsey Rd., Hemel Hempstead, Herts HP2 4SS, England. Ed. Alec Gee.

625.19 US ISSN 0026-7341
TF197
MODEL RAILROADER. 1934. m. $34.95 (foreign $45). Kalmbach Publishing Co., Box 1612, Waukesha, WI 53187-1612. TEL 414-796-8776. FAX 414-796-0126. Ed. Russell Larson. adv.; bk.rev.; charts; illus.; index. circ. 224,000. **Indexed:** Consum.Ind., Ind.How To Do It (1990-), Mag.Ind. —UnCover; UMI.
 Description: Informs and entertains, with how-to model railroad projects, drawings and data, and visits to model railroads across the country. New model railroading products are presented and reviewed.

625.19 UK
MODEL RAILWAYS. 1909. m. £20.40. Argus Specialist Publications Ltd., Argus House, Boundary Way, Hemel Hempstead, Herts. HP2 7ST, England. TEL 0442-66551. FAX 0442-66998. (Subscr. to: Argus Subscription Services, Queensway House, 2 Queensway, Redhill, Surrey, England. TEL 0737-768611) Ed. Dave Lowery. adv.; bk.rev.; charts; illus.; index. **Indexed:** Ind.How To Do It (1979-). **Document type:** consumer publication.
 Formerly: Your Model Railway; Incorporates (as of 1984): Model Railways (ISSN 0026-7368)
 Description: Provides the latest news, reviews, and developments in building model railways.

MODEL RETAILER. see BUSINESS AND ECONOMICS — Marketing And Purchasing

629.133 US
MODEL ROCKET NEWS. 1961. irreg. (3-4/yr.). free to qualified personnel. Estes Industries, Penrose, CO 81240. TEL 719-372-6565. FAX 719-372-3419. Ed. Michael Hellmund. adv.; charts; illus.; tr.lit.; circ. controlled.
 Formerly: Model Rocket News Magazine.

623.820 US ISSN 0199-7068
MODEL SHIP BUILDER; world's largest model ships & boats magazine. 1979. bi-m. $23. Phoenix Publications, Inc., Box 128, Cedarburg, WI 53012. TEL 414-377-7888. Ed. Jeffrey A. Phillips. adv.; bk.rev.; index. circ. 14,000. (back issues avail.) **Document type:** consumer publication.
 Description: Provides building instruction for model ships for both beginners and experts.

623.820 US ISSN 0264-2220
MODEL SHIPWRIGHT; a quarterly journal of ships and ship models. 1972. q. £21($36) Brassey's (UK) Ltd., 1st Fl., 165 Great Dover St., London SE1 4YA, England, England. TEL 071-334-4922. FAX 071-334-4913. (Subscr. to: Turpin Distribution Services, Blackhorse Rd., Letchworth, Herts. SG1 1HN, England. TEL 0462-672555) Ed. John L. Bowen. adv.; bk.rev. circ. 3,500. **Document type:** consumer publication.

625 US
MODEL TRAIN TRADER. 1990. m. $12 (Canada $30). (Oaks Hobby Shop Buyers Co-Op) R-Mac Publications, Inc., Rte. 3, Box 425, Jasper, FL 32052. TEL 904-792-2480. FAX 904-792-3230. Ed. Robert B. Marvin; Pub. Robert B. Marvin. adv.: B&W page $200; trim 8 1/2 x 11. circ. 4,000 (paid).
 Description: Covers model trains and model railroading and related technical subjects.

625.19 DK ISSN 0107-5330
MODELBANEN. 1981. q. DKK 35. c/o Ove Larsen, Maagevaenget 4, 4700 Naestved, Denmark. illus.

HOBBIES

745.5   NE   ISSN 0026-7384
MODELBOUWER; tijdschrift voor modelbouw. 1937. 10/yr. fl.80 (effective 1993). Nederlandse Vereniging van Modelbouwers, Van der Helstlaan 5, 1412 HG Naarden, Netherlands. (Subscr. to: N.V.M., Antwoordnummer 6151, 1380 WB Weesp, Netherlands) Ed. J. Esveldt. adv.; bk.rev.; charts; illus. circ. 7,500. (back issues avail.)
    Description: Covers scale modelling and model engineering, model shipbuilding, live steam, woodwork, and workshop topics.

629.133   FR   ISSN 0026-7392
MODELE MAGAZINE; revue des modeles d'avions. 1949. m. 285 F. (foreign 340 F.). Editions Lariviere, 15-17 Quai de l'Oise, 75166 Paris Cedex 19, France. TEL 1-40-34-22-07. FAX 1-40-35-84-41. TELEX 211 678 F. Ed. Philippe David. adv.; bk.rev.; illus. circ. 21,000.

629.133   FR   ISSN 0026-7406
MODELE REDUIT D'AVION. 1936. m. 270 F. (foreign 315 F.). Weka Presse, 82 rue Curial, 75019 Paris, France. TEL 40-35-36-00. FAX 40-35-80-05. TELEX 210 504 F. Ed. Jerome Clair. adv.: B&W page 4800 F., color page 6700 F.; 280 x 190; adv. contact: Mauricette Le Bouhellec. charts; illus. circ. 25,000.

623.82   FR   ISSN 0026-7414
MODELE REDUIT DE BATEAU. 1942. m. 270 F. (foreign 315 F.). Weka Presse, 82 rue Curial, 75019 Paris, France. TEL 40-35-36-00. FAX 40-35-80-05. TELEX 210 504 F. Ed. Jerome Clair. adv.: B&W page 4800 F., color page 6700 F.; 280 x 190; adv. contact: Mauricette Le Bouhellec. charts; illus. circ. 25,000.

629.133   DK   ISSN 0105-6441
MODELFLYVE NYT.* 1968. bi-m. DKK 90. (Dansk Modelflyve Forbund) Fritflyvings Unionen, Copenhagen, Denmark. Ed. Per Grunnet. illus. circ. 4,600.

790.13   RM
MODELISM - SUPLIMENT TEHNIUM. q. Piata Presei Libere 1, 71341 Bucharest, Rumania. Ed. Ioan Eremia Albescu. circ. 60,000.

MODELIST - KONSTRUKTOR. see *CHILDREN AND YOUTH — For*

629.133   GW   ISSN 0540-5203
MODELL; Fachzeitschrft fuer Funkgesteuerte Modelle. 1958. m. DM.78. Neckar Verlag GmbH, Postfach 1820, 78008 Villingen-Schwenningen, Germany. TEL 07721-8987-0. FAX 07221-898750. circ. 35,000. (back issues avail.) **Document type**: consumer publication.

625.19   SZ   ISSN 0250-782X
MODELL-EISENBAHN. 1980. m. (except Jul., Aug.). 75 Fr. (foreign 90 Fr.). Fachpresse Goldach Hudson und Co., CH-9403 Goldach, Switzerland. TEL 071-416611. FAX 071-413881. TELEX 881 531 HUDS CH. Ed. Martin von Meyenburg. circ. 28,000. (back issues avail.)
    Description: For those interested in model railroads.

790.13   GW
MODELL FAHRZEUG. bi-m. DM.45.90 (foreign DM.60). Vereinigte Motor-Verlag GmbH und Co. KG, Leuschnerstr. 1, 70174 Stuttgart, Germany. TEL 0711-18201. FAX 0711-1821156. Ed. Andreas Berse; Pub. Helmut Luckner. adv. contact: Gerhard Merkel. circ. 25,000. **Document type**: consumer publication.

790.13   GW   ISSN 0341-5104
MODELL FAN. m. DM.72. Carl Ed. Schuenemann KG, Postfach 106067, 28060 Bremen, Germany. TEL 0421-36903-72. FAX 0421-36903-34. circ. 21,000. **Document type**: consumer publication.
—CCC.
    Description: Magazine for the model building people. Features all types: airplanes, cars, ships, figures, motorcycles and military objects. Includes readers comments, new products, mail-order addresses.

790.13   GW   ISSN 0343-0359
MODELL MAGAZIN. 1976. m. DM.84. Alba Publikationen Alf Teloeken, Roemerstr. 9, 40476 Duesseldorf, Germany. TEL 0211-469010. FAX 0211-484382. Ed. S. Gierich. circ. 14,091 (controlled). **Document type**: consumer publication.
—CCC.

625.19   GW   ISSN 0938-0213
MODELLBAHN START. 9/yr. DM.76.50 (foreign DM.80.50). M I B A-Verlag Werner Walter Weinstoetter GmbH und Co., Jakobstr. 7, 90402 Nuernberg, Germany. TEL 0911-2419251. FAX 0911-2419257. circ. 23,000.

629.133 623.820   GW   ISSN 0323-312X
MODELLBAU HEUTE; Zeitschrift fuer Flug-, Schiffs- und Automodellsport. 1970. m. DM.60. (Zentralvorstand der Gesellschaft fuer Sport und Technik) Militaerverlag der Deutschen Demokratischen Republik, Storkower Str. 158, 10407 Berlin, Germany. TEL 4300618. Ed. Georg Kerber.

625.19   GW   ISSN 0026-7422
MODELLEISENBAHNER; Zeitschrift fuer den Modelleisenbahner und alle Freunde der Eisenbahn. 1951. m. T und M Verlagsgesellschaft mbH, Borkumstr. 2, 13189 Berlin, Germany. TEL 030-47805-0. FAX 030-47805131. Ed. Fritz Borchert. adv. contact: Doris Hartmann. bk.rev.; abstr.; charts; illus.; mkt.; stat.; index. circ. 62,414. **Document type**: consumer publication.

629.22   UK   ISSN 0963-0945
MODELLER'S WORLD. 1991. q. £2.50 per no. Traplet Publications Ltd., Traplet House, Severn Dr., Upton-upon-Severn, Worcestershire WR8 OJL, England. TEL 0684-594505. FAX 0684-594586. (Dist. by: Comag Magazine Marketing, Tavistock Rd., W. Drayton, Middx. UB7 7QE, England. TEL 0895-444055. FAX 0895-445255; Subscr. in U.S. to: Box 167, Florham Park, NJ 07932) Ed.Bd. adv. contact: Jane Stephenson. index. (back issues avail.) **Document type**: consumer publication.

790.13   GR
MODELLING. 11/yr. Dr.4500. Blachothanasi 18, GR-117 44 Athens, Greece. TEL 30-1-90-18-683. FAX 30-1-90-28-582. **Document type**: consumer publication.
    Description: Covers all aspects of building plastic model ships and airplanes.

625.19   SW   ISSN 1101-0207
MODELLTAAG; en idebok foer miniatyrrallare. 1989. a. Allt om Hobby, P.O. Box 90133, S-120 21 Stockholm, Sweden. Ed. Freddy Stenbom.

623.820   GW   ISSN 0170-1819
MODELLWERFT. m. DM.109.80 (foreign DM.116.40). M I B A - Verlag Werner Walter Weinstoetter GmbH und Co., Senefelderstr. 11, 90409 Nuernberg, Germany. TEL 0911-51965-0. FAX 0911-5196540. **Document type**: consumer publication.

625.19   DK   ISSN 0107-6310
MODELTOGET. 1982. bi-m. membership. Foreningen Toget, Strandvejen 140, 2900 Hellerup, Denmark. illus.
    Formerly: Toget (ISSN 0106-9136)

790.13 052
MONEYTALK. 1977. m. $22. Moneytalk, Inc., 334 Highlark Dr., Larksville, PA 18704. TEL 717-287-6498. (Subscr. to: Box 1677, Kingston, PA 18704) Ed. Jean Kwiatkowski. circ. 25,000 (paid). **Document type**: consumer publication.

790   US   ISSN 0162-3451
MONEYTREE.* 1966. m. $8. J.B. Printing, c/o Claudine Moffatt, Ed., 901 Brookvale Terr., Manchester, MO 63021. adv.; illus.

790.13 686.2   AT   ISSN 0159-7191
MOROCCO BOUND. 1979. q. Aus.$24. Guild of Craft Bookbinders, P.O. Box 111, Glebe, N.S.W. 2037, Australia. FAX 08-4983522. Ed. Daphne Dobbyn. bk.rev.; abstr. circ. 500. (back issues avail.)
    Description: Imparts information on binding, restoration and associated book topics for hobbyists.

MOVIE COLLECTORS WORLD. see *COMMUNICATIONS — Video*

MUNDO FERROVIARIO. see *TRANSPORTATION — Railroads*

MUSIC BOX. see *MUSIC*

625.19   GW   ISSN 0937-7220
N-BAHN MAGAZIN. 1990. q. DM.28. Alba Publikationen Alf Teloeken, Roemerstr. 9, 40476 Duesseldorf, Germany. TEL 0211-469010. FAX 0211-484382. Ed. M. Erkelenz. circ. 12,412 (controlled). **Document type**: consumer publication.

002.075   US
N O B S NEWSLETTER. 1984. q. $20 membership. Northern Ohio Bibliophilic Society, c/o 538 Granger Rd., Medina, OH 44256. TEL 216-239-2222. Ed. Paul M. Duke. bk.rev. circ. 400. (back issues avail.) **Document type**: newsletter.
    Description: Articles and news on book collecting.

625.19   US   ISSN 0148-2122
TF197
NARROW GAUGE & SHORT LINE GAZETTE. 1975. bi-m. $24 (foreign $34). Benchmark Publications, Ltd., Box 26, Los Altos, CA 94023. TEL 415-941-3823. Ed. Robert W. Brown. adv. circ. 15,900.
—UnCover.
    Description: For narrow gauge and short line scale railroad enthusiasts.

NARROW GAUGE NEWS. see *TRANSPORTATION — Railroads*

NATIONAL AMATEUR. see *JOURNALISM*

NATIONAL ASSOCIATION OF WATCH AND CLOCK COLLECTORS. BULLETIN. see *JEWELRY, CLOCKS AND WATCHES*

391.45   US   ISSN 0027-884X
NATIONAL BUTTON BULLETIN; devoted to the promotion of the hobby of button collecting. 1942. 5/yr. $15 membership (foreign $20). National Button Society, c/o Lois Pool, Sec., 2733 Juno Pl., Akron, OH 44333-4317. TEL 216-864-3296. Ed. M.W. Speights. adv.; bk.rev.; illus.; index. circ. 3,500. (back issues avail.) **Document type**: bulletin.

790.13   US
NATIONAL HOBBY NEWS; a publication for small businesses and the hobbyist. 1980. q. $3.95. N H N Publishing, Box 612, New Philadelphia, OH 44663-0612. TEL 216-339-6338. Ed. Woody Russell. adv.; bk.rev. circ. 13,000. **Document type**: newspaper.
    Description: Publishes articles and features on hobbies, unusual pasttimes, mail-order business opportunities, travel and historical material relating to Ohio and other parts of the US.

NATIONAL HOME BUSINESS REPORT; news, information & guidance for homebased business owners. see *BUSINESS AND ECONOMICS — Small Business*

625.19   US   ISSN 0027-9722
NATIONAL MODEL RAILROAD ASSOCIATION. BULLETIN. 1935. m. $24. National Model Railroad Association, 4121 Cromwell Rd., Chattanooga, TN 37421. TEL 317-422-8613. Ed. Mike Carlson. adv.; bk.rev.; charts; illus.; tr.lit.; index. circ. 26,000. (also avail. in microfilm from UMI; reprint service avail. from UMI) **Document type**: bulletin.
—UMI.

790.13   US   ISSN 0747-5527
NATIONAL STAMPAGRAPHIC. 1982. q. $16 (foreign $20). 1952 Everett St., N. Valley Stream, NY 11580. TEL 516-285-5587. FAX 714-968-4446. Ed. Melody Stein. adv. contact: Andy Newman. bk.rev.; illus. circ. 3,000. **Document type**: consumer publication.
    Description: Provides "how-to" information on rubberstamping, profiles of artists, contests, fiction--everything relevant to art rubber stamping.

790.13   US   ISSN 1044-8896
NATIONAL VALENTINE COLLECTORS BULLETIN. 1977. q. $16 ($20 in Canada). National Valentine Collectors Association, Box 1404, Santa Ana, CA 92702. TEL 714-547-1355. Ed. Evalene Pulati. adv.; bk.rev.; circ. 350 (paid). (back issues avail.) **Document type**: newsletter.
    Description: News of interest to collectors of valentines and related materials. Serves as a forum for discussion among collectors.

NAUTICAL RESEARCH JOURNAL. see *TRANSPORTATION — Ships And Shipping*

HOBBIES

790.13   CN
NEW AGE PEN PAL CLUB. m. Can.$5 membership. 113-437 Martin St., No. 224, Penticton, BC V2A 5L1, Canada. Ed. Jade. Document type: newsletter.
Formerly: Travel View 1.
Description: Links penpals worldwide.

NEW GUN WEEK. see SPORTS AND GAMES

NEW LOVECRAFT COLLECTOR. see LITERATURE — *Science Fiction, Fantasy, Horror*

790.132   US
NEWES. 1950. irreg. International Newspaper Collectors' Club, Box 55744, Phoenix, AZ 85078. TEL 602-482-2105. Ed. Charles J. Smith. adv.; bk.rev.; illus. circ. 150. (processed)

790.13   US   ISSN 0164-3290
TT178
NUTSHELL NEWS; for miniatures hobbyists and collectors. 1970. m. $29.95 (foreign $40). Kalmbach Publishing Co., Box 1612, Waukesha, WI 53187-1612. TEL 414-796-8776. FAX 414-796-0126. Ed. Sybil Harp. circ. 40,000.
Indexed: Ind.How To Do It (1990-).
—UnCover.
Description: Reports on consumer and trade shows, profiles of craftspeople, coverage of collections, museums and places to see and buy fine miniatures. Offers craft techniques and tips to help hobbyists display their collections.

625.19   US   ISSN 0889-4167
O GAUGE RAILROADING. 1969. bi-m. $22. Myron J. Biggar Group Inc., Box 239, Nazareth, PA 18064. TEL 215-759-0406. adv.; cum.index: 1969-1992. circ. 25,000. (back issues avail.)
Description: Model railroading for hobby enthusiasts; covers products for the one quarter inch model builder and operator of Lionel type trains.

DER OESTERREICHISCHE FILMAMATEUR. see MOTION PICTURES

OFFICIAL RAINBOW GUIDE ANNUAL. see CHILDREN AND YOUTH — *For*

790.13   IS
OLAM HASUSIM. 8/yr. IS.20. Maerkaz Hapoal, Rehov Haarbaah 8, Tel Aviv 64 739, Israel. TEL 03-260181.

790.13   US
OPTIMISTIC PEZZIMIST. s-a.? $3 per no. Box 606, Dripping Springs, TX 78620. Ed. Mike Robertson.
Description: Presents articles on how to build a showcase for one's collection of candy dispensers.

790.023   US   ISSN 1067-1609
ORDERS AND MEDALS SOCIETY OF AMERICA. JOURNAL. 1950. 10/yr. $15 (foreign $30). Orders and Medals Society of America, c/o John E. Lelle, Box 484, Glassboro, NJ 08028. Ed. Albert F. Gleim. adv.; bk.rev.; bibl.; charts; illus.; stat.; index. circ. 1,500. Indexed: Numis.Lit.
Formerly (until Jan. 1990): Medal Collector (ISSN 0025-6633)

790.13   US   ISSN 0891-8872
Z1000
OVERSTREET COMIC BOOK PRICE GUIDE. 1970. a. $15. Overstreet Publications, Inc., Box 2610, Cleveland, TN 37320-2610. TEL 615-472-4135. (Dist. by: Avon Books, 1350 Ave. of the Americas, New York, NY 10019) Ed. Robert M. Overstreet. adv. contact: Carole M. Overstreet. illus.; stat.; tr.lit. circ. 150,000. Document type: consumer publication.
—BLDSC (6240.820000).
Formerly (until 1987): Comic Book Price Guide (ISSN 0730-2916)

790.13 810   US
OZ TRADING POST. 1970. 3/yr. $15 membership. International Wizard of Oz Club, 220 N. 11th St., Escanaba, MI 49829-3523. Ed. Fred M. Meyer. adv. circ. 3,000. (looseleaf format)
Description: Medium of exchange where club members may buy, sell or trade items relating to L. Frank Baum or Oz.

PAPER COLLECTOR'S MARKETPLACE. see ANTIQUES

790.132   US
PEN AND QUILL. 1966. bi-m. $22. Universal Autograph Collectors Club, Box 6181, Washington, DC 20044-6181. Ed. Bob Erickson. adv.; bk.rev. circ. 2,500. (back issues avail.)

790.13 741.61   US   ISSN 1045-1188
TS1262
PEN WORLD. 1987. bi-m. $42. World Publications (Kingwood), 2240 North Park Dr., Kingwood, TX 77339. TEL 713-359-4363. FAX 713-359-4468. (Subscr. to: Box 6007, Kingwood, TX 77325) Ed. Nancy Olson. adv. circ. 28,000. (back issues avail.)
Description: Covers collecting pens, both vintage and contemporary, writing and writing instruments.

790.13 741.61   US
PENFINDER. 1989. bi-m. $70. World Publications (Kingwood), 2240 North Park Dr., Kingwood, TX 77339. TEL 713-359-4363. FAX 713-359-4468. (Subscr. to: Box 6007, Kingwood, TX 77325) Ed. Nancy Olson. (back issues avail.)
Description: For pen collectors.

790.13   BG   ISSN 0379-0649
PENPALS. (Text in English) 1973. q. $3. Hobby International, G.P.O. Box 2032, Dhaka 2, Bangladesh. Ed. Hafizur Rahman. adv.; bk.rev.; illus. circ. 6,000. (also avail. in microform)
—CCC.

790.13   UK   ISSN 0144-8137
PICTURE POSTCARD MONTHLY. 1978. m. £18 (foreign £23). 15 Debdale Ln., Keyworth, Nottingham NG12 5HT, England. TEL 0602-374079. FAX 0602-376197. Ed. Brian Lund. adv.: B&W page £130. bk.rev.; illus.; stat. circ. 4,000. (looseleaf format; back issues avail.) Document type: consumer publication.

790.13   FI   ISSN 0784-7610
PIENOISMALLI. 1981. 8/yr. FIM 179. Erikoislehdet Oy, Sport, P.O. Box 16, SF-00381 Helsinki, Finland. TEL 358-0-120-5911. FAX 358-0-120-5959. Ed. Ola Pedersen. circ. 5,000.

790.023   US
PLASTIC FIGURE AND PLAYSET COLLECTOR. 1989. bi-m. $18. Specialty Publishing Co., Box 1355, La Crosse, WI 54602-1355. TEL 608-781-1894. Ed. Thomas P. Terry. adv.: B&W page $100; 7 1/2 x 10. bk.rev.; illus. circ. 2,200. Document type: consumer publication.

PLAYTHINGS; for today's merchandisers of toys, hobbies and crafts. see GIFTWARE AND TOYS

POINTER. see JEWELRY, CLOCKS AND WATCHES

790.13   US
POLYHEDRON NEWSZINE. 1981. m. $20 membership. (Role Playing Game Association Network) T S R, Inc., Box 509, Lake Geneva, WI 53147. (Subscr. to: Box 5695, Boston, MA 02206) Ed. Jean Rabe. circ. 12,000. Document type: consumer publication.
Description: Features articles on role-playing games, news about network activities and the game industry, previews of coming releases, and convention reports.

POOLWAYS; the magazine of outdoor living (year). see SPORTS AND GAMES

621.38 537.5   US
POPULAR ELECTRONICS HOBBYISTS HANDBOOK. 1988. a. $3.50. Gernsback Publications, Inc., 500-B Bi-County Blvd., Farmingdale, NY 11735. TEL 516-293-3000. FAX 516-293-3115. Ed. Carl Laron. adv.; bk.rev.; charts; illus. circ. 135,000. (back issues avail.)
Description: Collection of reprinted articles from Popular Electronics magazine.

790.13   US
POSITIVELY PEZ. bi-m. $18. LaFoe, 3851 Gable Lane Dr., No. 513, Indianapolis, IN 46208. Ed. Larry LaFoe. Document type: newsletter.

795.4   US   ISSN 0897-4020
POSTCARD CLASSICS; picture postcards & ephemera for enjoyment & investment. 1960. bi-m. $15 (foreign $18). Deltiologists of America, Box 8, Norwood, PA 19074. TEL 215-485-8572. Ed. James Lewis Lowe. adv.; bk.rev.; bibl.; charts; illus.; tr.lit.; index, cum.index: 1960-1965. circ. 820. (looseleaf format; back issues avail.)
Former titles (until vol.22, no.6, 1986): Deltiology; Better Postcard Collector.
Description: Picture postcard collecting for enjoyment and investment.

795.4   US   ISSN 0746-6102
POSTCARD COLLECTOR. 1982. m. $24.95. Jones Publishing, Inc., 121 N. Main St., Box 337, Iola, WI 54945. TEL 715-445-5000. FAX 715-445-4053. Ed. Deb Lengkeek. adv.; bk.rev. circ. 6,500. (also avail. in microform from UMI; back issues avail.)
Description: Provides general and specific information about the hobby of postcard collecting for all levels of collectors.

741.6   US   ISSN 1069-5206
THE POSTCARD EXAMINER. 1984. 5/yr. $5.50 (foreign $7.50). Box 4177, Carson City, NV 89702. TEL 702-882-5312. Ed. Ann Rusnak. circ. 100. Document type: newsletter.
Description: Discusses new and unusual findings in the field of modern postcard collecting, and illustrates new postcard designs.

795.4   US
POSTCARD HISTORY SOCIETY. NEWSLETTER. 1975. q. $5. Postcard History Society, c/o John H. McClintock, Dir., Box 1765, Manassas, VA 22110. TEL 703-368-2757. illus. circ. 361. Document type: bulletin.
Description: Information for collectors on postcards 1893-1945, including research, want lists and other subject.

PRESIDENT TRANSPORT WORLD. see TRANSPORTATION

PRESIDENTS' JOURNAL. see HISTORY — *History Of North And South America*

790.023 658.8 338   US
PROFITABLE CRAFT MERCHANDISING. 1965. m. $30. P J S Publications, Inc., News Plaza, Box 1790, Peoria, IL 61656. TEL 309-682-6626. Ed. Miriam Olson. adv.; bk.rev.; illus. circ. 33,000. Document type: consumer publication.
Formerly: Profitable Hobby Merchandising (ISSN 0033-0299)

PUPPEN UND SPIELZEUG; internationales Sammlermagazin. see GIFTWARE AND TOYS

790.13   IT
QUATTRORUOTINE. q. L.30000($40) Editoriale Domus, Via Achelle Grandi 5-7, 20089 Rozzano, Milan, Italy. TEL 02-824721. FAX 02-26863123. TELEX 313589 EDIDOM I. adv.

629.133   GW
R C - FREIZEIT; die 1. deutsche Modellbauzeitung. 1980. m. DM.48. R C - F Verlag, Postfach 102224, 86012 Augsburg, Germany. Ed. Rudolf Gulich. adv.; bk.rev. circ. 30,000. Document type: consumer publication.
Formerly: R C Fundgrube.

629   SP
R C MODEL. (Radio Controlled) 1981. m. 6600 ptas. (Europe 10740 ptas.; elsewhere 12480 ptas.) (effective 1994). Hobby Press, S.A., C. de los Ciruelos, 4, 28700 S. Sebastian de los Reyes (Madrid), Spain. TEL 1-654-81-99. FAX 1-654-86-92. Ed. Andres Aylagas. adv. contact: Felipe Ribagorda. circ. 25,000. Document type: consumer publication.
Description: Covers radio controlled model cars, airplanes, boats and more.

629.133   US   ISSN 0033-6866
TL770.A1
R-C MODELER. 1963. m. $24. R-C Modeler Corp., 144 W. Sierra Madre Blvd., Sierra Madre, CA 91024. TEL 818-355-1476. Ed. Patricia E. Crews. adv.; charts; illus.
—UnCover.

HOBBIES 3027

790.13 US
R C NEWS. (Radio Control) 1982. m. $30. Alta Publishing, Inc., Box 6246, Woodland, CA 91365. TEL 818-340-5750. Ed. Lori Peralta. circ. 175,000. (back issues avail.) **Document type:** consumer publication.
Description: Covers all areas of radio controlled cars, racing and related industry matters.

625.19 FR ISSN 0033-8737
R M F. (Rail Miniature Flash) 1962. m. 288 F. (foreign 348 F.). Weka Presse, 82 rue Curial, 75019 Paris, France. TEL 40-35-36-00. FAX 40-35-80-05. TELEX 210 504 F. Ed. Jerome Clair. adv.: B&W page 3900 F., color page 6300 F.; 190 x 280; adv. contact: Mauricette Le Bouhellec. bk.rev.; abstr.; bibl.; charts; illus.; mkt.; tr.lit.; index. circ. 25,000.

790.13 US
R M S BULLETIN; voice of the hobby: 1941. bi-m. $10. Rathkamp Matchcover Society, c/o John Williams, Sec., 1359 Surrey Rd., Vandalia, OH 45377-1646. TEL 513-890-8684. Ed. Bill Retskin. adv.; bk.rev. circ. 1,400. (looseleaf format) **Document type:** newsletter.
Description: Information on the hobby of matchcover collecting. Provides information on local groups around the U.S. and Canada.

790.13 US ISSN 1054-2256
RADIO CONTROL ACTION SERIES. 4/yr. $15.95. Air Age Publishing, Rt. 7, 251 Danbury Rd., Wilton, CT 06897. TEL 203-834-2900. FAX 203-762-9803. (Subscr. to: Box 578, Mt. Morris, Il 61054) circ. 48,000. **Document type:** consumer publication.

623.820 US ISSN 0890-0078
RADIO CONTROL BOAT MODELER. 1986. 7/yr. $19.95. Air Age Publishing, Rt. 7, 251 Danbury Rd., Wilton, CT 06897. TEL 203-834-2900. FAX 203-762-9803. (Subscr. to: Box 433, Mt. Morris, IL 61054. TEL 800-877-5160) Ed. Tom Atwood. circ. 30,000. **Document type:** consumer publication.
Formerly: American Boat Modeler.

623.820 UK ISSN 0268-5248
RADIO CONTROL BOAT MODELLER. 1985. bi-m. £9.60. Argus Specialist Publications Ltd., Argus House, Boundary Way, Hemel Hempstead, Herts. HP2 7ST, England. TEL 0442-66551. FAX 0442-66998. (Subscr. to: Argus Subscription Services, Queensway House, 2 Queensway, Redhill, Surrey, England. TEL 0737-768611) Ed. John Cundell. adv.; bk.rev. (back issues avail.) **Document type:** consumer publication.
Description: Offers practical advice, photo-features, reviews, product and plants for radio-controlled model boat builders.

790.13 US ISSN 0886-1609
RADIO CONTROL CAR ACTION. 1985. m. $29.95. Air Age Publishing, Rt. 7, 251 Danbury Rd., Wilton, CT 06897. TEL 203-834-2900. FAX 203-762-9803. (Subscr. to: Box 427, Mt. Morris, IL 61054. TEL 800-877-5169) Ed. Frank Masi. circ. 93,000. **Document type:** consumer publication.

629.133 UK ISSN 0968-3291
▼**RADIO CONTROL JET INTERNATIONAL.** 1993. q. £12($20) Traplet Publications Ltd., Traplet House, Severn Dr., Upton-upon-Severn, Worcestershire WR8 OJL, England. TEL 0684-594505. FAX 0684-594586. (Dist. by: Comag Magazine Marketing, Tavistock Rd., W. Drayton, Middx. UB7 7QE, England. TEL 0895-444055. FAX 0895-445255; Subscr. in U.S. to: Box 167, Florham Park, NJ 07932) Ed. Mike Cherry. adv. contact: Jane Stephenson. index. (back issues avail.) **Document type:** consumer publication.

629.221 UK ISSN 0953-0576
RADIO CONTROL MODEL CARS. 1980. m. £21. Argus Specialist Publications Ltd., Argus House, Boundary Way, Hemel Hempstead, Herts. HP2 7ST, England. TEL 0442-66551. FAX 0442-66998. (Subscr. to: Argus Subscruption Services, Queensway House, 2 Queensway, Redhill, Surrey, England. TEL 0737-768611) Ed. Alan Harman. adv.; bk.rev.; illus. (back issues avail.) **Document type:** consumer publication.
Former titles (until 1987): Model Cars Monthly (ISSN 0269-8315); (until 1984): Model Cars (ISSN 0260-762X).
Description: Features product news, reviews, race reports, letters, and advice for model car enthusiasts.

929.221 US ISSN 1061-7205
RADIO CONTROL MODEL CARS AND TRUCKS. 1985. m. $25. Gallant Models, Inc., 34249 Camino Capistrano, Capistrano Beach, CA 92624. TEL 714-496-5411. FAX 714-496-5427. adv.: B&W page $1085; trim 8 1/8 x 10 7/8. circ. 119,120. **Document type:** consumer publication.
Formerly (until 1990): Radio Control Model Cars (ISSN 0887-4689)
Description: Covers r.c. car and truck building and racing.

629.133 UK ISSN 0268-3342
RADIO CONTROL MODEL WORLD. 1985. m. £20($42) Traplet Publications Ltd., Traplet House, Severn Dr., Upton-upon-Severn, Worcestershire WR8 OJL, England. TEL 0684-594505. FAX 0684-594586. (Dist. by: Comag Magazine Marketing, Tavistock Rd., W. Drayton, Middx. UB7 7QE, England. TEL 0895-444055. FAX 0895-445255; Subscr. in U.S. to: Box 167, Florham Park, NJ 07932) Ed. Simon Rodway. adv. contact: Jane Stephenson. index. (back issues avail.) **Document type:** consumer publication.

621.38 UK ISSN 0033-7838
RADIO CONTROL MODELS & ELECTRONICS. Variant title: R C M & E. 1960. m. £20.40. Argus Specialist Publications Ltd., Argus House, Boundary Way, Hemel Hempstead, Herts. HP2 7ST, England. TEL 0442-66551. FAX 0442-66998. (Subscr. to: Argus Subscription Services, Queensway House, 2 Queensway, Redhill, Surrey, England. TEL 0737-768611) Ed. Kevin Crozoer. adv.; illus. **Indexed:** Ind.How To Do It (1979-). **Document type:** consumer publication.
Description: Covers the use of radio-control equipment in model airplanes and helicopters.

629.133 UK ISSN 0267-8101
RADIO CONTROL SCALE AIRCRAFT QUARTERLY. 1985. q. £15. Argus Specialist Publications Ltd., Argus House, Boundary Way, Hemel Hempstead, Herts. HP2 7ST, England. TEL 0442-66551. FAX 0442-66998. (Subscr. to: Argus Subscription Services, Queensway House, 2 Queensway, Redhill, Surrey, England. TEL 0737-768611) Ed. David Bopdington. adv.; bk.rev. (back issues avail.) **Document type:** consumer publication.
Description: Discusses the practical aspects of scale models that fly with radio control equipment.

790.13 US ISSN 1055-887X
RADIO FUN. 1991. m. $12.95. Wayne Green Inc., 70 Rte 202 N., Peterborough, NH 03458. TEL 603-924-0058. FAX 603-924-9327. circ. 25,000. **Document type:** consumer publication.

623.820 600 IT ISSN 0391-383X
RADIO KIT ELETTRONICA. 1978. m. L.58000 (foreign L.90000). C & C Edizioni Radioelettroniche, Via Naviglio 37-2, Faenza, Italy. TEL 0546 22112. FAX 0546-662046. Ed. Nerio Neri. adv.; bk.rev. circ. 55,000. **Document type:** consumer publication.

621.38 UK ISSN 0144-0713
RADIO MODELLER. m. £19.20. Argus Specialist Publications Ltd., Argus House, Boundary Way, Hemel Hempstead, Herts. HP2 7ST, England. TEL 0442-66551. FAX 0442-66998. (Subscr. to: Argus Subscription Services, Queensway House, 2 Queensway, Redhill, Surrey, England. TEL 0737-768611) Ed. Alec Gee. **Document type:** consumer publication.
Description: Covers every aspect of radio-controlled flight.

629.22 UK ISSN 0268-3334
RADIO RACE CAR INTERNATIONAL. 1985. m. £20 (Europe £28; rest of world £38). Traplet Publications Ltd., Traplet House, Severn Dr., Upton-upon-Severn, Worcestershire WR8 OJL, England. TEL 0684-594505. FAX 0684-594586. (Dist. by: Comag Magazine Marketing, Tavistock Rd., W. Drayton, Middx. UB7 7QE, England. TEL 0895-444055; Subscr. in U.S. to: Box 167, Florham Park, NJ 07932) Ed. Jonty Walkeden. adv. contact: Jane Stephenson. index. (back issues avail.) **Document type:** consumer publication.

790.13 770 US
RAILFAN PHOTOGRAPHER. 1989. q. $17. Box 787, Higley, AZ 85236-0787. Ed. Gregory Monroe. adv.; illus.
Description: Features photographs of trains.

625.19 US ISSN 0033-877X
RAILROAD MODEL CRAFTSMAN. 1933. m. $25. Carstens Publications, Inc., Box 700, Newton, NJ 07860. TEL 201-383-3355. FAX 201-383-4064. Ed. William Schaumburg. adv.; bk.rev.; illus.; index. circ. 95,000.

625.19 UK ISSN 0033-8931
RAILWAY MODELLER. 1949. m. £24. Peco Publications & Publicity Ltd., Beer, Seaton, Devon EX12 3NA, England. TEL 0297-20580. FAX 0297-20229. Ed. J. Brewer. adv.; bk.rev.; index. circ. 72,181.

790.13 US
RANCHERO COURIER. 1982. bi-m. (except Jul.-Aug.). $22 (foreign $25). Ranchero Club, 1339 Beverly Rd., Port Vue, PA 15133. Ed. Gene Makrancy. adv. circ. 500. (back issues avail.) **Document type:** newsletter.
Description: Discusses the Club's vehicles.

790.13 CN ISSN 0380-8114
RANDOM THOUGHTS. 1967. bi-m. Can.$7($6) International Plastic Modellers Society-Canada, Box 626, Station B, Ottawa, Ont. K1P 5P7, Canada. Ed. J. Sauve. adv.; bk.rev.; charts; illus.; index. circ. 1,900.

RECREATIONAL VEHICLE BLUE BOOK. see *TRANSPORTATION — Automobiles*

REMEMBER THAT SONG; newsletter for sheet music collectors. see *MUSIC*

736.2 US ISSN 0048-8453
QE420
ROCK & GEM. 1971. m. $18. Miller Magazines, Inc., 4880 Market St., Ventura, CA 93003-2888. TEL 805-644-3824. Ed. W.R.C. Shedenhelm. (reprint service avail. from UMI) **Indexed:** GeoRef.
Description: For amateur lapidary and mineral hobbyists. Rockhound field trips show best areas for collecting, mineral profiles, photo-stories show how to create jewelry, etc.

ROCKIN' RECORDS; buyers - sellers reference book and price guide. see *MUSIC*

ROLLER COASTER!. see *TRAVEL AND TOURISM*

RONDELL PROGRAMM. see *MOTION PICTURES*

ROTORCRAFT. see *AERONAUTICS AND SPACE FLIGHT*

RUBBERSTAMPMADNESS. see *ARTS AND HANDICRAFTS*

790.023 II ISSN 0035-9580
RUBY MAGAZINE. (Text in Urdu) 1966. m. 3583 Netaji-Subash Marg, Darya Ganj, P.O. Box 7014, Dew Delhi 110 002, India. TEL 11-271637. Ed. Rehman Nayyar. adv.; illus. circ. 23,000.

790.13 US ISSN 1045-4373
TT850
RUG HOOKING. 1989. 5/yr. $24.95. Commonwealth Communications Services, Inc., Cameron and Kelker Sts., Box 15760, Harrisburg, PA 17105. TEL 717-234-5091. FAX 717-234-1359. Ed. Mary Ellen Cooper. circ. 10,869.

625.19 US ISSN 0273-6241
S GAUGIAN. 1962. bi-m. $26 (foreign $32). Heimburger House Publishing Co., 7236 W. Madison St., Forest Park, IL 60130. TEL 312-366-1973. Ed. Donald J. Heimburger. adv.; bk.rev.; illus. circ. 5,000. (back issues avail.) **Document type:** consumer publication.
Description: How-to articles, photos, plans and product news on 1:64 scale model railroading.

790.132 CN ISSN 0048-895X
SADDLE AND STRIKER. 1962. 5/yr. Can.$5. Trans-Canada Matchcover Club, 100 Gillespie Cres., Ottawa, Ont. K1V 0J2, Canada. Ed. Rod Cook. adv.

745.5 CI ISSN 0350-7483
SAM; Jugoslavenski magazine za samograditelje. 1975. m. $64. Vjesnik, Avenija Bratstva i Jedinstva 4, 41000 Zagreb, Croatia. Ed. Ivan Kreutz.

H

3028 HOBBIES

790.13   US
SAND PAPER. 1988. q. $5 membership. International Sand Collectors Society, 43 Highview Ave., Old Greenwich, CT 06870. TEL 203-637-2801. bk.rev.; circ. 100 (paid). **Document type:** newsletter.
  Description: Collecting tips, member news, collection descriptions, "how-to" microphotography, using sand as an instructional medium for el-hi teachers.

790.13   GW   ISSN 0940-3418
SCALE. q. DM.36 (foreign DM.40). Verlag fuer Technik und Handwerk GmbH, Robert-Bosch-Str. 4, 76532 Baden-Baden, Germany. TEL 07221-5087-0. FAX 07221-508752. Ed. Frank Schwartz. **Document type:** consumer publication.

629.133   UK   ISSN 0956-1420
SCALE AIRCRAFT MODELLING. 1976. m. Hall Publications Ltd., Douglas House, Simpson Rd., Bletchley, Milton Keynes, Bucks. MK1 1BA, Englnad. TEL 0908-377559. FAX 0908-366744. adv. circ. 18,000. (back issues avail.)
  Description: Provides information on all types of aircraft in word and drawing for color scheme research. Reviews new kits and gives advice about improving basic aircraft model kits.

790.13   US   ISSN 0195-217X
SCALE AUTO ENTHUSIAST. 1979. bi-m. $15. Highland Productions Inc., N50 W 13605 Overview Dr., Monomonee Falls, WI 53051. TEL 414-476-5998. FAX 414-476-0511. Ed. Gary Schmidt. adv.; bk.rev.; illus. circ. 62,000. **Document type:** consumer publication.
  Description: Devoted to building and collecting static models of automobiles, trucks and motorcycles.

790.13   US   ISSN 0145-8213
TT178
SCALE CABINETMAKER. 1976. q. $22 (effective 1993). Dorsett Publications, 630 Depot St., Box 2038, Christiansburg, VA 24073. TEL 703-382-4651. Ed. James H. Dorsett. cum.index: 1976-1991. circ. 1,800. (back issues avail.)
  Description: For the serious amateur and commercial craftsmen. Covers all facets of scale modeling (miniatures), such as tools and workbench techniques, as well as the history of furniture styles.

625.19   UK
SCALE MODEL TRAINS. 1980. m. £20.60. (Kristall Productions) Wessex Publishing, Surdaw House, Station Rd., Gillingham, Dorset SP8 4PR, England. TEL 07476-3400. FAX 0747-823808. Ed. Chris Ellis. adv.; bk.rev.; illus. circ. 10,000. (reprint service avail. from UMI) **Document type:** consumer publication.
  Formerly (until 1984): Scale Trains (ISSN 0262-8406)

745.5   US   ISSN 0036-5424
TL770.A1
SCALE MODELER. 1965. m. $27.95. Challenge Publications, Inc., 7950 Deering Ave., Canoga Park, CA 91304. TEL 818-887-0550. FAX 818-883-1343. adv.; bk.rev.; illus. circ. 55,000. **Document type:** consumer publication.

629.221   UK   ISSN 0269-834X
SCALE MODELS INTERNATIONAL. 1969. m. £20.40. Argus Specialist Publications Ltd., Argus House, Boundary Way, Hemel Hempstead, Herts. HP2 7ST, England. TEL 0442-66651. FAX 0442-66998. (Subscr. to: Argus Subscription Services, Queensway House, 2 Queensway, Redhill, Surrey, England. TEL 0737-768611) Ed. Kelvin Barber. adv.; bk.rev.; charts; illus.; mkt. **Document type:** consumer publication.
  —BLDSC (8087.453000).
  Formerly: Scale Models (ISSN 0036-5432); Incorporates: P A M News International; Model (ISSN 0026-7317)
  Description: Covers all aspects of building static model aircraft, cars, trucks, and motorcycles straight out of the box, with modifications, and from scratch.

629.221   US   ISSN 0199-7327
SCALE R - C MODELER. (Radio-Controlled) m. Challenge Publications, Inc., 7950 Deering Ave., Canoga Park, CA 91304. TEL 818-887-0550. FAX 818-883-1343. Ed. Norm Goyer. **Document type:** consumer publication.

790.13   US
SCANDAL SHEET.* 1971. irreg. $2. Scandalous Bohemians of New Jersey, c/o Norman Nolan, 68 Crest Rd., Middletown, NJ 07748. Ed. Robert A.W. Lowndes. (back issues avail.)

623.820   GW   ISSN 0722-7108
SCHIFFS MODELL. 1978. m. DM.78. Neckar Verlag GmbH, Postfach 1820, 78008 Villingen-Schwenningen, Germany. TEL 07221-8987-0. FAX 07221-898750. adv.; bk.rev. circ. 25,000. (back issues avail.) **Document type:** consumer publication.

623.820   GW   ISSN 0179-3195
SCHIFFSPROPELLER; das Fachmagazin fuer den Schiffsmodellbauer. bi-m. DM.45 (foreign DM.51). Verlag fuer Technik und Handwerk GmbH, Robert-Bosch-Str. 4, 76532 Baden-Baden, Germany. TEL 07221-5087-0. FAX 07221-508752. Ed. Helmut Harhaus. **Document type:** consumer publication.

SCHOLAR'S MATE. see SPORTS AND GAMES

793   US
SCOUT MEMORABILIA. 1966. 5/yr. $5. Lawrence L. Lee Scouting Museum, Box 1121, Manchester, NH 03105. TEL 603-625-6431. (Co-sponsor: Max I. Silber Scouting Library) Ed. Edward Rowan. adv.; bk.rev.; bibl.; charts; illus. circ. 1,000. **Document type:** newsletter.

790.13   IT
SCUOLA DEL FARDASE.* 1981. m. L.24000. Curcio Periodici S.p.A., Via Arno 64, 00198 Rome, Italy. Ed. Rosanna Falconi. adv. circ. 135,000.

790.13   UK   ISSN 0955-9221
THE SEARCHER. 1985. m. £21. Searcher Publications, P.O. Box 43, Hindhead, Surrey GU26 6XG, England. TEL 0428-606109. Ed. Jan Bowdery. circ. 7,500.
  Description: Provides information on the hobby of metal detecting.

745.592 387   US   ISSN 1052-4975
VM298
THE SEAWAYS; journal of maritime history and research. 1990. bi-m. $24.95 (effective 1994). Seaways Publishing, Inc., 2271 Constitution Dr., San Jose, CA 95124. TEL 408-975-5657. Ed. Jim Raines. adv.: Full page $600; adv. contact: Michelle Raines. bk.rev.; illus.; index; circ. 5,500 (paid). **Indexed:** Amer.Hist.& Life, Hist.Abstr.
  Formerly: Seaways' Ships in Scale.
  Description: Provides a workwhop and research guide for ship modelers of all levels.

790   GW
SELBERMACHEN. 1974. m. Jahreszeiten Verlag GmbH, Possmoorweg 5, 22301 Hamburg, Germany. TEL 040-27170. FAX 040-27172056. TELEX 213214-JAG-D. Ed. Harald Apelt. adv. contact: Michael Scheible. illus. circ. 242,469. **Document type:** consumer publication.

SHORTWAVE RADIO TODAY; the DX radio magazine for active SWL'S. see COMMUNICATIONS — Radio

SIDE-SADDLE NEWS. see SPORTS AND GAMES — Horses And Horsemanship

388.3   CN   ISSN 0037-4601
SIDEMOUNT REPORTER. 1960. m. Can.$20. Manitoba Classic and Antique Auto Club, Box 1031, Winnipeg, MB R3C 2W2, Canada. Ed. Roy Zelinsky. adv.; bk.rev.; illus. circ. 211. (processed) **Document type:** newsletter.

659.1   FI   ISSN 0037-4970
SIGNAL INTERNATIONAL; for penpals, collectors and traders. (Text in English) 1960. irreg. (3-4/yr.). $20. Moniposti, Box 150, FIN-15111 Lahti, Finland. FAX 358-18-334799. Ed. Raimo Kaarna; Pub. Raimo Kaarna. adv.; bk.rev.; illus.; tr.lit. circ. 5,000.

790.13   UK
SILENT FLIGHT. bi-m. Argus Specialist Publications Ltd., Argus House, Boundary Way, Hemel Hempstead, Herts. HP2 7ST, England. TEL 0442-66551. FAX 0442-66998. (Subscr. to: Argus Subscription Services, Queensway House, 2 Queensway, Redhill, Surrey, England. TEL 0737-768611) **Document type:** consumer publication.
  Description: Covers all aspects of building and flying model gliders and aircraft powered by electric motors.

790.132   US
SILVER & GOLD. 1979. a. $4.95 per no. People's Publishing Co., Inc., 5440 Ericson Way, Arcata, CA 95521. TEL 707-822-8442. FAX 707-822-0973. Ed. Rosemary Anderson. circ. 20,000.
  Description: Covers the use of metal detectors for locating silver and gold.

790.13   JA
SILVER FLOWER/GINKA. (Text in Japanese) 1967. q. 10380 Yen. Bunka Publishing Bureau, 22-1, 3-chome, Yoyogi, Shibuya-ku, Tokyo, Japan. Ed. Fukiko Hosoi.

790.13   US   ISSN 0164-3509
SKINNED KNUCKLES; a journal of car restoration. 1976. m. $16. S K Publications, 175 May Ave., Monrovia, CA 91016. TEL 818-358-6255. Ed. Terry Cannon. adv.; bk.rev.; index. circ. 7,000. (back issues avail.) **Indexed:** Ind.How To Do It (1990-).
  Description: Covers the hobby of restoring, operating, and maintaining automobiles, antiques and certain types of machines.

790.13   US   ISSN 1058-8256
TJ1570
SLOT MACHINE - JUKE BOX COLLECTOR.* 1991. q. (Wordmarque Design Associates) Slot - Box Collector, Box 315, Clifton, VA 22024-0315.

790.132   US
SMURF COLLECTORS CLUB INTERNATIONAL NEWSLETTER. 1986. q. $15. Smurf Collectors Club, 24U Cabot Rd. W., Massapequa, NY 11758. TEL 516-799-3221. Ed. Suzanne Lipschitz. adv.; bk.rev.; index. circ. 800. (looseleaf format; back issues avail.) **Document type:** newsletter.
  Formerly: Smurf Collectors Club Newsletter.

790.13   US
SNOW BIZ; the newsletter for snowdome collectors. 1990. q. $10. Nancy McMichael, Ed. & Pub., Box 53262, Washington, DC 20009. adv.; page $60. circ. 800 (paid). (back issues avail.) **Document type:** newsletter.
  Description: Informs collectors of snowdomes of what's available and offers tips on how to best keep and display these items.

790.13   US
SN3 MODELER. 1984. s-a. $11 (foreign $17). Heimburger House Publishing Co., 7236 W. Madison St., Forest Park, IL 60130. TEL 312-366-1973. Ed. Donald J. Heimburger. adv.; bk.rev.; charts; film rev.; illus.; tr.lit. circ. 2,000. (back issues avail.) **Document type:** consumer publication.
  Description: How-to articles, photos, plans and product news on narrow gauge 1:64 scale model railroading.

795.4   US
SOUVENIR CARD JOURNAL.* 1981. q. $10. Souvenir Card Collectors Society, c/o Robin Ellis, Ed., Box 8468, San Antonio, TX 78208-0468. adv. circ. 800.

790.1   US
SPEEDWAY. 1991. bi-m. Ballstreet, Inc., 7200 Montgomery N.E., Ste. 356, Albuquerque, NM 87109. TEL 505-888-1515. FAX 505-888-0717. illus. circ. 10,000. **Document type:** consumer publication.
  Description: For the racing memorabilia collector; features 12 of the hottest cars and drivers.

SPEELGOED & HOBBY. see GIFTWARE AND TOYS

796.357 795.4   US
THE SPORT AMERICANA BASEBALL ADDRESS LIST. Variant title: Baseball Address List. irreg., no.6, 1990. $12.95. Beckett Publications, 4887 Alpha Rd., Ste. 200, Dallas, TX 75244. TEL 214-991-6657. FAX 214-991-8930. (Subscr. to: Box 1915, Marion, OH 43305-1915) Eds. R.J. "Jack" Smalling, Dennis W. Eckes. **Document type:** directory, consumer publication.
  Description: Over 10,000 mailing addresses for most major league players, both active and retired. Includes past and present managers, minor leaguers, and umpires.

HOBBIES

795.4 796.357   US
THE SPORT AMERICANA BASEBALL CARD PRICE GUIDE. Variant title: Baseball Card Price Guide. a., no.14, 1992. $15.95. Beckett Publications, 4887 Alpha Rd., Ste. 200, Dallas, TX 75244. TEL 214-991-6657. FAX 214-991-8930. (Subscr. to: Box 1915, Marion, OH 43305-1915) Ed. James Beckett. **Document type:** directory, consumer publication.
Description: Comprehensive price guide for virtually every baseball card in existence through 1992. Includes the history of card collecting, a guide to the hobby, and how to grade your cards.

795.4 796.323   US
THE SPORT AMERICANA BASKETBALL CARD PRICE GUIDE AND ALPHABETICAL CHECKLIST. Variant title: Basketball Card Price Guide and Alphabetical Checklist. 1991. a., no.2, 1992. $12.95. Beckett Publications, 4887 Alpha Rd., Ste. 200, Dallas, TX 75244. TEL 214-991-6657. FAX 214-991-8930. (Subscr. to: Box 1915, Marion, OH 43305-1915) Ed. James Beckett. illus. **Document type:** directory, consumer publication.
Description: Features two sections - one for prices of all basketball cards issued from 1948 through 1992; and another list all of a player's cards by manufacturer.

795.4 796.332   US
THE SPORT AMERICANA FOOTBALL CARD PRICE GUIDE. Variant title: Football Card Price Guide. a., no.9, 1992. $14.95. Beckett Publications, 4887 Alpha Rd., Ste. 200, Dallas, TX 75244. TEL 214-991-6657. FAX 214-991-8930. (Subscr. to: Box 1915, Marion, OH 43305-1915) Ed. James Beckett. **Document type:** directory, consumer publication.
Description: Covers all of football with over 155,000 current prices for the NFL, USFL, CFL and regional college sets.

795.4 796.962   US
THE SPORT AMERICANA HOCKEY CARD PRICE GUIDE. Variant title: Hockey Card Price Guide. (Introduction in English, French) 1991. a. $12.95. Beckett Publications, 4887 Alpha Rd., Ste. 200, Dallas, TX 75249. TEL 214-991-6657. FAX 214-991-8930. (Subscr. to: Box 1915, Marion, OH 43305-1915) Ed. James Beckett. illus. **Document type:** directory, consumer publication.
Description: Lists over 50,000 prices for all issues known to exist from 1910 through 1992.

395.4 796.357   US
THE SPORT AMERICANA PRICE GUIDE TO BASEBALL COLLECTIBLES. Variant title: Price Guide to Baseball Collectibles. 1987. irreg., no.2, 1992. $12.95. Beckett Publications, 4887 Alpha Rd., Ste. 200, Dallas, TX 75244. TEL 214-991-6657. FAX 214-991-8930. (Subscr. to: Box 1915, Marion, OH 43305-1915) Ed. James Beckett. **Document type:** directory, consumer publication.

795.4 796.357   US
THE SPORT AMERICANA TEAM BASEBALL CARD CHECKLIST. Variant title: Team Baseball Card Checklist. irreg. (approx. a.), no.5, 1990. $12.95. Beckett Publications, 4887 Alpha Rd., Ste. 200, Dallas, TX 75249. TEL 214-991-6657. FAX 214-992-8930. (Subscr. to: Box 1915, Marion, OH 43305-1915) Eds. Dennis W. Eckes, Jeff Fritsch. **Document type:** directory, consumer publication.
Description: Lists each player by team for each year and card company.

795.4 796.332   US
THE SPORT AMERICANA TEAM FOOTBALL AND BASKETBALL CARD CHECKLIST. Variant title: Team Football and Basketball Card Checklist. 1990. irreg., (approx. a.). $10.95. Beckett Publications, 4887 Alpha Rd., Ste. 200, Dallas, TX 75249. TEL 214-991-6657. FAX 214-991-8930. (Subscr. to: Box 1915, Marion, OH 43305-1915) Ed.Bd. **Document type:** directory, consumer publication.
Description: Contains all major national football and basketball issues. Lists card numbers for all players on a team by year and card company.

629.133   US
TL844
SPORT ROCKETRY; America's complete model rocketry magazine. 1958. 8/yr. $24. National Association of Rocketry, 1311 Edgewood Dr., Altoona, WI 54720. TEL 800-262-4872. Ed. Steve Weaver. adv.; bk.rev. circ. 5,500. **Document type:** consumer publication.
Formerly: American Spacemodeling (ISSN 0883-0991)
Description: For model rocket enthusiasts.

790.13   GW
SPORT UND DESIGN DRACHEN. 6/yr. DM.54 (foreign DM.60). Verlag fuer Technik und Handwerk GmbH, Robert-Bosch-Str. 4, 76532 Baden-Baden, Germany. TEL 07221-5087-0. FAX 07221-508752. Ed. Peter Wuttke. adv. contact: Michael Essig. circ. 25,000. **Document type:** consumer publication.

SPORTS & LEISURE RETAILER. see SPORTS AND GAMES

795.4 796.357   ISSN 1061-5512
SPORTS CARD PRICE GUIDE MONTHLY. 1988. m. $18.95. Krause Publications, Inc., 700 E. State St., Iola, WI 54990. TEL 715-445-2214. FAX 715-445-4087. TELEX 556461 KRAUSE PUB UD. adv. circ. 197,129.
Formerly (until 1992): Baseball Card Price Guide Monthly (ISSN 0896-7563)
Description: Lists current values of more than 45,000 sports cards, with emphasis on cards produced from 1948 to the present.

795.4   US
SPORTS CARDS. 1981. m. $18.95. Krause Publications, Inc., 700 E. State St., Iola, WI 54990. TEL 715-445-2214. FAX 715-445-4087. TELEX 556461 KRAUSE PUB UD. Ed. Scott Kelnhofer. adv.; bk.rev. circ. 184,650.
Formerly (until May 1993): Baseball Cards (ISSN 8750-5851)
Description: Features sports cards from all eras. Helpful monthly guide to card collecting for both beginners and advanced collectors. Includes updated 4-sport card price guide in each issue with offerings of tens of thousands of sports cards and related items. Contains in-depth articles on the subject.

790.13 796.357   US   ISSN 0278-2693
SPORTS COLLECTORS DIGEST. 1974. w. $49.95. Krause Publications, Inc., 700 E. State St., Iola, WI 54990. TEL 715-445-2214. FAX 715-445-4087. Ed. Tom Mortenson. adv.; illus. circ. 43,216. (also avail. in microform from UMI)
Description: News, articles, and buy, sell, and trade ads for difficult-to-find baseball cards and sports memorabilia, featuring up-to-date price guides on card values.

745   US
STAINED FINGER. 1981. q. $22.50 membership. Society of Inkwell Collectors, 5136 Thomas Ave. S., Minneapolis, MN 55410. TEL 612-922-2792. Ed. Vincent McGraw. adv.; bk.rev.; bibl.; charts; illus.; pat.; stat. circ. 600. (back issues avail.) **Document type:** newsletter.
Description: Features profiles of collectors, inkwells, repair and cleaning techniques, networking, auction listings, current values, and classifieds.

795.4   UK
STANLEY GIBBONS CATALOGUE OF TELEPHONE CARDS. 1990. irreg. price varies. Stanley Gibbons Publications Ltd., Unit 5 Parkside, Christchurch Rd., Ringwood, Hants. BH24 3SH, England. TEL 0425-472363. FAX 0425-470247. TELEX 41271-SGPPUB-G. Ed. S.E.R. Hiscocks. **Document type:** catalog.
Description: Worldwide catalogue for collectors of telephone cards.

790.13   PK
STAR INTERNATIONAL. q. $2 per no. Tharechani 65121, Via Panoakil, Distt. Sukkur, Sind, Pakistan. Ed. Indus Hob.
Description: A penpal, friendship network.

790.13 808.838   US
STAR WARS COLLECTION TRADING POST. 1989. q. $12. L.L. Kyro, Ed. & Pub., 6030 Magnolia Ave., St. Louis, MO 63139. TEL 314-645-6692. adv.; bk.rev. circ. 150. (looseleaf format; back issues avail.)
Description: For space and science fiction fans, movie buffs and collectors.

STEAM CLASSIC. see TRANSPORTATION — Railroads

790.13   US
STICKERS & STUFF. 1983. q. $10. Ira Friedman, Inc., 10 Columbus Circle, Ste. 1300, New York, NY 10019. TEL 212-541-7300.

808.836   GW   ISSN 0936-7802
STRIPSPIEGEL. 1982. bi-m. Edition Stripspiegel G.B.R. Comicverlag Waigel, Weitmann, Seidel und Rausch, Auweg 16, 89312 Guenzburg, Germany. TEL 08221-4182. illus. circ. 3,000. (back issues avail.)

SUGEI PAZURU. see MATHEMATICS

796   US   ISSN 8750-0124
SUPPLY LINE. 1984. bi-m. membership. Military Vehicle Preservation Association, Box 520378, Independence, MO 64052-0378. TEL 816-737-5111. FAX 816-737-5423. Ed. Jerry Cleveland. adv. circ. 6,000. **Document type:** newsletter.
Description: Features current news on military vehicle collecting.

SVENSK LEKSAKSREVY. see GIFTWARE AND TOYS

SWIMMING POOLS TODAY. see SPORTS AND GAMES — Outdoor Life

790.13 622   US   ISSN 1053-055X
T H - ERS EXPRESS. (Treasure Hunt); adventure bulletin. Variant title: Treasure Hunters News. 1965. q. $10 (foreign $15) (includes book catalog). Treasure Trove, 210 N. Main St., Ames, NE 68621. TEL 402-721-8588. FAX 402-727-7710. (Subscr. to: Box 448, Fremont, NE 68025) Ed. Paul Tainter. adv.; bk.rev. circ. 7,500. (back issues avail.) **Document type:** newspaper.
Formerly: Treasure Hunters Newspaper.
Description: Covers all aspects of treasure hunting and small-scale mining.

790.13   US
T T O S BULLETIN. bi-m. $37. Toy Train Operating Society, 25 W. Walnut St., Ste. 308, Pasadena, CA 91103. TEL 818-578-0673. FAX 818-578-0750.

790.13   US
T T O S ORDER BOARD. bi-m. $37. Toy Train Operating Society, 25 W. Walnut St., Ste. 308, Pasadena, CA 91103. TEL 818-578-0750. FAX 818-578-0750.
Description: Provides news and information on collecting, preserving, and operating antique and new toy trains.

T V COLLECTOR. see COMMUNICATIONS — Television And Cable

790.13   UK
TAMIYA MODEL MAGAZINE INTERNATIONAL. bi-m. Argus Specialist Publications Ltd., Argus House, Boundary Way, Hemel Hempstead, Herts. HP2 7ST, England. TEL 0442-66551. FAX 0442-66998. (Subscr. to: Argus Subscription Services, Queensway House, 2 Queensway, Redhill, Surrey, England. TEL 0737-768611) **Document type:** consumer publication.
Description: Reviews both static and radio-controlled working models from Tamiya.

790.13   UK
TANKETTE. 1965. bi-m. £5 (foreign £6). Miniature Armoured Fighting Vehicle Association (MAFVA), 15 Berwick Ave., Heaton Mersey, Stockport, Cheshire SK4 3AA, England. TEL 061-432-7574. Eds. Gary Williams, Spike Judd. adv.; bk.rev.; illus. circ. 7,250. **Document type:** consumer publication.
Description: Contains articles, photographs and drawings of tanks, self-propelled guns, half-tracks, armoured cars, trucks, artillery, uniforms, unit organisatons, and multi-view original scale plans.

790.13   US   ISSN 0745-7189
NK8740
TEDDY BEAR AND FRIENDS; clearinghouse for information on teddy bears. 1983. 6/yr. $17.95. Cumberland Publishing Co., 900 Frederick St., Cumberland, MD 21502. TEL 301-759-5853. Ed. Carolyn B. Cook. circ. 60,000.

3030 HOBBIES

790.13   US   ISSN 0890-4162
TEDDY BEAR REVIEW. 1986. bi-m. $19.97. Collector Communications Corp., 170 Fifth Ave., New York, NY 10010. TEL 212-989-8700. FAX 212-645-8976. (Subscr. to: Box 1948, Marion, OH 43305) Ed. Stephen Cronk. circ. 60,000.

790.13   US
TEDDY TRIBUNE; news and views of the bear world. 1980. 10/yr. $17. 254 W. Sidney, St. Paul, MN 55107. TEL 612-291-7571. Ed. Barbara Wolters. circ. 1,200. (back issues avail.)

TEHNIUM. see SCIENCES: COMPREHENSIVE WORKS

745.5   SW
TEKNIK FOER ALLA. 1940. m. (11/yr.). SEK 325. Svenska Pressfoerlaget AB, P.O. Box 83, 182 71 Stocksund, Sweden. TEL 46-8-85-01-90. FAX 46-8-85-32-70. Leif Gustavsson. adv. contact: Liselott Olofson. circ. 20,000. **Document type:** consumer publication, trade publication.

790.13   GW
TELEFONKARTEN JOURNAL. m. Evers Verlag GmbH, Ernst-Guenter-Str., 25704 Meldorf, Germany. TEL 04832-2007. FAX 04832-7244. Ed. Karsten Windfelder. adv. contact: Helmut Lemke. circ. 60,000. **Document type:** bulletin.

790.13   GW   ISSN 0943-6871
TELEFONKARTEN NEWS. m. DM.85 (foreign DM.110). Heinrich Gietl Verlag, Burgweg 15, 93128 Regenstauf, Germany. TEL 09402-5856. FAX 09402-6635. **Document type:** bulletin.

TIGHT LINES. see SPORTS AND GAMES

793   US
TIN TYPE. m. $15. Tin Container Collectors Association, Box 440101, Aurora, CO 80044-0101. Ed. Clark Secrest. illus.

TOP (BENNINGEN). see CHILDREN AND YOUTH — For

TOY & HOBBY RETAILER. see BUSINESS AND ECONOMICS — Marketing And Purchasing

TOY & HOBBY RETAILER. see GIFTWARE AND TOYS

TOY & HOBBY WORLD. see GIFTWARE AND TOYS

TOY & HOBBY WORLD LATIN AMERICA. see GIFTWARE AND TOYS

TOY BOOK. see GIFTWARE AND TOYS

790.132   US
TOY CAR. 1971. q. $5. Toy Car Press, Box 1534, San Jose, CA 95109. Ed. Dave Robison. bk.rev. circ. 200.

745.592   US   ISSN 0898-5650
TOY SHOP. 1988. m. $23.95. Krause Publications, Inc., 700 E. State St., Iola, WI 54990. TEL 715-445-2214. FAX 715-445-4087. TELEX 55 6461 KRAUSE PUB UD. circ. 28,147. (tabloid format)
 Description: Advertises collectible toys, models, dolls for sale or wanted, listed alphabetically by type of toy. Includes extensive calendar of toy shows.

703.23   US   ISSN 0747-8615
TOY SOLDIER REVIEW. 1984. q. $12. Vintage Castings, Inc., 127-74th St., North Bergen, NJ 07047. TEL 201-861-2979. FAX 201-854-1738. Ed. William Lango. adv.; bk.rev.; illus.; circ. 4,000 (paid).
 Description: Covers the worldwide adult hobby of collecting toy soldiers, model soldiers, and collectible military toys.

TOY TRADER. see GIFTWARE AND TOYS

TOY TRADER. see GIFTWARE AND TOYS

TOYS & GAMES. see GIFTWARE AND TOYS

795.4 796.3   US   ISSN 1060-9970
TRADING CARDS. 1991. m. $17.95 (foreign $27.95). Larry Flynt Publications, Inc., 9171 Wilshire Blvd., Ste. 300, Beverly Hills, CA 90210. TEL 310-858-7100. FAX 310-274-7985. Ed. Terry Melia. adv. circ. 20,000. **Document type:** consumer publication.
 Description: Covers the market of professional baseball, basketball, football and hockey cards.

790.13   US   ISSN 1043-7665
TRADING POST (GREENVILLE). 1938. q. $20 includes membership (foreign $25). American Society of Military Insignia Collectors, Inc. (ASMIC), c/o Donal J. Sexton, Pres., 400 Flamingo Circle, Greenville, TN 37743. (Subscr. to: George Duell, 526 Lafayette Ave., Palmerton, PA 18071) Ed. Chris Aleck. circ. 3,000. (also avail. in microfilm; back issues avail.) **Document type:** directory.
 Description: Provides articles pertaining to insignia and illustrations of cloth and metal military insignia, especially of the US armed forces.

625.19   US   ISSN 0041-0829
TF197
TRAIN COLLECTORS QUARTERLY. 1955. q. $12. Train Collectors Association, 213 Fannie Ave., Lancaster, PA 17602. TEL 717-687-8623. Ed. Bruce D. Manson, Jr. bk.rev.; illus.; index; circ. 26,500 (controlled). **Document type:** academic/scholarly publication.
 —UnCover.

790.1   US   ISSN 0049-4593
TREASURE. 1970. m. $39. Double Eagle Publishing, 31970 Yucaipa Blvd., Yucaipa, CA 92399. TEL 714-794-4612. FAX 714-794-9452. Ed. Jim Williams. adv.; bk.rev.; charts; illus.; tr.lit. circ. 26,000.
 Description: Covers bottles, dowsing, lost treasures, detector electronics, underwater treasures and how-to.

793   US   ISSN 1061-4648
G521
TREASURE FOUND. 1991. q. $14 (foreign $23.95). Double Eagle Publishing, 31970 Yucaipa Blvd., Yucaipa, CA 92399. TEL 714-794-4612; 800-545-9364. FAX 714-794-9452. Ed. Jim Williams. adv.; bk.rev.; charts; illus. circ. 45,000.
 Supersedes (1975-1989): Treasure Search - Found; Which was formed by the 1988 merger of: Treasure Found; Treasure Search.
 Description: Contains stories on the treasures found by hunters and the methods that were used for success.

790.13   UK   ISSN 0140-4539
TREASURE HUNTING. 1977. m. £29.15. Sovereign International, Sovereign House, Brentwood, Essex CM14 4SE, England. Ed. Lin Wieland. adv.; bk.rev. circ. 11,415.
 Incorporates: Metal Detecting (ISSN 0142-3215)

TRENI. see TRANSPORTATION — Railroads

591 790.023   US   ISSN 0041-3259
SF456
TROPICAL FISH HOBBYIST. 1952. m. $30. T.F.H. Publications, Inc., One T.F.H. Plaza, Third and Union Aves., Neptune City, NJ 07753. TEL 908-988-8400. FAX 908-988-5466. TELEX 132468 TFH. Ed. Raymond Hunziker. adv.; bk.rev.; charts; illus.; index. circ. 60,000.
 —Faxon; UnCover.
 Description: Covers both freshwater and marine life for both beginners and long-time hobbyists.

790.13   GW   ISSN 0944-5897
TRUCK MODELL. 6/yr. DM.54 (foreign DM.60). Verlag fuer Technik und Handwerk GmbH, Robert-Bosch-Str. 4, 76532 Baden-Baden, Germany. TEL 07221-5087-0. FAX 07221-508752. Ed. Gernot Greiner. **Document type:** consumer publication.

790.13   GW   ISSN 0940-5070
TRUCK TREFF. bi-m. DM.36 (foreign DM.42). Verlag fuer Technik und Handwerk GmbH, Robert-Bosch-Str. 4, 76532 Baden-Baden, Germany. TEL 07221-5087-0. FAX 07221-508752. **Document type:** consumer publication.

795.4   US   ISSN 1041-4258
TUFF STUFF. 1979. m. $29.95 (effective May 1994). Tuff Stuff Publishing, Inc., Box 1637, Glen Allen, VA 23060-0637. TEL 800-394-9445. FAX 804-266-4204. (Subscr. to: Box 1637, Glen Allen, VA 23060) Ed. Ernie White; Pub. James D. Causey. adv. contact: Randy Burton. circ. 170,000.
 Description: For collectors of sports cards and other trading cards.

623.820   US
U S BOAT AND SHIP MODELER. 1987. q. $14. Gallant Models, Inc., 34249 Camino Capistrano, Capistrano Beach, CA 92624. TEL 714-496-5411. FAX 714-496-5427. adv.: B&W page $1075, color page $1625; trim 8 1/4 x 10 7/8. circ. 65,082. **Document type:** consumer publication.
 Description: Delivers detailed construction projects complete with blueprints. Includes product reviews and racing information.

V R; mensile di videoregistrazione creativa. (Video Review) see COMMUNICATIONS — Video

VAN CONVERSION BLUE BOOK. see TRANSPORTATION — Automobiles

790.023   II   ISSN 0042-3238
VELKI; quarterly English magic magazine. 1969. q. Rs.3($1) Joy Dev Ray, 123-2 Acharya Prafulla Chandra Rd., Calcutta 6, India. Ed. Asoke Bose. adv.; illus.

DIE VOLIERE. see BIOLOGY — Ornithology

WARP & WEFT. see TEXTILE INDUSTRIES AND FABRICS

795.4   US   ISSN 0885-9027
WASHINGTON CROSSING CARD COLLECTORS CLUB NEWSLETTER. 1973. m. $7. Washington Crossing Card Collectors Club, Box 39, Washington Crossing, PA 18977. TEL 215-598-7534. Ed. Betty Davis. bk.rev.; cum.index: 1973-1993. circ. 190. (looseleaf format) **Document type:** newsletter.
 Description: Covers the collection of postcards and the subjects pictured on them for adults.

790.132   US   ISSN 0890-0876
G521
WESTERN & EASTERN TREASURES; the no. 1 magazine for the sport of treasure hunting. (Special supplement avail.: Silver & Gold) 1963. m. $19.95. People's Publishing Co., Inc., 5440 Ericson Way, Arcata, CA 95521. TEL 707-822-8442. FAX 707-822-0973. Ed. Rosemary Anderson. circ. 50,000. (back issues avail.) **Document type:** consumer publication.
 Formerly: Western Treasures.
 Description: How-to magazine, containing information on metal detecting techniques, gold prospecting and relic and bottle collecting.

790.13   US
WHERE-TO-SELL-IT DIRECTORY. 1979. irreg., latest 1993. $5.95. Pilot Books, 103 Cooper St., Babylon, NY 11702. TEL 516-422-2225. FAX 516-422-2227. **Document type:** directory.
 Description: Lists dealers and collectors who will buy almost anything by mail. Gives buyer's name and address and describes the products wanted in a wide range of categories.

790.132 917   US
WHO'S WHO IN INDIAN RELICS. 1960. quadrennial. $35. Ben W. Thompson Publishing Co., 1757 W. Adams, St. Louis, MO 63122. TEL 314-822-2409. Ed. Ben W. Thompson. illus. circ. 5,000.

795.4   US
WICHITA POSTCARD CLUB NEWS. 1979. m. $8 (foreign $15). Wichita Postcard Club, Box 780282, Wichita, KS 67278-0282. TEL 316-686-5574. Ed. Hal N. Ottaway. bk.rev: circ. 432. **Document type:** consumer publication.
 Description: Contains articles and news on the hobby of deltiology (postcard collecting), both old and new.

790.13   US   ISSN 0886-3407
WILDFOWL CARVING AND COLLECTING. 1985. q. $29.95. Commonwealth Communications Services, Inc., Cameron and Kelker Sts., Box 1831, Harrisburg, PA 17105. TEL 717-234-5091. FAX 717-234-1359. Ed. Cathy Hart. adv. circ. 10,000.

790.13 799.202   US
WINCHESTER COLLECTOR. 1977. q. $35 (renewal $25). Winchester Arms Collectors Association, Box 6754, Great Falls, MT 59406. TEL 406-761-8948. Ed. Richard Berg. adv.; bk.rev.; index. circ. 2,000.
 Description: Explores the relationship between firearms and American history.

WINE TRADER. see BEVERAGES

790.13   US
WINNING! (BIXBY). 1976. 12/yr. $21. NatCom, Inc., 15115 S. 76 E. Ave., Bixby, OK 74008. TEL 918-366-4441. FAX 918-366-4439. Ed. Lawrence Taylor. adv.: B&W page $2500; adv. contact: Ellie Shimer. bk.rev. circ. 100,000.
Document type: consumer publication.
Formerly: National Reporter.
Description: Guide to winning big money prizes in contests and sweepstakes, lotteries, bingo, slots, and other games of chance.

790.13   US   ISSN 0738-0143
WINNING SWEEPSTAKES NEWSLETTER. 1983. m. $24. Sebell Publishing Company, Inc., 965 Concord St., Box 1468, Framingham, MA 01701. TEL 508-820-1800. Eds. Jeffrey Sklar, Robin Sklar. charts; illus. circ. 100,000. (back issues avail.)
Document type: newsletter.
Description: Analyzes and rates chances of winning sweepstakes.

643   US
WOODWORKER PROJECTS & TECHNIQUES. 1960. bi-m. $20.97. Woodworker, Inc., 274 Riverside Ave., Westport, CT 06880-4823. TEL 203-222-1113. Ed. Chris Dorbandt. adv. circ. 135,000. (back issues avail.) **Indexed:** Ind.How To Do It (1978-).
Formerly: Woodworker (ISSN 0084-1188)

790.13   KO
WORLD FRIENDS. (Text in English) 1966. q. $10. International Friendship Society, C.P.O. Box 100, Seoul 100-601, S. Korea. TEL 02-461-2501. FAX 02-461-2503. Ed. Chung Joo Suh. adv.; illus. circ. 20,000. (also avail. in microform)
Formerly: Friendship.

793.8 791.34   CC
ZAJI YU MOSHU/ACROBATICS AND MAGIC. (Text in Chinese) 1980. bi-m. $16.70. China Acrobatic Artists Association, Wenlian Dalou, 10 Nongzhanguan Nanli, Beijing 100026, People's Republic of China. TEL 5005662. FAX 4018362. (Dist. outside China by: China International Book Trading Corp., P.O. Box 399, Beijing, P.R. China) Ed. Zheng Dexing. adv. contact: Yang Hong. bk.rev.

ZUMBERACKE NOVINE. see *ETHNIC INTERESTS*

625.19   US   ISSN 1047-9333
48 - FT: O SCALE NEWS; journal for 1/4" scale modelers. 1970. bi-m. $18. Gate VI Publishing Co., Box 51, Elmhurst, IL 60126-0051. TEL 708-833-3658. Ed. Dave Crevie. adv.: B&W page $248, color page $372; adv. contact: Tom Nixon. illus.; circ. 2,847 (paid). **Document type:** consumer publication.
Formerly: O Scale News: 48 - Ft. (ISSN 0899-7144)
Description: Contains news of the world of 1/4" scale manufacturers and dealers, product reviews, modeling tips, convention, swap meet and show schedules.

HOBBIES — Abstracting, Bibliographies, Statistics

020.75 011   UK   ISSN 0006-7237
Z990
BOOK COLLECTOR. 1952. q. £26($47) (effective 1993). Collector Ltd., 43 Gordon Sq., London WC1H 0PD, England. TEL 071-388-0846. FAX 071-388-0854. Ed. Nicolas Barker. adv.; bk.rev.; bibl.; illus.; index. (also avail. in microform from KTO; reprint service avail. from KTO) **Indexed:** Artbibl.Mod., Arts & Hum.Cit.Ind., Bk.Rev.Ind. (1965-), Br.Hum.Ind., Child.Bk.Rev.Ind. (1965-), Curr.Cont., Ind.Bk.Rev.Hum., Lib.Lit., Lib.Sci.Abstr., M.L.A.
—BLDSC (2248.009500); Faxon.

DESIGN AND APPLIED ARTS INDEX. see *ART — Abstracting, Bibliographies, Statistics*

790.13   US
DUNGEON ADVENTURES. bi-m. $18. T S R Inc., 201 Sheridan Springs Rd., Box 111, Lake Geneva, WI 53147. TEL 414-248-3625. FAX 414-248-0389. circ. 35,000. **Document type:** consumer publication.

790.13   DK   ISSN 0105-8134
GOER DET SELV INDEKS. 1977. a. DKK 273. Dansk BiblioteksCenter as, Tempovej 7-11, DK-2750 Ballerup, Denmark. TEL 45-44-97-40-00. FAX 45-44-68-24-42.

790.13   US
H I A'S CRAFT & HOBBY INDUSTRY CONSUMER SURVEY (YEAR). 1988. biennial. $400. Hobby Industry Association, 319 E. 54th St., Box 348, Elmwood Park, NJ 07407. TEL 201-794-1133. FAX 201-797-0657. Ed. Susan Brandt. circ. 4,000.
Description: Studies consumer purchase and usage habits concerning crafts and hobbies.

HANDICRAFT - HOBBY INDEX; a current periodical index to doing, making, and building. see *HOW-TO AND DO-IT-YOURSELF — Abstracting, Bibliographies, Statistics*

790.13 016   DK
HOBBYINDEKS FOR BOERNEBIBLIOTEKER. 1974. a. DKK 395. Dansk Bibliotekscenter ab, Tempovej 7-11, DK-2750 Ballerup, Denmark. TEL 45-44-97-40-00. FAX 45-44-68-24-42.

790.1   US
SIZE OF THE CRAFT - HOBBY INDUSTRY SURVEY. 1990. biennial. $500. Hobby Industry Association, 319 E. 54th St., Box 348, Elmwood Park, NJ 07407. TEL 201-794-1133. FAX 201-797-0657. Ed. Susan Brandt. circ. 1,000. (looseleaf format; back issues avail.)
Description: Reported craft-hobby component product sales by retailers and manufacturers, component product purchases by consumer.

HOME ECONOMICS

see also Interior Design and Decoration; Nutrition and Dietetics

640   US   ISSN 0194-7176
A H E A ACTION. 1974. 5/yr. $7.50 to non-members. American Home Economics Association, 1555 King St., Alexandria, VA 22314. TEL 703-706-4600. FAX 703-706-4663. Ed. Marjorie Harter. adv.; illus.; tr.lit. circ. 23,000. (tabloid format; also avail. in microfilm from UMI; reprint service avail. from UMI) —UMI.
Description: Contains organization news plus reviews of legislation and consumer research of interest to the profession.

641.5   IT   ISSN 0394-7181
A TAVOLA. 11/yr. L.61600. Rizzoli Editore-Corriere della Sera, Via A. Rizzoli 2, 20132 Milan, Italy. TEL 02-2588. FAX 2-272-014-85. TELEX 312119 RIZZM I. Ed. Germano Pellizzioni. circ. 70,000.

649
ABOVE RUBIES; a magazine to promote family life. 1977. s-a. donation. Box 351, Antioch, TN 37011. (Alt. addr.: P.O. Box 500, Broadbeach, Qld. 4218, Australia. TEL 075-307-024. FAX 075-307-024) Ed. Nancy Campbell. adv. contact: Val Stares. bk.rev. circ. 150,000. (back issues avail.)
Description: Encourages women in their roles as wives, mothers and home-makers.

640   CN   ISSN 0834-213X
ALBERTA HOME ECONOMICS ASSOCIATION NEWSLETTER. 1967. 4/yr. Can.$10 (foreign Can.$15). Alberta Home Economics Association, 1403 - 105 Ave. S.W., Calgary, AB T2W 0B5, Canada. Ed. Bernie Webb. bk.rev.; index. circ. 550. **Document type:** newsletter.
Formerly: A H E A Newsletter (ISSN 0044-7137)

641.5   US   ISSN 0736-170X
ALMOST FREE COOKBOOKS & RECIPES UPDATE. 1983. a. $4. Update Publicare Co., c/o Prosperity & Profits Unlimited, Box 416, Denver, CO 80201-0416. TEL 303-575-5676. Ed. A. Doyle. adv.; bibl. circ. 1,000. (looseleaf format; also avail. in microfiche) **Document type:** newsletter.

641.5   US
AMERICAN COOKERY.* 1985. bi-m. $30. American Taste, c/o Jean Frey, 7 Park Ave., New York, NY 10016-4330. Ed. Patricia McBride. adv. circ. 20,000.

640   II
ANAND DIGEST. (Text in Hindi) 1981. m. Govind Mitra Rd., Patna 800 004, India. TEL 50341. Ed. S.S. Singh. circ. 55,900.

HOME ECONOMICS   3031

641.5 642.5   IT
APPUNTI DI GASTRONOMIA. 1990. 3/yr. $50 (effective Jan. 1994). Condeco Editore s.r.l., Via Gioberti 5, 20123 Milan, Italy. TEL 02-4988773. FAX 02-4818624. Ed. Claudio Benporat. bk.rev. circ. 500. **Document type:** monographic series.
Description: Covers the history of Italian and European food, cookery and gastronomy.

642   US   ISSN 0895-6200
THE ART OF EATING. 1986. q. $25. Box 242, Peacham, VT 05862. Ed. Edward Behr. bk.rev.
Document type: consumer publication.
Description: In-depth essays on food and occasionally wine.

648   JA
ARURU. 1977. m. 6360 Yen. Shufu-to-Seikatsusha Ltd., 5-7, 3-chome, Kyobashi, Chuo-ku, Tokyo 104, Japan. Ed. Tadashi Matsuda.

THE AUSTRALIAN FAMILY. see *CHILDREN AND YOUTH — About*

AUSTRALIA'S PARENTS. see *CHILDREN AND YOUTH — About*

641.5   UK
B B C GOOD FOOD. 1989. m. £20. (British Broadcasting Corporation) Redwood Publishing Ltd., 101 Bayham St., London NW1 0AG, England. TEL 071-331-8000. FAX 071-331-8001. adv. circ. 491,178.
Description: Publishes recipes from TV and radio programs. Contains features on cookery, seasonal foods, food products, wine, diet and health, kitchen gardening, interviews with personalities and kitchen equipment.

BACK HOME; hands on and down to earth. see *GENERAL INTEREST PERIODICALS — United States*

BACKWOODS HOME MAGAZINE. see *GENERAL INTEREST PERIODICALS — United States*

BACKWOODSMAN. see *HISTORY — History Of North And South America*

640.73   US   ISSN 1053-2021
BARGAIN HUNTERS & BUDGETEERS OPPORTUNITY NEWSLETTER. 1990. biennial. $5. Continnuus, c/o Prosperity & Profits Unlimited, Box 416, Denver, CO 80201-0416. TEL 303-575-5676. Ed. A.C. Doyle. circ. 2,000. (looseleaf format) **Document type:** newsletter.
Description: Tips on saving money.

640   US   ISSN 0897-0386
BEST RECIPES. 1987. bi-m. $14.95. Stauffer Publishing Group, 1503 S.W. 42nd St., Topeka, KS 66609. TEL 913-274-4300. FAX 913-274-4305. Ed. Mike Rafferty. adv.: B&W page $3190; color page 4190; adv. contact: Keith Chartier. circ. 290,000. (back issues avail.)
Formerly: Grit Best Recipes.
Description: Presents simple, easy-to-prepare recipes for the person on the go.

BETTER HOMES AND GARDENS. see *INTERIOR DESIGN AND DECORATION*

641.5   US
BETTER HOMES AND GARDENS CHRISTMAS COOKIES. 1989. a. Meredith Corporation, Special Interest Publications, 1716 Locust St., Des Moines, IA 50309. TEL 515-284-3000. FAX 515-284-2700. Pub. Steve Levinson. adv.: B&W page $13450, color page $18350; trim 8 x 10 1/2; adv. contact: Pat Tomlinson. circ. 700,000.
Description: Contains recipes and tips for all kinds of cookies, plus successful baking advice.

747 200   US   ISSN 0405-6590
BETTER HOMES AND GARDENS CHRISTMAS IDEAS. 1952. a. $3.50. Meredith Corporation, Special Interest Publications, 1716 Locust St., Des Moines, IA 50336. TEL 515-284-3000. Pub. Steve Levinson. adv.: B&W page $22075, color page $29900; adv. contact: Pat Tomlinson. circ. 1,250,000.

HOME ECONOMICS

640 US ISSN 1044-0909
BETTER HOMES AND GARDENS COUNTRY KITCHEN IDEAS. Key Title: Country Kitchen Ideas. 1987. a. $3.50. Meredith Corporation, Special Interest Publications, 1716 Locust St., Des Moines, IA 50336. TEL 515-284-3000. Pub. Steve Levinson. adv.: B&W page $20025, color page $28775; adv. contact: Pat Tomlinson. circ. 450,000. **Document type:** consumer publication.

640 US
BETTER HOMES AND GARDENS DO-IT-YOURSELF. 1968. q. $2.95 per no. Meredith Corporation, Special Interest Publications, 1716 Locust St., Des Moines, IA 50336. TEL 515-284-3000. Pub. Steve Levinson. adv.: B&W page $20025, color page $28775; adv. contact: Pat Tomlinson. circ. 450,000.

BETTER HOMES AND GARDENS GARDEN IDEAS AND OUTDOOR LIVING. see GARDENING AND HORTICULTURE

641.5 US
BETTER HOMES AND GARDENS HOLIDAY APPETIZERS. 1987. a. $3.50 per no. Meredith Corporation, Special Interest Publications, 1716 Locust St., Des Moines, IA 50336. TEL 515-284-3000. Pub. Steve Levinson. adv.: B&W page $13450, color page $18350; adv. contact: Pat Tomlinson. circ. 500,000.

641.5 US
BETTER HOMES AND GARDENS HOLIDAY CELEBRATIONS. a. Meredith Corporation, Special Interest Publications, 1716 Locust St., Des Moines, IA 50336. TEL 515-284-3000. Pub. Steve Levinson. adv.: B&W page $13450, color page $18350; adv. contact: Pat Tomlinson. circ. 750,000.

640 635 US ISSN 0194-0627
BETTER HOMES AND GARDENS HOME PLAN IDEAS. Key Title: Home Plan Ideas. 1973. q. $3.50 per no. Meredith Corporation, Special Interest Publications, 1716 Locust St., Des Moines, IA 50336. TEL 515-284-3000. Pub. Steve Levinson. adv.: B&W page $20025, color page $28775; adv. contact: Pat Tomlinson. circ. 450,000. **Document type:** consumer publication.

BLACK & DECKER BUILD IT. see HOW-TO AND DO-IT-YOURSELF

640 TX633 US ISSN 0006-6990
BON APPETIT. 1956. m. $18. Bon Appetit Publishing Corp. (Subsidiary of: Knapp Communications Corp.), 6300 Wilshire Blvd., Los Angeles, CA 90048. TEL 213-965-3600. (Subscr. to: Box 10776, Des Moines, IA 50340-0776) Ed. William J. Garry. adv.; bk.rev.; illus.; index. circ. 1,294,945. **Indexed:** Access (1978-), CMI, PMR.
—Faxon; UnCover; UMI.
Description: Recipes and features on various cuisines and wines, as well as home entertaining and travel.

640 FR
BONHEUR - LA REVUE DES FAMILLES. 1928. m. E.S.F. Editeur, 17 rue Viete, 75017 Paris, France. adv.; illus.

641 FR ISSN 0006-713X
BONNE CUISINE; a la portee de tous. 1952. m. 125 F. Ami Des Jardins, S.A., 8-10 rue Pierre Brossolette, 92300 Levallois Perret, France. TEL 40-87-40-80. Ed. A. Audinot. adv.; illus. circ. 160,000.
Description: Features French recipes, profiles on well known French chefs.

BRAUT UND BRAEUTIGAM; wissenwertes ueber heiraten und wohnen. see WOMEN'S INTERESTS

641.5 US ISSN 1042-7139
BREAD PUDDING UPDATE. 1989. a. $5 (Canada $7; elsewhere $9). Continnuus, c/o Prosperity & Profits Unlimited, Box 416, Denver, CO 80201-0416. TEL 303-575-5676. Ed. A.C. Doyle. circ. 1,500. (looseleaf format) **Document type:** newsletter.

BRIDES & SETTING UP HOME. see MATRIMONY

640 US
BROOKLYN HOME JOURNAL. q. Brooklyn Journal Publications, Inc., 129 Montague St., Brooklyn, NY 11201. TEL 718-624-6033. FAX 718-875-5302.

647 US
BUENHOGAR. (Editions avail. for Central America, Chile, Colombia, Ecuador, Mexico, Peru, Puerto Rico, U.S., Venezuela) (Text in Spanish) 1966. bi-w. $49.85. Editorial America, S.A., Vanidades Continental Bldg., 6355 N.W. 36th St., Virginia Gardens, FL 33166. TEL 305-871-6400. FAX 305-871-8769. Ed. Nania Julia Ballarin. adv. circ. 150,000.

641.5 IT
BUONA CUCINA.* m. L.2000 per no. Curcio Periodici S.p.A., Via Arno 64, 00198 Rome, Italy. Ed. Rosanna Falconi. adv.; illus. circ. 138,000.

641.5 GW
BURDA MEINE GUTE KUECHE. q. Verlag Aenne Burda, Am Kestendamm 2, 77652 Offenburg, Germany. TEL 0781-8402. Ed. Elisabeth Klapper-Hund. circ. 150,000.

BURDA MODEN (GERMAN EDITION). see CLOTHING TRADE — Fashions

641.5 GW
BURDA WEIHNACHTSBACKEN. a. Verlag Aenne Burda, Am Kestendamm 2, 77652 Offenburg, Germany. TEL 0781-8402. Ed. Elisabeth Klapper-Hund. circ. 280,000.

C O F O FAMILY POLICY REPORT. (Consortium of Family Organizations) see MATRIMONY

C O F O MEMO. (Consortium of Family Organizations) see MATRIMONY

640 CN ISSN 0008-3763
CANADIAN HOME ECONOMICS JOURNAL/REVUE CANADIENNE D'ECONOMIE FAMILIALE. 1951. q. Can.$35 to individuals (US Can.$40, elsewhere Can.$44); institutions Can.$50 (US Can.$55, elsewhere Can.$59). Canadian Home Economics Association, Burnside Bldg. Suite 901, 151 Slater St., Ottawa, ON K1P 5H3, Canada. TEL 613-238-8817. FAX 613-238-1677. Ed. Glenda Everett. adv.: B&W page Can.$470, color page Can.$1345; trim 8 1/8 x 10 7/8. bk.rev.; abstr.; illus.; index, cum.index; circ. 3,100 (controlled). (also avail. in microform from UMI,MML; reprint service avail. from UMI, MML) **Indexed:** Can.Per.Ind., CMI, Nutr.Abstr., P.A.I.S., Potato Abstr. **Document type:** academic/scholarly publication.
—BLDSC (3027.380000); Faxon; UnCover; UMI. CCC.
Description: Articles on home management, including food, nutrition, clothing, education, and family studies.

640 CN
CANADIAN HOUSE & HOME. 1982. 8/yr. Can.$26. Canadian Home Publishers, 511 King St., W., Ste. 120, Toronto, ON M5V 2Z4, Canada. TEL 416-593-6310. FAX 416-591-1630. Ed. Cobi Ladner; Pub. Lynda Reeves. adv.; bk.rev. circ. 110,700. (back issues avail.) **Document type:** consumer publication.
Formerly: House & Home.
Description: Covers interior decorating, do-it-yourself projects.

640 US ISSN 0008-5510
CANDLE (MACOMB). 1915. s-a. $10 for 3 yrs. Phi Upsilon Omicron, Inc., 13545 N. 1050 Rd., Macomb, IL 61455. TEL 309-837-1794. Ed. Colleen Carlson. bk.rev.; illus. circ. 20,000. **Document type:** academic/scholarly publication.

643 IT
CASA & GIARDINO. 1966. m. (10/yr.). L.63000 (foreign L.119000) (effective 1994). Casa & Giardino Editrice s.r.l., Via Filippo Tommaso Marinetti 3, 20127 Milan, Italy. TEL 02-26140371. FAX 02-2826011. Ed. Paolo Arione. adv.: B&W page L.10500000, color page L.12000000; trim 240 x 312. circ. 73,200.
Formerly: Casa, Arredamento e Giardino (ISSN 0576-8519).
Description: For middle class families and the building and design sector.

CENTER FOR SELF-SUFFICIENCY UPDATE. see EDUCATION — Adult Education

CHEF. see FOOD AND FOOD INDUSTRIES

CHERITH. see WOMEN'S INTERESTS

640 US ISSN 1069-7985
CHILE PEPPER; spicy world cuisine. 1987. bi-m. $18.95. Out West Publishing (Albuquerque), 5106 Grand Ave., N.E., Box 4278, Albuquerque, NM 87110. TEL 505-266-8322. FAX 505-266-2127. Ed. Dave DeWitt. adv.; bk.rev. circ. 80,000. (back issues avail.) **Document type:** consumer publication.
Former titles (until Jan. 1990): Whole Chile Pepper (ISSN 0898-0020); Whole Chile Pepper Catalog.
Description: Covers spicy food cooking worldwide. Includes recipes and information on new food products for consumers.

640 US
CHRISTMAS HELPS & HOLIDAY BAKING. 1954. a. $2.95. New York Times Women's Magazines, Special Interest Publications, 110 Fifth Ave., 7th Fl., New York, NY 10011. TEL 212-463-1124. Ed. Sally Koslow. adv.; bk.rev.; index. circ. 1,200,0000. (back issues avail.) **Document type:** consumer publication.
Formerly: Family Circle Great Ideas Christmas Helps and Holiday Baking.
Description: Includes recipes, menus, plans and ideas, as well as elegant and innovative craft projects at all skill levels.

641.5 US
CLASSIC PILLSBURY COOKBOOKS. 1979. m. $24.95. Pillsbury Company, 200 S. Sixth St., M.S. 28M7, Minneapolis, MN 55402. TEL 612-330-4475. adv.: color page $11995; trim 5 5/8 x 9 1/4; adv. contact: Nancy Jones. illus. circ. 527,363. **Document type:** consumer publication.
Description: Contains a variety of recipes.

CLASSIC RANGES; parts, services, restoration, sales. see HOBBIES

641.5 CN
CLUB KNORR A LA CARTE JOURNAL. (Text in English, French) 1989. q. Can.$12.95 membership. (Best Foods Canada) Pierce Communications, 56 Scollard St., Toronto, ON M5R 1E9, Canada. TEL 416-961-5328. FAX 416-961-4251. Eds. Lynn Kahrkling, Margaret Swaine. circ. 5,000.
Description: Includes recipes, seasonal entertaining ideas and cooking tips.

640 SP
COMER Y BEBER. 1963. m. $96.92. H Y M S.A., Aribau 28, 08011 Barcelona, Spain. TEL 3237063. FAX 4541322. Ed. Jaime Beltran Solano. adv.; abstr.; illus.; tr.lit.; index. circ. 240,937.
Formerly: Cocina y Hogar (ISSN 0045-7248)

640 US
THE COMMUNIQUE (INDEPENDENCE).* s-a. National Association of Extension Home Economists, 2820 M 291 Frontage Rd., Independence, MO 64057-1214.

CONNECTICUT FAMILY; the magazine just for the Fairfield County parent. see CHILDREN AND YOUTH — About

CONSUMER - FARMER COOPERATOR. see HOUSING AND URBAN PLANNING

640 US ISSN 0010-826X
COOKBOOK DIGEST. 1978. bi-m. $21 (foreign $31). Grass Roots Publishing Co., Inc., 950 Third Ave., 16th Fl., New York, NY 10022. (Subscr. to: Box 7532, Red Oak, IA 51591-0532) Ed. Andrea DiNoto. adv. circ. 100,000.

641.5 US
▼**COOKBOOK REVIEW.** 1992. bi-m. $24 to individuals; institutions & libraries $37. 60 Kinnaird St., Cambridge, MA 02139. TEL 617-868-8857. Ed. Lise Stern. bk.rev.
Description: Presents author interviews and other food-related news. Contains sample tested recipes.

641.86 US
COOKIES; a newsletter devoted to cookies and cookie shaping. 1972. bi-m. $9. 5426 27th St., N.W., Washington, DC 20015. TEL 202-966-0869. Ed. Phyllis Wetherhill. bk.rev.; bibl.; illus. (back issues avail.) **Document type:** newsletter.
Description: For all cooks, from home bakers to food researchers. Includes recipes.

COOKING CONTEST CHRONICLE. see *FOOD AND FOOD INDUSTRIES*

641.1 641.5   US   ISSN 0886-4446
COOKING LIGHT; the magazine of food and fitness. 1987. 7/yr. $18 (effective 1993). Southern Progress, Corp., c/o H. Johnson, V.P. Circulation, 2100 Lakeshore Dr., Birmingham, AL 35209. TEL 205-877-6000. (Subscr. to: Box 830549, Birmingham, AL 35283) Ed. Douglas Crichton. adv.; bk.rev. circ. 1,100,000.
—UMI.
    Description: Presents articles on food, nutrition, and exercise implementing a positive approach to a healthier lifestyle. Moderation, variety, and balance emphasized.

CORDIALITY. see *GENERAL INTEREST PERIODICALS — United States*

COUNTRY ACCENTS. see *INTERIOR DESIGN AND DECORATION — Furniture And House Furnishings*

747   US
COUNTRY ALMANAC. 1981. q. $14.97. Harris Publications, Inc., 1115 Broadway, 8th fl., New York, NY 10010. TEL 212-807-7100. FAX 212-627-4678. Ed. Jack C. Davis. adv. circ. 400,000.

COUNTRY DECORATING IDEAS. see *INTERIOR DESIGN AND DECORATION*

COUNTRY GARDEN. see *AGRICULTURE*

COUNTRY HOME. see *INTERIOR DESIGN AND DECORATION*

COUNTRY HOMES & INTERIORS. see *INTERIOR DESIGN AND DECORATION*

COUNTRYSIDE AND SMALL STOCK JOURNAL. see *GENERAL INTEREST PERIODICALS — United States*

640   JA
CROISSANT. (Text in Japanese) 1977. bi-w. Magazine House, 3-13-10, Ginza, Chuo-ku, Tokyo 104, Japan. TEL 03-3545-7100. FAX 03-3546-0034. Ed. Noriko Noshimori. circ. 600,000.

640   HU   ISSN 0865-0047
CSALADI HAZ. 1989. bi-m. $15 (effective 1993). Kultura, P.O. Box 149, 1389 Budapest 62, Hungary. TEL 361-180-31-94. FAX 361-180-33-06. TELEX 20-2855 KULT H. Ed. Koszo Jozsef.

642   IT
LA CUCINA ITALIANA. 1929. m. L.66000 (foreign L.135000). Editrice Quadratum S.p.A., Piazza Aspromonte, 13-A, 20131 Milan, Italy. TEL 02-706421. FAX 02-70638544. Ed. Paola Ricas. adv. circ. 152,000.

642   IT   ISSN 1120-2009
CUCINA NATURALE. 1988. m. (11/yr.). L.60000 (effective 1993). Zanfi Editori s.r.l., Via Emilia Ovest 954, ang. Via T. Livio 1, 41100 Modena, Italy. TEL 059-891700. FAX 059-891701.
    Description: Promotes natural foods.

642   FR   ISSN 0989-3091
CUISINE ACTUELLE. 1987. m. Prisma Presse, 6 rue Daru, 75008 Paris, France. TEL 44-15-30-00. FAX 47-64-10-42. Ed. Irene Karsenty. adv.; illus. circ. 509,000. Document type: consumer publication.
    Description: Covers regional gastronomic specialties, cookware tests, basic and complex recipes, and wine selection and serving.

CUOCO. see *HOTELS AND RESTAURANTS*

640   NE   ISSN 0011-8370
DENKEN EN DOEN. 1913. m. fl.43.40. (Nederlandse Vereniging van Huisvrouwen) Bosch en Keuning N.V., Box 1, Baarn, Netherlands. Ed. Wilma ter Gast-Verwoest. adv.; bk.rev.; illus. circ. 61,000.

687   BL   ISSN 0021-7301
DESFILE. 1969. m. $42. Bloch Editores S.A., Rua do Russell 766-804, 20210-000 Rio de Janeiro, RJ, Brazil. TEL 021-5554000. FAX 021-2059998. TELEX 2121525 BLOC. Ed. Roberto Barreira. adv. circ. 120,000. Document type: consumer publication.
    Formerly: Joia.
    Description: Covers fashions, cooking, beauty and aesthetics.

640   US
DESSERTS!. q. $9.95. House of White Birches Publishing, 306 E. Parr Rd., Berne, IN 46711. TEL 219-589-8741. FAX 219-589-8093. Ed. Judi K. Merkel. Document type: consumer publication.
    Description: Includes recipes for cakes, cookies, pies, puddings, pastries and more.

640   NE   ISSN 0165-3032
DOEHETZELF. Cover title: Doe Het Zelf - Woonideeen. 1957. m. fl.69. Uitgeverij Spaarnestad B.V., Europalaan 93, 3526 KP Utrecht, Netherlands. TEL 030-822577. FAX 030-898388. Ed. J. Hoffmans. adv. circ. 142,000. Document type: consumer publication.

641.86   IT
DOLCI; per tutte le occasioni. m. (11/yr.). L.28000 (effective 1993). Zanfi Editori s.r.l., Via Emilia Ovest 954, ang. Via T. Livio 1, 41100 Modena, Italy. TEL 059-891700. FAX 059-891701. Document type: consumer publication.
    Description: Covers how-to for desserts and cakes.

EATING WELL; the magazine of food & health. see *NUTRITION AND DIETETICS*

640 677   AT
ECHO. 1976. s-a. membership. Victorian Home Economics & Textiles Teachers Association, 3 Windsor Ave., Mount Waverely, Vic. 3149, Australia. TEL 03-888-2240. bk.rev.; index. circ. 800.

640
ECHO NEWS. 1960. 8/yr. membership. Victorian Home Economics and Textiles Teacher's Association, 3 Winsor Ave., Mount Waverley, Vic. 3149, Australia. TEL 03-888-2240. bibl. circ. 1,100. (back issues avail.)

640   FR   ISSN 0397-8389
ECONOMIE FAMILIALE/HOME ECONOMICS. (Text in English, French, German) q. 80 F. International Federation for Home Economics, 5 av. de la Porte Brancion, 75015 Paris, France. bk.rev.; illus.
    Continues: International Federation for Home Economics - Federation Internationale pour l'Economie Familiale. Bulletin.

643   US   ISSN 0883-2811
TX1
EDUCATORS GUIDE TO FREE HOME ECONOMICS MATERIALS. 1984. a. $24.95. Educators Progress Service, Inc., 214 Center St., Randolph, WI 53956. TEL 414-326-3126. FAX 414-326-3127. Ed. Kathleen Suttles Nehmer.
    Description: Covers free films, filmstrips, slides, tapes and printed materials.

640   FI   ISSN 0013-6522
EMANTALEHTI. 1902. m. FIM 100. Marttaliitto r.y., Uudenmaank. 24, 00120 Helsinki, Finland. FAX 358-0-6801266. Ed. Maija Riihijarvi-Samuel. adv.; bk.rev.; illus.; index. circ. 30,200. Document type: consumer publication.

ENVIRONMENTAL NUTRITION; the newsletter of diet, nutrition and health. see *NUTRITION AND DIETETICS*

ESPECIALES TEENAGER INTERNACIONAL. see *CLOTHING TRADE — Fashions*

ESSEN UND TRINKEN. see *FOOD AND FOOD INDUSTRIES*

ESSENTIALS. see *WOMEN'S INTERESTS*

641.5   IT
EUROPA A TAVOLA. m. L.60000 (foreign L.120000). Valentini Editore s.r.l., 19 Via Fabbio Filzi, 20124 Milan, Italy. TEL 02-6696471. FAX 02-6697083. TELEX 330299 VALEDI I. Ed. Aldo Quinto Lazzari.

EVA. see *WOMEN'S INTERESTS*

EXTENSION CONNECTION. see *AGRICULTURE*

F S A WASHINGTON MEMO. (Family Service America, Inc.) see *MATRIMONY*

LA FAMILIA DE HOY. see *ETHNIC INTERESTS*

640   US   ISSN 0014-7206
AP2   CODEN: FACIBO
FAMILY CIRCLE. 1932. 17/yr. $15.98 (foreign $31.98). Family Circle, Inc. (Subsidiary of: New York Times Company, Inc.), 110 Fifth Ave., New York, NY 10011. TEL 212-463-1000. FAX 212-463-1553. (Subscr. to: Box 3156, Harlan, IA 51593-0347. TEL 800-627-4444) Ed. Susan Ungaro. adv.; illus. circ. 5,000,000. (also avail. in microfilm) Indexed: Access (1975-), Consum.Ind., Curr.Lit.Fam.Plan., Ind.How To Do It (1978-1984), MELSA.
—UnCover; UMI.
    Description: Covers women's home interests: fashion, cooking, decorating, parenting, and family travel.

640   UK
FAMILY CIRCLE. 1964. m. £14($55.90) I P C Magazines, Southbank Publishing Group (Subsidiary of: Reed International PLC), King's Reach Tower, Stamford St., London SE1 9LS, England. TEL 071-261-6195. FAX 0444-440619. TELEX 892084 REEDBP G. (Dist. by: Quadrant Subscription Services, Oakfield House, Perrymount Rd., Haywards Heath, W. Sussex RH16 3DH, England. TEL 0444-440421) Ed. Gilly Batterbee. adv. contact: Hayley Allan. circ. 843,104. Indexed: Consum.Ind. Document type: consumer publication.

747 640   US   ISSN 0163-1306
TX1
FAMILY CIRCLE'S GREAT IDEAS. (Each edition covers a different topic) 1975. 7/yr. $2.50 per no. Family Circle, Inc. (Subsidiary of: New York Times Company, Inc.), 110 Fifth Ave., New York, NY 10011. TEL 212-463-1636. adv. (back issues avail.)

FAMILY ECONOMICS REVIEW. see *CONSUMER EDUCATION AND PROTECTION*

640 051   US
FAMILY MAGAZINE. q. Minority Press Association, 5121 Parallel Parkway, Ste. 9, Kansas City, KS 66104. TEL 913-596-1007. Ed. Samuel F. Jordan.

FAMILY PERSPECTIVE. see *SOCIOLOGY*

FAMILY SAFETY & HEALTH. see *PUBLIC HEALTH AND SAFETY*

649   US   ISSN 1056-9243
FAMILY TIMES (EAU CLAIRE); the newspaper for Chippewa Valley parents. 1990. 6/yr. $9. Family Times Publishing, Box 932, Eau Claire, WI 54702. TEL 715-836-9306. Ed. Ann Gorton. adv.; bk.rev. circ. 15,000. Document type: newspaper.
    Description: Carries articles, art, photos, and reviews about parenting issues. Focuses on west central Wisconsin.

641.5   US   ISSN 1052-3898
FARE SHARE, THE FOOD LETTER AND COOKBOOK NEWS. 1983. bi-m. $15.50 (effective Jan. 1991). Fare Share Co., 4709 Weyhill Dr., Arlington, TX 76013. TEL 817-457-2273. Ed. Gail Curnutt. adv.; bk.rev.; index. circ. 5,000. (looseleaf format; back issues avail.)
    Incorporates: Fare Share's Cookbook News.
    Description: Features good home cooking and extends the time-honored country tradition of sharing food ideas and regional cookbooks.

FARMERS AND CONSUMERS MARKET BULLETIN. see *AGRICULTURE*

FASHION POETRY PATTERNS & RECITALS NEWS. see *WOMEN'S INTERESTS*

648   SW   ISSN 0345-326X
FASTIGHETSFOLKET. 1933. 11/yr. SEK 100. Fastighetsanstaelldas Foerbund, P.O. Box 70446, 107 25 Stockholm, Sweden. FAX 08-205989. Ed. Hans Hjaelte. adv.; bk.rev. circ. 42,000.
    Formerly (until 1966): Fastighetsarbetaren.

640   US
FAVORITE BRAND NAME RECIPES. m. $2.50 per no. Publications International, Ltd., 7373 N. Cicero Ave., Lincolnwood, IL 60646. TEL 708-676-3470. FAX 708-676-3671.
    Formerly: Favorite Recipes.

640   FR   ISSN 0014-9934
FEMMES AU VILLAGE. 1952. m. 10 F. Organisakous Agricole, 30 rue Paul Ligneul, 72000 Le Mans, France. Ed. Gabriel Lantin. adv.; charts; illus.; stat.; tr.lit. circ. 20,000.

HOME ECONOMICS

640   US   ISSN 1072-5121
▼**FINE COOKING**; for people who love to cook. 1994. 6/yr. $26 (effective 1994). Taunton Press, Inc., 63 S. Main St., Box 5506, Newtown, CT 06470-5506. TEL 203-426-8171. FAX 203-426-3434. Ed. Martha Holmberg. adv. contact: Tom Leihbacher. bk.rev.; illus. **Document type:** consumer publication.
    Description: Presents new ideas, recipes, cooking techniques and advice for enthusiastic home cooks. Covers cooking fundamentals, ingredients, specialty equipment, exotic menus and familiar dishes.

640   US   ISSN 1040-9467
FIRST FOR WOMEN. 1989. 17/yr. $27. Bauer Publishing Company, L.P., 270 Sylvan Ave., Box 1649, Englewood Cliffs, NJ 07632-2513. TEL 201-569-6699. Ed. Jane Traulsen. adv. circ. 1,500,000.
    Description: Features fashion, food, health and fitness, and things to do and make around the house.

FOOD & WINE. see *FOOD AND FOOD INDUSTRIES*

640   US   ISSN 1054-0768
FOOD FREE OR CHEAP NEWSLETTER. 1990. biennial. $7.50. Continnuus, c/o Prosperity & Profits Unlimited, Box 416, Denver, CO 80201-0416. TEL 303-575-5676. Ed. A. Doyle. circ. 5,000. (looseleaf format) **Document type:** newsletter.

FOOD NEWS FOR CONSUMERS. see *CONSUMER EDUCATION AND PROTECTION*

643   IT
FORME. (Supplement avail.: Speciale Forme) 1962. bi-m. L.50000 (foreign L.130000). Luigi Massoni, Editore & C. S.r.l., Via G. Cermenate 37, 22072 Cermenate, Como, Italy. TEL 031-772932. Ed. Francesco Massoni. adv. circ. 60,000.
    Former titles: Forme Selezione; Forme.
    Description: Forum devoted to Italian and foreign manufactures of gift articles, ornaments and articles for the home. Includes articles on the design and marketing of these products. Distributed to Italian and foreign tradesmen.

640   GW   ISSN 0016-1187
FREUNDIN; Leben im jungen Stil. 1948. fortn. $120. Burda Verlag GmbH, Postfach 1230, 77602 Offenburg, Germany. TEL 089-9250-0. FAX 089-92503519. (U.S. dist.: GLP International, 153 S. Dean St., Englewood, NJ 07631. TEL 201-871-1010. FAX 201-871-0870) Ed. Elisabeth Baer. adv.; bk.rev.; illus.; index. circ. 850,000. **Document type:** consumer publication.

640   JA
FUJIN GAHO/WOMEN'S GRAPHIC. (Text in Japanese) 1905. m. 10600 Yen. Fujin Gaho Sha, 9-1, 2-chome, Nishi-Shinbashi, Minato-ku, Tokyo, Japan. Ed. Tetsu Uchida.

FUJIN NO TOMO/WOMEN'S FRIEND. see *EDUCATION — Adult Education*

640   JA
FUKUI UNIVERSITY. FACULTY OF EDUCATION. MEMOIRS. SERIES 4: APPLIED SCIENCE AND HOME ECONOMICS. (Text in Japanese; summaries in English, Japanese) 1964. a. Fukui University, Faculty of Education, 9-1, 3-chome, Bunkyo, Fukui 910, Japan.

GASTRONOMIE & TOURISME. see *TRAVEL AND TOURISM*

GESTGJAFINN. see *FOOD AND FOOD INDUSTRIES*

640   UK
GIROSCOPE; Girobank's magazine for customers. 1972. s-a. free. (National Girobank) B.P.C.C. Consumer Magazines, Athene House, 66-73 Shoe Lane, London EC4P 4AB, England. Ed. Ned Halley. adv.; bk.rev. circ. 1,000,000.

646   UK
GLOSS MAGAZINE. 1985. m. £12. Gloss Ltd., Baltic Chambers, 50 Wellington St., Glasgow G2 6HJ, Scotland. TEL 041-221-2658. FAX 041-204-3655. Ed. Loraine Chassels. adv.; bk.rev. circ. 80,000. (back issues avail.)
    Description: Scottish women's-interest magazine including fashion, homeliving, leisure and style.

640   GW
GLUECKLICH LEBEN; Elektro- und Rezeptkalender. 1953. a. DM.9. Energie-Verlag GmbH, Haeusserstr. 36, 69115 Heidelberg, Germany. TEL 06221-90130. FAX 06221-901341. Ed. Rosel Heller. circ. 700,000. (looseleaf format) **Document type:** bulletin.

051   US   ISSN 0017-209X
TX1
GOOD HOUSEKEEPING. 1885. m. $17.97 (foreign $39.97). Hearst Corporation, Good Housekeeping, 959 Eighth Ave., New York, NY 10019. TEL 212-649-2200. FAX 212-265-3307. (Subscr. to: C.D.S., 1901 Bell Ave., Des Moines, IA 50315. TEL 800-888-7788) Ed. John Mack Carter. adv.; bk.rev.; illus. circ. 5,028,000. (also avail. in microfiche from UMI; reprint service avail. from UMI) Indexed: Abr.R.G., CINAHL, Consum.Ind., Hlth.Ind., Ind.How To Do It (1978-), Mag.Ind., MELSA, PMR, R.G., TOM. **Document type:** consumer publication.
—Faxon; UnCover.
    Description: Magazine covering women's issues with emphasis on home, family life, food, health, beauty, personalities, and social issues.

641.5   IT   ISSN 0017-2561
GOURMET CLUB.* 1967. m. (10/yr.). L.1200 per no. Via G. Di Vittorio 32, 20094 Corsico, Italy. adv.

641.5   GW
GOURMETIP INTERNATIONAL. 1988. q. DM.35. Druck und Verlag, Ohlenschlagerstr. 6, 81369 Munich, Germany. TEL 089-783071. FAX 089-7809928. circ. 120,000. (back issues avail.)

641.5   SP
GUIA COCINA. w. Rocafort 104, 08015 Barcelona, Spain. TEL 93-2233191. Dir. Alicia Villoldo de Botana.

641.5   IT
GUIDACUCINA. 1981. w. L.52000 (foreign L.85200). Arnoldo Mondadori Editore S.p.A., Casella Postale 1772, 20090 Segrate (Milan), Italy. TEL 3199345. Ed. Edvige Bernasconi. adv. circ. 160,000.

642   FR   ISSN 0767-8177
GUIDE CUISINE. 1983. m. Prisma Presse, 6 rue Daru, 75008 Paris, France. TEL 44-15-30-00. FAX 47-64-10-42. Ed. Irene Karsenty. adv.; illus. circ. 256,000. **Document type:** consumer publication.
    Description: Devoted to practical and gourmet cuisine. Offers 4 weeks of menus every month.

640   GW   ISSN 0017-582X
GUTER RAT. m. Verlag fuer die Frau GmbH, Friedrich-Ebert-Str. 76-78, 04109 Leipzig, Germany. TEL 0341-71790. FAX 0341-282588. Ed. Rainer Bieling; Pub. Elisabeth Baer. adv. contact: Walter Krey. bk.rev.; charts; illus. circ. 147,484. **Document type:** consumer publication.

640   GW
H T W PRAXIS. (Hauswirtschaft Textilarbeit Werken) 1948. m. DM.78.60. R. Oldenbourg Verlag GmbH, Rosenheimer Str. 145, 81671 Munich, Germany. TEL 089-4112-0. FAX 089-4112207. TELEX 529296-ROVER. (Subscr. to: Postfach 801360, 81613 Munich, Germany) Eds. I. Bruckert, M.-A. Kupka. adv.; bk.rev.; index. circ. 4,100. (back issues avail.) **Document type:** trade publication.
    Formerly: Handarbeiten und Hauswirtschaft (ISSN 0176-7437)

640   GW   ISSN 0017-8454
HAUSWIRTSCHAFT UND WISSENSCHAFT. (Text in German; summaries in English, German) 1961. 6/yr. DM.80. (Deutsche Gesellschaft fuer Hauswirtschaft e.V.) Schneider Verlag Hohengehren GmbH, Wilhelmstr. 13, 73666 Baltmannsweiler, Germany. TEL 07153-41206. FAX 07153-48761. adv.; bk.rev.; abstr.; illus.; stat.; index. circ. 1,800. **Document type:** academic/scholarly publication.

640   GW   ISSN 0342-5088
HAUSWIRTSCHAFTLICHE BILDUNG. q. DM.65. Schneider Verlag Hohengehren GmbH, Wilhelmstr. 13, 73666 Baltmannsweiler, Germany. TEL 07153-41206. FAX 07153-48761. Ed. Rainer Schneider. Indexed: Dok.Arbeitsmed. **Document type:** academic/scholarly publication.
—CCC.

640 747   GW
HEIM UND HOBBY; Magazin fuer Heimwerker. 1957. bi-m. DM.36. Gert Wohlfarth GmbH Verlag Fachtechnik und Mercator-Verlag, Stresemannstr. 20-22, 47051 Duisburg, Germany. TEL 0203-30527-0. FAX 0203-336675. Ed. Wolfgang Metzmacher. circ. 78,000. **Document type:** consumer publication.
    Formerly: Kluger Mann Baut Selbst.

640   SW   ISSN 0018-0254
HEM OCH SAMHAELLE; Husmoderfoerbundets tidskrift. 1926. 4/yr. SEK 50 (effective 1993). Husmodersfoerbundet, P.O. Box 19109, Surbrunnsgatan 42, S-104 32 Stockholm, Sweden. TEL 46-8-612-28-20. FAX 46-8-612-72-14. Ed. Birgit Tyreus.
    Former titles (until 1970): Husmodersfoerbundets Tidskrift; (until 1953): Husmodersfoerbundets Medlemsblad; (until Sept. 1928): S.H.R.s Tidskrift; (until Jan. 1928): Husmodersfoerbundets Medlemsblad.

640   SW   ISSN 0018-0327
HEMMETS JOURNAL. 1921. w. SEK 652. Hemmets Journal AB, S-21205 Malmoe, Sweden. Ed. Janne Walles. adv.; film rev.; illus. circ. 300,000. (also avail. in audio cassette)
    Incorporates (in 1987): Saxons.

640 375   DK   ISSN 0106-0279
HJEMKUNDSKAB (HVALSOE).* Variant title: Hjemkundskab (Horsens). 1973. 10/yr. DKK 100. Hjemkundskabslaererforeningen, Horsens, Denmark. Ed. Marianne Schioett. adv.; bk.rev. circ. 3,100.
    Formerly (until 1978): Skolekoekkenet.

640 613.7   JA   ISSN 0386-4901
Q77
HOKKAIDO KYOIKU DAIGAKU KIYO. DAI-2-BU, C. KATEI, TAIIKU- HEN/HOKKAIDO UNIVERSITY OF EDUCATION. JOURNAL. SECTION 2 C. HOME ECONOMICS, TEACHER TRAINING FOR SCHOOL HEALTH AND PHYSICAL EDUCATION. vol.32, 1982. s-a. exchange basis. Hokkaido University of Education - Hokkaido Kyoiku Daigaku, Ainosato 5-jo, 3-chome, Kita-ku, Sapporo 002, Hokkaido, Japan.

HOME AND COUNTRY. see *WOMEN'S INTERESTS*

641   UK   ISSN 0965-366X
HOME COOKING. 1974. m. Argus Specialist Publications Ltd., Argus House, Boundary Way, Hemel Hempstead, Herts. HP2 7ST, England. TEL 0442-66551. FAX 0442-66998. (Subscr. to: Argus Subscription Services, Queensway House, 2 Queensway, Redhill, Surrey, England. TEL 0737-768611) adv.; bk.rev. **Document type:** consumer publication.
    Formerly (until 1992): Home and Freezer Digest (ISSN 0305-8751); Which incorporates: Your Home and Freezer.
    Description: Covers all culinary matters concerning food and drink, including diet and nutrition, and features kitchen product reviews.

640   US   ISSN 1071-4782
HOME COOKING. 1973. m. $9.95. House of White Birches Publishing, 306 E. Parr Rd., Berne, IN 46711. TEL 219-589-8741. Ed. Judi Merkel. adv.; bk.rev.; charts; illus. circ. 55,364. (back issues avail.) **Document type:** consumer publication.
    Formerly: Women's Circle Home Cooking (ISSN 0195-2439)
    Description: Contains 1,000 recipes each year, swaps, contests, low-budget meal ideas and foreign, exotic dishes.

HOME DECOR. see *PAINTS AND PROTECTIVE COATINGS*

640 641.1   AT
HOME ECONOMICS ASSOCIATION OF VICTORIA. NEWSLETTER. 1927. q. Aus.$40. Home Economics Association of Victoria, P.O. Box 143, Carlton South, Vic. 3058, Australia. bk.rev. circ. 250.

HOME ECONOMICS EDUCATOR. see *EDUCATION*

HOME ECONOMICS

640   AT
HOME ECONOMICS INSTITUTE OF AUSTRALIA. JOURNAL. 1969. 4/yr. Aus.$35. Home Economics Institute of Australia Inc., Q U T, Kelvin Grove Campus, Locked Bad No. 2, Red Hill, Qld., 4059, Australia. TEL 07-864-3522. FAX 07-864-3369. Eds. Jan Reynolds, Donna Pendergast. adv.; bk.rev. circ. 1,000. **Document type:** bulletin.
    Formerly: Home Economics Association of Australia. Journal (ISSN 0158-6912)
    Description: Reflects at national and international levels, the knowledge, skills and processes relevant to the discipline of home economics and allied fields.

640   US   ISSN 0046-7774
TX1   CODEN: HERSA
HOME ECONOMICS RESEARCH JOURNAL. 1972. q. $45 to individuals; institutions $80 (effective 1994). (American Home Economics Association) Sage Publications, Inc., 2455 Teller Rd., Thousand Oaks, CA 91320. TEL 805-499-0721. FAX 805-706-0871. (Subscr. to: Sage Publications, Inc., Box 5084, Thousand Oaks, CA 91359; Overseas subscr. to: Sage Publications, Ltd., 6 Bonhill St., London EC2 4PU, England; Sage Publications India Pvt. Ltd., P.O. Box 4215, New Delhi 110 048, India) Ed. Rodney Cate. adv.; bk.rev.; charts; illus.; stat.; index. circ. 2,300. (also avail. in microform from UMI; reprint service avail. from UMI) **Indexed:** Art & Archaeol.Tech.Abstr., C.I.J.E., Child Devel.Abstr., Ergon.Abstr., Mid.East: Abstr.& Ind., Nutr.Abstr., Psychol.Abstr., Text.Tech.Dig. **Document type:** academic/scholarly publication.
—BLDSC (4326.034000); Faxon; UnCover; SWETS; UMI.
    Incorporates (1962-1991): Titles of Dissertations and Theses Completed in Home Economics (ISSN 0082-4534)
    Description: Presents scholarly articles on a variety of issues and research in home economics.

640   UK   ISSN 0261-1384
HOME ECONOMIST JOURNAL. 1981. q. £21 (foreign £25). Institute of Home Economics, Hobart House, 40 Grosvenor Pl., London SW1X 7AE, England. TEL 071-823-1109. (Dist. by: I O P Ltd., 7 Great Western Way, Bristol BS1 6HE, England) Ed. Frances Vines. adv.; bk.rev.; index. circ. 2,200. **Document type:** academic/scholarly publication.
—BLDSC (4326.040400). CCC.
    Description: Publishes original scientific papers on home economics, including food, textiles, fuel and energy, home management, design marketing, health, and social issues.
    Refereed Serial

640   JA
HOME GRAPHIC/KATEI-GAHO. (Text in Japanese) 1958. m. 10560 Yen. Sekai Bunka Publishing Inc., 2-29, 4-chome, Kudan-Kita, Chiyoda-ku, Tokyo 102, Japan. Ed. Mamoru Tsuchiya.

647   UK
HOME QUARTERLY; a review of policies as seen from the home. 1947. q. £8. Home Publications, Bodifyr, off Lonpobty, Bangor, Gwynedd LL57 1HT, Wales. TEL 0248-3629634. (Subscr. to: Bloomfield Books, 26 Meadow Lane, Sudbury, Suffolk CO10 6TD, England) Ed. E.S. Dobbs.
    Formerly: Housewives Today.
    Description: A review of policy affecting home and family, supporting the family in its traditional role in society.

640   UK
HOMEC - HOME ECONOMICS YEARBOOK. 1981. a. £7.50. Maypole Press Ltd., The Tower, 10 Blackall Ind. Estate, South Woodham Ferrers, Chelmsford, Essex CM3 5UW, England. TEL 0245-323130. FAX 0245-323466. Ed. James Robinson. adv.; bk.rev. circ. 3,000.
    Formerly: Home Economics Yearbook.

HOMEMAKERS NETWORK NEWSLETTER. see WOMEN'S INTERESTS

640   CN   ISSN 0018-4209
HOMEMAKERS'S MAGAZINE/MADAME AU FOYER. (Text in English and French) 1966. 8/yr. Can.$4.95. Telemedia Procom Inc., 50 Holly St., Toronto, Ont. M4S 3B3, Canada. TEL 416-482-9399. FAX 416-482-3975. Ed. Sally Armstrong. adv.; charts; illus.; tr.lit.; circ. 1,600,000 (controlled). **Indexed:** Can.Per.Ind., CMI.

640   CE
HONEY. (Text in English) 1976. w. Independent Newspaper Ltd., 5 Gunasena Mawatha, Colombo 12, Sri Lanka. TEL 1-23882.
    Description: Illustrated family magazine.

640   SW   ISSN 0284-3773
HUS & HEM. 1987. m. SEK 319. I C A Foerlaget AB, Stora Gatan 41, S-721 85 Vaesteraas, Sweden. TEL 46-21-19-40-00. FAX 46-21-19-41-36.

640   DK
HUSMODEREN. bi-m. Danske Husmoderforeninger, Berggreensgade 32, 2100 Copenhagen OE, Denmark. Ed. Bente Gaunt. adv. circ. 28,850.

HUSMORBLADET. see WOMEN'S INTERESTS

640   SW   ISSN 0345-5068
I C A - KURIREN. 1942. 46/yr. SEK 429 (effective 1991). I C A - Foerlaget AB, Storagt. 41, 721 85 Vaesteraas, Sweden. TEL 46-21-19-40-00. FAX 46-21-19-41-36. TELEX 40486. Ed. Lena Bjoerk. adv. circ. 541,859. (also avail. in audio cassette)

645   US
IDEAS PARA SU HOGAR. (Editions avail. for Central America, Chile, Colombia, Ecuador, Mexico, Peru, Puerto Rico, U.S., Venezuela) (Text in Spanish) 1978. m. $22.50. Editorial America, S.A., Vanidades Continental Bldg., 6355 N.W. 36th St., Virginia Gardens, FL 33166. TEL 305-871-6400. FAX 305-871-8769. Ed. Gloria Ramos. adv. circ. 111,000.

640   II   ISSN 0970-2733
INDIAN JOURNAL OF HOME SCIENCE. (Text in English) 1967. s-a. Rs.100($8) Home Science Association of India, c/o Dr. Ms. N. Ogale, Faculty of Home Sciences, University Rd., Baroda 390 002, India. Ed. Padma S. Chari. adv.; bk.rev. circ. 500. (back issues avail.)

640   FR   ISSN 0074-3712
INTERNATIONAL CONGRESS OF HOME ECONOMICS. REPORT. (Text in English, French, German) quadrennial; 17th, 1992, Hanover, Germany. 50 F. International Federation for Home Economics, 5 av. de la Porte Brancion, 75015 Paris, France.

642 647.95   US
INTERNATIONAL ENTERTAINING.* 1990. bi-m. $12.50. Premier Publishing (San Francisco), 1740 Broadway, Ste. 503, San Francisco, CA 94109-2413. TEL 415-777-0399. FAX 415-777-0720. adv.; B&W page $6490, color page $9045; trim 8 3/8 x 10 7/8. circ. 200,627.

IOWA AGRICULTURE AND HOME ECONOMICS EXPERIMENT STATION. RESEARCH BULLETIN. see AGRICULTURE

ISENKRAMBRANCHEN. see CERAMICS, GLASS AND POTTERY

649   MP
JARGALAN/HAPPINESS. (Text in Mongolian) 1980. a. Executive Committee of Mongolian Red Cross, Marksyn Orgon Choloo 4, Ulan Bator, Mongolia. TEL 20635. Ed. N. Shura. illus. circ. 10,000.
    Description: Covers child care.

640   CC
JIATING/FAMILY. (Text in Chinese) m. $41.30. Guangdong Sheng Funu Lianhehui, Xihepu Shenglu, Dongshan, Guangzhou, Guangdong 510080, People's Republic of China. TEL 777718. (Dist. in US by: China Books & Periodicals, Inc., 2929 24th St., San Francisco, CA 94110. TEL 415-282-2994) Ed. Li Jun.

640   CC
JIATING SHENGHUO ZHINAN/FAMILY LIFE GUIDE. (Text in Chinese) m. Heilongjiang Sheng Kexue Jishu Xiehui, 204, Zhongshan Lu, Harbin, Heilongjiang 150001, People's Republic of China. TEL 221940. Ed. Yu Tongxi.

647   FR   ISSN 0755-9895
JOURNAL DES MENAGERES. 1901. w. 300 F. 23-25 rue de la Fidelite, 68200 Mulhouse, France. Ed. Regine Deharvengt. adv.; illus.

JOURNAL OF DIETETICS AND HOME ECONOMICS/TYDSKRIF VIR DIEET- EN HUISHOUDKUNDE. see NUTRITION AND DIETETICS

640   US   ISSN 0022-1570
TX1
JOURNAL OF HOME ECONOMICS. 1909. q. $20. American Home Economics Association, 1555 King St., Alexandria, VA 22314. TEL 703-706-4600. FAX 703-706-4663. Ed. Marjorie Harter. abstr.; bibl.; charts; illus.; tr.lit.; index. circ. 25,000. (also avail. in microfilm from UMI; reprint service avail. from UMI) **Indexed:** Biol.Abstr., Bk.Rev.Dig., Bk.Rev.Ind. (1965-), C.I.J.E., Chem.Abstr., Child.Bk.Rev.Ind. (1965-), Dairy Sci.Abstr., Educ.Ind., Farm & Garden Ind., Intl.Polym.Sci.& Tech., Media Rev.Dig., Nutr.Abstr., P.A.I.S., Sage Fam.Stud.Abstr., Soc.Work Res.& Abstr., Text.Tech.Dig.
—BLDSC (5002.900000); Faxon; UnCover; SWETS; UMI.
    Description: Covers family relations, children, food and nutrition, household affairs, and teaching methods.

KALNIRNAY. see ASTROLOGY

640 301.414   IO
KELUARGA. fortn. Jalan Sangaji 11, Jakarta, Indonesia. Ed. S. Dahono.

KEUKEN. see HOTELS AND RESTAURANTS

640   US
KITCHEN TIMES. 1975. m. $66. Howard Wilson & Co., Inc., 185 Marlborough, Boston, MA 02116. FAX 617-437-9983. Ed. Howard Wilson. bk.rev.; bibl.; illus. circ. 350. **Document type:** newsletter.
    Description: Information on restaurants, cooks, packaged goods, and wines. Emphasis is on "simple" recipes, not haute cuisine.

640   JA   ISSN 0389-584X
    CODEN: KJDKDJ
KOBE WOMEN'S UNIVERSITY. FACULTY OF HOME ECONOMICS. BULLETIN. (Text in English and Japanese; summaries in English) 1967. a. members only. Kobe Women's University, Faculty of Home Economics - Kobe Joshi Daigaku Kaseigakubu, Aoyama, Suma-ku, Kobe-shi 654, Japan. TEL 078-731-4416. FAX 078-732-5161. Ed. Kazuo Iwai. circ. 1,400. (back issues avail.) **Document type:** academic/scholarly publication.
—BLDSC (5100.577100).

641.5   GW
KOCHEN MIT MIKROWELLE. 1989. w. DM4.20 per no. c/o Marshall Cavendish, Paulstr. 3, 20095 Hamburg, Germany. TEL 040-322175. FAX 040-338769.

640   FI   ISSN 0355-1555
KOTI. 1939. m. FIM 150 (effective Jan. 1994). (Maatalouskeskusten Liitto) Maa- ja Kotitalousnaisten Keskus, Lonnrotinkatu 13, SF-00120 Helsinki, Finland. TEL 90-680-700. FAX 90-680-70270. Ed. Taina Harmoinen. adv.: B&W page FIM 5500, color page FIM 9000; trim220 x 270. circ. 25,365. circ. 25,365 (controlled). **Document type:** trade publication.

640   FI   ISSN 0023-4281
KOTILIESI. 1923. bi-m. FIM 428. Yhtyneet Kuvalehdet Oy, Maistraantinportti 1, FIN-00240 Helsinki, Finland. TEL 358-0-156-6524. FAX 358-0-156-6505. TELEX 121364. Ed. Elina Simonen. adv.; B&W page FIM 21800, color page FIM 32100. bk.rev.; play rev.; illus.; index. circ. 200,393.

640   FI   ISSN 0047-3685
KOTITALOUS. 1936. 12/yr. FIM 220. Koti-ja Laitostalousalan Opettajat, Ruusulankatu 19 A 16, 00250 Helsinki, Finland. TEL 358-0-491528. FAX 358-0-441757. (Kotitalousopettajien Liitto) Ed. Leena Loeyttyniemi. adv.: B&W page FIM 4500, color page FIM 8000; trim 158 x 230; adv. contact: Sirpa Forsman. bk.rev.; stat.; index. circ. 3,500. (back issues avail.) **Document type:** trade publication.

640   UK
KOUZINA/KITCHEN;* quarterly review for a better home life. (Text in Greek) 1982. q. Dr.1200($25) K. Korovilas & Co., c/o Robert G. Horsfield, Daisy Bank, Chinley via Stockport, England. Ed. Dina Korovilas. adv.; bk.rev. circ. 16,000. (back issues avail.)

L A PARENT; magazine for Southern California families. **see** CHILDREN AND YOUTH — About

LADIES HOME JOURNAL (INKPRINT EDITION). see WOMEN'S INTERESTS

HOME ECONOMICS

LADIES' HOME JOURNAL PARENT'S DIGEST. see *WOMEN'S INTERESTS*

641.5   US
▼**LAND O'LAKES COLLECTION OF CLASSIC RECIPES COOKBOOK.** 1992. bi-m. Russ Moore and Associates Inc., 4151 Knob Dr., Ste. 200, St. Paul, MN 55122. TEL 612-452-0571. FAX 612-454-5791. Ed. Diane Steen. adv.: B&W page $5200, color page $6800; trim 4 1/2 x 7 5/8. circ. 240,000.
    Description: Offers easy-to-follow, step-by-step recipes from their test kitchens.

641.5   FR   ISSN 0988-4343
LETTRE HEBDO DES CUISINISTES, DES BAINISTES ET DES ELECTROMENAGISTES. w. Officiel, S.A., B.P. 9037, 34041 Montpellier Cedex, France. TEL 67-58-82-28. FAX 67-92-38-86.

641.5 664   JA
LETTUCE CLUB. (Text in Japanese) 1987. s-m. S.S. Communications Inc., SSC Bldg., 11, Niban-cho, Chiyoda-ku, Tokyo 102, Japan. TEL 03-5276-2151. FAX 03-5276-2149. Ed. Kazuko Sasaki. circ. 820,000. **Document type:** consumer publication.
    Description: Covers consumer news, cooking methods, fashion, household items and culture.

641.5   HK
LISA'S KITCHEN BI-WEEKLY. (Text in Chinese) 1984. w. B2, 14-F Fuk Keung Ind. Bldg., 66-68 Tong Mei Rd., Taikoktsui, Kowloon, Hong Kong. TEL 3910668. FAX 7893869. Ed. Vincent Leung. circ. 75,000.

052   UK   ISSN 0024-5224
LIVING. 1967. m. £4($55) I P C Magazines, Southbank Publishing Group (Subsidiary of: Reed International PLC), King's Reach Tower, Stamford St., London SE1 9LS, England. TEL 071-261-5854. FAX 0444-440619. TELEX 892084 REEDBP G. (Dist. by) Quadrant Subscription Services, Oakfield House, Perrymount Rd., Haywards Heath, W. Sussex RH16 3DH, England. TEL 0444-440421) Ed. Olwen Rice. adv. contact: Louise Dickinson. charts; illus.; tr.lit. circ. 611,213. **Document type:** consumer publication.

M & M. see *WOMEN'S INTERESTS*

MCCALL'S. see *WOMEN'S INTERESTS*

640   US
▼**MCCALL'S FAVORITE CHRISTMAS IDEAS.** 1992. a. newsstand price: $2.95. New York Times Women's Magazines, Special Interest Publications, 110 Fifth Ave., New York, NY 10011. TEL 212-463-1275. FAX 212-463-1553. adv.: B&W page $17560, color page $22430; trim 8 x 10 1/2. circ. 1,000,000. **Document type:** consumer publication.

MADRE. see *WOMEN'S INTERESTS*

MAGAZIN POLOVNIKA. see *SPORTS AND GAMES — Outdoor Life*

MAGAZINE OF AMERICA'S BEST RECIPES. see *FOOD AND FOOD INDUSTRIES*

640   JA
MAMIRU. (Text in Japanese) 1972. m. 3600 Yen. Kosei Publishing Co. Ltd., 7-1, 2-chome, Wada, Suginami-ku, Tokyo 166, Japan. Ed. Sotaro Sasaki.

MANEQUIM. see *CLOTHING TRADE — Fashions*

640   IT
MANI DI FATA; per la donna, la casa, il bambino. 1925. m. L.36000 (foreign L.70000). Casa Editrice Mani di Fata, Via Vettabbia 7, Milan, Italy. Ed. Alfredo Canetta. adv. circ. 200,000.

641.5   MX
MARIA ORSINI; el arte del buen comer. bi-m. Mex.$69.60($45) Promocion e Imagen, S.A., Colima 368 A, Roma, 06700 Mexico D.F., Mexico. TEL 533-07-00. FAX 533-35-20. Ed. Maria Orsini. illus.; circ. 20,500 (paid). **Document type:** consumer publication.

641.5   US
MARTHA STEWART LIVING. 1990. bi-m. $12 (effective 1994). Time Inc. Ventures, 11 W. 42nd St., 24th Fl., New York, NY 10036. TEL 212-522-7800. FAX 212-522-7815. (Subscr. to: Box 53096, Boulder, CO 80322-3056) Ed. Martha Stewart. adv. contact: Suzanne Sobel. illus. **Document type:** consumer publication.

641.5   JA
MERU. 1979. bi-m. 2340 Yen. Gakken Co. Ltd., 40-5, 4-chome, Kamiikedai, Ohta-ku, Tokyo 145, Japan. Ed. Yusuki Takahashi.

METROPOLITAN HOME; style for our generation. see *INTERIOR DESIGN AND DECORATION*

643 641.53   US
MICROWAVE TIMES. 1975. bi-m. $11.95. Recipes Unlimited, Inc., Box 1271, Burnville, MN 55337. TEL 612-890-6655. FAX 612-890-6033. Ed. Janet Sadlack. index. circ. 160,000. (back issues avail.) **Document type:** consumer publication.
    Description: Recipes and hints for microwave cooking.

640 747   JA
MODERN LIVING. (Text in Japanese) 1951. bi-m. 7800 Yen. Fujin Gaho Sha, 9-1, 2-chome, Nishi-Shinbashi, Minato-ku, Tokyo, Japan. Ed. Semeru Saito.

DIE MODERNE KUECHE. see *INTERIOR DESIGN AND DECORATION — Furniture And House Furnishings*

640 646   UK   ISSN 0264-9683
MODUS. 1928. 8/yr. £28. National Association of Teachers of Home Economics and Technology, Hamilton House, Mabledon Pl., London WC1H 9BJ, England. TEL 071-387-1441. FAX 071-383-7230. Ed. Geoffrey Thompson. adv.; bk.rev.; charts; illus.; tr.lit.; index. circ. 5,500. **Document type:** academic/scholarly publication.
—BLDSC (5900.370000).
    Formerly (until Dec. 1982): Housecraft (ISSN 0018-6503)
    Description: Covers all aspects of health, nutrition and textiles, with coverage of curricular changes, technology and developments.

MONEYTREE. see *HOBBIES*

640   US
MOVING HOME. 1990. s-a. Doing It Right Communications, 6198 Butler Pike, Blue Bell, PA 19422. TEL 215-653-0810. FAX 215-653-0817. Ed. Gerard Dunwoody. adv.: color page $10000; trim 8 1/2 x 10 7/8. circ. 250,000.
    Description: Contains information for families preparing to move.

640   JA
MRS/MISESU. (Text in Japanese) 1961. m. 17980 Yen. Bunka Publishing Bureau, 22-1, 3-chome, Yoyogi, Shibuya-ku, Tokyo, Japan. Ed. Toyotaka Manabe.

640   CR
MUJER Y HOGAR. 1943. w. Apartado 89, Avda. 15, Casa 1916, Barrio Aranjuez, San Jose, Costa Rica. TEL 36-3128. Dir. Carmen Cornejo Mendez. circ. 15,000.

MY BABY. see *CHILDREN AND YOUTH — About*

640   FI   ISSN 1235-7995
▼**NAISEN MAAILMA.** 1992. 12/yr. FIM 220. Yhtyneet Kuvalehdet Oy - United Magazines Ltd., Maistraatinportti 1, SF-00240 Helsinki, Finland. TEL 358-0-156-6524. FAX 358-0-156-6505. Ed. Aila Pervonsuo. adv.: B&W page FIM 12900, color page FIM 1900; trim 217 x 280; adv. contact: Kauko Kanerva. circ. 100,000. **Document type:** consumer publication.
    Description: Directed to women who look for self-fulfillment in doing things themselves, everything from making food to decorating.

NATIONWIDE DIRECTORY OF GIFT, HOUSEWARES & HOME TEXTILE BUYERS. see *GIFTWARE AND TOYS*

NEUE HEIM UND WELT. see *WOMEN'S INTERESTS*

NEUES WOHNEN (BERLIN). see *INTERIOR DESIGN AND DECORATION*

640   US   ISSN 0748-4674
NEW CONNECTIONS; your guide to living in Manhattan from New York Telephone. 1984. a. Reuben H. Donnelley (Subsidiary of: Dun & Bradstreet), 711 Third Ave., New York, NY 10017. TEL 212-972-7100. Ed. Georgia Orcutt. adv.

340   US
NEW FAMILY. 1988. s-a. Hachette Magazines, Inc., 1633 Broadway, 45th Fl., New York, NY 10009. TEL 212-767-6000. Ed. Sally Koslow. adv.

640   UK
NEW HOME MAGAZINE. 1977. q. £0.50 per no. Gildea & Co. Ltd., Monkscoole House, Ste. 14D, Rathcoole, Co. Antrim BT37 9DA, N. Ireland. Ed. Andrew Gildea. adv. circ. 4,000.

640 635 745.5   AT   ISSN 0819-9981
NEW IDEA. 1902. w. Aus.$93.60 (foreign Aus.$130). Southdown Press, 32 Walsh Street, Melbourne, Vic., 3000, Australia. TEL 03-320-700. FAX 03-320-7410. Ed. D. Boling. adv.; bk.rev.; illus. circ. 1,003,223.
    Description: Articles on homemaking, crafts, cooking, gardening.

NEWS & VIEWS (BELMONT). see *AGRICULTURE*

640   JA   ISSN 0913-5227
TX1   CODEN: NKGAEB
NIHON KASEI GAKKAISHI/JOURNAL OF HOME ECONOMICS OF JAPAN. (Text in English, Japanese; summaries in English) 1950. m. 12000 Yen. Japan Society of Home Economics - Nihon Kasei Gakkai, No. 502, Gakuendai - Haitsu, 1-15, Otsuka 2-chome, Bunkyo-ku, Tokyo 112, Japan. TEL 03-3947-2627. (Subscr. to: Maruzen Co. Ltd., Export Department, P.O. Box 5050. Tokyo International 100-31, Japan) circ. 5,350. (back issues avail) **Indexed:** Soyabean Abstr.
—BLDSC (5002.955000); CASDDS. **CCC.**
    Formerly (until 1986): Kaseigaku Zasshi (ISSN 0449-9069)

NORTH COUNTRY FARM NEWS. see *AGRICULTURE*

NUTRITION AND FOOD SCIENCE. see *NUTRITION AND DIETETICS*

641.5 664   UK   ISSN 0142-7857
P P C. (Petits Propos Culinaires) 1979. 3/yr. £11 (foreign £13.50; $23.50 in US). Prospect Books Ltd., 45 Lamont Rd., London SW10 OHU, England. TEL 071-352-4209. FAX 071-351-1242. Ed. Alan Davidson. bk.rev.; cum.index: nos.1-15, 16-25, 26-35. circ. 1,000. **Indexed:** Art.Hosp.& Tour.
—BLDSC (6430.343000).

PARENTING. see *CHILDREN AND YOUTH — About*

PARENTING MAGAZINE OF ORANGE COUNTY. see *CHILDREN AND YOUTH — About*

PARENTS; on rearing children from crib to college. see *CHILDREN AND YOUTH — About*

641.5   CC   ISSN 1004-5783
PENGTIAO ZHISHI/COOK KNOWLEDGE. (Text in Chinese) 1983. m. Pengtiao Zhishi Zazhishe, 1 Bingzhou Lu, Taiyuan, Shanxi 030001, People's Republic of China. TEL 86-351-3030852. (Subscr. in U.S. to: China Books & Periodicals, Inc., 2929 24th St., San Francisco, CA 94110. TEL 415-282-2994; Dist. overseas by Jiangsu Publications Import & Export Corp., 56 Gao Yun Ling, Nanjing, Jiangsu, P.R.C.) Ed. Xue Huilin. adv. contact: Xing Daquan.

PETRA. see *WOMEN'S INTERESTS*

640   JA
PLANNING FOR LIVING/KURASHI NO SEKKEI. Variant title: Better Homemaking. (Text in Japanese) 1963. bi-m. 12750 Yen. Chuokoron-Sha, Inc., 2-8-7 Kyobashi, Chuo-ku, Tokyo 104, Japan. Ed. Yoichi Ikeda.

643.7 690.24   US
PRACTICAL HOMEOWNER'S DO-IT-YOURSELF ANNUAL. a. $19.95. Rodale Press, Inc., 33 E. Minor St., Emmaus, PA 18098. TEL 215-967-5171.

PRAIRIE NEWS. see *FOOD AND FOOD INDUSTRIES*

640   US
▼**PREVENTION'S QUICK & HEALTHY COOKING.** 1992. 3/yr. Rodale Press, Inc., 33 E. Minor St., Emmaus, PA 18098. TEL 215-967-5171. circ. 152,000.
    Description: Recipes and suggestions for health conscious families.

HOME ECONOMICS

641.1   PL   ISSN 0033-2119
PRZEGLAD GASTRONOMICZNY. 1945. m. $36. Wydawnictwo Czasopism i Ksiazek Technicznych SIGMA - NOT, Ul. Ratuszowa 11, P.O. Box 1004, 00-950 Warsaw, Poland. TEL 48-22-180918. FAX 48-22-192187. TELEX 814550 SIGMA PL. (Dist. by: SIGMA NOT Ltd., Ul. Bartycka 20, 00-716 Warsaw, Poland) Ed. Anna Szarejko. adv.: B&W $1010. bk.rev.; charts; illus.; stat. circ. 700.
    Formerly: Przemysl Gastronomiczny.

641.5   US
QUICK 'N EASY COUNTRY COOKIN'. 1986. bi-m. $12.95. Parkside Publishing, Box 66, Davis, SD 57021. TEL 605-238-5704. FAX 605-238-5339. Ed. Pam Schrag. adv.: B&W page $250, color page $390; trim 8 1/8 x 10 7/8; adv. contact: Pam Schrag. circ. 40,000. **Document type:** consumer publication.
    Formerly: Quick 'n Easy Cookin' (ISSN 0893-2247)
    Description: Edited for the "active" homemaker. Articles on quick and easy cooking. Includes craft and sewing ideas, poetry, low cholesterol and diabetic recipes.

RAAD & ROEN/ADVICE AND RESULTS. see GENERAL INTEREST PERIODICALS — Scandinavia

643   IT   ISSN 0393-0203
RASSEGNA. 1968. q. L.130000. Via Matteo Bandello 20, 20123 Milan, Italy. TEL 4814141. FAX 4814143. Ed. Vittorio Gregotti. adv. circ. 15,000.
—SWETS.
    Formerly: Rassegna Modi di Abitare Oggi.

640   GW   ISSN 0341-5295
RATIONELLE HAUSWIRTSCHAFT; die Hauswirtschaftsmeisterin. 1964. m. DM.66 (foreign DM.72). Verlag Neuer Merkur GmbH, Ingolstaedter Str. 63a, 80939 Munich, Germany. TEL 089-318905-0. FAX 089-31890553. Ed. Alexandra Gronski. bibl.; charts; illus.; mkt.; index. circ. 8,500. (tabloid format) **Document type:** newsletter.
    Formerly: Hauswirtschaftsmeisterin (ISSN 0017-8462)

641.5 642   US
RECIPE ANNUAL. a. $24.99. Sunset Publishing Corp., 80 Willow Rd., Menlo Park, CA 94025. TEL 415-321-3600. FAX 415-321-0551. (Subscr. to: Sunset Publishing, Box 56656, Boulder, CO 80322-6656) Ed.Bd. **Document type:** consumer publication.

640 745.5   US   ISSN 1053-7171
RECIPE GREETINGS UPDATE. 1990. a. $5 (Canada $7; elsewhere $8.50). Recipe Greeting Press, Box 416, Denver, CO 80201. Ed. A. Doyle. circ. 4,000. (looseleaf format) **Document type:** newsletter.
    Description: Provides verses for creating rhyming telephone answering machine greetings.

641.5 664   US
RECIPE YEARBOOK (YEAR). a. $12.95. Bon Appetit Publishing Corp., 5900 Wilshire Blvd., Los Angeles, CA 90036. TEL 213-965-3600.

RECIPES FOR SALE. see FOOD AND FOOD INDUSTRIES

640   US   ISSN 0736-1688
REFUNDING UPDATE. 1983. s-a. $4. Update Publicare Co., c/o Prosperity & Profits Unlimited, Box 416, Denver, CO 80201-0416. TEL 303-575-5676. Ed. A. Doyle. adv.; bibl. circ. 3,000. (looseleaf format; also avail. in microfiche; back issues avail.) **Document type:** newsletter.

640   US
THE REPORTER (INDEPENDENCE).* q. National Association of Extension Home Economists, 2820 M 291 Frontage Rd., Independence, VA 22360.

REZEPTE MIT PFIFF. see WOMEN'S INTERESTS

ROOI ROSE. see WOMEN'S INTERESTS

SADIE'S CHATTER. see LITERATURE

641.5   IT
SALE E PEPE. m. L.54000 (foreign L.64800). Arnoldo Mondadori Editore S.p.A., Palazzo Canovea, 20090 Milan - Segrate, Italy. TEL 02-75421. Ed. GianCarlo Barbieri. circ. 174,000.

SAN DIEGO PARENT. see CHILDREN AND YOUTH — About

640   BN   ISSN 0036-5203
SAVREMENO DOMACINSTVO. 1961. q. 20 din. Zavod za Unapredjenje Domacinstva Bosne i Hercegovine, Skenderija 70, Sarajevo, Bosnia Hercegovina. Ed. Mileva Vidovic.

641.5   MX
SAYROLS Y LA COCINA. bi-m. Consorcio Sayrols, Mier y Pesado 126, Col. del Valle, 03100 Mexico D.F., Mexico. TEL 525-543-49-94. FAX 525-523-7045. Ed. Patricia Olivera. **Document type:** consumer publication.

SCHOENER WOHNEN. see INTERIOR DESIGN AND DECORATION

640   US   ISSN 0883-475X
TX1
SCHOLASTIC CHOICES; personal development & living skills. 1956. m. (Sep.-May). $5.95. Scholastic Inc., 555 Broadway, New York, NY 10012-3999. TEL 212-343-6100. Ed. Lauren Tarshis. adv.; index. circ. 180,000. (also avail. in microform from UMI; reprint service avail. from UMI) **Indexed:** Ind.Child.Mag., Mag.Ind.
●Also available online. Vendor(s): DIALOG Information Services, Inc.
—UnCover; UMI.
    Incorporates (in 1991): Forecast for the Home Economist (ISSN 0890-9849); Which was formerly (until 1986): Forecast for Home Economics (ISSN 0015-7090); (1963-1966): Practical Forecast for Home Economics (ISSN 0742-8693); Supersedes (in 1984): Co-Ed (ISSN 0009-9724)
    Description: Aimed at adolescents.

640 640.73   GW   ISSN 0170-5768
SCHRIFTTUMS FUER DEN BEREICH HAUSHALT UND VERBAUCH. BIBLIOGRAPHIE. 1969. a. DM.14. Bundesforschungsanstalt fuer Ernaehrung, Institut fuer Ernaehrungsoekonomie und -soziologie, Garbenstr. 13, 70599 Stuttgart, Germany. TEL 0711-455063. FAX 0711-4569355. Ed. Hans-Joachim Ulrich. bk.rev. circ. 500. (back issues avail.) **Document type:** bibliography.

SCOTTISH HOME AND COUNTRY. see WOMEN'S INTERESTS

641.5   IT
SCUOLA DI CUCINA.* 1978. m. L.30000. Curcio Periodici S.p.A., Via Arno 64, 00198 Rome, Italy. Ed. Rosanna Falconi. adv.; illus. circ. 130,000.

641.5   PO
SEGREDOS DE COZINHA. w. Impala Sociedade Editorial, Lda., Rua Cristino da Silva, 1 r-c, 2745 Queluz, Portugal. TEL 439-02-34. FAX 439-02-33. **Document type:** consumer publication.

SEIVA. see AGRICULTURE

SELECT HOME DESIGNS. see BUILDING AND CONSTRUCTION

SEW IT SEAMS. see NEEDLEWORK

641.5   JA
SHIKI NO AJI/COOKING FOR FOUR SEASONS. (Text in Japanese) 1973. q. 7600 Yen. Kamakura Shobo Publishing Co. Ltd, 21 Sanai-cho, Ichigaya, Shinjuku-ku, Tokyo 162, Japan. Ed. Jiro Morisu. **Document type:** consumer publication.

642   CC   ISSN 1004-2083
SICHUAN PENGREN/SICHUAN CUISINE. (Text in Chinese) 1983. bi-m. Y1.80 per no. (Sichuan Shucai Yinshi Fuwu Gongsi) Sichuan Pengren Bianjibu, 4, Renmin Zhonglu 3 Duan, Chengdu, Sichuan 610031, People's Republic of China. TEL 028-6641387. adv.; illus. circ. 40,000. **Document type:** consumer publication.

641.5 639.2   US
SIMPLY SEAFOOD. 1991. q. $10. Waterfront Press, 1115 N.W. 46th St., Seattle, WA 98107. TEL 206-789-6506. FAX 206-789-9193. Ed. Peter Redmayne. adv. circ. 150,000.
    Description: Contains articles on seafood farming and production, with profiles of leading chefs, and columns on seafood cooking and wines.

SMART DADS. see SOCIOLOGY

SO-EN. see CLOTHING TRADE — Fashions

SOUTH AFRICAN BRIDE TO BE: FIRST HOME. see MATRIMONY

640   US
SOUTHERN LIVING HOME FOR THE HOLIDAYS. 1989. a. $3.95. Southern Progress Corp. (Subsidiary of: Time, Inc. Magazine Co.), c/o H. Johnson, V.P. Circulation, 2100 Lakeshore Dr., Birmingham, AL 35209. TEL 205-877-6000. FAX 205-877-6422. adv.: B&W page $8520, color page $12000; trim 8 1/8 x 10 7/8. circ. 600,000.

640   US
▼**SOUTHERN LIVING SUMMERTIME.** 1992. a. $3.95. Southern Progress Corp., c/o H. Johnson, V.P. Circulation, 2100 Lakeshore Dr., Birmingham, AL 35209. TEL 205-877-6000. FAX 205-877-6422. adv.: B&W page $7100, color page $10000; trim 8 1/8 x 10 7/8. circ. 500,000.

SOUTHWEST INTERNACIONAL WINE & FOOD REVIEW. see BEVERAGES

SUNSET; the magazine of Western living. see GENERAL INTEREST PERIODICALS — United States

643   FR   ISSN 0039-8012
SYSTEME D; la revue des bricoleurs. 1924. m. 334 F. Publications Georges Ventillard, 2-12 rue de Bellevue, 75940 Paris Cedex 19, France. TEL 42-00-33-05. FAX 42-41-89-40. TELEX 220 409 F. Ed. A. Valence. adv.; charts; illus.; index. circ. 200,000.

640   SA   ISSN 0039-8640
T W A U NEWS/T V L U NUUS. (Text in Afrikaans, English) 1962. m. membership. Transvaal Women's Agricultural Union, P.O. Box 11226, Brooklyn, Pretoria 0011, South Africa. TEL 012-466534. FAX 012-435144. Ed. Anna Boshoff. adv.; bk.rev.; illus. circ. 10,000. **Document type:** newsletter.

641   US   ISSN 1071-5878
▼**TASTE OF HOME.** 1993. bi-m. $16.98. Reiman Publications, Inc., 5400 S. 60th St., Greendale, WI 53129. TEL 414-423-0100. FAX 414-423-1143. (Subscr. to: Box 986, Greendale, WI 53129) Ed. Kathy Pohl. illus.; circ. 1,500,000 (paid). **Document type:** consumer publication.

TEEN TIMES. see CHILDREN AND YOUTH — For

640   FI   ISSN 0355-2527
TEHO B. (Text in Finnish; summaries in English) 1946. 2/yr. FIM 53 (foreign FIM 65) (effective 1994). Tyotehoseura R.Y., P.O. Box 28, Melkonkatu 16 A, FIN-00211 Helsinki, Finland. TEL 90-6922445. FAX 90-6922084. Ed. Tarmo Luoma. circ. 5,469. (back issues avail.) **Indexed:** Agri.Eng.Abstr. **Document type:** academic/scholarly publication, consumer publication.
    Description: Deals with the rationalization of work related to home economics, ergonomics, economics, and consumer education.

640 370   FI   ISSN 0355-8991
TEKSTIILIOPETTAJA/TEXTILLARAREN. (Text in Finnish and Swedish) 1957. q. Fmk.100. Tekstiiliopettajaliitto - Trade Union of Finnish Textile Teachers, Mannerheimintie 132 B 31, SF-00270 Helsinki, Finland. Ed. Salla Virtanen. adv. contact: Minna Matinlauri. bk.rev.; circ. 1,500 (controlled). **Document type:** academic/scholarly publication.

640   GW
TINA. 1975. w. (Thu.). DM.114.40. Heinrich Bauer Verlag, Burchardstr. 11, 20095 Hamburg, Germany. TEL 040-3019-0. FAX 040-323866. Ed. Hartmut Klemann. adv. contact: Goesta Ahrweiler. illus. circ. 1,689,329. **Document type:** consumer publication.
    Description: Concentrates on fashion, cosmetics, home economics, nutrition, advice and entertainment.

640   NE
TIP; 't lekkerste blad. 1977. m. (13/yr.) fl.4.95 per no. Uitgeverij Spaarnestad B.V. (Haarlem), P.O. Box 1, 2000 MA Haarlem, Netherlands. TEL 31-23-304304. FAX 31-23-350621. TELEX 41371 NL. Ed. Franska Stuy. adv.; illus. **Document type:** consumer publication.

HOME ECONOMICS — ABSTRACTING, BIBLIOGRAPHIES, STATISTICS

640   JA
TOKYO KASEI DAIGAKU KENKYU KIYO/TOKYO KASEI UNIVERSITY. BULLETIN. Variant English title: Tokyo College of Domestic Science. Bulletin. (Text and summaries in English and Japanese) 1960. a. Tokyo Kasei Daigaku - Tokyo Kasei University, 18-1 Kaga 1-chome, Itabashi-ku, Tokyo 173, Japan. **Indexed:** Chem.Abstr., Psychol.Abstr. **Document type:** bulletin.

640   US   ISSN 0073-3113
TX1   CODEN: XAHEAU
U.S. DEPARTMENT OF AGRICULTURE. HOME ECONOMICS RESEARCH REPORT. 1957. irreg. U.S. Department of Agriculture, Washington, DC 20250-1300. TEL 202-720-2791. **Indexed:** Nutr.Abstr. **Document type:** government publication.

640   US
THE UNMENTIONABLE. irreg., no.14, Fall 1992. $2 per no. Box 7219, Santa Cruz, CA 95061. (Also avail. through: Backlist Mailorder, 475 Valencia St., San Francisco, CA 94103. TEL 415-255-0388) Ed. Kelina Lobo. circ. 1,000 (paid). **Document type:** newsletter.
    Description: Provides new ideas for homemakers, including recipes and hints for needlework, in addition to stories.

641.5   US   ISSN 1061-2548
THE UPPERCRUST; food: procurement, preparation, & news from a practical point of view with a gourmet touch. 1987. bi-m. $12. Upper Crust Publications, 361 Virginia St., Crystal Lake, IL 60014. TEL 815-459-1000. Ed. Sharon R. Myers. bk.rev. circ. 5,700. (tabloid format; back issues avail.) **Document type:** newsletter.
    Description: Appeals to both novice and experienced chef alike with recipes featuring fresh ingredients rather than artificial or prepared mixes. *Refereed Serial*

640   US   ISSN 1065-2728
▼**VEGGIE LIFE;** growing, eating, cooking green. 1993. bi-m. $17. E G W Publishing Co., 1041 Shary Circle, Concord, CA 94520. TEL 510-671-9852. FAX 510-671-0692. Ed. David Camp. circ. 25,000.

VESTIDAL; moda y patrones. see *CLOTHING TRADE — Fashions*

641.5   IT
VIAGGI INTORNO ALLA TAVOLA. 1975. irreg. Edizioni Il Formichiere s.r.l., Via del Lauro 3, 20121 Milan, Italy.

VINTAGE; the international magazine of wine spirits. see *BEVERAGES*

640   CN   ISSN 0382-0289
VISTA (SASKATOON). 2/yr. Can.$25. (Saskatchewan Home Economics Teachers' Association) Saskatchewan Teachers' Federation, Box 1108, Saskatoon, SK S7K 3N3, Canada. TEL 306-525-0368. Ed. Sharon Baker. illus.

WEDDING AND HOME. see *MATRIMONY*

WESTCHESTER FAMILY; the magazine just for the Westchester County parent. see *CHILDREN AND YOUTH — About*

640   AT
WESTWARD HOME. 1968. q. Aus.$25. Home Economics Institute of Australia, West Australian Division, P.O. Box 196, Subiaco, W.A. 6008, Australia. FAX 09-386-2258. Ed. Anne Bonnett. bk.rev. circ. 350. **Document type:** newsletter.

640   US   ISSN 0043-4590
TX1
WHAT'S NEW IN HOME ECONOMICS. 1936. 5/yr. (Sep.-June.) $29 (foreign $47) (effective 1993). University Publishing, Inc., 1429 Walnut St., 10th Fl., Philadelphia, PA 19102. TEL 215-563-3501. Ed. Christine Weiser; Pub. Michele Sokoloff. adv.; bk.rev.; charts; illus.; tr.lit.; index. circ. 17,000. (also avail. in microform from UMI) **Document type:** trade publication.
    —UnCover; UMI.
    Description: Reports on products, services, technologies, and applications for professional home economists.

WILTON YEARBOOK OF BAKING AND CAKE DECORATING. see *FOOD AND FOOD INDUSTRIES — Bakers And Confectioners*

WINE & FOOD COMPANION. see *FOOD AND FOOD INDUSTRIES*

WINING & DINING; eating out and entertaining in. see *HOTELS AND RESTAURANTS*

051 641   US   ISSN 0043-7336
AP2
WOMAN'S DAY. 1937. 17/yr. $14.95. Hachette Magazines, Inc., 1633 Broadway, 45th Fl., New York, NY 10009. TEL 212-767-6000. Ed. Jane Chestnut. adv.; illus. circ. 4,500,000. (also avail. in microform from UMI) **Indexed:** Access (1975-), Ind.How To Do It (1978-1984), Mag.Ind., MELSA.
    —UnCover; UMI.
    Description: Articles on women's issues, emphasizing the home, covering food, decorating, crafts, fashion, family travel, parenting.

641.5   US   ISSN 0195-6299
WOMAN'S DAY GREAT HOLIDAY BAKING. 1977. a. $2.95 per no. Hachette Magazines, Inc., Woman's Day Special Publications, 1633 Broadway, 45th Fl., New York, NY 10019. TEL 212-767-6000. Ed. Rowann Gilman. adv. circ. 750,000. **Document type:** consumer publication.
    Description: Concentrates on the preparation of traditional and unusual holiday foods for the autumn and winter seasons.

641.5   US
WOMAN'S DAY LIGHT MEALS IN MINUTES. 1977. a. $2.95 per no. Hachette Magazines, Inc., Woman's Day Special Publications, 1633 Broadway, 45th Fl., New York, NY 10019. TEL 212-767-6000. Ed. Rowann Gilman. adv. circ. 450,000.
    Formerly: Woman's Day Simply Delicious Meals in Minutes.
    Description: Economical cooking ideas to make good, but quick, food.

641.5   US
▼**WOMAN'S DAY LOW FAT MEALS.** 1992. s-a. $2.95 per no. Hachette Magazines, Inc., Woman's Day Special Publications, 1633 Broadway, 45th Fl., New York, NY 10019. TEL 212-767-6745. FAX 212-767-5612. adv.: B&W page $11665, color page $16200; trim 7 7/8 x 10 1/2. circ. 450,000. **Document type:** consumer publication.

WOMAN'S JOURNAL. see *WOMEN'S INTERESTS*

WORK-AT-HOME SOURCEBOOK; how to find "at-home" work that's right for you. see *OCCUPATIONS AND CAREERS*

WORKING MOTHER. see *WOMEN'S INTERESTS*

640   US
WORLD OF COOKBOOKS. 1987. q. $40. 1645 S. Vineyard Ave., Los Angeles, CA 90019. TEL 213-933-1645. Ed. Grace Kirschenbaum. bk.rev.; illus.
    Description: Reviews cookbooks from other countries, as well as American cookbooks.

306.8   CC   ISSN 1000-4300
AP95.C4
XIANDAI JIATING/MODERN FAMILY. (Text in Chinese) 1985. m. $37.70. (Shanghai Funu Lianhehui) Weile Haizi Zazhishe, 7, 101 Lane, Songshan Lu, Shanghai 200021, People's Republic of China. TEL 3264961. (Dist. in US by: China Books & Periodicals, Inc., 2929 24th St., San Francisco, CA 94110. TEL 415-282-2994)

XIANDAI SHENGHUO YONGPIN/MODERN DAILY NECESSITIES. see *CONSUMER EDUCATION AND PROTECTION*

641.5   CC   ISSN 1000-1115
ZHONGGUO PENGREN/CHINESE COOKERY. (Text in Chinese) 1980. m. Y18($13.32) (Shangye Bu, Jingji Yanjiusuo - Ministry of Commerce, Economic Research Institute) Zhongguo Shangye Chubanshe - China Commercial Publishing House, Shangye-bu Dalou, 45 Fuxingmennei Jie, Xidan, Beijing 100801, People's Republic of China. TEL 668581-2455. (Dist. in US by: China Books & Periodicals, Inc., 2929 24th St., San Francisco, CA 94110. TEL 415-282-2994) Eds. Wang Yan, Wang Dihuan. adv.; bibl.; charts; illus.; stat.; tr.lit. circ. 120,000. (back issues avail.)
    Description: For cooks, historians of cookery, and housewives. Provides recipes, covers regional cuisines, cooking technology, and cooking history.

641.5   US
ZHONGGUO SHIPIN/CHINESE FOOD. (Text in Chinese) m. $36.80. China Books & Periodicals, Inc., 2929 24th St., San Francisco, CA 94110. TEL 415-282-2994. FAX 415-282-0994.

ZHONGGUO SHIPIN BAO/CHINA'S FOOD NEWS. see *FOOD AND FOOD INDUSTRIES*

HOME ECONOMICS — Abstracting, Bibliographies, Statistics

640   AT
AUSTRALIA. BUREAU OF STATISTICS. QUEENSLAND OFFICE. HOUSEHOLD EXPENDITURE SURVEY, QUEENSLAND. 1984. every 5 yrs. Aus.$1.80. Australian Bureau of Statistics, Queensland Office, 313 Adelaide St., Brisbane, Qld. 4000, Australia. TEL 07-222-6022. FAX 07-229-6171. TELEX AA 40271.
    Description: Household expenditure by selected household characteristics. Expenditure patterns by type of commodity or service; household size and composition; sources of income; other socio-economic characteristics of the household.

640   AT   ISSN 1036-3920
AUSTRALIA. BUREAU OF STATISTICS. TASMANIAN OFFICE. HOUSEHOLD EXPENDITURE SURVEY AT A GLANCE, TASMANIA. 1991. irreg., latest 1991. Aus.$1 per no. Australian Bureau of Statistics, Tasmanian Office, G.P.O. Box 66A, Hobart, Tas. 7001, Australia. **Document type:** government publication.
    Description: Covers expenditure patterns, household composition and other socio-economic characteristics of the household.

301.5 645   CN   ISSN 0318-5273
HD7305.A3
CANADA. STATISTICS CANADA. HOUSEHOLD FACILITIES AND EQUIPMENT. (Catalogue 64-202) (Text in English and French) 1947. a. Can.$28($34) (foreign $39). Statistics Canada, Publications Sales and Services, Ottawa, Ont. K1A 0T6, Canada. TEL 613-951-7277. FAX 613-951-1584. (also avail. in microform from MML)
    Description: Presents estimates from sample surveys of household facilities that are taken in the spring of each year of: heating, water, cooking and bathroom facilities; home appliances in Canadian homes.

640 011   US   ISSN 0731-8634
Z5776.G2
COOK'S INDEX; an index of cookery periodicals and cookbooks. 1989. triennial. $55. John Gordon Burke Publisher, Inc., Box 1492, Evanston, IL 60204-1492. TEL 708-866-8625. **Document type:** abstracting/indexing.
    ●Also available online.
    Description: Provides an index to cookery periodicals and cookbooks from approximately 1970 to present.

640   ES
EL SALVADOR. MINISTERIO DE PLANIFICACION Y COORDINACION DEL DESARROLLO ECONOMICO Y SOCIAL. ENCUESTA NACIONAL DE INGRESOS Y GASTOS DE LOS HOGARES URBANOS. a. Ministerio de Planificacion y Coordinacion del Desarrollo Economico y Social, Casa Presidential, San Salvador, El Salvador. **Document type:** government publication.

640 314   HU   ISSN 0439-9285
HC267.S2
HUNGARY. KOZPONTI STATISZTIKAI HIVATAL. HAZTARTASSTATISZTIKA. s-a. 80 Ft. Statisztikai Kiado Vallalat, Kaszasdulo u. 2, Box 99, 1300 Budapest 3, Hungary. TEL 688-635. TELEX 22-6699. (Subscr. to: Kultura, Box 149, H-1389 Budapest, Hungary)
    —BLDSC (4274.464530).

640   MF
MAURITIUS. CENTRAL STATISTICAL OFFICE. HOUSEHOLD EXPENDITURE SURVEY. 1983. irreg. Rs.100 per no. Central Statistical Office, Port-Louis, Mauritius. (Subscr. to: G.P.O., La Tour Koenig, Port-Louis, Mauritius)

310   PP
PAPUA NEW GUINEA. NATIONAL STATISTICAL OFFICE. HOUSEHOLD EXPENDITURE SURVEY. PRELIMINARY BULLETIN. (Text in English) 1975. irreg. National Statistical Office, P.O. Wards Strip, Papua New Guinea. FAX 675-255057. TELEX FINANCE NE 22312. Ed. Nick Suvulo. charts; stat. **Document type:** bulletin.

315 640   SI   ISSN 0217-9563
SINGAPORE. DEPARTMENT OF STATISTICS. REPORT ON THE HOUSEHOLD EXPENDITURE SURVEY. 1972. quinquennial. S.$10.70. Department of Statistics, 8 Shenton Way 10-01 Treasuru Bldg., Singapore 0106, Singapore. TEL 3209702. FAX 3209689. TELEX RS 63001 STAT. charts; stat.
  Description: Includes information on household consumption expenditure, income and consumer durables.

HOMOSEXUALITY

A S P E. (Agenzia di Stampa sui Problemi dell'Emarginazione) see SOCIAL SERVICES AND WELFARE

301.415 200   AT
ACCEPTANCE NEWSLETTER. 1975. m. Aus.$25 membership. Acceptance Melbourne Inc., P.O. Box 276, Carlton South, Vic. 3053, Australia. TEL 03-329-6862. bk.rev. circ. 300. (back issues avail.) **Document type:** newsletter.
  Description: For gay Catholics and Christians.

052   US
ACT UP - L A NEWS.* 1988. bi-m. free. 3924 W. Sunset Blvd., No. 2, Los Angeles, CA 90029-2242. illus.; index.
  Formerly: Act Up Los Angeles Newsletter.

301.415   GW
ADAM; das Original. 1970. m. $150. Foerster-Verlag GmbH, Alte Gasse 26, 60313 Darmstadt, Germany. TEL 069-2978681. FAX 069-2978567. circ. 28,000. **Document type:** bulletin.

ADAM EROTOMIC. see MEN'S INTERESTS

301.1   US
ADVENT. 1979. q. $30. Lutherans Concerned - San Francisco, 566 Vallejo St., Ste. 25, San Francisco, CA 94133. TEL 415-956-2069. Ed. Mark Lieu. adv. circ. 700. **Document type:** newsletter.
  Formerly: Adventus.
  Description: Promotes gay and lesbian understanding in Lutheran churches.

301.4157   US   ISSN 0001-8996
HQ76.8.U5
THE ADVOCATE (LOS ANGELES, 1967). 1967. 26/yr. $39.97. Liberation Publications, Inc., 6922 Hollywood Blvd., 10th Fl., Los Angeles, CA 90028. TEL 213-871-1225. FAX 213-467-0173. (Subscr. to: Box 541, Mt. Morris, IL 61054-7846. TEL 815-734-1157) Ed. Jeff Yarbrough. adv.; bk.rev.; film rev.; play rev.; illus. circ. 80,000. (also avail. in microform) **Indexed:** Alt.Press Ind.
  Description: National news and lifestyle magazine for the nation's gay and lesbian community.

ADVOCATE MEN. see MEN'S INTERESTS

370 200   US
AFFINITY. 1977. m. $20. Affirmation: Gay & Lesbian Mormons, Box 46022, Los Angeles, CA 90046. TEL 213-255-7251. circ. 750.
  Description: Publication in support of gay and lesbian Mormons; focuses on education of authorities and lay members regarding homosexuality.

ALICE REPORTS. see POLITICAL SCIENCE

ALL MAN. see MEN'S INTERESTS

363.49   US
AMERICAN FEDERATION OF TEACHERS. NATIONAL GAY AND LESBIAN CAUCUS. NEWSLETTER. 1990. q. membership. American Federation of Teachers, National Gay and Lesbian Caucus, Box 19856, Cincinnati, OH 45219. Eds. Lyle Rossman, Jan Smith. **Document type:** newsletter.

AMERICAN GAY & LESBIAN ATHEIST. see PHILOSOPHY

301.4157   SZ   ISSN 0259-5419
ANDERSCHUME - KONTIKI; das Schweizer Magazin fuer den schwulen Mann. (Text mainly in German; occasionally in French) 1985. q. 40 SFr. Postfach 7656, CH-8023 Zurich, Switzerland. TEL 054-7202402. Ed. D.P. Wiedmer. adv.; bk.rev.; film rev.; play rev.; video rev.; illus. circ. 6,900. (back issues avail.)
  Formed by the 1985 merger of: Anderschume & Kontiki.

301.4157   CN   ISSN 0824-2100
ANGLES; the magazine of Vancouver's lesbian, gay and bisexual communities. 1983. m. Can.$20($30) Lavender Publishing Society of British Columbia, 1170 Bute St., Vancouver, BC V6E 1Z6, Canada. TEL 604-688-0265. FAX 604-688-5405. adv.; bk.rev.; film rev.; play rev.; abstr.; illus. circ. 15,000. (back issues avail.) **Document type:** consumer publication.
  Description: Community magazine which offers a gay-lesbian perspective on contemporary events, politics, arts and entertainment.

301.415   FR
ARCHIVES, RECHERCHES ET CULTURES LESBIENNES. FEUILLE D'INFO. 1993. q. 200 F. Archives, Recherches et Cultures Lesbiennes, B.P. 362, 75526 Paris Cedex 11, France.

301.4157   US
ASSOCIATION OF GAY AND LESBIAN PSYCHIATRISTS. NEWSLETTER. 1978. q. $15 to non-members. Association of Gay and Lesbian Psychiatrists, c/o David Scasta, Ed., 1439 Pineville Rd., New Hope, PA 18938. adv.; bk.rev. circ. 400. **Document type:** newsletter.
  Formerly: American Psychiatric Association Gay Caucus. Newsletter.

ATALANTA. see WOMEN'S INTERESTS

AUF - EINE FRAUENZEITSCHRIFT. see WOMEN'S INTERESTS

AUSTRALASIAN GAY AND LESBIAN LAW JOURNAL. see LAW

363.49   US
B & G MAGAZINE; a different point of view. 1990. 11/yr. $18. B G Publishing, Box 1511, Cooper Sta., New York, NY 10276. Eds. Joseph Cornell, Yvette Anderson.

051   US   ISSN 1070-6550
▼**B-MEN.** 1993. m. Blk Publishing Company, Box 83912, Los Angeles, CA 90083-0912. TEL 310-410-0808. FAX 310-410-9250. adv.; circ. 42,000 (controlled). (back issues avail.) **Document type:** consumer publication.

B W M T - ATLANTA NEWSLETTER. (Black & White Men Together - Atlanta) see GENERAL INTEREST PERIODICALS — United States

301.412   US
BAD ATTITUDE; a lesbian sex magazine. 1984. 6/yr. $30. Bad Attitude, Inc., Box 390-110, Cambridge, MA 02139. TEL 508-372-6247. adv.; bk.rev.; illus. circ. 5,000. (back issues avail.)
  Description: Features erotic art, fiction, non-fiction, poetry, and erotic photography.

301.4157   US
BAY AREA REPORTER. 1971. w. $125. Benro Enterprises, Inc., 395 Ninth St., San Francisco, CA 94103-3831. TEL 415-861-5019. adv.; bk.rev.; circ. 37,500 (controlled). (tabloid format; also avail. in microfilm) **Document type:** newspaper.

301.4157   US   ISSN 0883-4334
BAY WINDOWS. 1983. w. $35. Bay Windows, Inc., 1523 Washington St., Boston, MA 02118. TEL 617-266-6670. Ed. Jeff Epperly; Pub. James G. Hoover. adv. contact: Ken Fulk. bk.rev.; film rev.; play rev. circ. 46,000. (tabloid format; back issues avail.) **Document type:** newspaper.

BEAU. see MEN'S INTERESTS

301.4157   GW
BERLIN & EX-DDR VON HINTEN; das Schwule Reisebuch. 1981. every 18 months. DM.16.80. Bruno Gmuender Verlag, Dessauerstr. 1-2, 10963 Berlin, Germany. TEL 030-25498200. FAX 030-2629162. Ed. Ralf Waldau. circ. 12,000. **Document type:** directory.
  Formerly: Berlin von Hinten (ISSN 0932-4887)

301.4157   NE
BEST GUIDE TO AMSTERDAM & THE BENELUX; for gay men and lesbians, with country and city maps. (Text in English) 1986. biennial. $16.95. Bookscene, P.O. Box 22320, 1100 CH Amsterdam, Netherlands. TEL 31-20-6002087. FAX 31-20-6950907. Ed. Brian Crawford. circ. 9,500.
  Former titles: Best Guide to Amsterdam and Benelux Venues; Best Guide to Amsterdam (for Gay Men).
  Description: Tourist guide to Amsterdam and other major cities in the Netherlands, Luxembourg and Belgium for gay and lesbian visitors.

301.415 919.04   NE
BEST GUIDE TO ASIA, AUSTRALASIA, AND SOUTH PACIFIC ISLANDS; for gay men, with country and city maps. (Text in English) 1989. biennial. $15.95. Bookscene, P.O. Box 22320, 1100 CH Amsterdam, Netherlands. TEL 31-20-6002087. FAX 31-20-6950907. Ed. Brian Crawford. charts; illus. circ. 7,500.
  Description: Tourist guide for the gay visitor to the Asian and South Pacific areas.

301.415 918.04   NE
▼**BEST GUIDE TO CARIBBEAN, CENTRAL AND SOUTH AMERICAN LANDS;** for gay men, with country and city maps. (Text in English) 1992. biennial. $16.95. Bookscene, P.O. Box 22320, 1100 CH Amsterdam, Netherlands. TEL 31-20-6002087. FAX 31-20-6950907. Ed. Brian Crawford. charts; illus. circ. 5,000.
  Description: Tourist guide for the gay visitor to the Caribbean, Central and South American countries.

301.415 914.4   NE
▼**BEST GUIDE TO FRANCE, SPAIN, AND PORTUGAL;** for gay men, with country and city maps. (Text in English) 1992. biennial. $16.95. Bookscene, P.O. Box 22320, 1100 CH Amsterdam, Netherlands. TEL 31-20-6002087. FAX 31-20-6950907. Ed. Brian Crawford. charts; illus. circ. 5,000.
  Description: Tourist guide for the gay visitor to France, Spain and Portugal.

301.4157   NE
BEST GUIDE TO GREAT BRITAIN; for gay men, with city maps. (Text in English) 1987. biennial. $11.95. Bookscene, P.O. Box 22320, 1100 CH Amsterdam, Netherlands. TEL 31-20-6002087. FAX 31-20-6950907. circ. 5,000.
  Description: Tourist guide to Great Britain for gay visitors.

301.415 910.202   NE
▼**BEST GUIDE TO MEDITERRANEAN LANDS;** for gay men, with country and city maps. (Text in English) 1992. biennial. $16.95. Bookscene, P.O. Box 22320, 1100 CH Amsterdam, Netherlands. TEL 31-20-6002087. FAX 31-20-6950907. Ed. Brian Crawford. charts; illus. circ. 5,000.
  Description: Tourist guide for the gay visitor to the countries on the Mediterranean.

301.415 915.04   NE
BEST GUIDE TO THE NORTH PACIFIC AND ORIENT; for gay men, with country and city maps. (Text in English) 1989. biennial. $16.95. Bookscene, P.O. Box 22320, 1100 CH Amsterdam, Netherlands. TEL 31-20-6002087. FAX 31-20-6950907. Ed. Brian Crawford. charts; illus. circ. 5,000.
  Description: Tourist guide for the gay visitor to China, Hawaii, Japan, Laos, Malaysia, Koreas, Taiwan, Myanmar (Burma), Indonesia, Macua, Hong Kong, Singapore, Philippines, Thailand, Vietnam, Cambodia, the Marshall Islands and Micronesia.

051   US   ISSN 1049-3298
BLACK LACE. 1991. q. $20 (foreign $36). Blk Publishing Company, Box 83912, Los Angeles, CA 90083-0912. TEL 213-410-0808. FAX 213-410-9250. Ed. Alycee J. Lane. circ. 4,500. (reprint service avail.) **Document type:** consumer publication.
  Description: Erotic magazine for black lesbians.

HOMOSEXUALITY

051 US ISSN 1049-3271
▼**BLACKFIRE**. 1992. bi-m. $30 (foreign $54). Blk Publishing Company, Box 83912, Los Angeles, CA 90083-0912. TEL 213-410-0808. FAX 213-410-9250. Ed. Alan Bell. adv.; bk.rev. circ. 15,000. (back issues avail.) **Document type:** consumer publication.
 Description: Erotic magazine for black gay men.

051 US ISSN 1043-0075
HQ75
BLK; the national black lesbian and gay newsmagazine. 1988. m. $18 (foreign $29). Blk Publishing Company, Box 83912, Los Angeles, CA 90083-0912. TEL 213-410-0808. FAX 213-410-9250. Ed. Don Thomas. adv. circ. 37,000. (also avail. in microfilm; reprint service avail.) Indexed: Alt.Press Ind. **Document type:** consumer publication.
 —UMI.
 Description: National newsmagazine for for black lesbians and gay men. Includes news, feature stories, a media column, calendar of events, cartoons and resource listing.

301.415 US ISSN 0279-3733
BLUEBOY. 1975. bi-m. $47.40. Hautaur Publishing, 519 8th Ave., New York, NY 10018. TEL 212-967-6262. Ed. Dana Bryan. adv.; bk.rev. circ. 100,000.

301.415 051 US
BOLD GAY LIFE STYLE. vol.2, no.1, 1991. 12/yr. $17. True T M Publishing, Inc., 2609 S. Highland, Box 18000-5, Las Vegas, NV 89109. TEL 702-796-9966. FAX 702-796-5655. Ed. R. Diamond.

282 US
BONDINGS. 1978. q. $10 (foreign $15) in an envelope. New Ways Ministry, 4012 29th St., Mt. Rainier, MD 20712. TEL 301-277-5674. Ed. Greg Link. bk.rev.; circ. 3,000 (paid); 2,000 (controlled). (tabloid format; back issues avail.)
 Description: Addresses issues relating to homosexuality and the Catholic Church.

BOOKS BOHEMIAN; hard-to-find, out-of-print, used. see *LITERATURE*

BOOKS FOR MEN. see *LITERATURE*

363.49 US ISSN 1070-0161
BRAVE NEW TICK. 1985. m. Graftographic Press, Box 24, S. Grafton, MA 01560-0024. TEL 508-799-3769. Ed. Paul N. Dion-Deitch. adv. circ. 85. (back issues avail.) **Document type:** newsletter.
 Formerly (until 1993): Bloated Tick.
 Description: Covers gay issues, rights, art, poetry, reviews and commentary.

BRIDGES: A JOURNAL FOR JEWISH FEMINISTS AND OUR FRIENDS. see *WOMEN'S STUDIES*

301.4157 CN
C L G R O NEWSLETTER. 1975. q. Can.$25. Coalition for Lesbian and Gay Rights in Ontario, Box 822, Sta. A, Toronto, ON M5W 1G3, Canada. TEL 416-533-6824. circ. 500. **Document type:** newsletter.
 Formerly: C G R O Newsletter.
 Description: Outreach to members of the coalition.

301.4157 028.1 US ISSN 1043-383X
PN56.H57
CABIRION: GAY BOOKS BULLETIN. 1978. 2/yr. $6. Gay Academic Union, Inc., Scholarship Committee, Box 480, Lenox Hill Station, New York, NY 10021. TEL 212-864-0361. Ed. Wayne Dynes. bk.rev. circ. 500. (back issues avail.) Indexed: M.L.A.
 Formerly: Gay Books Bulletin.

301.4157 AT
CAMPAIGN AUSTRALIA. 1975. m. Aus.$50 (foreign Aus.$75). Worlander Publishing, P.O. Box A228, Sydney South, N.S.W. 2000, Australia. TEL 02-332-3620. FAX 02-361-5962. Ed. Greg Callaghan. adv. contact: Dario Burgel. bk.rev.; film rev, play rev, illus. circ. 16,500. (back issues avail.)
 Description: Offers a forum for Australia's gay creative writers, journalists, and gay activists, to write articles dealing with the gay lifestyle.

157.734 UK
CAPITAL GAY. 1981. w. £29. Stonewall Press Ltd., Units 58-60, 49 Effra Rd., London SW2 1BZ, England. TEL 071-738-7010. FAX 071-924-9174. (Subscr. to: G.C.O.D.S., P.O. Box 44, Welwyn Garden City AL7 2DE, England) Ed. Gillian Rodgerson. adv.; bk.rev.; film rev.; play rev.; circ. 20,247 (controlled). (tabloid format) **Document type:** newspaper.

363.49 UK
CAPITOL GAY. w. Capitol Gay, 38 Mount Pleasant, London WC1X OAP, England. adv.; illus.

CELEBRASIAN. see *ETHNIC INTERESTS*

CENTER STAGE (NEW YORK). see *THEATER*

301 US ISSN 0894-8984
CENTER VOICE. 1985. m. $25. Lesbian & Gay Community Services Center, Inc., 208 W. 13th St., New York, NY 10011. TEL 212-620-7310. Ed. Richard Burns. adv. circ. 23,000. (back issues avail.)
 Description: Newsletter of activities, announcements, events and financial affairs of the Center.

051 US ISSN 0277-1675
CHALLENGE (CONVENT STATION). 1975. m. $15 (effective Oct. 1991). Gay Activist Alliance in Morris County, Box 137, Convent Station, NJ 07961. TEL 908-534-6347. FAX 201-285-5590. adv.; bk.rev. circ. 450. (looseleaf format) **Document type:** newsletter.
 Description: Provides information about events of the organization and the community.

301.415 US
CHIRON RISING; entertainment for mature men and admirers. q. $5 per no. Box 2589, Victorville, CA 92393.
 Description: Contains drawings, photos, and stories for gay men.

CHRISTOPHER STREET. see *LITERARY AND POLITICAL REVIEWS*

301.4157 US
CLUB GOLDENROD. q. $45. Continental Spectator, Box 278, Canal St. Sta., New York, NY 10013. TEL 800-325-4122. Ed. Randy Rushmore.
 Description: Contains contact ads, stories, and articles.

301.4157 301.412 US ISSN 0891-6969
COMMON LIVES - LESBIAN LIVES. 1981. q. $15 to individuals; institutions $25. Box 1553, Iowa City, IA 52244. Ed.Bd. adv.; bk.rev. circ. 3,000.
 Description: Seeks to document the experiences and thoughts of lesbians past, present, and future, by providing a forum for developing and clarifying lesbian - defined social and political relationships.

301.4157 US
COMMUNITY NEWS (SALEM). 1977. m. $10. Chuck Simpson, Pub., Box 663, Salem, OR 97308-0663. TEL 503-363-0006. Ed. Don Mathews. adv. contact: Linda Evans. bk.rev.; film rev. circ. 7,500. (tabloid format; back issues avail.) **Document type:** newspaper.
 Description: Non-profit gay-lesbian newspaper.

301.4157 US
COMMUNITY YELLOW PAGES. (In 3 eds.: Los Angeles, Long Beach - Orange County, and San Diego) 1982. a. free. 2305 Canyon Dr., Los Angeles, CA 90068-2411. TEL 213-469-4454. FAX 213-469-2531. Ed. Jeanne Cordova. adv. circ. 160,000 (100,000 LA ed.; 35,000 Long Beach - Orange County ed.; 25,000 San Diego ed.). (back issues avail.) **Document type:** directory.
 Description: Directory of organizations, businesses and professional services owned, operated and staffed by gays and lesbians welcoming gay and lesbian clientele.

301 US ISSN 0741-9872
CONCORD. 1976. q. $20. Lutherans Concerned North America, Box 10461, Fort Dearborn Sta., Chicago, IL 60610. Ed. Jim Kocher. circ. 1,200. **Document type:** newsletter.

301.4157 US
CRUISE ENTERTAINMENT MAGAZINE. 1979. w. $60. Tony Rome Enterprises, Inc., Box 398, Royal Oak, MI 48068. TEL 313-369-1900. Ed. Phillip O'Jibway. adv. contact: Tony Rome. bk.rev. circ. 5,000. **Document type:** consumer publication.
 Description: Information on gay-lesbian activities in Michigan-Ohio area.

CUNT. see *WOMEN'S INTERESTS*

157.734 US
D P F NEWSLETTER. 1981. bi-m. $25. Diaper Pail Friends, 38 Miller Ave., Ste. 127, Mill Valley, CA 94941. Ed. Thomas E. Siegel. circ. 1,500. (back issues avail.) **Document type:** newsletter.
 Description: For people interested in the adult baby games.

DAMRON ADDRESS BOOK. see *TRAVEL AND TOURISM*

DAMRON ROAD ATLAS. see *TRAVEL AND TOURISM*

301.415 AT
DARWIN GAY AND LESBIAN NEWSLETTER. 1985. m.? Aus.$5. Darwin Gay Society, P.O. Box 3926, Darwin, N.T. 0801, Australia. TEL 089-816812. Ed. Mark Wilson. adv.; bk.rev. circ. 230. **Document type:** newsletter.
 Formerly: Darwin Gay Informer (ISSN 1030-5025)
 Description: News about social events and AIDS reports.

051 US
DENEUVE. 1991. bi-m. $24. Outspoken Enterprises, Inc., 2336 Market St., No. 15, San Francisco, CA 94114. TEL 415-863-6538. FAX 415-863-1609. Ed. Katie Brown. adv. contact: Lisa Tripp. bk.rev.; illus. circ. 45,000. **Document type:** consumer publication.
 Description: Covers a wide variety of topics for the lesbian community.

301.4157 808.8
011 US
A DIFFERENT LIGHT REVIEW; a catalog of gay and lesbian literature. 1979. 3/yr. free. A Different Light Bookstores, 151 W. 19th St., New York, NY 10011. TEL 212-989-4850. FAX 212-989-2158. Ed. Water Vatter. bk.rev.; index; circ. 30,000 (controlled). **Document type:** catalog.
 Formerly (until 1990): Booked for Brunch?
 Description: Review of gay and lesbian literature featuring newly published titles with descriptions.

DIGEST ON GAY RIGHTS; I: human - civil rights. see *LAW*

301 US ISSN 0147-1139
DIGNITY - U S A. 1969. q. $20. Dignity - U S A, 1500 Massachusetts Ave. N.W., Ste. 11, Washington, DC 20005. TEL 202-861-0017. Ed. Michael J. Bushek. bk.rev.; tr.lit. circ. 5,000.

301.4157 301.412 US
DINAH. 1976. q. $10. Lesbian Activist Bureau, Inc., Box 1485, Cincinnati, OH 45201. Ed. Karen Phebe Beiser. adv.; bk.rev.; illus. circ. 500.

023 US ISSN 1051-547X
Z720.A4
DIRECTORY OF GAY AND LESBIAN LIBRARY WORKERS. 1990. a. American Library Association, Gay & Lesbian Task Force, c/o Office of Outreach Services, ALA, 50 E. Huron St., Chicago, IL 60611. **Document type:** directory.

301 US
DIRECTORY OF HOMOSEXUAL ORGANIZATIONS AND PUBLICATIONS. irreg. $6. Homosexual Information Center, 115 Monroe St., Bossier City, LA 71111. TEL 318-742-4709. (Alt. addr.: Box 8252, Universal City, CA 91608) Ed. Ursula Enters Copely. (back issues avail.) **Document type:** directory.
 Description: Guide to the homosexual movement in the US; access to sources and services.

301.415 GW
DON & ADONIS; Deutschlands Magazin von Maennern fuer Maenner. 1970. bi-m. $80. Foerster-Verlag GmbH, Alte Gasse 26, 60313 Frankfurt a.M., Germany. TEL 069-2978681. FAX 069-2978567. adv.; bk.rev.; play rev.; circ. 23,000 (controlled). **Document type:** consumer publication.
 Formerly: Don.

HOMOSEXUALITY

301.4157 US ISSN 1055-7415
DRUMMER. 1975. m. $70. Desmodus Inc., Box 410390, San Francisco, CA 94141-0390. TEL 415-252-1195. Ed. Mercus - Jay Wonacott. adv.; bk.rev.; film rev.; play rev.; illus. circ. 45,000. (back issues avail.)

157.734 374 US
DUNGEONMASTER. 1979. q. $24. Desmodus Inc., Box 410390, San Francisco, CA 94141-0390. TEL 415-252-1195. Ed. Marcus - Jay Wonacott. adv.; bk.rev.; illus. circ. 16,500. (back issues avail.)

301.4157 301.412 US
DYKE DIANNIC WICCA SEPARATIST AMAZON MAGICK. irreg. $3 per no. Box 486, Berkeley, CA 94701-0486. Ed. Amethyst-Artemis.

EDUCATIONAL T V CHANNEL NEWSLETTER. see *CLUBS*

EIDOS; sexual freedom and erotic entertainment for women, men and couples. see *WOMEN'S INTERESTS*

200 051 US ISSN 0892-1490
EMERGE!; a journal for Christian Scientists supporting lesbians, bisexuals, and gay men. 1986. bi-m. $25. (Emergence International) Kentner Scott, Ed.& Pub., Box 9161, San Rafael, CA 94912-9161. TEL 415-485-1881. FAX 415-459-0544. bk.rev.; circ. 300 (paid).
  Formerly: Emergence.
  Description: Contains articles, poems and reports of spiritual healing.

301.415 362.8 US ISSN 1047-9074
HQ76.5
EMPATHY; an interdisciplinary journal for persons working to end oppression on the basis of sexual identities. 1988. s-a. $15 to individuals; institutions $20; libraries $25 (effective Sep. 1992). Gay and Lesbian Advocacy Research Project, Inc., Box 5085, Columbia, SC 29250. TEL 803-791-1607. Ed. James T. Sears. adv.; bk.rev.; bibl.; illus. circ. 2,000. (back issues avail.) Document type: academic/scholarly publication.
  —UnCover.
  Description: Contains original essays and selected articles from gay, lesbian and bisexual publications. Includes prose and poetry, practitioner articles, anecdotes, research reports and photography. For workers in education, counseling, health care, social work and the ministry.
  Refereed Serial

301.4157 US
EMPTY CLOSET; gay, lesbian and bisexual newspaper for Rochester-Genesee Valley. 1971. m. $10. Gay Alliance of Genesee Valley, Inc., 179 Atlantic Ave., Rochester, NY 14607-1255. TEL 716-244-9030. Ed. Susan Jordan. adv.; bk.rev.; illus. circ. 4,500. (tabloid format) Document type: newspaper.

301.4157 US
EQUAL TIME NEWSPAPER; a non-profit community newspaper for lesbians, gay men and bisexuals. 1982. w. $80. Lavender Inc., 310 E. 38th St., Ste. 207, Minneapolis, MN 55409. TEL 612-823-3836. FAX 612-823-2615. Ed. Robyn Dochterman. adv.; bk.rev.; film rev.; play rev. circ. 24,500. (tabloid format; also avail. in microfilm; back issues avail.) Document type: newspaper.

EROTIC EARTHBODY; sacred sexuality, eros and the life force - networking our way toward evolution. see *WOMEN'S INTERESTS*

THE EVERGREEN CHRONICLES; a journal of gay and lesbian arts and cultures. see *LITERATURE*

F L G C NEWSLETTER. (Friends for Lesbian and Gay Concerns) see *RELIGIONS AND THEOLOGY*

301.4157 US ISSN 0046-3167
HQ76.5
FAG RAG. 1970. s-a. $10. Fag Rag, Inc., Box 15331, Kenmore Sta., Boston, MA 02215. TEL 617-661-7534. Ed.Bd. bk.rev.; illus. circ. 5,000. (tabloid format; also avail. in microform from UMI; back issues avail.) Indexed: Abstr.Pop.Cult.; Alt.Press Ind.

301.415 US
FAMILY RESEARCH REPORT. 1984. bi-m. $20 (effective July 1992). Family Research Institute, Inc., Box 2091, Washington, DC 20013. TEL 703-690-8536. Ed. Paul Cameron. circ. 6,500. Document type: newsletter.
  Description: Covers sexual social policy and gay rights.

301.4157 US
FAT APPLE REVIEW. 1978. m. $35 membership. Girth & Mirth Club of New York, Inc., Box 10, Pelham, NY 10803. TEL 914-699-7735. Ed. Buzz Kolwyck. adv. circ. 500. (looseleaf format) Document type: newsletter.
  Description: Provides news of interest to gay chubby men and their admirers.

301.4157 910.202 US
FERRARI'S PLACES FOR MEN (YEAR). (Text in English; introduction in French, German, Italian, Spanish) 1985. a. $13.95. Ferrari Publications, Inc., Box 37887, Phoenix, AZ 85069. TEL 602-863-2408. Ed. Marianne Ferrari.
  Formerly: Places for Men (Year).

301.4157 910.202 US
FERRARI'S PLACES FOR WOMEN: USA AND WORLDWIDE. a. $12. Ferrari Publications, Inc., Box 37887, Phoenix, AZ 85069. TEL 602-863-2408. adv. circ. 20,000.
  Former titles: Places for Women: USA and Worldwide; Places of Interest to Women: USA and Worldwide (ISSN 0731-0951); Places of Interest to Women: USA and Canada.
  Description: International lesbian travel guide.

301.4157 910.202 US
FERRARI'S PLACES OF INTEREST (YEAR); worldwide gay and lesbian guide. 1980. a. $14.95. Ferrari Publications, Inc., Box 37887, Phoenix, AZ 85069. TEL 602-863-2408. Ed. Marianne Ferrari. adv. circ. 25,000.
  Formerly: Places of Interest (Year) (ISSN 0731-096X)
  Description: Gay travel guide with feature articles written by the gay and lesbian press worldwide.

301.4157 US ISSN 0744-6349
FIRSTHAND MAGAZINE; experiences for loving men. 1980. m. $48. FirstHand Ltd., 310 Cedar Lane, Teaneck, NJ 07666. TEL 201-836-9177. FAX 201-836-5055. Ed. Bob Harris. adv.; bk.rev.; film rev.; play rev.; rec.rev.; illus. circ. 80,000. (back issues avail.)
  Description: Covers erotic fiction, articles and art.

301.4157 US
FOOT FRATERNITY. 1980. q. $45. Box 24102, Cleveland, OH 44124. TEL 216-449-4114. FAX 216-449-0114. Ed. Doug Gaines. adv.; bk.rev.; film rev.; illus.; stat. circ. 3,000.
  Description: Listing of men with a boot, foot, shoe, or sock fetish; helps people find others with similar interests.

808.8 UK
FORMALLY INC..* 1975. q. Millivres Ltd., 238 Camden High St., London NW1 7BX, England. circ. 1,000.
  Formerly: Gay World.

301 GW ISSN 0931-4091
PN56.H57
FORUM HOMOSEXUALITAET UND LITERATUR. 1987. 3/yr. DM.30. Universitaet - Gesamthochschule Siegen, Fachbereich 3, Postfach 101240, 57012 Siegen, Germany. TEL 0271-7402159. FAX 0271-7402330. Ed. Wolfgang Popp. adv.; bk.rev. circ. 1,100. Document type: academic/scholarly publication.

FRAMELINE NEWS. see *MOTION PICTURES*

301.4157 GW
FRANKFURT - RHEIN MAIN NECKAR SAAR VON HINTEN. 1981. every 18 mos. DM.16.80. Bruno Gmuender Verlag, Dessaustr. 1-2, 10963 Berlin, Germany. TEL 030-25498200. FAX 030-2629162. Ed. Ralf Waldau. circ. 5,000. Document type: directory.
  Formerly: Frankfurt von Hinten (ISSN 0932-4909)

FRAU OHNE HERZ; eine Zeitschrift fuer Frauen und andere Lesben. see *WOMEN'S INTERESTS*

FRIGHTEN THE HORSES; a document of the sexual revolution. see *SOCIOLOGY*

323.4 US
FRONT PAGE. 1979. s-m. $35. Bugle Publishing, Box 27928, Raleigh, NC 27611. TEL 919-829-0181. FAX 919-829-0830. Ed. Rog Faggart. adv.; bk.rev. circ. 12,000. (tabloid format; back issues avail.) Document type: newspaper.
  Description: Provides local news and features of interest to the gay and lesbian community.

051 US
FRONTIERS. 1982. bi-w. $39. Mercury Capital, Inc., 7985 Santa Monica Blvd., Ste. 109, W. Hollywood, CA 90046. TEL 213-848-2222. FAX 213-656-8784. Ed. Bill Geiger. adv.; bk.rev. circ. 42,000.

301.4157 CN ISSN 0831-1625
FUGUES. (Text mainly in French, occasionally English) 1983. m. Can.$30($35) Editions Nitram Inc., C.P. 335, Succ. C, Montreal, PQ H2L 4K3, Canada. TEL 514-848-1854. FAX 514-845-7645. Ed. Martin Hamel. adv.: B&W and color; B&W page Can.$495; 4 3/4 x 7 1/4; adv. contact: Tim Nugent. circ. 35,000. (back issues avail.)

363.49 US
G L A A D BULLETIN. bi-m. $35 for individual membership. Gay and Lesbian Alliance Against Defamation, 150 W. 26th St., Ste. 503, New York, NY 10001-6813. Ed. Ellen Carton. Document type: bulletin.

301.4157 378 US
G L A S OF (YEAR). 1972. q. free. Gay and Lesbian Alliance at Stanford, Box 8265, Stanford, CA 94305-0215. TEL 415-723-1488. adv.; bk.rev. circ. 500. (back issues avail.)

301.4157 323.4 US ISSN 1059-065X
G L B AMES NEWSLETTER. 1980. m. $7. (Gays, Lesbians and Bisexuals of Ames) G L A, Inc., Box 1761, Ames, IA 50010-1761. TEL 515-382-3223. Ed. Allan Beatty. adv.; bk.rev.; film rev. circ. 125. (back issues avail.) Document type: newsletter.
  Formerly: G L A Newsletter (ISSN 1041-7729)

301.4157 US
G L I B NEWS. (Gaymen and Lesbians in Brookhaven) 1981. bi-m. $10 contribution. Old South Haven Presbyterian Church, Box 203, Brookhaven, NY 11719. TEL 516-286-6867. Ed. J. DuRell Fleming. bk.rev. circ. 580. (looseleaf format) Document type: newsletter.
  Former titles: G L I B Notes; G L I B Newsletter.
  Description: Provides information about GLIB events, programs and news of interest to the gay community on Long Island.

301.415 US ISSN 1064-2684
HQ75 CODEN: JLGSES
▼**G L Q.** (Gay and Lesbian Quarterly); a journal of lesbian and gay studies. 1993. 4/yr. 29 ECU (effective 1993). Gordon & Breach Science Publishers, 820 Town Center Dr., Langhorne, PA 19047. TEL 215-750-2642. FAX 215-750-6343. (UK subscr. to: P.O. Box 90, Reading, Berkshire RG1 8JL, England. TEL 0734-560-080) (also avail. in microform)
  —CCC.
  Description: Publishes scholarship, criticism and commentary in the rapidly expanding interdisciplinary field of gay and lesbian studies.

363.49 020 US ISSN 1045-2893
G L T F NEWSLETTER. 1988. q. $5. American Library Association, Gay and Lesbian Task Force of the Social Responsibilities Round Table, Office of Library Outreach Services, 50 E. Huron St., Chicago, IL 60611. TEL 800-545-2433. FAX 312-440-9374. TELEX 490992000 ALA UI. adv.; bk.rev.; index. circ. 400. Document type: newsletter.
  Description: Information on library services to gay and lesbian library users and on issues related to gay and lesbian librarians and librarianship.

301.415 FR ISSN 0755-0251
GAI PIED HEBDO. 1979. w. 728 F. Editions du Triangle Rose, 45 rue Sedaine, 75557 Paris Cedex 11, France. TEL 43-57-52-05. FAX 43-57-80-40. Ed. Yves Charfe. adv.; bk.rev. circ. 43,000. (also avail. in microfilm; back issues avail.)
  Description: Includes information about cultural, political and sociological points of interest for the gay community.

HOMOSEXUALITY

301.4157 910.4 UK
GAIA'S GUIDE. 1973. a. $9.50. 11 Northington St., London WC1, England. Ed. Sandy Horn. adv.; bk.rev. circ. 8,000.
  Description: International guidebook for gay women. Lists bars, clubs, publications, centers, switchboards and bookstores.

301.1 150 US
GANYMEDIA. 1985. m. $25. Integrity - Chicago, Inc., Box 2516, Chicago, IL 60690. TEL 312-477-4196. Ed. David Lochman. bk.rev.; abstr. circ. 300. (tabloid format)

301.415 387.7 US
▼**GAY AIRLINE & TRAVEL CLUB NEWSLETTER.** 1993. q. $29 (effective Jan. 1993). (Gay Airline & Travel Club) Fan Club Publishing, Box 69A04, Dept. UL, W. Hollywood, CA 90069. TEL 213-650-5112. Ed. Louis Wendruck. adv.: page $800. bk.rev. circ. 10,000. (back issues avail.) **Document type:** newsletter.
  Formerly: Gay Airline Club Newsletter.
  Description: Provides a social organization for gay airline or travel industry employees, travelers, and collectors of airline memorabilia.

301.4157 US
GAY BOOK. 1981. s-a. $18. Rainbow Ventures, Inc., 584 Castro, Ste. 632, San Francisco, CA 94114. TEL 415-928-1859. Ed. Norman F. Bruce. adv.; bk.rev.; video rev. circ. 50,000. **Document type:** directory.
  Description: Business - resource - yellow-page type directory for the Gay - Lesbian community. Features a comprehensive resource guide of information for clubs, organizations, and AIDS. Includes women's business listings.

301.4157 US
GAY CHICAGO MAGAZINE. 1976. w. $96. Gernhardt Publications, Inc., 3121 N. Broadway, Chicago, IL 60657-4522. TEL 312-327-7271. FAX 312-327-0112. Ed. Ralph Gernhardt. adv.; bk.rev. circ. 22,000.

301 323 US ISSN 0147-0728
HQ75
GAY COMMUNITY NEWS (BOSTON); * the national weekly for lesbians and gay men. 1973. w. $39 to individuals; institutions $55. Bromfield Street Educational Foundation, Inc., 25 West St., Boston, MA 02111-1213. TEL 617-426-4469. FAX 617-426-2723. adv.; bk.rev.; film rev.; play rev.; illus.; index. circ. 15,000. (tabloid format; also avail. in microfilm; back issues avail.) **Indexed:** Alt.Press Ind.

301.415 GW
GAY EXPRESS. 1984. m. Verlag W.D. Fritsch, Zimmerstr. 38a, 22085 Hamburg, Germany. TEL 040-2204001. Ed. Bernd Schuemann. circ. 25,000.

301.41 US ISSN 0163-9897
GAY INSURGENT; * a gay left journal. no.4-5, 1979. 2/yr. $5. Alternative Distribution, Box 28977, Santa Ana, CA 92799-8977. Ed. Daniel Tsang. adv.; bk.rev.; bibl. circ. 2,000. (also avail. in microfilm from UMI) **Indexed:** Alt.Press Ind., CALL.
  Formerly: Midwest Gay Academic Journal.

323.4 UK ISSN 0307-9813
GAY LEFT; a socialist journal produced by gay people. 1975. s-a. 50p.($2) per issue. Gay Left Collective, 38 Chalcot Rd., London N.W. 1., England. Ed.Bd. bk.rev.; film rev.; illus. circ. 3,000. (also avail. in microfiche) **Indexed:** Alt.Press Ind.

051 US
GAY PEOPLES CHRONICLE. 1984. fortn. $40 (effective 1993). K W I R Publications, Box 5426, Cleveland, OH 44101. TEL 216-621-5280. FAX 216-621-5282. Ed. Kevin J. Beaney. adv. contact: Patricia Harris. bk.rev. circ. 15,000. (back issues avail.) **Document type:** newspaper.
  Description: Covers news, announcements and events of interest to the gay, lesbian and bisexual communities of northern Ohio.

301.4157 US ISSN 0016-5298
GAY SCENE. 1970. m. $16. Regiment Publications, Box 247, Grand Central Station, New York, NY 10163. Ed. Bruce King. adv.; bk.rev.; film rev.; charts; illus.

157.734 323.4 UK ISSN 0142-0313
GAY SCOTLAND; for lesbians, gays & bisexuals. Short title: G S. 1978. m. £29.20 to the U.S. and Canada. 58A Broughton St., Edinburgh EH1 3SA, Scotland. TEL 031-557-2625. FAX 041-333-1949. Ed. Dominic d'Angelo. adv. contact: John Wilkes. bk.rev.; circ. 5,600 (paid). (back issues avail.) **Document type:** consumer publication.
  ●Also available online.

301.41 UK
GAY STAR. 1976. q. £5($15) Sean McGouran, Ed. & Pub., 33 Athol St., Belfast BT12 4GX, N. Ireland. adv.; bk.rev. circ. 1,000. (also avail. in microform; back issues avail.) **Document type:** bulletin.
  Former titles: Northern Gay; N I G R A News.

301.415 UK ISSN 0950-6101
GAY TIMES. 1974. m. £18 (foreign £32). Millivres Ltd., Worldwide House, Ground Fl., 116-134 Bayham St., London NW1 0BA, England. TEL 071-482-2576. FAX 071-284-0329. Ed. John Marshall. adv.; bk.rev.; film rev.; play rev. circ. 41,000.
  Incorporates (in 1983): Gay News.
  Description: Contains news, interviews, and features affecting the life and interests of the gay community.

301.4157 320 US
GAY VOTE. 1978. m. $30. Harvey Milk Lesbian & Gay Democratic Club, Box 14368, San Francisco, CA 94114. TEL 415-773-9545. Ed. Geoffrey Kors. adv.; bk.rev. circ. 25,000. (back issues avail.)

301.4157 028.5 US
GAY YOUTH COMMUNITY NEWS. 1979. irreg. $5. Gay Youth Community Coalition, Box 846, San Francisco, CA 94101. TEL 415-386-4297. Ed. Michael Nulty. adv.; illus, stat. circ. 10,000. (tabloid format; back issues avail.) **Document type:** newspaper.

380.1 301.4157 US ISSN 0363-826X
GAYELLOW PAGES; classified directory of lesbian and gay U S A and Canada organizations and businesses. 1973. a. $12. Box 533, Village Station, New York, NY 10014-0533. TEL 212-674-0120. Ed. Frances Green. adv. circ. 50,000. **Document type:** directory.

363.49 US ISSN 1071-8427
▼**GAYME.** 1993. s-a. $10 (foreign $15). Zymurgy, Box 15645, Kenmore Sta., Boston, MA 02215. TEL 617-695-8015. Ed. Bill Andriette. adv.; B&W page $400. circ. 4,000. (back issues avail.)
  Description: Gay journal focusing on youth culture and sexuality.

301.4 US
GAYPAPER. Variant title: Baltimore Gay Paper. 1979. bi-m. $45. Gay and Lesbian Community Center of Baltimore, Ltd., Box 22575, Baltimore, MD 21203. TEL 301-837-7748. FAX 301-837-8512. Ed. Mike Chase. adv.; bk.rev. circ. 15,000. (also avail. in microfiche)

301.415 AT ISSN 0813-7196
GAYZETTE; newsletter of the mixed gay movement. 1984. m. Aus.$15 (foreign Aus.$ 27). P.O. Box 108, Carlton North, Vic. 3054, Australia. Ed.Bd. bk.rev. circ. 200. **Document type:** newsletter.

GENRE (NEW YORK). see *MEN'S INTERESTS*

GIRL JOCK. see *LITERATURE*

GLAD RAG. see *MEN'S INTERESTS*

301.4157 301.412 US
GRAPEVINE (SEASIDE). * q. membership. c/o L.J. Allen, Ed., 2829 W. Carolina Ave., Chickasha, OK 73018-6258.

301.415 323.4 US ISSN 1047-8906
THE GUIDE: GAY TRAVEL, ENTERTAINMENT, POLITICS, AND SEX. 1980. m. $25. Fidelity Publishing, Box 593, Boston, MA 02199. TEL 617-266-8557. FAX 617-266-1125. Ed. French Wall. adv.; bk.rev.; film rev. circ. 30,000. (back issues avail.) **Document type:** consumer publication.
  Formerly: Guide to the Gay Northeast.
  Description: To inform and entertain the gay community about travel, politics, sexuality, and gay history.

301.4157 US
GUIDE MAGAZINE (SEATTLE). 1986. m. $15.95. One in Ten Publishing Co., Box 23070, Seattle, WA 98102. TEL 206-323-7374. Ed. Roger Sandon. adv.; bk.rev.; film rev.; play rev.; illus. circ. 11,000. (back issues avail.)
  Description: Humor pieces, poetry, feature stories and interpretive essays examining personalities, politics, science, religion, current events and art as they relate to gay and lesbian life.

301.4157 US
GUYS. 1988. m. $52. FirstHand Ltd., 310 Cedar Lane, Box 1314, Teaneck, NJ 07666. TEL 201-836-9177. FAX 201-836-5055. Ed. William Spencer. adv. circ. 60,000. (back issues avail.)
  Description: Covers erotic fiction.

301.4157 CN
H A L O NEWSLETTER. (Text in English) 1978. m. Can.$15. Homophile Association of London Ontario, 649 Colborne St., London, Ont. N6A 3Z2, Canada. TEL 519-433-3762. Ed. Richard Hudler. adv.: Page $32.10; 6 1/4 x 7 1/2. bk.rev. circ. 275. (back issues avail.) **Document type:** newsletter.
  Description: Keeps members informed about activities at HALO and in the London gay and lesbian communities, and provides a forum for discussion.

301.4157 GW
HAMBURG - NORDDEUTSCHLAND VON HINTEN; das schwule Reisebuch. 1981. every 18 mos. DM.16.80. Bruno Gmuender Verlag, Dessauerstr. 1-2, 10963 Berlin, Germany. TEL 030-25498200. FAX 030-2629162. Ed. Ralf Waldau. circ. 5,000. **Document type:** directory.
  Former titles: Norddeutschland von Hinten; Hamburg und Sylt von Hinten (ISSN 0932-4917)

616.858 370 360 US
HAWAII'S NATIONAL GAY COMMUNITY NEWS; Hawaii and Western States. 1973. q. $25 contribution. Gay Community News, Box 37083, Honolulu, HI 96837-0083. TEL 808-521-6000. Ed. William E. Woods. adv.; bk.rev. circ. 20,000. **Document type:** newspaper.
  Former titles: Gay Community News (Honolulu) (ISSN 1044-3002); Gay Community Center Newsletter; (until 1987): Sexual Identity Center Newsletter.
  Description: Centers on gay and AIDS issues, task force work, upcoming events. Includes a state community services directory, classifieds, announcements, and news from western states.

HEAT. see *MEN'S INTERESTS*

HERA; Binghamton's women's newspaper. see *WOMEN'S INTERESTS*

305 US
HOLY TITCLAMPS. * 1989. irreg. $3 per issue. Larry-Bob, Box 591275, San Francisco, CA 94159-1275. circ. 1,500.

HOMO XTRA. see *MEN'S INTERESTS*

363.49 NE ISSN 0166-0993
HQ75
HOMOLOGIE. 1978. bi-m. fl.40. Stichting Homologie, P.O. Box 16584, 1001 RB Amsterdam, Netherlands. TEL 31-20-6380345. Ed.Bd. adv.; bk.rev.; bibl.; illus. circ. 5,000.
  —SWETS.
  Description: Features articles about the cultural, historical, social and political contexts of gay and lesbian life in the Netherlands and other countries

323.4 301 US
HOMOSEXUAL INFORMATION CENTER. NEWSLETTER. irreg. free. Homosexual Information Center, 115 Monroe St., Bossier City, LA 71111. TEL 318-742-4709. (Alt. addr.: Box 8252, Universal City, CA 91608) bk.rev. (back issues avail.) **Document type:** newsletter.

HONCHO. see *MEN'S INTERESTS*

HONCHO OVERLOAD; two handed man to man action. see *MEN'S INTERESTS*

HOMOSEXUALITY 3043

301.4157   US   ISSN 0885-6117
HOT SHOTS (SAN DIEGO). 1986. m. $33. Sunshine Publishing Co., 7060 Convoy Ct., San Diego, CA 92111. TEL 800-333-9345. FAX 619-278-9081. Ed. Ralph Cobar. adv. circ. 45,000. (back issues avail.)
    Description: Dedicated to sexual fantasies of life among the gay community. Includes personals, letters and video reviews.

HOTHEAD PAISAN; homicidal lesbian terrorist. see *WOMEN'S INTERESTS*

HUMAN SEXUALITY. see *BIOLOGY — Physiology*

303.4157 574   US   ISSN 0898-2805
HUMBOLDT SOCIETY NEWSLETTER. 1982. bi-m. $10. Humboldt Society, Lesbian & Gay Naturalists of Philadelphia, 2030 Fitzwater St., Philadelphia, PA 19146-1333. TEL 215-985-1456. Eds. Michael J. LoFurno, Bob Wendelgass. bk.rev. circ. 125. (back issues avail.) **Document type:** newsletter.
    Description: Articles on natural sciences and ecology from a gay-lesbian perspective. Includes field trip reports.

323.4   BE   ISSN 0281-627X
I L G A BULLETIN. (Text in English, Spanish) 1981. bi-m. £60($90) to individuals; institutions £100($160). International Lesbian and Gay Association, c/o Antenne Rose, 81, rue Marche-au-Charbon, B-1000 Brussels, Belgium. TEL 32-2-502-24-71. Ed. Micha Ramakers. bk.rev.; bibl. circ. 800. (back issues avail.) **Document type:** bulletin.
    Description: Covers association activities and international lesbian and gay movement news.

301.415   US
IMAGES (NEW YORK). q. $35 for individual membership. Gay and Lesbian Alliance Against Defamation, 150 W. 26th St., Ste. 503, New York, NY 10001-6813. **Document type:** newsletter.

301.4157   US   ISSN 0744-8341
IN TOUCH FOR MEN. 1973. m. $47.50. In Touch International, Inc., 13122 Saticoy St., North Hollywood, CA 91605-3402. TEL 818-764-2288. FAX 818-764-2307. Ed. Doug DiFranco. adv.; bk.rev. circ. 70,000. (back issues avail.) **Document type:** consumer publication.

INCHES. see *MEN'S INTERESTS*

301.4157 910.202   US
INN PLACES (YEAR). 1988. a. $14.95. Ferrari Publications, Inc., Box 37887, Phoenix, AZ 85069. TEL 602-863-2408. Ed. Marianne Ferrari. circ. 10,000.
    Description: Worldwide gay and lesbian accommodations, bed and breakfast guide.

301.41   NE
ITCH. 1979. 3/yr. fl.5 per no. Hemelkrijken 10, 5612 LD Eindhoven, Netherlands. Ed.Bd. bk.rev. circ. 1,000.
    Formerly: Verkeerde Krant.

301.4157 808   US   ISSN 0891-5393
PS536.2
JAMES WHITE REVIEW; a gay men's literary quarterly. 1983. q. $12 (Canada $14; foreign $17). James White Review Association, Box 3356, Butter Quarter Sat., Minneapolis, MN 55403. TEL 612-339-8317. Ed. Bayne Holley; Pub. Phil Willkie. adv.; bk.rev.; circ. 4,500 (paid). **Indexed:** Amer.Hum.Ind., Ind.Amer.Per.Verse.
    Description: Contains poetry, prose and sketches that relate to gay men's interests.

157.734 360 616.8   US   ISSN 0891-7140
RC558   CODEN: JGLPE9
JOURNAL OF GAY & LESBIAN PSYCHOTHERAPY. 1988. q. $32 to individuals; institutions $48; libraries $75. Haworth Press, Inc., 10 Alice St., Binghamton, NY 13904. TEL 607-722-5857; 800-342-9678. FAX 607-722-1424. Ed. Dr. David Scasta. adv.; bk.rev. circ. 1,129. (also avail. in microfilm; microfiche from UMI; reprint service avail. from HAW,ISI) **Indexed:** Psychol.Abstr., Soc.Work Res.& Abstr.
  —BLDSC (4987.640000); UnCover.
    Description: Multidisciplinary professional forum for discussion of issues relating to the use of psychotherapy for gay, lesbian and bisexual clients. Goal is to facilitate the quality of life for gays and foster effective therapy for those who require support.
    Refereed Serial

JOURNAL OF GAY & LESBIAN SOCIAL SERVICES. see *SOCIAL SERVICES AND WELFARE*

301.415   US   ISSN 0091-8369
HQ75   CODEN: JOHOD7
JOURNAL OF HOMOSEXUALITY. 1974. q. $38 to individuals; institutions $160; libraries $185. (San Francisco State University, Center for Research and Education in Sexuality) Haworth Press, Inc., 10 Alice St., Binghamton, NY 13904. TEL 607-722-5857; 800-342-9678. FAX 607-722-1424. Ed. John P. De Cecco. adv.; bk.rev.; abstr.; bibl.; charts; index. circ. 895. (also avail. in microfiche from UMI; back issues avail.; reprint service avail. from HAW) **Indexed:** Abstr.Anthropol., Adol.Ment.Hlth.Abstr., Alt.Press Ind., ASSIA, Biol.Abstr., Bull.Signal., CERDIC, Crim.Just.Abstr., Curr.Cont., Excerp.Med., Human Resour.Abstr., Ind.Med., Ind.Per.Art.Relat.Law, Mag.Ind., Mid.East: Abstr.& Ind., P.A.I.S., Packag.Sci.Tech., Past.Care & Couns.Abstr., Psychol.Abstr., Psychol.R.G., Sage Fam.Stud.Abstr., Soc.Work Res.& Abstr., Sociol.Abstr., SSCI, Wom.Stud.Abstr.
  —BLDSC (5002.970000); Faxon; UnCover; SWETS.
    Description: Covers theoretical, empirical, and historical research on homosexuality, heterosexuality, sexual identity, social sex roles, and the sexual relationships of both men and women.
    Refereed Serial

JOURNAL OF SEXUAL LIBERTY. see *LAW — Civil Law*

363.49   US
JUST OUT. 1983. s-m. $35. Box 14400, Portland, OR 97214. adv.; music rev.; play rev. (tabloid format; back issues avail., reprint service avail.) **Document type:** newspaper.

KINESIS. see *PHILOSOPHY*

301.4157   GW
KOELN - RHEINLAND VON HINTEN; das schwule Reisebuch. 1981. every 18 months. DM.16.80. Bruno Gmuender Verlag, Dessauerstr. 1-2, 10963 Berlin, Germany. TEL 030-25498200. FAX 030-2629162. Ed. Ralf Waldau. adv. circ. 10,000. **Document type:** directory.
    Former titles: Nordrhein-Westfalen von Hinten; Koeln-Duesseldorf von Hinten (ISSN 0932-4879)

051   US   ISSN 1049-328X
KUUMBA. 1991. s-a. $7.50 (foreign $11.50). Blk Publishing Company, Box 83912, Los Angeles, CA 90083-0912. TEL 213-410-0808. FAX 213-410-9250. Eds. Terri L. Jewell, G. Winston James. circ. 1,500. **Document type:** consumer publication.
    Description: Poetry journal for black lesbians and gay men.

301.41   DK   ISSN 0108-1888
KVINDER, KVINDER. 1972. a. Lesbisk Bevaegelse, Kvindehuset, Gothersgade 37, 1153 Copenhagen K, Denmark. illus.

L G L C NEWSLETTER. (Libertarians for Gay and Lesbian Concerns) see *LITERATURE*

301.4157 800   US   ISSN 1064-5950
L G S N: LESBIAN AND GAY STUDIES NEWSLETTER. 1973. 3/yr. Can.$14($12) (foreign $15) to individuals; institutions $20 (effective Mar. 1992). Gay and Lesbian Caucus for the Modern Languages, c/o Shelton Waldrep, Mng. Ed., Dept. of English, Duke University, Box 90021, Durham, NC 27708-0021. TEL 919-684-6508. FAX 919-684-4871. Ed. Margaret Morrison. adv.; bk.rev. circ. 700. (also avail. in microfilm) **Indexed:** M.L.A. **Document type:** academic/scholarly publication.
  —CCC.
    Formerly: G S N.

028.1   US   ISSN 1048-9487
PN56.H57
LAMBDA BOOK REPORT; a review of contemporary gay and lesbian literature. 1987. bi-m. $19.95. Lambda Rising, Inc., 1625 Connecticut Ave., N.W., Washington, DC 20009-1013. TEL 202-462-7924. FAX 202-462-7257. Ed. Jim Marks. adv.; bk.rev. circ. 11,000. (back issues avail.) **Indexed:** Alt.Press Ind., Bk.Rev.Ind. (1990-), Child.Bk.Rev.Ind. (1990-). **Document type:** consumer publication.
  —UnCover; UMI.
    Formerly (until 1991): Lambda Rising Book Report (ISSN 0894-1416)
    Description: Reviews all gay and lesbian books published nationally. Includes author interviews, essays, trade news, and best-seller lists.

LAMBDA FINANCIAL ADVISOR. see *BUSINESS AND ECONOMICS — Investments*

301.415   US   ISSN 1053-363X
LAMBDA RISING NEWS. (Supplement to: Whole Gay Catalog) 1989. q. $2. Lambda Rising, Inc., 1625 Connecticut Ave., NW, Washington, DC 20009. TEL 202-462-6969. Ed. John Myers. **Document type:** catalog.

301   US   ISSN 1058-949X
KF4754.5.A15
LAMBDA UPDATE. 1976. q. $40. Lambda Legal Defense & Education Fund, Inc., 666 Broadway, New York, NY 10012-2317. TEL 212-995-8585. Ed. Penny Perkins. adv.; bk.rev.; illus. circ. 20,000. (looseleaf format; back issues avail.) **Document type:** newsletter.
    Description: Pursues litigation to counter discrimination against gay men and lesbians. Contains legal docket of cases and educational articles on the state of gay and lesbian legal and civil rights. Contains articles and analysis on current legislature and political topics concerning gays, lesbians, and AIDS.

LATIN MEN. see *MEN'S INTERESTS*

363.49   US
LAVENDER GODZILLA. q. $15. Gay Asian Pacific Alliance, Box 421884, San Francisco, CA 94142-1884. Ed.Bd. adv.; illus.

301.4157 301.412   US
LAVENDER MORNING; a lesbian newsletter for lesbians. 1980. m. $18. c/o Editor, Box 50729, Kalamazoo, MI 49005. adv.; bk.rev.; illus. circ. 300. **Document type:** newsletter.

301.4157 301.412   US
LAVENDER PRAIRIE NEWS. 1976. 12/yr. $10. Lavender Prairie Collective, Box 2096, Station A, Champaign, IL 61820. adv.; bk.rev. circ. 150.
    Description: Monthly publication with news of interest to the lesbian community of Central Illinois.

LAW & SEXUALITY; a review of lesbian and gay legal issues. see *LAW*

301.415 301.412   AU
LESBENRUNDBRIEF. (Text in German) 1982. irreg. S.30 per no. Hosi Lesbengruppe, Novaragasse 40, A-1020 Vienna, Austria. bk.rev.; film rev.; play rev.; illus. circ. 250.

301.4157   GW
LESBENSTICH; das Lesbenmagazin fuer den aufrechten Gang. 1980. q. DM.20 (foreign DM.25). LesbenStich-Presse-Verlag, Postfach 360549, 10975 Berlin, Germany. (Dist. by: Anares Nord, Otto-Heise-Str. 2, 3163 Sehnde-Ilten, Germany. TEL 05132-7415) Eds. A. Droege, C. Schoppmann. adv.; bk.rev. circ. 1,000. (back issues avail.)
    Description: For lesbians in Germany and other German-speaking nations.

HOMOSEXUALITY

301.415   FR   ISSN 0754-944X
LESBIA MAGAZINE. 1982. m. 250 F. (Europe 350 F.; elsewhere 450 F.). Association Lesbia, B.P. 35, 75521 Paris Cedex 11, France. TEL 43-48-89-54. FAX 43-48-89-54. Ed. Christine Lemoine. adv.: Page 3000 F. bk.rev. circ. 10,000. (back issues avail.)
 Description: Covers lesbian rights and culture in France and abroad.

301.4157 157.734   AT
LESBIAN AND GAY COUNSELLING NEWS. 1980. a. Aus.$30($3) Gay and Lesbian Counselling Service of N.S.W., G.P.O. Box 334, Darlinghurst, N.S.W. 2010, Australia. TEL 02-360-3063. Ed. Ralph W. Moore. bk.rev. circ. 350. (back issues avail.)
 Formerly: Gay Counselling (ISSN 0705-5935)

301.4157 370
LESBIAN & GAY TEACHER'S ASSOCIATION NEWSLETTER. 1978. m. $25. Lesbian and Gay Teacher's Association, Box 021052, Brooklyn, NY 11202-0023. TEL 718-258-4102. Ed. Tim Kultenecker. adv.; bk.rev.; film rev. circ. 600. (back issues avail.) **Document type:** newsletter.
 Formerly: Gay Teachers Association Newsletter.

301.4157 301.412
LESBIAN CENTER NEWS. 1975. bi-m. $4. (Ambitious Amazons) Elsie Publishing Institute, Box 811, E. Lansing, MI 48826. TEL 517-371-5257. adv. circ. 1,200.

301.4157 323.4   US
LESBIAN CONNECTION. 1974. bi-m. $18 suggested donation. (Ambitious Amazons) Elsie Publishing Institute, Box 811, E. Lansing, MI 48826. TEL 517-371-5257. Ed.Bd. adv.; bk.rev. circ. 19,000. (back issues avail.)
 Description: Nationwide forum of news and ideas for, by, and about lesbians.

LESBIAN CONTRADICTION; a journal of irreverent feminism. see *WOMEN'S INTERESTS*

301 170   US   ISSN 8755-5352
LESBIAN ETHICS. 1984. 2/yr. $14 for 3 nos. to individuals (foreign $16); institutions $18 (foreign $20). Lesbian Ethics Publications, Box 4723, Albuquerque, NM 87196. Ed. Jeanette Silveira. circ. 1,550.
 —BLDSC (5183.567300); UnCover.
 Description: Forum for radical lesbian ethics and philosophy with emphasis on how lesbians behave with each other.

LESBIAN - GAY LAW NOTES. see *LAW*

301.4157   US   ISSN 1064-0819
LESBIAN HERSTORY ARCHIVES NEWSLETTER. 1975. irreg. donation. Lesbian Herstory Educational Foundation, Inc., Box 1258, New York, NY 10116. TEL 718-768-3953. FAX 718-768-4663. bibl. circ. 8,000. **Indexed:** Alt.Press Ind. **Document type:** newsletter.
 Description: Newsletter of archives' research projects, activities, bibliographies, and other documentation on the history and culture of lesbian women.

323.42   US   ISSN 0739-1803
LESBIAN NEWS. 1975. m. $35. Deborah Bergman, Ed. & Pub., Box 1430, Twentynine Palms, CA 92277. TEL 213-658-0258. Ed.Bd. adv.; bk.rev.; film rev.; circ. 27,000 (controlled). **Document type:** consumer publication.
 Description: Feature and news stories on lesbian issues and trends.

363.49 070.5   US
LESBIANLINE. 1987. q. $2. Clothespin Fever Press, 655 Fourth Ave., Ste. 34, San Diego, CA 92101. TEL 619-234-2656. Ed. Jenny Wrenn. tr.lit. circ. 5,000. (tabloid format; also avail. in diskette format; back issues avail.)
 Description: Book publishing by women, lesbians in particular. Activities around lesbian studies in libraries. Current news affecting availability of lesbian materials.

301.4157 301.412   US
LESBIANS RISING. s-a. Hunter College, 695 Park Ave., Rm. 245, New York, NY 10027.

301.4157   NE
LESBISCH INFORMATIEBOEKJE. 1983. a. fl.6.75. Nederlandse Vereniging tot Integratie van Homoseksualiteit C.O.C., Rozenstraat 8, 1016 NX Amsterdam, Netherlands. TEL 31-20-6231192. FAX 31-20-6267795. Ed. Ina van Diepen. circ. 750.

301.415   NO   ISSN 0800-014X
LOEVETANN. 1977. bi-m. NOK 200. Loevetann, P.O. Box 6745 St. Olavs Plass, N-0130 Oslo, Norway. TEL 47-22-36-00-78. FAX 47-22-20-61-75. adv.; bk.rev. circ. 2,000. (back issues avail.)

301.4157 100 800   US
LOVING BROTHERHOOD NEWSLETTER; a journal for personal and planetary transformation. 1977. m. $15 to non-members. (Loving Brotherhood, Inc.) Lightning Press, Box 556, Sussex, NJ 07461. TEL 201-875-4710. Ed. Robertbruce Walker. adv.; bk.rev.; illus. circ. 500. (back issues avail.) **Document type:** newsletter.
 Description: Directed to gay men; keeps members posted on the growing process and expanding impact of love worldwide. Includes information abpout members, letters from readers, news of workshops and editorials.

301.4157   NE   ISSN 0168-8413
LUST & GRATIE; lesbisch cultureel universeel tijdschrift. 1983. 4/yr. fl.54. P.O. Box 18199, 1001 ZB Amsterdam, Netherlands. TEL 31-20-6622261. Ed.Bd. adv. circ. 1,200. (back issues avail.) **Document type:** consumer publication.
 Description: Lesbian, feminist, cultural magazine. Includes essays, prose, poetry, graphic arts and photography.

M O H R NEWS. (Michigan Organization for Human Rights) see *POLITICAL SCIENCE — Civil Rights*

301.4157   US
MACH. 1979. q. $26. Desmodus Inc., Box 410390, San Francisco, CA 94141-0390. TEL 415-252-1195. Ed. Marcus - Jay Wonacott. adv.; illus. circ. 25,000.

301   US
MADISON AREA'S GAY - LESBIAN CALENDAR AND GUIDE. 1984. m. free. Madison Gay - Lesbian Resource Center, Box 1722, Madison, WI 53701. adv. circ. 700.

380 363.49   US
MADISON GAY LESBIAN RESOURCE CENTER. DIRECTORY; a guide to organizations serving Madison's gay/lesbian/bisexual community. 1988. a. free. Madison Gay - Lesbian Resource Center, Box 1722, Madison, WI 53701. adv. circ. 3,500. **Document type:** directory.

301.4157   GW   ISSN 0935-8838
MAENNER AKTUELL. 1987. m. DM.12.80 per no. Bruno Gmuender Verlag, Dessauerstr. 1-2, 10963 Berlin, Germany. TEL 030-25498200. FAX 030-2629162. Ed. Frank Herrmann. adv.; bk.rev. circ. 20,000. (back issues avail.) **Document type:** consumer publication.
 Formerly: Maenner.

301.415   GW   ISSN 0936-9090
MAGNUS. 1989. m. DM.96. (Verein zur Foerderung Schwuler Kultur in den Medien e.V.) Magnus Medien Verlags GmbH, Monumentenstr. 33-34, 10829 Berlin, Germany. TEL 030-7843031. FAX 030-7820453. adv.; bk.rev. circ. 18,000. **Document type:** consumer publication.

301.4157 301.412   US
MAINE LESBIAN FEMINIST NEWSLETTER.* m. $5 per no. Box 125, Belfast, ME 04915. **Document type:** newsletter.

301.415   US
MALCHUS; the nation's lesbian & gay Christian monthly. 1990. m. $18. Malchus, 6036 Richmond Hwy., Ste. 301, Alexandria, VA 22303. TEL 703-329-7896. FAX 703-329-77896. Ed. C. Alexis Tancibok. circ. 1,100.

MALE INSIDER. see *MEN'S INTERESTS*

301 305.31   CN   ISSN 1188-4932
MALEBOX. 1991. bi-m. Can.$20($30) MaleBox, Box 4639, Sta. E, Ottawa, ON K1S 5H8, Canada. TEL 613-232-4191. FAX 613-232-4191. Eds. Frank Shane. adv. circ. 10,000.
 Description: Erotic fiction, photography, entertainment for gay men.

301.4157   NE
MAN TO MAN GUIDE; gay-lesbian guide to Holland. (Text in Dutch, English, French, German and Italian) 1975. a. fl.9.50($10) City Map Produkties, P.O. Box 10419, 1001 EK Amsterdam, Netherlands. TEL 31-20-6260702. FAX 31-20-6203264. Ed. S.R. Korper. adv. circ. 12,000.

310.4157   US   ISSN 0360-1005
MANDATE; the international magazine of entertainment & eros. 1974. m. $39.95. Mandate Publications, Ltd. (Subsidiary of: Mavety Media Group Ltd.), 462 Broadway, Ste. 4000, New York, NY 10013. TEL 212-966-8400. (Dist. by: Flynt Distributing Co., 9171 Wilshire Blvd., Ste. 300, Beverly Hills, CA 90210) .Ed. Sam Staggs. adv.; bk.rev.; film rev.; play rev.; illus. circ. 75,000. (back issues avail.)

052 808.838   US
MANIFEST READER. 1980. bi-m. $30. Alternate Publishing, Box 1069, Forestville, CA 95436. TEL 707-823-0322. FAX 707-823-5403. Ed. Robert Payna. adv. contact: Gloria Pegoraro. circ. 10,000 (paid). (back issues avail.) **Document type:** consumer publication.
 Description: Fiction for gay males.

301.4157 808.838   US
MANSCAPE. 1984. 12/yr. $48. FirstHand Ltd., 310 Cedar Lane, Box 1314, Teaneck, NJ 07666. TEL 201-836-9177. FAX 201-836-5055. Ed. Dave Babbitt. circ. 60,000. (back issues avail.)
 Description: Covers erotic fiction.

301.4157 070   US
MEDIA REPORTER. 1981. q. free. Gay & Lesbian Press Association, Box 8185, Universal City, CA 91608-0185. TEL 818-902-1476. Ed. R.J. Curry. adv. circ. 1,000. (looseleaf format)
 Description: News and information for and about the gay media and those who work in it.

301.4157   AT   ISSN 0816-4290
MELBOURNE STAR OBSERVER. 1985. s-m. Aus.$30. Oz Media Pty. Ltd., P.O. Box 192, Fitzroy, Vic. 3065, Australia. FAX 03-419-9877. Eds. Kelly Gardiner, Crusader Hillis. adv.; bk.rev. circ. 9,000. (back issues avail.) **Document type:** newspaper.

392   US
METROLINE. 1972. bi-w. $38. Metro Publications Ltd., 495 Farmington Ave., Hartford, CT 06105-3105. TEL 203-236-7813. FAX 203-231-8503. Eds. William J. Mann, Surina A. Khan. adv.; bk.rev. circ. 20,000.
 Formerly: M C C News.
 Description: News, features, profiles and commentary for the gay-lesbian community of Connecticut, Western Massachusetts, Vermont and Rhode Island, as well as a section on national news.

301.415 367   US
▼**MILITARY AND POLICE UNIFORM ASSOCIATION NEWSLETTER**. 1993. q. $29 (effective Jan. 1993). (Military and Police Uniform Association) Fan Club Publishing, Box 69A04, Dept. UL, W. Hollywood, CA 90069. TEL 213-650-5112. Ed. Louis Wendruck. adv.: page $800. bk.rev. circ. 10,000. (back issues avail.) **Document type:** newsletter.
 Description: Presents a social organization for gay men interested in meeting other gay men who are interested in military and police uniforms and videos.

301.415   US
MOM GUESS WHAT NEWSPAPER. Short title: M G W Newspaper. 1977. bi-w. $25. 1725 L St., Sacramento, CA 95814. TEL 916-441-6397. Ed. Linda D. Birner. adv.; bk.rev. circ. 7,000. (tabloid format; back issues avail.) **Document type:** newspaper.
 Description: News, announcements, features, and items of interest to the contemporary lesbian community in Sacramento, California.

MOM'S APPLE PIE. see *WOMEN'S INTERESTS*

HOMOSEXUALITY

285 322.4　　US　　ISSN 0889-3985
MORE LIGHT UPDATE. 1980. m. (combined June-July). $10 to non-members. Presbyterians for Lesbian & Gay Concerns, Inc., Box 38, New Brunswick, NJ 08903-0038. TEL 908-249-1016. Ed. James D. Anderson. adv.; bk.rev. circ. 4,500. (also avail. in microfilm; back issues avail.) **Document type:** newsletter.
● Also available online.
Description: Focuses on the concerns of lesbians and gay men in the Presbyterian Church.

301.4157　　　　GW
MUENCHEN & BAYERN VON HINTEN; das schwule Reisebuch. 1981. every 18 months. DM.16.80. Bruno Gmuender Verlag, Dessauerstr. 1-2, 10963 Berlin, Germany. TEL 030-25498200. FAX 030-2629162. Ed. Ralf Waldau. adv. circ. 8,000. **Document type:** directory.
Formerly: Muenchen von Hinten (ISSN 0932-4895)

301.4157　　US　　ISSN 1055-1689
N A M B L A BULLETIN. 1980. 10/yr. $25 (foreign $40). North American Man-Boy Love Association, Box 174, Midtown Sta., New York, NY 10018. TEL 212-807-8578. Ed. Bill Andriette. adv.; bk.rev.; film rev.; play rev.; illus.; tr.lit. circ. 2,000. (back issues avail.) **Document type:** newsletter.
Description: Supports intergenerational relationships.

301　　US
N.Y.C. PARENTS - F L A G NEWSLETTER. 1975. m. $10. New York City Parents and Friends of Lesbians and Gays, Box 553, Lenox Hill Sta., New York, NY 10021-0034. TEL 212-463-0629. Ed. R Ashworth. adv. circ. 350. **Document type:** newsletter.
Description: Provides information to parents and friends of lesbians and gays about current issues regarding homosexuality and events that concern the New York chapter.

NASHVILLE WOMEN'S ALLIANCE. NEWSLETTER. see *WOMEN'S INTERESTS*

323.4　　US　　ISSN 0896-3649
NATIONAL GAY AND LESBIAN TASK FORCE. TASK FORCE REPORTS. 1973. 4/yr. $35 membership. National Gay & Lesbian Task Force, Inc., 1734 14th St., N.W., Washington, DC 20009-4309. TEL 202-332-6483. Ed. Robert Bray. adv.; illus. circ. 17,000.
Former titles: National Gay Task Force. Task Force Report; It's Time.
Description: Covers gay and lesbian issues including AIDS and anti-gay violence.

301.4157　301.412　US
NEW DAWN. 1980. q. $48. Box 1849, Alexandria, VA 22313-1849. adv.; bk.rev. circ. 2,000.

301　　US
NEW ENGLAND COMMUNITY GUIDE FOR GAY MALES AND LESBIANS. 1980. a. $5.95. M. Kennedy Publishing, 105 Charles St., Ste. 283, Boston, MA 02114. TEL 617-723-5130. FAX 617-723-9582. adv.; B&W page $995; 4 x 7. circ. 50,000. (reprint service avail.) **Document type:** directory.

NEW POETS SERIES - CHESTNUT HILLS PRESS. see *LITERATURE — Poetry*

NEW SINS. see *LITERATURE — Poetry*

301.4157　051　US
THE NEW VOICE. 1980. w. $49. Community Publishing Co., 408 Avondale, Houston, TX 77006. TEL 713-529-8490. FAX 713-529-9531. Ed. Jim Cheek. film rev.; circ. 13,000 (controlled). (tabloid format; back issues avail.)
Formerly: Montrose Voice.

301.4157　　US　　ISSN 0744-060X
NEW YORK NATIVE. fortn. $29. That New Magazine, Inc., 28 W. 25th St., 4th Fl., New York, NY 10010. TEL 212-627-2120. FAX 212-727-9321. Ed. Patrick Merla. adv.; bk.rev.; film rev.

301.4157　　US
NIGHTLIFE. 1968. fortn. $30. Data-Boy Enterprises, Inc., 7626 Santa Monica Blvd., Los Angeles, CA 90046. TEL 213-656-2960. FAX 213-656-7312. Ed. Dave Hodgson. adv.; bk.rev.; circ. 44,000 (controlled).
Former titles: Data-Boy - Nightlife & Data-Boy Magazine.
Description: Covers entertainment in Southern California.

157.734 614.58　US　ISSN 0895-5239
NINTH STREET CENTER JOURNAL. 1974. s-a. Ninth Street Center, Inc., 151 First Ave., Ste. 25, New York, NY 10003. TEL 212-228-5153. Ed. Dean Hannotte. bk.rev. (back issues avail.) **Document type:** academic/scholarly publication.
Description: Forum for ideas on social progress and human development, with emphasis on psychological polarity.

301.4157　　US
NORTHWEST GAY GUIDE; directory of gay - lesbian businesses. a. One in Ten Publishing Co., Box 23070, Seattle, WA 98102. TEL 206-323-7374. **Document type:** directory.

ODYSSEUS; an accommodations & travel guide for the gay community, USA & international. see *TRAVEL AND TOURISM*

301.412　　US　　ISSN 0890-2224
HQ75
ON OUR BACKS; entertainment for the adventurous lesbian. 1984. bi-m. $34.95. Blush Entertainment, 526 Castro, San Francisco, CA 94114. TEL 415-861-4723. Ed. Heather Findlay. adv. contact: Marnie Dubouis. bk.rev. circ. 15,000. (back issues avail.)
Description: Explores lesbian sexuality. Contains stories, opinions, advice and photos concerning lesbians.

301.4157　　US
ONELETTER. 1956. 12/yr. $35 membership. ONE, Inc., 3340 Country Club Dr., Los Angeles, CA 90019. TEL 213-735-5252. adv.; bk.rev. circ. 500. **Document type:** newsletter.

OPEN HANDS; resources for ministries affirming the diversity of human sexuality. see *RELIGIONS AND THEOLOGY — Protestant*

051　　US
OPTIONS (PORT CHESTER). 1981. 10/yr. $19.90. A J A Publishing Corp., Box 470, Port Chester, NY 10573. Ed. Don Stone. adv.; film rev. circ. 75,000. (back issues avail.) **Document type:** consumer publication.
Description: Emphasizes safe, loving relationships. Covers sexual interactions between homosexuals, bisexuals, and lesbians.

OTHER BLACK WOMAN; an international magazine for women. see *ETHNIC INTERESTS*

363.49 910.03　　US
OTHER COUNTRIES: BLACK GAY VOICES. 1988. a. $6.95 to individuals; institutions $11. Cultural Council Foundation, Box 3142, New York, NY 10008-3142. Eds. Gary Alan Johnson, Daniel Garrett. illus.

301.4157　　CK
EL OTRO; de las sexualidades y la contracultura. 1977. irreg., no.10, 1986. donation. Apdo. Aereo 6525, Medellin, Colombia. TEL 238-2691. Ed. BenHur Leon Zuleta Ruiz. circ. 1,000. (looseleaf format)

051　　US
OUR OWN. 1976. m. $14. 739 Yarmouth St., Norfolk, VA 23510-1512. TEL 804-625-0700. FAX 804-625-6024. Ed. Kathleen Vickory; Pub. Alicia Herr. adv.; bk.rev. circ. 10,000. **Document type:** newspaper.

301.4157　　US　　ISSN 1053-296X
OUR STORIES. 1985. 3/yr. $30 individual membership; institutions $50 (effective 1990). Gay & Lesbian Historical Society of Northern California, Box 424280, San Francisco, CA 94142. TEL 415-626-0980. adv.; bk.rev. circ. 1,500. **Document type:** newsletter.
Formerly (until vol.5, 1990): San Francisco Bay Area Gay and Lesbian Historical Society. Newsletter (ISSN 0896-162X)
Description: Covers the history of lesbians, gay men and other sexual minorities in Northern California, including work by contemporary historians.

301.4157 910.09　US　ISSN 1044-6699
G149
OUR WORLD; the international gay travel magazine. 1989. 10/yr. $35 (foreign $70). Our World Publishing, 1104 N. Nova Rd., Ste. 251, Daytona Beach, FL 32117. TEL 904-441-5367. FAX 904-441-5604. (Dist. by: Inland Book Co., Box 120261, E. Haven, CT 06512) Ed. Wayne Whiston. adv.; bk.rev.; illus. circ. 20,000. **Document type:** consumer publication.
Description: Gay and lesbian travel magazine with color photos, feature articles, reviews and news on gay hotels, restaurants, tours, cruises and festivals.

301.41　　NZ　　ISSN 0110-4454
OUT !. 1976. bi-m. $40 (foreign $75). Lawrence Publishing Co. N.Z. Ltd., Private Bag 92126, Auckland 1, New Zealand. TEL 64-9-377-7767. FAX 64-9-377-7767. Ed. Brett Sheppard; Pub. Tony Katavich. adv.; B&W page NZ.$375; trim 275 X 205; adv. contact: Brett Sheppad. bk.rev. circ. 10,000. Indexed: Alt.Press Ind.
Formerly: New Zealand Gay News (ISSN 0110-0238)
Description: Covers gay community scene and news in New Zealand and the South Pacific.

051　　US　　ISSN 1062-7928
HQ75
▼**OUT.** 1992. 10/yr. $24.95. Out Publishing Inc., 110 Greene St., Apt. 800, New York, NY 10012-3836. TEL 212-334-9119. FAX 212-334-9227. (Subscr. to: Box 15307, N. Hollywood, CA 91615-9852) Ed. Michael Goff. adv.; B&W page $4175; trim 8 1/8 x 10 7/8; adv. contact: Harry Taylor. bk.rev.; illus.; circ. 85,000 (paid). (also avail. in microform from UMI) **Document type:** consumer publication.
Description: Upscale general interest magazine for the gay and lesbian community.

051　　US
OUT IN THE MOUNTAINS; Vermont's newspaper for lesbians, gay men & bisexuals. 1986. m. $20. Box 177, Burlington, VT 05402. Ed. Deborah Lashmann. adv. **Document type:** newsletter.
Description: News, resources and activities for Vermont's gay, lesbian and bisexual communities.

301.4157 323.4　　US
OUTLINES; the voice of the gay and lesbian community. 1987. m. $32. Lambda Publications, Inc., 3059 N. Southport, Chicago, IL 60657. TEL 312-871-7610. FAX 312-871-7609. Ed. Tracy Baim. adv.; bk.rev.; film rev.; play rev. circ. 25,000. (back issues avail.) **Document type:** newspaper.
Description: Contains news, features, and entertainment for gays and lesbians.

301.4157　　AT　　ISSN 0811-2169
OUTRAGE. 1983. m. Aus.$58 (foreign Aus.$110). Designer Publications Pty. Ltd., P.O. Box 205, Fitzroy, Vic. 3065, Australia. TEL 61-3-419-9877. FAX 61-3-419-0827. Ed. Martyn Goddard. adv.; B&W page Aus.$895, color page Aus.$1495; adv. contact: Anthony L'Huillier. bk.rev.; circ. 10,500 (paid). (back issues avail.)
Description: Covers news, reviews, previews, interviews, photography and features of interest to gay men.

157.734　　NE　　ISSN 0167-5907
PAIDIKA; the journal of paedophilia. (Text in English) 1987. 2/yr. fl.95($57) to individuals; libraries $110. Stichting Paidika Foundation, Postbus 15463, 1001 ML Amsterdam, Netherlands. Ed. Joseph Geraci. adv.; bk.rev. circ. 1,000. (back issues avail.) **Document type:** academic/scholarly publication.
Description: Documents opposing viewpoints concerning child sexuality, paedophilia, precocious sexuality.

HOMOSEXUALITY

301.415   DK   ISSN 0902-347X
PAN BLADET. (Text in Danish) 1954. 10/yr. $50. Aktieselskabet Pan, Knabrostraede 3, P.O. Box 1023, DK-1007 Copenhagen K, Denmark. TEL 45-33-11-19-61. FAX 45-33-91-03-48. Ed. Inge-Lise Paulsen. adv.; bk.rev. circ. 9,000. (back issues avail.)
   Description: Focuses on the homosexual situation in Denmark as well as internationally. Features interviews, questions on civil rights, culture and health.

301
PARENTS AND FRIENDS OF LESBIAN AND GAYS NEWSLETTER. 1980. m. $6. Parents and Friends of Lesbians and Gays, Box 15711, Philadelphia, PA 19103. TEL 215-572-1833. bk.rev. circ. 450. (looseleaf format) **Document type:** newsletter.

323.4   US
PHILADELPHIA GAY NEWS. 1976. w. $110. 254 S. 11th St., Philadelphia, PA 19107. TEL 215-625-8501. FAX 215-925-6437. Ed. Al Patrick; Pub. Mark Segal. adv. contact: Tony Lombardo. bk.rev.; film rev.; play rev.; illus. circ. 40,000. (tabloid format; back issues avail.) **Document type:** newspaper.
   Formerly: Gay News.

363.49   UK
THE PINK PAPER; the national newspaper for lesbians and gay men. 1989. w. £39. 77 Garden Row, London N1 8EZ, England. Ed. Alison Gregory. adv.; illus. **Document type:** newspaper.

PLAYGUY. see *MEN'S INTERESTS*

QUEST MAGAZINE. see *ART*

301.415   US   ISSN 0149-709X
R F D; a country journal for gay men everywhere. 1974. q. $18 (foreign $25). (Gay Community Social Services) Short Mountain Collective, Box 68, Liberty, TN 37095. TEL 615-536-5176. Ed.Bd. adv.; bk.rev.; illus. circ. 3,300. (also avail. in microfilm; back issues avail.) **Indexed:** Alt.Press Ind.

301.4157   CN
R G. (Text in French) 1981. m. $50. Editions H.M.X. Inc., C.P. 5245, Succ. C, Montreal, PQ H2X 3M4, Canada. TEL 514-523-9463. FAX 514-523-2214. Ed. Alain Bouchard. adv.; bk.rev.; film rev.; play rev.; charts; illus. circ. 35,000. (back issues avail.)
   Formerly: Rencontres Gaies (ISSN 0712-838X)

301.4157 200   US
RECORD (NEW YORK, 1976). Issued with: Review (New York, 1976). 1976. q. free. Evangelicals Concerned, Inc., c/o Dr. Ralph Blair, Ed., 311 E. 72nd St., Ste. 1G, New York, NY 10021. TEL 212-517-3171. bk.rev. circ. 2,000. (looseleaf format; back issues avail.)

301.4157 200   US
REVIEW (NEW YORK). 1976. q. free. Evangelicals Concerned, Inc., c/o Dr. Ralph Blair, Ed., 311 E. 72nd St., Ste. 1G, New York, NY 10021. TEL 212-517-3171. bk.rev. circ. 2,000. (looseleaf format; back issues avail.)

301.4157 301.412   US
RICHMOND LESBIAN FEMINIST FLYER. 1973. m. $10. Richmond Lesbian Feminists, Box 7216, Richmond, VA 23221-0216. TEL 804-379-6422. Ed.Bd. adv.; bk.rev. circ. 700. **Document type:** newsletter.

DE ROZELINKS. see *POLITICAL SCIENCE — Civil Rights*

301.4157 155.5   US   ISSN 0895-3120
S M Y A L NEWS. 1987. q. $25. Sexual Minority Youth Assistance League, Inc., 333 1/2 Pennsylvania Ave. S.E., 3rd. Fl., Washington, DC 20003-1148. TEL 202-546-5940. FAX 202-544-1306. bk.rev. circ. 2,700. (back issues avail.) **Document type:** newsletter.

051   US
SAN FRANCISCO BAY TIMES; the gay-lesbian-bisexual newspaper and calendar of events for the Bay Area. 1979. s-w. $56. San Francisco Bay Times, 288 7th St., San Francisco, CA 94103-4004. TEL 415-626-8121. FAX 415-626-0629. Ed. Kim Corsaro. adv.; bk.rev. circ. 40,700. **Document type:** newspaper.
   Formerly (until vol.10, 1989): Coming Up!

301.4157   US
SAN FRANCISCO SENTINEL. 1974. w. $85 (foreign $200). 285 Shipley St., San Francisco, CA 94107-1010. TEL 415-861-8100. FAX 415-861-8431. Ed. Ray Chalker. adv.; bk.rev. circ. 50,000. **Document type:** newspaper.
   Formerly: Sentinel U S A.
   Description: Discusses news and topics of interest to the greater San Francisco area gay and lesbian community.

301.4157   UK   ISSN 0960-5754
SCENE OUT.* 1978. m. £15. Archway Publishing Ltd., 194 Musuell Hill, Broadway, London N10 3SA, England. TEL 061-953-4045. FAX 061-953-4001. Ed. Lee Allum. adv.; bk.rev.; film rev.; play rev.; illus.; stat. circ. 6,000. (back issues avail.)
   Former titles (until 1989): Gay Life Magazine; (until 1986): Mancunian Gay.
   Description: Reviews new films, plays, music. Contains celebrity interviews and personals.

301.4157   GW   ISSN 0932-4925
SCHWULE MAENNER. 1985. a. DM.12.80. Bruno Gmuender Verlag, Dessauerstr. 1-2, 10963 Berlin, Germany. TEL 030-25498200. FAX 030-2629162. Ed. Bruno Gmuender. adv. circ. 17,000. **Document type:** directory.
   Description: Pocket calendar and gay guide for German speaking countries.

051   US
SEATTLE GAY NEWS. 1973. w. Box 22007, Seattle, WA 98122-0007. TEL 206-324-4297. FAX 206-322-7188. circ. 30,000 (paid). **Document type:** newspaper.

200   US   ISSN 1047-3971
THE SECOND STONE; the national newspaper for gay and lesbian Christians. 1988. bi-m. $15 (effective Jan. 1993). Bailey Communications, Box 8340, New Orleans, LA 70182. TEL 504-899-4014. FAX 504-891-7555. Ed. Jim Bailey. adv.; bk.rev.; film rev. circ. 3,000. (tabloid format; back issues avail.)

301.4157   US
SENTINEL (SAN FRANCISCO). 1974. 52/yr. $85. 285 Shipley St., San Francisco, CA 94107-1010. TEL 415-281-3745. FAX 415-281-3745. adv.; bk.rev. circ. 115,000. (tabloid format)

301.415   FI   ISSN 0355-1407
SETA. (Text in Finnish) 1975. 5/yr. FIM 80($27) Seksuaalinen Tasavertaisuus ry, P.O. Box 55, FIN-00531 Helsinki, Finland. TEL 0-135-8302. FAX 0-135-8306. Ed. Kalle-Ville Lahtinen. adv.; bk.rev. circ. 3,000. (back issues avail.)

301.4157 157.734   RU
SIBIRSKII VARIANT. 1991. m. 40 Rub.($15) (Barnaul'skaya Assotsiatsiya Gomoseksualistov i Lesbiyanok) Sibirskii Variant, P.O. Box 73, 656099 Barnaul 99, Russia. TEL 385-2-425156. Ed. A. Khorshev. circ. 2,000.

301.4157 301.412   US
SISTERS UNITED. 1979. q. $7. Woman Prints Enterprises, 118 W. Sparks St., Galena, KS 66739. Eds. Ruth Lang, Jean Mallatt. adv.; illus.

301.4157   US
SKIPPER'S MATES FRIENDSHIP CLUB. 1969. m. $10. Skipper's Guides, Box 264, Bellbrook, OH 45305. Ed. T.R. Roy. circ. 2,200. (looseleaf format; back issues avail.)
   Former titles (until 1984): Skipper's Mates; (until 1972): Skipper's Newsletter.

051   US
SOUTHERN CALIFORNIA UPDATE. fortn. Box 204, Hollywood, CA 90028. TEL 213-467-2230. Ed. Harold Fairbanks. circ. 20,000.

301.405 910.202   GW
SPARTACUS INTERNATIONAL GAY GUIDE. (Text in English, French, German, Italian and Spanish) 1971. a. DM.45($29.95) Bruno Gmuender Verlag, Dessauerstr. 1-2, 10963 Berlin, Germany. TEL 030-25498200. FAX 030-2629162. Ed.Bd. adv.; illus. circ. 76,000. **Document type:** directory.

301.415   UK
SQUARE PEG. 1983. q. £9($20) BM Square Peg, London WC1N 3XX, England. TEL 081-691-3622. film rev.; illus.; play rev. circ. 5,000. (back issues avail.)

STALLION; the new breed of rugged male. see *MEN'S INTERESTS*

301.4157 378
323.4
STANFORD GAY AND LESBIAN AWARENESS WEEK PROGRAM. 1982. a. free. Gay and Lesbian Alliance at Stanford, Box 8265, Stanford, CA 94305-0215. TEL 415-723-1488. circ. 700. (back issues avail.)

363.49   US
STRANGE LOOKING EXILE; the all cartoon zine for queer dudes and babes. 1991. s-a. $4.25 per no. Giant Ass Publications, Box 214, New Haven, CT 06502. circ. 1,000.

301.4157 360   SZ
SWISS GAY; Blatt fuer sexuelle Variation, Politik und Kultur. (Text in German) 1984. m. 30 SFr. Arcados Verlag, Rheingasse 69, CH-4002 Basel, Switzerland. TEL 061-6813132. FAX 061-6816656. Ed. Peter Thommen. adv. circ. 2,000. (back issues avail.) **Document type:** bulletin.
   Former titles (until 1994): Come Out; (until 1988): Abendblatt.
   Description: Provides a regional forum for the social and political problems facing gays and lesbians.

301.415   AT   ISSN 0155-5936
SYDNEY GAY GUIDE. 1975. a. Gay Society of the University of NSW, Union Box 67, P.O. Box 1, Kensington, NSW 2033, Australia. circ. 5,000.

T V - T S TAPESTRY; the journal for persons interested in crossdressing & transsexualism. see *PSYCHOLOGY*

363.49   US   ISSN 0898-1477
T W N; the weekly news. 1977. w. $78. The Weekly News, Inc., 901 N.E. 79th St., Miami, FL 33138-4715. TEL 305-757-6333. FAX 305-756-6458. Ed. Steven Biller. adv. contact: Bill Watson. circ. 22,250. (tabloid format; also avail. in microfilm) **Document type:** newspaper.
   Description: Covers news of interest to the southern Florida gay community.

051   US
TASK FORCE FOR GAY & LESBIAN COUPLES. 1986. irreg. $10.50. Sweet Corn Productions, Box 9685, Seattle, WA 98109-0685. TEL 206-935-1206. Eds. Steve Bryant, Demian. adv.; bk.rev. **Document type:** consumer publication.
   Formerly (until 1993): Partners (Seattle) (ISSN 0891-1738)
   Description: Supports the diverse community of committed gay and lesbian couples with information and ideas.

TELEWOMAN. see *LITERATURE*

363.49   US
TEMA INTERNATIONAL. 1991. q. $15 to members. International Gay and Lesbian Human Rights Commission, 2978 Folsom St., San Francisco, CA 94110. Ed. Marsha Gessen.

917.306 301.4157   US
THIRD WORLD WOMAN'S GAY-ZETTE. 1976. m. Salsa-Soul Sisters, c/o Candice Boyce, 41-11 Parsons Blvd., Flushing, NY 11355.

301   US
THIS MONTH IN MISSISSIPPI. 1973. m. $15. Mississippi Gay - Lesbian Alliance, Inc., Box 8342, Jackson, MS 39284. TEL 601-371-1318. adv.; bk.rev. circ. 1,000. **Document type:** newsletter.

301.4157 323.4   US
THIS WEEK IN TEXAS. 1975. w. $69. Texas Weekly Times Newspaper Company, 811 Westheimer, Ste. 106, Houston, TX 77006. TEL 713-527-9111. FAX 713-527-8948. Ed. Richard Herbert. adv.; bk.rev. (back issues avail.)
   Description: News and entertainment oriented to the gay life-style.

TORSO; the new era in all-male erotica. see *MEN'S INTERESTS*

157.734   US
TRANSSEXUAL VOICE. 1981. bi-m. $18. Phoebe Smith, Ed. & Pub., Box 16314, Atlanta, GA 30321. adv.; bk.rev. circ. 300. (looseleaf format; back issues avail.) **Document type:** newsletter.

TRIBE; an American gay journal. see *LITERATURE — Poetry*

301.4157   US   ISSN 1042-735X
TRIKONE; gay and lesbian South Asians. 1986. q. $10. Box 21354, San Jose, CA 95151. TEL 408-270-8776. Ed. Arvind Kumar. bk.rev. circ. 500. (back issues avail.)
  Formerly: Trikon.

301.4157   US
TWIN CITIES GAZE;* the news weekly for the gay and lesbian community. 1985. bi-w. $12. Gaze Media, 2344 Nicollet Ave., Ste. 370, Minneapolis, MN 55404-3354. TEL 612-336-4006. FAX 612-338-5292. Ed. Brad Theissen. adv.; bk.rev. circ. 33,000. (looseleaf format; back issues avail.)

UNCUT; the magazine of the natural man. see *MEN'S INTERESTS*

301   US
UNITY: UNITED NEWSLETTER. 1984. bi-m. membership. Madison Community United, Box 310, Madison, WI 53701. TEL 608-255-8582. (Alt. addr.: 310 E. Wilson, Madison WI 53701) Ed. Jane Vanderbosch. bk.rev. circ. 1,500. (looseleaf format) **Document type**: newsletter.
  Formerly: United Newsletter.
  Description: Publishes articles on gay, lesbian and bisexual issues.

VALLEY WOMEN'S VOICE; a chronicle of feminist thought and action. see *WOMEN'S INTERESTS*

301.415   UK
VULCAN. 1971. bi-m. £24.95 (foreign £35). Millivres Ltd., Worldwide House, 116-134 Bayham St., London NW1 0BA, England. TEL 071-482-2576. FAX 071-284-0329. Ed. Nigel Hatton. adv. contact: Terry Deal. circ. 12,000. (back issues avail.) **Document type**: consumer publication.

301   US
WALKING WITH INTEGRITY. 1978. irreg. (6-12/yr.). $15 to non-members. Integrity - Washington, Inc., Box 19561, Washington, DC 20036-0561. TEL 301-953-9421. Ed.Bd. bk.rev. circ. 300. **Document type**: newsletter.
  Formerly (until Apr. 1994): Gayspring (ISSN 0896-5773)
  Description: Official newsletter of Integrity-Washington, Inc., an organization of gay and lesbian Episcopalians and their friends.

301.4157   US   ISSN 0278-9892
THE WASHINGTON BLADE; the gay weekly newspaper of the nation's capital. 1969. w. $30. 1408 U St., N.W., 2nd Fl., Washington, DC 20009-3916. TEL 202-797-7000. FAX 202-797-7040. Ed. Lisa M. Keen; Pub. Donald Michaels. adv.; bk.rev. circ. 42,000. (also avail. in microfilm from UMI; reprint service avail. from UMI) **Document type**: newspaper.

051   US
WINDY CITY TIMES. w. Sentury Publications, Inc., 970 W. Montana, Chicago, IL 60614-2409. TEL 312-935-1970. FAX 312-935-1853. Ed. Daniel Perreten. adv. circ. 24,000. **Document type**: newspaper.

301.412   US
WISHING WELL. 1974. bi-m. $25 membership in U.S., Canada, Mexico; elsewhere $30. Laddie Hosler, Ed. & Pub., Box 713090, Santee, CA 92072-3090. TEL 619-443-4818. adv.; B&W page $100; trim 8 x 6. bk.rev.; illus. circ. 5,000. (back issues avail.) **Document type**: newsletter.
  Description: Provides singles and couples listings for women-loving women. Includes letters, poetry, photos, resources and reviews.

WOMEN'S NETWORK; national newsletter for women. see *WOMEN'S INTERESTS*

WOMEN'S TRAVELLER. see *TRAVEL AND TOURISM*

301.4157   NE   ISSN 0927-5827
X L. 1971. 11/yr. fl.6.95. Nederlandse Vereniging tot Integratie van Homoseksualiteit C.O.C., Rozenstraat 8, 1016 NX Amsterdam, Netherlands. TEL 31-20-6231192. FAX 31-20-6267795. adv.; bk.rev.; film rev.; play rev. circ. 12,000. (also avail. in talking book)
  Formerly (until 1992): S E K - Lesbisch en Homoblad (ISSN 0166-1973)

301.4157 917.1   CN   ISSN 0829-3384
XTRA!; your gay & lesbian guide to Toronto. 1984. bi-w. Can.$45.95($52.95) (effective Jan. 1993). Pink Triangle Press, Box 7289, Sta. A, Toronto, ON M5W 1X9, Canada. TEL 416-925-6665. FAX 416-925-6674. Ed. Dayne Ogilvie. adv.; bk.rev.; film rev.; play rev.; illus.; circ. 28,000 (controlled). (back issues avail.) **Document type**: newspaper.

HA-YONAH/DOVE. see *ETHNIC INTERESTS*

301.4157   US
YOUNG GAY - LESBIAN LIFE. 1990. m. $15.95. One in Ten Publishing Co., Box 23070, Seattle, WA 98102. TEL 206-323-7374. Ed. Jenny Peterson. adv.
  Description: Looks at coming-out issues, working with parents, friends, schools.

ZIPPER. see *MEN'S INTERESTS*

301.415   US
▼**10 PERCENT**. 1992. q. $19.95 for 6 nos. Browning - Grace Communications, 54 Mint St., Ste. 200, San Francisco, CA 94103. TEL 415-905-8500. FAX 415-227-0463. Ed. Carlos Stelmach. adv.: B&W page $4500, color page $6000; trim 7 x 10. circ. 70,000. **Document type**: consumer publication.
  Description: Covers the interests, concerns and lifestyle of the lesbian and gay professional community.

HOMOSEXUALITY — Abstracting, Bibliographies, Statistics

LESBIAN HERSTORY ARCHIVES NEWSLETTER. see *HOMOSEXUALITY*

301.4157 011   NE
LESBISCH ARCHIVARIA. 1982. irreg. Anna Blaman House, Zuidvliet 118, P.O. Box 4062, 8901 EB Leeuwarden, Netherlands. TEL (058)121829. circ. 500.

011 301   US
SELECTED BIBLIOGRAPHY OF HOMOSEXUALITY. irreg. $0.50. Homosexual Information Center, 115 Monroe St., Bossier City, LA 71111. TEL 318-742-4709. (Alt. addr.: Box 8252, Universal City, CA 91608) Ed. Leslie Colfax. (back issues avail.) **Document type**: bibliography.

HORSES AND HORSEMANSHIP

see *Sports and Games–Horses and Horsemanship*

HOSPITALS

see also *Medical Sciences; Nutrition and Dietetics*

658 610.73   AT
A C O R N JOURNAL. 1976. bi-m. Aus.$50. (Australian Confederation of Operating Room Nurses) Associated Business Publications Pty. Ltd., 104-3 Smail St., Ultimo, N.S.W. 2007, Australia. TEL 02-212-2789. (Subscr. to: Subscription Manager, G.P.O. Box 2368, Sydney, N.S.W. 2001, Australia) Ed. Lynne Redknap. circ. 3,600. **Indexed**: CINAHL. **Document type**: bulletin.
  Former titles: Forceps, Snippets and A C O R N News; Forceps (ISSN 0156-3491)

658   US   ISSN 0891-6608
A H A NEWS. 1987. w. $100 to non-members (foreign $150); members $45 (foreign $95). American Hospital Publishing, Inc. (Subsidiary of: American Hospital Association Company), 737 N. Michigan Ave., Ste. 700, Chicago, IL 60611. TEL 312-440-6800. FAX 312-951-8491. Ed. Barbara J. Varro. circ. 28,600. (tabloid format; back issues avail.) **Document type**: newsletter.
  Description: Directed towards healthcare management, hospital trustees, and hospital program directors.

362.1   AT   ISSN 1031-010X
A H A SPECIAL MONOGRAPHS. irreg. Aus.$7.50 to non-members; members Aus.$4 (per issue). Australian Hospital Association, 42 Thesiger Court, Deakin, A.C.T. 2600, Australia. **Document type**: monographic series.
  Formerly: A H A Health Services Monographs.
  Description: Geared towards individuals involved in health care policymaking and administration.

A H R A RECORD. (Alberta Health Records Association) see *MEDICAL SCIENCES*

362   US
A M S A A NEWSLETTER. 1974. m. $25 to non-members. Ambulance and Medical Service Association of America, Box 14178, Hartford, CT 06114. adv.; illus. circ. 9,276. **Indexed**: Hosp.Lit.Ind. **Document type**: newsletter.
  Supersedes: Aid Newsletter (ISSN 0002-2063)

362   US   ISSN 1058-6385
A O H A. 1957. m. $28. American Osteopathic Hospital Association, 5301 Wisconsin Ave., N.W., Ste. 630, Washington, DC 20015-2015. TEL 202-686-1700. FAX 202-686-7615. Ed. Amy Miller Jackson. adv.; bk.rev.; charts; illus.; stat. circ. 1,859. (also avail. in microfilm from UMI; reprint service avail. from UMI) **Indexed**: Abstr.Hosp.Manage.Stud., C.I.N.L., Hosp.Lit.Ind., MEDSOC.
  Former titles (until 1991): A O H A Today (ISSN 1044-1980); (until 1989): Osteopathic Hospital Leadership; (until Jan. 1985): Osteopathic Hospitals; O H Osteopathic Hospitals (ISSN 0161-0007); Osteopathic Hospital (ISSN 0048-2293)
  Refereed Serial

362   US
A O H A ANNUAL DIRECTORY. a. $125 to non-members. American Osteopathic Hospital Association, 5301 Wisconsin Ave., N.W., Ste. 630, Washington, DC 20015-2015. TEL 202-686-1700. FAX 202-686-7615. **Document type**: directory.

658 628.44   US
A S H E S ANNUAL CONFERENCE. PROCEEDINGS MANUAL. 1985. a. $29.95 to members; non-members $39.95. (American Society for Healthcare Environmental Services) American Hospital Association, 840 N. Lake Shore Dr., Chicago, IL 60611. TEL 312-280-4458. FAX 312-280-4152. Ed. Katherine Suedman. circ. 1,500. **Document type**: proceedings.

650   FR   ISSN 1155-3839
ABSTRACT HOPITAL. 1989. m. Abstract Medical International, 25 bis, av. Pierre Grenier, 92100 Boulogne, France. TEL 49-10-06-06. Ed. Patricia Thelliez. circ. 15,000.
  Formerly (until 1990): Abstract Maladies Infectieuses (ISSN 0997-1785)

362   BE   ISSN 0044-6009
ACTA HOSPITALIA. (Text in Dutch, English, French; summaries in English) 1961. q. 1900 BEF($47) Katholieke Universiteit te Leuven, Centrum voor Ziekenhuiswetenschap, Kapucijnenvoer 35, B-3000 Leuven, Belgium. TEL 32-16-336973. FAX 32-16-336970. Ed. P. Quaethoven. adv.; bk.rev.; bibl.; cum.index. circ. 750. **Indexed**: Excerp.Med., Hosp.Abstr., Med. Care Rev. **Document type**: academic/scholarly publication.
  —BLDSC (0624.410000); SWETS.

ACTION KIT FOR HOSPITAL LAW. see *LAW*

658 340   US
ACTION KIT FOR HOSPITAL TRUSTEES. 1971. bi-m. $295. Action Kit Publications, 4614 Fifth Ave., Pittsburgh, PA 15213. TEL 800-245-1205. Ed. John Horty. (looseleaf format)
  Description: Helps hospital management and governing board members understand the legal and regulatory changes that affect hospitals.

ADMINISTRATION & MANAGEMENT SPECIAL INTEREST SECTION NEWSLETTER. see *OCCUPATIONAL HEALTH AND SAFETY*

HOSPITALS

362   **CN**   **ISSN 0317-3739**
ADMINISTRATION HOSPITALIERE ET SOCIALE.* 1955. 10/yr. Can.$10($12) Federation des Administrateurs des Services de Sante et des Services Sociaux du Quebec, 950 rue Victoria, Bur. 150, Greenfield Park, Que. J4V 1M9, Canada. Ed. Claude Magnan. adv.; bk.rev.; charts; illus.; stat.; index. circ. 3,500. **Indexed**: Pt.de Rep. (1983-), RADAR.
    Formerly: Hopital d'Aujourd'hui (ISSN 0018-4853)

ADMINISTRATIVE RADIOLOGY; the journal of medical imaging administration & management. see *MEDICAL SCIENCES — Radiology And Nuclear Medicine*

ADULT DAY CARE LETTER. see *GERONTOLOGY AND GERIATRICS*

658   **JA**   **ISSN 0911-1549**
AKAHIGE/TAKKO TOWN HOSPITAL. ANNUAL REPORT. (Text in Japanese; summaries in English, Japanese) 1984. a. Takko Choritsu Takko Byoin - Takko Town Hospital, 2-17, Maeda, Takko, Takkomachi, Sannohe-gun, Aomori-ken 039-02, Japan.

ALTENHEIM LEITFADEN FUER DEN EINKAUF. see *GERONTOLOGY AND GERIATRICS*

362.18   **UK**
AMBULANCE SERVICE JOURNAL; a professional journal for ambulance and first aid personnel. q. £1. Institute of Certified Ambulance Personnel, c/o F. Thornley, 64 Pen-y-fro, Dunvant, Wales. Ed. Nan Berger. circ. 1,200.
    Incorporating: Ambulance (ISSN 0044-7455)

362.18   **UK**
AMBULANCE U K. 1986. 5/yr. £10 (foreign $15). Media Publishing Co., Erith Business Centre, High St., Unit 14, Erith, Kent DA8 1RT, England. TEL 0322-332109. FAX 0332-336027. Ed. L. Caple. circ. 45,000. (back issues avail.)
    Description: Provides information about all matters related to the United Kingdom Ambulance Service, including the production of goods and services, communications and medicine.

AMERICAN ANIMAL HOSPITAL ASSOCIATION. ANNUAL MEETING SCIENTIFIC PROCEEDINGS. see *VETERINARY SCIENCE*

AMERICAN ANIMAL HOSPITAL ASSOCIATION JOURNAL. see *VETERINARY SCIENCE*

AMERICAN ASSOCIATION OF BLOOD BANKS. NEWS BRIEFS. see *MEDICAL SCIENCES*

362   **US**
AMERICAN COLLEGE OF HEALTHCARE EXECUTIVES. DIRECTORY. 1960. biennial. $150 to non-affiliates; affiliates $100. American College of Healthcare Executives, 840 N. Lake Shore Dr., Chicago, IL 60611. TEL 312-943-0544. FAX 312-943-3791. (Subscr. to: Order Processing Center, 1951 Cornell Ave., Melrose Park, IL 60160-1001) circ. 2,300. **Document type**: directory.
    Formerly: American College of Hospital Administrators. Directory (ISSN 0065-7794)
    Description: Contains complete professional information on affiliates, including education, the college status, past positions and addresses.

AMERICAN JOURNAL OF HOSPITAL PHARMACY. see *PHARMACY AND PHARMACOLOGY*

362   **US**
AMERICAN PROTESTANT HEALTH ASSOCIATION. BULLETIN. vol.30, 1966. q. membership. American Protestant Health Association, 1701 E. Woodfield Rd., Schaumburg, IL 60195. Ed. Dr. Charles D. Phillips. adv.; illus. circ. 3,000. (tabloid format; also avail. in microform from UMI) **Indexed**: C.I.N.L., Hosp.Lit.Ind., Rel.Ind.One. **Document type**: bulletin.
    —CCC.
    Formerly: American Protestant Hospital Association. Bulletin (ISSN 0003-0635)

AMERICAN SCHOOL AND HOSPITAL MAINTENANCE. see *EDUCATION — School Organization And Administration*

658 621   **US**
AMERICAN SOCIETY FOR HOSPITAL ENGINEERING TECHNICAL DOCUMENT SERIES. 1982. m. membership. American Hospital Association, 840 N. Lake Shore Dr., Chicago, IL 60611. TEL 312-280-3335. FAX 312-280-4152. Ed. Kerry Hacker. charts; illus. circ. 6,100. (back issues avail.) **Document type**: bulletin.
    Description: Detailed study of areas of selected topics written for facilities managers of health care institutions.

658   **US**
AMERICAN SOCIETY FOR HOSPITAL MATERIALS MANAGEMENT. CONFERENCE PROCEEDINGS. a. American Hospital Association, American Society for Hospital Materials Management, 840 N. Lake Shore Dr., Chicago, IL 60611. TEL 312-280-6137. index. (back issues avail.)
    Description: Provides materials managers with information on how to track opportunities, develop action plans and implement those plans to improve materials management operations.

610   **FR**   **ISSN 0066-3298**
ANNUAIRE MEDICAL DE L'HOSPITALISATION FRANCAISE.. 1949. a. 690 Fr. Edi-Publi-France - Rosenwald, 10, rue Vineuse, 75116 Paris, France. TEL 44-30-81-00. FAX 44-30-81-11. Ed. Marie-Jeanne Fiant. adv. **Document type**: directory.
    Description: Provides names and adresses of clinics and hospitals with the number of beds, types of specialization and medical equipment.

658   **JA**
AOMORI KENRITSU BYOIN NENPO/AOMORI PREFECTURAL HOSPITALS. ANNUAL REPORTS. (Text in Japanese) a. Aomoriken Kankyo Hokenbu - Aomori Prefectural Government, Environmental Health Division, 1-1, Nagashima 1-chome, Aomori-shi, Aomori-ken 030, Japan.

658   **JA**   **ISSN 0387-0138**
AOMORI KENRITSU CHUO BYOIN ISHI/AOMORI PREFECTURAL CENTRAL HOSPITAL. MEDICAL JOURNAL. (Text in English, Japanese) 1956. q. Aomori Kenritsu Chuo Byoin - Aomori Prefectural Central Hospital, 2-24, Nagashima 1-chome, Aomori-shi, Aomori-ken 030, Japan. **Indexed**: INIS Atomind.

AOMORIKEN JICHITAI IGAKKAISHI/AOMORI MUNICIPAL HOSPITAL ESTABLISHMENT ASSOCIATION. JOURNAL. see *MEDICAL SCIENCES*

APOTHEKE UND KRANKENHAUS. see *PHARMACY AND PHARMACOLOGY*

362.11   **CN**
ARBUTUS SOCIETY FOR CHILDREN. ANNUAL REPORT. 1927. a. Can.$6. Arbutus Society for Children, 2400 Arbutus Road, Victoria, B.C. V8N 1V7, Canada. TEL 604-477-1826. FAX 604-721-6837. Ed. Joy Spencer-Barry. circ. 1,000. (processed)
    Former titles: Queen Alexandra Hospital for Children. Annual Report; Queen Alexandra Solarium for Crippled Children Annual Report (ISSN 0085-526X)

658   **US**
ARKANSAS HOSPITAL ASSOCIATION. PRESIDENT'S LETTER. 1973. w. $700. Arkansas Hospital Association, 419 Natural Resources Dr., Little Rock, AR 72205. TEL 501-224-7878. FAX 501-224-0519. Ed. Roger Busfield. circ. 190. (looseleaf format; back issues avail.)

362   **BL**   **ISSN 0018-5442**
ARQUIVOS DOS HOSPITAIS E DA FACULDADE DE CIENCIAS MEDICAS DA SANTA CASA DE SAO PAULO. (Text in Portuguese; summaries in English) 1954. q. $20. Faculdade de Ciencias Medicas da Santa Casa de Sao Paulo - School of Medicine of Santa Casa of Sao Paulo, Rua Dr. Cesario Motta Jr. 112, 01221 Sao Paulo, Brazil. adv.; bk.rev.; abstr.; bibl.; charts; illus.; stat.; index.

658   **CN**
ARTERE. (Text in French) 1983. m. (10/yr.). Can.$69.34. Quebec Hospital Association, 505 Blvd. de Maisonneuve W., Ste. 400, Montreal, PQ H3A 3C2, Canada. TEL 514-282-4225. FAX 514-282-4289. Ed. Raymond Roberge. adv.: B&W & color, B&W page Can.$1950; trim 11 3/4 x 16 1/2. bk.rev. circ. 7,202. (tabloid format; back issues avail.) **Document type**: trade publication.
    Description: Information for hospital administrators, field personnel. Technical news and operation methods.

658 340   **US**
ARTHUR ANDERSEN WASHINGTON HEALTHCARE NEWSLETTER. 11/yr. free. Arthur Andersen & Co., 1666 K St., N.W., Washington, DC 20006. TEL 202-862-6732. FAX 202-862-7098. Ed. Don Yesukaitis. **Document type**: newsletter.

ASAHIKAWA SHIRITSU BYOIN ISHI/ASAHIKAWA CITY HOSPITAL. JOURNAL. see *MEDICAL SCIENCES*

ASIAN HOSPITAL. see *MEDICAL SCIENCES*

658   **UK**   **ISSN 0958-8167**
ASPEL'S GAZETTE. 1989. m. £48. Aspel Publishing Ltd., 27 Wyndham & Argyle Sts., Kingston-upon-Hull HU3 1JH, England. TEL 44-482-26373. FAX 44-482-225124. Ed. Hilary Ryan. adv. circ. 1,000. (back issues avail.) **Document type**: bulletin.
    Description: Lists surplus medical and other technical equipment for sale.

362.1   **AT**   **ISSN 0156-5788**
AUSTRALIAN HEALTH REVIEW. 1978. q. Aus.$50 to non-members; members Aus.$20. Australian Hospital Association, 42 Thesiger Court, Deakin, A.C.T. 2600, Australia. Ed. R. O'Sullivan. adv.; bk.rev.; index. circ. 3,100. **Indexed**: Excerp.Med., Hosp.Lit.Ind.
    Description: Geared towards hospital administrators, medical and nursing directors and students.
    Refereed Serial

362   **AT**
AUSTRALIAN HOSPITAL. 1972. bi-m. $75. (Australian Institute of Hospital Administrators) Peter Isaacson Publications Pty. Ltd., 45-50 Porter St., Prahran, Vic. 3181, Australia. TEL 03-245-7777. FAX 03-245-7606. Ed. Valerie Colyer-Farfalla. adv.; bk.rev.; illus. circ. 3,224. (tabloid format; also avail. in microform from UMI; reprint service avail. from UMI)
    Supersedes: Hospital and Health Administration (ISSN 0301-2190); Which was formerly: Hospital and Health Care (ISSN 0018-5515)

AUSTRALIAN JOURNAL OF HOSPITAL PHARMACY. see *PHARMACY AND PHARMACOLOGY*

362   **US**
B M C NEWS.* 1942. bi-m. free. Baptist Medical Centers, Box 830605, Birmingham, AL 35283-0605. TEL 205-322-9300. Ed. Ann K. Wetzel. illus. circ. 6,000. (back issues avail.)

658   **UK**
BARTS JOURNAL. 1893. q. £8 (foreign £10). St. Bartholomew's Hospital Medical College, West Smithfield, London EC1A 7BE, England. TEL 071-601-8871. FAX 071-796-3753. Ed. Richard Hook. adv.; bk.rev.; bibl.; charts; illus. circ. 1,200. (also avail. in microform from UMI; back issues avail.; reprint service avail. from UMI) **Document type**: newsletter.
    Formerly: St. Bartholomew's Hospital Journal (ISSN 0036-2778)
    Description: Articles and comment on health matters, especially matters relevant to St. Bartholomew's.

362   **US**
BAYLOR PROGRESS. 1948. m. free. Baylor Medical Center, 3500 Gaston Ave., Dallas, TX 75246. TEL 214-820-2116. Ed. Robin Stricklin. circ. 9,000.

362   **UK**
BELL - U C M S M STUDENTS' MAGAZINE. 1897. 3/yr. £3. University College and Middlesex School of Medicine, Cleveland St., London W1, England. Ed.Bd. adv.; bk.rev.; charts; illus.; index. circ. 1,500. **Indexed**: GeoRef.
    Formerly: Middlesex Hospital Journal (ISSN 0026-3222)

HOSPITALS 3049

BETHLEM AND MAUDSLEY GAZETTE. see *MEDICAL SCIENCES — Psychiatry And Neurology*

658 610 US
BIRMINGHAM HEALTHCARE REVIEW & FORECAST ANNUAL. 1990. a. $8.95. First Publishing Inc., 2100 Riverchase Center, Ste. 110, Birmingham, AL 35244. TEL 205-733-1970. FAX 205-733-1974. Ed. Mitzi McWhorter. adv. circ. 18,100. (back issues avail.)
   Description: Reviews challenges facing the healthcare industry in Birmingham.

610 GW
BLAETTER AUS DEM HENRIETTENSTIFT. 1868. s-a. Henriettenstiftung Hannover, Marienstr. 80, 30171 Hannover, Germany. Ed. Wolfgang Helbig. charts; illus.; stat. circ. 6,500.

658 GW
BLAUE DATEI DER KRANKENHAUSLIEFERANTEN. 1979. a. DM.61. Baumann Fachzeitschriftenverlag, E.C.-Baumann-Str. 5, 95326 Kulmbach, Germany. Ed. Jutta Lange. adv. circ. 5,000. **Document type:** directory.
   Formerly: Blaue Datei der Krankenhauslieferanten mit Krankenhausverzeichnis.

BOMBAY HOSPITAL JOURNAL. see *MEDICAL SCIENCES*

658 BL
BRAZIL. COORDENACAO DE ASSISTENCIA MEDICA E HOSPITALAR. CADASTRO DE ESTABELECIMENTOS DE SAUDE.* 1973. irreg. free. Ministerio da Saude, Secretaria Nacional de Acoes Basicas em Saude, Esplanada dos Ministerios, Bloco 11, 70058 Brasilia D.F., Brazil. stat. circ. 1,000.
   Formerly: Brazil. Coordenacao de Assistencia Medica e Hospitalar. Cadastro Hospitalar Brasileiro.

658 613 US
▼**BRIEFINGS ON HOSPITAL SAFETY**; the newsletter for hospital safety committees. 1993. m. $177. Opus Communications, Box 1168, Marblehead, MA 01945. TEL 617-639-1872. FAX 617-639-2982. (looseleaf format) **Document type:** newsletter.
   Description: Covers safety management issues, including planning, regulations. Offers practical information on how to improve safety.

658 US ISSN 1054-6995
BRIEFINGS ON J C A H O. (Joint Commission on Accreditation of Healthcare Organizations); alternative perspectives on accreditation. (Includes q. supplement: Briefings on C Q I) 1990. m. $292 (effective 1994). Opus Communications, Box 1168, Marblehead, MA 01945. TEL 617-639-1872. FAX 617-639-2982. Ed. James B. Flanagan. bk.rev.; index. circ. 2,300. (looseleaf format; back issues avail.) **Document type:** newsletter.
   Description: Covers issues and procedures in health care accreditation and compliance, quality improvement and related issues.

362 610 US
▼**BRIEFINGS ON LONG-TERM CARE**. 1993. m. $147. Opus Communications, Box 1168, Marblehead, MA 01945. TEL 617-639-1872. FAX 617-639-2982. (looseleaf format) **Document type:** newsletter.
   Description: Covers news and developments affecting administrators of long-term care facilities, including regulations, reimbursement, management issues and clinical procedures.

BRIEFINGS ON PRACTICE MANAGEMENT. see *MEDICAL SCIENCES*

BRITISH JOURNAL OF HOSPITAL MEDICINE. see *MEDICAL SCIENCES*

BRITISH JOURNAL OF MEDICAL ECONOMICS. see *MEDICAL SCIENCES*

362 US
BROOKDALE HOSPITAL MEDICAL CENTER NEWS-SCOPE. 1972. q. free. The Brookdale Hospital Medical Center, Linden Blvd. at Brookdale Plaza, Brooklyn, NY 11212. TEL 718-240-5345. illus. circ. 11,000. (tabloid format)
   Formerly: Brookdale Hospital Medical Center News.
   Description: Contains news and information about Brookdale Hospital, physicians, services, and staff for distribution internally and externally.

658 616.863 US
BROWN UNIVERSITY LONG-TERM CARE QUALITY LETTER. 1988. s-m. $197 to individuals (Canada $212; elsewhere $222); institutions $247 (Canada $262; elsewhere $272). Manisses Communications Group, Inc., Box 3357, Providence, RI 02906-0757. TEL 800-333-7771. FAX 401-861-6370. Eds. Drs. Barry Fogel, Vincent Mor. **Document type:** newsletter. —CCC.
   Formerly (until 1992): Brown University Long-Term Care Letter (ISSN 1042-1386)
   Description: Practical reports for administrators and clinical directors of long-term care facilities.

362 380.1 US
BUYERS GUIDE FOR THE HEALTH CARE MARKET; a directory of products and service for health care institutions. a. $14.95. American Hospital Publishing, Inc. (Subsidiary of: American Hospital Association Company), 737 N. Michigan Ave., Ste. 700, Chicago, IL 60611. TEL 312-440-6800. FAX 312-951-8491. circ. 76,700. **Document type:** directory.
   Former titles: Buyers Guide for the Health Care Industry; Buyers Guide for the Health Care Institutions.

658 JA ISSN 0385-2377
BYOIN/HOSPITAL. (Text in Japanese) 1949. m. 2200 Yen per no. Igaku Shoin Ltd., 5-24-3 Hongo, Bunkyo-ku, Tokyo 113-91, Japan. TEL 03-3817-5719. Ed.Bd. circ. 6,500.

BYOIN, CHIIKI SEISHIN IGAKU/JAPANESE JOURNAL OF HOSPITAL AND COMMUNITY PSYCHIATRY. see *MEDICAL SCIENCES — Psychiatry And Neurology*

658 JA ISSN 0386-9571
BYOIN KANRI/HOSPITAL ADMINISTRATION. (Text in Japanese; summaries in English) 1964. q. 5200 Yen($28) Japanese Society on Hospital Administration, c/o National Institute of Health Services Management, 23-1 Toyama, Shinjuku-ku, Tokyo 162, Japan. TEL 03-3203-5327. FAX 03-3203-6853. adv. circ. 1,300. (back issues avail.)

658 JA ISSN 0385-3454
BYOIN KANRI KENKYUJO KIYO/NATIONAL INSTITUTE OF HOSPITAL ADMINISTRATION. BULLETIN. (Text in Japanese) 1962. a. Koseisho, Byoin Kanri Kenkyujo - Ministry of Health and Welfare, National Institute of Hospital Administration, 21-13, Tayama 1-chome, Shinjuku-ku, Tokyo 162, Japan. **Document type:** bulletin.

658 JA ISSN 0525-3268
BYOIN KANRI KENKYUJO NENPO/NATIONAL INSTITUTE OF HOSPITAL ADMINISTRATION. ANNUAL REPORT. (Text in Japanese) 1961. a. Koseisho, Byoin Kanri Kenkyujo - Ministry of Health and Welfare, National Institute of Hospital Administration, 21-13, Toyama 1-chome, Shinjuku-ku, Tokyo 162, Japan.

362 JA ISSN 0408-0904
BYOIN YORAN/JAPANESE HOSPITAL DIRECTORY. (Text in Japanese) 1952-1964; resumed 1989. irreg. 15000 Yen. (Ministry of Health and Welfare) Igaku-Shoin Ltd., 5-24-3 Hongo, Bunkyo-ku, Tokyo 113-91, Japan. TEL 03-3817-5600. Ed.Bd. circ. 5,000. **Document type:** directory.

362.16 US
C C C N. (California Community Care News) 1965. m. $45. Box 163270, Sacramento, CA 95816. TEL 916-455-0723. FAX 916-455-7201. Ed. Charles W. Skoien, Jr. adv.; bk.rev. circ. 10,000. (tabloid format) **Document type:** trade publication.
   Formerly (until 1969): C A R C H News (ISSN 0163-2213)
   Description: Covers regulations, new legislation; includes information concerning operation, licensure and maintenance of community residential care home.

610 CN ISSN 0822-8426
C H A C INFO/INFO A C C S. (Text in English and French) 1983. q. membership. Catholic Health Association of Canada, 1247 Kilborn Pl., Ottawa, ON K1H 6K9, Canada. TEL 613-731-7148. FAX 613-731-7797. Ed. Freda Fraser. circ. 1,240 (controlled). **Document type:** newsletter.

362 CN ISSN 0226-5923
C H A C REVIEW. French edition: Revue A C C S (ISSN 0226-5931) (Text in English) 1958. 3/yr. Can.$30($35) Catholic Health Association of Canada, 1247 Kilborn Pl., Ottawa, ON K1H 6K9, Canada. TEL 613-731-7148. FAX 613-731-7797. Ed. Freda Fraser. adv.; bk.rev. circ. 1,607. **Document type:** academic/scholarly publication.
   Former titles (until 1973): Catholic Hospital (ISSN 0008-8099); C H A C Bulletin.

CALIFORNIA JOURNAL OF HOSPITAL PHARMACY. see *PHARMACY AND PHARMACOLOGY*

362.1 US
CALIFORNIA STATE HEALTH PLAN. 1980. a. $15. Office of Statewide Health Planning and Development, 1600 Ninth St., Rm. 440, Sacramento, CA 95814. TEL 916-654-2080. FAX 916-654-3138. Ed. Larry Meeks. stat. circ. 5,000. **Indexed:** Ind.Med. **Document type:** government publication.
   Former titles (until 1955): California State Plan for Hospital and Health Center Construction (ISSN 0098-9983); California State Plan for Hospitals and Related Health Facilities (ISSN 0526-9288); California State Plan for Hospitals (ISSN 0575-2221)
   Description: Contains an overview of the health care industry in California, an assessment of the current financial condition of hospitals, and identification of health care issues facing the State over the long-term planning horizon.

362.18 CN ISSN 0847-947X
CANADIAN EMERGENCY NEWS. vol.2, 1978. 11/yr. Can.$30 (foreign $45). Pendragon Publishing Ltd., Box 54087, 2640- 52nd St N.E., Calgary, AB T1Y 6S6, Canada. TEL 403-248-0755. FAX 403-248-7856. Ed. Kevin Blades. adv.: B&W page Can.$1290, color page Can.$1865; trim 8 1/4 x 10 7/8; adv. contact: Lyle Blumhagen. illus. circ. 4,000.
   Formerly: Canadian Emergency Services News (ISSN 0706-9278)
   Description: Covers emergency response - police, fire, rescue, paramedics and suppliers to the industry.

CANADIAN JOURNAL OF HOSPITAL PHARMACY. see *PHARMACY AND PHARMACOLOGY*

362.15 CN ISSN 0847-5520
CANADIAN NURSING HOME JOURNAL. 1985. q. Can.$15($20) Health Media Inc., 14453 29A Ave., White Rock, B.C. V4A 9K8, Canada. TEL 604-535-7933. Ed. Frank Fagan. circ. 4,000.
   Formerly (until 1989): Ontario Nursing Home Journal (ISSN 0829-6340)

362 US
CAPSULE (WYANDOTTE); a magazine about your health. 1961. q. free. Wyandotte Hospital and Medical Center, 2333 Biddle Ave., Wyandotte, MI 48192. TEL 313-284-2400. Ed. Mary Ellen McLeod. circ. 20,000.
   Formerly (until 1974): Capsule Comments.
   Description: News and human interest articles on health, profiles of patients and descriptions of hospital programs.

362 200 US
CATHOLIC HEALTH ASSOCIATION MEMBERS (YEAR). a. Catholic Health Association of the United States, 4455 Woodson Rd., St. Louis, MO 63134-3797. TEL 314-427-2500. FAX 314-427-0029.
   Former titles: Catholic Health Association of the United States. Guidebook; Guidebook of Catholic Hospitals (ISSN 0090-2535)
   Description: Guidebook to membership.

362 200 US ISSN 8756-4068
CATHOLIC HEALTH WORLD. 1985. 24/yr. $24 (foreign $28). Catholic Health Association of the United States, 4455 Woodson Rd., St. Louis, MO 63134-3797. TEL 314-427-2500. FAX 314-427-0029. Ed. Suzy Farren. adv. circ. 6,100.
   Description: Contains national and regional news, features, human interest items, articles on people and health care legislation, and reports of events.

3050 HOSPITALS

362   US   ISSN 0008-8684
CEDARS - SINAI MEDICAL CENTER COMPASS. Variant title: Cedars-Sinai Compass. 1957. q. free. Cedars - Sinai Medical Center, Public Relations Department, 8700 Beverly Blvd., Box 48750, Los Angeles, CA 90048. TEL 310-855-4767. FAX 310-657-9614. Ed. Jorian Clair. charts; illus. circ. 27,000.
  Supersedes (in 1962): Cedars of Lebanon Compass.

CHESHIRE SMILE. see HANDICAPPED — Physically Impaired

CHILDREN'S HOSPICE INTERNATIONAL NEWSLETTER. see MEDICAL SCIENCES — Pediatrics

362   US
CHILDREN'S WORLD. 1962. q. free. Children's Hospital, Boston, Public Affairs Dept., 300 Longwood Ave., Boston, MA 02115. TEL 617-735-6420. circ. 25,000.
  Formerly: Children's Hospital Medical Center, Boston. News (ISSN 0006-7938)

CHUBU BYOIN IGAKU ZASSHI/OKINAWA CHUBU HOSPITAL. BULLETIN. see MEDICAL SCIENCES

658   JA   ISSN 0389-4894
CHUSEI SOGO BYOIN ZASSHI/CHUSEI GENERAL HOSPITAL. JOURNAL. (Text in Japanese) 1978. biennial. Chusei Sogo Byoin, 28-30, Kanbe 8-chome, Suzuka-shi, Mie-ken 513, Japan.

CLINICAL ENGINEERING SECTION NEWSLETTER. see INSTRUMENTS

CLINICAL LABORATORY PRODUCT COMPARISON SYSTEM. see MEDICAL SCIENCES — Experimental Medicine, Laboratory Technique

THE CLINICIAN IN MANAGEMENT. see MEDICAL SCIENCES

658   AU
CLINICUM. 10/yr. S.370 (foreign S.420). Manstein Verlag GmbH, Brunner Feldstr. 45, A-2380 Perchtoldsdorf, Austria. TEL 0222-81608-0. FAX 0222-8160880. Ed. Dr. Angelika Rosenberger-Spitzy. adv.: B&W page S.24800, color page S.33800; trim 188 x 252; adv. contact: Peter Sudra. circ. 11,500. **Document type:** trade publication.

642.59   ISSN 0742-9800
CODING CLINIC FOR ICD-9-CM. 1984. q. $160 to non-members; members $105. American Hospital Association, 840 N. Lake Shore Dr., Chicago, IL 60611. TEL 312-280-6656. FAX 312-280-5995. Ed. Donna Pickett. circ. 5,000. (back issues avail.) **Document type:** newsletter.
  Description: Coding information and advice to assist in improving the quality of ICD-9-CM coding, especially for use in hospital prospective pricing, utilization management, and quality assurance programs.

658   US   ISSN 1063-1720
▼**COMPARATIVE PERFORMANCE OF U.S. HOSPITALS: THE SOURCEBOOK.** 1992. a. $439. H C I A Inc., 300 E. Lombard St., Baltimore, MD 21202. TEL 410-576-9600. FAX 410-783-0575. (Co-publisher: Deloitte & Touche)
  Description: Features more than 160 hospital comparison groups, including analysis by state, bond rating, system affiliation, ownership and bed size. Information tables and explanatory analyses cover the 52 most important measures of hospital performance, including occupancy rates, profit margins, staffing levels, and debt service coverage ratios.

658   US
▼**COMPARING QUALITY & FINANCIAL PERFORMANCE OF ACCREDITED HOSPITALS.** 1992. irreg. $195. (Joint Commission on Accreditation of Healthcare Organizations) H C I A Inc., 300 E. Lombard St., Baltimore, MD 21202. TEL 410-576-9600. FAX 410-783-0575.
  Formerly: Health Care Quality and Financial Measures: Comparative Performance of Accredited Hospitals.
  Description: Compares quality data from Joint Commission hospital surveys to the profitablity information from HCIA's hospital data base.

COMPUTERS IN HEALTHCARE. see MEDICAL SCIENCES — Computer Applications

362   IT   ISSN 0589-3267
CONGRESSO EUROPEO DI STORIA OSPITALIERA. ATTI. 1960. irreg., latest no.15. L.34000 (foreign L.42000). Centro Italiano di Storia Sanitaria e Ospitaliera, Biblioteca, Viale Risorgimento, 30, 42100 Reggio Emilia, Italy. TEL 0522-24252.

658 632.15   US
CONNECTIONS (LARGO). 1991. 3/yr. free. Hospice of the Florida Suncoast, 300 E. Bay Dr., Largo, FL 34640. TEL 813-586-4432. FAX 813-586-5213. Ed. Karen Cunningham. circ. 5,000. **Document type:** newsletter.
  Description: Informs professionals on medical, psychosocial and administrative issues related to terminal illness and hospice care.

658   US   ISSN 8750-9652
CONTEMPORARY LONG-TERM CARE. 1978. m. $32 (foreign $60). Bill Communications, Inc., 355 Park Ave. S., New York, NY 10010-1789. TEL 212-592-6275. FAX 212-592-6489. Ed. Ron Sympson. adv.; bk.rev. circ. 33,564. **Document type:** trade publication.
  —BLDSC (3425.191100); Faxon; UMI. **CCC.**
  Formerly: Contemporary Administrator (ISSN 0191-9873)
  Description: For administrators, directors of nursing, medical directors, pharmacists and other professionals responsible for management and patient care at nursing facilities, residential care centers, and hospitals with long-term care.

658   US
CONTEMPORARY LONG-TERM CARE REIMBURSEMENT BULLETIN. 1988. s-m. $297 (foreign $307). Bill Communications, Inc., 355 Park Ave. S., New York, NY 10010-1789. TEL 212-592-6275. FAX 212-592-6489. **Document type:** trade publication.
  Description: For administrators, financial executives and owners of nursing facilities, residential care centers, and hospitals with long-term care. Provides current news on US national, state and private pay medical reimbursement policies for the chronically ill patients.

658 360   US   ISSN 1057-428X
CONTINUING CARE; supporting the transition into post hospital care. 1982. m. $72 (subscr. includes a Buyer's Guide). Stevens Publishing Corporation, 225 N. New Rd., Waco, TX 76710. TEL 817-776-9000. FAX 817-776-9018. Ed. Stephanie McIntosh. adv.; bk.rev.; charts; illus.; tr.lit.; index. circ. 21,000. (back issues avail.)
  —CCC.
  Former titles: Continuing Care Coordinator & Coordinator (Los Angeles).

658 610   US   ISSN 1069-482X
▼**D R G HANDBOOK.** (Diagnosis Related Group); comparative clinical and financial standards. 1992. a. $399. H C I A Inc., 300 E. Lombard St., Baltimore, MD 21202. TEL 410-576-9600. FAX 410-783-0575. (Co-publisher: Ernst & Young)
  Formerly: Medicare D R G Handbook.
  Description: Compiles data based on 11 million Medicare patients and focuses on clinical and financial measures for 50 highest volume DRGs.

362.11   DK   ISSN 0106-6706
D S I NOTAT.* 1979. irreg. price varies. Dansk Sygehus Institut - Danish Hospital Institute, Nyropsgade 18, DK-1602 Copenhagen V, Denmark. illus. circ. 1,000.
  —BLDSC (6155.225000).

362.795   DK   ISSN 0108-5352
DAGPLEJE-HJEMMET.* 1982. bi-m. DKK 114. Dagplejehjemmet, Nyborg, Denmark. illus.

658   JA
DAIDO BYOIN NENPO/DAIDO HOSPITAL. ANNUAL REPORT. (Text in Japanese) 1982. a. Kojunkai Daido Byoin - Kojunkai Daido Hospital, 9, Hakusuicho, Minami-ku, Nagoya-shi, Aichi-ken 457, Japan.

610   GW
DEUTSCHE KRANKENHAUSGESELLSCHAFT. JAHRESBERICHT. biennial. free. Deutsche Krankenhausgesellschaft, Tersteegenstr. 9, 40474 Duesseldorf, Germany.

658   GW
DEUTSCHES KRANKENHAUS ADRESSBUCH. 1962. a. DM.119. Rombach GmbH Verlagshaus, Loerracherstr. 3, 79115 Freiburg, Germany. TEL 0761-4500-0. FAX 0761-4500-212. adv.; index. circ. 11,000. **Document type:** directory.
  Description: Brief editorials, mainly hospital addresses for Germany, Austria and Switzerland; includes supplier's register.

658   MX
DICCIONARIO DE TECNOLOGIA E INSUMOS MEDICOS. 1991. a. Ediciones P L M, S.A. de C.V., San Bernadino 17, Col. del Valle, 03100 Mexico, D.F., Mexico. TEL 687-1766. FAX 536-5027. Ed. Dr. Jose Luis Gonzalez. circ. 2,000.

658   US
DIRECTIONS (COLUMBUS); the technical journal for health care material management. 1986. s-a. membership. Health Care Material Management Society, 99 E. Weber Rd., Columbus, OH 43202. TEL 614-263-5927. Ed. S. Anne Sostrom. circ. 1,400.
  Description: Covers warehousing, purchasing, sterilization and reuse, and inventory control.

658   UK
DIRECTORY OF HOSPITAL TELEPHONE NUMBERS (YEAR). 1991. a. £15. C M A Medical Data Ltd., Cambridge Research Laboratories, 181A Huntingdon Rd., Cambridge CB3 0DJ, England. TEL 0223-277709. FAX 0223-276444. **Document type:** directory.
  Description: Contains over 2000 telephone numbers covering all NHS and independent hospitals. The hospitals are listed alphabetically and include the name of the town and the regional Health Authority in which the hospital is located.

DIRECTORY OF HOSPITALS (YEAR). see BUSINESS AND ECONOMICS — Trade And Industrial Directories

610   UK
DIRECTORY OF INDEPENDENT HOSPITALS AND HEALTH SERVICES; a comprehensive guide to the independent health care sector in the U.K. a. £90. Longman Group UK Ltd., Westgate House, 6th Fl., The High, Harlow, Essex CM20 1YR, England. TEL 0279-442601. FAX 0279-444501. TELEX 817484. adv. circ. 3,250. **Document type:** directory.
  —BLDSC (3594.266000).
  Formerly: Directory of Private Hospitals and Health Services (ISSN 0260-8820)

658 371.42   AT   ISSN 0157-2784
DIRECTORY OF INTERNSHIPS, RESIDENCIES AND REGISTRARSHIPS AVAILABLE IN VICTORIAN HOSPITALS. 1967. a. Aus.$15. Victorian Medical Postgraduate Foundation Inc., P.O. Box 27, Parkville, Vic. 3052, Australia. TEL 03-347-9633. FAX 03-347-4547. Ed. N. Gialouris. circ. 900. **Document type:** directory.
  —CCC.

362.1   US
RA977
DIRECTORY OF INVESTOR-OWNED HOSPITALS, RESIDENTIAL TREATMENT FACILITIES AND CENTERS, HOSPITAL MANAGEMENT COMPANIES AND HEALTH SYSTEMS. a. $60. F A H S Review, Inc., 1405 N. Pierce St., Ste. 308, Little Rock, AR 72207. TEL 501-661-9555. FAX 501-663-4903. (reprint service avail. from UMI) **Document type:** directory.
  Former titles: Directory of Investor-Owned Hospitals, Hospital Management Companies and Health Systems; Directory of Investor-Owned Hospitals and Hospital Management Companies (ISSN 0095-5191)

362   US
DIRECTORY OF OSTEOPATHIC POSTDOCTORIAL EDUCATION. a. $40 to non-members; members $12; free to students. American Osteopathic Hospital Association, 5301 Wisconsin Ave., N.W., Ste. 630, Washington, DC 20015-2015. TEL 202-686-1700. FAX 202-686-7615. Ed. Amy Miller Jackson. circ. 3,000. **Document type:** directory.

DIRECTORY OF RETIREMENT FACILITIES. see GERONTOLOGY AND GERIATRICS

HOSPITALS

658 US ISSN 1062-1946
▼DIRECTORY OF U S HOSPITALS. 1992. a. $219. H C I A Inc., 300 E. Lombard St., Baltimore, MD 21202. TEL 410-576-9600. FAX 410-783-0575. **Document type:** directory.
Description: Provides hospital-specific data for 30 key measures of descriptive, financial and clinical information for every U.S. hospital.

362 US ISSN 0276-4652
  CODEN: DPUPEH
DISCHARGE PLANNING UPDATE. 1980. bi-m. $57 non-members; members $47. American Hospital Association, 840 N. Lake Shore Dr., Chicago, IL 60611-2431. TEL 312-280-6414. FAX 312-280-4152. Ed. Salvinija Kernaghan. bk.rev. circ. 1,600. (back issues avail.) **Indexed:** CINAHL, Hosp.Lit.Ind. **Document type:** newsletter.
Description: Multidisciplinary approach to the hospital discharge planning process and the delivery of posthospital care.

DOAI IGAKU ZASSHI/FRATERNITY MEMORIAL HOSPITAL. MEDICAL JOURNAL. see *MEDICAL SCIENCES*

658 US ISSN 0882-5807
ECONOMIC TRENDS (CHICAGO). 1985. q. $135 to non-members; members $85. American Hospital Association, 840 N. Lake Shore Dr., Chicago, IL 60611. TEL 312-280-6494. FAX 312-280-4151. Ed. Karen McGannon. circ. 1,000. **Document type:** newsletter.
Description: Data on and analysis of US hospital finances, utilization, and staffing trends.

658 HU ISSN 0013-2276
EGESZSEGUGYI GAZDASAGI SZEMLE. (Text in Hungarian; summaries in English, German) 1963. bi-m. $22. (Nepjoleti Miniszterium - Ministry of Welfare) Egeszsegugyi Gazdasagi Vezetok Egyesulete, PO Box 1, 1361 Budapest, Hungary. TEL 361-1323100. Ed. E. Kovesi. adv.; bk.rev. circ. 1,000. **Indexed:** Excerp.Med., Hosp.Abstr. **Document type:** academic/scholarly publication.
—BLDSC (3664.195000).
Description: Covers managerial information for health institutions.

ELDERLY HEALTH SERVICES LETTER. see *GERONTOLOGY AND GERIATRICS*

649 362.7 FR
ETABLISSEMENTS MEDICAUX POUR ENFANTS. bi-m. Federation Francaise des Etablissements de Soins, de Cure et de Prevention pour Enfants, 34 rue Brunesseau, 75629 Paris Cedex 13, France. TEL 1-44-24-51-11. FAX 1-44-24-56-45. Ed. Fernand Bitterly. circ. 3,500.

658 GW
EUROPEAN HOSPITAL. 4/yr. DM.64 for 2 yrs. Beta Verlag GmbH, Postfach 140121, 53056 Bonn, Germany. TEL 0228-252061. FAX 0228-252067. TELEX 8869536-BETA-D. Ed. Dr. Paul Weiss. circ. 27,000. **Document type:** trade publication.

EXECUTIVE HOUSEKEEPING TODAY. see *OCCUPATIONAL HEALTH AND SAFETY*

658 US ISSN 0898-9753
EXECUTIVE REPORT ON MANAGED CARE. 1988. 12/yr. $157. American Business Publishing, 3100 Hwy. 138, Box 1442, Wall Township, NJ 07719-1442. TEL 908-681-1133. FAX 908-681-0490. Ed. Robert K. Jenkins. (back issues avail.)
—CCC.
Description: News of how major employers are implementing managed care programs. Helps companies prepare to evaluate and monitor various managed care proposals in terms of cost-effectiveness, quality and liability to the employer.

658 GW ISSN 0175-4548
F & W - FUEHREN UND WIRTSCHAFTEN IM KRANKENHAUS. 1984. bi-m. DM.80.40. Bibiomed - Medizinische Verlagsgesellschaft mbH, Postfach 150, 34201 Melsungen, Germany. adv.; bk.rev.; index. circ. 4,000.
—BLDSC (3858.000000).

FAMILY PRACTICE MANAGEMENT. see *MEDICAL SCIENCES*

FAR EAST HEALTH. see *PUBLIC HEALTH AND SAFETY*

362 CN ISSN 1185-5428
FAX PLUS. 1963. 5/yr. free. Montreal Children's Hospital, 2300 Tupper St., Ste. E-203, Montreal, PQ H3H 1P3, Canada. TEL 514-934-4307. Ed. Arlette Cote. adv.; circ. 1,500 (controlled). **Document type:** newsletter.
Formerly (until 1991): Montreal Children's Hospital. Children's News (ISSN 0047-8059)
Description: News of interest to staff and friends of Montreal Children's Hospital.

FITZHUGH DIRECTORY OF INDEPENDENT HEALTHCARE. FINANCIAL INFORMATION. ACUTE SECTOR. see *MEDICAL SCIENCES*

FITZHUGH DIRECTORY OF LONG TERM CARE FINANCIAL INFORMATION. see *MEDICAL SCIENCES*

FLORIDA BAR. HEALTH LAW SECTION. NEWSLETTER. see *LAW*

355.72 387.7 AT
FLYING DOCTOR YEARBOOK. 1976. a. Aus.$5 (effective 1994). Royal Flying Doctor Service of Australia, 379 Queen St., Brisbane, Qld. 4000, Australia. Ed. Ken Leckenby. adv. contact: Barry Cole. circ. 9,000.

658 UK
FREE PRESS. w. free. Royal Free Hospital Students Union, Clinical Sciences Building, Pond St., Hampstead, London NW3 2PE, England. Ed. Leela Biant. circ. 180. (looseleaf format)
Description: Contains organization news.

613.194 US ISSN 0748-8157
RA971
FRONTIERS OF HEALTH SERVICES MANAGEMENT. 1984. q. $60 (foreign $70). (Foundation of the American College of Healthcare Executives) Health Administration Press, 1021 E. Huron St., Ann Arbor, MI 48104-9990. TEL 312-943-0544. FAX 708-450-1618. (Subscr. to: Order Processing Center, 1951 Cornell, Melrose Park, IL 60160) Ed. Douglas A. Conrad. circ. 2,500. (also avail. in microform from UMI; reprint service avail. from UMI) **Indexed:** ABI Inform, Abstr.Health Care Manage.Stud., Excerp.Med. **Document type:** academic/scholarly publication.
—BLDSC (4042.023000); Faxon; UnCover; UMI. CCC.
Description: Focuses on directions in health services management and policy. Each issue examines a single topic in depth.

362 CN
GENERALLY SPEAKING. 1960. q. Montreal General Hospital, Rm. 618, 1650 Cedar Ave., Montreal, Que. H3G 1A4, Canada. TEL 514-937-6011. FAX 514-937-3023. Ed. Joan Lamontagne. bk.rev.; illus. circ. 4,500.
Formerly: Montreal General Hospital News (ISSN 0027-0709)

GERIATRIC CARE. see *GERONTOLOGY AND GERIATRICS*

658 SP ISSN 0214-8919
GESTION HOSPITALARIA. 1990. 4/yr. 4000 ptas.($80) (Europe 4500 ptas.). (Sociedad Espanola de Directores y Gerentes de Hospitales y Planificacion Sanitaria) Alpe Editores, S.A., Pedro Rico, 27, 28029 Madrid, Spain. TEL 733-88-11. FAX 315-96-52. Dir. A. Bartolome Sanchez. adv.: B&W page 100000 ptas.; color page 150000 ptas.; 210 x 280. circ. 6,500 (controlled).

362 FR ISSN 0016-9218
GESTIONS HOSPITALIERES. (Includes special nos.) 1960. m. 540 F. 44 rue Jules Ferry, 94400 Vitry sur Seine, France. TEL 42-66-15-26. FAX 47-42-44-66. Ed. Rene Bandelier. adv.; bk.rev. circ. 4,728. **Indexed:** Excerp.Med.
—BLDSC (4163.800000). CCC.

658 657.832 BE
GEZONDHEIDSZORG, BELEID EN ORGANIZATIE. (Supplement avail.) (Text in Flemish) s-m. 4134 BEF. C E D Samsom (Subsidiary of: Wolters Samsom Belgie n.v.), Kouterveld 14, B-1831 Diegem, Belgium. TEL 32-2-7231111.
Description: Provides detailed and professional advice on the organizational, fiscal and personnel aspects of running hospitals, retirement homes, sanitaria and rehabilitation centers.

362.11 UK
GREAT BRITAIN. DEPARTMENT OF HEALTH AND SOCIAL SECURITY. HEALTH BUILDING NOTES. 1961. irreg. price varies. H.M.S.O., P.O. Box 276, London SW8 5DT, England. (reprint service avail. from UMI)
Document type: government publication.
Formerly: Great Britain. Department of Health and Social Security. Hospital Building Notes (ISSN 0072-601X)

362.11 UK ISSN 0141-1403
GREAT BRITAIN. DEPARTMENT OF HEALTH AND SOCIAL SECURITY. HEALTH EQUIPMENT NOTES. 1975. irreg. price varies. H.M.S.O., P.O. Box 276, London SW8 5DT, England. (reprint service avail. from UMI)
Document type: government publication.
—CCC.
Formerly: Great Britain. Department of Health and Social Security. Hospital Equipment Notes (ISSN 0072-6028)

GROUP PRACTICE JOURNAL. see *MEDICAL SCIENCES*

362 CN ISSN 1195-0110
GUIDE TO CANADIAN HEALTH CARE FACILITIES/GUIDE DES ETABLISSEMENTS DE SANTE DU CANADA. (Text in English, French) 1953. a. Can.$112. Canadian Hospital Association, 17 York St., Ste. 100, Ottawa, ON K1N 9J6, Canada. TEL 613-241-8005. FAX 613-241-5055. Ed. Indra Seegobin. adv. circ. 2,000. (reprint service avail. from UMI) **Document type:** directory.
Formerly (until 1993): Canadian Hospital Directory (ISSN 0068-8932)
Description: Lists all hospitals and long-term care facilities in Canada; includes key personnel, budgets and numbers of beds.

658 US
▼**GUIDE TO FEDERAL FUNDING FOR HOSPITALS & HEALTH CENTERS.** 1993. a. $305.50. Government Information Services, 4301 N. Fairfax Dr., Ste. 875, Arlington, VA 22203-1627. TEL 703-528-1000. FAX 703-528-6060. Eds. Amy McAuliffe, Charles Edwards. (looseleaf format)
Description: Describes about 150 federal grant and loan programs for hospitals, health centers, and other agencies involved in administering health services.

658 362.6 US ISSN 1062-8258
▼**GUIDE TO THE NURSING HOME INDUSTRY.** 1992. a. $249. H C I A Inc., 300 E. Lombard St., Baltimore, MD 21202. TEL 410-576-9600. FAX 410-783-0575. (Co-publisher: Arthur Andersen & Co.)
Description: Provides aggregate financial and operating performance data on more than 15,000 nursing homes state-by-state.

658 US
GUIDELINES FOR HEALTH SUPERVISION II. 1985. irreg., 2nd ed., 1988. $41.95. American Academy of Pediatrics, 141 Northwest Point Blvd., Box 927, Elk Grove Village, IL 60009-0927. TEL 708-228-5005; 800-433-9016. FAX 708-228-1281. **Document type:** monographic series.
Description: Guidelines for patient visits from the prenatal visit to age twenty.

GUIDELINES FOR PERINATAL CARE. see *MEDICAL SCIENCES — Obstetrics And Gynecology*

362 UK ISSN 0017-5870
GUY'S HOSPITAL GAZETTE. 1872. m. £15. Guy's Hospital, Boland House, St. Thomas' Street, Guy's Hospital, London SE1 9RT, England. TEL 071-955-5000 ext. 5413. Ed. Fuad F. Hussain. adv.; bk.rev.; play rev.; illus.; stat.; index. circ. 3,000. **Indexed:** Chem.Abstr.

HOSPITALS

658 170   NE   ISSN 0956-2737
R724   CODEN: HEFOE8
H E C FORUM. (HealthCare Ethics Committee); an interdisciplinary journal on hospitals' ethical and legal issues. 1989. 6/yr. fl.219($114.50) (effective 1994). Kluwer Academic Publishers, Postbus 17, 3300 AA Dordrecht, Netherlands.
TEL 31-78-334911. FAX 31-78-334254. TELEX 29245 KAPG NL. (Dist by: Kluwer Academic Publishers Group, P.O. Box 322, 3300 AH Dordrecht, Netherlands. TEL 31-78-524400. FAX 31-78-524474; N. America dist. addr.: Box 358, Accord Sta., Hingham, MA 02018-0358. TEL 617-871-6600. FAX 617-871-6528) Eds. Stuart F. Spicker, Judith Wilson Ross. (also avail. in microform from UMI; reprint service avail. from SWZ)
—BLDSC (4275.247788); UMI. **CCC.**
Description: Focuses on ethical and legal issues as they pertain to hospitals. Responds to the increasingly complex issues addressed by hospital ethics committees, including administrative and policy issues and philosophical dilemmas.
Refereed Serial

658   NO   ISSN 0803-2556
H M T. HELSETJENESTEN - MEDICINSK TEKNIKK. 1928. m. (10/yr.). NOK 240. (Helsetjenestens Administrasjons Forbund) Selvig Publishing A-S, P.O. Box 9070, Gronland, N-0133 Oslo, Norway. Ed. P. Oivind Selvig. adv.; bk.rev. circ. 2,436.
—CCC.
Formed by the 1991 merger of: Medisinsk Teknikk (ISSN 0800-5656) & Helsetjenesten (ISSN 0333-3299); Which was formerly (until 1982): Norsk Sykehustidende (ISSN 0377-1792)

HACHINOHE SHIRITSU SHIMIN BYOIN ISHI/HACHINOHE CITY HOSPITAL. MEDICAL JOURNAL. see *MEDICAL SCIENCES*

362 658.8   US
HAYES DIRECTORY OF MEDICAL SUPPLY HOUSES. 1935. a. $200. Edward N. Hayes, Publisher, 4229 Birch St., Newport Beach, CA 92660.
TEL 714-756-9063. **Document type:** directory.
Formerly: Hayes Directory of Physician and Hospital Supply Houses (ISSN 0073-1412)

362   II   ISSN 0970-471X
HEALTH ACTION. (Text in English) 1959. m. Rs.60 to individuals; institutions Rs.80; foreign $50. Catholic Hospital Association of India, P.B. 2153, 157/6 Staff Road, Gunrock Enclave, Secunderabad 500 003, India. TEL 848293. TELEX 0425 6674 CHAI IN. Ed. C.M. Francis. adv.; bk.rev.; charts; illus.; tr.lit. circ. 35,000.
Formerly (until 1988): Medical Service (ISSN 0008-8102)

HEALTH BULLETIN. see *MEDICAL SCIENCES*

HEALTH CARE AND THE LAW. see *LAW*

362   US   ISSN 1049-2577
RA407.4.N7
HEALTH CARE ANNUAL: AN UPDATE ON TRENDS AND FACILITIES IN NEW YORK. a. $20. United Hospital Fund of New York, 55 Fifth Ave., New York, NY 10003. TEL 212-645-2500. FAX 212-727-2471. stat. **Document type:** academic/scholarly publication.
Formed by the merger of: Health and Health Care in New York City: Local, State, and National Perspectives (ISSN 0889-0331); Health Facilities in Southern New York: A Guide to Inpatient, Outpatient, and Long-Term Care (ISSN 0888-7039)
Description: Chartbook depicting most recent trends in population, health status, availability, and use of health facilities, health employment, education, and finances for New York and the nation.

362.1   UK   ISSN 0967-3881
HEALTH CARE BUYERS' GUIDE. 1966. a. £69 (overseas £84). Benn Business Information Services Ltd. (Subsidiary of: Morgan-Grampian plc), Riverbank House, Angel Ln., Tonbridge, Kent TN9 1SE, England. TEL 0732-362666. FAX 0732-770483. TELEX 95162-BENTON-G. Ed.Bd. **Document type:** directory.
—BLDSC (4274.937900).
Former titles: Health Service Buyers Guide (ISSN 0140-5748); Sell's Health Service Buyers Guide (ISSN 0308-7107); Sell's Hospital and Surgical Supplies (ISSN 0073-3458)
Description: Covers health care products, equipment, and supplies.

614.8 658   US   ISSN 0886-2095
HEALTH CARE COMPETITION WEEK. 1983. bi-w. $438 (foreign $462). Capitol Publications Inc., 1101 King St., Ste. 444, Alexandria, VA 22314.
TEL 703-683-4100. FAX 703-739-6517. (back issues avail.) **Document type:** newsletter.
●Also available online. Vendor(s): NewsNet (HH11).
—CCC.
Incorporates: Washington Actions on Health (ISSN 0194-5416)
Description: Critical coverage of the health care services business, marketing and management strategies.

658   US
HEALTH CARE CONSTRUCTION REPORT. m. $250. American Hospital Publishing, Inc. (Subsidiary of: American Hospital Association Company), 737 N. Michigan Ave., Ste. 700, Chicago, IL 60611. TEL 312-440-6800. FAX 312-951-8491. **Document type:** bulletin.
Description: Report of new and planned construction and renovation projects.

HEALTH CARE COSTS. see *BUSINESS AND ECONOMICS — Economic Situation And Conditions*

658   US
HEALTH CARE FACILITY MANAGEMENT. 1990. bi-w. $570. Commerce Clearing House, Inc., 4025 W. Peterson Ave., Chicago, IL 60646.
TEL 312-583-8500. Ed. D. Newquist. (looseleaf format)

658   US
HEALTH CARE FINANCING ADMINISTRATION MANUALS. Short title: H C F A Manuals. irreg. price varies. (Department of Health and Human Services) U.S. National Technical Information Service, 5825 Port Royal Rd., Springfield, VA 22161.
TEL 703-487-4630.
Description: Provides policies and procedures developed by the HCFA for providers of health care services. Includes information on the processing of medicaid and medicare claims.

610   US   ISSN 0197-3738
KF3580.H4
HEALTH CARE LABOR MANUAL. 1974. bi-m. $620 (foreign $744). Aspen Publishers, Inc., 200 Orchard Ridge Dr., Gaithersburg, MD 20878.
TEL 800-638-8437. FAX 301-417-7550. (Subscr. to: 7201 McKinney Circle, Frederick, MD 21701-9782) circ. 1,652. (looseleaf format)
Formerly: Health Care Labor Review.

HEALTH CARE LAW NEWSLETTER. see *LAW*

658.91 614.7   US   ISSN 0361-6274
RA393
HEALTH CARE MANAGEMENT REVIEW. 1976. q. $110 (foreign $132). Aspen Publishers, Inc., 200 Orchard Ridge Dr., Gaithersburg, MD 20878.
TEL 301-417-7500. FAX 301-417-7550. (also avail. in microform from UMI; reprint service avail. from UMI) **Indexed:** ABI Inform, Abstr.Health Care Manage.Stud., B.P.I, BPIA, Bus.Ind., CINAHL, Excerp.Med., Hlth.Ind., I.P.A., Ind.Med., Med.Care Rev., Tr.& Indus.Ind.
●Also available online.
—BLDSC (4274.943000); Faxon; UnCover; SWETS; UMI. **CCC.**

658.91 614.7   US   ISSN 1069-6571
▼**HEALTH CARE MANAGEMENT: STATE OF THE ART REVIEWS.** 1994. 3/yr. $66 (foreign $76). Hanley & Belfus, Inc., 210 S. 13th St., Philadelphia, PA 19107. TEL 215-546-7293. FAX 215-790-9330. Ed. Harvey Jolt.
Description: Covers the management of health care delivery systems, their organizational structure and administration.

HEALTH CARE NEWSLETTER. see *OCCUPATIONAL HEALTH AND SAFETY*

658 613.7   US   ISSN 0742-1478
HEALTH CARE STRATEGIC MANAGEMENT; the newsletter for hospital strategists. 1983. m. $187 (foreign $205). Business Word Inc., 5350 S. Roslyn St., Ste. 400, Englewood, CO 80111-2145. TEL 303-290-8500. FAX 303-290-9025. Ed. Alan Karia. adv.; bk.rev. circ. 1,500. **Indexed:** CINAHL. **Document type:** trade publication.
—BLDSC (4274.949200); Faxon; UMI.

658 610   CN   ISSN 0828-203X
HEALTH CAREER POST. 1987. m. Can.$20. Oakwood Publications Ltd., 55 Costain Ct., Kitchener, Ont. N2N 3A5, Canada. TEL 519-742-1099.
FAX 519-745-1289. Ed. John Prno. adv. circ. 9,800. (tabloid format; back issues avail.)
Description: Lists employment vacancies in Canada for health care professionals.

HEALTH DEVICES SOURCEBOOK. see *MEDICAL SCIENCES*

HEALTH EMPLOYMENT LAW UPDATE. see *BUSINESS AND ECONOMICS — Labor And Industrial Relations*

362.1   UK   ISSN 0957-7742
HEALTH ESTATE JOURNAL. 1946. 10/yr. £48 (overseas £53)(effective 1994). Institute of Hospital Engineering, 2 Abingdon House, Cumberland Business Centre, Northumberland Rd., Portsmouth PO5 1DS, England. TEL 0705-823186.
FAX 0705-815927. Ed. Sandy Ratcliffe. adv.; bk.rev.; charts; illus. circ. 3,000. (tabloid format) **Indexed:** Abstr.Health Care Manage.Stud., Sci.Abstr., W.R.C.Inf.
—BLDSC (4275.015400).
Former titles (until Jan. 1990): Institute of Hospital Engineering. Journal (ISSN 0953-1211); (until Sept. 1987): Hospital Engineering (ISSN 0309-7498); Hospital Engineer.

658   US   ISSN 0272-8443
HEALTH FACILITIES ENERGY REPORT. 1980. 12/yr. $157. Health Resources Publishing, Brinley Professional Plaza, 3100 Hwy. 138, Box 1442, Wall Township, NJ 07719-1442. TEL 908-681-1133. FAX 908-681-0490. Ed. Robert K. Jenkins. index. (back issues avail.)
Description: For hospital administrators, directors of engineering and energy specialists. Covers current developments in energy conservation - specifically for hospitals.

658   US   ISSN 0899-6210
RA971
HEALTH FACILITIES MANAGEMENT. m. $30 (foreign $50). American Hospital Publishing, Inc. (Subsidiary of: American Hospital Association Company), 737 N. Michigan Ave., Ste. 700, Chicago, IL 60611. TEL 312-440-6800. FAX 312-951-8491. Ed. Michael Hemmes. circ. 37,900. **Document type:** trade publication.
—BLDSC (4275.015700); UMI.

657.832   US   ISSN 0193-7928
HEALTH FUNDS DEVELOPMENT LETTER. 1978. 12/yr. $157. Health Resources Publishing, Brinley Professional Plaza, 3100 Hwy. 138, Box 1442, Wall Township, NJ 07719-1442. TEL 908-681-1133. FAX 908-681-0490. Ed. Robert K. Jenkins. index. (back issues avail.)
—CCC.
Description: For development directors and grants officers. Covers current news and trends in funding from government and private source.

HEALTH INDUSTRY TODAY; the market letter for health care industry vendors. see *MEDICAL SCIENCES*

331   US   ISSN 0148-4761
HEALTH LABOR RELATIONS REPORTS. 1976. 24/yr. $149. Interwood Publications, Box 20241, Cincinnati, OH 45220. TEL 513-221-3715. Ed. Frank J. Bardack; Pub. Frank J. Bardack. charts; stat. (looseleaf format; back issues avail.) **Document type:** newsletter.
Description: Covers court and National Labor Review Board decisions, including wrongful discharge, employment-at-will, contract settlements, arbitration awards and discrimination.

HEALTH LAW NEWS. see *LAW*

HEALTH LAW WEEK. see *LAW*

HOSPITALS

658 US ISSN 0891-3250
RA971 CODEN: HMAQEB
HEALTH MANAGEMENT QUARTERLY. Short title: H M Q. 1979. q. free. Baxter Foundation, One Baxter Parkway, Deerfield, IL 60015. TEL 708-948-2000. FAX 708-948-2887. Ed. George Couch. circ. 10,000 (controlled.) (back issues avail.) **Document type:** academic/scholarly publication.
—BLDSC (4275.052130).
Formerly (until 1984): Hospital Management Quarterly (ISSN 0891-9941)
Description: Management issues for health-care managers in hospitals and other medical facilities.

HEALTH PAGES. see *MEDICAL SCIENCES*

362 US ISSN 0882-1577
RA960
HEALTH PROGRESS. 1920. m. (10/yr.). $35. Catholic Health Association of the United States, 4455 Woodson Rd., St. Louis, MO 63134-3797. TEL 314-427-2500. FAX 314-427-0029. Ed. Judy Cassidy. adv.; bk.rev.; bibl.; charts; illus.; index. circ. 13,800. (also avail. in microform from UMI; reprint service avail. from UMI) **Indexed:** Abstr.Health Care Manage.Stud., Abstr.Hosp.Manage.Stud., Abstr.Soc.Geront., C.I.N.L., Cath.Ind., CERDIC, CLOA, Excerp.Med., Hosp.Lit.Ind, I.P.A., Ind.Med., Med. Care Rev., MEDSOC, Rehabil.Lit., Soc.Work Res.& Abstr.
●Also available online.
—BLDSC (4275.105150); UnCover; SWETS; UMI.
Formerly (until 1984): Hospital Progress (ISSN 0018-5817)
Description: Coverage of legislative, ethical, administrative, and legal issues among others for administrators, religious sponsors, department heads, trustees, physicians, nurses and other personnel in US Catholic health facilities.
Refereed Serial

362 UK ISSN 0952-2271
RA427 CODEN: HSJOEO
HEALTH SERVICE JOURNAL; for people involved in management. 1892. w. £49.50 to individuals; institutions £68. Macmillan Magazines Ltd., 4 Little Essex St., London WC2R 3LF, England. TEL 071-836-6633. Ed. Peter Davies. adv.; bk.rev.; abstr.; charts; illus.; stat. circ. 16,659. **Indexed:** Abstr.Health Care Manage.Stud., Abstr.Hyg., Build.Manage.Abstr., CINAHL, Excerp.Med., Hosp.Lit.Ind., Ind.Med., Nutr.Abstr., Trop.Dis.Bull. **Document type:** academic/scholarly publication.
—BLDSC (4275.107200); SWETS; UMI. **CCC.**
Formerly: Health and Social Service Journal (ISSN 0300-8347); Which incorporates: Medical Officer (ISSN 0025-7400); Community Medicine.

362 UK ISSN 0953-8534
CODEN: HSEMER
HEALTH SERVICES MANAGEMENT. (Former name of issuing body: Institute of Health Service Administrators) 1904. 6/yr. £95($99) Institute of Health Services Management, 39 Chalton St., London NW1 1JD, England. Ed. H. Goad. adv.; bk.rev.; illus.; index. circ. 6,232. (also avail. in microform from UMI; reprint service avail. from UMI) **Indexed:** Account.& Data Proc.Abstr., Curr.Adv.Ecol.Sci., Excerp.Med., Hosp.Abstr., Hosp.Abstr.Serv., Hosp.Lit.Ind., I.P.A., Intl.Mgmt.Info. **Document type:** trade publication.
—BLDSC (4275.108100); Faxon; SWETS; UMI. **CCC.**
Former titles: Hospital and Health Services Review (ISSN 0308-0234); Hospital (ISSN 0018-5477)

HEALTH SYSTEMS MANAGEMENT. see *PUBLIC HEALTH AND SAFETY*

362 US ISSN 1055-7466
HEALTH SYSTEMS REVIEW. 1967. bi-m. $20. F A H S Review, Inc., 1405 N. Pierce St., Ste. 308, Little Rock, AR 72207. TEL 501-661-9555. FAX 501-663-4903. Ed. John Herrmann. adv. contact: Bonnie Moneypenny. charts; illus.; stat.; tr.lit.; circ. 35,000. (also avail. in microform from UMI; reprint service avail. from UMI) **Indexed:** ABI Inform, Excerp.Med., Hosp.Lit.Ind., Med.Care Rev. **Document type:** trade publication.
—BLDSC (4275.215000); UnCover; UMI.
Former titles (until 1990): Federation of American Health Systems. Review (ISSN 0891-0200); (until 1986): Federation of American Hospitals. Review (ISSN 0148-9496); (until 1976): Investor-Owned Hospital Review (ISSN 0093-7312); (until 1973): F A H Review (ISSN 0046-3558)

362 US
HEALTH TEXAS. 1944. m. $36 (members $26). Texas Hospital Association, 6225 U.S. Hwy. 290 East, Box 15587, Austin, TX 78761-5587. TEL 512-465-1050. FAX 512-465-1090. Ed. Margaret Harrist. adv.; bk.rev.; charts; illus.; tr.lit.; index. circ. 7,000. (also avail. in microform from UMI; reprint service avail.) **Indexed:** Abstr.Health Care Manage.Stud. **Document type:** trade publication.
Formerly (until 1989): Texas Hospitals (ISSN 0040-4357)

658 CN
HEALTHCARE ADVOCATE. 1962. m. (10/yr.). Can.$21.40. Alberta Healthcare Association, 10009 108th St., Edmonton, AB T5J 3C5, Canada. TEL 403-498-8400. FAX 403-498-8465. Ed. Clay Adams. adv.; B&W page Can.$600; trim 7 1/2 x 9 1/2. bk.rev. circ. 2,800. (back issues avail.)
Former titles (until 1993): HospitAlta (ISSN 1187-7405); (until 1991): Alberta Hospital Association's HospitAlta (ISSN 0821-2015); HospitAlta (ISSN 0701-9076)

658 US
HEALTHCARE EDUCATION DATELINE. 1991. q. membership. American Hospital Association, 840 N. Lake Shore Dr., Chicago, IL 60611-2431. TEL 312-280-6113. FAX 312-280-4152. Ed. Mary Hudson. circ. 1,700. **Document type:** newsletter.

658 628.44 US
HEALTHCARE ENVIRONMENTAL SERVICES. 1986. bi-m. membership. (American Society for Healthcare Environmental Services) American Hospital Association, 840 N. Lake Shore Dr., Chicago, IL 60611. TEL 312-280-4458. FAX 312-280-4152. Ed. Katherine Svedman. adv.; bk.rev.; charts; illus. circ. 1,400. (back issues avail.) **Document type:** newsletter.
Description: Articles on trends and developments in environmental services, housekeeping, laundry, interior design, recycling, and waste management provided by healthcare institutions.

362 US ISSN 0883-5381
RA971 CODEN: HEEXEU
HEALTHCARE EXECUTIVE. 1985. 6/yr. $45 (foreign $60). American College of Healthcare Executives, 840 N. Lake Shore Dr., Chicago, IL 60611. TEL 312-943-0544. FAX 312-943-3791. (Subscr. to: Order Processing Center, 1951 Cornell Ave., Melrose Park, IL 60160) Ed. Walter Wachel; Pub. Lynn D. Kahn. adv. circ. 28,000. (back issues avail.; reprint service avail. from UMI) **Document type:** trade publication.
—BLDSC (4275.247790); Faxon; UnCover; UMI. **CCC.**
Description: Each issue focuses on a single critical management issue, such as human resources, physician roles, governance, technology, information systems, and career planning.

658 US
HEALTHCARE FINANCIAL BRIEFS. 1977. m. $150. Silver & Cherner, Ltd., Box 35425, Phoenix, AZ 85069-9908. TEL 602-995-9447. FAX 602-995-9458. Ed. Robert Cherner. (looseleaf format)
Description: Provides economic news, analyzes new developments and reviews studies.

657.832 US ISSN 0735-0732
HF5686.H7 CODEN: HFMAD7
HEALTHCARE FINANCIAL MANAGEMENT. 1947. m. $70. Healthcare Financial Management Association, Two Westbrook Corporate Center, Ste. 700, Westchester, IL 60154. TEL 708-531-9600. FAX 708-531-0032. Ed. Cheryl T. Stachura. adv.; bk.rev.; illus.; index. circ. 31,738. (also avail. in microform from UMI; reprint service avail. from UMI) **Indexed:** ABI Inform., Abstr.Health Care Manage.Stud., Account.& Data Proc.Abstr., Account.Ind. (1974-), B.P.I., BPIA, Bus.Ind., CINAHL, Excerp.Med., Hosp.Lit.Ind., I.P.A., Manage.Cont., Sci.Abstr., Tr.& Indus.Ind. **Document type:** academic/scholarly publication, trade publication.
●Also available online. Vendor(s): DIALOG Information Services, Inc.
—BLDSC (4275.247800); Faxon; UnCover; SWETS; UMI.
Former titles (until 1982): Hospital Financial Management; (until 1968): Hospital Accounting (ISSN 0018-5639)
Description: Covers management and finance of healthcare organizations, application of new procedures and systems in accounting, financial reporting, information systems, patient accounts management, financing of alternative delivery systems, reimbursement issues and legislation.

HEALTHCARE FINANCIAL RELATIONSHIPS. see *MEDICAL SCIENCES*

HEALTHCARE FOODSERVICE MAGAZINE. see *FOOD AND FOOD INDUSTRIES*

HEALTHCARE FOODSERVICE WHO'S WHO. see *BUSINESS AND ECONOMICS — Trade And Industrial Directories*

362 US ISSN 0899-9287
HOFOA6
HEALTHCARE FORUM JOURNAL; leadership strategies for healthcare executives. 1958. bi-m. $45 (effective 1991). Healthcare Forum, 830 Market St., San Francisco, CA 94102. TEL 415-421-8810. FAX 415-421-8837. Ed. Susan Anthony. adv.; bk.rev.; charts; illus.; tr.lit.; index. circ. 24,500. (also avail. in microform from UMI; reprint service avail. from UMI) **Indexed:** ABI Inform, Abstr.Health Care Manage.Stud., Abstr.Hosp.Manage.Stud., C.I.N.L., Excerp.Med., Hosp.Lit.Ind., I.P.A. **Document type:** trade publication.
—BLDSC (4275.247840); UnCover; UMI.
Former titles: Healthcare Forum (ISSN 0885-257X); Hospital Forum (ISSN 0018-5663)
Description: Presents commentary and critical analysis of key healthcare issues.

657.832 US
HEALTHCARE FUND RAISING NEWSLETTER. 1979. 6/yr. $77. Health Resources Publishing, Brinley Professional Plaza, 3100 Hwy. 138, Box 1442, Wall Township, NJ 07719-1442. TEL 908-681-1133. FAX 908-681-0490. Ed. Robert K. Jenkins. index. circ. 400. (back issues avail.) **Document type:** newsletter.
—CCC.
Formerly: Hospital Fund Raising Newsletter (ISSN 0193-9939)
Description: Exchange of information among hospitals, summarizing ways they are raising funds to meet competitive pressures and demands for services.

658 US ISSN 1060-9253
▼**HEALTHCARE HUMAN RESOURCES.** 1992. m. $128. C O R Research Inc., Box 40959, Santa Barbara, CA 93140. TEL 805-564-2177. Ed. Paul Engstrom. bk.rev. **Document type:** newsletter.
—CCC.
Description: Case studies and analysis of trends in the strategic management of human resources in hospitals and other healthcare organizations.

658 001.6 621.381 US
HEALTHCARE INFORMATION MANAGEMENT. 1987. q. membership only. Healthcare Information and Management Systems Society (Subsidiary of: American Hospital Association), 840 N. Lake Shore Dr., Chicago, IL 60657. TEL 312-280-6118. FAX 312-280-4152. Ed. Bonnie Million. bk.rev. circ. 8,000.
Formerly: Health Care Systems.

HOSPITALS

658 US ISSN 0749-6672
HEALTHCARE MATERIALS MANAGEMENT NEWS. 1974. q. membership. American Hospital Association, 840 N. Lake Shore Dr., Chicago, IL 60611. TEL 312-280-6137. FAX 312-280-4152. Ed. Shelly Johnson. bk.rev.; index. circ. 2,300. (back issues avail.) **Document type:** newsletter.
Formerly: American Society for Hospital Materials Management. Perspectives.

HEALTHSPAN; the report of health business and law. see BUSINESS AND ECONOMICS — Management

362 US
HEARTBEAT OF ST. JOSEPH'S MEDICAL CENTER. 1968. q. free. St. Joseph's Medical Center, 523 N. Third St., Brainerd, MN 56401. TEL 218-829-2861. illus. circ. 85,000. (tabloid format)
Formerly: Heartbeat of St. Joseph's Hospital (ISSN 0017-9272)

HEIM UND PFLEGE. see GERONTOLOGY AND GERIATRICS

610 US ISSN 0018-0416
R11 CODEN: HFHJA6
HENRY FORD HOSPITAL MEDICAL JOURNAL. 1953. q. free. Henry Ford Hospital, Editorial Office, 411-413 New CenterPavilion, 2921 W. Grand Blvd., Detroit, MI 48202. TEL 313-876-2028. Ed. Dr. Raymond C. Mellinger. bk.rev.; abstr.; charts; illus.; index. 20-yr. cum. index, 1972. circ. 10,000. (also avail. in microfilm from UMI; back issues avail.; reprint service avail. from UMI) **Indexed:** Biol.Abstr., C.I.S. Abstr., Chem.Abstr., Curr.Cont, Excerp.Med., Ind.Med.
—Faxon; UnCover; UMI; CASDDS.
Formerly: Henry Ford Hospital Medical Bulletin (ISSN 0096-1868)

658 JA ISSN 0914-8019
HIMEJI SEKIJUJI BYOINSHI/HIMEJI RED CROSS HOSPITAL. JOURNAL. (Text in English, Japanese; summaries in English) 1977. a. Himeji Sekijui Byoin, 30-1, Tatsunomachi 5-chome, Himeji-shi, Hyogo-ken 670, Japan.

658 JA ISSN 0912-7089
HIRATA SHIRITSU BYOIN NENPO/HIRATA MUNICIPAL HOSPITAL. JOURNAL. (Text in Japanese) 1984. a. Hirata Shiritsu Byoin, 613, Nadabuncho, Hirata-shi, Shimane-ken 691, Japan.

HIROSHIMA KENRITSU BYOIN ISHI/HIROSHIMA PREFECTURAL HOSPITAL. MEDICAL JOURNAL. see MEDICAL SCIENCES

900 GW ISSN 0440-9043
HISTORIA HOSPITALIUM. 1966. biennial. DM.45. Deutsche Gesellschaft fuer Krankenhausgeschichte e.V., c/o Abteilung fuer Geschichte der Medizin und des Krankenhauswesens, R W T H Aachen, Wendlingweg, 52057 Aachen, Germany. TEL 0241-8088095. Eds. Axel Hinrich Murken, Gerlind Buesche-Schmidt. bk.rev. circ. 600. **Document type:** academic/scholarly publication, monographic series.
Description: Studies the history of hospitals and nursing.

658 JA ISSN 0916-9547
HOKKAIDORITSU MIDORIGAOKA BYOIN NENPO/HOKKAIDO PREFECTURAL MIDORIGAOKA HOSPITAL. ANNUAL REPORT. (Text in Japanese) 1991. a. Hokkaidoritsu Midorigaoka, 1, Midorigaoka, Otofukecho, Kato-gun, Hokkaido 080-01, Japan.

362.15 US
HOME HEALTH CARE DEALER. 1989. bi-m. Curant Communications, Inc., 4676 Admiralty Way, Ste. 202, Marina Del Rey, CA 90292-6603. TEL 213-479-1769. FAX 213-301-3329. adv. circ. 12,000.
Description: For home care dealers and home care pharmacies.

658 US ISSN 0162-1424
RA645.3
HOME HEALTH CARE SERVICES QUARTERLY. 1980. q. $40 to individuals; institutions $180; libraries $250. Haworth Press, Inc., 10 Alice St., Binghamton, NY 13904. TEL 607-722-5857; 800-342-5857. FAX 607-722-1424. Ed. Brahna Trager. adv.; bk.rev.; stat. circ. 410. (also avail. in microfiche from HAW; reprint service avail. from HAW) **Indexed:** Abstr.Health Care Manage.Stud., Abstr.Soc.Geront., CINAHL, Excerp.Med., Hosp.Lit.Ind., Psychol.Abstr., Rehabil.Lit., Soc.Work Res.& Abstr., Sociol.Abstr.
—BLDSC (4326.053000); Faxon; UnCover; SWETS.
Description: Covers major areas of concern to policy makers, planners, and providers of home health care and related services. Focuses on research and policy issues.
Refereed Serial

658 BE
L'HOPITAL BELGE/BELGISCH ZIEKENHUIS. (Text in Flemish, French) 1923. 4/yr. 2600 BEF. Association Belge des Hopitaux, Route de Lennik 808, 1070 Brussels, Belgium. TEL 02-555-32144. FAX 02-555-45099. TELEX 65123. Ed. Dr. A. de Wever. adv.; bk.rev.; charts; illus. circ. 1,000. **Indexed:** Excerp.Med.
Description: Serves to improve Belgian hospitals and hospital management.

610 JA ISSN 0915-7344
HOSHI SOGO BYOIN NENPO/HOSHI GENERAL HOSPITAL. ANNUAL REPORT. (Text in Japanese) 1988. a. Hoshi Sogo Byoin, 1-16, Omachi 2-chome, Koriyama-shi, Fukushima-ken 963, Japan.

HOSPICE. see ALTERNATIVE MEDICINE

362.15 US ISSN 0742-969X
R726.8
HOSPICE JOURNAL; physical, psychosocial, and pastoral care of dying. 1985. q. $38 to individuals; institutions $90; libraries $150. Haworth Press, Inc., 10 Alice St., Binghamton, NY 13904. TEL 607-722-5857; 800-342-9678. FAX 607-722-1424. Ed. Madalon O'Rawe Amenta. adv.; bk.rev. (also avail. in microfiche from HAW; reprint service avail. from HAW) **Indexed:** Abstr.Health Care Manage.Stud., Abstr.Soc.Geront., CINAHL, CLOA, Excerp.Med., Nurs.Abstr., Past.Care & Couns.Abstr., Psychol.Abstr., Soc.Work Res.& Abstr.
—BLDSC (4333.030000); Faxon; UnCover.
Description: Contains clinical and research articles from all aspects of care for the dying, focusing on terminal and palliative care.
Refereed Serial

362 US ISSN 0913-6681
HOSPICE LETTER. 1979. 12/yr. $137. Health Resources Publishing, Brinley Professional Plaza, 3100 Hwy. 138, Box 1442, Wall Township, NJ 07719-1442. TEL 908-681-1133. FAX 908-681-0490. Ed. Robert K. Jenkins. index. (back issues avail.)
—CCC.
Description: Covers developments in the care of the terminally ill through hospice.

HOSPITAIS CIVIS DE LISBOA. BOLETIM CLINICO. see MEDICAL SCIENCES

EL HOSPITAL (CINCINNATI). see MEDICAL SCIENCES

362 II ISSN 0018-5531
HOSPITAL ADMINISTRATION. (Text in English) 1964. q. Rs.80($50) Indian Hospital Association, B-401, Sarita Vihar, New Delhi 110044, India. TEL 6835648. Ed. Dr. A.K. Khokhar. adv.; bk.rev. circ. 1,000. **Indexed:** Excerp.Med., Hosp.Lit.Ind.

642.59 US
HOSPITAL ADMITTING MONTHLY. 1982. m. $259. American Health Consultants, Inc., Six Piedmont Center, Ste. 400, Atlanta, GA 30305. TEL 404-262-7436; 800-688-2421. FAX 800-284-3291. Ed. Lourdes Dumke. circ. 1,400. (back issues avail.; reprint service avail.) **Document type:** newsletter.
●Also available online. Vendor(s): Mead Data Central, Inc.

HOSPITAL AND COMMUNITY PSYCHIATRY. see MEDICAL SCIENCES — Psychiatry And Neurology

658 US
HOSPITAL AND HEALTH CARE REPORT. a. $840. (Executive Compensation Service (ECS)) Wyatt Data Services, 218 Rte. 17, N., Roselle Park, NJ 07662-9832. TEL 201-843-1177. FAX 201-843-0101. charts. **Document type:** trade publication.
Description: Provides a wide variety of analyses to compare rates to other facilities in the area of size and type.

362 US ISSN 8750-3735
RA971
HOSPITAL & HEALTH SERVICES ADMINISTRATION. 1956. q. $50 (foreign $60). (Foundation of the American College of Healthcare Executives) Health Administration Press, 1021 E. Huron St., Ann Arbor, MI 48104-9990. TEL 312-943-0544. FAX 708-450-1618. (Subscr. to: Order Processing Center, 1951 Cornell Ave., Melrose Park, IL 60160; Alt. addr.: 840 N. Lake Shore Dr., Chicago, IL 60611) Ed. Richard Kurz. bk.rev. circ. 26,000. (also avail. in microform from UMI; reprint service avail. from UMI; avail. online) **Indexed:** ABI Inform, Abstr.Health Care Manage.Stud., Account.Ind. (1974-), BPIA, Bus.Ind., CINAHL, Curr.Cont., Excerp.Med., Hlth.Ind., Hosp.Lit.Ind., I.P.A., Med.Care Rev, Rehabil.Lit., SSCI, Tr.& Indus.Ind. **Document type:** academic/scholarly publication.
—BLDSC (4333.121000); Faxon; UnCover; SWETS; UMI. **CCC.**
Formerly: Hospital Administration (ISSN 0018-5523)
Description: Provides information on the latest trends, developments, and innovations in the health services field.

658 AT ISSN 0813-7471
HOSPITAL AND HEALTHCARE AUSTRALIA. 1932. m. Aus.$35 (foreign Aus.$90) (effective Jul. 1993). Yaffa Publishing Group, 17-21 Bellevue St., Surry Hills, N.S.W. 2010, Australia. TEL 02-281-2333. FAX 02-281-2750. (Subscr. to: Box 606 G.P.O., Sydney, N.S.W., Australia) Ed. M. Woods. adv.; B&W page Aus.$1905, color page Aus.$2660; trim 297 x 210. bk.rev. circ. 4,603. **Document type:** trade publication.
Formerly (until 1983): Hospital Journal of Australia.
Description: Publication of interest to public and private hospital and nursing home executives throughout Australia.

362 US ISSN 0018-5574
HOSPITAL ASSOCIATION OF NEW YORK STATE. NEWS. 1969. w. $150 to non-members; members $50. Hospital Association of New York State, 74 N. Pearl St., Albany, NY 12207. TEL 518-434-7600. FAX 518-434-7915. circ. 2,000.
Description: Contains organization news.

658 US ISSN 1047-6903
RA981.A2
HOSPITAL BLUE BOOK (OFFICIAL NATIONAL EDITION). a. $99.50. Billian Publishing, Inc., 2100 Powers Ferry Rd., Ste. 300, Atlanta, GA 30339. TEL 404-955-5656. FAX 404-952-0669.

658 US ISSN 1047-6911
HOSPITAL BLUE BOOK (OFFICIAL SOUTHERN EDITION). 1934. a. $35. Billian Publishing, Inc., 2100 Powers Ferry Rd., Ste. 300, Atlanta, GA 30339. TEL 404-955-5656. FAX 404-952-0669. circ. 10,654 (controlled). **Indexed:** CINAHL.
Formerly: Clarks' Directory of Southern Hospitals.

362.1 AT ISSN 0817-5675
HOSPITAL BRIEF. 1968. bi-m. membership only. Australian Hospital Association, 42 Thesiger Court, Deakin, A.C.T. 2600, Australia. Ed. B. Lamb. circ. 1,000. **Document type:** newsletter.
Formerly: Australian Hospital Newsletter (ISSN 0084-7410)
Description: Contains information relevant to health care providers and administrators.

658 US
▼**HOSPITAL CASE MANAGEMENT.** 1993. m. $219. American Health Consultants, Inc., Six Piedmont Center, Ste. 400, Atlanta, GA 30305. TEL 404-262-7436; 800-688-2421. FAX 800-284-3291. Ed. Betsy Bean. circ. 2,310. **Document type:** newsletter.

HOSPITALS

658 US
HOSPITAL CONTRACTS MANUAL. a. (plus s-a. supplements). $399 (foreign $499). Aspen Publishers, Inc., 200 Orchard Ridge Dr., Gaithersburg, MD 20878. TEL 301-417-7500. FAX 301-417-7550.

657.832 US ISSN 1045-1765
HOSPITAL COST MANAGEMENT AND ACCOUNTING. 1985. m. $205 (foreign $246). Aspen Publishers, Inc., 200 Orchard Ridge Dr., Gaithersburg, MD 20878. TEL 301-417-7500. FAX 301-417-7550. Ed. Steven Finkler. **Document type:** newsletter.
—UMI.
Formerly (until **1988**): Hospital Cost Accounting Advisor (ISSN 8756-7288)

HOSPITAL DE NINOS. REVISTA. see *MEDICAL SCIENCES — Pediatrics*

690.55 UK ISSN 0300-5720
HOSPITAL DEVELOPMENT. 1968. 11/yr. £52($175) (foreign £90). Wilmington Publishing, Wilmington House, Church Hill, Dartford, Kent UA2 7EF, England. TEL 0322-277788. FAX 0322-276476. (Subscr. to : Ferrari House, 258 Field End Rd., Ruislip, Middx HA4 9UX. TEL 081-868-4499) Ed. Melanie Armstrong. adv.; charts; illus.; stat.; circ. 8,635 (controlled). **Indexed:** Build.Manage.Abstr., Excerp.Med.
—SWETS.
Formerly: Hospital Building and Engineering (ISSN 0018-5582)

HOSPITAL DOCTOR. see *MEDICAL SCIENCES*

658 070 US ISSN 1046-1647
HOSPITAL EDITORS' IDEA EXCHANGE. 1990. m. $98. Editors' Forum Publishing Co., Box 411806, Kansas City, MO 64141. Ed. William R. Brinton. bk.rev. circ. 560. (looseleaf format; back issues avail.) **Document type:** newsletter.
Description: Contains tips and ideas on how hospital newsletter editors and publication specialists can improve their publications.

658 US ISSN 0744-6470
HOSPITAL EMPLOYEE HEALTH. 1982. m. $279. American Health Consultants, Inc., Six Piedmont Center, Ste. 400, Atlanta, GA 30305. TEL 404-262-7436; 800-688-2421. FAX 800-284-3291. Ed. Barrie Rissman. circ. 2,340. (back issues avail.; reprint service avail.) **Indexed:** CINAHL. **Document type:** newsletter.
●Also available online. Vendor(s): Mead Data Central, Inc.
—BLDSC (4333.148800). **CCC.**

362 JA
HOSPITAL ENGINEERING ASSOCIATION OF JAPAN. JOURNAL/BYOIN SETSUBI. (Text in Japanese) 1959. bi-m. 1000 Yen. Hospital Engineering Association of Japan - Nihon Byoin Setsubi Kyokai, Hongo Kasuga Mansion 403, 30-16 Hongo 1-chome, Bunkyo-ku, Tokyo 113, Japan. Ed.Bd. adv.; bk.rev.; abstr.; charts; index. circ. 2,000. (processed) **Indexed:** Excerp.Med.
Formerly: Hospital Equipment (ISSN 0007-764X)

362 UK ISSN 0018-5620
HOSPITAL EQUIPMENT & SUPPLIES. 1955. m. £44($214) (foreign £108). Wilmington Publishing, Wilmington House, Church Hill, Dartford, Kent UA2 7EF, England. TEL 0322-277788. FAX 0322-276476. (Subscr. to: Ferrari House, 258 Field End Rd., Ruislip, Middx HA4 9UX. TEL 081-868-4499) Ed. Melanie Armstrong. adv.; charts; illus. circ. 10,490.
—BLDSC (4333.158000).

012 AT ISSN 0159-9100
HOSPITAL EQUIPMENT AND SUPPLIES (YEAR). 1978. biennial. Aus.$141. M I M S Australia, 48 Albany St., Crows Nest, N.S.W. 2065, Australia. TEL 02-438-3588. FAX 02-906-3955. Ed. Marian Borland. circ. 4,500. (back issues avail.) **Document type:** directory.
Description: Purchasing reference for equipment officers in hospitals and nursing homes.

658 BL
HOSPITAL-ESCOLA SAO CAMILO E SAO LUIS. BOLETIM. a. Hospital-Escola Sao Camilo e Sao Luis, Macapa, Brazil.

657.832 170 US ISSN 8756-8519
HOSPITAL ETHICS. 1985. bi-m. $135 (members $85). American Hospital Association, 840 N. Lake Shore Dr., Chicago, IL 60611. TEL 312-280-6232. FAX 312-280-4182. Ed. Donald F. Phillips. circ. 1,800. (back issues avail.) **Document type:** newsletter.
Description: Review of the latest information in the field of hospital ethics, which reports news and opinions, defines their implications, and provides suggestions and strategies for resolving specific ethical concerns.

658 664 US ISSN 0747-7376
HOSPITAL FOOD & NUTRITION FOCUS. 1984. m. $136 (foreign $163). Aspen Publishers, Inc., 200 Orchard Ridge Dr., Gaithersburg, MD 20878. TEL 301-417-7500. FAX 301-417-7550. **Document type:** newsletter.
—BLDSC (4333.175000); UMI.

658 US
▼**HOSPITAL FOOD SERVICE MANAGEMENT.** 1993. m. $189. American Health Consultants, Inc., Six Piedmont Center, Ste. 400, Atlanta, GA 30305. TEL 404-262-7436; 800-688-2421. FAX 800-284-3291. Ed. Rosann Kent. circ. 230. **Document type:** newsletter.

HOSPITAL FOR SICK CHILDREN, TORONTO. RESEARCH INSTITUTE. ANNUAL REPORT. see *MEDICAL SCIENCES*

658 US
▼**HOSPITAL FUNDRAISING.** 1993. m. $219. American Health Consultants, Inc., Six Piedmont Center, Ste. 400, Atlanta, GA 30305. TEL 404-262-7436; 800-688-2421. FAX 800-284-3291. Ed. Ann Schrauth. circ. 435. **Document type:** newsletter.
Description: Crucial advice on keeping up with changing regulations and tax rulings, researching and writing effective grant proposals, and developing marketing and community relations strategies.

HOSPITAL HEALTH SCENE; journal of wellness and good health care. see *PHYSICAL FITNESS AND HYGIENE*

362.15 US ISSN 0884-8521
HOSPITAL HOME HEALTH; the monthly update for executives and health care professionals. 1984. m. $279. American Health Consultants, Inc., Six Piedmont Center, Ste. 400, Atlanta, GA 30305. TEL 404-262-7436; 800-688-2421. FAX 800-284-3291. Ed. Joyce Case. circ. 1,010. (back issues avail.; reprint service avail.) **Indexed:** CINAHL. **Document type:** newsletter.
—BLDSC (4333.189940).

658 JA
HOSPITAL IDENTITY. (Text in Japanese) 1989. m. Nihon H I S Kenkyukai, Sapoto Senta - Japan Hospital Identity System Association, Support Center, Shiokoji Agaru, Horikawa Dori, Shimogyo-ku, Kyoto 600, Japan.

658 US
THE HOSPITAL INDUSTRY AND ITS ENVIRONMENT. 1990. irreg., 5th ed., 1992. $395. Dun & Bradstreet Information Services (Murray Hill) (Subsidiary of: Dun & Bradstreet, Inc.), One Diamond Hill Rd., Murray Hill, NJ 07974. TEL 908-665-5224. FAX 908-771-7599. Ed. Paulette Roberts.
Description: Provides information on the hospital industry, including performance trends, third-party payers, demographic trends, national health expenditures, history, financial analysis and the outlook for the 1990's.

618.92 MX ISSN 0539-6115
CODEN: BMHIAK
HOSPITAL INFANTIL DE MEXICO. BOLETIN MEDICO. (Text in Spanish; summaries in English and Spanish) 1944. m. Mex.$120($70) (effective Jan. 1994). Hospital Infantil de Mexico Federico Gomez, Departamento de Ediciones Medicas, Calle Dr. Marquez 162, Col. Doctores, Deleg. Cuauhtemoc, 06720 Mexico D.F., Mexico. TEL 761-03-33. FAX 95-7-61-89-74. Ed. Dr. Luis Velasquez-Jones. adv.; bk.rev.; index, cum.index: 1959-1973; circ. 5,000 (paid). (back issues avail.) **Indexed:** Biol.Abstr., Child Devel.Abstr., Curr.Adv.Ecol.Sci., Dairy Sci.Abstr., Excerp.Med., Ind.Med., Nutr.Abstr., Protozool.Abstr. **Document type:** academic/scholarly publication, bulletin.
—BLDSC (2207.540000); SWETS; CASDDS.
Description: Covers pediatrics and health services.

610 US ISSN 0098-180X
HOSPITAL INFECTION CONTROL. 1974. m. $249. American Health Consultants, Inc., Six Piedmont Center, Ste. 400, Atlanta, GA 30305. TEL 404-262-7436; 800-688-2421. FAX 800-284-3291. Ed. Gary Evans. bk.rev.; bibl.; index. circ. 4,170. (also avail. in microform from UMI; back issues avail.; reprint service avail.) **Indexed:** CINAHL, Hosp.Lit.Ind., Ind.Med. **Document type:** newsletter.
●Also available online. Vendor(s): Mead Data Central, Inc.
—BLDSC (4333.192000); SWETS; UMI. **CCC.**

658 US
▼**HOSPITAL INTEGRATED CARE REPORT.** 1993. m. $219. American Health Consultants, Inc., Six Piedmont Center, Ste. 400, Atlanta, GA 30305. TEL 404-262-7436; 800-688-2421. FAX 800-284-3291. Ed. Allyson Harris. circ. 150. **Document type:** newsletter.

HOSPITAL LAW MANUAL. ADMINISTRATORS. see *LAW*

HOSPITAL LAW MANUAL. ATTORNEYS. see *LAW*

658 340 US ISSN 0738-0984
KF3825.A15
HOSPITAL LAW NEWSLETTER. 1984. m. $270 (foreign $324). Aspen Publishers, Inc., 200 Orchard Ridge Dr., Gaithersburg, MD 20878. TEL 301-417-7500. FAX 301-417-7550. **Document type:** newsletter.
—UMI.

658 US ISSN 1048-5201
KF3825.A15
HOSPITAL LITIGATION REPORTER. 1990. m. $294. Strafford Publications, Inc., 590 Dutch Valley Rd., N.E., Drawer 13729, Atlanta, GA 30324-0729. TEL 404-881-1141. FAX 404-881-0074. Ed. Nancy Johnson. cum.index: 1990-1991. (looseleaf format; back issues avail.) **Document type:** trade publication.
Description: Digest of judicial decisions that specifically concern or affect the hospital environment. For hospital attorneys and administrators, as well as risk-management professionals.

658 681 UK
HOSPITAL MAGAZINE. bi-m. £30. Mark Allen Publishing Ltd., Croxted Mews, 288 Croxted Rd., London SE24 9DA, England. TEL 081-671-7521. FAX 0815-971-1722. **Document type:** trade publication.

658 IT
HOSPITAL MANAGEMENT. 1981. m. Systems Communicazioni, Via Olanda, 6, 20083 Gaggiano (MI), Italy. TEL 02-90841814. FAX 02-90841682. Ed. L. Stella. adv.: B&W page L.3160000, color page L.4500000; trim 180 x 240. circ. 20,888.

658 UK ISSN 0953-9743
HOSPITAL MANAGEMENT INTERNATIONAL. 1984. a. membership. (International Hospital Federation) Sterling Publications Ltd. (Subsidiary of: Sterling Publishing Group Plc.), P.O. Box 839, London W2 2YW, England. TEL 071-915-9600. Ed. Leslie Paine. adv. contact: Simon Oldfield. circ. 10,000. **Document type:** trade publication.
—BLDSC (4333.204800).
Formerly: International Hospital Federation. Official Handbook (ISSN 0265-1874)

658 US ISSN 0737-903X
HOSPITAL MANAGEMENT REVIEW. 1982. m. (except July). $87. C O R Research Inc., Box 40959, Santa Barbara, CA 93140. TEL 805-564-2177. Ed. Dean H. Anderson. bk.rev. **Document type:** newsletter.
—SWETS. **CCC.**
Description: Informative summaries of articles selected from more than 140 healthcare management periodicals.

HOSPITALS

362.11 US ISSN 0888-3068
HOSPITAL MATERIALS MANAGEMENT; the newsletter for materials management and group purchasing. 1976. m. $187 (foreign $205). Business Word Inc., 5350 S. Roslyn St., Ste. 400, Englewood, CO 80111-2145. TEL 303-290-8500. FAX 303-290-9025. Ed. Curt Werner. adv.; bk.rev.; illus. **Indexed:** Excerp.Med., I.P.A. **Document type:** newsletter, trade publication.
—BLDSC (4333.205180); UMI.
Formerly: Hospital Purchasing Management (ISSN 0163-1322)
Description: Contains news about hospital group purchasing organizations; articles on materials management issues.

658 US ISSN 0192-2262
RA971.33
HOSPITAL MATERIEL MANAGEMENT QUARTERLY. 1979. q. $107 (foreign $128). Aspen Publishers, Inc., 200 Orchard Ridge Dr., Gaithersburg, MD 20878. TEL 301-417-7500. FAX 301-417-7550. Ed. Charles E. Housley. (also avail. in microform from UMI; reprint service avail. from UMI) **Indexed:** Abstr.Health Care Manage.Stud., BPIA, Bus.Ind., Excerp.Med., Manage.Cont. **Document type:** academic/scholarly publication.
—BLDSC (4333.205200); Faxon; UnCover; SWETS; UMI. **CCC.**
Formerly: Topics in Health Care Materiel Management.

HOSPITAL MEDICAL PRACTICE. see *MEDICAL SCIENCES*

HOSPITAL MEDICINE; for primary care physicians. see *MEDICAL SCIENCES*

658 610.73 US
HOSPITAL NEWS DELAWARE VALLEY. 1986. m. $36. H. Robert Jacobs Publishing Co., Inc., 2022 E. Allegheny Ave., Philadelphia, PA 19134. TEL 215-739-2033. FAX 215-426-4438. Ed. Marybeth Caracci. adv.; circ. 46,700 (controlled). (tabloid format)
Formerly: Hospital News.
Description: General interest healthcare journal focused on hospital-based regional healthcare issues, and practitioners.

658 CN
HOSPITAL NEWS - S W ONTARIO.* m. 123 Pleasant Dr., Stratford, ON N5A 4X5, Canada. TEL 519-425-0957. FAX 519-425-0958. Ed. Carl Page. circ. 20,000.

658 CN
HOSPITAL NEWS - TORONTO AND REGION. 1987. m. Can.$26.50. Auto Mart Magazine Ltd., 23 Apex Rd., Toronto, ON M6A 2V6, Canada. TEL 416-781-5516. FAX 416-781-5499. Ed. Donna Kell. adv. contact: Esther Dalys. circ. 50,000. (tabloid format; back issues avail.) **Document type:** newspaper.
Formed by merger of: Hospital News Downtown Toronto; Hospital News Greater Toronto.

642.59 US ISSN 0899-8957
HOSPITAL PATIENT RELATIONS REPORT; practical resources for service, marketing and community relations. 1980. m. $276 (effective Sep. 1992). Business Publishers, Inc., 951 Pershing Dr., Silver Spring, MD 20910-4464. TEL 301-587-6300. FAX 301-585-9075. Ed. Carl Ayers. (looseleaf format) **Document type:** newsletter.
●Also available online. Vendor(s): NewsNet.
Formerly: Hospital Guest Relations Report.
Description: Advice for hospital administrators on methods to improve satisfaction of patients and patients' families.

657.832 338.476 US
HOSPITAL PAYMENT AND INFORMATION MANAGEMENT. 1983. m. $349. American Health Consultants, Inc., 3525 Piedmont Rd., N.E., Six Piedmont Center, Ste. 400, Atlanta, GA 30305. TEL 404-262-7436. FAX 800-284-3291. (Subscr. to: Department L100, Box 740056, Atlanta, GA 30374-9822. TEL 800-688-2421) Ed. Reba Griffith. circ. 2,100. (reprint service avail.) **Document type:** trade publication.
●Also available online. Vendor(s): Mead Data Central, Inc., NewsNet.
—**CCC.**
Formerly (until 1994): Medicare Policy and Payment Report; (until 1992): Prospective Payment Survival (ISSN 0746-4703)

362.11 US ISSN 0149-2632
HOSPITAL PEER REVIEW. 1976. m. $239. American Health Consultants, Inc., Six Piedmont Center, Ste. 400, Atlanta, GA 30305. TEL 404-262-7436; 800-688-2421. FAX 800-284-3291. Ed. Warren Causey. bk.rev. circ. 2,990. (also avail. in microform from UMI; reprint service avail.) **Indexed:** Hosp.Lit.Ind., Ind.Med. **Document type:** newsletter.
●Also available online. Vendor(s): Mead Data Central, Inc.
—UMI. **CCC.**

HOSPITAL PHARMACIST REPORT. see *PHARMACY AND PHARMACOLOGY*

HOSPITAL PHARMACY. see *PHARMACY AND PHARMACOLOGY*

HOSPITAL PHARMACY IN ONTARIO. see *PHARMACY AND PHARMACOLOGY*

HOSPITAL PHARMACY PRACTICE. see *PHARMACY AND PHARMACOLOGY*

HOSPITAL PHARMACY SERVICE INSTANT UP-DATE. see *PHARMACY AND PHARMACOLOGY*

HOSPITAL PHYSICIAN. see *MEDICAL SCIENCES*

HOSPITAL PODIATRIST. see *MEDICAL SCIENCES — Orthopedics And Traumatology*

HOSPITAL PRACTICE. see *MEDICAL SCIENCES*

HOSPITAL PRACTICE (EDICION ESPANOLA). see *MEDICAL SCIENCES*

658 US
HOSPITAL PRODUCT COMPARISON SYSTEM. 1982. m. $695. (Emergency Care Research Institute) E C R I, 5200 Butler Pike, Plymouth Meeting, PA 19462. TEL 215-825-6000. FAX 215-834-1275. Ed. Garrett Hayner. (looseleaf format)
●Also available on CD-ROM. Producer(s): DIALOG Information Services, Inc.
Description: Designed for overall hospital technology purchasing and capital equipment planning. Topics covered range from anesthesia units to wheelchairs.
Refereed Serial

658 US
HOSPITAL PRODUCT LINE REPORT. m. St. Anthony Publishing, Inc., 500 Montgomery St., No. 700, Alexandria, VA 22314-1560. TEL 800-632-0123. Ed. Marletta Jones.

658.8 US ISSN 0279-4799
HOSPITAL PURCHASING NEWS; a magazine for hospital materials management. 1977. m. $44.95 (Canada $54.95, elsewhere $59.95). McKnight Medical Communications Co. (Subsidiary of: Medical Economics Publishing Co., Inc.), Two Northfield Plaza, Ste.300, Northfield, IL 60093. TEL 708-441-3700. Ed. Mark Thill. adv. contact: Deborah Tobiaski. charts; stat.; tr.lit. circ. 26,448. (tabloid format; back issues avail.)
—UMI. **CCC.**
Formerly: Purchasing Administration (ISSN 0192-4311)

362 SA ISSN 0018-5833
HOSPITAL R.S.A.* (Text in Afrikaans and English) 1962. bi-m. R.0.50. (Hospital Employees Association) Adlodorum, PO Box 3194, Pretoria, South Africa. Ed. Uld Walt.

658 US ISSN 1068-5294
▼**HOSPITAL REHAB.** 1992. m. $199. American Health Consultants, Inc., Six Piedmont Center, Ste. 400, Atlanta, GA 30305. TEL 404-262-7436; 800-688-2421. FAX 800-284-3291. Ed. Marcie O'Koon. circ. 845. **Document type:** newsletter.
Description: Covers reimbursement issues, legal problems, legislative action, regulatory changes, industry trends, and personnel issues.

658 340 US
HOSPITAL RISK CONTROL; an information and consultation system. (In four volumes) 1981. m. $695 (renewal $545). (Emergency Care Research Institute) E C R I, 5200 Butler Pike, Plymouth Meeting, PA 19462. TEL 610-825-6000. FAX 610-834-1275. Ed. Susan Bastnagel. bk.rev.; film rev.; abstr.; index. (looseleaf format) **Document type:** newsletter.
●Also available online.
Description: Covers hospital risk management and quality of care, safety, law and regulations.
Refereed Serial

658 US ISSN 0199-6312
HOSPITAL RISK MANAGEMENT. 1979. m. $279. American Health Consultants, Inc., Six Piedmont Center, Ste. 400, Atlanta, GA 30305. TEL 404-262-7436; 800-688-2421. FAX 800-284-3291. Ed. Bryan Powell. bk.rev. circ. 2,260. (also avail. in microfilm from UMI; back issues avail.; reprint service avail.) **Indexed:** CINAHL. **Document type:** newsletter.
●Also available online. Vendor(s): Mead Data Central, Inc.
—UMI. **CCC.**

658 US ISSN 0276-2323
HOSPITAL SAFETY INFORMATION SERVICE. 1979. bi-m. $98 (typically set in July). Scientific Enterprises, Inc., 5104 Randolph Rd., N. Little Rock, AR 72116. TEL 501-771-1775. FAX 501-771-1775. Ed. Dr. James O. Wear. bk.rev.; charts; illus.; stat.; index. (looseleaf format; back issues avail.) **Document type:** newsletter.
Description: Covers topics such as JCAHO and OSHA information, FDA recalls and examples of hazards for safety personnel.

HOSPITAL SECURITY AND SAFETY MANAGEMENT. see *CRIMINOLOGY AND LAW ENFORCEMENT — Security*

658 US
HOSPITAL STRATEGY REPORT. 1985. m. $192 (foreign $230). Aspen Publishers, Inc., 200 Orchard Ridge Dr., Gaithersburg, MD 20878. TEL 301-417-7500. FAX 301-417-7550. **Document type:** newsletter.
Formerly: Hospital Entrepreneur's Newsletter.

658 600 US ISSN 0888-711X
HOSPITAL TECHNOLOGY SERIES. (Four-part Series: Executive Briefing, Technology Scanner, Guideline Reports; Special Reports) 1981. m. $295 to non-members; members $195. American Hospital Association, 840 N. Lake Shore Dr., Chicago, IL 60611. TEL 312-280-5226. FAX 312-280-4151. Ed. Suzanna Hoppszallern. **Document type:** newsletter.
Formerly (until 1982): A H A Hospital Technology Series (ISSN 0735-4681)
Description: Covers trends and developments in medical technology and technology management that have strategic planning implications.

658 US ISSN 0018-5868
RA960
HOSPITAL TOPICS. 1922. q. $28 to individuals; institutions $51. Heldref Publications, 1319 Eighteenth St., N.W., Washington, DC 20036. TEL 202-296-6267. FAX 202-296-5149. Ed. Lisa Culp Neikirk. adv. contact: Raymond Rallo. bk.rev. circ. 7,200. (also avail. in microform from UMI; reprint service avail. from UMI) **Indexed:** Abstr.Health Care Manage.Stud., ASSIA, CINAHL, Excerp.Med., Hosp.Lit.Ind., I.P.A., Ind. Med. **Document type:** academic/scholarly publication.
●Also available online.
—BLDSC (4333.210000); Faxon; UnCover; UMI. **CCC.**
Formerly: Hospital Topics and Buyer's Guide (ISSN 0093-173X)
Refereed Serial

HOSPITALS

658   UK   ISSN 0305-4136
HOSPITAL UPDATE; the journal of continuing education for hospital doctors. 1974. m. £47 (free to qualified personnel). Reed Business Publishing Group, Reed Healthcare Communications (Subsidiary of: Reed Elsevier group), Quadrant House, The Quadrant, Sutton, Surrey SM2 5AS, England. TEL 081-652-8879. FAX 081-652-8946. Ed. Caley Montgomery. adv.; index. circ. 36,000. **Document type:** trade publication.
—BLDSC (4333.212000); SWETS.
   Formerly: Teach-in.
   Description: Keeps young doctors, consultants and senior registrars in touch with the latest developments in thinking and practice in every major medical specialty.

HOSPITAL VARGAS. ARCHIVOS. see *MEDICAL SCIENCES*

362   US   ISSN 1049-3662
HOSPITAL WATCH; a quarterly report on hospitals in New York City. 1990. q. free. United Hospital Fund of New York, 55 Fifth Ave., New York, NY 10003. TEL 212-645-2500. FAX 212-727-2471. Ed. Avery Hudson. **Document type:** newsletter.
   Description: Discusses trends in use, operations, and financial performance of voluntary and municipal hospitals in New York City.

362 331.88   UK
HOSPITAL WORKER. 1972. m. £24. c/o Clare Croft-White, Ed., 81a Minet Ave., London NW10, England. bk.rev.; charts; illus.; stat. circ. 5,000.

362   BE   ISSN 0018-5914
HOSPITALIA. (Text in Flemish) 1956. q. 1000 BEF. Verbond der Verzorgingsinstellingen, Guimardstraat 1, B-1040 Brussels, Belgium. FAX 02-513-52-69. Ed. A. Aernoudt. adv.; bk.rev.; bibl.; charts; illus. circ. 2,000. **Indexed:** Excerp.Med.

362   SZ   ISSN 0018-5930
HOSPITALIS. (Text in French, German) 1930. m. 74 SFr. Hospitalis Verlag AG, Hermetschloostr. 75, Postfach 1632, CH-8048 Zurich, Switzerland. TEL 01-4330080. FAX 01-4330242. Ed. Dr. N. Satz. adv. contact: Ernst Muerner. illus.; circ. 12,600 (controlled). **Indexed:** Med.Care Rev. **Document type:** trade publication.
●Also available online. Vendor(s): DIALOG Information Services, Inc.
—BLDSC (4333.230000).

658   FR   ISSN 0751-5766
HOSPITALISATION NOUVELLE. 1971. m. (10/yr.). 590 F. Union Hospitaliere Privee, 148 Bd. Malesherbes, 75017 Paris, France. Ed. Alain Coulomb. adv.; bk.rev. circ. 5,000. **Document type:** trade publication.

658   FR   ISSN 0439-6162
HOSPITALISATION PRIVEE; revue d'information hospitaliere. 1962. m. 420 F. Federation Intersyndicale des Maisons de Sante Privees de France et d'Outre-mer, 81 rue de Monceau, 75008 Paris, France. TEL 45-63-22-08. FAX 45-63-30-66. Ed. Dr. Louis Serfaty. adv. contact: H. Buffet. bk.rev.; illus.; stat. circ. 4,300. **Document type:** bulletin.

362   US   ISSN 1068-8838
RA960   CODEN: HHNEE5
HOSPITALS AND HEALTH NETWORKS. 1936. s-m. $65 (foreign $110). American Hospital Publishing, Inc. (Subsidiary of: American Hospital Association Company), 737 N. Michigan Ave., Ste. 700, Chicago, IL 60611. TEL 312-440-6800. FAX 312-951-8491. Ed. Mary Grayson. adv.; bk.rev.; illus.; index. circ. 114,900. (also avail. in microform from UMI; microfiche from CIS; reprint service avail. from UMI) **Indexed:** ABI Inform., Abstr.Health Care Manage.Stud., Account.Ind. (1974-), B.P.I., BPIA, C.I.N.L., Chem.Abstr., Curr.Cont., Excerp.Med., Pers.Lit., PSI, Sci.Cit.Ind., SRI, Tr.& Indus.Ind. **Document type:** trade publication.
●Also available online. Vendor(s): DIALOG Information Services, Inc., Mead Data Central, Inc.
—BLDSC (4333.270000); Faxon; UnCover; SWETS; UMI.
   Formerly: Hospitals (ISSN 0018-5973)

362.1   AT
HOSPITALS AND HEALTH SERVICES YEARBOOK AND BUYERS GUIDE. 1975. a. Aus.$140 per no. (University of New South Wales, School of Health Administration) Peter Isaacson Publications Pty. Ltd., 45-50 Porter St., Prahran, Vic. 3181, Australia. TEL 03-245-7777. FAX 03-245-7606. Pub. Kate Bowler.
   Former titles: Hospitals and Health Services Yearbook and Equipment Catalogue (ISSN 0817-5004); (until 1987): Hospitals and Health Services Yearbook (ISSN 0810-7513); Hospitals and Health Services Yearbook, Australia (ISSN 0156-3718); (until 1977): Australian Hospitals and Health Services Yearbook (ISSN 0312-5599); (until 1975): Australian and New Zealand Hospitals and Health Services Yearbook (ISSN 0084-7208).

658   JA   ISSN 0389-696X
HOSUPITARU/FUKUOKA HOSPITAL ASSOCIATION. JOURNAL. (Text in Japanese) 1973. m. 5000 Yen. Fukuokaken Byoin Kyokai, 14-5, Akasaka 1-chome, Chuo-ku, Fukuoka-shi, Fukuoka-ken 810, Japan.

362 614   US   ISSN 0046-8169
HUMAN ECOLOGY (PARK RIDGE). 1969. 2/yr. free. Lutheran General Health System, 1775 Dempster St., Park Ridge, IL 60068. Ed. Tina Weinheimer. adv. circ. 18,000. (also avail. in microfilm from JSC) **Indexed:** Biol.Abstr., Poult.Abstr., Protozool.Abstr., Rural Devel.Abstr., SSCI.

362 614.8   US
HUMAN RESOURCES ADMINISTRATOR. 1964. bi-m. $15 to non-members. (American Society for Healthcare Human Resources Administration) American Hospital Association, 840 N. Lake Shore Dr., Chicago, IL 60611. TEL 312-280-6434. FAX 312-280-4152. Ed. Catherine Futrell. circ. 2,900. **Document type:** newsletter.
   Formerly: Hospital Personnel Administration.
   Description: Information on human resources trends and issues in the health care field. Topics include management, recruitment, outplacement, legislation, benefits, and employee relations.

658   US
HUMANA HOSPITAL - MICHAEL REESE NEWS. 1974. bi-m. free. Humana Hospital - Michael Reese, Corporate Communications Department, 2816 S. Ellis Ave., Chicago, IL 60616. TEL 312-791-4462. Ed. Gretchen L. Holmberg. bk.rev.; illus.; circ. 16,000 (controlled).
   Formerly (until 1990): Michael Reese News; Which superseded: Michael Reese Mirror.

658   JA   ISSN 0913-7262
HYOGO KENRITSU KODOMO BYOIN NENPO/HYOGO PREFECTURAL KOBE CHILDREN'S HOSPITAL. ANNUAL REPORT. (Text in Japanese) a. Hyogo Kenritsu Kodomo Byoin, 1-1, Takakuradai 1-chome, Suma-ku, Kobe-shi, Hyogo-ken 654, Japan.

658   US   ISSN 0897-6198
I C C N - OUTPATIENT CARE. 1985. 6/yr. $40 (foreign $60) (free to qualified personnel). Reilly Publishing Co., 532 Busse Hwy., Park Ridge, IL 60068. TEL 312-693-3773. FAX 708-696-0946. Ed. Paula Ficara. circ. 36,087. (tabloid format)
   Description: Trade magazine serving physician specialists, chief medical officers, administrators, business managers and others concerned with product evaluation and procurement in freestanding ambulatory, diagnostic and surgical centers, group practices, HMOs and PPOs.

658 362.6   UK
I H A BULLETIN. (Former name of issuing body: Independent Hospital Group) m. membership. Independent Healthcare Association, 22 Little Russell St., London WC1A 2HT, England. TEL 44-71-430-0537. FAX 44-71-242-2681. Ed. Fiona Campbell. circ. controlled. **Document type:** bulletin.
   Supersedes: I H G Newsletter.

I N F A PRESS AND ADVERTISERS YEAR BOOK. (India News and Feature Alliance) see *ADVERTISING AND PUBLIC RELATIONS*

IBARAKI KENRITSU BYOIN IGAKU ZASSHI/IBARAKI PREFECTURAL HOSPITAL. MEDICAL JOURNAL. see *MEDICAL SCIENCES*

658   US   ISSN 1068-5286
▼**THE IDEA LETTER**. 1992. m. $129. American Health Consultants, Inc., Six Piedmont Center, Ste. 400, Atlanta, GA 30305. TEL 404-262-7436; 800-688-2421. FAX 800-284-3291. Ed. Steve Lewis. circ. 1,130. **Document type:** newsletter.
   Description: Offers ways to boost revenues, expand hospital services, integrate continuous quality improvement, streamline scheduling, and enhance interdepartmental communications.

658   FR   ISSN 0180-2224
INFIRMIERS. 1977. m. 280 F. Sopepharm, 15 rue du Nord, 95100 Argenteuil, France. TEL 39-82-02-02. FAX 39-80-84-60. Ed. Dr. Claude Richir. adv. circ. 5,000.
—BLDSC (4478.843500).
   Description: Information for black African French-speaking nurses.

658 610.73   GW   ISSN 0341-0595
INFORMATIONSDIENST KRANKENHAUSWESEN/HEALTH CARE INFORMATION SERVICE. (Text and summaries in English, German) 1969. bi-m. DM.195. Technische Universitaet Berlin, Institut fuer Gesundheitswesen, Str. des 17. Juni 135, 10623 Berlin, Germany. TEL 030-31423980. FAX 030-31424743. Ed. Ruediger Schneemann. bk.rev.; cum.index. circ. 400. (back issues avail.) **Document type:** abstracting/indexing.
●Also available online. Vendor(s): DIMDI.

658   US
INNOVATIONS (YEAR). a. price varies. American College of Physician Executives, Two Urban Centre, Ste. 200, 4890 W. Kennedy Blvd., Tampa, FL 33609. TEL 813-287-2000. FAX 813-287-8993.
   Description: Recognizes outstanding achievements in medical quality and cost management. Contains summaries of all the entries for 1993 determined innovative.

INPATIENT HOSPITAL USE IN NEW YORK CITY (YEAR). see *HOSPITALS — Abstracting, Bibliographies, Statistics*

658   SZ
DER INSELBOTE. q. Inselspital Bern, CH-3010 Bern, Switzerland. TEL 031-642974. circ. 5,750.

INTENSIVE CARING UNLIMITED. see *CHILDREN AND YOUTH — About*

362   NE
INTRAMURALE GEZONDHEIDSZORG. 1947. m. fl.10.($3.) Romeostr. 64, Amersfoort, Netherlands. Ed. H.J. Poots. adv.; bk.rev.; illus. circ. 5,500.
   Formerly: Protestantse Gezondheidszorg.

658   IE
IRISH HOSPITAL. 6/yr. McCann - McGuirk Presentations, 7 Greenmount House, Harold's Cross Rd., Dublin 6, Ireland. TEL 532497. FAX 544179. Ed. Lindie Naughton. bk.rev. circ. 3,005.

362   JA   ISSN 0021-1699
     CODEN: IRYOAV
IRYO (TOKYO, 1946)/JAPANESE JOURNAL OF NATIONAL MEDICAL SERVICES. Variant title: Therapeutics. (Text in Japanese; summaries in English, Japanese) 1946. m. Kokuritsu Iryo Gakkai - Japanese Society of National Medical Services, Koseisho Hoken Iryokyoku, 2-2, Kasumigaseki 1-chome, Chiyoda-ku, Tokyo 100, Japan. (Co-Sponsor: National Hospitals and Sanatoria of Japan) Ed. H. Hamada. adv.; charts; illus.; stat. circ. 5,000. **Indexed:** Biol.Abstr., Chem.Abstr., Excerp.Med., Excerp.Med., I.P.A., Ind.Med., INIS Atomind.
—BLDSC (4582.000000); CASDDS.

ISHIKAWA KENRITSU CHUO BYOIN IGAKUSHI/ISHIKAWA PREFECTURAL CENTRAL HOSPITAL. MEDICAL JOURNAL. see *MEDICAL SCIENCES*

ISRAEL. CENTRAL BUREAU OF STATISTICS. DIAGNOSTIC STATISTICS OF HOSPITALIZED PATIENTS. see *SOCIAL SERVICES AND WELFARE*

658   JA   ISSN 0916-3387
IWAKI KYORITSU BYOIN IHO/IWAKI KYORITSU GENERAL HOSPITAL. JOURNAL. (Text in English, Japanese) 1978. irreg. Iwaki Shiritsu Sogo Iwaki Kyoritsu Byoin, 16, Kusehara, Uchigomimayamachi, Iwaki-shi, Fukushima-ken 973, Japan.

HOSPITALS

658   JA   ISSN 0289-1484
IWAMIZAWA SHIRITSU SOGO BYOIN ISHI/IWAMIZAWA MUNICIPAL GENERAL HOSPITAL. JOURNAL. (Text in Japanese) 1975. a. Iwamizawa Shiritsu Sogo Byoin, Nishi 7-chome, 9-jo, Iwamizawa-shi, Hokkaido 068, Japan.

IWATE KENRITSU BYOIN IGAKKAI ZASSHI/IWATE PREFECTURAL HOSPITAL. MEDICAL JOURNAL. see *MEDICAL SCIENCES*

IWATE KENRITSU MIYAKO BYOIN IGAKU ZASSHI/IWATE PREFECTURAL MIYAKO HOSPITAL. MEDICAL JOURNAL. see *MEDICAL SCIENCES*

IYAKUHIN SOGO SAYO KENKYU/RESEARCH ON DRUG ACTIONS AND INTERACTIONS. see *PHARMACY AND PHARMACOLOGY*

658   US
RA399.A3
THE JOINT COMMISSION JOURNAL ON QUALITY IMPROVEMENT. 1974. m. $115 (foreign $125). Joint Commission on Accreditation of Healthcare Organizations, 1 Renaissance Blvd., Oakbrook Terrace, IL 60181. TEL 708-916-5600. FAX 708-916-5644. Ed. Steven Berman. bk.rev.; abstr.; bibl.; illus. circ. 7,000. also avail. in microform from UMI **Indexed:** Abstr.Health Care Manage.Stud., Abstr.Hosp.Manage.Stud., CINAHL, Excerp.Med. (until 1993), Hosp.Abstr., Hosp.Lit.Ind., Ind.Med., Int.Nurs.Ind., Med.Care Rev., Rehabil.Lit., Soc.Work.Res.& Abstr., Sociol.Abstr.
●Also available online. Vendor(s): Mead Data Central, Inc.
—Faxon; UnCover; UMI.
Formerly (until 1993): Q R B - Quality Review Bulletin (ISSN 0097-5990)

658   ISSN 1062-2551
JOURNAL FOR HEALTHCARE QUALITY. 1979. bi-m. $90. National Association for Healthcare Quality, 5700 Old Orchard Rd., Skokie, IL 60077-1057. TEL 708-965-2776. FAX 708-966-9418. Ed. Marylane Wade Koch. adv.; B&W page $925, color page $1720; trim 8 1/2 x 11. bk.rev. circ. 7,750. **Document type:** academic/scholarly publication.
—BLDSC (4996.872300).

610   US   ISSN 0148-9917
RA411
JOURNAL OF AMBULATORY CARE MANAGEMENT. 1978. q. $105 (foreign $126). Aspen Publishers, Inc., 200 Orchard Ridge Dr., Gaithersburg, MD 20878. TEL 301-417-7500. FAX 301-417-7550. (also avail. in microform from UMI; reprint service avail. from UMI) **Indexed:** Abstr.Health Care Manage.Stud., CINAHL, Excerp.Med., Med.Care Rev.
—BLDSC (4927.220000); Faxon; UnCover; UMI. **CCC.**

JOURNAL OF CASE MANAGEMENT. see *MEDICAL SCIENCES*

658   US   ISSN 0735-6722
RA440.6
JOURNAL OF HEALTH ADMINISTRATION EDUCATION. (Text in English; summaries in Spanish) 1983. q. $55 (foreign $60). Association of University Programs in Health Administration, 1911 N. Fort Myer Dr., Ste. 503, Arlington, VA 22209. TEL 703-524-5500. FAX 703-525-4791. Ed. Stephen Loebs. bk.rev.; bibl.; charts; illus.; stat. circ. 1,500. (back issues avail.; reprint service avail.) **Indexed:** Abstr.Health Care Manage.Stud., Hosp.Lit.Ind. **Document type:** academic/scholarly publication.
—BLDSC (4996.690000); Faxon; UnCover.

658 614.8   US   ISSN 0160-4198
RA1
JOURNAL OF HEALTH AND HUMAN RESOURCES ADMINISTRATION. 1978. q. $31 to individuals; libraries $50. Southern Public Administration Education Foundation, Pennsylvania State University at Harrisburg, Division of Public Affairs, Middletown, PA 17057. TEL 717-948-6363. FAX 717-540-1383. Eds. Jack Rabin, Thomas Vocino. bk.rev.; index. circ. 800. (back issues avail.) **Indexed:** Abstr.Health Care Manage.Stud., CINAHL, Excerp.Med., Manage.Cont., Med.Care Rev., Rehabil.Lit., Soc.Work Res.& Abstr. **Document type:** academic/scholarly publication.
—BLDSC (4996.703000); Faxon; UnCover.

JOURNAL OF HEALTH ECONOMICS. see *PUBLIC HEALTH AND SAFETY*

JOURNAL OF HEALTH INFORMATION & MEDICAL RECORDS OFFICERS. see *MEDICAL SCIENCES*

JOURNAL OF HEALTH POLITICS, POLICY AND LAW. see *MEDICAL SCIENCES*

658   US   ISSN 0889-2482
JOURNAL OF HEALTHCARE MATERIEL MANAGEMENT. 1983. 12/yr. $39 in U.S.: Canada $50; (foreign $98). Mayworm Associates, Inc., 507 N. Milwaukee Ave., Libertyville, IL 60048-2018. TEL 708-680-7878. FAX 708-680-8180. Ed. Marilyn Ferdinand. adv.; bk.rev. circ. 23,000. **Indexed:** Hosp.Lit.Ind. **Document type:** trade publication.
—BLDSC (4996.871000).
Formerly: Journal of Hospital Supply, Processing and Distribution (ISSN 0738-2928)
Description: Focuses on serving the specific educational and informational needs of materiel management, central service, purchasing, operating room, infection control and other personnel charged with the responsibility of purchasing, reprocessing and distributing supplies and equipment throughout the healthcare facility.

364.4   US   ISSN 0891-7930
JOURNAL OF HEALTHCARE PROTECTION MANAGEMENT. 1985? 2/yr. $25 (foreign $45). International Association for Healthcare Security and Safety, Box 190, Port Washington, NY 11050. TEL 516-883-1440. FAX 516-883-1683. Eds. Susan Krivin, Robert R. Rusting. adv. circ. 1,500. **Document type:** newsletter.
—BLDSC (4996.872000).

658 368.392   US
JOURNAL OF HEALTHCARE RISK MANAGEMENT. 1981. q. membership only. (American Society for Healthcare Risk Management) American Hospital Association, 840 N. Lake Shore Dr., Chicago, IL 60611. TEL 312-280-6198. FAX 312-280-5995. Ed. Margaret Veach. circ. 2,900. (back issues avail.) **Document type:** trade publication.
Former titles: Perspectives in Healthcare Risk Management (ISSN 0899-1073); (until 1987): Perspectives in Hospital Risk Management.
Description: Information on quality assurance, professional liability claims management, loss prevention, risk financing, risk management program development, workers' compensation, and risk management legislation and legal issues.

362.15   US   ISSN 0897-8018
RA645.3
JOURNAL OF HOME HEALTH CARE PRACTICE. 1988. 4/yr. $64 (foreign $77). Aspen Publishers, Inc., 200 Orchard Ridge Dr., Gaithersburg, MD 20878. TEL 301-417-7500. FAX 301-417-7550. **Indexed:** CINAHL, Nurs.Abstr.
—BLDSC (5002.956000); Faxon; UMI. **CCC.**

JOURNAL OF HOSPITAL MARKETING. see *BUSINESS AND ECONOMICS — Marketing And Purchasing*

JOURNAL OF J.J. GROUP OF HOSPITALS AND GRANT MEDICAL COLLEGE. see *MEDICAL SCIENCES*

618.9   US
JOURNAL OF LONG TERM HOME HEALTH CARE. 1982. q. $39 to individuals (foreign $44); institutions $74 (foreign $85). St. Vincent's Hospital, Pride Institute, 153 W. 11th St., New York, NY 10011. TEL 212-790-8864. Ed. Dr. Philip W. Brickner. (back issues avail.) **Indexed:** Psychol.Abstr., Soc.Work Res.& Abstr. **Document type:** trade publication.
—BLDSC (6612.889200); Faxon; UnCover.
Former titles: Pride Institute Journal of Long Term Home Health Care; Pride Institute Journal of Long Term Health Care (ISSN 0743-5088)
Description: Specialists and researchers describe their programs, examine important policy issues, and provide insight into practical matters of concern to service providers.

JOURNAL OF PALLIATIVE CARE. see *MEDICAL SCIENCES*

JOURNAL OF PUBLIC HEALTH POLICY. see *PUBLIC HEALTH AND SAFETY*

658   US
JUST FOR YOU. 1986. q. free. Kase Publications, Inc., 83 N. Central Ave., Ramsey, NJ 07446. TEL 201-818-9507. Ed. John E. Baer. adv.; bk.rev. circ. 190,000.

658   GW
K B - KRANKENHAUSBESCHAFFUNG. bi-m. DM.66. (Fachverband Einkauf und Materialwirtschaft im Krankenhaus e.V.) Beta Verlag GmbH, Postfach 140121, 53056 Bonn, Germany. TEL 0228-252061. FAX 0228-252067. TELEX 8869536-BETA-D. Ed. Ernst Heymann. circ. 4,000. **Document type:** trade publication.

KALEIDOSCOPE (TORONTO). see *MEDICAL SCIENCES — Pediatrics*

658   JA
KAWASAKI SHIRITSU IDA BYOIN NENPO/KAWASAKI MUNICIPAL IDA HOSPITAL. ANNUAL REPORT. (Text in Japanese) 1971. a. Kawasaki Shiritsu Ida Byoin, 1272 Ida, Nakahara-ku, Kawasaki-shi, Kanagawa-ken 211, Japan.

658   JA
KAWASAKI SHIRITSU KAWASAKI BYOIN NENPO/KAWASAKI MUNICIPAL HOSPITAL. ANNUAL REPORT. (Text in Japanese) 1965. a. Kawasaki Shiritsu Kawasaki Byoin, 12-1, Shinkawa Dori, Kawasaki-ku, Kawasaki-shi, Kanagawa-ken 210, Japan.

KING'S GAZETTE; the journal of King's College Hospital. see *MEDICAL SCIENCES*

362   GW   ISSN 0023-4486
KRANKENDIENST; Zeitschrift fuer kath. Krankenhaeuser, Sozialstationen und Pflegeberufe. 1920. m. DM.54 (foreign DM.69). (Katholischer Krankenhausverband Deutschlands e.V.) Lambertus-Verlag GmbH, Woelflinstr. 4, 79104 Freiburg, Germany. TEL 0761-36825-25. FAX 0761-37064. Ed. Werner Lauer. adv.; bk.rev.; index. circ. 4,000. (processed) **Document type:** bulletin.

658   GW   ISSN 0340-3602
DAS KRANKENHAUS. 1909. m. DM.272. (Deutsche Krankenhausgesellschaft) W. Kohlhammer GmbH, Hessbruehlstr. 69, 70565 Stuttgart, Germany. TEL 0711-7863-1. Ed. Peter Ossen. (back issues avail.; reprint service avail.) **Document type:** trade publication.
—BLDSC (5118.138000). **CCC.**

658   GW   ISSN 0720-3373
KRANKENHAUS-HYGIENE & INFEKTIONSVERHUETUNG. 1979. 6/yr. DM.100 (students DM.78). Verlag fuer Medizin Dr. Ewald Fischer GmbH, Fritz-Frey-Str. 21, 69121 Heidelberg, Germany. TEL 06221-4062-0. Eds. Schmidt-Burbach, B. Wille. circ. 5,500. **Document type:** academic/scholarly publication.
—BLDSC (5118.141000).

658   GW   ISSN 0720-3977
KRANKENHAUS TECHNIK; Zeitschrift fuer Verwaltung/Beschaffung/Haus- und Medizintechnik. 1976. m. DM.108. (Fachvereinigung Krankenhaustechnik e.V.) Ecomed Verlagsgesellschaft mbH und Co. KG, Rudolf-Diesel-Str. 3, 86899 Landsberg-Lech, Germany. TEL 08191-125-0. FAX 08191-125513. adv.: B&W page DM.3920; trim 190 x 270; adv. contact: Imke Ridder. circ. 9,000. (back issues avail.) **Document type:** bulletin.

362   GW   ISSN 0023-4508
KRANKENHAUS UMSCHAU; das Hospital Management Magazin. 1927. m. DM.246. (Krankenhausdirektoren Deutschland) Baumann Fachzeitschriftenverlag, E.C.-Baumann-Str. 5, 95326 Kulmbach, Germany. Ed. Jutta Lange. adv.; bk.rev.; charts; illus.; tr.lit.; index, cum.index: 1949-1962. circ. 4,300. **Indexed:** Excerp.Med. **Document type:** trade publication.

362   GW   ISSN 0023-4516
KRANKENHAUSARZT. 1927. 10/yr. DM.79 (foreign DM.99). Verlag G. Braun GmbH, Karl-Friedrich-Str. 14-18, 76133 Karlsruhe, Germany. TEL 0721-165-0. FAX 0721-165-227. Ed. H. Spaeth. adv.; bk.rev.; abstr.; bibl.; charts; illus.; index. circ. 20,000. **Indexed:** Dok.Arbeitsmed., Excerp.Med. (1994-). **Document type:** bulletin.
—BLDSC (5118.144000).

KUECHE IN KRANKENHAUS UND ALTENHEIM. see *FOOD AND FOOD INDUSTRIES*

HOSPITALS

362.11 DK ISSN 0107-1165
LAEGESTILLINGER OG SENGEPLADSER PAA INSTITUTIONER. 1974. a. DKK 75. Sundhedstyrelsen, Amaliegade 13, DK-1012 Copenhagen K, Denmark. (Subscr. to: Statens Information, P.O. Box 1103, 1009 Copenhagen K, Denmark)
Formerly: Normerede og Besatte Laegestillinger Samt Sengepladser paa Institutioner.

THE LATEST WORD. see MEDICAL SCIENCES

362 CN
LEADERSHIP IN HEALTH SERVICES. 1924. 8/yr. Can.$46($55) Canadian Hospital Association, 17 York St., Suite 100, Ottawa, Ont. K1N 9J6, Canada. TEL 613-238-8005. FAX 613-238-6924. Ed. Diane Bakker. adv.; bk.rev.; charts; illus.; mkt.; tr.lit. circ. 12,500. (also avail. in microfilm from UMI; back issues avail.; reprint service avail. from UMI) **Indexed:** Abstr.Health Care Manage.Stud., C.I.N.L., Can.B.P.I., Can.Per.Ind., Hosp.Abstr.Serv., Hosp.Lit.Ind., I.P.A., Ind.Med., Med.Care Rev.
●Also available online.
—Faxon; UnCover; UMI.
Formed by the 1992 merger of: Hospital Trustee (ISSN 0704-0407) & Dimensions in Health Service (ISSN 0317-7645); Which was formerly: Canadian Hospital (ISSN 0008-3798)
Description: Trade journal for Canada's health care managers.

LENGTH OF STAY BY D R G AND PAYMENT SOURCE. see HOSPITALS — Abstracting, Bibliographies, Statistics

658 US
LIMITED MOBILITY & IMMOBILIZED PATIENT PRODUCTS. 1987. q. Card-Zine Communications, Inc., 8912 Ewing Ave. Ste. A, Evanston, IL 60203-1907. TEL 708-933-0407. FAX 708-933-0217. adv.: B&W page $5610; 6 x 10 7/8. circ. 75,128.
Description: For healthcare professionals who evaluate and purchase products for hospitals, nursing homes, and home healthcare environments.

LIST OF APPROVED HOSPITALS AND RECOGNISED HOUSE OFFICER POSTS. see HOSPITALS — Abstracting, Bibliographies, Statistics

658 US
M G H NEWS. 1942. 9/yr. free. Massachusetts General Hospital Corp., Fruit St., Boston, MA 02114. TEL 617-726-2206. FAX 617-726-7475. Ed. Susan NcGreevey. bk.rev. circ. 25,000. (back issues avail.) **Document type:** bulletin.
Description: Covers recent research, developments, trends in health care and other medical information for the lay public and physicians.

M I M S ASSIST. see SOCIAL SERVICES AND WELFARE

658 659.2 US
M P R EXCHANGE. 1974. bi-m. membership. (American Society for Health Care Marketing and Public Relations) American Hospital Association, 840 N. Lake Shore Dr., Chicago, IL 60611. TEL 312-280-6358. FAX 312-280-5923. Ed. Lauren Barnett. circ. 3,000. **Document type:** newsletter.
Former titles: Hospital Marketing and Public Relations; Hospital Public Relations.
Description: Information on public relations and marketing for hospitals.

MANAGED CARE; a guide for physicians. see MEDICAL SCIENCES

MANAGED CARE LAW OUTLOOK. see MEDICAL SCIENCES

MANAGED CARE OUTLOOK; the insider's business briefing on managed health care. see MEDICAL SCIENCES

658 610 US ISSN 1064-5454
RA413
▼**MANAGED CARE QUARTERLY**. 1993. q. $94 (foreign $112). Aspen Publishers, Inc., 200 Orchard Ridge Dr., Gaithersburg, MD 20878. TEL 301-417-7500. FAX 301-417-7550. Ed. Lenda P. Hill. adv.; illus. (also avail. in microfilm from UMI; reprint service avail. from UMI)
—BLDSC (5358.630000). **CCC**.

MANAGED CARE WEEK. see MEDICAL SCIENCES

658 US ISSN 1072-2815
RA413.5.U5
MANAGED HEALTH CARE DIRECTORY. 1991. a. $250. American Managed Care and Review Association, 1227 25th St., N.W., Ste. 610, Washington, DC 20037-1156. TEL 202-728-0506. FAX 202-728-0609. index. circ. 500. (back issues avail.) **Document type:** directory.
Formed by the merger of (1985-1991): P P O Directory (Directory of Preferred Provider Organizations and the Industry Report on P P O Development) (ISSN 0894-9891); (1986-1991): H M O Directory (Directory of Health Maintenance Organizations) (ISSN 0894-9905)
Description: Lists HMOs, PPOs, UROs, IPAs, FMCs, addresses, phone and fax numbers, service, enrollment, provider contracts, and more.

658 US ISSN 1060-1392
RA413.5.U5
MANAGED HEALTHCARE NEWS; the newspaper for managers of healthcare costs and quality. 1990. m. $59 (foreign $117). Advanstar Communications, Inc., 7500 Old Oak Blvd., Cleveland, OH 44130. TEL 216-826-2839. FAX 216-891-2726. (Subscr. to: 1 E. First St., Duluth, MN 55082. TEL 800-346-0085) Ed. Jeff Schier. adv. circ. 30,000. (back issues avail.) **Document type:** newspaper, trade publication.
—CCC.
Description: Directed towards healthcare benefits managers, managed healthcare organizations, and providers of healthcare services. Covers issues of concern for managers responsible for controlling employee healthcare costs and quality; news, benefits management, legislative and regulatory issues, utilization patterns, and pharmaceutical trends.

658 US
MANAGEMENT BRIEFS. 1979. m. $37. Clinical Laboratory Management Association, 9 Old Lincoln Hwy., Ste. 201, Malvern, PA 19355-2135. TEL 215-647-8970. FAX 215-889-9731. Ed. Patricia A. Bergbauer. adv.; circ. 7,500 (controlled). **Indexed:** Excerp.Med.
Formerly (until 1989): Clinical Laboratory Management Newsletter.
Description: To keep association members updated on general healthcare management issues.

658 GW
MANAGEMENT UND KRANKENHAUS; Informationsdienst fuer alle Fuehrungskraefte im Gesundheitswesen. 1982. 10/yr. DM.132 (students DM.66). G I T Verlag GmbH, Roesslerstr. 90, 64293 Darmstadt, Germany. TEL 06151-8090-0. FAX 06151-809045. Ed. Brigitte Pfeiff. adv.: B&W page DM.7850, color page DM.10970; trim 185 x 260; adv. contact: Helga Dreschler. circ. 40,000. **Document type:** trade publication.

658 US ISSN 1059-4531
▼**MATERIALS MANAGEMENT IN HEALTH CARE**. 1992. m. $30 (foreign $50). (American Society for Hospital Materials Management) American Hospital Publishing, Inc. (Subsidiary of: American Hospital Association Company), 737 N. Michigan Ave., Ste. 700, Chicago, IL 60611-2615. TEL 312-440-6800. FAX 312-951-8491. (Co-sponsor: American Society for Hospital Central Service Personnel) Ed. Laura Souhrada. circ. 26,000. **Document type:** trade publication.
—UMI.
Description: Covers the selection, purchase and distribution of healthcare supplies, materials, and services.

658 FR
MEDECINE HOSPITALIERE/HOSPITAL MEDICINE. 1964. 6/yr. Syndicat National des Medecins, 56 rue de Vowille, 75015 Paris, France. TEL 45-33-01-71. FAX 45-33-42-09. Ed. Dr. Etienne Weill. adv. circ. 3,500. (also avail. in microfilm from UMI) **Indexed:** Excerp.Med.
Description: Information on trade-unionism.

MEDIA PROFILES: HEALTH SCIENCES EDITION. see MEDICAL SCIENCES

MEDICAL GROUP MANAGEMENT JOURNAL. see MEDICAL SCIENCES

658 US ISSN 1052-4924
MEDICAL RECORDS BRIEFING. 1986. m. $167 (effective 1994). Opus Communications, Box 1168, Marblehead, MA 01945. TEL 617-639-1872. FAX 617-639-2982. Ed. Susan Crawford. bk.rev.; charts; stat.; index. circ. 2,800. (looseleaf format; back issues avail.) **Document type:** newsletter.
Description: Covers issues, procedures and regulations affecting medical records management.

MEDICAL STAFF BRIEFING; the newsletter for volunteer/elected medical staff leaders. see MEDICAL SCIENCES

360 US ISSN 1041-6501
MEDICAL STAFF LEADER. vol.7, 1978. m. $22 (foreign $35). American Hospital Publishing, Inc. (Subsidiary of: American Hospital Association Company), 737 N. Michigan Ave., Ste. 700, Chicago, IL 60611. TEL 312-440-6800. FAX 312-951-8491. Ed. Jim Montague. circ. 14,000. (also avail. in microform from UMI; reprint service avail. from UMI) **Indexed:** Abstr.Health Care Manage.Stud., Excerp.Med. **Document type:** trade publication.
—UMI.
Former titles: Medical Staff News; (until 1985): Hospital Medical Staff (ISSN 0090-0710)

658 US
▼**MEDICAL STAFF STRATEGY REPORT**. 1992. m. $186. C O R Research Inc., Box 40959, Santa Barbara, CA 93140. TEL 805-564-2177. Ed. Therese M. Droste. **Document type:** newsletter.
Description: Case studies and articles on hospital-physician integration and strategies for medical staff development in hospitals.

MEDICINA OSPEDALIERA ROMANA. see MEDICAL SCIENCES

658 SW ISSN 1102-8068
MEDICINSK EKONOMI PLUS TEKNIK. 1924. 8/yr. SEK 200 (foreign SEK 296). E plus T Foerlaget, Jovisgatan 4, S-151 72 Soedertaelje, Sweden. TEL 46-8-55060554. FAX 46-8-55060664. Ed. Sten-Erik Jensen. adv.; bk.rev.; illus. circ. 10,000.
Formerly (until 1992): Sjukhuset (ISSN 0346-1130)
Description: Disseminates information on medical health administration, technology, economics as well as other related topics.

MEDICO OSPEDALIERO. see MEDICAL SCIENCES

658 GW ISSN 0721-6076
MEDIZIN IN BERLIN (WEST); aktuelle Anschriften und Telefonnummern des Berliner Gesundheitswesens. 1936. a. DM.32.64. Verlag Joachim Kugler, Machnower Str. 7a, 14133 Berlin, Germany. Ed.Bd. adv. circ. 4,200.

658 US ISSN 0160-7480
RA960
MODERN HEALTHCARE (YEAR); the newsmagazine for administrators and managers in hospitals, and other healthcare institutions. 1974. w. $110. Crain Communications, Inc. (Chicago), 740 N. Rush St., Chicago, IL 60611-2590. TEL 312-649-5341. FAX 312-280-3189. (Subscr. to: 965 E. Jefferson Ave., Detroit, MI 48207-3185. TEL 800-678-9595) Ed. Clark Bell. adv.; circ. 84,939 (controlled). (back issues avail.) **Indexed:** ABI Inform, Abstr.Health Care Manage.Stud., Account.Ind. (1974-), BPIA, Bus.Ind., CINAHL, Excerp.Med., Hlth.Ind., Hosp.Lit.Ind., I.P.A., Ind.Med., Int.Nurs.Ind., PROMT, PSI, Tr.& Indus.Ind.
●Also available online.
—BLDSC (5886.798000); Faxon; UnCover; SWETS; UMI. **CCC**.
Incorporates: Modern Healthcare (Long-Term Care) (ISSN 0093-7053) & Modern Healthcare (Short-Term Care) (ISSN 0093-7061); Modern Hospital (ISSN 0026-783X); Modern Nursing Home (ISSN 0026-8178)
Description: Contains information on healthcare management. Regular columns include news, technology, financial and legal briefs, new products, literature and a professional exchange.

HOSPITALS

658 610   US
MONITOR (WASHINGTON, 1970). 1970. 6/yr. $125. American Managed Care & Review Association, 1227 25th St., N.W., Ste. 610, Washington, DC 20037. TEL 202-728-0506. FAX 202-728-0609. Ed. Amanda M. Orr. bk.rev. circ. 1,000. (back issues avail.) **Document type:** newsletter.
   Former titles (until Oct. 1992): A M C R A's Managed Care Monitor; (until Dec. 1990): A M C R A Newsletter.
   Description: Discusses managed health care and delivery of services. Includes special original articles in each issue on particular aspects of managed health care, including state and national updates, legal viewpoint, educational programs and research programs.

MOUNT SINAI JOURNAL OF MEDICINE. see *MEDICAL SCIENCES*

362   US   ISSN 1057-3526
N A H A M MANAGEMENT JOURNAL. 1975. q. $90. National Association of Healthcare Access Management, 1101 Connecticut Ave., N.W., Ste. 700, Washington, DC 20036. TEL 202-857-1125. FAX 202-223-4579. Ed. Dale Konrad. adv.; bk.rev. circ. 1,400. **Indexed:** Ind.Med.
   Former titles (until 1991): Admitting Management Journal (ISSN 0894-1068); Journal for Hospital Admitting Management.
   Description: Information on hospital admissions and patient access services management, including systems and personnel.

N H O NEWSLINE. (National Hospice Organization) see *ALTERNATIVE MEDICINE*

NACHRICHTEN AUS DER AERZTLICHEN MISSION. see *RELIGIONS AND THEOLOGY*

362.15   US   ISSN 1047-5494
RA645.35
NATIONAL HOMECARE AND HOSPICE DIRECTORY. 1985. a. $135. National Association for Home Care, 519 C St., N.E., Washington, DC 20002-5809. TEL 202-547-7424. FAX 202-547-3540. adv. circ. 3,000. **Document type:** directory.
   Description: Lists over 15000 homecare and hospices nationwide.

362.1 340   US
NEW JERSEY STATE BAR ASSOCIATION. HEALTH AND HOSPITAL LAW SECTION. NEWSLETTER. 1987. irreg. membership only. New Jersey State Bar Association, Health and Hospital Law Section, 1 Constitution Sq., New Brunswick, NJ 08901-1500. TEL 908-249-5000. FAX 908-249-2815. Ed. Brian P. Blatz. circ. 400. **Document type:** newsletter.

658 362.2   US
NEW YORK (STATE). COMMISSION ON QUALITY OF CARE FOR THE MENTALLY DISABLED. ANNUAL REPORT. 1979. a. $4. Commission on Quality of Care for the Mentally Disabled, 99 Washington Ave., Albany, NY 12210. TEL 518-473-6304. FAX 518-473-6302. Ed. Marcus A. Gigliotti. circ. 11,000. **Document type:** government publication.

362   NZ   ISSN 0114-3727
NEW ZEALAND HEALTH & HOSPITAL. bi-m. $52. (New Zealand Health & Hospital Service) C. Rex Monigatti Publishing, 25 Braithwaite St., Wellington, New Zealand. TEL 64-4-476-7318. FAX 64-4-476-3898. adv.; bk.rev.; charts; illus. circ. 2,200. **Indexed:** Excerp.Med., I.P.A.
   —BLDSC (6092.263000). **CCC**.
   Formerly: New Zealand Hospital (ISSN 0028-8217).

NEWSPAPER ASSOCIATION OF AMERICA. NEWSPAPER ADVERTISING PLANBOOK. see *ADVERTISING AND PUBLIC RELATIONS*

NEWSPAPER MARKETING. see *BUSINESS AND ECONOMICS — Marketing And Purchasing*

658 610   JA
NIKKEI HEALTH BUSINESS. (Text in Japanese) 1987. w. 135000 Yen. Nikkei Business Publications, Inc. (Subsidiary of: Nihon Keizai Shimbun, Inc.), 2-7-6 Hirakawa-cho, Chiyoda-ku, Tokyo 102, Japan. TEL 02-5210-8502. FAX 03-5210-8119. Ed. Tatsuya Kawaguchi. **Document type:** newsletter.
   Description: Newsletter on the health care industry.

658 610   JA
NIKKEI HEALTHCARE. (Text in Japanese) 1989. m. 19500 Yen. Nikkei Business Publications, Inc. (Subsidiary of: Nihon Keizai Shimbun, Inc.), 2-7-6 Hirakawa-cho, Chiyoda-ku, Tokyo 102, Japan. TEL 03-5210-8502. FAX 03-5210-8119. Ed. Yutaka Ito. adv. contact: Takeshi Yamanaka. circ. 13,613. **Document type:** trade publication.
   Description: Provides guidelines for healthcare management. Includes extensive coverage of technological, sociological, and demographic trends.

658   JA   ISSN 0914-8574
NISHINOMIYA SHIRITSU CHUO BYOIN KIYO/NISHINOMIYA MUNICIPAL CENTRAL HOSPITAL. BULLETIN. (Text in Japanese) 1986. irreg. Nishinomiya Shiritsu Chuo Byoin, 8-24, Hayashidacho, Nishinomiya-shi, Hyogo-ken 663, Japan.

362   FR   ISSN 1150-8116
NOUVEL HOSPITALIER. 1947. bi-m. membership. Syndicat National des Cadres Hospitaliers, 44 rue Jules Ferry, 94400 Vitry-sur-Seine, France. TEL 42-34-81-01. FAX 43-26-86-98. Ed. Jean Paul Bastianelli. adv.; bibl.; charts; stat.; index, cum.index. circ. 2,500. (tabloid format)
   Formerly (until 1990): Hospitalier (ISSN 0754-5134)

642.54   SP
NUTRICION HOSPITALARIA. 7/yr. Antonio Lopez Aguado 4, 28029 Madrid, Spain. TEL 1-314-43-38. FAX 1-314-44-99. Ed. A. Garcia de Lorenzo.

O A C A O NEWSLETTER. (Older Adult Centres Association of Ontario) see *GERONTOLOGY AND GERIATRICS*

O H L A NEWSLINE. (Ontario Hospital Libraries Association) see *LIBRARY AND INFORMATION SCIENCES*

658   US   ISSN 8756-8047
O R MANAGER. (Operating Room) 1985. m. $68 (foreign $78) (effective 1994). O R Manager, Inc., Box 17487, Boulder, CO 80308-0487. TEL 303-442-1661; 800-442-9918. FAX 303-442-5960. Ed. Pat Patterson; Pub. Elinor S. Schrader. adv.; bk.rev.; circ. 3,000 (paid). **Indexed:** CINAHL. **Document type:** trade publication.
   —BLDSC (6277.375000). **CCC**.
   Description: Covers personnel management, budgeting and financial management, equipment and supplies, new technology, operating room nursing issues, and professional development.

657.832   DK
OEKONOMAEN. 1936. 22/yr. free. Oekonomaforeningen, Norre Voldgade 90, 1358 Copenhagen K, Denmark. adv. circ. 6,500.

362   AU   ISSN 0029-876X
OESTERREICHISCHE KRANKENHAUS ZEITUNG. 1960. m. S.1040. Verlag Dieter Goeschl GmbH, Hernalser Hauptstr. 213, A-1170 Vienna, Austria. TEL 01-464240. FAX 01-454902. adv.; bk.rev.; charts; illus.; stat.; index. circ. 2,090. **Indexed:** Excerp.Med. **Document type:** bulletin.

OKLAHOMA PUBLISHER. see *PUBLISHING AND BOOK TRADE*

658   DK   ISSN 0109-9957
OPERATIONSMOENSTERET PAA DANSKE SYGEHUSE. 1982. biennial. DKK 100. Sundehdsstyrelsen - National Board of Health, Amaliegade 13, P.O. Box 2020, 1012 Copenhagen K, Denmark. (Subscr. to: Statens Information, P.O. Box 1103, 1009 Copenhagen)

362   IT   ISSN 0030-6231
OSPEDALE. 1948. m. L.36000. Associazione Nazionale Medici Direttori di Ospedali, Istituto di Igiene, Via Santena 5-Bis, 10126 Turin, Italy. adv.; bk.rev. circ. 1,000.

658 610   IT   ISSN 0030-624X
OSPEDALE AL MARE. ARCHIVIO.* vol.22, 1970. q. L.3000. Ospedale al Mare, Lido di Venezia, Italy. Ed.Bd. adv.; bk.rev.; bibl.; charts; illus.; index. **Indexed:** Biol.Abstr., Excerp.Med.

362   IT   ISSN 0030-6258
OSPEDALI D'ITALIA. 1964. m. Federazione Italiana Associazioni Regionali Ospedaliere, Via dei Prefetti 46, 00186 Rome, Italy. Dir. Avv. D. Lanni. circ. 2,000. **Indexed:** Ind.Med.

658 617   US   ISSN 0270-207X
OUTREACH (CHICAGO). 1980. bi-m. $85 to non-members; members $65. (Society for Ambulatory Care Professionals) American Hospital Association, 840 N. Lake Shore Dr., Chicago, IL 60611. TEL 312-280-6046. FAX 312-280-5995. Ed. Tod Tappert. bk.rev.; charts; stat.; index. circ. 10,000. (back issues avail.) **Indexed:** Abstr.Health Care Manage.Stud. **Document type:** newsletter.
   Description: Information on ambulatory care, ambulatory surgery, emergency services, freestanding facilities, group practice, health maintenance organizations, preventive care, occupational health, home care, hospices, and primary care.

657.832   US
PATIENT ACCOUNTS. m. $75 to non-members; members $40. Healthcare Financial Management Association, 2 Westbrook Corporate Center, Ste. 700, Westchester, IL 60154-5700. TEL 708-531-9600. FAX 708-531-0032. adv. circ. 2,000. **Document type:** newsletter.
   Description: For healthcare professionals who are responsible for patient financial services in hospitals in the United States.

PATIENT CARE LAW. see *LAW*

658   US
▼**PATIENT-FOCUSED CARE**. 1993. m. $249. American Health Consultants, Inc., Six Piedmont Center, Ste. 400, Atlanta, GA 30305. TEL 404-262-7436; 800-688-2421. FAX 800-284-3291. Ed. Judy McGinnis. circ. 330. **Document type:** newsletter.

642.59   II
PATIENT HOSPITAL RELATIONS. 1991. bi-m. Rs.570($38) K.K. Roy (Private) Ltd., 55 Gariahat Road, P.O. Box 10210, Calcutta 700 019, India. Ed. K.K. Roy. adv.; abstr., bibl.; index. circ. 1,990.

658   US
PATIENT REPRESENTATION AND CONSUMER AFFAIRS. 1973. bi-m. membership. American Hospital Association, 840 N. Lake Shore Dr., Chicago, IL 60611-2431. TEL 312-280-6232. FAX 312-280-4182. Ed. Donald Phillips. circ. 1,100. **Document type:** newsletter.

PATIENTENPOST. see *CHILDREN AND YOUTH — For*

658 340   US
PATIENTS' RIGHTS REPORTER. 1983. m. Cox Publications, Box 20316, Billings, MT 59104-0316. TEL 406-256-8822. Ed. Meridith B. Cox. circ. 255. ●Available only online.
   Formerly: Patients' Rights in California (ISSN 0736-2544)
   Description: Keeps patients, their families and those providing pastoral care in health care settings aware of legislative and court decisions affecting patients' rights.

PEDIATRIC CLINICS OF INDIA. see *MEDICAL SCIENCES — Pediatrics*

658   US
PERSPECTIVES IN MEDICAL MANAGEMENT (YEAR). a. price varies. American College of Physician Executives, Two Urban Centre, Ste. 200, 4890 W. Kennedy Blvd., Tampa, FL 33609. TEL 813-287-2000. FAX 813-287-8993.

362.15   FR
PERSPECTIVES SANITAIRE ET SOCIALES. 6/yr. 10 rue de la Resiere, 75015 Paris, France. TEL 45-78-65-59. Ed. Jean Savy. circ. 5,000.

PHARMACIEN HOSPITALIER. see *PHARMACY AND PHARMACOLOGY*

PHILANTHROPIC DIGEST. see *SOCIAL SERVICES AND WELFARE*

HOSPITALS

658 US
PHYSICIAN EXECUTIVE; journal of management. m. $48 to non-members (foreign $60). American College of Physician Executives, Two Urban Centre, Ste. 200, 4890 W. Kennedy Blvd., Tampa, FL 33609. TEL 813-287-2000. FAX 813-287-8993.
 Description: Contains timely updates on health economics, clinical technology, health law, health services research, career management, health and business relations, and health policy reform.
 Refereed Serial

PRACTICE STANDARDS OF A S H P (YEAR). (American Society of Hospital Pharmacists) see *PHARMACY AND PHARMACOLOGY*

PREHOSPITAL AND DISASTER MEDICINE; an international journal. see *MEDICAL SCIENCES*

658 US
PRICE; the newsletter for physicians concerned about medical costs. q. $15 non-members. American College of Physician Executives, 4890 W. Kennedy Blvd., Ste. 200, Tampa, FL 33609. TEL 813-287-2000. FAX 813-287-8993. **Document type:** newsletter.
 Description: Provides a national forum for the exchange of ideas on clinical cost-effectiveness and for sharing work in development.

362 US ISSN 0033-0612
PROGRESS & CARE; at the Medical Center Hospital. 1953. q. free. Medical Center Hospital of Vermont, Colchester Ave., Burlington, VT 05401. TEL 802-656-2886. Ed. Beverly A. Rutherford. bk.rev.; illus. circ. 18,000.

PROVIDERS; the journal of long term care. see *MEDICAL SCIENCES — Nurses And Nursing*

PSYCHIATRIC HOSPITAL. see *MEDICAL SCIENCES — Psychiatry And Neurology*

800 613 PR
PUERTO RICO. DEPARTMENT OF HEALTH. INFORME ESTADISTICO DE FACILIDADES DE SALUD. (Text in Spanish) 1979. a. free. Department of Health, Health Facilities and Services Administration, Office of Health Statistics, Box 9342, Santurce, PR 00908. TEL 809-729-4707. FAX 809-729-4712. circ. 500.
 Formerly: Puerto Rico. Department of Health. Informe Anual de Facilidades de Salud.
 Description: Contains information on public and private hospitals' resources and services.

362 PR
PUERTO RICO. DIVISION OF HEALTH FACILITIES. PLAN FOR HOSPITAL AND MEDICAL FACILITIES. (Text and summaries in English) 1949. a. Department of Health, Division of Health Facilities, Stop 19, Santurce, PR 00907. circ. 250. (processed)

658 US
Q I - T Q M. (Quality Improvement - Total Quality Management) 1991. m. $269. American Health Consultants, Inc., Six Piedmont Center, Ste. 400, Atlanta, GA 30305. TEL 404-262-7436; 800-688-2421. FAX 800-284-3291. Ed. Warren Causey. circ. 2,300. **Document type:** newsletter.
 Description: Provides practical advice to hospital executives on implementation of the various continuous quality improvement models.

658 368.302 US ISSN 0747-3384
Q R C ADVISOR. (Quality, Risk & Cost); managing hospital quality, risk & cost. 1984. m. $199 (foreign $239). Aspen Publishers, Inc., 200 Orchard Ridge Dr., Gaithersburg, MD 20878. TEL 301-417-7500. FAX 301-417-7550. **Document type:** newsletter.
 —UMI.

658 US
QUALITY & RISK MANAGEMENT IN HEALTH CARE; an information service. 1990. s-a. $260 (foreign $312). Aspen Publishers, Inc., 200 Orchard Ridge Dr., Gaithersburg, MD 20878. TEL 301-417-7500. FAX 301-417-7550.
 Description: Covers new techniques, laws, regulations, program models, and guidelines from the discipline.

362 US ISSN 0892-6174
QUALITY CARE ADVOCATE. 1986. 6/yr. $45. National Citizens Coalition for Nursing Home Reform, 1224 M St., N.W., No. 301, Washington, DC 20005-5183. FAX 202-393-4122. bk.rev. circ. 6,000. **Document type:** newsletter.
 Description: Reports on federal legislation and regulatory developments, policy implementation and other current events affecting quality of care in nursing homes.

658 US
R A P S NEWS. m. Regulatory Affairs Professionals Society, 1230 Twinbrook Pkwy., Ste. 630, Rockville, MD 20852. TEL 301-770-2920. FAX 301-770-2924. (In Europe: 83 av. E. Mounier, 1200 Brussels, Belgium. TEL 32-2-7729247. FAX 32-2-7727237) Ed. Margaret C. Deegan. adv.; B&W page $1500; trim 8 1/2 x 11. **Document type:** newsletter.
 Description: News, information, publications and meetings of interest to health care regulatory professionals.

658 US ISSN 0300-6654
R H G H VITAL SIGNS. 1971. 6/yr. free. Richmond Heights General Hospital, 27100 Chardon Rd., Cleveland, OH 44143. TEL 216-585-6456. Ed. Peggy Walsh. illus. circ. 3,000. **Indexed:** Int.Nurs.Ind.

658 615.842 US ISSN 0198-7097
RA975.5.R3
RADIOLOGY MANAGEMENT. 1979. q. $36 (Canada $41; elsewhere $46). American Healthcare Radiology Administrators, 111 Boston Post Rd., Box 334, Sudbury, MA 01776-0003. TEL 508-443-7591. Ed. Mel L. Allen. adv.; bk.rev. circ. 3,407. (back issues avail.)
 —BLDSC (7238.160000).
 Description: Articles relating to management of the non-medical aspects of radiology.

REGAN REPORT ON HOSPITAL LAW. see *LAW*

658 US ISSN 1043-2752
REGULATORY AFFAIRS. 1989. q. $120 (foreign $145) (effective 1994). Regulatory Affairs Professionals Society, 12300 Twinbrook Pkwy., Ste. 630, Rockville, MD 20852. TEL 301-770-2920. FAX 301-770-2924.
 —BLDSC (7349.500000).
 Description: Provides a worldwide forum for communication, education, and development for health care regulatory professionals in industry and government.
 Refereed Serial

REHAB & COMMUNITY CARE MANAGEMENT. see *MEDICAL SCIENCES — Physical Medicine And Rehabilitation*

658 332 US ISSN 0884-2795
REIMBURSEMENT ADVISOR. 1985. m. $208 (foreign $250). Aspen Publishers, Inc., 200 Orchard Ridge Dr., Gaithersburg, MD 20878. TEL 301-417-7500. FAX 301-417-7550. circ. 1,200.
 —UMI.
 Description: Contains news and information concerning health care reimbursement.

REIMBURSEMENT UPDATE. see *BUSINESS AND ECONOMICS — Economic Situation And Conditions*

362.15 200 FR
RELIGIEUSES DANS LES PROFESSIONS DE SANTE. 1938. S N O C S S, 106 rue du Bac, 75005 Paris, France. Ed. M. Leroux. adv. circ. 6,556.
 Formerly: Religieuses d'Action Hospitaliere et Social.

REPORTS ON LONG TERM CARE. see *MEDICAL SCIENCES — Nurses And Nursing*

362 US ISSN 0034-5555
RESIDENT AND STAFF PHYSICIAN. 1955. m. $55 (foreign $92). Romaine Pierson Publishers, Inc., 80 Shore Rd., Port Washington, NY 11050. TEL 516-883-6350. FAX 516-883-6609. Ed. Dr. Alfred Bollet; Pub. Carl M. Roselle. adv. contact: Ann Hussey. illus.; tr.lit.; index. circ. 101,292. (also avail. in microform from UMI; back issues avail.; reprint service avail.) **Indexed:** Curr.Lit.Fam.Plan.
 —BLDSC (7777.243000); UMI.
 Formerly: Resident Physician.

RESPIRATORY CARE MANAGER. see *MEDICAL SCIENCES — Respiratory Diseases*

658 FR ISSN 0397-4626
REVUE HOSPITALIERE DE FRANCE. 6/yr. 435 F. (foreign 610 F.). Federation Hospitaliere de France, 33 av. d'Italie, 75013 Paris, France. TEL 44-06-84-44. FAX 44-06-84-45. Ed. M. Philippe Cadene. adv. circ. 4,500. **Indexed:** C.I.S. Abstr., Excerp.Med.

658 US ISSN 1062-2624
▼**RISK MANAGER'S LAW ALERT.** 1992. m. $199 (foreign $239). Aspen Publishers, Inc., 200 Orchard Ridge Dr., Gaithersburg, MD 20878. TEL 301-417-7500. FAX 301-417-7550. Ed. Audrey Covner. (looseleaf format) **Document type:** newsletter.

362 CN
S A H O NEWS. 1976. bi-m. free. Saskatchewan Association of Health Organizations, 1445 Park St., Regina, SK S4N 4C5, Canada. TEL 306-347-5526. FAX 306-525-1960. Ed. Loretta Fritz. circ. 3,500. (back issues avail.) **Document type:** newsletter.
 Formerly (until 1993): Continuum of Care.
 Description: Covers health care news and innovations in health care delivery.

658 US
S S M NETWORK. 1984. q. free. S S M Health Care System, 477 N. Lindbergh Blvd., St. Louis, MO 63141. TEL 314-994-7800. FAX 314-994-7900. Ed. Carol Bales. circ. 15,000. (tabloid format; back issues avail.)
 Description: Communicates the goals, vision, philosophy and mission of the SSM Health Care System.

658 US
ST. AGNES NEWS. 1961. bi-m. free to qualified personnel. St. Agnes Hospital, 900 Caton Ave, Baltimore, MD 21229. TEL 410-368-2170. FAX 410-368-2947. Ed. Helen Becker. circ. 6,000. (tabloid format)
 Description: Covers articles relating to the hospital's events, programs, and employees.

610 UK ISSN 0036-2840
SAINT GEORGE'S HOSPITAL GAZETTE. 1893. a. £1.50. St. George's Hospital, Medical School, Cranmer Terrace, Tooting, London SW17 0RE, England. adv.; bk.rev.; charts; illus.; cum.index. circ. 750.
 Formerly: New St. George Hospital Gazette.

362 UK
ST. THOMAS'S HOSPITAL GAZETTE. 1891. 3/yr. $13. St. Thomas's Hospital Medical School, c/o Medical School Library, London SE1 7EH, England. TEL 01-928-9292. Ed. I. Phillips. adv.; bk.rev.; bibl.; illus. circ. 1,500.
 Former titles: St. Thomas's Gazette (ISSN 0306-3860); St. Thomas's Hospital Gazette (ISSN 0036-3200)

362 FI ISSN 0036-326X
SAIRAALA.* (Text in Finnish; summaries in Swedish) 1928. 10/yr. Fmk.160. Infoteam Oy, Nervanderinkatu 5 D 41, FIN-00100 Helsinki, Finland. Ed. Pentti Vaananen. adv.; bk.rev.; bibl.; charts; illus. circ. 4,500.

658 SZ
DIE SANITAET. m. Wankdorffeldstr. 109, CH-3014 Bern, Switzerland. TEL 031-412342. circ. 4,000.

362 SZ
SCHWEIZER SPITAL; schweizerische Spitalzeitschrift/revue hospitaliere suisse. (Text in French, German, Italian) 1937. m. 80 SFr. for Western Europe and Turkey (foreign 100 SFr.). Veska Verlag, Postfach 4202, CH-5001 Aarau, Switzerland. TEL 064-241222. FAX 064-223335. adv.: B&W page 1450 SFr., color page 2635 SFr.; trim 182 x 259. bk.rev. circ. 3,000. **Indexed:** Dok.Arbeitsmed., Excerp.Med. **Document type:** consumer publication.
 Former titles: Schweizer Spital-Veska; Veska.

SCOPE (YORK). see *PHYSICS*

362 US ISSN 1063-4371
SERVICE QUALITY CONNECTION. 1989. bi-m. $125 to non-members; members $75. American Hospital Association, 840 N. Lake Shore Dr., Chicago, IL 60611-2431. TEL 312-280-7384. FAX 312-280-4182. Ed. Dianne V. Spenner. circ. 600. **Document type:** newsletter.
 Description: Presents ideas and programs to increase high-quality service in health care facilities.

3062 HOSPITALS

658 617.7 616.21 AT
SIGHT AND SOUND NEWS. 1950. q. free. Royal Victorian Eye and Ear Hospital, 32 Gisborne St., E. Melbourne, Vic. 3002, Australia. TEL 03-665-9376. FAX 03-663-7203. Ed. D.M. McGee. bk.rev. circ. 8,000. **Document type:** newsletter.

362 US ISSN 0037-5535
SINAI HOSPITAL OF DETROIT. BULLETIN. 1953. m. free. Sinai Hospital of Detroit, Committee on Hospital Publications, 6767 W. Outer Drive, Detroit, MI 48235. TEL 313-493-6824. Ed. Herbert J. Bloom. bk.rev.; abstr.; bibl.; charts; illus.; stat.; cum.index. circ. 3,700. **Indexed:** Biol.Abstr., Curr.Cont. **Document type:** bulletin.

SINGAPORE JOURNAL OF OBSTETRICS & GYNAECOLOGY. see *MEDICAL SCIENCES — Obstetrics And Gynecology*

SJUKHUSFARMACI. see *PHARMACY AND PHARMACOLOGY*

658 US
SMALL OR RURAL HOSPITALS UPDATE. 1977. irreg. free. American Hospital Association, Section for Small or Rural Hospitals, 840 N. Lake Shore Dr., Chicago, IL 60611. TEL 312-280-6395. FAX 312-280-6252. Eds. John Supplitt, Jane Gibson. circ. 3,500. (back issues avail.) **Document type:** bulletin.
Formerly (until 1989): Small or Rural Hospital Report.

SOCIEDAD ESPANOLA DE FARMACEUTICOS DE HOSPITALES. BOLETIN INFORMATIVO. see *PHARMACY AND PHARMACOLOGY*

355.72 UK ISSN 0038-9846
STAR AND GARTER MAGAZINE. 1921. q. £1. Star and Garter Home for Disabled Sailors, Soldiers and Airmen, Richmond Upon Thames, Surrey, England. Ed. C.F. Groves. adv.; charts; illus. circ. 2,000.

362 US ISSN 0895-688X
RA982.N49
STATE OF NEW YORK CITY'S MUNICIPAL HOSPITAL SYSTEM; report of the City Hospital Visiting Committee. a. $10. United Hospital Fund of New York, 55 Fifth Ave., New York, NY 10003. TEL 212-645-2500. FAX 212-727-2471. (Co-sponsor: City Hospital Visiting Committee) **Document type:** academic/scholarly publication.
Description: Reports findings that are based on a century-old citizens' group on the conditions affecting patient care in New York City's public hospitals. Includes overview of management, financial conditions, staffing, and individual facilities.

STRATEGIC HEALTH CARE MARKETING. see *BUSINESS AND ECONOMICS — Marketing And Purchasing*

658 US ISSN 1058-7829
STRATEGIES FOR HEALTHCARE EXCELLENCE. 1988. m. $197. C O R Research Inc., Box 40959, Santa Barbara, CA 93140-0959. TEL 805-564-2177. Ed. Susan J. Anthony. bk.rev. **Document type:** newsletter.
—CCC.
Former titles: Healthcare Productivity Report (ISSN 1043-1306); Healthcare Organization Report.
Description: Case studies and commentary on quality, efficiency, and productivity in healthcare delivery.

362.11 DK
RA989.D4
SYGDOMSMOENSTERET FOR INDLAGTE PATIENTER. 1979. biennial. DKK 100. Sundhedstyrelsen, Amaliegade 13, P.O. Box 1009, 1012 Copenhagen K, Denmark. (Subscr. to: Statens Informationstjeneste, P.O. Box 1103, 1009 Copenhagen K, Denmark).
Formerly: Sygdomsmoensteret ved Somatiske Sygehusafdelinger (ISSN 0107-8380)

362.11 DK ISSN 0107-508X
SYGEHUSKLASSIFIKATION OG KOMMUNEKODER. 1974. a. DKK 70. Sundhedsstyrelsen, Amaliegade 13, DK-1012 Copenhagen K, Denmark. (Subscr. to: Statens Informationstjeneste, P.O. Box 1103, 1009 Copenhagen K, Denmark)

362 FR ISSN 0040-1374
TECHNIQUES HOSPITALIERES, MEDICO-SOCIALES ET SANITAIRES. (Summaries in English, German, Italian, Spanish) 1945. 10/yr. 455 F. Association des Hautes Etudes Hospitalieres, 33 av. d'Italie, 75013 Paris, France. TEL 45-82-65-65. Ed. Pierre Raynaud. adv.; bk.rev. circ. 6,500. **Indexed:** Excerp.Med.
—SWETS. **CCC.**

362 IT ISSN 0392-4831
TECNICA OSPEDALIERA. 1971. m. L.85000 (foreign L.210000) (effective 1994). Tecniche Nuove s.p.a., Via C. Menotti 14, 20129 Milan, Italy. TEL 02-75701. FAX 02-7610351. Ed. Enzo Guaglione. adv.; B&W page L.1680000, color page L.2460000; trim 185 x 266. charts; illus. circ. 5,000.
Formerly: Nuova Tecnica Ospedaliera (ISSN 0029-6252)
Description: Covers hospital management and technical matters.

TEXAS HOSPITAL LAW. see *LAW*

362 UK ISSN 0308-7808
THERAPY WEEKLY; the newspaper for the remedial professions. 1974. w. £41.50 (free to qualified personnel). Macmillan Magazines Ltd., 4 Little Essex St., London WC2R 3LF, England. TEL 071-836-6633. FAX 071-836-0798. Ed. Carol Harris. adv.; bk.rev. circ. 10,000. (also avail. in microform from UMI; reprint service avail. from UMI) **Document type:** newspaper.
—BLDSC (8814.768000); UMI.
Incorporates: Remedial Therapist.

TIDSKRIFT FOER YNGRE LAEKARE. see *BUSINESS AND ECONOMICS — Labor And Industrial Relations*

362 DK ISSN 0040-702X
TIDSSKRIFT FOR DANSKE SYGEHUSE. (Text in Danish, Norwegian and Swedish) 1924. 10/yr. DKK 690. (Foreningen af Sygehusadministratorer i Danmark) Forlaget John Vaboe A-S, Hartmannsvej 47-49, DK-2920 Charlottenlund, Denmark. TEL 39-40-80-00. FAX 39-40-82-80. Ed. Preben Hauser. adv.; bk.rev.; bibl.; charts; illus.; stat. circ. 2,278. **Indexed:** Excerp.Med.

658 SP ISSN 0212-1972
TODO HOSPITAL. 1982. 10/yr. Publicaciones Nacionales Tecnicas y Extranjeras, S.A. (Puntex), C. Mare de Deu del Coll 14, Apdo. de Correos 5258, 08023 Barcelona, Spain. TEL 3-237-71-24. FAX 3-217-57-83. TELEX 97131 GPMM E. Ed. Ramon Marti. circ. 50,000.

657.832 330 US ISSN 0095-3814
RA410.A1 CODEN: THCFDG
TOPICS IN HEALTH CARE FINANCING. 1974. q. $110 (foreign $132). Aspen Publishers, Inc., 200 Orchard Ridge Dr., Gaithersburg, MD 20878. TEL 301-417-7500. FAX 301-417-7550. (also avail. in microform) **Indexed:** ABI Inform., Abstr.Health Care Manage.Stud., B.P.I., BPIA, Bus.Ind., CINAHL, Excerp.Med., Hlth.Ind., Ind.Med., Med.Care Rev., Tr.& Indus.Ind.
—BLDSC (8867.443000); Faxon; UnCover; UMI. **CCC.**

658 US ISSN 1065-0989
TOPICS IN HEALTH INFORMATION MANAGEMENT. 1980. q. $88 (foreign $106). Aspen Publishers, Inc., 200 Orchard Ridge Dr., Gaithersburg, MD 20878. TEL 800-638-8437. FAX 301-417-9550. (Subscr. to: 7201 McKinney Circle, Frederick, MD 21701) Ed. Carole Estey. circ. 3,000. **Indexed:** Abstr.Health Care Manage.Stud., BPIA, Bus.Ind., CINAHL, Comput.Cont.
—BLDSC (8867.443200); Faxon; UnCover; UMI. **CCC.**
Formerly (until 1991): Topics in Health Record Management (ISSN 0270-5230)

610 SP
TRIBUNA MEDICA HOSPITALES. 1987. m. 2000 ptas.($30) Editorial Garsi, S.A., Londres, 17, 28028 Madrid, Spain. TEL 256-08-00. FAX 361-10-07. Ed. Jesus Ibanez Montoya. circ. 20,000.

658 SP
TRIBUNA SANITARIA. 12/yr. Avda. Menendez Pelayo, 93, 28007 Madrid, Spain. TEL 1-522-66-04. Ed. A. Cusajus Lamperez. circ. 21,000.

362 US ISSN 0041-3674
RA960 CODEN: TRSTB
TRUSTEE; the magazine for hospital governing boards. 1947. m. $25 (foreign $40). American Hospital Publishing, Inc. (Subsidiary of: American Hospital Association Company), 737 N. Michigan Ave., Ste. 700, Chicago, IL 60611. TEL 312-440-6800. FAX 312-951-8491. Ed. Karen Gardner. adv.; bk.rev.; index. circ. 37,400. (also avail. in microform from UMI) **Indexed:** ABI Inform., Abstr.Health Care Manage.Stud., Excerp.Med., Hosp.Lit.Ind. **Document type:** trade publication.
—UMI.

U.S. NATIONAL CENTER FOR HEALTH STATISTICS. VITAL AND HEALTH STATISTICS. SERIES 13. DATA ON HEALTH RESOURCES UTILIZATION. see *PUBLIC HEALTH AND SAFETY*

UNIVERSIDADE DE SAO PAULO. HOSPITAL DAS CLINICAS. REVISTA. see *MEDICAL SCIENCES*

610 US
V A MEDICAL CENTER DIRECTORY. (Supplement to: V A Practitioner (ISSN 0883-5721)) a. Excerpta Medica, Inc. (Subsidiary of: Reed Elsevier Medical group), 105 Raider Blvd., Belle Mead, NJ 08502. TEL 908-874-8550. FAX 908-874-8419. (Subscr. to: 44 Cook St., Denver, CO 80206-5191. TEL 800-662-7776) **Document type:** directory.

360 AT ISSN 1030-8873
VICTORIA. HEALTH & COMMUNITY SERVICES. ANNUAL REPORT. 1979. a. free. Health & Community Services, 2nd Fl., 555 Collins St., Melbourne, Vic. 3000, Australia. TEL 616-7777. circ. 2,000.
Former titles (until 1993): Victoria. Health Department. Annual Report; Victoria. Health Commission. Annual Report; Victoria. Hospitals and Charities Commission. Annual Report.
Description: Review of the department's performance.

362.15 610 IT ISSN 0391-1470
VITA OSPEDALIERA. (Summaries in English) 1946. irreg. L.30000($22.50) Fatebenefratelli della Provincia Romana, Via Cassia 600, Rome, Italy. TEL 59.05.35. Dir. Giuseppe Magliozzi. circ. 5,000.

362 US ISSN 0005-1861
VOLUNTEER LEADER. 1960. q. $8 (foreign $10). American Hospital Publishing, Inc. (Subsidiary of: American Hospital Association Company), 737 N. Michigan Ave., Ste. 700, Chicago, IL 60611. TEL 312-440-6800. FAX 312-951-8491. Ed. Mary Grayson. adv.; bk.rev.; index. circ. 6,000. (also avail. in microform from UMI) **Indexed:** Hosp.Lit.Ind. **Document type:** bulletin.
—BLDSC (9254.585800); UMI.
Formerly: Auxillary Leader.

658 UK ISSN 0266-0776
RA987.W2
WELSH HOSPITAL WAITING LIST BULLETIN. 1984. s-a. £4 per issue. Welsh Office, Statistical Directorate, New Crown Building, Cathays Park, Cardiff CF1 3NQ, Wales. TEL 0222-825044. FAX 0222-825350. TELEX 498228. Ed. E. Swires-Hennessy. circ. 1,750. **Document type:** government publication.
—BLDSC (9294.568000). **CCC.**

WESTERN JOURNAL OF NURSING RESEARCH; An international forum for communciating nursing research. see *MEDICAL SCIENCES — Nurses And Nursing*

WHO'S WHO IN THE EMERGENCY & RESCUE SERVICES (YEAR). see *PUBLIC HEALTH AND SAFETY*

658 US
WINDOW (NEW YORK). 1981. irreg., (4-5/yr.), latest vol.13, no.3. free. New York Hospital - Cornell Medical Center, Office of Public Affairs, 525 E. 68th St., New York, NY 10021. TEL 212-821-0560. FAX 212-821-0576. Ed. Felicia E. Narvaez. circ. 17,000. (tabloid format)

362 UK ISSN 0512-3135
WORLD HOSPITALS. 1964. 3/yr. £59 (effective Jan. 1994). International Hospital Federation, 4 Abbots Pl., London NW6 4NP, England. TEL 071-372-7181. FAX 071-328-7433. Ed. Dr. Errol Pickering. adv.; bk.rev.; index, cum.index every 3 yrs. circ. 2,500. (also avail. in microform from UMI) **Indexed:** ASSIA, Br.Hum.Ind., CINAHL, Dok.Arbeitsmed., Excerp.Med., I.P.A., Med.Care Rev. **Document type:** academic/scholarly publication.
●Also available online.
—BLDSC (9356.065000); UnCover; SWETS; UMI. *Refereed Serial*

658 JA
YOKOHAMA MINAMI KYOSAI BYOIN NENPO/YOKOHAMA MINAMI MUTUAL AID ASSOCIATION HOSPITAL. ANNUAL REPORT. (Text in Japanese) 1979. a. Yokohama Minami Kyosai Byoin, 500, Mutsuuracho, Kanazawa-ku, Yokohama-shi, Kanagawa-ken 236, Japan.

658 CC ISSN 1001-5329
ZHONGGUO YIYUAN GUANLI/CHINESE HOSPITAL MANAGEMENT. (Text in Chinese) m. Heilongjiang Sheng Weishengting, 27, Xiangshun Jie, Xiangfang-qu, Harbin, Heilongjiang 150036, People's Republic of China. TEL 53359. Ed. Li Yihe.

ZHONGGUO YIYUAN YAOXUE ZAZHI/CHINESE JOURNAL OF HOSPITAL PHARMACY. see *PHARMACY AND PHARMACOLOGY*

362 NE ISSN 0044-4715
HET ZIEKENHUIS. 1970. 23/yr. fl.120 (effective 1992). (Nederlandse Zorgfederatie) C. Misset B.V., Postbus 4, 7000 BA Doetinchem, Netherlands. TEL 31-8340-49731. FAX 31-8340-63638. adv.: B&W page fl.1875, color page fl.4200; trim 210 x 297; adv. contact: Cor van Nek. bk.rev.; charts; illus.; index. circ. 5,350. **Indexed:** Ind.Med., Key to Econ.Sci. **Document type:** trade publication.
—BLDSC (9513.050000); SWETS.
Description: Professional journal for decision-makers, managers and executives in hospitals and health care.

1199 **NEWS.** see *LABOR UNIONS*

HOSPITALS — Abstracting, Bibliographies, Statistics

362 US
A H A HOSPITAL STATISTICS (YEAR). Key Title: Hospital Statistics. 1946. a. $139 to non-members; members $59. American Hospital Association, 840 N. Lake Shore Dr., Chicago, IL 60611. TEL 312-280-6225. FAX 312-280-4151. Ed. Jane Olson. charts; stat.; index. circ. 15,000. (also avail. in microfiche from CIS) **Indexed:** SRI. **Document type:** directory.
Former titles: Hospital Statistics; Data from American Hospital Association Annual Survey (ISSN 0090-6662); Survey of Hospital Charges (ISSN 0360-9316)
Description: Compilation of detailed statistical data on U.S. hospitals, including data on utilization, personnel, finances, facilities and services, approvals, affiliations, and revenue.

362 US ISSN 0094-8969
RA977.A1
AMERICAN HOSPITAL ASSOCIATION GUIDE TO THE HEALTH CARE FIELD. 1945. a. $195 to non-members; members $75. American Hospital Association, 840 N. Lake Shore Dr., Chicago, IL 60611. TEL 312-280-6225. FAX 312-280-4151. Ed. Jane Olson. adv.; stat.; tr.lit. circ. 30,000. (also avail. in microfiche from CIS) **Indexed:** SRI. **Document type:** directory.
Description: Directory listing registered hospitals, with selected data: health care systems, American Hospital Association institutional members, international, national, and regional organizations, and state organizations and agencies.

AUSTRALIA. BUREAU OF STATISTICS. QUEENSLAND OFFICE. HOSPITAL MORBIDITY, QUEENSLAND. see *POPULATION STUDIES — Abstracting, Bibliographies, Statistics*

658 AT ISSN 0814-4362
AUSTRALIA. BUREAU OF STATISTICS. VICTORIAN OFFICE. PUBLIC HOSPITAL MORBIDITY, VICTORIA. 1982. a. Aus.$8. Australian Bureau of Statistics, Victorian Office, G.P.O. Box 2796Y, Melbourne, Vic. 3001, Australia. **Document type:** government publication.
Description: Contains details on in-patient separations from Victorian public hospitals.

658 JA
BYOIN KANRI KENKYUJO KENKYU SHUDANKAI ENDAI SHOROKU/NATIONAL INSTITUTE OF HOSPITAL ADMINISTRATION. ABSTRACTS OF THE MEETING. (Text in Japanese) a. Koseisho, Byoin Kanri Kenkyujo - Ministry of Health and Welfare, National Institute of Hospital Administration, 21-13, Toyama 1-chome, Shinjuku-ku, Tokyo 162, Japan. **Document type:** abstracting/indexing.

658 CL
ESTADISTICAS DE SALUD. EGRESOS HOSPITALARIOS. 1971. a. Instituto Nacional de Estadisticas, Av. Bulnes 418, Casilla 498, Correo 3 Santiago, Chile.

613 016 NE ISSN 0921-8068
RA410.A1
EXCERPTA MEDICA. SECTION 36: HEALTH POLICY, ECONOMICS AND MANAGEMENT. 1971. 6/yr. fl.1062($574) (effective 1994). Excerpta Medica (Subsidiary of: Elsevier Science B.V.), P.O. Box 548, 1000 AM Amsterdam, Netherlands. TEL 31-20-5803911. FAX 31-20-5803222. TELEX 18582 ESPA NL. (Dist. by: Elsevier Science Ireland Ltd., P.O. Box 85, Limerick, Ireland. TEL 353-61-471944. FAX 353-61-472144; Subscr. in U.S. and Canada to: Elsevier Science Inc., Box 882, Madison Sq. Sta., New York, NY 10159. TEL 212-989-5800. FAX 212-633-3990) adv.; charts; index, cum.index. **Document type:** abstracting/indexing.
●Also available online. Vendor(s): BRS Online Products, DIMDI, Data-Star, DIALOG Information Services, Inc., JICST.
Also available on CD-ROM. Producer(s): SilverPlatter Information, Inc.
—BLDSC (3835.835500). **CCC.**
Former titles: Excerpta Medica. Section 36: Health Economics and Hospital Management (ISSN 0300-5321); Excerpta Medica. Section 36: Health Economics.
Description: Covers the economic, social and political aspects of health care and its organization, and includes hospital management, health care marketing, hospital automation, and the assessment of new technology for the health care industry.

658 310 US ISSN 0891-2173
RA981.A2
GERIATRIC LENGTH OF STAY BY DIAGNOSIS AND OPERATION, UNITED STATES. 1964. a. price varies. H C I A Inc., 300 E. Lombard St., Baltimore, MD 21202. TEL 410-576-9600. FAX 410-783-0575. stat. (also avail. in microfiche; magnetic tape; diskette format; back issues avail.)

658 US ISSN 0891-5016
HEALTHCARE MARKETING ABSTRACTS. 1986. m. $96. C O R Research Inc., Box 40959, Santa Barbara, CA 93140. TEL 805-564-2177. Ed. Therese Droste. bk.rev. **Document type:** abstracting/indexing.
—CCC.
Description: Informative abstracts of healthcare marketing articles selected from more than 140 periodicals.

362 016 US ISSN 0018-5736
Z6675.H75
HOSPITAL LITERATURE INDEX. 1945. q. (with a. cum.). $290 to non-members; members $225. American Hospital Association, 840 N. Lake Shore Dr., Chicago, IL 60611. TEL 312-280-6258. FAX 312-280-5979. Ed. Eloise Foster. index. circ. 2,500. (also avail. in microform from UMI) **Document type:** abstracting/indexing.
●Also available online. Vendor(s): DIMDI, National Library of Medicine.
—UMI.
Formerly: Hospital Periodical Literature Index.
Description: Author-subject index of periodical literature on the development and delivery of medical care and related subjects.

362 US ISSN 0894-8151
INPATIENT HOSPITAL USE IN NEW YORK CITY (YEAR). 1982. irreg., approx. every 2-3 yrs. $125 for 3 vols. United Hospital Fund of New York, 55 Fifth Ave., New York, NY 10003. TEL 212-645-2500. FAX 212-727-2471. stat. **Document type:** academic/scholarly publication.
Description: Supplies data showing overall patterns of hospital use by residents of each borough and by nonresident patients. Provides detailed community profiles showing the specific hospitals at which residents of each zip code area received care, the clinical service used, and the patients' insurance coverage.

KEY STATISTICAL INDICATORS FOR NATIONAL HEALTH SERVICE MANAGEMENT IN WALES. see *PUBLIC HEALTH AND SAFETY — Abstracting, Bibliographies, Statistics*

658 US ISSN 1043-9285
LENGTH OF STAY BY D R G AND PAYMENT SOURCE. (Diagnosis Related Group) (Editions avail.: United States Western Region, Southern Region, Northcentral Region, and Northeastern Region) 1988. a. price varies. H C I A Inc., 300 E. Lombard St., Baltimore, MD 21202-0303. TEL 410-576-9600. FAX 410-783-0575. (also avail. in microfiche; magnetic tape; back issues avail.)

658 310 US ISSN 0895-982X
LENGTH OF STAY BY DIAGNOSIS & OPERATION, UNITED STATES. 1964. a. price varies. H C I A Inc., 300 E. Lombard St., Baltimore, MD 21202. TEL 410-576-9600. FAX 410-783-0575. stat. (also avail. in microfiche; magnetic tape; diskette format; back issues avail.)
Formerly: Length of Stay by Diagnosis, United States (ISSN 0891-2149); Incorporates: Length of Stay by Operation, United States (ISSN 0891-2203)

658 310 US ISSN 0895-9846
LENGTH OF STAY BY DIAGNOSIS & OPERATION, UNITED STATES, NORTH CENTRAL REGION. 1964. a. price varies. H C I A Inc., 300 E. Lombard St., Baltimore, MD 21202. TEL 410-576-9600. FAX 410-783-0575. stat. (also avail. in microfiche; magnetic tape; diskette format; back issues avail.)
Formerly: Length of Stay by Diagnosis, United States, North Central Region (ISSN 0891-2165); Incorporates: Length of Stay by Operation, United States, North Central Region (ISSN 0891-222X)

658 310 US ISSN 0895-9838
LENGTH OF STAY BY DIAGNOSIS & OPERATION, UNITED STATES, NORTHEASTERN REGION. 1964. a. price varies. H C I A Inc., 300 E. Lombard St., Baltimore, MD 21202. TEL 410-576-9600. FAX 410-783-0575. stat. (also avail. in microfiche; magnetic tape; diskette format; back issues avail.)
Formerly: Length of Stay by Diagnosis, United States, Northeastern Region (ISSN 0891-2122); Incorporates: Length of Stay by Operation, United States, Northeastern Region (ISSN 0888-2673)

658 310 US ISSN 0895-9854
LENGTH OF STAY BY DIAGNOSIS & OPERATION, UNITED STATES, SOUTHERN REGION. 1964. a. price varies. H C I A Inc., 300 E. Lombard St., Baltimore, MD 21202. TEL 410-576-9600. FAX 410-783-0575. stat. (also avail. in microfiche; magnetic tape; diskette format; back issues avail.)
Formerly: Length of Stay by Diagnosis, United States, Southern Region (ISSN 0891-2130); Incorporates: Length of Stay by Operation, United States, Southern Region (ISSN 0891-219X)

658 310 US ISSN 0895-9862
LENGTH OF STAY BY DIAGNOSIS & OPERATION, UNITED STATES, WESTERN REGION. 1964. a. price varies. H C I A Inc., 300 E. Lombard St., Baltimore, MD 21202. TEL 410-576-9600. FAX 410-783-0575. stat. (also avail. in microfiche; magnetic tape; diskette format; back issues avail.)
Formerly: Length of Stay by Diagnosis, United States, Western Region (ISSN 0891-2157); Incorporates: Length of Stay by Operation, United States, Western Region (ISSN 0891-2211)

362.11 UK
LIST OF APPROVED HOSPITALS AND RECOGNISED HOUSE OFFICER POSTS. 1952. irreg. £10. General Medical Council, 44 Hallam St., London W1N 6AE, England. TEL 071-580-7642. FAX 071-436-1384.

HOSPITALS — COMPUTER APPLICATIONS

362 NZ
RA407.5.N4
NEW ZEALAND HEALTH INFORMATION SERVICE. HOSPITAL AND SELECTED MORBIDITY DATA. a. NZ.$30. New Zealand Health Information Service, Ministry of Health, 133 Molesworth St., P.O. Box 5013, Wellington, New Zealand. TEL 04-496-2188. FAX 04-496-2340.
 Formerly: New Zealand. Health Statistical Services. Hospital and Selected Morbidity Data (ISSN 0548-9938)

617 362 US ISSN 1065-8173
▼ **O R REPORTS.** 1992. bi-m. $88 (Canada $98; elsewhere $98). O R Manager, Inc., Box 17487, Boulder, CO 80308-0487. TEL 303-442-1661; 800-442-9918. FAX 303-442-5960. Ed. Pat Patterson; Pub. Elinor Schrader. circ. 1,000 (paid). **Document type:** trade publication.
 Description: Abstracts of scientific articles relating to the operating room environment and relevant standards and regulations.

658 310 US ISSN 0891-1223
RJ27.2
PEDIATRIC LENGTH OF STAY BY DIAGNOSIS AND OPERATION, UNITED STATES. 1964. a. price varies. H C I A Inc., 300 E. Lombard St., Baltimore, MD 21202. TEL 410-576-9600. FAX 410-783-0575. stat. (also avail. in microfiche; magnetic tape; diskette format; back issues avail.)

658 DK ISSN 0107-1173
RA989.D4
PERSONALE- OG OEKONOMISTATISTIK FOR SYGEHUSVAESENET. (Included in the series: Sygehusstatistik) 1976. a. DKK 60. Sundhedsstyrelsen, Amaliegade 13, DK-1012 Copenhagen K, Denmark. (Subscr. to: Statens Informationstjeneste, P.O. Box 1103, 1009 Copenhagen K, Denmark)
 Formerly: Personale og Sengepladser ved de Sygedomsbehandlende Institutioner.

362.1 316.8 SA
SOUTH AFRICA. CENTRAL STATISTICAL SERVICE. CENSUS OF HOSPITALS, CLINICS, AND OTHER HEALTH SERVICE ESTABLISHMENTS. (Report No. 93-01-01) triennial. latest 1990. R.15 (foreign R.18.75). Central Statistical Service - Sentrale Statistiekdiens, Private Bag X44, Pretoria 0001, South Africa. TEL 27-12-310-8911. FAX 27-12-310-8500. (Orders to: Government Printing Works, Private Bag X85, Pretoria 0001, South Africa) **Document type:** government publication.

362.1 316.8 SA
SOUTH AFRICA. CENTRAL STATISTICAL SERVICE. STATISTICAL RELEASE. CENSUS OF HOSPITALS, CLINICS AND OTHER HEALTH SERVICE ESTABLISHMENTS (YEAR). (No. P9301) irreg., latest 1990. free. Central Statistical Service - Sentrale Statistiekdiens, Private Bag X44, Pretoria 0001, South Africa. TEL 27-12-310-8911. FAX 27-12-310-8500. **Document type:** government publication.

362.11 DK ISSN 0109-3002
RA645.37.D4
STATISTIK OM HJEMMESSYGEPLEJERKEVIRKSOMHEDEN. (Subseries: Primaer Sundhedstjenestatistik) 1980. a. DKK 60. Sundhedsstyrelsen, Amaliegade 13, 1012 Copenhagen K, Denmark. (Subscr. to: Statens Informationsjeneste, P.O. Box 1103, 1009 Copenhagen K, Denmark)

310 614.8 DK ISSN 0107-749X
SUNDHEDSSTYRELSEN VITALSTATISTIK. (Includes: Doedsaarsagerne (ISSN: 0108-5646); Medicinsk Foedsels og Misdannelsesstatistik (ISSN: 0109-1966); Statistik om Praevention og Aborter (ISSN: 0106-7729)) 1983. a. DKK 125. Sundhedsstyrelsen, Amaliegade 13, 1012 Copenhagen K, Denmark. (Subscr. to: Statens Informationstjeneste, P.O. Box 1103, 1009 Copenhagen K, Denmark)

362.11 DK
SYGEHUSSTATISTIK. (Includes: Personale- og Oekonomistik for Sygehusvaesenet (ISSN: 0107-1173); Virksomheden ved Sygehuse) 1979. a. Sundhedsstyrelsen, Amaliegade 13, 1012 Copenhagen K, Denmark. (Orders to: Statens Informationstjeneste, P.O. Box 1103, 1009 Copenhagen K, Denmark)
 Formerly: Sygehusvaesenet (ISSN 0107-4954)

362 UY ISSN 0041-8455
UNIVERSIDAD DE LA REPUBLICA. HOSPITAL DE CLINICAS. INFORME ESTATISTICO. 1962. a. $1. Hospital de Clinicas "Dr. Manuel Quintela", Universidad de la Republica, Avda. Italia S-N, Montevideo, Uruguay. Ed. Bd. circ. 400.

658 DK ISSN 0903-8086
RA989.D4
VIRKSOMHEDEN VED SYGEHUSE. 1986. a. DKK 100. Sundhedsstyrelsen, Amaliegade 13, DK-1012 Copenhagen K, Denmark. (Subscr. to: Statens Informationstjeneste, P.O. Box 1103, 1009 Copenhagen K, Denmark)

WELSH HOSPITAL WAITING LIST BULLETIN. see *HOSPITALS*

HOSPITALS — Computer Applications

658.2 US ISSN 1066-3037
▼ **B B I'S MONITOR OF TECHNOLOGY ASSESSMENT AND REIMBURSEMENT**; cost, outcome and payment data critical to medical product markets. 1992. m. $420. Biomedical Business International (Subsidiary of: Macmillan Inc.), 1524 Brookhollow Dr., Santa Ana, CA 92705-5426. TEL 714-755-5757. FAX 714-755-5724.
 Description: Analysis of medical reimbursement, coverage decisions and clinical and procedure assessments, including product and therapy assessments, payer decisions, and provider programs impacting medical product and service markets.

HOTELS AND RESTAURANTS

see also Nutrition and Dietetics; Travel and Tourism

A B A NEWSLETTER. (American Bartenders' Association) see *BEVERAGES*

647.94 US
A H & M A REPORTS. 1984. 10/yr. membership. American Hotel & Motel Association, 1201 New York Ave., N.W., Washington, DC 20005-3931. TEL 202-289-3100. FAX 202-289-3199. Ed. Kathryn L. Cochran. circ. 12,000 (controlled). **Document type:** newsletter.
 Description: Covers a wide spectrum of topics in the lodging industry.

647.9 US
A H & M A'S SOURCE BOOK. 1976. a. American Hotel and Motel Association, 1201 New York Ave., N.W., Washington, DC 20005-3917. TEL 202-289-3165. adv.; illus. circ. 30,000. **Document type:** directory.
 Formerly: American Hotel and Motel Association. Buyers Guide for Hotels and Motels; Supersedes: American Hotel and Motel Association. Product News (ISSN 0032-9789)

642.5 US
A LA CARTE; a menu guide to the restaurants of western North Carolina. 1983. a. $4. Mountain Meadows Publications, 959 Merrimon Ave., Box 1513, Asheville, NC 28802. TEL 704-253-9299. Ed. Bobbi Cannon. adv. circ. 10,000.
 Description: Annual presentation of restaurant menus and recommended bed and breakfast and country inns in Western North Carolina.

642.5 AU
A LA CARTE. 8/yr. Wickenburggasse 13, A-1080 Vienna, Austria. TEL 01-4885710. FAX 01-48857188. Ed. Christian Gruenwald. circ. 35,000.

ABEL VALUE NEWS; panem et circenses/bread and circuses. see *THEATER*

ACCOMMODATION AUSTRALIA GUIDE. see *TRAVEL AND TOURISM*

647.94 917.04 CN
ACCOMMODATOR; the magazine of Ontario's hospitality industry. 1949. q. membership. Motels Ontario, 347 Pido Rd., Unit 2, R.R. 6, Peterborough, ON K9J 6X7, Canada. TEL 705-745-4982. FAX 705-745-4983. Ed. Bruce M. Gravel. adv.; index; circ. 1,300 (controlled).
 Description: For operators and suppliers in Ontario's accommodation and foodservice industries.

647.94 910.09 SP
ACTUALIDAD HOSTELERA Y TURISTICA. 26/yr. Loeches 6, Apdo. 45075, 28008 Madrid, Spain. TEL 1-247-00-52. FAX 1-542-90-60. TELEX 44651 FJAB E. Ed. Francisco J. Abello.

647 910 UK
AGENT'S HOTEL GAZETTEER: AMERICA. a. £22.50. C.H.G. Travel Publications, Waterside House, West Common, Gerrards Cross, Bucks, England.

647 UK
AGENT'S HOTEL GAZETTEER: CITIES OF EUROPE. a. £24. C.H.G. Travel Publications, Waterside House, West Common, Gerrards Cross, Bucks, England. illus.
 Formerly: Agent's Hotel Gazetteer: Tourist Cities (ISSN 0308-9584)

647 910 UK
AGENT'S HOTEL GAZETTEER: RESORTS OF EUROPE. a. £25.50. C.H.G. Travel Publications, Waterside House, West Common, Gerrards Cross, Bucks, England. illus.
 Formerly: Agent's Hotel Gazetteer: Resorts.

ALIMENTARIA; revista de tecnologia e higiene de los alimentos. see *FOOD AND FOOD INDUSTRIES*

647.9 GW ISSN 0002-5895
ALLGEMEINE HOTEL- UND GASTSTAETTEN-ZEITUNG; Deutsche Hotel-Nachrichten. 1946. w. DM.362.40. (Deutscher Hotel- und Gaststaettenverband e.V. (DEHOGA)) Matthaes Verlag GmbH, Olgastr. 87, 70180 Stuttgart, Germany. TEL 0711-2133-0. Ed.Bd. adv.; illus. circ. 31,000. **Document type:** newspaper.

647.94 US
▼ **ALMANAC.** 1992. a. $50. Penton Publishing, 1100 Superior Ave., Cleveland, OH 44114. TEL 216-696-7000. FAX 216-696-7658. Ed. Edward Watkins. adv.: B&W or color page $5300; trim 7 7/8 x 10 3/4. circ. 49,100.

642.5 SW ISSN 0283-3387
APERITIF; hotell, restaurang och matkultur. (Includes Innkoepshandboken) 1963. 9/yr. SEK 285. Trappgaveln Foerlags AB, Kistavaegan 2 C, 191 70 Sollentuna, Sweden. FAX 08-6268321. Ed. Bengt-Olov Bjoerlesjoe. adv.; bk.rev. circ. 6,000.
 Former titles (until 1981): Aperitif med Bar-Nytt; (until vol.2, 1963): Bar-Nytt.

APPUNTI DI GASTRONOMIA. see *HOME ECONOMICS*

642.5 664 US
ASIA PACIFIC FOODSERVICE PRODUCT NEWS.* 1990. 6/yr. $60 (effective 1992). Young - Conway Publications, 1101 Richmond Ave., Ste. 201, Point Pleasant Beach, NJ 08742-3049. adv.; circ. 29,921 (controlled).
 Description: Provides restaurant owners, managers, and chefs with information on new products, equipment and supplies.

647.94 HK
ASIAN HOTEL & CATERING TIMES. (Text in English) 1976. m. HK.$170 in Hong Kong; Asia $45; elsewhere $55. Thomson Press Hong Kong Ltd., 202-203 Hollywood Centre, 233 Hollywood Rd., Hong Kong. TEL 815-9111. FAX 851-1933. Ed. Glen Roger. adv. (back issues avail.) **Document type:** trade publication.
 Formerly: Asian Hotelkeeper and Catering Times.
 Description: Reviews hotel trade developments in Asia, Australia, and the Pacific.

647.94 SZ
ASSOCIATION HOTELIERE DU VALAIS. BULLETIN D'INFORMATION. 5/yr. Association Hoteliere du Valais, Case Postale 42, CH-1951 Sion, Switzerland. TEL 027-229922. Ed. Eric Biselx. circ. 800. **Document type:** bulletin.

ATLANTIC CITY ACTION. see *BUSINESS AND ECONOMICS — Investments*

HOTELS AND RESTAURANTS

647.94   CN
ATLANTIC HOSPITALITY & FOODSERVICE. (Supplement avail.: Atlantic Hospitality (ISSN 1183-532X)) irreg. (10-12/yr.). Can.$18 for 12 issues. Box 5000, Bridgewater, NS B4Y 3R7, Canada. TEL 902-543-5694. FAX 902-543-5694. Ed. Juan C. Canales. circ. 7,000. **Document type:** trade publication.
    Former titles (until 1992): Maritime Food and Beverage (ISSN 0827-6994); (until 1990): Food and Beverage (ISSN 0847-9852); (until 1989): Food and Beverage News (ISSN 1183-5397)

910.09 663   AT   ISSN 0813-7544
AUSTRALIAN HOTELIER. 1984. m. Aus.$60. (Australian Hotels Association) National Publishing Group Pty. Ltd., P.O. Box 8, Strawberry Hills, N.S.W. 2008, Australia. TEL 02-319-1888. FAX 02-319-6623. Ed. Jenny Berich. adv.; bk.rev.; tr.lit.; index. circ. 7,245. (back issues avail.) **Document type:** trade publication.
    Description: Covers all aspects of hotel management and the tourist and food and beverage industries in Australia.

647.94 647.95   FI   ISSN 0783-0041
AVEC ARCTIA. 2/yr. Erikoislehdet Oy Business Publications, P.O. Box 16, SF-00381 Helsinki, Finland. Ed. Marketta Rentola. circ. 30,000.

642.57   IT   ISSN 0392-2707
B A R GIORNALE. (Bar Alberghi Ristorazione) (Supplement avail.: Hotel Business and Management) 1979. m. (except Aug.). L.70000 (foreign L.140000). Agepe s.r.l., Via Domenico Trentacoste, 9, 20134 Milan, Italy. TEL 02-215621. FAX 02-2640330. TELEX 351491. Ed. Alberto Schieppati. adv.; B&W page L.24050000, color page L.43300000; trim 255 x 370. bk.rev.; circ. 246,244 (controlled). **Document type:** trade publication.
    Description: Features articles written for bar, cafe, hotel and restaurant entrepreneurs in Italy. Includes articles on tourism.

642.5   SZ
BAERNER CHANNE.* q. Postfach 766, CH-3000 Bern 22, Switzerland. Ed. M. Glanzmann. circ. 3,000.

642.5   GW
DIE BAR. bi-m. DM.51.60. Rhenania-Fachverlag GmbH, Possmoorweg 5, 22301 Hamburg, Germany. FAX 040-2717-2069. TELEX 213214. circ. 3,692. **Document type:** trade publication.

BAY FOOD. see *FOOD AND FOOD INDUSTRIES*

642.5   NO   ISSN 0803-219X
BEDRE STORKJOEKKEN; tidsskrift for storhusholdning og reiseliv. 1969. 10/yr. NOK 425. Vanebo Fagpresse A-S, P.O. Box 130, 2261 Kirkenaer, Norway. Ed. Odd H. Vanebo. adv.; illus. circ. 5,200.
    Former titles (until 1991): S K - Storkjoekken (ISSN 0800-1405); (until 1982): Storkjoekken (ISSN 0039-1956)

642.57   GW   ISSN 0937-7646
DAS BETRIEBSRESTAURANT; Fach-Illustrierte fuer Verpflegung in Industrie, oeffentlichem Dienst und BAB-Gastronomie. 1990. bi-m. DM.50. ProPress Verlag GmbH, Am Buschhof 8, 53227 Bonn, Germany. TEL 0228-970970. FAX 0228-444296. circ. 8,000. **Document type:** trade publication.

BILL OF FARE. see *FOOD AND FOOD INDUSTRIES*

647.9   UK   ISSN 0006-4351
BLACKPOOL HOTEL & GUEST HOUSE ASSOCIATION. JOURNAL.* 1924. w. 25p. Blackpool Hotel and Guest House Association Ltd., 87a Coronation St., Blackpool FY1 4PD, Lancastershire, England. Ed. Eric Pollitt. adv.; illus.; tr.lit.; circ. controlled.

642.47   FR
BOISSON RESTAURATION ACTUALITES. 11/yr. 167 Av. Victor Hugo, 75116 Paris, France. TEL 45-53-01-97. FAX 45-53-17-99. Ed. France Marie Pouilevet. circ. 60,000.

BOTTOMLINE (AUSTIN). see *BUSINESS AND ECONOMICS — Accounting*

642.47 658.8   UK
BRITAIN'S CATERING INDUSTRY. 1984. biennial. £125. Jordan Publishing Ltd., 21 St. Thomas St., Bristol BS1 6JS, England. TEL 0272-230600. FAX 0272-250486. TELEX 449119. **Document type:** directory.
    Formerly: Catering (London, 1984).

647.94   UK
▼**BRITAIN'S OLD INNS AND COUNTRY HOUSE HOTELS;** the comprehensive guide to Britain's recommended inns and hotels. 1994. a. £6.95. Peerage Publications, 9 Mortlake Terr., Kew Green, Richmond-upon-Thames, Surrey TW9 3DT, England. TEL 081-747-0385. Ed. Sara Marden-King; Pub. Bruce Duncan. adv.: B&W page £450, color page £575; trim 210 x 148. **Document type:** directory.

647.94   CN
BRITISH COLUMBIA & YUKON HOTELS ASSOCIATION. MEMBERSHIP DIRECTORY & BUYERS GUIDE. 1976. a. Naylor Communications Ltd., 124 W. 8th St., North Vancouver, BC V7M 3H2, Canada. TEL 604-985-8711. FAX 604-985-7399. Ed. Jim Hutson. adv. circ. 1,550. **Document type:** directory.

674.94   NE
BRUSSELS HILTON MAGAZINE. (Text in English) 1968. 6/yr. free to Brussels Hilton guests. (Hilton Hotels (Brussels)) Delta Publicity International Publications BV, Keizergracht 255, 1016 EB Amsterdam, Netherlands. Ed. David Deeley. adv. circ. 12,000.

642.5
BUCKHEAD LIFE. vol.10, 1991. q. free. Buckhead Life Restaurant Group, One Buckhead Plaza, 3060 Peachtree St., Ste. 930, Atlanta, GA 30305. TEL 404-237-2060.

647 910.09   GR
BUSINESS OF TOURISM. (Text in Greek) 1989. m. Dr.2750. Business Press SA, 44 Syngrou Ave., 117 42 Athens, Greece. TEL 9238672. FAX 9216847. Ed. Spiros Zougris. circ. 10,000.
    Description: For hotel and tourist trade professionals. Covers national and international developments affecting the Greek tourist trade.

C V R HOTEL GUIDE TO SOUTHERN AFRICA. see *TRAVEL AND TOURISM*

647.9   DK
CAFETERIA BLADET. 1939. m. Danmarks Cafeteriaforening, Vesterbrogade 18, 1620 Copenhagen V, Denmark. Ed. Bertha Juul. adv. circ. 1,794.
    Formerly: Cafeteria Motel Bladet (ISSN 0007-9545)

647.94   SZ
CAFETIER. 10/yr. 42 SFr. Schweizer Cafetier Verband, Bleicherweg 54, Postfach, CH-8039 Zurich, Switzerland. TEL 2016777. FAX 2016877.
    Former titles: Schweizer Cafetiers; Gaststaette.

647.9   FR
CAFETIER, RESTAURATEUR PARISIEN. 1946. m. 30 F. Syndicat des Cafetiers, Restaurateurs de Paris et Banlieues, 27 rue Hermel, 75018 Paris, France. TEL 42-64-86-11. FAX 42-64-08-09. Eds. Jean Biron, J.L. Delatte. adv.; illus. circ. 15,000.

647.94   US
CALIFORNIA INNTOUCH. 1981. bi-m. $28.95 to non-members. California Hotel - Motel Association, Box 160405, Sacramento, CA 95816-0405. TEL 916-444-5780. FAX 916-444-5848. Ed. William Howe. adv. contact: Laura Hellenthal. circ. 7,100. **Document type:** trade publication.
    Description: Features industry news, legislative updates, advice for hospitality businesses on improvements, innovations, and other developments.

CAMERON'S FOODSERVICE MARKETING REPORTER. see *FOOD AND FOOD INDUSTRIES*

647.9   CN   ISSN 0008-3801
                                                  CODEN: CAHREC
CANADIAN HOTEL & RESTAURANT. 1923. m. Can.$32. Kostuch Communications Ltd., 980 Yonge St., Ste. 400, Toronto, ON M4W 2J8, Canada. TEL 416-923-8888. FAX 416-923-6114. Ed. Jerry Tutunjian. adv.; bk.rev.; charts; illus.; tr.lit.; index. circ. 37,000. **Indexed:** Art.Hosp.& Tour., Can.B.P.I., Food Sci.& Tech.Abstr.
   —BLDSC (3027.500000).
    Formerly: Canadian Hotel Review and Restaurant.

CANADIAN HOTEL, RESTAURANT, INSTITUTION & STORE EQUIPMENT DIRECTORY. see *BUSINESS AND ECONOMICS — Trade And Industrial Directories*

647.95   PR
CARIBBEAN REPORTER. bi-m. Caribbean Hotel Association, 18 Marseilles St., Suite 1-A, Santurce, PR 00907. TEL 809-725-9139.

CARIBOO CHILCOTIN COAST TRAVEL GUIDE. see *TRAVEL AND TOURISM*

CASINO CHRONICLE. see *SPORTS AND GAMES*

642.47   UK
CATERING. 1981. m. Morgan-Grampian Farming Press Ltd. (Subsidiary of: Morgan-Grampian plc), Morgan-Grampian House, 30 Calderwood St., London SE18 6QH, England. TEL 081-855-7777. FAX 081-854-7476. Ed. Christian Davies. adv. contact: Mike Shinn. **Document type:** trade publication.

642.47   BA
CATERING AND HOTEL NEWS INTERNATIONAL. (Text in English) 26/yr. $200. Al Hilal Publishing & Marketing Group, P.O. Box 224, Manama, Bahrain. TEL 973-293131. FAX 973-293400. TELEX 8981 HILAL BN. (In U.K.: Hilal International (UK) Ltd., Crescent Ct., 102 Victor Rd., Teddington, Middx TW11 8SS, England. TEL 44-81-943-3630) Ed. Cecilia Ow. adv.: B&W page £2800, color page $3920; 400 x 275. circ. 4,930. (tabloid format; back issues avail.) **Document type:** trade publication.
    Supersedes: Catering and Hotel News (ISSN 0129-2935)
    Description: For senior personnel in the Middle East and South East Asia food service and manufacturing, catering and hotel industries.

642.47   UK
CATERING & LICENSING REVIEW. 1976. m. £16. Jemma Publications (N.I.) Ltd., 151 University St., Belfast BT7 1HR, N. Ireland. Ed. Linda Giles. adv. circ. 3,812.

642.5   UK
CATERING IN SCOTLAND. bi-m. £10. Scottish County Press Ltd., Sherwood Industrial Estate, Bonnyrigg, Midlothian EH19 3LW, Scotland. TEL 031-663-2404. FAX 031-663-6863. Ed. Jane Ambrose. adv. contact: Alan McVicar. circ. 11,008. **Document type:** trade publication.

CATERING TODAY. see *FOOD AND FOOD INDUSTRIES*

642.47   UK   ISSN 0269-7696
CATERING UPDATE. 1985. m. £25($65) Reed Business Publishing Group (Subsidiary of: Reed Elsevier group), Quadrant House, The Quadrant, Sutton, Surrey SM2 5AS, England. TEL 081-661-3500. FAX 081-661-8946. (Subscr. to: Oakfield House, Perrymount Rd., Haywards Heath, W. Sussex RH16 3DH, England) Ed. Mike Sawyer. adv.; bk.rev. circ. 70,183. (back issues avail.) **Document type:** trade publication.
   —BLDSC (3092.956000).
    Description: Product magazine covering all types of food service equipment, food, furnishings, technology for the food service industry.

642.5   UK
CATERNEWS. 1984. q. Barry Spouge, Ed. & Pub., 66 Bracondale, Norwich NR1 2BE, England. TEL 0603-623303. FAX 0603-666238. adv.; circ. 20,000 (controlled). **Document type:** trade publication.

CELLAR NOTES. see *BEVERAGES*

642.47   UI
CHANNEL ISLANDS CATERING NEWS. m. £1.50. Killowen, St. Aubin's Rd., St. Helier, Jersey, Channel Islands.

642.5   AT
CHEAP EATS IN SYDNEY. biennial. Aus.$6.95. Universal Magazines Pty. Ltd., 64 Talavera Rd., Macquarie Park, N.S.W. 2113, Australia. TEL 02-803-0399. FAX 02-805-0714.

CHEF. see *FOOD AND FOOD INDUSTRIES*

CHEF. see *FOOD AND FOOD INDUSTRIES*

CLEFS D'OR. see *LABOR UNIONS*

3066 HOTELS AND RESTAURANTS

642.57 910.09 SP
CLUB DE GOURMETS; gastronomy & travel magazine - gastronomia y viajes. 1976. m. 3520 ptas.($30) Club G., S.A., Cuesta San Vicente, 4-6a, 28008 Madrid, Spain. TEL 91-542-76-60. FAX 91-559-45-75. Ed. Francisco Lopez Canis. adv.; bk.rev.; bibl.; index. circ. 30,000. (back issues avail.)
 Description: Covers cooking, wines and travel.

642.5 US
COLORADO GUIDE TO SMOKE-FREE DINING. biennial. $1 contribution. Group to Alleviate Smoking Pollution (GASP), 2885 Aurora Ave., No. 37, Boulder, CO 80303-2252. TEL 303-444-9799. circ. 40,000. **Document type**: directory.
 Formerly: Guide to Smoke-Free Dining in Colorado.

CONSULTANT (LOUISVILLE). see FOOD AND FOOD INDUSTRIES

COOKING FOR PROFIT. see FOOD AND FOOD INDUSTRIES

647.9 US ISSN 0010-8804
TX901 CODEN: CHRQA2
THE CORNELL HOTEL & RESTAURANT ADMINISTRATION QUARTERLY. 1960. 6/yr. $130 (foreign $165) (effective 1994). (Cornell University, School of Hotel Administration) Elsevier Science Inc., Box 882, Madison Sq. Sta., New York, NY 10159. TEL 212-989-5800. FAX 212-633-3990. TELEX 420643 AEP UI. Ed. Glenn Withiam. bk.rev.; bibl.; charts; illus.; tr.lit.; index. circ. 8,000. (also avail. in microfilm; reprint service avail. from UMI) **Indexed**: ABI Inform., Account.Ind. (1974-), Art.Hosp.& Tour., B.P.I., BPIA, Bus.Ind., Food Sci.& Tech.Abstr., P.A.I.S., Rural Recreat.Tour.Abstr., Tr.& Dev.Alert, Tr.& Indus.Ind., World Agri.Econ.& Rural Sociol.Abstr. **Document type**: academic/scholarly publication.
—BLDSC (3470.943000); Faxon; UnCover; SWETS; UMI. **CCC**.
 Description: Covers management trends and principles relevant to the hospitality and food service industries.
 Refereed Serial

647.9 CK
CORPORACION HOTELERA DE COLOMBIA. BOLETIN INFORMATIVO. 1972. m. free. Corporacion Hotelera de Colombia, Carrera 7a 60-92, Apartado Aereo 29692, Bogota, Colombia. TEL 3103617. FAX 3103509. Dir. Elias Henao. bk.rev.

642.47 UK
CRONER'S CATERING. 1981. bi-m. £89.40 (subscr. includes m. newsletter) (effective 1993). Croner Publications Ltd., Croner House, London Rd., Kingston, Surrey KT2 6SR, England. TEL 081-547-3333. FAX 081-547-2637. Ed. Paula Quinn. (looseleaf format) **Document type**: trade publication.
 Description: Guidance on the law and proper management practices for those working in the hotel and catering trade.

642.5 FR ISSN 0045-9208
CUISINE COLLECTIVE;* la revue professionnelle des responsables de la restauration collective. 1960. 10/yr. 110 F. Editions Sonedis, 22-24 rue du President Wilson, 92532 Levallois-Perret Cedex, France. TEL 47-39-34-81. FAX 47-39-34-79. Ed. Emmanuelle Couturier. adv.; illus.; pat.; stat. circ. 21,000.

647.95 US
CULINARIAN. m. Chefs Association of the Pacific Coast, Inc., 1550 Bryant St., Ste. 810, San Francisco, CA 94103-4832. TEL 415-864-5627. Ed. Mary F. Forslund. adv. circ. 1,500.

647.95 US ISSN 1057-3453
TX901 CODEN: CUTRE8
CULINARY TRENDS. 1990. q. $21.60. Culinary Trends Publication, 6285 Spring St., Ste. 107, Long Beach, CA 90808. TEL 310-496-2558. FAX 310-982-1432. Ed. Tim Linden; Pub. Fred Mensinga. adv.; bk.rev. circ. 5,700. **Document type**: trade publication.
 Description: Serves the culinary industry with emphasis towards executives and working chefs, food and beverage directors, proprietors and general managers of hotels, resorts, private clubs, high-end catering establishments and fine restaurants.

642.57 641.5 IT
CUOCO. 1958. bi-m. L.6000 (free to qualified personnel). Federazione Italiana Cuochi - Italian Federation of Chefs, Via Monte di Pieta 1, 20121 Milan, Italy. TEL 2-804-468. Ed. Carlo Re. adv. circ. 12,000.

647.94 GW
D E H O G A JAHRESBERICHT. 1949. a. Deutscher Hotel- und Gaststaettenverband e.V., Kronprinzenstr. 46, 53173 Bonn, Germany. TEL 0228-820080. FAX 0228-8200846. **Document type**: trade publication.

647 GW
D G DAS HESSISCHE GASTGEWERBE. 1975. w. DM.102. Gastgewerbe Verlag, Postfach 1135, 4000 Duesseldorf 1, Germany. TEL 089-12607-0. Ed.Bd. bk.rev. circ. 32,120.

647.95 GW
D G DEUTSCHE GASTSTAETTE - DEUTSCHE HOTEL-ZEITUNG GASTWIRT UND HOTELIER; Fachzeitschrift fuer das gesamte Hotel- und Gaststaettenwesen. 1948. w. Gastgewerbe Verlag GmbH, 40196 Duesseldorf, Germany. TEL 0211-5050. Ed.Bd. adv.; bk.rev. circ. 44,455. **Document type**: trade publication.
 Incorporates: Deutsche Hotel Zeitung (ISSN 0012-0286); Gastgewerbe (ISSN 0046-547X); Gastwirt und Hotelier (ISSN 0016-5166)

642.5 AU
DACHSTEIN - TAUERN GAESTEZEITUNG. 1979. bi-m. Roseggerstr. 226, A-8970 Schladming, Austria. TEL 03687-23475. FAX 03687-22955. Ed. Wolfgang Pitzer. adv.; B&W page S.15000; trim 195 x 280. circ. 25,000. **Document type**: newsletter.

DAWSONS VENUE DIRECTORY. see TRAVEL AND TOURISM

647.94 UK
DE VERE HOTELS MAGAZINE. 1989. s-a. C P R Publishing, Northern Rock House, 20 Market Pl., Guisborough, Cleveland TS14 6HF, England. TEL 0287-639111. FAX 0287-637201. circ. 30,000 (controlled). **Document type**: trade publication.

642.5 UK ISSN 0144-655X
DINE OUT. 1980. 3/yr. £2.40. R. Engel Madison, Ed. & Pub., 314 Dukes Mews, London N10 2QF, England. adv.; bk.rev.; illus.

DIRECTORY OF CHAIN RESTAURANT OPERATORS (YEAR); includes: leading chain hotel companies operating foodservice units. see BUSINESS AND ECONOMICS — Trade And Industrial Directories

DIRECTORY OF HIGH VOLUME INDEPENDENT RESTAURANTS (YEAR). see BUSINESS AND ECONOMICS — Trade And Industrial Directories

647 US
DIRECTORY OF HOTEL AND MOTEL COMPANIES. a. $75. American Hotel and Motel Association, 1201 New York Ave., N.W., Washington, DC 20005-3917. TEL 202-289-3100. **Document type**: directory.
 Formerly: Directory of Hotel and Motel Systems.

647.94 SZ
EDEN. q. Schweizer Hotelier-Verein, Monbijoustr. 130, Postfach, CH-3001 Bern, Switzerland. TEL 031-462395. Ed. Stefan Sarbach. circ. 24,000.
 Formerly: Hotel Revue Special.

642.5 US
EMPIRE STATE FOOD SERVICE NEWS. 1975. m. $24. Wood Publishing, Box 89, Skaneateles, NY 13152. TEL 315-685-3300. Ed. J. Lee Wood. adv.; circ. 16,010 (controlled). **Document type**: trade publication.
 Description: Contains articles of interest to professionals in the food service industry in New York State.

642.5 CN
ENJOY. 1987. bi-m. Plymouth Publications, Inc., 1685 Inglewood Ave., Burnaby, B.C. V5C 4L8, Canada. TEL 604-294-8310. Ed. Jan Paskett.

647.95 US
EPICUREAN RENDEZVOUS.* a. Epicurean Rendezvous, Inc., 75 Howell Ave., Larchmont, NY 10538-3227. TEL 415-777-2676. adv.: B&W or color page $38120.

642.5 910.202 US ISSN 0895-738X
EPICUREAN REVUE; a confidential gastronomical & tourism letter. 1983. m. $79. Epicurean Revue, Inc., 4619 Higel Ave., Box 35128, Sarasota, FL 34242. TEL 813-346-2224. FAX 8130349-4370. TELEX 71-650-244-7440. Eds. Jean Noel, Georges Prade. bk.rev. circ. 9,836. (looseleaf format; back issues avail.) **Document type**: newsletter.

647.94 647.95 PO
EQUIPOTEL; revista de industria do turismo. 1971. 4/yr. Esc.1100($20) Publiotel Ltd., Rua Marechal Saldanha, 4-1o, 1200 Lisbon, Portugal. TEL 35113475201. FAX 3511327718. TELEX 3460045. Ed. Delmiro Santos. adv. circ. 6,500.
 Description: Covers food and beverage, equipment, design and management.

ESPANA HOSTELERA Y TURISTICA. see TRAVEL AND TOURISM

647.95 SP
EUROBUILDING 2. 52/yr. Editorial J.S. Publicaciones Especiales, Santa Susana 55, 5o 1 y 2, 28033 Madrid, Spain. TEL 1-763-34-01. adv.: B&W page 60000 ptas., color page 90000 ptas.; trim 258 x 185.

642.5 US
▼**EUROPEAN GOURMET**;* the grand dining tour of Europe. 1992. a. $22.95 (effective 1992). (American Airlines) European Gourmet, Ltd., 331 W. 57th St., No. 379, New York, NY 10019-3101. TEL 800-523-5503. Ed. Douglas Easton. illus. circ. 100,000.
 Description: In-depth reviews of more than 200 selected restaurants in Western Europe, for up-scale travellers.

647.94 658.8 UK ISSN 0967-361X
▼**EUROPEAN HOTEL AND CATERING MARKETING DIRECTORY**. 1992. irreg. £160($335) Euromonitor, 87-88 Turnmill St., London EC1M 5QU, England. TEL 071-251-8024. FAX 071-608-3149. (Addr. in N. America: Euromonitor International, 111 W. Washington St., Ste. 920, Chicago, IL 60602. TEL 312-541-8024. FAX 312-541-1567) stat. **Document type**: directory.
 Description: Analyzes marketing trends in the European hotel and catering industry.

647.93 SP
EUROSUITES. (Text in English, Spanish) s-a. Editorial J.S. Publicaciones Especiales, Santa Susana 55, 5o 1 y 2, 28033 Madrid, Spain. TEL 1-7633401. adv.: B&W page 60000 ptas., color page 90000 ptas.; trim 258 x 185.

EXECUTIVE HOUSEKEEPING TODAY. see OCCUPATIONAL HEALTH AND SAFETY

647.95 US
F E D A NEWS & VIEWS. bi-m. Foodservice Equipment Distributors Association, 332 S. Michigan Ave., Chicago, IL 60604-4301. TEL 312-427-9605. FAX 312-427-9607. Ed. Ray Herrick. adv. circ. 1,100.

647.9 US ISSN 0739-7011
TX901
F I U HOSPITALITY REVIEW. 1983. s-a. $10. Florida International University, North Miami Campus, 151st St. and Biscayne Blvd., North Miami, FL 33181. TEL 305-948-4500. Ed. William O'Brien. **Document type**: academic/scholarly publication.
—BLDSC (3948.449700).

647.94 SZ
FERIENBOTE. q. Schweizerische Verein fuer Familienherbergen, Poststr. 1, CH-4460 Gelterkinden, Switzerland. TEL 991747.

674.94 UK
FINANCIAL SURVEY COMPANY DATA FOR SUCCESS. HOTELS & LEISURE COMPLEXES. a. I C C Financial Surveys Ltd., Field House, 72 Oldfield Rd., Hampton, Middlesex TW12 2HQ, England. TEL 081-783-0977. FAX 081-783-1940.
 Formerly (until 1991): Financial Survey Company Directory. Hotels and Leisure Complexes (ISSN 0952-1259)

HOTELS AND RESTAURANTS

647.9   UK   ISSN 0308-8464
TX907
FINANCIAL TIMES INTERNATIONAL YEAR BOOKS: WORLD HOTEL DIRECTORY. 1975. a. £96. Longman Group UK Ltd., Westgate House, 6th Fl., The High, Harlow, Essex CM20 1YR, England. TEL 0279-442601. FAX 0279-444501. adv.: B&W page £575, color page £870; 202 x 154. **Document type:** directory.
—BLDSC (3927.035700). **CCC.**

647.94   GW   ISSN 0939-8414
FIRST CLASS; Fachmagazin fuer Hotels und Restaurants. 1983. m. DM.76 (foreign DM.96). Gildefachverlag GmbH & Co. KG, Postfach 1351, 31043 Alfeld, Germany. TEL 05181-80040. Ed. Susanne Stauss. circ. 12,114. **Document type:** trade publication.

647.94   US   ISSN 8750-6807
FLORIDA HOTEL & MOTEL JOURNAL. 1978. m. $24 (foreign $30). (Florida Hotel & Motel Association) Accommodations, Inc., 200 W. College Ave., Box 1529, Tallahassee, FL 32302. TEL 904-224-2888. FAX 904-222-3462. Ed. Jayleen Woods. adv.; bk.rev.; charts; illus.; pat.; stat. circ. 6,700. **Document type:** trade publication.
  Formerly (until Jan. 1985): Florida Hotel and Motel News (ISSN 0192-3498)
  Description: Provides management advice to hotel owners and managers.

642.47   NZ
FOOD AND BEVERAGE; hotels, motels, restaurants, industrial canteens, clubs, institutions, fast food. Short title: F & B. 1965. m. NZ.$60. T.P.L. Media (Trade Publications), 308 Great South Rd., 1st Fl., Greenlane, Auckland, New Zealand. TEL 0064-09-529-3000. FAX 0064-09-529-3001. (Dist. addr.: P.O. Box 9596, Newmarket, Auckland, New Zealand) Ed. Karry Tyack. adv.: B&W page NZ.$1495, color page NZ.$1950; trim 297 x 210; adv. contact: Fay Murray. bk.rev.; illus. circ. 9,000. **Indexed:** Art.Hosp.& Tour., Food Sci.& Tech.Abstr. **Document type:** trade publication.
  Former titles: Catering and Accomodation Management (ISSN 0113-2326); Pacific Catering and Accomodation Management (ISSN 0112-7144)
  Description: Features news and information from a wide range of hospitality industry professional associatons and liquor.

647.94   SZ
FOOD & BEVERAGE. 1898. 6/yr. 69 SFr. Societe Suisse des Cuisiniers, Adligenswilenstr. 22, CH-6002 Lucerne, Switzerland. TEL 041-592460. FAX 041-592471. **Document type:** trade publication.
  Formerly: Hotellerie.

642.5   US   ISSN 0891-0154
FOOD & SERVICE. 1940. 11/yr. $175 membership. Texas Restaurant Association, 1400 Lavaca St., Austin, TX 78701. TEL 512-472-3666; 800-395-2872. Ed. Julie Stephen Sherrier. adv.; bk.rev.; illus.; tr.lit.; index. circ. 5,600.
  Former titles: Texas Food and Service News; Chuck Wagon (ISSN 0009-6210)
  Description: Examines fast food trends, employee relations, management for foodservice business, Texas foodservice news, government legislation and service education. Includes marketplace items.

647.95   US   ISSN 1042-9123
TX945   CODEN: FOARE6
FOOD ARTS; the magazine for professionals. 1988. m. $30 (free to qualified personnel). M. Shanken Communications, Inc., 387 Park Ave. S., New York, NY 10016. TEL 212-684-4224. FAX 212-684-5424. TELEX 422687 MSHANK UI. circ. 51,968. (back issues avail.)
  Description: Deals with national and international trends in the restaurant industry.

FOOD INDUSTRY NEWS. see *FOOD AND FOOD INDUSTRIES — Grocery Trade*

642.5   US   ISSN 1062-0192
THE FOOD PAPER. (In 2 eds.: Los Angeles and San Francisco) 1991. q. $12. Gault Millau Inc., 5900 Wilshire Blvd., Ste. 590, Los Angeles, CA 90036. TEL 213-965-3529. FAX 213-936-2883. (Editorial addr.: 555 Fulton St., Ste. 215, San Francisco, CA 94102. TEL 415-552-4664) Ed. Andre Gayot. circ. 100,000 each edition. **Document type:** consumer publication.
  Description: Contains articles on food and wine.

647.95   642.5   JA
FOOD SERVICE MANAGEMENT/GEKKAN SYOKUDO. 1951. m. Shibata Publishing Co., 3-33-5 Hongo, Bunkyo-ku, Tokyo, Japan. Ed. Muneaki Ikdea. adv. circ. 80,000.

647.9   CN   ISSN 0007-8972
FOODSERVICE AND HOSPITALITY; Canada's hospitality business magazine. (Text in English) 1968. m. Can.$45 (foreign Can.$60). Kostuch Communications Ltd., 980 Yonge St., Ste. 400, Toronto, ON M4W 2J8, Canada. TEL 416-923-8888. FAX 416-923-6114. Ed. Rosanna Caira. adv.; bk.rev.; charts; illus.; stat. circ. 25,000. **Indexed:** Can.B.P.I. **Document type:** trade publication.
—**CCC.**
  Formerly: C R A Magazine.

647.9   US   ISSN 0885-6877
FOODSERVICE EAST. 1926. 7/yr. $20 (effective Jan. 1992). Newbury Street Group, Inc., 76 Summer St., Boston, MA 02110. TEL 617-695-9080. Ed. Susan Holaday; Pub. Richard E. Dolby. adv.; circ. 25,000. (controlled). **Document type:** trade publication.
  Former titles (until vol.60, no.3): Lodging and Food Service East; Lodging and Food Service News (ISSN 0024-5755); Hotel and Restaurant News.

642.5   US   ISSN 0888-8515
FOODSERVICE EQUIPMENT & SUPPLIES SPECIALIST. 1947. m. $69.95 (Canada $114.95; Mexico $107.95; elsewhere $129.95). Cahners Publishing Company (Des Plaines), Division of Reed Elsevier Inc., 1350 E. Touhy Ave., Box 5080, Des Plaines, IL 60017-5080. TEL 708-635-8800. FAX 708-635-6856. (Subscr. to: 44 Cook St., Denver, CO 80206. TEL 800-662-7776) Ed. Gregory Richards. adv.; bk.rev. circ. 22,116.
—UnCover; UMI. **CCC.**
  Former titles: Foodservice Equipment Specialist (ISSN 0148-4958); Foodservice Equipment Dealer.
  Description: For buyers, specifiers and distributors of equipment and supplies for commercial and institutional use. Includes new products, kitchen design and decor, distribution, sales and marketing.

642.5 664   US   ISSN 0199-7696
FOODSERVICE PRODUCT NEWS.* 1967. 12/yr. $36 (free to qualified food service operators)(effective 1992). Young - Conway Publications, 1101 Richmond Ave., Ste. 201, Point Pleasant Beach, NJ 08742-3049. Ed. Judy Young. adv.; bk.rev.; illus.; tr.lit.; circ. 132,000 (controlled). (tabloid format)
  Formerly (until 1980): Food and Equipment Product News (ISSN 0015-6280)
  Description: Covers manufacturer services and new products and literature for the foodservice market.

642.5   UK
FORTE NEWS. 1974. m. Prescom Publications, 90 High St., Harrow-on-the-Hill, Harrow, Middlesex HA1 3LP, England. TEL 081-422-2040. FAX 081-423-4230. Ed. Tam McDonald. circ. 35,000. **Document type:** newspaper.

642.5   GW   ISSN 0015-9964
FRANKFURTER GASTRONOMIE. 1962. m. membership. (Hotel- und Gaststaetten-Vereinigung Frankfurt am Main e.V.) Verlag Bodet & Partner, Speyererstr. 2-4, 60327 Frankfurt a.M., Germany. TEL 069-730536. FAX 069-735536. Ed. C. H. Bodet. bk.rev. circ. 3,000.

647.94   GW
G H GASTROTEL; Unabhaengiges Fachmagazin fuer Unternehmer und Manager in Hotellerie und Gastronomie. 1985. m. DM.12. G W Verlag GmbH, Zeughausstr. 28-38, 50667 Cologne, Germany. TEL 0221-120242. circ. 107,000. **Document type:** trade publication.

642.5   GW
GAST UND KUECHE. 1991. bi-m. DM.19.85 (foreign DM.20.95). Deutscher Fachverlag GmbH, Mainzer Landst. 251, 60326 Frankfurt a.M., Germany. TEL 069-7595-01. FAX 069-77-5952999. circ. 15,000. **Document type:** trade publication.
  Formerly (until 1993): Imbiss.

647.94   AU
GASTEIN AKTUELL INTERESSENGEMEINSCHAFT. 9/yr. Gasteinertal, A-5630 Bad Hofgastein, Austria. TEL 6432-64820. Ed. Sissi Graf. circ. 6,600.

647.94   GW
GASTGEWERBE. 1947. w. DM.211.20. Gastgewerbe Verlag GmbH, 40196 Duesseldorf, Germany. TEL 0211-5050. Ed. Wolfgang Habedank. index. **Document type:** trade publication.

642.5   SZ
GASTRO MANAGEMENT. (Text in French, German) 1961. m. Hohmadstr. 14, Postfach 1180, CH-3601 Thun, Switzerland. TEL 033-233609. FAX 033-233145. Ed. Hanspeter Frey. circ. 38,386. **Document type:** trade publication.

647.95
GASTRO SHOW; Zeitschrift fuer junge Leute in der Gastronomie. 1991. q. DM.36. Sisu Steinschulte Verlag, Bismarckallee 10, 53173 Bonn, Germany. TEL 0228-361063. FAX 0228-351130. circ. 50,000. **Document type:** trade publication.

642.5   GW   ISSN 0323-4762
GASTRONOMIE; Fachzeitschrift fuer Restaurant, Kueche und Hotel. 1970. m. DM.14. Verlag Die Wirtschaft GmbH, Am Friedrichshain 22, 10407 Berlin, Germany. TEL 030-4287464. FAX 030-4287234. Ed. Heidi Reinhardt. adv.; bk.rev. **Document type:** trade publication.

642.5   GW   ISSN 0936-5397
GASTRONOMIE UND HOTEL IMPULSE. 1979. 10/yr. DM.70. (Brillat Savarin-Stiftung) Melcher Verlag GmbH, Im Breitspiel 11, 69126 Heidelberg, Germany. Ed. Arne Krueger. circ. 15,000. **Document type:** trade publication.
  Formerly (until 1988): Gastronomie Impulse (ISSN 0720-3853)
  Description: News for hotel and restaurant management, training courses for cooks.

642.5   GW   ISSN 0016-5158
GASTWIRT. 1966. q. DM.48($20) Zeitungs- und Zeitschriftenverlag Heinrichs, Brueggekamp 1, 30890 Barsinghausen, Germany. TEL 05105-2289. Ed. G. Heinrichs. adv.; bk.rev.; charts; stat.; tr.lit. circ. 4,950. (tabloid format) **Document type:** trade publication.

642.5   AU
GASTWIRT - HOTELIER - CAFETIER. m. S.920. Zeitungsverlag Kuhn and Co. GmbH, Kutschkergasse 42, A-1180 Vienna, Austria. TEL 01-47686. FAX 01-4768621. Ed. Otto Hartmann. adv.: B&W page S.39000, color page S.55000; trim 255 x 185; adv. contact: Reinhard Furcht. circ. 20,600. **Document type:** trade publication.

647.94   GW
GAULT MILLAU GUIDE DEUTSCHLAND. 1983. a. DM.52. Wilhelm Heyne Verlag, Tuerkenstr. 5-7, 80333 Munich, Germany. TEL 089-231717-0. FAX 089-2800943. Ed. Johannes Heyne. (back issues avail.) **Document type:** consumer publication.

GAULT - MILLAU MAGAZINE. see *TRAVEL AND TOURISM*

647.9   FR
GAZETTE HOTELIERE. 1904. m. 10 place Gutenberg, 67000 Strasbourg, France. TEL 88-32-00-68. Ed. Andre Fahrer. adv. circ. 4,700.

642.5   SZ
GIORNALE ESERCENTI ALBERGATORI TICINO. 25/yr. Via Gemmo 11, CH-6900 Lugano, Switzerland. TEL 091-561751. FAX 091-563243. circ. 2,567.

647.94   CN   ISSN 0705-7520
GITE. (Text in French) 6/yr. P.O. Box 67, St. Joseph, Beauce, Que. G0S 2V0, Canada. adv.

647.94   UK
GOFF'S GUIDE TO MOTELS AND MOTORWAYS IN GREAT BRITAIN AND IRELAND.* 1963. a. Eastern Counties Newspaper Ltd., Rm. 120, Temple Chambers, Temple Ave., London EC4Y 0DT, England. Ed. R. De Young. adv. circ. 30,000.
  Formerly: Goff's Guide to Motels in Great Britain and Europe (ISSN 0072-4890)

642.5 664 663.2   IT
LA GOLA. 1991. 10/yr. L.90000 (foreign L.110000). Nibbio Italia s.r.l., Via Torino 46, 20123 Milan, Italy. TEL 02-72010241. Ed. Alberto Capatti. adv.

HOTELS AND RESTAURANTS

647.95   UK   ISSN 0072-5005
THE GOOD FOOD GUIDE. 1951. a. £14.95. Consumers' Association, 2 Marylebone Rd., London NW1 4DF, England. TEL 071-830-6000. FAX 071-830-6220. (Orders to: Consumers' Association, Castlemead, Gascoyne Way, Hertford SG14 1LH, England) Ed. Tom Jaine. circ. 60,000. (also avail. in microfiche)

647.94   SI
GOODWOOD JOURNAL. 1975. q. free. (Goodwood Park Hotel Limited) Couture Publishing Pte. Ltd., 809 French Rd., No. 07-164, Singapore 0820, Singapore. TEL 293-0268. FAX 293-4270. Ed. Colin Smith. adv. circ. 14,000. **Document type:** consumer publication.

647.9   NE   ISSN 0017-2529
GOUDEN SLEUTELS.* bi-m. Nederlandse Hotelportiers Vereniging, Postbus 10571, Amsterdam, Netherlands. Ed. J. Kilkens. adv.; illus.

642.5   SZ
GOURMET. m. Walchstr. 35, CH-3073 Guemligen, Switzerland. Ed. Rene Frech. circ. 22,000. **Document type:** consumer publication.

642.57 910.09   SP
GOURMETOUR; gastronomy & tourist guide. 1979. a. 3100 ptas.($20) Club G., S.A., Cuesta San Vicente, 4-6a, 28008 Madrid, Spain. TEL 91-542-76-60. FAX 91-542-45-75. Ed. Francisco Lopez Canis. adv.; bk.rev.; bibl. circ. 50,000. (back issues avail.) **Description:** Monuments, museums, restaurants, hotels, bars, discoteques and specialized shops.

642.5 663.2   SP
GRAN RESERVA; revista del buen vivir. 1986. 11/yr. 5000 ptas. (foreign 8000 ptas.) (effective 1993). Servivi, S.A., Almirante 15, 28004 Madrid, Spain. TEL 1-521-40-49. FAX 1-521-11-97. Ed. Pilar Molestina. adv.: B&W page 250000 ptas., color page 305000 ptas.; 285 x 420; adv. contact: Rafael Fonseca. bk.rev.; circ. 25,000 (controlled). **Description:** Covers gastronomy and oenology as important aspects of culture and society. Includes current events, anthropology, travel, leisure and music.

642.5   IT
GRAND GOURMET. 4/yr. L.44500. Elemond Periodici s.r.l., Via D. Trentacoste, 7, 20134 Milan, Italy. TEL 02-215631. FAX 02-26410847. Ed. Enrico Guagnini. circ. 34,000.

642.47   FR   ISSN 0985-1461
GRANDES CUISINES. 4/yr. 650 F. (foreign 920 F.). Editions Max Brezol, 9 rue Labie, 75838 Paris, France. TEL 45-74-21-62. FAX 45-74-01-03. Ed. Georges Golan. circ. 3,000.

642.5   UK   ISSN 0960-247X
GREAT HOSPITALITY. 1990. 4/yr. £18. London House, 19 Old Court Pl., London W8 4PF, England. TEL 071-938-2222. FAX 071-937-7293. Ed. Ian Fairservice. adv.; bk.rev. circ. 25,000. **Document type:** trade publication.

642.5   US
GREATER BOSTON RESTAURANT GUIDE.* 1983. a. Greater Boston Publishing, Inc., 550 Cochituate Rd., CC East, Framingham, MA 01701-4600. TEL 617-933-7100. Ed. Sandy Cohen. adv. circ. 110,000.

GREENSCENE; the only magazine for young vegetarians. see *NUTRITION AND DIETETICS*

647.94   GW
GUT SPEISEN UND REISEN. 1979. m. (Tourotel - Germany) Verlag Laterna Magica GmbH & Co. (Subsidiary of: Weinerwald Holding AG), Stridbeckstr. 48, 8000 Munich 71, Germany. Ed. Frederick Jahn. adv. circ. 270,000.

647.9   LU
H O R E S C A - INFORMATIONS. (Text in French and German) 1984. m. 1200 Fr. Federation Nationale des Hoteliers, Restaurateurs et Cafetiers du Grand-Duche de Luxembourg, 9 rue des Trevires, B.P. 2524, L-1025 Luxembourg, Luxembourg. TEL 487165. FAX 487156. Ed. Philippe Eschenauer. adv. contact: Jean Thielen. bk.rev. circ. 6,000. **Description:** Covers the hotel and restaurant trade, including tourism and gastronomy.

H S M A I MARKETING REVIEW. (Hospitality Sales and Marketing Association International) see *BUSINESS AND ECONOMICS — Marketing And Purchasing*

HANDELSHOCHSCHULE LEIPZIG. WISSENSCHAFTLICHE ZEITSCHRIFT. see *BUSINESS AND ECONOMICS*

647.94   II   ISSN 0073-0386
HARDY'S ENCYCLOPAEDIA HOTELS OF INDIA AND NEPAL.* (Text in English) 1964. a. price varies. Hardy & Ally, 8-44 Regal Bldg., Box 184, Connaught Place, New Delhi 1, India. Ed. K. N. Malhotra.

647.94   GW
HAUS ECHO. 1956. 4/yr. free. (Park Hotel Bremen) Kunstverlag Krebs & Co., Am Markt 11, 28195 Bremen, Germany. Ed. K.H. Krebs. adv. circ. 5,000.

HEALTH AND WELFARE LIBRARIES QUARTERLY. see *LIBRARY AND INFORMATION SCIENCES*

919.4   AT   ISSN 0085-1485
HERALD MOTEL GUIDE. 1965. a. Aus.$1. Herald Travel Bureau, Newspaper House, 247 Collins St., Melbourne, Vic. 3000, Australia. Ed. D.H. Day.

647.94   CK
HILTON COLOMBIA. 1985. 3/yr. Emiro Aristizabal, Pub., Av. 32, no. 14-16, Bogota, Colombia. TEL 245-4757. TELEX 45299 PANIB CO. Ed. Maria de Abello. circ. 25,000.

647.94   GR
HILTON GREECE. 1965. m. (Hilton Hotels - Athens) Vitos International, 16 Anapiron Polemou St., Athens, Greece. Ed. George Vitos. adv.

647.94   NE
HILTON - HOLLAND LIFE. (Text in English) m. (Hilton Hotels - Netherlands) Delta Publicity International Publications BV, Keizergracht 255, 1016 EB Amsterdam, Netherlands. Ed. Victor Thorne. adv. circ. 16,250.

647   UK
HILTON INTERNATIONAL (U.K.) MAGAZINE. 1963. q. International Court, 2-3 Rhodes Way, Watford, Herts WD2 4WY, England. adv.; bk.rev.; film rev.; play rev.; illus. circ. 50,000.
Formerly (until 1982): Stratford-Upon-Avon Hilton Magazine; Supersedes (in 1981): London Hilton Magazine (ISSN 0024-6042)

HOLIDAY. see *TRAVEL AND TOURISM*

647.9   GW   ISSN 0931-5179
HOLIDAY INN LIVE. 1987. s-a. (Holiday Inns (Germany) Inc.) E R M I Guide Orschel KG, Malvenweg 4, 51061 Cologne, Germany. TEL 0221-634091. FAX 0221-634677. **Document type:** trade publication.

647.9   NE   ISSN 0169-1325
HORECA. 1942. w. fl.181. Uitgeversmaatschappij C. Misset B. V., Hanzestr. 1, 7006 RH Doetinchem, Netherlands. TEL 31-8340-49911. FAX 31-8340-43839. TELEX 45481. (Subscr. to: Postbus 4, 7000 BA Doetinchem, Netherlands) Ed. R. Deutekom. adv.: B&W page fl.3765, color page fl.6410; trim 215 x 285; adv. contact: Cor van Nek. bk.rev.; charts; illus. circ. 19,850. **Indexed:** Key to Econ.Sci. **Document type:** trade publication.
Former titles: Missets Horeca (ISSN 0026-5950); Horeca (1942) (ISSN 0165-2893)
Description: Covers the entire catering industry.

HORECA NEWS (BRUSSELS, 1971); hotels - restaurants - cafes - traiteurs - fast food - night-club - collectives. see *FOOD AND FOOD INDUSTRIES*

647   SP
HORECO; revista mensual para hoteles, restaurantes, cafeterias y colectividades. 1984. m. 12500 ptas. (effective 1994). Grupo Arte y Cemento, S.A., C. Zancoeta, 9, 5 y 7, 48013 Bilbao, Spain. TEL 344-441-0766. FAX 344-441-9590. Ed. Ignacio Echevarria. adv. circ. 12,500. **Document type:** trade publication.

642   LU
HORESCA - INFORMATIONS. 1984. m. 1200 Fr. 9 rue des Trevires, B.P. 2524, L-1025 Luxembourg, Luxembourg. TEL 48-71-65. FAX 48-71-56. Ed. Philippe Eschenauer. adv. **Document type:** consumer publication.
Description: Covers the hotel trade, tourism and gastronomy.

647.94   CN   ISSN 0704-6359
L'HOSPITALITE. (Text in French) 1977. 6/yr. Can.$32 (foreign Can.$68). Communications Vero Inc., 1600 Henri-Bourassa W., Ste. 420, Montreal, PQ H3M 3E2, Canada. TEL 514-332-8376. FAX 514-332-2666. Ed. Francoise Pitt. adv. circ. 15,219.

647.9   UK   ISSN 0144-3704
HOSPITALITY. 1972. m. £23 (foreign £32)(effective 1992). Hotel Catering & Institutional Management Association, 191 Trinity Road, London, SW17 7HN, England. TEL 081-672-4251. FAX 081-682-1707. Ed. Alan Sutton. adv.; bk.rev.; charts; illus.; stat.; index. circ. 21,312. **Indexed:** Art.Hosp.& Tour., Food Sci.& Tech.Abstr. **Document type:** trade publication. —BLDSC (4333.243000).
Formerly (until Jan. 1980): H C I M A Journal; Which was formed by the merger of: H C I Journal (ISSN 0017-6141); Institutional Management (ISSN 0020-3602)
Description: Topics of interest to managers in the hotel and catering industry in the U.K. and, occasionally, elsewhere.

HOSPITALITY. see *FOOD AND FOOD INDUSTRIES — Bakers And Confectioners*

642.47   NZ
HOSPITALITY. 11/yr. (plus a. cumulation). NZ.$60 (including annual directory). T.P.L. Media (Trade Publications), 308 Great South Rd., 1st Fl., Greenlane, Auckland, New Zealand. TEL 0064-09-529-300. FAX 0064-09-529-3001. Ed. Malcom Wall. adv.: B&W page NZ.$1495, color NZ.$2085; trim 297 x 210; adv. contact: Deborah Cobb. **Document type:** trade publication.
Description: Encompasses news and views of restaurants and hotels, food catering, tourism, industry training. Features personality profiles, marketing and better operational articles.

HOSPITALITY & TOURISM EDUCATOR. see *EDUCATION — Adult Education*

HOSPITALITY DESIGN. see *INTERIOR DESIGN AND DECORATION*

647.9   AT
HOSPITALITY FOODSERVICE; national monthly newspaper of the accommodation, food service and convention industries. 1967. m. $65. Peter Isaacson Publications Pty. Ltd., 45-50 Porter St., Prahran, Vic. 3181, Australia. TEL 03-245-7777. FAX 03-245-7606. Ed. Ian Ross. adv.; bk.rev.; charts; illus. circ. 13,933. (tabloid format)
Former titles: Hospitality and Convention News; Hospitality (ISSN 0018-5949)

647.9   AT
HOSPITALITY GAZETTE OF SOUTH AUSTRALIA. 1930. m. Aus.$50. Hotel & Hospitality Industry Association, 4th Fl., 60 Hindmarsh Sq., Adelaide, S.A. 5000, Australia. FAX 08-232-4979. Ed. R.G. Acott. adv.; illus.; tr.lit. circ. 1,400.
Formerly: Hotel Gazette of South Australia (ISSN 0018-6139)

650 640   AT   ISSN 0817-0398
HOSPITALITY INDUSTRY SUPPLIERS INDEX. a. $45. Peter Isaacson Publications Pty. Ltd., 45-50 Porter St., Prahran, Vic. 3181, Australia. TEL 03-245-7777. FAX 03-245-7606.
Former titles: Hospitality Buyers Guide (ISSN 0156-3688); Hospitality Buyers Guide and Diary (ISSN 0314-1551); Hospitality Yearbook (ISSN 0311-2969)

647.94   US   ISSN 0889-5414
KF2042.H6
HOSPITALITY LAW; the preventive-law information service for the lodging industry. 1986. m. $197. Magna Publications, Inc., 2718 Dryden Dr., Madison, WI 53704. TEL 608-246-3580; 800-433-0499. FAX 608-246-3597. Ed. Mike McGreevy; Pub. Karen Stocker. bk.rev.; stat. circ. 1,200. (back issues avail.) **Document type:** newsletter. —CCC.
Description: Helps lodging managers understand the legal environment and reduce their risk of going to court. Covers legal issues and key cases.

658.91 US
HOSPITALITY MANAGEMENT. 1981. bi-m. $18. Delmont Communications, Inc., 1700 Livingston Ave., St. Paul, MN 55118. TEL 612-457-2289. FAX 612-457-7787. Ed. Joe Delmont. adv. circ. 11,500.
  Formerly (until 1990): Hospitality Scene.

380 642.5
HOSPITALITY MANAGER. 1985. m. $21. Kassis Communications, 120 Hayward, Ames, IA 50010. TEL 515-296-2400. Ed. Terry Lowman. circ. 10,000. (tabloid format) **Document type:** trade publication.

658.91 US
TX911.3.M27
HOSPITALITY RESEARCH JOURNAL. 1976. 3/yr. $50. Council on Hotel, Restaurant and Institutional Education, 1200 17th St., N.W., Washington, DC 20036-3097. TEL 202-331-5990. FAX 202-785-2511. Eds. Carolyn Lambert, Carl Reigel. bk.rev.; charts; illus.; stat. circ. 1,300. (back issues avail.) **Indexed:** Art.Hosp.& Tour.
—Faxon.
  Former titles: Hospitality Education and Research Journal (ISSN 0741-5095); Journal of Hospitality Education.
  Description: Contains articles related to hospitality, tourism, education and research.

HOSPITALITY WORLD. see JOURNALISM

647.94 SP
HOSTELERIA (YEAR). 12/yr. free. Asociacion de Empresarios de Hosteleria de Navarra, Perdo l, 1, 1o, 31007 Pamplona, Spain. TEL 948-26-84-12. FAX 948-17-25-56. Ed. Jorge Sauleda. adv.: B&W page 42900 ptas., color page 55000 ptas. circ. 2,500. **Document type:** trade publication.

647.94 SP
HOSTELERIA VALLISOLETANA. 6/yr. Plaza de la Universidad 4, bajo, 47002 Valladolid, Spain. TEL 39-12-77. Ed. J. Rubio Velasco.

647.94 SP
HOTEL. 12/yr. Segrimi S.A., Trav. de Gracia 18, 1o 4o, 08021 Barcelona, Spain. TEL 3-209-98-00. FAX 3-202-32-06. Ed. R. Grifoll Oliva.

642.47 IE
HOTEL AND CATERING REVIEW. m. £20. 22 Brookfield Ave., Blackrock, Co. Dublin, Ireland. TEL 886946. FAX 881098. (Subscr. to: P.O. Box 1973, Rathmines, Dublin 6, Ireland) Ed. Frank Corr. adv.: bk.rev. circ. 3,215. **Indexed:** Art.Hosp.& Tour.
  Formerly: Irish Catering Review (ISSN 0021-1095)

647.9 US ISSN 0018-6082
TX911.3.M27
HOTEL AND MOTEL MANAGEMENT. 1875. 21/yr. $35. Advanstar Communications, Inc., 7500 Old Oak Blvd., Cleveland, OH 44130. TEL 216-826-2839. FAX 216-891-2675. (Subscr. to: 131 W. First St., Duluth, MN 55802. TEL 800-346-0085) Ed. Robert A. Nozar. adv.; bk.rev.; charts; illus.; stat.; tr.lit.; index. circ. 45,613. (tabloid format; also avail. in microform) **Indexed:** Account.Ind. (1974-), Art.Hosp.& Tour., B.P.I., Bus.Ind., Tr.& Indus.Ind. **Document type:** trade publication.
●Also available online. Vendor(s): DIALOG Information Services, Inc.
—BLDSC (4333.570000); UnCover; SWETS; UMI. CCC.
  Incorporates: Motor Inn Journal (ISSN 0164-5617)
  Description: Covers marketing hotel and hotel services: lodging, food, beverages, meeting facilities. News about new products, business management, security and investor outlooks.

647.9 US
▼**HOTEL AND MOTEL MANAGEMENT - INTERNATIONAL EDITION;** newspaper for the international hospitality industry. (In 3 regional eds.: Europe, Africa, Middle East; Caribbean, Latin America; Asia, Pacific) 1992. 15/yr. $75 per region (foreign $90); all 3 regions $200 (foreign $240). Advanstar Communications, Inc., 7500 Old Oak Blvd., Cleveland, OH 44130. TEL 216-243-8100. FAX 216-891-2726. (Subscr. to: 1313 W. First St., Duluth, MN 55802. TEL 218-723-9477) adv.: B&W page $11490; trim 10 7/8 x 15. circ. 68,000. (tabloid format) **Document type:** newspaper, trade publication.
  Description: Reports current news and analyzes business trends affecting the industry throughout the world.

647.94 US ISSN 0073-3490
TX907
HOTEL AND MOTEL RED BOOK.* 1886. a. $59. American Hotel and Motel Association, 1201 New York Ave., N.W., Washington, DC 20005. Ed. Valerie A. Dow. circ. 75,000.

647.94 US ISSN 0149-3639
HOTEL & RESORT INDUSTRY. 1978. m. $50. Coastal Communications Corporation, 488 Madison Ave., New York, NY 10022. TEL 212-888-1500. FAX 212-888-8008. Ed. Stefani O'Connor. adv.; circ. 50,175 (controlled). **Document type:** trade publication.

642.5 UK
HOTEL & RESTAURANT MAGAZINE. 10/yr. £30 (foreign £60). Quantum Publishing Ltd., 29-31 Lower Coombe St., Croydon, Surrey CR9 1LX, England. TEL 081-681-2099. FAX 081-680-8828. Ed. Mark Hayes. adv.: B&W page £1600, color page £2400; trim 297 x 210. circ. 25,251. **Indexed:** Art.Hosp.& Tour. **Document type:** trade publication.
  Formed by 1992 merger of: Hotel Management (ISSN 0959-5414) & Restaurant Magazine.

647.9 910.2 US ISSN 0162-9972
CODEN: HTINDM
HOTEL AND TRAVEL INDEX; the world wide hotel directory. 1939. q. $89 (Canada $95; Central & S. America $150; elsewhere $299). Reed Travel Group, Part of the Reed Elsevier group (Subsidiary of: Reed Telepublishing), 500 Plaza Dr., Secaucus, NJ 07096. TEL 201-902-1600. FAX 201-319-1628. Ed. Roberta Bianchi. adv.; bk.rev.; illus. circ. 71,000. **Document type:** directory.
—CASDDS.
  Formerly: Travel Index.

647.94 US
HOTEL & TRAVEL INDEX - A B C INTERNATIONAL EDITION. 1941. q. $125 in Europe, Asia, Australia & Africa; elsewhere $299. Reed Travel Group, Part of the Reed Elsevier group (Subsidiary of: Reed Telepublishing), 500 Plaza Dr., Secaucus, NJ 07096. TEL 201-902-1600. FAX 201-319-1628. (UK addr.: Church St., Dunstable, Bedfordshire LU5 4HB, England. TEL 0582-600111) Ed. Lesley Krautheim. adv. circ. 62,000.
  Supersedes (in 1991): A B C Worldwide Hotel Guide; **Former titles (until 1985):** A - Z Worldwide Hotel Guide; A B C Hotel Guide (ISSN 0141-6251)

647.94 US
▼**HOTEL BUSINESS.** 1992. m. $25. I C D Publications, 1393 Veterans Hwy., Ste. 116 N., Hauppauge, NY 11788. TEL 516-979-7878. Ed. Peter Rameo. adv.: B&W page $6900. circ. 45,000 (controlled). (tabloid format)
  Description: Focuses on industry-related issues, such as legislation, analyses of statistics and finances.

647.94 IT
HOTEL BUSINESS AND MANAGEMENT. bi-m. Agepe s.r.l., Via Domenico Trentacoste, 9, 20134 Milan, Italy. TEL 02-215621. FAX 02-2640330. TELEX 351491. adv.: B&W page L.7000000, color page L.12600000; trim 237 x 347. circ. 43,163. **Document type:** trade publication.

647.94 IT ISSN 1121-0001
HOTEL DOMANI. 1973. m. L.70000 (foreign L.180000) (effective 1994). Tecniche Nuove s.p.a., Via C. Menotti, 14, 20129 Milan, Italy. TEL 02-75701. FAX 02-7610351. adv.: B&W page L.4400000, color page L.4400000; trim 210 x 297.

647.93 SP
HOTEL EMPERADOR. (Text in English, Spanish) s-a. Editorial J.S. Publicaciones Especiales, Santa Susana 55, 5o 1 y 2, 28033 Madrid, Spain. TEL 1-763-34-01. adv.: B&W page 60000 ptas., color page 90000 ptas.; trim 258 x 185.

647.94 SP
HOTEL EUROBUILDING. (Text in English, Spanish) 4/yr. Editorial J.S. Publicaciones Especiales, Santa Susana 55, 5o 1 y 2, 28003 Madrid, Spain. TEL 1-763-34-01. Ed. Jaime Sanchez Villar. adv.: B&W page 80000 ptas., color page 100000 ptas.; trim 258 x 185.

647.94 JA
HOTEL MANAGEMENT/HOTEL RYOKAN. 1951. m. Shibata Publishing Co., 3-33-5 Hongo, Bunkyo-ku, Tokyo, Japan. Ed. Muneaki Ikdea. adv. circ. 46,000.

647.94 SP
HOTEL MINDANAO. (Text in English, Spanish) s-a. Editorial J.S. Publicaciones Especiales, Santa Susana 55, 5o 1 y 2, 28033 Madrid, Spain. TEL 1-763-34-01. adv.: B&W page 60000 ptas., color page 90000 ptas.; trim 258 x 185.

647.94 GW
HOTEL MOSAIK. 1955. 4/yr. Sueddeutscher Verlag GmbH, Magazine Dept., Thomas-Dehler-Str. 27, 81737 Munich, Germany. TEL 089-678040. FAX 089-678014-192. TELEX 5216148-EFV-D. adv. circ. 40,000. **Document type:** trade publication.

647.94 364.4 US ISSN 8750-5126
HOTEL - MOTEL SECURITY AND SAFETY MANAGEMENT; a newsletter of loss prevention, crime prevention, and accident prevention. 1982. m. $169 (foreign $194). Rusting Publications, 402 Main St., Box 190, Port Washington, NY 11050. TEL 516-883-1440. FAX 516-883-1683. Ed. Robert R. Rusting. circ. 750. (looseleaf format) **Document type:** newsletter.
—UnCover.

647.94 IT
HOTEL PROFESSIONAL. 6/yr. Corso Italia 38, 20122 Milan, Italy. TEL 2-864-526-96. FAX 2-890-06-70. Ed. Luciano Dogliotti. circ. 11,000.

647.94 UK ISSN 0964-055X
HOTEL PROPRIETOR. q. £12. Unit 7, Edison Rd., Highfield Ind., Hampden Park, Eastbourne, E. Sussex BN21 3XE, England. TEL 0323-52112. FAX 0323-509306. Ed. Tony Clarke. adv. contact: Helen Roberts. circ. 10,000 (paid). **Document type:** trade publication.

647 IT
HOTEL - RESTAURANT. 9/yr. L.60000. Ediman s.r.l., Corso San Gottardo, 39, 20136 Milan, Italy. TEL 02-58103791. FAX 02-58103789. adv.; bk.rev.; illus. circ. 19,000. (tabloid format)

647.9 642.5 DK ISSN 0907-7529
HOTEL RESTAURANT & FRITID. 1884. m. DKK 550. Association of the Hotel, Restaurant and Leisure Industry in Denmark, Vodroffsvej 46, DK-1900 Frederiksberg C, Denmark. TEL 45-31-35-60-88. FAX 45-31-35-15-10. Ed. Henrik Uhre-Prahl. adv. circ. 16,000. **Document type:** trade publication.
  Former titles: Hotel og Restaurant (ISSN 0018-6201); Hotel og Restaurations Tidende.

647.94 747 UK
HOTEL SPECIFICATION INTERNATIONAL. 1987. a. £50($115) Pennington Publications Ltd., Carlton House, 20 Dudley Rd., Tunbridge Wells, Kent TN1 1LF, England. TEL 0892-536685. FAX 0892-510899. TELEX PPRESS-957187. Ed. Gaye Philpott. adv. contact: Steve Hardiman. circ. 10,000. **Document type:** directory.

647.94 SP
HOTEL - SUR. 12/yr. Camino de Ronda 84, 1o, 18004 Granada, Spain. TEL 58-25-82-00. FAX 58-25-86-67. circ. 15,000.
  Description: Covers the hotel industry in Andalusia.

3070 HOTELS AND RESTAURANTS

647.9   SZ   ISSN 0035-9920
HOTEL UND GASTGEWERBE; unabhaengiges Fachorgan fuer Hotellerie, Gastronomie, und Gemeinschaftsverpflegung. 1960. 10/yr. 76 SFr. (foreign 110 SFr.). S H Z Fachverlag AG, Alte Landstr. 43, CH-8700 Kuesnacht, Switzerland. TEL 01-9108022. FAX 01-9105155. Ed. Rudolf Humbel. adv.; bk.rev.; charts; illus.; stat.; circ. 10,000. (controlled). (processed) **Document type:** trade publication.
   Formerly: Hotel und Gastgewerbe Rundschau.

647.94   910.09   AU
HOTEL & TOURISTIK. m. S.400. Manstein Verlag GmbH, Brunner Landstr. 45, A-2380 Perchtoldsdorf, Austria. TEL 01-81608-0. circ. 16,000. **Document type:** trade publication.
   Former titles: Hotel und Touristik-Magazin; Hotelmagazin.

647.94   SZ
HOTEL UND TOURISTIK REVUE. 1892. w. 110 SFr. (foreign 146 SFr.). Schweizer Hotelier-Verein, Monbijoustr. 130, Postfach, CH-3001 Bern, Switzerland. TEL 031-462395. adv.; bk.rev. circ. 18,447. **Document type:** trade publication.

647.94   US
HOTEL UPDATE NEWSLETTER. 1990. m. $24. Entertainment Publications, Inc., 2125 Butterfield Rd., Troy, MI 48084. TEL 313-637-8432. FAX 313-637-2035. Ed. Robert McHenry. **Document type:** newsletter.
   Description: Provides information of attractive industry offerings for lodging, dining, leisure activities and travel.

647.94   SP
HOTEL WELLINGTON. (Text in English, Spanish) s-a. Editorial J.S. Publicaciones Especiales, Santa Susana 55, 5o 1 y 2, 28033 Madrid, Spain. TEL 1-763-34-01. adv.: B&W page 60000 ptas., color page 100000 ptas.; trim 258 x 185.

647   PL   ISSN 0137-7612
HOTELARZ. 1970. m. 250 Zl. Zrzeszenie Polskich Hoteli Turystycznych, Krolewska 27a, 00-060 Warsaw, Poland. Ed. Zygmunt Balkowski. adv.; bk.rev.

647.94   IT
HOTELDOMANI. (Text in English, Italian) 1976. 9/yr. L.15000. Hoteldomani s.r.l., Via Vitruvio 47, 20124 Milan, Italy. TEL 2-66-98-73-29. FAX 2-66-98-20-69. TELEX 333258 EMOMI I. Ed. Rodolfo Malfasi. adv.; bk.rev. circ. 8,000.

647.9   CK   ISSN 0018-6279
HOTELES DE COLOMBIA. 1955-1971; resumed 1975. m. Corporacion Hotelera de Colombia, Carrera 7a 70-92, Apartado Aereo 29692, Bogota, Colombia. TEL 3103640. FAX 3103509.

647.94   SP
HOTELES DE ESPANA. 12/yr. Comercio 4, Esc. 1a 1o A, 28007 Madrid, Spain. TEL 1-433-67-00. Ed. Javier Perez Serna.

647.9   GW   ISSN 0018-6287
HOTELIER. 1966. q. DM.48($20) Zeitungs- und Zeitschriftenverlag Heinrichs, Brueggekamp 1, 30890 Barsinghausen, Germany. TEL 05105-2289. Ed. G. Heinrichs. adv.; bk.rev.; charts; stat.; tr.lit. circ. 8,900. (tabloid format) **Document type:** trade publication.

647.94   CN
HOTELIER. 6/yr. $15 (foreign Can.$30). Kostuch Communications Ltd., 980 Yonge St., Ste. 400, Toronto, ON M4W 2J8, Canada. TEL 416-923-8888. FAX 416-923-6114. Ed. Rosanna Caira. adv. circ. 8,300. **Document type:** trade publication.

647.94   FR
HOTELIER. m. 110.50 F. Chambre Syndicale des Hoteliers Cafetiers, Restaurateurs de Paris et de sa Region, 41 rue Meslay, 75003 Paris, France. TEL 42-72-83-20. Ed. Louis Cot. circ. 6,000.

647.9   SA   ISSN 0018-6295
HOTELIER & CATERER (CAPE TOWN). 1935. m. R.130. Ramsay, Son & Parker (Pty) Ltd., P.O. Box 180, Howard Place 7450, Cape Town, South Africa. TEL 27-21-5311391. FAX 27-21-5313333. Ed. Andrew Moth. adv.; illus. circ. 7,000. **Indexed:** Food Sci.& Tech.Abstr., Packag.Sci.Tech. **Document type:** trade publication.
   —BLDSC (4333.770000).
   Incorporates: Hotelier and Caterer Buyer's Guide; Formed by the merger of: National Hotelier; S.A. Hotel Review.
   Description: Carries news and features on the hotel and catering industry in South Africa.

642.47   KE
HOTELIER & CATERER (NAIROBI). 1987. EAs.200($30) (Kenya Association of Hotelkeepers and Caterers) News Publishers Ltd., P.O. Box 30339, Nairobi, Kenya. Ed. Clive Mutiso. circ. 2,000.

647.94   UK
HOTELIERS INFORMATION JOURNAL. 1981. w. membership. Blackpool Hotel and Guest House Association, 87A Coronation St., Blackpool, Lancs. FY1 4PD, England. TEL 0253-21891. FAX 0253-23041. Ed. J.F. Donovan. adv. **Document type:** newsletter.
   Description: Updates organization members on important legislative changes and provides news of forthcoming events.

647.94   AU
HOTELINFORMATIONEN. q. Linke Wienzeile 5, A-1060 Vienna, Austria. TEL 01-5874487. Ed. Walter Gebetsberger. circ. 5,000.

647.9   NO
HOTELL OG RESTAURANT. 1907. m. (11/yr). NOK 300. Norsk Hotell og Restaurantforbund, Box 9551 Egertorget, 0128 Oslo 1, Norway. FAX 1-336675. Ed. Carl Johan Berg. adv. circ. 5,000.
   Formerly (until 1989): Norsk Hotell og Restaurantblad.

647.9   FR
L'HOTELLERIE. l'hebdo de la profession. (Supplements avail.: La Restauration, Service Compris, Resto-Flash, L'Hotellerie Madame, Boissons) 1923. 50/yr. 520 F. (includes the supplements). Societe d'Editions et de Periodiques Techniques, B.P. 152, 92203 Neuilly-Seine cedex, France. TEL 1-46-40-08-08. FAX 1-46-40-00-74. TELEX 612 009 F. (Subscr. to: 5 rue Antoine Bourdelle, 75737 Paris Cedex 15. TEL 45-48-64-64. FAX 45-48-04-23) adv.; bk.rev.; illus.; index. circ. 62,000.

647.9   BL   ISSN 0018-6333
HOTELNEWS. 1959. m. $300. Hotelnews Edicoes e Promocoes Ltda., Rua Camuirano, 96, Botafogo, 22270-020 Rio de Janeiro RJ, Brazil. TEL 021-286-2218. FAX 021-286-2179. TELEX 21-34148. Ed. Miriam Hauch. adv.: B&W page $2600, color page $3200; trim 210 x 280; adv. contact: Roberto Rodriques. charts; illus.; circ. 18,000 (controlled). **Document type:** trade publication.

647.9 642.5   US   ISSN 1047-2975 TX901
HOTELS. 1966. m. $74.95 (Canada $112.30; Mexico $104.95; elsewhere $134.95). (International Hotel Association) Cahners Publishing Company (Des Plaines), Division of Reed Elsevier Inc, 1350 E. Touhy Ave., Box 5080, Des Plaines, IL 60017-5080. TEL 708-635-8800. FAX 708-635-6856. (Subscr. to: 44 Cook St., Denver, CO 80206-5800. TEL 800-635-6089) Ed. James Carper. adv.; bk.rev. circ. 58,000. (back issues avail.) **Indexed:** Art.Hosp.& Tour., Bus.Ind., Food Sci.& Tech.Abstr., Key to Econ.Sci., Tr.& Indus.Ind.
   —BLDSC (4333.775000); UnCover; UMI. **CCC**.
   Formerly (until Oct. 1989): Hotels and Restaurants International (ISSN 0744-3897); Incorporates (in 1982): International Hotel Review (ISSN 0020-6911); Which was formerly: Service World International (ISSN 0049-0237).
   Description: For hotel, foodservice, resort and tourism industries, provides information in marketing, new business development, investment, interior design, hospitality and foodservice.

647.94   UK
HOTELS. m. 27 Paul St., London EC2A 4JU, England. TEL 071-628-7030. FAX 071-628-5984. Ed. James Carpenter. circ. 41,200.

674.94   UK
HOTELS AND RESTAURANTS OF BRITAIN. 1920. a. £12.95. Product Communication Ltd., 12 Fouberts Pl., London W1V 1HH, England. TEL 071-437-8395. FAX 071-439-8806. (Dist. in U.K. by: World Leisure Marketing Ltd., 117 The Hollow, Littleover, Derby DE3 7BS, England. TEL 0332-272020. FAX 0332-774287; Dist. in U.S. by: Globe Pequot Press, 6 Business Park Rd., Old Saybrook, CT 06475. TEL 203-395-0440. FAX 203-395-0312) Ed. Tabitha Dmochowska. adv. circ. 18,500. **Document type:** directory.
   Former titles: Official Guide to Hotels and Restaurants in Great Britain, Ireland and Overseas (ISSN 0307-062X); B H R C A Guide to Hotels and Restaurants (ISSN 0068-2128)

647.94   SP
HUSA PRINCESA. (Text in English, Spanish) q. Editorial J.S. Publicaciones Especiales, Santa Susana 55, 5o 1 y 2, 28033 Madrid, Spain. TEL 1-7633401. adv.: B&W page 80000 ptas., color page 100000 ptas.; trim 258 x 185.
   Formerly: Plaza Hoteles.

I A H A INFOLINE. (International Association of Hospitality Accountants) see *BUSINESS AND ECONOMICS — Accounting*

642.5   UK
I F C A QUARTERLY REVIEW. q. 33 Eaton Park Rd., Cobham, Surrey KT11 2JJ, England. TEL 0276-691261. FAX 0276-692427. Ed. W.M. Seeman.

647.95   US
ILLINOIS FOOD SERVICE NEWS.* 1939. 4/yr. $15. Illinois Restaurant Association, 350 W. Ontario, 7th Fl., Chicago, IL 60610-4017. adv. circ. 4,000.
   Formerly (until 1982): C I R A Scope (Chicago and Illinois Restaurant Association) (ISSN 0191-6769)

647.9   GW   ISSN 0931-5187
IMPRESSIONEN; Gaestemagazin der Guennewig Hotels und Restaurants. 1983. s-a. E R M I Guide Orschel KG, Malvenweg 4, 51061 Cologne, Germany. TEL 0221-634091. FAX 0221-634677. Ed. Gerhard Guennewig. **Document type:** trade publication.

642.5   UK   ISSN 0965-4720
INDEPENDENT CATERING. 1988. m. £55 in the UK; Europe £75; elsewhere £100. I M L Group plc, Blair House, High St., Tonbridge, Kent TN9 1BQ, England. TEL 0732-359990. FAX 0732-770049. Ed. Caroline Scoular. adv.; bk.rev. circ. 41,168. **Document type:** trade publication.

647.94   UK
INDEPENDENT HOTELIER. m. £15 (effective Jan. 1993). Argus Press, 256 Ipswich Rd., Slough, Bucks. SL1 4EP, England. TEL 44-753-551995. Ed. Jackie Mitchell. stat. circ. 16,500. (tabloid format; back issues avail.)
   Formerly: Hotelier and Caterer UK.
   Description: Informs the independent hotelier about everything he or she needs to know, from finance to product knowledge to doing business effectively.

647.94   II
INDIAN HOTELKEEPER & TRAVELER. 1966. m. Rs.125($90) 90-91 Maidens Hotel, Delhi 110 054, India. TEL 2525697. FAX 238347. TELEX 31-78163-OMDL-IN. Ed. S.K. Ambarder. adv.; bk.rev. circ. 15,000.

647.9   FR   ISSN 1141-0078
INDUSTRIE HOTELIERE. 1950. m. (11/yr.). 120 F. (foreign 200 F.). Societe d'Editions et de Documentation de l'Industrie Hoteliere, 22-24 rue du Pat Wilson, 92300 Levallois-Perret, France. Ed. M. Jacques The. circ. 46,518. **Indexed:** Key to Econ.Sci.
   Formerly: Industrie Hoteliere de France et d'Outre Mer (ISSN 0019-9095)

647.94 CN ISSN 0821-7610
INN BUSINESS. 1965. 6/yr. Can.$30 (foreign Can.$40). Zanny Publications Ltd., 11966 Woodbine Ave., Gormley, ON L0H 1G0, Canada. TEL 905-887-4813. FAX 905-479-4839. Ed. Amy Margaret; Pub. Janet Gardiner. adv.; B&W page Can.$2420, color page Can.$3320; trim 8 1/4 x 10 3/4. circ. 10,268.
Description: Covers all aspects of management in the hotel, motel and resorts industry.

647.94 CN ISSN 1193-1922
INN - FOCUS. 1938. 4/yr. Naylor Communications Ltd., 124 W. 8th St., North Vancouver, BC V7M 3H2, Canada. TEL 604-985-8711. FAX 604-985-7399. (Subscr. to: 100 Sutherland Ave., Winnipeg, MB R2W 3C7) Ed. Jim Hutson. adv. circ. 2,100.
Former titles: B.C. Hotelier; B.C. Hotelman (ISSN 0380-9668)

647.94 US ISSN 0895-2965
TX907
THE INN GUIDE. 1980. a. $12.67. Golden Gate North, Box 3383, Santa Rosa, CA 95402. TEL 707-542-4667. Ed. Toby Smith. adv.; index. circ. 900. (back issues avail.)
Formerly (until 1986): California Inns (ISSN 0748-8203)
Description: Lists approximately 700 California bed and breakfast inns, small restored hotels, and period lodges and resorts.

674.94 910.09 US
INN MARKETING NEWSLETTER; country inns, small hotels and bed & breakfasts. 1982. m. $35 (subscr. includes a. directory-catalog). Norman Strasma, Pub., 105 E. Court St., Box 1789, Kankakee, IL 60901. TEL 815-939-3509. FAX 815-939-8320. Ed. Anne W. Miller. adv.; index. (back issues avail.) **Document type:** catalog, directory.
Former titles: Inn Business Review Newsletter; (until June 1990): Inn Review Newsletter (ISSN 0748-8408)
Description: Presents news of people, places, and events of the inn and bed and breakfast business.

647.94 US
INN TOUCH. m. Wisconsin InnKeepers Association, 509 W. Wisconsin Ave., No. 619, Milwaukee, WI 53203-2006. TEL 414-271-2851. FAX 414-271-3050. Ed. Barbara Kiezek. circ. 1,300.

647.94 US ISSN 0746-6498
INNKEEPING WORLD. 1979. 10/yr. $112 (foreign $144). Charles Nolte. Ed. & Pub., Box 84108, Seattle, WA 98124. stat. circ. 2,000.

647.94 US
INNSIDE GOVERNMENT. m. American Hotel and Motel Association, 1201 New York Ave., N.W., Washington, DC 20005-3931. TEL 202-289-3147. FAX 202-289-3155. Ed. Kevin Maher. circ. 12,000.
Description: Covers congressional and executive branch activities affecting the hotel, motel, travel and tourism industry.

INNSIDE ISSUES. see REAL ESTATE

INSIDE DINING. see FOOD AND FOOD INDUSTRIES

647.94 642.5 UK ISSN 0962-3957
INSIDE HOTELS. 10/yr. £80 (effective Oct. 1993). Quadrant House, The Quadrant, Sutton, Surrey SM2 5AS, England. TEL 081-652-3856. FAX 081-652-8938. Ed. Lisa Barnard. adv.; bk.rev. circ. 16,000. **Document type:** trade publication.
Description: Aimed at decision makers in the UK and European hotel industry. Covers the complexity of elements that make a hotel profitable and seeks to encourage enthusiasm within the profession.

INTERNATIONAL ENTERTAINING. see HOME ECONOMICS

INTERNATIONAL GUIDE. see TRAVEL AND TOURISM

647.94 FR ISSN 0074-624X
INTERNATIONAL HOTEL GUIDE. (Text in English, French) 1948. a. International Hotel Association, 80 rue de la Roquette, 75011 Paris, France. TEL 47-00-84-57. FAX 47-00-64-55. TELEX 216410. adv.
Description: Lists 2500 hotels in 140 countries: address, telephone, telefax and telex numbers, names of managers and facilities.

INTERNATIONAL JOURNAL OF HOSPITALITY MANAGEMENT. see TRAVEL AND TOURISM

INTERNATIONAL JOURNAL OF HYGIENE AND NUTRITION IN FOOD SERVICE AND CATERING. see FOOD AND FOOD INDUSTRIES

642.5 US ISSN 1051-7413
IOWA APPETIZER. 1935. m. $20 to non-members. Iowa Restaurant and Beverage Association, 3800 Merle Hay Rd., No. 606, Des Moines, IA 50310. TEL 515-276-1454. FAX 515-276-3660. Ed. Frank A. DeFazio. adv.; illus. circ. 1,100. **Document type:** trade publication.
Formerly: Appetizer.

J & W TRAVEL INTERNATIONAL; international guide for business travel and tourism. see COMMUNICATIONS — Telephone And Telegraph

JAGUAR ELECTRONIC TRAVEL DIRECTORIES. see BUSINESS AND ECONOMICS — Trade And Industrial Directories

647 JA ISSN 0446-6217
JAPAN HOTEL GUIDE.* (Text in English) irreg. Japan Tourist Association, c/o Kokusai Kanko Kaikan, 1-8-3 Marunouchi, Chiyoda-ku, Tokyo 100, Japan. illus.

647.94 647.95 FR
JOURNAL DE L'HOTELLERIE. w. 249 F. Societe d'Editions et de Periodiques Techniques (Paris), B.P. 152, 92203 Neuilly Seine Cedex, France. TEL 42-62-05-22. FAX 46-40-00-74. TELEX 612009F.

642.5 SZ
JOURNAL DES CAFETIERS, RESTAURATEURS ET HOTELIERS. w. Bd. St. Georges 72, Postfach 326, CH-1211 Geneva, Switzerland. TEL 022-299722. FAX 022-204025. Ed. Michel Jordan. circ. 7,600.

647.94 UK ISSN 0954-9234
TX911.3.M27
JOURNAL OF CONTEMPORARY HOSPITALITY MANAGEMENT. 1988. 6/yr. $699.95. M C B University Press Ltd., 60-62 Toller Ln., Bradford, W. Yorks BD8 9BY, England. TEL 0274-499821. FAX 0274-547143. TELEX 51317-MCBUNI-G. (N. American subscr. to: M C B University Press Limited, Box 10182, Birmingham, AL 35202) Ed. Richard E. Teare. Indexed: Anbar. **Document type:** academic/scholarly publication.
—CCC.
Description: Articles deal with hospitality methods, techniques and innovations, applied research, management and marketing.

JOURNAL OF CULINARY PRACTICE. see FOOD AND FOOD INDUSTRIES

674.94 658 US ISSN 1050-7051
TX911.3.M3 CODEN: JHLME7
▼**JOURNAL OF HOSPITALITY & LEISURE MARKETING.** 1992. q. $28 to individuals; institutions $36; libraries $48. Haworth Press, Inc., 10 Alice St., Binghamton, NY 13904-1580. TEL 607-722-5857; 800-342-9678. FAX 607-722-1424. TELEX 4932599. Ed. Bonnie Knutson. adv.; bk.rev. (also avail. in microfiche from UMI; reprint service avail. from HAW) Indexed: Cont.Pg.Educ., Cont.Pg.Manage., Human Resour.Abstr.
—UnCover.
Description: Examines marketing issues in the hospitality and leisure industries. Aims to improve the understanding of relationships between hospitality - leisure organizations and their customers, and to improve the management of those relationships.
Refereed Serial

642.5 658 US ISSN 1052-214X
CODEN: JRFMED
▼**JOURNAL OF RESTAURANT & FOODSERVICE MARKETING.** 1992. q. $28 to individuals; institutions $36; libraries $48. Haworth Press, Inc., 10 Alice St., Binghamton, NY 13904. TEL 607-722-5857; 800-342-9678. FAX 607-722-1424. TELEX 4932599. Ed. Simon Crawford-Welch. adv.; bk.rev. (also avail. in microfiche from UMI; reprint service avail. from HAW) Indexed: Food Sci.&Tech.Abstr.
Description: Presents new developments in the field and provides state of the art knowledge on restaurant and foodservice marketing.
Refereed Serial

HOTELS AND RESTAURANTS 3071

647.954 UK
JUST A BITE;* Egon Ronay's Lucas guide for gourmets on a family budget. 1979. a. £4.50($6.95) Egon Ronay's Guides, Fanum House, Basingstoke, Hants RG2 2GA, England. (Dist. in U.S. & Canada by: St. Martin's Press, 175 Fifth Ave., New York, NY 10010)

642.5 US ISSN 0022-8753
KANSAS RESTAURANT. 1938. bi-m. membership. Kansas Restaurant Association, 359 S. Hydraulic, Wichita, KS 67211. TEL 316-267-8383. Ed. Trish Phelps. adv.; bk.rev.; film rev.; circ. 1,500 (controlled).

647.94 GW
KEMPINSKI JOURNAL. 4/yr. Marketing Ableitung des Kempinski AG, Kurfuerstendamm 27, 10719 Berlin, Germany. adv. circ. 40,000.

642.5 NE ISSN 0023-0731
KEUKEN. 1961. bi-m. fl.31.46. Nederlandse Club voor Chef-Koks, Postbus 1198, Amsterdam, Netherlands. Ed. M. Paulissen. adv.; charts; illus.

KEY MAGAZINE. THIS WEEK IN LOS ANGELES AND SOUTHERN CALIFORNIA; the leading weekly magazine of Southern entertainment & dining. see TRAVEL AND TOURISM

KITCHEN TIMES. see HOME ECONOMICS

642.5 US
KNIFE & FORK.* bi-m. Performance Network, 331 Dante Ct., Ste. B, Holbrook, CT 11741-3800. TEL 516-226-1000. FAX 516-226-0116. Ed. Richard A. Neste. circ. 1,200,000.

642 GW ISSN 0450-6235
KOCHPRAXIS UND GEMEINSCHAFTSVERPFLEGUNG; die Diaetkueche. m. DM.106.80. Matthaes Verlag GmbH, Olgastr. 87, 70180 Stuttgart, Germany. TEL 0711-2133-0. circ. 5,000. **Document type:** newspaper.

642.5 GW ISSN 0344-4376
KUECHE; Fachzeitschrift fuer aktuelle Kochkunst, Gastlichkeit und Ernaehrung. 1896. m. DM.62.40. (Verband der Koeche Deutschlands e.V.) Rhenania-Fachverlag GmbH, Possmoorweg 5, 22301 Hamburg, Germany. FAX 040-2717-2069. TELEX 213214. Ed. Hans-Herbert Seng. adv.; bk.rev.; illus. circ. 16,235. **Document type:** trade publication.

647.94 GW
LANDESVERBAND DES HOTEL- UND GASTSTAETTENGEWERBES IN BADEN-WUERTTEMBERG. MITTEILUNGEN. m. membership. Matthaes Verlag GmbH, Olgastr. 87, 70180 Stuttgart, Germany. TEL 0711-2133-0. circ. 12,100. **Document type:** newspaper.

LAS VEGAS INSIDER. see TRAVEL AND TOURISM

642.5 UK
THE LEADER. q. F S W Publications, 66 Bracondale, Norwich NR1 2BE, England. TEL 0603-623303. FAX 0603-666238. Ed. G. Cooper. adv. contact: K. O'Gorman. **Document type:** trade publication.

647.94 GW
LEBENDIGES DARMSTADT. STADTFUEHRER GASTRONOMIE UND UNTERHALTUNG. 1976. a. Verkehrsamt der Stadt Darmstadt, Luisenplatz 5, 64283 Darmstadt, Germany. **Document type:** directory.
Description: Provides a guide to restaurants and places of interest in the city of Darmstadt.

647.94 US
LEGISLATIVE MEMORANDA.* irreg. Foodservice and Lodging Institute, 1101 Connecticut Ave., Ste. 700, Washington, DC 20036-4303. TEL 202-659-9060.

647.94 FR ISSN 0767-6379
LETTRE DE LA PIERRE. bi-m. 2965 F. L'Agence Innovapresse, 29 rue du Faubourg Poissonniere, 75009 Paris, France. TEL 48-24-08-97. FAX 42-47-00-76. Ed. Antoine Loubiere.
Description: Studies hotel industry trends and statistics.

HOTELS AND RESTAURANTS

642.5   FR   ISSN 0024-3612
LIMONADIER DE PARIS. N.S. no.256, 1968. m. Syndicat Patronal des Cafes, 28 rue Beaurepaire, 75010 Paris, France. Ed. J. Blat. adv.; charts; stat.; tr.lit.

647   FR
LIMONADIER - RESTAURANTEUR HOTELIER. 11/yr. 9 place Saint-Andre-des-Arts, 75006 Paris, France. TEL 43-26-89-36. Ed. Yves Le Sergent. circ. 12,000.

647.94 910.09 388.411   GW   ISSN 0343-4192
LINKS UND RECHTS DER AUTOBAHN; der Reisefuehrer und Reiseatlas speziell fuer die Autobahn. 1961. a. DM.7.50. Verlag Holger Stuenings, Luisenstr. 100, 47799 Krefeld, Germany. adv.; charts. circ. 185,000. (back issues avail.)

647   US   ISSN 0360-9235
TX901
LODGING. 1975. m. $35. American Hotel Association Directory Corp., 1201 New York Ave., N.W., Ste. 600, Washington, DC 20005-3931. TEL 202-289-3164. FAX 202-289-3199. Ed. Dennis Jay. adv.: B&W page $2950, color page $3900; trim 8 3/8 x 10 7/8. illus. **Indexed**: Art.Hosp.& Tour.
—BLDSC (5292.178000); Faxon; UnCover.

647.9   US   ISSN 0148-0766
TX901
LODGING HOSPITALITY; management magazine for hotels, motels and resorts. 1949. m. $60 (free to qualified personnel). Penton Publishing (Subsidiary of: Pittway Company), 1100 Superior Ave., Cleveland, OH 44114-2543. TEL 216-696-7000. FAX 216-696-8765. (Subscr. to: Box 95759, Cleveland, OH 44101) Ed. Ed Watkins. adv.; charts; stat.; circ. 49,000 (controlled). (also avail. in microform from UMI; microfiche from CIS; back issues avail.; reprint service avail. from UMI) **Indexed**: Account.Ind. (1974-), Art.Hosp.& Tour., B.P.I., Bus.Ind., SRI, Tr.& Indus.Ind.
●Also available online. Vendor(s): DIALOG Information Services, Inc.
—BLDSC (5292.180000); Faxon; UMI. **CCC**.
Former titles: Hospitality Lodging; Hospitality-Food and Lodging (ISSN 0015-6302); Hospitality-Restaurant and Lodging; American Motel Magazine.
Description: Focuses on site selection, design and decor, financing, building, personnel, maintenance, sanitation, computerization, merchandizing and renovation.

647   FR
LOGIS DE FRANCE. 10/yr. 83 Av. d'Italie, 75013 Paris, France. TEL 45-84-70-00. FAX 44-24-08-74. TELEX LOGIAUB 202 030 F.

647.94   CN
M A A NEWS BULLETIN. bi-m. membership. Motel Association of Alberta, P.O. Box 3677, Sta. D, Edmonton, AB T5L 4J7, Canada. TEL 403-429-3321. FAX 403-429-3695. adv. **Document type**: newsletter.

MACAO. DIRECCAO DOS SERVICOS DE ESTATISTICA E CENSOS. RECENSEAMENTO AOS RESTAURANTES, HOTEIS E ESTABELECIMENTOS SIMILARES/MACAO. CENSUS AND STATISTICS DEPARTMENT. CENSUS OF RESTAURANTS, HOTELS AND SIMILAR ESTABLISHMENTS. see HOTELS AND RESTAURANTS — Abstracting, Bibliographies, Statistics

642.5   IT
MANGIARBERE OGGI. m. L.35000. Valentini Editore, Via Fabio Filzi 19, Milan, Italy. TEL 02-6696471. FAX 02-6697083. TELEX 330229 VALIDI I. Ed. Aldo Quinto Lazzari.

647.95   CN   ISSN 1184-1605
MANITOBA RESTAURANT NEWS. 1989. q. Can.$18($16) Mercury Publications Ltd., 945 King Edward Ave., Winnipeg, MB R3H 0P8, Canada. TEL 204-775-0387. FAX 204-775-7830. Ed. Kelly Grey. adv. contact: Frank Yeo. circ. 2,220.

642.5   UK
MARDEK GUIDE TO THE U K CATERING TRADE. a. William Reed Ltd., Broadfield Park, Crawley, W. Sussex RH11 9RT, England. TEL 0293-613400. FAX 0293-613304. **Document type**: directory.

697.9   US
MARKETSHARE. 1987. q. $95. Source Strategies, Inc., Box 120055, San Antonio, TX 78212. TEL 512-734-3434. Ed. Bruce Walker. circ. 300. (back issues avail.)
Description: Measures the marketshares of hotel chains and management.

642.56   NO
MAT.* bi-m. Norske Kokkemesteres Landsforening, P.O. Box 735, NO-4006 Stavanger, Norwayrammen, Norway. adv. circ. 2,500.

MEXICO CITY DAILY BULLETIN. see TRAVEL AND TOURISM

MICHELIN RED GUIDE SERIES: GREATER LONDON. see TRAVEL AND TOURISM

642.5   US   ISSN 0161-6447
MICHIGAN RESTAURATEUR. 1935. bi-m. $24. Michigan Restaurant Association, 225 W. Washington, Lansing, MI 48933. TEL 517-349-0272. FAX 517-482-5344. Ed. Kim Ohlemacher. adv.; bk.rev.; tr.lit. circ. 3,500. (back issues avail.) **Document type**: trade publication.
Formerly: Michigan Hospitality.

647.95   US
MIDSOUTHWEST RESTAURANT. 1938. bi-m. $25. Oklahoma Restaurant Association, 3800 N. Portland Ave., Oklahoma City, OK 73112. TEL 405-942-8181. Ed. Michele Clark. adv.; bk.rev.; charts; illus.; stat.; index. circ. 2,000.

642.5   US
MIDWEST FOOD SERVICE. 1983. bi-m. $18. Target Publishing Co., Inc. (Columbus), 2470 E. Main St., Columbus, OH 43209. TEL 614-235-1022. FAX 614-235-3584. Ed. Terri Stone-Corrath. adv. contact: Linda Katz. stat.; tr.lit. circ. 20,600. (tabloid format) **Document type**: trade publication.
Formerly (until vol.7, no.12, 1989): Ohio Restaurant News.
Description: Serves the restaurant business and its suppliers.

647.9   BE
MISSET HORECA MAGAZINE. (Editions in Flemish and French) 11/yr. Misset Belgium, Savaanstraat 92, 9000 Ghent, Belgium. adv. circ. 33,000.

647.95   US
MISSOURI RESTAURANT. 1916. 10/yr. $15 to non-members; members $10. Missouri Restaurant Association, 4049 Pennsylvania, Ste. 201, Kansas City, MO 64111. TEL 816-753-5222. FAX 816-753-6993. Ed. Michelle A. Holden. circ. 3,800. **Document type**: trade publication.

647.94   GW   ISSN 0937-2768
MODERNE HOTEL TECHNIK. 1990. q. DM.70. A T Fachverlag GmbH, Postfach 500180, 70331 Stuttgart, Germany. TEL 0711-952951-0. FAX 0711-952951-99. Ed. F. Neeracher. illus. circ. 35,657. **Document type**: trade publication.

647.94   US
MOTEL NEWS.* Variant title: N M B. vol.10, 1981. bi-m. National Motel Brokers, 3 37th Ave., no.5, San Mateo, CA 94403-4457. TEL 415-349-1234. Ed. Alberta Sur. illus. circ. 5,400.

658.91   FR   ISSN 1169-8217
MOUVEMENT HOTELIER ET TOURISTIQUE. 1968. 11/yr. 11 bis av. de Lyon, 73000 Chambery, France. TEL 79-69-26-18. Ed. Jacques Jond. adv. circ. 6,000.

647.9   GW   ISSN 0930-2255
N G Z SERVICE MANAGER. (Neue Gastronomische Zeitschrift); neue gastronomische Zeitschrift fuer Fuehrungskraefte in Restaurant und Hotel. 1948. m. DM.163.45 (foreign DM.167). Deutscher Fachverlag GmbH, Mainzer Landstr. 251, 60326 Frankfurt a.M., Germany. TEL 069-759501. FAX 069-75952999. (Subscr. to: Postfach 100606, 60006 Frankfurt a.M., Germany) Ed. Karin Dircks. adv.; bk.rev.; illus. circ. 13,482. **Document type**: trade publication.
Formerly: N G Z (ISSN 0027-6529)

NATIONAL CULINARY REVIEW. see FOOD AND FOOD INDUSTRIES

647.94   US   ISSN 0146-3950
NATIONAL DIRECTORY OF BUDGET MOTELS; a nation-wide guide to low-cost chain motel accommodations. 1975. a. $5.95. Pilot Books, 103 Cooper St., Babylon, NY 11702. TEL 516-422-2225. FAX 516-422-2227. Ed. Raymond Carlson. **Document type**: directory.
Description: Guide to more than 2,200 low-cost chain motels throughout the U.S. and Canada.

647.95   CN
NATIONAL HOSPITALITY NEWS. m. Canadian Restaurant and Foodservices Association, 80 W. Bloor St., Suite 904, Toronto, Ont. M5S 2V1, Canada. TEL 416-923-8416.

642.5   US   ISSN 0028-0518
NATION'S RESTAURANT NEWS; the newspaper of the food service industry. w. $89. Lebhar-Friedman, Inc., 425 Park Ave., New York, NY 10022. TEL 212-756-5000. FAX 212-838-9487. Ed. Rick Van Warner. adv.; abstr.; charts; illus.; mkt.; stat. circ. 90,000. (tabloid format; also avail. in microform from UMI; microfiche from CIS; reprint service avail. from UMI) **Indexed**: Hlth.Ind., PROMT, SRI, Tr.& Indus.Ind.
●Also available online. Vendor(s): DIALOG Information Services, Inc., Mead Data Central, Inc.
—UMI. **CCC**.

647.95   FR   ISSN 1145-377X
NEO RESTAURATION. 1972. bi-m. 380 F. (foreign 535 F.). Groupe L S A, B.P. 142, 6 rue Marius Aufan, 92300 Levallois-Perret Cedex, France. TEL 47-58-20-00. FAX 47-58-72-00. Ed. Patrice Albert. adv.: B&W page 19500 F., color page 32000 F.; trim 204 x 276. illus.; stat.; index. circ. 17,400.
Former titles: Neo Restauration Hotellerie Collectives (ISSN 0291-8099); Neo Restauration Hotellerie.

NEW ORLEANS MENU; dining out and in. see FOOD AND FOOD INDUSTRIES

NIGERIA TOURIST BOARD. OFFICIAL TOURIST GUIDE. see TRAVEL AND TOURISM

647.95   US   ISSN 0893-4177
NIGHT CLUB & BAR MAGAZINE. 1984. m. $25. Oxford Publishing, 307 W. Jackson Ave., Oxford, MS 38655-2154. TEL 601-236-5510. FAX 601-236-5541. Ed. Ava Middleton. adv. circ. 20,000. **Document type**: trade publication.
Formerly (until 1987): Night Club and Bar (ISSN 0893-4169)

647.95   JA
NIKKEI RESTAURANTS. (Text in Japanese) 1988. 26/yr. 19800 Yen. Nikkei Business Publications, Inc. (Subsidiary of: Nihon Keizai Shimbun, Inc.), 2-7-6 Hirakawa-cho, Chiyoda-ku, Tokyo 102, Japan. TEL 03-5210-8502. FAX 03-5210-8119. Ed. Hideo Kato. adv. contact: Yoshihiko Shimada. circ. 25,253. **Document type**: trade publication.
Description: Covers developments in the food service industries, from restaurants and hotels to institutions.

642.5   US
NORTH EAST FOOD SERVICE BUYER'S GUIDE. 1982. a. $7.50. Trade Winds Publishing Co., Box 332, Braintree, MA 02184. TEL 617-848-5039. Ed. Dorothy Delano. adv. circ. 23,326.
Formerly (until 1986): New England Food Service Buyer's Guide.
Description: Lists suppliers of goods and services for the industry.

647.94   UK
NORTHERN HOTEL AND RESTAURANT. 26/yr. Wharncliffe House, Church St., Barnsley, S. Yorkshire S70 2AS, England. TEL 0226-734291. FAX 0226-734455. Ed. Keith Dixon. circ. 11,000.

642.5   DK
NYT DANMARKS RESTAURANTER. 12/yr. membership. Association of the Hotel, Restaurant and Leisure Industry in Denmark, Vodroffsvej 46, DK-Frederiksberg C, Denmark. TEL 45-31-35-60-88. FAX 45-31-35-15-10. Ed. Henrik Uhre-Prahl. adv. circ. 2,000. **Document type**: newsletter.
Formerly: Danmarks Restauranter.

THE OBEROI GROUP MAGAZINE. see TRAVEL AND TOURISM

HOTELS AND RESTAURANTS

647.94   AU
OE G Z STAMMTISCH. m. Nikolsdorfergasse 7-11, A-1051 Vienna, Austria. TEL 01-555585267. FAX 01-555585347. circ. 22,400.

642.5   AU
OESTERREICHISCHE GASTGEWERBE- UND HOTELZEITUNG. Short title: Oe G Z. 1946. w. S.1160. (Gast- und Schankbetriebe) Oesterreichischer Wirtschaftsverlag, Nikolsdorfer Gasse 7-11, A-1051 Vienna 5, Austria. TEL 0222-555585. TELEX 1-11669. Ed. Guenther Greul. adv.; bk.rev. circ. 22,400.
    Formerly: Oesterreichische Gastgewerbe-Zeitung (ISSN 0029-9103)

647   AU
OESTERREICHISCHE RESTAURANT & G V - PRAXIS; Fachzeitschrift fuer Gastronomie, Hotellerie und moderne Grossverpflegung. 1981. 11/yr. S.480. (Arbeitsgemeinschaft der Grosskuechen Oesterreichs) Deutscher Fachverlag GmbH, Verlag fuer Wirtschaftspraxis GmbH, Schrannengasse 4, Postfach 39, A-5027 Salzburg, Austria. TEL 0662-877108. FAX 0662-8771083. (Co-sponsor: Klub der Koeche Kaerntens) circ. 13,300. **Document type:** newspaper.

642.56   AU   ISSN 0029-9847
OESTERREICHISCHES CAFE JOURNAL; Fachblatt fuer Kaffeehaeuser, Caferestaurants, Espressi, Cafekonditoreien. vol.11, 1970. m. S.480. (Bundesinnung der Cafetiers) Oesterreichischer Wirtschaftsverlag, Nikolsdorfer Gasse 7-11, A-1051 Vienna, Austria. TEL 0222-555585. TELEX 1-11669. Ed. Guenther Greul. adv.; bk.rev.; illus.; index. circ. 5,600.

OFFICIAL GUIDE TO AMERICAN HISTORIC INNS; 1,100 bed & breakfast and country inns. see *TRAVEL AND TOURISM*

647.94   US
OFFICIAL HOTEL GUIDE. (Includes 18 geographical segments) 1963. a. (in 3 vols.). $219. Reed Travel Group, Part of the Reed Elsevier group (Subsidiary of: Reed Telepublishing), 500 Plaza Dr., Secaucus, NJ 07096. TEL 212-902-2000. adv. circ. 25,000. **Document type:** directory.
    Formerly (until 1992): Official Hotel and Resort Guide.

647.95   IT
OGGETTO IN TAVOLA. 2/yr. Agepe Gruppo Editoriale, Via Domenico Trentacoste 9, 20134 Milan, Italy. TEL 02-215621. FAX 02-2640330. Ed. Livia Artuffo. adv.: B&W page L.3400000, color page L.4200000; trim 204 x 295; adv. contact: Angelo Borrello. circ. 9,234. **Document type:** trade publication.

OHIO BEVERAGE JOURNAL; first trade journal of Ohio's beverage, restaurant and hotel industry. see *BEVERAGES*

647.97 917.1   CN
ONTARIO BED & BREAKFAST GUIDE. 1991. a. Can.$3.50. Charles Productions Inc., 240 Westwood Rd., Ste. 9B, Guelph, Ont. N1H 7W9, Canada. TEL 514-748-2547. FAX 519-748-0219. Ed. Ted Charles. adv. circ. 150,000. (tabloid format)

647.95   CN
ONTARIO RESTAURANT ASSOCIATION. MEMBERSHIP DIRECTORY & BUYERS' GUIDE. 1982. a. $200. Naylor Communications Ltd., 920 Yonge St., 6th Fl., Toronto, ON M4W 3C7, Canada. TEL 416-961-1028. FAX 416-924-4408. adv.

647.95   CN   ISSN 0834-0404
ONTARIO RESTAURANT NEWS; Ontario's hospitality business newspaper. (Includes quarterly supplement: Lodging Ontario) 1986. 12/yr. Can.$33.95. Ishcom Publications Inc., 169 The West Mall, Etobicoke, Ont. M9C 1C2, Canada. TEL 416-622-9332. FAX 416-622-6688. Ed. Steven Law; Pub. Steven Isherwood. adv.; bk.rev. circ. 17,200. (tabloid format; back issues avail.) **Document type:** newspaper.

647.95   AT
OPEN HOUSE. 1974. m. Aus.$40. (Australian Guild of Professional Cooks) Rank Publishing Co., 66 Chandos St., St. Leonards, N.S.W. 2065, Australia. (Co-sponsors: Academie Culinaire de France; Association of Professional Cooks and Chefs) Ed. Julia Newbould. adv. circ. 20,032.
    Description: Discusses the accomodation, foodservice and catering industries throughout Australia.

ORO VERDE. see *TRAVEL AND TOURISM*

658.91   NO
OSS VERTER IMELLOM.* m. (11/yr.). (Forbundet for Overnatting og Serveringnaeringen) Soelberg Trykk A-S, Kink Reklame A-S, P.O. Box 122, 2266 Arneberg, Norway. adv. circ. 1,900.

647.95   IT
OSTERIE D'ITALIA. a. L.36000 to non-members; members L.28000. Arcigola Slow Food Editore, Via della Mendicita istruita 14, 12042 Bra (CN), Italy. TEL 0172-426207. FAX 0172-421293.
    Description: Lists inns and taverns by region.

642.47   GW   ISSN 0343-7507
P V - REPORT. (Personal-Verpflegung); Catering - Operating - Versorgung. 1972. m. DM.60. (Internationale Kuechenmeister und Serviermeister Verband) E S Fachschriften Verlag GmbH, Paul-Gerhard-Allee 24, 81245 Munich, Germany. TEL 089-8347077. FAX 089-8341962. Ed. Elgo Schwaab. circ. 12,000. **Document type:** trade publication.

647.9 642.5   PK   ISSN 0250-4359
TX910.P35
PAKISTAN HOTEL AND RESTAURANT GUIDE. (Text in English) 1980. a. Rs.70($7) Maulai Enterprise, J-6-2, al-Naseer, Sharifabad, Federal B Area, Blk. No. 1, Karachi 75950, Pakistan. TEL 92-21-6322764. Ed. Syed Wali Ahmad Maulai. adv.; stat. circ. 5,000. **Document type:** directory.
    Incorporates (1973-1986): Pakistan Business and Shopping Guide (ISSN 0250-4340)

PAKISTAN HOTEL AND TRAVEL REVIEW. see *TRAVEL AND TOURISM*

647.9   PK   ISSN 0250-3654
PAKISTAN HOTEL GUIDE. (including business & shopping guide). (Text in English) 1957. a. Rs.70($7) Maulai Enterprise, J-6-2, al-Naseer, Federal B Area, Block No. 1, Karachi 75950, Pakistan. TEL 92-21-6322764. Ed. Syed Wali Ahmad Maulai. adv. contact: S.H. Fatimi. charts; stat. circ. 5,000. (back issues avail.) **Document type:** directory.

PALATE AND SPIRIT; the travel magazine for food lovers. see *TRAVEL AND TOURISM*

647.9   SP
PANORAMA DE HOSTELERIA. 24/yr. La Marina 61, 38001 Santa Cruz de Tenerife, Spain. TEL 22-28-89-02. Ed. F. Delgado Arbelo.

PENINSULA GROUP MAGAZINE. see *TRAVEL AND TOURISM*

914.1   UK
PINK PAGES; Scotland's premier guide to food and drink. 1977. m. £10. 123 Crown St., Aberdeen, Scotland. Ed. Bernard Holbrook. adv.; bk.rev. circ. 15,000.

647.95   IT
PIZZAPRESS. 10/yr. Futura International s.r.l., Via Alfieri 9, 20154 Milan, Italy. TEL 2-34-93-888. FAX 2-331-91-31. Ed. Antonio Primiceri. circ. 30,000.

642.5   FR   ISSN 0981-7301
PLAISIRS.* 1976. 10/yr. 70 F. 151 av. Charles de Gaulle, 92200 Neuilly, France. Ed. Rene Gessler. adv.; bk.rev.
    Former titles (until no.70, July-Aug. 1978): Gastronomie Magazine: l'Art Culinaire & Gastronomie (ISSN 0016-5115)

647.95   SP
LA POSADA. 12/yr. Circulo Gastonomico de Espana - Gastronomic Circle of Spain, Hermanos Garate 6, 5o B, 28020 Madrid, Spain. TEL 1-571-85-64. FAX 1-572-21-64.

647.9   CN
PRAIRIE HOTELIER. 1977. bi-m. Can.$18. Naylor Communications Ltd. (Winnipeg), 100 Sutherland Ave., Winnipeg, Man. R2W 3C7, Canada. TEL 604-985-8711. (Co-sponsors: Manitoba Hotel Association; Hotels Association of Saskatchewan; Alberta Hotel Association) Ed. Janis Connolly. adv.
    Formerly: Prairie Hotelman.

647.94   UK
PRESTIGE. 1972. 2/yr. (Prestige Hotels) Guest Publications Ltd., 25 Manchester Sq., London W1, England. Ed. June B. Quinn. adv.

PRESTIGE HOTEL AND RESTAURANT INTERIORS. see *INTERIOR DESIGN AND DECORATION*

PREVIEW BERMUDA. see *TRAVEL AND TOURISM*

PROGRESS IN TOURISM, RECREATION AND HOSPITALITY MANAGEMENT. see *TRAVEL AND TOURISM*

642.5   UK
PUB FOOD. 10/yr. Quantum Publishing Ltd., 29-31 Lower Coombe St., Croydon, Surrey CR9 1LX, England. TEL 081-681-2099. FAX 081-680-8828. Ed. Dominic Roskrow. adv. circ. 30,000. **Document type:** trade publication.
    Formerly (until 1993): Pub Food Business.

647.7   AT   ISSN 0818-9889
Q M A A NEWS. 1980. bi-m. Aus.$42. Queensland Motel & Accommodation Association Inc., 201 Wickham Terrace, Brisbane, Qld. 4000, Australia. TEL 07-831-8628. FAX 07-832-2983. Ed. C.M. Llewellyn. adv.; bk.rev. circ. 625.
    Description: General interest news to motel and accommodation property owners.

642.5   UK
RECEPTION. m. 46b Highgate, Kendal, Cumbria LA9 4TF, England. TEL 0539-730509. FAX 0539-740003. Ed. Julian Whittle.

RECOMMENDED COUNTRY INNS: MID-ATLANTIC AND CHESAPEAKE REGION. see *TRAVEL AND TOURISM*

RECOMMENDED COUNTRY INNS: NEW ENGLAND. see *TRAVEL AND TOURISM*

RECOMMENDED COUNTRY INNS: ROCKY MOUNTAIN REGION. see *TRAVEL AND TOURISM*

RECOMMENDED COUNTRY INNS: THE MIDWEST. see *TRAVEL AND TOURISM*

RECOMMENDED COUNTRY INNS: THE SOUTH. see *TRAVEL AND TOURISM*

RECOMMENDED COUNTRY INNS: THE SOUTHWEST. see *TRAVEL AND TOURISM*

RECOMMENDED COUNTRY INNS: THE WEST COAST. see *TRAVEL AND TOURISM*

REPORT ON INSTITUTIONAL FOODSERVICE. see *FOOD AND FOOD INDUSTRIES*

658.91   US   ISSN 1065-0849
RESORTS & PARKS PURCHASING GUIDE. 1965. a. $42.50. Klevens Publications, Inc., 7600 Ave. V, Littlerock, CA 93543. TEL 805-944-4111. FAX 805-944-1800. adv.; tr.lit. circ. 16,874.
    Description: Provides sources to purchase materials and products used in operation of family-oriented outdoor resort and recreation facilities.

647.95 647.94   GW   ISSN 0344-4422
RESTAURANT AND HOTEL MANAGEMENT; Magazin fuer Inhaber, Direktoren und Fuehrungskraefte der gehobenen Hotellerie und Gastronomie. m. DM.71.50. Rhenania-Fachverlag GmbH, Possmoorweg 5, 22301 Hamburg, Germany. FAX 040-2717-2069. TELEX 213214. Ed. Eberhard B. Freise. circ. 7,302. **Document type:** trade publication.

HOTELS AND RESTAURANTS

658.91   US   ISSN 0884-0695
RESTAURANT BRIEFING;* the restaurateur's news digest. 1975. m. $65. Walter Mathews Associates, Inc. (Subsidiary of: American Express, Co.), 799 Broadway, No. 309, New York, NY 10003-6811. TEL 212-921-4314. FAX 212-719-9382. (Subscr. to: Box 889, Midtown Sta., New York, NY 10018) bk.rev.; index. circ. 87,000. (looseleaf format; back issues avail.)
   Formerly: Briefing (New York).
   Description: Highlights the advertising, promotional, customer service, managerial, and legislative aspects of the restaurant industry.

642.57   US   ISSN 0097-8043
TP628   CODEN: RSBSAY
RESTAURANT BUSINESS. 1902. 18/yr. $79. Bill Communications, Inc., 355 Park Ave. S., 3rd Fl., New York, NY 10010-1789. TEL 212-592-6200. FAX 212-592-6509. Ed. Scott Allmenbinger. adv.; bk.rev.; illus.; tr.lit. circ. 130,000. (also avail. in microform from UMI; microfiche from CIS; reprint service avail. from UMI) **Indexed:** Art.Hosp.& Tour., B.P.I., Bus.Ind., Chic.Per.Ind., Food Sci.& Tech.Abstr., PROMT, SRI, Tr.& Indus.Ind.
  ●Also available online. Vendor(s): DIALOG Information Services, Inc., Mead Data Central, Inc.
  —BLDSC (7777.770000); Faxon; UnCover; UMI.
   Formerly: Fast Food (ISSN 0014-8725)
   Description: Information on food, equipment, supplies, services and personnel for restaurant chain executives and independent restaurateurs, hotel food and beverage executives, contact feeders, and foodservice in retail stores.

647.95   US
RESTAURANT DIGEST.* 1986. m. $12.75. Azusa Group, Inc., 15215 Shady Grove Rd., No. 305, Rockville, MD 20850-3235. TEL 202-328-3811. FAX 202-328-9742. adv. circ. 18,635.
   Description: Provides news, interviews and market information for the Mid-Atlantic states.

642.5   US
RESTAURANT EXCHANGE NEWS.* 1979. m. $18. Box 2507, Greenwich, CT 06836-2507. TEL 914-638-1108. Ed. Robert B. Melton. circ. 10,021.

642.5   US
RESTAURANT - FOOD REVIEW. 1988. w. $36. E W A Publications, 275 Bay 37th St., Brooklyn, NY 11214. TEL 718-996-5406. FAX 718-373-1352. Ed. Kenneth Brown. adv. contact: Adrienne Knoll. circ. 206,000. (tabloid format) **Document type:** newspaper.
   Description: Contains restaurant reviews, personality features, food stories, and general restaurant news.

642.5   US   ISSN 0147-9989
TX901   CODEN: RHOSDP
RESTAURANT HOSPITALITY. 1919. m. $55 (free to qualified personnel). Penton Publishing (Subsidiary of: Pittway Publishing), 1100 Superior Ave., Cleveland, OH 44114-2543. TEL 216-696-7000. FAX 216-696-8765. (Subscr. to: Box 95759, Cleveland, OH 44101) Ed. Michael Deluca. adv.; circ. 138,000 (controlled). (also avail. in microform from UMI; reprint service avail. from UMI) **Indexed:** ABI Inform., Account.Ind. (1974-), Art.Hosp.& Tour., Bus.Ind., Food Sci.& Tech.Abstr., PROMT, Tr.& Indus.Ind.
  —Faxon; UnCover; UMI. CCC.
   Former titles (until 1976): Hospitality, Restaurant (ISSN 0098-3292); (until 1967): American Restaurant Hospitality; (until 1962): American Restaurant Magazine; (until 1928): American Restaurant.
   Description: All phases of management in commercial food service operations.

647.95   AT
RESTAURANT HOTEL CLUB & CATERER. 1984. q. R L Gordon Nominees Pty Ltd, 25 Foss St., Palmyra, W.A. 6157, Australia. Ed. Bob Gordon.
   Incorporates: Western Australian Hotel, Club and Caterer.

642.5   US
RESTAURANT INDUSTRY OPERATIONS REPORT. 1973. a. $38 to non members; members $19. National Restaurant Association, 1200 17th St., N.W., Washington, DC 20036. TEL 202-331-5900. FAX 202-331-2429. Ed. Hudson Riehle. circ. 2,500. (also avail. in microfiche from CIS) **Indexed:** SRI.
   Former titles: Restaurant Operations Report for Tableservice Restaurants; (until 1978?): Tableservice Restaurant Operations Report; Restaurant Operations (ISSN 0190-9452)

642.5   GW   ISSN 0939-8406
RESTAURANT INTERNATIONAL. 1964. bi-m. DM.46 (foreign DM.58). Gildefachverlag GmbH & Co. KG, Postfach 1351, 31043 Alfeld, Germany. TEL 05181-80040. circ. 15,100. **Document type:** trade publication.
   Formerly (until 1990): Chef International (ISSN 0170-1800)

642.5   US
RESTAURANT JOURNAL. 1937. m. $48. Pennsylvania Restaurant Association, 100 State St., Harrisburg, PA 17011-1034. TEL 717-232-4433. Ed. Morna McEver Golletz. adv. contact: Brad Wastler. circ. 5,000. (back issues avail.) **Document type:** trade publication.
   Description: Covers legislative and business news affecting the restaurant industry.

647.95   US
RESTAURANT MANAGEMENT INSIDER. 1980. bi-w. $225. Walker Communications Inc., 1541 Morris Ave., Bronx, NY 10457-8702. TEL 718-583-8060. FAX 718-583-8258. Ed. Michael Schau. circ. 536. (reprint service avail. from UMI)
  —CCC.
   Former titles: Restaurant Management Today; Chain Restaurant Today; Chain Marketing and Management (ISSN 0733-012X)
   Description: For owners, managers and marketing executives in the restaurant, food service and hospitality industries.

642.5   US   ISSN 0048-7406
RESTAURANT NEWS.* 1950. m. $15. Hani Publications, 571 Whitaker Rd., La Grange, GA 30240-3779. Ed. Harold Fertig. adv.; bk.rev.; illus. circ. 15,000. (tabloid format; back issues avail.)
   Incorporates: Mobile and Industrial Catering.

647.95   US
RESTAURANT NEWS OF THE ROCKIES. 1986. m. $10. D & H Communications, 8962 E. Hampden Ave., Box 156, Denver, CO 80231-4911. TEL 303-751-5788. Ed. Harlan Ihrke. adv. circ. 13,489.
   Description: For owners and managers of foodservice operations in the Rocky Mountain region.

642.5   US
RESTAURANT REVIEW. 1979. w. $15. E W A Publications, 275 Bay 37th St., Brooklyn, NY 11214. TEL 718-996-5406. FAX 718-373-1352. Ed. Kenneth Brown. adv. contact: Adrienne Knoll. circ. 134,000. (tabloid format) **Document type:** newspaper.

647   US
RESTAURANT ROW MAGAZINE. 1983. m. $24. Restaurant Row Inc., Box 13109, Long Beach, CA 90803-8109. TEL 213-438-6565. Ed. Ron Hodges. adv. contact: Tom Bauder. circ. 35,000. **Document type:** consumer publication.
   Description: Covers the Los Angeles and Orange County markets with articles on restaurant dining, food, wines and spirits, and hotels and resorts.

674.95   US
RESTAURANT SHOW DAILY. 1985. a. free to convention attendees. Penton Publishing (Subsidiary of: Pittway Company), 1100 Superior Ave., Cleveland, OH 44114-2543. TEL 216-696-7000. FAX 216-696-8765. (Subscr. to: Box 95759, Cleveland, OH 44101) Ed. Mary Hofer-Clem. circ. 16,410. (tabloid format) **Document type:** trade publication.
   Description: Emphasis on marketing, finance, labor management, advertising, menu development, facility design, sanitation and facility exchange.

647.95   US   ISSN 1040-7030
RESTAURANT WINE; buying - selling - serving: the full service guide to on sale beverage profits. (Former name of issuing body: Wiegand and Boblitt) 1988. 6/yr. $99 in U.S.; Canada $112 (foreign $145). Wine Profits, Inc., 306 Randolph St., Box 222, Napa, CA 94559-0222. TEL 707-224-4777. FAX 707-224-6740. Ed. Ronn R. Wiegand. bk.rev. circ. 2,000.
   Description: Guide to wine service, sales, and marketing for the hospitality industry focusing on trends, innovative staff training ideas, wine marketing, and inventory control.

338.4   US   ISSN 0273-5520
TX1   CODEN: RINSDR
RESTAURANTS AND INSTITUTIONS. 1937. 24/yr. $104.95 (Canada $192.55; Mexico $179.95; elsewhere $234.95). Cahners Publishing Company (Des Plaines), Division of Reed Elsevier Inc., 1350 E. Touhy Ave., Box 5080, Des Plaines, IL 60017-5080. TEL 708-635-8800. FAX 708-299-8622. (Subscr. to: 44 Cook St., Denver, CO 80206. TEL 800-662-7776) Ed. Michael Bartlett. adv.; bk.rev.; illus.; tr.lit.; index. circ. 162,000. (also avail. in microfiche from CIS) **Indexed:** Art.Hosp.& Tour., Hlth.Ind., PROMT, SRI, Tr.& Indus.Ind. **Document type:** trade publication.
  —BLDSC (7777.778000); Faxon; UnCover; UMI. CCC.
   Incorporates (in 1986): Bar Business; **Former titles:** Institutions; Institutions - Volume Feeding (ISSN 0094-6745); Institutions - Volume Feeding Management (ISSN 0020-3610)
   Description: For the foodservice and lodging industry, features food trends, new products, recipes, menu concepts and merchandising ideas from the most successful restaurants and institutional foodservice operations around the US.

658.8   US
RESTAURANTS & INSTITUTIONS MARKETPLACE. 1987. 6/yr. $49.95 (Canada & Mexico $74.95; elsewhere $84.95). Cahners Publishing Company (Des Plaines), Division of Reed Elsevier Inc., 1350 E. Touhy Ave., Box 5080, Des Plaines, IL 60017-5080. TEL 708-635-8800. FAX 708-299-8622. (Subscr. to: 44 Cook St., Denver, CO 80206. TEL 800-662-7776) Ed. Molly Ingram. circ. 201,000. (tabloid format) **Document type:** trade publication.
   Description: Contains new product reviews, recipe cards and ideas for the foodservice industry.

647.95   US
RESTAURANTS, RESORTS & HOTELS. m. $30 (foreign $40). Trade Publishing, 41 Shea Terr., Stratford, CT 06497-2422. TEL 203-378-1223. FAX 203-378-7285. Ed. John Mortimer. adv.: B&W page $4975; adv. contact: Nick Glowatsky. circ. 91,000.
   Formerly (until Dec. 1993): Restaurant Merchandising News.

647.95   US   ISSN 0890-5584
TX901
RESTAURANTS U S A. 1919. m. (11/yr.). $125 to non-members. National Restaurant Association, 1200 17th St., N.W., Washington, DC 20036-3097. TEL 202-331-5900. Ed. Paul Moomaw. cum.index: 1982-1989. circ. 30,000. **Indexed:** Potato Abstr., PROMT. **Document type:** trade publication.
  —BLDSC (7777.790000); Faxon.
   Former titles: N R A News (ISSN 0465-7004); National Restaurant Association News.
   Description: Covers foodservice industry developments and trends. Includes feature stories and news columns.

642.5   US
RESTAURATEUR. 1947. q. $20. Restaurant Association of Metropolitan Washington, 7926 Jones Branch Dr., Ste. 530, McLean, VA 22102-3303. TEL 703-356-1315. FAX 703-893-4926. Ed. Cathy Jones. adv.; bk.rev.; charts; stat.; illus. circ. 4,000. **Document type:** trade publication.
   Formerly: Restaurant News.
   Description: Designed to enhance the knowledge of the food service professional by discussing areas of professional concern.

642.5 SW ISSN 0034-5814
RESTAURATOEREN. 1916. 10/yr. SEK 290. Sveriges Hotell- och Restaurangfoerbund - Swedish Hotels' and Restaurants' Association, P.O. Box 1158, 111 81 Stockholm, Sweden. (Co-sponsor: Sveriges Arbetsgivarefoerening Foer Hotell och Restauranger - Swedish Hotel and Restaurant Employers Association) Ed. Staffan Aakerlund. adv.; bk.rev. circ. 8,000.
Formerly (until 1945): Tidskrift foer Hotell- och Restaurangnaeringen; (until 1940): Restauratoeren.

647.954 DK ISSN 0906-4397
RESTAURATOEREN, DANMARK. Variant title: Restauratoeren, Jylland-Fyn. 1943. 6/yr. Restauratoerforeningen af 1883 for Fyns Amt, Odense, Fyn, Denmark.
Formerly (until 1991): Restauratoeren paa Fyen (ISSN 0906-4389); Incorporates (1982-1991): Restauratoeren (ISSN 0108-092X)

647.9 FR
RESTO-FLASH. (Supplement to: L'Hotellerie) 1965. 10/yr. avail. only with subscr to: L'Hotellerie. Societe d'Editions et de Periodiques Techniques, B.P. 152, 92203 Neuilly-Seine cedex, France. TEL 42-62-05-22. FAX 46-40-00-74. TELEX 612009F. Ed. Michel Milinaire. adv.; charts; illus.; stat.; index. circ. 7,000.
Formerly (until 1983): Prestige de l'Hotellerie, de la Restauration et de Tourism (ISSN 0032-7921)

663.2 SP
REVISTA DE GASTRONOMIA Y ENOLOGIA. 1985. m. 3750 ptas. Ediciones y Estudios, Grupo I.P., Plaza de Alfonso X el Sabio, 7, 1-4, 08025 Barcelona, Spain. TEL (93)347 59 00. TELEX 98662. Ed. Miguel de Haro.

642.5 CL
REVISTA DINERS - MUNDO. 1963. m. Diner's Club of Chile, Providencia 2653, Santiago, Chile. circ. 32,000.

647.9 910.2 FR ISSN 0035-3140
REVUE GENERALE DE L'HOTELLERIE, DE LA GASTRONOMIE ET DU TOURISME.* 1910. m. 100 F. Societe E G T, 6 rue de Reims, 94230 Cachan, France. TEL 46-63-27-43. Ed. J. Deit. adv.; bk.rev.; illus.; index.

647.9 FR
REVUE TECHNIQUE DES HOTELS, RESTAURANTS, COLLECTIVITES. 1948. m. 350 F. Nouvelles du Monde, 10 rue Beffroy, 92200 Neuilly sur Seine, France. TEL 46-40-01-01. FAX 46-40-19-49. Ed. Nelly Rioux. adv.; illus.; index. circ. 20,000.
Formerly: Revue Technique des Hotels, Restaurants, Bars, Brasseries, Limonadiers, Tabacs, Habitats Collectifs (ISSN 0035-4228)

647.94 GW
RHEINISCH-PFAELZISCHE HOTELS AND GASTSTAETTEN. m. (Bezirksverband Hotel- und Gaststaettengewerbe Rheinhessen-Pfalz e.V.) Hammerstein Verlag, Postfach 1213, 56172 Vallendar, Germany. TEL 0261-69872. FAX 0261-671204. **Document type:** bulletin.

647.94 IT
RIALTO - HOTEL MAGAZINE. 9/yr. S M & C s.r.l., Via Montecervino 4, 20149 Milan, Italy. TEL 2-48-17-782. FAX 2-48-19-34-05. Ed. Sergio Cesana. adv.: B&W or color page L.4600000; 210 x 297. circ. 9,521.

647.95 IT
RISTORANTE. 11/yr. Via Ramazzotti 20, 20052 Monza-Parco, Italy. TEL 39-49-30-01. FAX 39-49-31-02. Ed. Paolo Altieri. circ. 40,000.

647.95 IT ISSN 1120-6039
RISTORAZIONE COLLETIVA - CATERING. 1976. 10/yr. L.90000 (Europe L.155000) (effective 1994). Via A. Pestalozza 31, 20131 Milan, Italy. TEL 2-70-63-00-22. FAX 2-266-80-516. Ed. Luigi Porro. adv. circ. 24,500.

647.95 IT ISSN 1120-6144
RISTORAZIONE PIU. 1986. 10/yr. L.60000. Editrice Arti Poligrafiche Europee, Via Casella 16, 20156 Milan, Italy. TEL 02-330221. FAX 02-39214341. Ed. Antonio Ghiorzo. adv.: B&W page L.6650000, color page L.9500000; trim 266 x 392. charts; illus.; circ. 30,000 (controlled).

647.95 IT
RISTORAZIONE ROMANA. 12/yr. Corso Vittorio Emanuele II, 326, 00186 Rome, Italy. TEL 6-68-69-068. FAX 6-68-75-947. Ed. Giulio Somma.

ROBERT NOAH'S PARIS EN CUISINE NEWSLETTER; the insider's guide to gastronomic news of France. see *FOOD AND FOOD INDUSTRIES*

647.9 IR ISSN 0035-9262
ROYAL TEHRAN HILTON. 1963. q. Rs.350($5) Interpub Co. Ltd., 140 Abbasabad Ave., Passage Parvin (4th Floor), Teheran, Iran. Ed. A.M. Arbabi. adv.; bk.rev.; film rev.; play rev.; illus. circ. 5,000.

647.94 AU
RUND UM DEN GAST. 1983. 8/yr. Maclean Hunter GmbH, Loquaiplatz 12, A-1061 Vienna, Austria. TEL 01-599600. FAX 01-5996021. Ed. Wolfgang Daehnhard. circ. 11,200. **Document type:** trade publication.

642.5 SZ
SALZ & PFEFFER. 11/yr. Postfach 351, CH-8401 Winterthur, Switzerland. TEL 052-252593. FAX 052-252735. Ed. Daniel Eggli. circ. 15,000.

642.5 US
SCHOOL FOOD SERVICE NEWS. bi-m. free to qualified personnel. Department of Public Instruction, 125 S. Webster St., Madison, WI 53702. TEL 608-267-9228.

642.5 SZ
SCHWEIZER CAFETIER. 10/yr. 50 SFr. A N A G Annoncen und Verlag AG, Winzerstr. 112, Postfach 132, CH-8049 Zurich, Switzerland. TEL 01-3413080. FAX 01-3411811. Ed. Charles Frei. circ. 5,200. **Document type:** trade publication.
Formerly: Cafeteria.

642.5 SZ
SCHWEIZER GASTRO REVUE. m. Polygon Marketing AG, Rosenbergstr. 51, CH-9000 St. Gallen, Switzerland. TEL 071-231823. FAX 071-231846. circ. 21,500.

642.5 SZ
SCHWEIZER GASTRONOMIE. 1895. w. 125 SFr. Schweizer Wirteverband, Blumenfeldstr. 20, CH-8046 Zurich, Switzerland. FAX 01-3721828. TELEX 817845. Ed. H. Keller. adv.; bk.rev. circ. 17,551. **Document type:** trade publication.
Formerly: Schweizerische Wirte-Zeitung (ISSN 0036-780X)

642.5 SZ ISSN 0048-9514
SCHWEIZER HOTEL JOURNAL. 1971. q. 75 SFr. Verlag Schweizer Journal AG, Kreuzstr. 11, CH-8712 Staefa, Switzerland. Ed. Judith Frey. adv.; illus. **Document type:** trade publication.

642.5 UK
SCOTTISH CATERER. m. £25.30. Peebles Publishing Group Ltd., Bergius House, Clifton St., Glasgow G3 7LA, Scotland. TEL 041-331-1022. FAX 041-331-1395. Ed. Margaret Hughes. circ. 14,000. **Document type:** trade publication.

647.9 UK
SCOTTISH YOUTH HOSTELS ASSOCIATION HANDBOOK. 1931. a. £0.95. Scottish Youth Hostels Association, 7 Glebe Crescent, Stirling FK8 2JA, Scotland. TEL 0786-451181. FAX 0786-450198. TELEX 779689. adv. circ. 50,000. **Document type:** bulletin.

647.9 SP
SEMANA HOSTELERA. 52/yr. P. Delicias 65, Bl.C, Esc. 3 2o, 28045 Madrid, Spain. TEL 1-468-27-12. FAX 1-467-10-17.

647.95 US
SERVER - PENNSYLVANIA. (In regional editions for eastern and western Pennsylvania.) 1979. m. $19.95. Group Publications, Inc., 1816 Brownsville Rd., Pittsburgh, PA 15210-3908. TEL 412-885-7600. FAX 412-885-7617. Ed. Lisa Stewart. adv. circ. 21,000. **Document type:** trade publication.
Description: Covers new products, marketing and promotion ideas, and success stories for the food, beverage and hospitality industry.

647 FR
SERVICE COMPRIS. m. Societe d'Edition et de Periodiques Techniques, 9 rue Ybry, B.P. 152, 92200 Neuilly sur Seine, France. TEL 46-40-08-08. FAX 46-40-00-74.

647 FR
SERVICE TRAITEUR. 5/yr. 4 rue Santerre, 75012 Paris, France. TEL 43-45-03-33. FAX 43-44-51-41. Ed. Serge Benard. circ. 20,000.

647.94 UK
SHERATON LONDON MAGAZINE. 1978. 4/yr. (Sheraton Hotels - London) E & N Associates Ltd., 20 Fouberts Place, London W1V 2JU, England. Ed. Julie White. adv. circ. 30,000.

SILENCE COURIER; Gaestezeitschrift der Silencehotels Deutschland. see *GENERAL INTEREST PERIODICALS* — Germany

647.94 SP
SOL MAGAZINE. 4/yr. C B B Ediciones S.A., Andres Borrego 19, 1o P.C., 28004 Madrid, Spain. TEL 1-523-12-60. FAX 1-523-15-01. Ed. Cristina B. Bafico.

SOMMELIERS. see *BEVERAGES*

SOPHISTICATED LEISURE TRAVEL DIRECTORY. see *TRAVEL AND TOURISM*

658.91 SA ISSN 0489-8567
SOUTH AFRICAN LICENSEE'S GUARDIAN. 1950. a. R.80. Ramsay, Son & Parker (Pty) Ltd., P.O. Box 180, Howard Place, 7450 Cape Town, South Africa. TEL 27-21-5311391. FAX 27-21-5313333. Ed. Mike Froud. adv.; stat.; tr.lit. circ. 700. **Document type:** trade publication, directory.
Description: Directory of the South African beer, wine and liquor industry, listing trade associations, producers, importers and wholesalers, products, as well as covering training courses, licences and other legal topics.

642.5 UK
SOUTH WALES CATERER. q. F S W Publications, 66 Bracondale, Norwich NR1 2BE, England. TEL 0603-623303. FAX 0603-666238. Ed. G. Cooper. adv. contact: K. O'Gorman. **Document type:** trade publication.

SOUTHEAST FOOD SERVICE NEWS. see *FOOD AND FOOD INDUSTRIES*

SOUTHERN CALIFORNIA GUIDE; the current directory of restaurants, art galleries, hotels, motels, entertainment, shopping, sightseeing, tourist attractions. see *TRAVEL AND TOURISM*

642.5 UK
SOUTHERN CATERER UPDATE. q. F S W Publications, 66 Bracondale, Norwich NR1 2BE, England. TEL 0603-623303. FAX 0603-666238. Ed. G. Cooper. adv. contact: K. O'Gorman. **Document type:** trade publication.

647 CN
SPA MANAGEMENT. 1990. q. $32. Publicom Inc., C.P. 365, Place d'Armes, Montreal, PQ H2Y 3H1, Canada. TEL 514-274-0004. FAX 514-274-5884. Ed. Guy Jonkman. adv. circ. 9,130.
Description: Trade publication for spa directors and spa resort executives located mainly in Canada and the US. Also distributed in Europe, Japan, Australia, New Zealand, Mexico and the Caribbean.

658.91 658 US
SPECIAL EVENTS. 1982. m. $36. Miramar Publishing Co., Box 3640, Culver City, CA 90231-3640. TEL 310-337-9717. Ed. Liese Gardner. adv. circ. 22,506.

647.94 GW
STEIGENBERGER JOURNAL. (Text in English, German) 1952. 4/yr. DM.18. Steigenberger Hotels AG, Hauptabteilung Konzern-Medien, Bethmannstr. 33, Postfach 160663, 60311 Frankfurt a.M., Germany. TEL 069-21550718. FAX 069-215540. Ed. Marina Colbatzky. adv. circ. 60,000. **Document type:** trade publication.
Description: Magazine of the Steigenberger hotel chain containing articles about hotels, health spas and cultural events of interest to tourists.

HOTELS AND RESTAURANTS

642.47 — UK
STEWARD. q. National Union of Club Stewards, Edwards Bldg., Regent St., Hinckley LL10 0BB, England. TEL 0455-614060.

SUNBELT FOODSERVICE. see *FOOD AND FOOD INDUSTRIES*

647.9 — SW — ISSN 0346-2137
SVENSK HOTELLREVY. 1918. m. SEK 120. Hotell- och Restaurangsanstaelldas Foerbund, P.O. Box 1143, S-111 81 Stockholm, Sweden. TEL 46-8-781-02-00. FAX 46-8-20-47-28. Ed. Kerstin Ekberg. adv.: B&W page SEK 18900, color page SEK 34700; trim 185 x 270. bk.rev.; film rev.; play rev.; illus. circ. 57,500. (back issues avail.)
Document type: trade publication.
Description: Deals with all aspects of the hotel, restaurant and tourism industries in Sweden.

642.5 — SZ
SWISS HOGA. a. Kuhn Annoncen AG, Koeschenruetistr. 109, CH-8052 Zurich, Switzerland. TEL 01-3021500. FAX 01-3022022. Ed. R. Kuhn. circ. 3,000.

642.5 — AT — ISSN 1039-2351
SYDNEY RESTAURANT SURVEY. 1990. a. Aus.$9.95. H W W Pty. Ltd. (Horan Wall & Walker), 15-19 Prospect St., Surry Hills, N.S.W. 2010, Australia. TEL 02-331-6600. FAX 02-380-5533. **Document type:** trade publication.
Formerly: Sydney Eats Out (ISSN 1035-7262)
Description: Restaurant guide.

647.94 — GW
T V PROGRAMM FUER NOBEL HOTELS. m. E R M I Guide Orschel KG, Malvenweg 4, 51061 Cologne, Germany. TEL 0221-634091. FAX 0221-634677. **Document type:** trade publication.

647.94 — CH
TAIPEI HILTON. 1977. 6/yr. (Taipei Hilton Hotel) Mei Ya Publications, 5-1 Lane 124, Ching-Chiang St., Taipei, Taiwan, Republic of China. Ed. F.C. Lu. adv. circ. 8,000.

642.5 — UK
TEAM (LONDON). q. free. 22-24 Worple Rd., Wimbledon, London SW19 4DD, England. TEL 081-947-3131. FAX 081-944-6552. Ed. Sharon Watson. adv.; bk.rev.; circ. 40,000. **Document type:** consumer publication, trade publication.
Formerly (until 1992): Five Star News.
Description: Contains information about food and leisure, hotels, food manufacturing, distribution and retail, leisure services, and professional sports.

647.9 — SP
TECNO HOSTELERIA. 11/yr. Gran Via Carlos III, 86 7o, 08028 Barcelona, Spain. TEL 3-330-70-52. FAX 3-330-74-96. Ed. D. Jorge Vila Fradera. circ. 10,214.

647 — SP
TECNO HOTEL; vida colectiva. Bound with: Editur. 1963. m. 10200 ptas. Ediciones Turisticas, S.A., Gran via Carlos III 86, Barcelona 28, Spain. Ed. Jorge Vila Fradera. adv.; bk.rev.; illus.

642.57 — IT
TECNOREST; metodi, tecnologia e cultura della ristorazione. 1978. bi-m. Iniziative Editoriali Esercizi Pubblici, Piazza Risorgimento 10, 20129 Milan, Italy. TEL 2-71-89-11. FAX 2-76-11-10-42. (Co-sponsor: Associazione Nazionale delle Aziende di Ristorazione Colletiva) Ed. Lino Arturo Cepollina. adv. circ. 6,860.

647.9 — SP
TENEDORES Y ESTRELLAS. 6/yr. Mazustegui 21, 4a planta, 48006 Bilbao, Spain. TEL 4-415-90-22. FAX 4-416-27-43. Ed. Teresa del Hoyo. circ. 7,000.

647.95 — US
TENNESSEE RESTAURANTEUR. bi-m. Images Publications, 505 Mulberry St., Loudon, TN 37774. TEL 615-458-3560. FAX 615-458-4095. Ed. Ronnie Hart. adv. circ. 1,600.

THIS WEEK IN THE POCONOS. see *TRAVEL AND TOURISM*

647 — FR
LA TOQUE ET LE VERRE. 3/yr. Editions P.P., 103 rue Bechevelin, B.P. 7235, 69354 Lyon Cedex 07, France. TEL 78-72-13-08. FAX 72-72-98-37. Ed. Jacques Freville. circ. 10,000.

642.47 — FR
TOQUES BLANCHES. 4/yr. 123 rue des Dames, 75017 Paris, France. TEL 43-87-73-70. FAX 43-87-68-29. Ed. Georges Prade. circ. 3,000.

642.56 — CN
TORONTO LIFE EPICURE. 1974. 4/yr. Toronto Life Publishing Co. Ltd., 59 Front St. E., Toronto, Ont. M5E 1B3, Canada. TEL 416-364-3333. Ed. Joseph Hoare. adv.; illus.
Former titles: Toronto Life Gourmet Guide & Toronto Life Restaurant and Gourmet Guide.

TOTAL FOOD SERVICE. see *FOOD AND FOOD INDUSTRIES*

658 — US — ISSN 1069-5591
TOTAL QUALITY IN HOSPITALITY; the manager's guide to building profits through customer satisfaction. 1988. m. $167. Magna Publications, Inc., 2718 Dryden Dr., Madison, WI 53704. TEL 608-246-3580; 800-433-0499. FAX 608-246-3597. Ed. Barbara Mulhern; Pub. Karen Stocker. charts; illus.; stat. circ. 800. (back issues avail.) **Document type:** trade publication.
—CCC.
Formerly (until 1993): Successful Hotel Marketer (ISSN 1040-600X)
Description: Offers practical hotel marketing strategies, creative ideas, and innovative techniques.

647 910 — FR
TOURISME ET GASTRONOMIE. 10/yr. S E T E G, 44 rue de la Garenne, 69005 Lyon, France. TEL 78-59-33-80. FAX 78-59-78-64. Ed. Louis Camus. circ. 28,000.

647.94 — FR — ISSN 0150-7540
TOUTES LES NOUVELLES DE L'HOTELLERIE ET DU TOURISME. 1971. m. 200 F. Sedotourmovico, 4 rue Barye, 75017 Paris, France. adv.; bk.rev. circ. 21,000.
Description: Aimed at professionals in the hotel and restaurant industry.

642.5 — IT
TRADIZIONE NELLA RISTORAZIONE ITALIANA. (Text in English, German, Italian) a. Ordine Ristoratori Professionisti Italiani, Via Quarto, 12, 16148 Genoa, Italy. (Co-sponsor: Ministero del Turismo e dello Spettacolo)

647.94 — CN
TRAVEL & ADVENTURE GUIDE IN B.C.. 1989. a. Can.$27 (foreign $33). Westcoast Publishing Ltd., 1496 West 72nd Ave., Vancouver, BC V6P 3C8, Canada. TEL 604-266-7433. FAX 604-263-8620. Ed. Brian Gauvin. adv. circ. 10,500.
Formerly: Westcoast Hospitality (ISSN 1182-2783)

TRAVEL AND HOSPITALITY CAREER DIRECTORY. see *OCCUPATIONS AND CAREERS*

TRAVEL NEWS ASIA. see *TRAVEL AND TOURISM*

TRAVEL TRADE GAZETTE EUROPA. see *TRAVEL AND TOURISM*

647.94 — US
TRENDS IN THE HOTEL INDUSTRY. Regional editions: New York City Report. Massachusetts Report. New Hampshire Report. Rhode Island Report. U S A Edition (ISSN 0276-5357) International Edition (US ISSN 0741-7985) 1936. m. $150 for New York City report; Massachusetts $100. Pannell Kerr Forster - P K F Consulting, 420 Lexington Ave., Ste. 2400, New York, NY 10170. TEL 212-867-8000. FAX 212-986-8162. **Document type:** newsletter.
Former titles (until 1980): Trends in the Hotel - Motel Business (ISSN 0741-7985); (until 1961): Trends in the Hotel Industry (ISSN 0741-7993)

TURISMOHOTEL. see *TRAVEL AND TOURISM*

647 — TU
TURKEY: HOTELS - CAMPING. (Text in English, French, German, Italian and Turkish) 1964. a. free. Ministry of Culture and Tourism - Turizm ve Tanitma Bakanligi, Gazi Mustafa Kemal Bulvari 33, Ankara, Turkey. adv. circ. 20,000.
Formerly: Hotel Guide to Turkey.

647.95 — US
TURTLE SOUP. m. $13.50. 7697 Ninth St., Buena Vista, CA 90621. TEL 714-994-4320. Ed. Orris Abbott. adv.; circ. 35,000 (paid). **Document type:** trade publication.

142.57 663 — IT
TUTTI AL BAR; mensile di informazione e di aggiornamento per i professionisti del bar. 1978. m. (11/yr.). L.5000 (foreign L.10000). Tuttopress Editrice s.r.l., Via Cagliero, 21, 20125 Milan, Italy. TEL 02-6682834. FAX 02-6072185. Ed. Silvano Rusmini. adv.; bk.rev.; circ. 170,000 (controlled). **Document type:** trade publication.

U T; revija za ugostiteljstvo i turizam. see *TRAVEL AND TOURISM*

647.94 — SZ
UNION HELVETIA. (Text in French, German, Italian) 1885. w. 115 SFr. Adligenswilerstr. 22, Postfach 4870, CH-6002 Luzern, Switzerland. TEL 041-592-222. FAX 041-592280. Ed. Esther Husler. adv.; bk.rev. circ. 21,358. (back issues avail.) **Document type:** trade publication, newspaper.
Description: For hotel and restaurant employees, including chefs, cooks, service persons, housekeeping and administrative staff.

UNITED VOICE. see *LABOR UNIONS*

647.94 — GW
V C H KURIER. 1984. s-a. Verband Christlicher Hotels, Wartenbergstr. 5, 78532 Tuttlingen, Germany. TEL 07461-12620. FAX 07461-13860. adv.
Formerly: Hospiz-Kurier.

647.94 — FR
VACANCES ACTIVES, VACANCES HIVER; guide Auberges de jeunesse. bi-m. Federation Unie des Auberges de Jeunesse, 6 Rue Mesnil, 75016 Paris, France. TEL 45-05-13-14.

642.56 — CN — ISSN 0706-5302
VANCOUVER GASTRONOMIC. 1977. a. $5 per no. Apogee Enterprises Ltd, Box 48525, Sta. Bentall, Vancouver, B.C. V7X 1A2, Canada. TEL 604-685-7798. Ed. Elliot Cristall. adv. circ. 20,000.

647 — DK — ISSN 0107-3796
VANDRERHJEM I DANMARK.* 1968. irreg. DKK 19. Landsforeningen Danmarks Vandrerhjem, Copenhagen, Denmark. (Co-sponsors: Danmarks Vandrerhjem; Landsforeningen Danmarks Vandrerhjem)

914.3 — GW — ISSN 0171-4767
VARTA - FUEHRER; ausgewaehlte Hotels und Restaurants in der Bundesrepublik Deutschland. 1957. a. DM.58. VARTA Aktiengesellschaft, Postfach 540, 30405 Hannover, Germany. TEL 0511-3401310. Ed.Bd. adv. circ. 120,000. **Document type:** trade publication.
Formerly: VARTA - Fuehrer durch Deutschland, Westlicher Teil und Berlin (ISSN 0083-5250)

VEGETARIAN HANDBOOK. see *NUTRITION AND DIETETICS*

647.94 — GW
VERMIETER UND GAST; Fremdenverkehr - Gastronomie - Unterhaltung - Information. 1977. m. DM.20. Verlag Gerd Spranger, Unterjettenberg 2, 83435 Bad Reichenhall, Germany. TEL 08651-5822. FAX 08651-67178. adv.; illus. circ. 15,000. (tabloid format)

642.5 — IT
VIAGGIARE CON DINERS/TRAVELLING WITH DINERS. 1961. biennial. free to Italian card holders. Diners Club Italia S.p.A., Piazza Cavour 25, 00193 Rome, Italy. TEL 06-35751. FAX 06-3212697. Ed. Claudio Chiodelli. adv.; bk.rev. circ. 175,000. **Document type:** directory.
Former titles: Guida ai Punti di Credito - Guide to the Establishments; Diners Club.

HOTELS AND RESTAURANTS — ABSTRACTING, BIBLIOGRAPHIES, STATISTICS

VISITOR VACATION GUIDE. see *TRAVEL AND TOURISM*

647.9   FI   ISSN 0357-749X
TX901
VITRIINI. (Text in Finnish; summaries in Swedish) 1928. 8/yr. FIM 360. Restaurateur's Syndicate Ltd., Merimiehenkatu 29, 00150 Helsinki, Finland. FAX 358-0-171430. Ed. Jutta Rydman. adv. contact: M. Siltanen. bk.rev. circ. 3,500. **Document type:** trade publication.
    Formerly (until 1979): Hotelli- ja Ravintolalehti (ISSN 0018-6317)

647.94   US
▼**VIVA ITALIA.** 1992. m. Amazon Enterprises, 303 Second St., Holland, MI 47541. TEL 812-536-4762. FAX 812-536-3110. Ed. Amy Lorton; Pub. Theresa Acles Cole. adv.: B&W page $3714, color page $4399; trim 8 1/8 x 10 7/8; adv. contact: Karla Beier. circ. 42,169 (controlled). **Document type:** trade publication.
    Description: Foodservice guide to pizza, pasta and profits.

647.9   UK
VOICE OF THE BRITISH HOSPITALITY ASSOCIATION. 10/yr. £30 to non-members. British Hospitality Association, 40 Duke St., London W1M 6HR, England. TEL 071-499-6641. FAX 071-355-4596. Ed. Ann Satchell. adv.; illus. circ. 5,000. **Indexed:** Art.Hosp.& Tour.
    Former titles: British Hotelier and Restauranteur; B H R A Journal (ISSN 0007-0807)

VOYAGER INTERNATIONAL. see *TRAVEL AND TOURISM*

642.5   GW
W WINTERN; Zeitschrift fuer alle Mitarbeiter des Wienerwaldes. 1964. bi-m. free. Wienerwald GmbH, Elsenheimerstr. 61, 80687 Muncih, Germany. Ed. Manfred Greil. adv.; bk.rev.; illus. circ. 6,000.
    Formerly: Geschichten aus dem Wienerwald (ISSN 0016-9064)

642.5   UK
WALES CATERERS GUIDE. m. 63 Cambrian Dr., Colwyn Bay, Clwyd LL28 4TA, Wales. TEL 0492-547057. Ed. G.E. Walters.

647.94 647.95   JA
WEEKLY HOTEL & RESTAURANT. (Text in Japanese) 1951. 48/yr. 48000 Yen. Ohta Publications Co., Ltd., Dame Ginza Bldg., 7-18 Ginza, 6-chome, Chuo-ku, Tokyo 104, Japan. TEL 03-3571-1181. FAX 03-3574-1650. Ed. Ryoji Matsuzawa. adv.; bk.rev. circ. 65,000.
    Description: Information in the form of market analyses, hard facts and figures, and new operating strategies. Ways to incorporate various seasonal attractions and events for business promotions.

WHERE (LONDON, 1975); your best guide to: shopping, dining, sightseeing and entertainment. see *TRAVEL AND TOURISM — Airline Inflight And Hotel Inroom*

642 917.1   CN   ISSN 0315-3088
WHERE TO EAT IN CANADA. 1971. a. $14.95. Oberon Press, 400 - 350 Sparks St., Ottawa, ON K1R 7S8, Canada. TEL 613-238-3275. Ed. Anne Hardy. circ. 5,000.
    Description: National restaurant guide that independently rates and reviews over 500 restaurants from coast to coast.

642   UK
WHERE TO EAT IN IRELAND. 1985. a. £2.95. Kingsclere Publications Ltd., Furlongs House, Peasemore, Newbury, Berks RG16 OJE, England. TEL 0635-247770. FAX 0635-247272. Ed. Diana Breadmore. adv. circ. 10,000. **Document type:** directory.
    Description: Guide to dining in Ireland.

647.95 914.2   UK
WHERE TO EAT IN NORTH WEST ENGLAND. 1985. a. £2.50. Kingsclere Publications Ltd., Furlongs House, Peasemore, Newbury, Berkshire RG16 OJE, England. TEL 0635-247770. FAX 0635-247272. Ed. Diana Breadmore. adv. circ. 10,000. **Document type:** directory.
    Formerly: Where to Eat in Greater Manchester and Cheshire.
    Description: Guide to dining in North West England.

642   UK
WHERE TO EAT IN SCOTLAND. 1985. a. £2.50. Kingsclere Publications Ltd., Furlongs House, Peasemore, Newbury, Berks RG16 OJE, England. TEL 0635-247770. FAX 0635-247272. Ed. Diana Breadmore. adv. circ. 10,000. **Document type:** directory.
    Supersedes: Where to Eat in Edinburgh, Fife and the Lothians; Where to Eat In and Around Glasgow.
    Description: Guide to dining in Scotland.

914.2 642.5   UK
WHERE TO EAT IN SOUTH AND SOUTHEAST ENGLAND. 1980. a. £2.50. Kingsclere Publications Ltd., Furlongs House, Peasemore, Newbury, Berkshire RG16 OJE, England. TEL 0635-247770. FAX 0635-247272. Ed. Diana Breadmore. adv. circ. 10,000. **Document type:** directory.
    Formerly (until 1993): Where to Eat in Berkshire; Incorporates (in 1993): Where to Eat in Kent & Where to Eat in Surrey & Where to Eat in Sussex.
    Description: Guide to dining in Berkshire, Hants, Surrey, East and West Sussex, and Kent.

914.2 642.5   UK
WHERE TO EAT IN THE CHANNEL ISLANDS. 1982. a. £1. Kingsclere Publications Ltd., Furlongs House, Peasemore, Newbury, Berkshire RG16 OJE, England. TEL 0635-247770. FAX 0635-247272. Ed. Diana Breadmore. adv. circ. 10,000. **Document type:** directory.
    Formerly: Where to Eat in Guernsey; Supersedes: Where to Eat in the Channel Islands.
    Description: Guide to dining on the islands of Jersey and Guernsey.

914.2 642.5   UK
WHERE TO EAT IN THE WEST COUNTRY AND WALES. 1981. a. £3.50. Kingsclere Publications Ltd., Furlongs House, Peasemore, Newbury, Berkshire RG16 OJE, England. TEL 0635-247770. FAX 0635-247272. Ed. Diana Breadmore. adv. circ. 10,000. **Document type:** directory.
    Formerly (until 1993): Where to Eat in Bristol, Bath and Avon; Incorporates (in 1993): Where to Eat in Cornwall; Where to Eat in Devon; Where to Eat in Dorset and South Wiltshire; Where to Eat in Gloucestershire, Oxfordshire and the Cotswolds; Where to Eat in Hampshire; Where to Eat in Somerset; Where to Eat in Wales.
    Description: Guide to dining in Avon, Devon, Cornwall, Gloucestershire, Somerset, Wiltshire and Wales.

647.95   UK
WHICH? HOTEL GUIDE. a. £14.99. Consumers' Association, 2 Marylebone Rd., London NW1 4DF, England. TEL 071-830-6000. FAX 071-830-6220. (Orders to: Consumers' Association, Castlemead, Gascoyne Way, Hertford, SG14 1LH, England) Ed. Patricia Yates. circ. 35,000.
    Formerly: Good Hotel Guide.
    Description: Seeks out value and excellence in establishments in all price brackets across Britain.

WHO'S WHO IN AMERICA'S RESTAURANTS; encyclopedia of America's dining establishments. see *ENCYCLOPEDIAS AND GENERAL ALMANACS*

647.94   US
WHO'S WHO IN THE LODGING INDUSTRY. a. $45. American Hotel and Motel Association, 1201 New York Ave., N.W., Washington, DC 20005-3917. TEL 202-289-3100. **Document type:** directory.

642.5   GW
WIENERWALD; Zeitung fuer alle Gaeste. 1965. bi-m. distributed free in all Wienerwald restaurants. Wienerwald GmbH, Marketing Service GmbH, 81479 Munich, Germany. Ed. M. Greil. adv.; bk.rev.; illus. circ. 130,000.

640   UK   ISSN 0261-3956
WINING & DINING; eating out and entertaining in. 1980. m. £9.50. H S Publishing, 16 Ennismore Ave., Chiswick, London W.4., England. Ed. Helene Hodge. illus.
    Incorporates: Wine and Dine.

642.5   US   ISSN 0274-7452
WISCONSIN RESTAURATEUR. 1933. bi-m. $17.50. Wisconsin Restaurant Association, 31 S. Henry, No. 300, Madison, WI 53703. TEL 608-251-3663. FAX 608-251-3666. Ed. Sonya Knecht Bice. adv. contact: Kerry Koppen. bk.rev. circ. 4,200. (reprint service avail.) **Document type:** trade publication.

642.47   JA
WORLD HOTEL AND CONVENTION DIRECTORY. (Text in Japanese) a. 12000 Yen($145) Ohta Publications Co., Ltd., Dame Ginza Bldg., 7-18 Ginza, 6-chome, Chuo-ku, Tokyo 104, Japan. TEL 03-3571-1181. FAX 03-3574-1650. Ed. Hiroyuki Takagishi. circ. 10,000.
    Description: Listings of over 13,000 hotels around the globe with description of property facilities and locations. Information on world's convention facilities.

642.47   JA
WORLD HOTEL INDEX. (Text in English, Japanese) 1964. 2/yr. 16000 Yen. Travel Consultants of Japan, Ltd., Dai-ichi Akiyama Bldg., 7F, 2-3-22 Toranomon, Minato-ku, Tokyo 105, Japan. TEL 03-3506-8311. FAX 03-3506-8326. Ed. Mari Kono. adv.; index. circ. 12,000. (back issues avail.)

642.5 664   US   ISSN 0195-2552
YANKEE FOOD SERVICE. 1979. m. $35. Griffin Publishing Company, Inc., 1099 Hingham St., Rockland, MA 02370. TEL 617-878-5300. FAX 617-871-4721. adv. circ. 21,000. (tabloid format; back issues avail.) **Document type:** trade publication.

647   YU
YUGOSLAVIA: HOTEL AND TOURIST DIRECTORY. Spine title: Hotelsko-Turisticki Adresar. (Text in English, French, German, Serbo-Croatian) irreg. Privredni Pregled, Marsala Birjuzova 3-5, 11000 Belgrade, Serbia, Yugoslavia. illus.

ZAKENREIS/BUSINESS TRAVEL. see *TRAVEL AND TOURISM*

ZHONGGUO SHIPIN/CHINESE FOOD. see *HOME ECONOMICS*

642.5   SZ
ZUERCHER WIRTE NACHRICHTEN. m. Blumenfeldstr. 22, CH-8040 Zurich, Switzerland. TEL 01-3720666. FAX 01-3720667. Ed. Kurt Ulrich. circ. 3,500.

HOTELS AND RESTAURANTS — Abstracting, Bibliographies, Statistics

642.47 910   UK   ISSN 0268-0858
ARTICLES IN HOSPITALITY AND TOURISM. 1985. m. £60. University of Surrey, George Edwards Library, Guildford, Surrey GU2 5XH, England. TEL 0483-300800. (Subscr. to: Geoff Cole, Library, Oxford Polytechnic, Gipsy Ln., Oxford OX3 0BP, England. TEL 0865-819137) Ed. Ruth Mitchell. circ. 90. **Document type:** abstracting/indexing.

647.94   AT   ISSN 1031-2897
AUSTRALIA. BUREAU OF STATISTICS. NEW SOUTH WALES OFFICE. TOURIST ACCOMMODATION, NEW SOUTH WALES. 1975. q. Aus.$20 per no. Australian Bureau of Statistics, New South Wales Office, St. Andrews House, Sydney Square, George St., Sydney, N.S.W. 2000, Australia. **Document type:** government publication.
    Description: Covers hotels, motels, caravan parks, holiday flats and units and visitor hostels, showing capacity, occupancy rates and takings from accommodation for each month.

647.94   AT   ISSN 0157-1354
AUSTRALIA. BUREAU OF STATISTICS. NORTHERN TERRITORY OFFICE. TOURIST ACCOMMODATION, NORTHERN TERRITORY. 1977. q. Aus.$12 per no. Australian Bureau of Statistics, Northern Territory Office, MLC Bldg., 6th Fl., 81 Smith St., Darwin, N.T. 0800, Australia. **Document type:** government publication.
    Description: Contains information about hotels, motels, caravan parks, holiday flats, units and visitor hostels, occupancy rates and takings from accommodation for each month by type of establishment.

647.97   AT   ISSN 0725-394X
AUSTRALIA. BUREAU OF STATISTICS. QUEENSLAND OFFICE. TOURIST ACCOMMODATION, QUEENSLAND. 1975. q. Aus.$20 per no. Australian Bureau of Statistics, Queensland Office, 313 Adelaide St., Brisbane, Qld. 4000, Australia. TEL 07-222-6022. FAX 07-229-6171. TELEX AA 40271. **Document type:** government publication.
    Description: Covers hotels, motels, caravan parks, holiday flats and occupancy rates.

HOUSING AND URBAN PLANNING

647.94   AT   ISSN 0312-6900
AUSTRALIA. BUREAU OF STATISTICS. TASMANIAN OFFICE. TOURIST ACCOMMODATION, TASMANIA. 1974. q. Aus.$20 per no. Australian Bureau of Statistics, Tasmanian Office, G.P.O. Box 66A, Hobart, Tas. 7001, Australia. **Document type:** government publication.
    Description: Contains information about hotels, motels, caravan parks, holiday flats and units, occupancy rates and takings from accommodation for each month by type of establishment.

647.94   AT   ISSN 1031-0770
AUSTRALIA. BUREAU OF STATISTICS. TOURIST ACCOMMODATION, AUSTRALIA. 1975. q. Aus.$20 per no. Australian Bureau of Statistics, P.O. Box 10, Belconnen, A.C.T. 2616, Australia. **Document type:** government publication.
    Description: Covers hotels, motels, caravan parks, holiday flats and units, and visitor hostels, including their showing capacity, occupancy rates and takings from accommodation for each month.

647.94   AT   ISSN 1032-0490
AUSTRALIA. BUREAU OF STATISTICS. TOURIST ACCOMMODATION, AUSTRALIAN CAPITAL TERRITORY. 1988. q. Aus.$8 per no. Australian Bureau of Statistics, P.O. Box 10, Belconnen, A.C.T. 2616, Australia. **Document type:** government publication.
    Incorporates (in 1990): Australia. Bureau of Statistics. Tourist Accommodation: Selected Establishments, Australian Capital Territory (ISSN 1034-2486)
    Description: Covers hotels and motels by star grading and holiday flats and units showing capacity, occupancy rates and takings from accommodation for each month.

647.94   AT   ISSN 0727-2243
AUSTRALIA. BUREAU OF STATISTICS. TOURIST ACCOMMODATION, WESTERN AUSTRALIA. 1975. q. Aus.$20 per no. Australian Bureau of Statistics, Western Australian Office, 30 Terrace Rd., E. Perth, W.A. 6004, Australia. **Document type:** government publication.
    Description: Provides information about hotels, motels, caravan parks, holiday flats and units, occupancy rates and takings from accommodation for each month by type of establishment.

647.94   AT   ISSN 1031-2900
AUSTRALIA. BUREAU OF STATISTICS. VICTORIAN OFFICE. TOURIST ACCOMMODATION, VICTORIA. 1975. q. Aus.$20. Australian Bureau of Statistics, Victorian Office, G.P.O. Box 2796Y, Melbourne, Vic. 3001, Australia. **Document type:** government publication.
    Description: Covers hotels, motels, caravan parks, holiday flats and units, and visitor hostels, showing capacity, occupancy rates and takings from accommodation for each month.

642.5   CN   ISSN 0226-2320
TX910.C2
CANADA. STATISTICS CANADA. RESTAURANT, CATERER AND TAVERN STATISTICS. (Catalogue 63-011) (Text in English and French) 1967. m. Can.$61($73) (foreign $85). Statistics Canada, Publications Sales and Services, Ottawa, Ont. K1A 0T6, Canada. TEL 613-951-7277. FAX 613-951-1584. (also avail. in microform from MML)
    Formerly: Canada. Statistics Canada. Restaurant Statistics (ISSN 0008-2627)
    Description: Presents the monthly estimates of total receipts of restaurants, caterers and taverns both at the national and provincial levels.

647.9 016   UK
H C I M A QUARTERLY CURRENT AWARENESS BULLETIN FOR HOSPITALITY MANAGEMENT. 1980. q. £58 (foreign £70). Hotel Catering and Institutional Management Association, 191 Trinity Rd., London SW17 7HN, England. TEL 081-672-4251. FAX 081-682-1707. circ. 130. **Document type:** trade publication.
    Formerly: H C I M A Quarterly Bibliography of Hotel and Catering Management (ISSN 0144-7580)

HONG KONG. CENSUS AND STATISTICS DEPARTMENT. WHOLESALE, RETAIL AND IMPORT - EXPORT TRADES, RESTAURANTS AND HOTELS. SURVEY. see BUSINESS AND ECONOMICS — Abstracting, Bibliographies, Statistics

647   US
HOSPITALITY INDEX; an index for the hotel, foodservice and travel industries. a. (plus q. updates). $79.95 ($149 with updates). Cornell University, School of Hotel Administration, Stouffer Hotels Library, Statler Hall, Ithaca, NY 14853-6901. TEL 607-254-4503. FAX 202-289-3199. (Co-sponsor: American Hotel and Motel Association) Ed. Nancy Young.
● Also available on CD-ROM.
    Description: Provides complete bibliographic citations of journals in the hospitality field.

658.91   IS   ISSN 0333-7715
ISRAEL. CENTRAL BUREAU OF STATISTICS. HOTELS; income, expenditures and product. (Text in English, Hebrew) irreg. Government Publishing House, 25 David Elazar St., Hakirya, Tel Aviv 61070, Israel.

647.94 642.5   US   ISSN 0894-5128
LODGING AND RESTAURANT INDEX. 1985. q. $150. Hotel and Institutional Management Institute, Purdue University, West Lafayette, IN 47907-1002. TEL 317-494-2914. Ed. Priscilla C. Geahigan. circ. 200. (also avail. in diskette format) **Document type:** abstracting/indexing.
    Description: Indexes 52 professional, trade and scholarly journals in hotel, restaurant, food service and travel fields.

642.5   MH
MACAO. DIRECCAO DOS SERVICOS DE ESTATISTICA E CENSOS. RECENSEAMENTO AOS RESTAURANTES, HOTEIS E ESTABELECIMENTOS SIMILARES/MACAO. CENSUS AND STATISTICS DEPARTMENT. CENSUS OF RESTAURANTS, HOTELS AND SIMILAR ESTABLISHMENTS. (Text in Chinese, Portuguese) 1986. a. free. Direccao dos Servicos de Estatistica e Censos, Rua Inacio Baptista, No.4-6, P.O. Box 3022, Macao. TEL 3995311. FAX 307825. **Document type:** government publication.
    Description: Presents principal statistics in areas such as persons engaged, number of establishments, total incomes and expenditures by activity and classification of establishments.

N Z T B PRODUCT RESEARCH SERIES. see TRAVEL AND TOURISM — Abstracting, Bibliographies, Statistics

647   SI
SINGAPORE. DEPARTMENT OF STATISTICS. REPORT ON THE SURVEY OF WHOLESALE TRADE, RETAIL TRADE, RESTAURANTS & HOTELS (YEAR). a. S.$12.70. Department of Statistics, 8 Shenton Way 10-01 Treasury Bldg., Singapore 0106, Singapore. TEL 3209702. FAX 3209689. TELEX RS 63001 STAT.
    Formerly: Singapore. Department of Statistics. Report on the Census of Wholesale, Retail Trades, Restaurants and Hotels (ISSN 0129-6760)

642.5 316.8   SA
SOUTH AFRICA. CENTRAL STATISTICAL SERVICE. CENSUS OF CATERING AND ACCOMMODATION SERVICES. (Report No. 63-01-01) irreg., latest 1983. R.4.40 (foreign R.5.50). Central Statistical Service - Sentrale Statistiekdiens, Private Bag X44, Pretoria 0001, South Africa. TEL 27-12-310-8911. FAX 27-12-310-8500. (Orders to: Government Printing Works, Private Bag X85, Pretoria 0001, South Africa) **Document type:** government publication.
    Supersedes: Census of Accomodation Establishments.

647.94 316.8   SA
SOUTH AFRICA. CENTRAL STATISTICAL SERVICE. STATISTICAL RELEASE. REGISTERED HOTELS - FINANCIAL STATISTICS. (No. P6443) q. free. Central Statistical Service - Sentrale Statistiekdiens, Private Bag X44, Pretoria 0001, South Africa. TEL 27-12-310-8911. FAX 27-12-310-8500. **Document type:** government publication.

647.94 316.8   SA
SOUTH AFRICA. CENTRAL STATISTICAL SERVICE. STATISTICAL RELEASE. STATISTICS OF REGISTERED HOTELS. (No. P6441) m. free. Central Statistical Service - Sentrale Statistiekdiens, Private Bag X44, Pretoria 0001, South Africa. TEL 27-12-310-8911. FAX 27-12-310-8500. **Document type:** government publication.
    Description: Statistics on trading revenues and bed occupancy by tourism region.

647.94 316.8   SA
SOUTH AFRICA. CENTRAL STATISTICAL SERVICE. STATISTICAL RELEASE. STATISTICS OF REGISTERED HOTELS: BEDNIGHTS - FOREIGN TOURISTS. (No. P6442) m. free. Central Statistical Service - Sentrale Statistiekdiens, Private Bag X44, Pretoria 0001, South Africa. TEL 27-12-310-8911. FAX 27-12-310-8500. **Document type:** government publication.
    Formerly: South Africa. Central Statistical Service. Statistical News Release. Statistics of Registered Hotels: Foreign Tourists.

315.61   TU
TURKEY. DEVLET ISTATISTIK ENSTITUSU. TICARET, OTEL, LOKANTA VE HIZMET ISTATISTIKLERI/TURKEY. STATE INSTITUTE OF STATISTICS. STATISTICS OF TRADE, HOTELS, RESTAURANTS AND SERVICES. (Text in English, Turkish) 1991. a. $30. Devlet Istatistik Enstitusu - State Institute of Statistics, Necatibey Caddesi No. 114, 06100 Ankara, Turkey. TEL 90-312-4185027. FAX 90-312-4180432. **Document type:** government publication.

HOUSING AND URBAN PLANNING

see also Building and Construction; Real Estate

362.6 352.7   US
A A R P HOUSING REPORT. q. American Association of Retired Persons, Consumer Affairs, 601 E St., N.W., Washington, DC 20049. TEL 202-662-4842. circ. 5,500. **Document type:** bulletin.
    Description: Provides updates on housing issues facing older people.

352.7   US
A I C P ROSTER. biennial. American Institute of Certified Planners, 1776 Massachussets Ave., N.W., Washington, DC 20036. TEL 202-872-0611. FAX 202-872-0643. **Document type:** directory.
    Description: Also lists universities with accredited programs.

352   US   ISSN 0160-8266
NA9108
A P A PLANNING ADVISORY SERVICE REPORTS. 1949. 8/yr. price varies. American Planning Association, 1313 E. 60th St., Chicago, IL 60637. TEL 312-955-9100. FAX 312-955-8312. (And: 1776 Massachusetts Ave., N.W., Washington, DC 20036. TEL 202-872-0611) Dir. James Hecimovich. bibl.; charts; illus.; stat.; index. circ. 1,750. (also avail. in microfilm from UMI; microfiche; back issues avail.; reprint service avail. from UMI) **Indexed:** P.A.I.S.
—UMI.
    Formerly: American Society of Planning Officials. A S P O Planning Advisory Service (ISSN 0044-8044); Incorporates: Planning Advisory Service Reports (ISSN 0048-430X)

352   US
A R C ACTION. 1971. bi-m. free. Atlanta Regional Commission, 3715 Northside Pkwy., Bldg. 200, Ste. 300, Atlanta, GA 30327. TEL 404-364-2500. Ed. Julie Ralston. bk.rev.; illus. circ. 6,000. **Document type:** newsletter.

352.7   US
A S C P DIRECTORY. a. American Society of Consulting Planners, 1015 15th St., N.W., Ste. 600, Washington, DC 20005. TEL 202-289-6797. FAX 202-289-6797.

388.3   AT   ISSN 0155-8234
ACTION FOR PUBLIC TRANSPORT NEWSLETTER. 1976. q. Aus.$12 (foreign Aus.$15). P.O. Box K606, Haymarket, N.S.W. 2000, Australia. TEL 61-2-4168459. Ed. Jim Donovan. bk.rev. circ. 500. **Document type:** newsletter.
    Description: Advocates improvement of city and national public transport for economic, social and environmental reasons.

ACTION MUNICIPALE; organe de defense et d'information des mairies. see PUBLIC ADMINISTRATION — Municipal Government

HOUSING AND URBAN PLANNING

350.865   FR
ACTUALITES H L M. (Habitations a Loyer Modere) 1970. 24/yr. 1260 F. to non-members; members 690 F. (foreign 1315 F.) (effective Jan. 1993). Union Nationale des Federations d'Organismes d'Habitations a Loyer Modere, Editions Department, 14 rue Lord Byron, 75384 Paris Cedex 08, France. TEL 40-75-78-00. FAX 40-75-79-83. adv.; bk.rev.; stat. circ. 4,000.

333.77   IT
AD ARNUM QUADERNI. 1989. irreg. irreg. Assessorato all'Urbanistica e Assetto del Territorio, Via Cavour, 1, 50129 Florence, Italy. TEL 055-27601. FAX 055-2760360. **Document type:** monographic series.

ADVISER. see *SOCIAL SERVICES AND WELFARE*

AFRICAN URBAN STUDIES. see *ETHNIC INTERESTS*

711.4   US
ALASKA HOUSING FINANCE CORPORATION. ANNUAL REPORT. 1945. a. free. Alaska State Housing Authority, 520 E. 34th St., Anchorage, AK 99503. TEL 907-561-1900. FAX 907-561-0364. Ed. Margaret Nelson. circ. 1,000 (controlled). **Document type:** corporate report.
    Former titles (until 1991): Alaska. State Housing Authority. Annual Report; Alaska. State Building Authority. Annual Report; Alaska. State Housing Authority. Annual Report.

352.7   US   ISSN 1063-374X
HD7303.A4
ALASKA HOUSING MARKET INDICATOR. q. free. Department of Labor, Research & Analysis Section, Box 25501, Juneau, AK 99802-5501. TEL 907-465-6031. FAX 907-465-2101. (Co-sponsor: Alaska Housing Finance Corporation) **Document type:** government publication.
    Description: Details statistics relating to Alaska's housing market. Provides information on housing loans and structure characteristics by census area.

352.7 690   JA
ALL OF HOUSING/KATEI-BAN HYAKKA SERIES.* (Text in Japanese) 1972. m. 19800 Yen. Sankei Publishing Ltd., Sankei-Honsha Bldg., 1-7-2 Otemachi, Chiyoda-ku, Tokyo, 100, Japan. Ed. Seizo Sano.

352.7   DK
HD7288.78.D4
ALMENNYTTIGE BOLIGAFDELINGERS REGNSKABER. 1978. a. DKK 100. Boligministeriet - Ministry of Housing, Departementets 4 Kontor, Slotholmsgade 12, 1216 Copenhagen K, Denmark. (Dist. by: Statens Informationstjeneste, Nr. Farimagsgade 65, P.O. Box 1103, DK-1364 Copenhagen K, Denmark) **Document type:** government publication.
    Former titles (until 1988): Almennyttige Boligselskabers Regnskaber (ISSN 0107-1572); (until 1977): Beretning om de Almennyttige Boligselskabers Regnskaber.

352.7 352   GW   ISSN 0170-9364
HT101
DIE ALTE STADT. 1974. q. DM.146 to individuals; students DM.110. W. Kohlhammer GmbH, Hessbruehlstr. 69, 70565 Stuttgart, Germany. TEL 0711-7863-1. Ed.Bd. bk.rev.; bibl. **Indexed:** Amer.Hist.& Life (until 1992), Avery Ind.Archit.Per., Hist.Abstr. (until 1992). **Document type:** bulletin.
    —CCC.
    Former title: Zeitschrift fuer Stadtgeschichte, Stadtsoziologie und Denkmalpflege.

711   IT   ISSN 1122-0937
AMBIENTE STORICO; studi di storia urbana e del territorio. 1990. irreg. no.4, 1993. price varies. Casa Editrice Leo S. Olschki, Casella Postale 66, 50100 Florence, Italy. TEL 055-6530584. FAX 055-6530214. **Document type:** monographic series.

AMENAGEMENT ET NATURE. see *CONSERVATION*

352.7   US
AMERICAN ASSOCIATION OF HOUSING EDUCATORS. NEWSLETTER. 3/yr. American Association of Housing Educators, c/o College of Architecture, Texas A & M University, College Station, TX 77843-3137. FAX 409-845-4491.

352.7   US
AMERICAN ASSOCIATION OF HOUSING EDUCATORS. PROCEEDINGS. 1974. a. membership. American Association of Housing Educators, College of Architecture, Texas A & M University, College Station, TX 77843-3137. FAX 409-845-4491. TELEX 510-892-7689. bk.rev. circ. 350. **Document type:** proceedings.

352 711   US   ISSN 0194-4363
HD87.5   CODEN: JAPAD9
AMERICAN PLANNING ASSOCIATION. JOURNAL. 1925. q. $36 to non-members (foreign $50); members $23 (foreign $30). American Planning Association, 1313 E. 60th, Chicago, IL 60637. TEL 312-955-9100. FAX 312-955-8312. (And: 1776 Massachusetts Ave., N.W., Wasington, DC 20036. TEL 202-872-0611) adv.; bk.rev.; abstr.; bibl.; charts; illus.; maps; cum.index. circ. 13,000. (also avail. in microform from UMI; reprint service avail. from KTO,UMI) **Indexed:** A.B.C.Pol.Sci., ABI Inform., Amer.Hist.& Life, Art Ind., ASSIA, Avery Ind.Archit.Per., BPIA, Br.Tech.Ind., Bus.Ind., Curr.Cont., Educ.Admin.Abstr., Environ.Abstr., Environ.Per.Bibl. (1989-), Excerpt.Med., Geo.Abstr., Hist.Abstr., HRIS, I D A, INIS Atomind., Intl.Civil Eng.Abstr., Manage Cont., Med.Care Rev., Mid.East: Abstr.& Ind., P.A.I.S., PSI, Soc.Sci.Ind., Soft.Abstr.Eng., SSCI.
    —BLDSC (4691.700000); CIS; Faxon; UnCover; SWETS; UMI.
    Former titles (until 1979): Planners Journal; American Institute of Planners. Journal (ISSN 0002-8991)
    Description: Focuses on city planning issues.

AMERICAN REAL ESTATE AND URBAN ECONOMICS ASSOCIATION. JOURNAL. see *REAL ESTATE*

352.7 301.15 949.5   GR
ANCIENT GREEK CITIES REPORT. 1971. irreg. price varies. Athens Center of Ekistics, 24 Syndesmou St., Box 3471, Athens 102 10, Greece. Ed. P. Psomopoulos.

352.7   UK   ISSN 0261-5932
ANGUS DISTRICT COUNCIL. HOUSING PLANS AND PROGRAMMES. 1979. 4/yr., latest 1993, for the the period 1994-1999. £2.50. Angus District Council, Housing Department, County Buildings, Forfar DD8 3LG, Scotland. TEL 44-307-465101. FAX 44-307-464834. circ. 300.

352.9   FR   ISSN 0180-930X
HT101
ANNALES DE LA RECHERCHE URBAINE. (Text in French; abstracts in English, Spanish) 1979. 4 /yr. 350 F. to individuals; institutions 550 F. Dunod, 15 rue Gossin, 92543 Montrouge Cedex, France. TEL 1-46-56-52-66. FAX 1-47-46-81-21. TELEX 270 004. (Subscr. to: Centrale des Revues, 11 rue Gossin, 92543 Montrouge Cedex, France) Ed. Anne Querrien. bk.rev. circ. 1,600.
    —BLDSC (0995.310000); SWETS. **CCC.**
    Description: Contains results of research and discussions regarding contemporary urban problems both from a theoretical and a practical perspective.

ANNALS OF REGIONAL SCIENCE; international journal of urban, regional and environmental research and policy. see *BUSINESS AND ECONOMICS*

352.7 360   FR
ANNUAIRE H L M. (Habitations a Loyer Modere) 1968. a. 470 F. to non-members; members 280 F. Union Nationale des Federations d'Organismes d'Habitations a Loyer Modere, Editions Department, 14 rue Lord Byron, 75384 Paris Cedex 08, France. TEL 40-75-78-00. FAX 40-75-79-83. adv.; index. circ. 5,600.

ANNUARIO EUROPEO DELL'AMBIENTE. see *ENVIRONMENTAL STUDIES*

352.7   US   ISSN 0192-0030
HD1361
APARTMENT AGE; the voice of the industry. 1967. m. $41. Apartment Association of Greater Los Angeles, 621 S. Westmoreland Ave., Los Angeles, CA 90005. TEL 213-384-4131. FAX 213-382-3970. Ed. Kevin B. Postema. adv.: B&W page $2446. bk.rev.; index. circ. 40,300. **Document type:** trade publication.
    Description: Covers multi-housing issues including legal, legislative, political, management, financial and maintenance issues for apartment owners.

333.33   US   ISSN 0192-1576
APARTMENT OWNER - BUILDER. (In 5 Los Angeles Area editions) 1959. m. $9. Apartment News Publications, Inc., 3220 E. Willow, Long Beach, CA 90806. TEL 310-424-8674. FAX 213-636-8353. Ed. Chris Callard. adv.; charts; illus.; stat. circ. 60,000. **Document type:** trade publication.
    Formerly: Apartment News (ISSN 0044-8400)
    Description: Covers legal, political, management, and maintenance issues for the apartment owners of Los Anegels and Orange Counties.

ARCHI ECHOS. see *ARCHITECTURE*

ARCHIS. see *ARCHITECTURE*

ARCHITECT. see *ARCHITECTURE*

ARCHITECTUS. see *ARCHITECTURE*

711   IT   ISSN 0004-0177
HT101
ARCHIVIO DI STUDI URBANI E REGIONALI. 1970. 3/yr. L.75000 (foreign L.95000) (effective 1993). Franco Angeli Editore, Viale Monza 106, Casella Postale 17175, 20100 Milan, Italy. TEL 02-2827651. Ed.Bd.
    Formerly: Collana di Studi Urbani e Regionali.

352.9   KE
ARDHI: JOURNAL OF LAND DEVELOPMENT. (Text in English) 1982. s-a. $2. University of Nairobi, Department of Land Development, P.O. Box 30197, Nairobi, Kenya. Eds. George K. King'drian, S.S. Yahya. bk.rev. circ. 500.

711 711.4   IT
AREA. (Editions in English, Italian) 1990. q. L.100000($95) (effective 1992). Azzurra Editrice s.r.l., Via della Moscova, 49, 20121 Milan, Italy. TEL 02-6552498. FAX 02-29002192. adv. circ. 20,000.
    Description: Reviews project culture, architecture, design, and visual communication.

352.7   JA
AREA DEVELOPMENT IN JAPAN. (Text in English) 1968. s-a. 750 Yen. Japan Center for Area Development Research - Nihon Chiiki Kaihatsu Senta, lino Bldg., 2-1-1 Uchisaiwai-cho, Chiyoda-ku, Tokyo 100, Japan. TEL 03-501-6856. FAX 03-501-6855. Ed. Ikumi Hoshino. charts. circ. 1,000.

ARHITECTURA. see *ARCHITECTURE*

388.3   US   ISSN 0004-1564
ARIZONA MOBILE CITIZEN. 1948. w. $14.50. Arizona Trailer Publications, (Subsidiary of: Sun State Publishing Co., Inc.), Box 5397, Phoenix, AZ 85010. TEL 602-275-1776. Ed. Ruth C. Kaseman. adv.; bk.rev.; illus.; stat. circ. 20,000. (tabloid format)
    Description: Aimed at mobile and manufactured home owners, RV owners, and trade.

ARKITEKTUR OG SKIPULAG. see *ARCHITECTURE*

ARQUISUR. see *ARCHITECTURE*

ARQUITECTURA Y URBANISMO. see *ARCHITECTURE*

352.7   SP
ASOCIACION NACIONAL DE PROMOTORES CONSTRUCTORES DE EDIFICIOS URBANOS. ANNUAL REPORT. a. Asociacion Nacional de Promotores Constructores de Edificios Urbanos, Diego de Leon, 50, 28006 Madrid, Spain. TEL 5624033.

352.7   SP
ASOCIACION NACIONAL DE PROMOTORES CONSTRUCTORES DE EDIFICIOS URBANOS. PROMOCION. bi-m. Asociacion Nacional de Promotores Constructores de Edificios Urbanos, Diego de Leon, 50, 28006 Madrid, Spain. TEL 2624033.

711   GR   ISSN 0067-0073
ATHENS CENTER OF EKISTICS. RESEARCH REPORT. 1967. irreg., no.13, 1973. price varies. Athens Center of Ekistics, 24, Strat. Syndesmou Street, P.O. Box 3471, Athens 102 10, Greece. Ed. P. Psomopoulos. circ. 275.

352   US   ISSN 0732-1805
ATLANTA REGIONAL COMMISSION. ANNUAL REPORT. 1973. a. Atlanta Regional Commission, 3715 Northside Pkwy., Bldg. 200, Ste. 300, Atlanta, GA 30327. TEL 404-364-2500.

HOUSING AND URBAN PLANNING

352.7　　　　　AT　ISSN 1033-1662
AUSTPLAN. 6/yr. Aus.$45 (foreign Aus.$50). Royal Australian Planning Institute Inc., Rapi House, 615 Burwood Rd., Hawthorn, Vic. 3122, Australia. TEL 03-819-0728. FAX 03-819-0676. Ed. Diana Marks. adv. **Document type:** newsletter.
Description: Covers Australian planning; for planners residing and working in Australia.

AUSTRALIA. DEPARTMENT OF HEALTH, HOUSING, LOCAL GOVERNMENT AND COMMUNITY SERVICES. ANNUAL REPORT. see *PUBLIC HEALTH AND SAFETY*

352　　　　　AT　ISSN 0729-3682
AUSTRALIAN PLANNER. 1958. q. Aus.$65 (foreign Aus.$70). Royal Australian Planning Institute Inc., Rapi House, 615 Burwood Rd., Hawthorn, Vic. 3122, Australia. TEL 03-819-0728. FAX 03-819-0676. Ed. Richard Cardew. adv. contact: Rosalba Druhmond. bk.rev.; charts; illus.; index. circ. 3,000. (back issues avail.) **Indexed:** Aus.P.A.I.S., Aus.Rd.Ind. **Document type:** academic/scholarly publication.
—BLDSC (1817.860000).
Former titles: Australian Planning Institute Journal; Royal Australian Planning Institute Journal (ISSN 0004-9999)

AUSTRALIAN PLANNING APPEAL DECISIONS. see *LAW*

352.7　　　　　AT　ISSN 0310-7930
AUSTRALIAN URBAN STUDIES. 1972. q. $33 (effective 1994). Australian Institute of Urban Studies, Queensland Division, Inc., P.O. Box 122, St. Lucia, Qld. 4067, Australia. TEL 07-376-2255. FAX 07-368-9229. Ed. Maurice W. Milburn. bk.rev.; bibl.; charts; illus. circ. 600. **Document type:** newsletter.
—BLDSC (1823.900000).

388.3　　　　　US
AUTOMATED BUILDER ANNUAL BUYERS' GUIDE. 1977. a. C M N Publications (Subsidiary of: C M N Associates), 4371 Carpinteria Ave., Box 120, Carpinteria, CA 93014. TEL 805-684-7659. FAX 805-684-1765. adv. circ. 25,000. (also avail. in microfilm from UMI; reprint service avail. from UMI) **Document type:** trade publication.
Former titles: Automation in Housing and Manufactured Home Dealer Annual Buyers' Guide; Automation in Housing-Systems Building News Annual Buyers' Guide.

350　　　　　GW　ISSN 0173-6566
B F L R MITTEILUNGEN. 1980. bi-m. free. Bundesforschungsanstalt fuer Landeskunde und Raumordnung, Am Michaelshof 8, 53173 Bonn, Germany. TEL 0228-826-0. FAX 0228-826266. Eds. W. Strubelt, H.-P. Gatzweiler. circ. 4,000. **Document type:** government publication.

B S A - C M L PARLIAMENTARY CUTTING SERVICE. (Building Societies Association) see *REAL ESTATE*

B S A DIRECTORY OF MEMBERS. (Building Societies Association) see *REAL ESTATE*

350.865　　　　DK　ISSN 0108-2582
BEBOERBLADET. 1963. q. DKK 100 (includes Boligen). Boligselskabernes Landsforening, Studiestraede 50, DK-1554 Copenhagen V, Denmark. TEL 45-33-11-11-22. FAX 45-33-93-37-47. Eds. John Apelroth, Helge Moeller. adv. circ. 472,000.
Formerly (until 1981): Beboerbladet Boligen (ISSN 0108-2574)

352.7　　　　　SZ
BERICHTE ZUR ORTS-, REGIONAL- UND LANDESPLANUNG. 1968. irreg. price varies. Eidgenoessische Technische Hochschule, Institut fuer Orts-, Regional- und Landesplanung, Redaktion DISP - Swiss Federal Institute of Technology, Institute for Local, Regional and National Planning, CH-8093 Zurich, Switzerland. TEL 01-3772956. FAX 01-3720486. Ed. Michael Koch. **Document type:** academic/scholarly publication.

309.2 352　　　　AU　ISSN 0005-9102
HC261
BERICHTE ZUR RAUMFORSCHUNG UND RAUMPLANUNG. (Text in German; summaries in English, French, Russian) 1954. bi-m. S.444($14.20) Oesterreichische Gesellschaft fuer Raumforschung und Raumplanung, Karlsplatz 13, A-1040 Vienna, Austria. (Dist. in US by: Springer-Verlag, 175 Fifth Ave., New York, NY 10010) Eds. Dr. Peter Faller, Dr. Rudolf Wurzer. bk.rev.; abstr.; charts; illus.; stat.; index, cum.index. circ. 1,500. **Indexed:** Bibl.Cart., Dok.Str., Geo.Abstr., P.A.I.S.For.Lang.Ind.
—CCC.

352.7　　　　　US　ISSN 1047-5192
HT390
BERKELEY PLANNING JOURNAL. 1985. a. $10 to individuals; institutions $25. University of California, Berkeley, Department of City and Regional Planning, Graduate Students, 228 Wurster Hall, Berkeley, CA 94720. TEL 415-642-3256. FAX 510-643-9576. bk.rev. **Indexed:** Environ.Per.Bibl. (1989-).
—UnCover.

BERLINER HAUS- UND GRUNDBESITZ. see *REAL ESTATE*

352.7　　　　　GW
BERLINER HAUSBESITZER-MAGAZIN. 1958. s-m. DM.46. Verlag Adalbert Bestgen, Spessartstr. 13, 14197 Berlin, Germany. adv.; bk.rev. circ. 4,000. (looseleaf format)
Formerly (until 1986): Berliner Hausbesitz.

BEST-SELLING HOME PLANS. see *ARCHITECTURE*

352.7　　　　　VI
BLOCK AID. m. Planning Office, Community Development Program, Box 2606, St. Thomas, VI 00801.

352.7　　　　　AG　ISSN 0326-7857
HT127.5
BOLETIN DE MEDIO AMBIENTE Y URBANIZACION. 1982. 4/yr. Arg.$30 ($35 in Latin America; elsewhere $50). Instituto Internacional de Medio Ambiente y Desarrollo, IIED - America Latina, Corrientes 2835, Cuerpo A, Piso 6 B, 1193 Buenos Aires, Argentina. TEL 961-3050. FAX 541-961-1854. (Co-sponsor: Canadian International Development Agency) Ed. Jorge Hardoy. adv.; bk.rev.; index. circ. 1,500. **Document type:** academic/scholarly publication.

350.865 728　　　DK
BOLIGEN. 1932. m. (11/yr.). DKK 100 (includes Beboerbladet). Boligselskabernes Landsforening, Stuediestraede 50, DK-1554 Copenhagen V, Denmark. TEL 45-33-11-11-22.
FAX 45-33-93-37-47. Ed.Bd. adv. circ. 28,200.

352　　　　　NE　ISSN 0006-8381
BOUWONDERNEMER. 1932. q. free. Nederlandse Vereniging van Bouwondernemers, Parkweg 162, 2271 AM Voorburg, Netherlands. TEL 31-70-3860204. Ed. F.A.H. Nuss. adv. circ. 6,000.

352.7 338.40　　　XO
BRATISLAVA. (Text in Czech or Slovak; summaries in English, Russian) q. $30. (National Committee of Bratislava) Obzor, Ceskoslovenskej Armady 35, 815 85 Bratislava, Slovakia.

309.26　　　　BL
BRAZIL. SUPERINTENDENCIA DO DESENVOLVIMENTO DO NORDESTE. S U D E N E PLANO DE ACAO. Cover title: S U D E N E Plano de Acao. irreg. Superintendencia do Desenvolvimento do Nordeste, Praca Ministro J. Goncalves de Souza, Edf. Sudene, Cidade Universitaria, 50670-900 Recife PE, Brazil. TEL 2711044. FAX 4531277. illus.

352.7　　　　　CN　ISSN 0225-509X
HD7305.B7
BRITISH COLUMBIA. HOUSING MANAGEMENT COMMISSION. ANNUAL REPORT. 1978. a. free. B.C. Housing Management Commission, Ste. 1701, 4330 Kingsway, Burnaby, BC V5H 4G7, Canada. TEL 604-433-1711. FAX 604-433-3295. Ed. Janet E.M. Austin. illus. circ. 2,500. **Document type:** government publication.

350.86　　　　US
BUCKS COUNTY PLANNING COMMISSION. PLANNING PROGRESS. 1955. q. free. Bucks County Planning Commission, Almshouse, Neshaminy Manor Center, Doylestown, PA 18901. TEL 215-345-3431. FAX 215-345-3886. Ed. Cheryl Zabinski. circ. 3,000. (tabloid format; back issues avail.) **Document type:** newsletter.
Description: To aquaint citizens and municipal government with the work of the planning commission.

BUILDING MANAGEMENT & DESIGN; for the design, construction, facilities & building management industry. see *REAL ESTATE*

352.7 340　　　US　ISSN 1055-193X
KF5701.A15
BUILDING PERMITS LAW BULLETIN. 1989. m. $63. Quinlan Publishing Co., Inc., 23 Drydock Ave., Boston, MA 02110. TEL 617-542-0048; 800-229-2084. FAX 617-345-9646. index. (looseleaf format; back issues avail.) **Document type:** newsletter.
—UMI. CCC.
Formerly: Municipal Planners and Contractors Law Bulletin.
Description: Case law summaries about building permits, code requirements, appeals procedures, environmental impact, and more.

BUILDING SOCIETIES YEARBOOK. see *REAL ESTATE*

BUILDING SOCIETY ANNUAL ACCOUNTS DATA. see *REAL ESTATE*

352　　　　　GW　ISSN 0007-5884
BUNDESBAUBLATT; Zeitschrift fuer Wohnungswesen, Staedtebau, Raumordnung, Baurecht, Bautechnik, Bauforschung. 1952. m. DM.262 (foreign DM.304). (Bundesministerium fuer Raumordnung, Bauwesen und Staedtebau) Bauverlag GmbH, Postfach 1460, 65004 Wiesbaden, Germany. TEL 06123-700-0. FAX 06123-700122. Ed. H. Wendt. adv. contact: A. Mayer. bk.rev.; abstr.; charts; illus.; stat.; tr.lit.; index. circ. 8,500. **Indexed:** Excerp.Med., INIS Atomind. **Document type:** government publication, trade publication.
—BLDSC (2930.120000).
Description: Covers all aspects and areas of building, environmental planning, and housing. Contains some technical information, readers' comments.

350.865　　　　NO
BYGGE OG BO. 1958. 5/yr. membership. Bergen og Omegn Boligbyggelag, Postboks 1990 Nordnes, 5024 Bergen, Norway. TEL 05-327750. FAX 05-234536. Ed. Tone Hartvedt. adv. circ. 41,000.
Description: News about corporate housing.

BYGGFORSKNING. see *BUILDING AND CONSTRUCTION*

352 711　　　　DK　ISSN 0007-7658
BYPLAN. 1948. 6/yr. DKK 385. Arkitektens Forlag, Nyhavn 43, DK-1051 Copenhagen K, Denmark. TEL 33-13-62-00. FAX 33-91-27-70. Ed. Arne Gaardmand. adv.; bk.rev.; charts; illus.; maps; index, cum.index every 5 yrs. circ. 2,300. **Indexed:** Geo.Abstr.
Description: Journal on town planning, regional and national planning.

352.7　　　　　US　ISSN 1050-3811
C D - HOUSING REGISTER. 1983. s-m. $369. (Community Development Services, Inc.) C D Publications, 8204 Fenton St., Silver Spring, MD 20910. TEL 301-588-6380. FAX 301-588-6385. Ed. Dave Kittross. (looseleaf format; back issues avail.) **Document type:** newsletter.
Description: Packets of individually reprinted items from the Federal Register regulations affecting housing, community economics, rural development, housing for the elderly, and mortgage finance, construction and materials.

HOUSING AND URBAN PLANNING

334 338.91 US ISSN 0895-5735
C H F NEWSBRIEFS. 1964. 2/yr. free. Cooperative Housing Foundation, 1010 Wayne Ave., Ste. 240, Silver Spring, MD 20910. TEL 301-587-4700. FAX 301-587-2626. TELEX 440271 CHF UI. Ed. Alicia J. George. illus. circ. 5,500. (processed) Document type: newsletter.
 Formerly: F C H News Briefs (ISSN 0014-570X)
 Description: News items on activities to support cooperative housing and community improvement and development in low-income and needy areas throughout the world.

C M L ANNUAL REPORT. (Council of Mortgage Lenders) see REAL ESTATE

C M L - B S A MORTGAGE WEEKLY. see REAL ESTATE

C M L DIRECTORY OF MEMBERS. see REAL ESTATE

C M L JOURNALS INDEX. see REAL ESTATE

C M L LIBRARY BULLETIN. see REAL ESTATE

C M L MARKET BRIEFING. see REAL ESTATE

350.086 US
C P L DIRECTORY OF PLANNING AND URBAN AFFAIRS. irreg. Council of Planning Librarians, Publications Office, 1313 E. 60th St., Chicago, IL 60637-2897. TEL 312-955-9100. FAX 312-955-8312. Document type: directory.

350.086 US ISSN 0045-8791
C P L NEWSLETTER. 1966. m. membership. Council of Planning Librarians, Publications Office, 1313 E. 60th St., Chicago, IL 60637-2897. TEL 312-955-9100. FAX 312-955-8312. Ed. Thelma Helyar. bk.rev.; bibl. circ. 175. (processed) Document type: newsletter.

C P M ASPECTS. (Certified Property Manager) see REAL ESTATE

352.9 US
C R A REPORTER. 1987. q. $30 (free to qualified personnel). Center for Community Change, 1000 Wisconsin Ave., N.W., Washington, DC 20007. TEL 202-342-0567. FAX 202-342-1132. Ed. Debby Goldberg. bk.rev. circ. 1,200. Document type: newsletter.
 Description: News on the interpretation and enforcement of the regulatory guidelines of the Community Reinvestment Act requiring that federal financial institutions help meet the credit needs of their entire communities, including low income areas.

711.4 333.77 US
C R P C INFO. 1967. m. free. Capital Region Planning Commission, 333 N. 19th St., Box 3355, Baton Rouge, LA 70821. TEL 504-383-5203. Dir. Sidney L. Gray. circ. 719.

352.7 BG
C U S BULLETIN. (Text in English) 1973. biennial. $10. Centre for Urban Studies, c/o Dept. of Geography, University of Dhaka, Ramna, Dhaka 2, Bangladesh. FAX 880-2-863060. adv.; bk.rev. circ. 1,000.

352.7 FR ISSN 0980-8442
CAHIERS DE L'HABITAT. 1986. q. 200 F. (foreign 300 F.). (Ministere de l'Equipement, du Logement, des Transports et de l'Espace, Direction de la Construction) Imprimerie Nationale, B.P. 514, 59505 Douai Cedex, France. TEL 27-93-70-70. FAX 27-93-70-96. TELEX 120 389 F.
 Description: Provides a forum for social and economic discussions of housing and urban planning.

352 US
CALIFORNIA NEIGHBORHOODS. 1975. q. free. Department of Housing and Community Development, Box 952050, Sacramento, CA 94252-2050. TEL 916-445-4782. illus. circ. 6,000. (tabloid format) Indexed: Cal.Per.Ind. (1986-).
 Former titles: California Communities (ISSN 0194-2913); Communities; Which supersedes: Housing and Community Development News (ISSN 0300-8754)

CALIFORNIA PLANNING AND DEVELOPMENT REPORT. see PUBLIC ADMINISTRATION

711 720 UK
CAMBRIDGE URBAN AND ARCHITECTURAL STUDIES. 1972. irreg., no.11, 1986. price varies. (Cambridge University, Cambridge School of Architecture) Cambridge University Press, Edinburgh Bldg., Shaftesbury Rd., Cambridge CB2 2RU, England. TEL 0223-312393. FAX 0223-315052. TELEX 851817256. (N. American addr.: Cambridge University Press, Journals Dept., 40 W. 20th St., New York, NY 10011. TEL 212-924-3900. FAX 212-691-3239) Eds. Leslie Martin, Lionel March. Document type: monographic series.

352 CN ISSN 0226-0336
CANADA MORTGAGE AND HOUSING CORPORATION. ANNUAL REPORT. a. Canada Mortgage and Housing Corporation, 700 Montreal Rd., Ottawa, Ont. K1A 0P7, Canada. TEL 613-748-2367. FAX 613-748-4069.
 Formerly: Central Mortgage and Housing Corporation. Annual Report.

352.7 BL ISSN 0104-0251
CARAMELO. 1990. s-a. Rua do Lago 876, Cidade Universitaria, 05508-900 Sao Paulo SP, Brazil. TEL 011-813-3222 ext. 3141.

CARAVAN HOLIDAYS. see TRAVEL AND TOURISM

333.77 US ISSN 0164-0070
HT393.N8
CAROLINA PLANNING. 1975. s-a. $12. University of North Carolina at Chapel Hill, Department of City and Regional Planning, CB 3140 East, Chapel Hill, NC 27599-3140. TEL 919-962-1475. Ed.Bd. adv.; bk.rev. circ. 1,100. Indexed: P.A.I.S.

352.7 UK
CATHOLIC HOUSING AID SOCIETY. ANNUAL REPORT. 1956. a. free. Catholic Housing Aid Society, 189A Old Brompton Rd., London SW5 OAR, England. Ed. Robina Rafferty. circ. 5,000.

352.7 338 US ISSN 0891-1029
CENTER CITY REPORT. 1978. q. $50. International Downtown Association, 915 15th St., N.W., Ste. 600, Washington, DC 20005. TEL 202-783-4963. FAX 202-347-2161. Ed. Dale Doyle. adv.; bk.rev. circ. 1,000. Document type: newsletter.

352.7 US
CENTRAL MISSISSIPPI PLANNING AND DEVELOPMENT DISTRICT. ANNUAL REPORT. a. free. Central Mississippi Planning and Development District, 2675 River Ridge Rd., Box 4935, Jackson, MS 39216. TEL 601-981-1511. Ed. M.L. Smith. circ. 700.

352.7 UK ISSN 0952-2603
CENTRE FOR HOUSING RESEARCH. DISCUSSION PAPER. 1985. irreg., no. 43, 1993. £4.50 per no. Centre for Housing Research, University of Glasgow, 25 Bute Gardens, Glasgow G12 8RS, Scotland. TEL 041-339 8855. FAX 041-330-4983. Ed. Keith Kintren. circ. 200. (back issues avail.) Document type: academic/scholarly publication.
 —BLDSC (3597.783300).

312 301 352.7 CN ISSN 0316-4691
CENTRE FOR URBAN AND COMMUNITY STUDIES. BIBLIOGRAPHIC SERIES. 1969. irreg. (approx. 2/yr.). Centre for Urban and Community Studies, University of Toronto, 455 Spadina Ave., Toronto, ON M5S 2G8, Canada. TEL 416-978-2072. FAX 416-978-7162. Indexed: Urb.Aff.Abstr. Document type: bibliography.
 —BLDSC (1970.300000).
 Description: Covers housing and planning, sociology, geography and population studies.

312 301 352.7 CN ISSN 0319-4620
CENTRE FOR URBAN AND COMMUNITY STUDIES. MAJOR REPORT SERIES. 1974. irreg. (1-2/yr.). price varies. Centre for Urban and Community Studies, University of Toronto, 455 Spadina Ave., Toronto, ON M5S 2G8, Canada. TEL 416-978-2072. FAX 416-978-7162. Indexed: Urb.Aff.Abstr.
 Description: Covers housing and planning, sociology, geography and population studies.

312 301 352.7 CN ISSN 0316-0068
CENTRE FOR URBAN AND COMMUNITY STUDIES. RESEARCH PAPERS. 1968. irreg. (5-10/yr.). price varies. Centre for Urban and Community Studies, 455 Spadina Ave., University of Toronto, Toronto, ON M5S 2G8, Canada. TEL 416-978-2072. FAX 416-978-7162.
 Description: Covers housing and planning, sociology, geography and population studies.

352.7 UK
CENTRE FOR URBAN AND REGIONAL RESEARCH. WORKING PAPER. 1973. irreg., no.75, 1991. Centre for Urban and Regional Research, Arts Bldg. B, University of Sussex, Falmer, Brighton BN1 9QN, England. TEL 44-273-606755. Document type: academic/scholarly publication, monographic series.

352.7 US
CERRO GORDO TOWN FORUM. 1974. q. $15. Town Forum, Inc., Box 569, Cottage Grove, OR 97424. TEL 503-942-7720. Ed. Christopher Canfield. adv.; bk.rev. circ. 750. (back issues avail.)
 Formerly: Cerro Gordo News.

350.086 330.9 CC
CHENGSHI GAIGE YU FAZHAN/URBAN REFORM AND DEVELOPMENT. (Text in Chinese) bi-m. Chengdu Shi Tizhi Gaige Weiyuanhui, 75, Madao Jie, Chengdu, Sichuan 610015, People's Republic of China. TEL 667240. Ed. Zhang Xueguo.

711 CC ISSN 1002-1329
CHENGSHI GUIHUA. English edition: China City Planning Review. (Text in Chinese) bi-m. $7.98. (Zhongguo Chengshi Guihua Xuehhui - Urban Planning Society of China) China Academy of Urban Planning and Design, Academic Information Center, No. 9 Sanlihe Road, Beijing 100037, People's Republic of China. TEL 8329944. TELEX 222302 MURC CN. Ed. Wu Liangyong. circ. 15,000.
 —UnCover.

CHENGSHI GUIHUA HUIKAN. see ENGINEERING — Civil Engineering

350.086 CC
CHENGXIANG JIANSHE/URBAN AND RURAL CONSTRUCTION. (Text in Chinese) m. Y1.30. (Ministry of Construction - Jianshe Bu) Jianshe Zazhishe, Baiwanzhuang, Beijing 100835, People's Republic of China. TEL 8315217. (Dist. outside China by: China International Book Trading Corp., P.O. Box 399, Beijing, P.R.C.) Ed. Sun Qinghua.

711 CC ISSN 1002-8447
CHINA CITY PLANNING REVIEW. Chinese edition: Chengshi Guihua. (Text in English) q. $60. (Zhongguo Chengshi Guihua Xuehui - Urban Planning Society of China) China Academy of Urban Planning and Design, Academic Information Center, No. 9 Sanlihe Road, Beijing 100037, People's Republic of China. TEL 8329944. TELEX 222302 MURC CN. Ed. Chen Zhanxiang. circ. 500.

352 US ISSN 0009-7535
CITIES AND VILLAGES. Variant title: Ohio Cities and Villages. 1953. 11/yr. $10. Ohio Municipal League, 175 S. Third St., Ste. 510, Columbus, OH 43215-5134. TEL 614-221-4349. FAX 614-221-4390. Ed. John K. Mahoney. adv.; B&W page $502. bk.rev.; charts; illus.; stat.; tr.lit.; index. circ. 9,400. Document type: trade publication.

301.3 IT ISSN 0009-7640
CITTA E SOCIETA; studi e analisi sui problemi delle comunita urbane. 1966. bi-m. Piazza S. Ambrogio 15, 20123 Milan, Italy. Ed. Vittorino Colombo. adv.; bk.rev.; abstr.; bibl.; charts; illus.; cum.index.

690.87 US
CITY COMMERCIAL CODES. (Section of: Directory of Buildings & Regulations) irreg., latest 1991. $37.50. National Conference of States on Building Codes and Standards, Inc., 505 Huntmar Pk. Dr., Ste. 210, Herndon, VA 22070. TEL 703-437-0100. FAX 703-481-3596. Document type: directory.
 Description: Covers building, mechanical, plumbing, electrical, accessibility, energy, fire prevention and life safety codes applicable in commercial buildings in 50 major US cities, with contact names for city building officials.

HOUSING AND URBAN PLANNING

325.7   US   ISSN 0199-0330
HN79.N43
CITY LIMITS. 1976. 10/yr. $20 to individuals; institutions $35. City Limits Community Information Service, Inc., 40 Prince St., New York, NY 10012. TEL 212-925-9820. FAX 212-966-3407. Ed. Andrew White. adv.: B&W page $400. bk.rev.; circ. 3,000 (paid); 1,000 (controlled). (also avail. in microform from UMI; back issues avail.) **Indexed:** Alt.Press Ind., Avery Ind.Archit.Per. —UnCover.
    Description: Provides news, investigative reports and analysis of current urban issues.

690.87   US
CITY RESIDENTIAL CODES. (Section of: Directory of Building Codes & Regulations) irreg., latest 1991. $20. National Conference of States on Building Codes and Standards, Inc., 505 Huntmar Pk. Dr., Ste. 210, Herndon, VA 22070. TEL 703-437-0100. FAX 703-481-3596. **Document type:** directory.
    Description: Covers the residential codes of 50 major US cities, including name and edition of code adopted, contacts for promulgation and enforcement for one and two-family dwellings, modular homes and mobile home parks.

352.7   SP   ISSN 1133-6579
▼**CIUDADES.** 1993. irreg. 1500 ptas. Universidad de Valladolid, Secretariado de Publicaciones, Instituto de Urbanistica, C. Juan Mambrilla 14, 47003 Valladolid, Spain. TEL 983-423000. FAX 34-83-290300. **Document type:** monographic series, academic/scholarly publication.

352.7   US
CLASSICS IN URBAN HISTORY. 1958. irreg., latest 1993. price varies. University of California Press, 2120 Berkeley Way, Berkeley, CA 94720. TEL 510-642-4247. FAX 510-643-7127. (Orders to: California-Princeton Fulfillment Services, 1445 Lower Ferry Rd., Ewing, NJ 08618. TEL 800-777-4726. FAX 800-999-1958) Ed. Michael H. Ebner. (back issues avail.) **Document type:** monographic series.
    Description: Reissues seminal historic texts on urban studies.
    Refereed Serial

352.7   US
COASTAL BEND COUNCIL OF GOVERNMENTS. MONTHLY UPDATE. 1969. q. membership. Coastal Bend Council of Governments, Box 9909, Corpus Christi, TX 78469. TEL 512-883-5743. Ed. Juliet K. Wenger. illus. circ. 1,100.
    Formerly (until 1987): Costal Bend Council of Governments. State of the Region.
    Description: Examines regional planning.

690.87   US   ISSN 0889-3616
CODES & STANDARDS. 1980. m. $75. Kelly P. Reynolds & Associates Inc., 1105 W. Chicago Ave., Ste. 302, Chicago, IL 60622. TEL 312-829-6000; 800-950-2633. FAX 312-829-8855. Ed. Kelly P. Reynolds. bk.rev. (looseleaf format) **Document type:** newsletter.
    Description: Covers new trends, developments, case law and interpretation of fire and building codes.

352.7   UK
COMMUNITY ACTION MAGAZINE. 1972. bi-m. £3 to individuals; £7.50 to libraries. Community Action Magazine Ltd., 27 Clerkenwell Close, London E.C.1., England. adv.; bk.rev.; bibl.; illus. circ. 4,000. (also avail. in microfiche; back issues avail.) **Indexed:** ASSIA, Stud.Wom.Abstr.

COMMUNITY AFFAIRS. see *PUBLIC ADMINISTRATION*

350.865   US   ISSN 0190-1192
KF581.A15
COMMUNITY ASSOCIATION LAW REPORTER. 1978. m. $150 to non-members; members $125. Community Associations Institute (Alexandria), 1630 Duke St., Alexandria, VA 22314. TEL 703-548-8600. FAX 703-684-1581. (Subscr. to: Box 25037, Alexandria, VA 22313-5037) Ed. Wayne S. Hyatt. index. circ. 4,000. (looseleaf format) **Document type:** newsletter.
    Description: News articles on legislation and judicial proceedings pertaining to establishing, financing, operating, and maintaining condominiums, cooperatives, and homeowner associations.

COMMUNITY CHANGE. see *BUSINESS AND ECONOMICS — Economic Situation And Conditions*

690   US   ISSN 0094-2324
COMMUNITY DEVELOPMENT DIGEST; development, planning, infrastructure, financing. 1965. s-m. $369. (Community Development Services, Inc.) C D Publications, 8204 Fenton St., Silver Spring, MD 20910. TEL 301-588-6380. FAX 301-588-6385. Ed. Tom Bryan. bk.rev.; abstr.; bibl.; s-a. index. (back issues avail.) **Document type:** newsletter.
    Incorporates (1978-1991): Economic Growth Report (ISSN 1048-5848); Which was formerly titled: Economic Growth and Revitalization; Local Economic Growth and Neighborhood Reinvestment Report; Which was formed by the merger of (1979-1982): Local Economic Growth Letter; Neighborhood Reinvestment Report; Which was formerly titled: Neighborhood and Rehab Report (ISSN 0193-6794); Economic Growth and Revitalization Report; Incorporates (in 1991): Economic Development Monitor; Which was formerly: Report on Development Financing; Industrial Development News (ISSN 1040-3345); Incorporates (1983-1985): Urban and Housing Research Report; Formerly: Housing and Renewal Index (ISSN 0018-6597).
    Description: Covers U.S. community development programs.

COMMUNITY DEVELOPMENT SOCIETY. JOURNAL. see *SOCIAL SERVICES AND WELFARE*

COMMUNITY ECONOMICS. see *BUSINESS AND ECONOMICS — Cooperatives*

COMMUNITY INVESTMENT AND AFFORDABLE HOUSING. see *BUSINESS AND ECONOMICS — Investments*

COMMUNITY QUARTERLY; leading journal of community development case studies. see *SOCIOLOGY*

352.7   CN
COMPENDIUM OF RESEARCH. (Text in English and French) 1984. a. free. Canada Mortgage & Housing Corporation, 700 Montreal Rd., Ottawa, Ont. K1A 0P7, Canada. TEL 613-748-2367. FAX 613-748-4069.

352.7   US
COMPILATION OF NATIONALLY AVERAGED RENTAL RATES. 1951. a. $32.50. Associated Equipment Distributors, 615 W. 22nd St., Oak Brook, IL 60521. TEL 708-574-0650. Ed. C. David Loftus. circ. 15,000. (back issues avail.)

350.865   CN   ISSN 0849-6714
CONDOMINIUM. 1976. 12/yr. Can.$65. Shelter Publications, 366 Adelaide St. W., Ste. 501, Toronto, Ont. M5V 1R5, Canada. TEL 416-585-2552. FAX 416-585-9741. adv.: B&W page $850, color page $1350. circ. 6,000. (tabloid format)
    Formerly (until 1989): Condominium Magazine (ISSN 0826-502X)
    Description: Trade magazine for condominium development and administration industries.

352.7   US
CONNECTICUT HOUSING MARKET. ANNUAL REPORT.*
1980. a. $5. Department of Housing, Research Unit, 505 Hudson St., Hartford, CT 06106-2502. TEL 203-566-4682. FAX 203-566-8600. Ed. Sandy Bergin. circ. 3,500.

CONSTRUCTION REVIEW. see *BUILDING AND CONSTRUCTION*

352.7   US
CONSUMER - FARMER COOPERATOR. 1938. a. free. Consumer - Farmer Foundation, Inc., 121 6th Ave., Ste. 501, New York, NY 10003. TEL 212-431-9783. Ed. Harry DeRienzo. charts; illus. circ. 5,000.

352   BL
CONTRIBUICOES EM DESENVOLVIMENTO URBANO. irreg. Editora Campus Ltda. (Subsidiary of: Elsevier Science Publishers B.V.), Rua Sete de Setembro 111-16 andar, 50020-02 Centro, Rio de Janeiro RJ, Brazil. TEL 021-221-5340. FAX 021-252-2904.

352.7   US   ISSN 0097-9759
COOPERATIVE HOUSING BULLETIN. 1950. 6/yr. $35 (includes Cooperative Housing Journal). National Association of Housing Cooperatives, 1614 King St., Alexandria, VA 22314. TEL 703-549-5201. FAX 703-549-5204. Ed. Katharine Law. bk.rev. circ. 3,200. (looseleaf format; back issues avail.) **Document type:** newsletter.
    Description: Publishes articles on the creation and effective operation of housing cooperatives.

352.7   US   ISSN 0589-6355
COOPERATIVE HOUSING JOURNAL. resumed 1963. a. $35 (includes Cooperative Housing Bulletin). National Association of Housing Cooperatives, 1614 King St., Alexandria, VA 22314. TEL 703-549-5201. FAX 703-549-5204. Ed. Katharine Law. adv.; bk.rev. circ. 1,500. (back issues avail.) **Document type:** trade publication.
    Description: Covers issues relating to the creation and effective operation of housing cooperatives.

352.7 334   CN   ISSN 0226-8531
CO-OPSERVATIONS. (Text in English, French) 3/yr. free. Co-operative Housing Federation of Canada - Federation de l'Habitation Cooperative du Canada, 225 Metcalfe St., Ste. 311, Ottawa, ON K2P 1P9, Canada. TEL 613-230-2201. FAX 613-230-2231. Ed. Lyse Huot. adv.; illus. circ. 45,000. (tabloid format) **Document type:** newsletter, newspaper.
    Description: Reports on issues of interest to co-op housing households across Canada.

333.77   US
CORNELL UNIVERSITY. DEPARTMENT OF CITY AND REGIONAL PLANNING. REGIONAL SCIENCE DISSERTATION AND MONOGRAPH SERIES. 1972. irreg., latest 1982. Cornell University, Department of City and Regional Planning, College of Architecture, Art, and Planning, 106 W. Sibley Hall, Ithaca, NY 14853-6701. (reprint service avail. from UMI) **Document type:** monographic series.

352.7 333.77   US
CORNELL UNIVERSITY. DEPARTMENT OF CITY AND REGIONAL PLANNING. RESEARCH REPORTS. 1955. irreg., latest 1981. Cornell University, Department of City and Regional Planning, College of Architecture, Art, and Planning, 106 W. Sibley Hall, Ithaca, NY 14853-6701. (reprint service avail. from UMI)
    Formerly: Cornell University. Program in Urban and Regional Studies. Research Reports; Supersedes (in 1970): Cornell University. Center for Housing and Environmental Studies. Research Reports (ISSN 0070-0061)

333.77   US
CORNELL UNIVERSITY. DEPARTMENT OF CITY AND REGIONAL PLANNING. WORKING PAPERS IN PLANNING. 1974. irreg., no.98, 1990. Cornell University, Department of City and Regional Planning, College of Architecture, Art, and Planning, 106 W. Sibley Hall, Ithaca, NY 14853-6701. (reprint service avail. from UMI)
    Former titles (until 1979): Cornell University. City and Regional Planning Publications. Occasional Papers; Cornell University. Program in Urban and Regional Studies. Occasional Papers; Supersedes (in 1976): Cornell University. Center for Urban Development Research. Occasional Papers.

352.7 690   US
COUNCIL ON TALL BUILDINGS AND URBAN HABITAT. COLLECTED PAPERS. irreg., 4th World Congress, Hong Kong, 1990. $48 (foreign $51.75). Council on Tall Buildings and Urban Society, Fritz Lab, 13 E. Packer Ave., Lehigh University, Bethlehem, PA 18015. TEL 215-758-3515. FAX 215-758-4522. Ed. Lynn S. Bralle. **Document type:** proceedings.

352.7 690   US
COUNCIL ON TALL BUILDINGS AND URBAN HABITAT. PROCEEDINGS. irreg., 4th World Congress, Hong Kong, 1990. $60 (foreign $64.25). Council on Tall Buildings and Urban Habitat, Lehigh University, 13 E. Packer Ave., Bethlehem, PA 18015. TEL 215-758-3515. FAX 215-758-4522. illus. **Document type:** proceedings.

352.7   UK
COUNTY PLANNING DEPARTMENT. SURREY COUNTY COUNCIL. TECHNICAL REPORT.. m. £5 per issue. County Planning Department, Surrey County Council, County Hall, Penrhyn Rd., Kingston-upon-Thames KT1 2DT, England.

CRONER'S PREMISES MANAGEMENT. see *BUSINESS AND ECONOMICS — Management*

333.77   PE   ISSN 4001-4029
CUADERNOS PARA EL DEBATE REGIONAL. irreg., no.4030, 1988. price varies. Centro de Estudios Regionales Andinos "Bartolome de Las Casas", Apdo. 477, Cusco, Peru. TEL 084-236494. FAX 084-238255.

---

352 690   US   ISSN 0896-6702
CURRENT CONSTRUCTION REPORTS: HOUSING COMPLETIONS. (Series C22) 1970. m. $20 (foreign $25). U.S. Bureau of the Census, Data User Services Division, Washington, DC 20233. TEL 301-763-4100. (Subscr. to: Superintendent of Documents, U.S. Government Printing Office, Box 371954, Pittsburgh, PA 15250-7954. TEL 202-783-3238. FAX 202-512-2233) charts; stat. (also avail. in microfiche from CIS; back issues avail.; reprint service avail. from CIS) **Document type:** government publication.
  Formerly (until 1987): Construction Reports: Housing Completions (ISSN 0363-8804).
  Description: Compiles statistics on the number of new private housing units completed and under construction.

---

352 690   US   ISSN 0896-6761
CURRENT CONSTRUCTION REPORTS: HOUSING STARTS. (Series C20) 1959. m. $20 (foreign £25). U.S. Bureau of the Census, Data User Services Division, Washington, DC 20233. TEL 310-763-4100. (Subscr. to: Superintendent of Documents, U.S. Government Printing Office, Box 371954, Pittsburgh, PA 15250-7954. TEL 202-783-3238. FAX 202-512-2233) charts; stat. (also avail. in microfiche from CIS; back issues avail.; reprint service avail. from CIS) **Indexed:** Amer.Stat.Ind. (1973-). **Document type:** government publication.
  ●Also available online. Vendor(s): CompuServe, Inc., DIALOG Information Services, Inc.
  Formerly (until 1987): Construction Reports: Housing Starts (ISSN 0498-8442).
  Description: Compiles data on the number of nonfarm and total housing units started, by ownership, location, and type of structure.

301.5   US   ISSN 0896-9221
HD7293.A1
CURRENT CONSTRUCTION REPORTS: HOUSING UNITS AUTHORIZED BY BUILDING PERMITS; states and selected metropolitan areas. (Series C40) 1967. m. (plus a. supplement). $70 (foreign $87.50). U.S. Bureau of the Census, Data User Services Division, Washington, DC 20233. TEL 301-763-4100. (Subscr. to: Superintendent of Documents, U.S. Government Printing Office, Box 371954, Pittsburgh, PA 15250-7954. TEL 202-783-3238. FAX 202-512-2233) charts; stat. (also avail. in microfiche from CIS; back issues avail.; reprint service avail. from CIS) **Indexed:** Amer.Stat.Ind. (1973-) **Document type:** government publication.
  ●Also available online. Vendor(s): CompuServe, Inc., DIALOG Information Services, Inc.
  Former titles (until 1987): Construction Reports: Housing Units Authorized by Building Permits (ISSN 0896-923X); (until 1986): Current Construction Reports: Housing Units Authorized by Building Permits (ISSN 0897-540X); (until 1980): Current Construction Reports: Housing Units Authorized by Building Permits and Public Contracts (ISSN 0363-8790); Which incorporates (in 1969): Construction Reports: Housing Units Authorized by Building Permits and Public Contracts, States, and Selected Standard Metropolitan Areas (Series C42) (ISSN 0091-4762)

---

352 690   US
CURRENT CONSTRUCTION REPORTS: NEW ONE-FAMILY HOUSES SOLD. (Series C25) 1971. m. (plus a. supplement). $25 (foreign $31.25). U.S. Bureau of the Census, Data User Services Division, Washington, DC 20233. TEL 301-763-4100. (Subscr. to: Superintendent of Documents, U.S. Government Printing Office, Box 371954, Pittsburgh, PA 15250-7954. TEL 202-783-3238. FAX 202-512-2233) charts; stat. (also avail. in microfiche from CIS; back issues avail.; reprint service avail. from CIS) **Document type:** government publication.
  ●Also available online. Vendor(s): CompuServe, Inc., DIALOG Information Services, Inc.
  Former titles (until 1990): Construction Reports: New One-Family Houses Sold and for Sale (ISSN 0896-9248); (until 1987): Current Construction Reports: New One-Family Homes Sold and for Sale (ISSN 0363-8537)
  Description: Provides preliminary information regarding new privately owned one-family houses sold during the month and for sale at the end of the month.

---

352 690   US   ISSN 0896-6737
CURRENT CONSTRUCTION REPORTS: NEW RESIDENTIAL CONSTRUCTION IN SELECTED METROPOLITAN AREAS. (Series C21) q. $9 (foreign $11.25). U.S. Bureau of the Census, Data User Services Division, Washington, DC 20233. TEL 301-763-4100. (Subscr. to: Superintendent of Documents, U.S. Government Printing Office, Box 371954, Pittsburgh, PA 15250-7954. TEL 202-783-3238. FAX 202-512-2233) charts; stat. (also avail. in microfiche from CIS; back issues avail.; reprint service avail. from CIS) **Document type:** government publication.
  ●Also available online. Vendor(s): CompuServe, Inc., DIALOG Information Services, Inc.
  Formerly (until 1987): Construction Reports: New Residential Construction in Selected Standard Metropolitan Statistical Areas (ISSN 0145-0212).
  Description: Compiles data on new housing construction in various metropolitan areas.

---

352 690   US   ISSN 0896-6745
CURRENT CONSTRUCTION REPORTS: VALUE OF NEW CONSTRUCTION PUT IN PLACE. (Series C30) m. $27 (foreign $33.75). U.S. Bureau of the Census, Data User Services Division, Washington, DC 20233. TEL 301-763-4100. (Subscr. to: Superintendent of Documents, U.S. Government Printing Office, Box 371954, Pittsburgh, PA 15250-7954. TEL 202-783-3238. FAX 202-512-2233) charts. (also avail. in microfiche from CIS; back issues avail.; reprint service avail. from CIS) **Indexed:** Amer.Stat.Ind. (1973-). **Document type:** government publication.
  ●Also available online. Vendor(s): CompuServe, Inc., DIALOG Information Services, Inc.
  Former titles (until 1987): Construction Reports: Value of New Construction Put in Place (ISSN 0896-6753); (until 1986): Current Construction Reports: Value of New Construction Put in Place (ISSN 0897-5396); (until 1985): Construction Reports: Value of New Construction Put in Place (ISSN 0363-8294)

333.33   US
CURRENT HOUSING REPORTS: AMERICAN HOUSING SURVEY FOR METROPOLITAN AREAS. (Series H-170) a. price varies. U.S. Bureau of the Census, Data User Services Division, Washington, DC 20233. TEL 301-763-4100. (Subscr. to: Superintendent of Documents, U.S. Government Printing Office, Box 371954, Pittsburgh, PA 15250-7954. TEL 202-783-3238. FAX 202-512-2233) stat.; index. (also avail. in microfiche; back issues avail.) **Document type:** government publication.
  Formerly: Current Housing Reports: Annual Housing Survey: Metropolitan Areas.

333.33   US
CURRENT HOUSING REPORTS: AMERICAN HOUSING SURVEY FOR THE UNITED STATES. (Series H-150) biennial. price varies. U.S. Bureau of the Census, Data User Services Division, Washington, DC 20233. TEL 301-763-4100. (Subscr. to: Superintendent of Documents, U.S. Government Printing Office, Box 371954, Pittsburgh, PA 15250-7954. TEL 202-783-3238. FAX 202-512-2233) stat.; index. (also avail. in microfiche; back issues avail.) **Document type:** government publication.
  Former titles: Current Housing Reports: American Housing Survey for the United States and Regions; Current Housing Reports: Annual Housing Survey: United States and Regions.

---

352 690   US   ISSN 0896-9264
HD9715.U5
CURRENT HOUSING REPORTS: EXPENDITURES FOR RESIDENTIAL IMPROVEMENTS AND REPAIRS. (Series C50) 1961. q. $7 (foreign $8.75). U.S. Bureau of the Census, Data User Services Division, Washington, DC 20233. TEL 301-763-4100. (Subscr. to: Superintendent of Documents, U.S. Government Printing Office, Box 371954, Pittsburgh, PA 15250-7954. TEL 202-783-3238. FAX 202-512-2233) charts; stat. (also avail. in microfiche from CIS; back issues avail.; reprint service avail. from CIS) **Document type:** government publication.
  Formerly (until 1987): Construction Reports: Residential Alterations and Repair (ISSN 0501-7645)
  Description: Estimates expenditures by property owners for maintenance and repairs, additions, alterations, and major replacements to their homes.

---

352 301.5   US   ISSN 0498-8450
CURRENT HOUSING REPORTS: HOUSING CHARACTERISTICS. (Series H-121) irreg. U.S. Bureau of the Census, Data User Services Division, Washington, DC 20233. TEL 301-763-4100. (Subscr. to: Superintendent of Documents, U.S. Government Printing Office, Box 371954, Pittsburgh, PA 15250-7954. TEL 202-783-3238. FAX 202-512-2233) stat.; index. (also avail. in microform; back issues avail.) **Document type:** government publication.

301.5   US   ISSN 0498-8469
CURRENT HOUSING REPORTS: HOUSING VACANCIES. Quarterly reports are titled: Housing Vacancies and Homeownership. Annual reports are titled: Housing Vacancies and Homeownership Annual Statistics. (Series H-111; order ID: CHR) q. (plus a. issue). $12 (foreign $15). U.S. Bureau of the Census, Data User Services Division, Washington, DC 20233. TEL 301-763-4100. (Subscr. to: Superintendent of Documents, U.S. Government Printing Office, Box 371954, Pittsburgh, PA 15250-7954. TEL 202-783-3238. FAX 202-512-2233) stat.; index. (also avail. in microfiche from CIS; back issues avail.; reprint service avail. from CIS) **Indexed:** Amer.Stat.Ind. (1974-). **Document type:** government publication.
  ●Also available online. Vendor(s): CompuServe, Inc., DIALOG Information Services, Inc.

301.5 331.83   US   ISSN 0363-8286
HD7287.6.U5
CURRENT HOUSING REPORTS: MARKET ABSORPTION OF APARTMENTS. (Series H-130; order ID: CHMA) q. (plus a. issue). $8.50 (foreign $10.65). U.S. Bureau of the Census, Data User Services Division, Washington, DC 20233. TEL 301-763-4100. (Subscr. to: Superintendent of Documents, U.S. Government Printing Office, Box 371954, Pittsburgh, PA 15250-7954. TEL 202-783-3238. FAX 202-512-2233) (Co-sponsor: U.S. Department of Housing and Urban Development) index. (also avail. in microfiche from CIS; back issues avail.; reprint service avail. from CIS) **Indexed:** Amer.Stat.Ind. (1973-). **Document type:** government publication.

352.7   PL   ISSN 0137-3617
CZLOWIEK I SRODOWISKO. 1977. q. Instytut Gospodarki Przestrzennej i Komunalnej, Ul. Krzywickiego 9, 02-078 Warsaw, Poland. TEL 48-22-250937. Ed. Zofia Debowska. circ. 650.
  Description: Covers spatial planning, building apartments, communal economy.

HOUSING AND URBAN PLANNING

350.865   DK   ISSN 0108-4585
D A B INFORMATION. 1982. bi-m. free. Dansk Almennyttigt Boligselskab af 1942 s.m.b.a., Finsenvej 35, 2000 Frederiksberg, Denmark. FAX 31-197383. Eds. Niels Chr. Knutzon, Michael Frisch-Jensen. illus.

D E S W O S - BRIEF. (Deutsche Entwicklungshilfe fuer Soziales Wohnungs- und Siedlungswesen e.V.) see BUSINESS AND ECONOMICS — *International Development And Assistance*

352.7 338.9   SZ   ISSN 0251-3625
D I S P. (Dokumente und Informationen zur Schweizerischen Orts-, Regional- und Landesplanung) (Text in English, French, German, Italian) 1965. 4/yr. Eidgenoessische Technische Hochschule, Institut fuer Orts-, Regional- und Landesplanung, Redaktion DISP, CH-8093 Zurich, Switzerland. TEL 01-3772956. FAX 01-3720486. Ed. Michael Koch. charts; cum.index. circ. 3,000. **Indexed:** Dok.Str. **Document type:** academic/scholarly publication.
—BLDSC (3616.435000).
    Formerly: Informationen zur Orts-, Regional- und Landesplanung (ISSN 0300-3981)

352   AU   ISSN 0011-5320
DAHEIM BEI DER W A G; Mieterzeitung. 1964. s-a. Wohnungsaktiengesellschaft Linz, Dr. Oswald Kratochwill, Stadlerstr. 3, A-4026 Linz, Austria.

DALLAS - FORT WORTH HOME BUYER'S GUIDE. see *REAL ESTATE*

352.7   US
DALLAS TENANTS NEWS. 1978. q. $15 (includes handbook of Tenants' Rights in English, Spanish). Dallas Tenants' Association, 2906 Swiss Ave., Dallas, TX 75204. TEL 214-824-0728. Ed. Dorothy Masterson. circ. 2,000.

DANMARKS TEKNISKE HOEJSKOLE. INSTITUTET FOR VEJE, TRAFIK OG BYPLAN. NOTAT/TECHNICAL UNIVERSITY OF DENMARK. INSTITUTE OF ROADS, TRANSPORT AND TOWN PLANNING. PAPER. see *TRANSPORTATION — Roads And Traffic*

333.77   PE
DEBATES URBANO REGIONALES. irreg., latest no.7002. $20. Centro de Estudios Regionales Andinos "Bartolome de Las Casas", Apdo. 477, Cusco, Peru. TEL 084-236494. FAX 084-238255.

711   FR   ISSN 0982-0671
DECIDEURS D'ILE-DE-FRANCE; et du bassin parisien. w. 3500 F. L'Agence Innovapresse, 29 rue du Faubourg Poisonniere, 75009 Paris, France. TEL 48-24-08-97. FAX 42-47-00-76. Ed. Antoine Loubiere.
    Description: Studies city planning.

DEFENSE HOUSING. see *MILITARY*

333.77   DK   ISSN 0108-6901
DENMARK. MILJOEMINISTERIET. MILJOEMINISTERENS REDEGOERELSE OM LANDSPLANLAEGNING. 1975. a. DKK 85. Miljoeministeriet, Landsplanafdelingen - Ministry of the Environment, Slotsholmsgade 12, DK-1216 Copenhagen K, Denmark.
    Formerly: Denmark. Miljoeministeriet. Redegoerelse fra Miljoeministeren om Landsplanlaegning.

DENVER HOUSING GUIDE. see *REAL ESTATE*

DEPARTMENT OF TOWN AND COUNTRY PLANNING. WORKING PAPER SERIES. see *PUBLIC ADMINISTRATION*

DESIGN RESEARCH NEWS. see *ARCHITECTURE*

711 352   GW   ISSN 0011-9822
DEUTSCHE AKADEMIE FUER STAEDTEBAU UND LANDESPLANUNG. MITTEILUNGEN. 1957. s-a. price varies. Deutsche Akademie fuer Staedtebau und Landesplanung, Kurfuerstendamm 188-189, 10707 Berlin, Germany. TEL 030-8854936. Ed. Lothar Juckel. bk.rev. circ. 800. **Indexed:** P.A.I.S.For.Lang.Ind.
—BLDSC (5839.070000).

DEVELOPMENT PLANS IN THE PIPELINE. see *REAL ESTATE*

352.7   US
DEVELOPMENTS; news magazine for the resort-recreational real estate and community development industries. 1978. m. membership only. American Resort Development Association, 1220 L St., N.W., Ste. 510, Washington, DC 20005. TEL 202-371-6700. FAX 202-289-8544. Ed. Sheila Morris. adv.: B&W page $1075, color page $1575; adv. contact: Sheila Morris. bk.rev. circ. 2,000. (back issues avail.) **Document type:** trade publication.

711.4   NE   ISSN 0923-8131
DEVELOPMENTS IN LANDSCAPE MANAGEMENT AND URBAN PLANNING. (Text in English) 1982. irreg., vol.6E, 1994. price varies. Elsevier Science B.V., Books Division, P.O. Box 211, 1000 AE Amsterdam, Netherlands. TEL 31-20-5803911. FAX 31-20-5803705. TELEX 18582 ESPA NL. (Subscr. in U.S. and Canada to: Elsevier Science Inc., Box 882, Madison Sq. Sta., New York, NY 10159. TEL 212-989-5800) (back issues avail.) **Document type:** monographic series.
—BLDSC (3579.084000).
Refereed Serial

352.7   FR   ISSN 0338-0610
DIAGONAL. 1973. 6/yr. 180 F. Villes et Territoires, Arche de la Defense, 92055 Paris la Defense Cedex 04, France. TEL 40-81-15-52. FAX 40-81-15-99. TELEX 610 835 F. Ed. Marie-Claude Diebold.

690.87   US
DIRECTORY OF BUILDING CODES & REGULATIONS. (Consists of 4 vols.: State Commercial Codes, State Residential Codes, City Commercial Codes, City Residential Codes) irreg., latest 1991. $100. National Conference of States on Building Codes and Standards, Inc., 505 Huntmark Pk. Dr., Ste. 210, Herndon, VA 22070. TEL 703-437-0100. FAX 703-481-3596. **Document type:** directory.
    Description: Lists code information for single and multi-family residential and commercial building and safety codes (including regulations governing mobile home parks) for all 50 states, Washington DC, Puerto Rico and the US Virgin Islands with names and addresses of officials, name and edition of code adopted, with amendments and commentary.

DISCUSSIONS IN ENVIRONMENTAL HEALTH PLANNING. see *ENVIRONMENTAL STUDIES*

333.77   PE
DOCUMENTOS REGIONALES. 1990. irreg., no.4103, 1990. price varies. Centro de Estudios Regionales Andinos "Bartolome de las Casas", Apdo. 477, Cusco, Peru. TEL 084-236494. FAX 084-238255.

711 301 658.8   US   ISSN 0012-5822
DOWNTOWN IDEA EXCHANGE. 1954. s-m. $133. (Downtown Research & Development Center) Alexander Research & Communications, Inc., 215 Park Ave., S., Ste. 1301, New York, NY 10003. TEL 212-228-0246. FAX 212-228-0376. Ed. Laurence A. Alexander. bk.rev.; charts; illus. **Document type:** newsletter.
    Description: Newsletter of downtown revitalization for downtown leaders and officials in local and state government.

DOWNTOWN PROMOTION REPORTER. see *ADVERTISING AND PUBLIC RELATIONS*

ECONOMIC DEVELOPMENT AND LAW CENTER REPORT. see *BUSINESS AND ECONOMICS — Economic Situation And Conditions*

352.7   US
ECOVILLAGE NEWSLETTER. q. $15. EcoVillage at Ithaca, Anabel Taylor Hall, Cornell University, Ithaca, NY 14853. TEL 607-255-8276. Ed. Liz Walker. circ. 500 (paid) (paid). **Document type:** newsletter.
    Supersedes (in 1991): Foot Prints.
    Description: Contains information about EcoVillage at Ithaca, a new environment-orientedorganization which is building a community for 500 people based on co-housing principles, land preservation, intensive organic agriculture and energy efficiency.

352.7   SZ
EIDGENOESSISCHE TECHNISCHE HOCHSCHULE. INSTITUT FUER ORTS-, REGIONAL- UND LANDESPLANUNG. LEHRMITTEL. 1978. irreg., latest 1989. price varies. Eidgenoessische Technische Hochschule, Institut fuer Orts-, Regional- und Landesplanung - Swiss Federal Institute of Technology, CH-8093 Zurich, Switzerland. FAX 01-3720486. **Document type:** academic/scholarly publication.

350.865   GW   ISSN 0722-2815
DIE EIGENTUMSWOHNUNG; Vorteilhaft erwerben, nutzen und verwalten. 1982. bi-m. DM.98. Wirtschaft Recht und Steuern Verlag, Fraunhoferstr. 5, 82152 Planegg, Germany. TEL 089-89517-0. FAX 089-89517250. (Subscr. to: Postfach 1363, 82142 Planegg, Germany) (looseleaf format) **Document type:** bulletin.

301 720 HN1   GR   ISSN 0013-2942
EKISTICS; problems and science of human settlements. 1955. bi-m. $80 to individuals; students $48. Athens Technological Organization, Athens Center of Ekistics, 24 Syndemou St., 106-73 Athens, Greece. TEL 30-1-3623-216. FAX 30-1-3633-395. TELEX 215227. Ed. Panayotis C. Psomopoulos. abstr.; bibl.; charts; illus.; stat.; index. circ. 2,000. (also avail. in microform from UMI; back issues avail.; reprint service avail. from UMI) **Indexed:** A.I.Abstr., Archit.Per.Ind., ASSIA, Avery Ind.Archit.Per., Avery Ind.Archit.Per., Br.Tech.Ind., Chem.Abstr., Curr.Cont., Ekist.Ind., Energy Ind., Energy Info.Abstr., Environ.Abstr., Environ.Ind., Excerp.Med., Fut.Surv., Geo.Abstr., HRIS, I D A, Int.Lab.Doc., Mid.East: Abstr.& Ind., Rural Recreat.Tour.Abstr., Sage Urb.Stud.Abstr., Soc.Sci.Ind., SSCI, Urb.Aff.Abstr, World Agri.Econ.& Rural Sociol.Abstr.
—BLDSC (3668.600000); Faxon; UnCover; SWETS; UMI.

352.7   MX
EN CONCRETO. 1963. 6/yr. (Instituto Nacional de Planificacion Integral) D'Pastrana Editores, S.A., Kelper No. 147-A, Mexico 5, D.F., Mexico. adv. circ. 12,000.

696   US
ENERGY DIRECTORY. irreg., latest 1991. $47.50. National Conference of States on Building Codes and Standards, Inc., 505 Huntmar Pk. Dr., Ste. 210, Herndon, VA 22070. TEL 703-437-0100. FAX 703-481-3596. **Document type:** directory.
    Description: Technical and administrative requirements of energy codes used in each state, with criteria for low-rise and high-rise residential buildings and commercial buildings.

ENVIRONMENT & DEVELOPMENT. see *ENVIRONMENTAL STUDIES*

301 352 711 HT166   UK   ISSN 0308-518X
ENVIRONMENT AND PLANNING A. 1969. m. $620. Pion Ltd., 207 Brondesbury Park, London NW2 5JN, England. TEL 081-459-0066. FAX 081-451-6454. Eds. A. Wilson, N. Thrift. adv.; bk.rev.; index. **Indexed:** AESIS, Avery Ind.Archit.Per., Bibl.Cart., Curr.Adv.Ecol.Sci., Curr.Cont., E.I., Energy Rev., Environ.Per.Bibl. (1990-), Excerp.Med., Geo.Abstr., HRIS, I D A, Intl.Civil Eng.Abstr., J.of Econ.Lit., Popul.Ind., Rural Recreat.Tour.Abstr., Sage Pub.Admin.Abstr., Sage Urb.Stud.Abstr., Sel.Water Res.Abstr., Soft.Abstr.Eng., SSCI, Trans.Res.Abstr., World Agri.Econ. & Rural Sociol.Abstr. **Document type:** academic/scholarly publication.
—BLDSC (3791.105200); Faxon; UnCover; SWETS.
    Formerly: Environment and Planning (ISSN 0013-9173)
    Description: Concerned with the analysis and planning of cities and regions. Covers geography, economics, planning and regional science.
Refereed Serial

301 720 711 UK ISSN 0265-8135
NA2005 CODEN: EPBDEX
ENVIRONMENT AND PLANNING B: PLANNING & DESIGN. 1974. bi-m. $225. Pion Ltd., 207 Brondesbury Park, London NW2 5JN, England. TEL 081-459-0066. FAX 081-451-6454. Eds. M. Batty, M. Breheny. adv. contact: Diana Mallett. bk.rev.; index. **Indexed:** Avery Ind.Archit.Per., Bibl.Cart., Energy Ind., Energy Info.Abstr., Energy Rev., Environ.Per.Bibl., HRIS, I D A, Risk Abstr., SSCI. **Document type:** academic/scholarly publication.
—BLDSC (3791.105500); Faxon; UnCover; SWETS.
Description: Research in urban systems analysis and design science in the field of urban and regional planning.
Refereed Serial

352.7 301 UK ISSN 0263-7758
H1
ENVIRONMENT AND PLANNING D: SOCIETY & SPACE. 1983. 4/yr. $225. Pion Ltd., 207 Brondesbury Park, London NW2 5JN, England. TEL 081-459-0066. FAX 081-451-6454. Ed. G. Pratt. adv. contact: Diana Mallett. bk.rev.; index. **Indexed:** Energy Rev., I D A, SSCI. **Document type:** academic/scholarly publication.
—BLDSC (3791.105700); Faxon; UnCover; SWETS.
Description: Focuses on the convergence between social theory and human geography, in the development of time-space relationships.
Refereed Serial

ENVIRONMENTAL AND URBAN ISSUES. see *ENVIRONMENTAL STUDIES*

ENVIRONMENTAL DESIGN RESEARCH ASSOCIATION. ANNUAL CONFERENCE PROCEEDINGS. see *ARCHITECTURE*

ENVIRONMENTAL PLANNING. see *ENVIRONMENTAL STUDIES*

ENVIRONMENTS; a journal of interdisciplinary studies. see *ENVIRONMENTAL STUDIES*

333.5 DK ISSN 0108-3775
ERHVERVSLEJEREN. 1981. q. membership. Erhvervslejernes Landsorganisation (ELO), Frederiksbergsgade 2, DK-1459 Copenhagen K, Denmark. illus.

ESTATES GAZETTE PLANNING LAW REPORTS. see *REAL ESTATE*

720 962 UA ISSN 1110-2497
ETUDES URBAINES. (Text in French) 1989. irreg., vol.3, 1993. price varies. Institut Francais d'Archeologie Orientale du Caire, P.O. Box 11562 Kasr-el-Aini, 37 Sharia Sheikh Aly Youssef, Mounira, Cairo, Egypt. TEL 20-2-3548245. FAX 20-2-3544635. (Dist. outside Egypt by: Imprimerie Nationale - D A C F, 27 rue de la Convention, 75732 Paris Cedex 15, France. TEL 33-1-40-58-32-92. FAX 33-1-40-58-30-57) (back issues avail.) **Document type:** monographic series.
Description: Publishes conference proceedings and scholarly studies of historical topics relating to housing, habitat, and the architecture of cities in Egypt and neighboring regions.

711 614.7 IT
EUPOLIS; rivista critica di ecologia territoriale. 1990. bi-m. (Consulta delle Piccole Citta dell'Italia Centrale) Edizioni Nuovi Quaderni, Pancole 57, 53037 S. Gimignano (Si), Italy. TEL 0577-95-50-26. Ed. Pietro M. Toesca.

EUROPEAN COMMUNITY MORTGAGE BULLETIN. see *REAL ESTATE*

352.7 UK ISSN 0965-4313
▼**EUROPEAN PLANNING STUDIES.** 1993. q. $90 to individuals; institutions $222 (effective 1994). Carfax Publishing Co., P.O. Box 25, Abingdon, Oxon. OX14 3UE, England. TEL 44-235-555335. FAX 44-235-555335. (N. American subscr. to: Carfax Publishing Co., Box 2025, Dunnellon, FL 34430-2025) Ed. Philip Cook. adv.; bk.rev.; index. (also avail. in microfiche; back issues avail.) **Document type:** academic/scholarly publication.
—BLDSC (3829.780000).

309.26 UK ISSN 0960-6130
EUROPEAN RESEARCH IN REGIONAL SCIENCE. 1969. a. $35. (British Section of Regional Science Association) Pion Ltd., 207 Brondesbury Park, London NW2 5JN, England. TEL 081-459-0066. FAX 081-451-6454. Ed. P. Batey. **Document type:** academic/scholarly publication.
—BLDSC (3829.924100).
Formerly (until 1990): London Papers in Regional Science (ISSN 0076-0633)
Refereed Serial

352.7 GW ISSN 1022-534X
EUROPOLIS - N U R E C WORKING PAPERS. 1991. irreg., no.2, 1992. DM.10 (5 ECU). Network on Urban Research in the European Community, c/o Stadt Duisburg, Amt fuer Statistik, Stadtforschung und Europaangelegenheiten, Bismarckstr. 150-158, 47049 Duisburg, Germany. TEL 0203-2832058. FAX 0203-2834404. Ed.Bd. **Document type:** monographic series.

352.7 DK
F S B - BEBOEREN. 1954. bi-m. Frederikssundsvej 123, 2700 Broenshoej, Denmark. TEL 01-800637. Ed. Karin Peilusen. adv. circ. 12,000.

352.7 US
FAIR HOUSING: DISCRIMINATION IN REAL ESTATE, COMMUNITY DEVELOPMENT AND REVITALIZATION. 1987. base vol. (plus a. suppl.). $95. Shepard's - McGraw-Hill, Inc., Box 35300, Colorado Springs, CO 80935-3530. TEL 800-525-2474.
Description: Comprehensive, systematic treatment of current laws regulating nondiscrimination in housing and community development.

331.83 FJ
FIJI. HOUSING AUTHORITY. REPORT. (Subseries of: Fiji Parliament. Parliamentary Paper) 1959. a. $2. Housing Authority, Box 1263, Suva, Fiji. circ. 550.

FORECAST OF HOUSING ACTIVITY. see *BUSINESS AND ECONOMICS — Economic Situation And Conditions*

352.7 FR ISSN 1140-5597
FORMES ET STRUCTURES. (Text in English, French) 1966. q. 600 F. (foreign 900 F.). Art et Maitrise Publicite, 9, rue de Trevise, 75009 Paris, France. TEL 47-70-50-01. FAX 48-00-98-11. Ed. Simone Tayeb. adv.: B&W page 22000 F., color page 27000 F.; adv. contact: S. Tayeb. circ. 5,000. **Indexed:** Br.Tech.Ind. **Document type:** trade publication.
—BLDSC (4008.371500).
Formerly (until 1989): Mur Vivant.
Description: By and for architects.

350 GW ISSN 0341-244X
FORSCHUNGEN ZUR RAUMENTWICKLUNG. 1975. irreg., vol.22, 1993. price varies. Bundesforschungsanstalt fuer Landeskunde und Raumordnung, Am Michaelshof 8, 53177 Bonn, Germany. TEL 0228-826-0. FAX 0228-826266. Ed.Bd. **Document type:** government publication.
—BLDSC (4010.512000).
Supersedes (1953-1974): Institut fuer Raumordnung. Mitteilungen.

352.7 FR
FRANCE. MINISTERE DE L'EQUIPEMENT ET DU LOGEMENT. ACTIVITE ET EMPLOI DANS LE B T P. 4/yr. 360 F. (foreign 400 F.). Documentation Francaise, 29-31 Quai Voltaire, 75340 Paris Cedex 07, France. TEL 1-40-15-70-00. (Subscr. to: 124 rue Henri Barbusse, 9308 Aubervilliers Cedex, France. TEL 48-39-56-00. FAX 48-39-56-01) stat. (also avail. in microfiche from DFR) **Document type:** government publication.
Former titles: France. Ministere de l'Urbanisme et du Logement. Tableau de Bord du Batiment du Logement et des Travaux Publics (ISSN 0243-8828); France. Ministere de l'Amenagement du Territoire, de l'Equipement du Logement et des Transports. Tableau de Bord Conjoncturel du Logement.

350.865 GW
FREIBURGER HAUSBESITZER ZEITUNG. 1926. m. Verband der Haus-, Wohnungs- und Grundeigentuemer e.V., Erbprinzenstr. 7, 79098 Freiburg, Germany. TEL 0761-22464. Ed. Erwin Fedeler. (looseleaf format)

G S D NEWS. (Harvard University Graduate School of Design) see *ARCHITECTURE*

GEOMETRIA. see *ARCHITECTURE*

352 GW
GESCHICHTE - ERZIEHUNG - POLITIK. 1959. 11/yr. DM.64.90. Paedagogischer Zeitschriftenverlag, Postfach 269, 10107 Berlin, Germany. TEL 030-20343431. FAX 030-20343432. Ed. Wolfgang Heidler. bk.rev.; charts; illus.; index. circ. 12,000. **Document type:** academic/scholarly publication.
Formerly: Geschichtsunterricht und Staatsbuergerkunde (ISSN 0016-9072)

690.87 UK
GLASS'S GUIDE TO CARAVAN VALUES. 1971. q. £65. Glass's Guide Service Ltd., Elgin House, St. George's Ave., Weybridge, Surrey KT13 0BX, England. TEL 0932-853211. FAX 0932-849299. (Subscr. to: Sales and Marketing, St. Martins Ct., 37 Queens Rd., Weybridge, Surrey KT13 9TU, England. TEL 0932-823823. FAX 0932-864564) adv. **Document type:** trade publication.

352 SW
THE GLOBAL TENANT. 1958. q. free. International Union of Tenants - Internationella Hyresgaestalliansen, P.O. Box 7514, S-103 92 Stockholm, Sweden. TEL 46-8-791250. FAX 46-8-205324. Ed. Nic Nilsson. bk.rev.; illus. circ. 600. **Document type:** bulletin.
Former titles (until 1993): International Union of Tenants. International Information (ISSN 0345-5440); Supersedes (in 1970): Internationale Informationen.

GOLD BOOK OF MULTIHOUSING. see *BUILDING AND CONSTRUCTION*

GRANT ALERT. see *BUSINESS AND ECONOMICS — Public Finance, Taxation*

301.36 309.26 GW
GRAUE LITERATUR ZUR STADT-, REGIONAL- UND LANDESPLANUNG; Gutachten, Forschungs- und Planungsberichte. 1975. s-a. DM.60. Deutsches Institut fuer Urbanistik, Str. des 17. Juni 112, 10623 Berlin, Germany. TEL 030-390010. FAX 030-39001100. circ. 500. **Document type:** bulletin.
Formerly: Graue Literatur zur Orts Regional- und Landesplanung (ISSN 0340-112X)

GRUENSTIFT (BERLIN); das Umweltmagazin fuer Berlin und Brandenburg. see *CONSERVATION*

301.54 FR
GUIDE DE L'HABITAT ET DU DEVELOPPEMENT LOCAL. 1967. a. Federation Nationale de l'Habitat Rural et de l'Amenagement du Territoire Rural, 27 rue La Rochefoucauld, 75009 Paris, France. TEL 45-26-69-66. FAX 1-40-82-90-77. Eds. Philippe Pierret, Pierre Coulmin.
Former titles: Guide de l'Habitat et de l'Amenagement Rural; Guide de l'Habitat Rural; Annuaire des Organismes d'Habitat Rural (ISSN 0066-2917)

GUIDE TO FEDERAL FUNDING FOR GOVERNMENTS AND NONPROFITS. see *PUBLIC ADMINISTRATION — Municipal Government*

352.7 US
H A C NEWS. bi-w. free. Housing Assistance Council, 1025 Vermont Ave., N.W., Ste. 606, Washington, DC 20005. TEL 202-842-8600. FAX 202-347-3441. Ed. Jennifer Garner. **Document type:** newsletter.
Description: Includes information on the most recent legislation, research and other news affecting rural housing for low-income individuals.

350.865 FR
H L M AUJOURD'HUI. (Habitations a Loyer Modere) 1975. q. 400 F. to non-members; members 350 F. (foreign 470 F.) (effective Jan. 1993). Union Nationale des Federations d'Organismes d'Habitations a Loyer Modere, Editions Department, 14 rue Lord Byron, 75384 Paris Cedex 08, France. TEL 40-75-78-00. FAX 40-75-79-83. Ed. Soraya Mehiri. adv.; illus. circ. 10,000.
Formerly (until 1986): H (ISSN 0338-2842)

HOUSING AND URBAN PLANNING

352.7 333.33   CN   ISSN 0700-5040
HABITABEC MONTREAL; pour mieux se loger - everything about the house. (Text in English, French) 1976. w. Can.$125. Habitabec Inc., 8594 rue Berri, Montreal, PQ H2P 2G4, Canada. TEL 514-389-5944. FAX 514-385-6282. Ed. Jacques Dery. adv.: page Can.$4060; 14 x 10. bk.rev.; stat. circ. 105,509. (tabloid format; also avail. in microfilm from BNQ) **Document type:** newspaper.
   Description: Provides news, information, advice and views on interest rates, market trends, home ownership options, renovation and interior decorating.

352.7 333.33   CN   ISSN 0844-2487
HABITABEC QUEBEC; pour mieux se loger. 1984. w. Habitabec Inc., 8594 Berri St., Montreal, PQ H2P 2G4, Canada. TEL 514-389-5944. FAX 514-385-6282. Ed. Jacques Dery. adv.: page Can.$1820; 14 x 10. circ. 26,000. (tabloid format; also avail. in microfilm from BNQ) **Document type:** newspaper.
   Description: Provides information for prospective home buyers.

352.7   US   ISSN 0272-9946
HABITAT. (Subseries of: S I R S Social Issues (ISSN 0740-3127)) 1975. a. price varies. Social Issues Resources Series, Box 2348, Boca Raton, FL 33427-2348. TEL 407-994-0079; 800-232-7477. FAX 407-994-4704. (looseleaf format; also avail. in microfiche; back issues avail.)
   Description: Reprints articles that describe living conditions in various parts of the world and explores such philosophical questions as quality of life.

352.7   US   ISSN 0890-958X
HD7287.95
HABITAT WORLD. 1984. bi-m. donations. Habitat for Humanity International, Inc., 121 Habitat St., Americus, GA 31709-3498. TEL 912-924-6935. FAX 912-924-6541. Ed Nancy Cardwell. circ. 750,000. (tabloid format) **Document type:** newspaper.
   Formerly: Habitat Happenings.
   Description: Ecumenical Christian program of volunteer efforts to build non-profit, no-interest housing.

352.7   GW
HAEUSER. 1979. bi-m. DM.78 (Europe DM.97.20; elsewhere DM.153). Gruner und Jahr AG & Co., Am Baumwall 11, 20459 Hamburg, Germany. TEL 040-3703-0. FAX 040-37035606. Ed. Angelika Jahr. circ. 82,000. **Document type:** consumer publication.

301.363   US
HARVARD STUDIES IN URBAN HISTORY. irreg., latest 1985. price varies. Harvard University Press, 79 Garden St., Cambridge, MA 02138. TEL 617-495-2600. FAX 617-495-5898. **Document type:** monographic series.
   Refereed Serial

352.7   GW
DAS HAUSEIGENTUM; Zeitschrift fuer Recht und Praxis im Wohnungswesen. 1990. m. DM.51. Grundeigentum Verlag GmbH, Eichborndamm 141-165, 13403 Berlin, Germany. TEL 030-4116031. FAX 030-4113025. Ed. Dieter Bluemmel. circ. 7,000. **Document type:** trade publication.
   Formerly: Haus und Wohnung.

711   GW
HESSISCHE STAEDTE- UND GEMEINDE-ZEITUNG. 1948. m. DM.56. Hessischer Staedte- und Gemeindebund, Henri-Dunant-Str. 3, 63165 Muehlheim a. M., Germany. adv. circ. 2,300.

333.7   KE
HIGHLANDS FIELD STATION REPORT. 1978. irreg., latest no.2. University of Nairobi, Department of Urban and Regional Planning, Box 30197, Nairobi, Kenya.

711   US
HIGHLIGHTS (EDWARDSVILLE). 1983. q. free. Southern Illinois University, Edwardsville, Regional Research and Development Services, Campus Box 1456, Edwardsville, IL 62026-1456. TEL 618-692-3500. FAX 618-692-2886. circ. 1,000 (controlled).

HISTORIC PRESERVATION FORUM. see *ARCHITECTURE*

HOME FINDERS GUIDEBOOK. see *REAL ESTATE*

352.7   US   ISSN 1053-0762
HOME GROUND. 1991. q. $20 membership. Home Habitat Society, 11824 Taneytown Pke., Taneytown, MD 21787. **Document type:** academic/scholarly publication.

690   US   ISSN 0018-6554
HD7293.A1
HOUSING AFFAIRS LETTER; weekly Washington report on housing. 1961. w. $354. (Community Development Services, Inc.) C D Publications, 8204 Fenton St., Silver Spring, MD 20910. TEL 301-588-6380. FAX 301-588-6385. Ed. Tom Bryan. abstr.; charts; mkt.; stat.; s-a. index. (back issues avail.) **Document type:** newsletter.
   Incorporates (1985-1992): Mortgage Market Insight (ISSN 1050-3226)
   Description: Covers the housing market, its legislation and regulations.

331.83   US   ISSN 0091-5939
KF5729.A1
HOUSING AND DEVELOPMENT REPORTER - CURRENT DEVELOPMENTS. 1973. bi-w. $602.95 (overseas $765). Warren Gorham Lamont, One Penn Plaza, New York, NY 10119. TEL 212-971-5000. FAX 212-971-5240. (Subscr. to: The Park Square Bldg., 31 St. James Ave., Boston, MA 02116-4112. TEL 800-950-1207) Ed.Bd. bk.rev.; abstr.; index. (looseleaf format) **Document type:** newsletter.
   —CCC.
   Description: Reports on legislative developments, administrative actions, and judicial opinions affecting housing and urban affairs and community development. Provides comprehensive coverage.

352.7 330.9   JM
HOUSING & FINANCE - JAMAICA. 1980. s-a. free. Building Societies Association of Jamaica, Ltd., 17 Belmont Rd., P.O. Box 141, Kingston 10, Jamaica, W.I. TEL 809-96-83855. Ed.Bd. adv. circ. 3,000.
   Description: Describes and analyzes current developments in shelter and urban planning policies.

711 352   UK
HOUSING AND PLANNING REVIEW. bi-m. £18 (foreign £20). National Housing and Town Planning Council, 14-18 Old St., London EC1V 9AB, England. Ed. Chris Griffin. adv.; charts; illus. circ. 2,300. **Indexed:** ASSIA, Avery Ind.Archit.Per., J.of Ferroc., RICS.
—BLDSC (4335.092000).
   Former titles: Housing and Planning Bulletin; Housing and Planning Review (ISSN 0018-6589)
   Description: Current issues in housing, planning and the environment.

352.7 312   MF
HOUSING AND POPULATION CENSUS OF MAURITIUS. a. R.75. Central Statistical Office, Port-Louis, Mauritius. (Subscr. to: G.P.O., La Tour Koenig, Port-Louis, Mauritius)

350.86   US   ISSN 0888-2746
HOUSING AND SOCIETY. 1974. 3/yr. $50 to individuals; libraries $60; students $15. American Association of Housing Educators, c/o Paul Woods, Associate Ed., Texas A & M University, College of Architecture, College Station, TX 77843-3137. FAX 409-845-4491. TELEX 510-892-7689. Ed. Marjorie Inman. bk.rev.; abstr.; illus. circ. 450. (back issues avail.) **Indexed:** P.A.I.S.
—UnCover.
   Description: Research on home ownership, energy conservation, residential property management, social, psychological, and economics aspects of housing.

352.7   SW
HOUSING AND URBAN PLANNING IN SWEDEN. ANNUAL REPORT/SVENSKA BOSTAEDER. AARSREDOVISNING. a. SB Svenska Bostaeder, Vaellingbyplan 2, P.O. Box 95, 16212 Vaellingby, Sweden. illus.; stat.

711.4   UK
HOUSING ASSOCIATIONS DIRECTORY AND YEARBOOK. 1982. a. £45. National Federation of Housing Associations, 175 Gray's Inn Rd., London WC1X 8UP, England. TEL 071-278-6571. FAX 071-955-5696. circ. 10,000. **Document type:** directory.

711.4   UK
HOUSING ASSOCIATIONS WEEKLY. 1987. w. £54 (foreign £95). National Federation of Housing Associations, 175 Gray's Inn Rd., London WC1X 8UP, England. TEL 071-278-6571. FAX 071-955-5696. Ed. Chris Bazlinton. adv.; bk.rev.; illus. circ. 12,000. **Document type:** newsletter.

352   US   ISSN 0018-6627
HOUSING AUTHORITY JOURNAL. 1970. m. free. Housing Authority, 250 Broadway, Rm. 901, New York, NY 10007. TEL 212-306-3453. FAX 212-306-6482. Ed. Andres Roura. bk.rev.; charts; illus. circ. 230,000. **Document type:** newspaper, government publication.

352.7   UK   ISSN 0260-4094
HOUSING CORPORATION. QUARTERLY REVIEW. 1979. q. Housing Corporation, 7 Noel St., London W1V 3PB, England.

HOUSING ECONOMICS. see *BUSINESS AND ECONOMICS — Economic Situation And Conditions*

HOUSING FINANCE. see *REAL ESTATE*

352.7 332   KE
HOUSING FINANCE COMPANY OF KENYA. ANNUAL REPORT AND ACCOUNTS. 1970. a. Housing Finance Company of Kenya, Rehani House, Kenyatta Ave., P.O. Box 30088, Nairobi, Kenya. circ. 1,000.

352.7   SA
HOUSING IN SOUTHERN AFRICA/BEHUISING IN SUIDELIKE AFRIKA. (Text in Afrikaans and English) 1974. 11/yr. R.15. (Institute for Housing of Southern Africa) Unified Communications C.C., P.O. Box 344, Westhoven 2142, South Africa. TEL 27-11-477-9760. FAX 27-11-673-6218. (Co-sponsor: National Association of Home-Builders) Ed. J. Maclean. adv.; B&W page R.2010, color page R.2510; trim 260 x 180. bk.rev.; circ. 4,000 (controlled). **Document type:** trade publication.
   Supersedes: Housing in South Africa - Behuising in Suid-Afrika.
   Description: Informs readers of all aspects of housing, especially mass housing, including government policy, planning and construction, financial and management subjects, new products, research and technology, and related aspects of infrastructure development.

352.7   US   ISSN 0277-8491
KF5722
HOUSING LAW BULLETIN. 1971. bi-m. $50 (free to qualified personnel). National Housing Law Project, Inc., 2201 Broadway Ste. 815, Oakland, CA 94612-3024. TEL 510-251-9400. FAX 510-251-0600. Ed. Katherine Castro. bk.rev.; index. circ. 1,500. **Document type:** bulletin.
   Formerly (until 1978): National Housing Law Project. Law Project Bulletin.
   Description: Includes judicial, statutory and regulatory developments relating to the operation, maintenance and preservation of public, subsidized, and other low-income housing; also covers issues of discrimination and homelessness.

HOUSING LAW MONITOR. see *LAW*

HOUSING LAW REPORTS. see *LAW*

352.7   UK
HOUSING MAGAZINE. 1936. 10/yr. Inside Communications, 9 White Lion St., Islington, London N1 9XJ, England. TEL 071-837-8727. FAX 071-837-7124. Ed. Savvas Eleftheriades. adv.: B&W page £855; trim 297 x 210. circ. 10,841.

690   US   ISSN 0363-4744
HD7293.A1
HOUSING MARKET REPORT. 1976. s-m. $299. (Community Development Services, Inc.) C D Publications, 8204 Fenton St., Silver Spring, MD 20910. TEL 301-588-6380. FAX 301-588-6385. Ed. Joe Poduska. **Document type:** newsletter.
   Description: Focuses on national and regional markets. Includes monthly forecasts of starts, interests rates, and other key indicators.

HOUSING AND URBAN PLANNING

711.4 350.865   US   ISSN 0898-7653
HOUSING MATTERS. 1986. q. $15 to individuals; non-profit groups $22; corporate $32. Massachusetts Law Reform Institute, 69 Canal St., Boston, MA 02114. TEL 617-742-9250. FAX 617-742-1983. Ed. Annette Duke. **Document type:** newsletter.
    Description: Reports on local initiatives and strategies being used to provide affordable housing. Includes interviews, legislation news and events.

352.7   US   ISSN 1051-1482
HD7293.A1
HOUSING POLICY DEBATE. 1990. q. free. (Fannie Mae, Office of Housing Policy Research) Federal National Mortgage Association, 3900 Wisconsin Ave., N.W., Washington, DC 20016-2899. TEL 202-752-4422. FAX 202-752-4933. Ed. James H. Carr. adv.; charts; illus.; circ. 4,000 (controlled). (also avail. in microform from UMI; back issues avail.) **Indexed:** ABI Inform., P.A.I.S., World Bank.Abstr. **Document type:** academic/scholarly publication.
—BLDSC (4335.139600); UnCover; UMI.
    Description: Stimulates thoughtful and insightful discussion on a broad range of housing issues, including public policy, home mortgage finance and international housing finance.
    Refereed Serial

354.4   UK   ISSN 0018-6651
HOUSING REVIEW. 1952. bi-m. £27 to individuals; libraries £35. Housing Centre Trust, 20-22 Vestry St., London N1 7RE, England. TEL 071-253-6103. FAX 071-608-1304. Ed. Joan Ash. adv. contact: Marjorie Cleaver. bk.rev.; charts; illus.; index. circ. 2,500. (also avail. in microfilm from UMI; reprint service avail. from UMI) **Indexed:** Archit.Per.Ind., ASSIA, Avery Ind.Archit.Per., Build.Manage.Abstr., RICS. **Document type:** academic/scholarly publication.
—BLDSC (4335.145000).

711.4   UK   ISSN 0267-3037
HOUSING STUDIES. 1986. q. $58 to individuals; institutions $134 (effective 1994). Carfax Publishing Co., P.O. Box 25, Abingdon, Oxon. OX14 3UE, England. TEL 44-235-555335. FAX 44-235-553559. (N. American subscr. to: Carfax Publishing Co., Box 2025, Dunnellon, FL 34430-2025) Ed. Alan Murie. adv.; bk.rev.; index. circ. 800. (also avail. in microfiche; back issues avail.) **Indexed:** ASSIA, Stud.Wom.Abstr. **Document type:** academic/scholarly publication.
—BLDSC (4335.152130); UnCover; UMI. **CCC.**
    Refereed Serial

362.6   US   ISSN 1050-3234
HD7287.92.U5
HOUSING THE ELDERLY REPORT. 1982. m. $157. (Community Development Services, Inc.) C D Publications, 8204 Fenton St., Silver Spring, MD 20910. TEL 301-588-6380. FAX 301-588-6385. Ed. Frank Cavaliere. index. **Document type:** newsletter.
    Description: News and advice for sponsors, managers of retirement homes, projects and nursing homes.

350.865   II
HOUSING TIMES. (Text in English) 1965. m. Rs.20($3) Bombay Thane Districts Co-Operative Housing Federation Ltd., 19 Bell Bldg., Sir P. Mehta Rd. Fort, Bombay 400001, India. Ed. D.S. Borwankar. adv.; bk.rev.; charts; illus.; stat. circ. 4,700.

HOUSING VICTORIA - TASMANIA. see *BUILDING AND CONSTRUCTION*

352.7   UK   ISSN 0264-5181
HOUSING YEAR BOOK. 1983. a. £65. Longman Group UK Ltd., Westgate House, 6th Fl., The High, Harlow, Essex CM20 1YR, England. TEL 0279-442601. FAX 0279-444501. adv.: B&W page £395, color page £795; 203 x 128; adv. contact: Clare Mills. **Document type:** directory.
—BLDSC (4335.152280).

352.7   DK   ISSN 0108-562X
HUMAN SETTLEMENTS SITUATION AND RELATED TRENDS AND POLICIES. 1982. quinquennial. DKK 75. Boligministeriet, Slotsholmsgade 12, 1216 Copenhagen K, Denmark. (Dist. by: Danske Boghendleres Kommissionsanstalt, Siljangade 6, 2300 Copenhagen S, Denmark) (Co-sponsor: Danish National Agency for Physical Planning) **Document type:** government publication.

352   SW   ISSN 0018-8360
HYRESGAESTEN. 1962. 7/yr. free. Hyresgaesternas Riksfoerbund, P.O. Box 7514, S-103 92 Stockholm, Sweden. TEL 8-791-0200. FAX 8-205324. Ed. Peder Palmstierna. illus. circ. 23,000.

352.7   US   ISSN 0090-3248
HD7303.I3
ILLINOIS. HOUSING DEVELOPMENT AUTHORITY. ANNUAL REPORT. 1970. a. free. Housing Development Authority, 401 N. Michigan Ave., Chicago, IL 60611. TEL 312-836-5200. FAX 312-527-2509. Ed. Tom Laue. charts; illus.; stat.; circ. 5,000 (controlled).

352.7   US
IN-HOUSE (COLLEGE STATION). vol.14, 1990. q. American Association of Housing Educators, College of Architecture, Texas A&M University, College Station, TX 77843-3137. TEL 409-845-0986. FAX 409-845-4491. TELEX 510-892-7689. Ed. Paul Woods.

352.7 336   US
INCENTIVE TAXATION. 1974. 8/yr. $15. Center for the Study of Economics, 2000 Century Plaza (238), Columbia, MD 21044. TEL 410-740-1177. FAX 410-740-3279. Ed. Steven B. Cord. cum.index; circ. 5,400. (back issues avail.) **Document type:** bulletin.
    Description: Presents objective research on how cities can promote economic development at no extra tax cost by shifting the property tax from buildings to land.

INDIAN ARCHITECT; a magazine for the architect, town planner and construction engineer. see *ARCHITECTURE*

331.83   IO
INDONESIA. DIREKTORAT PERUMAHAN RAKJAT. LAPORAN KERDJA. 1970. a. free. Direktorat Perumahan Rakjat, Jalan Wijaya I-68, Kebayoran Baru, Jakarta, Indonesia. circ. controlled.

352.7   GW   ISSN 0340-1774
DD91
INFORMATIONEN ZUR MODERNEN STADTGESCHICHTE (I M S). 1970. s-a. DM.40. Deutsches Institut fuer Urbanistik, Str. des 17. Juni 112, 10623 Berlin, Germany. TEL 030-390010. FAX 030-39001100. bibl. circ. 800. **Document type:** bulletin.

350   GW   ISSN 0303-2493
HT395.G4
INFORMATIONEN ZUR RAUMENTWICKLUNG. 1973. m. DM.66. Bundesforschungsanstalt fuer Landeskunde und Raumordnung, Am Michaelshof 8, 53173 Bonn, Germany. TEL 0228-826-0. FAX 0228-826266. abstr.; bibl.; charts; illus.; stat.; index. circ. 2,200. (back issues avail.) **Indexed:** Dok.Raum., Dok.Str., Excerp.Med., Geo.Abstr., INIS Atomind., P.A.I.S.For.Lang.Ind. **Document type:** academic/scholarly publication.
—BLDSC (4496.479000).
    Formed by the merger of: Institut fuer Landeskunde. Rundbrief & Institut fuer Raumordnung. Informationen (ISSN 0020-2312)

711 350.865   IT
INFORMAZIONI S U N I A. 1978. q. Sindicato Unitario Nazionale Inquilini Assegnatari, Via Monzermone, 14, 42100 Reggio Emilia, Italy. TEL 0522-434757. Ed. Malaguti Secondo.
    Description: Forum dedicated to tenants. Includes articles on living conditions throughout Italy, legislative topics related to housing and action to improve housing in Italy.

352.7   UK   ISSN 0950-3358
INSIDE HOUSING. 1984. w. £35. Inside Communications Ltd., 9 White Lion St., London N1 9XJ, England. TEL 071-837-8727. FAX 071-837-7124. Ed. Rosalind Bayley. adv.; bk.rev.; index. circ. 16,000.

301 352   FR   ISSN 0153-6184
HT166
INSTITUT D'AMENAGEMENT ET D'URBANISME DE LA REGION D'ILE DE FRANCE. CAHIERS. 1964. 4/yr. 515 F. (foreign 580 F.). Institut d'Amenagement et d'Urbanisme de la Region d'Ile de France, 251, rue de Vaugirard, 75015 Paris Cedex 15, France. TEL 1-40-43-70-70. FAX 40-43-76-02. TELEX 203 987. (Dist. by: Documentation Francaise, 124 rue Henri Barbusse, 93308 Aubervilliers Cedex, France. TEL 48-39-56-00. FAX 48-39-56-01) bibl.; charts; illus.; stat. circ. 3,000. (also avail. in microfiche from DFR) **Indexed:** Avery Ind.Archit.Per., P.A.I.S.For.Lang.Ind.
—BLDSC (2948.308000); SWETS.
    Formerly: Institut d'Amenagement et d'Urbanisme de la Region Parisienne. Cahiers (ISSN 0020-2207)

INSTITUT ZA ARHITEKTURU I URBANIZAM SRBIJE. ZBORNIK RADOVA. see *ARCHITECTURE*

711   II   ISSN 0537-9679
HT169.I5
INSTITUTE OF TOWN PLANNERS, INDIA. JOURNAL. (Text in English) 1955. q. Rs.100($45) Institute of Town Planners, India, 4-A Ring Rd., Indraprastha Estate, New Delhi 110 002, India. TEL 331-8571. Ed. J.B. Kshirsagar. adv. **Indexed:** Geo.Abstr. **Document type:** trade publication.

352.7 614.7   CN   ISSN 1182-9281
INSTITUTE OF URBAN STUDIES. (Supplement avail.: Sustainable Cities) 3/yr. free. University of Winnipeg, Institute of Urban Studies, 515 Portage Ave., Winnipeg, MB R3B 2E9, Canada. TEL 204-786-9409. FAX 204-786-1824. Ed. Mary Ann Beavis. adv. circ. 2,300. (also avail. in microform from MML; back issues avail.) **Document type:** newsletter.
    Formerly (until 1990): Institute of Urban Studies. Newsletter (ISSN 0843-2872)
    Description: Articles and announcements of interest to urban researchers, municipal officials, academics, students, local community.

INSTITUTION OF CIVIL ENGINEERS. PROCEEDINGS. MUNICIPAL ENGINEER. see *ENGINEERING — Civil Engineering*

352.7   SA   ISSN 0257-1978
INSTITUTION OF MUNICIPAL ENGINEERS OF SOUTHERN AFRICA. JOURNAL. Short title: I M I E S A Journal. (Text in Afrikaans, English) 1976. m. R.27.50 (typically set in Jan.). Preference Publications (Pty) Ltd., 403 Sasbo House, 97 Simmonds St., Braamfontein, Johannesburg, South Africa. TEL 403-2720. FAX 403-2722. (Subscr. to: P.O. Box 3387, Johannesburg 2000, South Africa) Ed. John R. Shorten. charts;illus. circ. 2,780. (back issues avail.)
    Description: Original and technical articles relative to the whole wide scope of municipal engineering.

INTERNATIONAL CONFERENCE OF BUILDING OFFICIALS. EVALUATION REPORTS. see *BUILDING AND CONSTRUCTION*

301.5   NE
INTERNATIONAL FEDERATION FOR HOUSING AND PLANNING. DIRECTORY. (Text in English, French or German) 1972. irreg., latest 1994. membership only. International Federation for Housing and Planning, Wassenaarseweg 43, 2596 CG The Hague, Netherlands. circ. 1,500 (controlled). **Document type:** directory.
    Former titles: International Federation for Housing and Planning. Yearbook; International Federation for Housing and Planning. List of Members.

301   US   ISSN 0146-6518
HD7285   CODEN: IJHADL
INTERNATIONAL JOURNAL FOR HOUSING SCIENCE AND ITS APPLICATIONS; housing planning. 1977. q. $190. (International Association for Housing Science) Ural and Associates, Inc., Box 340525, Coral Gables, FL 33134. TEL 305-348-3797. FAX 305-446-9462. Ed. Oktay Ural. adv.; bk.rev. circ. 550. (also avail. in microform from MIM,UMI; back issues avail.; reprint service avail. from UMI) **Indexed:** Br.Tech.Ind., Concr.Abstr., J.of Ferroc.
—BLDSC (4542.285000); EI; SWETS. **CCC.**

INTERNATIONAL JOURNAL OF ENVIRONMENTAL STUDIES. SECTIONS A & B. see *ENVIRONMENTAL STUDIES*

HOUSING AND URBAN PLANNING

352.7   UK   ISSN 0309-1317
HT101
INTERNATIONAL JOURNAL OF URBAN AND REGIONAL RESEARCH. 1976. q. £41($70) to individuals; institutions £76($141). Basil Blackwell Ltd., 108 Cowley Rd., Oxford OX4 1JF, England. TEL 0865-791100. FAX 0865-791347. Ed. M. Harloe. **Indexed:** A.B.C.Pol.Sci., Asian-Pac.Econ.Lit., ASSIA, Avery Ind.Archit.Per., Chic.Per.Ind., E.I., Energy Ind., Energy Info.Abstr., Geo.Abstr., I D A, Lang.& Lang.Behav.Abstr., Mult.Ed.Abstr., P.A.I.S., Rural Recreat.Tour.Abstr., Sage Pub.Admin.Abstr., Sage Urb.Stud.Abstr., Sociol.Abstr. (1980-), SSCI, World Agri.Econ.& Rural Sociol.Abstr.
—BLDSC (4542.697000); Faxon; UnCover; SWETS; UMI. **CCC.**
Description: Takes an interdisciplinary approach to the study of conflicting interests in the urban and regional development, demonstrating the social basis of various approaches to planning and state intervention.

333.77   US
INTERNATIONAL STUDIES IN PLANNING. 1978. irreg. Cornell University, Department of City and Regional Planning, College of Architecture, Art, and Planning, 106 W. Sibley Hall, Ithaca, NY 14853-6701. (reprint service avail. from UMI)

711   JA   ISSN 0074-8897
INTERNATIONAL SYMPOSIUM ON REGIONAL DEVELOPMENT. PAPERS AND PROCEEDINGS. (Text in English) 1967. irreg., 4th, 1974. 3700 Yen. Japan Center for Area Development Research - Nihon Chiiki Kaihatsu Senta, Iino Bldg., 2-1-1 Uchisaiwaicho, Chiyoda-ku, Tokyo 100, Japan. TEL 03-501-6856. FAX 03-501-6855. circ. 500. **Document type:** proceedings.

333.77   UK
INTERNATIONAL YEARBOOK OF RURAL PLANNING. 1980. irreg., latest 1988. price varies. Elsevier Science Ltd., Books Division, P.O. Box 800, Kidlington, Oxford OX5 1DX, England. TEL 44-865-843000. FAX 44-865-843010. (Subscr. in U.S. and Canada to: Elsevier Science, 660 White Plains Rd., Tarrytown, NY 10591-5153. TEL 914-524-9200) Ed. A.W. Gilg. **Indexed:** Br.Archaeol.Abstr., Geo.Abstr., Rural Recreat.Tour.Abstr., World Agri.Econ. & Rural Sociol.Abstr. **Document type:** academic/scholarly publication.
Formerly (until 1987): Countryside Planning Yearbook (ISSN 0143-8190)
Description: Comprehensive guide to the year's events in legislation and literature.
Refereed Serial

INVESTICNI VYSTAVBA; casopis pro popularizaci technickoekonomickych poznatku v oboru investicni cinnosti. see *BUILDING AND CONSTRUCTION*

301.54   IS   ISSN 0075-109X
ISRAEL. CENTRAL BUREAU OF STATISTICS. SURVEY OF HOUSING CONDITIONS. (Subseries of its Special Series) (Text in English and Hebrew) 1963. irreg., no.641, 1978. price varies. Central Bureau of Statistics, P.O. Box 13015, Jerusalem, Israel. TEL 02-21 12 11.

352.7   IS   ISSN 0302-8267
ISRAEL. MINISTRY OF THE INTERIOR. CITY AND REGION - IR VE EZOR.* (Text in Hebrew; summaries in English) 1972. q. Ministry of the Interior, Jerusalem, Israel. Ed. Moshe Weiss. bk.rev.; charts.

352.7   US
ISSUE BRIEF. 1974. q. membership. Metropolitan Planning Council, 220 S. State St., Ste. 1800, Chicago, IL 60604-2103. TEL 312-922-5616. FAX 312-922-5619. Ed. Molly Bartlett. circ. 1,600.
Formerly: Planning Reporter.

ISTITUTO DI ARCHITETTURA E URBANISTICA. RASSEGNA. see *ARCHITECTURE*

352.7   US
J P C NEWSLETTER. 1971. bi-m. free. Joint Planning Commission, Lehigh - Northampton Counties, 961 Marcon Blvd., Ste. 310, Allentown, PA 18103-9397. TEL 215-264-4544. Ed. Frederic Brock. circ. 1,600 (controlled). (looseleaf format) **Document type:** newsletter.
Formerly: J P C Planner.

JAMAICA. MINISTRY OF CONSTRUCTION (WORKS). JAMAICA BUDGET (YEAR). see *BUILDING AND CONSTRUCTION*

338.7   JM   ISSN 0304-8373
JAMAICA. URBAN DEVELOPMENT CORPORATION. ANNUAL REPORT. 1970. a. free. Urban Development Corporation, 12 Ocean Blvd., Kingston, Jamaica, W.I. TEL 809-922-8310. FAX 809-922-9326. TELEX 2281 UNDECOR. Eds. G. Royale-Davis, B. Josephs. illus. circ. 500. **Document type:** government publication.

JERUSALEM URBAN STUDIES. see *SOCIOLOGY*

309.26   US   ISSN 0075-3947
JOINT CENTER FOR URBAN STUDIES. PUBLICATIONS. irreg. Harvard University Press, 79 Garden St., Cambridge, MA 02138. TEL 617-495-2600. FAX 617-495-5898. (Co-publisher: M I T Press)
Refereed Serial

352.7   US   ISSN 1061-4354
▼**JOURNAL OF AFFORDABLE HOUSING AND COMMUNITY DEVELOPMENT LAW.** 1992. q. $40. American Bar Association, 750 N. Lake Shore Dr., Chicago, IL 60611. TEL 312-988-5000. Ed. Jeffrey Kuta. circ. 1,300 (controlled). (back issues avail.)
Description: Reviews developments in affordable housing and community development law and practice.

352 711   UK   ISSN 0964-0568
NA9000
JOURNAL OF ENVIRONMENTAL PLANNING AND MANAGEMENT. 1948. q. $88 to individuals; institutions $292 (effective 1994). (University of Newcastle-upon-Tyne, Department of Town and Country Planning) Carfax Publishing Co., P.O. Box 25, Abingdon, Oxon. OX14 3UE, England. TEL 44-235-555335. FAX 44-235-553559. (U.S. subscr.to: Carfax Publishing Co., Box 2025, Dunnellon, FL 34430-2025) Ed. John Benson. adv.; bk.rev.; bibl.; illus. circ. 500. **Indexed:** Avery Ind.Archit.Per., Br.Hum.Ind., Environ.Abstr., Environ.Per.Bibl. (1985-), Geo.Abstr., I D A, Rural Recreat.Tour.Abstr., World Agri.Econ. & Rural Sociol.Abstr. **Document type:** academic/scholarly publication.
—BLDSC (4979.384900); Faxon; SWETS. **CCC.**
Formerly (until 1992): Planning Studies (ISSN 0032-0714)
Description: Covers issues of environmental policy, planning, management, regulatory aspects of natural resources, environmental protection, conservation, and human-environment interactions.
Refereed Serial

352   US   ISSN 0272-7374
HD7285   CODEN: JOHOA4
JOURNAL OF HOUSING. 1944. bi-m. $24 (Canada $26; elsewhere $30). National Association of Housing and Redevelopment Officials, 1320 18th St., N.W., Washington, DC 20036. TEL 202-429-2960. FAX 202-429-9684. Ed. Terence Cooper. adv.: B&W page $1320, color page $2270. bk.rev.; film rev.; charts; illus.; tr.lit.; index. circ. 12,000. (also avail. in microfilm from UMI; reprint service avail. from UMI) **Indexed:** ABI Inform., Avery Ind.Archit.Per., BPIA, Environ.Abstr., Geo.Abstr., Manage.Cont., P.A.I.S., PSI, Sage Pub.Admin.Abstr., Soc.Sci.Ind., SSCI, Tr.& Indus.Ind. **Document type:** trade publication.
—Faxon; UnCover; UMI.
Formerly: J O H: Journal of Housing (ISSN 0164-646X)

352.7   US   ISSN 1051-1377
JOURNAL OF HOUSING ECONOMICS. 1991. q. $110 (foreign $135). Academic Press, Inc., Journal Division, 525 B St., Ste. 1900, San Diego, CA 92101-4495. TEL 619-230-1840. FAX 619-699-6800. (Subscr. to: Box 620000, Orlando, FL 32891-8340. TEL 800-543-9534) Ed. Henry O. Pollakowski. **Document type:** academic/scholarly publication.
—BLDSC (5003.411000); UnCover. **CCC.**
Description: Provides a focal point for the publication of economic research related to housing.

352.7   US   ISSN 1052-7001
HD7293.A1
JOURNAL OF HOUSING RESEARCH. 1990. s-a. free. (Fannie Mae, Office of Housing Policy Research) Federal National Mortgage Association, 3900 Wisconsin Ave., N.W., Washington, DC 20016-2899. TEL 202-752-4422. FAX 202-752-4933. Ed. James H. Carr. adv.; charts; illus.; circ. 3,200 (controlled). (back issues avail.) **Document type:** academic/scholarly publication.
—BLDSC (5003.412500); UnCover; UMI.
Description: Provides an outlet for theoretical and empirical research on a broad range of housing issues, including housing policy, home mortgage finance and international housing finance.
Refereed Serial

JOURNAL OF PLANNING AND ENVIRONMENT LAW. see *LAW*

711   US   ISSN 0739-456X
HT392
JOURNAL OF PLANNING EDUCATION AND RESEARCH. 1981. 3/yr. $20 to individuals (foreign $25); institutions $60 (foreign $65); students $15 (foreign $20). Association of Collegiate Schools of Planning, Florida State University, Dept. of Urban and Regional Planning R-117, Tallahassee, FL 32306. TEL 904-644-9653. FAX 904-644-6041. Eds. Charles Connerly, Bruce Stiflel. adv.; bk.rev. circ. 2,000. (back issues avail.) **Indexed:** Avery Ind.Archit.Per., Environ.Abstr., Environ.Per.Bibl. (1991-), Geo.Abstr., I D A, P.A.I.S. **Document type:** academic/scholarly publication.
—BLDSC (5040.440000); CIS; Faxon; UnCover; SWETS.

333.77   US   ISSN 0885-4122
Z5942
JOURNAL OF PLANNING LITERATURE. 1986. q. $44 to individuals; institutions $113 (effective 1994). (Ohio State University, Department of City and Regional Planning) Sage Publications, Inc., 2455 Teller Rd., Thousand Oaks, CA 91320. TEL 805-499-0721. FAX 805-499-0871. (Subscr. to: Sage Publications, Inc., Box 5084, Thousand Oaks, CA 91359; Overseas subscr. to: Sage Publications, Ltd., 6 Bonhill St., London EC2A, England; Sage Publications India Pvt. Ltd., P.O. Box 4125, New Delhi 110 048, India) Ed. Kenneth Pearlman. bk.rev.; abstr.; index. circ. 900. (also avail. in microform from UMI; back issues avail.) **Document type:** academic/scholarly publication.
—BLDSC (5040.460000); UnCover; SWETS. **CCC.**
Description: Reviews current literature on city and regional planning, with listings of titles.
Refereed Serial

352.7   UK   ISSN 0959-9916
HD251
JOURNAL OF PROPERTY RESEARCH. 1984. 3/yr. £120 (foreign £130). (Land Development Education Trust) E. & F.N. Spon, 2-6 Boundary Row, London SE1 8HN, England. TEL 071-865-0066. FAX 071-522-9623. (Dist. by: International Thomson Publishing Services, Ltd., N. Way, Andover, Hampshire SP10 5BE. TEL 0264-342919; U.S. addr.: Chapman & Hall, One Penn Plaza, 41st Fl., New York, NY 10119. TEL 212-564-1060. FAX 212-564-1505) Ed.Bd. **Document type:** trade publication.
—BLDSC (5042.781000); Faxon; UMI.
Formerly: Land Development Studies (ISSN 0264-0821)
Description: Serves professional practitioners in planning and development, researchers in colleges, university and other institutes concerning property investment portfolios and land development.

JOURNAL OF REAL ESTATE FINANCE AND ECONOMICS. see *REAL ESTATE*

338 350   US   ISSN 0022-4146
H62
JOURNAL OF REGIONAL SCIENCE. 1958. 4/yr. $53 to individuals in N. America (elsewhere $61); institutions in N. America $78 (elsewhere $90.50) (effective 1994). (Regional Science Research Institute) Basil Blackwell Inc., 238 Main St., Cambridge, MA 02142. TEL 617-547-7110; 800-835-6670. FAX 617-547-0789. adv.: rate page $300; trim 5 x 8. bk.rev.; bibl.; charts; index, cum.index. circ. 2,200. (also avail. in microform from UMI; back issues avail.; reprint service avail. from KTO,UMI) **Indexed:** ABI Inform., Avery Ind.Archit.Per., Biostat., BPIA, Bus.Ind., C.R.E.J., Curr.Cont., Geo.Abstr., I D A, INIS Atomind., Intl.Civil Eng.Abstr., J.of Econ.Lit., Key to Econ.Sci., Manage.Cont., Mid.East: Abstr.& Ind., Oper.Res.Manage.Sci., Popul.Ind., Qual.Contr.Appl.Stat., Rural Recreat.Tour.Abstr., Sage Pub.Admin.Abstr., Sage Urb.Stud.Abstr., Soc.Sci.Ind., Soft.Abstr.Eng., SSCI, World Agri.Econ.& Rural Sociol.Abstr. **Document type:** academic/scholarly publication.
—BLDSC (5048.700000); Faxon; UnCover; SWETS; UMI. **CCC.**
Description: Presents papers applying locational and spatial approaches to socio-economic phenomena; publishes research on abstract and neoclassical location theory, and papers on migration, housing, and urban problems and on regional economic growth and development.
Refereed Serial

JOURNAL OF THE NETWORK OF AFRICAN COUNTRIES ON LOCAL BUILDING MATERIALS AND TECHNOLOGIES. see *BUILDING AND CONSTRUCTION*

352.7   US   ISSN 0735-2166
HT101   CODEN: JUAFEM
JOURNAL OF URBAN AFFAIRS. 1976. q. $60 to individuals (foreign $70); institutions $145 (foreign $165). J A I Press Inc., 55 Old Post Rd., No.2, Box 1678, Greenwich, CT 06836-1678. TEL 203-661-7602. FAX 203-661-0792. (Addr. in Europe: J A I Press Ltd., The Courtyard, 28 High St., Hampton Hill, Mddx. TW12 1PD, England. TEL 44-81-943-9296. FAX 44-81-943-9317) Eds. Scott B. Cummings, Knowlton W. Johnson. adv.; bk.rev. circ. 530. (also avail. in microfiche; back issues avail.) **Indexed:** Amer.Hist.& Life, Hist.Abstr., Int.Polit.Sci.Abstr., Polit.Sci.Abstr., Soc.Work Res.& Abstr., Sociol.Abstr. **Document type:** academic/scholarly publication.
—BLDSC (5071.549500); Faxon; UnCover. **CCC.**
Formed by the 1982 merger of: Urban Affairs Papers; Urban Interest Journal (ISSN 0192-4974)

352   US
HT101
JOURNAL OF URBAN ANALYSIS AND PUBLIC MANAGEMENT. 1972. 8/yr. (in 2 vols., 4 nos./vol.). 164 ECU per vol. (effective 1993). Gordon and Breach Science Publishers, 820 Town Center Dr., Langhorne, PA 19047. TEL 215-750-2642. FAX 215-750-6343. (UK subscr. to: P.O. Box 90, Reading, Berkshire RG1 8JL, England. TEL 0734-560-080) Ed. Stanley M. Altman. adv.; bk.rev.; illus.; index. (also avail. in microform) **Indexed:** ASSIA, Avery Ind.Archit.Per., Bus.Ind., Curr.Cont., Geo.Abstr., Mid.East: Abstr.& Ind., Sci.Abstr.
—**CCC.**
Former titles: Urban Analysis and Public Management (ISSN 0883-6027); Journal of Urban Analysis (ISSN 0091-1909)
Refereed Serial

624   US   ISSN 0733-9488
NA9000   CODEN: JUPDDM
JOURNAL OF URBAN PLANNING AND DEVELOPMENT. 1956. q. $88 to non-members (foreign $94); members $22 (foreign $28). American Society of Civil Engineers, Urban Planning and Development Division, 345 E. 47th St., New York, NY 10017-2398. TEL 212-705-7288. FAX 212-980-4681. Ed. R. Lan Kingham. circ. 3,900. (reprint service avail. from UMI) **Indexed:** A.S.& T.Ind., Br.Rail.Bd., CAD CAM Abstr., Curr.Cont., Deep Sea Res.& Oceanogr.Abstr., Eng.Ind., Environ.Abstr., Fluidex, GeoRef., HRIS, Intl.Civil Eng.Abstr., Soft.Abstr.Eng., SSCI, W.R.C.Inf. **Document type:** academic/scholarly publication.
—BLDSC (5071.680000); CIS; EI; Faxon; UnCover; SWETS; UMI. **CCC.**
Formerly (until 1982): American Society of Civil Engineers. Urban Planning and Development Division. Journal (ISSN 0569-8081)
Description: Covers the application of civil engineering to such aspects of urban planning as area-wide transportation, the coordination of planning and programming of public works and utilities, and the development and redevelopment of urban areas.

352.7   JA
JUTAKU SANGYO HANDBOOK; statistical handbook for Japanese housing industry. (Text in Japanese) 1976. a. 3000 Yen. Jutaku Sangyo Johoh Services, 23 Mori Bldg., 1-23-7, Toranomon, Minato-ku, Tokyo 105, Japan. Ed. Tsuneshi Miwa. adv. (back issues avail.)
Formerly: Jutaku Sangyo Handobukku.

690   SW   ISSN 0022-7293
K B S - RAPPORTER. (Kungliga Byggnadsstyrelsen) 1961. irreg. (5-15/yr.). price varies. Byggnadsstyrelsen - National Board of Public Building, S-106 43 Stockholm, Sweden. FAX 8-7831180.

354.4   SW
K B S TEKNISKA FOERESKRIFTER/K B S TECHNICAL REGULATIONS; krav och raad/requirements and recommendations. (In four parts) 1966. irreg. (4-5/yr.). price varies. Byggnadsstyrelsen - National Board of Public Building, S-106 43 Stockholm 27, Sweden. FAX 8-783-1180.
Supersedes (in 1979): K B S Anvisningar - K B S Directions (ISSN 0022-7285)

333.7   IS   ISSN 0302-6248
HD951.P3
KARKA/LAND. (Text in Hebrew; summaries in English) 1971. q. $10 (effective 1994). Land Use Research Institute - Keren Kayemeth Leisrael, King George St. 43, P.O. Box 283, Jerusalem 91002, Israel. TEL 972-2-246828. FAX 972-2-231612. Ed. Alexander Poznanski. bk.rev. circ. 1,000.
Description: Examines regional planning.

352.7   KE
KENYA. MINISTRY OF HOUSING. ANNUAL REPORT. 1967. a. Government Printing and Stationery Department, P.O. Box 30128, Nairobi, Kenya.
Supersedes in part: Kenya. Ministry of Health and Housing. Annual Report (ISSN 0075-5877)

350.865   KE
KENYA. NATIONAL HOUSING CORPORATION. ANNUAL REPORT. 1958. a. free. National Housing Corporation, P.O. Box 30257, Nairobi, Kenya. TEL 270623. charts; illus.; stat. circ. 1,000.
Description: Statistical periodical on the operations of the corporation.

333 350.08   US
KEYNOTES (TRENTON). (Supplement avail.: Lenderlink) 1987. q. free. New Jersey Housing and Mortgage Finance Agency, Division of Planning and Intergovernmental Relations, 3625 Quakerbridge Rd., CN-18550, Trenton, NJ 08650-2085. TEL 609-890-8900. FAX 609-890-0414. Ed.Bd. circ. 7,500. **Document type:** government publication, newsletter.
Description: Highlights of the Agency's single-family and multifamily housing programs, and issues affecting its role as a producer of affordable housing for low- and moderate-income families.

350.086   IS
KIBBUTZ PLANNING BULLETIN. 1981. q. free. United Kibbutz Movement, Planning Department, 27 Soutine St., Tel Aviv 64 684, Israel. TEL 972-3-245271. Ed. Amos Rodner. adv. circ. 2,000. **Document type:** bulletin.

352.7 720   SU   ISSN 1018-3604
KING SAUD UNIVERSITY. JOURNAL. ARCHITECTURE AND PLANNING. Key Title: Majallat Jami'at al-Malik Sa'ud, al-Imarah wal-Takhtit. (Other sections avail.: Administrative Sciences, Agricultural Sciences, Arts, Computer and Information Sciences, Educational Sciences and Islamic Studies, Engineering Sciences, Sciences) (Text in Arabic, English) 1989. a. $10. King Saud University, University Libraries, P.O. Box 22480, Riyadh 11495, Saudi Arabia. TEL 966-1-4676148. FAX 966-1-4676162. TELEX 401019 KSU SJ. Ed. Tarik M. Al-Soliman. charts; illus. **Document type:** academic/scholarly publication.
Refereed Serial

352.7   DK   ISSN 0573-9799
KOEBENHAVN BOLIGKOMMISSIONEN. AARSBERETNING. 1940. a. free. Koebenhavs Boligkommission - Copenhagen's Housing Commission, Ottiliavej 3, DK-2500 Valby, Denmark. TEL 45-33-66-53-70. FAX 45-31-17-70-74. circ. 1,900.

352.7   GW   ISSN 0340-1170
KOMMUNALWISSENSCHAFTLICHE DISSERTATIONEN. 1970. a. DM.30. Deutsches Institut fuer Urbanistik, Str. des 17. Juni 112, 10623 Berlin, Germany. TEL 030-390010. FAX 030-39001100. circ. 500. **Document type:** bulletin.

334   YU   ISSN 0023-3161
HT101
KOMUNA (BELGRADE); casopis za pitanja teorije i prakse komunalnih zajednica. 1954. bi-m. 180 din. Stalna Konferencija Gradova i Opstina Yugoslavije, Makedonska 22-X, P.O. Box 414, Belgrade, Serbia, Yugoslavia. FAX 11-321-015. Ed. Bosko Markovic. adv.; bk.rev. circ. 2,000.

334   FI   ISSN 0023-5385
KUNNALLISTEKNIIKKA/KOMMUNALTEKNIK. (Text in Finnish or Swedish; summaries in English and Swedish) 1946. 6/yr. FIM 150 (typically set in Jan.). Suomen Kunnallisteknillinen Yhdistys r.y., P.O. Box 51, 00131 Helsinki 13, Finland. FAX 358-0-771-2296. Ed. Kari Ojala. adv.; bk.rev.; bibl.; charts; illus.; stat.; index. circ. 1,239.
Description: Provides information on the development of municipal techniques.

KUNST UND STADT. see *ARCHITECTURE*

KWARTALNIK ARCHITEKTURY I URBANISTYKI. see *ARCHITECTURE*

L A CO-OPS AND THE SHARED HOUSING NETWORKER. see *SOCIAL SERVICES AND WELFARE*

333   US   ISSN 0023-768X
LAND USE DIGEST. 1968. m. membership only. Urban Land Institute, 625 Indiana Ave., N.W., Ste. 400, Washington, DC 20004-2930. TEL 202-624-7000. FAX 202-624-7140. Ed. David Muluihill. stat. circ. 13,500. (looseleaf format; reprint service avail. from UMI) **Document type:** newsletter.

333.77   US   ISSN 1064-0401
LAND USE LAW REPORT. 1973. bi-w. $273 (effective Sep. 1992). Business Publishers, Inc., 951 Pershing Dr., Silver Spring, MD 20910-4464. TEL 301-587-6300. FAX 301-585-9075. Ed. James Lawlor. bk.rev. (looseleaf format) **Document type:** newsletter.
●Also available online. Vendor(s): NewsNet (EVO2).
—**CCC.**
Formerly: Land Use Planning Report (ISSN 0093-3864); Incorporates: Land and the Environment.
Description: Presents rulings on land use, especially as related to US and state environmental regulations; lender liability emphasized.

HOUSING AND URBAN PLANNING

352.7 — UK — ISSN 0264-8377
HD101
LAND USE POLICY. 1984. q. £165 in UK and Europe; elsewhere £178. Butterworth - Heinemann (Subsidiary of: Reed International PLC), Linacre House, Jordan Hill, Oxford OX2 8DP, England. TEL 0865-310366. FAX 0865-310898. TELEX 83111 BHPOXF G. (Subscr. to: Turpin Transactions Ltd., Distribution Centre, Blackhorse Rd., Letchworth, Herts SG6 1HN, England. TEL 0462-672555) Ed. Penny Street. index. (also avail. in microform from UMI; back issues avail.) **Indexed:** Avery Ind.Archit.Per., Field Crop Abstr., Forest.Abstr., Herb.Abstr., I D A, Irr.& Drain.Abstr., P.A.I.S., Rice Abstr., Rural Devel.Abstr., Soils & Fert., Soyabean Abstr., World Agri.Econ.& Rural Sociol.Abstr. **Document type:** academic/scholarly publication.
—BLDSC (5146.958700); Faxon; UnCover; SWETS; UMI. **CCC.**
 Description: Examines geography, agriculture, forestry, irrigation, environmental conservation, housing, urban development and transport in both developed and developing countries.
Refereed Serial

352.7 350 — GW — ISSN 0342-2259
DER LANDKREIS. Bavarian State Edition (ISSN 0340-9880); Hessian State Edition (ISSN 0340-3246); Rheinland-Pfalz Edition (ISSN 0172-9640) 1930. m. DM.151. (Deutscher Landkreistag) W. Kohlhammer GmbH, Hessbruehlstr. 69, 70565 Stuttgart, Germany. TEL 0711-7863-1. Ed. Arnim Franke. adv.; bk.rev.; bibl.; illus.; tr.lit. **Indexed:** Geo.Abstr., INIS Atomind. **Document type:** bulletin.
—CCC.

LANDLINE IN AUSTRALIA. see *REAL ESTATE*

LENDERLINK. see *BUSINESS AND ECONOMICS — Investments*

LIGUE URBAINE ET RURALE CAHIERS. see *ENVIRONMENTAL STUDIES*

352.7 — US
LIVABILITY. 2/yr. $35 membership. Partners for Livable Places, 1429 21st St., N.W., Washington, DC 20036. TEL 202-887-5990. FAX 202-466-4845. **Document type:** newsletter.
 Description: Discusses quality of life issues thoughout the U.S. Reports on the organization's programs and initiatives.

352.7 — UK — ISSN 0260-3756
LOCAL AUTHORITY SPECIFIERS' REFERENCE BOOK AND BUYERS GUIDE. a. £20. (District Council Technical Association) Sterling Publications Ltd., 86-88 Edgware Rd., London W2 2YW, England. TEL 01-258 0066.
 Formerly: Housing Managers Buyers Guide.

LOCAL SELF-GOVERNMENT. see *PUBLIC ADMINISTRATION — Municipal Government*

LOCAL - STATE FUNDING REPORT. see *BUSINESS AND ECONOMICS — Public Finance, Taxation*

352.7 — US
LOFTY TIMES. no.3, 1977. m. free. Lofty Times, Inc., 497 Broome St., New York, NY 10013. Ed. Donald McPherson. adv.; illus.

LOG CABIN NEWS. see *BUILDING AND CONSTRUCTION*

352 — UK — ISSN 0954-6685
LONDON SOCIETY. JOURNAL. Key Title: Journal of the London Society. 1913. s-a. £9 (foreign £12). London Society, Senate House, 4th Fl., Malet St., London WC1E 7HU, England. TEL 071-580-5537. Ed. I. Brown. bk.rev.; illus.; index. circ. 600. **Indexed:** Br.Hum.Ind. **Document type:** bulletin.

352.7 — US
M H F A NEWSLETTER. q. free. Massachusetts Housing Finance Agency, 50 Milk St., Boston, MA 02109. TEL 617-451-3480. Ed. Martha Vaananen. charts; illus. **Document type:** newsletter.
 Description: Provides information about agency activities and housing programs for people of varied economic means.

352.7 747 — US — ISSN 1047-1359
M I N FAX. 1965. m. $125. Marketing Information Network, 1 Irving Place, Irvington, NY 10533. TEL 914-674-2705. Ed. Edward C. Birkner. index. circ. 500. (looseleaf format; back issues avail.)
 Incorporating: Span.
 Description: Information digest addressing housing, real estate, and community design and planning.

M L A NEWS (RALEIGH). (Multi-housing Laundry Association) see *CLEANING AND DYEING*

352.7 — US
M S H D A REVIEW; better housing for Michigan people. 1978. q. free. State Housing Development Authority, Plaza One, 4th Fl., 401 S. Washington Sq., Box 30044, Lansing, MI 48909. TEL 517-373-8370. FAX 517-373-7657. Ed. Kathleen Fagan. illus.
 Description: Provides information about state sponsored housing programs for low and moderate income families.

352.7 — US
MAINTENANCE AND MODERNIZATION SUPERVISOR. 1981. m. $24. Weil Communications and Marketing, Inc., Box 535, Olney, MD 20832. TEL 301-924-5490. Ed. Stephen A. Weil. adv.; bk.rev. circ. 9,500. (tabloid format)
 Description: Focuses on the maintenance, operation, and renovation of government housing facilities, particularly those managed by city and county public housing authorities and military housing commands.

352.7 — MW
MALAWI. NATIONAL STATISTICAL OFFICE. URBAN HOUSING SURVEY. 1987. irreg. K.10. National Statistical Office, P.O. Box 333, Zomba, Malawi. **Document type:** government publication.

331.83 — MW — ISSN 0581-0892
MALAWI HOUSING CORPORATION. ANNUAL REPORT AND ACCOUNTS. 1964. a. free. Malawi Housing Corporation, P.O. Box 414, Blantyre, Malawi. circ. 500.

MAN - ENVIRONMENT SYSTEMS. see *ENVIRONMENTAL STUDIES*

690 — US — ISSN 0193-6808
MANAGING HOUSING LETTER. 1978. m. $134. (Community Development Services, Inc.) C D Publications, 8204 Fenton St., Silver Spring, MD 20910. TEL 301-588-6380. FAX 301-588-6385. Ed. Joe Poduska. index. (back issues avail.) **Document type:** newsletter.
 Incorporates (1984-1993): Landlord - Tenant Relations Report (ISSN 1050-3196); (1991-1992): Private Multifamily Manager (ISSN 1057-1426)
 Description: News and advice for owners and managers of public, private, and subsidized rental housing. Includes news from Washington plus practical management tips.

388.3 690.87 — US — ISSN 1047-2967
HD7395.M6
MANUFACTURED HOME MERCHANDISER. 1952. m. $36 (free to qualified personnel). R L D Group, Inc., 203 N. Wabash, Ste. 800, Chicago, IL 60601-2476. TEL 312-236-3528. Ed. Bob Overend; Pub. Herb Tieder. adv.; stat.; circ. 15,000 (controlled). (also avail. in microform from UMI) **Indexed:** Bus.Ind., Tr.& Indus.Ind. **Document type:** trade publication.
—UMI.
 Former titles: Mobile - Manufactured Home Merchandiser (ISSN 0191-9768); Mobile Home Merchandiser; Mobile and Recreational Housing Merchandiser (ISSN 0026-7120); Mobilehomes' Merchandiser.

352.7 — US
MANUFACTURED HOUSING QUARTERLY. q. Manufactured Housing Institute, 1745 Jefferson Davis Hwy., Ste. 511, Arlington, VA 22202.

MANUFACTURED HOUSING TRADE DIGEST. see *BUILDING AND CONSTRUCTION*

352.7 690 — US
MARYLAND BUILDER. 1960. bi-m. $20 to non-members. Home Builders Association of Maryland, 1502 Woodlawn Dr., Baltimore, MD 21207. TEL 410-265-7400. FAX 410-265-6529. Ed. Cindy Wick. adv.: B&W page $570; trim 8 1/2 x 11. bk.rev.; charts; stat. circ. 3,000. (back issues avail.)
 Formerly: Maryland Home and Apartment Journal.
 Description: Reports current industry trends, important developments, and local, state and national news.

352.7 310 — US
MARYLAND TOMORROW. 1985. q. Department of State Planning, 301 W. Preston St., Rm. 1101, Baltimore, MD 21201. TEL 301-225-4500. Ed. Ann Wilmer. stat. circ. 3,000.

331.83 — US — ISSN 0076-499X
MASSACHUSETTS HOUSING FINANCE AGENCY. ANNUAL REPORT. 1969. a. free. Massachusetts Housing Finance Agency, 50 Milk St., Boston, MA 02109. TEL 617-451-3480. FAX 617-4510859. Ed. Martha Vaananen. charts; illus.; stat. circ. 8,000. **Document type:** corporate report.
 Description: Describes programs and highlights the agency's fiscal year activities and achievements for people of varied economic means.

711.4 — GW — ISSN 0938-6335
MATERIALEN ZUR RAUMENTWICKLUNG. 1981. irreg., vol.53, 1993. price varies. Bundesforschungsanstalt fuer Landeskunde und Raumordnung, Am Michaelshof 8, 53173 Bonn, Germany. TEL 0228-826-0. FAX 0228-826266. Ed.Bd. **Document type:** monographic series.
 Formerly: Bundesforschungsanstalt fuer Landeskunde und Raumordnung. Seminare - Symposien - Arbeitspapiere (ISSN 0930-3839)

DER MAUERANKER. see *ARCHITECTURE*

333 711 — MF — ISSN 0076-552X
MAURITIUS. MINISTRY OF HOUSING, LANDS AND TOWN AND COUNTRY PLANNING. ANNUAL REPORTS. a. price varies. Government Printing Office, Elizabeth II Ave., Port Louis, Mauritius.

352.7 — MF
MAURITIUS HOUSING CORPORATION. REPORT AND ACCOUNTS. (Text in English) 1964. a. Mauritius Housing Corporation, P.O. Box 478, Port Louis, Mauritius. Ed.Bd. circ. 500.

MESTNYI PROIZVODSTVENNYI OPYT V STROITEL'STVE/LOCAL LEVEL EXPERIENCE IN THE CONSTRUCTION INDUSTRY; nauchno-tekhnicheskii referativnyi sbornik. see *BUILDING AND CONSTRUCTION*

353.9 — US
MICHIGAN STATE HOUSING DEVELOPMENT AUTHORITY. ANNUAL REPORT. 1970. a. State Housing Development Authority, Plaza One, 4th Fl., 401 S. Washington Sq., Box 30044, Lansing, MI 48909. TEL 517-373-8370. Ed. Kathleen Fagan. illus.; stat. circ. 7,500.
 Description: Report of activities and financial status of Michigan State Housing Development Authority housing production data.

352.7 — GW
MIETERECHO. 1956. bi-m. Berliner Mietergemeinschaft e.V., Moeckernstr. 92, 10963 Berlin, Germany. TEL 030-2168001. Eds. Gerhard Hess, Sabine Loehr. bk.rev. circ. 20,000. (back issues avail.)

360 — GW
MIETERZEITUNG. 1951. m. DM.15. (Deutscher Mieterbund e.V.) Verlagsgesellschaft des Deutschen Mieterbundes mbH, Postfach 410269, 50862 Cologne, Germany. TEL 0221-40083-0. FAX 0221-4008322. Ed. H. Schlich. adv.; bk.rev. circ. 450,000. **Document type:** newspaper.

352.7 333.33 — IT
MINIAPPARTAMENTI. 1980. s-a. Di Baio Editore s.r.l., Via Settembre, 11, 20124 Milan, Italy. TEL 6692254-5. FAX 02-6709257. Ed. Giuseppe Maria Jonghi Lavarini.

352.7   GW
MITTEILUNGEN DER HEIMSTAETTEN UND LANDESENTWICKLUNGSGESELLSCHAFTEN. 1958. q. Bundesvereinigung der Landesentwicklungsgesellschaften und Heimstaetten e.V., Meckenheimer Allee 128, 53115 Bonn, Germany. TEL 0228-631386. FAX 0228-659560. circ. 5,000. **Document type:** newsletter.

388.3   UK   ISSN 0268-4594
MOBILE & HOLIDAY HOMES. 1960. m. £30.10. Link House Magazines Ltd., Link House, Dingwall Ave., Croydon, Surrey CR9 2TA, England. TEL 081-686-2599. FAX 081-760-0973. (Subscr. to: C P G, 120-126 Lavender Ave., Mitcham, Surrey CR2 4HP, England) Ed. Anne Webb. adv.; bk.rev.; illus. **Document type:** consumer publication.
   Former titles: Mobile Home and Holiday Caravan (ISSN 0306-5839); Mobile Home (ISSN 0026-7139)
   Description: For owners of caravan holiday homes and-or residential park (mobile) homes.

388.3 340   US
MOBILE HOMES AND MOBILE HOME PARKS. 1975. base vol. (plus a. suppl.). $95. Shepard's - McGraw-Hill, Inc., Box 35300, Colorado Springs, CO 80935-3530. TEL 800-525-2474.
   Description: Provides information on the laws and multiple regulations applicable to mobile homes, mobile home parks and recreational vehicles.

388.3   US   ISSN 0026-7198
MOBILE LIVING.* 1953. irreg. membership. National Association of Trailer Owners, Inc., 2015 Tuttle, Box 1418, Sarasota, FL 34230. TEL 813-953-2730. Ed. Frances Neel. adv.; charts; illus.; tr.lit. circ. 42,000.

352.7   BO
MONOGRAFIAS URBANAS. 1975. irreg., no.3, 1985. $12. Centro de Investigaciones Sociales, Casilla 6931 - C.C., La Paz, Bolivia. **Document type:** monographic series.

MONTANA AND THE SKY. see TRANSPORTATION — Air Transport

MORTGAGE FINANCE MONTHLY. see REAL ESTATE

352.7   CN   ISSN 0702-7206
KE5295.A45
MUNICIPAL AND PLANNING LAW REPORTS (2ND SERIES). 1976. 12/yr. (in 5 vols.). Can.$120. Carswell, One Corporate Plaza, 2075 Kennedy Rd., Scarborough, ON M1T 3V4, Canada. TEL 416-609-8000. FAX 416-298-5094. Ed. Stanley M. Makuch. adv. contact: M. Lalani. **Indexed:** C.L.I., Ind.Can.L.P.L., L.R.I.
   Description: Features municipal law decisions from the courts and planning tribunals of all Canadian jurisdictions selected by experts in the field.

350.086   US   ISSN 0194-9268
N A H R O MONITOR; a semimonthly report on issues in housing and community development. 1979. s-m. membership only. National Association of Housing and Redevelopment Officials, 1320 18th St., N.W., Washington, DC 20036. TEL 202-429-2960. FAX 202-429-9684. Ed. Julie Gaskill. circ. 7,500. (also avail. in microform from UMI; reprint service avail. from UMI) **Document type:** trade publication.
   Supersedes (1967-1979): N A H R O Letter (ISSN 0300-6409)

352.7   US
N A N BULLETIN. 1975. q. $25. National Association of Neighborhoods, 1651 Fuller St., N.W., Washington, DC 20009. TEL 202-332-7766. FAX 202-332-2314. Ed. Althea Gatewood. adv.; bk.rev. circ. 3,000. **Document type:** newsletter, bulletin.

N A T A T'S REPORTER. see PUBLIC ADMINISTRATION — Municipal Government

690.87   US
N C S B C S NEWS. 1977. bi-m. $35. National Conference of States on Building Codes and Standards, Inc., 505 Huntmar Pk. Dr., Ste. 210, Herndon, VA 22070. TEL 703-437-0100. FAX 703-481-3596. Ed. Deborah Brettner. bk.rev. circ. 700. (back issues avail.) **Document type:** newsletter.
   Incorporates (in July 1987): National Conference of States on Buildings and Codes and Standards. Legislative Bulletin.

352.7   UN   ISSN 0257-7313
N G O NEWS ON HUMAN SETTLEMENTS. (Non-governmental Organizations) 1987. 3/yr. free. (United Nations Centre for Human Settlements (Habitat)) Habitat International Coalition, Cordobanes 24, 03900 Col. San Jose Insurgentes, Mexico D.F., Mexico. TEL 651-68-07. FAX 545-32-63. TELEX 117 64 54 MAFOME. (Subscr. to: UNCHS (Habitat), Box 30030, Nairobi, Kenya) Ed. Jodi Grahl. bk.rev. **Document type:** newsletter.
   Description: Serves as a forum for non-governmental organizations concerned with issues related to human settlements at the international and national levels.

350.086   PH
N H A ANNUAL REPORT. a. free. National Housing Authority, Quezon Memorial Circle, Elliptical Rd., Diliman, Quezon City, Philippines. TEL 921-4066. FAX 632-921-0444. circ. 500.

352.7 624   US   ISSN 1071-9466
N T I S ALERTS: REGIONAL & URBAN PLANNING & TECHNOLOGY. w. $160 (outside N. America $225). U.S. National Technical Information Service, 5285 Port Royal Rd., Springfield, VA 22161. TEL 703-487-4650. FAX 703-321-8547. TELEX 64617. bibl. **Document type:** newsletter, government publication.

NASHRAT AL-ISKAN WAL-ASHGHAL/WORKS AND HOUSING BULLETIN. see PUBLIC ADMINISTRATION

309.2   US   ISSN 0098-308X
HT394.W3
NATIONAL CAPITAL PLANNING COMMISSION. QUARTERLY REVIEW OF COMMISSION PROCEEDINGS. Key Title: Quarterly Review of Commission Proceedings. Running title: N C P C Quarterly. 1974. q. free. U.S. National Capital Planning Commission, 1325 G St., N.W., Washington, DC 20576. TEL 202-724-0174. illus.; index. circ. 700. **Document type:** proceedings.

690.87   US
NATIONAL CONFERENCE OF STATES ON BUILDING CODES AND STANDARDS. ANNUAL CONFERENCE PROCEEDINGS. a. National Conference of States on Building Codes and Standards, 505 Huntmar Park Dr., Ste. 210, Herndon, VA 22070. TEL 703-437-0100. FAX 703-481-3596. **Document type:** proceedings.

352.7   US
NATIONAL HOUSING & REHABILITATION ASSOCIATION. NEWSLETTER. m. membership only. National Housing & Rehabilitation Association, 1726 18th St., N.W., Washington, DC 20009. TEL 202-328-9171. FAX 202-265-4435. **Document type:** newsletter.

352.7   UK   ISSN 0264-9829
NATIONAL HOUSING AND TOWN PLANNING COUNCIL. CONFERENCE AND EXHIBITION GUIDE. 1952. a. National Housing and Town Planning Council, 14-18 Old St., London EC1V 9AB, England. adv. circ. 1,200.
   Description: Agendas, descriptions of exhibits, floor plans, and lists of speakers and participants in this conference.

NATIONAL HOUSING DIRECTORY FOR PEOPLE WITH DISABILITIES. see HANDICAPPED

352.7   US   ISSN 1059-3071
NATIONAL HOUSING REGISTER. 1991. irreg., approx. q. free to qualified personnel. William D. Diemer, Ed. & Pub., 27239 Meadowbrook Dr., Davis, CA 95616-5049. TEL 916-757-6403. FAX 916-753-1768. circ. 40 (controlled). (back issues avail.) **Document type:** newsletter.
   Description: Discusses the need for a National Housing Register listing every structure in the United States, strategies and measures appropriate to the design, development and maintenance of this list, and serves as a clearinghouse for information of interest to professionals and government officials.

352.7   US
NATIONAL LEASED HOUSING ASSOCIATION. BULLETIN. 1972. m. membership. National Leased Housing Association, 2300 M St., N.W., Ste. 260, Washington, DC 20037. TEL 202-785-8888. FAX 202-785-2008. Ed. Denise Muha. circ. 800. **Document type:** bulletin.
   Description: Covers government-related programs.

301.36   US
NATIONAL URBAN LEAGUE ANNUAL REPORT. a. $1. National Urban League, 500 E. 62nd St., New York, NY 10021. TEL 212-310-9000. illus.
   Formerly: National Urban League Progress Report (ISSN 0098-7735)

NEBELHORN; Regionalmagazin fuer Politik und Kultur. see BUSINESS AND ECONOMICS — Labor And Industrial Relations

333.77 531.64
614.7   US   ISSN 0193-791X
NEIGHBORHOOD WORKS. 1978. 6/yr. (plus 2 special issues). $30. Center for Neighborhood Technology, 2125 W. North Ave., Chicago, IL 60647. TEL 312-278-4800. FAX 312-278-3840. Ed. Patti Wolter. adv. contact: Bridget Torres. bk.rev.; charts; illus.; index. circ. 2,500. (back issues avail.) **Indexed:** Alt.Press Ind.
   Description: Covers housing, energy, economic and environmental concerns from the perspective of how these issues affect city neighborhoods, and what residents, acting through community organizations, can do about them.

352.7   NE   ISSN 0920-1580
NETHERLANDS JOURNAL OF HOUSING AND ENVIRONMENTAL RESEARCH. (Text in English) 1986. q. fl.120. (N I R O V, O T B, Delft) Delft University Press, Stevinweg 1, 2628 CN Delft, Netherlands. TEL 31-15-783254. FAX 31-15-781661. Ed. H. Priemus. index. (back issues avail.)
   —UnCover; SWETS.

352.7 645   GW
NEUES WOHNEN (HAMBURG). 1956. m. DM.38.40 (Europe DM.64.80; elsewhere DM.115.80). Gruner und Jahr AG & Co., Am Baumwall 11, 20459 Hamburg, Germany. TEL 040-3703-0. FAX 040-37035606. circ. 272,897. **Document type:** consumer publication.

NEW HAMPSHIRE MUNICIPAL PRACTICE SERIES. VOLS. 1 AND 1A: LAND USE AND PLANNING. see PUBLIC ADMINISTRATION — Municipal Government

711.4 352.7   US
NEW HAMPSHIRE PLANNING AND LAND USE REGULATION. a. $16. Butterworth Legal Publishers (Salem) (Subsidiary of: Reed Elsevier plc), 8 Industrial Way, Bldg. C, Salem, NH 03079. TEL 800-548-4001. FAX 603-898-9858. Ed.Bd.

352.7   JA
NEW HOME DESIGN/ATRASHI SUMAI-NO SEKKAI.* (Text in Japanese) 1961. m. 7800 Yen. Sankei Publishing Ltd., Sankei-Honsha Bldg., 1-7-2 Otemachi, Chiyoda-ku, Tokyo, 100, Japan. Ed. Sei Segawa.

333 350.08   US
NEW JERSEY HOUSING AND MORTGAGE FINANCE AGENCY ANNUAL REPORT. 1967. a. free. New Jersey Housing and Mortgage Finance Agency, Division of Planning and Intergovernmental Relations, 3625 Quakerbridge Rd., CN-18550, Trenton, NJ 08650-2085. TEL 609-890-8900. FAX 609-890-0414. Ed.Bd. circ. 6,500. **Document type:** government publication.
   Description: Covers yearly highlights of the Agency's activities in promoting safe and affordable housing in New Jersey by providing low-interest construction and permanent loans for single-family and multifamily housing for eligible low- and moderate-income households.

352.7   AT   ISSN 0819-6028
NEW SOUTH WALES. DEPARTMENT OF HOUSING. ANNUAL REPORT. 1986. a. Department of Housing, Information and Publications Services, 23-31 Moore St., Liverpool, N.S.W. 2170, Australia. FAX 02-821-6901. illus. circ. 3,000. **Document type:** government publication.
   Formed by the merger of (1942-1985): New South Wales. Housing Commission. Annual Report (ISSN 0727-9558); (1977-1985): New South Wales. Land Commission. Annual Report (ISSN 0155-2074)

NEW YORK CITY HOUSING MAINTENANCE CODE. see LAW

NEW YORK HABITAT TIMES. see SOCIAL SERVICES AND WELFARE

HOUSING AND URBAN PLANNING

NEW YORK LANDLORD AND TENANT HANDBOOK. see *LAW — Civil Law*

NEW YORK MULTIPLE DWELLING LAW. see *LAW*

352 US
NEW YORK PLANNING NEWS. 1937. bi-m. membership. New York Planning Federation, 488 Broadway, Ste. 313, Albany, NY 12207. FAX 518-427-8625. Ed. David Church. adv.; bk.rev. circ. 11,000.
Formerly: New York State Planning News (ISSN 0028-7679)

352 NZ ISSN 0111-9435
NEW ZEALAND PLANNING INSTITUTE. PLANNING QUARTERLY. Key Title: Planning Quarterly. 1965. q. NZ.$45 (foreign NZ.$60). (New Zealand Planning Institute) Associated Group Media Ltd., Private Beg 99-915, Newmarket, Auckland, New Zealand. TEL 09-795-393. FAX 09-379-5393. Ed. Cathy Sheehan. adv.; bk.rev.; charts; illus.; cum.index every 4 yrs. circ. 1,200. Indexed: Sage Urb.Stud.Abstr. Document type: trade publication.
—BLDSC (6509.253000). CCC.
Formerly (until 1982): New Zealand Planning Institute. Town Planning Quarterly (ISSN 0041-0012)

352 NZ ISSN 1171-1884
NEW ZEALAND RESOURCE MANAGEMENT APPEALS. 1956. 10/yr. Butterworths of New Zealand Ltd., P.O. Box 472, 205-207 Victoria St., Wellington, New Zealand. TEL 04-385-1479. FAX 04-385-1598. Ed. Peter Haig.
—CCC.
Former titles (until 1992): New Zealand Town Planning Appeals (ISSN 0110-1390); (until 1972): Town and Country Planning Appeals (ISSN 0495-971X)
Description: Selected decisions of the Planning Tribunal, High Court and Court of Appeal on town planning, environmental, and local government issues.

352.7 UK ISSN 0262-0383
NORTHERN ECONOMIC REVIEW. 1981. s-a. £15. University of Durham, Department of Sociology and Social Polidy, University of Durham, Durham DH1 3JT, England. TEL 44-91-3742308. (Co-sponsor: University of Newcastle upon Tyne, Centre for Urban and Regional Development, Newcastle upon Tyne NE1 7RU, England) Ed. Fred Robinson. bk.rev.; charts; illus. circ. 500. Indexed: C.R.E.J. Document type: academic/scholarly publication.
—BLDSC (6150.740000).
Description: Covers a wide variety of economic issues of the northern United Kingdom in detail.
Refereed Serial

711 CK
NOTICIERO I.D.U.N.. 1976. irreg. Instituto de Desarrollo Urbano, Division de Documentacion, Comunicacion y Archivo, Apartado Aereo 034176, Bogota, Colombia.

352.7 690 MX
OBRAS. 1973. m. $162 (typically set in Jan.). Expansion, S. de R.L. de C.V. (Subsidiary of: Capital Cities - A B C, Inc.), Salamanca No. 35, 06700 Mexico D.F., Mexico. TEL 208-96-09. FAX 208-28-19. Ed. Enrique Chao. adv. contact: Elena Bayardo. illus. circ. 10,623.
Description: Cover the construction industry in Mexico.

OBRAS PUBLICAS. see *PUBLIC ADMINISTRATION*

309.26 301 AU
OESTERREICHISCHES INSTITUT FUER RAUMPLANUNG. OE I R - FORUM. 1957. irreg. price varies. Oesterreichisches Institut fuer Raumplanung, Franz Josefs Kai 27, A-1011 Vienna, Austria. TEL 5338747.
Formerly (until 1982): Oesterreichisches Institut fuer Raumplanung. Veroeffentlichungen (ISSN 0078-3625)

301.54 CN ISSN 0835-0213
HD7305.A3
ONTARIO. MINISTRY OF HOUSING. ANNUAL REPORT. 1966. a. Can.$2.50 per no. Ministry of Housing, 777 Bay St., 17th Fl., Toronto, Ont. M5G 2E5, Canada. TEL 416-585-7020. circ. 2,000.
Formerly (until 1985): Ontario. Ministry of Municipal Affairs and Housing. Annual Report (ISSN 0078-4885)

352.7 UK ISSN 0168-2601
OPEN HOUSE INTERNATIONAL; the journal of an association of institutes and individuals concerned with housing, design and development in the built environment. 1976. q. £68. Open House International Association, School of Architecture, The University, Newcastle-upon-Tyne NE1 7RU, England. TEL 091-222-6008. FAX 091-261-1182. TELEX 53654-UNINEW-G. (Subscr. to: N.B.S. Services Ltd., Mansion House Chambers, The Close, Newcastle-upon-Tyne NE1 3RE, England) Ed. Nicholas Wilkinson. adv.: B&W page £200. bk.rev. Document type: academic/scholarly publication.
—BLDSC (6265.960400); UnCover.
Formerly (until 1983): Open House (ISSN 0921-3864)
Description: Interdisiciplinary journal on housing and design, focusing on theories, tools and practice, with special emphasis on the local scale. Examines user participation and community roles in these processes, government or private sector, in both developed and developing countries.
Refereed Serial

352.7 US
P A S MEMO. (Planning Advisory Service) m. price varies. American Planning Association, 1313 E. 60th St., Chicago, IL 60637. TEL 312-955-9100. FAX 312-955-8312. (And: 1776 Massachusetts Ave., N.W., Washington, DC 20036. TEL 202-872-0611) Ed. Jim Hecimovich. (reprint service avail. from UMI)

350.86 CN ISSN 0048-4326
P I B C NEWS. 1959. 5/yr. Can.$35 to non-members. Planning Institute of British Columbia, 10551 Shellbridge Way, Ste. 20, Richmond, BC V6X 2W9, Canada. TEL 604-947-2300. FAX 604-947-2377. Ed. Bob Burgess. adv.; bk.rev. circ. 600. (also avail. in microfiche from MML) Document type: newsletter.
Description: Presents articles and news of local events of interest to the practicing urban and regional planners of British Columbia.

350.86 PR ISSN 0048-4466
H8
P L E R U S. (Planning: Economic, Regional, Urban, Social) (Text in English and Spanish) 1967. a. $5 (effective 1994). Universidad de Puerto Rico, Escuela Graduada de Planificacion, Apartado B.E., Rio Piedras, PR 00931. TEL 809-764-0000. Ed. Jose A. Vega Lopez. adv.; bk.rev. circ. 700. Document type: academic/scholarly publication.
●Also available online.
Description: Devoted to the discussion of issues relevant to planning as a scientific discipline and a professional practice. Focuses on major issues in urban, economic, social and environmental planning.

352.7 UK
P S A SPECIFICATIONS. 3/yr. £120. Property Services Agency, Apollo House, 36 Wellesley Rd., Croydon CR9 3RR, England. TEL 081-760-8590.

352.7 IT ISSN 1120-3544
NA9203
PAESAGGIO URBANO; dossier di cultura e progetto della citta. 1990. bi-m. L.120000 to individuals; institutions L.165000 (effective 1994). Maggioli Editore, Viale Vespucci 12-n, Casella Postale 290, 47037 Rimini, Italy. TEL 0541-626777. FAX 0541-622020. Ed.Bd. adv.: B&W page L.2000000, color page L.3100000; trim 160 x 265.

352.7 PN
PANAMA. MINISTERIO DE VIVIENDA. MEMORIA. a. Ministerio de Vivienda, Apdo. 5228, Panama 5, Panama. TEL 02-5960. FAX 62-9250. illus.; stat. Document type: government publication.
Supersedes (in 1973): Instituto de Vivienda y Urbanismo. Memoria Presentada por el Director General.

PARAMETRO; international review of architecture and town planning. see *ARCHITECTURE*

711 FR
PARIS PROJET; amenagement urbanisme avenir. 1969. irreg. 350 F. (foreign 400 F.). Atelier Parisien d'Urbanisme, 9 place de l'Hotel de Ville, 75004 Paris, France. TEL 42-71-28-14. FAX 42-76-24-05. Ed. Nathan Starkman. adv. circ. 15,000. (back issues avail.)

PARLIAMENTARY HOUSING NEWS. see *LAW*

301.54 SP ISSN 0067-4168
PATRONATO MUNICIPAL DE LA VIVIENDA DE BARCELONA. MEMORIA. 1947. a. free. Patronato Municipal de la Vivienda, Plaza F. de Lesseps, 12, Barcelona 6, Spain. bk.rev.; index. circ. 1,500.

352.7 AU
PERSPEKTIVEN. 10/yr. Jenullgasse 4, A-1141 Vienna, Austria. TEL 01-8946449. FAX 01-8946523. TELEX 133832. Ed. Jutta Fahnler. circ. 10,000.

711 309.26 PH ISSN 0048-3850
HT169. P6
PHILIPPINE PLANNING JOURNAL. 1969. s-a. $12. University of the Philippines, School of Urban and Regional Planning, E. Jacinto St., Diliman, Quezon City 3004, Philippines. FAX 632-98-35-95. Ed.Bd. adv.; bk.rev.; charts; index, cum.index. circ. 1,000. Indexed: Ind.Phil.Per. Document type: academic/scholarly publication.

PLACE. see *ARCHITECTURE*

PLACES; a quarterly journal of environmental design. see *ARCHITECTURE*

352.7 333.33 US
PLACES RATED ALMANAC. 1981. irreg. approx. every 2 yrs., latest 1993. $20. Prentice Hall (Subsidiary of: Simon & Schuster), 15 Columbus Cir., New York, NY 10023. TEL 212-375-8500; 800-223-2348. Document type: consumer publication.
Formerly: Rand McNally Places Rated Almanac.

352 711 SW ISSN 0032-0560
HT169.S8
PLAN; tidskrift foer planering av landsbygd och taetorter/the Swedish town and country planning review. (Text in Swedish; abstracts in English) 1947. 6/yr. SEK 310 in Nordic countries; rest of Europe SEK 410; elsewhere SEK 430 (typically set in May). Foereningen foer Samhaellsplanering - Swedish Society for Town and Country Planning, P.O. Box 15013, S-800 15 Gaevle, Sweden. TEL 46-26-687500. FAX 46-26-611536. Ed. Goeran Cars. adv.; bk.rev.; charts; illus.; index. circ. 3,000. Indexed: Geo.Abstr.
Description: Covers issues relating to the general planning of urban and rural areas. Seeks to provide a forum for discussion between experts, representatives of central and local government, the business community, and the general public.

352 711 CN ISSN 0032-0544
NA9000
PLAN CANADA. (Text and summaries in English and French) 1959. 6/yr. Can.$58.85 to individuals (foreign Can.$61.60); institutions Can.$65.91 (foreign Can.$77). Canadian Institute of Planners, H L R & Associates - Institut Canadien des Urbanistes, 51 Ottawa St., Arnprior, ON K7S 1W9, Canada. TEL 613-623-6975. FAX 613-623-5179. Ed. Heather Lang-Runtz. adv.: B&W page Can.$750; 7 1/2 x 9 1/2; adv. contact: Tracy Sparling. bk.rev.; illus.; cum.index. circ. 4,700. (also avail. in microfilm; reprint service avail. from MML) Indexed: Avery Ind.Archit.Per., Can.Per.Ind., CMI, P.A.I.S.
—BLDSC (6508.122000); Faxon. CCC.
Formerly: Plan.
Description: Looks at Canadian planning practice and theory, urban and rural planning, sustainable development and social, economic and evironmental aspects of planning.

352.7 US
PLANNERS NETWORK NEWSLETTER. 1975. bi-m. membership. Planners Network, 1601 Connecticut Ave., N.W., Washington, DC 20009. TEL 202-347-1457. FAX 202-638-2095. Ed. Prentice Bowsher. bk.rev. circ. 700. Document type: newsletter.
Description: For professionals, activists, academics, and students involved in physical, social, economic, and environmental planning in urban and rural areas, who promote fundamental change in our political and economic system.

711 II
PLANNERS' NEWSLETTER. q. free to members. Institute of Town Planners, India, 4-A Ring Rd., Indraprastha Estate, New Delhi 110 002, India. TEL 331-8571. Document type: newsletter.

HOUSING AND URBAN PLANNING 3093

352 US ISSN 0001-2610
HC101 CODEN: PLNNDB
PLANNING. 1972. m. $40 (foreign $55); or membership. American Planning Association, 1313 E. 60th St., Chicago, IL 60637. TEL 312-955-9100. FAX 312-955-8312. (And: 1776 Massachusetts Ave., N.W., Washington, DC 20036. TEL 202-872-0611) Ed. Sylvia Lewis. adv.: B&W page $1560. bk.rev.; bibl.; charts; illus.; index. circ. 30,000. (also avail. in microform from UMI; reprint service avail. from UMI) **Indexed:** ABI Inform., Avery Ind.Archit.Per., BPIA, Bus.Ind., Energy Rev., Environ.Abstr., Environ.Ind., Environ.Per.Bibl. (1977-), Excerp.Med., Geo.Abstr., Manage.Cont., P.A.I.S., PSI, Tr.& Indus.Ind.
—BLDSC (6508.923000); Faxon; UnCover; SWETS; UMI.
Formerly: American Society of Planning Officials. A S P O Newsletter; Which superseded (in 1978) Practicing Planner; (in 1971): Planner's Notebook (ISSN 0048-4296)

352.7 NE ISSN 0167-3572
PLANNING; methodiek en toepassing. 1976. 3/yr. fl.10. Instituut voor Ruimtelijke Organisatie - Institute of Spatial Organization, Postbus 6041, 2600 JA Delft, Netherlands. FAX 31-15-624341. Ed. H. Duel. bk.rev.; software rev. **Indexed:** P.A.I.S., Sage Pub.Admin.Abstr., Sage Urb.Stud.Abstr. **Document type:** academic/scholarly publication.
—BLDSC (6509.085000); SWETS.

350.86 US
PLANNING AND PUBLIC POLICY. 1975-1988; resumed 1990. s-a. $5 (overseas $6). University of Illinois at Urbana-Champaign, Department of Urban and Regional Planning, 907 W. Nevada St., Urbana, IL 61801. TEL 217-333-3890. FAX 217-244-1717. Ed. Lewis Hopkins. circ. 4,500. (looseleaf format) **Document type:** newsletter.
Supersedes: Illinois University. Department of Urban and Regional Planning. Research Bureau. Newsletter (ISSN 0046-8630)
Description: Discusses how federal and state laws affect urban planning.

352.7 323.11 US
PLANNING AND THE BLACK COMMUNITY. q. U.S. Department of the Army, Box C-3755, Seattle, WA 98124-2255. TEL 206-764-3614. **Document type:** newsletter.
Description: Covers issues concerning planning in black communities.

352 UK ISSN 0964-0177
PLANNING & TRANSPORT NEWS. bi-w. £92 (foreign £104). London Research Centre, Research Library, Parliament House, 81 Black Prince Rd., London SE1 7SZ, England. TEL 071-627-9661. FAX 071-627-9664.
Description: Covers all aspects of urban and regional planning and transportation.

711 352 US ISSN 0738-114X
HD211.M5
PLANNING & ZONING NEWS. 1982. m. $140 (effective 1993). Planning & Zoning Center, Inc., 302 S. Waverly Rd., Lansing, MI 48917. TEL 517-886-0555. FAX 517-886-0564. Ed. Mark A. Wyckoff. bk.rev.; cum.index. circ. 2,300. (back issues avail.)

352.7 US ISSN 1058-5605
PLANNING COMMISSIONERS JOURNAL; for America's municipal & county planning boards. 1991. 4/yr. $40. Champlain Planning Press, Box 4295, Burlington, VT 05406. TEL 802-864-9083. FAX 802-862-1882. Ed. Wayne M. Senville. circ. 3,000. **Document type:** newsletter.
Description: Aimed at local planning commissioners across the country, and others interested in local planning. Covers wide range of planning issues including transportation, land use, zoning, housing, and urban design.

711
PLANNING HISTORY PRESENT. 1987. q. membership. Society for American City and Regional Planning History, 3655 Darbyshire Dr., Hilliard, OH 43026-2534. bk.rev.
Description: Presents information on history of city planning.

352.7 US ISSN 0048-4318
PLANNING IN NORTHEASTERN ILLINOIS.* 1963. q. free. Northeastern Illinois Planning Commission, 222 S. Riverside Plz., Ste. 1800, Chicago, IL 60606-6001. TEL 312-454-0400. FAX 312-454-0411. Ed. Alexandra Radtke. bk.rev.; charts; illus.; stat.; circ. 9,500 (controlled). (looseleaf format)

350.86 UK ISSN 1352-8424
HT169.G7
PLANNING WEEK. 1914. 51/yr. £55 (rest of Europe £60; N. America, Africa, Middle East £75; Asia. Australia £85). (Royal Town Planning Institute) Hay Market Publishing Ltd., 38-42 Hampton Rd., Teddington, Mddx. TW11 OJE, England. TEL 081-943-5045. FAX 081-943-5098. Ed. Vicky Browning; Pub. Nigel Roby. adv. contact: Suzie Ellis. bk.rev.; bibl.; charts; illus.; tr.lit.; index. circ. 18,000. **Indexed:** Br.Hum.Ind., Br.Tech.Ind., Excerp.Med., Geo.Abstr., Intl.Civil Eng.Abstr., Rural Recreat.Tour.Abstr., Sage Urb.Stud.Abstr., Soft.Abstr.Eng., World Agri.Econ.& Rural Sociol.Abstr. **Document type:** trade publication.
—Faxon; SWETS.
Former titles (until 1993): Planner (ISSN 0309-1384); Royal Town Planning Institute Journal (ISSN 0048-8739)

352.7 CN
POLICY ISSUES & PLANNING RESPONSES. 1981. irreg. University of British Columbia, Centre for Human Settlements, 2206 East Mall, Vancouver, BC V6T 1W5, Canada. TEL 604-228-3276. circ. 150.
Supersedes (in 1993): U B C Planning Papers; University of British Columbia. School of Community and Regional Planning. Planning Papers; Formerly: University of British Columbia. School of Community and Regional Planning. Occasional Papers.

711.4 PL ISSN 0079-3493
POLSKA AKADEMIA NAUK. KOMITET PRZESTRZENNEGO ZAGOSPODAROWANIA KRAJU. BIULETYN. 1960. irreg., vol.166, 1993. price varies. Wydawnictwo Naukowe P W N, Ul. Miodowa 10, 00-251 Warsaw, Poland. TEL 48-22-312738. FAX 48-22-267163. TELEX 813763 PWN PL. Ed. Ryszrd Domanski. index. circ. 1,300.

711 PL ISSN 0860-3375
POLSKA AKADEMIA NAUK. KOMITET PRZESTRZENNEGO ZAGOSPODAROWANIA KRAJU. STUDIA REGIONALIA. (Text in English, French, Polish or Russian: summaries in English and Russian) 1961. irreg., vol.101, 1993. price varies. Wydawnictwo Naukowe P W N - Polish Scientific Publishers P W N Ltd., Ul. Miodowa 10, 00-251 Warsaw, Poland. TEL 48-22-260207. FAX 48-22-267163. Ed. Ryszard Domanski.
Formerly (until 1986): Polska Akademia Nauk. Komitet Przestrzennego Zagospodarowania Kraju. Studia (ISSN 0079-3507)

POLSKA AKADEMIA NAUK. ODDZIAL W KRAKOWIE. KOMISJA URBANISTYKI I ARCHITEKTURY. TEKA. see ARCHITECTURE

350.086 CL
PONTIFICIA UNIVERSIDAD CATOLICA DE CHILE. INSTITUTO DE ESTUDIOS URBANOS. DOCUMENTOS DE TRABAJO. 1969. irreg., no.251, 1984. price varies. Pontificia Universidad Catolica de Chile, Instituto de Estudios Urbanos, Los Navegantes 1919, Casilla 16002-Correo 9, Santiago, Chile.
Formerly: Universidad Catolica de Chile. Instituto de Planificacion del Desarrollo Urbano. Documentos de Trabajo.

PORTABLE DWELLING. see SPORTS AND GAMES — Outdoor Life

350.086 US ISSN 0163-8602
HT123
PRESIDENT'S NATIONAL URBAN POLICY REPORT. 1978. biennial. U.S. Department of Housing and Urban Development, Washington, DC 20410. TEL 202-655-4000.

PREVISIONS GLISSANTES DETAILLEES EN PERSPECTIVES SECTORIELLES (VOL.27): LOGEMENT. see BUSINESS AND ECONOMICS — Economic Situation And Conditions

352.7 DK ISSN 0904-4477
PRIVATBOLIGEN.* 1989. bi-m. DKK 109.80. Foreningernes Forlag ApS, Sankt Peders Straede 28A, 1453 Copenhagen K, Denmark. illus.
Formed by the merger of (1982-1989): Andels-Boligen (ISSN 0109-033X); (1987-1989): Andels- og Ejerboligen (ISSN 0903-4234); (1985-1989): Ejerboligen (ISSN 0901-0076)

PROA; urbanismo, arquitectura, industrias. see ARCHITECTURE

PROBLEMY BOL'SHIKH GORODOV/PROBLEMS OF LARGE METROPOLITAN AREAS; obzornaya informatsiya. see ENVIRONMENTAL STUDIES

711 309.62 UK ISSN 0305-9006
HT166
PROGRESS IN PLANNING. 1973. 6/yr. (in 2 vols., 3 nos./vol.). £183($280) (effective 1994). Elsevier Science Ltd., Pergamon, P.O. Box 800, Kidlington, Oxford OX5 1DX, England. TEL 44-865-843000. FAX 44-865-843010. (Subscr. in U.S. and Canada to: Elsevier Science, 660 White Plains Rd., Tarrytown, NY 10591-5153. TEL 914-524-9200. FAX 914-333-2444) Ed.Bd. (also avail. in microfilm from UMI) **Indexed:** ASSIA, Geo.Abstr., HRIS, I D A, Sage Urb.Stud.Abstr., SSCI. **Document type:** academic/scholarly publication, monographic series.
—BLDSC (6873.550000); SWETS; UMI. **CCC.**
Description: Publishes extended papers reviewing recent international research in planning.
Refereed Serial

352 NE ISSN 0926-0005
PROJECT ANALYSE. (Supplement to: Bouw) 1990. 6/yr. fl.49.90. Keesing, P.O. Box 1118, 1000 BE Amsterdam, Netherlands.

711.4 690 US
PROJECT PLANNING AND CONTROL FOR CONSTRUCTION. 1988. irreg. $59.95. R.S. Means Company, Inc., 100 Construction Plaza, Kingston, MA 02364. TEL 617-585-7880. Ed. Bd.

352.7 PE
PROPUESTAS PARA EL DESARROLLO. 1983. bi-m. Asociacion Nacional de Centros, 285 Jesus Maria, Lima, Peru.

352 711 NE
PROSPECT. (Text in English, French and German) 1961. 4/yr. fl.130. International Federation for Housing and Planning, Wassenaarseweg 43, 2596 CG The Hague, Netherlands. TEL 31-70-3244557. FAX 31-70-3282085. Ed. I Hesper. bk.rev. circ. 1,300. **Indexed:** Avery Ind.Archit.Per., Geo.Abstr., Mid.East: Abstr.& Ind. **Document type:** academic/scholarly publication.
Former titles (until 1988): I F H P News Sheet; International Federation for Housing and Planning Bulletin (ISSN 0020-6660)

PROVINCIA NUOVA. see PUBLIC ADMINISTRATION

352.7 US ISSN 0887-4468
PUBLIC INNOVATION ABROAD. (Former name of issuing body: Council for International Urban Liaison) 1977. m. $48 (foreign $60). Academy for State and Local Government, 444 N. Capitol St., N.W., Ste. 349, Washington, DC 20001. TEL 202-638-1445. Ed. George G. Wynne. bk.rev. circ. 9,000. (reprint service avail. from UMI) **Indexed:** Sage Pub.Admin.Abstr. **Document type:** newsletter.
—BLDSC (6967.090000).
Formerly: Urban Innovation Abroad (ISSN 0163-6499); Incorporates: Urban Transportation Abroad; Which was formerly titled (1977-1985): Urban Transit Abroad (ISSN 0163-6529)
Description: Provides leaders at the state and local levels with information from throughout the world on new ideas, new concepts and new technologies that are working to improve service delivery, quality of life and cost-effectiveness for sub-national units of government.

350.086 PR
PUERTO RICO. DEPARTAMENTO DE LA VIVIENDA. SECRETARIA AUXILIAR DE PLANIFICACION Y PROGRAMACION. INFORME ANUAL. 1953. a. free. Department of Housing, Urban Renewal and Housing Corporation, 606 Barbosa Ave., Apdo. 21365, Rio Piedras, PR 00928. circ. 2,000.

352.7   UK
QUEEN'S UNIVERSITY OF BELFAST. DEPARTMENT OF ARCHITECTURE AND PLANNING. OCCASIONAL PAPER. irreg. £2 per no. Queen's University of Belfast, Department of Architecture and Planning, 2 Lennoxvale, Belfast BT9 5BY, N. Ireland. TEL 0232-245133. FAX 0232-682475.

352   AT
QUEENSLAND PLANNER. 1961. q. Aus.$35. Royal Australian Planning Institute, Queensland Division, 223 Brisbane Albert St., N. Quay, Qld. 4002, Australia. TEL 07-870-3562. Ed. Phil Day. adv.; bk.rev.; abstr.; bibl.; charts; illus.; stat.; index, cum.index. circ. 700. **Indexed:** Aus.P.A.I.S., High.Educ.Curr.Aware.Bull., Sage Pub.Admin.Abstr., Sage Urb.Stud.Abstr.
    Formerly: Planner (ISSN 0032-0676)
    Description: Publishes professional and academic articles, practice notes, institute affairs, editorial comment.

R O M MAGAZINE; vaktijdschrift voor ruimtelijke ordening en milieubeheer. see *ENVIRONMENTAL STUDIES*

352.7   US
R P C DATA FILE.* 1972. m. $0.25 per no. Regional Planning Commission of Cuyahoga County, 323 Lakeside Ave. W., No. 400, Cleveland, OH 44113-1009. TEL 216-861-6805. index. circ. 900.

363.5 347   SW   ISSN 0347-7150
RAETTSFALL FRAAN BOSTADSDOMSTOLEN. Variant title: R B D. 1971. a. SEK 280 (effective 1991). (Domstolsverket) Fritzes, S-106 47 Stockholm, Sweden. TEL 08-739-96-30. FAX 08-205021.
    Formerly (until 1975): Praxis i Hyresmaal.

RAKENNUSLEHTI. see *BUILDING AND CONSTRUCTION*

352.7   AU
RAUM; oesterreichische Zeitschrift fuer Raumplanung und Regionalpolitik. 1991. a. S.360. Oesterreichisches Institut fuer Raumplanung, Franz Josefs Kai 27, A-1011 Vienna, Austria. TEL 5338747. FAX 533874766.

352.7 614   SZ
RAUMPLANUNG UND UMWELTSCHUTZ IM KANTON ZURICH. (Text in German) 1964. irreg., no.18, 1992. 20 SFr. Amt fuer Raumplanung, Stampfenbachstr. 14, CH-8090 Zurich, Switzerland. TEL 01-2593046. bibl.; charts; illus. circ. 5,000. **Document type:** government publication.
    Formerly (until no.7, 1971): Regionalplanung in Kanton Zurich.

REAL ESTATE NEWS AND BUYERS GUIDE. see *REAL ESTATE*

352.7   CN
RECENT RESEARCH FUNDED BY C M H C. (Text in English and French) 1979. q. free. Canada Mortgage and Housing Corporation, 682 Montreal Rd., Ottawa, Ont. K1A 0P7, Canada. TEL 613-748-2367. FAX 613-748-4069.

309.26   FR
RECHERCHE URBAINE. 1973. irreg. price varies. Editions de l' Ecole des Hautes Etudes en Sciences Sociales, 131 bd. St-Michel, 75005 Paris, France. TEL 43-54-47-15. FAX 43-54-80-73. (Dist. by: Centre Interinstitutionnel pour la Diffusion de Publications en Sciences Humaines, 131 bd. St-Michel, 75005 Paris, France)

RECHERCHES REGIONALES (ALPES MARITIME ET CONTREE LIMITROPHE). see *HISTORY — History Of Europe*

352.7   EI
REGIONAL DEVELOPMENT STUDIES. (Text in English, French) irreg., no.6, 1993. (Commission of the European Communities, Directorate-General for Regional Policies) Office for Official Publications of the European Communities, 2985 Luxembourg, Luxembourg. **Document type:** monographic series.

352   US   ISSN 1066-5935
▼**REGIONAL PLAN ASSOCIATION. WORKING PAPER.*** 1992. irreg. $10 per no. to non-members. Regional Plan Association, Inc., 570 Lexington Ave., 20th Fl., New York, NY 10022-6824. TEL 212-398-1140. **Document type:** academic/scholarly publication.

330   NE   ISSN 0166-0462
HB9   CODEN: RSUEDM
REGIONAL SCIENCE & URBAN ECONOMICS. (Text in English) 1971. 6/yr. fl.734($397) (effective 1994). North-Holland (Subsidiary of: Elsevier Science B.V.), P.O. Box 211, 1000 AE Amsterdam, Netherlands. TEL 31-20-5803911. FAX 31-20-5803598. TELEX 18582 ESPA NL. (Subscr. in U.S. and Canada to: Elsevier Science Inc., Box 882, Madison Sq. Sta., New York, NY 10159. TEL 212-989-5800. FAX 212-633-3990) Eds. J.M. Quigley, K.O. Stahl. adv.; index. (also avail. in microform from UMI; back issues avail.; reprint service avail. from ISI,SWZ) **Indexed:** A.B.C.Pol.Sci., ABI Inform., Asian-Pac.Econ.Lit., BPIA, Bus.Ind., C.R.E.J., Curr.Cont., Environ.Per.Bibl., Geo.Abstr., HRIS, J.of Econ.Lit., Sage Urb.Stud.Abstr., SSCI, Tr.& Indus.Ind., World Bank.Abstr. **Document type:** academic/scholarly publication.
    —BLDSC (7336.714000); Faxon; UnCover; SWETS; UMI. **CCC.**
    Formerly: Regional and Urban Economics - Operational Methods (ISSN 0034-3331)
    Description: Publishes original research papers in spatial economics, economic geography and related disciplines.
    Refereed Serial

REGIONAL SCIENCE ASSOCIATION NEWSLETTER. see *SOCIAL SCIENCES: COMPREHENSIVE WORKS*

500   US   ISSN 0485-8255
REGIONAL SCIENCE RESEARCH INSTITUTE. DISCUSSION PAPER SERIES. 1963. irreg. $10 per no. Regional Science Research Institute, Box 329, Hightstown, NJ 08520. TEL 609-448-6966. FAX 609-448-6966. Ed. Benjamin H. Stevens. bibl. circ. 150. (back issues avail.) **Indexed:** Geo.Abstr., GeoRef. **Document type:** academic/scholarly publication.
    Description: Studies the human perception of the environment, the preservation and value of open space, the economic effects of development, related technical issues in regional economic modeling, and selected topics in location theory.

350   US
REGIONAL SCIENCE REVIEW. 1971. a. $8.50. Northeast Regional Science Association, School of Management, State University of New York at Binghamton, Binghamton, NY 13901. TEL 607-777-2475. FAX 607-777-4422. Ed. Manas Chatterji. (back issues avail.) **Document type:** academic/scholarly publication.
    Former titles: Northeast Regional Science Review; Regional Science Review.

352   UK   ISSN 0034-3404
HT390   CODEN: REGSAT
REGIONAL STUDIES. 1966. 8/yr. $116 to individuals; institutions $340 (effective 1994). (Regional Studies Association) Carfax Publishing Co., P.O. Box 25, Abingdon, Oxon. OX14 3UE, England. TEL 44-235-555335. FAX 44-235-553559. (U.S. subscr. to: Carfax Publishing Co., Box 2025, Dunnellon, FL 34430-2025) Ed P. McGregor. adv.; bk.rev.; charts. (also avail. in microform from UMI; back issues avail.; reprint service avail. from SWZ) **Indexed:** Abstr.Health Care Manage.Stud., ASSIA, Avery Ind.Archit.Per., C.R.E.J., Cont.Pg.Manage., Curr.Cont., Excerp.Med., Geo.Abstr., I D A, Int.Lab.Doc., J.of Econ.Lit., Lang.& Lang.Behav.Abstr., Mid.East: Abstr.& Ind., P.A.I.S., Popul.Ind., Sage Urb.Stud.Abstr., SSCI, World Agri.Econ.& Rural Sociol.Abstr., World Bank.Abstr. **Document type:** academic/scholarly publication.
    —BLDSC (7336.730000); Faxon; UnCover; SWETS. **CCC.**
    Description: Presents original research on such topics as industrial, retail and office location, labor markets, housing, migration, recreation, and transport.
    Refereed Serial

352   IT   ISSN 0034-3412
REGIONE E POTERE LOCALE. 1969. m. Piazza S. Ambrogio 15, Casella Postale 2, 20123 Milan, Italy. Ed. Vittorino Colombo. bk.rev.; index.

352   US   ISSN 0034-3420
REGION'S AGENDA.* 1970; N.S. 1992. irreg., no.4, 1993. $5 per no. to non-members. Regional Plan Association, Inc., 570 Lexington Ave., 20th Fl., New York, NY 10022-6824. TEL 212-398-1140. **Document type:** academic/scholarly publication.
    Description: Reports issued upon completion of projects sponsored by the association.

728 643.7   CN   ISSN 0845-5341
RENEW; Canada's magazine of residential renovation and restoration. 1987. 5/yr. Can.$16.50 (foreign Can.$26.50). Bluestone House, Inc., 12 Mill St. S., Port Hope, ON L1A 2S5, Canada. TEL 905-885-2449. FAX 905-885-5355. Ed. T. Cruickshank. adv.; bk.rev. circ. 30,000. (back issues avail.) **Document type:** consumer publication.

RENT REVIEW AND LEASE RENEWAL. see *REAL ESTATE*

RESEARCH IN URBAN ECONOMICS. see *PUBLIC ADMINISTRATION — Municipal Government*

352.7   US
RESEARCH IN URBAN POLICY. 1985. a. $63.50 to institutions. J A I Press Inc., 55 Old Post Rd., No. 2, Box 1678, Greenwich, CT 06836-1678. TEL 203-661-7602. Ed. Terry Nichols Clark.

711.59
RESTAURO. 1972. q. L.84000 to individuals; institutions L.100000; foreign L.120000 (effective 1993). Edizioni Scientifiche Italiane S.p.A., Via Chiatamone, 7, 80121 Naples, Italy. TEL 081-7645768. FAX 081-7646477. Ed. Roberto Di Stefano. adv. circ. 1,000.

352.7 362.6   US
RETIREMENT PLACES RATED. 1983. irreg., latest 1990. $16.95. Prentice Hall (Subsidiary of: Simon & Schuster), 15 Columbus Cir., New York, NY 10023. TEL 212-373-8500; 800-223-2348. **Document type:** consumer publication.
    Former titles: Rand McNally Retirement Places Rated; Rand McNally Places Rated Retirement Guide.

309.26   US   ISSN 0048-749X
HT390
REVIEW OF REGIONAL STUDIES. 1970. 3/yr. $30. Southern Regional Science Association, 505A Stokely Management Center, The University of Tennessee, Knoxville, TN 37996-0550. TEL 615-974-3303. FAX 615-974-4601. Eds. Henry W. Herzog, Alan M. Schlottmann. adv. circ. 500. (also avail. in microform) **Indexed:** J.of Econ.Lit., Popul.Ind. **Document type:** academic/scholarly publication.
    —BLDSC (7794.192000); Faxon; UnCover.

352.7   RH   ISSN 1016-2240
HT395.A356
REVIEW OF RURAL AND URBAN PLANNING IN EASTERN AND SOUTHERN AFRICA. 1989. a. Association of Rural & Urban Planners in Eastern & Southern Africa, c/o University of Zimbabwe, Dept. of Rural & Urban Planning, P.O. Box MP 167, Mt. Pleasant, Harare, Zimbabwe. **Indexed:** Documentatieblad, P.L.E.S.A. (1989-). **Document type:** academic/scholarly publication.

REVISTA DA CONSTRUCAO CIVIL. see *BUILDING AND CONSTRUCTION*

REVISTA DE ADMINISTRACAO MUNICIPAL. see *PUBLIC ADMINISTRATION — Municipal Government*

350.086   CL   ISSN 0250-7161
HT127.5
REVISTA LATINOAMERICANA DE ESTUDIOS URBANO REGIONALES. 1970. q. Esc.1000($57) to individuals; institutions $5. Pontificia Universidad Catolica de Chile, Instituto de Estudios Urbanos, Los Navegantes 1919, Casilla 16002, Correo 9, Santiago, Chile. Ed. Gladys Rubio. circ. 1,000. **Indexed:** Hisp.Amer.Per.Ind., P.A.I.S.For.Lang.Ind., Rural Devel.Abstr.
    —SWETS.
    Supersedes (1969-1970): Cuadernos de Desarrollo Urbano Regional.

352   CN   ISSN 0035-3728
REVUE MUNICIPALE. 1923. m. Can.$25. Communications Vero Inc., 1600 Henri Bourassa Blvd., W., No. 420, Montreal, PQ H3M 3E2, Canada. TEL 514-332-8376. FAX 514-332-2666. Ed. Jean-Guy Thibault. adv.: B&W page $1445, color page $2075. bk.rev.; charts; illus.; index. circ. 8,936. **Indexed:** Pt.de Rep. (1983-).
    Incorporates: Mart (ISSN 0319-2709)

HOUSING AND URBAN PLANNING

352 US
RHODE ISLAND DIVISION OF PLANNING MONTHLY PROGRESS REPORT. 1965. m. free. Division of Planning, Department of Administration, 1 Capitol Hill, 4th Fl., Providence, RI 02908-5870. TEL 401-277-1220. FAX 401-277-2083. Ed. Carol Ciotola. circ. 250. (processed) **Document type:** government publication.
 Formerly: Rhode Island Statewide Planning Program Monthly Progress Report (ISSN 0300-6468)

352.7 US
RIGHT TO HOUSING REPORT. 2/yr. $25 membership. Interfaith Assembly on Homelessness and Housing, 1047 Amsterdam Ave. at 112th St., New York, NY 10025. TEL 212-316-3171.

RIVISTA GIURIDICA DI URBANISTICA; trimestrale di giurisprudenza, dottrina e legislazione. see *PUBLIC ADMINISTRATION* — Municipal Government

350.086 UK ISSN 0307-6911
ROOF. 1976. bi-m. £21 to individuals; institutions £42. (National Campaign for the Homeless) Shelter Publications, 88 Old St., London EC1V 9HU, England. TEL 071-253-0202. FAX 071-490-8918. **Indexed:** ASSIA, Geo.Abstr. **Document type:** bulletin.
—BLDSC (8021.900000).

ROYAL TROPICAL INSTITUTE. BULLETIN. see *AGRICULTURE*

354 AT
RURAL ADJUSTMENT AND FINANCE CORPORATION OF WESTERN AUSTRALIA. ANNUAL REPORT. 1972. a. free. Rural Adjustment and Finance Corporation of Western Australia, May Holman Centre, 32 St. George's Terrace, Perth, W.A. 6000, Australia. stat.
 Former titles: Rural Adjustment of Western Australia. Annual Report; Rural Reconstruction Authority of Western Australia. Annual Report (ISSN 0310-4923)

352.7 US ISSN 0584-4266
HT393.W6
S E W R P C NEWSLETTER. Key Title: Newsletter - Southeastern Wisconsin Regional Planning Commission. 1961. bi-m. $2. Southeastern Wisconsin Regional Planning Commission, 916 N. East Ave., Box 1607, Waukesha, WI 53187-1607. TEL 414-547-6721. FAX 414-547-1103. Ed. Kurt W. Bauer. bk.rev.; charts; illus.; stat. circ. 2,460.

352.7 GW
S I N - STAEDTEBAUINSTITUT. INFORMATION. Short title: S I N Information. irreg. DM.10 per no. S I N - Staedtebauinstitut Forschungsgesellschaft mbH, Neutorgraben 1A, D-8500 Nuremberg 111, Germany. (looseleaf format)

352.7 GW
S I N - STAEDTEBAUINSTITUT. JAHRESBERICHTE. Short title: S I N Jahresberichte. a. free. S I N - Staedtebauinstitut Forschungsgesellschaft mbH, Neutorgraben 1A, 90419 Nuremberg, Germany.

711 690 GW ISSN 0078-2807
S I N - STAEDTEBAUINSTITUT. SCHRIFTENREIHE. 1965. irreg. price varies. S I N - Staedtebauinstitut Forschungsgesellschaft mbH, Neutorgraben 1A, D-8500 Nuremberg 111, Germany. Ed. Gerhard G. Dittrich.

711 690 GW ISSN 0078-2815
S I N - STAEDTEBAUINSTITUT. STUDIENHEFTE. 1965. irreg. price varies. S I N - Staedtebauinstitut Forschungsgesellschaft mbH, Neutorgraben 1A, 90419 Nuremberg, Germany. Ed. Gerhard G. Dittrich.

711 690 GW ISSN 0078-2823
S I N - STAEDTEBAUINSTITUT. WERKBERICHTE. 1968. irreg. price varies. S I N - Staedtebauinstitut Forschungsgesellschaft mbH, Neutorgraben 1A, D-8500 Nuremberg 111, Germany. Ed. Gerhard G. Dittrich.

SAFETY NETWORK. see *SOCIAL SERVICES AND WELFARE*

352.7 360 US
SANTA CRUZ ACTION NETWORK. NEWSLETTER. Abbreviated title: S C A N Newsletter. 1982. m. $15. Santa Cruz Action Network (SCAN), 108 Loucst St., No.13, Santa Cruz, CA 95060-3930. TEL 408-458-9425. Eds. John Malkin, Nancy Aebersol. adv. circ. 1,000. **Document type:** newsletter.

338.7 CN
SASKATCHEWAN MUNICIPAL GOVERNMENT. ANNUAL REPORT. 1973. a. free. Department of Municipal Government, Housing Division, 900-2500 Victoria Ave., Regina, SK S4P 3V7, Canada. TEL 306-787-4177. FAX 306-787-8571. Ed.Bd. illus.; stat. circ. 2,000. (reprint service avail.) **Document type:** government publication.
 Former titles: Saskatchewan Community Services. Annual Report; Saskatchewan Housing Corporation. Annual Report.

711 CN
SASKATCHEWAN PLANNING NEWS. 1949. s-a. Can.$20 membership. Community Planning Association, Saskatchewan Division, 2837 Dewdy Ave., Regina, SK S4T 0X8, Canada. TEL 306-569-1611. FAX 306-569-1611. Ed. Ralph K. Leibel. bk.rev.; charts; illus.; stat. circ. 250. (looseleaf format)
 Description: Examines all areas of planning: social, economic, physical.

352.7 NO ISSN 0281-5737
SCANDINAVIAN HOUSING & PLANNING RESEARCH. (Supplements avail.) (Text and summaries in English) 1984. q. NOK 725 in the Nordic countries; elsewhere NOK 750. (National Swedish Institute for Building Research) Scandinavian University Press, P.O. Box 2959 Toeyen, N-0608 Oslo, Norway. TEL 472-67-7600. FAX 472-67-7575. (U.S. addr.: Scandinavian University Press, 200 Meacham Ave., Elmont, NY 11003. TEL 516-352-7300) Ed.Bd. bk.rev. circ. 400. (back issues avail.)
—BLDSC (8087.476500); UnCover.
 Description: Presents interdisciplinary social research on housing and planning in Scandinavia and beyond.

352.7 SZ
SCHRIFTENREIHE ZUR ORTS-, REGIONAL- UND LANDESPLANUNG. 1969. irreg. price varies. Eidgenoessische Technische Hochschule, Institut fuer Orts-, Regional- und Landesplanung, Redaktion DISP - Swiss Federal Institute of Technology, Institute for Local, Regional and National Planning, CH-8093 Zurich, Switzerland. TEL 01-3772956. FAX 01-3720486. **Document type:** academic/scholarly publication.

352.7 UK ISSN 0143-8972
SCOTTISH PLANNING APPEAL DECISIONS. 1976. m. £175 to non-members; members £145. Planning Exchange, 186 Bath St., Glasgow G2 4HG, Scotland. TEL 041-332-8541. FAX 041-332-8277. **Document type:** abstracting/indexing.
 Description: Summary of all Scottish Office planning appeal decisions.

SCOTTISH PLANNING LAW & PRACTICE. see *LAW — Estate Planning*

SEARCH (YORK). see *SOCIAL SERVICES AND WELFARE*

711.59 CN
SELECT HOMES RENOVATION IDEAS. s-a. Telemedia Publishing Inc., 50 Holly St., Toronto, Ont. M4S 3B3, Canada. TEL 416-482-8260. FAX 416-482-1239. (Subscr. to: 797 Don Mills Rd., 13th Fl., Don Mills, Ont. M3C 1V2, Canada) Ed. Diane McDougall.
 Description: Presents actual case studies of renovations performed in Southern Ontario, complete with approximate costs and names of suppliers and contractors.

SHARED HOUSING QUARTERLY. see *SOCIAL SERVICES AND WELFARE*

350.865 US
SHELBY COUNTY URBAN DEVELOPMENT REPORT. 1979. a. Memphis and Shelby County Office of Planning and Development, 125 Mid America Mall N., Memphis, TN 38103-2084. FAX 901-576-6418. Ed. Jerry Sexton. circ. 500.
 Supersedes: Urban Growth Indicators and Residential Activity Permit Report.

352.7 US ISSN 0885-9612
HD7293.A1
SHELTERFORCE; a national housing publication. 1975. bi-m. $24 to individuals; institutions $30; foreign $40. National Housing Institute, 439 Main St., Orange, NJ 07050. TEL 201-678-3110. FAX 201-678-0014. E-mail: hn0344@handsnet.org. Ed. Patrick Morrissy. adv.; bk.rev.; charts; illus.; stat.; tr.lit. circ. 3,000. (also avail. in microfilm; back issues avail.; reprint service avail. from UMI) **Indexed:** Alt.Press Ind.
—BLDSC (8256.366300).
 Description: Serves a network of housing advocates and professionals with information about affordable housing strategies, industry issues, events and forecasts.

352.7 AU
SIEDLUNG UND EIGENHEIM. bi-m. Oesterreichischer Siedlerverband, Siebenbrunnenfeldgasse 1D, A-1050 Vienna, Austria. TEL 01-543736. Ed. Erwin Miggl. circ. 65,000.

350.086 SI
SINGAPORE. HOUSING AND DEVELOPMENT BOARD. ANNUAL REPORT.* (Text in English) 1960. a. S.$20. Housing and Development Board, 3451 Jalan Bukit Merah, Singapore 0315, Singapore. TEL 2739090. TELEX SINHDB-RS-22020. charts; illus.; stat.; circ. controlled. (back issues avail.)

352.7 IT ISSN 0393-5493
SISTEMI URBANI; rivista quadrimestrale di scienza della citta e del territorio. (Text in English or Italian) 1988. 3/yr. L.180000 (foreign L.290000) (effective 1992). (Italian National Research Council) Guida Editori S.p.A., Via D. Morelli 16-B, 80121 Naples, Italy. TEL 081-7644278. FAX 081-7644414. Ed. C.S. Bertuglia.
 Description: Deals with all aspects of urban planning and living, ranging from architecture to urban geography, economics and statistics.

352.7 US ISSN 0196-1683
HT101
SMALL TOWN. 1969. bi-m. $35 to individuals; institutions $40; foreign $45. Small Towns Institute, Box 517, Ellensburg, WA 98926. TEL 509-925-1830. FAX 509-963-1753. Ed.Bd. bk.rev.; illus. circ. 1,800. **Indexed:** Sage Pub.Admin.Abstr.
—Faxon; UnCover.

352.7 UK ISSN 1351-4288
SOCIAL HOUSING; the journal of new initiatives in housing finance. 1988. m. £120. Financial Information Co. Ltd., Finsbury Business Centre, 122 Hemmingford Rd., London N1 1DE, England. TEL 071-700-4199. FAX 071-607-5092. Ed. Tim Roberts. adv.; bk.rev. **Document type:** newsletter.

352.7 AG
SOCIEDAD INTERAMERICANA DE PLANIFICACION. EDICIONES S I A P. 1974. irreg. (Sociedad Interamericana de Planificacion) Ediciones S.I.A.P., Chenaut 1968, 1426 Buenos Aires, Argentina. (Dist. by: Ediciones Nueva Vision, Viamonte 494, Buenos Aires, Argentina) Dir. Martha S. de Kaplan. circ. 3,000.

SOCIETY FOR THE STUDY OF ARCHITECTURE IN CANADA. BULLETIN/SOCIETE POUR L'ETUDE DE L'ARCHITECTURE AU CANADA. BULLETIN. see *ARCHITECTURE*

352.7 323.4 US
SOUTHERN COMMUNITIES. 1977. bi-m. $15. Southern Neighborhoods Network, Box 121133, Nashville, TN 37212-1133. TEL 615-292-1798. Ed. Verna M. Fausey. bk.rev. circ. 475. (back issues avail.) **Document type:** newsletter.
 Formerly: Southern Neighborhoods (ISSN 0735-8644)

HOUSING AND URBAN PLANNING

711 332.6   US
SOUTHERN ILLINOIS UNIVERSITY, EDWARDSVILLE. REGIONAL RESEARCH AND DEVELOPMENT SERVICES. REPORT: PRIVATE SECTOR INVESTMENTS. 1969. irreg., no.10, 1979. Southern Illinois University, Edwardsville, Regional Research and Development Services, Campus Box 1456, Edwardsville, IL 62026-1456. TEL 618-692-3500. FAX 618-692-2886. circ. 100 (controlled). **Document type:** monographic series.
    Former titles: Southern Illinois University, Edwardsville. Regional Research and Development Services. Report; (until 1985): Southern Illinois University, Edwardsville. Center for Urban and Environmental Research and Services. C U E R S Report (ISSN 0073-4993)

350   AT   ISSN 0310-0189
SPACE. 1973. q. Aus.$20. Town and Country Planning Association of Victoria, FIT Urban Studies Unit, 2nd Fl., Ross House, 247 Flinders Lane, Melbourne, Vic. 3000. TEL 03-650-7142. Ed. W.S. Logan. bk.rev. circ. 500.
    Formerly: Plan News Review.

352.7   SP   ISSN 0490-3323
SPAIN. MINISTERIO DE LA VIVIENDA. BOLETIN OFICIAL. m. 500 ptas. Ministerio de la Vivienda, Servicio Central de Publicaciones, Plaza de San Juan de la Cruz 1, Madrid 3, Spain. charts; stat. **Document type:** government publication.

352 711   GW
DIE STADT. 1972. irreg. price varies. S I N - Staedtebauinstitut Forschungsgesellschaft mbH, Neutorgraben 1A, 90419 Nuremberg, Germany. Ed. Gerhard G. Dittrich. adv. **Indexed:** Avery Ind.Archit.Per.

690.87   US
STATE COMMERCIAL CODES. irreg., latest 1991. $37.50. National Conference of States on Building Codes and Standards, Inc., 505 Huntmar Pk. Dr., Ste. 210, Herndon, VA 22070. TEL 703-437-0100. FAX 703-487-3596. **Document type:** directory.
    Description: Building, mechanical, plumbing, electrical, accessibility, energy, fire and life safety codes applicable in commercial buildings in all 50 states, Washington DC, Puerto Rico and the US Virgin Islands, with notes on anticipated changes and unique conditions.

690.87   US
STATE RESIDENTIAL CODES. (Section of: Directory of Building Codes & Regulations) irreg., latest 1991. $20. National Conference of States on Building Codes and Standards, Inc., 505 Huntmar Pk. Dr., Ste. 210, Herndon, VA 22070. TEL 703-437-0100. FAX 703-481-3596. **Document type:** directory.
    Description: Complete information on residential codes for all 50 states, Washington DC, Puerto Rico and the U.S. Virgin Islands, with names and addresses of code officials, name and edition of the code adopted, with notes on amendments.

352 301   NE   ISSN 0039-0879
STEDEBOUW EN VOLKSHUISVESTING. Short title: S en V. 1920. 6/yr. fl.143. (Nederlands Instituut voor Ruimtelijke Ordening en Volkshuisvesting) Delwel Uitgeverij B.V., Postbus 19110, 2500 CC The Hague, Netherlands. TEL 31-70-3624800. FAX 31-70-3605606. Ed.Bd. adv.; bk.rev.; illus.; maps; index. circ. 3,428. **Indexed:** Avery Ind.Archit.Per., Excerp.Med., Key to Econ.Sci. —SWETS.
    Description: Publishes analytical reviews of issues in urban planning, administration and related concerns.

352.7   IT
STORIA DELLA CITTA; rivista internazionale di storia urbana e territoriale. (Text in English, French, German, Italian) q. L.85000($50) Elemond Periodici s.r.l., Via Trentacoste 7, 20134 Milan, Italy. Ed. Enrico Guidoni. **Indexed:** Avery Ind.Archit.Per., Bibl.Cart., RILA.

352.7   IT
STORIA URBANA; rivista di studi sulle trasformazioni delle citta e del territorio in eta moderna. 1977. 4/yr. L.98000 (foreign L.130000) (effective 1993). Franco Angeli Editore, Viale Monza 106, 20127 Milan, Italy. TEL 02-28-27-651. Ed.Bd.

352.7   US
STREETSCAPE EQUIPMENT SOURCEBOOK. irreg. Center for Design Planning, 1208 N. McKinley St., Albany, GA 31701. TEL 912-888-1606.
    Description: Lists street signs and traffic control lights, as selected by a panel of professionals in urban design.

350.86   GW
STRUCTUR; Zeitschrift fuer Planung, Entwicklung und Umwelt. 1967. m. DM.92. Structur-Verlag, Haidaer Str. 1, 53359 Rheinbach, Germany. Ed.Bd. bk.rev.; abstr.; bibl.; charts; illus.
    Formerly: Raum und Siedlung (ISSN 0048-6825)

STUDIA I MATERIALY DO TEORII I HISTORII ARCHITEKTURY I URBANISTYKI. see *ARCHITECTURE*

352.7   GW
SUEDDEUTSCHE HAUS- UND WOHNWIRTSCHAFT. 1949. m. DM.30. Jedermann Verlag, Hans-Boeckler-Str. 4, 69115 Heidelberg, Germany. TEL 06221-28145. FAX 06221-27870. Ed. Paul Well. adv. circ. 40,000.

SWEDEN. STATENS RAAD FOER BYGGNADSFORSKNING. DOCUMENT. see *BUILDING AND CONSTRUCTION*

SWEDEN. STATENS RAAD FOER BYGGNADSFORSKNING. RAPPORT. see *BUILDING AND CONSTRUCTION*

350.865   UK   ISSN 0261-197X
T P A S NOTES. 1980. irreg. price varies. Tenant Participation Advisory Service, 20 St. Andrews St., Glasgow G1 5PD, Scotland. Eds. Robina Goodlad, Roger Popplewell. circ. 1,000. (back issues avail.)

TAIPEI PICTORIAL/TAIPEI HUA K'AN. see *GENERAL INTEREST PERIODICALS — Taiwan*

350.086   TZ
TANZANIA. CAPITAL DEVELOPMENT AUTHORITY. REPORT AND ACCOUNTS. 1974. a. EAs.100. Capital Development Authority, P.O. Box 913, Dodoma, Tanzania. TELEX 53177 CDA TZ. illus. circ. 110.

354   TZ
TANZANIA. MINISTRY OF LANDS, HOUSING AND URBAN DEVELOPMENT. URBAN PLANNING DIVISION. ANNUAL REPORT. 1974. a. Ministry of Lands, Housing and Urban Development, Urban Planning Division, P.O. Box 20671, Dar es Salaam, Tanzania. Ed. I.J. Mitiro.

TECHNICAL UNIVERSITY OF DENMARK. INSTITUTE OF ROADS, TRANSPORT AND TOWN PLANNING. REPORT. see *TRANSPORTATION — Roads And Traffic*

352.7   SP
TECNOLOGIA Y ARQUITECTURA. 4/yr. Joaquim Ma. Lopez 23, 4o D, 28015 Madrid, Spain. TEL 1-543-61-48. FAX 1-544-75-70. Ed. Javier Mozas.

711   HU   ISSN 0040-2680
TELEPULESTUDOMANYI KOZLEMENYEK. (Text in Hungarian; summaries in English, German, Russian) 1952. a. free. (Budapesti Muszaki Egyetem, Varosepitesi Tanszek) Magyar Urbanisztikai Tarsasag, Rakoczi Ut 7, 1088 Budapest, Hungary. (Co-sponsor: Varosepitesi Tudomanyos es Terverzo Interet) Ed. Dr. Kalman Farago. bk.rev.; bibl.; charts; illus. circ. 1,030.
    Description: Budapest-based legal journal.

352   US   ISSN 0040-3083
TENANT/INQUILINO. (Text in English and Spanish) 1971. m. (11/yr.) $2.50 to individuals; institutions $5. Met Council, Inc., 102 Fulton St., Ste. 302, New York, NY 10038-2525. TEL 212-693-0550. FAX 212-693-0555. Ed. Judy Pasternak. adv.; bk.rev.; charts; illus. circ. 3,500. **Document type:** newspaper.

352.7   CN
TENANT TIMES. 6/yr. $4. Cleveland Tenants Organization, Artcraft Bldg., 2nd Fl., 2530 Superior Ave., Cleveland, OH 44114.

TENANTS' BULLETIN. see *REAL ESTATE*

TERRITOIRES; la revue des acteurs locaux. see *PUBLIC ADMINISTRATION — Municipal Government*

TEXAS MUNICIPAL ZONING LAW. see *LAW*

352.7 690   US   ISSN 1061-5121
TIMES (BETHLEHEM). 1969. irreg. (3-4/yr.). $60. Council on Tall Buildings and Urban Habitat, Lehigh University, 13 E. Packer Ave., Bethlehem, PA 18015. TEL 215-758-3515. FAX 215-758-4522. Ed. Lynn S. Beedle. illus.; stat. circ. 1,500. (back issues avail.)
    Description: News, research reviews, and items of interest on the architecture of tall buildings and their surrounding urban habitat.

352.7   JA
TOSHI KENKYU HOKOKU/REPORT ON URBAN RESEARCH. (Text in Japanese) 1969. irreg. free. Tokyo Metropolitan University, Center for Urban Studies, 1-1 Minami Ohsawa, Hachioji, Tokyo 192-03, Japan. TEL 0426-77-2351. FAX 0426-77-2352. Dir. Yorifusa Isida. illus. **Document type:** academic/scholarly publication.

352   UK   ISSN 0040-9960
NA9000
TOWN AND COUNTRY PLANNING. 1904. m. £51 (foreign £63). Town and Country Planning Association, 17 Carlton House Terrace, London SW1Y 5AS, England. Ed. Nick Matthews. adv.; bk.rev.; bibl.; charts; stat.; index. circ. 4,000. (also avail. in microform from UMI; reprint service avail. from UMI) **Indexed:** Art Ind., ASSIA, Br.Hum.Ind., Br.Tech.Ind., Excerp.Med., Geo.Abstr., P.A.I.S., RICS, Rural Recreat.Tour.Abstr., Soc.Sci.Ind., World Agri.Econ.& Rural Sociol.Abstr. **Document type:** bulletin.
    —BLDSC (8872.000000); Faxon; UnCover; SWETS; UMI.

309.2   UK   ISSN 0308-082X
HT169.G7
TOWN AND COUNTRY PLANNING ASSOCIATION. ANNUAL REPORT. 1899. a. £3. Town and Country Planning Association, 17 Carlton House Terrace, London SW1Y 5AS, England. Ed. Nick Matthews. **Document type:** bulletin.

352.7   UK   ISSN 0495-9728
TOWN & COUNTRY PLANNING ASSOCIATION. PLANNING BULLETIN. 1947. w. (48/yr.). £50 (foreign £62). Town & Country Planning Association, 17 Carlton House Terrace, London SW1Y 5AS, England. Ed. Helen Dwyer. adv.; cum.index. circ. 500. **Document type:** bulletin.

711   UK   ISSN 0078-2114
TOWN AND COUNTRY PLANNING SUMMER SCHOOL: REPORT OF PROCEEDINGS. Issued with: Planner (ISSN 0309-1384) 1936. a. Royal Town Planning Institute, 26 Portland Place, London W1N 4BE, England. TEL 071-636-9107. FAX 071-323-1582. Ed. Anthony Fyson. circ. 15,606. **Document type:** proceedings.

TOWN CRIER. see *PUBLIC ADMINISTRATION — Municipal Government*

TOWN PLANNING AND LOCAL GOVERNMENT GUIDE. see *PUBLIC ADMINISTRATION — Municipal Government*

352   UK   ISSN 0041-0020
NA9000
TOWN PLANNING REVIEW. 1910. q. £30($60) to individuals; institutions £80($160). (University of Liverpool, Department of Civic Design) Liverpool University Press, P.O. Box 147, Liverpool L69 3BX, England. TEL 051-794-2235. FAX 051-708-6502. TELEX 627095-UNIPL-G. Ed. David Massey. adv.; bk.rev.; bibl.; illus.; index. circ. 1,500. (back issues avail.; reprint service avail. from KTO) **Indexed:** Art Ind., ASCA, ASSIA, Avery Ind.Archit.Per., Br.Archaeol.Abstr., Br.Hum.Ind., Br.Tech.Ind., Cont.Pg.Manage., Curr.Cont., Environ.Abstr., Environ.Per.Bibl. (1977-), Excerp.Med., Geo.Abstr., Intl.Civil Eng.Abstr., Mid.East: Abstr.& Ind., P.A.I.S., Risk Abstr., Rural Recreat.Tour.Abstr., Sage Fam.Stud.Abstr., Sage Pub.Admin.Abstr., Soft.Abstr.Eng., SSCI, World Agri.Econ.& Rural Sociol.Abstr. **Document type:** academic/scholarly publication.
    —BLDSC (8873.000000); CIS; Faxon; UnCover; SWETS. CCC.
    Description: Covers city and regional planning and associated disciplines.

TRADITIONAL DWELLINGS AND SETTLEMENTS REVIEW. see *ARCHITECTURE*

HOUSING AND URBAN PLANNING

352.7 US ISSN 0300-6026
HD7293.A1
TRENDS IN HOUSING.* 1956. bi-m. $18. National Committee Against Discrimination in Housing, Inc., 331 5th St., S.E., Washington, DC 20003. Ed. Natalie P. Shear. bk.rev. circ. 16,000.

352.7 GW ISSN 0724-6234
TRIALOG; Zeitschrift fuer das Planen und Bauen in der Dritten Welt. (Text in English and German) 1983. q. DM.60. Vereinigung zur Wissenschaftlichen Erforschung des Planens und Bauens in Entwicklungslaendern e.V., Postfach 6380, 76043 Karlsruhe, Germany. (Distr. by: Magazin Verlag, Schweffelstr. 6, 24118 Kiel, Germany. TEL 0431-565899) Ed. Kosta Mathey. adv.; bk.rev.; abstr.; charts; illus. circ. 1,000. (back issues avail.) **Indexed:** Abstr.Rural Dev.Trop. **Document type:** academic/scholarly publication, trade publication. —BLDSC (9050.080000).
Description: Academic and professional discussion of planning issues in developing countries.

TVAI; periodical for architecture, town planning, industrial design & the plastic arts. see *ARCHITECTURE*

309.2 350.86 UN ISSN 1014-8108
HD7285
U N C H S (HABITAT) SHELTER BULLETIN. (Text and summaries in English, French) 1988. 3/yr. free. United Nations Centre for Human Settlements (Habitat), Box 30030, Nairobi, Kenya. TEL 254-2-621234. FAX 254-2-624266. TELEX 22996 UNHAB KE. Ed. Ellen Kitonga. circ. 10,500. **Document type:** bulletin.
Formerly (until 1989): U N C H S Shelter Bulletin (ISSN 1012-7828)
Description: Provides highlights of news and developments pertaining to various aspects of shelter and related infrastructure and services for the homeless, the poor, and the disadvantaged.

309.2 350.86 UN ISSN 0255-271X
U N C H S HABITAT NEWS. (Text in Arabic, English, French and Spanish) 1979. 3/yr. free. United Nations Centre for Human Settlements (Habitat), P.O. Box 30030, Nairobi, Kenya. TEL 254-2-621234. FAX 254-2-226473. TELEX 22996 UNHABIT. Ed. Ellen Kitonga. bk.rev. circ. 10,500. (processed) **Indexed:** Avery Ind.Archit.Per., Mid.East: Abstr.& Ind., Risk Abstr. **Document type:** newsletter.
Former titles: Habitat News (ISSN 0251-7205); Human Settlements (ISSN 0046-8231)
Description: Provides information on human settlement related activities of the Centre, as well as a calendar of events, publications and courses.

350.086 US ISSN 0890-8648
U S A. 1970. 6/yr. $10. Association of Community Organizations for Reform Now, 1024 Elysian Fields, New Orleans, LA 70117. TEL 504-943-0044. Ed. Bill Klinke. adv.; bk.rev.; charts; illus. circ. 60,000. (tabloid format; back issues avail.)

350.865 US ISSN 0565-2820
U.S. DEPARTMENT OF HOUSING AND URBAN DEVELOPMENT. ANNUAL REPORT. 1965. a. U.S. Department of Housing and Urban Development, Washington, DC 20410. TEL 202-655-4000. **Document type:** government publication.

352.7 US
U.S. DEPARTMENT OF HOUSING AND URBAN DEVELOPMENT. CHARACTERISTICS OF F H A SINGLE-FAMILY MORTGAGES: SELECTED SECTIONS OF NATIONAL HOUSING ACT. a. U.S. Department of Housing and Urban Development, Federal Housing Administration, 451 Seventh St., S.W., Washington, DC 20410. (Subscr. to: Superintendent of Documents, U.S. Government Printing Office, Box 371954, Pittsburgh, PA 15250-7954. TEL 202-783-3238. FAX 202-512-2233) stat. **Document type:** government publication.
Description: Compiles statistics for Federal Housing Administration mortgages.

352.7 US ISSN 0275-1267
HD7293.A49
U.S. DEPARTMENT OF HOUSING AND URBAN DEVELOPMENT. F H A HOMES; data for states on characteristics of FHA operations under Section 203. Key Title: F.H.A. Homes. (Supplement avail.) 1956. irreg. U.S. Department of Housing and Urban Development, Federal Housing Administration, Information Systems Division, 451 Seventh St., S.W., Washington, DC 20410-8000. TEL 202-755-5995. (Avail. from: Superintendent of Documents, U.S. Government Printing Office, Box 371954, Pittsburgh, PA 15250-7954. TEL 202-783-3238. FAX 202-512-2233) stat. circ. 1,500. **Document type:** government publication.

352.7 368 US ISSN 0743-4464
HG2040.5.U5
U.S. DEPARTMENT OF HOUSING AND URBAN DEVELOPMENT. F H A HOME MORTGAGE INSURANCE OPERATIONS: STATE, COUNTY AND M S A - P M S A. Key Title: F.H.A. Home Mortgage Insurance Operations. 1974. a. U.S. Department of Housing and Urban Development, Federal Housing Administration, Information Systems Division, 451 Seventh St., S.W., Washington, DC 20410-8000. TEL 202-755-5995. (Subscr. to: Superintendent of Documents, U.S. Government Printing Office, Box 371954, Pittsburgh, PA 15250-7954. TEL 202-783-3238. FAX 202-512-2233) stat. **Document type:** government publication.

352.7 US
U.S. DEPARTMENT OF HOUSING AND URBAN DEVELOPMENT. F H A HOMES (SUPPLEMENT). Key Title: F.H.A. Homes (Supplement). a. U.S. Department of Housing and Urban Development, Federal Housing Administration, Information Systems Division, 451 Seventh St., S.W., Washington, DC 20410-8000. TEL 202-755-5995. (Subscr. to: Superintendent of Documents, U.S. Government Printing Office, Box 371954, Pittsburgh, PA 15250. TEL 202-783-3238. FAX 202-512-2233) charts; stat. **Document type:** government publication.
Description: Compiles home mortgage statistics by state.

352.7 368 US ISSN 0145-5656
U.S. DEPARTMENT OF HOUSING AND URBAN DEVELOPMENT. F H A MONTHLY REPORT OF OPERATIONS. PROJECT INSURANCE PROGRAMS. Key Title: F.H.A. Monthly Report of Operations. Project Insurance Programs. 1975. a. U.S. Department of Housing and Urban Development, Federal Housing Administration, Housing Production and Mortgage Credit, Management Information Systems Division, Multifamily Activities Branch, 451 Seventh St., S.W., Washington, DC 20410-8000. (Subscr. to: Superintendent of Documents, U.S. Government Printing Office, Box 371954, Pittsburgh, PA 15250-7954. TEL 202-783-3238. FAX 202-512-2233) **Document type:** government publication.

352.7 368 US
U.S. DEPARTMENT OF HOUSING AND URBAN DEVELOPMENT. F H A REPORT OF INSURANCE OPERATIONS UNDER HOME MORTGAGE PROGRAMS FOR (MONTH). Variant title: F.H.A. Report of Insurance Operations Under Home Mortgage Programs for (Month). m. U.S. Department of Housing and Urban Development, Federal Housing Administration, F H A Comptroller, Office of Evaluation, Information Systems Division, 451 Seventh St., S.W., Washington, DC 20410-8000. TEL 202-755-5995. (Subscr. to: Superintendent of Documents, U.S. Government Printing Office, Box 371954, Pittsburgh, PA 15250-7954. TEL 202-783-3238. FAX 202-512-2233) charts; stat. **Document type:** government publication.
Description: Provides statistics on F.H.A.-insured mortgages for each month.

352.7 US ISSN 0364-2666
U.S. DEPARTMENT OF HOUSING AND URBAN DEVELOPMENT. F H A TRENDS OF HOME MORTGAGE CHARACTERISTICS. Key Title: F.H.A. Trends of Home Mortgage Characteristics. a. U.S. Department of Housing and Urban Development, Federal Housing Administration, F H A Comptroller, Information Systems Division, 451 Seventh St., S.W., Washington, DC 20410-8000. TEL 202-755-5995. (Subscr. to: Superintendent of Documents, U.S. Government Printing Office, Box 371954, Pittsburgh, PA 15250-7954. TEL 202-783-3238. FAX 202-512-2233) charts; stat. **Document type:** government publication.
Description: Reports on F.H.A.-insured mortgages for the year, by states and by MSA-PMSAs.

352.7 340 US
UNITS. 1977. 9/yr. $18 to non-members; members $15. National Apartment Association, 1111 Fourteenth St., N.W., Ste. 900, Washington, DC 20005. TEL 202-842-4050. FAX 202-842-4056. Ed. Stephanie Oetjen. adv.; circ. 32,000 (controlled). **Document type:** trade publication.
Description: Covers multifamily housing ownership and management.

309 711.4 UK ISSN 0067-8953
UNIVERSITY OF BIRMINGHAM. CENTRE FOR URBAN AND REGIONAL STUDIES. OCCASIONAL PAPERS. 1968; N.S. 1981. irreg., no.4, 1982. University of Birmingham, Centre for Urban and Regional Studies, J.G. Smith Bldg., P.O. Box 363, Birmingham B15 2TT, England. TEL 021-414-5011. FAX 021-414-4989. TELEX 333762 UOBHAM.
Description: Discusses rental housing, policies and problems.

309 711.4 UK ISSN 0306-4034
UNIVERSITY OF BIRMINGHAM. CENTRE FOR URBAN AND REGIONAL STUDIES. RESEARCH MEMORANDUM. irreg., no.87, 1981. price varies. University of Birmingham, Centre for Urban and Regional Studies, J.G. Smith Bldg., Box 363, Birmingham B15 2TT, England. **Indexed:** Geo.Abstr.

309 711.4 UK ISSN 0067-8961
UNIVERSITY OF BIRMINGHAM. CENTRE FOR URBAN AND REGIONAL STUDIES. URBAN AND REGIONAL STUDIES. 1971. irreg., no.11, 1984. University of Birmingham, Centre for Urban and Regional Studies, J.G. Smith Bldg., Box 363, Birmingham B15 2TT. (U.S. addr.: Allen & Unwin Inc., 8 Winchester Place, Winchester, MA 01890) **Indexed:** Geo.Abstr.

309 711.4 UK
UNIVERSITY OF BIRMINGHAM. CENTRE FOR URBAN AND REGIONAL STUDIES. WORKING PAPER. irreg. price varies. University of Birmingham, Centre for Urban and Regional Studies, J.G. Smith Bldg., Box 363, Birmingham B15 2TT, England. **Indexed:** Rural Recreat.Tour.Abstr., World Agri.Econ. & Rural Sociol.Abstr.

352.7 UK
UNIVERSITY OF MANCHESTER. DEPARTMENT OF PLANNING AND LANDSCAPE. OCCASIONAL PAPERS. irreg., vol.36, 1993. University of Manchester, Department of Planning and Landscape, Oxford Rd., Manchester M13 9PL, England. TEL 061-275-6904. FAX 061-275-6893. Ed. Gwyn Williams.

352.7
UNIVERSITY OF PENNSYLVANIA. DEPARTMENT OF CITY AND REGIONAL PLANNING. RESEARCH REPORTS SERIES. 1983. irreg. (approx. 6/yr.). price varies. University of Pennsylvania, Department of City and Regional Planning, Philadelphia, PA 19104. TEL 215-898-5731. Ed. Robert E. Coughlin. circ. 250.

UNIVERSITY OF WATERLOO. SCHOOL OF URBAN AND REGIONAL PLANNING. WORKING PAPERS SERIES. see *ENVIRONMENTAL STUDIES*

711.4 301.3 US ISSN 0083-4688
HT108
URBAN AFFAIRS ANNUAL REVIEWS. 1967. irreg., vol.41, Sep. 1993. $22.50 (hardcover ed. $48) (effective 1994). Sage Publications, Inc., 2455 Teller Rd., Thousand Oaks, CA 91320. TEL 805-499-0721. FAX 805-499-0871. (And: Sage Publications, Ltd., 6 Bonhill St., London EC2A 4PU, England) (back issues avail.) **Document type:** monographic series.
—BLDSC (9123.160000).

HOUSING AND URBAN PLANNING

352.7 301   US
URBAN AFFAIRS ASSOCIATION. NEWSLETTER. 1971. 5/yr. $45 membership (includes Journal of Urban Affairs). Urban Affairs Association, University of Delaware, Newark, DE 19716. Ed. Mary Helen Callahan. **Document type:** academic/scholarly publication, newsletter.
   Formerly (until 1991): Urban Affairs Association Communication.
   Refereed Serial

352.7 300   US
URBAN AFFAIRS JOURNAL. 1971. q. $45 membership (includes Newsletter). Urban Affairs Association, University of Delaware, Newark, DE 19716. Ed. Mary Helen Callahan. **Document type:** academic/scholarly publication.
   Refereed Serial

711 323   US   ISSN 0042-0816
HT101
URBAN AFFAIRS QUARTERLY. 1965. q. $50 to individuals; institutions $150 (effective 1994). Sage Publications, Inc., 2455 Teller Rd., Thousand Oaks, CA 91320. TEL 805-499-0721. FAX 805-499-0871. (Subscr. to: Sage Publications, Inc., Box 5084, Thousand Oaks, CA 91359; Overseas subscr. to: Sage Publications, Ltd., 6 Bonhill St., London EC2A 4PU, England; Sage Publications India Pvt. Ltd., P.O. Box 4215, New Delhi 110 048, India) Eds. Dennis R. Judd, Donald Phares. adv.; bk.rev.; charts; index. circ. 1,900. (also avail. in microfilm from UMI; back issues avail.) **Indexed:** A.B.C.Pol.Sci., Abstr.Soc.Work, Amer.Hist.& Life, ASSIA, Avery Ind.Archit.Per., C.I.J.E., Chic.Per.Ind., Curr.Cont., Educ.Admin.Abstr., Environ.Abstr., Excerp.Med., Geo.Abstr., Hist.Abstr., Int.Polit.Sci.Abstr., Lang.& Lang.Behav.Abstr., Mag.Ind., Mid.East: Abstr.& Ind., P.A.I.S., Risk Abstr., Sage Pub.Admin.Abstr., Sage Urb.Stud.Abstr., Soc.Sci.Ind., Soc.Work Res.& Abstr., Sociol.Abstr., SSCI, Stud.Wom.Abstr., Urb.Aff.Abstr. **Document type:** academic/scholarly publication.
  —BLDSC (9123.180000); Faxon; UnCover; SWETS; UMI. **CCC.**
   Description: Emphasizes state-of-the-art research and scholarly analysis of urban studies; covers political, social, economic, and historic topics.

URBAN AND SOCIAL CHANGE REVIEW. see *SOCIAL SERVICES AND WELFARE*

352.7 720   US   ISSN 0898-5049
URBAN DESIGN AND PRESERVATION QUARTERLY.* 1978. q. $20. American Planning Association, Urban Design and Preservation, 1776 Massachusetts Ave. N.W., Washington, DC 20036. Ed. Hamid Shirvani. bk.rev.; illus. circ. 1,350. **Document type:** academic/scholarly publication.
  —UnCover.
   Formerly (until 1987): U D Review.
   Description: Contains scholarly articles and project reports on urban planning.
   Refereed Serial

URBAN DESIGN UPDATE. see *ARCHITECTURE*

352.7   UK
URBAN DEVELOPMENT INFORMATION SERVICE. 6/yr. £175 to non-members; members £110. Planning Exchange, 186 Bath St., Glasgow G2 4HG, Scotland. TEL 041-332-8541. FAX 041-332-8277.

352.7   SA   ISSN 1015-3802
URBAN FORUM; a journal of housing, infrastructure and planning. 1990. s-a. $50. Witwatersrand University Press, Wits 2050, South Africa. TEL 011-339-3559. TELEX 4-27125 SA. Eds. Robert McCutcheon, Richard Tomlinson. **Document type:** academic/scholarly publication.
   Description: Scholarly articles and topical commentary on urban and rural development planning, architecture and engineering.

333.77   US   ISSN 0272-3638
GF125
URBAN GEOGRAPHY. 1980. 8/yr. $275 (foreign $314). V.H. Winston & Son, Inc., c/o Bellwether Publishing. Ltd., 8640 Guidford Rd., Columbia, MD 21046. TEL 410-290-3870. FAX 410-290-8726. Eds. Jim Wheeler, Robert Lake. bk.rev.; abstr.; charts; illus.; stat.; index. **Indexed:** Asian-Pac.Econ.Lit., ASSIA, E.I., Geo.Abstr., Sage Urb.Stud.Abstr., Stud.Wom.Abstr., World Agri.Econ.& Rural Sociol.Abstr. **Document type:** academic/scholarly publication.
  —BLDSC (9123.378000); Faxon; UnCover; SWETS. **CCC.**

711   II   ISSN 0970-9045
URBAN INDIA. 1981. s-a. Rs.100($15) National Institute of Urban Affairs, 11 Nyaya Marg, Chanakyapuri, New Delhi 110021, India. TEL 91-11-3014580. FAX 91-11-3792961. Ed. Gangadhar Jha. adv.; bk.rev. circ. 500. (back issues avail.)
   Description: Covers urbanization, urban development, urban infrastructure management, financing and other related aspects.

352.7   UK
▼**URBAN INNOVATION.** 1992. irreg. Sage Publications Ltd., 6 Bonhill St., London EC2A 4PU, England. TEL 071-374-0645. FAX 071-374-8741.

711   AT
URBAN ISSUES.* 1970. irreg. Aus.$5 to libraries. Australian Institute of Urban Studies, Queensland Division, c/o Austalian Sociological Association, La Trobe University, Bundoora, Vic. 3083, Australia. Ed. J.H.A. Dick. **Indexed:** Aus.P.A.I.S.

301 352   US   ISSN 0042-0891
NA9000
URBAN LAND. 1941. m. membership only. Urban Land Institute, 625 Indiana Ave., N.W., Ste. 400, Washington, DC 20004-2930. TEL 202-624-7000. FAX 202-624-7140. Ed. Libby Howland. adv.; B&W page $3095; adv. contact: John McKenzie. bk.rev.; charts; illus.; stat.; index. circ. 13,500. (also avail. in microform from UMI; back issues avail.; reprint service avail. from UMI) **Indexed:** Avery Ind.Archit.Per., Br.Tech.Ind., Environ.Abstr., Environ.Ind., HRIS, Mid.East: Abstr.& Ind., P.A.I.S. **Document type:** trade publication.
  —BLDSC (9123.688000); Faxon; UnCover; UMI.

352.7 333.33   US
URBAN LAND INSTITUTE PROJECT REFERENCE FILE. 1971. 20/yr. $85 to non-members; members $70. Urban Land Institute, 625 Indiana Ave., N.W., Ste. 400, Washington, DC 20004-2930. TEL 202-624-7000. FAX 202-624-7140. Ed. Scott Middleton. illus.; stat. (reprint service avail. from UMI) **Document type:** monographic series.

301   US   ISSN 0732-8265
NA9000
URBAN OUTLOOK. 1977. s-m. $157. Government Information Services, 4301 Fairfax Dr., Ste. 875, Arlington, VA 22203-1627. TEL 703-528-1000. FAX 703-528-6060. Ed. Laurence A. Alexander. **Document type:** newsletter.
  Incorporates: Urban Futures Idea Exchange (ISSN 0147-7137)
   Description: For professionals concerned with meeting the unique challenges of today's urban areas. Focuses on planning and land use, energy and environment, urban technology, infrastructure, health, economic development, demographics and lifestyles, taxes and finance, education, housing, grants and funding, crime and security.

352.7   KE   ISSN 1052-729X
URBAN PERSPECTIVES. 1985. q. free. U.S. Agency for International Development, Regional Housing and Urban Development Office for East and Southern Africa, P.O. Box 30261, Nairobi, Kenya. FAX 2-337304. TELEX 22964-AMEMB-KE. Ed. Richard Martin. bk.rev. circ. 800.
   Formerly (until 1990): Housing and Urban Development Digest.

352.7   AT   ISSN 0811-1146
URBAN POLICY & RESEARCH; an Australian guide to urban affairs. 1982. q. Aus.$45. Urban Policy and Research, P.O. Box 2620W, Melbourne, Vic. 3001, Australia. TEL 03-660-2226. bk.rev. circ. 300.
  —BLDSC (9123.688800).
   Description: Brings together a wide variety of viewpoints on urban issues and promotes active dialogue between researchers, policy makers and practitioners, particularly at the state and local levels.
   Refereed Serial

301   UK   ISSN 0042-0980
HT103
URBAN STUDIES. 1964. 10/yr. $98 to individuals; institutions $318 (effective 1994). Carfax Publishing Co., P.O. Box 25, Abingdon, Oxon. OX14 3UE, England. TEL 44-235-555335. FAX 44-235-553559. (U.S. subscr. to: Carfax Publishing Co., Box 2025, Dunnellon, FL 32630) Ed.Bd. adv.; bk.rev.; abstr.; bibl.; charts; illus.; stat.; index, cum.index. (also avail. in microfiche; back issues avail.; reprint service avail. from KTO) **Indexed:** Amer.Hist.& Life, ASSIA, Avery Ind.Archit.Per., Br.Hum.Ind., Br.Tech.Ind., C.R.E.J., Curr.Cont., E.I., Energy Ind., Energy Info.Abstr. (until 1994), Excerp.Med., Geo.Abstr., Hist.Abstr., HRIS, I D A, J.of Econ.Lit., Lang.& Lang.Behav.Abstr., Mid.East: Abstr.& Ind., P.A.I.S., RICS, Sage Fam.Stud.Abstr., Sage Pub.Admin.Abstr., Sage Urb.Stud.Abstr., Soc.Sci.Ind., SSCI, Stud.Wom.Abstr. **Document type:** academic/scholarly publication.
  —BLDSC (9123.690000); Faxon; UnCover; SWETS. **CCC.**
   Refereed Serial

352.7   UK
▼**URBAN TRENDS.** 1992. irreg., no.1, 1992. Policy Studies Institute, 100 Park Village East, London NW1 3SR, England. TEL 071-387-2171. FAX 071-388-0914. (Dist. by: BEBC Distribution Ltd., P.O. Box 1496, Poole, Dorset BH12 3YD, England) Eds. Peter Willmott, Robert Hutchison. **Document type:** monographic series.

301   FR   ISSN 0042-1014
NA9000
URBANISME; revue francaise. 1932. 10/yr. 57 rue de Seine, 75006 Paris, France. TEL 40-51-04-04. FAX 46-33-49-13. TELEX 680 876 F. Ed. M. Sarazin. adv.; bk.rev.; charts; illus.; pat.; tr.mk.; index. circ. 8,475. **Indexed:** Avery Ind.Archit.Per., Excerp.Med.
  —Faxon; SWETS; UMI.
   Former titles (until 1993): Urbanismes et Architecture (ISSN 1145-5187); (until 1989): Urbanisme (ISSN 1240-0874)

352.7   SP
URBANISMO C O A M. 3/yr. Colegio Oficial de Arquitectos de Madrid - Madrid Official College of Architects, Barquillo 12, 28004 Madrid, Spain. TEL 1-521-82-00 220. Ed. Abel Anguita Puebla.

352.7   FR   ISSN 0336-9722
URBAPRESS INFORMATIONS; la lettre confidentielle de l'amenagement et des villes. (Supplement avail.: Prospectives) 1975. w. 4975 F. L'Agence Innovapresse, 29, rue du Faubourg Poissonniere, 75009 Paris, France. TEL 48-24-08-97. FAX 42-47-00-76. TELEX 280 114 F. Ed. Antoine Loubiere. adv.; bk.rev.
   Formerly: Urbapress; **Incorporates:** Lettre du Moniteur.
   Description: Concerned with town and country planning.

352.7   SW   ISSN 0042-2002
VAAR BOSTAD/OUR DWELLING. 1924. 11/yr. SEK 95. (H S Bs Riksfoerebund) Hyresgerstarnas Foerlags AB, Kungsbroplan 3A, 112 27 Stockholm, Sweden. TEL 8-654-17-80. FAX 08-785-36-77. (Co-sponsor: Hyresgestarnas Riksfoerbund) Ed. Oesten Johansson. adv.; illus. circ. 945,845. (also avail. in audio cassette)

VANGUARD (MILWAUKEE). see *SOCIAL SERVICES AND WELFARE*

352.7   GW
VEBA WOHNEN MAGAZIN; Informationen fuer Mieter und Kunden. 1986. q. Veba Wohnen, Philippstr. 3, 44803 Bochum, Germany. TEL 0234-314528. FAX 0234-314314. Ed. Eberhard Schmitt. circ. 145,000.

HOUSING AND URBAN PLANNING — ABSTRACTING, BIBLIOGRAPHIES, STATISTICS

VENEZUELA. MINISTERIO DE HACIENDA. MEMORIA. see *PUBLIC ADMINISTRATION*

690.87   US
VENTILATION DIRECTORY. irreg., latest 1990. $20. National Conference of States on Building Codes and Standards, Inc., 505 Huntmar Pk. Dr., Ste. 210, Herndon, VA 22070. TEL 703-437-0100. FAX 703-481-3596. stat. **Document type:** directory.
    Description: Summarizes the ventilation requirements of the 1990 National, Uniform and Standard Building Codes, ASHRAE Standards, and special provisions in Massachusetts, New York, southern Florida, and Wisconsin.

VERMONT NATURAL RESOURCES COUNCIL. BULLETIN. see *ENVIRONMENTAL STUDIES*

352.7   AT
VICTORIA. DEPARTMENT OF PLANNING AND HOUSING. ANNUAL REPORT. HOUSING AND CONSTRUCTION VICTORIA. 1938. a. Department of Planning and Housing, 250 Elizabeth St., Melbourne, Vic. 3000, Australia. illus. circ. 2,000. **Document type:** government publication.
    Former titles: Victoria. Department of Planning and Construction. Annual Report. Housing and Construction Victoria; Victoria. Ministry of Housing and Construction. Annual Report; (until 1983): Victoria. Housing Commision. Annual Report (ISSN 0810-4972)

VIE PUBLIQUE; le journal des elus et des administrateurs locaux. see *PUBLIC ADMINISTRATION — Municipal Government*

350.865   HU
VILLAGE/FALU; settlement policy, village development, architecture. 1985. q. 500 Ft.($20) Agroinform Kiado es Nyomda Kft., Kitaibel Pal u. 4, 1024 Budapest II, Hungary. TEL 0135-1927. FAX 135-0344. Ed. Tibor Ferenczi. **Document type:** newsletter.

352.7   US
VIRGINIA HOUSING. 1975. q. free. Virginia Housing Development Authority, 601 S. Belvedere St., Richmond, VA 23220. TEL 804-782-1986. FAX 804-783-6749. Ed. Michael Anderson. circ. 7,000.

352.7   BE
VLAAMSE HUISVESTINGSMAATSCHAPPIJ. JAARVERSLAG. (Text in Dutch) 1934. a. free. Vlaamse Huisvestingsmaatschappij, Breydelstraat 12. TEL 32-2-2305125. FAX 32-2-2304690. **Document type:** government publication.
    Formerly: Nationale Maatschappij voor de Huisvesting. Jaarverslag (ISSN 0522-7739)

352   UK
VOLUNTARY HOUSING. 1935. m. £54 (foreign £95) (effective 1993). National Federation of Housing Associations, 175 Gray's Inn Rd., London WC1X 8UP, England. TEL 071-278-6571. FAX 071-955-5696. Ed. Chris Bazlinton. adv.; bk.rev.; illus. circ. 12,000. **Indexed:** RICS. **Document type:** bulletin.
    Formerly: National Federation of Housing Societies. Quarterly Bulletin (ISSN 0027-9234)

VYSTAVBA A ARCHITEKTURA. see *ARCHITECTURE*

352   AU   ISSN 0042-9562
W B F O. (Wohnbauforschung in Oesterreich) 1956. bi-m. S.570. Forschungsgesellschaft fuer Wohnen, Bauen und Planen, Loewengasse 47, A-1030 Vienna 3, Austria. TEL 0222-726251. Ed. Hermann Lebeda. adv.; bk.rev.; charts; illus.; stat.; tr.lit.; index. circ. 1,000. **Document type:** bulletin.

352.7   GW
WACKENBERGER ECHO. 1976. bi-m. Paedagogisch - Soziale Aktionsgemeinschaft e.V., Rubensstr. 78, 66119 Saarbruecken, Germany. TEL 0681-853514. Ed. Armin Kuphal. adv. circ. 2,000. **Document type:** bulletin.

352.7   US   ISSN 0733-0677
WATERFRONT WORLD SPOTLIGHT. 1982. 4/yr. $60. Waterfront Center, 1536 44th St., N.W., Washington, DC 20007. TEL 202-337-0356. FAX 202-625-1654. Eds. Ann Breen, Dick Rigby. adv.; bk.rev.; bibl.; charts. circ. 10,000. (back issues avail.) **Document type:** newsletter.
    Description: Covers urban waterfront developments, including views of private investors, citizen's organizations, environmentalists and municipal officials.

388.3   US   ISSN 0043-3942
WESTERN MOBILE NEWS. 1951. bi-w. $7.50. (Modern Housing Inc.) Coast Media, Inc., 4043 Irving Place, Culver City, CA 90230. TEL 213-839-5271. Ed. Edward B. Ely. adv.; bk.rev.; illus. circ. 26,000. (tabloid format)
    Formerly: Western Mobile Home News.

WETTBEWERBE AKTUELL; architectural competitions in Germany. see *ARCHITECTURE*

352   AU
WOHNEN PLUS; Zeitschrift der gemeinnuetzigen Bauvereinigungen in Oesterreich. 1961. q. S.150. Oesterreichischer Verband Gemeinnuetziger Bauvereinigungen, Boesendorferstr. 7, A-1010 Vienna, Austria. TEL 0222-5055824. adv.; bk.rev.; stat.; index. circ. 5,000. **Document type:** trade publication.
    —BLDSC (9342.540000).
    Formerly (until 1990): Wohnen und Siedeln (ISSN 0043-7158)

WOHNRECHTLICHE BLAETTER. see *LAW*

352.7   GW   ISSN 0179-745X
WOHNUNGSWIRTSCHAFT. 1947. m. DM.84. Nordweststr. 50, 63128 Dietzenbach, Germany. Ed. Christian Bauer. adv. contact: Dieter Mueller.

WOHNUNGSWIRTSCHAFT UND MIETRECHT. see *LAW*

352.7   US
YOUR HOME. 1987. m. $15. Housing Resource Center, 1820 W. 48th St., Cleveland, OH 44102. TEL 216-281-4663. FAX 216-651-0914. bk.rev. circ. 4,500. (back issues avail.) **Document type:** newsletter.
    Description: Features home improvement information.

YOUR REGION. see *PUBLIC ADMINISTRATION — Municipal Government*

352.7   GW
Z O V. (Zeitschrift fuer Offene Vermoegensfragen) 1991. bi-mo. DM.90. Grundeigentum Verlag GmbH, Eichborndamm 141-165, 13403 Berlin, Germany. TEL 030-4116031. FAX 030-4113025. Ed. Dieter Bluemmel. circ. 3,000. **Document type:** trade publication.

711   CC
ZHONGZHOU JIANSHE/ZHONGZHOU CONSTRUCTION. (Text in Chinese) 1987. q. Y8 (foreign $12). Henan Sheng Jianshe Ting - Henan Provincial Department of Urban & Rural Construction, No. 102, Jinshui Lu, Zhengzhou, Henan 450003, People's Republic of China. TEL 0371-229147. (Co-sponsor: Henan Provincial Society of Urban Science) Ed. Cao Jiangshui. adv.: B&W page Y1000, color page Y2000; adv. contact: Kai Zhao. circ. 1,000. **Document type:** academic/scholarly publication.
    Formerly (until 1993): Zhongzhou Chengshi Yanjiu - Zhongzhou Urban Research.
    Description: Covers academic researches, scientific and technical information, and national construction policies.

352.7   US
ZONING AND PLANNING LAW HANDBOOK. a. $75. Clark - Boardman - Callaghan Company Ltd., 375 Hudson St., New York, NY 10014. TEL 212-929-7500; 800-221-9428. FAX 212-924-0460. Ed. Kenneth H. Young.
    Description: Covers emerging and projected trends, significant developments, and case law in the field of zoning and land use law.

352.7   US   ISSN 0161-8113
KF5697.A15
ZONING AND PLANNING LAW REPORT. 1978. m. (11/yr.). $185. Clark - Boardman - Callaghan Company Ltd., 375 Hudson St., New York, NY 10014. TEL 212-929-7500; 800-221-9428. FAX 212-924-0460. Ed. Kenneth H. Young. index. (looseleaf format; back issues avail.) **Indexed:** C.L.I., L.R.I. **Document type:** newsletter.
    Description: Details critical developments in zoning and planning law through timely articles, reviews of recent cases, and succinct, practical treatment of other important developments.

352.7   333.33 920
614.7
ZONING NEWS. 1984. m. $45 (foreign $54). American Planning Association, 1313 E. 60th St., Chicago, IL 60637. TEL 312-955-9100. FAX 312-955-8312. (And: 1776 Massachusetts Ave., N.W., Washington, DC 20036. TEL 202-872-0611) Ed. James Schwab. circ. 3,800. (back issues avail.)

ZUKUNFTSFORSCHUNG. see *SOCIAL SCIENCES: COMPREHENSIVE WORKS*

HOUSING AND URBAN PLANNING — Abstracting, Bibliographies, Statistics

352.7   600 016   US   ISSN 0163-1535
ABSTRACT NEWSLETTER: URBAN AND REGIONAL TECHNOLOGY AND DEVELOPMENT. w. $95 (foreign $135). U.S. National Technical Information Service, 5285 Port Royal Rd., Springfield, VA 22161. TEL 703-487-4630. index. (back issues avail.)
    Former titles: Weekly Abstract Newsletter: Urban and Regional Technology and Development; Weekly Government Abstracts. Urban and Regional Technology and Development; Weekly Government Abstracts. Urban Technology (ISSN 0363-7417)

352.7   AT   ISSN 1030-6048
ANNUAL REVIEW OF MAJOR RESIDENTIAL MARKETS IN AUSTRALIA. 1978. a. Aus.$50. Real Estate Institute of Australia, Real Estate House, 16 Thesiger Court, Deakin, A.C.T. 2600, Australia. TEL 06-282-4277. FAX 06-285-2444. Ed. Julian Robertson. charts; stat. circ. 1,000. (back issues avail.)
    Formerly (until 1986): Annual Review of the Residential Property Market (ISSN 0155-9508)

352.7   AT   ISSN 0728-375X
AUSTRALIA. BUREAU OF STATISTICS. BUILDING ACTIVITY, AUSTRALIA. 1948. q. Aus.$14 per no. Australian Bureau of Statistics, P.O. Box 10, Belconnen, A.C.T. 2616, Australia. **Document type:** government publication.
    Description: Contains the number of dwelling units and value of residential buildings, value of alterations and additions to residential buildings, and value of non-residential buildings.

352.7 690   AT   ISSN 1031-0177
AUSTRALIA. BUREAU OF STATISTICS. BUILDING APPROVALS, AUSTRALIA. 1960. m. Aus.$13 per no. Australian Bureau of Statistics, P.O. Box 10, Belconnen, A.C.T. 2616, Australia. **Document type:** government publication.
    Description: Contains number of dwelling units and value of residential buildings approved for both private and public sectors, value of alterations and additions to residential buildings and value of non-residential buildings.

352.7   AT   ISSN 1032-0865
AUSTRALIA. BUREAU OF STATISTICS. DIRECTORY OF HOUSING RELATED STATISTICS. 1988. irreg., latest 1991. Aus.$30 per no. Australian Bureau of Statistics., P.O. Box 10, Belconnen, A.C.T. 2616, Australia. **Document type:** government publication, directory.
    Description: Presents details of housing related statistics produced by both government and non-government sources.

352.7   AT   ISSN 0158-3263
AUSTRALIA. BUREAU OF STATISTICS. NEW SOUTH WALES OFFICE. BUILDING APPROVALS, NEW SOUTH WALES. 1957. m. Aus.$10.50 per no. Australian Bureau of Statistics, New South Wales Office, St. Andrews House, Sydney Square, George St., Sydney, N.S.W. 2000, Australia. **Document type:** government publication.
    Description: Provides number of dwelling units and value of residential buildings approved for both private and public sectors.

HOUSING AND URBAN PLANNING — ABSTRACTING, BIBLIOGRAPHIES, STATISTICS

AUSTRALIA. BUREAU OF STATISTICS. NEW SOUTH WALES OFFICE. BUILDING ACTIVITY, NEW SOUTH WALES. see *BUILDING AND CONSTRUCTION — Abstracting, Bibliographies, Statistics*

352.7 AT ISSN 0814-7957
AUSTRALIA. BUREAU OF STATISTICS. NEW SOUTH WALES OFFICE. DWELLING UNIT COMMENCEMENTS REPORTED BY APPROVING AUTHORITIES, NEW SOUTH WALES. 1948. q. Aus.$10.50 per no. Australian Bureau of Statistics, New South Wales Office, St. Andrews House, Sydney Square, George St., Sydney, N.S.W. 2000, Australia. **Document type:** government publication.
   Description: Contains details on the number of dwellings commenced as reported by approving authorities in local government areas.

AUSTRALIA. BUREAU OF STATISTICS. NORTHERN TERRITORY OFFICE. BUILDING ACTIVITY, NORTHERN TERRITORY. see *BUILDING AND CONSTRUCTION — Abstracting, Bibliographies, Statistics*

352.7 AT ISSN 0813-1260
AUSTRALIA. BUREAU OF STATISTICS. NORTHERN TERRITORY OFFICE. BUILDING APPROVALS, NORTHERN TERRITORY. 1982. m. Aus.$7 per no. Australian Bureau of Statistics, Northern Territory Office, MLC Bldg., 6th Fl., 81 Smith St., Darwin, N.T. 0800, Australia. **Document type:** government publication.
   Description: Contains number of dwelling units and value of residential buildings approved for both private and public sectors, value of alterations and additions to residential buildings, and values of non-residential buildings.

AUSTRALIA. BUREAU OF STATISTICS. QUEENSLAND OFFICE. BUILDING ACTIVITY, QUEENSLAND. see *BUILDING AND CONSTRUCTION — Abstracting, Bibliographies, Statistics*

352.7 AT ISSN 1031-198X
AUSTRALIA. BUREAU OF STATISTICS. QUEENSLAND OFFICE. BUILDING APPROVALS, QUEENSLAND. 1947. m. Aus.$10.50 per no. Australian Bureau of Statistics, Queensland Office, 313 Adelaide St., Brisbane, Qld. 4000, Australia. TEL 07-222-6022. FAX 07-229-6171. TELEX AA 40271. **Document type:** government publication.
   Description: Contains summary of building work approved by statistical divisions of local areas and districts.

352.7 AT ISSN 0728-6546
AUSTRALIA. BUREAU OF STATISTICS. QUEENSLAND OFFICE. BUILDING APPROVALS: SMALL AREA STATISTICS, QUEENSLAND. 1980. a. Aus.$10.50. Australian Bureau of Statistics, Queensland Office, 313 Adelaide St., Brisbane, Qld. 4000, Australia. TEL 07-222-6022. FAX 07-229-6171. TELEX AA 40271. **Document type:** government publication.
   Formerly: Australia. Bureau of Statistics. Queensland Office. Building Operations: Small Area Statistics (ISSN 0155-5731)
   Description: Provides data on the number and value of approved dwelling units in new residential buildings of Brisbane city.

352.7 AT ISSN 0814-8023
AUSTRALIA. BUREAU OF STATISTICS. QUEENSLAND OFFICE. DWELLING COMMENCEMENTS REPORTED BY APPROVING AUTHORITIES, QUEENSLAND. 1980. m. Aus.$10.50 per no. Australian Bureau of Statistics, Queensland Office, 313 Adelaide St., Brisbane, Qld. 4000, Australia. TEL 07-222-6022. FAX 07-229-6171. TELEX AA 40271. **Document type:** government publication.
   Formerly (until 1984): Australia. Bureau of Statistics. Queensland Office. Number of New Dwellings Commenced in Queensland (ISSN 0726-1861)
   Description: Provides data on the number of dwelling units commenced by type of residential building in statistical divisions and subdivisions.

352.7 AT ISSN 1030-9683
AUSTRALIA. BUREAU OF STATISTICS. QUEENSLAND OFFICE. DWELLING UNIT COMMENCEMENTS: SMALL AREA STATISTICS, QUEENSLAND. 1986. a. Aus.$10.50. Australian Bureau of Statistics, Queensland Office, 313 Adelaide St., Brisbane, Qld. 4000, Australia. TEL 07-222-6022. FAX 07-229-6171. TELEX AA 40271. **Document type:** government publication.
   Description: Provides statistics on the number of dwelling units commenced by type of residential building in local areas (suburbs) of Brisbane City.

AUSTRALIA. BUREAU OF STATISTICS. SOUTH AUSTRALIAN OFFICE. BUILDING ACTIVITY, SOUTH AUSTRALIA. see *BUILDING AND CONSTRUCTION — Abstracting, Bibliographies, Statistics*

352.7 AT ISSN 0810-4743
AUSTRALIA. BUREAU OF STATISTICS. SOUTH AUSTRALIAN OFFICE. BUILDING APPROVALS, SOUTH AUSTRALIA. 1961. m. Aus.$10.50 per no. Australian Bureau of Statistics, South Australian Office, G.P.O. Box 2272, Adelaide, S.A. 5001, Australia. **Document type:** government publication.
   Description: Contains number and value of residential buildings approved for private and public sectors, value of alterations and additions to residential buildings and value of classes of non-residential buildings approved.

352.7 690 AT ISSN 1031-2226
AUSTRALIA. BUREAU OF STATISTICS. SOUTH AUSTRALIAN OFFICE. DWELLING UNIT COMMENCEMENTS REPORTED BY APPROVING AUTHORITIES, SOUTH AUSTRALIA. 1980. m. Aus.$10.70 per no. Australian Bureau of Statistics, South Australian Office, G.P.O. Box 2272, Adelaide, S.A. 5001, Australia. **Document type:** government publication.
   Incorportes (1983-1990): Australia. Bureau of Statistics. South Australian Office. Dwelling Unit Commencements Reported by Approving Authorities, South Australia, Preliminary (ISSN 0815-1849)
   Description: Contains number of dwelling unit commencements (houses and other residential buildings) as reported by approving authorities.

AUSTRALIA. BUREAU OF STATISTICS. TASMANIAN OFFICE. BUILDING ACTIVITY, TASMANIA. see *BUILDING AND CONSTRUCTION — Abstracting, Bibliographies, Statistics*

352.7 AT ISSN 0156-7861
AUSTRALIA. BUREAU OF STATISTICS. TASMANIAN OFFICE. BUILDING APPROVALS, TASMANIA. 1971. m. Aus.$10.50 per no. Australian Bureau of Statistics, Tasmanian Office, G.P.O. Box 66A, Hobart, Tas. 7001, Australia. **Document type:** government publication.
   Description: Contains number of dwelling units and value of residential buildings approved for both private and public sectors.

AUSTRALIA. BUREAU OF STATISTICS. VICTORIAN OFFICE. BUILDING ACTIVITY, VICTORIA. see *BUILDING AND CONSTRUCTION — Abstracting, Bibliographies, Statistics*

352.7 690 AT
AUSTRALIA. BUREAU OF STATISTICS. VICTORIAN OFFICE. BUILDING APPROVALS BY STATISTICAL LOCAL AREAS, VICTORIA - SMALL AREA SUMMARY DATA REPORTS. 1986. a. Aus.$8.20. Australian Bureau of Statistics, Victorian Office, G.P.O. Box 2796Y, Melbourne, Vic. 3001, Australia. **Document type:** government publication.
   Formerly: Australia. Bureau of Statistics. Victorian Office. Building Approvals, Small Area Summary, Victoria (ISSN 1037-1079)
   Description: Contains annual summary of housing number, value of new houses and other residential buildings, and value of alterations.

352.7 690 AT ISSN 1031-1998
AUSTRALIA. BUREAU OF STATISTICS. VICTORIAN OFFICE. BUILDING APPROVALS, VICTORIA. 1959. m. Aus.$10.70 per no. Australian Bureau of Statistics, Victorian Office, G.P.O. Box 2796Y, Melbourne, Vic. 3001, Australia. **Document type:** government publication.
   Description: Contains number of dwelling units and value of residential buildings approved for both private and public sectors, value of alterations and additions to residential buildings and value of non-residential buildings.

352.7 AT ISSN 0814-236X
AUSTRALIA. BUREAU OF STATISTICS. VICTORIAN OFFICE. DWELLING UNIT COMMENCEMENTS REPORTED BY APPROVING AUTHORITIES, VICTORIA. 1985. m. Aus.$10.70 per no. Australian Bureau of Statistics, Victorian Office, G.P.O. Box 2796Y, Melbourne, Vic. 3001, Australia. **Document type:** government publication.
   Description: Contains number of dwelling unit commencements as reported by approving local authorities. Also includes trend estimates and seasonal adjustment data.

352.7 AT ISSN 0819-405X
AUSTRALIA. BUREAU OF STATISTICS. WESTERN AUSTRALIAN OFFICE. BUILDING APPROVALS - PRIVATE SECTOR, PERTH STATISTICAL DIVISION. 1986. m. Aus.$5.10 per no. Australian Bureau of Statistics, Western Australian Office, 30 Terrace Rd., E. Perth, W.A. 6004, Australia. **Document type:** government publication.
   Description: Contains private sector building approvals for Perth Statistical Division.

352.7 AT ISSN 0727-2278
AUSTRALIA. BUREAU OF STATISTICS. WESTERN AUSTRALIAN OFFICE. BUILDING APPROVALS, WESTERN AUSTRALIA. 1944. m. Aus.$10.70 per no. Australian Bureau of Statistics, Western Australian Office, 30 Terrace Rd., E. Perth, W.A. 6004, Australia. **Document type:** government publication.
   Description: Contains number of dwelling units and value of residential buildings approved for both private and public sectors.

352.7 AT ISSN 0728-4055
AUSTRALIA. BUREAU OF STATISTICS. WESTERN AUSTRALIAN OFFICE. BUILDING ACTIVITY, WESTERN AUSTRALIA. 1946. q. Aus.$10.70 per no. Australian Bureau of Statistics, Western Australian Office, 30 Terrace Rd., E. Perth, W.A. 6004, Australia. **Document type:** government publication.
   Description: Contains the number of dwelling units and value of residential buildings, value of alterations, and value of non-residential buildings.

352.7 690 AT ISSN 1036-5761
AUSTRALIA. BUREAU OF STATISTICS. WESTERN AUSTRALIAN OFFICE. DWELLING UNIT COMMENCEMENTS, WESTERN AUSTRALIA. 1983. m. Aus.$10.70 per no. Australian Bureau of Statistics, Western Australian Office, 30 Terrace Rd., E. Perth, W.A. 6004, Australia. **Document type:** government publication.
   Description: Contains number of dwelling unit commencements as reported by authorities and number of new houses commenced by material of outer walls and ownership.

352.7 GW ISSN 0930-4274
BOCHUM. AMT FUER STATISTIK, STADTFORSCHUNG UND WAHLEN. SONDERBERICHTE. 1954. 3/yr. DM.13. Amt fuer Statistik, Stadtforschung und Wahlen, 44777 Bochum, Germany. TEL 0234-9108510. FAX 0234-9108512. charts; illus. **Document type:** government publication.

352.7 GW ISSN 0067-9437
BOCHUM. AMT FUER STATISTIK, STADTFORSCHUNG UND WAHLEN. STATISTICAL YEARBOOK. 1954. a. DM.20. Amt fuer Statistik, Stadtforschung und Wahlen, 44777 Bochum, Germany. TEL 0234-9108510. FAX 0234-9108512. charts; index. circ. 750. **Document type:** government publication.

352.7 GW ISSN 0931-2900
BOCHUM. AMT FUER STATISTIK, STADTFORSCHUNG UND WAHLEN. VERWALTUNGSBERICHT. 1912. a. DM.20. Amt fuer Statistik, Stadtforschung und Wahlen, 44777 Bochum, Germany. TEL 0234-9108510. FAX 0234-9108512. index. circ. 115. **Document type:** government publication.

352.7 GW
BOCHUM. AMT FUER STATISTIK, STADTFORSCHUNG UND WAHLEN. ZUR STADTENTWICKLUNG. 1969. irreg. DM.20. Amt fuer Statistik, Stadtforschung und Wahlen, 44777 Bochum, Germany. TEL 0234-9108510. FAX 0234-9108512. bibl.; charts. circ. 700. **Document type:** government publication.

011 020 US
C P L BIBLIOGRAPHIES. 1957. 12/yr. $285. Council of Planning Librarians, Publications Office, 1313 E. 60th St., Chicago, IL 60637-2897. TEL 312-955-9100. FAX 312-955-8312. (And: 1776 Massachusetts Ave., N.W., Washington, DC 20036) Ed. Deborah Thompson-Wise. (also avail. in microfiche from BHP; microfilm from PMC) **Document type:** bibliography.
Description: Provides a forum for the exchange of information among those interested in problems of library organization and research; disseminates information about city and regional planning.

301.54 CN ISSN 0068-8940
CANADIAN HOUSING STATISTICS. 1955. a. (plus m. supplements). Can.$10. Canada Mortgage and Housing Corporation, 700 Montreal Rd., Ottawa, Ont. K1A 0P7, Canada. TEL 613-748-2068. FAX 613-748-4069.
Formerly: Housing in Canada.

352.7 UK ISSN 0144-4514
HV4546
CHARTERED INSTITUTE OF PUBLIC FINANCE AND ACCOUNTANCY. HOMELESSNESS STATISTICS. 1980. a. £37. Chartered Institute of Public Finance and Accountancy, 3 Robert St., London WC2N 6BH, England. TEL 071-895-8823. FAX 071-895-8825. (back issues avail.)
—BLDSC (4326.175700).

352.7 UK ISSN 0967-8441
CHARTERED INSTITUTE OF PUBLIC FINANCE AND ACCOUNTANCY. HOUSING REVENUE ACCOUNT STATISTICS. ESTIMATES & ACTUALS. 1975. a. £75. Chartered Institute of Public Finance and Accountancy, 3 Robert St., London WC2N 6BH, England. TEL 071-895-8823. FAX 071-895-8825. (back issues avail.)
—BLDSC (4335.144400).
Formed by the 1990 merger of: Chartered Institute of Public Finance and Accountancy. Housing Revenue Account Statistics. Actuals (ISSN 0260-4078) & Chartered Institute of Public Finance and Accountancy. Housing Revenue Statistics. Estimates (ISSN 0260-4086); Which was formerly (until 1979): Chartered Institute of Public Finance and Accountancy. Housing Statistics. England and Wales. Housing Revenue Account Estimates; Actuals superseded in part (in 1980): Chartered Institute of Public Finance and Accountancy. Housing Statistics. England and Wales. Part 2. Housing Revenue Account (ISSN 0309-6238); Which was formerly (1969-1974): Chartered Institute of Public Finance and Accountancy. Housing Statistics. England and Wales. Part 2. Housing Revenue and Repairs Accounts (ISSN 0307-1316); Which superseded: Housing Statistics (ISSN 0443-3777).

352.7 UK ISSN 0260-406X
CHARTERED INSTITUTE OF PUBLIC FINANCE AND ACCOUNTANCY. HOUSING RENTS STATISTICS. ACTUALS. 1969. a. £55. Chartered Institute of Public Finance and Accountancy, 3 Robert St., London WC2N 6BH, England. TEL 071-895-8823. FAX 071-895-8825. (back issues avail.)
Formerly: Chartered Institute of Public Finance and Accountancy. Housing Part 1: Rents. Actuals Statistics (ISSN 0307-1308).

352.7 UK ISSN 0964-5446
HT169.G72
CHARTERED INSTITUTE OF PUBLIC FINANCE AND ACCOUNTANCY. PLANNING AND DEVELOPMENT STATISTICS. ESTIMATES & ACTUALS. 1977. a. £40. Chartered Institute of Public Finance and Accountancy, 3 Robert St., London WC2N 6BH, England. TEL 071-895-8823. FAX 071-895-8825. (back issues avail.)
Formerly: Chartered Institute of Public Finance and Accountancy. Planning and Development Statistics. Estimates (ISSN 0144-901X); Which supersedes in part: Chartered Institute of Public Finance and Accountancy. Planning Estimates Statistics. Actuals (ISSN 0307-8329).

EKISTIC INDEX. see SOCIOLOGY — Abstracting, Bibliographies, Statistics

352.7 310 FR ISSN 0184-6892
HD9715.F7
FRANCE. MINISTERE DE L'URBANISME ET DU LOGEMENT. STATISTIQUES ET ETUDES GENERALES. 10/yr. Documentation Francaise, 29-31 Quai Voltaire, 75340 Paris Cedex 07, France. TEL 1-40-15-70-00. FAX 40-15-72-30. TELEX 215 666 DOCFRAN. (Subscr. to: 124 rue Henri Barbusse, 93308 Aubervilliers Cedex, France. TEL 48-39-56-00. FAX 48-39-56-01) stat. (also avail. in microfiche from DFR; back issues avail.) **Document type:** government publication.
Former titles: France. Direction du Batiment, des Travaux Publics et de la Conjoncture. Etudes Statistiques sur la Construction et l'Equipement; France. Direction du Batiment, des Travaux Publics et de la Conjoncture. Etudes Statistiques de l'Equipement.

314.2 332.7 UK
GREAT BRITAIN. DEPARTMENT OF THE ENVIRONMENT. LOCAL HOUSING STATISTICS: ENGLAND AND WALES. (Joint publication with the Welsh Office) 1966. q. price varies. (Department of the Environment) H.M.S.O. Books, Publications Centre, 51 Nine Elms Ln., London SW8 5DR, England. TEL 071-873-0011. FAX 071-873-8463. (Subscr. to: H.M.S.O. Books, P.O. Box 276, London SW8 5DT, England. TEL 071-873-9090. FAX 071-973-8200) stat. (back issues avail.) **Document type:** government publication.

HOME LOAN AFFORDABILITY IN AUSTRALIA. see REAL ESTATE — Abstracting, Bibliographies, Statistics

352.7 318 HO
HONDURAS. SECRETARIA DE PLANIFICACION COORDINACION Y PRESUPUESTO. DIRECCION GENERAL DE ESTADISTICA Y CENSOS. ENCUESTA PERMANENTE DE HOGARES DE PROPOSITOS MULTIPLES. a. Secretaria de Planificacion Coordinacion y Presupuesto, Direccion General de Estadistica y Censos, Tegucigalpa D.C., Honduras. circ. 100.

352.7 UK ISSN 0952-8156
HOUSING ABSTRACTS (H A B S). 1987. fortn. £92. London Research Centre, Parliament House, 81 Black Prince Rd., London SE1 7SZ, England. TEL 071-627-9666. FAX 071-627-9674. Ed. Judith Barton. circ. 570. (back issues avail.) **Document type:** abstracting/indexing.
Description: Summarizes press reports and press notices on housing issues, as well as abstracts of new reports, journal articles and pamphlets.

352.7 UK ISSN 0267-0054
HOUSING INFORMATION DIGEST. 1984. m. £95 to non-member; members £60. Planning Exchange, 186 Bath St., Glasgow G2 4HG, Scotland. TEL 041-332-8541. FAX 041-332-8277. **Document type:** abstracting/indexing.
Description: Abstracts of current literature in the housing field.

HOUSING MARKET STATISTICS. see BUSINESS AND ECONOMICS — Abstracting, Bibliographies, Statistics

352.7 UK
HOUSING NEEDS AND RESOURCES (YEAR); analysis of Housing Investments Programme. 1980. a. £20. London Research Centre, Parliament House, 81 Black Prince Rd., London SE1 7SZ, England. TEL 071-735-4250. FAX 071-627-9606. (back issues avail.)
Description: Presents statistics from HIP submissions and analysis of allocations for the year.

352.7 310 JA
HOUSING SURVEY OF JAPAN (YEAR). 1990. 1/5 yrs. 8800 Yen. Nihon Tokei Kyokai - Japan Statistical Association, Crest 21, 6-21, Yocho-machi, Shinjuku-ku, Tokyo 162, Japan. (Co-sponsor: Somu-cho Tokei-kyoku - Statistics Bureau, Management and Coordination Agency)

350.86 310 UN
HUMAN SETTLEMENTS BASIC STATISTICS/STATISTIQUES DE BASE ETABLISSEMENTS HUMAINS/ESTADISTICAS BASICAS DE ASENTAMIENTOS HUMANOS. (Text and summaries in Arabic, English, French, Spanish) 1990. irreg. free. United Nations Centre for Human Settlements (Habitat) - Centre des Nations Unies pour les Etablissements Humains, P.O. Box 30030, Nairobi, Kenya. TEL 254-2-621234. FAX 254-2-226473. TELEX 22996 UNHABITAT. charts.
Description: Provides a quick and easy source of general information on human settlements statistics for policy-makers, researchers and the general public.

350 016 US ISSN 0046-8908
Z7165.U5
INDEX TO CURRENT URBAN DOCUMENTS. 1972. q. (with a. cumulation). $350. Greenwood Press, Inc. (Subsidiary of: Greenwood Publishing Group Inc.), 88 Post Rd. W., Box 5007, Westport, CT 06881-5007. TEL 203-226-3571. FAX 203-222-1502. Ed. Laura Kaminsky. index. **Document type:** academic/scholarly publication.
● Also available online.

352.7 SP ISSN 1130-3700
INDICE ESPANOL DE CIENCIAS SOCIALES. SERIES E: URBAN PLANNING. 1979. a. 10000 ptas. or exchange basis (effective 1994). Centro de Informacion y Documentacion Cientifica (Cindoc), Pinar, 25, 3, 28006 Madrid, Spain. TEL 1-5635482. FAX 1-5642644. **Document type:** abstracting/indexing.
● Also available online.
Also available on CD-ROM.
Supersedes in part (in 1982): Indice Espanol de Ciencias Sociales (ISSN 0211-1373).

350.865 MH
MACAO. DIRECCAO DOS SERVICOS DE ESTATISTICA E CENSOS. RECENSEAMENTO GERAL A HABITACAO/MACAO. CENSUS AND STATISTICS DEPARTMENT. GENERAL CENSUS OF HOUSING. (Text in Chinese, Portuguese) 1970. every ten yrs. Direccao dos Servicos de Estatistica e Censos, P.O. Box 3022, Macao. TEL 3995311. FAX 307825. **Document type:** government publication.

MARKET FACTS. see REAL ESTATE — Abstracting, Bibliographies, Statistics

MARKET FACTS (NORTHERN TERRITORY: DARWIN - ALICE SPRINGS). see REAL ESTATE — Abstracting, Bibliographies, Statistics

352.7 310 NR ISSN 0794-4055
NIGERIA. FEDERAL OFFICE OF STATISTICS. REPORT ON GENERAL HOUSEHOLD SURVEY. a. £N2. Federal Office of Statistics, P.M.B. 12528, Lagos, Nigeria.
Formerly: Nigeria. Federal Office of Statistics. Report on Rural Household Survey.

352.7 310 NR
NIGERIA. FEDERAL OFFICE OF STATISTICS. REPORT ON URBAN HOUSEHOLD SURVEY. a. Federal Office of Statistics, P.M.B. 12528, Lagos, Nigeria.
Incorporates: Nigeria. Federal Office of Statistics. Report on Rural Household Survey; Nigeria. Federal Office of Statistics. Report on Rural Economic Survey; Nigeria. Federal Office of Statistics. Report on Rural Consumer Survey; Nigeria. Federal Office of Statistics. Report on Urban Consumer Survey; Nigeria. Federal Office of Statistics. Report on Urban Household Survey.

OMAHA - COUNCIL BLUFFS METROPOLITAN AREA PLANNING AGENCY. POPULATION AND HOUSING UNIT ESTIMATES. see POPULATION STUDIES — Abstracting, Bibliographies, Statistics

301.54 PL ISSN 0079-2659
POLAND. GLOWNY URZAD STATYSTYCZNY. ROCZNIK STATYSTYCZNY GOSPODARSKI MIESZKANIOWEJ I KOMUNALNEJ. (Subseries of: Statystyka Polski) 1967. irreg., latest 1988. 39 Zl. Zaklad Wydawnictw Statystycznych, Al. Niepodleglosci 208, 00-925 Warsaw, Poland. TEL 48 22 25-03-45.

HOW-TO AND DO-IT-YOURSELF

352 GW ISSN 0034-0111
RAUMFORSCHUNG UND RAUMORDNUNG. 1942. bi-m. DM.105. (Bundesforschungsanstalt fuer Landeskunde und Raumordnung) Carl Heymanns Verlag KG, Luxemburgerstr. 449, 50939 Cologne, Germany. TEL 0221-46010-0. FAX 0221-4601069. (Co-sponsor: Akademie fuer Raumforschung und Landesplannung, Hannover) Ed.Bd. adv.; bk.rev.; charts; illus.; index. circ. 1,900. **Indexed:** Bibl.Cart., Dok.Str., Excerp.Med., Geo.Abstr., Int.Lab.Doc., P.A.I.S.For.Lang.Ind. **Document type:** government publication.
—BLDSC (7296.000000); Faxon.

REFERATEBLATT ZUR RAUMENTWICKLUNG. see *PUBLIC ADMINISTRATION — Abstracting, Bibliographies, Statistics*

352.7 016 US ISSN 0090-5747
HT51
SAGE URBAN STUDIES ABSTRACTS. 1973. q. $87 to individuals; institutions $267 (effective 1994). Sage Publications, Inc., 2455 Teller Rd., Thousand Oaks, CA 91320. TEL 805-499-0721. FAX 805-499-0871. (Subscr. to: Sage Publications, Inc., Box 5084, Thousand Oaks, CA 91359; Overseas subscr. to: Sage Publications, Ltd., 6 Bonhill St., London EC2A 4PU, England; Sage Publications India Pvt. Ltd., P.O. Box 4215, New Delhi 110 048, India) Ed. Paul McDowell. adv.; index. circ. 750. (back issues avail.) **Document type:** abstracting/indexing.
—UnCover; UMI.
Description: Publishes cross-indexed abstracts of important recent literature on all aspects of urban studies, from public policy to planning and design.

352.7 US
SAN DIEGO REGION. INFO BULLETIN. POPULATION & HOUSING ESTIMATES. 1965. a. $3. San Diego Association of Governments (SANDAG), 401 B St., Ste. 800, San Diego, CA 92101. TEL 619-595-5300. (looseleaf format) **Document type:** bulletin.
Former titles: San Diego County. Department of Planning and Land Use. County Data Base; San Diego County Planning Department. Planning Data.

SEARCH (DEVON); the magazine index for architecture, interiors, and housing magazines. see *ARCHITECTURE — Abstracting, Bibliographies, Statistics*

352.7 SA
SOUTH AFRICA. CENTRAL STATISTICAL SERVICE. CENSUS OF TOWNSHIP DEVELOPMENT. (Report No. 83-04-01) (Text in Afrikaans and English) triennial, latest 1988. R.4.40 (foreign R.5.50). Central Statistical Service - Sentrale Statistiekdiens, Private Bag X44, Pretoria, South Africa. TEL 27-12-310-8911. FAX 27-12-310-8500. (Orders to: Government Printing Works, Private Bag X85, Pretoria 0001, South Africa) stat. **Document type:** government publication.
Former titles: South Africa. Central Statistical Service. Township Developers; South Africa. Department of Statistics. Census of Township Developers.

352.7 316.8 SA
SOUTH AFRICA. CENTRAL STATISTICAL SERVICE. STATISTICAL RELEASE. SURVEY OF FLATS. (No. P0102) a. free. Central Statistical Service - Sentrale Statistiekdiens, Private Bag X44, Pretoria 0001, South Africa. TEL 27-12-310-8911. FAX 27-12-310-8500. **Document type:** government publication.
Description: Sampling collected for calculation of the consumer price index.

352.7 316.8 SA
SOUTH AFRICA. CENTRAL STATISTICAL SERVICE. STATISTICAL RELEASE. SURVEY OF HOUSES, SECTIONAL TITLE UNITS AND DOMESTIC WORKERS. (No. P0101) (Text in Afrikaans, English) a. free. Central Statistical Service - Sentrale Statistiekdiens, Private Bag X44, Pretoria 0001, South Africa. TEL 27-12-310-8911. FAX 27-12-310-8500. **Document type:** government publication.
Former titles: South Africa. Central Statistical Service. Statistics of Houses and Domestic Servants and of Flats; South Africa. Department of Statistics. Statistics of Houses and Domestic Servants and of Flats.

526.9 US ISSN 1057-3623
HA203
STATE RANKINGS; a statistical view of the 50 United States. Key Title: State Rankings (Lawrence, Kan.). 1967. a. $43.95. Morgan Quitno Corporation, Box 1656, Lawrence, KS 66044. TEL 913-841-3534. FAX 913-841-3568. Ed. Kathleen Morgan.
Formerly: U.S. Statistikal Rankings (ISSN 0743-0833)

352.7 UN ISSN 0257-7216
UNITED NATIONS CENTRE FOR HUMAN SETTLEMENTS. BIBLIOGRAPHIC NOTES. (Text in English) 1983. 2/yr. free. United Nations Centre for Human Settlements (Habitat), Box 30030, Nairobi, Kenya. TEL 254-2-621234. FAX 254-2-624266. TELEX 22996 UNHABITAT.
Description: Provides abstracts of various kinds of materials on the subjects in the field of human settlements.

352.7 US ISSN 1049-0507
HT169.5
U.S. AGENCY FOR INTERNATIONAL DEVELOPMENT. OFFICE OF HOUSING AND URBAN PROGRAMS. ABSTRACTS. 1989. s-a. U.S. Agency for International Development, Office of Housing and Urban Programs, Room 401, SA-2, Washington, DC 20523-0214.

301.54 US ISSN 0082-9366
U.S. BUREAU OF THE CENSUS. CENSUS OF HOUSING. (Issued in several series) 1940. decennial. price varies. U.S. Bureau of the Census, Data User Services Division, Washington, DC 20233. TEL 301-763-4100. (Subscr. to: Superintendent of Documents, U.S. Government Printing Office, Box 371954, Pittsburgh, PA 15250-7954. TEL 202-783-3238. FAX 202-512-2233) **Document type:** government publication.

314 IT ISSN 0041-896X
UNIVERSITA DEGLI STUDI DI FIRENZE. ISTITUTO DI STATISTICA. DOCUMENTAZIONE; ricerca sul problema delle abitazioni in Italia. (Text in Italian; summaries in English and French) 1965. irreg. price varies. Universita degli Studi di Firenze, Istituto di Statistica, Via Curtatone N.1, Florence, Italy. (Co-sponsor: Consiglio Nazionale delle Ricerche) Ed. Renzo Ricci. circ. 500. (processed)

310 VE
VENEZUELA. MINISTERIO DE HACIENDA. BOLETIN ESTADISTICO. q. Ministerio de Hacienda, Centro Simon Bolivar, Edificio Norte, Caracas, Venezuela. charts. **Document type:** government publication.

HOW-TO AND DO-IT-YOURSELF

690 US
▼**AMERICAN HOW-TO.** 1993. bi-m. $30. (Handyman Club of America) North American Outdoor Group, Inc., 12301 Whitewater Dr., Box 3401, Minnetonka, MN 55343. TEL 612-936-9333. FAX 612-936-9755. Ed. Tom Sweeney. adv.: B&W page $4290. circ. 195,000. **Document type:** consumer publication.

684 US ISSN 8750-9318
TT194
AMERICAN WOODWORKER. 1985. bi-m. $24. Rodale Press, Inc., 33 E. Minor St., Emmaus, PA 18098. TEL 215-967-5171. TELEX 847338. Ed. David Sloan. adv.; bk.rev. circ. 100,000. (back issues avail.) **Indexed:** Ind.How To Do It (1989-).
—UMI.
Description: How-to magazine covering all aspects of small-shop woodworking for the serious amateur woodworker.

BETTER HOMES AND GARDENS HOME PRODUCTS GUIDE. see *BUILDING AND CONSTRUCTION*

BETTER HOMES AND GARDENS PRIZEWINNING REMODELING. see *INTERIOR DESIGN AND DECORATION*

684 US ISSN 0743-894X
BETTER HOMES AND GARDENS WOOD. Variant title: Wood. 1984. 9/yr. $24.97 (foreign $38). Meredith Corporation, 1716 Locust St., Des Moines, IA 50336. TEL 515-284-3000. adv. circ. 600,000. **Indexed:** Ind.How To Do It (1984-). **Document type:** consumer publication.
Description: Covers woodworking projects for homeowners.

690 790.13 US
BLACK & DECKER BUILD IT. 1984. a. Agua-Field Publications, Inc., 66 W. Gilbert St., Shrewsbury, NJ 07702. TEL 908-842-8300. adv. circ. 167,633.

684 694 CN ISSN 0704-0717
CANADIAN WORKSHOP; the do-it-yourself magazine. 1977. m. Can.$25.95. (Canadian Workshop Magazine) Camar Publications Ltd., 130 Spy Court, Markham, Ont. L3R 5H6, Canada. TEL 416-475-8440. FAX 416-475-9246. Ed. Erina Kelly. adv.; bk.rev.; illus. circ. 125,000. **Indexed:** CMI, Ind.How To Do It (1980-).

CHILTON'S HARDWARE AGE; serving the North American hardware - home center market. see *BUILDING AND CONSTRUCTION — Hardware*

CONSUMER HOME AND GARDEN. see *GARDENING AND HORTICULTURE*

690 UK ISSN 0950-6500
D I Y REPORT. 1978-1986; resumed 1988. irreg. £375($750) Euromonitor, 87-88 Turnmill St., London EC1M 5QU, England. TEL 071-251 8024. FAX 071-608-3149. **Document type:** trade publication.
●Also available online.
Former titles: Do-It-Yourself Report (ISSN 0263-5437); Euromonitor Reports on D I Y and Home Improvement Markets (ISSN 0260-6542)
Description: Offers assessment of the U.K. do-it-yourself market.

690 638 UK
D I Y SUPERSTORE. (Do It Yourself) m. £40 (foreign £60). Wesley Barker Ltd., Colebrook House, Ducklington Rd., Witney, Oxon OX8 7TT, England. TEL 0993-706848. FAX 0993-706955. Ed. Andrew Ross. circ. 7,000. **Document type:** trade publication.
Description: Concerns the hardware industry.

683 UK ISSN 0954-8823
D I Y WEEK. (Do-It-Yourself) 1874. fortn. £58 (foreign £85). Benn Publications Ltd. (Subsidiary of: Morgan-Grampian plc), Benn House, Sovereign Way, Tonbridge, Kent TN9 1RW, England. TEL 0732-364422. FAX 0723-361534. Ed. Colin Petty. adv. contact: Christine Kemp. charts; illus.; mkt.; stat.; tr.lit.; tr.mk.; index. circ. 16,744. **Indexed:** Key to Econ.Sci. **Document type:** trade publication.
Incorporates: Hardware Trade Journal (ISSN 0017-7741); Domestic Electrical Appliances; Ironmonger; Hardware Merchandiser; Ironmongery and Hardware; Domestic Electrical Appliances, Lighting, Mercantile Guardian; Do-It-Yourself Retailing.

690 UK
DO-IT-YOURSELF (HAMPTON). 6th edt., 1987. every 18 mos. £155 per no. Key Note Publications Ltd., Field House, Old Field Rd., Hampton TW12 2HQ, England. TEL 01-783-0755.
Description: Review of the do-it-yourself industry of the U.K., including industry structure, market size and trends, recent developments and future prospects.

683 US ISSN 0889-2989
TS200
DO-IT-YOURSELF RETAILING; hardware, home centers, lumberyards. 1901. m. $15. National Retail Hardware Association, 5822 W. 74th St., Indianapolis, IN 46278. TEL 317-297-1190. FAX 317-328-4354. Ed. Mark Parrott. adv.; bk.rev.; charts; illus.; tr.lit.; index. circ. 70,000. **Indexed:** Bus.Ind., Tr.& Indus.Ind. **Document type:** trade publication.
Former titles (until Sep. 1984): Hardware Retailing (ISSN 0164-7695); Hardware Retailer (ISSN 0017-7725)

ECONOMIC HOME OWNER. see *BUILDING AND CONSTRUCTION*

ELECTRONIC SERVICING & TECHNOLOGY; the how-to magazine of electronics. see *ELECTRONICS*

ELEKTOR - ELECTRONIQUE. see *ELECTRONICS*

690 070.483 HU
EZERMESTER. 1957. m. $22. Dessewffy u.34, 1066 Budapest, Hungary. TEL 132-0542. TELEX 22-6423. Ed. J. Szucs. circ. 135,000.
Description: Covers do-it-yourself projects.

HUMANITIES: COMPREHENSIVE WORKS

690 US ISSN 0014-7230
TX323
FAMILY HANDYMAN; the do-it-yourself home improvement magazine. 1951. 10/yr. $19.97. Home Service Publications, Inc., 7900 International Dr., Ste. 950, Minneapolis, MN 55425. TEL 612-854-3000. FAX 612-854-8009. Ed. Gary Havens. adv.; bk.rev.; illus.; index. circ. 1,000,000. **Indexed:** Consum.Ind., Ind.How To Do It (1964-), Mag.Ind., MELSA, Pinpointer, PMR, R.G.
—Faxon; UnCover; UMI.
Incorporates: Home Garden (ISSN 0015-4482)
Description: Covers home remodeling and repairs for the do-it-yourself handy person. Includes auto and appliance repair, woodworking projects, new product reviews, and answers to reader problems.

690 DK ISSN 0901-4241
GOER DET SELV. m. DKK 34.50. Bonniers Specialmagasiner A-S, Strandboulevarden 130, 2100 Copenhagen OE, Denmark. Ed. Tim Johnson. illus.
Former titles: Goer det Selv i Hjemmet; Goer det Selv (ISSN 0107-6876)
Description: Do it yourself magazine on building, repair, tools and materials.

690 US ISSN 8755-0423
T1
HOME MECHANIX; managing your home. 1928. 10/yr. $13.94 (foreign $21.94). Times Mirror Magazines, Inc., 2 Park Ave., New York, NY 10016-5601. TEL 212-779-5000. FAX 212-779-5468. (Subscr. to: Box 54320, Boulder, CO 80322-4320. TEL 800-456-6369) Ed. Michael Chotinerk. adv.; bk.rev.; charts; illus.; pat. circ. 1,000,000. (also avail. in microform from UMI; back issues avail.; reprint service avail. from UMI) **Indexed:** Biog.Ind., Ind.How To Do It (1963-), Mag.Ind., MELSA, PMR, R.G., TOM. **Document type:** consumer publication.
—Faxon; UnCover; UMI.
Formerly (until 1985): Mechanix Illustrated (ISSN 0025-6587); **Incorporates:** Electronics Illustrated (ISSN 0013-5178)

HOME POWER; the hands-on journal of home-made power. see ENERGY

684 AT ISSN 1037-1354
HOUSE AND HOME WORKER. 1990. q. Aus.$12 (foreign Aus.$22.50). Skills Book Publishing Pty. Ltd., 40-44 Red Lion St., Rozelle, N.S.W. 2039, Australia. TEL 02-810-6222. FAX 02-818-5675. Ed. Arthur Burrows. adv. circ. 18,000. (back issues avail.) **Document type:** consumer publication.
Formerly (until 1991): Australian Home Woodworker (ISSN 1035-1108)
Description: Covers all aspects of home extension, renovation and improvement.

HOW; the magazine of ideas and techniques in graphic design. see PRINTING

684 SP ISSN 1133-1445
▼**MANERAS D**; hacer bricolage. 1993. m. 3400 ptas. Editorial Resistor, S.A., C. Maudes 15, entlo. C, 28003 Madrid, Spain. TEL 1-53-44-666. FAX 1-534-47-51. adv.; B&W page 200000 ptas. circ. 40,000. **Document type:** consumer publication.
Description: Covers bricolage and do-it-yourself projects.

690 FR
NEGOCE - CONSTRUCTION, AMENAGEMENT, DECORATION. 10/yr. Editions S E R I P, 40 rue Guy Moquet, 94501 Champigny sur Marne, France. TEL 48-81-91-91. FAX 48-81-81-77. Ed. Frances-Xavier Hermelin. circ. 12,000.

690 UK
NEW D I Y; for the practical man about the house. 1957. m. £29.70. Link House Magazines Ltd., Link House, Dingwall Ave., Croydon, Surrey CR9 2TA, England. TEL 081-686-2599. FAX 081-760-0973. (Subscr. to: C P G, 120-126 Lavender Ave., Mitcham, Surrey CR4 3HP, England) Ed. John McGowan. adv.; bk.rev.; charts; illus. **Document type:** consumer publication.
Formerly: Do It Yourself (ISSN 0012-4370)
Description: News about home improvement, maintenance and modernization. Includes product reviews and technical advice.

OWNER BUILDER MAGAZINE. see BUILDING AND CONSTRUCTION

620 US ISSN 0360-2273
TT155
POPULAR MECHANICS DO-IT-YOURSELF YEARBOOK. a. Hearst Magazines, Popular Mechanics, 224 W. 57th St., New York, NY 10019. illus.

PRATIQUE. see INTERIOR DESIGN AND DECORATION — Furniture And House Furnishings

691 FR
PROFESSION NEGOCIANT BRICOLAGE. 1987. 9/yr. 345 F. (foreign 435 F.). Publications du Moniteur, 17, Rue d'Uzes, 75002 Paris, France. TEL 1-40-13-30-30. FAX 1-40-26-55-87. TELEX UPRESSE 680876F. Ed. Gerard Pillet. circ. 12,000.
Formerly: Profession Negoce et Bricolage.

643.7 GW ISSN 0930-7133
PROFITIPS FUER SELBERMACHER; das aktuelle Bau- und Modernisierungsmagazin. m. DM.45 (foreign DM.57). Fachschriften Verlag GmbH, Hoehenstr. 17, 70736 Fellbach, Germany. TEL 0711-5206-256. FAX 0711-5281424. Ed. Elmar Haag-Schwilk; Pub. Ottmar Strebel. adv. contact: Wolfgang Kriwan. **Document type:** consumer publication.

R C C SERVICE MANUALS. (Radio College of Canada) see ELECTRONICS

690 CN ISSN 0381-0992
RENOVATION BRICOLAGE. (Text in French) 1976. m. Can.$27.95. Publicor Inc., 7 Chemin Bates, Outremont, Que. H2V 1A6, Canada. TEL 514-270-1100. FAX 514-270-6900. Ed. Andre Vilder. adv. circ. 72,493. **Indexed:** Pt.de Rep. (1981-).

690 GW
SELBST IST DER MANN. m. DM.64.80. Heinrich Bauer Spezialzeitschriftenverlag, Industriestr. 16, 50735 Cologne, Germany. TEL 0221-7709102. FAX 0221-714153. Ed. Ernst-Heinrich Schlichting. adv. contact: Sven Schrader. circ. 215,259. **Document type:** consumer publication.

690 FR ISSN 0151-3648
SPECIAL BRICOLAGE. q. 397 F. Societe d'Edition et de Presse, 106 bd. Malesherbes, 75017 Paris, France. adv.

VAKBLAD MIX. see BUILDING AND CONSTRUCTION — Hardware

747 US
▼**WEEKEND DECORATOR.** 1992. a. New York Times Company, Magazine Group, 110 Fifth Ave., New York, NY 10011. TEL 212-463-1574. adv.; illus. circ. 600,000. **Document type:** consumer publication.

684 US
WEEKEND WOODWORKING PROJECTS; neat things you can build in a hurry. 1987. bi-m. $24.97. Meredith Corporation, 1912 Grand Ave., Des Moines, IA 50309-3379. TEL 515-284-3000. Ed. Larry Clayton. circ. 200,000. **Indexed:** Ind.How To Do It (1988-). **Document type:** consumer publication.

684 US ISSN 1045-3040
TT180
WOODWORK. 1989. bi-m. $15 (effective Jan. 1992). Ross Periodicals, 42 Digital Dr., No. 5, Novato, CA 94949. TEL 415-382-0580. Ed. John McDonald. adv. contact: Stan Michelman. circ. 90,000. **Indexed:** Ind.How To Do It (1989-). **Document type:** consumer publication.
Description: How-to articles and plans for reproduction for all ages and ability. Includes woodworking techniques.

684 US ISSN 0199-1892
WOODWORKER'S JOURNAL. 1977. bi-m. $17.95. Madrigal Publishing Co., Inc., 517 Litchfield Rd., Box 1629, New Milford, CT 06776. TEL 203-355-2694. FAX 203-350-2165. Ed. James J. McQuillan. adv.; B&W page $3969, color page $5160; adv. contact: Lynda Morris. circ. 140,000. **Indexed:** Ind.How to Do It (1977-). **Document type:** consumer publication.
—UnCover.
Description: Gives project plans, techniques, step-by-step instruction, and practical information on machinery, tools and supplies for both hobbyists and professionals. Gives project plans and how-to articles for hobbyist wooodworkers.

684 US ISSN 0043-8057
GV1201
WORKBENCH; the do-it-yourself home improvement and woodworking magazine. 1946. bi-m. $12.95. K C Publishing Inc., 700 W. 74th St., Ste. 310, Kansas City, MO 64112. TEL 816-531-5730. FAX 816-531-3873. Ed. Robert N. Hoffman. adv.: B&W page $14200, color page $17500; trim77/8 x 103/4. bk.rev.; illus.; tr.lit.; index. circ. 816,733. (also avail. in microfilm from UMI; reprint service avail. from UMI) **Indexed:** Ind.How To Do It (1963-), Jun.High.Mag.Abstr., Mag.Ind., MELSA, PMR, R.G., TOM. **Document type:** consumer publication.
●Also available online. Vendor(s): DIALOG Information Services, Inc.
—Faxon; UnCover; UMI.
Description: Covers do-it-yourself home improvement and woodworking projects. Guides readers with with photos, drawings and detailed instructions.

WORLD SCANNER REPORT; a journal of VHF-UHF scanner technology & engineering. see COMMUNICATIONS — Radio

HOW-TO AND DO-IT-YOURSELF — Abstracting, Bibliographies, Statistics

745.5 US ISSN 0730-6466
HANDICRAFT - HOBBY INDEX; a current periodical index to doing, making, and building. 1980. bi-m. $78 (typically set in Nov.). Metropolitan Library Service Agency, 201 Hamline Park Plaza Bldg., 570 Asbury St., St. Paul, MN 55104. TEL 612-645-5731. FAX 612-649-3169. Ed. Sylvia Welygan. cum.index. circ. 250. (microfiche) **Document type:** abstracting/indexing.
Formerly (until 1984): M E L S A Do It Index.
Description: Gives a current, cumulative, annotated guide to how-to-do-it information located in over 30 popular and specialized periodicals.

011 US ISSN 0073-5930
Z7913
INDEX TO HOW TO DO IT INFORMATION; a periodical index. 1963. a. $35 (cum.index $50). Norman Lathrop Enterprises, 2342 Star Dr., Box 198, Wooster, OH 44691. TEL 216-262-5587. Ed. Norman Lathrop. cum.index: 1963-1989. **Document type:** abstracting/indexing.
Description: Annotated subject guide to "how-to" articles appearing in craft, hobby and how-to magazines.

HUMANITIES: COMPREHENSIVE WORKS

001.3 US ISSN 0065-7972
AS36
A C L S ANNUAL REPORT. 1957. a. free. American Council of Learned Societies, 228 E. 45th St., New York, NY 10017. TEL 212-697-1505. circ. 2,000. **Document type:** corporate report.

001.3
A C L S OCCASIONAL PAPERS. 1987. irreg. free. American Council of Learned Societies, 228 E. 45th St., New York, NY 10017. TEL 212-697-1505. Ed. Candace Frede. circ. 6,000. **Indexed:** Anthropol.Lit.

917 300 CN ISSN 0714-2579
A C S NEWSLETTER/A E C BULLETIN. (Text in English, French) 1978. q. Can.$40($45) to individuals; institutions Can.$75($80). Association for Canadian Studies, P.O. Box 8888, Sta. "A", Montreal, PQ H3C 3P8, Canada. TEL 514-987-7784. FAX 514-987-8210. Ed. Maryann Farkas. adv.: page Can.$400; adv. contact: Susan Hoeltken. bibl.; illus.; stat. circ. 950. (back issues avail.) **Indexed:** Can.Per.Ind. **Document type:** newsletter.
Description: Post-secondary Canadian teaching research.

A G B U ARARAT; quarterly journal of Armenian literature, history and the arts. (Armenian General Benevolent Union) see LITERATURE

001.3 US
A M S STUDIES IN CULTURAL HISTORY. irreg., no.3, 1993. (Abrahams Magazine Service) A M S Press, Inc., 56 E. 13th St., New York, NY 10003. TEL 212-777-4700. FAX 212-995-5413. **Document type:** academic/scholarly publication, monographic series.

HUMANITIES: COMPREHENSIVE WORKS

001.3 GW ISSN 0724-9624
DAS ABENDLAND; Forschungen zur Geschichte europaeischen Geisteslebens. Neue Folge. 1972. irreg., vol.21, 1993. price varies. Vittorio Klostermann, Frauenlobstr. 22, 60487 Frankfurt a.M., Germany. TEL 069-774011. FAX 069-708038. (Subscr. to: Postfach 900601, 60446 Frankfurt a.M., Germany) Eds. E. Heftrich. **Document type:** monographic series.

001.3 BE
ACADEMIAE ANALECTA. KLASSE DER LETTEREN. (Text in Dutch and English; summaries in English) 1938. 2/yr. price varies. Koninklijke Academie voor Wetenschappen, Letteren en Schone Kunsten van Belgie, 1 Hertogsstraat, B 1000 Brussels, Belgium. FAX 32-2-5110143. (Dist. by: N.V. Brepols, Steenweg op Tielen 68, 2300 Turnhout, Belgium) TEL 32-14-415463. FAX 32-14-428919) Ed. G. Verbeke. circ. 700. (back issues avail.) **Document type:** academic/scholarly publication.
  Former titles (until 1980): Koninklijke Academie voor Wetenschappen, Letteren en Schone Kunsten. Mededelingen. Klasse der Letteren (ISSN 0770-1241); (until 1972): Koninklijke Vlaamse Academie voor Wetenschappen, Letteren en Schone Kunsten. Mededelingen. Klasse der Letteren (ISSN 0770-1292)

ACADEMIE MALGACHE. BULLETIN D'INFORMATION ET DE LIAISON. see *SCIENCES: COMPREHENSIVE WORKS*

001.3 967 BE ISSN 0776-2933
ACADEMIE ROYALE DES SCIENCES D'OUTRE MER. CLASSE DES SCIENCES MORALES ET POLITIQUES. MEMOIRES IN 8/KONINKLIJKE ACADEMIE VOOR OVERZEESE WETENSCHAPPEN. KLASSE DER MORELE EN POLITIEKE WETENSCHAPPEN. VERHANDELINGEN IN 8. 1933; N.S. 1955. irreg., vol.51, no.2, 1991. price varies. Academie Royale des Sciences d'Outre-Mer - Koninklijke Academie voor Overzeese Wetenschappen, B.P. 3, 1 rue Defacqz, 1050 Brussels, Belgium. (Dist. by: Librairie Transatlantique, Chaussee de Wavre 126, 1050 Brussels) TEL 32-2-5124930) (back issues avail) **Document type:** monographic series.
  Former titles (until 1983): Academie Royale des Sciences d'Outre-Mer. Classe des Sciences Morales et Politiques. Collection in 8 (ISSN 0770-1799); (until 1963): Academie Royale des Sciences d'Outre-Mer. Classe des Sciences Morales et Politiques. Memoires in 8 (ISSN 0770-1845); (until 1960): Academie Royale des Sciences Coloniales. Classe des Sciences Morales et Politiques. Memoires in 8 (ISSN 0770-6510); (until 1954): Institut Royal Colonial Belge. Section des Sciences Morales et Politiques. Memoires - Collection in 8 (ISSN 0770-6669).

001.3 500 BE
ACADEMIE ROYALE DES SCIENCES, DES LETTRES ET DES BEAUX-ARTS DE BELGIQUE. ANNUAIRE. 1835. a. Academie Royale des Sciences, des Lettres et des Beaux-Arts de Belgique, Palais des Academies, 1 rue Ducale, 1000 Brussels, Belgium. (Subscr. to: Le Libraire Alain Ferraton, 162 Ch. de Charleroi, 1060 Brussels, Belgium) **Indexed:** Bibl.Ling.

001.3 BE ISSN 0378-0716
ACADEMIE ROYALE DES SCIENCES, DES LETTRES ET DES BEAUX-ARTS DE BELGIQUE. CLASSE DES BEAUX-ARTS. BULLETIN. 1846. m. 1000 BEF (foreign 1200 BEF). Academie Royale des Sciences, des Lettres et des Beaux-Arts de Belgique, Classe des Beaux-Arts, Palais des Academies, 1 rue Ducale, B-1000 Brussels, Belgium. (Dist. by: Le Libraire Alain Ferraton, 162 Ch. de Charleroi, B-1060 Brussels, Belgium) circ. 500. **Indexed:** RILA. **Document type:** bulletin.

001.3 BE
ACADEMIE ROYALE DES SCIENCES, DES LETTRES ET DES BEAUX-ARTS DE BELGIQUE. CLASSE DES LETTRES ET DES SCIENCES MORALES ET POLITIQUES. MEMOIRES. 1904. irreg. price varies. Academie Royale des Sciences, des Lettres et des Beaux-Arts de Belgique, Classe des Lettres et des Science Morales et Politiques, Palais des Academies, 1 rue Ducale, 1000 Brussels, Belgium. (Dist. by: Librarie Alain Ferration, 162 Ch. de Charleroi, 1060 Brussels, Belgium) Ed.Bd. circ. 1,000.

800 300 BE ISSN 0001-4133
ACADEMIE ROYALE DES SCIENCES, DES LETTRES ET DES BEAUX-ARTS DE BELGIQUE. CLASSE DES LETTRES ET SCIENCES MORALES ET POLITIQUES. BULLETIN. 1919. m. Academie Royale des Sciences, des Lettres et des Beaux-Arts de Belgique, Classe des Lettres et Sciences Morale et Politiques, Palais des Academies, 1 rue Ducale, 1000 Brussels. (Dist. by: Librairie Alain Ferraton, 162 Ch. de Charleroi, 1060- Brussels Belgium) illus.; index. circ. 700. **Indexed:** Bibl.Ling.

001.3 IT ISSN 1122-1380
ACCADEMIA DELLE SCIENZE DI TORINO. ATTI. PART 2. CLASSE DI SCIENZE MORALI, STORICHE E FILOLOGICHE. 1865. 2/yr. price varies. Accademia delle Scienze di Torino, Via Maria Vittoria 3, 10123 Turin, Italy. (Subscr. to: Bottega d'Erasmo via G. Ferrari 9, 10124 Turin, Italy) Ed. Silvio Romano. illus. circ. 700. **Indexed:** Bibl.Ling.
  Which supersedes in part (in 1928): Reale Accademia delle Scienze di Torino. Atti; **Former titles (until 1946):** Reale Accademia delle Scienze di Torino. Atti. Part 2. Classe di Scienze Morali, Storiche e Filologiche.

001.3 IT ISSN 1120-1622
ACCADEMIA DELLE SCIENZE DI TORINO. MEMORIE. PART 2. CLASSE DI SCIENZE MORALI, STORICHE E FILOLOGICHE. 1759. q. price varies. Accademia delle Scienze di Torino, Via Maria Vittoria 3, 10123 Turin, Italy. (Subscr. to: Bottega d'Erasmo, via G. Ferrari 9, 10124 Turin, Italy) Ed. Silvio Romano. illus. circ. 500.
  Formerly: Reale Accademia delle Scienze di Torino. Memorie. Part 2. Classe di Scienze Morali, Storiche e Filologiche (1926-1942) (ISSN 1120-1606); Which supersedes in part: Reale Accademia delle Scienze di Torino. Memorie (ISSN 1120-1592); Which was formerly (until 1818): Academie Royale des Sciences de Turin. Memoires (ISSN 1120-1576), which was formed by the 1813 merger of: Academie Impriale des Sciences Littrature et Beaux-Arts de Turin. Memoires. Sciences Physiques et Mathematiques (ISSN 1120-1568) and Academie Impriale des Sciences Littrature et Beaux-Arts de Turin. Memoires. Littrature et Beaux-Arts (ISSN 1120-1584).

ACCADEMIA LIGURE DI SCIENZE E LETTERE. ATTI. see *SCIENCES: COMPREHENSIVE WORKS*

001.3 IT ISSN 0393-2397
ACCADEMIA PETRARCA DI LETTERE, ARTI E SCIENZA. ATTI E MEMORIE. 1920. irreg., vol.58, 1993. price varies. Casa Editrice Leo S. Olschki, Casella Postale 66, 50100 Florence, Italy. TEL 055-6530684. FAX 055-6530214. **Document type:** academic/scholarly publication, proceedings.
  Description: Deals with literature, the arts and the sciences.

001.3 PL ISSN 0239-8605
ACCADEMIA POLACCA DELLE SCIENZE. CONFERENZE. Key Title: Conferenze - Accademia Polacca delle Scienze (1978). (Text in French or Italian) 1958. irreg., vol.100, 1992. price varies. (Polska Akademia Nauk, Stacja Naukowa w Rzymie, IT - Accademia Polacca delle Scienze, Centro Scientifico in Roma) Ossolineum, Publishing House of the Polish Academy of Sciences, Rynek 9, 50-106 Wroclaw, Poland. TEL 48-71-368-25. FAX 48-71-448-103. TELEX 0712771 OSS PL. **Indexed:** Math.R. **Document type:** monographic series.
  Former titles (until 1978): Accademia Polacca delle Scienze. Conferenze e Studi (ISSN 0208-5623); (until 1977): Accademia Polacca delle Scienze. Conferenze (ISSN 0079-3167)
  Description: Dissemination of Polish culture and scholarship abroad.

001.3 SW ISSN 0072-4823
ACTA REGIAE SOCIETATIS SCIENTIARUM ET LITTERARUM GOTHOBURGENSIS. HUMANIORA. (Contributions in various languages) 1967. irreg., no.31, 1990. price varies; also exchange basis. Kungliga Vetenskaps- och Vitterhets-Samhaellet i Goeteborg, c/o Goeteborgs Universitetsbibliotek, Box 5096, S-402 22 Goeteborg, Sweden. **Document type:** monographic series.
  Supersedes in part: Goeteborgs Kungliga Vetenskaps- och Vitterhets-Samhaelle. Handlingar.

001.3 500 SW ISSN 0347-4925
ACTA REGIAE SOCIETATIS SCIENTIARUM ET LITTERARUM GOTHOBURGENSIS. INTERDISCIPLINARIA. 1977. irreg., no.2, 1979. price varies; also exchange basis. Kungliga Vetenskaps- och Vitterhets-Samhaellet i Goeteborg, c/o Goeteborgs Universitetsbibliotek, Box 5096, S-402 22 Goeteborg, Sweden. **Document type:** monographic series.

001.3 PL ISSN 0860-7435
ACTA UNIVERSITATIS LODZIENSIS: FOLIA LIBRORUM. (Text in Polish; summaries in various languages) irreg. Wydawnictwo Uniwersytetu Lodzkiego, Ul. Jaracza 34, Lodz, Poland. TEL 331671. (Dist. by: Ars Polona-Ruch, Krakowskie Przedmiescie 7, Warsaw, Poland) **Document type:** academic/scholarly publication.
—BLDSC (0585.207250).
  Supersedes in part (in 1989): Acta Universitatis Lodziensis: Folia Scientiarum Artium et Librorum.

001.3 370 PL ISSN 0860-7443
ACTA UNIVERSITATIS LODZIENSIS: FOLIA SCIENTIAE ARTIUM ET LITTERARUM. (Text in Polish; summaries in various languages) irreg. Wydawnictwo Uniwersytetu Lodzkiego, Ul. Jaracza 34, Lodz, Poland. TEL 331671. (Dist. by: Ars Polona-Ruch, Krakowskie Przedmiescie 7, Warsaw, Poland) **Document type:** academic/scholarly publication.
—BLDSC (0585.208600).
  Supersedes in part (in 1989): Acta Universitatis Lodziensis: Folia Scientiarum Artium et Librorum.
  Description: Presents articles about history of theatre, drama and film.

001.3 PL
▼**ACTA UNIVERSITATIS WRATISLAVIENSIS. NIEMCOZNAWSTWO.** (Text in Polish; summaries in English or German) 1993. irreg. price varies. (Uniwersytet Wroclawski) Wydawnictwo Uniwersytetu Wroclawskiego, Pl. Uniwersytecki 9-13, 50-137 Wroclaw, Poland. TEL 44-10-06. (Dist. by: Ksiegarnia Uniwersytetu Wroclawskiego, Pl. Uniwersytecki 9-13, 50-137 Wroclaw, Poland) Ed. Karol Fiedor. circ. 300. **Document type:** academic/scholarly publication.

001.3 PL ISSN 0860-6668
ACTA UNIVERSITATIS WRATISLAVIENSIS. PRACE KULTUROZNAWCZE. (Text in Polish; summaries in English) 1987. irreg. price varies. (Uniwersytet Wroclawski) Wydawnictwo Uniwersytetu Wroclawskiego, Pl. Uniwersytecki 9-13, 50-137 Wroclaw, Poland. TEL 44-10-06. (Dist. by: Ksiagarnia Uniwersytetu Wroclawskiego, Pl. Uniwersytecki 9-13, 50-137 Wroclaw, Poland) Ed. Stanislaw Pietraszko. circ. 300. **Document type:** academic/scholarly publication.

ACTA WASAENSIA. see *BUSINESS AND ECONOMICS — Economic Systems And Theories, Economic History*

001.3 SJ ISSN 0302-8844
ADDAB JOURNAL. (Text in English, French) 1972. a. (University of Khartoum, Faculty of Arts) Khartoum University Press, P.O. Box 321, Khartoum, Sudan. Ed. Ali Abdalla Abbas. bk.rev.

AFRICA 2001; dialogue with the future. see *SOCIAL SCIENCES: COMPREHENSIVE WORKS*

001.3 US
AITIA MAGAZINE; humanities magazine. 1972. 3/yr. $14 for 2 yrs. to individuals; institutions 16. State University of New York at Farmingdale, Center for Philosophy, Law, Citizenship, Knapp Hall 15, Farmingdale, NY 11735. TEL 516-420-2050. FAX 516-420-2698. Ed. James P. Friel. adv.: B&W page $100; 5 1/2 x 8 1/2. bk.rev.; film rev.; play rev.; abstr.; bibl.; illus.; stat.; circ. 3,000 (controlled). (back issues avail.) **Document type:** academic/scholarly publication.
  Description: Contains course outlines and articles about the environment.

001.3 ER ISSN 0235-7771
AKADEEMIA. (Text in Estonian; summaries in English) 1989. m. $30. (Ministry of Culture and Education) Kirjastus Perioodika, Parnu mnt.8, 0090 Tallinn, Estonia. TEL 441-262. FAX 442-484. (Subscr. to: Akadeemia, Postkast 80, Kuutri 1, EE 2400 Tartu, Estonia) Ed. Ain Kaalep. adv.; bk.rev.; abstr.; bibl.; charts; illus.; index. circ. 3,400.

HUMANITIES: COMPREHENSIVE WORKS

300 001.3   GW   ISSN 0002-2977
AS182
AKADEMIE DER WISSENSCHAFTEN UND DER LITERATUR. GEISTES- UND SOZIALWISSENSCHAFTLICHE KLASSE. ABHANDLUNGEN. 1950. irreg. price varies. Franz Steiner Verlag Wiesbaden GmbH, Birkenwaldstr. 44, 70919 Stuttgart, Germany. TEL 0711-2582-0. FAX 0711-2582290. TELEX 723636-DAZ-D. (Subscr. to: Postfach 101061, 70009 Stuttgart, Germany) bibl.; charts; illus.; index. **Indexed:** Bibl.Ling. **Document type:** monographic series.
—Faxon.

AKADEMIE DER WISSENSCHAFTEN UND DER LITERATUR, MAINZ. JAHRBUCH. see *SCIENCES: COMPREHENSIVE WORKS*

001.3 370   VE
ALBARREGAS.* 1976. irreg. Universidad de los Andes, Facultad de Humanidades y Educacion, Via los Chorras de Milla, C.P. 5101, Merida, Venezuela. (Dist. by: Oficina Distribucion de Publicaciones, Av. Andres Bello-Via la Parroquia, Merida, Venezuela) Ed. Ramon Palomares. circ. 2,500.

001.3 378   GW   ISSN 0342-6785
AS911
ALEXANDER VON HUMBOLDT FOUNDATION. ANNUAL REPORT. German edition: Alexander von Humboldt-Stiftung. Jahresbericht (ISSN 0172-3111) (Text in English) 1954. a. free. Alexander von Humboldt-Stiftung, Jean-Paul-Str. 12, 53173 Bonn, Germany. TEL 0228-833-0. FAX 0228-833-199. TELEX 885627. Ed. Heinrich Pfeiffer. index, cum.index: 1953-1993. **Document type:** corporate report.
Description: Report on the activities of the framework of the foundation's international research promotion.

001.3   GW   ISSN 0344-0354
ALEXANDER VON HUMBOLDT-STIFTUNG. MITTEILUNGEN. 1958. s-a. Alexander von Humboldt-Stiftung, Jean-Paul-Str. 12, 53173 Bonn, Germany. TEL 0228-833-0. FAX 0228-833199. Ed. Heinrich Pfeiffer. bibl.; illus. circ. 22,000. **Document type:** newsletter.
Description: News and other information about the foundation's actual researchers' results and the AvH follow-up program.

001.3   IT
ALMANACCO DELLA CALABRIA. 1991. a. Casella Postale 86, 88046 Lamezia Terme (CZ), Italy. TEL 0698-27473. Ed. Giuseppe Grisolia.

001.3 061   US
AS36
AMERICAN ACADEMY OF ARTS AND LETTERS. PROCEEDINGS. 1951. a. $15 to individuals; libraries $12. American Academy of Arts and Letters, 633 W. 155th St., New York, NY 10032. TEL 212-368-5900. FAX 212-491-4615. circ. 650. (back issues avail.) **Indexed:** Curr.Cont. **Document type:** proceedings.
—Faxon.
Former titles: American Academy and Institute of Arts and Letters. Proceedings (ISSN 0145-8493); American Academy of Arts and Letters. Proceedings (ISSN 0065-6836)
Description: Includes citations of new members and award winners, tributes to deceased members, and transcript of annual induction and award ceremony.

001.3 500   US   ISSN 0002-712X
AS36
AMERICAN ACADEMY OF ARTS AND SCIENCES. BULLETIN. 1948. 8/yr. $8. American Academy of Arts and Sciences, 136 Irving St., Cambridge, MA 02138. TEL 617-492-8800. FAX 617-576-5088. Ed. Alexandra Oleson. circ. 3,500. (also avail. in microform from UMI; reprint service avail. from UMI) **Indexed:** Amer.Hist.& Life (until 1991), Hist.Abstr. (until 1991).
—BLDSC (2385.200000); UMI.

AMERICAN BOOK REVIEW. see *LITERARY AND POLITICAL REVIEWS*

001.3   US   ISSN 1041-5963
AS36
AMERICAN COUNCIL OF LEARNED SOCIETIES. NEWSLETTER. Short title: A C L S Newsletter. 1987. q. free. American Council of Learned Societies, 228 E. 45th St., New York, NY 10017. TEL 212-697-1505. Ed. Candace Frede. circ. 10,000. **Indexed:** Anthropol.Lit., P.A.I.S., Sociol.Abstr. **Document type:** newsletter.

001.3 300   US   ISSN 0277-7126
P99
AMERICAN JOURNAL OF SEMIOTICS. 1981. q. $30. Semiotic Society of America, c/o Dean MacCannell, Applied Behavioral Sciences, University of California, Davis, CA 95616. TEL 916-752-6437. Eds. Dean MacCannell, Juliet Flower MacCannell. bk.rev. circ. 810. **Indexed:** Arts & Hum.Cit.Ind., Bibl.Ling., Curr.Cont., Lang.& Lang.Behav.Abstr., M.L.A., Sociol.Abstr.
—BLDSC (0838.130000); UnCover.

AMERICAN PHILOSOPHICAL SOCIETY. PROCEEDINGS. see *HISTORY*

970 300   US   ISSN 0003-0678
AP2
AMERICAN QUARTERLY. 1949. q. $59 to institutions (foreign $68). (American Studies Association) Johns Hopkins University Press, Journals Publishing Division, 2715 N. Charles St., Baltimore, MD 21218. TEL 410-516-6987. FAX 410-516-6968. Eds. Gary Kulik, Mary Corbin Sies. adv.; bk.rev.; bibl.; charts; illus.; cum.index. circ. 5,010. (also avail. in microform from MIM,UMI; reprint service avail. from KTO) **Indexed:** Abstr.Engl.Stud., Acad.Ind., Amer.Hist.& Life, Arts & Hum.Cit.Ind., Bk.Rev.Ind. (1990-), CERDIC, Child.Bk.Rev.Ind. (1990-), Curr.Cont., Film Lit.Ind. (1990-), Hist.Abstr., Hum.Ind., LCR, M.L.A., Mid.East: Abstr.& Ind., Rel.Ind.One.
—BLDSC (0853.440000); Faxon; UnCover; SWETS. CCC.
Description: Serves as a guide to studies in the culture of the United States. Promotes a broad humanistic understanding of American culture, encourages scholars from diverse disciplines to exchange ideas on America, and examines the ways American life relates to world society.

AMERICAN STUDIES. see *SOCIAL SCIENCES: COMPREHENSIVE WORKS*

970 300   US   ISSN 0883-105X
AP2
AMERICAN STUDIES INTERNATIONAL. 1962. 2/yr. journal and 2/yr. newsletter. $22 to individuals; institutions and foreign $30. George Washington University, American Studies Program, 2108 G St. N.W., Washington, DC 20052. TEL 202-994-7368. FAX 202-994-8651. TELEX 3730526. Eds. Bernard Mergen, Lisa Johnson Bedell. adv.; bk.rev.; illus. circ. 1,000. (also avail. in microform from UMI) **Indexed:** A.B.C.Pol.Sci., Amer.Hist.& Life, Arts & Hum.Cit.Ind., Curr.Cont., Hist.Abstr., Hum.Ind., M.L.A. **Document type:** academic/scholarly publication, newsletter.
—Faxon; UnCover; SWETS; UMI.
Formerly: American Studies News.

300 980 970   US   ISSN 0379-0940
F1401
AMERICAS. Spanish edition (ISSN 0379-0975) 1949. bi-m. $15. (Organization of American States) Americas Magazine, 19th St. & Constitution Ave., N.W., Ste. 300, Washington, DC 20006. TEL 202-458-3278. FAX 202-458-6217. (Subscr. to: Box 2103, Knoxville, IA 50198. TEL 800-284-6746) Ed. Rebecca Medrano. bk.rev.; illus. circ. 50,000 (combined). (microfilm; also avail. in microform from UMI) **Indexed:** Abr.R.G., Acad.Ind., Amer.Hist.& Life, Arts & Hum.Cit.Ind., Bk.Rev.Ind., Curr.Cont., Hisp.Amer.Per.Ind., Hist.Abstr., Hum.Ind., Ind.Bk.Rev.Hum., Key to Econ.Sci., M.L.A., Mag.Ind., Peace Res.Abstr, PMR, R.G., SSCI.
● Also available on CD-ROM.
—UnCover; UMI.
Description: Presents cultural interests in the western world.

AMNESTY INTERNATIONAL. CANADIAN SECTION (ENGLISH SPEAKING). BULLETIN. see *POLITICAL SCIENCE — Civil Rights*

001.3   NE   ISSN 0926-5600
AMSTERDAM MONOGRAPHS IN AMERICAN STUDIES. (Text in English) 1991. irreg. price varies. Editions Rodopi B.V., Keizersgracht 302-304, 1016 EX Amsterdam, Netherlands. TEL 31-20-6227507. FAX 31-20-6380948. (In N. America: 233 Peachtree Rd., N.E., Ste. 404, Atlanta, GA 30303-1504. TEL 800-225-3998) Ed. Bob Kroes. **Document type:** monographic series.
Description: Covers topics in American studies. *Refereed Serial*

001.3   CU
ANALES DEL CARIBE. a. $12 in S. America; N. America $14; elsewhere $16. Ediciones Cubanas, Obispo No. 527, Apdo. 605, Havana, Cuba.

060   US   ISSN 0066-1694
AS911
ANDREW W. MELLON FOUNDATION. REPORT. 1969. a. free. Andrew W. Mellon Foundation, 140 E. 62nd St., New York, NY 10021. TEL 212-838-8400. circ. 3,000. **Document type:** newsletter.
Supersedes: Avalon Foundation. Report; Old Dominion Foundation. Report.

ANGLES. see *LINGUISTICS*

001.3   GW   ISSN 0344-8266
ANGLISTIK UND ENGLISCHUNTERRICHT. (Text in English, German) 1977. 3/yr. DM.60 (students DM.50). Universitaetsverlag C. Winter Heidelberg GmbH, Hans-Bunte-Str. 18, 69123 Heidelberg, Germany. Ed.Bd. circ. 800. (back issues avail.) **Indexed:** M.L.A. **Document type:** academic/scholarly publication.
—BLDSC (0902.777200).

ANGLO-SAXON ENGLAND. see *HISTORY — History Of Europe*

ANIMA; the journal of human experience. see *NEW AGE PUBLICATIONS*

ANIMA. see *PSYCHOLOGY*

001.3   FI   ISSN 0355-113X
ANNALES ACADEMIAE SCIENTIARUM FENNICAE. DISSERTATIONES HUMANARUM LITTERARUM. (Text in English, French, German and Latin) 1973. irreg. (3-5/yr.). price varies. Suomalainen Tiedeakatemia - Academia Scientiarum Fennicae, Mariankatu 5, FIN-00170 Helsinki, Finland. FAX 358-0-622-1121. (Dist. by: The Bookstore Tiedekirja, Kirkkokatu 14, SF-00170 Helsinki, Finland) Ed. Heikki Palva. circ. 250. (reprint service avail. from UMI) **Indexed:** M.L.A.

001.3   FI   ISSN 0066-2011
Q60
ANNALES ACADEMIAE SCIENTIARUM FENNICAE. SERIES B. (Text in English, French, German) 1909. irreg. (5-6/yr.). price varies. Suomalainen Tiedeakatemia - Academia Scientiarum Fennica, Mariankatu 5, FIN-00170 Helsinki, Finland. (Orders to: The Bookstore Tiedekirja, Kirkkokatu 14, SF-00170 Helsinki, Finland) Ed. Pekka Suvanto. cum.index: 1909-1968 in vol.150. circ. 300. (back issues avail.; reprint service avail. from UMI) **Indexed:** Abstr.Engl.Stud., Amer.Hist.& Life, Bibl.Ling., Bull.Signal., Hist.Abstr., Lang.& Lang.Behav.Abstr., Psychol.Abstr.

900 940   SZ   ISSN 0263-7383
PQ2211.C24
ANNALES BENJAMIN CONSTANT. 1980. a. 45 SFr. Institut Benjamin Constant, Universite de Lausanne, CH-1015 Lausanne, Switzerland. FAX 021-6923230. bk.rev. circ. 500. (back issues avail.) **Document type:** academic/scholarly publication.

HUMANITIES: COMPREHENSIVE WORKS

001.3   US   ISSN 0192-2858
AS30
ANNALS OF SCHOLARSHIP; an international quarterly in the humanities and social sciences. 1980. q. $32 to individuals; institutions $60 (effective through 1995). Wayne State University Press, The Leonard N. Simons Bldg., 5959 Woodward Ave., Detroit, MI 48202. TEL 313-577-6120. FAX 313-577-6131. Ed. Marie Rose Logan. adv.; bk.rev. circ. 500. (back issues avail.) **Indexed:** M.L.A. **Document type:** academic/scholarly publication.
—BLDSC (1043.950000); Faxon; UnCover.
    Description: Deals with the Connections among philosophy, history, sociology, literature, and the arts. Explores the history and current development of disciplinary criteria and the ways in which research influences and is influenced by institutional, political or social factors.

ANSTOESSE; aus der Arbeit der Evangelischen Akademie Hofgeismar. see *RELIGIONS AND THEOLOGY*

001.3 020   SP   ISSN 0211-5611
Z2685
ANTHROPOS; revista de documentacion cientifica de la cultura. 1981. 12/yr. 9714 ptas. (foreign 10700 ptas.). Promat, Sociedad Cooperativa Ltda., Apdo. 387, 08190 Sant Cugat del Valles (Barcelona), Spain. TEL 93-674-60-04. FAX 93-674-17-33. Dir. Ramon Gabarros Cardona. adv.; bk.rev. circ. 10,000. **Indexed:** SSCI.
    Description: Investigates and documents the leading creative cultural agents and producers of thought in Spain.

001.3 020   SP   ISSN 1130-4936
DP48
ANTHROPOS. DOCUMENTOS A; genealogia cientifica de la cultura. 1990. s-a. 4680 ptas. (foreign 5300 ptas.). Promat, Sociedad Cooperativa, Ltda., Apdo. 387, 08190 Sant Cugat del Valles (Barcelona), Spain. TEL 93-674-60-04. FAX 93-674-17-33. adv.; bk.rev. circ. 5,000.
    Description: Covers significant subjects or influential works that shape contemporary culture.

001.3 020   SP   ISSN 1130-2089
ANTHROPOS. SUPLEMENTOS. 1988. 6/yr. 10573 ptas. (foreign 11100 ptas.). Promat, Sociedad Cooperativa, Ltda., Apdo. 387, 08190 Sant Cugat del Valles (Barcelona), Spain. TEL 93-674-60-04. FAX 93-674-17-33. Dir. Ramon Gabarros Cardona.
    Description: Contains further information on subjects covered in Anthropos.

001.3   LY
AOUZOU. a. Sebha University, P.O. Box 18758, Sebha, Libya. TEL 71-21575. TELEX 30622.

001.3   BL
AQUIRI; caderno de cultura. 1989. irreg. Fundacao Cultural do Acre, Rua Rio Grande do Sul s/n, 69900 Rio Branco, Acre, Brazil. TEL 068-224-6890.

ARCHIVAL ISSUES. see *HISTORY*

001.3   CK   ISSN 0570-7293
AP63
ARCO; revista de temas de actualidad. 1959. m. Col.500($50) Promotora de Medios de Comunicacion Social, Carrera 6 no. 35-39, Apdo. Aereo 8624, Bogota D.E., Colombia. TEL 285-1500. TELEX 45153. Dir. Alvaro Valencia Tovar. adv.; illus. circ. 10,000.

L'ARCO DI GIANO; revista di medical humanities. see *MEDICAL SCIENCES*

001.3   PE
ARETE. 1990. s-a. $24. Pontificia Universidad Catolica del Peru, Departamento de Humanidades, Fondo Editorial, Apdo. 1761, Lima 100, Peru. TEL 626390. FAX 5114-611785. Ed. Pepa Patron.

700 800   IS   ISSN 0004-1343
AP8
ARIEL (ENGLISH EDITION); the Israeli review of arts and letters. Finnish edition (ISSN 0333-6409); French edition (ISSN 0334-4916); German edition (ISSN 0334-2719); Spanish edition (ISSN 0334-4967) (Arabic, Russian editions also avail.) 1962. q. $27 (effective 1993). (Ministry for Foreign Affairs) Youval Tal Ltd., P.O. Box 2160, Jerusalem 91021, Israel. FAX 972-2-380626. (Editorial addr.: 214 Jaffa St., Jerusalem 91130, Israel. TEL 972-2-381515) Ed. Asher Weill. bk.rev.; illus. circ. 35,000. (also avail. in microfiche from IDC) **Indexed:** Arts & Hum.Cit.Ind., Ind.Jew.Per., M.L.A.
—Faxon.
    Description: Publishes articles on literature, archaeology, architecture, film, theater, music, the arts and general culture in Israel, as well as fiction and poetry.

ARION; a journal of humanities and the classics. see *CLASSICAL STUDIES*

001.3 500   PH   ISSN 0115-6950
ARTS & SCIENCES JOURNAL. (Text in English) 1981-1982; resumed. s-a. (Mindanao State University, College of Arts & Sciences) Mindanao State University, Mamitua Saber Research Center, P.O. Box 5594, Iligan City 9200, Philippines. circ. 500 (controlled). **Document type:** academic/scholarly publication.

001.3   FR   ISSN 0181-1835
ARTUS. 1979. q. 150 F.($20) Artus, P.O. Box 26, 56200 La Gacilly, France. (Subscr. to: P.O. Box 27, 44007 Nantes Cedex 01, France) Ed. Herve Giot. bk.rev. circ. 3,000. (back issues avail.)

ASIAN THOUGHT AND SOCIETY: AN INTERNATIONAL REVIEW. see *SOCIAL SCIENCES: COMPREHENSIVE WORKS*

001.3   II
ASSAM ACADEMY REVIEW. (Text in English) s-a. Assam Academy for Cultural Relations, Chandmari, Guwahati 781003, India. Ed. Pradip Jyoti Mahanta.

500 800 700   CL   ISSN 0716-1840
AP63
ATENEA (YEAR); revista de ciencia, arte y literatura. (Text in Spanish) 1924. s-a. $24. Universidad de Concepcion, Biblioteca Central Campus Universitario, Casilla 1557, Concepcion, Chile. Ed. Tito Castillo. adv.; bk.rev.; illus. circ. 2,000. **Indexed:** Amer.Hist.& Life, Hisp.Amer.Per.Ind., Hist.Abstr.
—BLDSC (1765.860000); UnCover.
    Former titles: Nueva Atenea; Atenea (ISSN 0004-6507)

020   US   ISSN 0067-057X
AUGUSTANA LIBRARY PUBLICATIONS. Variant title: Augustana College Library Publications. 1898. irreg., no.36, 1992. price varies. Augustana College, Library, Rock Island, IL 61201. TEL 309-794-7266. FAX 309-794-7230. circ. 1,000. **Document type:** monographic series.

AULA. see *EDUCATION*

001.3   AT   ISSN 1320-243X
▼**AUSTRALIAN ACADEMY OF THE HUMANITIES. LECTURE SERIES (NO.)**. 1993. irreg. price varies. Australian Academy of the Humanities, G.P.O. Box 93, Canberra, A.C.T. 2601, Australia. TEL 6-06-248774. FAX 6-06-2486287. E-mail: aah@anu.edu.au. Ed. Christine Alexander. illus.

001.3   AT
AUSTRALIAN ACADEMY OF THE HUMANITIES. OCCASIONAL PAPERS (NO.). 1972. irreg. price varies. Australian Academy of the Humanities, G.P.O. Box 93, Canberra, A.C.T. 2601, Australia. TEL 6-06-2487744. FAX 6-06-2486287. E-mail: aah@anu.edu.au. Ed.Bd. illus.; maps.

001.3   AT   ISSN 0067-1592
AUSTRALIAN ACADEMY OF THE HUMANITIES. PROCEEDINGS. 1970. a. price varies. Australian Academy of the Humanities, G.P.O. Box 93, Canberra, A.C.T. 2601, Australia. TEL 6-06-2487744. FAX 6-06-2486287. E-mail: aah@anu.edu.au. Ed. H.H.R. Love. circ. 1,000. **Document type:** proceedings.

001.3   AT   ISSN 0818-8149
AUSTRALIAN SLAVONIC AND EAST EUROPEAN STUDIES. (Text in English and Russian) 1967. s-a. Aus.$25. University of Melbourne, Department of Russian, Parkville, Vic. 3052, Australia. TEL 03-344-5193. FAX 03-344-7821. Ed. Paul Cubberley. adv.; bk.rev. circ. 150. (also avail. in microfilm from UMI) **Indexed:** Bibl.Ling., M.L.A. **Document type:** academic/scholarly publication.
—BLDSC (1820.330000); UnCover.
    Formerly: Melbourne Slavonic Studies (ISSN 0076-6267)
    Description: Publishes scholarly articles, review articles and short reviews on all aspects of Slovonic and East European studies, in particular language, literature, history and political science; also art and social science.

B C STUDIES. see *SOCIAL SCIENCES: COMPREHENSIVE WORKS*

BANCO DE LA REPUBLICA. BIBLIOTECA LUIS ANGEL ARANGO. BOLETIN CULTURAL Y BIBLIOGRAFICO. see *BIBLIOGRAPHIES*

BAR-ILAN: ANNUAL OF BAR-ILAN UNIVERSITY. see *RELIGIONS AND THEOLOGY* — *Judaic*

BASIS; majalah bulanan kebudayaan umum/monthly for culture in general. see *ART*

900   GW   ISSN 0005-710X
AS182
BAYERISCHE AKADEMIE DER WISSENSCHAFTEN. PHILOSOPHISCH-HISTORISCHE KLASSE. ABHANDLUNGEN, N.F.. 1929. irreg. price varies. Bayerische Akademie der Wissenschaften, Marstallplatz 8, 80539 Munich, Germany. FAX 089-23031-100. circ. 700. **Indexed:** Anthropol.Lit., Bibl.Ling. **Document type:** academic/scholarly publication.

900   GW   ISSN 0342-5991
AS182
BAYERISCHE AKADEMIE DER WISSENSCHAFTEN. PHILOSOPHISCH-HISTORISCHE KLASSE. SITZUNGSBERICHTE. irreg. (3-6/yr.). Bayerische Akademie der Wissenschaften, Marstallplatz 8, 80539 Munich, Germany. FAX 089-23031100. **Indexed:** Bibl.Ling., M.L.A. **Document type:** academic/scholarly publication.

001.531   CC   ISSN 1000-3541
AS452.H3194
BEIFANG LUNCONG/NORTHERN FORUM. (Text in Chinese; table of contents in English) 1979. bi-m. Y9 (effective since 1989). (Harbin Shifan Daxue - Harbin Normal University) Beifang Luncong Bianjibu, 24 Hexing Lu, Nangang Qu, Harbin, Heilongjiang 150080, People's Republic of China. (Dist. outside China by: China International Book Trading Corp., P.O. Box 399, Beijing, P.R.C.) Ed. Qi Liangzu. adv.; bk.rev.
    Description: Contains papers on literature, psychology, sociology, linguistics. Also includes news of academic activities.

001.3   CC   ISSN 1000-5919
BEIJING DAXUE XUEBAO (ZHEXUE SHEHUI KEXUE BAN)/BEIJING UNIVERSITY. JOURNAL (PHILOSOPHY AND SOCIAL SCIENCE EDITION). (Text in Chinese; table of contents in English, Russian) 1955. bi-m. (Beijing University) Beijing University Press, Haidian Qu, Beijing 100871, People's Republic of China. TEL 86-1-2501216. bibl. circ. 6,500. **Document type:** academic/scholarly publication.
—BLDSC (4839.636000).
    Description: Contains research papers and dissertations in the fields of philosophy and social sciences.

001.3   SP   ISSN 0210-8550
BERCEO. 1946. s-a. 1200 ptas. (foreign 1500 ptas.). Instituto de Estudios Riojanos, C. Calvo Sotelo 15, 26071 Logrono, Spain. TEL 41-29-13-05. FAX 41-29-13-07. Dir. Jose Miguel Delgado Idarreta. illus. **Document type:** academic/scholarly publication.
    Description: Covers archaeology, architecture, the arts, anthropology, ethnology, law, geography, history, linguistics, literature, music, philosophy, political science and sociology.

BHAVAN'S JOURNAL. see *LITERATURE*

BIBLION. see *LIBRARY AND INFORMATION SCIENCES*

080   IT   ISSN 0067-7434
BIBLIOTECA DI LABEO. 1964. irreg. price varies. Casa Editrice Dott. Eugenio Jovene, Via Mezzocannone, 109, 80134 Naples, Italy. TEL 081-5521019. FAX 081-5520687. Ed.Bd. bk.rev.

080   IT   ISSN 0067-7469
BIBLIOTECA DO EDUCADOR PROFISSIONAL. 1968. irreg., no.130, 1993. price varies. Livros Horizonte, Lda., Rua das Chagas, 17, 1121 Lisbon Codex, Portugal. TEL 1-3466917. FAX 1-3426921. Ed. Rogerio Mendes de Moura.

001.3   SP
BIBLIOTECA N T; coleccion cultural de bolsillo. 1975. irreg., no.121, 1990. price varies. Ediciones Universidad de Navarra, S.A., Apdo. 396, 31080 Pamplona, Spain. TEL 94 825 6850.
   Formerly: Temas N T.

800 011   CU   ISSN 0006-1727
Z897
BIBLIOTECA NACIONAL JOSE MARTI. REVISTA. 1909; N.S. 1959. 3/yr. $15. Biblioteca Nacional Jose Marti, Plaza de la Revolucion, Apdo. 6881, Havana, Cuba. TEL 79-6091. TELEX 511963. Distr. by: Ediciones Cubanas, Obispo No. 527, Apdo. 605, Havana, Cuba) Ed. Julio Le Riverend. bk.rev.; bibl.; illus. circ. 2,000. (tabloid format; also avail. in microfilm) **Indexed**: Amer.Hist.& Life, Hisp.Amer.Per.Ind., Hist.Abstr., Lib.Lit.
   —BLDSC (7804.735000).

BIDRAG TILL KAENNEDOM AV FINLANDS NATUR OCH FOLK. see *SOCIAL SCIENCES: COMPREHENSIVE WORKS*

800   IS   ISSN 0084-9456
BIKORET VEPARSHANUT/CRITICISM AND INTERPRETATION; journal for literature, linguistics, history and aesthetics. (Text in Hebrew; summaries in English) 1970. s-a. $14 per no. (Bar-Ilan University) Bar-Ilan University Press, Ramat Gan 52900, Israel. TEL 972-3-5318401. Ed. H. Weiss. (back issues avail.) **Indexed**: Ind.Heb.Per. **Document type**: academic/scholarly publication.

001.3   SP
BOLETIN ACEPRENSA. 1970. w. 14300 ptas.($110) (effective 1994). Aceprensa, S.A., Nunez de Balboa, 125, 28006 Madrid, Spain. TEL 341-5628712. FAX 341-563-7243. Ed. Ignacio Arechaga. bk.rev.; film rev.; index. circ. 3,200. (looseleaf format; back issues avail.) **Document type**: newsletter.

BOOK FORUM. see *PUBLISHING AND BOOK TRADE*

001.3   US   ISSN 0276-9220
AS30
BORDERLANDS JOURNAL. 1977. s-a. $8 to individuals; institutions $16. Texas Southmost College, Border Research Department, 80 Fort Brown, Brownsville, TX 78520. TEL 512-544-8225. (Co-sponsor: South Texas Institute of Latin and Mexican American Research) Ed. Anthony N. Zavaleta. bk.rev. circ. 500. **Indexed**: Hisp.Amer.Per.Ind.
   Formerly: South Texas Journal of Research and the Humanities (ISSN 0198-7542)

700   NE   ISSN 0006-8624
BRABANTIA. 1952. 10/yr. fl.55. Noordbrabants Genootschap, P.O. Box 1104, 5200 BD 's-Hertogenbosch, Netherlands. TEL 31-73-139484. Ed. Th. Hoogbergen. adv.; bk.rev. circ. 1,700.
   —SWETS.

001.3   PO
BRIGANTIA; revista de cultura. 1981. q. Esc.700. Secretaria da Assembleia Distrital, Arquivo Distrital, Apdto. 125, 5300 Braganca, Portugal. Ed. Belarmino Afonso.

800 300   US   ISSN 0007-0106
AS30
BRIGHAM YOUNG UNIVERSITY STUDIES. 1959. q. $15. Brigham Young University, 2246 SFLC, Provo, UT 84602. TEL 801-378-6691. Ed. John W. Welch. bk.rev.; bibl.; charts; illus.; index. circ. 4,000. (also avail. in microform from UMI; reprint service avail. from UMI) **Indexed**: Abstr.Engl.Stud., Amer.Hist.& Life, Arts & Hum.Cit.Ind., Arts & Hum.Cit.Ind., Curr.Cont., Hist.Abstr., M.L.A., Rel.Ind.One. **Document type**: academic/scholarly publication.
   —Faxon; UnCover.
   Description: Scholarly articles reflecting a Latter-day Saint point of view.

001.3   NE   ISSN 0920-8607
BRILL'S STUDIES IN INTELLECTUAL HISTORY. 1987. irreg., no.51, 1994. price varies. E.J. Brill, P.O. Box 9000, 2300 PA Leiden, Netherlands. TEL 31-71-312624. FAX 31-71-317532. TELEX 39296 BRILL NL. (In N. America: E.J. Brill, 24 Hudson St., Kinderhook, NY 12106. TEL 800-962-4406. FAX 518-758-1959) (back issues avail.) **Document type**: monographic series.
   —BLDSC (2284.130000).
   Refereed Serial

900   UK
BRITISH JOURNAL FOR EIGHTEENTH-CENTURY STUDIES. 1978. 2/yr. £30. Voltaire Foundation, Taylor Institution, St. Giles, Oxford OX1 3NA, England. TEL 0865-270250. FAX 0865-270740. Ed. Brean Hammond. (also avail. in microfiche from VFN; back issues avail.) **Indexed**: RILA. **Document type**: academic/scholarly publication.

001.3   PO   ISSN 0870-7618
BROTERIA; revista de cultura. 1925. bi-m. Esc.2500. Edicoes Broteria, Rua Maestro Antonio Taborda, 14, 1200 Lisbon, Portugal. TEL 1-3961660. Ed. Antonio da Silva. circ. 2,100. (back issues avail.)

BUCKNELL REVIEW; a scholarly journal of letters, arts and science. see *SCIENCES: COMPREHENSIVE WORKS*

BULLETIN AGIR. see *POLITICAL SCIENCE — Civil Rights*

001.3   US   ISSN 0095-4608
DF503
BYZANTINE STUDIES/ETUDES BYZANTINES. (Text in English, French, German, and Russian) 1974. 2/yr. $15 to individuals; institutions $20. c/o Walter K. Hanak, Department of History, Shepherd College, Shepherdstown, WV 25443. adv.; bk.rev.; index. circ. 300. (back issues avail.) **Indexed**: Amer.Hist.& Life, Arts & Hum.Cit.Ind., Curr.Cont., Hist.Abstr., RILA.

001.3 407   CL   ISSN 0716-2138
PA5225
BYZANTION NEA HELLAS. 1970. a. free. Universidad de Chile, Centro de Estudios Bizantinos y Neohelenicos Fotios Malleros, Facultad de Filosofia y Humanidades, Cap. Ignacio Carrers Pinto, no. 1025, Casilla 10136, Santiago, Chile. Ed. Miguel Castillo Didier. bk.rev. circ. 1,000. **Indexed**: M.L.A. **Document type**: academic/scholarly publication.

700 800 500   US   ISSN 0162-0177
AS30
C R: CENTENNIAL REVIEW. 1957. 3/yr. $12. Michigan State University, College of Arts & Letters, 312 Linton Hall, E. Lansing, MI 48824-1044. TEL 517-355-1905. FAX 517-336-1858. Ed. R.K. Meiners. adv. contact: Cherylee Finney. index. circ. 1,000. (also avail. in microform from UMI; reprint service avail. from UMI) **Indexed**: A.I.P.P., Abstr.Engl.Stud., Amer.Bibl.Slavic & E.Eur.Stud., Amer.Hist.& Life, Amer.Hum.Ind., Arts & Hum.Cit.Ind., Curr.Cont., Hist.Abstr., Ind.Bk.Rev.Hum., Lang.& Lang.Behav.Abstr., M.L.A. **Document type**: academic/scholarly publication.
   —BLDSC (3104.200000); Faxon; UnCover; UMI.
   Former titles: Centennial Review (ISSN 0008-901X); Centennial Review of Arts and Science.

C S D - S W O BULLETIN. (Centre for Science Development - Sentrum vir Wetenskapontwikkeling) see *SOCIAL SCIENCES: COMPREHENSIVE WORKS*

001.3 330   FR
CAHIERS D'ECONOMIE APPLIQUEE AUX SCIENCES HUMAINES. Short title: C E A S H. irreg. Universite de Montpellier (Universite Paul Valery), B.P. 5043, 43032 Montpellier Cedex 1, France. TEL 67-14-20-00. Ed. Genevieve Duche.

300 800   TI   ISSN 0008-0012
DT241
CAHIERS DE TUNISIE; revue de sciences humaines et sociales. 1953. q. 200 F. (£40). Faculte des Sciences Humaines et Sociales de Tunis, 94 Bd. du 9 Avril, Tunis, Tunisia. Eds. Mohamed Hedi Cherif, Hassen Annabi. bk.rev.; bibl.; charts; illus.; stat.; index. circ. 1,300. **Indexed**: A.I.C.P., Amer.Hist.& Life (until 1986, 1991-), Bibl.Ling., Curr.Cont.Africa, Documentatieblad, Hist.Abstr. (until 1986, 1991-), Numis.Lit. **Document type**: academic/scholarly publication.
   —BLDSC (2952.380000).

001.3   IT
CAMPI IMMAGINABILI; rivista quadrimestrale di cultura. 3/yr. L.40000 (foreign L.60000). Marra Editore, c/o Bosco Sottano, Pal "Domus Apta", 87100 Cosenza, Italy. TEL 0984-394265.

001.3   CN
CANADIAN ASSOCIATION FOR AMERICAN STUDIES. NEWSLETTER. 1980. a. membership. Canadian Association for American Studies, University of Montreal, Montreal, Que., Canada. Ed. Robert Martin. circ. 400. **Document type**: newsletter.
   Description: Looks at humanities in Canada.

940 947   CN   ISSN 0381-6133
CANADIAN ASSOCIATION OF SLAVISTS NEWSLETTER. (Text mainly in English; occasionally in French) 1961. 2/yr. Can.$6 to non-members. Canadian Association of Slavists - Association Canadienne des Slavistes, c/o Gust Olson, Slavic Department, University of Alberta, Edmonton, AB T6G 2E6, Canada. TEL 403-492-3537. FAX 403-492-5086. adv.; circ. 400 (controlled). (processed) **Document type**: newsletter.

001.3   CN   ISSN 0707-8048
CANADIAN FEDERATION FOR THE HUMANITIES. BULLETIN. (Text in English, French) 1978. irreg. (3-4/yr.). Canadian Federation for the Humanities, 151 Slater St., Ste. 407, Ottawa, Ont. K1P 5H3, Canada. TEL 613-236-4686. FAX 613-238-4853. **Document type**: bulletin.
   Formerly: Humanities Research Council of Canada. Bulletin (ISSN 0315-9566)

917 300   CN   ISSN 0318-8442
CANADIAN ISSUES/THEMES CANADIENS. (Text in English, French) 1975. a. Can.$15 to non-members. Association for Canadian Studies, P.O. Box 8888, Sta. "A", Montreal, PQ H3C 3P8, Canada. TEL 514-987-7784. FAX 514-987-8210. Ed. Vincent Masciotra. abstr.; bibl. circ. 1,000. (also avail. in microform from MML; back issues avail.) **Indexed**: Amer.Hist.& Life (1993-), Can.Per.Ind., Hist.Abstr. (1993-), Int.Polit.Sci.Abstr., Pt.de Rep. **Document type**: proceedings, academic/scholarly publication, monographic series.
   Description: Selection of papers presented at the annual conference, dealing with Canadian society, government, history, economy.
   Refereed Serial

001.3 800 890 941   CN   ISSN 0703-1459
PR8700
CANADIAN JOURNAL OF IRISH STUDIES. (Text mainly in English; occasionally in French) 1975. s-a. $13.50 (foreign $16.50). Canadian Association for Irish Studies, c/o Univ. of Saskatchewan, Dept. of English, Saskatoon, Sask. S7N 0W0. FAX 306-966-8839. Ed. Ron Marken. adv.: B&W page Can.$300. bk.rev. circ. 600. (back issues avail.) **Indexed**: M.L.A.
   —BLDSC (3031.760000).
   Description: Scholarly journal of Irish culture.
   Refereed Serial

378 001.3   CN   ISSN 0576-5803
CANADIAN NOTES & QUERIES/QUESTIONS & REPONSES CANADIENNES. (Contributions in English and French) 1968. 2/yr. Can.$10($10) Canadian Notes & Queries Association, Special Collections, Douglas Library, Queen's University, Kingston, Ont. K7L 5C4, Canada. TEL 613-545-2528. FAX 613-545-6300. Eds. William F.E. Morley, Barbara Teatero. adv. circ. 400.
   Description: International exchange of ideas between scholars in Canadian studies.

CANADIAN REVIEW OF STUDIES IN NATIONALISM. see *HISTORY*

940 947   CN   ISSN 0008-5006
PG6
CANADIAN SLAVONIC PAPERS/REVUE CANADIENNE DES SLAVISTES. (Text in English, French) 1956. q. Can.$40 (foreign Can.$45). Canadian Association of Slavists, Dept. of Comparative Literature, University of Alberta, 347 Arts Building, Edmonton, Alta. T6G 2E6, Canada. TEL 403-492-2566. FAX 403-492-9112. Ed. E. Mozejko. adv.; bk.rev.; cum.index: 1956-1973, 1974-1987. circ. 800. (back issues avail.) **Indexed**: Amer.Bibl.Slavic & E.Eur.Stud., Amer.Hist. & Life, Arts & Hum.Cit.Ind., Bibl.Ling., Curr.Cont., Hist.Abstr., Lang.& Lang.Behav.Abstr., M.L.A., P.A.I.S., SSCI. **Document type**: academic/scholarly publication.
   —Faxon; UnCover.

HUMANITIES: COMPREHENSIVE WORKS

700   IT   ISSN 0008-5618
CANNOCCHIALE; rivista di cultura. 3/yr. L.55000 to individuals; institutions L.72000; foreign L.88000 (effective 1993). Edizioni Scientifiche Italiane S.p.A., Via Chiatamone 7, 80121 Naples, Italy. TEL 081-7645768. FAX 081-7646477. Ed. Angelo G. Sabatini. bk.rev.; bibl.; index. circ. 500.

CARIBBEAN STUDIES. see SOCIAL SCIENCES: COMPREHENSIVE WORKS

CARINDEX: SOCIAL SCIENCES AND HUMANITIES. see SOCIAL SCIENCES: COMPREHENSIVE WORKS — Abstracting, Bibliographies, Statistics

CARNEGIE CORPORATION OF NEW YORK ANNUAL REPORT. see SOCIAL SERVICES AND WELFARE

CARNEGIE QUARTERLY. see SOCIAL SERVICES AND WELFARE

CAROLO-WILHELMINA MITTEILUNGEN. see TECHNOLOGY: COMPREHENSIVE WORKS

001.3   US   ISSN 0098-0900
CENTER FOR HERMENEUTICAL STUDIES. PROTOCOL SERIES OF THE COLLOQUIES. 1970. 2-4/yr. $8.50 per no. Center for Hermeneutical Studies, 2400 Ridge Rd., Berkeley, CA 94709. TEL 415-649-2479. (Co-Sponsors: Graduate Theological Union; University of California, Berkeley) Ed. Christopher Ocker. circ. 200. (back issues avail.) **Indexed:** New Test.Abstr. **Document type:** academic/scholarly publication.
  Description: Provides interdisciplinary dialogue for scholars from the Graduate Theological Union and the University of California at Berkeley whose interests focus on interpretation of texts and culture, past and present.

378 200   FR   ISSN 0008-9605
CENTRE CATHOLIQUE DES INTELLECTUELS FRANCAIS. RECHERCHES ET DEBATS. 4/yr. 110 F. Centre Catholique des Intellectuels Francais, 61 rue Madame, 75006 Paris, France. Ed. Desdee De Brouwer.

001.3   FR
CENTRE CULTUREL PORTUGAIS. ACTES DES COLLOQUES. irreg. price varies. Centre Culturel Portugais, Fondation Calouste Gulbenkian, 51 av. d'lena, 75116 Paris, France. TEL 1-47-20-86-84. FAX 1-40-70-98-79. (Subscr. to: Jean Touzot, 38 rue Saint-Sulpice, 75006 Paris, France. TEL 43-26-03-88)

001.3   NQ
CENTRO DE ESTUDIOS INTERNACIONALES. BOLETIN. 1991. s-a. C.$20($20) Centro de Estudios Internacionales, Apdo. Postal 1747, Managua, Nicaragua. TEL 505-2-785413. FAX 505-2-670517. circ. 200. **Document type:** bulletin.
  Description: Publishes information on research in progress.

001.3   BL   ISSN 0101-7934
CENTRO DE ESTUDOS PORTUGUESES. BOLETIM. (Text in Portuguese; summaries in Portuguese and English, French or Spanish) 1969. s-a. $8. Universidade Federal de Minas Gerais, Centro de Estudos Portugueses, Av. Antonio Carlos 6627, SL 2047, 31270-910 Belo Horizonte, MG, Brazil. TEL 031-4485134. Ed. Lelia Parreira Duarte. bk.rev. **Document type:** bulletin.
  Description: Contains reviews on Portuguese language and literature.

CENTRO DI RICERCHE INFORMATICHE PER I BENI CULTURALI. QUADERNI. see LIBRARY AND INFORMATION SCIENCES

001.3   US
CHARLES ELIOT NORTON LECTURES. 1939. irreg. Harvard University Press, 79 Garden St., Cambridge, MA 02138. TEL 617-495-2600. FAX 617-495-5898.
  Refereed Serial

051   US   ISSN 0069-2786
CHARTER; Gonzaga University's journal of liberal arts. 1961. a. free. Gonzaga University, Spokane, WA 99258. TEL 509-328-4220. FAX 509-484-2818. circ. 2,000.
  Description: Examines philosophical topics with contributions by both faculty and students.

001.3   RU   ISSN 0236-2007
B821.A1
CHELOVEK. 1990. 6/yr. 39 Rub. per issue. Rossiskaya Akademiya Nauk, Presidium, Maronovskii per., d.26, 117810 Moscow, Russia. TEL 238-2300. Ed. B.G. Yudin. adv.; bk.rev. circ. 48,000.

CIMARRON REVIEW. see LITERATURE

CIMBEBASIA. see SCIENCES: COMPREHENSIVE WORKS

CIMBEBASIA. MEMOIR. see SCIENCES: COMPREHENSIVE WORKS

700   US   ISSN 0009-7349
F1408.3
CIRCULO; revista de cultura. (Text in English and Spanish) 1970. a. $15 to individuals; institutions $25. Circulo de Cultura Panamericano, 16 Malvern Pl., Verona, NJ 07044. TEL 201-239-3125. Ed. Elio Alba-Buffill. adv.; bk.rev.; abstr.; bibl.; cum.index. circ. 800. **Indexed:** M.L.A. **Document type:** academic/scholarly publication.

CITHARA; essays in Judaeo-Christian tradition. see RELIGIONS AND THEOLOGY

001.3   IT
▼**CIVILTA BRESCIANA**. 1992. q. L.20000. (Fondazione Civilta Bresciana) Editrice la Rosa, Via Filippo Lippi 6, Brescia, Italy. TEL 2304666. Ed. Antonio Fappani.

001.3   VE   ISSN 0069-5114
COLECCION "HUMANISMO Y CIENCIA". (Some vols. issued in more than one part) irreg., no.12, 1977. Universidad Central de Venezuela, Direccion de Cultura, Biblioteca, Piso 10, Ciudad Universitaria, Caracas, Venezuela.

001.3   MX
COLECCION 500 ANOS DESPUES. 1990. irreg., no.16, 1993. price varies. Universidad Nacional Autonoma de Mexico, Centro Coordinador y Difusor de Estudios Latinoamericanos, Torre I de Humanidades, 2o piso, Ciudad Universitario, 04510 Mexico D.F., Mexico. TEL 622-1902. FAX 548-9662. **Document type:** monographic series.
  Description: Contains studies on the discovery, philosophy and history of Latin America.

COLLOQUY (SAN FRANCISCO). see EDUCATION — Teaching Methods And Curriculum

001.3   FI   ISSN 0069-6587
P9
COMMENTATIONES HUMANARUM LITTERARUM. (Text in English, French, German) 1923. irreg. price varies. Societas Scientiarum Fennica - Finnish Society of Sciences and Letters, Marieg 5, FIN-00170 Helsinki, Finland. TEL 358-0-633-005. FAX 358-0-661-065. Ed. Holger Thesleff. circ. 1,000. **Indexed:** Abstr.Engl.Stud., Bull.Signal., Lang.& Lang.Behav.Abstr., M.L.A.

COMMONWEALTH NOVEL IN ENGLISH. see LITERATURE

COMMUNITY SPIRIT MAGAZINE (CARMEL). see ENVIRONMENTAL STUDIES

COMPARATIVE CIVILIZATIONS REVIEW. see SOCIAL SCIENCES: COMPREHENSIVE WORKS

001.3   IT   ISSN 1121-6875
▼**CONCERTINO**; trimestrale di varia cultura. 1992. q. L.32000 (foreign L.64000) (effective 1994). Via Mose Bianchi 59, 20149 Milan, Italy. TEL 02-435679. Ed. Giancarlo Buzzi. adv.: page L.600000. circ. 1,000 (paid). **Document type:** consumer publication.
  Description: Covers literature, art and human sciences.

CONFLUENCES, MEDITERRANEE. see POLITICAL SCIENCE — International Relations

CONNECTICUT ACADEMY OF ARTS AND SCIENCES. MEMOIRS. see SCIENCES: COMPREHENSIVE WORKS

700 060 500   US   ISSN 0069-8989
Q11   CODEN: TCAAAL
CONNECTICUT ACADEMY OF ARTS AND SCIENCES. TRANSACTIONS. 1866. irreg., vol.51, 1992. price varies. Connecticut Academy of Arts and Sciences, Box 208211, New Haven, CT 06520-8211. TEL 203-432-3113. Ed. Catherine Skinner. cum.index in vol.38, 1949. **Indexed:** Biol.Abstr., GeoRef.
  Refereed Serial

CONTEMPORARY FRANCE; a review of interdisciplinary studies. see HISTORY — History Of Europe

001.3   US
CONTINUUM. 1990. 3/yr. $40. Crossroad - Continuum Publishing, 370 Lexington Ave., New York, NY 10017. TEL 212-532-3650. Ed. Justus George Lawler.
  Description: Multidisciplinary journal of history, hermeneutics, and social concerns.

001.5   SP
CORRESPONDANCE. (Text in French, Spanish) 1990. irreg. Universidad de Extremadura, Servicio de Publicaciones, Calle Pizarro, 8, 10071 Caceres, Spain. TEL 927-247650. illus.
  Description: Presents the exchange of culture (literature, art, theory, and creation) between Spain and Belgium.

001.3   IT   ISSN 1122-0864
CORRISPONDENZE LETTERARIE, SCIENTIFICHE ED ERUDITE DAL RINASCIMENTO ALL'ETA MODERNA. 1987. irreg., no.5, 1993. price varies. Casa Editrice Leo S. Olschki, Casella Postale 66, 50100 Florence, Italy. TEL 055-6530684. FAX 055-6530214. **Document type:** monographic series.

001.3   IT
COSCIENZA DEL TEMPO. irreg., latest vol.18. price varies. Edizioni Studium, Via Cassiodoro 14, 00193 Rome, Italy. **Document type:** monographic series.

COURIER (PARIS). see POLITICAL SCIENCE — International Relations

001.3 659.1   US   ISSN 0277-6723
COVER; arts New York. 1979. m. $10 to individuals; institutions $15. Arts New York, Box 1215, Cooper Sta., New York, NY 10276. TEL 212-673-1152. FAX 212-431-4057. Ed. Jeff Wright. adv.; bk.rev. circ. 25,000. (back issues avail.) **Document type:** consumer publication.
  Description: Covers all the arts including painting, photography, music, dance, theater, poetry, literature and film.

CRISI E LETTERATURA; periodico di lettere filosofia arti. see LITERATURE

055.1   IT   ISSN 0011-1449
CRISTALLO; rassegna di varia umanita. 1959. 3/yr. membership. Centro di Cultura dell'Alto Adige, Via Napoli 1, 39100 Bolzano, Italy. TEL 0471-201354. Ed. Giuseppe Negri. adv.; bk.rev.; bibl. circ. 3,000. **Indexed:** M.L.A.

001.3   MX
CRITERIO UNIVERSITARIO. irreg., no.8, 1978. Universidad Autonoma de Chiapas, 2a Poniente Sur 118, Tuxtla Gutierrez, Chiapas, Mexico.

700 282   US   ISSN 0011-149X
CRITIC (CHICAGO); a Catholic review of culture and the arts. 1942-1981; resumed 1985. q. $17. Thomas More Association, 205 W. Monroe St., 6th Fl., Chicago, IL 60606. TEL 312-609-8880. FAX 312-609-8891. Ed. John L. Sprague. illus. circ. 2,500. (also avail. in microform from UMI; reprint service avail. from UMI) **Indexed:** Bk.Rev.Dig., Bk.Rev.Ind. (1965-1983), Cath.Ind., Child.Bk.Rev.Ind. (1965-1983), Hum.Ind. —Faxon; UMI.

CRITICISM; a quarterly for literature and the arts. see LITERATURE

CROSSROADS (DEKALB); an interdisciplinary journal of Southeast Asian studies. see HISTORY — History Of Asia

001.3   PR
CRUZ ANSATA. 1978. a. $10. Universidad Central de Bayamon, Bayamon, PR 00960-1725. FAX 809-786-3030. Dir. Jose R. Ortiz. circ. 600. **Document type:** academic/scholarly publication.

001.3 CK
CUADERNOS DE CIENCIAS HUMANAS. 1983. s-a. Universidad de Antioquia, Facultad de Ciencias Humanas, A.A. 1226, Medellin, Colombia.

001.3 UY ISSN 0185-061X
CUADERNOS DE MARCHA. 1967. m. $66 in Latin America; N. America $78; Europe $84; elsewhere $90. Centro de Estudios Uruguay-America Latina, Piedras 524, 11000 Montevideo, Uruguay. TEL 5982-95-79-73. FAX 5982-95-31-34. Eds. Jose M. Quijano, Mercedes Quijano. circ. 10,000. —BLDSC (3490.732000).

001.3 SP ISSN 1130-8354
CUADERNOS EUROPEO DE DEUSTO. 1988. s-a. 2000 ptas.($25) Universidad de Deusto, Instituto de Estudios Europeos, Avda. de las Universidades, s/n, 48007 Bilbao, Spain. Ed. Nicolas Mariscal.

001.3 SP
CUADERNOS N T. 1975. irreg., no.9, 1980. price varies. Ediciones Universidad de Navarra, S.A., Apdo. 396, 31080 Pamplona, Spain. TEL 94 825 6850.

001.3 BL
CULTURA. (Editions in English, French, Portuguese) 1971. q. free. Ministerio da Cultura, Coordenadoia de Comunicacao Social, Esplanada dos Ministerios, Bloco L, 9 andar s-905, 70047 Brasilia D.F., Brazil. Ed. Paulo Nunes. adv.; illus. **Indexed:** Hisp.Amer.Per.Ind.

001.3 IT
CULTURA (BOLOGNA). 1881. 3/yr. L.110000. Societa Editrice Il Mulino, Strada Maggiore, 37, 40125 Bologna, Italy. TEL 051-256011. FAX 051-256034. Ed. Gennaro Sasso. circ. 1,500.

001.3 IT ISSN 0391-8505
CULTURA (ROME). 1974. irreg., latest no.53. price varies. Edizioni Studium, Via Cassiodoro 14, 00193 Rome, Italy. **Document type:** monographic series.

001.3 VE
CULTURA UNIVERSITARIA. no.98-99, 1968. 3/yr. Universidad Central de Venezuela, Direccion de Cultura, Biblioteca, Piso 10, Ciudad Universitaria, Caracas, Venezuela. bibl.

001.3 US ISSN 1063-634X
CB3
▼**CULTUREFRONT**; a magazine for the humanities. 1992. 3/yr. $15 to individuals (foreign $26); institutions $25 (foreign $35). New York Council for the Humanities, 198 Broadway, 10th Fl., New York, NY 10038. TEL 212-233-1131. FAX 212-233-4607. Ed. Jay Kaplan. adv.: B&W page $1250; adv. contact: Lisa Vecchione. bk.rev.; film rev.; illus. **Document type:** academic/scholarly publication.
Description: Presents news and a variety of views on the production, interpretation and politics of culture. Each issue includes interviews, articles on cultural topics, and a special section with a thematic focus.

001.3 PH ISSN 0115-6594
D L S U DIALOGUE. 1965. s-a. P.60($4.40) (De La Salle University) De La Salle University Press, 2401 Taft Ave., Manila, Philippines. TEL 2-59-48-32. FAX 632-521-9094. Ed. Cirilo Bautista. adv.; bk.rev.; film rev.; play rev.; bibl.; charts; illus.; stat. circ. 1,000. **Document type:** academic/scholarly publication.
Formerly: Dialogue.
Description: Publishes scholarly articles reflecting significant quantitative or qualitative research. Includes speeches, research reports, and "state of the art" papers.

300 500 US ISSN 0011-5266
Q11 CODEN: DAEDAU
DAEDALUS. 1846. q. $25 to individuals (foreign $30); institutions $40 (foreign $45). American Academy of Arts and Sciences, Norton's Woods, 136 Irving St., Cambridge, MA 02138. TEL 617-492-8800. (Subscr. to: Box 515, Canton, MA 02021) Ed. Stephen R. Graubard. charts; illus.; index. circ. 20,000. (also avail. in microform from UMI; back issues avail.; reprint service avail. from UMI) **Indexed:** A.B.C.Pol.Sci., Acad.Ind., Amer.Hist.& Life, Arts & Hum.Cit.Ind., Biol.Abstr., Bk.Rev.Ind. (1976-1990), Br.Archaeol.Abstr., Chem.Abstr., Chic.Per.Ind., Child.Bk.Rev.Ind. (1976-1990), CLOSS, Deep Sea Res.& Oceanogr.Abstr., Fut.Surv., G.Soc.Sci.& Rel.Per.Lit., Geo.Abstr., GeoRef., Hist.Abstr., Hum.Ind., INIS Atomind., Lang.& Lang.Behav.Abstr., Mag.Ind., Met.Abstr., Mid.East: Abstr.& Ind., P.A.I.S., Psychol.Abstr., Res.High.Educ.Abstr., RILA, Sci.Abstr. —BLDSC (3509.990000); Faxon; UnCover; SWETS; UMI. **CCC.**
Formerly: American Academy of Arts and Sciences. Proceedings (ISSN 0199-9818)

001.3 US
DALLAS INSTITUTE OF HUMANITIES AND CULTURE. INSTITUTE NEWSLETTER. 1981. a. $5. Dallas Institute of Humanities and Culture, 2719 Routh St., Dallas, TX 75201. TEL 214-871-2440. FAX 214-969-1884. Ed. Mary Bonifield. circ. 10,000. **Document type:** newsletter.

001.3 370 PH
DANYAG; journal of studies in the humanities, education and the sciences, basic and applied. 1976. s-a. University of the Philippines in the Visayas, College of Arts and Sciences, Iloilo City 5000, Philippines.
Description: Covers a variety of academic fields with special attention to the western Visayas region.

001.3 FR ISSN 0246-2346
AP20
DEBAT. 1980. 5/yr. 323 F. Editions Gallimard, 5 rue Sebastien-Bottin, 75007 Paris, France. TEL 33-1-46-59-89-00. Ed. Pierre Nora. circ. 10,000. **Indexed:** Amer.Hist.& Life (until 1989), Hist.Abstr. (until 1989).
—BLDSC (3535.960800); SWETS.

001.3 US ISSN 0965-156X
DEBATTE; a new journal for the new Germany. £18($25) to individuals; institutions £50 ($75) (effective 1994). Berg Publishers, Attn: Annette Emerson, 221 Waterman St., Providence, RI 02906. (N. American subscr. to: Carfax Publishing Co., Box 2025, Dunnellon, FL 34430-2025. FAX 904-489-6996; Elsewhere: Carfax Publishing Co., P.O. Box 25, Abingdon, Oxon. OX14 3UE. TEL 44-235-521154. FAX 44-235-553559) (back issues avail.) **Document type:** academic/scholarly publication.
Description: Combines scholarly analysis of various topics in German studies with documentation of German sources in translation, covering humanistic studies ranging from policy to media studies, from cultural trends to economics.

700 US ISSN 0011-8869
AP2
DENVER QUARTERLY. 1966. q. $15 to individuals (foreign $18); institutions $18. University of Denver, Department of English, University Park, Denver, CO 80208. TEL 303-871-2892. FAX 303-871-2853. Ed. Donald Revell. adv.; bk.rev.; index. circ. 1,000. (also avail. in microform from UMI; back issues avail.; reprint service avail. from UMI) **Indexed:** Amer.Hum.Ind., Ind.Amer.Per.Verse, Ind.Bk.Rev.Hum., M.L.A., Mid.East: Abstr.& Ind.
—BLDSC (3553.568000); Faxon; UnCover; UMI.

800 900 GW ISSN 0012-0936
PN4
DEUTSCHE VIERTELJAHRSSCHRIFT FUER LITERATURWISSENSCHAFT UND GEISTESGESCHICHTE. 1923. q. DM.160 (DM.122 to students). J.B. Metzlersche Verlagsbuchhandlung, Kernerstr. 43, 70182 Stuttgart, Germany. adv.; bk.rev.; bibl.; charts; index, cum.index. circ. 1,800. **Indexed:** Arts & Hum.Cit.Ind., Bibl.Ling., Can.Rev.Comp.Lit., Curr.Cont., M.L.A., Phil.Ind., RILA.
—Faxon; UnCover; SWETS.

300 500 BG
DHAKA UNIVERSITY STUDIES. PART A: ARTS, HUMANITIES, AND SOCIAL SCIENCE. (Text in English) vol.18, 1970. University of Dhaka, Registrar, Ramna, Dhaka 2, Bangladesh. bibl.; charts. **Indexed:** Amer.Hist.& Life, Hist.Abstr.
Formerly: Dacca University Studies. Part A: Humanities (ISSN 0011-5223)

001.3 500 JO ISSN 0255-8033
AS593.J35 CODEN: DSNJDI
DIRASAT. SERIES A: HUMANITIES. (Consists of Series A: Humanities, Series B: Pure and Applied Sciences (ISSN 0253-424X)) (Text in Arabic and English) 1974. 5/yr. $60 (Series A&B $120). University of Jordan, Deanship of Academic Research, Amman, Jordan. FAX 962-6-832318. TELEX UNVJ JO 21629. Ed. Dr. Humam B. Ghassib. bk.rev.; index, cum.index: 1974-1984; circ. 1,000 (controlled). (back issues avail.) **Indexed:** Agroforest.Abstr., Bibl.Ling., Biol.Abstr., Crop Physiol.Abstr., Dairy Sci.Abstr., Field Crop Abstr., Geo.Abstr., Herb.Abstr., I D A, Ind.Vet., Irr.& Drain.Abstr, Mid.East: Abstr.& Ind., Ornam.Hort., Per.Islam. (1991-), Plant Grow.Reg.Abstr., Poult.Abstr., Psychol.Abstr., Seed Abstr., Soyabean Abstr., Triticale Abstr., Vet.Bull. **Document type:** academic/scholarly publication.
—BLDSC (3589.590000).
Description: Presents original research papers and articles in the different disciplines in the humanities. *Refereed Serial*

DISCOURSE; journal for theoretical studies in media and culture. see COMMUNICATIONS

DISCRETIO. see LITERARY AND POLITICAL REVIEWS

001.3 US
DISCUSSION PAPERS IN THE AFRICAN HUMANITIES. 1989. irreg., no.23, 1992. $4 per no. Boston University, African Studies Center, 270 Bay State Rd., Boston, MA 02215. TEL 617-353-3673. FAX 617-353-4975. TELEX 9103501947 BUASC.

900 001.3 800 IS ISSN 0334-2816
DIVREI HA-AKADEMIA HA-LEUMIT HA-YISRAELIT LEMADAIM. (Text in Hebrew) 1964. irreg. price varies. Israel Academy of Sciences and Humanities, 43 Jabotinski St., P.O. Box 4040, Jerusalem 91040, Israel. TEL 02-636211. FAX 02-666059. circ. 900. (back issues avail.) **Indexed:** Ind.Heb.Per.
Description: Reprints of papers read at meetings of the Academy, mostly focused on Judaism.

940 FR ISSN 0070-6760
CB411
DIX-HUITIEME SIECLE. 1969. a. 230 F. (Societe Francaise d'Etude du Dix-Huitieme Siecle) Presses Universitaires de France, Departement des Revues, 14 av. du Bois-de-l'Epine, 91003 Evry Cedex, France. TEL 1-60-77-82-05. FAX 1-60-79-20-45. TELEX PUF 600 474 F. (Subscr. to: Robert Granderoute, Residence Aspin II, 12, av du Stade-Nautique, 64000 Pau, France) Ed. Roland Desne. adv.; bk.rev. circ. 2,500. **Indexed:** M.L.A.

DOCTOR - PATIENT STUDIES. see PHILOSOPHY

001.3 US ISSN 0196-7134
DOCUMENTARY EDITING. 1979. q. $25. Association for Documentary Editing, c/o Henry Laurens Papers, History Dept., Univ. of South Carolina, Columbia, SC 29208. TEL 803-777-6526. FAX 803-777-4494. (Subscr. to: c/o Harriet F. Simon, Center for Dewey Studies, Southern Illinois University, Carbondale, IL 62901) Ed. C. James Taylor. adv.; bk.rev.; bibl.; illus.; index, cum.index: 1979-1989; circ. 475 (paid). (also avail. in microfiche; back issues avail.) **Document type:** academic/scholarly publication.
Description: Publishes articles on editorial method and technique.

DOKUMENTATION OSTMITTELEUROPA. see SOCIAL SCIENCES: COMPREHENSIVE WORKS

001.4 US ISSN 0419-8050
DUKE ENDOWMENT. ANNUAL REPORT. 1925. a. free. Duke Endowment, 100 N. Tryon St., Ste. 3500, Charlotte, NC 28202-4012. TEL 704-376-0291. FAX 704-376-9336. Ed. Elizabeth H. Locke. illus. circ. 7,500.

HUMANITIES: COMPREHENSIVE WORKS

001.3 — US
DUKE ENDOWMENT. ISSUES. 1984. s-a. free. Duke Endowment, 100 N. Tryon St., Ste. 3500, Charlotte, NC 28202-4012. TEL 704-376-0291. FAX 704-376-9336. Ed. Elizabeth H. Locke. illus. circ. 10,000.

EAST AND MAGHREB. see *ETHNIC INTERESTS*

EDIZIONI PER LA CONSERVAZIONE; periodico internazionale di prevenzione e conservazione. see *ENVIRONMENTAL STUDIES*

EDUCATION, SCIENCE ET CULTURE/UBUREZI, UBUHANGA N'UMUCO. see *EDUCATION*

001.3 350 — II
EDUCATIONAL BOOK REVIEW. (Text in English) 1975. bi-m. Rs.120($24) P.O. Box 8807, FC1, Chembur, Bombay 400074, India. TEL 022-5522240. Ed. K. Gurprakash; Pub. W.B./Singh. adv. contact: H.S. Khanna. bk.rev. circ. 5,500. **Document type:** academic/scholarly publication, newsletter.

941.5 — US — ISSN 0013-2683
EIRE - IRELAND; a journal of Irish studies. 1966. q. $26 (foreign $32) (effective 1994). Irish American Cultural Institute, 2115 Summit Ave., No. 5026, St. Paul, MN 55105-1096. TEL 612-962-6040. FAX 612-962-6043. Ed. Tom Redshaw. adv.; bk.rev.; rec.rev.; bibl.; index. circ. 8,731. (also avail. in microform from UMI; reprint service avail. from UMI) **Indexed:** Abstr.Engl.Stud., Amer.Hist.& Life, Amer.Hum.Ind., Arts & Hum.Cit.Ind., Curr.Cont., Hist.Abstr., Ind.Bk.Rev.Hum., M.L.A., Numis.Lit. **Document type:** academic/scholarly publication.
—BLDSC (3666.753000); Faxon; UnCover.

001.3 491.7 — US — ISSN 1064-6663
CODEN: ESSSEE
▼**ELEMENTA;** journal of Slavic studies and comparative cultural semiotics. 1993. q. Harwood Academic Publishers, 820 Town Center Dr., Langhorne, PA 19047. TEL 215-750-2642. FAX 215-750-6343. (UK subscr. to: P.O. Box 90, Reading, Berkshire RG1 8JL, England. TEL 0734-560-080) Ed. Vyacheslav Ivanov. (also avail. in microform)
—CCC.
Description: Concerned with problems of sign systems and results of the comparison of different semiotic systems and texts with particular application to Slavic traditions.

300 — NQ — ISSN 0424-9674
ENCUENTRO. Variant title: Revista Encuentro. 1968. 3/yr. $30. Universidad Centroamericana, Apdo. 69, 70352 Managua, Nicaragua. TEL 505-2-670352. FAX 505-2-670106. bk.rev.; illus. circ. 1,500. **Indexed:** Hisp.Amer.Per.Ind., Int.Lab.Doc.
Description: Covers the social sciences and humanities in Nicaragua.

820 — SA — ISSN 0013-8398
PR1
ENGLISH STUDIES IN AFRICA; a journal of the humanities. 1958. s-a. $17.50 to individuals; institutions $35. Witwatersrand University Press, Wits 2050, South Africa. FAX 011-339-3559. TELEX 4-27125 SA. Ed. G. Hughes. adv.; bibl.; index. circ. 350. (also avail. in microform from UMI; back issues avail.; reprint service avail. from UMI) **Indexed:** Abstr.Engl.Stud., Arts & Hum.Cit.Ind., Curr.Cont., Hum.Ind., Ind.Bk.Rev.Hum., Ind.S.A.Per., Lang.& Lang.Behav.Abstr., M.L.A.
—BLDSC (3775.120000); Faxon; UnCover; UMI.
Description: Critical articles on English literature world-wide with special focus on African literature in English.

100 — CN — ISSN 0318-3319
ERASMUS STUDIES. 1973. irreg. price varies. University of Toronto Press, 5201 Dufferin St., Downsview, ON M3H 5T8, Canada. TEL 416-667-7791. FAX 416-667-7832. (U.S. addr.: 340 Nagel Dr., Cheektowaga, NY 14225) **Document type:** academic/scholarly publication.

001.3 — SP
ESPACIO - ESPACO ESCRITO. (Text in Spanish, Portuguese) s-a. 1400 ptas. Diputacion Provincial de Badajoz, Felipe Checa 15, 06701 Badajoz, Spain. TEL 924-21-24-52. FAX 924-21-24-80. Dir. Angel Campos Pampano. circ. 3,000.
Description: Presents the literature, philosophy, and culture of Spain and Portugal.

001.3 — PE
ESPACIO Y DESARROLLO. 1990. s-a. $16. Pontifica Universidad Catolica del Peru, Departamento de Humanidades, Fondo Editorial, Apdo. 1761, Lima 100, Peru. TEL 626390. FAX 5114-611785. Ed. Hildegardo Cordova.

ESSAYS IN ARTS AND SCIENCES. see *SCIENCES: COMPREHENSIVE WORKS*

001.3 — PY — ISSN 1012-2478
F2670
ESTUDIOS; revista de cultura. 1987. 10/yr. $30. (Centro Paraguayo de Estudios Sociologicos) Distribuidor Internacional Publicaciones Paraguayas, P.O. Box 2507, Ayoreos e-4a y 5a, Asuncion, Paraguay. TEL 595-21-495367. FAX 595-21-447460. Ed. Luis Maria Martinez. adv.; bk.rev. circ. 2,000.

001.3 — UY — ISSN 0256-3061
ESTUDIOS DE CIENCIAS Y LETRAS. 1981. irreg., latest no.10. Universidad Catolica del Uruguay "Damaso Antonio Larranaga", Instituto de Filosofia, Ciencias y Letras, Avda. 8 de Octubre 2738, Montevideo, Uruguay. bk.rev. circ. 1,000.

001.3 — BL — ISSN 0104-0049
ESTUDOS PORTUGUESES. 1989. a. Associacao de Estudos Portugueses Jordao Emerenciano, c/o UFP - Dept. de Letras, Av. Academico Helio Ramos, Cidade Universitaria, 50739 Recife, Pernambuco, Brazil. Ed. Jose Rodrigues de Paiva. **Document type:** academic/scholarly publication.

001.3 — GW
▼**EUROPEAN CULTURES.** (Text in English) 1993. irreg., vol.1, 1993. DM.98. Walter de Gruyter und Co., Genthiner Str. 13, 10785 Berlin, Germany. TEL 030-26005-0. FAX 030-26005251. **Document type:** monographic series.

EUROPEAN STUDIES NEWSLETTER. see *SOCIAL SCIENCES: COMPREHENSIVE WORKS*

001.3 940 — US — ISSN 0098-2474
CB361
EXPLORATIONS IN RENAISSANCE CULTURE. 1974. a. $10. (University of Southwestern Louisiana, Department of English) South-Central Renaissance Conference, Box 44612, USL Sta., Lafayette, LA 70504. TEL 318-231-6857. FAX 318-231-6195. Ed. Albert W. Fields. charts; illus.; stat. circ. 300. (back issues avail.) **Indexed:** M.L.A. **Document type:** academic/scholarly publication.
Description: Contains academic articles in language and literature, music, history, philosophy, and art history.

001.3 100 — IR — ISSN 1017-4117
FARHANG. (Text in Farsi) 1987. 4/yr. $25 (effective 1993). Mu'assasah-i Mutala'at va-Tahqiqat-i Farhangi, Mo'asseseh Bldg., 64 St., Seyyed Jamal-eddin Ave., Tehran 14374, Iran. TEL 98-21-688037. FAX 98-21-686317. bk.rev. circ. 2,000. **Document type:** academic/scholarly publication.
Description: Publishes contributions in philosophy, linguistics, literature and the social sciences.

001.3 — US — ISSN 8756-0313
FLAT EARTH NEWS; the last iconoclast. 1972. q. $25 for 2 yrs. (Covenant Peoples Church) Flat Earth Research, Box 2533, Lancaster, CA 93539. TEL 805-727-1635. Ed. Charles K. Johnson. adv.; bk.rev. circ. 3,500. (tabloid format) **Document type:** newsletter.
Description: Focuses on tenets of this hoax (globe theory) and espouses skepticism of accepted scientific claim.

FOLIA HUMANISTICA; ciencias, artes, letras. see *SCIENCES: COMPREHENSIVE WORKS*

001.3 890 — US — ISSN 0882-3030
FOLIO (BROCKPORT); essays on foreign languages and literature. (Text in English, French, Spanish) 1970. irreg., no.16, 1984. $8. State University of New York, Department of Foreign Languages, Brockport, NY 14420. TEL 716-395-2269. Ed. Martha O'Nan. adv.; bk.rev. circ. 500. (back issues avail.) **Indexed:** M.L.A.

FORD FOUNDATION ANNUAL REPORT. see *SOCIAL SCIENCES: COMPREHENSIVE WORKS*

FORD FOUNDATION REPORT. see *SOCIAL SCIENCES: COMPREHENSIVE WORKS*

FORT HARE PAPERS. see *SCIENCES: COMPREHENSIVE WORKS*

001.3 — IT
LA FORTEZZA; rivista di studi. 1990. s-a. L.25000. (Liceo Classico Machiavelli, Fortezza da Basso) Diaspro Edizioni Polistampa, Via S. Maria 27, Florence, Italy. Ed. Saverio Orlando.

FORUM FUER INTERDISZIPLINAERE FORSCHUNG. see *PHILOSOPHY*

001.3 — US — ISSN 1071-7269
▼**FREETHOUGHT HISTORY.** 1992. q. $10. People's Culture, Box 5224, Kansas City, KS 66119. TEL 913-588-1996. Ed. Fred Whitehead. adv.; bk.rev.; film rev. circ. 200. (looseleaf format; back issues avail.) **Document type:** newsletter.
Description: Presents information on topics relating to agnosticism, atheism and liberal thought.

940 335 — GW — ISSN 0409-1477
FREIE UNIVERSITAET BERLIN. OSTEUROPA-INSTITUT. BERICHTE. 1952. irreg. price varies. Freie Universitaet Berlin, Osteuropa-Institut, Garystr. 55, 14195 Berlin, Germany. FAX 030-8383788. circ. 300. **Document type:** proceedings.

FRENCH AMERICAN REVIEW. see *LITERATURE*

001.3 — US — ISSN 1069-5656
FRINGE WARE REVIEW. q. $12. FringeWare Inc., Box 49921, Austin, TX 78765. E-mail: fringeware@wixer.bga.com. Eds. Paco Xander Nathan, Jon Lebkowsky. **Document type:** consumer publication, catalog.
Description: Covers marginal culture. Contains essays, fiction, interviews, tutorials, comics and reviews.

FUJIAN LUNTAN (JINGJI BAN)/FUJIAN TRIBUNE (ECONOMICS EDITION). see *BUSINESS AND ECONOMICS — Economic Situation And Conditions*

001.3 — CC — ISSN 1000-8659
FUJIAN LUNTAN (WEN SHI ZHE BAN)/FUJIAN TRIBUNE (LITERATURE, HISTORY AND PHILOSOPHY EDITION). (Text in Chinese) 1981. m. $27. Fujian Shehui Kexueyuan - Fujian Academy of Social Sciences, Xiao Liu Cun, Fuzhou, Fujian 350001, People's Republic of China. TEL 7550401. FAX 7550371. (Subscr. to: China International Book Trading Corp., P.O. Box 399, P.R. China) Ed. Lin Qiping. circ. 18,000. **Document type:** academic/scholarly publication.

001.3 — US
FURMAN HUMANITIES REVIEW. 1988. a. free. Furman University, 3300 Poinsett Hwy., Greenville, SC 29613-0666. TEL 803-294-3177. FAX 803-294-3001. Ed. David H. Bost. circ. 1,250. **Document type:** academic/scholarly publication.
Description: Contains undergraduate papers in the humanities.

001.3 — US — ISSN 0190-4701
AS36
FURMAN STUDIES. 1912. a. free. Furman University, 3300 Poinsett Hwy., Greenville, SC 29613-0666. TEL 803-294-3072. FAX 803-294-3001. Ed. Marion E. Strobel. circ. 1,250. **Indexed:** M.L.A. **Document type:** academic/scholarly publication.
Formerly: Furman University Bulletin. Furman Studies Issue.
Description: Scholarly research on contemporary intellectual movements in the humanities.

001.3 — IT — ISSN 1122-083X
GABINETTO SCIENTIFICO E LETTERARIO G.P. VIEUSSEUX. 1985. irreg., no.5, 1991. price varies. Casa Editrice Leo S. Olschki, Casella Postale 66, 50100 Florence, Italy. TEL 055-6530684. FAX 055-6530214. **Document type:** monographic series.

001.3 — IT
GAZZETTA DI GAETA. 1973. m. L.20000($25) Gaetano Andrisani, Ed. & Pub., Via Bologna 15, 04024 Gaeta, Italy.

GENDERS. see *WOMEN'S STUDIES*

HUMANITIES: COMPREHENSIVE WORKS

001.3 100 FR
GENRE HUMAN. 1981. 2/yr. 320 F. (foreign 360 F.). Editions du Seuil, 27 rue Jacob, 75006 Paris, France. (Subscr. to: Service des Abonnement, B.P.29, 91162 Longjumeau Cedex, France. TEL 69-09-24-09) adv.; bk.rev.
Description: Tracks all forms of racism, especially those that manifest themselves in the name of science.

001.3 US
GEORGIA HUMANITIES. 1981. q. free. Georgia Humanities Council, 50 Hurt Plaza, S.E., Ste. 440, Atlanta, GA 30303-2936. Ed. Susan Wynne Brown. circ. 6,000 (controlled). **Document type:** newsletter.
Description: Provides a forum to foster understanding and appreciation of the humanities among the citizens of Georgia.

GERMANIC NOTES AND REVIEWS. see *LINGUISTICS*

057.8 YU ISSN 0017-1166
GLEDISTA. (Text in Serbo-Croatian; contents page in English) 1960. m. 200 din. Univerzitet u Beogradu, Marsala Tita 16, Belgrade, Serbia, Yugoslavia. (Co-sponsor: Republicka Konferencija Saveza Omladine Srbije) Eds. Dr. Oskar Kovac, Vladimir Goati. bk.rev.; index.

551 SW ISSN 0436-113X
GOETEBORGS KUNGLIGA VETENSKAPS- OCH VITTERHETS-SAMHAELLE. AARSBOK. 1967. a. SEK 40 or exchange basis. Kungliga Vetenskaps- och Vitterhets-Samhaellet i Goeteborg, P.O. Box 5096, S-402 22 Goeteborg, Sweden.
Formerly: Goeteborgs Kungliga Vetenskaps- och Vitterhets-Samhaelle. Handlingar Bihang.

001.3 SP ISSN 0017-4181
GRIAL; revista gallega de cultura. (Text in Gallegan) 1951-1952; resumed 1963. q. 3350 ptas. (foreign 4000 ptas.). Editorial Galaxia, S.A., Reconquista 1, 36201 Vigo, Spain. TEL 986-43-21-00. FAX 986-22-32-05. Ed. Carlos Casares. bk.rev. circ. 2,000. **Indexed:** M.L.A.
Description: Informs readers of Galician cultural events and incorporates universal culture within Galicia.

GUIDE TO FUNDING FOR ARTS & CULTURE. see *ART*

001.3 JA ISSN 0367-4061 CODEN: GDKKAX
GUNMA JOURNAL OF LIBERAL ARTS AND SCIENCES. 1967. a. exchange basis. Gunma University, Faculty of General Studies, Gunma University Library, 4-2 Aramaki, Maebashi, Gunma 371, Japan. Ed.Bd. circ. 640.

001.3 JA ISSN 0386-4294 AS552.G8
GUNMA UNIVERSITY. FACULTY OF EDUCATION. ANNUAL REPORT: CULTURAL SCIENCE SERIES. 1950. a. exchange basis. Gunma University, Faculty of Education - Gunma Daigaku Kyoikubu, Gunma University Library, 4-2 Aramaki, Maebashi, Gunma 371, Japan. **Indexed:** M.L.A.
—UnCover.

HSRC-RGN IN FOCUS. (Human Sciences Research Council) see *SOCIAL SCIENCES: COMPREHENSIVE WORKS*

001.3 US ISSN 0198-6449
HALCYON; a journal of the humanities. 1979. a. free. Nevada Humanities Committee, Box 8029, Reno, NV 89507. TEL 702-784-6587. FAX 702-895-4097. (Co-sponsor: University of Nevada, Department of History) Ed. Thomas C. Wright. circ. 2,000. (back issues avail.) **Indexed:** Amer.Hist.& Life, Hist.Abstr.
—BLDSC (4238.615000).
Description: Publishes essays and research articles on topics in history and the humanities, including regional history, literary, social and cultural criticism.
Refereed Serial

001.3 CC ISSN 1001-0661 PL1281
HANZI WENHUA/CHINESE CULTURE. (Text in Chinese) 1989. 4/yr. Y11($16.20) (Beijing Guoji Hanzi Yanjiuhui - Beijing International Society for Chinese Character Research) Hanzi Wenhua Zazhishe, P.O. Box 2214, Beijing, People's Republic of China. TEL 605-6376. (Dist. outside China by: China International Book Trading Corp., P.O. Box 399, Beijing, P.R.C.. TEL 8413063; Dist. in US by: China Books & Periodicals, Inc., 2929 24th St., San Francisco, CA 94110. TEL 415-282-2994) Eds. Yuan Xiaoyuan, Xu Dejiang. circ. 5,000. **Document type:** academic/scholarly publication.
—BLDSC (3180.274200).
Description: Publishes academic research papers on Chinese character research and teaching, and on Linguistics.

001.3 US AS30
HARVARD REVIEW. 1992. 2/yr. $12. Harvard College Library, Poetry Room, Cambridge, MA 02138. TEL 617-495-2454. FAX 617-496-3692. Ed. Stratis Haviaras. adv. contact: Joyce Wilson. circ. 3,000.
Description: Reviews literary monographs, publishes original poetry, fiction, literary non-fiction, letters from abroad.

HEBREW ANNUAL REVIEW; a journal of biblical and Hebraic studies. see *LITERATURE*

HELLENIKA; Zeitschrift fuer deutsch-griechische kulturelle und wirtschaftliche Zusammenarbeit. see *LITERATURE*

001.3 SP ISSN 0018-0114
HELMANTICA; revista de filologia clasica y hebrea. 1950. 3/yr. 4000 ptas.($50) Universidad Pontificia, Departamento de Ediciones y Publicaciones, Apdo. de Correos 541, 37080 Salamanca, Spain. TEL 923-21-51-40. FAX 923-21-34-50. Ed. Dr. Jose Oroz. bk.rev.; abstr.; bibl.; index. circ. 650. **Indexed:** Bibl.Ling.

001.6 CC ISSN 1000-5242
HENAN DAXUE XUEBAO (SHEHUI KEXUE BAN)/HENAN UNIVERSITY. JOURNAL (SOCIAL SCIENCE EDITION). (Text in Chinese) 1934-19??; resumed 1956. bi-m. $60. Henan Daxue, Xuebao Bianjibu, Kaifeng, Henan 475001, People's Republic of China. TELEX 551029. (Dist. overseas by: China International Book Trading Corp., P.O. Box 399, Beijing, P.R.C.) Ed. Wang Zhenduo. bk.rev. circ. 3,000. **Document type:** academic/scholarly publication.
Description: Covers history, literature and liguistics, political theory, and education. Each issue deals with a specific topic.

378.1 IE ISSN 0018-0750 AS121
HERMATHENA. 1873. s-a. I£20 (foreign I£25). Trinity College, Classics Department, Dublin 2, Ireland. TEL 01-7021092. FAX 01-772646. Ed. B.C. McGing. adv.; bk.rev.; illus.; index, cum.index. circ. 600. (also avail. in microform from UMI; reprint service avail. from UMI) **Indexed:** Abstr.Engl.Stud., Amer.Hist.& Life, Arts & Hum.Cit.Ind., Bibl.Ling., Br.Hum.Ind., Curr.Cont., Hist.Abstr., Hum.Ind., M.L.A., Old Test.Abstr., Phil.Ind. **Document type:** academic/scholarly publication.
—BLDSC (4300.073000); Faxon; UnCover; UMI.

001.3 JA ISSN 0910-3023
HERMES. (Text in Japanese) 1984. bi-m. 10000 Yen. Iwanami Shoten Publishers, 2-5-5 Hitotsubashi, Chiyoda-ku, Tokyo 101-02, Japan. FAX 03-3239-9618. (Dist. overseas by: Japan Publications Trading Co., Ltd., Box 5030, Tokyo International, Tokyo 100-31, Japan; Or: 1255 Howard St., San Francisco, CA 94103) Ed.Bd. adv.; bk.rev.; illus.
Description: Covers architecture, literature, music, philosophy, and anthropology.

001.3 FI ISSN 0073-2702 PT9205
HISTORISKA OCH LITTERATURHISTORISKA STUDIER. (Subseries of: Svenska Litteratursaellskapet i Finland. Skrifter) (Text in Swedish) 1925. a. FIM 150. Svenska Litteratursaellskapet i Finland, Marieg. 8, 00170 Helsinki 17, Finland. FAX 358-0-632820. Ed. Helena Solstrand-Pipping. **Indexed:** Amer.Hist.& Life, Hist.Abstr., M.L.A. **Document type:** academic/scholarly publication, monographic series.

HITOTSUBASHI JOURNAL OF ARTS AND SCIENCES. see *SCIENCES: COMPREHENSIVE WORKS*

001.3 JA ISSN 0386-4472
HOKKAIDO KYOIKU DAIGAKU KIYO. DAI-1-BU, A. JINBUN HEN/HOKKAIDO UNIVERSITY OF EDUCATION. JOURNAL. SECTION 1 A. HUMANITIES. vol.32, 1982. s-a. exchange basis. Hokkaido University of Education - Hokkaido Kyoiku Daigaku, Ainosato 5-jo, 3-chome, Kita-ku, Sapporo 002, Hokkaido, Japan.

001.3 917.106 CN ISSN 0827-1569
HORIZONS INTERCULTURELS. (Text in English, French) 1985. s-a. Can.$6.70 (foreign Can.$8.50). Interculturel Institute of Montreal - Institut Interculturel de Montreal, 4917 St. Urbain, Montreal, PQ H2T 2W1, Canada. TEL 514-288-7229. FAX 514-844-6800. bk.rev. circ. 3,000.
Supersedes (in 1985): Monchanin Cross-Cultural Center News Bulletin.
Description: Reports on ethnocultural communities and reviews of cross-cultural events.

378.1 PR ISSN 0018-5027
HORIZONTES. (Text mainly in Spanish; occasionally in English) 1957. s-a. $7.50 (foreign $8.50). Universidad Catolica de Puerto Rico, Ponce, PR 00732. Ed. Maria de los Milagros Perez. bk.rev.; bibl.; index. circ. 1,100. **Indexed:** Amer.Hist.& Life, Hist.Abstr., M.L.A.

300 001.3 SA
HUMAN SCIENCES RESEARCH COUNCIL. ANNUAL REPORT. (Text in Afrikaans, English) 1969. a. free. Human Sciences Research Council, Private Bag X41, Pretoria 0001, South Africa. TEL 27-12-202724. FAX 27-12-2022892. TELEX 321710 SA. circ. 1,400. **Document type:** corporate report.

001.3 US
HUMAN TIES. q. free. Utah Humanities Council, 350 S. 400 E., Ste. 110, Salt Lake City, UT 84111-2946. TEL 801-531-7868. FAX 801-531-7869. Ed. Cynthia Buckingham. bk.rev. circ. 4,500. (looseleaf format; back issues avail.)
Formerly: Utah Humanities News.
Description: Contains information about public humanities programs supported by the Utah Humanities Council and National Endowment for the Humanities, as well the availably of grants. Also provides technical assistance for community program planning.

300 700 800 GT ISSN 0018-7356
HUMANIDADES. vol.8, 1970. irreg. (2-3/yr.). Universidad de San Carlos de Guatemala, Ciudad Universitaria, Guatemala 12, Guatemala. Ed.Bd. bk.rev.; bibl.

001.3 BL ISSN 0102-9479 AS80.A1
HUMANIDADES. 1982. q. $40 to individuals; institutions $50. (Airton Lugarinho de Lima Camara) Editora Universidade de Brasilia, Caixa Postal 04551, 70919-970 Brasilia D.F., Brazil. FAX 061-274-5352. TELEX 61-1083 UNBS BR. adv.; bk.rev. circ. 16,000.
Description: Geared toward specialists and laymen. Includes articles written by Brazilian professors.

001.3 DK ISSN 0107-9573
HUMANIST. 1982. irreg. (approx. 15/yr.). free. Koebenhavns Universitet, Humanistisk Facultets Kontor - University of Copenhagen, Faculty of Humanities, Njalsgade 80, 2300 Copenhagen S, Denmark. FAX 45-31-54-32-11. Eds. Karsten Borup, Lise Tolstrup Kristensen. bk.rev.; illus. circ. 4,000. **Indexed:** Acad.Ind.

300 700 800 US ISSN 0018-7526 LB2301
HUMANITIES. 1980. bi-m. $11. U.S. National Endowment for the Humanities, 1100 Pennsylvania Ave., N.W., Washington, DC 20506. (Orders to: Supt. of Documents, Washington, DC 20402) Ed. Mary Lou Beatty. circ. 4,000. (also avail. in microfilm from UMI; reprint service avail. for UMI) **Indexed:** Ind.U.S.Gov.Per.
—BLDSC (4336.567000); Faxon; UnCover; UMI.
Description: Articles by major writers on issues in the humanities; listing of all recent NEH grants; application deadlines; and endowment projects.

HUMANITIES: COMPREHENSIVE WORKS

001.3   AT   ISSN 0312-5041
HUMANITIES RESEARCH CENTRE BULLETIN. 1975. q. free. Australian National University, G.P.O. Box 4, Canberra, A.C.T. 2601, Australia. FAX 062-48-0054. TELEX AA 61670. Ed. B.J. Parvey. circ. 2,000. (back issues avail.)

001.3   II
HUMANITIES REVIEW. (Text in English) 1979. q. Rs.20($20) Nahal, Chaman Nahal, 2-1 Kalkaji Extension, New Delhi 110019, India.

001.3 300   HU   ISSN 0236-6568
DB901
HUNGARIAN STUDIES. (Text in English, French, German) 1985. s-a. $56 (effective 1992). (International Association of Hungarian Studies) Akademiai Kiado, Publishing House of the Hungarian Academy of Sciences, P.O. Box 245, H-1519 Budapest, Hungary. TEL 181-2134. FAX 166-6466. TELEX 22-6228 AKNYO H. Ed. Mihaly Szegedi-Maszak. **Indexed:** Bibl.Ling.
—BLDSC (4337.093000). **CCC.**
Description: Offers an independent, international forum for original papers in the humanities and social sciences: literature, philology, ethnology, folklore, musicology, history, sociology, etc.

300   SG   ISSN 0018-9642
DT1
I F A N BULLETIN. SERIE B: SCIENCES HUMAINES. (Text in French; occasionally in English or other languages) 1954. q. 190 F. Institut Fondamental d'Afrique Noire - Cheikh Anta Diop, B.P. 206, Dakar, Senegal. Ed. Abdoulaye Bara Diop. bk.rev.; charts; illus. circ. 1,000. **Indexed:** Amer.Hist.& Life, Anthropol.Lit., Bibl.Ling., Deep Sea Res.& Oceanogr.Abstr., Documentatieblad, Hist.Abstr.

I I A S OCCASIONAL PAPERS. (Indian Institute of Advanced Study) see *EDUCATION — Higher Education*

001.3   US   ISSN 1068-0454
IDEAS FROM THE NATIONAL HUMANITIES CENTER. 1979. 2/yr. free. National Humanities Center, Box 12256, Research Triangle Park, NC 27709-2256. TEL 919-549-0661. FAX 919-990-8535. Ed. Jean Anne Leuchtenburg. circ. 4,000. **Document type:** newsletter.
Supersedes (in 1992): National Humanities Center Newsletter (ISSN 0196-1721); Which supersedes (in 1980): Ideas.

001.3   VE
IMAGEN; artes letras espectaculos. irreg. Consejo Nacional de la Cultura, Apdo. 50995, Caracas, Venezuela. TEL 77-46-61. Ed. Juan Calzadilla.

001.3   FR   ISSN 0019-2899
AS161
IMPACTS. 1967. q. 200 F. (effective 1993). (Universite Catholique de l'Ouest) Association Saint-Yves, 3 Place Andre-Leroy B.P. 808, 49008 Angers Cedex 01, France. Ed. Louis Collin. adv.; bk.rev.; abstr.; bibl. circ. 850.
—BLDSC (4371.030000).

001.3   US   ISSN 0277-8432
IMPRIMIS. 1972. m. free. Hillsdale College, Center for Constructive Alternatives, Hillsdale, MI 49242. TEL 517-437-7341. FAX 517-437-3923. Eds. Ronald Trowbridge, Lissa Roche. adv. circ. 510,000. (back issues avail.) **Indexed:** P.A.I.S.

001.3   US   ISSN 0923-7135
INCOGNITA; international journal for cognitive studies in the humanities. 1990. s-a. fl.72($46.39) to individuals; institutions fl.117 ($67). c/o Prof. D.A. Miller, 10848 S. Hoyne, Chicago, IL 60643. **Document type:** academic/scholarly publication.
—CCC.
Description: Transdisciplinary journal for bringing into the study of humanities the benefits of the "cognitive revolution" and for creating intellectual bridges between linguistics, history, philosophy, literature, archaeology, and the study of religion in past and present civilizations.
Refereed Serial

L'INCONTRO DELLE GENTI; rivista di scienze lettere ed arte. see *ART*

001.3 060   II   ISSN 0073-6465
INDIAN INSTITUTE OF ADVANCED STUDY. TRANSACTIONS AND MONOGRAPHS. Variant title: Indian Institute of Advanced Study. Transactions. 1965. irreg. price varies. Indian Institute of Advanced Study, Rashtrapati Nivas, Summer Hill, Simla 171005, India.

001.3   II
INDIAN INSTITUTE OF WORLD CULTURE. ANNUAL REPORT. no.18, 1977. a. Indian Institute of World Culture, 6 Shri B.P. Wadia Rd., P.O. Box 402, Basavangudi, Bangalore 560 004, India.

001.3   II   ISSN 0251-1630
INDIAN INSTITUTE OF WORLD CULTURE. BULLETIN. 1981. m. Rs.25. Indian Institute of World Culture, 6 Shri B P Wadia Road, P.O. Box 402, Basavangudi, Bangalore 560 004, India.

054 001.3   FR   ISSN 0980-3637
INSTITUT D'ETUDES SLAVES INFORMATIONS. 1969. irreg. free to members and universities. Institut d'Etudes Slaves, 9 rue Michelet, 75006 Paris, France. bibl. **Document type:** newsletter.
Formerly: I N E S Informations (ISSN 0339-4212)

980 972   FR   ISSN 0993-5878
INSTITUT DES HAUTES ETUDES DE L'AMERIQUE LATINE. COLLECTION DES TRAVAUX ET MEMOIRES. 1957. a. price varies. Institut des Hautes Etudes de l'Amerique Latine, 28 rue Saint-Guillaume, 75007 Paris, France. **Indexed:** Amer.Hist.& Life, Hist.Abstr.
Formerly: Institut des Hautes Etudes de l'Amerique Latine. Travaux et Memoires (ISSN 0073-8298)

054.1   SZ
INSTITUT NATIONAL GENEVOIS. ACTS. 1853. irreg. free. Institut National Genevois, 1, Promenade du Pin, Geneva, Switzerland.

001.3   BL
INSTITUTO BRASILEIRO DO PATRIMONIO CULTURAL. GOVERNMENT CULTURAL PUBLICATIONS. 1937. irreg. Secretaria do Patrimonio Historico e Artistico Nacional, Avda. Rio Branco 46, 3o andar, 20090-002 Rio de Janeiro RJ, Brazil. TEL 021-253-4276. FAX 021-263-5677. Dir. Renato Soeiro. bibl.; charts; illus. **Document type:** government publication, monographic series.
Formerly: Instituto do Patrimonio Historico e Artistico Nacional. Publicacoes.

001.3   CK
INSTITUTO CARO Y CUERVO. PUBLICACIONES. 1944. irreg., no.89, 1990. price varies. Instituto Caro y Cuervo, Seccion de Publicaciones, Apdo. Aereo 51502, Botoga, Colombia. (back issues avail.) **Indexed:** Bibl.Ling.

378.1   PR   ISSN 0020-3815
F1951
INSTITUTO DE CULTURA PUERTORRIQUENA. REVISTA. 1958. q. $10. Instituto de Cultura Puertorriquena, Division de Publicaciones 4184, Apdo. 4184, San Juan, PR 00902-4184. TEL 809-724-0700. Dir. Jose Miguel Barcelo. illus. circ. 1,000.
—BLDSC (7817.450000).

001.3   SP   ISSN 0584-6374
DP302.M1
INSTITUTO DE ESTUDIOS MADRILENOS. ANALES. 1966. irreg., no.30, 1991. price varies. Consejo Superior de Investigaciones Cientificas (C.S.I.C.), Instituto de Estudios Madrilenos, Prudencio Ibanez Campos, Cerro del Viso 16, Torrejon de Ardoz, Madrid, Spain. **Indexed:** Amer.Hist.& Life, Hist.Abstr.

001.3   UY
INSTITUTO DE FILOSOFIA, CIENCIAS Y LETRAS. CUADERNOS. no.6, 1980. irreg. Universidad Catolica del Uruguay "Damaso Antonio Larranaga", Instituto de Filosofia, Ciencias y Letras, Av. 8 de Octubre 2738, Montevideo, Uruguay. circ. 1,000.

001.3   PO
INSTITUTO NACIONAL DE INVESTIGACAO CIENTIFICA. TEXTOS HUMANISTICOS PORTUGUESES. vol.6, 1988. a. (Instituto Nacional de Investigacao Cientifica, Centro de Linguistica) Universidade de Coimbra, Centro de Estudos Classicos e Humanisticos, Faculdade de Letras, Coimbra, Portugal.

001.3 917.106   CN   ISSN 0828-797X
INTERCULTURE; exploring the frontiers of cross-cultural understanding. French edition (ISSN 0712-1571) (Text in English) 1968. q. Can.$23 to individuals; institutions Can.$37. Intercultural Institute of Montreal - Institut Interculturel de Montreal, 4917 St. Urbain, Montreal, PQ H2T 2W1, Canada. TEL 514-288-7229. FAX 514-844-6800. Ed.Bd. bk.rev.; bibl.; index, cum.index. circ. 1,000. (also avail. in microfilm from WMP; back issues avail.) **Indexed:** I D A, Pt.de Rep. (1991-), Rel.& Theol.Abstr. (1989-), Rel.Ind.One. **Document type:** academic/scholarly publication.
—BLDSC (4533.356070).
Formerly (until July 1981): Revue Monchanin Journal.
Description: Information on contemporary cultures, exploring current intercultural issues.

001.3 375   US   ISSN 1056-6139
AZ183.U5
INTERDISCIPLINARY HUMANITIES. 1984. q. $20. National Association for Humanities Education, c/o Interdisciplinary Programs, University of Minnesota, Duluth, MN 55812. TEL 218-726-8548. Ed. Fred E.H. Schroeder. adv.; bk.rev.; abstr. circ. 500. (also avail. in microform from UMI) **Indexed:** ERIC. **Document type:** academic/scholarly publication.
Formerly (until vol.9, 1992): Humanities Education (ISSN 0882-5475); Supersedes (1967-1979): Humanities Journal (ISSN 0046-8266)
Description: Dedicated to the teaching of integrated studies among the humanities, arts and related fields in schools, colleges and cultural institutions.

INTERNATIONAL CONFERENCE OF ORIENTALISTS IN JAPAN. TRANSACTIONS. see *ORIENTAL STUDIES*

001.3 300   KO
INTERNATIONAL CULTURAL SOCIETY OF KOREA. NEWSLETTER. (Text in English) 1990. q. free to qualified personnel. International Cultural Society of Korea, Daewoo Foundation Bldg., 526, 5-ga, Namdaemunno, C.P.O. Box 2147, Chung-gu, Seoul, S. Korea. TEL 753-6464. FAX 757-2049. Ed. Hyuck-In Lew. **Document type:** newsletter.

900   UK   ISSN 0066-3247
INTERNATIONAL DIRECTORY OF EIGHTEENTH-CENTURY STUDIES/REPERTOIRE INTERNATIONAL DES DIX-HUITIEMISTES. 1969. quadrennial. Voltaire Foundation, Taylor Institution, St. Giles, Oxford OX1 3NA, England. TEL 0865-270250. FAX 0865-270740. adv. circ. 5,000. **Document type:** directory.

001.3   US   ISSN 1042-4032
AS9   CODEN: IJHAEM
INTERNATIONAL JOURNAL OF HUMANITIES AND PEACE; synergy, synthesis, transformation. 1983. q. $18 to individuals; institutions $25; Canada $20.50; elsewhere $24. Vasant V. Merchant, Ed. & Pub., 1436 N. Evergreen Dr., Flagstaff, AZ 86001. TEL 602-774-4793. bk.rev.; film rev.; bibl. circ. 1,000. (back issues avail.) **Document type:** academic/scholarly publication.
—UnCover.
Formerly (until 1988): Arizona Humanities Association Journal.
Refereed Serial

INTERNATIONAL JOURNAL OF INDIAN STUDIES; a journal devoted to the study of Indian culture, society and tradition. see *ORIENTAL STUDIES*

INTERNATIONAL JOURNAL OF THE CLASSICAL TRADITION. see *CLASSICAL STUDIES*

001.3   FR   ISSN 0074-6819
INTERNATIONAL LITERARY AND ARTISTIC ASSOCIATION. PROCEEDINGS AND REPORTS OF CONGRESS. (Text in English and French) irreg., 54th, 1972, Paris. International Literary and Artistic Association, c/o A. Francon, 55 rue des Mathurins, 75008 Paris, France. **Document type:** proceedings.

001.3 320   US
INTERNATIONAL REVIEW OF THIRD WORLD CULTURE AND ISSUES. q. $10. Box 1785, Palm Springs, CA 92263. Ed. Joe Beaver.

HUMANITIES: COMPREHENSIVE WORKS

001.3   US   ISSN 1055-7180
INTERNATIONAL STUDIES IN GLOBAL CHANGE. irreg. Harwood Academic Publishers, 820 Town Center Dr., Langhorne, PA 19047. TEL 215-750-2642. FAX 215-750-6343. (U.K. subscr. to: Box 90, Reading, Berkshire RG1 8JL, England. TEL 0734-560-080) Eds. Tom Burns, Thomas Dietz. (also avail. in microform)
Refereed Serial

IRIS: A JOURNAL ABOUT WOMEN. see *WOMEN'S INTERESTS*

500 600   IS   ISSN 0578-9230
ISRAEL ACADEMY OF SCIENCES AND HUMANITIES. SECTION OF HUMANITIES. PROCEEDINGS. (Supersedes in part the Academy's Proceedings) (Text in English and French) 1967. irreg. price varies. Israel Academy of Sciences and Humanities, 43 Jabotinski St., P.O. Box 4040, Jerusalem 91040, Israel. TEL 02-636211. FAX 02-666059. circ. 900. (back issues avail.) **Indexed:** Ind.Heb.Per. **Document type:** proceedings.
Description: Reprints of papers on the humanities read at meetings of the Academy.

ISTITUTO GIAPPONESE DI CULTURA IN ROMA. ANNUARIO. see *HISTORY — History Of Europe*

870   IT
ISTITUTO NAZIONALE DI STUDI ROMANI. RASSEGNA D'INFORMAZIONI. 1933. m. free. Istituto Nazionale di Studi Romani, Piazza dei Cavalieri di Malta 2, 00153 Rome, Italy. adv.; bibl.
Formerly: Istituto di Studi Romani. Rassegna d'Informazioni (ISSN 0021-2474)

001.3   CR
▼**ISTMICA.** 1994. s-a. Col.1000($10) in Latin America; U.S. $20. Universidad Nacional Autonoma, Facultad de Filosofia y Letras, Apdo. Postal 86, 3000 Heredia, Costa Rica. TEL 506-237-6363 ext. 429. Ed. Joseph Richey. bk.rev. circ. 2,500. **Document type:** academic/scholarly publication.
Description: Covers philosophy, literature, politics, religion and art.

IWATE MEDICAL UNIVERSITY SCHOOL OF LIBERAL ARTS & SCIENCES. ANNUAL REPORT/IWATE IKA DAIGAKU KYOYOBU NENPO. see *SCIENCES: COMPREHENSIVE WORKS*

001.3   II
J & K RESEARCH BIANNUAL. (Jammu and Kashmir) (Text in English) 1976. s-a. Directorate of Libraries, Research, Museums, and Archaeology, Srinager, Jammu and Kashmir, India.

001.3   BG
JAHANGIRNAGAR REVIEW. PART C. (Text in Bangla and English) 1987. a. Tk.30($5) Jahangirnagar University, Department of English, Rm. 223, Savar, Dhaka, Bangladesh. Ed. Nurul Islam. circ. 500.

001.3   GW
JAHRBUCH KREIS EUSKIRCHEN. 1951. a. DM.7. Kreis Euskirchen, Julicher Ring 32, 53879 Euskirchen, Germany. adv. circ. 7,000.

JAHRBUCH LANDKREIS KASSEL. see *HISTORY — History Of Europe*

001.3   TS   ISSN 1021-9889
JAMI'AT AL-IMARAT AL-ARABIYYAH AL-MUTTAHIDAH. KULLIYYAT AL-AADAAB. MAJALLAH/UNITED ARAB EMIRATES UNIVERSITY. FACULTY OF ARTS. JOURNAL. (Text in Arabic, English) 1985. a. exchange basis. Jami'at al-Imarat al-Arabiyyah al-Muttahidah, Kulliyyat al-Aadaab - United Arab Emirates University, Faculty of Arts, P.O. Box 17771, Al-Ain, United Arab Emirates. TEL 678007. FAX 671612. TELEX 33521 JAMEAH EM. Ed. Fuad Shaban. bk.rev. circ. 1,000. **Document type:** academic/scholarly publication.
Description: Publishes research papers in the humanities and social sciences.
Refereed Serial

001.3   JA
JAPAN FOUNDATION ANNUAL REPORT. (Text in English) a. free. Japan Foundation, Park Bldg., 3-6, Kioi-cho, Chiyoda-ku, Tokyo 102, Japan. TEL 03-3263-4491. FAX 03-3234-7884. **Document type:** corporate report.

JEWS AND THE JEWISH PEOPLE - JEWISH SAMIZDAT/EVREI I EVREISKI NAROD - EVREISKII SAMIZDAT. see *ETHNIC INTERESTS*

001.3 300   JA   ISSN 0495-8012
JINBUN SHIZEN KAGAKU RONSHU/JOURNAL OF HUMANITIES AND NATURAL SCIENCES. (Text mainly in Japanese, partly in English) 1962. 3/yr. Tokyo Keizai University - Tokyo Keizai Daigaku, 7 Minamicho 1-chome, Kokubunji, Tokyo 185, Japan. FAX 0423-27-9834. Ed.Bd. bk.rev. circ. 2,200. —BLDSC (5003.475000).

020   UK   ISSN 0301-102X
JOHN RYLANDS UNIVERSITY LIBRARY OF MANCHESTER. BULLETIN. 1903. 3/yr. £37.50($60) John Rylands University Library, Manchester M13 9PP, England. FAX 061-273-7488. Ed. Dorothy Clayton. adv.; illus.; cum.index: vols.1-25, 26-50, 51-60. circ. 700. (also avail. in microform; reprint service avail. from KTO) **Indexed:** Abstr.Engl.Stud., Amer.Hist.& Life, Arts & Hum.Cit.Ind., Bibl.Ling., Br.Hum.Ind., Curr.Cont., Hist.Abstr., LISA, M.L.A., New Test.Abstr., Old Test.Abstr., Rel.& Theol.Abstr. (1968-), Rel.Ind.One, RILA. **Document type:** bulletin. —BLDSC (2597.410000); Faxon; UnCover; UMI.
Formerly: John Rylands Library. Bulletin (ISSN 0021-7239)
Description: Examines material about the humanities, social sicences, and on the history and the philospohy of the natural and physical sciences. One issue per year devoted to catalogs and/or archival book collections held by the library.

378.0025   JA   ISSN 0385-1478
JOHO KODO KAGAKU KENKYU/STUDIES IN INFORMATION AND BEHAVIORAL SCIENCES. (Text and summaries in English and Japanese) 1975. a. exchange only. Hiroshima Daigaku, Sogo Kagakubu - Hiroshima University, Faculty of Integrated Arts and Sciences, 1-89 Higashisenda-cho 1-chome, Naka-ku, Hiroshima-shi, Hiroshima-ken 730, Japan. circ. 200. (back issues avail.)

001.3 500 613   JA   ISSN 0914-9775
JOSAI DAIGAKU KENKYU NENPO. SHIZEN KAGAKU HEN/JOSAI UNIVERSITY BULLETIN OF LIBERAL ARTS. NATURAL SCIENCE, HEALTH AND PHYSICAL EDUCATION. (Text and summaries in Japanese) 1977. a. Josai University - Josai Daigaku, 1-1 Keyakidai, Sakado-shi, Saitama-ken 350-02, Japan.

001.3   FR   ISSN 1145-6396
JOURNAL DES ECONOMISTES ET DES ETUDES HUMAINES; bilingual journal of interdisciplinary studies. (Text in English, French) irreg. Universite Aix-Marseille III, Institut Europeen des Etudes Humaines, 3 ave. Robert Schuman, 13628 Aix-en-Provence Cedex, France. Ed. Pierre Garello.

JOURNAL FOR GENERAL PHILOSOPHY OF SCIENCE/ZEITSCHRIFT FUER ALLGEMEINE WISSENSCHAFTSTHEORIE. see *SCIENCES: COMPREHENSIVE WORKS*

001.3 300   GW   ISSN 0944-9094
▼**JOURNAL FOR THE STUDY OF BRITISH CULTURES.** (Text in English) 1994. a. DM.48 to individuals; institutions DM.58. Gunter Narr Verlag, Postfach 2567, 72015 Tuebingen, Germany. TEL 07071-78091. FAX 07071-75288. Ed.Bd. **Document type:** academic/scholarly publication.

305.896 970   US   ISSN 1051-1865
▼**JOURNAL OF AFRO-LATIN AMERICAN STUDIES AND LITERATURES.** 1993. 2/yr. $20 to individuals; institutions $45 (effective 1994). c/o Dept. of Modern Languages & Literatures, Howard University, 2400 Sixth St., N.W. - Locke Hall, Washington, DC 20059. TEL 202-806-6758. Ed. Rosangela Maria Vieira. (back issues avail.) **Document type:** academic/scholarly publication.
Description: Promotes the scientific investigation of issues faced by African-Latin Americans from colonial times to the present, and their contribtuions to the life, culture and arts of the Americas.
Refereed Serial

001.3   JA   ISSN 0914-8035
JOURNAL OF AMERICAN AND CANADIAN STUDIES. (Text in English, Japanese) 1988. s-a. Sophia University, Institute of American and Canadian Studies, 7-1 Kioi-cho, Chiyoda-ku, Tokyo 102, Japan. TEL 03-3238-3908. FAX 03-3238-3908. Ed. Kimitada Miwa. bk.rev. circ. 2,000. —BLDSC (4927.230600).
Description: Covers research results by the American and Canadian studies specialists in various disciplines, and interdisciplinary studies on American and Canadian affairs and their relations with Japanese affairs.

917   CN   ISSN 0021-9495
F1001
JOURNAL OF CANADIAN STUDIES/REVUE D'ETUDES CANADIENNES. (Text in French, English) 1966. q. Can.$28 to individuals; Can.$45 to institutions. Trent University, Peterborough, ON K9J 7B8, Canada. TEL 705-748-1279. FAX 705-748-1655. Ed. Michael Peterman. adv.; bk.rev.; index. circ. 1,400. (also avail. in microform from MML; back issues avail.; reprint service avail. from MMI) **Indexed:** Abstr.Anthropol., Abstr.Engl.Stud., Amer.Hist.& Life, Arts & Hum.Cit.Ind., Can.Lit.Ind., Can.Per.Ind., CMI, Curr.Cont., Hist.Abstr., Hum.Ind., Ind.Bk.Rev.Hum., Mar.Aff.Bibl., Mid.East: Abstr.& Ind., SSCI.
—BLDSC (4954.760000); Faxon; UnCover; SWETS. CCC.

060   JA   ISSN 0521-7903
JOURNAL OF CULTURAL SCIENCES/BUNKA KAGAKU KIYO. (Text in Japanese) 1959. a. Chiba University, Faculty of Humanities and Social Sciences, 1-33 Yayoicho, Chiba 280, Japan.

JOURNAL OF DEVELOPING SOCIETIES; a forum for developmental issues in developing and developed societies. see *SOCIAL SCIENCES: COMPREHENSIVE WORKS*

001.3   KO   ISSN 0537-7137
JOURNAL OF HUMANISTIC STUDIES/INMUN KWAHAK. (Text in English and Korean) 1957. s-a. 3000 Won. (Yonsei University, Institute of Humanistic Studies) Yonsei University Press, 134 Sinchon-Dong, Seodaemoon-Ku, Seoul, S. Korea. Ed. Chong- Young Lee. illus.; cum.index: vols.1-20 and vols.21-30 (2 vols). **Indexed:** M.L.A.

001.3   MW   ISSN 1016-0728
JOURNAL OF HUMANITIES. (Text in English, French; summaries in English) 1987. a. K.15($15) to individuals; institutions K.10($10). University of Malawi, Institute of Education for Faculty of Humanities, Chancellor College, P.O. Box 280, Zomba, Malawi. TEL 265-522-622. FAX 265-522-046. TELEX 4742 CHANCOL MI. Ed. D.N. Kaphagawani. bk.rev. circ. 500. (back issues avail.) **Indexed:** P.L.E.S.A (1990-). —BLDSC (5003.474000).

JOURNAL OF INTERDISCIPLINARY HISTORY. see *HISTORY*

001.3 300   US   ISSN 0890-0132
BD255   CODEN: JISTE2
JOURNAL OF INTERDISCIPLINARY STUDIES; an international journal of interdisciplinary and interfaith dialogue. (Text in English, French, German) 1989. a. $15 to individuals (foreign $20); institutions $25 (foreign $30); students $10 (foreign $15). Institute for Interdisciplinary Research, 2828 Third St., Ste. 11, Santa Monica, CA 90405-4150. TEL 310-396-0517. (Co-sponsor: International Christian Studies Association) Ed. Oskar Gruenwald. adv.; bk.rev.; index, cum.index. circ. 1,700. (back issues avail.) **Indexed:** Int.Polit.Sci.Abstr., Rel.& Theol.Abstr. (1989-), Rel.Ind.One, Sociol.Abstr. **Document type:** academic/scholarly publication. —UnCover; UMI.
Description: Offers a scholarly forum for recovering the lost unity of Renaissance learning while affirming transcendental values and faith.

001.3   IQ   ISSN 1012-3377
JOURNAL OF IRAQI DISSERTATION ABSTRACTS. PART A: HUMANITIES AND SOCIAL SCIENCES. (Editions in Arabic, English) 1985. irreg. free. Scientific Research Council, Jadiriyah P.O. Box 2441, Baghdad, Iraq. TELEX 213976 SR IK. Ed. Radhwan K. Abdul-Halim. circ. 500.

HUMANITIES: COMPREHENSIVE WORKS

909 US ISSN 0047-2573
CB351
JOURNAL OF MEDIEVAL AND RENAISSANCE STUDIES.
1971. 3/yr. $32 to individuals (foreign $38); institutions $72 (foreign $78). Duke University Press, Box 90660, Durham, NC 27708-0660. TEL 919-687-3600. FAX 919-688-4574. Eds. Marcel Tetel, Annabel Patterson. adv.; bibl. circ. 900. (also avail. in microform from MIM,UMI; reprint service avail. from ISI,UMI) Indexed: Amer.Hist.& Life, Arts & Hum.Cit.Ind., Curr.Cont., Hist.Abstr., M.L.A., RILA.
—BLDSC (5017.550000); Faxon; SWETS; UMI. CCC.
Refereed Serial

956 MM ISSN 1016-3476
DE1 CODEN: JMESEP
JOURNAL OF MEDITERRANEAN STUDIES; history, culture and society in the Mediterranean world. (Text and summaries mainly in English; occasional articles and summaries in French, Italian) 1991. s-a. £25 to individuals; institutions £50 (effective 1994). (University of Malta, Mediterranean Institute) University of Malta Services Ltd., Msida MSD 06, Malta. TEL 356-333903. (Dist. by: Turpin Distribution Services Ltd., Blackhorse Rd., Letchworth, Hertfordshire SG6 1HN, England. TEL 44-462-672555) Ed. Paul Sant Cassia. adv.: B&W page £150; adv. contact: R. Bartolo. abstr.; illus.; cum.index every 5 yrs. (back issues avail.) Indexed: Amer.Hist.& Life (1991-), Anthropol.Lit., Hist.Abstr. (1991-), Sociol.Abstr. Document type: academic/scholarly publication.
—BLDSC (5017.583000); UnCover.
Description: Interdisciplinary journal devoted to the Mediterranean, publishing original scholarship in anthropology, archaeology and the history, literature, religions, culture and society of Southern Europe and North Africa in both historical and modern periods.
Refereed Serial

001.3 300 JA ISSN 0386-8729
JOURNAL OF SOCIAL SCIENCES AND HUMANITIES/JINBUN GAKUHO.* 1944. a. Tokyo-toritsu Daigaku, Jinbun Gakubu - Tokyo Metropolitan University, Faculty of Social Sciences and Humanities, 1-1 Minamiosawa, Hachioji-shi, Tokyo 192-03, Japan. circ. 650. Indexed: Amer.Hist.& Life, Hist.Abstr.

JOURNAL OF SPIRITUAL FORMATION. see *RELIGIONS AND THEOLOGY*

900 100 300 US ISSN 0022-5037
B1
JOURNAL OF THE HISTORY OF IDEAS; a quarterly devoted to cultural and intellectual history. 1940. q. $21 to individuals; institutions $42. Johns Hopkins University Press, Journals Publishing Division, 2715 N. Charles St., Baltimore, MD 21218-4319. TEL 410-516-6987. FAX 410-516-6968. Ed. Donald R. Kelley. adv.; bk.rev.; bibl.; index, cum.index: 1940-1964, 1965-1969, 1970-1974, 1975-1979, 1980-1984. circ. 3,200. (also avail. in microform from MIM,UMI,KTO,PMC; back issues avail.; reprint service avail. from UMI) Indexed: Abstr.Engl.Stud., Acad.Ind., Amer.Hist.& Life, Arts & Hum.Cit.Ind., Bk.Rev.Ind. (1965-), Chem.Abstr., Child.Bk.Rev.Ind. (1965-), Curr.Cont., Deep Sea Res.& Oceanogr.Abstr., Hist.Abstr., Hum.Ind., M.L.A., Mid.East: Abstr.& Ind., Phil.Ind., Rel.Ind.One, RILA, SSCI. Document type: academic/scholarly publication.
—BLDSC (5000.900000); Faxon; UnCover; SWETS; UMI. CCC.
Description: Examines the evolution of ideas and their influence on historical developments

700 UK ISSN 0075-4390
AS122 CODEN: JWCIAH
JOURNAL OF THE WARBURG AND COURTAULD INSTITUTES. 1937. a. £50. Warburg Institute, University of London, Woburn Sq., London WC1H 0AB, England. TEL 071-580-9663. FAX 071-436-2852. Ed.Bd. index. circ. 1,400. Indexed: Artbibl.Mod., Arts & Hum.Cit.Ind., Avery Ind.Archit.Per., Curr.Cont., RILA. Document type: academic/scholarly publication.
—BLDSC (4912.700000); Faxon; UnCover; SWETS.
Description: Provides a common forum for historians of art, religion, science, literature, philosophy and anthropology.

JOURNAL OF THOUGHT. see *SOCIAL SCIENCES: COMPREHENSIVE WORKS*

001.3 300 CE
KALYANI; journal of humanities and social sciences of the University of Kelaniya. 1982. a. Rs.100($15) University of Kelaniya, c/o Librarian, Kelaniya, Sri Lanka. FAX 521485. Ed.Bd. bk.rev. circ. 550.

089 JA ISSN 0287-7082
KANAGAWA UNIVERSITY. INSTITUTE FOR HUMANITIES RESEARCH. BULLETIN. (Text in Japanese; summaries in English) 1965. a. 1000 Yen. Kanagawa University, Institute for Humanities Research, 3-chome Rokkaku-bashi, Kanagawa-ku, Yokahama 221, Japan. Ed. Shigeo Takano. bk.rev. circ. 800.
Formerly: Kanagawa University. Institute of Humanities. Bulletin.

810 US ISSN 0022-8745
AP2
KANSAS QUARTERLY. 1968. q. $20 (effective 1993). Kansas Quarterly Association, Kansas State University, English Department, Manhattan, KS 66506-0703. TEL 913-532-6716. Ed.Bd. adv.; illus.; index. circ. 1,200. (back issues avail.) Indexed: A.I.P.P., Abstr.Engl.Stud., Amer.Hist.& Life, Amer.Hum.Ind., Hist.Abstr., Ind.Amer.Per.Verse., M.L.A.
—Faxon; UnCover.
Supersedes (1872-1968): Kansas Magazine.
Description: Focuses on the culture, history, lifestyle, art, and writing of Mid-America.

001.3 II ISSN 0075-515X
AS472.K33
KARNATAK UNIVERSITY, DHARWAD, INDIA. JOURNAL. HUMANITIES. (Text mainly in English; occasionally in French, German and Sanskrit) 1957. a. Rs.8($4) Karnatak University, Director, Prasaranga, Dharwad 580003, Karnataka, India. Ed. C.G. Dubey. circ. 500.

001.3 080 US ISSN 0075-5265
KATHERINE ASHER ENGEL LECTURES. 1958. irreg., latest 1984. price varies. Smith College, Department of History, Wright Hall, Northampton, MA 01063-0001. TEL 413-585-3715. (reprint service avail. from UMI) Document type: academic/scholarly publication.

001.3 US ISSN 0191-1031
AS30
KENTUCKY REVIEW. 1979. 3/yr. $10. University of Kentucky, Library Associates, Lexington, KY 40506-0039. TEL 606-257-3801. FAX 606-257-1563. Eds. G. Hogg, B. Carrington. circ. 900. Indexed: Amer.Hum.Ind, M.L.A., RILA. Document type: academic/scholarly publication.
Description: Examines American, English, and world literature, history, philosophy, art, architecture, music, folklore, typography, cinema, and other topics in the discipline of humanities.
Refereed Serial

001.3 KE
KENYA NATIONAL ACADEMY FOR ADVANCEMENT OF ARTS AND SCIENCES. FOUNDATION LECTURES. 1965. irreg.no.6, 1974. Kenya National Academy for Advancement of Arts and Sciences, P.O. Box 47288, Nairobi, Kenya.
Formerly: East African Academy. Foundation Lectures.

001.3 060 KE
CODEN: PSEADA
KENYA NATIONAL ACADEMY FOR ADVANCEMENT OF ARTS AND SCIENCES. PROCEEDINGS. 1964. a. EAs.70($9) Kenya National Academy for Advancement of Arts and Sciences, Box 47288, Nairobi, Kenya. Document type: proceedings.
—CASDDS.
Formerly: East African Academy. Proceedings (ISSN 0070-7945)

001.3 YU ISSN 0350-4115
KNJIZEVNA REC; list za knjizevnost, umetnost, kulturu i drustvena pitanja. (Text in Serbo-Croatian) 1972. s-m. 8000 din.($20) Knjizevna Omladina Srbije - Serbian Literary Youth, Knjizevna Rec, Marsala Tita 16, 11000 Beograd, Yugoslavia. circ. 6,000.
Description: Articles on Yugoslavia and world literature, translations of literary criticism.

KNOWLEDGE AND SOCIETY; studies in the sociology of culture past and present. see *SOCIOLOGY*

001.3 300 JA
KOBE UNIVERSITY OF MERCANTILE MARINE. REVIEW. PART 1. STUDIES IN HUMANITIES AND SOCIAL SCIENCE. (Text in Japanese; summaries in English) 1952. a. Kobe University of Mercantile Marine, 1-1, Fukae-Minami-machi 5-chome, Higashi-Nada-ku, Kobe-shi, Hyogo-ken 658, Japan.

001.3 SZ ISSN 0075-6520
KOELNER ROMANISTISCHE ARBEITEN. (Text in German) irreg., no.67, 1992. price varies. (Universitaet zu Koeln, Romanisches Seminar, GW) Librairie Droz S.A., 11, rue Massot, CH-1211 Geneva 12, Switzerland. TEL 022-3466666. FAX 022-3472391. circ. 500. Document type: monographic series.
—CCC.

KOERS; bulletin vir Christelike wetenskap - bulletin for Christian scholarship. see *RELIGIONS AND THEOLOGY*

001.3 100 DK ISSN 0106-0481
AS281
KONGELIGE DANSKE VIDENSKABERNES SELSKAB. HISTORISK - FILOSOFISKE MEDDELELSER. (Text in Danish and English; summaries in English) 1917. irreg., vol.66, 1992. price varies. Kongelige Danske Videnskabernes Selskab - Royal Danish Academy of Sciences and Letters, H.C. Andersens Blvd. 35, DK-1553 Copenhagen V, Denmark. TEL 33128570. FAX 33129387. (Orders to: Munksgaard Export and Subscription Service, P.O. Box 2148, Noerre Soegade 35, DK-1060 Copenhagen K, Denmark) bibl. circ. 800. (back issues avail.) Indexed: M.L.A. Document type: monographic series.

001.3 DK ISSN 0023-3307
KONGELIGE DANSKE VIDENSKABERNES SELSKAB. HISTORISK - FILOSOFISKE SKRIFTER. (Text mainly in English) 1940. irreg., vol.16, 1992. price varies. Kongelige Danske Videnskabernes Selskab - Royal Danish Academy of Sciences and Letters, H.C. Andersens Blvd. 35, DK-1553 Copenhagen V, Denmark. TEL 33128570. FAX 33129387. (Orders to: Munksgaard Export and Subscription Service, P.O. Box 2148, Noerre Soegade 35, DK-1060 Copenhagen K, Denmark) bibl.; illus.; index. Document type: monographic series.

001.3 DK ISSN 0368-7201
KONGELIGE DANSKE VIDENSKABERNES SELSKAB. OVERSIGT OVER SELSKABETS VIRKSOMHED. ANNUAL REPORT. (Text in Danish; summary in English) 1814. a. Kongelige Danske Videnskabernes Selskab - Royal Danish Academy of Sciences and Letters, H.C. Andersens Blvd. 35, DK-1553 Copenhagen V, Denmark. TEL 33128570. FAX 33129387. (Orders to: Munksgaard Export and Subscription Service, P.O. Box 2148, Noerre Soegade 35, DK-1060 Copenhagen K, Denmark) illus. Indexed: Biol.Abstr., Chem.Abstr. Document type: monographic series.

KONGELIGE NORSKE VIDENSKABERS SELSKAB. FORHANDLINGER. see *SCIENCES: COMPREHENSIVE WORKS*

KONGELIGE NORSKE VIDENSKABERS SELSKAB. SKRIFTER/ROYAL NORWEGIAN SOCIETY OF SCIENCES. PUBLICATIONS. see *SCIENCES: COMPREHENSIVE WORKS*

001.3 BE ISSN 0770-0997
KONINKLIJKE ACADEMIE VOOR WETENSCHAPPEN, LETTEREN EN SCHONE KUNSTEN VAN BELGIE. VERHANDELINGEN. KLASSE DER LETTEREN. (Text in Dutch, English, French) 1941. irreg., no.145, 1992. price varies. Koninklijke Academie voor Wetenschappen, Letteren en Schone Kunsten van Belgie, 1 Hertogsstraat, B-1000 Brussels, Belgium. (Dist. by: N.V. Brepols, Steenweg op Tielen 68, 2300 Turnhout, Belgium. TEL 32-14-420500. FAX 32-14-428919) (back issues avail.) Document type: monographic series.
Formerly (until 1972): Koninklijke Vlaamse Academie voor Wetenschappen, Letteren en Schone Kunsten van Belgie. Verhandelingen. Klasse der Letteren (ISSN 0770-1047)

HUMANITIES: COMPREHENSIVE WORKS

001.3 NE ISSN 0065-5511
AS244
KONINKLIJKE NEDERLANDSE AKADEMIE VAN WETENSCHAPPEN. AFDELING LETTERKUNDE. VERHANDELINGEN. NIEUWE REEKS. (Text in Dutch, English, French and German) 1896. irreg., vol.153, 1993. price varies. Elsevier Science B.V., Books Division, P.O. Box 211, 1000 AE Amsterdam, Netherlands. TEL 31-20-5803911. FAX 31-20-5803705. TELEX 18582 ESPA NL. (Subscr. in U.S. and Canada to: Elsevier Science Inc., Box 882, Madison Sq. Sta., New York, NY 10159. TEL 212-989-5800) Ed. A.M. Verheggen. adv.; bk.rev. circ. 1,000. (also avail. in microform from PMC) **Document type:** monographic series.
Refereed Serial

KONKURSBUCH; Zeitschrift fuer Vernunftkritik. see *PHILOSOPHY*

KOREA FOUNDATION NEWSLETTER. see *ORIENTAL STUDIES*

001.3 US ISSN 0361-6584
AS30
KRONOS; a journal of interdisciplinary synthesis. 1975. 3/yr. $20. Kronos Press, Box 343, Wynnewood, PA 19096. Ed. Lewis Greenberg. adv.; bk.rev. circ. 2,000. **Indexed:** Ind.S.A.Per.

001.3 PL ISSN 0075-7179
KSIAZKA W DAWNEJ KULTURZE POLSKIEJ. 1951. irreg., vol.17, 1990. price varies. (Polska Akademia Nauk, Instytut Badan Literackich) Ossolineum, Publishing House of the Polish Academy of Sciences, Rynek 9, 50-106 Wroclaw, Poland. TEL 48-71-386-25. FAX 48-71-448-103. TELEX 0712771 OSS PL. **Document type:** monographic series.
Description: Bibliographies, dictionaries and monographs devoted to old Polish books, printers and authors.

001.3 DK ISSN 0107-3591
KULTUR OG SAMFUND; tekster. 1979. irreg. free. Postboks 260, 4000 Roskile, Denmark. FAX 46-757401. Eds. Michel Olsen, Kim Schroeder. illus. circ. 300.

001.3 GW
KULTUR- UND GEISTESGESCHICHTLICHE OSTMITTELEUROPA STUDIEN. irreg., no.4, 1992. DM.52. N.G. Elwert Verlag, Reitgasse 7-9, 35037 Marburg, Germany. TEL 06421-25023. FAX 06421-15487. **Document type:** monographic series.

KULTURA; casopis za teoriju i sociologiju kulture i kulturnu politiku. see *SOCIOLOGY*

001.3 RU
KUL'TURA. w. Ul. Novoslobodskaya 73, 101484 Moscow, Russia. TEL (095) 285-78-02. Ed. A.A. Belyaev.
Formerly: Sovetskaya Kul'tura.

001.3 CI ISSN 0023-5253
AP56
KULTURNI RADNIK. (Text in Croatian; summaries in English) 1948. bi-m. $15. Kulturno-Prosvjetni Sabor Hrvatske, Socijalisticke Revolucije 17-III, P.O. Box 462, 41000 Zagreb, Croatia. TEL 41-412-536. Ed. Sinisa Zrinscak. adv.; bk.rev. circ. 1,100.
Description: Disseminates various philosophical and socio-economic ideologies.

001.3 LI ISSN 0134-3106
AP95.L5
KULTUROS BARAI. (Text in Lithuanian; summaries in English) 1965. m. $32. (Ministry of Culture and Education) Kulturos Barai, Universiteto 6, Vilnius 2600, Lithuania. TEL 011-70122-616696. Ed. Bronys Savukynas. adv.; B&W page $70. bk.rev.; circ. 2,600 (paid).
Description: Covers history of culture, philosophy, literature, philology, history of Lithuania.

001.3 JA ISSN 0075-7381
KYOTO-FURITSU DAIGAKU GAKUJUTSU HOKOKU: JINBUN/KYOTO PREFECTURAL UNIVERSITY. SCIENTIFIC REPORTS: HUMANITIES. (Text in Japanese; summaries in English) 1952. irreg., no.28, 1976. exchange basis. Kyoto Prefectural University - Kyoto-furitsu Daigaku, Shimogamo Hangi-cho, Sakyo-ku, Kyoto 606, Japan. Ed. Z. Hayashino.

001.3 JA ISSN 0453-0349
300
KYUSHU INSTITUTE OF TECHNOLOGY. BULLETIN: HUMANITIES, SOCIAL SCIENCES/KYUSHU KOGYO DAIGAKU KENKYU HOKOKU: JINBUN-SHAKAI-KAGAKU. (Text in Japanese, English or German) 1953. a. exchange basis. Kyushu Institute of Technology - Kyushu Kogyo Daigaku, 1-1 Sensui-cho, Tobata, Kitakyushu 804, Japan. (reprint service avail. from JICST)
—BLDSC (2601.520000).

001.3 US ISSN 0275-410X
AS30
LAMAR JOURNAL OF THE HUMANITIES. 1974. s-a. $6. Lamar University, Department of English and Foreign Languages, Box 10023, Beaumont, TX 77710. TEL 409-880-8558. Eds. Ronald Fritze, Lloyd Daigrepont. bk.rev. circ. 350. **Indexed:** Abstr.Engl.Stud., Amer.Hist.& Life, Hist.Abstr., M.L.A. **Document type:** academic/scholarly publication.
—BLDSC (5143.972700).
Description: Interdisciplinary papers in the fields of literature, history, contemporary culture and the fine arts.

LATIN AMERICAN MONOGRAPH AND DOCUMENT SERIES. see *SOCIAL SCIENCES: COMPREHENSIVE WORKS*

001.3 II
LATIN AMERICAN STUDIES IN ASIA. 1991. q. Rs.598($115) K.K. Roy (Private) Ltd., 55 Gariahat Road, P.O. Box 10210, Calcutta 700 019, India. Ed. K.K. Roy. adv.; abstr.; bibl.; index. circ. 1,980.

378.1 AO
LAVRA & OFICINA; literary monthly. 1953. m. Esc.12($6.50) Uniao dos Escritores Angolanos, C.P. 2767-C, Luanda, Angola. TEL 322155. bk.rev.; bibl.; illus.; mkt.; cum.index: nos.1-20, 21-31. circ. 5,000. **Indexed:** Amer.Hist.& Life, Hist.Abstr.
Former titles: Uniao dos Escritores Angolanos. Boletim; Instituto de Angola. Boletim (ISSN 0020-3726)

001.3 GH
LEGON JOURNAL OF THE HUMANITIES. 1974. irreg. NC.600($10) to individuals; institutions NC.2000($20). University of Ghana, Faculty of Arts, P.O. Box 25, Legon, Ghana. TEL 775381. (Subscr. to: University of Ghana, Faculty of Arts, Office of the Dean, Legon, Ghana) Ed. J.N.D. Dodoo. adv.; bk.rev. circ. 1,000. (back issues avail.) **Indexed:** M.L.A. **Document type:** academic/scholarly publication.

001.3 SP ISSN 0210-3516
LETRAS DE DEUSTO. (Text mainly in Spanish; occasionally in Basque, English, French, German, Italian) 1971. 4/yr. 5000 ptas.($60) (effective 1994). Universidad de Deusto, Facultad de la Filosofia y Letras, Departamento de Publicaciones, Apdo. 1, 48080 Bilbao, Spain. TEL 34-4-4453100. FAX 34-4-445-8916. TELEX 34221 UDDE. (Distr. by: Editorial Mesajero, Sancho Azpeitia 2, 48014 Bilbao, Spain. TEL 94-447-03-58) Ed. Roberto Perez. adv.; bk.rev.; bibl.; circ. 700 (controlled). **Indexed:** Amer.Hist.& Life, Arts & Hum.Cit.Ind., Curr.Cont., Hist.Abstr., M.L.A. **Document type:** academic/scholarly publication.
—Faxon.
Formerly: Universidad de Deusto. Publicaciones. Filosofia.
Description: Devoted to the humanities: literature, linguistics, history, philosophy, and education.
Refereed Serial

001.3 US ISSN 0730-9066
LIFTOFF; a world commonwealth of education, science and culture. 1947. bi-m. $35 membership. World University Roundtable, Box 2470, Benson, AZ 85602-2470. TEL 602-586-2985. Ed. Howard John Zitko. bk.rev. circ. 1,000. (back issues avail.) **Indexed:** Refug.Abstr. **Document type:** newsletter.
Formerly: World University. International Newsletter.

001.3 IT ISSN 1122-0813
LINEA VENETA NELLA CULTURA CONTEMPORANEA. 1982. irreg., no.10, 1993. price varies. (Fondazione Giorgio Cini) Casa Editrice Leo S. Olschki, Casella Postale 66, 50100 Florence, Italy. TEL 055-6530684. FAX 055-6530214. **Document type:** monographic series.

LITERATURE - FILM QUARTERLY. see *MOTION PICTURES*

001.3 US
LIVABLE CITY. irreg. membership. Municipal Art Society, 457 Madison Ave., New York, NY 10022. TEL 212-935-3960. FAX 212-753-1816. Ed. Linda Cox. bk.rev. circ. 9,000.
Description: Covers all aspects of New York City's physical environment.

001.3 SP
LLETRA DE CANVI. (Text in Catalan) 1988. m. 5000 ptas. Montesinos Editor, S.A., Maignon 26, 3o, 08024 Barcelona, Spain. TEL 93-219-92-11. Dir. Julia Guilamon. circ. 7,000.
Description: Covers Catalonian literary culture. Includes interviews, trends and new works.

001.3 500 PL ISSN 0208-628X
LODZKIE TOWARZYSTWO NAUKOWE. SPRAWOZDANIA Z CZYNNOSCI I POSIEDZEN NAUKOWYCH. 1946. a. price varies. Lodzkie Towarzystwo Naukowe, Ul. Piotrowska 179, 90-447 Lodz, Poland. TEL 48-42-361026. FAX 48-42-362415. TELEX 884519 PAN PL. Ed. Jerzy Starnowski. **Document type:** proceedings.
—BLDSC (8420.050000).
Formerly: Lodzkie Towarzystwo Naukowe. Sprawozdania z Posiedzen (ISSN 0303-5263)

LONDON MAGAZINE. see *LITERARY AND POLITICAL REVIEWS*

001.3 700 BE ISSN 0779-5815
NX553.A1
▼**THE LOW COUNTRIES;** arts and society in Flanders and The Netherlands: a yearbook. (Text in English) 1993. a. fl.85. Stichting Ons Erfdeel v.z.w., Murissonstraat 60, B-8931 Rekken, Belgium. TEL 32-56-411201. FAX 32-56-414707. Ed. Jozef Deleu.
Description: Covers the cultural traditions and contemporary life and culture of the Low Countries.

300 500 AI ISSN 0320-8117
LRABER HASARAKAKAN GITUT'YUNNERI/VESTNIK OBSHCHESTVENNYKH NAUK/HERALD OF SOCIAL SCIENCES. m. 19.20 Rub. Akademiya Nauk Armenii, Pr. Marshala Bagramayana, 24, 375019 Erevan, Armenia. TEL 52-45-80. TELEX 243344. Ed.Bd. bk.rev.; bibl.; charts; stat. circ. 930. **Indexed:** Bibl.Ling., Numis.Lit.

001.3 PL ISSN 0208-4996
LUBELSKIE TOWARZYSTWO NAUKOWE. WYDZIAL HUMANISTYCZNY. PRACE. MONOGRAFIE. irreg., latest vol.29, no.2. Lubelskie Towarzystwo Naukowe, Plac Litewski 2, Palac Czartoryskich, 20-080 Lublin, Poland. (Dist. by: Ars Polona, Krakowskie Przedmiescie 7, 00-068 Warsaw, Poland) Ed. L. Jablonski. bibl. circ. 470. **Document type:** monographic series.

LUZO - BRAZILIAN REVIEW; devoted to the culture of the Portuguese speaking world. see *LITERARY AND POLITICAL REVIEWS*

001.3 AG
LA MAGA; noticias de cultura. 1991. fortn. Arg.$25000 per no. (Taller Escuela Agencia) Ediciones Periodismo x Periodistas, Lavalle 2083, 1051 Buenos Aires, Argentina. Ed. Carlos Ares.

MAHARAJA SAYAJIRAO UNIVERSITY OF BARODA. JOURNAL. see *SCIENCES: COMPREHENSIVE WORKS*

MAISON FRANCO-JAPONAISE. BULLETIN. see *ORIENTAL STUDIES*

001.3 059.915 IR
MAJALLAH-I DANISHNAMAH. (Text in Persian) 1990. q. IRl.2000. Danishgah-i Azad-i Islami - Islamic Azad University of Iran, P.O. Box 19395-1775, Tehran, Iran. **Document type:** academic/scholarly publication.
Description: Scholarly research in the humanities and social sciences.

MAKEDONSKA AKADEMIJA NA NAUKITE I UMETNOSTITE. LETOPIS. see *SCIENCES: COMPREHENSIVE WORKS*

HUMANITIES: COMPREHENSIVE WORKS

001.3   PH   ISSN 0115-6195
AS539.5
MALAY; dyornal ng humanidades at agham panlipunan - journal of humanities and social sciences. (Text in Filipino) 1981. s-a. P.60($4.40) (De La Salle University) De La Salle University Press, 2401 Taft Ave., Manila, Philippines. TEL 2-59-48-32. FAX 632-521-9094. adv.; bk.rev.; film rev. circ. 500. **Document type:** academic/scholarly publication.
   Description: Publishes scholarly articles reflecting significant quantitative or qualitative research. Includes speeches, research reports, and "state of the art" papers. Welcomes contributions.

MARATHWADA UNIVERSITY JOURNAL. see *EDUCATION — Higher Education*

001.3 300   US   ISSN 0160-8797
Z5055.U5
MASTER'S THESES IN THE ARTS AND SOCIAL SCIENCES. 1976. a. $40. Master's Theses Directories, Box 92, Cedar Falls, IA 50613. TEL 319-273-6412. FAX 319-273-2742. Ed. H.M. Silvey.

001.3   US   ISSN 0892-2772
MEDICAL HUMANITIES REVIEW. 1986. s-a. $20 to individuals (foreign $25); institutions $40 (foreign $45). University of Texas Medical Branch, Galveston, TX 77555-1311. FAX 409-772-5640. Eds. Ronald A. Carson, Thomas H. Murray. adv.; bk.rev. circ. 900. **Indexed:** Bk.Rev.Ind. (1990-), Child.Bk.Rev.Ind. (1990-). **Document type:** academic/scholarly publication.
—BLDSC (5527.517000).

MEDIEVAL ACADEMY REPRINTS FOR TEACHING. see *HISTORY — History Of Europe*

001.3 972   US   ISSN 0742-9797
F1201
MEXICAN STUDIES/ESTUDIOS MEXICANOS. (Text in English, Spanish) 1985. s-a. $21 to individuals (foreign $25); institutions $43 (foreign $47) (effective 1994). University of California Press, Journals Division, 2120 Berkeley Way, Berkeley, CA 94720. TEL 510-643-7154. FAX 510-642-9917. (Subscr. in Mexico only: Universidad Nacional Autonoma de Mexico, Instituto de Investigaciones Historicas, Alvaro Obregon 04510, Ciudad Universitaria, Mexico D.F., Mexico) (Co-sponsor: Universidad Nacional Autonoma de Mexico) Ed. Jaime E. Rodriguez. adv.; index. circ. 1,300. (also avail. in microform from UMI; back issues avail.) **Indexed:** Amer.Hist.& Life, Curr.Cont., Hisp.Amer.Per.Ind., Hist.Abstr., Human Resour.Abstr., Int.Polit.Sci.Abstr., Soc.Sci.Ind. **Document type:** academic/scholarly publication.
—BLDSC (5750.582000); Faxon; UnCover; UMI. CCC.
   Description: Focuses on Mexico and its people.
Refereed Serial

MICHIGAN ACADEMICIAN. see *SCIENCES: COMPREHENSIVE WORKS*

100   US   ISSN 0026-3451
AS30
MIDWEST QUARTERLY; a journal of contemporary thought. 1959. 4/yr. $12 (foreign $16). Pittsburg State University, Midwest Quarterly, Pittsburg, KS 66762. TEL 316-235-4317. FAX 316-232-7515. Ed. James B.M. Schick. bk.rev.; index. circ. 750. (also avail. in microfiche from UMI; reprint service avail. from UMI) **Indexed:** A.I.P.P., Abstr.Engl.Stud., Amer.Hist.& Life, Arts & Hum.Cit.Ind., Curr.Cont., Hist.Abstr., Hum.Ind., Ind.Bk.Rev.Hum., Lang.& Lang.Behav.Abstr., P.A.I.S. **Document type:** academic/scholarly publication.
—BLDSC (5761.446000); Faxon; UnCover; UMI.

MINAMI-KYUSHU DAIGAKU ENGEIGAKUBU KENKYU HOKOKU. SHIZEN KAGAKU, JINBUN SHAKAI KAGAKU/MINAMI KYUSHU UNIVERSITY. FACULTY OF HORTICULTURE. BULLETIN. NATURAL SCIENCE, CULTURAL SCIENCE, AND SOCIAL SCIENCE. see *GARDENING AND HORTICULTURE*

001.3   IT
MITTELEUROPA; Austria Cecoslovacchia Italia Jugoslavia Ungheria. (Text in Italian) q. L.30000 in Central Europe; elsewhere L.50000. Marsilio Editore S.p.A., Marittima - Fabbricato 205, 30135 Venice, Italy. TEL 041-5227822. FAX 041-5238352. Ed. Cesare Tomasetig.

001.3   UK
MODERN HUMANITIES RESEARCH ASSOCIATION. PUBLICATIONS. 1969. irreg. price varies. Modern Humanities Research Association, King's College, Strand, London WC2R 2LS, England. **Document type:** monographic series.
   Formerly: Modern Humanities Research Association. Monograph (ISSN 0076-9983)

001.3   US
▼**MODERNISM - MODERNITY.** 1994. 3/yr. $25 to individuals; institutions $50. Johns Hopkins University Press, Journals Publishing Division, 701 W. 40th St., Ste. 275, Baltimore, MD 21211. TEL 410-516-6980. FAX 410-516-6998.

060   VE   ISSN 0252-9076
MONTALBAN. 1972. a. $16 or on exchange basis. Universidad Catolica Andres Bello, Facultad de Letras, Departamento de Humanidades, Apdo. 29068, Caracas 1021, Venezuela. TEL 4419511. FAX 442-3897. Ed. Angelina Pollak-Eltz. bk.rev. circ. 1,200. **Indexed:** A.I.C.P., Amer.Hist.& Life, Anthropol.Lit., Hisp.Amer.Per.Ind., Hist.Abstr., Lang.& Lang.Behav.Abstr. **Document type:** academic/scholarly publication.
   Description: Covers history, ethno-history, ethnology, archaeology, folklore, ethno-linguistics. Most papers deal with Venezuela and its adjacent areas.

001.3   GO   ISSN 0768-9403
DT16.B2
MUNTU; revue scientifique et culturelle. (Text in English, French, Portuguese, Spanish) 1984. s-a. 200 F.($35) Centre International des Civilisations Bantu, B.P. 770, Libreville, Gabon. TEL 70-09-52. (Co-sponsor: Presence Africaine) circ. 2,000. (back issues avail.) **Indexed:** Bibl.Ling., Documentatieblad.

001.3 300   BE   ISSN 0065-4124
MUSEE ROYAL DE L'AFRIQUE CENTRALE. ANNALES - SCIENCES HUMAINES. SERIE IN 8/KONINKLIJK MUSEUM VOOR MIDDEN-AFRIKA. ANNALEN - MENSELIJKE WETENSCHAPPEN. SERIE IN 8. 1951. irreg., no.136, 1992. price varies. Musee Royal de l'Afrique Centrale - Koninklijk Museum voor Midden-Afrika, 13 Steenweg op Leuven, B-3080 Tervuren, Belgium. TEL 32-2-7675401. FAX 32-2-7670242. **Indexed:** Lang.& Lang.Behav.Abstr. **Document type:** monographic series.
—BLDSC (0933.954200).
   Description: Scholarly research and studies in ethnography, ethnomusicology, anthropology and linguistics relating to central Africa, with an emphasis on Zaire, Rwanda and Burundi.

MUSICAL INTERPRETATION RESEARCH. see *MUSIC*

001.3   JO   ISSN 1021-6804
MU'TAH LIL-BUHUTH WAL-DIRASAT. AL-SILSILAH A: AL-'ULUM AL-INSANIYYAH WAL-IJTIMA'IYYAH/MU'TAH LIL-BUHUTH WAL-DIRASAT. SERIES A: HUMAN AND SOCIAL SCIENCES. Spine Title: Mu'tah Journal for Research and Studies. (Text in Arabic, English) 1986. q. Mu'tah University, Deanship of Scientific Research and Graduate Studies - Jami'at Mu'tah, 'Imadat al-Buhuth al-'Ilmi wal-Dirasat al-'Ulya, P.O. Box 7, Mu'tah, Jordan. **Document type:** academic/scholarly publication.
Refereed Serial

001.3 069   CI   ISSN 0352-1443
MUZEJ BRODSKOG POSAVLJA. VIJESTI; godisnjak. 1959-1983; resumed 1991. a. $6. Muzej Brodskog Posavlja, Starceviceva 8, 55000 Slovonski Brod, Croatia. TEL 055-232415. FAX 055-232243. bk.rev. circ. 500.
   Description: Publishes original scientific papers on archeology, history, history of art, ethnology, paleontology, geology and ecology.

001.3   US   ISSN 0741-1804
E29.N3
N A; the magazine for the cross-culturally aware. 1983. q. $16 to individuals; institutions $35. Network Africa, Box 81, Pratt Sta., Brooklyn, NY 11205. TEL 718-875-7448. Ed. Shirley Ademu-John. adv. circ. 2,000. (back issues avail.)
   Description: Cross-cultural experiences related to Africa. Includes poetry, short stories and interviews.

001.3   US   ISSN 0895-7576
NANCY'S MAGAZINE. 1983. a. $6 for 2 nos. N'S M Publications, Box 02108, Columbus, OH 43202. TEL 614-294-7935. Ed. Nancy Bonnell-Kangas. adv.; bk.rev.; play rev.; charts; illus. circ. 1,000. (back issues avail.) **Indexed:** A.I.P.P.
   Description: Variety magazine for generalists. Includes poetry, cartoons, essays, recipes, and miscellaneous humor.

001.3 070   IR   ISSN 0259-9090
NASHR-I DANISH. (Text in Persian) 1980. bi-m. IRl.700 (Middle East £26; Europe £30; elsewhere £34). Markaz-i Nashr-i Danishgahi - Iran University Press, 85 Park Ave., Dr. Bihishti Ave., P.O. Box 15875-4748, Tehran, Iran. TEL 98-21-623232. FAX 98-21-8861749. TELEX 213636-8-D5300. Ed. Nasrollah Pourjavady. bk.rev.; bibl. circ. 8,000. **Document type:** academic/scholarly publication.
   Description: Publishes articles and extensive book reviews and other items relating to the field of scholarly publishing in Iran and elsewhere.

001.3   US   ISSN 0083-2111
LB2301
NATIONAL ENDOWMENT FOR THE HUMANITIES. ANNUAL REPORT. 1966. a. U.S. National Endowment for the Humanities, 1100 Pennsylvania Ave., N.W., Washington, DC 20506. TEL 202-786-0438. circ. 3,000.

001.3   US   ISSN 1040-130X
AZ513.N8
NATIONAL HUMANITIES CENTER. REPORT. 1980. a. National Humanities Center, 7 Alexander Dr., Box 12256, Research Triangle Park, NC 27709-2256. TEL 919-549-0661. FAX 919-990-8535. Ed. Jean Anne Leuchtenburg. **Document type:** corporate report.

NATIONALITIES PAPERS. see *SOCIAL SCIENCES: COMPREHENSIVE WORKS*

NATURES - SCIENCES - SOCIETES. see *EARTH SCIENCES*

001.3   PY   ISSN 0254-8178
NEMITY; revista bilingue de cultura. (Text in Guarani, Spanish) 1977. 3/yr. $30. (Centro Paraguayo de Estudios Sociologicos) Distribuidor Internacional Publicaciones Paraguayas, P.O. Box 2507, Ayoreos e-4a y 5a, Asuncion, Paraguay. TEL 595-21-495367. FAX 595-21-447460. Ed. Natalia K. de Canese. bk.rev. circ. 1,000.

001.3   IT
NEOCLASSICO. s-a. L.40000 (foreign L.80000) (effective 1994). (Archivio Europeo del Neoclassico di Trieste) Marsilio Editori S.p.A., Marittime - Fabbricato 205, 30135 Venice, Italy. TEL 041-5227822. FAX 041-5238352.
   Description: Presents research on art, architecture and literature of the neoclassic period.

DAS NEUE ERLANGEN; Zeitschrift fuer Wissenschaft, Wirtschaft und kulturelles Leben. see *SCIENCES: COMPREHENSIVE WORKS*

001.3   US
▼**NEW DIRECTIONS IN CULTURAL ANALYSIS.** 1992. irreg., vol.2, 1993. price varies. University of California Press, 2120 Berkeley Way, Berkeley, CA 94720. TEL 510-642-4247. FAX 510-643-7127. (Orders to: California-Princeton Fulfillment Services, 1445 Lower Ferry Rd., Ewing, NJ 08618. TEL 800-777-4796. FAX 800-999-1958) (back issues avail.) **Document type:** monographic series.
   Description: Examines such topics as the meaning of culture and the politics of ideology in a world of change.
Refereed Serial

001.3 943   US   ISSN 1043-5808
NEW GERMAN-AMERICAN STUDIES/NEUE DEUTSCHE-AMERIKANISCHE STUDIEN. (Text in English, German) irreg. Peter Lang Publishing, Inc., 62 W. 45th St., 4th Fl., New York, NY 10036. TEL 212-302-6740. FAX 212-302-7574. Ed. Don Heinrich Tolzmann. **Document type:** academic/scholarly publication.
—BLDSC (6084.214500).
   Description: Deals with topics in the humanities, or social sciences pertaining to the German-American experience.

HUMANITIES: COMPREHENSIVE WORKS

430 830   US   ISSN 0094-033X
PT1
NEW GERMAN CRITIQUE; an interdisciplinary journal of German studies. 1973. 3/yr. $28 to individuals; institutions $65. (Cornell University, Department of German Literature) Telos Press Ltd., 431 E. 12th St., New York, NY 10009. TEL 212-228-6479. FAX 212-228-6379. Ed. David Bathrick. adv.; bk.rev. circ. 3,000. (also avail. in microform from UMI; back issues avail.; reprint service avail. from UMI) **Indexed**: Alt.Press Ind., Amer.Bibl.Slavic & E.Eur.Stud., Amer.Hist.& Life, Arts & Hum.Cit.Ind., Curr.Cont., Film Lit.Ind. (1990-), Hist.Abstr., Lang.& Lang.Behav.Abstr., Left Ind. (1986-), M.L.A., Mid.East: Abstr.& Ind. **Document type**: academic/scholarly publication.
—BLDSC (6084.215000); Faxon; UnCover; SWETS.

001.3   US
NEW JERSEY HUMANITIES. 1974. irreg. (3-4/yr.) free. New Jersey Committee for the Humanities, 390 George St., Ste. 602, New Brunswick, NJ 08901-2018. TEL 201-932-7726. Ed. Georgia Whidden. bibl. circ. 12,000. **Indexed**: Mid.East: Abstr.& Ind. **Document type**: newsletter.
Former titles: Humanitas (New Jersey); N J C H Memo; Humanitems; New Jersey Committee for the Humanities Newsletter.
Description: Describes activities of the Committee, grants awarded, grant application procedures.

491 940 300   NZ   ISSN 0028-8683
NEW ZEALAND SLAVONIC JOURNAL. (Text in English, Russian) 1967. a. NZ.$40. Victoria University of Wellington, School of European Languages, Russian Section, c/o Veronika Romankin-Arndt, Secretary, P.O. Box 600, Wellington, New Zealand. TEL 64-4-471-5322. FAX 64-4-496-5419. Eds. I. Zohrab, C. Dowsett. bk.rev.; play rev. circ. 175. (processed) **Indexed**: Amer.Hist.& Life, Bibl.Ling., Hist.Abstr., Ind.N.Z.Per., M.L.A.

001.3   NQ   ISSN 0252-8800
NICARAUAC. 1980. q. Ministerio de Cultura, Apdo. Postal 3514, Managua, Nicaragua. Ed. Ernesto Cardenal. bk.rev. circ. 10,000. **Document type**: government publication.

NIEUWE WEST INDISCHE GIDS/NEW WEST INDIAN GUIDE. see SOCIAL SCIENCES: COMPREHENSIVE WORKS

001.3   SW   ISSN 0078-0901
NOBEL SYMPOSIUM SERIES. (Publisher varies) 1966. irreg., no.82, 1990. price varies. Nobel Foundation, Nobel House, P.O. Box 5232, S-102 45 Stockholm, Sweden. TEL 468-663-09-20. FAX 468-660-38-47. TELEX 12382 NOBHAUS S. (US and Canada subscr. to: Cambridge University Press, 32 East 57th St., New York, NY 10022) Ed. Gunilla Berg. **Indexed**: Biol.Abstr., Chem.Abstr.

001.3   US   ISSN 1050-9917
NOMAD; an interdisciplinary journal of the humanities, arts & sciences. 1990. s-a. $9 to individuals; institutions $16. Nomad Publication, 406 Williams Hall, Florida State University, Tallahassee, FL 32306. Ed. Hope Kurtz. bk.rev. **Document type**: academic/scholarly publication.
Description: Publishes articles about interdisciplinary interests, intermedia artwork, and experimental writing.

378.1 300   US   ISSN 0029-277X
AS36
NORTH DAKOTA QUARTERLY. 1910. q. $15 to individuals (foreign $23); institutions $20 (foreign $28). University of North Dakota, Box 7209, Grand Forks, ND 58202. TEL 701-777-3321. FAX 701-777-3650. Ed. Robert W. Lewis. adv.; bk.rev.; charts; illus.; index, cum.index. circ. 800. (also avail. in microfiche) **Indexed**: Abstr.Engl.Stud., Amer.Hist.& Life, Amer.Hum.Ind., CERDIC, Film Lit.Ind. (1986-), Hist.Abstr., M.L.A., Mid.East: Abstr.& Ind. **Document type**: academic/scholarly publication.
—BLDSC (6149.394000); Faxon; UnCover.

NORTHERN ILLINOIS UNIVERSITY. CENTER FOR SOUTHEAST ASIAN STUDIES. OCCASIONAL PAPERS SERIES. see HISTORY — History Of Asia

NORTHERN ILLINOIS UNIVERSITY. CENTER FOR SOUTHEAST ASIAN STUDIES. SPECIAL REPORT SERIES. see HISTORY — History Of Asia

001.3 500   US   ISSN 0894-3362
NORTHERN REVIEW; a journal of essays, articles, fiction, poetry, and art. 1987. s-a. $8. University of Wisconsin at Stevens Point, Academic Achievement Center, Rm. 018 LRC, Stevens Point, WI 54481. TEL 715-346-3568. Ed. Richard Behm. adv.; bk.rev. circ. 1,000. (back issues avail.) **Indexed**: Amer.Hum.Ind. **Document type**: academic/scholarly publication.
Description: Covers Northern issues and themes.

001.3 300   CN   ISSN 0835-3433
NORTHERN REVIEW. 1988. s-a. Can.$24 to individuals; institutions Can.$36. Yukon College, P.O. Box 2799, Whitehorse, YT Y1A 5K4, Canada. TEL 403-668-8736. FAX 403-668-8828. Ed. Amanda Graham. adv.; bk.rev.; film rev.; charts; illus. circ. 350. (also avail. in microfiche from MML) **Document type**: academic/scholarly publication.
Description: Devoted to the promotion of discussion about human experience in, and thought about the North. Articles encompass the humanities, fine arts, social sciences, human ecology, geography, law, environmental studies, social services.
Refereed Serial

001.3   UK   ISSN 0308-4809
NORTHUMBRIANA; True Northumberland's own magazine. (Text in English and Northumbrian) 1975. irreg., no.45, 1994. price varies. Morpeth Northumbrian Gathering Committee, Westgate House, Dogger Bank, Morpeth, Northumberland NE61 1RF, England. TEL 0670 513308. Ed. Roland Bibby. adv.; bk.rev. circ. 700. **Document type**: academic/scholarly publication.
Description: Discusses dialect and writings, history, lore and legend, landscape, architecture, balladry, song, music, dance & crafts.

001.3   IT
NOTE E DISCUSSIONI ERUDITE. 1951. irreg., no.20, 1989. price varies. Edizioni di Storia e Letteratura s.r.l., Via Lancellotti, 18, 00186 Rome, Italy. TEL 6540556. FAX 06-6872567. Ed. Augusto Campana.

NOTRE DAME JOURNAL. see EDUCATION

930 800 001.3   MX
NOVA TELLUS. (Text in Greek, Latin, Spanish) 1983. a. Mex.$35. Universidad Nacional Autonoma de Mexico, Centro de Estudios Clasicos, Ciudad Universitaria, 04510 Mexico D.F., Mexico. (back issues avail.)

001.3   XO   ISSN 0546-8051
NOVE OBZORY. 1959. a. price varies. (Vlastivedne Muzeum v Presove) Vychodoslovenske Vydavatel'stvo v Kosiciach, Alejova 3, 040 01 Kosice 1, Slovakia. TEL 657-10. (Dist. by: Slovart, nam. Svobody 6, 817 64 Bratislava, Slovakia) Ed. I. Sedlak. bk.rev. circ. 800. **Indexed**: Bibl.Ling.

001.3   CI   ISSN 0352-7417
NOVOGRADISKI ZBORNIK. 1986. a. Narodno Sveuciliste "Matija Antun Reljkovic", Rljkoviceva 4, 55400 Nova Gradiska, Croatia. TEL 055 63-762.

001.3   AG   ISSN 0325-4453
NUDOS EN LA CULTURA ARGENTINA. 1977-1985 (no.15); resumed. 3/yr. $30. Parana 63, 1er piso, 1017 Buenos Aires, Argentina. TEL 38-3313. Ed. Jorge Reinaldo Brega. adv.; bk.rev. circ. 3,000.
Supersedes (in 1978): Posta de Arte y Literatura.
Description: Covers narrative, poetry, plastics arts, theater, films, esthetics, visual arts, popular culture, and native, historical and Latinamerican issues. Each issue is illustrated by a prominent Argentine artist.

001.3   IT
NUOVA EUROPA; rivista internazionale di cultura. 1991. bi-m. R.C. Edizioni s.r.l., Villa Ambiveri, Via Tasca 36, 24068 Seriate (BG), Italy. TEL 035-294021. Ed. Romano Scalfi.

OESTERREICHISCHE AKADEMIE DER WISSENSCHAFTEN. ALMANACH. see SCIENCES: COMPREHENSIVE WORKS

001.3 300   US   ISSN 0730-1502
OFFSHOOTS OF ORGONOMY. 1980. s-a. $15. Offshoots Publications, Box 987, Valley Forge, PA 19481. Ed. Marjorie Gruff. bk.rev. circ. 1,000. (back issues avail.)
Description: Based on Wilhelm Reich's Orgone (cosmic life energy) theories covering childrearing, education, art, orgonomic devices.

100 001.3 830   GW   ISSN 0078-5539
OPUSCULA - AUS WISSENSCHAFT UND DICHTUNG. 1962. irreg., no.51, 1989. DM.10.80. Verlag Guenther Neske, Kloster, 72793 Pfullingen, Germany. TEL 07121-71339. FAX 07121-79581.

001.3   GW
ORDEN POUR LE MERITE FUER WISSENSCHAFTEN UND KUENSTE. REDEN UND GEDENKWORTE. 1955. a. DM.39. Verlag Lambert Schneider GmbH, Postfach 100123, 70826 Gerlingen, Germany. TEL 07156-4308-0. FAX 07156-430840. **Document type**: academic/scholarly publication.

001.3   US   ISSN 0294-1945
ORDRES SOCIAUX. 1982. irreg. Gordon & Breach Science Publishers, 820 Town Center Dr., Langhorne, PA 19047. TEL 215-750-2642. FAX 215-750-6343. (UK subscr. to: Box 90, Reading, Berkshire RG1 8JL, England. TEL 0734-560-080) Eds. M. Auge, J. Revel. **Document type**: monographic series.

055.1   IT
ORIENTE E OCCIDENTE; revista quadrimestrale. 1978. 3/yr. L.5500($10) Via Sappusi 12, 91025 Marsala, Italy. Dir. Giuseppe Pipitone. **Indexed**: Chem.Abstr., Psychol.Abstr.
Supersedes (1963-1978): Vidya (ISSN 0042-5311)

001.3   JA   ISSN 0030-6134
AS552.O775
OSAKA KOGYO DAIGAKU KIYO. JINBUN HEN/OSAKA INSTITUTE OF TECHNOLOGY. MEMOIRS. SERIES B: LIBERAL ARTS. (Text in English and Japanese) 1955. 2/yr. Osaka Kogyo Daigaku - Osaka Institute of Technology, 16-1 Omiya 5-chome, Asahi-ku, Osaka 535, Japan.
—BLDSC (5629.533000).

OTHER DIMENSIONS; the journal of multimedia horror. see MOTION PICTURES

700   UK
OXFORD-WARBURG STUDIES. 1963. irreg. price varies. (Warburg Institute) Oxford University Press, Oxford Journals, Walton St., Oxford OX2 6DP, England. TEL 0865-56767. FAX 0865-56646. TELEX 837330-OXPRES-G. (U.S. subscr. to: Oxford University Press Inc., 2001 Evans Rd., Cary, NC 27513. TEL 919-677-0977) (Co-sponsor: Clarendon Press) **Document type**: academic/scholarly publication.
Formerly: Warburg Institute. Oxford-Warburg Studies.

800 001.3   MX   ISSN 0185-5727
PALABRA Y EL HOMBRE. 1957; N.S. 1972. q. Mex.$100 (U.S. $75; other America $100; Europe $120). Universidad Veracruzana, Direccion Editorial, Apdo. Postal 97, Xalapa, Ver., Mexico. TEL 281-72954. Dir. Raul Hernandez Viveros. bk.rev.; bibl.; tr.lit. circ. 2,000. **Indexed**: Arts & Hum.Cit.Ind., Curr.Cont., Hisp.Amer.Per.Ind., M.L.A.

001.3 300   II
PANJAB UNIVERSITY RESEARCH BULLETIN (ARTS). (Text in English) 1951. s-a. $6. Panjab University, Publication Bureau, Chandigarh 160014, Union Territory, India. Ed. Nirmal Mukirji. bk.rev. circ. 500. **Indexed**: Curr.Adv.Ecol.Sci., Deep Sea Res.& Oceanogr.Abstr., GeoRef, M.L.A., Math.R.

001.3   HO
PARADISO; literatura - ciencia - arte. 1990. q. L.30. Producciones Culturales Libreria Paradiso, S. de R.L., Apdo. Postal 2037, Tegucigalpa, Honduras. Ed. Iris Pineda Van Dyke.

001.3   VE   ISSN 0798-278X
PARAMILLO. 1983. a. Bs.120. Universidad Catolica del Tachira, Centro de Estudios Interdisciplinarios, Carrera 14 con Calle 14, San Cristobal, Estado Tachira, Venezuela. TEL 076-432080. FAX 076-446183. TELEX 076-76499. bk.rev. circ. 1,000.
Description: Publishes research and studies on human sciences in Venezuela: history, geography, linguistics, philosophy, and anthropology.

001.3   SP
PARERGA. 1970. irreg., no.10, 1973. price varies. Ediciones Universidad de Navarra, S.A., Apdo. 396, 31080 Pamplona, Spain. TEL 94 825 6850.

HUMANITIES: COMPREHENSIVE WORKS

001.3 480   GR   ISSN 0048-301X
PA5201
PARNASSOS; an annual literary journal. (Text in Greek; occasionally in English, French, Italian) 1865; N.S. 1959. a. $80. Parnassos Literary Society - Filologikos Silogos Parnassos, 8, St. George Karytsis Sq., 105 61 Athens, Greece. TEL 30-1-322-1917. FAX 30-1-324-9398. Ed. D. Kalamakis. bk.rev.; play rev.; bibl.; tr.lit.; index, cum.index. circ. 2,500. **Indexed:** M.L.A. **Document type:** academic/scholarly publication.
  Description: Multidisciplinary study of the culture and history of Greece.

001.3   UY
▼**PATRIMONIO CULTURAL.** 1992. s-a.? Ministerio de Educacion y Cultura, Comision del Patrimonio Historico, Artistico y Cultural de la Nacion, Ituzaingo 1255, Montevideo, Uruguay. TEL 95-79-42.

PEACE & FREEDOM (SPALDING). see *LITERATURE*

320 001.3   US
PEACE DEVELOPMENTS. 1981. 3/yr. free. Peace Development Fund, 44 N. Prospect St., Box 1280, Amherst, MA 01004. TEL 413-256-8306. FAX 413-256-8871. Ed. Isabella Halsted. circ. 7,000. (tabloid format; back issues avail.) **Document type:** newsletter.
  Description: Provides details on grant awards made to peace groups each funding cycle and articles on the American peace movement.

001.3   AT
PEASANTS IN HISTORY AND LITERATURE. 1981. a. Aus.$3. Australian Academy of the Humanities, G.P.O. Box 93, Canberra, A.C.T. 2601, Australia. FAX 6-06-2486287. E-mail: aah@anu.edu.au. Ed. H.H.R. Love.

THE PEN WOMAN. see *LITERATURE*

001.3   AT
PEOPLING OF THE BRITISH PERIPHERIES IN THE EIGHTEENTH CENTURY. SERIES: ESSO LECTURE: NO.2. 1988. triennial. price varies. Australian Academy of the Humanities, G.P.O. Box 93, Canberra, A.C.T. 2601, Australia. FAX 062-486287. E-mail: aah@anu.edu.au. Ed. H.H.R. Love.

001.3   DR
PEQUENO UNIVERSO.* 1971. q. Universidad Autonoma de Santo Domingo, Facultad de Humanidades, Santo Domingo, Dominican Republic. bk.rev.; abstr.; bibl.; illus.

001.3 300   HU   ISSN 1216-0555
▼**PERIODICA POLYTECHNICA. HUMANITIES AND SOCIAL SCIENCES.** (Text in English) 1993. s-a. $8. Budapesti Muszaki Egyetem - Technical University of Budapest, Periodica Polytechnica, 1521 Budapest, Hungary. FAX 361-166-6808. TELEX 22-5931 MUEGY H. (Subscr. to: Kultura, P.O. Box 149, 1389 Budapest, Hungary. FAX 361-201-3207) Ed. Gy. Licsko. bk.rev. circ. 400. **Document type:** academic/scholarly publication.

309.1   SP   ISSN 0210-0436
PERSPECTIVA SOCIAL. (Text in Catalan, French or Spanish) 1973. s-a. 1500 ptas. (typically set in Jan.). Institut Catolic d'Estudis Socials de Barcelona, Enric Granados, 2, 08007 Barcelona, Spain. TEL 93-4532800. FAX 93-4513708. Dir. Joaquim Novella. adv.; bk.rev.; bibl.; charts; illus. circ. 500. **Indexed:** CERDIC.

PHI SIGMA IOTA FORUM. see *LINGUISTICS*

001.3   PH   ISSN 0115-0243
DS651
PHILIPPINE QUARTERLY OF CULTURE AND SOCIETY. 1973. q. P.280($28) in SE Asia; elsewhere $30. (University of San Carlos) San Carlos Publications, 6000 Cebu City, Philippines. Ed. Joseph Baumgartner. bk.rev.; bibl.; charts; illus.; index. circ. 360. **Indexed:** A.I.C.P., Abstr.Rural Dev.Trop., Agroforest.Abstr., Anthropol.Lit., Ind.Phil.Per., M.L.A., World Agri.Econ.& Rural Sociol.Abstr. **Document type:** academic/scholarly publication.
  Description: Publishes articles on subjects pertaining to Philippine culture and society.

001.3   PH   ISSN 0031-7837
DS651
PHILIPPINE STUDIES; quarterly publication of Philippine thought and culture. 1953. q. P.225($30) (Ateneo de Manila University) Ateneo de Manila University Press, P.O. Box 154, 1099 Manila, Philippines. TEL 632-9244495. FAX 632-9244690. Ed. Joseph A. Galdon. adv.; bk.rev.; illus.; index, cum.index. 1953-1962, 1963-1977. circ. 650. **Indexed:** Amer.Hist.& Life, Cath.Ind, Hist.Abstr., Ind.Phil.Per., M.L.A., Mid.East: Abstr.& Ind.
  —UnCover; SWETS.
  Description: Publishes articles, notes, and reviews in the humanities, literature, history, social sciences, philosophy, and Philippine arts.

200 300 100   UK   ISSN 0191-4537
AS30
PHILOSOPHY AND SOCIAL CRITICISM. 1973. 4/yr. £25 to individuals; institutions £80. Sage Publications Ltd., 6 Bonhill St., London EC2A 4PU, England. TEL 071-374-0645. FAX 071-374-8741. Ed. David Rasmussen. adv.; B&W page £190; trim 183 x 114; adv. contact: Bernie Folan. bk.rev.; index. circ. 1,000. **Indexed:** Lang.& Lang.Behav.Abstr., Left Ind. (1986-), Phil.Ind, Sociol.Abstr, SSCI. **Document type:** academic/scholarly publication.
  —BLDSC (6464.810000); Faxon; UnCover; SWETS.
  Formerly: Cultural Hermeneutics (ISSN 0011-2860)
  Refereed Serial

001.3   IR
PIZHUHISH/RESEARCH. (Text in Farsi) irreg., no.3, 1986. University of Tabriz, Research Affairs Administration, P.O. Box 711-51664, Tabriz, Iran.

001.3   JA
THE PLAZA; a space for global human relations. (Text in English, Japanese) 1985. q. 550 Yen. U - Kan Inc., Yoyogi 2-32-1, Shibuya-ku, Tokyo 151, Japan. TEL 03-3379-3881. FAX 03-3379-3882.

366   UK   ISSN 0032-2326
POINT 3. 1968. m. £3.60. Toc H, 1 Forest Close, Wendover, Aylesbury, Bucks HP22 6BT, England. TEL 0296-623911. FAX 0296-696137. Ed. Ruth Boyd. adv.; bk.rev.; illus.; index. circ. 5,000. **Document type:** academic/scholarly publication.

001.3   IT   ISSN 0391-2647
POLICORDO;* revista quadrimestale di cultura, letteratura, arte. 1977. q. L.20800. Via Capranica 35, 73020 Cavallino, Italy. Ed. Dante Maffia. adv.; bk.rev.

POLONIAN. see *GENERAL INTEREST PERIODICALS — United States*

001.3   PL   ISSN 0079-3531
POLSKA AKADEMIA NAUK. ODDZIAL W KRAKOWIE. ROCZNIK. 1959. a. price varies. Ossolineum, Publishing House of the Polish Academy of Sciences, Rynek 9, 50-106 Wroclaw, Poland. TEL 48-71-386-25. FAX 48-71-448-103. TELEX 0712771 OSS PL. Ed. Krystyna Stachowska. **Document type:** proceedings.
  Description: Information on the activity of the Cracow Branch of the Polish Academy of Sciences, list of members and bibliography of books published every year.

POLSKIE TOWARZYSTWO NAUKOWE NA OBCZYZNIE. ROCZNIK. see *SCIENCES: COMPREHENSIVE WORKS*

001.3   US   ISSN 1057-1515
DP532
PORTUGUESE STUDIES REVIEW. 1991. s-a. $24 to individuals; institutions $49. International Conference Group on Portugal, Univ. of New Hampshire, Dept. of History, HSCC 408, Durham, NH 03824. TEL 603-862-3018. FAX 603-868-6935. Ed. Douglas L. Wheeler. bk.rev. circ. 350. **Document type:** academic/scholarly publication.
  Description: Covers the social sciences and humanities including current and historical material, articles and research news for Africa, Asia and the Americas.

001.3   US   ISSN 0277-9897
PN1995
POST SCRIPT (COMMERCE); essays in film and the humanities. 1981. 3/yr. $12 to individuals; institutions $20. Post Script, Inc., Department of Literature and Languages, East Texas State University, Commerce, TX 75429. TEL 903-886-5260. FAX 903-886-5980. Ed. Gerald Duchovnay. adv.; bk.rev.; bibl.; circ. 400. (back issues avail.) **Indexed:** Bk.Rev.Ind. (1983-), Child.Bk.Rev.Ind. (1983-), Film Lit.Ind. (1982-), Ind.Bk.Rev.Hum., Int.Ind.Film Per., Intl.Ind.TV., M.L.A. **Document type:** academic/scholarly publication.
  —BLDSC (6559.500000); Faxon.

001.3   SA   ISSN 0079-4333
POTCHEFSTROOM UNIVERSITY FOR CHRISTIAN HIGHER EDUCATION. WETENSKAPLIKE BYDRAES. REEKS A: GEESTESWETENSKAPPE. (Text in Afrikaans and English) 1971. irreg. price varies. Potchefstroom University for Christian Higher Education - Potchefstroomse Universiteit vir Christelike Hoer Onderwys, Potchefstroom, South Africa. circ. 350. **Document type:** monographic series.

001.3   NE   ISSN 0165-4373
PRANA; tijdschrift voor geestelijke verruiming en randgebieden der wetenschappen. 1975. bi-m. fl.57. Uitgeverij Ankh-Hermes B.V., Smyrnastraat 5, 7413 BA Deventer, Netherlands. TEL 05700-33355. FAX 05700-24632. Ed.Bd. adv.; bk.rev.; bibl.

001.5 407   US   ISSN 0731-0714
P301
PRE-TEXT; a journal of rhetorical theory. 1980. q. $15 to individuals; institutions $45; foreign $60. Victor J. Vitanza, Ed. & Pub., c/o University of Texas, Dept. of English, Box 19035, Arlington, TX 76019-0035. adv.; bk.rev.; index. circ. 600. (back issues avail.) **Indexed:** M.L.A., Sociol.Abstr.
  —BLDSC (6603.630000); Faxon; UnCover.

PRESENTATIONS. see *SOCIAL SERVICES AND WELFARE*

001.3   AT
PRESS, THE LAW AND BEYOND. SERIES: ESSO LECTURE: NO.1; a view from the press council. 1985. triennial. price varies. Australian Academy of the Humanities, G.P.O. Box 93, Canberra, A.C.T. 2601, Australia. TEL 6-06-2487744. FAX 6-06-2486287. E-mail: aah@anu.edu.au. Ed. H.H.R. Love.

001.3 701.18   US
PRINCETON ESSAYS ON THE ARTS. 1975. irreg. price varies. Princeton University Press, 41 William St., Princeton, NJ 08540. TEL 609-258-4900. FAX 609-258-6305. (reprint service avail. from UMI) **Document type:** monographic series.

001.3 900   US
PRINCETON SERIES IN CULTURE - POWER - HISTORY. irreg. price varies. Princeton University Press, 41 William St., Princeton, NJ 08540. TEL 609-258-4900. FAX 609-258-6305. **Document type:** monographic series.

001.3 300 500   US   ISSN 0032-8456
Z733.P93
PRINCETON UNIVERSITY LIBRARY CHRONICLE. 1939. 3/yr. $50 membership; $30 to institutions. (Friends of the Princeton University Library) Princeton University Library, 1 Washington Rd., Princeton, NJ 08544. TEL 609-452-3184. FAX 609-258-4105. Ed. Patricia H. Marks. adv.; bibl.; illus.; cum.index: vols.1-25 (1939-1964); circ. 2,000 (paid). (also avail. in microfilm from UMI) **Indexed:** Abstr.Engl.Stud., Amer.Hist.& Life, Curr.Cont., Hist.Abstr., Hum.Ind., Lib.Lit., M.L.A. **Document type:** academic/scholarly publication.
  —Faxon; UnCover; UMI.
  Description: Publishes articles of scholarly importance and general interest written for the educated non-specialist and based upon research conducted in the Department of Rare Books and the Special Collections of the Princeton University Libraries.

PROBLEMATA. see *PHILOSOPHY*

HUMANITIES: COMPREHENSIVE WORKS

001.3   IT   ISSN 0391-836X
PROSPETTIVE SETTANTA. 1975. q. L.100000 (foreign L.190000) (effective 1992). Guida Editori S.p.A., Via D. Morelli 16-B, 80121 Naples, Italy. TEL 081-7644288. FAX 081-7644414. Ed. Giuseppe Galasso.
    Description: Deals with topics of general interest in the humanities focusing above all on history, philosophy, sociology and literature.

001.3   CN   ISSN 0300-3523
PROTEE. 1971. q. Can.$34 in US Can.$44; elsewhere Can.$49. Universite du Quebec a Chicoutimi, Departement des Arts et Lettres, 555 bd. de l'Universite, Chicoutimi, PQ, Canada. TEL 418-545-5396. FAX 418-545-5012. Ed. Francine Belle-Isle. adv.; bk.rev.; charts; illus.; stat.; index. circ. 500. **Indexed:** Amer.Hist.& Life, Hist.Abstr., Periodex, Pt.de Rep. (1982-), RADAR. **Document type:** academic/scholarly publication.

001.3   PL   ISSN 0552-4245
PRZEGLAD ZACHODNIOPOMORSKI. (Text in Polish; summaries in German) 1957. q. 40000 Zl. per issue. (Uniwersytet Szczecinski) Wydawnictwo Naukowe Universytetu Szczecinskiego, Ul. Mickiewicza 64, Szczecin, Poland. TEL 48-91-560-31. (Dist. by: Ars Polona - Ruch, Krakowskie Przedmiescie 7, Warsaw, Poland) Ed. Tadeusz Bialecki. bk.rev.; bibl. circ. 550.
—BLDSC (6944.932000).

PSICOTERAPIA E SCIENZE UMANE. see *MEDICAL SCIENCES — Psychiatry And Neurology*

PUBLIC CULTURE. see *LITERARY AND POLITICAL REVIEWS*

001.3   IT
PUNTO D'INCONTRO; rivista di attualita politica, di economia, cultura, costume. 1978. q. L.8000. Via V. Veneto 5, 66034 Lanciano (Chieti), Italy. Ed. Mario Micozzi. adv.; illus. circ. 35,000.

001.3   IT
QUADERNI DI CULTURA FRANCESE. 1959; N.S. 1982; N.S. 1991. irreg., no.26, 1992. price varies. (Fondazione Primoli) Edizioni di Storia e Letteratura s.r.l., Via Lancellotti 18, 00186 Rome, Italy. TEL 65-40-556. FAX 06-6872567. Ed. Massimo Colesanti.

001.3   IT   ISSN 1120-9232
QUADERNI EMILIANI; e questioni di stile. 1978. 3/yr. L.45000 (foreign L.70000). Editrice C L U E B, Via Marsala 24, 40126 Bologna, Italy. TEL 051-220736. FAX 051-237758. Ed. Roberto Fregna.

QUADERNI SARDI DI FILOSOFIA E SCIENZE UMANE. see *PHILOSOPHY*

001.3   US
QUANTUM BOOKS SERIES. no.4, 1974. irreg., no.32, 1992. price varies. University of California Press, 2120 Berkeley Way, Berkeley, CA 94720. TEL 510-642-4247. FAX 510-643-7127. (Orders to: California-Princeton Fulfillment Services, 1445 Lower Ferry Rd., Ewing, NJ 08618. TEL 800-777-4726. FAX 800-999-1958) (back issues avail.) **Document type:** monographic series.
    Description: Covers a variety of topics and issues in the humanities.

QUORUM; literary journal. see *LITERATURE*

001.3   IT
R S U. (Rivista di Studi Ungheresi) 1986. a. L.20000 (foreign L.25000). (Centro Interuniversitario per gli Studi Ungheresi in Italia) Carucci Editore, Viale Trastevere, 60, 00153 Rome, Italy. TEL 06-5806274.

RAKUNO GAKUEN DAIGAKU KIYO. JINBUN SHAKAI KAGAKU HEN/RAKUNO GAKUEN UNIVERSITY. JOURNAL: CULTURAL AND SOCIAL SCIENCES. see *AGRICULTURE*

700 800   II   ISSN 0033-9156
RAMAKRISHNA MISSION INSTITUTE OF CULTURE. BULLETIN. (Text in English) 1950. m. Rs.30 (foreign $24). Ramakrishna Mission Institute of Culture, Gol Park, Calcutta 700 029, India. TEL 46-3431. Ed. Swami Lokeswarananda. adv.; bk.rev.; index. circ. 3,400.

914.6   IT   ISSN 0392-4777
RASSEGNA IBERISTICA. 1978. 3/yr. (Universita degli Studi di Venezia, Dipartimento di Iberistica) Bulzoni Editore, Via dei Liburni 14, 00185 Rome, Italy. FAX 06-4450355. (Edit. addr.: S. Marco 3417, 30124 Venice, Italy) Eds. Franco Meregalli, Guiseppe Bellini. bibl.

001.3   SP   ISSN 0034-0235
AP60
RAZON Y FE; revista hispano-americana de cultura. 1901. 10/yr. 4900 ptas.($58) (effective 1994). Centro Loyola de Estudios y Comunicacion Social, Pablo Aranda, 3, 28006 Madrid, Spain. FAX 341-563-40-73. adv.; bk.rev.; abstr.; index, cum.index: 1901-1952, 1953-1975. circ. 6,000. **Indexed:** Cath.Ind., CERDIC, M.L.A., New Test.Abstr.
—Faxon.

RAZVITOK. see *LITERATURE*

700 800   US   ISSN 1054-5212
RE: ARTS AND LETTERS. Cover title: R E A L. 1968. s-a. $8 to individuals; institutions $10. Stephen F. Austin State University, School of Liberal Arts, Box 13007, SFA Sta., Nacogdoches, TX 75962. TEL 409-568-2101. Ed. Lee Schultz. charts; illus. circ. 450. **Indexed:** Abstr.Engl.Stud., M.L.A.
—BLDSC (7300.258000); UnCover.
    Supersedes: Re: Artes Liberales; Formerly (until 1972): Re: Arts and Letters (ISSN 0034-0286)

REGENSBURGER UNIVERSITAETSZEITUNG. see *COLLEGE AND ALUMNI*

001.3   UK   ISSN 0486-3720
AS121
RENAISSANCE AND MODERN STUDIES. 1957. a. £6. (University of Nottingham) Sisson & Parker, 25 Wheeler Gate, Nottingham NG1 2NF, England. (Co-sponsor: Renaissance & Modern Studies) Eds. R.A. Cardwell, M.C.E. Jones. adv.; bibl. circ. 500. (also avail. in microform from UMI; reprint service avail. from UMI) **Indexed:** Amer.Hist.& Life, Br.Hum.Ind., Hist.Abstr., M.L.A.
—BLDSC (7356.865000); Faxon.

378.1 700 800   US   ISSN 0034-4400
AS30
RENDEZVOUS; a journal of arts and letters. (Text mainly in English, occasionally in French, German, Spanish) 1966. 2/yr. $7. (Idaho State University, College of Arts and Sciences) Idaho State University Press, Box 8113, Pocatello, ID 83209-0009. TEL 208-236-2845. Ed.Bd. bk.rev.; charts; illus. circ. 200. **Indexed:** Abstr.Engl.Stud., Amer.Hist.& Life, Hist.Abstr. **Document type:** academic/scholarly publication.
—Faxon; UnCover.

001.3   CC   ISSN 0447-662X
RENWEN ZAZHI/JOURNAL OF HUMANITIES. (Text in Chinese; table of contents in English) 1957. bi-m. Y7.20($53.40) (Shaanxi Sheng Shehui Kexueyuan - Shaanxi Academy of Social Sciences) Renwen Zazhishe, 7 Lingyuan S. Rd., Xi'an, Shaanxi 710061, People's Republic of China. TEL 54004. (Dist. outside China by: Guoji Shudian - China International Book Trading Corp., P.O. Box 399, Beijing, P.R.C.; Dist. in US by: China Books & Periodicals, Inc., 2929 24th St., San Francisco, CA 94110. TEL 415-282-2994) (Co-sponsor: Shaanxi Sheng Shehui Kexue Xuehui, Lianhehui) Ed. Wang Yuliang. **Document type:** academic/scholarly publication.
—BLDSC (5003.473400); UnCover.

001.3   FR   ISSN 0987-6030
REPERTOIRE. (Text in English, French) 1985. biennial. Universite de Montpellier (Universite Paul Valery), B.P. 5043, 34032 Montpellier Cedex 1, France. TEL 67-14-20-00. bk.rev. circ. 500.
    Description: Descriptive catalog of French periodicals of English and American studies.

REPERTOIRE INTERNATIONAL DES MEDIEVISTES. see *HISTORY — History Of Europe*

001.3   US   ISSN 0734-6018
NX1   CODEN: RPREEL
REPRESENTATIONS. 1983. q. $33 to individuals (foreign $39); institutions $62 (foreign $68); students $23 (foreign $29) (effective 1994). University of California Press, Journals Division, 2120 Berkeley Way, Berkeley, CA 94720. TEL 510-643-7154. FAX 510-642-9917. Eds. Stephen Greenblatt, Svetlana Alpers. adv.; illus. circ. 2,900. (also avail. in microform from UMI; back issues avail.) **Indexed:** Amer.Hum.Ind., Artbibl.Mod., Arts & Hum.Cit.Ind., Curr.Cont., Film Lit.Ind. (1989-), M.L.A., RILA. **Document type:** academic/scholarly publication.
—BLDSC (7690.800000); Faxon; UnCover; SWETS; UMI. **CCC.**
    Description: Provides a forum for new work in cultural studies, art, history, literature, anthropology, and social history.
    Refereed Serial

REPUBLIC OF CHINA. NATIONAL SCIENCE COUNCIL. PROCEEDINGS. PART C: HUMANITIES AND SOCIAL SCIENCES. see *SOCIAL SCIENCES: COMPREHENSIVE WORKS*

378.54   II
RESEARCH JOURNAL: HUMANITIES AND SOCIAL SCIENCES. (Text in English and Hindi) 1972. irreg. Rs.5. University of Indore, University House, Indore 452001, Madhya Pradesh, India. bibl.; illus.

001.3   PE
▼**RETABLO ARTE Y CULTURA.** 1993. q. Lluvia Editores, Av. Garcilaso de la Vega 1976, Of. 501, Lima, Peru. TEL 822029. (Edit. addr.: Jr. Cahuide 400, Puca Cruz, Ayacucho, Peru) Ed. Edilberto Jimenez Quispe.

001.3   JA
REVIEW ON LIBERAL ARTS/KYOYO RONSHU. (Text in English or Japanese) 1975. irreg. Kokushikan University, Society of Liberal Arts - Kokushikan Daigaku Kyoyo Gakkai, 4-28-1 Setagaya, Setagaya-ku, Tokyo 154, Japan.

001.3 500   RM
REVISTA ACADEMICA. 1990. bi-m. Academia Romana, Str. Dr. Marcovici Nr. 9, Sectorul 6, Bucharest, Rumania. Dir. Mihai Draganescu.

001.3 056.1   PR   ISSN 0378-7974
PC4001
REVISTA DE ESTUDIOS HISPANICOS; estudios de lengua y literatura. (Text in English, French, Spanish) 1971. a. $9 to individuals; students $6; institutions $18.50. University of Puerto Rico, Seminario de Estudios Hispanicos "Federico de Onis", P.O. Box 21787, Rio Piedras, PR 00931. TEL 809-764-0000. (Subscr. to: Oficina de Publicaciones, Facultad de Humanidades, Universidad de Puerto Rico, Rio Piedras, PR 00931) Ed. Mercedes Lopez-Baralt. adv.; bk.rev.; bibl. circ. 1,000. (also avail. in microform from UMI; reprint service avail. from UMI) **Indexed:** Chic.Per.Ind., M.L.A. **Document type:** academic/scholarly publication.
—BLDSC (7854.507100).

001.3   PN
REVISTA NACIONAL DE CULTURA. 1975. q. Instituto Nacional de Cultura, Apdo. Postal 662, Panama 1, Panama. TEL 62-3497. Eds. Ramon Oviero, Reymundo Gurdion G. illus. **Indexed:** Abstr.Engl.Stud., Amer.Hist.& Life, Hist.Abstr.

001.3   VE   ISSN 0035-0230
AS90.A1
REVISTA NACIONAL DE CULTURA.* 1938. irreg., no.246, 1981. Consejo Nacional de la Cultura, Centro Simon Bolivar, Torre Norte, piso 16, Apdo. 50995, Caracas, Venezuela. Ed. Francisco Perez Perdomo. adv. **Indexed:** Abstr.Engl.Stud., Hisp.Amer.Per.Ind.

001.3   PN
REVISTA VICEVERSA. 1991. 3/yr. Instituto Nacional de Cultura, Departamento de Letras, Apdo. 662, Panama 1, Panama. Ed. Reymundo Gurdion G.

001.3   FR
REVUE DE PAU ET DU BEARN. 1973. a. 100 F. Societe de Sciences, Lettres et Arts de Pau, Archives Departementales, bd. Tourasse, 64000 Pau, France. Ed.Bd. bibl.; illus. **Indexed:** Amer.Hist.& Life, Hist.Abstr.

HUMANITIES: COMPREHENSIVE WORKS

940 RM ISSN 0035-2063
DR1
REVUE DES ETUDES SUD-EST EUROPEENNES. (Text in English, French, German, Italian and Russian) 1963. q. 200 lei($62) (Institutul de Studii Sud-Est Europene) Editura Academiei Romane, Calea Victoriei 125, 79717 Bucharest, Rumania. (Dist. by: Rompresfilatelia, Calea Grivitei 64-66, P.O. Box 12-201, 78104 Bucharest, Rumania) Ed. A. Dutzu. bk.rev.; illus.; index. circ. 1,200. **Indexed:** Amer.Hist.& Life, Bibl.Ling., Hist.Abstr., Lang.& Lang.Behav.Abstr., Numis.Lit.

REVUE DES SOCIETES SAVANTES DE HAUTE NORMANDIE. see SCIENCES: COMPREHENSIVE WORKS

001.3 297 FR ISSN 0997-1327
DT160
REVUE DU MONDE MUSULMAN DE LA MEDITERRANEE. 1981. q. 320 F. (Association pour l'Etude des Sciences Humaines en Afrique du Nord (AESHAN)) Edisud, La Calade, RN 7, 13090 Aix-en-Provence, France. TEL 42-21-61-44. FAX 42-21-56-20. TELEX 305551 BSCEDISUD. adv.; bk.rev. (back issues avail.) **Indexed:** Documentatieblad.

001.3 BE ISSN 0770-8602
AP22
REVUE GENERALE. 1865. 10/yr. 2300 BEF (effective 1992). Imprimerie Dieu-Brichart, Chaussee de la Croix 47, B-1340 Ottignies, Belgium. TEL 10-866629. FAX 10-866691. (Editorial addr.: Chaussee de Louvain 41, B-5990 Hamme-Mille, Belgium) Ed.Bd. adv.; bk.rev.; bibl.; illus.; index. circ. 8,000.
—Faxon.
Formerly: Revue Generale pour l'Humanisme des Temps Nouveax; Supersedes: Revue Generale: Lettres, Arts, Sciences Humaines; Which was formerly: Revue Generale: Perspectives Europeennes des Sciences Humaines; Which superseded: Revue Generale Belge (ISSN 0035-3078)

001.3
RICERCA IN CAMPO; letteratura, arti, scienze, critica. q.? Edizioni Piero Manni, Via Braccio Martello 36, 73100 Lecce, Italy. TEL 0832-315929. FAX 0832-314834.

001.3 US ISSN 0882-3731
THE RIGHT OF AESTHETIC REALISM TO BE KNOWN. 1973. w. $9 (Canada and Mexico $14; elsewhere $20) for six mos. Aesthetic Realism Foundation, 141 Greene St., New York, NY 10012. TEL 212-777-4490. FAX 212-777-4426. Ed. Ellen Reiss. bk.rev. (back issues avail.)
Description: Contains works by Eli Siegel, founder of Aesthetic Realism; commentary by Ellen Reiss; articles by Aesthetic Realism consultants. Explains world events and questions of self on an aesthetic basis.

001.3 IT ISSN 0080-3073
DG533.A1
RINASCIMENTO. (Supplement avail.) (Text in English, French, German and Italian) 1950. a. L.97000 (foreign L.113000) (effective 1993). (Istituto Nazionale di Studi sul Rinascimento) Casa Editrice Leo S. Olschki, Viuzzo del Pozzetto, Casella Postale 66, 50100 Florence, Italy. TEL 055-6530684. FAX 055-6530214. Eds. Eugenio Garin, Cesare Vasoli. cum.index. circ. 800. **Indexed:** Amer.Hist.& Life, Arts & Hum.Cit.Ind., Hist.Abstr., RILA. **Document type:** academic/scholarly publication.
—SWETS.
Supersedes (1938-1944): Rinascita.

001.3 IT ISSN 0394-4387
RINASCIMENTO. QUADERNI. 1965. irreg., no.20, 1993. price varies. (Istituto Nazionale di Studi sul Rinascimento) Casa Editrice Leo S. Olschki, Casella Postale 66, 50100 Florence, Italy. TEL 055-6530684. FAX 055-6530214. **Document type:** monographic series.

055.1 IT ISSN 0035-5739
RIVISTA ABRUZZESE; rassegna trimestrale di cultura. 1947. q. L.40000($60) (foreign L.80000) (effective 1994). Via Fagiani 37, Casella Postale 325, 66034 Lanciano, Italy. TEL 0872-49445. Ed. Dr. Emiliano Giancristofaro. bk.rev.; abstr.; bibl.; charts; illus.; tr.lit.; index, cum.index. circ. 650. (tabloid format)
Description: Covers literature, cultural anthropology, regional history, political news, and the humanities.

001.3 IT ISSN 1120-8856
RIVISTA PASCOLIANA. 1989. a. L.50000 (effective 1991). (Accademia Pascoliana di San Mauro) Patron Editore, Via Badini 12, 40127 Quarto Inferiore (BO), Italy. (Edit. addr.: Dipartmento di Italianistica, Via Zamboni 32, 40100 Bologna, Italy) Ed. Mario Pazzaglia.

001.3 PL
ROCZNIKI HUMANISTYCZNE. (In six parts: 1. Polish Literature; 2. History; 3. Classical Philology; 4. History of Arts; 5. Linguistics; 6. Neophilology) (Text in Polish: summaries in French) 1949. 6/yr. price varies. Katolicki Uniwersytet Lubelski, Towarzystwo Naukowe, Ul. Gliniana 21, 20-616 Lublin, Poland. index. circ. 670. **Indexed:** Amer.Hist.& Life, Bibl.Ling., Hist.Abstr., M.L.A.

001.3 IT
ROMAGNA ARTE E STORIA. 1981. 3/yr. L.25000($25) Via San Giuliano 69, Rimini, C.A.P. 47037, Italy. charts; illus.; cum.index. circ. 10,000. (back issues avail.)

THE RUSSIAN REVIEW; an American quarterly devoted to Russia past and present. see HISTORY — History Of Europe

001.3 500 US
S I I A S NEWS. q. $25. Staten Island Institute of Arts and Sciences, 75 Stuyvesant Place, Staten Island, NY 10301. TEL 717-727-1135. FAX 718-273-5683. Ed. Edward Gregory. circ. 9,000. (back issues avail.)
Description: Examines the broad spectrum of public programs that affect the residents of Staten Island.

001.3 AG
S Y C. 1989. s-a. Torre Abolida, Corrientes 2063, of. 6, 1045 Buenos Aires C.F., Argentina. Ed. Noe Jitrik.

SAECULA SPIRITALIA. see HISTORY

060 II ISSN 0080-5416
SAHITYA AKADEMI, NEW DELHI. REPORT. (Text in English) 1954. a. free. National Academy of Letters - Sahitya Akademi, Rabindra Bhavan, New Delhi 110001, India. TEL 38 20 50.
Description: Annual report of the archives of Sahitya Akademi and the National Academy of Letters in New Delhi.

001.3 500 PH ISSN 0036-3014
AS540.S34
SAINT LOUIS UNIVERSITY RESEARCH JOURNAL; an interdisciplinary journal in the sciences and the humanities. (Text mainly in English) 1963. s-a. $52. Saint Louis University, Graduate School of Arts and Sciences, Box 71, Baguio City 2600, Philippines. Ed. Felino L. Lorente. adv.; bk.rev.; charts; illus.; circ. 1,000 (controlled). (also avail. in microform from KTO) **Indexed:** Curr.Cont., Ind.Phil.Per., Mid.East: Abstr.& Ind. **Document type:** academic/scholarly publication.
—Faxon; UnCover.
Formerly (until 1969): Saint Louis Quarterly.

300 700 800 US ISSN 0036-3529
SALMAGUNDI; a quarterly of the humanities & social sciences. 1965. q. $15 to individuals; institutions $25. Skidmore College, Saratoga Springs, NY 12866. TEL 518-584-5000. FAX 518-581-7400. Eds. Robert & Peggy Boyers. adv.; bk.rev.; film rev.; play rev.; illus.; index, cum.index: 1965-1975. circ. 4,800. (also avail. in microfilm from UMI; reprint service avail. from UMI) **Indexed:** A.I.P.P., Abstr.Engl.Stud., Amer.Hum.Ind., Arts & Hum.Cit.Ind., Curr.Cont., Film Lit.Ind. (1990-), Ind.Amer.Per.Verse, Ind.Bk.Rev.Hum., M.L.A., Sociol.Abstr. **Document type:** academic/scholarly publication.
—BLDSC (8070.930000); UnCover; UMI.
Description: Articles on contemporary art and culture. Presents poetry by contemporary writers.

001.3 PH
SAN CARLOS PUBLICATIONS. SERIES A: HUMANITIES. (Text in English) 1964. irreg., no.18, 1989. P.498.50($21.75) (University of San Carlos) San Carlos Publications, 6000 Cebu City, Philippines. (Dist. in U.S. by: Cellar Book Shop, 18090 Wyoming, Detroit, MI 48221) Ed. Joseph Baumgartner. circ. 547.
—BLDSC (4336.580450).
Formerly: University of San Carlos. Series A: Humanities (ISSN 0069-1321)

300 500 US ISSN 0097-8051
AS36.C17
SAN JOSE STUDIES. 1975. 3/yr. $12 to individuals; institutions $18. San Jose State University, One Washington Sq., San Jose, CA 95192-0149. TEL 408-924-4476. Eds. J. Engell, D. Mesher. illus. circ. 500. (also avail. in microform from UMI; reprint service avail. from UMI) **Indexed:** A.I.P.P., Abstr.Engl.Stud., Amer.Hist.& Life, Amer.Hum.Ind., Biol.Abstr., Hist.Abstr., Lang. & Lang.Behav.Abstr., M.L.A., Sociol.Abstr., Wom.Stud.Abstr. **Document type:** academic/scholarly publication.
—BLDSC (8072.925000); UnCover; UMI.
Description: Publishes scholarship, essays, fiction and poetry with a special focus on California and Bay Area cultures.

SAN MARCOS. see ART

001.3 RU
AS262
SANKT-PETERBURGSKII UNIVERSITET. VESTNIK. SERIYA: FILOSOFIYA, POLITOLOGIYA, SOTSIOLOGIYA, PSIKHOLOGIYA, PRAVO. (Text in Russian; contents page and summaries in English) 1946. q. 18.60 Rub. Sankt-Peterburgskii Universitet, Universitetskaya Nab., 7-9, St. Petersburg V-164, Russia. (Subscr. to: Mezhdunarodnaya Kniga, ul. Dimitrova 39, Moscow G-200, Russia) Ed. N.A. Belyaev. bibl.; illus.; index.
Former titles (until June 1991): Leningradskii Universitet. Vestnik. Seriya: Filosofiya, Politologiya, Teoriya i Istoriya Sotsializma, Sotsiologiya, Psikhologiya, Pravo; (until 1990): Leningradskii Universitet. Vestnik. Seriya: Istoriya K P S S , Nauchnyi Kommunizm, Filosofiya, Pravo (ISSN 0233-7541); Supersedes in part (in 1985): Leningradskii Universitet. Vestnik. Seriya: Ekonomika, Filosofiya i Pravo (ISSN 0024-0818)

001.3 IT ISSN 0581-4758
SANSKRITI. (Text in Hindi) 1958. q. Rs.4. Ministry of Education and Social Welfare, Department of Education, Shastri Bhavan, New Delhi 110001, India. (Order from: Assistant Educational Adviser (Publications), Ministry of Human Resource Development, Department of Education, Ex. AFO Hutments, Dr. Rajendra Prasad Road, New Delhi 110001, India) (back issues avail.)

001.3 500 JA ISSN 0389-3944
CODEN: SIDKDW
SAPPORO IKA DAIGAKU JINBUN SHIZEN KAGAKU KIYO/SAPPORO MEDICAL COLLEGE. JOURNAL OF LIBERAL ARTS AND SCIENCES. (Text and summaries in English and Japanese) 1960. a. Sapporo Ika Daigaku - Sapporo Medical College, Nishi-17-chome, Minami-1-jo, Chuo-ku, Sapporo-shi, Hokkaido 060, Japan. **Indexed:** Biol.Abstr., Chem.Abstr., Jap.Per.Ind.
—BLDSC (5010.310000); CASDDS.

001.3 IT
SAVENNA SETTA SAMBRO; rivista semestrale di storia, cultura e ambiente. 1991. s-a. (Grupo di Studi delle Valli Savena, Setta, Sambro) Litosei s.r.l., Via Bellini 22-4, Sesto di Rastignano, Bologna, Italy. TEL 051-744539. FAX 051-742312. Ed. Daniele Ravaglia.

001.3 IT ISSN 1122-6323
SCHEDE UMANISTICHE. 1991. s-a. L.42000 (foreign L.68000) (effective 1994). Cooperativa Libraria Universitaria Editrice Bologna, Via Marsala 24, 40126 Bologna, Italy. TEL 051-220736. FAX 051-237758.

SCHLESIEN; arts, science, folklore. see SCIENCES: COMPREHENSIVE WORKS

001.3 US ISSN 1047-6377
SCHOLARLY RESEARCH AND REVIEW. q. $19.95 to individuals; institutions $29.95. Edwin Mellen Press, 415 Ridge St., Box 450, Lewiston, NY 14092. TEL 716-754-2788. FAX 716-754-4056.
Description: Covers research notes and reviews in all fields.

001.3 US ISSN 0161-7729
SCHOLARS' FACSIMILES & REPRINTS. 1936. irreg., vol.476, 1993. price varies. Academic Resources Corporation, Box 344, Delmar, NY 12054. Ed. Norman Mangouni. (also avail. in microfiche; back issues avail.) **Document type:** academic/scholarly publication.

SCHOLASTIC ART. see ART

HUMANITIES: COMPREHENSIVE WORKS

SCIENCE AND ARTS - RESEARCH STUDIES/ULUM WA FUNUN - DIRASAT WA BUHUTH. see *SCIENCES: COMPREHENSIVE WORKS*

SCIENCE, TECHNOLOGY & HUMAN VALUES. see *SCIENCES: COMPREHENSIVE WORKS*

040   IS   ISSN 0080-8369
SCRIPTA HIEROSOLYMITANA. (Text in English) 1954. irreg., vol.33, 1992. price varies. (Hebrew University of Jerusalem) Magnes Press, Hebrew University, Jerusalem, P.O. Box 7695, Jerusalem 91076, Israel. (back issues avail.) **Indexed:** Biol.Abstr. **Document type:** academic/scholarly publication, monographic series.

001.3 100   IT   ISSN 0392-095X
AS222
SCUOLA NORMALE SUPERIORE DI PISA. ANNALI. CLASSE DI LETTERE E FILOSOFIA. (Text in English, French, German, Italian, Spanish) 1873. q. L.80000 (foreign L.150000). Scuola Normale Superiore di Pisa, Piazza dei Cavalieri 7, 56100 Pisa, Italy. TEL 050-597111. FAX 050-563513. Ed. Giuseppe Nenci. bk.rev.; illus.; index. circ. 1,300. (also avail. in microfilm from BHP; back issues avail.) **Indexed:** Amer.Hist.& Life, Bibl.Ling., Hist.Abstr., M.L.A. —Faxon.
Formerly: Scuola Normale Superiore di Pisa. Annali. Lettere, Storia e Filosofia (ISSN 0036-990X)

001.3   IT
SEGUSIUM. vol.23, 1987. s-a. Societa di Ricerche e Studi Valsusini, Casella Postale 43, 10059 Susa, Italy. Ed. Ferruccio Pari.

001.3   JA   ISSN 0037-1084
SEISHIN STUDIES. (Text in English and Japanese) 1952. s-a. 900 Yen($5) University of the Sacred Heart, Hiroo, 4-3-1 Shibuya-ku, Tokyo, Japan. FAX 03-5485-3884. Ed.Bd. bk.rev.; illus.; index, cum.index every 2 yrs. circ. 1,000. **Indexed:** Jap.Per.Ind.
—BLDSC (8219.983000).

SEMIOTEXT(E). see *LITERARY AND POLITICAL REVIEWS*

001.3   CN   ISSN 0847-1622
SEMIOTIC REVIEW OF BOOKS. 1990. 3/yr. Can.$23($23) to individuals; institutions Can.$30. Toronto Semiotic Circle, Victoria Park, 73 Queen's Park Cres. E., Toronto, Ont. M5S 1S3, Canada. TEL 416-585-4456. FAX 416-585-4584. Ed. Paul Bouissac. circ. 2,000. **Document type:** academic/scholarly publication.
Description: A multidisciplinary journal publishing exclusively review articles in humanities, social and natural sciences.
Refereed Serial

001.3   FR   ISSN 0085-6037
SEMITICA. 1948. irreg., latest vol.41-42, 1993. 196 F. (Universite de Paris III (Sorbonne-Nouvelle), Institut d'Etudes Semitiques) Editions d'Amerique et d'Orient, 11 rue St. Sulpice, 75006 Paris, France. TEL 43-26-86-35. FAX 33-1-43-54-59-54. (Co-sponsor: Centre National de la Recherche Scientifique) Ed.Bd. **Indexed:** Bibl.Ling., Old Test.Abstr.
—BLDSC (8239.507000).

001.3   MX
SERIE NUESTRA AMERICA. 1981. irreg., no.36, 1992. price varies. Universidad Nacional Autonoma de Mexico, Centro Coordinador y Difusor de Estudios Latinoamericanos, Torre I de Humanidades, 2o piso, Ciudad Universitario, 04510 Mexico D.F., Mexico. TEL 622-1902. FAX 548-9662. **Document type:** monographic series.
Description: Contains studies on Central and South America.

001.6   CC   ISSN 1000-260X
SHENZHEN DAXUE XUEBAO (RENWEN SHEKE BAN)/SHENZHEN UNIVERSITY. JOURNAL (HUMANITIES, SOCIAL SCIENCES EDITION). (Text in Chinese; summaries in English) 1984. 4/yr. Y12. Shenzhen Daxue, Xuebao Bianjibu, Shenzhen, Guangdong 518060, People's Republic of China. TEL 6660277. Ed. Zheng Tianlun. **Document type:** academic/scholarly publication.
Description: Contains academic papers. Aims to reflect research results in education and to promote academic exchange.

001 300   JA   ISSN 0386-2755
AS551
SHISO/THOUGHT. (Text in Japanese) 1921. m. 10000 Yen. Iwanami Shoten Publishers, 2-5-5 Hitotsubashi, Chiyoda-ku, Tokyo 101-02, Japan. TEL 03-3265-4111. FAX 03-3221-8998. TELEX 39495. (Dist. overseas by: Japan Publications Trading Co., Ltd., Box 5030, Tokyo International, Tokyo 100-31, Japan; Or: 1255 Howard St., San Francisco, CA 94103)

001.3 500   II   ISSN 0368-4199
SHIVAJI UNIVERSITY. JOURNAL (HUMANITIES). (Text in English) 1968. Rs.60. Shivaji University, Registrar, Shivaji University, Vidyanagar, Kolhapur (Maharashtra) 416 004, India. TEL 0231-25068. FAX 0231-24033. Ed. S. N. Pawar. bk.rev. circ. 377. **Indexed:** Biol.Abstr., Chem.Abstr. **Document type:** academic/scholarly publication.

001.3 300   JA
SHIZUOKA DAIGAKU KYOIKUGAKUBU KENKYU HOKOKU. JINBUN KAGAKU HEN/SHIZUOKA UNIVERSITY. FACULTY OF EDUCATION. BULLETIN. LIBERAL ARTS AND SOCIAL SCIENCES SERIES. (Text in English, Japanese) a. Shizuoko Daigaku, Kyoikugakubu, 836 Oya, Shizuoka-shi, Shizuoka-ken 422, Japan. TEL 054-237-1170. FAX 054-237-9376. **Document type:** academic/scholarly publication.

001.3   II
SHRI RAMAKRISHNA JYOT; a Gujarati monthly of the Ramakrishna Order. 1989. m. Rs.40 (foreign Rs.175). Sri Ramakrishna Ashrama, Dr. Yagnik Rd., Rajkot 360 001, India.

SIAM SOCIETY. JOURNAL. see *SOCIAL SCIENCES: COMPREHENSIVE WORKS*

SICHUAN DAXUE XUEBAO (SHEHUI KEXUE BAN)/SICHUAN UNIVERSITY. JOURNAL (SOCIAL SCIENCES EDITION). see *SOCIAL SCIENCES: COMPREHENSIVE WORKS*

800 100   IT   ISSN 0037-458X
AS221
SICULORUM GYMNASIUM. 1948. s-a. L.75000($7.50) Universita degli Studi di Catania, Facolta di Lettere e Filosofia, Catania, Italy. **Indexed:** Bibl.Ling., M.L.A.

SILLIMAN JOURNAL; a quarterly of investigation and discussion in the humanities and in the sciences. see *SCIENCES: COMPREHENSIVE WORKS*

001.3 300   AT   ISSN 0816-2735
SIR ROBERT MADGWICK LECTURE SERIES (NO.). 1984. a. free. University of New England, Faculty of Arts, Armidale, N.S.W. 2351, Australia. TEL 067-732223. FAX 067-733317. circ. 400.
Description: Lectures by distinguished scholars in the humanities and social sciences who through their work have furthered the ideals of liberal education.

001.3   IT
SLAVIA; rivista trimestrale di cultura. q. L.30000 (effective 1992). Istituto di Cultura e Lingua Russa, Piazza della Repubblica 47, 00185 Rome, Italy. TEL 06-48-81-411. FAX 06-48-84-106. TELEX 62-11-12. Ed. Bernardino Bernardini.

001.3   BE   ISSN 0085-6169
SNOECK'S ALMANACH. 1782. a. 110 BEF. Snoeck-Ducaju en Zoon N.V., Begijnhoflaan 464, B-9000 Ghent, Belgium. Ed. Serge Snoeck. adv. circ. 100,000. **Document type:** directory.

001.3   BE   ISSN 0085-6177
SNOECK'S: LITERATUUR KUNST FILM TONEEL MODE REIZEN. 1923. a. 150 BEF. Snoeck-Ducaju en Zoon N.V., Begijnhoflaan 464, B-9000 Ghent, Belgium. Ed. Serge Snoeck. adv.; bk.rev. circ. 150,000.

SOCIAL EPISTEMOLOGY; a journal of knowledge, culture and policy. see *PHILOSOPHY*

800 300   HO   ISSN 0049-1276
SOL.* 1971. m. Instituto Hondureno de Cultura Interamericana, Avda. 2 No. 511, Comayaguela, D.C., Apdo 201, Tegucigalpa, Honduras. Ed. Mariana Zepeda. adv.; illus.

001.3   EC
SOLOTEXTOS; revista de cultura. 1991. s-a.? Casa de la Cultura Ecuatoriana, Nucleo del Azuay, Aptdo. 4907, Cuenca, Ecuador.

001.3   CH   ISSN 1010-0733
SOOCHOW JOURNAL OF HUMANITIES. Key Title: Dongwu Wenshi Xuebao. 1976. a. $15 per no. Soochow University, Wai Shuang Hsi, Shih Lin, Taipei, Taiwan, Republic of China. FAX 886-02-8812317. (reprint service avail.) **Document type:** academic/scholarly publication.

001.3   JA   ISSN 0489-6432
SOPHIA (TOKYO, 1952); interdisciplinary studies on cultural exchange. (Text in Japanese) 1952. q. 500 Yen. Sophia University - Jochi Daigaku, 7-1 Kioi-cho, Chiyoda-ku, Tokyo 102, Japan. Ed. Naoji Kimura. bk.rev.; index, cum.index. circ. 2,000.

001.3 300   US   ISSN 0038-1861
BV1460
SOUNDINGS (KNOXVILLE); an interdisciplinary journal. 1968. q. $18 to individuals; institutions $27. University of Tennessee, 306 Alumni Hall, Knoxville, TN 37996-0530. TEL 615-974-8252.
(Co-publisher: Society for Values in Higher Education) Ed. Ralph V. Norman. adv.; index. circ. 1,700. (also avail. in microform from MIM,KTO,UMI; reprint service avail. from UMI) **Indexed:** Amer.Hist.& Life, Arts & Hum.Cit.Ind., C.I.J.E., Curr.Cont., Film Lit.Ind., Hist.Abstr., Hum.Ind., Lang.& Lang.Behav.Abstr., New Test.Abstr., Old Test.Abstr., Rel.& Theol.Abstr. (1969-), Rel.Ind.One, Rel.Per., Sociol.Abstr.
—BLDSC (8330.550000); Faxon; UnCover; UMI.
Supersedes: Christian Scholar.

001.3   NQ
SOUTH - SOUTH BULLETIN. (Text in English and Spanish) 3/yr. $15. Centro de Estudios Internacionales, Apdo. postal 1747, Managua, Nicaragua. TEL 505-2-785413. FAX 505-2-670517.

300 700 800   US   ISSN 0038-4186
AS36.A86
SOUTHERN HUMANITIES REVIEW. 1967. q. $15. Auburn University, 9088 Haley Center, Auburn, AL 36849. TEL 205-844-9088. FAX 205-844-2378. (Co-sponsor: Southern Humanities Council) Eds. Dan R. Latimer, R.T. Smith. adv.; bk.rev. circ. 700. (also avail. in microform from UMI; reprint service avail. from UMI) **Indexed:** A.I.P.P., Abstr.Engl.Stud., Amer.Hist.& Life, Amer.Hum.Ind., Arts & Hum.Cit.Ind., Bk.Rev.Ind. (1984-), Child.Bk.Rev.Ind. (1984-), Curr.Cont., Film Lit.Ind. (1990-), Hist.Abstr., Ind.Bk.Rev.Hum., LCR, M.L.A., Ref.Sour. **Document type:** academic/scholarly publication.
—BLDSC (8354.170000); Faxon; UnCover; UMI.

700 800 300   US   ISSN 0038-4496
AS30
SOUTHERN QUARTERLY; a journal of the arts in the South. 1962. q. $10 to individuals; institutions $25. University of Southern Mississippi, Box 5078, Southern Sta., Hattiesburg, MS 39406-5078. TEL 601-266-4370. FAX 601-266-4410. Ed. Stephen Flinn Young. adv.; bk.rev.; film rev.; play rev.; charts; index. circ. 950. (also avail. in microform from UMI; reprint service avail. from ISI,UMI) **Indexed:** Abstr.Engl.Stud., Amer.Hist.& Life, Amer.Hum.Ind., Arts & Hum.Cit.Ind., Curr.Cont., Film Lit.Ind. (1986-), Hist.Abstr., Ind.Bk.Rev.Hum., Lang.& Lang.Behav.Abstr., M.L.A., Sociol.Abstr. **Document type:** academic/scholarly publication.
—BLDSC (8354.655000); Faxon; UnCover; UMI.
Description: Interdisciplinary journal of Southern culture and society with an emphasis on the arts.

SOUTHERN STUDIES: AN INTERDISCIPLINARY JOURNAL OF THE SOUTH. see *SOCIAL SCIENCES: COMPREHENSIVE WORKS*

059.91   AI   ISSN 0038-500X
SOVETAKAN ARVEST. 1932. m. 10.80 Rub. Ministerstvo Kul'tury, Ul. Isahakian, 28, Erevan, Armenia. Ed. S. Baiandur. adv.; bk.rev.; film rev.; play rev.; charts; illus.; stat. circ. 9,000.

001.3   CN   ISSN 0225-9044
SPIRALE; art lettres spectacles, sciences humaines. 1979. 9/yr. Can.$28 to individuals (foreign Can.$35); institutions Can.$40; students Can.$20. 426 rue Sherbrooke est, 2eme etage, Montreal, PQ H2L 1J6, Canada. TEL 514-982-3725. Ed.Bd. adv.; bk.rev. circ. 1,500. (also avail. in microfilm from BNQ) **Indexed:** Pt.de Rep. (1983-), RADAR.

HUMANITIES: COMPREHENSIVE WORKS

001.3   IT   ISSN 0490-4788
SPOLETIUM; rivista di arte storia cultura. 1954. a. L.60000 (effective 1994). Accademia Spoletina, Palazzo Mauri, Via Brignone 14, 06049 Spoleto (PG), Italy. TEL 0743-221203. Ed. Giovanni Antonelli. adv.; circ. 1,500 (controlled). **Document type:** academic/scholarly publication.

059.91   LE   ISSN 0038-8696
SPURK.* (Text in Armenian) vol.7, 1967. w. £L25. Box 2669, Beirut, Lebanon. Ed. S. Simonian. adv.; bk.rev.; charts; illus.

300 700 800   CE
SRI LANKA JOURNAL OF THE HUMANITIES. (Text in English) 1970. s-a. Rs.100($8.50) University of Peradeniya, P.O. Box 35, Perandeniya, Sri Lanka. Ed. Merlin Peris. adv.; bk.rev. circ. 500. **Indexed:** Abstr.Engl.Stud., Sri Lanka Sci.Ind. **Document type:** academic/scholarly publication.
     Formerly: Ceylon Journal of the Humanities (ISSN 0009-0840)

001.3 500   YU   ISSN 0081-4032
SRPSKA AKADEMIJA NAUKA I UMETNOSTI SPOMENICA. (Text in Serbo-Croatian; summaries in English, French, German or Russian) 1888. irreg. price varies. Srpska Akademija Nauka i Umetnosti, Knez Mihailova 35, 11001 Belgrade, Serbia, Yugoslavia. FAX 38-11-182-825. TELEX 72593 SANU YU. (Dist. by: Prosveta, Terazije 16, Belgrade, Serbia, Yugoslavia) circ. 700.

001.3 100   CH   ISSN 0258-8412
AS455.A1
SSU YU YEN/THOUGHT AND WORDS; journal of the humanities and social sciences. Key Title: Si yu Yan. (Text in Chinese) 1963. q. NT.$500 in ROC (students NT.$250); foreign $30. Thought and Words Association - Ssu yu Yen Tsa Chih She, 7F, No.3, Chinshan S. Rd. Sec. 2, Taipei, Taiwan, Republic of China. TEL 02-396-6685. FAX 02-363-4857. Ed.Bd. bk.rev.; bibl.; index. circ. 1,000. (back issues avail.) **Indexed:** Amer.Hist.& Life, Hist.Abstr.

001.3   US   ISSN 1048-3721
AS30
STANFORD HUMANITIES REVIEW. 1989. 2/yr. $20 to individuals; institutions $40. Stanford University, Humanities Center, Mariposa House, Stanford, CA 94305-8630. TEL 415-725-6747. FAX 415-723-1895. Eds. Stefano Franchi, Gueven Guezeldere. adv.: B&W page $100; adv. contact: Anahid Kassabian. bk.rev.; illus. circ. 200. **Document type:** academic/scholarly publication.
     Description: Interdisciplinary literary review.

STRATEGIES (LOS ANGELES); a journal of theory, culture and politics. see POLITICAL SCIENCE — International Relations

STREVEN. see LITERARY AND POLITICAL REVIEWS

STUDI PIEMONTESI. see LITERATURE

001.3   IT   ISSN 0393-9944
STUDI SCIACCHIANI. 1985. s-a. L.60000 (foreign $50) (effective 1994). Edizioni dell' Arcipelago s.a.s., Casella Postale 997, 16100 Genova, Italy. TEL 010-27-22-431. Eds. Maria A. Raschini, Pier P. Ottonello. bk.rev. **Document type:** academic/scholarly publication.

001.3   IT
STUDI UMANISTICI PICENI; atti dei congressi internazionali di studi umanistici. 1981. a. Istituto Internazionale di Studi Piceni, Piazza Matteotti, 60047 Sassoferrato (AN), Italy. TEL 0732-9465.

001.3   PL   ISSN 0039-3355
STUDIA SLASKIE/SILESIAN STUDIES. (Text in Polish; summaries in English, German) 1958. a. 100000 Zl.($10) Instytut Slaski w Opolu, Ul. Piastowska 17, 45-082 Opole, Poland. TEL 364-41. FAX 330-81. bk.rev. circ. 600. (back issues avail.)

001.3   SP   ISSN 0211-1837
STUDIA ZAMORENSIA. 1980. a. 1500 ptas. Ediciones Universidad de Salamanca, Apdo. 325, 37080 Salamanca, Spain. TEL 923-26-14-54. Dir. Jose Antonio Perez Bowie. **Document type:** academic/scholarly publication.
     Description: Contains studies on the city of Zamora and general humanities.

STUDIES; an Irish quarterly review. see SCIENCES: COMPREHENSIVE WORKS

001.3 900   US   ISSN 0360-2370
STUDIES IN EIGHTEENTH CENTURY CULTURE. 1975. irreg., no.22, 1990. (American Society for Eighteenth Century Studies) Boydell & Brewer Inc., Box 41026, Rochester, NY 14604. TEL 716-275-0419. FAX 716-271-8778. (Subscr. to: Colleague Press Inc., Box 4007, E. Lansing, MI 48823) (reprint service avail. from UMI) **Indexed:** Amer.Hist.& Life, Hist.Abstr., M.L.A.
—BLDSC (8490.473000).

STUDIES IN HISTORY AND CULTURE. see HISTORY

001.3 500   US
STUDIES IN SCIENCE AND THE HUMANITIES. 1988. irreg., vol.3, 1992. price varies. University of Notre Dame Press, Notre Dame, IN 46556. TEL 219-631-6346. FAX 219-631-8148. (Orders to: Box 635, South Bend, IN 46624) **Document type:** academic/scholarly publication.

300 700 800   US   ISSN 0039-3800
AS36.I5
STUDIES IN THE HUMANITIES (INDIANA). 1969. s-a. $5 to individuals; institutions $12. Indiana University of Pennsylvania, English Department, Indiana, PA 15705. TEL 412-357-2322. FAX 412-357-6213. Ed. Malcolm Hayward. bk.rev. circ. 300. **Indexed:** Abstr.Engl.Stud., Amer.Bibl.Slavic & E.Eur.Stud., Amer.Hum.Ind., Film Lit.Ind. (1982-), Ind.Bk.Rev.Hum., M.L.A.
—BLDSC (8490.701000); Faxon; UnCover.
     Description: Multidisciplinary journal of investigations in literature, film and aesthetics.

001.3   US   ISSN 0742-6712
STUDIES IN THE HUMANITIES (NEW YORK); literature, politics, society. 1985. irreg. Peter Lang Publishing, Inc., 62 W. 45th St., 4th Fl., New York, NY 10036. TEL 212-302-6740. FAX 212-302-7574. Ed. Guy Mermier. **Document type:** academic/scholarly publication.

001.3 500 300   SJ   ISSN 0453-8129
DT118
SUDAN RESEARCH INFORMATION BULLETIN. (Issued in two sections) 1965. irreg. University of Khartoum, Sudan Unit, Box 321, Khartoum, Sudan.

001.3   YU   ISSN 0488-7557
SVETLOSC. 1952. bi-m. 8400 din.($60) N I U "Ruske Slovo", Bul. 23, Oktobra 31, 21000 Novi Sad, Yugoslavia. TEL 621-555. Ed. Djura Papharhaji. bk.rev.; index. circ. 850. (back issues avail.)

100   BL   ISSN 0039-7695
SYMPOSIUM. 1959. 2/yr. 1800($6) or exchange. Universidade Catolica de Pernambuco, Biblioteca Central, Rua do Principe, 526, 50050-900 Recife, Pernambuco, Brazil. FAX 081-2164204. TELEX 81-2776 UVCP. Ed. Ferdinand Azevedo S.J. bibl.; charts; illus. circ. 600. **Indexed:** Hum.Ind., M.L.A., Soc.Sci.Ind. **Document type:** academic/scholarly publication.
—BLDSC (8582.877000).
     Description: Interdisciplinary approach to the study of humanities.

020
SYRACUSE UNIVERSITY LIBRARY ASSOCIATES COURIER. 1958. s-a. $30. Syracuse University Associates, 600 Bird Library, Syracuse, NY 13244. TEL 315-443-2697. FAX 315-443-9510. Ed. Mary Beth Hinton. illus. circ. 600. (back issues avail) **Indexed:** M.L.A. **Document type:** academic/scholarly publication.
     Formerly (until 1984): Courier (ISSN 0011-0418)

001.3
T H R C NEWSLETTER. 1991. q. free. Texas Humanities Resource Center, Banister Pl. A, 3809 S. Second St., Austin, TX 78704. TEL 512-441-0288.

001.3   IT   ISSN 1120-6683
TALENTO; rivista di attualita culturale. 1974. bi-m. L.30000 (foreign L.50000) (effective 1991). Lorenzo Editore, Via Monza 6, 10152 Turin, Italy. TEL 011-248-53-87. Ed. Lorenzo Masetta.
     Formerly (until 1990): Controcampo (ISSN 0393-7992)

001.3   IS
TEL AVIV UNIVERSITY. FACULTY OF THE HUMANITIES AND SOCIAL SCIENCES. YEDION. (Text in Hebrew) a. Tel Aviv University, Faculty of Humanities and Social Sciences, Ramat Aviv, P.O. Box 39040, Tel Aviv 69978. TEL 972-3-6409733. FAX 972-3-6409518.

001.3   IT
TELLUS; quadrimestrale di critica della cultura. 3/yr. L.18000 (foreign L.30000). Volpicella M.F., Vicolo Scenaia, 1, Morbegno, Italy. TEL 0342-610862. **Document type:** consumer publication.

001.3   PR
TERTULIA. 1988. s-a. (Corporacion de las Artes y la Cultura del Manatuabon (Artcuma)) Ediciones del Chorro, Apdo. 846, Manati, PR 00701.
     Description: Covers local literature, culture and history.

001.3   GW   ISSN 0165-4888
P302
TEXT; an interdisciplinary journal for the study of discourse. 1981. q. DM.122 to individuals; institutions DM.318. Walter de Gruyter und Co., Mouton de Gruyter, Genthiner Str. 13, 10785 Berlin, Germany. TEL 030-26005-0. FAX 030-26005251. TELEX 184027. (U.S. address: Walter de Gruyter, Inc., 200 Saw Mill River Rd., Hawthorne, NY 10532) Ed. Teun A. van-Dijk. circ. 500. (back issues avail.) **Indexed:** Bibl.Ling., Lang.& Lang.Behav.Abstr. (1981-). **Document type:** academic/scholarly publication.
—BLDSC (8800.614000); Faxon; UnCover; SWETS. CCC.

TEXTUAL STUDIES IN CANADA; Canada's journal of cultural literacy. see LITERARY AND POLITICAL REVIEWS

001.3   US
THE NEW HISTORICISM: STUDIES IN CULTURAL POETICS. 1987. irreg., no.26, 1993. price varies. University of California Press, 2120 Berkeley Way, Berkeley, CA 94720. TEL 510-642-4247. FAX 510-643-7127. (Orders to: California-Princeton Fulfillment Services, 1445 Lower Ferry Rd., Ewing, NJ 08618. TEL 800-777-4726. FAX 800-999-1958) Ed. Stephen Greenblatt. (back issues avail.) **Document type:** monographic series.
     Description: Examines the interrelationship of art, literature, scholarship, politics and economics through history.
     Refereed Serial

700 300 800   SA   ISSN 0040-5817
AS615
THEORIA; a journal of studies in the arts, humanities and social sciences. 1947. s-a. R.25($25) to individuals; institutions R.35($35) (effective 1994). University of Natal Press, P.O. Box 375, Pietermaritzburg, South Africa. TEL 27-331-260226. FAX 27-331-260599. Ed. R. de Kadt. bk.rev.; cum.index. circ. 300. (also avail. in microfilm from JAI; microfiche from UMI) **Indexed:** Ind.S.A.Per., M.L.A., Phil.Ind. **Document type:** academic/scholarly publication.
—BLDSC (8814.585000); UnCover.
     Description: Encourages reflection on, and engagement with, significant intellectual issues and social, artistic and political events shaping the contemporary world.
     Refereed Serial

THEORY CULTURE & SOCIETY; explorations in critical social science. see SOCIOLOGY

001.3   JA   ISSN 0285-3825
TOHOKU INSTITUTE OF TECHNOLOGY. MEMOIRS. SERIES 2: HUMANITIES AND SOCIAL SCIENCE. (Text in English or Japanese; summaries in English) 1981. a. exchange basis only. Tohoku Institute of Technology, 35-1 Yagiyama-Kasumi-cho, Taihaku-ku, Sendai 982, Japan. (back issues avail.)

040   JA   ISSN 0495-7601
TOKUSHIMA DAIGAKU GAKUGEI KIYO/TOKUSHIMA UNIVERSITY. JOURNAL OF GAKUGEI. (Text in Japanese; summaries in English) 1951. a. Tokushima Daigaku, Kyoikugakubu - Tokushima University, Faculty of Education, Tokushima-shi, Tokushima-ken 770, Japan. circ. 450. **Indexed:** Biol.Abstr.
     Formerly: Journal of Cultural Sciences.

HUMANITIES: COMPREHENSIVE WORKS

300 700 800   US   ISSN 0049-4127
AS30
TOPIC (WASHINGTON); a journal of the liberal arts. 1961. a. $3. Washington & Jefferson College, 60 S. Lincoln St., Washington, PA 15301. TEL 412-222-4400. circ. 1,000. Indexed: Abstr.Engl.Stud., Amer.Bibl.Slavic & E.Eur.Stud., M.L.A. **Document type:** academic/scholarly publication.
—BLDSC (8867.375000); UnCover.

001.3   US
TOUCHSTONE (NASHVILLE). 1978. 3/yr. free in Tennessee; elsewhere $10. Tennessee Humanities Council, 1003 18th Ave. S., Box 24767, Nashville, TN 37202. TEL 615-320-7001. Ed. Robert Cheatham. bk.rev. circ. 12,000.
Supersedes (1978-1984): Cross-Reference.

TRADITIO; studies in ancient and medieval history, thought, and religion. see HISTORY — History Of Europe

001.3   PO
TRES CONTINENTES. 1980. m. Esc.380. Apart. 4152, Av. do Uruguai, 11 c-v, 1500 Lisbon, Portugal. Ed. J. Fernandes Ribeiro.

001.3   CL   ISSN 0716-0356
TRILOGIA; ciencia-tecnica-espiritu. 1981. s-a. $20 or exchange basis. Instituto Profesional de Santiago, Dieciocho 161, Casilla 9845 Correo Central, Santiago, Chile. TEL 56-6994722. Ed. Laura Torres Deramond. adv.; bk.rev.; charts; bibl.; illus.; cum.index. circ. 3,400. Indexed: Lib.Sci.Abstr., LISA.
Description: Scholarly research in science, technology and social sciences.

TURK KULTURU ARASTIRMALARI. see ORIENTAL STUDIES

TURKIYAT MECMUASI. see HISTORY — History Of The Near East

001.3   FI   ISSN 0082-6987
TURUN YLIOPISTO. JULKAISUJA. SARJA B. HUMANIORA. (Latin title: Annales Universitatis Turkuensis) (Text in English, Finnish, French, German) 1923. irreg. price varies. Turun Yliopisto - University of Turku, SF-20500 Turku 50, Finland.
FAX 358-21-6335050. TELEX 62123 TYK SF.
Description: Covers history, linguistics, political history, law and education.

001.3 500   FI   ISSN 0082-6995
TURUN YLIOPISTO. JULKAISUJA. SARJA C. SCRIPTA LINGUA FENNICA EDITA. (Latin title: Annales Universitatis Turkuensis) (Text in Finnish; summaries in English, French, German) 1965. irreg. price varies. Turun Yliopisto, SF-20500 Turku 50, Finland. FAX 358-21-6335050. TELEX 62123 TYK SF.

001.3   SW   ISSN 0348-7997
TVAERSNITT. 1979. q. SEK 96 (effective 1992). (Humanistisk-Samhaellsvetenskapliga Forskningraadet - Swedish Humanistic Research Council) Swedish Science Press, P.O. Box 118, S-751 04 Uppsala, Sweden. TEL 090-16-5201. FAX 090-14-3374. Ed. Kjell Jonsson. adv.; bk.rev.; illus. circ. 6,000.
Formerly (until 1978): Humanistisk Forskning.

300 700 800   SA   ISSN 0041-4751
AS611
TYDSK.RIF VIR GEESTESWETENSKAPPE. (Text in Afrikaans; summaries in English, French, German) 1961. q. R.44 (effective 1994). Suid-Afrikaanse Akademie vir Wetenskap en Kuns, P.O. Box 538, Pretoria 0001, South Africa. TEL 27-12-285082. FAX 27-12-285091. Ed. E. Raidt. bk.rev.; bibl.; index. circ. 1,000. Indexed: Bibl.Ling., Documentatieblad, Ind.S.A.Per., M.L.A. **Document type:** academic/scholarly publication.

001.3   SW   ISSN 0345-0155
UMEAA STUDIES IN THE HUMANITIES. (Subseries of Acta Universitatis Umensis) 1975. irreg. price varies. A W I International AB, P.O. Box 4627, S-116 91 Stockholm, Sweden. TEL 468-640-8800. FAX 468-41-1180. Ed. Per G. Raberg. Indexed: Bibl.Ling.

001.3   US
UNA'S LECTURES. 1974. irreg., vol.6, 1992. price varies. University of California Press, 2120 Berkeley Way, Berkeley, CA 94720. TEL 510-643-7127. FAX 510-643-7127. (Orders to: California-Princeton Fulfillment Services, 1445 Lower Ferry Rd., Ewing, NJ 08618. TEL 800-777-4726. FAX 800-999-1958) (back issues avail.) **Document type:** monographic series.
Description: Covers a wide variety of literary, political, and historical topics.
Refereed Serial

001.3   UN   ISSN 0049-5204
L13
UNESCO. CENTRO DE DOCUMENTACION CULTURAL, HAVANA. INFORMACIONES TRIMESTRALES. (Text in Spanish) 1966. q. free. Unesco, Centro de Documentacion Cultural, Havana - Regional Office for Culture in Latin America and the Caribbean, Calzada 551, Esq. a D, Vedado, Apdo. 4158, Havana, Cuba. TEL 32-1787. FAX 53-7-33-3144. TELEX 51-2154 UNESCO CU. Ed. Blanca Patallo Emperador. bk.rev. circ. 1,000. **Document type:** newsletter.

001.3   UN
UNESCO. COMISION NACIONAL CUBANA. BOLETIN. 3/yr. Unesco, Comision Nacional Cubana, Ave. de Kohly No. 151, Nuevo Vedado, Havana, Cuba. TELEX 51-2154 UNISCO CU. Ed. Perha Verdura.

060   BE   ISSN 0074-9346
UNION ACADEMIQUE INTERNATIONALE. COMPTE RENDU DE LA SESSION ANNUELLE DU COMITE. 1920. irreg., 57th, 1983. (International Union of Academies) Office International de Librairie, 30 av. Marnix, B-1050 Brussels, Belgium.

001.3   SQ   ISSN 1017-7442
UNISWA RESEARCH JOURNAL. (Text in English) 1988. irreg., vol.6, 1992. University of Swaziland, Private Bag Kwaluseni, Swaziland. TELEX 2087 WD. Ed. J.C. Norman. bk.rev.; abstr.; bibl. **Document type:** academic/scholarly publication.
Description: Publishes original research results, review articles, policy papers, analyses of problems or phenomena of interest, and accounts of professional practice with relevance to Swaziland. Certain volumes are devoted to papers in a single specific discipline.

700 500   PH   ISSN 0041-7149
LH7.M28
UNITAS; a quarterly review for the arts and sciences. 1922. q. $18. University of Santo Tomas, Espana St., Manila, Philippines. Ed. Maximo Marina. adv.; bk.rev.; bibl.; charts; illus.; index. circ. 2,000. **Indexed:** Amer.Hist.& Life, Hist.Abstr., Ind.Phil.Per.

001.3 500   TS
UNITED ARAB EMIRATES UNIVERSITY. JOURNAL/JAMI'AT AL-IMARAT AL-ARABIYYAH AL-MUTTAHIDAH. MAJALLAH.* (Text in Arabic, English) 1983. s-a. exchange basis. United Arab Emirates University, Deanship of Graduate Study and Research and Scientific Publishing, P.O. Box 17771, Al-Ain, United Arab Emirates. TEL 642500. TELEX 33521 JAMEAH EM. circ. 1,000.
Description: Publishes research papers in the humanities, social sciences, and in both natural and applied sciences.

378.1   AG   ISSN 0041-8234
AP63
UNIVERSIDAD.* 1935. q. Arg.$1000. Universidad Nacional del Litoral, Boulevar Pellegrini 2750, 3000 Santa Fe, Argentina. TEL 042-34461. Dir. Dr. Eneas C. Murua. bk.rev.; abstr.; bibl. circ. 1,800.

378.1   MX   ISSN 0186-7180
UNIVERSIDAD AUTONOMA DE YUCATAN. REVISTA. 1958. q. $10 per no. Universidad Autonoma de Yucatan, Direccion General de Difusion y Comunicacion, Calle 64 No. 411 con 49 y 47-A, C.P. 97000, Merida, Yucatan, Mexico. TEL 24-72-14. bk.rev.; bibl.; illus.; cum.index. circ. 5,000.
Formerly: Universidad de Yucatan. Revista (ISSN 0041-8536)
Description: Covers the history, philosophy, medicine, sociology, education and agriculture of Latin America, with emphasis on Mexico.

001.3   VE
UNIVERSIDAD CATOLICA DEL TACHIRA. PAGINA CULTURAL E INFORMATIVA. m. $12. Universidad Catolica del Tachira, Carrera 14 con calle 14, Apdo. 366, San Cristobal, Venezuela. TEL 076-432080. FAX 076-446183.

001.3   CK
UNIVERSIDAD DE ANTIOQUIA. DEPARTAMENTO DE HISTORIA. COLECCION PAPELES DE TRABAJO. 1977. irreg. Universidad de Antioquia, Departamento de Historia, Medellin, Colombia.
Formerly: Universidad de Antioquia. Departamento de Humanidades. Coleccion Papeles de Trabajo.

001.3   CK   ISSN 0120-2367
AP63
UNIVERSIDAD DE ANTIOQUIA. REVISTA. 1935. 4/yr. Col.$3200($54) Universidad de Antioquia, Departamento de Publicaciones, Bloque 22, Cuidad Universitaria, Apdo. Aereo 1226, Medellin, Colombia. TEL 2631311. FAX 2105010. Dir. Hector Abad Faciolince. adv.; bk.rev. circ. 4,000. (also avail. in microform) **Document type:** academic/scholarly publication.

001.3   SP   ISSN 0072-5382
UNIVERSIDAD DE GRANADA. COLECCION MONOGRAFICA. 1970. irreg., no.92, 1989. price varies. Universidad de Granada, Departamento de Historia del Arte, Secretariado de Publicaciones, Granada, Spain. **Document type:** monographic series.

001.3   GT
UNIVERSIDAD DE SAN CARLOS ANUAL. 1945. a. Universidad de San Carlos de Guatemala, Ciudad Universitaria, Guatemala 12, Guatemala. Ed.Bd. bk.rev.; bibl. **Indexed:** Amer.Hist.& Life, Hist.Abstr.

UNIVERSIDAD DE SEVILLA. SERIE: FILOSOFIA Y LETRAS. see PHILOSOPHY

001.3   VE   ISSN 0041-8811
UNIVERSIDAD DEL ZULIA. REVISTA. 1947; N.S. 1958. irreg. Universidad del Zulia, Direccion de Cultura, Apartado 526, Maracaibo, Venezuela. Indexed: Biol.Abstr.

001.3   CK   ISSN 0120-095X
UNIVERSIDAD INDUSTRIAL DE SANTANDER. REVISTA - HUMANIDADES. (Text in Spanish; summaries in English, French, German and Spanish) 1959. s-a. Col.$6000($8) for 2 yrs. Universidad Industrial de Santander, Apdo. Aereo 678, Bucaramanga, Santander, Colombia. FAX 5776-351946. adv.; bk.rev.; bibl.; charts; illus.; cum.index every 5 yrs. **Document type:** academic/scholarly publication.
Supersedes in part (in 1969): Universidad Industrial de Santander. Revista.

UNIVERSIDAD INDUSTRIAL DE SANTANDER. REVISTA - INVESTIGACIONES. see ENGINEERING

001.3   CR
UNIVERSIDAD NACIONAL. CENTRO DE ESTUDIOS GENERALES. CUADERNO DE ESTUDIO. m. Universidad Nacional, Centro de Estudios Generales, Heredia, Costa Rica. circ. 150.

001.3   MX   ISSN 0188-0861
UNIVERSIDAD NACIONAL AUTONOMA DE MEXICO. INSTITUTO DE INVESTIGACIONES ESTETICAS. MONOGRAFIAS. SERIE MAYOR. 1977. irreg., latest 1982. price varies. Universidad Nacional Autonoma de Mexico, Instituto de Investigaciones Esteticas, Circuito Mtro. Mario de la Cueva, Ciudad de la Investigacion en Humanidades, 04000 Mexico, D.F., Mexico.

001.3   CK   ISSN 0121-0890
UNIVERSIDAD NACIONAL DE COLOMBIA. REVISTA. 1985. bi-m. Col.$1900. Universidad Nacional de Colombia, Biblioteca Central-Seccion de Canje, Bogota, Colombia. TELEX AA37855. Dir. Ruben Sierra Mejia. bk.rev. circ. 4,000.

378.1   AG   ISSN 0041-8625
UNIVERSIDAD NACIONAL DE LA PLATA. REVISTA. 1957. s-a. free. Universidad Nacional de la Plata, Plaza Rocha 137, 1900 La Plata, Argentina. bk.rev.; charts; illus.; cum.index. circ. 1,700. (also avail. in diskette format) **Document type:** academic/scholarly publication.

HUMANITIES: COMPREHENSIVE WORKS

060   AG   ISSN 0564-4070
UNIVERSIDAD NACIONAL DE TUCUMAN. FACULTAD DE FILOSOFIA Y LETRAS. CUADERNOS DE HUMANITAS.* 1959. irreg., no.58, 1982. price varies. Universidad Nacional de Tucuman, Facultad de Filosofia y Letras, Avda. Benjamim Araoz, 750, 4000 San Miguel de Tucuman, Argentina. Ed. Bd. bibl. circ. 400.

060   IT
UNIVERSITA DEGLI STUDI DI CAGLIARI. FACOLTA DI LETTERE - FILOSOFIA. ANNALI. 1976. a. L.25000. Universita degli Studi di Cagliari, Facolta di Lettere-Filosofia, Cagliari, Italy. abstr.; illus. circ. 425.
    Supersedes in part (1936-1975): Universita di Cagliari. Facolta di Lettere - Filosofia e Magistero. Annali.

060   IT
UNIVERSITA DEGLI STUDI DI CAGLIARI. FACOLTA DI MAGISTERO. ANNALI. 1976. irreg., no.2, 1977. Universita degli Studi di Cagliari, Facolta di Magistero, 09100 Cagliari, Italy. abstr.; illus. circ. 425.
    Supersedes in part (1936-1975): Universita di Cagliari. Facolta di Lettere - Filosofia e Magistero. Annali.

001.3 100   IT
UNIVERSITA DI MESSINA. FACOLTA DI MAGISTERO. NUOVI ANNALI. 1983. a. L.120000. Herder Editrice e Libreria s.r.l., Piazza Montecitorio 117-120, 00186 Rome, Italy. TEL 67-94-628. FAX 678-47-51. TELEX 621427 NATEL. Ed. Antonio Mazzarino. **Document type:** academic/scholarly publication.

001.3   CH   ISSN 1015-8383
UNIVERSITAS; monthly review of philosophy and culture. Key Title: Zhexue yu Wenhua Yuekan. (Partnership with magazine Universitas in Stuttgart, Germany) (Text mainly in Chinese; table of contents in English) 1964. m. NT.$700 (students NT.$500); in Hong Kong HK.$270 (students HK.$220); elsewhere $40 (students $32). 94 Loli Rd., Taipei, Taiwan 10668, Republic of China. TEL 02-903-1111. (In Hong Kong, orders to: Catholic Centre, Grand Bldg., 15-18 Connaught Rd., Central, Hong Kong; In Singapore and Malaysia: Mr. Ting Shu-jen, 225-B Queen St., Singapore; Editorial addr.: 4F, Literature Yuan, Fu Jen University, Chung Cheng Rd., Hsinchuang, Taipei Hsien, Taiwan, R.O.C.) Ed.Bd. bk.rev.; bibl.; index. circ. 800.
—UnCover.
    Formerly (until 1974): Hsien Tai Hsueh Yuan (ISSN 0018-6929)

001.3   BL   ISSN 0102-5678
UNIVERSITAS. CULTURA. 1968. q. Universidade Federal da Bahia, Centro Editorial e Didatico, Rua Augusto Viana s-n, Canela, 40000 Salvador, Bahia, Brazil. TEL 071-245-2811. bk.rev.; illus.; cum.index; circ. 500 (controlled).
    Supersedes in part (in 1985): Universitas (ISSN 0041-9052)

085   RM
UNIVERSITATEA DIN CRAIOVA. ANALE. SERIA: ISTORIE, GEOGRAFIE, FILOLOGIE. (Text in Rumanian; summaries in French and/or English, German, Italian, Russian) 1972. irreg. $10. Universitatea din Craiova, Str. A.I. Cuza Nr. 13, 1100 Craiova, Rumania. (Dist. by: ILEXIM, Str. 13 Decembrie Nr. 3, P.O. Box 136-137, Bucharest, Rumania) illus.

001.3   BE   ISSN 0076-1222
UNIVERSITE CATHOLIQUE DE LOUVAIN. FACULTE DE PHILOSOPHIE ET LETTRES. TRAVAUX. Abbreviated title: Travaux de la Faculte de Philosophie et Lettres U C L. 1967. irreg. Universite Catholique de Louvain, Faculte de Philosophie et Lettres, College Erasme, Place Blaise Pascal, 1, B-1348 Louvain-la-Neuve, Belgium. TEL 32-10-474972. FAX 32-10-472579. (Subscr. to: Librairie A. Ferraton, 162 Chaussee de Charleroi, B-1060 Brussels, Belgium. TEL 32-2-538-6917. FAX 32-2-5374606) **Document type:** academic/scholarly publication.

001.3   BE   ISSN 0770-0962
BD638
UNIVERSITE DE BRUXELLES. REVUE. 2/yr. 1600 BEF. Editions de l'Universite de Bruxelles, Av. Paul Heger 26 - C.P. 163, B-1050 Brussels, Belgium. TEL 32-2-6503799. FAX 32-2-6503794. TELEX 23069 UNILIB BRUX. Ed.Bd. **Indexed:** Amer.Hist.& Life (until 1993), Hist.Abstr. (until 1993).

001.3   BE
UNIVERSITE DE LIEGE. FACULTE DE PHILOSOPHIE ET LETTRES. PUBLICATIONS. 1897. irreg. Universite de Liege, Faculte de Philosophie et Lettres, 7 Place du 20-Aout, 4000 Liege, Belgium. (Dist. by: Librairie Droz S.A., 11 rue Massot, Geneva, Switzerland) **Document type:** academic/scholarly publication.

001.3   FR   ISSN 0751-4239
PT2
UNIVERSITE DE PROVENCE. CENTRE D'AIX. CAHIERS D'ETUDES GERMANIQUES. 1972. s-a. 150 F. Universite de Provence, Centre d'Aix, 29 Avenue Robert Schuman, 13621 Aix-en-Provence Cedex 1, France. TEL 42-64-39-28. FAX 42-20-33-33. TELEX AMIUP 402 014.
—BLDSC (2948.922500).

001.3   FR   ISSN 0223-9469
UNIVERSITE DE SAINT ETIENNE. CENTRE JEAN PALERNE. MEMOIRES. 1978. irreg. price varies. Universite de Jean-Monnet, Saint Etienne, Centre Jean Palerne, 35 reu du Onze Novembre, 42100 Saint Etienne, France. TEL 77-42-16-60. FAX 77-42-17-99. **Document type:** proceedings.
    Description: Studies scientific and technological aspects of ancient times.

UNIVERSITE DE STRASBOURG II. INSTITUT DE PHONETIQUE. TRAVAUX. see *LINGUISTICS*

800 300 700   IR   ISSN 0041-9192
UNIVERSITE DE TEHRAN. FACULTE DES LETTRES ET DES SCIENCES HUMAINES. REVUE.* 1953. bi-m. $3. University of Teheran, Faculty of Letters and Humanities, Englehab Ave., Teheran, Iran. Ed. Dr. S.H. Nasr. bk.rev.; bibl.; charts; illus.; index, cum.index.

001.3   BE
UNIVERSITE LIBRE DE BRUXELLES. FACULTE DE PHILOSOPHIE ET LETTRES. TRAVAUX. 1930. irreg. Editions de l'Universite de Bruxelles, Av. Paul Heger 26 - C.P. 163, B-1050 Brussels, Belgium. TEL 32-2-6503799. FAX 32-2-6503794. TELEX 23069 UNILIB BRUX. **Document type:** monographic series.

001.3   US
UNIVERSITY OF CALIFORNIA AT LOS ANGELES. CLARK LIBRARY PROFESSORSHIP. MONOGRAPHIC SERIES. no.2, 1975. irreg., no.12, 1991. price varies. (Clark Library) University of California Press, 2120 Berkeley Way, Berkeley, CA 94720. TEL 510-642-4247. FAX 510-643-7127. (Orders to: California-Princeton Fulfillment Services, 1445 Lower Ferry Rd., Ewing, NJ 08618. TEL 800-777-4726. FAX 800-999-1958) (back issues avail.) **Document type:** monographic series.
    Description: Discusses English history, thought, science, and literature.
Refereed Serial

001.3   US   ISSN 0071-6189
UNIVERSITY OF FLORIDA MONOGRAPHS. HUMANITIES. (Text in English, French and Spanish) 1959. irreg., no.67, 1993. price varies. University Press of Florida, 15 N.W. 15th St., Gainesville, FL 32603. TEL 904-392-1351. FAX 904-392-7302. Ed. Raymond Gay-Crosier. **Document type:** monographic series.

001.3   NR
UNIVERSITY OF IFE. FACULTY OF ARTS. LECTURE SERIES. 1974. irreg. University of Ife, Faculty of Arts, Ile-Ife, Nigeria.

001.3   US   ISSN 0085-2473
UNIVERSITY OF KANSAS HUMANISTIC STUDIES. 1987. irreg. (approx. a.). price varies. (University of Kansas, Hall Center for the Humanities) Peter Lang Publishing, Inc., 62 W. 45th St., 4th Fl., New York, NY 10036. TEL 212-302-6740. FAX 212-302-7574. Ed. David Bergeron. **Document type:** academic/scholarly publication.

001.3   NR   ISSN 0075-7675
UNIVERSITY OF LAGOS. HUMANITIES SERIES.* 1971. irreg. price varies. University of Lagos, Centre for Cultural Studies, Akoba, Yaba, Miseha, Nigeria.

001.3   NR   ISSN 0075-7659
UNIVERSITY OF LAGOS. INAUGURAL LECTURE SERIES. Title varies: Lagos University. Annual Lectures. 1968. irreg. price varies. (University of Lagos) Lagos University Press, P.O. Box 132, Akoka, Yaba, Lagos, Nigeria.
    Description: Lectures delivered by professors at the University of Lagos.

001.3   UK   ISSN 0041-977X
PJ3
UNIVERSITY OF LONDON. SCHOOL OF ORIENTAL AND AFRICAN STUDIES. BULLETIN. Key Title: Bulletin of the School of Oriental and African Studies. Abbreviated title: B S O A S. 1917. 3/yr. £58($110) (School of Oriental and African Studies) Oxford University Press, Oxford Journals, Walton St., Oxford OX2 6DP, England. TEL 0865-56767. FAX 0865-56646. TELEX 837330-OXPRES-G. (U.S. subscr. to: Oxford University Press Inc., 2001 Evans Rd., Cary, NC 27513. TEL 919-677-0977) Ed. J.C. Wright. adv. contact: Jane Parker. bk.rev.; index. circ. 900. (back issues avail.; reprint service avail. from KTO) **Indexed:** A.I.C.P., Anthropol.Lit., Arts & Hum.Cit.Ind., Bibl.Ling., Curr.Cont., M.L.A. **Document type:** academic/scholarly publication, bulletin.
—BLDSC (2702.560000); Faxon; UnCover; SWETS. CCC.
    Description: Contains contributions to the knowledge of Asian and African languages, culture, history, and literature.
Refereed Serial

UNIVERSITY OF MICHIGAN. DIVISION OF RESEARCH DEVELOPMENT AND ADMINISTRATION. RESEARCH NEWS. see *EDUCATION — Higher Education*

001.3   US   ISSN 0077-6386
UNIVERSITY OF NEBRASKA STUDIES. NEW SERIES. 1946. irreg., no.67, 1984. available on exchange basis only. University of Nebraska, Lincoln, Committee on Scholarly Publications, Serials Department, Lincoln, NE 68588-0410. TEL 402-472-3874. Ed. Susan Rosowski. circ. 600. (also avail. in microfilm) **Indexed:** M.L.A.

001.3 060   SA   ISSN 0079-3957
UNIVERSITY OF PORT ELIZABETH. PUBLICATIONS. GENERAL SERIES. (Text in Afrikaans, English) 1965. irreg., no.A16, 1984. price varies. University of Port Elizabeth, Publications Committee, U P E Library, Private Bag X6058, Port Elizabeth 6000, South Africa. TEL 041-504-2281. FAX 041-504-2280. TELEX 243342. Ed.Bd.
    Description: Monographs on topics of general academic interest.

001.3   SA   ISSN 0085-5022
UNIVERSITY OF PORT ELIZABETH. PUBLICATIONS. INAUGURAL AND EMERITUS ADDRESSES. (Text in Afrikaans, English) 1971. irreg., latest 1990. price varies. University of Port Elizabeth, Publications Committee, U P E Library, Private Bag X6058, Port Elizabeth 6000, South Africa. TEL 041-504-2281. FAX 041-504-2280. TELEX 243342. Ed.Bd.
    Description: Covers inaugural lectures delivered before the University of Port Elizabeth.

001.3 060   SA   ISSN 0079-3965
UNIVERSITY OF PORT ELIZABETH. PUBLICATIONS. RESEARCH PAPERS. (Text in Afrikaans, English) 1970. irreg., no.C26, 1991. price varies. University of Port Elizabeth, Publications Committee, U P E Library, Private Bag X6058, Port Elizabeth 6000, South Africa. TEL 041-504-2281. FAX 041-504-2280. TELEX 243342. Ed. Bd. circ. 500. **Document type:** monographic series.
    Description: Research monographs on a variety of topics.

001.3 060   SA
UNIVERSITY OF PORT ELIZABETH. PUBLICATIONS. SYMPOSIA, SEMINARS, AND LECTURES. (Text in Afrikaans, English) 1969. irreg., no.B18, 1991. price varies. University of Port Elizabeth, Publications Committee, U P E Library, Private Bag X6058, Port Elizabeth 6000, South Africa. TEL 041-504-2281. FAX 041-504-2280. TELEX 243342. Ed.Bd.
    Formerly: University of Port Elizabeth. Publications. Symposia and Seminars (ISSN 0079-3973)

UNIVERSITY OF PORTLAND REVIEW; journal of arts and sciences. see *SCIENCES: COMPREHENSIVE WORKS*

UNIVERSITY OF SANTO TOMAS. GRADUATE SCHOOL. JOURNAL OF GRADUATE RESEARCH. see *SOCIAL SCIENCES: COMPREHENSIVE WORKS*

HUMANITIES: COMPREHENSIVE WORKS

001.3 IR
UNIVERSITY OF TABRIZ. FACULTY OF HUMAN AND SOCIAL SCIENCES. PUBLICATION/DANESHGAH-E TABRIZ. DANESHKADE-YE ULUME ENSANI VA IJTIMA'I. NASHRIYEH. (Text in Farsi) 1948. q. University of Tabriz, Faculty of Human and Social Sciences, Tabriz 711-51664, Iran. TEL 041-30081. FAX 041-34013. TELEX 412045. Ed.Bd.
 Formerly: University of Azarabadegan. Faculty of Letters and Humanities. Publication - Danegash-e Azarabadegan. Daneshkade-ye Adabiyyat va 'Olume Ensani. Nashriyeh - Universite d'Azarabadegan. Faculte des Lettres et Sciences Humaines. Revue.

001.3 PK ISSN 0555-7666
UNIVERSITY OF THE PUNJAB. JOURNAL OF RESEARCH: HUMANITIES. (Text in English) 1966. s-a. Rs.25($10) University of the Punjab, Department of English Language and Literature, 1 Shahrah-e-al-Beruni, Lahore 2, Pakistan. Ed. M.I. Bhatti.

378.1 700 800 CN ISSN 0042-0247
UNIVERSITY OF TORONTO QUARTERLY; a Canadian journal of the humanities. (Text in English, French) 1931. q. $32 to individuals; institutions $57.50. University of Toronto Press, Journals Department, 5201 Dufferin St., Downsview, ON M3H 5T8, Canada. TEL 416-667-7782. FAX 416-667-7803. Ed. Alan Bewell. adv.; bk.rev.; index. circ. 1,100. (also avail. in microform from JAI,MIM,UMI) **Indexed:** Abstr.Engl.Stud., Amer.Bibl.Slavic & E.Eur.Stud., Amer.Hist.& Life, C.I.J.E., Can.Lit.Ind., Can.Per.Ind., Can.Rev.Comp.Lit., CMI, Curr.Cont., Hist.Abstr., Hum.Ind., Ind.Bk.Rev.Hum., LCR, M.L.A., RILA.
 —BLDSC (9119.205000); Faxon; UnCover; SWETS; UMI. **CCC.**

UNIVERSITY OF VAASA. PROCEEDINGS. DISCUSSION PAPERS. see *BUSINESS AND ECONOMICS — Economic Systems And Theories, Economic History*

001.3 PL ISSN 0208-4740
UNIWERSYTET GDANSKI. WYDZIAL HUMANISTYCZNY. ZESZYTY NAUKOWE. SLAWISTYKA. (Text in Polish; summaries in English and Russian) 1978. irreg., latest no.6. price varies. Uniwersytet Gdanski, Wydzial Humanistyczny, c/o Biblioteka Glowna, Ul. Armii Krajowej 110, 81-824 Sopot, Poland. TEL 51-0061. TELEX 051 2247 BMOR PL. (Dist. by: Ars Polona-Ruch, Krakowskie Przedmiescie 7, 00-680 Warsaw, Poland) Ed. Leszek Moszynski. circ. 250. **Document type:** academic/scholarly publication.
 Description: Contains articles on Slavic studies. Includes reports of conferences and chronicles of the Slavonic Languages Department of the Russian Philology Institute.

001.3 PL ISSN 0076-034X
UNIWERSYTET LODZKI. PRACE. irreg. price varies. Wydawnictwo Uniwersytetu Lodzkiego, Ul. Jaracza 34, Lodz, Poland. TEL 331671. (Dist. by: Ars Polona-Ruch, Krakowskie Przedmiescie 7, Warsaw, Poland) **Document type:** academic/scholarly publication.

VAASAN YLIOPISTO. JULKAISUJA. TUTKIMUKSIA/UNIVERSITY OF VAASA. PROCEEDINGS. RESEARCH PAPERS. see *BUSINESS AND ECONOMICS — Economic Systems And Theories, Economic History*

001.3 US ISSN 1069-7144
VEERY. 1991. 2/yr. $13 to individuals; institutions $26. Foxglove Co., 333 N. Michigan Ave., Ste. 2032, Chicago, IL 60601. TEL 312-804-0777. Eds. R.H. Crane, Steven Vita. bk.rev.
 Description: An intellectual study through unique, analytical interviews of what links and separates minds.

001.3 IT
VENEZIA CINQUECENTO; studi di storia dell'arte e della cultura. 1991. s-a.? Bulzoni Editore, Via del Liburni 14, 00185 Rome, Italy. TEL 06-4455207. FAX 06-4450355.

VENEZUELAN LITERATURE AND ARTS JOURNAL/REVISTA DE LITERATURA Y ARTES VENEZOLANAS. see *LITERATURE*

001.3 IT
VERIFICHE E PROPOSTE. 1975. irreg. Tringale Editore, Via Vecchia Ognina 90, 95129 Catania, Italy. Ed. Ermanno Scuderi. **Document type:** monographic series.

001.3 301.16 BL ISSN 0103-1414
F2510
VERSO E REVERSO. 1987. s-a. $20 or exchange basis. (Universidade do Vale do Rio dos Sinos) Unisinos, Av. Unisinos, 950, 93010 Sao Leopoldo RS, Brazil. TEL 051-5926333. FAX 0512-921035. TELEX 524076. Ed. Sergio Farina. bibl. **Document type:** academic/scholarly publication.

300 700 500 US ISSN 0042-5222
PR1
VICTORIAN STUDIES; a journal of the humanities, arts and sciences. 1957. q. $25 to individuals; institutions $40. Indiana University Press, 601 N. Morton, Bloomington, IN 47404.
 TEL 812-855-9449. Ed. Donald Gray. adv.; bk.rev.; bibl.; illus.; index. circ. 3,000. (also avail. in microform from UMI; reprint service avail. from UMI,KTO) **Indexed:** Abstr.Engl.Stud., Amer.Hist.& Life, Arts & Hum.Cit.Ind., Bk.Rev.Ind. (1976-), Child.Bk.Rev.Ind. (1976-), Curr.Cont., Hist.Abstr., Hum.Ind., Ind.Bk.Rev.Hum., LCR, M.L.A., Ref.Sour., RILA.
 —BLDSC (9232.710000); Faxon; UnCover; SWETS; UMI.

001.3 300
VIDYA BHARATHI.* (Text in English) 1975. s-a. Rs.10. Bangalore University, Department of Publications and Extension Lectures, Bangalore 560056, India.
 Description: Contains research articles on humanities and social sciences.

301.2 AG ISSN 0042-594X
VIGENCIA. 1968. m. Arg.$6000($30) Editorial Belgrano, Teodoro Garcia 2090, Buenos Aires, Argentina. Ed. Enrique Pugliese. adv.; bk.rev.; abstr.; bibl.; charts; illus. circ. 15,000. (tabloid format)

001.3 700 FR ISSN 0151-3605
VISAGES DU VINGTIEME SIECLE; revue de "La Legion Violette". 1952. 5/yr. 150 F. Association Culturelle des Membres de la Legion d'Honneur, Palmes Academiques, Arts et Lettres, c/o Michel Beau, 12 av. Foch, 93150 Blanc-Mesnil, France. adv.; bk.rev.; illus.
 Formerly: Legion Violette.
 Description: Research articles covering the arts in the twentieth century.

001.3 II ISSN 0507-1410
PK101
VISHVESHVARANAND INDOLOGICAL JOURNAL. (Text in English) 1963. s-a. Rs.40($10) Vishveshvaranand Vedic Research Institute, P.O. Sadhu Ashram, Hoshiarpur 146021, Punjab, India. Ed. S. Bhaskaran Nair. bk.rev. (back issues avail.) **Indexed:** Bibl.Ling., M.L.A.
 Description: Research organ of the institute.

VISIBLE LANGUAGE; the quarterly concerned with all that is involved in our being literate. see *COMMUNICATIONS*

VITA SOCIALE. see *RELIGIONS AND THEOLOGY — Roman Catholic*

001.3 II
VIVEKANANDA KENDRA PATRIKA; distinctive cultural magazine of India. (Text in English) 1972. s-a. Rs.160. Vivekananda Kendra Prakashan, 3 Singarachari St., Triplicane, Madras 600005, India. (Co-sponsor: Swami Vivekananda Centenary Celebration) Ed. Dr. Lakshmikumari. adv.; bibl.; charts; illus.

001.3 IT
VOCE DELLA MARTINELLA; mensile di arte, cultura e vita cittadina. m. L.5000 (foreign L.100000). Edilibraria Carrobbio, Via Martiri della Liberta, 1, Locate Triulzi (MI), Italy. TEL 02-575-10-361. Ed. Giuseppe Molinari.

W E S AUTHORS' AND PUBLISHERS' SERVICE NEWSLETTER. (Watman Educational Services) see *EDUCATION*

001.3 UK ISSN 0083-7199
WARBURG INSTITUTE. STUDIES. 1939. irreg. price varies. Warburg Institute, University of London, Woburn Sq., London WC1H OAB, England.
 TEL 071-580-9663. FAX 071-436-2852. **Document type:** academic/scholarly publication, monographic series.
 Description: Monograph series in Medieval and Renaissance philosophy, science, literature and art.

700 UK ISSN 0266-1772
WARBURG INSTITUTE. SURVEYS AND TEXTS. 1963. irreg. price varies. Warburg Institute, University of London, Woburn Sq., London WC1H OAB, England. TEL 071-580-9663. FAX 071-436-2852. **Document type:** academic/scholarly publication.
 —BLDSC (9261.818210).
 Formerly: Warburg Institute. Surveys (ISSN 0083-7202)
 Description: Presents texts, survey studies and colloquium papers in the field of medieval and Renaissance philosophy, science, literature and art.

WAS UNS BETRIFFT; Zeitschrift fuer Kriegsdienstverweigerer und Zivildienstleistende. see *POLITICAL SCIENCE — Civil Rights*

WASHINGTON INTERNATIONAL ARTS LETTER. see *ART*

300 US ISSN 0891-8899
AS30
WEBER STUDIES: AN INTERDISCIPLINARY HUMANITIES JOURNAL. 1984. 3/yr. $10 to individuals; institutions $20 (effective Jan. 1992). Weber State University, Ogden, UT 84408-1214. TEL 801-626-6473. FAX 801-626-7130. Ed. Neila C. Seshachari. adv.; bk.rev. circ. 1,000. (back issues avail.) **Indexed:** Abstr.Engl.Stud., Amer.Hum.Ind., Ind.Amer.Per.Verse, M.L.A., Sociol.Abstr. **Document type:** academic/scholarly publication.
 —BLDSC (9284.010000); UnCover.
 Formerly (until 1987): Weber Studies.
 Description: For educated readers and scholars in literature, philosophy, history, sociology, political science and science. Includes critical essays, biography, fiction and poetry.

001.3 895.1 CC ISSN 0511-4721
WEN SHI ZHE/JOURNAL OF LITERATURE, HISTORY AND PHILOSOPHY. Key Title: Wenshizhe. (Text in Chinese; table of contents in English) 1951. bi-m. Y7.20. Shandong Daxue, Wen Shi Zhe Bianjibu, No. 27, Shanda Nanlu, Jinan, Shandong 250100, People's Republic of China. TEL 0531-890386. FAX 0531-8902167. (Dist. outside China by: China International Book Trading Corp., P.O. Box 2820, Beijing, P.R.C.) Ed. Han Lingxuan. **Document type:** academic/scholarly publication.
 —UnCover.

WESTERN HUMANITIES REVIEW. see *LITERATURE*

WORKS AND DAYS; essays in the socio-historical dimensions of literature and the arts. see *LITERATURE*

001.3 PL ISSN 0084-3016
WROCLAWSKIE TOWARZYSTWO NAUKOWE. PRACE. SERIA A. HUMANISTYKA. (Text in English, French, German and Polish; summaries in English, French and German) 1947. irreg., no.244, 1989. price varies. Ossolineum, Publishing House of the Polish Academy of Sciences, Rynek 9, 50-106 Wroclaw, Poland. TEL 48-71-386-25. FAX 48-71-448-103. TELEX 0712771 OSS PL. **Indexed:** Math.R. **Document type:** monographic series.
 Description: Covers all provinces of humanities and social sciences.

001.3 PL ISSN 0084-3024
WROCLAWSKIE TOWARZYSTWO NAUKOWE. PRACE. SERIA B. NAUKI SCISLE. (Text in Polish; summaries in English, French, and German) 1947. a. price varies. Ossolineum, Publishing House of the Polish Academy of Sciences, Rynek 9, 50-106 Wroclaw, Poland. TEL 48-71-386-25. FAX 48-71-448-103. TELEX 0712771 OSS PL. Ed. J. Kolbuszewski. **Document type:** monographic series.
 —BLDSC (6588.797000).

001.3 PL ISSN 0239-6025
WYZSZA SZKOLA PEDAGOGICZNA IM. KOMISJI EDUKACJI NARODOWEJ W KRAKOWIE. PRACE MONOGRAFICZNE/ECOLE NORMALE SUPERIEURE A CRACOVIE. ETUDES MONOGRAPHIQUES. 1964. irreg., no.139, 1991. price varies. Wydawnictwo Naukowe W S P, Ul. Karmelicka 41, 31-128 Krakow, Poland. TEL 33-78-20. (Co-sponsor: Ministerstwo Edukacji Narodowej)

HUMANITIES: COMPREHENSIVE WORKS — ABSTRACTING, BIBLIOGRAPHIES, STATISTICS

001.3   PL   ISSN 0078-544X
WYZSZA SZKOLA PEDAGOGICZNA, OPOLE. ZESZYTY NAUKOWE. SERIA B. STUDIA I MONOGRAFIE. (Text in Polish; summaries in English, German, Polish, Russian) 1956. irreg., no.178, 1990. price varies. Wyzsza Szkola Pedagogiczna, Opole, Oleska 48, 48 77 383-87 Opole, Poland. TEL 48-77-383-87. (Dist. by: Ars Polona-Ruch, Krakowskie Przedmiescie 7, Warsaw, Poland) bk.rev. **Document type:** academic/scholarly publication, monographic series.

XAVIER REVIEW. see *LITERATURE*

XI'OU YANJIU/WESTERN EUROPEAN STUDIES. see *SOCIAL SCIENCES: COMPREHENSIVE WORKS*

YA MKOBE. see *SCIENCES: COMPREHENSIVE WORKS*

YAGL-AMBU; Papua New Guinea journal of the social sciences and humanities. see *SOCIAL SCIENCES: COMPREHENSIVE WORKS*

001.3 080   US   ISSN 0084-3318
YALE COLLEGE SERIES. 1964. irreg., no.14, 1976. price varies. Yale University Press, Box 209040, New Haven, CT 06520. TEL 203-432-0940. **Document type:** monographic series.

001.3   US   ISSN 1041-6374
K29
YALE JOURNAL OF LAW & THE HUMANITIES. 1988. s-a. $15 to individuals (foreign $25); institutions $30 (foreign $40). Yale University, School of Law, Box 401A, Yale Sta., New Haven, CT 06520. TEL 203-432-4037. FAX 203-432-2592. adv. circ. 525. (back issues avail.)
—Faxon; UnCover.
Description: Articles of an interdisciplinary nature which contribute to the debate about the relationships between law and recent theoretical developments in the humanities.

001.3   JA   ISSN 0085-834X
TA4   CODEN: YDKKAR
YAMAGATA DAIGAKU KIYO/YAMAGATA UNIVERSITY. BULLETIN. (Bulletin issued in 7 parts) (Text in English, German, Japanese; summaries in English and German) 1950. a. Yamagata Daigaku - Yamagata University, Main Library, Kojirakawa-machi, Yamagata-shi, Yamagata-ken 990, Japan. **Indexed:** Biol.Abstr., Chem.Abstr., INIS Atomind., Jap.Per.Ind., Sci.Abstr.
—BLDSC (2821.880000).

001.3 500   CC
YANTAI DAXUE XUEBAO/YANTAI UNIVERSITY. JOURNAL. (Text in Chinese) 1988. q. Y7.20. Yantai Daxue - Yantai University, Yantai, Shandong 264005, People's Republic of China. (Dist. overseas by: China Publications Foreign Trade Corp., P.O. Box 782, Beijing, P.R.C.)
Description: Contains research papers in all areas of arts and sciences.

001.3 800   UK   ISSN 0306-2473
YEARBOOK OF ENGLISH STUDIES. 1971. a. $86. Modern Humanities Research Association, King's College, Strand, London WC2R 2CS, England. Ed. A.J. Gurr. bk.rev.; bibl. **Indexed:** Abstr.Engl.Stud., Ind.Bk.Rev.Hum., M.L.A.
—UnCover.

YEARBOOK ON HUMAN RIGHTS. see *POLITICAL SCIENCE — Civil Rights*

001.3   AI
YEREVAN BANBER. HASARAKAKAN GITUT'YUNNER. HAMALSARANI. (Text in Armenian, Russian) 1967. 3/yr. 3.60 Rub. Erevanskii Gosudarstvennyi Universitet, Ul. Mraviana 1, Erevan, Armenia. bk.rev.; index. circ. 1,000. **Indexed:** Bibl.Ling.
Description: Publishes articles on Armenian history, philology, philosophy and economy.

296   US
YIVO NEWS/YEDIES FUN YIVO. (Text in English, Yiddish) 1943. s-a. membership. Yivo Institute for Jewish Research, 1048 Fifth Ave., New York, NY 10028. TEL 212-535-6700. FAX 212-734-1062. Ed. Andrea Raab. circ. 9,000. **Document type:** newsletter.
Formerly: News of the Yivo (ISSN 0028-9302)
Description: Provides information on Yivo projects, programs, events and personnel.

001.3 060   JA
ZINBVN. (Text in various languages; not Japanese) 1957. a. Kyoto University, Institute for Research in Humanities - Kyoto Daigaku Jinbun Kagaku Kenkyusho, Ushinomiya-cho, Yoshida, Sakyo-ku, Kyoto 606, Japan. circ. controlled. **Document type:** academic/scholarly publication.
—UnCover.
Formerly: Jinbun (ISSN 0084-5515)

HUMANITIES: COMPREHENSIVE WORKS — Abstracting, Bibliographies, Statistics

011   US
ACADEMIC INDEX. (Not avail. in printed format) updated m. $93 per hour on BRS; $90 on DIALOG; CD-ROM $2700. Information Access Company, 362 Lakeside Dr., Foster City, CA 94404. TEL 415-378-5200; 800-227-8431. FAX 415-378-5369. **Document type:** abstracting/indexing.
●Also available online. Vendor(s): BRS Online Products (ACAD), DIALOG Information Services, Inc. (File no.88), Information Access Co.
Also available on CD-ROM.
Description: Indexes about 550 scholarly and general interest journals covering the arts, education, history, literature, popular science, psychology, economics and cultural studies.

016 810   US   ISSN 0361-0144
AI3
AMERICAN HUMANITIES INDEX. 1975. a. $250. Whitston Publishing Co. Inc., Box 958, Troy, NY 12181. TEL 518-283-4363. FAX 518-283-4363. Ed. Jean Goode. bibl.; cum.index. circ. 200. (back issues avail.) **Document type:** academic/scholarly publication, abstracting/indexing.
—BLDSC (0819.260000).
Description: Index to some 500 creative, critical and scholarly serials in the arts and humanities.

ARTS & HUMANITIES CITATION INDEX. see *ART — Abstracting, Bibliographies, Statistics*

700   UK   ISSN 0966-8772
B H I PLUS. (British Humanities Index) q. $1300. Bowker - Saur Ltd., A Reed Reference Publishing Company, Part of the Reed Elsevier group, Maypole House, Maypole Rd., E. Grinstead, W. Sussex RH19 1HH, England. TEL 0342-330-100. FAX 0342-330-191. (Subscr. to: c/o Butterworths Service Co., Borough Green, Sevenoaks, Kent TN15 8PH, England. TEL 0732-884567) Ed. Lyn Duffus. (avail. for MS-DOS version) **Document type:** abstracting/indexing.
●Available only on CD-ROM. Producer(s): Bowker - Saur Ltd.
Description: Delivers information about the arts, economics, history, philosophy, politics, religion, and society. Features 135,000 indexed articles from over 320 key periodicals from 1985 to present.

001.3   GW   ISSN 0933-131X
BIBLIOGRAPHIA HUMBOLDTIANA. (Text in English and German) 1977. a. free. Alexander von Humboldt-Stiftung, Jean-Paul-Str. 12, 53173 Bonn, Germany. TEL 0228-833-0. FAX 0228-833199. Ed. Heinrich Pfeiffer. circ. 5,000. **Document type:** bibliography.
Formerly (until 1987): Humboldtiana (ISSN 0171-2063)
Description: Bibliographical entries of all relevant new research publications of former Humboldt fellows and awardees.

001.3 016   SZ   ISSN 0067-7000
Z6207.R4
BIBLIOGRAPHIE INTERNATIONALE DE L'HUMANISME ET DE LA RENAISSANCE. 1965. a. price varies. (International Federation of Societies and Institutes for the Study of the Renaissance) Librairie Droz S.A., 11, rue Massot, CH-1211 Geneva 12, Switzerland. TEL 022-3466666. FAX 022-3472391. circ. 1,200. **Document type:** bibliography.
—CCC.

700 800 016   UK   ISSN 0007-0815
AI3
BRITISH HUMANITIES INDEX. 1915. q. (plus a. cumulation). £385($720) (foreign £425). Bowker - Saur Ltd., A Reed Reference Publishing Company, Part of the Reed Elsevier group, Maypole House, Maypole Rd., E. Grinstead, W. Sussex RH19 1HH, England. TEL 0342-330-100. FAX 0342-330-191. (Subscr. to: c/o Baileys, 127 Sandgate Rd., Folkestone, Kent, CT20 2BL. TEL 0303-850801) Ed. L. Duffus. **Document type:** abstracting/indexing.
●Also available on CD-ROM. Producer(s): Bowker - Saur Ltd.
—BLDSC (2301.700000).
Description: Indexes and indexes humanities-related articles published by British newspapers and journals. Covers the arts, economics, history, philosophy, politics, religion and society.

301 016   MX
Z7163
C L A S E. (Citas Latinoamericanas en Ciencias Sociales y Humanidades) 1976. q. $190. Universidad Nacional Autonoma de Mexico, Centro de Informacion Cientifica y Humanistica, Ciudad Universitaria, Apdo. Postal 70-392, C.P. 04510 Mexico, D.F., Mexico. **Indexed:** P.A.I.S.For.Lang.Ind. **Document type:** abstracting/indexing.
●Also available online.
Also available on CD-ROM.
Formerly (until 1986): C L A S E. Citas Latinoamericanas en Sociologia, Economia, y Humanidades (ISSN 0185-0903)

CLIO BIBLIOGRAPHY SERIES. see *HISTORY — Abstracting, Bibliographies, Statistics*

001.3 016   US   ISSN 0163-3155
CURRENT CONTENTS: ARTS & HUMANITIES. Short title: C C: A & H. (Includes Author Index and Address Directory, Current Book Contents, and Title Word Index) 1979. fortn. $442. Institute for Scientific Information, 3501 Market St., Philadelphia, PA 19104. TEL 215-386-0100. FAX 215-386-2991. (And: Brunel Science Park, Brunel University, Uxbridge UB8 3PQ, England) (also avail. in magnetic tape) **Indexed:** SSCI. **Document type:** abstracting/indexing.
●Also available online. Vendor(s): BRS Online Products (CTOC,CBIB,ARTS), DIALOG Information Services, Inc. (File no.440).
—BLDSC (3496.127000).
Description: Tables of contents of the world's leading publications covering art and architecture, performing arts, music, literature, language and linguistics, history, philosophy, religion and theology.

001.3   UK   ISSN 0267-1972
AZ188.G7
CURRENT RESEARCH IN BRITAIN. HUMANITIES. (Other vols. avail.: Biological Sciences, Physical Sciences, Social Sciences) 1986. biennial. £50 (foreign £55). Longman Cartermill Ltd., Technology Centre, St. Andrews, Fife KY16 9EA, Scotland. TEL 0937-843434. FAX 0937-546333. TELEX 557381. Ed. Mike Bate. **Document type:** abstracting/indexing.
●Also available online. Vendor(s): Orbit Search Service (CRIB).

DIRECTORY OF PUBLISHED PROCEEDINGS. SERIES S S H - SOCIAL SCIENCES - HUMANITIES. see *MEETINGS AND CONGRESSES — Abstracting, Bibliographies, Statistics*

378   US
DISSERTATION ABSTRACTS. 1986. q. $1965. University Microfilms International, 300 N. Zeeb Rd., Ann Arbor, MI 48016-1304. TEL 313-761-4700; 821-521-0600. FAX 313-761-1203. Ed. Dorie Mickelson. (also avail. in microfilm; microfiche; magnetic tape; back issues avail.) **Document type:** abstracting/indexing.
●Also available online. Vendor(s): BRS Online Products (DISS), Data-Star, DIALOG Information Services, Inc., STN International.
Also available on CD-ROM. Producer(s): University Microfilms International.
Description: Contains over one million citations and abstracts of U.S., Canadian, and European doctoral dissertations and masters theses.

HUMANITIES: COMPREHENSIVE WORKS — COMPUTER APPLICATIONS

300 016   US   ISSN 0419-4209
Z5053
DISSERTATION ABSTRACTS INTERNATIONAL. SECTION A: HUMANITIES AND SOCIAL SCIENCES. 1938. m. $475. University Microfilms International, 300 N. Zeeb Rd., Ann Arbor, MI 48106.
TEL 313-761-4700; 800-521-0600.
FAX 313-761-1203. index. (also avail. in microfiche from UMI; reprint service avail. from UMI) Indexed: Agri.Eng.Abstr., Agroforest.Abstr., Bibl.Ling., Biol.Abstr., Chem.Abstr., Cott.& Trop.Fibr.Abstr., Dairy Sci.Abstr., Field Crop Abstr., Forest Prod.Abstr., GeoRef, Geotech.Abstr., Herb.Abstr., Irr.& Drain.Abstr., M.L.A., Maize Abstr., Music Ind., Pig News & Info., Popul.Ind., Poult.Abstr., Psychol.Abstr., RAPRA, Rice Abstr., Rural Devel.Abstr., Rural Ext.Educ.& Tr.Abstr., Rural Recreat.Tour.Abstr., Soyabean Abstr., Triticale Abstr., Trop.Oil Seeds Abstr., World Agri.Econ.& Rural Sociol.Abstr., Yrbk.Assoc.Educ.& Rehab.Blind. **Document type:** abstracting/indexing.
●Also available online. Vendor(s): BRS Online Products (DISS), Data-Star, DIALOG Information Services, Inc. (File no.35), STN International.
Also available on CD-ROM. Producer(s): University Microfilms International.
—BLDSC (3599.030000); UMI.
Formerly (until 1969): Dissertation Abstracts. Section A: Humanities and Social Sciences (ISSN 0095-9154); Supersedes in part (in 1966): Dissertation Abstracts (ISSN 0099-3123).

016   US   ISSN 1042-7279
Z5053   CODEN: DAICDG
DISSERTATION ABSTRACTS INTERNATIONAL. SECTION C: WORLDWIDE. 1976. q. $750. University Microfilms International, 300 N. Zeeb Rd., Ann Arbor, MI 48106. TEL 313-761-4700; 800-521-0600.
FAX 313-761-1203. Indexed: Br.Archaeol.Abstr., Dairy Sci.Abstr., E&P Hlth. (1993-), Field Crop Abstr., Food Sci.& Tech.Abstr., Gas Process.& Ppl. (1993-), GeoRef, Geotech.Abstr., Herb.Abstr., Ind.Vet., Nutr.Abstr., Off.Tech. (1993-), Petrol.Abstr. (1980-), Rural Recreat.Tour.Abstr., Vet.Bull., Weed Abstr., World Agri.Econ.& Rural Sociol.Abstr.
Document type: abstracting/indexing.
●Also available online. Vendor(s): BRS Online Products (DISS), DIALOG Information Services, Inc. (File no.35), STN International.
Also available on CD-ROM. Producer(s): University Microfilms International.
—BLDSC (3599.041000).
Formerly: Dissertation Abstracts International. Section C: European Abstracts (ISSN 0307-6075).

001.3   US   ISSN 0095-5981
AI3
HUMANITIES INDEX. 1974. q., plus a. cumulations. service basis. H.W. Wilson Co., 950 University Ave., Bronx, NY 10452. TEL 800-367-6770.
FAX 718-590-1617. TELEX 4990003HWILSON. Ed. Joanna Greenspon. (also avail. in magnetic tape) **Document type:** abstracting/indexing.
●Also available online. Vendor(s): BRS Online Products (WHUM), Wilsonline (File HUM).
Also available on CD-ROM. Producer(s): H.W. Wilson (WILSONDISC).
—BLDSC (4336.579000).
Supersedes in part: Social Sciences and Humanities Index (ISSN 0037-7899)
Description: Author and subject index to periodicals in the fields of archaeology and classical studies, area studies, folklore, history, language and literature, literary and political criticism, performing arts, philosophy, religion and theology, and related subjects.

INDEX TO SOCIAL SCIENCES & HUMANITIES PROCEEDINGS. see *SOCIAL SCIENCES: COMPREHENSIVE WORKS — Abstracting, Bibliographies, Statistics*

020 011   US   ISSN 0020-4994
HC121
INTER-AMERICAN REVIEW OF BIBLIOGRAPHY/REVISTA INTERAMERICANA DE BIBLIOGRAFIA. (Text in English, French, Portuguese and Spanish) 1951. q. $12. (Inter-American Committee on Bibliography) Organization of American States, General Secretariat, Department of Publications, 1889 F St., N.W., Washington, DC 20006. TEL 703-941-1617. bk.rev.; bibl.; illus.; index. circ. 3,000. (also avail. in microform from UMI; reprint service avail. from UMI) Indexed: Amer.Hist.& Life, Arts & Hum.Cit.Ind., Curr.Cont., Hisp.Amer.Per.Ind., Hist.Abstr., Ind.Bk.Rev.Hum., Lib.Lit. **Document type:** bibliography.
—Faxon; UnCover; UMI.

001.3 314   PL
POLAND. GLOWNY URZAD STATYSTYCZNY. ROCZNIK STATYSTYCZNY KULTURY/POLAND. CENTRAL STATISTICS OFFICE. STATISTICAL YEARBOOK OF CULTURE. (Subseries of its: Statystyka Polski) 1969. irreg., latest 1990. Zaklad Wydawnictw Statystycznych, Al. Niepodleglosci 208, 00-925 Warsaw, Poland. TEL 48 22 25-03-45.
Formerly: Poland. Glowny Urzad Statystyczny. Kultura (ISSN 0079-2713)

REFERENCE SOURCES FOR THE SOCIAL SCIENCES AND HUMANITIES. see *SOCIAL SCIENCES: COMPREHENSIVE WORKS — Abstracting, Bibliographies, Statistics*

RESEARCH AND STUDIES. see *EDUCATION — Abstracting, Bibliographies, Statistics*

001.3 016   XR
STATNI VEDECKA KNIHOVNA. VYBER NOVINEK. SERIE E: KULTURA. 1974. 6/yr. 18 Kcs. (35 Kcs. for 7 vols. series: A-G). Statni Vedecka Knihovna, Kounicova 5-7, 601 87 Brno, Czech Republic. Ed. Ivana Ruzickova. circ. 300.

THESIS ABSTRACTS. see *AGRICULTURE — Abstracting, Bibliographies, Statistics*

U P RESEARCH MONITOR. (University of the Philippines) see *SCIENCES: COMPREHENSIVE WORKS — Abstracting, Bibliographies, Statistics*

U P THESIS AND DISSERTATION ABSTRACTS. (University of the Philippines) see *EDUCATION — Abstracting, Bibliographies, Statistics*

060   SA
UNIVERSITY OF PORT ELIZABETH. PUBLICATIONS. BIBLIOGRAPHIES. (Text in Afrikaans, English) 1977. irreg., no.E3, 1986. University of Port Elizabeth, Publications Committee, U P E Library, Private Bag X6508, Port Elizabeth 6000, South Africa. TEL 041-504-2281. FAX 041-504-2280. TELEX 243342. Ed.Bd. **Document type:** bibliography.

300 016   JA   ISSN 0021-5341
ZASSHI KIJI SAKUIN. JINBUN SHAKAI HEN/JAPANESE PERIODICALS INDEX. HUMANITIES AND SOCIAL SCIENCE SECTION. (Text in Japanese) 1948. q. 21200 Yen. National Diet Library - Kokuritsu Kokkai Toshokan, 1-10-1 Nagata-cho, Chiyoda-ku, Tokyo 100, Japan. TEL 03-3581-2331.
FAX 03-3597-9104. index. circ. 1,180. **Document type:** abstracting/indexing.

HUMANITIES: COMPREHENSIVE WORKS — Computer Applications

001   US   ISSN 0190-6631
A C H NEWSLETTER. 1979. q. $60 includes Computers & Humanities. Association for Computers and the Humanities, c/o Humanities Computing Facility, Univ. of California, Santa Barbara, CA 93106-3170. Ed. Eric Dahlin. bk.rev.; software rev. circ. 350.
Indexed: Comput.Lit.Ind.
Description: For students and humanities teachers interested in computer-aided research and instruction.

001.3   US   ISSN 0891-2955
BITS & BYTES REVIEW; reviews and news of products and resources for academic computing. Short title: B & B Review. 1987. 4/yr. $55 to individuals (foreign $70); institutions $70 (foreign $85). Bits and Bytes Computer Resources, 623 N. Iowa Ave., Whitefish, MT 59937. TEL 406-862-7280.
FAX 406-862-1124. Ed. John J. Hughes. bk.rev.; index. circ. 2,000. (looseleaf format; back issues avail.) **Indexed:** Sci.Abstr. **Document type:** newsletter.
—BLDSC (2096.326000).
Description: Provides moderately technical, detailed product reviews and reports on a broad spectrum of computing-related activities.

CARIBBEAN JOURNAL OF SCIENCE. see *BIOLOGY*

COMPUTERS AND PEOPLE SERIES. see *COMPUTERS*

651.8 001.3   NE   ISSN 0010-4817
Z699.5.H8   CODEN: COHUAD
COMPUTERS AND THE HUMANITIES. (Text in English) 1966. 6/yr. fl.432($225) (effective 1994). (Association for Computers and the Humanities) Kluwer Academic Publishers, Postbus 17, 3300 AA Dordrecht, Netherlands. TEL 31-78-334911.
FAX 31-78-334254. TELEX 29245 KAPG NL. (Dist. by: Kluwer Academic Publishers Group, P.O. Box 322, 3300 AH Dordrecht, Netherlands. TEL 31-78-524400. FAX 31-78-524474; N. America dist. addr.: Box 358, Accord Sta., Hingham, MA 02018-0358. TEL 617-871-6600. FAX 617-871-6528) Ed. Glyn Holmes. adv.; bk.rev.; bibl.; charts; illus.; index, cum.index: vols.1-5. (also avail. in microform from UMI; back issues avail.) Indexed: Abstr.Engl.Stud., Amer.Bibl.Slavic & E.Eur.Stud., Amer.Hist.& Life, Amer.Hum.Ind., Arts & Hum.Cit.Ind., Bk.Rev.Ind. (1984-), Br.Archaeol.Abstr., Child.Bk.Rev.Ind. (1984-), Compumath, Comput.Cont., Comput.Lit.Ind., Comput.Rev., Curr.Cont., High.Educ.Curr.Aware.Bull., Hist.Abstr., Hum.Ind., INSPEC, Lang.& Lang.Behav.Abstr., Lit.Automat., M.L.A., Music Ind., RILM, Sci.Abstr., Sci.Cit.Ind., SSCI. **Document type:** academic/scholarly publication.
—BLDSC (3394.710000); Faxon; UnCover; SWETS; UMI. CCC.
Description: Contains papers on computer-aided studies applications, automation and computer-assisted instruction.
Refereed Serial

F R A N C I S. 603: INFORMATIQUE ET SCIENCES JURIDIQUES. see *LAW — Computer Applications*

001.3   UK   ISSN 0956-9782
Z699.5.H8
THE HUMANITIES COMPUTING YEARBOOK. a. varies. Oxford University Press, Oxford Journals, Walton St., Oxford OX2 6DP, England. TEL 0865-56767.
FAX 0865-267773. TELEX 837330-OXPRES-G. (U.S. subscr. to: Oxford University Press Inc., 2001 Evans Rd., Cary, NC 27513. TEL 919-677-0977) Ed. Ian Lancashire. **Document type:** academic/scholarly publication.
—BLDSC (4336.577500).
Description: Comprehensive guides to the use of computers in all disciplines of the humanities.

3128 HYDRAULIC ENGINEERING

HYDRAULIC ENGINEERING

see Engineering–Hydraulic Engineering

HYDROELECTRICAL ENERGY

see Energy–Hydroelectrical Energy

HYDROLOGY

see Earth Sciences–Hydrology

HYPNOSIS

see Medical Sciences–Hypnosis

INDUSTRIAL ENGINEERING

see Engineering–Industrial Engineering

INFORMATION SCIENCE AND INFORMATION THEORY

see Computers–Information Science and Information Theory

INORGANIC CHEMISTRY

see Chemistry–Inorganic Chemistry

INSTRUMENTS

see also Jewelry, Clocks and Watches; Metrology and Standardization

681   US   ISSN 0739-0270
A A M I NEWS. bi-m. $75. Association for the Advancement of Medical Instrumentation, 3330 Washington Blvd., Ste. 400, Arlington, VA 22201-4598. TEL 703-525-4890. circ. 5,500. (back issues avail.)
   Description: Keeps readers informed of government standards, and AAMI activities regarding medical instrumentation.

681.2   US   ISSN 1054-0032
TA165   CODEN: AINCEV
ADVANCES IN INSTRUMENTATION AND CONTROL. (Consists of: Instrument Society of America. International Conference Proceedings) 1964. a. price varies. Instrument Society of America, 67 Alexander Dr., Box 12277, Research Triangle Park, NC 27709. TEL 919-549-8411. FAX 919-549-8288. TELEX 802540 ISA DURM. (reprint service avail. from ISI,UMI) **Indexed:** Chem.Abstr., Excerp.Med. **Document type:** proceedings.
   —BLDSC (0709.241000); EI; Faxon; SWETS; CASDDS. **CCC.**
   Former titles (until 1989): Advances in Instrumentation (ISSN 0065-2814); (until 1967): Instrument Society of America. Annual Conference Proceedings (ISSN 0097-675X)
   Refereed Serial

681   US   ISSN 0882-5785
   CODEN: AINSB8
ANALYSIS INSTRUMENTATION. (Includes: Analysis Instrumentation Symposium Proceedings) 1963. a. price varies. Instrument Society of America, 67 Alexander Dr., Box 12277, Research Triangle Park, NC 27709. TEL 919-549-8411. FAX 919-549-8288. TELEX 802540 ISA DURM. (reprint service avail. from ISI,UMI) **Indexed:** INIS Atomind. **Document type:** proceedings.
   —**CCC.**
   Refereed Serial

681.2 643   UK   ISSN 0265-3435
ANALYTICAL INSTRUMENT INDUSTRY REPORT. 1984. s-m. £295($545) A I I Report, P.O. Box 78, E. Grinstead, W. Sussex RH19 2YW, England. TEL 44-342-323382. FAX 44-342-315939. Ed. Gordon Wilkinson. bk.rev. (back issues avail.) **Document type:** newsletter.
   ●Also available online.
   Description: Provides market information on laboratory equipment and analytical instrument business.

ATOMIZATION AND SPRAYS. see ENGINEERING — Chemical Engineering

681   AT   ISSN 0045-0626
QC53   CODEN: AJICA9
AUSTRALIAN JOURNAL OF INSTRUMENTATION AND CONTROL. 1944-1985; N.S. 1986. q. Aus.$25($7.50) South Australian Institute of Technology, Measurement and Instrumentation Systems Centre, P.O. Box 1, Ingle Farm, South Australia, Australia. TEL (08)343 3342. (Co-sponsor: Institute of Instumentation and Control, Australia (I.I.C.A.)) Ed. David Aspinall. adv.; bk.rev. circ. 850. **Indexed:** Aus.Rd.Ind., Aus.Sci.Ind., Chem.Abstr., Curr.Cont., Sci.Abstr.
   —BLDSC (1809.100000); EI; Faxon.
   Description: Covers control instrumentation and data systems for manufacturing and non-manufacturing industries.

681   GW   ISSN 0178-2320
TJ212
AUTOMATISIERUNGSTECHNISCHE PRAXIS; Zeitschrift fuer Mess- und Automatisierungstechnik. 1959. m. DM.149. R. Oldenbourg Verlag GmbH, Rosehheimerstr. 145, 81671 Munich, Germany. TEL 089-4112-232. FAX 089-4112207. (Subscr. to: Postfach 801360, 81613 Munich, Germany) Ed. K.F. Frueh. adv.; bk.rev.; charts; illus.; tr.lit.; index. circ. 8,000. **Indexed:** Appl.Mech.Rev., Chem.Abstr., Cyb.Abstr., Eng.Ind., Excerp.Med., Fluidex, INIS Atomind., Sci.Abstr. **Document type:** academic/scholarly publication.
   —BLDSC (1831.584400); SWETS. **CCC.**
   Incorporates (in 1991): Messen - Steuern - Regeln (ISSN 0026-0347); **Formerly:** Regelungstechnik Praxis (ISSN 0340-4730)
   Description: Articles on the use of automatic controls and automation in industrial processes. Includes software applications, detailed descriptions of actual automated systems, industry news, new products.

AUTOMATIZALAS/AUTOMATION. see ENGINEERING — Mechanical Engineering

681   IT   ISSN 0393-3911
AUTOMAZIONE INTEGRATA. 1968. 11/yr. L.75000 (foreign L.185000) (effective 1994). Tecniche Nuove s.p.a., Via Menotti 14, 20129 Milan, Italy. TEL 02-75701. FAX 02-7610351. Ed. G. Nardella. adv.: B&W page L.2130000, color page L.2910000; trim 185 x 266. bk.rev.; abstr.; charts; illus.; pat.; tr.lit. circ. 7,045. **Indexed:** Cyb.Abstr.
   Former titles: Controlli Numerici Macchine a C N Robot Industriali (ISSN 0392-6036); Controlli Numerici e Macchine (ISSN 0010-8081)
   Description: Articles on advanced automation factories with employees, flexible working systems and robotics.

681   GW   ISSN 0005-755X
   CODEN: BECRBZ
BECKMAN REPORT. 1959. 2/yr. free. Beckman Instruments GmbH, Frankfurter Ring 115, 80807 Munich, Germany. TEL 089-3887-1. FAX 089-3887-490. TELEX 5215761. Ed. B. Maneck. adv.; bk.rev.; charts; stat. circ. 17,000. **Indexed:** Chem.Abstr. **Document type:** consumer publication.
   —CASDDS.
   Description: Reports on research and development of new products in analytical measurement systems for biochemistry and biotechnology, lab automation systems and systems for laboratory data management.

BIOMEDICAL SCIENCES INSTRUMENTATION. see MEDICAL SCIENCES

681   BL   ISSN 0101-0794
C & I.* (Controle & Instrumentacao - Automatizacao) 1972. m. $85. Editora Gruenwald Ltda., Rua Consorcio 59, 04535 Sao Paulo, Brazil. FAX 011-829-0042. TELEX 1130410. adv.; bk.rev.; tr.lit. circ. 26,000.

681   CN
C I I M S NEWSLETTER. 1973. q. Can.$45. Canadian Information and Image Management Society, 86 Wilson St., Oakville, Ont. L6K 3G5, Canada. TEL 416-842-6067. Ed. D.F. Donoahue. adv.; bk.rev. circ. 500. **Document type:** newsletter.
   Former titles: Canadian Information and Management Society. Newsletters; Canadian Information and Image Management Society. Micro Notes; Canadian Micrographic Society. Micro Notes (ISSN 0315-9337)

C L R. (Clinical Laboratory Reference) see MEDICAL SCIENCES — Experimental Medicine, Laboratory Technique

CHEMICAL MONITOR. see CHEMISTRY — Analytical Chemistry

681   US
CLINICAL ENGINEERING SECTION NEWSLETTER. 1987. bi-m. membership. (American Society for Hospital Engineering) American Hospital Association, 840 N. Lake Shore Dr., Chicago, IL 60611. TEL 312-280-3335. FAX 312-280-4152. Ed. Kerry Hacker. charts; illus. circ. 6,100. (back issues avail.) **Document type:** newsletter.
   Description: Information on the maintenance and upkeep of diagnostic equipment in hospitals. Geared toward clinical engineers and biomedical equipment technicians.

681   II
   CODEN: CSIOBT
COMMUNICATIONS IN INSTRUMENTATION. (Text in English) 1974. q. Rs.100($25) Central Scientific Instruments Organization, Sector 30, Chandigarh 160 020, India. TEL 0172-40090. FAX 0172-40527. TELEX 0395-7300 CSIO IN. (Affiliate: Council of Scientific and Industrial Research) Ed. M.G. Joshi; Pub. G.S. Dhillon. adv.; bk.rev.; illus.; index. circ. 250. (back issues avail.) **Indexed:** Eng.Ind., Excerp.Med., Indian Sci.Abstr., Indian Sci.Ind., Phys.Ber., Sci.Abstr. **Document type:** academic/scholarly publication.
   —BLDSC (3490.186000).
   Formerly (until 1993): C S I O Communications (ISSN 0304-9841)

CONFERENCE ON PRECISION ELECTROMAGNETIC MEASUREMENTS. DIGEST. see ENGINEERING — Electrical Engineering

681   US
CONTROL (CHICAGO). 1988. 12/yr. Putman Publishing Co., 301 E. Erie St., Chicago, IL 60611. TEL 312-644-2020. Ed. Peggy Smedley. circ. 75,000.
   Description: Covers all aspects of instrumentation and process control through features and news.

681   US
CONTROL AD - LITS. 1988. q. Putman Publishing Co., 301 E. Erie St., Chicago, IL 60611. TEL 312-644-2020. FAX 312-644-1131. Ed. Nick Cappelletti. adv. circ. 75,026.
   Description: Contains literature and reviews of process control industries products and services.

681   GW
DIAGNOSTIK DIGEST. 1991. 3/yr. free. Beckman Instruments GmbH, Frankfurter Ring 115, 80807 Munich, Germany. TEL 089-3887-1. FAX 089-3887490. Ed. Bernd Maneck. circ. 8,500. **Document type:** trade publication.
   Description: Reports on research and development of new products in diagnostic measurement systems and reagents for the clinical laboratory.

681.2   CC   ISSN 1001-1390
DIANCE YU YIBIAO/ELECTRONIC MEASURING AND METERS. (Text in Chinese) m. Harbin Diangong Yibiao Yanjiusuo - Harbin Institute of Electrical Engineering and Instruments, 1 Gongli Chu, Haping Lu, Harbin, Heilongjiang 150040, People's Republic of China. TEL 63097. Ed. Wang Yi.

DRUG AND DEVICE PRODUCT APPROVAL LIST. see MEDICAL SCIENCES — Experimental Medicine, Laboratory Technique

ENVIRONMENTAL SENSORS. see *ENVIRONMENTAL STUDIES*

EQUIPOS MEDICOS. see *MEDICAL SCIENCES*

681   UK
EUROPEAN MEDICAL DEVICE MANUFACTURER. 1990. bi-m. free. Canon Communications, Inc., 46 Watergate St., Chester CH1 2LA, England. TEL 0244-342-112. FAX 0244-317-837. (N. America addr.: Canon Communications, Inc., 3340 Ocean Park Blvd., Ste. 1000, Santa Monica, CA 90405. TEL 310-392-5509) Document type: trade publication.
   Formerly: International Medical Device and Diagnostic Industry.
   Description: Written exclusively for the European medical device and diagnostic industry. Provides timely and concise information on the latest materials, components, equipment, and service of interest to designers of medical products in Europe.

EXPERIMENTAL ASTRONOMY; an international journal on astronomical instrumentation and data analysis. see *ASTRONOMY*

681   HU   ISSN 0231-2662
TS176   CODEN: FNMKAY
FINOMMECHANIKA, MIKROTECHNIKA. 1961. m. $26. (Optikai, Akusztikai es Filmtechnikai Egyesulet) Lapkiado Vallalat, Lenin korut 9-11, 1073 Budapest 7, Hungary. TEL 222-408. (Subscr. to: Kultura, Box 149, H-1389 Budapest, Hungary) illus. **Indexed:** Excerp.Med., INIS Atomind., Sci.Abstr.
   Formerly: Finommechanika.

681.2   UK   ISSN 0955-5986
TA357.5.M43   CODEN: FMEIEJ
FLOW MEASUREMENT AND INSTRUMENTATION. 1989. q. £145 in UK and Europe; elsewhere £155. Butterworth - Heinemann (Subsidiary of: Reed International PLC), Linacre House, Jordan Hill, Oxford OX2 8DP, England. TEL 0865-310366. FAX 0865-310898. TELEX 83111 BHPOXF G. (Subscr. to: Turpin Transactions Ltd., Distribution Centre, Blackhorse Rd., Letchworth, Herts SG6 1HN, England. TEL 0462-672555) Ed. Michael Sanderson. (also avail. in microform from UMI; back issues avail.) **Indexed:** E&P Hlth. (1993-), Gas Process.& Ppl. (1993-), Off.Tech. (1993-), Petrol.Abstr. (1992-). **Document type:** academic/scholarly publication.
—BLDSC (3958.300000); EI; SWETS; UMI; CASDDS. **CCC.**
   Description: International journal containing refereed technical papers, review articles and case studies on the latest advances in flowmeters and the theory of their operation.
   Refereed Serial

681   US   ISSN 0196-626X
KF3827.M4
THE G M P LETTER. (Good Manufacturing Practice) 1980. m. $337. Washington Business Information, Inc., c/o Karen Harrington, 1117 N. 19th St., Ste. 200, Arlington, VA 22209. TEL 703-247-3434. FAX 703-247-3421. Ed. Samuel Gilston. bk.rev. (looseleaf format) **Document type:** newsletter.
●Also available online. Vendor(s): BRS Online Products (DIOG), Data-Star, DIALOG Information Services, Inc.
—SWETS. **CCC.**
   Description: Covers Good Manufacturing Practice according to FDA rules dictating controls on production and quality control.

681   688.7   ISSN 1120-5849
GADGET. q. Editrice di Lombardo Giuseppa & C., Via Lombardia 83, 95045 Misterbianco (CT), Italy. TEL 095-399305. FAX 095-399398. adv.: B&W page L.1800000, color page L.3000000; trim 190 x 270. circ. 6,702.

681.2   621.329   CC
GUANGXUE YIQI/OPTICAL INSTRUMENTS. (Text in Chinese) bi-m. Shanghai Guangxue Yiqi Yanjiusuo, 115 Changling Lu, Shanghai 200093, People's Republic of China. TEL 5433311. Ed. Peng Dingsang.

681   MX
GUIA DE LA INDUSTRIA: LABORATORIOS DE ESPECIALIDADES Y CONTROL. 1963. a. Mex.$100000($50) Informatica Cosmos, S.A. de C.V., Fernandez Arrieta 5-101, Col. Los Cipreses, 04830 Mexico D.F., Mexico. TEL 677-48-68. FAX 679-35-75. Dir. Cesar Macazaga Orodono. circ. 5,000.

GUIDE TO BIOTECHNOLOGY PRODUCTS AND INSTRUMENTS. see *BIOLOGY — Biotechnology*

539.2   541.3   NE
HANDBOOK ON SYNCHROTRON RADIATION. (Text in English) 1983. irreg., vol.4, 1991. price varies. Elsevier Science B.V., Books Division, P.O. Box 211, 1000 AE Amsterdam, Netherlands. TEL 31-20-5803911. FAX 31-20-5803705. TELEX 18582 ESPA NL. (Subscr. in U.S. and Canada to: Elsevier Science Inc., Box 882, Madison Sq. Sta., New York, NY 10159. TEL 212-989-5800) Eds. D.E. Eastman, Y. Farge. (back issues avail.) **Document type:** monographic series.
   Refereed Serial

681   NE   ISSN 0020-4358
HONEYWELL INSTRUMENTATIE NIEUWS. 1965. q. free. Honeywell B.V., Marketing Division, Postbus 12683, 1100 AR Amsterdam, Netherlands. illus. circ. 5,000.

HOSPITAL MAGAZINE. see *HOSPITALS*

681   GW
I C F A INSTRUMENTATION BULLETIN. (Text in English) 1986. 2/yr. free. International Committee for Future Accelerators, c/o University of Siegen, Physics Department, Adolf-Reichwein-Str., 57076 Siegen, Germany. TEL 0271-740-4140. FAX 0271-74515. TELEX 872337. Ed. A.H. Walenta. adv.; bk.rev. circ. 2,000.
   Formerly: Instrumentation Bulletin.
   Description: Reports on research and progress in the field of instrumentation, with emphasis on application.

681   US
I E C O N: INTERNATIONAL CONFERENCE ON INDUSTRIAL ELECTRONICS, CONTROL AND INSTRUMENTATION. PROCEEDINGS. Variant title: I E E E Industrial Electronics Society Conference. (Former name of issuing body: Industrial Electronics and Control Instrumentation Society) a. (I E E E, Industrial Electronics Society) Institute of Electrical and Electronics Engineers, Inc., 345 E. 47th St., New York, NY 10017. TEL 212-705-7900. FAX 212-705-7682. (Subscr. to: 445 Hoes Lane, Box 1331, Piscataway, NJ 08855-1331) **Document type:** proceedings.
   Former titles (until 1983): I E E E - I E C O N. Proceedings; (until 1981): I E C I Industrial and Control Applications of Microprocessors. Proceedings; Industrial Applications of Microprocessors.
   Description: Covers the enhancement of industrial and manufacturing processes through the application of electronics and electrical sciences.

681.2   US
I E E E INSTRUMENTATION AND MEASUREMENT TECHNOLOGY CONFERENCE. PROCEEDINGS.. Short title: I M T C. 1984. a. price varies. (I E E E, Instrumentation and Measurement Society) Institute of Electrical and Electronics Engineers, Inc., 345 E. 47th St., New York, NY 10017-2394. FAX 908-981-9667. (Subscr. to: Box 1331, 445 Hoes Lane, Piscataway, NJ 08855-1331. TEL 908-981-1393) **Document type:** proceedings.

681   US   ISSN 0272-8141
HD9706.6.U6
I S A DIRECTORY OF INSTRUMENTATION. (Instrument Society of America) 1979. a. $100. I S A Services, Inc., 67 Alexander Dr., Box 12277, Research Triangle Park, NC 27709. TEL 919-549-8411. FAX 919-549-8288. TELEX 802540 ISA DURM. Ed. Susan M. Organ. adv. circ. 50,000. **Document type:** directory.
—**CCC.**
   Incorporates: I S A Transducer Compendium.

681   610   JA   ISSN 0019-1736
IKAKIKAI GAKU ZASSHI/JOURNAL OF MEDICAL INSTRUMENTS. (Text in Japanese) 1923. m. 6000 Yen. Medical Instrument Society of Japan - Nihon Ikakikai Gakkai, 3-39-15 Hongo, Bunkyo-ku, Tokyo 113, Japan. Ed. Muramatsu Atsuyoshi.

681   UK
INDUSTRIAL & SCIENTIFIC INSTRUMENTS. 1960. m. £30($139) (foreign £70). Wilmington Publishing, Wilmington House, Church Hill, Dartford, Kent UA2 7EF, England. TEL 0332-277788. FAX 0322-276476. (Subscr. to: Ferrari House, 258 Field End Rd., Ruislip, Middx HA4 9AU. TEL 081-868-4499) adv. circ. 22,000. **Indexed:** BMT, Br.Ceram.Abstr., Fluidex, Met.Abstr., World Alum.Abstr.

681.2   UK   ISSN 0142-3312
TJ212   CODEN: TICODG
INSTITUTE OF MEASUREMENT AND CONTROL. TRANSACTIONS. 1979. 5/yr. £146 (foreign £178). Institute of Measurement and Control, 87 Gower St., London WC1E 6AA, England. TEL 44-71-387-4949. FAX 44-71-388-8431. TELEX 946797-PRONTO-G. Ed. C. Carter. **Indexed:** Br.Tech.Ind., Chem.Eng.Abstr., Cyb.Abstr., Fluidex, ISMEC, Sci.Abstr., Sh.& Vib.Dig., T.C.E.A. **Document type:** academic/scholarly publication.
—BLDSC (8940.500000); EI; UnCover; SWETS.
   Description: Presents a selection of technical papers covering a wide range of topics in the control and instrumentation industry.
   Refereed Serial

681.2   UK
INSTRUMENT ENGINEER'S YEARBOOK; manufacturers' - users' guide to instrumentation & control. 1985. a. £35 to non-members. Institute of Measurement and Control, 87 Gower St., London WC1E 6AA, England. TEL 44-71-387-4949. FAX 44-71-388-8431. TELEX 946797-PRONTO-G. Ed. B. Watson. tr.mk. **Document type:** directory.
   Description: Lists companies in the control and instrumentation industry, including trade names, distributors, and products and services.

681   US   ISSN 1072-2742
Q184
INSTRUMENTATION & AUTOMATION NEWS; instruments, scientific equipment, electronic and mechanical components. 1953. m. $35. Chilton Co., Chilton Way, Radnor, PA 19089. TEL 215-964-4419. FAX 215-964-2919. (Subscr. to: Box 2005, Radnor, PA 19089) Ed. Patricia Pool. adv.; illus.; tr.lit. circ. 117,227. (tabloid format; also avail. in microfilm from UMI; microfiche from UMI; reprint service avail. from UMI) **Indexed:** Bus.Ind., Tr.& Indus.Ind.
—UMI. **CCC.**
   Former titles: Chilton's I A N; Chilton's Instrument and Apparatus News (ISSN 0193-6174); Instrument and Apparatus News (ISSN 0020-4293)
   Description: Presents news, state-of-the-art products, plus applications for existing products for the instrumentation and control engineer.

681   US
TA165   CODEN: CHISDY
INSTRUMENTATION AND CONTROL SYSTEMS; the publication of control technology for engineers and engineering management. 1928. m. $60. Chilton Co., Chilton Way, Radnor, PA 19089. TEL 215-964-4417. FAX 215-964-2919. (Subscr. to: Box 2026, Radnor, PA 19080-9526) Ed. John E. Hickey Jr. adv.; bk.rev.; charts; illus.; tr.lit.; index. circ. 92,603. (also avail. in microfilm from UMI,PMC; microfiche from UMI; reprint service avail. from UMI) **Indexed:** A.S.& T.Ind., API Abstr., API Catal., API Hlth.& Environ., API Oil., API Pet.Ref., API Pet.Subst., API Transport., Appl.Mech.Rev., Biol.Abstr., Ceram.Abstr., Chem.Abstr., Chem.Eng.Abstr., Comput.Cont., Comput.Dtbs., Curr.Cont., Cyb.Abstr., Deep Sea Res.& Oceanogr.Abstr., Eng.Ind., Excerp.Med., Fluidex, Fuel & Energy Abstr., Met.Abstr., PROMT, Robomat. (until 1992), Sci.Abstr.
●Also available online. Vendor(s): DIALOG Information Services, Inc.
—EI; Faxon; UnCover; SWETS; UMI. **CCC.**
   Former titles: Chilton's I and C S (ISSN 0746-2395); (until 1983): Chilton's Instruments and Control Systems (ISSN 0164-0089); Instruments and Control Systems (ISSN 0020-4404)
   Description: Technical features on engineering applications related to control technology.

3130 INSTRUMENTS

681.2   US
TP157
INSTRUMENTATION FOR THE PROCESS INDUSTRIES.
35th, 1980. a. price varies. Instrument Society of America, 67 Alexander Dr., Box 12277, Research Triangle Park, NC 27709. TEL 919-549-8411. FAX 919-549-8288. TELEX 802540-ISA DURM. (reprint service avail. from ISI,UMI) **Indexed:** Chem.Abstr. **Document type:** proceedings.
—BLDSC (1534.955500). **CCC.**
   Formerly: Instrumentation Symposium for the Process Industries (ISSN 0738-3231)
   Refereed Serial

681 660   US   ISSN 0074-0551
TP157   CODEN: INCPAW
INSTRUMENTATION IN THE CHEMICAL AND PETROLEUM INDUSTRIES. (Includes: International Instrument Society of America Chemical and Petroleum Instrumentation Symposium Proceedings) 1965. a. price varies. Instrument Society of America, 67 Alexander Dr., Box 12277, Research Triangle Park, NC 27709. TEL 919-549-8411. FAX 919-549-8288. TELEX 802-540 ISA DURM. (reprint service avail. from ISI,UMI) **Indexed:** API Catal., API Hlth.& Environ., API Oil., API Pet.Ref., API Pet.Subst., API Transport. **Document type:** proceedings.
—BLDSC (4529.012000); Faxon. **CCC**
   Refereed Serial

681 664   US
TP373   CODEN: IFDBB8
INSTRUMENTATION IN THE FOOD AND PHARMACEUTICAL INDUSTRIES. irreg., vol.3, 1980. price varies. Instrument Society of America, 67 Alexander Dr., Box 12277, Research Triangle Park, NC 27709. TEL 919-549-8411. FAX 919-832-0237. TELEX 802540 ISA DURM. (reprint service avail. from ISI,UMI) **Document type:** proceedings.
—**CCC.**
   Formerly: Instrumentation in the Food Industry (ISSN 0095-0777)
   Refereed Serial

681.7   US   ISSN 0074-056X
TJ5   CODEN: IPWIAN
INSTRUMENTATION IN THE POWER INDUSTRY. (Includes: International Instrument Society of America Power Symposium Proceedings) 1967. a. price varies. Instrument Society of America, 67 Alexander Dr., Box 12277, Research Triangle Park, NC 27709. TEL 919-549-8411. FAX 919-549-8288. TELEX 802540 ISA DURM. (reprint service avail. from UMI,ISI) **Indexed:** INIS Atomind. **Document type:** proceedings.
—**CCC.**
   Refereed Serial

681   US
INSTRUMENTATION NEWSLETTER. q. National Instruments Corporation, 6504 Bridge Point Pkwy., Austin, TX 78730. TEL 512-794-0100. FAX 512-338-9119. Ed. Traci Hensley. circ. 130,000. **Document type:** newsletter.

681   FR
INSTRUMENTATION SYSTEMS. m. 370 F. (foreign 500 F.). Promotion Presse International, 7 ter, Tour des Petites-Ecuries, 75010 Paris, France. Ed. H. Thiron. adv. circ. 9,000.

681   US
INSTRUMENTOS Y CONTROLES INTERNACIONALES. (Editions in Spanish, English) q. Keller International Publishing Corp., 150 Great Neck Rd., Great Neck, NY 11021-3309. TEL 516-829-9210. FAX 516-829-5414. Ed. Felicia Morales. circ. 62,000.

681   US   ISSN 0020-4412
QC53   CODEN: INETAK
INSTRUMENTS AND EXPERIMENTAL TECHNIQUES. English translation of: Pribory i Tekhnika Eksperimenta (RU ISSN 0032-8162) 1958. m. $1295 (foreign $1515) (effective 1994). (Russian Academy of Sciences, RU) Plenum Publishing Corp, Consultants Bureau, 233 Spring St., New York, NY 10013-1578. TEL 212-620-8468. FAX 212-463-0742. TELEX 23-421139. Ed. M.S. Khaikin. (also avail. in microfilm from JSC; back issues avail.) **Indexed:** Appl.Mech.Rev., Cadscan, Chem.Titles, Comput.Abstr., Comput.& Info.Sys., Curr.Cont., Electron.& Communic.Abstr.J., Energy Res.Abstr., Eng.Ind., INIS Atomind., Lead Abstr., Mass Spectr.Bull., Solid St.Abstr., Zincscan. **Document type:** academic/scholarly publication.
—BLDSC (0412.700000); Faxon; UnCover; SWETS; UMI. **CCC.**
   Refereed Serial

681   II   ISSN 0047-0376
CODEN: ISIDBS
INSTRUMENTS INDIA. Variant title: I M D A Journal. (Text in English) 1957. bi-m. Rs.30. All India Instrument Manufacturers and Dealers Association, A-32 Navyug Niwas, 167, Dr. D. Bhadkamkar Rd., Bombay 400007, India. Ed. V.K. Vasudevan. adv.; bk.rev. circ. 2,000. **Indexed:** Sci.Abstr.

681   US   ISSN 0192-303X
TA165   CODEN: INTCDD
INTECH; the international journal of instrumentation and control. 1954. m. $65 (foreign $100). (Instrument Society of America) I S A Services, Inc., 67 Alexander Dr., Box 12277, Research Triangle Park, NC 27709. TEL 919-549-8411. FAX 919-549-8288. TELEX 802540 ISA DURM. Ed. Robert C. Waterbury. adv.; bk.rev.; charts; illus.; tr.lit.; index. circ. 53,000. (also avail. in microfilm from UMI; reprint service avail. from ISI,UMI) **Indexed:** A.S.& T.Ind., Abstr.Bull.Inst.Pap.Chem., API Catal., API Hlth.& Environ., API Oil., API Pet.Ref., API Pet.Subst., API Transport., Appl.Mech.Rev., Biol.Abstr., Chem.Abstr., Chem.Eng.Abstr., Comput.Cont., Comput.Dtbs., Comput.Rev., Curr.Cont., Deep Sea Res.& Oceanogr.Abstr., Eng.Ind., Excerp.Med., Fluidex, Fuel & Energy Abstr., Gas Abstr., Ind.Sci.Rev., Met.Abstr., Ocean.Abstr., Petrol.Abstr., Pollut.Abstr., PROMT, Risk Abstr., Sci.Abstr., Sci.Cit.Ind., Sh.& Vib.Dig., World Alum.Abstr.
—BLDSC (4531.804000); Faxon; UnCover; SWETS; UMI; CASDDS. **CCC.**
   Former titles: Instrumentation Technology (ISSN 0020-4382); I S A Journal (ISSN 0096-0810)

681.2 540   UK
INTERNATIONAL GUIDE TO SCIENTIFIC INSTRUMENTS & CHEMICALS. 1976. a. £70. International Labmate Ltd., 12 Alban Park, Hatfield Rd., St. Albans AL4 0JJ, England. TEL 0727-55574. Ed. M.H. Pattison. circ. 45,000. (back issues avail.) **Document type:** trade publication.

681   US
INTERNATIONAL INSTRUMENTATION & CONTROLS. 1975. 6/yr. Keller International Publishing Corporation, 150 Great Neck Rd., Great Neck, NY 11021. TEL 516-829-9210. FAX 516-829-7265. TELEX 221 574 KELLE. Ed. Felicia M. Morales. adv.; abstr.; illus. circ. 30,052. (tabloid format) **Indexed:** Mass Spectr.Bull. **Document type:** trade publication.
   Formerly: International Instrumentation - Instrumentacion Internacional.

INTERNATIONAL JOURNAL OF REMOTE SENSING. see *EARTH SCIENCES*

INTERNATIONAL LABMATE. see *MEDICAL SCIENCES — Experimental Medicine, Laboratory Technique*

681 542   II   ISSN 0047-1070
INTERNATIONAL PRESS CUTTING SERVICE: SCIENTIFIC INSTRUMENTS, LABORATORY EQUIPMENT & CHEMICALS. 1970. w. $65. International Press Cutting Service, Box 63, Allahabad 211001, India. Ed. N. Khanna. bk.rev.; index. circ. 1,200. (processed)

681   RU   ISSN 0368-1025
CODEN: IZTEAW
IZMERITEL'NAYA TEKHNIKA. English translation: Measurement Techniques (US ISSN 0543-1972) 1939. m. 31.80 Rub. Gosudarstvennyi Komitet Standartov Mer i Izmeritel'nykh Priborov, Shchusseva 4, Moscow K-1, Russia. Ed. G.D. Burdun. bk.rev.; charts; index. **Indexed:** Chem.Abstr., INIS Atomind., ISMEC, Sci.Abstr.
—BLDSC (0085.000000); CASDDS.

681   RU   ISSN 0021-3454
CODEN: IVUBAY
IZVESTIYA VYSSHIKH UCHEBNYKH ZAVEDENII. SERIYA PRIBOROSTROENIE. 1958. m. 10.80 Rub. Leningradskii Institut Tochnoi Mekhaniki i Optiki, Leningrad, Russia. Ed. L.F. Porfiriev. charts; illus.; index. circ. 2,500. (tabloid format) **Indexed:** Chem.Abstr., INIS Atomind., Sci.Abstr.
—CASDDS.

681   JA   ISSN 0385-4418
CODEN: JNAIDF
J E O L NEWS: ANALYTICAL INSTRUMENTATION. (Text in English) 1963. 2/yr. exchange basis. Japan Electron Optics Laboratory News - Nihon Denshi K.K., 1-2, Musashino 3-chome, Akishima-shi, Tokyo 196, Japan. TEL 0425-42-2161. FAX 0425-46-3353. TELEX 0-2842-135. Ed. Shunichi Enomoto. circ. 12,000. **Indexed:** Chem.Abstr., INIS Atomind., Mass Spectr.Bull., Sci.Abstr. **Document type:** academic/scholarly publication.
—BLDSC (4665.280000); CASDDS.
   Formerly: J E O L News - Analytical Instruments: Application.

629   JA   ISSN 0385-4426
CODEN: JNEIDZ
J E O L NEWS: ELECTRON OPTICS INSTRUMENTATION. (Text in English) 1963. 2/yr. exchange basis. J E O L Ltd. - Nihon Denshi K.K., 1-2, Musashino 3-chome, Akishima-shi, Tokyo 196, Japan. TEL 0425-42-2161. FAX 0425-46-3353. TELEX 0-2842-135. Ed. Shunichi Enomoto. circ. 18,000. **Indexed:** Mass Spectr.Bull. **Document type:** academic/scholarly publication.
—BLDSC (4665.300000); CASDDS.
   Formerly: J E O L News - Electron Optics Instruments - Application.

JAPAN SOCIETY FOR PRECISION ENGINEERING. INTERNATIONAL JOURNAL. see *ENGINEERING*

JOURNAL OF ELECTROPHYSIOLOGICAL TECHNOLOGY. see *BIOLOGY — Biophysics*

JOURNAL OF OPTICAL TECHNOLOGY. see *PHYSICS — Optics*

KEISOKU TO SEIGYO/SOCIETY OF INSTRUMENT AND CONTROL ENGINEERS. JOURNAL. see *METROLOGY AND STANDARDIZATION*

KYOWA ENGINEERING NEWS/KYOWA GIHO. see *ENGINEERING*

681 540   JA   ISSN 0916-0892
KYUSHU DAIGAKU CHUO BUNSEKI SENTA HOKOKU/KYUSHU UNIVERSITY. CENTER OF ADVANCED INSTRUMENTAL ANALYSIS. REPORT. (Text in Japanese; summaries in English) 1983. a. Kyushu Daigaku, Chuo Bunseki Senta - Kyushu University, Center of Advanced Instrumental Analysis, 6-1, Kasuga Koen, Kasuga-shi, Fukuoka-ken 816, Japan.

681 540   JA
KYUSHU DAIGAKU CHUO BUNSEKI SENTA NYUSU/KYUSHU UNIVERSITY. CENTER OF ADVANCED INSTRUMENTAL ANALYSIS. NEWS. (Text in Japanese) 1983. q. Kyushu Daigaku, Chuo Bunseki Senta - Kyushu University, Center of Advanced Instrumental Analysis, 6-1, Kasuga Koen, Kasuga-shi, Fukuoka-ken 816, Japan.

681.2   CC
L S I ZHIZHAO YU CESHI. (Text in Chinese) bi-m. Shanghai Yibiao Dianxunju, Guangxue Hangye Chu, Room 201, 450 Jiangxi Zhonglu, Shanghai 200020, People's Republic of China. TEL 3230383. Ed. Zhuang Songlin.

LABORATORIUM PRAKTIJK. see *MEDICAL SCIENCES — Experimental Medicine, Laboratory Technique*

INSTRUMENTS

338.4   UK
LABORATORY EQUIPMENT BUYERS' GUIDE. 1972. a. £70 (overseas £85). Benn Business Information Services Ltd. (Subsidiary of: Morgan-Grampian plc), Riverbank House, Angel Ln, Tonbridge, Kent TN9 1SE, England. TEL 0732-362666. FAX 0732-767301. TELEX 957829 BENTON G. Ed.Bd. circ. 1,500. **Document type:** directory.
    Former titles: Laboratory Equipment Directory (ISSN 0141-8963); Laboratory Equipment Directory and Buyers Guide.

681.2 607   US
LASER QUEST. 1971. a. free. Metrologic Instruments Inc., Coles Rd. at Rte. 42, Blackwood, NJ 08012. TEL 609-228-8100. FAX 609-228-6673. Ed. Herbert H. Gottlieb. adv.; bk.rev.; charts; illus. circ. 5,000.
    Formerly: Education News from Metrologic (ISSN 0046-144X)

621   US
M & C DATA ACQUISITION AND RECORDER HANDBOOK & BUYERS GUIDE. 1982. a. $15. Measurements & Data Corp., 2994 W. Liberty Ave., Pittsburgh, PA 15216. TEL 412-343-9666. Eds. Harish Saluja, Elisa Behnk. adv. circ. 10,000.
    Former titles: M and C Temperature Handbook and Buyers Guide; M and C Pressure and Force Handbook Buyers Guide.

681   UK   ISSN 0966-4378
MARCONI INSTRUMENTS MEASURE TEST; international newsletter. 1967. q. free. Marconi Instruments Ltd., Longacres, St. Albans, Herts. AL4 0JN, England. TEL 0727-859292. FAX 0727-857481. (U.S. subscr. addr.: 3 Pearl Court, Allendale, NJ 07401) Ed. Nitin Dahad. circ. 30,000. **Document type:** newsletter.
    Formerly (until 1991): M I Contact (ISSN 0024-8207)

681.2   UK   ISSN 0020-2940
TJ212   CODEN: MEACBX
MEASUREMENT AND CONTROL. 1968. m. (10/yr.). £89 (foreign £117). Institute of Measurement and Control, 87 Gower St, London WC1E 6AA, England. TEL 44-71-387-4949. FAX 44-71-388-8431. TELEX 946797-PRONTO-G. Ed. B. Watson. adv.; bk.rev.; charts; illus.; index. circ. 6,560. **Indexed:** Br.Tech.Ind., Chem.Eng.Abstr., Cyb.Abstr., Eng.Ind., Fluidex, Fuel & Energy Abstr., ISMEC, Met.Abstr., Sci.Abstr., T.C.E.A., World Text.Abstr. **Document type:** academic/scholarly publication.
    —BLDSC (5413.560000); EI; Faxon; UnCover; SWETS.
    Supersedes: Society of Instrument Technology. Transactions.
    Description: Covers a variety of subjects relevant to the measurement and control industry.

681 530   UK   ISSN 0957-0233
QC39   CODEN: MSTCEP
MEASUREMENT SCIENCE AND TECHNOLOGY. 1968. m. £370($759) (effective 1994). (Institute of Physics) I O P Publishing, Techno House, Redcliffe Way, Bristol BS1 6NX, England. TEL 0272-297481. FAX 0272-294318. TELEX 449149-INSTP-G. (Subscr. to: I O P Circulation Centre, Readerlink, Audit House, 260 Field End Rd., Eastcote, Ruislip, Mddx. HA4 9LT, England. TEL 081-868-4499. FAX 081-428-3117; U.S. addr.: American Institute of Physics, Member and Subscriber Services, 500 Sunnyside Blvd., Woodbury, NY 11797-2999. TEL 516-576-2200) Ed. J.D.C. Jones. adv.; bk.rev.; bibl.; charts; illus.; index. (also avail. in microfiche from AIP; microfilm from AIP; back issues avail.) **Indexed:** A.S.& T.Ind., Abstr.Bull.Inst.Pap.Chem., AESIS, Agri.Eng.Abstr., Anal.Abstr., Appl.Mech.Rev., Biol.Abstr., Biol.Abstr., BMT, Br.Ceram.Abstr., Br.Tech.Ind., C.I.S.Abstr., Chem.Abstr., Chem.Eng.Abstr., Curr.Cont., Deep Sea Res.& Oceanogr.Abstr., Eng.Ind., Excerp.Med., Fluidex, Fuel & Energy Abstr., GeoRef, Hort.Abstr., Ind.Sci.Rev., Ind.Vet., INIS Atomind., Int.Aerosp.Abstr., Int.Build.Serv.Abstr., Mass.Spectr.Bull., Met.Abstr., Nutr.Abstr., Phys.Ber., Sci.Abstr., Sh.& Vib.Dig., Soils & Fert., T.C.E.A., W.R.C.Inf., World Alum.Abstr., World Text.Abstr. **Document type:** academic/scholarly publication.
    —BLDSC (5413.568000); EI; Faxon; UnCover; SWETS; CASDDS. **CCC.**
    Former titles (until 1990): Journal of Physics E: Scientific Instruments (ISSN 0022-3735); Journal of Scientific Instruments (ISSN 0368-4253)
    Description: Discusses the construction of new instruments for industry and research laboratories.

681   US   ISSN 0148-0057
T50
MEASUREMENTS AND CONTROL. (Supplement avail.: M & C: Measurement & Control News.) 1967. bi-m. $22. Measurements & Data Corp., 2994 W. Liberty Ave., Pittsburgh, PA 15216. TEL 412-343-9666. Ed. Harish Saluja. adv.; bk.rev.; illus.; cum.index. circ. 100,000. (reprint service avail. from UMI) **Indexed:** Excerp.Med., Petrol.Abstr.
    —Faxon; SWETS; UMI.
    Formerly: Measurements and Data (ISSN 0025-6323)
    Refereed Serial

681   US   ISSN 0194-1461
MEASUREMENTS & CONTROL NEWS. (Supplement to: Measurements & Control) 6/yr. Measurements & Data Corp., 2994 W. Liberty Ave., Pittsburgh, PA 15216. TEL 412-343-9666. Ed. Harish C. Saluja. (reprint service avail. from UMI)

681   US   ISSN 0194-844X
                             CODEN: MDIIDI
MEDICAL DEVICE & DIAGNOSTIC INDUSTRY. 1979. m. free to qualified personnel. Canon Communications, Inc., 3340 Ocean Park Blvd., Ste. 1000, Santa Monica, CA 90405-3207. TEL 310-392-5509. FAX 310-392-4920. Ed. John Bethune. adv.; charts; illus.; pat.; tr.lit.; index. circ. 35,000. (back issues avail.) **Indexed:** Chem.Abstr., Curr.Adv.Ecol.Sci., Curr.Pack.Abstr., Telegen. **Document type:** trade publication.
    —BLDSC (5527.055000); EI; CASDDS.
    Description: Emphasizes applied technology in product design, manufacturing and marketing. Covers market trends, business news, regulatory and legal issues and management for manufacturers of medical devices and medical electronics.

681 610   UK   ISSN 1352-4402
▼**MEDICAL DEVICE COMPANIES ANALYSIS.** 1992. m. £795. M D I S Publications Ltd., MDIS House, 8 Eastgate Sq., Chichester, W. Sussex PO19 1JN, England. TEL 0243-533322. FAX 0243-533418. **Document type:** directory.

MEDICAL DEVICES, DIAGNOSTICS & INSTRUMENTATION REPORTS: THE GRAY SHEET. see *MEDICAL SCIENCES*

681 610   US
MEDICAL EQUIPMENT DESIGNER. bi-m. Huebcore Communications, Inc., 29100 Aurora Rd., Ste. 200, Cleveland, OH 44139. TEL 216-248-1125. FAX 216-248-0187. Ed. Michael F. Malley. circ. 12,000.

MEDICAL INDUSTRY EXECUTIVE. see *MEDICAL SCIENCES*

681 338   US   ISSN 0893-6250
R856.A1
MEDICAL PRODUCT MANUFACTURING NEWS. 1985. 10/yr. free to qualified personnel. Canon Communications, Inc., 3340 Ocean Park Blvd., Ste. 1000, Santa Monica, CA 90405-3207. TEL 310-392-5509. FAX 310-392-4920. Ed. John Bethune. adv. circ. 30,000. (tabloid format; back issues avail.) **Indexed:** Telegen. **Document type:** trade publication.
    Description: Covers product news of equipment, materials, components, and services for original equipment manufacturers of medical devices and medical electronics.

MEDICAL PRODUCTS SALES. see *MEDICAL SCIENCES*

681.2   UK
MEDINDEX. a. £18. Reed Business Publishing Group, Reed Healthcare Communications (Subsidiary of: Reed Elsevier group), Quadrant House, The Quadrant, Sutton, Surrey SM2 5AS, England. TEL 081-652-8879. FAX 081-652-8946. circ. 6,000. **Document type:** directory.

681   SZ   ISSN 0026-2854
QC81   CODEN: MITCAJ
MICROTECNIC. (Includes Micro-News) (Text in English, French and German) 1947. q. 205 SFr. Agifa Verlag AG, Bruggacherstr. 26, CH-8117 Faellanden, Switzerland. TEL 01-8256464. Ed. Rudolf Weber. adv.; bk.rev.; abstr.; bibl.; illus.; stat.; index, cum.index. circ. 7,000. (also avail. in microfilm from UMI; reprint service avail. from UMI) **Indexed:** C.I.S.Abstr., Chem.Abstr., Curr.Cont., Eng.Ind., Fluidex, ISMEC, Sci.Abstr., Sh.& Vib.Dig. **Document type:** academic/scholarly publication.
    —BLDSC (5761.000000); EI; SWETS; UMI.

681   RU   ISSN 0236-3933
MOSKOVSKII GOSUDARSTVENNYI TEKHNICHESKII UNIVERSITET. VESTNIK. PRIBOROSTROENIE/MOSCOW STATE TECHNICAL UNIVERSITY. PROCEEDINGS. INSTRUMENT ENGINEERING. (Text in Russian; summaries in English, Russian) 1990. q. $200. Moskovskii Gosudarstvennyi Tekhnicheskii Universitet - Moscow State Technical University, 2-ya Baumanskaya, 5 MGTU, 107005 Moscow, Russia. TEL 263-60-45. FAX 95-267-98-93. Ed. Igor Borisovich Feodorov. adv. circ. 1,000. **Document type:** proceedings.

MUSIQUE ET INSTRUMENTS; la revue des editeurs de musique et des facteurs d'instruments. see *MUSIC*

N R A O NEWSLETTER. (National Radio Astronomy Observatory) see *ASTRONOMY*

681.2   PL   ISSN 0257-3881
Q184   CODEN: NAAPEO
NAUCHNAYA APPARATURA/SCIENTIFIC INSTRUMENTATION. (Text in English, Russian) 1986. q. $48. Polska Akademia Nauk, Instytut Chemii Fizycznej - Polish Academy of Sciences, Institute of Physical Chemistry, Kasprzaka 44-52, 10-224 Warsaw, Poland. TEL 386-25. Ed. Wojciech Zielenkiewicz.
    —CASDDS.
    Description: Forum for the exchange of experiences between the academies of sciences of the socialist countries in the field of production of research instrumentation and laboratory equipment.

NEWSMETER. see *ADVERTISING AND PUBLIC RELATIONS*

681 621.9   US
NOTICIARIO DE TESTES E LABORATORIOS. (Text in Portuguese) 3/yr. Thomas Publishing Company, Five Penn Plaza, 8th Fl., New York, NY 10001. TEL 212-629-1549. FAX 212-629-1542. adv. circ. 12,000.
    Description: Covers the Brazilian market of analytical instruments, information systems, statistical quality control products, and measurement and inspection equipment.

OPTIKO-MEKHANICHESKAYA PROMYSHLENNOST'. see *PHYSICS — Optics*

OPTOELECTRONICS, INSTRUMENTATION AND DATA PROCESSING. see *ELECTRONICS*

681   SZ   ISSN 0255-6944
PRECISION; Fachzeitschrift fuer Automation, Industrie-Elektronik, Pruefen und Messen, Praezisionstechnik und Zulieferindustrie. (Text in French and German) 1927. m. 103 SFr. Vogt-Schild Ag, Zuchwilerstr. 21, CH-4501 Solothurn 1, Switzerland. TEL 065-247247. FAX 065-247235. Ed. Robert Meier. adv.; bk.rev.; bibl.; charts; illus.; stat.; index. circ. 11,000. **Document type:** trade publication.
    —CCC.
    Former titles: Uhren Rundschau; Schweizer Uhr (ISSN 0036-7478)

681   RU   ISSN 0032-8162
QC53   CODEN: PRTEAJ
PRIBORY I TEKHNIKA EKSPERIMENTA. English translation: Instruments and Experimental Techniques (US ISSN 0020-4412) 1963. bi-m. 54.90 Rub. (Rossiiskaya Akademiya Nauk) Izdatel'stvo Nauka, 90 Profsoyuznaya ul., 117864 Moscow, Russia. Ed. A.I. Shal'nikov. index. (tabloid format) **Indexed:** Chem.Abstr., Sci.Abstr.
    —BLDSC (0131.700000); CASDDS. **CCC.**

REMOTE SENSING OF ENVIRONMENT. see *GEOGRAPHY*

INSTRUMENTS — ABSTRACTING, BIBLIOGRAPHIES, STATISTICS

681　　　　　US　　ISSN 0034-6748
Q184　　　　　　　　CODEN: RSINAK
REVIEW OF SCIENTIFIC INSTRUMENTS. 1930. m. $800. American Institute of Physics, One Physics Ellipse, College Park, MD 20740-3843. TEL 301-209-3000. (Subscr. to: AIP Member and Subscriber Services, 500 Sunnyside Blvd., Woodbury, NY 11797-2999. TEL 516-576-2270) Ed. Thomas H. Braid. adv.; bk.rev.; bibl.; illus.; index, cum.index. (also avail. in microfiche from AIP; back issues avail.) Indexed: A.S.& T.Ind., Abstr.Bull.Inst.Pap.Chem., Agri.Eng.Abstr., Anal.Abstr., Appl.Mech.Rev., Biol.Abstr., Br.Ceram.Abstr., C.P.I., Chem.Abstr., Curr.Cont., Deep Sea Res.& Oceanogr.Abstr., Eng.Ind., Excerp.Med., Fluidex, Fuel & Energy Abstr., Gas Abstr., Gen.Phys.Adv.Abstr., GeoRef., Int.Aerosp.Abstr., Mass Spectr.Bull., Met.Abstr., Meteor.& Geoastrophys.Abstr., Phys.Ber., Psychol.Abstr., RAPRA, Sci.Abstr., Sh.& Vib.Dig., World Alum.Abstr. **Document type:** academic/scholarly publication.
—BLDSC (7795.000000); EI; Faxon; UnCover; SWETS; CASDDS. **CCC.**
Refereed Serial

681.2　918　　　US
SCIENTIFIC INSTRUMENTS: LATIN AMERICAN INDUSTRIAL REPORT. 1985. a. $235 per country report. Aquino Productions, Box 15760, Stamford, CT 06901. TEL 203-325-3138. Ed. Andres C. Aquino.

SEIMITSU KOGAKKAI TAIKAI GAKUJUTSU KOENKAI KOEN RONBUNSHU/JAPAN SOCIETY OF PRECISION ENGINEERING. PROCEEDINGS OF THE MEETING. see *ENGINEERING*

SEIMITSU KOGAKKAISHI/JAPAN SOCIETY FOR PRECISION ENGINEERING. JOURNAL. see *ENGINEERING*

681　　　　　GW　　ISSN 0179-9592
SENSOR REPORT; Sensorik Messtechnik Automatisierung. 1985. bi-m. DM.147.66 (foreign DM.194.40). P. Keppler GmbH und Co. KG, Industrie. 2, 63150 Heusenstamm, Germany. TEL 06104-6060. FAX 06104-606333. TELEX 410131. Ed. Dr. G.A. Weissler. adv.; bk.rev.; illus.; circ. 10,000 (controlled). **Document type:** trade publication.

681 001.53　　US　　ISSN 0746-9462
TA165
SENSORS; the journal of applied sensing technology. 1984. m. $55 (free to qualified personnel). Helmers Publishing, Inc., 174 Concord St., Box 874, Peterborough, NH 03458-0874. TEL 603-924-9631. FAX 603-924-2076. Ed. Dorothy Rosa. adv.; tr.lit. circ. 63,000. **Indexed:** A.I.Abstr. (until 1992), CAD CAM Abstr. (until 1992), Robomat. (until 1992), Telegen (until 1989).
—BLDSC (8241.784500); EI; Faxon; UnCover; SWETS. **CCC.**
Description: For users of sensing devices and related products for use in product design and manufacture.
Refereed Serial

681 001.53　　US
SENSOR'S BUYERS GUIDE. 1984. a. Helmers Publishing, Inc., 174 Concord St., Peterborough, NH 03458. TEL 603-924-9631. FAX 603-924-7408. adv.: B&W page $3840; trim 8 1/8 x 10 7/8. circ. 63,000.
Description: Contains information on over 1400 companies in the sensor industry.

SEPARATION. see *MEDICAL SCIENCES — Experimental Medicine, Laboratory Technique*

681　　　　　UK
SIRA REVIEW ANNUAL BROCHURE. 1980. a. Sira Ltd., South Hill, Chislehurst, Kent BR7 5EH, England. TEL 081-467-2636. FAX 081-467-6515. TELEX 896649-SIRA-G. circ. 3,000.
Formerly: Sira Review.

681 629.8 681　　　UK
SIRA SPOTLIGHT. 1971. 2/yr. free to qualified personnel. Sira Ltd., South Hill, Chislehurst, Kent BR7 5EH, England. TEL 081-467-2636. FAX 081-467-6515. TELEX 896649-SIRA-G. Ed. F.E. Jones. charts. circ. 10,000. **Indexed:** Br.Ceram.Abstr., Fluidex, World Surf.Coat., World Text.Abstr.
Incorporates: Measurement and Automation News; Which supersedes: Sira Limited. Annual Report; Which was formerly: British Scientific Instrument Research Association. Annual Report.
Description: Provides information on automation application in scientific and industrial measurement. Areas covered include process instrumentation, software programs, industrial instrumentation and sensors.

SOLID STATE NUCLEAR MAGNETIC RESONANCE; an international journal. see *CHEMISTRY — Analytical Chemistry*

681.2　　　　FR
SPECTRA ANALYSE; la revue scientifique d'actualite sur l'instrumentation d'analyse de mesure et de controle. (Text in French; summaries in English, French) 1972. 6/yr. 350 F. (foreign 527 F.). P C I, B.P. 268, 54512 Vandoeuvre Cedex, France. TEL 83-44-88-00. FAX 83-44-12-90. TELEX 960 568 F BIOTECK. Ed. Robert Brisart. adv. contact: Frederic Reux. bk.rev.; bibl.; illus. circ. 5,000. **Indexed:** Anal.Abstr., Mass Spectr.Bull.
Formerly: Spectra 2000 (ISSN 0399-1172)
Description: Covers physico-chemistry, physics, optics and biology used in university and research labs, as well as quality control labs.

SPECTRUM. see *PHYSICS — Optics*

681.2　　　US　　ISSN 1042-6019
TA165
STANDARDS AND PRACTICES FOR INSTRUMENTATION AND CONTROL. 1963. biennial. price varies. Instrument Society of America, 67 Alexander Dr., Box 12277, Research Triangle Park, NC 27709. TEL 919-549-8411. FAX 919-549-8288. TELEX 802540-ISA-DURM. (Dist. in Japan by: Intercontinental Marketing Corp., I.P.O. Box 5056, Tokyo 100-31, Japan) index. **Document type:** proceedings.
Formerly (until 1989): Standards and Practices for Instrumentation (ISSN 0074-0527)

STANKI I INSTRUMENTY. see *ENGINEERING — Mechanical Engineering*

681　　　　　GW　　ISSN 0171-8096
TA165　　　　　　　　CODEN: TMTMDL
TECHNISCHES MESSEN - T M. 1931. m. DM.218. (Archiv fuer Technisches Messen) R. Oldenbourg Verlag GmbH, Rosenheimerstr. 145, 81671 Munich, Germany. TEL 089-4112-0. FAX 089-4112207. (Subscr. to: Postfach 801360, 81613 Munich, Germany) Ed. Prof. Hesse. adv.; bk.rev.; charts; illus.; tr.lit.; index. circ. 4,000. **Indexed:** Appl.Mech.Rev., ASCA, C.I.S.Abstr., Chem.Abstr., Curr.Cont., Eng.Ind., Excerp.Med., Met.Abstr., Sci.Abstr., Sh.& Vib.Dig. **Document type:** academic/scholarly publication.
—BLDSC (8753.780000); SWETS; CASDDS. **CCC.**
Former titles: Technisches Messen - A T M (ISSN 0340-837X); A T M und Messtechnische Praxis; Archiv fuer Technisches Messen - A T M (ISSN 0003-9411)
Description: Devoted to new developments in measurement techniques. News on surface analysis, signal processing, temperature and pressure measurement technology and new products.

001.64 681.2　　　UK
TEST; state of the art review. 1975. m. (9/yr.). £46($174) in Europe; elsewhere £58 (effective 1994). Angel Publishing Ltd., Kingsland House, 361 City Rd., London EC1V 1LR, England. TEL 071-417-7400. FAX 071-417-7500. Ed. David Evans. adv.; bk.rev.; illus.; tr.lit. circ. 11,000. (tabloid format) **Document type:** trade publication.
—BLDSC (8796.327400). **CCC.**
Former titles: Test-Cadmat; Test (ISSN 0143-2397); (until Feb. 1979): Journal of A T E (ISSN 0307-2649)

TEST & MEASUREMENT WORLD BUYER'S GUIDE. see *ENGINEERING — Electrical Engineering*

681　　　　　GW
UHREN; Journal fuer Sammler klassischer Zeitmesser. 1978. bi-m. DM.132 (students DM.97.20). Callwey Verlag, Postfach 800409, 81604 Munich, Germany. TEL 089-436005-0. FAX 089-43600513. Ed. Ch. Pfeiffer-Belli. adv.; bk.rev. circ. 6,000. **Document type:** trade publication.
—SWETS. **CCC.**
Former titles (until 1992): Alte Uhren und Moderne Zeitmessung (ISSN 0932-2655); Alte Uhren (ISSN 0343-7140)

681　　　　　US
▼**ULTRAPRODUCT FOCUS.** 1992. 4/yr. Cahners Publishing Company (Des Plaines), Division of Reed Elsevier Inc., 1350 E. Touhy Ave., Box 5080, Des Plaines, IL 60017-5080. TEL 708-635-8800. FAX 708-390-2770. Ed. Betty Newboe. adv.: B&W page $5750; trim 10 7/8 x 14 3/4. circ. 65,000. (tabloid format)
Description: Showcases the leading-edge equipment and materials required to develop and manufacture high-tech products.

V W D - MASCHINEN. see *BUSINESS AND ECONOMICS — Investments*

681　　　　　US　　ISSN 1072-9933
V X I JOURNAL. bi-m. 25875 Jefferson, St. Clair Shores, MI 48081. TEL 313-774-8180. FAX 313-774-8182. Ed. Wayne Kristoff. circ. 5,000.

WEIGHING & MEASURING DIRECTORY; buyers guide. see *ENGINEERING*

WHAT'S NEW IN PROCESSING. see *ENGINEERING — Chemical Engineering*

681　　　　　CC
YIBIAO JISHU/TECHNOLOGY OF METERS AND INSTRUMENTS. (Text in Chinese) bi-m. Shanghai Yiqi Yibiao Yanjiusuo - Shanghai Instrument and Meter Research Institute, 225 Longjiang Lu, Shanghai 200082, People's Republic of China. TEL 5417350. Ed. Ding Yinyun.

681.2 001.6　　CC　　ISSN 1000-0380
ZIDONGHUA YIBIAO. (Text in Chinese) 1968. m. $13.32. Shanghai Gongye Zidonghua Yibiao Yanjiusuo - Shanghai Institute of Process Automation Instrumentation, 103 Caobao Lu, Shanghai 200233, People's Republic of China. TEL 4368180. (Dist. overseas by: China International Books Trading Corp., P.O. Box 399, Beijing, P.R. China) (Co-sponsor: China Instrument Society) Ed. Fan Jianrwen. adv. circ. 18,600. **Document type:** academic/scholarly publication.
Description: Covers scientific research, new products and technologies in the field of process automation instrumentation.

INSTRUMENTS — Abstracting, Bibliographies, Statistics

AUTOMATIZALASI, SZAMITASTECHNIKAI ES MERESTECHNIKAI SZAKIRODALMI TAJEKOZTATO/AUTOMATION, COMPUTING, COMPUTERS & MEASUREMENT ABSTRACTS. see *PHYSICS — Abstracting, Bibliographies, Statistics*

681.2　　　US　　ISSN 0195-4938
　　　　　　　　　CODEN: CCHIDW
C A SELECTS. CHEMICAL INSTRUMENTATION. s-w. $210 (effective Jan. 1994). Chemical Abstracts Service (Subsidiary of: American Chemical Society), 2540 Olentangy River Rd., Box 3012, Columbus, OH 43210-0012. TEL 614-447-3600. FAX 614-447-3713. TELEX 6842086. **Document type:** abstracting/indexing.
Description: Covers the use of analyzers, detectors, and meters in chemistry related areas; and the construction and modification of such instrumentation.

681 016　　　RU　　ISSN 0131-7997
EKSPRESS-INFORMATSIYA. ISPYTATEL'NYE PRIBORY I STENDY. 1961. 48/yr. 52.80 Rub. Vsesoyuznyi Institut Nauchno-Tekhnicheskoi Informatsii (VINITI), Baltiiskaya ul., 14, Moscow A-219, Russia. (Subscr. to: Mezhdunarodnaya Kniga, Dimitrova ul. 39, 113095 Moscow, Russia)

681 016   RU   ISSN 0131-0224
**EKSPRESS-INFORMATSIYA.
KONTROL'NO-IZMERITEL'NAYA TEKHNIKA.** 1957. 48/yr. 52.80 Rub. Vsesoyuznyi Institut Nauchno-Tekhnicheskoi Informatsii (VINITI), Baltiiskaya ul., 14, Moscow A-219, Russia. (Subscr. to: Mezhdunarodnaya Kniga, Dimitrova ul. 39, 113095 Moscow, Russia)

EXCERPTA MEDICA. SECTION 27: BIOPHYSICS, BIO-ENGINEERING AND MEDICAL INSTRUMENTATION. see *MEDICAL SCIENCES — Abstracting, Bibliographies, Statistics*

KEY ABSTRACTS - MEASUREMENTS IN PHYSICS. see *METROLOGY AND STANDARDIZATION — Abstracting, Bibliographies, Statistics*

SACHGUETERERZEUGUNG SCHNELLBERICHT. see *CERAMICS, GLASS AND POTTERY — Abstracting, Bibliographies, Statistics*

INSURANCE

368   US
A A I S VIEWPOINT. 1976. q. free. American Association of Insurance Services, 1035 S. York Rd., Bensenville, IL 60106. TEL 708-595-3225. FAX 708-595-4647. Ed. Carol Poynter. circ. 1,500. (back issues avail.) Document type: trade publication.
   Description: Discusses property and casualty insurance issues.

A A P P O JOURNAL. (American Association of Preferred Provider Organizations) see *BUSINESS AND ECONOMICS*

368   AT   ISSN 0314-8580
A I I JOURNAL. 1919. 5/yr. Aus.$35. Australian Insurance Institute, 31 Queen St., Melbourne, Vic. 3000, Australia. TEL 03-629-4021. FAX 03-629-4204. Ed. M.J. Sheehan. adv.: B&W page Aus.$2990. bk.rev. circ. 17,000. Document type: academic/scholarly publication.
   Formerly: Australian Insurance Institute Journal (ISSN 0084-7453)

368   US
A L F I NEWS. (Auto, Life, Fire, Insurance) 1936. bi-w. State Farm Insurance Cos., One State Farm Plaza, Bloomington, IL 61710. TEL 309-766-2628. Ed. Davina Frazier. circ. 8,000. Document type: newsletter.
   Description: Information for employees at State Farm's home office.

368   US
A L I C O NEWS; Caribbean, Americas, Europe & New Zealand. 1964. 3/yr. American Life Insurance Co., One ALICO Plaza, Box 2226, Wilmington, DE 19899. TEL 301-594-2900. Ed. Ellen J. Roberts. circ. 5,000.
   Description: Conveys company and industry news to worldwide field force.

A P P A DIGEST. (American Professional Practice Association) see *BUSINESS AND ECONOMICS — Investments*

A S P A FLASH. (American Salvage Pool Association) see *TRANSPORTATION — Automobiles*

A S P A REPORT. (American Salvage Pool Association) see *TRANSPORTATION — Automobiles*

368   US   ISSN 0001-3730
ACACIA CLARION. 1940. bi-m. Acacia Mutual Life Insurance Co., 51 Louisiana Ave. N.W., Washington, DC 20001. TEL 202-628-4506. adv.; bk.rev.; charts; illus.; stat. circ. 2,000.

ACCIDENTS CLAIMS JOURNAL. see *LAW*

ACCOUNTANCY, BUSINESS & INSURANCE REVIEW. see *BUSINESS AND ECONOMICS — Accounting*

ACCOUNTANTS' LIABILITY REVIEW. see *BUSINESS AND ECONOMICS — Accounting*

368   FR   ISSN 0761-7593
ACTU'A G F. 1970. bi-m. free. Assurances Generales de France, 87 rue de Richelieu, 75002 Paris, France. TEL 42-44-19-50. FAX 42-44-19-56. Eds. Alain de la Baume, Dimitri Thanassekos. bk.rev. circ. 18,000.
   Formerly: Assurances Generales de France. Informations (ISSN 0066-989X)

368   SP   ISSN 0012-947X
ACTUALIDAD ASEGURADORA; el eco del seguro. 1891. w. 22000 ptas.($80) I N E S E, Santa Engracia, 151, 28003 Madrid, Spain. Ed. Manuel Maestro Lopez. adv.; bk.rev. 12,000.

368 332.6   MX
ACTUALIDAD EN SEGUROS Y FIANZAS. q. Comision Nacional de Seguros y Fianzas, Av. de los Insurgentes Sur 1971, Plaza Inn, Torre 2 N., 2o piso, 01020 Mexico DF, Mexico. Document type: government publication.
   Description: Dissertation and analysis of the activities of the insurance and surety bonds sector. Includes information on companies' financial situations and legal modifications about the insurance business.

368   US
ACTUARIAL DIGEST. 1982. bi-m. $24. Actuarial Digest Publishing Company, Box 1127, Ponte Vedra Beach, FL 32004-1127. TEL 904-273-1245. Ed. Gene Hubbard; Pub. Eric R. Hubbard. adv. contact: Bob Green. circ. 14,000.
   Description: Articles of interest to the working professional actuary.

368 657   US
ACTUARIAL UPDATE. 1972. m. membership. American Academy of Actuaries, 1720 I St., N.W., 7th Fl., Washington, DC 20006. TEL 202-223-8196. FAX 202-872-1948. (Subscr. to: 475 N. Martingale Rd., Ste. 800, Schaumburg, IL 60173) Ed. Jeffrey Speicher. circ. 11,000. (back issues avail.) Document type: government publication, newsletter.
   Description: Covers insurance, pensions and employee benefits.

368.01   NE
ACTUARIEEL GENOOTSCHAP. MEDEDELINGENBLAD. 1963. 6/yr. membership. Actuarieel Genootschap - Actuarial Society of the Netherlands, Postbus 259, 1000 AG Amsterdam, Netherlands. TEL 31-20-5942685. FAX 31-20-6937968. bibl. circ. 765. (looseleaf format) Document type: proceedings.

368.01   NE   ISSN 0929-4562
▼**DE ACTUARIS.** (Text mainly in Dutch) 1993. 6/yr. fl.120 (effective 1994). Actuarieel Genootschap - Actuarial Society of the Netherlands, Postbus 259, 1000 AG Amsterdam, Netherlands. FAX 31-20-6937968. Ed. W. Dullemond. adv.: B&W page fl.1500. circ. 1,400. (back issues avail.) Document type: academic/scholarly publication, bulletin.
   Description: Publishes articles on topics of interest to actuaries, as well as activities of the society and sections and interviews.

368.01   US   ISSN 0001-7825
ACTUARY. 1967. m. (Sep.-Jun.). $15 (foreign $22.50)(effective 1991). Society of Actuaries, 475 N. Martingale, No. 800, Schaumburg, IL 60173-2226. TEL 708-706-3500. FAX 708-706-3599. Ed. Linda Emory. adv. circ. 14,000.
   Description: Publishes articles on professional issues and SOA activities.

368   US
ADJUSTERS' REFERENCE GUIDE. 1960. q. $425 ($190 for 4 supplements). Insurance Field Company, Box 24244, Louisville, KY 40224-0244. TEL 502-491-5857. FAX 502-491-5905. Eds. Ralph Wm. Bourne, Ron Anderson. (looseleaf format)

368.012
ADVANCED UNDERWRITING SERVICE. 1935. 7 base vols. plus m. updates. $429 (renewals $214) (effective 1993). Dearborn - R & R Newkirk, 520 N. Dearborn St., Chicago, IL 60610-4354. TEL 312-836-4400. FAX 312-836-1021. (Subscr. to: Box 830350, Birmingham, AL 35283-0350. TEL 800-633-4931) circ. 3,400. (looseleaf format)

368.3   US   ISSN 0001-9585
AETNAIZER. vol.52,1970. bi-m. free. Aetna Life and Casualty, 151 Farmington Ave., RWAB, Hartford, CT 06156. TEL 203-273-7973. Ed. Mary DiLeo. adv.; charts; illus.; circ. 18,000 (controlled). Document type: corporate report.
   Description: For independent insurance agents representing Aetna products and services.

368   SA
AFRICAN INSURANCE & FINANCE RECORD. 1924. m. R.24. P.O. Box 2651, Cape Town 8001, South Africa. TEL 021 46-6932. Ed. Fred Roffey. adv.; bk.rev.; charts; illus. circ. 3,000. Indexed: Ind.S.A.Per.
   Incorporates: African Insurance Record (ISSN 0002-001X)

368.4   SZ   ISSN 0379-7074
HD7237
AFRICAN NEWS SHEET. French edition: Nouvelles Africaines de Securite Sociale. 1967. irreg. International Social Security Association, Case Postale 1, CH-1211 Geneva 22, Switzerland. (Dist. by: I S S A Regional Office for Africa, Boite Postale 10113, Lome, Togo) Document type: bulletin.
   Formerly: African Social Security Series (ISSN 0065-4043)
   Description: News and information on ISSA's activities in the region, and on developments in African social security schemes.

368   US
AGENCY NEWS. 1905. bi-w. free to qualified personnel. Equitable Life Assurance Society of the U.S., 787 Seventh Ave., Area 39N, New York, NY 10019. TEL 212-554-2100. Ed. Tom Donlon. adv.; charts; illus. circ. 15,000.
   Former titles: Agency News Items; Agency Items (ISSN 0002-0788)

AGENT NEWSLETTER. see *AGRICULTURE — Agricultural Economics*

368   US
AGENTS INFORMATION SERVICE. 1984. m. $27. Insurance Field Company, Box 24244, Louisville, KY 40224. TEL 502-491-5857. FAX 502-491-5905. Ed. Tad De Santo. charts; illus.; stat.; tr.lit. circ. 5,500. (looseleaf format; back issues avail.)
   Description: Marketing tool for insurance companies, excess and surplus lines brokers, and MGAs.

368   US
AIM (BOSTON). 1977. bi-m. membership only. Commercial Union Insurance Companies, One Beacon St., Boston, MA 02108. TEL 617-725-6000. Ed. Susan Kaplovitz. charts; illus.; stat. circ. 10,000.
   Description: Contains information of the Company's insurance products for the salesforce.

ALBERTA HAIL AND CROP INSURANCE CORPORATION. ANNUAL REPORT. see *AGRICULTURE — Crop Production And Soil*

368   CN   ISSN 0712-9343
ALBERTA INSURANCE DIRECTORY; insurance companies, agents and adjusters. 1982. a. Can.$20. Arbutus Publications Ltd., P.O. Box 35070, Sta. E., Vancouver, BC V6M 4G1, Canada. TEL 604-687-8003. Ed. W.D.S. Earle. adv. circ. 1,000.

368.4   NE   ISSN 0401-331X
ALGEMEEN WERKLOOSHEIDSFONDS. JAARVERSLAG. 1949. a. Bureau Centrale Fondsen - Social Security Council, Postbus 100, 2700 AC Zoetermeer, Netherlands. Document type: corporate report.

368   US   ISSN 1044-9426
RA395.A3
ALL ABOUT MEDICARE. 1987. a. $7.95. National Underwriter Co., 505 Gest St., Cincinnati, OH 45203. TEL 513-721-2140. FAX 513-721-0126.
   Description: Provides comprehensive information on Medicare benefits and costs in a question and answer format.

368   BE   ISSN 0772-4764
ALLE RISICO'S. (Text in Flemish) s-m. 1990 BEF. C E D Samsom (Subsidiary of: Wolters Samsom Belgie n.v.), Kouterveld 14, B-1831 Diegem, Belgium. TEL 32-2-7231111.
   Description: Reports on various aspects of the insurance industry.

ALLENSBACHER MARKT-ANALYSE - WERBETRAEGER-ANALYSE. see *BUSINESS AND ECONOMICS — Marketing And Purchasing*

INSURANCE

368   GW   ISSN 0943-4569
TJ3   CODEN: MSCNA3
ALLIANZ REPORT; fuer Risiko und Sicherheit. (Text in German; summaries in Dutch, English, French, Italian) 1924. bi-m. DM.130. Allianz Versicherungs-AG, Koeniginstr. 28, 80802 Munich, Germany. TEL 089-3800-2163. Eds. E. Siepe, J.M. Zimmer. bk.rev.; illus. circ. 4,000. **Indexed:** C.I.S. Abstr., Cadscan, Chem.Abstr., Eng.Ind., Excerp.Med., Fuel & Energy Abstr., INIS Atomind., Lead Abstr., Met.Abstr., Sci.Abstr., Sh.& Vib.Dig., World Alum.Abstr., Zincscan. **Document type:** bulletin.
—BLDSC (0792.600500); SWETS; CASDDS.
  Formerly (until 1993): Maschinenschaden (ISSN 0025-4517).

368   GW
ALLIANZ ZEITUNG; Zeitschrift fuer den Aussen- und Innendienst der Allianz-Gesellschaften. 1919. m. free. Allianz Versicherungs-AG, Koeniginstr. 28, 80802 Munich, Germany. TEL 089-3800-2163. Ed.Bd. **Document type:** newsletter.

368.01   US   ISSN 0569-2032
HG8754
AMERICAN ACADEMY OF ACTUARIES. YEARBOOK. a. $25. American Academy of Actuaries, 1720 I St., N.W., 7th Fl., Washington, DC 20006. TEL 202-223-8196. FAX 202-872-1948. (Subscr. to: 475 N. Martingale Rd., Ste. 800, Schaumburg, IL 60173) index. circ. 11,000. **Document type:** directory, government publication.
  Description: Directory of the Academy's board of directors and committees. Includes bylaws, qualification standards, and guides to professional conduct.

368   US   ISSN 0002-7200
HG9651
AMERICAN AGENT AND BROKER. 1929. m. $24 (free to qualified personnel). Commerce Publishing Co., 330 N. Fourth St., St. Louis, MO 63102-2036. TEL 314-421-5445. Ed. George Williams. adv. contact: Dee Severino. bk.rev.; illus. circ. 39,125. (also avail. in microfilm from UMI) **Indexed:** ABI Inform. **Document type:** trade publication.
—UMI.
  Formerly: Local Agent.
  Description: Provides sales management information to help multi-line independent insurance agents serve their clients better.

AMERICAN ASSOCIATION OF CROP INSURERS WASHINGTON UPDATE. see AGRICULTURE — Agricultural Economics

AMERICAN JOURNAL OF MEDICAL QUALITY. see BUSINESS AND ECONOMICS — Management

AMERICAN MARITIME CASES. see LAW — Maritime Law

AMERICAN SOCIETY OF APPRAISERS. NEWSLINE. see BUSINESS AND ECONOMICS — Banking And Finance

368.32   US   ISSN 1052-2875
HG8751
AMERICAN SOCIETY OF C L U & CH F C. JOURNAL. (Chartered Life Underwriters) 1946. bi-m. $32 (foreign $57). American Society of C L U & Ch F C, 270 Bryn Mawr Ave., Bryn Mawr, PA 19010. TEL 215-526-2500. FAX 215-526-2538. Ed. Kenneth Black. adv.; bk.rev.; charts; illus.; stat.; index, cum.index. circ. 42,000. (also avail. in microform from UMI; back issues avail.; reprint service avail. from UMI,WSH) **Indexed:** ABI Inform., B.P.I., BPIA, Bus.Ind., C.L.I., L.R.I., Leg.Per., P.A.I.S., PSI, Tr.& Indus.Ind. **Document type:** trade publication.
—BLDSC (4692.660000); Faxon; UnCover; UMI.
  Former titles (until 1986): American Society of C L U. Journal (ISSN 0742-9517); C L U Journal (ISSN 0007-8573).

AMERISURE SAFETY NEWS. see PUBLIC HEALTH AND SAFETY

346   NE
▼**AMSTERDAM FINANCIAL SERIES. INSURANCE AND E E C LAW: COMMENTARY.** (Text in English) 1994. base vol. (plus irreg. updates). Kluwer Law and Taxation Publishers (Subsidiary of: Wolters Kluwer N.V.), P.O. Box 23, 7400 GA Deventer, Netherlands. TEL 31-5700-47261. FAX 31-5700-22244. TELEX 49295 KLUDV NL. (Dist. by: Libresso Distribution Centre, P.O. Box 23, 7400 GA Deventer, Netherlands. TEL 31-5700-33155. FAX 31-5700-33834; In N. America: Kluwer Law and Taxation Publishers, 675 Massachusetts Ave., Cambridge, MA 02139. TEL 617-354-0140. FAX 617-354-8595) Eds. Martijn van Empel, Hubert Drabbe. (looseleaf format)
  Description: Discusses the impact of EC directives on the insurance industry, both on day-to-day business and at the intracommunity level.

DIE ANGESTELLTENVERSICHERUNG. see PUBLIC ADMINISTRATION

368   FR   ISSN 0299-5514
ANNUAIRE DES ASSURANCES. 1909. a. 930 F. (effective July 1992). 2 rue de Chateaudun, 75009 Paris, France. FAX 48-78-36-59. TELEX 643 040 F.
  Formerly (until 1986): Annuaire des Assurances et l'Assureur-Conseil (ISSN 0183-7923)

368   IT   ISSN 0084-6635
ANNUARIO ITALIANO DELLE IMPRESE ASSICURATRICI. 1925. a. L.150000. Associazione Nazionale fra le Imprese Assicuratrici, Via della Frezza, 70, 00186 Rome, Italy. TEL 06-326881. FAX 06-3227135. Ed. Fabrizio Moretti. circ. 5,000. **Document type:** directory.

368   SP   ISSN 0211-125X
ANUARIO ESPANOL DE SEGUROS. 1910. a. 18000 ptas. I N E S E, Santa Engracia, 151, 28003 Madrid, Spain. circ. 7,500.

APPRAISERS' INFORMATION EXCHANGE. see BUSINESS AND ECONOMICS — Investments

368.4   NE
ARBEIDSONGESCHIKTHEIDSFONDS EN ALGEMEEN ARBEIDSONGESCHIKTHEIDSFONDS. JAARVERSLAG. 1977. a. Bureau Centrale Fondsen - Social Security Council, Postbus 100, 2700 AC Zoetermeer, Netherlands. **Document type:** corporate report.
  Former titles: Algemeen Arbeidsongeschiktheidsfonds. Jaarverslag; Arbeidsongeschiktheidsfonds. Jaarverslag.

368.4   AG   ISSN 0004-1025
ARGENTINA. DIRECCION NACIONAL DE ASISTENCIA NACIONAL. DAS.* 1961. q. Direccion Nacional de Asistencia Nacional, Cangallo 524, Buenos Aires, Argentina. Ed.Bd. bibl.; illus.

368   FR   ISSN 0150-6854
L'ARGUS ET LA SEMAINE; journal international des assurances. 1877. w. 990 F. Securitas, 2 rue de Chateaudun, 75009 Paris, France. TEL 45-96-13-00. FAX 1-48-78-36-59. Ed. Brigitte Raymond. adv.; bk.rev.; bibl.; charts; stat.; index. circ. 22,809.
  Formed by the merger of: Argus (ISSN 0004-1173); Semaine (ISSN 0150-6846)

368   SP   ISSN 0004-430X
ASEGURADORES. 1968. 10/yr. 3500 ptas. Colegios de Agentes y Corredores de Seguros, Consejo General, Nunez de Balboa 116, 28006 Madrid, Spain. FAX 2622702. TELEX 43779 CACS E. Dir. Jose Espinosa Gasco. adv.; bk.rev.; illus.; stat.; circ. 29,000 (controlled).

368   SP
ASESOR. 6/yr. Marques de San Esteban 1, 5o, Gijon (Asturias), Spain. TEL 85-34-81-04. Ed. Jose R. Llana Garcia. circ. 90,000.

368   SZ   ISSN 0518-8881
HD7090
ASIAN NEWS SHEET. (Text in English) 1972. s-a. free. International Social Security Association, Case Postale 1, CH-1211 Geneva 22, Switzerland. (Dist. by: I S S A Regional Office for Asia and the Pacific, c/o ILO Area Office, 7 Sardar Patel Marg, New Delhi 110 021, India) **Indexed:** World Bibl.Soc.Sec. **Document type:** bulletin.
  Formerly: Social Security Series for Asia and Oceania.
  Description: Information on social security in Asia and the Pacific, also giving information about ISSA activities in the region.

368.32   US
ASSETS (BRYN MAWR). (Former name of issuing body: American Society of Chartered Life Underwriters) 1980. bi-m. membership. American Society of C L U & Ch F C, 270 Bryn Mawr Ave., Bryn Mawr, PA 19010. TEL 215-526-2500. Ed. Carl L. Hall Jr. circ. 1,200. **Document type:** trade publication.

368   IT   ISSN 0004-511X
ASSICURAZIONI; rivista di diritto, economia e finanza delle assicurazioni private. 1934. bi-m. L.95000. Istituto Nazionale delle Assicurazioni, S.p.A., Via Sallustiana 51, 00187 Rome, Italy. TEL 06-4882497. FAX 06-47224595. TELEX 610336 INA RM1. (Subscr. to: Periodici Le Monnier, Via Antonio Meucci, 2, 50015 Grassina (Florence), Italy) Ed. Brando Battistig. adv.; bk.rev.; abstr.; tr.lit.; index. circ. 2,600.

368.3   US   ISSN 0066-9598
ASSOCIATION OF LIFE INSURANCE MEDICAL DIRECTORS OF AMERICA. TRANSACTIONS. 1889. a. $15. Association of Life Insurance Medical Directors of America, Southeastern Head Office, Metropolitan Plaza, Tampa, FL 33607. Ed. Dr. Walter S. Clough. cum.index every 5 yrs.; circ. 1,000 (controlled). (also avail. in microform from UMI) **Indexed:** Ind.Med.
—BLDSC (8903.000000); UMI.

368   FR   ISSN 0004-6019
ASSURANCE FRANCAISE. 1947. 22/yr. 940 F. Societe d'Editions et de Publications l'Assurance Francaise, 55 rue de Chateaudun, 75009 Paris, France. TEL 45-26-89-00. FAX 42-80-45-93. TELEX 283 392F. Ed. Genevieve Morin. adv.; bk.rev. circ. 9,500.

368   FR
ASSURANCE MUTUELLE. (Text in French) 1925. q. free. Reunion des Organismes d'Assurance Mutuelle, 114 rue la Boetie, 75008 Paris, France. TEL 1-42-25-59-37. FAX 1-42-56-04-49. Ed. M. Belembert. bk.rev. circ. 4,500. **Document type:** corporate report.

368   CN   ISSN 0004-6027
HG8015
ASSURANCES; revue trimestrielle des assurances. (Text mainly in French; occasionally in English) 1933. q. Can.$50 (foreign Can.$54. Sodarcan Inc., 1140 Ouest, Blvd. de Maisonneuve, 7e etage, Montreal, Que. H3A 3H1, Canada. TEL 514-282-1112. FAX 514-282-9841. Ed. Remi Moreau. adv.: B&W page Can.$175; trim 6 x 9. bk.rev.; bibl.; charts. circ. 1,000. **Indexed:** Can.Per.Ind., Ind.Can.L.P.L., P.A.I.S.For.Lang.Ind., P.A.I.S., Pt.de Rep. (1983-).
—BLDSC (1746.790000).

368   DK   ISSN 0109-1875
ASSURANDOEREN. 1964. m. DKK 200 to non-members. Centralforeningen for Danske Assurandoerer, Strandvejen 32 D, 2100 Copenhagen, Denmark. TEL 45-39-27-30-33. FAX 45-39-27-55-77. Ed. Peter Hemicke. adv.; illus. circ. 2,800.
  Former titles (until 1983): Danske Assurandoerer (ISSN 0109-1468); (until 1982): Tidsskrift for Danske Assurandoerer (ISSN 0109-145X)

368   NE   ISSN 0167-3882
ASSURANTIE MAGAZINE. (Text in Dutch) 1979. bi-w. fl.89. Samsom BedrijfsInformatie, Postbus 4, Prinses Margrietlaan 3, 2404 MA Alphen aan den Rijn, Netherlands. TEL 01720-66571. FAX 01720-22892. TELEX 39682. Ed. Richard Vroom. adv.; bk.rev.; circ. 30,000 (controlled).

INSURANCE

368   UK   ISSN 0515-0361
ASTIN BULLETIN. (Text in English or French) 1958. s-a. £25($49) (International Actuarial Association, Astin Section) Tieto Ltd., Bank House, 8A Hill Rd., Clevedon, Bristol BS21 7HH, England. Eds. H. Buhlmann, D.H. Reid. adv.; bk.rev.; index. circ. 2,000. (back issues avail.) **Indexed:** World Bank.Abstr.
—BLDSC (1747.065000); SWETS.

368.01   US
ATLANTIC STATES INSURANCE.★ 1986. bi-m. $20. Independent Insurance Agents Association of Maryland, Pennsylvania, Delaware & Washington, D.C., 2408 Peppermill Dr., Glen Burnie, MD 21061-3257. (Subscr. to: Chase Communications Group, 495 New Rochelle Rd., Bronxville, NY 10708) Ed. George Boue. adv. circ. 4,000. (back issues avail.)
Formerly (until vol.2, 1987): I Magazine.

ATTORNEY'S GUIDE TO SOCIAL SECURITY DISABILITY CLAIMS. see LAW — Legal Aid

368   GW   ISSN 0933-8357
AUSSENDIENST INFORMATIONEN; Trainingskurs fuer systematische Akquisition. (Text in Danish, Dutch, English, Finnish, French, German, Italian, Norwegian, Spanish, Swedish) 1969. fortn. DM.259.20. Verlag Norbert Mueller AG und Co. KG, Ingolstaedterstr. 20, 80807 Munich, Germany. TEL 089-3509302. FAX 089-35093218. Ed. Renate vom Hofe. cum.index: 1985-1991. circ. 19,000. (back issues avail.) **Document type:** trade publication.

368   US   ISSN 0279-9006
AUSTIN INSURANCE REPORT. ADMINISTRATIVE EDITION. 1956. 51/yr. $70. Report Publications, Inc., Box 12368, Austin, TX 78711. TEL 512-478-5663. FAX 512-478-2345. Eds. Bill Kidd, Homer Olsen. circ. 500.

368 610   AT   ISSN 0815-1008
HD7102.A8
AUSTRALIA. DEPARTMENT OF HEALTH. OPERATIONS OF THE REGISTERED HEALTH INSURANCE ORGANIZATIONS. ANNUAL REPORT. 1984. a. Australian Government Publishing Service, G.P.O. Box 84, Canberra, A.C.T. 2601, Australia. **Document type:** government publication.

368.4   AT
AUSTRALIA. DEPARTMENT OF SOCIAL SECURITY. ANNUAL REPORT OF THE DIRECTOR-GENERAL. 1972. a. price varies. Australian Government Publishing Service, Publishing Branch, G.P.O. Box 84, Canberra, A.C.T. 2601, Australia. TEL 61-6-295-4612. FAX 61-6-295-4500. illus.; stat. **Document type:** government publication.

328.94 368.9   AT   ISSN 1032-1020
AUSTRALIA. INSURANCE AND SUPERANNUATION COMMISSION. ANNUAL REPORT. (Supplement avail.: Industry Statistics (Canberra) (ISSN 1032-1039)) 1974. a. price varies. Australian Government Publishing Service, G.P.O. Box 84, Canberra, A.C.T. 2601, Australia. TEL 61-6-295-4612. FAX 61-6-295-4500. illus.; stat. **Document type:** government publication.
Formerly (until 1988): Australia. Insurance Commissioner. Annual Report (ISSN 0311-8967)

368   AT   ISSN 1031-7937
AUSTRALIA. LIFE INSURANCE GROUP. HALF YEARLY FINANCIAL BULLETIN ON LIFE INSURANCE. s-a. Aus.$2.25 per no. Australian Government Publishing Service, G.P.O. Box 84, Canberra, A.C.T. 2601, Australia. TEL 61-6-295-4612. FAX 61-6-295-4500. Ed.Bd. circ. 1,020. **Document type:** government publication.
—CCC.
Formerly (until 1987): Australia. Office of the Life Insurance Commissioner. Half Yearly Financial and Statistical Bulletin (ISSN 0728-6864)

368   AU
AUSTRALIAN AND NEW ZEALAND INSURANCE REPORTER. (In 3 vols.) 1979. 12/yr. $ C C H Australia Ltd., P.O. Box 230, North Ryde, N.S.W. 2113, Australia. TEL 888-2555. FAX 02-888-7324. (looseleaf format)

AUSTRALIAN SUPERANNUATION LAW & PRACTICE. see SOCIAL SERVICES AND WELFARE

368.3   US   ISSN 0093-0466
HG9970.A5
AUTOMOBILE INSURANCE LOSSES, COLLISION COVERAGES, VARIATIONS BY MAKE AND SERIES. (Subseries of its Research Report) 1972. s-a. free. Highway Loss Data Institute, c/o Stephen L. Oesch, General Counsel, Sec.-Treas., 1005 N. Glebe Rd., Ste. 800, Arlington, VA 22201. TEL 703-247-1600. FAX 703-247-1678. illus.; stat. circ. 2,500. **Indexed:** SRI.

368   US
KFN5298.A8P52
AUTOMOBILE LIABILITY NEWSLETTER. 1991. s-a. $10 to non-members (effective 1994). New York State Bar Association, Insurance, Negligence and Compensation Law Section, 1 Elk St., Albany, NY 12207. TEL 518-463-3200. FAX 518-487-5699. Ed. Eric Dranoff. adv.; bk.rev.; circ. 4,050 (controlled). **Document type:** academic/scholarly publication, newsletter.

368   CN   ISSN 0707-7114
B.C. AGENT. 1949. bi-m. Can.$15 to non-members. (Insurance Agents' Association of British Columbia) Arbutus Publications Ltd., P.O. Box 35070, Sta. E, Vancouver, B.C. V6M 4G1, Canada. TEL 604-687-8003. Ed. William D. S. Earle. adv.; illus. circ. 1,100.

368   CN
B.C. BROKER. (British Columbia) 1949. 6/yr. Insurance Publications Ltd., Box 35070, Sta. E, Vancouver, B.C. V6M 4G1, Canada. TEL 604-687-8003. FAX 604-687-2733. Ed. Patrick Durrant. adv.

368   GW   ISSN 0723-7561
DIE B G; Fachzeitschrift fuer Arbeitssicherheit und Unfallversicherung. 1876. m. DM.117.60. (Hauptverband der Gewerblichen Berufsgenossenschaften e.V.) Erich Schmidt Verlag GmbH & Co. (Bielefeld), Viktoriastr. 44A, 33602 Bielefeld, Germany. TEL 0521-583080. (Subscr. to: Postfach 102451, 33524 Bielefeld, Germany) Ed. Dr. Sokoll. adv.; bk.rev. **Indexed:** INIS Atomind., World Bibl.Soc.Sec. **Document type:** trade publication.
—BLDSC (1947.487000); SWETS. **CCC**.
Formerly: Berufsgenossenschaft (ISSN 0005-9544)

368   GW   ISSN 0937-0811
B G W MITTEILUNGEN. 1970. q. Berufsgenossenschaft fuer Gesundheitsdienst und Wohlfahrtspflege, Pappelallee 35-37, 22089 Hamburg, Germany. TEL 040-202070. FAX 040-20207-525. TELEX 2174949. Ed. Gerhard Mehrtens. **Document type:** newsletter.
Formerly (until 1988): B G W Mitteilungsblatt (ISSN 0178-8574)

B I F U REPORT. (Banking Insurance & Finance Union) see BUSINESS AND ECONOMICS — Banking And Finance

B N A PENSION & BENEFITS REPORTER. see BUSINESS AND ECONOMICS — Labor And Industrial Relations

368 331   US
▼**B W C NEWS**. 1992. q. Ohio Bureau of Workers' Compensation, Communications Department, 30 W. Spring St., 3rd Fl., Columbus, OH 43266-0581. TEL 614-466-1320. Ed. Robert Loomis. **Document type:** newsletter.
Description: News and information on workers' compensation and related issues for Ohio employers.

368   US   ISSN 8756-5374
BAD FAITH LAW REPORT. 1985. 10/yr. $240. Stratton Press, Box 22391, San Francisco, CA 94122. (Subscr. to: Box 96, San Ramon, CA 94583) Ed. Stephen Ashley. index; circ. 900 (paid). (back issues avail.) **Document type:** newsletter.
Description: A compendium of recent developments in the law of bad faith relating to insurance claims settlement practice, including summaries of all related United States appellate decisions.

BANK INSURANCE AND PROTECTION BULLETIN. see BUSINESS AND ECONOMICS — Banking And Finance

BANKINSURANCE NEWS. see BUSINESS AND ECONOMICS — Banking And Finance

BANKS IN INSURANCE REPORT. see BUSINESS AND ECONOMICS — Banking And Finance

368   US
KFC290.A15C3
BARCLAYS INSURANCE LAW REPORT (CALIFORNIA EDITION). 1990. m. $225. Barclays Law Publishers, 400 Oyster Point Blvd., Ste. 500, S. San Francisco, CA 94080. TEL 415-588-1155. FAX 415-244-6619. Ed. George Lydon. q. index. (looseleaf format; back issues avail.) **Document type:** newsletter.

368   GW
BARMER. 1928. 4/yr. free. Barmer Ersatzkasse, Redaktion, 42271 Wuppertal, Germany. TEL 0202-568-0. FAX 0202-5681459. Ed. Susanne Ruesberg-Uhrig. bk.rev.; charts; illus.; index. circ. 5,600,000. **Document type:** trade publication.
Formerly: Barmer Ersatzkasse (ISSN 0005-5980)

368   GW
BARMER BRUECKE; Zeitschrift fuer die Vertrauensleute der Barmer Ersatzkasse. 1951. 4/yr. free. Barmer Ersatzkasse, Redaktion, 42271 Wuppertal, Germany. TEL 0202-568-0. FAX 0202-5681459. Ed. Susanne Ruesberg-Uhrig. bk.rev.; charts; illus.; index. circ. 180,000. **Document type:** trade publication.
Formerly: B E K - Bruecke (ISSN 0005-8238)

368   BE   ISSN 0046-9726
BELGIUM. INSTITUT NATIONAL D'ASSURANCE MALADIE INVALIDITE. I.N.A.M.I. BULLETIN D'INFORMATION/BELGIUM. RIJKSINSTITUUT VOOR ZIEKTE- EN INVALIDITEITSVERZEKERING. R.I.Z.I.V. INFORMATIEBLAD. (Editions in Dutch, French) 1964. 6/yr. 800 BEF (effective 1993). Institut National d'Assurance Maladie-Invalidite - Rijksinstituut voor Ziekte- en Invaliditeitsverzekering, Av. de Tervuren 211, B-1150 Brussels, Belgium. TEL 32-2-739-71-11. FAX 32-2-739-72-91. Ed. Raphael Chutyser. bk.rev.; charts; stat.; index, cum.index. circ. 4,600 (2,150 Dutch ed.; 2,450 French ed.) **Document type:** bulletin, government publication.
Description: Provides a detailed review of the activities and policies of the institute.

368.4   BE
BELGIUM. INSTITUT NATIONAL D'ASSURANCES SOCIALES POUR TRAVAILLEURS INDEPENDANTS. RAPPORT ANNUEL. Flemish edition: Belgium. Rijksinstituut voor de Sociale Verzekeringen der Zelfstandigen. Jaarverslag. 1970. a. free. Institut National d'Assurances Sociales pour Travailleurs Independants, Bibliotheque - Bureau 4-7 (Wat.), Place Jean Jacobs 6, B-1000 Brussels, Belgium. TEL 32-2-507-6211. FAX 32-2-511-2153. **Document type:** government publication.
Description: Details activities for each branch of the institute.

331.252 368   UK   ISSN 0268-764X
BENEFITS & COMPENSATION INTERNATIONAL. 1971. 10/yr. $400 (foreign £230) (effective 1994). Pension Publications Ltd., East Wing, 4th Fl., Hope House, 45 Great Peter St., London SW1P 3LT, England. TEL 071-222-0288. FAX 071-799-2163. Ed. Irena St. John-Brooks. adv.; bk.rev.; charts; index. circ. 1,190. (also avail. in microform from UMI; back issues avail.) **Indexed:** ABI Inform., BPIA, Bus.Ind., Manage.Cont., World Bibl.Soc.Sec. **Document type:** trade publication.
—BLDSC (1891.467000); SWETS.
Formerly (until 1985): Benefits International (ISSN 0045-172X)
Description: Covers international employee benefits and compensation trends. Emphasis is on design of private pension plans and pension fund investment.

BENEFITS LAW JOURNAL. see LAW — Legal Aid

368 622   GW   ISSN 0933-0127
BERGBAU-BERUFSGENOSSENSCHAFT. JAHRESBERICHT. 1887. a. free. Bergbau-Berufsgenossenschaft, Hunscheidtstr. 18, 44789 Bochum, Germany. TEL 0234-316352. FAX 0234-316300. adv.; bk.rev.; stat. circ. 1,600. **Indexed:** GeoRef. **Document type:** corporate report.
Formerly: Bergbau-Berufsgenossenschaft. Geschaeftsbericht (ISSN 0343-0510)
Description: Annual and statistical report of insurance companies for the mining industry. Covers mine accidents, work related illnesses, injuries, and workers' compensation.

BEST OF THE YEAR. see BUSINESS AND ECONOMICS — Banking And Finance

INSURANCE

368 US ISSN 0094-9973
HG8943
BEST'S AGENTS GUIDE TO LIFE INSURANCE COMPANIES.
1974. a. $95. A.M. Best Co., Ambest Rd., Oldwick,
NJ 08858. TEL 908-439-2200.
FAX 908-439-3296. Ed. Larry Mayewski. stat.
Document type: directory.
—CCC.

368 US ISSN 1075-8682
**BEST'S AGGREGATES AND AVERAGES: LIFE - HEALTH
EDITION.** 1981. a. $95. A.M. Best Co., Ambest Rd.,
Oldwick, NJ 08858. TEL 908-439-2200.
FAX 908-439-3296. Ed. Larry Mayewski. **Document
type:** directory.
Description: Statistics on companies, groups,
business lines, peer groupings, and industry.

368 US ISSN 0270-5974
**BEST'S AGGREGATES AND AVERAGES: PROPERTY -
CASUALTY EDITION.** 1940. a. $285. A.M. Best Co.,
Ambest Rd., Oldwick, NJ 08858.
TEL 908-439-2200. FAX 908-439-3296. Ed. John
Snyder. **Document type:** directory.
Description: Statistics on companies, groups,
business lines, peer groupings, and industry.

368 US ISSN 0271-0927
HG8525
**BEST'S DIRECTORY OF RECOMMENDED INSURANCE
ADJUSTERS.** 1930. a. $65. A.M. Best Co., Ambest
Rd., Oldwick, NJ 08858. TEL 908-439-2200.
FAX 908-439-3296. Ed. E.C. Krisak. **Document type:**
directory.
Former titles (until 1980): Best's Recommended
Independent Insurance Adjusters (ISSN
0091-830X); Best's Recommended Insurance
Adjusters.

368 US ISSN 0277-1551
KF195.I5
**BEST'S DIRECTORY OF RECOMMENDED INSURANCE
ATTORNEYS.** 1928. a. $75. A.M. Best Co., Ambest
Rd., Oldwick, NJ 08858. TEL 908-439-2200.
FAX 908-439-3296. Ed. E.C. Krisak. **Document type:**
directory.
Formerly: Best's Recommended Insurance
Attorneys.

368 US ISSN 1071-7722
HG8881
BEST'S FLITCRAFT COMPEND. 1887. a. (with q.
updates). $55. A.M. Best Co., Ambest Rd., Oldwick,
NJ 08858. TEL 908-439-2200.
FAX 908-439-3296. Ed. Andrew Gold. (also avail. in
diskette format) **Document type:** directory.
Formerly (until 1968): Flitcraft Compend (ISSN
0733-9631)
Description: Third-party comparison of life
insurance contracts.

368 US ISSN 0884-4313
BEST'S INSURANCE REPORTS - INTERNATIONAL. 1985.
a. $600. A.M. Best Co., Ambest Rd., Oldwick, NJ
08858. TEL 908-439-2200. FAX 908-439-3296.
Ed. C. Burton Kellogg II. **Document type:** directory.
Description: Ratings and financial data for
international insurance companies.

368 US ISSN 1075-8690
BEST'S INSURANCE REPORTS: LIFE - HEALTH. 1905. a.
$600. A.M. Best Co., Ambest Rd., Oldwick, NJ
08858. TEL 908-439-2200. FAX 908-439-3296.
Ed. Larry Mayewski. stat. **Document type:** bulletin.
●Also available on CD-ROM.

368 US ISSN 0148-3218
HG9655
BEST'S INSURANCE REPORTS: PROPERTY - CASUALTY.
1900. a. $600. A.M. Best Co., Ambest Rd., Oldwick,
NJ 08858. TEL 908-439-2200.
FAX 908-439-3296. Ed. John Snyder. stat.
Document type: bulletin.
●Also available on CD-ROM.
—CCC.
Formerly: Best's Insurance Reports: Property -
Liability.

368 US ISSN 1064-7376
BEST'S KEY RATING GUIDE: LIFE - HEALTH EDITION.
1991. q. $95. A.M. Best Co., Ambest Rd., Oldwick,
NJ 08858. TEL 908-439-2200.
FAX 908-439-3296. Ed. Larry Mayewski. (also avail.
in diskette format) **Document type:** directory.
Description: Ratings and financial information for
life and health insurers.

368 US ISSN 0148-3064
**BEST'S KEY RATING GUIDE: PROPERTY - CASUALTY
EDITION.** 1906. q. $95. A.M. Best Co., Ambest Rd.,
Oldwick, NJ 08858. TEL 908-439-2200.
FAX 908-439-3296. Ed. John Snyder. (also avail. in
diskette format) **Document type:** directory.
Description: Ratings and financial information for
property and casualty insurers.

368 US
BEST'S LOSS CONTROL ENGINEERING MANUAL. 1968.
3/yr. $500. A.M. Best Co., Ambest Rd., Oldwick, NJ
08858. TEL 908-439-2200. FAX 908-439-3296.
Ed. Mary Beth Iannaccone. (reprints avail. from A.M.
Best Co.) **Document type:** bulletin.
Description: Inspection and investigation checklists
for safety engineers and field inspectors.

368 US ISSN 1075-8712
▼**BEST'S MANAGED CARE REPORTS - H M O.** 1993. a.
$65. A.M. Best Co., Ambest Rd., Oldwick, NJ
08858. TEL 908-439-2200; 908-439-3296. Ed.
Manfred Nowacki. **Document type:** directory.
Description: Financial data and performance ratios
for HMOs in the U.S.

368 US ISSN 0572-6301
BEST'S MARKET GUIDE. (Vol.1: Corporate Stocks; Vol.2:
Corporate Bonds; Vol.3: Municipal Bonds) 1969. a.
(in 3 vols.) $1575 (Vol.1 $500; Vol.2 $625; Vol.3
$625). A.M. Best Co., Ambest Rd., Oldwick, NJ
08858. TEL 908-439-2200. FAX 908-439-3296.
Ed. Kenneth Millroy. (also avail. in diskette format)
Document type: directory.
Description: Details insurance company
investments.

368 US ISSN 0197-2405
HD7106.U5
BEST'S RETIREMENT INCOME GUIDE. 1979. s-a. $65.
A.M. Best Co., Ambest Rd., Oldwick, NJ 08858.
TEL 908-439-2200. FAX 908-439-3296. Ed. A.D.
Gold. **Document type:** bulletin.

368 US ISSN 0005-9706
HG8751 CODEN: BRLHB5
BEST'S REVIEW. LIFE - HEALTH INSURANCE EDITION.
1899. m. $21. A.M. Best Co., Ambest Rd., Oldwick,
NJ 08858. TEL 908-439-2200.
FAX 908-439-3296. Ed. Mark Schussel. adv.;
bk.rev.; charts; illus.; stat. circ. 35,900. (also avail.
in microform from UMI; microfiche from CIS; reprint
service avail. from A.M. Best Co.) **Indexed:** ABI
Inform., Account.Ind. (1974-), B.P.I., BPIA, Bus.Ind.,
Comput.Lit.Ind., Data Process.Dig., Hlth.Ind., L.I.I.,
Pers.Lit., PROMT, PSI, Sci.Abstr., SRI, Tr.& Indus.Ind.,
Work Rel.Abstr. **Document type:** bulletin.
●Also available online. Vendor(s): DIALOG
Information Services, Inc.
—BLDSC (1942.387000); Faxon; UnCover; SWETS;
UMI. **CCC.**
Formerly: Best's Insurance News. Life Edition.

368 US ISSN 0161-7745
HG8011 CODEN: BRPIDU
**BEST'S REVIEW. PROPERTY - CASUALTY INSURANCE
EDITION.** 1899. m. $21. A.M. Best Co., Ambest Rd.,
Oldwick, NJ 08858. TEL 908-439-2200.
FAX 908-439-3296. Ed. Mark Schussel. adv.;
bk.rev.; charts; illus.; stat.; tr.lit.; index, cum.index.
circ. 40,900. (also avail. in microform from UMI;
microfiche from CIS; reprint service avail. from UMI)
Indexed: ABI Inform., Account.Ind. (1974-), B.P.I.,
BPIA, Bus.Ind., Comput.Lit.Ind., Data Process.Dig.,
PSI, Sci.Abstr., SRI, Tr.& Indus.Ind. **Document type:**
bulletin.
●Also available online. Vendor(s): DIALOG
Information Services, Inc.
—BLDSC (1942.389000); Faxon; UMI. **CCC.**
Former titles: Best's Review. Property - Liability
Insurance Edition (ISSN 0005-9714); Best's
Insurance News. Fire and Casualty Edition.
Description: Highlights property and casualty
coverage.

368 US
BEST'S UNDERWRITING GUIDE. 1975. q. $500. A.M.
Best Co., Ambest Rd., Oldwick, NJ 08858.
TEL 908-439-2200. FAX 908-439-3296. Ed. Mary
Beth Iannaccone. illus. (also avail. in diskette format)
Document type: bulletin.
●Also available online.
Also available on CD-ROM.
Description: Detailed descriptions of commercial
risk classifications.

368 US ISSN 1075-8739
BEST'S UNDERWRITING NEWSLETTER. 1972. m. $65.
A.M. Best Co., Ambest Rd., Oldwick, NJ 08858.
TEL 908-439-2200. FAX 908-439-3296. Ed.
Joseph Mangan. **Document type:** newsletter.
Description: Reports on latest developments and
changes that affect underwriting.

368 US ISSN 1075-8747
BESTWEEK: LIFE - HEALTH EDITION. 1957. w. $390.
A.M. Best Co., Ambest Rd., Oldwick, NJ 08858.
TEL 908-439-2200. FAX 908-439-3296. Ed.
Christopher Winans. charts; stat. **Document type:**
bulletin.
Former titles (until 1993): Best's Insurance
Management Reports: Life - Health Edition; (until
1979): Best's Insurance News Digest: Life - Health
Edition; Best's Weekly Digest (ISSN 0005-9722)

368 US ISSN 1075-8747
BESTWEEK: PROPERTY - CASUALTY EDITION. 1957. w.
$390. A.M. Best Co., Ambest Rd., Oldwick, NJ
08858. TEL 908-439-2200. FAX 908-439-3296.
Ed. Christopher Winans. charts; stat. **Document type:**
bulletin.
Former titles (until 1993): Best's Insurance
Management Reports: Property - Casualty Edition;
(until 1979): Best's Insurance News Digest: Property
- Casualty Edition.

368.4 GW ISSN 0005-9951
BETRIEBLICHE ALTERSVERSORGUNG. 1946. 8/yr.
membership. Arbeitsgemeinschaft fuer Betriebliche
Altersversorgung e.V., Postfach 101208, 69002
Heidelberg, Germany. TEL 06221-21422.
FAX 06221-24210. Ed. Michael Lubnow. bk.rev.
circ. 1,900. **Indexed:** World Bibl.Soc.Sec. **Document
type:** bulletin.

368.4 GW ISSN 0342-0817
DIE BETRIEBSKRANKENKASSE. 1908. m. DM.62.40.
Bundesverband der Betriebskrankenkassen,
Kronprinzenstr. 6, 45128 Essen, Germany.
TEL 0201-1791140. FAX 0201-1791003. adv.;
bk.rev. circ. 7,500. (also avail. in microfiche)
Indexed: World Bibl.Soc.Sec. **Document type:** bulletin.

368 NE ISSN 0006-0313
BEURSBENGEL. 1938. m. (11/yr.). fl.30. Stichting
Vakontwikkeling Verzekeringsbedrijf, Postbus 9791,
3506 GT Utrecht, Netherlands. (Co-sponsor:
Federatie van Vereniginen tot Bevordering van de
Assurantie-Wetenschap) Ed. J.C. Mijnarends. adv.;
bk.rev.; bibl.; index. circ. 30,000.
—SWETS.

368.382 GW ISSN 0172-0805
BLEIB GESUND. 1960. bi-m. DM.5.
(AOK-Bundesverband) Wirtschaftsdienst Gesellschaft
fuer Medien & Kommunikation mbH & Co. OHG,
Lange Str. 13, 60311 Frankfurt a.M., Germany. Ed.
Werner Stuetzel. circ. 12,861,600. **Document type:**
bulletin.

368 CN ISSN 0831-6503
BLUE CHART REPORT. 1984. a. Can.$22.50 (foreign
Can.$25.50). Stone and Cox Ltd., 111 Peter St.,
Ste. 202, Toronto, Ont. M5V 2H1, Canada.
TEL 416-599-0772. FAX 416-599-0867. Ed. John
D. Wyndham.
Suepresedes: Underwriting Results: The Blue Chart.
Description: Performance and solvency ratios for
Canadian property and casualty insurance
companies.

368 IT
BLUGREEN. 4/yr. Via G.B. Morgagni 30 E, 00161
Rome, Italy. TEL 6-88-30-209. FAX 6-88-30-118.
circ. 70,000.

368 EC
BOLETIN DE SEGUROS. a. Superintendencia de Bancos,
Avda. 12 de Octubre 1561, Apdo. de Correos
17-17-770, Quito, Ecuador. FAX 563-652. TELEX
21102 SUPBAN ED. circ. controlled.

368.4 SP
**BOLETIN INFORMATIVO DE LA SEGURIDAD SOCIAL.
GESTION ECONOMICA.** m. 12000 ptas. Ministerio de
Trabajo y Seguridad Social, Centro de Publicaciones,
Agustin de Bethencourt 11, 28003 Madrid, Spain.
TEL 554-34-00. FAX 533-06-91. **Document type:**
government publication.

INSURANCE

368   **CK**
BOLIVAR. 1941. q. Compania de Seguros Bolivar, Medellin, Colombia. **Indexed:** Amer.Hist.& Life, Hist.Abstr.

BOND. see RELIGIONS AND THEOLOGY — Protestant

368   **US**   **ISSN 0006-9256**
BRATRSKY VESTNIK/FRATERNAL HERALD. 1897. m. $10. Western Fraternal Life Association, 1900 First Ave., N.E., Cedar Rapids, IA 52402. TEL 319-363-2653. Pub. Cathy M. Langer. bk.rev.; stat. circ. 50,000.

368   **US**   **ISSN 0006-9779**
BRICKBATS & BOUQUETS. Short title: B & B. 1934. bi-m. free to qualified personnel. Employers Insurance of Texas, Box 2759, Dallas, TX 75221. TEL 214-760-6282. FAX 214-760-3751. Ed. Denise Brooke. illus.; circ. 2,100 (controlled).

BRIEF (CHICAGO). see LAW

368.4   **CN**
BRITISH COLUMBIA. WORKERS' COMPENSATION BOARD. WORKERS' COMPENSATION REPORTER. 1973. irreg. Can.$50 per vol. Workers' Compensation Board, Community Relations Department, 6951 Westminster Highway, Richmond, B.C. V7C 1C6, Canada. TEL 604-276-3068. FAX 604-276-7406. circ. 1,522.
    Description: Covers matters of policy and interpretation of the British Columbia Workers Compensation Act.

BRITISH COLUMBIA DECISIONS - INSURANCE LAW CASES. see LAW

368   **CN**   **ISSN 0068-1598**
BRITISH COLUMBIA INSURANCE DIRECTORY. INSURANCE COMPANIES, AGENTS AND ADJUSTERS. 1964. a. Can.$23. Arbutus Publications Ltd., P.O. Box 35070, Sta. E, Vancouver, B.C. V6M 4G1, Canada. TEL 604-687-8003. Ed. W.D.S. Earle. adv.; bk.rev. circ. 1,400.

368   **UK**
BROKER. 1977. q. £12. Lloyd's List International, 1 Singer Street, London EC2A 4LQ, England. TEL 071-250-1500. FAX 071-250-0998. TELEX 987321 LLOYDS G. Ed. Edward Ion. adv.; bk.rev.; bibl.; tr.lit. circ. 20,000.
    Formerly (until 1988): British Insurance Broker (ISSN 0141-6197)

368   **US**
THE BROKER. 1933? bi-m. Western Association of Insurance Brokers, 235 Montgomery St., Rm. 962, San Francisco, CA 94104-3002. TEL 415-392-5383. FAX 415-392-5644. Ed. Michael S. Cabot. adv.; circ. 1,200 (controlled).

368   **US**   **ISSN 0273-6551**
BROKER WORLD. 1980. m. $6. Insurance Publications, Inc., 10709 Barkley, Ste. 3, Overland Park, KS 66211. TEL 800-762-3387. FAX 913-383-1247. Ed. Sharon Chace. adv. circ. 26,631. (back issues avail.)
—UMI.
    Description: Contains information pertinent to independent life and health insurance agents and brokers.

368   **UK**   **ISSN 0260-2385**
BROKERS' MONTHLY & INSURANCE ADVISER. 1950. m. £31 (foreign £58). Insurance Publishing & Printing Co., 7 Stourbridge Rd., Lye, Stourbridge, W. Midlands DY9 7DG, England. Ed. Brian Susman. adv.; bk.rev.; charts; illus.; mkt.; tr.lit.; index, cum.index. circ. 8,500.
—BLDSC (2349.490000).
    Formerly: Insurance Brokers' Monthly (ISSN 0020-4633)

368   **CN**   **ISSN 0585-3680**
HG8550.A4
THE BROWN CHART. PROVINCIAL RESULTS. Short title: Brown Chart. (Text in English, French) 1935. a. Can.$68. Stone & Cox Ltd., 111 Peter St., Ste. 202, Toronto, ON M5V 2H1, Canada. TEL 416-599-0772. FAX 416-599-0867. Ed. John D. Wyndham. circ. 500. (also avail. in diskette format)
    Incorporates: Provincial Results in Canada of Fire and Casualty Companies & Provincial Results in Canada of General Insurance Companies; **Formerly:** Brown Chart for All Lines of General Insurance. Provincial Results. Reports (ISSN 0227-437X)
    Description: Breakdown of business in each province by class of insurance for Canadian property-casualty companies.

368   **AG**
BRUJULA. Variant title: Compania Argentina de Seguros. Memoria y Balance General. no.14, 1975. irreg. Compania Argentina de Seguros, San Martin 439, Buenos Aires, Argentina.

368   **US**   **ISSN 0007-3261**
BUILDER (COLUMBUS). 1909. 6/yr. free. Midland Mutual Life Insurance Company, 250 E. Broad St., Columbus, OH 43215. TEL 614-228-2001. Ed. M. Pollman. illus.; tr.lit.; circ. 1,300 (controlled).

368.32   **US**   **ISSN 0739-9413**
HD7653
BUSINESS AND HEALTH. 1983. 12/yr. $99 (foreign $136). Medical Economics Publishing Co., Inc., Five Paragon Dr., Montvale, NJ 07645. TEL 201-358-7208. FAX 201-573-1045. Ed. Joe Burns. adv.; bk.rev.; circ. 5,000 (paid); 38,000 (controlled). **Indexed:** ABI Inform., Abstr.Health Care Manage.Stud., Abstr.Soc.Geront., B.P.I.
—BLDSC (2933.205000); Faxon; UMI. **CCC**.
    Description: Examines the full range of managed healthcare concerns affecting purchasers and providers, including cost management, quality assurance, health promotion and wellness, disability, workers' compensation, utilization review, pharmacy benefits, dental and vision care.

368   **US**   **ISSN 0007-6864**
HG8011   **CODEN: BUINEW**
BUSINESS INSURANCE; news magazine for corporate risk, employee benefit and financial executives. 1967. w. $80. Crain Communications, Inc. (Chicago), 740 Rush St., Chicago, IL 60611. TEL 312-649-5286. FAX 312-280-3174. (Subscr. to: 965 E. Jefferson Ave., Detroit, MI 48207-9966. TEL 800-992-9970) Ed. Jim Burcke. bk.rev. circ. 50,176. (tabloid format; also avail. in microform from UMI,MIM; reprint service avail. from UMI) **Indexed:** ABI Inform., B.P.I., BPIA, Bus.Ind., CINAHL, Hlth.Ind., L.I.I., PROMT, PSI, Tr.& Indus.Ind.
●Also available online. Vendor(s): Mead Data Central, Inc.
—BLDSC (2933.830000); SWETS; UMI; CASDDS. **CCC**.

368 346   **CN**
BUTTERWORTHS WORKERS' COMPENSATION IN ONTARIO SERVICE. irreg. Can.$120. Butterworths Canada Ltd., Part of the Reed Elsevier group, 75 Clegg Rd., Markham, ON L6G 1A1, Canada. TEL 905-479-2265. FAX 905-479-2826. (looseleaf format)

368   **US**   **ISSN 0199-2414**
C A L UNDERWRITER. 1970. m. $5. California Association of Life Underwriters, 70 Washington St., Ste. 325, Oakland, CA 94607. TEL 510-834-2258. FAX 510-834-1453. Ed. Dan Crouch. adv.; bk.rev. circ. 11,000. (reprint service avail.) Document type: trade publication.
    Description: News and articles on legislative, regulatory, tax, and political issues of interest to the California Association of Life Underwriters. Includes regular columns on membership benefits, public relations, education, trends and sales techniques.

368.5   **US**
C G L REPORTER. (Comprehensive - General Liability); the insurance coverage litigation handbook. 1983. s-a. $175. International Risk Management Institute, Inc., 12222 Merit Dr., Ste. 1660, Dallas, TX 75251-2217. TEL 214-960-7693. FAX 214-960-6037. Ed. Bonnie Rogers. cum.index: 1983-1993. (looseleaf format)
    Description: Provides case-by-case annotations of important federal and regional court decisions involving commercial general liability and other business-related policies for attorneys and insurance professionals.

368.01   **UK**   **ISSN 0957-4883**
C I I JOURNAL. 1976. bi-m. £18 to non-members (effective 1994). Chartered Insurance Institute, 20 Aldermanbury, London EC2V 7HY, England. TEL 071-606-3835. FAX 071-726-0131. Ed. P. Knight. adv.; bk.rev. circ. 62,000. **Indexed:** RICS. Document type: trade publication.
—BLDSC (4725.200000).
    Formerly: Chartered Institute, London. Journal (ISSN 0309-4928)
    Description: Provides information on CII activities and articles on matters of interest to insurance people.

368   **US**
C O I LETTER. m. free. National Conference of Insurance Legislators, Box 217, Brookfield, WI 53008. TEL 414-782-6669. FAX 414-782-9607. Ed. Charles O. Davis. circ. 500. (back issues avail.)

368   **US**   **ISSN 0007-8883**
C P C U NEWS. 1952. m. (except May-June & Sep.-Oct. combined). Society of Chartered Property & Casualty Underwriters, Box 3009, 720 Providence Rd., Malvern, PA 19355. TEL 215-251-2743. Ed. Lisa A. Fittipaldi. circ. 23,000. (tabloid format; avail. on records) **Indexed:** P.L.I.I. Document type: trade publication.

368   **US**
C S R CONNECTION. (Customer Service Representative) q. $35. National Association of Professional Agents, 400 N. Washington St., Alexandria, VA 22314-2312. TEL 703-836-9340. Ed. Kathy Mc Carty. Document type: newsletter.

368   **SZ**
C S S ZEITUNG. (Chretienne Sociale Suisse) (Text in French, German) bi-m. C S S Assurance, Roesslimattstr. 40, CH-6002 Luzern, Switzerland. TEL 041-490483. FAX 041-442822. Ed. Guido Fuerer. circ. 520,000.

368   **BL**   **ISSN 0101-5818**
CADERNOS DE SEGURO. 1981. bi-m. $30. Fundacao Escola Nacional de Seguros, Rua Senador Dantas 74, 5 e 11 andar, 20031 Rio de Janeiro RJ, Brazil. TEL 021-532-3322. FAX 021-262-32-48. TELEX 21-39481. Ed. Cristina Amaral. adv. contact: Sonia Kraucher. bk.rev. circ. 2,000. Document type: monographic series.

368.4 355.115
CAL - VET INSURANCE PLANS. ANNUAL REPORT. 1980. a. Department of Veterans Affairs, 1227 O St., Sacramento, CA 95814. TEL 916-322-1796.

CALIFORNIA COMPENSATION CASES. see LAW

CALIFORNIA INSURANCE LAW AND PRACTICE. see LAW

368   **US**   **ISSN 1047-6466**
KFC290.A15C348
CALIFORNIA INSURANCE LAW AND REGULATION REPORTER. 1989. m. $355. Shepard's - McGraw-Hill, Inc., Box 35300, Colorado Springs, CO 80935-3530. TEL 719-475-7230. FAX 800-525-0053. Ed. John DiMugno. (looseleaf format)

368   **US**   **ISSN 0890-4871**
KFC290.A15C35
CALIFORNIA INSURANCE REPORT. 1986. m. $217. Data Research, Inc., 4635 Nicols Rd., Ste. 100, Eagan, MN 55122. TEL 612-452-8267. FAX 612-452-8694. (Subscr. to: Box 490, Rosemount, MN 55068) Ed. Warren Cody. Document type: newsletter.

CALIFORNIA LAW OF EMPLOYEE INJURIES AND WORKMEN'S COMPENSATION. see LAW

INSURANCE

332 368   CN   ISSN 0068-7383
CANADA. DEPARTMENT OF INSURANCE. REPORT. CO-OPERATIVE CREDIT ASSOCIATIONS. 1956. a. price varies. (Department of Insurance) Supply and Services Canada, Publishing Centre, Ottawa, Ont. K1A 0S9, Canada. TEL 819-997-2560.

368   CN   ISSN 0068-7405
HG8550
CANADA. DEPARTMENT OF INSURANCE. REPORT OF THE SUPERINTENDENT OF INSURANCE. (In 3 vols.) a. price varies. (Department of Insurance) Supply and Services Canada, Publishing Centre, Ottawa, Ont. K7A 0S9, Canada. TEL 819-997-2560.

332   CN   ISSN 0068-7413
CANADA. DEPARTMENT OF INSURANCE. REPORT. SMALL LOANS COMPANIES AND MONEY-LENDERS. a. price varies. (Department of Insurance) Supply and Services Canada, Publishing Centre, Ottawa, Ont. K1A 0S9, Canada. TEL 819-997-2560.

332.1 368   CN   ISSN 0068-7391
CANADA. DEPARTMENT OF INSURANCE. REPORT. TRUST AND LOAN COMPANIES. a. price varies. (Department of Insurance) Supply and Services Canada, Publishing Centre, Ottawa, Ont. K1A 0S9, Canada. TEL 819-997-2560.

368.4 340   CN
CANADIAN BENEFITS ADMINISTRATION MANUAL. 1989. bi-m. Can.$205. Carswell, One Corporate Plaza, 2075 Kennedy Rd., Scarborough, ON M1T 3V4, Canada. TEL 416-609-8000. FAX 416-298-5094. Ed. Jacques Benedavid. circ. 1,300. (looseleaf format; back issues avail.)
   Description: Provides quick and effective help in dealing with everyday problems arising from the administration of all government and private benefits programs, such as hiring, birth, death, illness, retirement or termination.

CANADIAN CASES ON THE LAW OF INSURANCE (2ND SERIES). see *LAW*

368 331.8   CN
CANADIAN EMPLOYMENT BENEFITS & PENSION GUIDE. m. Can.$645. C C H Canadian Ltd., 6 Garamond Ct., North York, ON M3C 1Z5, Canada. TEL 416-441-2992. FAX 416-444-9011.
   Formerly: Canadian Employment Benefits and Pension Guide Reports.
   Description: Canada and Quebec pension plans and provincial legislation regulating private pension plans.

CANADIAN HEALTH CARE MANAGEMENT. see *MEDICAL SCIENCES*

368   CN   ISSN 0008-3828
CANADIAN INDEPENDENT ADJUSTER. (Text in English and French) 1958. q. Can.$5. (Canadian Independent Adjusters' Conference) Journal Management, 216 Market Square, Newmarket, Ont. L3Y 4A8, Canada. Ed. Vernn Newton. adv.; bk.rev.; circ. 3,400 (controlled). (processed)

368   CN   ISSN 0008-3879
HG8015
CANADIAN INSURANCE. 1905. m. (13/yr.) Can.$30 (foreign $44). Stone and Cox Ltd., 111 Peter St., Ste. 202, Toronto, ON M5V 2H1, Canada. TEL 416-599-0772. FAX 416-599-0867. Ed. Sally Praskey; Pub. J. Kent Chisholm. adv.: page $3195; trim 8 1/8 x 10 7/8. illus.; stat. circ. 11,041. **Indexed:** ABI Inform., BPIA, Can.B.P.I.
—UMI.
   Incorporates: Corporate Insurance in Canada (ISSN 0315-8098); Insurance Agent and Broker in Canada (ISSN 0020-4595)
   Description: Industry magazine for the insurance industry, covers statistics, computerization, marine, reinsurance and office management.

368.014   CN   ISSN 0318-0352
CANADIAN INSURANCE CLAIMS DIRECTORY. 1932. a. $37.50. University of Toronto Press, Directories Department, 10 St. Mary St., Ste. 700, Toronto, ON M4Y 2W8, Canada. TEL 705-833-2882. FAX 705-833-2451. Ed. Gwen Peroni. adv. **Document type:** directory.
   Description: Facilitates the forwarding of insurance claims throughout Canada and the US. Lists 1600 independent adjusting offices.

368.91   CN   ISSN 0068-9033
CANADIAN INSURANCE LAW BULLETIN SERVICE. 1929. m. Can.$175. Stone & Cox Ltd., 11 Peter St., Ste. 202, Toronto, Ont. M5V 2H1, Canada. TEL 416-599-0772. FAX 416-599-0867. Ed. Blair C.F. Fraser. circ. 800.
   Description: Statute law and bulletin service covering the laws and regulations governing insurance enterprises in Canada and the provinces.

CANADIAN INSURANCE LAW REPORTER. see *LAW*

CANADIAN INSURANCE LAW REVIEW. see *LAW*

368   CN   ISSN 0822-109X
KE1142
CANADIAN JOURNAL OF INSURANCE LAW. 1983. 6/yr. Can.$180. Butterworths Canada Ltd., Part of the Reed Elsevier group, 75 Clegg Rd., Markham, ON L6G 1A1, Canada. TEL 905-479-2665. FAX 905-479-2826. Ed. Lazar Sarna. (back issues avail.) **Indexed:** Ind.Can.L.P.L.
   Description: Covers insurance, pensions and benefits; reviews recent laws and cases. For insurance professionals and legal practitioners.

368.3   CN   ISSN 0706-5582
CANADIAN JOURNAL OF LIFE INSURANCE. 1978. irreg. (approx. q.) Can.$62 (US Can.$59, elsewhere Can.$65). P.M.L.R. Publications, Box 365, Elmira, Ont. N3B 2Z7, Canada. TEL 519-669-2693. Ed. R. Alastair Rickard. bk.rev. (also avail. in microfilm) **Indexed:** Can.B.P.I.

368   CN   ISSN 0068-9157
CANADIAN LIFE AND HEALTH INSURANCE FACTS; an authoritative source of factual information about life and health insurance in Canada. (Editions in English, French) 1955. a. Can.$5.50. Canadian Life and Health Insurance Association Inc., Communications Department - Association Canadienne des Compagnies d'Assurances de Personnes Inc., 1 Queen St., E., Ste. 1700, Toronto, ON M5C 2X9, Canada. TEL 416-777-2221. FAX 416-777-1895. Ed. Lydia Boyko. stat. circ. 7,000. **Indexed:** CS Ind. **Document type:** trade publication.
   Formed by the 1986 merger of: Canadian Health Insurance Facts & Canadian Life Insurance Facts.

368   CN   ISSN 0008-5251
CANADIAN UNDERWRITER. (Includes annual number: Statistical Issue) 1934. 13/yr. Can.$26.70($40) Southam Magazine Group, 1450 Don Mills Rd., Don Mills, ON M3B 2X7, Canada. TEL 416-445-6641. Ed. Lawrence Welsh. adv.; bk.rev.; charts; illus.; stat.; tr.lit.; index. circ. 7,500. **Indexed:** Can.B.P.I.
●Also available online. Vendor(s): Southam Electronic Publishing.
—UMI.
   Description: Committed to the Canadian insurance industry.

368   US   ISSN 1056-814X
CAPTIVE INSURANCE COMPANY DIRECTORY (YEAR). (Was formerly part of (1974-1979): Risk Management Reports (ISSN 0199-6827)) 1974. a. $175 foreign $180 or £105. Tillinghast (Subsidiary of: Towers Perrin), Financial Centre, Ste. 600, 695 E. Main St., Stamford, CT 06901. TEL 203-326-5400. Ed. Corinne E. Ramming. **Document type:** directory.

368   US   ISSN 1056-8158
CAPTIVE INSURANCE COMPANY REPORTS. Variant title: C I C R. 1977. m. Tillinghast (Subsidiary of: Towers Perrin), Financial Centre, Ste. 600, 695 E. Main St., Stamford, CT 06901. TEL 203-326-5400. **Document type:** trade publication.
—UMI.

368   UK   ISSN 0262-7701
CAPTIVE INSURANCE COMPANY REVIEW. 1981. m. £245($450) Risk & Insurance Research Group Ltd., 4 Henrietta St., Covent Garden, London WC2E 8PS, England. TEL 071-836-0614. FAX 071-379-6355. Ed. C.F. Best. bk.rev. **Document type:** trade publication.

368   US   ISSN 1065-1292
CAROLINA AGENT. q. $18 to non-members; members $14. (Carolinas Association of Professional Insurance Agents) C A P I A Services Corp., 3109 Charles B. Root Wynd, Raleigh, NC 27612. TEL 919-782-5807. FAX 919-781-6189. Ed. Sally R. Sherman. adv. circ. 1,050. **Document type:** trade publication.

CASE MANAGER. see *MEDICAL SCIENCES*

368   US
CASUALTY INVESTIGATION CHECKLISTS. a. $62.50. Clark - Boardman - Callaghan Company Ltd., 375 Hudson St., New York, NY 10014. TEL 212-929-7500; 800-221-9428. FAX 212-924-0460. Ed. Pat Magarick.
   Description: Provides crucial information needed by investigators, supervisors, and attorneys in order to effectively and efficiently conduct a casualty investigation.

368 282   US
CATHOLIC AID NEWS. 1895. m. membership. Catholic Aid Association, 3499 N. Lexington Ave., St. Paul, MN 55126-8098. TEL 612-490-0170. FAX 612-490-0746. Ed. David E. Brown. circ. 38,000. **Document type:** newspaper.
   Description: News articles and announcements pertaining to the members and activities of this association.

CATHOLIC FORESTER. see *GENERAL INTEREST PERIODICALS — United States*

368   US
CATHOLIC KNIGHT MAGAZINE. 1909. q. membership. Catholic Knights Insurance Society, 1100 W. Wells St., Box 05900, Milwaukee, WI 53205-0900. TEL 414-273-6266. FAX 414-223-3201. Ed. Dorothy Deer. circ. 57,000.
   Description: News, announcements, insurance product information, and features pertaining to the members and activities of this society.

368   UK   ISSN 0269-5804
CHARTERED INSURANCE INSTITUTE. SOCIETY OF FELLOWS. JOURNAL. 1986. 2/yr. £10. Chartered Insurance Institute, Society of Fellows, 20 Aldermanbury, London EC2V 7HY. TEL 44-71-606-3835. FAX 44-71-726-0131. Ed. D.W. Cloughton. bk.rev.; circ. 4,000 (controlled). (back issues avail.) **Document type:** academic/scholarly publication.
—BLDSC (4887.350000).
   Description: Contains articles about insurance, the law, and marketing as they pertain to insurance, reinsurance, and financial services at the postgraduate level.
Refereed Serial

368   SZ
CHRETIENNE SOCIALE SUISSE. (Text in French, German, Italian) 10/yr. C S S Assurance, Roesslimattstr. 40, CH-6002 Luzern, Switzerland. TEL 041-490111. FAX 041-442822. Ed. Guido Fuerer. circ. 145,000.

368   MX
CIRCULARES DE SEGUROS. a. Comision Nacional de Seguros y Fianzas, Av. de los Insurgentes Sur 1971, Plaza Inn, Torre 2 N., 2o piso, 01020 Mexico DF, Mexico. **Document type:** government publication.
   Description: Official communications on insurance law reforms.

368   US
CLAIMS. 1953. m. $38. 1001 Fourth Ave. Plaza, Ste. 3029, Seattle, WA 98154. TEL 206-624-6965. FAX 206-624-5021. Ed. Bill Thorness. adv.; bk.rev.; illus. circ. 8,012.
   Formerly: Insurance Adjuster (ISSN 0020-4579)

THE CLAIMS FORUM. see *BUSINESS AND ECONOMICS — Labor And Industrial Relations*

368.014   US
CLAIMS NETWORK NEWSLETTER. 1982. m. Insurance Field Company, Box 24244, Louisville, KY 40224-0244. TEL 502-491-5857. FAX 502-491-5905. Ed. Charles Kaltenthaler. adv. circ. 1,500. (back issues avail.) **Document type:** newsletter.
   Formerly: Kentucky Claims Association Newsletter.
   Description: Reports the activities of six professional claims organizations within Kentucky and Indiana. Contains items of local legal interest and general national news.

368   SA
COLIMPEX INSURANCE BROKERS EXECUPAD. (Text in Afrikaans and English) a. Colimpex Africa (Pty.) Ltd., P.O. Box 5838, Johannesburg 2000, South Africa. adv.

INSURANCE

368.01   US
COLLEGE OF INSURANCE. ACADEMIC BULLETIN. 1962. biennial. free. College of Insurance, 101 Murray St., New York, NY 10007. TEL 212-962-4111. FAX 212-964-3381. circ. 20,000.
    Formerly: College of Insurance. General Bulletin (ISSN 0069-5718)

COLOMBIA. MINISTERIO DE TRABAJO Y SEGURIDAD SOCIAL. CARTA INFORMATIVA. see *BUSINESS AND ECONOMICS* — Labor And Industrial Relations

COLOMBIA. MINISTERIO DE TRABAJO Y SEGURIDAD SOCIAL. MEMORIA AL CONGRESO NACIONAL. see *BUSINESS AND ECONOMICS* — Labor And Industrial Relations

COLOMBIA. SUPERINTENDENCIA BANCARIA. SEGUROS Y CAPITALIZACION. see *BUSINESS AND ECONOMICS*

368   US
COLUMNS (MINNEAPOLIS). 1990. fortn. free. Northwestern National Life Insurance Companies, Inc., 20 Washington Ave., S., Minneapolis, MN 55401. TEL 612-372-5628. FAX 612-342-3002. Ed. Ruth Weber. circ. 3,500. (back issues avail.)
    Document type: newsletter.
    Description: Provides news of the companies' activities, and financial information.

368   CN   ISSN 0382-7038
COMMENT. Variant title: C L U Comment. French edition: Commentaires (ISSN 0382-7046) 1967. 6/yr. (Canadian Institute Chartered Life Underwriters) Life Underwriters Association of Canada, 41 Lesmill Rd., Don Mills, ON M3B 2T3, Canada. TEL 416-444-5251. (Co-sponsor: Chartered Financial Consultants) cum.index every 5 yrs. circ. 29,000.

368   CN   ISSN 0382-7046
COMMENTAIRES. English edition: Comment (ISSN 0382-7038) 1967. bi-m. Can.$71.58. Institut Canadien des Assureurs-Vie Agrees et des Conseillers Financiers Agrees - Canadian Institute of Chartered Life Underwriters and Chartered Financial Consultants, 41 Lesmill, Don Mills, Ont. M3B 2T3, Canada. TEL 416-444-5251. FAX 416-444-8031. Ed.Bd. circ. 5,000.
    Description: Examines financial planning.

368   US
▼**COMMERCIAL AUTO INSURANCE.** 1993. q. $199. International Risk Management Institute, Inc., 12222 Merit Dr., Ste. 1660, Dallas, TX 75251-2217. TEL 214-960-7693. FAX 214-960-6037. Ed. Maureen C. McLendon. charts; illus.; cum.index. (looseleaf format; cc)
    Description: Discusses and interprets standard business auto, garage and truckers insurance policies, summarizes state uninsured motorist and no-fault statutes.

368   US
COMMERCIAL LIABILITY INSURANCE. 1985. q. $265. International Risk Management Institute, Inc., 12222 Merit Dr., Ste. 1660, Dallas, TX 75251-2217. TEL 214-960-7693. FAX 214-960-6037. Ed. Jeff Woodward. (looseleaf format)
    Description: Interpretes general liability and umbrella liability insurance policy language and makes recommendations as to how to alter policy language to improve coverage.

368   US
COMMERCIAL PROPERTY INSURANCE. 1989. q. $239. International Risk Management Institute, Inc., 12222 Merit Dr., Ste. 1660, Dallas, TX 75251-2217. TEL 214-960-7693. FAX 214-960-6037. Ed. Linda G. Robinson. (looseleaf format)
    Description: For insurance and risk management professionals. Provides coverage interpretations and advice on arranging property, inland, marine, crime, boiler and machinery, and package insurances.

COMPANY LAW INSTITUTE OF INDIA. REPORTS OF COMPANY CASES INCLUDING BANKING & INSURANCE. see *LAW* — Corporate Law

368   US
COMPARISON OF STATE UNEMPLOYMENT INSURANCE LAWS. 1938. s-a. $45 (foreign $56.25). U.S. Department of Labor, Unemployment Insurance Service, Frances Perkins Bldg., 200 Constitution Ave., N.W., Washington, DC 20210. TEL 202-219-5200. (Subscr. to: Superintendent of Documents, U.S. Government Printing Office, Box 371954, Pittsburgh, PA 15250-7954. TEL 202-783-3238. FAX 202-512-2233) circ. 3,000.
    Document type: government publication.
    Description: Publishes revisions reflecting changes in state unemployment insurance laws.

COMPENSATION & BENEFITS MANAGEMENT. see *BUSINESS AND ECONOMICS* — Personnel Management

368   MX
COMPORTAMIENTO DEL SISTEMA ASEGURADOR MEXICANO. q. plus a. cum. Comision Nacional de Seguros y Fianzas, Av. de los Insurgentes Sur 1971, Plaza Inn, Torre 2 N., 2o piso, 01020 Mexico DF, Mexico. Document type: government publication.
    Description: Presents financial information about groups of companies of the insurance sector, their growth in nominal and real terms. Annual issue contains information on the behavior and historical development of the market during the previous 5 years.

368.32   US   ISSN 0010-5287
CONCORDIA TORCH. 1909. q. membership. Concordia Mutual Life Association, 3041 Woodcreek Dr., Downers Grove, IL 60515. TEL 312-971-8000. Ed. Lee Strouse. circ. 17,000.

368 340   US
CONNECTICUT INSURANCE LAW REVIEW. 1981. a. $15. Yules & Yules, Box 3597, Hartford, CT 06103. Ed. Robert B. Yules. index. circ. 2,000. (back issues avail.)

368   US
CONNECTICUT - RHODE ISLAND TELEPHONE TICKLER FOR INSURANCE MEN & WOMEN. 1982. a. $7. Underwriter Printing and Publishing Co., 50 E. Palisade Ave., Englewood, NJ 07631. TEL 201-569-8808. Ed. Donald E. Wolff. adv.; circ. 11,000 (paid). Document type: directory.
    Description: Lists the names, addresses, and telephone numbers of insurance companies, agents, brokers, and related suppliers throughout Connecticut and Rhode Island.

368   FR
CONSEILLER DES ASSURANCES ET DE LA FINANCE. 1879. m. 60 F. 129 bd. St. Michel, 75005 Paris, France. TEL 43-25-92-50. Ed. Rene Colin.

CONSTRUCTION RISK MANAGEMENT. see *BUILDING AND CONSTRUCTION*

CONSUMERS FOR HEALTH CARE REFORM NEWSLETTER. see *CONSUMER EDUCATION AND PROTECTION*

368   US   ISSN 0010-7697
CONTINENTAL BULLETIN. 1903. 4/yr. free. Continental Corp., Corporate Communications, 180 Maiden Lane, New York, NY 10038. TEL 212-440-7735. FAX 212-440-3263. Ed. Abbe Bates. illus. circ. 23,000. Document type: bulletin.

368   US
CONTINGENCIES. 1989. bi-m. $24. American Academy of Actuaries, 1720 I St., N.W., Washington, DC 20006. TEL 202-223-8196. FAX 202-872-1948. Ed. Dana Murphy. circ. 22,000 (controlled).
    Document type: government publication, newsletter.
    Description: Reports on and analyzes actuarial trends in insurance and business.

368 340   BE
COORDINATION OFFICIEUSE DES TEXTES LEGAUX RELATIFS AU STATUT SOCIAL DES TRAVAILLEURS INDEPENDANTS ET COMMENTAIRES. Flemish edition: Officieuze Coordinatie van de Wetteksten Betreffende het Sociaal Statuut der Zelfstandigen en Kommentaar. (Text in French) 6 base vols. (plus irreg. updates). 11300 BEF. Institut National d'Assurances Sociales pour Travailleurs Independants, Bibliotheque - Bureau 4-7 (Wat.), Place Jean Jacobs 6, B-1000 Brussels, Belgium. TEL 32-2-507-6307. FAX 32-2-511-2153.
    Document type: government publication.

368   UK
CORPORATE COVER. 1989. m. £75 (Europe £85). Reactions Publishing Group Ltd., 39-41 North Rd., London N7 9DP, England. TEL 071-609-8661. FAX 071-609-0139. Ed. Tony Dowding. adv.: B&W page £1980, color page £2970; adv. contact: Andy Smith. bk.rev. circ. 14,000. (back issues avail.)
    Document type: trade publication.

368 366   US   ISSN 0364-1066
RA626
CORRESPONDENT (APPLETON). 1904. q. membership. Aid Association for Lutherans, 4321 N. Ballard Rd., Appleton, WI 54919. TEL 414-734-5721. FAX 414-730-3757. Ed. Cindy S. Zirbel. circ. 920,000 (controlled).

368   AT
COVER NOTE. 1975. w. Aus.$395 (effective Jan. 1993). Newsletter Information Services, P.O. Box 693, Manly, Sydney, N.S.W. 2095, Australia. FAX 02-977-3310. Ed. Michael Burns. adv.; bk.rev. circ. 700. (back issues avail.)
    Description: Provides reports on all facets both life and general insurance. Includes coverage on risk management, superannuation, selfinsurance, workers compensation and captive insurance companies.

368   US
COVERAGE. 1940. m. membership. National Association of Insurance Brokers, Inc., 1401 New York Ave., N.W., No. 720, Washington, DC 20005. TEL 202-628-6700. Ed. Enno Hobbing. stat.; circ. controlled. Document type: trade publication.
    Formerly (until 1992): Friday Flash (ISSN 0016-1233)

368   US
CRITTENDEN EXCESS & SURPLUS INSIDER. w. Crittenden Publishing, Inc., Box 1150, Novato, CA 94948-1150. TEL 415-382-2458. FAX 415-382-2476. Ed. James Church. circ. 10,000.

368   US
CRITTENDEN INSURANCE MARKETS NEWSLETTER. w. Crittenden Publishing, Inc., Box 1150, Novato, CA 94948-1150. TEL 415-382-2440. FAX 415-382-2416. Ed. Colleen Pestana.

368   SZ   ISSN 0379-0290
HD7088
CURRENT RESEARCH IN SOCIAL SECURITY/RECHERCHES EN SECURITE SOCIALE/FORSCHUNG IN DER SOZIALEN SICHERHEIT/INVESTIGACIONES EN LA SEGURIDAD SOCIAL. (Text in English, French, German and Spanish) 1978. s-a. free. International Social Security Association, Case Postale 1, CH-1211 Geneva 22, Switzerland. FAX 022-7986385. circ. 1,500. Indexed: Abstr.Hyg., HR Rep. Document type: bulletin.
    —BLDSC (3501.994000).
    Description: Summaries of projects undertaken by social security institutions, government departments, research institutes and universities, includes results of research and addresses of those in charge of research projects.

CYPRUS. MINISTRY OF LABOUR AND SOCIAL INSURANCE. ANNUAL REPORT. see *BUSINESS AND ECONOMICS* — Labor And Industrial Relations

D O K: POLITIK - PRAXIS RECHT. see *LAW*

368   DK   ISSN 0106-2735
DANSK FORSIKRINGS - AARBOG. Variant title: Dansk Forsikringsaarbog. 1904. a. DKK 325. (Forsikringserhvervet) Forlaget Forsikring, Amaliegade 10, DK-1256 Copenhagen K, Denmark. TEL 45-33-13-75-55. FAX 45-33-11-23-53. Ed. Kirsten Skov Johansen. adv.: B&W page DKK 2575. circ. 1,800.

332.6   US   ISSN 1062-6123
DATA BASE OF DEFINED CONTRIBUTION AND DEFINED BENEFIT PLANS. 1990. a. price varies. Judy Diamond Associates, Inc., 1730 M St., N.W., Ste. 1025, Washington, DC 20036. TEL 202-728-0840. FAX 202-728-0845. Ed. Judy Diamond. (looseleaf format; also avail. in magnetic tape; diskette format; back issues avail.) Document type: trade publication.

INSURANCE

368   DK   ISSN 0907-9947
DENMARK. FINANSTILSYNET. HOVEDTAL. 1990. a. DKK 25. Finanstilsynet, Gl. Kongevej 74 A, DK-1850 Frederiksberg C, Denmark. TEL 45-31-23-11-88. FAX 45-31-23-04-41. (Dist. By: D B K Bogdistribution, Siljangade 2-8, DK-2300 Copenhagen S., Denmark) **Document type:** government publication.

368   DK   ISSN 0907-3698
HG8655
DENMARK. FINANSTILSYNET. STATISTISK MATERIALE. PENGEINSTITUTTER M.V.. (Text in Danish, English and French) 1989. a. DKK 55. Finanstilsynet, Gl. Kongevej 74A, DK-1850 Frederiksberg C, Denmark. TEL 45-31-23-11-88. FAX 45-31-23-04-41. (Dist. by: D B K - Bogdistribution, Siljangade 6, 2300 Copenhagen S, Denmark) circ. 1,500.
Formerly (until 1991): Denmark. Finanstilsynet. Beretning. Bilag 1: Pengeinstitutter m.v.

368.8   II   ISSN 0304-6966
HG1662.I4
DEPOSIT INSURANCE CORPORATION. ANNUAL REPORT: DIRECTORS' REPORT, BALANCE SHEET AND ACCOUNTS. (Text in English) 1962. a. Deposit Insurance & Credit Guarantee Corp., New India Centre, 17 Cooperage Rd., Bombay 400039, India. TEL 202-02-99. circ. 4,000.

368   GW   ISSN 0012-0200
DEUTSCHE GESELLSCHAFT FUER VERSICHERUNGSMATHEMATIK. BLAETTER. 1950. s-a. DM.57. Deutsche Gesellschaft fuer Versicherungsmathematik e.V., Walter-Flex-Str. 3, 53113 Bonn, Germany. TEL 0228-9162210. FAX 0228-9162211. Ed. E. Neuburger. bk.rev.; abstr.; charts. circ. 1,550. **Document type:** trade publication.
—BLDSC (2109.100000).

368   GW   ISSN 0070-4237
DIE DEUTSCHE LEBENSVERSICHERUNG. JAHRBUCH. a. free. Verband der Lebensversicherungs Unternehmen e.V., Eduard-Pflueger-Str. 55, 53113 Bonn, Germany. TEL 0228-5300841. FAX 0228-5300867. (Subscr. to: Verlag Versicherungswirtschaft e.V., Klosestr. 22, 76137 Karlsruhe, Germany) Ed. Michael Glueck. circ. 23,000. (back issues avail.) **Document type:** trade publication.

368.4   GW   ISSN 0012-0618
DEUTSCHE RENTENVERSICHERUNG. 1929. m. DM.192. (Verband Deutscher Rentenversicherungstraeger) Wirtschaftsdienst Gesellschaft fuer Medien & Kommunikation mbH & Co. OHG, Lange Str. 13, 60311 Frankfurt a.M., Germany. Ed. Franz Ruland. adv.; bk.rev.; charts; illus.; index. circ. 3,350. **Indexed:** World Bibl.Soc.Sec. **Document type:** bulletin.

DEVELOPMENTS IN HEALTH ECONOMICS AND PUBLIC POLICY. see *PUBLIC HEALTH AND SAFETY*

DEVELOPPEURS. see *BUSINESS AND ECONOMICS*

368 658   FR
DIRECTIONS. 4/yr. 4 bd. Poissonniere, 75009 Paris, France. TEL 44-79-94-44. FAX 44-79-94-58. TELEX 648 559 CAPA F. Ed. Anne-Francoise Khanine. circ. 3,058.

368   HK
DIRECTORY OF HONG KONG INSURANCE SERVICES.* a. HK.$200. Hong Kong Trade and Industry Promotion Centre, c/o Hong Kong Trade Development Council, 36th-39th Fl., Office Tower, Convention Plaza, 1 Harbor Rd., Wanchai, Hong Kong. TEL 3-882708. FAX 3-7716438.

368   US   ISSN 0070-5691
DIRECTORY OF INSURANCE COMPANIES LICENSED IN NEW YORK STATE. a. $1 per no. (single copies free to NY residents). Insurance Department, Publications Unit, Empire State Plaza, Agency Bldg. No. 1, Albany, NY 12257. circ. 5,000.

DIRITTO E PRATICA NELL'ASSICURAZIONE. see *LAW*

DIRITTO E TECNICA DELLA CIRCOLAZIONE STRADALE E ASSICURAZIONE OBBLIGATORIA DI R C A. see *LAW*

368.012   US   ISSN 0742-5619
HG9336
DISABILITY INCOME AND HEALTH INSURANCE; time saver. a. $25.95. National Underwriter Co., 505 Gest St., Cincinnati, OH 45203. TEL 513-721-2140. FAX 513-721-0126. Ed. Price Gaines. stat.

368.4   SZ   ISSN 0250-6041
DOCUMENTACION DE LA SEGURIDAD SOCIAL AMERICANA. (Text in Spanish) 1980. a. 15 SFr. per no. International Social Security Association, Publications, Case Postale 1, CH-1211 Geneva 22, Switzerland. FAX 022-7986385. Ed.Bd. **Document type:** bulletin.
Description: Includes regional reports, round tables and other meetings' proceedings on Social Security.

346.71   CN   ISSN 0706-8964
DUNHILL LIABILITY LOSS REPORT. 1977. bi-m. Can.$115. Dunhill Publishing Company, 6389 Coburg Rd., Halifax, NS B3H 2A5, Canada. TEL 902-429-7272. FAX 902-425-2191. **Document type:** newsletter.

346.71   CN
DUNHILL PERSONAL INJURY & DEATH REPORTS. 1976. bi-m. Can.$115. Dunhill Publishing Company, 6389 Coburg Rd., Halifax, NS B3H 2A5, Canada. TEL 902-429-7272. FAX 902-425-2191. **Document type:** newsletter.
Former titles: Dunhill Personal Injury Awards Annotator; Dunhill Insurance Law Report (ISSN 0706-8956)

368.012   US
E & S MARKET NEWS. (Excess and Surplus) 1979. bi-w. $387. Merritt Company, 1661 Ninth St., Box 955, Santa Monica, CA 90406. TEL 310-450-7234. FAX 310-396-4563. Ed. Juan Hovey. circ. 1,155. (looseleaf format) **Document type:** newsletter.
Formerly: Excess Express (ISSN 0740-1388)
Description: Information on excess and surplus insurance, specialty insurance and unique insurance coverages.

E B R I ISSUE BRIEF. (Employee Benefit Research Institute) see *BUSINESS AND ECONOMICS — Personnel Management*

368   UK   ISSN 0965-9676
EAST EUROPEAN INSURANCE REPORT. m. £375($621) (overseas £375) (effective 1993). Financial Times Business Information Ltd., 126 Jermyn St., London SW1Y 4UJ, England. TEL 071-411-4414. FAX 071-411-4115. stat. **Document type:** newsletter.
Description: Provides international service for East Europe's insurance and reinsurance management.

368   US
EMPLOYERS' HEALTH BENEFITS BULLETIN. 1987. m. $227. Thompson Publishing Group, 1725 K St., N.W., Ste. 200, Washington, DC 20006. TEL 202-872-4000. FAX 301-543-2921. Ed. John Ortman. (looseleaf format; back issues avail.) **Document type:** bulletin, newsletter.

368   US   ISSN 0740-9087
EMPLOYERS' HEALTH COSTS SAVINGS LETTER. 1983. m. $157. American Business Publishing, 3100 Hwy. 138, Box 1442, Wall Township, NJ 07719-1442. TEL 908-681-1133. FAX 908-681-0490. Ed. Robert K. Jenkins. index. (back issues avail.) —CCC.
Description: For business and industry vice presidents, personnel, fringe benefit managers and other executives. Provides current information on how to save money in health care costs.

368   CN   ISSN 0707-901X
HD7096.C2
EMPLOYMENT AND IMMIGRATION CANADA. ANNUAL REPORT/EMPLOI ET IMMIGRATION CANADA. RAPPORT ANNUEL. (Text in English and French) 1978. a. free. Public Enquiries Centre, Employment and Immigration Canada, Ottawa, ON K1A 0J9, Canada. charts; stat. circ. 10,000. **Document type:** corporate report.
Incorporates: Employment and Immigration Commission. Annual Report; Unemployment Insurance Canada. Annual Report (ISSN 0576-4157)

EMPLOYMENT SERVICE AND UNEMPLOYMENT INSURANCE OPERATIONS; a monthly summary. see *OCCUPATIONS AND CAREERS*

EN MARCHE; journal bimensuel d'information pour les beneficiaires des soins de sante. see *PHYSICAL FITNESS AND HYGIENE*

368 657   US
ENROLLED ACTUARIES REPORT. 1976. q. membership. American Academy of Actuaries, 1720 I St., N.W., 7th Fl., Washington, DC 20006. TEL 202-223-8196. FAX 202-872-1948. Ed. Jeffrey Speicher. circ. 5,000. (back issues avail.) **Document type:** government publication, newsletter.
Description: Newsletter for pension actuaries on pension and employee benefit topics.

368   US
ENTERPRISE (NEW YORK). 1956. fortn. free to qualified personnel. Equitable Life Assurance Society of the U.S., Corporate Communications Department, Internal Communications Division, 787 Seventh Ave., Area 37K, New York, NY 10019. TEL 212-554-4738. Ed. James Lacey. charts; illus. circ. 22,000.
Formerly: Equinews (ISSN 0013-984X)

ENVIRONMENTAL COMPLIANCE & LITIGATION STRATEGY. see *LAW*

340   US
ENVIRONMENTAL INSURANCE COVERAGE; state law and regulation. 1991. base vol. (plus a. suppl.). $125. Butterworth Legal Publishers (Salem) (Subsidiary of: Reed Elsevier plc), 8 Industrial Way, Bldg. C, Salem, NH 03079. TEL 800-548-4001. FAX 603-898-9858. Ed. Mitchell L. Lathrop. (looseleaf format)
Description: Overview of judicial decisions involving insurance coverage arising from environmental and toxic tort claims.

368.4   SZ   ISSN 0379-0266
HD7088
ESTUDIOS DE LA SEGURIDAD SOCIAL. (Text in Spanish) irreg. price varies. International Social Security Association, Publications, Case Postale 1, CH-1211 Geneva 22, Switzerland. FAX 022-7986385. (Orders to: Oficina para las Americas de la A I S S, Zuviria 20, Temperley 1834, Buenos Aires, Argentina) (Co-sponsors: Secretariat of State for Social Security of Argentina; Family Allowances Fund for Industrial Personnel, Dockers and Commercial Employees.) Ed.Bd. **Document type:** bulletin.

368   UK   ISSN 0960-0981
EUROPEAN INSURANCE MARKET. 1989. m. £230($460) D Y P Insurance & Reinsurance Research Group Ltd., Bridge House, 181 Queen Victoria St., London EC4V 4DD, England. TEL 071-236-2175. FAX 071-489-1487. Ed. Julius S. Bannister. charts; stat. **Document type:** newsletter.
Description: Keeps insurance executives informed of developments in the European insurance market.

368   UK
EXECUTIVES' AND DIRECTORS' PENSIONS (YEAR). 1976. a. £45($82) (overseas £48) (effective 1994). Financial Times Business Information Ltd., 102 Clerkenwell Rd., London EC1M 5SA, England. TEL 071-814-9770. FAX 071-814-9778. (Avail. from: F T Management Reports, Customer Services, P.O. Box 6, Camborne TR14 9EQ, England. TEL 0209-711928. FAX 0209-612493) Ed. David Lewis. adv.: B&W page £2150; color page £2600; adv. contact: Colin Clarke. circ. 4,500. (tabloid format) **Document type:** directory.
Formerly: Executive Pensions.
Description: Focuses on more than 100 plans available in the U.K. to executives and directors wishing to make pension arrangements through a company scheme.

EXPATRIATE. see *BUSINESS AND ECONOMICS — Labor And Industrial Relations*

368   SZ   ISSN 0014-4932
EXPERIODICA. Issued with: Sigma (ISSN 0037-4857) (Editions in English, German, French, Spanish) 1960. irreg. (6-7/yr.). free. Schweizerische Rueckversicherungs-Gesellschaft - Swiss Reinsurance Company, Economic Department, Mythenquai 50-60, CH-8022 Zurich, Switzerland. TEL 01-2852551. FAX 01-2852999. TELEX 815722-SRE-CH. abstr. **Document type:** newsletter.
Description: Topical news items pertaining to the international insurance press.

INSURANCE

368 NO
F F-AVISEN. bi-m. Forsikringsfunksjonaerenes Landsforbund, Bygdoe Alle 19, Oslo 2, Norway. adv. circ. 4,800.

368.08 UK ISSN 0071-3686
FACULTY OF ACTUARIES IN SCOTLAND. TRANSACTIONS. 1901. irreg. (approx. 2/yr.) £9 per issue to non-members. Faculty of Actuaries, 23 St. Andrew Sq., Edinburgh EH2 1AQ, Scotland. TEL 031-557-1575. FAX 031-557-6702. Ed. Leslie J.G. Purdie. bk.rev.; index. circ. 1,100. Document type: proceedings.
  Description: Publishes actuarial papers and discussions from the Faculty's sessional meetings.

368 282 US
THE FAMILY FRIEND. 1905. q. Catholic Family Life Insurance, Box 11563, Milwaukee, WI 53211. TEL 414-961-0500. FAX 414-961-2059. Ed. David L. Springob. circ. 25,000. (back issues avail.)

368.4 US ISSN 1073-1474
FAST FACTS AND FIGURES ABOUT SOCIAL SECURITY (YEAR). 1986. a. U.S. Social Security Administration, Office of Research and Statistics, Publications Staff, Van Ness Center, Rm. 209, 4301 Connecticut Ave., N.W., Washington, DC 20008. TEL 202-282-7161. FAX 202-282-7219. (Subscr. to: Superintendent of Documents, U.S. Government Printing Office, Box 371954, Pittsburgh, PA 15250-7954. TEL 202-783-3238. FAX 202-512-2233) charts; stat. Document type: government publication.
  Description: Answers the most frequently asked questions on OASDI beneficiaries and SSI recipients, as well as the Medicare, Medicaid, and AFDC programs.

368 US
FEDERAL & STATE INSURANCE WEEK. 1987. 48/yr. $347. J R Publishing, Box 6654, McLean, VA 22106. TEL 703-532-2235. Ed. John V. Reistrup. Document type: newsletter.
  ●Also available online. Vendor(s): NewsNet (IN04).

368.32 355.15 US
FEDERAL BENEFITS FOR VETERANS AND DEPENDENTS. a. U.S. Veterans Administration, Department of Veterans Affairs, Office of Public Affairs (80D), 810 Vermont Ave., Washington, DC 20420. (Orders to: Superintendent of Documents, Mail Stop: SSOP, Washington, DC 20402-9328) Document type: government publication.
  Formerly: Government Life Insurance Programs for Veterans and Members of the Services. Annual Report.
  Description: Outlines and describes benefits and services available to U.S. veterans. Also lists V.A. facilities nationwide.

FEDERAL BENEFITS FOR VETERANS AND DEPENDENTS, IS-1 FACT SHEET. see *MILITARY*

FEDERAL RESERVE BANK OF CLEVELAND. WORKING PAPER. see *BUSINESS AND ECONOMICS — Banking And Finance*

368.4 US
FEDERAL SOCIAL SECURITY LAWS. 1986. irreg. West Publishing Corp., 620 Opperman Dr., Eagan, MN 55123. TEL 612-687-8000; 800-328-9352. FAX 612-687-7302. Document type: trade publication.

FEDERAL TAXATION OF INSURANCE COMPANIES. see *BUSINESS AND ECONOMICS — Public Finance, Taxation*

368.4 NE ISSN 0071-4151
HC321
FEDERATIE VAN BEDRIJFSVERENIGINGEN. JAARVERSLAG. 1930. a. free. Federatie van Bedrijfsverenigingen, Postbus 8300, 1005 C A Amsterdam, Netherlands. TEL 020-879111. circ. 400.
  Description: Covers unemployment law, insurance, union dues, salaries, work environment, legal protection, scientific research, international affairs, financial situation and more.

FEDERATION OF INSURANCE AND CORPORATE COUNSEL QUARTERLY. see *LAW — Corporate Law*

368 MG
FEON'NY MAMA. m. B.P. 185, 101 Antananarivo, Malagasy Republic. TEL 25433. Ed. Richard Ramanandraibe. circ. 2,500.

FIDELITY AND SURETY NEWS. see *LAW*

368 332 US ISSN 1053-4407
FIELD GUIDE TO ESTATE PLANNING, BUSINESS PLANNING & EMPLOYEE BENEFITS. 1989. a. $23.95. National Underwriter Co., 505 Gest St., Cincinnati, OH 45203. TEL 513-721-2140. FAX 513-721-0126.
  Description: Practical guide to the uses of life insurance in estate planning, business planning, and employee benefits.

FINANCE, INSURANCE AND REAL ESTATE U S A. see *BUSINESS AND ECONOMICS — Abstracting, Bibliographies, Statistics*

368 UK ISSN 0964-4695
FINANCIAL REINSURANCE NEWSLETTER. 1991. m. £225($450) D Y P Insurance & Reinsurance Group Ltd., Bridge House, 181 Queen Victoria St., London EC4V 4DD. TEL 071-236-2175. FAX 071-489-1487. Ed. Julius S. Banister. stat.; charts. Document type: newsletter.
  Description: Covers the technicalities of the financial reinsurance sector and how it can affect other insurance companies.

368 US ISSN 0270-5656
FINANCIAL REVIEW OF ALIEN INSURERS. a. $275. National Association of Insurance Commissioners, 120 W. 12th St., Kansas City, MO 64105. TEL 816-374-7259. (Subscr. to: N A I C Publications, Box 263 Department 42, Kansas City, MO 64193-0042)
  Description: Provides current financial and corporate data for alien insurance companies.

368 332 US
FINANCIAL SERVICES DOCUMENT WATCH - INSURANCE EDITION. (Consists of 4 eds.: Banking; Insurance; Public Finance; Thrift) m. $180. American Banker - Bond Buyer, Newsletter Division (Subsidiary of: Thomson Financial Services Company), One State St. Plaza, New York, NY 10004-1549. TEL 800-733-4371. FAX 212-943-2224. (Subscr. to: Box 28315, Washington, DC 20038-8315. TEL 202-347-2665) Document type: newsletter.
  Supersedes in part: Insurance Document Watch.
  Description: Real-time delivery of key documents in the insurance sector.

368 UK ISSN 0309-751X
FINANCIAL TIMES INTERNATIONAL YEAR BOOKS: WORLD INSURANCE. a. £140. Longman Group UK Ltd., Westgate House, 6th Fl., The High, Harlow, Essex CM20 1YR, England. TEL 0279-442601. FAX 0279-444501. adv.; B&W page £715, color page £1150; 202 x 154. Document type: directory.

368 CN ISSN 0832-0659
FINANCIAL TIMES OF CANADA. R R S PS (YEAR). French edition: R E E R. Regime Enregistre d'Epargne Retraite (ISSN 1187-6557) 1983. a. Can.$14.95. Financial Times of Canada, 440 Front St. W., Toronto, ON M5V 3E6, Canada. TEL 416-585-5000. FAX 416-585-5547.
  Former titles (until 1986): No-Nonsense Guide to R R S Ps (ISSN 0832-0667); (until 1983): Financial Times of Canada. Guide to R R S Ps (ISSN 0712-1482)

368 CN
FINK AND BORSTEIN WORKERS' COMPENSATION NEWSLETTER. 1986. 4/yr. Can.$75. Fink and Bornstein, Barristers & Solicitors, 466 Dupont St., Toronto, ON M5R 1W6, Canada. TEL 416-537-0108. FAX 416-537-1604. circ. 200. Document type: newsletter.

368.38 610 FI ISSN 0355-4813
FINLAND. KANSANELAKELAITOS. JULKAISUJA. SARJA AL. (Text in English and Finnish; summaries in English) 1975. irreg., no. AL36, 1993. Kansanelakelaitos - Social Insurance Institution of Finland, Research and Development Centre, P.O. Box 78, FIN-00381 Helsinki 38, Finland.

368.38 610 FI ISSN 0355-4856
FINLAND. KANSANELAKELAITOS. JULKAISUJA. SARJA EL. (Text in English and Finnish; summaries in English) 1973. irreg., no. EL88, 1992. Kansanelakelaitos - Social Insurance Institution of Finland, Research and Development Centre, P.O. Box 78, FIN-00381 Helsinki 38, Finland. Ed. Kaino Laaksonen.

368.38 610 FI ISSN 0355-483X
FINLAND. KANSANELAKELAITOS. JULKAISUJA. SARJA ML. (Text in Finnish and English; summaries in English) 1973. irreg., no.ML126, 1993. Kansanelakelaitos - Social Insurance Institution of Finland, Research and Development Centre, P.O. Box 78, SF-00381 Helsinki 38, Finland.

368 US
FIRE, CASUALTY & SURETY BULLETIN. 5 base vols. (plus m. updates). $267.50. National Underwriter Co., 505 Gest St., Cincinnati, OH 45203. TEL 513-721-2140. FAX 513-721-0126.
  Description: Provides current information on all aspects of property and casualty insurance.

368.11 US
FIRE MARK CIRCLE OF THE AMERICAS JOURNAL. 1985. a. $30 membership. Fire Mark Circle of the Americas, 2859 Marlin Dr., Chamblee, GA 30341-5119. TEL 404-451-2651. Ed. Edward R. Tufts. circ. 350. (tabloid format; back issues avail.)

368.11 US
FIRE MARK CIRCLE OF THE AMERICAS NEWSLETTER. q. Fire Mark Circle of the Americas, 2859 Marlin Dr., Chamblee, GA 30341-5119. TEL 404-451-2651. Document type: newsletter.

FLOOD REPORT. see *EARTH SCIENCES — Hydrology*

368 US ISSN 0743-3441
FLORIDA UNDERWRITER. 1984. m. $16.50. National Underwriter Co., 505 Gest St., Cincinnati, OH 45203. TEL 513-721-2140. FAX 513-721-0126. Ed. James Seymour. adv. circ. 10,000. (reprint service avail.)
  Description: Covers the insurance industry in Florida, including regulatory and legislative decisions and trends.

368 US
FOCUS (AUSTIN).* 1956. q. membership only. (Professional Insurance Agents of Texas) Turnkey Publishing, Inc., Box 200549, Austin, TX 78720-0549. TEL 512-345-5316. Ed. Becky Sloan. adv. circ. 3,000.
  Description: Covers news and issues of interest to independent insurance agents in Texas.

368 SW ISSN 0015-7880
HG8015
FOERSAAKRINGSTIDNINGEN. 1946. 10/yr. SEK 400. Sveriges Foersaekringsfoerbund, P.O. Box 1436, S-111 84 Stockholm, Sweden. FAX 46-8-723-03-08. Ed. Margareta Lindqvist. adv.; bk.rev.; illus. circ. 4,700.

368 SW ISSN 0345-3901
FOERSAEKRINGS VAERLDEN. 1945. m. (10/yr). SEK 150. Foersaekringsjaenstemannafoerbundet, Box 45166, 104 30 Stockholm, Sweden. TEL 08-247455. FAX 08-102271. Ed. Peter Hennix. adv. circ. 20,294. (also avail. in microfiche)

368 SW ISSN 0345-3898
FOERSAEKRINGSANSTAELLD. Alternate title: F A. 1919. m. (11/yr.). SEK 60 (effective 1991). Foersaekringsanstaelldas Foerbund, Vasagatan 44, P.O. Box 1119, 111 81 Stockholm, Sweden. adv. circ. 23,150. (also avail. in audio cassette)
  Formerly (until 1969): Foersaekringsfunktionaeren.

368 FI ISSN 0355-7308
FOERSAEKRINGSTIDNING. (Text in Swedish) 1935. 4/yr. FIM 277 in the Nordic countries; elsewhere FIM 346. Vakuutussanomia Oy, Bulevardi 28, 00120 Helsinki 12, Finland. TEL 358-0-680-401. FAX 358-0-640-469. Ed. Reijo Ollikainen. adv. circ. 1,000.

368 CN
FOREFRONT. 1976. m. free. Sun Life Assurance Company of Canada, Agency Communications, 225 King St. W., Toronto, ON M5V 3C5, Canada. TEL 416-408-7644. FAX 416-974-9298. Ed. Carol Bingham. circ. 5,000.
  Former titles (until 1984): Sunbeat; Sun Life Assurance Company of Canada. Field News.

368 UK ISSN 0141-2027
FORESIGHT (LONDON); the journal of insurance and risk management. 1975. m. £230. Risk & Insurance Research Group Ltd., 4 Henrietta St., Covent Garden, London WC2E 8PS, England. TEL 071-836-0614. FAX 071-379-6355. Document type: trade publication.

INSURANCE

368   DK   ISSN 0105-4260
FORSIKRING. 1969. fortn. (except July). DKK 485. Forlaget Forsikring, Amaliegade 10, DK-1256 Copenhagen K, Denmark. TEL 45-33-13 75 55. FAX 45-33-33-02-71. Ed. Soeren P. Espersen. adv.; bk.rev.; bibl.; charts; illus.; stat.; index; circ. 3,000 (controlled). **Document type:** trade publication.
    Formerly: Dansk Forsikrings Tidende - Assurandoeren (ISSN 0300-4732)

368   NO   ISSN 0015-7929
FORSIKRINGSTIDENDE. 1897. 10/yr. NOK 340. Forsikringslitteratur, Box 2473, Solli, 0202 Oslo 2, Norway. Ed. Egil Tannaes. adv.; bk.rev.; charts; illus. circ. 3,785.
  —CCC.

368   US   ISSN 0013-6743
FORUM (SYRACUSE). 1927. m. $24. Independent Insurance Agents Association of New York State, Inc., Box 9001, Mt. Vernon, NY 10552. TEL 914-699-2020. FAX 914-664-1503. Stephen H. Acunto. adv.; bk.rev.; illus.; circ. 3,000 (controlled). (back issues avail.)
    Formerly: Empire State Agency Forum.

346 368   FR   ISSN 0760-0305
HC271
FRANCE. MINISTERE DE L'ECONOMIE, DES FINANCES ET DU BUDGET. BULLETIN OFFICIEL DE L'ADMINISTRATION CENTRALE. Abbreviated title: B O A C. q. Ministere de l'Economie, des Finances et du Budget, Imprimerie Nationale, B.P. 514, 59505 Douai Cedex, France.
    Former titles: Ministere de l'Economie et des Finances. Bulletin Administratif des Assurances (ISSN 0243-7910); France. Office des Assurances. Bulletin (ISSN 0243-7902)

FRAT. see HANDICAPPED — Hearing Impaired

368   US   ISSN 0016-0105
FRATERNAL MONITOR. 1890. m. $23 (effective 1993). Dearborn - R & R Newkirk, 520 N. Dearborn St., Chicago, IL 60610-4354. TEL 312-836-4400. FAX 312-836-1021. (Subscr. to: Box 830350, Birmingham, AL 35283-0350. TEL 800-633-4931) Ed. James A. Ballew. adv.; illus. circ. 5,000.

FRIENDLY EXCHANGE. see GENERAL INTEREST PERIODICALS — United States

368   US   ISSN 0016-1748
FROM THE STATE CAPITALS. INSURANCE REGULATION. Variant title: Insurance Regulation from the State Capitals. 1946. w. $215 (foreign $235) (effective Dec. 1990). Wakeman-Walworth, Inc., 300 N. Washington St., Alexandria, VA 22314. TEL 703-549-8606. FAX 703-549-1372. (processed)
  ●Also available online. Vendor(s): West Services, Inc.
  —CCC.
    Description: Regulation of policy, rates and benefits for all types of insurance - life, health, automobile, homeowner, malpractice. Covers self-insurance and innovations such as life style considerations.

368   AU   ISSN 0016-2728
FUNDAMENT; das Erste Allgemeine Generali-Magazin. 1951. 6/yr. membership. Erste Allgemeine Versicherungs-AG, Generali Allgemeine Lebensversicherung AG, Landskrongasse 1-3, A-1011 Vienna, Austria. FAX 53401-593. (Co-sponsor: Generali Rueckversicherung AG) Ed. Beate Manndorff. bk.rev. circ. 8,000. **Document type:** trade publication.

368   US
G A M A NEWS JOURNAL. 1983. bi-m. $20. General Agents and Managers Association, 1922 F St., N.W., Washington, DC 20006-4389. TEL 202-331-6088. FAX 202-785-5712. adv.; bk.rev. circ. 9,000.
    Description: Provides information on the art and science of agency management.

368 914.306   US
G B U REPORTER. 1893. bi-m. free. Greater Beneficial Union of Pittsburgh, 4254 Clairton Blvd., Pittsburgh, PA 15227-3394. TEL 412-884-5100. FAX 412-884-9815. Ed. Frederick W. Schwesinger. circ. 10,700. (also avail. in microfiche) **Document type:** newsletter.
    Formerly (until 1958): Union Reporter.
    Description: Contains news of members of the society and of insurance products available to them.

G D S - ZEITUNG. (Gewerkschaft der Sozialversicherung) see LABOR UNIONS

368   US
G E I C O DIRECT. 1986. q. (Government Employees Insurance Company) Maxwell Custom Publishing, 1999 Shepard Rd., St. Paul, MN 55666. TEL 612-690-7200. FAX 612-690-7357. Ed. Sharon Ross. circ. controlled.

368   SP
G E S. BOLETIN DE INFORMACION. Running title: General Espanola de Seguros. Boletin de Informacion. 1940. q. free. General Espanola de Seguros, S.A., Plaza de las Cortes, 2, Madrid 28014, Spain. charts; illus.; stat.; circ. 1,500 (controlled).

368   AG
GALICIA Y RIO DE LA PLATA. COMPANIA DE SEGUROS. MEMORIA Y BALANCE GENERAL. 1974. a. Compania de Seguros, Rivadavia 717, Buenos Aires, Argentina. stat.

368   FR
GAZETTE DES ASSUREURS CONSEILS. 11/yr. Syndicat Francais des Assureurs - Conseils, 14 rue Grange Bateliere, 75009 Paris, France. TEL 45-23-25-26. FAX 48-00-93-01. Ed. Yolanda de Clairval. circ. 1,200.

368   US   ISSN 0926-4957
HG8015
GENEVA PAPERS ON RISK AND INSURANCE THEORY. 1975. 2/yr. fl.179($93.50) (effective 1994). (Geneva Association) Kluwer Academic Publishers Boston, Box 358, Accord Sta., Hingham, MA 02018-0358. TEL 617-871-6600. FAX 617-871-6528. TELEX 200190. (Dist. outside N. America by: Kluwer Academic Publishers Group, P.O. Box 322, 3300 AH Dordrecht, Netherlands. TEL 31-78-524400. FAX 31-78-524474) Eds. Henri Louberge, Harris Schlesinger. (also avail. in microform from UMI) **Document type:** academic/scholarly publication.
  —BLDSC (4115.562000); Faxon. **CCC.**
    Formerly (until 1992): Geneva Papers on Risk and Insurance (ISSN 0252-1148)
    Description: Publishes theoretical, empirical and experimental articles on the economics of risk, uncertainty and insurance.
  Refereed Serial

368   GW   ISSN 0302-5608
GERMANY (FEDERAL REPUBLIC, 1949-). BUNDESAUFSICHTSAMT FUER DAS VERSICHERUNGSWESEN. GESCHAEFTSBERICHT. 1953. a. DM.50. Bundesaufsichtsamt fuer das Versicherungswesen, Ludwigkirchplatz 3-4, 10719 Berlin, Germany. TEL 030-88930. FAX 030-8893494. bk.rev.; stat.; index. circ. 2,000. **Document type:** government publication.

368   GW   ISSN 0170-236X
GERMANY (FEDERAL REPUBLIC, 1949-) BUNDESAUFSICHTSAMT FUER DAS VERSICHERUNGSWESEN. VEROEFFENTLICHUNGEN. m. DM.72. Bundesaufsichtsamt fuer das Versicherungswesen, Ludwigkirchplatz 3-4, 10719 Berlin, Germany. TEL 030-88930. FAX 030-8893494. circ. 2,800. **Document type:** government publication.

368   SZ
GESUNDHEIT. bi-m. Postfach, CH-4502 Solothurn, Switzerland. TEL 065-204204. Ed. U.O. Mueller. circ. 30,000.

368   IT
GIORNALE DELLE ASSICURAZIONI - ESPANSION; mensile di finanza e assicurazioni. 1981. m. L.81000 (foreign L.82200). Arnoldo Mondadori Editore S.p.A., Casella Postale 1833, 20101 Milan, Italy. Ed. Redento Mori. circ. 10,000.

368 355   US
GOVERNMENTAL RISK MANAGEMENT MANUAL. 1976. bi-m. $150 (renewal $100) (effective 1993). Risk Management Publishing Co., 2030 E. Broadway, Ste. 106, Tucson, AZ 85719. TEL 602-622-5174. FAX 602-629-9924. Ed. Barry Cole. cum.index: 1976-1989. circ. 1,000. (looseleaf format; back issues avail.) **Document type:** newsletter.

368   US
GOVERNORS' JOURNAL. 1971. s-a. free. International Insurance Society, Inc., Tuscaloosa, AL 35487. TEL 205-348-8974. FAX 205-348-8973. Ed. Mary B. Silberberg. circ. 2,000. **Document type:** newsletter.

368   UK   ISSN 0308-499X
GREAT BRITAIN. DEPARTMENT OF TRADE. INSURANCE BUSINESS: ANNUAL REPORT. a. (Department of Trade) H.M.S.O., P.O.Box 276, London SW8 5DT, England. stat. (reprint service avail. from UMI) **Document type:** government publication.
  —BLDSC (4531.691600).
    Supersedes: Great Britain. Board of Trade. Insurance Business: Annual Report (ISSN 0072-5684)

368 610   US
▼**GUIDE TO THE MANAGED CARE INDUSTRY.** 1992. a. $199. H C I A Inc., 300 E. Lombard St., Baltimore, MD 21202. TEL 410-576-9600. FAX 410-783-0575.
    Formerly: H M O Performance Almanac (ISSN 1063-1704)
    Description: Provides information on financial ratios, enrollment, liquidity and membership for some HMOs in the U.S.

368.382 610   US   ISSN 1050-9038
H M O MAGAZINE. (Health Maintenance Organization) 1959. 6/yr. $75 (effective Jan. 1994). Group Health Association of America, Inc., 1129 Twentieth St., N.W., Ste. 600, Washington, DC 20036. TEL 202-778-3247. FAX 202-331-7487. Ed. Lisa Lopez. bk.rev. circ. 5,000. **Indexed:** Med.Care Rev. **Document type:** trade publication.
    Former titles (until vol.31, no.2, 1990): G H A A News (ISSN 0887-9087); (until Dec. 1986): Group Health News (ISSN 0164-0542); (until Dec. 1975): Group Health and Welfare News (ISSN 0017-470X)
    Description: Provides analysis and news on HMO market trends and legislative and regulatory issues. Includes ideas on management information systems, pharmacy benefits, and health care finances.

368.382   IS
HADASHOT KUPOT HOLIM. m. (General Labor Federation of Israel) Kupot Holim, 101 Arlozorof St., Tel Aviv 62 098, Israel. TEL 03-433340. Ed. David Tagar.

368   US   ISSN 0073-1110
HAWAII. INSURANCE DIVISION. REPORT OF THE INSURANCE COMMISSIONER OF HAWAII. 1903. a. free. Department of Commerce and Consumer Affairs, Insurance Division, Box 3614, Honolulu, HI 96811. TEL 808-586-2790. circ. 1,000.
    Description: Presents the official transactions of the Division and condensed financial statements and insurance transactions in Hawaii every fiscal year.

HEALTH AFFAIRS; the journal of the health policy sphere. see PUBLIC HEALTH AND SAFETY

HEALTH CARE FINANCING ADMINISTRATION MANUALS. see HOSPITALS

368.382   US
HEALTH CARE FINANCING NOTES. irreg. free. Health Care Financing Administration, Office of Research and Demonstrations, Oak Meadows Bldg., Rm. 2230, 6325 Security Blvd., Baltimore, MD 21207. TEL 301-966-6584. (Subscr. to: Supt. of Documents, Washington, DC 20402. TEL 202-783-3238)
    Description: Presents data highlights or selected summary information on various aspects of the Medicare and Medicaid programs.

368.3   US   ISSN 0017-9019
HG9371
HEALTH INSURANCE UNDERWRITER. 1951. m. (except July-Aug. combined). $40 to non-members; members $18. National Association of Health Underwriters, 1000 Connecticut Ave., N.W., Ste. 1111, Washington, DC 20036. TEL 202-223-5533. FAX 202-785-2274. Ed. Michelle D. Esmacher. adv. contact: Allan F. Johnson. illus.; circ. 1,200 (paid). **Document type:** trade publication.
    Description: Provides information, instruction, facts and opinions of interest to individuals and corporations selling health and disability insurance products.

HIGHLIGHTS OF STATE UNEMPLOYMENT COMPENSATIONS LAWS. see LAW — Legal Aid

368 629.222 US
HIGHWAY LOSS DATA INSTITUTE. VEHICLE DESCRIPTIONS. 1983. a. free. Highway Loss Data Institute, c/o Stephen L. Oesch, General Counsel, Sec.-Treas., 1005 N. Glebe Rd., Ste. 800, Arlington, VA 22201. TEL 703-247-1600. FAX 703-247-1678.

368 US
HINE'S DIRECTORY OF INSURANCE ADJUSTERS. 1936. a. $25. Hine's Legal Directory, Inc., Box 280, Glen Ellyn, IL 60138. TEL 708-462-9670. Ed. James R. Collins. circ. 6,000 (controlled). **Document type:** catalog.
Description: Lists selected independent insurance adjuster offices in US and Canada.

HINE'S INSURANCE COUNSEL. see *LAW*

368 GW ISSN 0073-3350
HOPPENSTEDT VERSICHERUNGS-JAHRBUCH. 1958. a. DM.583. Verlag Hoppenstedt GmbH, Havelstr. 9, 64295 Darmstadt, Germany. TEL 06151-380-0. FAX 06151-380-360. adv. **Document type:** bulletin.

368 US
HUEBNER FOUNDATION MONOGRAPH. 1972. irreg. price varies. University of Pennsylvania, Wharton School, S.S. Huebner Foundation for Insurance, 430 Vance Hall, Philadelphia, PA 19104-6301. TEL 215-898-9631. FAX 215-573-2218. (Dist. by: Boyertown Publishing, Boyertown, PA 195512) Ed. J. David Cummins. circ. 1,000. **Indexed:** J.of Econ.Lit. **Document type:** monographic series.
Description: Presents scholarly research studies in risk and insurance.

368 NE
HUEBNER SERIES IN RISK AND INSURANCE. (Text in English) irreg., vol.18, 1994. price varies. Kluwer Academic Publishers, Postbus 17, 3300 AA Dordrecht, Netherlands. TEL 31-78-334911. FAX 31-78-334254. TELEX 29214 KAPG NL. (Dist. by: Kluwer Academic Publishers Group, P.O. Box 322, 3300 AH Dordrecht, Netherlands. TEL 31-78-524400. FAX 31-78-524474; N. America dist. addr.: Box 358, Accord Sta., Hingham, MA 02018-0358. TEL 617-871-6600. FAX 617-871-6528) **Document type:** monographic series.
Refereed Serial

368 US
I A D A SERVICE DIRECTORY. 1965. q. free. Independent Automotive Damage Appraisers Association, 710 E. Ogden Ave., Ste. 113, Naperville, IL 60563-8603. TEL 800-369-4232. FAX 708-369-2488. adv. circ. 20,000. **Document type:** directory.
Formerly: I A D A Bulletin.

368.4 US
I A I A B C NEWSLETTER. 1914. m. $500 membership. International Association of Industrial Accident Boards, 1575 Aviation Ctr. Pkwy., Ste. 512, Daytona Beach, FL 32114. TEL 904-252-2915. FAX 904-258-9965. Ed. R.B. Collyer. circ. 1,200. (tabloid format; back issues avail.) **Document type:** newsletter.

368 360 US
I B I S REVIEW. 1986. m. $90 (foreign $110). (International Benefits Information Service) Charles D. Spencer & Associates, Inc., 250 S. Wacker Dr., Ste. 600, Chicago, IL 60606. TEL 312-993-7900. FAX 312-993-7910. Eds. Bruce F. Spencer, Laurie W. Letts. adv.: B&W page $1040, color page $1750; trim 5 7/8 x 8 3/4. charts; stat.; index. circ. 2,200. (back issues avail.)
Description: Provides descriptions and commentary on topics of importance to international benefits specialists, such as pensions, death benefits and health care.

368 AT
I C A BULLETIN. 1975. q. Insurance Council of Australia Inc., 31 Queen St., 5th Fl., Melbourne, Vic. 3000, Australia. Ed. Judy Robertson. circ. 4,800. (back issues avail.)

368.382 GW ISSN 0945-3482
I K K STUTTGART AKTUELL. 1985. q. DM.2. Volker Rothfuss Verlag, Wollgrasweg 31, 70599 Stuttgart, Germany. TEL 0711-4567179. FAX 0711-4567180. Ed. Volker Rothfuss. circ. 45,000. **Document type:** consumer publication.

368 US ISSN 1071-5509
I O M A'S MONTHLY REPORT ON PROPERTY - CASUALTY RATES & RATINGS. m. $245. Institute of Management and Administration, 29 W. 25th St., 5th Fl., New York, NY 10001-2299. TEL 212-244-0360. FAX 212-564-0465. Ed. Catherine Henry.

368 BL ISSN 0019-0446
I R B REVISTA. 1940. 4/yr. free. Instituto de Resseguros do Brasil, Secretaria Geral da Presidencia (SECR-GP), Av. Marechal Camara 171-8, Rio de Janeiro, Brazil. TEL 021-2720317. FAX 021-2406261. TELEX IRBR 021-21019, 21237,30105. Ed. Lilia Maria G. Ferreira Leite. adv.; bk.rev.; charts; illus.; index. circ. 6,000.

368 US
I R M I'S ACCOUNT HANDLING SYSTEM. 1978. q. $160. International Risk Management Institute, Inc., 12222 Merit Dr., Ste. 1660, Dallas, TX 75251-2217. TEL 214-960-7693. FAX 214-960-6037. Ed. Natlia Stigers Duval. (looseleaf format)
Description: Contains a detailed exposure survey questionnaire and master insurance coverage checklists applicable to any commercial entity. Includes general liability, automobile, workers compensation, property, crime, umbrella, D&O, EIL, B&M, excess WC and aircraft.

368.4 SZ ISSN 0255-7592
I S S A. COMMITTEE ON PROVIDENT FUNDS. REPORTS. (Text in English) 1977. irreg., no.10, 1992. 10 SFr. International Social Security Association, Publications, Case Postale 1, CH-1211 Geneva 22, Switzerland. FAX 022-7986385. Ed.Bd. **Document type:** monographic series.
Description: Details aspects of converting provident to pension funds, training and capital investment.

368.4 SZ ISSN 0254-0576
I S S A. SOCIAL SECURITY DOCUMENTATION. CARIBBEAN SERIES. (Text in English) 1984. irreg., no.6, 1993. 15 SFr. per no. International Social Security Association, Publications, Case Postale 1, CH-1211 Geneva 22, Switzerland. FAX 022-7986385. Ed.Bd. **Document type:** monographic series.

368 US
I T T HARTFORD AGENT. 1909. 6/yr. (plus bulletins as needed). free to qualified personnel. I T T Hartford Insurance Group, Hartford Plaza, Hartford, CT 06115. TEL 203-547-4959. FAX 203-547-3799. Ed. Robert R. Proctor. charts; illus.; circ. 7,000 (controlled).
Formerly: Hartford Agent (ISSN 0017-7962)
Description: Provides current information about ITT Hartford and its products and services, and insurance issues in general for agents.

368 US
ILLINOIS BROKER. 1990. q. $12. Broker Publishing, Inc., 18101 Martin Ave., Homewood, IL 60430. TEL 708-799-2572. FAX 708-799-0425. Ed. Wendy Luna. adv.: B&W page $2176; trim 11 x 17. circ. 52,329. **Document type:** newspaper.

368 US ISSN 0094-7660 HG8538.I3
ILLINOIS INSURANCE. 1969. bi-m. free. Department of Insurance, 320 W. Washington St., Springfield, IL 62767. TEL 217-782-4515. Ed. Nan Nases. circ. 5,000. (also avail. in microform from UMI; reprint service avail. from UMI) **Document type:** newsletter, government publication.
—UMI.
Description: Regulatory newsletter of the Illinois Department of Insurance.

IMPULS; Zeitung fuer Sicherheit im Betrieb. see *BUSINESS AND ECONOMICS — Management*

368 CN ISSN 0848-1342
IN ONTARIO. 1976. q. membership. Insurance Institute of Ontario, 18 King St., E., 6th Fl., Toronto, ON M5C 1C4, Canada. TEL 416-362-8586. FAX 416-362-1126. Ed. Zina Tofano. bk.rev.; circ. 13,000 (controlled). **Document type:** newsletter.
Formerly: Insurance Institute of Ontario. Newsletter (ISSN 0225-1701)
Description: Provides course schedules and other educational opportunities offered by the Institute.

368.4 US ISSN 1073-1423
INCOME OF THE POPULATION 55 OR OLDER. 1976. biennial. U.S. Social Security Administration, Office of Research and Statistics, Publications Staff, Van Ness Center, Rm. 209, 4301 Connecticut Ave., N.W., Washington, DC 20008. TEL 202-282-7161. FAX 202-282-7219. (Subscr. to: Superintendent of Documents, U.S. Government Printing Office, Box 371954, Pittsburgh, PA 15250-7954. TEL 202-783-3238. FAX 202-512-2233) charts; stat. **Document type:** government publication.
Description: Presents a broad income picture of a cross-section of the population age 55 and over, with emphasis on several aspects of the income of populations age 65 and older.

368 US ISSN 0019-3658
INDEPENDENT ADJUSTER.* vol.35, 1970. q. free. National Association of Independent Insurance Adjusters, 300 W. Washington St., No. 805, Chicago, IL 60606-2001. TEL 312-427-7965. Ed. Richard Christopher. adv.; charts; illus.

368 US ISSN 0002-7197 HG9651
INDEPENDENT AGENT. 1903. m. $24. Independent Insurance Agents of America - M S I, 127 S. Peyton St., Alexandria, VA 22314. TEL 703-683-IIAA. FAX 703-683-7556. Ed. Maureen P. Wall. adv.; bk.rev.; charts; illus. circ. 55,000. (also avail. in microform from UMI; reprint service avail. from UMI) **Document type:** trade publication.
—UMI.
Formerly: American Agency Bulletin.
Description: Deals with insurance marketplace, agency management, marketing and sales, and IIAA's latest news.

368 US
INDEX OF INSURANCE AND EMPLOYEE BENEFITS PROCEEDINGS. 1982. a. $50. Badger Infosearch, Box 11943, Milwaukee, WI 53211. TEL 414-964-2377. Ed. Darlene E. Waterstreet. (looseleaf format; back issues avail.)

368.012 US ISSN 0195-7805
INDIANA UNDERWRITER. 1979. m. $16.50. National Underwriter Co., 505 Gest St., Cincinnati, OH 45203. TEL 513-721-2140. FAX 513-721-0126. Ed. Marianne Coil. circ. 10,000.
Description: Covers the insurance industry in Indiana, including regulatory and legislative decisions and trends.

INDIVIDUAL INVESTOR'S GUIDE TO LOW-LOAD INSURANCE PRODUCTS. see *BUSINESS AND ECONOMICS — Investments*

368 US
INDUSTRY WATCH; a summary of current financial trends affecting the property and casualty industy. q. Society of Chartered Property & Casualty Underwriters, Box 3009, 720 Providence Rd., Malvern, PA 19355. TEL 215-251-2728. Ed. Lisa A. Fittipaldi. **Document type:** trade publication.
Formerly: C P C U Update.

368 340 CK ISSN 0120-1875
INFORMATIVO JURIDICO. 1977. bi-m. $35. Union de Aseguradores Colombianos, Carrera 7a. No. 26-20, Piso 11, Apdo. Aereo 5233, Bogota, Colombia. circ. 800.
Description: Contains main pieces of Colombian legislation relevant to the insurance sector.

INJURY VALUATION REPORTS AND SPECIAL RESEARCH REPORTS. see *LAW*

INSIGHT (CHATSWORTH). see *LAW*

368 FR ISSN 0007-4438
INSTITUT DE SCIENCE FINANCIERE ET D'ASSURANCES. BULLETIN DES ACTUAIRES DIPLOMES.* 1958. s-a. 500 F. (foreign 480 F.). F I C O M, 5 av. de l'Opera, 75001 Paris, France. Ed. J. Dulac. index.

368 UK ISSN 0020-2681
INSTITUTE OF ACTUARIES. JOURNAL. 1851. 3/yr. £15 per copy. Institute of Actuaries, Staple Inn Hall, High Holborn, London WC1E 7QJ, England. TEL 071-242-0106. FAX 071-405-2482. Ed. A.D. Dart. adv.; bk.rev.; charts; stat.; index. cum.index. circ. 9,000. **Indexed:** Abstr.Hyg., Popul.Ind., Trop.Dis.Bull., World Bank.Abstr. **Document type:** academic/scholarly publication.
—BLDSC (4769.900000); SWETS.

INSURANCE

368.4 EC
INSTITUTO ECUATORIANO DE SEGURIDAD SOCIAL. BOLETIN. NORMAS RESOLUCIONES Y JURISPRUDENCIAS. 1938. s-a. exchange basis. Instituto Ecuatoriano de Seguridad Social, Apdo. Postal 2640, Quito, Ecuador. circ. 10,000.
Supersedes (in 1970): Boletin de Informaciones y de Estudios Sociales y Economicos.

368.4 HO ISSN 0074-0233
INSTITUTO HONDURENO DE SEGURIDAD SOCIAL. DEPARTAMENTO DE ESTADISTICA Y PROCESAMIENTO DE DATOS. ANUARIO ESTADISTICO. a. (with supplements). exchange basis. Instituto Hondureno de Seguridad Social, Departamento de Estadistica y Actuarial, Apdo. 555, Tegucigalpa, D.C., Honduras.

368.4 CR
INSTITUTO NACIONAL DE SEGUROS MEMORIA ANUAL. 1934. a. free. Instituto Nacional de Seguros, Apdo. 10061, San Jose, Costa Rica. charts; illus.; stat. circ. 2,000.
Former titles: Instituto Nacional de Seguros. Memoria Anual I.N.S; Instituto Nacional de Seguros. Informe Anual (ISSN 0074-0268).

368.382 GW ISSN 0945-3490
INSTRUKTIV. 1990. q. DM.8. Volker Rothfuss Verlag, Wollgrasweg 31, 70599 Stuttgart, Germany. TEL 0711-4567179. FAX 0711-4567180. Ed. Volker Rothfuss. circ. 4,000. **Document type:** consumer publication.

368 US
INSURANCE ACCOUNTANT. 48/yr. $625 for new subscr. (foreign $675); renewal $695 (foreign $745). American Banker - Bond Buyer, Newsletter Division (Subsidiary of: Thomson Financial Services Company), One State St. Plaza, New York, NY 10004-1549. TEL 800-733-4371. FAX 212-943-2224. (Subscr. to: Box 28315, Washington, DC 20038-8315. TEL 202-347-2665) **Document type:** newsletter.
Description: Concentrates on the regulatory, legislative and accounting policy developments affecting the insurance industry accounting practices. Covers all relevant major developments within the National Association of Insurance Commissioners, the AICPA, the FASB, the IRS, and the SEC, as well as relevant court cases impacting insurance accounting.

368 US ISSN 0020-4587
INSURANCE ADVOCATE. 1889. w. $40. Roberts Publishing Corp., Box 9001, Mt. Vernon, NY 10552-9001. TEL 914-699-2020. FAX 914-664-1503. Ed. Emanuel Levy. adv.; bk.rev.; illus.; stat.; tr.lit. circ. 8,500. (also avail. in microform from UMI; back issues avail.; reprint service avail. from UMI) **Indexed:** P.L.I.I.
—UMI.
Description: Covers all aspects of the insurance business, including feature articles for insurance specialists and professionals. Provides stock listings of 60 insurers, reinsurers and publicly held brokers.

368 UK ISSN 0142-6265
INSURANCE AGE. 1979. m. £50 (foreign £75). E M A P Business Publishing, 33-39 Bowling Green Ln., London EC1R 0DA, England. TEL 071-837-1212. Ed. John Jackson. circ. 19,636. (tabloid format) **Document type:** trade publication.

368 US ISSN 0074-0675
INSURANCE ALMANAC; WHO, WHAT, WHEN AND WHERE IN INSURANCE. 1912. a. $115. Underwriter Printing and Publishing Co., 50 E. Palisade Ave., Englewood, NJ 07631. TEL 201-569-8808. Ed. Donald E. Wolff. adv. circ. 10,000. **Document type:** directory.
Description: Lists 2,000 agencies and brokerages; more than 3,000 U.S. and Canadian insurance companies; and adjusters, auditors, investigators, insurance officials, and organizations.

368 US ISSN 0736-0126
HG8011
INSURANCE AND FINANCIAL REVIEW. 1978. m. $365. Philo Smith & Co., Inc., 2950 Summer St., Stamford, CT 06905-4303. TEL 203-348-7365. FAX 203-348-4307. TELEX 317785. Ed. James A. Amen. circ. 1,000.
Former titles: Insurance Review (Stamford); Insurance Stock Review (ISSN 0579-529X).
Description: Short analytical progress reports discussing current results and point of view on insurance and other financial service companies.

INSURANCE AND FINANCIAL SERVICES CAREERS. see OCCUPATIONS AND CAREERS

368 UK ISSN 0950-5377
INSURANCE AND REINSURANCE SOLVENCY REPORT. 1986. m. £230($460) D Y P Insurance & Reinsurance Group Ltd., Bridge House, 181 Queen Victoria St., London EC4V 4DD, England. TEL 071-236-2175. FAX 071-489-1487. Ed. Julius S. Banister. **Document type:** newsletter.
Description: Examines the solvency of insurance and reinsurance firms in detail. Also presents licensing and regulation requirements for transacting insurance and reinsurance overseas.

368 332.6 US ISSN 0892-5887
INSURANCE AND RISK MANAGEMENT. 1987. bi-w. $398 (foreign $420). Buraff Publications (Subsidiary of: Millin Publications, Inc.), 1350 Connecticut Ave. N.W., Ste. 1000, Washington, DC 20036. TEL 800-333-1291. FAX 202-862-0999. Ed. George Kimmerling. (back issues avail.) **Document type:** newsletter.
—CCC.
Description: Covers risk management and loss prevention and control, including news briefs, tax tips, state developments, and coverage of specific insurance and risk management topics.

368 AT ISSN 0314-3236
INSURANCE BROKER. 1977. bi-m. Aus.$45 (foreign Aus.$105). National Insurance Brokers Association, 2 Jocelyn Ct., Doncaster East, Vic. 3109, Australia. TEL 61-3-848-9540. FAX 61-3-848-6908. (Subscr. in New Zealand to: Corporation of Insurance Brokers of New Zealand: 3rd Fl. Ferry Bldg., Quay St., Auckland 1, New Zealand. TEL 09-309-4343. FAX 09-307-1285) Ed. John Heath. adv.; B&W page Aus.$1705, color page Aus.$2305; trim 297 x 210. bk.rev. circ. 3,800. (back issues avail.) **Document type:** trade publication.
Description: Covers current topics in insurance, insurance broking and related fields in Australia, New Zealand and Asia.

INSURANCE CASE LAW DIGEST. see LAW

368 629.222 US ISSN 1054-2892
INSURANCE COLLISION REPORT PASSENGER CARS, CARGO VANS, PICKUPS, AND UTILITY VEHICLES. 1976. a. free. Highway Loss Data Institute, c/o Stephen L. Oesch, General Counsel, Sec.-Treas., 1005 N. Glebe Rd., Ste. 800, Arlington, VA 22201. TEL 703-247-1600. FAX 703-247-1678.

368 PH
INSURANCE COMPANY PROFILE. 1982. biennial. price varies. Philippine Insurance Commission, Statistics and Research Division - Ministry ng Pananalapi, Komisyon ng Seguro, Insurance Commission Bldg., 1071 United Nations Ave., P.O. Box 3589, Manila, Philippines. TEL 02-599221. FAX 02-522-1434. circ. 300. (back issues avail.)
Description: Provides a brief history of each company authorized to transact insurance business in the Philippines, including comparative highlights on the financial situation, operating results, and business done.

INSURANCE CONFERENCE PLANNER. see MEETINGS AND CONGRESSES

368 UK ISSN 0074-0691
INSURANCE DIRECTORY AND YEAR BOOK. (In 4 vols.) 1841. a. £269. Buckley Press, 58 Fleet St., London EC4Y 1JU, England. TEL 071-353-4881. FAX 071-583-6069. adv.; charts. **Document type:** directory.
Formerly: Post Magazine Almanack. Insurance Directory.

368 NZ ISSN 1172-3076
INSURANCE DIRECTORY OF NEW ZEALAND. 1965. a. NZ.$12. Mercantile Gazette Marketing Ltd., P.O. Box 20-034, Christchurch 5, New Zealand. Ed. G. Everts.

368 US ISSN 0020-4684
INSURANCE FIELD. 1888. a. free. Insurance Field Company, Box 24244, Louisville, KY 40224-0244. TEL 502-491-5857. FAX 502-491-5905. Ed. Charles Kaltenthaler. adv.; bk.rev.; illus.; stat.; circ. 3,000. (controlled).
Description: Covers the American Association of Managing General Agents annual convention.

368 US ISSN 0095-2923
HG8501
INSURANCE FORUM. 1974. m. $60. Insurance Forum, Inc., Box 245, Ellettsville, IN 47429. Ed. Joseph M. Belth. bk.rev.; index. (also avail. in microform from UMI; reprint service avail. from UMI) **Indexed:** L.I.I.

368.3 US ISSN 1062-919X
INSURANCE HANDBOOK; nationwide health insurance billing directory. 1990. a. $49.95. Med - Index, 5225 Wiley Post Way, Ste. 500, Salt Lake City, UT 84116. TEL 801-536-1700. FAX 801-536-1009. Ed. Linda Carrabotta. **Document type:** directory.

368 AT
INSURANCE IN AUSTRALIA. 1966. a. Aus.$45. Craftsman Publishing Pty. Ltd., 125 Highbury Rd., Burwood, Vic. 3000, Australia. TEL 03-808-9622. FAX 03-808-0317. Ed. Edward Morgan. adv.; bk.rev. circ. 1,000.
Formerly: Insurance in Australia and New Zealand (ISSN 0811-0905).

368 FI ISSN 0356-9993
INSURANCE IN FINLAND. (Text in English) s-a. FIM 66. Vakuutussanomia Oy - Insurance News Ltd., Bulvardi 28, 00120 Helsinki 12, Finland. TEL 358-0-68-04-02-58. FAX 90-64-04-69. TELEX 123511 VAKES SF. Ed. Eeva Koskinen. circ. 5,000.
Description: Covers a broad range of insurance related topics for a non-specialist audience.

368 IE ISSN 0791-7201
▼**INSURANCE INDUSTRY INTERNATIONAL.** 1992. m. I£499. Lafferty Publications Ltd., The Tower, IDA Enterprise Centre, Pearse St., Dublin 2, Ireland. TEL 01-6718022. FAX 01-6718520. (U.S. subscr. to: 2970 Clairmont Rd., Ste. 800, Atlanta, GA 30329. TEL 404-636-6610) Ed. Ciara Linnane. **Document type:** bulletin.

368 US
INSURANCE INDUSTRY NEWSLETTER. 1969. w. $117. Insurance Field Company, Box 24244, Louisville, KY 40224-0244. TEL 502-491-5905. FAX 502-491-5905. Ed. George V.R. Smith. bk.rev. circ. 450. (looseleaf format) **Document type:** newsletter.
Description: Condensation of a wide range of reading matter on the insurance industry.

368 629.222 US
INSURANCE INJURY REPORT PASSENGER CARS, CARGO VANS, PICKUPS, AND UTILITY VEHICLES. 1973. a. free. Highway Loss Data Institute, c/o Stephen L. Oesch, General Counsel, Sec.-Treas., 1005 N. Glebe Rd., Ste. 800, Arlington, VA 22201. TEL 703-247-1600. FAX 703-247-1678.

368.012 US
INSURANCE INSTITUTE OF AMERICA. INSTITUTE INSIGHTS. s-a. Insurance Institute of America, 720 Providence Rd., Box 3016, Malvern, PA 19355-0716. TEL 215-644-2100. FAX 215-251-9995. Ed. Anne Swigart. circ. 4,000. (back issues avail.) **Document type:** newsletter.

368 US
INSURANCE INSTITUTE OF AMERICA. KEY INFORMATION. 1970. a. Insurance Institute of America, 720 Providence Rd., Box 3016, Malvern, PA 19355-0716. TEL 215-644-2100. FAX 215-251-9995. Ed. Anne Swigart. circ. 300,000. **Document type:** catalog.
Description: Describes objectives, content, study materials, and national exams for each of 18 educational programs.

368 CN ISSN 0843-0977
INSURANCE INSTITUTE OF CANADA. PERSPECTIVES. 1972. q. membership. Insurance Institute of Canada, 18 King St. E., 6th Fl., Toronto, ON M5C 1C4, Canada. TEL 416-362-8586. FAX 416-362-1126. Eds. Ella Kolm, Walter Braddock. bk.rev. circ. 29,000. **Document type:** newsletter.
Former titles: Insurance Institute of Canada. Newsletter (ISSN 0225-168X); Insurance Institute of Canada. Report (ISSN 0074-0721).

INSURANCE

368   II
INSURANCE INSTITUTE OF INDIA. JOURNAL. 1975. s-a. Rs.15 per issue. Insurance Institute of India, 6th Fl., Universal Insurance Bldg., Sir Pherozshah Mehta Rd., Bombay 400 001, India. TEL 22-2872923. TELEX 11-85705-INST-IN. Ed. V.H.P. Pinto. bk.rev. circ. 15,000. **Document type:** academic/scholarly publication.
    Formerly (until 1987): Federation of Insurance Institutes Journal.
    Description: Explores insurance education, training and research in India and neighboring countries.

368   US
INSURANCE ISSUES UPDATE. m. $75. Insurance Information Institute, 110 William St., New York, NY 10038. TEL 212-669-9200. FAX 212-732-1916.
●Also available online. Vendor(s): Mead Data Central, Inc.
    Former titles: Data Base Reports; Data Base Plus.

368.9   BG
INSURANCE JOURNAL. (Text in English) 1975. m. Tk.150($8) Bangladesh Insurance Academy, 53 Mohakhali Commercial Area, Dhaka 1212, Bangladesh. Ed. C.M. Rahman. adv.
    Formerly: Bangladesh Insurance Academy. Journal.

INSURANCE LAW & PRACTICE. see *LAW*

368   US   ISSN 0892-4422
K9
INSURANCE LAW ANTHOLOGY. 1986. a. $149.95. International Library Law Book Publishers, Inc., 101 Lakeforest Blvd., Ste. 270, Gaithersburg, MD 20877. TEL 301-990-7755. FAX 301-990-7642. Ed. Allison P. Zabriskie. bibl.; index. **Document type:** monographic series.
    Description: Selected best U.S. law review articles, printed in their entirety, in the field of insurance culled from over 900 U.S. law review journals.

INSURANCE LAW CITATIONS. see *LAW*

INSURANCE LAW JOURNAL. see *LAW*

368   UK   ISSN 0957-0888
INSURANCE LAW MONTHLY. m. £134 (foreign £156). Monitor Press, Rectory Rd., Great Waldingfield, Sudbury, Suffolk CO10 0TL, England. TEL 0787-378607. FAX 0787-880201. (back issues avail.) **Document type:** newsletter.
    Description: Covers pending and new legislation and developments on insurance law.

368 340   US   ISSN 0020-4730
INSURANCE LAW REPORTS: FIRE & CASUALTY. 1929. fortn. $870. Commerce Clearing House, Inc., 4025 W. Peterson Ave., Chicago, IL 60646. TEL 312-583-8500. charts; stat. (looseleaf format)

368 340   US
INSURANCE LAW REPORTS: LIFE, HEALTH & ACCIDENT. 1975. m. $835. Commerce Clearing House, Inc., 4025 W. Peterson Ave., Chicago, IL 60646. TEL 312-583-8500. charts; stat. (looseleaf format)

368   US
INSURANCE LAW REVIEW. a. $95. Clark - Boardman - Callaghan Company Ltd., 375 Hudson St., New York, NY 10014. TEL 212-929-7500; 800-221-9428. FAX 212-924-0460. Ed. Pat Magarick.
    Description: Discusses a wide variety of insurance topics within the scope of the casualty-tort field.

INSURANCE LITIGATION REPORTER; recent decisions of national significance. see *LAW*

368   UK   ISSN 0020-4773
INSURANCE MAIL. 1904. m. £12. Stone & Cox (Publications) Ltd., 44 Fleet St., London EC4Y 1BS, England. Ed. Richard Blausten. adv.; bk.rev.
    Description: Sales and marketing magazine for the insurance industry.

368   US   ISSN 0892-1458
INSURANCE MARKETING INSIDER. 1987. m. $132. Standard Publishing Corp., 155 Federal St., Boston, MA 02110. TEL 617-457-0600. FAX 617-457-0608. Ed. Diana Montgomery. circ. 1,760. (back issues avail.) **Document type:** trade publication.
    Description: Insurance marketing information for insurance professionals.

368   US   ISSN 0538-2629
HG8523
INSURANCE MARKETPLACE; the agents and brokers guide to non-standard & specialty lines, aviation, marine & international insurance. 1962. a. $6.50. Rough Notes Co., Inc., 1200 N. Meridian, Box 564, Indianapolis, IN 46206. TEL 800-428-4384. FAX 317-634-1041. Ed. Wallace L. Clapp, Jr. circ. 50,000.
—UMI.

368 510   NE   ISSN 0167-6687
CODEN: IMECDX
INSURANCE: MATHEMATICS & ECONOMICS. (Text in English) 1982. 6/yr. (in 2 vols.; 3 nos./vol.). fl.874($472) (effective 1994). North-Holland (Subsidiary of: Elsevier Science B.V.), P.O. Box 211, 1000 AE Amsterdam, Netherlands. TEL 31-20-5803911. FAX 31-20-5803598. TELEX 18582 ESPA NL. (Subscr. in U.S. and Canada to: Elsevier Science Inc., Box 882, Madison Sq. Sta., New York, NY 10159. TEL 212-989-5800. FAX 212-633-3990) Ed. F. De Vylder. adv.; bk.rev.; index. circ. 1,000. (also avail. in microform; back issues avail.) **Indexed:** ABI Inform., BPIA, Bus.Ind., Compumath, Int.Abstr.Oper.Res., Manage.Cont., Math.R., Phys.Abstr., Risk Abstr., SSCI. **Document type:** academic/scholarly publication.
—Faxon; UnCover; SWETS; UMI. **CCC.**
    Description: Includes the theory, models and computational methods of life insurance, non-life insurance, and of reinsurance and other risk-sharing arrangements.
Refereed Serial

368.32
INSURANCE PRODUCT NEWS. q. $12.95. Investment Dealers' Digest, Two World Trade Center, 18th Fl., New York, NY 10048. TEL 212-227-1200. FAX 212-321-2336. Ed. Gail Brown. adv. circ. 22,692.
    Description: Contains new product information for life insurance salespeople.

368   US
INSURANCE PULSE. a. $35. Insurance Information Institute, 110 William St., New York, NY 10038. TEL 212-699-9200. FAX 212-732-1916.

368   US   ISSN 0020-4803
INSURANCE RECORD. 1934. fortn. $15. Record Publishing Co. (Dallas), Box 225770, Dallas, TX 75222. TEL 214-630-0687. FAX 214-631-2476. Ed. Glen E. Hargis. adv.; illus. circ. 2,100.

368 368   AT   ISSN 0725-4644
INSURANCE RECORD OF AUSTRALIA & NEW ZEALAND; journal of insurance, banking and finance. 1877. m. (except Jan.). Aus.$55. Craftsman Publishing Pty. Ltd., 125 Highbury Rd., Burwood, Vic. 3165, Australia. TEL 03-808-9622. FAX 03-808-0317. Ed. Edward Morgan. adv.; bk.rev.; mkt.; stat.; index. circ. 1,200.
    Former titles: Insurance and Banking Record (ISSN 0311-0192); Australasian Insurance and Banking Record (ISSN 0004-8372).

368   US
INSURANCE REGULATOR. 48/yr. $675 for new subscr. (foreign $725): renewal $750 (foreign $800). American Banker - Bond Buyer, Newsletter Division (Subsidiary of: Thompson Financial Services Company), One State St. Plaza, New York, NY 10004-1549. TEL 800-733-4371. FAX 212-943-2224. (Subscr. to: Box 28315, Washington, DC 20038-8315. TEL 202-347-2665) **Document type:** newsletter.
    Description: Covers state regulation and gives a national overview of developing trends in the industry. Includes a ledger of state commissions' activities, and a "Behind the Scenes" column presenting the opinions and actions of newsmakers involved in the policy affecting insurance.

368   PK   ISSN 0020-4811
INSURANCE REVIEW. (Text in English) 1964. q. Rs.10($2) Pakistan Insurance Corporation, Pakistan Insurance Bldg., Bunder Rd., Karachi 2, Pakistan. Ed. Jauher Hussain. adv.; charts; illus. **Indexed:** Tr.& Indus.Ind.

368   RH
INSURANCE REVIEW. 1955. m. Z.$21.70 (foreign Z.$30.25). (Insurance Institute, Zimbabwe) Thomson Publications Zimbabwe (Pvt) Ltd., Thomson House, P.O. Box 1683, Harare, Zimbabwe. TEL 736835. FAX 752390. TELEX 24705 ZW.
    Formerly: Rhodesian Insurance Review (ISSN 0035-4805)

368   US   ISSN 0749-8667
HG9956   CODEN: INRVER
INSURANCE REVIEW (NEW YORK). 1940. m. $42. Journal of Commerce - Knight-Ridder Inc., 2 World Trade Center, 27th Fl., New York, NY 10048. TEL 212-837-7090. FAX 212-837-7035. Ed. Olga B. Sciortino. adv.: B&W page $3310; trim 7 x 10; adv. contact: William Lavner. charts; illus.; index; circ. 62,500 (controlled). (also avail. in microfilm from UMI; reprint service avail. from UMI) **Indexed:** ABI Inform., BPIA, Bus.Ind., HRIS, P.A.I.S., Tr.& Indus.Ind. **Document type:** trade publication.
—BLDSC (4531.766000); Faxon; UnCover. **CCC.**
    Former titles (until 1983): Journal of Insurance (ISSN 0022-1929); Journal of Insurance Information.
    Description: Covers important news, issues and developments affecting the property and casualty and life and health insurance industry. Assists agents, brokers and corporate policy makers in responding to legal, financial, regulatory and consumer concerns.

368   US   ISSN 1057-0349
INSURANCE SOUTH MAGAZINE. 1991. bi-m. Ronald W. Vinson, Ed. & Pub., 8517 Cherry Valley, Alexandria, VA 22309. TEL 703-799-1430.

368 629.222   US
INSURANCE SPECIAL REPORT: VARIOUS TOPICS. 1974. a. free. Highway Loss Data Institute, c/o Stephen L. Oesch, General Counsel, Sec.-Treas., 1005 N. Glebe Rd., Ste. 800, Arlington, VA 22201. TEL 703-247-1600. FAX 703-247-1648.

368 629.222   US   ISSN 0276-6280
INSURANCE THEFT REPORT PASSENGER CARS, CARGO VANS, PICKUPS, AND UTILITY VEHICLES. 1979. a. free. Highway Loss Data Institute, c/o Stephen L. Oesch, General Counsel, Sec.-Treas., 1005 N. Glebe Rd., Ste. 800, Arlington, VA 22201. TEL 703-247-1600. FAX 703-247-1678.

368   US   ISSN 0888-4935
INSURANCE TIMES. 1982. bi-w. $39.95. 20 Park Plz., Ste. 1101, Boston, MA 02116-4303. TEL 617-292-7117. FAX 617-292-0111. Ed. Andrew Simpson. adv.; circ. 6,500 (controlled). (reprint service avail.) **Document type:** newspaper.
    Formerly: New England Insurance Times.
    Description: Insurance newspaper covering Northeast region.

368   US   ISSN 0020-4846
INSURANCEWEEK. 1933. w. $30. I W Publications, Inc., 1001 Fourth Ave. Plaza, Ste. 3029, Seattle, WA 98154. TEL 206-624-6965. FAX 206-624-5021. Ed. Richard Rambeck. adv.; illus. circ. 9,000.
    Description: Western States property and casualty news weekly.

368   UK
INTERBEN. 1983. m. $285. Interben Publications, Westwood, Westbourne Dr., Lancaster LA1 5EE, England. TEL 44-524-32880. Ed. Peter A. Boylan. bk.rev. circ. 110. **Document type:** newsletter.

368   GW   ISSN 0177-8722
INTERN (WIESBADEN): Nachrichten fuer die Mitarbeiter. 1935. bi-m. D B V Versicherungen, Frankfurterstr. 50, 65189 Wiesbaden, Germany. TEL 0611-3632593. FAX 0611-3634161. circ. 20,000.

368   SZ   ISSN 0074-1647
INTERNATIONAL ASSOCIATION OF HAIL INSURERS. CONGRESS REPORT. biennial, 21st Vienna, 1991. membership. International Association of Hail Insurers - Association Internationale des Assureurs contre la Grele, c/o R.M. Regnault de Beaucaron, Sec.-Treas., 61 Seilergraben, CH-8023 Zurich, Switzerland. TEL 41-1-2517172. FAX 41-1-2611021. circ. controlled. **Document type:** proceedings.
    Supersedes: International Association of Hail Insurance Companies. Congress Report.

INSURANCE

368   **UK**
THE INTERNATIONAL BROKER. m. £275($450) Risk & Insurance Research Group Ltd., 4 Henrietta St., Covent Garden, London WC2E 8PS, England. TEL 071-836-0614. FAX 071-379-6355. **Document type:** trade publication.

368   **US**
INTERNATIONAL CLAIM ASSOCIATION PROCEEDINGS. 1910. a. $12. International Claim Association, c/o Ernest Beane, Modern Woodmen of America, Mississippi River at 17th St., Rock Island, IL 61201. (Dist. by: Professional Book Distributors, Inc., Box 100120, Roswell, GA 30077) Ed. James F. Adams. circ. 3,000 (paid). **Document type:** proceedings.

368   **US**
INTERNATIONAL CONFERENCE OF INSURANCE REGULATORY OFFICIALS. PROCEEDINGS. a. $100. National Association of Insurance Commissioners, 120 W. 12th St., Kansas City, MO 64105. TEL 816-374-7259. (Subscr. to: N A I C Publications, Box 263 Department 42, Kansas City, MO 64193-0042) **Document type:** proceedings.
  Description: Publishes papers on international insurance topics submitted during the annual conference.

368.4   **SZ**   ISSN 0444-1583
INTERNATIONAL CONFERENCE OF SOCIAL SECURITY ACTUARIES AND STATISTICIANS. REPORTS. (Text and summaries in English, French, German, Spanish) fifth, 1971. irreg., no.9, 1990. 40 SFr. per no. International Social Security Association, Publications, Case Postale 1, Ch-1211 Geneva 22, Switzerland. FAX 022-7986385. Ed.Bd. **Document type:** bulletin.

368.4   **SZ**   ISSN 0251-7469
INTERNATIONAL CONFERENCE ON DATA PROCESSING IN THE FIELD OF SOCIAL SECURITY. REPORTS. (Text and summaries in English, French, German, Spanish) second, 1978. quadrennial. 25 SFr. per no. International Social Security Association, Publications, Case Postale 1, CH-1211 Geneva 22, Switzerland. FAX 022-7986385. Ed.Bd. **Document type:** bulletin.

346   **NE**
▼**INTERNATIONAL ENCYCLOPAEDIA OF LAWS. INSURANCE LAW.** (Text in English) 1992. base vol. (plus irreg. updates). fl.295($160) (effective 1994). Kluwer Law and Taxation Publishers (Subsidiary of: Wolters Kluwer N.V.), P.O. Box 23, 7400 GA Deventer, Netherlands. TEL 31-5700-47261. FAX 31-5700-22244. TELEX 49295 KLUDV NL. (Dist. by: Libresso Distribution Centre, P.O. Box 23, 7400 GA Deventer, Netherlands. TEL 31-5700-33155. FAX 31-5700-33834; In N. America: Kluwer Law and Taxation Publishers, 675 Massachusetts Ave., Cambridge, MA 02139. TEL 617-354-0140. FAX 617-354-8595) Eds. S. Fredericq, H. Cousy. (looseleaf format) **Document type:** monographic series.
  Description: Covers national and international insurance law, including international organizations in the field of insurance, EC law with respect to private insurance, and discussions of the principles and practice of insurance law in individual countries.

344   **NE**
▼**INTERNATIONAL ENCYCLOPAEDIA OF LAWS. SOCIAL SECURITY LAW.** (Text in English) 1994. base vol. (plus irreg. updates). fl.200($115) (effective 1994). Kluwer Law and Taxation Publishers (Subsidiary of: Wolters Kluwer N.V.), P.O. Box 23, 7400 GA Deventer, Netherlands. TEL 31-5700-47261. FAX 31-5700-22244. TELEX 49295 KLUDV NL. (Dist. by: Libresso Distribution Centre, P.O. Box 23, 7400 GA Deventer, Netherlands. TEL 31-5700-33155. FAX 31-5700-33834; In N. America: Kluwer Law and Taxation Publishers, 675 Massachusetts Ave., Cambridge, MA 02139. TEL 617-354-0140. FAX 617-354-8595) Ed. Jef van Langendonck. (looseleaf format) **Document type:** monographic series.
  Description: Covers national and international issues in social security law, including comprehensive discussion of individual countries' social security systems and law, the international texts regulating social security in industrialized nations, and a review of international organizations such as the ILO, EEC, Council of Europe and the Nordic Council.

INTERNATIONAL FOUNDATION OF EMPLOYEE BENEFIT PLANS. DIGEST. see BUSINESS AND ECONOMICS — Labor And Industrial Relations

368   **US**   ISSN 0020-6997
HG8011
INTERNATIONAL INSURANCE MONITOR. 1947. m. $25 (foreign $35). International Insurance Monitor, Box 9001, Mt. Vernon, NY 10552. TEL 914-699-2020. Ed. M. Martin. adv.; bk.rev. circ. 3,200. (also avail. in microform from UMI; reprint service avail. from UMI) **Indexed:** ABI Inform., BPIA.
—BLDSC (4541.430000); UMI.

368   **UK**
INTERNATIONAL INSURANCE REPORT. 1986. m. £245. Risk & Insurance Research Group Ltd., 4 Henrietta St., Covent Garden, London WC2E 8PS, England. TEL 071-836-0614. FAX 071-379-6355. **Document type:** trade publication.

368.4   **SZ**   ISSN 0251-1339
INTERNATIONAL SOCIAL SECURITY ASSOCIATION. REPORTS OF THE GENERAL ASSEMBLIES OF THE ISSA. triennial, 24th, 1992, Acapulco. price varies. International Social Security Association, Case Postale 1, CH-1211 Geneva 22, Switzerland. FAX 022-7986385. **Document type:** proceedings.
  Formerly: International Social Security Association. Technical Reports of Assemblies (ISSN 0074-8439)
  Description: International comparative studies dealing with different branches or aspects of social security.

368.4   **SZ**
INTERNATIONAL SOCIAL SECURITY ASSOCIATION. STUDIES AND RESEARCH. (Editions in English and French) 1970. irreg. (1-2/yr.). 25 SFr. per no. International Social Security Association, Case Postale 1, CH-1211 Geneva 22, Switzerland. FAX 022-7986385. **Document type:** bulletin.
  Description: Specialized conferences and meetings organized by the ISSA.

368.4   **SZ**   ISSN 0020-871X
HD7090
INTERNATIONAL SOCIAL SECURITY REVIEW. French edition: Revue Internationale de Securite Sociale (ISSN 0379-0312); German edition: Internationale Revue fuer Sociale Sicherheit (ISSN 0379-0282); Spanish edition: Revista Internacional de Seguridad Social (ISSN 0250-605X) (Text in English) 1947. q. 50 SFr. International Social Security Association, Secretariat General, Case Postale 1, CH-1211 Geneva 22, Switzerland. FAX 022-7996617. FAX 022-7986385. Ed. Michael Gautrey. bk.rev.; bibl.; charts; illus.; stat.; index. circ. 5,000. (back issues avail.; reprint service avail. from SCH) **Indexed:** Abstr.Hyg., ASSIA, C.I.S. Abstr., CERDIC, CLOA, Excerp.Med., Int.Lab.Doc., Med.Care Rev., Mid.East: Abstr.& Ind., P.A.I.S., Soc.Work Res.& Abstr., Stud.Wom.Abstr., Trop.Dis.Bull. **Document type:** bulletin.
—BLDSC (4549.470000); Faxon; UnCover; SWETS; UMI.
  Formerly: International Social Security Association Bulletin.
  Description: Articles and studies of social security around the world. Includes analyses of technical and administrative aspects of social insurance and commments on new social security legislation.

INTERNATIONAL SOCIETY FOR LABOR LAW AND SOCIAL SECURITY. BULLETIN. see BUSINESS AND ECONOMICS — Labor And Industrial Relations

368 332.6   **US**
INVESTMENT BULLETIN; survey of mortgage commitments on commercial properties. 1965. q. $65. American Council of Life Insurance, 1001 Pennsylvania Ave. N.W., Washington, DC 20004. TEL 202-624-2000. Ed. Rich Maier. circ. 1,100. (looseleaf format; back issues avail.) **Document type:** bulletin.
  Formerly (until 1992): Investment Topics.
  Description: Reports survey results of life insurers mortgage commitment activity on income producing properties.

368   **IE**   ISSN 0790-3677
IRISH INSURANCE BROKER. 12/yr. (Irish Brokers Association) Holyrood Publications Ltd., 139a Lower Drumcondra Rd., Dublin 9, Ireland. TEL 718-022. FAX 360624. Ed. Frank McQuaid. adv. contact: Mandy McCarthy. **Document type:** trade publication.

368   **IT**   ISSN 0021-2482
ISTITUTO ITALIANO DEGLI ATTUARI. GIORNALE. (Text mainly in Italian; occasionally in other languages) 1930. s-a. L.65000 (foreign L.75000) (effective 1993). Istituto Italiano degli Attuari, Via del Corea 3, 00186 Rome, Italy. Ed. Luciano Daboni. bk.rev. circ. 700. **Document type:** academic/scholarly publication.
  Description: Publishes papers on actuarial subjects; life, non-life, social security, pension funs, financial matters.

368   **IT**   ISSN 0021-2520
HD7182
ISTITUTO NAZIONALE DELLA PREVIDENZA SOCIALE. ATTI UFFICIALI. 1925. m. L.45000. Istituto Nazionale della Previdenza Sociale, Via Ciro II Grande 21, 00144 Rome, Italy. index. circ. 8,500.

368   **GW**
J O. (Junge Ortskrankenkasse) 1974. bi-m. DM.6. (AOK-Bundesverband) Wirtschaftsdienst Gesellschaft fuer Medien & Kommunikation mbH & Co. OHG, Lange Str. 13, 60311 Frankfurt a.M., Germany. Ed. Wolfgang Frenken. adv. circ. 1,250,000. **Document type:** bulletin.

368   **JM**
JAMAICA. MINISTRY OF SOCIAL SECURITY. REPORT. irreg. free. Ministry of Social Security, 14 National Heroes Circle, Box 10, Kingston 5, Jamaica, W.I.
  Formerly: Jamaica. Ministry of Pensions and Social Security. Report; Incorporates: Jamaica. National Insurance Scheme. Annual Reports (ISSN 0077-5053)

368   **JA**   ISSN 0910-4534
JAPAN INSURANCE NEWS. (Text in English) 1974. bi-m. 8100 Yen($82) (effective Jan. 1994). Hoken Kenkyujo Ltd. - Insurance Research Institute Ltd., 17-3 Hon-machi 1-chome, Shibuya-ku, Tokyo, Japan. TEL 03-3376-3331. FAX 03-3376-7125. Ed. Toshiaki Shirai. adv.; bk.rev. circ. 3,000.
—BLDSC (4648.317000).

THE JEWELRY APPRAISER. see JEWELRY, CLOCKS AND WATCHES

368   **CC**
JIANGSU BAOXIAN/JIANGSU INSURANCE. (Text in Chinese) bi-m. Jiangsu Baoxian Xuehui - Jiangsu Insurance Association, 57 Beijing Donglu, Nanjing, Jiangsu 210018, People's Republic of China. TEL 714055. (Co-sponsor: Zhongguo Renmin Baoxian Gongsi Jiangsu Fengongsi) Ed. Li Jiming.

JISHIN SAIGAI YOSOKU NO KENKYU/SEISMICITY AND SEISMIC HAZARD. see EARTH SCIENCES — Geophysics

368   **US**   ISSN 0021-7204
JOHN LINER LETTER. 1963. m. $159. Standard Publishing Corp., 155 Federal St., Boston, MA 02110. TEL 617-457-0600. FAX 617-457-0608. Ed. Robert Montgomery. index. circ. 6,000. **Document type:** newsletter.

368 332.6   **US**   ISSN 0894-1807
JOHN LINER REVIEW. 1987. q. $98. Standard Publishing Corp., 155 Federal St., Boston, MA 02110. TEL 617-457-0600. FAX 617-457-0608. Ed. Roger Pierce. adv. contact: Frank Eaton. circ. 2,000. **Document type:** trade publication.
—UMI.

368   **FR**   ISSN 1149-6452
JOURNAL DE L'ASSURANCE. 11/yr. Edicop, 15 bis, rue Ernest-Renan, B.P. 62, 92133 Issy-les-Moulineaux, France. TEL 40-93-01-02. FAX 42-66-93-07. Ed. Michel Goue. circ. 5,150.
  Description: Information about the insurance world, its people, products and the market.

368   **CN**
▼**JOURNAL DE L'ASSURANCE.** 1992. m. Can.$39.50 (US Can.$49.95). Editions du Journal de l'Assurance Inc., 105 de Champagne, St.-Lambert, PQ J4S 1E5, Canada. TEL 514-923-8935. FAX 514-671-8126. Ed. Serge Therrien. adv.; B&W page Can.$2300, color page Can.$3600; trim 8 1/8 x 10 7/8. circ. 15,000.

JOURNAL OF FINANCIAL SERVICES RESEARCH. see BUSINESS AND ECONOMICS — Banking And Finance

JOURNAL OF HEALTHCARE RISK MANAGEMENT. see HOSPITALS

INSURANCE

368 610 US ISSN 0743-6661
CODEN: JINNER
JOURNAL OF INSURANCE MEDICINE. 1969. q. $45 (foreign $55) (effective 1993). American Academy of Insurance Medicine, Box 82446, Kenmore, WA 98028-0446. Ed. Dr. Roger H. Butz. adv. circ. 1,200. **Document type:** academic/scholarly publication.
—BLDSC (5007.535000).
   Description: Original articles concerning insurance medicine, including actuariomedical analysis for development of life table, mortality, morbidity, and survival data, underwriting, claims, disability and health insurance issues.

368 US ISSN 0736-248X
K10
JOURNAL OF INSURANCE REGULATION. 1983. q. $50 (foreign $65). National Association of Insurance Commissioners, 120 W. 12th St., Kansas City, MO 64105. TEL 816-374-7259. (Subscr. to: N A I C Publications, Box 263 Department 42, Kansas City, MO 64193-0042) Ed. Gregory Krohm. cum.index: 1983-1986. circ. 2,200. (also avail. in microfilm from UMI, back issues avail.) **Document type:** academic/scholarly publication.
—BLDSC (5007.536000); UMI.
   Description: Covers current insurance topics. Includes case studies and legal reviews.
   Refereed Serial

368 JA ISSN 0387-2939
JOURNAL OF INSURANCE SCIENCE. 1895. q. 5000 Yen. Japanese Society of Insurance Science, Life Insurance Association of Japan, 3-4-1 Marunouchi, Chiyoda-ku, Tokyo 100, Japan. TEL 03-3286-2734. Ed. Y. Kuroda. **Document type:** academic/scholarly publication.

368 US ISSN 0022-4367
HG8011
JOURNAL OF RISK AND INSURANCE. 1933. q. $90 in US and Canada; elsewhere $95. American Risk and Insurance Association, c/o Dr. Patricia Cheshier, Executive Director, California State University, Sacramento, School of Business, BUS-3059, 6000 J St., Sacramento, CA 95819-6088. Ed. J. David Cummins. adv.; bk.rev.; abstr.; bibl.; charts; index, cum.index: 1932-1967, 1968-1975. circ. 2,200. (also avail. in microform from UMI; reprint service avail. from ISI,UMI) **Indexed:** ABI Inform., B.P.I., BPIA, Bus.Ind., Cont.Pg.Manage., Curr.Cont., J.of Econ.Lit., L.I.I., Manage.Cont., Med.Care Rev., P.A.I.S., Risk Abstr., SSCI, Tr.& Indus.Ind. **Document type:** academic/scholarly publication.
● Also available online. Vendor(s): DIALOG Information Services, Inc.
—BLDSC (5052.100000); Faxon; UnCover; SWETS; UMI.
   Formerly: Journal of Insurance.
   Description: Presents scholarly articles on theory and practice relevant to insurance and related areas.

368.4 331 US ISSN 1059-4167
HD7103.65.U6
JOURNAL OF WORKERS COMPENSATION. 1991. q. (John Liner Organization) Standard Publishing Corp., 155 Federal St., Boston, MA 02110. TEL 617-457-0600. FAX 617-457-0608. adv. contact: Frank Eaton. circ. 2,500. **Document type:** trade publication.
   Description: Gives information and advice on workers compensation management.

368 FR ISSN 0022-6823
JURISPRUDENCE AUTOMOBILE. 1929. m. 495 F. L' Argus, 2 rue de Chateaudun, 75441 Paris Cedex 09, France. TEL 45-96-13-00. FAX 48-78-36-59. Ed. Gerard DeFrance. adv.; bk.rev.; charts; tr.lit.; index. circ. 2,200.

368.382 GW
K K H NACHRICHTEN; Informations- und Beratungsdienst der Kaufmaennischen Krankenkasse fuer Firmen. 1967. q. Kaufmaennische Krankenkasse Hauptverwaltung, Hindenburgstr. 43-45, 30175 Hannover, Germany. TEL 0511-28020. FAX 0511-2802-232. **Document type:** bulletin.

368 US
KANSAS INSURANCE AGENT & BROKER. 1979. bi-m. $30. Professional Independent Insurance Agents of Kansas, 817 S.W. Topeka Ave., Topeka, KS 66612. TEL 913-232-0561. FAX 913-232-6817. Ed. Elaine Spencer. adv.; stat. circ. 930. (back issues avail.) **Document type:** trade publication.
   Formerly (until 1992): Kansas Insurance (ISSN 0194-634X)
   Description: Official magazine of professional and independent insurance agents in Kansas who belong to the association.

368 GW
KARLSRUHER GREIF. 1955. m. Karlsruher Lebensversicherung AG, Friedrich-Scholl-Platz, Postfach 3649, 76137 Karlshue, Germany. TEL 0721-1392232. FAX 0721-1392699. Ed. Werner Hampel. adv.; bk.rev. (back issues avail.)

368.3 US
KEMPER INSURANCE MAGAZINE. bi-m. Kemper National Insurance Cos., Public Affairs and Communications, F-3, 1 Kemper Dr., Long Grove, IL 60049. FAX 708-540-4279. Ed. Derrick K. Baker. circ. 17,000 (controlled). (back issues avail.)

368.3 JA ISSN 0022-989X
KENPO NYUSU. (Text in Japanese) 1957. 3/m. 10800 Yen. National Federation of Health Insurance Societies, 1-24-4 Minami-Aoyama, Minato-ku, Tokyo, Japan. FAX 03-5410-2091. adv.; bk.rev.; stat.; index.

KENTUCKY INSURANCE DIRECTORY. see *BUSINESS AND ECONOMICS — Trade And Industrial Directories*

KIKAI NO SONGAI/MACHINERY DAMAGE. see *MACHINERY*

368 622 GW ISSN 0342-0809
KOMPASS; Zeitschrift fuer Sozialversicherung im Bergbau. 1886. m. DM.85.70. (Bergbau-Berufsgenossenschaft) Verlag Glueckauf GmbH, Postfach 103945, 45039 Essen, Germany. FAX 0201-293630. **Indexed:** World Bibl.Soc.Sec.
—BLDSC (5105.600000).
   Description: Covers insurance for the mining industry (accident, medical, retirement and social security). Includes information on the prevention of accidents and illness, association news, and a list of events.

368 KO
KOREA NON-LIFE INSURANCE. (Text in English) 1979. a. free. Korea Non-Life Insurance Association, 80 Soosong-dong, 6th Fl., Chongno-ku, Seoul, S. Korea. Ed. Su-Ung Cho. circ. 1,500.
   Formerly: Korea Non-Life Insurance Industry.

368 GW ISSN 0301-4835
HD7102.G3
DIE KRANKENVERSICHERUNG. 1949. m. DM.143.40. (I K K - Bundesverband) Erich Schmidt Verlag GmbH & Co. (Bielefeld), Viktoriastr. 44A, 33602 Bielefeld, Germany. TEL 0521-58308-0. (Subscr. to: Postfach 102451, 33524 Bielefeld, Germany) illus. **Indexed:** World Bibl.Soc.Sec. **Document type:** trade publication.
—CCC.

368 US ISSN 0889-0986
L I M R A'S MARKETFACTS. 1982. bi-m. $95 to non-members (foreign $105); members $50 (foreign $60). Life Insurance Marketing and Research Association (LIMRA), Box 208, Hartford, CT 06141. TEL 203-674-4267. Ed. Heather Waldron. bk.rev. circ. 9,000. **Indexed:** ABI Inform.
—BLDSC (5220.080000); UMI.
   Formerly: Marketfacts.

368 US
L.O.M.A. RESOURCE. 1974. m. $36. Life Office Management Association, Inc., 5770 Powers Ferry Rd., Atlanta, GA 30327. TEL 404-951-1770. FAX 404-984-0441. Ed. Ron Clark. adv.; bk.rev.; charts; illus. circ. 26,000.
   Incorporates: Life Office Management Association. Annual Conference. Proceedings of Concurrent Sessions; Which was formerly: Life Office Management Association. Annual Conference. Highlights; **Supersedes:** Systems and Procedures Review (ISSN 0024-3191); Personnel Quarterly (ISSN 0031-5834); Life Office Management Association. Bulletin (ISSN 0024-3183); Former titles: Keynotes (ISSN 0023-0979); Group Administration Topics.
   Description: Articles of interest to life insurance management personnel.

368.32 CN ISSN 0380-3147
L U A C FORUM. 1914. 10/yr. Can.$30. Life Underwriters Association of Canada, 41 Lesmill Rd., Don Mills, ON M3B 2T3, Canada. TEL 416-444-5251. FAX 416-444-8031. Ed. Valarie Osborne. adv.; bk.rev.; illus. circ. 18,000. **Indexed:** L.I.I.
   Incorporates: Revue des Assureurs-Vie.

LABOUR AND NATIONAL INSURANCE/AVODA UBITUACH LEUMI. see *BUSINESS AND ECONOMICS — Labor And Industrial Relations*

368 GW ISSN 0023-7922
LANDESVERSICHERUNGSANSTALT HESSEN. NACHRICHTEN. 1951. 6/yr. free. Landesversicherungsanstalt Hessen, Staedelstr. 28, 60596 Frankfurt a.M., Germany. Ed. Manfred Brenda. bk.rev.; illus.; stat.; index. circ. 22,000. **Document type:** government publication.

368 340 US
LEGAL ADVISORY.* 1983. irreg. free to members. Workers' Compensation Reinsurance Association, 445 Minnesota St., Ste. 600, St. Paul, MN 55101-2125. TEL 612-293-0999. FAX 612-293-0719. Ed. Robert Clayton. circ. 1,200. (back issues avail.)
   Description: Covers issues arising under Minnesota Workers' Compensation Law.

368 US ISSN 0094-0623
KF1164.A1
LEGAL NOTES FOR INSURANCE. 1982. m. $106. Data Research, Inc., 4635 Nicols Rd., Ste. 100, Eagan, MN 55122. TEL 612-452-8267. FAX 612-452-8694. (Subscr. to: Box 490, Rosemount, MN 55068. TEL 800-365-4900) Ed. David Greven. index. circ. 1,000.
   Description: Reports recent state and federal court decisions and legislation affecting insurance.

369 US
LEGISLATIVE REPORTER. 1945. fortn. membership only. National Association of Independent Insurers, 2600 River Rd., Des Plaines, IL 60018. TEL 708-297-7800. Ed. Robert Witt. circ. 750. (looseleaf format)
   Description: Provides comprehensive coverage of state legislative actions affecting the property-casualty insurance industry.

LESLIE AND BRITTS: MOTOR VEHICLE LAW IN N.S.W.. see *LAW*

368 FR
LETTRE DE L'ASSURANCE. 24/yr. 54 rue de Verneuil, 75007 Paris, France. TEL 42-61-24-25. FAX 49-27-93-18. Ed. Jean Luc Bengel. circ. 1,500.

368 UK ISSN 0960-099X
LIABILITY RISK & INSURANCE. 1989. m. £220($440) D Y P Insurance & Reinsurance Research Group Ltd., Bridge House, 181 Queen Victoria St., London EC4V 4DD, England. TEL 071-236-2175. FAX 071-489-1487. Ed. Julius S. Bannister. charts; stat. **Document type:** newsletter.
   Description: Provides accurate summaries of key legal cases and liability developments from around the world.

368 US
KF1246.A3L53
LIABILITY WEEK. 1986. 48/yr. $495. J R Publishing Inc., Box 6654, McLean, VA 22106. TEL 703-532-2235. FAX 703-532-2236. Ed. John V. Reistrup. (back issues avail.)
● Also available online. Vendor(s): NewsNet.

INSURANCE

368 KF1165 US ISSN 0742-5120
LICENSING, COUNTERSIGNING AND SURPLUS LINE LAWS. a. $17. National Underwriter Co., 505 Gest St., Cincinnati, OH 45203. TEL 513-721-2140. FAX 513-721-0126. Ed. Michael McCracken.
  Description: Compilation of the laws and regulations governing licensing and countersigning requirements of insurance agents for all 50 states, Puerto Rico and Virgin Islands.

368.3 HG8751 US ISSN 1053-2838
LIFE & HEALTH INSURANCE SALES. 1878. m. $25 (foreign $35). Rough Notes Co., Inc., 1200 N. Meridian, Box 564, Indianapolis, IN 46206. TEL 800-428-4384. FAX 317-634-1041. Ed. Phil Zinkewicz. adv.; bk.rev.; illus.; s-a. index. circ. 20,000. **Indexed:** ABI Inform., L.I.I., PSI.
  —BLDSC (5208.913500); UnCover; UMI.
  Former titles (until 1990): Insurance Sales (ISSN 0199-4581); Insurance Salesman (ISSN 0020-482X)

368.32 HG8751 US ISSN 0024-3078
LIFE ASSOCIATION NEWS. 1906. m. $6 to non-members (foreign $22). National Association of Life Underwriters, 1922 F St., N.W., Washington, DC 20006. TEL 202-331-6070. FAX 202-835-9068. Ed. Ian MacKenzie. adv. contact: Afsoon Namini. bk.rev.; illus.; index. circ. 144,000. (also avail. in microform from UMI) **Indexed:** ABI Inform., BPIA, L.I.I., PSI. **Document type:** trade publication.
  —BLDSC (5208.916500); Faxon; UMI.
  Incorporates (1956-1986): Probe (Rockville Centre) (ISSN 0032-9193)

368 CH
LIFE INSURANCE BUSINESS IN TAIWAN (YEAR). (Text in Chinese, English) 1972. a. free. Taipei Life Insurance Association, Ste. 152, 5th Fl., Sung Chiang Rd., Taipei, Taiwan, Republic of China. Ed.Bd.
  Formerly: Annual Report of Life Insurance, Republic of China.

368.3 HG8943 US ISSN 0075-9406
LIFE INSURANCE FACT BOOK. 1946. biennial. single copy free; additional copies $1 per no. American Council of Life Insurance, 1001 Pennsylvania Ave., N.W., Washington, DC 20004-2599. TEL 202-624-2000. Ed. Suzanne K. Stemnock. circ. 40,000. (also avail. in microfiche from CIS; diskette format) **Indexed:** L.I.I., SRI. **Document type:** monographic series.

368.32 IE
LIFE INSURANCE INTERNATIONAL. m. I£499. Lafferty Publications Ltd., The Tower, IDA Enterprise Centre, Pearse St., Dublin 2, Ireland. TEL 01-6718022. FAX 01-6718520. (US subscr. to: 2970 Clairmount Rd., Ste. 800, Atlanta, GA 30329. TEL 404-636-6610) Ed. Gerard Lysaght. **Document type:** bulletin.
  Description: Bulletin for senior executives of financial institutions that provide life insurance and other forms of contractual savings products.

368.32 US ISSN 0024-3132
LIFE INSURANCE PLANNING. 1966. base vol. (plus m. updates; s-m. Life Insurance Planning Ideas) $261. Maxwell Macmillan, Professional and Business Reference Publishing, 910 Sylvan Ave., Englewood Cliffs, NJ 07632. TEL 800-562-0245. FAX 201-816-3569. (looseleaf format)

368.32 HG8751 US ISSN 0024-3140
LIFE INSURANCE SELLING. 1926. m. $12. Commerce Publishing Co., 330 N. Fourth St., St. Louis, MO 63102-2036. TEL 314-421-5445. Ed. Chuck Hirsch. adv. contact: Dee Severino. bk.rev.; illus. circ. 43,528. (also avail. in microform from UMI) **Indexed:** L.I.I. **Document type:** trade publication.
  Description: Information for life insurance salespeople to serve clients better, increase sales and profits.

368.32 US
LIFE LINES. free. Monumental Life Insurance Company, 2 E. Chase St., Baltimore, MD 21202. TEL 301-685-2900. FAX 301-347-8666. Ed. Chris Boerner. circ. 850 (controlled). **Document type:** newsletter.
  Formerly: Monumental News.
  Description: Company news for employees and retirees.

368 US
LIFETIME. m. Kansas City Life Insurance Company, Box 419139, Kansas City, MO 64141. TEL 816-753-7000. Ed. Eileen Jenkins. index. circ. 2,500. (back issues avail.)
  Description: Articles on issues affecting the insurance industry for members of the agency force of the Kansas City Life Insurance Company.

368.32 US ISSN 0194-4312
LIFETIMES. 1962. bi-m. $3 to non-members. Tennessee Association of Life Underwriters, 500 Interstate Blvd. S., Ste. 310, Box 100745, Nashville, TN 37224. TEL 615-256-8258. Ed. Terry Scalos. adv.; illus. circ. 4,200.
  Formerly: Tennessee Life Insurance News (ISSN 0040-330X)

LITIGATION AND PREVENTION OF INSURER BAD FAITH. see LAW — Civil Law

368 GW
LLOYD REPORT. 1959. bi-m. free. Deutscher Lloyd Versicherungen, Karlstr. 10, 80333 Munich, Germany. TEL 089-5908415. FAX 089-5908203. Ed. Peter Frank. bk.rev. circ. 6,800. **Document type:** corporate report.

368 US
LLOYD'S INSURANCE INTERNATIONAL. 1987. w. $325 (foreign $365). Lloyd's of London Press, Inc., 611 Broadway, Ste. 308, New York, NY 10012-2608. TEL 212-529-9500. FAX 212-529-9826.
  Description: Offers in-depth coverage of world news as it relates to the insurance industry. Includes timely coverage of developments in insurance and reinsurance including property, casualty, aviation, fire, automotive, professional and product liability, accident and natural disasters.

LLOYD'S LIST INTERNATIONAL. see TRANSPORTATION — Ships And Shipping

368 UK ISSN 0963-6617
LLOYD'S MARKET. (170) a. £85. D Y P Insurance and Reinsurance Research Group Ltd., Bridge House, 181 Queen Victoria St., London EC4V 4DD, England. TEL 071-236-2175. FAX 071-489-1487.
  —BLDSC (5287.276400).

368.2 387 US ISSN 0047-4908
LLOYD'S WEEKLY CASUALTY REPORTS. vol.207, 1972. w. (4 vols./yr.). $645. Lloyd's of London Press Ltd., Sheepen Place, Colchester, Essex CO3 3LP, England. TEL 0206-772277. FAX 0206-46273. TELEX 987321 LLOYDS G. (US subscr. to: 611 Broadway, Ste. 308, New York, NY 10012. TEL 212-529-9500) q. index.
  Description: Provides information on marine, non-marine aviation and miscellaneous casualties, port conditions and weather information.

368 UK ISSN 0265-8356
LONDON MARKET NEWSLETTER. s-m. £280($550) D Y P Insurance & Reinsurance Group Ltd., Bridge House, 181 Queen Victoria St., London EC4V 4DD, England. TEL 071-236-2175. FAX 071-489-1487. Ed. Julius S. Banister. bk.rev. **Document type:** newsletter.
  Description: Compiles statistics on the London insurance market and reports on all important developments.

368 US
LONG ISLAND TELEPHONE TICKLER FOR INSURANCE MEN & WOMEN. 1982. a. $7. Underwriter Printing and Publishing Co., 50 E. Palisade Ave., Englewood, NJ 07631. TEL 201-569-8808. Ed. Donald E. Wolff. adv. circ. 17,000. **Document type:** directory.
  Description: Lists names, addresses and telephone numbers of insurance companies, agents, brokers, and related suppliers in the Long Island, NY, area.

LOUISIANA - MISSISSIPPI INSURANCE DIRECTORY. see BUSINESS AND ECONOMICS — Trade And Industrial Directories

368 US
LOUISIANA SURPLUS LINE REPORTER. m. Reporter Publishing Company, Box 52193, New Orleans, LA 70152-2193. TEL 504-366-8797. Ed. Carol J. DeGraw.

368.4 LU
LUXEMBOURG. INSPECTION GENERALE DE LA SECURITE SOCIALE. APERCU SUR LA LEGISLATION DE LA SECURITE SOCIALE AU GRAND-DUCHE DE LUXEMBOURG. 1991. a. 165 Fr. Inspection Generale de la Securite Sociale, Ministere de la Securite Sociale, B.P. 1308, L-1013 Luxembourg, Luxembourg. FAX 352-478-6225. TELEX 2985 MINTSS LU. circ. 2,000. **Document type:** government publication.

368 US
M D R T ANNUAL MEETING. PROCEEDINGS. 1927. a. $20. Million Dollar Round Table, 325 Touhy, Park Ridge, IL 60068. TEL 708-692-6378. FAX 708-518-8921. Ed. H. William Woulfe. circ. 20,000. (audio cassette; video cassette) **Indexed:** L.I.I. **Document type:** proceedings.
  Description: Presents motivational and technical life insurance sessions from annual meetings.

368 US ISSN 0024-8282
M O N Y NEWS; for its employees and field force. 1959. fortn. Mutual of New York Life Insurance Co., Public Relations Department, 1740 Broadway, New York, NY 10019. TEL 212-708-2000. Ed. Georgianna Hinsch. charts; illus.; stat. circ. 13,000. **Document type:** newspaper.

368 MW ISSN 0076-3349
MALAWI. REGISTRAR OF INSURANCE. REPORT. a., latest 1972. K.0.50. Government Printer, P.O. Box 37, Zomba, Malawi.

368 650 HG8751 US ISSN 0025-1968
MANAGER'S MAGAZINE. 1926. m. $65 to non-members; members $45. Life Insurance Marketing and Research Association (LIMRA), Box 208, Hartford, CT 06141. TEL 203-677-0033. Ed. Daniel J. Nahorney. bk.rev.; illus.; index. circ. 10,000. **Indexed:** ABI Inform., BPIA, Bus.Ind., Manage.Cont.
  —BLDSC (5359.280000); Faxon; UnCover; UMI.

368 631 HG9968.C75 CN ISSN 0542-5395
MANITOBA CROP INSURANCE CORPORATION. ANNUAL REPORT. 1962. a. free. Manitoba Crop Insurance Corporation, 25 Tupper St., N., Portage la Prairie, Man. R1N 3K1, Canada. FAX 204-239-3401. charts. circ. 325. **Document type:** corporate report.

368 US
MANUFACTURING RISK MANAGEMENT & INSURANCE. 1988. q. $218. International Risk Management Institute, Inc., 12222 Merit Dr., Ste. 1660, Dallas, TX 75251-2217. TEL 214-960-7693. FAX 214-960-6037. Ed. Jeff Woodward. (looseleaf format)
  Description: Gives insurance and risk management considerations for manufacturers. Designed for agents, brokers and underwriters to help design better insurance and risk management programs.

368 UK ISSN 0265-8410
MARINE & AVIATION INSURANCE REPORT. 1984. m. £230(£460) D Y P Group, Bridge House, 181 Queen Victoria St., London EC4V 4DD, England. TEL 071-236-2175. FAX 071-489-1487. Ed. Julius S. Bannister. bk.rev.; charts; stat. (back issues avail.) **Document type:** newsletter.
  Description: Covers the marine, aviation, and transport insurance market segment.

MATECON; materiali di finanza, credito e assicurazioni. see BUSINESS AND ECONOMICS — Banking And Finance

368 MF
MAURITIUS. MINISTRY OF FINANCE. INSURANCE UNIT. CONTROLLER OF INSURANCE. REPORT. 1972. a. Rs.50. Ministry of Finance, Insurance Unit, Controller of Insurance, 7 Leoville l'Homme St., Port Louis, Mauritius. FAX 088622. TELEX 4249 EXTERN 1W. (Dist. by: Government Printing Office, Elizabeth II Ave., Port Louis, Mauritius) stat. **Document type:** government publication.
  Formerly: Mauritius. Registrar of Insurance. Annual Report.

INSURANCE 3149

MEALEY'S LITIGATION REPORT: ASBESTOS. see *LAW — Civil Law*

MEALEY'S LITIGATION REPORT: BAD FAITH. see *LAW — Civil Law*

MEALEY'S LITIGATION REPORT: BREAST IMPLANTS. see *LAW — Civil Law*

MEALEY'S LITIGATION REPORT: INSURANCE. see *LAW — Civil Law*

MEALEY'S LITIGATION REPORT: INSURANCE FRAUD. see *LAW — Civil Law*

MEALEY'S LITIGATION REPORT: INSURANCE INSOLVENCY. see *LAW — Civil Law*

MEALEY'S LITIGATION REPORT: PUNITIVE DAMAGES AND TORT REFORM. see *LAW — Civil Law*

MEALEY'S LITIGATION REPORT: REINSURANCE. see *LAW — Civil Law*

MEDICAL LIABILITY ADVISORY SERVICE. see *LAW — Civil Law*

346.73   US   ISSN 0732-9636
MEDICAL LIABILITY MONITOR; newsletter on professional liability and risk management. (Supplement avail.) 1975. m. $150. Malpractice Lifeline, Inc., Box 316, Glenview, IL 60025-0316. TEL 708-996-3000. FAX 708-998-1930. Ed. Carol Brierly Golin. bk.rev.; index. circ. 1,750. **Document type:** newsletter.
    Formerly (until 1981): Malpractice Lifeline (ISSN 0361-8412)
    Description: News updates on legal and policy issues that affect premiums for malpractice insurance.

MEDICAL LIABILITY REPORTER; recent decisions of national significance. see *LAW — Civil Law*

MEDICAL OFFICE REPORT. see *MEDICAL SCIENCES*

368.382 340   US   ISSN 1061-4192
▼**MEDICAL RECORD RISKS: CLAIMS & LITIGATION.** 1992. m. $250. Cox Publications, Box 20316, Billings, MT 59104-0316. TEL 406-256-8822. Ed. Meridith B. Cox. circ. controlled.
    Description: For those who review medical records for claims and litigation.

368 610   US   ISSN 0897-9634
MEDICARE ADVISOR. 1986. m. $125. Shannon Publications, Inc., 9441 Lyndon B. Johnson Fwy., Ste. 510, Box 2, Dallas, TX 75243-4541. TEL 214-644-0159. FAX 214-644-1538. Ed. Ellen L. Bradley. (back issues avail.) **Document type:** newsletter.
    Description: Discusses Medicare coverage and reimbursement for nursing and long-term care facilities. Advises about policy changes from H.C.F.A. and covers subacute trends and health care reform.

368.382   US
MEDICARE AND MEDICAID DATA BOOK. a. Health Care Financing Administration, Office of Research and Demonstrations, Oak Meadows Bldg., Rm. 2230, 6325 Security Blvd., Baltimore, MD 21207. TEL 301-966-6584. (Subscr. to: Supt. of Documents, Washington, DC 20402. TEL 202-783-3238) stat.
    Formerly: Data on the Medicaid Program: Eligibility - Service - Expenditures.
    Description: Provides an overview, descriptive and comparative data and analyses of the Medicare and Medicaid programs. Includes trends and statistics on enrolees, recipients, utilization and expenditures.

368.382 610   US
MEDICARE COMPLIANCE ALERT. (Supplement avail.: Civil Money Penalties Reporter) 1989. bi-w. $370. United Communications Group, 11300 Rockville Pike, Ste. 1100, Rockville, MD 20852-3030. TEL 301-816-8950. FAX 301-816-8945. Ed. Carol Sardinha.
    Formerly: Medicare Compliance Report.
    Description: Examines enforcement trends in Medicare and Medicaid fraud, abuse law and billing practices. Also gives health care providers and attorneys analysis of administrative law rulings in Civil Money Penalties Reporter.

368 610   US   ISSN 1068-2465
MEDICARE MANAGER. 1990. m. $117. Shannon Publications, Inc., 9441 Lyndon B. Johnson Fwy., Ste. 510, Box 2, Dallas, TX 75243-4541. TEL 214-644-0159. FAX 214-644-1538. Ed. Ellen L. Bradley. (back issues avail.) **Document type:** newsletter.
    Description: Contains tips, solutions, and applications to help clear up the confusion caused by Medicare's constant changes.

368.382   US
MEDICARE - MEDICAID GUIDE. 1969. w. $1140. Commerce Clearing House, Inc., 4025 W. Peterson Ave., Chicago, IL 60646. TEL 312-583-8500. Ed. D. Newquist. (looseleaf format)

368 610   US   ISSN 0885-0925
MEDICARE REVIEW. 1984. m. $175. Shannon Publications, Inc., 9441 Lyndon B. Johnson Fwy., No. 510, Box 2, Dallas, TX 75243-4541. TEL 214-644-0159. FAX 214-644-1538. Ed. Ellen L. Bradley. (back issues avail.) **Document type:** newsletter.
    Description: Provides in-depth coverage of billing-coding policies, coverage issues, reimbursements, and legislation, as well as updates on health care reform.

368 364.4   SP
MERCADO PREVISOR. 22/yr. Plaza Conde Valle Suchil 3, 28015 Madrid, Spain. TEL 1-447-51-51. Ed. Jose Luis Morillo. circ. 12,000.

368   CN   ISSN 0714-6914
MERCER BULLETIN. 1951. m. free. William M. Mercer Ltd., BCE Place, 161 Bay St., P.O. Box 501, Toronto, ON M5J 2S5. TEL 416-868-2892. FAX 416-868-7694. Ed. Gordon M. Hall. circ. 8,500. Indexed: World Bibl.Soc.Sec. **Document type:** bulletin.
    Formerly (until Jan. 1982): Mercer Actuarial Bulletin (ISSN 0025-9845)

368   US   ISSN 0742-3446
MERRITT RISK MANAGEMENT REVIEW. 1983. fortn. $397. Merritt Company, 1661 Ninth St., Box 955, Santa Monica, CA 90406. TEL 310-450-7234. FAX 310-396-4563. Eds. Juan Hovey, James Walsh. circ. 3,000. (looseleaf format) **Document type:** newsletter.
    Description: Commentary on risk management and insurance.

368   US
MESSENGER REPORTER. vol.13, 1977. 10/yr. free. (Council of Insurance Brokers of Greater New York) Chase Communications Group, Inc., c/o Linda S. Warren, Asst. VP, 25-35 Beechwood Ave., Mount Vernon, NY 10550. TEL 914-699-2020. FAX 914-664-1503. adv.; illus. circ. 800.
    Incorporating: Brooklyn Insurance Brokers Association. Bulletin (ISSN 0007-2354)

368   US   ISSN 1061-2610
MICHIGAN INSURANCE HANDBOOK. 1989. biennial. $30 (for 1993-1994 ed.). (Citizen's Insurance Co. of America) Public Sector Consultants, Inc., Knapp's Centre, Ste. 401, 300 S. Washington Sq., Lansing, MI 48933. TEL 517-484-4954. FAX 517-484-6549. Ed. Wilma Harrison.
    Description: Provides an objective examination of insurance issues in Michigan, for consumers, businesses, insurers, and government.

368 331   US   ISSN 0746-1461
KFM4542.A59
MICHIGAN WORKERS' COMP DIGEST. 1982. m. $70. Pathfinder Associates, Inc., 1906 Mills Ave., Box 5240, North Muskegon, MI 49445. TEL 616-744-8462. FAX 616-744-0509. Ed. Ronald E. Hauxwell. adv. circ. 400. (back issues avail.)
    Description: Offers a summary of Michigan workers' compensation cases and laws.

368   US   ISSN 0026-2935
MID-AMERICA INSURANCE. 1891. m. $10. Insurance Publications, Inc., Box 11310, Overland Park, KS 66207. FAX 913-383-1247. Ed. James M. Willman. adv.; charts; illus.; stat. circ. 13,227. Indexed: ABI Inform.
—UMI.

368   US
MINNESOTA CLAIMS. 1991. bi-m. $15. Meusey Communications, 1107 Hazeltine Blvd., Ste. 478, Chaska, MN 55318. TEL 612-488-8816. adv.: B&W page $398; trim 8 1/2 x 11. circ. 2,000.
    Description: Reports on issues, people and events in the insurance claim business.

368   US
MINNESOTA INSURANCE.* 1982. m. $14. Meusey Communications, 1107 Hazeltine Blvd., Ste. 478, Chaska, MN 55318-1008. TEL 612-544-8666. Ed. Jack Meusey. adv. circ. 4,500.
    Description: Covers people, events, and issues affecting insurance in Minnesota.

368.2 340   US
MINNESOTA NO-FAULT AUTOMOBILE INSURANCE. 2nd ed., 1989. 2 base vols. (plus suppl.). $140. Butterworth Legal Publishers (Salem) (Subsidiary of: Reed Elsevier plc), 8 Industrial Way, Bldg. C, Salem, NH 03079. TEL 800-548-4001. FAX 603-898-9858. Ed. Michael K. Steenson. (looseleaf format)
    Description: Reviews the history, amendment and development of the no-fault statute since 1974 and discusses the case law that has arisen under the act.

368   US
MISSOURI. DEPARTMENT OF INSURANCE. ANNUAL REPORT AND STATISTICAL DATA. 1870. a. $10. Department of Insurance, Statistics Section, Box 690, Jefferson City, MO 65102. TEL 314-751-4439. FAX 314-751-1165. stat. circ. 750. **Document type:** corporate report.
    Formerly: Missouri. Division of Insurance. Annual Report and Statistical Data.
    Description: Contains department operations summaries and listing of insurance companies licensed in Missouri.

368   UK
MITSUBISHI FINANCE RISK DIRECTORY (YEAR); a guide to risk management products and services worldwide. 1991. a. (Mitsubishi Finance International plc) Risk Magazine, 104-112 Marylebone Ln., London W1M 5FU, England. TEL 44-71-487-5326. FAX 11-71-486-0879. **Document type:** directory.
    Description: Lists banks, brokerages, and consulting firms involved in finance insurance.

368   BE   ISSN 0772-5817
LE MONDE DES ASSURANCES. Dutch edition: Verzekeringswereld (ISSN 0772-5825) 1910. m. 1995 BEF. (Office des Assureurs de Belgique) Kluwer Editorial, Excelsiorlaan 18, 1930 Zaventem, Belgium. TEL 32-2-7191511. FAX 32-2-7191559. Ed. Frank Claes. adv.; bk.rev.; bibl. circ. 5,200.
    Supersedes: Moniteur des Assurances; Which was formerly: Petit Moniteur des Assurances (ISSN 0031-627X)

MONITOR (WASHINGTON, 1970). see *HOSPITALS*

368   UK   ISSN 0965-8629
▼**MOTOR INSURANCE MARKET.** 1992. m. £150($300) D Y P Insurance & Reinsurance Research Group Ltd., Bridge House, 181 Queen Victoria St., London EC4V 4DD, England. TEL 071-236-2175. FAX 071-489-1487. Ed. Julius S. Bannister. charts; stat. **Document type:** newsletter.
    Description: Covers developments in motor vehicle insurance.

368   US
MUTUAL PIPER. irreg. Professional Insurance Communicators of America, Box 68700, Indianapolis, IN 46268. TEL 317-875-5250. FAX 317-879-8408.
    Formerly: Communique.

368   FR   ISSN 0027-5239
HG8057
MUTUALITE/GEGEN - SEITIGKEIT/MUTUALISMO/MUTUALITY. (Text in English, French, German, Spanish) 1965. s-a. free. Association Internationale des Societes d'Assurance Mutuelle - International Association of Mutual Insurance Companies, 114 rue la Boetie, 75008 Paris, France. FAX 1-42-56-04-49. Ed. R. Choplin. bk.rev.; bibl.; illus.; circ. 2,500 (controlled). **Document type:** bulletin.

N A D E ADVOCATE. (National Association of Disability Examiners) see *SOCIAL SERVICES AND WELFARE*

INSURANCE

368   US   ISSN 0741-0727
HG8501
N A I C NEWSLETTER. 1983. m. $150. National Association of Insurance Commissioners, 120 W. 12th St., Kansas City, MO 64105. TEL 816-374-7259. (Subscr. to: N A I C Publications, Box 263 Department 42, Kansas City, MO 64193-0042) **Document type**: newsletter.
    Description: Provides summaries of insurance regulatory activities.

N A I F A CONVENTION. PROCEEDINGS. (National Association of Independent Fee Appraisers) see *REAL ESTATE*

N A I F A TECHNICAL MANUAL. (National Association of Independent Fee Appraisers) see *REAL ESTATE*

368   US   ISSN 1051-0958
HG8501
N A M I C MAGAZINE. 1895. m. $18 (effective 1994). National Association of Mutual Insurance Companies, 3601 Vincennes Rd., Box 68700, Indianapolis, IN 46268. TEL 317-875-5250. FAX 317-879-8408. Ed. Janet Wright. adv.; bk.rev.; illus.; circ. 3,000 (paid). **Document type**: trade publication.
    Formerly: Mutual Insurance Bulletin.

368 340   UK
N A P F PENSIONS LEGISLATION SERVICE. 2 base vols. (plus updates 3/yr.). $324. (National Association of Pension Funds) Butterworth & Co. (Publishers) Ltd. (Subsidiary of: Reed Elsevier plc), 88 Kingsway, London WC2B 6AB, England. TEL 71-405-6900. FAX 71-405-1332. (US addr.: Butterworth Legal Publishers, 90 Stiles Rd., Salem, NH 03079-9981. TEL 603-898-9664) (looseleaf format)
    Description: Contains the amended texts of all the relevant statues and statutory instruments, as well as nonstatutory materials relating to pensions.

368   US   ISSN 0027-5964
N A P I A BULLETIN.* vol.13, 1970. q. membership. National Association of Public Insurance Adjusters, 1767 Busines Center Dr., Ste. 200, Reston, VA 22090-5332. TEL 202-371-1258. FAX 202-371-1090. adv. circ. 900. **Document type**: bulletin.

N A R I STETHOSCOPE. (National Association of Residents and Interns) see *BUSINESS AND ECONOMICS — Investments*

N F R A NEWSLETTER. (National Forest Recreation Association) see *CONSERVATION*

368   SW   ISSN 0348-6516
N F T/SCANDINAVIAN INSURANCE QUARTERLY. (Jointly edited by the Insurance Societies of Denmark, Finland, France, German, Norwegian or Swedish) (Text in Danish, English, French, German, Norwegian or Swedish) 1921. q. SEK 100($12) Svenska Foersaekringsfoereningen - Swedish Insurance Society, Sloejdgatan 9, S-115 87 Stockholm, Sweden. TEL 46-8-24-28-60. FAX 46-8-24-13-20. Eds. Anders Kleverman, Charlotta Friborg. adv.; bk.rev.; illus.; cum.index every 5 yrs. circ. 9,000. (processed) **Document type**: trade publication.
    —BLDSC (6119.250000).
    Formerly (until 1977): Nordisk Foersaekringstidskrift (ISSN 0029-1358)

368   US
N R R A NEWS. m. National Risk Retention Association, 3421 M St., N.W., Box 1740, Washington, DC 20007. TEL 800-999-4505. Ed. Leslea Dummer.

368.32   US   ISSN 0027-7142
N Y L I C REVIEW. 1933. m. free. New York Life Insurance Co., Agency Dept. for the Field Representatives, 51 Madison Ave., New York, NY 10010. TEL 212-567-7000. Ed. Douglas S. Davin. bk.rev.; charts; illus.; index. circ. 16,500.

368   US
NATIONAL ASSOCIATION OF INSURANCE COMMISSIONERS. COMPILATION OF REPORTS. q. $250 (effective Jan. 1993). National Association of Insurance Commissioners, 120 W. 12th St., Kansas City, MO 64105. TEL 816-374-7259. (Subscr. to: N A I C Publications, Box 263 Department 42, Kansas City, MO 64193-0042) (looseleaf format) **Document type**: proceedings.
    Description: Provides immediate access to meeting minutes.

368   US
NATIONAL ASSOCIATION OF INSURANCE COMMISSIONERS. LIFE AND HEALTH ACTUARIAL REPORT. m. $200 (effective Jan. 1992). National Association of Insurance Commissioners, 120 W. 12th St., Kansas City, MO 64105. TEL 816-374-7259. (Subscr. to: N A I C Publications, Box 263 Department 42, Kansas City, MO 64193-0042)
    Description: Provides reports of task force research studies and meetings.

368   US
NATIONAL ASSOCIATION OF INSURANCE COMMISSIONERS. LISTING OF COMPANIES. s-a. $150 (effective Jan. 1992). National Association of Insurance Commissioners, 120 W. 12th St., Kansas City, MO 64105. TEL 816-374-9259. (Subscr. to: N A I C Publications, Box 263 Department 42, Kansas City, MO 64193-0042) (also avail. in diskette format) **Document type**: directory.
    Description: Provides demographic information and code numbers on more than 5,000 insurance companies.

368   US   ISSN 0363-0358
HG8016
NATIONAL ASSOCIATION OF INSURANCE COMMISSIONERS. PROCEEDINGS. 1871. q. $300. National Association of Insurance Commissioners, 120 W. 12th St., Kansas City, MO 64105. TEL 816-374-7259. (Subscr. to: N A I C Publications, Box 263 Department 42, Kansas City, MO 64193-0042) Ed. Karen Montalto. charts; stat.; cum.index: 1950-1970, 1970-1979, 1980-1989. circ. 800. (back issues avail.) **Document type**: proceedings.
    ●Also available online. Vendor(s): Mead Data Central, Inc.
    Description: Official record of transactions from all of the association's meetings.

368.382 610   US   ISSN 0897-3059
NATIONAL DIRECTORY OF H M OS. Key Title: G H A A's National Directory of H M Os. 1986. a. $125. Group Health Association of America, Inc., 1129 20th St., N.W., Ste. 600, Washington, DC 20036. TEL 202-778-3247. FAX 202-331-7487. **Document type**: directory.

368   TZ
NATIONAL INSURANCE CORPORATION OF TANZANIA. ANNUAL REPORT AND ACCOUNTS. (Text in English) a. National Insurance Corporation of Tanzania Ltd., Corporate Planning & Marketing, P.O. Box 9264, Dar es Salaam, Tanzania. Ed. S.A. Shamis. **Document type**: corporate report.

368.01   IS   ISSN 0075-1324
NATIONAL INSURANCE INSTITUTE, JERUSALEM. FULL ACTUARIAL REPORT. (Text in English and Hebrew) triennial. price varies. National Insurance Institute, 13 Sderot Weizman, Jerusalem, Israel. **Document type**: corporate report.

NATIONAL INSURANCE LAW REVIEW. see *LAW*

368   US   ISSN 0028-033X
HG8751
NATIONAL UNDERWRITER. LIFE & HEALTH INSURANCE EDITION. w. $75 (foreign $167). National Underwriter Co., 505 Gest St., Cincinnati, OH 45203. TEL 513-721-2140. FAX 513-721-0126. Ed. Tom Slattery. adv.; charts; illus.; stat. circ. 30,695. (also avail. in microfilm from UMI; reprint service avail. from UMI) **Indexed**: ABI Inform., B.P.I., BPIA, Bus.Ind., Hlth.Ind., L.I.I., PSI, Tr.& Indus.Ind.
    Description: News on legislation, products and general facts on the life, health and financial services industries.

368.012   US   ISSN 1042-6841
HG8011   CODEN: NUCEE5
NATIONAL UNDERWRITER. PROPERTY & CASUALTY - RISK & BENEFITS MANAGEMENT EDITION. 1896. w. $75 (foreign $187). National Underwriter Co., 505 Gest St., Cincinnati, OH 45203. TEL 513-721-2410. FAX 513-721-0126. Ed. Tom Slattery. circ. 41,670. (also avail. in microform from UMI; reprint service avail. from UMI) **Indexed**: ABI Inform., B.P.I, BPIA, Bus.Ind., Hlth.Ind., P.L.I.I., PSI, Tr.& Indus.Ind.
    —BLDSC (6033.235000); UnCover; UMI.
    Former titles (until 1989): National Underwriter. Property and Casualty - Employee Benefits Edition (ISSN 0898-8897); (until 1986): National Underwriter. Property and Casualty Insurance Edition (ISSN 0163-8912)
    Description: Discusses products, market, legislation, risk management and employee benefits.

368.382   US   ISSN 1050-6357
HG9956
NATIONAL UNDERWRITER PROFILES. HEALTH INSURERS. 1962. a. National Underwriter Co., 505 Gest St., Cincinnati, OH 45203. TEL 513-721-2140. FAX 513-721-0126.
    Formerly (until 1989): Argus Chart of Health Insurers (ISSN 0897-6732)

368.32   US   ISSN 1050-5857
HG8955
NATIONAL UNDERWRITER PROFILES. LIFE INSURERS. 1976. a. National Underwriter Co., 505 Gest St., Cincinnati, OH 45203. TEL 513-721-2140. FAX 513-721-0126.
    Formerly (until 1989): Life Financial Reports, Financial and Operating Results of Life Insurers (ISSN 0271-1559)

368.1   US   ISSN 1050-6365
HG9765
NATIONAL UNDERWRITER PROFILES. PROPERTY - CASUALTY INSURERS. a. $36.50. National Underwriter Co., 505 Gest St., Cinncinnati, OH 45203. TEL 513-721-2140. FAX 513-721-0126.
    Former titles (until 1989): Argus F C and S Chart (ISSN 0360-8921); (until 1964): Argus Chart. Fire (ISSN 0737-9846); And (until 1951): Argus Fire Chart (ISSN 0737-9854).
    Description: Provides financial information on insurance companies' performances.

368   UK
NATIONAL UNION OF INSURANCE WORKERS. PRUDENTIAL SECTION. GAZETTE. 4/w. National Union of Insurance Workers, Prudential Section, 27 Old Gloucester St., London WC1N 3AF, England. TEL 071-405-6798. FAX 071-404-8150. circ. 13,000.
    Supersedes: Prudential Staff Gazette.

368   NE   ISSN 0077-5975
NATIONALE-NEDERLANDEN. ANNUAL REPORT. (Text in Dutch and English) 1963. a. free. Nationale-Nederlanden N.V., Johan de Wittlaan 3, Box 29701, 2502 LS The Hague, Netherlands. TEL 70-581210. circ. 37,000.

368   GW
NESSELBLATT. 1971. bi-m. Provinzial Versicherungen, Sophienblatt 33, 24114 Kiel, Germany. FAX 0431-6032804. TELEX 292977. Ed. Guenther Jesumann. bk.rev. circ. 4,500. **Document type**: newsletter.
    Description: Insurance company publication including annual report, reports of meetings and events, company news, and list of exhibitions.

368 340   US
▼**NEW HAMPSHIRE INSURANCE LAWS (YEAR)**. 1992. a. $35. Butterworth Legal Publishers (Salem) (Subsidiary of: Reed Elsevier plc), 8 Industrial Way, Bldg. C, Salem, NH 03079. TEL 800-548-4001. FAX 603-898-9858. Ed.Bd.

NEW HAMPSHIRE PRACTICE SERIES. VOLS. 8 AND 9: PERSONAL INJURY - TORT AND INSURANCE PRACTICE. see *LAW — Civil Law*

NEW HORIZON. see *BUSINESS AND ECONOMICS — Banking And Finance*

NEW JERSEY INSURANCE DIRECTORY. see *BUSINESS AND ECONOMICS — Trade And Industrial Directories*

INSURANCE 3151

368   US
NEW YORK (STATE). INSURANCE DEPARTMENT. ANNUAL REPORT OF THE SUPERINTENDENT OF INSURANCE TO THE NEW YORK LEGISLATURE. a. free. Insurance Department, Publications Unit, Empire State Plaza, Agency Bldg. No. 1, Albany, NY 12257. circ. 2,000. **Indexed:** SRI. **Document type:** corporate report.

368   US
NEW YORK (STATE). INSURANCE DEPARTMENT. BULLETIN. 1961. m. free. Insurance Department, Research Bureau, 160 W. Broadway, 21st Fl., New York, NY 10013. TEL 212-602-0473. FAX 212-602-0437. Ed. Wayne Cotter. circ. 5,000 (controlled). (back issues avail.) **Document type:** government publication.

368   US
NEW YORK (STATE). INSURANCE DEPARTMENT. FEES AND TAXES CHARGED INSURANCE COMPANIES UNDER THE LAWS OF NEW YORK TOGETHER WITH ABSTRACTS OF FEES, TAXES AND OTHER REQUIREMENTS OF OTHER STATES. 1906. a. $2.50. Insurance Department, Publications Unit, Empire State Plaza, Agency Bldg. No. 1, Albany, NY 12257. circ. 1,000. **Document type:** government publication.

368.32   US   ISSN 0024-3221
NEW YORK CITY ASSOCIATION OF LIFE UNDERWRITERS. BULLETIN. 1922. m. $15. New York City Association of Life Underwriters, Inc., 500 Fifth Ave., New York, NY 10110. FAX 212-764-8693. Ed. C. Jennings. adv.; bk.rev.; charts; illus.; stat. circ. 3,400. **Document type:** bulletin.

NEW YORK INSURANCE DIRECTORY. see *BUSINESS AND ECONOMICS — Trade And Industrial Directories*

NEW YORK NO-FAULT ARBITRATION REPORTS. see *LAW*

368   US
NEW YORK TELEPHONE TICKLER FOR INSURANCE MEN AND WOMEN. 1949. a. $14.95. Underwriter Printing and Publishing Co., 50 E. Palisade Ave., Englewood, NJ 07631. TEL 201-569-8808. Ed. Donald E. Wolff. adv. circ. 27,500. **Document type:** directory.
  Formerly: Telephone Tickler for Insurance Men and Women (ISSN 0082-2663)
  Description: Lists names, addresses, and telephone numbers of insurance companies, agents, brokers, and related suppliers in the New York City area.

368   ZR
NGABU; revue Zairoise des assurances. 1973. q. £120. Societe Nationale d'Assurance, Sonas Sankuru Bldg., Blvd. du 30 Juin, P.O. Box 3443, Kinshasa-Gombe, Zaire. TEL 23051. TELEX 21653. Ed. Utshudiema Luhaka. adv.; illus.

368.9   TZ   ISSN 0856-1222
NGAO. (Text in English) 1972. q. National Insurance Corporation of Tanzania Ltd., Corporate Planning & Marketing, P.O. Box 9264, Dar es Salaam, Tanzania. Ed. S.A. Shamis. illus. circ. 3,000.

368   NR   ISSN 0048-0398
NIGERIAN INSURANCE MONITOR.* 1971. m. EAs.34. Nara Advertising Ltd., 30 Idoluwo St., Box 4236, Lagos, Nigeria. Ed. Obiora Okeke. adv.; illus.

368   KO
NON-LIFE INSURANCE. (Text in English) 1961. m. free. Korea Non-Life Insurance Association, 80 Soosong-dong, 6th floor, Chongno-ku, Seoul, S. Korea. Ed. Su-Ung Cho. circ. 9,000.

368   JA
NON-LIFE INSURANCE IN JAPAN. FACT BOOK. (Text in English) 1975. a. 820 Yen($7.5) (effective 1992; typically set in Dec.). Marine & Fire Insurance Association of Japan Inc., Information Service Office, Non-Life Insurance Bldg., 9, Kanda Awajicho 2-chome, Chiyoda-ku, Tokyo 101, Japan. TEL 03-3255-1437. FAX 03-3255-1234. TELEX 222-4829 SONPO J. Ed. Yoshiki Amamoto. circ. 4,500.
  Description: General market report on the Japanese non-life insurance business.

368   US
NORTH JERSEY TELEPHONE TICKLER FOR INSURANCE MEN & WOMEN. 1982. a. $7. Underwriter Printing and Publishing Co., 50 E. Palisade Ave., Englewood, NJ 07631. TEL 201-569-8808. Ed. Donald E. Wolff. adv. circ. 17,000. **Document type:** directory.
  Description: Lists names, addresses, and telephone numbers of insurance companies, agents, brokers, and related suppliers in northern New Jersey.

NORTH - SOUTH CAROLINA INSURANCE DIRECTORY. see *BUSINESS AND ECONOMICS — Trade And Industrial Directories*

NORTH TEXAS INSURANCE DIRECTORY. see *BUSINESS AND ECONOMICS — Trade And Industrial Directories*

368   IT
NOTIZIARIO ASSICURATIVO. 1919. m. L.60000. Publiass s.r.l., Via Dei Gracchi, 30, 20146 Milan, Italy. TEL 39-2-58313538. FAX 39-2-58313730. Ed. Sergio Scotti. adv.; bk.rev. circ. 16,800.

NOTIZIARIO DEL LAVORO E PREVIDENZA. see *LAW — Corporate Law*

368   NE   ISSN 0165-8220
NU. 1971. m. free. Nationale-Nederlanden N.V., Johan de Wittlaan 3, Box 29701, 2502 LS The Hague, Netherlands. TEL 70-581726. Ed. Anneke Rijk. circ. 19,000.

368.4   US   ISSN 1073-1482
HD7123
O A S D I BENEFICIARIES BY STATE AND COUNTY. (Old Age, Survivors, Disability Insurance) 1976. a. U.S. Social Security Administration, Office of Research and Statistics, Publications Staff, Van Ness Center, Rm. 209, 4301 Connecticut Ave., N.W., Washington, DC 20008. TEL 202-282-7161. FAX 202-282-7219. (Subscr. to: Superintendent of Documents, U.S. Government Printing Office, Box 371954, Pittsburgh, PA 15250-7954. TEL 202-783-3238. FAX 202-512-2233) charts; stat. **Document type:** government publication.
  Formerly (until 1986): Social Security Benefits by State and County (ISSN 0888-8302)
  Description: Presents information on the number of persons receiving O.A.S.D.I. benefits, the type of benefit received, and the total each state, county, and U.S. possession paid out in December of the year in question.

368.4 331   UK   ISSN 0952-231X
OCCUPATIONAL PENSIONS. 1987. 12/yr. £99 (foreign £110). Eclipse Publications Ltd., 18-20 Highbury Place, London N5 1QP, England. TEL 071-354-5858. FAX 071-359-4000. Ed. Colin Sherwood. circ. 1,000. (back issues avail.)
—BLDSC (6229.760000).
  Description: Provides guidelines on new legislation and changes to regulations. Includes comprehensive surveys on named organizations.

368   US
OHIO AGENT. m. $15. (Professional Insurance Agents of Ohio) Zimmerman Publishing Company, Inc., 929 Harrison Ave., Ste. 202, Columbus, OH 43215. TEL 614-294-8878. FAX 614-294-4831. Ed. Eric D. Wygle. adv. circ. 2,300. **Document type:** trade publication.

368   US   ISSN 0198-683X
OHIO UNDERWRITER; insurance news of Ohio. 1967. m. $16.50. National Underwriter Co., 505 Gest St., Cincinnati, OH 45203. TEL 513-721-2410. FAX 513-721-0126. Ed. Gilbert McLean. adv.; bk.rev.; stat.; tr.lit. circ. 10,000. (tabloid format; also avail. in microform from UMI; back issues avail.; reprint service avail. from UMI)
  Formerly (until 1980): State Underwriter (ISSN 0039-0178)
  Description: Covers the insurance industry in Ohio, including regulatory and legislative decisions and trends.

368 331   RU   ISSN 0131-2618
OKHRANA TRUDA I SOTSIAL'NOE STRAKHOVANIE. 1913. m. $65 (foreign $87). (Vsesoyuznyi Tsentral'nyi Sovet Professional'nykh Soyuzov) Profizdat, Ul. Myasnitskaya 13, 101000 Moscow, Russia. (Dist. in U.S. by: Victor Kamkin Inc., 4956 Boiling Brook Pkwy, Rockville, MD 20852) Ed. K.S. Khromov. adv.; bk.rev.; charts; illus.; stat. circ. 560,000. **Indexed:** World Bibl.Soc.Sec.

368   NE
ONDERNEMINGSANALYSES VERZEKERINGSMAATSCHAPPIJEN. a. fl.72. Delwel Uitgeverij B.V., Postbus 19110, 2500 CC The Hague, Netherlands. TEL 31-70-3624800. FAX 31-70-3605606.
  Description: Financial and economic information on the insurance industry in the Netherlands.

368   CN   ISSN 0829-9838
ONTARIO INSURANCE DIRECTORY; a comprehensive listing of Ontario brokers, general and reinsurance company personnel, adjusters, appraisers, associations, and buyers guide. 1959. a. Can.$32.20. (Toronto Insurance Conference) Southam Magazine Group, 1450 Don Mills Rd., Don Mills, ON M3B 2X7, Canada. TEL 416-445-6641. FAX 416-442-2261. Ed. Nancy Campbell. adv. contact: Janice Dumphie. circ. 3,000. **Document type:** directory.
  Formerly (until 1984): Toronto Insurance Directory (ISSN 0315-8330)
  Description: Lists insurance companies, brokers and adjusters, providing addresses and telephone numbers.

368.4   US
OPINION MANUAL LETTERS (CHRONOLOGICAL). q. $100 in US, Canada, Mexico; elsewhere $200. (Pension Benefit Guaranty Corporation) U.S. National Technical Information Service, 5825 Port Royal Rd., Springfield, VA 22161. TEL 703-487-4630. (back issues avail.)
  Description: Consists of issuances that are responses to issues raised under Employee Retirement Income Security Act (ERISA.)

368.4   US
OPINION MANUAL UPDATES (SECTIONAL). q. $100 in US, Canada, Mexico; elsewhere $200. (Pension Benefit Guaranty Corporation) U.S. National Technical Information Service, 5825 Port Royal Rd., Springfield, VA 22161. TEL 703-487-4630.

368.4   FR
ORGANIC INFORMATIONS. 4/yr. Editions Roger Franck, 9 rue Godotde-Mauroy, 75009 Paris, France. TEL 44-66-91-66. Ed. Henri Charvon. circ. 150,000.
  Description: Covers state pensions for the self-employed in industry and commerce.

368   CI   ISSN 0030-6193
OSIGURANJE I PRIVREDA; casopis za teoriju i praksu osiguranja. (Text in Croatian; summaries in English, French or German) 1960. m. 600 din.($30) Croatia Osiguranje, d.d., Savska 41, 4100 Zagreb, Croatia. TEL 041-630-622. FAX 041-535-616. TELEX 21216. Ed. Vladimir Miletic. adv.; bk.rev.; index. circ. 3,000.

368   US   ISSN 0030-6932
OUR PAPER. 1913. m. free. Grain Dealers Mutual Insurance Co., 1752 N. Meridian St., Box 1747, Indianapolis, IN 46206. TEL 317-923-2453. Ed. John C. Knox. illus. circ. 2,500.

368   US
OUR VOICE.* (Text in English and Slovenian) 1910. s-m. membership. American Mutual Life Association, 19424 S. Waterloo Rd., Cleveland, OH 44119-3250. Ed. Margot Ann Klima. adv.; circ. 8,500 (controlled). (tabloid format; back issues avail.)

368 387   UK   ISSN 0950-4044
HE964.5.G7
P & I INTERNATIONAL. (Protection & Indemnity); monthly review of mutual insurance. 1987. m. £154 (foreign £176). Lloyd's of London Press Ltd., Sheepen Place, Colchester, Essex CO3 3LP, England. TEL 0206-772277. FAX 0206-46273. TELEX 987321 LLOYDS G. (US subscr. to: 611 Broadway, Ste. 308, New York, NY 10012. TEL 212-529-9500) Ed. Bill Robertson. bk.rev. (back issues avail.) **Document type:** trade publication. —BLDSC (6327.107000).
  Description: Covers developments affecting insurance companies, brokers, and adjusters, including legislation, case law, personal injury, cargo, pollution, and more.

P I P E R. (Pensions & Investments Performance Evaluation Reports) see *BUSINESS AND ECONOMICS — Investments*

3152 INSURANCE

368.3 GW ISSN 0343-9321
P K V INFORMATIONDIENST. (Private Krankenversicherung) 1946. w. DM.536. Egon Siller Verlag, Tussmannstr. 17, 40477 Dusseldorf, Germany. Ed. H.U. Hill. circ. 200. (looseleaf format)
  Formerly: Informationsdienst fuer die Private Krankenversicherung (ISSN 0020-031X)

368 GW ISSN 0176-3261
P K V PUBLIK. 1964. 9/yr. DM.6.30. (Verband der Privaten Krankenversicherung e.V.) Verlag Versicherungswirtschaft e.V., Klosestr. 20-24, 76137 Karlsruhe, Germany. TEL 0721-3509-0. FAX 0721-31833. Ed. Christoph Uleer. charts.
  Document type: trade publication.
  Formerly: Private Krankenversicherung.

P P O LETTER. (Preferred Provider Organizations) see BUSINESS AND ECONOMICS

368.382 610 US ISSN 0893-8121
PART B NEWS. 1987. fortn. $426. United Communications Group, 11300 Rockville Pike, Ste.1100, Rockville, MD 20852-3030. TEL 301-816-8950. FAX 301-816-8945. Ed. Carol Monaco. (back issues avail.)
  Description: Reports on the changes in Medicare insurance reimbursement rules for physicians, plus ways they can get their share of "Part B" dollars.

368 338 US
THE PENSION ACTUARY. 1966. m. membership. American Society of Pension Actuaries, 4350 N. Fairfax Dr., Ste. 820, Arlington, VA 22203. TEL 703-516-9300. FAX 703-519-9308. Ed. Richard Block. circ. 4,200 (controlled). (back issues avail.)
  Description: Issues and topics of interest to retirement planners and small business pension companies.

362.6 UK ISSN 0140-6647
PENSION FUNDS & THEIR ADVISERS. 1978. a. £69. A P Information Services, Roman House, 296 Golders Green Rd., London NW11 9PZ, England. TEL 081-455-4550. FAX 081-455-6381. (Dist. in U.S. by: Money Market Directories Inc., 300 Eastmarket St., Charlottesville, VA 22901) Ed. Alan Philipp. adv. circ. 3,500. (also avail. in diskette format) **Document type:** directory.
  —BLDSC (6422.710000).

368 331 US
PENSION PLAN GUIDE. w. $955. Commerce Clearing House, Inc., 4025 W. Peterson Ave., Chicago, IL 60646. TEL 312-583-8500.
  Supersedes: Pension Plan Guide Summary.

PENSION WORLD. see BUSINESS AND ECONOMICS — Banking And Finance

368 UK ISSN 0140-8526
PENSIONS TODAY. 1979. m. £165 (foreign £187). Monitor Press, Rectory Rd., Great Waldingfield, Sudbury, Suffolk CO10 0TL, England. TEL 0787-378607. FAX 0787-880201. (back issues avail.) **Document type:** newsletter.
  Description: For pension-fund managers, trustees, company secretaries, pensions specialists in broking and insurance companies.

368 UK ISSN 0307-191X
PENSIONS WORLD. 1972. m. £46. (National Association of Pension Funds) Tolley Publishing Co. Ltd., Tolley House, 2 Addiscombe Rd., Croydon, Surrey CR9 5AF, England. TEL 081-686-9141. FAX 081-686-3155. Ed. Stephanie Hawthorne. adv.; bk.rev.; stat.; index. circ. 9,500. **Indexed:** Account.& Data Proc.Abstr., Account.Ind. (1974-), Anbar, Work Rel.Abstr. **Document type:** bulletin.
  —BLDSC (6422.720500).

PERSONAL INJURY NEWSLETTER. see LAW

PERSONAL INJURY VALUATION HANDBOOKS; injury valuation & special research reports. see LAW

368.5 US
PERSONAL INJURY VERDICT REVIEWS. 1982. w. $375. L R P Publications, 747 Dresher Rd., Box 980, Horsham, PA 19044. TEL 800-341-7874. (back issues avail.)
  Description: Up-to-date case examples and research provided on various liability areas in personal damage litigation.

368.5 US
PERSONAL INJURY VERDICT SURVEY. (Edition for the 50 US States) a. $29.50. L R P Publications, 747 Dresher Rd., Box 980, Horsham, PA 19044. TEL 800-341-7874. (back issues avail.)
  Description: Analysis of personal damage verdict trends by state.

368 UK
PERSONAL PENSIONS (YEAR). 1975. a. £45($48) (overseas £48). Financial Times Business Information Ltd., 102 Clerkenwell Rd., London EC1M 5SA, England. TEL 071-814-9770. FAX 071-814-9778. (Avail. from: F T Management Reports, Customer Services, P.O. Box 6, Camborne TR14 9EQ, England. TEL 0209-711928. FAX 0209-612493) Ed. Janet Walford. adv.: B&W page £2150; color page £2600; adv. contact: Colin Clarke. circ. 3,500. (tabloid format) **Document type:** directory.
  Former titles: Self-Employed Pensions; Handbook of Self-Employed Pensions.
  Description: Provides a detailed technical analysis of almost every available personal pension plan in the U.K. Includes information on taxation aspects and other factors affecting selection of a suitable plan; summary tables compare the performance of the policies.

368 US ISSN 0737-6839
PERSONAL PROPERTY SECTION NEWS. 1980. q. $45 membership. International Association of Assessing Officers, 130 E. Randolph, Ste. 850, Chicago, IL 60601. TEL 312-947-2042. Ed. Dean McQuown. circ. 655. (back issues avail.)

368 PH ISSN 0117-5394
PHILIPPINE INSURANCE COMMISSION ANNUAL REPORT. 1949. a. P.350($40) Insurance Commission, Insurance Commission Bldg., 1071 United Nations Ave., P.O. Box 3589, Manila, Philippines. TEL 632-599-221. FAX 632-522-1434. circ. 300 (controlled).
  Description: Provides the insurance industry and the public with information on the results of business operations in the country and other related information.

368 XR ISSN 0032-2393
POJISTNY OBZOR. 1923. m. 18 Kcs.($15.40) (Ceska Statni Pojistovna, Prague) Nakladatelstvi Technicke Literatury, Spalena 51, 113 02 Prague 1, Czech Republic. (Dist. by: Artia, Ve Smeckach 30, 111 27 Prague 1, Czech Republic) (Co-sponsor: Slovenska Statni Pojistovna, Bratislava) Ed. Eva Trojanova. bk.rev. circ. 4,800.

365 US
POLICIES IN REVIEW. 1988? m. $227.50. Standard Publishing Corp., 155 Federal St., Boston, MA 02110. TEL 617-457-0600. Ed. Roger Peirce.

368 UK ISSN 0263-6700
POLICY MARKET. 1902. m. £24. Stone and Cox (Publications) Ltd., 44 Fleet St., London EC4Y 1BS, England. Ed. David Vaughan-Williams. adv.; illus.; stat.; index.
  Formerly: Policy (ISSN 0032-2652)
  Description: Covers life and non-life insurance industries, of special interest to the broker.

PONTE. see AGRICULTURE

368 UK ISSN 0032-5252
HG8013
POST MAGAZINE AND INSURANCE MONITOR. 1840. w. £85. Buckley Press, 58 Fleet St., London EC4Y 1JU, England. TEL 071-383-4880. FAX 071-583-6069. Ed. V.J.F. Betson. adv.; charts; illus.; stat. **Document type:** trade publication.
  —BLDSC (6558.879000).

368 610 YU ISSN 0032-5880
POVRATAK U ZIVOT. 1952. bi-m. $4.80. Institut za Rehabilitaciju, Belgrade, Sokobanjska, Belgrade, Yugoslavia. Ed. Zivojin Zec.

368.4 IT ISSN 0032-8065
HD7090
PREVIDENZA SOCIALE. (Text in Italian; summaries in English) 1945. bi-m. L.30000. Istituto Nazionale della Previdenza Sociale, Via Ciro Il Grande 21, Rome, Italy. Ed. Aldo Stranges. adv.; bk.rev.; bibl.; stat.; index. circ. 6,000. **Indexed:** P.A.I.S.For.Lang.Ind., World Bibl.Soc.Sec.

368 IT ISSN 0032-809X
PREVIDENZA SOCIALE NELL'ARTIGIANATO. vol.11, 1970. bi-m. L.3000. Confederazione delle Libere Associazioni Artigiane Italiane, Piazzetta Pattari 4, Milan, Italy. Ed. Gabriele Maria Lanfredini. bk.rev.; abstr.

PREVISIONS GLISSANTES DETAILLEES EN PERSPECTIVES SECTORIELLES (VOL.34): ASSURANCES. see BUSINESS AND ECONOMICS — Economic Situation And Conditions

PRINCIPAL'S REPORT. see BUSINESS AND ECONOMICS — Management

368.382 GW
PRO B K K. 1951. m. DM.26.40. Bundesverband der Betriebskrankenkassen, Kronprinzenstr. 6, 45128 Essen, Germany. TEL 0201-1791140. FAX 0201-1791003. circ. 12,800. (back issues avail.) **Document type:** trade publication.
  Formerly (until 1993): Selbstverwaltung und Selbstverantwortung (ISSN 0342-1988)

368.014 380.5 US
PROCLAIM (FORT WASHINGTON). 1984. q. $40. (Certified Claims Professional Accreditation Council) Silesia Companies Inc., 619 Broadcreek Dr., Ft. Washington, MD 20711. TEL 301-292-1970. FAX 301-292-1787. adv.; bk.rev. circ. 300. **Document type:** newsletter.
  Description: Discusses transportation insurance claims.

368 US
PRODUCER NEWS. 1976. m. $27. Insurance Field Company, Box 24244, Louisville, KY 40224-0244. TEL 502-491-5857. FAX 502-491-5905. Ed. George V.R. Smith. circ. 16,350. (looseleaf format; back issues avail.) **Document type:** newsletter.
  Description: Newsletter for independent insurance agents.

368 GW ISSN 0723-3604
PRODUKTHAFTPFLICHT INTERNATIONAL. 1982. bi-m. DM.170. Koelnische Rueckversicherungs Gesellschaft AG, Theodor-Heuss-Ring 11, 50668 Cologne, Germany. Ed. Wilhelm Zeller. bk.rev.; index. circ. 1,000. (back issues avail.) **Document type:** academic/scholarly publication.
  Description: Covers product liability and related matters.

368 US ISSN 0148-8899
HG8011
PROFESSIONAL AGENT. 1937. m. $24 to non-members; members $12. National Association of Professional Insurance Agents, 400 N. Washington St., Alexandria, VA 22314. TEL 703-836-9340. FAX 703-836-1279. Ed. Alan Prochoroff. adv.; bk.rev.; charts; illus.; stat. circ. 30,414. **Document type:** trade publication.
—UMI.
  Formerly (until 1976): Mutual Review (ISSN 0027-5204)

368.01 US
PROFESSIONAL INSURANCE AGENTS OF NEW YORK - NEW JERSEY - CONNECTICUT. 1948. m. (except July). $25. P I A Management Services, Inc., Box 997, Glenmont, NY 12077-0997. TEL 518-434-3111. FAX 518-434-2342. Ed. Mary Vanniere. adv. contact: Cindy Wlazio. index. circ. 5,000. **Document type:** trade publication.
  Description: Covers technical subjects, general business management information, and Association activities.

368 US
PROFESSIONAL LIABILITY INSURANCE. 1990. q. $231. International Risk Management Institute, Inc., 12222 Merit Dr., Ste. 1660, Dallas, TX 75251-2217. TEL 214-960-7693. FAX 214-960-6037. Ed. Robert Bregman. (looseleaf format; back issues avail.)
  Description: Analyzes the liability exposures and coverages written for major professions including doctors, lawyers, accountants, architects, engineers, corporate and non-profit directors and officers.

INSURANCE 3153

368.5 UK ISSN 0268-9669
PROFESSIONAL LIABILITY TODAY. 1986. m. $392. Lloyds' of London Press Ltd., Sheepen Pl., Colchester, Essex CO3 3LP, England. TEL 0206-772277. FAX 0206-46273. TELEX 987321-LLOYDS-G. (US subscr. to: 611 Broadway, New York, NY 10012. TEL 212-529-9500) Ed. J.S. Ashworth. (back issues avail.)
—BLDSC (6859.528000).
  Description: Advises on law, insurance, and practical means to avoid and minimize liability.

368 UK
PROSPECT (LONDON). 1974. m. membership only. (Life Insurance Association) Harrington Publications Ltd., 14 Stoneleigh Park Rd., Ewell, Epsom, Surrey KT19 0TN, England. TEL 02357-4012. FAX 02357-65693. Ed. Stewart Farr. adv.; bk.rev.; circ. 11,500 (controlled). **Document type:** trade publication.
  Description: Focuses on technical knowledge, business and selling strategies and motivational aspects relating to the sale of life insurance, pensions and allied investments.

368 CN
PROSPECTIVE. (Text in English, French) 1989. 9/yr. Can.$45. Association des Intermediares en Assurance de Personnes du Quebec, 1 Westmount Sq., Ste. 500, Montreal, PQ H3Z 2P9, Canada. TEL 514-932-4277; 800-361-9989. FAX 514-932-6400. Ed. Louis Garneau. adv.: B&W page Can.$1625, color page Can.$2500; trim 8 1/8 x 10 7/8. circ. 13,000. **Document type:** trade publication.

PUBLIC RISK. see *PUBLIC ADMINISTRATION*

Q R C ADVISOR; managing hospital quality, risk & cost. (Quality, Risk & Cost) see *HOSPITALS*

368 US
QUARTERLY LISTING OF ALIEN INSURERS. q. $150 (with supplement $250). National Association of Insurance Commissioners, 120 W. 12th St., Kansas City, MO 64105. TEL 816-374-7259. (Subscr. to: N A I C Publications, Box 263, Department 42, Kansas City, MO 64193-0042) stat. **Document type:** directory.
  Description: Provides information on alien insurance companies.

368 CN ISSN 0701-5666
HG1662.C3
QUEBEC (PROVINCE). REGIE DE L'ASSURANCE-DEPOTS DU QUEBEC. RAPPORT ANNUEL. a. Can.$2. Ministere des Communications, Direction Generale des Publications Gouvernementales, 9e etage, 1279 boul. Charest Ouest, Quebec, PQ G1N 4K7, Canada. TEL 413-643-5150. **Document type:** government publication.

368 US ISSN 0033-6270
QUERY (BRYN MAWR). (Former name of issuing body: American Society of Chartered Life Underwriters) 1946. bi-m. membership. American Society of C L U & Ch F C, 270 Bryn Mawr Ave., Bryn Mawr, PA 19010. TEL 215-526-2500. Ed. Carl L. Hall, Jr. **Document type:** trade publication.

368.4 FR ISSN 0223-5838
QUESTIONS DE SECURITE SOCIALE.* 1948. m. 472 F. 3 rue Chabanais, 75002 Paris, France. TEL 42-60-30-58. FAX 42-60-32-34. Ed. Laurence Granet. adv. circ. 5,000. Indexed: World Bibl.Soc.Sec.
—BLDSC (7216.370000).

368 US
R E I D QUARTERLY. (Real Estate Investment Quarterly) 1973. q. free. Prudential Insurance Co. of America, Public Relations & Advertising Dept., 5 Plaza, Newark, NJ 07101. TEL 201-877-6000. Ed. Carol Abaya. circ. 3,000 (controlled).
  Supersedes: Mirror.

368 GW
R UND V GRUPPENBILD. 1985. m. R und V Versicherung, Taunusstr. 1, 65193 Wiesbaden, Germany. TEL 0611-5330. FAX 0611-533375. Ed. Renate Killmer. bk.rev. circ. 14,000. (back issues avail.) **Document type:** newsletter.

368 GW
R UND V REPORT. 1986. q. free. R und V Versicherung, Taunusstr. 1, 65193 Wiesbaden, Germany. TEL 0611-533-4672. FAX 0611-533375. Ed. Renate Killmer. index. circ. 33,000. **Document type:** corporate report.

368.382 US
R V S FEE SCHEDULE. (Relative Value Scale) base vol. (plus updates 9/yr.). $370. United Communications Group, 11300 Rockville Pike, Ste. 1100, Rockville, MD 20852-3030. TEL 301-816-8950. FAX 301-816-8945. Ed. Carol Monaco.
  Description: Examines the Medicare payment system for physicians; includes data and worksheet to calculate reimbursement.

346 SW
RAETTSFALL FRAAN FOERSAEKRINGSOEVERDOMSTOLEN. 1967. irreg. (6-7/yr. plus a. cumulation). SEK 360 (effective 1991). Domstolsverket, S-552 81 Joenkoeping, Sweden. (Dist. by: Allmaenna Foerlaget AB, S-106 47 Stockholm, Sweden) **Document type:** government publication.
  ●Also available online.
  Formerly (until 1992): Raettsfall fraan Foersaekringsoeverdomstolen och Foersaekringsraetterna (ISSN 0283-1872)

368 US
RALPH H. BLANCHARD MEMORIAL ENDOWMENT SERIES. 1977. irreg. $10. University of Pennsylvania, Wharton School of Finance and Commerce, Pension Research Council, Colonial Penn Center, Philadelphia, PA 19104-6218. **Document type:** monographic series.

368.3 GW ISSN 0033-9989
DER RATGEBER; Monatshefte fuer die Aus- und Fortbildung der Krankenkassenangestellten. m. DM.29.40. Verlag der Ratgeber, Postfach 3004, 65020 Wiesbaden, Germany. Ed. H.A. Aye. bk.rev.; index. (also avail. in record)

368 UK ISSN 0953-5640
REACTIONS. 1979. m. £165 (Europe £185). ReActions Publishing Group Ltd., 39-41 North Rd., London N7 9DP, England. TEL 071-609-8661. FAX 071-609-0139. TELEX 27142-REACT-G. Ed. Richard Schwarzt. adv. contact: John Walsh. bk.rev. circ. 5,592. **Document type:** trade publication.
—BLDSC (7300.280200); UMI.

368 UK
REACTIONS INTERNATIONAL INSURANCE AND REINSURANCE YEARBOOK. a. ReActions Publishing Group, 39-41 North Rd., London N7 9DP, England. TEL 071-609-8661. FAX 071-609-0139. TELEX 27142-REACT-G. Ed. Richard Newell. adv. contact: Kevin Kibble. **Document type:** trade publication.

366 UK
THE RECHABITE NEWS. 1840. q. free. Independent Order of Rechabites, Rechabite Bldgs., One N. Parade, Deansgate, Manchester 3, England. TEL 061-832-4821. Ed. K. Bradley. circ. 3,000.
  Formerly: Rechabite (ISSN 0034-1215)

RECUEIL JURIDIQUE DE L'EST SECURITE SOCIALE; doctrine jurisprudence, documents administratifs. see *LAW*

368 US
RED SHIELD NEWS. 1940. m. free to employees. Royal Insurance, Corporate Communications Dept., 9300 Arrowpoint Blvd., Charlotte, NC 28217. TEL 704-522-2000. FAX 704-522-2055. Ed. Dene Hellman. charts; illus.; stat. circ. 10,000. **Document type:** newsletter.
  Formerly: Red Shield (ISSN 0034-2041)

368 NE ISSN 0034-2947
REFLECTOR. 1949. m. fl.60. Nederlandse Vereniging van Makelaars in Assurantien en Assurantieadviseurs, Postbus 235, 3800 AE Amersfoort, Netherlands. TEL 033-631414. FAX 033-634133. Ed. H.A.M. Kuijpers. adv.; bk.rev.; illus. circ. 4,000. **Document type:** corporate report.

368 CK
▼**REGIMEN DE SEGUROS.** 1992. base vol. (plus irreg. updates). $80 for base vol.; updates $30. Union de Aseguradores Colombianos, Carrera 7a No. 26-20, Piso 11, Apdo. Aereo 5233, Bogota, Colombia. circ. 200.
  Description: Contains insurance legislation in Colombia.

369 US
REGULATORY REPORTER. 1986. 4/yr. membership. National Association of Independent Insurers, 2600 River Rd., Des Plaines, IL 60018. TEL 708-297-7800. FAX 708-297-5064. Ed. Robert Zeman. circ. 800. (back issues avail.) **Document type:** newsletter.

REIMBURSEMENT ADVISOR. see *HOSPITALS*

368 UK ISSN 0048-7171
HG8059.R4
REINSURANCE; the monthly international reinsurance magazine. 1969. m. £55. Buckley Press, 58 Fleet St., London EC4Y 1JU, England. TEL 071-353-4881. FAX 071-583-6069. Ed. V.J.F. Betson. adv.; charts; illus.; stat. Indexed: P.A.I.S. **Document type:** trade publication.
—BLDSC (7351.800000).

368 US ISSN 0747-5276
HG8083
REINSURANCE DIRECTORY; Bermuda, Canada, & the U.S.A. 1984. a. $95. Robert W. Strain Publishing & Seminars, Box 1520, Athens, TX 75751. TEL 914-677-5974. Ed. Robert W. Strain. adv.; index; circ. 1,000 (paid). **Document type:** directory.

368 US ISSN 1053-5934
REINSURANCE EDUCATOR. 1990. bi-m. $240. Reinsurance Educator, 10808 Des Moines Ave., Northridge, CA 91326. TEL 818-366-9826. Ed. Anthony Leonard. **Document type:** newsletter.

368 UK ISSN 0266-8653
REINSURANCE MARKET REPORT. 1983. fortn. £255($510) D Y P Insurance & Reinsurance Research Group Ltd., Bridge House, 181 Queen Victoria St., London EC4V 4DD, England. TEL 071-236-2175. FAX 071-489-1487. Ed. Julius S. Bannister. bk.rev.; charts; stat. (back issues avail.) **Document type:** newsletter.
  Description: Interprets key events that can affect the insurance business. Tracks all major professional reinsurers and brokers, featuring their results and activities.

368 US ISSN 0034-3641
REINSURANCE REPORTER. 1958. q. free. Lincoln National Reinsurance Cos., One Reinsurance Plaza, P.O. Box 7808, Fort Wayne, IN 46801. FAX 219-455-2738. Ed. Barbara A. Wachtman. adv.; charts; illus.; stat. circ. 3,500.

368 GW ISSN 0340-5753
DIE RENTENVERSICHERUNG. 1959. m. DM.80. Asgard-Verlag Dr. Werner Hippe KG, Einsteinstr. 10, 53757 St. Augustin, Germany. TEL 02241-3164-0. Ed. W. Hippe. adv.; bk.rev.; bibl. circ. 1,000.

RESIDENTIAL BUILDING COST GUIDE (YEAR). see *BUILDING AND CONSTRUCTION*

368 340 US
RESPONSIBILITIES OF INSURANCE AGENTS AND BROKERS. 1974. s-a. $640. Matthew Bender & Co., Inc., 11 Penn Plaza, New York, NY 10001. TEL 212-967-7707. (Subscr. to: 1275 Broadway, Box 989, Albany, NY 12201) Ed. Bertram Harnett. index, cum.index: 1974-1988. circ. 1,683.
  Description: Updates to comprehensive treatises on insurance agency law.

368 UK ISSN 0034-6349
HG8013
REVIEW: WORLDWIDE REINSURANCE. 1869. m. £95 (foreign £115). E M A P Business Publishing, 33-39 Bowling Green Ln., London EC1R 0DA, England. TEL 071-837-1212. Ed. Nick Morgan. adv.; charts; stat.; index. **Document type:** trade publication.

REVISTA DE TRABAJO Y SEGURIDAD SOCIAL. see *BUSINESS AND ECONOMICS — Labor And Industrial Relations*

INSURANCE

368   CK   ISSN 0120-1972
REVISTA FASECOLDA. 1977. bi-m. $35. Union de Aseguradores Colombianos, Carrera 7a. No. 26-20, Piso. 11, Apdo. Aereo 5233, Bogota, Colombia. circ. 1,000.
   Incorporates (1977-1992): Informativo Tecnico; Which was formerly: Informativo Fasecolda (ISSN 0120-1921); Formerly: Fasecolda.

368   FR   ISSN 1146-6316
REVUE DU COURTAGE. 1923. m. 320 F. Federation Francaise des Courtiers d'Assurances et de Reassurances, 31 rue d'Amsterdam, 75008 Paris, France. TEL 33-1-48-74-19-12. FAX 42-82-91-10. Ed. Alain Farshian. adv.; bk.rev.; bibl.; illus.; index. circ. 2,000.
   Former titles: Revue l'Assureur Conseil; Assureur Counseil (ISSN 0004-6043)
   Description: Deals with insurance, security and prevention, risk management, pensions, law and cases, international relations, insurance companies and products, broking.

368   FR   ISSN 0035-3167
REVUE GENERALE DES ASSURANCES TERRESTRES. 1930. q. 600 F. (foreign 630 F.). (Librairie Generale de Droit et de Jurisprudence) Editions Juridiques Associees, 26 rue Vercingetorix, 75014 Paris, France. TEL 1-43-35-01-67. FAX 43-20-07-42. TELEX EJA 203 918 F. Ed. Jean Bigot. bk.rev. circ. 1,350.
   —BLDSC (7905.600000); SWETS. **CCC.**
   Description: Presents articles, chronicles, miscellanea and jurisprudence of insurance.

368   US
RIMSCOPE. 24/yr. membership. Risk & Insurance Management Society, Inc., 205 E. 42nd St., New York, NY 10017. TEL 212-286-9292. FAX 212-986-9716. Ed. Thomas Johnson. circ. 8,000. **Document type:** newsletter.
   Description: Covers property, casualty and liability insurance, risk management and employee benefits issues of interest to members.

368   US
RISK AND BENEFITS JOURNAL. 1991. bi-m. Curant Communications, Inc., 1849 Sawtelle Blvd., Ste. 770, Los Angeles, CA 90025. TEL 213-479-1769. FAX 213-479-6275. adv. circ. 14,000.
   Description: Includes case histories, features, industry news, legislative information and pragmatic information for risk and benefits managers.

368   US   ISSN 1050-9232
HG8054.5
RISK & INSURANCE. 1990. m. Axon Group, 747 Dresher Rd., Ste. 500, Box 980, Horsham, PA 19044. TEL 215-784-0860. FAX 215-784-0870. Ed. Linda Wasserman. circ. 43,000. (tabloid format) **Document type:** trade publication.
   —CCC.
   Description: For insurance industry executives and risk and insurance managers at corporations, nonprofit institutions and government agencies. Covers professional liability, environmental liability, captive administration, health benefits and workers' compensation.

368   US
RISK FINANCING. 1983. q. $204. International Risk Management Institute, Inc., 12222 Merit Dr., Ste. 1660, Dallas, TX 75251-2217. TEL 214-960-7693. FAX 214-960-6037. Ed. Bob Bregman. (looseleaf format)
   Description: Explores variations in risk funding approaches to workers compensation and liability insurance. Gives tax and accounting ramifications of each type of plan.

368   US   ISSN 0035-5593
HG8059.C7   CODEN: RMGTDN
RISK MANAGEMENT. 1954. 12/yr. $48. (Risk and Insurance Management Society) Risk Management Society Publishing, Inc., 205 E. 42nd St., New York, NY 10017. TEL 212-986-9364. FAX 212-986-9716. TELEX 968289. Ed. Alice Oshins. adv.; bk.rev.; charts; mkt.; index. circ. 10,700. (also avail. in microfilm from UMI; reprint service avail. from UMI; back issues avail.) **Indexed:** ABI Inform., Account.Ind. (1974-), BPIA, Bus.Ind., Hlth.Ind., Manage.Cont., PROMT, Sci.Abstr., Tr.& Indus.Ind. **Document type:** trade publication.
   ●Also available on CD-ROM.
   —BLDSC (7972.600000); Faxon; UnCover; UMI.
   Formerly: National Insurance Buyer.
   Description: Official publication of the Risk and Insurance Management Society with how-to and interpretive articles relating to risk analysis and funding techniques, safety and loss prevention, employee benefits planning, and federal/state legislative and regulatory developments.

368   US   ISSN 0732-2666
RISK MANAGEMENT FOR EXECUTIVE WOMEN. 1982-1985; resumed 1990. m. $100 (effective Jan. 1994). Cox Publications, Box 20316, Billings, MT 59104-0316. TEL 406-256-8822. Ed. Meridith B. Cox. circ. 470 (controlled). **Document type:** trade publication.
   Formerly (until 1983): California Risk Management Report: For the Female Executive.
   Description: Reports on court decisions affecting insurance, personnel, health records and safety issues which expand liability or set up new areas of risk.

368   US
RISK MANAGEMENT NEWS AND REVIEW. fortn. $397. Merritt Company, 1661 Ninth St., Box 955, Santa Monica, CA 90406. TEL 310-450-7234. FAX 310-396-4563. Ed. James Walsh. **Document type:** newsletter, trade publication.
   Formerly: Risk Management Newsletter (ISSN 0740-1396)

368   US   ISSN 0199-6827
RISK MANAGEMENT REPORTS. (Included (1974-1980): Captive Insurance Company Directory (ISSN 0199-6827)) 1974. bi-m. Seawrack, 61 Ealy's Ferry Rd., Lyme, CT 06371. TEL 203-434-2917. FAX 203-434-3917. **Document type:** trade publication.

RISK MANAGER LAW BULLETIN. see LAW — Corporate Law

368   US
RISK REPORT. 1978. m. $149. International Risk Management Institute, Inc., 12222 Merit Dr., Ste. 1660, Dallas, TX 75251-2217. TEL 214-960-7693. FAX 214-960-6037. Ed. Jack P. Gibson.
   Description: Detailed articles explore property insurance, casualty insurance and risk managment topics.

368   US   ISSN 1063-357X
RISK RETENTION REPORTER. 1987. m. $245 (foreign $265) (effective 1993). Insurance Communications, Box 50147, Pasadena, CA 91115. TEL 818-796-4972. FAX 818-796-2363. Ed. Karen Cutts.
   Description: Covers liability insurance concerns.

368   UK   ISSN 0952-1984
RISK UPDATE. 1987. m. £185($370) D Y P Insurance & Reinsurance Group Ltd., Bridge House, 181 Queen Victoria St., London EC4V 4DD, England. TEL 071-236-2175. FAX 071-489-1487. Ed. Julius S. Bannister. **Document type:** newsletter.
   Description: Provides clear technical detail on risk management and loss prevention.

368 450   US
RISKWATCH. 1985. m. $125. Public Risk Management Association, 1117 N. 19th St., Ste. 900, Arlington, VA 22209. TEL 703-528-7701. FAX 703-528-7966. Ed. Kathleen M. Rakestraw. circ. 2,500. **Document type:** newsletter.
   Description: A current events watchdog for public sector risk managers.

368   US   ISSN 0035-8525
HG8011
ROUGH NOTES; property, casualty, surety. 1878. m. $25 (foreign $35). Rough Notes Co., Inc., 1200 N. Meridian, Box 564, Indianapolis, IN 46206. TEL 800-428-4384. FAX 317-634-1041. Ed. Thomas McCoy. adv.; bk.rev.; illus.; index. circ. 40,000. **Indexed:** ABI Inform.
   —BLDSC (8025.750000); Faxon; UnCover; UMI.

368   US
ROUND THE TABLE. 1973. bi-m. $10. Million Dollar Round Table, 325 Touhy, Park Ridge, IL 60068. TEL 708-692-6378. FAX 708-518-8921. Ed. Mary Kay Ams. bk.rev.; charts; illus.; tr.lit. circ. 21,000. (back issues avail.) **Indexed:** L.I.I.
   Description: Contains sales ideas and organizational information for life underwriters.

368   UK
ROYAL INSURANCE NEWSLETTER. m. Royal Insurance, P.O. Box 144, New Hall Place, Liverpool L69 3EN, England. Ed. Bill Curran. **Document type:** newsletter.

368   GW
DER RUNDE TISCH. 1956. bi-m. Vereinte Versicherungen, 80291 Munich, Germany. TEL 089-67852152. FAX 089-67852158. illus. **Document type:** bulletin.

368.4   US   ISSN 1073-1407
S S I RECIPIENTS BY STATE AND COUNTY (YEAR). (Social Security Insurance) a. U.S. Social Security Administration, Office of Research and Statistics, Publications Staff, Van Ness Center, Rm. 209, 4301 Connecticut Ave., N.W., Washington, DC 20008. TEL 202-282-7161. FAX 202-282-7219. (Subscr. to: Superintendent of Documents, U.S. Government Printing Office, Box 371954, Pittsburgh, PA 15250-7954. TEL 202-783-3238. FAX 202-512-2233) charts; stat. **Document type:** government publication.
   Description: Presents statistical data on the distribution of federally administered Social Security payments to the elderly and disabled children and adults by state and county.

368   US   ISSN 0036-2409
SAFECO AGENT. 1923. bi-m. free. (Safeco Insurance Companies) Safeco Corporation, Safeco Plaza, Seattle, WA 98185. TEL 206-545-6009. Ed. Dan Pedersen. adv.; charts; illus.; stat.; circ. 11,000 (controlled). **Document type:** trade publication.

ST. ANTHONY'S CODING FOR GENERAL SURGERY REIMBURSEMENT. see MEDICAL SCIENCES — Surgery

ST. ANTHONY'S CODING FOR OPHTHALMOLOGY REIMBURSEMENT. see MEDICAL SCIENCES — Ophthalmology And Optometry

368   US   ISSN 0036-3669
SALVAGE BIDS. 1963. fortn. $410. John B. Tamke, Ed. & Pub., Box 5, Laconia, NH 03246. TEL 603-528-3039. FAX 603-366-5734. charts; tr.lit. circ. 1,322. (looseleaf format)
   Description: Compilation of major industrial actions worldwide.

368.3   CN
HD7102.C22
SASKATCHEWAN HEALTH. ANNUAL REPORT. (Supplements avail.: Saskatchewan Health. Mental Health Service Branch; Saskatchewan Health. Medical Care Insurance Branch; Saskatchewan Health. Labor and Distribution Control Branch; Saskatchewan Health. Community Health - Preventitive Service Branch; Saskatchewan Health. Hospital Service Branch; Saskatchewan Health. Continuing Care Branch; Saskatchewan Health. Prescription Drug Service Branch; Saskatchewan Health. Vital Statistics Branch.) 1962. a. free. Medical Care Insurance Branch, T.C. Douglas Bldg., 3475 Albert St., Regina, Sask. S4S 6X6, Canada. TEL 306-787-3475. FAX 306-787-9000. circ. 2,500. **Document type:** corporate report.
   Incorporates: Saskatchewan Health. Medical Care Insurance Branch. Annual Report; Which was formerly: Saskatchewan. Medical Care Insurance Commission. Annual Report (ISSN 0080-6544)

368   UK   ISSN 0308-1729
SAVINGS MARKET. 1976. q. £2. United Trade Press Ltd., U.T.P. House, 33-35 Bowling Green Lane, London EC1R 0DA, England. TEL 01-837 1212. Ed. Mike Hockings.

INSURANCE

368.01 NO ISSN 0346-1238
HG8751 CODEN: SAJODI
SCANDINAVIAN ACTUARIAL JOURNAL. (Supplements avail.) (Text in English) 1918. s-a. NOK 385 in the Nordic countries; elsewhere NOK 405. (Scandinavian Societies of Actuaries) Scandinavian University Press, P.O. Box 2959 Toeyen, N-0608 Oslo, Norway. TEL 472-67-7600. FAX 472-67-7575. (U.S. addr.: Scandinavian University Press, 200 Meacham Ave., Elmont, NY11003. TEL 516-352-7300) Ed.Bd. adv.; bk.rev. circ. 1,500. (tabloid format) **Indexed:** Comput.Abstr., J.Cont.Quant.Meth., Math.R.
—BLDSC (8087.468000); Faxon; SWETS.
Formerly: Skandinavisk Aktuarietidskrift (ISSN 0037-606X)
Description: Deals, in theory and application, with mathematical methods for insurance and related matters.

368 SZ
SCHWEIZER VERSICHERUNG; Magazin fuer Fuehrungskraefte aus der Versicherungswirtschaft. 1988. 6/yr. 54 SFr. (foreign 68 SFr.). S H Z Fachverlag AG, Alte Landstr. 43, CH-8700 Kuesnacht, Switzerland. TEL 01-9108022. FAX 01-9105155. circ. 10,000. **Document type:** trade publication.

368 SZ ISSN 0042-3815
SCHWEIZERISCHE VEREINIGUNG DER VERSICHERUNGSMATHEMATIKER. MITTEILUNGEN. (Text and summaries in English, French and German) 1901. s-a. 160 SFr.($105) Staempfli und Cie AG, Hallerstr. 7-9, CH-3001 Bern, Switzerland. TEL 031-276666. FAX 031-3006688. Ed. Hans Buehlman. bk.rev. **Document type:** bulletin.
—CCC.

368 SZ
SCHWEIZERISCHE VERSICHERUNGSZEITSCHRIFT/REVUE SUISSE D'ASSURANCES. (Text in French and German) 1933. bi-m. 84 SFr. (foreign 92 SFr.). Verlag Peter Lang AG, Jupiterstr. 15, CH-3000 Bern 15, Switzerland. TEL 031-9411122. FAX 031-9411131. TELEX 912651-PELA-CH. Ed.Bd. adv.; B&W page 660 SFr.; trim 170 x 240. bk.rev.; bibl.; index. circ. 2,000. **Indexed:** World Bibl.Soc.Sec. **Document type:** trade publication.

368 SZ
SCHWEIZERISCHER VERSICHERUNGS KURIER. bi-m. Aumattweg 10, CH-3032 Hinterklappen, Switzerland. Ed. R. Schaer. circ. 3,300.

SECURE RETIREMENT. see *GERONTOLOGY AND GERIATRICS*

368.4 CK
SEGURIDAD SOCIAL. 1948. q. Instituto Colombiana de Seguros Sociales, Transversal 17, no. 25-39, Bogota, Colombia.

368.4 BO
SEGURIDAD SOCIAL. 1938. m. Caja Nacional de Seguridad Social, Casilla 697, Plaza Murillo, Esquina Ingavi, La Paz, Bolivia. bibl.
Formerly (1938-1954): Proteccion Social.

368 UY
SEGUROS. 1975. irreg. Banco de Seguros, Av. Libertador Brigadier General Juan A. Lavalleja No. 1465, Montevideo, Uruguay. illus.
Formerly: Bancoseguros.

368 CC
SHANDONG BAOXIAN/SHANDONG INSURANCE. (Text in Chinese) m. Shandong Sheng Baoxian Gongsi - Shandong Insurance Company, No. 4, Gongqingtuan Lu, Jinan, Shandong 250012, People's Republic of China. TEL 25103. Ed. Huang Shanhua.

368 CC
SHANGHAI BAOXIAN/SHANGHAI INSURANCE. (Text in Chinese) m. Zhongguo Renmin Baoxian Gongsi, Shanghai Fengongsi, Baoxian Yanjiusuo - China People's Insurance Company, Shanghai Branch, Insurance Research Institute, No.1, Alley 590, Room 101, Yuanping Nanlu, Shanghai 200030, People's Republic of China. TEL 4386301. Ed. Wu Yue.

SHEPARD'S INSURANCE LAW CITATIONS. see *LAW*

368.012 US
SHORTCUT. 1948. q. $720. National Underwriter Co., 505 Gest St., Cincinnati, OH 45203. TEL 513-721-2140. FAX 513-721-0126. adv. (also avail. in diskette format)
Formerly (until 1986): Agent's and Buyer's Guide (ISSN 0065-4272)
Description: Provides data on available markets for standard, excess and surplus insurance coverages on a state by state basis, as well as those markets with binding authority.

368 CC
SICHUAN BAOXIAN/SICHUAN INSURANCE. (Text in Chinese) bi-m. Zhongguo Renmin Baoxian Gongsi, Sichuan Fengongsi - China People's Insurance Company, Sichuan Branch, Baoxian Dalou, Donggan Dao, Chengdu, Sichuan 610016, People's Republic of China. TEL 25738. Ed. Zheng Zhenhua.

368 IT
SICURTA. 1945. m. L.12000. Nuova Mercurio S.p.A., Via S. Paolo 15, 20121 Milan, Italy. Ed. Luigi Giudice. adv. circ. 12,000.

368 SZ ISSN 0037-4857
SIGMA. Issued with: Experiodica (ISSN 0014-4932) (Editions in English, French, German, Italian) 1958. irreg. (6-7/yr.) free. Schweizerische Rueckversicherungs-Gesellschaft - Swiss Reinsurance Company, Economic Department, Mythenquai 50-60, CH-8022 Zurich, Switzerland. TEL 01-2852551. FAX 01-2852999. TELEX 815722-SRE-CH. charts; stat. **Document type:** newsletter.
Description: Studies of problems concerning the economics and insurance fields.

368 MX
SINTESIS EMPRESARIAL DEL SECTOR ASEGURADOR. q. Comision Nacional de Seguros y Fianzas, Av. de los Insurgentes Sur 1971, Plaza Inn, Torre 2 N., 2o piso, 01020 Mexico DF, Mexico. **Document type:** government publication.
Description: Presents information on the insurance companies, their classification by level, including financial statements, direct premiums issue and financial ratios.

368.4 US
▼**SMART'S CALIFORNIA WORKERS' COMP BULLETIN.** 1992. 50/yr. $195. Smart's Publishing Group, 1 Waters Park Dr., Ste. 104, San Mateo, CA 94403. TEL 415-341-2432. FAX 415-341-3304. Ed. Fred Pilot. circ. 250. **Document type:** newsletter.
Formerly: Smart's Insurance Bulletin: Workers' Compensation Edition.
Description: Focuses on California workers' compensation developments.

368 US ISSN 0736-8348
SMART'S INSURANCE BULLETIN. 1956. 50/yr. $245. Smart's Publishing Group, 1 Waters Park Dr., No.104, San Mateo, CA 94403-1137. TEL 415-982-1480. FAX 415-982-3504. Ed. Fred Pilot. charts; stat.; tr.lit.; q. index. circ. 1,000. (looseleaf format) **Document type:** newsletter.
—CCC.
Description: Contains California legislative, regulatory, judicial news and opinion relating to insurance.

368.4 IS
SOCIAL SECURITY; journal of welfare and social security studies. (Text in Hebrew; summaries in English) 1971. s-a. IS.30. National Insurance Institute, 13 Sderot Weizman, Jerusalem, Israel. Ed.Bd. bibl.; cum.index. circ. 500. (tabloid format; back issues avail.) **Indexed:** Ind.Heb.Per., World Bibl.Soc.Sec. **Document type:** academic/scholarly publication.
Description: Discusses contemporary social security problems from sociological, economic and legal perspectives.

368.4 US ISSN 0037-7910
HD7123 CODEN: SSYBA
SOCIAL SECURITY BULLETIN. 1937. q. (plus a. supplement). $13 (foreign $16.25) (includes q. and a. supplements). U.S. Social Security Administration, Office of Research and Statistics, Publications Staff, Van Ness Center, Rm. 209, 4301 Connecticut Ave., N.W., Washington, DC 20008. TEL 202-282-7161. FAX 202-282-7219. (Subscr. to: Superintendent of Documents, U.S. Government Printing Office, Box 371954, Pittsburgh, PA 15250-7954. TEL 202-783-3238. FAX 202-512-2233) Ed. Marilyn R. Thomas. adv.; bk.rev.; bibl.; charts; stat.; index, cum.index: 1938-1979, 1980-1988. (also avail. in microform from MIM,UMI,PMC; microfiche from CIS; reprint service avail. from CIS,UMI) **Indexed:** ABI Inform., Abstr.Soc.Geront., Amer.Stat.Ind. (1973-), ASCA, B.P.I., Bus.Ind., C.L.I., CLOA, Excerp.Med., Ind.Med., Ind.U.S.Gov.Per., J.of Econ.Lit., L.I.I., L.R.I., Leg.Per., Med.Care Rev., MEDOC, P.A.I.S., Pers.Lit., PROMT, Rehabil.Lit., Soc.Work Res.& Abstr., SSCI, Tr.& Indus.Ind., Work Rel.Abstr., World Bibl.Soc.Sec. **Document type:** government publication.
●Also available online. Vendor(s): DIALOG Information Services, Inc.
—BLDSC (8318.195100); Faxon; UnCover; SWETS; UMI.
Description: Presents the results of the agency's research and statistics program with subjects including the economic status of the aged, the disability program, and overviews of the nation's income-security system.

368 SZ ISSN 0379-704X
SOCIAL SECURITY DOCUMENTATION: AFRICAN SERIES. 1977. irreg. 15 SFr. per no. International Social Security Association, Case Postale 1, CH-1211 Geneva 22, Switzerland. FAX 022-7986385. **Indexed:** Int.Lab.Doc. **Document type:** monographic series.
—BLDSC (8318.195500).
Description: Includes reports of regional conferences, round tables and study groups, as well as articles and studies on regional problems.

368 SZ ISSN 0250-4057
SOCIAL SECURITY DOCUMENTATION: ASIAN SERIES. 1979. irreg. 15 SFr. per no. International Social Security Association, Case Postale 1, CH-1211 Geneva 22, Switzerland. FAX 022-7986385. **Document type:** monographic series.
Description: Includes reports of regional conferences, round tables and other meetings, as well as studies on problems specific to the region.

368 SZ
SOCIAL SECURITY DOCUMENTATION: EUROPEAN SERIES. (Editions in English, French, German, Spanish) 1979. irreg. 20 SFr. per no. International Social Security Association, Case Postale 1, CH-1211 Geneva 22, Switzerland. FAX 022-7986385. **Indexed:** World Agri.Econ.& Rural Sociol.Abstr. **Document type:** monographic series.
Description: Studies and reports of meetings concerning aspects of social security which are of special interest to industrialized countries.

368.4 US
SOCIAL SECURITY LAW & PRACTICE. 9 base vols. (plus q. updates). $1025. Clark - Boardman - Callaghan Company Ltd., 375 Hudson St., New York, NY 10014. TEL 212-929-7500; 800-221-9428. FAX 212-924-0460. (looseleaf format)
Description: Offers analysis of social security law, citing controlling cases and pertinent statutory provisions, regulations, rulings, and agency manuals.

368.4 US
SOCIAL SECURITY LAW & PRACTICE NEWSLETTER. 8/yr. Clark - Boardman - Callaghan Company Ltd., 375 Hudson St., New York, NY 10014. TEL 212-929-7500; 800-221-9428. FAX 212-924-0460. **Document type:** newsletter.

360 UK
SOCIAL SECURITY LIBRARY BULLETIN. 1971. m. £9. Departments of Health and Social Security, Adelphi, 1-11, John Adam St., London WC2N 6HT, England. (Subscr. to: D H Publications Unit, No. 2 Site, Manchester Rd., Heywood, Lancs. OL10 2PZ, England) Ed. Lynwen John. circ. 800. **Indexed:** L.R.I. **Document type:** abstracting/indexing, government publication.
Formerly: Current Literature on Social Security.

INSURANCE

368 US
SOCIAL SECURITY MANUAL. a. $11.95. National Underwriter Co., 505 Gest St., Cincinnati, OH 45203. TEL 513-721-2140. FAX 513-721-0126.
Description: Guide providing explanations of rules and rights under Social Security in a question and answer format.

368.4 US
SOCIAL SECURITY PRACTICE GUIDE. (Issued in 4 base vols. with supplements) 1984. irreg. $750. Matthew Bender & Co., Inc., 11 Penn Plaza, New York, NY 10001. TEL 212-967-7707. (looseleaf format)
Description: Comprehensive information on understanding Social Security regulations pertaining to the standards used in evaluating medical and vocational aspects of disability claims.

368.4 US
SOCIAL SECURITY RULINGS, ACQUIESCENCE RULINGS ON FEDERAL OLD-AGE, SURVIVORS, DISABILITY, SUPPLEMENTAL SECURITY INCOME AND BLACK LUNG BENEFITS. 1961. q. (plus annual cum.). $9.50. U.S. Social Security Administration, 6401 Security Blvd., Baltimore, MD 21235. TEL 202-953-3600. (Subscr. to: Superintendent of Documents, U.S. Government Printing Office, Box 371954, Pittsburgh, PA 15250-7954. TEL 202-783-3238. FAX 202-512-2233) **Document type:** government publication.
Former titles (until 1987): Social Security Rulings on Federal Old-Age, Survivors, Disability, Supplemental Security Income and Black Lung Benefits; Social Security Rulings on Federal Old-Age, Survivors, Disability and Health Insurance, Supplemental Security Income and Miners Benefits.

368 DK ISSN 0107-5047
SOCIALE YDELSER, HVEM, HVAD, OG HVORNAAR; en kort oversigt over Danmarks sociale lovgivning med regler og ydelser. 1968. a. DKK 30. (Forsikringsoplysningen) Forlaget Forsikring, Amaliegade 10, DK-1256 Copenhagen K, Denmark. TEL 45-33-13-75-55. FAX 45-33-11-23-53. illus. **Document type:** consumer publication.

SOCIALNA POLITIKA. see *SOCIAL SCIENCES: COMPREHENSIVE WORKS*

SOCIETA LOMBARDA DI MEDICINA LEGALE E DELLE ASSICURAZIONI. ARCHIVIO. see *MEDICAL SCIENCES — Forensic Sciences*

368 US
SOCIETY OF ACTUARIES. RECORD. 1975. q. $60 (foreign $90)(effective 1991). Society of Actuaries, 475 N. Martingale, No. 800, Schaumburg, IL 60173-2226. TEL 708-706-3500. FAX 708-706-3599. Ed. James G. Cochran. circ. 14,000.
Description: Contains the proceedings of spring and annual meetings of the SOA, including session discussions.

368 US ISSN 0037-9794
HG8754
SOCIETY OF ACTUARIES. TRANSACTIONS (GENERAL). 1949. a. $55 (foreign $82.50). Society of Actuaries, 475 N. Martingale, Ste. 800, Schaumburg, IL 60173-2226. TEL 708-706-3500. FAX 708-706-3599. Ed. Jerry Enoch. bk.rev.; abstr.; bibl.; charts; index, cum.index every 5 yrs. circ. 14,000. (also avail. in microform from UMI) **Indexed:** L.I.I.
Description: Prosents formal and scholarly papers contributed by SOA members.
Refereed Serial

368 US
SOCIETY OF ACTUARIES. TRANSACTIONS: REPORTS OF MORTALITY AND MORBIDITY EXPERIENCE. 1951. a. $50 (foreign $75)(effective 1991). Society of Actuaries, 475 N. Martingale, Ste. 800, Schaumburg, IL 60173-2226. TEL 708-706-3500. FAX 708-706-3599. charts; index. circ. 14,000.
Description: Presents the results of experience studies.

368 US
SOCIETY OF ACTUARIES. YEARBOOK. 1950. a. $25 (foreign $37) (effective 1991). Society of Actuaries, 475 N. Martingale, Ste. 800, Schaumburg, IL 60173-2226. TEL 708-706-3500. FAX 708-706-3599. Ed. Barbara A. Simmons. index. circ. 14,000.
Description: Lists officers, committees, members, constitution and by-laws, and other items of insterest to SOA members.

368 US ISSN 0162-2706
HG8011
SOCIETY OF CHARTERED PROPERTY AND CASUALTY UNDERWRITERS. JOURNAL. Short title: C P C U Journal. 1949. q. $20 (foreign $25). Society of Chartered Property & Casualty Underwriters, Box 3009, 720 Providence Rd., Malvern, PA 19355. TEL 215-251-2743. adv.; bk.rev.; charts; stat.; index. circ. 25,000. **Indexed:** ABI Inform., BPIA, P.L.I.I. **Document type:** trade publication.
—BLDSC (3486.190000); Faxon; UnCover; UMI.
Formerly: Society of Chartered Property and Casualty Underwriters. Annals (ISSN 0037-9824)

368 US ISSN 0038-0075
SOCIETY PAGE. (Former name of issuing body: American Society of Chartered Life Underwriters) 1961. bi-m. membership. American Society of C L U & Ch F C, 270 Bryn Mawr Ave., Bryn Mawr, PA 19010. TEL 215-526-2500. Ed. Carl L. Hall, Jr. charts; illus.; stat. circ. 35,000. **Document type:** trade publication.

SOSIAL TRYGD. see *SOCIAL SERVICES AND WELFARE*

368.38 US ISSN 0073-148X
HG9396
SOURCE BOOK OF HEALTH INSURANCE DATA. 1959. a. single copy free. Health Insurance Association of America, 1025 Connecticut Ave., N.W., Washington, DC 20036-3998. index. circ. 45,000. (also avail. in microfiche from CIS) **Indexed:** SRI.

368.4 331.2 SA
SOUTH AFRICA. UNEMPLOYMENT INSURANCE FUND. REPORT/SOUTH AFRICA. WERKLOOSHEIDVERSEKERINGSFONDS. VERSLAG. (Text in Afrikaans, English) a. R.1. Unemployment Insurance Fund, Box 1851, Pretoria 0001, South Africa. **Document type:** government publication.
Description: Report of the Unemployment Insurance Fund consisting of the balance sheet and income and expenditure accounts for the year.

SOUTH TEXAS INSURANCE DIRECTORY. see *BUSINESS AND ECONOMICS — Trade And Industrial Directories*

368 US
SOUTHERN INSURANCE. m. Chase Communications, Box 9001, Mt. Vernon, NY 10552-9001. TEL 212-320-2727. FAX 914-699-2025. Ed. Stephen Acunto. circ. 3,400.

368 GW ISSN 0038-6057
SOZIALE SELBSTVERWALTUNG; Informationsdienst fuer Mitglieder der Selbstverwaltung in der Sozialversicherung. 1953. m. DM.30.60. (Bundesvereinigung der Deutschen Arbeitgeberverbaende e.V.) Heider Verlag GmbH, Postfach 200540, 51435 Bergisch Gladbach, Germany. TEL 02202-53047. FAX 02202-21531. Eds. J. Husmann, E. Mueller. adv.; bk.rev. circ. 5,400. **Document type:** bulletin.
—CCC.

368.43 AU ISSN 0038-6065
HD7090
SOZIALE SICHERHEIT; Fachzeitschrift fuer die Oesterreichische Sozialversicherung. 1948. m. S.298.50. Hauptverband der Oesterreichischen Sozialversicherungstraeger, Kundmanngasse 21, A-1030 Vienna 3, Austria. TEL 0222-71132. FAX 0222-71132-3777. Ed. Ralph Mace. adv.; bk.rev.; charts; illus.; stat.; index, cum.index. circ. 7,500. **Indexed:** World Bibl.Soc.Sec. **Document type:** government publication.
Description: Covers social insurance in Austria.

368 UK ISSN 0957-0063
SPACE INSURANCE REPORT. 1989. m. £255($510) D Y P Insurance & Reinsurance Research Group Ltd., Bridge House, 181 Queen Victoria St., London EC4V 4DD, England. TEL 071-236-2175. FAX 071-489-1487. Ed. Julius S. Bannister. charts; stat. **Document type:** newsletter.
Description: Keeps underwriters and brokers fully informed of developments in the space insurance market segment. Explains the intricacies of space hardware.

SPAIN. MINISTERIO DE TRABAJO Y SEGURIDAD SOCIAL. BOLETIN; jurisprudencia laboral y de seguridad social. see *BUSINESS AND ECONOMICS — Labor And Industrial Relations*

368.3 US
SPECIALTY COVERAGE MARKET REPORTS. m. $70. Rough Notes Co., Inc., 1200 N. Meridian, Indianapolis, IN 46204. TEL 317-634-1541. FAX 317-634-1041. Ed. Wallace Clapp. circ. 1,000. (looseleaf format) **Document type:** bulletin.

368 UK ISSN 0038-8637
SPRINKLER BULLETIN. 1892. every 6-9 mos. Mather and Platt Ltd., Park Works, Manchester M10 6BA, England. Ed. M.L.A. Jones. charts; illus.; stat.; circ. 10,000. (controlled).

368 US ISSN 0038-9390
HG9651
THE STANDARD (BOSTON); New England's insurance weekly. 1865. w. $35. Standard Publishing Corp., 155 Federal St., Boston, MA 02110-1727. TEL 617-457-0604. FAX 617-482-7820. Ed. Frank R. Pote, Jr. adv. contact: Barbara Crockett. bk.rev.; illus.; stat.; index; circ. 5,675 (paid). (also avail. in microform from UMI; back issues avail.; reprint service avail. from UMI) **Indexed:** P.L.I.I. **Document type:** trade publication.
—UMI.
Description: Covers legislative, regulatory hearings, court cases, insurance meetings, and conventions geared toward those who sell insurance products.

368 US
STANDARD'S SUMMARY LIFE REPORT AND RATIO ANALYSIS.* 1988. a. $5. Standard Analytical Services, Inc., 5960 Howdershell Rd., Ste. 101, Hazelwood, MO 63042-1115. TEL 314-727-5151. FAX 314-727-4167. Ed. John B. LaMacchia, Jr.
Description: Reports on individual insurance companies featuring financial information compared with that of the 25 largest companies.

368 US
STANDARD'S SUMMARY REPRODUCTIONS.* 1988. a. $5. Standard Analytical Services, Inc., 5960 Howdershell Rd., Ste. 101, Hazelwood, MO 63042-1115. TEL 314-727-5151. Ed. John B. LaMacchia, Jr.
Description: Financial summary sheets from annual statements of insurance companies, showing the financial conditions of individual companies.

368.4 US ISSN 0099-2100
HD7102.U5
STATE HEALTH BENEFITS PROGRAM OF NEW JERSEY. ANNUAL REPORT.* a. Department of the Treasury, Division of Pensions, State House, 1st Fl., CN 002, Trenton, NJ 08625. TEL 609-292-7060.

368 BE
STATUT SOCIAL DES TRAVAILLEURS INDEPENDANTS. Flemish edition: Sociaal Statuut der Zelfstandigen. (Text in French) a. 300 BEF (effective 1993). Institut National d'Assurances Sociales pour Travailleurs Independants, Bibliotheque - Bureau 4-7 (Wat.), Place Jean Jacobs, 6, B-1000 Brussels, Belgium. TEL 32-2-507-6211. FAX 32-2-511-2153. **Document type:** government publication.

INSURANCE

368   CN   ISSN 0380-223X
HG9783
STONE AND COX GENERAL INSURANCE REGISTER. 1920. a. Can.$34. Stone and Cox Ltd., 111 Peter St., Suite 202, Toronto, Ont. M5V 2H1, Canada. TEL 416-599-0772. FAX 416-599-0867. Ed. John D. Wyndham. adv. circ. 4,230. **Document type:** directory.
  Formerly: Stone and Cox General Insurance Year Book (ISSN 0081-5772)
  Description: Directory of property-casualty services in Canada: companies and management groups, adjusters, appraisers, legal counsel, brokers and agents, includes financial supplement.

368.3   CN   ISSN 0835-2933
STONE AND COX LIFE INSURANCE TABLES. (Text in English, French) 1912. a. Can.$27.50. Stone and Cox Ltd., 111 Peter St., Suite 202, Toronto, Ont. M5V 2H1, Canada. TEL 416-599-0772. FAX 416-599-0867. Ed. John D. Wyndham. adv. circ. 3,700.
  Description: Life insurance rates, values, dividends and special features of plans for the top 60 writers of individual life insurance in Canada.

368   UK
STONE AND COX ORDINARY BRANCH LIFE ASSURANCE HANDBOOK (AND UP-DATES). 1953. m. £60 including monthly up-date sheets. Stone and Cox (Publications) Ltd., 44 Fleet St., London EC4Y 1BS, England. TEL 01-353 1622. (Subscr. to: 73-75 Gammons Lane, Watford, Herts WD2 5HU, England) Ed. Ernest Holland. adv. (looseleaf format; back issues avail.) **Document type:** directory.
  Formerly: Stone and Cox Ordinary Branch Life Assurance Tables.
  Description: Covers nearly all UK and Irish life insurance offices.

368   UK
STONE AND COX UNIT LINKED LIFE ASSURANCE HANDBOOK (AND UP-DATES). 1970. m. £56 including monthly up-date sheets. Stone & Cox (Publications) Ltd., 44 Fleet St., London EC4Y 1BS, England. (Subscr. to: 73-75 Gammons Ln., Watford, Herts WD2 5HU, England) (looseleaf format) **Document type:** directory.
  Formerly: Stone and Cox Unit Linked Assurance and Annuity Tables.
  Description: Covers UK and Irish life insurance offices.

368   PL   ISSN 0137-9704
STUDIA UBEZPIECZENIOWE. (Text in Polish; summaries in English, Russian) 1973. irreg., vol.10, 1989. price varies. Polskie Towarzystwo Ekonomiczne, Oddzial w Poznaniu, Ul. Marchlewskiego 146-150, 60-957 Poznan, Poland. Ed. Tadeusz Sangowski. bibl.; illus.

STUDIES IN RISK AND UNCERTAINTY. see BUSINESS AND ECONOMICS — Economic Systems And Theories, Economic History

SUEDDEUTSCHE METALL-BERUFSGENOSSENSCHAFT. MITTEILUNGEN. see OCCUPATIONAL HEALTH AND SAFETY

368.3   JA
SUKOYAKA KENPO. (Text in Japanese) 1959. m. 780 Yen. National Federation of Health Insurance Societies, 1-24-4 Minami-Aoyama, Minato-ku, Tokyo, Japan. FAX 03-5410-2091. Ed. Tesuo Yagi. adv.; bk.rev.; film rev.; abstr.; bibl.; stat. circ. 7,200.
  Formerly: Kenko Hoken Shinbun (ISSN 0022-992X)

368   FI   ISSN 0356-7826
SUOMEN VAKUUTUSVUOSIKIRJA/FINNISH INSURANCE YEARBOOK. Swedish edition: Foersakringsaarsbok foer Finland (ISSN 0356-7834) (Text in Finnish, Swedish) 1912. a. FIM 235. Suomen Vakuutusyhdistys - Finnish Insurance Society, Bulevardi 28, 00120 Helsinki 12, Finland. FAX 358-0-68040235. adv.; stat. circ. 800 (Finnish ed.); 400 (Swedish ed.).

368   AT   ISSN 0729-3828
SUPERFUNDS. 1962. q. Aus.$66. (Association of Superannuation Funds of Australia) Rala Information Service Pty. Ltd., 203-205 Darling St., Balmain, N.S.W. 2041, Australia. (Subscr. to: Federal Secretary, ASFA, 8th Floor, 37 York St., Sydney, N.S.W. 2000, Aus) Ed.Bd. adv.; bk.rev.; index. circ. 2,400. Indexed: Aus.P.A.I.S.

368 333.33   CN
HG8550
SUPERINTENDENT OF INSURANCE ANNUAL REPORT. 1976. a. free. Alberta Consumer and Corporate Affairs, 10025 Jasper Ave., Edmonton, Alta. T5J 3Z5, Canada. TEL 403-422-1592. FAX 403-422-0775. stat. circ. 600. **Document type:** corporate report.
  Former titles: Alberta Insurance Report (ISSN 0229-7108); (until 1984): Alberta. Office of the Superintendent of Insurance and Real Estate. Annual Report (ISSN 0705-596X)

368   US
SURPLUS LINE REPORTER. 1978. m. $20. Reporter Publishing Co., Box 52193, New Orleans, LA 70152. TEL 504-366-8797. Ed. Carol DeGraw. circ. 3,100. (tabloid format; back issues avail.)

368   SW   ISSN 1102-1330
SVENSK FOERSAEKRING/SWEDISH INSURANCE; aarsbok. Variant title: Svensk Foersaekringsaarsbok. 1891. a. SEK 260. Svenska Foersaekringsfoereningen - Swedish Insurance Society, Sloejdgatan 9, S-115 87 Stockholm, Sweden. TEL 46-8-24-28-60. FAX 46-8-24-13-20. Ed. Tage Larsson. adv. circ. 1,600.
  Former titles (until 1986): Svensk Foersaekring-Aarsbok (ISSN 0081-9794); (until 1916): Meddelanden Angaaende Foersaekringsvaesendet i Sverige.

368.4   SW   ISSN 0082-0075
HA1521
SWEDEN. RIKSFOERSAEKRINGSVERKET. ALLMAEN FOERSAEKRING. (Text in Swedish; summaries in English) 1963. a. SEK 142. Riksfoersaekringsverket - National Social Insurance Board, S-103 51 Stockholm, Sweden. (Dist. by: Liber Foerlag, S-162 89 Stockholm, Sweden) circ. 1,200. **Document type:** government publication.

368   US
TARGET ARSON: UPDATE. m. q. Insurance Committee for Arson Control, 110 William St., 4th Fl., New York, NY 10038-3901. TEL 212-669-9245. Ed. Dahlia Wachs. circ. 1,500. **Document type:** newsletter.

368   US
TAX FACTS 1; taxation on life insurance. a. $15.95. National Underwriter Co., 505 Gest St., Cincinnati, OH 45203. TEL 513-721-2140. FAX 513-721-0126. (also avail. in microform from UMI) **Indexed:** L.I.I.
  Formerly: Tax Facts on Life Insurance (ISSN 0145-1847)
  Description: Provides answers to federal, income, estate and gift tax questions.

368   US
TENNESSEE AGENT. 1951. bi-m. $15. Professional Insurance Agents of Tennessee, 500 Wilson Pike Cir., No. 212, Brentwood, TN 37027-5252. Ed. Lochiel Gaines. adv.; bk.rev. circ. 800.

TENNESSEE INSURANCE DIRECTORY. see BUSINESS AND ECONOMICS — Trade And Industrial Directories

TEXAS INSURANCE LAW JOURNAL. see LAW

368   US
TEXAS INSUROR. 1923. bi-m. $20. Box 684488, Austin, TX 78767. TEL 512-476-6281. FAX 512-469-9512. Ed. Amy B. Wick. adv. contact: Evelyn Pankratz. circ. 4,000. **Document type:** trade publication.
  Description: Explores political, regulatory, and management issues of interest to independent property and casualty insurance agents.

368   US
TEXAS SURPLUS LINE REPORTER. 1984. m. $20. Reporter Publishing Co., Box 52193, New Orleans, LA 70152. TEL 504-366-8797. Ed. Carol DeGraw. circ. 5,100. (tabloid format; back issues avail.)
  Description: Local coverage of political and financial organizations.

368   US
TITLE MANAGEMENT TODAY; the independent newsmonthly for title company officers, managers, and counsel. 1991. m. $189. M. Lee Smith Publishers & Printers, 162 Fourth Ave. N., Box 2678, Nashville, TN 37219. Ed. Lewis Laska. (back issues avail.) **Document type:** trade publication.
  Description: Covers litigation, regulation, marketing, and management of title insurance offices.

368   US   ISSN 0892-4414
TODAY'S INSURANCE WOMAN. 1946. bi-m. $15. National Association of Insurance Women (International), 1847 E. 15th St., Box 4410, Tulsa, OK 74159. TEL 918-744-5195. FAX 914-743-1968. Ed. Stephanie Darling. adv.: B&W page $1200; trim 8 5/8 x 10 7/8; adv. contact: Denise Griggs. circ. 14,500 (paid). **Document type:** trade publication.
  Description: Articles focus on insurance industry issues as well as professional and personal development.

TOXIC TORTS; litigation of hazardous substance cases. see PUBLIC HEALTH AND SAFETY

TRAFFIC SAFETY SERIES. see TRANSPORTATION — Roads And Traffic

368   US   ISSN 0041-2384
TRENDS IN ADJUSTING. 1962. 3/yr. free to qualified personnel. Daynard & Van Thunen Co., Inc., 1 World Trade Center, Ste. 7967, New York, NY 10048. TEL 212-432-1100. Ed. William C. Van Thunen. bk.rev.; tr.lit. circ. 500. (processed) **Document type:** newsletter.

368   FR
TRESORERIE. 10/yr. 22 rue Chauchat, 75009 Paris, France. TEL 40-22-06-74. FAX 40-22-09-72. Ed. Herve Labrid. circ. 10,000.

368   FR   ISSN 0395-9406
TRIBUNE DE L'ASSURANCE. 1946. 14/yr. 790 F. La Tribune de l'Assurance, 39 rue de Trevise, 75009 Paris, France. TEL 1-48-01-01-10. FAX 1-48-01-04-35. Ed. Michel Goue. adv. contact: Aline Berard. bk.rev. circ. 12,000. **Document type:** trade publication.
  Description: Studies strategy and management of insurance companies, brokers and agents.

368   XN   ISSN 0041-3445
TRUDOV INVALID. (Text in Macedonian) vol.8, 1966. m. $2 din. per no. Sojuzot na Trudovite Invalidi na Makedonija, Marsala Tita, Box 437, Skopje, Macedonia. Ed. Blagoja Trajkovski.

368   AG
TUTORA. MEMORIA Y BALANCE GENERAL. no.13, 1975. a. Compania Sudamericana de Seguros, Rivadavia 717, Buenos Aires, Argentina.

368   NE   ISSN 0041-4581
TWEE N. 1937. m. free. Nationale-Nederlanden N.V., Johan de Wittlaan 3, Box 29701, 2502 LS The Hague, Netherlands. TEL 70-581726. Ed. Anneke Rijk. circ. 9,700.

U C A N S S. BULLETIN JURIDIQUE. (Union des Caisses Nationales de Securite Sociale) see LAW

368 331.8   US   ISSN 0041-5189
U L L I C O BULLETIN. 1938. q. membership. Union Labor Life Insurance Co., 111 Massachusetts Ave., N.W., Washington, DC 20001. TEL 202-682-4907. Ed. Doyle Niemann. illus. circ. 25,000. **Document type:** bulletin.

368   US
UMBRELLA ANALYZER. 1989. s-a. $698. International Risk Management Institute, Inc., 12222 Merit Dr., Ste. 1660, Dallas, TX 75251-2217. TEL 214-960-7693. FAX 214-960-6037. Eds. Maureen McLendon, Jack P. Gibson. (also avail. in diskette format)
  Description: In-depth coverage analysis of over 150 umbrella and excess coverage forms. Allows comparisons on screen of two umbrella/excess and up to 4 policies in printed form.

INSURANCE

368 US
UNDERWRITERS' HANDBOOK. a. $39.50. National Underwriter Co., 505 Gest St., Cincinnati, OH 45203. TEL 513-721-2140. FAX 513-721-0126.
   Description: Provides comprehensive information about the US domestic insurance market.

368.012 US ISSN 0041-6622
UNDERWRITERS' REPORT; the West's weekly insurance newsmagazine. 1905. w. $45 (foreign $80) (effective 1993). Underwriters' Report, Inc., 657 Mission St., San Francisco, CA 94105. TEL 415-896-2660. FAX 415-974-5041. Ed. Roy Pasini. adv.; charts; illus.; circ. 5,918 (paid). **Document type:** trade publication.
   —UMI.

UNEMPLOYMENT INSURANCE ACTUARIAL STUDY & FINANCIAL HANDBOOK (YEAR). see BUSINESS AND ECONOMICS — Labor And Industrial Relations

368.331 US
UNEMPLOYMENT INSURANCE REPORTS WITH SOCIAL SECURITY. 1934. w. $2025. Commerce Clearing House, Inc., 4025 W. Peterson Ave., Chicago, IL 60646. TEL 312-583-8500. Ed. J. Rooney. (looseleaf format)

UNITED CHURCH OF CHRIST. PENSION BOARDS (ANNUAL REPORT). see RELIGIONS AND THEOLOGY — Other Denominations And Sects

UNITED RETIREMENT BULLETIN. see GERONTOLOGY AND GERIATRICS

U.S. CHAMBER OF COMMERCE. ANALYSIS OF WORKERS' COMPENSATION LAWS. see BUSINESS AND ECONOMICS — Labor And Industrial Relations

U.S. DEPARTMENT OF HOUSING AND URBAN DEVELOPMENT. F H A HOME MORTGAGE INSURANCE OPERATIONS: STATE, COUNTY AND M S A - P M S A. (Federal Housing Administration) see HOUSING AND URBAN PLANNING

U.S. DEPARTMENT OF HOUSING AND URBAN DEVELOPMENT. F H A MONTHLY REPORT OF OPERATIONS. PROJECT INSURANCE PROGRAMS. (Federal Housing Administration) see HOUSING AND URBAN PLANNING

U.S. DEPARTMENT OF HOUSING AND URBAN DEVELOPMENT. F H A REPORT OF INSURANCE OPERATIONS UNDER HOME MORTGAGE PROGRAMS FOR (MONTH). (Federal Housing Administration) see HOUSING AND URBAN PLANNING

U.S. DEPARTMENT OF LABOR. EMPLOYEE RETIREMENT INCOME SECURITY ACT. REPORT TO CONGRESS. see BUSINESS AND ECONOMICS — Labor And Industrial Relations

332.17 368.85 US ISSN 0083-0658
U.S. FEDERAL DEPOSIT INSURANCE CORPORATION. ANNUAL REPORT. 1934. a. U.S. Federal Deposit Insurance Corporation, 550 17th St., N.W., Washington, DC 20429. TEL 202-393-8400.

U.S. VETERANS ADMINISTRATION. ANNUAL REPORT. see MILITARY

368 US
UPPER CASE. q. National Life Insurance Company of Vermont, Montpelier, VT 05604. TEL 802-229-3333. Ed. Jack Fehr. bk.rev.; charts; illus.; stat.; index; circ. 3,000 (controlled).
   Supersedes (until 1983): National Messenger (ISSN 0027-9714)
   Description: Geared toward Vermont's insurance agents. Includes articles and information on industry developments and issues.

368 332.6 US ISSN 1049-6173
V A R D S REPORT. (Variable Annuity Research & Data Service) 1988. m. $698. Financial Planning Resources, Inc., Box 1927, Roswell, GA 30077-1927. TEL 404-998-5186. FAX 404-998-5187. Ed. R.H. Rick Carey. circ. 500. **Document type:** academic/scholarly publication.
   ●Also available online.
   Description: Reports on essential elements of variable annuity analysis - investment performance and contract features, as well as the industry as a whole.

368 GW ISSN 0170-9690
V G A NACHRICHTEN. 1952. bi-m. DM.60. Bundesverband der Geschaeftsstellenleiter der Assekuranz, Kaiser-Wilhelm-Ring 15, 50672 Cologne, Germany. TEL 0221-527321. FAX 0221-523615. adv.; B&W page DM.1000; trim 171 x 250. bk.rev. circ. 1,500. (back issues avail.) **Document type:** newsletter.

368 NE ISSN 0923-6066
VADEMECUM VOOR HET VERZEKERINGSWEZEN. a. fl.343.50. Nijgh Periodieken B.V., Postbus 122, 3100 AC Schiedam, Netherlands. TEL 31-10-4274100. FAX 31-10-4739911. adv.: B&W page fl.1600, color page fl.3790; trim 148 x 210; adv. contact: Bert Niewold. circ. 1,500. **Document type:** directory.
   Formed by the merger of: Vademecum voor Het Nederlandse Verzekeringswezen; Jaarboek voor Het Assurantie- en Hypotheekwezen.

368 FI ISSN 0355-7294
VAKUUTUSSANOMAT. 1903. 8/yr. FIM 222 in the Nordic countries; elsewhere FIM 277. Vakuutussanomia Oy, Bulevardi 28, 00120 Helsinki 12, Finland. TEL 358-0-680-401. FAX 358-0-640-469. Ed. Reijo Ollikainen. adv. circ. 9,000.

VALUATION. see BUSINESS AND ECONOMICS — Banking And Finance

368 GW ISSN 0178-9813
VERSICHERUNGS BETRIEBSWIRT. 1966. bi-m. DM.60. Vereinigung der Versicherungs Betriebswirte e.V., Postfach 2240, 50152 Kerpen, Germany. TEL 02237-52145. FAX 02237-2651. Ed. Rudolf Slate. adv.; bk.rev. circ. 1,600. **Document type:** trade publication.

368 GW ISSN 0344-6379
VERSICHERUNGSBETRIEBE; journal fuer Automation Betriebsorganisation und Einrichtung. 1970. 6/yr. DM.112 (foreign DM.122.80). Hans Holzmann Verlag GmbH, Gewerbestr. 2, 86825 Bad Woerishofen, Germany. TEL 08247-35401. FAX 08247-354170. Ed. Erwin Stroebele. adv. circ. 4,312. **Document type:** trade publication.

368.01 GW ISSN 0049-6006
VERSICHERUNGSKAUFMANN; Fachmagazin fuer die Versicherungsbranche. 1954. m. DM.138 (foreign DM.162). Betriebswirtschaftlicher Verlag Dr. Th. Gabler GmbH, Taunusstr. 54, 65183 Wiesbaden, Germany. TEL 0611-534-0. FAX 0611-534400. bk.rev.; abstr.; bibl.; illus.; stat.; tr.lit.; index. **Document type:** trade publication.
   —CCC.

368 GW ISSN 0342-2429
VERSICHERUNGSRECHT; Juristische Rundschau fuer die Individualversicherung. 1950. 36/yr. DM.323.12. Verlag Versicherungswirtschaft e.V., Klosestr. 20-24, 76137 Karlsruhe, Germany. TEL 0721-3509126. FAX 0721-31833. Eds. Egon Lorenz, Karl-Heinz Rehnert. adv.; bk.rev.; bibl.; index. circ. 8,000. (back issues avail.; reprint service avail. from SCH) Indexed: ELLIS. **Document type:** trade publication.
   ●Also available online.
   —SWETS.

368 GW ISSN 0049-6014
VERSICHERUNGSVERMITTLUNG; Zeitschrift selbstaendiger Versicherungskaufleute und Bausparkaufleute. 1901. m. DM.102. Bundesverband Deutscher Versicherungskaufleute (BVK), Kekulestr. 12, 53115 Bonn, Germany. TEL 0228-224315. FAX 0228-261157. Ed. Hans-Dieter Schaefer. adv.; bk.rev. circ. 19,000. **Document type:** trade publication.

368 GW ISSN 0042-4358
VERSICHERUNGSWIRTSCHAFT. 1946. fortn. DM.159.24. Verlag Versicherungswirtschaft e.V., Klosestr. 20-24, 76137 Karlsruhe, Germany. TEL 0721-3509-0. FAX 0721-31833. Ed. Karl-Heinz Rehnert. adv.; bk.rev.; charts; illus. circ. 11,600. (back issues avail.) **Document type:** trade publication.
   —SWETS.

368 NE ISSN 0042-4528
VERZEKERINGS-ARCHIEF. (Text in Dutch, English and French) 1920. q. (Nederlandse Vereniging ter Bevordering van het Levensverzekeringwezen) Kluwer Academic Publishers, Postbus 17, 3300 AA Dordrecht, Netherlands. TEL 31-78-334911. FAX 31-78-334254. TELEX 29245 KAPG NL. (Dist. by: Kluwer Academic Publishers Group, P.O. Box 322, 3300 AH Dordrecht, Netherlands. TEL 31-78-524400; N. America dist. addr.: Box 358, Accord Sta., Hingham, MA 02018-0358. TEL 617-871-6600) Ed.Bd. bk.rev.; bibl.; index. **Indexed:** Excerp.Med., Math.R.
   —SWETS.

368 NE ISSN 0925-3440
VERZEKERINGS MAGAZINE V V P. w. fl.147.50 (effective 1994). Nijgh Periodieken B.V., Postbus 122, 3100 AC Schiedam, Netherlands. TEL 31-10-4274100. FAX 31-10-4739911. adv.: B&W page fl.1985, color page fl.3981; trim 210 x 297; adv. contact: Bert Niewold. circ. 5,742. **Document type:** trade publication.
   Former titles (until 1991): V V P Magazine (ISSN 0922-7415); (until 1988): Verenigde Verzekeringspers (ISSN 0169-0841)

368 BE
VERZEKERINGNIEUWS. (Supplement avail.) (Text in Flemish) s-m. 4558 BEF. C E D Samsom (Subsidiary of: Wolters Samsom Belgie n.v.), Kouterveld 14, B-1831 Diegem, Belgium. TEL 32-2-7231111.
   Description: Insurance industry news from national and European Community perspectives.

VIERTELJAHRESSCHRIFT FUER SOZIALRECHT. see LAW

VIRGINIA INSURANCE DIRECTORY. see BUSINESS AND ECONOMICS — Trade And Industrial Directories

368 SA ISSN 0259-0026
VITAE; the South African insurance magazine. (Text in English) 1980. bi-m. R.95. Vitae Insurance Publications (Pty) Ltd., P.O. Box 849, Highlands North 2037, South Africa. TEL 27-11-882-6105. FAX 27-11-882-6104. Ed. S.W. Bishop. adv.; bk.rev.; index. circ. 2,000. **Document type:** trade publication.
   Incorporates (March 1982): S.A. Insurance Magazine.
   Description: Motivational and educational material for life insurance salespersons and managers.

368 US ISSN 1061-1444
W B F IN ACTION. 1906. bi-m. $1. Workmen's Benefit Fund of the United States of America, 99 N. Broadway, Hicksville, NY 11801-2936. TEL 516-938-6060. Ed. Charles Grossman. bk.rev.; charts; illus.; tr.lit.; circ. 15,000. **Indexed:** Abstr.Engl.Stud. **Document type:** newsletter.
   Formerly (until 1991): Solidarity (Hicksville) (ISSN 0038-1152)

368.4 CN
W C B NEWS. q. Workers' Compensation Board, 6951 Westminster Hwy., Richmond, BC V7C 1C6, Canada. TEL 604-279-7572. FAX 604-279-7406. Ed. Kathy Eccles. circ. 25,000. (back issues avail.) **Document type:** newsletter.
   Description: Provides information on policies and operations of the WCB, for employers and labor organizations.

WASHINGTON INSURANCE LAW LETTER. see LAW

368 US
WAVELENGTH (NEWPORT BEACH). 1966? 6/yr. free. Pacific Mutual Life Insurance, 700 Newport Center Dr., Newport Beach, CA 92663. TEL 714-640-3768. Ed. Barbara Assadi. illus.
   Formerly (until 1989): Soundings (Newport Beach); Supersedes: P M L - Life (ISSN 0030-8765)

368 US
WHO WRITES WHAT IN LIFE AND HEALTH INSURANCE. a. $22.95. National Underwriter Co., 505 Gest St., Cincinnati, OH 45203. TEL 513-721-2140. FAX 513-721-0126. adv.
   Description: Provides information for coverages and services for unusual and hard to place risks.

INSURANCE — ABSTRACTING, BIBLIOGRAPHIES, STATISTICS

368   US   ISSN 0083-9574
HG8523
WHO'S WHO IN INSURANCE. 1942. a. $115. Underwriter Printing and Publishing Co., 50 E. Palisade Ave., Englewood, NJ 07631. TEL 201-569-8808. Ed. Donald E. Wolff. circ. 6,000. **Document type:** directory.
    Description: Contains more than 5,000 biographies of insurance officials, leading agents and brokers, and high-ranking company officers. Each biography includes position-title, educational background, club and professional associations, and career synopses.

368   US
WHO'S WHO IN RISK MANAGEMENT. 1971. a. $65. Underwriter Printing and Publishing Co., 50 E. Palisade Ave., Englewood, NJ 07631. TEL 201-569-8808. Ed. Donald E. Wolff. circ. 10,000. **Document type:** directory.
    Description: Contains specialized biographies of insurance buyers for large business and industrial firms throughout the U.S. Includes indexes by company and location.

368.32   AT
WICKEN'S THE LAW OF LIFE INSURANCE IN AUSTRALIA. 4/yr. Aus.$310 with updates. Law Book Co. Ltd., 44-50 Waterloo Rd., North Ryde, N.S.W. 2113, Australia. TEL 02-887-0177. FAX 02-888-9706. TELEX ASBOOK 27995. Eds. Brian Sharpe, Cathy Manolios. (looseleaf format)
    Description: Examines the law of life insurance including taxation, mortgages on policies, trusts and trustees, agency and brokers and reinsurance.

368   GW
WIR (COLOGNE). 1932. q. Berlin-Koelnische Versicherungen, Clever Str. 36, 50668 Cologne, Germany. TEL 0221-7724-0. FAX 0221-7724-200. Ed. Rudolf A.P. Slate. bk.rev. circ. 4,500. **Document type:** bulletin.
    Formerly: Bruecke (Cologne).

368   US
WISCONSIN INSUROR.* vol.40, 1977. m. $10. Independent Insurance Agents of Wisconsin, 725 John Nolen Dr., Madison, WI 53713-1421. Ed. Robert C. Jartz. adv.; charts; illus.; stat. circ. 1,200.
    Former titles: Wisconsin Insurance; Wisconsinsuror (ISSN 0043-6704)

368   CN   ISSN 0833-1278
WITHOUT PREJUDICE. 1936. 10/yr.(Sept.-June). Can.$60 to non-members; (foreign Can.$75). Ontario Insurance Adjusters Association, c/o C. W. Gibula, Ed., 55 Devins Dr., Aurora, Ont. L4G 2Z3, Canada. TEL 416-542-0576. FAX 416-542-1301. (Subscr. to: Business Manager, OIAA, 132 Bonham Blvd., Mississauga, Ont. L5M 1C7, Canada) adv.; charts. circ. 1,300.

368   US   ISSN 1069-1790
HS1510.W78
WOODMEN. 1890. bi-m. $3. Woodmen of the World Life Insurance Society, c/o Billie Jo Foust, Asst. Ed., 170 Farnam St., Omaha, NE 68102. TEL 402-342-1890. FAX 402-271-7269. bk.rev.; illus.; circ. 495,000 (controlled). **Document type:** trade publication.
    Formerly: Woodmen of the World Magazine (ISSN 0043-7751)
    Description: Contains articles on insurance, Woodmen of the World operations, health, lodges and fraternal activities.

368 331   US   ISSN 1066-2669
▼**WORKERS' COMP MANAGED CARE.** 1992. m. $228. Business Information Services, Inc. (Laurel), 12811 N. Point Ln., Laurel, MD 20708. TEL 301-604-4001. FAX 301-604-5126. Ed. James H. Gutman. **Document type:** newsletter.
—CCC.
    Description: Deals with business-related developments and trends on the medical side of workers' compensation as they affect managed health care firms, insurers, providers, employers and government.

368   US
WORKERS' COMPENSATION - BUSINESS MANAGEMENT GUIDE. 1939. a. (plus fortn. updates). $474. Commerce Clearing House, Inc., 4025 W. Peterson Ave., Chicago, IL 60646. TEL 312-583-8500. FAX 708-940-0113. Ed. James Rooney. (looseleaf format)
    Formerly (until 1993): Workers' Compensation Law Reporter.

368 331   US
▼**WORKERS' COMPENSATION COST CONTROL.** 1992. m. $93 (effective 1993). Quinlan Publishing Co., Inc., 23 Drydock Ave., Boston, MA 02210-2387. TEL 617-542-0048; 800-229-2084. FAX 617-345-9646. index. (looseleaf format; back issues avail.) **Document type:** newsletter.
    Description: Articles, research and ides for dealing with workers' compensation cost management.

WORKERS' COMPENSATION LAW BULLETIN. see BUSINESS AND ECONOMICS — Labor And Industrial Relations

368.014   US
WORKERS' COMPENSATION LAW REVIEW. Variant title: Workmens' Compensation Law Review. 1974. a. $72. William S. Hein & Co., Inc., 1285 Main St., Buffalo, NY 14209. TEL 800-828-7571. FAX 716-883-8100. TELEX 91-209 WU 7 HEIN BUF. Ed. William Moran. circ. 300. **Document type:** academic/scholarly publication.
    Description: Legal articles on workers' compensation.

WORKERS' COMPENSATION LAWS OF CALIFORNIA. see LAW

368   UK   ISSN 0306-3445
WORLD INSURANCE REPORT. s-m. £565($939) (overseas £587) (effective 1993). Financial Times Business Information Ltd., 126 Jermyn St., London SW1Y 4UJ, England. TEL 071-411-4414. FAX 071-411-4415. **Document type:** newsletter.
—UMI.
    Description: International service for the world's insurance and reinsurance management.

368   UK   ISSN 0955-4831
WORLD POLICY GUIDE; a monthly analysis of insurance policies available in the U.K. 1983. m. £723($1,187) (overseas £742) (effective 1993). Financial Times Business Information Ltd., 126 Jermyn St., London SW1Y 4UJ, England. TEL 071-411-4414. FAX 071-411-4415. Ed. Sue Copeman.
●Also available online.
—UMI.
    Former titles: F T London Policy Guide (ISSN 0263-5569); World Policy Checklist.
    Description: Provides analysis of commercial, corporate, and group insurances offered by UK-based insurers.

368 333.33   NP
WORLDWIDE INSURANCE AND REAL ESTATE. 1980. a. Siveast Consultants, Inc., USA, P.O. Box 8510, Kathmandu, Nepal. TEL 418-864. (Alt. addr.: G.P.O. Box 29, 9-11-1, Goutami Nagar, Kovvur 534 350, West Godavari District, Andhra Pradesh, India) Ed. C.V. Ramasastry.
    Description: Lists worldwide reputed insurance companies. Examines the insurance business in light of real estate and other market forces.

368   NP
WORLDWIDE MOTOR, FIRE, MARINE AND AIR CARGO INSURANCE SURVEYORS AND CLAIMS SETTLING AGENTS. 1980. a. $50. Siveast Consultants, Inc., USA, P.O. Box 8510, Kathmandu, Nepal. TEL 418-864. Ed. C.V. Ramasastry. adv.
    Description: Lists worldwide experienced insurance surveyors with high professional ethics.

368   NE
WORLDWIDE NEWS. (Text in English) 1962. 5/yr. free. Nationale-Nederlanden N.V., Johan de Wittlaan 3, Box 29701, 2502 LS The Hague, Netherlands. TEL 70-3581315. Ed. Sharon Lewis. bk.rev. circ. 13,000.

368   XR   ISSN 0044-1708
ZABRANA SKOD; damage prevention: fire prevention, road safety, work safety, agriculture and industry protection. 1953. m. 12 Kcs.($11.45) (Ceska Statni Pojistovna, Prague) Nakladatelstvi Technicke Literatury, Spalena 51, 113 02 Prague 1, Czech Republic. (Dist. by: Artia, Ve Smecckach 30, 111 27 Prague 1, Czech Republic) (Slovenska Statni Pojistovna, Bratislava) Ed. Eva Trojanova. circ. 10,000.
—BLDSC (9425.100000).

368   ZA
ZAMBIA STATE INSURANCE CORPORATION. REPORT AND ACCOUNTS. 1971. a. Zambia State Insurance Corporation, Box 894, Lusaka, Zambia. circ. 3,000.

368   GW   ISSN 0044-2585
HG8015
ZEITSCHRIFT FUER DIE GESAMTE VERSICHERUNGSWISSENSCHAFT. 1901. q. DM.127. (Deutscher Verein fuer Versicherungswissenschaft e.V.) Duncker und Humblot GmbH, Postfach 410329, 12113 Berlin, Germany. TEL 030-7900060. FAX 030-79000631. (And: Verlag Versicherungswirtschaft e.V., Klosestr. 20-24, 76137 Karlsruhe, Germany. TEL 0721-3509-0) bk.rev.; bibl.; index. (tabloid format) **Document type:** academic/scholarly publication.
—CCC.

368   GW
ZEITSCHRIFT FUER VERSICHERUNGSWESEN. (Text in English and German) 1950. s.m. DM.197.73. Allgemeiner Fachverlag Rolf Mathern GmbH, Agnesstr. 1, 22301 Hamburg, Germany. TEL 040-473500. FAX 040-4605870. Ed. Marc Surminski. circ. 6,000. **Document type:** trade publication.

368   CC   ISSN 1001-4489
ZHONGGUO BAOXIAN/INSURANCE IN CHINA. (Text in Chinese) m. Zhongguo Renmin Baoxian Gongsi - China People's Insurance Company, 22 Xijiaominxiang, Beijing 100031, People's Republic of China. TEL 654231. Ed. Pan Lufu.

INSURANCE — Abstracting, Bibliographies, Statistics

368   US   ISSN 1046-5081
ACTUARIAL REVIEW. 1973. q. $10 to non-members. Casualty Actuarial Society, 1100 N. Glebe Rd., Ste. 600, Arlington, VA 22201. TEL 703-276-3100. bk.rev.; charts.
—UMI.

368.382   AT   ISSN 0727-1611
AUSTRALIA. BUREAU OF STATISTICS. HEALTH INSURANCE SURVEY, AUSTRALIA. 1979. irreg., latest 1990. Aus.$15 per no. Australian Bureau of Statistics, P.O. Box 10, Belconnen, A.C.T. 2616, Australia. **Document type:** government publication.
    Description: Contains statistics showing the level of private health insurance of contributor units and persons, cross-classified by: type of insurance covered, contribution rate, composition and income of contributor unit.

AUSTRALIA. LIFE INSURANCE GROUP. HALF YEARLY FINANCIAL BULLETIN ON LIFE INSURANCE. see INSURANCE

368 319 332   HO
BANCO CENTRAL DE HONDURAS. DIVISION DE SEGUROS. BOLETIN DE ESTADISTICAS DE SEGUROS. 1974. a. free. Banco Central de Honduras, Division de Seguros, Tegucigalpa, M.D.C., Honduras. FAX 504-37-1791. TELEX 1121 BANTRAL HO. charts; illus.; stat. circ. 250.
    Description: Covers insurance market statistics.

INSURANCE — ABSTRACTING, BIBLIOGRAPHIES, STATISTICS

368   BE
BELGIUM. INSTITUT NATIONAL D'ASSURANCES SOCIALES POUR TRAVAILLEURS INDEPENDANTS. STATISTIQUES DES BENEFICIAIRES DE PRESTATIONS DE RETRAITE ET DE SURVIE/BELGIUM. RIJKSINSTITUUT VOOR DE SOCIALE VERZEKERINGEN DER ZELFSTANDIGEN. STATISTIEK VAN DE PERSONEN DIE EEN RUST- EN OVERLEVINGSPRESTATIE GENIETEN. (Text in Flemish and French) 1970. a. free. Institut National d'Assurances Sociales pour Travailleurs Independants, Bibliotheque - Bureau 4-7 (Wat.), Place Jean Jacobs, 6, B-1000 Brussels, Belgium. TEL 32-2-507-6211. FAX 32-2-511-2153. **Document type:** government publication.

314 368.4   BE
BELGIUM. INSTITUT NATIONAL D'ASSURANCES SOCIALES POUR TRAVAILLEURS INDEPENDANTS. STATISTIQUE DES ENFANTS BENEFICIAIRES D'ALLOCATIONS FAMILIALES/BELGIUM. RIJKSINSTITUUT VOOR DE SOCIALE VERZEKERINGEN DER ZELFSTANDIGEN. STATISTIEK VAN DE KINDEREN DIE RECHT GEVEN OP KINDERBIJSLAG. (Text in Dutch and French) 1970. a. Institut National d'Assurances Sociales pour Travailleurs Independants, 6 place Jean Jacobs, B-1000 Brussels, Belgium. TEL 32-2-507-6211. FAX 32-2-511-2153. **Document type:** government publication.

368.4   BE
BELGIUM. INSTITUT NATIONAL D'ASSURANCES SOCIALES POUR TRAVAILLEURS INDEPENDANTS. STATISTIQUES DES PERSONNES ASSUJETTIES AU STATUT SOCIAL DES TRAVAILLEURS INDEPENDANTS/BELGIUM. RIJKSINSTITUUT VOOR DE SOCIALE VERZEKERINGEN DER ZELFSTANDIGEN. STATISTIEK VAN DE PERSONEN DIE ONDER DE TOEPASSING VALLEN VAN HET SOCIAAL STATUUT VAN DE ZELFSTANDIGEN. (Text in Flemish and French) 1970. a. free. Institut National d'Assurances Sociales pour Travailleurs Independants, Biblotheque - Bureau 4-7 (Wat.), Place Jean Jacobs, 6, B-1000 Brussels, Belgium. TEL 32-2-507-6211. FAX 32-2-511-2153. **Document type:** government publication.
Description: Employment statistics covering a wide variety of professions.

368   CN   ISSN 0701-5488
HD7106.C2
CANADA. STATISTICS CANADA. PENSION PLANS IN CANADA. (Catalogue 74-401) (Text in English and French) 1970. biennial. Can.$35($42) (foreign $42) per issue. Statistics Canada, Publications Sales and Services, Ottawa, Ont. K1A 0T6, Canada. TEL 613-951-7277. FAX 613-951-1584. (also avail. in microform from MML) **Document type:** government publication.
Description: Includes all occupational pension plans sponsored by employers in both the public and private sectors. Includes sections on recipients of pension benefits and contributors to RRSPs.

368   CN   ISSN 0068-9025
CANADIAN INSURANCE. ANNUAL STATISTICAL ISSUE. 1905. a. Can.$32. Stone and Cox Ltd., 111 Peter St., Ste. 202, Toronto, Ont. M5V 2H1, Canada. TEL 416-599-0772. FAX 416-599-0867. Ed. M. Steeler. adv. circ. 11,338. (back issues avail.)
Description: Round-up of the underwriting statistics for the Canadian property-casualty and life insurance industry, with informed comment.

368   US
CASUALTY ACTUARIAL SOCIETY. DISCUSSION PAPER PROGRAM. 1982. a. price varies. Casualty Actuarial Society, 1100 N. Glebe Rd., Ste. 600, Arlington, VA 22201. TEL 703-276-3100.

368   US
CASUALTY ACTUARIAL SOCIETY. FORUM. 1987. s-a. $30. Casualty Actuarial Society, 1100 N. Glebe Rd., Ste. 600, Arlington, VA 22201. TEL 703-276-3100.

368.01   US   ISSN 0893-2980
CASUALTY ACTUARIAL SOCIETY. PROCEEDINGS. 1914. a. $50. Casualty Actuarial Society, 11009 N. Glebe Rd., Ste. 600, Arlington, VA 22201. TEL 703-276-3100. (also avail. in microform from UMI; reprint service avail. from UMI) **Document type:** proceedings.

368   US   ISSN 0895-6022
CASUALTY ACTUARIAL SOCIETY. YEARBOOK. a. $40 (effective 1991). Casualty Actuarial Society, 1100 N. Glebe Rd., Ste. 600, Arlington, VA 22201. TEL 703-276-3100.

368.4   CL
CHILE. SUPERINTENDENCIA DE SEGURIDAD SOCIAL. SEGURIDAD SOCIAL: ESTADISTICAS. 1969. irreg. exchange basis. Superintendenica de Seguridad Social, Santiago, Chile.
Formerly: Chile. Superintendencia de Seguridad Social. Boletin de Estadisticas de Seguridad.

368   CK
DATASEGUROS. 1987. a. $60 (diskette $100). Union de Aseguradores Colombianos, Carrera 7a No. 26-20, Piso 11, Apdo. Aereo 5233, Bogota, Colombia. circ. 150. (also avail. in diskette format)
Description: Contains statistics organized by insurance company, balance sheets and insurance lines.

368   ES
HG8555.A4
EL SALVADOR. SUPERINTENDENCIA DEL SISTEMA FINANCIERO. JUNTA MONETARIA. ANUARIO ESTADISTICO. 1963. a. free. Superintendencia del Sistema Financiero, Asesoria Actuarial y Estadistica, Junta Monetaria, Apdo. Postal 2942, San Salvador, El Salvador. Dir. Jose Roberto Navarro Escobar. stat. circ. 500. **Document type:** government publication.
Formerly (until no.14, 1976): El Salvador. Superintendencia de Bancos y Otras Instituciones Financieras. Estadisticas (ISSN 0067-3234)

368.4 314   FI   ISSN 0071-5247
FINLAND. KANSANELAKELAITOS. TILASTOLLINEN VUOSIKIRJA/FINLAND. FOLKPENSIONSANSTALT. STATISTISK AARSBOK/FINLAND. SOCIAL INSURANCE INSTITUTION. STATISTICAL YEARBOOK. (Subseries of its Julkaisuja. Series T: 1) (Text in Finnish, Swedish; summaries in English) 1965. a. Kansanelakelaitos - Social Insurance Institution of Finland, Estimating and Statistics Department, Nordenskioldinkatu 12, FIN-00250 Helsinki 25, Finland. Ed. K. Lindroos. charts; stat. circ. 4,000. **Document type:** government publication.

368 314   GW   ISSN 0435-7442
GESAMTSTATISTIK DER KRAFTFAHRTVERSICHERUNG. 1958. a. free. Verband der Haftpflicht-, Unfall- und Kraftverkehrsversicherer e.V., Glockengiesserwall 1, 20095 Hamburg, Germany. stat.; circ. controlled. **Document type:** trade publication.

368   GY
GUYANA. NATIONAL INSURANCE BOARD. ANNUAL REPORT: GUYANA NATIONAL INSURANCE SCHEME. 1970. a. free. National Insurance Board, Brickdam and Winter Place, Georgetown, Guyana. TEL 592-02-66797. FAX 592-02-52273. stat. circ. 300.
Description: Yearly information and tabular statistics on the activities of the board, focusing on employers and employees, benefit branches, claims adjudication issues, training and staffing, income and expenditure, audited accounts with an annex of tabular statistics.

368 314   AU
HANDBUCH DER OESTERREICHISCHEN SOZIALVERSICHERUNG. 1971. a. (2 vols.). S.135. Hauptverband der Oesterreichischen Sozialversicherungstraeger, Kundmanngasse 21, A-1030 Vienna, Austria. TEL 0222-71132. FAX 0222-71132-3777. **Document type:** government publication.
Formerly: Statistisches Handbuch der Oesterreichischen Sozialversicherung; Which superseded in part: Jahrbuch der Oesterreichischen Sozialversicherung.

368 314   IT   ISSN 0021-2539
I N A I L NOTIZIARIO STATISTICO. 1951. q. L.16320. Istituto Nazionale per l'Assicurazione Contro gli Infortuni sul Lavoro, Via 4 Novembre 144, 00187 Rome, Italy. Ed. Carla Maciocci. charts; index. circ. 2,500.
Description: Statistics on work accidents.

368.4 331   US
INDIANA. DEPARTMENT OF EMPLOYMENT AND TRAINING SERVICES. UNEMPLOYMENT INSURANCE CLAIMS BY AREA. w. free. Department of Employment and Training Services, Statistical Services, 10 Senate Ave., Rm. 313, Indianapolis, IN 46204. TEL 317-232-7704. FAX 317-232-6950. **Document type:** government publication.
Description: Tabulates initial and continued claims under the State and Federal Unemployment Insurance programs for all local offices.

368.4 331   US
INDIANA. DEPARTMENT OF EMPLOYMENT AND TRAINING SERVICES. UNEMPLOYMENT INSURANCE PAYMENTS BY INDUSTRY. m. free. Department of Employment and Training Services, Statistical Services, 10 Senate Ave., Rm. 313, Indianapolis, IN 46204. TEL 317-232-7704. FAX 317-232-6950. **Document type:** government publication.
Description: Reports number and amount of State Unemployment Insurance payments by selected industries.

368   CK
INDUSTRIA ASEGURADORA COLOMBIANA. ESTADISTICAS ANUALES. 1976. a. $30 (diskette $60). Union de Aseguradores Colombianos, Carrera 7a. No. 26-20, Piso 11, Apdo. Aereo 5233, Bogota, Colombia. TEL 571-287-6611. FAX 571-287-5764. (also avail. in diskette format)
Description: Principal data from balance sheets and statistics on Colombian businesses.

016 368   NE   ISSN 0167-8558
INSURANCE ABSTRACTS AND REVIEWS. (Text in English) 1982. q. fl.220($88) to individuals; institutions fl.220 ($88). Nationale - Nederlanden N.V., P.O. Box 29701, 2502 LS The Hague, Netherlands. Ed. G.W. de Wit.
—CCC.

368 016   US   ISSN 0735-3944
INSURANCE AND EMPLOYEE BENEFITS LITERATURE. 1950. bi-m. Can.$15($15) (foreign $20). Special Libraries Association, Insurance and Employee Benefits Division, c/o Jennifer Silverman, Marsh & McLennan, 1156 Ave. of the Americas, New York, NY 10036. FAX 212-345-3776. Ed. Laurie Meyers. bk.rev.; bibl. circ. 375. **Document type:** bibliography.
Formerly: Insurance Literature (ISSN 0020-4765)
Description: Features an annoted current bibliography and buying guide regarding books, pamphlets and government documents concerning insurance and employee benefits.

368   UK
▼**INSURANCE JOURNALS INDEX.** 1992. m. £495. Legal Information Resources Ltd., Elphin House, 1 New Rd., Mytholmroyd, Hebden Bridge, W. Yorkshire HX7 5DZ, England. TEL 0422-886277. FAX 0422-886250. Ed.Bd. cum.index. (also avail. in magnetic tape; back issues avail.) **Document type:** abstracting/indexing.
Description: Covers over 100 journals on insurance, risk management and all related topics. Contains information on insurance and reinsurance companies and brokers, cases, legislation, and new products pertinent to insurance.

368 016   US   ISSN 0074-073X
HG8011
INSURANCE PERIODICALS INDEX. 1962. a. $100. (Special Libraries Association, Insurance and Employee Benefits Division) N I L S Publishing Company, 21625 Prairie St., Box 2507, Chatsworth, CA 91311. TEL 818-998-8830. FAX 818-718-8482. (Addr. of Association: 1700 19th St., N.W., Washington, DC 20009) Ed. Oriole Anderson. circ. 450. (back issues avail.) **Document type:** abstracting/indexing.
●Also available online. Vendor(s): DIALOG Information Services, Inc. (File no.169), Mead Data Central, Inc. (NEXIS/LEXIS), West Services, Inc.
Description: Indexes the 35 most significant journals in insurance. Online databases include abstracts.

INSURANCE — ABSTRACTING, BIBLIOGRAPHIES, STATISTICS

368 US
INSURANCE REGULATORY INFORMATION SYSTEM RATIO RESULTS. a. $100. National Association of Insurance Commissioners, 120 W. 12th St., Kansas City, MO 64105. TEL 816-374-7259. (Subscr. to: N A I C Publications, Box 263 Department 42, Kansas City, MO 64193-0042) stat. (also avail. in magnetic tape; diskette format)
Description: Provides statistical reports on the financial condition of 5,000 insurance companies.

368 319 FJ
INSURANCE REPORT AND STATISTICS OF FIJI. 1969. a. free. Commissioner of Insurance, Government Printer, Box 1220, Suva, Fiji. TEL 679 301688. stat. circ. 200.
Formerly: Insurance Statistics of Fiji.

368 UK ISSN 0950-3668
INSURANCE STATISTICS (YEARS). 1952. a. free. Association of British Insurers, 51 Gresham St., London EC2V 7HQ, England. TEL 071-600-3333. FAX 071-696-8999. circ. 10,000.
—BLDSC (4531.770800).
Supersedes (in 1985): Insurance Facts and Figures & Life Insurance in the United Kingdom.

THE INSURANCE TAX REVIEW. see BUSINESS AND ECONOMICS — Public Finance, Taxation

368 315 IS ISSN 0074-0705
ISRAEL. CENTRAL BUREAU OF STATISTICS. INSURANCE IN ISRAEL/ISKE HA-BITUAH BE-YISRAEL. (Subseries of the Bureau's Special Series) (Text in English, Hebrew) 1950. a. price varies. Central Bureau of Statistics, P.O. Box 13015, Jerusalem 91 130, Israel. TEL 02-21 12 11.

368.382 315 JA ISSN 0911-8454
JAPAN. MINISTRY OF HEALTH AND WELFARE. STATISTICS AND INFORMATION DEPARTMENT. REPORT ON SURVEY OF NATIONAL MEDICAL CARE INSURANCE SERVICES. Key Title: Shakai Iryo Shinryo Koibetsu Chosa Hokoku. (Text in Japanese) 1976. a. (in 2 vols.) 3600 Yen for vol.1; vol.2 6400 Yen. Ministry of Health and Welfare, Statistics and Information Department - Koseisho Daijin Kanbo Tokei Johobu, 7-3 Ichigaya-Honmura-cho, Shinjuku-ku, Tokyo 162, Japan. TEL 03-3260-3181. FAX 03-3260-7292. (Subscr. to: Health & Welfare Statistics Association, 5-13-14 Roppongi, Minato-ku, Tokyo, Japan. TEL 03-3586-3361. FAX 03-3584-4710) **Document type:** government publication.

368 LU ISSN 0259-8108
LUXEMBOURG. INSPECTION GENERALE DE LA SECURITE SOCIALE. RAPPORT GENERAL SUR LA SECURITE SOCIALE AU GRAND-DUCHE DE LUXEMBOURG. 1974. a. 1000 Fr. Inspection Generale de la Securite Sociale, Ministere de la Securite Sociale, B.P. 1308, L-1013 Luxembourg, Luxembourg. FAX 478-6225. TELEX 2985 MINTSS LU. circ. 900. **Document type:** government publication.
Description: Covers statistics on demography, economics, and finances.

368 016 US ISSN 0743-8079
MEDICAL BENEFITS. 1984. s-m. $172. Panel Publishers, Inc., Box 1007, Charlottesville, VA 22902. TEL 804-979-4947. FAX 804-979-5164. Ed. Bruce G. Carveth. charts.

368.4 613.62 MX
MEXICO. CENTRO DE INFORMACION TECNICA Y DOCUMENTACION. INDICE DE ARTICULOS SOBRE SEGURIDAD E HIGIENE INDUSTRIAL. 1979. 3/yr. Mex.$140($13) (Centro de Informacion Tecnica y Documentacion) Mexico. Servicio Nacional de Adiestramiento Rapido de la Mano de Obra en la Industria, Calzada Atzcapotzalco-la Villa 209, Apdo. 16-099, Mexico 16, D.F., Mexico. Ed. Javier Pedraza Garcia. circ. 2,000.

368 MX
MEXICO. COMISION NACIONAL DE SEGUROS Y FIANZAS. ANUARIO ESTADISTICO DE SEGUROS. 1945. a. free. Comision Nacional de Seguros y Fianzas, Av. de los Insurgentes 1971, Plaza Inn, Torre 2 Norte, 2o Piso, 01020 Mexico, D.F., Mexico. stat.; index. **Document type:** government publication.
Formerly: Mexico. Comision Nacional Bancaria y de Seguros. Anuario Estadistico de Seguros.
Description: Contains statistical information on the insurance sector: life, accident, health and property-casualty, and on reinsurance.

310 IS
NATIONAL INSURANCE INSTITUTE, JERUSALEM. ANNUAL SURVEY. 1981. a. free. National Insurance Institute, 13 Sderot Weizman, Jerusalem, Israel. Ed. Lea Achdud. circ. 1,000.
Formerly: National Insurance Institute, Jerusalem. Statistical Abstracts.

368.4 314 NE ISSN 0168-4108
NETHERLANDS. CENTRAAL BUREAU VOOR DE STATISTIEK. DIAGNOSESTATISTIEK BEDRIJFSVERENIGINGEN (OMSLAGLEDEN). (Text in Dutch and English) 1958. a. Centraal Bureau voor de Statistiek, Prinses Beatrixlaan 428, Voorburg, Netherlands. (Dist. by: SDU - Publishers, Christoffel Plantijnstraat, The Hague, Netherlands) **Document type:** government publication.

368 317 US
NEW YORK (STATE). INSURANCE DEPARTMENT. STATISTICAL TABLES FROM ANNUAL STATEMENTS. 1944. a. $11.50 (single copy free to NY residents). Insurance Department, Publications Unit, Empire State Plaza, Agency Bldg. No. 1, Albany, NY 12257. circ. 1,000. (back issues avail.) **Document type:** government publication.

368 NZ ISSN 0111-0225
HG8784.N45
NEW ZEALAND. DEPARTMENT OF STATISTICS. NEW ZEALAND LIFE TABLES. quinquennial. NZ.$30.65. Department of Statistics, P.O. Box 2922, Wellington, New Zealand.
Formerly: New Zealand. Department of Statistics. Life Annuity Tables.

368.4 PP
PAPUA NEW GUINEA. DEPARTMENT OF LABOUR AND EMPLOYMENT. WORKER'S COMPENSATION CLAIMS. (Text in English) 1966. a. K.1.50. Department of Labour and Employment, Publication Section, P.O. Box 417, Papua New Guinea. circ. 110. **Document type:** government publication.
Former titles: Papua New Guinea. National Statistical Office. Worker's Compensation Claims & Papua New Guinea. Bureau of Statistics. Industrial Accidents; Papua New Guinea. Bureau of Statistics. Workers' Compensation Statistics (ISSN 0078-9267)
Description: Contains tables on the value of workers' compensation premiums collected and claims paid; number of claims lodged, by age, sex and occupation of claimant, location and nature of injury, cause of accident, duration of absence from work, industry of employer, and province.

PENSIONS JOURNALS INDEX. see BUSINESS AND ECONOMICS — Abstracting, Bibliographies, Statistics

368 314 PL ISSN 0079-2853
POLAND. GLOWNY URZAD STATYSTYCZNY. UBEZPIECZENIA MAJATKOWE I OSOBOWE/POLAND. CENTRAL STATISTICS OFFICE. PROPERTY AND PERSONAL INSURANCE. 1969. a. Zaklad Wydawnictw Statystycznych, Al. Niepodleglosci 208, 00-925 Warsaw, Poland. TEL 48 22 25-03-45.

368 US
PROFITABILITY BY LINE BY STATE. a. $125. National Association of Insurance Commissioners, 120 W. 12th St., Kansas City, MO 64105. TEL 816-374-7259. (Subscr. to: N A I C Publications, Box 263 Department 42, Kansas City, MO 64193-0042) stat.
Description: Provides comparative statistics for evaluating insurance company performance.

368.01 US ISSN 1050-4710
HG8523
PROPERTY - CASUALTY INSURANCE FACTS. 1961. a. $22.50. Insurance Information Institute, 110 William St., New York NY 10038. TEL 212-669-9200. circ. 7,500. (also avail. in microfiche from CIS) **Indexed:** SRI.
Formerly: Insurance Facts (ISSN 0074-0713)
Description: Comprehensive statistical yearbook about property-liability insurance business.

368.4 317 CN ISSN 0226-5346
HD7102.C2
QUEBEC (PROVINCE). REGIE DE L'ASSURANCE-MALADIE. STATISTIQUES ANNUELLES. (Text in French) 1971. a. free. Regie de l'Assurance-Maladie, Case Postale 6600, Quebec, Que. G1K 7T3, Canada. TEL 418-682-5168. FAX 418-643-7312. Ed.Bd. circ. 1,000.

SASKATCHEWAN HEALTH. PRESCRIPTION DRUG SERVICES BRANCH. ANNUAL STATISTICAL REPORT. see PHARMACY AND PHARMACOLOGY — Abstracting, Bibliographies, Statistics

368 MX
SISTEMA DE INFORMACION FIANCIERA GRAFICA TRIMESTRAL. q. Comision Nacional de Seguros y Fianzas, Av. de los Insurgentes 1971, Plaza Inn, Torre 2 N., 2o piso, 01020 Mexico DF, Mexico. (diskette format) **Document type:** government publication.
Description: Contains graphic information on the insurance sector from the previous eight quarters.

368 IT
STATISTICHE PER LA PREVENZIONE. 1974. s-a. L.16320. Istituto Nazionale per l'Assicurazione Contro gli Infortuni sul Lavoro, Via 4 Novembre 144, 00187 Rome, Italy. Ed. Carla Maciocci. charts; stat.; index. circ. 2,000.

368 310 JA ISSN 0910-5727
STATISTICS OF JAPANESE NON-LIFE INSURANCE BUSINESS. Key Title: Insurance. Songai Hoken Tokubetsu Tokei-go. (Text in English, Japanese) 1948. a. 3000 Yen. Hoken Kenkyujo Ltd. - Insurance Research Institute Ltd., 17-3, Hon-machi 1-chome, Shibuya-ku, Tokyo, Japan. TEL 03-3376-3331. FAX 03-3376-7125. Ed. Kazuaki Shimada. circ. 10,000.
Formerly: Japanese Insurance Business Statistics: Non-Life; Which supersedes in part: Insurance - Non-Life Annual Statistics (ISSN 0085-1930)
Description: Annual business figures for the non-life industry and all domestic individual companies.

368 JA ISSN 0910-5719
STATISTICS OF LIFE INSURANCE BUSINESS IN JAPAN. Key Title: Insurance. Seimei Hoken Tokei-go. (Text in English and Japanese) 1948. a. 3000 Yen. Hoken Kenkyujo Ltd. - Insurance Research Institute Ltd., 17-3, Hon-machi 1-chome, Shibuya-ku, Tokyo, Japan. TEL 03-3376-3331. FAX 03-3376-7125. Ed. Kazuaki Shimada. circ. 10,000.
Formerly: Japanese Insurance Business Statistics: Life; Which supersedes in part: Insurance - Non-Life Annual Statistics (ISSN 0085-1930)
Description: Annual business figures for the life industry and all domestic individual companies.

368 FR
STATISTICS ON INSURANCE. (Text and summaries in English, French) 1983. a. free. Organization for Economic Cooperation and Development, 2 rue Andre Pascal, 75775 Paris Cedex 16, France. (U.S. orders to: O.E.C.D. Publications and Information Center, 2001 L St., N.W., Ste. 700, Washington, DC 20036-4910. TEL 202-785-6323) stat. (back issues avail.)
Description: Comparitive tables of insurance statistics covering 24 OECD member countries.

368.382 314 DK ISSN 0107-8437
SYGESIKRINGSSTATISTIK. 1981. a. free. Sygesikringens Forhandlingsudvalg, c/o Amtsraadsforeningen i Danmark, Landmaerket 10, 1119 Copenhagen K, Denmark. TEL 33-912161. FAX 33-15-12-44. Ed. Ejnar Lomholt. circ. 500. **Document type:** government publication.
Formerly: Statistik over Afregning af Ydelser Inden for den Offentlige Sygesikring.
Description: Statistical information about public expenditure on health security.

368.32 US ISSN 0739-4691
HG8961.T4
TEXAS BLUE BOOK OF LIFE INSURANCE STATISTICS. 1944. a. $34. Record Publishing Co. (Dallas), Box 225770, Dallas, TX 75222. TEL 214-630-0687. FAX 214-631-2476. Ed. John H. Leslie. circ. 1,300.

333.33 016 368 US ISSN 0040-8190
TITLE NEWS. 1925. bi-m. $30. American Land Title Association, 1828 L St. N.W., Washington, DC 20036. TEL 202-296-3671. FAX 202-223-5843. Ed. Adina Conn. adv.; bk.rev.; charts; illus.; pat.; tr.mk.; index. circ. 4,600. **Indexed:** C.L.I., L.R.I., Leg.Per., P.A.I.S., Tr.& Indus.Ind.

368 UK
WORLDWIDE INSURANCE ABSTRACTS. m. £258($420) Risk & Insurance Research Group Ltd., 4 Henrietta St., Covent Garden, London WC2E 8PS, England. TEL 071-836-0614. FAX 071-379-6355. **Document type:** abstracting/indexing.

INSURANCE — COMPUTER APPLICATIONS

368 RH ISSN 0556-8692
ZIMBABWE. REGISTRAR OF INSURANCE. REPORT. (Text in English) 1974. a. Z.$4.50. Registrar of Insurance, Private Bag 7705, Causeway, Harare, Zimbabwe. stat. circ. 500. **Document type:** government publication.
Supersedes: Rhodesia. Central Statistical Office. Insurance Statistics.

INSURANCE — Computer Applications

368 US ISSN 1054-0733
HG8075 CODEN: INSREK
INSURANCE AND TECHNOLOGY. 1976. m. $48 in the U.S.; Canada $60; elsewhere $105. Miller Freeman Inc. (New York) (Subsidiary of: United Newspapers Group), 1515 Broadway, New York, NY 10036. TEL 212-869-1300. FAX 212-302-6273. Ed. Kathleen Burger. adv.; charts; illus.; stat.; tr.lit. circ. 18,000. (back issues avail.) **Indexed:** ABI Inform., Comput.Cont., Comput.Lit.Ind.
—UMI. CCC.
Former titles: Insurance Software Review (ISSN 0892-8533); Interface. Insurance Industry (ISSN 0745-0419); Insurance Industry (ISSN 0362-8817)
Description: Articles on information strategies for insurance management.

368 UK ISSN 0268-1935
INSURANCE SYSTEMS BULLETIN; the essential international monthly management review of information technology in the insurance industry. 1985. m. £269($538) I B C Publishing, c/o Helen Cruickshank, Gilmoora House, 57-61 Mortimer St., London W1N 7TD. TEL 071-637-4383. FAX 071-636-6414. (Subscr. in U.S. to: IBC (USA), 290 Eliot St., Box 91004, Ashland, MA 01721-9104) Ed. Derek Austin. bk.rev. (tabloid format; back issues avail.) **Document type:** newsletter.
—UMI.

INTERIOR DESIGN AND DECORATION

see also Interior Design and Decoration–Furniture and House Furnishings

747 720 SP
A D. (Arquitectura Diseno) 6/yr. Publicaciones Heres, S.A., Gran Via Carlos III, 124 5o, 08034 Barcelona, Spain. TEL 3-280-00-88. FAX 3-280-55-55. TELEX 97834 PUER E. Ed. Magda Broto.

747 US
A D ARCHITECTURAL DIGEST, EDIZIONE ITALIANA. (Text in Italian) 1980. m. Conde Nast Publications Inc., Attn.: Editorial Dept., 6300 Wilshire Blvd., Los Angeles, CA 90046. TEL 213-965-3700. FAX 213-937-1458. TELEX 901-321-2437. adv. circ. 120,000.

A D ARCHITECTURE. (Architectural Digest) see *ARCHITECTURE*

A I T. (Architektur, Innenarchitektur, Technischer Ausbau) see *ARCHITECTURE*

747 US
A S I D REPORT. 1975. bi-m. membership only. American Society of Interior Designers, 608 Massachusetts Ave., N.E., Washington, DC 20002-6006. TEL 202-546-3480. FAX 202-546-3240. Ed. Joseph Pryweller; Pub. Ann Schwartz. bk.rev.; circ. 35,000 (controlled). **Document type:** trade publication.

ABITARE. see *ARCHITECTURE*

747 US
ACCESSORY MERCHANDISING. 1980. q. $10. Market Place Publications, 170 World Trade Center, Box 58421, Dallas, TX 75258. TEL 214-747-4274. Ed. Nancy Miller. adv. circ. 17,000.

747 GW
AMBIENTE. 1980. 10/yr. $120. Burda Verlag GmbH, Postfach 1230, 77602 Offenburg, Germany. TEL 089-9250-0. FAX 089-9250-3519. (U.S. dist.: GLP International, 153 S. Dean St., Englewood, NJ 07631. TEL 201-871-1010. FAX 201-871-0870) **Indexed:** Excerp.Med. **Document type:** consumer publication.

747 IT ISSN 0392-5730
L'AMBIENTE CUCINA. (Text in English and Italian) 1979. bi-m. L.44000($77) Editoriale P E G SpA, Via Statuto 4, 20121 Milan, Italy. TEL 02-29004927. FAX 02-29003015. TELEX 323088 PEGMOS I. Ed. Fabrizio Gomarasca. adv.: B&W page L.3950000, color page L.6320000; trim 270 x 370. circ. 22,100.
Description: Covers kitchen interior design, surveys on updated production, reports from main sectorial exhibitions in Italy and abroad.

747 US ISSN 1052-0236
T223.V1
AMERICAN CORPORATE IDENTITY. 1986. a. $44.95. Art Direction Book Company, 10 E. 39th St., New York, NY 10016. TEL 212-889-6100. FAX 212-889-6504. circ. 6,000. **Document type:** trade publication.
Description: Reports corporations' visual identities, such as signage, stationary, trademarks, and packaging.

747 US
AMERICAN HOMESTYLE. 1986. 8/yr. $9.97. Family Circle, Inc. (Subsidiary of: New York Times Company, Inc.), 110 Fifth Ave., New York, NY 10011. TEL 212-463-1636. Eds. Catherine George, Karen Saks. adv. circ. 684,447.
Formerly (until 1993): Decorating Remodeling; Which was formed by the merger of: Remodeling Made Easy; Decorating Made Easy; Which was formerly titled: Family Circle's Home Decorating Guide (ISSN 0090-8630)

747 US
APPLIANCES: LATIN AMERICAN INDUSTRIAL REPORT. (Avail. for each of 22 Latin American countries) 1985. a. $435 per country report. Aquino Productions, Box 15760, Stamford, CT 06901. TEL 203-325-3138.

AN APPROACH TO BARRIER FREE DESIGN. see *HANDICAPPED — Physically Impaired*

747 FR ISSN 0294-8567
ARCHI-CREE. bi-m. 710.09 F. (foreign 725 F.). Societe d'Edition et de Presse, 106 bd. Malesherbes, 75017 Paris, France. adv. circ. 20,000. **Indexed:** Avery Ind.Archit.Per.
—SWETS.
Formerly: Architecture Interieure.
Description: International architecture magazine that covers the development of architecture, draftmanship, building details and interior arrangements.

ARCHIMAGE. see *ARCHITECTURE*

ARCHITECT. see *ARCHITECTURE*

ARCHITECTURAL DESIGNS. see *ARCHITECTURE*

747 US ISSN 0003-8520
NA730.C2
ARCHITECTURAL DIGEST; the international magazine of fine interior design. 1920. m. $39.95. Conde Nast Publications Inc., c/o Editorial Dept., 6300 Wilshire Blvd., Los Angeles, CA 90048. TEL 213-965-3700. FAX 213-937-5643. TELEX 901-321-2437. (Subscr. to: Box 59061, Boulder, CO 80322-9061) Ed. Paige Rense. adv.; bk.rev.; illus. circ. 750,000. **Indexed:** Access, Art & Archaeol.Tech.Abstr., Arts & Hum.Cit.Ind., Avery Ind.Archit.Per., Curr.Cont., Curr.Pack.Abstr., Gard.Lit. (1992-), Mag.Ind., PMR, Search (1988-).
—BLDSC (1600.070000); Faxon; UnCover; SWETS; UMI.
Description: Profiles current projects and ideas in interior design. Includes both contemporary and period work.

ARCHITECTURAL LIGHTING. see *ARCHITECTURE*

ARCHITEKTUR UND LADENBAU; europaeische Fachzeitschrift fuer modernen Ladenbau, Schaufenster und Auslage. see *ARCHITECTURE*

746 NE ISSN 0165-4535
ARIADNE. 1947. m. fl.63. Uitgeverij Spaarnestad B.V., Europalaan 93, 3526 KP Utrecht, Netherlands. TEL 31-30-822511. FAX 31-30-898388. Ed. Rozemarijn de Witte. adv.; index. circ. 144,000. **Document type:** consumer publication.
Formerly: Handwerken Ariadne (ISSN 0017-7415)
Description: Resource for creative leisure activities including home decoration, cooking, crafts, sewing, fashions for children and adults, and more.

747 SZ
ART & DECORATION. 8/yr. Zaehringerstr. 26, CH-8001 Zurich, Switzerland. TEL 01-2526970. FAX 01-2614134. circ. 23,000. **Document type:** consumer publication.

747 FR ISSN 0004-3168
N2
ART ET DECORATION; la revue de la maison. 1897. 8/yr. 146 F. (foreign 220 F.). Editions Charles Massin, 16-18 rue de l'Amiral Mouchez, 75686 Paris Cedex 14, France. TEL 1-45-65-48-48. FAX 1-45-65-47-00. TELEX 240 918 TRACE. adv.; bk.rev.; illus.; index. circ. 451,443. **Indexed:** Art Ind.
—SWETS.

747 US ISSN 1063-1593
ATLANTA HOMES AND LIFESTYLES. 1983. 7/yr. $16.95. Wiesner Publishing, 5775-B Glenridge Dr., Ste. 580, Atlanta, GA 30328. TEL 404-252-6670. FAX 404-252-6673. Ed. Barbara Tapp. adv. contact: Gina Schreiber. bk.rev. circ. 50,000. **Document type:** consumer publication.
Formerly (until 1991): Southern Homes (ISSN 0887-1523)
Description: Contains many ideas about interior decorating and design, architecture, remodeling kitchens and baths, gardening, and cooking and entertaining, as well as stories abouut people who live in Atlanta.

747 AT
AUSTRALIAN DESIGN SERIES. 1981. m. Aus.$73.50 (foreign Aus.$153). 54 Park St., Sydney, N.S.W. 2000, Australia. TEL 02-282-8450. FAX 02-264-5001. Ed. Stephanie King. circ. 24,000. **Document type:** consumer publication.
Description: Covers domestic and commercial design and interiors.

747 AT ISSN 0004-928X
AUSTRALIAN HOME BEAUTIFUL. 1926. m. Aus.$42 (foreign Aus.$60). Southdown Press, 32 Walsh St., Melbourne, Vic. 3000, Australia. Ed. Tony Fawcett. adv.; bk.rev.; charts; illus. circ. 151,000. **Indexed:** Pinpointer. **Document type:** consumer publication.

747 AT ISSN 0004-931X
AUSTRALIAN HOUSE AND GARDEN. 1948. m. Aus.$50.40. A C P Publishing Pty. Ltd., 54-58 Park St., Sydney, N.S.W. 2000, Australia. TEL 02-282-8456. FAX 02-267-4912. Ed. Stephanie King; Pub. Richard Walsh. adv. contact: Peter Miller. bk.rev.; illus.; tr.lit.; index. circ. 120,000. **Indexed:** Pinpointer. **Document type:** consumer publication.
Description: Covers building, furnishing, decorating, handicrafts, gardening, and entertaining.

645 AT ISSN 0814-107X
AUSTRALIANA. 1978. q. Aus.$35 (effective 1993). Australiana Society Inc., P.O. Box 288, Lindfield N.S.W. 2070, Sydney, Australia. FAX 02-569-7246. Ed. Kevin Fahy. adv.; bk.rev.; index. circ. 74. (back issues avail.) **Document type:** academic/scholarly publication.

AUTO OG BOLIG MONTERING. see *INTERIOR DESIGN AND DECORATION — Furniture And House Furnishings*

747 FI ISSN 0355-2950
AVOTAKKA. 1948. m. FIM 420. A-Lehdet Oy, Hitsaajankatu 7, 00810 Helsinki 81, Finland. FAX 0-783-582. Ed. Anja Tuomi. adv.; illus. circ. 49,392. **Document type:** consumer publication.
Formerly: Kaunis Koti (ISSN 0022-9482)
Description: Devoted to housing and interior decoration.

747 JA
AXIS; world design journal. (Text in English, Japanese) 1947. q. 1800 Yen. Axis Inc., 5-17-1, Roppongi, Minato-ku, Tokyo 106, Japan. TEL 03-3587-2781. FAX 03-3586-5246. Ed. Yasuko Seki.

INTERIOR DESIGN AND DECORATION

747 CN ISSN 0829-982X
AZURE MAGAZINE. 1985. 6/yr. Can.$18 (foreign Can.$34). Azure Publishing Inc., 2 Silver Ave., Toronto, ON M6R 3A2, Canada. TEL 416-588-2588. FAX 416-588-2357. Ed. Nelda Rodger. adv.; bk.rev.; abstr.; illus. circ. 10,000. (back issues avail.) **Document type:** consumer publication.
Description: Covers interior, graphic and industrial design, architecture and art.

747 CN ISSN 1196-006X
▼**B C HOME DIGEST.** 1992. 4/yr. Can.$6.95. Canada Wide Magazines Ltd., 4180 Lougheed Hwy., Ste. 401, Burnaby, BC V5C 6A7, Canada. TEL 604-299-7311. FAX 604-299-9188. Ed. Nancy Ryder. adv.: B&W page Can.$5625, color page Can.$7500; trim 8 1/8 x 10 7/8. circ. 110,000. **Document type:** consumer publication.

747 IT
BAGNO & BAGNI. 4/yr. Via Montecervino 4, 20149 Milan, Italy. TEL 2-48-17-82. FAX 2-481-93-405. Ed. Paolo Pedrizzetti.

747 IT
BAGNO & BAGNI INTERNATIONAL. 2/yr. Via Montecervino 4, 20149 Milan, Italy. TEL 2-48-17-82. FAX 2-481-93-405. Ed. Paolo Pedrizzetti.

744 728 IT ISSN 1120-5407
BAGNO E CUCINA ARCHITETTURA E INTERIOR DESIGN. q. L.25000 (foreign L.70000) (effective 1994). Tecniche Nuove s.p.a., Via C. Mennotti, 14, 20129 Milan, Italy. TEL 02-75701. FAX 02-7610351. adv.: B&W page L.3470000, color page L.5552000; 210 x 297. circ. 21,327.

747 IT ISSN 0392-2715
IL BAGNO OGGI E DOMANI/BAIN AUJOURD'HUI ET DEMAIN/BATHROOM TODAY AND TOMORROW/BAD HEUTE UND MORGEN. (Text in English, French, German and Italian) 1974. m. (9/yr.). L.77000($134) Editoriale P E G SpA, Via Statuto 4, 20121 Milan, Italy. TEL 02-29004927. FAX 02-29003015. TELEX 323088 PEGMOS I. Ed. Oscar G. Colli. adv.: B&W page L.4650000, color page L.7440000; trim 240 x 320. illus. circ. 25,200.
Description: Covers bathroom interior design, surveys on updated production, reports from main sectorial exhibitions in Italy and abroad.

747 IT
BAGNOGUIDA/BATHROOM GUIDE. 1978. a. L.25000 (foreign L.35000). Gruppo Editoriale Faenza Editrice s.p.a., Via Pier de Crescenzi no.44, 48018 Faenza (RA), Italy. TEL 0546 663488. adv. **Document type:** consumer publication.

747 IT
BAGNONEWS. 1990. 6/yr. L.8000($32) Editoriale P E G SpA, Via Statuto 4, 20121 Milan, Italy. TEL 2-29004927. FAX 2-29003015. TELEX 323088 PEGMOS I. Ed. Oscar G. Colli. adv.: page L.3500000; trim 240 x 340. circ. 15,100.

747 690 UK
BARBOUR INDEX BUILDING PRODUCT COMPENDIUM. 1977. a. £75 free to qualified personnel. Barbour Index plc, New Lodge, Drift Rd., Windsor, Berks. SL4 4RQ, England. FAX 0344-884845. Ed. Carol Barnes. adv. circ. 20,000. (also avail. in microfiche from BAR) **Document type:** directory.
Formerly: Barbour Compendium Building Products (ISSN 0260-9169)

749 UK ISSN 0950-0197
BATHROOMS. 1986. m. £45. Maclean Hunter Ltd., Maclean Hunter House, Chalk Lane, Cockfosters Rd., Barnet, Herts EN4 0BU, England. TEL 081-242-3132. FAX 081-242-3134. TELEX 299072 MACHUN G. Ed. D. Smithers. circ. 6,794.

BEAUTIFUL HOMES. see *ARCHITECTURE*

747 US
BEDROOMS & BATHS. 3/yr. Harris Publications, Inc., 1115 Broadway, New York, NY 10010-2803. TEL 212-807-7100. FAX 212-627-4678. Ed. Barbara Jacksier.

747 AT ISSN 0310-1452
BELLE. 1972. bi-m. Aus.$34.80. A C P Publishing Pty. Ltd., 54-58 Park St., Sydney, N.S.W. 2000, Australia. TEL 02-282-8258. FAX 02-267-8037. Ed. Michaela Dunworth; Pub. Richard Walsh. adv. contact: Peter Miller. bk.rev. circ. 44,000. (back issues avail.) **Document type:** consumer publication.

747 641 US ISSN 0006-0151
NA7100
BETTER HOMES AND GARDENS. (Regional editions: New England, Middle Atlantic (including Metro New York), East North Central, West North Central, Central, Southwest and Pacific) 1922. m. $17. Meredith Corporation, 1716 Locust St., Des Moines, IA 50336. TEL 515-284-3000. Ed. Jean LaMon. adv. circ. 7,600,000. (also avail. in microform from UMI; reprint service avail. from UMI) **Indexed:** CINAHL, Hlth.Ind., Ind.How To Do It (1971-), Jun.High.Mag.Abstr., Mag.Ind., MELSA, PMR, R.G., TOM. **Document type:** consumer publication.
—Faxon; UnCover; UMI.
Description: Provides ideas and how-to-information on interior decorating, landscape design, home entertainment, parenting, food, money, automotives.

747 US
BETTER HOMES AND GARDENS BEDROOM AND BATH IDEAS. 1988. q. $3.50. Meredith Corporation, Special Interest Publications, 1716 Locust St., Des Moines, IA 50336. TEL 515-284-3000. Pub. Steve Levinson. adv.: B&W page $22225, color page $31775; adv. contact: Pat Tomlinson. illus. circ. 500,000.
Supersedes (1977-1983): Better Homes and Gardens Bedroom and Bath Decorating Ideas (ISSN 0164-0186)

747 US
BETTER HOMES AND GARDENS DECORATING. 1941. q. $3.50 per no. Meredith Corporation, Special Interest Publications, 1716 Locust St., Des Moines, IA 50336. TEL 515-284-3000. Pub. Steve Levinson. adv.: B&W page $22225, color page $31775; adv. contact: Pat Tomlinson. illus. circ. 500,000.
Former titles: Better Homes and Gardens Decorating Ideas (ISSN 0731-7441); Better Homes and Gardens Furnishings and Decorating Ideas (ISSN 0092-7961)

643.3 US ISSN 0731-5600
TH4816
BETTER HOMES AND GARDENS KITCHEN & BATH IDEAS. 1973. q. $3.50 per no. Meredith Corporation, Special Interest Publications, 1716 Locust St., Des Moines, IA 50336. TEL 515-284-3000. Pub. Steve Levinson. adv.: B&W page $20025, color page $28775; adv. contact: Pat Tomlinson. illus. circ. 450,000.

747 US
BETTER HOMES AND GARDENS KITCHEN AND BATH PLANNING GUIDE. a. Meredith Corporation, Special Interest Corporation, 1716 Locust St., Des Moines, IA 50336. TEL 515-284-3000. Pub. Steve Levinson. adv.: B&W page $20025, color page $28775; adv. contact: Pat Tomlinson. circ. 450,000.

747 US
▼**BETTER HOMES AND GARDENS PRIZEWINNING REMODELING.** 1992. a. Meredith Corporation, 1716 Locust St., Des Moines, IA 50309. TEL 515-284-3000. FAX 515-284-2700. adv.: B&W page $17200, color page $24725; trim 8 x 10 1/2. circ. 450,000.
Description: Focuses on top winners of the magazine's home improvement contests. Contains before and after photos and product information.

747 US ISSN 0277-836X
NK2121
BETTER HOMES AND GARDENS WINDOW & WALL IDEAS. Key Title: Window & Wall Ideas. 1975. q. $3.50 per no. Meredith Corporation, Special Interest Publications, 1716 Locust St., Des Moines, IA 50336. TEL 515-284-3000. Pub. Steve Levinson. adv.: B&W page $22225, color page $31775; adv. contact: Pat Tomlinson. illus. circ. 500,000. **Document type:** consumer publication.
Formerly: Window and Wall Decorating Ideas (ISSN 0363-5406)

747 696 IT
BLU E ROSSO. m. (9/yr.). (National Association of Plumbers Merchants and Bathroom Retailers) S M & C s.r.l., Via Montecervino 4, 20149 Milan, Italy. TEL 2-48-16-965. FAX 2-48-19-34-05. adv.: B&W page L.4500000, color page L.4500000; 210 x 297. circ. 5,177.

747 DK ISSN 0006-5285
BO BEDRE. 1961. m. DKK 34.50. Bonniers Specialmagasiner A-S, Strandboulevarden 130, 2100 Copenhagen OE, Denmark. TEL 45-31-29-55-00. FAX 45-31-29-01-99. Ed. Karen Lyager Horve. **Document type:** consumer publication.
Description: Home decorating, design gardening and cooking for the Danish family.

747 GW ISSN 0006-5463
BODEN, WAND, DECKE. 1954. m. DM.156. Lobrecht Verlag Max Rauscher GmbH & Co. KG, Postfach 1454, 86817 Bad Woerishofen, Germany. FAX 08247-5894. Ed. Max Rauscher. adv.; bk.rev.; charts; illus.; mkt.; pat.; tr.lit.; index. circ. 7,500. **Document type:** trade publication.
—CCC.
Description: Information on coverings for ceilings, floors and walls.

747 NO ISSN 0800-1936
BONYTT/DESIGN FOR LIVING; norsk spesialblad for arkitektur boliginnredning. 1941. 10/yr. NOK 350. Forlaget Bonytt AS, Bygdoey Alle 9, 0257 Oslo 2, Norway. Ed. Tore Giljane. adv. circ. 70,000.
—CCC.
Former titles: Nye Bonytt (ISSN 0029-6783); Bonytt (ISSN 0006-7199)

747 UK
BRITISH DECORATOR. 1930. bi-m. £12 (overseas £20). British Decorators Association, 32 Coton Rd., Nuneaton, Warks. CV11 5TW, England. TEL 0203-353776. Ed. S.M. Broughton. adv.; charts; illus.; stat.; tr.lit. circ. 2,500. **Indexed:** World Surf.Coat. **Document type:** trade publication.
—BLDSC (2298.750000).
Formerly: Masterpainter (ISSN 0025-5092)

747 UK ISSN 0263-2047
BRITISH INSTITUTE OF INTERIOR DESIGN MEMBERS' REFERENCE BOOK. 1983. a. £20. Sterling Publications Ltd., 86-88 Edgware Road, London, W2 2YW, England. TEL 01-258 0066. adv.

BROOKLYN HOME JOURNAL. see *HOME ECONOMICS*

747 US
BUDGET WISE HOME PLANS. a. Archway Press, Inc., 19 W. 44th St., New York, NY 10036. TEL 212-757-5580.

BUILDER'S BEST HOME DESIGNS. see *BUILDING AND CONSTRUCTION*

C A U S NEWS; color, design, fashion, marketing. (Color Association of the United States) see *CLOTHING TRADE*

CAMINO. see *ARCHITECTURE*

747 651 CN ISSN 1193-7505
CANADIAN FACILITY MANAGEMENT & DESIGN. 1987. 6/yr. Can.$30. C F M Communications, 62 Olsen Dr., Don Mills, ON M3A 3J3, Canada. TEL 416-447-3417. FAX 416-447-4410. Ed. Victor von Buchstab. adv. contact: Arvid Stonkus. circ. 6,000. (controlled). **Document type:** trade publication.
Formerly: Canadian Facility Management (ISSN 0838-0139)

747 CN
CANADIAN HOME STYLE MAGAZINE. 1989. 6/yr. Can.$30 (foreign Can.$50). Lorell Communications Inc., 598 Stillwater Ct., Burlington, ON L7T 4G7, Canada. TEL 416-681-7932. FAX 416-681-2141. Ed. Laurie O'Halloran. adv.: B&W page Can.$2310, color page Can.$3135; trim 8 1/8 x 10 7/8; adv. contact: Michael O'Hallorar. circ. 7,600.

INTERIOR DESIGN AND DECORATION

747   CN   ISSN 0008-3887
CANADIAN INTERIORS. 1964. 6/yr. Can.$38 (foreign Can.$84). 113 Davenport Rd., Toronto, ON M5R 1H8, Canada. TEL 416-966-9944. FAX 416-966-9946. Ed. Sheri Craig. adv.: B&W page Can.$3290, color page Can.$4588; trim 8 x 10 3/4. bk.rev.; charts; illus.; index. circ. 11,302. (also avail. in microform from UMI; reprint service avail. from UMI). **Indexed:** CMI.
—UnCover.

CARTER'S ANTIQUES & COLLECTABLES MAGAZINE. see *ANTIQUES*

CARTER'S PRICE GUIDE TO ANTIQUES IN AUSTRALIA. see *ANTIQUES*

747 720   BL   ISSN 0104-1711
CASA CLAUDIA; a revista para morar melhor. 1977. m. $120. Editora Abril, S.A., R. Geraldo Flausino Gomes, 61, 04573-900 Sao Paulo SP, Brazil. TEL 011-8239222. FAX 011-8643796. (Subscr. to: Rua do Curtume, 769, 05065-900 Sao Paulo SP, Brazil. TEL 011-823-9100) Ed. Elda Muller. adv.; charts; illus. circ. 133,000. **Document type:** consumer publication.
    Description: Profiles current projects and ideas in interior design.

747   BL
CASA E JARDIM. 1953. m. Rua Felizbelo Freire 671, 20071 Rio de Janeiro, RJ, Brazil. TEL 21-270-6262. Ed. Milton Madeira. illus. circ. 80,000.

699   IT
CASA STILE. 1962. m. L.110000. Agenzia Gestione Periodici, Via D. Trentacoste 9, 20134 Milan, Italy. TEL 02-215621. FAX 02-2640330. TELEX 3351491 AGEPE I. Ed. Livia Artuffo; Pub. G. Artuffo. adv.: B&W page L.3400000, color page L.4200000; trim 190 x 255; adv. contact: Ana Moroni. bk.rev.; charts; illus.; stat.; circ. 12,000 (controlled). **Document type:** trade publication.
    Former titles: Stile Casa (ISSN 0039-1441); Casalinghi Stile.

747   IT   ISSN 0008-7173
CASA VOGUE. 1969. m. L.61600 (foreign L.120150). Edizioni Conde Nast S.p.A., Piazza Castello 27, 20121 Milan, Italy. TEL 02-85611. FAX 02-870686. Ed. Paola Carpineti. adv.; charts; illus. circ. 51,322. **Indexed:** Artbibl.Mod. **Document type:** consumer publication.

747   IT
CASARREDO & CONTRACT. (Text in English, French, German, Spanish) 1977. q. L.30000. Editore RIMA s.r.l., Via Vincenzo Da Filicaia 7, 20162 Milan, Italy. TEL 02-66103539. FAX 02-66103558. adv. circ. 17,500.
    Formerly: Casarredo International.
    Description: Covers Italian design, office and contract furniture.

CASE AL MARE. see *ARCHITECTURE*

CASE DI CAMPAGNA. see *ARCHITECTURE*

CASE DI MONTAGNA. see *ARCHITECTURE*

747   CN   ISSN 0838-9330
CENTURY HOME. (Text in English) 1983. 7/yr. Can.$19.95. Bluestone House Inc., 12 Mill St. S., Port Hope, ON L1A 2S5, Canada. TEL 905-885-2449. FAX 905-885-5355. Ed. Joan Rumgay. adv.; bk.rev. circ. 35. (back issues avail.) **Document type:** consumer publication.
    Formerly: Canada Century Home (ISSN 0821-5774)

747   CN   ISSN 0715-5689
CITY & COUNTRY HOME. (Supplement to: Chatelaine) 1982. 6/yr. Maclean-Hunter Ltd., 777 Bay St., 8th Fl., Toronto, ON M5W 1A7, Canada. TEL 416-596-5936. FAX 416-593-3197. Ed. Anita Draycott. adv.; illus. circ. 115,000. **Indexed:** CMI.
    Former titles: Home Decor Canada; Canadian Home Decor.

747   FR
CLUB MAISON. 1978. 4/yr. 48 F. (foreign 60 F.). Publications Conde Nast S.A., 10 Bd. du Montparnasse, 75724 Paris Cedex 15, France. TEL 45-67-35-05. FAX 45-67-99-60. TELEX 204 191. Ed. Francoise Labro.

COLONIAL HOMES. see *BUILDING AND CONSTRUCTION*

747 635 301   US   ISSN 0272-6904
TX301
COLORADO HOMES & LIFESTYLES. 1980. bi-m. $15. Wiesner Publishing, Inc., 7009 S. Potomac St., Englewood, CO 80112. TEL 303-397-7600. FAX 303-397-7619. Ed. Laura Lund. adv.; bk.rev. circ. 24,041. **Document type:** trade publication.
—UnCover.

747   CN
CONDOS DE REVES. 1991. a. Can.$2.95. Groupe Magazines, 877 rue St. Pierre, Terrebonne, PQ J6W 1E6, Canada. TEL 514-968-1978. FAX 514-964-2327. Ed. Marthe Leonard; Pub. Denis Clermont. adv.: B&W or color page Can.$2995. circ. 35,000. **Document type:** consumer publication.

729 747   SW   ISSN 0347-2078
CONTRACT. 1975. 3/yr. SEK 285 (effective 1991). Per Olssons Konsult AB, P.O. Box 1083, S-26901 Baastad, Sweden.

747   US   ISSN 1053-5632
TS840
CONTRACT DESIGN; the business magazine of commercial and institutional interior design and architecture, planning and construction. 1960. m. $65 (Canada & Mexico $70; elsewhere $90). Miller Freeman Inc. (New York) (Subsidiary of: United Newspapers Group), 1515 Broadway, New York, NY 10036. TEL 212-869-1300. FAX 212-302-6273. Ed. Roger Yee. adv.; illus.; tr.lit.; index. circ. 29,500. (also avail. in microform from UMI) **Indexed:** Search (1990-). **Document type:** trade publication.
—UnCover; UMI. **CCC**.
    Formerly (until 1991): Contract (ISSN 0010-7832)

747   GW
COUNTRY. (Text in German; summaries in English) 1988. q. DM.56. Jahreszeiten Verlag GmbH, Possmoorweg 5, 22301 Hamburg, Germany. TEL 040-27170. FAX 040-27172056. Ed. Christa von Hantelmann. (back issues avail.)

COUNTRY ALMANAC. see *HOME ECONOMICS*

747   US
COUNTRY DECORATING IDEAS. 1980. q. $8. Harris Publications, Inc., 1115 Broadway, 8th fl., New York, NY 10010. TEL 212-807-7100. adv. **Document type:** consumer publication.

747   US
THE COUNTRY DECORATOR. q. G C R Publishing Group, 1700 Broadway, New York, NY 10019-5905. TEL 212-541-7100. FAX 212-245-1241. Ed. Marilyn Hansen. **Document type:** trade publication.

747   US   ISSN 0737-3740
TH4850
COUNTRY HOME. 1979. 6/yr. $18. Meredith Corporation, 1716 Locust St., Des Moines, IA 50309-3023. TEL 515-284-3000. FAX 515-284-2700. Ed. Molly Cullbertson. circ. 1,000,000. **Indexed:** Access (1984-), Gard.Lit. (1992-).

747 745.1   UK   ISSN 0951-3019
COUNTRY HOMES & INTERIORS. 1986. m. £23.40 (foreign £33). I P C Magazines, Southbank Publishing Group (Subsidiary of: Reed Elsevier plc), King's Reach Tower, Stamford St., London SE1 9LS, England. TEL 071-261-6434. FAX 0444-440619. TELEX 892084 REEDBP G. (Dist. by: Quadrant Subscription Services, Oakfield House, Perrymount Rd., Haywards Heath, W. Sussex RH16 3DH, England. TEL 0444-440421) Ed. Julia Watson. adv. contact: Alison Woodrow. bk.rev. circ. 100,700. (back issues avail.) **Document type:** consumer publication.

747   US
COUNTRY KITCHENS. 3/yr. Harris Publications, Inc., 1115 Broadway, New York, NY 10010-2803. TEL 212-807-7100. FAX 212-627-4678. Ed. Kathleen Fredrick.

747   US   ISSN 0732-2569
TX1
COUNTRY LIVING (NEW YORK). 1978. m. $17.97 (foreign $33.97). Hearst Magazines, Country Living, 224 W. 57th St., New York, NY 10019. TEL 212-649-3500. (Subscr. to: C.D.S., 1901 Bell Ave., Des Moines, IA 50315) Ed. Rachel Newman. adv. circ. 1,700,000. **Indexed:** Gard.Lit. (1992-), PMR.
    Formerly: Good Housekeeping's Country Living (ISSN 0274-4791)

747   US
COUNTRY LIVING REMODELING. a. $2.95 per no. Hearst Magazines, 250 W. 55th St., New York, NY 10019. TEL 212-649-4203.

747   US
COUNTRY VICTORIAN ACCENTS. bi-m. $3.50 per no. G C R Publishing Group, Inc., 1700 Broadway, 34th Fl., New York, NY 10019. TEL 212-541-7100. FAX 212-245-1241.

747   US
COUNTRY VICTORIAN DECORATING. q. G C R Publishing Group, 1700 Broadway, New York, NY 10019-5905. TEL 212-541-7100. FAX 212-245-1241. Ed. Marilyn Hansen.

747   CN
CUISINES ET SALLES DE BAINS. a. Publicor Inc., 7 Chemin Bates, Outremont, Que. H2V 1A6, Canada. TEL 514-270-1100. FAX 514-270-6900.
    Description: Features new designs in kitchen and bathroom furnishing and accessories.

747   GW   ISSN 0172-2867
D L W NACHRICHTEN; Zeitschrift fuer Architektur und Innenausbau. (Text in English, French and German) 1927. a. free. D L W Aktiengesellschaft, Postfach 140, 72406 Bietigheim, Germany. Ed. Frank Werner. bk.rev.; bibl.; illus. circ. 35,000. **Document type:** trade publication.
    Formerly: D L W Informationen zur Bau- und Einrichtungspraxis (ISSN 0011-5002)

747   GW   ISSN 0942-0983
DECO; Wohnen mit Textilien. 1979. a. DM.14. Peter Winkler Verlag, Maximiliansplatz 9, 80539 Munich, Germany. TEL 089-555701. FAX 089-553752. circ. 40,000. **Document type:** trade publication.

747   UK   ISSN 0070-3192
DECORATING CONTRACTOR ANNUAL DIRECTORY. 1903. a. £13.50. Kingslea Press Ltd., 137 Newhall St., Birmingham B3 1SF, England. TEL 021-236-8112. FAX 021-200-1480. Ed. Sam Ichbia. adv.; bk.rev. circ. 1,000. **Document type:** directory.

747   US   ISSN 1064-3095
DECORATING DIGEST CRAFT & HOME PROJECTS. 1987. bi-m. $21. Women's Publishing Company, 950 Third Ave., 16th Fl., New York, NY 10022. TEL 212-888-1855. FAX 212-838-8420. (Subscr. to: Box 11276, Des Moines, IA 50340-1276) Ed. Christine Burns Roth. circ. 450,000. (back issues avail.) **Document type:** consumer publication.
    Formerly: Decorating Digest (ISSN 0889-2210)

676.284   US
DECORATING PRODUCTS RETAIL SALES REPORT; an analysis of sales through decorating products dealers. a. $850. National Decorating Products Association, 1050 N. Lindbergh Blvd., St. Louis, MO 63132. TEL 314-991-3470. FAX 314-991-5039. Ed. David Weiss. circ. 400.
    Former titles: Decorating Products Sales Report.

747   US
DECORATING REMODELING BEST KITCHEN PLAN DESIGNS. 1990. 3/yr. New York Times Company, Magazine Group, 110 Fifth Ave., New York, NY 10011. TEL 212-463-1574. adv. circ. 450,000.
    Description: Features popular configurations, island plans, L-shapes, U-shapes, and galleys.

676.284   US   ISSN 0011-7404
DECORATING RETAILER. 1964. m. $45. National Decorating Products Association, 1050 N. Lindbergh Blvd., St. Louis, MO 63132. TEL 314-991-3470. FAX 314-991-5039. Ed. Diane Capuano. adv.: B&W page $1015, color page $2670; 8 3/16 x 11 1/8. charts; illus.; index. circ. 32,786. **Document type:** trade publication.

INTERIOR DESIGN AND DECORATION

747 US
▼**DECORATING RETAILER'S DECORATING REGISTRY.**
1992. a. $9. National Decorating Products Association, 1050 N. Lindbergh Blvd., St. Louis, MO 63132. TEL 314-991-3470. FAX 314-991-5039. Ed. Kristin Pratt. adv. circ. 32,786. **Document type:** directory.
   Description: Provides information on manufacturers, distributors and suppliers serving the decorating products industry.

676.284 US
DECORATING RETAILER'S DIRECTORY OF THE WALLCOVERING INDUSTRY; the gold book. 1972. a. $25. National Decorating Products Association, 1050 N. Lindbergh Blvd., St. Louis, MO 63132. TEL 314-991-3470. FAX 314-991-5039. Ed. Kristin Pratt. adv. circ. 8,000. (back issues avail.) **Document type:** directory.
   Description: Source of wallcoverings from manufacturer to distributor. Current collections and their distributors listed for dealers.

745 FR
DECORATION. 9/yr. 360 F. (foreign 432 F.). Editions Rusconi, 90 rue de Flandre, 75019 Paris, France.

747 GW
DECORATION. 1989. q. DM.34 (Europe DM.50; elsewhere DM.115.20). Gruner und Jahr AG & Co., Am Baumwall 11, 20459 Hamburg, Germany. TEL 040-3703-0. FAX 040-37035606. circ. 140,000. **Document type:** consumer publication.

747 CN ISSN 0705-1093
DECORATION CHEZ-SOI. 1977. 10/yr. Can.$44 for 48 issues. Publicor Inc., 7 Chemin Bates, Outremont, Que. H2V 1A6, Canada. TEL 514-270-1100. Ed. Andre Vilder. adv.; illus. circ. 70,000.

747 CN ISSN 0315-047X
DECORMAG. (Text in French) 1972. 10/yr. Can.$23.05. Editions du Feu Vert, Inc., 5148 St. Laurent Blvd., Montreal, PQ H2T 1R8, Canada. TEL 514-273-9773. FAX 514-273-9034. Ed. Karine Vilder. adv. contact: Liette Brosseau. bk.rev.; illus. circ. 60,000. Indexed: Pt.de Rep. (1981-). **Document type:** consumer publication.

747 CN
DEL CONDOMINIUM LIFE. 1986. 4/yr. Can.$10. Del Property Management Inc., 4800 Dufferin St., Downsview, Ont. M3H 5S9, Canada. TEL 416-661-3640. FAX 416-661-8923. Ed. Patricia Mackellar. adv.; circ. 25,000 (controlled).

DESIGN. see ART

DESIGN BOOK REVIEW. see ARCHITECTURE

DESIGN FIRM DIRECTORY; a listing of firms and consultants in industrial and graphic design in the U.S. and Canada. see BUSINESS AND ECONOMICS — Trade And Industrial Directories

747 DK ISSN 0108-0695
NK1457.A1
DESIGN FROM SCANDINAVIA; a Scandinavian production in furniture, textiles, illumination, arts and crafts and industrial design. (Text in English, French, German and Scandinavian languages) 1966. a. $19. World Pictures, Martinsvej 8, DK-1926 Frederiksberg C, Denmark. FAX 31-270481. (U.S. dist by: Eastern News Distributors, Inc., 250 W. 55th St., New York, NY 10019) Ed. Kirsten Bjerregaard. illus. circ. 50,000.
   Formerly: Design from Denmark.

747 FI ISSN 0782-4327
DESIGN IN FINLAND. 1960. a. FIM 60. Finnish Foreign Trade Association, P.O. Box 908, 00101 Helsinki, Finland. illus. circ. 55,000.
   Formerly: Designed in Finland (ISSN 0418-7717)

DESIGN LINE. see ARCHITECTURE

DESIGN QUARTERLY. see ARCHITECTURE

747 720 US ISSN 0277-3538
NA2750
DESIGN SOLUTIONS.* 1981. q. $18. Architectural Woodwork Institute, Box 1550, Centerville, VA 22020-8550. TEL 703-222-1100. FAX 703-222-2499. Ed. Elaine Ferri. adv. circ. 25,000. Indexed: Avery Ind.Archit.Per.
   Description: Devoted to interior design solutions and custom use of wood, metals, plastics, and fabrics. Combines interior design and structural architecture with detailed dragings.

747 720 US ISSN 1041-0422
DESIGN TIMES; beautiful interiors of the Northeast. 1988. bi-m. $30 (effective Jan. 1992). Regis Publishing, Inc., 715 Boylston St., Boston, MA 02116. TEL 617-859-9690. FAX 617-859-0002. Ed. Louis Postel. adv.; bk.rev. circ. 15,000. **Document type:** consumer publication.

DESIGN WORLD. see TECHNOLOGY: COMPREHENSIVE WORKS

747 728 US
DESIGNER HOME PLANS. 1986. 2/yr. $15.95 (includes Architectural Designs). Woodworker, Inc., 274 Riverside Ave., Westport, CT 06880-4823. TEL 203-222-1113. Ed. Chris Dorbandt. circ. 75,000.

DESIGNERS' COLLECTION HOME PLANS. see BUILDING AND CONSTRUCTION

747 301 US
DESIGNERS ILLUSTRATED. bi-m. $15.95. Select Communications, Inc., 4410 El Camino Real, Ste. 111, Los Altos, CA 94022. TEL 415-941-6200. FAX 415-941-6263. Ed. Paul D. Nyberg. adv.; illus.
   Description: Resource guide for interior design and home furnishings for consumers.

747 728 UK ISSN 0264-8148
NK2043
DESIGNERS' JOURNAL. 1983. 10/yr. £30. Architectural Press Ltd., 9 Queen Anne's Gate, London SW1H 9BY, England. TEL 01-222-4333. FAX 01-222-5196. TELEX 8953505-MBC-QAG-G. Ed. Alastair Best. adv.; bk.rev.; illus. circ. 13,000. Indexed: Art.Hosp.& Tour., Artbibl.Mod., Avery Ind.Archit.Per., Ergon.Abstr.
—UnCover.

745 724 US ISSN 0192-1487
NK2004
DESIGNERS WEST.* 1953. m. $30 (includes annual Resource Directory). Designers World Corp., 3255 Wilshire Blvd., Ste. 1100, Los Angeles, CA 90010-1415. TEL 310-657-8231. Ed. Carol King. adv.; bk.rev.; tr.lit. circ. 36,789. **Document type:** trade publication.
—UnCover.
   Description: For interior designers, architects and industrial designers professionally interested in the United States Sunbelt states.

645 520 US ISSN 0192-1487
DESIGNERS WEST RESOURCE DIRECTORY.* (Supplement to: Designers West) 1973. a. $10 (for single copy). Designers World Corp., 3255 Wilshire Blvd., Ste. 1100, Los Angeles, CA 90010-1415. TEL 310-657-8231. Ed. Carol S. King. adv.; index. circ. 38,564. **Document type:** trade publication.

747 US ISSN 1057-8277
NK1700
DESIGNERS WORLD.* 1991. m. $30. Designers World Corp., 3255 Wilshire Blvd., Ste. 1100, Los Angeles, CA 90010-1415. TEL 310-657-8231. Ed. Carol King.
   Description: Provides the southern and southwestern design professional with an expanded and comprehensive pictorial portfolio of outstanding hospitality, residential, and corporate design projects.

747 728 US
DESIGNMENT. 1986. a. (Simpson Door Company) Northwest Home Designing, Inc., N H D Marketing Division, 4928 109th St., S.W., Tacoma, WA 98499. TEL 206-584-6309. FAX 206-588-0607. Ed. Todd Lord. adv.; bk.rev.; illus. circ. 120,000. (back issues avail.)
   Description: Discusses home plans.

747 CN ISSN 0835-2526
DESIGNS. (Text English in French) 1986. 4/yr. Can.$8 (foreign Can.$16). Association Communication Innovation Designs 4, C.P. 692, succ. Place D'Armes, Montreal, Que. H2Y 3H8, Canada. TEL 514-842-4436. FAX 514-848-9730. Ed. Bill Taillefer. adv.: B&W page Can.$2800, color page Can.$3600; trim 8 1/2 x 11. circ. 13,900 (controlled). **Document type:** trade publication.
   Description: Addressed to architects, interior and industrial designers, graphists, manufacturers, retailers, government agencies.

DIRECTORY OF CONTRACT WALLCOVERINGS AND SPECIFICATIONS. see BUSINESS AND ECONOMICS — Trade And Industrial Directories

747 II
DIRECTORY OF INTERIOR DESIGNERS & FURNITURE MAKERS. (Text in English) 1984. irreg. $15. Architects Publishing Corp. of India, 51 Sujata, Ground Floor, Rani Sati Marg, Malad East, Bombay 400 097, India. TEL 8404442. Ed. A.K. Gupta. adv.; charts; illus. circ. 5,000. **Document type:** directory.
   Formerly: Directory of Interior Designers (ISSN 0256-4025)
   Description: Listing of professional interior designers, manufacturers, dealers and contractors.

747 620 IT
DISEGNO. 12/yr. Edizioni ESSE s.r.l., Viale Renato Serra 14, 20148 Milan, Italy. TEL 2-32-70-337. Ed. Roberto Salardi. circ. 30,000.

747 SP
DISENO INTERIOR. 12/yr. Infanta Mercedes, 90 8o, 28020 Madrid, Spain. TEL 1-571-75-55. FAX 1-572-25-08. Ed. M. Perez Bodegas.

747 US ISSN 1049-9172
DISPLAY & DESIGN IDEAS. 1988. m. $57. Shore Communications, Inc., 6255 Barfield Rd., N.E., Ste. 200, Atlanta, GA 30328-4300. TEL 404-252-8831. FAX 404-252-4436. Ed. Kari Hudson. adv.; bk.rev.; circ. 18,039 (controlled). **Document type:** trade publication.
   Description: Discusses new products and display ideas in the visual merchandising and store design field.

DOM. see ARCHITECTURE

747 XR ISSN 0012-5369
DOMOV. 1960. m. 300 Kcs. F T V Premiera, spol. s.r.o., Radlicka 103, 150 02 Prague 5, Czech Republic. TEL 422-536679. FAX 422-24510270. Ed. Eva Polackova. circ. 50,000.

DOMUS; architettura arredamento arte. see ARCHITECTURE

DOSSIER COMPONENTI; international lighting technology and lighting accessories magazine. see ENGINEERING — Electrical Engineering

747 US ISSN 0279-4918
DRAPERIES & WINDOW COVERINGS. 1981. 13/yr. $33 (Canada and Mexico $33; elsewhere $100). L.C. Clark Publishing Co., Inc., 450 Skokie Blvd., Ste. 507, Northbrook, IL 60062. FAX 407-627-3447. (Or: 840 US Hwy. 1, Ste. 330, North Palm Beach, FL 33408-3833) Ed. Katie Sosnowchik. adv.; tr.lit. circ. 25,115. (reprint service avail.) **Document type:** trade publication.

EARLY AMERICAN LIFE; magazine of authentic colonial design, decorating, fine crafts and reproductions. see INTERIOR DESIGN AND DECORATION — Furniture And House Furnishings

747 NE ISSN 0165-3083
EIGEN HUIS EN INTERIEUR. 1967. m. fl.42. Uitgeverij Spaarnestad B.V., Postbus 2252, 3500 MD Utrecht, Netherlands. TEL 31-30-822511. FAX 31-30-898388. Ed. M. de Haas. adv.; bk.rev.; charts; illus. circ. 91,400. Indexed: Key to Econ.Sci. **Document type:** consumer publication.
   Formerly: Eigen Huis (ISSN 0013-2519)

747 641 UK
ESSEX HOMES & LIVING. 1988. m. £10. Essex County Newspapers, Wickham House, 1 Northgate St., Colchester, Essex CO1 1HA, England. TEL 0206-714255. FAX 0206-561806. Ed. Christine Beeson. circ. 25,000 (paid). (back issues avail.) **Document type:** consumer publication.

INTERIOR DESIGN AND DECORATION

747   SZ
FACHKOLLEGE. 6/yr. Oberdorfstr. 4, CH-9512 Rossrute, Switzerland. TEL 073-001676. Ed. Renate Kissling. circ. 500.

747 658   UK
FACILITY DESIGN AND MANAGEMENT. 1986. m. £30. Maple Publishing Ltd., 952A Brighton Rd., Purley, Surrey CR8 2LP, England. TEL 081-763-0552. FAX 081-763-2994. Ed. Laura Blair. adv.; bk.rev. circ. 9,500. **Document type:** trade publication.
    Formerly: Facility Management.
    Description: Discusses all the individual elements that create the modern office environment.

747   FR   ISSN 0181-9461
FLASH CONTACT. 1977. 4/yr. Dinat, 34 rue Lucien-Jeannin, 92250 La Garenne-Columbes, France. TEL 47-84-23-68. FAX 47-86-26-41. Ed. Michel Anzou. circ. 18,000.
    Description: Covers interior design and decoration.

747   US   ISSN 1045-5116
FLOOR COVERING NEWS - U.S.A. 1986. bi-w. $20. Altron Communications, Inc., 29-10 Thomson Ave., Long Island City, NY 11101. TEL 718-706-7830. Ed. Albert Wahnon. adv. circ. 912.
    Formerly (until 1989): Floor Covering News (ISSN 0899-9961)

747   CN   ISSN 1193-8781
FLOOR COVERING PLUS. 1955. 6/yr. Can.$20($30) Style Communications Inc., 1448 Lawrence Ave. E., Ste. 302, Toronto, ON M4A 4V6, Canada. TEL 416-755-5199. FAX 416-755-9123. Ed. Jill Sawyer. adv. circ. 6,294. **Document type:** trade publication.
    Formerly (until 1992): Floor Covering News (ISSN 0319-616X)

747.4   US   ISSN 1064-7627
▼**FLOOR FOCUS.** 1992. 10/yr. $29.95. Floor Focus, Inc., 10 S. Division St., New Rochelle, NY 10805. TEL 914-636-0633. FAX 914-636-0809. Ed. Frank O'Neill. adv.: B&W page $1230, color page $2140; trim 8 1/4 x 10 7/8; adv. contact: Harold O'Keefe. circ. 6,800. **Document type:** trade publication.

747   UK   ISSN 0263-7693
FLOORS. 1982. m. £20. Maple Publishing Ltd., 952A Brighton Rd., Purley, Surrey CR8 2LP, England. TEL 081-763-0552. FAX 081-763-2994. Ed. Malcolm Bowen. adv.; bk.rev. circ. 14,000. (tabloid format)
    Formerly (until 1987): Floor and Flooring.
    Description: Information on new products and developments within the flooring industry for the retail and commercial purchasing sectors, retail outlets and buyers for distributors in the U.K.

051 635   US   ISSN 0898-9494
FLORIDA HOME & GARDEN. 1984. m. $24 (foreign $39). Florida Media Affiliates, Inc. (Subsidiary of: Micromedia Affiliates), 600 Brickell Ave., Ste. 207, Miami, FL 33131. TEL 305-445-4500. FAX 305-374-7691. (Subscr. to: Box 2052, Marion, OH 44306) Ed. Kathryn Howard. adv.; bk.rev. circ. 80,000.
    Formerly: South Florida Home and Garden (ISSN 0743-863X)
    Description: Features home interior design, gardening, homecare and travel.

747   GW   ISSN 0015-7678
FORM; Zeitschrift fuer Gestaltung. 1957. q. DM.65. Verlag Form GmbH, Ernsthoefer Str. 12, 64342 Seeheim-Jugenheim, Germany. TEL 06257-81395. FAX 06257-85324. Ed. Karl-Heinz Krug. adv.; bk.rev.; illus.; mkt.; index. circ. 12,000. **Indexed:** Graph.Arts Lit.Abstr. **Document type:** trade publication.
—SWETS.

745.5 720   SW   ISSN 0015-766X
FORM; designtidskriften. (Text in Swedish; summaries in English; editions in English) 1905. 6/yr. SEK 425 in Nordic countries; elsewhere SEK 715. Foereningen Svensk Form - Swedish Society of Crafts and Design, Renstiernas Gata 12, S-116 28 Stockholm, Sweden. TEL 8-6443303. FAX 8-6442285. Ed. Ulf Beckman. adv.; bk.rev.; illus.; index, cum.index. circ. 11,000.
—BLDSC (4008.300000).
    Formerly (until 1932): Svenska Sloejdfoereningens Tidskrift (ISSN 0284-0340)

FORM & ZWECK; Fachzeitschrift fuer industrielle Formgestaltung. see BUILDING AND CONSTRUCTION

747 700   FI   ISSN 0358-8904
NK1471.F5
FORM FUNCTION FINLAND. (Text in English) 1980. q. FIM 130($50) in Finland and Scandinavia; elsewhere FIM 180. (Finnish Society of Crafts and Design) Design Forum Finland, Korkeavuoenkatu 19 A 4 b, SF-00130 Helsinki 13, Finland. TEL 358-0-171 621. FAX 358-0-651449. (U.S. addr.: Art Consulting: Scandinavia, 25777 Punto de Vista Dr., Calabasas, CA 91302-2155. TEL 818-222-2088) Eds. Barbro Kulvik, Liisa Aula. adv.: B&W & color page FIM 9000; adv. contact: Liisa Aula. bk.rev.; index. circ. 6,000. (back issues avail.) **Document type:** bulletin.
—BLDSC (4008.307000); SWETS.
    Description: Promotes the image of the Finnish design and environmental culture abroad.

FRAMING AND ART. see ART

FRANK LLOYD WRIGHT QUARTERLY. see ARCHITECTURE

747   US
FURNITURE: LATIN AMERICAN INDUSTRIAL REPORT. (Avail. for each of 22 Latin American countries) 1985. a. $435 per country report. Aquino Productions, Box 15760, Stamford, CT 06901. TEL 203-325-3138. Ed. Andres C. Aquino.

747   IT   ISSN 0393-4500
GIORNALE DELL'ARREDAMENTO. 1982. m. L.70000. Editore Rima s.r.l., Via Vincenzo Da Filicaia 7, 20162 Milan, Italy. TEL 02-66103539. FAX 02-66103558. Ed. Flavio Maestrini. circ. 16,000.
    Description: Covers modern interior design.

747   UK
GLASS INTERIORS. 1989. q. £12. Spotlight Publications Ltd. (Subsidiary of: Morgan-Grampian plc), Ludgate House, 245 Blackfriars Rd., London SE1 9UZ, England. TEL 071-620-3636. FAX 071-401-8035. Ed. Peter Butler. adv. contact: Martin Gray. circ. 4,300. **Document type:** trade publication.
    Description: Provides information on the creative use of glass in interior design.

747   US
▼**GOOD HOUSEKEEPING DECORATING AND HOME IMPROVEMENTS.** 1993. a. $2.95. Hearst Corporation, Good Housekeeping, 959 Eighth Ave., New York, NY 10019. TEL 212-649-2200. FAX 212-265-3307. adv.: B&W page $13400, color page $20000; trim 8 x 10 3/4. circ. 400,000. **Document type:** consumer publication.

747   US
THE GUILD: THE DESIGNER'S REFERENCE BOOK OF ARTISTS. a. $35. Kraus Sikes Inc., 228 State St., Madison, WI 53703. TEL 608-256-1990. FAX 608-256-1938. **Document type:** directory.
    Supersedes in part: Guild: A Sourcebook of Artists and Artisans; Which was formerly (until 1990): Guild: A Sourcebook of American Craft Artists (ISSN 0885-3975)

747 651.2   IT   ISSN 1120-236X
HABITAT UFFICIO. (Text in English and Italian) 1981. 6/yr. $80. Alberto Greco Editore, Via del Fusaro 8, 20146 Milan, Italy. TEL 02-4819086. FAX 02-4819091. Ed. Paola Pianzola. circ. 21,500.

HARDWOOD FLOORS. see BUILDING AND CONSTRUCTION — Carpentry And Woodwork

747   GW
DAS HAUS. 10/yr. $40. Burda Verlag GmbH, Postfach 1230, 77602 Offenburg, Germany. TEL 089-9250-0. FAX 089-92503519. (U.S. dist.: GLP International, 153 S. Dean St., Englewood, NJ 07631. TEL 201-871-1010. FAX 201-871-0870) **Document type:** consumer publication.

747   US
HAUT DECOR. 1990. bi-m. $14.95. Haut Decor, Inc., Box 2426, Fort Lauderdale, FL 33303-2426. TEL 305-568-9444. FAX 305-568-9445. Ed. Janet Verdeguer. adv. contact: Lisa M. Collins. bk.rev.; circ. 15,000 (controlled). (tabloid format; back issues avail.) **Document type:** trade publication.
    Description: Reports on the upper-end furnishings community, both residential and commercial, for professional interior designers.

HEIM UND HOBBY; Magazin fuer Heimwerker. see HOME ECONOMICS

747   GW   ISSN 0017-9876
HEIMTEX; trade journal for interior decoration. 1949. m. DM.144. (Fachverband des Deutschen Teppich- und Gardinenhandels e.V.) Westdeutsche Verlagsanstalt GmbH, Ahmser Str. 190, 32052 Herford, Germany. TEL 05221-775-0. FAX 05221-775215. Ed. H. Russ. adv.; illus. **Document type:** trade publication.
—CCC.
    Description: Focuses on interior decoration and trading with carpets.

HOME; creative ideas for home design. see ARCHITECTURE

747   IT
HOME; tessile d'arredamento nell'architettura d'interni. (Text in English and Italian) m. (10/yr.) L.70000 (foreign L.95000). Editoriale Galfa s.r.l., Viale Monza 57, 20125 Milan, Italy. TEL 02-2840574. FAX 2610923. TELEX 315614 SISTAR. adv.: B&W page L.2780000, color page L.3500000; trim 178 x 253. circ. 6,967. **Document type:** trade publication.
    Formerly: Ambientare Home.
    Description: Trade magazine covering the furnishing textiles and interior design industry.

688   US
HOME ACCENTS TODAY; the merchandising and fashion news magazine of the home accent industry. 1986. 8/yr. $19.95. Cahners Business Newspapers, Division of Reed Elsevier Inc., 7025 Albert Pick Rd., Greensboro, NC 27409. TEL 910-605-0121. FAX 910-605-1143. Ed. Judith Z. Cushman. adv. circ. 25,000. **Document type:** trade publication.
    Formerly: Accessories - Today.
    Description: Aimed at decorative accessory, specialty home accent, and major gift buyers shopping the major furniture markets in High Point, Dallas, Atlanta, and San Francisco; and gift markets in New York, Los Angeles, Atlanta, Dallas, and Chicago.

747   UK
▼**HOME & IDEAS.** 1993. m. I P C Magazines, Southbank Publishing Group (Subsidiary of: Reed Elsevier plc), King's Reach Tower, Stamford St., London SE1 9LS, England. TEL 071-261-7325. FAX 0444-440619. TELEX 892084 REEDBP G. (Dist. by: Quadrant Subscription Services, Oakfield House, Perrymount Rd., Haywards Heath, W. Sussex RH16 3DH, England. TEL 0444-440421) adv. contact: Allison Woodrow. **Document type:** consumer publication.
    Description: For women between the ages 25-54; provides the latest ideas for the home; includes decorating, furniture, food and everything that makes a home.

747 641   UK
HOME FLAIR. 1990. m. £12. Hamerville Magazines Ltd., Regal House, Regal Way, Watford, Herts. WD2 4YJ, England. TEL 0923-237799. FAX 0923-246901. Ed. Terry Smith. adv. circ. 100,644. **Document type:** consumer publication.
    Description: Presents a forum for stylish yet obtainable and affordable ideas for home interior decorating.

HOME FURNISHINGS REVIEW. see INTERIOR DESIGN AND DECORATION — Furniture And House Furnishings

747   HK
HOME JOURNAL. 1980. m. HK.$250. Communication Management Ltd., 1811, Hong Kong Plaza, 188 Connaught Rd. W., Hong Kong. TEL 547-7117. FAX 858-2671. Ed. Lina Ross. adv. circ. 302,800.

747   US
HOME PLANS. 3/yr. $3.95 per no. New York Times Company, Magazine Group, 110 Fifth Ave., New York, NY 10011. TEL 212-463-1124.

INTERIOR DESIGN AND DECORATION

747 635   UK   ISSN 0018-4233
HOMES AND GARDENS. 1919. m. £25($49.50) (foreign £34). I P C Magazines, Southbank Publishing Group (Subsidiary of: Reed International PLC), King's Reach Tower, Stamford St., London SE1 9LS, England. TEL 071-261-5678. FAX 0444-4406191. (Dist. by: Quadrant Subscription Services, Oakfield House, Perrymount Rd., Haywards Heath, W. Sussex RH16 3DH, England. TEL 0444-440421; US subscr. to: ISI, Box 186, N. Bergen, NJ 07047, USA) Ed. Amanda Evans. adv. contact: Jean Thorpe. bk.rev.; illus.; index. circ. 192,000. (back issues avail.) **Document type:** consumer publication.
—CCC.
Formerly: Our Homes and Gardens; Incorporates: Home.

747   CN
HOMES AND IDEAS MAGAZINE.* 6/yr. Can.$12.75. N H R Publishing Ltd., Box 91824, West Vancouver, BC V7V 4S1, Canada. TEL 604-926-0333. FAX 604-926-1313. Ed. John Hromyk. adv. circ. 203,272.

747   US   ISSN 1062-9254
NA7800
HOSPITALITY DESIGN.* 1979. 12/yr. $40 (foreign $90). Bill Communications, Inc., 355 Park Ave. S., 3rd Fl., New York, NY 10010-1706. TEL 212-592-6200. Ed. M.J. Madigan. adv.; charts; illus. circ. 36,000. (also avail. in microform from UMI; reprint service avail. from UMI) **Indexed:** Bus.Ind., Search (1993-), Tr.& Indus.Ind.
—Faxon; UnCover; UMI.
Former titles: Restaurant - Hotel Design International (ISSN 0898-9079); (until 1987): Restaurant and Hotel Design (ISSN 0745-4929); (until 1982): Restaurant Design (ISSN 0191-345X)
Description: Edited for interior designers and architects of hotels, restaurants, clubs, and senior living facilities and for the developers, owners, and operators of such projects.

HOTEL SPECIFICATION INTERNATIONAL. see *HOTELS AND RESTAURANTS*

747   FR
HOTELLERIE DECORATION. 8/yr. 9 rue Ybry, 92200 Neuilly-sur-Seine, France. TEL 46-40-08-08. FAX 46-40-00-74. circ. 71,986.

HOUSE & BUNGALOW; quarterly journal of the Architectural Service Planning Partnership. see *ARCHITECTURE*

747 641   UK   ISSN 0043-5759
HOUSE & GARDEN (LONDON). 1934. 12/yr. £30 (Europe and N. America £42; elsewhere £48). Conde Nast Publications Ltd., Vogue House, Hanover Sq., London W1R 0AD, England. TEL 071-499-9080. FAX 071-493-1345. (Subscr. to: Quadrant Subscription Services, Oakfield House, Perrymount Rd., Haywards Heath, W. Sussex RH16 3DH, England) Ed. Susan Crewe; Pub. Deborah Gresty. adv.; bk.rev.; illus.; index. circ. 150,627. **Indexed:** Artbibl.Mod., Br.Tech.Ind. **Document type:** consumer publication.
Incorporates: Wine and Food.

747   JA
HOUSE & HOME. (Text in Japanese) 1981. bi-m. 5280 Yen. Gakken Co. Ltd., 40-5, 4-chome, Kamiikedai, Ohta-ku, Tokyo 145, Japan. Ed. Takanari Taguchi.

747   US   ISSN 0018-6422
NA7100
HOUSE BEAUTIFUL. 1896. m. $17.97 (foreign $33.97). Hearst Magazines, House Beautiful, 1700 Broadway, New York, NY 10019-5970. TEL 212-903-5000. FAX 212-765-8292. (Subscr. to: C.D.S., 1901 Bell Ave., Des Moines, IA 50315. TEL 515-282-1508) Ed. Louis O. Gropp. adv.; bk.rev.; illus.; tr.lit. circ. 1,000,000. (also avail. in microform from UMI; reprint service avail. from UMI) **Indexed:** Access (1978-1988), Avery Ind.Archit.Per., Consum.Ind., Gard.Lit. (1992-), Mag.Ind., PMR, R.G.
—Faxon; UnCover.

HOUSE BEAUTIFUL'S HOME BUILDING. see *BUILDING AND CONSTRUCTION*

747   US
HOUSE BEAUTIFUL'S HOME REMODELING & DECORATING. 1964. q. $2.95 per no. Hearst Corporation, 1700 Broadway, Ste. 2801, New York, NY 10019. TEL 212-903-5050. FAX 212-262-9401. Ed. John Driemen. adv.; illus. circ. 250,000.
Formed by the 1987 merger of: House Beautiful's Home Decorating (ISSN 0018-6457) & House Beautiful's Home Remodeling (ISSN 0018-6465)

747   US
HOUSE BEAUTIFUL'S KITCHENS - BATHS. 1980. 3/yr. $2.95 per no. Hearst Corporation, 1700 Broadway, Ste. 2801, New York, NY 10019. TEL 212-903-5050. FAX 212-262-9401. Ed. Timothy Drew. adv. circ. 250,000.

747   US
HOUSE PLAN FAVORITES. s-a. $2.95 per no. Archway Press, Inc., 19 W. 44th St., New York, NY 10036. TEL 212-757-5580.

747   US
HOUSE PLANS & PRODUCTS. 6/yr. Cahners Publishing Company (Des Plaines), Division of Reed Elsevier Inc., 1350 E. Touhy Ave., Box 5080, Des Plaines, IL 60017-5080. TEL 708-635-8800. FAX 708-635-9950. Ed. Ed Fitch. circ. 100,000 (paid), 99,000 (controlled). **Document type:** consumer publication.
Description: Offers new home designs for sale and up-to-date building products.

747 645   IC   ISSN 1021-8327
HUS & HIBYLI. 1973. bi-m. ISK 2390($46) Samutgafan Korpus hf, Armula 20-22, 108 Reykjavik, Iceland. TEL 354-1-813122. FAX 354-1-680102. Ed. Thorarinn J. Magnusson. adv. contact: Helga Moeller. circ. 14,000. (back issues avail.)

747   US   ISSN 0161-1895
I.D.E.A.S.. (Interiors, Design, Environment, Arts, Structures) 1976. q. $20. DoDi Publishing Corporation Inc., Box 343392, Coral Gables, FL 33114-3392. TEL 305-238-0557. Ed. Dorothy Rachline. adv.; illus. circ. 27,500 (paid).

747 658.788   US   ISSN 0894-5373
TS1
I D: INTERNATIONAL DESIGN MAGAZINE; planning-design-marketing. Alternative title: I D Magazine of International Design. (Includes: Annual Design Review) 1954. bi-m. $55. Design Publications, Inc., 250 W. 57th St., New York, NY 10107. TEL 212-956-0535. FAX 212-246-3891. Ed. Annetta Hanna. adv.: B&W page $3150, color page $4200; trim 9 x 10 7/8. bk.rev.; charts; illus.; tr.lit.; index. circ. 16,343. (also avail. in microfilm from UMI; back issues avail.; reprint service avail. from UMI) **Indexed:** A.S.& T.Ind., Art Ind., Artbibl.Mod., Avery Ind.Archit.Per., Ind.Sci.Rev.
—BLDSC (4362.217000); Faxon; UnCover; UMI.
CCC.
Former titles (until 1984): Industrial Design (ISSN 0883-8267); (until 1983): Industrial Design Magazine (ISSN 0192-3021); (until vol. 26, 1979): Industrial Design (ISSN 0019-8110)

747   DK   ISSN 0109-4505
IDE-NYT: TIL LEJLIGHEDER I ETAGEBEBYGGELSE. Variant title: Ide-nyt Til Lejligheder. q. free. Forlaget Ide-nyt A-S, Klausdalsbrovej 495, DK-2730 Herlev, Denmark. TEL 45-44-53-40-00. FAX 44-92-11-21. adv.: B&W page DKK 76100, color page DKK 77800. charts; illus.; stat.; tr.lit. circ. 850,000. **Document type:** consumer publication.
Formerly: Ide-nyt Hus og Have til Villa - Raekkehuse.
Description: Provides tips on improving the lifestyle of Danish apartment dwellers. Includes recipes and occasionally patterns.

747 635   DK   ISSN 0906-0952
IDE-NYT: TIL VILLA, RAEKKEHUSE OG JORDBRUGERE. 1959. q. free. Forlaget Ide-Nyt AS, Gl. Klausdalsbrovej 495, DK-7230 Herlev, Denmark. TEL 45-44-53-40-00. FAX 45-44-92-11-21. Ed. Suzanne LeMaire. adv.; charts; illus.; stat.; tr.lit. circ. 1,600,000. **Document type:** consumer publication.
Formed by the 1984 merger of: Ide-nyt: Til Jordbrugere (ISSN 0109-4513); (1973-1984): Ide-nyt: Til Villa og Raekkehuse (ISSN 0107-007X); Which incorporates (1959-1982): Vi Med Hus og Have (ISSN 0109-3983)
Description: Provides ideas and information to people living in single-home houses or row houses, either with or without gardens.

747   UK   ISSN 0019-1361
IDEAL HOME. 1920. m. £19.95 (foreign £21.15). I P C Magazines, Southbank Publishing Group (Subsidiary of: Reed International PLC), King's Reach Tower, Stamford St., London SE1 9LS. TEL 071-261-6474. FAX 0444-440619. TELEX 892084 REEDBP G. (Dist. by: Quadrant Subscription Services, Oakfield House, Perrymount Rd., Haywards Heath, W. Sussex RH16 3DH, England. TEL 0444-440421) Ed. Terence Whelan. adv. contact: Adrienne Moyce. bk.rev.; illus. circ. 282,429. **Document type:** consumer publication.
—BLDSC (4362.373500). CCC.

747   US
IDEAL HOME PLANS. 1989. a. $1.95. Archway Press, Inc., 19 W. 44th St., New York, NY 10036. TEL 212-757-5580. circ. 75,000. (back issues avail.)
Description: Provides complete description of single family detached homes including floor plans and perspective elevations.

747 645   SZ
IDEALES HEIM/SCHWEIZER WOHNMAGAZIN. 1928. m. 81 SFr. Novapress AG, Rieterstr. 35, CH-8002 Zurich, Switzerland. TEL 01-2019120. FAX 01-2019123. adv. contact: Emil Bisig. circ. 27,500. (back issues avail.) **Document type:** consumer publication.

747 332.6   US
IDEAS FOR BETTER LIVING. 1945. m. free to qualified personnel. Boulevard Publications, 3380 Tremont Rd., Columbus, OH 43221-2112. TEL 614-451-6548. FAX 614-451-6554. Ed. Steve Bulkley. adv. contact: Drew M. West. bk.rev.; illus.; circ. 250,000 (controlled). **Document type:** consumer publication.
Description: Includes home decorating articles, as well as articles on health, pets, good money sense, travel, interesting hobbies (available commercially), and gardening.

747   CN   ISSN 0840-8130
IDEES DE MA MAISON. 1983. 10/yr. Can.$44 for 24 issues. Publicor Inc., 7 Chemin Bates, Outremont, Que. H2V 1A6, Canada. TEL 514-270-1100. FAX 514-270-6900. adv. circ. 86,118.

ILLUMINOTECNICA; international lighting magazine. see *ENGINEERING — Electrical Engineering*

747   CN
IMAGE. (Text in French) 1986. q. membership. Societe des Decorateurs Ensembliers du Quebec, 20 rue Elmira, etage E, C.P. 1122, Place Bonaventure, Montreal, Que. H5A 1G4, Canada. TEL 514-397-1770. FAX 514-397-9601. adv.: B&W page Can.$1000; trim 8 1/2 x 11; adv. contact: Edgar Donelle. circ. 1,500.

INDIVIDUAL HOMES; designing, building & renovating your own home. see *BUILDING AND CONSTRUCTION*

747   II   ISSN 0970-1761
NK2076.A1
INSIDE - OUTSIDE; the Indian design magazine. (Text in English) 1977. m. Rs.180($68) Business India Group of Publications, Wadia Bldg., 17-19 Dalal St., Bombay 400 023, India. TEL 22-274161. FAX 22-2875671. TELEX 118-3557-BZIN-IN. Ed. Sheila Shahani. adv.; illus. circ. 47,115. **Indexed:** Br.Tech.Ind.

INTERIOR DESIGN AND DECORATION

747 — **CN**
INSITE (DOWNSVIEW). (Text in English, French) 1981. bi-m. Can.$32 (US $55, elsewhere $96). Manor Communications, 312 Dolomite Dr., Ste. 217, Downsview, ON M3J 2N2, Canada. TEL 416-667-9609. FAX 416-667-9715. Ed. Lisa Rochon. adv.; B&W page Can.$2700, color page Can.$3600; trim 9 1/2 x 12 1/2. tr.lit. circ. 11,000. (back issues avail.) **Document type:** consumer publication.
   Former titles (until 1993): International Contract (ISSN 1183-9708); (until 1991): Contract (ISSN 1184-2512); (until 1990): Contract Magazine (ISSN 0833-9406); (until 1986): Canada's Contract Magazine (ISSN 0714-6108)
   Description: Aims to educate employees, suppliers and readers about advanced design and to inspire excellence through a comprehensive understanding of design and architecture as they relate to quality of life, health, dignity, the vitality of culture and the sustenance of the individual, the collective and the global environment.

747 643.6 — **DK**
INTERIEUR. 1925. m. (9/yr.). DKK 250 (typically set in Oct.); free to qualified personnel. NOVA Kommunikation A-S, Box 146, Solvang 23, DK-3450 Alleroed, Denmark. TEL 45-42-27-00-78. FAX 45-42-27-13-65. Ed. Poul Jacobsen. adv.; circ. 7,000 (controlled).
   Formerly: Huset Ude og Inde (ISSN 0108-9072)

747 — **US**
NK1705
INTERIOR DECORATORS' HANDBOOK. 1922. 3/yr. $30. Columbia Communications, Inc., 370 Lexington Ave., New York, NY 10017. TEL 212-532-9290. FAX 212-779-8345. Ed. Eileen Roether. adv.; illus.; circ. 20,000 (controlled). **Document type:** trade publication.
   Former titles (until 1992): I D H, The Handbook (ISSN 1055-5013); (until 1989): Interior Decorators' Handbook (ISSN 0733-8511)

747 — **UK** **ISSN 0020-5494**
INTERIOR DESIGN. 1957. m. £25. A G B Publications Ltd., Audit House, Field End Rd., Ruislip, Middx HA4 9LT, England. TEL 01-868-4499. FAX 01-429-3117. TELEX 926726. Ed. Katherine Tickle. adv.; bk.rev.; charts; illus.; tr.lit.; index. circ. 9,736. **Indexed:** Artbibl.Mod., Br.Tech.Ind., Bus.Ind., Tr.& Indus.Ind. **Document type:** trade publication.
   ●Also available online. Vendor(s): DIALOG Information Services, Inc.
   —UnCover. **CCC.**
   Incorporating: Decor and Contract Furnishing (ISSN 0010-2946)
   Description: Professional facts for the designer working in the commercial interior field.

747 — **US** **ISSN 0020-5508**
NK1700
INTERIOR DESIGN. 1932. 17/yr. $39.95 (Canada $63.95; elsewhere $149.95). Cahners Publishing Company (New York), Design Devision, Division of Reed Elsevier Inc., 249 W. 17th St., New York, NY 10011. TEL 212-463-6706. FAX 212-463-6667. (Subscr. to: Box 52331, Boulder, CO 80323-2331) Ed. Stanley Abercrombie. adv.; bk.rev.; illus. circ. 57,000. (also avail. in microform from UMI; microfiche from CIS; reprint service avail. from UMI) **Indexed:** Art Ind., Artbibl.Mod., Avery Ind.Archit.Per., Bus.Ind., Search (1988-), SRI, Tr.& Indus.Ind. **Document type:** trade publication.
   —Faxon; UnCover; SWETS; UMI. **CCC.**
   Description: For the professional designer; provides information on trends and new products.

INTERIOR DESIGN BUYERS GUIDE. see BUSINESS AND ECONOMICS — Trade And Industrial Directories

747 — **CN** **ISSN 0836-3803**
INTERIOR DESIGN ONTARIO. 1985. 8/yr. membership. Association of Registered Interior Designers of Ontario (ARIDO), 717 Church St., Toronto, ON M4W 2M5, Canada. TEL 416-921-2127. FAX 416-921-3660. Ed. Phillip Moody; Pub. Reva Karstadt. adv. contact: Laurie Watson. bk.rev. circ. 6,400. **Document type:** trade publication.
   Description: Devoted to the encouragement of the design industry and the enhancement of the profession.

747 — **UK** **ISSN 0956-988X**
INTERIOR DESIGNER'S HANDBOOK. 1981. a. £55 (overseas £60). Cheerman Ltd., Halpern House, 301-305 Euston Rd., London NW1 3SS, England. TEL 071-383-5757. FAX 071-383-3181. Ed. Jill Blake. adv. circ. 10,000. **Document type:** trade publication.

INTERIOR LANDSCAPE. see GARDENING AND HORTICULTURE

747 — **US** **ISSN 0164-8470**
TS1300
INTERIORS: FOR THE CONTRACT DESIGN PROFESSIONAL. Key Title: Interiors (New York, 1978). 1888. m. $35. B P I Communicatins, Inc. (New York), 1515 Broadway, 39th Fl., New York, NY 10036. TEL 212-764-7300; 800-BPI-4100. FAX 212-944-1719. Ed. Paula Rice Jackson. adv.; bk.rev.; illus.; tr.lit.; index. circ. 29,200. (also avail. in microform from UMI,MIM) **Indexed:** Art Ind., Artbibl.Mod., Avery Ind.Archit.Per., Br.Tech.Ind., Search (1988-). **Document type:** trade publication.
   —BLDSC (4534.350000); Faxon; UnCover; SWETS; UMI. **CCC.**
   Former titles: Contract Interiors (ISSN 0148-012X); Interiors (ISSN 0020-5516)
   Description: Complete coverage of the commercial design industry for the design professionals and students.

747 — **AT**
INTERIORS MAGAZINE. 1984. bi-m. Aus.$3.95. Magazine Group Pty. Ltd., 3 Montague St., Balmain, N.S.W. 2041, Australia. TEL 02-555-1455. FAX 02-555-7822. Eds. Patsy Hollis, Mandy Nolan. circ. 70,000.
   Former titles: Gabriel's Interiors Magazine & Gabriel's Interiors Annual.
   Description: Details domestic decorating, building and furnishings. Reviews global trends and their application to Australia.

747 — **US** **ISSN 0744-8635**
INTERIORSCAPE.* 1977. 6/yr. $12. Brantwood Publications, Inc., 3023 Eastland Blvd., Ste. 103, Clearwater, FL 34621-4106. TEL 813-796-3877. Ed. Jeffrey A. Morey. adv.; bk.rev.; circ. 7,500 (controlled).

747 — **US** **ISSN 1043-4100**
NK1980
INTERNATIONAL CONTRACT DESIGN. 1988. biennial. Abbeville Press, Inc., 488 Madison Ave., New York, NY 10022.

INTERNATIONAL LIGHTING REVIEW. see BUILDING AND CONSTRUCTION

747 — **IT** **ISSN 0020-9538**
NK1700
INTERNI; la rivista dell'arredamento. (Includes annual supplement) 1954. m. (10/yr.). L.144000 (foreign L.250000) (effective 1992). Elemond Periodici s.r.l., Via D. Trentacoste 7, 20134 Milano, Italy. TEL 02-215631. FAX 02-26410847. TELEX 350523 ELEPER I. Ed. Dorothea Balluff. adv.; charts; illus.; tr.lit. circ. 60,000.
   —SWETS.
   Formerly (until 1966): Rivista dell'Arredamento (ISSN 0392-8462)

747 — **US** **ISSN 1064-6906**
NA7235.H3
ISLAND HOME. 1991. bi-m. $20 (effective 1993). Pacific Publishing, 1221 Kapiolani Blvd., Penthouse 40, Honolulu, HI 96814-3503. TEL 808-593-2800. FAX 808-593-2900. circ. 7,800.
   Formerly (until Jan. 1992): Hawaiian Island Home (ISSN 1051-3787)
   Description: Architecture, design and decoration magazine featuring exclusive Hawaiian residences, art and collectibles, with coverage of restaurants, travel and leisure activities.

ITALIAN LIGHTING. see ENGINEERING — Electrical Engineering

747 — **FR** **ISSN 0750-3288**
JOURNAL DE LA MAISON.* 1968. m. 138 F. 20 rue Billancourt, 92103 Boulogne-Billancourt Cedex, France. Ed. Jean Yves Bonhommet. adv. circ. 20,300.

JOURNAL OF DESIGN HISTORY. see ART.

747 — **US**
NK1700
JOURNAL OF INTERIOR DESIGN. 1976. s-a. $35 to individuals; institutions $50; students $20. Interior Design Educators Council, Inc., c/o Paul Eshelman, Ed., Design & Env. Analysis, MVR Hall, Cornell University, Ithaca, NY 14853. TEL 607-255-1811. bk.rev.; cum.index: 1976-1988. circ. 700. (back issues avail.) **Document type:** academic/scholarly publication.
   —UnCover.
   Formerly: Journal of Interior Design Education and Research (ISSN 0147-0418)
   Description: Focuses on research in interior design profession and education, including related fields. *Refereed Serial*

643.3 — **US**
KITCHEN & BATH DESIGN NEWS.* 1983. 12/yr. free. K B C Publications, Inc., 1 Horizon Rd., No. 68, Fort Lee, NJ 07024-6505. TEL 201-487-7800. Ed. Tom Garry. adv.; tr.lit. circ. 41,700. (reprint service avail.)

747 — **US**
KITCHEN PLANS. s-a. $3.95 per no. New York Times Company, Magazine Group, 110 Fifth Ave., New York, NY 10011. TEL 212-463-1018.

749 — **UK**
KITCHENS & BATHROOMS. 1975. m. £20. A G B Publications Ltd., Audit House, Field End Rd., Ruislip, Middx. HA4 9LT, England. TEL 01-868-4499. Ed. Grahame Morrison. adv.; bk.rev. circ. 11,902.

747 — **GW** **ISSN 0722-9917**
KUECHENPLANER; Partner des Kuechen-Fachhandels. 1966. bi-m. DM.53. Verlag A. Strobel KG, Postfach 5654, 59806 Arnsberg, Germany. TEL 02931-8900-0. FAX 02931-890048. Ed. Hilmar Dueppel. circ. 2,900. (back issues avail.) **Document type:** trade publication.
   Description: Trade journal for planning, furnishing and mounting of kitchens and household appliances and techniques.

L D & A. (Lighting Design & Application) see ENGINEERING — Electrical Engineering

747 — **HU** **ISSN 0047-391X**
LAKASKULTURA. 1966. 6/yr. $24.50. (Belkereskedelmi Miniszterium) Lapkiado Vallalat, Lenin korut 9-11, 1073 Budapest 7, Hungary. TEL 222-408. (Subscr. to: Kultura, Box 149, H-1389 Budapest, Hungary) Ed. Maria Pataki. adv. circ. 130,000.

747 — **IT**
LIBRO DI CASA. 1935. a. Editoriale Domus, Via Grandi 5-7, 20089 Rozzano (MI), Italy. TEL 02-82472527. FAX 02-8255033. adv.

LICHT; vakblad voor beslissers over verlichting. see ENGINEERING — Electrical Engineering

LIGHTING DESIGN. see ENGINEERING — Electrical Engineering

LIGHTING DIMENSIONS. see ARCHITECTURE

747 — **US**
LIGHTING YOUR LIFE. 1986. irreg. $2. American Lighting Association, Box 580168, Dallas, TX 75258-0168. TEL 214-698-9898; 800-60L-IGHT.
   Description: Covers types of lighting, shapes and forms of lighting, lighting control, light sources, energy savings, design of indoor and outdoor lighting as well as track and recessed lighting.

LUMI DECOR. see PHYSICS — Electricity

747 — **US**
LUXURY HOMES. 4/yr. Cahners Publishing Company (Des Plaines), Division of Reed Elsevier Inc., 1350 E. Touhy Ave., Box 5080, Des Plaines, IL 60017-5080. TEL 708-635-8800. FAX 708-635-9950. (Subscr. to: 44 Cook St., Denver, CO 80206-5800. TEL 800-635-6089) Ed. Ed Fitch. circ. 100,000 (paid); 45,000 (controlled). **Document type:** consumer publication.
   Formerly (until 1992): Luxury Home Ideas.
   Description: Aimed at custom home buying consumers.

INTERIOR DESIGN AND DECORATION

747   GW   ISSN 0343-0642
M D. (Moebel Interior Design) (Text in English, French and German) 1955. m. DM.214.80 (foreign DM.223.80). Konradin Verlag Robert Kohlhammer GmbH, Ernst-Mey-Str. 8, 70771 Leinfelden-Echterdingen, Germany. TEL 0711-7594-0. FAX 0711-7594-390. Ed. Gisela Schultz. adv.; B&W page DM.5980; trim 205 x 283. bk.rev.; illus. circ. 14,716. (back issues avail.) **Indexed:** Artbibl.Mod., Br.Tech.Ind., CERDIC. **Document type:** trade publication.
—BLDSC (5413.509200); SWETS. **CCC.**
    Formerly: M D Moebel Interior Design (ISSN 0024-8029); Formed by the merger of: Innenarchitektur und Moebel; Decoration.
    Description: Offers a unique editorial and advertising platform for trendsetting problems and solutions in the fields of furniture, interior furnishings and design.

M I N FAX. (Marketing Information Network) see *HOUSING AND URBAN PLANNING*

747   UK
MAGAZINE FOR LONDON LIVING.* 1982. m. £15. Magazine Publishing Co. Ltd., 147-149 Wardour St., 1st. Fl., London W1V 3T13, England. TEL 01-485-0975. Ed. Lucy Tuck. adv.; bk.rev.; film rev.; play rev. circ. 65,000.

747   FR   ISSN 0025-0945
MAISON ET JARDIN. (Supplement avail.: Maison et Jardin Hors Serie) 1950. 10/yr. 250 F.($59) (foreign 400 F.)(effective Aug. 1990). Publications Conde Nast S.A., 10 bd. du Montparnasse, 75724 Paris Cedex 15, France. TEL 1-45-67-35-05. FAX 1-45-67-99-60. TELEX 204 191. (Subscr. to: 60732 Sainte-Genevieve Cedex, France. TEL 16-44-03-44-00; In U.S. subscr. to: International Subscriptions Inc., 1305 Paterson Plank Rd., North Bergen, NJ 07047-1890. TEL 201-867-9381) Ed. Patrick Delcroix. index. circ. 97,524.

747   FR
MAISON ET JARDIN HORS SERIE. (Supplement to: Maison et Jardin (ISSN 0025-0945)) 1978. 2/yr. 310 F.($59) Publications Conde Nast S.A., 4 place du Palais-Bourbon, 75341 Paris Cedex 07, France. (Subscr. to: 60732 Sainte-Genevieve Cedex, France. TEL 16-44-03-44-00; In U.S. subscr. to: International Subscriptions Inc., 1305 Paterson Plank Rd., North Bergen, NJ 07047-1890. TEL 201-867-9381) Ed. Patrick Delcroix. adv.; illus.
    Formerly: Maison Magazine.

747   FR   ISSN 0025-0953
TX1
MAISON FRANCAISE. 1946. m. 340 F. (foreign 396 F.). Publications du Moniteur, 17 rue d'Uzes, 75002 Paris, France. TEL 40-13-30-30. FAX 40-26-10-97. TELEX 680876. Ed. Claude Berthod. adv.; bk.rev.; charts; illus. circ. 93,476. **Indexed:** Avery Ind.Archit.Per.

747   FR
MAISON INDIVIDUELLE. 1970. 9/yr. 160 F. (foreign 250 F.). Publications du Moniteur, 17 rue d'Uzes, 75002 Paris, France. TEL 40-13-30-30. FAX 40-26-10-97. TELEX UPRESSE 680876F. Ed. Beatrice Talpaert. circ. 160,000.

747   FR   ISSN 0180-4561
MAISONS & DECORS MEDITERRANEE. 1974. bi-m. 151 Fr. Compagnie Mediterraneene d'Edition, Collines de Cuque, Av. de l'Armee d'Afrique, 13100 Aix en Provence, France. TEL 42-27-29-53. adv.

747   CN
MANDARIN HOME. bi-m. Home - Sweet - Home Publishing Inc., 226 Esna Park Dr., Ste. 202, Markham, Ont. L3R 1H3, Canada. TEL 416-479-5666. FAX 416-479-5667. Ed. Roks Lam. circ. 12,000.

747   CN
MANITOBA LIVING GUIDE. q. 826 Erin St., Winnipeg, Man. R3G 2W4, Canada. TEL 204-775-8918. Ed. Frank Chalmers. adv. circ. 36,666.

MANUEL GENERAL DE LA PEINTURE ET DE LA DECORATION. see *PAINTS AND PROTECTIVE COATINGS*

MEANS INTERIOR COST DATA (YEAR). see *BUILDING AND CONSTRUCTION*

747   US   ISSN 1058-7233
METRO (ORLANDO).* 1989. m. $14. NewTech Solutions, Inc., 800 N. Magnolia Ave., Ste. 1650, Winter Park, FL 32803-3256. TEL 407-629-2393. FAX 407-629-5448. Ed. Carole Engle-Avriett. adv. circ. 25,000.
    Formerly (until 1991): Metro - Orlando Home (ISSN 1047-9856)

METROPOLIS; the urban magazine of architecture and design. see *ARCHITECTURE*

747   US   ISSN 0273-2858
NK1700
METROPOLITAN HOME; style for our generation. 1969. m. $14.95. Hachette Magazines, Inc., 1633 Broadway, 43rd Fl., New York, NY 10009. TEL 212-767-6000. Ed. Donna Warner. adv.; bk.rev.; bibl.; charts; illus.; tr.lit. circ. 600,000. (also avail. in microform from UMI) **Indexed:** Access (1984-), Ind.How To Do It (1978-1980), Mag.Ind., PMR, Search (1988-).
—UnCover; UMI.
    Former titles (until 1981): Apartment Life (ISSN 0092-0444); (until 1970): Apartment Ideas (ISSN 0003-6366)
    Description: Articles on home design and entertainment. Includes product profiles and menu ideas.

747   IT
LA MIA CASA - MENSILE DI ARREDAMENTO. 1968. m. (10/yr.). L.50000. Alberto Peruzzo Editore, Viale Marelli 165, 20099 Sesto S. Giovanni, Milan, Italy. TEL 02 24202284. FAX 2402723. TELEX 314386 APER I. Ed. Alessandra Burgiana. adv. circ. 55,000.

747   NE   ISSN 0165-5302
MOBILIA; vakblad voor interieurspecialisten. 1959. 11/yr. (foreign fl.123). Uitgeverij Mobilia BV, Prof. Tulpstr. 17, 1018 GZ Amsterdam, Netherlands. TEL 31-20-6206934. FAX 31-20-6207624. Ed. Olga Smalhout-Holst; Pub. Monica Kaltenschnee. adv. contact: Peter Huiberts. bk.rev. circ. 6,300. **Document type:** trade publication.

MODERN LIVING. see *HOME ECONOMICS*

747   SZ   ISSN 0026-8712
MODERNES WOHNEN/HABITATION MODERNE.* 1958. q. 20 Fr. Verlag H. G. Franke, 8126 Zumikon, Switzerland. adv.; charts.

747   AU
MOEBEL RAUM DESIGN. q. Nikolsdorfergasse 7-11, A-1051 Vienna, Austria. TEL 01-555585228. FAX 01-555585347. TELEX 111669. Ed. Konrad Fischer. circ. 6,500.

N Y HABITAT; for co-op, condominium and loft living. see *REAL ESTATE*

747   UK
NATIONAL FEDERATION OF PAINTING AND DECORATING CONTRACTORS YEAR BOOK. 1982. a. Comprint Ltd., 177 Hagden Lane, Watford WD1 8LW, England. adv.

747   IT
NEGOZIO MODERNO. 1981. 8/yr. L.20000. EDIBA Editrice Varese, Via Ponte Rotto, 21056 Induno Olona, Italy. TEL 332-201-101. FAX 332-201-700. Ed. Antonio Bagnasco. adv. circ. 40,000.

747 640   GW   ISSN 0863-4076
NEUES WOHNEN (BERLIN). Polish edition: Moje Mieszkanie. 1956. m. DM.70.80. Verlagsgesellschaft Neues Wohnen mbH, Karl-Liebknecht-Str. 29, 10178 Berlin, Germany. TEL 030-23275270. FAX 030-23276325. (Subscr. to: Deutscher Pressevertrieb, Postfach 101602, 20010 Hamburg, Germany) Ed. Cornelia Schreier. adv.; B&W page DM.11344, color page DM.17016; trim 232 x 300; adv. contact: Bernd-Rainer Buettner. bk.rev. circ. 184,079. **Document type:** consumer publication.
—BLDSC (6080.619200).
    Formerly (until 1990): Kultur im Heim (ISSN 0323-4967)
    Description: Devoted to new design in interior furnishings, interior decorating, architecture and interior architecture, renovations, and artwork; includes tips.

THE NEW YORK COOPERATOR. see *REAL ESTATE*

NEW ZEALAND HOME AND BUILDING. see *BUILDING AND CONSTRUCTION*

747   DK
NORDIC CONTRACT; commercial furnishings and interior design. (Text in English, French and German) 1983. a. DKK 75. N O V A Kommunikation A-S, Solvang 23, P.O. Box 146, DK-3450 Alleroed, Denmark. TEL 42-27-00-78. FAX 42-27-13-05. Ed. Poul Jacobson. adv.; illus.; circ. 22,000 (controlled). **Document type:** consumer publication.
    Formerly: Danish Contract (ISSN 0108-982X)

NUESTRA ARQUITECTURA. see *ARCHITECTURE*

747   IT   ISSN 1120-2386
OFFICE FURNITURE; annual of Italian design for the office. (Supplement to: Habitat Ufficio) 1986. a. $30. Alberto Greco Editore, Via del Fusaro 8, 20146 Milan, Italy. TEL 02-4819086. FAX 02-4819091. Ed. Paola Pianzola. adv. circ. 21,500.

747   IT   ISSN 0391-7487
OTTAGONO; industrial design. 1966. q. L.50000 (foreign L.70000). CO.P.IN.A, Via Melzi d'Eril 26, 20154 Milan, Italy. TEL 315508. FAX 3494731. Ed. Aldo Colonetti. adv.; bk.rev. circ. 24,000. (back issues avail.) **Indexed:** Artbibl.Mod., Avery Ind.Archit.Per., Br.Tech.Ind.
—SWETS.

PAINTER & ALLIED TRADES JOURNAL. see *LABOR UNIONS*

747   UK   ISSN 0956-9227
PAINTING & DECORATING.* 1880. 6/yr. £12.30. (National Federation of Painting & Decorating Contractors) David Pescod Associates, The Old Forge, 9b Vicarage Ln., Kings Langley, Herts WD4 9HF, England. Ed. Alison Davis. adv.; bk.rev. circ. 3,850. **Indexed:** World Surf.Coat.
    Formerly: Painting and Decorating Journal (ISSN 0030-9559)

PAINTING AND WALLCOVERING CONTRACTOR. see *PAINTS AND PROTECTIVE COATINGS*

747 330   US
PATHWAYS TO PROFITABILITY; a financial analysis of the decorating products centers in the U.S. a. $140. National Decorating Products Association, 1050 N. Lindbergh Blvd., St. Louis, MO 63132. TEL 314-991-3470. FAX 314-991-5039. Ed. Donald A. Boetcher. circ. 400.
    Former titles: Sales and Operations Comparison; Pathways to Retail Profits; Cost of Doing Business Study.

747 635   US   ISSN 0270-9341
TX311
PHOENIX HOME & GARDEN. 1980. m. $19. P H G, Inc., Box 34308, Phoenix, AZ 85067. TEL 602-234-0840. FAX 602-277-7857. Ed. Mary Chesterfield. adv.; bk.rev. circ. 38,249. **Document type:** consumer publication.

PICTURE HOUSE. see *MOTION PICTURES*

747   CN
PISCINES, TERRASSES ET PATIOS. a. Publicor Inc., 7 Chemin Bates, Outremont, Que. H2V 1A6, Canada. TEL 514-270-1100. FAX 514-270-6900. Ed. Andre Vilder. adv. contact: Lyane Blackman. circ. 25,000.
    Description: Focuses on exterior design, landscaping and outdoor furniture.

PLANAHOME GUIDE. see *BUILDING AND CONSTRUCTION*

747 333.33   CN   ISSN 0826-4392
PLANS DE MAISONS DU QUEBEC. 4/yr. Can.$2 per no. Quebecor Inc., 7 Chemin Bates, Outremont, Que. H2V 1A6, Canada. TEL 514-270-1100. adv.; illus. **Indexed:** Pt.de Rep. (1981-).
    Formerly (until 1983): Maisons du Quebec.

747   IT
POSATORE. 2/yr. Edipubblicita s.n.c., Via Nicolodi 15, 20161 Milan, Italy. TEL 2-6456661. FAX 2-66200318. Ed. V. Barsotti. circ. 7,000.

PRACTICAL HOUSEHOLDER. see *BUILDING AND CONSTRUCTION*

INTERIOR DESIGN AND DECORATION

747   UK
PRESTIGE HOTEL AND RESTAURANT INTERIORS. 1988. bi-m. £24. Albatross Publications, P.O. Box 193, Dorking, Surrey RH5 5YF, England. Ed. Carol Andrews. adv. circ. 4,000. (back issues avail.) **Document type:** trade publication.
    Former titles: Professional Hotel and Restaurant Interiors; Professional Interiors.

PRODESIGN. see *ART*

747   UK   ISSN 0956-9235
PROFESSIONAL PAINTER AND DECORATOR.* 6/yr. David Pescod Associates, The Old Forge, 9b Vicarage Ln., King's Langley, Herts WD4 9HF, England. TEL 0923-260083. FAX 0923-260085.
    —BLDSC (6860.870000).

QUEST: MANHATTAN PROPERTIES & COUNTRY ESTATES. see *REAL ESTATE*

RAKAM; mensile di moda e lavori femminili. see *WOMEN'S INTERESTS*

747   IT   ISSN 1120-0219
RASSEGNA BAGNO CUCINA. 1979. 4/yr. $55. Alberto Greco Editore, Via del Fusaro 8, 20146 Milan, Italy. TEL 02-4819086. FAX 02-4819091. Ed. Ezio Corti. adv. circ. 45,000.
    Formerly (until 1988): Rassegna del Bagno (ISSN 1120-4044)
    Description: Discusses furniture and accessories for bath and kitchen.

747   US
REMODELED HOMES. 6/yr. Cahners Publishing Company (Des Plaines), Division of Reed Elsevier Inc., 1350 E. Touhy Ave., Box 5080, Des Plaines, IL 60017-5080. TEL 708-635-8800. FAX 708-635-9950. Ed. Ed Fitch. circ. 100,000 (paid); 100,000 (controlled). **Document type:** consumer publication.
    Description: Offers residential remodeling ideas for the consumer.

747 694   US
RENOVATOR'S SUPPLY. 1978. 6/yr. $3 per no. Renovator's Supply, Inc., Renovator's Old Mill, Millers Falls, MA 01349. TEL 413-659-2241. FAX 413-659-3796. adv.
    Description: Concentrates on products for decorating, remodeling, restoring and building.

547 720   CN
RESIDENCES. (Text in English, French) 1990. 5/yr. Can.$17.50. Marketing U.S.P. Inc., 233 rue du Limousin, Saint-Lambert, PQ J4S 1X5, Canada. TEL 514-923-3492. FAX 514-923-0470. Ed. Regine Thomasset; Pub. Daniele Adam. adv. contact: James Dawe, Michel Carriere. circ. 71,053.
    Description: Focuses on topics related to lifestyles, interior decoration and garden design.

747   US   ISSN 1047-8841
RETAIL STORE IMAGE. 1990. bi-m. $35 (foreign $75). Argus Inc., 6151 Powers Ferry Rd., N.W., Atlanta, GA 30339-2941. TEL 404-955-2500. FAX 404-9550-0400. Ed. Katherine Field. adv. circ. 22,000. (also avail. in microform from UMI; reprint service avail. from UMI) **Document type:** trade publication.
    —UMI. **CCC.**
    Description: For store planners, visual merchandisers, interior designers, architects, retail headquarter executives, and store owners who create and implement an image for national and local retail stores. Focuses on the in-line and freestanding store.

747   BE
REVUE DES PEINTURES BELGES. (Editions in Flemish and French) bi-m. (Federation Nationale Belge des Entrepreneurs de Peinture, de Decoration et de Recouvrement des Murs et du Sol.) Editions Coppieters, S.P.R.L., Bd. de Smet de Nayer 393, Boite 5, B-1090 Brussels, Belgium. TEL 02-478-40-98. FAX 02-478-35-02. adv. circ. 2,000.

747   CN
RICKY MCMOUNTAIN BUYER'S GUIDE; the home and lifesytle magazine. 1988. 5/yr. Can.$4.95. Ricky McMountain Enterprises, Ltd., 2256A Sheppard Ave. W., Toronto, ON M9M 1L7, Canada. TEL 416-744-7030. FAX 416-744-7133. Ed. Ylva Van Buuren. adv.: Color page Can.$12800; trim 5 3/8 x 7 3/8; adv. contact: John McGouran. circ. 700,000. **Document type:** consumer publication.

747 635   US
SAN DIEGO HOME - GARDEN LIFESTYLES. 1979. m. $16. McKinnon Enterprises, Box 719001, San Diego, CA 92171-9001. TEL 619-571-1818. FAX 619-571-1889. Ed. Dick Sutro; Pub. Laurence Bame. adv. contact: Marc Baker. bk.rev. circ. 45,000. (also avail. in microfiche) **Document type:** consumer publication.
    Formerly (until 1993): San Diego Home - Garden.
    Description: Covers fine homes, gardens, food, furniture, and art; profiles interesting people; and discusses local and regional issues, travel, arts, and recreation.

640 747   GW
SCHOENER WOHNEN. 1960. m. DM.72 (Europe DM.118.20; elsewhere DM.211.20). Gruner und Jahr AG & Co., Am Baumwall 11, 20459 Hamburg, Germany. TEL 040-3703-0. FAX 040-37035606. Ed. Angelika Jahr. adv.; illus. circ. 430,000. (also avail. in microfilm from UMI; reprint service avail. from UMI) **Document type:** consumer publication.

747   GW
SCHOENER WOHNEN DECORATION. q. Gruner und Jahr AG & Co., Am Baumwall 11, 20459 Hamburg, Germany. TEL 040-3703-0. FAX 040-37035604. Ed. Angelika Jahr. adv. contact: Bernd-Rainer Buettner. circ. 140,000. **Document type:** consumer publication.

747   SZ
SCHWEIZERISCHE KAMINFEGERMEISTER ZEITUNG. (Text in French, German, Italian) m. 50 SFr. Renggerstr. 44, CH-5000 Aarau, Switzerland. TEL 064-224445. FAX 064-248627. adv.; bk.rev. circ. 1,000.

747   CC
SHINEI SHEJI/INTERIOR DESIGN. (Text in Chinese) q. (Chongqing Jianzhu Gongcheng Xueyuan - Chongqing Architectural and Civil Engineering Institute) Zhongguo Jianzhu Gongye Chubanshe - China Architectural Industry Press, Shapingba, Chongqing, Sichuan 630045, People's Republic of China. TEL 661989. (Co-sponsor: Chongqing Jianzhu Kance Sheji Yanjiuyuan)

747   IT
SHOP & DECORATION.* q. S D & D, Via Venini, 20127 Milan, Italy. TEL 02-733240. FAX 02-782483. Ed. Ramon R. Vidal y Plana. circ. 30,000.

747   US
SINGLE FAMILY HOME PLANS. s-a. $2 per no. Archway Press, Inc., 19 W. 44th St., New York, NY 10036. TEL 212-757-5580.

SKOENA HEM - ALLT I HEMMET. see *INTERIOR DESIGN AND DECORATION — Furniture And House Furnishings*

SLOVENIJALES; glasilo mednarondega podjetja za trgovino, inzeniring, proizvodnjo, zastopanje in konsignacijo. see *BUSINESS AND ECONOMICS*

SOL ET MURS MAGAZINE. see *TECHNOLOGY: COMPREHENSIVE WORKS*

SOUTH AFRICAN GARDEN & HOME. see *GARDENING AND HORTICULTURE*

747 635   US   ISSN 0149-516X
NK2002
SOUTHERN ACCENTS. 1977. bi-m. $24.95 (foreign $30)(effective Jan. 1992). Southern Progress Corp. (Subsidiary of: Time, Inc. Magazine Co.), c/o H. Johnson, V.P. Circulation, 2100 Lakeshore Dr., Birmingham, AL 35209. TEL 205-877-6263. (Subscr. to: Box 10411, Birmingham, AL 35202) Ed. Karen Phillips Irons. adv.; bk.rev.; illus.; tr.lit. circ. 265,000. **Indexed:** Avery Ind.Archit.Per., Gard.Lit., Search (1988-1989).
    —UMI.

SPACIOLOGY. see *ARCHITECTURE*

STORE EQUIPMENT AND DESIGN. see *FOOD AND FOOD INDUSTRIES — Grocery Trade*

747   US   ISSN 0896-8772
STORE PLANNING & DESIGN REVIEW. 1941. m. $399 (effective 1994). Retail Reporting Bureau, 302 Fifth Ave., New York, NY 10001. TEL 212-279-7000; 800-251-4545. FAX 212-279-7014. illus. **Document type:** trade publication.
    Supersedes: Store Planning Service (ISSN 0039-1859)

747.85   US   ISSN 0192-8732
NK2195.S89
STORES OF THE YEAR; a pictorial report on store interiors. 1980. biennial. Retail Reporting Bureau, 302 Fifth Ave., New York, NY 10001. TEL 212-279-7000; 800-251-4545. FAX 212-279-7014. illus.

747   US
SWEET'S CONTRACT INTERIORS FILE. a. $39.80 to qualified personnel. Sweet's Catalog Files (Subsidiary of: McGraw-Hill, Inc.), 1221 Ave. of the Americas, New York, NY 10020. TEL 212-512-4750. FAX 212-512-2348. circ. 10,000.

749.63   US
SWEET'S LIGHT SOURCE. 1906. a. Sweet's Catalog Files, 1221 Ave. of the Americas, New York, NY 10020. TEL 212-512-6566. adv. circ. 21,000.

SYNTHESIS/COMPOSITION. see *CLOTHING TRADE*

747   IT
TEX HOME; mensile della biancheria per la casa. (Text in English and Italian) 1971. m. (10/yr.) L.70000 (foreign L.95000). Editoriale Galfa s.r.l., Viale Monza 57, 20125 Milan, Italy. TEL 02-2840574. FAX 2610923. TELEX 315614 SISTAR I. Ed. Franco Battaglini. adv.: B&W page L.2780000, color page L.3500000; trim 185 x 250. **Document type:** trade publication.
    Former titles: Tessilcasa Tex Home; Tex Home.
    Description: Covers the household linen industry.

747 666   IT
TILE ITALIA. 1990. 6/yr. L.30000 (foreign L.50000). Via Circonvallazione N-E 165-1, 41049 Sassuolo, Italy. TEL 536-80-71-21. FAX 536-80-29-09. Ed. Graziano Sezzi. adv. circ. 13,000.

TILE NEWS. see *CERAMICS, GLASS AND POTTERY*

720 651 747   US   ISSN 1059-0307
NA4170
TODAY'S FACILITY MANAGER; the magazine of facilities - interior planning team. 1982. 10/yr. $30. Group C Communications, 121 Monmouth St., Box 2060, Red Bank, NJ 07701. TEL 800-524-0337. FAX 908-758-6634. Ed. Heidi Schwartz. adv. contact: Susan L. Coene. bk.rev.; illus. circ. 35,000. (tabloid format; back issues avail.) **Document type:** trade publication.
    —CCC.
    Formerly (1988-1990): Business Interiors (ISSN 1044-3584); Incorporates (1987-1987): Corporate Design (ISSN 0894-3575); Which was formerly (1984-1987): Corporate Design and Realty (ISSN 8750-8206); (1982-1984): Corporate Design (ISSN 0744-2750)

TODAY'S FAMILY HOME PLANS. see *ARCHITECTURE*

747   HK
TODAY'S LIVING. (Text in Chinese, English) 1987. m. HK.$336 (Asia HK.$753; elsewhere HK$903). Press Mark Media Ltd., Flat D, 1-F Prospect Mansion, 66-72 Paterson St., Causeway Bay, Hong Kong. TEL 852-8822230. FAX 852-8823949. TELEX 49505 EMART HK. Ed. Kenneth Li Kam Man. adv.: color page HK$15500; adv. contact: Jackie Ho. circ. 35,000. **Document type:** consumer publication.
    Description: Covers all aspects of interior design, furniture, carpets, draperies, wall-coverings, lighting, and kitchen and bathroom fixtures.

TOKYO NO IKEBANA. see *ARTS AND HANDICRAFTS*

747   CN
TORONTO LIFE HOMES. 1978. 4/yr. Toronto Life Publishing Co., 59 Front St. E., Toronto, Ont. M5E 1B3, Canada. TEL 416-364-3333. Ed. Marq de Villiers. adv.; illus. circ. 103,000.
    Formerly: Toronto Life Design and Decor Guide.

INTERIOR DESIGN AND DECORATION

TOY AND DECORATION FAIR DIRECTORY. see *BUSINESS AND ECONOMICS — Trade And Industrial Directories*

747   US   ISSN 0883-4660
NK2002
TRADITIONAL HOME. 1978. 6/yr. $17.97 (foreign $23.97). Meredith Corporation (Des Moines), 1716 Locust St., Des Moines, IA 50336. TEL 515-284-3000. FAX 515-284-2083. Ed. Karol DeWulf Nickell. adv. circ. 675,000. **Document type:** consumer publication.
   Former titles: Better Homes and Gardens Traditional Home; Traditional Home Ideas (ISSN 0162-1386)

TRE OG MOEBLER. see *INTERIOR DESIGN AND DECORATION — Furniture And House Furnishings*

TUTTOVILLE. see *INTERIOR DESIGN AND DECORATION — Furniture And House Furnishings*

747   751.2   IT   ISSN 0503-0455
UFFICIOSTILE. (Text in English, Italian) 1968. m. (7/yr.) L.68000($118) Editoriale P E G SpA, Via Statuto 4, 20121 Milan, Italy. TEL 02-29003009. FAX 02-29003015. TELEX 323088 PEGMOS I. adv.: B&W page L.5000000, color page L.7600000; trim 210 x 294. circ. 17,000.

747   AU
UMBAUEN UND MODERNISIEREN. bi-m. DM.36 (foreign DM.42). C P Z Verlagsgesellschaft mbH, Wilhelminenstr. 80, A-1160 Vienna, Austria. TEL 01-454001. FAX 01-460287. Eds. Klaus Vetterle, Ute Cramer. adv. contact: Peter Ross. circ. 50,248. **Document type:** consumer publication.

UNIVERSITA DEGLI STUDI DI PARMA. ISTITUTO DI STORIA DELL'ARTE. CATALOGHI. see *ART*

747   US   ISSN 1040-8150
VERANDA; a gallery of Southern style. 1987. q. $12. 455 E. Paces Ferry Rd., Ste. 216, Atlanta, GA 30305. TEL 404-261-3603. FAX 404-233-5635. Ed. Lisa Newsom. adv.; bk.rev. circ. 95,000. **Document type:** consumer publication.
   Description: Covers Southern interior decorating, antiques and gracious living.

747   US   ISSN 0744-415X
NK2115.5.V53
VICTORIAN HOMES. 1982. bi-m. $18. Vintage Publications, Inc., Box 61, Millers Falls, MA 01349. TEL 413-659-3785. FAX 413-659-3113. Ed. Carolyn Flaherty; Pub. Donna Jeanloz. adv.; bk.rev.; illus.; circ. 100,000 (paid). (back issues avail.) Indexed: Avery Ind.Archit.Per., Gard.Lit. (1992-). **Document type:** consumer publication.
   —UnCover.
   Description: For owners and lovers of homes built in the late 19th and early 20th centuries. Provides how-to information on decorating.

747   BL
VIDA DOMESTICA. m. Carlos Goncalves Fidalgo, Ed. & Pub., Rua Riachuelo 414, Rio de Janeiro GB, Brazil.

747   FR   ISSN 0042-8973
VOTRE MAISON; l'officiel de la maison individuelle et de la decoration. (Text in French, German, Italian, Japanese, Portuguese and Spanish) 1947. bi-m. $20. Editions du Croissant, 6 av. Delcasse, 75008 Paris, France. (Dist. by: European Publishers, 11-03 46th Avenue, Long Island City, N.Y. 11101) Dir. Felix M. Portal. adv.; bk.rev.; charts; illus. circ. 315,000.

747   US   ISSN 0273-6837
THE WALL PAPER; the only monthly journal serving the wallcovering trade exclusively. 1980. m $21 (Canada $35; elsewhere $65). Wall Publications, Inc., 570 7th Ave., Ste. 500, New York, NY 10018. TEL 212-869-4960. FAX 212-869-1141. Ed. Marita Thomas. adv.; bk.rev.; illus. circ. 18,000. (tabloid format; back issues avail.) **Document type:** trade publication.
   Description: Edited for wallcovering dealers and others in the industry. Reports on product selling, merchandising, sales training, advertising, promotions, new products, and procedures.

747   US
WALLCOVERINGS LETTER. m. Publishing Dynamics, Inc., 15 Bank St., Ste.101, Stamford, CT 06901-3017. TEL 203-357-0028. FAX 203-357-0075. Ed. Martin Johnson. circ. 500. **Document type:** trade publication.

747   US   ISSN 1055-4394
HD9843.U6
WALLCOVERINGS, WINDOWS & INTERIOR FASHION. 1919. m. $18. Publishing Dynamics Inc., 15 Bank St., Ste. 101, Stamford, CT 06901. TEL 203-357-0028. FAX 203-357-0075. Ed. G. Lisa Cutler. adv.; illus.; stat.; tr.lit. circ. 17,000. (back issues avail.) **Document type:** trade publication.
   Former titles (until 1991): Wallcoverings Magazine (ISSN 8750-8184); Wallpaper and Wallcoverings (ISSN 0043-0145)

747   US   ISSN 1065-3317
▼**WALLPAPER REPRODUCTION NEWS.** 1990. q. $20. W R N Associates, Box 187, Lee, MA 01238-0187. TEL 413-243-3489. Ed. Robert Kelly. bk.rev. **Document type:** trade publication.
   Description: Primarily for the professional markets dealing with reproduction wallpaper including: screen printers, decorators, designers, architects, and museum professionals, especially of historic houses. Reports on new methods.

747   JA
WATASHI NO HEYA/MY ROOM. (Text in Japanese) 1972. bi-m. 5460 Yen. Fujin Seikatsu Sha, 19-5, 2-chome, Yushima, Bunkyo-ku, Tokyo, Japan. Ed. Hanaho Yagi.

WEEKEND DECORATOR. see *HOW-TO AND DO-IT-YOURSELF*

WEST COAST PEDDLER; oldest journal of antiques, art & collectibles in the Pacific states. see *ANTIQUES*

747   380.1   UK   ISSN 0262-2742
WHAT'S NEW IN INTERIORS. q. £20($40) Morgan-Grampian (Construction Press) Ltd. (Subsidiary of: Morgan-Grampian plc), Morgan-Grampian House, 30 Calderwood St., London SE18 6QH, England. TEL 081-855-7777. FAX 081-316-3169. Ed. Anthea Bain. adv. contact: Ian Witham. circ. 18,000. **Document type:** trade publication.

747   US
WINDOW & WALL IDEAS. q. Harris Publications, Inc., 1115 Broadway, New York, NY 10010-2803. TEL 212-807-7100. FAX 212-627-4678. Ed. Kathleen Fredrick.

747   US   ISSN 1074-813X
WINDOW TECHNOLOGY. 1991. 9/yr. $28. R C M Enterprises, Inc., Twelve Oaks Center, Ste. 922, Wayzata, MN 55391. TEL 612-473-5088. FAX 612-473-7068. Ed. Joe Pawlowski; Pub. Robert C. Mead. adv. circ. 1,500. (back issues avail) **Document type:** trade publication.
   Formerly: Win-Tech.
   Description: Covers materials, equipment and technology used in the production and application of window covering products and accessories.

WOHN DESIGN. see *ARCHITECTURE*

747   GW
WOHNIDEE; wohnen und leben. 1984. m. DM.57.60 (foreign DM.100.20). Heinrich Bauer Verlag, Burchardstr. 11, 20095 Hamburg, Germany. TEL 040-30195273. FAX 040-324636. Ed. Ute Stahmann. adv. contact: Goesta Ahrweiler. circ. 278,022. **Document type:** consumer publication.

747   AU
WOHNKULTUR. bi-m. Verlag Lorenz, Ebendorferstr. 10, A-1010 Vienna, Austria. TEL 0222-426695. FAX 0222-438693. Ed. Christian Lorenz. circ. 5,050. **Document type:** trade publication.

747   SZ
WOHNREVUE. 8/yr. B & L Verlags AG, Steinwiesenstr. 3, CH-8952 Schlieren, Switzerland. TEL 01-7304066. FAX 01-7305841. Ed. Peter Boll. circ. 20,000. **Document type:** consumer publication.

747.05   US   ISSN 0361-638X
TX311
WOMAN'S DAY HOME DECORATING IDEAS. Short title: Home Decorating Ideas. 3/yr. $2.25. Hachette Magazines, Inc., Woman's Day Special Publications, 1633 Broadway, 45th Fl., New York, NY 10019. TEL 212-767-6000. adv.; illus. **Document type:** consumer publication.

747   US
WOMAN'S DAY HOME IMPROVEMENTS. 1984. q. $2.75 per no. Hachette Magazines, Inc., Woman's Day Special Publications, 1633 Broadway, 45th Fl., New York, NY 10019. TEL 212-767-6818. FAX 212-767-5612. Carolyn M. Gatto. adv. circ. 450,000.
   Description: Covers various aspects of maintaining and upgrading the home.

WOMAN'S DAY KITCHEN & BATH NEW PRODUCT IDEAS. see *INTERIOR DESIGN AND DECORATION — Furniture And House Furnishings*

747   US
WOMAN'S DAY KITCHENS AND BATHS. 1971. q. $2.75 per no. Hachette Magazines, Inc., Woman's Day Special Publications, 1633 Broadway, 45th Fl., New York, NY 10019. TEL 212-719-6000. adv.
   Description: Concentrates on the remodeling and decorating of the kitchen and bath.

747   UK   ISSN 0264-083X
NK1700
THE WORLD OF INTERIORS. 1981. m. £33 (Europe and N. America £52; elsewhere £58). Conde Nast Publications Ltd., 234 King's Rd., London SW3 5UA, England. FAX 351-3709. TELEX 914549-INTMAG-G. (Subsr. to: Quadrant Subscriptions Services, Oakfield House, Perrymount Rd., Haywards Heath, W. Sussex RH16 3DH, England) Ed. Min Hogg; Pub. Tony Willett. adv.; bk.rev. circ. 63,341. (back issues avail.) Indexed: Artbibl.Mod., Avery Ind.Archit.Per. **Document type:** consumer publication.
   —BLDSC (9356.071480).

747   CC
XIANDAI ZHUANGSHI/MODERN DECORATION. (Text in Chinese) 1985. q. Y9.60 (HK$20) per no. Shenzhen Zhuangshi Gongcheng Gongye Zonggongsi - Shenzhen Corporation of Interior Design Engineering Industy, Zhuangshi Gongye Dasha, 2nd Floor, Baguailing 10 Dong, Shenzhen, Guangdong 518029, People's Republic of China. TEL 0755-263855. Ed. Gao Shouquan.

YISHU - SHENGHUO/ART - LIFE. see *ARTS AND HANDICRAFTS*

747   NZ   ISSN 1170-3229
YOUR HOME. 1990. 6/yr. NZ.$24.95. Associated Group Media Ltd., Private Bag 99-915, Newmarket, Auckland, New Zealand. TEL 09-379-5393. FAX 09-3089-523. Ed. Sharon Newey. adv.; charts; illus.; tr.lit. circ. 23,500. **Document type:** consumer publication.
   Description: Seasonal coverage of topics pertinent to people in their first year living in a different home, including redecorating, finances, new products, home improvements, working with contractors and professionals.

747   JA
ZAKKA CATALOG. (Text in Japanese) 1985. q. 5200 Yen. Shugunotomo Co., Ltd., 2-9 Kanda Surugadai, Chiyoda-ku, Tokyo 101, Japan. TEL 81-3-3294-1134. FAX 81-3-3294-1169. Ed. Makiko Ishigami. circ. 200,000. **Document type:** consumer publication, catalog.
   Description: Features Japanese and foreign handy or decorative items for the home.

747   GW   ISSN 0941-1070
ZUHAUSE WOHNEN. 1967. m. DM.60 (foreign DM.80.40). Jahreszeiten Verlag GmbH, Possmoorweg 5, 22301 Hamburg, Germany. TEL 040-27170. FAX 040-27172056. TELEX 213214-JAG-D. Ed. Barbara Friedrich. adv. contact: Michael Scheible. circ. 232,472. **Document type:** consumer publication.
   Formerly (until 1991): Zuhause (ISSN 0342-6750)

INTERIOR DESIGN AND DECORATION — Abstracting, Bibliographies, Statistics

643.3 US
ASSOCIATION OF HOME APPLIANCE MANUFACTURERS. M A C A P STATISTICAL REPORT. a. free (SASE required). Association of Home Appliance Manufacturers, Major Appliance Consumer Action Panel, 20 N. Wacker Dr., Chicago, IL 60606. TEL 312-984-5800. FAX 312-984-5823. circ. 700. **Document type:** trade publication.

338.4 US
CARPET AND RUG INDUSTRY REVIEW. a. $15. Carpet and Rug Institute, 310 Holiday Ave., S., Box 2048, Dalton, GA 30720-2048. TEL 404-278-3176. FAX 404-278-8835. (also avail. in microfiche from CIS) **Indexed:** SRI.
Formerly: Carpet and Rug Institute. Review-State of the Industry (ISSN 0092-0495)

680 FR
FRANCE. SERVICE D'ETUDE DES STRATEGIES ET DES STATISTIQUES INDUSTRIELLES. RESULTATS MENSUELS DES ENQUETES DE BRANCHE. AMEUBLEMENT. m. 260 F. (foreign 310 F.)(effective 1991). Service d'Etude des Strategies et des Statistiques Industrielles (SESSI), 85 Bd. du Montparnasse, 75270 Paris Cedex 06, France. TEL 45-56-42-34. FAX 45-56-40-71. stat.
Document type: government publication.
Description: Follows developments in the furnishings industry through the performance of selected indicators.

680 FR
FRANCE. SERVICE D'ETUDE DES STRATEGIES ET DES STATISTIQUES INDUSTRIELLES. RESULTATS TRIMESTRIELS DES ENQUETES DE BRANCHE. INDUSTRIE DE L'AMEUBLEMENT. q. 180 F. (foreign 210 F.)(effective 1991). Service d'Etude des Strategies et des Statistiques Industrielles (SESSI), 85 Bd. du Montparnasse, 75270 Paris Cedex 06, France. TEL 45-56-42-34. FAX 45-56-40-71. stat.
Document type: government publication.
Description: Provides detailed industry-wide performance statistics for comparative evaluations.

684 016 RU ISSN 0484-2286
REFERATIVNYI ZHURNAL. KOMMUNAL'NOE, BYTOVOE I TORGOVOE OBORUDOVANIE. 1959. m. 50.40 Rub. (52.50 Rub. including index). Vsesoyuznyi Institut Nauchno-Tekhnicheskoi Informatsii (VINITI), Baltiiskaya ul., 14, Moscow A-219, Russia. (Subscr. to: Mezhdunarodnaya Kniga, Dimitrova ul. 39, 113095 Moscow, Russia) **Document type:** abstracting/indexing.

INTERIOR DESIGN AND DECORATION — Furniture And House Furnishings

749 US
A & D BUSINESS.* (Architects & Designers) bi-m. Aztex Inc., Box 5059, Hoboken, NJ 07030-1501. TEL 212-545-0055. FAX 212-545-0119. Ed. Laura A. Fentress.

684.1 GW
A B I T INTERNATIONAL. 1987. a. DM.10. Verlagsanstalt Alexander Koch GmbH, Fasanenweg 18, 70771 Leinfelden-Echterdingen, Germany. TEL 0711-7591-1. FAX 0711-7591-266. Ed. Dietmar Danner. **Document type:** trade publication.
Formerly (until 1993): European Office Furniture.

690 664 US
A H A M MAJOR APPLIANCE FACTORY SHIPMENT REPORT. m. $50 to non-members by mail; by fax $100. Association of Home Appliance Manufacturers, 20 N. Wacker Dr., Chicago, IL 60606. TEL 312-984-5800. FAX 312-984-5823. Ed. Joyce Viso. circ. 1,000. (looseleaf format) **Document type:** newsletter.
Description: Factory unit shipments on major appliances, by month, year-to-date, and quarterly (in "units" for current periods and "percent change" from year-ago periods) for 12 product categories.

690 664 US
A H A M MAJOR APPLIANCE INDUSTRY FACTS BOOK (YEAR). a. $45 to non-members; members $35. Association of Home Appliance Manufacturers, 20 N. Wacker Dr., Chicago, IL 60606.
TEL 312-984-5800. FAX 312-984-5823. charts; illus. **Document type:** trade publication.
Description: Comprehensive reference book on the United States' major home appliance industry. Discusses industry market and products.

645 IT
AD. 1981. 12/yr. L.72000 (foreign L.140000). Editoriale Giorgio Mondadori S.p.A., Via A. Ponti, 10, 20143 Milan, Italy. TEL 02-891661. FAX 02-89125888. Ed. Ettore Mocchetti. adv.; bk.rev.; charts; illus. circ. 140,000. **Indexed:** CERDIC.

645 790.132 US
AMERICAN COUNTRY COLLECTIBLES. 1991. q. G C R Publishing Group, Inc., 1700 Broadway, New York, NY 10019. TEL 212-541-7100. (Subscr. to: Box 486, Mt. Morris, IL 61054-7891) Ed. Florina McCain. adv. **Document type:** consumer publication.

747 US
THE AMERICAN DREAM.* 1984. a. $3.95 free. Yorktown Publishing, 125 Union Pl., Lynbrook, NY 11563-4116. TEL 914-962-2565. adv.: B&W page $2150 (Fairfield Ed.), $2480 (Westchester Ed.), $1890 (Rockland Ed., Dutchess & Putnam Ed.); trim 8 x 10 3/4. circ. 11,350 (controlled).
Description: For new homeowners in Westchester, Fairfield, Rockland, Dutches and Putnam counties.

AMI DES JARDINS ET DE LA MAISON. see GARDENING AND HORTICULTURE

684 FR
ANNUAIRE DE L'AMEUBLEMENT. 1908. a. 600 F. Editions Louis Johanet, 68 rue Boursault, 75017 Paris, France.
Former titles: Annuaire de l'Ameublement et des Industries s'y Rattachant (ISSN 0066-2615); Annuaire de l'Ameublement.

645 666 IT
ANNUARIO ARTICOLI CASALINGHI E ARTICOLI REGALO. (Editions in English, French and Italian) 1980. a. L.16000($30) Edispe s.n.c., Via Melchiorre Gioia 71, 20144 Milan, Italy. Ed. Vincenzo Vaccaro. adv. circ. 9,500.

684.1 GW
ANZEIGEN BEOBACHTER MOEBEL. 1978. m. DM.1176. Team Work Werbung & Verlag GmbH, Heinrich-Heine-Str. 1, 61118 Bad Vilbel, Germany. TEL 06101-64007. FAX 06101-7918. stat. circ. 190. (back issues avail.) **Document type:** consumer publication.

645 GW
ARCADE. 1990. 6/yr. DM.135. Ferdinand Holzmann Verlag GmbH, Mexikoring 37, 22297 Hamburg, Germany. TEL 040-632018-0. FAX 040-6307510. Eds. Joern Holzmann, Jochen Holzmann. **Document type:** trade publication.

645.1 US ISSN 0044-8974
ARMSTRONG LOGIC. 1915. 4/yr. free to qualified personnel. Armstrong World Industries, Inc., Floor Division, Box 3001, Lancaster, PA 17604. TEL 717-397-0611. Ed. Shannon M. Oates. charts; illus.; circ. 80,000 (controlled). (tabloid format)
Description: Provides selling tips and installation information to flooring retailers, contractors and installers.

749 IT ISSN 0004-2854
ARREDORAMA. 1969. m. L.80000 (foreign L.160000) (effective 1994). Industria del Mobile s.r.l., Via Giambologna 21, 20136 Milan, Italy. TEL 02-8394780. FAX 02-8372547. adv.; illus. circ. 18,000.
Description: Review of information for the furnishings sector.

749 IT
ARTICOLI CASALINGHI ED ELETTROCASALINGHI. 1958. m. L.160000. Pubbliemme International s.r.l., Via Caracciolo 77, 20155 Milan, Italy. TEL 02-33100954. FAX 02-313864. Ed. Massimo Martini. adv.; bk.rev.; illus.; index. circ. 17,600. **Document type:** trade publication.
Formerly: Articoli Casalinghi (ISSN 0004-3672)

ASIAN SOURCES GIFTS & HOME PRODUCTS. see GIFTWARE AND TOYS

AUDIO - VIDEO INTERIORS. see ELECTRONICS

645 AT
AUSTRALASIAN FURNISHING TRADE JOURNAL. 1949. bi-m. Aus.$46. (Furnishing Society of Victoria) Furnishing Publications Pty. Ltd., 5 Faigh St., Mulgrave, Vic. 3170, Australia. TEL 03-562-5844. FAX 03-562-5412. Ed. Keith Dunn. adv.; illus. circ. 4,400. **Document type:** trade publication.
Formerly: Australian Furnishing Trade Journal (ISSN 0810-3151)
Description: For retailers, manufacturers, distributors, suppliers and affiliated industres.

645 AT
AUSTRALIAN CONTRACT FURNISHING CYCLOPAEDIA. 1972. a. Aus.$50. Furnishing Publications Pty. Ltd., 5 Faigh St., Mulgrave, Vic. 3170, Australia. TEL 03-562-5844. FAX 03-562-5412. Ed. Keith Dunn. adv.; illus.; pat.; tr.lit. circ. 5,951.
Formerly: Australian Contract Yearbook.
Description: For manufacturers, suppliers and retailers of commercial furniture, flooring and furnishings as well as architects, specifiers and government departments federal, state and local.

747 DK ISSN 0903-3947
AUTO OG BOLIG MONTERING.* 1898. m. DKK 42. Sadelmager- og Tapetmestrelaget i Danmark, Fortunstraede 5, 1065 Copenhagen K, Denmark. TEL 45-33-13-80-38. Ed. Frithiof Larsen. adv.; index; circ. 3,200 (controlled).
Formerly (until 1987): Sadelmager og Tapetserer Tidende (ISSN 0036-228X)

AVOTAKKA. see INTERIOR DESIGN AND DECORATION

670 676 GW
B T H - TAPETENZEITUNG. (Boden - Tapeten - Heimtextilien) 1888. 11/yr. DM.156 (foreign DM.168). S N Verlag Michael Steinert, An der Alster 21, 20099 Hamburg, Germany. TEL 040-240852. TELEX 2165704-AFZF-D. adv.; bk.rev.; charts; illus.; mkt.; pat.; stat.; tr.lit. circ. 6,000.
Formerly: B T H Fussboden-Forum - Tapetenzeitung; Incorporates: Tapetenzeitung (ISSN 0720-6593); Fussboden-Zeitung; Tapetenzeitung Tapete und Bodenbelag (ISSN 0039-9566)

747 TS
BAIT AL-IMARAT/EMIRATES HOME. (Text in Arabic) 1987. q. International Publications, P.O. Box 6872, Sharjah, United Arab Emirates. TEL 595777. TELEX 68715. Ed. Abdullah Ahmed Ibrahim. circ. 1,000.

684.16 GW ISSN 0341-3659
BAU- UND MOEBELSCHREINER. (Abbreviated Title: B M) 1946. m. DM.174 (foreign DM.188.40). (Verband des Holz- und Kunststoffverarbeitenden Handwerks) Konradin Verlag Robert Kohlhammer GmbH, Ernst-Mey-Str. 8, 70771 Leinfelden-Echterdingen, Germany. TEL 0711-7594-0. FAX 0711-7594-390. Eds. Peter Nagel, Manfred Maier. adv.; B&W page DM.7520; color page DM.10920; trim 190 x 270. bk.rev.; charts; illus. circ. 28,780. (back issues avail.) **Indexed:** Excerp.Med. **Document type:** trade publication.
—SWETS.
Description: Trade publication for the furniture and building industry. Covers building materials, construction, manufacturing, interior design, architecture, and marketing. Includes events and exhibitions, and positions available.

BAUSPAR-JOURNAL. see BUILDING AND CONSTRUCTION

747.77 UK ISSN 0966-6524
BEDROOMS MAGAZINE. 6/yr. Chalk Lane, Cockfosters Rd., Barnet, Herts EN4 0BU, England. TEL 081-975-9759. FAX 081-975-9753. TELEX 299072-MACHUN-G. Ed. Grahame Morrisson. circ. 6,000. **Document type:** trade publication.
Description: Directed to bedroom retailers, merchants, distributors, manufacturers, and developers.

INTERIOR DESIGN AND DECORATION — FURNITURE AND HOUSE FURNISHINGS

684.15 US ISSN 0893-5556
TX315 CODEN: BEDTEF
BEDTIMES. 1917. m. $35 (foreign $40). International Sleep Products Association, 333 Commerce St., Alexandria, VA 22314-2801. TEL 703-683-8371. FAX 703-683-4503. Ed. Andrea Herman. adv.; bk.rev.; charts; illus.; mkt.; pat.; tr.lit.; tr.mk. circ. 3,000. (back issues avail.) **Indexed:** Text.Tech.Dig. **Document type:** trade publication.
 Formerly: Bedding (ISSN 0005-7568)
 Description: Geared towards mattress manufacturing industry and its suppliers, and other related sleep products trades.

645 US
▼**BETTER HOMES AND GARDENS HOME FURNISHINGS PRODUCTS GUIDE.** 1992. a. Meredith Corporation, 1716 Locust St., Des Moines, IA 50309. TEL 515-284-3000. FAX 515-284-2700. adv.: B&W page $19100, color page $27300; trim 8 x 10 1/2. circ. 450,000.
 Description: Surveys what is available in home furnishings for consumers and professionals.

645 US
BETTER HOMES AND GARDENS KITCHEN AND BATH PRODUCTS GUIDE. 1990. s-a. $3.50. Meredith Corporation, Special Interest Publications, 1716 Locust St., Des Moines, IA 50309. TEL 515-284-3000. FAX 515-284-2700. Pub. Steve Levinson. adv.: B&W page $20025, color page $28775; trim 8 x 10 1/2; adv. contact: Pat Tomlinson. circ. 450,000.
 Description: Lists products in categories, including: cabinetry, appliances, sinks and faucets, bath fixtures, tile, flooring, lighting, laundry equipment and accessories.

747.3 UK ISSN 0305-733X
BLINDS AND SHUTTERS. 1952. q. £38. (British Blind & Shutter Association) Turret Group Plc., Turret House, 171 High St., Rickmansworth, Herts WD3 1SN, England. TEL 0923-777000. FAX 0923-771297. Ed. Debra Clay. adv.; bk.rev. circ. 3,200. **Document type:** consumer publication.
 Formerly: Blindmaker (ISSN 0006-4874)

679.6 US
BROOM, BRUSH & MOP. 1912. m. $20. Don Rankin, Ed. & Pub., 118 E. Main, Arcola, IL 61910. TEL 217-268-4950. FAX 217-268-4815. (Subscr. to: Box 130, Arcola, IL 61910) adv.; tr.lit.; stat. circ. 1,200. **Document type:** trade publication.
 Formerly: Broom and Broom Corn News (ISSN 0007-2400)
 Description: Covers industry news, sales analysis, market conditions, supplier's surveys, new product news and monthly import and export figures on both raw materials and finished products.

BRUSHWARE. see BUILDING AND CONSTRUCTION — Hardware

684.16 UK
CABINET MAKER. 1880. w. £73 (foreign £98). Benn Publications Ltd. (Subsidiary of: Morgan-Grampian plc), Benn House, Sovereign Way, Tonbridge, Kent TN9 1RW, England. TEL 0732-364422. FAX 0732-361534. Ed. Sandra Danby. adv. contact: John Walker. bk.rev.; charts; illus.; mkt.; tr.lit. circ. 8,289. **Indexed:** Key to Econ.Sci. **Document type:** trade publication.
 Former titles: Cabinet Maker and Retail Furnisher (ISSN 0007-9278); Carpet World & Furniture Record; Incorporates: Furnishing World (ISSN 0016-3015)

684.1 US ISSN 1048-0196
CABINETMAKER. 1987. bi-m. $55 (foreign $100) (free to qualified personnel). Delta Communications Inc. (Subsidiary of: Cahners Publishing Company), Division of Reed Elsevier Inc., 455 N. Cityfront Plaza Dr., 24th Fl., Chicago, IL 60611. TEL 312-222-2000. FAX 312-222-2026. TELEX 210012 UR. Ed. Bruce Plantz; Pub. S.L. (Sandy) Berliner. adv.: B&W page $3495, color page $3790; trim 7 7/8 x 10 3/4; adv. contact: Julie Okon. circ. 25,000. **Document type:** trade publication.
 —CCC.

381 AG
CAMARA DE COMERCIANTES EN ARTEFACTOS PARA EL HOGAR. REVISTA. irreg. Camara de Comerciantes en Artefactos para el Hogar, Bartolome Mitre 2162, Buenos Aires, Argentina. illus.

684.1 CN ISSN 0711-0030
CANADA'S FURNITURE MAGAZINE. (Text in English, French) 1981. 4/yr. Can.$16 for 2 yrs. Manor Publishing Co. Ltd., 312 Dolomite Dr., Ste. 217, Downsview, Ont. M3J 2N2, Canada. TEL 416-667-9609. FAX 416-667-9715. Ed. Don Douloff. adv.: B&W page Can.$2241, color page Can.$3213; trim 9 1/2 x 12 1/2; adv. contact: Victor Sibilia. circ. 11,000. (back issues avail.)

CANADIAN FURNITURE & FURNISHINGS DIRECTORY. see BUSINESS AND ECONOMICS — Trade And Industrial Directories

CARE AND REPAIR. see BUILDING AND CONSTRUCTION

670 747.4 UK ISSN 0263-4236
CARPET & FLOORCOVERINGS REVIEW. 1946. fortn. £55 (foreign £73). Benn Publications Ltd. (Subsidiary of: Morgan-Grampian plc), Benn House, Sovereign Way, Tonbridge, Kent TN9 1RW, England. TEL 0732-364422. FAX 0732-361534. Ed. Joy Lawrence. adv. contact: Brian Crittenden. bk.rev.; illus.; stat.; tr.lit.; tr.mk.; index. circ. 5,720. **Indexed:** World Text.Abstr. **Document type:** trade publication.
 Former titles: Carpet Review Weekly (ISSN 0308-4507); Carpet Review (ISSN 0008-6851)

CARPET & RUG INDUSTRY. see TEXTILE INDUSTRIES AND FABRICS

747 PO
CASA E DECORACAO. 1967. 10/yr. Esc.7800. Meriberica - Liber Editores, Lda., Rua D. Filipa de Vilhena, 8, 3o Dto., 1000 Lisbon, Portugal. TEL 01-3530485. FAX 01-576344. circ. 10,000.
 Description: Covers art, architecture, design, decoration, rebuilding and garden.

747 635 PO
CASA E JARDIM. 1978. m. Esc.8250 (in Europe Esc.14500; elsewhere Esc.16000). Edicoes Projardim, Lda., Rua da Misericordia 137, s-l esq., 1200 Lisbon, Portugal. TEL 01-347-21-27. FAX 01-342-14-90. Dir. Eduardo Fortunato de Almeida. circ. 20,000.

747 IT ISSN 0394-882X
CASA TESSIL REPORTER. 12/yr. L.160000 (effective until Aug. 1993). Edi Team s.n.c., Via Montecassino 1, 20021 Baranzate di Bollate (MI), Italy. TEL 2-38-200-080. FAX 2-38-200-082. Ed. Lia di Clemente. circ. 25,000. **Document type:** trade publication.

747 AG ISSN 0008-7203
CASAS Y JARDINES. 1932. 6/yr. $30. Editorial Contempora s.r.l., Sarmiento 643, Piso 5, 1382 Buenos Aires, Argentina. TEL 1-45-1793. Ed. Norberto M. Muzio. adv. circ. 35,000.

645 IT
CASAVIVA. 1973. m. L.60000 (foreign L.84600). Arnoldo Mondadori Editore S.p.A., Casella Postale 1833, 20101 Milan, Italy. TEL 3199345. Ed. Maria Pia Rosignoli. circ. 299,000.

749 US
CASUAL LIVING. 1960. m. $20. Columbia Communications, Inc., 370 Lexington Ave., New York, NY 10017. TEL 212-532-9290. FAX 212-779-8345. Ed. Eileen Smith. adv.; charts; illus.; stat.; tr.lit. circ. 11,500.
 Formerly: Casual Living and Summer and Casual Furniture (ISSN 0008-7564)

CATALOG CONNECTION. see GIFTWARE AND TOYS

645 CN
CHAMBRES A COUCHER. a. Publicor Inc., 7 Chemin Bates, Outremont, Que. H2V 1A6, Canada. TEL 514-270-1100. FAX 514-270-6900.
 Description: Features new designs in bedroom furnishing and accessories.

749 US ISSN 1054-9080
NK2668
CLASSICAL CHINESE FURNITURE SOCIETY. JOURNAL. 1991. q. $60. Classical Chinese Furniture Society, Box 707, Renaissance, CA 95962. TEL 916-692-3143. FAX 916-692-1596. Ed. Jeanne Chapman. circ. 1,500. **Document type:** academic/scholarly publication.
 Description: Studies Chinese hardwood furniture of the Ming and Early Qing dynasties.

645 US
CONTACT (HIGH POINT). vol.26, 1989. m. $18. International Home Furnishings Representatives Association, 209 S. Main St., Space M1215, Box 670, High Point, NC 27261. TEL 919-889-3920. Ed. Robert A. Hall. circ. 3,700. **Document type:** trade publication.
 Description: For home furnishings representatives. Gives facts on taxes, markets, legislation and membership benefits and ideas on how to enhance sales.

645 US
COUNTRY ACCENTS. 1986. bi-m. $13. G C R Publishing Group, Inc., 1700 Broadway, 34th Fl., New York, NY 10019. TEL 212-541-7100. FAX 212-245-1241. Ed. Sally Clark. adv. circ. 300,000.

COUNTRY ALMANAC. see HOME ECONOMICS

COUNTRY DECORATING IDEAS. see INTERIOR DESIGN AND DECORATION

COUNTRY HOME. see INTERIOR DESIGN AND DECORATION

747 US
▼**COUNTRY SAMPLER'S DECORATING IDEAS.** 1993. bi-m. $19.95. Sampler Publications, Inc., 707 Kautz Rd., St. Charles, IL 60174. TEL 708-377-8000. FAX 708-377-8194. (Subscr. to: Box 628, Mt. Morris, IL 61054) adv.: B&W or color page $3750; trim 8 1/8 x 10 3/4. circ. 125,000.

747.3 FR ISSN 1169-0704
COURRIER DU MEUBLE ET DE L'HABITAT. 1957. w. 650 F. (foreign 1030 F.). Editions du Tigre, 23 rue Joubert, 75009 Paris, France. TEL 48-74-52-50. FAX 1-40-16-43-65. TELEX COUMEUB 283769F. adv. circ. 9,600.
 Formerly (until 1990): Courrier du Meuble (ISSN 0751-6320)

643.3 IT
CUCINA BELLA E BUONA. 1978. 4/yr. L.6500. Di Baio Editore s.r.l., Via Settembrini 11, 20124 Milan, Italy. TEL 2-66-92-254. FAX 2-670-9257. Ed. Giuseppe Maria Jonghi-Lavarini. adv. circ. 80,000.
 Formerly: Cucina Bella.

643.3 FR
CUISIGN. 5/yr. Societe de Gestion de Publications, 72 rue du Dr. Decorse, 94410 St-Maurice, France. TEL 43-76-65-29. FAX 43-76-54-68. TELEX 699 559 COMA. Ed. Jean-Pierre Picamal. circ. 6,000.

684.1 GW ISSN 0341-8839
D D S - DER DEUTSCHER SCHREINER UND TISCHLER; Fachzeitschrift fuer die Holz- und Kunststoffverarbeitung. 1901. m. DM.171 (foreign DM.183). Deutsche Verlags-Anstalt GmbH, Postfach 106012, 70049 Stuttgart, Germany. TEL 0711-2631-0. FAX 0711-2859623. Ed. Ulrich Mueller. adv.: B&W page DM.4860, color page DM.8700; trim 269 x 185. bk.rev.; charts; illus.; tr.lit.; index. circ. 21,454. **Document type:** trade publication.
 —CCC.
 Former titles: Deutscher Schreiner (ISSN 0012-0685); Deutsche Moebel- und Bauschreiner.
 Description: Trade publication for the wood and plastics industry. Features design and construction, technology, materials, business, economics, and education. Includes positions available.

643 658.8 UK
D I Y: THE INTERNATIONAL MARKET. (Do-It-Yourself) a. £1375($2750) Euromonitor, 87-88 Turnmill St., London EC1M 5QU, England. TEL 071-251-8024. FAX 071-608-3149. (Addr. in N. America: Euromonitor International, 111 W. Washington St., Chicago, IL 60602. TEL 312-541-8024. FAX 312-541-1567) (looseleaf format) **Document type:** trade publication.
 ●Also available online. Vendor(s): Data-Star, DIALOG Information Services, Inc.
 Description: Analyzes the market for products and supplies geared toward handypersons for France, Germany, Italy, Spain, the U.K., the U.S., and Japan.

747.5 US
DALTON CARPET JOURNAL. 1981. m. $12. Daily Citizen-News, 308 S. Thornton Ave., Dalton, GA 30720. TEL 404-278-1011. Ed. Louise Hackney. adv.; bk.rev. circ. 20,000.

INTERIOR DESIGN AND DECORATION — FURNITURE AND HOUSE FURNISHINGS

684.1   IT   ISSN 0393-330X
DATALIGNUM. (Text in English, German and Italian) 1982. m. L.80000($100) Milla Editrice srl, Via Mugello 6, 20137 Milan, Italy. TEL 02-7610878. FAX 02-7490037. TELEX 322210 MILLA I. Ed. Pietro Stroppa. adv.; bk.rev. circ. 9,000.

DEALERSCOPE MERCHANDISING; the marketing magazine for consumer electronics and major appliance retailing. see *ELECTRONICS*

749   US   ISSN 0011-7358
N8610
DECOR; the magazine of fine interior accessories. 1880. m. $20. Commerce Publishing Co., 330 N. Fourth St., St. Louis, MO 63102-2036. TEL 314-421-5445. Ed. Gary Goldman. adv. contact: Dee Severino. illus.; mkt. circ. 22,122. **Document type:** trade publication.
    Formerly: Picture and Gift Journal.
    Description: Provides merchandizing and operating ideas to help retailers of art, frames and related materials increase sales.

347.5   US   ISSN 1045-8816
THE DECORATIVE RUG. 1987. m. $48. Oriental Rug Auction Review, Inc., Box 709, Meredith, NH 03253. TEL 603-744-9191. FAX 603-744-6933. Ed. Ron O'Callaghan. adv.; bk.rev.; illus. circ. 10,000. **Document type:** trade publication.
    Formerly: Decorative Rug Review.
    Description: Covers new oriental rugs at the wholesale and retail levels.

747   BE   ISSN 0773-4034
DECORS NEW EDITIONS. (Editions in French and Dutch) 1965. q. 2000 Fr. Decors New Editions S.A., Av. des Mimosas 33, B-1150 Brussels, Belgium. Ed. Euroset. circ. 40,000.
    Former titles: Decors; S.A. Decors New Editions; Meubles et Decors (ISSN 0026-1653)

747   IT
DESIGN AND CONTRACT. 4/yr. Editore RIMA s.r.l., Via da Filicaia, 20162 Milan, Italy. TEL 2-10-35-39. FAX 2-66-103-558. Ed. Flavio Maestrini. circ. 16,200.

645.4   US
DIGEST FOR HOME FURNISHERS.* 1919. q. $3.50. Minnesota 300, 300 Prairie Center Dr., Ste. 210, Eden Prairie, MN 55344. Ed. Richard L. English. adv. circ. 3,000.
    Formerly: Furniture Digest.

DIRECTORY OF HOME CENTER OPERATORS & HARDWARE CHAINS (YEAR); includes: home center warehouses, lumber/building material outlets, farm & home stores & specialty paint chains. see *BUSINESS AND ECONOMICS — Trade And Industrial Directories*

DIRECTORY OF HOME FURNISHINGS RETAILERS (YEAR); includes: full-line home furnishing stores, furniture stores, bedding stores, wholesalers and distributors. see *BUSINESS AND ECONOMICS — Trade And Industrial Directories*

DIRECTORY OF MATERIALS SUPPLIERS. see *FIRE PREVENTION*

684.1   UK   ISSN 0070-6604
DIRECTORY TO THE FURNISHING TRADE. 1957. a. £95 (foreign £105). Benn Business Information Services Ltd. (Subsidiary of: Morgan-Grampian plc), Riverbank House, Angel Ln., Tonbridge, Kent TN9 1SE, England. TEL 0732-362666. FAX 0732-367301. TELEX 957829 BENTON G. Ed.Bd. adv.; index. circ. 2,000. **Document type:** directory.
    Formerly: Cabinet Maker and Retail Furnisher Directory to the Furnishing Trade.
    Description: Features manufacturers and wholesalers, classified buyers, retailers, and agents. Also includes business information and related trade associations.

747   IT
DOMINA. 9/yr. L.120000($110) Domina s.r.l., Via Cavour 2, 22012 Cernobbio (CO), Italy. TEL 31-51-34-34. FAX 31-34-07-53. Ed. Stefania Bosco di Camastra. adv. contact: Damiana Danieli. circ. 18,000. **Document type:** trade publication.

DOMOV. see *INTERIOR DESIGN AND DECORATION*

749.63   GW
E R C O LICHTBERICHT. 1977. 3/yr. E R C O Leuchten GmbH, Postfach 2460, 58505 Luedenscheid, Germany. TEL 02351-551-0. illus. circ. 40,000. **Document type:** bulletin.

645   GW
▼**E Z HAUSRAT.** 1993. 20/yr. DM.108. Eisenwaren-Zeitung GmbH, Rheinwallgraben 11, 41460 Neuss, Germany. TEL 02131-273028. FAX 02131-271516. Ed. Georg Fremdling. adv.: B&W page DM.3620, color page DM.6404; trim 185 x 260. circ. 12,000. **Document type:** trade publication.
    Supersedes in part (in 1992): E Z - Eisenwaren und Hausrat (ISSN 0938-2011)

749   US   ISSN 0012-8155
E162
EARLY AMERICAN LIFE; magazine of authentic colonial design, decorating, fine crafts and reproductions. 1970. bi-m. $19.97 (foreign $22.95). (Early American Society) Cowles Magazines, Inc. (Subsidiary of: Cowles Media Company), 6405 Flank Dr., Box 8200, Harrisburg, PA 17105-8200. TEL 717-657-9555. FAX 717-657-9526. (Subscr. to: Box 1620, Mt. Morris, IL 61054. TEL 800-435-9601) Ed. Mimi Handler. adv.; bk.rev.; illus.; tr.lit. circ. 124,729. (also avail. in microform from UMI; reprint service avail. from UMI) **Indexed:** Access (1976-), Amer.Hist.& Life, Hist.Abstr., Ind.How To Do It (1977-), Mag.Ind. **Document type:** consumer publication.
    —UnCover; UMI.

747.4   US
EASTERN FLOORS. 1990. q. $20. Specialist Publications, Inc., 17835 Ventura Blvd., Ste. 312, Encino, CA 91316. TEL 818-345-3550. FAX 818-344-9647. Ed. Howard Olansky. circ. 17,500.
    Description: For floor covering and tile retailers, distributors, agents and manufacturers in the eastern half of the United States, with an emphasis on markets, shows, conventions and industry meetings.

645   BE   ISSN 0772-6287
ECHO DU MEUBLE/MEUBEL ECHO. (Text in Flemish, French) 24/yr. 1500 BEF. Hayez S.A., Rue Fin 4, 1080 Brussels, Belgium. TEL 32-2-4240064. FAX 32-2-4240378. TELEX 63467 HAYEZ B. Ed. Geert Degrande; Pub. Geert Degrande. adv. contact: Karin Lamberts. circ. 2,500 (paid). **Document type:** trade publication.
    Supersedes: Meubel Echo (ISSN 0772-6279)

EIGEN HUIS EN INTERIEUR. see *INTERIOR DESIGN AND DECORATION*

645   AU
EISEN - METALL - KUECHEN - GERAET. m. Zeitungverlag Kuhn und Co., Kutschkergasse 42, A-1180 Vienna, Austria. TEL 01-341503. FAX 01-3130121. Ed. Gerd Volker Weege. circ. 5,400. **Document type:** trade publication.

643.3   SW
ELECTROLUX. ANNUAL REPORT. (Text in English) a. free to qualified personnel. Electrolux, Lilla Essingen, S-10545 Stockholm, Sweden. **Document type:** corporate report.
    Description: Reports on electrical appliances.

645   US   ISSN 1046-1957
NK1700
ELLE DECOR. (American edition) 1989. 6/yr. $18. Elle Publishing (Subsidiary of: Hachette Filipacchi Magazines), 1633 Broadway, New York, NY 10019. TEL 212-767-5800. FAX 212-489-4241. (Subscr. to: Box 55851, Boulder, CO 80322. TEL 800-274-4687) Ed. Marian McEvoy. adv.; bk.rev. circ. 400,000. **Indexed:** Access (1991-). **Document type:** consumer publication.
    —UnCover.
    Description: Provides an international design showcase of home products. Encourages readers to use their own creativity.

747   IT   ISSN 1120-4400
ELLE DECOR. 1990. 10/yr. Rizzoli Editore-Corriere della Sera, Via Angelo Rizzoli 2, 20132 Milan, Italy. TEL 39-02-25841. adv.: color page L.19800000; 287 x 230. circ. 51,435.

747   FR   ISSN 0988-1476
ELLE DECORATION. 1987. 9/yr. 30 F. (foreign 307 F./yr.). Hachette Filipacchi Publications, 6 rue Ancelle, 92525 Neuilly-sur-Seine Cedex, France. TEL 40-88-72-59. FAX 40-88-72-62. (Subscr. to: 90 rue de Flandre, 75947 Paris Cedex 19, France. TEL 40-34-35-00) adv.: B&W page 48500 F., color page 73500 F.; trim 227 x 297. circ. 175,072.

747   GW   ISSN 0941-7303
ELLE DECORATION. 1990. q. DM.32. Burda GmbH and F.E.P., Arabellastr. 23, 81925 Munich, Germany. TEL 089-9250-3040. FAX 089-92503332. Ed. Renate Rosenthal; Pubs. Hubert Burda, Daniel Filipacchi. adv.: B&W page DM.15000, color page DM.21830; trim 230 x 285; adv. contact: Stephanie Albrecht. circ. 75,000. **Document type:** consumer publication.

643.3   SP
EQUIPO DOMESTICO - ELECTRODOMESTICOS; revista especializada del mundo de los aparatos que dan confort al hogar. 7/yr. 6180 ptas. (foreign 10000 ptas.). Ediciones de Prensa Duarte, S.L., Fermin Caballero 64 (Larra 1), 6o D, 28034 Madrid, Spain. TEL 91-378-04-70. Ed. Antonio Duarte Palomero. adv.: B&W page 175000 ptas., color page 190000 ptas.; 210 x 297. charts; illus.; stat. circ. 5,600. **Document type:** trade publication.

ESSEX HOMES & LIVING. see *INTERIOR DESIGN AND DECORATION*

684.1   SP   ISSN 0210-5489
EUROMUEBLE. 1965. m. $45. Editorial Ofice, German Perez Carrasco, 63, 28027 Madrid, Spain. Ed. Ch.G. Robba. circ. 10,000. (back issues avail.)

645   GW
EUROPAEISCHER WIRTSCHAFTSDIENST. EINKAUFSBERATER FUER DIE MOEBELINDUSTRIE. m. DM.390. Casimir Katz Verlag, Bleichstr. 20-22, 76593 Gernsbach, Germany. TEL 07224-9397-0. FAX 07224-939750. TELEX 78915-DBV-D. **Document type:** trade publication.

684.1   GW
EUROPAEISCHER WIRTSCHAFTSDIENST. MOEBEL-DIENST. 1926. w. DM.450. Casimir Katz Verlag, Bleichstr. 20-22, 76593 Gernsbach, Germany. TEL 07224-9397-0. FAX 07224-939750. TELEX 78915-DBV-D. Eds. Richard Barth, Stefan Lang. circ. 980. **Document type:** trade publication.

645   HK
▼**EUROPEAN FURNITURE.** (Text in English) 1992. a. HK.$198. Press Mark Media Ltd., Flat D, 1-F Prospect Mansion, 66-72 Paterson St., Causeway Bay, Hong Kong. TEL 852-8822-230. FAX 852-8823-949. TELEX 49505 EMART HX. Ed. Kenneth Li Kam Man. adv.: color page HK$18000. circ. 20,000. **Document type:** consumer publication.
    Description: Covers the latest design of furniture, lighting, art pieces and decorations from Milan.

380.1   GW
EUROPEAN FURNITURE REVIEW. (Text in English, French, German) a. $63. A B C Publishing Group, Postfach 100262, 64202 Darmstadt, Germany. TEL 06151-3892-0. FAX 06151-33164. (Dist. in US by: Western Hemisphere Publishing Corp., Box 847, Hillsboro, OR 97123. TEL 503-640-3736. FAX 503-640-2748) adv. **Document type:** directory.
    Description: Reviews European furniture export industries.

684.1   GW
EUROPEAN WOODWORKING MACHINERY AND ACCESSORIES. (Text in English) 1986. a. free. D R W-Verlag Weinbrenner GmbH & Co., Fasanenweg 18, 70771 Leinfelden-Echterdingen, Germany. TEL 0711-7591-1. Ed. Karl-Heinz Weinbrenner. circ. 25,000. **Document type:** trade publication.

INTERIOR DESIGN AND DECORATION — FURNITURE AND HOUSE FURNISHINGS

684.1 US ISSN 0192-8058
TS880
F D M - FURNITURE DESIGN & MANUFACTURING. 1959. m. $55 (foreign $100) (free to qualified personnel). Delta Communications Inc. (Subsidiary of: Cahners Publishing Company), Division of Reed Elsevier Inc., 455 N. Cityfront Plaza Dr., 24th Fl., Chicago, IL 60611. TEL 312-222-2000. FAX 312-222-2026. TELEX 210012 UR. Ed. Michael Chazin; Pub. S.L. (Sandy) Berliner. adv.: B&W page $4225, color page $4620; trim 7 7/8 x 10 3/4; adv. contact: Julie Okon. illus.; tr.lit. circ. 50,000. (also avail. in microform from UMI,MIM) **Indexed:** Key to Econ.Sci. **Document type:** trade publication.
 —UnCover; UMI. CCC.
 Formerly: Furniture Design and Manufacturing (ISSN 0016-304X)
 Description: Articles on the furniture, bedding and upholstering industries.

684.1 UK ISSN 0014-5904
TS840
F I R A BULLETIN; the quarterly for the furniture industry. 1962. q. £55 to non-members (foreign £68). Furniture Industry Research Association (F I R A), Maxwell Rd., Stevenage, Herts. SG1 2EW, England. TEL 0438-313433. FAX 0438-727607. TELEX 827653 FIRA G. Ed. P.R. Hinton. adv.; abstr.; illus. circ. 1,000. **Indexed:** Br.Ceram.Abstr., C.I.S. Abstr., Fluidex, Forest.Abstr., World Surf.Coat., World Text.Abstr. **Document type:** bulletin.
 Formerly: F I R A Technical Bulletin.
 Description: Contains articles on developments in the industry.

747.4 US ISSN 0015-3761
FLOOR COVERING WEEKLY. 1952. w. $34. Hearst Business Communications, Inc., F C W Division, 645 Stewart Ave., Garden City, NY 11530-4709. Ed. Janey Morgan Daly. adv.; bk.rev.; illus. circ. 19,000. (tabloid format) **Indexed:** Text.Tech.Dig. **Document type:** trade publication.

747.4 US
FLOOR COVERING WEEKLY. ANNUAL DIRECTORY. 1977. a. $25. Hearst Business Communications, Inc., F C W Division, 645 Stewart Ave., Garden City, NY 11530-4709. Ed. Janet Morgan Daly. **Document type:** trade publication.
 Former titles: Specifier's Guide to Contract Floor Coverings; Handbook of Contract Floor Covering.

747.4 US
FLOOR COVERING WEEKLY MARKET GUIDE SERIES. 1979. s-a. Hearst Business Communications, Inc., F C W Division, 645 Stewart Ave., Garden City, NY 11530-4709. Ed. Janey Morgan Daly. circ. 19,000. (tabloid format) **Document type:** trade publication.

747.4 US
FLOOR COVERINGS INTERNATIONAL. 1980. s-a. Hearst Business Communications, Inc., F C W Division, 645 Stewart Ave., Garden City, NY 11530-4709. (Subscr. to: Floor Covering Weekly, 645 Stewart Ave., Garden City, NY 11530) Ed. Janey Morgan Daly. **Document type:** trade publication.

747.4 US ISSN 0162-881X
TH2521
FLOORING; the magazine of interior surfaces. (Publishes Flooring Buying & Resource Guide annually as the Oct. issue) 1931. m. $37 (foreign $97). Leo Douglas, Inc., 9609 Gayton Rd., Ste. 100, Richmond, VA 23233. TEL 804-741-6704. FAX 804-750-2399. Ed. Mark S. Kuhar. adv. contact: Milhe Korsonsky. circ. 24,546. **Indexed:** Text.Tech.Dig. **Document type:** trade publication.
 Description: Contains in-depth feature stories, as well as the latest industry news, and information on all the latest products and services in areas such as: wood flooring, ceramic tile, carpet, vinyl flooring, and accessories.

FORESTA; Rumanian wood and furniture review. see *FORESTS AND FORESTRY — Lumber And Wood*

FRAMES ARCHITETTURA DEI SERRAMENTI; rivista internazionale degli infissi e dei sistemi di chiusura nell'edilizia. see *BUILDING AND CONSTRUCTION*

FRAMES BOOK (YEAR), see *BUSINESS AND ECONOMICS — Trade And Industrial Directories*

645 UK
FURNISHING (MIDDLESEX). 1989. 12/yr. Times House, Station Approach, Ruislip, Middlesex HA4 8NB, England. TEL 0895-677677. FAX 0895-676027. Ed. Lisa Burcher. adv. circ. 10,552. **Document type:** trade publication.
 Description: Highlights information for retail furnishers.

747.4 AT ISSN 0816-5947
FURNISHING FLOORS. DOMESTIC AND CONTRACT; national magazine for the flooring trade. 6/yr. Aus.$44. Furnishing Publications Pty. Ltd., 5 Faigh St., Mulgrave, Vic. 3170, Australia. TEL 03-562-5844. FAX 03-562-5412. Ed. Keith Dunn. adv.; illus.; pat.; tr.lit. circ. 4,800.
 Former titles (until 1984): Interior Design (ISSN 0314-0156); (until 1976): Floor.
 Description: For floor covering industry both domestic and commercial, suppliers, manufacturers, retailers, architects, specifiers, and government departments, federal, state and local.

684.3 IE
FURNISHING RETAILER & CONTRACTOR. 1975. m. Acorn Publishing Co. Ltd., 105 Aradara Ave., Raheny, Dublin 13, Ireland. Ed. David Collins. adv.

747 677 UK
FURNISHINGS RECORD. 1981. s-a. free with Drapers Record. International Thomson Business Publishing, 100 Avenue Road, London NW3 3TP, England. TEL 01-935-6611. Ed. Cliff Waller. adv.; illus.; stat.
 Former titles (until 1986): Furnishings International; Home Furnishings International.

645 PH
FURNITURE. 6/yr. $12. Leverage International (Consultants) Inc., PS Bank Bldg. 5F, C.P.O. Box 2296, Ayala Ave., Makati MM, Philippines. FAX 632-8101594. Ed. Cecilia Sanchez.

645 GW
FURNITURE/MOEBEL. (Text in English, French, German) 1952. a. $55. Industrieschau-Verlagsgesellschaft mbH, Berliner Allee 8, 64295 Darmstadt, Germany. TEL 06151-38920. FAX 06151-33164. (U.S. subscr. to: Western Hemisphere Publishing Corp., Box 847, Hillsboro, OR 97123-0847. TEL 503-640-3736. FAX 503-640-2748) Ed. Margit Selka. circ. 8,000. **Document type:** directory.
 ●Also available online.
 Also available on CD-ROM.

684.1 UK
FURNITURE COMPONENTS INTERNATIONAL. 1991. m. £20 (Europe £37; elsewhere £41). Nigel Gearing Ltd., No.4 Red Barn Mews, High St., Battle, E. Sussex TN33 0AG, England. TEL 0424-774982. FAX 0424-774321. Ed. John Legg. adv. circ. 11,000. **Document type:** trade publication.
 Formerly (until 1993): Furniture Components and Production International (ISSN 0964-0940)

684.1 US
THE FURNITURE EXECUTIVE. 1983. m. membership. American Furniture Manufacturers Association, Box HP-7, High Point, NC 27261. TEL 919-884-5000. Ed. Nancy High. circ. 2,500. **Document type:** trade publication, newsletter.

749 UK ISSN 0016-3058
NK2528
FURNITURE HISTORY. 1965. a. £16 (U.S. $20; Europe £18) (subscr. includes q. newsletter). Furniture History Society, c/o B. Austen, One Mercedes Cottages, St. John's Rd., Haywards Heath, W. Sussex RH16 4EH, England. TEL 0444-413845. Ed. Sarah Medlam. adv. contact: Brian Austen. bk.rev.; abstr.; bibl.; illus.; cum.index every 10 yrs. circ. 1,500. (tabloid format; back issues avail.) **Indexed:** Artbibl.Mod., Avery Ind.Archit.Per., Br.Archaeol.Abstr., RILA. **Document type:** academic/scholarly publication.
 —UnCover.
 Description: Includes information about antiques, art, interior design, and decoration, furniture and house furnishing.

684.1 UK ISSN 0306-0519
FURNITURE MANUFACTURER; the international journal for the furniture manufacturer. 1935. m. £72. Publex International Ltd., 110 Station Rd. E., Oxted, Surrey RH8 0QA, England. TEL 0883-717755. FAX 0883-714554. Ed. Ann Von Klosst-Dohna. adv.; bk.rev.; illus. circ. 7,495. **Indexed:** Key to Econ.Sci., PROMT. **Document type:** trade publication.
 —BLDSC (4059.239500).
 Formerly: Furniture and Bedding Production.

749 658 US
FURNITURE RETAILER (GREENSBORO). 1927. m. $48. Pace Communications Inc., 1301 Carolina St., Greensboro, NC 27401. TEL 919-378-6065. FAX 919-275-2864. Ed. Patricia N. Bowling. adv.; charts; illus.; stat.; tr.lit. circ. 16,780. **Document type:** trade publication.
 Former titles (until 1989): Competitivedge (ISSN 0149-2276); N H F A Reports (ISSN 0027-6944); N R F A Reports.
 Description: For the home furnishings retail trade.

749 US ISSN 0194-360X
FURNITURE - TODAY; the weekly business newspaper of the furniture industry. 1976. w. $79.95. Cahners Business Newspapers, Division of Reed Elsevier Inc., 7025 Albert Pick Rd., Greensboro, NC 27409. TEL 910-605-0121. FAX 910-605-1143. (Subscr. to: Box 1424, Riverton, NJ 08077) Ed. Lester Craft. adv.; bk.rev.; charts; illus.; stat. circ. 27,500. (tabloid format; also avail. in microform from UMI; back issues avail.) **Document type:** trade publication.
 —UMI. CCC.
 Description: Edited for the furniture retailer and manufacturer in the home furnishing industry.

749 US ISSN 0738-890X
FURNITURE WORLD. 1870. 13/yr. $16. Towse Publishing Co., 530 Fifth Ave., Pelham, NY 10803. TEL 914-738-6744. FAX 914-738-6820. Ed. B.I. Bienenstock. adv.; illus. circ. 20,100. **Document type:** trade publication.
 Formerly (until 1982): Furniture World and Furniture Buyer and Decorator (ISSN 0016-3104); Incorporates: Furniture South (ISSN 0016-3074)
 Description: Contains information on finance, operations, marketing and sales management for homefurnishings retailers.

677 NE ISSN 0923-3660
GAAF GOED; vakblad voor de interieur-textiel-branche. Short title: G G. (Text in Dutch) 1986. 6/yr. fl.89. Uitgeverij Cobbenhage B.V., Treubstraat 1N, Postbus 1890, 2280 DW Rijswick. TEL 31-70-3995108. FAX 31-70-3902488. Ed. J.W. Wunnink. adv.; circ. 5,075 (paid); 2,600 (controlled). (tabloid format; back issues avail.) **Document type:** trade publication.
 Description: Business magazine for home decorating retailers and the home textile market.

645 IT
GAP CASA. m. (10/yr.). L.115000 in Europe; America L.160000. Publimedia Societa Editrice, Corso Venezia 18, 20121 Milan, Italy. TEL 02-77521. FAX 02-781068. Ed. Francesco Buffa di Perrero. adv. circ. 20,000.

643.3 US
GLOBAL APPLIANCE REPORT. 1990. m. $350 to non-members; members $250. Association of Home Appliance Manufacturers, 20 N. Wacker Dr., Chicago, IL 60606. TEL 312-984-5800. FAX 312-984-5823. Ed. Craig Schulz. (looseleaf format) **Document type:** newsletter.
 Description: Digest of international news affecting the home appliance industry.

747.5 SW ISSN 0345-3979
GOLV TILL TAK; Skandinavisk tidskrift om golv, vaeggar och tak/Scandinavian magazine for floor coverings, wallcoverings and ceilings. Alternate title: Tidskriften Golf till Tak. (Text in Swedish; summaries in English) 1972. 8/yr. SEK 300. (Golventreprenoerernas Branschorganisation) Foerlags AB Golv till Tak, P.O. Box 4604, 116 91 Stockholm, Sweden. TEL 08-644 09 05. FAX 08-643-98-11. (Co-sponsor: Sveriges Golvhandlares Riksfoerbund) Ed. Inger Rosengren. adv. circ. 3,708.

645 IT
GUIDA: ANNUARIO DEI FORNITORI DELL'INDUSTRIA DEL MOBILE. a. L.60000. Industria del Mobile s.r.l., Via Giambologna 21, 20136 Milan, Italy. TEL 02-8394780. FAX 02-8372547.

INTERIOR DESIGN AND DECORATION — FURNITURE AND HOUSE FURNISHINGS

749 US ISSN 0746-7885
HF5001
H F D. (Home Furnishing Daily) 1929. w. $44.95 to trade groups and companies; institutions $44.95 (effective 1992). Fairchild Fashion & Merchandising Group (Subsidiary of: Capital Cities - A B C, Inc.), 7 W. 34th St., New York, NY 10001. TEL 212-630-4000. FAX 212-630-3675. (Subscr. to: 55 Fifth Ave., New York, NY 10001) Ed. Geri Brin. adv.; illus.; mkt. circ. 52,000. (tabloid format; also avail. in microform) Indexed: Bus.Ind., PROMT, Text.Tech.Dig., Tr.& Indus.Ind. **Document type:** newspaper.
● Also available online. Vendor(s): DIALOG Information Services, Inc., Mead Data Central, Inc. —BLDSC (4303.415000). **CCC.**
  Former titles: H F D - Retailing Home Furnishings (ISSN 0162-9158); (until 1976): Home Furnishings Daily (ISSN 0018-4047)
  Description: Ideas for retailers, wholesalers, manufacturers and suppliers, covers furniture, bedding, floor coverings, giftware and housewares.

645 IT ISSN 0394-1132
HARPER'S GRAN BAZAAR. Key Title: Gran Bazaar. 1978. 6/yr. L.40000. Edizioni S Y D S Italia s.r.l., Viale Stelvio 57, 20159 Milan, Italy. Ed. Giuseppe Della Schiava. adv. circ. 44,000.

684.1 GW
HAUSTEX. 1950. m. DM.108. Westdeutsche Verlagsanstalt GmbH, Ahmser Str. 190, 32052 Herford, Germany. TEL 05221-775-0. FAX 05221-775215. Ed. H. Russ. adv.; illus. **Document type:** consumer publication.
  Formerly: Aussteuer Bett und Couch (ISSN 0004-8259)
  Description: Information, insider news on interior design and decoration.

HEARTH & HOME; the magazine of specialty retailing. see ENERGY

684.1 GW
HIGHLIGHT; technical magazine for lighting. 1990. q. DM.52. Verlag Matthias Ritthammer GmbH, Andernacherstr. 5a, 90019 Nuernberg, Germany. TEL 0911-955780. FAX 0911-9557811. Ed. Ruediger Zeitz. circ. 10,000. **Document type:** consumer publication.

684.1 AU ISSN 0018-3776
HOLZ IM HANDWERK; oesterreichische Moebelzeitschrift. 1959. m. S.480. Zeitungsverlag Kuhn und Co. GmbH, Kutschkergasse 42, A-1180 Vienna, Austria. TEL 0222-47686. FAX 0222-4768621. **Document type:** trade publication.

684.1 GW
TS840
HOLZ- UND MOEBELINDUSTRIE. (Text in English, German) 1965. 11/yr. DM.183.70. D R W-Verlag Weinbrenner GmbH & Co., Fasanenweg 18, 70771 Leinfelden-Echterdingen, Germany. TEL 0711-7591-1. Ed. Karl-Heinz Weinbrenner. adv.; bk.rev.; bibl.; illus.; stat. circ. 8,500. **Indexed:** Packag.Sci.Tech. **Document type:** trade publication. —**CCC.**
  Former titles: Holz- und Kunststoffverarbeitung (ISSN 0721-2585); Moderne Holzverarbeitung.

747 SI
HOME & DECOR. 1981. bi-m. S.58. Times Periodicals Private Ltd., 422 Thomson Rd., Time Industrial Bldg., Singapore 1129, Singapore. TEL 2550011. FAX 2568016. Ed. Sophie Kho. illus. circ. 20,000.
  Formerly: Decor Guide (ISSN 0129-8194)
  Description: A guide to home designing and decor, features on decor trends and ideas.

645 BE ISSN 0773-557X
HOME DIGEST. Dutch edition (ISSN 0773-5588) (Text in French) 1985. 10/yr. Mema N.V., Wielewaalstraat 20, B-2610 Wilrijk, Belgium. TEL 32-3-4480827. FAX 32-3-4480832. Ed. Piet Germeys. adv.: B&W page 52100 BEF, color page 66700 BEF; trim 297 x 210; adv. contact: P. Germeys. illus.; circ. 11,000 (controlled). **Document type:** trade publication.
  Description: For professionals in the housewares industry and retail trade.

684.3 US ISSN 0896-7962
TS1760
HOME FASHIONS MAGAZINE. 1979. m. $30 (foreign $60) (effective 1992). Fairchild Fashion & Merchandising Group (Subsidiary of: Capital Cities - A B C, Inc.), 7 W. 34th St., New York, NY 10001. TEL 212-630-4199. FAX 212-630-4201. adv. circ. 11,000.
  Formerly (until 1987): Home Fashion Textiles (ISSN 0195-654X)

HOME FLAIR. see INTERIOR DESIGN AND DECORATION

658.8 684.1 US
HOME FURNISHINGS REVIEW. 1927. m. $36. Home Furnishings International Association, 110 World Trade Center, Box 581207, Dallas, TX 75258. TEL 800-942-4663. FAX 214-742-9103. Ed. Milton Kessel. adv.; bk.rev.; charts; illus.; mkt.; tr.lit.; index. circ. 4,800.
  Former titles: Home Furnishings; Southwest Homefurnishings News (ISSN 0199-8854); Southwest Furniture News (ISSN 0038-4666)
  Description: Presents business information drawn from a variety of publitions and other sources, digested into brief articles aimed at helping the home furnishings retailer operate a more profitable business.

644.3 US ISSN 0162-9077
HOME LIGHTING & ACCESSORIES. 1923. m. $30 (effective Jan. 1991). Doctorow Communications, Inc., 1033 Clifton Ave., Clifton, NJ 07013. TEL 201-779-1600. FAX 201-779-3242. Ed. Peter Wulff. adv.; bk.rev.; charts; illus.; mkt.; pat.; tr.lit. circ. 10,300.
—**CCC.**
  Formerly: Lamp Journal (ISSN 0023-7426)
  Description: Describes lamps and fixtures.

747 US
HOMEMARKET TRENDS. 6/yr. Lebhar-Friedman, Inc., 425 Park Ave., New York, NY 10022. TEL 212-756-5000. Ed. Tony Lisanti. adv. circ. 14,329.
  Description: Covers the home fashions industry. Includes furniture, bed and bath, table top and window treatments.

645 US
HOMEWORLD BUSINESS;* the newspaper for the housewares decision maker. 1989. m. $25 (Canada $35; elsewhere $200). I C D Publications, 1393 Veterans Hwy, Ste. 116 N, Hauppauge, NY 11788. TEL 516-979-7878. FAX 516-979-8182. Ed. Ian Gittlitz. adv.; circ. 12,800 (controlled). (tabloid format)
  Description: Provides statistical analysis and coverage of the houseware industry.

HOUSE BEAUTIFUL. see INTERIOR DESIGN AND DECORATION

645 UK
HOUSE BEAUTIFUL. 1989. m. £16.80. National Magazine Co. Ltd., 72 Broadwick St., London W1V 2BP, England. TEL 071-439-5000. FAX 071-439-5179. Ed. Pat Roberts. circ. 344,466. **Document type:** consumer publication.

643.6 UK ISSN 0264-8563
HOUSEWARES. 1983. 11/yr. £36 (foreign £52). Benn Publications Ltd. (Subsidiary of: Morgan-Grampian plc), Benn House, Sovereign Way, Tonbridge, Kent TN9 1RW, England. TEL 0732-364422. FAX 0732-361534. Ed. Bridget Gill. adv. contact: Alexandra Hobson. circ. 9,250. **Document type:** trade publication.

645 CN ISSN 0829-9889
HOUSEWARES CANADA. 1985. bi-m.
Can.$21.40($38.50) (foreign $38.50). Centre Publications Ltd. (Subsidiary of: Southam Communications), 1450 Don Mills Rd., Don Mills, Ont. M3B 2X7, Canada. TEL 416-438-1153. Ed. Laurie Merckel. adv. circ. 18,000.

643 658.8 UK
HOUSEWARES: THE INTERNATIONAL MARKET. a. £1375($2750) Euromonitor, 87-88 Turnmill St., London EC1M 5QU, England. TEL 071-251-8024. FAX 071-608-3146. (Addr. in N. America: Euromonitor International, 111 W. Washington St., Ste. 920, Chicago, IL 60602. TEL 312-541-8024. FAX 312-541-1567) (looseleaf format) **Document type:** trade publication.
● Also available online. Vendor(s): Data-Star, DIALOG Information Services, Inc.
  Description: Analyzes the housewares market for France, Germany, Italy, Spain, the U.K., the U.S., and Japan.

HUS & HIBYLI. see INTERIOR DESIGN AND DECORATION

IDEALES HEIM/SCHWEIZER WOHNMAGAZIN. see INTERIOR DESIGN AND DECORATION

747 US
IDEAS (CORAL GABLES). q. Dodi Publishing, Box 343392, Coral Gables, FL 33134. TEL 305-238-0557. Ed. Sam Hirsch. circ. 17,000.

684.1 IT ISSN 0019-753X
INDUSTRIA DEL MOBILE. (Includes a. industry directory) 1959. m. L.120000 (foreign L.240000) (effective 1994). Industria del Mobile s.r.l., Via Giambologna, 21, 20136 Milan, Italy. TEL 02-8394780. FAX 02-8372547. adv.; illus. circ. 6,000.

INDUSTRIEL SUR BOIS. see BUILDING AND CONSTRUCTION — Carpentry And Woodwork

684.1 GW
INSIDE. 1974. s-m. DM.332.98. Inside-Verlag, Kaiserstr. 12, Postfach 440328, 80801 Munchen, Germany. Ed. Peter Wulff.

747.4 US ISSN 0192-1657
TS1779.5
INSTALLATION & CLEANING SPECIALIST. 1963. m. $22. Specialist Publications, Inc., 17835 Ventura Blvd., Ste. 312, Encino, CA 91316. TEL 213-873-1411. FAX 818-344-9647. Ed. Howard Olansky. adv. circ. 16,639.
  Formerly: Installation Specialist (ISSN 0446-3161)

INTERIEUR. see INTERIOR DESIGN AND DECORATION

747 US
INTERIOR DESIGN MARKET. 3/yr. Cahners Publishing Company (New York), Interior Design Group, Division of Reed Elsevier Inc., 249 W. 17th St., New York, NY 10011. TEL 212-645-0067. FAX 212-645-5409. (Subscr. to: Box 1970, Marion, OH 43305) Ed. Stanley Abercrombie. circ. 47,122. **Document type:** trade publication.

747 US ISSN 1059-5287
INTERIORS & SOURCES. 1990. bi-m. $18. L C Clark Publishing, 840 US Highway One, 330, N. Palm Beach, FL 33408. TEL 407-627-3393. FAX 407-627-3447. (Subscr. to: Box 13079, N. Palm Beach, FL 33408-7079) Ed. Katie Sosnowchick. adv.; bk.rev. circ. 18,780. **Document type:** trade publication.

INTERIORS MAGAZINE. see INTERIOR DESIGN AND DECORATION

INTERNI; la rivista dell'arredamento. see INTERIOR DESIGN AND DECORATION

645 GW
▼**JUNGES WOHNEN.** (Supplement to: Spot Markt and Moebel Kultur) 1993. 4/yr. Ferdinand Holzmann Verlag GmbH, Mexikoring 37, 22297 Hamburg, Germany. TEL 040-632018-0. FAX 040-6307510. Eds. Joern Holzmann, Jochen Holzmann. **Document type:** trade publication.

684 US ISSN 0022-7161
HD9999.I473
JUVENILE MERCHANDISING. 1946. m. $20. Columbia Communications, Inc., 370 Lexington Ave., New York, NY 10017. TEL 212-532-9290. FAX 212-779-8345. Ed. Claudia Desimone. adv.; charts; illus.; mkt.; tr.lit. circ. 12,000.

643.3 UK
K B B REVIEW.* 12/yr. Times House, Station Approach, Ruislip, Middlesex HA4 8NB, England. Ed. Sarah Carlile. circ. 13,000.

INTERIOR DESIGN AND DECORATION — FURNITURE AND HOUSE FURNISHINGS

643.3 NE
KEUKEN & INTERIEUR MAGAZINE. 1983. bi-m. Bruil Tijdschriften, Keppelsweg 44, Postbus 100, 7000 AC Doetinchem, Netherlands. TEL 31-8340-24033. FAX 31-8340-33433. Ed. Bert Bruil. adv. circ. 5,200. **Document type:** trade publication.
Description: For kitchen and interior design specialists.

643.3 NE
KEUKEN MAGAZINE. bi-m. Bruil Tijdschriften, Keppelsweg 44, Postbus 100, 7000 AC Doetinchem, Netherlands. TEL 31-8340-24033. FAX 31-8340-33433. Ed. Bert Bruil. adv. **Document type:** consumer publication.
Description: For consumers wishing to buy a kitchen.

KITCHEN & BATH DESIGN NEWS. see *INTERIOR DESIGN AND DECORATION*

643.3 UK
KITCHEN BATHROOM BEDROOM BUSINESS MONTHLY. 10/yr. £28 (Europe £50; elsewhere £64). Kingsland House, 361 City Rd., London EC1V 1LR, England. TEL 071-417-7400. FAX 071-417-7500. Ed. Maureen Browne. **Document type:** trade publication.

KITCHENS & BATHROOMS. see *INTERIOR DESIGN AND DECORATION*

KOMPASS PROFESSIONNEL. BATIMENT ET GENIE CIVIL, MANUTENTION - LEVAGE, BOIS - MEUBLES. see *BUSINESS AND ECONOMICS — Trade And Industrial Directories*

643.3 GW
KUECHENPROFI; Moebel, Geraete, Zubehoer. 1988. s-a. free. Ferdinand Holzmann Verlag GmbH, Mexikoring 37, 22297 Hamburg, Germany. TEL 040-632018-0. FAX 040-6307510. Ed. Dieter Reinbender. circ. 10,500. **Document type:** trade publication.
Description: News for the kitchen furniture and appliance trade.

677 US ISSN 0892-743X
HD9850.1
L D B INTERIOR TEXTILES. 1928. m. $35. Columbia Communications Inc., 370 Lexington Ave., New York, NY 10017. TEL 212-532-9290. FAX 212-779-8345. Ed. Renee Bennett. adv.; illus.; stat.; index. circ. 32,000. (back issues avail.) **Indexed:** Text.Tech.Dig. **Document type:** consumer publication.
Formed by the 1988 merger of: Interior Textiles; *Which was formerly:* Curtain, Drapery and Bedspread Magazine (ISSN 0011-4065) & Linens, Domestics and Bath Products (ISSN 0024-3833); *Which was formerly:* Linens and Domestics.
Description: Retailing magazine for home furnishing, textiles and bath products, including linens.

674 IT
L M L'INDUSTRIA DEL LEGNO E DEL MOBILE. 1949. bi-m. L.160000. Centro Studi Industria Leggera, Via Gesu 17, 20121 Milan, Italy. TEL 02-79-66-30. FAX 2-78-07-03. Ed. Renata D'Antoni. adv.; bk.rev.; illus.; stat.; tr.lit.; cum.index. circ. 4,000. **Indexed:** Chem.Abstr.
Formerly: Industria del Legno e del Mobile (ISSN 0019-7521)

749.63 GW
▼**LICHT UND ARCHITEKTUR**. (Text in English, German) 1993. q. DM.76.40. Bertelsmann Fachzeitschriften GmbH, Postfach 120, 33311 Guetersloh, Germany. TEL 05241-802332. FAX 05241-8060660. adv.: B&W page DM.9480, color page DM.15290; trim 189 x 279. circ. 23,850. **Document type:** trade publication.
Description: Covers all aspects of lighting, including indoor and outdoor lighting, engineering, design, reports on trends, and new products.

749.63 621.32 UK ISSN 0024-3418
LIGHTING EQUIPMENT NEWS. 1967. m. £55. Maclean Hunter Ltd., Maclean Hunter House, Chalk Lane, Cockfosters Rd., Barnet, Herts EN4 0BU, England. TEL 081-242-3000. FAX 081-242-3185. TELEX 299072-MACHUN-G. Ed. Judy Sewell. adv.; bk.rev.; illus. circ. 12,782. **Indexed:** C.I.S. Abstr., Int.Build.Serv.Abstr., Sci.Abstr. **Document type:** trade publication.
—BLDSC (5214.400000); SWETS.

621.32 658.7 CN ISSN 0832-574X
LIGHTING MAGAZINE. 1987. 6/yr. Can.$25.68($48) Kerrwil Publications Ltd., 395 Matheson Blvd. E., Mississauga, ON L4Z 2H2, Canada. TEL 905-890-1846. FAX 905-890-5769. Ed. Bryan S. Rogers. adv. circ. 8,000. **Document type:** trade publication.
Description: For purchasers and specifiers of lighting products.

677 US
LINENS, DOMESTICS & BATH - INTERIOR TEXTILE ANNUAL DIRECTORY. 1927. a. $20. Columbia Communications, Inc., 370 Lexington Ave., New York, NY 10017. TEL 212-532-9290. FAX 212-779-8345. adv. circ. 18,000. **Document type:** directory.
Former titles: Curtain, Drapery and Bedspread National Buyers Guide (ISSN 0084-9502); (until 1987): Linens, Domestics and Bath Products Annual Directory; *Incorporates* (1987): Interior Textiles National Buyers Guide.

644.3 749.63 FR
LUMINAIRES ET ECLAIRAGE. 4/yr. 370 F. Editions Bernard Begassat, 17 rue du Louvre, 75001 Paris, France. TEL 42-36-05-13. FAX 40-13-98-51. adv. circ. 8,000.

LYS; miljoe-design-teknik. see *ENGINEERING — Electrical Engineering*

643.3 US
M A C A P CONSUMER BULLETINS. irreg., latest no.13. $0.25. Association of Home Appliance Manufacturers, Major Appliance Consumer Action Panel, 20 N. Wacker Dr., Chicago, IL 60606. TEL 312-984-5800. FAX 312-984-5823. **Document type:** bulletin.

684.1 IT
MACCHINE ACCESSORI COMPONENTI. Short title: M A C. 1977. m. L.50000. Editore RIMA s.r.l., Via Vincenzo Da Filicaia 7, 20162 Milan, Italy. TEL 02-66103539. FAX 02-66103558. adv. circ. 16,000. **Document type:** trade publication.
Formerly: Informobili (ISSN 0393-4403)
Description: For the furniture and accessories industry.

LA MADERA. see *FORESTS AND FORESTRY — Lumber And Wood*

684.1 FR ISSN 0025-3537
MARKET; commerce de l'equipement du cadre de vie. 1969. m. 200 F. Editions Presse Professionnelle, 96 rue de la Victoire, 75009 Paris, France. Ed. Jacqueline Peron. adv. circ. 62,000.
Formerly: Equipment des Jardins; *Incorporates:* Quincaillier Equipement Menager.

684.1 GW
MATERIAL UND TECHNIK. 1985. 4/yr. DM.7 per no. Verlag Matthias Ritthammer GmbH, Andernacherstr. 5a, 90019 Nuernberg, Germany. TEL 0911-955780. FAX 0911-9557811. Ed. Otmar Kamp. circ. 17,000. **Document type:** consumer publication.

METROPOLITAN HOME; style for our generation. see *INTERIOR DESIGN AND DECORATION*

684.1 NE ISSN 0165-4543
MEUBEL; the weekly business newspaper for the furnishing market. (Text in Dutch) 1919. w. fl.170 (foreign fl.420). Uitgeverij Lakerveld B.V., Mangaanstraat 86, Postbus 43250, 2504 AG The Hague, Netherlands. TEL 31-70-3218218. FAX 31-70-3298744. Ed. Reinold Vugs. adv.; bk.rev.; illus. circ. 7,000. (back issues avail.) **Indexed:** Key to Econ.Sci. **Document type:** trade publication.
Formerly: Vakblad voor de Meubelindustrie (ISSN 0042-2231)

MIDWEST RETAILER. see *BUSINESS AND ECONOMICS — Marketing And Purchasing*

747.8 US
MIRROR NEWS MAGAZINE.* q. Market Power, Inc., 103 2nd St., Hopkins, MN 55343-9276. TEL 612-935-3666. W.L. Tiller. bk.rev. circ. 93,321.

684.1 IT ISSN 0026-7112
IL MOBILE; quindicinale indipendente di economia e informazione. 1957. s-m. L.120000($81) Mobile s.r.l., Viale Renato Serra 14, 20148 Milan, Italy. TEL 3270337. FAX 02-39210192. Ed. Roberto Salardi. adv.; bk.rev. circ. 12,000. (tabloid format)

747 FR
MOBILIS AGENCEMENT. 9/yr. 19 rue du Docteur Goujon, 75012 Paris, France. TEL 43-42-08-08. FAX 43-43-39-62. Ed. Yves Perennou. circ. 12,000.
Description: Covers furnishing, decoration, design and distribution.

684.1 US ISSN 1055-4440
TS840
MODERN WOODWORKING. 1954. m. $24 (free to qualified personnel) (foreign $36). Associations Publications, Inc., Box 640, Collierville, TN 38027-9986. TEL 901-853-7470. FAX 901-853-6437. adv.; bk.rev. circ. 53,300.
Formerly: Cutting Tool Business; *Incorporates* (in 1988): Furniture and Cabinet Manufacturing (ISSN 0894-8348); Which was formerly: Furniture Manufacturing Management (ISSN 0192-799X); (until 1978): Furniture Methods and Materials.

643.3 GW ISSN 0026-864X
DIE MODERNE KUECHE. 1958. bi-m. DM.50. (Arbeitsgemeinschaft die Moderne Kueche) Die Planung Verlagsgesellschaft mbH, Holzhofallee 25-31, 64295 Darmstadt, Germany. TEL 06151-314104. FAX 06151-387525. Ed. Horst Bach. adv.; charts; illus.; tr.lit. circ. 4,500. **Document type:** consumer publication.
Description: Covers remodeling and appliances.

684 GW ISSN 0077-0205
DIE MOEBEL-INDUSTRIE UND IHRE HELFER. 1957. a. $47. Industrieschau-Verlagsgesellschaft mbH, Postfach 100262, 64202 Darmstadt, Germany. TEL 06151-3892-0. FAX 06151-33164. (U.S. subscr. to: Western Hemisphere Publishing Corp., Box 847, Hillsboro, OR 97123-0847. TEL 503-640-3736. FAX 503-640-2748) Ed. Margit Selka. circ. 10,000. **Document type:** directory.
●Also available online.
Also available on CD-ROM.

684.1 GW ISSN 0047-7796
MOEBEL-KULTUR; Fachzeitschrift fuer die Moebelwirtschaft. 1949. m. DM.310. Ferdinand Holzmann Verlag GmbH, Mexikoring 37, 22297 Hamburg, Germany. TEL 040-6307510-0. FAX 040-6307510. Eds. Joern Holzmann, Jochen Holzmann. adv.; bk.rev.; index; circ. controlled. **Document type:** trade publication.

684.1 GW
MOEBELFERTIGUNG. (Text in English and German) 1985. s-a. free. Ferdinand Holzmann Verlag GmbH, Mexikoring 37, 22297 Hamburg, Germany. TEL 040-632018-0. FAX 040-6307510. Eds. Joern Holzmann, Jochen Holzmann. **Document type:** trade publication.
Description: Covers furniture production, from concept to market place.

684.1 NO ISSN 0333-354X
MOEBELHANDLEREN. 1929. m. (10/yr.). NOK 350. Moebelhandlernes Landsforbund, Drammensvn. 30, 0255 Oslo 2, Norway. Ed. Jan Erik Bjeorn. adv. circ. 4,500. **Document type:** trade publication.

684.1 GW
MOEBELMARKT. 1960. m. DM.162. Verlag Matthias Ritthammer GmbH, Andernacherstr. 5a, 90019 Nuernberg, Germany. TEL 0911-955780. FAX 0911-9557811. Ed. Franz Schaefer. adv.; bk.rev.; abstr.; illus.; stat.; index; circ. 12,800 (controlled). **Document type:** consumer publication.

684.1 SW ISSN 0345-7737
MOEBLER, MILJOE. Variant title: Moebler och Miljoe. 1921. m. SEK 395. Sveriges Moebelhandlares Centralfoerbund - Swedish Furniture Retailers' Association, Kungsgatan 21, S-105 61 Stockholm, Sweden. Ed. Birgit Johansson. adv.; bk.rev. circ. 4,616. **Document type:** trade publication.
Formerly (until 1974): Moebelvaerlden (ISSN 0026-7090)

684.1 US
MONDAY MORNING MESSAGE. 1966. w. $88. John H. Tobin, Ed. & Pub., Box 6415, High Point, NC 27262-6415. TEL 919-884-5732. FAX 919-884-4038. bk.rev. circ. 5,000.

INTERIOR DESIGN AND DECORATION — FURNITURE AND HOUSE FURNISHINGS

MONDOCUCINA. see *BUILDING AND CONSTRUCTION*

747.4   AT
NATIONAL MASTER PAINTERS AND DECORATORS TRADE JOURNAL. 1990. bi-m. Aus.$33. (Federation of Master Painters and Decorators Association of Australia) Furnishing Publications Pty. Ltd., 5 Faigh St., Mulgrave, Vic. 3170, Australia. TEL 03-562-5844. FAX 03-562-5412. circ. 2,900. **Document type:** trade publication.
    Formerly: Master Painter and Decorations Trade Journal.

NATIONWIDE DIRECTORY OF GIFT, HOUSEWARES & HOME TEXTILE BUYERS. see *GIFTWARE AND TOYS*

NEUES WOHNEN (HAMBURG). see *HOUSING AND URBAN PLANNING*

684   UK
NURSERY TRADER. 1874. q. £20 (foreign £27.50). Millhouse Ltd., Cryers Hill, High Wycombe, Bucks HP15 6LJ, England. Ed. Alison Davis. adv.; bk.rev. illus. circ. 3,726.
    Former titles (until 1983): Pram and Nursery Trader (ISSN 0032-6844); Pram World; Nursery Times International.

749   AU   ISSN 0029-9081
OESTERREICHISCHE FUSSBODENZEITUNG.* 1965. bi-m. S.48. Verlag Piletzky, Nikolsdorfer Gasse 7, A-1050 Vienna, Austria. Ed. Heinrich Piletzky. adv.; charts; illus.; stat. circ. 4,300.
    Description: Concerns floor coverings.

749 684.1   AU   ISSN 0029-9405
OESTERREICHISCHE RAUMAUSSTATTERZEITUNG.* 1966. bi-m. S.48. Verlag Piletzky, Nikolsdorfer Gasse 7, 1050 Vienna, Austria. Ed. Heinrich Piletzky. adv.; charts; illus.; stat. circ. 4,100.

OFFICIEL DU BOIS (EDITION ROUGE). see *BUILDING AND CONSTRUCTION — Carpentry And Woodwork*

677.643   US   ISSN 0030-5332
ORIENTAL RUG. 1928. q. $15 (Canada & Mexico $20; elsewhere $40). Oriental Rug Importers Association of America, 15 E. 30th St., No.4-W, New York, NY 10016. Ed. Archie Cherkezian. adv. contact: Lucille J. Lauffer. bk.rev.; illus.; stat.; tr.lit. circ. 8,000. **Document type:** trade publication.
    Description: For retailers and others in the home furnishings industry. Contains educational articles about all types of oriental rugs, with wholesale and retail market analysis, and more.

747.5   US   ISSN 1044-4807
NK2808
ORIENTAL RUG REVIEW. 1981. bi-m. $48. Oriental Rug Auction Review, Inc., Box 709, Meredith, NH 03253. TEL 603-744-9191. FAX 603-744-6933. Ed. Ron O'Callaghan. adv.; bk.rev.; illus. circ. 4,500.
    Description: Covers oriental rugs and other textiles for collectors and dealers.

684.1   US   ISSN 0048-2633
PACIFIC MARKETER;* the Northwest's only home furnishings magazine. 1926. bi-m. $4. Northwest Furniture Retailers' Association, 12233 Ashwoth N., No. 15, Seattle, WA 98133. TEL 206-623-1510. Ed. Lucy Hazelton. adv.; illus. circ. 4,000.

747.4   GW   ISSN 0934-9014
PARKETT MAGAZIN. 1988. 6/yr. DM.80 (foreign DM.86). S N Verlag Michael Steinert, An der Alster 21, 20099 Hamburg, Germany. TEL 040-240852. FAX 040-2803788.

747.4   FR   ISSN 1165-1059
▼**PARQUETS LAMBRIS REVETEMENTS.** 1992. q. 120 F. Editions Bernard Begassat, 17 rue du Louvre, 75001 Paris, France. TEL 42-36-05-13. FAX 40-13-98-51. circ. 7,000.

684.1   UK   ISSN 0964-0959
PINE NEWS INTERNATIONAL. 1986. m. £25 (Europe £31; elsewhere £36). Nigel Gearing Ltd., No.4 Red Barn Mews, High St., Battle, E. Sussex TN33 0AG, England. TEL 0424-774982. FAX 0424-774321. Ed. John Legg. adv. circ. 4,000. **Document type:** trade publication.
    Description: News and information on all aspects of the pine furniture industry and related softwood markets.

684.1   GW
POLSTER-FASHION. 1991. s-a. DM.14 per no. Verlag Matthias Ritthammer GmbH, Andernacherstr. 5a, 90019 Nuernberg, Germany. TEL 0911-955780. FAX 0911-9557811. Ed. Otmar Kamp. circ. 15,000. **Document type:** consumer publication.

645   FR
PRATIQUE. 1966. m. 95 F. S.E.B.A.M., 42 rue de Louvre, Paris, France. Ed. J.P. Renau. adv.; bk.rev. circ. 90,000.
    Former titles: Bricolage; Bricolage Maison Pratique.

PREVISIONS GLISSANTES DETAILLEES EN PERSPECTIVES SECTORIELLES (VOL.4): INDUSTRIES DU BOIS ET DE L'AMEUBLEMENT. see *BUSINESS AND ECONOMICS — Economic Situation And Conditions*

747.5   US   ISSN 1043-4232
PROFESSIONAL CLEANING JOURNAL.* 1981. m. $15 (effective Jan. 1991). Target Trade, Box 796575, Dallas, TX 75379-6575. TEL 214-484-4474. FAX 214-484-4280. Ed. Keven Todd. adv. circ. 9,800. **Document type:** trade publication.
    Formerly: Southwest Cleaning (ISSN 0744-7124)
    Description: Business and technical information on the carpet, drapery and upholstery cleaning industry.

645   SP
▼**PUERICULTURA MARKET;** revista profesional de los productos para bebes y 1a infancia. 1992. bi-m. 4000 ptas.($50) (effective 1994). Ediciones Just, S.A., C. San German 5, 1a, 08004 Barcelona, Spain. TEL 93-325-32-87. FAX 93-424-44-60. Dir. Fernando Cortes. Pub. M. Dolores Just. circ. 4,000. **Document type:** trade publication.
    Supersedes (in 1994): Express Puericultura.
    Description: Covers the industry of products for babies and toddlers.

REMODELING. see *BUILDING AND CONSTRUCTION*

749.63   US
▼**RESIDENTIAL LIGHTING.** 1993. m. Vance Publishing Corporation, 400 Knightsbridge Pkwy., Lincolnshire, IL 60069. TEL 708-634-2600. FAX 708-634-4379. adv.: B&W page $1350, color page $2050; trim 10 5/8 x 14 1/8. circ. 10,600. **Document type:** trade publication.

643.3   US
RETAIL OBSERVER. 1990. m. $5. 1442 Sierra Creek Way, San Jose, CA 95132. TEL 408-272-8974. FAX 408-251-6511. adv.; circ. 3,888 (controlled). **Document type:** trade publication.
    Description: Covers the retailing of appliances, electronics, and kitchen and bath items.

684.1   FR   ISSN 0242-8903
REVUE DE L'AMEUBLEMENT. (Includes Centre de Liaison et d'Ameublement des Fournisseurs de l'Ameublement et de la Literie. Cahier Mensuel) vol.65, 1977. 10/yr. 500 F. (foreign 950 F.). Editions du Tigre, 23 rue Joubert, 75009 Paris, France. TEL 48-74-52-50. FAX 1-40-16-43-65. TELEX COUMEUB 283769F. Ed. Francois Prevot. adv.; illus.

747   FR
REVUE PROFESSIONNELLE DES METIERS DE L'AMEUBLEMENT ET DE LA DECORATION. 4/yr. 38 rue Pascal, 75013 Paris, France. TEL 43-31-57-27. FAX 45-35-33-76. TELEX 480 746 OFFISOD. Ed. Rene Heutte. adv. circ. 3,500.

747   IT
RIVISTA ARREDOS; rivista mensile specializzata nel settore dell'arredamento. (Text in English, Italian) m. Stampacolor, Via Grazia Deledda 13, 07100 Sassari, Italy. TEL 079-241215. TELEX 315528 SIAP MI I. Ed. Dott. Sebastiano Ibba. adv.

747   SP
SALA BANO; revista bimestral de decoracion. (Text in Italian, Spanish) 1981. bi-m. 15000 ptas. Faenza Editrice Iberica S.L., C. San vicente, 62 entlo., 12001 Castellon, Spain. TEL 964-21-65-70. FAX 964-24-10-10. (In Italy: Via Pier de Crescenzi 44, 48018 Faenza (RA), Italy) Ed. Benjamin Cervera. adv.; bk.rev. circ. 300. (back issues avail.)

643   NE
▼**DE SANITAIR SPECIALIST.** 1992. 6/yr. Bruil Tijdschriften, Keppelsweg 44, Postbus 100, 7000 AC Doetinchem, Netherlands. TEL 31-8340-24033. FAX 31-8340-33433. Ed. Bert Bruil. adv. circ. 5,250. **Document type:** trade publication.

747   SP
SANITARISTAS. 6/yr. Via Augusta 59 8o Ofic. 812, 08006 Barcelona, Spain. TEL 3-237-11-98. FAX 3-415-86-88. Ed. S. Beltran Nunez. circ. 10,000.

SCHORNSTEINFEGERHANDWERK. see *BUILDING AND CONSTRUCTION*

SCHWEIZERISCHE SCHREINERZEITUNG. see *BUILDING AND CONSTRUCTION — Carpentry And Woodwork*

747   SP
SELECCIONES DE FORNITURAS; y complementos para la industria de la confeccion. 4/yr. Vilamari 81, 08015 Barcelona, Spain. TEL 3-226-32-98. Ed. A. Palazon Serrano.

749.63   IT
SHOWCASE. (Text in English, Italian) 1989. 3/yr. L.70000 (typically set in Sep.). Editrice Habitat s.r.l., Via M.M. de Taddei, 3, 20147 Milan, Itlay. TEL 48-14-800. FAX 48-19-3013. adv. circ. 50,000.
    Description: For entrepeneurs in the design sector, including import-exporters, dealers, architects, and designers.

749   SW
SKOENA HEM — ALLT I HEMMET. (Text in Swedish; summaries in English) 1956. m. SEK 414. Bonniers Maanads Tidningar, Sveavaegen 53, S-105 44 Stockholm, Sweden. TEL 08-7365300. FAX 08-346908. TELEX 10043-BONMAG-S. Ed. Bjoern Vingaard. adv.; charts; illus.; mkt. circ. 126,800. **Document type:** consumer publication.
    Formed by the 1992 merger of: Skoena Hem & Allt i Hemmet (ISSN 0002-6182)

645 659   US
SLEEP CONNECTION; an information resource for the bedding industry. 1984. bi-m. membership. National Waterbed Retailers Association, 36 S. State St., Ste. 1212, Chicago, IL 60603. TEL 312-236-6662. FAX 312-236-1140. Ed. Ken/Bauder. adv. contact: Ken Bauder. **Document type:** newsletter.
    Description: News of industry and marketing developments affecting the retail waterbed business, including announcements of upcoming conventions and exhibitions.

SLOVENIJALES; glasilo mednarodnega podjetja za trgovino, inzeniring, proizvodnjo, zastopanje in konsignacijo. see *BUSINESS AND ECONOMICS*

684   US   ISSN 0037-7260
SMALL WORLD; the magazine of nursery furniture, wheel goods, toys and accessories. 1949. m. $18. Earnshaw Publications, Inc., 225 W. 34th St., Ste. 1212, New York, NY 10001. TEL 212-563-2742. Ed. Thomas W. Hudson. adv.; bk.rev.; charts; illus.; mkt.; tr.lit.; index. circ. 10,200.

747   IT   ISSN 0394-1442
SPAZIO ABITATO. 1975. bi-m. L.30000 (foreign L.40000). Editore Rima s.r.l., Via Vincenzo Da Filicaia 7, 20162 Milan, Italy. TEL 02-66103539. FAX 02-66103558. Ed. Flavio Maestrini. circ. 15,000.

747 635.9   IT   ISSN 1120-4516
SPAZIO CASA. 1989. m. L.57600 (foreign L.95000). Rusconi Editori S.p.A., Viale Sarca 235, 20126 Milan, Italy. TEL 02-66191. FAX 02-6619-2686. Ed. Isabella Orsenigo. adv.; bk.rev. circ. 126,679.
    Description: Covers furniture for the home and gardening.

645   GW
▼**SPOT MARKT.** 1992. 20/yr. DM.496. Ferdinand Holzmann Verlag GmbH, Mexikoring 37, 22297 Hamburg, Germany. TEL 040-632018-0. FAX 040-6307510. Eds. Joern Holzmann, Jochen Holzmann. **Document type:** trade publication.

747.4   US
THE SQUARE YARD. American Floorcovering Association, 13-154 Merchandise Mart, Chicago, IL 60654. TEL 312-644-1243. FAX 312-644-2787. Ed. Susan Ing. adv. contact: Susan Ing. (back issues avail.) **Document type:** newsletter, trade publication.
    Description: Educates floor covering retailers.

645 677 UK ISSN 0950-5032
STOCKLISTS COLOUR MAGAZINE. a. Mayville Publishing Co., Ltd., Mayville House, 142 Park Rd., Timperley, Altrincham WA15 6QT, England. TEL 061-973-8858. Ed. Roy P. Spragg. circ. 13,000.

747.4 US ISSN 0895-934X
SUN BELT FLOOR COVERING.* 1963. m. $14. Target Trade, Box 796575, Dallas, TX 75379-6575. TEL 214-484-4474. FAX 214-484-4280. Ed. Howard Clark. adv. circ. 21,897.
Formed by the 1987 merger of: Southeast Floor Covering (ISSN 0894-5047) & Southwest Floor Covering (ISSN 0279-6902); Which was formerly: Southwest Floor Covering News (ISSN 0192-9186)

SUPPLIERS SANITARY - TABLEWARE BOOK. see *HEATING, PLUMBING AND REFRIGERATION*

747.4 CN
SURFACE. (Text in French) 1985. 8/yr. free. Federation Quebecoise des REvetemetns de Sol Inc., 9420 rue Pascal Gagnon, St-Leonard, Montreal, Que. H1P 1Z7. TEL 514-323-8480. FAX 514-323-1511. adv. circ. 4,500.
Description: Discusses such floor covering topics as ceramic, fiber, wood, natural stone, carpet and vinyl, installation and resiliency.

747.5 SW ISSN 0039-6753
SVENSK TAPETSERARETIDNING.* 1923. bi-m. SEK 225 (effective 1990). Sveriges Tapetseraremaestare Centralfoerening, c/o Curt Bodin Annonsservice, P.O. Box 6083, 18306 Taeby, Sweden. adv.; illus. **Document type:** trade publication.
Former titles (until vol.8, 1932): Svensk Saddelmakare-Tapesteraretidning; (until 1931): Svensk Tapesteraretidning.

642.7 666 FR ISSN 0039-8780
TABLE ET CADEAU. (Editions in English, French, German, Italian, Spanish) 1961. 10/yr. 380 F. (foreign 525 F.). Editions Ampere, Groupe C.E.P.P., 25, rue Dagorno, 75012 Paris, France. TEL 43-47-30-20. FAX 43-47-30-80. TELEX GMPPAR 216219F. circ. 6,000.
Formerly: Arts et Decor de la Table et du Foyer.

749 CH
TAIWAN FURNITURE. (Text in English) irreg. (approx. 3/yr.). NT.$1400($60) for Middle East, Asia, Oceania; elsewhere $70. China Economic News Service, 561 Chung Hsiao E. Rd. Sec. 4, Taipei, Taiwan 10516, Republic of China. TEL 2-642-2629. FAX 2-642-7422. TELEX 27710-CENSPC. (Subscr. to: P.O. Box 43-60, Taipei, Taiwan, R.O.C.)

749.63 CH
TAIWAN LIGHTING. (Text in English) q. NT.$1600($70) in Asia, Middle East, Oceania; elsewhere $80. China Economic News Service, 561 Chunghsiao E. Rd. Sec. 4, Taipei, Taiwan 10516, Republic of China. TEL 02-642-2629. FAX 02-642-7422. TELEX 27710-CENSPC.

645 AU
TAPEZIERER UND RAUMAUSSTATTER. m. Verlag Lorenz, Ebendorferstr. 10, A-1010 Vienna, Austria. TEL 0222-426695. FAX 0222-438693. Ed. Christian Lorenz. circ. 2,300. **Document type:** trade publication.

747.5 IT
TAPPEZZIERE IN STOFFA. 1952. q. (Associazione Tappezzori in Stoffa e Affini) Refernces s.r.l., Viale Europa, 20090 Lodovecchio (MI), Italy. TEL 371-752-522. FAX 371-754-022. adv. circ. 10,000.

TORONTO LIFE HOMES. see *INTERIOR DESIGN AND DECORATION*

684.1 NO
TRE OG MOEBLER. 1969. m. (10/yr.). NOK 250 in Nordic countries; elsewhere NOK 350. (Norske Trevarefabrikkers Landsforbund) John A. Antonsen A-S, Postboks 78 Sentrum, 0101 Oslo 1, Norway. TEL 02-33-67-76. FAX 02-33-23-61. (Co-sponsor: Moebelprodusentenes Landsforbund) Ed. John A. Antonsen. adv. circ. 2,528. **Document type:** trade publication.
Description: Directed to the woodworking and furniture industry, building and furniture architects, and furniture trade and agents.

749 IT ISSN 0041-445X
TUTTOVILLE. 1967. q. L.16000. Gruppo Editoriale Electa Periodici s.r.l., Via Goldoni 1, 20129 Milano, Italy. adv.; illus. circ. 9,000.
Supersedes: Furniture Arredamento - Furniture Italy.

U F A C (YEAR). (Upholstered Furniture Action Council) see *FIRE PREVENTION*

U F A C VOLUNTEER. (Upholstered Furniture Action Council) see *FIRE PREVENTION*

UNIVERSIDADE DE SAO PAULO. MUSEU PAULISTA. COLECAO. SERIE DE MOBILIARIO. see *MUSEUMS AND ART GALLERIES*

747.5 US ISSN 1056-2052
UPHOLSTERY DESIGN & MANUFACTURING. Short title: U D M. 1988. m. $55 (foreign $100)(free to qualified personnel). Delta Communications Inc. (Subsidiary of: Cahners Publishing Company), Division of Reed Elsevier Inc., 455 N. Cityfront Plaza Dr., 24th Fl., Chicago, IL 60611. TEL 312-222-2000. FAX 312-222-2026. TELEX 210012 UR. Ed. Michael Chazin; Pub. S.L. (Sandy) Berliner. adv.: B&W page $2995, color page $4320; trim 7 7/8 x 10 3/4; adv. contact: Julie Okon. tr.lit. circ. 18,000. **Document type:** trade publication.
—CCC.
Incorporates (in 1990): Upholstery Manufacturing.

V D T A NEWS. (Vacuum Dealers Trade Association) see *BUSINESS AND ECONOMICS — Marketing And Purchasing*

V D T A PHONE DIRECTORY AND PRODUCT GUIDE. (Vacuum Dealers Trade Association) see *BUSINESS AND ECONOMICS — Marketing And Purchasing*

747 AT ISSN 0042-8035
VOGUE LIVING. 1967. 6/yr. Aus.$30 (foreign Aus.$45) (effective Jun. 1994). Conde Nast Publications Pty. Ltd., 170 Pacific Highway, Greenwich, N.S.W. 2065, Australia. TEL 02-964-3888. FAX 02-964-3882. (U.S. and Canada subscr. to: International Subscriptions Inc., 30 Montgomery St., 7th Fl., Jersey City, NJ 07302) Ed. Ilsa Konrads. adv.; bk.rev. circ. 62,570. Indexed: Gdlns. **Document type:** consumer publication.
Formerly: Vogue's Guide to Living.

WATASHI NO HEYA/MY ROOM. see *INTERIOR DESIGN AND DECORATION*

747.3 US ISSN 0886-9669
WINDOW FASHIONS. 1981. m. $30. G & W McNamara Publishing, Inc., 4225 White Bear Pky., Ste. 400, St. Paul, MN 55110-3349. TEL 612-293-1544. FAX 612-293-9497. Ed. Linnea C. Addison. adv. contact: Karen Fischer. charts; illus.; stat. circ. 23,000. (back issues avail.) **Document type:** trade publication.
Former titles: W E S: Voice of the Window Treatment Industry (ISSN 0746-7400); (until 1983): Window Energy Systems (ISSN 0277-0709)
Description: Articles and information on design, decoration, and treatment (motorized and mechanical shading), with installation and sales advice, business prospects, and an advertisement index.

645 GW ISSN 0178-2509
WOHNBADEN. s-a. DM.25.20. Krammer Verlag, Hermannstr. 3, 40233 Duesseldorf, Germany. TEL 0211-67972-0. FAX 0211-6797231. TELEX 8586639-KRVG-D. Ed.Bd. adv. contact: Heinz Martin. **Document type:** trade publication.
Description: Bathroom, kitchen and heating industry news and features. Includes latest designs, practical information, new ideas.

645 GW
WOHNMAGAZIN. 1959. 10/yr. DM.85 (foreign DM.128). Wohnteam-Verlag, Deutz-Muelheimer-Str. 30, 50679 Cologne, Germany. TEL 0221-813353. FAX 0221-814732. Ed. Josef Nuxoll. adv. circ. 4,000.

WOMAN'S DAY HOME DECORATING IDEAS. see *INTERIOR DESIGN AND DECORATION*

643 US
WOMAN'S DAY KITCHEN & BATH NEW PRODUCT IDEAS. 1990. a. $3.50. Hachette Magazines, Inc., Woman's Day Special Publications, 1633 Broadway, New York, NY 10019. TEL 212-767-6000. adv. circ. 450,000. **Document type:** consumer publication.
Description: Provides information about products that are available to help in remodeling kitchens or baths.

XIANDAI SHENGHUO YONGPIN/MODERN DAILY NECESSITIES. see *CONSUMER EDUCATION AND PROTECTION*

ZUHAUSE WOHNEN. see *INTERIOR DESIGN AND DECORATION*

INTERNAL MEDICINE

see *Medical Sciences–Internal Medicine*

INTERNATIONAL COMMERCE

see *Business and Economics–International Commerce*

INTERNATIONAL DEVELOPMENT AND ASSISTANCE

see *Business and Economics–International Development and Assistance*

INTERNATIONAL EDUCATION PROGRAMS

see *Education–International Education Programs*

INTERNATIONAL LAW

see *Law–International Law*

INTERNATIONAL RELATIONS

see *Political Science–International Relations*

INVESTMENTS

see *Business and Economics–Investments*

ISLAM

see *Religions and Theology–Islamic*

JEWELRY, CLOCKS AND WATCHES

739 US ISSN 0192-7507
ACCENT (NEW YORK). 1976. m. $36. Larkin Pluznick-Larkin, Inc., 100 Wells Ave., Newton, MA 02159. TEL 617-964-5100. FAX 617-964-2752. Ed. Lauren Parker. adv. circ. 15,000. (also avail. in microfilm from UMI; microfiche from UMI; reprint service avail. from UMI) **Document type:** trade publication.
—UMI. **CCC.**
Description: Primarily targeted to users of fashion jewelry and fashion watches - fashion forward editorials.

553.8 US
AMERICAN DIAMOND INDUSTRY ASSOCIATION NEWSLETTER. 1982. irreg. free to qualified personnel. American Diamond Industry Association Inc., 71 W. 47th St., New York, NY 10023. TEL 212-575-0525. FAX 212-869-3721. Ed. Lloyd Jaffe. circ. 16,000. **Document type:** trade publication.

JEWELRY, CLOCKS AND WATCHES

739.27 US ISSN 0002-9041
AMERICAN JEWELRY MANUFACTURER. 1956. m. $36 (Canada & Central America £46; elsewhere $74). (Manufacturing Jewelers and Silversmiths of America, Inc) Chilton Co., Chilton Way, Radnor, PA 19089. TEL 215-964-4037. Ed. Mitch Plotnick. adv.; charts; illus.; stat. circ. 5,600. (reprint service avail. from UMI) **Document type:** trade publication.
—BLDSC (0820.910000).
Description: Includes jewelry manufacturing technology, management and marketing topics, industry trends and news.

681.11 IT
▼**ANNUARIO OROLOGI.** 1992. a. L.18000. Technimedia s.r.l., Via Carlo Perrier 9, 00157 Rome, Italy. TEL 396-418921. FAX 396-41732169. Ed. Marco Marinacci. adv. circ. 70,000. (back issues avail.)

681.11 UK ISSN 0003-5785
ANTIQUARIAN HOROLOGY AND THE PROCEEDINGS OF THE ANTIQUARIAN HOROLOGICAL SOCIETY. 1953. q. £35($60) to members in the U.K. and Europe (U.S. and Canada £45 ($67); elsewhere £47 ($80)) (prices set in Oct.). Antiquarian Horological Society, New House, High St., Ticehurst, Wadhurst, Sussex TN5 7AL, England. TEL 0580 200155. Ed. Denys Vanghan. adv.; bk.rev.; illus.; index. circ. 3,000. **Document type:** trade publication, proceedings.
—BLDSC (1549.900000).
Description: Presents scholarly articles on all facets of antique clocks, reports on lectures, and a calendar of events of interest to society members.

ANTIQUE COMB COLLECTOR. see *ANTIQUES*

ART AUREA; Schmuck Mensch Objekte. see *ART*

739.27 681.11 SP
ARTE Y JOYA INTERNATIONAL. 5/yr. $160. Publicaciones Joyeras S.A., Via Layetana 71, pral 2a, 08003 Barcelona, Spain. TEL 3-318-07-10. FAX 3-318-59-84. Ed. Eva Gabarros. circ. 6,000. **Document type:** catalog.

739.27 681.11 SP
ARTE Y PRESTIGIO. 5/yr. Provenza 374, entlo. 1a, 08037 Barcelona, Spain. TEL 3-258-56-18. FAX 3-257-95-40. circ. 4,800.

739.27 681.11 IT
ARTEREGALO ORO ARGENTO; trimestrale inviato in abbonamento agli operatori commerciali dei settori oreficeria, gioielleria, argenteria. 1984. q. L.130000. Pubbliemme International s.r.l., Via Caracciolo 77, 20155 Milan, Italy. TEL 02-33100954. FAX 02-313864. Dir. Massimo Martini. adv. circ. 12,700. **Document type:** trade publication.
Formerly: Arteregalo - Oreficeria, Argenteria, Vetri d'Arte.
Description: Covers production of jewelry, silverware, and watches.

681.11 US ISSN 0254-1173
ASIAN SOURCES TIMEPIECES. 1980. m. $60. Asian Sources Trade Journals, c/o Wordright Enterprises Inc., 1020 Church St., Evanston, IL 60201. TEL 708-475-1900. FAX 708-475-2794. (Subscr. in Asia to: ASIMAG Ltd., P.O. Box 12367, Hong Kong) adv. circ. 19,700.

739.27 BE
AURIFEX. 1978. irreg., vol.7, 1988. price varies. Association des Diplomes Histoire Art et Archeologie, Centre d'Archeologie Grecque, College Erasme, Place Blaise Plascal 1, B-1348 Louvain-la-Neuve, Belgium. FAX 32-10-472579. Ed. T. Hackens. **Document type:** monographic series.

739.27 553.8 AT ISSN 0004-9174
CODEN: AGMLB2
AUSTRALIAN GEMMOLOGIST. 1958. q. Aus.$20. Gemmological Association of Australia, P.O. Box 35, South Yarra, Vic. 3141, Australia. TEL 03-826-9003. Ed. W.H. Hicks. adv.; bk.rev.; index, cum.index. circ. 2,356. (tabloid format; back issues avail.) **Indexed:** AESIS, Chem.Abstr., GeoRef., Mineral.Abstr.
—CASDDS.

BEAD FORUM. see *ARCHAEOLOGY*

BEADS. see *ANTHROPOLOGY*

739.27 700 US
THE BEST IN MODERN JEWELERY DESIGN. a. $55. Watson - Guptill Publications, 1515 Broadway, New York, NY 10036. (Subscr. to: 1695 Oak St., Lakewood, NJ 08701. TEL 800-451-1741. FAX 908-363-0338) illus.

739.27 681.11 FR ISSN 0766-6934
BIJOUTIER. 1940. m. 480 F. Pierre Johanet et ses Fils, 7 av. Franklin D. Roosevelt, 75008 Paris, France. TEL 43-59-08-91. FAX 42-25-59-47. adv.; illus.
Formerly (until 1985): Revue Francaise des Bijoutiers Horlogers (ISSN 0035-2993)

745 SP ISSN 1130-4359
BISUTERIA Y BISUTEROS. w. 5000 ptas. (foreign 9000 ptas.). Tecnipublicaciones, S.A., Fernando VI, 27, 28004 Madrid, Spain. TEL 91-419-90-66. FAX 91-410-2041.
Formerly: Catalogo Bisuteria y Bisuteros.

739.27 681.11 UK
BRITISH JEWELLER & WATCH BUYER. 1933. m. £36. E M A P Response Publishing Ltd., Wentworth House, Wentworth St., Peterborough PE1 1DS, England. TEL 0733-63100. FAX 0733-62656. Ed. Alison Marshall. adv.; bk.rev.; illus.; mkt.; stat. circ. 7,000.
Formerly: British Jeweller (ISSN 0007-0866)

681.11 UK
BRITISH JEWELLER & WATCH BUYER. YEARBOOK. a. £20. E M A P Response Publishing Ltd., Wentworth House, Wentworth St., Peterborough PE1 1DS, England. TEL 0733-63100. FAX 0733-62656. Ed. Alison Marshall. circ. 7,000.
Former titles: British Jeweller. Yearbook; British Jeweller. Buyer's Guide.

551 739.27 CN ISSN 0226-7446
CANADIAN GEMMOLOGIST. 1976. q. Can.$25($25) (typically set in Jan.). Canadian Gemmological Association, 21 Dundas Square, Ste. 1209, Toronto, ON M5B 1B7, Canada. TEL 416-603-0451. FAX 416-603-0456. Ed. Willow Wight. adv.; bk.rev.; index. circ. 600. (back issues avail.) **Document type:** trade publication.
Description: Covers all aspects of gemmology, new gemstones and localities.
Refereed Serial

739.27 CN ISSN 0008-3917
CANADIAN JEWELLER. 1879. 7/yr. Can.$22 (foreign Can.$42). Style Communications Inc., 1448 Lawrence Ave. E., Ste. 302, Toronto, ON M4A 2V6, Canada. TEL 416-755-5199. FAX 416-755-9123. Ed. Carol Besler. adv.; B&W page Can.$2787, color page Can.$3952; trim 8 x 10 3/4; adv. contact: John Peters. charts; illus.; tr.lit. circ. 6,376. **Indexed:** Can.B.P.I. **Document type:** trade publication.
—UMI.

CANADIAN JEWELLERY & GIFTWARE DIRECTORY. see *BUSINESS AND ECONOMICS — Trade And Industrial Directories*

CATALOG CONNECTION. see *GIFTWARE AND TOYS*

681.11 SP
CATALOGO RELOJES Y RELOJEROS. a. 3250 ptas. Tecnipublicaciones, S.A., Fernando VI, 27, 28004 Madrid, Spain. TEL 91-319-7889. FAX 91-319-7089.

681.11 US
CATALYST (LONG BEACH); happenings of the Self Winding Clock Association. 1979. q. $25 membership. (Self Winding Clock Association) S W C Publications (Long Beach), 1161 E. Marcellus St., Long Beach, CA 90807-1609. TEL 310-427-8001. Ed. Bengt E. Honning. bk.rev.; cum.index. circ. 250. (looseleaf format) **Indexed:** Amer.Hist.& Life, Hist.Abstr.
Description: Presents technical information and articles on the self-winding clock and other electro-mechanical and related horological items.

739.27 US ISSN 0194-2905
TS720
CHILTON'S JEWELERS' CIRCULAR-KEYSTONE. 1869. 14/yr. $31.95. Chilton Co., Chilton Way, Radnor, PA 19089. TEL 215-964-4474. FAX 215-964-4481. Ed. George Holmes. adv. contact: Lee Lawrence. bk.rev.; charts; illus.; mkt.; pat.; tr.lit.; index. circ. 37,000. (also avail. in microfilm from UMI; microfiche from UMI,CIS; reprint service avail. from UMI) **Indexed:** Bus.Ind., SRI, Tr.& Indus.Ind. **Document type:** trade publication.
●Also available online. Vendor(s): DIALOG Information Services, Inc.
—CCC.
Formerly: Jewelers' Circular-Keystone (ISSN 0021-6267)
Description: Covers store management, design and repair of jewelry and watches and trends in the industry.

739.27 IT ISSN 0009-8752
CLESSIDRA. 1945. m. L.100000. Sothis Editrice srl, Via Pietro Maestri 3, 00191 Rome, Italy. TEL 06-3295642. FAX 06-3295624. Ed. Gianfranco di Mario. adv.; bk.rev. circ. 20,000. **Document type:** trade publication.
Description: Focuses on the jewelry and watch industry. Advertises the latest trends in the jewelry market. Covers trade shows and various related events.

745.5 629.288 UK ISSN 0968-2384
CLOCKS. 1978. m. £28.80($56) Argus Specialist Publications Ltd., Argus House, Boundary Way, Hemel Hempstad, Herts. HP2 7ST, England. TEL 0442-66551. FAX 0442-66998. (Subscr. to: Argus Subscription Services, Queensway House, 2 Queensway, Redhill, Surrey, England. TEL 0737-786111) Ed. John Hunter. adv. **Document type:** consumer publication.
Former titles (until 1991): Antique Clocks (ISSN 0954-593X); (until 1988): Clocks (ISSN 0141-5107)
Description: Contains articles of interest to collectors of fine time pieces; also discusses restoration techniques.

739.27 622 US ISSN 1046-462X
COLORED STONE; the international reporter of the gemstone trade. 1988. bi-m. $18. Lapidary Journal, Inc., c/o Cindi Willcox, Circ. Dir., 60 Chestnut Ave., Ste. 201, Devon, PA 19333. TEL 215-293-1112. FAX 215-293-1717. Ed. Elana Verbin. adv. circ. 10,000. (back issues avail.) **Document type:** trade publication.

681.11 SP
CRONOMETRIA. 4/yr. Pizarro 14, 46004 Valencia, Spain. TEL 6-322-79-70. Ed. J. Leon Roca.

DAIYAMONDO SHINPOJUMU KOEN YOSHISHU/ABSTRACTS OF DIAMOND SYMPOSIUM. see *CHEMISTRY — Abstracting, Bibliographies, Statistics*

553.8 GW ISSN 0343-7892
DEUTSCHE GEMMOLOGISCHE GESELLSCHAFT. ZEITSCHRIFT. 1951. a. DM.86. E. Schweizerbart'sche Verlagsbuchhandlung, Johannesstr. 3A, 70176 Stuttgart, Germany. TEL 0711-625001. FAX 0711-625005. TELEX 723363-SCHB-D. Eds. H. Bank, U. Henn. adv.; charts; illus.; index. **Indexed:** GeoRef. **Document type:** academic/scholarly publication.
—CCC.

681.1 GW ISSN 0070-4040
DEUTSCHE GESELLSCHAFT FUER CHRONOMETRIE. JAHRBUCH. 1950. a. DM.35. Deutsche Gesellschaft fuer Chronometrie e.V., Christophstr. 5, 70178 Stuttgart, Germany.

739.27 BE
DIAMANT. (Text in Dutch, English, French) 1958. m. 2000 BEF($75) Consciencestraat 7, 2018 Antwerp, Belgium. TEL 32-3-239-2250. FAX 32-3-239-4354. Ed. Daphne Ringer. adv.: B&W page 33000 BEF. illus. circ. 3,000.
Description: Covers all aspects of the international diamond market, for the wholesale, retail and manufacturing sectors of the jewelry trade.

JEWELRY, CLOCKS AND WATCHES

553.8 US ISSN 1073-7316
▼**DIAMOND INDUSTRY WEEK.** 1994. w. (48/yr.). $377. Superconductivity Publications, 710 Easton Ave., Ste. C, Somerset, NJ 08873-1855. TEL 908-846-2002. FAX 908-846-2050. E-mail: 74130.650@COMPUSERVE.COM. pat. **Document type:** trade publication.
  Description: Covers all aspects of industrial diamonds and related materials. Includes news of business and technical developments, as well as government contract announcements and awards.

739.27 382 US ISSN 0954-5581
DIAMOND INSIGHT; penetrating the multi-faceted world of diamonds. 1988. 11/yr. $295 (effective 1994). Tryon Mercantile Inc., 790 Madison Ave., Ste. 602, New York, NY 10021. TEL 212-570-4180. FAX 212-772-1286. Ed. Guido Giovannini-Torelli. bk.rev.; abstr.; bibl.; charts; stat.; index, cum.index; circ. 260 (paid). (looseleaf format; back issues avail.) **Document type:** newsletter, trade publication.
  Description: Provides intelligence on the world's most important diamonds, future price indicators and key individuals in the industry.

739.27 US ISSN 0199-9753
DIAMOND REGISTRY. BULLETIN. 1969. m. $97 (foreign $125). Diamond Registry, 580 Fifth Ave., New York, NY 10036. TEL 212-575-0444. FAX 212-575-0722. Ed. Joseph Schlussel. bk.rev. (back issues avail.) **Document type:** bulletin.
  Description: Provides information, forecasts trends, wholesale diamond prices, and diamond jewelry news.

739 II ISSN 0970-7727
DIAMOND WORLD. (Text in English) 1973. bi-m. Rs.200($55) Diamond World, A-95 Journal House, Janta Colony, Jaipur 302 004, India. TEL 91-141-44398. FAX 91-141-42937. TELEX 365 2410 KALA IN. Ed. Vidya Vinod Kala. adv.: B&W page $900, color page $1200; trim 22.5 x 17.5. illus.; stat.; tr.lit. **Document type:** trade publication.
  Description: Contains news, views and developments in the diamond industry all over the world.

739.27 IS ISSN 0333-5380
DIAMOND WORLD REVIEW. (Text in English) 1974. 6/yr. $78. (World Federation of Diamond Bourses) International Diamond Publications Ltd., P.O. Box 3237, Ramat Gan 52131, Israel. TEL 972-3-7512165. FAX 972-3-5752201. TELEX 341730 SPEED IL. Ed. Joseph Sela; Pub. Itzchak Arikna. adv. contact: Yola Avidan. bk.rev. circ. 6,400. **Document type:** trade publication.

DIRECTORY OF JAPANESE JEWELERS (YEAR). see BUSINESS AND ECONOMICS — Trade And Industrial Directories

739.27 SP
DUPLEX BIJOUX. 3/yr. Duplex Creativos S.A., Via Layetana, 71 pral 1a, 08003 Barcelona, Spain. TEL 3-318-37-38. FAX 3-318-59-84. Ed. Pedro Perez. circ. 6,000. **Document type:** catalog.

739.27 669 NE
EDELMETAAL. m. Centraal Orgaan voor de Detailhandel in Juwelen, Goud, Zilver, Uurwerken en Aanver Wante Artikelen en het Uuwerkmakersambacht, Treubstraat 25, 2288 Rijswijk, Netherlands.

681.11 NE
EDELMETAAL UURWERKEN EDELSTENEN. 1946. m. avail. on request. Federatie Goud en Zilver, Van der Spiegelstraat 3, 2518 ES The Hague, Netherlands. TEL 31-70-3469607. FAX 31-70-3643431. Ed. P.L. Renes. adv.; bk.rev.; bibl.; illus.; stat. circ. 4,500. **Indexed:** Key to Econ.Sci.

739.27 IT
ELENCO DETTAGLIANTI D'ITALIA. 2/yr. Globo Editoriale s.r.l., Via S. Calimero 1, 20122 Milan, Italy. TEL 2-58-320-97-44. FAX 2-58-30-97-39. Ed. Ciro Borgonovi. circ. 6,000.

739.27 681.11 IT
ELENCO NAZIONALE MARCHI D'IDENTIFICAZIONE. 2/yr. Globo Editoriale s.r.l., Via S. Calimero 1, 20122 Milan, Italy. TEL 2-58-30-97-44. FAX 2-58-30-97-39. Ed. Ciro Borgonovi. circ. 10,000.

739.27 SZ ISSN 0014-2603
EUROPA STAR - INTERNATIONAL JEWELLERY MAGAZINE. (6 eds. avail.) bi-m. $50. Hugo Buchser S.A., Route des Acacias 25, P.O. Box 30, CH-1211 Geneva 24, Switzerland. TEL 022-3003737. FAX 022-3003748. adv.; bk.rev.; illus. circ. 38,000. **Document type:** trade publication.

688.2 US ISSN 0014-8644
FASHION ACCESSORIES. 1951. m. $22 in U.S.; Canada & Mexico $32; elsewhere $38. S.C.M. Publications, Inc., 65 W. Main St., Bergenfield, NJ 07621-1696. TEL 201-384-3336. FAX 201-384-6776. Ed. Samuel Mendelson. adv.; bk.rev.; illus.; stat. circ. 8,000. (tabloid format; back issues avail.) **Document type:** trade publication.
  Description: Directed to manufacturing and wholesaling jewlery executives.

739.27 CH
FASHION JEWELRY & ACCESSORIES. m. $60. Taiwan Trade Pages Corp., P.O. Box 72-50, Taipei, Taiwan, Republic of China. TEL 02-3050759. FAX 866-2-3071000. TELEX 24838 TRADEPAG. Eds. Michelle Cheng, Jennifer Yeh.
  Formerly: Gifts and Sundries.

739.27 669 NE
FEDERATIE GOUD EN ZILVER. VADEMECUM. a. Federatie Goud en Zilver, Van de Spiegelstraat 3, 2518 The Hague, Netherlands. TEL 31-70-3469607. FAX 31-70-3643431. **Document type:** directory.

681.11 SZ
FEDERATION DE L'INDUSTRIE HORLOGERE SUISSE. ANNUAL REPORT. (Text in French and German) 1925. a. free. Federation de l'Industrie Horlogere Suisse - Federation of the Swiss Watch Industry, 6 rue d'Argent, CH-2501 Bienne, Switzerland. TEL 032-225911. FAX 032-233197. (Dist. in U.S. by: Watchmakers of Switzerland Information Center, Inc., 608 Fifth Ave., 8th Fl., NY 10020) circ. 3,300. **Document type:** corporate report.
  Formerly: Federation Horlogere Suisse. Annual Report (ISSN 0071-4259)

681.11 SZ
FEDERATION DE L'INDUSTRIE HORLOGERE SUISSE. REVUE. Short title: Revue F H. (Text in French and German) fortn. (22/yr.). 360 SFr. Federation de l'Industrie Horlogere Suisse - Federation of the Swiss Watch Industry, 6 rue d'Argent, CH-2501 Bienne, Switzerland. TEL 032-225911. FAX 032-233197. **Document type:** trade publication.
  Formerly: Federation Horlogere Suisse. Bulletin.

FINE METAL GAZETTE. see METALLURGY

681.11 739.27 FR ISSN 0015-9573
FRANCE HORLOGERE; revue de l'horlogerie, bijouterie, orfevrerie cadeaux. 1901. 10/yr. 550 F. Societe d'Editions Millot et Cie, 20 rue Gambetta, B.P. 169, 25014 Besancon Cedex, France. TEL 81-82-14-90. FAX 81-83-36-82. adv.; bk.rev.; illus.; stat.; tr.lit. circ. 6,525.

739.27 UK ISSN 0964-6736
GEM & JEWELLERY NEWS. 1991. q. Gemmological Association and Gem Testing Laboratory of Great Britain, 27 Greenville St., London EC1N 8SU, England. TEL 071-404-3334. FAX 071-404-8843. Ed. E.A. Jobbins.

736 553.8 II
GEM & JEWELLERY YEARBOOK. 1974. a. Rs.300($55) International Journal House, A-95 Journal House, Janta Colony, Jaipur 302 004, India. TEL 91-141-44398. FAX 91-141-42973. TELEX 365 2410 KALA IN. Eds. Vidya Vinod Kala, Alok Kala. adv.: B&W page $600, color page $1000; trim 22 x 14.5. bk.rev.; charts; illus.; stat.; tr.lit. circ. 4,500.

553.8 US ISSN 0016-626X
TS720 CODEN: GEGEA2
GEMS & GEMOLOGY. 1934. q. $54.95. Gemological Institute of America, 1660 Stewart St., Santa Monica, CA 90404. TEL 310-829-2991. FAX 310-453-4478. Ed. Alice S. Keller. bk.rev.; charts; illus.; index; circ. 10,000 (paid). **Indexed:** AESIS, Chem.Abstr., GeoRef. **Document type:** trade publication.
  —Faxon; UnCover.
  Description: Industry news and technological and historical information on gems.

739.2 GW ISSN 0017-1573
GOLD UND SILBER - UHREN UND SCHMUCK. 1948. m. DM.194.40 (foreign DM.210). Konradin Verlag Robert Kohlhammer GmbH, Ernst-Mey-Str. 8, 70771 Leinfelden-Echterdingen, Germany. TEL 0711-7594-0. FAX 0711-7594-390. Ed. Klaus Hallwass. adv.: B&W page DM.3780; trim 205 x 283; adv. contact: Anna Waskala. bk.rev.; charts; illus.; pat.; tr.lit. circ. 10,140. (back issues avail.) **Document type:** trade publication.
  —CCC.
  Formed by merger of: Gold und Silber & Uhren und Schmuck (ISSN 0041-5847)
  Description: Trade publication for the watch and jewelry industry. Covers the latest trends in designs and styles. Includes reports and announcements of exhibitions and events, list of courses, and positions available.

739 681 GW
GOLDSCHMIEDE- UND UHRMACHER-JAHRBUCH. 1903. a. DM.23. Ruehle-Diebener Verlag GmbH und Co. KG, Postfach 700450, 70574 Stuttgart, Germany. TEL 0711-97667-0. FAX 0711-97667-49. adv. circ. 2,500. **Document type:** trade publication.
  Formerly: Diebeners Goldschmiede- und Uhrmacher-Jahrbuch (ISSN 0070-4814)

739.27 GW ISSN 0932-464X
GOLDSCHMIEDE UND UHRMACHER ZEITUNG - EUROPEAN JEWELER. (Supplements avail.). 1892. m. DM.180.40. (Zentralverband fuer das Juwelier-, Gold- und Silberschmiedhandwerk) Ruehle-Diebener Verlag GmbH und Co. KG, Postfach 700450, 70574 Stuttgart, Germany. TEL 0711-97667-0. FAX 0711-97667-49. adv.: B&W page DM.4100, color page DM.6164; trim 280 x 212. bk.rev.; illus.; tr.lit. circ. 15,100. **Indexed:** Chem.Abstr. **Document type:** trade publication.
  Formerly: Goldschmiede Zeitung - European Jeweler und Uhrmacherzeitschrift (ISSN 0017-1689); Which incorporated: Deutsche Urmacher-Zeitschrift (ISSN 0012-0863)

739.27 DK ISSN 0017-5544
GULDSMEDEBLADET. 1917. m. (11/yr.). DKK 620 (effective 1994). Guldsmedefagets Faellesraad, DK-4894 Oester Ulslev, Denmark. TEL 53-86-55-66. FAX 53-86-55-69. Ed. Bendix Bech-Thostrup. adv.; bk.rev.; bibl.; illus.; stat.; index, cum.index; circ. 1,400. (controlled). **Document type:** trade publication.

739.2 SW ISSN 0282-4175
GULDSMEDSTIDNINGEN. 1915. m. (8/yr.). SEK 475 in Nordic countries; elsewhere SEK 650. Sveriges Juvelerare- och Guldsmedsfoerbund - Swedish Jewellers and Goldsmiths Association, Gamla Brogatan 19, S-111 20 Stockholm, Sweden. TEL 46-820-51-95. FAX 46-824-80-25. Ed. Eric Form. adv. contact: Lisbet Wadelius. bk.rev.; illus.; index; circ. 1,250 (controlled). **Document type:** trade publication.
  Formerly (until 1984): Svensk Guldsmedstidning (ISSN 0039-6559)

739.27 NO ISSN 0046-6603
GULLSMEDKUNST. 1910. 11/yr. NOK 275. Norges Gullsmedforbund - Norwegian Goldsmiths' Association, Storgaten 14, 0184 Oslo 1, Norway. Ed. Berit Roehne. adv.; bk.rev.; index. circ. 1,825. (back issues avail.) **Document type:** trade publication.
  —CCC.

HENRY'S AUKTIONEN. see ANTIQUES

739.27 681.11 HK
HONG KONG JEWELLERY COLLECTION. (Text in English) 1985. s-a. $40 (free to qualified personnel). Hong Kong Trade Development Council, 36-39th Fl., Office Tower, Convention Plaza, 1 Harbour Rd., Wanchai, Hong Kong. TEL 584-4333. FAX 824-0249. Ed. Saul Lockhart. circ. 20,000.
  Former titles: Hong Kong Jewellery Bi-Annual; Hong Kong Jewellery Annual; Which superseded in part: Hong Kong Jewellery and Watches.

739.27 HK
HONG KONG JEWELLERY MAGAZINE. (Text in Chinese, English) 1978. q. HK.$140($18) Ridgeville Ltd., Flat A, 12th Fl., Kaiser Estate Phase 1, 41 Man Yue St. Hunghom, Kowloon, Hong Kong. TEL 3344311. FAX 852-7641956. Ed. Catherine Chan. circ. 15,000. **Document type:** trade publication.
  Description: Professional & trade magazine about the jewellery industry and allied trade. Aimed at jewellers and jewelry trades throughout the world.

I J K

JEWELRY, CLOCKS AND WATCHES

681.11   HK
HONG KONG WATCHES & CLOCKS. (Text in English) 1988. s-a. $40 (free to qualified personnel). Hong Kong Trade Development Council, 36-39th Fl., Office Tower, Convention Plaza, 1 Harbour Rd., Wanchai, Hong Kong. TEL 584-4333. FAX 824-0249. Ed. Saul Lockhart. circ. 20,000.
    Supersedes in part: Hong Kong Jewellery and Watches.

681.11   US   ISSN 0145-9546
TS540
HOROLOGICAL TIMES. 1977. m. $45. American Watchmakers Institute, 3700 Harrison Ave., Box 11011, Cincinnati, OH 45211. TEL 513-661-3838. FAX 513-661-3131. Ed. Milton C. Stevens. adv.; bk.rev. circ. 7,500. **Document type:** trade publication.

HOSEKI GAKKAISHI/GEMMOLOGICAL SOCIETY OF JAPAN. JOURNAL. see CHEMISTRY — Crystallography

I M R SOURCEBOOK UPDATE. (Institute of Metal Repair) see METALLURGY

681.11   SP
IDEAS PARA REGALO. 24/yr. Ramon Patuel, 3 L-8, 28017 Madrid, Spain. TEL 1-255-00-45. Ed. I. Garcia Rodriguez.

739.27   IT   ISSN 0393-0076
INDUSTRIA ORAFA ITALIANA; mensile di arte orafa, orologi, argento. 1917. m. L.60000. Globo Editoriale s.r.l., Via S. Calimero, 1, 20122 Milan, Italy. TEL 02-58309823. FAX 02-58309739. adv. circ. 8,000.

681.11   US
INTERNATIONAL WRIST WATCH. bi-m. $30. International Publishers Group, 242 West Ave., Darien, CT 06820-4111. TEL 203-656-3913. FAX 203-656-2774.

681.11   JA
▼**INTERNATIONAL WRIST WATCH (JAPANESE EDITION).** (Text in Japanese) 1993. q. 6770 Yen. Nigensha Publishing Co., Ltd., 22, Kanda-Jimbocho, Chiyoda-ku, Tokyo 101, Japan. TEL 81-3-5210-4706. FAX 81-3-5210-4726. adv.; B&W page 35000 Yen, color page 700000 Yen; trim 210 x 270; adv. contact: R. Ohkoshi.
    Description: Provides local and international news and articles for wrist watch enthusiasts.

739.27   IS   ISSN 0021-2016
ISRAEL DIAMONDS. (Text in English) 1966. bi-m. $78. International Diamond Publications Ltd., P.O. Box 3237, Ramat Gan 52131, Israel. TEL 972-3-7512165. FAX 972-3-5752201. TELEX 341730 SPEED IL. Ed. Joseph Sela; Pub. Itzchak Arikna. adv. contact: Yola Avidan. bk.rev.; illus. circ. 4,500. **Document type:** trade publication.

739.27   IT
ITALIA ORAFA. 11/yr. (Goldsmiths Association of Lombardy) Lombardoro Servizi s.r.l., Piazza Pio XI 1, 20123 Milan, Italy. TEL 2-805-88-18. FAX 2-86-90-113. Ed. Emanuele de Giovanni. circ. 20,000.

739.27   US
J C K'S JEWELERS' DIRECTORY. (Jewelers' Circular - Keystone) a. Chilton Co., Jewelers' Circular - Keystone, One Chilton Way, Radnor, PA 19089. TEL 610-964-4470. FAX 610-964-4481. TELEX 173223 CHILTON UT. (Subscr. to: Box 2088, Radnor, PA 19080-9485. TEL 610-964-4148) adv.; circ. 29,256 (paid). **Document type:** directory.
    Description: Listing of manufacturers and suppliers of jewelry trade by types of products.

739.27   CN   ISSN 0823-1346
J W PLUS. 1982. 6/yr. $65 (foreign $100). Jewellery World Ltd., 20 Eglinton Ave. W., Ste. 1108, Toronto, ON M4R 1K8, Canada. TEL 416-480-1450. FAX 416-480-2342. Ed. Jonathon Reid. adv.; circ. 7,000. (tabloid format)

745.594   US
JEWELERS' BOOK CLUB NEWS. 1979. q. (Jewelers' Book Club) Chilton Co. (Subsidiary of: A B C, Inc.), Chilton Way, Radnor, PA 19089-0140. TEL 215-964-4470. FAX 215-964-4481. Ed. Donald S. McNeil. bk.rev. circ. 7,000.
    Description: Geared to retail and manufacturing jewelers. Offers educational and coffee table publications pertinent to the industry.

739.27   US
JEWELERS, INC.. 1910. m. $24. Trades Publishing Co., Box 42, Rochford, SD 57778-0042. TEL 507-373-2316. FAX 507-373-0605. Ed. Patti Reick. adv. circ. 48,000. **Document type:** trade publication.
    Formerly: Northwestern Jeweler (ISSN 0029-3490)
    Description: Features convention news, seminars, selling techniques, new products, regional items about various jewelers, and state association news for professionals.

739.27   AT
JEWELLERS ASSOCIATION OF AUSTRALIA. NATIONAL NEWSLETTER. 1968. q. free to members (foreign Aus.$75). Jewellers Association of Australia Limited, P.O. Box E 446, Queen Victoria Terrace, Canberra, A.C.T. 2600, Australia. TEL 06-282-3211. FAX 06-282-2725. Ed. Kim Hilliard. adv.; bk.rev. circ. 1,500. **Document type:** trade publication, newsletter.
    Former titles: Jewellers Association of Australia. Federal Newsletter (ISSN 0816-6706); Australian Jewellers Association. Federal Newsletter; Australian Jewellers Association. Jewellers News.

681.1 739.27   UK
JEWELLERS' REFERENCE BOOK.* 1931. a. £19.50. Nexus Business Communications Ltd., Warwick House, Azalea Dr., Swanley, Kent BR8 8HY, England. adv.
    Formerly (until 1986): Watchmaker, Jeweller and Silversmith Directory of Trade Names and Punch Marks (ISSN 0083-7628)

745.594   UK
JEWELLERY. 6th ed., 1987. every 18 mos. £155 per no. Key Note Publications Ltd., Field House, Old Field Rd., Hampton TW12 2HQ, England. TEL 01-783-0755. **Document type:** trade publication.
    Description: Review of the jewelry industry in the U.K., including industry structure, market size and trends, recent developments, prospects and company profiles.

739.27   HK
JEWELLERY AND GEMSTONE DIRECTORY OF ASIA. (Text in English) 1991. a. $90. Jewellery News Asia Ltd., Guardian House, Rm. 601, 32 Oi Kwan Rd., Wanchai, Hong Kong. TEL 852-8322011. FAX 852-8329208. Ed. Peter Brindisi. circ. 5,000. **Document type:** directory.
    Description: Lists companies in the jewellery and gemstone industries in 10 countries in Asia.

739.27   IE
JEWELLERY & GIFTWARE IRELAND. 6/yr. Sandyford Office Park, Unit 9, Sandyford, Dublin 18, Ireland. TEL 958069. FAX 958065. Ed. P. Codyre. circ. 1,500.

739.27   HK
JEWELLERY NEWS ASIA. (Text in English) 1983. m. HK.$340($112) Jewellery News Asia Ltd., Guardian House, Rm. 601, 32 Oi Kwan Rd., Wanchai, Hong Kong. TEL 852-8322011. FAX 852-8329208. Ed. Peter Brindisi. adv.; bk.rev.; charts; illus.; stat.; tr.lit. circ. 9,118. (back issues avail.) **Document type:** trade publication.
    Description: Covers new products, manufacturing and marketing techniques for executives in jewlry, gemstone, watch and clock trades.

681.11   NZ   ISSN 1170-9960
JEWELLERY TIME. 1925. bi-m. NZ.$96. (Jewellers and Watchmakers of NZ Inc.) Ink Link Publications, Box 46-218, Herne Bay, Auckland, New Zealand. TEL 09-378-1222. FAX 09-378-1270. (Co-sponsor: Jewellery Manufacturers Federation of New Zealand Inc.) Ed. Carol Bucknell; Pub. D.E. Whiting. adv.; B&W page NZ$800, color page NZ$1000; trim 275 x210. bk.rev.; circ. 1,200 (controlled). **Document type:** trade publication.
    Former titles (until 1991): New Zealand Jeweller and Watchmaker; (1962-1982): New Zealand Horological Journal (ISSN 0028-8195)

745.594   CN   ISSN 0383-9818
JEWELLERY WORLD. 1976. 6/yr. Can.$65 (foreign Can.$100). Jewellery World Ltd., 20 Eglinton Ave. W., Ste. 1108, Toronto, ON M4R 1K8, Canada. TEL 416-480-1450. FAX 416-480-2342. Ed. Jonathon Reid. adv. circ. 7,000.

681.11   AT   ISSN 0811-2274
JEWELLERY WORLD. 1981. bi-m. Aus.$24($40) Jewellery World Pty. Ltd., P.O. Box 63, Eastwood, N.S.W. 2122, Australia. TEL 2-804-6517. FAX 2-804-6517. Ed. D.D. Michel. adv. circ. 3,050.

688.2   US   ISSN 0883-7929
JEWELRY AD REVIEW. 1936. m. $250 (effective 1994). Retail Reporting Bureau, 302 Fifth Ave., New York, NY 10001. TEL 212-279-7000; 800-251-4545. FAX 212-279-7014. illus. **Document type:** trade publication.
    Former titles: Costume Jewelry Review; Jewelry Clip Review (ISSN 0021-6283)

553   US
THE JEWELRY APPRAISER. 1980. q. membership only. National Association of Jewelry Appraisers, Box 6558, Annapolis, MD 21401-0558. TEL 301-261-8270. Ed. James V. Jolliff. adv.; bk.rev.; circ. 800 (controlled). (back issues avail.) **Document type:** newsletter.
    Description: Discusses the value and evaluation techniques of jewels and gems.

739.27   SP
JEWELRY DUPLEX. 2/yr. Duplex Creativos S.A., Via Layetana, 71 pral 1a, 08003 Barcelona, Spain. TEL 3-318-37-38. FAX 3-318-59-84. Ed. Pedro Perez. circ. 15,000. **Document type:** catalog.

681   US   ISSN 0738-7261
JEWELRY NEWSLETTER INTERNATIONAL. 1973. m. $250. Newsletters International, Inc., 2600 S. Gessner Rd., Houston, TX 77063. TEL 713-783-0100. Ed. Len Fox. **Document type:** newsletter.

736.2   II   ISSN 0022-1244
TS720
JOURNAL OF GEM INDUSTRY. (Editions in English, Hindi) 1963. bi-m. Rs.125($50) Journal of Gem Industry, A-95 Journal House, Janta Colony, Jaipur 302 004, India. TEL 44398. FAX 91-141-42973. TELEX 365-2410-KALA-IN. Ed. Alok Kala. adv.: B&W page Rs.600, color page Rs.1000; trim 22.5 x 17.5. bk.rev.; charts; illus.; stat. **Document type:** trade publication.
    Description: Covers the import and export, and latest technological advances in equipment and prcessing in the field of gems and jewellery.

553.8   UK   ISSN 0022-1252
                                                                                                CODEN: JGEAAR
JOURNAL OF GEMMOLOGY. 1947. q. £130 (overseas £155) (includes subscr. to Gem & Jewellery News) (effective 1994). Gemmological Association and Gem Testing Laboratory of Great Britain, 27 Greville St., London EC1N 8SU, England. TEL 071-404-3334. FAX 071-404-8843. Ed. E.A. Jobbins. adv. contact: Mary Burland. bk.rev.; abstr.; bibl.; cum.index every 2 yrs. circ. 4,000. (also avail. in microform from UMI; reprint service avail. from UMI) **Indexed:** AESIS, Chem.Abstr., GeoRef. **Document type:** newsletter, academic/scholarly publication.
—BLDSC (4987.650000); UMI; CASDDS.
    Formerly: Journal of Gemmology and Proceedings of the Gemmological Association of Great Britain (ISSN 0375-6734)

739.27   SP   ISSN 0213-120X
JOYAS & JOYEROS; revista independiente para el profesional de la joyeria relojeria y orfebreria. 1985. bi-m. 6500 ptas. (foreign 10000 ptas). Tecnipublicaciones, S.A., Fernando VI, 27, 28004 Madrid, Spain. TEL 91-319-7889. FAX 91-319-7089. adv. circ. 10,000.
    Incorporates: Diamantes Oro.

739.27   SP
JOYAS DEL MUNDO. 2/yr. Grassot 83, 08025 Barcelona, Spain. TEL 3-207-11-00. FAX 3-459-05-24. Ed. Rosa Carmen Macia.

739.27   SP
JOYASOL. 12/yr. Plaza Uncibay-3, 5o Of. 8, 29008 Malaga, Spain. TEL 52-22-62-23. FAX 52-21-70-28. Ed. Sebastian M. Molina.

JEWELRY, CLOCKS AND WATCHES

681   FI   ISSN 1236-4169
KELLO- JA KULTASEPANALA/WATCH AND GOLDSMITH BRANCH. 1926. 8/yr. FIM 290. Suomen Kultaseppien Liitto r. y. - Finnnish Goldsmith Association, Vuorikatu 3 A 10, 00100 Helsinki 10, Finland. TEL 358-0-660-562. FAX 358-0-660-230. (Co-sponsor: Finnish Watchmakers Association) Eds. Pekka Kautto, Paula Holmen. adv.: B&W page FIM 3700, color page FIM 7000. bk.rev.; index. circ. 2,600. Document type: trade publication.
    Formed by the July 1992 merger of: Kultaseppien Lehti (ISSN 0085-2600) & Kelloseppa (ISSN 0355-7588)

LAPIDARY JOURNAL. see *HOBBIES*

LAPIS; die aktuelle Monatsschrift fuer Liebhaber und Sammler von Mineralien und Edelsteinen. see *MINES AND MINING INDUSTRY*

745.594   FR   ISSN 0760-2146
LETTRE D'ORION. 1983. s-m. 410 F. Publicat, 17 bd. Poissonniere, 75002 Paris, France. TEL 40-39-13-13. FAX 42-21-02-50. (tabloid format) Document type: trade publication.

745.594   FR   ISSN 0987-3872
LETTRE D'ORION (MAGAZINE). 1983. bi-m. 410 F. 17 bd. Poissonniere, 75002 Paris, France. TEL 40-39-13-13. FAX 42-21-02-50. Ed. Nathalie Coupez. adv. circ. 5,000. Document type: trade publication.

739.27   US
M J S A BENCHMARK. 1990. bi-m. membership. Manufacturing Jewelers and Silversmiths of America, 100 India St., Providence, RI 02903. TEL 401-274-3840. Document type: newsletter.

739.27 301   US   ISSN 0892-1989
MARGARETOLOGIST. 1985. s-a. $15. Center for Beads Research, 4 Essex St., Lake Placid, NY 12946. TEL 518-523-1794. Ed. Peter Francis, Jr. bk.rev. circ. 200. Document type: newsletter.
    Description: Devoted exclusively to the scientific study of beads in the human context.

739.27 681.11   US   ISSN 0193-208X
MODERN JEWELER. NATIONAL EXECUTIVE. 1901. m. $25 (foreign $100). Vance Publishing Corporation, 7950 College Blvd., Shawnee Mission, KS 66210. TEL 913-451-2200. FAX 913-451-5821. Ed. Joseph Thompson. adv.; bk.rev.; illus.; mkt.; index. circ. 38,000. (also avail. in microform from UMI)
    Supersedes in part: Modern Jeweler (ISSN 0026-7864)

739.27   US   ISSN 0744-2513
HD9747.U5
MODERN JEWELER NATIONAL. 1901. m. $35 (foreign $100). Vance Publishing Corporation, 7950 College Blvd., Shawnee Mission, KS 66210. TEL 913-451-2200. (Subscr. to: Box 1416, Lincolnshire, IL 60069) Ed. Joseph Thompson. circ. 38,000 (controlled). (also avail. in microfilm; back issues avail.)
    —UMI. **CCC.**

739.27   IT   ISSN 0392-6079
MONDO DEI GIOIELLI. (Text in English and Italian) 1977. 3/yr. L.40000 (foreign L.110000) (effective 1992). Mastermaind s.n.c., Via delle Groane 13, Arese (MI), Italy. adv.: B&W page L.3500000, color page L.4250000; trim 220 x 304. illus. circ. 14,000.
    Formerly: Alam al Mugiauharat.
    Description: Information on the exhibitions and collections of Italian goldsmiths and jewelers.

332.743   UK   ISSN 0047-9020
N.P.A. JOURNAL. 1959. bi-m. £2. National Pawnbrokers Association (Inc.), Park 1 Bell Yard, London WC2, England.

681.11   US   ISSN 0027-8688
NK11
NATIONAL ASSOCIATION OF WATCH AND CLOCK COLLECTORS. BULLETIN. 1946. 6/yr. $25. National Association of Watch and Clock Collectors, Inc., 514 Poplar St., Columbia, PA 17512. TEL 717-684-8261. FAX 717-684-0878. Ed. Kathy I. Everett. bk.rev.; abstr.; charts; illus.; index, cum.index every 9 to 10 yrs. circ. 35,000. (back issues avail.) Document type: bulletin.

739.27 681.11   US   ISSN 0027-9544
HD9747.U54
NATIONAL JEWELER. 1906. bi-m. $480. Miller Freeman Inc. (New York) (Subsidiary of: United Newspapers Group), 1515 Broadway, New York, NY 10036. TEL 212-869-1300. FAX 212-302-6273. Ed. Lynn Diamond. adv.; bk.rev.; charts; illus.; mkt.; tr.lit.; index. circ. 34,700.
    ●Also available online.
    —CCC.
    Formerly: National Jeweler and National Watchmaker.

NEW DIAMOND. see *CHEMISTRY — Crystallography*

739.27   IS
NEW YORK DIAMONDS. (Text in English) 1988. q. $36 in U.S. (elsewhere $44). International Diamond Publications Ltd., P.O. Box 3237, Ramat Gan 52131, Israel. TEL 972-3-7512165. FAX 972-3-5752201. TELEX 341730 SPEED IL. Ed. Joseph Sela; Pub. Itzchak Arikna. adv. contact: Yola Avidan. circ. 18,500. Document type: trade publication.
    Description: Reports on the diamond business in New York, the U.S. and worldwide, from mining and manufacturing to trade news.

681.11   JA   ISSN 0029-0416
NIHON TOKEI GAKKAISHI/HOROLOGICAL INSTITUTE OF JAPAN. JOURNAL. (Text in Japanese; summaries in English) 1957. q. 2000 Yen. Nihon Gakkai Jimu Senta, c/o Copyright Council of the Academic Societies, 704-42-6 Akasaka 9-chome, Minato-ku, Tokyo 107, Japan. TEL 81-3-3475-4621. FAX 81-2-3403-1738. Ed. Y. Jimbo. adv. **Indexed:** JTA, Sci.Abstr. Document type: academic/scholarly publication.
    —BLDSC (4758.600000).

739.27   JA
NIKKEI JEWELLERY. (Text in Japanese) 1991. m. 22000 Yen. Nikkei Business Publications, Inc. (Subsidiary of: Nihon Keizai Shimbun, Inc.), 2-7-6 Hirakawa-cho, Chiyoda-ku, Tokyo 102, Japan. TEL 03-5210-8502. FAX 03-5210-8119. Ed. Osamu Hasuike. adv. contact: Tohru Matsuura. circ. 6,644. Document type: trade publication.
    Description: Covers information for retailers, wholesalers, and other specialists in all areas of Japan's jewelry market. Includes management methods, new trends, consumer survey results and more.

739.27 681.11   JA   ISSN 0029-0653
NIPPON KIKINZOKU TOKEI SHINBUN/JAPAN PRECIOUS METALS AND WATCH NEWS. (Text in Japanese) every 10 days. 5000 Yen. Nippon Kikinzoku Tokei Shinbunsha, Tokyo Kikokaikan Bldg., 2-19-16 Negishi, Taito-ku, Tokyo 110, Japan. Ed. Chosaburo Someya. adv.

NOTES FROM A BEADERWORKER'S JOURNAL. see *ARTS AND HANDICRAFTS*

NYU DAIYAMONDO. see *CHEMISTRY — Crystallography*

739.27   IT   ISSN 0471-7376
ORAFO ITALIANO. 1947. m. (11/yr.). L.200. L'Orafo Italiano S.r.l., Via Nervesa 2, 20139 Milan, Italy. TEL 92-5392288. FAX 92-5695814. Ed. Gianni Roggini. adv.: B&W page L.2500000, color page L.4100000; trim 180 x 220. illus. circ. 7,985.
    Description: Includes color editorials on jewelry, precious stones, watches and trade fairs.

739   IT   ISSN 0473-1174
ORAFO ITALIANO NEL MONDO/ITALIAN GOLDSMITH IN THE WORLD. (Text in English and Italian) 1956. 3/yr. free. L'Orafo Italiano S.r.l., Via Nervesa 2, 20139 Milan, Italy. TEL 92-5392288. FAX 92-5695814. adv.; charts; illus. circ. 20,000.
    Description: Includes color editorials on jewelry, precious stones, watches and production methods.

681.11   IT   ISSN 0030-4182
ORAFO OROLOGIAIO. 1945. bi-m. L.10000. Associazione Piemontese Orafi Orologiai, Via Bogino N. 1, 10123 Turin, Italy. Ed. Italo Ambrosio. adv.; charts; illus. circ. 2,500.

745.5   US   ISSN 0148-3897
NK7300
ORNAMENT; a quarterly of jewelry and personal adornment. 1974. q. $26 (foreign $30) (effective 1993). Ornament Inc., Box 2349, San Marcos, CA 92079-2349. TEL 619-599-0222. FAX 619-599-0228. Eds. Robert K. Liu, Carolyn L.E. Benesh. adv. contact: Simone Trifunovic. bk.rev. circ. 45,000. (back issues avail.) **Indexed:** A.I.C.P., Art Ind., Artbibl.Mod., Br.Archaeol.Abstr. Document type: consumer publication.
    —BLDSC (6291.750000); Faxon; UnCover.
    Formerly (until 1979): Bead Journal (ISSN 0094-2448)
    Description: Covers ancient, ethnic, and contemporary jewelry, costumes and artist-made clothing.

681.11   IT
OROLOGI; le misure del tempo. 1987. m. (11/yr.). L.64000 (Europe L.165000; America L.230000). Technimedia s.r.l., Via Carlo Perrier, 9, 00157 Rome, Italy. TEL 396-418921. FAX 396-41732169. Ed. Marco Marinacci. adv. circ. 70,000. (back issues avail.)

745.594   IT
OROLOGI DA POLSO. 1987. bi-m. L.40000 (foreign L.80000). Studio Zeta S.r.l., Via S. Fruttuoso, 10, 20052 Monza, Italy. TEL 39-731952. FAX 39-736500. Ed. Eugenio Zigliotto. circ. 27,000.

681.11   IT
OROLOGI E NON SOLO. 12/yr. Editore s.r.l., Viale Mazzini 117, 00195 Rome, Italy. TEL 06-38-35-39. FAX 06-38-90-51. Ed. Vincenzo Bruno. circ. 45,000.

681.1   NO
PAA SEKUNDET. 1908. 11/yr. NOK 650 to non-members; members NOK 500. (Urmakerforbundets Rasjonaliseringselskap) TidsPress A-S, P.O. Box 81, N-4363 Brusand, Norway. TEL 47-51-43-93-88. FAX 47-51-43-93-53. Ed. Inger Johanne Mola. adv. contact: Paul Lunde.

PLATINUM (YEAR). see *MINES AND MINING INDUSTRY*

736.2   AT
POINTER.* q. Combined Victorian Gem Clubs Association, G.P.O. Box 4076, Melbourne, Vic. 3001, Australia. adv. **Indexed:** Educ.Ind.

739.27 669   US   ISSN 0730-1901
PRECIOUS METALS NEWS AND REVIEW. 1977. 7/yr. $24. International Precious Metals Institute, 4905 Tilghman St., Ste. 160, Allentown, PA 18104. TEL 610-395-9700. FAX 610-395-5855. Ed. Roger J. Runck. circ. 1,200 (paid). Document type: newsletter.
    Description: Offers information about mining, recovery, refining, applications, analyses, economics, environmental problems.

739.27   US   ISSN 0746-9829
RAPAPORT DIAMOND REPORT. 1976. w. $180 (foreign $250). Rapaport Corp., 15 W. 47th St., Ste. 700, New York, NY 10036. TEL 212-354-0575. FAX 212-840-0243. Ed. Jane Everhart; Pub. Martin Rapaport. adv. (back issues avail.)
    ●Also available online.
    Description: News for the jewelry and gemstone industries, including current diamond prices.

681.11   SP
RELOJES. 12/yr. Aviacion y Turismo S.A., German Perez Carrasco 81 bajo, 28027 Madrid, Spain. TEL 1-377-46-40. FAX 1-377-42-86. Ed. Hipolito Navarro. circ. 12,000.

739.27 669   US
REPAIRING METALWARE. m. Institute of Metal Repair, 1558 S. Redwood St., Escondido, CA 92025. TEL 619-747-5978. Document type: bulletin.

JEWELRY, CLOCKS AND WATCHES — ABSTRACTING, BIBLIOGRAPHIES, STATISTICS

739.27 681.11 UK ISSN 0034-6063
RETAIL JEWELLER; for retailers, wholesalers and manufacturers of jewelry, clocks, watches, silverware, etc., dealers and designers. 1963. fortn. £58.40($95.19) International Thomson Business Publishing, 100 Avenue Road, London NW3 3TP, England. TEL 01-935-6611. Ed. Jill Bousoulengas. adv.; bk.rev.; illus. circ. 10,031. (also avail. in microfilm from UMI) **Document type:** newspaper.
  Incorporates: Gemmologist; Goldsmiths Journal & Horological Review.

SAN FRANCISCO GIFTCENTER AND JEWELRYMART BUYER'S GUIDE. see *GIFTWARE AND TOYS*

739.27 GW ISSN 0341-9002
SCHMUCK UND UHREN. 1947. 6/yr. DM.85.80 (including special insert DM.151.80). Ebner Verlag GmbH, Postfach 3060, 89020 Ulm, Germany. TEL 0731-152028. FAX 0731-152071. Ed. R.J. Ludwig. adv.; bk.rev.; bibl.; charts; illus.; mkt.; pat.; tr.lit.; index. circ. 20,000. **Document type:** trade publication.
  Formerly: Neue Uhrmacher-Zeitung (ISSN 0028-341X)

739.27 GW
SCHMUCKSZENE (YEAR). a. Verein zur Foerderung des Handwerks e.V., Max-Joseph-Str. 4, 80333 Munich, Germany. TEL 089-5119240. **Document type:** catalog.

681.11 SZ
SCHWEIZERISCHE UHRMACHER- UND GOLDSCHMIEDE-ZEITUNG/JOURNAL SUISSE DES HORLOGERS ET DES BIJOUTIERS-ORFEVRES. (Text in French, German) 1878. m. 140 SFr. (Zentralverband Schweizerischer Uhrmacher) Editions Scriptar S.A., Ch. Creux de Corsy 25, CH-1093 La Conversion-Lausanne, Switzerland. TEL 021-7911065. FAX 021-7914084. (Co-sponsor: Vereinigung Schweizerischer Juwelen- und Edelmetallbranchen) adv.; bk.rev.; charts; illus.; index. circ. 2,500. **Document type:** trade publication.
  Formerly: Schweizerische Uhrmacher Zeitung (ISSN 0036-7761)

681.11 SW
STJAERNURMAKAREN. 1887. 8/yr. SEK 350. (Sveriges Urmakarefoerbund) Ohlsson Reklam Information AB, Everoed 13, S-273 00 Tomelilla, Sweden. Ed. Elbe Oldenburg. adv.; bk.rev.; charts; illus.; tr.lit.; index. circ. 1,800.
  Former titles: Svensk Urmakartidning (ISSN 0284-2300); (until 1987): Ur, Optik; (until 1979): Svensk Ur-Optik Tidning (ISSN 0039-680X); (until 1962): Svensk Urmakeritidning.

I J K

681.11 739.27 SZ ISSN 0039-7520
SWISS WATCH AND JEWELRY JOURNAL. 1876. bi-m. 80 SFr.($56) (European Watch, Clocks and Jewellery Fair) Editions Scriptar S.A., Ch. Creux de Corsy 25, CH-1093 La Conversion-Lausanne, Switzerland. TEL 021-7911065. FAX 021-7914084. adv.; bk.rev.; illus. circ. 20,000. **Document type:** trade publication.

TAIWAN GIFTS & HOUSEWARES. see *BUSINESS AND ECONOMICS — Trade And Industrial Directories*

745.594 BE
TECHNICA. 1948. m. 3000 BEF. Comite National de la Bijouterie, Horlogerie, Joaillerie, Orfevrerie, Blvd. de Smet de Naeyer 290a, 1090 Brussels, Belgium. TEL 32-2-4282245. FAX 32-2-4283078. adv.: B&W page 30000 BEF, color page 45000 BEF. bk.rev. circ. 2,400. **Document type:** trade publication.

681.11 617.752 DK
TID OG SYN. m. (except Aug.). DKK 320. Urmagernes- og Optikernes Landssammenslutning, Upsalagade 20, 4, DK-2100 Copenhagen Oe, Denmark. TEL 45-35-26-54-19. FAX 35-43-21-04. Ed. Per Bjerre. adv.: B&W page DKK 2700, color page DKK 6300; trim 263 x 184. circ. 1,900. **Document type:** trade publication.
  Description: Directed to members of the trade union for watchmakers and opticians.

TODAY'S HOSPITAL GIFT SHOP BUSINESS. see *BUSINESS AND ECONOMICS — Marketing And Purchasing*

739.27 IS
TOKYO DIAMONDS. (Text in Japanese, summaries in English) 1991. 4/yr. $36. International Diamond Publications Ltd., P.O. Box 3237, Ramat Gan 52131, Israel. TEL 972-3-7512165. FAX 972-3-5752201. TELEX 341730 SPEED IL. (Co-publisher: Matsubara-Kashiwa Books, Tokyo) Ed. Joseph Sela; Pub. Itzchak Arikna. adv. contact: Yola Avidan. circ. 8,000. **Document type:** trade publication.
  Description: Covers the diamond trade in Japan and worldwide.

681.11 SZ
U S F B INFORMATIONS. 1968. m. (10/yr.). $25. Union Suisse des Fabricants de Boites de Montres, Case Postale 75, 2500 Bienne 4, Switzerland. stat. circ. controlled.

UHREN; Journal fuer Sammler klassischer Zeitmesser. see *INSTRUMENTS*

739.27 AU ISSN 0041-5839
UHREN JUWELEN. 1960. m. S.780. Oesterreichischer Wirtschaftsverlag, Nikolsdorfer Gasse 7-11, A-1050 Vienna, Austria. TEL 0222-555585. TELEX 1-11669. tr.mk.; index. circ. 3,400.
  Formerly: Ein- und Verkaufsfuehrer der Oesterreichischen Uhren- und Schmuckwirtschaft (ISSN 0013-2632)

739.2 GW
UHREN - JUWELEN - SCHMUCK. 1946. s-m. DM.160. Bielefelder Verlagsanstalt GmbH & Co. KG, Niederwall 53, 33602 Bielefeld, Germany. TEL 0521-595-520. adv.; bk.rev.; charts; illus.; mkt.; pat.; tr.lit.; index. circ. 9,000. **Document type:** trade publication.
  Formerly: Uhr (ISSN 0041-5820)

681.11 GW
UHREN UND SCHMUCK JOURNAL. 1950. m. DM.27.50. (Bundesgrosshandelsverband fuer Uhren- und Uhrentechnischen Bedarf e.V.) MC Wolf GmbH und Co., Fabrikstr. 17, 44629 Heide, Germany. Ed. J.P. Polzin. adv.; bk.rev. circ. 5,200.
  Formerly: Uhrenjournel (ISSN 0041-5855)

681.11 SZ ISSN 0049-5042
UHRENFACHGESCHAEFT/MAGASIN D'HORLOGERIE SPECIALISE. vol.22, 1971. bi-m. 16 Fr. to non-members. (Verband Schweizerischer Uhrenfachgeschaefte - Swiss Watch Shops Association) Buchdruckerei K. Furter, Scheidgasse 48, CH-3800 Unterseen-Interlaken, Switzerland. adv.; charts; illus. circ. 1,250.

681.11 NO ISSN 0332-5547
UR.* 1908. 11/yr. NOK 350. Urmakerforbundets Rasjionaliseringsselskap, Kr. Robins vei 13, N-0978 Oslo, Norway. Ed. Steinar Opstad. adv.; charts; illus. circ. 956.
  Formerly (until 1971): Norges Urmakerforbunds Tidskrift (ISSN 0332-9895)

739.27 DK ISSN 0106-7869
URE & OPTIK. 1893. m. (10/yr.). DKK 250. A-Reklame, Autoriseret Reklamebureau A-S - A-Reklame, Authorized Advertising Co., Ltd., Lillehoejvej 10, Postbox 306, DK-8600 Silkeborg, Denmark. Ed. Harry Krojgaard. adv.; bk.rev.; bibl.; charts; illus.; stat.; tr.lit.; index. circ. 1,300.
  Former titles (until Jan. 1979): Urmager-Tidende (ISSN 0042-1081); Dansk Tidsskrift for Urmagere.

739.2 IT
VALENZA GIOIELLI. 1958. q. L.75000. (Associazione Orafa Valenzana) A O V Service s.r.l., Piazza Don Minzoni 1, 15048 Valenza, Italy. TEL 31-941851. FAX 31-946609. (Subscr. to: A I E, Via Gadames, 89, I-20152 Milan, Italy) Dir. Rosanna Comi. adv. circ. 16,000.
  Formerly (until Jan. 1987): Orafo Valenzano (ISSN 0030-4190)

745.594 IT
VICENZAORO MAGAZINE. (Text in English and Italian) 1984. 3/yr. L.30000 (foreign L.55000). (Vicenza Trade Fair Board) Pentastudio, Corso Palladio 114, 36100 Vicenza, Italy. TEL 0444-54-31-33. FAX 0444-54-34-66. TELEX 481542 FIERVI I. (Subscr. to: Ente Fiera di Vicenza, Via dell'Oreficeria, 36100 Vicenza, Italy. TEL 0444-969111. FAX 0444-563954) Ed. Paolo Dalla Chiara. adv. contact: Graziella Pivato. circ. 15,000. **Document type:** trade publication.
  Description: For Italian and foreign jewelers, designers and manufacturers.

745.594 681.11 FR
646.7
VIE DES METIERS HORLOGERIE, MODE, COIFFURE, BIJOUTERIE. 10/yr. Practice Editions, 21 rue Baudin, 34000 Montpellier, France. TEL 67-58-61-09. Ed. Alain Vogel-Singer. circ. 1,000.

739.27 IT ISSN 1120-7817
VOGUE GIOIELLO. s-a. L.21000 (foreign L.37950). Edizioni Conde Nast S.p.A., Piazza Castello 27, 20121 Milan, Italy. TEL 02-85611. FAX 02-870686. Ed. A. Milella. adv. circ. 45,000. **Document type:** consumer publication.

681.11 739.27 US ISSN 0279-6198
TS540
WATCH AND CLOCK REVIEW. 1936. m. $15. Bell Publications, 2403 Champa St., Denver, CO 80205. TEL 303-296-1600. Ed. Jayne Barrick. adv.; illus. circ. 14,000. (also avail. in microform from UMI) —UnCover; UMI.
  Formerly (until 1981): American Horologist and Jeweler (ISSN 0002-8797)

739.27 TH
▼**WATCH & JEWELLERY.** (Text in Thai) 1992. bi-m. B.400. Grand Prix International Co., Ltd., 129-133 Rim Klong Prapar, Prachachuen Rd., Bangsue, Bangkok 10800, Thailand. TEL 662-02-587-0101. FAX 662-02-587-6567. Dir. Prachin Eamlumnow. circ. 20,000. **Document type:** consumer publication.

739.27 380.1 HK
WORLD JEWELOGUE (YEAR). (Text and summaries in English) 1986. a. HK.$199($40) Headway International Publications Co., 907 Great Eagle Centre, 23 Harbour Rd., Hong Kong. TEL 852-827-5121. FAX 852-827-7064. TELEX 72554 HEWAY HX. (Dist. in U.S. by: Leonard Estrin Publications, 20832 Roscoe Blvd., Canoga Park, CA 91304) Ed. Doreen Wong. pat.; tr.lit.; cum.index: 1986-1993. circ. 100,000. (back issues avail.) **Document type:** trade publication.
  Description: Color catalogue with references and order guides for the international jewelry industry.

681.11 380.1 HK
WORLD TIME CATALOGUE (YEAR). (Text and summaries in English) 1987. a. HK.$190($38) Headway International Publications Co., 907 Great Eagle Centre, 23 Harbour Rd., Hong Kong. TEL 852-827-5121. FAX 852-827-7064. TELEX 72554 HEWAY HX. (Dist. in U.S. by: Leonard Estrin Publications, 20832 Roscoe Blvd., Canoga Park, CA 91304) Ed. Doreen Wong. illus.; pat.; tr.lit.; cum.index: 1987-1993. circ. 50,000. (back issues avail.) **Document type:** trade publication.
  Description: Color catalogue with references and order guides for the international horological industry.

739.27 IT
18 KARATI GOLD & FASHION. (Text in English, French, German, Italian and Spanish) 1971. bi-m. $85. Edizioni Gold s.r.l., Viale Zara, 7-9, 20159 Milan, Italy. TEL 02-680189. FAX 02-606298. TELEX 311271 MIPP. Ed. Florinda Gaudio. adv.

JEWELRY, CLOCKS AND WATCHES — Abstracting, Bibliographies, Statistics

739.27 US
JEWELERS' BOOK CLUB CATALOG. 1979. a. $3. (Jewelers' Book Club) Chilton Co. (Subsidiary of: A B C, Inc.), Chilton Way, Radnor, PA 19089. TEL 215-964-4490. FAX 215-964-4481. Ed. Donald S. McNeil. bk.rev. circ. 12,000. **Document type:** catalog.
  Description: Geared to the retail and manufacturing jeweler, offering educational and coffee table publications pertinent to the industry.

JEWELERS' BOOK CLUB NEWS. see *JEWELRY, CLOCKS AND WATCHES*

JOURNALISM

A A F COMMUNICATOR. (American Advertising Federation) see *ADVERTISING AND PUBLIC RELATIONS*

JOURNALISM

070   UK
A B C CIRCULATION REVIEW. 1931. s-a. membership. Audit Bureau of Circulations, 207-209 High St., Berkhamsted, Herts HP4 1AD, England. TEL 44-442-870800. FAX 44-442-877407.

070.172 347.9   US
A C C N BULLETIN.* q. (Associated Court and Commercial Newspapers) Daily Journal of Commerce, Box 10127, Portland, OR 97210. TEL 503-226-1311. Ed. Stutz Maul. circ. 100. (looseleaf format; back issues avail.)
Description: Information regarding newspaper issues and Associated Court and Commercial Newspapers' activities.

070   US   ISSN 0738-7792
A I M REPORT. 1972. s-m. $22.95. Accuracy in Media, Inc., 445 Connecticut Ave., Ste. 330, Washington, DC 20008. TEL 202-364-4401. FAX 202-364-4098. Ed. Reed J. Irvine. index. circ. 18,000. (back issues avail.; reprint service avail.)
●Also available online.

070   SP
A N I G PUBLICACION. 6/yr. National Association of Press Reporters, Espronceda 32, 6o, 28010 Madrid, Spain. TEL 1-442-08-97. Ed. Da. de la Torre Lainez.

070 659.1   US
A P A MEMBER BULLETIN. w. $30. Arkansas Press Association, 1701 Broadway, Little Rock, AR 72206-1249. TEL 501-374-1500. FAX 501-374-7509. Ed. Dennis Schick. adv. circ. 250. (looseleaf format; back issues avail.) **Document type:** bulletin.
Description: Covers current activities, postal information, legislation, and how to provide training. Includes how-to articles on sales, advertising, writing.

070   US   ISSN 0193-4562
A P F REPORTER. 1977. q. free. Alicia Patterson Foundation, 1001 Pennsylvania Ave., N.W., Ste. 1250, Washington, DC 20004. TEL 202-393-5995. FAX 301-951-8512. Ed. Margaret Engel. circ. 3,200 (controlled). (back issues avail. Online. Vendor(s): CompuServe, Inc., DIALOG Information Services, Inc., Mead Data Central, Inc., VU/TEXT Information Services, Inc.
—CCC.
Description: Investigative reporting and photojournalism based on the year-long research projects of the foundation's fellows.

808.02 371.3   US
A W P CHRONICLE. 1970. 6/yr. $18. Associated Writing Programs, Norfolk, VA 23529-0079. TEL 804-683-3839. Ed. D.W. Fenza. adv.; bk.rev. circ. 12,000. (tabloid format) **Document type:** newsletter.
Formerly: A W P Newsletter (ISSN 0194-6498)

AARETS PRESSEFOTO. see *PHOTOGRAPHY*

070   GW   ISSN 0065-0323
ABHANDLUNGEN UND MATERIALEN ZUR PUBLIZISTIK. 1962. irreg. price varies. (Freie Universitaet Berlin, Institut fuer Publizistik) Colloquium Verlag, Luetzowstr. 105, 10785 Berlin, Germany. Ed. Bernd Soesemann. circ. 1,000.

070 301.16   KE
AFRICA MEDIA MONOGRAPH SERIES. 1986. irreg., latest no.9, 1991. $13 (outside Africa $16). African Council for Communication Education, P.O. Box 47495, Nairobi, Kenya. TEL 227043. TELEX 25148 ACCE KE. **Document type:** monographic series.
Description: Presents various issues related to journalism and communication by African and other communication scholars, researchers and practitioners.

070   SZ
AFRIKA BULLETIN. (Text in German) 1976. q. 15 SFr.($8) Afrika Komitee, Postfach 1072, CH-4001 Basel, Switzerland. FAX 061-2616222. Ed.Bd. adv.; bk.rev. circ. 1,200. (back issues avail.) **Document type:** bulletin.

AGENDA IN BRIEF. see *ETHNIC INTERESTS*

AIR ACCIDENTS & THE NEWS MEDIA. see *AERONAUTICS AND SPACE FLIGHT*

070   US   ISSN 1046-0470
AMERICAN AMATEUR JOURNALIST. 1936. bi-m. membership only. American Amateur Press Association, c/o Leslie W. Boyer, Ed., 535 Kickerillo Dr., Houston, TX 77079. circ. 340. (back issues avail.)
Description: Covers writing and printing for fun; any age, any level of experience, any subject, any technology.

070 617.6   US
AMERICAN ASSOCIATION OF DENTAL EDITORS. JOURNAL - NEWSLETTER. 1973. q. $25 (foreign $40). American Association of Dental Editors, 1100 Lake St., Ste. 240, Oak Park, IL 60301. TEL 708-445-0322. FAX 708-445-0321. Ed. Joanna Carey. circ. 325 (controlled). (back issues avail.) **Document type:** trade publication.

070   US   ISSN 0882-1127
PN4700
AMERICAN JOURNALISM. 1982. q. $25 (typically set in Oct.). American Journalism Historians Association, Univ. of Georgia, Grady College of Journalism, Athens, GA 30602. TEL 404-542-1704. Ed. Wallace Eberhard. adv.; bk.rev. circ. 350. **Indexed:** Amer.Hist.& Life (1993-), Hist.Abstr. (1993-).
—BLDSC (0840.135000); Faxon; UnCover.
Description: Publishes articles, and research notes on the history of journalism and mass communication.

070   US   ISSN 1067-8654
AP2
AMERICAN JOURNALISM REVIEW. Short title: A J R. 1977. m. $24. (University of Maryland, College of Journalism) American Journalism Review, 8701 Adelphi Rd., Adelphi, MD 20783. TEL 301-431-4771. FAX 301-431-0097. Ed. Rem Rieder. adv.; bk.rev. circ. 25,000. (also avail. in microform from UMI; back issues avail.) **Indexed:** Access (1980-), Bk.Rev.Ind. (1981-), Child.Bk.Rev.Ind. (1981-), Dent.Abstr. **Document type:** trade publication.
—BLDSC (0840.138000); Faxon; UnCover; UMI.
Former titles (until Mar. 1993): Washington Journalism Review (ISSN 0741-8876); (until 1983): W J R (ISSN 0743-9881); (until 1981): Washington Journalism Review (ISSN 0149-1172)
Description: Covers issues relating to print and broadcast journalism in the U.S.

070 369   US   ISSN 0002-9742
AMERICAN LEGION PRESS ASSOCIATION NEWS-LETTER. 1946. bi-m. membership. National American Legion Press Association, Box 1184, Decatur, GA 30031-1184. TEL 404-377-5602. Ed. George W. Hooten. bk.rev. circ. 2,600. **Document type:** newsletter.

808.02 617.585   US
AMERICAN PODIATRIC MEDICAL WRITERS ASSOCIATION. NEWSLETTER. 1985. bi-m. $12 to non-members; free to members. American Podiatric Medical Writers Association, Box 50, Island Sta., New York, NY 10044. TEL 212-355-5216. FAX 212-486-7706. Ed. Barry Block. adv.; bk.rev. circ. 200. (back issues avail.) **Document type:** newsletter.
Description: For professional writers of podiatric literature.

070   US   ISSN 0003-1178
PN4700
AMERICAN SOCIETY OF NEWSPAPER EDITORS. BULLETIN. 1926. 9/yr. $20. American Society of Newspaper Editors, Box 4090, Reston, VA 22090-1700. TEL 703-648-1144. Ed. Richard Aregood. index. circ. 2,500. (back issues avail.)
—UnCover.
Description: Forum for the editors of daily newspapers to discuss their work.

ARCHIV FUER PRESSERECHT; Zeitschrift fuer das gesamte Medienrecht. see *LAW*

338.025 070   US
ARKANSAS PRESS ASSOCIATION DIRECTORY. 1940. a. $25. Arkansas Press Association, 1701 Broadway, Little Rock, AR 72206-1249. TEL 501-374-1500. FAX 501-374-7509. Ed. Dennis Schick. circ. 1,000. **Document type:** directory.
Description: Lists newspapers, ad agencies, and other publications.

070 659.1   US
ARKANSAS PUBLISHER. 1927. q. $30. Arkansas Press Association, 1701 Broadway, Little Rock, AR 72206-1249. TEL 501-374-1500. FAX 501-374-7509. Ed. Dennis Schick. adv. circ. 1,000. (back issues avail.) **Document type:** bulletin.
Description: Photo and word history of the association in action.

079   KO
ASIAN PRESS.* a. $3. Institute for Communication Research, Readership Research Center, Seoul National University, Dong Song-dong, Seoul, S. Korea. illus.

ASSOCIATION DES JOURNALISTES AGRICOLES. ANNUAIRE. see *AGRICULTURE*

070   US
AURORA ADVERTISER. 3/w. $16 (outside the state $19). (Missouri Press Association) Aurora Advertiser, 32 W. Olive, Box 509, Aurora, MO 65605. TEL 417-678-2115. Ed. J.Kim McCully. adv.; B&W & color, color page $90; adv. contact: Jewel Bagby. circ. 5,600.

AUSTRALIAN JOURNAL OF COMMUNICATION. see *COMMUNICATIONS*

070   AT   ISSN 0810-2686
PN4701
AUSTRALIAN JOURNALISM REVIEW. 1979. a. Aus.$20 to individuals; institutions Aus.$40. Journalism Education Association, c/o School of Media and Journalism, Queensland University of Technology, G.P.O. Box 2434, Birsbane, Qld. 4001, Australia. TEL 07-864-2656. FAX 07-864-1810. E-mail: L.GRANATO@QUT.edu.au. Ed. Len Granato. adv.; bk.rev. circ. 500. **Document type:** academic/scholarly publication.

AUTHORS & ARTISTS FOR YOUNG ADULTS. see *CHILDREN AND YOUTH — For*

AUTOMATIC I D NEWS. see *COMPUTERS — Automation*

AUTOMATIC I D NEWS EUROPE. see *COMPUTERS — Automation*

070   UK   ISSN 0306-1000
B A I E NEWS. 1972. m. £20. British Association of Industrial Editors, 3 Locks Yard, High St., Sevenoaks, Kent TN13 1LT, England. FAX 0732-4617574. adv.; bk.rev. circ. 1,250.

070 895.1   CC   ISSN 0257-0149
BAOGAO WENXUE/REPORTAGE LITERATURE. (Text in Chinese) 1984. m. $56.70. Renmin Ribao Chubanshe - People's Daily Publishing House, 2, Jintai Xilu, Chaoyangmenwai, Beijing 100733, People's Republic of China. (Dist. in US by: China Books & Periodicals, Inc., 2929 24th St., San Francisco, CA 94110. TEL 415-282-2994)

BEITRAEGE ZUR KOMMUNIKATIONSWISSENSCHAFT UND MEDIENFORSCHUNG. see *COMMUNICATIONS*

070   UK
BENN'S MEDIA: EUROPE. 1846. a. £99. Benn Business Information Services Ltd. (Subsidiary of: Morgan-Grampian plc), Riverbank House, Angel Ln., Tonbridge, Kent TN9 1SE, England. TEL 0732-362666. FAX 0732-367301. TELEX 957829 BENTON G. adv.; index. circ. 5,700. **Document type:** directory.
—BLDSC (1892.053000).
Formerly: Benn's Media Directory. Europe (ISSN 0964-6167); Which supersedes in part (in 1992): Benn's Media Directory. International (ISSN 0269-8366); Which was formerly (until 1985): Benn's Press Directory. Volume 2: Overseas (ISSN 0141-6170); Which supersedes in part (in 1978): Newspaper Press Directory (ISSN 0078-043X)

070   UK
BENN'S MEDIA: UNITED KINGDOM. 1846. a. £99. Benn Business Information Services Ltd. (Subsidiary of: Morgan-Grampian plc), Riverbank House, Angel Ln., Tonbridge, Kent TN9 1SE, England. TEL 0732-362666. FAX 0732-367301. TELEX 957829 BENTON G. adv.; index. circ. 5,700. **Document type:** directory.
Former titles: Benn's Media Directory. United Kingdom (ISSN 0269-8358); (until 1986): Benn's Press Directory. Volume 1: United Kingdom (ISSN 0141-1772); Which supersedes in part (in 1978): Newspaper Press Directory (ISSN 0078-043X)

JOURNALISM

070
BENN'S MEDIA: WORLD. 1846. a. £99. Benn Business Information Services Ltd. (Subsidiary of: Morgan-Grampian plc), Riverbank House, Angel Ln., Tonbridge, Kent TN9 1SE, England. TEL 0732-362666. FAX 0732-767301. TELEX 957829 BENTON G. adv.; index. circ. 5,700. **Document type:** directory.
—BLDSC (1892.053000).
 Formerly: Benn's Media Directory. World (ISSN 0964-6175); Which supersedes in part (in 1992): Benn's Media Directory. International (ISSN 0269-8366); Which was formerly (until 1985): Benn's Press Directory. Volume 2: Overseas (ISSN 0141-6170); Which supersedes in part (in 1978): Newspaper Press Directory (ISSN 0078-043X)

808.42   US   ISSN 1056-8034
BEST AMERICAN SPORTS WRITING. a. $10.95 (cloth ed. $22.95). Ticknor & Fields (Subsidiary of: Houghton Mifflin Co.), 215 Park Ave. S., New York, NY 10003. TEL 212-420-5800. (Dist. by: Houghton Mifflin Co., Wayside Rd., Burlington, MA 01803. TEL 800-225-3362)

081   US   ISSN 0195-895X
PN4726
BEST NEWSPAPER WRITING; winners, the American Society of Newspaper Editors' competition. 1979. a. $11.95 (typically set. in Apr.). (American Society of Newspaper Editors) Poynter Institute for Media Studies, 801 Third St. S., St. Petersburg, FL 33701. TEL 813-821-9494. FAX 813-821-0583. (Dist. by: Bonus Books, Inc. 160 E. Illinois St., Chicago, IL 6011. TEL 312-467-0580. FAX 312-467-9271) bibl.; circ. 5,000 (paid). (back issues avail.)
 Description: Publishes reprinted articles by the winning writers, with selected articles by finalists in each category, interviews with winning writers, observations and study questions, judges' comments.

081   US   ISSN 0737-2612
Z253.5
BEST OF NEWSPAPER DESIGN. 1979. a. price varies. Society of Newspaper Design, c/o Newspaper Center, Box 4075, Reston, VA 22090. TEL 703-620-1083. FAX 703-620-4557. circ. 7,000. **Document type:** trade publication.
 Description: Features winners of the society's newspaper design and graphics competition.

BETWEEN THE LINES (WASHINGTON). see *POLITICAL SCIENCE*

070   CC   ISSN 1001-4314
BIANJI XUEBAO/ACTA EDITOLOGICA. (Text in Chinese; table of contents and a few abstracts in English) 1989. q. Y46. (Zhongguo Kexue Jishu Qikan Bianji Xuehui - China Editology Society of Science Periodicals) Science Press, Marketing and Sales Department, 16 Donghuangchenggen Beijie, Beijing 100707, People's Republic of China. TEL 4010642. FAX 4012180. TELEX 210247 SPBJ CN. Ed. Wang Yong-qing.
 Description: Covers the science of editing sci-tech journals.

BIANJI ZHI YOU/COMPILERS' FRIEND. see *PUBLISHING AND BOOK TRADE*

BILL PALMER'S WORD WATCHING. see *LINGUISTICS*

BORDER WATCH. see *PRINTING*

808.02   GW   ISSN 0939-3498
BRIEF BERATER. 1991. q. DM.199.80. Verlag Norman Rentrop, Theodor-Heuss-Str. 4, 53177 Bonn, Germany. TEL 0228-8205-0. FAX 0228-364411. (looseleaf format) **Document type:** bulletin.

070   UK   ISSN 0007-0238
BRITISH AMATEUR JOURNALIST. 1890. 3/yr. £5 membership. British Amateur Press Association, Cimarron Close, South Woodham Ferrers, Essex CM3 5PB, England. Ed. Allan Bula. bk.rev. circ. 200.
 Description: Includes articles, stories, poems and line drawings by Association members.

070   UK   ISSN 0956-4748
BRITISH JOURNALISM REVIEW. 1990. q. £25 to individuals (foreign £30 ($50)); institutions £50 (foreign £60 ($100)). Cassell plc, Villiers House, 41-47 Strand, London WC2N 5JE, England. TEL 071-839-4900. FAX 071-839-4900. (U.S. dist.: Cassell, 387 Park Ave. S., 5th Fl., New York, NY 10016-8810) Ed. Geoffrey Goodman. bk.rev.
—BLDSC (2326.450000).
 Description: Discusses current issues in print and broadcast journalism.

070 940 070   BU   ISSN 0323-956X
BULGARSKI ZHURNALIST/BULGARIAN JOURNALIST. 1959. m. 50 lv.($47) (Suiz na Bulgarskite Zhurnalisti - Union of Bulgarian Journalists) Bulgarian Journalist, Editor's Office, Bogdanovets 2, Sofia 1606, Bulgaria. TEL 35-92-525348. FAX 35-92-883047. TELEX 022635. Ed. Yordanka Blagoeva. adv.; bk.rev. circ. 5,000.

BULLDOG WEEKLY. see *COLLEGE AND ALUMNI*

070.172   GW
BUNDESVERBAND DEUTSCHER ZEITUNGSVERLEGER. ZEITUNG. 1973. m. Bundesverband Deutscher Zeitungsverleger, Riemenschneiderstr. 10, 53175 Bonn, Germany. TEL 0228-810040. FAX 0228-8100415. TELEX 885461. bk.rev. circ. 12,000. **Document type:** newsletter.

070   US   ISSN 1055-3568
BUSINESS SPEAKER'S DIGEST. 1990. bi-m. $195. Lime Rock Press, Inc., Box 363, Salisbury, CT 06068. TEL 800-228-5297. FAX 203-435-8937.
 Description: Contains digests of speeches and articles.

808.02   US   ISSN 0744-4249
BYLINE. 1981. m. (Jul.-Aug. combined). $20. Marcia Preston, Ed. & Pub., Box 130596, Edmond, OK 73013. TEL 405-348-5591. adv.; circ. 3,000 (paid). **Document type:** trade publication.
 Description: Offers information and encouragement for writers.

070 302.44   US   ISSN 1056-8093
PN4735
C P J UPDATE.* q. Committee to Protect Journalists, Inc., 330 Seventh Ave., 12th Fl., New York, NY 10001-5010.

070   UK
C P U NEWS. 1968. 6/yr. £12 (foreign £20). Commonwealth Press Union, Studio House, 184 Fleet St., London EC4A 2DU, England. FAX 01-831-4923. Ed. Eric Blott. adv.; bk.rev. circ. 1,800.
 Formerly (until 1989): C P U Quarterly.

070   XR   ISSN 0590-501X
C T K DOKUMENTACNI PREHLED. 1967. fortn. (plus 2-3 supplements per yr.). $156. Ceska Tiskova Kancelar, Dokumentacni Redakce - Czech News Agency, Opletalova 5, 111 44 Prague 1, Czech Republic. Ed. Pavel Hanus. circ. 1,000. (processed)

070   US
CALIFORNIA NEWSPAPER PUBLISHERS ASSOCIATION. DIRECTORY AND RATE BOOK. 1923. a. $50. California Newspaper Publishers Association, Inc., 1311 I St., Ste. 200, Sacramento, CA 95814-2913. TEL 916-443-5991. FAX 916-443-6447. Ed. John Bates. adv. circ. 2,800. **Document type:** directory.
 Formerly: California Newspaper Publishers' Association. Newspaper Directory; Which supersedes: California Newspaper Directory (ISSN 0068-5763)

070   US   ISSN 0008-1434
PN4700
CALIFORNIA PUBLISHER. 1918. bi-m. $15. California Newspaper Publishers Association, Inc., 1311 I St., Ste. 200, Sacramento, CA 95814-2912. TEL 916-443-5991. FAX 916-443-6447. adv.; bk.rev.; illus.; tr.lit. circ. 1,700. (tabloid format)

070.4 283   US
CATHEDRAL. 1986. q. $10. Cathedral Church of St. John the Divine, 1047 Amsterdam Ave. at 112th St., New York, NY 10025. TEL 212-316-7564. FAX 212-932-7348. Ed. William Bryant Logan. circ. 13,000 (controlled). **Document type:** newsletter.
 Formerly: Heights.

070 282   US   ISSN 0008-8129
CATHOLIC JOURNALIST. 1945. m. $12. Catholic Press Association (Rockville Center), 119 North Park Ave., Rockville Centre, NY 11570. TEL 516-766-3400. Ed. Owen P. Govern. adv.; bk.rev.; illus.; stat.; tr.lit. circ. 2,700. (tabloid format) **Indexed:** Cath.Ind.

070   US
CENSORED: THE PROJECT CENSORED YEARBOOK; the news you need to know. a. $12.95. (Project Censored) Four Walls Eight Windows, 39 W. 14th St., Ste. 503, New York, NY 10011. TEL 212-206-8965. FAX 919-206-8799. circ. 20,000. **Document type:** academic/scholarly publication.
 Description: Reviews the current state of media control and censorship as practiced today in the U.S. and reviews the top censored stories of the preceding year.

342   US   ISSN 0749-6001
CENSORSHIP NEWS. 1975. q. $30. National Coalition Against Censorship, 275 Seventh Ave., 20th Fl., New York, NY 10001. TEL 212-807-6222. FAX 212-807-6245. Ed. Roz Udow. bk.rev. circ. 14,000. (back issues avail.) **Document type:** newsletter.
 Description: Covers current school book censorship controversies, including threats to the free flow of information, obscenity laws, sexual expression, creationism and school textbooks.

070   US   ISSN 0887-0594
CENTRAL AMERICA NEWSPAK; a bi-weekly news & resource update. 1986. fortn. $38. Documentation Exchange, Box 2327, Austin, TX 78768. TEL 512-476-9841. Eds. Sara Buttrey, Billy Pope. circ. 325. (back issues avail.)

794.1   US
CHESS JOURNALIST.* 1972. 4/yr. $5. Chess Journalists of America, c/o Bill Merrell, 13 Gloria Lane, St. Peters, MO 63376. TEL 215-449-4294. (Subscr. to: Bill Wall, 626-B Perimeter Rd., Mountain View, CA 94043) Ed. John Hillery.

070   IT
CHI E' CHI DEL GIORNALISMO DELL'AUTO. (Text in English, Italian) 1986. a. L.40000. Crisalide Editrice, Via Brusuglio 66, 20161 Milan, Italy. TEL 6464663. Ed. Bianca Carretto. circ. 50,000.

070   US
CHICAGO MEDIA DIRECTORY. 1989. a. $5 to non-members. Chicago Convention and Tourism Bureau, Inc., McCormick Place on the Lake, Chicago, IL 60616. TEL 312-567-8500. FAX 312-567-8533. Ed. Kate Haymaker. circ. 1,000. **Document type:** directory.

CHINA NEWS ANALYSIS. see *GENERAL INTEREST PERIODICALS — China*

070   US   ISSN 1045-2958
CHIPS OFF THE WRITER'S BLOCK. 1986. bi-m. $15. Chips Off the Writer's Block, Box 83371, Los Angeles, CA 90083. Ed. Wanda Windham. adv.; bk.rev. circ. 500. (back issues avail.) **Document type:** newsletter.
 Description: How-to articles and inspiration for writers, with market and contest information.

070   BL
COLECAO JORNALISMO CATARINENSE. 1978. irreg. (Sindicato dos Jornalistas) Editora Lunardelli, Rua Victor Meirelles 28, 880000 Florianopolis SC, Brazil.

COLLECTIBLE NEWSPAPERS. see *HOBBIES*

070 378   US   ISSN 0739-1056
COLLEGE MEDIA REVIEW. 1956. q. $15 to non-members. College Media Advisers, c/o Department of Journalism, Memphis State University, Memphis, TN 38152. TEL 901-678-2403. Ed. Wayne Maikranz. adv.; bk.rev.; illus.; stat.; cum.index: 1959-1972. circ. 1,000. (also avail. in microfilm) **Indexed:** Coll.Stud.Pers.Abstr. **Document type:** academic/scholarly publication.
 Formerly: College Press Review (ISSN 0010-1117)

COLLEGE PRESS SERVICE. see *EDUCATION — Higher Education*

070   US   ISSN 0010-1567
COLORADO EDITOR. 1926. m. $5. Colorado Press Association, 1336 Glenarm Place, Denver, CO 80204. TEL 303-571-5117. FAX 303-571-1803. Ed. Marge Easton. adv.; bk.rev.; illus. circ. 948.

070 378   US   ISSN 0010-194X
PN4700
COLUMBIA JOURNALISM REVIEW. 1961. bi-m. $19.95. Columbia University, Graduate School of Journalism, 700 Journalism Bldg., New York, NY 10027. TEL 212-854-1881. FAX 212-854-8580. (Subscr. to: Box 1943, Marion OH 43302) Ed. Suzanne Braun Levine. adv.; bk.rev.; illus. circ. 31,000. (also avail. in microform from UMI,MIM; reprint service avail. from UMI,WSH) **Indexed:** Acad.Ind., Amer.Bibl.Slavic & E.Eur.Stud., Bk.Rev.Ind. (1980-), C.L.I., Child.Bk.Rev.Ind. (1980-), Curr.Cont., Film Lit.Ind. (1976-), HR Rep., Hum.Ind., Leg.Per., Mid.East: Abstr.& Ind., P.A.I.S., PMR, SSCI. —BLDSC (3323.220000); Faxon; UnCover; SWETS; UMI.
Incorporates: More Magazine & Public Interest Alert; Media and Consumer (ISSN 0047-6439)
Description: Reports and comments critically on developments and trends in the world of journalism.

COMMUNICARE; journal of communication sciences. see *COMMUNICATIONS*

COMMUNICATION. see *COMMUNICATIONS*

COMMUNICATION: JOURNALISM EDUCATION TODAY. see *EDUCATION*

COMMUNICATIONS MANAGER; practical ideas and methods for publications, PR and desktop publishing managers. see *ADVERTISING AND PUBLIC RELATIONS*

070 659.1   US
COMMUNICATOR'S NOTEBOOK. 1981. bi-w. $196. Box 1312, New York, NY 10018-0724. TEL 212-979-7395. FAX 212-877-2213. Ed. Robert Miko. bk.rev. circ. 500. **Document type:** newsletter.
Description: Monitor of international corporate communicator.

070   US
COMMUNITY COLLEGE JOURNALIST. 1972. q. $35 to individuals; libraries $40. Community College Journalism Association, c/o Tom Pasqua, Ed., Southwestern College, 900 Otay Lakes Rd., Chula Vista, CA 91910. TEL 619-421-6700. FAX 619-482-6412. (Subscr. to: c/o W.B. Daugherty, San Antonio College, 1300 San Pedro Ave., San Antonio, TX 78284) adv.; bk.rev. circ. 250. (also avail. in microform from EDR) **Indexed:** ERIC.
Formerly: Junior College Journalist.

COMPUTERITER; microcomputer news and views for the writer-editor. see *COMPUTERS — Personal Computers*

CONGRES INTERNATIONAL D'HISTOIRE DES SCIENCES. ACTES. see *SCIENCES: COMPREHENSIVE WORKS*

070   RM   ISSN 1016-7609
AP86
CONTRAPAUNCT. 1990. w. Uniunea Scriitorilor din Romania, c/o Rompresfilatelia, Sectorul Export-Import Presa, P.O. Box 12-201, Bucuresti, Rumania.

070 051   US
CONVERSATIONS WITH WRITERS. 1977. irreg. $50 per vol. Gale Research Inc., 835 Penobscot Bldg., Detroit, MI 48226. TEL 313-961-2242. FAX 313-961-6083. TELEX 810-221-7086. Ed.Bd. illus.

070   II
COOPERATIVE PRESS IN SOUTH-EAST ASIA. 1965. irreg. Rs.7.50($1) International Co-Operative Alliance, Regional Office and Education Centre for South-East Asia, Box 3312, 43 Friends Colony, New Delhi 110014, India.

070   US   ISSN 1049-3190
PN4784.C75   CODEN: CPDIE2
COPY EDITOR; the national newsletter for professional copy editors. 1990. bi-m. $69. Box 604, Ansonia Sta., New York, NY 10023-0604. TEL 212-757-2645. Ed. Mary Beth Protomastro. bk.rev. circ. 1,500. **Document type:** newsletter.

COPYRIGHT (GOETEBORG); tidskrift foer press- och dokumentaerfotografi. see *PHOTOGRAPHY*

CORPORATE ANNUAL REPORT NEWSLETTER. see *COMMUNICATIONS*

070.43   FR
CORRESPONDANCE DE LA PRESSE; quotidien d'information et documentation professionnelles. 1951. d. 19150 F. (foreign 20450 F.) Societe Generale de Presse et d'Editions, 13 av. de l'Opera, 75001 Paris, France. TEL 40-15-17-89. FAX 40-15-17-15. TELEX SOGPRESS 230023. Ed. Etienne Lacour; Pub. Marianne Berard Quelin. adv.
Description: Provides professional news and data on the media industry.

CRITERION (RIVERSIDE). see *COLLEGE AND ALUMNI*

CRITIC. see *MOTION PICTURES*

CROSS AND QUILL; Christian writers newsletter. see *RELIGIONS AND THEOLOGY*

070   SP
CUADERNOS. 12/yr. Silva 22, 3o izda., 28004 Madrid, Spain. TEL 1-522-48-10. FAX 1-522-26-82. circ. 3,000.

070   NO   ISSN 0011-5304
DAGSPRESSEN. 1924. 18/yr. NOK 350 (foreign NOK 500)(typically set in Aug.-Sep.). Norwegian Newspapers Association, Storgaten 32, Oslo 1, Norway. FAX 02-171127. (Co-sponsor: Association of Norwegian Newspaper Editors) Ed. Helge Iversen. adv.; bk.rev.; illus. circ. 4,100.
—CCC.

DANMARKS JOURNALISTHOEJSKOLE. BERETNING. see *EDUCATION — Higher Education*

070   MG
DANS LES MEDIA, DEMAIN; hebdomadaire independant d'information & d'analyse. 1986. m. FMG.150000($265) 58 rue Tsiombikibo Ambatovinaky, B.P. 1734, 101 Antananarivo, Malagasy Republic. TEL 277-88. FAX 359-79. TELEX 22225. Ed. Voahangy Rakotoarivelo. adv.: color page FMG.315000 ($165); adv. contact: Honore S. Razafintsalama. circ. 2,800.

070 658.8   DK   ISSN 0106-5343
AP42
DANSK PRESSE. 1918. 10/yr. DKK 310. Danske Dagblades Forening - Danish Newspapers Association, Pressens Hus, Skindergade 7, 1159 Copenhagen K, Denmark. TEL 45-33-122115. FAX 45-33-142325. Ed. Hans Joergen Vonsild. adv.; bk.rev.; index. circ. 8,000.

070 327   US
DEADLINE. 1986. q. $25 includes membership. Center for War, Peace, and the News Media, 10 Washington Place, New York, NY 10003. TEL 212-998-7960. FAX 212-995-4143. circ. 6,000. (back issues avail.)
Description: Press criticism of US media coverage of US-Soviet relations, the Soviet Union, arms control, and international security.

072.9415   US
DEMOCRAT. 1966. w. Observer Newspapers Ltd., Irish St., Dungannon, N. Ireland. TEL 22557. Ed. D. Mallon. **Document type:** newspaper.

070   XR   ISSN 0011-8214
DEMOCRATIC JOURNALIST. French edition: Journaliste Democratique. Russian edition: Demokratischeskii Zhurnalist. Spanish edition: Periodista Democrata. (Editions in English, French, Spanish and Russian) 1953. m. $10. International Organization of Journalists, Parizska 9, 110 01 Prague 1, Czech Republic. TEL 0422-341533. FAX 2320426. (Subscr. to: Rooseveltova 18, 160 00 Prague 6, Czech Republic) adv.; bk.rev.; illus.; index. circ. 15,000.
—Faxon; UnCover.
Description: Analyses the development of communication media in different countries and regions of the world, the status of journalist, activities of their organizations.

070   GR
DEMOSIOGRAFIKI/JOURNALISM. (Text in English and Greek) 1987. m. Dr.1000($10) 7-9 Prokopion St., 171 24 N. Smyrni, Greece. TEL 973-1388. Ed. John Menounos. bk.rev. circ. 3,000.

070   PH
DEPTHNEWS. 1969. w. $2500. Press Foundation of Asia, Box 1843, Manila, Philippines. Ed. M. Jara. bibl.; illus.
Formerly: Press Forum (ISSN 0048-5209)

073   GW   ISSN 0933-2995
DEUTSCHE PRESSEFORSCHUNG. 1958. irreg., vol.28, 1992. DM.168. (Deutsche Presseforschung e.V.) K.G. Saur Verlag KG, A Reed Reference Publishing Company, Part of the Reed Elsevier group, Ortlerstr. 8, 81373 Munich, Germany. TEL 089-76902-0. FAX 089-76902150. TELEX 5212067-SAUR-D. (Subscr. to: Postfach 701620, 81316 Munich, Germany) Ed. Elger Bluehm. **Document type:** academic/scholarly publication.
Formerly (until 1985): Studien zur Publizistik. Bremer Reihe (ISSN 0585-6175)

DHARMA COMBAT; a magazine about spirituality, metaphysics, reality and other conspiracies. see *RELIGIONS AND THEOLOGY*

070   US
▼**DIALOGUE: A JOURNAL FOR WRITING SPECIALISTS.** 1993. s-a. $20 to individuals; institutions $25. Northwestern State University of Louisiana, 203 Russell Hall, Natchitoches, LA 71457. Eds. S. Hunter, R. Wallace.

070.43   BE   ISSN 0417-5271
DIRECT LINE. French edition (ISSN 0773-7386); German edition (ISSN 0258-4344); Spanish Edition (ISSN 0258-4352) (Text in English) 1963. m. free. International Federation of Journalists, International Press Centre, 1 Bd. Charlemagne, Bte. 5, B-1041 Brussels, Belgium. TEL 02-2380951. FAX 02-2303633. TELEX 61275 IPC. Ed. Aidan White. bk.rev. circ. 2,500. (back issues avail.)
Description: Consists of short news and information of federation activities.

070 658   US
DIRECTORY OF FLORIDA & GEORGIA MARKETS FOR WRITERS AND P R PROFESSIONALS. 1982. a. $19.95. (Florida & Georgia Freelance Writers Association) C N W Publishing, Maple Ridge Rd., N. Sandwich, NH 03259-9999. TEL 603-284-6367. FAX 603-284-6648. Ed. Dana K. Cassell. circ. 1,000. **Document type:** directory.
Formerly (until 1992): Directory of Florida Markets for Writers and P R Professionals.
Description: Guide to 700 publications and book publishers located in or pertaining to the state of Florida; 300 in Georgia.

073   GW   ISSN 0417-9994
DORTMUNDER BEITRAEGE ZUR ZEITUNGSFORSCHUNG. 1958. irreg., vol.5, 1993. price varies. (Institut fuer Zeitsforschung der Stadt Dortmund) K.G. Saur Verlag KG (Subsidiary of: Reed Reference Publishing), Ortlerstr. 8, 81373 Munich, Germany. TEL 089-76902-0. FAX 089-76902150. TELEX 5212067-SAUR-D. (Subscr. to: Postfach 701620, 81316 Munich, Germany) Ed. Kurt Koszyk.

070   US
DOW JONES NEWSPAPER FUND. ADVISER UPDATE. 1970. s-a. free. Dow Jones Newspaper Fund, Box 300, Princeton, NJ 08543-0300. TEL 609-452-2820. FAX 609-520-5804. Ed. Elaine Reed. circ. 1,500.
Description: Covers scholastic journalism.

070   US
THE EAST SIDE HERALD. 1935. w. $20. East Side Communication Corp., 4309 E. Michigan St., Box 11042, Indianapolis, IN 46201. TEL 317-356-2487. Ed. William K. Thoele. adv.; circ. 19,000 (controlled). (back issues avail.)

070   FR   ISSN 0012-9232
ECHO DE LA PRESSE ET DE LA PUBLICITE.* 1945. w. 1370 F. Editions Jacquemart, Maison du Livre en Bourgogne, 14 rue Chaptal, B.P. 82, 92303 Levallois-Perret Cedex, France. Ed. Noel Jacquemart. adv.; illus.; index. circ. 8,100.
Incorporates: Echo de l'Imprimerie et des Arts Graphiques (ISSN 0012-9259)

070.172   SP
ECO DE SITGES. 1886. w. 40 ptas. Bonaire 6, D.L.B. 2908-1960, Sitges, Spain. Dir. J.M. Soler.

JOURNALISM

070   FR   ISSN 0070-8321
ECOLE FRANCAISE DES ATTACHES DE PRESSE. ASSOCIATION DES ANCIENS ELEVES. ANNUAIRE. 2nd ed., 1962. a. price varies. Association des Anciens Eleves de l'Ecole Francaise des Attaches de Presse, 61 rue Pierre-Charron, 75008 Paris, France. adv. circ. 5,000.

070   SA   ISSN 0256-0054
ECQUID NOVI; journal for journalism in Southern Africa/tydskrif vir joernalistiek in Suider-Afrika. (Text in Afrikaans, English) 1980. s-a. $20 to individuals; institutions $30. Institute for Communication Research, Potchefstroom University, Potchefstroom 2520, South Africa. TEL 27-148-991651. FAX 27-148-992799. TELEX 267666 SA. (Subscr. to: Argo Publications, P.O. Box 1475, Johannesburg 2000, South Africa) Ed. Arnold S. de Beer. adv.; bk.rev.; bibl.; illus. circ. 800. (also avail. in microfiche; back issues avail.) Indexed: Ind.S.A.Per. **Document type:** academic/scholarly publication.
•Also available online.
Refereed Serial

EDITOR & PUBLISHER INTERNATIONAL YEAR BOOK; encyclopedia of the newspaper industry. see *COMMUNICATIONS*

070 800   US
EDITOR & PUBLISHER SYNDICATE DIRECTORY; annual directory of syndicate services. 1925. a. $7. Editor & Publisher Co., Inc., 11 W. 19th St., New York, NY 10011. TEL 212-675-4380. FAX 212-929-1259. Ed. Collin Philips. circ. 28,000. **Document type:** directory.
Description: Lists syndicates, syndicated features, syndicated cartoonists, columnists by subject. Used by newspaper industry and others.

070 659.1   US   ISSN 0013-094X
PN4700
EDITOR & PUBLISHER - THE FOURTH ESTATE; spot news and features about newspapers, advertisers & agencies. (Annual Numbers: International Year Book; Market Guide; Syndicate Directory) 1884. w. $55. Editor & Publisher Co., Inc., 11 W. 19th St., New York, NY 10011. TEL 212-675-4380. FAX 212-929-1259. Ed. Robert U. Brown. adv.; B&W page $2630, color page $3700; trim 8 1/4 x 11 1/8. bk.rev.; illus. circ. 27,641. (also avail. in microform from UMI,MIM; reprint service avail. from UMI) Indexed: B.P.I., Chic.Per.Ind., Graph.Arts Lit.Abstr. **Document type:** trade publication.
•Also available online.
—BLDSC (3661.077000); UnCover; SWETS; UMI.

THE EDITORIAL EYE; focusing on publications standards and practices. see *PUBLISHING AND BOOK TRADE*

070
EDITORIAL PACE. (Text in English, Spanish) 1955. s-a. free. Derus Media Service, Inc., 500 N. Dearborn, Chicago, IL 60610. TEL 312-644-4360. Ed. Pat Derus. adv.; bk.rev.; charts; illus.; tr.lit.; circ. 10,000 (controlled). (tabloid format) **Document type:** catalog.

070   US
EDITORS' EXCHANGE. 1978. 11/yr. $11. American Society of Newspaper Editors, Box 4090, Reston, VA 22090-1700. TEL 703-648-1147. Ed. Elise Burroughs. circ. 2,100. (back issues avail.)
Description: Ideas of interest to editors of daily newspapers.

070   US   ISSN 0746-3014
EDITORS' FORUM. 1980. m. $86.50. Editors' Forum Publishing Co., Box 411806, Kansas City, MO 64141. TEL 913-384-2555. Ed. William R. Brinton. adv.; bk.rev.; illus. circ. 1,500.
Formerly (until 1985): Newsletter Forum.
Description: Educational journal which deals with writing, editing, proofreading, layout and design.

EDITORS' NOTES. see *PUBLISHING AND BOOK TRADE*

070   US   ISSN 0735-8490
EDITORS ONLY. 1982. m. $89 (Canada $95; elsewhere $105). Editors Only Publications, Box 17108, Fountain Hills, AZ 85269. TEL 602-837-6492. FAX 602-837-6872. Ed. William Dunkerley. bk.rev. circ. 450. (back issues avail.) **Document type:** newsletter.
•Also available online. Vendor(s): NewsNet (PB13).

070 370   US
EDITOR'S REVENGE. 1979. m. $10 in US, Canada and Mexico; elsewhere $12. Box 805, Morristown, NJ 07960. Ed. John T. Harding. circ. 500.
Description: Memorandum on the use, misuse and abuse of the English language in America.

070   US
EDITOR'S WORKSHOP NEWSLETTER. 1984. w. $119. Lawrence Ragan Communications, Inc., 212 W. Superior St., Ste. 200, Chicago, IL 60610-3533. TEL 312-335-0037. Ed. Charles Shields. bk.rev. circ. 6,000. **Document type:** newsletter.

070
EIGHT BALL. 1947. m. (plus a. edition). membership. Greater Los Angeles Press Club, 2005 N. Highland Ave., Los Angeles, CA 90068-3272. TEL 213-874-3003. FAX 213-874-3005. adv.; bk.rev. circ. 2,500. (tabloid format)

070.4 330   FR
ENTREPRESSE. 1976. q. 200 F. Union des Journaux et Journalistes d'Entreprise de France (UJJEF), 63 Ave. de la Bourdonnais, 75007 Paris, France. FAX 47-05-22-54. Ed. Jacques Dehedin. adv. circ. 1,500.

EUROP. see *LITERARY AND POLITICAL REVIEWS*

070   FR   ISSN 0071-2299
EUROPA. REVUE DE PRESSE EUROPEENNE.* 1969. irreg. 0.50 f. each. Cercle Europe de la Faculte de Droit et des Sciences Economiques de Paris, 92 rue d'Assas, 75006 Paris, France. Indexed: Amer.Hist.& Life, Hist.Abstr.

EUROPEAN ECONOMICS EDITOR; news for managers and economic journalists. see *BUSINESS AND ECONOMICS — Management*

070.5   US   ISSN 0145-3939
EXTRA! 1987. 6/yr. $30 to individuals; institutions $40. Fairness & Accuracy In Reporting (F.A.I.R.), 130 W. 25th St., New York, NY 10001. TEL 212-633-6700. FAX 212-727-7668. (Subscr. to: Box 3000, Dept. FAR, Denville, NJ 07834. TEL 800-847-3993) Ed. Jim Naureckas. adv.; bk.rev. circ. 13,000.
Description: Contains media criticism, focusing on corporate control, dominance of establishment views and exclusion of alternative voices.

070.43   US
F O I A UPDATE. (Freedom of Information Act) 1979. q. $5 (foreign $6.25; government agencies free). U.S. Department of Justice, Office of Information and Privacy, Constitution Ave. & 10th Sts., N.W., Washington, DC 20530. TEL 202-514-5105. FAX 202-514-1009. (Subscr. to: Superintendent of Documents, U.S. Government Printing Office, Box 371954, Pittsburgh, PA 15250-7954. TEL 202 783 3238. FAX 202-512-2233) Ed. Pamela Maida. circ. 5,000. (also avail. in microfiche) Indexed: Ind.U.S.Gov.Per. **Document type:** government publication.
•Also available online.
Description: Provides information and guidance to federal agencies on FOIA legislation under consideration, relevant court rulings, and other related issues.

070   DK   ISSN 0905-670X
FAGPRESSEN. 1932. 4/yr. DKK 175. Dansk Fagpresse Service ApS, Sommerstedgade 7, 1718 Copenhagen V, Denmark. Ed. John Hjarsoe. adv.; bk.rev.; illus.; index. circ. 4,329. **Document type:** trade publication.
Former titles (until 1989): Dansk Fagpresse (ISSN 0106-0120); (until 1976): Nordisk Fagpresse (ISSN 0029-1331)

070.5   FJ   ISSN 0377-4422
FIJI. PRINTING DEPARTMENT REPORT. Key Title: Report - Printing Department (Suva). (Text in English) a. price varies. Government Printing Department, P.O. Box 98, Suva, Fiji. **Document type:** government publication.

070   US   ISSN 0739-0033
FILLERS FOR PUBLICATIONS; the editorial tool that eliminates deadline pressures. 1956. m. $72. Publications Co., 7015 Prospect Pl., N.E., Albuquerque, NM 87110. TEL 505-884-7636. FAX 505-888-0477. Ed. Pat Johnston. (back issues avail.)
Description: Publishes short articles, cartoons, clip art and puzzles.

070   FI   ISSN 0071-5301
FINLAND. POSTI-JA LENNATINLAITOS. ULKOMAISTEN SANOMALEHTIEN HINNASTO. UTLANDSK TIDNINGSTAXA. (Text in Finnish and Swedish) 1853. a. FIM 7. Posti- ja Lennatinlaitos - General Direction of Posts and Telegraphs, Mannerheimintie 11, SF-00100 Helsinki 10, Finland. index.

070   US   ISSN 0888-3955
FOLLOW UP FILE. 1975. w. $144. Editorial Services, Inc., 24 Vinka Ln., Irvington, NY 10333-2333. FAX 914-591-6526. Ed. Steve Hess. index. (tabloid format; back issues avail.)
Description: News idea service for radio and TV stations, newspaper, and magazines.

070   JA   ISSN 0387-5040
FOREIGN PRESS CENTER JAPAN. PRESS GUIDE. 12/yr. Foreign Press Center - Forin Puresu Senta, Nippon Press Center Bldg., 2-1 Uchisaiwai-cho 2-chome, Chiyoda-ku, Tokyo 100, Japan. TEL 03-501-3401. FAX 03-501-3622.

070   CN   ISSN 0015-9190
FOURTH ESTATE; Canada's national press journal. 1967. m. Fourth Estate Partnership, P.O. Box 971, Cornwall, P.E.I. C0A 1H0, Canada. Ed. A.L. O'Neill. bk.rev.; circ. 1,500 (controlled).
•Also available online.

070 700   UK   ISSN 0016-0385
FREE-LANCE WRITING & PHOTOGRAPHY. 1965. 6/yr. £16.50. Weavers Press Publishing, Tregeraint House, Zennor, St. Ives, Cornwall TR26 3DB, England. TEL 0736-797061. Ed. John T. Wilson. adv.; bk.rev. (back issues avail.) **Document type:** trade publication.
Formerly: Free-Lance Writing.
Description: Practical articles and features to help freelance writers and photographers into print.

070 384.54 323.4   US
FREE PRESS NETWORK. 1982. q. $25. Free Press Association, Box 15548, Columbus, OH 43215. TEL 614-291-1441. Ed. Michael Grossberg. adv.; bk.rev. circ. 400. (looseleaf format; back issues avail.)
Description: Debates First Amendment issues and reports on controversies in the area of communication.

070   US
FREEDOM MAGAZINE. 1968. m. $22.50. Church of Scientology International, 6331 Hollywood Blvd., Ste. 1200, Los Angeles, CA 90028. TEL 213-960-3500. FAX 213-960-3508. Ed. Thomas G. Whittle. bk.rev.; illus. circ. 110,000.

808.02   US   ISSN 1064-9050
FREELANCE WRITER'S NEWSLETTER. irreg. $100 lifetime subscr. Fine Arts Press, Box 3491, Knoxville, TN 37927. TEL 615-637-9243. **Document type:** newsletter.
Description: Contains the latest news, ideas, advice and inside information for writers, editors and publishers.

808.02 070.5 659.1   US   ISSN 0731-549X
FREELANCE WRITER'S REPORT. 1982. m. $39. C N W Publishing, Maple Ridge Rd., N. Sandwich, NH 03259-9999. TEL 603-284-6367. FAX 603-284-6648. Ed. Dana K. Cassell. bk.rev. circ. 1,000. (looseleaf format)
Description: Contains market information, news of interest and how-to features for the professional.

FRONTPAGE. see *LABOR UNIONS*

070   US
G C GOVERNMENT COMMUNICATIONS. 1976. 10/yr. $50. National Association of Government Communicators, 669 S. Washington St., Alexandria, VA 22304. TEL 703-519-3902. FAX 703-519-7732. Ed. Michael Stirens. adv. circ. 1,000.
Former titles (until 1992): Communicator; Journal of Public Communication and Membership Directory; Journal of Public Communication.

GADNEY'S GUIDES TO INTERNATIONAL CONTESTS, FESTIVALS & GRANTS IN FILM & VIDEO, PHOTOGRAPHY, TV-RADIO BROADCASTING, WRITING & JOURNALISM. see *COMMUNICATIONS*

070 301.16   NE   ISSN 0016-5492
PN4699   CODEN: GIJMAZ
GAZETTE; international journal for mass communication studies. (Text in English) 1955. 6/yr. fl.418($219) (effective 1994). (Institute of the Science of the Press) Kluwer Academic Publishers, Postbus 17, 3300 AA Dordrecht, Netherlands. TEL 31-78-334911. FAX 31-78-334254. TELEX 29245 KAPG NL. (Dist. by: Kluwer Academic Publishers Group, P.O. Box 322, 3300 AH Dordrecht, Netherlands. TEL 31-78-524400. FAX 31-78-524474; N. America dist. addr.: Box 358, Accord Sta., Hingham, MA 02018-0358. TEL 617-871-6600. FAX 617-871-6528) Ed. Wim Noomen. adv.; bk.rev.; bibl.; charts; illus.; index. (also avail. in microform from SWZ,UMI; reprint service avail. from SWZ) **Indexed:** Abstr.Rural Dev.Trop., Amer.Hist.& Life (until 1992), Commun.Abstr., E.I., Hist.Abstr. (until 1992), P.A.I.S. **Document type:** academic/scholarly publication.
—BLDSC (4092.700000); Faxon; UnCover; SWETS; UMI. **CCC.**
Refereed Serial

070   FR   ISSN 0398-9887
GAZETTE DE LA PRESSE DE LANGUE FRANCAISE. 1974. bi-m. 250 F. Union Internationale des Journalistes et de la Presse de Langue Francaise, 3 Cite Bergere, 75009 Paris, France. TEL 47-70-02-80. FAX 48-24-26-32. TELEX 219 000. Ed. Georges Gros. adv.; bk.rev. circ. 15,000.

GAZETTE OF LAW JOURNALISM. see *LAW*

GENERAL DIRECTORY OF THE PRESS AND PERIODICALS IN JORDAN AND KUWAIT. see *PUBLISHING AND BOOK TRADE*

GENERAL DIRECTORY OF THE PRESS AND PERIODICALS IN SYRIA. see *PUBLISHING AND BOOK TRADE*

070   IT
GIORNALISMO. m. L.5000. Viale Montesanto, 7, 20124 Milan, Italy. TEL 02-6552874. Ed. Giorgio Santerini. circ. 15,000.

070   IT   ISSN 0017-0518
GIORNALISMO EUROPEO. (Text in French, German and Italian) 1966. bi-m. Comunita Europea dei Giornalisti, Via Venti Settembre 26, 00187 Rome, Italy. Ed. Karol Kleszczynski. circ. 10,000.

070   US   ISSN 0017-3541
GRASSROOTS EDITOR. 1960. q. $14. International Society of Weekly Newspaper Editors, Box 2235, South Dakota State University, Brookings, SD 57007-0596. TEL 605-688-4171. FAX 605-688-6516. Ed. Richard W. Lee. circ. 1,000. (also avail. in microform from UMI; reprint service avail. from UMI)
—Faxon; UnCover; UMI.
Formerly: Grassroots (Carbondale) (ISSN 0046-6328)
Description: Geared to those interested in community journalism.

GUIDE TO FLORIDA, GEORGIA, TEXAS & OTHER WRITERS. see *BUSINESS AND ECONOMICS* — *Trade And Industrial Directories*

GUILD OF AGRICULTURAL JOURNALISTS YEAR BOOK. see *AGRICULTURE*

070   UK
GUILD OF BRITISH NEWSPAPER EDITORS GUILD JOURNAL. 1947. 4/yr. membership. Guild of British Newspaper Editors, Bloomsbury House, Bloomsbury Sq., 74-77 Great Russell St., London WC1B 3DA, England. TEL 071-636-7014. FAX 071-631-5119. Ed. E. Price. adv.; bk.rev. circ. 450.

GUILD REPORTER. see *LABOR UNIONS*

070   UK   ISSN 0954-9021
HEADLINES (LONDON). 1981. 6/yr. £18 (Europe £29; other countries £43.50). Newspaper Society, Bloomsbury House, 74-77 Gt. Russell St., London WC1B 3DA, England. TEL 071-636-7014. FAX 071-631-5119. Ed. Gary Cullum. adv.; illus.; charts; circ. 8,000 (controlled). (tabloid format) **Indexed:** Print.Abstr. **Document type:** trade publication.
Formerly (until 1988): Newstime (London) (ISSN 0262-6373); Which was formed by the merger of: Newspaper Society News; Newspaper Sales; Talking Points.
Description: Articles about the local and regional press.

070   US   ISSN 0742-5538
HISTORICAL GUIDES TO THE WORLD'S PERIODICALS AND NEWSPAPERS. 1982. irreg. price varies. Greenwood Press, Inc. (Subsidiary of: Greenwood Publishing Group Inc.), 88 Post Rd. W., Box 5007, Westport, CT 06881-5007. TEL 203-226-3511. FAX 203-222-1502.

370   US
HOME SCHOOL GAZETTE.* bi-m. $20. Brackin and Sons Publishing, 3512 Fontaine St., Plano, TX 75075-6213. TEL 301-421-1473.
Description: Christian-oriented student newspaper written by home-schooled students under the guidance of professional journalists.

070.4   US
▼**HORA DE CIERRA.** (Text in Spanish) 1992. q. Inter American Press Association, 2911 N.W. 39th St., Miami, FL 33142. TEL 305-634-2465. FAX 305-635-2272. Ed. Harry Caicedo. adv.: B&W page $1200, color page $2000; trim 8 3/8 x 10 7/8. circ. 15,000 (controlled). **Document type:** newspaper.
Description: For editors, publishers and top managers in the editorial, production, advertising, promotion, personnel and circulation departments of Latin American newspapers and magazines.

HOSPITAL EDITORS' IDEA EXCHANGE. see *HOSPITALS*

070   US
HOSPITALITY WORLD. 1986. m. $48 (effective 1993). International Food, Wine & Travel Writers Association, Box 13110, Long Beach, CA 90803-8110. TEL 213-433-5969. circ. 600. **Document type:** newsletter.
Description: International information on food, wine and travel story opportunities for writers and interested industry executives.

070   AA
HOSTENI/AIGUILLON, reviste politike, satiro-humoristike. 1945. fortn. $14. Bashkimi i Gazetareve te Shqiperise - Union of Journalists of Albania, Punetoret e Rilindjes St., Tirana, Albania. TEL 75-10. Ed. Niko Nikolla. circ. 30,000. **Indexed:** Apic.Abstr.

070 340   US   ISSN 1049-1724
KF5753.Z9
HOW TO USE THE FEDERAL F O I ACT. 1979. a. $4. Reporters Committee for Freedom of the Press, 1735 Eye St., N.W., Rm. 504, Washington, DC 20005.

070   CC
HUBEI FANGZHI. (Text in Chinese) bi-m. Hubei Sheng Difangzhi Bianzuan Weiyuanhui Bangongshi, Wuchang, Hubei 430071, People's Republic of China. Eds. Ren Ping, Zhao Hui.
Description: Covers the editing and compilation of local records.

070   US   ISSN 1046-8110
PN4784.N5
HUDSON'S SUBSCRIPTION NEWSLETTER DIRECTORY. 1977. a. $128. Hudson Associates, 44 W. Market St., Box 311, Rhinebeck, NY 12572. TEL 914-876-2081. FAX 914-876-2561. adv. **Document type:** directory.
—BLDSC (4335.832300).
Former titles: Hudson's Newsletter Directory (ISSN 1041-9195); Hudson's Directory; Newsletter Yearbook Directory.
Description: Lists 4,139 business, professional and consumer newsletters worldwide in 52 major subject headings, broken down into 169 categories.

070   US   ISSN 0441-389X
Z6953.W5
HUDSON'S WASHINGTON NEWS MEDIA CONTACTS DIRECTORY. 1968. a. $155. Hudson Associates, 44 W. Market St., Box 311, Rhinebeck, NY 12572. TEL 914-876-2081. FAX 914-876-2561. Ed. Howard Penn Hudson. adv. **Document type:** directory.
Description: Comprehensive listing of Washington Press Corps (1989) 4,145 newspapers, magazines, radio-TV, 4,529 correspondents and editors, with names, assignments, addresses and phone numbers.

070   US   ISSN 0018-8409
PN4712
I A P A NEWS. no.216, April-May, 1973. m. $60 to non-members. Inter American Press Association, 2911 N.W. 39th St., Miami, FL 33142. TEL 305-634-2465. TELEX 522873. Ed.Bd. bibl.; illus. **Indexed:** HR Rep.
Formerly: Bulletin Press of the Americas.

070   US   ISSN 0018-8824
P87
I C B.* (International Communication Bulletin) 1966. q. $4. Association for Education in Journalism, International Division, Box 820172, Tuscaloosa, Box 1482, AL 35487-0172. TEL 301-454-2228. adv.; bk.rev.; abstr.; bibl. circ. 1,600. (looseleaf format)

I E E E TRANSACTIONS ON PROFESSIONAL COMMUNICATION. see *ENGINEERING* — *Electrical Engineering*

070.43   BE
I F J INFORMATION. (Text in English, French, Spanish) 1953. a. free. International Federation of Journalists, International Press Centre, 1 Bd. Charlemagne, Bte. 5, B-1041 Brussels, Belgium. TEL 02-2380951. FAX 02-2303633. TELEX 61275 IPC. Ed. Aidan White. bk.rev. (tabloid format; back issues avail.)
Description: Contains studies of relevance to professionals, including freelancers' working conditions, freedom of the press and licensing.

070 331   US
I L C A REPORTER. (Former name of issuing body: International Labor Press Association) 1956. m. membership only. International Labor Communications Association, 815 16th St., N.W., Washington, DC 20006. TEL 202-637-5068. circ. 850.
Formerly: I L P A Reporter (ISSN 0018-9995)

070   XR
I O J NEWSLETTER. French edition: Nouvelles de l'O I J. German edition: I O J Nachrichten. Spanish edition: Correo de la O I P. (Editions also in Arabic, Portuguese and Russian) 1974. fortn. $12.50 to non-members. International Organization of Journalists, Parizska 9, 110 01 Prague 1, Czech Republic. TELEX 122631.
Formerly (until 1980): Journalists' Affairs.
Description: Provides up-to-date information about the activities of IOJ, its member organizations and clubs.

070   AU   ISSN 0019-0314
I P I REPORT. 1952. m. 200 Fr. International Press Institute, Spiegelgasse 2-29, A-1010 Vienna, Austria. TEL 01-5129011. FAX 01-5129014. (Subscr. to: International Press Institute, Wydlerweg 10, CH-8047 Zurich, Switzerland) Ed. Adam Feinstein. adv.; bk.rev.; illus.; index, cum.index. circ. 2,000. **Indexed:** HR Rep. **Document type:** trade publication.
—UnCover.
Description: Coverage of journalists and journalism, both print and broadcast.

070   US
I S W N E NEWSLETTER. 1976. m. (10/yr.). $30 membership. International Society of Weekly Newspaper Editors, Box 2235, South Dakota State University, Brookings, SD 57007-0596. TEL 605-688-4171. FAX 605-688-6516. Ed. Richard W. Lee. circ. 350. **Document type:** newsletter.
Description: Covers developments in community journalism.

I W I NEWSLETTER. (Illinois Writers, Inc.) see *LITERATURE*

070   US
IDEAS UNLIMITED; for company editors. m. $137. Newsletter Services, Inc., 1545 New York Ave., N.E., Washington, DC 20002. TEL 202-529-5700. FAX 202-636-3992. (back issues avail.)
Description: Contains camera-ready art and helpful editorial features and information on safety, health, good work and business practices for incorporation in to company newsletters and publications.

070   US
THE ILLINOIS PUBLISHER. 1917. q. $4. Illinois Press Association, Inc., 701 S. Grand Ave., W., Springfield, IL 62704. TEL 217-523-5092. FAX 217-523-5103. Ed. David Porter. adv.; bk.rev.; circ. 2,000 (paid). (back issues avail.) **Document type:** trade publication.

JOURNALISM

IMPRESOR; al servicio de las artes graficas. see *PRINTING*

070   AU
IMPRESSUM. q. Verlag Robert Hammerl, Seeboeckgasse 15, A-1160 Vienna, Austria. TEL 01-464636. circ. 1,700.

070   US   ISSN 1067-5132
IN PRINT. 1934. 12/yr. $12 (students $8). New Jersey Press Association, 206 W. State St., Trenton, NJ 08608-1095. TEL 609-695-3366. FAX 609-695-8729. Ed. Elisabeth Hagen. adv.; bk.rev.; illus. circ. 1,000. **Document type**: trade publication.
    Formerly (until Dec. 1989, vol.57, no.9): Jersey Publisher (ISSN 0021-5961)
    Description: Covers events, issues and personalities in the New Jersey newspaper industry.

070 900   US   ISSN 1056-3504
INCITE INFORMATION; inquiry and commentary. 1990. bi-m. $10. Incite Information, Box 326, Arlington, VA 22210. Ed. Mark Hand. bk.rev. circ. 200. (back issues avail.) **Document type**: newsletter.
    Description: Offers news and analysis, commentary and investigation. Focuses on current and historical events ignored by mainstream press. Intended for readers dissatisfied with traditional perspectives.

INDEPENDENT NATIONAL EDITION; a monthly journal for thoughtful Canadians. see *ENVIRONMENTAL STUDIES*

079   II
INDIAN & EASTERN NEWSPAPER SOCIETY PRESS HANDBOOK. Spine title: I.E.N.S. Press Handbook. (Text in English) irreg. Rs.25. Indian and Eastern Newspaper Society, I.E.N.S. Bldgs., Rafi Marg, New Delhi 110001, India.

070   II   ISSN 0445-801X
INDIAN PRESS. 1962-1964; N.S. March 1974. m. Rs.25($20) Indian and Eastern Newspaper Society, I.E.N.S. Bldgs., Rafi Marg, New Delhi 110001, India. Ed.Bd. adv.; illus. (also avail. in microfilm from UMI; reprint service avail. from UMI)

070   US   ISSN 0019-6711
PN4700
INDIANA PUBLISHER. 1936. w. $25. Hoosier State Press Association, Inc., 300 Consolidated Building, 1 Virginia Ave., Ste. 701, Indianapolis, IN 46204-3616. TEL 317-637-3966. FAX 317-624-4428. Ed. Cheryl L. Matthews. adv. contact: Marsha K. Guillaum. bk.rev.; circ. controlled. **Document type**: newspaper.

070   UK
INFORMATION SOURCES FOR THE PRESS AND BROADCAST MEDIA. 1991. irreg. £41($70) Bowker - Saur Ltd., A Reed Reference Publishing Company, Part of the Reed Elsevier group, Maypole House, Maypole Rd., E. Grinstead, W. Sussex RH19 1HH, England. TEL 0342-330100. FAX 0342-330191. (Subscr. to: c/o Butterworths Service Co., Borough Green, Sevenoaks, Kent TN15 8PH, England. TEL 9732-884567) Ed. Selwyn Eagle. **Document type**: directory.
    Description: Provides a comprehensive listing of sources essential to those who produce newspapers and news-oriented magazines and radio and television programs.

070   AU
INFORMATION UND MEINUNG. 1970. q. S.280. Leo Karner Verlags GmbH, A-3100 Neidling 23, Austria. TEL 02742-51567. FAX 02742-515674. Ed. Leo Karner. circ. 2,000. **Document type**: bulletin.

INKWORLD. see *LABOR UNIONS*

INTER AMERICAN PRESS ASSOCIATION. COMMITTEE ON FREEDOM ON THE PRESS. REPORT. see *POLITICAL SCIENCE*

070   US
INTER AMERICAN PRESS ASSOCIATION. MINUTES OF THE ANNUAL MEETING. a. $100. Inter American Press Association, 2911 N.W. 39th St., Miami, FL 33142. TEL 305-634-2465. TELEX 522873.

INTERCOM; revista brasileira de comunicacao. see *COMMUNICATIONS*

INTERNATIONAL FEDERATION OF JOURNALISTS AND TRAVEL WRITERS. OFFICIAL LIST/REPERTOIRE OFFICIEL. see *TRAVEL AND TOURISM*

070   US   ISSN 0020-837X
INTERNATIONAL PRESS JOURNAL; international press news and views. 1957. q. $20. Drawer G, Kenmore, NY 14217. Ed. Edward Howard Barr. adv.; bk.rev.; illus. circ. 7,000. (tabloid format)

070.43   US   ISSN 0164-7016
INVESTIGATIVE REPORTERS & EDITORS JOURNAL. 1978. bi-m. $25 (foreign $40). Investigative Reporters & Editors, Inc., 100 Neff Hall, School of Journalism, University of Missouri, Columbia, MO 65211. TEL 314-882-2042. FAX 314-882-5431. E-mail: mvcgw.jourtlb@ssgate.missouri.edu. Ed. Steve Weinberg. bk.rev. circ. 5,000. (also avail. in microfiche from UMI) **Document type**: trade publication.
    —Faxon; UnCover; UMI.
    Description: Devoted to issues and techniques of information-gathering in journalism.

070 378   US   ISSN 0897-0696
                           CODEN: ISWRE7
ISSUES IN WRITING; education, government, arts and humanities, business and industry, science and technology. 1988. s-a. $12 (foreign $15) (typically set in Sep.). University of Wisconsin at Stevens Point, Department of English, Stevens Point, WI 54481. TEL 715-346-4333. FAX 715-346-4215. Eds. Roberta Stokes, David Holborn. adv.; bk.rev.; index. **Indexed**: Lang.& Lang.Behav.Abstr. **Document type**: academic/scholarly publication.
    —UnCover.
    Refereed Serial

070 301.16   US   ISSN 0196-3031
PN4700
J Q: JOURNALISM QUARTERLY; devoted to research in journalism and mass communication. 1924. q. $40 to individuals (foreign $50); institutions $50 (foreign $60). Association for Education in Journalism and Mass Communication, 1621 College St., University of South Carolina, Columbia, SC 29208-0251. TEL 803-777-2005. Ed. Jean Folkerts. adv.; bk.rev.; bibl.; charts; index, cum.index. circ. 4,100. (also avail. in microform from UMI; reprint service avail. from UMI) **Indexed**: Acad.Ind., Amer.Bibl.Slavic & E.Eur.Stud., Amer.Hist.& Life, Bk.Rev.Ind. (1976-), C.I.J.E., Chic.Per.Ind., Child.Bk.Rev.Ind. (1976-), Commun.Abstr., Cont.Pg.Educ., Curr.Cont., E.I., Hist.Abstr., Hum.Ind., Lang.& Lang.Behav.Abstr., M.L.A., Mid.East: Abstr.& Ind., P.A.I.S., Psychol.Abstr., Ref.Sour., Sage Pub.Admin.Abstr., Sage Urb.Stud.Abstr., SSCI. **Document type**: academic/scholarly publication.
    —BLDSC (5072.860000); Faxon; UnCover; SWETS; UMI.
    Formerly: Journalism Quarterly (ISSN 0022-5533)

070   GW
JAHRBUCH DER KOELNER JUGENDPRESSE. 1974. biennial. DM.5.20. Junge Presse Koeln Arbeitsgemeinschaft, Postfach 420390, 50897 Cologne, Germany. TEL 0221-835852. FAX 0221-835824. adv.; bk.rev. circ. 1,000. **Document type**: bulletin.

070   JA
THE JAPANESE PRESS. (Text in English) 1949. a. $52.80. Japan Newspaper Publishers & Editors Association, Nippon Press Center Bldg., 2-2-1 Uchisaiwaicho, Chiyoda-ku, Tokyo 100, Japan. TEL 03-3591-4401. FAX 03-3591-6149. (Dist. by: Intercontinental Marketing Corp., I.P.O. Box 5056, Tokyo 100-30, Japan. TEL 81-3-3661-7458. FAX 81-3-3667-9646) Ed. Izumi Tadokoro.

JEWISH WORLD. see *ETHNIC INTERESTS*

070   II   ISSN 0021-6976
JIWAN DHARA. (Text in Hindi; summaries in English and Hindi) 1966. 8/yr. Rs.5. Ram Ballabh Tapuriah, Pub., Naya Shaher, Sikar, Rajasthan, India. adv.; illus.

070   CC
JIZHE YAOLAN/JOURNALISTS CRADLE. (Text in Chinese) m. Liaoning Ribao, Xinwen Yanjiusuo - Liaoning Daily, Journalism Institute, 339 Zhongshan Lu, Shenhe Qu, Shenyang, Liaoning 110014, People's Republic of China. TEL 472417. Ed. Li Qingmin.

070   GW
JOJO. (Journal der Fachjournalisten); Geschichte und Geschichten. 1985. s-a. free. c/o Siegfried Quandt, Pub., Justus-Liebig-Universitaet Giessen, Fachbereich 08, 6300 Giessen, Germany. TEL 0641-7025505. FAX 0641-48199. Ed. Gunter Stemmler. circ. 1,500.

071   CN   ISSN 0380-2051
JOURNAL DU NORD-OUEST. 1974. d. Can.$1.50. Publications du Nord-Ouest, 167 Dallaire, c.p. 490, Rouyn, Que. J9X 4T3, Canada. illus.

JOURNAL OF COMMUNICATION. see *COMMUNICATIONS*

JOURNAL OF MEDIATED COMMUNICATION. see *COMMUNICATIONS — Computer Applications*

070 371.0025   US   ISSN 0895-6545
PN4788
JOURNALISM AND MASS COMMUNICATION DIRECTORY. 1983. a. $20 (foreign $30). Association for Education in Journalism and Mass Communication, University of South Carolina, 1621 College St., Columbia, SC 29208-0251. TEL 803-777-2005. adv. circ. 2,500. (also avail. in microfilm) **Document type**: directory.
    Formerly: J D: Journalism Directory (ISSN 0735-3103)

070.07 370   US   ISSN 0022-5517
PN4788
JOURNALISM EDUCATOR. 1945. q. $30 to individuals; institutions $35 (foreign $40). Association for Education in Journalism and Mass Communication, 1621 College St., University of South Carolina, Columbia, SC 29208-0251. TEL 803-777-2005. Ed. Jim Crook. bk.rev.; stat. circ. 2,500. (also avail. in microform from UMI; microfiche from CIS; reprint service avail. from UMI) **Indexed**: C.I.J.E., Commun.Abstr., Cont.Pg.Educ., Educ.Ind., SRI. **Document type**: academic/scholarly publication.
    —BLDSC (5072.827000); Faxon; UnCover; SWETS; UMI.

070   US   ISSN 0094-7679
PN4700
JOURNALISM HISTORY. 1974. q. $15 to individuals; institutions $35. Greenspun School of Communication, University of Nevada, Las Vegas, NV 89154-5007. TEL 702-895-3964. FAX 702-895-4805. Ed. Barbara Cloud. adv.; bk.rev.; bibl. circ. 600. (also avail. in microform from UMI; reprint service avail. from UMI) **Indexed**: Amer.Hist.& Life, Hist.Abstr., Hum.Ind., Mid.East: Abstr.& Ind. **Document type**: academic/scholarly publication.
    —UnCover; UMI.

070   US   ISSN 0022-5525
PN4722
JOURNALISM MONOGRAPHS. 1966. 6/yr. $30 to individuals (foreign $35); institutions $35 (foreign $40). Association for Education in Journalism and Mass Communication, 1621 College St., University of South Carolina, Columbia, SC 29208-0251. TEL 803-777-2005. Ed. James Tankard. circ. 2,300. (also avail. in microform from UMI; reprint service avail. from UMI,ERIC) **Indexed**: Amer.Hist.& Life, Commun.Abstr., ERIC, Hist.Abstr. **Document type**: monographic series, academic/scholarly publication.
    —BLDSC (5072.840000); UnCover; UMI.

070   IS   ISSN 0334-2948
JOURNALISM YEARBOOK. a. Association of Journalists, 4 Kaplan St., Tel Aviv, Israel. TEL 03-256141. Ed. Dov Atzman.

070   GW   ISSN 0022-5576
PN4703
JOURNALIST. 1950. m. DM.192. (Deutscher Journalisten-Verband e.V) Verlag Rommerskirchen und Co. KG, Bennauerstr. 60, 53115 Bonn, Germany. TEL 0228-222974. FAX 0228-214917. TELEX 886567-JOUR-D. Ed. Ulrike Kaiser. adv.; bk.rev.; illus.; cum.index. circ. 33,000. **Document type**: trade publication.

070　　　　　　　NE　ISSN 0022-555X
PN4705
JOURNALIST. 1946. a. fl.165. Nederlandse Vereniging van Journalisten - Netherlands Association of Journalists, Postbus 75997, 1070 AZ Amsterdam, Netherlands. TEL 31-20-6766771. FAX 31-20-6624901. Ed. W. Verbei. adv.; bk.rev. circ. 8,500. **Indexed:** Key to Econ.Sci.
—SWETS.
　Description: Articles cover freedom of the press, newspaper managing, publishing, and schooling. Includes Association news, and positions available.

070　　　　　　　UK　ISSN 0022-5541
JOURNALIST. 1908. bi-m. £9.50 (foreign £13). National Union of Journalists, 314-320 Grays Inn Rd., London WC1X 8DP, England. TEL 071-278-7916. FAX 071-837-8143. adv.; bk.rev.; illus. circ. 30,000. **Document type:** bulletin.

070　　　　　　　SW　ISSN 0022-5592
JOURNALISTEN. 1904. 39/yr. SEK 400. Svenska Journalistfoerbundet - Swedish Association of Journalists, Vasagatan 50, 111 20 Stockholm, Sweden. Ed. Lars-G. Holmstroem. adv.; bk.rev.; illus.; stat. circ. 16,141.

070　　　　　　　NO　ISSN 0332-7108
JOURNALISTEN. 1917. 20/yr. NOK 350. Norwegian Union of Journalists, Box 8793, Youngstorget, 0028 Oslo 1, Norway. TEL 02-173825. FAX 02-171783. Ed. Jan Otto Hauge. adv.; bk.rev. circ. 7,500.

070 301.16　　　GW　ISSN 0176-9707
JOURNALISTEN JAHRBUCH. 1983. a. DM.39.80. Verlag Oelschlaeger GmbH, Kegelhofstr. 54, 20251 Hamburg, Germany. TEL 040-470081. FAX 040-474676. Ed. Bernd-Juergen Martini. adv. circ. 3,000. (back issues avail.)

070　　　　　　　AU
JOURNALISTEN NEWS. q. Privat Press, Wiesengasse 1, A-2440 Neu Mitterndorf, Austria. TEL 2234-8681. circ. 8,000.

070　　　　　　　FI　ISSN 1236-3596
JOURNALISTI/JOURNALISTEN. (Text in Finnish, Swedish) 1924. 22/yr. FIM 230. Suomen Journalistiliitto, Hietalahdenkatu 2B22, 00180 Helsinki, Finland. TEL 647-326. FAX 640-361. Eds. Timo Vuortama, Pertti Kangas. adv.; bk.rev.; illus. circ. 10,500. **Document type:** trade publication.
　Formerly (until 1993): Sanomalehtimies (ISSN 0036-4479)

070 621.384　　UK　ISSN 0269-1736
JOURNALIST'S HANDBOOK. 1985. q. £10 to non-U.K. journalists. Carrick Media, 2-7 Galt House, 31 Bank St., Irvine KA12 0LL, Scotland. TEL 0294-311322. Ed. Fiona MacDonald. adv.; bk.rev./; circ. 2,600 (controlled). **Document type:** trade publication.
　Description: Presents a review of the media for English journalists.

070　　　　　　　US
JOURNALIST'S ROAD TO SUCCESS. 1962. a. $3 per no. Dow Jones Newspaper Fund, Inc., Box 300, Princeton, NJ 08543-0300. TEL 609-452-2820; 800-DOW-FUND. FAX 609-520-5804. bibl.; stat.; index.
　Former titles: Journalism Career and Scholarship Guide; Journalism Scholarship Guide (ISSN 0449-3362)
　Description: Provides information on career preparation, salary data, list of more than 450 schools offering degrees and financial aid for journalism study.

JUGENDPRESSEREPORT; Magazin fuer engagierte Schueler und Nachwuchsjournalisten. see CHILDREN AND YOUTH — For

808.02 740　　　US
JUNIOR AUTHORS AND ILLUSTRATORS SERIES. 1951. irreg., 6th ed., 1989. price varies. H.W. Wilson Co., 950 University Ave., Bronx, NY 10452. TEL 800-367-6770. FAX 718-590-1617. TELEX 4990003HWILSON. Ed. Sally Holmes Holtze. index.
　Description: Biographical sketches of outstanding creators of children's literature.

070.48　　　　　US
KAPPA TAU ALPHA. NEWSLETTER; national society honoring scholarship in journalism and communication. 1983. irreg. (1-2/yr.). membership. Kappa Tau Alpha, U M School of Journalism, Box 838, Columbia, MO 65205. TEL 314-882-7685. FAX 314-882-4823. Ed. Keith Sanders. circ. 500 (controlled). **Document type:** newsletter.
　Description: Covers news in journalism and mass communications.

070　　　　　　　US　ISSN 0023-0324
KENTUCKY PRESS. 1929. m. $4. Kentucky Press Association, 101 Consumer Lane, Frankfort, KY 40601. TEL 502-223-8821. FAX 502-875-2624. Ed. Pam Shingler. adv.; bk.rev. circ. 638.

070　　　　　　　SP
KIOSKO. 11/yr. Sanchez Barcaiztegui 38 1o, jardin 5, 28007 Madrid, Spain. TEL 1-4336405. FAX 1-4338354. Ed. Jorge las Heras. circ. 2,000.

073　　　　　　　GW　ISSN 0941-7982
KOMMUNIKATION UND POLITIK. irreg., no.25, 1991. DM.68. K.G. Saur Verlag KG (Subsidiary of: Reed Reference Publishing), Ortlerstr. 8, 81373 Munich, Germany. TEL 089-76902-0. FAX 089-76902150. TELEX 5212067-SAUR-D. (Subscr. to: Postfach 701620, 81316 Munich, Germany) Ed.Bd.

070　　　　　　　KO
KOREAN PRESS. Korean edition: Korean Press Annual. (Text in English) 1984. a. free. Korean Press Institute, Korea Press Center Bldg., 12th Fl., 1-25 Taepyung-ro, Chung-ku, Seoul, S. Korea. TEL 02-398-1601. FAX 02-737-7170. Ed. Kim Ok-Jo.
　Description: Introduces Korean press to both domestic and foreign countries.

070.43　　　　　KO
KOREAN PRESS ANNUAL/HANGUK SINMUN PANGSONG YONGAM. English edition: Korean Press. (Text in Korean) 1977. a. 50000 Won (effective 1993). Korean Press Institute, Korea Press Center Bldg., 12th Fl., 1-25 Taepyung-ro, Chung-ku, Seoul, S. Korea. TEL 02-398-1601. FAX 02-737-7170. Ed. Kim Ok-Jo. adv. circ. 1,000.
　Description: Includes up-to-date statistics of journalism-related information and Who's Who of the Korean press. Also covers activities of domestic media for the past one year.

070　　　　　　　UZ
KORRESPONDENT. (Editions in Russian and Uzbek) 1918. m. (Soyuz Zhurnalistov Uzbekistana) Izdatel'stvo Kommunisticheskaya Partiya Uzbekistana, Ul. Pravdy Vostoka, 26, Tashkent 700000, Uzbekistan. Ed. N. Uvarov. illus. circ. 1,123.

070　　　　　　　PL　ISSN 0137-2998
PN5355.P6
KWARTALNIK HISTORII PRASY POLSKIEJ. 1962. q. $40. (Polska Akademia Nauk, Instytut Badan Literackich) Ossolineum, Publishing House of the Polish Academy of Sciences, Rynek 9, 50-106 Wroclaw, Poland. TEL 48-71-386-25. FAX 48-71-448-103. TELEX 0712771 OSS PL. Ed. J. Myslinski. bk.rev.; abstr.; bibl.; charts; illus.; cum.index: 1962-1974. circ. 640. **Document type:** academic/scholarly publication.
　Formerly: Rocznik Historii Czasopismiennictwa Polskiego (ISSN 0035-7669)
　Description: History of Polish dailies and periodicals.

070　　　　　　　GW
LANDBOTE. 1952. 5/yr. DM.20. Junge Presse Baden -Wuerttemberg e.V., Postfach 1127, 71611 Ludwigsburg, Germany. TEL 6221-384765.

918　　　　　　　AU
LATEINAMERIKA PRESSESPIEGEL. 1981. 5/yr. S.100. Oesterreichisches Lateinamerika Institut, Schmerlingplatz 8, A-1010 Vienna, Austria. TEL 0222-5233315. **Document type:** trade publication.

JOURNALISM 3191

070.172 301　　US　ISSN 1046-7912
PN4888.P6
LIES OF OUR TIMES; a journal to correct the record. 1990. 10/yr. $28 in US; Canada & Mexico $36; elsewhere $40. (Institute for Media Analysis) Sheridan Square Press, 145 W. Fourth St., New York, NY 10012. TEL 212-254-1061. FAX 212-254-9598. TELEX 650-305-3524. Ed. Edward S. Herman. bk.rev. circ. 9,000. (also avail. in microfiche from UMI) **Indexed:** Alt.Press Ind.
—UMI.
　Description: A forum for media criticism. Encompasses subjects that have been ignored as well as hypocrasies, misleading emphases, and hidden premises.

070 929　　　　US
LIFESTORY; America's only magazine of writing personal and family history. 1991. m. $21. 3591 Letter Rock Rd., Manhattan, KS 66502. TEL 800-685-7330. Ed. Charley Kempthorne. adv.; illus.

LITERARY AGENTS OF NORTH AMERICA. see LITERATURE

LITERARY MAGAZINE REVIEW. see LITERATURE

070　　　　　　　US
M P A BULLETIN. m. free to qualified personnel. Maine Press Association, 5743 Lord Hall, University of Maine, Orono, ME 04469-5743. TEL 207-581-1283. Ed. Steve Reiley. stat.; tr.lit. circ. 300. (looseleaf format; back issues avail.)

070 659.1　　　UK
MACCLESFIELD EXPRESS ADVERTISER. 1811. w. Lancashire and Cheshire County Newspapers Ltd., 37 Chestergate, Macclesfield, Cheshire, England. TEL 0625-24445. Ed. D.J. Pickford. circ. 18,000.

070　　　　　　　US　ISSN 0025-5122
PN4700
THE MASTHEAD. 1948. q. $25 to non-members. National Conference of Editorial Writers, 6223 Executive Blvd., Rockville, MD 20852. TEL 301-984-3015. FAX 301-231-0026. Ed. Keith Runyon. bk.rev. circ. 1,000. (back issues avail.) **Indexed:** Amer.Hist.& Life, Hist.Abstr. **Document type:** trade publication.
—Faxon; UnCover.
　Description: Devoted to all aspects of producing editorials in all media, from determining editorial policy to writing, design and presentation.

MASTHEAD; the magazine about magazines. see PUBLISHING AND BOOK TRADE

070　　　　　　　CN　ISSN 1198-2209
MEDIA. (Text in English, French) 1978. q. Can.$60 membership; libraries Can.$14.98. Canadian Association of Journalism, Carleton University, St. Patrick's Bldg., 1125 Colonel By Dr., Ottawa, ON K1S 5B6, Canada. FAX 613-788-5604. Ed. David McKie. adv. contact: John Stevens. bk.rev. circ. 2,500. (also avail. in microform from MML) **Document type:** trade publication.
　Former titles: C A J Bulletin (ISSN 1184-0641); C I J Bulletin (ISSN 0822-207X)
　Description: Reports on news from behind the scenes, written for journalists by journalists.

MEDIA; Asia's media & marketing newspaper. see ADVERTISING AND PUBLIC RELATIONS

MEDIA ASIA. see COMMUNICATIONS

MEDIA CULTURE REVIEW. see COMMUNICATIONS — Television And Cable

MEDIA OWNERSHIP IN AUSTRALIA. see BUSINESS AND ECONOMICS — Trade And Industrial Directories

070　　　　　　　UK　ISSN 0309-0256
PN4701
MEDIA REPORTER. 1976. q. Brennan Publications, 148 Birchover Way, Allestree, Derby DE22 2RW, England. Ed. J. Brennan. adv.; bk.rev. circ. 15,000. **Indexed:** Intl.Ind.TV.
　Description: Covers the mass media: professional standards and education and training in all media.

MEDIA REPORTER. see HOMOSEXUALITY

MEDIACOM; Central and Eastern Europe. see COMMUNICATIONS

JOURNALISM

MEDIAFILE. see *COMMUNICATIONS*

070   FR
MEDIAS POUVOIRS.* 1955. 9/yr. 315 F. 9 bis, rue Abel Hovelcque, 75013 Paris, France. TEL 47-23-61-88. FAX 40-70-17-19. Ed. Jean-Marie Charon. bk.rev.; abstr.; charts; illus. circ. 5,000.
    Formerly: Presse Actualite (ISSN 0032-7832)

070.43 320   US   ISSN 1053-8321
MEDIAWATCH. 1987. m. $29. Media Research Center, 113 S. West St., 2nd Fl., Alexandria, VA 22314. TEL 703-683-9733. FAX 703-683-9736. Ed. Brent H. Baker. circ. 15,000.
    Description: Analyzes the liberal political bias in reporting from major media outlets, especially the television networks.

MEDIEN-KRITIK. see *COMMUNICATIONS — Television And Cable*

070   GW   ISSN 0932-7886
MEDIEN UND PUBLICUM; Medien fuer den Dialog mit den Medien. 1987. m. DM.34.80. (Studienzentrum fuer Publizistische Bildung) Publicum Verlagsgesellschaft mbH, Otto-Hahn-Str. 10, 71726 Benningen, Germany. TEL 07144-18002. (back issues avail.)

070   US
MEDIUM RARE. q. $50 to non-member individuals; institutions $100; members free. Native American Journalists Association, 1433 Franklin Ave. E., Minneapolis, MN 55404. TEL 612-376-0441. FAX 612-376-0448. Ed. Gordon Regguinti. circ. 2,000. **Document type:** newsletter.

MENSCHEN - MACHEN - MEDIEN. see *COMMUNICATIONS*

070   US   ISSN 0026-6671
MISSOURI PRESS NEWS. 1938. m. $7.50. Missouri Press Association, Eighth and Locust, Columbia, MO 65201. TEL 314-449-4167. FAX 314-874-5894. Ed. Kent M. Ford. adv.; bk.rev.; illus.; index. circ. 1,000. (also avail. in microfilm) **Document type:** trade publication.

070   RU
MOSKOVSKII UNIVERSITET. VESTNIK. SERIYA 11: ZHURNALISTIKA. (Text in Russian; table of contents in English) bi-m. 13.50 Rub. Moskovskii Universitet, Ul. Gertsena 5-7, 103009 Moscow, Russia. bk.rev.; bibl.; index.

070.43   US
▼**MUCKRAKER.** 1992. q. $20 to individuals (foreign $30); institutions $40 (foreign $50); students $15 (foreign $25). Center for Investigative Reporting, 568 Howard St., 5th Fl., San Francisco, CA 94105-3008. TEL 415-543-1200. FAX 415-543-8311. circ. 1,000 (paid).
    Description: Presents articles of investigative reporting on the government, lobbyists and environmental issues.

MUNDO ISRAELITA; actualidad de la semana en Israel y en el mundo judio. see *GENERAL INTEREST PERIODICALS — Israel*

N A B J JOURNAL. (National Association of Black Journalists) see *ETHNIC INTERESTS*

070.172   US
N N A NATIONAL DIRECTORY OF WEEKLY NEWSPAPERS. 1921. a. $50. National Newspaper Association, 1627 K St., N.W., Ste. 400, Washington, DC 20006. TEL 202-466-7200. adv.; charts; stat. circ. 3,000. **Document type:** directory.
    Description: Lists more than 7,000 weekly newspapers by city, state and county groupings.

070.172   JA   ISSN 0916-295X
N S K NEWS BULLETIN. (Nihon Shinbun Kyokai) (Text in English) 1978. q. 2000 Yen. Japan Newspaper Publishers and Editors Association, Nippon Press Center Bldg., 2-2-1, Uchisaiwai-cho 2-chome, Chiyoda-ku, Tokyo 100, Japan. TEL 03-3591-4401. FAX 03-3591-6149. Dir. Hyde Sakata. circ. 1,200. **Document type:** bulletin.

070   UK
N U J FREELANCE DIRECTORY. biennial. £10. National Union of Journalists, Acorn House, 314-320 Grays Inn Rd., London WC1X 8DP, England. TEL 071-278-7916. FAX 071-837-8143. **Document type:** directory.

808.02   US
N W C MARKET UPDATE. 1978. 6/yr. $18. National Writers Club, 1450 S. Havana, Ste. 424, Aurora, CO 80012. TEL 303-751-7844. FAX 303-751-8593. Ed. Sandy Whelchel. circ. 6,000. (back issues avail.) **Document type:** newsletter.
    Formerly (until 1984): Freelancers Market.

070   US   ISSN 0342-9148
NACHRICHTENTECHNIK. (Text in German) 1977. irreg. price varies. Springer-Verlag, 175 Fifth Ave., New York, NY 10010. TEL 212-460-1500. FAX 212-473-6272. (Also: Berlin, Heidelberg, Tokyo and Vienna) Ed. H. Marko. (reprint service avail. from ISI) **Document type:** academic/scholarly publication.

070   YU   ISSN 0027-8149
NASA STAMPA. (Text in Serbo-Croation) 1951. m. 400 din. Savez Novinara Jugoslavije, Trg Republike 5, Belgrade, Yugoslavia. Ed. Miodrag Avramovic.

070 790.13   US   ISSN 0027-8521
NATIONAL AMATEUR. 1878. q. membership. National Amateur Press Association, c/o David Warner, 12311 Winding Ln., Bowie, MD 20715. bk.rev.; charts. circ. 400.

808.02 694   US
NATIONAL ASSOCIATION OF HOME AND WORKSHOP WRITERS NEWSLETTER. Short title: N A H W W Newsletter. 1973. q. $25 membership only. National Association of Home and Workshop Writers, c/o Richard Day, Man. Ed., Box 10, Palomar Mountain, CA 92060-0010. E-mail: oberreck@ext24.oes.orst.edu. bk.rev. circ. 100. **Document type:** newsletter.
    Description: Presents marketing and other information for home and workshop writers.

070   US   ISSN 0027-9927
NATIONAL PRESS CLUB RECORD. 1949. 48/yr. membership only. National Press Club, National Press Bldg., Washington, DC 20045. TEL 202-662-7500. circ. 5,500. **Document type:** newsletter.
    Description: Covers activities and events of the Club. Includes a listing of employment opportunities.

070   US   ISSN 0028-1913
PN4700
NEBRASKA NEWSPAPER. 1949. bi-m. $10.50. Nebraska Press Association, 1120 K St., Lincoln, NE 68508. TEL 402-476-2851. FAX 402-476-2942. Ed. MaryJo Chatelain. adv.; bk.rev.; illus. circ. 568.

NELLA GALASSIA DELL'INFORMAZIONE. see *LABOR UNIONS*

808.02 301.412   US   ISSN 1044-1476
NETWORK (NEW YORK); an alliance and network for those connected to the written word. 1980. bi-m. $35 (foreign $45). International Women's Writing Guild, Box 810, Gracie Sta., New York, NY 10028. TEL 212-737-7536. FAX 212-737-9469. Ed. Tatoama Stoumen. adv. circ. 3,500. **Indexed:** Abstr.Hyg. **Document type:** newsletter.
    Description: News of and by women writers.

NEWES. see *HOBBIES*

070   XK   ISSN 1010-5735
NEWS ADVERTISER. 1985. q. $10. A L K I M Communication Production Company, Box MA 020, Marchand Post Office, Castries, St. Lucia, W.I. Ed. Albert De Terville. adv. circ. 5,000.
—CCC.

070   US   ISSN 1054-3791
Z6951
NEWS BUREAU CONTACTS (YEAR). a. (plus m. updates). $120. B P I Communications, Inc. (New York), 1515 Broadway, New York, NY 10036. TEL 212-536-5261; 800-BPI-4100. FAX 212-536-5294. Ed. Mitch Tebo. circ. 350. (back issues avail.) **Document type:** directory.
    Description: Lists publications, newspapers, trade magazines with news bureau.

070 340   US   ISSN 0149-0737
KF2750.A15
NEWS MEDIA AND THE LAW. 1973. 4/yr. $25 (foreign $40). Reporters Committee for Freedom of the Press, 1735 Eye St. N.W., Rm. 504, Washington, DC 20006. TEL 202-466-6312. Ed. Jane E. Kirtley. adv. circ. 3,500. (also avail. in microform from UMI; back issues avail.; reprint service avail. from UMI,WSH) **Indexed:** C.L.I., HR Rep., L.R.I., Leg.Per.—Faxon; UnCover; UMI.
    Supersedes (as of 1977): Press Censorship Newsletter.

070   US
NEWSLETTER DESIGN. 1987. 12/yr. $95. Newsletter Clearinghouse (Rhinebeck), 44 W. Market St., Box 311, Rhinebeck, NY 12572. TEL 914-876-2081. FAX 914-876-2561. illus.
    Description: News and reviews for the desktop generation. Features illustrated critiques of 20 newsletters chosen from those entered in the Newsletter Clearinghouse's annual award competition.

070   US   ISSN 0028-9507
NEWSLETTER ON NEWSLETTERS; reporting on the newsletter world: editing, graphics, management, promotion, newsletter reviews, and surveys. 1964. s-m. $120 (foreign $140). Newsletter Clearinghouse (Rhinebeck), 44 W. Market St., Box 311, Rhinebeck, NY 12572. TEL 914-876-2081. FAX 914-876-2561. Ed. Howard Penn Hudson. bk.rev. (looseleaf format) **Document type:** newsletter.

070   II   ISSN 0028-9531
NEWSMAN.* (Text in English) vol.9, 1968. m. Madras Reporters Guild, Government Estate, Madras 2, India. Ed. V. Ramakrishna Aiyar. adv.

070   KO
NEWSPAPER AND BROADCASTING. (Text in Korean) 1964. m. 15000 Won (effective 1993). Korean Press Institute, Korea Press Center Bldg., 12th Fl., 1-25 Taepyung-ro, Chung-ku, Seoul, S. Korea. TEL 02-398-1601. FAX 02-737-7170. circ. 2,850.
    Description: Comprises specific issues and feature stories along with activities of Korean media and data related to journalism and mass communication.

NEWSPAPER FINANCIAL EXECUTIVES JOURNAL. see *BUSINESS AND ECONOMICS — Management*

070   US
NEWSPAPER FUND ADVISER UPDATE. vol.15, 1974. 2/yr. (during school year). free. Dow Jones Newspaper Fund, Inc., Box 300, Princeton, NJ 08543-0300. TEL 609-452-2820. FAX 609-520-5804. Ed. Elaine Wells Reed. bk.rev. circ. 1,500.
    Formerly: Newspaper Fund Newsletter.
    Description: Aimed at high school journalism teachers, publication advisers and others interested in scholastic journalism.

070.4   US   ISSN 0090-2209
HD6515.N4
NEWSPAPER GUILD. ANNUAL T.N.G. CONVENTION OFFICERS' REPORT. Key Title: Annual T N G Convention Officers' Report. a. Newspaper Guild, AFL-CIO, CLC., 8611 Second Ave., Silver Spring, MD 20910. TEL 301-585-2990. **Document type:** proceedings.

070.4   US   ISSN 0741-7950
HD6515.N4
NEWSPAPER GUILD. PROCEEDINGS OF THE ANNUAL CONVENTION. 1940. a. Newspaper Guild, AFL-CIO, 8611 Second Ave., Silver Spring, MD 20910. TEL 301-585-2990. (also avail. in microform from UMI; reprint service avail. from UMI) **Document type:** proceedings.
—UMI.

070   UK
NEWSPAPER PUBLISHERS HANDBOOK. a. £15. E C N Special Publications, 69 Thorpe Rd., Norwich, Norfolk NR1 1TB, England. FAX 0603-615973. circ. 4,000.

070.172 US
NEWSPAPER RESEARCH JOURNAL. 1979. q. $20 to individuals; institutions $30; libraries $40. Association for Education in Journalism and Mass Communication, 1621 College St., University of South Carolina, Columbia, SC 29208-0251. TEL 803-777-2005. (Subscr. to: School of Journalism, Ohio University, Athens, OH 45701) Ed. Ralph Izard. bk.rev. circ. 900. (also avail. in microform from UMI; reprint service avail. from UMI) **Indexed:** Commun.Abstr., Sage Urb.Stud.Abstr. **Document type:** academic/scholarly publication.

070.172 US
NEWSPAPERS & TECHNOLOGY.* m. Media Business Corp., 1786 Platte St., Denver, CO 80202. TEL 303-355-2101. FAX 303-355-2144. Ed. Chuck Moozahis. adv. circ. 18,900.

070 US
NEWSPAPERS AND VOICE. 1991. m. Virgo Publishing, Inc., 4141 N. Scottsdale Rd., No. 316, Scottsdale, AZ 85251. TEL 602-990-1101. FAX 602-990-0819. adv.: B&W page $2270; trim 8 1/8 x 10 7/8. circ. 10,000.
Description: Covers voice services offered by the international newspaper community.

NEWSPAPERS, DIVERSITY AND YOU. see *OCCUPATIONS AND CAREERS*

070 378 US
NEWSWIRE (MANHATTAN). 1972. 4/yr. $35 to individuals; institutions $40. Journalism Education Association, Inc., Kedzie Hall 103, Kansas State University, Manhattan, KS 66506. TEL 913-532-5532. FAX 913-532-7309. Ed. Nancy Hall. adv. circ. 2,000. (reprint service avail. from ERIC)

070 US ISSN 0028-9817
PN4700
NIEMAN REPORTS. 1947. q. $20 (foreign $30). Nieman Foundation, Harvard University, 1 Francis Ave., Cambridge, MA 02138. TEL 617-495-2237. FAX 617-495-8976. (Subscr. to: Box 4951, Manchester, NH 03108) Ed. Robert H. Phelps. bk.rev. circ. 1,349. (also avail. in microform from UMI; microform from IAC; reprint service avail. from UMI, IAC) **Indexed:** Mid.East: Abstr.& Ind. **Document type:** academic/scholarly publication.
●Also available on CD-ROM. Producer(s): University Microfilms International.
—Faxon; UnCover; UMI.
Description: Provides a forum for discussion of media-related issues by journalists, educators, and public figures.

070.172 JA
NIHON KAIJI SHIMBUN/JAPAN MARITIME DAILY. 1942. d. (Mon.-Fri.). Nihon Kaiji Shimbunsha, 13-4, Shimbashi 5-chome, Minato-ku, Tokyo, Japan. TEL 03-3436-3221. FAX 03-3436-6553. Ed. Minoru Takashimizu; Pub. Takaaki Ohyma. adv.: page 1300000 Yen; adv. contact: Hideo Sakon. **Document type:** newspaper.

NORTHERN ADVOCATE. see *ADVERTISING AND PUBLIC RELATIONS*

070 301.16 YU ISSN 0029-5175
NOVINARSTVO. (Text in Serbo-Croatian; abstract in English) 1965. q. 10000 din. Jugoslovenski Institut za Novinarstvo Beograd, Njegoseva 72, Box 541, 11000 Belgrade, Yugoslavia. TEL 11-444-22-51. FAX 11-444-842. Ed. Zdravko Lekovic. adv.; bk.rev.; bibl.; stat.; index, cum.index. circ. 3,000.

070 DK ISSN 0109-5072
NU!. Variant title: Udenrigsmagasinet Nu! 1983. bi-m. DKK 35 per no. Danmarks Journalisthoejskole, Olof Palmes Alle 11, DK-8200 Aarhus N, Denmark. TEL 86-161122. FAX 86-168910. Ed. Hans-Henrik Holm. illus. circ. 1,000.

NURSE AUTHOR AND EDITOR. see *MEDICAL SCIENCES — Nurses And Nursing*

070 IT
O G INFORMAZIONE. bi-m. Consiglio Nazionale dell'Ordine dei Giornalisti - National Council of Journalists, Via Lungotevere Cenci, 8, Rome, Italy. TEL 06-6565908. Ed. Liami Faustini. adv.; bk.rev. circ. 65,000.

OBSCURE PUBLICATIONS AND VIDEO. see *PUBLISHING AND BOOK TRADE*

070 AU
OESTERREICHISCHE JOURNALIST. bi-m. Mayrwies 149, A-5023 Salzburg, Austria. TEL 0662-661073. Ed. Johann Oberauer. circ. 5,000.

058.81 DK ISSN 0901-2869
OGSAA EN AVIS. 1973. 8/yr. DKK 50. Danmarks Journalisthoejskole - Danish School of Journalism, Olof Palmes Alle 11, DK-8200 Aarhus N., Denmark. FAX 45-86-16-89-10. Ed. Flemming Soerensen. adv. circ. 2,700. **Document type:** newspaper.

OHIO STATE LANTERN. see *COLLEGE AND ALUMNI*

OREGON PUBLISHER. see *PUBLISHING AND BOOK TRADE*

070.48 XO ISSN 0322-7049
OTAZKY ZURNALISTIKY. 1958. q. $29. (Journalist Study Institute) Obzor, Ceskoslovenskej Armady 35, 815 85 Bratislava, Slovakia.

070.4 US ISSN 0195-6124
PN4871
OUTDOOR WRITERS ASSOCIATION OF AMERICA. DIRECTORY. a. Outdoor Writers Association of America, Inc., 2017 Cato Ave., Ste. 101, State College, PA 16801. TEL 814-234-1011. **Document type:** directory.
Formerly: O W A A Outdoor Writers Directory.

OUTDOORS UNLIMITED. see *CONSERVATION*

070 US
OVERSEAS PRESS CLUB BULLETIN.* vol.28, 1973. s-m. membership. Overseas Press Club of America, Inc., 320 E. 42nd St., Mezz, New York, NY 10017-5900. TEL 212-983-4655. adv.; bk.rev.; illus.; tr.lit. circ. 1,700.
Formerly: Overseas Press Bulletin (ISSN 0048-2544).

059.95 JA ISSN 0910-4607
BJ1545
P H P INTERSECT.* (Peace, Happiness and Prosperity) (Text in English) 1970. m. 3600 Yen($18) P H P Institute International, Inc., International Division, 3-10 Sanban-cho, Chiyoda-ku, Tokyo 102, Japan. TEL 03-239-6238. Ed. Robert J. Wargo. adv.; bk.rev. circ. 70,000.
—UnCover.
Formerly (until 1985): P H P (ISSN 0030-798X)
Description: Intended to promote mutual understanding and trust between the U.S. and Japan. Offers valuable insight into Japan and the Japanese people. Touches on problems - and their possible solutions - that affect the two countries.

070 US ISSN 0030-8196
P N P A PRESS. 1929. 10/yr. $17.75. Pennsylvania Newspaper Publishers Association, 2717 N. Front St., Harrisburg, PA 17110. TEL 717-234-4067. FAX 717-234-0746. Ed. Amy H. Smith. adv.; bk.rev.; illus. circ. 985. **Document type:** trade publication.
Description: Provides information and in-depth commentary on all aspects of the newspaper business, including editorial, advertising, production and legal matters.

070.1 CN ISSN 0845-8499
P.W.A.CONTACT. 1976. bi-m. Can.$55 to non-members; students Can.$27.50. Periodical Writers Association of Canada, 24 Ryerson Ave., Toronto, Ont. M5T 2P3, Canada. TEL 416-868-6913. Ed. Kathe Lieber. adv. circ. 550. **Document type:** newsletter.
Former titles (until 1988): P.W.A.C. National Newsletter (ISSN 0822-4706); P.W.A.C. Newsletter (ISSN 0711-5946); (until 1979): Periodical Writers Association Newsletter (ISSN 0701-0826)

070 US ISSN 0883-6752
PAGES; editorial and filler service. 1969. 12/yr. $185 (diskette service $235). Berry Publishing Company, 300 N. State St., Chicago, IL 60610. TEL 312-222-9245. FAX 312-222-9637. bk.rev.; illus. circ. 5,000. (also avail. in diskette format)
Description: Contains editorial filler articles, statistics and artwork for newsletter editors.

070 808.8 US ISSN 0895-0180
PEN IN HAND. 1987. m. $25. Brooklyn Writers' Network, 2509 Avenue K, Brooklyn, NY 11210. TEL 718-377-4945. Ed. Vicki Karen Hershkowitz. adv. circ. 500. (back issues avail.)

070.1 CN ISSN 0829-0857
PERIODICAL WRITERS ASSOCIATION OF CANADA. DIRECTORY OF MEMBERS. 1982. a. Can.$18.24. Periodical Writers Association of Canada, 24 Ryerson Ave., Toronto, ON M5T 2P3, Canada. TEL 416-868-6913. circ. 1,500. **Document type:** directory.
Formerly: Periodical Writers Association of Canada. Directory.
Description: Listing of 350 of Canada's freelance magazine writers listed geographically, by area of specialty and related skills, and in alphabetical index.

070.1 CN
PERIODICAL WRITERS ASSOCIATION OF CANADA. WHO PAYS WHAT. 1979. biennial. Can.$17.50. Periodical Writers Association of Canada, 24 Ryerson Ave., Toronto, ON M5T 2P3, Canada. TEL 416-868-6913. circ. 1,500. **Document type:** directory.
Former titles: Periodical Writers Association of Canada. Magazine Markets and Fees (ISSN 0829-0865); Periodical Writers Association of Canada. Fees Survey.
Description: Guide to over 300 Canadian magazines with rates and requirements.

070 VE ISSN 0048-3370
PERIODISTA. 1967. bi-m. Bs.2. Colegio Nacional de Periodistas, Casa Nacional del Periodista, Avda. Andres Bello, Caracas, Venezuela. Ed.Bd. adv.; bk.rev.; charts; illus. circ. 500. (also avail. in microform)

PHOTOJOURNALIST (NEWARK). see *PHOTOGRAPHY*

PIMS EUROPEAN CONSUMER DIRECTORY. see *BIBLIOGRAPHIES*

PIMS EUROPEAN NEWSPAPERS DIRECTORY. see *BIBLIOGRAPHIES*

PIMS MEDIA TOWNSLIST. see *PUBLISHING AND BOOK TRADE*

PIMS U K MEDIA DIRECTORY. see *PUBLISHING AND BOOK TRADE*

PIMS U S A CONSUMER DIRECTORY. see *BIBLIOGRAPHIES*

PIMS U S A NEWSPAPER DIRECTORY. see *BIBLIOGRAPHIES*

PIMS U S A TRADE & TECHNICAL DIRECTORY. see *BIBLIOGRAPHIES*

070 236 US
PITTSBURGH JEWISH CHRONICLE. 1961. w. $26 in PA; states east of Mississippi River $28; west of Miss. R. and FL $30; foreign $50. Pittsburgh Jewish Publication and Education Foundation, 5600 Baum Blvd., Pittsburgh, PA 15206. TEL 412-687-1000. FAX 412-687-5119. Ed. Joel Roteman; Pub. Barbara Befferman. adv. contact: Rosalie Caplan. bk.rev. circ. 3,000. **Document type:** newspaper.
Formerly: American Jewish Press Association. Bulletin.

070 323.44 II
PRESS COUNCIL OF INDIA REVIEW. (Text in English) 1980. q. free. Press Council of India, Faridkot House, Copernicus Marg, New Delhi 110 001, India. TEL 388885. Ed. G.L. Ahuja. illus. circ. 2,000.
Description: Covers the press world, articles and adjudications of the Council.

070 CH
PRESS COUNCIL OF THE REPUBLIC OF CHINA. 1967. m. National Press Council of the Republic of China, Nanchang Rd. Sec. 1, Lane 9, No. 4, 3rd Fl., Taipei, Taiwan 107, Republic of China. Ed.Bd. circ. 4,000 (controlled).
Formerly: P C O T Bulletin.

070 CN ISSN 0706-9286
PRESS REVIEW. 1976. 4/yr. Can.$20. Press Review Ltd., Box 368, Sta. A, Toronto, ON M5W 1C2, Canada. TEL 416-368-0512. FAX 416-366-0104. Ed. Michael Cassidy. adv.; bk.rev. circ. 16,000.

JOURNALISM

070 US ISSN 0032-7824
PRESS WOMAN. 1937. bi-m. $20. National Federation of Press Women, Inc., c/o Lois Lauer Wolfe, Ed., 1105 Main St., Box 99, Blue Springs, MO 64013. TEL 816-229-1666. FAX 816-229-8877. adv. contact: Lois Lauer Wolf. bk.rev.; illus.; circ. 4,000 (paid). **Document type:** trade publication.
—Faxon.

070.1 BE ISSN 0478-1546
PRESSE/PERS. (Text in Dutch, French) 1954. q. 700 Fr. Association Belge des Editeurs de Journaux, Rue Belliard 20, B-1040 Brussels, Belgium. TEL 02-512-17-32. FAX 02-511-9969. Ed. J. Hoet. adv.; bk.rev.; bibl. circ. 1,500.

PRESSE REPORT; Magazin fuer den Presseeinzelhandel. see *PUBLISHING AND BOOK TRADE*

070.172 GW
PRESSE UND SPRACHE. (Text in English, French and German) 1959. m. DM.21. Eilers und Schuenemann Verlag GmbH und Co., II Schlachtpforte 7, Postfach 106067, 28195 Bremen, Germany. TEL 0421-3690347. FAX 0421-3690348.
Formerly: Unsere Zeitung.
Description: Press review with articles from German newspapers with explanations or translations of difficult words in English and French.

PRESSEHANDBUCH (YEAR). see *PUBLISHING AND BOOK TRADE*

070 SW ISSN 0032-7883
PRESSENS TIDNING. 1920. 20/yr. SEK 395 (effective 1994). (Svenska Tidningsutgivarefoereningen - Swedish Newspaper Publishers Association) TU: S Foerlags AB, P.O. Box 22500, 104 22 Stockholm, Sweden. Ed. Mats Lundman. adv.; bk.rev. circ. 18,087.

070 US
PRESSNEWS. 1947. q. $5. Maryland-Delaware-D.C. Press Association, 275 West St., Ste. 310, Annapolis, MD 21401. TEL 410-263-7878. FAX 410-263-7878. Ed. Patricia Marshall. adv.; illus. circ. 250. (also avail. in microfilm) **Document type:** newsletter.
Former titles: Md De D C Press News (ISSN 0025-4215); Maryland-Delaware Press News.
Description: Articles and announcements on the newspaper industry, largely in the Maryland-Delaware-D.C. area.

070.172 686.2 US ISSN 0194-3243
PN4700
PRESSTIME. 1979. m. $100 (foreign $135). Newspaper Association of America, 11600 Sunrise Valley Dr., Reston, VA 22090. TEL 703-648-1000. FAX 703-620-4557. Ed. Terence Polltrack. adv.; bk.rev.; charts; illus.; stat.; index. circ. 15,000. (also avail. in microfiche from CIS) **Indexed:** Abstr.Bull.Inst.Pap.Chem., Graph.Arts Lit.Abstr., SRI. —BLDSC (6612.555000); Faxon; UnCover.
Supersedes (1979): American Newspaper Publishers Association, Research Institute. R I Bulletins (ISSN 0001-205X)
Description: Covers all aspects of the newspaper business, including technology, telecommunications, computers, public policy, news-editorial, research, readership, circulation, advertising, employee relations, diversity, training and newsprint.

PRIMA COMUNICAZIONE. see *COMMUNICATIONS*

070 US
PRINT'S REGIONAL DESIGN ANNUAL. a. newsstand price: $32. R C Publications, Inc., 104 Fifth Ave., 19th Fl., New York, NY 10011-6901. TEL 212-463-0600. FAX 212-989-9891. Ed. Martin Fox; Pub. Howard Cadel.

PRODUCTION JOURNAL. see *PRINTING*

070 800 US
PROFESSIONAL FREELANCE WRITERS DIRECTORY. 1970. a. $15. National Writers Club, 1450 S. Havana, Ste. 424, Aurora, CO 80012. TEL 303-751-7844. FAX 303-751-8593. Ed. Sandy Whelchel. circ. 1,500. (processed; back issues avail.) **Indexed:** Text.Tech.Dig. **Document type:** directory.
Supersedes: National Writers Club. Bulletin for Professional Members (ISSN 0028-0429)

PUBLIC OPINION REPORT. see *POLITICAL SCIENCE*

070 US ISSN 0048-5942
PN4700
PUBLISHERS' AUXILIARY. 1865. fortn. $55. National Newspaper Association, 1627 K St., N.W., Ste. 400, Washington, DC 20006. TEL 202-466-7200. Ed. Chuck Holahan. adv. contact: Sharon McFarland. bk.rev.; charts; illus.; tr.lit. circ. 9,000. (tabloid format) **Indexed:** Graph.Arts Lit.Abstr. **Document type:** trade publication.

PUBLIZISTIK. see *COMMUNICATIONS*

070 GW
PUBLIZISTIK UND KUNST. 1951. m. DM.48. Industriegewerkschaft Medien, Postfach 102451, 70020 Stuttgart, Germany. TEL 0711-2018-0. FAX 0711-2018199. Ed.Bd. adv.; bk.rev.; illus.; index. circ. 11,000. **Document type:** trade publication.
Formerly (until 1990): Feder (ISSN 0014-8970)

070 US ISSN 1051-8126
▼**PULSO**; del periodismo. (Text in Spanish; table of contents in English) 1990. q. $15. Universidad Internacional de la Florida, Miami, Programa Centroamericano de Periodismo - Florida International Univeristy, Central American Journalism Program, Biscayne Blvd. at N.E. 151st St., North Miami, FL 33181. TEL 305-940-5672. FAX 305-956-5498. (And: Apdo. 1253-1002, San Jose, Costa Rica. TEL 506-533-280) Ed. Gerardo Bolanos. adv. contact: Mike Leonard. bk.rev.; circ. 4,500 (controlled). (back issues avail.) **Document type:** trade publication.
Description: Covers problems in journalism emphasizing Latin American media.

070 IS
QESHER/CONNECTION. (Text in Hebrew; summaries in English) 1987. s-a. $22 per no. (effective 1992). Tel Aviv University, Institute for Research of the Jewish Press, Journalism Studies Program, P.O. Box 39040, Tel Aviv 69978, Israel. TEL 03-6413404. FAX 03-6422318. Ed. Mordecai Naor.
Description: Covers the history of Jewish journalism and journalists throughout the world.

QINGNIAN ZUOJIA/YOUNG WRITERS; wenxue shuang yuekan. see *LITERATURE*

070 IT ISSN 0302-5063
QUARTO POTERE; rassegna di storia, tecnica ed esperienze del giornalismo. 1973. q. Via Bartolomeo Gosio 59, 00191 Rome, Italy. Ed. Gino Pallotta.

070 US ISSN 0033-6475
QUILL (GREENCASTLE); the magazine for journalists. 1912. m. $29 (foreign $30). Society of Professional Journalists, Box 77, Greencastle, IN 46135-0077. TEL 317-653-3333. FAX 317-653-4631. Ed. Brian L. Steffens. adv. contact: Greg Christopher. bk.rev.; charts; illus.; stat.; tr.lit.; index; circ. 18,000 (paid). (also avail. in microform from UMI) **Indexed:** Hum.Ind. **Document type:** trade publication.
●Also available online. Vendor(s): DIALOG Information Services, Inc., Information Access Co. Also available on CD-ROM.
—Faxon; UnCover; UMI.
Description: Publishes news, commentary and critique of the news media, both print and broadcast, and trends, research and professional issues concerning journalism.

070 373 US ISSN 0033-6505
QUILL AND SCROLL. 1926. 4/yr. $12. (International Honorary Society for High School Journalists) Quill & Scroll Society, School of Journalism and Mass Communication, Univ. of Iowa, Iowa City, IA 52242. TEL 319-335-5795. FAX 319-335-5210. Ed. Richard P. Johns. adv.; bk.rev.; illus.; circ. 13,500 (paid). (also avail. in microform from UMI; reprint service avail. from UMI) **Indexed:** C.I.J.E.
—Faxon; UnCover; UMI.

070 200 US ISSN 0034-4109
R N A NEWSLETTER.* 1953. bi-m. $5. Religion Newswriters Association, c/o Ben Kaufman, Cincinnati Enquirer, 617 Vine St., Cincinnati, OH 45202. circ. 125. (processed) **Document type:** newsletter.

R T N D A COMMUNICATOR. (Radio - Television News Directors Association) see *COMMUNICATIONS — Radio*

070 RU ISSN 0033-9318
RASPROSTRANENIE PECHATI. 1929. m. 15.60 Rub. (Komitet po Pechati Soveta Ministrov) Izdatel'stvo Kniga, 50, Gorky St., 125047 Moscow, Russia. Ed. K.F. Takoyev.

070 BE
REDACTUEL. 1979. bi-m. membership. Association Belge de la Presse d'Enterprise, Hammeveld 2, B-1785 Hamme, Belgium. FAX 02-210-07-02. Ed. Christiane Asselberghs. bk.rev. circ. 200.
Formerly: Informations pour Journalistes d'Entreprise - Informatie voor Bedrijfsjournalisten.

808.02 US
REGISTERED WRITER'S COMMUNIQUE - CONTACTS AND ASSIGNMENTS; magazine for professional freelance writers. 1986. m. $18. (Registered Writer's Guild) Gibbs Publishing Company, Box 600927, N. Miami Beach, FL 33160. Ed. James Calvin Gibbs. adv.; bk.rev. **Document type:** trade publication.
Formerly: Registered Writer's Forum - Assignments.

070 RU
REPORTER. 1990. w. Soyuz Zhurnalistov S.S.S.R., Kemerovskaya Oblastnaya Organizatsiya, Pr. Lenina 124, 650056 Kemerovo, Russia. TEL 55-81-21. Ed. Aleksandr Kosvintsev. circ. 50,000.

REPORTER - YOUR EDITORIAL ASSISTANT. see *EDUCATION*

070 UK
REPORTERS SANS FRONTIERES. ANNUAL REPORT. 1985. a. £15. John Libbey & Company Ltd., 13 Smiths Yard, Summerley St., London SW18 4HR, England. TEL 081-947-2777. FAX 081-947-2664. **Document type:** corporate report.
Description: Reports on freedom of the press throughout the world.

070 MG
REVUE DE LA PRESSE DE L'OCEAN INDIEN. (Text in French) 1981. bi-m. $23. Communication and Media Ocean Indien, B.P. 46, Antananarivo, Malagasy Republic. Ed. Georges Ranaivosoa. adv.; bk.rev. circ. 3,000.

070 BE
REVUE DE LA PRESSE PERIODIQUE/TIJDSCHRIFT VOOR DE PERIODIEKE PERS. (Text in English, French) 1900. 4/yr. 500 BEF. (Association des Journalistes Periodiques Belges et Etrangers) F. Lepeer, Ed. & Pub., 110 av. de Heyn, B-1090 Brussels, Belgium. circ. 1,500.

REVUE TUNISIENNE DE COMMUNICATION. see *COMMUNICATIONS*

808.06 978 US
PS374.W4
THE ROUNDUP MAGAZINE. 1953. bi-m. $30. Texas Christian University Press for Western Writers of America, Inc., 416 Bedford Rd., El Paso, TX 79922-1204. TEL 817-921-7822. FAX 915-544-9967. Ed. S. Gail Miller. bk.rev. circ. 700. **Document type:** trade publication.
Formerly (until Sep. 1993): Roundup (El Paso) (ISSN 0035-855X)
Description: Examines literature and history as it relates to the American West.

070 AT
ROY MORGAN MAGAZINE & NEWSPAPER SURVEY. 1971. s-a. Roy Morgan Research Centre Pty. Ltd., Box 2282U, Melbourne, Vic. 3001, Australia. FAX 03-629-1250.

808.02 070.5 US
RUSS VON HOELSCHER PUBLISHING REPORT. 1980. 6/yr. $49. Publishers Media, 1136 Broadway, Ste. 8, Box 1295, El Cajon, CA 92022-1295. Ed. Russ A. von Hoelscher. adv.; bk.rev. circ. 3,300.
Former titles (until 1992): Independent Publishing Report; (until 1984): Free Lance Writing and Publishing.

JOURNALISM

070 US ISSN 0036-2972
PN4899.S25
ST. LOUIS JOURNALISM REVIEW. 1970. m. (except Dec.-Jan. and Jul.-Aug. combined). $25. Charles L. Klotzer, Ed. & Pub., 8380 Olive Blvd., St. Louis, MO 63132. TEL 314-991-1698. FAX 314-997-1898. adv.; bk.rev.; illus.; circ. 5,000 (paid). (tabloid format; back issues avail.) **Indexed:** Alt.Press Ind., Amer.Hist.& Life, Hist.Abstr., Mid.East: Abstr.& Ind., P.A.I.S.
● Also available on CD-ROM.
—CCC.
Incorporates (after no.95, 1984): Focus - Midwest (ISSN 0015-508X)
Description: Evaluates media print, broadcast, communications, advertising, and public relations, and issues ignored by media.

070 BU ISSN 0205-1656
P87
SAVREMENNA ZHURNALISTIKA/MODERN JOURNALISM. 1982. q. 10 lv. Research and Information Centre of Journalism, Editor's Office, Bratya Miladinovi 12, Sofia 1000, Bulgaria. TEL 88 42 33. TELEX 022635. (Co-sponsor: Union of Bulgarian Journalists) Ed. Todor Abazov. bk.rev. circ. 1,000.

SCAVENGER'S NEWSLETTER. see LITERATURE — Science Fiction, Fantasy, Horror

070 SZ
SCHWEIZER FACHPRESSE/PRESSE SPECIALISEE SUISSE/STAMPA SPECIALIZATA SVIZZERA. (Text in French, German and Italian) 1925. bi-m. 18 SFr. Schweizerischer Fachpresse-Verband - Union Suisse de la Presse Specialisee, Secretariat, Hintere Hauptgasse 9, Postfach 2, CH-4800 Zofingen, Switzerland. Ed. Jaroslaw Trachsel. adv.; B&W page 546 SFr.; trim 185 x 265; adv. contact: Uta Buhl. bk.rev. circ. 1,100.
Formerly: Fachpresse (ISSN 0014-6382)

SE LA VIE WRITER'S JOURNAL. see LITERATURE — Poetry

070 MP
SETGUULCH/JOURNALIST. (Text in Mongolian) 1982. bi-m. Union of Journalists, Ulan Bator, Mongolia. TEL 25388. Ed. T. Baasansuren. circ. 4,000.
Description: Covers journalism, politics, literature, art and economy.

070 KO
SHIN DONG-A/NEW EAST ASIA. 1931. m. Dong-A Ilbo, 17 Yeoido-dong, Yongdeungpo-ku, Seoul 150 010, S. Korea. TEL 02-781-0611. FAX 02-785-4547. Ed. Kwon O-Kie. circ. 335,000.

070 CC
SICHUAN XINWEN TUPIAN/SICHUAN NEWS PHOTO PRESS. (Text in Chinese) 1980. q. $0.60. Sichuan Xiwen Tupianshe - Sichuan News Photo Agency, Chongqing, Sichuan 630010, People's Republic of China. TEL 45856. circ. 50,000.
Formerly (until 1992): Sichuan News Photo.

070.48 500 US ISSN 0737-0350
SIPISCOPE. 1970. q. free. Scientists' Institute for Public Information, 355 Lexington Ave., New York, NY 10017. TEL 212-661-9110. FAX 212-599-6432. Ed. fred Jerome. circ. 10,000. **Document type:** newsletter.
Description: Discusses media coverage of science and technology.

070.48 796.93 US
SKI WRITERS BULLETIN. 1964. q. membership. United States Ski Writers Association, 7 Kensington Rd., Glens Falls, NY 12801. TEL 518-793-1201. circ. 350. **Document type:** trade publication.

SMALL PRESS REVIEW - SMALL MAGAZINE REVIEW. see PUBLISHING AND BOOK TRADE

SOCIAL RESPONSIBILITY: BUSINESS, JOURNALISM, LAW, MEDICINE. see PHILOSOPHY

070 FR
SOCIETE GENERALE DE PRESSE ET D'EDITIONS. INDEX; revue quotidienne de la presse francaise. d. 18500 F. (foreign 19800 F.). Societe Generale de Presse et d'Editions, 13 Avenue de l'Opera, 75001 Paris, France. TEL 40-15-17-89. FAX 40-15-17-15. TELEX SOGPRES 230023.

EL SOL. see ETHNIC INTERESTS

070 378 US ISSN 0038-3716
SOUTHEASTERNER. 1965. m. (Sep.-May). free. University of Kentucky, Southeast Community College, Cumberland, KY 40823. TEL 606-589-2145. Ed. Ed Boggs. adv.; illus.; circ. 2,500 (paid); 3,500 (controlled). **Document type:** newspaper.

SPECTRUM (OLATHE); a guide to the independent press and informative organizations. see LIBRARY AND INFORMATION SCIENCES

808.02 330 US ISSN 0272-8079
SPEECHWRITER'S NEWSLETTER. 1980. w. $287. Lawrence Ragan Communications, Inc., 212 W. Superior St., Ste. 200, Chicago, IL 60610-3533. TEL 312-335-0037. Ed. John Cowan. bk.rev. circ. 1,500. **Document type:** newsletter.

070 370 US
LB3621.A2
STUDENT PRESS REVIEW. 1925. q. $22. Columbia Scholastic Press Association, Columbia Univ., Central Mail Room, Box 11, New York, NY 10027-6969. TEL 212-854-9400. FAX 212-854-9401. Ed. Helen F. Smith. adv.; bk.rev.; charts; illus. circ. 7,000. (also avail. in microform from UMI; reprint service avail. from UMI) **Indexed:** ERIC. **Document type:** trade publication.
—UnCover.
Formerly (until 1991): School Press Review (ISSN 0036-6730)
Description: Covers journalism in schools and colleges.

070 FI ISSN 0039-5587
SUOMEN LEHDISTO/FINLANDS PRESS. (Text in Finnish; summaries in Swedish) 1930. m. $54. Sanomalehtien Liitto - Tidningarnas Foerbund (Finnish Newspaper Publishers Association), Lonnrotenkatu 11, FIN-00120 Helsinki, Finland. TEL 358-0-2287-7300. Ed. Olavi Rantalainen. adv. contact: Vieno Sauri. bk.rev.; circ. 3,788 (controlled).

070 US ISSN 1055-2723
PN4888.S9
SYNDICATED COLUMNIST CONTACTS (YEAR). 1975. a. (plus m. updates). $120. B P I Communications, Inc. (New York), 1515 Broadway, New York, NY 10036. TEL 212-536-5261; 800-BPI-4100. FAX 212-536-5294. Ed. Mitch Tebo. bibl. circ. 1,000. **Document type:** directory.
Formerly (until 1989): Syndicated Columnists (ISSN 1046-6738)
Description: Provides contact information for syndicated columnists in 37 different editorial areas.

SYNDICATED COLUMNISTS WEEKLY. see HANDICAPPED — Visually Impaired

070 330 US
T J F R BUSINESS NEWS REPORTER. 1987. s-m. $575 (effective Jan. 1991). T J F R Publishing Co., 545 N. Maple Ave., Ridgewood, NJ 07450. TEL 201-444-6061. FAX 201-444-5919. Ed. Dean Rotbart. bk.rev.; index. (back issues avail.)
Formerly: Journalist and Financial Report.
Description: Directed to corporate communications executives who seek a better understanding of business media.

070 US
T P A MESSENGER. 1926. m. $6. Texas Press Association, 718 W. Fifth St., Austin, TX 78701. TEL 512-477-6755. Ed. Lyndell Williams. adv.; bk.rev.; charts; illus. circ. 1,015. (tabloid format)
Formerly (until vol.64, no.77, 1979): Texas Press Messenger (ISSN 0040-4624)

070 IT
TABLOID. 12/yr. Board of Journalists of Lombardy, Viale Monte Santo 7, 20124 Milan, Italy. TEL 02-65-97-163. FAX 02-65-54-307. Ed. Franco Abruzzo.

TASCHENBUCH FUER AGRARJOURNALISTEN. see AGRICULTURE

810 760 US ISSN 0492-3901
TAYLOR TALK; the yearbook magazine. 1960. 3/yr. $12. Taylor Publishing Co., 1550 W. Mockingbird Lane, Dallas, TX 75235. TEL 800-677-2800. FAX 214-819-8131. Ed. Leigh-Ellen Clark. illus. circ. 25,000. **Document type:** academic/scholarly publication.

TECHNICAL COMMUNICATION. see COMMUNICATIONS

070 UK ISSN 0959-7808
TEES VALLEY WRITER. 1990. s-a. £1.90 (foreign £3.30). 57 the Avenue, Linthorpe, Middlesbrough, Cleveland TS5 6QU, England. TEL 0642-819102. Ed. Derek Gregory. adv.; bk.rev. circ. 1,000.
Description: Provides an outlet for creative writers from the Northeast.

070 SZ
TELEX. 6/yr. Churfirstenweg 22, CH-8200 Schaffhausen, Switzerland. TEL 053-247588. Ed. Martin Edlin. circ. 6,995.

070 US ISSN 1053-900X
TEXT TECHNOLOGY. 1991. q. $72. Dakota State University, Madison, SD 57042. TEL 605-256-5270. Ed. Eric Johnson. bk.rev. circ. 800. **Document type:** academic/scholarly publication.
Description: Publishes articles and reviews on computer applications to communications, and text analysis.

THEATRE RECORD. see THEATER

TITRA; le journal des journaux africains. see GENERAL INTEREST PERIODICALS — Africa

070 TZ ISSN 0856-0595
TORCH (DAR ES SALAAM). (Text in English) 1975. m. free. Tanzania School of Journalism, Box 4067, Dar es Salaam, Tanzania. TELEX 41344-MASCOMTZ-TZ. adv.; bk.rev. circ. 5,000.
Formerly (until 1978): Tanzanian Journalist.

TRAVEL JOURNALIST/JOURNALISTE DE TOURISME. see TRAVEL AND TOURISM

070.48 910 US
TRAVEL WRITER. 1959. 10/yr. membership. Society of American Travel Writers, 1155 Connecticut Ave., Ste. 500, Washington, DC 20036. TEL 202-429-6639. circ. 1,000. (looseleaf format)

808.02 910 US ISSN 0738-9094
TRAVELWRITER MARKETLETTER. 1979. m. $60 (foreign $70). At the Waldorf-Astoria, Ste. 1850, New York, NY 10022. TEL 212-759-6744. FAX 212-758-9209. Ed. Robert Scott Milne. bk.rev. circ. 1,000. **Document type:** newsletter.
—CCC.
Description: Marketing information for travel writers and photographers. Includes information on free trips for professionals.

070 028.5 GW
TREFFPUNKT JUGENDPRESSE. 1960. s-a. Junge Presse Koeln Arbeitsgemeinschaft, Postfach 420390, 50897 Cologne, Germany. TEL 0221-835852. FAX 0221-835852. Ed. Thomas Roessler. adv.; bk.rev.; film rev.; play rev.; bibl.; charts; illus.; stat. circ. 500. **Document type:** bulletin.

070 370 US
LB3620
TRENDS IN COLLEGE MEDIA. 1921. 3/yr. $12. National Scholastic Press Association, 620 Rarig Center, 330 21st Ave. S., University of Minnesota, Minneapolis, MN 55455. TEL 612-625-8335. FAX 612-626-0720. (Co-sponsor: Associated College Press) Ed. Tom E. Rolnicki. adv.; bk.rev.; charts; illus.; index. circ. 2,300. (processed; also avail. in microform from UMI; reprint service avail. from UMI)
Supersedes in part: Scholastic Editor's Trends in Publications (ISSN 0745-2357); Former titles (until 1982): Scholastic Editor; (until Sep. 1975): Scholastic Editor Graphics - Communications (ISSN 0036-6390)

070 370 US ISSN 1046-2155
LB3621.5
TRENDS IN HIGH SCHOOL MEDIA. 4/yr. $15. National Scholastic Press Association, 620 Rarig Center, 330 21st Ave. S., University of Minnesota, Minneapolis, MN 55455. TEL 612-625-8335. FAX 612-626-0720.
—UMI.
Supersedes in part: Scholastic Editor's Trends in Publications (ISSN 0745-2357)

070 AA
TRIBUNA E GAZETARIT. 1964. bi-m. $14. Bashkimi i Gazetareve te Shqiperise - Union of Journalists of Albania, Punetoret e Rilindjes St., Tirana, Albania. TEL 27977.

JOURNALISM

070   IT
TRIBUNA STAMPA. 1965. m. (9/yr.). L.30000 (foreign L.50000) (effective 1994). Tribuna Stampa Cooperativa Giornalisti, Via Egadi 3-5, 20144 Milan, Italy. TEL 2-4693495. Ed. Jole Zangari. adv. contact: Luigi Madia. bk.rev. circ. 32,000. **Document type:** newspaper.

THE TYNDALL REPORT. see COMMUNICATIONS — Television And Cable

070   UK   ISSN 0041-5170
U K PRESS GAZETTE; journalism's newspaper. 1965. w. £53.75. Maclean Hunter Ltd., Maclean Hunter House, Chalk Lane, Cockfosters Rd., Barnet, Herts EN4 0BU, England. TEL 081-243-3000. FAX 081-242-3185. Ed. T. Loynes. adv.; bk.rev.; charts; illus. circ. 9,283. **Document type:** newspaper. Incorporates (1990): Magazine Week (UK).

U S B W A TIP-OFF. (United States Basketball Writers Association) see SPORTS AND GAMES — Ball Games

070.48 796.93   US
U S SKI WRITERS ASSOCIATION NEWSLETTER. 1963. bi-m. membership. United States Ski Writers Association, 7 Kensington Rd., Glens Falls, NY 12801. TEL 518-793-1201. circ. 400.
    Description: News of interest to ski journalist members.

070   SP
UNIVERSIDAD DE NAVARRA. FACULTAD DE CIENCIAS DE LA INFORMACION. COLECCION DE TRABAJO. 1964. irreg., no.56, 1990. price varies. Ediciones Universidad de Navarra, S.A., Apdo. 396, 31080 Pamplona, Spain. TEL 94 825 6850.

070   SP   ISSN 0078-8783
UNIVERSIDAD DE NAVARRA. FACULTAD DE CIENCIAS DE LA INFORMACION. MANUALES: PERIODISMO. 1967. irreg., no.13, 1988. price varies. Ediciones Universidad de Navarra, S.A., Apdo. 396, 31080 Pamplona, Spain. TEL 94 825 6850.

070   US   ISSN 0077-6378
UNIVERSITY OF NEBRASKA. SCHOOL OF JOURNALISM. DEPTH REPORT. 1961. a. free. University of Nebraska, Lincoln, College of Journalism, Lincoln, NE 68508. TEL 402-472-3047. Ed. Daryl Frazell. circ. 2,500.

070   XO   ISSN 0083-422X
UNIVERZITA KOMENSKEHO. FILOZOFICKA FAKULTA. ZBORNIK: ZURNALISTIKA. (Text in Slovak; summaries in German and Russian) 1968. irreg. exchange basis. Univerzita Komenskeho, Filozoficka Fakulta, c/o Ustredna Kniznica Filozofickej Fakulty, Gondova 2, 818 01 Bratislava, Slovakia. Ed. Lubos Sefcak. circ. 600. **Document type:** academic/scholarly publication.

070 800   US   ISSN 0709-4698
PN5124.P4
VICTORIAN PERIODICALS REVIEW. 1968. q. $18 to individuals (foreign $22); institutions $23 (foreign $27). (Research Society for Victorian Periodicals) University Press of Colorado, Box 849, Niwot, CO 80544. TEL 303-530-5337. FAX 303-530-5306. (Editorial addr.: c/o Clark College, 1800 E. McLoughlin Blvd., Vancouver, WA 98663. TEL 206-699-0217. FAX 206-690-7149) Ed. Richard D. Fulton. adv.; bk.rev.; stat. circ. 650. (also avail. in microfilm from UMI; reprint service avail. from UMI) **Indexed:** Amer.Hist.& Life, Amer.Hum.Ind., Hist.Abstr., M.L.A. **Document type:** academic/scholarly publication.
—Faxon; UnCover; UMI.
    Formerly: Victorian Periodicals Newsletter (ISSN 0049-6189)

070   US   ISSN 0887-5227
VIRGINIA'S PRESS. 1918. w. $20 to non-members. Virginia Press Association, Inc., Box 85613, Richmond, VA 23285-5613. TEL 804-550-2361. FAX 804-550-2407. Ed. Ray Hall. adv.; bk.rev.; illus. circ. 894. **Document type:** newsletter.
    Formerly: Virginia Publisher and Printer (ISSN 0042-6741)

320.9 051   US   ISSN 0042-742X
PN6121
VITAL SPEECHES OF THE DAY. 1934. s-m. $37.50 (foreign $42). City News Publishing Co. Inc., Box 1247, Mt. Pleasant, SC 29465-1247. TEL 803-881-8733. FAX 803-881-4007. Ed. Thomas F. Daly III. index, cum.index: 1934-1959; 1960-1984. circ. 14,000. (also avail. in microfilm from PMC; microfiche from PMC) **Indexed:** ABI Inform., Acad.Ind., BPIA, Bus.Ind., Fut.Surv., Hlth.Ind., Mag.Ind., Manage.Cont., Mid.East: Abstr.& Ind., Pers.Lit., PMR, PSI, R.G., TOM. **Document type:** academic/scholarly publication, newsletter.
—BLDSC (9241.855000); Faxon; UnCover; SWETS; UMI.

070   II
VRITTA VIDYA; experimental journal. (Text in English and Marathi) 1965. bi-m. free. University of Poona, Department of Communication and Journalism, Ranade Institute, Poona 411 004, India. Ed. P.N. Paranjpe. adv.; bk.rev.; film rev.; play rev. circ. 600. (tabloid format)

070   XO
VYBER. 1968. w. $78. Union of Slovak Journalists, Oktobrove nam. 7, 814 76 Bratislava, Slovakia. TEL 42-7-316640. FAX 42-7-334534. Ed. Igor Slobodnik. circ. 25,000. **Indexed:** Sci.Abstr.

070   US   ISSN 0043-0684
WASHINGTON NEWSPAPER. 1914. bi-m. $8 to non-member Washington residents; others $10. Washington Newspaper Publishers Association, Inc., 3838 Stone Way North, Seattle, WA 98103. TEL 206-634-3838. FAX 206-634-3842. Ed. Diana Kramer. adv.; tr.lit. circ. 700. **Document type:** newspaper.

WASHINGTON STATE UNIVERSITY DAILY EVERGREEN. see COLLEGE AND ALUMNI

070   US
WEST VIRGINIA FOURTH ESTATESMAN. 1941. q. West Virginia University, School of Journalism, 112 Martin Hall, Box 6010, Morgantown, WV 26506-6010. TEL 304-293-3505. FAX 304-293-3505. Ed. Emery L. Sasser. circ. 3,400 (controlled). **Document type:** newsletter.

WEST WORD. see LITERATURE

WHO'S WHO OF AUSTRALIAN WRITERS. see BIOGRAPHY

WILLIAM WINTER COMMENTS; a twice monthly personal newsletter on current world affairs. see POLITICAL SCIENCE — International Relations

WOMEN'S WRITING; the early modern period. see WOMEN'S STUDIES

070   US
WORD UP! (WASHINGTON). q. African American Writers Guild, Box 43874, Columbia Sta., Washington, DC 20010. TEL 202-678-8462. **Document type:** newsletter.

070.43   II
WORKING JOURNALIST. (Text in English) 1955. m. Rs.12. Indian Federation of Working Journalists, Fl. 101, M.S. Apt., Kasturba Gandhi Marg, New Delhi 110001, India. TEL 384956. Ed. K. Vikram Rao. adv.; bk.rev. circ. 25,000.

070   US   ISSN 0084-1323
Z6951
WORKING PRESS OF THE NATION. (Issued in 4 vols.: Vol.1 The Newspaper Directory, Vol.2 The Magazine and Internal Publications Directory, Vol.3 The Radio and Television Directory, Vol.4 The Feature Writers, Photographers, and Professional Speakers Directory) 1949. a. $385. National Register Publishing, A Reed Reference Publishing Company, Part of the Reed Elsevier group, 121 Chanlon Rd., NJ 07974. TEL 908-464-6800. FAX 908-665-6688. TELEX 138 755. (Subscr. to: Order Dept., Box 31, New Providence, NJ 07974-9903. TEL 800-521-8110) (also avail. in magnetic tape) **Document type:** directory.
    Description: Provides the names of writers, reporters, editors and executives, as well as phone numbers, materials requirements, deadlines, and more for newspapers, magazines, TV, and radio.

808.02 011   US   ISSN 1065-335X
WORLD LEADER UPDATE. 1990. q. $25. MinRef Press, 8379 Langtree Way, Sacramento, CA 95823-5645. TEL 916-424-8465. Ed. Rick Lawler.
    Formerly: How to Write to World Leaders.
    Description: Provides information on how to contact world leaders. Gives profiles of world leaders, information on new nations, environmental action alerts and listings of global organizations.

070   AU
WORLD PRESS FREEDOM REVIEW. 1952. a. International Press Institute, Spiegelgasse 2-29, A-1010 Vienna, Austria. TEL 01-5129011. FAX 01-5129014. (Subscr. to: International Press Institute, Wydlerweg 10, CH-8047 Zurich, Switzerland) **Document type:** trade publication.
    Former titles: Annual Review of World Press Freedom; International Press Institute. Survey (ISSN 0085-2198)

070   UK
WORLD PRESS JOURNAL.* q. £25. Johnsons Publishing Ltd., Grayson House, 12-16 Clerkenwell Rd., London EC1M 5PQ, England. Ed. Leonard Stall.
    Description: Presents information for international publishing executives and general readers who are interested in keeping up with trends, developments, and informed comment about the publishing and ancilliary trade.

WRITERS CONNECTION. see PUBLISHING AND BOOK TRADE

070 800   US   ISSN 0043-9525
PN101
WRITER'S DIGEST. 1920. m. $24. F & W Publications, Inc., 1507 Dana Ave., Cincinnati, OH 45207. TEL 513-531-2222. (Subscr. to: Box 2123, Harlan, IA 51593) Ed. Bruce Woods. adv.; bk.rev.; illus.; mkt.; index. circ. 247,640. (also avail. in microform from UMI,MIM; reprint service avail. from UMI) **Indexed:** Access (1979-), Ind.How To Do It (1990-), Mag.Ind., Pop.Per.Ind., R.G.
—BLDSC (9364.681000); Faxon; UnCover; UMI.
    Description: Provides "how-to" instruction, information and inspiration for people who love to write. Includes advice from bestselling authors, tips and techniques for creating better manuscripts, and information on how and where to sell fiction, nonfiction, poetry and scripts.

808.42   US   ISSN 1057-0756
WRITER'S FORUM (CINCINNATI). q. F & W Publications, Inc., 1507 Dana Ave., Cincinnati, OH 45207. TEL 513-531-2222. FAX 513-531-1843. Ed. Thomas Clark. **Document type:** newsletter.
    Formerly (until 1991): W D S Forum (ISSN 0275-9748)
    Description: For students of Writer's Digest School. Includes articles on how to improve your writing and marketing efforts, as well as notices of students' successes.

808.02   US   ISSN 1053-1793
WRITER'S GUIDELINES MAGAZINE; a roundtable for writers and editors. 1988. bi-m. $18. Salaki Publishing, Box 608, Pittsburg, MO 65724. TEL 417-993-5544. FAX 417-993-5544. Ed. Susan Salaki. adv.; bk.rev.; circ. 1,000 (paid). (back issues avail.) **Document type:** newsletter.
—CCC.
    Former titles: Guidelines Magazine (ISSN 1046-9184); Guidelines Newsletter.
    Description: Provides inspiration and support for writers and a guideline service in which 300 editors supply current guidelines.

WRITERS GUILD OF AMERICA, WEST. JOURNAL. see LITERATURE

070   US   ISSN 0891-8759
WRITERS' JOURNAL.* 1980. bi-m. $14.97 (foreign $36). Minnesota Ink, Inc., 3585 Lexington Ave. N, Ste. 328, St. Paul, MN 55126-8056. TEL 612-225-1306. Ed. Valerie Hockert. adv.; B&W page $845. bk.rev.; index. circ. 45,000. (back issues avail.; reprint service avail.)
    Incorporates (in 1990): Minnesota Ink; **Former titles:** Inkling Literary Journal; Inkling (ISSN 0734-7138)
    Description: Information, news, and practical advice for freelance writers, communicators, and consultants.

WRITERS NEWS. see LITERATURE

JOURNALISM — ABSTRACTING, BIBLIOGRAPHIES, STATISTICS

070   US   ISSN 0890-9504
WRITER'S NOOK NEWS. 1985. q. $18. Writer's Nook Press, 38114 Third St., Ste. 181, Willoughby, OH 44094. TEL 216-953-9292. FAX 216-354-6403. Ed. Eugene Ortiz. adv.; bk.rev.; index. circ. 1,000. **Document type:** newsletter.
     Description: Contains news and tips for working and aspiring writers.

WRITING (MIDDLETOWN); the continuing guide to written communication. see *LITERATURE*

070   US   ISSN 1050-4788
WRITING CONCEPTS; the newsletter on writing & editing. 1990. m. $77 (foreign $107). Communication Concepts, Inc., 2100 National Press Bldg., Ste. 202, Washington, DC 20045. TEL 703-425-7751. FAX 703-425-8930. (Subscr. to: Box 1608, Springfield, VA 22151-0608) **Document type:** newsletter.
     Description: Provides practical advice from peers for nonfiction writers and editors and addresses new problems they are facing.

808.02   US
XIE ZUO/WRITING. (Text in Chinese) m. $36.80. China Books & Periodicals, Inc., 2929 24th St., San Francisco, CA 94110. TEL 415-282-2994. FAX 415-282-0994.

070   CC
XINWEN JIZHE/JOURNALISTS. (Text in Chinese) m. Shanghai Shehui Kexueyuan, Xinwen Yanjiusuo - Shanghai Academy of Social Sciences, Institute of Journalism, No. 20, Lane 18, Gao'an Road, Shanghai 200030, People's Republic of China. TEL 4337049. Ed. Wei Yongzheng.

070 808.02   CC
XINWEN XUEKAN. (Text in Chinese) bi-m. Y1.20 per no. (Zhongguo Xinwen Xuehui, Lianhehui) Xinwen Xuekan Bianjibu, 2, Jintai Xilu, Beijing, People's Republic of China. (Subscr. to: P.O. Box 8811, Beijing 100733, P.R.C.) (Co-sponsor: Zhongguo Shehui Kexueyuan, Xinwen Yanjiusuo) Ed. Qian Xinbo.
     Description: Examines issues related to journalism and the news media.

070   CC
XINWEN YANJIU ZILIAO/JOURNALISM RESEARCH MATERIALS. (Text in Chinese) q. Zhongguo Shehui Kexueyuan, Xinwen Yanjiusuo - Chinese Academy of Social Sciences, Institute of Journalism, 2, Jintan Xilu, Beixiang, Bldg. No. 9, Beijing 100026, People's Republic of China. TEL 5022868. Ed. Yan Huanshu. **Document type:** academic/scholarly publication.

070   CC
XINWEN YU CHENGCAI. (Text in Chinese) m. Jiefangjun Baoshe, 34, Fuchengmenwai Dajie, Beijing 100832, People's Republic of China. TEL 6846991. Ed. Yuan Liang.

070   CC
XINWEN YU XIEZUO/JOURNALISM AND WRITING. (Text in Chinese) m. Beijing Ribao - Beijing Daily, 34, Biaobei Hutong, Dongdan, Beijing 100734, People's Republic of China. TEL 546218. Ed. Qi Shoucheng.

070 796   CC   ISSN 0257-5930
XINWEN ZHANXIAN. (Text in Chinese) m. Y12($36.80). People's Daily Publishing House - Renmin Ribao Chubanshe, 2, Jintai Xilu, Chaoyang Menwai, Beijing 100733, People's Republic of China. (Dist. outside China by: China International Book Trading Corp., P.O. Box 2820, Beijing, P.R.C.; Dist. in US by: China Books & Periodicals, Inc., 2929 24th St., San Francisco, CA 94110. TEL 415-272-2994) Ed. Cao Xianwen. adv.

070   CC
XINWENJIE/PRESS CIRCLES. (Text in Chinese) bi-m. Sichuan Daily, Sichuan Ribaoshe, Hongxing Zhonglu Erduan (Sec. 2), Chengdu, Sichuan 610012, People's Republic of China. TEL 667450. (Co-sponsor: Sichuan Journalists Association)

070   GR
YEARBOOK OF GREEK PRESS. 1965. a. free. Secretariat General of Press and Information, Zalokosta 10, Athens, Greece. Ed.Bd. index. circ. 2,000. (tabloid format)

070   CC
ZHONGGUO JIZHE/CHINESE JOURNALIST. (Text in Chinese) m. $42.20. Xinhua Tongxunshe - Xinhua News Agency, 57 Xuanwumen Xidajie, Beijing 100803, People's Republic of China. TEL 3073780. (Dist. in US by: China Books & Periodicals, Inc., 2929 24th St., San Francisco, CA 94110. TEL 415-282-2994) Ed. Yu Zhenpeng.

070   RU   ISSN 0022-5568
ZHURNALIST. 1920. m. $80. (Soyuz Zhurnalistov) Zhurnalist, Bumazhny pre. 14, 101453 Moscow, Russia. TEL 095-257-3058. FAX 095-257-3589. (Dist. in U.S. by: Victor Kamkin Inc., 4956 Boiling Brook Pkwy, Rockville, MD 20852. TEL 301-881-5973) Ed. D.S. Avraamov. adv. contact: S.B. Dubisnkaya. bk.rev.; abstr.; bibl.; illus.; stat. circ. 10,000. **Indexed:** Curr.Dig.Sov.Press.
     Supersedes (in 1967): Sovetskaya Pechat'

070   GW   ISSN 0179-762X
ZIMPEL. TEIL 1: ZEITUNGEN. m. Verlag Dieter Zimpel, Angererstr. 36, 80796 Munich, Germany. TEL 089-2722356. FAX 089-302409. Ed. Ingrid Finsterwald. **Document type:** directory.
     Formerly (until 1986): Deutschen Vollredaktionen. Teil 1. Zeitungen (ISSN 0173-1033)

070 296 956.940   IS
ZSHURNALIST. (Text in Yiddish) 1974. irreg. World Federation of Jewish Journalists, P.O. Box 7009, Tel Aviv 64734, Israel. (Co-sponsor: World Zionist Organization. Information Department)

070   US
10 BEST CENSORED STORIES. 1976. a. free with SASE. Project Censored, Sonoma State University, Rohnert Park, CA 94928. TEL 707-664-2500. FAX 707-664-2505.
     Description: Top 10 censored stories of the previous year are capsulized. A combination of journalism review and bibliographic listing, and an innovative approach to constructive media criticism.

JOURNALISM — Abstracting, Bibliographies, Statistics

A B C NEWS INDEX. see *COMMUNICATIONS — Abstracting, Bibliographies, Statistics*

011   UA   ISSN 0303-2728
AL-AHRAM INDEX/KASHSHAF AL-AHRAM. (Text in Arabic) 1974. m. $100 in N. America (effective 1994). Mu'assasat al-Ahram, Sharia al-Galaa, Cairo, Egypt. TEL 02-758333. FAX 02-745888. TELEX 20185 AHRAM UN. (In N. America: Al-Ahram International, 405 Lexington Ave., New York, NY 10174. TEL 212-972-6440. FAX 212-286-0285) Ed. Muhammed M. Daoud. adv. circ. 300. (also avail. in microfilm) **Document type:** abstracting/indexing.
     Description: Index analysis of every item (articles, news) of Al-Ahram daily newspaper.

070   AU
AUSTRIAN JOURNALISTS INDEX; lists 8200 journalists. (Text in German) 1983. s-a. S.980($94) Presseverlag Wien, Frimmelgasse 41, A-1190 Vienna, Austria. TEL 01-371577. FAX 01-374693. Ed. Peter Hoffer. adv.; index. circ. 1,200. (back issues avail.) **Document type:** abstracting/indexing.

070   US   ISSN 0893-2727
BOSTON GLOBE INDEX. a. $860. University Microfilms International, 300 N. Zeeb Rd., Ann Arbor, MI 48106. TEL 313-761-4700; 800-521-0600. FAX 313-761-1203. **Document type:** abstracting/indexing.
     ●Also available online. Vendor(s): DIALOG Information Services, Inc. (file no. 484).

CALIFORNIA NEWSPAPER PUBLISHERS ASSOCIATION. DIRECTORY AND RATE BOOK. see *JOURNALISM*

070 011   US   ISSN 0893-245X
AI21.C462
CHRISTIAN SCIENCE MONITOR INDEX. 1945. m. (plus q. & a. cumulations). $375. University Microfilms International, 300 N. Zeeb Rd., Ann Arbor, MI 48106-1346. TEL 313-761-4700; 800-521-0600. FAX 313-761-1203. **Indexed:** Bk.Rev.Ind., Bus.Ind., Child.Bk.Rev.Ind., Tr.& Indus.Ind. **Document type:** abstracting/indexing.
     ●Also available online. Vendor(s): DIALOG Information Services, Inc.
     Former titles: Index to the Christian Science Monitor (ISSN 0098-1184); Christian Science Monitor. Cumulated Index (ISSN 0578-0152)

070.172   UK
CLOVER NEWSPAPER INDEX. 1986. 46/yr. £172 (foreign £295). Clover Publications, 32 Ickwell Rd., Northill, Biggleswade, Beds. SG18 9AB, England. TEL 0767-627363. **Document type:** abstracting/indexing.
     Description: Indexes articles from daily and Sunday newspapers.

070 011   MX
COLEGIO DE MEXICO. BIBLIOTECA. LISTA DE OBRAS EN CANJE. PUBLICACIONES PERIODICAS. 1973. q. free. Colegio de Mexico, Biblioteca, Camino al Ajusco 20, Mexico 20, D.F., Mexico. FAX 645-45-84. bibl. circ. 300. **Document type:** bibliography.

CURRENT DIGEST OF THE POST-SOVIET PRESS. see *POLITICAL SCIENCE — Abstracting, Bibliographies, Statistics*

070 915.2   JA
DAILY SUMMARY OF THE JAPANESE PRESS. d. Embassy of the United States in Japan, 1-10-5 Akasaka, Minato-ku, Tokyo, Japan. (also avail. in microfilm)

011   DK   ISSN 0106-147X
DANSK ARTIKELINDEKS: AVISER OG TIDSSKRIFTER/DANISH INDEX OF ARTICLES: NEWSPAPERS AND PERIODICALS. 1940. m. (plus a. cum.). DKK 8570. Dansk BiblioteksCenter as, Tempovej 7-11, DK-2750 Ballerup, Denmark. TEL 45-44-97-40-00. FAX 45-44-68-24-42. bibl.; index. circ. 300. (back issues avail.)
     ●Also available online.
     Formed by the merger of: Avis-Kronik-Index (ISSN 0005-2280); Dansk Tidsskrift Index.

070   DK   ISSN 0109-0968
DANSK FAGPRESSEKATALOG. 1984. a. DKK 225. Dansk Fagpresse Service ApS, Sommerstedgade 7, 1718 Copenhagen V, Denmark. circ. 4,329.
     Description: Gives facts on media data, prices, sizes, circulation and members per year.

070   US   ISSN 0893-2441
AI21.D44
DENVER POST INDEX. 1979. m. (plus q. & a. cumulations). $680. University Microfilms International, 300 N. Zeeb Rd., Ann Arbor, MI 48106-1346. TEL 313-761-4700; 800-521-0600. FAX 313-761-1203. **Document type:** abstracting/indexing.
     ●Also available online. Vendor(s): DIALOG Information Services, Inc.
     Formerly: Index to the Denver Post (ISSN 0195-6434)

070 011   US   ISSN 0893-2433
AI21.D46
DETROIT NEWS INDEX. 1976. m. (plus q. & a. cumulations). $680. University Microfilms International, 300 N. Zeeb Rd., Ann Arbor, MI 48106-1346. TEL 313-761-4700; 800-521-0600. FAX 313-761-1203. **Document type:** abstracting/indexing.
     ●Also available online. Vendor(s): DIALOG Information Services, Inc.
     Former titles: Index to the Detroit News; Detroit News. Newspaper Index (ISSN 0361-6983)

071 016   US   ISSN 0013-0966
D839
EDITORIALS ON FILE; newspaper editorial reference service with index. 1970. s-m. $365. Facts on File Inc., 460 Park Ave. S., New York, NY 10016. TEL 212-683-2244. Ed. Oliver Trager. cum.index. circ. 1,500. (looseleaf format; also avail. in microfiche)
     Description: Covers the top eight to twelve stories of the day and furnishes a selection of editorial cartoons.

JOURNALISM — ABSTRACTING, BIBLIOGRAPHIES, STATISTICS

070 016 FR
FICHIERS-PRESSE. 1971. 5/yr. price varies for each category. Argus des Fichiers Presse, 19 bd. Montmartre, 75002 Paris, France. TEL 40-20-02-59. FAX 42-86-04-61. Ed. Stephanie Duriez. (looseleaf format) **Document type:** directory.

070 JM ISSN 0259-0336
GLEANER INDEX. 1975. q. $101. National Library of Jamaica, 12 East St., P.O. Box 823, Kingston, Jamaica, W.I. TEL 809-92-20620. FAX 809-92-25567. TELEX 596. Ed. Valerie G. Francis. circ. 35. **Document type:** abstracting/indexing.
  Formerly: Airs - Index to the Daily Gleaner.
  Description: Personal name and subject index of articles of political, social, economic or cultural significance to Jamaica and the West Indies, appearing in the Gleaner.

070 CC
GUANGMING RIBAO SUOYIN/INDEX TO THE GUANGMING RIBAO. (Text in Chinese) m. $21.50. Guangming Ribao Chubanshe, 106, Yong'an Lu, Beijing 100050, People's Republic of China. (Dist. outside China by: China International Book Trading Corp., P.O. Box 2820, Beijing, P.R.C.; Dist. in US by: China Books & Periodicals, Inc., 2929 24th St., San Francisco, CA 94110. TEL 415-282-2994) **Document type:** abstracting/indexing.

070 011 US ISSN 0893-2476
AI21.H68
HOUSTON POST INDEX. 1976. m. (plus q. & a. cumulations). $680. University Microfilms International, 300 N. Zeeb Rd., Ann Arbor, MI 48106-1346. TEL 313-761-4700; 800-521-0600. FAX 313-761-1203. **Document type:** abstracting/indexing.
  ●Also available online. Vendor(s): DIALOG Information Services, Inc.
  Former titles: Index to the Houston Post; Houston Post. Newspaper Index (ISSN 0363-7824)

011 MY ISSN 0126-9062
AI3
INDEKS SURATKHABAR MALAYSIA. English edition: Malaysian Newspaper Index (ISSN 0127-7448) (Text in Bahasa Malaysia) 1979. q. M.$30 (foreign M.$40) per no. National Library of Malaysia, Bibliography and Indexing Division, 1st Fl., East Block, 232 Jalan Tun Razak, 50572 Kuala Lumpur, Malaysia. TEL 2922144. FAX 03-2927899. (Subscr. to: University of Malaya Co-operative Bookshop Ltd., Library Building, University of Malaya, 59100 Kuala Lumpur, Malaysia) Ed. Zahariah Sharoon. circ. 160. **Document type:** abstracting/indexing.
  Description: Covers all significant news items pertaining to Malaysia.

070 US ISSN 0741-5281
AI21.B63
INDEX TO THE BOSTON GLOBE. 1983. m. (plus a. cumulation). $860. University Microfilms International, 300 N. Zeeb Rd., Ann Arbor, MI 48106. TEL 313-761-4700; 800-521-2128. FAX 313-761-1203. **Document type:** abstracting/indexing.
  ●Also available online. Vendor(s): DIALOG Information Services, Inc. (File no. 484).

011 US
INDEX TO THE NATIONAL OBSERVER. irreg. University Microfilms International, 300 N. Zeeb Rd., Ann Arbor, MI 48106-1346. TEL 313-761-4700; 800-521-0600. FAX 313-761-1203. (back issues avail.) **Document type:** abstracting/indexing.
  Formerly: National Observer Newspaper Index (ISSN 0363-7832)

011 US
INDEX TO THE ST. PAUL PIONEER PRESS. 1967. m. (plus a. cumulation). $212 to non tax-exempt organizations. St. Paul Public Library, 90 W. Fourth St., St. Paul, MN 55102. TEL 612-292-6306. FAX 612-292-6141. Ed. Norman Lathrop. bk.rev. circ. 36. (looseleaf format; back issues avail.) **Document type:** abstracting/indexing.
  Former titles: Index to the St. Paul Pioneer Press and Dispatch; St. Paul Dispatch and Pioneer Press Newspaper Index (ISSN 0048-900X)

954 015 II ISSN 0019-6177
AI3
INDIAN PRESS INDEX. (Text in English) 1968. m. Rs.300($70) Delhi Library Association, Box 1270, c/o Hardinge Public Library, Queen's Gardens, New Delhi 6, India. Ed. Shri C.P. Vashisth. index. **Document type:** abstracting/indexing.

070 US
JIEFANG RIBAO HEDINGBEN/LIBERATION DAILY BOUND INDEX. (Text in Chinese) m. $402.40. China Books & Periodicals, Inc., 2929 24th St., San Francisco, CA 94110. TEL 415-282-2994. FAX 415-282-0994. **Document type:** abstracting/indexing.
  Formerly: Jiefang Ribao Suoyin Hedingben.

070 016 US ISSN 0075-4412
PN4725
JOURNALISM ABSTRACTS; M.A., M.S., and Ph.D. theses in journalism and mass communication. 1963. a. $15 to individuals (foreign $25); institutions $20 (foreign $30). Association for Education in Journalism and Mass Communication, 1621 College St., University of South Carolina, Columbia, SC 29208-0251. TEL 803-777-2005. Ed. Gilbert Fowler. circ. 700. (also avail. in microform from UMI; reprint service avail. from UMI) **Document type:** abstracting/indexing.
  —UMI.

070 011 US ISSN 0742-4817
AI21.L65
LOS ANGELES TIMES INDEX. 1972. m. (plus q. & a. cumulations). $680. University Microfilms International, 300 N. Zeeb Rd., Ann Arbor, MI 48106-1346. TEL 313-761-4700; 800-521-0600. FAX 313-761-1203. **Indexed:** Art & Archaeol.Tech.Abstr., Bus.Ind., Med.Care Rev. **Document type:** abstracting/indexing.
  ●Also available online. Vendor(s): DIALOG Information Services, Inc.
  Former titles: Index to the Los Angeles Times (ISSN 0195-6418); Los Angeles Times. Newspaper Index (ISSN 0098-1192)

070 GW ISSN 0170-4192
Z6956.G3
MEDIA DATEN: FACHZEITSCHRIFTEN. 7/yr. DM.650. Media Daten Verlag GmbH, Klingenweg 4, 65396 Walluf, Germany. TEL 06123-700-0. **Document type:** directory.
  —SWETS.

070 GW ISSN 0170-4176
Z6956.G3
MEDIA DATEN: ZEITSCHRIFTEN. 7/yr. DM.650. Media Daten Verlag GmbH, Klingenweg 4, 65396 Walluf, Germany. TEL 06123-700-0. **Document type:** directory.
  —SWETS.

070 GW ISSN 0931-3265
MEDIA DATEN: ZEITUNGEN. (Text in German) 1961. 7/yr. DM.650. Media Daten Verlag Gmbh, Klingenweg 4, 6229 Walluf, Germany. TEL 06123-700-0. adv. circ. 2,580. **Document type:** directory.
  Formerly: Media Daten (ISSN 0038-951X)

011 UK ISSN 0953-7171
AI21
LE MONDE INDEX. (Text in French) m. £360. Research Publications International Ltd., P.O. Box 45, Reading RG1 8HF, England. TEL 0734-583247. FAX 0734-591325. (Dist. in the Americas by: Research Publications Inc., 12 Lunar Dr., Drawer AB, Woodbridge, CT 06525. TEL 203-397-2600) **Document type:** abstracting/indexing.
  ●Also available on CD-ROM.

MONTHLY INDEX TO THE FINANCIAL TIMES. see BUSINESS AND ECONOMICS — Abstracting, Bibliographies, Statistics

NATIONAL NEWSPAPER INDEX. see ABSTRACTING AND INDEXING SERVICES

070 011 US ISSN 0893-2484
AI21.T66
NEW ORLEANS TIMES - PICAYUNE INDEX. 1972. m. (plus q. & a. cumulations). $680. University Microfilms International, 300 N. Zeeb Rd., Ann Arbor, MI 48106-1346. TEL 313-761-4700; 800-521-0600. FAX 313-761-1203. **Document type:** abstracting/indexing.
  Former titles: Index to the New Orleans Times-Picayune (ISSN 0195-640X); New Orleans Times-Picayune. Newspaper Index (ISSN 0098-1206)

070 US ISSN 0147-538X
AI21
NEW YORK TIMES INDEX. 1913. s-m. (plus 3 q. & a. cumulations). $995 for s-m., q., & a; s-m. $650; a. $690 (includes New York Times Index Highlights). (New York Times Company) University Microfilms International, 300 N. Zeeb Rd., Ann Arbor, MI 48106. TEL 313-761-4700; 800-521-0600. FAX 313-761-1203. **Document type:** abstracting/indexing.
  ●Also available online.
  Also available on CD-ROM.

070 016 US
NEW YORK TIMES INDEX HIGHLIGHTS. 1977. q. free to New York Times Index subscribers. (New York Times Company) University Microfilms International, 300 N. Zeeb Rd., Ann Arbor, MI 48106. TEL 313-761-4700; 800-521-0600. FAX 313-761-1203.

OFFICIAL INDEX TO THE FINANCIAL TIMES. see BUSINESS AND ECONOMICS — Abstracting, Bibliographies, Statistics

011 UK
OFFICIAL INDEX TO THE INDEPENDENT. m. £420. Research Publications International Ltd., P.O. Box 45, Reading RG1 8HF, England. TEL 0734-583247. FAX 0734-591325. (Dist. in the Americas by: Research Publications Inc., 12 Lunar Dr., Drawer AB, Woodbridge, CT 06525. TEL 203-397-2600) **Document type:** abstracting/indexing.
  ●Also available on CD-ROM.

070 PP
P N G POST-COURIER INDEX. 1972. a. price varies. National Research Institute, P.O. Box 5854, Boroko, NCD, Papua New Guinea. TEL 675-26-0300. FAX 675-26-0312. **Document type:** abstracting/indexing.

070 PP
P N G TIMES INDEX. 1980. irreg. price varies. National Research Institute, P.O. Box 5854, Boroko, NCD, Papua New Guinea. TEL 675-26-0300. FAX 675-26-0312. **Document type:** abstracting/indexing.

P O M P I. (Popular Music Periodicals Index) see MUSIC — Abstracting, Bibliographies, Statistics

PROGRESSIVE PERIODICALS DIRECTORY. see PUBLISHING AND BOOK TRADE — Abstracting, Bibliographies, Statistics

070 CC
RENMIN RIBAO SUOYIN/PEOPLE'S DAILY. INDEX. (Text in Chinese) m. $32.30. People's Daily Publishing House - Renmin Ribao Chubanshe, 2 Jintai Xilu, Chaoyangmenwai, Beijing 100733, People's Republic of China. (Dist. in US by: China Books & Periodicals, Inc., 2929 24th St., San Francisco, CA 94019. TEL 415-282-0994) **Document type:** abstracting/indexing.

070 US
THE RUNDOWN. 1981. w. $325. Standish Publishing Co., P.O. Box 335, Ardmore, PA 19003. TEL 215-664-3322. FAX 215-667-5148. Ed. Kim Standish. circ. 400. (looseleaf format) **Document type:** newsletter.
  Description: Reports on trends in local television news and information programming and on television news management issues.

070   US   ISSN 0893-2417
AI21.S79
ST. LOUIS POST - DISPATCH INDEX. Variant title: Index to the St. Louis Post-Dispatch. 1980. m. (plus q. & a. cum.). $680. University Microfilms International, 300 N. Zeeb Rd., Ann Arbor, MI 48106-1346. TEL 313-761-4700; 800-521-0600. FAX 313-761-1203. **Document type:** abstracting/indexing.
  Formerly: Bell & Howell Newspaper Index to the St. Louis Post-Dispatch (ISSN 0275-858X)

070 011   US   ISSN 0893-2425
AI21.S25
SAN FRANCISCO CHRONICLE INDEX. 1976. m. (plus q. & a. cumulations). $680. University Microfilms International, 300 N. Zeeb Rd., Ann Arbor, MI 48106-1346. TEL 313-761-4700; 800-521-0600. FAX 313-761-1203. **Document type:** abstracting/indexing.
  Former titles: Index to the San Francisco Chronicle (ISSN 0195-6396); San Francisco Chronicle. Newspaper Index (ISSN 0363-7816)

011   MF
SUBJECT INDEX TO ARTICLES IN NEWSPAPERS IN MAURITIUS. Cover title: Newspapers Index: Mauritius. (Text in English) publication begun and suspended 1978; resumed 1983. s-a. City Library, City Hall, Port Louis, Mauritius.

948 011   FI   ISSN 0355-4074
SUOMEN SANOMALEHTIEN MIKROFILMIT/MICROFILMED NEWSPAPERS OF FINLAND. (Text in English, Finnish, Swedish) 1971. quinquennial. free. Helsingin Yliopiston Kirjasto - Helsinki University Library, Box 15, Unioninkatu 36, SF-00014, University of Helsinki, Finland. circ. 300. **Document type:** bibliography.
  Description: Contains bibliographic data on Finnish newspapers microfilmed by Helsinki University Library.

011   UK
TIMES INDEX. 1906. m. £510. Research Publications International Ltd., P.O. Box 45, Reading RG1 8HF, England. TEL 0734-583247. FAX 0734-5912325. (Dist. in U.S. by: Research Publications Inc., 12 Lunar Dr., Drawer AB, Woodbridge, CT 06525) index. circ. 1,000. (also avail. in microfilm) **Indexed:** Ind.Bus.Rep. **Document type:** abstracting/indexing.
  Formerly: Index to the Times (ISSN 0046-8924)

070 011   US   ISSN 0041-1116
Z7403
TRANSDEX INDEX. Key Title: Transdex. Variant title: Bell and Howell Transdex. 1974. m. (plus microform a. cumulation). $885. University Microfilms International, Research Information Services, 300 N. Zeeb Rd., Ann Arbor, MI 48106-1346. TEL 313-761-4700; 800-521-0600. FAX 313-761-1203. **Document type:** abstracting/indexing.

070   US   ISSN 0893-2409
AI21.U8
U S A TODAY INDEX. 1982. m. (plus q. & a. cumulations). $265. University Microfilms International, 300 N. Zeeb Rd., Ann Arbor, MI 48106-1346. TEL 313-761-4700; 800-521-0600. FAX 313-761-1203. **Document type:** abstracting/indexing.
  Formerly: Index to USA Today (ISSN 0736-9999)

071   US   ISSN 1041-1534
AI21.W33
WASHINGTON POST INDEX. 1979. m. $895. University Microfilms International, 300 N. Zeeb Rd., Ann Arbor, MI 48106. TEL 313-761-4700; 800-521-0600. FAX 313-761-1203. **Document type:** abstracting/indexing.
  Supersedes (in 1989): Official Washington Post Index (ISSN 0193-9580)

WHO'S WHO IN WRITERS, EDITORS & POETS IN THE UNITED STATES & CANADA; a biographical directory. see LITERATURE — Abstracting, Bibliographies, Statistics

053 073 015   GW   ISSN 0340-0107
ZEITUNGS - INDEX; Verzeichnis wichtiger Aufsaetze aus deutschsprachigen Zeitungen. (Supplement: Buchrezensionen) 1974. q. DM.448. K.G. Saur Verlag KG (Subsidiary of: Reed Reference Publishing), Ortlerstr. 8, 81373 Munich, Germany. TEL 089-76902-0. FAX 089-76902150. TELEX 5212067-SAUR-D. (Subscr. to: Postfach 701620, 81316 Munich, Germany) Ed. Willi Gorzny. index. circ. 1,000. **Document type:** abstracting/indexing.
  ●Also available on CD-ROM.
  —CCC.
  Description: Indexes 19 German-language daily and weekly newspapers.

JUDAISM

see Religions and Theology—Judaic

JUDICIAL SYSTEMS

see Law—Judicial Systems

LABOR AND INDUSTRIAL RELATIONS

see Business and Economics—Labor and Industrial Relations

LABOR UNIONS

see also Business and Economics—Labor and Industrial Relations

331.8   US   ISSN 0001-009X
HD6856
A A L C REPORTER. (Editions in Arabic, English, French) 1965(English, French); 1977(Arabic). bi-m. free. African-American Labor Center, A F L - C I O, 1400 K St., Ste. 700, Washington, DC 20005. TEL 202-789-1020. FAX 202-842-0730. TELEX 710-822-1115. Ed. Mary Ann Forbes. illus.; cum.index: 1970-1974; 1975-1977; 1978-1980; 1981-84; 1985-89; circ. 3,850 (controlled). **Indexed:** HR Rep. **Document type:** newsletter.
  Description: Reports on the activities and policies of the center in its cooperative program with African labor movements to promote free and democratic labor.

331.8   BE   ISSN 0778-8762
A C W VISIE; weekblad van de christelijke arbeidersbeweging. Key Title: Visie. 1945. w. 1025 BEF (foreign 1130 BEF) (effective 1994). Algemeen Christelijk Werknemersverbond - Catholic Workers Movement, Wetstraat 121, B-1040 Brussels, Belgium. TEL 32-2-2373111. FAX 32-2-2373700. Ed. Leo Pauwels. bk.rev. circ. 1,118,800.
  Formerly (until 1992): Volksmacht (ISSN 0042-854X)

331.8 327   US   ISSN 0890-6165
A F L - C I O. DEPARTMENT OF INTERNATIONAL AFFAIRS. BULLETIN. m. American Federation of Labor - Congress of Industrial Organizations, Department of International Affairs, 815 16th St., N.W., Washington, DC 20006. Dir. Tom Kahn.

331.8   US
A F L - C I O CONVENTION PROCEEDINGS. 1955. biennial. $15. A F L - C I O, 815 16th St., N.W., Washington, DC 20006. TEL 202-637-5041. index. circ. 5,000. (back issues avail.) **Document type:** proceedings.

331.88   US   ISSN 0001-1185
A F L - C I O NEWS. 1956. bi-w. $10. American Federation of Labor - Congress of Industrial Organizations, 815 16th St., N.W., Washington, DC 20006. TEL 202-637-5010. FAX 202-637-5058. Ed. Michael Byrne. bk.rev.; illus. circ. 75,000. (tabloid format; also avail. in microform from UMI) **Indexed:** Med.Care Rev., Pers.Lit. **Document type:** newspaper.
  ●Also available online. Vendor(s): DIALOG Information Services, Inc.
  —UMI.

LABOR UNIONS 3199

331.88 370   US
A F T ISSUES BULLETIN. irreg. American Federation of Teachers, 555 New Jersey Ave., N.W., Washington, DC 20001. TEL 202-879-4400. (reprint service avail. from UMI)

331.88 384.5 US   ISSN 0044-7676
A F T R A. 1968. q. free. American Federation of Television and Radio Artists, 260 Madison Ave., 7th Fl., New York, NY 10016-2401. Ed. Dick Moore. adv.; bk.rev.; charts; illus. circ. 80,000.
  Formerly: American Federation of Television and Radio Artists. A F T R A.

791   US
A G V A NEWSLETTER.* 1958. irreg. membership. American Guild of Variety Artists, 184 Fifth Ave., New York, NY 10010. TEL 212-675-1003. adv.; bk.rev.; illus. circ. 16,500.
  Formerly: A G V A News (ISSN 0001-1371)

331.3   SP
A HOMBROS DE TRABAJADORES. m. Workers Union of Central Madrid, Juan de Austria 9, 28010 Madrid, Spain. TEL 91-4464290. Dir. Juan Gonzalez Castejon.

331.88 650   UK
A P E X. 1908. 6/yr. £5 (foreign £7). Association of Professional, Executive, Clerical and Computer Staff, 22 Worple Rd., Wimbledon, London SW19 4DF, England. Ed. Neil Hamilton. adv.; bk.rev.; abstr.; illus. circ. 60,000.
  Formerly: Clerk (ISSN 0009-8744)

331.88 384.5 US   ISSN 0001-2289
A R A LOG.* 1949. 2/yr. membership only. American Radio Association, 17 Battery Pl., No. 1443, New York, NY 10004-1101. Ed. W.R. Steinberg. adv.; bk.rev.; charts; illus.; stat. circ. 3,000.

331.8   AT   ISSN 1038-4812
A S U NATIONAL. 1986. q. Aus.$10 to non-members. Australian Services Union, National Executive, 2nd Fl., 116-124 Queensberry St., Carlton South, Vic. 3053, Australia. TEL 03-348-1788. FAX 03-349-1108. Ed. S.P. Gibbs. bk.rev.; circ. 80,000 (controlled). (back issues avail.) **Document type:** newspaper.
  Formerly (until July, 1991): Foreword (ISSN 0819-2006)

A T F ANNUAL REPORT. (Australian Teachers Union) see EDUCATION

331.3   AO
A VOZ DO TRABALHADOR. m. Uniao Nacional de Trabalhadores Angolanos, CP 28, Luanda, Angola.

331.88   FR   ISSN 0181-2874
ACTION JURIDIQUE (PARIS, 1978). 1978. bi-m. 250 F. (foreign 307 F.)(effective Jan. 1992). Confederation Francaise Democratique du Travail, 4 Blvd. de la Villette, 75955 Paris Cedex 19, France. TEL 42-03-81-40. Ed. Loic Richard.

THE ADVOCATE (PITTSBURGH). see EDUCATION

629.1
AERO MECHANIC.* 1939. m. $4. Machinists District Lodge 751, 9125 15th Pl., South, Seattle, WA 98108-5100. TEL 206-763-1300. FAX 206-764-0303. Ed. Connie Kelliher. bk.rev. circ. 55,000. (tabloid format) **Document type:** newspaper, trade publication.

AEROVOZ. see AERONAUTICS AND SPACE FLIGHT

331.88   LB   ISSN 0002-0044
AFRICAN LABOUR NEWS.* vol.3, 1967. w. International Confederation of Free Trade Unions, African Regional Organisation, P.O.B. 415, Monrovia, Liberia. Ed. Gab Atitsogbui. illus. (tabloid format)

331.88   TG
AFRICAN TRADE UNION NEWS. bi-m. Regional Economic Research and Documentation Center, Box 7138, Lome, Togo. **Indexed:** HR Rep.

331.88 387   US   ISSN 0002-2411
AIR LINE EMPLOYEE. 1952. bi-m. $7 or membership. Air Line Employees Association, 5600 S. Central, Chicago, IL 60638. TEL 312-767-3333. Ed. Quentin David. illus. circ. 12,000.

AIR LINE PILOT; the magazine of professional flight deck crews. see AERONAUTICS AND SPACE FLIGHT

3200 LABOR UNIONS

331.8   US
ALABAMA A F L - C I O. 1957. w. Alabama Labor Council, 297 W. Valley Ave., Birmingham, AL 35209. TEL 205-942-5260. FAX 205-945-8207. Ed. James E. Albright. circ. 2,158. **Document type:** newspaper.

331.88 780   US   ISSN 0002-5704
ML1
ALLEGRO. 1921. 11/yr. $23 to non-members. Associated Musicians of Greater New York, Local 802, A F M, 322 W. 48th St., New York, NY 10036. TEL 212-245-4802. FAX 212-245-6255. Ed. Tim Ledwith. adv.; bk.rev.; illus.; circ. 17,000 (controlled). (also avail. in microfilm) **Document type:** newspaper.
    Description: Presents articles on music as it relates to the members.

L'ALLIANCE (MONTREAL). see *EDUCATION*

350   CN   ISSN 0838-7990
ALLIANCE (OTTAWA). French edition (ISSN 0838-8008) 1966. q. free. Public Service Alliance of Canada, 233 Gilmour St., Ottawa, ON K2P 0P1, Canada. TEL 613-560-4200. FAX 613-236-1654. Eds. Nancy Mitchell, Francine Filion. charts; illus.; circ. 130,000 (controlled).
    Formerly: Argus-Journal (ISSN 0004-1211)

331.88   US   ISSN 0002-6107
ALLIED INDUSTRIAL WORKER. 1956. m. $6. Allied Industrial Workers of America, A F L - C I O, Box 343913, Milwaukee, WI 53234. TEL 414-645-9500. FAX 414-645-5530. Ed. Nick Serraglio. bk.rev.; illus. circ. 70,000. (tabloid format)

331.8   US
ALUMINUM WORKERS NEWS. 1952. q. free. Local 3911 U.S.W.A., 5722 W. 63rd, Chicago, IL 60638. TEL 312-581-1033. Ed. Gus Wilson. **Document type:** newspaper.

331.8   US   ISSN 0279-7968
AMERICAN AERONAUT. 1941. m. $5. I A M & A W, District 727, 2600 W. Victory Blvd., Burbank, CA 91505. TEL 818-845-7401. Ed. Don Nakamoto. circ. 15,000. **Document type:** newspaper.

AMERICAN DIRECTORY OF ORGANIZED LABOR; unions, locals, agreements and employers. see *BUSINESS AND ECONOMICS — Labor And Industrial Relations*

AMERICAN EDUCATOR. see *EDUCATION*

331.88 371.1   US   ISSN 0894-8208
AMERICAN FEDERATION OF TEACHERS. ACTION. w. American Federation of Teachers, 555 New Jersey Ave., N.W., Washington, DC 20001. TEL 202-879-4400. Ed. Trish Gorman. (reprint service avail. from UMI)
    Former titles: A F T - Action; A F T in Action.

331.88   US   ISSN 0002-8525
HD6350.G5
AMERICAN FLINT. 1909. m. membership. American Flint Glass Workers' Union, 1440 S. Byrne Rd., Toledo, OH 43614. TEL 419-385-6687. FAX 419-385-8839. Ed. Richard Morgan. circ. 12,000. **Document type:** newspaper.

331.88 387.5   US   ISSN 0002-9882
AMERICAN MARITIME OFFICER. 1970. m. free. Marine Engineers Beneficial Association - Associated Maritime Officers, A F L - C I O, District 2, 650 Fourth Ave., Brooklyn, NY 11232. TEL 718-965-6705. FAX 718-965-1766. Ed. Paul Doell. adv.; charts; illus. circ. 21,000. (tabloid format) **Document type:** newspaper.

AMERICAN POSTAL WORKER. see *COMMUNICATIONS — Postal Affairs*

331.88 370   US   ISSN 0003-1380
L11
AMERICAN TEACHER. 1916. 8/yr. $12 or membership. American Federation of Teachers, 555 New Jersey Ave., N.W., Washington, DC 20001. TEL 202-879-4430. Ed. Trish Gorman. adv. contact: Sharon Wright. bk.rev.; illus. circ. 750,000. (tabloid format; also avail. in microform from UMI; reprint service avail. from UMI) **Indexed:** Biog.Ind., Educ.Ind. **Document type:** newspaper.
    —UMI.

331.8   GW   ISSN 0341-017X
ANGESTELLTEN MAGAZIN; Wirtschaft und Wissen. 1950. m. DM.30. (Deutscher Gewerkschaftsbund) Bund-Verlag GmbH, Postfach 900840, 51118 Cologne, Germany. Ed. Hermann A. Grontzki. adv.; bk.rev.; abstr.; charts; illus.; stat. circ. 360,000. **Document type:** bulletin.
    —CCC.
    Formerly: Wirtschaft und Wissen (ISSN 0043-616X)

331.8   AU   ISSN 0003-7656
HD4809
ARBEIT UND WIRTSCHAFT. 1923. m. S.142($14) Oesterreichischer Gewerkschaftsbund, Hohenstaufengasse 10-12, A-1010 Vienna, Austria. Ed. Kurt Horak. bk.rev.; charts; illus.; index. circ. 30,000. **Indexed:** C.I.S. Abstr., ELLIS, Int.Lab.Doc.

331.8   GW   ISSN 0344-8223
ARBEITNEHMER. 1953. m. DM.10.50. Arbeitskammer des Saarlandes, Fritz-Dobisch-Str. 6-8, 66111 Saarbruecken, Germany. TEL 0681-4005-0. FAX 0681-4005-401. Ed. Hans-Arthur Klein. adv.; bk.rev.; charts; illus.; stat.; tr.lit. circ. 23,000. **Indexed:** Dok.Arbeitsmed.
    Former titles (until 1976): Saarlaendischer Arbeitnehmer (ISSN 0003-7737); (until 1968): Arbeitskammer.

331.8 948.5   SW   ISSN 0281-7446
ARBETARHISTORIA. 1977. 4/yr. SEK 150. Arbetarroerelsens Arkiv och Bibliotek, P.O. Box 1124, S-111 81 Stockholm, Sweden. TEL 46-84-54-65-00. FAX 8-21-55-60. Ed. Marie Hedstroem. bk.rev.; illus. circ. 2,500. **Indexed:** Amer.Hist.& Life, Hist.Abstr.
    Formerly: Arbetarroerelsens Arkiv och Bibliotek. Meddelande.
    Description: Presents research carried out in the history of labor movements and labor history.

331.8   SW   ISSN 0003-7842
ARBETSLEDAREN; foer chefer i produktionen. 1908. 11/yr. SEK 200 (typically set in Jan.). Sveriges Arbetsledarefoerbund (SALF), P.O. Box 12069, 102 22 Stockholm 12, Sweden. FAX 08-539968. Ed. Ingrid Askeberg. adv.; bk.rev.; illus.; stat.; circ. 93,000 (controlled). (also avail. in microform)
    Formerly (until 1926): Sveriges Verkmaestaretidning.

ARC-BOUTANT; organe d'information des questions scolaires et familiales. see *SOCIAL SERVICES AND WELFARE*

331 630   LY
AL-ARDH. w. Agricultural Trade Union, P.O. Box 7528, Tripoli, Libya.

331.88 690   US   ISSN 0004-4245
HD6515.A55
ASBESTOS WORKER. 1916. q. free. International Association of Asbestos Workers, Machinists Bldg., 1776 Massachusetts Ave. N.W., Ste. 301, Washington, DC 20036. TEL 202-785-2388. Ed. Andrew T. Haaf. illus.; circ. controlled.

331.8   II
ASIAN AND PACIFIC LABOUR. (Text in English) 1963. bi-m. Rs.48($25) International Confederation of Free Trade Unions (ICFTU), Asian and Pacific Regional Organization, P-20, Green Park Extension, Delhi 110016, India. Ed. V.S. Mathur. adv.; bk.rev.; illus.; stat. circ. 25,000.
    Formerly: Asian Labour (ISSN 0004-4601)

792.028 331.88   AG
ASOCIACION ARGENTINA DE ACTORES. MEMORIA Y BALANCE. no.58, 1977. a. free. Asociacion Argentina de Actores, Alsina 1766, Buenos Aires, Argentina. circ. 3,000.

331.88   II   ISSN 0970-8626
ASSOCIATION OF SCIENTIFIC WORKERS OF INDIA. BULLETIN. (Text in English) 1947. 9/yr. Rs.10. Association of Scientific Workers of India, 10 Rajendra Park, New Delhi 110 060, India. TEL 11-587625. Ed. Ram Prasad. adv.; bk.rev. circ. 2,000.
    Formerly (until 1968): Vijnan Karmee.

331.8   GW   ISSN 0004-8119
AUSBLICK (DUSSELDORF). 1948. m. DM.10. Gewerkschaft Handel, Banken und Versicherungen, Tersteegenstr. 30, 40474 Dusseldorf, Germany. TEL 0211-4582-0. FAX 0211-4582239. TELEX 08584653. Ed. Detlef Feldhoff. bk.rev.; film rev.; play rev.; abstr.; charts; illus.; mkt.; stat. circ. 400,000. **Indexed:** M.L.A.

331   AT
AUSTRALIAN CONGRESS OF TRADE UNIONS. DECISIONS. biennial. Aus.$10. Australian Council of Trade Unions, 393-397 Swanston St., Melbourne, Vic. 3000, Australia.

AUSTRALIAN EDUCATOR. see *EDUCATION*

331 385   AT
AUSTRALIAN RAILWAYS UNION. FEDERAL OFFICE NEWS. 1960. q. free. Percival Publishing Co. Pty. Ltd., 862-870 Elizabeth St., Waterloo, N.S.W. 2017, Australia.

331.88   AT
AUSTRALIAN WORKER. 1994. bi-m. Aus.$45 (effective 1994). A W U - F I M E Amalgameted Union, 245 Chalmers St., Ste. 15, Redfern, N.S.W. 2016, Australia. TEL 02-690-1022. FAX 02-6901020. TELEX AA73231. Ed.Bd. adv. circ. 105,000. (tabloid format)
    Formerd by the merger of (1991-1994): Federation of Industrial, Manufacturing and Engineering Employees. Labor News; Which was formerly (1945-1991): Federated Ironworkers' Association of Australia. Labor News (ISSN 0014-9276); (1891-1991): Australian Worker (ISSN 0045-0979); Which incorporated: Queensland Worker (ISSN 0043-8065)

AUTOTECNICA. see *TRANSPORTATION — Automobiles*

331.88 664   US   ISSN 0163-447X
B C & T NEWS. 1969. 10/yr. free to qualified personnel. Bakery, Confectionery and Tobacco Workers International Union, 10401 Connecticut Ave., Kensington, MD 20895. TEL 301-933-8600. FAX 301-946-8452. Ed. Frank Hurt. bk.rev.; illus. circ. 135,000. (tabloid format) **Document type:** newspaper.
    Supersedes: B and C News (ISSN 0001-043X); Which was formed by the merger of: A B C News; Bakers and Confectioners Journal.

331.88   US   ISSN 1049-3921
HD6350.R43
B M W E RAILWAY JOURNAL. 1892. m. (10/yr.). $16. Brotherhood of Maintenance of Way Employes, 26555 Evergreen Rd., Ste. 200, Southfield, MI 48076-4225. TEL 313-868-0490. Ed. Mac A. Fleming. illus. circ. 65,000. **Document type:** trade publication.
    Former titles: B M W E Railway Journal (ISSN 0146-0625); Brotherhood of Maintenance of Way Employes. Journal (ISSN 0007-2443)

B N A (YEAR) SOURCEBOOK ON COLLECTIVE BARGAINING AND EMPLOYEE RELATIONS. see *BUSINESS AND ECONOMICS — Labor And Industrial Relations*

331.8   IS
BAMAARACHOT. m. Technical Engineers Union, 93 Arlozorov St., Tel Aviv 62 098, Israel.

331.88 332.1   II   ISSN 0005-5077
BANK KARAMCHARI. (Text in English) 1963. m. Rs.5($3.) All India Bank Employees Federation, c/o V.N. Sekhri, 26-104 Birhana Rd., Kanpur 208001, India. Ed. Shri V.K. Agarwal. adv.; bk.rev. circ. 2,000.

BANKVAERLDEN. see *BUSINESS AND ECONOMICS — Banking And Finance*

331.8   US
BANNER (GARY). 1966. q. membership. United Steel Workers of America, Local Union 1066, 1221 E. 37th Ave., Gary, IN 46409. TEL 219-887-0591. FAX 219-887-0593. Eds. Linda Watson, Robert Watson. circ. 5,000. (tabloid format) **Document type:** newspaper.

331.8   ML
BARAKELA. m. Union Nationale des Travailleurs du Mali, Bamako, Mali.

331.8   GW   ISSN 0933-0615
BEAMTE HEUTE. 1949. m. DM.24. (Deutscher Gewerkschaftsbund) Bund-Verlag GmbH, Postfach 900840, 51118 Cologne, Germany. Ed. Dieter Benthien. adv.; bk.rev.; abstr.; index. circ. 94,000. **Document type:** trade publication.
—CCC.
   Formerly: Deutsche Beamte (ISSN 0011-9938)

331.8   GW
DER BEAMTE IN DER BUNDESANSTALT FUER ARBEIT. 1954. bi-m. membership. Verband der Beamten der Bundesanstalt fuer Arbeit, Pellergasse 9A, 90475 Nuernberg, Germany. adv.; bk.rev. circ. 10,000. **Document type:** newsletter.

BEFALSBLADET. see *MILITARY*

331.3   CC
BEIJING GONGREN/BEIJING WORKERS. (Text in Chinese) m. Beijing Shi Zonggonghui, 2, Taijichang Santiao, Beijing 100005, People's Republic of China. TEL 544207. Ed. Zheng Shouting.

331.8   IS
BEMOATZA. bi-m. Jerusalem Labour Federation, 17 Strauss St., Jerusalem 91 000, Israel. TEL 02-233863.

331   US   ISSN 1065-2426
HD6350.A2
▼**BEYOND BORDERS**; a forum for labor in action around the globe. 1992. q. $16. Beyond Borders, Inc., 4677 30th St., Ste. 214, San Diego, CA 92116. TEL 619-281-2009. Ed. Mary E. Tong. bk.rev.; film rev.; video rev. circ. 2,500. (back issues avail.) **Document type:** trade publication.
   Description: Written by labor organizers and community activists for organizers and educators. Reports news of the global economy and organizational efforts to build cross-border ties to improve living and working conditions. Contents emphasizes how-to's of organizing, informs readers of available resources.

331.8   XR   ISSN 0006-0453
BEZPECNOST A HYGIENA PRACE/SAFETY AND HYGIENE OF WORK.* 1951. m. $39.20. Prace, Publishing House of the Trade Union Movement, c/o Artia, Ve Smeckach 30, 111 37 Prague 1, Czech Republic. Ed. Jiri Pehe. adv.; bk.rev. circ. 48,000. **Indexed:** C.I.S.Abstr.

331   US
BOILERMAKER REPORTER. 1961? 6/yr. $1.50. International Brotherhood of Boilermakers, Iron Ship Builders, Blacksmiths, Forgers and Helpers, 753 State Ave., Ste. 565, Kansas City, KS 66101. TEL 913-371-2640. FAX 913-371-8482. Ed. Charles W. Jones. index. circ. 85,000. (tabloid format; back issues avail.) **Document type:** newspaper.
   Formerly: Boilermakers - Blacksmiths Reporter.
   Description: AFL-CIO, CFL union membership newspaper.

331.88   SZ
BUILDING AND WOOD.* q. International Federation of Building and Woodworkers, c/o Ulf Asp, ICC Building A, 20 route de Pre-Bois, Postfach 733, 1215 Geneve 15 Aeorport, Switzerland.

690 331.88   US   ISSN 0007-3717
BUILDING TRADESMAN. 1952. fortn. $15. Greater Detroit Building Trade Council, 1640 Porter St., Detroit, MI 48216. TEL 313-961-3800. FAX 313-961-2467. Ed. Martin Mulcahy. adv.; illus. circ. 46,000. **Document type:** newspaper.
   Description: Includes articles of interest to building trades union members in Detroit and Michigan.

331.88   BU   ISSN 0007-3954
BULGARIAN TRADE UNIONS. 1948. bi-m. $5. (Bulgarski Profesionalni Suiuzi) Izdatelstvo Profizdat, 82, Dondukov Blvd., Sofia, Bulgaria. (Dist. by: Hemus, 6, Rouski Blvd., 1000 Sofia Bulgaria) Ed. Kiril Panauotov. illus. circ. 3,850. **Indexed:** BSL Econ.

331.88   II   ISSN 0045-348X
BULLET. (Text in English or Hindi) no.19, 1971. m. Rs.1.20. All India Administrative Offices Employees Union, C-1-2 Baird Rd., New Delhi 110001, India. Ed. L.A. Prasad. adv.; stat. circ. 7,500.

331.8   FR   ISSN 0294-8397
C F D T AUJOURD'HUI. 1973. bi-m. 309 F. (foreign 349 F.)(effective Jan. 1992). Confederation Francaise Democratique du Travail, 4 Blvd. de la Villette, 75955 Paris Cedex 19, France. TEL 42-03-81-40. Ed. A. Mercier.

C H C G PULSE. (Canadian Health Care Guild) see *MEDICAL SCIENCES — Nurses And Nursing*

331   SR
C L O BULLETIN. 1973. irreg. Centrale Landsdienaren Organisatie, Gemenelandsweg 95, Paramaribo, Surinam.

331.88 384   US   ISSN 0007-9227
C W A NEWS. 1948. m. $2. Communications Workers of America, 501 Third St., N.W., Washington, DC 20001. TEL 202-434-1100. FAX 202-434-1482. Ed. Jeffery M. Miller. bk.rev.; charts; illus. circ. 525,000. (also avail. in microform from UMI; microfilm from KTO; reprint service avail. from UMI) **Document type:** newspaper.
—UMI.

331.88   FR   ISSN 0398-3145
CADRES C F D T. 1948. bi-m. 280 F. Union Confederale des Ingenieurs et Cadres, 47 av. Simon Bolivar, 75950 Paris Cedex 19, France. FAX 42-02-48-58. Ed. Marie-Noelle Auberger-Barre. adv.; bk.rev. circ. 30,000.
   Formerly: Cadres and Profession (ISSN 0007-9472)

CAHIERS D'ETUDE ET DE RECHERCHE. see *BUSINESS AND ECONOMICS — Economic Systems And Theories, Economic History*

331.88   BG
CALAMANA.* (Text in Bengali) q. Tk.1. Chalaman Sanskritik Sibir, Kendriya Samsada, S-1 Nurjahan Rd., Mohammadpur, Dhaka 7, Bangladesh.

331.116   CN   ISSN 0381-4130
CALENDAR OF EXPIRING COLLECTIVE AGREEMENTS (YEAR). a. Can.$10.75. Ministry of Skills, Training & Labour, Parliament Bldgs., Victoria, BC V8V 1X4, Canada. (Subscr. to: Crown Publications, 546 Yates St., Victoria, BC V8W 1K8, Canada. TEL 604-386-4636)
   Description: Compiles major collective agreements in BC which are scheduled to expire in the coming year.

331.88   US   ISSN 0008-0802
CALIFORNIA A F L - C I O NEWS. 1959. w. $10 to individuals; corporations $20. California Labor Federation, A F L - C I O, 417 Montgomery St., San Francisco, CA 94104. TEL 415-986-3535. FAX 415-392-8505. Ed. Floyd Tucker. bk.rev.; stat. circ. 5,200.

CALIFORNIA LABOR & EMPLOYMENT LAW QUARTERLY. see *LAW*

353.93   US
CALIFORNIA PRIDE. 1931. bi-m. $10. California State Employees Association, 1108 O St., Sacramento, CA 95814. TEL 916-326-4293. FAX 916-326-4215. Ed. Robert Striegel. adv.; bk.rev.; illus. circ. 60,000. **Indexed:** Cal.Per.Ind. (1990-). **Document type:** trade publication.
   Formerly: California State Employee (ISSN 0008-1566)

CALIFORNIA TEACHER. see *EDUCATION*

331.8   CN   ISSN 0841-6060
CANADA WORKS!. (Text in English, French) 1971. bi-m. Service Employees International, One Credit Union Dr., Toronto, ON M4A 2S6, Canada. TEL 416-752-4770. FAX 416-752-1966. Ed. Ellen Gardner. circ. 45,000. (back issues avail.)
   Formerly (until 1989): Canadian Service Employee (ISSN 0229-3609)

CANADIAN EMPLOYMENT BENEFITS & PENSION GUIDE. see *INSURANCE*

383   CN   ISSN 0008-4794
CANADIAN POSTMASTER/MAITRE DE POSTE CANADIEN. (Text in English, French) 1926. 4/yr. membership. Canadian Postmasters and Assistants Association, 281 Queen Mary, Ottawa, Ont. K1K 1X1, Canada. TEL 613-745-2095. FAX 613-745-5559. Ed. G.J. Bourque. circ. 11,000.

CANADIAN TRANSPORT. see *TRANSPORTATION*

350   CN
CANADIAN UNION OF PUBLIC EMPLOYEES. THE PUBLIC EMPLOYEE. 1964. m. membership. Canadian Union of Public Employees, 21 Florence St., Ottawa, Ont. K2P 0W6, Canada. TEL 613-237-1590. Ed. Fred Tabachnick. bk.rev. circ. 11,000.
   Formerly: Canadian Union of Public Employees. Journal (ISSN 0045-5512)

331.8   BB
CARIBBEAN CONGRESS OF LABOUR. LABOUR VIEWPOINT. q. Caribbean Congress of Labour, Norman Centre, Rm. 405, Broad St., Bridgetown, Barbados, W.I.
   Formerly: Caribbean Congress of Labour. Perspectives on Caribbean Labour.
   Description: Reports on trade union developments and economic factors affecting the Caribbean.

331.8   BB   ISSN 0576-7547
CARIBBEAN CONGRESS OF LABOUR. REPORT. 1962. triennial. Caribbean Congress of Labour, Norman Centre, Rm. 405, Broad St., Bridgetown, Barbados, W.I.
   Description: Reports on the activities of the congress.

CARPENTER. see *BUILDING AND CONSTRUCTION — Carpentry And Woodwork*

331.88 642.5   US   ISSN 0008-7815
CATERING INDUSTRY EMPLOYEE. 1890. bi-m $5 (foreign $7). Hotel Employees & Restaurant Employees International Union, A F L - C I O, 1219 28th St., N.W., Washington, DC 20007-3316. TEL 202-393-4373. FAX 202-333-0468. Ed. Herman Leavitt. illus.; index. circ. 250,000. **Document type:** newspaper.
   Description: Provides news and features of the Union, other unions and overall labor issues, both domestic and international.

CESKOSLOVENSKY HORNIK A ENERGETIK. see *MINES AND MINING INDUSTRY*

331.88 660   US   ISSN 0162-637X
CHEMICAL WORKER. 1944. m. $12 for non-members; $2 for libraries and schools. International Chemical Workers Union, International Chemical Workers Bldg., 1655 W. Market St., Akron, OH 44313. TEL 216-867-2444. FAX 216-867-0544. Ed. Frank D. Martino. bk.rev.; illus. circ. 85,000. (tabloid format)
   Formerly: International Chemical Worker (ISSN 0020-6334)

331.88 385   SZ   ISSN 0009-2916
CHEMINOT. (Text in French) 1919. w. 30 Fr. (foreign 34 Fr.). Schweizerischer Eisenbahnerverband - Federation Suisse des Cheminots, Steinerstr. 35, Case Postale 186, 3000 Berne 16, Switzerland. Ed. Michel Beguelin. adv.; charts; illus.

385 331.88   FR   ISSN 0245-7318
CHEMINOT DE FRANCE. 1917. bi-m. 50 F. Federation des Cheminots, 22 rue Pajol, 75018 Paris, France. TEL 46-07-15-19. FAX 40-38-49-11. Dir. Y. Tasserie. adv.
   Description: Publication of the railway transportation organization.

385 331.88   FR
CHEMINOT RETRAITE. 1945. m. (10/yr.). 72 F. membership. Federation Generale des Retraites des Chemins de Fer de France et d'Outre-Mer, 138 rue La Fayette, 75010 Paris, France. TEL 40-37-31-21. adv. circ. 100,000.
   Description: Covers the interests of retired railroad workers and their widows.

331.8   US
CHRONICLER. q.? $2. Cincinnati A F L - C I O Labor Council, 35 E. Seventh St., Ste. 200, Cincinnati, OH 45202. TEL 513-421-1846. FAX 513-421-1614. Ed. Harriet Applegate. circ. 1,500. **Document type:** newspaper.

CIVIL AVIATION NEWS; the paper that unites all aviation workers. see *TRANSPORTATION — Air Transport*

331.795   MF
CIVIL SERVICE NEWS. (Text in English or French) m. Federation of Civil Service Unions, 10, La Chausee, Port Louis, Mauritius.

LABOR UNIONS

331.8   SP
CLARIDAD. bi-m. 1500 ptas. Secretaria de Comunicacion e Imagen de U G T, Hortaleza 86-88, 28004 Madrid, Spain. TEL 91-589-76-00. Ed. Miguel Angel Ordonez. adv. contact: Lola Paredero. bk.rev. circ. 5,000.
    Description: Aims to be an open forum for reflection, study, research and controversy of all questions relating to the workers' movement.

647.94 331.88   FR
CLEFS D'OR. 4/yr. Union Professionnelle des Portiers des Grands Hotels, 12 rue Cambon, 75001 Paris, France. TEL 42-60-77-57. TELEX 214 965 F CLEFSOR. Ed. Jose Rabadan. adv. circ. 8,200.

CLEVELAND CITIZEN. see BUILDING AND CONSTRUCTION

687 331.8   SA
CLOTHES LINE. (Text in English) 1979. w. membership. Garment Workers Union of the Western Province, 350 Victoria Rd., Box 194, Salt River 7925, Cape Town, South Africa. Ed. C.E. Petersen. adv. circ. 53,000.

COLLECTIVE BARGAINING IN HIGHER EDUCATION AND THE PROFESSIONS. ANNUAL BIBLIOGRAPHY. see EDUCATION — Higher Education

331.116   CN   ISSN 1184-8073
COLLECTIVE BARGAINING INFORMATION MONTHLY SUMMARY. m. Can.$39.59. Labour Relations Board, 1125 Howe St., Vancouver BC V6Z 2K8, Canada. (Subscr. to: Crown Publications, 546 Yates St., Victoria, BC V8W 1K8, Canada. TEL 604-386-4636) **Document type:** government publication.
    Formerly: Collective Bargaining Information (ISSN 0826-8800)
    Description: Contains information of wage settlement, work stoppages and collective agreement settlements.

331.8   US
COLORADO LABOR ADVOCATE. 1923. s-m. $12 in state; out-of-state $15. 35 W. Fourth Ave., Denver, CO 80223. TEL 303-744-1731. FAX 303-238-1909. Ed. Michael K. Osborne. circ. 19,000. **Document type:** newspaper.

331.8   EI
COMMISSION OF THE EUROPEAN COMMUNITIES. TRADE UNION INFORMATION BULLETIN. (Text in various languages) bi-m. Commission of the European Communities, L-2985 Luxembourg, Luxembourg. circ. 20,000. (tabloid format; also avail. in microfiche from CIS; back issues avail.) **Indexed:** IIS. **Document type:** newsletter.
    Formerly (until 1968): Information Service of the European Communities. Trade Union News (ISSN 0073-7909)

331.88 350   IE
COMMUNICATIONS WORKER. 1923. m. membership. Communications Workers Union, 575 N. Circular Rd., Dublin 1, Ireland. Ed. D. Begg. adv.; bk.rev.; stat. circ. 18,000. (tabloid format) **Document type:** trade publication.
    Former titles (until 1991): Postal and Telecommunications Journal (ISSN 0790-6277); (until 1983): Postal Worker (ISSN 0032-5392)

COMMUNITY COLLEGE COUNCIL PERSPECTIVE. see EDUCATION — Higher Education

331.88   CE   ISSN 0045-6217
CONGRESS NEWS. (Text in English) vol.4, 1971. s-m. free. Ceylon Workers' Congress, P.O. Box 1294, 72 Ananda Coomaraswamy Mawatha, Colombo 7, Sri Lanka. Ed. Ponniah Krishnaswamy. circ. 5,000. (processed)

331.88   IT   ISSN 0010-6348
CONQUISTE DEL LAVORO. 1948. 312/yr. L.16000. (Confederazione Italiana Sindacati Lavoratori - Italian Workers' Trade Union) Editrice Finlavoro, Via Po 21, 00198 Rome, Italy. TEL 06-84-731. Dir. Bruno Storti. bk.rev.; film rev.; illus.; index. circ. 150,000. (tabloid format)

331.88   AG   ISSN 0589-5081
CONTACTO. 1968. m. (Federacion Argentina de Trabajadores de Luz y Fuerza) Editorial Sleil S.A., Calao 1764, Buenos Aires, Argentina. (Dist. by: Macht y Cla S.R.L. Carlos Calvo, 2426 Argentina) Ed. Carlos Garcia Martinez. illus. **Indexed:** Excerp.Med.

331.8   NE   ISSN 0921-500X
CONTRIBUTIONS TO THE HISTORY OF LABOR AND SOCIETY. (Text in English) 1988. irreg., vol.4, 1993. price varies. E.J. Brill, P.O. Box 9000, 2300 PA Leiden, Netherlands. TEL 31-71-312624. FAX 31-71-317532. TELEX 39296 BRILL NL. (In N. America: E.J. Brill, 24 Hudson St., Kinderhook, NY 12106. TEL 800-962-4406. FAX 518-758-1959) (back issues avail.) **Document type:** monographic series.
—BLDSC (3458.623000).
    Refereed Serial

331   AT
COUNSELLOR. 1965. q. Aus.$0.05 per no. Federated Municipal and Shire Council Employees' Union of Australia, Victorian Division, 1-3 O'Connell St., N. Melbourne, Vic. 3051, Australia. TEL 03-3266001. Ed. Paul Slape. adv.; bk.rev. circ. 15,000.

331.8   US
CRAFTSMAN. q. Graphic Communications, 204 S. Ashland Ave., Chicago, IL 60607. TEL 312-738-4200. FAX 312-738-1517. Ed. Stanley Mucha. **Document type:** newspaper.

331.8 327   US   ISSN 1062-7863
HD6854
CRITIQUE OF TRADE UNION RIGHTS IN COUNTRIES AFFILIATED WITH THE LEAGUE OF ARAB STATES. (Documentation Supplement avail.) 1989. a. $5. Jewish Labor Committee, 25 E. 21st St., New York, NY 10010. TEL 212-477-0707. FAX 212-477-1918. E s. Arieh Lebowitz, Michael S. Perry. bibl. circ. 5,000. (back issues avail.) **Document type:** academic/scholarly publication.
    Description: Comprehensive country-by-country review of labor policies, practices and conditions in the Arab countries of the Middle East and North Africa, compiled from ILO and U.S. State Department reports as well as newspaper, radio and broadcast news sources.

331.8   GW   ISSN 0935-6592
D A G - JOURNAL. 1948. 6/yr. DM.55. Deutsche Angestellten-Gewerkschaft, Karl-Muck-Platz 1, 20355 Hamburg, Germany. TEL 040-34915-1. FAX 040-34915-400. TELEX 211642-AGHV-D. adv.; index. circ. 500,000. **Document type:** bulletin.
    Former titles: Angestellten (ISSN 0028-307X); Neue Angestellte.

331.8   GW
D B B MAGAZIN. 1949. m. DM.12.80. (Deutscher Beamtenbund) Deutscher Beamtenverlag GmbH, Peter-Hensen-Str. 5-7, 53175 Bonn, Germany. TEL 0228-811-0. FAX 0228-811171. Eds. W. Schmitz, F.J. Schmitz. adv.: B&W page DM.14418, color page DM.25700; trim 185 x 270. bk.rev.; illus. circ. 449,403. **Document type:** newsletter.
    Formerly (until 1991): Der Beamten-Bund (ISSN 0405-1033)

331.8   US
D G A NEWS. 1990. bi-m. $24 (foreign $35). Directors Guild of America, 7920 Sunset Blvd., Hollywood, CA 90046. TEL 310-289-2029. FAX 310-289-2029. Ed. Tomm Carroll. adv.: page $1990; adv. contact: Scott Burnell. bk.rev.

331.8   US   ISSN 0749-7113
THE DAILY REPORTER (MILWAUKEE). 1897. d. (Mon.-Fri.). $9. Daily Reporter Associates, 633 W. Wisconsin Ave., Ste. 301, Milwaukee, WI 53203. TEL 414-276-0273. FAX 414-276-8057. circ. 2,000. **Document type:** newspaper.

331.8   US   ISSN 0740-1213
DALLAS CRAFTSMAN. 1913. m. $22.50. Reilly Echols Printing, Inc., 1710 S. Harwood, Box 152358, Dallas, TX 75215. TEL 214-428-8385. Ed. Amelia Reilly. adv. contact: Carol Echols. circ. 5,000. **Document type:** newsletter, trade publication.

331.88 355.133   FR
DEFENSE DES GRADES DE LA POLICE NATIONALE. m. 20 F. Syndicat des Grades de la Police Nationale, 11 rue des Ursins, 75004 Paris, France.

331.8   XV   ISSN 0011-7722
DELAVSKA ENOTNOST. (Text in Slovenian) 1942. w. 10400 din.($23) T.O.Z.D. Delavska Enotnost, CGP Delo, n.sol.o., Celovska 43, 61001 Ljubljana, Slovenia. Eds. Dusan Gacnik, Francek Kavcic. adv.; bk.rev.

331.88 658.87   US   ISSN 0011-8915
DEPARTMENT STORE WORKERS' UNION. LOCAL 1-S NEWS. 1949. m. $6 to members. Department Store Workers' Union, Local 1- S, Retail, Wholesale and Dept. Store Union, A F L - C I O, 140 W. 31st St., New York, NY 10001. Eds. Joseph Pascarella, Harold H. Hollabaugh. circ. 10,000 (controlled). (tabloid format; also avail. in microfilm from UMI) —UMI.

331.3   US
DESERT EDGE. 1972. m. membership. Bleiweiss Communications, Inc., Box 1167, Bloomington, CA 92316. TEL 714-877-5000. FAX 714-877-5986. (And: 4391 Park Milano, Calabasas, CA 91302. TEL 818-883-5141) circ. 13,000. (tabloid format) **Document type:** newspaper.

331.8   US
DETROIT LABOR NEWS. 1914. bi-w. $11. Metropolitan Detroit A F L - C I O, 2550 W. Grand Blvd., Detroit, MI 48208. TEL 313-896-2600. FAX 313-896-1078. Eds. Aldo Vagnozzi, David Hecker. adv.; bk.rev. circ. 4,500. (tabloid format; also avail. in microform from UMI; back issues avail.; reprint service avail. from UMI) **Document type:** newspaper.

DETROIT TEACHER. see EDUCATION

331.88 383   GW   ISSN 0012-0596
DEUTSCHE POST (FRANKFURT). 1949. m. DM.36 to non-members. Deutsche Postgewerkschaft, Rhonestr. 2, 60528 Frankfurt a.M., Germany. TEL 069-6695-0. FAX 069-6695-6941. Ed. Rudi Vetter. circ. 586,000. **Document type:** trade publication.

331.116   FR
DICTIONNAIRE PERMANENT CONVENTIONS COLLECTIVES. m. 1950 F. base vols. (m. updates 450 F.). Editions Legislatives et Administratives, 80 av. de la Marne, 92546 Montrouge Cedex, France. TEL 40-92-68-68. FAX 46-56-00-15. TELEX 632 855 F. Ed. Michel Vaillant. (looseleaf format)
    Description: Covers collective bargaining.

331.88   IT
DIMENSIONE LAVORO. 1980. m. L.15000. Editrice Dimensione Lavoro, Via Cavour 108, 00184 Rome, Italy. TEL 4755774. adv.; bk.rev. circ. 120,000.

331.8   US
PN1998.A1
DIRECTORS GUILD OF AMERICA. DIRECTORY OF MEMBERS. 1967. a. $22. Directors Guild of America, 7920 Sunset Blvd., Hollywood, CA 90046. TEL 310-289-2000. FAX 310-289-2029. adv.: page $660. circ. 15,000. **Document type:** directory.

DIRECTORY OF FACULTY CONTRACTS AND BARGAINING AGENTS IN INSTITUTIONS OF HIGHER EDUCATION. see EDUCATION — Higher Education

331.8   US
DIRECTORY OF KENTUCKY LABOR ORGANIZATIONS. a. $5. Labor Cabinet, Office of Labor-Management Relations, 1049 US 127 S., Frankfort, KY 40601. TEL 502-564-7127. FAX 502-564-5387. **Document type:** directory, government publication.
    Formerly: Directory of Labor Organizations.

331.8   US
DIRECTORY OF LABOR UNIONS AND EMPLOYEE ORGANIZATIONS IN NEW YORK STATE. 1948. biennial. $15. Department of Labor, Division of Research and Statistics, One Main St., Brooklyn, NY 11201. Ed. Eileen DeVeau. circ. 5,000. **Document type:** directory, government publication.
    Formerly: Directory of Labor Organizations in New York State.

LABOR UNIONS

331.88   CN   ISSN 0075-7578
DIRECTORY OF LABOUR ORGANIZATIONS IN CANADA/REPERTOIRE DES ORGANISATIONS DE TRAVAILLEURS ET TRAVAILLEUSES AU CANADA. (Catalog no. L2-2-1990) (Text in English and French) 1911. a. Can.$21 (foreign $25.20). Canada Communiation Group, Publishing Division, Ottawa, Ont. K1A 0S9, Canada. TEL 819-956-2560. circ. 6,000. **Document type:** directory.
   Description: Names of officials, telephone numbers, and addresses of all labor organizations in Canada with data on union membership and international affiliations.

331.8   US
DIRECTORY OF MAINE LABOR ORGANIZATIONS. (Subseries of: Maine. Bureau of Labor Standards. B L S Bulletin) 1969. a. Department of Labor, Bureau of Labor Standards, Division of Research & Statistics, State House Station 45, Augusta, ME 04333-0045. TEL 207-624-6440. FAX 207-624-6449. Ed. Terry M. Hathaway. circ. 800. **Document type:** government publication, directory.

331.8   US   ISSN 0734-6786
HD6504
DIRECTORY OF U.S. LABOR ORGANIZATIONS (YEAR). 1982. biennial. $35. B N A Books (Subsidiary of: The Bureau of National Affairs, Inc.), 1250 23rd St., N.W., Washington, DC 20037. TEL 202-833-7470; 800-372-1033. FAX 202-833-7490. (Subscr. to: BNA Books Distribution Center, 30 Raritan Center Pkwy., Box 7816, Edison, NJ 08818-7816. TEL 908-225-1900. FAX 908-417-0482) Ed. Courtney D. Gifford.
—CCC.

DIREKTE AKTION; anarchosyndikalistische Zeitung. see BUSINESS AND ECONOMICS — Economic Situation And Conditions

331.88   US   ISSN 0012-3765
DISPATCHER (SAN FRANCISCO, 1942). 1942. m. $2.50 membership or exchange basis. International Longshoremen's & Warehousemen's Union, 1188 Franklin St., 4th Fl., San Francisco, CA 94109. TEL 415-775-0533. FAX 415-775-1302. Ed. Zack Nauth. bk.rev.; charts; illus. circ. 42,000. (tabloid format; also avail. in microform from UMI) **Document type:** newspaper.

331.88   DK   ISSN 0107-6981
DJOEF - BLADET. 1918. s-m. DKK 360. Danmarks Jurist og Oekonomforbund, Gothersgade 133, 1123 Copenhagen K, Denmark.
   Supersedes in part: Juristen og Oekonomen (ISSN 0108-2817); Which was formed by the 1976 merger of: Juristen (ISSN 0022-6874); Oekonomen (ISSN 0108-2809)

331.8 385   BE
DYNAMIC. vol.52, 1971. s-m. membership. Christelijke Vakbond van Communicatiemiddelen en Cultuur, Oudergemselaan 26-32, 1040 Brussels, Belgium. Ed. Michel Bovy. film rev.; stat. circ. 40,000.
   Formerly: Rechte Lijn (ISSN 0048-6949)

331.8   US   ISSN 0012-8422
EAST BAY LABOR JOURNAL. 1919. m. membership. Alameda County Central Labor Council, 7992 Capwell Dr., Oakland, CA 94621. TEL 510-632-4242. FAX 510-632-3993. Ed. Lincoln Smith. circ. 6,000 (controlled). **Document type:** newspaper.

ECHO. see EDUCATION

370.7 331.88   FR   ISSN 0982-5339
ECOLE DU GRAND PARIS. 1922. m. (during academic year). 3 F. Syndicat National des Instituteurs et Professeurs du College, 69 rue du Faubourg St. Martin, 75010 Paris, France. adv.

331.88 621   US   ISSN 0041-686X
ELECTRICAL UNION WORLD. 1940. m. $1. International Brotherhood of Electrical Workers, A F L - C I O, Local Union No. 3, 158-11 Harry Van Arsdale Jr. Ave., Flushing, NY 11365. TEL 718-591-4000. FAX 718-380-8998. Ed. Thomas Van Arsdale. adv.; bk.rev.; illus.; circ. 50,000 (controlled). (also avail. in microform from UMI) **Document type:** newspaper.

331.88   SA
EMPLO REVIEW/TYDSKRIF. (Text in Afrikaans and English) 1935. m. membership. South African Railways and Harbours Employees' Union, Boston House, Rm. 335, Waterkant St., Cape Town 8001, South Africa. Ed. G. Janse van Rensburg. adv.; illus.; circ. 10,000 (controlled).
   Formerly: S.A.R. and H. Employees' Review (ISSN 0036-0929)

EMPLOYERS NEGOTIATING SERVICE. see EDUCATION — School Organization And Administration

023   UK   ISSN 0963-5548
EMPLOYMENT NEWS. 1978. 2/yr. free. Library Association, Professional Practice Division, 7 Ridgmount St., London WC1E 7AE, England. TEL 071-636-7543. FAX 071-436-7218. Ed. V.E. Fraser. bk.rev. circ. 4,500.
   Formerly (until 1991): L A Trade Union News (ISSN 0144-6827)
   Description: Contains news and informational articles on a range of topics which have implications for library and information staff who have an interest in trade union matters across all library sectors including job-sharing arrangements and equal employment opportunities.

624   US
ENGINEERS NEWS. 1942. m. membership. International Union of Operating Engineers, Local No. 3, 1620 S. Loop Rd., Alameda, CA 94502. TEL 510-748-7400. FAX 510-748-7401. Ed. James Earp. circ. 35,000 (controlled). (tabloid format) **Document type:** newspaper.

331.8   AG
ENGRANAJES. 1991. q.? Centro de Estudios y Formacion Sindical, Hipolito Yrigoyen 3150, PB 3, 1207 Buenos Aires, Argentina. TEL 97-8017.

ERZIEHUNG UND WISSENSCHAFT NIEDERSACHSEN. see EDUCATION

ESSOR DE L'ELECTRICITE ET DE L'ELECTRONIQUE. see ENGINEERING — Electrical Engineering

ESTANDARTE OBRERO. see BUSINESS AND ECONOMICS — Labor And Industrial Relations

EUROPEAN INFORMATION BULLETIN; a quarterly publication for European Trade Unionists. see BUSINESS AND ECONOMICS — Labor And Industrial Relations

331.8   UK
F D A NEWS. 1980. m. membership. Association of First Division Civil Servants, 2 Caxton St., London SW1H 0QH, England. TEL 071-222-6242. FAX 071-222-5926. Ed. Jonathan Baume. adv.; bk.rev. circ. 10,600. (back issues avail.) **Document type:** newsletter.
   Description: Keeps members up to date on all issues related to their work and well-being.

331   NE
F N V - MAGAZINE (WOERDEN). 1881. fortn. fl.44.25 (free to members). F N U Dienstenbond, P.O. Box 550, 3440 AN Woerden, Netherlands. TEL 31-3480-87788. FAX 31-3480-31498. Ed. P. Boss. adv.; illus.; circ. 90,000 (controlled). **Document type:** newspaper.
   Formerly (until 1978): Mercurius (ISSN 0025-9950)

331.88   NE
F N V NEWS. (Text in English) 1977. 3/yr. free. Federatie Nederlandse Vakbeweging - Confederation Netherlands Trade Union Movement, Maritaweg 10, Amsterdam, Netherlands. FAX 20-6844541. TELEX 16660 FNV NL. bk.rev. circ. 550.
   Supersedes: Netherlands Federation of Trade Unions. Information Bulletin (ISSN 0466-7530)

F Q P P U UNIVERSITE. (Federation Quebecoise des Professeures et Professeurs d'Universite) see EDUCATION — Higher Education

331.88   CN   ISSN 0705-856X
FACTS. 1978. 10/yr. free. Canadian Union of Public Employees, 21 Florence St., Ottawa, Ont. K2P 0W6, Canada. TEL 613-237-1590.

331.8   US
FAIRLESS UNION NEWS. 1954. q. membership. United Steel Workers of America, 920 Trenton Rd., Fairless Hills, PA 19030. TEL 215-945-2930. FAX 215-945-2930. Ed. Lew Dopson. circ. 2,500. (tabloid format) **Document type:** newspaper.

331.88   BL   ISSN 0100-2120
FEDERACAO DOS TRABALHADORES NA AGRICULTURA DO ESTADO DO PARANA. RELATORIO. irreg. Federacao dos Trabalhadores na Agricultura do Estado do Parana, Curitiba, Brazil.

331.88   UK   ISSN 0014-9411
FEDERATION NEWS. 1950. irreg. (3-4/yr.). free. General Federation of Trade Unions, Central House, Upper Woburn Pl., London WC1H 0HY, England. TEL 071-387-2578. FAX 071-383-0820. bk.rev.; charts; illus. stat. circ. 1,000.

331.88   US   ISSN 0014-942X
FEDERATION NEWS (CHICAGO). vol.85, 1973. m. $3. Chicago Federation of Labor and Industrial Union Council, 130 E. Randolph, Ste. 1710, Chicago, IL 60601-6221. FAX 312-565-6769. Ed. Robert L. Kite. adv.; bk.rev.; illus. circ. 3,800. **Document type:** newspaper.

331.88   US   ISSN 0738-0550
FEDERATION NEWS (LOS ANGELES). (Supplement avail.: Labor Review) 1896. m. Los Angeles County Federation of Labor, A F L - C I O, 2130 W. 9th St., Box 20630, Los Angeles, CA 90630. TEL 213-381-5611. Ed. Dan Swinton. adv.; bk.rev.; illus. circ. 5,500. (tabloid format) **Document type:** newspaper.
   Formerly (until 1983): Los Angeles Citizen (ISSN 0024-6549)

331.8 350   US   ISSN 0430-2761
FEDNEWS.* 1962. q. $2.40. National Association of Government Employees, 159 Burgin Pkwy., Quincy, MA 02169-4213. TEL 617-268-5002. FAX 617-268-2142. Ed Ed Gillooly. adv. circ. 35,000. (tabloid format) **Indexed:** Pers.Lit.

331.8   MG
FEON'NY MPIASA. (Text in Malagasy) m. Lot M8, Isotry, 101 Antananarivo, Malagasy Republic. Ed. M. Razakanaivo. circ. 2,000.

331.88 385   SZ   ISSN 0015-0215
FERROVIERE. w. 30 Fr. (foreign 34 Fr.). Schweizerischer Eisenbahnerverband - Federation Suisse des Cheminots, Steinerstr. 35, Case Postale 186, 3000 Berne 16, Switzerland. Ed. Franco Robbiani. adv.; charts; illus.; stat.

331.88   US
FIRE LINES. vol.12, 1973. m. membership. Uniformed Firefighters Association of Greater New York, Local 94, 225 Broadway, New York, NY 10007. TEL 212-233-4234. Ed. Robert di Virgilio. adv.; charts; illus.

331.8   BE
FLASH. (Text in Dutch, English, French, German, Spanish) fortn. 250 BEF($6) (effective 1992). World Confederation of Labour, 33 rue de Treves, B-1040 Brussels, Belgium. TEL 32-2-2306295. FAX 32-2-2308722. TELEX 26966.

331.88   XR
FLASHES FROM THE TRADE UNIONS. (Editions in English, French, Spanish) 1972. bi-m. $24. World Federation of Trade Unions, Branicka 112, 140 00 Prague 4, Czech Republic. TEL 46-21-40. FAX 46-13-78. illus. circ. 4,000.
   Formerly: Trade Union Press (ISSN 0041-0527)
   Description: Monitors the activities of trade unions world-wide. Covers congresses, sessions, meetings, seminars, strikes and demonstrations.

FLIGHTLOG. see TRANSPORTATION — Air Transport

331.8 350   SZ
FONCTION PUBLIQUE. (Text in French, Italian) 1927. m. 7.50 SFr. (Union Romande et Tessinoise des Societes de Fonctionaires Cantonaux) Presses Centrale Lausanne SA, Rue de Geneve 7, CH-1003 Lausanne, Switzerland. TEL 021-7289977. Ed. Gerard Laurent. adv.; charts; illus.; stat. circ. 11,500. **Document type:** bulletin.

LABOR UNIONS

331.88   SA   ISSN 0015-6809
FOOTPLATE/VOETPLAAT. (Text in Afrikaans, English) 1925. m. membership. South African Footplate Staff Association - Suid Afrikaanse Voetplaatpersoneelvereniging, P.O. Box 31100, Braamfontein, Johannesburg 2001, South Africa. FAX 339-2888. Ed. H.C. Kidson. adv. circ. 9,000.
Description: Covers news of the different divisions within the trade union.

331.8   BL
FORCA SINDICAL. 1991. m.? Central de Trabaalhadores Forca Sindical, Rua Cel. Oscar Porto, 841, Bairro do Paraiso, 04003 Sao Paulo SP, Brazil. TEL 011-885-3217. FAX 011-885-0890.

331.8   US
FOREFRONT (MINEOLA). 1953. m. membership. Amalgamated Meatcutters Union, Local 342-50, 166 E. Jericho Tpke., Mineola, NY 11501. TEL 516-747-5980. FAX 516-294-9608. Ed. Jan Miner. **Document type:** newspaper.

FRANKFURTER LEHRERZEITUNG. see *EDUCATION — School Organization And Administration*

331.88   BE   ISSN 0016-0350
FREE LABOUR WORLD. Spanish edition: Mundo del Trabajo Libre (ISSN 0027-3260) (Editions in English, French, German, Spanish) 1950. m. 1000 BEF. International Confederation of Free Trade Unions (ICFTU), 37-41 rue Montagne aux Herbes Potageres, B-1000 Brussels, Belgium. TEL 32-2-2178085. FAX 32-2-2188415. TELEX 26785 ICFTU B. Ed. B. Russell. bk.rev.; illus.; index. circ. 16,000. (tabloid format) **Indexed:** HR Rep., Mid.East: Abstr.& Ind., P.A.I.S. **Document type:** newspaper.

331.88 070   US   ISSN 0016-2183
FRONTPAGE. 1942. irreg. $5. Newspaper Guild of New York, A F L - C I O, C L C, 133 W. 44th St., New York, NY 10036. TEL 212-575-1580. Ed. Dona Fowler. charts; illus.; stat.; circ. 5,000 (controlled). (tabloid format) **Document type:** newspaper.
Description: Covers news and activities of the guild and related unions, with international and local developments of interest to labor.

331.8 368.4   GW   ISSN 0173-2323
G D S - ZEITUNG. 1971. m. DM.78. (Gewerkschaft der Sozialversicherung) Deutscher Gemeindeverlag GmbH, Postfach 400263, 50832 Cologne, Germany. TEL 02234-1060. Ed. G. Paetz. adv. (reprint service avail.) **Document type:** newspaper.
—CCC.
Formerly: Sozialversicherungs-Beamte und -Angestellte BSBA (ISSN 0340-367X)

G E O: GRASSROOTS ECONOMIC ORGANIZING NEWSLETTER. see *OCCUPATIONS AND CAREERS*

331.88 350   UK
G M B WORKING TOGETHER. 1924. m. free. G M B, Thorne House, Ruxley Ridge, Esher, Surrey KT10 OTL, England. FAX 0372-67164. Ed.Bd. adv.; bk.rev.; charts; illus. circ. 80,000.
Former titles: General, Municipal, Boilermakers and Allied Trades Union Journal; General and Municipal Workers' Union (ISSN 0016-6499)

331.8   US   ISSN 1065-1640
HD9623.U45
G M P HORIZONS. 1982. m. Glass, Molders, Pottery, Plastics and Allied Workers, 608 E. Baltimore Pike, Media, PA 19063. TEL 215-565-5051. Ed. Richard Kline. circ. 85,000. **Document type:** newspaper.
Formerly (until 1988): G P P A W Horizons (ISSN 0745-0761)

G R E M I. see *PRINTING*

331.88 687   US   ISSN 0016-4712
GARMENT WORKER.* 1902. m. membership. United Garment Workers of America, 4207 Lebanon Rd., Hermitage, TN 37076. Ed. Catherine C. Peters. illus. (tabloid format; also avail. in microform from UMI)

LA GAUCHE. see *POLITICAL SCIENCE*

331.15 331.8   GW   ISSN 0016-9447
HD4809
GEWERKSCHAFTLICHE MONATSHEFTE. 1950. m. DM.132. (Deutscher Gewerkschaftsbund) Bund-Verlag GmbH, Postfach 900840, 51118 Cologne, Germany. Ed. Hans Otto Hemmer. adv.; bk.rev.; abstr.; bibl.; index. circ. 6,100. **Indexed:** INIS Atomind., Key to Econ.Sci., P.A.I.S.For.Lang.Ind. **Document type:** bulletin.
—BLDSC (4165.595000); SWETS. **CCC.**

331.88   SZ   ISSN 0016-9455
GEWERKSCHAFTLICHE RUNDSCHAU. 1909. 4/yr. 36 SFr. Schweizerischer Gewerkschaftsbund - Swiss Federation of Trade Unions, Monbijoustr. 61, CH-3000 Bern 23, Switzerland. TEL 031-3715666. FAX 031-3710837. Ed. Ewald Ackermann. bk.rev.; bibl.; charts; stat.; index. circ. 5,000. **Indexed:** Chem.Abstr., World Bibl.Soc.Sec. **Document type:** bulletin.

331.88 282   BE
DE GIDS OP MAATSCHAPPELIJK GEBIED; tijdschrift voor syndicale, culturele en sociale problemen. 1902. 10/yr. 1300 BEF. (Algemeen Christelijk Werknemersverbond - Catholic Workers Movement) V.Z.W. Vormingscentrum Ter Munk, Wetstraat 121, 1040 Brussels, Belgium. TEL 32-2-2373111. FAX 32-2-2373700. TELEX 61770 CSC ACV. Ed. A. Vanempten. bk.rev. **Indexed:** Key to Econ.Sci.

GLOS NAUCZYCIELSKI. see *EDUCATION*

331.88 350   US   ISSN 1041-5335
GOVERNMENT STANDARD. 1933. 4/yr. membership. American Federation of Government Employees, A F L - C I O, 80 F St., N.W., Washington, DC 20001. TEL 202-639-6423. FAX 202-639-6441. Ed. Magda Lynn Seymour. illus. circ. 222,000. (tabloid format) **Indexed:** Pers.Lit. **Document type:** bulletin.
Description: Covers working conditions, legislation; and organizing regarding federal and DC employees.

331.88 655   US   ISSN 0746-3626
GRAPHICOMMUNICATOR. 1908. 8/yr. $12 in US and Canada; elsewhere $15. Graphic Communications International Union, 1900 L St., N.W., Washington, DC 20036. TEL 202-462-1400. FAX 202-331-9516. Ed. Harold Grandstaff. adv.; charts; illus. circ. 160,000. (tabloid format; also avail. in microform from UMI; reprint service avail. from UMI) **Indexed:** Chem.Abstr., Graph.Arts Lit.Abstr. **Document type:** newspaper.
Formerly (until June 1983): Union Tabloid (ISSN 0275-8342); Which superseded (in 1978): Graphic Arts Unionist (ISSN 0017-3363); Which was formed by the 1964 merger of: International Bookbinder; American Photo-Engraver (ISSN 0097-3297); Lithographer Journal; Also supersedes (in 1983): International Printing and Graphic Communications Union. News and Views; Which was formerly: International Printing Pressmen and Assistants Union of North America. News and Views (ISSN 0020-8388).
Description: Contains news of the union and its members in the printing and publishing industry.

331.88 665.538   SP
GREMIO DE ESTACIONES DE SERVICIO. REVISTA PROFESIONAL. Short title: A E S D I. vol.8, 1978. m. 800 ptas.($10) Gremio de Estaciones de Servicio, Torre de Madrid Plt. 8, Madrid, Spain. Ed. Julio Carpallo Abadia. adv.; bibl.; illus.

331.8   CN
GUARDIAN. 1952. m. Can.$10. Guardian of Windsor Inc., 1855 Turner Rd., Windsor, Ont. N8W 3K2, Canada. TEL 519-258-6400. Ed. Tom Burton. circ. 35,000.

331.88 070   US   ISSN 0017-5404
HD6350.N4
GUILD REPORTER. 1933. m. $20. Newspaper Guild, AFL-CIO, CLC, 8611 Second Ave., Silver Spring, MD 20910. TEL 301-585-2990. FAX 301-585-0668. Ed. Brian Williams. bk.rev.; charts; illus.; stat. circ. 32,000. (tabloid format; also avail. in microform from UMI; reprint service avail. from UMI) **Indexed:** HR Rep.
—UMI. **Document type:** newspaper.

GURU MALAYSIA. see *EDUCATION*

331.88 655   SZ   ISSN 0017-5811
LE GUTENBERG; relieur et cartonnier. 1871. w. 30 Fr. Syndicat du Livre et du Papier, Monbijoustrasse 33, 3011 Berne, Switzerland. Ed. Florence Rouiller. adv.; bk.rev.; charts; illus.; stat. circ. 7,000.

331.8 381   SW   ISSN 0017-7326
HANDELSNYTT. 1908. 11/yr. SEK 70 (effective 1990). Handelsanstaelldas Foerbund, Fack 5074, 200 71 Malmoe, Sweden. Ed. Lars Jonson. circ. 161,000. (tabloid format)
Incorporates (in 1989): Spegeln; **Former titles (until 1955):** Handelsnytt, Handelsarbetaren; (until 1951): Handelsarbetaren.

331.8   LU
HANDWIERK. (Text in French and German) 1945. m. 450 Fr. Federation des Artisans, 2, circuit de la Foire Internationale, L-1347 Luxembourg, Luxembourg. TEL 40-00-22-1. FAX 48-97-02. TELEX 2215. (Co-sponsor: Chambre des Metiers) Ed.Bd. adv.; bk.rev. circ. 7,500. **Indexed:** Key to Econ.Sci.

331.8   US
HARMONY HIGHLIGHTS. 1969. bi-m. membership. International Association of Machinists and Aerospace Workers A F L - C I O, Local No. 831, 222 Propect Pl., S.W., Cedar Rapids, IA 52404. TEL 319-364-2459. FAX 319-364-1037. Ed. Robert Northrup. circ. 2,500. **Document type:** newspaper.

331.88   US
HAWAII A F L - C I O NUPEPA. 1966. m. membership. Hawaii State A F L - C I O, 320 Ward Ave., Ste. 205, Honolulu, HI 96814. TEL 808-536-4945. Ed. Roy M. Takumi. adv.; bk.rev.; illus. circ. 300.
Former titles: Hawaii A F L - C I O News (ISSN 0017-8535); Hawaii State Fed. News.

778.5 331.88   AG
HECHOS DE MASCARA.* m. free. Asociacion Argentina de Actores, Alsina 1766, Buenos Aires, Argentina. Ed. Victor Bruno. adv.; illus. circ. 6,500.

331.8 664   BU
HELPER TO TRADE UNION'S MEMBERS. 1955. bi-m. 60 lv. Bulgarian Federation of Independent Agricultural Trade Unions, 29, Dimo H. Dimov St., 1606 Sofia, Bulgaria. TEL 52-11-77. FAX 52-25-03. circ. 1,500.
Former titles: Bulgarian Federation of Agricultural Workers' Independent Unions. Bulletin; U A F I W Bulletin.

HESSISCHE BEITRAEGE ZUR GESCHICHTE DER ARBEITERBEWEGUNG. see *HISTORY — History Of Europe*

331.88   II   ISSN 0073-2273
HIND MAZDOOR SABHA. REPORT OF THE ANNUAL CONVENTION. 1952. a. price varies. Hind Mazdoor Sabha, Nagindas Chambers, 167 P. d'Mello Rd., Bombay 400001, India.

331.3 700   HU   ISSN 1217-0992
HIRMAGAZIN - MAGYAR IPARSZOVETSEG. 1956. fortn. 600 Ft.($75) for 3 mos. (Hungarian Industrial Association) Econ-Soft Ltd., 16 Maglodi ut, 1106 Budapest, Hungary. TEL 261-6669. FAX 261-9004. Ed. Tibor Bartha. adv.; B&W page 20000 Ft.($200), color page 40000 Ft.($400); trim 175 x 260; adv. contact: Tibor Barany. bk.rev. circ. 12,000.
Former titles (until 1992): Szovetkezeti Hirmagazin (ISSN 0238-5775); (until 1988): Szovetkezeti Magazin (ISSN 0238-0749); Szovetkezeti Hirlap (ISSN 0557-9686)

331.88   GW   ISSN 0018-3806
HOLZARBEITER-ZEITUNG. Abbreviated title: H Z. 1893. m. DM.25 to non-members. Gewerkschaft Holz und Kunststoff, Postfach 102562, 40016 Duesseldorf, Germany. Ed. Klaus Brands. adv.; bk.rev.; illus.; stat. circ. 160,000. **Document type:** bulletin.

331.8 385   SA
HOOFLIG/HEADLIGHT.* (Text in Afrikaans and English) 1930. m. Transport Worker's Union of S.A., P.O.B. 31415, Braamfontein 2017, South Africa. Ed. Mari Gerber. adv. circ. 7,000. (back issues avail.)

HOSPITAL WORKER. see *HOSPITALS*

LABOR UNIONS

331.88 642.55   US
HOTEL VOICE. (Text in English and Spanish) 1940. w. $10. Hotel, Motel & Club Employees Union Local 6, AFL-CIO, 707 Eighth Ave., New York, NY 10036. TEL 212-245-8100. (Co-sponsor: New York Hotel and Motel Trades Council) Ed.Bd. illus. circ. 28,000.
Former titles: Motel, Restaurant Voice; Hotel Voice; Hotel and Club Voice (ISSN 0018-6074); Hotel (ISSN 0018-6066)

HUMAN RESOURCES REPORT. see BUSINESS AND ECONOMICS — Personnel Management

331.88   HU   ISSN 0018-778X
HUNGARIAN TRADE UNION NEWS.* (Text in English. Editions in six languages.) 1957. m. free. Szakszervezetek Orszagos Tanacsa, Rakoczi utca 54, 1964 Budapest, Hungary. TEL 2-122-4810. Ed. Emoke Nandori. charts; illus.; stat.

331.88 621   US   ISSN 0018-859X
IBEW-AFL-CIO. LOCAL 1470 JOURNAL. 1952. m. free. International Brotherhood of Electrical Workers, AFL-CIO, Local 1470, 60 Central Ave., Kearny, NJ 07032. TEL 201-589-3605. FAX 201-589-3606. Ed. Jim Fitzgerald. bk.rev.; bibl.; charts; illus.; stat. circ. 500. (tabloid format)
Document type: newspaper.

331.88 621   US   ISSN 0897-2826
HD6350.E3
IBEW JOURNAL. 1893. m. $4. International Brotherhood of Electrical Workers, AFL-CIO, 1125 15th St., N.W., Washington, DC 20005. TEL 202-833-7000. FAX 202-728-7664. Ed. J.J. Barry. illus. circ. 900,000.
—UnCover.
Formerly: Electrical Workers' Journal (ISSN 0013-4449)

331.88   SY   ISSN 0018-8816
ICATU REVIEW.* (Text in English) 1968. m. International Confederation of Arab Trade Unions, P.O. Box 3225, Sahat al-Tahrir, Damascus, Syria. Ed. El-Sayed. charts; illus.

331.88   MX
ICFTU-ORIT INTER-AMERICAN LABOR NEWS. (Text in English and Spanish) bi-m. free to qualified personnel. Organizacion Regional Interamericana de Trabajadores, Vallarta 8, 3 Piso, Mexico, D.F. 06030, Mexico. FAX 592-73-29. TELEX 1771699 ORITME. Ed. Luis A. Anderson. illus. circ. 3,000.
Supersedes (in 1984): Revista Sindical Interamericana.

IEA-NEA ADVOCATE. (Illinois Education Association, National Education Association) see EDUCATION

331.8   US
ILA NEWSLETTER. 1-2/yr. membership. International Longshoremen's Association, 17 Battery Pl., New York, NY 10004. TEL 212-425-1200. FAX 212-429-2928. Ed. James A. McNamara. circ. 85,000. (tabloid format) **Document type:** newsletter.

331.88   UK
ITF NEWS. (Editions in English, French, German, Spanish and Swedish) 1905. m. International Transport Workers' Federation, 133-135 Great Suffolk St., London SE1 1PD, England. TEL 01-403 2733. index. circ. 1,500 (English ed.); 205 (French ed.); 1,000 (German ed.); 510 (Spanish ed.); 400 (Swedish ed.).
Formerly: ITF Newsletter (ISSN 0019-0799)
Description: Industrial and labor issues of interest to transport workers.

331.88 655   US   ISSN 0019-0853
ITU REVIEW.* 1958. w. free. International Typographical Union, 316 Wilcox St., Castle Rock, CO 80104-2441. Ed. Robert S. McMichen. bk.rev.; illus. circ. 35,000.

331.8   US
IUD ACTION. 6/yr. AFL-CIO, Industrial Union Department, 815 16th St., N.W., Washington, DC 20006. TEL 202-842-2800.
Formerly: IUD Digest (ISSN 0199-3704)

331.88 621   US   ISSN 0019-0861
HD6350.E3
IUE NEWS. 1949. m. $2. International Union of Electronic, Electrical, Salaried, Machine and Furniture Workers, AFL-CIO, 1126 16th St., N.W., Washington, DC 20036. TEL 202-296-1200. FAX 202-785-4563. Ed. Carmen DelleDonne. charts; illus.; stat. circ. 160,000. (tabloid format; also avail. in microform from UMI; reprint service avail. from UMI) **Document type:** newspaper.
—UMI.

331.88 940   GW   ISSN 0046-8428
HD8448
IWK. (Internationale Wissenschaftliche Korrespondenz zur Geschichte der Deutschen Arbeiterbewegung) (Text in English, French and German) 1965. 4/yr. DM.72 to individuals; students DM.45. Historische Kommission zu Berlin, Kirchweg 33, 14129 Berlin, Germany. TEL 030-81600141. FAX 030-81600134. Ed. Henryk Skrzypczak. adv.; bk.rev.; abstr. circ. 1,400. **Indexed:** A.B.C.Pol.Sci., Amer.Hist.& Life, Hist.Abstr. **Document type:** academic/scholarly publication.
—BLDSC (4554.960000); SWETS.

IZA. (Illustrierte Zeitschrift fuer Arbeitssicherheit) see OCCUPATIONAL HEALTH AND SAFETY

IDEAS & ACTION. see BUSINESS AND ECONOMICS — Labor And Industrial Relations

331.3   RM
IFJUMUNKAS. (Text in Hungarian) 1957. w. Piata Presei Libere 1, 71341 Bucharest, Rumania. Ed. Jozsef Varga. circ. 22,000.

ILLINOIS LABOR HISTORY SOCIETY REPORTER. see BUSINESS AND ECONOMICS — Labor And Industrial Relations

331.88 686   FR
IMPRIMERIE SYNDICALISTE. 1949. bi-m. Federation Force Ouvriere du Livre, 198 Av. du Maine, 75014 Paris, France.

331.88   NZ   ISSN 0019-3054
IMPRINT. 1934. q. free. New Zealand Printing & Related Trades Industrial Union of Workers, Central Chambers, 3 Eva St., P.O. Box 6413, Wellington, New Zealand. FAX 04-382-8577. Ed. P.J. Tolich. adv.; bk.rev.; charts; illus.; tr.lit. circ. 9,000.
—CCC.

331.88   US   ISSN 0019-3291
IN TRANSIT. 1892. m. $5. Amalgamated Transit Union, 5025 Wisconsin Ave., N.W., Washington, DC 20016. TEL 202-537-1645. FAX 202-244-7824. Ed. Shawn Perry. illus. circ. 160,000. (tabloid format) **Document type:** newspaper.
Incorporates: Union Leader (ISSN 0161-9292)

331.88   II   ISSN 0537-2682
INDIAN WORKER; English weekly journal of labour movement in India led by INTUC. (Text in English) vol.20, 1972. w. Rs.100($9) Indian National Trade Union Congress, 1-B Maulana Azad Rd., New Delhi 110011, India. Ed. S.N. Rao. adv.; charts; illus.

311.3   PN
INFORMATIVO INDUSTRIAL. m. Sindicato de Industriales de Panama, Apdo. 6-4798, El Dorado, Panama City 1, Panama. TEL 60-0077. FAX 36-0166. Ed. Jose Chirino R.

331.88 070   II   ISSN 0377-0087
PN4701
INKWORLD. (Text in English) 1972. q. Rs.24. National Union of Journalists (India), 7 Jantar Mantar Rd., New Delhi 110 001, India. Ed. K.N. Gupta. adv.; bk.rev.; illus. circ. 2,000.

331.8 370   US
INSIDER'S REPORT; a special bulletin for leaders. 1983. 3/yr. free. Concerned Educators Against Forced Unionism, 8001 Braddock Rd., Ste. 500, Springfield, VA 22160. TEL 703-321-8519. Ed. Cathy Jones. circ. 7,500. **Document type:** newsletter.
Description: Discusses coercive unionism in education, in relation to legislation, litigation and other areas.

943 331 327   GW   ISSN 0173-2471
INSTITUT ZUR ERFORSCHUNG DER EUROPAEISCHEN ARBEITERBEWEGUNG. MITTEILUNGSBLATT. 1987. 2/yr. DM.56 for 4 nos. (Ruhr-Universitaet, Institut zur Erforschung der Europaeischen Arbeiterbewegung) Klartext Verlag, Dickmannstr. 2-4, 45143 Essen, Germany. TEL 0201-8620631. FAX 0201-8620622. bk.rev. circ. 500. **Document type:** bulletin.

331.88   FR
INTENDANCE ET SYNDICALISME. 1953. 8/yr. 60 F. S.N.I.E.N., 22 bis rue de Paradis, 75010 Paris, France. TEL 48-24-70-90. FAX 45-23-33-11. Ed. Marc Ripoll. adv.; bk.rev. circ. 91,000.

331.88 385   US   ISSN 0885-5889
INTERCHANGE (ROCKVILLE). 1901. bi-m. $5. Transportation Communications International Union, 3 Research Pl., Rockville, MD 20850. TEL 301-948-4910. FAX 301-948-1369. Ed. R.A. Scardelletti. charts; illus.; mkt. circ. 125,000. **Document type:** newspaper.
Former titles (until 1985): Railway Clerk - Interchange (ISSN 0033-8869); Railway Clerk.

331.88 790   US   ISSN 0020-5885
INTERNATIONAL ALLIANCE OF THEATRICAL STAGE EMPLOYEES AND MOVING PICTURE MACHINE OPERATORS OF THE UNITED STATES AND CANADA. OFFICIAL BULLETIN. 1910. q. $3. International Alliance of Theatrical Stage Employees and Moving Picture Machine Operators of the United States and Canada, 1515 Broadway, Ste. 601, New York, NY 10036. TEL 212-730-1770. FAX 212-921-7699. Ed. Thomas C. Short. bk.rev.; illus. circ. 70,000. **Document type:** bulletin.

331.8   BE   ISSN 0074-2872
INTERNATIONAL CONFEDERATION OF FREE TRADE UNIONS. WORLD CONGRESS REPORTS. 1949. quadrennial, 14th, 1988, Melbourne. 1000 BEF. International Confederation of Free Trade Unions (ICFTU), 37-41 rue Montagne aux Herbes Potageres, B-1000 Brussels, Belgium. TEL 32-2-2178085. FAX 32-2-2188415. TELEX 26785 ICFTU B. Ed. Enzo Friso. circ. 1,500.

331.88   SZ
INTERNATIONAL FEDERATION OF COMMERCIAL CLERICAL, PROFESSIONAL AND TECHNICAL EMPLOYEES. NEWSLETTER. (Editions in English, French, German and Spanish) 1974. 10/yr. International Federation of Commercial Clerical, Professional and Technical Employees, 15, Avenue de Balexert, 1219 Chatelaine-Geneva, Switzerland. FAX 022-7965321. TELEX 418736-FIET-CH. Ed. Philip Jennings. charts; illus.; stat. circ. 4,000. **Document type:** newsletter.
Formerly: International Federation of Commercial Clerical and Technical Employees. Newsletter; Which superseded: Non-Manual Worker in the Free Labour World (ISSN 0029-1056); International Non-Manual Workers Bulletin.

INTERNATIONAL FEDERATION OF PLANTATION, AGRICULTURAL AND ALLIED WORKERS. REPORT OF THE SECRETARIAT TO THE IFPAAW WORLD CONGRESS. see AGRICULTURE — Agricultural Economics

331.88   BE   ISSN 0074-6177
INTERNATIONAL GRAPHICAL FEDERATION. REPORT OF ACTIVITIES. (Text in English, French, German, Spanish and Swedish) 1950. triennial. International Graphical Federation, Rue des Fripiers 17, Bloc 2, Galerie du Centre, 1000 Brussels, Belgium. TEL 32-2-223-18-14. FAX 32-2-223-02-20. circ. 1,800. **Document type:** corporate report.

INTERNATIONAL MUSICIAN. see MUSIC

331.8   US   ISSN 0020-8159
INTERNATIONAL OPERATING ENGINEER. 1896. bi-m. $5. International Union of Operating Engineers, 1125 17th St. N.W., Washington, DC 20036. TEL 202-429-9100. FAX 202-429-0316. Ed. N.B. Coutts. illus.; circ. 4,000 (paid).
—UnCover.

INTERNATIONAL TRADE CONFERENCE OF WORKERS OF THE BUILDING, WOOD AND BUILDING MATERIALS INDUSTRIES. (BROCHURE). see BUILDING AND CONSTRUCTION

LABOR UNIONS

331.88   UK   ISSN 0539-0915
INTERNATIONAL TRANSPORT WORKERS' FEDERATION REPORT ON ACTIVITIES. (Editions in English, French, German, Spanish and Swedish) 1897. 4/yr. International Transport Workers' Federation, 133-135 Great Suffolk St., London SE1 1PD, England. circ. 500 (controlled).

331.88 691   US   ISSN 0362-3696
HD6350.B9
INTERNATIONAL UNION OF BRICKLAYERS AND ALLIED CRAFTSMEN. JOURNAL. 1898. m. $1.50. International Union of Bricklayers and Allied Craftsmen, 815 15th St., N.W., Washington, DC 20005. TEL 202-783-3788. Ed. Mary T. Dresser. adv.; charts; illus. circ. 105,000.
    Former titles (until 1975): Bricklayers', Masons' and Plasterers' International Union of America. Journal (ISSN 0360-6058); Bricklayer, Mason and Plasterer.

331.88 664   SZ
INTERNATIONAL UNION OF FOOD, AGRICULTURAL, HOTEL, RESTAURANT, CATERING, TOBACCO AND ALLIED WORKERS' ASSOCIATIONS. MEETING OF THE EXECUTIVE COMMITTEE. I. DOCUMENTS OF THE SECRETARIAT. II. SUMMARY REPORT. a. 180 SFr. International Union of Food, Agricultural, Hotel, Restaurant, Catering, Tobacco and Allied Workers' Associations - Union Internationale des Travailleurs de l'Alimentation, de l'Agriculture, de l'Hotellerie-Restauration, du Tabac et des Branches Connexes, Secretariat, Rampe du Pont-Rouge 8, CH-1213 Petit-Lancy - Geneva, Switzerland. **Document type:** proceedings.
    Formerly (until 1993): International Union of Food and Allied Workers' Associations. Meeting of the Executive Committee. I. Documents of the Secretariat. II. Summary Report (ISSN 0579-8299)

331.88 664   SZ
INTERNATIONAL UNION OF FOOD, AGRICULTURAL, HOTEL, RESTAURANT, CATERING, TOBACCO AND ALLIED WORKERS' ASSOCIATIONS. NEWS BULLETIN. (Editions in a Scandinavian language, English, French, German, Spanish) 1920. bi-m. 180 SFr. International Union of Food, Agricultural, Hotel, Restaurant, Catering, Tobacco and Allied Workers' Associations - Union Internationale des Travailleurs de l'Alimentation, de l'Agriculture, de l'Hotellerie-Restauration, du Tabac et des Branches Connexes, Secretariat, Rampe du Pont-Rouge 8, CH-1213 Petit-Lancy - Geneva, Switzerland. Ed. Dan Gallin. index. **Document type:** bulletin.
    Formerly (until 1993): International Union of Food and Allied Workers' Associations. News Bulletin (ISSN 0020-9074)

331.8   US
IOWA A F L - C I O NEWS. 1970. q. $2. Iowa A F L - C I O, 2000 Walker St., Des Moines, IA 50317. TEL 515-262-9571. circ. 80,000. **Document type:** newspaper.

331.88   US   ISSN 0021-163X
HD6350.I5
IRONWORKER. 1901. m. $15 or membership. Ironworkers International, 1750 New York Ave., N.W., Ste. 700, Washington, DC 20006. TEL 202-383-4800. FAX 202-638-4856. Ed. Martin T. Byrne. bk.rev.; charts; illus. circ. 136,000. **Document type:** newspaper.

331.88   MM   ISSN 0021-2725
IT-TORCA. (Text in Maltese) 1944. w. £23.40 (effective 1994). (General Workers Union) Union Print Co., Ltd., South St., Valletta, Malta. TEL 356-242996. FAX 356-243454. TELEX 1724 UNWOR RAW. Ed. Louis Chuchi. adv. contact: Anthony Ciappara. bk.rev.; film rev.; play rev. circ. 30,000. (tabloid format) **Document type:** newspaper.

331.8 622   FR   ISSN 0397-1511
JOURNAL DU MINEUR. no.96, 1975. m. 12 F. Federation Nationale des Mineurs CFDT, 35 rue des Ferronniers, 59500 Douai, France. Ed. M. Provost Jean-Gerant. charts; stat. (tabloid format)

JOURNAL OF COMMUNICATION BETWEEN RURAL COMMUNITIES AND TOWNS/NOSON TO TOSHI O MUSUBU. see AGRICULTURE — Agricultural Economics

331.8   US   ISSN 0745-4228
JOURNAL OF LABOR. 1896. bi-w. $10. Georgia State A F L - C I O, Electric Plaza Bldg., Ste. 549, 501 Pulliam St., S.W., Atlanta, GA 30312. TEL 404-525-2793. FAX 404-525-5983. Ed. Elizabeth Wilson. adv. circ. 10,000. (tabloid format) **Document type:** newspaper.

JOURNAL OF LABOR RESEARCH. see BUSINESS AND ECONOMICS — Labor And Industrial Relations

331.88 687   US   ISSN 0022-7013
HD6350.C6
JUSTICE. Spanish edition: Justicia (ISSN 0195-3737) 1919. 8/yr. $2. International Ladies' Garment Workers' Union, 1710 Broadway, New York, NY 10019. TEL 212-265-7000. Ed. Dwight Burton. illus. circ. 280,000. (tabloid format; also avail. in microfilm from BHP,KTO) **Indexed:** HR Rep.

331.88 687   US   ISSN 0195-3737
JUSTICIA. English edition: Justice (ISSN 0022-7013) 8/yr. $2. International Ladies' Garment Workers' Union, 1710 Broadway, New York, NY 10019. TEL 212-265-7000. Ed. Felicita Vargas. illus. circ. 35,000. (tabloid format)

331.88   XO
KALENDAR ODBORARA. a. 17 Sk. Praca, Spol. s r.o., Odborarske Nam. 3, 812 71 Bratislava, Slovakia. TEL 42-7-650-60. FAX 42-7-212-985. Ed. Jozef Gerboc.

331   US   ISSN 0023-0251
KENTUCKY LABOR NEWS.* 1942. bi-m. $10.50. Kentucky State A F L - C I O, Box 5445, Louisville, KY 40205-0445. Ed. Tom Brimm. adv.; bk.rev.; charts; illus.; stat. circ. 10,000.

331.8   RU   ISSN 0023-219X
KLUB I KHUDOZHESTVENNAYA SAMODEYATEL'NOST'.* 1951. s-m. 26.40 Rub. (Vsesoyuznyi Tsentral'nyi Sovet Professional'nykh Soyuzov) Profizdat, Ul. Myasnitskaya 13, 101000 Moscow, Russia. TEL 095-924-5740. adv.; bk.rev.; bibl.; illus.; index. circ. 92,000.

331.88   KN   ISSN 0454-4196
HD6835.6
KOREAN TRADE UNIONS.* (Text in English) no.142, 1974. m. General Federation of Trade Unions of Korea, Central Committee, Pyongyang, N. Korea. illus.

331.88   DK   ISSN 0109-2057
KRISTELIG FAGFORENING. MEDLEMSBLAD. vol.41, 1984. m. free. Kristelig Fagforening, Postbox 239, 8900 Randers, Denmark. FAX 86-417301. Ed. Per Boysen. bk.rev. circ. 36,000.
    Supersedes in part: Kristelig Fagforening, Kristelig Funktionaer-Organisation. Medlemsblad (ISSN 0109-2936); Which was formerly: Kristelig Fagforening og K F O (ISSN 0107-8860)

331.88   DK   ISSN 0109-1131
KRISTELIG FUNKTIONAER-ORGANISATION. MEDLEMSBLAD. vol.14, 1984. m. free. Kristelig Funktionaer-Organisation, Postbox 239, 8900 Randers, Denmark. FAX 86-417301. Ed. Per Boysen. illus. circ. 27,000.
    Supersedes in part: Kristelig Fagforening, Kristelig Funktionaer-Organisation. Medlemsblad (ISSN 0109-2936); Which was formerly: Kristelig Fagforening og K F O (ISSN 0107-8860)

DIE KUENSTLERGILDE; Mitteilungsblatt fuer unsere Mitglieder und Freunde. see ART

331.3   KN
KULLOJA/WORKERS. (Text in Korean) 1946. m. Central Committee of the Korean Workers' Party, 1 Munshin Dong, Tongdaewon, Pyongyang, N. Korea. Ed. Li Jong-Nam. circ. 300,000.

331.8   DK   ISSN 0105-032X
HD8542
L O BLADET. 1904. 24/yr. DKK 100 (typically set in Jan.). Landsorganisationen i Danmark - Danish Federation of Trade Unions, Danasvej 7, 1910 Frederiksberg C, Denmark. FAX 45-31-31-79-89. Ed. Finn Thorgrimson. bk.rev.; charts; illus.; stat.; index. circ. 36,000. (tabloid format) **Indexed:** C.I.S.Abstr.
    Formerly: Lon og Virke (ISSN 0024-5976)

331.8   US
LA CROSSE UNION HERALD. 1951. m. $5. 1920 Ward Ave., La Crosse, WI 54601. TEL 608-788-9590. Ed. John Roesler. adv.; bk.rev. circ. 5,000. (tabloid format) **Document type:** newspaper.

331.8   US
LABEL LETTER. 1975. bi-m. free. Union Label and Service Trades, 815 16th St., N.W., Washington, DC 20036. TEL 202-628-2131. FAX 202-638-1602. Ed. Richard Perry. circ. 40,000. **Document type:** newspaper.

LABOR AND EMPLOYMENT LAW ANTHOLOGY. see LAW

LABOR ARBITRATION ADVOCACY; effective tactics and techniques. see LAW

340   US   ISSN 1071-7404
LABOR LAW PERSONNEL NOTES. m. $70. Nyper Publications, Box 662, Latham, NY 12110. TEL 800-281-8582. FAX 518-456-1654. Ed. Harvey Randall.

LABOR LAW REPORTS. see LAW

331.8   US   ISSN 0023-6594
LABOR LEADER.* 1906. m. $10. San Diego-Imperial Counties Labor Council, 4265 Fairmount Ave., San Diego, CA 92105-1265. Ed. Gabe DeNunzio. adv.; bk.rev.; film rev.; circ. 33,000 (controlled). (tabloid format)

331.8   US
THE LABOR PAGE; news for Boston area workers. 1982. bi-m. $8. Workplace Committee of City Life - Vida Urbana, 335 Lamerine St., Jamaica Plains, MA 02130. TEL 617-524-3541. circ. 3,500.

331.8   US   ISSN 1067-5019
THE LABOR PAPER (KENOSHA). 1936. w. $26. Joseph A. Schackelman, Ed. & Pub., 3030 39th Ave., Kenosha, WI 53140-0655. TEL 414-657-6116. adv.; bk.rev.; circ. 15,000 (paid). (tabloid format) **Document type:** newspaper.
    Formerly: Kenosha Labor.

LABOR PAPER (PEORIA). see BUSINESS AND ECONOMICS — Labor And Industrial Relations

331.88   BE
LABOR PRESS AND INFORMATION; revue on trade union information and training. (Editions in Dutch, English, French, German, Spanish) 1971. 8/yr. 600 BEF($15) World Confederation of Labour, 33 rue de Treves, 1040 Brussels, Belgium. TEL 32-2-2306295. FAX 32-2-2308722. TELEX 26966. Ed.Bd. charts. circ. 2,700.
    Formed by the merger of: Labor (ISSN 0047-3871) & World Confederation of Labour. Information Bulletin.

331.8   US
LABOR TIMES. 1977. q. Amalgamated Clothing and Textile Workers Union, 333 S. Ashland Ave., Chicago, IL 60607. TEL 312-738-6100. FAX 312-738-0784. Ed. Libby Saries. circ. 17,500. **Document type:** newspaper.

331.88 687   US   ISSN 0271-5848
LABOR UNITY. (Text in English, French, Spanish) 1976. q. $1.50 domestic; Canada $1.75. Amalgamated Clothing and Textile Workers Union, A F L - C I O, 15 Union Sq., New York, NY 10003. TEL 212-242-0700. FAX 212-255-7230. Ed. Jack Womack. bk.rev.; illus. circ. 225,000. **Indexed:** Text.Tech.Dig. **Document type:** newspaper.
    Incorporates: Textile Labour - Canadian Edition (ISSN 0049-3562); Formed by the merger of: Advance (New York) (ISSN 0001-8597); Textile Labor (ISSN 0040-5027)

331.88   US   ISSN 0023-6667
LABOR WORLD. 1896. bi-w. $10. (Duluth A F L - C I O Central Labor Body) Labor World, Inc., 2002 London Rd., Rm. 108, Duluth, MN 55812. TEL 218-728-4469. FAX 218-728-1651. Ed. Larry Sillanpa. adv.; bk.rev. circ. 14,000. (tabloid format; also avail. in microfilm) **Document type:** newspaper.

331.88   US   ISSN 0023-6888
HD6350.B89
LABORER. 1947. bi-m. $2. Laborers' International Union of North America, 905 16th St., N.W., Washington, DC 20006. TEL 202-737-8320. FAX 202-737-2754. Ed. Arhtur A.Coia. bk.rev. circ. 500,000.

LABOUR/TRAVAIL; journal of Canadian labour studies - revue d'etudes ouvrieres canadiennes. see BUSINESS AND ECONOMICS — Labor And Industrial Relations

320.531   UK   ISSN 0953-3494
LABOUR & TRADE UNION REVIEW. 1988. bi-m. £11 in U.K.; Europe £13; elsewhere £18. 23 Morland Close, Hampton, Mddsx. TW12 3YX, England. Ed. Dick Barry. adv.; bk.rev. circ. 1,000.
  Formerly: Socialist; Supersedes: Communist.

LABOUR ARBITRATION. see LAW

331.8   IS   ISSN 0023-6969
LABOUR IN ISRAEL. French edition: Israel au Travail (ISSN 0021-1966); German edition: Histadrut Nachrichten (ISSN 0333-7782); Spanish edition: Trabajo en Israel (ISSN 0041-0225) 1947. irreg. (3-4/yr.). free. Histadrut, 93 Arlosoroff St., 62 098 Tel Aviv, Israel. TEL 03-431111. TELEX 342-488-HISTD-IL. Ed. Raffel Benkler-Barkan. illus. circ. 24,000 (9,000 English ed.; 3,500 French ed.; 3,500 German ed.; 8,000 Spanish ed.).
  Description: News about trade unions in Israel and socio-economic issues.

331.88   CN   ISSN 0383-3437
HD6529.N63
LABOUR ORGANIZATIONS IN NOVA SCOTIA. 1970. a. free. Department of Labour, Research Division, P.O. Box 697, Halifax, NS B3J 2T8, Canada. TEL 902-424-4313. FAX 902-424-3239. (processed) Document type: directory.
  Formerly: Directory of Labour Unions in Nova Scotia.
  Description: Directory of union locals in the province of Nova Scotia.

331.8   CN
LABOUR REPORTER. 1985. m. membership. Saskatchewan Federation of Labour, 2709 12th Ave., No. 103, Regina, SK S4T 1J3, Canada. TEL 306-525-0197. FAX 306-525-8960. Ed. Garnet Dishaw. charts; illus.; stat. circ. 6,000.
  Description: Covers labor legislation, strikes and lock-outs, organizing efforts and politics.

LABOUR RESOURCER. see BUSINESS AND ECONOMICS — Labor And Industrial Relations

LAND CONTRACTOR. see AGRICULTURE

LANDWORKER. see AGRICULTURE

331.88   US   ISSN 0023-8384
LANSING LABOR NEWS. 1945. fortn. $13 to non-members. U.A.W., 342 Clare St., Lansing, MI 48917. TEL 517-484-7408. Ed. Harold Foster. adv.; bk.rev.; illus. circ. 29,000. (tabloid format)

331.3   LS
LAO DONG/LABOR. (Text in Lao) 1986. fortn. Lao Federation of Trade Unions, 87 ave Lane Xang, BP 780, Vientiane, Laos. circ. 46,000.

331.8   IT
IL LAVORO. 1946. a. free. Camera Confederale del Lavoro UIL, V. Polonio, 5, 34100 Trieste, Italy. TEL 040-302633. Dir. Carlo Fabricci.
  Description: Focuses on labor union activities in the Trieste economic area.

331.8 340   IT   ISSN 1120-947X
LAVORO E DIRITTO. 1987. 4/yr. L.120000. Societa Editrice Il Mulino, Strada Maggiore, 37, 40125 Bologna, Italy. TEL 051-256011. FAX 051-256034. Ed. Umberto Romagnoli. adv.; index. circ. 900. (back issues avail.)

331.8   IT   ISSN 0023-9089
LAVORO ITALIANO.* vol.18, 1966. fortn. L.5000. Unione Italiana del Lavoro, Via Cavour 108, 00184 Rome, Italy. Ed. Camillo Benevento. charts; illus.; stat.

331.3 350   CN   ISSN 0845-5031
LEADER (OTTAWA, 1986). 1986. bi-m. Canadian Union of Public Employees, 21 Florence St., Ottawa, Ont. K2P 0W6, Canada. TEL 613-234-8477. Ed. Ron Verzuh. circ. 50,000.

331.8 664.752   US   ISSN 8750-9903
LOCAL 3 BAKERY WORKERS NEWS. 1955. m. Local 3 Bakery Workers, 41-07 Crescent St., Long Island City, NY 11101. TEL 718-784-3476. Ed. Joseph Rodriguez. circ. 8,000. (tabloid format) Document type: newspaper.

331.8   US
LOCAL 1010 STEELWORKER. 1957. m. membership. U S W A Local 1010, 3703 Euclid Ave., E. Chicago, IN 46312. TEL 219-398-3100. FAX 219-397-5968. Ed. Dan C. Stevenson. tr.lit.; circ. 23,000 (controlled). (tabloid format) Document type: newspaper.

331.8   US
LOCAL 11. 1955. q. membership. Hotel & Restaurant Employees & Bartenders Union, Local 11 A F L - C I O, 321 S. Bixel St., Los Angeles, CA 90017. TEL 213-481-8530. Ed. Karen Massorian. circ. 12,000. Document type: newspaper.

624
LOCAL 138 NEWS. m. free to members. International Union of Operating Engineers, Local 138, 1389, 138b, Gazza Blvd., Box 206, Framingdale, NY 11735. TEL 516-694-2480. Ed. James J. Duffy, Jr. circ. 2,500. Document type: newspaper.

331.8   US
LOCAL 73 JOURNAL. 1966. bi-m. membership. Service Employees International Union, Local 73, 1640 N. Wells St., Chicago, IL 60614. TEL 312-787-5868. FAX 312-337-7768. Ed. Dino Pigoni. circ. 25,000 (controlled). Document type: newspaper.

LOCOMOTIVE ENGINEER NEWSLETTER. see TRANSPORTATION — Railroads

LOCOMOTIVE ENGINEERS JOURNAL. see TRANSPORTATION — Railroads

LOCOMOTIVE JOURNAL. see TRANSPORTATION — Railroads

331.88 387   US   ISSN 0160-2047
HD6350.S4
LOG (CAMP SPRINGS). (Annual supplement avail.: Tax Tips for Seamen) 1939. m. free. Seafarers' International Union, A F L - C I O, 5201 Auth Way, Camp Springs, MD 20746. TEL 301-899-0675. FAX 301-899-7355. Ed. Jessica Smith. bk.rev.; charts; illus. circ. 45,000. (tabloid format; also avail. in microfilm from BHP) Indexed: Rehabil.Lit. Document type: newspaper.
  Formerly (until 1976): Seafarer's Log (ISSN 0037-0096).
  Description: Concerned with issues that matter to those involved with U.S. shipping industry, including public policy, personnel, elected officials, maritime industry analysis, plus information about retired civilian mariners.

331.8   US   ISSN 0190-7573
LOS ANGELES FIREFIGHTER. bi-m. (A F L - C I O - C L C, I A F F Local 112) United Firefighters, 1571 Beverly Blvd., Los Angeles, CA 90026. TEL 213-489-1300. FAX 213-651-8092. Ed. Jim Perry. adv.; illus. circ. 6,300. (tabloid format) Document type: newspaper.
  Description: Discusses labor news and other issues affecting or of interest to firefighters in Los Angeles.

385 331.3   RM
LUPTA C F R. 1932. w. Rumanian Railway Workers (C F R), Bd. Dinicu Golescu 38, Bucharest, Rumania. Ed. Ionel Chiru. circ. 150,000.

620   UK
M S F JOURNAL.* 1914. m. £7 to non-members. Manufacturing, Science and Finance Union, Transport House, Smith Sq., London SW1P 3JP, England. adv.; bk.rev.; charts; illus. circ. 400,000.
  Former titles: Tass News and Journal; Tass Journal (ISSN 0307-3424); Data Journal (ISSN 0011-6823)

331.8 630   FI
MAASEUTUTYOVAEN VIESTI. m. Suomen Maaseututyovaen Liitto - Finnish Forest and Agricultural Workers Union, Haapaniemenk 7-9, SF-00530 Helsinki 53, Finland.

MAJOR COLLECTIVE BARGAINING SETTLEMENTS IN PRIVATE INDUSTRY. see BUSINESS AND ECONOMICS — Economic Situation And Conditions

331 614.7   US   ISSN 0731-0323
MALCRIADO. (Text in English, Spanish) 1964-1990; N.S. 1992. m. $5. United Farm Workers of America, Box 62, La Paz, Keene, CA 93531. TEL 805-822-5571. FAX 805-822-6537. adv. circ. 25,000.

331.8   US   ISSN 0161-9373
HE730
MARITIME NEWSLETTER. 1967. m. $2.50. A F L - C I O, Maritime Trades Department, 815 16th St., N.W., Rm. 510, Washington, DC 20006. TEL 202-628-6300. FAX 202-347-1137. Ed. Max Hall. charts; illus.; stat. Document type: newsletter.
  Formerly (until 1976): Maritime (ISSN 0025-3391)

MARITIME WORKER. see TRANSPORTATION — Ships And Shipping

331.8   SP
MAS. 11/yr. Hermandades del Trabajo - Union of Workers, Juan de Austria 6, 28010 Madrid, Spain. TEL 1-4473000. FAX 1-4464292. Ed. Jose Lorenzo Lopez. circ. 5,700.

MASARYKOVA UNIVERSITA. FILOZOFICKA FAKULTA. SBORNIK PRACI. G: RADA SOCIALNEVEDNA. see SOCIOLOGY

331.88   US
MASSACHUSETTS LABOR LEADER. q. membership. Massachusetts State Labor Council, A F L - C I O, 8 Beacon St., 3rd Fl., Boston, MA 02108. TEL 617-227-8260. FAX 617-227-2010. Ed. Joseph Fagherty. circ. 1,000. Document type: newspaper.

331.88   US   ISSN 0025-4894
MASSACHUSETTS STATE LABOR COUNCIL A F L - C I O NEWSLETTER. 1960. m. free. Massachusetts State Labor Council, A F L - C I O, 8 Beacon St., 3rd Fl., Boston, MA 02108. TEL 617-227-8260. FAX 617-227-2010. Ed. Margaret F. O'Connor. circ. 8,000 (controlled). Document type: newsletter.

331.8 623.8   US
MASTER. m. membership. International Organization of Masters, Mates & Pilots, 700 Maritime Blvd., Linthicum Heights, MD 21090. TEL 410-850-8700. FAX 410-850-8725. Ed. Ron Schoop. bk.rev. circ. 22,000. (tabloid format) Document type: newspaper.

MEATWORKER. see FOOD AND FOOD INDUSTRIES

MEDECINE HOSPITALIERE/HOSPITAL MEDICINE. see HOSPITALS

331.1 677   SW
MEDLEMSTIDNINGEN INDUSTRIFACKET. 1944. 18/yr. SEK 125. Industrifacket, P.O. Box 1120, S-111 81 Stockholm, Sweden. TEL 46-8-786-85-95. FAX 46-8-21-28-72. Ed. Margaretha Holmqvist. adv.; charts; illus.; circ. 125,000 (controlled). (also avail. in audio cassette) Document type: trade publication.
  Former titles (until 1993): Beklaednadsfolket - Fabriksarbetaren; Which was formed by the merger of: Beklaednadsfolket (ISSN 0005-8262) & Fabriksarbetaren (ISSN 0014-6234)

331.88   US   ISSN 0047-679X
MESSAGE (BRONX).* 1972. m. Union of Telephone Workers, 702 Rhinelander Ave., Bronx, NY 10462. Ed. H. Curran. charts; illus.

670   DK   ISSN 0026-0517
METAL. 1912. 3/w. DKK 100. Dansk Metalarbejderforbund, Nyropsgade 38, 1602 Copenhagen V, Denmark. TEL 33 12 82 12. FAX 33-12-82-28. Ed. Kjeld Hammer. adv.; bk.rev.; index. circ. 150,000.

338.11   AT   ISSN 0727-1115
METAL WORKER. 1939. m. membership. Automotive, Metals and Engineering Union, National Council, 136 Chalmers St., Surry Hills, N.S.W. 2010, Australia. FAX 02-6987516. Ed. Chris Lindsay. bk.rev. circ. 191,000.
  Former titles: A M W S U Journal; A M W U Journal; A E U Monthly Journal.

331.88 670   US   ISSN 0047-6870
METALETTER. vol.3, 1972. m. free. A F L - C I O, Metal Trades Department, 815 16th St., N.W., Washington, DC 20006. TEL 202-637-5000. Ed.Bd. charts.

METALLARBETAREN. see METALLURGY

LABOR UNIONS

331.88 US ISSN 0026-1998
MICHIGAN A F L - C I O NEWS. 1939. m. $2.50. Michigan A F L - C I O News, Inc., 419 Washington Square South, Ste. 200, Lansing, MI 48933. TEL 517-487-5966. Ed. Jon Ogar. adv.; bk.rev.; illus.; stat. circ. 30,000. (tabloid format; also avail. in microfilm from UMI; reprint service avail. from UMI) **Document type:** newspaper.
—UMI.
Description: Articles and news on issues affecting the Michigan labor movement.

331.8 US
MILWAUKEE LABOR PRESS, A F L - C I O. 1942. m. $9. Milwaukee County Labor Council, A F L - C I O, 633 S. Hawley Rd., Milwaukee, WI 53214. TEL 414-771-7070. FAX 414-771-0509. Ed. Carole Casamento. adv. circ. 76,800. (tabloid format) **Document type:** newspaper.

331.8 US ISSN 0274-9017
MINNEAPOLIS LABOR REVIEW. 1907. s-m. $10. Minneapolis Central Labor Union Council, 312 Central Ave., Rm. 526, Minneapoli, MN 55414. TEL 612-379-4206. FAX 612-379-1307. Ed. Wallace Nelson. adv.; circ. 50,000 (controlled). (tabloid format) **Document type:** newspaper.

331.8 US ISSN 1061-8449
MINNESOTA PUBLIC EMPLOYEE. 1947. bi-m. membership. Minnesota State Employees Union, 265 Lafayette Rd., S., St. Paul, MN 55107. TEL 612-291-1020. FAX 612-221-0045. Ed. Don J. Dinndorf. circ. 42,000. **Document type:** newspaper.

331.88 US ISSN 0026-6728
MISSOURI TEAMSTER.* 1963. q. $3. Teamsters Joint Council No. 13, 300 S. Grand Blvd., Rm. 215, St. Louis, MO 63103-2432. TEL 314-647-2002. Ed. Gus Lumpe. bk.rev.; charts; illus.; stat. circ. 42,000. (tabloid format; back issues avail.)

331.3 RM
MUNKASELET. (Text in Hungarian) 1957. w. General Trade Union Confederation, Piata Presei Libere 1, 41917 Bucharest, Rumania. TEL 185795. Ed. Aurel Moja. circ. 12,000.

331.88 380.5 FR ISSN 0182-726X
MUTUALISTE R A T P. 1947. q. Societe Mutualiste du Personnel de la Regie Autonome des Transports Parisiens, 18 rue de Naples, 75381 Paris Cedex 8, France. adv.; illus.
Formerly (until 1977): Mutualiste du Metro (ISSN 0182-7251)

331.88 384 US ISSN 0027-5697
HD6350.B86
N A B E T NEWS.* vol.24, 1975. bi-m. $2. National Association of Broadcast Employees and Technicians, A F L - C I O, 501 Third Ave., N.W., Washington, DC 20001-2760. TEL 301-659-8420. FAX 301-657-9478. Ed. John J. Krieger. illus. circ. 9,500. **Document type:** newspaper.

N E A ADVOCATE; a publication for NEA members in higher education. (National Education Association of the United States) see EDUCATION — Higher Education

N E A ALMANAC OF HIGHER EDUCATION. (National Education Association of the United States) see EDUCATION — Higher Education

331.88 US ISSN 0279-540X
HD8009.03
N T E U BULLETIN. 1973. m. membership. National Treasury Employees Union, 901 E St., N.W., Ste. 600, Washington, DC 20004. TEL 202-783-4444. FAX 202-783-4085. Ed. Eve Berton. illus.; stat. circ. 81,000. (tabloid format) **Document type:** newspaper, bulletin.
Formerly: National Treasury Employees Union. Bulletin (ISSN 0095-4748); Continues the bulletin issued by the union under its earlier name: National Association of Internal Revenue Employees.

331 US
N T L NEWS. 1986. q. membership. International Brotherhood of Boilermakers, Iron Ship Builders, Blacksmiths, Forgers and Helpers, National Transient Lodge, 753 State Ave., Ste. 765, Kansas City, KS 66101. TEL 913-371-2640. FAX 913-371-8482. Ed. George Santos. circ. 4,000.

331.8 US
N T U BULLETIN. m. free. Newark Teachers Union, No. 481 A F T, A F L - C I O, 1019 Broad St., Newark, NJ 07102. TEL 201-643-8430. Ed. Don Nicholas. bk.rev.; illus. circ. 10,000. (tabloid format) **Document type:** newspaper.

331.88 350 US ISSN 0027-8513
HE6499
NATIONAL ALLIANCE (WASHINGTON). 1917. m. $10. National Alliance of Postal and Federal Employees, National Executive Board, 1628 11th St., N.W., Washington, DC 20001. TEL 202-939-6325. FAX 800-939-6389. Ed. Jacquelyn C. Moore. adv.; illus. circ. 15,000.
Formerly: Postal Alliance.

NATIONAL CENTER FOR THE STUDY OF COLLECTIVE BARGAINING IN HIGHER EDUCATION AND THE PROFESSIONS. ANNUAL CONFERENCE PROCEEDINGS. see EDUCATION — Higher Education

331.8 622 JA
NATIONAL UNION OF COAL MINE WORKERS. JOURNAL. q. National Union of Coal Mine Workers, 20-12 Shiba, 2-chome, Minato-ku, Tokyo 105, Japan.

331.88 070 IT
NELLA GALASSIA DELL'INFORMAZIONE. 1945. m. L.80000. Federazione Nazionale Stampa Italiana, Corso Vittorio Emanuele 349, 00186 Rome, Italy. TEL 06-6833879. TELEX 06-6871444. (Co-sponsor: Sindacato dei Giornalisti Italiani) Dir. Giorgio Santerini. bk.rev.; charts; illus. circ. 25,000. **Document type:** trade publication.
Former titles (until Nov. 1985): Numero Zero; Stampa Italiana.

NEW JERSEY EDUCATION LAW REPORT; the authority on labor relations in New Jersey schools. see EDUCATION

NEW JERSEY LABOR UNIONS. see BUSINESS AND ECONOMICS — Trade And Industrial Directories

331.88 US
HD6350.A76
NEW TEAMSTER. 1903. 8/yr. $12. International Brotherhood of Teamsters, A F L - C I O, 25 Louisiana Ave., N.W., Washington, DC 20001. TEL 202-624-6911. FAX 202-624-6918. Ed. Matt Witt. bk.rev.; charts; illus. circ. 1,800,000. (also avail. in microform from UMI; reprint service avail. from UMI)
—Faxon; UnCover.
Formerly: International Teamster (ISSN 0020-8892)

621.38 US ISSN 0028-7245
NEW YORK GENERATOR. 1960. m. $2. Communications Workers of America, Local 1101, C W A, A F L - C I O, 275 Seventh Ave., 17th Fl., New York, NY 10001. TEL 212-683-2666. Eds. Angel Feliciano, Cecilia E. Mallia. adv.; bk.rev.; illus. circ. 14,000.

331.88 350 US ISSN 0028-7342
NEW YORK LETTER CARRIERS' OUTLOOK. 1939. m. $6. National Association of Letter Carriers, N Y L C Branch 36, 249 W. 49th St., New York, NY 10019. TEL 212-956-3110. Eds. Lenny Goldman, Sid Klein. adv.; illus. circ. 9,200. (tabloid format)

331.88 370 US
NEW YORK TEACHER. 1917. bi-w. $8. New York State United Teachers, 159 Wolf Rd., Box 15-008, Albany, NY 11212-5008. (Or: 260 Park Ave. S., New York, NY 10010. TEL 212-254-7660) Ed. Deborah Hormel Ward. adv.; bk.rev.; charts; illus.; stat. circ. 326,000. **Document type:** newspaper.
Formerly: United Teacher (ISSN 0041-8161)

331.88 686.2 US ISSN 0049-4968
NEW YORK TYPOGRAPHICAL UNION NUMBER SIX. BULLETIN. 1898. irreg. membership. New York Typographical Union Number Six, 817 Broadway, New York, NY 10003. TEL 212-533-2000. FAX 212-475-0536. Ed. Gunnar Janger. bk.rev.; charts; illus. circ. 9,000. **Document type:** newspaper.

331.88 NZ ISSN 1170-7887
NEW ZEALAND COUNCIL OF TRADE UNIONS. DIRECTORY. Key Title: N Z C T U Directory. 1971. a. free. New Zealand Council of Trade Unions, P.O. Box 6645, Wellington, New Zealand. FAX 3856-051. Ed.Bd. adv. circ. 4,000. **Document type:** directory.
Former titles (until 1991): New Zealand Council of Trade Unions. Official Trade Union Directory (ISSN 0114-9296); N Z C T U Official Directory (ISSN 0114-6246)

331.8 US
NEWS & VIEWS OF LOCAL 23. 1983. bi-m. free. United Food and Commercial Workers, Local 23, 951 Penn Ave., Pittsburgh, PA 15222. TEL 412-261-0301. FAX 412-261-4429. Ed. James R. Bond. circ. 23,000 (controlled). (tabloid format) **Document type:** newspaper.

331.8 US ISSN 0164-1395
NEWS HI-LITES. 1959. q. free. Virginia State A F L - C I O, 3315 W. Broad St., Richmond, VA 23230. TEL 804-355-7444. FAX 804-353-0442. Ed. K. Scott Reynolds. tr.lit. circ. 112,000. (tabloid format) **Document type:** newsletter.

331 AT ISSN 0728-4845
NEWSMONTH. 1981. 8/yr. Aus.$38. New South Wales Independent Teachers Association, G.P.O. Box 116, Sydney, N.S.W. 2001, Australia. TEL 02-202-2600. FAX 02-261-8860. Eds. Dick Shearman, Leith Hamilton. adv.: page Aus.$1200. bk.rev. circ. 16,000. (tabloid format; back issues avail.) **Document type:** newspaper.
Formerly: I T A Newsletter.
Description: Contains news tories, salary scales and information on member benefits.

383 331.88 US
NEWSPAPER AND MAIL DELIVERERS' UNION BULLETIN. vol.73, 1976. m. membership. Newspaper and Mail Deliverers' Union, 41-18 27th St., Long Island City, NY 11101. TEL 718-392-8367. charts. circ. 4,000.

331.8 NR
NIGERIAN WORKER. m? United Labour Congress, 97 Herbert Macaulay St., Lagos, Nigeria. Ed. Lawrence Borha.

NIKKYOSO KYOIKU SHINBUN. see EDUCATION

331.88 SW
NORDISKA SAMARBETSORGAN. 1975. irreg. Nordisk Raad, Tyrgatan 7, P.O. Box 19506, S-104 32 Stockholm, Sweden.

NORSK SJOEMANNSFORBUND. MEDLEMSBLAD. see TRANSPORTATION — Ships And Shipping

331.8 331 US ISSN 0894-444X
NORTHWEST LABOR PRESS. 1900. s-m. $10. Oregon Labor Press Publishing Co., 4313 N.E. Tillamook, Ste. 206, Box 13150, Portland, OR 97213. TEL 503-288-3311. FAX 503-288-3320. Ed. Michael Gutwig. adv. circ. 52,000. (tabloid format; also avail. in microfilm)
Description: Covers issues of interest to labor.

NOUVEAU CENTRE DE SANTE. see MEDICAL SCIENCES

331.8 IT
NUOVA RASSEGNA SINDACALE. 1956. w. L.120000 (foreign L.260000) (effective 1993). (Confederazione Generale Italiana di Lavoro - Italian General Confederation of Work) Edit Coop., Via dei Frentani, 4-A, 00185 Rome, Italy. TEL 06-448701. FAX 06-4481260. Ed. Renato d'Agostini. adv.; bk.rev.; charts; illus.; stat.; index. circ. 30,000.
Formerly: Rassegna Sindacale (ISSN 0033-9849)

331.88 US ISSN 8756-1727
HD6350.P415
O C A W REPORTER. 1944. bi-m. $6. Oil, Chemical and Atomic Workers International Union, Box 281200, Lakewood, CO 80228-8200. TEL 303-987-2229. Ed. Rodney Rogers. bk.rev.; illus. circ. 120,000. (tabloid format; also avail. in microfilm from UMI; reprint service avail. from UMI) **Document type:** newspaper.
—UMI.
Formerly (until 1984): Oil, Chemical and Atomic Workers International Union. Union News (ISSN 0030-1426)

LABOR UNIONS

331.8   LU
O G B - L AKTUELL/O G B - L ACTUALITES. 1919. m. 300 F. to non-members. Confederation of Independent Trade Unions of Luxembourg, 4002 Esch-sur-Alzette, P.O. Box 149, Luxembourg. TEL 54-05-45. FAX 54-16-20. TELEX 1368. Ed. Jean-Marie Grober. bk.rev. circ. 38,000.

O P S E U NEWS. (Ontario Public Service Employees Union) see BUSINESS AND ECONOMICS — Labor And Industrial Relations

OBRERO FERROVIARIO. see TRANSPORTATION — Railroads

331.88   US   ISSN 0030-0772
OHIO A F L - C I O NEWS AND VIEWS. 1958. s-m. free. Ohio A F L - C I O, 271 E. State St., Columbus, OH 43215. TEL 614-224-8271. FAX 614-224-2671. Ed. Kent Darr. stat.; circ. 11,500 (controlled). (processed) Document type: newsletter.

OHIO LABOR CITIZEN. see BUILDING AND CONSTRUCTION

331.88   II   ISSN 0030-1329
OIL & CHEMICAL WORKER. (Text in English) 1965. m. National Federation of Petroleum Workers, Tel-Rasayan Bhavan, Tilak Rd., Dadar, Bombay 400 014, India. (Co-sponsor: Indian National Chemical Workers' Federation) Ed. Raja Kulkarni. adv.; stat. circ. 500. (avail. in talking book)

662 665.5   TU
OIL CHEMICAL RUBBER WORKERS TRADE UNION OF TURKEY. YEARBOOK. a. Turkiye Petrol, Kimya, Lastik Iscileeri Sendikasi - Oil Chemical Rubber Workers Trade Union of Turkey, Yildiz, Posta Cad P.O. Box 284, Evren Sitesi Gayrettepe, Istanbul 80280, Turkey. TEL 1748896. FAX 1747446.

331.88   US   ISSN 0030-4840
OREGON TEAMSTER. 1946. m. membership. Joint Council of Teamsters No. 37, 1872 N.E. 162nd Ave., Portland, OR 97230-5642. TEL 503-251-2339. FAX 503-251-2303. Ed. Frank Flori. bk.rev. circ. 34,000. Document type: newspaper.

OSIM INYAN. see SOCIAL SERVICES AND WELFARE

331.88 687   US   ISSN 0048-2390
OUR LOCAL SIXTY SIX.* vol.24, 1971. q. membership. International Ladies Garment Workers Union, Local 66, 1710 Broadway, NY 10019. Ed. Rafael Martinez. charts; illus.

331.8   CN   ISSN 0822-6377
OUR TIMES MAGAZINE; independent Canadian labour magazine. 1981. 6/yr. Can.$20 to individuals; institutions Can.$32. Our Times Publishing Ltd., 390 Dufferin St., Toronto, ON M6K 2A3, Canada. TEL 416-531-5762. FAX 416-533-2397. Ed. Lorraine Endicott. adv.; B&W page Can.$900, color page Can.$1824; trim 8 1/2 x 11; adv. contact: Mike Edwards. bk.rev. circ. 5,000. (also avail. in microfilm; back issues avail., reprint service avail. from MML) Indexed: Alt.Press Ind., Can.Per.Ind., CMI.
Description: Reports and opinions, profiles and interviews, creative writing and photography, reflecting the current state of the union movement in Canada.

331.8   US
P E D FORUM. 1975. q. free. A F L - C I O, Public Employee Department, 816 16th St., N.W., Ste. 308, Washington, DC 20006. TEL 202-393-2820. FAX 202-347-1825. Ed. Laura Ginsburg. bk.rev. circ. 3,500. Document type: newsletter.
Formerly: In Public Service (ISSN 0161-9330)

P E I T F NEWSLETTER. (Prince Edward Island Teachers Federation) see EDUCATION

331.8   CN
P S A C UNION UPDATE. French edition: Parlons Syndicat (ISSN 0849-0260) 1976. fortn. free. Public Service Alliance of Canada, 233 Gilmour St., Ottawa, ON K2P 0P1, Canada. TEL 613-560-4241. FAX 613-236-1654. Eds. Francine Filion, Nancy Mitchell. stat.; illus. circ. 30,000 (controlled). (back issues avail.) Document type: newsletter.
Former titles: Your Union; P S A C Newsletter (ISSN 0849-0295); (until 1989): Public Service Alliance of Canada. Weekly Newsletter (ISSN 0700-6063)

331.8   AT   ISSN 1038-4030
P S A INDUSTRIAL BULLETIN. 1988. s-m. Public Service Association of New South Wales, G.P.O. Box 3365, Sydney, N.S.W. 2001, Australia. TEL 02-290-1555. FAX 02-262-1623. Ed. Les Carr. circ. 7,000.
Description: Reports on current industrial issues.

331.8   AT   ISSN 0812-7573
P S A REPORTER. 1983. s-m. Public Service Association of New South Wales, G.P.O. Box 3365, Sydney, N.S.W. 2001, Australia. TEL 02-290-1555. FAX 02-262-1623. Ed. Les Carr. circ. 7,000.
Description: Reports of decisions and industrial disputes.

P S C CLARION. (Professional Staff Congress) see EDUCATION — Higher Education

331.8   FR
PAGES JURIDIQUES DE LA VIE OUVRIERE. a. Vie Ouvriere, 33 rue Bouret, 75940 Paris cedex, France.

331.88 698   US   ISSN 0030-9532
HD6350.P2
PAINTER & ALLIED TRADES JOURNAL. 1887. m. membership. International Brotherhood of Painters & Allied Trades, 1750 New York Ave., N.W., Washington, DC 20006-5393. TEL 202-637-0700. FAX 202-637-0771. Ed. A.L. Monroe. illus. circ. 175,000. Document type: newspaper.
Formerly: Painter and Decorator.

331.88 676   US   ISSN 0363-6437
HD6350.P27
PAPERWORKER. 1972. m. membership. United Paperworkers International Union, 3340 Perimeter Hill Dr., Box 1475, Nashville, TN 37202. TEL 615-834-8590. FAX 615-333-6667. Ed. Dick Blin. bk.rev.; illus.; stat. circ. 265,000. (tabloid format; back issues avail.) Document type: newspaper.
Supersedes: Pulp and Paper Worker; United Paper (ISSN 0041-7459)

331.8   HU
PEDAGOGUSOK LAPJA. fortn. $21. Hungarian Union of Teachers, Gorkij fasor 10, 1068 Budapest, Hungary. circ. 20,000.

331.8   US
PENNSYLVANIA A F L - C I O NEWS. 1960. m. $2.50. c/o David H. Wilderman, Dir., 230 State St., Harrisburg, PA 17101. TEL 717-238-9351. FAX 717-238-8541. Ed. Jim Deegan. bk.rev.; circ. 10,000 (controlled). Document type: newspaper.

PENNSYLVANIA EDUCATION LAW REPORT. see EDUCATION

331.88   FR   ISSN 0031-661X
PEUPLE. 1921. bi-m. 615 F. (Confederation Generale du Travail) Edition de Publications et Journaux Syndicaux, 263 rue de Paris, Case 432, 93516 Montreuil Cedex, France. TEL 48-18-83-06. FAX 48-59-28-31. TELEX 235091F. Ed. Marie-Laure Herges. stat.; index. circ. 23,500.

331.8 384.54   UK
PHI PI EPSILON STAGE SCREEN & RADIO. 1946. m. £20. Broadcasting, Entertainment, Cinematograph, and Theatre Union, 111 Wardour St., London W1V 4AY, England. TEL 071-437-8506. FAX 071-437-8268. Ed. Janice Turner. adv.; bk.rev. circ. 55,000. Document type: newsletter.
Former titles: Phi Pi Epsilon B E T A News; B E T A News; Which incorporates (in 1985): A B Stract; Nattke News.
Description: Includes association news, radio, television and cinema industry and theatre news.

331.8   US
PIPELINES. 1958. m. membership. Plumbers - Steamfitters U A Local 38, 1621 Market St., San Francisco, CA 94103. TEL 415-626-2000. Ed. Rob Weinstein. tr.lit./ circ. 3,000 (controlled). (tabloid format) Document type: newspaper.

331.8   US   ISSN 0032-1036
PLASTERER AND CEMENT MASON. 1951. m. membership. Plasterers & Cement Masons International, 1125 17th St., N.W., Washington, DC 20036. TEL 202-393-6569. FAX 202-393-2514. Ed. Dominic Martell. adv.; circ. 40,000 (controlled). Document type: newspaper.

331.88   PE
PONTIFICIA UNIVERSIDAD CATOLICA. TALLER DE ESTUDIOS URBANO INDUSTRIALES. SERIE: ESTUDIOS SINDICALES. no.3, 1976. irreg. Pontificia Universidad Catolica, Taller de Estudios Urbanos Industriales, Fundo Pando s-n, Lima, Peru.

331.8 620.85   US
PORTLAND ALLIANCE. (Text in English, Spanish) 1981. m. $20. Northwest Alliance for Alternative Media & Education, 2807 S.E. Stark, Portland, OR 97214. TEL 503-239-4991. Ed. Norm Diamond. adv.; bk.rev.; film rev.; play rev.; illus. circ. 7,500. (back issues avail.) Document type: newspaper.
Description: Covers local and regional political, cultural and environmental issues from a radical perspective.

331.88 350   US   ISSN 0032-5376
HD6350.P75
POSTAL RECORD. 1888. m. $16. National Association of Letter Carriers, A F L - C I O, 100 Indiana Ave., N.W., Washington, DC 20001. TEL 202-393-4695. FAX 202-737-1540. Ed. Lorraine Swerdloff. illus. circ. 315,000.

POTRAVINAR. see NUTRITION AND DIETETICS

POWER. see BUSINESS AND ECONOMICS — Labor And Industrial Relations

331.8   NO
PRAUSIS. 1905. 10/yr. NOK 50. Arbeidernes Ungdomsfylking, Arbeidersamfunnets Plass 1, Oslo 1, Norway. Ed. Jens Ove Kristiansen. adv.; bk.rev. circ. 31,811.
Formerly: Arbeidrungdommen.

331.8 364   US
PRECINCT REPORTER. 1965. w. $20. Brian Townsend, Ed. & Pub., 1677 W. Baseline St., San Bernardino, CA 92411. FAX 714-889-1706. circ. 55,000. Document type: newspaper.

PROCESSED WORLD. see COMPUTERS

331.8   RU
PROFSOYUZY. 1917. m. $115. (Vsesoyuznyi Tsentral'nyi Sovet Professional'nykh Soyuzov) Profizdat, Ul. Myasnitskaya 13, 101000 Moscow, Russia. (Dist. by: Mezhdunarodnaya Kniga, Moscow, G-200, Russia; Dist. in U.S. by: Victor Kamkin Inc., 4956 Boiling Brook Pkwy, Rockville, MD 20852. TEL 301-881-5973) Ed. M.P. Mudrov. bk.rev.; illus. circ. 269,970.
Formerly: Sovetskie Profsoyuzy (ISSN 0132-1196)

331.8   US   ISSN 1062-5992
HD8008.A1
PUBLIC EMPLOYEE MAGAZINE. 1935. 8/yr. membership. American Federation of State, County & Municipal Employees, A F L - C I O, 1625 L St., N.W., Washington, DC 20036-5687. TEL 202-429-1144. FAX 202-429-1084. Ed. Marshall O. Donley. bk.rev. circ. 1,400,000. (also avail. in microform from UMI) Indexed: Pers.Lit. Document type: trade publication. —UnCover.
Formerly (until 1991): Public Employee (Washington) (ISSN 0161-7494)
Description: Official publication with matters of interest to the American Federation of State, County and Municipal Employees.

331.88 350   US   ISSN 0033-345X
PUBLIC EMPLOYEE PRESS. 1959. fortn. (m. in Jan., July, Aug.). $15 to non-members. American Federation of State, County & Municipal Employees, A F L - C I O, District Council 37, 125 Barclay St., New York, NY 10007. TEL 212-815-1000. FAX 212-815-7535. Ed. Walter Balcerak. bk.rev.; illus. circ. 160,000. (tabloid format) Document type: newspaper.

331.88   AT
PUBLIC SECTOR VOICE. 1914. 10/yr. Aus.$2 to members only. State Public Services Federation, Queensland, P.O. Box 175, Level 2-3, 96 Albert St., Brisbane, Qld. 4000, Australia. TEL 07-210-0544. FAX 07-210-0525. Ed. Jeni Eastwood. adv. circ. 13,000. Document type: government publication.
Supersedes (in Jan. 1993): Professional Officer (ISSN 0048-5454)

PUBLIC SERVICE ASSOCIATION JOURNAL. see PUBLIC ADMINISTRATION

3210 LABOR UNIONS

331.88   PR
PUERTO RICO. DEPARTMENT OF LABOR. DIRECTORIO DE ORGANIZACIONES DEL TRABAJO. 1965. a. free. Department of Labor, Bureau of Labor Statistics, 505 Munoz Rivera Ave., Hato Rey, PR 00918. Ed. Federico Irizarry. circ. 900. (also avail. in microform) **Document type:** government publication.

331.8   AA
PUNA/TRAVAIL. (Editions in Albanian and French) q. $1.54. Unions Professionnelles d'Albanie, Tirana, Albania.

QUARTERNOTE. see *MUSIC*

331.8   GW   ISSN 0033-6246
HD4809
DIE QUELLE; Funktionaerzeitschrift des Deutschen Gewerkschaftsbundes. 1951. m. DM.24. (Deutscher Gewerkschaftsbund) Bund-Verlag GmbH, Postfach 900840, 51118 Cologne, Germany. adv.; bk.rev.; illus. circ. 200,000. **Indexed:** Dok.Arbeitsmed. **Document type:** bulletin.
—BLDSC (7216.100000). **CCC**.

331.8 621.3   IC
R.S.I. BLADID; felagsblad rafidnadarmanna. 1988. s-a. membership. Rafidnadarsamband Islands, Haaleitisbraut 68, 103 Reykjavik, Iceland. TEL 354-1-681433. FAX 354-1-39097. Ed. Boedvar Bjarki Petursson. circ. 3,000. (back issues avail.)
Description: Concerned with issues of interest to labor unions such as wages and insurance, as well as politics and technical news for workers in the electricity branch.

331.88   US   ISSN 0033-7196
R W D S U RECORD. 1954. bi-m. $3. Retail Wholesale and Department Store Union, AFL-CIO, CLC, 30 E. 29th St., New York, NY 10016. TEL 212-684-5300. Ed. Stuart Applebaum. bk.rev.; charts; illus. circ. 140,000. (tabloid format; also avail. in microform from UMI; reprint service avail. from UMI) **Document type:** newspaper.
—UMI.
Description: Concerns union activites at the local level.

331.8   US
RACINE LABOR; Racine's voice of working people. 1941. w. $23.50. Union Labor Publishing Co., Inc., 1840 Sycamore Ave., Racine, WI 53406. TEL 414-634-7186. Ed. Jim McNeill. adv. circ. 12,225. (tabloid format; back issues avail.) **Document type:** newspaper.
Description: Covers local and national labor issues.

331.8   YU   ISSN 0033-7463
RAD. 1945. a. 320 din. Savez Sindikata Jugoslavije, Trg Marksa i Engelsa 5, 11000 Belgrade, Yugoslavia. Ed. Stanislav Marinkovic. (also avail. in microfilm from NRP) **Indexed:** Math.R.

385   FR
RAIL SYNDICALISTE. 1947. m. Federation Syndicale Force Ouvriere des Cheminots, 60 rue Vergniand, 75640 Paris Cedex 13, France. adv.

RASANT; Zeitschrift der D A G-Jugend. see *CHILDREN AND YOUTH — For*

331.88   US   ISSN 0034-1541
THE RECORD (NEW YORK, 1940). 1940. m. free. Utility Workers Union of America, A F L - C I O, Local 1-2, 386 Park Ave. S., New York, NY 10016. TEL 212-532-7110. FAX 212-684-3987. Ed. Joseph Flaherty. illus. **Indexed:** Rehabil.Lit.

331.8   US
THE RECORDER (SAN FRANCISCO). 1877. d. (Mon.-Fri.). $295 to small firms and individuals; large firms $475. Am Law Newspaper Co., 625 Polk St., Ste. 500, San Francisco, CA 94102. TEL 415-749-5400. FAX 415-749-5449. Ed. Craig Madden. circ. 6,250. **Document type:** newspaper.

331.8   AT   ISSN 1030-0740
RED TAPE. bi-m. Aus.$20. Public Service Association of New South Wales, G.P.O. Box 3365, Sydney, N.S.W. 2001, Australia. TEL 02-290-1555. FAX 02-262-1623. Ed. Les Carr. circ. 45,000. (tabloid format)
Description: Covers wages, conditions of public sector employees and broader industrial and political issues for union members.

REEL. see *MOTION PICTURES*

331.9   US
RETAIL UNIONIST. q. membership. Retail Clerks Union No.648, 1980 Mission St., San Francisco, CA 94103. TEL 415-861-7840. Ed. Joseph F. Grech. circ. 6,000. **Document type:** newspaper.

331.8   AG
REVISTA GREMIAL. 1991. m. Arg.$20000 per no. Producciones Periodisticas Independientes, Alberti 93, piso 6o D, 1082 Buenos Aires, Argentina. TEL 953-5638. Dirs. Jose di Mauro, Oscar Benini.

331.8   SZ   ISSN 0035-421X
REVUE SYNDICALE SUISSE. 1909. 6/yr. 35 SFr. Union Syndicale Suisse - Swiss Federation of Trade Unions, Monbijoustr. 61, CH-3000 Bern 23, Switzerland. FAX 031-3710837. Ed. Fernand Quartenoud. bk.rev.; index. **Indexed:** C.I.S.Abstr., World Bibl.Soc.Sec. **Document type:** bulletin.

331.8 340   IT   ISSN 0392-7229
RIVISTA GIURIDICA DEL LAVORO E DELLA PREVIDENZA SOCIALE. DOTTRINA. 1949. q. L.130000 (foreign L.230000) (effective 1994). Ediesse s.r.l., Via dei Frentani, 4-A, 00185 Rome, Italy. TEL 06-448701. FAX 06-4481260. index. circ. 2,000. (back issues avail.)
—BLDSC (7986.620000).

331.88   XO   ISSN 0557-1693
ROCENKA ODBORARA. a. 15 Kcs. (Slovenska Odborova Rada) Praca, spol. s r.o., Odborarske Nam. 3, 812 71 Bratislava, Slovakia. TEL 42-7-650-60. FAX 42-7-212-985. Ed. Michal Zaleta.

331.88   US   ISSN 0887-7920
ROCHESTER A F L - C I O LABOR NEWS. Key Title: Labor News (Rochester, N.Y.). 1945. s-m. $7. A F L - C I O, Rochester Labor Council, 509 N. Goodman St., Rochester, NY 14609. TEL 716-232-7018. Ed. Ronald K. Barlow. adv. contact: Ron Barlow. circ. 10,000. (tabloid format) **Document type:** newspaper.

331.8   SW   ISSN 0347-0342
S A C O - S R-TIDNINGEN.* 1954. 8/yr. SEK 110. Centralorganisationen S A C O-S R - Swedish Confederation of Professional Associations, P.O. Box 2206, 114 89 Stockholm, Sweden. FAX 08-20-40-49. TELEX 810-52-25. Ed. Lars-Goeran Heldt. adv.; charts; illus.; stat. circ. 35,000.
Formerly: S A C O Tidningen (ISSN 0036-0597)

331.88   SA   ISSN 0036-1011
S.A. WORKER/S.A. WERKER. (Text in Afrikaans and English) 1941. m. R.12. South African Iron, Steel and Allied Industries Union, 430 Church St. W., P.O. Box 19299, Pretoria, South Africa. Ed. J.A. van Niekerk-Venter. adv.; bk.rev. circ. 28,000. **Document type:** trade publication, newspaper.

331.88   US
S E I U UPDATE. (Building Service, Office Worker Healthcare, Public and Industrial & Allied Division Editions) 1977. q. free. Service Employees International Union, AFL-CIO, CLC, 1313 L St., N.W., Washington, DC 20005. TEL 202-898-3200. FAX 202-898-3438. Ed. Joyce Moscato. circ. 50,000 (controlled). **Document type:** government publication.
Formerly (until 1986): S E I U Leadership News Update.
Description: Consists of five quarterly news magazines for union leaders in the building service, clerical, health care, public sector and other industries.

331.88   SW   ISSN 0349-4438
S I F - TIDNINGEN. 1921. 20/yr. Svenska Industritjaenstemannafoerbundet - Swedish Union of Clerical & Technical Employees in Industry, S-105 32 Stockholm, Sweden. Ed. Bengt Rolfer. adv.; bk.rev.; abstr.; illus.; stat.; index. circ. 303,000.
Former titles (until 1980): S I F
Industritjaenstemannen; (until 1971):
Industritjaenstemannen; (until 1932): S.V.T.

331.88   US
S P E E A SPOTLITE. 1963. m. $53 membership. Seattle Professional Engineering Employees Association, 15205 52nd Ave. S., Seattle, WA 98188. TEL 206-433-0995. FAX 206-248-3990. Ed. Robbi Alberts. adv.; charts; stat.; circ. 18,000 (controlled). (back issues avail.) **Document type:** newsletter.
Description: Discusses labor union issues for engineers, scientists, and technical employees.

331.88   US   ISSN 0036-2247
HD6517.C2
SACRAMENTO VALLEY UNION LABOR BULLETIN. 1928. m. $10. Sacramento Area Central Labor Council, Building Trades Council, 2840 El Centro Rd., No. 109, Sacramento, CA 95833-9700. TEL 916-646-4007. Ed. Rita A. Carroll. adv. contact: Linda Bedrosian. bk.rev.; charts; illus.; stat. circ. 14,000. (tabloid format) **Document type:** bulletin, newsletter.

331.88   US
ST. LOUIS - SOUTHERN ILLINOIS LABOR TRIBUNE; the official weekly A F L - C I O newspaper. 1937. w. $25. Labor Tribune Publishing Co., 505 S. Ewing Ave., St. Louis, MO 63103. TEL 314-535-9660. FAX 314-535-9013. Ed. Sherwood Kerker. adv. circ. 90,000. (tabloid format; also avail. in microfilm) **Document type:** newspaper.
Formerly: St. Louis Labor Tribune (ISSN 0190-0870); Incorporates: Southern Illinois Labor Tribune (ISSN 0490-0200)

331.8 780   US   ISSN 0036-407X
SAN DIEGO SOUND POST. 1945. bi-m. $12. American Federation of Musicians, Musicians Association of San Diego County Local 325, 1717 Morena Blvd., San Diego, CA 92110. TEL 619-276-4324. FAX 619-276-4876. Ed. Edward C. Arias. adv.; illus. circ. 1,200. **Document type:** newspaper.

331.8 780.65   YU
SAVEZ ORGANIZACIJA KOMPOZITORA JUGOSLAVIJE. BILTEN. English edition: Union of Yugoslav Composers' Organizations. Bulletin. (Text in Serbo-Croatian) 1971. m. free. Savez Organizacija Kompozitora Jugoslavije (SOKOJ), Misarska 12-14, 11000 Belgrade, Yugoslavia. TEL 38-11-334771. FAX 33-11-336-168. Ed. Ivan Kovac. circ. 1,500.
Description: Publishes news on union's activities in the country and abroad.

331.8   YU
SAVEZ SINDIKATA JUGOSLAVIJE. VECA S S J. BILTEN. 1953. m. Savez Sindikata Jugoslavije, Veca S S J, Trg Marksa i Engelsa 5, Belgrade, Yugoslavia. Ed. Radovan Vukovic. circ. 5,000.
Formerly: Savez Sindikata Jugoslavije. Centralni Vec. Bilten (ISSN 0006-2561)

331.8   SJ
SAWT AL UMMAL/WORKER'S VOICE. m. £S025 per no. Sudan Federation of Trade Unions, P.O. Box 2285, Khartoum, Sudan.

331.8   US   ISSN 8750-1708
SCANNER KING COUNTY LABOR NEWS. bi-m. $7. King County Labor Council, 2800 1st Ave., Rm. 206, Seattle, WA 98121. TEL 206-441-7102. FAX 206-441-7103. Ed. Ron Judd. circ. 80,000. **Document type:** newspaper.

331.8 791   US   ISSN 0036-956X
PN1993
SCREEN ACTOR. 1934. q. $7. Screen Actors Guild, 5757 Wilshire Blvd., Los Angeles, CA 90036-3600. TEL 213-549-6652. FAX 213-549-6698. Ed. Harry Medred. adv.; bk.rev.; illus. circ. 90,000. (back issues avail.) **Indexed:** Film Lit.Ind. (1982-). **Document type:** trade publication.
Formerly (until 1959): Screen Actor News (ISSN 0745-7243)
Description: Official publication with news and events of the Screen Actors Guild. Includes articles of general interest about motion pictures.

331.88 387   UK   ISSN 0037-0142
SEAMAN. 1911. m. membership. National Union of Rail, Maritime and Transport Workers, Maritime House, Old Town, Clapham, London SW4 0JP, England. TEL 071-622-5581. FAX 071-738-8636. Ed. Jim Jump. adv.; bk.rev.; illus.; index. circ. 13,000.

LABOR UNIONS

331.88 669.142   CN   ISSN 0037-041X
SEARCHER. vol.7, 1970. m. membership. United Steelworkers of America, Local 6500, 92 Frood Rd., Sudbury, Ont., Canada. TEL 705-675-1383. Ed. Ron MacDonald. illus.

331.88   US
SERVICE EMPLOYEES INTERNATIONAL UNION. INTERNATIONAL CONVENTION OFFICIAL PROCEEDINGS. 17th ed., 1980. quadrennial. Service Employees International Union, 1313 L St., N.W., Washington, DC 20005. TEL 202-898-3200. **Document type:** government publication, proceedings.

331.8   US   ISSN 1041-7400
SERVICE EMPLOYEES NEWS. 1953. bi-m. membership. Service Employees International Union, Local 79, 2604 Fourth St., Detroit, MI 48201. TEL 313-965-9450. FAX 313-965-0422. Ed. Paul Policicchio. circ. 20,000. **Document type:** newspaper.

331.88   US
SERVICE EMPLOYEES UNION. 1921. q. $12 to non-members. Service Employees International Union, AFL-CIO, CLC, 1313 L St., N.W., Washington, DC 20005. TEL 202-898-3200. FAX 202-898-3438. Ed. Susan Calhoun. bk.rev.; film rev.; illus.; circ. 950,000 (controlled). **Document type:** government publication.
Formerly (until 1986): Service Employees (ISSN 0037-2609).
Description: Features opinions, advice and news of interest to union and non-union workers.

331.88   IS   ISSN 0037-413X
SHUROTE. 1938. m. $4.50. General Federation of Labour, P.O. Box 303, Tel Aviv, Israel. Ed. Hayim Yaari. adv. circ. 20,000.

331.88 385   US   ISSN 0037-5020
HD6350.R39
SIGNALMAN'S JOURNAL. 1920. bi-m. $10. Brotherhood of Railroad Signalmen, Box U, Mt. Prospect, IL 60056-9048. TEL 708-439-3732. Ed. J.L. Mattingly. adv.; bk.rev.; charts; illus.; tr.lit.; index. circ. 18,000. (also avail. in microfilm)

331.8   IT   ISSN 0037-5543
SINDACATO MODERNO.* vol.6, 1969. m. L.2000. Federazione Impiegati Operai Metallurgici, Via Maroncelli 34, 47100 Forli, Italy. Ed. Alberto Bellocchio. bk.rev.; charts; illus.

331.8   SP
SINDICALISMO EN ESPANA/TRADE UNIONISM IN SPAIN.* (Text in English, French, Spanish) bi-m. Servicio de Relaciones Exteriores Sindicales, Paseo del Prado, 18-20, Madrid-14, Spain. illus.

331.88   SI
SINGAPOREAN. (Supplements) 1980. fortn. S.$10($1) National Trades Union Congress, Trade Union House, Shenton Way, Singapore 1, Singapore. adv.; abstr.; charts; illus. circ. 25,000. (looseleaf format)
Formerly (until vol.4, 1980): N.T.U.C. Perjuangan (ISSN 0031-5443); Incorporates: Afro-Asian Labour Bulletin (ISSN 0002-063X)

331.88   US
SKILL; the UAW's international magazine for skilled trades members. 1981. q. $5 to non-members. United Automobile, Aerospace, and Agricultural Implement Workers of America, 8000 E. Jefferson, Detroit, MI 48214. TEL 313-926-5277. Ed. D. Elsila. circ. 180,000.

SLUZBA LIDU. see BUSINESS AND ECONOMICS — Management

SOCIAL ACTUALITE; bulletin de la protection sociale. see SOCIAL SERVICES AND WELFARE

SOCIALIST CHALLENGE. see POLITICAL SCIENCE

331.8   US   ISSN 0164-856X
SOLIDARITY (DETROIT). 1958. 10/yr. $5. International, United Automobile, Aerospace and Agricultural Implement Workers of America, 8000 E. Jefferson, Detroit, MI 48114. TEL 313-926-5291. FAX 313-331-1520. Ed. David Elsila. bk.rev.; charts; illus. circ. 1,327,708. **Document type:** consumer publication.
Description: News of the labor movement; economic and political reports.

331.8   MG
SOSIALISMA MPIASA. 1979. m. B.P. 1128, 101 Antananarivo, Malagasy Republic. TEL 21989. Ed. Paul Rabemananjara. circ. 5,000.

SOUTH AFRICAN JOURNAL OF LABOUR RELATIONS. see BUSINESS AND ECONOMICS — Labor And Industrial Relations

331.8 655   SA   ISSN 0038-2787
Z119
SOUTH AFRICAN TYPOGRAPHICAL JOURNAL/SUID-AFRIKAANSE TIPOGRAFIESE JOERNAAL. (Text in Afrikaans and English) 1898. m. R.1.80. South African Typographical Union, P.O. Box 1993, 166 Visagie St., Pretoria, South Africa. Ed. E. Van Tonder. adv.; bk.rev.; illus. circ. 18,000.

SOUTH INDIAN TEACHER. see EDUCATION

331.88   US   ISSN 0038-3953
SOUTHERN CALIFORNIA TEAMSTER. 1941. 12/yr. $5. Joint Council of Teamsters No. 42, 1616 W. Ninth St., Los Angeles, CA 90015. TEL 213-383-4242. Ed. Paul J. Mihalow. bk.rev.; charts; illus. circ. 160,000. (tabloid format)

331.8   LU
SOZIALE FORTSCHRITT; progres social. (Text in French, German) 1920. fortn. 500 Fr. Letzeburger Chreschtleche Gewerkschaftsbond - Confederation of Christian Trade Unions of Luxembourg, 11 rue du Commerce, B.P. 1208, L-1012 Luxembourg, Luxembourg. TEL 49-94-24-1, FAX 49-94-24-49. TELEX 2116 LCGB. Ed. Robert Weber. adv. circ. 25,000. (back issues avail.)

SPLINTER. see CHILDREN AND YOUTH — For

791.4 331.8   UK   ISSN 0969-6652
STAGE SCREEN & RADIO. 1935. m. £20.00 per no. (typically set in Jan.). Broadcasting Entertainment and Cinematograph Theatre Union, 111 Wardour St., London W1V 4AY, England. FAX 437-8268. Ed. Janice Turner. adv.; bk.rev.; illus.; index. circ. 58,000. **Document type:** trade publication.
Former titles (until 1992): F T T and Beta News (ISSN 0015-1106); Film and Television Technician.

331.88 621   US
STAND BY. 1954. bi-m. free to members. Electrical Workers Local 369, Box 36275, Louisville, KY 40233. TEL 502-368-2568. FAX 502-368-1270. Ed. James F. McNay. tr.lit.; circ. 2,000 (controlled). (tabloid format) **Document type:** newspaper.

331.8   GW   ISSN 0172-9527
DER STANDPUNKT (HAMBURG). (Supplement to D A G Journal) 1962. 6/yr. DM.55. Deutsche Angestellten-Gewerkschaft, Karl-Muck-Platz 1, 20355 Hamburg, Germany. TEL 040-34915-1. FAX 040-34915400. Ed. Peter Stueber. bk.rev.; bibl.; charts; illus.; index. circ. 55,000. **Indexed:** CERDIC. **Document type:** trade publication.

331.8   AT
STATE SERVICE; the official journal of the Queensland State Service Union. 1904. m. membership. Queensland State Service Union (Q.S.S.U.), 96 Albert St., Brisbane, Qld. 4000, Australia. TEL 07-221-1633. FAX 07-221-5250. Ed. L.M.J. Gillespie. adv. circ. 17,000. (back issues avail.)
Description: Industrial issues of interest to union members.

STAVEBNIK. see BUILDING AND CONSTRUCTION

331.88 669.142   US   ISSN 0883-3141
STEELABOR. (Text in English, French, Spanish) 1936. bi-m. $5. United Steelworkers of America, Five Gateway Center, Pittsburgh, PA 15222. TEL 412-562-2442. FAX 412-562-2445. Ed. Gary Hubbard. bk.rev.; illus. circ. 950,000. **Document type:** newspaper.
Formerly: Steel Labor (ISSN 0039-0941)

331.88   SW
STUDIER I ARBETARROERELSENS HISTORIA. irreg. Saellskapet foer Studier i Arbetarroerelsens Historia, P.O. Box 16 393, Stockholm, Sweden.

331.88   MY   ISSN 0126-7191
SUARA BURUH. (Text in English) 1956. m. $7.20. Malaysian Trades Union Congress, 19 Jalan Barat, 3rd Fl., P.O. Box 38, Petaling Jaya, Selangor, Malaysia. TEL 03-7560224. Ed. V. David. adv.; charts; illus. circ. 50,000. (tabloid format)
Description: Labor, trade unions and related news.

332.1 331.88   MY   ISSN 0126-947X
SUARA N U B E. (Text in English) 1968. bi-m. free. National Union of Bank Employees, 114 Jalan Tuanku Abdul Rahman, Nube Bldg., 5th Fl., P.O. Box 12488, 50780 Kuala Lumpur, Malaysia. TEL 2927616. FAX 2910050. Ed. K. Sanmugam. charts; illus. circ. 12,000. (tabloid format)

SUGAR WORLD; a newsletter on issues of concern to sugar workers. see FOOD AND FOOD INDUSTRIES

331.88   FR
SYNDICALISME HEBDO. w. 307 F. (foreign 446 F.) (effective Jan. 1992). Confederation Francaise Democratique du Travail, 4 Blvd. de la Villette, 75955 Paris Cedex 19, France. TEL 42-03-81-40. Ed. Loic Richard. charts; illus.; stat.
Former titles: Syndicalisme C F D T; Syndicalisme Hebdo (ISSN 0039-7741)

331.8   FR
SYNDICALISTE FORAIN. 24/yr. 14 rue de Bretagne, 75003 Paris, France. TEL 48-87-43-80. FAX 48-87-58-40. Ed. Claude Cornoueil. circ. 25,200.

331.8   VN   ISSN 0049-2744
SYNDICATS VIETNAMIENS.* (Editions in English and French) vol.13, 1971. q. Federation des Syndicats du Vietnam, 82 Tran Hung Dao, Hanoi, Socialist Republic of Vietnam. charts; illus.

331.8   UK
T & G RECORD. 1922. m. free. Transport and General Workers Union, Transport House, Smith Sq., London SW1P 3JB, England. Ed. Chris Kaufman. circ. 200,000. (tabloid format) **Document type:** newsletter.
Formerly: T G W U Record.

331.88   GH
T U C NEWS. vol.4, 1970. m. $0.15 per copy. Trades Union Congress of Ghana, Hall of Trade Unions, P.O. Box 701, Accra, Ghana. Ed. C.A. Quansah. adv.; illus.; circ. 10,000 (controlled).
Former titles: T U C Newsletter; Ghana Workers' Bulletin (ISSN 0016-9617)

331.88 630 634   RU
T U I A F P W INFORMATION. (Text in Arabic, English, French, Russian, Spanish) 1974. bi-m. exchange basis. Trade Union International of Agricultural, Forestry and Plantation Workers, Bol'shaya Serpokhovskaya, 44, 113093 Moscow, Russia. TEL 230-2070. TELEX 411040 UISAG SU. illus.

331.88   US   ISSN 0039-8659
T W U EXPRESS. 1949. m. $2. Transport Workers Union of America, 80 West End Ave., New York, NY 10023. TEL 212-873-6000. FAX 212-721-2527. Ed. Jim Gannon. bk.rev.; illus. circ. 120,000. (tabloid format; also avail. in microform from UNW) **Document type:** newspaper.

331.8   IS   ISSN 0002-4074
TA'AWUN; cooperation, economics and social welfare. (Text in Arabic) 1960. irreg. (2-3/yr.). Histadrut, Arab Workers' Department, P.O. Box 303, Tel Aviv, Israel. TEL 03-431111. TELEX 342-488-HISTD-IL. Ed. Mahmoied Youners.

371.3 331.8   AT   ISSN 1320-7431
TASMANIAN EDUCATION REVIEW. 1918. 8/yr. Aus.$20. Australian Education Union, Tasmanian Branch, 32 Patrick St., Hobart, Tas., Australia. TEL 002-349500. FAX 002-343052. Ed. C. Duhig. adv.; bk.rev.; illus. circ. 6,400.
Former titles (until Aug. 1993): Teacher (ISSN 0813-6580); (until 1983): Tasmanian Teacher (ISSN 0039-9868)

TEACHERS OF THE WORLD; international pedagogical and trade union review. see EDUCATION

TEACHING TODAY. see EDUCATION

LABOR UNIONS

331.8   US
TEAMSTER CONVOY DISPATCH. 1976. 9/yr. $35. Teamsters for a Democratic Union, Box 10128, Detroit, MI 48210. TEL 313-842-2600. circ. 60,000. (tabloid format; back issues avail.)

TECHNICKY TYDENIK; casopis pro novou techniku a otazky zlepsovatelskeho a vynalezcovskeho hnuti. see TECHNOLOGY: COMPREHENSIVE WORKS

621.38 331.8   NO
TELE TJENESTEN. 10/yr. Norsk Tele Tjeneste Forbund, Moellergt. 10, 0179 Oslo 1, Norway. TEL 02-202-843. Ed. Asbjoern Gardsjord. adv. circ. 14,000.

TELLING IT LIKE IT IS. see TRANSPORTATION — Railroads

331.8   US
TEXAS A F L - C I O NEWS. m. membership. American Federation of Labor - Congress of Industrial Organizations, Texas Division, 1106 Lavaca, No. 200, Austin, TX 78701. TEL 512-477-6195. FAX 512-477-2962. Ed. Christopher Cook. circ. 7,000. **Document type:** newspaper.

331.88 642.5   ISSN 0040-6546
THREE HUNDRED THIRTY-EIGHT NEWS; labor monthly of the food service industry. 1940. bi-m. $3. Retail, Wholesale and Department Store Union, 30 E. 29th St., New York, NY 10016. TEL 212-684-5300. adv.; bk.rev.; rec.rev.; illus. circ. 12,000. (tabloid format) **Document type:** newspaper.

331.8   DK   ISSN 0906-124X
TOLDTIDENDE. 1990. m. membership. D T S - Dansk Told- og Skatteforbund, Tjenestemaendenes Hus, Bredgade 21, DK-1260 Copenhagen K, Denmark. Ed.Bd. circ. 2,300.
    Formed by merger of (1963-1990): Toldbladet (ISSN 0040-9049); (1903-1990): Dansk Toldtidende (ISSN 0901-3415)

331.3   US   ISSN 1058-0557
TRADE UNION ADVISOR. bi-w. (23/yr.) $225 (Canada $235; elsewhere $250) (effective 1993). Labor Research Association, 145 W. 28th St., 6th Fl., New York, NY 10001-6191. TEL 212-714-1677. FAX 212-714-1674. **Document type:** newsletter.

331.88   US   ISSN 0041-0497
TRADE UNION COURIER.* 1936. m. $18.50. (New York Teamsters Joint Council, Carpenters District Council) Socio-Economic Publications, Inc., 386 Park Ave. S., Ste. 1108, New York, NY 10016. Ed. Maxwell C. Raddock. adv.; bk.rev.; charts; illus.; stat. (tabloid format)

331.8   US   ISSN 1053-7007
TRADE UNION HANDBOOK. 1950. a. $25 (effective 1992). New York City Central Labor Council, A F L - C I O, 386 Park Ave. S., New York, NY 10016. TEL 212-685-9552. FAX 212-685-9557. Ed. Ted H. Jacobsen.
    Formerly: New York City Trade Union Handbook (ISSN 0545-6061)
    Description: Contains current information on American labor history, scholarships, publications and services of the AFL-CIO affiliated unions in New York City and State, as well as names and addresses of officers of AFL-CIO unions at city, state, national and international levels.

331.8   SW   ISSN 0284-6403
TRADE UNION NEWS; fackliga nyheter paa engelska. (Editions in Arabic, English, Serbo-Croatian, Spanish) 1983. 4/yr. SEK 50. L O - Landsorganisationen i Sverige, Barnhusgatan 18, 105 53 Stockholm, Sweden. FAX 08-200358. TELEX 19145-LO-PRESS. Ed. Pentti Lehto. adv.; bk.rev. circ. 15,000. (back issues avail.; reprint service avail.) **Document type:** trade publication.
    Formerly: Sindikalistika Nea (ISSN 0281-0557)

331.88   II   ISSN 0445-6289
TRADE UNIONS IN INDIA. (Text in English) biennial. Rs.34($12.24) Labour Bureau, Simla 171004, India. (Order from: Controller of Publications, Government of India, Civil Lines, Delhi 110054, India)
    Supersedes: Review on the Working of the Trade Unions Act, 1926.

TRADE UNIONS INTERNATIONAL OF AGRICULTURAL, FORESTRY AND PLANTATION WORKERS. BULLETIN. see FORESTS AND FORESTRY

943.9   HU
TRADE UNIONS INTERNATIONAL OF CHEMICAL, OIL AND ALLIED WORKERS. INFORMATION BULLETIN. q. Trade Unions International of Chemical, Oil and Allied Workers, Benczur ut 45, 1415 Budapest VI, Hungary.

331.88   HU   ISSN 0084-1544
TRADE UNIONS INTERNATIONAL OF CHEMICAL, OIL AND ALLIED WORKERS. INTERNATIONAL TRADE CONFERENCE. DOCUMENTS. irreg., 7th, Tarnow, Poland. free. Trade Unions International of Chemical, Oil and Allied Workers, Benczur u. 45, Budapest 6, Hungary.

331.88   UK
TRADES UNION CONGRESS. REPORT. Cover title: T U C Report. 1868. a. £38. Trades Union Congress, Congress House, Great Russell St., London WC1B 3LS, England. FAX 071-636-0632. TELEX 268-328-TUC-G. Ed. M.J. Smith. circ. 1,000. (also avail. in microfilm) **Document type:** proceedings.

331.88 385   US   ISSN 0041-0837
HD6350.R318
TRAIN DISPATCHER. 1919. 4/yr. $12 to non-members; members $5. American Train Dispatchers Association, 1401 S. Harlem Ave., Berwyn, IL 60402. TEL 708-795-5656. FAX 708-795-0832. Ed. R.L. Rafferty. adv.; bk.rev.; illus. circ. 3,550. **Document type:** newspaper.
    Formerly: Transit.

331.88 380.5   HU
TRANSPORT WORKERS OF THE WORLD.* (Editions in English, French, Spanish) 1973. q. $15. Trade Unions International of Transport Workers, Koztarsasag ter 3, 1428 Budapest, Hungary. TEL 209-601. Ed. K.C. Mathew. charts; illus. circ. 2,000.

331.8   GV
TRAVAILLEUR DE GUINEE. m. Conakry, Guinea.

LE TRAVAILLEUR DU LIVRE. see PUBLISHING AND BOOK TRADE

331.8   UK   ISSN 0041-2821
TRIBUNE. 1937. w. £1 per no. Tribune Publications Ltd., 308 Grays Inn Rd., London WC1X 8DY, England. Ed. Mark Seddon. adv. contact: George Osgenby. bk.rev.; illus. circ. 40,000. (also avail. in microform) **Document type:** newsletter.

331.8   XN   ISSN 0041-3437
TRUDBENIK; vesnik na sindikalnite organizacii vo Makedonija. (Text in Macedonian) 1945. w. 50 din. Sojuzot na Sindikatite na Makedonija, 12 Udarne brigade 3 a, Skopje, Macedonia. Ed. Simo Ivanovski.

TRUDOVOI TIRASPOL. see POLITICAL SCIENCE — Civil Rights

331.8   PL   ISSN 0866-9198
TYGODNIK GDANSKI. 1989. w. (Zarzad Regionu N S Z Z Solidarnosc) Przekaz, Sp. z o.o., Ul. Waly Piastowskie 24 p. 105-107, 80-855 Gdansk, Poland. TEL 48-58-317612. FAX 48-31-317121. Ed. Andrzej Liberadzki. circ. 50,000.
    Description: Labor union publication. Covers politics, social life, culture, economy.

331.88 630   PL   ISSN 0860-9950
TYGODNIK ROLNIKOW - SOLIDARNOSC. 1989. w. N S Z Z Rolnikow Indywidualnych "Solidornosc", Ul. Dabrowskiego 3, 00-057 Warsaw, Poland. TEL 48-269817. Ed. Adam Wieczorek. circ. 30,000.

TYGODNIK SOLIDARNOSC/SOLIDARITY WEEKLY. see BUSINESS AND ECONOMICS — Economic Situation And Conditions

331.88 655   US   ISSN 0041-4832
TYPOGRAPHICAL JOURNAL.* 1889. m. $6 to non-members. International Typographical Union, 316 Wilcox St., Castle Rock, CO 80104-2441. Ed. Thomas W. Kopeck. adv.; bk.rev.; illus. circ. 75,000. **Indexed:** Graph.Arts Lit.Abstr.
    Incorporates (1912-1979): International Typographical Union. Bulletin.

331.88   US
U A W AMMO. 1960. m. $1.50. United Automobile, Aerospace, and Agricultural Implement Workers of America, 8000 E. Jefferson Ave., Detroit, MI 48214. TEL 313-926-5291. Ed. Frank Joyce. circ. 180,000.
    Formerly: U A W Ammunition (ISSN 0502-9392)

331.88   US   ISSN 0041-4980
U A W WASHINGTON REPORT. vol.9, 1969. w. free. United Automobile, Aerospace, and Agricultural Implement Workers of America (Washington), 1757 N St., N.W., Washington, DC 20036. Ed. Frank Wallick. bk.rev.; charts; illus.; index. circ. 60,000.

331.88 350   UK
U C W JOURNAL. 1920. m. Union of Communication Workers, U.C.W. House, Crescent Ln., Clapham, London SW4 9RN, England. FAX 01-720-6853. Ed. Julia Simpson. adv.; bk.rev. circ. 180,000. **Document type:** bulletin.
    Formerly (until 1993): Post (ISSN 0032-5236)

331.88   US   ISSN 0041-5065
U E NEWS. 1937. every 3 wks. $5 to individuals; institutions $10. United Electrical, Radio & Machine Workers of America, 2400 Oliver Bldg., 535 Smithfield St., Pittsburgh, PA 15222-2304. TEL 412-471-8919. FAX 412-471-8999. Ed. Peter Gilmore. bk.rev.; charts; illus. (also avail. in microfilm) **Document type:** newspaper, trade publication.

331.88   CN
U E NEWS MAGAZINE. vol.33, 1970. bi-m. free. United Electrical Radio and Machine Workers of Canada, 10 Codeco Court, Don Mills, Ont. M3A 1A2, Canada. TEL 416-447-5196. FAX 416-447-5709. Ed. Elias Stavrides. adv.; bk.rev.; charts; illus. circ. 10,000. (also avail. in microfilm)
    Former titles (until 1990): U E News (ISSN 0041-5049); U E Canadian News.

331.88 664.9   US   ISSN 0195-0363
U F C W ACTION. 1979. 6/yr. membership. United Food and Commercial Workers International Union, 1775 K St., N.W., Washington, DC 20006. TEL 202-223-3111. FAX 202-466-1562. Ed. Susan Phillips. illus.; circ. 1,300,000 (controlled). **Document type:** newspaper.
—UMI.
    Incorporates (1989-1979): Retail Clerks Advocate (ISSN 0034-6039); (1911-1979): Butcher Workman (ISSN 0007-7267)

331.8   US
U F C W LOCAL 1500. q. free to members. United Food and Commercial Workers Union, Retail Food Clerks Union, Local 1500, 221-10 Jamaica Ave., Jamaica, Queens Village, NY 11428. TEL 718-479-8700. FAX 718-217-7316. Ed. Charles Michelson. circ. 18,000. (tabloid format) **Document type:** newspaper.

331.88   US
U F C W LOCAL 174. 1967. bi-m. membership. United Food & Commercial Workers, Local 174, 540 W. 48th St., New York, NY 10036. TEL 212-307-7007. FAX 212-307-9390. Ed. Olga Pla. circ. 7,500. (tabloid format) **Document type:** newspaper.

331.8 664   US
U F C W LOCAL 27 REPORTER. (Supplement avail. q.: Retiree Roundup) 1956. bi-m. membership. United Food & Commercial Workers, Local 27, 21 West Rd., Baltimore, MD 21204. TEL 301-337-2700. FAX 301-337-0849. Ed. Tom Russow. circ. 30,000. **Document type:** newspaper.

331.88 690   FI
U I T B B BULLETIN. (Text in English) 1955. q. Trade Unions International of Workers of the Building, Wood and Building Materials Industries, P.O. Box 281, 00101 Helsinki 10, Finland. charts; illus.
    Formerly: U I T B B Information (ISSN 0356-8105)

U L L I C O BULLETIN. (Union Labor Life Insurance Co.) see INSURANCE

331.88 350   US   ISSN 0041-5464
U S A RECORD. vol.10, 1973. m. membership. Uniformed Sanitationmen's Association, 23-25 Cliff St., New York, NY 10038. TEL 212-964-8900. Ed. Edward T. Ostrowski. charts; illus.

LABOR UNIONS 3213

331.88   UK
U S D A W TODAY. 1973. m. £15. Union of Shop Distributive and Allied Workers, Oakley, 188 Wilmslow Rd., Fallowfield, Manchester, England. TEL 061-224-2804. FAX 061-257-2566. Ed. P.H. Jones. adv.; bk.rev.; charts; illus.; stat.; index. circ. 90,000. **Document type:** newsletter.
    Formerly: Dawn; **Supersedes:** New Dawn (ISSN 0028-4521)

331.8   UA
AL-UMMAL. w. Egyptian Trade Union Federation, 90 Sharia Galal, Cairo, Egypt. TEL 02-740362. TELEX 93255. Ed. Ahmed Hara.

UNIFICACION. see *TRANSPORTATION — Railroads*

331.1   US
UNION DEMOCRACY REVIEW. 1972. bi-m. $10 to individuals; institutions $15. Association for Union Democracy, Inc., 500 State St., Brooklyn, NY 11217. TEL 718-855-6650. Ed. Herman Benson. bk.rev. circ. 3,000. **Document type:** newsletter.
    Supersedes: Union Democracy in Action (ISSN 0041-6835)
    Description: Reports movements for reform and development in law affecting union democracy and movements against corruption in labor unions.

331.8   SP
UNION GENERAL DE TRABAJADORES. REVISTA. 26/yr. Union General de Trabajadores - General Workers' Union, Hortaleza 86-88, 28004 Madrid, Spain. TEL 1-589-76-00-01. Ed. Miguel Angel Ordonez.

331.88 630   MY   ISSN 0049-528X
HD6820.6.Z6
UNION HERALD. (Text in English) vol.65, 1985. m. M.$0.50 per no. National Union of Plantation Workers, Plantation Workers House, P.O. Box 73, 46700 Petaling Jaya, Selangor, Malaysia. TEL 7927861. Ed.Bd. bk.rev.; abstr.; stat. circ. 1,000. (processed)
    Description: Provides news about agriculture for plantation workers in Southeast Asia.

331.8   US
UNION LABOR JOURNAL. 1903. q. $3. Kern-Inyo-Mono County Central Labor Council, 200 W. Jeffrey, Bakersfield, CA 93305. TEL 805-324-6451. circ. 6,300.

331.88   US   ISSN 0041-6924
UNION LABOR NEWS. 1937. m. $6. Union Labor News Publishers, Ltd., 1602 S. Park, Rm. 228, Madison, WI 53715. TEL 608-256-5111. Ed. James A. Cavanaugh. adv.; bk.rev.; illus. circ. 16,000. (tabloid format; also avail. in microform) **Document type:** newspaper.

UNION LABOR REPORT. see *BUSINESS AND ECONOMICS — Labor And Industrial Relations*

UNION LABOR REPORT WEEKLY NEWSLETTER. see *BUSINESS AND ECONOMICS — Labor And Industrial Relations*

UNION LABOR REPORT'S ON THE LINE; a guide for union stewards. see *BUSINESS AND ECONOMICS — Labor And Industrial Relations*

331.8   US
UNION MAGAZINE. (Supplement avail.) 1921. q. membership. Service Employees International Union, 1313 L St., N.W., Washington, DC 20005. TEL 202-898-3200. FAX 202-898-3438. Ed. Karen Gutloff. bk.rev. circ. 1,000,000. **Document type:** newspaper.

331.88   CN
UNION MATTERS. 1927. 6/yr. free. Saskatchewan Government Employees' Union, 1440 Broadway Ave., Regina, Sask. S4P 1E2, Canada. TEL 306-522-8571. FAX 306-352-1969. Ed. Beth Smillie. charts; illus.; stat.; circ. 17,500 (controlled).
    Former titles: Common Ground; (until 1986): Dome (ISSN 0319-8588)

331.8   SZ   ISSN 0503-2334
UNION MONDIALE DES ORGANISATIONS SYNDICALES SUR BASES ECONOMIQUE ET SOCIALE LIBERALES. CONFERENCES: RAPPORT. 1960. a. World Union of Liberal Trade Union Organisations, 41 Badenerstr., CH-8004 Zurich, Switzerland.

331.8   UK
UNION NEWS. 1952. q. Amalgamated Engineering and Electrical Union, Electrical, Electronic and Telecommunications - Plumbing Union Section, W. Common Rd., Hayes, Bromley, Kent, England. FAX 081-462-4959. Ed. Gavin H. Laird. adv.; bk.rev.; abstr.; charts; illus.; stat.; tr.lit.; index. circ. 830,000. **Document type:** newspaper.
    Former titles (until 1993): Contact (Bromley); Electron (ISSN 0010-7255)

331.8 674   US   ISSN 0274-970X
UNION REGISTER. 1937. m. $9. Western Council of Industrial Workers Union, 721 S.W. Oak, Portland, OR 97205. TEL 503-228-0780. FAX 503-228-0245. Ed. Merle A. Reinikka. circ. 22,000. (tabloid format) **Document type:** newspaper.

331.8   US
UNION TOPICS. 1949. q. membership. Amalgamated Transit Union, Local 1300, 126 W. 25th St., Baltimore, MD 21218. TEL 410-889-3566. FAX 410-243-5541. Ed. Lawrence Prince Lloyd. adv.; bk.rev. circ. 2,700. (tabloid format) **Document type:** newspaper.

331.8   IT   ISSN 0394-8390
L'UNIONE DEI SEGRETARI. 1952; N.S. 1987. bi-m. L.90000. (Unione dei Segretari) Maggioli Editore, Viale Vespucci 12-n, Casella Postale 290, 47037 Rimini, Italy. TEL 0541-626777. FAX 0541-622020. Ed. Antonino Saija.

331.2   US
THE UNIONEER. 1961. q. $15. C W A, 1408 N. Washington, Dallas, TX 75204. TEL 214-826-6215. Ed. Connie Gloyen. circ. 5,000. (tabloid format) **Document type:** newspaper.

331.88 360   US   ISSN 0041-7092
UNIONIST. 1965. m. membership. Social Service Employees Union, Local 371, District Council 37, A F S C M E , A F L - C I O, 817 Broadway, New York, NY 10003. TEL 212-677-3900. Ed. Martin Fishgold. bk.rev.; illus. circ. 17,000.
    Formerly: S S E U News.

331.8   US
THE UNIONIST. 1945. m. $6.50. 1309 N.W. Radial Hwy., Omaha, NE 68132. TEL 402-558-9500. Ed. Larry L. Maupin. circ. 30,000. **Document type:** newspaper.

331.88 696.1   US   ISSN 0041-7181
UNITED ASSOCIATION JOURNAL. 1889. m. free. United Association of Journeymen and Apprentices of the Plumbing and Pipe Fitting Industry of the United States and Canada, 901 Massachusetts Ave., N.W., Washington, DC 20001. TEL 202-628-5823. FAX 202-628-5024. Ed. Marion A. Lee. charts; illus. circ. 300,000. **Document type:** trade publication.

331.8 664   US
UNITED FOOD & COMMERCIAL WORKERS UNION LOCAL 876. 1964. bi-m. free to members. United Food & Commercial Workers, Local 876, 876 Horace Brown Dr., Madison Heights, MI 48071. TEL 313-585-9671. FAX 313-585-0509. Ed. Ronald L. Brown. circ. 24,000. **Document type:** newspaper.

331.88 622   US   ISSN 0041-7327
HD6350.M6
UNITED MINE WORKERS JOURNAL. 1891. m. $10 to individuals; institutions $25; corporations $100. United Mine Workers, 900 15th St., N.W., Washington, DC 20005. TEL 202-842-7200. Ed. Greg Hawthorne. bk.rev.; film rev. circ. 200,000. (also avail. in microform; back issues avail.) —UnCover.

331.88 678   US   ISSN 0162-3869
HD6350.R9
UNITED RUBBER WORKER. 1935. bi-m. $10 for 12 nos. to non-members. United Rubber, Cork, Linoleum, & Plastic Workers of America, AFL-CIO, CLC, Public Relations Office, 570 White Pond Dr., Akron, OH 44320-1156. TEL 216-869-0320. FAX 216-869-5627. Ed. Kenneth L. Coss. bk.rev. circ. 150,000. **Document type:** trade publication.

331.88 669.142   CN   ISSN 0566-0963
UNITED STEELWORKERS OF AMERICA. INFORMATION. (Text in English and French) bi-m. United Steelworkers of America, 92 Frood Rd., Sudbury, Ont., Canada. TEL 705-675-1383. illus.

331.8 647.9   US
UNITED VOICE. 1942. bi-m. membership. Hotel Employees Union & Restaurant Employees Union, 515 N. Cabrillo Park Dr., Ste. 205, Santa Ana, CA 92701. TEL 714-542-3119. FAX 714-542-3182. Ed. Angela J. Keefe. **Document type:** newspaper.
    Formerly (until 1991): Serving America.

331.88 312
UNITY. 1968. q. membership. Society of Registration Officers, Civic Centre, Barras Bridge, Newcastle upon Tyne NE1 8PS, England. TEL 091-232-8520. Ed. David Morgan. adv. circ. 700. (processed) **Document type:** trade publication.

331.8
UNITY (ALBANY). 1984. m. free. New York State A F L - C I O, 100 S. Swan St., Albany, NY 12210. TEL 518-436-8516. (And: c/o Mario Cilento, Pubic Relations, 48 E. 21st St., 12th Fl., New York, NY 10010. TEL 212-777-6040) Ed. Edward J. Cleary. circ. 5,000. **Document type:** newspaper.

UNIVERSITETSLAERAREN. see *EDUCATION*

331.8   GW   ISSN 0941-9233
UNTERNEHMEN UND GESELLSCHAFT. 4/yr. DM.73.45. (Institut der Deutschen Wirtschaft) Deutscher Instituts Verlag GmbH, Postfach 510670, 50942 Cologne, Germany. TEL 0221-3708341. FAX 0221-3708191. TELEX 8882768-IWKD. **Document type:** trade publication.
    Former titles (until 1991): Institut der Deutschen Wirtschaft. Gewerkschaftsreport (ISSN 0084-9782); Deutsches Industrieinstitut. Berichte zu Gewerkschaftsfragen.

331.8   US   ISSN 0190-4965
UTILITY REPORTER. 1941. m. membership. International Brotherhood of Electrical Workers, Local Union 1245, 3063 Citrus Circle, Box 4790, Walnut Creek, CA 94596. TEL 510-933-6060. FAX 510-933-0115. Ed. Eric Wolfe. bk.rev. circ. 22,000. (tabloid format) **Document type:** newspaper.

331.8   SZ
V O REALITES. (Text in French) 1944. w. 100 Fr. Parti Suisse du Travail, 4-6, rue du Pre-Jerome, 1205 Geneva, Switzerland. TEL 022-206335.
    Formerly (until 1986): Voix Ouvriere.

331.8   FR   ISSN 0980-7217
V R P SYNDICALISTE. (Voyageur Representant Placier) 7/yr. 270 F. for 12 nos. Federation Nationale des Syndicats, V R P et Commerciaux F O, 6 rue Albert Bayet, 75013 Paris, France. TEL 45-70-75-90. FAX 44-24-35-69. Ed. Henry Dupille. adv.: B&W page 19000 F., color page 27300 F.; trim 275 x 190. illus. circ. 22,000.

331.88 621.3   FI   ISSN 0049-5883
VASAMA. 1957. s-m. FIM 105. Suomen Sahkoalantyontekijain Liitto - Finnish Electric Workers' Union, P.O. Box 747, 33101 Tampere, Finland. TEL 358-31-2520-111. FAX 358-31-2520-210. Ed. Seppo Salisma. adv.; charts; illus.; circ. 31,238 (controlled). (tabloid format) **Document type:** trade publication.

331.88   FR   ISSN 1240-9367
VIE A DEFENDRE. 1965. m. 100 F. Confederation Francaise des Travailleurs Chretiens, 13 rue des Ecluses Saint-Martin, 75483 Paris Cedex 10, France. TEL 44-52-49-00. FAX 44-52-49-18. Ed. G. Drilleaud. adv. contact: Pierre Cabaret. bk.rev.; charts; illus. circ. 200,000.
    Formerly: Syndicalisme C F T C (ISSN 0039-775X)

VIE DE LA RECHERCHE SCIENTIFIQUE. see *SCIENCES: COMPREHENSIVE WORKS*

331.8   FR   ISSN 0399-1164
VIE OUVRIERE. 1909. w. 550 F. (foreign 760 F.). (Confederation Generale du Travail) Vie Ouvriere, 33 rue Bouret, 75940 Paris Cedex 19, France. TEL 40-40-36-51. FAX 42-09-99-65. Ed. Roger Guilbert. adv.; bk.rev. circ. 264,555. **Indexed:** RADAR.

331.8   IT   ISSN 0042-7357
VITA SINDACALE BERGAMASCA. 1960. fortn. Unione Sindacale Provinciale, G. Paglia 16, 24100 Bergamo, Italy. Ed. Dir. Dino T. Donadoni. illus. (tabloid format)

LABOR UNIONS — ABSTRACTING, BIBLIOGRAPHIES, STATISTICS

331.8   IT
LA VOCE DELLA U I L. 1961. m. free. Unione Italiana del Lavoro, Piazzetta Padenna, 26, 48100 Ravenna, Italy. TEL 0544-36059. FAX 0544-36899. stat.; tr.lit.; index.
    Formerly: Nessuno.
    Description: Covers various topics on the Italian labor union.

331.88   JO
VOICE OF JORDANIAN LABOURERS/SAWT UMMAL AL-URDON.* (Text in Arabic) 1973. m. General Federation of Jordania Trade Unions, Wadi as-Sir Rd., P.O. Box 1065, Amman, Jordan. Ed. Salim Jedoun.

331.8   US
VOICE OF LOCAL ONE. 1957. q. free. United Food and Commercial Workers Union, Local One, 106 Memorial Pkwy., Utica, NY 13501. TEL 315-797-9600. FAX 315-797-0576. Ed. Paul Lameo. circ. 32,000. **Document type:** newspaper.

331.8   US
VOICE OF LOCAL 399. (Supplements avail.: Accion, 399 Organizer) 1976. m. membership. Hospital & Service Employees Union, Local 399, 1247 W. Seventh St., Los Angeles, CA 90017. TEL 213-680-9567. FAX 213-488-0328. Ed. Tom Ramsay. bk.rev. circ. 30,000. (tabloid format; back issues avail.) **Document type:** newspaper.

331.8   US   ISSN 0741-3742
VOICE OF LOCAL 880. 1983. m. free. United Food and Commercial Workers, Local 880, 2828 Euclid, Cleveland, OH 44115. TEL 216-241-5930. FAX 216-241-2826. Ed. James B. Jerele. circ. 20,000. (tabloid format) **Document type:** newspaper.
    Supersedes (1979-1983): Voice (Akron) (ISSN 0199-2821)

VOICE OF THE UNIONS. see BUSINESS AND ECONOMICS — Labor And Industrial Relations

331.8   US
VOICE OF 1319. q. free. Voice of 1319, 67 Public Sq., IBEW Bldg., Rm. 1217, Wilkes Barre, PA 18701. TEL 717-823-2078. FAX 717-824-9025. Ed. Anthony Harzinski. circ. 800. **Document type:** newspaper.

331.8   CF
VOIX DE LA CLASSE OUVRIERE. Short title: Voco. 6/yr. B.P. 2311, Brazzaville, Congo. TEL 83-36-66. Ed. Marie-Joseph Tsengou. circ. 4,500.

331.88 655.55   AU   ISSN 0042-8930
VORWAERTS. 1867. m. membership. Gewerkschaft Druck und Papier, Seidengasse 15, A-1070 Vienna, Austria. Ed. Josef Keller. bk.rev.; illus. circ. 26,000.

331.8   RU
VREMYA. 1990. w. 10.44 Rub. Nezavisimye Profsoyuzy Kuzbassa, Pr. Sovetskii 56, Kemerovo, Russia. circ. 24,799. **Document type:** newspaper.
    Formerly (until Oct. 1990): Profsoyuzy i Vremya.

331.8   RU   ISSN 0201-7628
VSEMIRNOE PROFSOYUZNOE DVIZHENIE.* (Editions in several languages) 1949. m. 7.20 Rub. (World Federation of Trade Unions) Profizdat, Ul. Myasnitskaya 13, 101000 Moscow, Russia. TEL 095-924-5740. (Dist. by: Mezhdunarodnaya Kniga, Moscow, G-200, Russia) Ed. A.V. Byhovskii. illus.; stat.

331.116 664.9   AT
W.A. MEAT WORKER. s-a. free. Australasian Meat Industry Employees' Union, W.A. Branch, 1 St. Floor, 102 Beaufort St., Perth, W.A. 6000, Australia. Ed. D.J. Beaton.

W B F IN ACTION. (Workmen's Benefit Fund of the United States of America) see INSURANCE

W S I MITTEILUNGEN. (Wirtschafts- und Sozialwissenschaftliches Institut) see SOCIAL SCIENCES: COMPREHENSIVE WORKS

331.8   US
WEST VIRGINIA A F L - C I O OBSERVER. 1967. q. free. West Virginia Labor Federation, A F L - C I O, 501 Broad St., Charleston, WV 25301. TEL 304-344-3550. FAX 304-344-3550. Ed. Lee Beard. circ. 72,000. **Document type:** newspaper.

331.8 674   CN   ISSN 0049-7371
WESTERN CANADIAN LUMBER WORKER. 1939. m. Can.$2. International Woodworkers of America, 1285 W. Pender St., 500, Vancouver, BC V6E 4B2, Canada. TEL 604-683-1117. Ed. Clay Perry. adv.; bk.rev. circ. 34,000. (tabloid format; also avail. in microfilm)

WESTERN TEACHER. see EDUCATION

331.88   US   ISSN 0043-4876
WHITE COLLAR. no.322, May 1973. q. $1 per no. Office and Professional Employees International Union, AFL-CIO, CLC, Rm. 610, 265 W. 14th St., New York, NY 10011. Ed. John Kelly. charts; illus.; stat. circ. 120,000.

331.8   US   ISSN 1070-2415
▼**THE WINNING EDGE.** 1993. q. Transportation Communications International Union, 3 Research Pl., Rockville, MD 20850. TEL 301-948-4910. FAX 301-948-1369. Ed. R. Scardelletti. circ. 2,300 (controlled). **Document type:** newsletter.
    Description: Examines economic trends, arbitration decisions and collective bargaining agreements affecting members employed in the transportation industry, especially railroads.

331.4   AT   ISSN 0818-6154
WOMEN'S CONTACT BULLETIN. 1986. irreg. Public Service Association of New South Wales, G.P.O. Box 3365, Sydney, N.S.W. 2001, Australia. TEL 02-290-1555. FAX 02-262-1623. Ed. Les Carr. circ. 9,000.
    Description: Covers industrial relations of particular importance to women.

331.88 694   US   ISSN 0894-7481
WOODWORKER. 1942. 6/yr. $5. International Woodworkers of America, U.S. - A F L - C I O, 25 Cornell Ave., Gladstone, OR 97027-2547. Ed. Glenn Blaylock. adv.; bk.rev.; illus. circ. 26,000. (tabloid format) **Document type:** newspaper.
    Formerly (until 1987): International Woodworker (ISSN 0020-9139)

WORK IN PROGRESS. see POLITICAL SCIENCE — Civil Rights

WORKERS COMPENSATION REPORT. see BUSINESS AND ECONOMICS — Labor And Industrial Relations

WORKER'S DEMOCRACY. see POLITICAL SCIENCE

331.88   ZA
WORKERS VOICE. 1972. fortn. 2000 n. per no. Zambia Congress of Trade Unions, P.O. Box 20652, Kitwe, Zambia. TEL 211446. Ed. Reuben S. Muchimba. adv.; bk.rev.; illus. circ. 15,000.

331.88   II   ISSN 0377-6611
WORKING CLASS. 1971. m. Rs.20. Centre of Indian Trade Unions, 6 Talkatora Rd., New Delhi 110001, India. TEL 384071. Ed. P.K. Ganguly. adv.; bk.rev.; charts; illus.; index. circ. 5,000.

331.8   AT   ISSN 1036-5117
WORKPLACE. 1991. q. Aus.$10. Australian Council of Trade Unions, 393-397 Swanston St., Melbourne, Vic. 300, Australia. TEL 03-663-5266. Ed. Andrew Casey.
    Description: Presents union movement perspectives on industrial, economic, social and other issues.

YA'AD. see POLITICAL SCIENCE

YORKSHIRE MINER. see MINES AND MINING INDUSTRY

331.8   CN
YOUR UNION LOCAL 480 U S W A. 1974. m. Local 480 U S W A, 910 Portland St., Trail, B.C. V1R 3X7, Canada. TEL 604-368-9131. FAX 604-368-5568. Ed. Jim Hill. adv. circ. 2,000. (back issues avail.)
    Description: Discusses membership information, safety, health and grievance issues and affairs of provincial and national interest.

331.88   YU   ISSN 0044-135X
YUGOSLAV TRADE UNIONS. (Editions in English, French, Russian, Spanish) 1960. bi-m. Savez Sindikata Jugoslavije, Trg Marksa i Engelsa 5, 11000 Belgrade, Yugoslavia. Ed. Milos Marinovic. illus. circ. 10,000. **Indexed:** P.A.I.S.

331.88   YU   ISSN 0022-6041
YUGOSLAVSKIE PROFSOYUZY; gazeta Soyuza profsoyuzov Yugoslavii. (Text in Russian) 1960. bi-m. 9 Kop.per no. Savez Sindikata Jugoslavije, Trg Marksa i Engelsa 5, 11000 Belgrade, Yugoslavia. Ed. Milos Marinovic.

331.8   GW   ISSN 0934-9677
ZEITSCHRIFT FUER PERSONAL VERTRETUNGSRECHT. bi-m. DM.52. (Deutscher Beamtenbund) Deutscher Beamtenverlag GmbH, Peter-Hensen-Str. 5-7, 53175 Bonn, Germany. TEL 0228-81123. FAX 0228-379621. Ed. Wilhelm Ilbertz. **Document type:** bulletin.

331.8 664   BU
ZEMIA. d. 11 Avgust St., 1000 Sofia, Bulgaria. TEL 835033.
    Formerly (until 1990): Cooperative Village.

331.3   CC
ZHONGGUO GONGYUN XUEYUAN XUEBAO/CHINESE INSTITUTE OF LABOR MOVEMENT. JOURNAL. (Text in Chinese) bi-m. Zhongguo Gongyun Xueyuan, 2, Huayuancun, Fucheng Lu, Beijing 100037, People's Republic of China. TEL 8314477. Ed. Yu Shixiong. **Document type:** academic/scholarly publication.

331.88   US   ISSN 0192-2343
32B - 32J. 1936. m. membership. Service Employees International Union, A F L - C I O, Local 32B - 32J, 101 Ave. of the Americas, New York, NY 10013. TEL 212-490-9688. Ed. J.J. McGrath. circ. 67,000. (tabloid format) **Document type:** newspaper.

331.3   US
32E EVENTS. q. membership. Service Employees International Union, Local 32E, 4234 Bronx Blvd., Bronx, NY 10466-2611. TEL 718-324-6556. FAX 718-994-4910. Ed. Diana D. DeGroat. circ. 10,000.
    Description: Contains information for members and retirees; covers benefits, union events; and lists contacts.

331.8   US
328 UNION VOICE. 1983. q. free. United Food & Commercial Workers Union, Local 328, 278 Silver Spring St., Providence, RI 02904. TEL 401-861-0300. Ed. Frank McCarthy. **Document type:** newspaper.

331.88 615   US   ISSN 0012-6535
1199 NEWS. 1965. 10/yr. $15. (National Health and Human Service Employees Union) Local 1199, 310 W. 43d St., New York, NY 10036. TEL 212-582-1890. Ed. Daniel North. bk.rev.; illus. circ. 100,000.

331.8   US   ISSN 0190-4744
1262 BANNER. 1941. m. Retail Store Employees Union Local 1262, 1389 Broad St., Clifton, NJ 07013. TEL 201-777-3700. FAX 201-778-1725. Eds. Joeseph Rizzo, Frank Margiotta. circ. 38,000. **Document type:** newspaper.

331.88   US
1814 UNION NEWS. 1960. q. free. International Longshoremen's Association, A F L - C I O, Local 1814, 343 Court St., Brooklyn, NY 11231. TEL 718-834-7800. Ed. Jon Visel. bk.rev.; illus. circ. 15,750.
    Formerly (until 1978): Brooklyn Longshoreman (ISSN 0007-2370)

LABOR UNIONS — Abstracting, Bibliographies, Statistics

331.8 011   US   ISSN 0001-1150
A F L - C I O LIBRARY ACQUISITION LIST. 1967. bi-m. free. A F L - C I O, Library, 815 16th St., N.W., Washington, DC 20006. TEL 202-637-5000. bibl. (processed)

331.8   AT   ISSN 0312-1437
AUSTRALIA. BUREAU OF STATISTICS. TRADE UNION STATISTICS, AUSTRALIA. 1969. a. Aus.$10.50. Australian Bureau of Statistics, P.O. Box 10, Belconnen, A.C.T. 2616, Australia. TEL 062-527911. FAX 062-516009. illus. circ. 413. **Document type:** government publication.
    Description: Contains information on separate trade unions, financial and total members classified by state, territory and sex, proportion of employed wage and salary earners who were members of unions.

331.8 011 US
CRITIQUE OF TRADE UNION RIGHTS IN COUNTRIES AFFILIATED WITH THE LEAGUE OF ARAB STATES. DOCUMENTATION SUPPLEMENT. 1989. a. $5. Jewish Labor Committee, 25 E. 21st St., New York, NY 10010. TEL 212-477-0707. FAX 212-477-1918. Ed. Michael S. Perry. circ. 500. (back issues avail.) **Document type:** academic/scholarly publication.
Description: Bibliography of sources and actual documentation used in annual review of labor policies, practices, and conditions in Arab countries of the Middle East and North Africa.

FUNDHEFT FUER ARBEITS- UND SOZIALRECHT; systematischer Nachweis der Gesetzgebung, Rechtsprechung, Buecher und Aufsaetze. see *LAW — Abstracting, Bibliographies, Statistics*

NATIONAL TRADE AND PROFESSIONAL ASSOCIATIONS OF THE UNITED STATES AND LABOR UNIONS. see *BUSINESS AND ECONOMICS — Trade And Industrial Directories*

331.8 BL ISSN 0103-4723
HD6611
SINDICATOS; indicadores sociais. 1987. a. Fundacao Instituto Brasileiro de Geografia e Estatistica, Av. Franklin Roosevelt, 166 - Centro, 20021 Rio de Janeiro RJ, Brazil. TEL 021-284-7690. FAX 021-228-9575. (Subscr. to: Divisao de Comercializacao e Promocao, Rua General Canbarro, 666, Bloco B 2o andar, Maracana, CEP 20271 Rio de Janeiro RJ, Brazil)

331.881 314 NE ISSN 0168-4035
STATISTIEK DER VAKBEWEGING IN NEDERLAND/STATISTICS OF THE TRADE UNIONS IN THE NETHERLANDS. (Text in Dutch and English) 1946. a. Centraal Bureau voor de Statistiek, Prinses Beatrixlaan 428, Voorburg, Netherlands. (Orders to: SDU - Publishers, Christoffel Plantijnstraat, The Hague, Netherlands) **Document type:** government publication.
Formerly: Omvang der Vakbeweging in Nederland (ISSN 0077-6904)

331.11 US
UNION LABOR IN CALIFORNIA. 1939. biennial. free. Department of Industrial Relations, Division of Labor Statistics and Research, Box 420603, San Francisco, CA 94142-0603. TEL 415-703-3451.

LABORATORY TECHNIQUE

see *Medical Sciences–Experimental Medicine, Laboratory Technique*

LAW

see also *Law–Civil Law; Law–Computer Applications; Law–Constitutional Law; Law–Corporate Law; Law–Criminal Law; Law–Estate Planning; Law–Family and Matrimonial Law; Law–International Law; Law–Judicial Systems; Law–Legal Aid; Law–Maritime Law; Law–Military Law; Criminology and Law Enforcement; Patents, Trademarks and Copyrights*

345.01 US
A A A ANNUAL REPORT. a. American Arbitration Association, 140 W. 51st St., New York, NY 10020-1203. TEL 212-484-4009. FAX 212-541-4841.

020 US
A A L L DIRECTORY AND HANDBOOK. 1946. a. $60. American Association of Law Libraries, 53 W. Jackson Blvd., Ste. 940, Chicago, IL 60604. TEL 312-939-4764. FAX 312-431-1097. Ed.Bd. circ. 4,700. **Document type:** directory.
Formerly: Directory of Law Libraries.

020 US ISSN 0065-7255
A A L L PUBLICATIONS SERIES. 1960. irreg., no.44, 1993. price varies. (American Association of Law Libraries) Fred B. Rothman & Co., 10368 W. Centennial Rd., Littleton, CO 80127. TEL 303-979-5657. FAX 303-978-1457. (back issues avail.)

A A M P LIFIER. (American Association of Meat Processors) see *AGRICULTURE — Poultry And Livestock*

340 US
▼**A A U REPORTER.** (Administrative Appeals Unit) 1992. bi-m. $285 to non-members; members $225. American Immigration Lawyers Association, 1400 I St., N.W., Ste. 1200, Washington, DC 20005. TEL 202-371-9377. FAX 202-371-9449. Ed. Allen E. Kaye. index. (looseleaf format) **Document type:** newsletter.
Description: Contains decisions and case summaries of the INS Administrative Appeals Unit.

340 US ISSN 0740-4050
A B A - B N A LAWYERS' MANUAL ON PROFESSIONAL CONDUCT. (Subseries of: Trial Practice Series) 1984. bi-w. $634. (American Bar Association) The Bureau of National Affairs, Inc., 1231 25th St., N.W., Washington, DC 20037. TEL 202-452-4200. FAX 202-822-8092. TELEX 285656 BNAI WSH. (Subscr. to: 9435 Key West Ave., Rockville, MD 20850. TEL 800-372-1033) Ed. Robert A. Robbins. bk.rev.; index, cum.index. (looseleaf format) back issues avail.
—CCC.
Description: Notification and reference service covering a broad range of issues dealing with ethics and professional responsibiliity.

A B A BANK COMPLIANCE. (American Bankers Association) see *BUSINESS AND ECONOMICS — Banking And Finance*

340 US ISSN 0747-0088
K1
A B A JOURNAL; the lawyer's magazine. 1915. 12/yr. $66 to non-members (effective June 1991). American Bar Association, 750 N. Lake Shore Dr., Chicago, IL 60611. TEL 312-988-5000. FAX 312-988-6014. Ed. Gary A. Hengstler. adv.; bk.rev.; illus.; index; 50 yr. cum.index. circ. 431,000. (also avail. in microfilm from UMI; microfiche from UMI) **Indexed:** Amer.Bibl.Slavic & E.Eur.Stud., Amer.Hist.& Life, Bk.Rev.Ind. (1990-), C.L.I., Child.Bk.Rev.Ind. (1990-), CJPI, Crim.Just.Abstr., Curr.Cont., Hist.Abstr., Hlth.Ind., L.R.I., Law Ofc.Info.Svc., Leg.Cont., Leg.Per., P.A.I.S., Pers.Lit., Risk Abstr., SSCI. **Document type:** trade publication.
●Also available online. Vendor(s): Mead Data Central, Inc., West Services, Inc.
—BLDSC (0537.721400); Faxon; UnCover; SWETS; UMI.
Formerly (until 1983): American Bar Association Journal (ISSN 0002-7596)

A B A JOURNAL ANNUAL BUYERS GUIDE. see *BUSINESS AND ECONOMICS — Trade And Industrial Directories*

A B A JUVENILE AND CHILD WELFARE LAW REPORTER. (American Bar Association) see *CHILDREN AND YOUTH — About*

340 US ISSN 0516-9968
KF200
A B A WASHINGTON LETTER. m. $30 to non-members; members $25. American Bar Association, Governmental Affairs Office, 1800 M St., N.W., Washington, DC 20036. TEL 202-331-2609. Ed. Kevin O'Scanniain. circ. 5,000. **Document type:** newsletter.
●Also available online.
Description: Reports congressional actions on legislative issues of interest to the legal profession.

A C A UPDATE; news for arts leaders. (American Council for the Arts) see *ART*

A C C N BULLETIN. (Associated Court and Commercial Newspapers) see *JOURNALISM*

A C R A ALERT. (American Car Rental Association) see *TRANSPORTATION — Automobiles*

A C R A REPORT. (American Car Rental Association) see *TRANSPORTATION — Automobiles*

340 GW
A D A C HANDBUCH: REISERECHT ENTSCHEIDUNGEN. irreg. DM.48. (Allgemeiner Deutscher Automobil-Club e.V.) A D A C GmbH, Am Westpark 8, Postfach 70 01 26, D-8000 Munich, Germany. TEL 089-7676-0.

340 GW
A D A C HANDBUCH: SCHADENERSATZ BEI VERLETZUNG. irreg. DM.48. (Allgemeiner Deutscher Automobil-Club e.V.) A D A C GmbH, Am Westpark 8, Postfach 70 01 26, D-8000 Munich, Germany. TEL 089-7676-0.

340 GW
A D A C HANDBUCH: UNFALL IM AUSLAND - SCHADENSREGULIERUNG. irreg. DM.38. (Allgemeiner Deutscher Automobil-Club e.V.) A D A C GmbH, Am Westpark 8, 81373 Munich, Germany. TEL 089-7676-0.

340 GW
A D A C HANDBUCH: UNFALL RATGEBER. irreg. DM.34. (Allgemeiner Deutscher Automobil-Club e.V.) A D A C GmbH, Am Westpark 8, Postfach 70 01 26, D-8000 Munich, Germany. TEL 089-7676-0.

A D A COMPLIANCE MANUAL FOR EMPLOYERS. (Americans with Disabilities Act) see *BUSINESS AND ECONOMICS — Labor And Industrial Relations*

340 296 US
A D L LAW REPORT. 1965. irreg. (1-2/yr.). Anti-Defamation League, 823 United Nations Plaza, New York, NY 10017. TEL 212-490-2525. Ed.Bd. circ. 5,000 (controlled). (reprint service avail. from UMI) **Document type:** bulletin.
Formerly: Law (ISSN 0023-916X)

346 US ISSN 0090-2411
K1
A E LEGAL NEWSLETTER. (Architects and Engineers) 1973. 10/yr. $200. Victor O. Schinnerer & Co., Two Wisconsin Circle, Chevy Chase, MD 20815. TEL 301-961-9800. Ed. Milton F. Lunch. bk.rev. circ. 500. (looseleaf format) **Document type:** newsletter.

A F R A ADVICE SHEET. (Association for Rural Advancement) see *POLITICAL SCIENCE — Civil Rights*

340 US
A G BULLETIN. 1981. 10/yr. $55. National Association of Attorneys General, 444 N. Capitol St., N.W., Ste. 403, Washington, DC 20001. TEL 202-628-0435. FAX 202-434-8008. Ed. Robert Biesenbach. circ. 200. (back issues avail.)
Formerly: A G Report.

340 US
A I L A BUSINESS IMMIGRATION NEWS. q. $50 for 25 copies. American Immigration Lawyers Association, 1400 I St., N.W., Ste. 1200, Washington, DC 20005. TEL 202-371-9377. FAX 202-371-9449. Ed. Warren R. Leiden. **Document type:** newsletter.

340 US ISSN 0898-1663
KF4802
A I L A MONTHLY MAILING. 1982. m. $295. American Immigration Lawyers Association, 1400 I St., N.W., Ste. 1200, Washington, DC 20005-2208. TEL 202-371-9377. circ. 3,000. (back issues avail.) **Document type:** newsletter.
Description: Covers recent developments in immigration law.

340 US
A I L T O INSIDER. 1986. q. membership. American Institute for Law Training within the Office, 4025 Chestnut St., Philadelphia, PA 19104. TEL 215-243-1614. FAX 215-243-1664. Ed. Leslie Belasco. bk.rev.; video rev. (back issues avail.) **Document type:** newsletter.

340 608.7 US
A I P L A BULLETIN. 5/yr. $40 to non-members (foreign $70). American Intellectual Property Law Association, 2001 Jefferson Davis Hwy., Ste. 203, Arlington, VA 22202. FAX 703-415-0786. Ed. Michael W. Blommer. circ. 7,500. **Document type:** bulletin.

LAW

346 US ISSN 0883-6078
K1
A I P L A QUARTERLY JOURNAL. 1972. q. $45. American Intellectual Property Law Association, 2001 Jefferson Hwy., Ste. 203, Arlington, VA 22202. FAX 703-415-0786. Ed. Donald Chisum. illus. circ. 4,700. (also avail. in microform from WSH; reprint service avail. from WSH) **Indexed:** C.L.I., L.R.I., Leg.Per.
—UnCover.
Formerly: A P L A Quarterly Journal (American Patent Law Association) (ISSN 0091-0538)

347 US
A J A BENCHMARK. q. $25 (includes subscr. to: Court Review). (American Judges Association) National Center for State Courts, 300 Newport Ave., Williamsburg, VA 23187-8798. TEL 804-253-2000. FAX 804-220-0449. Ed. Joseph Burtell. circ. 2,800.
Description: Notifies members of the association's activities.

375 340 US
A L A NEWS. 1960. 4/yr. membership. American Lawyers Auxiliary, 750 N. Lake Shore Dr., Chicago, IL 60611. TEL 312-988-6387. Ed. Susan Hendricks. circ. 2,000.

342 US ISSN 1045-1153
A L A NEWS. 1970. bi-m. $36 to non-members. Association of Legal Administrators, 175 E. Hawthorn Pkwy., Ste. 325, Vernon Hills, IL 60061-1428. TEL 708-816-1212. FAX 708-816-1213. Ed. Jay Strother. adv. circ. 8,000. (reprint service avail.)

340 US ISSN 0044-7560
A L I - A B A - C L E REVIEW. 1970. m. free. American Law Institute - American Bar Association, Committee on Continuing Professional Education, 4025 Chestnut St., Philadelphia, PA 19104. TEL 215-243-1604. FAX 215-243-1664. Ed. Mark T. Carroll. adv.; bk.rev. circ. 60,000. (also avail. in microform from UMI) **Document type:** newsletter.
—UMI.
Description: Looks at courses, books, humor, reviews, lawyer news and other educational materials for lawyers.

340 US ISSN 0145-6342
K1
A L I - A B A COURSE MATERIALS JOURNAL. 1976. bi-m. $40. American Law Institute - American Bar Association, Committee on Continuing Professional Education, 4025 Chestnut St., Philadelphia, PA 19104. TEL 215-243-1604. FAX 215-243-1664. Ed. Mark T. Carroll. adv.; bibl.; cum.index. circ. 4,500. (back issues avail.; reprint service avail. from UMI) **Indexed:** C.L.I., L.R.I., Law Ofc.Info.Svc., Leg.Per. **Document type:** trade publication.
—UnCover; UMI.
Description: Collections of outlines presented at various ALI-ABA courses.

340 US ISSN 0164-5757
KF200
A L I REPORTER. 1978. q. free to qualified personnel. American Law Institute, 4025 Chestnut St., Philadelphia, PA 19104. TEL 215-243-1600. FAX 215-243-1664. Ed. Michael Greenwald. circ. 3,300. **Document type:** newsletter.
Description: Information on the institute, its projects and members.

A L L A NEWSLETTER. (Atlanta Law Libraries Association) see LIBRARY AND INFORMATION SCIENCES

A L L - S I S NEWSLETTER. (Academic Law Libraries S I S) see LIBRARY AND INFORMATION SCIENCES

340 AT
A L R C REPORT SERIES. (Australia Law Reform Commission) 1975. irreg. price varies. Australian Government Publishing Service, G.P.O. Box 84, Canberra, A.C.T. 2601, Australia. TEL 61-6-295-4612. FAX 61-6-295-4500. **Indexed:** Aus.Leg.Mon.Dig. **Document type:** government publication.

A L T A CAPITAL COMMENT. (American Land Title Association) see REAL ESTATE

A M P L A BULLETIN. (Australian Mining and Petroleum Law Association Ltd.) see MINES AND MINING INDUSTRY

A M P L A YEARBOOK. (Australian Mining and Petroleum Law Association Ltd.) see MINES AND MINING INDUSTRY

340 US
A M S A LAW DIGEST. 1979. q. $50 to non-members. Association of Metropolitan Sewerage Agencies, 1000 Connecticut Ave., N.W., Ste. 1006, Washington, DC 20036. TEL 202-833-2672. FAX 202-833-4657. Ed. Ken Kirk. circ. 200. (back issues avail.) **Document type:** newsletter.

A M S STUDIES IN CRIMINAL JUSTICE. see CRIMINOLOGY AND LAW ENFORCEMENT

340 IT
A N D I G. 1990. irreg., no.3, 1991. price varies. (Associazione Nazionale Docenti Informatica Giuridica) Liguori Editore s.r.l., Via Mezzocannone 19, 80134 Naples, Italy. TEL 081-5527139. Ed. Vittorio Frosini. **Document type:** monographic series.

340 UK
A P A S NEWS. 1924. 4/yr. free. Association of Personal Assistants and Secretaries Ltd., 14 Victoria Terrace, Leamington Spa, Warwickshire, England. FAX 0926-451988. Ed. Jacqueline Cameron. bk.rev. circ. 1,000.

340 US
A P I NEWSBRIEFS. 1981. m. $50 to non-members. American Prepaid Legal Services Institute, 541 N. Fairbanks Court, Chicago, IL 60611. TEL 312-988-5751. FAX 312-988-5032. Ed. Alec M. Schwartz. circ. 650. (back issues avail.) **Document type:** newsletter.

A S A E ASSOCIATION LAW AND POLICY. (American Society of Association Executives) see BUSINESS AND ECONOMICS — Management

A S C P WASHINGTON REPORT ON NATIONAL AND STATE ISSUES. (American Society of Clinical Pathologists) see MEDICAL SCIENCES

340 613 US ISSN 1048-907X
A S H SMOKING AND HEALTH REVIEW. vol.8, 1968. 6/yr. $15 (foreign $25). Action on Smoking & Health, 2013 H St., N.W., Washington, DC 20006. TEL 202-659-4310. FAX 202-833-3921. Ed. John F. Banzhaf, III. illus. circ. 32,000.
Formerly: A S H Newsletter.

976 340 US
KF352.A1
A S L H NEWSLETTER. 1970. s-a. $35 to individuals (foreign $40); institutions $50 (foreign $55). American Society for Legal History, Department of History, University of Mississippi, University, MS 38677. TEL 601-232-7148. FAX 601-232-7033. Ed. Robert J. Haws. circ. 1,300. **Document type:** newsletter.
Description: Provides members with news about the society and other items of interest to legal historians.

340 US ISSN 0746-4177
A T L A ADVOCATE. 1977. 10/yr. membership. Association of Trial Lawyers of America, 1050 31st St., N.W., Washington, DC 20007. TEL 202-965-3500. FAX 202-965-0030. Ed. Donald C. Dilworth. circ. 60,000.
Formerly (until 1983): A T L A Bar News (ISSN 0164-8160)

340 US
A T L A ADVOCATE (LITTLE ROCK). bi-m. Arkansas Trial Lawyers Association, 225 E. Markham, Ste. 200, Little Rock, AR 72201. TEL 501-376-2852. FAX 501-372-0951. Ed. Carol Utley. circ. 1,000. **Document type:** newsletter.

340 US
K1.T56
A T L A DOCKET. q. Arkansas Trial Lawyers Association, 225 E. Markham, Ste. 200, Little Rock, AR 72201. TEL 501-376-2852. FAX 501-372-0951. Ed. Carol Utley. circ. 1,000. **Document type:** newsletter.

340 US ISSN 1043-0393
A T L A PROFESSIONAL NEGLIGENCE LAW REPORTER. 1986. 10/yr. $195 to non-members; members $110. Association of Trial Lawyers of America, 1050 31st St., N.W., Washington, DC 20007. TEL 202-965-3500. FAX 202-965-0030. Ed. Liane Leshne. index. (looseleaf format) **Document type:** newsletter.
Formerly (until 1988): Professional Negligence Law Reporter (ISSN 0890-3913)

340 US
A U L BRIEFING MEMO. 1990. irreg. Americans United for Life, 343 S. Dearborn St., Ste. 1804, Chicago, IL 60604. TEL 312-786-9494. FAX 312-786-2131. Ed. Melodie Schlenker Gage. **Document type:** newsletter.

340 US
A U L INSIGHTS. 4/yr. price varies. Americans United for Life, 343 S. Dearborn St., Ste. 1804, Chicago, IL 60604. TEL 312-786-9494. Ed. Melodie Schlenker Gage. (back issues avail.)
Description: Factual review of pro-life topics.

340 US
A U L STUDIES IN LAW, MEDICINE & SOCIETY. irreg. $3. Americans United for Life, 343 S. Dearborn St., Ste. 1804, Chicago, IL 60604. TEL 312-786-9494. Ed. Melodie Schlenker Gage. (back issues avail.) **Document type:** monographic series.
Description: Monograph series on issues involving the human right to life.

A V A ADVISOR. (Asbestos Victims of America) see MEDICAL SCIENCES — Oncology

A - V & MICROGRAPHICS S I S NEWSLETTER. (Audio - Visual) see LIBRARY AND INFORMATION SCIENCES

340 US
LA ABOGADA INTERNACIONAL.* biennial. International Federation of Women Lawyers, 440 Park Ave. S., 12th Fl., New York, NY 10016-8012. TEL 212-206-1666.

340 US
LA ABOGADA NEWSLETTER.* q. International Federation of Women Lawyers, 440 Park Ave. S., 12th Fl., New York, NY 10016-8012. TEL 212-206-1666. **Document type:** newsletter.
Description: Aims to advance the practice of law in various countries and protect women's interests.

ACADEMIA DE STIINTE A REPUBLICA MOLDOVA. REVISTA FILOSOFIE SI DREPT/AKADEMIYA NAUK MOLDAVSKOI RESPUBLIKI. VOPROSY FILOSOFII I PRAVA. see PHILOSOPHY

340 500 AG ISSN 0325-5425
ACADEMIA NACIONAL DE DERECHO Y CIENCIAS SOCIALES DE CORDOBA. ANALES. 1943. a. Academia Nacional de Derecho y Ciencias Sociales de Cordoba, Gral. Artigas 74, 5000 Cordoba, Argentina. TEL 051-44929.

347 II
ACADEMY LAW REVIEW. (Text in English) 1977. s-a. Rs.60($12) (effective vol.14, 1990). Kerala Law Academy, Punnen Rd, Trivandrum 695 039, India. TEL 62378. Ed. K. Parameswaran. bk.rev. circ. 5,000.

340 US ISSN 1057-4212
KF320.A9
ACCESS (CHICAGO, 1990). 1990. biennial. American Bar Association, 750 N. Lake Shore Dr., Chicago, IL 60611. TEL 312-988-5555.

340 AT
ACCIDENT COMPENSATION VICTORIA. 6/yr. $455. Butterworths, 271-273 Lane Cove Rd., P.O. Box 345, North Ryde, N.S.W. 2113, Australia. TEL 02-335-4444. FAX 02-335-4655. (looseleaf format)

340 614.19   US   ISSN 1057-8153
ACCIDENT RECONSTRUCTION JOURNAL. 1989. bi-m.
$39. 3004 Charleton Ct., Waldorf, MD
20602-2527. TEL 301-843-1371.
FAX 301-884-5066. (Subscr. to: Box 234, Waldorf,
MD 20604-0234) Ed. Victor T. Craig. adv.; index.
circ. 3,200. (back issues avail.) **Document type:** trade
publication.
—BLDSC (0573.301500).
   Description: Covers traffic accident investigation
and reconstruction, traffic safety news, safety recalls
and related legal developments.

340 368   II   ISSN 0001-4583
ACCIDENTS CLAIMS JOURNAL. (Text in English) 1966.
m. Rs.450 (typically set in Jan.). 12 Malka Ganj,
Delhi 110007, India. TEL 2917483. Ed. R.L. Kumar.
adv. circ. 6,000.

ACCOUNTANCY LAW REPORTS. see *BUSINESS AND
ECONOMICS — Accounting*

ACCOUNTING FOR BANKS. see *BUSINESS AND
ECONOMICS — Accounting*

ACCOUNTING FOR LAW FIRMS. see *BUSINESS AND
ECONOMICS — Accounting*

ACCOUNTING SYSTEMS FOR LAW OFFICES. see
BUSINESS AND ECONOMICS — Accounting

ACQUISITION ISSUES. see *BUILDING AND
CONSTRUCTION*

340   US
ACROSS THE BAR. 1990. bi-m. membership. Tennessee
Bar Association, c/o Mary M. Tucker, 3622 West
End Ave., Nashville, TN 37205.
TEL 615-383-7421. FAX 615-297-8058. Ed. Julie
Gamble Warner. **Document type:** newsletter.

340 320   HU   ISSN 0524-904X
**ACTA FACULTATIS POLITICO-JURIDICAE UNIVERSITATIS
SCIENTIARUM BUDAPESTIENSIS DE ROLANDO
EOTVOS NOMINATAE.** (Text in Hungarian; summaries
in German and Russian) 1959. irreg. Eotvos Lorand
Tudomanyegyetem, Allam- es Jogtudomanyi Kar, Pf.
109, 1364 Budapest, Hungary. TEL 1-174-930.
FAX 1-1174-114. TELEX 225467. **Indexed:**
Amer.Hist.& Life, Hist.Abstr.

340   SA   ISSN 0065-1346
LAW
ACTA JURIDICA. 1947. a. R.75. Juta & Co. Ltd., P.O.
Box 14373, Kenwyn 7790, South Africa.
TEL 021-797-5101. FAX 021-761-5010. Ed.Bd.
circ. 500. **Indexed:** Ind.S.A.Per., Leg.Per.,
P.A.I.S.For.Lang.Ind.
   Formerly (until 1959): Butterworths South African
Law Review.
   Description: Articles and discussions on recent
legal problems in South Africa.

349   HU   ISSN 1216-2574
ACTA JURIDICA HUNGARICA. (Text in English) 1959. q.
$80 (effective 1992). (Magyar Tudomanyos
Akademia) Akademiai Kiado, Publishing House of
the Hungarian Academy of Sciences, P.O. Box 245,
1519 Budapest, Hungary. TEL 181-2134.
FAX 166-6466. TELEX 22-6228 AKNYO H. Ed.
Vilmos Peschka. adv.; bk.rev.; index. **Indexed:**
Abstr.Crim.& Pen., P.A.I.S.For.Lang.Ind.
—CCC.
   Formerly: Academia Scientiarum Hungarica. Acta
Juridica (ISSN 0001-592X)
   Description: Publishes papers in the field of
jurisprudence: constitutional law, administrative law,
civil law, and constitutional and legal theory.

ACTA TECNOLOGIAE ET LEGIS MEDICAMENTI. see
MEDICAL SCIENCES

340 320   HU   ISSN 0563-0606
**ACTA UNIVERSITATIS DE ATTILA JOZSEF NOMINATAE.
ACTA IURIDICA ET POLITICA.** (Text in English, French,
German, Hungarian or Russian) 1955. a. exchange
basis. Attila Jozsef University, c/o E. Szabo,
Exchange Librarian, Dugonics ter 13, P.O.B. 393,
Szeged H-6701, Hungary. (Subscr. to: Kultura, Box
149, H-1389 Budapest, Hungary) Ed.Bd. circ. 500.
   Description: Law and political science with special
reference to Hungary and the socialist countries.

340 370   PL   ISSN 0208-6069
K1
ACTA UNIVERSITATIS LODZIENSIS: FOLIA IURIDICA.
(Text in Polish; summaries in various languages)
1955-1974; N.S. 1980. irreg. Wydawnictwo
Uniwersytetu Lodzkiego, Ul. Jaracza 34, Lodz,
Poland. TEL 331671. (Dist. by: Ars Polona-Ruch,
Krakowskie Przedmiescie 7, Warsaw, Poland)
Document type: academic/scholarly publication.
—BLDSC (0585.207200).
   Supersedes in part: Uniwersytet Lodzki. Zeszyty
Naukowe. Seria 1: Nauki Humanistyczno-Spoleczne
(ISSN 0076-0358)
   Description: Separate issues include sets of
articles, monographs or conference papers of
particular branches of law.

340   PL   ISSN 0208-5283
ACTA UNIVERSITATIS NICOLAI COPERNICI. PRAWO.
1961. irreg. price varies. Uniwersytet Mikolaja
Kopernika, Biblioteka Uniwerytecka, Ul. Gagarina 13,
87-100 Torun, Poland. TEL 233-52. TELEX
552382. (Dist. by: Osrodek Rozpowszechniania
Wydawnictw Naukowych PAN, Palac Kultury i Nauki,
00-901 Warsaw, Poland)
   Formerly: Uniwersytet Mikolaja Kopernika, Torun.
Nauki Humanistyczno-Spoleczne. Prawo (ISSN
0083-4513)

340 310.412   US   ISSN 1053-4083
ACTION ALERT (WASHINGTON, 1980). 1980. m. $25
to non-members; members $20. American
Association of University Women, 1111 16th St.,
N.W., Washington, DC 20036. TEL 202-785-7700.
FAX 202-872-1425. Ed. Carolin Head. index. circ.
1,500. (back issues avail.) **Document type:**
newsletter.
—BLDSC (0537.065000).
   Description: Covers pending legislation, regulations
and court decisions affecting women's issues, with
emphasis on education, work and family issues.

658 340   US
ACTION KIT FOR HOSPITAL LAW. 1972. m. $495.
Action Kit Publications, 4614 Fifth Ave., Pittsburgh,
PA 15213. TEL 800-245-1205. Ed. John Horty.
circ. 2,000. (looseleaf format)

ACTION KIT FOR HOSPITAL TRUSTEES. see *HOSPITALS*

345   US
**ACTS AND CASES BY POPULAR NAMES, FEDERAL AND
STATE.** 1968. base vol. (plus supplements 6/yr.).
$316. Shepard's - McGraw-Hill, Inc., Box 35300,
Colorado Springs, CO 80935-3530.
TEL 800-525-2474.
   Formerly (until 1979): Shepard's Acts and Cases
by Popular Names, Federal and State (ISSN
0080-9233)

340   CK   ISSN 0211-5603
ACTUALIDAD JURIDICA. 1975. m. Avda. Jimenez
12-42, Apdo. Aereo 27248, Bogota, Colombia. Ed.
Carlos A. Useque.

340   SP   ISSN 1132-0257
ACTUALIDAD JURIDICA ARANZADI; pliego semanal de
actualidad juridica. 1991. w. free to qualified
personnel. Editorial Aranzadi, S.A., Avda. Carlos III,
34, Apdo. 111, 31080 Pamplona, Spain.
TEL 948-331212. FAX 948-330919. Ed. Juan
Miguel Perez. illus.

340   FR   ISSN 0044-6157
ACTUALITE FIDUCIAIRE. 1927. 11/yr. 276 F. (foreign
345 F.). Nouvelles Editions Fiduciaires, 2 bis rue de
Villiers, 92300 Levallois-Perret, France. Ed. Sodie
Robert. adv.; bk.rev. circ. 26,000.
—CCC.

349 333   FR
L'ACTUALITE JURIDIQUE: DROIT ADMINISTRATIF. 1945.
m. 620 F. (foreign 690 F.). Publications du
Moniteur, 17 rue d'Uzes, 75002 Paris, France.
TEL 40-13-30-30. FAX 40-26-04-01. TELEX 680
876 F. Ed. Jerome Chapuisat. adv.; bk.rev.; abstr.;
bibl.; index. circ. 6,513. (reprint service avail. from
SCH) **Indexed:** ELLIS.
—SWETS.
   Formerly: Actualite Juridique: Edition Droit
Administratif (ISSN 0001-7728); Incorporates:
Actualite Juridique: Edition Propriete Immobiliere
(ISSN 0001-7736)
   Description: Property and real estate from a
juridical and economical point of view.

340   FR   ISSN 0001-7736
ACTUALITE JURIDIQUE PROPRIETE IMMOBILIERE. 1950.
m. 725 F. (foreign 800 F.). Publications du
Moniteur, 17 rue d'Uzes, 75002 Paris, France.
TEL 1-40-13-30-30. FAX 1-40-26-04-01. TELEX
UPRESSE 680876F. Ed. Bernard Boussageon. circ.
5,506.

340   FR   ISSN 0753-874X
ACTUALITE LEGISLATIVE DALLOZ. 1918. bi-m. 530 F.
(foreign 670 F.). Editions Dalloz, 11 rue Soufflot,
75240 Paris Cedex 05, France. (Subscr. to: 35, rue
Tournefort, 75240 Paris Cedex 05, France. TEL
45-87-37-48) Ed. Philippe Weiss. bk.rev.; index.
Indexed: ELLIS.
   Formerly (until 1983): Bulletin Legislatif Dalloz
(ISSN 0755-2424)

340   FR   ISSN 1011-923X
ACTUALITES COMMUNAUTAIRES; bulletin mensuel du
dictionnaire du Marche Commun. vol.11, 1979. m.
800 F. G L N - Joly Editions, 1 av. Franklin D.
Roosevelt, 75008 Paris, France. TEL 44-95-16-20.
FAX 1-45-63-89-39. Eds. Xavier de Roux,
Dominique Voillemot. circ. 700.
   Formerly: Notes d'Informations Communautaires
(ISSN 0339-6460)

330 297   TS
AL-ADALAH/JUSTICE. (Text in Arabic) 1975. q. Ministry
of Justice, P.O. Box 260, Abu Dhabi, United Arab
Emirates. TEL 652224. FAX 664944. Ed. Khalifa
Sultan al-Aqroubi. circ. 3,000.
   Description: Covers the revival of the Islamic legal
heritage, contemporary legal scholarship, foreign
legal research, and important legal cases in the UAE.

340   US   ISSN 0884-514X
ADDENDUM; newsletter of the Indiana State Bar
Association. 1985. bi-m. membership only. Indiana
State Bar Association, 230 E. Ohio St., Indianapolis,
IN 46204. TEL 317-639-5465.
FAX 317-266-2588. Ed. Susan J. Ferrer. **Document
type:** newsletter.
   Description: Professional news and announcements
of interest to lawyers in Indiana.

340   AT   ISSN 0065-1915
LAW
ADELAIDE LAW REVIEW. 1960. 2/yr. $40. Adelaide
Law Review Association, c/o Department of Law,
University of Adelaide, Adelaide, S.A. 5000,
Australia. TEL 08-228-5063. FAX 08-232-4679.
(Dist. in U.S. by: William S. Hein & Co., 1285 Main
St., Buffalo, NY 14209) Ed.Bd. adv.; bk.rev.; index.
circ. 500. (also avail. in microform from UMI)
Indexed: Aus.P.A.I.S., C.L.I., L.R.I., Leg.Per. **Document
type:** academic/scholarly publication.
—BLDSC (0680.300000); UnCover; UMI.

340   US   ISSN 8756-3630
ADELPHIA LAW JOURNAL.* 1972-19??; resumed 1982.
a. $10. Sigma Nu Phi Legal Fraternity, 9700
Fernwood Rd., W. Bethesda, Washington, DC 20817.
bk.rev.; cum.index: 1982-1984. circ. 2,000. (back
issues avail.) **Indexed:** Leg.Per. **Document type:**
academic/scholarly publication.
   Formerly: Adelphia.

340   US   ISSN 0147-3603
ADMINISTRATION OF JUSTICE MEMORANDA. 1975.
irreg. price varies. University of North Carolina at
Chapel Hill, Institute of Government, Knapp Bldg., CB
3330, Chapel Hill, NC 27599-3330.
TEL 919-966-4119. FAX 919-962-2707. Ed.
Robert L. Farb. circ. 400. **Document type:**
academic/scholarly publication, bulletin.
   Description: Discusses current issues of concern to
North Carolina law enforcement and judicial officials.

340 364   US
ADMINISTRATION OF JUVENILE JUSTICE IN CALIFORNIA.
Department of Justice, Division of Law Enforcement,
4949 Broadway, Box 13427, Sacramento, CA
95813.

342   BE   ISSN 0771-4084
ADMINISTRATION PUBLIQUE. 1976. q. 3800 BEF
(foreign 4000 BEF). Institut Belge des Sciences
Administratives - Belgian Institute of Administrative
Sciences, Rue Saint-Bernard, 98, B-1060 Brussels,
Belgium. TEL 02-536-59-38. FAX 02-536-59-11.
Indexed: ELLIS.
—SWETS.
   Formerly: Recueil de Jurisprudence de Droit
Administrative et du Conseil d'Etat.

LAW

340   AT   ISSN 0813-779X
ADMINISTRATIVE APPEAL REPORTS. 1984. m. price varies. Law Book Co. Ltd., 44-50 Waterloo Rd., North Ryde, N.S.W. 2113, Australia. TEL 02-887-0177. FAX 02-888-9706. TELEX ASBOOK 27995. Ed. Matthew Smith. cum.index. (back issues avail.)
Description: Provides reports of decisions of the Administrative Appeals Tribunal.

346.066   US
ADMINISTRATIVE INTERPRETATIONS OF THE UNIFORM CONSUMER CREDIT CODE. 1989. base vol. (plus suppl.). $110. Butterworth Legal Publishers (Salem) (Subsidiary of: Reed Elsevier plc), 8 Industrial Way, Bldg. C, Salem, NH 03079. TEL 800-548-4001. FAX 603-898-9858. Ed. Fred H. Miller. (looseleaf format)

340   US   ISSN 1064-394X
ADMINISTRATIVE JUDICIARY NEWS AND JOURNAL. 1978. q. membership only. American Bar Association, National Conference of Administrative Law Judges, 750 N. Lake Shore Dr., Chicago, IL 60611. TEL 312-988-5000. Ed. John M. Vittone. circ. 450.
Formerly: American Bar Association. Conference of Administrative Law Judges. Newsletter.

340   US
ADMINISTRATIVE LAW. 1977. 6 base vols. (plus irreg. supplements). $1035. Matthew Bender & Co., Inc., 11 Penn Plaza, New York, NY 10001. TEL 212-967-7707. Ed. Glenn A. Mitchell. (looseleaf format)
Description: Analyzes all aspects of administrative law and the administrative process.

342
KFI1640.A15I44   US
ADMINISTRATIVE LAW (SPRINGFIELD). 1971. q. $12 to members. Illinois State Bar Association, Section on Administrative Law, Illinois Bar Center, Springfield, IL 62701. TEL 217-525-1760. FAX 217-525-0712. Eds. Paul Freehling, Robert Kane. circ. 450. (looseleaf format; back issues avail.) **Document type**: newsletter.

340   AT   ISSN 0726-5816
ADMINISTRATIVE LAW DECISIONS. 1976. irreg. Aus.$350 per vol. Butterworths, 271-273 Lane Cove Rd., North Ryde, N.S.W. 2113, Australia. TEL 02-335-4444. FAX 02-335-4655. (Subscr. to: P.O. Box 345, North Ryde, N.S.W. 2113, Australia) Ed. D.C. Pearce.

342   US
ADMINISTRATIVE LAW LETTER. 1989. q. membership. Arkansas Trial Lawyers Association, 225 E. Markham, Ste. 200, Little Rock, AR 72201. TEL 501-376-2852. FAX 501-372-0951. Ed. Carol Utley. circ. 200. **Document type**: newsletter.

340   US   ISSN 0567-9494
LAW
ADMINISTRATIVE LAW NEWS. 1974. q. membership only. American Bar Association, Administrative Law and Regulatory Practice Section, 750 N. Lake Shore Dr., Chicago, IL 60611. TEL 312-988-6068. Ed. William Funk. circ. 8,000. **Indexed**: C.L.I., L.R.I. **Document type**: newsletter.
Description: Provides information about meetings, committees, and council activities; chairman's report; and decisions of interest on the practice of administrative law.

342   US
ADMINISTRATIVE LAW QUARTERLY DIGEST. q. $21 to non-members; law students $12. District of Columbia Bar, 1707 L St., N.W., 6th Fl., Washington, DC 20036-4202. TEL 202-331-4364. index. (looseleaf format) **Document type**: newsletter.

340   CN   ISSN 0824-2615
KE5015.A49
ADMINISTRATIVE LAW REPORTS. 1983. 12/yr. (in 6 vols.). Can.$125. Carswell, Corporate Plaza, 2075 Kennedy Rd., Scarborough, ON M1T 3V4, Canada. TEL 416-609-8000. FAX 416-298-5094. Ed. David J. Mullan. adv. contact: M. Lalani. **Indexed**: Ind.Can.L.P.L.
Description: Features decisions in administrative law from all Canadian jurisdictions selected by experts in the field. Includes cases on the availability of and grounds for judicial review of decisions of administrative tribunals, delegation of legislative powers, remedies on judicial review, and articles, annotations and case comments.

340   UK   ISSN 0957-9710
ADMINISTRATIVE LAW REPORTS. 1989. 26/yr. £96.50. Barry Rose Law Periodicals, Little London, Chichester, W. Sussex PO19 1PG, England. TEL 0243-787841. FAX 0243-779278. Ed. Ian McLeod. **Document type**: academic/scholarly publication.
Description: Reports on recent developments in administrative law in England.

340   US   ISSN 0001-8368
LAW
ADMINISTRATIVE LAW REVIEW. 1973. q. $35 to non-members (foreign $40). American Bar Association, Administrative Law and Regulatory Practice Section, 750 N. Lake Shore Dr., Chicago, IL 60611. TEL 312-988-6068. Ed. Charles H. Koch, Jr. adv.; abstr.; cum.index. circ. 8,000. (reprint service avail. from RRI) **Indexed**: Abstr.Bk.Rev.Curr.Leg.Per., BPIA, Bus.Ind., C.L.I., Curr.Cont., Energy Ind., Energy Info.Abstr., L.R.I., Leg.Cont., Leg.Per., Pers.Lit., SSCI. **Document type**: academic/scholarly publication.
—BLDSC (0696.450000); Faxon; UnCover; SWETS.
Description: Scholarly approach to the study of developments in the field of administrative law.

340   US
ADMINISTRATIVE RULEMAKING. 1983. base vol. (plus a. suppl.). $95. Shepard's - McGraw-Hill, Inc., Box 35300, Colorado Springs, CO 80935-3530. TEL 800-525-2474.
Description: Addresses the development of rulemaking. Covers the petition process, OMB input and includes regulatory analysis and judicial reviews.

340   II   ISSN 0970-1060
LAW
ADMINISTRATIVE TRIBUNALS CASES. (Text in English) 1986. fortn. $96. Eastern Book Company, 34 Lalbagh, Lucknow 226 001, India. FAX 0091-522-244328. Ed. Surendra Malik. adv.; bk.rev. circ. 1,000. (back issues avail.)
Description: Contains the decisions of the Central Administrative Tribunals, and of the Supreme Court of India.

ADOPTION. see SOCIAL SERVICES AND WELFARE

ADOPTION AND FOSTERING. see SOCIAL SERVICES AND WELFARE

ADOPTION FACTBOOK; United States data, issues, regulations and resources. see SOCIAL SERVICES AND WELFARE

340   US
ADVANCES SESSION LAWS. 1932. irreg. price varies. Commerce Clearing House, Inc., 4025 W. Peterson Ave., Chicago, IL 60646. TEL 312-583-8500. Ed. D. Newquist.

ADVERTISING COMPLIANCE SERVICE NEWSLETTER. see ADVERTISING AND PUBLIC RELATIONS

346.066   US   ISSN 0093-1985
ADVERTISING LAW ANTHOLOGY. 1973. s-a. $149.95 per no. International Library Law Book Publishers, Inc., 101 Lakeforest Blvd., Ste. 270, Gaithersburg, MD 20877. TEL 301-990-7755. FAX 301-990-7642. Ed. Donald J. Hoyes. bibl.; index, cum.index. **Document type**: monographic series.
Description: Contains selected best U.S. law review articles, printed in their entirety, in the field of advertising, culled from more than 900 American law review journals.

ADVERTISING TOPICS. see ADVERTISING AND PUBLIC RELATIONS

340   US
ADVOCACY: THE ART OF PLEADING A CAUSE, 2-E. 1980. base vol. (plus a. suppl.). $95. Shepard's - McGraw-Hill, Inc., Box 35300, Colorado Springs, CO 80935-3530. TEL 800-525-2474.
Description: Provides "how-to" information on eliciting truthful answers from various types of witnesses.

340   US
ADVOCATE (BALTIMORE). q. membership. Maryland State Bar Association, Young Lawyers Section, 520 W. Fayette St., Baltimore, MD 21201. TEL 410-685-7878. FAX 410-837-0518. Eds. Susan Land, Anne-Marie Gering. circ. 4,500. **Document type**: newsletter.

340 975   US   ISSN 0515-4987
KF200
THE ADVOCATE (BOISE). 1957. m. $30. Idaho State Bar, 525 Jefferson St., Box 895, Boise, ID 83701. TEL 208-342-8958. FAX 208-342-3799. Ed. Jeannie M. Ornel. adv. contact: Lori Barck. bk.rev. circ. 3,500. (also avail. in microfiche; back issues avail.) **Indexed**: C.L.I. **Document type**: trade publication.
—UnCover.

340   US
THE ADVOCATE (BRONX). 1954; N.S. 1992. q. membership. Bronx County Bar Association, 851 Grand Concourse, Rm. 124, Bronx, NY 10451. TEL 718-293-5600. Ed. Stuart L. Davis. adv.
Former titles: Bronx County Bar Journal (ISSN 8755-6081); (until 1983): Advocate (ISSN 0400-6216)
Description: Publishes articles discussing issues in criminal, civil and international law and relevant professional issues.

THE ADVOCATE (INDIANAPOLIS). see POLITICAL SCIENCE — Civil Rights

347.91   US   ISSN 0199-1876
KFC1025.A15
ADVOCATE (LOS ANGELES, 1973). 1973. m. $50. Los Angeles Trial Lawyers Association, 3435 Wilshire Blvd., Ste. 2870, Los Angeles, CA 90010-1912. TEL 213-487-1212. FAX 213-487-1224. Ed. Christine Spagnoli. adv. circ. 3,100.
Description: Covers both substantive law and practice tips.

340   US
ADVOCATE (TALLAHASSEE). 1975. irreg. (3-4/yr.). membership. Florida Bar, Trial Lawyers Section, 650 Apalachee Pkwy., Tallahassee, FL 32399-2300. TEL 904-561-5628. circ. 6,300. **Document type**: newsletter.

340   CN   ISSN 0382-456X
ADVOCATE (TORONTO). 1964. irreg. University of Toronto, Faculty of Law, Toronto, Ont. M5S 2C5, Canada. TEL 416-978-3725.

340   CN   ISSN 0044-6416
ADVOCATE (WEST VANCOUVER). 1943. bi-m. Can.$20. Vancouver Bar Association, 4765 Pilot House Rd., W. Vancouver, BC V7W 1J2, Canada. TEL 604-925-2122. FAX 604-925-2065. Ed. David Roberts. adv.; bk.rev.; cum.index: 1943-1986. circ. 8,500. (back issues avail.) **Indexed**: Ind.Can.L.P.L.
—UnCover.

340   NO   ISSN 0801-3020
ADVOKATBLADET. 1921. m. (10/yr.). NOK 250. Norske Advokatforening - Norwegian Bar Association, Juristenes Hus, Kristian Augusts gate 9, N-0167 Oslo 1, Norway. TEL 47 2 11 68 68. FAX 47-2-11-53-25. Ed. Per Wang. adv. circ. 4,700.
Formerly (until 1985): Norsk Advokatblad (ISSN 0332-5466); (until 1965): Norsk Sakfoererblad (ISSN 0332-9186); (until 1931): Norske Sakfoerforeningsblad Medlemsblad (ISSN 0802-555X)

349   SW   ISSN 0281-3505
LAW
ADVOKATEN. m. (8/yr.). SEK 350. Sveriges Advokatsamfund - Swedish Bar Association, P.O. Box 27321, S-102 54 Stockholm, Sweden. Ed. Lars Bentelius. adv.; charts.
Formerly: Sveriges Advokatsamfund. Tidskrift (ISSN 0040-6902)

340   DK   ISSN 0107-5616
ADVOKATEN. 1921. 11/yr. free to members. Danske Advokatsamfund - Danish Law Society, Kronprinsessegade 28, 1306 Copenhagen K, Denmark. TEL 33-93-49-50. FAX 33-321831. Ed. Ole Stig Andersen. adv.; bk.rev.; index; circ. 5,500 (controlled). **Indexed:** ELLIS. **Document type:** academic/scholarly publication.
  Former titles (until 1980): Advokatbladet (ISSN 0106-4398); (until 1958): Sagfoererbladet (ISSN 0106-3820)

349   YU   ISSN 0017-0933
ADVOKATSKA KOMORA VOJVODINE. GLASNIK; Chasopis za pravnu teoriju i praksu. (Text in Serbo-Croatian) 1928. m. 246000 din. Advokatska Komora Vojvodine, Zmaj Jovina 20, 21000 Novi Sad, Yugoslavia. TEL 021 29-459. (Co-sponsor: Samoupravna Interesna Zajednica za Naucni Rad Vojvodine) Ed. Miroslav Zdjelar. adv.; bk.rev. circ. 1,000.
  Description: Provides articles on law theory and practice.

340   YU   ISSN 0350-087X
ADVOKATURA. 1975. q. 60 din. Advokatska Komora Srbije, Mose Pijade 13, Belgrade, Yugoslavia. Ed. Aleksander Mikulic.
  Formerly (until 1991): Branic (ISSN 0353-9644)

347   BN
ADVOKATURA BOSNE I HERCEGOVINE. 1975. q. 150 din. Advokatska Komora Bosne i Hercegovine, Saloma Albaharija 2, Sarajevo, Bosnia Hercegovina. Ed. Seid Hadziselimovic.

340   AG   ISSN 0327-8972
▼**AEQUITAS.** 1993. a. $40. Universidad del Salvador, Facultad de Ciencias Juridicas, Rodriguez Pena 770, 2o piso, 1020 Buenos Aires, Argentina. TEL 42-1381. FAX 42-0631. **Document type:** academic/scholarly publication.
  Description: Devoted to legal science.

AEROSPACE MANAGEMENT AND LAW. see AERONAUTICS AND SPACE FLIGHT

340   US   ISSN 0360-5485
KF325.26
AFFILIATE. 19755. 6/yr. $15 (free to qualified personnel). American Bar Association, Young Lawyers Division, Affiliate Outreach Committees, 750 N. Lake Shore Dr., Chicago, IL 60611. TEL 312-988-5555. FAX 312-988-6281. Ed. Richard Bright.

340   US   ISSN 1071-7390
AFFIRMATIVE ACTION - E E O NOTES. m. $70. Nyper Publications, Box 662, Latham, NY 12110. TEL 518-786-1654. FAX 518-456-8582. Ed. Harvey Randall. (back issues avail.) **Document type:** newsletter.

347   AF
AFGHANISTAN. MINISTRY OF JUSTICE. LAW JOURNAL. (Text in Persian or Pushto) 1976. m. $3. Ministry of Justice, Darrul Aman, Kabul, Afghanistan.

342   AF
AFGHANISTAN. MINISTRY OF JUSTICE. OFFICIAL GAZETTE/RASMI JARIDAH. (Text in Persian) irreg. AF.21. Ministry of Justice, Judicial Relations and Planning Department, Darrul Aman, Kabul, Afghanistan. circ. 10,500.

349   ET   ISSN 0002-0052
LAW
AFRICAN LAW DIGEST. (Name of issuing body varies: Haile Sellassie I University, University of Addis Ababa, National University) 1966. 3/yr. Eth.$15($40) Addis Ababa University, Faculty of Law, P.O. Box 1176, Addis Ababa, Ethiopia. Ed. Yeshak Teshome. bibl.; index. circ. 250. (processed; also avail. in microfiche from SWZ; reprint service avail. from SWZ)
  Description: Summaries of important African legislation and inter-African treaties.

610 355.115   US
AGENT ORANGE REVIEW; for veterans who served in Vietnam. 1982. irreg. (approx. 2-3/yr.). free. U.S. Department of Veterans Affairs, Automation Center (200-397), 1615 Woodward St., Austin, TX 78772-0001. TEL 202-535-7183. Ed. Donald J. Rosenblum. circ. controlled. (looseleaf format) **Document type:** government publication, newsletter.
  Description: Provides information on Agent Orange exposure, examination, compensation, and other related matters including legislation for Vietnam veterans, families, and others concerned about the effects of herbicides used in Vietnam.

AGGRESSIVE TAX AVOIDANCE FOR REAL ESTATE INVESTORS. see REAL ESTATE

AGRARRECHT. see AGRICULTURE

340 630   US
AGRICULTURAL LAW. 1980. 15 base vols. (plus irreg. supplements). $1830. Matthew Bender & Co. Inc., 11 Penn Plaza, New York, NY 10001. TEL 212-967-7760. (looseleaf format)
  Description: Covers the pertinence of all case and statutory law to farms, ranches, and other agricultural interests.

AGRICULTURAL LAW (SPRINGFIELD). see AGRICULTURE

AGRICULTURAL LAW DIGEST. see AGRICULTURE

340 630   US
AGRICULTURAL LAW MANUAL. 1985. base vol. (plus irreg. supplements). Matthew Bender & Co., Inc., 11 Penn Plaza, New York, NY 10001. TEL 212-967-7707. (looseleaf format)
  Description: Covers taxation of farm income, government regulation of agriculture, agricultural estate and business planning, agricultural cooperatives, farm bankruptcy and foreclosure and organizing the farm or ranch.

AGRICULTURAL LAW NEWSLETTER. see AGRICULTURE

AGRICULTURAL LAW UPDATE. see AGRICULTURE — Agricultural Economics

340 630   US   ISSN 0002-1741
LAW
AGRICULTURE DECISIONS. 1942. m. U.S. Department of Agriculture, Office of Administrative Law Judges, 14th St. & Independence Ave., S.W., Washington, DC 20250-1300. TEL 202-720-2791. (also avail. in microform from UMI) **Document type:** government publication.
  —UMI.

347   US   ISSN 0098-9738
KFH510.A73
AHA'ILONO; to report the news. vol.6, 1978. bi-m. free. Hawaii State Judiciary, Public Information Office, Box 2560, Honolulu, HI 96804. TEL 808-548-4634. FAX 808-548-6002. Ed. Chapman Lam. illus. circ. 4,500.
  Description: Reports current events and departmental updates for the Hawaii State Judiciary.

340 616.9   US
AIDS & FLORIDA LAW. 1989. 2 base vols. (plus suppl.). $120. Butterworth Legal Publishers (Salem) (Subsidiary of: Reed Elsevier plc), 8 Industrial Way, Bldg. C, Salem, NH 03079. TEL 800-548-4001. FAX 603-898-9858. (looseleaf format)

AIDS & PUBLIC POLICY JOURNAL. see MEDICAL SCIENCES — Communicable Diseases

610 340   US
AIDS LAW & LITIGATION REPORTER. (Acquired Immune Deficiency Syndrome) q., plus a. update. $2500 (update only $495). University Publishing Group, Inc., 107 E. Church St., Frederick, MD 21701. TEL 800-654-8188. **Document type:** academic/scholarly publication.
  Description: Presents complete, retrospective, full-text decisions from federal, state, and local courts, surveys proposed and enacted legislation. Provides an analysis of current thinking on crucial issues.

340 610   US   ISSN 0899-1464
KF3803.A54
AIDS LITIGATION REPORTER. (Acquired Immune Deficiency Syndrome); the national journal of record of AIDS-related litigation. 1987. s-m. $700. Andrews Publications, 1646 West Chester Pike, Box 1000, Westtown, PA 19395. TEL 215-399-6600. FAX 215-399-6610. Ed. Ronald V. Baker. s-a. index. (looseleaf format; back issues avail.) **Document type:** newsletter.

344.043 614   US   ISSN 0887-1493
KF3803.A54
AIDS POLICY AND LAW. (Acquired Immune Deficiency Syndrome); the bi-weekly newsletter on legislation, regulation, and litigation concerning AIDS. 1986. bi-w. $487 (foreign $509). Buraff Publications (Subsidiary of: Millin Publications, Inc.), 1350 Connecticut Ave. N.W., Ste. 1000, Washington, DC 20036. TEL 800-333-1291. FAX 202-862-0999. Ed. Richard M. Hagan. index. (back issues avail.) **Document type:** newsletter.
  ●Also available online. Vendor(s): Human Resources Information Network (CDD, HDD).
  —CCC.
  Description: Covers legal issues & regulatory aspects of AIDS & HIV. Includes the latest developments on the federal, state and local levels, fair employment practices, litigation, legislation, regulation, policy guidelines, case studies, and interviews.

AIDS UPDATE (NEW YORK). see MEDICAL SCIENCES — Communicable Diseases

340 629.1   US   ISSN 0747-7449
KF2400.A15
AIR AND SPACE LAWYER. 1984. q. $20 membership. American Bar Association, Forum on Air and Space Law, 541 N. Fairbanks Ct., Chicago, IL 60611. TEL 312-988-5522. FAX 312-988-5531. (Subscr. to: Publication Orders, Box 10892, Chicago, IL 60610-0892) Ed. Robert J. O'Connell. **Document type:** academic/scholarly publication.
  Description: News on significant developments in air and space law, as well as reports of committee activities.

AIR SAFETY WEEK; the newsletter of air safety regulation. see AERONAUTICS AND SPACE FLIGHT

AIR TRAFFIC CONTROL ASSOCIATION. BULLETIN. see TRANSPORTATION — Air Transport

340   BL
AJURIS. 1974. irreg. (Associacao dos Juizes do Rio Grande do Sul) Livraria Sulina, Av. Borges de Medeiros 1030-1036, Porto Alegre, Brazil.

AKADEMIYA NAUK AZERBAIJANA. IZVESTIA. SERIYA ISTORIYA, FILOSOFIYA I PRAVO. see HISTORY

340   US   ISSN 0002-371X
K1
AKRON LAW REVIEW. 1967. 4/yr. $20. University of Akron, School of Law, Akron, OH 44325. TEL 216-972-7335. FAX 216-258-2343. adv.; bk.rev. circ. 1,500. (also avail. in microfilm from PMC,WSH; microfiche from WSH; back issues avail.; reprint service avail. from WSH) **Indexed:** C.C.L.P., C.L.I., L.R.I., Leg.Cont., Leg.Per., R.G. **Document type:** academic/scholarly publication.
  —BLDSC (0785.641000); UnCover.

340   US
AKRON LEGAL NEWS. 1921. d. (Mon.-Fri.). $65. 60 S. Summit St., Akron, OH 44308. TEL 216-376-0917; 216-376-0917. Ed. J.L. Bueleson. adv. circ. 1,100. (tabloid format) **Document type:** newspaper.

349   SW   ISSN 0349-3520
AKTUELL JURIDIK. 1978. q. SEK 900 (effective 1994). Fritzes, S-106 47 Stockholm, Sweden. TEL 08-739-96-30. FAX 08-739-95-48.

340   US
KFA45.A25
ALABAMA BAR REPORTER. 26/yr. $120. Alabama State Bar Foundation, 415 Dexter Ave., Montgomery, AL 36101. TEL 205-269-1515. FAX 205-261-6310. **Document type:** newsletter.

3220 LAW

340 331   US   ISSN 1049-9369
ALABAMA EMPLOYMENT LAW LETTER. 1990. m. $92. (Lehr, Middlebrooks, & Procter) M. Lee Smith Publishers & Printers, 162 Fourth Ave., N., Box 198867, Nashville, TN 37219-8867. TEL 615-242-7395; 800-274-6774. FAX 615-256-6601. Ed.Bd. **Document type:** newsletter.
   Description: Reports the latest Alabama employment law developments that affect Alabama companies.

340 613.1   US   ISSN 1066-1131
▼**ALABAMA ENVIRONMENTAL COMPLIANCE UPDATE.** 1993. m. $137. (Sirote & Permutt) M. Lee Smith Publishers & Printers, 162 Fourth Ave., N., Box 198867, Nashville, TN 37219-8867. TEL 615-242-7395; 800-274-6774. FAX 615-256-6601. Eds. Charles Driggars, Kaye Houser Turberville. **Document type:** newsletter.
   Description: Reports the latest state-specific environmental law developments that affect companies in Alabama.

340   US   ISSN 0002-4279
K1
ALABAMA LAW REVIEW. 1948. 3/yr. $24. University of Alabama, School of Law, Box 870382, University, AL 35487-0382. TEL 205-348-7191. bk.rev.; index, cum.index every 5 yrs. circ. 1,500. (also avail. in microform from WSH; reprint service avail. from WSH) **Indexed:** C.I.I., Crim.Just.Abstr., L.R.I., Leg.Cont., Leg.Per., P.A.I.S.
   ●Also available online. Vendor(s): West Services, Inc..
   —BLDSC (0786.521500); Faxon; UnCover.

340   US   ISSN 0002-4287
KF200
ALABAMA LAWYER. 1940. q. $15. State Bar of Alabama, Lock Box 4156, Montgomery, AL 36101. TEL 205-269-1515. Ed. Margaret Lacey. adv.; bk.rev.; index, cum.index: vols.1-25. circ. 9,000. **Indexed:** C.I.I., L.R.I., Leg.Per.
   ●Also available online. Vendor(s): West Services, Inc..
   —BLDSC (0786.522000); UnCover.

ALABAMA TODAY. see BUSINESS AND ECONOMICS — Chamber Of Commerce Publications

340   US
ALAMEDA COUNTY BAR ASSOCIATION BULLETIN. vol.24, 1993. 10/yr. $2. Alameda County Bar Association, 360 22nd St., Ste. 800, Oakland, CA 94612. TEL 510-893-7160. Ed. Thomas M. Singman. adv.; illus. **Document type:** bulletin.
   Description: News of association activities and programs, and other items of interest to lawyers in the Oakland area.

340   US
ALASKA BANKRUPTCY REPORTS. 1989. m. $295. Montana Law Week, 33 S. Benton, Helena, MT 59601. TEL 406-443-5312. FAX 406-443-5364. Ed. Frank Adams. (looseleaf format; back issues avail.)

340   US
ALASKA BAR RAG. 1963. bi-m. $25. Alaska Bar Association, Box 100279, Anchorage, AK 99510. TEL 907-272-7469. Ed.Bd. adv.; bk.rev.; index. circ. 3,000. (looseleaf format)
   Former titles: Alaska Bar Brief (ISSN 0093-1039); Alaska Law Journal (ISSN 0002-452X)

340   US   ISSN 0883-0568
K1
ALASKA LAW REVIEW. vol.8, 1991. s-a. $20 (foreign $23). Duke University, School of Law, Box 90364, Durham, NC 27708-0364. TEL 919-684-5966. FAX 919-684-3417. (also avail. in microfilm from RRI; reprint service avail. from RRI) **Document type:** academic/scholarly publication.
   —UnCover.

340   US   ISSN 0002-4678
LAW
ALBANY LAW REVIEW. 1931. 4/yr. $25. Albany Law School, 80 New Scotland Ave., Albany, NY 12208. TEL 518-445-2375. FAX 518-445-2315. Ed. Alicia R. Ovellette. adv.; bk.rev.; index. circ. 1,000. (also avail. in microfilm from PMC,WSH; back issues avail.) **Indexed:** Abstr.Bk.Rev.Curr.Leg.Per., C.I.I., Crim.Just.Abstr., Geo.Abstr., L.R.I., Leg.Cont., Leg.Per. **Document type:** academic/scholarly publication.
   —BLDSC (0786.568000); Faxon; UnCover; UMI. **CCC.**

340   CN
ALBERTA CORPORATIONS LAW GUIDE. bi-m. Can.$540. C C H Canadian Ltd., 6 Garamond Ct., North York, ON M3C 1Z5, Canada. TEL 416-441-2992. FAX 416-444-9011.
   Description: Covers Alberta business corporations act and regulations.

342   CN   ISSN 0824-7277
ALBERTA DECISIONS. RULES AND STATUTE CITATOR. 1981. m. Can.$115. Western Legal Publications, 301-1 Alexander St., Vancouver, BC V6A 1B2, Canada. TEL 604-687-5671. FAX 604-687-2796. (looseleaf format)
   Description: Provides notes on all current judgements of the Supreme Court of Canada and the Alberta Courts, and case citations for all decisions of the Alberta Courts in which an Alberta Rule of Court or statute was cited.

340   CN   ISSN 0319-7980
ALBERTA DECISIONS, CIVIL AND CRIMINAL CASES. 1974. m. Can.$335. Western Legal Publications, 301-1 Alexander St., Vancouver, BC V6A 1B2, Canada. TEL 604-687-5671. FAX 604-687-2796.
   ●Also available online.
   Description: Provides detailed summaries of judgements from the Alberta Court of Appeals, Court of Queen's Bench and selected decisions of the Provincial Courts of Alberta.

340   CN
ALBERTA LAW REFORM INSTITUTE. REPORT. 1968. irreg. free. Alberta Law Reform Institute, 402 Law Centre, University of Alberta, Edmonton, AB T6G 2H5, Canada. TEL 403-492-5291. FAX 403-492-1790. (also avail. in microfiche)
   Formerly: Institute of Law Research and Reform. Report (ISSN 0317-1604)

340   CN   ISSN 0703-3117
LAW
ALBERTA LAW REPORTS (3RD SERIES). 1976. 8 vols./yr. Can.$120 per vol. Carswell, One Corporate Plaza, 2075 Kennedy Rd., Scarborough, ON M1T 3V4, Canada. TEL 416-609-8000. FAX 416-298-5094. Ed. Margaret James. adv. contact: M. Lalani. cum.index.
   Description: Contains full text of all decisions of significance from the courts of Alberta and appeals from those judgments to the Supreme Court of Canada, fully headnoted and topically indexed. Cases, statutes and rules judicially considered are listed in each headnote and cumulated in the parts and bound volumes.

340   CN   ISSN 0002-4821
ALBERTA LAW REVIEW. 1955. 4/yr. Can.$45. University of Alberta, Faculty of Law, Edmonton, AB T6G 2H5, Canada. TEL 403-492-5559. FAX 403-492-4924. adv.; bk.rev.; illus.; index. circ. 2,500. (also avail. in microform from UMI; reprint service avail. from UMI) **Indexed:** Abstr.Bk.Rev.Curr.Leg.Per., C.I.I., Can.Per.Ind., Ind.Can.L.P.L., L.R.I., Leg.Cont., Leg.Per., Mar.Aff.Bibl. **Document type:** academic/scholarly publication.
   —BLDSC (0786.587000); UnCover; UMI.

ALBERTA LEGAL TELEPHONE DIRECTORY. see BUSINESS AND ECONOMICS — Trade And Industrial Directories

340   CN
ALBERTA LIMITATIONS MANUAL. 2/yr. Can.$205. Butterworths Canada Ltd., Part of the Reed Elsevier group, 75 Clegg Rd., Markham, ON L6G 1A1, Canada. TEL 905-479-2665. FAX 905-479-2826. (looseleaf format)
   Description: A reference of time limits specified in Alberta's legal statutes.

340   CN   ISSN 0703-3109
ALBERTA REPORTS. 1976. irreg., latest vol.137. Can.$124 per vol. Maritime Law Book Ltd., Box 302, Fredericton, NB E3B 4Y9, Canada. TEL 506-453-9921; 800-561-0220. FAX 506-453-9525. (back issues avail.)
   ●Also available online. Vendor(s): QL Systems Ltd.
   Description: Contains all of the judgments of the Alberta Court of Appeal plus selected trial court judgments.

343   CN   ISSN 0715-3155
ALBERTA, SASKATCHEWAN, MANITOBA - CRIMINAL CONVICTION CASES. 1976. m. Can.$175. Western Legal Publications, 301-1 Alexander St., Vancouver, BC V6A 1B2, Canada. TEL 604-687-5671. FAX 604-687-2796. q. index. (looseleaf format)
   Description: Summaries of criminal conviction decisions made available by the Appellate and Trial Divisions of the Superior Courts of Alberta, Saskatchewan and Manitoba.

340   CN   ISSN 0713-892X
ALBERTA WEEKLY LAW DIGEST. 1982. w. (50/yr.). Can.$385. Carswell, One Corporate Plaza, 2075 Kennedy Rd., Scarborough, ON M1T 3V4, Canada. TEL 416-609-8000. FAX 416-298-5094. Ed. Margaret James. cum.index.
   Description: Pre-reporting service of digests of all available judgments of the courts of Alberta plus decisions of the Supreme Court of Canada and the Federal Court in cases originating in the province. Refusals of leave of appeal to the Supreme Court are also noted.

ALCOHOL ISSUES INSIGHTS. see BEVERAGES

344.73   US   ISSN 0098-0757
KF3919
ALCOHOL, TOBACCO AND FIREARMS BULLETIN. q. $12 (foreign $15). U.S. Department of the Treasury, Bureau of Alcohol, Tobacco and Firearms, 650 Massachusetts Ave., N.W., Washington, DC 20226. TEL 202-927-7777. (Subscr. to: Superintendent of Documents, U.S. Government Printing Office, Box 371954, Pittsburgh, PA 15250-7954. TEL 202-783-3238. FAX 202-512-2233) (back issues avail.) **Document type:** bulletin, government publication.
   Description: Announces all new laws, regulations, codes and rulings or changes relating to alcohol, tobacco or firearms.

ALERT (LOS ANGELES). see SOCIAL SERVICES AND WELFARE

340   BE
ALGEMENE PRACTISCHE RECHTVERZAMELING. Short title: A P R. 1972. irreg. price varies. Kluwer Editions Juridiques Belgique, E. Story-Scientia (Subsidiary of: Wolters Kluwer N.V.), 230 bd. Emile Bockstael, B-1020 Brussels, Belgium. TEL 32-2-4223911. FAX 32-2-4223979.

ALIMENTALEX; international food law review - revue internationale de droit de l'alimentation - revista internacional de derecho alimentario. see FOOD AND FOOD INDUSTRIES

340   CN   ISSN 0705-1360
ALL CANADA WEEKLY SUMMARIES - NATIONAL. 1977. w. Can.$147. Canada Law Book Inc., 240 Edward St., Aurora, ON L4G 3S9, Canada. TEL 905-841-6472. FAX 905-841-5085. adv. contact: Mary Cull.
   ●Also available online.

349   II   ISSN 0002-5593
ALL INDIA REPORTER; full reports of all reportable (civil, criminal and revenue) cases of the High Courts and Supreme Court in India. 1922. m. Rs.540($168) All India Reporter Ltd., P.O. Box 209, Nagpur 440012, India. Ed. V.R. Manohar. adv.; bk.rev.; index. circ. 34,000.

340   II
ALL INDIA SERVICES LAW JOURNAL; the journal that serves those in service. (Text in English) 1973. m. Rs.640 (effective 1993). Bahri Brothers, Box 2032, 742 Lajpat Rai Market, Delhi 110006, India. adv.; bk.rev.; index. circ. 2,000.
   Description: Reports important service rules, amendments orders, clarifications and decisions of Indian government

340   PK   ISSN 0030-9958
ALL PAKISTAN LEGAL DECISIONS. 1949. m. Rs.640($42) (effective 1993). P.L.D. Publishers, 35 Nabha Rd., Lahore 1, Pakistan. TEL 92-42-213497. Ed. Malik Muhammad Saeed. (back issues avail.; reprint service avail. from UMI)

LAW

340 350   HU   ISSN 0324-7171
JA26
ALLAM ES IGAZGATAS. 1951. m. $22.50. (Minisztertanacs) Lapkiado Vallalat, Lenin korut 9-11, 1073 Budapest 7, Hungary. TEL 222-408. (Subscr. to: Kultura, Box 149, H-1389 Budapest, Hungary) Ed. Tibor Kovacs. adv.; bk.rev.; bibl. **Indexed:** Rural Recreat.Tour.Abstr., World Agri.Econ.& Rural Sociol.Abstr.

349 320   HU   ISSN 0002-564X
ALLAM- ES JOGTUDOMANY/POLITICAL SCIENCE AND JURISPRUDENCE. (Text in Hungarian; summaries in French and Russian) 1957. q. 600 Ft. (Magyar Tudomanyos Akademia, Allam-es Jogtudomanyi Intezet) Akademiai Kiado, Publishing House of the Hungarian Academy of Sciences, P.O. Box 245, H-1519 Budapest, Hungary. TEL 181-2134. FAX 166-6466. TELEX 22-6228 AKNYO H. Eds. I. Szabo, F. Madl. adv.; bk.rev.; index. **Indexed:** Rural Recreat.Tour.Abstr., World Agri.Econ.& Rural Sociol.Abstr.

340   US
ALLEGHENY LAWYER. 1959. m. free to members. Allegheny County Bar Association, 436 7th Ave., Ste. 400, Pittsburgh, PA 15219-1818. TEL 412-261-6161. FAX 412-261-3622. Ed. James I. Smith. circ. 6,300. (back issues avail.) **Description:** Membership news of the Allegheny County Bar Association.

340   US
KF9084.A15A472
ALTERNATIVE DISPUTE RESOLUTION NEWSALERT. 1991. bi-m. $150. Bancroft-Whitney Company, Box 7005, San Francisco, CA 94120-7005. TEL 415-986-4410. Ed. Dan Smith. index. (looseleaf format) **Document type:** newsletter.

340   AT   ISSN 1037-969X
ALTERNATIVE LAW JOURNAL. 1974. bi-m. Aus.$63 (foreign $85). Legal Service Bulletin Co., Ltd., c/o Monash University, Faculty of Law, Wellington Rd., Clayton, Vic. 3168, Australia. TEL 64-3-544-0974. FAX 64-3-565-5305. bk.rev.; cum.index. circ. 2,000. (back issues avail.) **Indexed:** C.L.I. **Document type:** academic/scholarly publication.
●Also available online. Vendor(s): Info-One International Pty Ltd..
—UnCover.
Formerly (until 1992): Legal Service Bulletin (ISSN 0817-3516); Incorporates: Aboriginal Law Bulletin (ISSN 0728-5671)

340   US
KF9084.A15A47
ALTERNATIVES NEWSLETTER. 1987. 3/yr. $12. American Bar Association, Young Lawyers Division, 750 N. Lake Shore Dr., Chicago, IL 60611. TEL 312-988-5000. FAX 312-988-6281. **Document type:** newsletter.
Description: Features editorials on the subject of Alternative Dispute Resolution, articles on young lawyers and ADR programs in operation, as well as federal and state case law updates.

340   US   ISSN 0736-3613
KF9084.A15A44
ALTERNATIVES TO THE HIGH COST OF LITIGATION. 1983. m. $175. Center for Public Resources, Legal Program, 366 Madison Ave., New York, NY 10017. TEL 212-949-6490. FAX 212-949-8859. Ed. Deborah Jacobs. bk.rev.; index. circ. 1,800. (looseleaf format; back issues avail.; reprint service avail.) **Document type:** newsletter.

AMERICAN ACADEMY OF PSYCHIATRY AND THE LAW. BULLETIN. see *MEDICAL SCIENCES — Psychiatry And Neurology*

340 616.8   US   ISSN 0896-5633
KF8922
AMERICAN ACADEMY OF PSYCHIATRY AND THE LAW. NEWSLETTER. 1975. 3/yr. $25. American Academy of Psychiatry and the Law, Box 30, Bloomfield, CT 06002-0030. TEL 203-242-5450. FAX 203-286-0787. Ed. Dr. Robert Miller. circ. 1,750. **Document type:** academic/scholarly publication, newsletter.
Description: Law and practice in psychiatry and forensic psychiatry.

AMERICAN ASSOCIATION OF LEGAL NURSE CONSULTANTS NETWORK; news for the legal nurse consultant. see *MEDICAL SCIENCES — Nurses And Nursing*

AMERICAN AUTOMOBILE ASSOCIATION. DIGEST OF MOTOR LAWS. see *TRANSPORTATION — Automobiles*

340   US   ISSN 0027-9048
K1
AMERICAN BANKRUPTCY LAW JOURNAL. 1927. q. $50. National Conference of Bankruptcy Judges, 235 Secret Cove Dr., Lexington, SC 29072. TEL 803-957-6225. Ed. Sam Bufford. bk.rev.; illus.; index, cum.index: vols.24-27 (1950-1973). circ. 3,408. (also avail. in microfilm from UMI; reprint service avail. from WSH) **Indexed:** Bank.Lit.Ind., C.L.I., Curr.Cont., L.R.I., Leg.Cont., Leg.Per., SSCI. **Document type:** academic/scholarly publication.
—BLDSC (0810.723000); Faxon; UnCover; UMI.
Formerly: National Conference of Referees in Bankruptcy. Journal (ISSN 0197-2669)

340   US
AMERICAN BAR ASSOCIATION. OFFICE OF POLICY ADMINISTRATION. SUMMARY AND REPORTS. s-a. $10. American Bar Association, Office of Policy Administration, 750 N. Lake Shore Dr., Chicago, IL 60611. TEL 312-988-5169. FAX 312-988-5153. **Document type:** proceedings.
Description: Contains recommendations and informational reports to and summary of actions of the ABA House of Delegates.

340 336   US   ISSN 0277-2361
KF6272
AMERICAN BAR ASSOCIATION. SECTION OF TAXATION. NEWSLETTER. q. $15 to non-members. American Bar Association, Taxation Section, 1800 M St., N.W., 2nd Fl., S. Lobby, Washington, DC 20036-5886. TEL 202-331-2231. FAX 202-331-2220. Ed. Phyllis Horn Epstein. (looseleaf format; back issues avail.) **Indexed:** C.L.I., Leg.Per. **Document type:** newsletter.
Description: Update on current tax developments, committee projects, meeting information.

340 352   US   ISSN 0569-3349
KF2077
AMERICAN BAR ASSOCIATION. UTILITY SECTION. NEWSLETTER. 1960. q. membership only. American Bar Association, Public Utility Law Section, 750 N. Lake Shore Dr., Chicago, IL 60611. TEL 312-988-5602. **Indexed:** C.L.I.
Description: Articles pertaining to the field of public utility law.

340   US   ISSN 0094-3584
LAW
AMERICAN BAR - THE CANADIAN BAR - THE INTERNATIONAL BAR. 1919. a. $275. Forster-Long, Inc., 3280 Ramos Circle, Sacramento, CA 95827. TEL 916-362-3276. FAX 916-362-5643. Ed. Marie Finn. circ. 40,000. **Document type:** directory.
Description: Biographical directory of preeminent lawyers of the world with abridged handbook.

347.9   US
AMERICAN BENCH; judges of the nation. 1977. biennial. $275. Forster-Long, Inc., 3280 Ramos Circle, Sacramento, CA 95827. TEL 916-362-3276. FAX 916-362-5643. Ed. Marie Finn. maps. **Document type:** directory.
Description: Biographical reference guide listing approximately 18,000 judges serving all levels of federal, state and local courts.

AMERICAN CRIMINAL LAW REVIEW. see *CRIMINOLOGY AND LAW ENFORCEMENT*

AMERICAN GROUP PRACTICE ASSOCIATION. EXECUTIVE NEWS SERVICE. see *MEDICAL SCIENCES*

340   US
AMERICAN INDIAN COURTLINE. 1986. irreg. membership. American Indian Court Clerks Association, 1000 Connecticut Ave., N.W., Ste. 1206, Washington, DC 20036. TEL 202-296-0685. Ed. Thomas Colisimo. **Document type:** newsletter.

AMERICAN INDIAN JOURNAL. see *HISTORY — History Of North And South America*

340 970.1   US   ISSN 0094-002X
K1
AMERICAN INDIAN LAW REVIEW. 1973. s-a. $20. University of Oklahoma, College of Law, 300 Timberdell Rd., Norman, OK 73019. TEL 405-325-2840. Ed. Sandra Lee Nowack. adv.; bk.rev. circ. 700. (also avail. in microfilm from WSH,PMC; reprint service avail. from WSH) **Indexed:** C.L.I., L.R.I., Leg.Cont., Leg.Per., Sel.Water Res.Abstr. **Document type:** academic/scholarly publication.
●Also available online. Vendor(s): West Services, Inc.
—Faxon.
Description: Contains articles, student notes and federal developments on American Indian law and education.

AMERICAN JOURNAL OF CRIMINAL LAW. see *CRIMINOLOGY AND LAW ENFORCEMENT*

AMERICAN JOURNAL OF FORENSIC PSYCHIATRY. see *MEDICAL SCIENCES — Forensic Sciences*

AMERICAN JOURNAL OF FORENSIC PSYCHOLOGY; interfacing issues of psychology and law. see *PSYCHOLOGY*

340   US   ISSN 0065-8995
K14
AMERICAN JOURNAL OF JURISPRUDENCE. 1956. a. $20 to individuals; institutions $25. University of Notre Dame, Law School, Notre Dame, IN 46556. TEL 219-255-2938. Eds. Charles E. Rice, Robert E. Rodes. adv.; bk.rev. circ. 1,100. (also avail. in microfilm from UMI,WSH,PMC; back issues avail.; reprint service avail. from UMI,WSH) **Indexed:** A.B.C.Pol.Sci., C.L.I., Cath.Ind., L.R.I., Leg.Cont., Leg.Per.
—BLDSC (0826.850000); UnCover; SWETS.
Formerly: Natural Law Forum.

340 610   US   ISSN 0098-8588
K1   CODEN: AJLMDN
AMERICAN JOURNAL OF LAW & MEDICINE. 1975. q. $70 (foreign $100). American Society of Law, Medicine & Ethics, 765 Commonwealth Ave., Ste. 1634, Boston, MA 02215. TEL 617-262-4990. FAX 617-437-7596. (Co-sponsor: Boston University, School of Law) Ed. Lawrence O. Gostin. bk.rev.; bibl. circ. 5,000. (also avail. in microfilm from WSH,PMC; reprint service avail. from WSH) **Indexed:** Abstr.Bk.Rev.Curr.Leg.Per., Abstr.Health Care Manage.Stud., Biol.Abstr., C.L.I., Curr.Cont., Dok.Arbeitsmed., Excerp.Med., Hlth.Ind., Hosp.Lit.Ind., Ind.Med., INIS Atomind., L.R.I., Leg.Cont., Leg.Per., Med.Care Rev., SSCI, Telegen.
—BLDSC (0826.880000); Faxon; UnCover; SWETS; UMI. CCC.
Description: Interdisciplinary law review providing in-depth legal analysis of current medicolegal issues. *Refereed Serial*

340   US   ISSN 0002-9319
AMERICAN JOURNAL OF LEGAL HISTORY. 1957. q. $25. Temple University, School of Law, Philadelphia, PA 19122. TEL 215-787-1256. FAX 215-787-1785. Ed. John Lindsey. adv.; bk.rev.; bibl.; charts; index, cum.index every 5 yrs. circ. 1,200. (also avail. in microfilm from RRI; reprint service avail. from RRI) **Indexed:** A.B.C.Pol.Sci., Abstr.Bk.Rev.Curr.Leg.Per., Amer.Hist.& Life, C.L.I., Chic.Per.Ind., Hist.Abstr., L.R.I., Leg.Cont., Leg.Per., SSCI. **Document type:** academic/scholarly publication.
●Also available online. Vendor(s): West Services, Inc.
—BLDSC (0826.900000); Faxon; UnCover; SWETS.

347.91   US   ISSN 0160-0281
K1
AMERICAN JOURNAL OF TRIAL ADVOCACY. 1977. 3/yr. $24. Samford University, Cumberland School of Law, 800 Lakeshore Dr., ROBH 305D, Birmingham, AL 35229. TEL 205-870-2959. FAX 205-870-2673. Ed.Bd. bk.rev.; index. circ. 1,500. (also avail. in microfilm from UMI; reprint service avail. from RRI) **Indexed:** C.C.L.P., C.L.I., CJPI, Hlth.Ind., L.R.I., Leg.Cont., Leg.Per. **Document type:** academic/scholarly publication.
—BLDSC (0838.900000); UnCover; UMI.

340   US   ISSN 0732-1031
KF294.A4
AMERICAN JUDICATURE SOCIETY. ANNUAL REPORT. 1917. a. free. American Judicature Society, 25 E. Washington, Ste. 1600, Chicago, IL 60602-1805. Ed. Ira Pilchen. circ. 15,000. **Document type:** corporate report.

LAW

340 US ISSN 0065-9045
AMERICAN LAW INSTITUTE. ANNUAL MEETING. PROCEEDINGS. 1923. a. price varies. American Law Institute, 4025 Chestnut St., Philadelphia, PA 19104. TEL 215-243-1600. FAX 215-243-1664. Ed. Todd David Feldman. index from 1967. (also avail. in microfiche from BHP) **Document type:** proceedings.
   Description: Edited transcript of the American Law Institute's annual meeting, the American Law Institute's Annual Reports and additional information on ALI and ALI-ABA projects.

340 US ISSN 0162-3397
K1
THE AMERICAN LAWYER. 1979. m. (10/yr.). $56550. American Lawyer Media, L.P. (New York), 600 Third Ave., 2nd Fl., New York, NY 10016. TEL 212-973-2800. FAX 212-972-6258. Ed. John Morris. adv. contact: Amy Doering. bk.rev. circ. 17,000. (tabloid format) **Indexed:** Access (1981-), C.L.I., L.R.I., Leg.Info.Manage.Ind., Leg.Per.
   ●Also available online. Vendor(s): Mead Data Central, Inc.
   —UnCover. **CCC.**
   Description: News and features about the legal profession including the people and management issues shaping the legal field.

340 US
AMERICAN LAWYER MANAGEMENT SERVICE. 1984. 3 base vols. (plus q. updates). $295 for set; q. update $135. American Lawyer Media, L.P. (San Francisco), 625 Polk, Ste. 500, San Francisco, CA 94102. TEL 415-749-5407. Ed. Sara Seigel.
   Description: Practical management advice for law firm partners and adminstration.

347 US ISSN 0044-7773
AMERICAN NOTARY. 1965. bi-m. $9. American Society of Notaries, 918 16th St., N.W., Washington, DC 20006. TEL 202-955-6162. FAX 202-785-3209. Ed. Eugene E. Hines. adv.; bk.rev.; circ. 22,000 (controlled). (also avail. in microform from UMI) **Document type:** newsletter.
   —UMI.

AMERICAN SOCIETY OF CORPORATE SECRETARIES. LOS ANGELES CHAPTER. NEWSLETTER. see *BUSINESS AND ECONOMICS — Management*

340 US ISSN 0003-1453
LAW
AMERICAN UNIVERSITY LAW REVIEW. 1952. 4/yr. $30. American University, Washington College of Law, 4400 Massachusetts Ave., N.W., Washington, DC 20016. TEL 202-885-2652. Ed. Douglas Sheehy. adv.; bk.rev.; index. circ. 1,600. (also avail. in microform from UMI) **Indexed:** C.L.I., CJPI, Crim.Just.Abstr., L.R.I., Leg.Cont., Leg.Per. **Document type:** bulletin.
   ●Also available online. Vendor(s): West Services, Inc.
   —BLDSC (0858.070000); Faxon; UnCover; SWETS; UMI.

342 940 US ISSN 0740-0470
AMERICAN UNIVERSITY STUDIES. SERIES 10. POLITICAL SCIENCE. 1983. irreg. Peter Lang Publishing, Inc., 62 W. 45th St., 4th Fl., New York, NY 10036. TEL 212-302-6740. Ed. Kathryn Earle. **Document type:** academic/scholarly publication.
   —BLDSC (0858.078400).

AMISTAD. see *HISTORY — History Of North And South America*

340 GW
AMTLICHE BEKANNTMACHUNGEN DER UNIVERSITAET GESAMTHOCHSCHULE ESSEN. 1972. m. Universitaet Gesamthochschule Essen, Universitaetsstr. 2, 45141 Essen, Germany. TEL 0201-183-2075. TELEX 859091-UNIE-D. circ. 500.

AMTLICHES SCHULBLATT FUER DEN REGIERUNGSBEZIRK DUESSELDORF. see *EDUCATION*

340 AU ISSN 0003-2220
AMTSBLATT DER OESTERREICHISCHEN JUSTIZVERWALTUNG. 1923. S.535. (Bundesministerium fuer Justiz) Oesterreichische Staatsdruckerei, Rennweg 12a, A-1037 Vienna, Austria. TEL 0222-79789333. index. circ. 1,400. **Document type:** government publication.

349 GW ISSN 0003-2336
DER AMTSVORMUND. 1927. m. DM.75. Deutsches Institut fuer Vormundschaftswesen e.V., Zaehringerstr. 10, 69115 Heidelberg, Germany. TEL 06221-9818-0. FAX 06221-981828. Ed. Walter Zarbock. adv.; bk.rev. circ. 1,500. **Document type:** bulletin.
   Description: Discusses legal problems involving minor children.

349 AG ISSN 0034-6985
LAW
ANALES DE LEGISLACION ARGENTINA. 1940. every 10 days (plus q. cum.). Arg.$150($600) Ediciones la Ley S.A., 1471 Tucuman, Buenos Aires, Argentina. adv.; abstr.; index, cum.index; circ. 11,000 (controlled).

ANALYSIS OF KEY S E C NO-ACTION LETTERS. see *BUSINESS AND ECONOMICS — Investments*

340 US
ANDERSON'S LAWRITER UNREPORTED OHIO APPELLATE CASES. q. $2195. Anderson Publishing Co., 2035 Reading Rd., Cincinnati, OH 45202. TEL 513-421-4142. FAX 513-562-8116.
   ●Available only on CD-ROM.
   Description: Presents all unreported Ohio appellate cases from 1981 to the present, and selected unreported Ohio appellate cases from Ohio Opinions from 1953-1980.

340 US
ANDREWS ADVISOR; quarterly newsletter for law librarians. 1989. q. Andrews Publications, 1646 West Chester Pike, Box 1000, Westtown, PA 19395. TEL 215-399-6600; 800-345-1101. FAX 215-399-6610. **Document type:** newsletter.

ANESTHESIA MALPRACTICE PROTECTOR. see *MEDICAL SCIENCES — Anaesthesiology*

ANESTHESIOLOGY MALPRACTICE REPORTER. see *MEDICAL SCIENCES — Anaesthesiology*

340 UK ISSN 0308-6569
K1
ANGLO-AMERICAN LAW REVIEW. 1972. q. £75 (typically set in Sep.). Barry Rose Law Periodicals, Little London, Chichester, W. Sussex PO19 1PG, England. TEL 0243-787841. FAX 0243-779278. Ed. Martin Partington. adv.; bk.rev. **Indexed:** C.L.I., L.R.I., Leg.Cont., Leg.Per. **Document type:** academic/scholarly publication.
   —BLDSC (0902.803000); UnCover. **CCC.**
   Description: Covers major legal issues in the U.K. and the U.S. and throughout the common law world.

340 US
KF3841.A15A55
ANIMAL LAW REPORT. 1987. s-a. $10. American Bar Association, Young Lawyers Division, 750 N. Lake Shore Dr., Chicago, IL 60611. TEL 312-988-5555. FAX 312-988-6281. Ed. Elinor Molbegott.
   Description: Summarizes recent legislation, case decisions, and literature.

343 DK ISSN 0108-7169
ANKLAGEMYNDIGHEDENS AARSBERETNING. 1973. a. free. Rigsadvokaturen, Rigspolitchefen, Christians Brygge 28, 3. sal t.v., 1559 Copenhagen V, Denmark. FAX 33-147008. circ. 3,000.

340 PL ISSN 0458-4317
ANNALES UNIVERSITATIS MARIAE CURIE-SKLODOWSKA. SECTIO G. IUS. (Text in English, French, German, Polish; summaries in French, German, Polish) 1954. a. price varies. Uniwersytet Marii Curie-Sklodowskiej, Wydawnictwo, Pl. M. Curie-Sklodowskiej 5, 20-031 Lublin, Poland. TEL 48-81-375304. FAX 48-81-336699. TELEX 0643223. Ed. Wieslaw Skrzydlo. circ. 500. **Indexed:** Amer.Hist.& Life, Hist.Abstr., World Agri.Econ.& Rural Sociol.Abstr. **Document type:** academic/scholarly publication.
   —BLDSC (0962.200000).

ANNALS OF AIR AND SPACE LAW/ANNALES DE DROIT AERIEN ET SPATIAL. see *AERONAUTICS AND SPACE FLIGHT*

340 CN
ANNOTATED BRITISH COLUMBIA LABOUR RELATIONS CODE. 4/yr. Can.$150. Butterworths Canada Ltd., Part of the Reed Elsevier group, 75 Clegg Rd., Markham, ON L6G 1A1, Canada. TEL 905-479-2665. FAX 905-479-2826. (looseleaf format)
   Former titles: British Columbia Annotated Industrial Relations Act; British Columbia Labour Code.
   Description: British Columbia Labour Court and Labour Board decisions.

340 FR ISSN 0242-6366
ANNOUNCES JUDICIAIRES ET LEGALES. (Supplement to: Gazette du Palais (ISSN 0242-6331)) 1971. irreg. Gazette du Palais, 3 bd du Palais, 75180 Paris Cedex 04, France. TEL 43-25-97-47. FAX 40-46-03-47. TELEX GAZPAL 200 621.
   Formerly (until 1976): Announces Legales (ISSN 0242-6374).

340 FR ISSN 0066-2658
ANNUAIRE DE LEGISLATION FRANCAISE ET ETRANGERE. a. price varies. (Centre National de la Recherche Scientifique, Service de Recherches Juridiques Comparatives) C N R S Editions, 20-22 rue St. Amand, 75105 Paris, France. TEL 45-33-16-00. FAX 45-33-92-13. TELEX 200 356 F. adv.; bk.rev.; index; circ. 1,250 (controlled).
   Description: Studies on the evolution and development of law in different countries.

345 622 US ISSN 0273-5253
KF1849.A2
ANNUAL INSTITUTE ON MINERAL LAW. 1954. a. $50. (Louisiana State University, Institute on Mineral Law) Louisiana State University Press, Paul M. Hebert Law Center, Baton Rouge, LA 70803-1025. TEL 504-388-8724. FAX 504-388-8202. TELEX 510-993-3414. Ed. Thomas A. Harrell. index. circ. 500. (reprint service avail. from UMI) **Indexed:** Leg.Per.
   —UnCover.
   Formerly (until 1956): Louisiana State University. Law School. Institute on Mineral Law. Proceedings (ISSN 0076-1087)

ANNUAL INSTITUTE ON SECURITIES REGULATION. see *BUSINESS AND ECONOMICS — Banking And Finance*

ANNUAL REVIEW OF BANKING LAW. see *BUSINESS AND ECONOMICS — Banking And Finance*

340 US
ANNUAL REVIEW OF POVERTY LAW. a. $15. National Clearinghouse for Legal Services, Inc., 205 W. Monroe, 2nd Fl., Chicago, IL 60606. TEL 312-263-3830. FAX 312-263-3846.

340 UK ISSN 0066-4405
ANNUAL SURVEY OF AFRICAN LAW. 1970. a. price varies. Rex Collings Ltd., 6 Paddington St., London W.1., England. Eds. N.N. Rubin, E. Cotran. index.

345 US ISSN 0066-4413
KF178
ANNUAL SURVEY OF AMERICAN LAW. 1945. a. price varies. (New York University, Law Publications) Oceana Publications, Inc., 75 Main St., Dobbs Ferry, New York, NY 10522. TEL 914-693-1320. FAX 914-693-0402. circ. 800. (back issues avail.) **Indexed:** C.L.I., L.R.I., Leg.Per. **Document type:** academic/scholarly publication.
   —BLDSC (1534.905000); UnCover; SWETS.
   Description: Focuses on developments and issues which affect the legal system in America.

340 US ISSN 0270-1464
ANNUAL SURVEY OF BANKRUPTCY LAW. 1979. a. $135. Clark - Boardman - Callaghan Company, Inc., 155 Pfingsten Rd., Deerfield, IL 60015. TEL 800-323-1336. Ed. Jean Maess. index. (back issues avail.)

340 II ISSN 0570-2666
LAW
ANNUAL SURVEY OF INDIAN LAW. (Text in English) 1965. a. $16. Indian Law Institute, Bhagwandas Rd., New Delhi 110001, India. bibl.

340.5   IT   ISSN 0003-5149
ANNUARIO DI DIRITTO COMPARATO E DI STUDI LEGISLATIVI. (Text in English, French and Italian) 1925. s-a. L.90000. (Istituto Italiano di Studi Legislativi) Maggioli Editore, Viale Vespucci 12-n, Casella Postale 290, 47037 Rimini, Italy. TEL 0541-626777. FAX 0541-622020. Dir. Gian Piero Orsello. adv.: B&W page L.2500000; trim 115 x 195. index. circ. 800.

ANNUARIO EUROPEO DELL'AMBIENTE. see *ENVIRONMENTAL STUDIES*

ANTITRUST & TRADE REGULATION REPORT. see *BUSINESS AND ECONOMICS — Production Of Goods And Services*

ANTITRUST FREEDOM OF INFORMATION LOG. see *BUSINESS AND ECONOMICS — International Commerce*

347.7   US   ISSN 0073-5000
KF1431.A15A5
ANTITRUST LAW NEWSLETTER. 1959. bi-m. $12 to members. Illinois State Bar Association, Section on Antitrust Law, Illinois Bar Center, Springfield, IL 62701. TEL 217-525-1760. FAX 217-525-0712. Eds. Don R. Sampen, C. Steven Baker. circ. 550 (controlled). (looseleaf format; back issues avail.) **Document type:** newsletter.

340   US   ISSN 1057-8919
KF1650.A58
ANTITRUST REPORT. 1980. bi-m. $145. National Association of Attorneys General, 444 N. Capitol St., Ste. 339, Washington, DC 20001. TEL 202-434-8000. FAX 202-434-8008. Ed. Clay Friedman. s-a. index. (looseleaf format) **Document type:** newsletter.

340   UY   ISSN 0797-0773
ANUARIO DE DERECHO CIVIL URUGUAYO. 1970. a. $89. Fundacion de Cultura Universitaria, 25 de Mayo, No. 568, Casilla de Correo No. 1155, Montevideo, Uruguay. TEL 961152. FAX 952549.

340   SP   ISSN 0210-3001
ANUARIO DE DERECHO PENAL Y CIENCIAS PENALES. 1948. a. (plus updates 3/yr.). 5000 ptas. (foreign 5400 ptas.). Ministerio de Justicia, Centro de Publicaciones, Secretaria General Tecnica, Gran Via, 76-8, 28013 Madrid, Spain. TEL 547-54-22. FAX 559-29-48. **Document type:** government publication.
—SWETS.

340 940   SP   ISSN 0304-4319
LAW
ANUARIO DE HISTORIA DEL DERECHO ESPANOL. 1924. a. 6420 ptas. (foreign 6500 ptas.). Ministerio de Justicia, Centro de Publicaciones, Secretaria General Tecnica, Gran Via, 76-8, 28013 Madrid, Spain. TEL 547-54-22. FAX 559-29-48. bk.rev.; bibl.; index. **Indexed:** Amer.Hist.& Life, Hist.Abstr. **Document type:** government publication.

340   MX   ISSN 0185-3295
ANUARIO JURIDICO. 1974. a. $30. Universidad Nacional Autonoma de Mexico, Instituto de Investigaciones Juridicas, Ciudad Universitaria, Delegacion Coyoacan, 04510 Mexico, DF, Mexico. Ed. Eugenio Hurtado Marquez. adv.; bk.rev.; abstr.; bibl.; index.

340   MX   ISSN 0188-0837
KGF292
ANUARIO MEXICANO DE HISTORIA DEL DERECHO. 1989. a. $20. Universidad Nacional Autonoma de Mexico, Instituto de Investigaciones Juridicas, Ciudad Universitaria, Coyoacan, 04510 Mexico D.F., Mexico. Dir. Jorge Madrazo.

340   GW   ISSN 0171-7227
ANWALTSBLATT. 1950. m. DM.165. (Deutscher Anwaltverein e.V.) Deutscher Anwaltverlag GmbH, Bocholder 259, 45369 Essen, Germany. TEL 0201-611114. Ed. P. Hamacher. adv.; bk.rev.; stat.; index. circ. 26,000. **Indexed:** ELLIS.

AOYAMA JOURNAL OF SOCIAL SCIENCES/AOYAMA SHAKAI KAGAKU KIYO. see *SOCIAL SCIENCES: COMPREHENSIVE WORKS*

APARTMENT AGE; the voice of the industry. see *HOUSING AND URBAN PLANNING*

346.066   US
APPEALS TO THE ELEVENTH CIRCUIT. 1984. 3 base vols. (plus suppl. 2-3/yr.). $120. Butterworth Legal Publishers (Salem) (Subsidiary of: Reed Elsevier plc), 8 Industrial Way, Bldg. C, Salem, NH 03079. TEL 800-548-4001. FAX 603-898-9858. (looseleaf format)

346.066   US
APPEALS TO THE FIFTH CIRCUIT. 1977. 2 base vols. (plus suppl. 1-2/yr.). $150. Butterworth Legal Publishers (Salem) (Subsidiary of: Reed Elsevier plc), 8 Industrial Way, Bldg. C, Salem, NH 03079. TEL 800-548-4001. FAX 603-898-9858. (looseleaf format)

346.066   US
APPEALS TO THE THIRD CIRCUIT. 1986. 2 base vols. (plus suppl.). $130. Butterworth Legal Publishers (Salem) (Subsidiary of: Reed Elsevier plc), 8 Industrial Way, Bldg. C, Salem, MA 03079. TEL 800-548-4001. FAX 603-898-9858. (looseleaf format)

340   CN
APPORTIONMENT OF LIABILITY IN BRITISH COLUMBIA. 4/yr. Can.$180. Butterworths Canada Ltd., Part of the Reed Elsevier group, 75 Clegg Rd., Markham, ON L6G 1A1, Canada. TEL 905-479-2665. FAX 905-479-2826. (looseleaf format)
Description: Practical digest of all the British Columbia cases that address liability in motor vehicle accidents.

APROPAA. see *CRIMINOLOGY AND LAW ENFORCEMENT*

340 300   SP   ISSN 1131-5369
ARANZADI SOCIAL. (Includes bound vols. with indexes.) 1991. w. 56000 ptas. (effective 1991). Editorial Aranzadi, S.A., Avda. Carlos III, 34, Apdo. 111, 31080 Pamplona, Spain. TEL 948-331212. FAX 948-330919. index.

ARBEIT UND ARBEITSRECHT; Zeitschrift fuer betriebliche Praxis. see *BUSINESS AND ECONOMICS — Labor And Industrial Relations*

347.9 331   GW   ISSN 0003-7648
ARBEIT UND RECHT; Zeitschrift fuer Arbeitsrechtspraxis. 1953. m. DM.163. (Deutscher Gewerkschaftsbund) Bund-Verlag GmbH, Postfach 900840, 51118 Cologne, Germany. Ed. Rudolf Buschmann. adv.; bk.rev.; index. circ. 3,600. **Indexed:** P.A.I.S.For.Lang.Ind. **Document type:** trade publication.
—SWETS. **CCC.**

340   GW   ISSN 0934-7100
ARBEITSRECHT-BLAETTER (A R); Handbuch fuer die Praxis. 1949. m. DM.398. Forkel Verlag GmbH, Im Weiher 10, 69121 Heidelberg, Germany. TEL 06221-489-0. FAX 06221-489476. Eds. Werner Oehmann, Thomas Dieterich. (looseleaf format; back issues avail.) **Document type:** abstracting/indexing.
Description: Compilation of verdicts and texts, with a list of reference texts.

ARBEITSRECHT DER GEGENWART. see *BUSINESS AND ECONOMICS — Labor And Industrial Relations*

ARBEITSRECHT IN STICHWORTEN; Arbeitsrechtliche Entscheidungssammlung. see *BUSINESS AND ECONOMICS — Labor And Industrial Relations*

ARBEJDSRETLIGT TIDSSKRIFT; arbejdsrettens domme, arbejdsretlige kendelser. see *BUSINESS AND ECONOMICS — Labor And Industrial Relations*

ARBITRATION & THE LAW. see *LAW — Corporate Law*

349   GW   ISSN 0003-8911
JA14
ARCHIV DES OEFFENTLICHEN RECHTS. 1886. q. DM.198. Verlag J.C.B. Mohr (Paul Siebeck), Wilhelmstr. 18, 72074 Tuebingen, Germany. TEL 07071-923-0. FAX 07071-51104. TELEX 7262872-MOHR-D. (Subscr. to: Postfach 2040, 72010 Tuebingen, Germany) Ed.Bd. adv.; bk.rev.; index. **Indexed:** A.B.C.Pol.Sci., INIS Atomind. **Document type:** academic/scholarly publication.
—SWETS. **CCC.**
Description: All aspects of German public law.

341   GW   ISSN 0003-892X
JX5
ARCHIV DES VOELKERRECHTS. 1948. q. DM.260. Verlag J.C.B. Mohr (Paul Siebeck), Wilhelmstr. 18, 72074 Tuebingen, Germany. TEL 07071-923-0. FAX 07071-51104. TELEX 7262872-MOHR-D. (Subscr. to: Postfach 2040, 72010 Tuebingen, Germany) Ed.Bd. adv.; bk.rev.; bibl.; index. **Indexed:** A.B.C.Pol.Sci., Amer.Hist.& Life, ELLIS, Hist.Abstr., INIS Atomind., Mar.Aff.Bibl., P.A.I.S.For.Lang.Ind. **Document type:** academic/scholarly publication.
—SWETS. **CCC.**
Description: Analysis and reports on international public law court decisions.

340 070.43   GW   ISSN 0341-5198
ARCHIV FUER PRESSERECHT; Zeitschrift fuer das gesamte Medienrecht. 1970. q. Verlagsgruppe Handelsblatt GmbH, Kasernenstr. 67, 40213 Duesseldorf, Germany. TEL 0211-8870. (Subscr. to: Postfach 102717, 40018 Duesseldorf, Germany) Ed. Georg Wallraf. (reprint service avail. from SCH) **Document type:** bulletin.

ARCHIV FUER RECHTS- UND SOZIALPHILOSOPHIE/ARCHIVES DE PHILOSOPHIE DU DROIT ET DE PHILOSOPHIE SOCIALE/ARCHIVES FOR PHILOSOPHY OF LAW AND SOCIAL PHILOSOPHY. see *PHILOSOPHY*

ARCHIV FUER RECHTS- UND SOZIALPHILOSOPHIE. BEIHEFTE. see *PHILOSOPHY*

340   SZ
ARCHIV FUER SCHWEIZERISCHES ABGABERECHT. m. Falkenhoeheweg 12a, CH-3012 Bern, Switzerland. Ed. Peter Locher. circ. 2,000. **Document type:** bulletin.

340   FR   ISSN 0066-6564
ARCHIVES DE PHILOSOPHIE DU DROIT. 1952. a. price varies. Editions Sirey-Diffusion Dalloz, 11 rue Soufflot, 75240 Paris Cedex 05, France. TEL 1-40-51-54-54. FAX 1-45-87-37-48. TELEX 206 446 F.
—SWETS. **CCC.**

340 388.31   IT
ARCHIVIO DELLA CIRCOLAZIONE E DEI SINISTRI STRADALI. 1955? m. L.100000 (Europe L.150000; elsewhere L.200000) (effective 1994). Casa Editrice la Tribuna, Via Don Minzoni, 51, 29100 Piacenza, Italy. TEL 0523-759015. FAX 0523-757219.
Description: Covers doctrine, jurisprudence and legislation of traffic and vehicular accident law.

340 333.3   IT   ISSN 0392-615X
ARCHIVIO DELLE LOCAZIONI E DEL CONDOMINIO. 1979. q. L.100000 (Europe L.150000; elsewhere L.200000) (effective 1994). Casa Editrice la Tribuna, Via Don Minzoni, 51, 29100 Piacenza, Italy. TEL 0523-759015. FAX 0523-757219.
Description: Covers doctrine, jurisprudence and legislation of tenancy and condominium law.

340 011   IT   ISSN 0391-5646
ARCHIVIO GIURIDICO. 1868. s-a. L.100000 (foreign L.120000). Mucchi Editore s.r.l., Via Emilia Est. 1527, 41100 Modena, Italy. adv. (back issues avail.)

340   PL   ISSN 0066-6882
ARCHIVUM IURIDICUM CRACOVIENSE. (Text in English, French and German) 1968. a. price varies. (Polska Akademia Nauk, Oddzial w Krakowie, Komisja Nauk Prawnych) Ossolineum, Publishing House of the Polish Academy of Sciences, Rynek 9, 50-106 Wroclaw, Poland. TEL 48-71-386-25. FAX 48-71-448-103. TELEX 0712771 OSS PL. Ed. Franciszek Studnicki. circ. 600. **Document type:** academic/scholarly publication.
Description: Legal theory and jurisprudence, constitutional, administrative, civil, penal laws, law of labor, international law, comparativistic studies.

L'ARGUS DE LA LEGISLATION LIBANAISE. see *PUBLIC ADMINISTRATION*

349   YU   ISSN 0004-1270
ARHIV ZA PRAVNE I DRUSTVENE NAUKE. (Text in Serbo-Croatian; summaries in English) 1906. a. $20. Savez Udruzenja Pravnika Jugoslavije, Proleterskih Brigada 74, P.O. Box 179, Belgrade, Yugoslavia. TEL 11-452-848. Ed. Jovan Dordevic. adv.; bk.rev. circ. 4,000. **Indexed:** Amer.Hist.& Life, Foreign Leg.Per., Hist.Abstr.

LAW

340   US   ISSN 0004-1386
ARIZONA ADVOCATE. 1966. 6/yr. free to qualified personnel. University of Arizona, College of Law, Tucson, AZ 85721. TEL 602-621-1373. Ed. Tracy Earl. adv.; bk.rev.; illus. circ. 700. (tabloid format; also avail. in microfilm; reprint service avail. from UMI)

340   US   ISSN 1040-4090
K1
ARIZONA ATTORNEY. 1965. 11/yr. $30. State Bar of Arizona, 363 N. First Ave., Phoenix, AZ 85003. TEL 602-252-4804. FAX 602-271-4930. Ed. Patricia Gannon. adv.; bk.rev.; stat. circ. 12,000. Indexed: C.L.I., L.R.I., Law Ofc.Info.Svc., Leg.Per. **Document type:** trade publication.
—UnCover; UMI.
   Formerly: Arizona Bar Journal (ISSN 0004-1424)
   Description: General interest publication for the Arizona legal profession.

340 613.1   US   ISSN 1070-4655
ARIZONA ENVIRONMENTAL COMPLIANCE UPDATE. 1990. m. $137. (Brown & Bain) M. Lee Smith Publishers & Printers, 162 Fourth Ave., N., Box 198867, Nashville, TN 37219-8867. TEL 615-242-7395; 800-274-6774. FAX 615-256-6601. Ed.Bd. **Document type:** newsletter.
   Formerly: Arizona Environmental Law Letter (ISSN 1049-9342)
   Description: Reports the latest state-specific environmental law developments that affect Arizona companies.

ARIZONA FARM BUREAU NEWS. see *AGRICULTURE*

340   US   ISSN 0004-153X
K1
ARIZONA LAW REVIEW. 1959. q. $26 (foreign $28). University of Arizona, College of Law, Tucson, AZ 85721. TEL 602-621-1764. FAX 602-621-9140. Ed. Sarah Jeffries Johnson. adv.; bk.rev.; index. circ. 2,000. (also avail. in microform from UMI; reprint service avail. from RRI,UMI) Indexed: C.L.I., Crim.Just.Abstr., INIS Atomind., L.R.I., Leg.Cont., Leg.Per.
—BLDSC (1668.439000); Faxon; UnCover.

348   US
KFA2431
ARIZONA LEGISLATIVE SERVICE. Cover title: A R S Legislative Service. irreg. West Publishing Corp., 620 Opperman Dr., Eagan, MN 55123. TEL 612-687-8000; 800-328-9352. FAX 612-687-7302. **Document type:** trade publication.

340   US   ISSN 0164-4297
K1
ARIZONA STATE LAW JOURNAL. 1969. q. $20. Arizona State University, College of Law, Tempe, AZ 85287. TEL 602-965-6287. FAX 602-965-2427. Ed.Bd. adv.; bk.rev.; bibl. circ. 1,500. (also avail. in microfilm from WSH,PMC) Indexed: C.L.I., L.R.I., Leg.Cont., Leg.Per., P.A.I.S. **Document type:** academic/scholarly publication.
●Also available online. Vendor(s): West Services, Inc.
—BLDSC (1668.530000); Faxon; UnCover; UMI.
   Supersedes: Law and the Social Order (ISSN 0023-9224)

340   US
ARKANSAS BAR ASSOCIATION. LEGISLATIVE NEWSLETTER. 1978. w. free to members. Arkansas Bar Association, 400 W. Marham, Little Rock, AR 72201. TEL 501-375-4605. FAX 501-375-4901. Ed. Sara Landas. **Document type:** newsletter.

340   US
ARKANSAS BAR ASSOCIATION. NEWS BULLETIN. 1975. bi-m. Arkansas Bar Association, 400 W. Markham, Little Rock, AR 72201. TEL 501-375-4605. Ed. Sara Landis. circ. 4,000. (back issues avail.) **Document type:** bulletin.

340   US   ISSN 0004-1831
K1
ARKANSAS LAW REVIEW. 1946. q. $15 (foreign $17.50). University of Arkansas, School of Law, Waterman Hall, Fayetteville, AR 72701. TEL 501-575-5609. Ed. Charles E. Harris. adv.; bk.rev.; index. circ. 5,000. (also avail. in microfilm from WSH,PMC; back issues avail.; reprint service avail. from WSH) Indexed: C.L.I., L.R.I., Leg.Cont., Leg.Per.
—BLDSC (1671.250000); Faxon; UnCover.

340   US
ARKANSAS LAWYER. 1967. q. $15. Arkansas Bar Association, 400 W. Markham, Little Rock, AR 72201. TEL 501-375-4605. Ed. Paige Markman. adv.; bk.rev.; charts; illus.; index. circ. 4,100. (back issues avail.) Indexed: C.L.I.

340   US
ARKANSAS REGISTER. 1977. m. $40. Office of the Secretary of State, State Capitol, Little Rock, AR 72201-1094. TEL 501-682-3578. FAX 501-682-1284. Ed. Ricky B. Hearne. cum.index: 1977-1985. circ. 300. (back issues avail.) **Document type:** government publication.

340   US
ARKANSAS TRIAL LAWYERS ASSOCIATION. LEGISLATIVE BULLETIN. 1987. w. during legislative sessions. $100 to non-members; free to members. Arkansas Trial Lawyers Association, 225 E. Markham, Ste. 200, Little Rock, AR 72201. TEL 501-376-2852. FAX 501-372-0951. Ed. Carol Utley. circ. 900. **Document type:** bulletin.
   Description: Contains Arkansas legislations of interest to trial lawyers.

ARMCHAIR ARCHAEOLOGIST. see *ARCHAEOLOGY*

340   US   ISSN 0364-1287
KF7209.A1
ARMY LAWYER. 1971. m. $19 (foreign $23.75). U.S. Army, Judge Advocate General's School, Charlottesville, VA 22903-1781. TEL 804-972-6395. (Subscr. to: Superintendent of Documents, U.S. Government Printing Office, Box 371954, Pittsburgh, PA 15250-7954. TEL 202-783-3238. FAX 202-512-2233) Ed. J.B. Jones. index. circ. 7,600. (also avail. in microfilm from MIM,UMI; back issues avail.) Indexed: C.L.I., Ind.U.S.Gov.Per., L.R.I., Leg.Cont., Leg.Per. **Document type:** government publication.
—UnCover; UMI.
   Description: Contains articles of interest to attorneys practicing military law.

349   NE   ISSN 0004-2870
ARS AEQUI; juridisch studentenblad. (Supplement avail.: Ars Aequi Katern (ISSN 0925-5443)) 1951. 11/yr. fl.47.85 (students fl.34.65). Stichting Ars Aequi, Postbus 1043, 6501 BA Nijmegen, Netherlands. TEL 31-80-223506. FAX 31-80-241108. Greke Gerrits. adv.; bk.rev.; index. circ. 28,000. Indexed: ELLIS, Excerp.Med.
—SWETS.

340   NE   ISSN 0925-5443
KKM70
ARS AEQUI KATERN. (Supplement to: Ars Aequi (ISSN 0004-2870)) 1981. q. Stichting Ars Aequi, Postbus 1043, 6501 BA Nijmegen, Netherlands. TEL 31-80-223506. FAX 31-80-241108.

340   US
ARSON REPORTER; arson cases and legislation. m. $16. American Bar Association, Young Lawyers Division, 750 N. Lake Shore Dr., Chicago, IL 60611. TEL 312-988-5555.
   Description: Reports on court decisions pertaining to arson and legislation at both the state and national level.

700 657   US   ISSN 0886-1013
KF4288.A15
ART LAW & ACCOUNTING REPORTER. 1982. q. $25. Texas Accountants & Lawyers for the Arts, 1540 Sul Ross, Houston, TX 77006. TEL 713-526-4876. FAX 731-526-1299. Ed.Bd. circ. 2,000 (paid). (back issues avail.) **Document type:** academic/scholarly publication.
   Description: Art-related legal and accounting articles for artists, attorneys, accountants, and other interested professionals.

ARTHUR ANDERSEN WASHINGTON HEALTHCARE NEWSLETTER. see *HOSPITALS*

340 006.3   NE   ISSN 0924-8463
K1   CODEN: AINLEO
▼**ARTIFICIAL INTELLIGENCE AND LAW;** an international journal. (Text in English) 1992. 4/yr. fl.372($194.50) (effective 1994). Kluwer Academic Publishers, Postbus 17, 3300 AA Dordrecht, Netherlands. TEL 31-78-334911. FAX 31-78-334254. TELEX 29245 KAPG NL. (Dist. by: Kluwer Academic Publishers Group, P.O. Box 322, 3300 AH Dordrecht, Netherlands. TEL 31-78-524400. FAX 31-78-524474; N. America dist. addr.: Box 358, Accord Sta., Hingham, MA 02018-0358. TEL 617-871-6600. FAX 617-871-6528) Eds. Donald H. Berman, Carole D. Hafner. (also avail. in microform from UMI; back issues avail.) **Document type:** academic/scholarly publication.
—BLDSC (1735.035250); UMI.
   Description: Publishes theoretical and empirical studies addressing the formulation of computational models of legal reasoning and knowledge, in-depth studies of artificial intelligence systems being used in the legal domain, and discussions of the ethical and social implications of the field of artificial intelligence and law.
   Refereed Serial

340 700   AT   ISSN 1038-510X
▼**ARTS AND ENTERTAINMENT LAW REVIEW.** 1992. bi-m. Aus.$125. Law Book Co. Ltd., 44-50 Waterloo Rd., North Ryde, N.S.W. 2113, Australia. TEL 02-887-0177. FAX 02-888-9706. TELEX ASHBOOK 27995. Ed. Colin Golvan.

ARZTRECHT; Kompendium des Gesamten Rechtes der Medizin. see *MEDICAL SCIENCES*

340   US
KF228.M33
ASBESTOS BANKRUPTCIES LITIGATION REPORTER; the national journal of record reporting details of the Johns-Manville Corporation and Hillsborough Holding Corp. bankruptcy proceedings. 1986. s-m. $1300. Andrews Publications, 1646 West Chester Pike, Box 1000, Westtown, PA 19395. TEL 215-399-6600; 800-345-1101. FAX 215-399-6610. Ed. Thomas Hennessey. (looseleaf format; back issues avail.) **Document type:** newsletter.
   Formed by merger of (1986-1993): Stockholders and Creditors News Service Concerning the Johns-Manville Corporation, et al (ISSN 1042-5780); (1990-1993): Stockholders and Creditors News Service Re: Hillsborough Holding Corporation (ISSN 1053-0215)

340 613.62   US
ASBESTOS CASE LAW QUARTERLY. q. $85. Butterworth Legal Publishers (Salem) (Subsidiary of: Reed Elsevier plc), 8 Industrial Way, Bldg. C, Salem, NH 03079. TEL 800-548-4001. FAX 603-898-9858. Ed. Jerry Nates.

340   US   ISSN 0273-3048
KF1297.A73
ASBESTOS LITIGATION REPORTER; the national journal of record of asbestos litigation. 1979. s-m. $950. Andrews Publications, 1646 West Chester Pike, Box 1000, Westtown, PA 19395. TEL 215-399-6600; 800-345-1101. FAX 215-399-6610. Ed. Thomas M. Hennessey. abstr.; bibl.; stat.; s-a. index. (looseleaf format; back issues avail.) **Document type:** newsletter.
   Description: Focuses on the most recent developments in suits alleging personal injuries from exposure to asbestos. Reports selected developments in suits brought or recover the cost of removing or encapsulating asbestos building materials.

340   US   ISSN 1059-6232
KF226
ASBESTOS M D L 875 UPDATE. 1991. s-m. $650. Andrews Publications, 1646 West Chester Pike, Box 1000, Westtown, PA 19395. TEL 215-399-6600; 800-345-1101. FAX 215-399-6610. Ed. Thomas Hennessey. bibl.; stat.; s-a. index. (looseleaf format; back issues avail.) **Document type:** newsletter.
   Description: Covers developments in the consolidated pretrial proceedings pending in Philadelphia before US District Court Judge Charles R. Weiner.

340 US
KF3964.A73M21
ASBESTOS PRODUCT LIABILITY LITIGATION M D L REPORTER. 1991. s-m. $650. McGuire Publications, Box 315, Springfield, PA 19064. TEL 215-328-4388. FAX 215-328-0566. Ed. Arthur McGuire. s-a. index. (looseleaf format) **Document type:** newsletter.

340 US ISSN 1041-5130
KF1950.A59
ASBESTOS PROPERTY LITIGATION REPORTER; the national journal of asbestos property litigation. 1988. s-m. $725. Andrews Publications, 1646 West Chester Pike, Box 1000, Westtown, PA 19395. TEL 215-399-6600; 800-345-1101. FAX 215-399-6610. Ed. Jay Steinberg. abstr.; bibl.; stat.; s-a. index. (looseleaf format; back issues avail.) **Document type:** newsletter.
  Incorporates: Asbestos Abatement Litigation Reporter (ISSN 1053-0231)
  Description: Covers current developments in suits brought to recover the cost of removing or encapsulating asbestos-containing building materials.

340 330 HK
ASIA LAW. (Text in English) 1989. 10/yr. HK.$2965($410) (effective Jan. 1994). Asia Law & Practice Ltd., 2-F, 29 Hollywood Rd., Central, Hong Kong. TEL 852-544-9918. FAX 852-543-7617. Ed. Eric Shiu. s-a.index. circ. 3,000. (back issues avail)
  Formerly: Asia Law and Practice (ISSN 1015-5562)
  Description: Publishes updates on business law developments in 13 Asian countries.

340 HK
▼**ASIA PACIFIC LAW REVIEW.** (Text in English) 1992. s-a. HK.$940 per no. (foreign $135). Longman Asia Ltd., Taikoo Place, 979 King's Rd., Quarry Bay, Hong Kong. TEL 852-866-6335. FAX 852-565-7440. TELEX 73051 LGHK HX. (Dist. in N. America by: Wm. W. Gaunt & Sons, Inc., Gaunt Bldg., 3011 Gulf Dr., Homes Beach, Florida 34217-2199. TEL 813-778-5211. FAX 813-778-5252) **Document type:** academic/scholarly publication.
  Description: Covers wide range of law and law related topics written by leading academics and practitioners in Asia.
  Refereed Serial

340 UY ISSN 0376-5024
ASOCIACION DE ESCRIBANOS DEL URUGUAY. REVISTA. 1904. s-a. price varies. Asociacion de Escribanos del Uruguay, Av. 18 de Julio 1730, Piso 11, Montevideo, Uruguay. TEL 40-64-00. FAX 42-19-43. Ed. Julia Siri Garcia. bk.rev.; bibl.; index. circ. 5,000. **Document type:** trade publication.
  Description: Covers all matters of Uruguayan law.

ASSET BASED FINANCING: A TRANSACTIONAL GUIDE. see BUSINESS AND ECONOMICS — Banking And Finance

ASSIA. see MEDICAL SCIENCES

ASSISTED HOUSING MANAGEMENT INSIDER. see REAL ESTATE

342 US
ASSOCIATION OF ADMINISTRATIVE LAW JUDGES NEWSLETTER. bi-m. free. Association of Administrative Law Judges, 310 W. Wisconsin Ave., Rm. 880, Milwaukee, WI 53203. TEL 414-297-3141. Ed. James D'Amico. bk.rev. circ. 350. **Document type:** newsletter.

340 US ISSN 0519-1025
ASSOCIATION OF AMERICAN LAW SCHOOLS. NEWSLETTER. 1964. 4/yr. $28. Association of American Law Schools, 1201 Connecticut Ave., N.W., Ste. 800, Washington, DC 20036. TEL 202-296-8851. Ed. Alice Gresham Bullock. circ. controlled. (processed) **Document type:** newsletter.

346 US ISSN 0066-9407
ASSOCIATION OF AMERICAN LAW SCHOOLS. PROCEEDINGS. 1901. a. $22.50. Association of American Law Schools, 1201 Connecticut Ave., N.W., Ste. 800, Washington, DC 20036. TEL 202-296-8851. Ed. Alice Gresham Bullock. 50 yr. cum.index. (processed; also avail. in microfiche from BHP) **Document type:** proceedings.

340 320 US ISSN 0885-7342
Z675.L2L36
ASSOCIATION OF COLLEGE AND RESEARCH LIBRARIES. LAW AND POLITICAL SCIENCE SECTION NEWS. 1985. s-a. membership. American Library Association, 50 E. Huron St., Chicago, IL 60611. TEL 800-545-2433. Ed. Cathy Doyle. (back issues avail.) **Document type:** newsletter.

ASSOCIATION OF FOOD AND DRUG OFFICIALS. JOURNAL. see FOOD AND FOOD INDUSTRIES

340 020 US ISSN 0197-4815
ASSOCIATION OF LAW LIBRARIES OF UPSTATE NEW YORK. NEWSLETTER. 1974. q. membership. Association of Law Libraries of Upstate New York, Inc., 75 State St., Box 459, Albany, NY 12201-0459. TEL 518-447-3266. FAX 518-426-4260. circ. 150. **Indexed:** Leg.Info.Manage.Ind. **Document type:** newsletter.

340 US
ASSOCIATION OF THE BAR OF THE CITY OF NEW YORK. LEGISLATIVE BULLETIN. irreg. (4-5/yr.). $70. Association of the Bar of the City of New York, 42 W. 44th St., New York, NY 10036. TEL 212-382-6655. FAX 212-354-7438. index. **Document type:** bulletin.

340 US ISSN 0004-5837
ASSOCIATION OF THE BAR OF THE CITY OF NEW YORK. RECORD. 1946. 8/yr. $65. Association of the Bar of the City of New York, 42 W. 44th St., New York, NY 10036. TEL 212-382-6650. FAX 212-398-6634. Ed.Bd. adv.; bibl.; index, cum.index every 3 yrs. circ. 19,600. (also avail. in microform from UMI; microfiche from WSH; reprint service avail. from UMI) **Indexed:** C.L.I., L.R.I., Law Ofc.Info.Svc., Leg.Info.Manage.Ind., Leg.Per., P.A.I.S.
—BLDSC (7313.500000); Faxon; UnCover; UMI.

340 US
AT ISSUE. q. membership. Pennsylvania Bar Association, Young Lawyers Division, 100 South St., Harrisburg, PA 17108. TEL 717-238-6715. FAX 717-238-7182. Ed. John McNally. **Document type:** newsletter.
  Formerly: Y L D News.

ATLANTIC LEGAL TELEPHONE DIRECTORY. see BUSINESS AND ECONOMICS — Trade And Industrial Directories

340 CN ISSN 0713-8970
ATLANTIC PROVINCES REPORTERS. 1974. irreg., latest vol.332. Can.$104 per vol. Maritime Law Book Ltd., Box 302, Fredericton, NB E3B 4Y9, Canada. TEL 506-453-9921; 800-561-0220. FAX 506-453-9525. (back issues avail.)
  Description: Combines the reports from New Brunswick, Nova Scotia, Newfoundland and Prince Edward Island.

ATOMIC ENERGY LAW JOURNAL. see ENERGY — Nuclear Energy

ATT ADOPTERA. see SOCIAL SERVICES AND WELFARE

340 US
ATTORNEY FEE AWARDS. base vol. (plus s-a. suppl.). $95 price varies. Shepard's - McGraw-Hill, Inc., Box 35300, Colorado Springs, CO 80935-3530. TEL 800-525-2474.
  Description: Analysis of federal fee opinion and fee award precedents.

340 US
ATTORNEY FEES IN WASHINGTON; annotated statutes, cases and commentary. 1991. base vol. (plus irreg. suppl.). $85. Butterworth Legal Publishers (Salem) (Subsidiary of: Reed Elsevier plc), 8 Industrial Way, Bldg. C, Salem, NH 03079. TEL 800-548-4001. FAX 603-898-9858. Ed. Philip A. Talmadge. (looseleaf format)
  Description: Complete guide to the granting or allowing of attorney fees in Washington. Contains statutes from the Washington State code concerning attorneys fees along with annotations, case summaries, and helpful commentary.

340 US
ATTORNEY'S FEES IN FLORIDA. 1989. 3 base vols. (plus suppl.). $120. Butterworth Legal Publishers (Salem) (Subsidiary of: Reed Elsevier plc), 8 Industrial Way, Bldg. C, Salem, MA 03079. TEL 800-548-4001. FAX 603-898-9858. (looseleaf format)

340 US ISSN 1047-997X
Z1223.Z7
ATTORNEY'S GUIDE TO GOVERNMENT STUDIES AND REPORTS. 1984. biennial. Matthew Bender & Co., Inc., 11 Penn Plaza, New York, NY 10001. TEL 212-967-7707.

340 US ISSN 1057-5596
KF302.Z95
ATTORNEY'S GUIDE TO STATE BAR ADMISSION REQUIREMENTS. 1991. a. Federal Reports, Inc., 1010 Vermont Ave. N.W., Ste. 408, Washington, DC 20005. **Document type:** directory.

ATTORNEY'S REPORT. see BUSINESS AND ECONOMICS — Accounting

346 NZ ISSN 0067-0510
K1
AUCKLAND UNIVERSITY LAW REVIEW. 1967. a. NZ.$25. Auckland University Law Students Society, Inc., c/o Faculty of Law, Private Bag 92019, Auckland, New Zealand. TEL 64-9-3737599. FAX 64-9-3737440. adv.: page NZ.$250; adv. contact: Chris Haynes. bk.rev. circ. 1,500. (back issues avail.) **Indexed:** C.L.I., L.R.I., Leg.Per. **Document type:** academic/scholarly publication.
—UnCover.
  Description: Publishes legislation notes, case notes, and articles on topics of current legal interest relevant to New Zealand, commonwealth and common law countries.

340 US
AUDIO LAWYER. 8/yr. $99. American Law Institute - American Bar Association, Committee on Continuing Professional Education, 4025 Chestnut St., Philadelphia, PA 19104. TEL 215-243-1697. FAX 215-243-1664. Ed. William S. Stevens. circ. 125. (audio cassette) **Document type:** trade publication.
  Description: Articles of practical interest to the general practitioner.

340 333.33 US
AUDIO REAL ESTATE LAWYER. 4/yr. $75. American Law Institute - American Bar Association, Committee on Continuing Professional Education, 4025 Chesnut St., Philadelphia, PA 19104. TEL 215-243-1697. FAX 215-243-1664. Ed. William S. Stevens. circ. 200. (audio cassette) **Document type:** trade publication.
  Description: Collection of articles of practical interest to attorneys specializing in real estate.

AUSSENWIRTSCHAFTSRECHT (YEAR); Einfuehrung - Fundstellen - Vorschriftentexte. see BUSINESS AND ECONOMICS — International Commerce

328.94 328.9 AT
AUSTRALASIAN AND PACIFIC REGIONAL PARLIAMENTARY SEMINAR. SUMMARY REPORT OF PROCEEDINGS. 1972. biennial. free. Commonwealth Parliamentary Association, Regional Secretariat, Canberra, A.C.T. 2600, Australia. TEL 61-62-774340. FAX 61-62-772000. TELEX 61884 PRO. circ. 250. **Document type:** proceedings.
  Former titles: Australasian and Pacific Parliamentary Seminar. Summary Report of Proceedings; (until 1980): Australia Parliamentary Seminar. Summary Report of Proceedings.

340 301.415 AT ISSN 1039-0987
▼**AUSTRALASIAN GAY AND LESBIAN LAW JOURNAL.** 1992. 2/yr. $22. Federation Press Pty. Ltd., P.O. Box 45, Annandale, N.S.W. 2038, Australia. (Dist. in N. America by: Wm. W. Gaunt & Sons, Inc., Law Book Dealers & Subscription Agents, Gaunt Bldg., 3011 Gulf Dr., Holmes Beach, Fl 34217-2199. TEL 813-889-5211. FAX 813-778-5252)
—UnCover.
  Formerly (until 1993): Australian Gay and Lesbian Law Journal.
  Description: Seeks to provide a forum for discussion of the law and to disseminate legal information on issues which may affect the lives of and-or be of interest to gay men and lesbians.

LAW

340   AT   ISSN 0312-6994
AUSTRALIA. LAW REFORM COMMISSION. ANNUAL REPORT. 1975. a. price varies. Australian Government Publishing Service, G.P.O. Box 84, Canberra, A.C.T. 2601, Australia. TEL 61-6-295-4500. FAX 61-6-295-4612. (also avail. in microform from PMC; back issues avail.) Indexed: Aus.Leg.Mon.Dig. Document type: government publication.
—CCC.

340   AT
AUSTRALIAN AND NEW ZEALAND EQUAL OPPORTUNITY LAW AND PRACTICE. (In 2 vols.) 1984. bi-m. C C H Australia Ltd., P.O. Box 230, North Ryde, N.S.W. 2113, Australia. TEL 02-888-2555. FAX 02-888-7324.
Description: Includes guidelines issued by various boards and authorities.

AUSTRALIAN AND NEW ZEALAND INSURANCE REPORTER. see *INSURANCE*

230   AT
AUSTRALIAN BANKRUPTCY LEGISLATION. 1989. irreg., as required for all legislative changes. C C H Australia Ltd., P.O. Box 230, North Ryde, N.S.W. 2113, Australia. TEL 02-888-2555. FAX 02-888-7324. (looseleaf format)

340   AT   ISSN 0814-8589
K1
AUSTRALIAN BAR REVIEW. 1986. 3/yr. Aus.$145. Butterworths, P.O. Box 345, North Ryde, N.S.W. 2113, Australia. TEL 02-335-4444. FAX 02-335-4655. Document type: academic/scholarly publication.

340 690   AT
AUSTRALIAN BUILDING REGULATION REPORTER. 1991. bi-m. C C H Australia Ltd., P.O. Box 230, North Ryde, N.S.W. 2113, Australia. TEL 02-888-2555. FAX 02-888-7324. (looseleaf format)

AUSTRALIAN BUSINESS LAW REVIEW. see *LAW — Corporate Law*

347 330   AT
AUSTRALIAN CONSUMER SALES AND CREDIT LAW REPORTER. (In 4 vols.) 1978. every 3 wks. C C H Australia Ltd., P.O. Box 230, North Ryde, N.S.W. 2113, Australia. TEL 888-2555. FAX 02-888-7324. charts. (looseleaf format)

346.066   AT
AUSTRALIAN CONTRACT LAW REPORTER. (In 2 vols.) 1991. q. C C H Australia Ltd., P.O. Box 230, North Ryde, N.S.W. 2113, Australia. TEL 02-888-2555. FAX 02-888-7324. (looseleaf format)
Description: Includes case reporting.

340   AT
AUSTRALIAN CORPORATION LAW. 6 base vols. (plus updates every 3 weeks). $745. Butterworths, 271-273 Lane Cove Rd., P.O. Box 345, North Ryde, N.S.W. 2113, Australia. TEL 02-335-4444. FAX 02-335-4655. (looseleaf format)
Formerly: Australian Company Law.

340 382   AT
AUSTRALIAN CUSTOMS LAW AND PRACTICE. 1990. 10/yr. C C H Australia Ltd., P.O. Box 230, North Ryde, N.S.W. 2113, Australia. TEL 02-888-2555. FAX 02-888-7324. (looseleaf format)

340   AT
AUSTRALIAN DE FACTO RELATIONSHIPS LAW. 1985. bi-m. C C H Australia Ltd., P.O. Box 230, North Ryde, N.S.W. 2113, Australia. TEL 02-888-2555. FAX 02-888-7324. (looseleaf format)
Description: Includes case reporting.

346   AT   ISSN 0067-1843
AUSTRALIAN DIGEST. 1988. irreg. price varies. Law Book Co. Ltd., 44-50 Waterloo Rd., North Ryde, N.S.W. 2113, Australia. TEL 02-887-0177. FAX 02-888-9706. TELEX ASBOOK 27995. Ed. J. Bennett.
Incorporates: Australian Digest Annual Supplement (ISSN 0813-5959)

340   AT   ISSN 1034-3059
AUSTRALIAN DISPUTE RESOLUTION JOURNAL. q. Aus.$165. Law Book Co. Ltd., 44-50 Waterloo Rd., North Ryde, N.S.W 2113, Australia. TEL 02-887-0177. FAX 02-888-9706. TELEX ASBOOK 27995. Eds. Micheline Dewdney, Ruth Charlton.
Description: Discusses and promotes the use of alternative dispute resolution processes in Australia and New Zealand.

340   AT
AUSTRALIAN HEALTH AND MEDICAL LAW REPORTER. 1988. bi-m. C C H Australia Ltd., P.O. Box 230, North Ryde, N.S.W. 2113, Australia. TEL 02-888-2555. FAX 02-888-7324. (looseleaf format)

342   AT
AUSTRALIAN HIGH COURT AND FEDERAL COURT PRACTICE. (In 2 vols.) 1980. every 5 wks. C C H Australia Ltd., P.O. Box 230, North Ryde, N.S.W. 2113, Australia. TEL 888-2555. FAX 02-888-7324. charts. (looseleaf format)

340 336   AT
AUSTRALIAN INCOME TAX RULINGS. (In 3 vols.) 1983. fortn. C C H Australia Ltd., P.O. Box 230, North Ryde, N.S.W. 2113, Australia. TEL 02-888-2555. FAX 02-888-7324. (looseleaf format)

340 338   AT
AUSTRALIAN INDUSTRIAL & INTELLECTUAL PROPERTY. (In 2 vols.) 1983. m. C C H Australia Ltd., P.O. Box 230, North Ryde, N.S.W. 2113, Australia. TEL 02-888-2555. FAX 02-888-7324. (looseleaf format)
Description: Includes full text case reporting of all court and patent office decisions.

AUSTRALIAN INDUSTRIAL SAFETY, HEALTH & WELFARE. see *OCCUPATIONAL HEALTH AND SAFETY*

340 336   AT
AUSTRALIAN INTERNATIONAL TAX AGREEMENTS. (In 2 vols.) 1982. irreg. C C H Australia Ltd., P.O. Box 230, North Ryde, N.S.W. 2113, Australia. TEL 02-888-2555. FAX 02-888-7324. (looseleaf format)

340   AT   ISSN 0729-3356
K1
AUSTRALIAN JOURNAL OF LAW AND SOCIETY. 1982. a. Aus.$12 to individuals; institutions Aus.$16. School of Law, Macquarie University, Sydney, N.S.W. 2109, Australia. FAX 612-805-7686. TELEX MACUNI AA122377. adv.; bk.rev. circ. 500. (back issues avail.) Indexed: C.L.I., Leg.Per.
—BLDSC (1809.140000).

348   AT   ISSN 0310-0014
LAW
AUSTRALIAN LAW REPORTS. fortn. Aus.$170 per vol. Butterworths, 271-273 Lane Cove Rd., North Ryde, N.S.W. 2113, Australia. TEL 02-335-4444. FAX 02-335-4655.

340   AT
AUSTRALIAN LAWYER. 1964. m. Aus.$55. Law Council of Australia, G.P.O. Box 1989, Canberra, A.C.T. 2601, Australia. TEL 062 47-3788. FAX 062-480-639. Ed. Barrie Virtue. adv. contact: Warren Spence. bk.rev. circ. 26,784. (back issues avail.)
—UMI.
Former titles (until Feb. 1993): Australian Law News (ISSN 0159-7531); Law Council of Australia. Law Council Newsletter (ISSN 0047-4177)
Description: Covers activities of the Law Council of Australia, national issues of interest to lawyers, case reports and more.

340 658.3   AT
AUSTRALIAN LEAVE & HOLIDAYS PRACTICE MANUAL. 1981. q. C C H Australia Ltd., P.O. Box 230, North Ryde, N.S.W. 2113, Australia. TEL 02-888-2555. FAX 02-888-7324. (looseleaf format)

AUSTRALIAN LEGAL DIRECTORY. see *BUSINESS AND ECONOMICS — Trade And Industrial Directories*

340   AT   ISSN 0728-6309
LAW
AUSTRALIAN PLANNING APPEAL DECISIONS. 1980. irreg. (approx. 16/yr.). price varies. Law Book Co. Ltd., 44-50 Waterloo Rd., North Ryde, N.S.W. 2113, Australia. TEL 02-887-0177. FAX 02-888-9706. TELEX ASBOOK 27995. Ed. Carolyn May. (back issues avail.)
Description: Covers all planning and environmental appeal decisions.

340 628   AT
AUSTRALIAN POLLUTION LAW (CONTROL). 1990. q. C C H Australia Ltd., P.O. Box 230, North Ryde, N.S.W. 2113, Australia. TEL 02-888-2555. FAX 02-888-7324. (looseleaf format)
Description: To be used together with Australian Pollution Law New South Wales and Australian Pollution Law Victoria.

340 628   AT
AUSTRALIAN POLLUTION LAW NEW SOUTH WALES. 1990. q. C C H Australia Ltd., P.O. Box 230, North Ryde, N.S.W. 2113, Australia. TEL 02-888-2555. FAX 02-888-7324. (looseleaf format)
Description: To be used together with Australian Pollution Law (Control).

340 628   AT
AUSTRALIAN POLLUTION LAW VICTORIA. 1990. q. C C P Australia Ltd., P.O. Box 230, North Ryde, N.S.W. 2113, Australia. TEL 02-888-2555. FAX 02-888-7324. (looseleaf format)
Description: To be used together with Australian Pollution Law (Control).

AUSTRALIAN SOCIAL SECURITY GUIDE. see *SOCIAL SERVICES AND WELFARE*

AUSTRALIAN TAX CASES. see *BUSINESS AND ECONOMICS — Public Finance, Taxation*

AUSTRALIAN TAX FORUM; a journal of taxation policy, law and reform. see *BUSINESS AND ECONOMICS — Public Finance, Taxation*

AUSTRALIAN TAX REVIEW. see *BUSINESS AND ECONOMICS — Public Finance, Taxation*

340   AT
AUSTRALIAN TENANCY PRACTICE & PRECEDENTS. 2 base vols. (plus s-a. updates). $235. Butterworths, 271-273 Lane Cove Rd., P.O. Box 345, North Ryde, N.S.W. 2113, Australia. TEL 02-335-4444. FAX 02-335-4655. (looseleaf format)

340   AT
AUSTRALIAN TORTS REPORTER. (In 3 vols.) 1984. 10/yr. C C H Australia Ltd., P.O. Box 230, North Ryde, N.S.W. 2113, Australia. TEL 888-2555. FAX 02-888-7324. (looseleaf format)
Description: Details relevant cases on the practice and procedure of the High Court, Federal Court and Administrative Appeals Tribunal.

AUSTRALIAN TRADE PRACTICES REPORTER. see *BUSINESS AND ECONOMICS*

340   NE
AUSTRIAN BUSINESS LAW; legal, accounting and tax aspects of business in Austria. (Text in English) 2nd ed., 1993. base vol. (plus a. updates). fl.225($122) (effective 1994). Kluwer Law and Taxation Publishers (Subsidiary of: Wolters Kluwer N.V.), P.O. Box 23, 7400 GA Deventer, Netherlands. TEL 31-5700-47261. FAX 31-5700-22244. (Dist. by: Libresso Distribution Centre, P.O. Box 23, 7400 GA Deventer, Netherlands. TEL 31-5700-33155. FAX 31-5700-333834; In N. America: Kluwer Law and Taxation Publishers, 675 Massachusetts Ave., Cambridge, MA 02139. TEL 617-354-0140. FAX 617-354-8595) (Co-publisher: Mainz, AU) (looseleaf format)
Description: Comprehensive guide to the fundamentals of conducting business in Austria.

AUTHORS GUILD BULLETIN. see *LITERATURE*

340 388   US
AUTOMOBILE DESIGN LIABILITY. 1970. a., 3rd ed., 1992. $310. Clark - Boardman - Callaghan Company Ltd., 375 Hudson St., New York, NY 10014. TEL 212-929-7500. FAX 212-924-0460. Ed. Richard M. Goodman.

LAW

340 US ISSN 0278-4726
AUTOMOTIVE LITIGATION REPORTER; the twice monthly national reporting service of litigation concerning common automotive defects. 1981. s-m. $825. Andrews Publications, 1646 West Chester Pike, Box 1000, Westtown, PA 19395. TEL 215-399-6600; 800-345-1101. FAX 215-399-6610. Ed. Nicholas W. Sullivan. bibl.; stat.; cum.index every 6 mos. (looseleaf format; back issues avail.) **Document type:** newsletter.

AVIATION LAW REPORTS. see *TRANSPORTATION — Air Transport*

340 629.13 US
AVIATION LITIGATION. 1986. base vol. (plus a. suppl.). $95. Shepard's - McGraw-Hill, Inc., Box 35300, Colorado Springs, CO 80935-3530. TEL 800-525-2474.
Description: Covers major commercial crashes as well as small aircraft and military accidents. Describes the substantive law of liability, the damages recoverable, the technical steps involved in aviation litigation, alternative theories and defenses of liability.

340 US ISSN 0737-7746
KF2454.A59
AVIATION LITIGATION REPORTER; the national journal of record of aviation litigation. 1983. s-m. $825. Andrews Publications, 1646 West Chester Pike, Box 1000, Westtown, PA 19395. TEL 215-399-6600; 800-345-1101. FAX 215-399-6610. Ed. Nicholas W. Sullivan. bibl.; stat.; cum.index every 6 mos. (looseleaf format; back issues avail.) **Document type:** newsletter.
Description: Covers developments in lawsuits arising from commercial carrier, military, private plane and helicopter crashes.

AZIONE NONVIOLENTA. see *CIVIL DEFENSE*

340 US
B A R - B R I BAR REVIEW. (Consists of 13 parts: Civil Procedure, Community Property, Constitutional Law, Contracts, Corporations, Criminal Law, Evidence, Professional Responsibility, Real Property, Remedies, Torts, Trusts, Wills) a. $1,295. B A R - B R I Bar Review, 3280 Motor Ave., Los Angeles, CA 90034-3710. TEL 213-477-2542.

346.73 US ISSN 0098-762X
KF801.Z9
B A R - B R I BAR REVIEW. CONTRACTS. a. $395. B A R - B R I Bar Review, 3280 Motor Ave., Los Angeles, CA 90034-3710. TEL 213-477-2542.

347.73 US
B A R - B R I BAR REVIEW. EVIDENCE. a. $395. B A R - B R I Bar Review, 3280 Motor Ave., Los Angeles, CA 90034-3710. TEL 213-477-2542.

174 US
B A R - B R I BAR REVIEW. PROFESSIONAL RESPONSIBILITY. a. $395. B A R - B R I Bar Review, 3280 Motor Ave., Los Angeles, CA 90034-3710. TEL 213-477-2542.
Formerly: Bay Area Review Course. Legal Ethics (ISSN 0098-7980)

346.73 US
B A R - B R I BAR REVIEW. REAL PROPERTY. a. $395. B A R - B R I Bar Review, 3280 Motor Ave., Los Angeles, CA 90034-3710. TEL 213-477-2542.

347 US ISSN 0098-7999
KF9010.Z9
B A R - B R I BAR REVIEW. REMEDIES. a. $395. B A R - B R I Bar Review, 3280 Motor Ave., Los Angeles, CA 90034-3710. TEL 213-477-2542.

346.066 GW ISSN 0340-9848
B B K BUCHFUEHRUNG, BILANZ, KOSTENRECHNUNG. 1954. fortn. DM.210. Verlag Neue Wirtschafts-Briefe GmbH, Eschstr. 22, 44629 Herne, Germany. circ. 20,000. **Document type:** trade publication.
—CCC.

340 CN
B C GAZETTE. PART 1. vol.26, 1986. w. Can.$114. Queen's Printer, Victoria, 563 Superior St., Victoria, B.C. V8V 1X4, Canada. (Dist. by: Crown Publications, 546 Yates St., Victoria, B.C. V8W 1K8, Canada. TEL 604-386-4636) index. (back issues avail.)
Description: Contains legal notices including forestry tenders, notices to creditors, changes of name and company incorporations.

340 CN
B C GAZETTE. PART 2. vol.29, 1986. fortn. Can.$72. Queen's Printer, Victoria, 563 Superior St., Victoria, B.C. V8V 1X4, Canada. (Dist. by: Crown Publications, 546 Yates St., Victoria, B.C. V8W 1K8, Canada. TEL 604-386-4636) (back issues avail.)
Description: Contains new B C regulations.

340 301.435 US ISSN 0888-1537
B I F O C A L (Bar Associations in Focus on Aging and the Law) Key Title: Bifocal. 1979. q. free. American Bar Association, Commission of Legal Problems of the Elderly, 1800 M St., N.W., Washington, DC 20036. TEL 202-331-2298. FAX 202-331-2220. Ed. Norma B. Gregerman. circ. 3,000. **Document type:** newsletter.

340 US
B N A ADMINISTRATIVE PRACTICE MANUAL. 1986. base vol. (plus a. suppl.). $245 includes Supplement. B N A Books (Subsidiary of: The Bureau of National Affairs, Inc.), 1250 23rd St., N.W., Washington, DC 20037. TEL 202-833-7470; 800-372-1033. FAX 202-833-7490. (Subscr. to: BNA Books Distribution Center, 30 Raritan Center Pkwy., Box 7816, Edison, NJ 08818-7816. TEL 908-225-1900. FAX 908-417-0482) Ed. Bertram R. Cottine. index. (looseleaf format)

340 US
B N A ADMINISTRATIVE PRACTICE MANUAL. SUPPLEMENT. 1989. a. $98. B N A Books (Subsidiary of: The Bureau of National Affairs, Inc.), 1250 23rd St., N.W., Washington, DC 20037. TEL 202-833-7470; 800-372-1033. FAX 202-833-7490. (Subscr. to: BNA Books Distribution Center, 30 Raritan Center Pkwy., Box 7816, Edison, NJ 08818-7816. TEL 908-225-1900. FAX 908-417-0482) Ed. Bertram Robert Cottine. (looseleaf format)
Description: Reflects changes in every area of administrative law.

B N A CALIFORNIA - ENVIRONMENT REPORTER. see *ENVIRONMENTAL STUDIES*

346.066 336 US ISSN 0891-0634
KF967
B N A'S BANKING REPORT; legal and regulatory developments in the financial services industry. 1965. w. $965. The Bureau of National Affairs, Inc., 1231 25th St., N.W., Washington, DC 20037. TEL 202-452-4200. FAX 202-822-8092. TELEX 285656 BNAI WSH. (Subscr. to: 9435 Key West Ave., Rockville, MD 20850. TEL 800-372-1033) Ed. Lise Simmons. index. (looseleaf format; back issues avail.) **Indexed:** Bank.Lit.Ind.
●Also available online. Vendor(s): Bureau of National Affairs, Human Resources Information Network (CDD,HDD), Mead Data Central, Inc. (BNABNK), West Services, Inc. (BNA-BNK).
—CCC.
Formerly (until 1987): Washington Financial Reports (ISSN 0511-3172)
Description: Covers major developments from Washington affecting financial institutions and their competitors.

340 US ISSN 1044-7474
KF1507
B N A'S BANKRUPTCY LAW REPORTER. 1989. w. $812. The Bureau of National Affairs, Inc., 1231 25th St., N.W., Washington, DC 20037. TEL 202-452-4200. FAX 202-822-8092. TELEX 285656 BNAI WSH. (Subscr. to: 9435 Key West Ave., Rockville, MD 20850. TEL 800-372-1033) Ed. Wendell Yee. index. (back issues avail.)
—CCC.
Description: Notification service covering various areas of bankruptcy law.

B N A'S CORPORATE COUNSEL WEEKLY. see *BUSINESS AND ECONOMICS — Management*

380 340 US
B N A'S DIRECTORY OF STATE & FEDERAL COURTS, JUDGES, AND CLERKS. irreg., 4th ed., 1992. $85. B N A Books (Subsidiary of: The Bureau of National Affairs, Inc.), 1231 25th St., N.W., Washington, DC 20037. TEL 202-833-7470; 800-372-1033. FAX 202-833-7490. (Subscr. to: BNA Books Distribution Center, 300 Raritan Center Parkway, Box 7816, Edison, NJ 08818-7816. TEL 908-225-1900. FAX 908-417-0482) Ed.Bd. **Document type:** directory.
Formerly: B N A's Directory of State Courts, Judges, and Clerks.
Description: Lists the names, addresses, and telephone numbers of 9,271 judges and 3,683 clerks and administrators, in more than 2,000 courts at the three highest levels of all US states and territories.

340 613.1 US ISSN 1073-5798
▼**B N A'S ENVIRONMENTAL COMPLIANCE BULLETIN.** 1993. bi-w. $464. The Bureau of National Affairs, Inc., 1231 25th St., N.W., Washington, DC 20037. TEL 202-452-4200. FAX 202-822-8092. TELEX 285656 BNAI WSH. (Subscr. to: 9435 Key West Ave., Rockville, MD 20850. TEL 800-372-1033) Ed. Karen S. Walker. (back issues avail.)
—CCC.

340 614.7 US
▼**B N A'S ENVIRONMENTAL DUE DILIGENCE GUIDE.** 1992. m. $628. The Bureau of National Affairs, Inc., 1231 25th St., N.W., Washington, DC 20037. TEL 202-452-4200. FAX 202-822-8092. TELEX 285656 BNAI WSH. (Subscr. to: 9435 Key West Ave., Rockville, MD 20850. TEL 800-372-1033) Ed. Anne M. Lange. (looseleaf format; back issues avail.)
Description: Reference manual which describes how environmental law affects real estate transactions and how "due diligence" can provide protection against Superfund (CERCLA) and RCRA cleanup liabilities.

610 340 US ISSN 1064-2137
KF3825.5.A15
▼**B N A'S HEALTH LAW REPORTER**; a weekly review of legislative, regulatory, and legal developments. 1992. w. $895. The Bureau of National Affairs, Inc., 1231 25th St., N.W., Washington, DC 20037. TEL 202-452-4200. FAX 202-822-8092. TELEX 285656 BNAI WSH. (Subscr. to: 9435 Key West Ave., Rockville, MD 20850. TEL 800-372-1033) Ed. Susan Webster. s-a. index. (back issues avail.)
—CCC.
Description: Provides comprehensive coverage of the wide range of legal, regulatory, and legislative developments that have an impact on health care attorneys and top-flight health care executives, in such areas as antitrust, tax, professional liability, insurance, fraud and abuse, reimbursement, medical health law, Medicare, Medicaid, and licensure.

B N A'S MEDICARE REPORT. see *MEDICAL SCIENCES*

340 613.1 US ISSN 1073-5798
▼**B N A'S NEW JERSEY ENVIRONMENTAL COMPLIANCE BULLETIN.** 1993. bi-w. The Bureau of National Affairs, Inc., 1231 25th St., N.W., Washington, DC 20037. TEL 202-452-4200. FAX 202-822-8092. TELEX 285656 BNAI WSH. (Subscr. to: 9435 Key West Ave., Rockville, MD 20850. TEL 800-372-1033) Ed. Karen S. Walker. (back issues avail.)

340 613.1 US ISSN 1073-5798
▼**B N A'S TEXAS ENVIRONMENTAL COMPLIANCE BULLETIN.** 1993. bi-w. The Bureau of National Affairs, Inc., 1231 25th St., N.W., Washington, DC 20037. TEL 202-452-4200. FAX 202-822-8092. TELEX 285656 BNAI WSH. (Subscr. to: 9435 Key West Ave., Rockville, MD 20850. TEL 800-372-1033) Ed. Karen S. Walker. (back issues avail.)

B N A'S WORKERS' COMPENSATION REPORT. see *BUSINESS AND ECONOMICS — Labor And Industrial Relations*

B O C A NATIONAL BUILDING CODE. (Building Officials and Code Administrators International) see *BUILDING AND CONSTRUCTION*

B O C A NATIONAL MECHANICAL CODE. see *BUILDING AND CONSTRUCTION*

3228 LAW

B O C A NATIONAL PLUMBING CODE. see *HEATING, PLUMBING AND REFRIGERATION*

B O C A NATIONAL PROPERTY MAINTENANCE CODE. see *BUILDING AND CONSTRUCTION*

340   GW   ISSN 0722-6934
B R A K - MITTEILUNGEN. 1969. q. DM.40. Verlag Dr. Otto Schmidt KG, Unter den Ulmen 96-98, 50968 Cologne, Germany. TEL 0221-9373801. FAX 0221-93738941. TELEX 8883381. index. circ. 66,150. (back issues avail.) **Document type:** bulletin.
—CCC.

340 333.33   AT   ISSN 0727-8047
BAALMAN & WELL'S LAND TITLES OFFICE PRACTICE. 1980. 3/yr. Aus.$310 with updates. Law Book Co. Ltd., 44-50 Waterloo Rd., N. Ryde, N.S.W. 2113, Australia. TEL 02-887-0177. FAX 02-888-9706. TELEX ASBOOK 27995. Ed. Kevin Nettle. (looseleaf format)
Description: Covers the practice of the land Titles Office, the preparation of conveyancing instruments aad official registration requirements.

BACK FORTY. see *CONSERVATION*

340   US
BACK HOME - THE NEWSLETTER OF THE NONRESIDENT LAWYERS DIVISION. 1990. irreg. (2-3/yr.) membership. State Bar of Wisconsin, Nonresident Lawyers Division, 402 W. Wilson St., Madison, WI 53703. TEL 608-257-3838. FAX 608-257-5502. Ed. Betty Braden. circ. 4,794. (back issues avail.) **Document type:** newsletter.

BAD FAITH LAW REPORT. see *INSURANCE*

340   US   ISSN 1045-9669
KF836.A59B33
BAD FAITH LAW UPDATE. 1986. m. $245. Matthew Bender & Co., Inc., 11 Penn Plaza, New York, NY 10001. TEL 212-967-7707. FAX 212-967-1069. index. (looseleaf format; back issues avail.) **Document type:** newsletter.

BALDWIN'S OHIO LEGISLATIVE SERVICE. see *PUBLIC ADMINISTRATION*

BALDWIN'S OHIO SCHOOL LAW JOURNAL. see *EDUCATION*

342   BG
BANGLADESH JATIYA AINJIBI SAMITY SOUVENIR. Variant title: Bangladesh Jatiya Ainjibi Samity. Annual Law Journal. (Text in English or Bengali) 1977. a. Tk.25. Bangladesh Jatiya Ainjibi Samity - National Bar Associaton of Bangladesh, Dhanmandi R.A. 87, Road 7A, Dhaka, Bangladesh. Ed. Mr.Sobhan. adv.; bk.rev. circ. 10,000.

342   BG
BANGLADESH SUPREME COURT REPORTS. (Text in English) 1975. q. $20. Bangladesh Institute of Law and International Affairs, 501 Dhanmondi Residential Area, Rd. No. 7, Dhaka 5, Bangladesh. (Dist. by: Karim International, Padmalochon Roy Lane, Mahuttuly, Dacca 1, Bangladesh) Ed.Bd. circ. 2,500.

BANK ASSET - LIABILITY MANAGEMENT. see *BUSINESS AND ECONOMICS — Banking And Finance*

BANK BAILOUT LITIGATION NEWS. see *BUSINESS AND ECONOMICS — Banking And Finance*

340 332.1   US
BANK HOLDING COMPANY COMPLIANCE MANUAL. 1986. base vol. (plus irreg. suppl.). $245. Matthew Bender & Co., Inc., 11 Penn Plaza, New York, NY 10001. TEL 212-967-7707. Ed. Joseph G. Beckford. (looseleaf format)
Description: Guide to the day-to-day compliance responsibilities faced by bank holding company line officers.

BANK INCOME TAX RETURN MANUAL. see *BUSINESS AND ECONOMICS — Banking And Finance*

BANK OFFICERS HANDBOOK OF COMMERCIAL BANKING LAW (SUPPLEMENT). see *BUSINESS AND ECONOMICS — Banking And Finance*

340   TU
BANKA VE TICARET HUKUKU DERGISI. 1961. s-a. TL.122400($25) Ankara Universitesi, Hukuk Fakultesi - University of Ankara, Faculty of Law, 06590 Cebeci - Ankara, Turkey. circ. 1,000. (back issues avail.) **Document type:** academic/scholarly publication.

BANKER'S LETTER OF THE LAW. see *BUSINESS AND ECONOMICS — Banking And Finance*

BANKING AND FINANCE LAW REVIEW/REVUE DE DROIT BANCAIRE ET DE FINANCE. see *BUSINESS AND ECONOMICS — Banking And Finance*

346.066   US
BANKING ATTORNEY. 48/yr. $650 for new subscr. (foreign $706); renewal $725. American Banker - Bond Buyer, Newsletter Division (Subsidiary of: Thomson Financial Services Company), One State St. Plaza, New York, NY 10004-1549. TEL 800-733-4371. FAX 212-943-2224. (Subscr. to: Box 28315, Washington, DC 20038-8315. TEL 202-347-2665) Ed. Dave Postal. adv. (back issues avail.) **Document type:** newsletter.
Formerly: Bank Attorney; Incorporates: Thrift Attorney.
Description: Provides analyses of legal issues, legal ruling, and litigation affecting all depository institutions. Reports on recent court decisions in bank-related cases, comments on the impact of those decisions, and provides a summary of upcoming court cases that will influence banking.

340 332.1   US
BANKING LAW. 1981. 12 base vols. (plus irreg. suppl.). $1700. Matthew Bender & Co., Inc., 11 Penn Plaza, New York, NY 10001. TEL 212-967-7707. (looseleaf format)
Description: Operational guidance for bank officers, with analysis of statutory law and agency regulations.

340 332.1   US   ISSN 0737-2159
K2
BANKING LAW ANTHOLOGY. 1983. a. $149.95. International Library Law Book Publishers, Inc., 101 Lakeforest Blvd., Ste. 270, Gaithersburg, MD 20877. TEL 301-990-7755. FAX 301-990-7642. Ed. Allison P. Zabriskie. bibl.; index, cum.index. **Indexed:** Leg.Per.
Description: Selected best U.S. law review articles, printed in their entirety, in the field of banking, selected from over 900 American law review journals.

BANKING LAW BRIEFS. see *BUSINESS AND ECONOMICS — Banking And Finance*

346.066   US
BANKING LAW IN THE UNITED STATES. 1988. base vol. (plus a. supplements). $95. Butterworth Legal Publishers (Salem) (Subsidiary of: Reed Elsevier plc), 8 Industrial Way, Bldg. C, Salem, NH 03079. TEL 800-548-4001. FAX 603-898-9858. Ed.Bd.
Description: Reviews and analyses of the laws and regulations governing banking practice in the US.

BANKING LAW JOURNAL. see *BUSINESS AND ECONOMICS — Banking And Finance*

BANKING LAW JOURNAL DIGEST (SUPPLEMENT). see *BUSINESS AND ECONOMICS — Banking And Finance*

340 332   US
BANKING LAW MANUAL: LEGAL GUIDE TO COMMERCIAL BANKS, THRIFT INSTITUTIONS AND CREDIT UNIONS. 1983. base vol. (plus irreg. suppl.). $185. Matthew Bender & Co., Inc., 11 Penn Plaza, New York, NY 10001. TEL 212-967-7707. (looseleaf format)
Description: Examines the basic legal issues related to financial institutions and the regulatory framework within which they operate. Includes a comparative analysis of the powers of various types of financial institutions.

BANKING LAW REVIEW; practical legal guidance for bankers and their attorneys. see *BUSINESS AND ECONOMICS — Banking And Finance*

340   US
BANKRUPTCY CODE, RULES AND FORMS. 1978. a. West Publishing Corp., 620 Opperman Dr., Eagan, MN 55123. TEL 612-687-8000; 800-328-9352. FAX 612-687-7302. **Document type:** trade publication.

340   US
KF1507.B347
BANKRUPTCY COUNSELLOR. 1988. 24/yr. $345. Counsellor Publications Inc., Box 19070, Alexandria, VA 22320. TEL 703-684-9156. FAX 703-739-0489. Ed. Gregory Lee. index. **Document type:** newsletter.

340   US   ISSN 1059-2873
BANKRUPTCY EVIDENCE MANUAL. 1987. a. West Publishing Corp., 620 Opperman Dr., Eagan, MN 55123-1308. TEL 612-687-8000; 800-328-9352. FAX 612-687-7302. **Document type:** trade publication.

340   US
BANKRUPTCY, INSOLVENCY - CREDITORS' RIGHTS NEWSLETTER. q. membership. State Bar of Wisconsin, Bankruptcy, Insolvency and Creditors' Rights Section, 402 W. Wilson St., Madison, WI 53703. TEL 608-257-3838. FAX 608-257-5502. circ. 830. **Document type:** newsletter.

BANKRUPTCY LAW LETTER. see *BUSINESS AND ECONOMICS — Banking And Finance*

340   CE
BAR ASSOCIATION OF SRI LANKA. NEWSLETTER. (Text in English) 1975. m. Bar Association of Sri Lanka, Law Library, Colombo 12, Sri Lanka. **Document type:** newsletter.

340   US   ISSN 0005-5824
LAW
BAR EXAMINER. 1931. 4/yr. free to judges and lawyers engaged in the field of admissions to the bar. National Conference of Bar Examiners, 333 N. Michigan Ave., Ste. 1025, Chicago, IL 60601-4090. TEL 312-641-0963. FAX 312-641-2052. Ed. Stuart Duhl. circ. 2,500. (also avail. in microform from UMI; reprint service avail. from UMI) **Indexed:** C.L.I., L.R.I., Leg.Per.
—UnCover; UMI.

340   IS   ISSN 0334-0716
K13
BAR-ILAN LAW STUDIES/MICHKARAI MISHPAT. (Text in Hebrew) a. $38. Bar-Ilan University Press, Ramat Gat 52900, Israel. TEL 03-5318401. (back issues avail.) **Document type:** academic/scholarly publication.
Description: Direct and theoretical studies of general and Jewish law.

340.06   US   ISSN 0099-1031
KF200
BAR LEADER. 1975. bi-m. $21 (free to qualified personnel). American Bar Association, Bar Services Division, 750 N. Lake Shore Dr., Chicago, IL 60611. TEL 312-988-5000. Ed. George Gold. illus. circ. 8,000. **Indexed:** C.L.I., L.R.I., Leg.Cont.
—UnCover.
Formed by the merger of: American Bar Association. Section of Bar Activities. Bar Activities; American Bar Association. Section of Bar Activities. Bar Keys; American Bar Association. Section of Bar Activities. Communications Coordinator.

340   US   ISSN 1044-0194
K2.A674
BARCLAYS CALIFORNIA LAW LIBRARY. Key Title: Barclays Law Library. 1979. m. $295. Barclays Law Publishers, 400 Oyster Point Blvd., Ste. 500, S. San Francisco, CA 94080. TEL 415-588-1155. FAX 415-244-6619. Ed. Frank Gomez. adv.
Former titles (until 1989): Barclays California Law Monthly (ISSN 8755-772X); (until 1984): Barclays Law Monthly (ISSN 0164-3835)

340 610   US
▼**BARCLAYS HEALTH LAW BULLETIN (CALIFORNIA EDITION).** 1992. m. $245. Barclays Law Publishers, 400 Oyster Point Blvd., Ste. 500, S. San Francisco, CA 94080. TEL 415-588-1155. FAX 415-244-6619. q. index. **Document type:** newsletter.

340   CE
KFC556.A3692B3
▼**BARCLAYS LABOR LAW BULLETIN (CALIFORNIA EDITION).** 1992. m. $195. Barclays Law Publishers, 400 Oyster Point Blvd., Ste. 500, S. San Francisco, CA 94080. TEL 415-588-1155. FAX 415-244-6619. Ed. Frank Gomez. q. index. (looseleaf format) **Document type:** newsletter.

LAW

342 US
BARCLAYS UNITED STATES EIGHTH CIRCUIT SERVICE. s-m. Barclays Law Publishers, 400 Oyster Point Blvd., Ste. 500, San Francisco, CA 94080. TEL 415-588-1155. **Document type:** newsletter.

342 US
BARCLAYS UNITED STATES TENTH CIRCUIT SERVICE. s-m. Barclays Law Publishers, 400 Oyster Point Blvd., Ste. 500, San Francisco, CA 94080. TEL 415-588-1155. **Document type:** newsletter.

BARNEN FRAMFOER ALLT/CHILDREN ABOVE ALL. see SOCIAL SERVICES AND WELFARE

340.1 NR ISSN 0331-0086
K2
BARRISTER. 1967; N.S. 1970. irreg. 6 n. University of Nigeria, Law Student's Association, Nsukka, Nigeria. Ed. Mr. Anyadike. adv.; bk.rev. circ. 2,000. **Indexed:** Leg.Per.
  Description: Articles by law students at the University of Nigeria, Enuqu Campus.

340 US ISSN 0094-5277
K2
BARRISTER (CHICAGO). 1973. q. $20. American Bar Association, Young Lawyers Division, 750 N. Lake Shore Dr., Chicago, IL 60611. TEL 312-988-6047. Ed. Anthony Monahan. adv.; bk.rev. circ. 151,421. (reprint service avail.) **Indexed:** Anbar, C.L.I., L.R.I., Law Ofc.Info.Svc., Leg.Cont., Leg.Per.
—BLDSC (1863.824000); UnCover.
  Incorporates: Law Notes (ISSN 0023-9305)
  Description: General articles about the legal profession, the law, and society.

340 US ISSN 0739-2494
KF200
BARRISTER (PHILADELPHIA). 1970. q. $32. Pennsylvania Trial Lawyers Association, 121 S. Broad St., Ste. 800, Philadelphia, PA 19107-4594. TEL 215-546-6451. FAX 215-546-5430. Ed. Lee C. Swartz. adv.; bk.rev.; cum.index. circ. 4,000. (back issues avail.) **Document type:** academic/scholarly publication.
  Description: Advice and information for advocates practicing trial law in Pennsylvania.

341.484 US ISSN 1058-5532
KF4819.3
BASIC IMMIGRATION LAW. 1989. a. Practising Law Institute, 810 Seventh Ave., New York, NY 10019. TEL 212-765-5700.

340 US ISSN 1053-5969
KF1030.E4
BASIC U C C SKILLS. ARTICLE 4A. 1990. a. Practising Law Institute, 810 Seventh Ave., New York, NY 10019.

340 SZ
BASLER JURISTISCHE MITTEILUNGEN. 6/yr. Elisabethenstr. 8, Postfach 135, CH-4010 Basel, Switzerland. TEL 061-232288. FAX 061-232206. TELEX 964348. Ed. K. Spiro. circ. 735.

340 SZ
BASLER STUDIEN ZUR RECHTSWISSENSCHAFT. 1932. irreg. price varies. Helbing und Lichtenhahn Verlag AG, Freie Str. 84, CH-4051 Basel, Switzerland. TEL 064-268626. FAX 064-245780. (Subscr. to: Sauerlaender AG, Postfach, CH-5001 Aarau, Switzerland) **Document type:** monographic series.

BAURECHT; Zeitschrift fuer das gesamte oeffentliche und zivile Baurecht. see BUILDING AND CONSTRUCTION

340 SZ ISSN 1017-0588
BAURECHT/DROIT DE LA CONSTRUCTION. (Text in French and German) 1979. q. 49 SFr. (Seminar fuer Schweizerisches Baurecht) Union Walter AG, Postfach, Kapuzinerstr. 6, CH-4502 Solothurn, Switzerland. TEL 065-238161. FAX 065-222931. Ed.Bd. adv.; bk.rev. circ. 3,900. (tabloid format; back issues avail.)

340 350 GW ISSN 0522-5377
BAYERISCHE VERWALTUNGSBLAETTER; Zeitschrift fuer oeffentliches Recht und oeffentliche Verwaltung. 1955. s-m. DM.362.40. Richard Boorberg Verlag (Stuttgart), Scharrstr. 2, 70563 Stuttgart, Germany. TEL 0711-7385-0. Ed. Herbert von Golitschek. **Indexed:** Dok.Str., ELLIS, INIS Atomind. **Document type:** bulletin.
—CCC.

349 GW ISSN 0005-7142
BAYERISCHES JUSTIZMINISTERIALBLATT. 1863. m. DM.50. Staatsministerium der Justiz, Justizpalast, 80097 Munich, Germany. FAX 089-55973566. (Subscr. to: J. Schweizer Sortiment, Lenbachplatz 1, 80333 Munich, Germany) index. circ. 2,300. **Document type:** government publication.

340 US ISSN 0005-7274
K2
BAYLOR LAW REVIEW. 1948. q. $28. Baylor University, Law School, 1400 S. 5th St., Waco, TX 76706. TEL 817-755-3487. (Subscr. to: Box 97156, Waco, TX 76798) Ed. Charles Wesky Rhodes IV. adv.; index, cum.index every 5 yrs.: vols.1-43 (1984-1991). circ. 1,200. (also avail. in microfilm from WSH,PMC) **Indexed:** C.L.I., Curr.Cont., L.R.I., Leg.Cont., Leg.Per., P.A.I.S., SSCI.
—BLDSC (1871.241500); Faxon; UnCover.

BEER MARKETER'S INSIGHTS. see BEVERAGES

BEHAVIORAL SCIENCES AND THE LAW. see PSYCHOLOGY

340 AU
BEITRAEGE ZUM UNIVERSITAETSRECHT. 1982. irreg., vol.15, 1992. price varies. Manzsche Verlags- und Universitaetsbuchhandlung, Kohlmarkt 16, A-1014 Vienna, Austria. TEL 0222-531610. FAX 0222-53161-181. Ed. Rudolf Strasser. circ. 1,500. **Document type:** monographic series.
  Description: Collects articles on university law.

343 BE
BELGIUM. COUR DE CASSATION. BULLETIN DES ARRETS.
Cover title: Arrets de la Cour de Cassation de Belgique. m. 8250 Fr. Etablissements Emile Bruylant, 67 rue de la Regence, B-1000 Brussels, Belgium. TEL 02-512-9845.
  Formerly: Belgium. Cour de Cassation. Bulletin.

340 US
KFI1708.A15B46
BENCH AND BAR. 1971. m. $12 to members. Illinois Bar Center, Section on Bench and Bar, Illinois Bar Center, Springfield, IL 62701. TEL 217-525-1760. FAX 217-525-0712. Eds. Dennis Dohm, Michael S. Jordan. circ. 475. (looseleaf format) **Document type:** newsletter.

340 US ISSN 0276-1505
KF200
BENCH & BAR OF MINNESOTA. 1931. 11/yr. $25 to non-members; members $15. Minnesota State Bar Association, 514 Nicollet Ave., Ste. 300, Minneapolis, MN 55402. TEL 612-333-1183. FAX 612-333-4927. Ed. Judson Haverkamp. adv.; bk.rev.; index. circ. 14,000. (also avail. in microform; back issues avail.) **Indexed:** C.L.I., L.R.I., Law Ofc.Info.Svc.
—UnCover.
  Description: Law related topics of interest to Minnesota lawyers.

340 US ISSN 0882-4312
K2
BERKELEY WOMEN'S LAW JOURNAL. 1986. a. $17 to individuals; institutions $38; students $9 (effective 1994). University of California Press, Journals Division, 2120 Berkeley Way, Berkeley, CA 94720. TEL 510-643-7154. FAX 510-642-9917. Ed.Bd. adv.; bk.rev. circ. 550. (also avail. in microform from UMI; back issues avail.) **Indexed:** Alt.Press Ind. **Document type:** academic/scholarly publication.
—BLDSC (1940.630000); Faxon; UnCover; UMI. CCC.
  Description: Explores racial, cultural, and socioeconomic issues concerning women and the law.
  Refereed Serial

340 GW ISSN 0930-3065
BERLINER ANWALTSBLATT. 1951. m. DM.132. C B Verlag Carl Boldt, Baseler Str. 80, 12205 Berlin, Germany. TEL 030-8337087. FAX 030-8339125. circ. 5,900. **Document type:** bulletin.

340 SZ
BERNISCHE VERWALTUNGSRECHTSPRECHUNG.* m. Geiger AG, Habsburgstr. 19, CH-3000 Bern 16, Switzerland. Ed. U. Zimmerli. circ. 1,350.

340 US ISSN 1067-4756
BEST LAWYERS IN AMERICA. 1983. biennial, latest 6th ed. $110. Woodward - White, Inc., 129 First Ave., Aiken, SC 29801. TEL 803-648-0300. Eds. Steven Naifeh, Gregory White Smith. **Document type:** directory.
  Description: Lists approximately 12,000 of the best attorneys in the U.S., as determined through a national poll of their peers.

658 340 GW ISSN 0340-7918
BETRIEBS-BERATER; Zeitschrift fuer Recht und Wirtschaft. 1946. 3/m. DM.417.60. Verlag Recht und Wirtschaft GmbH, Haeusserstr. 14, 69115 Heidelberg, Germany. TEL 06221-906-1. (Subscr. to: Postfach 105960, 69049 Heidelberg, Germany) adv.; bk.rev. circ. 20,000. **Indexed:** INIS Atomind., Key to Econ.Sci. **Document type:** trade publication.
—BLDSC (1946.830000); SWETS. CCC.

340 GW ISSN 0179-2776
K2
BETRIFFT JUSTIZ. 1985. q. DM.40($20) Neuthor-Verlag, P.O. Box 3402, 64715 Michelstadt, Germany. Ed.Bd. index. circ. 1,500. (back issues avail.)

340 US ISSN 1051-628X
BEVERLY HILLS BAR ASSOCIATION JOURNAL. vol.4, 1970. q. $40 (foreign $45). Beverly Hills Bar Association, 300 S. Beverly Dr., Ste. 201, Beverly Hills, CA 90212. TEL 213-553-6644. FAX 213-284-8290. adv.; bk.rev.; illus. circ. 3,000. (also avail. in microfiche) **Indexed:** C.L.I., L.R.I., Leg.Per. **Document type:** academic/scholarly publication.
  ●Also available online. Vendor(s): West Services, Inc.
—UnCover.
  Description: Scholarly journal dealing with substantive and procedural issues in the law.

BIANJI ZHI YOU/COMPILERS' FRIEND. see PUBLISHING AND BOOK TRADE

BIBLIOTHECA IURIDICA LATINA MEXICANA. see CLASSICAL STUDIES

BIJBLAD BIJ DE INDUSTRIELE EIGENDOM. see PATENTS, TRADEMARKS AND COPYRIGHTS

349 YU ISSN 0006-2731
BILTEN PRAVNE SLUZBE J N A. (Text in Serbo-Croatian) 1961. q. Savezni Sekretarijat za Narodnu Odbranu, Kneza Milosa 37, Belgrade, Yugoslavia. Ed. Vuko Gozze-Gucetic.

340 020 US ISSN 1048-8936
KF1
BIMONTHLY REVIEW OF LAW BOOKS. 1990. bi-m. $80. Fred B. Rothman & Co., 10368 W. Centennial Rd., Littleton, CO 80127. TEL 303-979-5657. FAX 303-978-1457. Eds. Edward Bander, Michael Rustad. (back issues avail.; reprint service avail. from RRI)
  Description: Provides law librarians, legal academics and lawyers with reviews of contemporary legal topics.

BIOETHICS YEARBOOK. see RELIGIONS AND THEOLOGY

BIOLAW: A LEGAL AND ETHICAL REPORTER ON MEDICINE, HEALTH CARE, AND BIOENGINEERING. see BIOLOGY — Bioengineering

340 660 UK ISSN 0261-6904
BIOTECHNOLOGY BULLETIN. m. £195($390) I B C Publishing, Gilmoora House, 57-61 Mortimer St., London W1N 7TD, England. TEL 071-637-4383. FAX 071-636-6414. (Subscr. in U.S. to: IBC (USA), 290 Eliot St., Box 91004, Ashland, MA 01721-9104. TEL 508-881-2800. FAX 508-881-0982) Ed. John Elkington. **Document type:** bulletin.
—BLDSC (2089.861000); SWETS.

BIOTECHNOLOGY LAW REPORT. see BIOLOGY — Biotechnology

340 US ISSN 0006-3711
BIRMINGHAM BAR ASSOCIATION. BULLETIN.* 1964. q. $10. Birmingham Bar Association, 109 N. 20th St., Birmingham, AL 35203. TEL 205-251-8006. Ed. Warren B. Lightfoot. adv.; bk.rev.; circ. 1,600 (controlled). (tabloid format)

LAW

340   SZ
BLAETTER FUER SCHULDBETREIBUNG UND KONKURS. 6/yr. Parkstr. 49, CH-3084 Wabern, Switzerland. Ed. Walter Ochsenbein. circ. 1,100.

349   SZ   ISSN 0006-4491
BLAETTER FUER ZUERCHERISCHE RECHTSPRECHUNG. 10/yr. 115 SFr. (foreign 133 SFr.). Schulthess Polygraphischer Verlag AG, Zwingliplatz 2, CH-8022 Zurich, Switzerland. TEL 01-2519336. FAX 01-2616394. Ed.Bd. adv. circ. 1,700. **Document type:** bulletin.
—CCC.

346.066 340   CN
BLAKES REPORT - INTELLECTUAL PROPERTY. 1986. q. Blake, Cassels & Graydon, Box 25, Commerce Court West, Toronto, Ont. M5L 1A9, Canada. TEL 416-863-2400. FAX 416-863-2653. TELEX 06-219687. Ed. Victor V. Butsky. index. circ. 5,500. (back issues avail.)

340   US
BLUE SKY COMPLIANCE MANUAL; a state-by-state guide. 1987. base vol. (plus suppl.). $75. Butterworth Legal Publishers (Salem) (Subsidiary of: Reed Elsevier plc), 8 Industrial Way, Bldg. C, Salem, NH 03079. TEL 800-548-4001. FAX 603-898-9858. Ed. Bobby G. Palmer. (looseleaf format)
Description: For attorneys, legal assistants, paralegal and legal secretaries; includes a directory of all state securities administrators' addresses and telephone numbers, necessary forms for compliance in every state and sample filings and cover letters.

BLUE SKY GUIDE. see *BUSINESS AND ECONOMICS — Investments*

340   US
BLUE SKY LAW REPORTS. 1928. s-m. $875. Commerce Clearing House, Inc., 4025 W. Peterson Ave., Chicago, IL 60646. TEL 312-583-8500. Ed. D. Newquist.

346.006   US
BOARD OF CONTRACT APPEALS BID PROTEST DECISIONS. m. $524. Federal Publications Inc., 1120 20th St., N.W., Ste. 500 S., Washington, DC 20036. TEL 202-337-7000. FAX 202-659-2233.
Description: Reports on government contracts.

340   US
BOHANNON'S NEW MEXICO ENVIRONMENTAL LAW HANDBOOK; a practical guide to New Mexico laws and regulations. 1990. base vol. (plus irreg. supplements). $95. Butterworth Legal Publishers (Salem) (Subsidiary of: Reed Elsevier plc), 8 Industrial Way, Bldg. C, Salem, NH 03079. TEL 800-548-4001. FAX 603-898-9858. Ed. Paul M. Bohannon. (looseleaf format)
Description: Provides a current review of all environmental programs operating in New Mexico.

340   EC
BOLETIN DE LEGISLACION E INFORMACION JURIDICA. no.20, 1979. m. Camara de Comercio de Quito, Avenidas Amazonas y de la Republica, Apdo. 202, Quito, Ecuador.

340.5   MX   ISSN 0041-8633
K2
BOLETIN MEXICANO DE DERECHO COMPARADO. 1948. 3/yr. Mex.$50($42) Universidad Nacional Autonoma de Mexico, Instituto de Investigaciones Juridicas, Delegacion Coyoacan, Ciudad Universitaria, 04510 Mexico, DF, Mexico. Ed. Eugenio Hurtado Marquez. adv.; bk.rev.; abstr.; bibl.; index. **Indexed:** A.B.C.Pol.Sci., HR Rep., Mar.Aff.Bibl.
Formerly: Universidad Nacional Autonoma de Mexico. Instituto de Investigaciones Juridicas. Boletin.

347   SP
BOLETIN OFICIAL DE LAS CORTES ESPANOLES. s-w. 38000 ptas. Congreso de los Diputados, C. Floridablanca s-n., 28014 Madrid, Spain.

340   IT   ISSN 0394-6592
BOLLETTINO DEL LAVORO E DEI TRIBUTI; settimanale di dottrina legislazione circolari giurisprudenza. 1971. w. L.440000 (effective 1994). Casa Editrice Edis s.r.l., Via S. Franca 60, 29100 Piacenza, Italy. TEL 0523-25684. FAX 0523-336782. Ed. Giuseppe Sgroi. (back issues avail.)
Formerly (until 1987): Bollettino del Lavoro (ISSN 0391-822X)

340   II
BOMBAY LAW REPORTER. (Text in English) 1899. m. Rs.200 (foreign Rs.400). Bombay Law Reporter Pvt. Ltd., Krishna Mahal 63, Marine Dr., Bombay 20, India. Eds. A.P. Yajnik, A.G. Joshi. adv.; bk.rev.; bibl.; index. circ. 2,500.

340   US
BOSTON BAR JOURNAL. 1959. 5/yr. $40. Boston Bar Association, 16 Beacon St., Boston, MA 02108. TEL 617-742-0615. FAX 617-523-0127. adv.; bk.rev. circ. 8,500. **Indexed:** C.L.I. **Document type:** academic/scholarly publication.

BOSTON COLLEGE ENVIRONMENTAL AFFAIRS LAW REVIEW. see *ENVIRONMENTAL STUDIES*

341.57   US   ISSN 0161-6587
K2
BOSTON COLLEGE LAW REVIEW. 1959. 5/yr. $20. Boston College, School of Law, 885 Centre St., Newton, MA 02159. TEL 617-552-8575. index, cum.index. circ. 600. (also avail. in microfiche from RRI; microfilm from RRI; reprint service from RRI) **Indexed:** Bank.Lit.Ind., BPIA, Bus.Ind., C.L.I., L.R.I., Leg.Per., Ocean.Abstr., P.A.I.S., Pollut.Abstr. **Document type:** academic/scholarly publication.
●Also available online. Vendor(s): West Services, Inc.
—BLDSC (2251.812300); Faxon; UnCover; UMI.
Formerly (until vol.19, 1977): Boston College Industrial and Commercial Law Review (ISSN 0006-7954)

340   US   ISSN 0006-8047
LAW
BOSTON UNIVERSITY LAW REVIEW. 1897. 5/yr. $25 (foreign $30). Boston University, School of Law, Law Review, 765 Commonwealth Ave., Boston, MA 02215. TEL 617-353-3118. FAX 617-353-6767. adv.; bk.rev.; index. cum.index: vols.1-26. circ. 3,000. (also avail. in microfiche from RRI; microfilm from RRI) **Indexed:** BPIA, Bus.Ind., C.L.I., Crim.Just.Abstr., Curr.Cont., L.R.I., Leg.Cont., Leg.Per., P.A.I.S., Risk Abstr., SSCI.
●Also available online. Vendor(s): Mead Data Central, Inc., West Services, Inc.
—BLDSC (2251.840000); Faxon; UnCover.

340   US
KFC77.B6
BOTTOM LINE (SAN FRANCISCO). 1979. bi-m. membership. State Bar of California, 555 Franklin St., San Francisco, CA 94102. TEL 415-561-8225. FAX 415-561-8228. **Document type:** newsletter.

340   US
KFI1277.B67
BOTTOM LINE (SPRINGFIELD). 1980. q. $14 to members. Illinois State Bar Association, Law Office Economics Section, Illinois Bar Center, Springfield, IL 62701. TEL 217-525-1760. FAX 217-525-0712. Eds. Jeffrey Simon, Dennis Norden. circ. 2,500. **Document type:** newsletter.

BOWHUNTING NEWS. see *SPORTS AND GAMES — Outdoor Life*

340   UK   ISSN 0308-4574
K2
BRACTON LAW JOURNAL. 1965-1973; resumed 1975. a. University of Exeter, Faculty of Law, Exeter EX4 4QJ, England. (Dist. in N. America by: Wm. W. Gaunt & Sons, Inc., Gaunt Bldg., 3011 Gulf Dr., Holmes Beach, FL 34217-2199. TEL 813-778-5211. FAX 813-778-5252) **Indexed:** C.L.I., L.R.I., Leg.Per.
—BLDSC (2265.895000); Faxon.

BRANDEIS UNIVERSITY. INSTITUTE FOR HEALTH POLICY. RESEARCH NEWS. see *MEDICAL SCIENCES*

340   BL
BRAZIL. SUPREMO TRIBUNAL FEDERAL. INDICES DE LEGISLACAO FEDERAL. (Subseries of: D.I.N.-Divulgacao) a. price varies. Supremo Tribunal Federal, Departamento de Imprensa Nacional, SIG -Quadra 6- Lote 800, CEP 70604 Brasilia-DF, Brazil.

340   BL
BRAZIL. SUPREMO TRIBUNAL FEDERAL. RELATORIO DOS TRABALHOS REALIZADOS. Title varies slightly. 1916. a. Supremo Tribunal Federal, Departamento de Imprensa Nacional, SIG - Quadra 6- Lote 800, CEP 70604 Brasilia-DF, Brazil.

340   BL   ISSN 0076-8855
BRAZIL. TRIBUNAL REGIONAL DO TRABALHO. TERCERA REGIAO. REVISTA. 1965. s-a. Cr.$15000. Tribunal Regional do Trabalho, Tercera Regiao, Rua Curitiba 835, 30000 Belo Horizonte, MG, Brazil. TELEX 31 11 76. Ed.Bd. bibl. circ. 1,000.

340 613.9   UK   ISSN 0309-7978
BREAKING CHAINS. 1977. q. £12 to members. Abortion Law Reform Association, 27-35 Mortimer St., London W1N 7RJ, England. TEL 071-637-7264. Ed.Bd. adv. bk.rev. circ. 2,000.
Formerly: A L R A Newsletter.
Description: Presents a pro-choice forum for the association.

340 610   US   ISSN 1062-1814
KF1297.M4
▼**BREAST IMPLANT LITIGATION REPORTER.** 1992. s-m. $650. Andrews Publications, 1646 West Chester Pike, Box 1000, Westtown, PA 19395. TEL 215-399-6600; 800-345-1101. FAX 215-399-6610. Ed. Robert Sullivan. **Document type:** newsletter.
Description: Provides current information on developments in breast implant suits nationally.

340   US   ISSN 1066-8411
K25
BRIDGEPORT LAW REVIEW. 1980. q. $32. (Quinnipiac Law Review Association) Quinnipiac College, School of Law, 303 University Ave., Bridgeport, CT 06601. Ed. Mona Ragheb. bk.rev. circ. 500. (also avail. in microfiche from WSH,PMC; microfilm from WSH,PMC; back issues avail.) **Indexed:** Leg.Cont.
●Also available online. Vendor(s): West Services, Inc.
—Faxon; UnCover.
Formerly: University of Bridgeport Law Review (ISSN 0735-2832)

BRIEF. see *LEISURE AND RECREATION*

368 340   US   ISSN 0273-0995
KF1164.A1
BRIEF (CHICAGO). q. $18 to non-members; members $4 per no. American Bar Association, Tort and Insurance Practice Section, 750 N. Lake Shore Dr., Chicago, IL 60611. TEL 312-988-5555. Ed. Lucia Ann Lockwood. (also avail. in microform)
●Also available online. Vendor(s): West Services, Inc. (BRIEF).
—UnCover.
Formerly: American Bar Association. Section of Insurance, Negligence and Compensation Law. I N C L Brief.
Description: News and features on current events in the fields of tort and insurance law.

BRIEFING PAPERS. see *BUSINESS AND ECONOMICS — Economic Situation And Conditions*

340   US
BRIEFLY ... (JEFFERSON CITY). m. free to qualified personnel. Missouri Bar, Communications Dept., Box 119, Jefferson City, MO 65102.
TEL 314-634-4128. FAX 314-635-2811. Ed. Gary P. Toohey. **Document type:** newsletter.

340 367   CN   ISSN 0715-3759
BRIEFLY SPEAKING. 1979. m. membership. Canadian Bar Association - Ontario, 20 Toronto St., Ste. 200, Toronto, Ont. M5C 2B8, Canada.
FAX 416-869-1390. Ed. Lucinda Falconer. circ. 16,000.

340.05   US   ISSN 0360-151X
K2
BRIGHAM YOUNG UNIVERSITY LAW REVIEW. 1975. q. $20. Brigham Young University, J. Reuben Clark Law School, 453 JRCB, Provo, UT 84602. TEL 801-378-5678. FAX 801-378-3595. adv.; bk.rev. circ. 850. (also avail. in microform from UMI; reprint service avail. from RRI,UMI) **Indexed:** C.L.I., L.R.I., Leg.Cont., Leg.Per.
●Also available online. Vendor(s): West Services, Inc.
—BLDSC (2283.976000); Faxon; UnCover; SWETS; UMI.

340   CN   ISSN 0381-2510
LAW
BRITISH COLUMBIA. LAW REFORM COMMISSION. ANNUAL REPORT. 1970. a. Law Reform Commission, 203-865 Hornby St., Vancouver, BC V6Z 2G3, Canada. TEL 604-660-2366. FAX 604-660-2378. Ed. Arthur L. Close. circ. 2,000 (controlled).

LAW

340 CN
BRITISH COLUMBIA. LAW REFORM COMMISSION. REPORTS. irreg. price varies. Law Reform Commission, 203-865 Hornby St., Vancouver, BC V6Z 2G3, Canada. TEL 604-660-2366. FAX 604-660-2378. (Subscr. to: Crown Publications, 546 Yates St., Victoria, BC V8W 1K8, Canada. TEL 604-386-4636) (back issues avail.)

340 CN
BRITISH COLUMBIA ANNUAL PRACTICE. a. Can.$75. Western Legal Publications, 301 One Alexander St., Vancouver, BC V6A 1B2, Canada. TEL 604-687-5671. FAX 604-687-2796.
Description: Provides access to the current text of the B.C. Rules of Court, fully annotated with more than 850 decisions, a History of the Rules and all available Practice Directions for the Rules of Court and the Court of Appeals Rules.

340 CN ISSN 1189-6302
BRITISH COLUMBIA APPEAL CASES. 1991. irreg., (approx. 8/yr.). Can.$90. Maritime Law Book Ltd., P.O. Box 302, Fredericton, NB E3B 4Y9, Canada. TEL 506-453-9921; 800-561-0220. FAX 506-453-9525. (back issues avail.)
Description: Includes all of the decisions of the British Columbia Court of Appeal.

340 CN
BRITISH COLUMBIA COURT FORMS. 2/yr. Can.$615. Butterworths Canada Ltd., Part of the Reed Elsevier group, 75 Clegg Rd., Markham, ON L6G 1A1, Canada. TEL 905-479-2665. FAX 905-479-2826. Eds. Beverly M. McLachlin, James P. Taylor. (looseleaf format)
Description: Precedents and court forms for important court procedures encountered by British Columbia lawyers.

340 368 CN ISSN 0824-720X
BRITISH COLUMBIA DECISIONS - INSURANCE LAW CASES. 1981. m. Can.$299.50. Western Legal Publications, 301-1 Alexander St., Vancouver, BC V6A 1B2, Canada. TEL 604-687-5671. FAX 604-687-2796. m.index. (looseleaf format)
●Also available online.
Description: Digests of cases concerning insurance, motor vehicle liability, personal injury damages, negligence and relevant practice issues are included.

BRITISH COLUMBIA DECISIONS - LABOUR ARBITRATION. see BUSINESS AND ECONOMICS — Labor And Industrial Relations

340 352 CN ISSN 0824-7188
BRITISH COLUMBIA DECISIONS - MUNICIPAL LAW CASES. 1980. m. Can.$85. Western Legal Publications, 301-1 Alexander St., Vancouver, BC V6A 1B2, Canada. TEL 604-687-5671. FAX 604-687-2796. m.index. (looseleaf format)
●Also available online.

342 CN ISSN 0715-4798
BRITISH COLUMBIA DECISIONS - STATUTE CITATOR. 1978. m. Can.$115. Western Legal Publications, 301-1 Alexander St., Vancouver, BC V6A 1B2, Canada. TEL 604-687-5671. FAX 604-687-2796. (looseleaf format)
Description: Provides all current judicial decisions pertaining to the interpretation and application of British Columbia statutes decided by the Supreme Court of Canada and the British Columbia Courts.

340 CN ISSN 0703-3060
KEB104
BRITISH COLUMBIA LAW REPORTS (2ND SERIES). 1976. 12/yr. Can.$112. Carswell, One Corporate Plaza, 2075 Kennedy Rd., Scarborough, ON M1T 3V4, Canada. TEL 416-609-8000. FAX 416-298-5094. Ed. Leanne Berry. adv. contact: M. Lalani. cum.index.
Description: Contains important judgments from the civil courts of BC, selected criminal decisions, and Supreme Court of Canada appeals from BC decisions. All judgments fully headnoted.

BRITISH COLUMBIA LEGAL TELEPHONE DIRECTORY. see BUSINESS AND ECONOMICS — Trade And Industrial Directories

340 CN
BRITISH COLUMBIA PRACTICE. a. Can.$475. Butterworths Canada Ltd., Part of the Reed Elsevier group, 75 Clegg Rd., Markham, ON L6G 1A1, Canada. TEL 905-479-2665. FAX 905-479-2826. Eds. Beverly M. McLachlin, James P. Taylor. (looseleaf format)
Description: Text of each rule and subrule of the Canadian Supreme Court and Court of Appeals.

BRITISH COLUMBIA REAL ESTATE LAW GUIDE. see REAL ESTATE

340 CN
BRITISH COLUMBIA RULES CITATOR. 1977. m. Can.$105. Western Legal Publications, 301 One Alexander St., Vancouver, BC V6A 1B2, Canada. TEL 604-687-5671. FAX 604-687-2796. (looseleaf format)
Description: Covers case citations for all decisions of the B.C. Courts since February 1977.

340 CN
BRITISH COLUMBIA STATUTE CITATOR. q. Can.$199. Canada Law Book Inc., 240 Edward St., Aurora, ON L4G 3S9, Canada. TEL 905-841-6472. FAX 905-841-5085. adv. contact: Mary Cull. (looseleaf format)

340 CN ISSN 0713-8865
BRITISH COLUMBIA WEEKLY LAW DIGEST. 1982. w. (50/yr.). Can.$510. Carswell, One Corporate Plaza, 2075 Kennedy Rd., Scarborough, ON M1T 3V4, Canada. TEL 416-609-8000. FAX 416-298-5094. Ed. Leanne Berry. cum.index.
Description: Summarizes available reserve and oral judgments of the BC Court of Appeals and BC decisions, and selected judgments from the Provincial Courts. Tracks all previously digested proceedings, includes BC Law Reports cites for reported proceedings and notes disposition of applications for leave to appeal.

164 UK
BRITISH INSTITUTE OF INTERNATIONAL AND COMPARATIVE LAW. COMPARATIVE LAW AND PRIVATE INTERNATIONAL LAW SERIES. (Subseries avail.: United Kingdom Comparative Law Series) 1961. irreg., vol.14, 1993. price varies. British Institute of International and Comparative Law, Charles Clore House, 17 Russel Sq., London WC1B 5DR, England. TEL 071-636-5802. FAX 071-323-2016. **Document type:** academic/scholarly publication.
Incorporates: British Institute of International and Comparative Law. Private International Law Series & British Institute of International and Comparative Law. Comparative Law Series (ISSN 0068-2160); Which was formerly: Common Market European and Comparative Law Series.

BROADCASTING AND THE LAW. see COMMUNICATIONS — Television And Cable

BROADCASTING LAW AND PRACTICE. see COMMUNICATIONS — Television And Cable

340 333.33 US
BROKER-DEALERS AND SECURITIES MARKETS. 1977. base vol. (plus a. supplement). $95. Shepard's - McGraw-Hill, Inc., Box 35300, Colorado Springs, CO 80935-3530. TEL 800-525-2474.
Description: Focuses on Securities and Exchange Commission rules, their various interpretations and their many relationships to the brokerage industry and regulatory process.

BRONX COOP CONDO CONVERSION DIGEST. see REAL ESTATE

340 US ISSN 0007-232X
BROOKLYN BARRISTER. 1950. q. $15 includes membership. Brooklyn Bar Association, 123 Remsen St., Brooklyn, NY 11201. TEL 718-624-0675. FAX 718-797-1713. Ed. John L. Leventhal. adv.; bk.rev.; index. circ. 2,600. (also avail. in microform from UMI; reprint service avail. from UMI) **Indexed:** C.L.I., Leg.Per. **Document type:** trade publication.
—UnCover; UMI.

340 US ISSN 0007-2362
K2
BROOKLYN LAW REVIEW. 1935. 4/yr. $18. Brooklyn Law School, 250 Joralemon St., Brooklyn, NY 11201. TEL 718-780-7968. bk.rev.; bibl.; index. circ. 3,000. (also avail. in microfilm from MIM,RRI; back issues avail.; reprint service avail. from RRI) **Indexed:** Abstr.Bk.Rev.Curr.Leg.Per., C.L.I., Crim.Just.Abstr., L.R.I., Leg.Cont., Leg.Per. **Document type:** academic/scholarly publication.
●Also available online. Vendor(s): Mead Data Central, Inc.
—BLDSC (2350.150000); Faxon; UnCover.
Description: Analyzes a wide variety of legal topics.

BROWARD REVIEW. see BUSINESS AND ECONOMICS

340 US ISSN 0407-5501
BUCKS COUNTY LAW REPORTER. 1951. w. $42. Bucks County Bar Association, 135 E. State St., Box 300, Doylestown, PA 18901. TEL 215-348-9413. Ed. Ann Marie Daly. adv.; cum.index. circ. 700. (also avail. in microfiche)

340 US ISSN 0197-4955
BUFFALO LAW JOURNAL. 1929. 2/w. $75. American City Business Journals (Charlotte), 128 S. Tryon St., Ste. 2200, Charlotte, NC 28202. Ed. Jack Connors. circ. 1,400. (tabloid format) **Document type:** newspaper.

340 US ISSN 0023-9356
K2
BUFFALO LAW REVIEW. 1951. 3/yr. $27 (overseas $32) (effective 1993). State University of New York at Buffalo, Buffalo Law Review, 605 John Lord O'Brian Hall, Amherst Campus, Amherst, NY 14260. TEL 716-645-2059. FAX 716-645-2064. bk.rev. circ. 600. (also avail. in microfilm from WSH,PMC; reprint service avail.; reprint service avail. from WSH) **Indexed:** Abstr.Bk.Rev.Curr.Leg.Per., C.L.I., Crim.Just.Abstr., Curr.Cont., Environ.Abstr., L.R.I., Lang.& Lang.Behav.Abstr., Leg.Cont., Leg.Per., Mar.Aff.Bibl., SSCI. **Document type:** academic/scholarly publication.
●Also available online. Vendor(s): West Services, Inc.
—BLDSC (2357.600000); Faxon; UnCover.
Description: Publishes scholarly writings addressing contemporary issues in all areas of law.

BUILDING AND CONSTRUCTION CONTRACTS IN AUSTRALIA. see BUILDING AND CONSTRUCTION

BUILDING AND CONSTRUCTION LAW. see BUILDING AND CONSTRUCTION

340 690 UK ISSN 0266-0628
BUILDING LAW MONTHLY. m. £135 (foreign £157). Monitor Press, Rectory Rd., Great Waldingfield, Sudbury, Suffolk CO10 OTL, England. TEL 0787-378607. FAX 0787-880201. (back issues avail.) **Document type:** newsletter.
Description: Advisory service for specialists in the building and construction industries.

340 690 UK ISSN 0141-5875
BUILDING LAW REPORTS. 1976. 5/yr. £151($284) (foreign £167). Longman Group UK Ltd., Longman House, Burnt Mill, Harlow, Essex CM2O 2JE, England. TEL 0279-426721. FAX 0279-431059. Ed.Bd. (back issues avail.)
Description: Comprehensive and up-to-date collection of legal construction cases for all those with a professional interest in construction law.

BUILDING LICENSING LAWS. see BUILDING AND CONSTRUCTION

BUILDING PERMITS LAW BULLETIN. see HOUSING AND URBAN PLANNING

340 690 AT
BUILDING SERVICE N.S.W. (BCA). 1974. base vol. (plus updates 5/yr.). Aus.$280 (renewal Aus.$230). Law Book Co. Ltd., 44-50 Waterloo Rd., N. Ryde, N.S.W. 2113, Australia. TEL 02-887-0177. FAX 02-888-9706. TELEX ASBOOK 27995. Ed. Stefani White. (looseleaf format; back issues avail.)
Formerly (until Jan. 1993): Local Government Ordinance 70 "Building" (New South Wales) (ISSN 0727-7997)
Description: Contains the building code of Australia, and all essential information relating to building standards and regulation in New South Wales.

340   FR   ISSN 0007-411X
BULLETIN ANNOTE DES LOIS ET DECRETS. 1825. m. 380 F. Publications Paul Dupont, 38 rue Croix des Petits Champs, 75001 Paris, France. TEL 42-36-06-87. FAX 40-39-01-23.

342 613.1   CN   ISSN 1188-682X
BULLETIN DE DROIT DE L'ENVIRONNEMENT. 10/yr. Can.$145. Les Editions Yvon Blais, 430 rue St-Pierre, Ste. 200, Montreal, PQ H2Y 2M5, Canada. TEL 514-842-3937. FAX 514-842-7144. (Subscr. to: C.P. 180, Cowansville, PQ J2K 3H6, Canada. TEL 514-263-1086) Eds. Pierre B. Meunier, Andre Durocher.
  Description: Contains author's commentary, digests of recent judgements, review of status of laws and regulations, bibliographies of recent publications in the field.

340   CN   ISSN 0829-1802
BULLETIN DE DROIT IMMOBILIER. 12/yr. Can.$140. Les Editions Yvon Blais, 430 rue St-Pierre, Ste. 200, Montreal, PQ H2Y 2M5, Canada. TEL 514-842-3937. FAX 514-842-7144. (Subscr. to: C.P. 180, Cowansville, PQ J2K 3H6, Canada. TEL 514-263-1086) Ed. Lise Szmigielski. (back issues avail.)

340   FR   ISSN 0007-4519
BULLETIN DES TRANSPORTS; et de la logistique. 1895. w. 980 F. (effective 1993). Lamy S.A., 187-189 Quai de Valmy, 75490 Paris, France. TEL 1-46-27-28-90. FAX 42-29-86-81. TELEX 214 398. adv.; charts; illus.; index. circ. 7,000.
  —CCC.
  Description: Covers the law, regulation, jurisprudence, and professional news of all forms of transport.

BULLETIN FIDUCIAIRE. see *BUSINESS AND ECONOMICS — Banking And Finance*

342   BE
BULLETIN LEGISLATIF BELGE. (Includes supplement: Tables Chronologiques et Alphabetiques du Moniteur Belge) w. 9450 BEF (effective 1993). Maison Ferdinand Larcier S.A., Rue des Minimes 39, 1000 Brussels, Belgium. TEL 32-2-5124712. FAX 32-2-5139009. **Document type:** bulletin.
  Description: Reports current legal developments, legislation and other relevant texts in Belgian and European Communities law.

BULLETIN OF COMPARATIVE LABOUR RELATIONS. see *BUSINESS AND ECONOMICS — Labor And Industrial Relations*

340   XR   ISSN 0323-2719
BULLETIN OF CZECHOSLOVAK LAW. (Text in English) 1960. q. $40. Asociace Pravniku C S F R - Association of Lawyers of the Czech and Slovak Federal Republic, Nam. Curieovych 7, 116 40 Prague 1, Czech Republic. (Dist. by: Pegas Press Distributor, Artia, Ve Smeckach 30, 111 27 Prague 1, Czech Republic) **Indexed:** Geo.Abstr.

340   US   ISSN 0362-3769
KF325.188
BULLETIN OF LAW, SCIENCE & TECHNOLOGY. 1976. bi-m. membership only. American Bar Association, Science and Technology Section, 750 N. Lake Shore Dr., Chicago, IL 60611. TEL 312-988-6067. FAX 312-988-6281. Ed. Marla Hillary. bk.rev. circ. 5,400. **Indexed:** C.L.I., L.R.I. **Document type:** newsletter.
  •Also available online. Vendor(s): BRS Online Products, DIALOG Information Services, Inc., Mead Data Central, Inc., West Services, Inc.
  Description: Developments in areas of science and technology, and related legal issues and court decisions; news of section activities.

340   UK   ISSN 0007-4969
BULLETIN OF LEGAL DEVELOPMENTS; a fortnightly survey of U.K., European, foreign, commonwealth and international legal events. 1966. fortn. £95($190) (effective 1994). British Institute of International and Comparative Law, Charles Clore House, 17 Russel Sq., London WC1B 5DR, England. TEL 071-636-5802. FAX 071-323-2016. Ed.Bd. s.a.index. circ. 350. **Indexed:** Ocean.Abstr., Pollut.Abstr. **Document type:** bulletin.
  —BLDSC (2865.600000).
  Description: Provides news on legal developments all over the world.

348   US   ISSN 0146-2989
BULLETIN OF MEDIEVAL CANON LAW. NEW SERIES. (Text in English, French, German, Italian, Latin and Spanish) 1971. a. $20. Institute of Medieval Canon Law, University of California, Berkeley, Box 23651, Oakland, CA 94623-0651. TEL 415-642-5094. Ed. Kenneth Pennington. bibl. circ. 500. (back issues avail.) **Indexed:** Canon Law Abstr., CERDIC. **Document type:** bulletin.
  —BLDSC (2870.170000).

320   UK   ISSN 0260-6550
K2
BULLETIN OF NORTHERN IRELAND LAW. 1981. 10/yr. £130. S L S Legal Publications, School of Law, Queens University of Belfast, Belfast BT7 1NN, N. Ireland. TEL 0232-245133. FAX 0232-247895. TELEX 74487. Ed. Deborah J. McBride. adv. circ. 650. **Document type:** bulletin.
  •Also available online. Vendor(s): Context Ltd..

340   RH
BULLETIN OF ZIMBABWEAN LAW. 1988. 3/yr. $150 (effective 1993). Legal Resources Foundation, P.O. Box 918, Harare, Zimbabwe. TEL 263-4-790947. FAX 263-4-728213. (back issues avail.) **Document type:** bulletin.
  Description: Up-to-date references to case law and legislation in Zimbabwe.

340   FR   ISSN 0750-0416
BULLETIN OFFICIEL DE LA JUSTICE. q. 240 F. (Ministere de la Justice) Direction des Journaux Officiels, 26 rue Desaix, 75727 Paris Cedex 15, France. TEL 45-78-61-44. **Document type:** government publication.
  Description: Provides ministerial directives, instructions, notes and responses covering interpretation of law and administrative procedures.

340   CN
BULLETIN ON CURRENT RESEARCH IN SOVIET AND EAST EUROPEAN LAW. 1970. 3/yr. $9 (effective Feb. 1991). University of Toronto, Centre for Russian and East European Studies, 100 St. George St., Toronto, ON M5S 1A1, Canada. TEL 416-978-3330. Ed. Peter Solomon, Jr. adv.; bk.rev.; bibl. circ. 200. (processed; back issues avail.) **Document type:** bulletin.

BULLETIN RAPIDE DE DROIT DES AFFAIRES. see *BUSINESS AND ECONOMICS — Management*

340   BE
BULLETIN USUEL DES LOIS ET ARRETES. 1850. fortn. 20000 Fr. Etablissements Emile Bruylant, 67 rue de la Regence, B-1000 Brussels, Belgium. TEL 02-512-9845.

340 351.06   GW
BUNDESWEHRVERWALTUNG; Fachzeitschrift fuer Administration. m. DM.150. Carl Heymanns Verlag KG, Luxemburgerstr. 449, 50939 Cologne, Germany. TEL 0221-46010-0. FAX 0221-4601069. **Document type:** bulletin.

BUREAU OF VOLUNTARY COMPLIANCE NEWSLETTERS. see *PHARMACY AND PHARMACOLOGY*

340   BD
BURUNDI. MINISTERE DE LA JUSTICE. BULLETIN OFFICIEL. (Text in French) vol.10, 1971. m. Ministere de la Justice, Bujumbura, Burundi. (Subscr. to: Impr. du Gouvernement, B.P. 991, Bujumbura, Burundi)

BUSINESS ACCOUNTING FOR LAWYERS NEWSLETTER; summary, analysis, and application of current accounting concepts in the practice of law. see *BUSINESS AND ECONOMICS — Accounting*

BUSINESS FRANCHISE GUIDE. see *BUSINESS AND ECONOMICS — Small Business*

340   UK   ISSN 0263-4430
BUSY SOLICITORS' DIGEST. 1982. m. £59($90) Longman Group Ltd., Law, Tax and Finance Division, 21-27 Lamb's Conduit St., London WC1N 3NJ, England. TEL 071-242-2548. FAX 071-831-8119. Eds. S. Vaulkhard, C. Spencer. **Document type:** trade publication.
  —UMI. **CCC.**
  Description: Changes and developments in the law for solicitors.

340   UK
BUTTERWORTHS ANNOTATED LEGISLATION SERVICE. irreg. (4-5/yr.). price varies. Butterworth & Co. (Publishers) Ltd. (Subsidiary of: Reed Elsevier plc), 88 Kingsway, London WC2B 6AB, England. TEL 71-405-6900. FAX 71-405-1332. (US addr.: Butterworths Legal Publishers, 90 Stiles Rd., Salem, NH 03079-9981. TEL 603-898-9664)

340   NZ
BUTTERWORTHS ANNOTATIONS TO THE NEW ZEALAND STATUTES. 4 base vols. (plus m. update). NZ.$360. Butterworths of New Zealand Ltd., 203-207 Victoria St., P.O. Box 472, Wellington, New Zealand. TEL 04-385-1479. FAX 04-385-1598. Ed. Moira Thompson. (looseleaf format)
  Description: Full text of all amendments to New Zealand public Acts, regularly updated, plus case notes and annotations.

340   NZ   ISSN 0113-115X
BUTTERWORTHS CONVEYANCING BULLETIN. 1982. 8/yr. NZ.$176. Butterworths of New Zealand Ltd., P.O. Box 472, 203-207 Victoria St., Wellington, New Zealand. TEL 04-385-1479. FAX 04-385-1598. Ed. John Cotte. **Document type:** bulletin.
  Formerly (until 1985): New Zealand Conveyancing Bulletin (ISSN 0111-9656)
  Description: Articles and case notes dealing with significant developments in conveyancing and property transactions.

390   UK
BUTTERWORTHS COSTS SERVICE. 2 base vols. (plus updates 3/yr.). $525. Butterworth & Co. (Publishers) Ltd. (Subsidiary of: Reed Elsevier plc), 88 Kingsway, London WC2B 6AB, England. TEL 71-405-6900. FAX 71-405-1332. (US addr.: Butterworths Legal Publishers, 90 Stiles Rd., Salem, NH 03079-9981. TEL 603-898-9664) Ed. Michael J. Cook. (looseleaf format)
  Description: Reference for for practitioners advising on costs, drafting bills of costs or appearing in taxation proceedings.

340   UK
BUTTERWORTHS COUNTY COURT PRECEDENTS & PLEADINGS. 2 base vols. (plus updates 3/yr.). $370. Butterworth & Co. (Publishers) Ltd. (Subsidiary of: Reed Elsevier plc), 88 Kingsway, London WC2B 6AB, England. TEL 71-405-6900. FAX 71-405-1332. (US addr.: Butterworth Legal Publishers, 90 Stiles Rd., Salem, NH 03079-9981. TEL 800-548-4001) Eds. Louise diMambro, Peter Thompson. (looseleaf format)
  Description: Covers the areas of law within the County Court jurisdiction.

340.093   NZ   ISSN 0110-070X
LAW
BUTTERWORTHS CURRENT LAW. 24/yr. NZ.$560. Butterworths of New Zealand Ltd., P.O. Box 472, 203-207 Victorian St., Wellington, New Zealand. TEL 04-385-1479. FAX 04-385-1598. Ed. Christine O'Brien. cum.index.
  —CCC.
  Description: Covers legislative changes, and cases of significance in New Zealand.

340   NZ   ISSN 0113-714X
BUTTERWORTHS DISTRICT COURT REPORTS. 1981. 18/yr. NZ.$648. Butterworths of New Zealand Ltd., P.O. Box 472, 203-207 Victoria St., Wellington, New Zealand. TEL 04-385-1479. FAX 04-385-1598. Ed. Judge Robert Kerr.
  —CCC.
  Formerly: New Zealand District Court Reports (ISSN 0111-4239)
  Description: Reports on a large selection of District Court cases from throughout New Zealand.

340 332   UK   ISSN 0269-2694
K2
BUTTERWORTHS JOURNAL OF INTERNATIONAL BANKING AND FINANCIAL LAW. 1986. m. £365($975) Butterworth & Co. (Publishers) Ltd. (Subsidiary of: Reed Elsevier plc), 88 Kingsway, London WC2B 6AB, England. TEL 71-405-6900. FAX 71-405-1332. (US addr.: Butterworth Legal Publishers, 90 Stiles Rd., Salem, NH 03079-9981. TEL 603-898-9664) Ed. Josephine McAfee. bk.rev. (back issues avail.) **Indexed:** World Bank.Abstr.
  —BLDSC (2935.632050); SWETS. **CCC.**
  Description: Presents news, comment and briefings from international financial centers.

340   **UK**
BUTTERWORTHS LAW DIRECTORY. 1985. a. £47. Martindale-Hubbell, Butterworths Law Directories (Subsidiary of: Reed Elsevier plc), Maypole House, Maypole Rd., E. Grinstead, W. Sussex RH19 1HH. TEL 0342-330100. FAX 0342-330191. (Subscr. to: c/o Butterworths Service Co., Borough Green, Sevenoaks, Kent TN15 8PH, England. TEL 0732-884567) Ed. Y. Dolling. circ. 10,000.
Document type: directory.
    Description: Provides a comprehensive listing of over 43,000 lawyers and 11,300 firms currently in private practice in England, Wales, Scotland, Northern Ireland, the Channel Islands, and also features information on corporate lawyers and barristers. Entries provide full contact information and the type of practice each firm is engaged in.

340   **UK**
BUTTERWORTHS LAW OF FOOD & DRUGS. 6 base vols. (plus updates 3/yr. and m. Butterworths Consumer Law Bulletin). $1190. Butterworth & Co. (Publishers) Ltd. (Subsidiary of: Reed Elsevier plc), 88 Kingsway, London WC2B 6AB, England. TEL 71-405-6900. FAX 71-405-1332. (US addr.: Butterworth Legal Publishers, 90 Stiles Rd., Salem, NH 03079-9981. TEL 603-898-9664) Ed. Anthony A. Painter. (looseleaf format)
    Description: Reference on food, medicines and related law. Contains all the national statutes, regulations and Orders in fully annotated form, together with the reports and recommendations of advisory committees and summaries of the principal cases.

340   **UK**
BUTTERWORTHS LEGAL SERVICES DIRECTORY. 1987. a. £25. Martindale-Hubbell, Butterworths Law Directories (Subsidiary of: Reed Elsevier plc), Maypole House, Maypole Rd., E. Grinstead, W. Sussex RH19 1HH, England. TEL 0342-330100. FAX 0342-330191. Ed. Y. Dolling. circ. 10,000.
Document type: directory.
    Description: Provides a comprehensive listing of investigators and other firms offering legal services in the United Kingdom.

340   **SA**
BUTTERWORTHS LEGISLATION SERVICE. MONTHLY BULLETIN. (Text in English) 1958. m. (plus q. update). price varies. Butterworth Publishers (Pty.) Ltd., P.O. Box 792, Durban 4000, South Africa. TEL 27-31-294247. FAX 27-31-283255. Ed. Anne Dawson. circ. 8,000. **Document type:** bulletin.
    Formerly: Butterworths Consolidated Legislation Service of South Africa. Monthly Bulletin (ISSN 0007-7321)

340 333.33   **UK**
BUTTERWORTHS PROPERTY LAW SERVICE. base vol. (plus updates 3/yr. and bi-m. bulletin). $320. Butterworth & Co. (Publishers) Ltd. (Subsidiary of: Reed Elsevier plc), 88 Kingsway, London WC2B 6AB, England. TEL 71-405-6900. FAX 71-405-1332. (US addr.: Butterworth Legal Publishers, 90 Stiles Rd., Salem, NH 03079-9981. TEL 603-898-9664) (looseleaf format)
    Formerly: Butterworths Property Law Handbook.
    Description: Deals chronologically with each stage of a conveyance transaction.

340 388.31   **UK**
BUTTERWORTHS ROAD TRAFFIC SERVICE. (Bi-monthly supplement avail.: Butterworths Road Traffic Service Bulletin) a. (plus 3 irreg. updates). £150. Butterworth & Co. (Publishers) Ltd. (Subsidiary of: Reed Elsevier plc), 88 Kingsway, London WC2B 6AB, England. TEL 071-405-6900. FAX 071-405-1332. (U.S. addr.: Butterworth Legal Publishers, 90 Stiles Rd., Salem, NH 03079. TEL 603-898-9664) Ed. Shaun Thorpe. (looseleaf format)
    Formerly: Mahaffy and Dodson on Road Traffic.

346.066   **UK**
BUTTERWORTHS TRADING AND CONSUMER LAW. 2 base vols. (plus updates 3/yr. and m. bulletin). $390. Butterworth & Co. (Publishers) Ltd. (Subsidiary of: Reed Elsevier plc), 88 Kingsway, London WC2B 6AB, England. TEL 71-405-6900. FAX 71-405-1332. (US addr.: Butterworth Legal Publishers, 90 Stiles Rd., Salem, NH 03079-9981. TEL 603-898-9664) Eds. Deborah L. Parry, Roland Rowell. (looseleaf format)
    Formerly: O'Keefe's Law Relating to Trade Descriptions.
    Description: Designed specifically for regular use by those whose daily business it is to enforce or to advise consumer protection legislation.

340 320   **US**
BYERS ELECTION LAW. a. $80. New York Legal Publishing Corp., 6 Charles Park, Guilderland, NY 12084. TEL 800-541-2681. FAX 518-456-0828.

340 323.4   **UK**
C A B NEWS. 1972. 4/yr. free. National Association of Citizens Advice Bureaux, 115 Pentonville Rd., London N1 9LZ, England. Ed. Stella Bland. circ. 6,000. **Indexed:** Ind.Child.Mag. **Document type:** newsletter.
    Formerly: Owl.

C A C S W NEWS. (Canadian Advisory Council on the Status of Women) see WOMEN'S INTERESTS

C A L L BULLETIN. (Chicago Association of Law Libraries) see LIBRARY AND INFORMATION SCIENCES

340   **US**   **ISSN 0892-1822**
KF200
C B A RECORD. 1987. m. (10/yr.). $25 to non-members; members $10. Chicago Bar Association, 321 S. Plymouth Ct., Chicago, IL 60604-3907. TEL 312-554-2000. Ed. Paul C. Kimball. adv.; bk.rev. circ. 19,000. (also avail. in microfilm; back issues avail.; reprint service avail. from RRI) **Indexed:** C.L.I., L.R.I., Law Ofc.Info.Svc., Leg.Per.
    ●Also available online. Vendor(s): West Services, Inc.
    —UnCover; UMI.
    Formerly (until 1987): Chicago Bar Record (ISSN 0009-3505)

C C A NEWS. (Consumer Credit Association) see BUSINESS AND ECONOMICS — Banking And Finance

340   **US**
▼**C C R NEWS.** 1992. q. Center for Constitutional Rights, 666 Broadway, 12th Fl., New York, NY 10012. TEL 212-614-6422. FAX 212-614-6499.

C E D E J EGYPTE - MONDE ARABE; droit, economie, societe. (Centre d'Etudes et de Documentation Economique, Juridique et Sociale) see POLITICAL SCIENCE

346.013   **PY**   **ISSN 1017-2785**
C E D H U. 1988. bi-m. $12. Centro de Estudios Humanitarios, Azara 3267, Asuncion, Paraguay. (Dist. by: D.I.P.P., Box 2507, Asuncion, Paraguay) Ed. Esther Prieto. circ. 500.

C E I UPDATE. (Competitive Enterprise Institute) see BUSINESS AND ECONOMICS

C G L REPORTER; the insurance coverage litigation handbook. (Comprehensive - General Liability) see INSURANCE

C H I L D NEWSLETTER. (Children's Healthcare Is a Legal Duty) see CHILDREN AND YOUTH — About

C L C LEGAL INFORMATION REVIEW. (Convention Liaison Council) see MEETINGS AND CONGRESSES

C L E A R EXAM REVIEW. (Council on Licensure, Enforcement & Regulation) see PUBLIC HEALTH AND SAFETY

340 378   **US**
KF275
C L E JOURNAL AND REGISTER. 1965. 6/yr. $75. American Law Institute - American Bar Association, Committee on Continuing Professional Education, 4025 Chestnut St., Philadelphia, PA 19104. TEL 215-243-1604. FAX 215-243-1664. Ed. Mark T. Carroll. circ. 480. **Document type:** trade publication.
    Former titles (until 1987): C L E Register (ISSN 0193-693X); (until 1979): C L E Catalog of Continuing Legal Education Programs in the United States.
    Description: Catalogue of continuing legal education courses for lawyers and articles on continuing legal education.

340   **US**
C L E T V. (Continuing Legal Education) (In 4 series: Law Practice Management, Estate and Financial Planning, Business Law, Civil Trial Practice) 1988. 4/yr. $295 for each series. American Law Institute - American Bar Association, Committee on Continuing Professional Education, 4025 Chestnut St., Philadelphia, PA 19104. TEL 215-243-1617. FAX 215-243-1664. Ed. Eileen Kenney. (video cassette) **Document type:** trade publication.
    Description: Video programs of practical interest.

340   **US**   **ISSN 1051-7030**
C L S NEWSLETTER ON THE CONFERENCE ON CRITICAL LEGAL STUDIES. Key Title: C L S. 1975. a. $35. Conference on Critical Legal Studies, c/o Prof. Gary Peller, Ed., Georgetown University Law Center, 600 New Jersey Ave., N.W., Washington, DC 20001. TEL 202-662-9000. FAX 202-662-9444. circ. 600. **Document type:** newsletter.

340 200   **US**   **ISSN 0736-0142**
KF200
C L S QUARTERLY. 1980. 4/yr. $20. Christian Legal Society, 4208 Evergreen Lane, Ste. 222, Annandale, VA 22003. TEL 703-642-1070. FAX 703-642-1075. Ed. Karen Heal. adv.; bk.rev. circ. 6,000. (also avail. in microform from UMI; back issues avail.; reprint service avail. from WSH) **Indexed:** C.L.I., L.R.I., Leg.Per. **Document type:** trade publication.
    —UnCover; UMI.
    Formerly (until 1981): Christian Legal Society Quarterly (ISSN 0275-6765); Which was formed by the merger of: Christian Legal Society Newsletter; Christian Lawyer.
    Description: Platform for views held by Christian attorneys, judges, law students and law professors.

C M A COMMUNICATOR. (Colorado Mining Association) see MINES AND MINING INDUSTRY

340 320 350   **US**   **ISSN 1059-6224**
KF4568.A15
C O G E L GUARDIAN. Key Title: Guardian (Lexington). 1980. bi-m. $60 to non-members; members $25. Council on Governmental Ethics Laws, Iron Works Pike, Box 11910, Lexington, KY 40578. TEL 606-231-1909. FAX 606-231-1858. Ed. Joyce Bullock. bk.rev.; abstr.; bibl.; stat. circ. 400.
Document type: newsletter.
    Formerly: C O G E L Newsletter.
    Description: Reports on campaign finance, conflict of interest and lobbying issues, legislation and litigation.

340 657   **US**   **ISSN 1047-5818**
C P A LITIGATION SERVICE COUNSELOR.* 1989. m. $196. C P A Services Inc., 1250 6th Ave., San Diego, CA 92101-4312. TEL 414-797-9999. FAX 414-782-7997. Ed. Corrine Anshus. bk.rev.; index. (looseleaf format; back issues avail.) **Document type:** newsletter.

C R I V SHEET. (Committee on Relations with Information Vendors) see LIBRARY AND INFORMATION SCIENCES

C S B S EXAMINER. (Conference of State Bank Supervisors) see BUSINESS AND ECONOMICS — Banking And Finance

340 350   **US**
C S I CONGRESSIONAL RECORD REPORT. d. (following session of Congress). price varies. (Capitol Services, Inc.) National Standards Association, 1200 Quince Orchard Blvd., Gaithersburg, MD 20878. Ed. Lisa Joy.

LAW

340 350   US
C S I FEDERAL REGISTER. d. price varies. (Capitol Services, Inc.) National Standards Association, 1200 Quince Orchard Blvd., Gaithersburg, MD 20878. Ed. Gregory Friedman.

C S P NEWSLETTER. (Contemporary Social Problems Special Interest Section) see LIBRARY AND INFORMATION SCIENCES

C T F A STRAIGHT TALK. (Committee for Truth in Farmland Assessment) see CONSERVATION

347.91   US   ISSN 0889-7751
KFC1025.A15
C T L A FORUM. 1979. 10/yr. $50 (avail. to law libraries only). California Trial Lawyers Association, 980 Ninth St., Ste. 200, Sacramento, CA 95814-2721. TEL 916-442-6902. Ed. Sharon E. Scott. adv. circ. 6,200. **Document type:** trade publication.
    Formerly: California Trial Lawyers Forum; Supersedes: California Trial Lawyers Association. Journal (ISSN 0730-4919); California Trial Lawyers Journal (ISSN 0575-6315)

340   US   ISSN 8750-944X
C Y L A QUARTERLY. 1984. q. membership. State Bar of California, Young Lawyers Association, 555 Franklin St., San Francisco, CA 94102. TEL 415-561-8219. FAX 415-561-8228. **Document type:** newsletter.

340 384.55   US
KF2844.A15
CABLE T V AND NEW MEDIA LAW & FINANCE. 1983. m. $195 (effective Sep. 1991). Leader Publications, Inc. (Subsidiary of: New York Law Publishing Co.), 111 Eighth Ave., Ste. 900, New York, NY 10011. TEL 800-888-8300. FAX 212-463-5523. Eds. Michael Botein, David M. Rice. bk.rev.
    Formerly: Cable T V Law and Finance (ISSN 0736-489X)
    Description: Interprets and analyzes the latest developments in cable and video.

CABLE T V LAW REPORTER. see COMMUNICATIONS — Television And Cable

CABLE T V PROGRAMMING; newsletter on programs for pay cable T V and analysis of basic cable networks. see COMMUNICATIONS — Television And Cable

340   BL
CADERNO DE DIREITO ECONOMICO. 1983. irreg. $15. Centro de Extensao Universitaria, R. Maestro Cardim 370, 01323-000 Sao Paulo SP, Brazil. TEL 011-251-5377. FAX 011-285-5373. circ. 1,000. **Document type:** academic/scholarly publication, monographic series.
    Description: Debates objective questions on an economic law doctrine theme.

340   BL
CADERNO DE DIREITO NATURAL. 1985. irreg. $10. Centro de Estudos de Extensao Universitaria, Rua Maestro Cardim 370, 01323-000 Sao Paulo, SP, Brazil. TEL 011-251-5373. FAX 011-285-5373. circ. 1,000. **Document type:** academic/scholarly publication, monographic series.
    Description: Discusses several views of a specific theme in natural law.

340   BL
CADERNO DE PESQUISAS TRIBUTARIAS. 1976. a. $45. Centro de Extensao Universitaria, Rua Maestro Cardim 370, 01323-000 Sao Paulo SP, Brazil. TEL 011-251-5377. FAX 011-285-5373. circ. 5,000. **Document type:** academic/scholarly publication, monographic series.
    Description: Debates objective questions on a theme of tributary law doctrine.

340   MG
CAHIERS D'HISTOIRE JURIDIQUE ET POLITIQUE. 1966. s-a. Universite de Madagascar, Etablissement d'Enseignement Superieur de Droit, d'Economie, de Gestion et de Sociologie, B.P. 905, Antananarivo, Malagasy Republic.
    Formerly (until no.10, 1974): Universite de Madagascar. Centre d'Etudes des Coutumes. Cahiers (ISSN 0496-8018)

340   CN   ISSN 0007-974X
LAW
CAHIERS DE DROIT. (Text in English and French) vol.1, 1954. q. Can.$42.80 to individuals; institutions Can.$53.50. (Universite Laval) Wilson et Lafleur Ltee., C.P. 24, Place d'Armes, Montreal, Que. H2Y 3L2, Canada. Ed. Pierre Verge. adv.; bk.rev.; bibl.; index, cum.index. circ. 1,200. (also avail. in microform from BNQ,UMI,MML; reprint service avail. from UMI,WSH) **Indexed:** C.L.I., Ind.Can.L.P.L., L.R.I., Leg.Per., Mar.Aff.Bibl., Pt.de Rep. (1982-). —BLDSC (2948.853000); UnCover; UMI.

340   FR
CAHIERS DE L'EXPERTISE JUDICIARE. 4/yr. 162 av. Lacassagne, 69003 Lyon, France. TEL 72-33-40-40. Ed. M. Dirand. circ. 2,500.

CAHIERS DE L'UNIVERSITE DE PERPIGNAN. see LITERATURE

340   CN   ISSN 0840-7266
CAHIERS DE PROPRIETE INTELLECTUELLE. 3/yr. Can.$75. Les Editions Yvon Blais, 430 rue St-Pierre, Ste. 200, Montreal, PQ H2Y 2M5, Canada. TEL 514-842-3937. FAX 514-842-7144. (Subscr. to: C.P. 180, Cowansville, PQ J2K 3H6, Canada. TEL 514-263-1086) **Indexed:** Ind.Can.L.P.L.
    Description: Covers legislative and jurisprudencial developments in intellectual property law.

CAHIERS DU TOURISME. SERIE E: LEGISLATION. see TRAVEL AND TOURISM

340   FR   ISSN 0981-1761
CAHIERS TERRITOIRES. 1983. 2/yr. 350 F. Association Territoires, 31, rue de la Cerisaie, 75004 Paris, France. TEL 4274-7461.
    Formerly: Territoires (ISSN 0761-7143)

CAISSES CENTRALES DE MUTUALITE SOCIALE AGRICOLE. STATISTIQUES. see BUSINESS AND ECONOMICS — Abstracting, Bibliographies, Statistics

340   II   ISSN 0045-3854
CALCUTTA WEEKLY NOTES; a journal of law notes of the Calcutta high court. (Text in English) 1896. w. Rs.55($16) Weekly Notes Printing Works, Pvt. Ltd., 34 Ballygunge Circular Rd., Calcutta 700019, India. Ed. Ranadeb Chaudhuri. adv.; bibl.
    Description: Law notes and reports of Calcutta High Court.

CALENDARS OF THE UNITED STATES HOUSE OF REPRESENTATIVES AND HISTORY OF LEGISLATION. see MEETINGS AND CONGRESSES

340   US
CALIFORNIA. LAW REVISION COMMISSION. REPORTS, RECOMMENDATIONS AND STUDIES. 1955. irreg., vol.22, 1992. pamphlets (price varies); bound vols. $50. Law Revision Commission, 4000 Middlefield Rd., Ste. D-2, Palo Alto, CA 94303-4739. TEL 415-494-1335. index. circ. 300. **Document type:** government publication.
    Description: Includes its Annual Reports, Recommendations and Studies issues as pamphlets, bound every two years.

CALIFORNIA. STATE BOARD OF BARBERING AND COSMETOLOGY. RULES AND REGULATIONS. see BEAUTY CULTURE

346.066   US
CALIFORNIA ADMINISTRATIVE AND ANTITRUST LAW; regulation of business, trades and professions. 1991. 2 base vols. (plus supplement). $160. Butterworth Legal Publishers (Salem) (Subsidiary of: Reed Elsevier plc), 8 Industrial Way, Bldg. C, Salem, NH 03079. TEL 800-548-4001. FAX 603-898-9858. Eds. Robert C. Fellmeth, Ralph H. Folsom. (looseleaf format)

340   US
CALIFORNIA AND NEVADA LEGAL SERVICES PROGRAMS DIRECTORY. 1974. a. $2.50. Western Center on Law and Poverty, Inc., 3701 Wilshire Blvd., Ste. 208, Los Angeles, CA 90010-2809. TEL 213-487-7211. circ. 120.

CALIFORNIA CABLLETTER; current community perspectives and directions. see COMMUNICATIONS

CALIFORNIA CLOSELY HELD CORPORATIONS: TAX PLANNING AND PRACTICE GUIDE. see BUSINESS AND ECONOMICS — Public Finance, Taxation

340 331   US
CALIFORNIA COMPENSATION CASES. a. (plus m. supplements). $215. Matthew Bender & Co., Inc., 11 Penn Plaza, New York, NY 10001. TEL 212-967-7707. Ed. W.H. Ryan.
    Description: Covers all en banc and selected panel decisions of Workers' Compensation Appeals Board. Includes digests of significant Appeals Board decisions denied judicial review and digests of related state and federal court opinions.

340 690   US
CALIFORNIA CONSTRUCTION LAW MANUAL, 3-E. 1990. base vol. (plus a. supplement). $95. Shepard's - McGraw-Hill, Inc., Box 35300, Colorado Springs, CO 80935-3530. TEL 800-525-2474.
    Description: For construction executives, architects, engineers and lawyers who work in California.

CALIFORNIA CONSTRUCTION LAW REPORTER. see BUILDING AND CONSTRUCTION

340 331   US   ISSN 1049-9334
CALIFORNIA EMPLOYMENT LAW LETTER. 1990. m. $95. (O'Melveny & Myers) M. Lee Smith Publishers & Printers, 162 Fourth Ave. N., Box 198867, Nashville, TN 37219-8867. TEL 615-242-7395; 800-274-6674. FAX 615-256-6601. Ed.Bd. **Document type:** newsletter.
    Description: Reports the latest California employment law developments that affect California employers.

CALIFORNIA ENVIRONMENTAL LAW AND REGULATION REPORTER. see ENVIRONMENTAL STUDIES

CALIFORNIA ENVIRONMENTAL LAW REPORTER. see ENVIRONMENTAL STUDIES

340 658.3   US
KFC570.A15C35
CALIFORNIA - FEDERAL PERSONNEL LAW UPDATE. 1985. m. $119. Council on Education in Management, 325 Lennon Ln., Walnut Creek, CA 94598. TEL 510-944-9444. FAX 510-944-0617. Ed. Julie Furer. circ. 2,500. (back issues avail.) **Document type:** newsletter.

347.91   US
CALIFORNIA FORMS OF JURY INSTRUCTION. 1985. 3 base vols. (plus irreg. supplements). $650. Matthew Bender & Co., Inc., 11 Penn Plaza, New York, NY 10001. TEL 212-967-7707. (looseleaf format)
    Description: Comprehensive source for jury instructions in contract, business tort and real property cases. Enables litigators to draft instructions that accurately reflect the law and are comprehensible to the average juror.

340 368   US
CALIFORNIA INSURANCE LAW AND PRACTICE. 1986. 4 base vols. (plus irreg. supplements). $645. Matthew Bender & Co., Inc., 11 Penn Plaza, New York, NY 10001. TEL 212-967-7707. Ed.Bd. (looseleaf format)
    Description: Provides detailed coverage of life, health and disability insurance, property and liability insurance, agents and brokers, and carriers. Examines common insurance law problems and considerations, with an analysis of California statutes, case law, regulations, and other administrative material.

340 331.8   US
CALIFORNIA LABOR & EMPLOYMENT LAW QUARTERLY. 1983. q. $30. State Bar of California, Labor & Employment Law Section, 555 Franklin St., San Francisco, CA 94102. TEL 415-561-8890. Ed. Ann S. Masters. adv.; bk.rev. circ. 3,600. (looseleaf format; back issues avail.) **Document type:** newsletter.
    Description: Covers current California labor law developments; includes articles written by labor law specialists.

340 331   US
CALIFORNIA LAW OF EMPLOYEE INJURIES AND WORKMEN'S COMPENSATION. 1953. 4 base vols. (plus irreg. supplements). $475. Matthew Bender & Co., Inc., 11 Penn Plaza, New York, NY 10001. TEL 212-967-7707. Ed.Bd. (looseleaf format)
    Description: Covers every stage of workers' compensation cases in California and all related proceedings. Includes principles of substantive law (California workers' compensation liability and federal and state law of employee injuries).

340   US   ISSN 0008-1221
K3   CODEN: CLARDJ
CALIFORNIA LAW REVIEW. 1912. 6/yr. $38 (effective 1994). (University of California at Berkeley, Boalt Hall School of Law) University of California Press, Journals Division, 2120 Berkeley Way, Berkeley, CA 94720. TEL 510-643-7154. FAX 510-642-9917. Ed.Bd. adv.; bk.rev.; bibl.; index. circ. 1,700. (also avail. in microfiche from RRI; microfilm from RRI; microform from UMI; back issues avail.; reprint service avail. from RRI) Indexed: A.B.C.Pol.Sci., ABI Inform, C.L.I., Commun.Abstr., Crim.Just.Abstr., Curr.Cont., L.R.I., Leg.Cont., Leg.Per., P.A.I.S., SSCI. Document type: academic/scholarly publication.
—BLDSC (3015.020000); Faxon; UnCover; SWETS; UMI. CCC.
  Description: Contains articles on problems and developments in all areas of the law.
  Refereed Serial

340   US   ISSN 0279-4063
KF200
CALIFORNIA LAWYER. 1928. m. $24. Daily Journal Corporation (San Francisco), 1390 Market St., Ste. 1016, San Francisco, CA 94102. TEL 415-558-9888. FAX 415-558-8469. Ed. Ray Reynolds. adv.; bk.rev.; bibl.; illus. circ. 120,00. (also avail. in microform from UMI,WSH,PMC; reprint service avail. from UMI,WSH) Indexed: C.L.I., Cal.Per.Ind. (1984-), L.R.I., Law Ofc.Info.Svc., Leg.Per., So.Pac.Per.Ind.
—BLDSC (3015.022000); Faxon; UnCover; UMI.
  Former titles (until 1981): California State Bar Journal (ISSN 0161-9241); State Bar of California. Journal (ISSN 0039-002X)
  Description: Discusses legal affairs, with news, analysis and practical advice on products and services.

CALIFORNIA LEAGUE OF SAVINGS INSTITUTIONS. REGULATORY CHECKLIST. see *BUSINESS AND ECONOMICS — Banking And Finance*

340   US
CALIFORNIA LITIGATION NEWS. 3/yr. $35 or membership. State Bar of California, Litigation Section, 555 Franklin St., San Francisco, CA 94102. TEL 415-561-8341. FAX 415-561-8228. Document type: newsletter.

340   US
CALIFORNIA NOTARY LAW PRIMER. a. $9.95. National Notary Association, 8236 Remmet Ave., Box 7184, Canoga Park, CA 91309-7184. TEL 818-713-4000. FAX 818-713-9061. Ed. Charles N. Faerber. (reprint service avail. from UMI) Document type: monographic series.

340   US
CALIFORNIA OFFICIAL REPORTS; official advance sheets of the Supreme Court, Courts of Appeal, and Appellate Departments of the Superior Court. 1850. 35/yr. $416.44. Bancroft-Whitney Company, Box 7005, San Francisco, CA 94120-7005. TEL 415-986-4410. Ed. Jay Nicolaisen. circ. 7,560.

340   US   ISSN 1040-2640
KF320.L4
CALIFORNIA PARALEGAL MAGAZINE. 1989. q. $22. California Paralegal Magazine, Box 6960, Los Osos, CA 93412. TEL 805-526-8705. Ed. Valerie Goodman-Plater. adv.; bk.rev. circ. 2,000.
  Description: Forum for paralegal networking. Contains updates on continuing education seminars and reports on paralegal literature.

340   US
CALIFORNIA POINTS AND AUTHORITIES. 1965. 24 base vols. (plus irreg. supplements). $2245. Matthew Bender & Co., Inc., 11 Penn Plaza, New York, NY 10001. TEL 212-967-7707. Ed.Bd. (looseleaf format)
  Description: Provides the necessary statutory and case law required in law and motion picture proceedings.

340 640.73   US
CALIFORNIA PRODUCTS LIABILITY ACTIONS. 1970. base vol. with supplements. $140. Matthew Bender & Co., Inc., 11 Penn Plaza, New York, NY 10001. TEL 212-967-7707. Ed.Bd. (looseleaf format)
  Description: Covers every aspect of California products liability law for both plaintiff and defendant: investigation, role of experts, pleadings, discovery, proof, defenses, damages and trials.

340 350   US
CALIFORNIA PUBLIC AGENCY PRACTICE. 1988. 3 base vols. (plus irreg. supplements). $390. Matthew Bender & Co., Inc., 11 Penn Plaza, New York, NY 10001. TEL 212-967-7707. Ed. Gregory L. Ogden. (looseleaf format)
  Description: Covers both the theoretical and practical aspects of administrative law practice in California.

340   US   ISSN 0739-7860
KFC430.A15
CALIFORNIA REGULATORY LAW REPORTER. 1981. q. $45. University of San Diego, School of Law, Center for Public Interest Law, 5998 Alcala Park, San Diego, CA 92110. TEL 619-260-4806. FAX 619-260-4753. Ed. Robert C. Fellmeth. index. circ. 1,000. (back issues avail.) Document type: newsletter.
—UnCover.
  Description: Provides information on 60 California administrative agencies that regulate business, trades and professions. Includes pending litigation and legislation, feature articles and commentaries.

CALIFORNIA SCHOOL LAW DIGEST. see *EDUCATION — School Organization And Administration*

CALIFORNIA TAX LAWYER. see *BUSINESS AND ECONOMICS — Public Finance, Taxation*

340   US   ISSN 0744-6756
CALIFORNIA TORT REPORTER. 1980. 10/yr. $290. Shepard's - McGraw-Hill, Inc., Box 35300, Colorado Spring, CO 80935-3530. TEL 719-475-7230. FAX 800-525-0053. Ed.Bd. (looseleaf format; back issues avail.) Document type: newsletter.

340 380   US
CALIFORNIA VEHICLE CODE. 1988. a. $15.95. Gould Publications, 1333 N. U.S. Hwy. 17-92, Longwood, FL 32750-3724. TEL 407-695-9500. FAX 407-695-2906. adv.; bk.rev. (looseleaf format)
  Description: Contains the motor vehicle laws of the state. Includes an addenda of pertinents related statutes and a comprehensive index.

340   US   ISSN 1053-4938
CALIFORNIA WATER LAW & POLICY REPORTER. 1990. m. $270. Shepard's - McGraw-Hill, Inc., 555 Middle Creek Pkwy., Colorado Springs, CO 80935-3530. TEL 719-488-3000. FAX 800-525-0053. Ed. Rafael Bernardino. index. (looseleaf format) Document type: newsletter.

340   US   ISSN 0008-1639
LAW
CALIFORNIA WESTERN LAW REVIEW. 1965. 2/yr. $20 (foreign $25). California Western School of Law, 350 Cedar St., San Diego, CA 92101. TEL 619-239-0391. FAX 619-696-9999. adv.; bk.rev. circ. 1,000. (also avail. in microfilm from RRI; reprint service avail. from RRI) Indexed: C.L.I., L.R.I., Leg.Cont., Leg.Per., P.A.I.S.
—BLDSC (3015.360000); Faxon; UnCover.

340 331   US   ISSN 0363-129X
KFC592.A15
CALIFORNIA WORKERS' COMPENSATION REPORTER. 1973. m. $260 (effective June 1993). California Workers' Compensation Reporter, Box 975, Berkeley, CA 94701. TEL 510-444-2454. Ed. Melvin S. Witt. bk.rev.; cum.index. circ. 1,350. (back issues avail.) Document type: newsletter.
  Description: News articles and briefs on legislative, policy, and judicial developments pertaining to the state law.

340   UK   ISSN 0084-8328
K3
CAMBRIAN LAW REVIEW. 1970. a. $20. University College of Wales, Aberystwyth, Department of Law, Aberystwyth, Wales. TEL 0970-62271. FAX 0970-622729. adv.; bk.rev.; illus. circ. 700. (also avail. in microfilm from WSH,PMC) Indexed: Abstr.Bk.Rev.Curr.Leg.Per., C.L.I., L.R.I., Leg.Per. Document type: academic/scholarly publication.
—BLDSC (3015.935000); Faxon; UnCover; UMI.

340   UK   ISSN 0008-1973
LAW
CAMBRIDGE LAW JOURNAL. 1921. 3/yr. £37($80) to institutions (overseas £50). (Cambridge University, Law Faculty) Cambridge University Press, Edinburgh Bldg., Shaftesbury Rd., Cambridge CB2 2RU, England. TEL 0223-312393. FAX 0223-315052. TELEX 851817256. (N. American addr.: Cambridge University Press, Journals Dept., 40 W. 20th St., New York, NY 10011. TEL 212-924-3900. FAX 212-691-3239) (Co-sponsors: Society of Public Teachers of Law; Association of Law Teachers) Ed. C.C. Turpin. adv.; bk.rev.; index. circ. 1,600. (also avail. in microform from UMI; back issues avail.) Indexed: Abstr.Bk.Rev.Curr.Leg.Per., BPIA, Br.Hum.Ind., Bus.Ind., C.L.I., ELLIS, L.R.I., Leg.Per., Soc.Work Res.& Abstr. Document type: academic/scholarly publication.
—BLDSC (3015.960000); Faxon; UnCover; SWETS; UMI.
  Description: Contains articles on issues such as tort, constitutional law, legal history, and criminal law, with emphasis on current developments.

340 341   UK   ISSN 0068-6751
CAMBRIDGE STUDIES IN INTERNATIONAL AND COMPARATIVE LAW. 1967; N.S. 1982. irreg. price varies. Cambridge University Press, Edinburgh Bldg., Shaftesbury Rd., Cambridge CB2 2RU, England. TEL 0223-312393. FAX 0223-315052. TELEX 851817256. (N. American addr.: Cambridge University Press, Journals Dept., 40 W. 20th St., New York, NY 10011. TEL 212-924-3900. FAX 212-691-3239) Document type: monographic series.

340   AT   ISSN 0729-2570
CAMERON: SUPREME AND DISTRICT COURTS PRACTICE N.S.W. 1982. 6/yr. in 3 vols. Aus.$425 with updates. Law Book Co. Ltd., 44-50 Waterloo Rd., N. Ryde, N.S.W. 2113, Australia. TEL 02-887-0177. FAX 02-888-9706. TELEX ASBOOK 27995. Ed. J. Lemaine. (looseleaf format; back issues avail.)
  Description: Covers courts, jurisdiction, offices, judgement and enforcement, admiralty rules.

340   US   ISSN 0198-8174
K3
CAMPBELL LAW REVIEW. 1979. 3/yr. $15. Campbell University, Box 1165, Buies Creek, NC 27506. TEL 919-893-4111. Ed. Donald Higley. adv.; bk.rev.; cum.index. circ. 1,000. (back issues avail.) Indexed: C.L.I., Leg.Per.
●Also available online. Vendor(s): West Services, Inc.
—Faxon; UnCover.

340   US   ISSN 0742-8987
CAMPBELL'S LIST; a directory of selected lawyers. 1879. a. (plus supplement). $10. Campbell's List, Inc., Campbell Bldg., 100 E. Ventris Ave., Maitland, FL 32751. TEL 407-644-8298. FAX 407-740-6494. Ed. John A. Campbell, Jr. circ. 10,000 (controlled).

CANADA. LABOUR CANADA. WOMEN'S BUREAU. WOMEN IN THE LABOUR FORCE. see *BUSINESS AND ECONOMICS — Labor And Industrial Relations*

340   CN   ISSN 0045-4192
CANADA GAZETTE: PART 1: GOVERNMENT, DIVORCE, BANKRUPTCY NOTICES, ETC. (Catalog no. SP2-1) (Text in English, French) w. Can.$135($162) Canada Communication Group, Publishing Division, Ottawa, Ont. K1A 0S9, Canada. TEL 819-997-2560. (also avail. in microfilm from MIM,UMI,BHP,KTO)

340   CN
CANADA GAZETTE: PART 2: STATUTORY INSTRUMENTS. (Catalog SP2-2) (Text in English, French) s-m. Can.$67.50($79.80) Canada Communication Group, Publishing Division, Ottawa, Ont. K1A 0S9, Canada. TEL 819-997-2560. (also avail. in microform from MIM,UMI)
  Formerly: Canada Gazette: Part 2: Statutory Orders and Regulations (ISSN 0045-4206)

CANADA LABOUR ARBITRATION. see *BUSINESS AND ECONOMICS — Labor And Industrial Relations*

CANADA LABOUR RELATIONS BOARD; an annotated guide. see *BUSINESS AND ECONOMICS — Labor And Industrial Relations*

LAW

340   CN
CANADA LEGAL DIRECTORY (YEAR)/ANNUAIRE JUDICIAIRE CANADIEN (YEAR). 1911. a. Can.$95. Carswell, One Corporate Plaza, 2075 Kennedy Rd., Scarborough, ON M1T 3V4, Canada. TEL 416-609-8000. FAX 416-298-5094. adv. contact: M. Lalani. circ. 3,000. (back issues avail.)
   Description: Includes alphabetical listing of law firms by province and city with addresses and phone numbers, separate finding list of individual lawyers, a listing of corporate "in-house" counsel, fax numbers and a comprehensive listing within each province of courts, officials, judicial districts, law societies.

340   CN
CANADA PENSION PLAN, OLD AGE SECURITY ACT AND PENSION BENEFITS STANDARDS ACT. irreg., 10th ed., 1993. Can.$24.95. C C H Canadian Ltd., 6 Garamond Ct., North York, ON M3C 1Z5, Canada. TEL 416-441-2992. FAX 416-444-9011.
   Formerly: Canada Pension and Old Age Security Legislation.

340   CN
CANADA STATUTE CITATOR. irreg. (4-5/yr.). Can.$183. Canada Law Book Inc., 240 Edward St., Aurora, ON L4G 3S9, Canada. TEL 905-841-6472. FAX 905-841-5085. (also avail. in looseleaf format)

340 336   CN
CANADA'S TAX TREATIES. s-a. Can.$365. Butterworths Canada Ltd., Part of the Reed Elsevier group, 75 Clegg Rd., Markham, ON L6G 1A1, Canada. TEL 905-479-2665. FAX 905-479-2826. (looseleaf format)
   Description: Reference guide for tax practitioners and companies involved in cross-border transactions.

340   CN   ISSN 0318-4935
CANADIAN BAR ASSOCIATION. ANNUAL REPORT OF PROCEEDINGS. a. Can.$45. Canadian Bar Foundation, 50 O'Connor, Suite 902, Ottawa, Ont. K1P 6L2, Canada. TEL 613-237-2925. FAX 613-237-0185.
   Description: Transcript of proceedings of Canadian Bar Association's annual meeting.

340   CN   ISSN 0384-5753
CANADIAN BAR ASSOCIATION. BRITISH COLUMBIA BRANCH. PROGRAM REPORT.* 1971. irreg. Canadian Bar Association, British Columbia Branch, 50 O'Connor St., Ottawa, Ont. K1P 6L2, Canada.
   Indexed: Ind.Can.L.P.L.

340   CN   ISSN 0008-3003
CANADIAN BAR REVIEW. 1923. q. Can.$100. Canadian Bar Foundation, 50 O'Connor, Ste. 902, Ottawa, Ont. K1P 6L2, Canada. TEL 613-237-2925. FAX 613-237-0185. Ed. A.J. MacClean. adv.; bk.rev.; index, cum.index. circ. 35,000. (also avail. in microfilm from WSH,PMC) **Indexed:** Amer.Bibl.Slavic & E.Eur.Stud., C.L.I., Crim.Just.Abstr., Ind.Can.L.P.L., L.R.I., Leg.Per., Refug.Abstr., Risk Abstr., SSCI, Tr.& Indus.Ind.
   —UnCover.

340
KE173
CANADIAN CASE CITATIONS. 20/yr. Can.$555 includes Canadian Current Law. Carswell, One Corporate Plaza, 2075 Kennedy Rd., Scarborough, ON M1T 3V4, Canada. TEL 416-609-8000. FAX 416-298-5094.
   Formerly: Canadian Citations (ISSN 0835-9776); Supersedes in part: Canadian Current Law and Canadian Citations.

340 658.3   CN
CANADIAN CASES ON EMPLOYMENT LAW. 1983. 5 vols./yr. Can.$118. Carswell, One Corporate Plaza, 2075 Kennedy Rd., Scarborough, ON M1T 3V4, Canada. TEL 416-609-8000. FAX 416-298-5094. Ed. David Harris. adv. contact: M. Lalani. **Indexed:** Ind.Can.L.P.L.
   Former titles: Canadian Cases on Employment Law Reports (ISSN 0824-2607); Employment Law Reports.
   Description: Features all important decisions in employment law, outside the collective bargaining process, from all Canadian jurisdictions. Includes wrongful dismissal, dismissal for cause, constructive dismissal, demotion, employment contracts and standards, mandatory retirement policies, wages and remuneration, pensions and profit sharing.

340 368   CN   ISSN 0824-2585
CANADIAN CASES ON THE LAW OF INSURANCE (2ND SERIES). 1983. 6/yr. Can.$118. Carswell, One Corporate Plaza, 2075 Kennedy Rd., Scarborough, ON M1T 3V4, Canada. TEL 416-609-8000. FAX 416-298-5094. Eds. Marvin G. Baer, James A. Rendall. adv. contact: M. Lalani. **Indexed:** Ind.Can.L.P.L.
   Description: Includes cases on interpretation of insurance contracts and insurance legislation; common insurance principals; insurable interest; insured's duty of disclosure; indemnity and subrogation; liability of agents, brokers and adjusters, annotations and case comments.

340   CN   ISSN 0701-1733
KE1232.A45
CANADIAN CASES ON THE LAW OF TORTS (2ND SERIES). 1976. 4/yr. Can.$120. Carswell, One Corporate Plaza, 2075 Kennedy Rd., Scarborough, ON M1T 3V4, Canada. TEL 416-609-8000. FAX 416-298-5094. Ed. John Irvine. adv. contact: M. Lalani. **Indexed:** C.L.I., Ind.Can.L.P.L., L.R.I.
   Description: Features all important decisions in tort law from Canadian jurisdictions selected by experts in the field. Includes cases on negligence principles, medical malpractice, professional negligence, personal injury contributory negligence, personal injury, contributory negligence, defamation, economic torts, products liability.

340   CN
CANADIAN CHARTER OF RIGHTS ANNOTATED. 9/yr. Can.$199. Canada Law Book Inc., 240 Edward St., Aurora, ON L4G 3S9, Canada. TEL 905-841-6472. FAX 905-841-5085. (looseleaf format)

342   CN   ISSN 0821-719X
CANADIAN CHARTER OF RIGHTS DECISIONS. 1982. fortn. Can.$400. Western Legal Publications, 301-1 Alexander St., Vancouver, BC V6A 1B2, Canada. TEL 604-687-5671. FAX 604-687-2796. index. (back issues avail.)
   Description: Information on all available decisions pertaining to the Canadian Charter of Rights and Freedoms and the Canadian Bill of Rights.

CANADIAN COMMERCIAL REAL ESTATE MANUAL. see *REAL ESTATE*

340   CN
CANADIAN COMPETITION LAW. q. Can.$345. Carswell, One Corporate Plaza, 2075 Kennedy Rd., Scarborough, ON M1T 3V4, Canada. TEL 416-609-8000. FAX 416-298-5094. (looseleaf format)
   Description: Offers complete coverage of all areas of business governed by the Competition Act including pricing practices, granting disproportionate advertising or display allowances, price maintenance, criminal offences, misleading advertising, agreements in restraint of trade, civil matter, foreign laws and directives.

340   CN
CANADIAN COMPETITION RECORD. 1980. q. Can.$250 to individuals; institutions Can.$125. Fraser & Beatty Legal Publications Inc., 180 Elgin St., Ste. 1201, Ottawa, ON K2P 2K7, Canada. TEL 613-235-0690. FAX 613-563-7800. Ed. Randal T. Hughes. bk.rev. circ. 280. (back issues avail.) **Indexed:** Can.Per.Ind., Ind.Can.L.P.L. **Document type:** academic/scholarly publication.
   Formerly: Canadian Competition Policy Record (ISSN 0228-1961)

CANADIAN CORPORATE SECRETARY'S GUIDE. see *BUSINESS AND ECONOMICS — Management*

340   CN   ISSN 0835-9768
KE173
CANADIAN CURRENT LAW. 1948. 28/yr. Can.$495 includes Canadian Citations. Carswell, One Corporate Plaza, 2075 Kennedy Rd., Scarborough, ON M1T 3V4, Canada. TEL 416-609-8000. FAX 416-298-5094. adv. contact: M. Lalani.
   Supersedes in part: Canadian Current Law and Canada Citations.

340 331   US   ISSN 1073-5720
▼**CANADIAN EMPLOYMENT LAW FOR U.S. COMPANIES.** 1994. m. $177. (McCarthy Tetrault) M. Lee Smith Publishers & Printers, 162 Fourth Ave., N., Box 198867, Nashville, TN 37219-8867. TEL 615-242-7395; 800-274-6774. FAX 615-256-6601. Eds. Nancy A. Eber, Brian Smeenk. **Document type:** newsletter.
   Description: Reports developments of Canadian employment law that affect U.S. companies.

347.9   CN
CANADIAN EMPLOYMENT LAW GUIDE. bi-m. Can.$245. C C H Canadian Ltd., 6 Garamond Ct., North York, ON M3C 1Z5, Canada. TEL 416-441-2992. FAX 416-444-9011.
   Description: Covers collective bargaining, minimum wage, personnel reports, work hours, overtime, payment of wages, vacations, holidays, leaves of absence, termination, human rights, equal pay and unemployment insurance.

346.066   CN
CANADIAN EMPLOYMENT LAW TODAY. fortn. Can.$278. M P L Communications Inc., 700-133 Richmond St. W., Toronto, ON M5H 3M8, Canada. TEL 416-869-1177. FAX 416-869-0456.
   Description: Focuses on the field of Canadian employment law and how it affects management-employee relations.

CANADIAN EMPLOYMENT SAFETY AND HEALTH GUIDE. see *OCCUPATIONAL HEALTH AND SAFETY*

340 614.7   CN
CANADIAN ENVIRONMENTAL LAW. 6/yr. Can.$870. Butterworths Canada Ltd., Part of the Reed Elsevier group, 75 Clegg Rd., Markham, ON L6G 1A1, Canada. TEL 905-479-2665. FAX 905-479-2826. Eds. Roger Cotton, Alastair R. Lucas. (looseleaf format)
   Description: Reference on waste management and other aspects of pollution control.

CANADIAN ENVIRONMENTAL LAW REPORTS. NEW SERIES. see *ENVIRONMENTAL STUDIES*

CANADIAN ENVIRONMENTAL PROTECTION. see *ENVIRONMENTAL STUDIES*

340 332.1   CN   ISSN 1183-8922
CANADIAN FINANCIAL SERVICES ALERT. 1988. 8/yr. Can.$235. Carswell, One Corporate Plaza, 2075 Kennedy Rd., Scarborough, ON M1T 3V4, Canada. TEL 416-609-8000. FAX 416-298-5094. Ed. John W. Teolis. circ. 175. **Document type:** newsletter.
   Formerly (until Jun.1991): Canadian Banking Law Newsletter.
   Description: Provides current news and views on rapidly changing Canadian financial services law. Offers Canadian, US and international perspectives.

340 330   CN
CANADIAN FRANCHISE GUIDE. m. Can.$350. Carswell, One Corporate Plaza, 2075 Kennedy Rd., Scarborough, ON M1T 3V4, Canada. TEL 416-609-8000. FAX 416-298-5094. (looseleaf format)
   Description: Designed for franchisers and professional advisers. Addresses legal considerations, tax considerations, current and future trends, marketing and finanical planning strategies as well as forms, documents, agreements and precedents.

340 614   CN
CANADIAN HEALTH FACILITIES LAW GUIDE. bi-m. Can.$530. C C H Canadian Ltd., 6 Garamond Ct., North York, ON M3C 1Z5, Canada. TEL 416-441-2992. FAX 416-444-9011. index.
   Description: Statutes and commentary related to health care facilities (i.e. hospitals, nursing homes, clinics, chronic care homes, etc.). Text of approximately 70 statutes and selected regulations are reproduced.

340 336   CN
CANADIAN INDUSTRIAL INCENTIVES LEGISLATION. 3/yr. Can.$175. Butterworths Canada Ltd., Part of the Reed Elsevier group, 75 Clegg Rd., Markham, ON L6G 1A1, Canada. TEL 905-479-2665. FAX 905-479-2826. Eds. Les Soloman, Jeff Carbell. (looseleaf format)
   Description: Both Federal and Provincial assistance and tax incentive programs. A reference for business and industry managers.

LAW

346.086   CN   ISSN 0045-4990
CANADIAN INSURANCE LAW REPORTER. m. Can.$490. C C H Canadian Ltd., 6 Garamond Ct., North York, ON M3C 1Z5, Canada. TEL 416-441-2992. FAX 416-444-9011. index.
   Description: Contains text decisions from provincial and federal courts on insurance contracts: life, health, accident, fire, casualty and automobiles. Comprehensive digests of tort decisions, quantum of damages chart.

346.066   CN   ISSN 0836-0456
CANADIAN INSURANCE LAW REVIEW. 1988. 3/yr. Can.$180. Carswell, One Corporate Plaza, 2075 Kennedy Rd., Scarborough, ON M1T 3V4, Canada. TEL 416-609-8000. FAX 416-298-5094. Ed. J.F. Graham. adv. contact: M. Lalani. cum.index. **Indexed:** Ind.Can.L.P.L.
   Description: Confronts the most topical issues being faced by the insurance industry today. Covers the law of insurance and regulation of the insurance industry.

CANADIAN INTELLECTUAL PROPERTY REVIEW. see *PATENTS, TRADEMARKS AND COPYRIGHTS*

340   CN   ISSN 0835-6742
K3
CANADIAN JOURNAL OF ADMINISTRATIVE LAW & PRACTICE. 1987. 3/yr. (plus bound vol.). Can.$128. (Council of Canadian Administrative Tribunals) Carswell, One Corporate Plaza, 2075 Kennedy Rd., Scarborough, ON M1T 3V4, Canada. TEL 416-609-8000. FAX 413-298-5094. Ed. Michael I. Jeffery. adv. contact: M. Lalani. bk.rev.; cum.index. **Indexed:** Ind.Can.L.P.L.
   Description: Provides a forum for in-depth discussion of administrative law issues and emphasizes the important role played by tribunals, boards and commissions in the administrative process.

CANADIAN JOURNAL OF INSURANCE LAW. see *INSURANCE*

345   CN   ISSN 0703-900X
K27
CANADIAN JOURNAL OF LAW & JURISPRUDENCE. 1961. s-a. Can.$32.10($26) to individuals; institutions Can.$57.78 ($46). University of Western Ontario, Faculty of Law, London, Ont. N6A 3K7, Canada. TEL 519-679-2111. FAX 519-661-3790. Eds. Richard Bronaugh, Peter Barton. adv.; bk.rev. circ. 600. (also avail. in microfilm from WSH,PMC) **Indexed:** C.L.I., Ind.Can.L.P.L., L.R.I., Leg.Cont., Leg.Per. **Document type:** academic/scholarly publication.
   —UnCover. **CCC.**
   Former titles (until 1988): Western Ontario Law Review (ISSN 0083-8950); University of Western Ontario Law Review.
   Description: Serves as a forum for the publication of scholarly writing in the area of general jurisprudence and legal philosophy.

350 301   CN   ISSN 0829-3201
K3   CODEN: CJLSEU
CANADIAN JOURNAL OF LAW AND SOCIETY/REVUE CANADIENNE DROIT ET SOCIETE. (Text in English, French) s-a. Can.$32 to individuals (foreign $30); institutions Can.$55 (foreign $50). University of Calgary Press, 2500 University Dr., N.W., Calgary, AB T2N 1N4, Canada. TEL 403-220-7578. FAX 403-282-0085. TELEX 03-821545. Ed. C. Thomasset. circ. 300. (back issues avail.) **Indexed:** Ind.Can.L.P.L.
   —BLDSC (3031.795000); UnCover.
   Description: Articles broadly relating to law and society.
   Refereed Serial

340 305.4   CN   ISSN 0832-8781
                   CODEN: CJWLEU
CANADIAN JOURNAL OF WOMEN AND THE LAW/REVUE FEMMES ET DROIT. (Text in English, French) 1986. s-a. Can.$42.80 to individuals; institutions Can.$69.55; students Can.$21.40. 575 King Edward Ave., Ottawa, ON K1N 6N5, Canada. TEL 613-564-5617. FAX 613-564-7190. Eds. Marlene Cano, Elizabeth A. Sheehy. bk.rev. circ. 1,250. (also avail. in microfilm from MML; back issues avail.) **Indexed:** C.L.I., Can.Per.Ind., Can.Wom.Per.Ind., Ind.Can.L.P.L., Leg.Per., Mult.Ed.Abstr, Stud.Wom.Abstr., Wom.Stud.Abstr. (1986-).
   —BLDSC (3036.750000); UnCover.

CANADIAN LABOUR ARBITRATION SUMMARIES. see *BUSINESS AND ECONOMICS — Labor And Industrial Relations*

CANADIAN LABOUR LAW REPORTER. see *BUSINESS AND ECONOMICS — Labor And Industrial Relations*

CANADIAN LABOUR RELATIONS BOARD REPORTS. see *BUSINESS AND ECONOMICS — Labor And Industrial Relations*

CANADIAN LAW LIBRARIES/BIBLIOTHEQUES DE DROIT CANADIENNES. see *LIBRARY AND INFORMATION SCIENCES*

340   CN   ISSN 0084-8573
CANADIAN LAW LIST. a. Can.$92. Canada Law Book Inc., 240 Edward St., Aurora, ON L4G 3S9, Canada. TEL 905-841-6472. FAX 905-841-5085. Ed. Patricia Egan. **Document type:** directory.
   Description: Lists all lawyers in Canada by province, municipality and firm. Also lists alphabetically by firm association and location.

340   CN   ISSN 0703-2129
K3
CANADIAN LAWYER. 1977. 10/yr. Can.$48 (foreign $58). Canada Law Book, 240 Edward St., Aurora, ON L4G 3S9, Canada. TEL 905-841-6480. FAX 905-841-5085. Ed. Catherine Kentridge. adv. contact: Jayne Townsend. bk.rev. circ. 30,000. (also avail. in microform from UMI; reprint service avail. from UMI) **Indexed:** C.L.I., Can.Per.Ind., CMI, Ind.Can.L.P.L., L.R.I., Law Ofc.Info.Svc.
   —UMI.
   Description: Provides commentary, insider gossip and profiles of leading lawyers and law firms.

340 330   US   ISSN 0740-1043
KE3298.A13C36
CANADIAN LEGAL & LEGISLATIVE BENEFITS REPORTER. 1984. 6/yr. membership. International Foundation of Employee Benefit Plans, Box 69, Brookfield, WI 53008-0069. TEL 414-786-6700. Ed. Raymond Koskie. (looseleaf format) **Document type:** newsletter.
   —CCC.

CANADIAN LEGAL FAX DIRECTORY. see *BUSINESS AND ECONOMICS — Trade And Industrial Directories*

450 917.106   CN   ISSN 0225-2279
KE7705.8
CANADIAN NATIVE LAW REPORTER. Short title: C N L R. 1977. q. Can.$55 (typically set in Nov.). University of Saskatchewan, Native Law Centre, Diefenbaker Centre, Saskatoon, SK S7N 0W0, Canada. TEL 306-966-6189. FAX 306-966-8517. Ed. Zandra Wilson. bk.rev.; cum.index. circ. 450. (back issues avail.) **Indexed:** C.L.I., Ind.Can.L.P.L.
   Description: Comprehensive coverage and full text reporting of Canadian native law judgments.

CANADIAN OCCUPATIONAL SAFETY & HEALTH LAW. see *OCCUPATIONAL HEALTH AND SAFETY*

CANADIAN OIL & GAS. see *PETROLEUM AND GAS*

340 608.7   CN   ISSN 0008-4689
CANADIAN PATENT REPORTER. 1942. fortn. Can.$250. Canada Law Book Inc., 240 Edward St., Aurora, ON L4G 3S9, Canada. TEL 905-841-6472. FAX 905-841-5085. Ed. G.F. Henderson. index. **Indexed:** Ind.Can.L.P.L.
   ●Also available online.

342 917.1   CN   ISSN 0715-4860
KE4381.5.A45
CANADIAN RIGHTS REPORTER. a.(6 parts and 6 vols.). Can.$720. Butterworths Canada Ltd., Part of the Reed Elsevier group, 75 Clegg Rd., Markham, ON L6G 1A1, Canada. TEL 905-479-2665. FAX 905-479-2826.
   Description: Reports of cases decided under the Canadian Charter of Rights and Freedoms.

346.092   CN   ISSN 0045-5342
CANADIAN SECURITIES LAW REPORTER. m. Can.$950. C C H Canadian Ltd., 6 Garamond Ct., North York, ON M3C 1Z5, Canada. TEL 416-441-2992. FAX 416-444-9011. index.
   Description: Full texts of provincial securities acts, regulations, related federal and provincial statutes. Policy statements by securities commissions. By-laws of self-regulatory bodies.

340   CN
CANADIAN SENTENCING DIGEST. 1980. irreg.(4-6/yr.). Can.$408. Carswell, One Corporate Plaza, 2075 Kennedy Rd., Scarborough, Ont. M1T 3V4, Canada. TEL 416-609-8000. FAX 416-298-5094. Eds. Paul Nadin-Davis, Clarey B. Sproule. (looseleaf format)
   Formerly: Nadin-Davis Canadian Sentencing Digest.
   Description: Offers digests of virtually all Canadian cases on quantum of sentence from 1970 to the present, organized according to statute and section.

340.6   CN   ISSN 0008-5030
                   CODEN: JCFSBP
CANADIAN SOCIETY OF FORENSIC SCIENCE JOURNAL/SOCIETE CANADIENNE DES SCIENCES JUDICIAIRES JOURNAL. 1967. q. Can.$50 (foreign Can.$60). Canadian Society of Forensic Science, 2660 Southvale Crescent, Ste. 215, Ottawa, Ont. K1B 4W5, Canada. TEL 613-731-2096. Ed. Brian T. Hodgson. adv.; bk.rev.; charts; illus. circ. 900. **Indexed:** Biol.Abstr., Chem.Abstr., Excerp.Med.
   —BLDSC (4723.120000); CASDDS. **CCC.**
   Supersedes: Canadian Society of Forensic Science Newsletter.
   Description: Includes forensic chemistry, blood alcohol analysis, forensic toxicology, questioned documents, forensic odontology, firearms examination, forensic pathology and forensic biology.

CANADIAN TAX OBJECTIONS AND APPEAL PROCEDURES. see *BUSINESS AND ECONOMICS — Public Finance, Taxation*

CANADIAN TRANSPORTATION LAW REPORTER. see *TRANSPORTATION*

340   CN   ISSN 0008-5308
CANADIAN WEEKLY LAW SHEET. 1959. w. Can.$300. Butterworths Canada Ltd., Part of the Reed Elsevier group, 75 Clegg Rd., Markham, ON L6G 1A1, Canada. TEL 905-292-1421. FAX 905-292-6970. Ed.Bd. q. index. circ. 650. (looseleaf format)
   Description: Digests reported cases on all fields of Canadian law.

340   CN
CANNONS OF CONSTRUCTION. 1970. q. free to qualified personnel. W. 234 Law Centre, University of Alberta, Edmonton, Alta. T6G 2H5, Canada. TEL 403-492-5121. FAX 403-492-4929. Ed. Paul T. Babie. adv.; bk.rev. circ. 1,600.

CAPITOL LINE-UP. see *AGRICULTURE — Poultry And Livestock*

CAPITULO CRIMINOLOGICO. see *CRIMINOLOGY AND LAW ENFORCEMENT*

340 301.16   US   ISSN 0736-7694
K3
CARDOZO ARTS & ENTERTAINMENT LAW JOURNAL. 1981. s-a. $20. Cardozo School of Law, 55 Fifth Ave., New York, NY 10003. TEL 212-790-0292. cum.index. circ. 1,300. (also avail. in microform from WSH; back issues avail.; reprint service avail. from WSH) **Indexed:** C.L.I., Film Lit.Ind. (1985-), Leg.Per.
   —BLDSC (3051.530000); Faxon; UnCover.
   Description: Covers current legal issues in the arts, entertainment, communications, intellectual property and sports.

340   US
CARDOZO LAW REVIEW. 1979. bi-m. $30. Cardozo School of Law, 55 Fifth Ave., New York, NY 10003. TEL 212-790-0324. (back issues avail.; reprint service avail. from RRI) **Indexed:** C.L.I., Leg.Per.

340 800   US   ISSN 1043-1500
K3
CARDOZO STUDIES IN LAW AND LITERATURE. 1989. s-a. $20 to individuals; institutions $50; students $18. Jacob Burns Institute for Advanced Legal Studies, Cardoza School of Law, Yeshiva University, 55 Fifth Ave., New York, NY 10003. TEL 212-790-0370. FAX 212-790-0345. Ed. Richard H. Weisberg. adv.; bk.rev.; index every 3 yrs. circ. 700. **Document type:** academic/scholarly publication.
   —UnCover.
   Refereed Serial

CAREER OPPORTUNITIES BULLETIN. see *OCCUPATIONS AND CAREERS*

LAW

340   CN   ISSN 0706-5388
KEO1115.8
CARSWELL'S PRACTICE CASES. (3RD SERIES). 1976. 10/yr. Can.$135 per vol. Carswell, One Corporate Plaza, 2075 Kennedy Rd., Scarborough, ON M1T 3V4, Canada. TEL 416-609-8000. FAX 416-298-5094. Ed. Michael McGowan. adv. contact: M. Lalani. (also avail. in looseleaf format) Indexed: C.L.I., Ind.Can.L.P.L., L.R.I.
   Description: Features all important decisions on practice in civil proceedings from all Canadian common law jurisdictions and all court levels. Includes cases on institution of proceedings, parties, pleadings, service, limitation of actions, third party proceedings, discovery, evidence, injunctions, judgments and orders, costs and appeals.

CARTA DE GERENCIA. see *BUSINESS AND ECONOMICS — Management*

CASE CITATIONS. see *EDUCATION — School Organization And Administration*

340   US   ISSN 0736-8240
KF9614.C37
CASE COMMENTARIES AND BRIEFS. 1981. 10/yr. free to members. National District Attorneys Association, 99 Canal Center Plaza, Ste. 510, Alexandria, VA 22314. TEL 703-549-9222. FAX 703-836-3195. Ed. James P. Manak. circ. 7,000. (looseleaf format; back issues avail.) Document type: newsletter.

340   US   ISSN 0008-7262
K3
CASE WESTERN RESERVE LAW REVIEW. 1948. 4/yr. $25. Case Western Reserve University, School of Law, 11075 East Blvd., Cleveland, OH 44106-7148. TEL 216-368-3304. FAX 216-369-6144. adv.; bk.rev.; charts; index. circ. 800. (also avail. in microfilm from RRI; microfilm from WSH; back issues avail.) Indexed: C.L.I., L.R.I., Leg.Per. Document type: academic/scholarly publication.
   ●Also available online. Vendor(s): West Services, Inc.
   —BLDSC (3058.244000); Faxon; UnCover.
   Formerly: Western Reserve Law Review (ISSN 0270-2150)

340   US
CASES AND MATERIALS ON TRADE REGULATION. irreg. price varies. Foundation Press, Inc., 615 Merrick Ave., Westbury, NY 11590-6607.

CASES IN POINT. see *EDUCATION — School Organization And Administration*

343   IT   ISSN 0008-7424
CASSAZIONE PENALE; rivista mensile di giurisprudenza. 1961. m. L.220000 (foreign L.330000). Casa Editrice Dott. A. Giuffre, Via Busto Arsizio 40, 20151 Milan, Italy. TEL 02-38000905. FAX 02-38009582. Ed. Giorgio Lattanzi. adv.; bk.rev.; index. circ. 5,500. (looseleaf format)

340   330   IT
CATALOGO LEGALE. 1886. q. Libreria Gozzini, Via Ricasoli 49-103r, 50122 Florence, Italy. TEL 55-212433. FAX 55-211105. circ. 3,500.

340   US   ISSN 0008-8137
K3
CATHOLIC LAWYER. 1955. q. $5. St. John's University, School of Law, 8000 Utopia Pkwy., Jamaica, NY 11439. TEL 718-990-6654. FAX 718-990-6649. Ed. Edward D. Cavanagh. bk.rev.; illus.; index, cum.index. circ. 2,500. (also avail. in microfilm from RRI; reprint service avail. from RRI) Indexed: C.L.I., Canon Law Abstr., Cath.Ind., CERDIC, L.R.I., Leg.Cont., Leg.Per. Document type: academic/scholarly publication.
   —BLDSC (3093.075000); UnCover.

340   US   ISSN 0008-8390
K3
CATHOLIC UNIVERSITY LAW REVIEW. 1950. q. $25 (foreign $30). Catholic University of America, Law School, Washington, DC 20064. TEL 202-319-5159. Ed. Scott B. Gilly. adv.; bk.rev.; index. circ. 1,200. (also avail. in microfilm from WSH,PMC; reprint service avail. from UMI,WSH) Indexed: Abstr.Bk.Rev.Curr.Leg.Per., C.L.I., Cath.Ind., Curr.Cont., L.R.I., Leg.Cont., Leg.Per., SSCI. Document type: academic/scholarly publication.
   ●Also available online. Vendor(s): Mead Data Central, Inc.
   —BLDSC (3093:249000); Faxon; UnCover.

340   US
CAUSES OF ACTION. a. $18.90. Shepard's - McGraw-Hill, Inc., Box 35300, Colorado Springs, CO 80935-3530. TEL 800-525-2474.
   Description: Analysis of issues involved in establishing or defending a "prima facie" case.

340   352   CJ
CAYMAN GAZETTE. (Issues usually accompanied by numbered supplements) 1975. fortn. C.$221($269.52) Government Information Service, Tower Bldg., Grand Cayman, Cayman Islands, British W.I. FAX 809-94-98487. TELEX 4260 CIGOVT CP. Ed. Pat Ebanks. circ. 500.
   Description: Official publication for government and other legal notices including liquidations, trade marks and probate.

CEMETERY BUSINESS & LEGAL GUIDE. see *FUNERALS*

CENTER FOR LAW AND EDUCATION. NEWSNOTES. see *EDUCATION*

CENTRO DE ESTUDIOS PUBLICOS. DOCUMENTO DE TRABAJO. see *BUSINESS AND ECONOMICS — Economic Situation And Conditions*

340   US   ISSN 0886-2435
KF8727.A15
CHANGE EXCHANGE; the newsletter for reduction of litigation cost and delay. 1985. q. $14 (free to qualified personnel). American Bar Association, Judicial Administration Division Lawyers Conference, 750 N. Lake Shore Dr., Chicago, IL 60611. TEL 312-988-5555. FAX 312-988-5704. circ. 4,000. Document type: newsletter.
   Description: News on programs from state courts.

340   630   US
CHAPTER 12: FARM REORGANIZATIONS. 1987. base vol. (plus a. suppl.). $110. Shepard's - McGraw-Hill, Inc., Box 35300, Colorado Springs, CO 80935-3500. TEL 800-525-2474. (looseleaf format)
   Description: Comprehensive review of theory and practice under Chapter 12, including examination of history, filing procedures, cram-down procedures against creditors and improved debtor protection.

340   US
CHAPTER 13: PRACTICE AND PROCEDURE. 1983. base vol. (plus a. suppl.). $95. Shepard's - McGraw-Hill, Inc., Box 35300, Colorado Springs, CO 80935-3530. TEL 800-525-2474. (looseleaf format)
   Description: Covers legal history, current practices and provides procedural advice.

CHEMICAL INFORMATION ALERT. see *CHEMISTRY*

CHEMICAL SUBSTANCES CONTROL; an advisory bulletin on industry practices, regulatory impact, and control techniques. see *CHEMISTRY*

CHEMICAL WASTE LITIGATION REPORTER. see *ENVIRONMENTAL STUDIES*

340   US   ISSN 0362-6148
CHICAGO DAILY LAW BULLETIN. 1854. d. (Mon.-Fri.). $150. Law Bulletin Publishing Co., 415 N. State St., Chicago, IL 60610-4674. TEL 312-644-7800. FAX 312-644-4255. Ed. Bernard Judge. adv.; bk.rev.; index. circ. 7,000. (also avail. in microfilm; back issues avail.) Indexed: C.L.I., Hlth.Ind., L.R.I. Document type: newspaper.

340   US
CHICAGO - KENT LAW REVIEW. 1923. 3/yr. $23. Chicago - Kent College of Law, 565 W. Adams St., Chicago, IL 60661-3691. TEL 312-906-5190. FAX 312-906-5280. Ed. Mary N. Cameli. adv.; bk.rev.; cum.index. circ. 1,800. (also avail. in microform from WSH,PMC; reprint service avail. from WSH) Indexed: C.L.I., L.R.I., Leg.Cont., Leg.Per. Document type: academic/scholarly publication.
   ●Also available online. Vendor(s): West Services, Inc. Also available on CD-ROM.
   —UnCover.
   Former titles: I I T Chicago - Kent Law Review; Chicago - Kent Law Review (ISSN 0009-3599)
   Description: Each issue is in symposium format, with one issue each year focusing on the US Court of Appeals for the 7th Circuit located in Chicago.

340   US   ISSN 0199-8374
K3
CHICAGO LAWYER.* 1978. m. $38. Chicago Lawyer Publishing, Inc., 703 W. Roscoe St., Ste. 2, Chicago, IL 60657-2416. Ed. Rob Warden. circ. 5,820. (back issues avail.)
   —UMI.)

340   US
CHICAGO MUNICIPAL CODE HANDBOOK. 1988. a. $17.95 (effective May 1992). Gould Publications (Binghamton), 199-300 State St., Binghamton, NY 13901. TEL 607-724-3000. FAX 607-723-4285. adv.; bk.rev. (looseleaf format)
   Description: Covers police operations, traffic, licensing, fire prevention, working conditions and more.

340   US
F548.54.C4
▼**CHICAGO TUNNEL LITIGATION REPORTER**. 1992. s-m. $400. 1943 Sherman Ave., Evanston, IL 60201. TEL 708-328-1662. FAX 708-328-0026. Ed. Julie Whitmore. Document type: newsletter.

340   US   ISSN 1061-8899
K3
CHICANO - LATINO LAW REVIEW. 1972. a. $10. (U C L A Chicano Studies Center) University of California, Los Angeles, School of Law, 405 Hilgard Ave., Los Angeles, CA 90024. TEL 213-825-2894. adv. circ. 600. (back issues avail.; reprint service avail. from RRI) Indexed: C.L.I., L.R.I., Leg.Per.
   ●Also available online. Vendor(s): West Services, Inc.
   —UnCover.
   Formerly: Chicano Law Review.

CHILDREN AND FAMILIES. see *CHILDREN AND YOUTH — About*

CHILDREN AND THE LAW. see *CHILDREN AND YOUTH — About*

340   HK
CHINA & HONG KONG LAW STUDIES SERIES. (Text in English) irreg. price varies. Longman Asia ltd., Taikoo Place, 979 King's Rd., Quarry Bay, Hong Kong. TEL 852-856-6335. FAX 852-565-7440. Document type: monographic series, academic/scholarly publication.
   Description: Law texts for law students and legal practitioners in Hong Kong.

CHINA BANKING & FINANCE. see *BUSINESS AND ECONOMICS — Banking And Finance*

340   HK   ISSN 1011-2359
LAW
CHINA CURRENT LAWS. (Text in English, Chinese) 1987. 4/yr. HK.$2250($300) (effective 1993). Longman Asia Ltd., Taikoo Place, 979 King's Rd., Quarry Bay, Hong Kong. TEL 852-856-6335. FAX 852-565-7440. TELEX 73051 LGHK HX. Ed.Bd. (back issues avail.) Document type: academic/scholarly publication.
   Description: Covers Chinese laws and regulations for lawyers and businesses involved in China trade and investment.

340   330   HK   ISSN 1012-6724
CHINA LAW & PRACTICE; documenting & analysing the Chinese legal system. (Text in English and Chinese, summaries in English) 1988. 10/yr. HK.$5950($792) (effective Jan. 1994). Asia Law & Practice Ltd., 2-F, 29 Hollywood Rd., Central, Hong Kong. TEL 852-544-9918. FAX 852-543-7617. s-a. index. (back issues avail.)
   —BLDSC (3180.186300).
   Description: Contains a digest, case studies, and full transactions of legal texts concerning business law developments for foreign investors in the People's Republic of China.

340   US   ISSN 0009-4609
K3
CHINESE LAW AND GOVERNMENT; a journal of translations. 1968. bi-m. $429 (foreign $472). M.E. Sharpe, Inc., 80 Business Park Dr., Armonk, NY 10504. TEL 914-273-1800. FAX 914-273-2106. Eds. Michael Y.M. Kau, James Tong. adv.; index. (also avail. in microfilm from PMC,WSH; back issues avail.; reprint service avail. from WSH) Indexed: C.L.I., Curr.Cont., Leg.Per., P.A.I.S., SSCI.
   —Faxon; UnCover; UMI.
   Refereed Serial

CHRONICLE OF PARLIAMENTARY ELECTIONS AND DEVELOPMENTS. see POLITICAL SCIENCE

340 320   HT
CHRONIQUE JUDICIAIRE D'HAITI; revue juridique et culturelle Haitienne. (Text in English and French) 1980. m. $24. Imprimerie des Antilles, P.O. Box 1453, Port-au-Prince, Haiti, W.I. Ed. Lucien Lacarriere. adv.; bk.rev. circ. 10,000. (back issues avail.)

349   JA   ISSN 0009-6296
CHUO LAW REVIEW/HOGAKU SHINPO. (Text in Japanese; title and contents page in English) 1891. m. exchange basis. Chuo Daigaku, Hogakubu - Chuo University, Faculty of Law, 3-9 Kanda-Surugadai, Chiyoda-ku, Tokyo, Japan. Ed. Toichiro Kigawa. index. circ. 650.

340 200   US
CHURCH LAW & TAX REPORT. 1987. q. $78. Christian Ministry Resources, c/o Bernice Bush Company, 15052 Springdale St., Huntington Beach, CA 92649-1178. TEL 714-891-3344. FAX 704-841-8059. (Subscr. to: Box 2301, Matthews, NC 28105. TEL 704-841-8059)

340   ES
CIENCIAS JURIDICAS Y SOCIALES.* 1947. s-a. Universidad de El Salvador, Associacion de Estudiantes de Derecho, Final 25 Avda Norte, Ciudad Universitaria, San Salvador, El Salvador.

340   US   ISSN 0009-6881
K25
CINCINNATI LAW REVIEW. Variant title: University of Cincinnati Law Review. 1932. q. $22.50 per no. (foreign $30). University of Cincinnati, College of Law, Rm. 300, Cincinnati, OH 45221-0040. TEL 513-556-5101. FAX 513-556-6265. Ed. Michael M. Neltner. adv.; bk.rev.; cum.index: vols.1-43. circ. 1,200. (also avail. in microform from RRI,WSH; reprint service avail. from RRI) **Indexed:** Abstr.Bk.Rev.Curr.Leg.Per., C.L.I., Curr.Cont., Energy Ind., Energy Info.Abstr., L.R.I., Leg.Cont., Leg.Per.
●Also available online. Vendor(s): West Services, Inc.
—BLDSC (9106.600000); Faxon; UnCover.

CITIZEN ACTION. see SOCIOLOGY

340   UK
CITIZENS ADVICE NOTES SERVICE. 1940. 3/yr. £90. C A N S Trust, 1 Stockwell Green, London SW9 9HP, England. TEL 071-326-0356. FAX 071-737-3237. Ed. Flavia Wade. circ. 3,200. (looseleaf format)
Description: Digest of British social legislation.

340 370   US
CITIZENSHIP EDUCATOR. 4/yr. free to members. Missouri Bar, Advisory Committee on Citizenship Education, Box 119, Jefferson City, MO 65102. TEL 314-635-4128. FAX 314-635-2811. Ed. Jack A. Wax. **Document type:** newsletter.

CITY OF CHICAGO BUILDING CODE. see BUILDING AND CONSTRUCTION

340   US
CITY OF NEW YORK COUNCIL DIGEST; a cumulative record of the councilmanic session. 1990. 24/yr. $600. New York Legal Publishing Corp., 6 Charles Park, Guilderland, NY 12084. TEL 800-541-2681. FAX 518-456-0828.
Description: Covers budget modifications, public hearing schedules, bills and local laws, zoning, landmarking, and land use issues.

340   US
CIVIL ACTIONS AGAINST THE UNITED STATES: ITS AGENCIES, OFFICES, AND EMPLOYEES. 1982. base vol. (plus a. suppl.). $95. Shepard's - McGraw-Hill, Inc., Box 35300, Colorado Springs, CO 80935-3530. TEL 800-525-2474.
Description: Covers the problems that arise when the United States is named a party defendant to a suit.

340 320 355 301   US
CIVILIAN CONGRESS; includes a directory of persons holding executive branch-military office in Congress contrary to constitutional prohibition (Art.1, Sec.6, Cl.2) of concurrent office-holding. 1964. biennial. $10. 2361 Mission St., Rm. 238, San Francisco, CA 94110-1868. TEL 415-695-1597. Ed. Jack Fitch. bk.rev. circ. 500. (looseleaf format; back issues avail.) **Document type:** directory.

THE CLAIMS FORUM. see BUSINESS AND ECONOMICS — Labor And Industrial Relations

340   UK
CLARKE HALL & MORRISON ON CHILDREN. 2 base vols. (plus updates 3/yr.). $390. Butterworth & Co. (Publishers) Ltd. (Subsidiary of: Reed Elsevier plc), 88 Kingsway, London WC2B 6AB, England. TEL 71-405-6900. FAX 71-405-1332. (US addr.: Butterworth Legal Publishers, 90 Stiles Rd., Salem, NH 03079-9981. TEL 603-898-9664) Ed. Richard White. (looseleaf format)
Description: Provides full coverage of the family courts and family proceedings courts and the criminal jurisdiction of the youth courts.

340   US   ISSN 0746-7168
K3.L36
CLASS ACTION REPORTS. 1972. 6/yr. $320. Class Action Reports, Inc., 4900 Massachusetts Ave. N.W., Ste. 230, Washington, DC 20016. TEL 202-364-1031. FAX 202-363-6912. Ed. Beverly C. Moore, Jr. adv. contact: Deanna Moore. bk.rev.; index. circ. 500. (back issues avail.) **Document type:** academic/scholarly publication.
—UnCover.
Description: Digests state and federal class action decisions in all areas of the law; also covers attorney fee awards in class actions; extensive bibliographies; articles; reports; commentary.

CLEARING UP: NORTHWEST ENERGY MARKETS. see ENERGY

340   US   ISSN 0009-868X
KF336
CLEARINGHOUSE REVIEW. 1969. m. $95 to individuals; institutions $125 (foreign $145). (Legal Services Corporation) National Clearinghouse for Legal Services, Inc., 205 W. Monroe, 2nd Fl., Chicago, IL 60606. TEL 312-263-3830. FAX 312-263-3846. Ed. Rita McLennon. bk.rev.; bibl.; tr.lit.; index, cum.index: 1967-1984. circ. 10,000. (looseleaf format; also avail. in microform from UMI) **Indexed:** Abstr.Health Care Manage.Stud., Bus.Ind., C.L.I., Hlth.Ind., L.R.I., Law Ofc.Info.Svc., Leg.Cont., Leg.Per., Med.Care Rev.
—BLDSC (3278.539000); Faxon; UnCover; UMI.

340   US   ISSN 0160-1598
CLEVELAND BAR JOURNAL. 1938. m. $12 to non-members. Cleveland Bar Association, 113 St. Clair Ave., N.E., Ste. 225, Cleveland, OH 44144-1253. TEL 216-696-3525. FAX 216-696-2413. Ed. Randy Orr. adv.; illus. circ. 5,400. **Document type:** academic/scholarly publication.
—UnCover.
Description: Covers current legal and professional issues of interest to Cleveland area lawyers.

340   US   ISSN 0009-8876
K3
CLEVELAND STATE LAW REVIEW. 1951. 4/yr. $20. Cleveland State University, Cleveland-Marshall College of Law, 1983 E. 24th St., Cleveland, OH 44115. TEL 216-687-2336. (also avail. in microfilm from PMC,WSH; microfiche from WSH) **Indexed:** C.L.I., L.R.I., Leg.Cont., Leg.Per.
●Also available online. Vendor(s): West Services, Inc.
—BLDSC (3278.655000); Faxon; UnCover.
Formerly: Cleveland-Marshall Law Review.

340   US
CLIENT UPDATE. q. $39.90 for 25 copies. (American Bar Association) A B A Press, 750 N. Lake Shore Dr., Chicago, IL 60611. TEL 312-988-6122. **Document type:** newsletter.
Description: Short items on the latest legal trends intended for laymen. Distributed by individual law offices to their clients.

CLINICAL MEDICAL ETHICS. see MEDICAL SCIENCES

340   US
CLOSING OFFICER'S GUIDE. 1983. base vol. (plus a. supplement). $70. Butterworth Legal Publishers (Salem) (Subsidiary of: Reed Elsevier plc), 8 Industrial Way, Bldg. C, Salem, NH 03079. TEL 800-548-4001. FAX 609-898-9858. Ed. Fred B. Phillips, Jr. (looseleaf format)

346.066   US
CODE AND REGULATIONS. 1946. m. $330. Commerce Clearing House, Inc., 4025 W. Peterson Ave., Chicago, IL 60646. TEL 312-583-8500. Ed. D. Newquist.

CODE GENERAL DES IMPOTS. see BUSINESS AND ECONOMICS — Public Finance, Taxation

CODE NEWS (CLEVELAND). see BUILDING AND CONSTRUCTION

353   US
CODE OF FEDERAL REGULATIONS. a. $829 for print ed. (foreign $1036.25); microfiche $244 (foreign $305). U.S. Office of the Federal Register, National Archives and Records Administration, 8th St. and Pennsylvania Ave., N.W., Washington, DC 20408. TEL 202-523-5230. (Subscr. to: Superintendent of Documents, U.S. Government Printing Office, Box 371954, Pittsburgh, PA 15250-7954. TEL 202-783-3238. FAX 202-512-2233) (also avail. in microfiche; microform from PMC) **Document type:** government publication.
●Also available on CD-ROM.
Description: Codifies the general and permanent rules published in the Federal Register.

353   US
CODE OF FEDERAL REGULATIONS, L S A, LIST OF C F R SECTIONS AFFECTED. m. $24 (foreign $30). U.S. Office of the Federal Registrar, National Archives and Records Administration, Eighth St. and Pennsylvania Ave., N.W., Washington, DC 20408. TEL 202-523-5230. (Subscr. to: Superintendent of Documents, U.S. Government Printing Office, Box 371954, Pittsburgh, PA 15250-7954. TEL 202-783-3238. FAX 202-512-2233) (back issues avail.) **Document type:** government publication.
Description: Lists amendatory actions published in the Federal Register.

CODE OF MARYLAND REGULATIONS. see PUBLIC ADMINISTRATION

349   BE   ISSN 0010-0188
CODES LARCIER. (In 5 vols.: Droit Civil, Judiciare et Commercial; Droit Penal; Droit Social; Droit Economique et Fiscal; Droit Public et Administratif) a. (base vols. plus q. updates). 8540 BEF for 1992 updates (base vols. 19300 BEF). Maison Ferdinand Larcier S.A., Rue des Minimes 39, 1000 Brussels, Belgium. TEL 32-2-5124712. FAX 32-2-5139009. charts; index.
Description: Compendium of Belgian legal codes.

349   SA   ISSN 0010-020X
CODICILLUS. (Text in Afrikaans, English) 1960. s-a. R.8 (overseas $7.50) (effective 1994). University of South Africa, Faculty of Law, P.O. Box 392, Pretoria 0001, South Africa. TEL 27-12-322-8944. FAX 27-12-429-3221. TELEX 350068. Ed. G.J. van Nickerk. adv.; bk.rev.; charts; illus. circ. 6,400. (also avail. in microform from UMI; reprint service avail. from UMI) **Indexed:** Ind.S.A.Per. **Document type:** academic/scholarly publication.
—UMI.
Description: Covers legal history and recent legislation.

340 320   US   ISSN 0741-9333
K3   CODEN: SWTEEN
COGITATIONS ON LAW AND GOVERNMENT. 1983. q. $16. (Cogitations on Law and Government, Inc.) Bill Keyes, Ed. & Pub., Drawer 6865, McLean, VA 22106-6865. Ed. Jonathan W. Emord. adv.; bk.rev. circ. 2,000. **Indexed:** Sage Pub.Admin.Abstr.

342   VE
COLECCION TEXTOS LEGISLATIVOS. a. Editorial Juridica Venezolana, Apdo. 17598 Parque Central, Caracas, Venezuela.

349   CR   ISSN 0010-0587
COLEGIO DE ABOGADOS. REVISTA.* vol.24, 1969. 3/yr. Colegio de Abogados, Apdo. 3161, San Jose, Costa Rica. Ed. Luis Antonio Murillo. charts; index.

349   AG   ISSN 0325-8955
COLEGIO DE ABOGADOS DE BUENOS AIRES. REVISTA. 1921. 3/yr. free. Colegio de Abogados de la Ciudad de Buenos Aires, Montevideo 640, 1019 Buenos Aires, Argentina. FAX 54-1-42-2690. Ed. Julian del Campo. adv.; bk.rev. circ. 1,200.

349   PR   ISSN 0010-0579
LAW
COLEGIO DE ABOGADOS DE PUERTO RICO. REVISTA. (Text in Spanish) 1914. q. $30. Colegio de Abogados de Puerto Rico, Box 1900, San Juan, PR 00902. TEL 809-721-3358. FAX 809-725-0330. Ed. Carmelo Delgado Cintron. adv.; bk.rev. circ. 7,000. **Indexed:** C.L.I., L.R.I., Leg.Per.

3240 LAW

340 378   US   ISSN 0192-1371
KF4225.A59
COLLEGE ADMINISTRATOR AND THE COURTS; briefs of selected court cases affecting the administration of institutions of higher education. 1977. q. $117.50. College Administration Publications, Inc., Box 15898, Asheville, NC 28813-0898. TEL 704-277-8777. Ed. Robert D. Bickel. index. circ. 1,200. **Document type:** newsletter.
   Description: Peer editorial research briefs on court cases that affect the administrative staff and activities of institutions of higher education, with a yearly cumulative index cross-referenced by case name, topic, and subject.

340 378   US   ISSN 0145-1472
KF4243.A59
COLLEGE STUDENT AND THE COURTS; briefs of selected court cases involving student-institutional relationships in higher education. 1973. q. $117.50. College Administration Publications, Inc., Box 15898, Asheville, NC 28813-0898. TEL 704-277-8777. Eds. D. Parker Young, Donald D. Gehring. index. circ. 2,200. (looseleaf format; back issues avail.) **Document type:** newsletter.
   Description: Peer editorial research briefs on court cases that affect the relationship between students and institutions in higher education, with a yearly cumulative index cross-referenced by case name, topic, and subject.

COLLIER BANKRUPTCY COMPENSATION GUIDE. see *BUSINESS AND ECONOMICS — Banking And Finance*

COLLIER BANKRUPTCY MANUAL. see *BUSINESS AND ECONOMICS — Banking And Finance*

COLLIER HANDBOOK FOR CREDITORS' COMMITTEES. see *BUSINESS AND ECONOMICS — Banking And Finance*

COLLIER LENDING INSTITUTIONS AND THE BANKRUPTCY CODE. see *BUSINESS AND ECONOMICS — Banking And Finance*

COLLIER ON BANKRUPTCY. see *BUSINESS AND ECONOMICS — Banking And Finance*

340   CE   ISSN 0069-5939
COLOMBO LAW REVIEW.* 1969. a. Rs.15($3) (Sri Lanka University Law Review Association) Hansa Publishers Ltd., 71 Havelock Rd., Colombo 5, Sri Lanka.

340   US   ISSN 1059-504X
▼**COLORADO EMPLOYMENT LAW LETTER.** 1992. m. $95. (Holland & Hart) M. Lee Smith Publishers & Printers, 162 Fourth Ave., N., Box 198867, Nashville, TN 37219. TEL 615-242-7395; 800-274-6774. FAX 615-256-6601. Ed.Bd. (back issues avail.) **Document type:** newsletter.
   Description: Reports the latest state-specific employment law developments that affect Colorado employers.

340 613.1   US   ISSN 1072-057X
COLORADO ENVIRONMENTAL COMPLIANCE UPDATE. m. $137. (Holme, Roberts & Owen) M. Lee Smith Publishers & Printers, 162 Fourth Ave., N., Box 198867, Nashville, TN 37219-8867. TEL 615-242-7395; 800-274-6774. FAX 615-256-6601. Eds. Edward J. McGrath, Thomas Cope. **Document type:** newsletter.
   Description: Reports the latest state-specific environmental law developments that affect companies in Colorado.

COLORADO LAWS ENACTED AFFECTING MUNICIPAL GOVERNMENTS. see *PUBLIC ADMINISTRATION — Municipal Government*

340   US   ISSN 0363-7867
K3
THE COLORADO LAWYER. 1971. m. $85 to individuals; libraries $35. Colorado Bar Association, Inc., 1900 Grant St., Ste. 940, Denver, CO 80203-4309. TEL 303-860-1118. FAX 303-830-3990. Ed. Arlene Abady. adv.; bk.rev.; index. circ. 12,000. (also avail. in microfiche from WSH) **Indexed:** C.L.I. **Document type:** trade publication.
   —BLDSC (3321.525000); Faxon; UnCover.
   Description: Provides practical information to the Colorado legal profession. Includes articles on substantive law, full appellate opinions, law-related features and certain federal court opinion summaries.

COLTIVATORE DIRETTO. see *AGRICULTURE*

382   US   ISSN 0898-0721
K3
COLUMBIA BUSINESS LAW REVIEW. 1986. 3/yr. $30. Columbia University, School of Law, 435 W. 116th St., New York, NY 10027. (also avail. in microform from WSH; back issues avail.; reprint service avail. from WSH) **Indexed:** C.L.I., Leg.Per.
   —BLDSC (3322.991000); Faxon; UnCover.

340   US   ISSN 0090-7944
K3
COLUMBIA HUMAN RIGHTS LAW REVIEW. 1967. 2/yr. $26. Columbia University, School of Law, 435 W. 116th St., New York, NY 10027. TEL 212-854-2171. FAX 212-854-7946. Ed. Ivan Sacks. bk.rev. circ. 600. (also avail. in microfiche from WSH; microfilm from PMC; back issues avail.) **Indexed:** C.L.I., Leg.Per.
   —BLDSC (3323.030000); Faxon; UnCover; SWETS; UMI.
   Description: Domestic and international issues in human and civil rights.

340   US   ISSN 0098-4582
K3   CODEN: CJELE8
COLUMBIA JOURNAL OF ENVIRONMENTAL LAW. 1973. s-a. $25. Columbia University, School of Law, Box B-28, 435 W. 116th St., New York, NY 10027. TEL 212-280-2539. adv.; bk.rev.; index. circ. 900. (also avail. in microfilm from PMC,WSH; back issues avail.; reprint service avail. from WSH) **Indexed:** Abstr.Bk.Rev.Curr.Leg.Per., C.L.I., Energy Ind., Energy Info.Abstr., Environ.Abstr., Environ.Per.Bibl., L.R.I., Leg.Cont., Leg.Per, Pollut.Abstr., Sel.Water Res.Abstr.
   —BLDSC (3323.040000); Faxon; SWETS. **CCC.**
   Description: Local, national and international issues in environmental and public health law.

340   US   ISSN 0010-1923
LAW
COLUMBIA JOURNAL OF LAW AND SOCIAL PROBLEMS. 1965. q. $35 (foreign $40). (Columbia University, School of Law) Darby Publishing, 435 W. 116th St., New York, NY 10027. TEL 212-663-8708. adv.; index. circ. 800. (also avail. in microfilm from PMC,WSH; microfiche from WSH) **Indexed:** A.B.C.Pol.Sci., Adol.Ment.Hlth.Abstr., C.L.I., Curr.Cont., L.R.I., Leg.Cont., Leg.Per., P.A.I.S., SSCI. **Document type:** academic/scholarly publication.
   —BLDSC (3323.050000); Faxon; UnCover; UMI.
   Description: General interest, student-written law journal.

340   US   ISSN 0093-304X
KF292.C6
COLUMBIA LAW ALUMNI OBSERVER. 1971. 5/yr. free. Columbia University, School of Law, 435 W. 116th St., New York, NY 10027. TEL 212-280-2156. Ed. C. Davidson. circ. 15,500. (tabloid format)
   Formerly: Columbia Law Observer.

340   US   ISSN 0010-1958
K3
COLUMBIA LAW REVIEW. 1901. m. (Oct.-Jan., Mar.-Jun.). $40 (foreign $46). Columbia Law Review Association, 435 W. 116th St., New York, NY 10027. TEL 212-854-4398. Ed. Joseph Liu. adv.; bk.rev.; index. circ. 3,000. (also avail. in microfiche from RRI; microfilm from RRI; reprint service avail. from RRI) **Indexed:** A.B.C.Pol.Sci., Abstr.Bk.Rev.Curr.Leg.Per., Account.Ind. (1974-), BPIA, Bus.Ind., C.L.I., Chic.Per.Ind., Crim.Just.Abstr., Curr.Cont., L.R.I., Leg.Per., Mar.Aff.Bibl., P.A.I.S., Pers.Lit., SSCI. **Document type:** academic/scholarly publication.
   ●Also available online. Vendor(s): Mead Data Central, Inc., West Services, Inc.
   —BLDSC (3323.250000); Faxon; UnCover; SWETS; UMI. **CCC.**

COLUMBIA LAW SCHOOL NEWS. see *COLLEGE AND ALUMNI*

COLUMBIA - V L A JOURNAL OF LAW & THE ARTS. see *ART*

340   US
K9.L478
COMMERCIAL, BANKING & BANKRUPTCY LAW. 1956. 6/yr. $16 to members. Illinois State Bar Association, Section on Commercial, Banking & Bankruptcy Law, Illinois Bar Center, Springfield, IL 62701. TEL 217-525-1760. FAX 217-525-0712. Eds. Kevin Stein, Thomas Sandquist. index. circ. 2,450. (looseleaf format; back issues avail.) **Document type:** newsletter.

340   CN   ISSN 0832-7688
KE1492
COMMERCIAL INSOLVENCY REPORTER. 1987. 6/yr. Can.$130. Butterworths Canada Ltd., Part of the Reed Elsevier group, 75 Clegg Rd., Markham, ON L6G 1A1, Canada. TEL 905-479-2665. FAX 905-479-2826. (back issues avail.)
   Description: For accounting professionals. Contains case digests and comments, legislation, analyses of secured transactions and creditors' rights.

346.066   US
COMMERCIAL LAW BULLETIN. bi-m. Commercial Law League of America, 175 W. Jackson, Ste. 1541, Chicago, IL 60604. TEL 312-431-1305. FAX 312-431-1669. Ed. Linda Saghir. **Document type:** bulletin.

340   US   ISSN 0010-3055
COMMERCIAL LAW JOURNAL. 1912. q. $75 (foreign $85). Commercial Law League of America, 175 W. Jackson Blvd., Ste. 1541, Chicago, IL 60604-2703. TEL 312-431-1305. FAX 312-431-1669. Ed. Linda Saghir. adv.; bk.rev.; bibl.; index. circ. 7,000. (also avail. in microform from UMI; microfilm from WSH) **Indexed:** ABI Inform., BPIA, Bus.Ind., C.L.I., L.R.I., Leg.Cont., Leg.Per. **Document type:** academic/scholarly publication.
   —BLDSC (3336.965000); Faxon; UnCover; SWETS; UMI.
   Description: Discusses legal aspects of business.

346.066 347.7   US   ISSN 1046-4751
KF872
COMMERCIAL LAW REPORT. 1987. m. $215. Matthew Bender & Co., Inc., 11 Penn Plaza, New York, NY 10001. TEL 212-967-7707. FAX 212-244-3188. Ed.Bd. index. (looseleaf format; back issues avail.) **Document type:** newsletter.

340   UK   ISSN 0141-7258
LAW
COMMERCIAL LAWS OF EUROPE. (Text in English and original language) 1978. m. £340. (European Law Centre Ltd.) Sweet & Maxwell, South Quay Plaza, 7th Fl., 183 Marsh Wall, London E14 9FT, England. TEL 071-538-8686. FAX 071-538-9508. Ed. Neville March Hunnings. adv. contact: Jackie Wood. index. (back issues avail.) **Document type:** bulletin.
   Description: Reports national and international legislation.

COMMERCIAL LEASE LAW INSIDER; the practical, plain-English, monthly newsletter for owners, managers, attorneys and other real estate professionals. see *REAL ESTATE*

COMMERCIAL LOAN DOCUMENTATION GUIDE. see *BUSINESS AND ECONOMICS — Banking And Finance*

340   US
COMMERCIAL PAPER AND PAYMENT SYSTEMS. 1990. 2 base vols. (plus a. suppl.). $150. Butterworth Legal Publishers (Salem) (Subsidiary of: Reed Elsevier plc), 8 Industrial Way, Bldg. C, Salem, NH 03079. TEL 800-548-4001. FAX 603-898-9858. Ed. William H. Lawrence. (looseleaf format)
   Description: Discusses traditional payment systems while analyzing the role of new, alternative payment methods as they complement or compete with historical modes of payment.

COMMISSION ROYALE DES ANCIENNES LOIS ET ORDONNANCES DE BELGIQUE. BULLETIN/KONINKLIJKE COMMISSIE VOOR DE UITGAVE DER OUDE WETTEN EN VERORDENINGEN VAN BELGIE. HANDELINGEN. see *HISTORY*

340 US ISSN 0887-784X
KF1085.A59
COMMODITIES LITIGATION REPORTER; the national journal of record of commodities litigation. 1985. m. $750. Andrews Publications, 1646 West Chester Pike, Box 1000, Westtown, PA 19395. TEL 215-399-6600; 800-345-1101. FAX 215-399-6610. Ed. Barbara Pizzirani. abstr.; bibl.; stat.; cum.index every 6 mos. (looseleaf format; back issues avail.) **Document type:** newsletter.
 Description: Covers reparations and enforcements actions involving the scope of the Commodity Exchange Act.

346.066 332.6 US
COMMODITY FUTURES LAW REPORTS. 1974. s-m. $705. Commerce Clearing House, Inc., 4025 W. Peterson Ave., Chicago, IL 60646. TEL 312-940-4600. Ed. D. Newquist.

COMMON GROUND (ALEXANDRIA). see *REAL ESTATE*

341 UK ISSN 0588-7445
COMMON MARKET LAW REPORTS. (Supplement avail.) 1962. w. £480 with supplement. (European Law Centre Ltd.) Sweet & Maxwell, South Quay Plaza, 7th Fl., 183 Marsh Wall, London E14 9FT, England. TEL 071-538-8686. FAX 071-538-9508. Ed. Neville March Hunnings. adv. contact: Jackie Wood. cum.index: vol. 1-50 (1962-1987). (back issues avail.) **Document type:** bulletin.
 —UnCover; SWETS.
 Description: Up-to-date reports of community case law.

340 UK ISSN 0953-4423
KJE6456.A7
COMMON MARKET LAW REPORTS ANTITRUST SUPPLEMENT. 1988. m. (European Law Centre Ltd.) Sweet & Maxwell, South Quay Plaza, 7th Fl., 183 Marsh Wall, London E14 9FT, England. TEL 071-538-8686. FAX 071-538-9508. Ed. Neville March Hunnings. adv. contact: Jackie Wood. **Document type:** bulletin.

340 UK ISSN 0305-0718
LAW
COMMONWEALTH LAW BULLETIN. q. £60. Commonwealth Secretariat, Publications Division, Carlton House Terrace, Pall Mall, London S1Y 5HX, England. TEL 071-839-3411. FAX 071-930-0827. **Indexed:** RICS. **Document type:** academic/scholarly publication.
 —BLDSC (3340.880000).

334 UK
COMMONWEALTH LAWYER. 1984. s-a. £60. Law Society, Commonwealth Lawyers Association, 50 Chancery Ln., London WC2A 1SX, England. TEL 071-242-1222. FAX 071-831-0057. Ed. Karen Brewer. bk.rev. **Document type:** bulletin.

340 UK ISSN 0307-6539
COMMONWEALTH MAGISTRATES' CONFERENCE. REPORT. 1972. irreg., vol.9, 1991 Australia. £25. Commonwealth Magistrates' and Judges' Association, 10 Duke St., London W1M 5AA, England. TEL 071-487-2886. FAX 071-487-4386. adv. circ. 500.

COMMUNICATIONS AND THE LAW. see *COMMUNICATIONS*

340 AT
COMMUNICATIONS LAW & POLICY IN AUSTRALIA. base vol. (plus q. update). $395. Butterworths, 271-273 Lane Cove Rd., P.O. Box 345, North Ryde, N.S.W. 2113, Australia. TEL 02-335-4444. FAX 02-335-4655. (looseleaf format)

340 301.16 US ISSN 0737-7622
KF2750.A15
COMMUNICATIONS LAWYER. 1983. 4/yr. $15 to non-members. (American Bar Association, Forum Committee on Communications Law) A B A Press, 750 N. Lake Shore Dr., Chicago, IL 60611. TEL 312-988-6067. FAX 312-988-6281. Ed. Marla Hillery. adv.; bk.rev.; bibl. circ. 2,020. **Document type:** newsletter.
 Description: Reviews significant activities and developments in communications law and reports on Forum Committee events.

COMMUNICATIONS UPDATE; a monthly round-up of media and communications. see *COMMUNICATIONS*

COMMUNITY ASSOCIATION LAW REPORTER. see *HOUSING AND URBAN PLANNING*

340 US
COMMUNITY LAW WEEK NEWSLETTER. irreg. $6. American Bar Association, Young Lawyers Division, 750 N. Lake Shore Dr., Chicago, IL 60611. TEL 312-988-5555.

360 FR
COMPAGNIE NATIONALE DES COMMISSAIRES AUX COMPTES. CONSEIL NATIONAL. BULLETIN. 1970. q. 420 F. Compagnie Nationale des Commissaires aux Comptes, 8 rue de l'Amiral de Coligny, 75001 Paris, France. FAX 42-61-37-73. TELEX CINACO 240564F. bk.rev.; index. circ. 20,000. **Document type:** bulletin.
 Formerly: Federation des Associations de Commissaires de Societes. Bulletin de Liason.

340 US ISSN 0069-7893
COMPARATIVE JURIDICAL REVIEW. (Text in English and Spanish) 1964. a. free. (Rainforth Foundation) Pan American Institute of Comparative Law, 3001 Ponce de Leon Blvd., Coral Gables, FL 33134. TEL 305-446-7856. Ed. David S. Willig. bk.rev.; cum.index in vol.11, 1973. circ. 1,000. **Indexed:** C.L.I., L.R.I.
 —Faxon; UnCover.

COMPARATIVE LABOR LAW JOURNAL. see *BUSINESS AND ECONOMICS — Labor And Industrial Relations*

340.5 JA ISSN 0010-4116
COMPARATIVE LAW REVIEW/HIKAKUHO ZASSHI. (Text in Japanese; summaries in English) 1951. q. 900 Yen per no. Institute of Comparative Law in Japan - Nihon Hikakuho Kenkyujo, c/o Chuo University, Higashinakano, Hachioji-shi, Tokyo 192-03, Japan. FAX 0426-74-3301. Ed. Yoshiaki Sanada. bk.rev.; bibl.; pat.; index, cum.index. circ. 1,000.

COMPARATIVE STATE POLITICS. see *POLITICAL SCIENCE*

COMPENSATION OF LEGAL AND RELATED JOBS (NON-LAW FIRMS). see *BUSINESS AND ECONOMICS — Labor And Industrial Relations*

COMPENSATION STRATEGY AND MANAGEMENT. see *BUSINESS AND ECONOMICS — Personnel Management*

340 US
COMPETITION (SAN FRANCISCO). 4/yr. $40 (effective 1993-1994). State Bar of California, Antitrust and Trade Regulation Law Section, 555 Franklin St., San Francisco, CA 94102. TEL 415-561-8854. FAX 415-561-8228. circ. 1,000. (looseleaf format) **Document type:** newsletter.

340 US
COMPILATION OF BAR EXAMINATION QUESTIONS & ANSWERS. 1968. s-a. $70. Institute for Bar Review Study, 86 Norwood Rd., West Hartford, CT 06117-2236. TEL 203-232-3100. Ed. Robert Whitman. circ. 220. (back issues avail.) **Document type:** academic/scholarly publication.
 Description: Study aid for the Bar exam.

340 US ISSN 0882-9136
KF1262.A29
COMPILATION OF STATE AND FEDERAL PRIVACY LAWS. (Annual supplement avail.) 1975. irreg., latest 1992. $29. (Privacy Journal) Robert Ellis Smith, Ed. & Pub., Box 28577, Providence, RI 02908. TEL 401-274-7861. circ. 2,000. **Indexed:** Comput.Lit.Ind.
 Description: Cites and describes state and federal laws protecting confidentiality of personal information.

340 US ISSN 0741-9066
K3
COMPLEAT LAWYER. 1984. q. $39.90. (American Bar Association) A B A Press, 750 N. Lake Shore Dr., Chicago, IL 60611. TEL 312-988-6122. Ed. Ray DeLong. adv. circ. 44,000. (back issues avail.) **Indexed:** C.L.I., L.R.I.
 —BLDSC (3364.203350); Faxon; UnCover.
 Formerly (until vol.19, no.3, 1983): Docket Call (Chicago) (ISSN 0569-3160)
 Description: Practical articles directed to the lay clients of general practitioners on substantive areas of law.

340 US
COMPLETE GUIDE TO MECHANIC'S AND MATERIALMAN'S LIEN LAWS OF TEXAS. base vol. (plus suppl. 1-2/yr.), 3rd ed., 1990. $115. Butterworth Legal Publishers (Salem) (Subsidiary of: Reed Elsevier plc), 8 Industrial Way, Bldg. C, Salem, NH 03079. TEL 800-548-4001. FAX 603-898-9858. Eds. Brenda T. Cubbage, Sterling W. Steves. (looseleaf format)

COMPLETE LEGISLATIVE SERVICE. see *PUBLIC ADMINISTRATION*

340 332.1 US
COMPLIANCE EXAMINATIONS UPDATE. 1985. bi-m. $278 (foreign $445.35) (effective 1994). (Consumer Bankers Association) Warren Gorham Lamont, One Penn Plaza, New York, NY 10119. TEL 212-971-5000. FAX 212-971-5240. (Subscr. to: The Park Square Bldg., 31 St. James Ave., Boston, MA 02116-4112. TEL 800-950-1207) (looseleaf format) **Document type:** trade publication.
 Description: Update service written by two lawyers covers the latest compliance violations in the industry. Offers helpful curing techniques to protect a compliance program.

COMPLIANCE PROGRAM GUIDANCE MANUALS. see *PUBLIC HEALTH AND SAFETY*

COMPTROLLER GENERAL'S PROCUREMENT DECISIONS. see *BUSINESS AND ECONOMICS — Economic Situation And Conditions*

340 001.6 621.381 AT
▼**COMPUTER CONTRACTS PRINCIPLES AND PRECEDENTS**. 1992. base vol. (plus updates 4/yr.). Aus.$295. Law Book Co. Ltd., 44-50 Waterloo Rd., North Ryde, N.S.W 2113, Australia. TEL 02-887-0177. FAX 02-888-9706. TELEX ASHBOOK 27995. Eds. G. Hughes, A. Sharpe. (looseleaf format)
 Description: Provides all the information necessary to negotiate, draft and advise on contracts for the sale or acquisition of computer products and computer-related services; contains precedent contracts.

COMPUTER COUNSEL; the journal of law office productivity and automation. see *COMPUTERS*

340 US ISSN 0740-1469
KF390.5.C6
COMPUTER INDUSTRY LITIGATION REPORTER; the national journal of record of computer industry litigation. 1983. s-m. $825. Andrews Publications, 1646 West Chester Pike, Box 1000, Westtown, PA 19395. TEL 215-399-6600; 800-345-1101. FAX 215-399-6610. Ed. Harry G. Armstrong. bibl.; stat.; cum.index every 6 mos. (looseleaf format; back issues avail.) **Document type:** newsletter.
 Description: Reports on copyright, patent and trademark claims, theft of secret cases, significant user - vendor contract-misrepresentation claims, consultant liability questions, and other evolving issues as they relate to the computer industry.

COMPUTER LAW & PRACTICE. see *COMPUTERS*

COMPUTER LAW & TAX REPORT; monthly newsletter covering computer-related law and tax issues. see *COMPUTERS*

COMPUTER-LAW JOURNAL; international journal of computer, communication and information law. see *COMPUTERS*

COMPUTER LAW MONITOR. see *COMPUTERS*

COMPUTER LAW REPORTER; a monthly journal of computer law and practice, intellectual property, copyright and trademark law. see *COMPUTERS*

COMPUTER LAW SERIES. see *COMPUTERS*

COMPUTER LAW STRATEGIST. see *COMPUTERS*

COMPUTER LAWYER. see *COMPUTERS*

COMPUTER SOFTWARE PROTECTION LAW. see *COMPUTERS — Software*

LAW

340 001.6 621.381 US
COMPUTER TECHNOLOGY AND THE LAW. 1983. base vol. (plus a. suppl.). $95. Shepard's - McGraw-Hill, Inc., Box 35300, Colorado Springs, CO 80935-3530.
 Description: Explores all facets of proprietary rights and contract issues. Discusses how computers affect principles of law and legal procedure, and how law and regulation affect the development, marketing and implementation of new data processing technologies.

COMPUTER UND RECHT; Forum fuer die Praxis des Rechts der Datenverarbeitung, Kommunikation und Automation. see COMPUTERS

COMPUTERREPORT DER NEUE JURISTISCHEN WOCHENSCHRIFT; Informationsmanagement und Bueroorganisation in der juristischen Praxis. see LAW — Computer Applications

340 SP
COMUNIDAD EUROPEA. (Includes q. bound vols.) 1974. m. (except Aug.). 16000 ptas. Editorial Aranzadi, S.A., Avda. Carlos III, 34, Apdo. 111, 31080 Pamplona, Spain. TEL 948-331212. FAX 948-330919. bibl.; index.

CONCERNS (WASHINGTON). see EDUCATION

CONDITIONS OF WORK DIGEST. see BUSINESS AND ECONOMICS — Labor And Industrial Relations

347.91 CN
CONDUCT OF CIVIL LITIGATION IN BRITISH COLUMBIA. s-a. Can.$475. Butterworths Canada Ltd., Part of the Reed Elsevier group, 75 Clegg Rd., Markham, ON L6G 1A1, Canada. TEL 905-479-2665. FAX 905-479-2826. Eds. Peter Fraser, John Horn. (looseleaf format)
 Description: A guide for practitioners and support staff in British Columbia.

349 PE ISSN 0573-4347
CONFERENCIA DE FACULTADES LATINOAMERICANAS DE DERECHO. (DOCUMENTOS OFICIALES).* 1959. a. Universidad Nacional, Apartado 524, Lima, Peru.

340 US
CONFIDENTIAL REPORT FOR ATTORNEYS. 1963. s-m. $195 (diskette $395). Confidential Report for Attorneys, Box 1476, Oceanside, CA 92051. TEL 619-721-3622. FAX 619-721-3683. Ed. Richard Neubauer. index. (looseleaf format; also avail. in diskette format) **Document type:** newsletter.

340 360 US ISSN 1064-0061
CONFLICT RESOLUTION NOTES. 1983. q. $20. Conflict Resolution Center International, Inc., 2205 E. Carson St., Pittsburgh, PA 15203-2107. TEL 412-481-5559. FAX 412-481-5559. Ed. Paul Wahrhaftig. adv.; bk.rev. circ. 600. (back issues avail.) **Document type:** newsletter.
 ●Also available online.
 Description: Presents short articles for researchers or practitioners of conflict resolution. Focuses on resolution of neighborhood, racial, ethnic and religious, and gender conflicts.

340 352 US
CONGRESSIONAL LEGISLATIVE REPORTING. 1937. irreg. price varies. Commerce Clearing House, Inc., 4025 W. Peterson Ave., Chicago, IL 60646. TEL 312-583-8500. Ed. D. Newquist.

340 US
CONGRESSIONAL RESEARCH SERVICE INDEX. 1975. a (plus q. updates). price varies. University Publications of America (Subsidiary of: Congressional Information Service), 4520 East-West Hwy., Ste. 800, Bethesda, MD 20814-3389. TEL 301-657-3200. FAX 301-657-3200. (microfiche) **Document type:** abstracting/indexing, bibliography.
 Description: Includes studies and issue briefs from important collections on key legal, environmental, economic, social, and international issues dated from 1916 to date in the United States.

353.9 US
KFC4108
CONNECTICUT. JUDICIAL BRANCH. BIENNIAL REPORT. Key Title: Report of the Judicial Branch, State of Connecticut. 1928. biennial. free. Judicial Branch, 231 Capitol Ave., Drawer N, Sta. A, Hartford, CT 06106. TEL 203-566-8219. FAX 203-566-3308. Ed. Faith Arkin. illus. **Document type:** government publication.
 Former titles: Connecticut. Judicial Department. Report (ISSN 0098-8138); (until 1974): Connecticut. Judicial Council. Report (ISSN 0190-7824)

320 US
CONNECTICUT. LAW REVISION COMMISSION. ANNUAL REPORT. 1976. a. Law Revision Commission, State Capitol, Rm. 509A, Hartford, CT 06106. TEL 203-240-0220. FAX 203-240-0322.

340 US
CONNECTICUT APPELLATE PRACTICE & PROCEDURE. 1989. base vol. (plus suppl.). $105. Butterworth Legal Publishers (Salem) (Subsidiary of: Reed Elsevier plc), 8 Industrial Way, Bldg. C, Salem, NH 03079. TEL 800-548-4001. FAX 603-898-9858. Ed. Colin C. Tait. (looseleaf format)
 Description: Covers appeals from the Superior Court to the Appellate Court and the Supreme Court, and appeals from the Appellate Court to the Supreme Court. Constitutional and statutory materials are discussed, as are matters within the original jurisdiction of the Supreme Court.

340 US
CONNECTICUT APPELLATE REPORTS. 4/yr. $21. Commission on Official Legal Publications, Office of Production and Distribution, 111 Phoenix Ave., Enfield, CT 06082. TEL 203-741-3027. FAX 203-745-2178.
 Description: Complete version of the opinions of the Connecticut Appellate Court, including headnotes, preliminary procedural summaries and names of counsel.

340 US ISSN 0010-6070
LAW
CONNECTICUT BAR JOURNAL. 1927. bi-m. $35. Connecticut Bar Association, 101 Corporate Pl., Rocky Hill, CT 06067. TEL 203-721-0025. Ed. William T. Burrante. adv.; bk.rev.; bibl.; index. circ. 11,000. (also avail. in microfilm from WSH) **Indexed:** C.L.I., L.R.I., Law Ofc.Info.Svc., Leg.Per. **Document type:** trade publication.
 —BLDSC (3417.615000); Faxon; UnCover.

CONNECTICUT EDUCATION ASSOCIATION. LEGISLATIVE BULLETIN. see EDUCATION

340 331 US ISSN 1064-4903
▼**CONNECTICUT EMPLOYMENT LAW LETTER.** 1993. m. $95. (Pepe & Hazard) M. Lee Smith Publishers & Printers, 162 Fourth Ave., N., Box 198867, Nashville, TN 37219-8867. TEL 615-242-7395; 800-274-6774. FAX 615-256-6601. Eds. Ann F. Bird, Henry J. Zaccardi. **Document type:** newsletter.
 Description: Reports the latest state-specific employment law developments that affect companies in Connecticut.

340 613.1 US ISSN 1064-2382
▼**CONNECTICUT ENVIRONMENTAL COMPLIANCE UPDATE.** 1992. m. $137. (Pepe & Hazard) M. Lee Smith Publishers & Printers, 162 Fourth Ave., N., Box 198867, Nashville, TN 37219-8867. TEL 615-242-7395; 800-274-6774. FAX 615-256-6601. Ed.Bd. **Document type:** newsletter.
 Description: Reports the latest state-specific environmental law developments that affect companies in Connecticut.

340 US ISSN 0737-920X
KFC3700.A15
CONNECTICUT FAMILY LAW JOURNAL. 1982. 6/yr. $95. Butterworth Legal Publishers (Salem) (Subsidiary of: Reed Elsevier plc), 8 Industrial Way, Bldg. C, Salem, NH 03079. TEL 800-548-4001. FAX 603-898-9858. Ed. Otis Dean. cum.index. (looseleaf format; back issues avail.) **Document type:** newsletter.
 Description: Family law articles, case comments, and Connecticut Superior Court decisions.

CONNECTICUT INSURANCE LAW REVIEW. see INSURANCE

340 US
CONNECTICUT LAW JOURNAL. 1935. w. $150. Commission on Official Legal Publications, Office of Production and Distribution, 111 Phoenix Ave., Enfield, CT 06082. TEL 203-741-3027. FAX 203-745-2178. Dir. Richard J. Hemenway.
 Description: Covers Supreme Court, appellate court and selected superior court decisions; practice book rule changes; administrative regulations; and legal notices.

340 US ISSN 0010-6151
CONNECTICUT LAW REVIEW. 1968. q. $23. Connecticut Law Review Association, 65 Elizabeth St., Hartford, CT 06105-2290. TEL 203-241-4607. FAX 203-241-7666. Ed. James F. Sullivan. adv.; bk.rev. circ. 1,600. (also avail. in microfilm; back issues avail.; reprint service avail. from RRI,UMI) **Indexed:** C.L.I., L.R.I., Leg.Cont., Leg.Per.
 ●Also available online. Vendor(s): West Services, Inc. —BLDSC (3417.653000); Faxon; UnCover; UMI.

340 US ISSN 0198-0289
K3
CONNECTICUT LAW TRIBUNE. w. $315. Connecticut Law Tribune Company (Subsidiary of: American Lawyer Media, L.P.), One Post Rd., Ste. 100, Fairfield, CT 06430-0215. TEL 203-256-3600. FAX 203-255-3319. Ed. Joseph Calve. adv.; bk.rev.; index. circ. 3,500. (back issues avail.)
 Description: Covers legal issues for the state of Connecticut.

340 US ISSN 1057-2384
CONNECTICUT LAWYER. 1969. 11/yr. membership. Connecticut Bar Association, 101 Corporate Pl., Rocky Hill, CT 06067-1894. TEL 203-721-0025. FAX 203-257-4125. Ed. Megan FitzGerald. adv.; illus. circ. 11,000. **Document type:** trade publication.
 Description: Provides a forum for discussion of current legal and professional concerns, with news of association activities and meetings.

340 US
CONNECTICUT NOTARY LAW PRIMER. a. $9.95. National Notary Association, 8236 Remmet Ave., Box 7184, Canoga Park, CA 91309-7184. TEL 818-713-4000. FAX 818-713-9061. Ed. Charles N. Faerber. (reprint service avail. from UMI) **Document type:** monographic series.

CONNECTICUT REAL ESTATE LAW JOURNAL. see REAL ESTATE

340 333.33 US
CONNECTICUT REAL PROPERTY STATUTES. (2nd ed., 1991) 1980. base vol. (plus supplements). $55. Butterworth Legal Publishers (Salem) (Subsidiary of: Reed Elsevier plc), 8 Industrial Way, Bldg. C, Salem, NH 03079. TEL 800-548-4001. FAX 603-898-9858. (looseleaf format)

340 US
CONNECTICUT REPORTS. (Supplement avail.: Connecticut Supplement) irreg. (approx. 4/yr.). price varies. Commission on Official Legal Publications, Office of Production and Distribution, 111 Phoenix Ave., Enfield, CT 06082. TEL 203-741-3027. FAX 203-745-2178.
 Description: Complete version of the opinions of the Connecticut Supreme Court, including headnotes, preliminary procedural summaries, orders on petitions for certification and names of counsel.

340 US
CONNECTICUT SUPPLEMENT. (Supplement to: Connecticut Reports) irreg. $21. Commission on Official Legal Publications, Office of Production and Distribution, 111 Phoenix Ave., Enfield, CT 06082. TEL 203-741-3027. FAX 203-745-2178.
 Description: Selected opinions of the Connecticut Superior Court, chosen by a committee of State Trial Referees (former Judges of the Superior Court) for their significance to the trial bench and bar.
 Refereed Serial

340 US
CONNECTICUT TIME LIMITATIONS. (2nd ed., 1991) 1984. base vol. (plus supplement). $55. Butterworth Legal Publishers (Salem) (Subsidiary of: Reed Elsevier plc), 8 Industrial Way, Bldg. C, Salem, NH 03079. TEL 800-548-4001. FAX 603-898-9858. (looseleaf format)

CONNECTICUT WORKERS' COMPENSATION REVIEW OPINIONS. see *BUSINESS AND ECONOMICS — Labor And Industrial Relations*

CONSCIOUS CONSUMER; products and services that help the earth and society. see *ENVIRONMENTAL STUDIES*

340   IT   ISSN 0010-6569
CONSIGLIO DI STATO; rassegna di giurisprudenza e dottrina. 1953. m. L.435000. Casa Editrice Italedi, Piazza Cavour 19, 00193 Rome, Italy. TEL 6-321-08-03. Ed. Ignazio Scotto. adv.; bk.rev.; bibl.; index, cum.index. circ. 5,000.

340   SA
CONSOLIDATED INDEX AND NOTER-UP TO THE SOUTH AFRICAN LAW REPORTS. Variant title: Gracie's Index. a. Butterworth Publishers (Pty.) Ltd., P.O. Box 792, Durban 4000, South Africa. TEL 27-31-294247. FAX 27-31-283255. Ed. Tom Coghlan. Document type: abstracting/indexing.
    Formerly: South African Law Reports, Index and Noter-Up.

342   II   ISSN 1049-4987
K3
CONSTITUTIONAL LAW JOURNAL. (Text in English) 1971. q. Rs.80($20) Law Academy, 1-9-322 Vidyanagar, Hyderabad 500044 (A.P.), India. Ed. G.S. Prasad Rao. adv.; bk.rev.
    —UnCover.
    Description: Covers Indian Supreme Court decisions and includes articles by eminent authorities.

CONSTRUCTION AND DESIGN LAW DIGEST. see *BUILDING AND CONSTRUCTION*

340 690   US   ISSN 0148-933X
KFN5230.B8A493
CONSTRUCTION & SURETY LAW NEWSLETTER. 1991. 2/yr. $10 to non-members. New York State Bar Association, 1 Elk St., Albany, NY 12207-1096. TEL 518-463-3200. FAX 518-487-5699. Ed. William R. Moriarity. adv.; bk.rev. circ. 500. Document type: newsletter.

CONSTRUCTION CLAIMS CITATOR. see *BUILDING AND CONSTRUCTION*

CONSTRUCTION CLAIMS MONTHLY; devoted exclusively to the problems of construction contracting. see *BUILDING AND CONSTRUCTION*

CONSTRUCTION CLAIMS TRAINING GUIDE. see *BUILDING AND CONSTRUCTION*

340 690   UK   ISSN 0269-0039
CONSTRUCTION INDUSTRY LAW LETTER. 10/yr. £150($300) I B C Publishing, Gilmoora House, 57-61 Mortimer St., London W1N 7TD, England. TEL 071-637-4383. FAX 071-636-6414. (Subscr. in U.S. to: IBC (USA), 290 Eliot St., Box 91004, Ashland, MA 01721-9104. TEL 508-881-2800. FAX 508-881-0982) Eds. Paul Darling, Louise Randall. Document type: newsletter.
    —BLDSC (3421.307600).

340 690   US   ISSN 1050-4060
CONSTRUCTION INJURY LIABILITY MONTHLY. 1989. m. $156. Business Publishers, Inc., 951 Pershing Dr., Silver Spring, MD 20910-4464. TEL 301-587-6300. FAX 301-587-1081. Ed. Tom Ramstack. (looseleaf format; back issues avail.) Document type: newsletter.
    •Also available online. Vendor(s): NewsNet.
    Description: Case studies to help construction managers avoid litigation.

CONSTRUCTION LAW ADVISER; monthly practical advice for lawyers and construction professionals. see *BUILDING AND CONSTRUCTION*

CONSTRUCTION LAW DIGEST. see *LAW — Abstracting, Bibliographies, Statistics*

CONSTRUCTION LAW JOURNAL. see *BUILDING AND CONSTRUCTION*

CONSTRUCTION LAW LETTER. see *BUILDING AND CONSTRUCTION*

690 340   CN   ISSN 0824-2593
CONSTRUCTION LAW REPORTS. 1983. 6 vols./yr. Can.$135. Carswell, One Corporate Plaza, 2075 Kennedy Rd., Scarborough, ON M1T 3V4, Canada. TEL 416-609-8000. FAX 416-298-5094. Ed. Harvey J. Kirsh. adv. contact: M. Lalani. Indexed: Ind.Can.L.P.I.
    Description: Features important construction law decisions from all Canadian jurisdictions selected by experts in the field. Includes cases on building contracts, remedies for their breach, construction liens and bonding issues, court actions involving architects, engineers, contractors.

CONSTRUCTION LAWYER. see *BUILDING AND CONSTRUCTION*

CONSTRUCTION LITIGATION REPORTER; recent decisions of national significance. see *BUILDING AND CONSTRUCTION*

340   US   ISSN 1058-3963
CONSUMER BANKRUPTCY NEWS. 1991. w. $255. L R P Publications, 747 Dresher Rd., Horsham, PA 19044. TEL 215-784-0860. FAX 215-784-0870. Ed. David Light. (looseleaf format; back issues avail.) Document type: newsletter.

340   US   ISSN 0300-6034
KF1039.A15
CONSUMER CREDIT & TRUTH IN LENDING COMPLIANCE REPORT. 1969. m. $176.75 (overseas $235.90). Warren Gorham Lamont, One Penn Plaza, New York, NY 10119. TEL 212-971-5000. FAX 212-971-5240. (Subscr. to: The Park Square Bldg., 31 St. James Ave., Boston, MA 02116-4112. TEL 800-950-1207) Ed. Earl Phillips. (also avail. in microform from UMI) Document type: newsletter.
    —CCC.
    Description: Focuses on the latest regulatory rulings and findings involving consumer lending and credit activity.

340   UK
CONSUMER CREDIT CONTROL. irreg. £267. Longman Group Ltd., Law, Tax and Finance Division, 21-27 Lambs Conduit St., London WC1N 3NJ, England. TEL 071-242-2548. FAX 071-831-8119. Ed. Frances Bennion. (looseleaf format) Document type: bulletin.
    Description: Analysis of the Consumer Credit Act.

640.73   US
CONSUMER CREDIT GUIDE REPORTS. 1969. bi-w. $900. Commerce Clearing House, Inc., 4025 W. Peterson Ave., Chicago, IL 60646. TEL 312-583-8500. FAX 708-940-0113. Ed. James Rooney. circ. 1,200. (looseleaf format)
    Description: Covers federal and state consumers credit, and disclosure rules.

340 640.73   UK   ISSN 0140-8518
CONSUMER LAW TODAY - THE FAIR TRADING MONITOR. 1977. m. £127 (foreign £149). Monitor Press, Rectory Rd., Great Waldingfield, Sudbury, Suffolk CO10 OTL, England. TEL 0787-378607. FAX 0787-880201. (back issues avail.) Document type: newsletter.
    Formerly (until 1993): Consumer Law Today.
    Description: For senior management who need to know about the latest developments and regulations that concern packaging and advertising, labelling, credit, pricing, contracts, guarantees, insurance and new moves on product liability.

340   US   ISSN 1052-9632
KF1296.A59
CONSUMER PRODUCT LITIGATION REPORTER. 1990. m. $500. Andrews Publications, 1646 West Chester Pike, Box 1000, Westtown, PA 19395. TEL 215-399-6600; 800-345-1101. FAX 215-399-6610. Ed. Mary Rhoads. adv.; bibl.; stat.; cum.index every 6 mos. (looseleaf format; back issues avail.) Document type: newsletter.
    Description: Covers product liability issues such as strict liability, adequacy of warning and merchantability. Also covers state and federal legislation.

340   UK   ISSN 1353-3592
▼**CONSUMER PROTECTION.** 1994. a. £17.50. Jordan Publishing Ltd., 21 St. Thomas St., Bristol BS1 6JS, England. TEL 0272-230600. FAX 0272-250486. Ed. Diana Jackson. Document type: academic/scholarly publication.

CONSUMER PROTECTION, ANTITRUST & UNFAIR BUSINESS PRACTICES NEWSLETTER. see *CONSUMER EDUCATION AND PROTECTION*

CONSUMER PROTECTION REPORT. see *CONSUMER EDUCATION AND PROTECTION*

CONTEMPORARY DRUG PROBLEMS. see *DRUG ABUSE AND ALCOHOLISM*

340   CN   ISSN 0381-0925
CONTINUUM. 1973. 2/yr. York University, Osgoode Hall Law School, Rm. 320, 4700 Keele St., North York, ON M3J 1P3, Canada. TEL 416-736-5638. Ed. John D. McCamus. illus. circ. 8,500. Indexed: C.I.J.E., Film Lit.Ind. (1989-). Document type: academic/scholarly publication.

340   US   ISSN 1063-4444
CONTRA COSTA LAWYER. 1988. m. membership. Contra Costa County Bar Association, 1001 Galaxy Way, Ste. 102, Concord, CA 94520. TEL 510-686-6900. Ed. Linda DeBene. adv.; illus.
    Formerly (until 1992): Contra Costa County Bar Association. Recorder (ISSN 1046-9028)
    Description: Covers association news and activities and legal topics of interest to lawyers in Contra Costa county.

340   US
CONTRACT APPEALS DECISIONS. 1956. bi-w. $890. Commerce Clearing House, Inc., 4025 W. Peterson Ave., Chicago, IL 60646. TEL 312-583-8500. Ed. D. Newquist.

340   US   ISSN 0147-1074
CONTRIBUTIONS IN LEGAL STUDIES. 1978. irreg., no.67, 1992. price varies. Greenwood Press, Inc. (Subsidiary of: Greenwood Publishing Group Inc.), 88 Post Rd. W., Box 5007, Westport, CT 06881-5007. TEL 203-226-3571. FAX 203-222-1502. Ed. Paul L. Murphy.
    —BLDSC (3458.870000).

CONVENTION LIAISON COUNCIL. LEGAL REVIEW. see *MEETINGS AND CONGRESSES*

CONVEYANCER AND PROPERTY LAWYER. see *REAL ESTATE*

340   UK   ISSN 1352-4534
▼**CONVEYANCING.** 1993. a. £17.50. Jordan Publishing Ltd., 21 St. Thomas St., Bristol BS1 6JS, England. TEL 0272-230600. FAX 0272-250486. Ed. Frances Silverman. Document type: academic/scholarly publication.

340   SA
CONVEYANCING BULLETIN. base vol. (plus q. supplement). R.100. Butterworth Publishers (Pty.) Ltd., P.O. Box 792, Durban 4000, South Africa. TEL 27-31-294247. FAX 27-31-283255. Ed. R.C. Laurens. (looseleaf format) Document type: bulletin.

340   AT
CONVEYANCING SERVICE NEW SOUTH WALES. 2 base vols. (plus updates 8/yr.). $655. Butterworths, 271-273 Lane Cove Rd., P.O. Box 345, North Ryde, N.S.W. 2113, Australia. TEL 02-335-4444. FAX 02-335-4655. (looseleaf format)

340   US   ISSN 0899-5621
KF292.C6884
COOLEY BENCHMARK. 1976. m. Thomas Cooley Law School, Box 13038, Lansing, MI 48901. TEL 517-371-5140. FAX 517-334-5718. Ed. Michelle L. Villas.
    Description: Features articles on trends in the law and on alumni.

COORDINATION OFFICIEUSE DES TEXTES LEGAUX RELATIFS AU STATUT SOCIAL DES TRAVAILLEURS INDEPENDANTS ET COMMENTAIRES. see *INSURANCE*

LAW

340   UN   ISSN 0010-8634
CODEN: UECBAP
COPYRIGHT BULLETIN; quarterly review. French edition: Bulletin du Droit d'Auteur (ISSN 0304-2928); Spanish edition: Boletin de Derecho de Autor (ISSN 0304-2936) (Text in English) 1948. q. 60 F.($25) Unesco, 7-9 Place de Fontenoy, 75700 Paris, France. TEL 45-77-16-10. (Dist. in U.S. by: Unipub, 4611-F Assembly Dr., Lanham, MD 20706-4391. TEL 800-274-4888) Ed. Evgueni Guerassimov. bibl.; charts. circ. 1,590. (also avail. in microform) **Indexed:** ELLIS, Mid.East: Abstr.& Ind., P.A.I.S. —BLDSC (3468.790000); Faxon; UnCover; SWETS; CASDDS.

340   US   ISSN 0010-8839
KF292.C6914
CORNELL LAW FORUM. 1949. 3/yr. free to qualified personnel. Cornell University, Law School, Myron Taylor Hall, Ithaca, NY 14853. TEL 607-255-7477. Eds. John A. Siliciano, Kathleen E. Rourke. illus.; pat.; tr.rvw. circ. 9,000. (reprint service avail. from WSH) **Indexed:** C.L.I., L.R.I., Leg.Per.
—UMI.

340   US   ISSN 0010-8847
K3
CORNELL LAW REVIEW. 1915. 6/yr. $35. Cornell University, Law School, Myron Taylor Hall, Ithaca, NY 14853. TEL 607-255-3387. Ed.Bd. adv.; bk.rev.; charts; illus.; index, cum.index: vol.1-15, 16-38. circ. 3,500. (also avail. in microfiche from RRI,WSH; microfilm from RRI,WSH; back issues avail.; reprint service avail. from RRI) **Indexed:** A.B.C.Pol.Sci., Account.Ind. (1974-), Bank.Lit.Ind., BPIA, C.L.I., Crim.Just.Abstr., Curr.Cont., L.R.I., Leg.Cont., Leg.Per., P.A.I.S., SSCI.
●Also available online. Vendor(s): Mead Data Central, Inc., West Services, Inc.
—BLDSC (3470.955500); Faxon; UnCover; SWETS.
Formerly: Cornell Law Quarterly.

340   IT
CORRIERE GIURIDICO. 12/yr. Strada 1, Palazzo F6, 20090 Assago Milanofiori (MI), Italy. TEL 2-82-47-61. Ed. Massimiliano Galioni. circ. 14,000.

340   US
COUNCIL FOR COURT EXCELLENCE ANNUAL REPORT. 1982. a. $50. Council for Court Excellence, 1800 M St., N.W., Ste. 750-S, Washington, DC 20036-5802. TEL 202-785-5917. FAX 202-785-5922. Ed. Samuel F. Harahan. circ. 2,000. (back issues avail.)
Description: Report of public interest group working to improve the administration of justice.

340   US   ISSN 0279-9626
KF200
COUNTY BAR UPDATE. 1981. m. membership. Los Angeles County Bar Association, Box 55020, Los Angeles, CA 90055. TEL 213-896-6410. FAX 213-896-6500. Ed. Karen King. circ. 24,000. (back issues avail.)

340   UK   ISSN 0269-3291
COUNTY COURT PRACTICE. a. $270. Butterworth & Co. (Publishers) Ltd. (Subsidiary of: Reed Elsevier plc), 88 Kingsway, London WC2B 6AB, England. TEL 71-405-6900. FAX 71-405-1332. (US addr.: Butterworth Legal Publishers, 90 Stiles Rd., Salem, NH 03079-9981. TEL 603-898-9664) Ed. P.J.K. Thompson.

340 026   US
COUNTY LAW LIBRARY PROGRAM BULLETIN. 1980. 5/yr. $6. Minnesota State Law Library, 25 Constitution Ave., St. Paul, MN 55155-6102. TEL 612-297-2087. FAX 612-296-6740. Ed. Barbara Golden. bk.rev. circ. 475. **Document type:** newsletter.

340   US
COUNTY LINE. 4/yr. free to qualified personnel. Pennsylvania Bar Association, 100 South St., Harrisburg, PA 17108. TEL 717-238-6715. FAX 717-238-7182. **Document type:** newsletter.

340   CN   ISSN 0316-1234
COURS DE PERFECTIONNEMENT DU NOTARIAT. 1962. s-a. Can.$40 per no. Chambre des Notaires du Quebec, 630 Blvd. Rene Levesque, Ste. 1700, Montreal, PQ H3B 1T6, Canada. TEL 514-879-1793. FAX 514-879-1923. bibl.; cum.index: 1962-1985. (also avail. in record; video cassette) **Indexed:** Ind.Can.L.P.L.

340 332   UK   ISSN 0954-0857
CREDIT & FINANCE LAW. 10/yr. £147($294) I B C Publishing, Gilmoora House, 57-61 Mortimer St., London W1N 7TD, England. TEL 071-637-4383. FAX 071-636-6414. (Subscr. in U.S. to: IBC (USA), 290 Eliot St., Box 91004, Ashland, MA 01721-9104. TEL 508-881-2800. FAX 508-881-0982) Ed. Watson Farley. **Document type:** newsletter.

CREDIT UNION WEEK. see BUSINESS AND ECONOMICS — Banking And Finance

340   US   ISSN 0011-1155
K3
CREIGHTON LAW REVIEW. 1963. q. $25. Creighton University, Creighton Law School, 2133 California St., Omaha, NE 68178. TEL 402-280-2980. (Dist. by: Fred B. Rothman & Co., 10368 W. Centennial Rd., Littleton, CO 80123) Ed. Michael A. LeMay. adv.; bk.rev.; index. circ. 3,840. (also avail. in microform from UMI; reprint service avail. from RRI,UMI) **Indexed:** C.L.I., L.R.I., Leg.Cont., Leg.Per. **Document type:** academic/scholarly publication.
●Also available online. Vendor(s): West Services, Inc. —BLDSC (3487.297000); Faxon; UnCover.

340   IT
CRITICA GIUDIZIARIA. bi-m. Via F. Turati 37, 40134 Bologna, Italy. Ed. Giuseppe Delfini.

347 945   IT
CRITICA PENALE.* q. Via Bassi 14, 40121 Bologna, Italy.

CRITICAL ISSUES. see POLITICAL SCIENCE

340 658.7   UK
CRONER'S BUYING AND SELLING LAW. 1982. bi-m. £81 effective 1992. Croner Publications Ltd., Croner House, London Road, Kingston, Surrey KT2 6SR, England. TEL 081-547-3333. FAX 081-547-2637. TELEX 267778. Ed. Robert Piper. (looseleaf format)
Description: Covers the essentials of all areas of the law relevant to buying and selling goods or services.

340 658.3   UK
CRONER'S EMPLOYMENT LAW. 1980. bi-m. £96.40 (effective 1992). Croner Publications Ltd., Croner House, London Road, Kingston, Surrey KT2 6SR, England. TEL 081-547-3333. FAX 081-547-2637. TELEX 267778. Ed. Clio Fisher. (looseleaf format)
Description: Details legislative requirements at each stage of employment from recruitment to termination.

CRONER'S HEALTH AND SAFETY AT WORK. see OCCUPATIONAL HEALTH AND SAFETY

340   UK   ISSN 0953-7643
CROWN OFFICE DIGEST. bi-m. £178. Sweet & Maxwell, South Quay Plaza, 7th Fl., 183 Marsh Wall, London E14 9FT, England. TEL 071-538-8686. FAX 071-538-9508. Ed. Nick O'Dell. adv. contact: Jackie Wood. **Document type:** bulletin.

342   AG
CUADERNOS DE LOS INSTITUTOS. 1957. irreg. Universidad Nacional de Cordoba, Instituto de Derecho Constitucional, Calle Obispo Trejo y Sanabria 242, Cordoba, Argentina.

340   SP   ISSN 1132-6700
▼**CUADERNOS JURIDICOS.** 1992. m. (11/yr.). $65. Editorial Fontalba, S.A., Valencia 359, 6o 1a, 08009 Barcelona, Spain.

340   US   ISSN 0360-8298
K3
CUMBERLAND LAW REVIEW. 1970. 3/yr. $24. Samford University, Cumberland School of Law, 800 Lakeshore Dr., ROBBH 305D, Birmingham, AL 35229. TEL 205-870-2757. FAX 205-870-2673. Ed.Bd. adv. contact: Christopher Drews. bk.rev. circ. 1,700. (also avail. in microfilm from UMI; back issues avail.; reprint service avail. from RRI,UMI) **Indexed:** C.L.I., L.R.I., Leg.Cont., Leg.Per. **Document type:** academic/scholarly publication.
●Also available online. Vendor(s): West Services, Inc. —Faxon; UnCover; UMI.
Formerly: Cumberland-Samford Law Review (ISSN 0045-9275)

340   US
CURRENT AWARD TRENDS. 1960. a. $39.50. Jury Verdict Research, Inc., 30700 Bainbridge Rd., Ste. H, Solon, OH 44139. TEL 800-321-6910. FAX 216-349-5879. TELEX 216-349-JURY. Ed. Brian Shenker. circ. 5,000.

340   II   ISSN 0253-6579
CURRENT CENTRAL LEGISLATION; central acts, ordinances, regulations, rules & notifications. (Text in English) 1975. m. $41. Eastern Book Company, 34 Lalbagh, Lucknow 226 001, India. TEL 91-522-244328. FAX 91-522-244328. Eds. P.L. Malik, K.K. Malik. adv.; bk.rev. circ. 2,500. (back issues avail.)

CURRENT INCOME TAX LAW. see BUSINESS AND ECONOMICS — Public Finance, Taxation

340   II   ISSN 0011-3573
CURRENT INDIAN STATUTES. (Text in English) 1923. m. Rs.300. 36, Sector 9-A, Chandigarh 160009, India. Ed. Lalit Mohan Suri. adv.; bk.rev.; index, cum.index. circ. 2,500. (back issues avail.)

340   UK   ISSN 0011-362X
CURRENT LAW. 1947. m. £246. Sweet & Maxwell, South Quay Plaza, 7th Fl., 183 Marsh Wall, London E14 9FT, England. TEL 071-538-8686. FAX 071-538-9508. adv. contact: Jackie Wood. **Indexed:** Leg.Per. **Document type:** bulletin. —SWETS.

340   SA
CURRENT LAW SERVICE. (Supplement to: Laws of South Africa) m. R.495. Butterworth Publishers (Pty.) Ltd., P.O. Box 792, Durban 4000, South Africa. TEL 27-31-294247. FAX 27-31-283255. (looseleaf format) **Document type:** proceedings.
Description: Details current developments in South African law.

CURRENT MUNICIPAL PROBLEMS. see PUBLIC ADMINISTRATION — Municipal Government

CUSTOMS BULLETIN AND DECISIONS; regulations, rulings, decisions, and notices concerning customs and related matters and decisions of Court of Customs and Patent Appeals and Customs Court. see BUSINESS AND ECONOMICS — Public Finance, Taxation

D A L L ADVANCE SHEET. (Dallas Association of Law Librarians) see LIBRARY AND INFORMATION SCIENCES

349   GW   ISSN 0012-1231
D A R. (Deutsches Autorecht) 1926. m. DM.132. (Allgemeiner Deutscher Automobil-Club e.V.) A D A C Verlag GmbH, 81365 Munich, Germany. TEL 089-7676-0. Ed. Dr. Gontard. adv.; bk.rev.; bibl. circ. 6,200. **Indexed:** Dok.Str. **Document type:** bulletin. —BLDSC (3576.287000). CCC.

D & O LIABILITY HANDBOOK: LAW, SAMPLE DOCUMENTS, FORMS. see BUSINESS AND ECONOMICS — Investments

340   US
D C B A BRIEF. 1987. 10/yr. $40. DuPage County Bar Association, 126 S. County Farm Rd., Wheaton, IL 60187. TEL 708-653-7779. FAX 708-653-7870. adv. circ. 1,532.
Description: Provides updates on current case law, tips on business management and on trial preparation.

D.C. CODE UPDATER. see PUBLIC ADMINISTRATION — Municipal Government

340   US   ISSN 0276-5675
KF1297.D7
D E S LITIGATION REPORTER; the national journal of record of diethylstilbestrol litigation. 1981. m. $800. Andrews Publications, 1646 West Chester Pike, Box 1000, Westtown, PA 19395. TEL 215-399-6600; 800-345-1101. FAX 215-399-6610. Ed. Edith McFall. bibl.; stat.; cum.index every 6 mos. (looseleaf format; back issues avail.) **Document type:** newsletter.

D I N. CATALOGUE OF TECHNICAL RULES. VOL. 1: GERMAN STANDARDS AND TECHNICAL RULES. (Deutsches Institut fuer Normung e.V. (D I N)) see TECHNOLOGY: COMPREHENSIVE WORKS

D I N. CATALOGUE OF TECHNICAL RULES. VOL. 2: INTERNATIONAL STANDARDS AND TECHNICAL RULES. (Deutsches Institut fuer Normung e.V. (D I N)) see *TECHNOLOGY: COMPREHENSIVE WORKS*

349   DK   ISSN 0108-3627
LAW
D J OE F - HAANDBOGEN; opslagsbog for tillidsrepraesentanter i D J OE F. 1981. biennial. DKK 201.30. Danmarks Jurist- og Oekonomforbund, Gothersgade 133, 1123 Copenhagen K, Denmark. TEL 45-33-14-29-20.

340   US
KF8228.N3L28
D N A NEWSLETTER. 1968. bi-m. free. D N A - People's Legal Services, Inc., Box 306, Window Rock, AZ 86515. TEL 602-871-4151. Ed. T.J. Holgate. adv.; charts; illus.; stat. circ. 4,500. (also avail. in microfilm from MCA) **Document type:** newsletter.
    Former titles: D N A in Action; Law in Action.

THE D.O.; a publication for osteopathic physicians and surgeons. (Doctor of Osteopath) see *MEDICAL SCIENCES — Chiropractic, Homeopathy, Osteopathy*

340   368   GW   ISSN 0936-6156
HD7102.G3
D O K: POLITIK - PRAXIS RECHT. 1914. s-m. DM.126. (A O K - Bundesverband) A O K - Verlag GmbH, Lilienthalstr. 1-3, Postfach 1120, 53424 Remagen, Germany. FAX 02642-931130. Ed. Michael Petter. adv.; bk.rev. circ. 7,000. (also avail. in microfilm) **Indexed:** World Bibl.Soc.Sec. **Document type:** academic/scholarly publication.
    Formerly: Ortskrankenkasse (ISSN 0030-5995)

342   610   170   301.2   CN   ISSN 0847-1797
D W D NEWSLETTER. 1983. q. membership. Dying with Dignity, 600 Eglinton Ave. E., Ste. 401, Toronto, ON M4P 1P3, Canada. TEL 416-486-3998. FAX 416-489-9010. Ed. Sheilagh Hickie. bk.rev.; charts; stat. circ. 6,500. **Document type:** newsletter.
    Description: Discusses issues related to end of life decision making. Looks at ethical, legal, moral and social aspects of life-death concerns of Canadians.

629.283   340   US   ISSN 0889-0234
KF2231.A15D85
D W I JOURNAL: LAW & SCIENCE. (Driving While Intoxicated) 1986. m. $255. Whitaker Newsletters Inc., 313 South Ave., Fanwood, NJ 07023. TEL 908-889-6339. FAX 908-889-6339. Ed. John Tarantino. bk.rev.; index. (looseleaf format; back issues avail.) **Document type:** newsletter.
    Description: Covers news and analysis pertaining to case law decisions on drunk driving defense.

340   330   US
DAILY BULLETIN (BROOKLYN); a daily newspaper serving professionals. 1975. d. $150. Brooklyn Journal Publications, Inc., 129 Montague St., Brooklyn, NY 11201. TEL 718-624-6033. FAX 718-875-5302. Ed. Edward Goldstein. adv.; bk.rev. circ. 5,200. **Document type:** newspaper.
    Formerly: Brooklyn Journal.

340   US
DAILY COURT REPORTER. 1977. d. (Mon.-Fri.). $75. 120 W. Second St., Dayton, OH 45402. TEL 513-222-6000. Ed. Jeffrey Foster. circ. 700. **Document type:** newspaper.

DAILY ENVIRONMENT REPORT. see *ENVIRONMENTAL STUDIES*

340   US
DAILY LEGAL NEWS. 1926. d. (Mon.-Fri.). $72. Richard F. Demko & J.T. Cover, Eds. & Pubs., 112 W. Commerce St., Ste. 1, Youngstown, OH 44503. TEL 216-747-7777. circ. 1,025. **Document type:** newspaper.

DAILY RECORD (KANSAS CITY). see *BUSINESS AND ECONOMICS*

THE DAILY RECORD (OMAHA). see *BUSINESS AND ECONOMICS*

340   332   US   ISSN 0360-9510
K4
DAILY REPORTER (SIOUX CITY). 1896. w. $139. Daily Reporter of Sioux City Inc., 518 Nebraska St., Sioux City, IA 51101-1306. TEL 712-255-8829. Ed. Jeffrey S. Scotsky. circ. 450.

DAILY TERRITORIAL. see *BUSINESS AND ECONOMICS*

DAILY TRANSCRIPT. see *REAL ESTATE*

340   US
K4.A523
DAILY WASHINGTON LAW REPORTER. 1874. d. (Mon.-Fri.). $180. Washington Law Reporter Co., 1001 Connecticut Ave., N.W., Ste. 238, Washington, DC 20036-5504. TEL 202-331-1700. FAX 202-785-8476. Ed. M. Dale Hill. adv.; s-a. index. (looseleaf format) **Document type:** newspaper.

340   JA
DAITO HOGAKU/JOURNAL OF LAW AND POLITICS. (Text in Japanese) 1974. a. free. Daito Bunka University, Law and Politics Society - Daito Bunka Daigaku Hogakkai, 1-9-1 Takashimadaira, Itabashi-ku, Tokyo, Japan. circ. 2,350.

340   CN   ISSN 0317-1663
K4
DALHOUSIE LAW JOURNAL. (Text in English and French) 1973. 2/yr. Can.$12.50 per no. Dalhousie University, Faculty of Law, Halifax, NS B3H 4H9, Canada. TEL 902-494-1006. FAX 902-494-1316. (Subscr. to: Carswell Co. Ltd., 2330 Midland Ave., Agincourt, ON M1S 1P7, Canada) Ed. F. Woodman. bk.rev. circ. 325. (back issues avail.) **Indexed:** Abstr.Bk.Rev.Curr.Leg.Per., C.L.I., Curr.Cont., Ind.Can.L.P.L., L.R.I., Leg.Per., Mar.Aff.Bibl. **Document type:** academic/scholarly publication.
    —BLDSC (3517.730000); Faxon; UnCover; UMI.

340   TZ   ISSN 0418-3770
DAR ES SALAAM UNIVERSITY LAW JOURNAL. Short title: D U L J. (Text in English) 1963-1987; N.S. 1991. q. $100. University of Dar es Salaam, Faculty of Law, P.O. Box 35034, Dar es Salaam, Tanzania. (Co-sponsor: Friedrich Gibert Stiftung) Ed. Kasimbazi, E.B.
    Formerly (until 1971): Denning Law Society. Journal.

340   US   ISSN 1068-1167
DAYTON BAR BRIEFS BULLETIN. vol.17, 1993. m. membership. Dayton Bar Association, 600 One First National Plaza, Dayton, OH 45402-1501. TEL 513-222-7902. FAX 513-222-1308. **Document type:** newsletter.

340   SA
DE JURE. (Text in Afrikaans, English) 2/yr. R.78. (Pretoria University, Faculty of Law) Butterworth Publishers (Pty.) Ltd., P.O. Box 792, Durban 4000, South Africa. TEL 27-31-294247. FAX 27-31-283255. Ed. N.J. Grove. **Document type:** academic/scholarly publication, newsletter.
    Description: Publishes articles, notes and case reviews on current and pertinent South African legal issues.

340   US   ISSN 0011-7188
DE PAUL LAW REVIEW. 1951. q. $21. DePaul University, College of Law, 25 E. Jackson Blvd., Chicago, IL 60604. TEL 312-362-8553. FAX 312-362-5931. Ed. Donna Welch. adv.; bk.rev.; index. circ. 2,300. (also avail. in microform from UMI,PMC; back issues avail.; reprint service avail. from ISI,UMI) **Indexed:** C.C.L.P., C.L.I., L.R.I., Leg.Per. **Document type:** academic/scholarly publication.
    ●Also available online. Vendor(s): West Services, Inc.
    —BLDSC (3535.948000); Faxon; UnCover; UMI.
    Description: Covers scholarly legal research and other areas of law.

340   US   ISSN 0011-7250
DECALOGUE JOURNAL.* 1950. q. $36. Decalogue Society of Lawyers, 39 S. La Salle St., Ste. 410, Chicago, IL 60603-1605. TEL 312-263-6493. Ed. Melvin Lewis. adv.; bk.rev. circ. 1,800. (also avail. in microform from UMI; reprint service avail. from UMI) **Indexed:** C.L.I., L.R.I.
    —UMI.

DECENCY REPORTER. see *SOCIOLOGY*

347
DECISIONS & DEVELOPMENTS. 1979. bi-m. $84. Box 342, Wayland, MA 01778. TEL 617-890-5678. Ed. Joseph S. Iandiorio.
    Description: Reports court decisions relating to intellectual property.

340   US   ISSN 0193-4007
KFD57.D44
DELAWARE LAW MONTHLY. 1978. m. $340. Delaware Law Monthly, Box 262, Wilmington, DE 19899. TEL 302-577-3836. Eds. Charles Oberly, Bartholomew Dalton. circ. 250.
    Incorporated in part: Delaware Corporate Law Reporter.
    Description: Covers decisions of Delaware State Courts, with emphasis on corporate and business decisions.

340   US   ISSN 0735-6595
DELAWARE LAWYER. 1982. q. (Delaware Bar Foundation) Suburban Marketing Associates, Inc., 3 Christina Centre, 201 N. Walnut St., Ste. 1204, Wilmington, DE 19801. TEL 302-656-8440. Ed. William E. Wiggin. adv.; illus.
    Description: Publishes opinions and review articles covering legal subjects of interest to Delaware judges, lawyers and the community at large.

340   US
DELAWARE LEGAL DIRECTORY. a. $45 to non-members; members $17. Delaware State Bar Association, 1225 N. King St., 10th Fl., Wilmington, DE 19801-3233. (looseleaf format) **Document type:** directory.
    Description: Provides names, addresses, phone and fax numbers for over 2300 Delaware judges and attorneys, along with their Supreme Court ID numbers and the year they were admitted to the Bar.

348   US   ISSN 0091-5564
KFD47
DELAWARE REPORTER. (Vol. numbering adopted from that of the Atlantic Reporter) 1968. irreg. West Publishing Corp., 620 Opperman Dr., Eagan, MN 55123. TEL 612-687-8000; 800-328-9352. FAX 612-687-7302. **Document type:** trade publication.
    Supersedes: Delaware. Court of Chancery. Delaware Chancery Reports; Delaware. Courts. Delaware Reports.

340   II   ISSN 0971-4936
DELHI LAW REVIEW. 1972. a. $20. University of Delhi, Faculty of Law, Delhi 110007, India. Ed. Tahir Mahmood. adv.; bk.rev. circ. 275.

349   II   ISSN 0011-7846
DELHI LAW TIMES. (Text in English) 1965. fortn. Rs.45. 36 Sector 9-A, Chandigarh 11, India. Eds. Ravinder Mohan Suri, Shashi Mohan Suri. adv.; bk.rev.; cum.index every 5 yrs.

DEMOCRATIC REPUBLIC OF THE SUDAN GAZETTE/AL-JARIDAH AL-RASMIYAH LI-JUMHURIYAT AL-SUDAN AL-DIMUQRATIYAH. see *PUBLIC ADMINISTRATION*

DEMOCRATIC REPUBLIC OF THE SUDAN GAZETTE. LEGISLATIVE SUPPLEMENT. see *PUBLIC ADMINISTRATION*

340   IT   ISSN 0416-9565
DEMOCRAZIA E DIRITTO/DEMOCRACY AND LAW. 1960. bi-m. L.61000 (foreign L.81000). Editori Riuniti, Via Serchio 9-11, 00198 Rome, Italy. TEL 06-866383. FAX 06-416096. TELEX EDIRIU I 625292. Ed. Pietro Barcellona. adv.; bk.rev. circ. 7,000.
    —BLDSC (3550.575000); SWETS.

DENMARK. LOVINFORMATION FRA MILJOESTYRELSEN. see *ENVIRONMENTAL STUDIES*

340   DK   ISSN 0109-1913
KJR3127.A12
DENMARK. MILJOEMINISTERIET. MILJOEMINISTERIETS LOVREGISTER; retsinformation, lovregister, stikordsregister. 1984. q. DKK 95 per no. (Miljoestyrelsen) Danish Environmental Protection Agency, Environmental Data and Information, Strandgade 29, DK-1401 Copenhagen K, Denmark. TEL 45-31-57-83-10. FAX 45-31-57-24-49. TELEX 31209 MILJOE DK. Ed. Birgitte Pedersen. circ. 150.
    Description: Provides an introduction to the department's regulations. Includes 1,000 key words to all of the agency's regulations.

LAW

340 UK ISSN 0269-1922
K4
DENNING LAW JOURNAL. 1986. a. £12.50. University of Buckingham, Faculty of Law, Buckingham, Bucks MK18 1EG, England. TEL 0280-814080. FAX 0280-822245. (Dist. in US by: Wm. W. Gaunt & Sons, Inc., Law Book Dealers & Subscription Agents, Gaunt Bldg., 3011 Gulf Dr., Holmes Beach, FL 34217-2199. TEL 813-778-5211) Ed. C.G. Hall. adv. (back issues avail.) **Indexed:** C.L.I., Leg.Per.
—BLDSC (3553.104500); Faxon; UnCover.

340 US
DENVER BAR ASSOCIATION. DOCKET. 11/yr. membership. Denver Bar Association, 1900 Grant St., Ste. 950, Denver, CO 90203. TEL 303-860-1112. FAX 303-894-0821. Ed. Diane Hartman. adv. circ. 5,300. (back issues avail.) **Document type:** newsletter.
Formerly: Denver Bar Association. Calendar.

340 US
DENVER UNIVERSITY LAW REVIEW. 1923. q. $23. University of Denver, College of Law, Porter Adm. Bldg., 7039 E. 18th Ave., Denver, CO 80220-1826. TEL 303-871-6171. Ed. Diana Cachey. adv.; bk.rev.; index, cum.index every 5 and 20 yrs. circ. 1,500. (also avail. in microfiche from WSH; microfilm from WSH,PMC) **Indexed:** C.L.I., Curr.Cont., L.R.I., Law Ofc.Info.Svc., Leg.Cont., Leg.Per., P.A.I.S., Sel.Water Res.Abstr., SSCI.
● Also available online. Vendor(s): West Services, Inc.
—BLDSC (3553.568600); UnCover.
Former titles: Denver Law Journal (ISSN 0011-8834); Dicta.

340 PE
DERECHO. 1944. a. $15. Pontificia Universidad Catolica del Peru, Facultad de Derecho, Fondo Editorial, Apdo. 1761, Lima 100, Peru. TEL 626390. FAX 5114-611785. Ed. Cesar Landa Arroyo. adv. circ. 2,000.

DERECHO DEL TRABAJO; revista critica mensual de jurisprudencia, doctrina y legislacion. see *BUSINESS AND ECONOMICS — Labor And Industrial Relations*

340 300 MX
DERECHO Y CIENCIAS SOCIALES. 1973. q. Universidad Autonoma de Nuevo Leon, Loma Redonda 1515-A, Col. Loma Larga, Monterrey, Mexico. illus.

DESKBOOK ENCYCLOPEDIA OF AMERICAN SCHOOL LAW. see *EDUCATION*

DETENTION REPORTER; a monthly resource for detention & corrections. see *CRIMINOLOGY AND LAW ENFORCEMENT*

340.05 US ISSN 0099-135X
K4
DETROIT COLLEGE OF LAW REVIEW. 1975. q. $28. Detroit College of Law, 130 E. Elizabeth St., Detroit, MI 48201. TEL 313-224-0151. Ed. Louise B. Machler. adv.; bk.rev. circ. 1,500. (also avail. in microfilm from MIM,WSH,PMC; reprint service avail. from WSH) **Indexed:** Abstr.Bk.Rev.Curr.Leg.Per., C.L.I., L.R.I., Leg.Per., Mar.Aff.Bibl. **Document type:** academic/scholarly publication.
—UnCover.

340 US ISSN 0739-9480
DETROIT LEGAL NEWS. 1895. d. (Mon.-Fri.). $100. Detroit Legal News. Co., 2001 W. Lafayette, Detroit, MI 48216. TEL 313-961-3940. FAX 313-961-7817. Ed. Eric Pope. circ. 2,500. **Document type:** newspaper.

340 GW ISSN 0937-9371
K4
DEUTSCH - DEUTSCHE RECHTS ZEITSCHRIFT. (Supplement to: Neue Juristische Wochenschrift) 1990. m. DM.112 (students DM.98). C.H. Beck'sche Verlagsbuchhandlung, Wilhelmstr. 9, 80801 Munich, Germany. TEL 089-38189338. FAX 089-38189398. TELEX 5215085-BECK-D. adv.: B&W page DM.2200, color DM.4400; trim 260 x 186. circ. 58,000. (back issues avail.) **Document type:** academic/scholarly publication.
● Also available on CD-ROM.
—SWETS.

340 GW ISSN 0138-1644
DEUTSCHE DEMOKRATISCHE REPUBLIK. GESETZBLATT;* Gesetze und andere allgemeinverbindliche Rechtsvorschriften mit Ausnahme von voelkerrechtlichen Vertraegen. 1949. irreg. DM.30. Staatsverlag der DDR, Otto-Grotewohlstr. 17, 1086 Berlin, Germany. Ed.Bd. **Indexed:** Agri.Eng.Abstr.

DEUTSCHE NOTAR-ZEITSCHRIFT. see *PUBLIC ADMINISTRATION*

340 GW ISSN 0340-8612
DEUTSCHE RICHTERZEITUNG. 1950. m. DM.82. (Deutscher Richterbund) Carl Heymanns Verlag KG, Luxemburgerstr. 449, 50939 Cologne, Germany. TEL 0221-46010-0. FAX 0221-4601069. index. circ. 1,300. (back issues avail.) **Document type:** newsletter.
—SWETS.

340 GW ISSN 0940-1555
DEUTSCHE ZEITSCHRIFT FUER WIRTSCHAFTSRECHT. 1991. m. DM.156 (students DM.96). Walter de Gruyter und Co., Genthiner Str. 13, 10785 Berlin, Germany. TEL 030-26005-0. FAX 030-26005251. TELEX 184027. (U.S. addr.: Walter de Gruyter, Inc., 200 Saw Mill Rd., Hawthorne, NY 10532. TEL 914-747-0110) Eds. H.W. Bayer, G.F. Bauer. circ. 1,000. **Document type:** academic/scholarly publication.

DEUTSCHES STEUERRECHT; Wochenschrift fuer Steuerrecht, Gesellschaftsrecht und Betriebswirtschaft. see *BUSINESS AND ECONOMICS — Public Finance, Taxation*

349 GW ISSN 0012-1363
DEUTSCHES VERWALTUNGSBLATT. (Includes: Verwaltungsarchiv) 1885. s-m. DM.418. Carl Heymanns Verlag KG, Luxemburgerstr. 449, 50939 Cologne, Germany. TEL 0221-46010-0. FAX 0221-4601069. Ed. C.H. Vle. adv.; bk.rev.; abstr.; charts; stat.; index. circ. 3,300. (reprint service avail. from SCH) **Indexed:** Dok.Str., ELLIS, INIS Atomind. **Document type:** bulletin.
—BLDSC (3578.300000); SWETS.

340 BG
DHAKA LAW REPORTS: CIVIL DIGEST. (Text in English) 1949-1984; N.S. 1986. irreg. $35. Dhaka Law Reports Office, Malibagh, Dhaka, Bangladesh. TEL 403909. Ed. Obaidul Huq. adv.; bk.rev. circ. 5,000.
Formerly: Up-to-Date Civil Reference.
Description: Contains commentaries and case laws of Bangladesh, India and Pakistan.

340 US ISSN 1063-7419
DICKINSON JOURNAL OF ENVIRONMENTAL LAW & POLICY. 1991. s-a. Dickinson School of Law, 150 S. College St., Carlisle, PA 17013. Ed. Phyllis L. Stockton.
—UnCover.
Formerly (until 1992): Journal of Environmental Law and Policy (ISSN 1063-7427)

340 US ISSN 0012-2459
LAW
DICKINSON LAW REVIEW. 1897. q. $35. Dickinson School of Law, 150 S. College St., Carlisle, PA 17013. TEL 717-243-4611. FAX 717-243-4443. Ed. Deneice Covert. adv.; bk.rev.; charts; index. circ. 1,500. (also avail. in microfilm from WSH,PMC) **Indexed:** C.C.L.P., C.L.I., Crim.Just.Abstr., L.R.I., Leg.Per., Mar.Aff.Bibl. **Document type:** academic/scholarly publication.
● Also available online. Vendor(s): West Services, Inc.
—BLDSC (3580.270000); Faxon; UnCover; SWETS.

340 US
DICTA; the lawyer's magazine. m. $30 to non-members; members $1.50. San Diego County Bar Association, 1333 Seventh Ave., San Diego, CA 92101-3283. TEL 619-231-0781. Ed. Gayle L. Eskridge. adv.; illus.
Description: Covers legal issues, including recent cases, professional concerns, financial planning and other matters of interest to San Diego area attorneys.

DICTIONNAIRE DU MARCHE COMMUN. see *BUSINESS AND ECONOMICS — International Commerce*

DICTIONNAIRE JOLY CONCURRENCE. see *BUSINESS AND ECONOMICS*

349 FR ISSN 0012-2475
DICTIONNAIRE PERMANENT DROIT DES AFFAIRES. 1963. fortn. 1720 F. base vols. (updates 600 F.). Editions Legislatives et Administratives, 80, ave. de la Marne, 92546 Montrouge Cedex, France. TEL 1-40-92-68-68. FAX 1-46-56-00-15. TELEX 632 855 F. bibl.; index, cum.index. circ. 9,000. (looseleaf format)
Description: Covers commercial, economic and business laws.

340 US
DICTUM. 1979. bi-m. membership. New Jersey State Bar Association, Young Lawyers Division, One Constitution Sq., New Brunswick, NJ 08901-1500. TEL 908-249-5000. FAX 908-4249-2815. Ed. Brian P. Blatz. bk.rev.; circ. 3,000. (controlled). (back issues avail.) **Document type:** newsletter.
Formerly: New Jersey State Bar Association. Young Lawyers Division Newsletter.

340 IT ISSN 0394-9036
LA DIFESA PENALE; rivista trimestrale di eloquenza, diritto e applicazione forense. 1983. q. L.100000($125) Edizioni Bucalo snc., Casella Postale 51, 04100 Latina, Italy. TEL 773-62-32-26. Dir. Enrico Baccino. adv.; bk.rev.; bibl.; cum.index. circ. 5,000.

DIGEST, BUSINESS & LAW JOURNAL. see *BUSINESS AND ECONOMICS — Banking And Finance*

340 331 II ISSN 0419-1293
DIGEST OF CURRENT INDUSTRIAL AND LABOUR LAW. (Text in English) vol.8, 1973. m. Rs.36. Current Law Publishers, PO Box 1268, Delhi 110006, India. Ed. J.D. Jain.

340 613.1 US
KF3775.A15D53
DIGEST OF ENVIRONMENTAL LAW. 1987. m. $240. National Property Law Digests, Inc., 7200 Wisconsin Ave., Ste. 314, Bethesda, MD 20814. TEL 301-654-8004. FAX 301-654-8894. Ed. Ian Portnoy. index. (looseleaf format; back issues avail.) **Document type:** newsletter.

347.9 II ISSN 0012-2750
DIGEST OF LABOUR CASES. (Text in English) 1960. m. Rs.20. V. Subramanian, Ed. & Pub., 337 Thambu Chetty St., Madras 600001, India. adv.; bk.rev.; index; circ. 280 (controlled).

340 US ISSN 0012-2777
DIGEST OF OPINIONS OF THE ATTORNEY GENERAL. 1965. q. $7.50. Attorney General's Office, Rm. 112, State Capitol, Oklahoma City, OK 73105. TEL 405-521-3921. FAX 405-521-6246. Ed. Cathy Margerum. circ. 780. (processed) **Document type:** government publication.

340 CN ISSN 0229-0812
DIGEST ON GAY RIGHTS; I: human - civil rights. 1977. a. free. Gays for Equality, P.O. Box 1661, Winnipeg, MB R3C 2Z6, Canada. TEL 204-772-8215. FAX 204-478-1160. Ed. Chris Vogel. circ. 500.

340 IS ISSN 0070-4903
K4
DINE ISRAEL; an annual of Jewish law: past and present. (Text in English and Hebrew) 1969. a. $40. Tel Aviv University, Faculty of Law, Ramat Aviv, Tel Aviv, Israel. Ed. Aaron Kirschenbaum. bk.rev. circ. 500. **Indexed:** Ind.Heb.Per. **Document type:** academic/scholarly publication.
Incorporates (no.8, 1969): Current Bibliography of Hebrew Law.

340 SP
DIRECCION GENERAL DE LOS REGISTROS Y DEL NOTARIADO. ANUARIO. a. 7000 ptas. Ministerio de Justicia, Centro de Publicaciones, Secretaria General Tecnica, Gran Via, 76-8, 28013 Madrid, Spain. TEL 547-54-22. FAX 559-29-48. **Document type:** government publication.

342 US
DIRECT CONFRONTATION.* 1984. m. $12. Constitutional Revival, Box 3182, Enfield, CT 06083-3182. TEL 203-745-2221. Ed. Andy Mel. circ. 2,000. (back issues avail.)

340 US ISSN 1061-1835
KF190
DIRECTORY OF ASSOCIATIONS OF WOMEN LAWYERS.
1985. a. $15. American Bar Association,
Commission on Women in the Profession, 750 N.
Lake Shore Dr., Chicago, IL 60611.
FAX 312-988-6281. **Document type:** directory.

340 US
**DIRECTORY OF BAY AREA PUBLIC INTEREST
ORGANIZATIONS.** 1980. triennial, 4th ed., 1991.
$25 to non-members; members $20. Public Interest
Clearinghouse, 200 McAllister St., San Francisco, CA
94102. TEL 415-565-4695. FAX 415-621-4859.
circ. 1,000.
 Formerly (until 1991): Public Interest
Clearinghouse Directory.
 Description: Comprehensive listing describing the
services, costs and publications of public interest
organizations in the San Francisco Bay Area.

340 EI ISSN 0257-5256
DIRECTORY OF COMMUNITY LEGISLATION IN FORCE. (In
2 vols.: Vol.I - Analytical Register; Vol.II -
Chronological Index, Alphabetical Index) 2/yr. $140.
(Commission of the European Communities, Legal
Service) Office for Official Publications of the
European Communities, L-2985 Luxembourg,
Luxembourg. (Dist. in the U.S. by: Unipub, 4611-F
Assembly Dr., Lanham, MD 20706-4391. TEL
800-274-4888. FAX 301-459-0056) **Document
type:** directory.
 ●Also available online. Vendor(s): Commission of the
European Communities.
 Description: Reference work which enables the
user to find the current instruments of Community
legislation.

**DIRECTORY OF CRIMINAL JUSTICE ISSUES IN THE
STATES.** see CRIMINOLOGY AND LAW
ENFORCEMENT

340 333.33 US
DIRECTORY OF INTELLECTUAL PROPERTY ATTORNEYS.
1989. a. Prentice Hall Law & Business, 270 Sylvan
Ave., Englewood Cliffs, NJ 07632.
TEL 201-894-8484. **Document type:** directory.

340 CN ISSN 0383-8358
KE280.D575
**DIRECTORY OF LAW TEACHERS/ANNUAIRE DES
PROFESSEURS DE DROIT.** (Text in English and
French) 1972. a. Can.$13.50. Canadian Association
of Canadian Law Teachers, c/o Canadian Bar
Association, 57 Copernicus, Ottawa, Ont. K1N 6N5,
Canada. Ed. Louis Perret. adv. circ. 500. **Document
type:** directory.

340 US
DIRECTORY OF LAWYER REFERRAL SERVICES. 1976. a.
$7.50. American Bar Association, Standing
Committee on Lawyer Referral and Information
Service, 750 N. Lake Shore Dr., Chicago, IL 60611.
TEL 312-988-5760. FAX 312-988-5664. circ.
1,000. **Document type:** directory.

340 US ISSN 0092-9174
KF193.S25
DIRECTORY OF SAN FRANCISCO ATTORNEYS. a. $54.25
to non-members. Bar Association of San Francisco,
685 Market St., Ste. 700, San Francisco, CA
94105. adv. circ. 10,000. **Document type:** directory.
 Description: Lists all attorneys in San Francisco
and notes which are members of the Bar
Association. Also lists San Francisco law firms,
federal, state and local courts and governments.

**DIRECTORY OF STATE COURT CLERKS & COUNTY
COURTHOUSES (YEAR).** see PUBLIC
ADMINISTRATION

**DIRECTORY OF WORKERS' COMPENSATION MANAGED
CARE ORGANIZATIONS.** see LAW — Corporate Law

340 PO
DIREITO. 4/yr. Rua Rodrigues Fonseca 149 4o, Lisbon,
Portugal.

340 PO
DIREITO ADMINISTRATIVO. 1980. s-m. Centelha
Promocao do Livro, S.A.R.L., Apartado 241, 3003
Coimbra Codex, Portugal.

340 BL
DIREITO & JUSTICA. 1979. s-a. Pontificia Universidade
Catolica do Rio Grande do Sul, Faculdade de Direito,
Av. Iparanga 6681, Caixa Postal 1429, Porto Alegre
RS, Brazil.

341.57 IT ISSN 0012-3390
DIRITTO AEREO; rivista di dottrina, giurisprudenza e
legislazione aeronautica dei trasporti intermodali e
del diritto spaziale. 1962, N.S. 1993. s-a.
L.60000($200) International Association of Lawyers
and Experts in Air and Intermodal Transports Law,
Via Prisciano 8, piano 4, 00136 Rome, Italy.
TEL 39-6-3450955. FAX 39-6-343470. Ed.
Adalberto Tempesta. adv.; bk.rev.; bibl.; index. circ.
500. (back issues avail.)
 Formerly: Diritto Aereo e dei Trasporti Intermodali.
 Description: Forum devoted to air and space law.
Includes law cases and articles in international
multimodal transport of goods, air traffic control and
rights of servitude.

DIRITTO DEL COMMERCIO INTERNAZIONALE. see
BUSINESS AND ECONOMICS — International
Commerce

347.9 IT ISSN 0012-3404
DIRITTO DEL LAVORO; rivista di dottrina e di
giurisprudenza. 1927. bi-m. L.115000 to
individuals; libraries L.75000. Fondazione Diritto del
Lavoro, Via Gramsci, 14, Rome, Italy. Ed. Raffaele
Foglia. bk.rev. circ. 1,500. **Indexed:** ELLIS,
P.A.I.S.For.Lang.Ind.
 —BLDSC (3595.413500).

DIRITTO DELL'AGRICOLTURA. see AGRICULTURE

340 US
DIRITTO DELL'INFORMAZIONE E DELL'INFORMATICA.
1985. 3/yr. L.90000 (foreign L.135000). Casa
Editrice Dott. A. Giuffre, Via Busto Arsizio 40,
20151 Milan, Italy. TEL 02-38000905.
FAX 02-38009582. **Indexed:** ELLIS.

340 IT ISSN 0012-3412
**DIRITTO DELLE RADIODIFFUSIONI E DELLE
TELECOMUNICAZIONI.** 1969. 3/yr. L.70000 (foreign
L.95000). E R I Edizioni R A I, Via Arsenale 41,
10121 Turin, Italy. TEL 011-8800.
FAX 011-534732. Ed. Emanuele Santoro. bk.rev.;
abstr.

DIRITTO DELLE RELAZIONI INDUSTRIALI. see BUSINESS
AND ECONOMICS — Labor And Industrial Relations

DIRITTO DI AUTORE. see PATENTS, TRADEMARKS AND
COPYRIGHTS

340 IT
DIRITTO DI FAMIGLIA E DELLE PERSONE. 1972. q.
L.100000 (foreign L.150000). Casa Editrice Dott.
A. Giuffre, Via Busto Arsizio 40, 20151 Milan, Italy.
TEL 02-38000905. FAX 02-38009582. Ed. V.
Lojacono. adv.; bk.rev.; bibl. circ. 2,600.

340 IT
DIRITTO E CULTURA. s-a. L.55000 to individuals;
institutions L.72000; foreign L.88000 (effective
1993). Edizioni Scientifiche Italiane S.p.A., Via
Chiatamone 7, 80121 Naples, Italy.
TEL 081-7645768. FAX 081-7646477.

349 IT ISSN 0012-3439
DIRITTO E GIURISPRUDENZA; rassegna trimestrale di
dottrina e di giurisprudenza civile. 1945. q.
L.100000. Casa Editrice Dott. Eugenio Jovene, Via
Mezzocannone 109, 80134 Naples, Italy.
TEL 081-5521019. FAX 081-5520687. Ed.
Antonio Guarino.

DIRITTO E PRATICA DELL'AVIAZIONE CIVILE. see
TRANSPORTATION — Air Transport

347 368 IT ISSN 0417-6766
DIRITTO E PRATICA NELL'ASSICURAZIONE. 1956. q.
L.80000 (foreign L.120000). (Centro Studi
Assicurativi of Milano) Casa Editrice Dott. A. Giuffre,
Via Busto Arsizio 40, 20151 Milan, Italy.
TEL 02-38000905. FAX 02-38009582. Ed. Emilio
Pasanisi. adv. circ. 3,800.

340 IT ISSN 0012-3447
DIRITTO E PRATICA TRIBUTARIA. 1929. bi-m.
L.450000 (foreign L.600000) (effective 1994).
Casa Editrice Dott. Antonio Milani, Via Jappelli 5,
35121 Padua, Italy. TEL 049-656677.
FAX 049-8752900. Dir. Victor Uckmar. bk.rev.;
index. circ. 3,000. **Indexed:** ELLIS.

340 IT
DIRITTO E SOCIETA (PADUA). 1973-1975; N.S. 1978.
q. L.145000 (foreign L.200000) (effective 1994).
Casa Editrice Dott. Antonio Milani, Via Jappelli 5,
35121 Padua, Italy. TEL 049-656677.
FAX 049-8752900. Ed. Leopoldo Mazzarolli. circ.
700.
 Description: Covers legal problems of the nation
and of democracy in the present age.

340 388.41 368.2 IT
▼**DIRITTO E TECNICA DELLA CIRCOLAZIONE STRADALE
E ASSICURAZIONE OBBLIGATORIA DI R C A.** 1993.
3/yr. L.50000 (foreign L.70000) (effective 1994).
Casa Editrice Dott. Antonio Milani, Via Jappelli 5,
35100 Padua, Italy. TEL 049-656677.
FAX 049-8752900. Ed. Giuseppe Marcon.
 Description: Contains updates and comments on
the new traffic codes.

340 330 IT ISSN 0394-8366
DIRITTO ED ECONOMIA; rivista-dibattito interdisciplinare
quadrimestrale. 1988. 3/yr. L.100000 (effective
1994). (Istituto di Diritto Pubblica) Maggioli Editore,
Viale Vespucci 12-n, Casella Postale 290, 47037
Rimini, Italy. TEL 0541-626777.
FAX 0541-622020. Eds. Carlo Ferrari, Gian Maria
Gros-Pietro. adv.; B&W page L.1200000, color page
L.1800000; trim 115 x 195.

340 IT
**DIRITTO FALLIMENTARE E DELLE SOCIETA
COMMERCIALI.** vol.26, 1951. bi-m. L.220000
(foreign L.27000) (effective 1994). Casa Editrice
Dott. Antonio Milani, Via Jappelli 5, 35121 Padua,
Italy. TEL 049-656677. FAX 049-8752900. Eds. A.
Bonsignori, G. Ragusa Maggiori. circ. 2,500.

347.75 IT ISSN 0012-348X
DIRITTO MARITTIMO; rivista trimestrale di dottrina
giurisprudenza legislazione italiana e straniera. (Text
in English, French, Italian) 1899. q. L.210000
(effective Jan. 1992). Dirmar, s.n.c., Via Roma 10-2,
Genoa, Italy. FAX 10-594805. TELEX 270687
DIRMAR. bk.rev.; index. circ. 750. **Indexed:**
Mar.Aff.Bibl.
 —SWETS.

340 IT
DIRITTO PROCESSUALE AMMINISTRATIVO. 1983. q.
L.70000 (foreign L.105000). Casa Editrice Dott. A.
Giuffre, Via Busto Arsizio 40, 20151 Milan, Italy.
TEL 02-38000905. FAX 02-38009582. Ed.
Ricardo Villata. adv.; bk.rev. circ. 1,500.

340 362.4 US
KF475.D57
DISABILITY ADVOCATES BULLETIN. 1977. bi-m. Pike
Institute for the Handicapped, c/o Boston University
School of Law, 765 Commonwealth Ave., Boston,
MA 02215. TEL 617-353-2904.
FAX 617-353-5995. Ed. Harry Beyer. circ. 550.
(looseleaf format; back issues avail.) **Document type:**
newsletter, bulletin.
 Formerly (until 1985): P and A Newsletter.

340 362.4 US ISSN 1055-9779
DISABILITY COMPLIANCE BULLETIN. 1991. s-m. $150.
L R P Publications, 747 Dresher Rd., Horsham, PA
19044. TEL 215-784-0860. FAX 215-784-9639.
Ed. Melinda Maloney. bk.rev. (looseleaf format; back
issues avail.)

DISABILITY LAW COMPLIANCE REPORT. see
HANDICAPPED

340 US
DISCOVERY IN ILLINOIS; federal and state practice.
1985. base vol. (plus suppl.). $80. Butterworth
Legal Publishers (Salem) (Subsidiary of: Reed
Elsevier plc), 8 Industrial Way, Bldg. C, Salem, NH
03079. TEL 800-548-4001. FAX 603-898-9858.
Eds. Robert G. Johnston, Kenneth Kandaras.
 Description: Practitioner's guide to the law of
discovery in Illinois state and federal courts; provides
both the theoretical basis and the practical
application of the rules.

LAW

340 — US
DISCOVERY PROCEEDINGS IN FEDERAL PRACTICE, 2-E. 1991. 2 base vol. (plus a. suppl.). $190. Shepard's - McGraw-Hill, Inc., Box 35300, Colorado Springs, CO 80935-3530. TEL 800-525-2474.
  Description: Provides a practical guide to the federal discovery rules and their applications in federal practice.

340 — AG
DISCREPANCIAS. 1983. m. Federacion Argentina de Colegios de Abogados, Av. de Mayo 651, Buenos Aires, Argentina. Ed. Gustavo Adolfo Blanco.

DISMISSAL AND EMPLOYMENT LAW DIGEST. see BUSINESS AND ECONOMICS — Labor And Industrial Relations

340 — US — ISSN 0271-2709
KF9084.A15
DISPUTE RESOLUTION. 1979. 4/yr. free. American Bar Association, Standing Committee on Dispute Resolution, 1800 M St., N.W., Washington, DC 20036. TEL 202-331-2258. FAX 202-331-2220. Ed. Mark Donberger. bk.rev. circ. 3,000.

340 — US
KF9084.A15D57
DISPUTE RESOLUTION FORUM. 1983. 4/yr. National Institute for Dispute Resolution, 1901 L St., N.W., Ste. 600, Washington, DC 20036. TEL 202-466-4764. FAX 202-466-4769. bk.rev. circ. 15,000. (back issues avail.) **Document type:** newsletter.

DISPUTE RESOLUTION JOURNAL. see BUSINESS AND ECONOMICS — Labor And Industrial Relations

340 — US — ISSN 0731-4833
KF9084.A15
DISPUTE RESOLUTION PROGRAM DIRECTORY (YEAR). 1982. irreg. $60. American Bar Association (Washington), 1800 M St., N.W., Washington, DC 20036. TEL 202-331-2257. FAX 202-331-2220. Ed. John Johnson. adv. circ. 2,000. **Document type:** directory.
  Description: Guide to mediation, conciliation and arbitration programs from around the country. Includes addresses and phone numbers.

340 333.33 — US
DISTRESSED BUSINESS AND REAL ESTATE NEWSLETTER. 1987. 8/yr. $90. Westlake Professional Publications, Inc., 31332 Via Colinas, Ste. 112, Westlake Village, CA 91362. TEL 818-889-1495. FAX 818-889-5107. Eds. Baxter Dunaway, Grant W. Newton. bk.rev.; index. (looseleaf format; back issues avail.) **Document type:** newsletter.

340 333.33 — US — ISSN 0892-4198
KF1507
DISTRESSED REAL ESTATE LAW ALERT. 1988. 6/yr. $250. Clark - Boardman - Callaghan Company Ltd., 375 Hudson St., New York, NY 10014. TEL 212-929-7500; 800-221-9428. FAX 212-924-0460. Ed. R. Kenneth Keim. (looseleaf format)
  Description: Each issue addresses an emerging topic affecting distressed real property - from real estate appraisal liability to westlands issues, with coverage of recent cases and upcoming conferences.

340 — AT
DISTRICT COURT PROCEDURE (N.S.W.). base vol. (plus updates 8/yr.). $255. Butterworths, 271-273 Lane Cove Rd., P.O. Box 345, North Ryde, N.S.W. 2113, Australia. TEL 02-335-4444. FAX 02-335-4655. (looseleaf format)
  Formerly: District Court Act and Rules: New South Wales.

340 — US
DISTRICT OF COLUMBIA BAR. BAR REPORT. vol.9, 1981. bi-m. $20. District of Columbia Bar, 1707 L St., N.W., Ste. 600, Washington, DC 20036-4203. TEL 202-331-3883. FAX 202-223-7726. Ed. Cynthia Kuhn. adv.; illus. circ. 62,000. (tabloid format) **Indexed:** C.L.I., Leg.Per.
  Description: Covers activities of the District of Columbia Bar.

340 — US
DISTRICT OF COLUMBIA COURTS. ANNUAL REPORT. a. District of Columbia Courts, Research and Development Division, 515 Fifth St., N.W., Washington, DC 20001. Eds. Anne P. Stygles, Anne B. Wicks.

DITCHLEY CONFERENCE REPORTS. see SOCIAL SCIENCES: COMPREHENSIVE WORKS

DITCHLEY NEWSLETTER. see SOCIAL SCIENCES: COMPREHENSIVE WORKS

DIVORCE CHATS. see SOCIOLOGY

340 — CU
DIVULGACION JURIDICA.* q. (Ministerio de Justica, Departamento de Divulgacion) Ediciones Cubanas, Obispo 57, Apdo. 605, Havana, Cuba.

340 — CU
DIVULGACION LEGISLATIVA. q. $15 in N. and S. America; Europe $16; elsewhere $18. (Ministerio de Justicia, Departamento de Divulgacion) Ediciones Cubanas, Obispo No. 527, Apdo. 605, Havana, Cuba.

340 — NZ
DIXON'S ROAD TRAFFIC LAW. 2 base vols. (plus updates 4/yr.). NZ.$396. Butterworths of New Zealand Ltd., 203-207 Victoria St., Box 472, Wellington, New Zealand. TEL 04-385-1479. FAX 04-385-1598. Ed. John Cottle. (looseleaf format)
  Formerly: Dixon and McVeagh's Road Traffic Law.
  Description: Statutes and regulations pertaining to road traffic law, with commentary and case notes.

340 — US
DOCKET (SACRAMENTO). 1963. m. $24. Sacramento County Bar Association, 901 H St., Ste. 101, Sacramento, CA 95814. TEL 916-448-1087. adv.: B&W page $510, color page $1000; trim 8 1/2 x 11. bk.rev. circ. 2,857.

340 — US — ISSN 0895-1659
THE DOCKET (TULSA). Variant title: N A L S Docket. 1952. 6/yr. $20 to non-members. National Association of Legal Secretaries, 2250 E. 73rd St., Ste. 550, Tulsa, OK 74136-6864. FAX 918-493-5784. Ed. Steven M. Wood. adv.: B&W page $1390; color page $2140; trim 8 1/4 x 10 3/4; adv. contact: Ami Bucher. bk.rev. circ. 16,500. **Indexed:** Law Ofc.Info.Svc. **Document type:** trade publication.
  Description: For legal secretaries and other non-attorney support personnel. Addresses trends and emerging issues in the legal field. Provides information that helps to achieve proficiency in the performance of legal services, and offers techniques for career growth and development.

340.05 — US
DOCKET CALL (RICHMOND). 1973. s-a. $1 per no. Virginia State Bar, Young Lawyers Conference, 707 E. Main St., Ste. 1500, Richmond, VA 27219-2803. TEL 804-775-0585. circ. 6,500. **Indexed:** C.L.I.
  Former titles: Virginia State Bar. Young Lawyers Conference. Newsletter; Virginia State Bar. Younger Members Conference. Newsletter (ISSN 0094-2251)

340 — BE
DOCTRINE JURIDIQUE BELGE. (Text in French) a. 2850 BEF (effective 1993). La Charte - Die Keure, Oude Gentweg 108, B-8000 Brugge, Belgium. FAX 32-50-34-37-68. index.

340 — FR — ISSN 0292-935X
DOCUMENTATION ORGANIQUE. (Supplement avail.: Supplement Diagonales (ISSN 0292-8280)) 1948. w. 1890 F. Documentation Organique, 11, rue de Teheran, 75008 Paris, France. TEL 45-62-54-35. FAX 1-44-13-82-85. adv. (looseleaf format)
—CCC.

340 — FR
DOCUMENTS D'ETUDES. (Includes 6 Series: Droit Constitutionnel et Institutions Politiques; Droit Administratif; Droit International Publiqu; Libertes Publiques; Finances Publiques; Jurisprudence du Conseil d'Etat) 1970. irreg. Documentation Francaise, 29-31 Quai Voltaire, 75340 Paris Cedex 07, France. TEL 1-40-15-70-00. FAX 40-15-72-30. TELEX 215 666 DOCFRAN. (Subscr. to: 124 rue Henri Barbusse, 93308 Aubervilliers Cedex, France. TEL 48-39-56-00. FAX 48-39-56-01) Ed. Jean Jenger. bibl. (also avail. in microfiche) **Document type:** government publication.

DOING BUSINESS IN AUSTRALIA. see BUSINESS AND ECONOMICS

DOING BUSINESS IN BRAZIL. see BUSINESS AND ECONOMICS

DOING BUSINESS IN CHINA. see BUSINESS AND ECONOMICS

DOING BUSINESS IN MEXICO. see BUSINESS AND ECONOMICS

349 — AU — ISSN 0012-5075
DOKUMENTATION DER GESETZE UND VERORDNUNGEN OSTEUROPAS. 1950. 15/yr. S.5800. Oesterreichisches Ost- und Suedosteuropa Institut, Josefsplatz 6, A-1010 Vienna, Austria. Ed. Ilona Slawinski. index. circ. 100. **Document type:** bulletin.

340 — GW — ISSN 0175-5293
DOKUMENTATION DEUTSCHE FINANZRECHTSPRECHUNG. 1968. s-a. DM.162. Stollfuess Verlag Bonn GmbH & Co. KG, Dechenstr. 7, 53115 Bonn, Germany.

DOLLARS & CENTS. see BUSINESS AND ECONOMICS — Management

340 — CN — ISSN 0012-5350
KE132
DOMINION LAW REPORTS. 1912. w. Can.$117. Canada Law Book Inc., 240 Edward St., Aurora, ON L4G 3S9, Canada. TEL 905-841-6472. FAX 905-841-5085. Ed. Bruce Dunlop. adv. contact: Mary Cull.
● Also available online.

340 — SW — ISSN 0347-5271
DOMSTOLSVERKETS FOERFATTNINGSSAMLING. 1977. irreg. (20-25/yr.). SEK 100 (effective 1990). Domstolsverket, S-551 81 Joenkoeping, Sweden. **Document type:** government publication.

DO'S AND DON'TS IN ADVERTISING. see ADVERTISING AND PUBLIC RELATIONS

DR. SAMUEL MUDD NEWSLETTER. see HISTORY — History Of North And South America

340 — US — ISSN 0012-5938
DRAKE LAW REVIEW. 1951. q. $25. Drake University, Law School, Cartwright Hall, Des Moines, IA 50311. TEL 515-271-2930. Ed.Bd. adv.; bk.rev. circ. 1,250. (also avail. in microform from MIM; microfilm from RRI; back issues avail., reprint service avail. from RRI) **Indexed:** C.C.L.P., C.L.I., L.R.I., Lang.& Lang.Behav.Abstr., Leg.Cont., Leg.Per. **Document type:** academic/scholarly publication.
● Also available online. Vendor(s): West Services, Inc. —BLDSC (3623.190000); Faxon; UnCover.

340 663.4 — US
KF1293.5.A59D73
DRAM SHOP AND ALCOHOL REPORTER. 1983. m. $95. Box 590, Falmouth, MA 02541. TEL 508-540-1606. Ed. Ronald S. Beitman. adv. (looseleaf format; back issues avail.)
  Formerly: Dram Shop Reporter.
  Description: Disseminated nationally to attorneys, bars, restaurants, package stores and insurance carriers who are concerned with liquor liability.

340 — AA — ISSN 0304-2731
DREJTESIA POPULLORE/JUSTICE POPULAIRE. 1948. q. $6.16. Cour Supreme et du Parquet General de la Republique Populaire Socialiste d'Albanie, Tirana, Albania. Ed. Eleni Selenica.

340 US
DRINKING DRIVER IN MINNESOTA. 1989. base vol. (plus suppl.). $88. Butterworth Legal Publishers (Salem) (Subsidiary of: Reed Elsevier plc), 8 Industrial Way, Bldg. C, Salem, NH 03079. TEL 800-548-4001. FAX 603-898-9858. Ed. Donald H. Nichols.
 Description: Practical analysis of Minnesota statutes and cases plus expert examination of the psychological, and pharmacological effects of alcohol.

DRINKING DRIVING LAW LETTER. see *TRANSPORTATION — Automobiles*

340 UA
DROIT/AL-HAQQ. (Text in Arabic and French) 1970. 3/yr. P.T.50 per no. Arab Lawyers Union - Itehad el Mohameen el Arab, 13, rue Itihad el Mohameen el Arab, Garden City, Cairo, Egypt. bk.rev. circ. 1,000.

DROIT AU LOGEMENT. see *REAL ESTATE*

340 613.1 FR ISSN 1145-2455
DROIT DE L'ENVIRONNEMENT. 1990. 6/yr. 370 F. Victoires - Editions, 38 rue Croix des Petits Champs, 75001 Paris, France. TEL 42-60-01-93. FAX 42-60-10-41. TELEX 615 887 F.

DROIT DE L'INFORMATIQUE ET DES TELECOMS. see *COMPUTERS*

340 BE
DROIT DE LA SECURITE SOCIALE. q. 4626 Fr. Maison Ferdinand Larcier S.A., Rue des Minimes 39, 1000 Brussels, Belgium.

DROIT DU SOUS SOL. see *MINES AND MINING INDUSTRY*

340 FR
DROIT ET AFFAIRES/RECHT & WITSCHAFT/ECONOMIA - DIRITTO. (Text in French, German, Spanish) 1962. bi-m. 700 F. Institut Jupiter, 71 rue du Faubourg St.-Honore, 75008 Paris, France. TEL 42-66-68-61. FAX 42-66-13-16. TELEX 280 097. Eds. Wolfgang Wenner, Cecile Foy. adv.; bk.rev. circ. 1,000.
 Former titles (until 1993): Droit et Affaires - CEE International (ISSN 0184-5926); Droit et Affaires (ISSN 0012-6403)

340 330 FR ISSN 0012-639X
DROIT ET ECONOMIE. 1958. 3/yr. 20 F. Association Nationale des Docteurs en Droit, 38 bis, rue Fabert, 75007 Paris, France. TEL 47-05-11-65. FAX 45-51-57-81. (Co-sponsor: Club International du Droit et de l'Economie) Ed. Pierre Prunet. adv.; bk.rev.; bibl.; charts; illus.; stat. circ. 2,500. Document type: bulletin.

340 FR ISSN 1165-4074
DROIT ET PATRIMOINE; journal des notaires et des avocats. 1808. m. 990 F. 26 av. de l'Europe, 78140 Velizy, France. Ed. Jean-Denis Errard. adv. circ. 7,900. **Indexed:** ELLIS.
 Former titles (until 1993): Journal des Notaires et des Avocats (ISSN 0751-6452); (until 1988): Journal des Notaires et des Avocats et Journal du Notariat (ISSN 1246-676X); Which was formed by the 1943 merger of: Journal des Notaires et des Avocats... et Jurisprudence du Notariat (ISSN 1243-2741); Journal du Notariat (ISSN 1246-6751).

340 301 FR
DROIT ET SOCIETE; revue international de theorie du droit et de sociologie juridique. 1926. 3/yr. 380 F. (foreign 400 F.). (Librairie Generale de Droit et de Jurisprudence) Editions Juridiques Associees, 26 rue Vercingetorix, 75014 Paris, France. TEL 1-43-35-01-67. FAX 43-20-07-42. TELEX EJA 203 918 F. bk.rev.

DROIT NUCLEAIRE. see *ENERGY — Nuclear Energy*

349 FR ISSN 0012-6438
DROIT SOCIAL. (Includes special numbers) 1938. m. 788.60 F. (foreign 928 F.). Editions Techniques et Economiques, 3 rue Soufflot, 75005 Paris, France. TEL 46-34-10-30. FAX 46-34-55-83. TELEX 260-717 F. Ed. Jean-Jacques Dupeyroux. adv.; bk.rev.; charts; stat.; index. circ. 6,700. (reprint service avail. from SCH) **Indexed:** ELLIS, Int.Lab.Doc., World Bibl.Soc.Sec.
 —BLDSC (3627.375000); SWETS.
 Description: Studies the problems of labor law, including social security, social policy and jurisprudence.

340 FR ISSN 0766-3838
DROITS; revue francaise de theorie juridique. s.a. 325 F. (foreign 375 F.). Presses Universitaires de France, Departement des Revues, 14 av. du Bois-de-l'Epine, 91003 Evry Cedex, France. TEL 1-60-77-82-05. FAX 1-60-79-20-45. TELEX PUF 600 474 F. Ed.Bd.
 —SWETS.

340 US
DRUG AND ALCOHOL TESTING; advising the employer. 1990. base vol. (plus a. supplement). $110. Butterworth Legal Publishers (Salem) (Subsidiary of: Reed Elsevier plc), 8 Industrial Way, Bldg. C, Salem, NH 03079. TEL 800-548-4001. FAX 603-898-9858. Ed. William D. Turkula. (looseleaf format)
 Description: Discusses the law, scientific methodology and practical applications of drug testing programs in the workplace.

DRUG LAW REPORT. see *DRUG ABUSE AND ALCOHOLISM*

DRUGS AND BIOLOGY GUIDANCE MANUAL. see *PUBLIC HEALTH AND SAFETY*

345.73 US ISSN 1045-9618
KF2231.A15D78
DRUNK DRIVING - LIQUOR LIABILITY REPORTER. 1987. m. $225. Matthew Bender & Co., Inc., 11 Penn Plaza, New York, NY 10001-2006. TEL 212-967-7707. FAX 212-967-1069. Ed. Laurie Wood. index. (looseleaf format; back issues avail.) Document type: newsletter.

340 IE
DUBLIN UNIVERSITY LAW JOURNAL. 1976. a. £15. Dublin University, Law School, Arts Bldg., Trinity College, Dublin 2, Ireland. TEL 01-772941. FAX 01-772694. Eds. Alex Schuster, Tony Kerr. adv.; bk.rev. circ. 700. **Indexed:** C.L.I., L.R.I., Leg.Per.

340 US ISSN 0012-7086
K4
DUKE LAW JOURNAL. 1951. 6/yr. $36 (foreign $42). Duke University, School of Law, Box 90364, Durham, NC 27708-0364. TEL 919-684-5966. FAX 919-684-3417. adv.; bk.rev.; cum.index. circ. 1,400. (processed; also avail. in microfilm from WSH,PMC; reprint service avail. from WSH) **Indexed:** Abstr.Health Care Manage.Stud., C.L.I., Commun.Abstr., Crim.Just.Abstr., Curr.Cont., L.R.I., Leg.Cont., Leg.Per., Rel.Per., SSCI. Document type: academic/scholarly publication.
 •Also available online. Vendor(s): Mead Data Central, Inc., West Services, Inc.
 —BLDSC (3630.950000); Faxon; UnCover; SWETS; UMI.

DUNHILL PERSONAL INJURY & DEATH REPORTS. see *INSURANCE*

340 US
DUNNELL MINNESOTA DIGEST. 1978. 47 base vols. (plus a. suppl.), 4th ed., 1991. $1350. Butterworth Legal Publishers (Salem) (Subsidiary of: Reed Elsevier plc), 8 Industrial Way, Bldg. C, Salem, NH 03079. TEL 800-548-4001. FAX 603-898-9858. Ed.Bd.
 Description: Covers all Minnesota Supreme Court and Court of Appeals cases as well as relevant Minnesota cases decided by the Federal Courts.

340 US ISSN 0093-3058
K4
DUQUESNE LAW REVIEW. 1963. q. $25 (effective 1994). Duquesne University, Duquesne School of Law, 900 Locust St., Pittsburgh, PA 15282. TEL 412-396-6297. FAX 412-396-6294. Ed. Linda S. Somerville. adv.; bk.rev.; index. circ. 1,700. (also avail. in microform from WSH; reprint service avail. from WSH) **Indexed:** Abstr.Bk.Rev.Curr.Leg.Per., C.L.I., Crim.Just.Abstr., L.R.I., Leg.Cont., Leg.Per., Mar.Aff.Bibl. Document type: academic/scholarly publication.
 •Also available online.
 Also available on CD-ROM.
 —BLDSC (3631.500000); Faxon; UnCover; UMI.
 Formerly: Duquesne University Law Review (ISSN 0012-7213)

340 US
E.A.S.L. NEWSLETTER. (Entertainment, Arts & Sports Law) 1988. irreg. (3-4/yr.). $20 to non-members. Florida Bar, 650 Apalachee Pkwy., Tallahassee, FL 32399-2300. TEL 904-561-5624. circ. 745 (controlled). (back issues avail.) Document type: newsletter.

340 UK ISSN 0144-3054
LAW
E C L R: EUROPEAN COMPETITION LAW REVIEW; a bi-monthly review. 1980. bi-m. £165. (E S C Publishing Ltd.) Sweet & Maxwell, South Quay Plaza, 7th Fl., 183 Marsh Wall, London E14 9FT, England. TEL 071-538-8686. FAX 071-538-8625. Ed. Cheri Evans. adv. contact: Jackie Wood. bk.rev.; index. circ. 400. (back issues avail.) **Indexed:** ELLIS. Document type: bulletin.
 —BLDSC (3829.637000); UnCover; SWETS.

E D F LETTER. (Environmental Defense Fund) see *ENVIRONMENTAL STUDIES*

E D I LAW REVIEW; legal aspects of paperless communication. (Electronic Data Interchange) see *COMPUTERS — Data Communications And Data Transmission Systems*

E D V & RECHT; Zeitschrift fuer das Recht der Datenverarbeitung. see *COMPUTERS*

346 333.79 US
▼**E M F LITIGATION NEWS.** 1993. m. $797. Litigation Reporting Service, Box 248, Chalfont, PA 18914. TEL 215-822-9158. FAX 215-822-9158. Ed. William Keough. bk.rev.; s-a. index. (looseleaf format; back issues avail.) Document type: newsletter.

E P A ADMINISTRATIVE LAW REPORTER. see *ENVIRONMENTAL STUDIES*

E P A FASTSEARCH; Environmental Protection Agency regulations. see *ENVIRONMENTAL STUDIES*

E P A POLICY ALERT. (Environmental Protection Agency) see *ENVIRONMENTAL STUDIES*

E P A WATCH. (Environmental Protection Agency) see *ENVIRONMENTAL STUDIES*

340 658.3 US
▼**E R I S A AND BENEFITS LAW JOURNAL.** (Employee Retirement Income Security Act) 1992. q. $125. Butterworth Legal Publishers (Salem) (Subsidiary of: Reed Elsevier plc), 8 Industrial Way, Bldg. C, Salem, NH 03079. TEL 800-548-4001. FAX 603-898-9858. Eds. Michael Macris, Arthur F. Woodward.

E R I S A: THE LAW AND THE CODE. (Employee Retirement Income Security Act) see *BUSINESS AND ECONOMICS — Labor And Industrial Relations*

340 362.4 US ISSN 1058-6482
EARLY CHILDHOOD REPORTER. 1990. m. $150. L R P Publications, 747 Dresher Rd., Horsham, PA 19044. TEL 215-784-0860. FAX 215-784-9639. Ed. Melinda Maloney. (looseleaf format; back issues avail.)
 Description: Concerned with Part H Early Intervention Program.

EARLY IRISH LAW SERIES. see *LINGUISTICS*

340 KE
EAST AFRICAN LAW JOURNAL. 2/yr. P.O. Box 30197, Nairobi, Kenya. Ed. G.K. Rukwaro. circ. 400.

LAW

349   TZ   ISSN 0012-8678
K5
EASTERN AFRICA LAW REVIEW; a journal of law and development. (Text in English) 1968. 2/yr. $25. (University of Dar es Salaam, Faculty of Law) Dar es Salaam University Press, P.O. Box 35093, Dar es Salaam, Tanzania. TEL 48336. Ed. N.N.N. Nditi. adv.; bk.rev.; bibl. circ. 1,000. (back issues avail.) **Document type:** academic/scholarly publication.

340   US   ISSN 0733-6098
KF1819.A2
EASTERN MINERAL LAW FOUNDATION. ANNUAL INSTITUTE. 1980. a. $105. Eastern Mineral Law Foundation, West Virginia University Law Center, Box 6130, Morgantown, WV 26506-6130. TEL 304-293-2470. FAX 304-293-7654. (Dist. by: Matthew Bender & Co., Inc., Box 989, Dept. D.M., Albany, NY 12214-1056) circ. 750. **Indexed:** Leg.Per.
    Description: Features news and program schedules.

340 622   US   ISSN 0749-7709
EASTERN MINERAL LAW FOUNDATION. CASE UPDATE. 1983. 3/yr. $100. Eastern Mineral Law Foundation, West Virginia University Law Center, Box 6130, Morgantown, WV 26506-6130. TEL 304-293-2470. FAX 304-293-7654. Ed. Sharon J. Daniels. (looseleaf format; back issues avail.) **Indexed:** C.L.I. **Document type:** newsletter.

340 549   US
EASTERN MINERAL LAW FOUNDATION NEWSLETTER. vol.8, 1988. q. Eastern Mineral Law Foundation, West Virginia University Law Center, Box 6130, Morgantown, WV 26506-6130. TEL 304-293-2470.
    Description: Discusses coal legislation and Institute conference topics.

614.7 340   US   ISSN 0046-1121
K5
ECOLOGY LAW QUARTERLY. 1971. q. $29 to individuals; institutions $48; students $21 (effective 1994). (Boalt Hall School of Law) University of California Press, Journals Division, 2120 Berkeley Way, Berkeley, CA 94720. TEL 510-643-7154. FAX 510-642-9917. Ed.Bd. adv.; bk.rev.; bibl.; index. circ. 1,300. (also avail. in microfilm from WSH,PMC; reprint service avail. from WSH) **Indexed:** Acid Pre.Dig., C.L.I., Curr.Adv.Ecol.Sci., Curr.Cont., Deep Sea Res.& Oceanogr.Abstr., Energy Rev., Environ.Abstr., Environ.Ind., Environ.Per.Bibl. (1972-), Excerp.Med., Geo.Abstr., GeoRef., Ind.Sci.Rev., INIS Atomind., L.R.I., Leg.Cont., Leg.Per., Mar.Aff.Bibl., P.A.I.S., Pollut.Abstr., Risk Abstr., Sage Pub.Admin.Abstr., Sci.Cit.Ind., Sel.Water Res.Abstr., SSCI. **Document type:** academic/scholarly publication. —BLDSC (3650.044000); CIS; Faxon; UnCover; SWETS; UMI. **CCC.**
    Description: Legal issues relating to environmental affairs.
    Refereed Serial

ECONOMIA E DIRITTO DEL TERZIARIO. see *BUSINESS AND ECONOMICS*

ECONOMIC DESIGN. see *BUSINESS AND ECONOMICS — Economic Systems And Theories, Economic History*

ECONOMIC DEVELOPMENT AND LAW CENTER REPORT. see *BUSINESS AND ECONOMICS — Economic Situation And Conditions*

ECONOMY AND LAW. see *BUSINESS AND ECONOMICS — Economic Systems And Theories, Economic History*

340   UK   ISSN 0953-9964
EDUCATION AND THE LAW. 1989. q. £35 to individuals; institutions £69. Longman Group UK Ltd., Longman House, Burnt Mill, Harlow, Essex CM20 2JE, England. TEL 0279-426721. FAX 0279-431059. Ed.Bd. adv.; bk.rev. **Indexed:** Mult.Ed.Abstr., SOMA. **Document type:** academic/scholarly publication. —BLDSC (3661.188200); UMI.
    Description: Covers all aspects of the law relating to primary, secondary, tertiary and higher education.

340 370   CN   ISSN 0838-2875
EDUCATION LAW JOURNAL. 1988. 3/yr. (plus bound vol.). Can.$140 per vol. Carswell, One Corporate Plaza, 2075 Kennedy Rd., Scarborough, ON M1T 3V4, Canada. TEL 416-609-8000. FAX 416-298-5094. Ed. Greg Dickinson. adv. contact: M. Lalani. bk.rev.; cum.index. **Indexed:** Ind.Can.L.P.L.
    Description: Focuses on issues arising from the interaction of law and education at the elementary, secondary and post-secondary levels. Provides articles and case comments which have direct application to school board trustees, university boards of governors, educational administrators, teachers, professors, students, parents and legal counsel for these parties.

340 370   UK   ISSN 1351-7570
EDUCATION LAW REPORTS. q. £60. Jordan Publishing Ltd., 21 St. Thomas St., Bristol BS1 6JS, England. TEL 0272-230600. FAX 0272-250486. Ed. Neville Harris. **Document type:** academic/scholarly publication.

EDUCATION PERSONNEL NEWS. see *EDUCATION — School Organization And Administration*

EDUCATIONEWS. see *EDUCATION — School Organization And Administration*

340   AU
EHE- UND FAMILIENRECHTLICHE ENTSCHEIDUNGEN. 1966. a. price varies. Manzsche Verlags- und Universitaetsbuchhandlung, Kohlmarkt 16, A-1014 Vienna, Austria. TEL 0222-531610. FAX 0222-53161-181. Eds. Wolfgang Melber, Anton Schwarz. circ. 2,500. **Document type:** bulletin.
    Description: Collects decisions on laws of domestic relations.

DIE EIGENTUMSWOHNUNG; Vorteilhaft erwerben, nutzen und verwalten. see *HOUSING AND URBAN PLANNING*

347.9   GW   ISSN 0341-2261
EILDIENST: BUNDESGERICHTLICHE ENTSCHEIDUNGEN. 1971. w. DM.386.40. Richard Boorberg Verlag (Stuttgart), Scharrstr. 2, 70563 Stuttgart, Germany. TEL 0711-7385-0. Ed. Max D. Kleiner. index. (back issues avail.) **Document type:** bulletin.
—CCC.

340   US
ELDER LAW ADVISORY. 1991. 12/yr. $13095. Clark - Boardman - Callaghan, 50 Broad St. E., Rochester, NY 14694. TEL 716-546-1490. Ed. Mick Cole. (looseleaf format; back issues avail.) **Document type:** newsletter.
    Description: For professionals concerned with delivering quality legal services for older and disabled clients.

340   US
ELDER LAW ATTORNEY. 1991. 2/yr. $30 to non-members. New York State Bar Association, Elder Law Section, One Elk St., Albany, NY 12207-1096. TEL 518-463-3200. FAX 518-487-5699. Ed. Michael Miller. adv. circ. 1,300. (back issues avail.) **Document type:** newsletter.

340 362.5   US
ELDER LAW NEWS. irreg. (2-4/yr.). membership. State Bar of Wisconsin, Elder Law Section, 402 W. Wilson St., Madison, WI 53703. TEL 608-257-3838. FAX 608-257-5502. circ. 630. (back issues avail.) **Document type:** newsletter.
    Description: Covers legal issues affecting senior citizens.

340   US   ISSN 1047-7055
KF390.A4E43
THE ELDER LAW REPORT. 1989. 11/yr. $109. Little, Brown and Company, Law Division, Law Division, 34 Beacon St., Boston, MA 02108. TEL 617-227-0730. FAX 617-859-0629. Ed. Harry Margolis. index. (looseleaf format; back issues avail.) **Document type:** newsletter.

340   US   ISSN 1056-1218
KF390.A4S48
ELDERCARE - LAW NEWSLETTER. 1991. m. $99. Shepard's - McGraw-Hill, Inc., 555 Middle Creek Pky., Colorado Springs, CO 80935-3530. TEL 719-488-3000. FAX 800-525-0053. Ed. Robert Wilkins. index. (looseleaf format; back issues avail.) **Document type:** newsletter.

342   US
ELECTION LAWS OF HAWAII HANDBOOK. a. free. Office of the Lieutenant Governor, State Capitol, Honolulu, HI 96813. TEL 808-586-0255. FAX 808-586-0231.
    Formerly: Election Laws of Hawaii (ISSN 0091-9101)

340   UK
EMDEN'S CONSTRUCTION LAW. 5 base vols. (plus updates 4/yr.). $700. Butterworth & Co. (Publishers) Ltd. (Subsidiary of: Reed Elsevier plc), 88 Kingsway, London WC2B 6AB, England. TEL 71-405-6900. FAX 71-405-1332. (US addr.: Butterworth Legal Publishers, 90 Stiles Rd., Salem, NH 03079-9981. TEL 603-898-9964) Ed.Bd. (looseleaf format)
    Formerly: Building Contracts and Practice.
    Description: Source of detailed information on the whole area of construction law.

340 610   US
EMERGENCY LEGAL BRIEFINGS. 1990. m. $149. American Health Consultants, Inc., Six Piedmont Center, Ste. 400, Atlanta, GA 30305. TEL 404-262-7436; 800-688-2421. FAX 800-284-3291. Ed. Debbie Lydon. circ. 860. **Document type:** newsletter.

EMERGENCY MEDICAL TECHNICIAN LEGAL BULLETIN. see *MEDICAL SCIENCES*

EMERGENCY MEDICINE REPORTS LEGAL BRIEFINGS. see *MEDICAL SCIENCES*

EMERGENCY NURSE LEGAL BULLETIN. see *MEDICAL SCIENCES — Nurses And Nursing*

EMERGENCY PHYSICIAN LEGAL BULLETIN. see *MEDICAL SCIENCES*

EMERGING TRENDS IN SECURITIES LAW. see *BUSINESS AND ECONOMICS — Investments*

340   US   ISSN 0094-4076
K10
EMORY LAW JOURNAL. 1952. q. $30. Emory University, School of Law, Gambrell Hall, Atlanta, GA 30322. TEL 404-727-6830. FAX 404-727-6820. Ed. Ann Beeson. adv.; bk.rev.; charts; index, cum.index every 5 yrs. circ. 1,100. (also avail. in microfilm from PMC,UMI,WSH; reprint service avail. from WSH) **Indexed:** A.B.C.Pol.Sci., C.L.I., Curr.Cont., L.R.I., Leg.Cont., Leg.Per., SSCI. **Document type:** academic/scholarly publication.
●Also available online. Vendor(s): West Services, Inc. —BLDSC (3733.560000); Faxon; UnCover; SWETS; UMI.
    Formerly (until 1974): Journal of Public Law (ISSN 0022-4014)
    Description: Illuminates the current state of the law and proposes novel concepts in the law.

EMPLOYEE DISCIPLINE LAW BULLETIN. see *BUSINESS AND ECONOMICS — Labor And Industrial Relations*

344.73   US   ISSN 0098-8898
K5   CODEN: ERLJDC
EMPLOYEE RELATIONS LAW JOURNAL. 1975. q. $198 in US and Canada; elsewhere $248. Executive Enterprises Publications Co., Inc., 22 W. 21st St., New York, NY 10010-6904. TEL 212-645-7880. FAX 212-645-1160. Ed. Jean Stephenson. (also avail. in microfilm from UMI,WSH,PMC; reprint service avail. from UMI,WSH) **Indexed:** ABI Inform., B.P.I., Bank.Lit.Ind., BPIA, Bus.Ind., C.L.I., Curr.Cont., L.R.I., Leg.Cont., Leg.Per., Manage.Cont., Pers.Lit., Risk Abstr., Sage Fam.Stud.Abstr., Tr.& Indus.Ind.
●Also available online. Vendor(s): DIALOG Information Services, Inc.
—BLDSC (3737.053000); Faxon; UnCover; UMI. **CCC.**
    Description: Designed to make employer and personnel manager proficient in handling EEO, occupational health and safety, labor-management relations, employee benefits and compensation problems.

EMPLOYEE TERMINATIONS LAW BULLETIN. see *BUSINESS AND ECONOMICS — Labor And Industrial Relations*

LAW

340 US
EMPLOYERS GUIDE TO LAW SCHOOLS. a. $80 to non-members. National Association for Law Placement, 1666 Connecticut Ave., Ste. 450, Washington, DC 20009. TEL 202-667-1666.
  Formerly: Employers Guide to A B A Approved N A L P Member Law Schools (ISSN 0275-2832)
  Description: Interprets student resumes, grading systems, standards for honors recognition, and lists law school placement office contacts.

EMPLOYMENT AND LABOUR LAW REPORTER. see BUSINESS AND ECONOMICS — Labor And Industrial Relations

EMPLOYMENT AT WILL REPORTER. see BUSINESS AND ECONOMICS — Labor And Industrial Relations

340 331 CN ISSN 1183-3076
EMPLOYMENT BULLETIN; legal issues in the workplace. 0836-2394. 8/yr. Can.$104. Canada Law Book Inc., 240 Edward St., Aurora, ON L4G 3S9, Canada. TEL 905-841-6472. FAX 905-841-5085. Ed. Brian A. Grosman. **Document type:** bulletin.
  Formerly (until 1990): Employment Letter (ISSN 0836-2394)
  Description: For lawyers, human resource professionals, union and management negotiators and corporate executives.

EMPLOYMENT DISCRIMINATION. see BUSINESS AND ECONOMICS — Personnel Management

EMPLOYMENT DISPUTES; law and stategies for representing the employer. see BUSINESS AND ECONOMICS — Labor And Industrial Relations

340 331.1 CN
EMPLOYMENT IN ALBERTA; a guide to conditions of work and employee benefits. s-a. Can.$100. Butterworths Canada Ltd., Part of the Reed Elsevier group, 75 Clegg Rd., Markham, ON L6G 1A1, Canada. TEL 905-479-2665. FAX 905-479-2826. Ed. Philip H. McLarren. (looseleaf format)
  Description: Information on laws, regulations, programs, plans and practices affecting conditions of work and employee benefits in the province of Alberta.

340 331.1 CN
EMPLOYMENT IN BRITISH COLUMBIA; a guide to conditions of work and employee benefits. s-a. Can.$100. Butterworths Canada Ltd., Part of the Reed Elsevier group, 75 Clegg Rd., Markham, ON L6G 1A1, Canada. TEL 905-479-2665. FAX 905-479-2826. Ed. Philip H. McLarren. (looseleaf format)
  Description: Information on laws, regulations, programs, plans and practices affecting conditions of work and employee benefits in the province of British Columbia.

EMPLOYMENT IN MISSOURI; a guide to employment practice and regulations. see BUSINESS AND ECONOMICS — Labor And Industrial Relations

340 331.1 CN
EMPLOYMENT IN ONTARIO; a guide to conditions of work and employee benefits. s-a. Can.$120. Butterworths Canada Ltd., Part of the Reed Elsevier group, 75 Clegg Rd., Markham, ON L6G 1A1, Canada. TEL 905-479-2665. FAX 905-479-2826. Ed. Phillip H. McLarren. (looseleaf format)
  Description: Information on laws, regulations, programs, plans and practices affecting conditions of work and employee benefits in the province of Ontario.

340 331 US
EMPLOYMENT LAW DESK BOOK FOR TENNESSEE EMPLOYERS. 1989. a. $89. M. Lee Smith Publishers & Printers, 162 Fourth Ave. N., Nashville, TN 37219-8867. TEL 615-242-7395. FAX 615-256-6601. Ed. John P. Phillips, Jr. **Document type:** directory.
  Description: Reference encyclopedia for all areas of employment law - both state and federal.

346.066 US
EMPLOYMENT LAW GUIDE (YEAR). a. $70 to non-members; members $35. Pennsylvania Chamber of Business and Industry, 222 N. Third St., Harrisburg, PA 17101. TEL 800-326-3252. FAX 717-255-3298.

340 IE ISSN 0791-2560
KDK802
EMPLOYMENT LAW REPORTS. 1990. q. I£110($165) The Round Hall Press, Kill Lane, Blackrock, Co. Dublin, Ireland. TEL 2892922. FAX 2893072. Ed. Eilis Barry. circ. 400 (controlled). **Document type:** bulletin.
  Description: Reports decisions of the Employment Appeals Tribunal and appeals therefrom to higher courts.

340 658.3 US ISSN 0890-9253
EMPLOYMENT LAW UPDATE. 1986. m. $97.50 (effective 1992). Rutkowski & Associates Inc., Box 15250, Evansville, IN 47716-0250. TEL 812-476-4520. Eds. Arthur D. Rutkowski, Barbara Lang Rutkowski. index. (back issues avail.) **Document type:** newsletter.
  Description: Provides timely news for human resources executives on relevant issues, including critical legislation and legal decisions, current trends, helpful policies and checklists, and authoritative legal analysis.

340 US ISSN 1055-6249
EMPLOYMENT LITIGATION REPORTER; the national journal of record for termination lawsuits alleging tort and contract claims against employers. 1986. s-m. $800. Andrews Publications, 1646 West Chester Pike, Box 1000, Westtown, PA 19395. TEL 215-399-6600; 800-345-1101. FAX 215-399-6610. Ed. Linda Coady. cum.index every 6 mos. (looseleaf format; back issues avail.) **Document type:** newsletter.
  Formerly: Wrongful Termination Litigation Reporter (ISSN 0888-1197)

EMPLOYMENT RELATIONS TODAY. see BUSINESS AND ECONOMICS — Labor And Industrial Relations

EMPLOYMENT SAFETY AND HEALTH GUIDE. see OCCUPATIONAL HEALTH AND SAFETY

340 658 CN
EMPLOYMENT STANDARDS HANDBOOK AND DIGEST SERVICE. base vol. (plus q. updates). Can.$140. Canada Law Book Inc., 240 Edward St., Aurora, ON L4G 3S9, Canada. TEL 905-841-6472. FAX 905-841-5085. Ed. Robert M. Parry. adv. contact: Mary Cull.

230 US ISSN 1065-2531
EMPLOYMENT TESTING; law and policy reporter. m. $295. University Publications of America (Subsidiary of: Congressional Information Service), 4520 East-West Hwy., Ste. 800, Bethesda, MD 20814-3389. TEL 301-657-3200. FAX 301-657-3203. Ed. Rosemary Orthman. cum.index. (looseleaf format) **Document type:** academic/scholarly publication.
  Description: Offers a forum for timely information on questions and debate concerning substance, integrity, aptitude, and intelligence testing in the workplace.

346.066 UK
ENCYCLOPEDIA OF BANKING LAW. 3 base vols. (plus updates 3/yr.) $790. Butterworth & Co. (Publishers) Ltd. (Subsidiary of: Reed Elsevier plc), 88 Kingsway, London WC2B 6AB, England. TEL 71-405-6900. FAX 71-405-1332. (US addr.: Butterworth Legal Publishers, 90 Stiles Rd., Salem, NH 03079-9981. TEL 603-898-9664) (looseleaf format)
  Description: Provides up-to-date information on the constant change and development in the law and practice of banking.

ENERGY INFORMATION BULLETIN. see ENERGY

340 333.79 US ISSN 0270-9163
K5
ENERGY LAW JOURNAL. 1980. s-a. $25 (Canada $36; elsewhere $42) (effective 1992). Federal Energy Bar Association, 1350 Connecticut Ave., N.W., Ste. 300, Washington, DC 20036. FAX 202-833-5566. Ed. William A. Mogel. adv.; bk.rev.; index, cum.index. circ. 2,500. (also avail. in microfilm; microfiche; back issues avail.) **Indexed:** C.L.I., INIS Atomind., L.R.I., Leg.Per. **Document type:** academic/scholarly publication.
  —BLDSC (3747.671700); Faxon; UnCover; UMI.

ENERGY MANAGEMENT AND FEDERAL ENERGY GUIDELINES. see ENERGY

ENFORCEMENT ALERT. see BUSINESS AND ECONOMICS — Banking And Finance

340 620 US
ENGINEERING EVIDENCE, 2-E. 1987. 2 base vols. (plus a. suppl.). $195. Shepard's - McGraw-Hill, Inc., Box 35300, Colorado Springs, CO 80935-3530. TEL 800-525-2474.
  Description: Covers every aspect of locating, obtaining, interpreting, understanding and preparing engineering evidence for use in litigation involving construction, products liability, catastrophic and transportation cases.

340 NE
ENGLISH LEGAL MANUSCRIPTS. (Includes printed guide and bibliography) 1975. irreg., latest section 5. fl.34430. I D C Microform Publishers B.V., P.O. Box 11205, 2301 EE Leiden, Netherlands. FAX 071-131721. (microfiche)
  Description: Collections of 16th and 17th century legal manuscripts from Lincoln's Inn, Gray's Inn, the Bodleian, Harvard and Yale libraries.

790 US ISSN 8756-3991
ENTERTAINMENT & SPORTS LAW REVIEW. 1983. s-a. $30. University of Miami, School of Law, Box 248087, Coral Gables, FL 33124-8087. TEL 305-284-6886. Ed. Michael Hanrahan. (back issues avail.)
  ●Also available online. Vendor(s): West Services, Inc. —UnCover.

340 790 US ISSN 0732-1880
KF4290.A15
ENTERTAINMENT AND SPORTS LAWYER. 1982. 4/yr. $30. (American Bar Association, Forum Committee on the Entertainment and Sports Industries) A B A Press, 750 N. Lake Shore Dr., Chicago, IL 60611. TEL 312-988-6068. Ed. Richard J. Greenston. circ. 2,946. (also avail. in microform) **Indexed:** C.L.I. **Document type:** newsletter.
  Description: Developments in entertainment and sports law.

340 US ISSN 1054-1047
ENTERTAINMENT, ARTS & SPORTS LAW. 1989. 3/yr. $35 to non-members. New York State Bar Association, Entertainment, Arts & Sports Law Section, 1 Elk St., Albany, NY 12207-1096. TEL 518-463-3200. FAX 518-487-5699. Ed. Howard Leib. circ. 1,000. (back issues avail.) **Document type:** newsletter.

340 US
▼**ENTERTAINMENT LAW.** 1992. 4 base vols. (plus a. suppl.). $525. Shepard's - McGraw-Hill, Inc., Box 35300, Colorado Springs, CO 80935-3530. TEL 800-525-2474. (looseleaf format)
  Description: Focuses on the legal principles and business realities that motivate the entertainment industry, with a systematic discussion and analysis of applicable case law.

346.066 US
ENTERTAINMENT LAW & BUSINESS. 1989. base vol. (plus suppl.). $119. Butterworth Legal Publishers (Salem) (Subsidiary of: Reed Elsevier plc), 8 Industrial Way, Bldg. C, Salem, NH 03079. TEL 800-548-4001. FAX 603-898-9858. Ed. David Sinacore-Guinn. (looseleaf format)

750 US ISSN 0883-2455
ENTERTAINMENT LAW & FINANCE. 1985. m. $185. New York Law Publishing Co., 345 Park Ave. S., New York, NY 10010. TEL 212-545-6220. FAX 212-696-1848. **Document type:** newsletter.
  Description: Legal and financial developments in music, film, theater, broadcasting, sports, publishing, video and related media arts.

340 US ISSN 0270-3831
KF4290.A59
ENTERTAINMENT LAW REPORTER; motion pictures, television, radio, music, theater, publishing, sports. 1979. m. $175 (effective May 1991). Entertainment Law Reporter Publishing Co., 2210 Wilshire Blvd., No. 311, Santa Monica, CA 90403. TEL 310-829-9335. Ed. Lionel S. Sobel. adv.; bk.rev.; index. circ. 825. **Indexed:** C.L.I., Leg Cont., Leg.Per. **Document type:** newsletter.

LAW

340   UK   ISSN 0959-3799
ENTERTAINMENT LAW REVIEW. 1990. bi-m. £180. (E S C Publishing Ltd.) Sweet & Maxwell, South Quay Plaza, 7th Fl., 183 Marsh Wall, London E14 9FT, England. TEL 071-538-8686. FAX 071-538-9508. Eds. Cheri Evans, Nick Gingell. adv. contact: Jackie Wood. **Document type:** bulletin.
—BLDSC (3776.655000).
    Description: Provides a regular update on developments in entertainment law.

340   US   ISSN 1047-4137
KF4290.A59
ENTERTAINMENT LITIGATION REPORTER; national journal of record covering critical issues in entertainment law field. 1989. m. $700. Andrews Publications, 1646 West Chester Pike, Box 1000, Westtown, PA 19395. TEL 215-399-6600; 800-345-1101. FAX 215-399-6610. Ed. Robert Sullivan. abstr.; bibl.; stat.; cum.index every 6 mos. (looseleaf format; back issues avail.) **Document type:** newsletter.

340   GW
ENTSCHEIDUNGEN DER OBERVERWALTUNGSGERICHTE FUER DAS LAND NORDRHEIN-WESTFALEN IN MUENSTER SOWIE FUER DIE LAENDER NIEDERSACHSEN UND SCHLESWIG-HOLSTEIN IN LUENEBURG. 1953. irreg., vol.41. DM.185. Aschendorffsche Verlagsbuchhandlung, Soesterstr. 13, 48155 Muenster, Germany. TEL 0251-690-0. FAX 0251-690143. circ. 1,000. **Document type:** monographic series.

340   GW   ISSN 0435-7124
KK7980.3
ENTSCHEIDUNGEN DES BUNDESGERICHTSHOFES IN ZIVILSACHEN. 1951. m. DM.54. Carl Heymanns Verlag KG, Luxemburgerstr. 449, 50939 Cologne, Germany. TEL 0221-460100. FAX 0221-4601069. (back issues avail.) **Document type:** bulletin.

340   GW   ISSN 0433-7646
ENTSCHEIDUNGEN DES BUNDESVERFASSUNGSGERICHTS. 1952. irreg. (1-2/yr.). DM.64 per vol. Verlag J.C.B. Mohr (Paul Siebeck), Wilhelmstr. 18, 72074 Tuebingen, Germany. TEL 07071-923-0. FAX 07071-51104. (Subscr. to: Postfach 2040, 72010 Tuebingen, Germany) **Document type:** academic/scholarly publication.
    Description: Decisions of the German Constitutional Court.

340   GW   ISSN 0013-9106
ENTSCHEIDUNGEN DES BUNDESVERWALTUNGSGERICHTS. 1955. irreg. DM.78. Carl Heymanns Verlag KG, Luxemburgerstr. 449, 50939 Cologne, Germany. TEL 0221-460100. FAX 0221-4601069. (back issues avail.) **Document type:** bulletin.

ENTSCHEIDUNGEN ZUM WIRTSCHAFTSRECHT - E W I R. see BUSINESS AND ECONOMICS — Economic Situation And Conditions

ENVIROACTION. see CONSERVATION

340 613.1   UK   ISSN 0959-0617
ENVIRONMENT LAW BRIEF. 10/yr. £117($234) (students £58.50($117)). I B C Publishing, Gilmoora House, 57-61 Mortimer St., London W1N 7TD, England. TEL 071-637-4383. FAX 071-636-6414. (Subscr. in U.S. to: IBC (USA), 290 Eliot St., Box 91004, Ashland, MA 01721-9104. TEL 508-881-2800. FAX 508-881-0982) Ed. Stephen Battersby. **Document type:** newsletter.
—BLDSC (3791.332000).

ENVIRONMENTAL AND LAND USE LAW. see ENVIRONMENTAL STUDIES

340 614.7   US
ENVIRONMENTAL AND NATURAL RESOURCES PERMITS; federal approval standards and procedures. 1991. base vol. (plus irreg. updates). $95. Butterworth Legal Publishers (Salem) (Subsidiary of: Reed Elsevier plc), 8 Industrial Way, Bldg. C, Salem, NH 03079. TEL 800-548-4001. FAX 603-898-9858. Ed. Robert L. Schmid. (looseleaf format)
    Description: Covers air pollution, water quality, hazardous waste, radiation material, mineral, timber, grazing and wildlife resources and land use and occupancy.

340 614.7   AT   ISSN 0813-300X
K5   CODEN: EPLJEX
ENVIRONMENTAL AND PLANNING LAW JOURNAL. 1984. 6/yr. Aus.$225. Law Book Co. Ltd., 44-50 Waterloo Rd., North Ryde, N.S.W. 2113, Australia. TEL 02-887-0177. FAX 02-888-9706. TELEX ASBOOK 27995. Ed. Gerry Bates. bk.rev. (back issues avail.) **Indexed:** Environ.Per.Bibl. (1990-), Sel.Water Res.Abstr.
—BLDSC (3791.383200).
    Description: Discusses environmental policy and administration, national parks and wildlife, cultural and natural heritage and environmental contaminants.

ENVIRONMENTAL APPROVALS IN CANADA; practice and procedure. see ENVIRONMENTAL STUDIES

ENVIRONMENTAL AUDITS. see ENVIRONMENTAL STUDIES

ENVIRONMENTAL BRIEFING. see ENVIRONMENTAL STUDIES

340   US
ENVIRONMENTAL CITIZEN SUITS. 1991. base vol. (plus a. supplement). $95. Butterworth Legal Publishers (Salem) (Subsidiary of: Reed Elsevier plc), 8 Industrial Way, Bldg. C, Salem, NH 03079. TEL 800-548-4001. FAX 603-898-9858. Ed. Michael D. Axline. (looseleaf format)
    Description: Provides both the experienced practitioner and the environmental law novice with information concerning the prosecution and defense of environmental citizen suits.

ENVIRONMENTAL CLAIMS JOURNAL. see ENVIRONMENTAL STUDIES

ENVIRONMENTAL COMPLIANCE. see ENVIRONMENTAL STUDIES

340   US
ENVIRONMENTAL COMPLIANCE & LITIGATION STRATEGY. 1985. m. $195. New York Law Publishing Co., 345 Park Ave. S., New York, NY 10010. TEL 212-545-6170. FAX 212-696-1848.
    Formerly (until 1993): Hazardous Waste and Toxic Torts Law and Strategy (ISSN 0884-3775)
    Description: Roundup of significant legislative and regulatory rulings of special interest to manufacturers, insurance companies, trial attorneys, government enforcement agencies, environmental consultants and corporate counsel.

ENVIRONMENTAL CONTROL LAW. see ENVIRONMENTAL STUDIES

ENVIRONMENTAL INSURANCE COVERAGE; state law and regulation. see INSURANCE

ENVIRONMENTAL LABORATORY WASHINGTON REPORT. see MEDICAL SCIENCES — Experimental Medicine, Laboratory Technique

ENVIRONMENTAL LAW (PORTLAND). see ENVIRONMENTAL STUDIES

344.73   US   ISSN 0748-8769
KF3775.A15
ENVIRONMENTAL LAW (WASHINGTON). 1973. 2/yr. $18 to institutions; free to individuals. American Bar Association, Standing Committee on Environmental Law, 1800 M St., N.W., Washington, DC 20036. TEL 202-331-2276. FAX 202-331-2220. Ed. Elissa C. Lichtenstein. bk.rev. circ. 6,600. (back issues avail.) **Indexed:** C.L.I., L.R.I., Sel.Water Res.Abstr. **Document type:** newsletter.
—UMI.
    Formerly: American Bar Association. Special Committee on Environmental Law. Quarterly Newsletter (ISSN 0093-7797)
    Description: Lists ABA programs and activities in environmental law, and presents articles on current issues.

340 614.7   CN   ISSN 0847-2068
ENVIRONMENTAL LAW ALERT. 1989. 6/yr. Can.$112. Canada Law Book Inc., 240 Edward St., Aurora, ON L4G 3S9, Canada. TEL 905-841-6472. FAX 905-841-5085. Eds. Robert Fishlock, Johnathan Kahn. adv. contact: Mary Cull.
    Description: Covers the environmental facts affecting corporations, businesses, natural resource companies and municipalities.

ENVIRONMENTAL LAW AND ENERGY JOURNAL. see ENERGY

340 614.7   UK   ISSN 1067-6058
    CODEN: ELAMER
ENVIRONMENTAL LAW AND MANAGEMENT. 1989. 6/yr. $295. John Wiley & Sons Ltd., Journals, Baffins Ln., Chichester, Sussex PO19 1UD, England. TEL 0243-779777. FAX 0243-775878. TELEX 86290-WIBOOK-G. Ed. Malcolm Forster. circ. 142. **Indexed:** Environ.Per.Bibl. (1990-). **Document type:** academic/scholarly publication.
—BLDSC (3791.515030); UMI.
    Formerly: Land Management and Environment Law Report.
    Description: Provides information on the entire spectrum of environmental issues in a cross-sectoral manner.

347   US
ENVIRONMENTAL LAW ANTHOLOGY. 1990. a. $149.95. International Library Law Book Publishers, Inc., 101 Lakeforest Blvd., Ste. 270, Gaithersburg, MD 20877. TEL 301-990-7755. FAX 301-990-7642. Ed. Allison P. Zabriskie. bibl.; index. **Document type:** monographic series.
    Description: Selected best U.S. law review articles, printed in their entirety, in the field of enviromental law culled from over 900 American law review journals.

ENVIRONMENTAL LAW HANDBOOK. see ENVIRONMENTAL STUDIES

ENVIRONMENTAL LAW IN NEW YORK; developments in federal and state law. see ENVIRONMENTAL STUDIES

340 614.7   US
KFT1554.A15
ENVIRONMENTAL LAW JOURNAL. 1969. q. $10. State Bar of Texas, Environmental and Natural Resources Section, Box 12487, Capitol Sta., Austin, TX 78711-2487. TEL 512-463-1463. FAX 512-463-1475. Ed. Jimmy Alan Hall. bk.rev. circ. 2,500. **Indexed:** C.L.I., L.R.I.
    Formerly: Environmental Law Newsletter (ISSN 0163-545X)
    Description: Provides current legal articles and recent developments and information pertaining to environmental and natural resources law.

340 613.1   UK   ISSN 0968-4794
▼**ENVIRONMENTAL LAW MONTHLY.** 1992. m. £115 (foreign £137). Monitor Press, Rectory Rd., Great Waldingfield, Sudbury, Suffolk CO10 0TL, England. TEL 0787-378607. FAX 0787-880201. **Document type:** newsletter.
—BLDSC (3791.515100).

ENVIRONMENTAL LAW NEWS. see ENVIRONMENTAL STUDIES

ENVIRONMENTAL LAW REPORTER. see ENVIRONMENTAL STUDIES

340 613.1   UK   ISSN 0966-2022
ENVIRONMENTAL LAW REPORTS. q. £145. Sweet & Maxwell, South Quay Plaza, 7th Fl., 183 Marsh Wall, London E14 9FT, England. TEL 071-538-8686. FAX 071-538-9508. Ed. Andrea Dowsett. adv. contact: Jackie Wood. **Document type:** bulletin.

346.066   US
ENVIRONMENTAL LIABILITY; law and strategy for businesses and corporations. 1990. base vol. (plus a. suppl.). $110. Butterworth Legal Publishers (Salem) (Subsidiary of: Reed Elsevier plc), 8 Industrial Way, Bldg. C, Salem, NH 03079. TEL 800-548-4001. FAX 603-898-9858. Ed. Lawrence P. Schnapf. (looseleaf format)
    Description: Provides guidance on environmental law issues for attorneys handling business venture start-ups and compliance with Superfund cleanup regulations. Includes the text of relevant federal and state environmental statutes.

340 613.1   UK   ISSN 0966-2030
ENVIRONMENTAL LIABILITY. bi-m. £195. Sweet & Maxwell, South Quay Plaza, 7th Fl., 183 Marsh Wall, London E14 9FT, England. TEL 071-538-8686. FAX 071-538-9508. Ed. Andrea Dowsett. adv. contact: Jackie Wood. **Document type:** bulletin.
—BLDSC (3791.517300).
    Description: Regular coverage of criminal and civil liability involving environmental issues.

ENVIRONMENTAL MANAGEMENT REVIEW. see ENVIRONMENTAL STUDIES

340 613.1   UK   ISSN 1350-7613
▼**ENVIRONMENTAL MANAGER.** 1993. 10/yr. £132 (foreign £154). Monitor Press, Rectory Rd., Great Waldingfield, Sudbury, Suffolk CO10 0TL, England. TEL 0787-378607. FAX 0787-880201. **Document type:** newsletter.

ENVIRONMENTAL POLICY AND LAW. see ENVIRONMENTAL STUDIES

340 620.85   AT
ENVIRONMENTAL RESPONSIBILITIES LAW (N.S.W.). base vol. (plus updates 4/yr.). Aus.$295. Law Book Co. Ltd., 44-50 Waterloo Rd., North Ryde, N.S.W. 2113, Australia. TEL 02-887-0177. FAX 02-888-2287. (looseleaf format)
   Description: Provides a comprehensive overview of environmental legislation in New South Wales.

ENVIRONMENTAL SPILL REPORTING MANUAL. see ENVIRONMENTAL STUDIES — Waste Management

ENVIRONMENTAL STATUTES. see ENVIRONMENTAL STUDIES

EPITESUGYI ERTESITO. see BUILDING AND CONSTRUCTION

340   US
EQUAL RIGHTS ADVOCATE. 1979. q. $25. Equal Rights Advocates, 1663 Mission St., Ste. 550, San Francisco, CA 94103. TEL 415-621-0672. FAX 415-621-6744. Ed. Wendell Ricketts. circ. 5,000. (back issues avail.) **Document type:** newsletter.

340   US   ISSN 0733-4303
EQUIPMENT LEASING NEWSLETTER. 1982. m. $275. New York Law Publishing Co., 345 Park Ave. S., New York, NY 10010. TEL 212-545-6170. FAX 212-696-1848. **Document type:** newsletter.
   Description: Legal, business, and tax developments affecting the equipment leasing industry.

347   US   ISSN 0743-247X
KF532.7.A15
EQUITABLE DISTRIBUTION JOURNAL; a monthly review of current developments. m. $105. National Legal Research Group, Inc., 2421 Ivy Rd., Box 7187, Charlottesville, VA 22906-7187. TEL 800-446-1870. FAX 804-295-4667. Ed. Joan L. Cobb.
   Description: Analyses of recent cases in equitable distribution.

340   US
EQUITABLE DISTRIBUTION OF PROPERTY. 1983. base vol. (plus a. suppl.). $70. Shepard's - McGraw-Hill, Inc., Box 35300, Colorado Springs, CO 80935-3530. TEL 800-525-2474.
   Description: Provides classification of marital and separate property and information on how to avoid malpractice. Covers valuation of property, the Uniform Marriage and Divorce Act, discovery techniques, and advocacy and litigation skills.

349   CK   ISSN 0014-1461
ESTUDIOS DE DERECHO. (Text mainly in Spanish; occasionally in English, French, Italian) 1939. s-a. $15. Universidad de Antioquia, Facultad de Derecho y Ciencias Politicas, Apdo. Aereo 1226, Medellin, Colombia. FAX 638282. Ed. Dr. Benigno Mantilla Pineda. adv.; bk.rev.; abstr.; bibl. circ. 2,000. (also avail. in microform) Indexed: Amer.Hist.& Life, Foreign Leg.Per., Hist.Abstr., P.A.I.S.For.Lang.Ind.

ESTUDIOS PUBLICOS. see BUSINESS AND ECONOMICS — Economic Situation And Conditions

340   BL   ISSN 0100-2538
ESTUDOS JURIDICOS. 1971. 3/yr. Cr.$40000($20) or exchange basis. (Universidade do Vale do Rio dos Sinos) Unisinos, Av. Unisinos, 950, 93010 Sao Leopoldo RS, Brazil. TEL 051-5926333. FAX 0512-921035. TELEX 524076. Ed. Bruno Hammes. bibl.; index, cum.index. circ. 250. (back issues avail.) **Document type:** academic/scholarly publication.

ETHIK IN DER MEDIZIN. see PHILOSOPHY

340   NR
ETHIOPE LAW SERIES. no.4, 1976. irreg. Ethiope Publishing Corporation, 34 Murtala Mohammed St., P.M.B. 1192, Benin City, Nigeria. Ed. T.O. Elias.

340   GW   ISSN 0341-9800
LAW
EUROPAEISCHE GRUNDRECHTE ZEITSCHRIFT. 1974. fortn. DM.314. N.P. Engel Verlag, Gutenbergstr. 29, 77694 Kehl, Germany. TEL 07851-2463. FAX 07851-4234. (Dist. in U.S. by: N.P. Engel, Publisher, 3608 S. 12th St., Arlington, VA 22204. TEL 703-920-3126. FAX 703-920-3127) Ed. N.P. Engel. adv.; index. circ. 1,400. Indexed: ELLIS, INIS Atomind., Refug.Abstr. **Document type:** bulletin.
—BLDSC (3829.345000); SWETS.
   Formerly (until 1977): Grundrechte; die Rechtsprechung in Europa (ISSN 0340-8906)
   Description: Articles, constitutional and Supreme Court decisions and reports, documentation and pending proceedings.

349 940   EI   ISSN 0531-2671
EUROPEAN ASPECTS, LAW SERIES; a collection of studies relating to European integration. 1962. irreg. Council of Europe, Publishing and Documentation Service, 67075 Strasbourg Cedex, France. (Dist. in U.S. by Manhattan Publishing Co., P.O. Box 650, Croton-on-Hudson, N.Y. 10520)

346.066   UK   ISSN 0959-6941
K5
EUROPEAN BUSINESS LAW REVIEW. 1990. 11/yr. £242($410) (effective 1994). Graham & Trotman Ltd. (Subsidiary of: Kluwer Academic Publishers Group), Sterling House, 66 Wilton Rd., London SW1V 1DE, England. (Dist. by: Kluwer Academic Publishers Group, P.O. Box 322, 3300 AH Dordrecht, Netherlands. TEL 31-78-524400. FAX 31-78-524474; N. America dist. addr.: Box 358, Accord Station, Hingham, MA 02018-0358. TEL 617-871-6600. FAX 617-871-6528) Ed. Susan Nicholas. adv.
—BLDSC (3829.552700); UnCover; UMI.
   Description: Publishes short, practical analyses of recent legal developments in European business law, including news on specific countries and coverage of EC directives, legislation, treaties, case notes and other related matters.

340   UK   ISSN 0141-7266
LAW
EUROPEAN COMMERCIAL CASES. 1978. bi-m. £330. (European Law Centre) Sweet & Maxwell, South Quay Plaza, 7th Floor, 183 Marsh Wall, London E14 9FT, England. TEL 071-538-8686. FAX 071-538-8625. Ed. Marina Milmo. adv. contact: Jackie Wood. **Document type:** newsletter.
—BLDSC (3829.618500); UnCover.
   Description: Major decisions of European national courts in certain areas of commercial law.

340   UK   ISSN 0950-7361
EUROPEAN COMMUNITIES LEGISLATION: CURRENT STATUS. a. (plus q. suppl.). price varies. Butterworth & Co. (Publishers) Ltd. (Subsidiary of: Reed Elsevier plc), 88 Kingsway, London WC2B 6AB, England. TEL 71-405-6900. FAX 71-405-1332. (US addr.: Butterworth Legal Publishers, 90 Stiles Rd., Salem, NH 03079-9981. TEL 603-898-9664)
—BLDSC (3829.629350).
   Description: Reference source of all Community secondary legislation published in the Official Journal of the European Communities since 1952.

340   UK   ISSN 0964-0037
KJC30
EUROPEAN CURRENT LAW. m. £330. Sweet & Maxwell, South Quay Plaza, 7th Fl., 183 Marsh Wall, London E14 9FT, England. TEL 071-538-8686. FAX 071-538-9508. Ed. Helen Wauchope. adv. contact: Jackie Wood. **Document type:** bulletin.
—UnCover.
   Description: Provides practitioners, research departments, academics and libraries with a comprehensive guide to legal developments throughout Europe.

340 628.5   UK   ISSN 0966-1646
KJC6242.A13
▼**EUROPEAN ENVIRONMENTAL LAW REVIEW.** (Includes: Country Reports, Eurobrief, View from America) 1992. 11/yr. £195($330) (effective 1994). Graham & Trotman Ltd. (Subsidiary of: Kluwer Academic Publishers Group), Sterling House, 66 Wilton Rd., London SW1 1DE, England. TEL 44-71-821-1123. FAX 44-71-630-5229. TELEX 298878-GRAMCO-G. (Dist. by: Kluwer Academic Publishers Group, P.O. Box 322, 3300 AH Dordrecht, Netherlands. TEL 31-78-524400. FAX 31-78-524474; N. America dist. addr.: Box 358, Accord Sta., Hingham, MA 02018-0358. TEL 617-871-6600. FAX 617-871-6528) Ed. Elizabeth Bramwell. adv.; bk.rev. (also avail. in microform from UMI; back issues avail.) **Document type:** academic/scholarly publication.
—BLDSC (3829.700600); SWETS.
   Description: Offers comprehensive coverage of developments in environmental law throughout Europe.
   Refereed Serial

EUROPEAN FOOD LAW REVIEW. see FOOD AND FOOD INDUSTRIES

EUROPEAN HUMAN RIGHTS. see POLITICAL SCIENCE — Civil Rights

340 323.4   UK   ISSN 0260-4868
LAW
EUROPEAN HUMAN RIGHTS REPORTS. 1979. m. £250. (European Law Centre Ltd.) Sweet & Maxwell, South Quay Plaza, 7th Floor, 183 Marsh Wall, London E14 9FT, England. TEL 071-538-8686. FAX 071-538-9508. Ed. Sarah Andrews. adv. contact: Jackie Wood. **Document type:** bulletin.
—BLDSC (3829.718500).
   Description: Includes articles on criminal procedure, property law and aliens control.

EUROPEAN JOURNAL OF HEALTH LAW. see MEDICAL SCIENCES

EUROPEAN JOURNAL OF LAW AND ECONOMICS. see BUSINESS AND ECONOMICS

340   UK   ISSN 1350-1968
▼**EUROPEAN LAW MONITOR.** 1993. m. £129 (foreign £151). Monitor Press, Rectory Rd., Great Waldingfield, Sudbury, Suffolk CO10 0TL, England. TEL 0787-378607. FAX 0787-880201. **Document type:** newsletter.

340   UK   ISSN 0307-5400
K5
EUROPEAN LAW REVIEW. 1975. 6/yr. £198. Sweet & Maxwell, South Quay Plaza, 7th Fl., 183 Marsh Wall, London E14 9FT, England. TEL 071-538-8686. FAX 071-538-9505. adv. contact: Jackie Wood. (reprint service avail. from RRI) Indexed: Abstr.Bk.Rev.Curr.Leg.Per., C.L.I., ELLIS, L.R.I., Leg.Per. **Document type:** bulletin.
—BLDSC (3829.748700); Faxon; UnCover; SWETS; UMI.

340   NE
EUROPEAN STUDIES IN LAW. 1977. irreg., vol.9, 1980. price varies. Elsevier Science B.V., Books Division, P.O. Box 211, 1000 AE Amsterdam, Netherlands. TEL 31-20-5803911. FAX 31-20-5803705. TELEX 18582 ESPA NL. (Subscr. in U.S. and Canada to: Elsevier Science Inc., Box 882, Madison Sq. Sta., New York, NY 10159. TEL 212-989-5800) Ed. A.G. Chloros. **Document type:** monographic series.
   Refereed Serial

EVANGELISCHE KIRCHE DER KIRCHENPROVINZ SACHSEN. AMTSBLATT. see RELIGIONS AND THEOLOGY — Protestant

340   US
EVIDENCE TRIAL MANUAL FOR TEXAS LAWYERS: CIVIL. (2nd ed., 1992) (Companion to: Evidence Trial Manual for Texas Lawyers - Criminal) 1986. 2 base vols. (plus irreg. supplements). $160. Butterworth Legal Publishers (Salem) (Subsidiary of: Reed Elsevier plc), 8 Industrial Way, Bldg. C, Salem, NH 03079. TEL 800-548-4001. FAX 603-898-9858. Ed. Murl A. Larkin. (looseleaf format)
   Description: Provides the full text of all state and federal evidence rules and statutes applicable in Texas.

LAW

340   US
EVIDENCE TRIAL MANUAL FOR TEXAS LAWYERS: CRIMINAL. (Companion to: Evidence Trial Manual for Texas Lawyers - Civil) 1986. base vol. (plus suppl. 1-2/yr.). $120. Butterworth Legal Publishers (Salem) (Subsidiary of: Reed Elsevier plc), 8 Industrial Way, Bldg. C, Salem, NH 03079. TEL 800-548-4001. FAX 603-898-9858. Ed. Murl A. Larkin. (looseleaf format)

THE EXCHANGE (SAN FRANCISCO). see *MEDICAL SCIENCES — Communicable Diseases*

346.066 336   US   ISSN 1043-3082
EXECUTIVE ACTION REPORT. w. (plus irreg. Special Reports). $234. Warren Gorham Lamont, One Penn Plaza, New York, NY 10119-4098. TEL 800-950-1201. FAX 617-423-1914.
  Description: Contains late-breaking news from Washington D.C., case studies, practical strategies, and tax-saving tips.

340   US
EXECUTIVE AND PROFESSIONAL EMPLOYMENT CONTRACTS; the major legal issues and forms. 1988. base vol. (plus suppl.). $105. Butterworth Legal Publishers (Salem) (Subsidiary of: Reed Elsevier plc), 8 Industrial Way, Bldg. C, Salem, NH 03079. TEL 800-548-4001. FAX 603-898-9858. Ed. L.J. Kutten. (looseleaf format)

347 617.1   US   ISSN 0891-0278
KF2915.E95
EXERCISE STANDARDS AND MALPRACTICE REPORTER. 1987. 6/yr. $39.95. Professional Reports Corporation, 4418 Belden Village St., N.W., Canton, OH 44718-2516. TEL 216-492-6063; 800-336-0083. FAX 216-492-6176. Eds. David L. Herbert, William G. Herbert. adv.; index. circ. 700. (looseleaf format; back issues avail.) **Document type:** newsletter.
  Description: Current standards of practice for exercise, wellness and health promotion programs. Malpractice and professional concerns and developments are examined.

340   US   ISSN 1054-3473
K5
EXPERIENCE. 1986. q. $34.95. (American Bar Association) A B A Press, 750 N. Lake Shore Dr., Chicago, IL 60611. TEL 312-988-6122. FAX 312-988-6281. Ed. Ray DeLong. adv.; bk.rev. circ. 7,500.
  —UnCover.
  Supersedes (in 1990): Senior Lawyer.
  Description: Articles on practice problems and aspects of retirement for lawyers 60 and older. Includes news of the division.

340   US   ISSN 0737-8726
THE EXPERT AND THE LAW. 1979. bi-m. $75. National Forensic Center, 17 Temple Terr., Lawrenceville, NJ 08648. TEL 609-883-0550. Ed. Betty Lipscher. **Document type:** newsletter.
  ●Also available online. Vendor(s): Mead Data Central, Inc.
  Description: Devoted to the application of scientific, medical, and technical knowledge to litigation.

340 150   UK   ISSN 0965-3643
▼**EXPERT EVIDENCE;** international digest of human behaviour science and law. 1992. 4/yr. £38 to individuals; institutions £76. S L E Publications Ltd., 77 Birdham Rd., Chichester, W. Sussex PO20 7DU, England. TEL 0243-532952. FAX 0243-786043. Eds. David Carson, Ray Bull. **Document type:** academic/scholarly publication.
  —BLDSC (3842.002950).

340   AT
▼**EXPERT EVIDENCE.** 1993. irreg. (in 4 vols.). Aus.$595. Law Book Co. Ltd., 44-50 Waterloo Rd., North Ryde, N.S.W. 2113, Australia. TEL 02-887-0177. FAX 02-888-9706. TELEX ASBOOK 27995. Eds. Ian Freckelton, Hugh Selby. (looseleaf format)
  Description: Detailed exposition and analysis of the law of expert evidence and explanation of over 55 specialist fields of expertise, both legal and technical.

340   FR
EXPERTS. 4/yr. C G N, 32 rue Saint-Marc, 75002 Paris, France. TEL 42-60-51-58. Ed. Albert Willemetz. circ. 5,130.

340   CK   ISSN 0121-4055
EXTERNADO REVISTA JURIDICA. 1935. s-a. Col.6000 per no. (effective July 1993). Universidad Externado de Colombia, Departamento de Publicaciones, C. 12, No. 0-46 Este, Apdo. Aereo 034141, Bogota, Colombia. TEL 341-2610. FAX 2843769. Eds. Fernando Hinestrosa, Camilo Calderon. adv.; bk.rev. circ. 2,500.
  Former titles (until 1986): Externado (ISSN 0120-5218); (until 1981): Universidad Externado de Colombia. Revista (ISSN 0041-8544); (until 1964): Universidad Externado de Colombia. Facultad de Derecho. Revista.

EXTRAORDINARY CONTRACTUAL RELIEF REPORTER. see *BUSINESS AND ECONOMICS — Economic Situation And Conditions*

340   US
EYEWITNESS TESTIMONY: STRATEGIES AND TACTICS. 1984. base vol. (plus a. suppl.). $195. Shepard's - McGraw-Hill, Inc., Box 35300, Colorado Springs, CO 80935-3530. TEL 800-525-2474.
  Description: Explains how and where errors in eyewitness perception can occur.

F C C REPORT; an exclusive report on domestic and international telecommunications policy and regulation. (Federal Communications Commission) see *COMMUNICATIONS*

F C N L WASHINGTON NEWSLETTER. (Friends Committee on National Legislation) see *POLITICAL SCIENCE*

340   US
F E L A REPORTER & RAILROAD LIABILITY MONITOR. (Federal Employees Liability Act) 1988. m. $350. M. Lee Smith Publishers & Printers, 162 Fourth Ave. N., Nashville, TN 37219-8867. TEL 615-242-7395. FAX 615-256-6601. Ed. Lewis L. Laska.
  Description: Summarizes current information about employment compensation cases involving railroads.

340   US   ISSN 0093-7630
HD4903.5.U58
F E P GUIDELINES. (Fair Employment Practices) m. $89.40. Bureau of Business Practice, 24 Rope Ferry Rd., Waterford, CT 06386. TEL 203-442-4365. FAX 203-434-3078. TELEX 966420. Ed. Ruso Case.

340   US
F I J ACTIVIST. 1989. q. $15 membership. Fully Informed Jury Association, Box 59, Helmville, MT 59843. TEL 406-793-5550; 800-TEL-JURY. Eds. Larry Dodge, Don Doig. bk.rev. circ. 4,000. **Document type:** newsletter.
  Description: Reports on the association's progress, grass roots activism, legislative activity. Covers theory and history of jury nullification (the common law right of jurors to judge the merits of the law itself).

F M A TODAY (JACKSONVILLE). (Florida Medical Association) see *MEDICAL SCIENCES*

F R V T A NEWS. (Florida Recreational Vehicle Trade Association) see *LEISURE AND RECREATION*

F T C FREEDOM OF INFORMATION LOG. (Federal Trade Commission) see *BUSINESS AND ECONOMICS — International Commerce*

340   BE
FACULTE DE DROIT DE NAMUR. TRAVAUX. no.12, 1975. irreg. price varies. (Societe d'Etudes Morales, Sociales et Juridiques) Maison Ferdinand Larcier S.A., Rue des Minimes 39, 1000 Brussels, Belgium.

340 900   FR   ISSN 0765-4847
KJV150.A15
FACULTES DE DROIT ET DE LA SCIENCE JURIDIQUE. REVUE D'HISTOIRE. 1984. s-a. 260 F. Societe pour l'Histoire des Facultes de Droit et de la Science Juridique, Universite de Paris V, 10 av. Pierre Larousse, 92241 Malakoff Cedex, France. (Dist. by: Librairie Generale de Droit et de Jurisprudence, 26 rue Vercingetorix, 75014 Paris, France) Ed. Jean-Marie Carbasse. bk.rev. (back issues avail.)
  Formerly (until 1987): Facultes de Droit et de la Science Juridique. Annales d'Histoire.

340   US   ISSN 0887-7807
KF971.3
FAILED BANK AND THRIFT LITIGATION REPORTER; the nationwide litigation report of failed national and state banks and savings and loan associations, including F D I C and F S L I C complaints and related actions among shareholders, officers, directors, institutions and insurers. 1986. s-m. $825. Andrews Publications, 1646 West Chester Pike, Box 1000, Westtown, PA 19395. TEL 215-399-6600; 800-345-1101. FAX 215-399-6610. Ed Barbara Murphy. abstr.; bibl.; stat.; s-a. index. (looseleaf format; back issues avail.) **Document type:** newsletter.

340   CC
FALU YU SHENGHUO/LAW & LIFE. (Text in Chinese) m. $41.30. Falu Chubanshe, Law Press, Taiping Lu, Haidian Qu, Beijing 100036, People's Republic of China. TEL 8217301. (Dist. in US by: China Books & Periodicals, Inc., 2929 24th St., San Francisco, CA 94110. TEL 415-282-2994) Ed. Xu Chang.

FAMILJEFOERENINGEN FOER INTERNATIONELL ADOPTION. see *SOCIAL SERVICES AND WELFARE*

340   PH   ISSN 0046-3272
LAW
FAR EASTERN LAW REVIEW. (Text in English) 2/yr. P.20($5) Far Eastern University, Institute of Law, Quezon Boulevard, Manila, Philippines. Ed. Faustino S. Cruz. (also avail. in microform from UMI; reprint service avail. from UMI) **Indexed:** Mar.Aff.Bibl.
  —BLDSC (3865.925000).
  Formerly: F E U Quarterly.

340   IR
FASLNAMAH-I HAQQ. 1985. q. Markaz-i Mutala'at-i Huquqi va Qaza'i-i Dadgustari-i, 57 Pasture Ave., Tehran, Iran.
  Description: Text and commentary on Iranian laws.

340   CC   ISSN 1000-4238
FAXUE/SCIENCE OF LAW. (Text in Chinese) m. Huadong Zhengfa Xueyuan - East China Institute of Law, 1575 Wanhangdu Lu, Shanghai 200042, People's Republic of China. TEL 2594295. Ed. Zhang Guoquan.

340   CC   ISSN 1002-896X
FAXUE YANJIU/STUDIES IN LAW. (Text in Chinese) 1979. bi-m. $33.80. Zhongguo Shehui Kexueyuan, Faxue Yanjiusuo - Chinese Academy of Social Science, Institute of Law, 15 Shatan Beijie, Beijing 100720, People's Republic of China. TEL 4035471. FAX 4014045. (Dist. in US by: China Books & Periodicals, 2929 24th St., San Francisco, CA 94110. TEL 415-282-2994) Ed. Wang Baoshu. adv.; bk.rev. **Document type:** academic/scholarly publication.
  —UnCover.

340   CC
FAXUE YICONG/TRANSLATED LAW LITERATURE. (Text in Chinese) bi-m. Zhongguo Shehui Kexueyuan, Faxueyanjiusuo, 15 Shatan Beijie, Beijing 100720, People's Republic of China. TEL 441580. Ed. Ren Yunzheng.

340   CC
FAXUE YU SHIJIAN/LAW AND PRACTICE. (Text in Chinese) bi-m. Heilongjiang Sheng Faxue Yanjiusuo - Heilongjiang Institute of Law, 43, Hongxia Jie, Daoli-qu, Harbin, Heilongjiang 150010, People's Republic of China. TEL 417707. (Co-sponsor: Heilongjiang Law Society) Ed. Wang Wei.

340   CC   ISSN 1001-618X
FAXUE ZAZHI/JOURNAL OF JURISPRUDENCE. (Text in Chinese) bi-m. $15.80. Beijing Faxuehui - Beijing Jurisprudence Society, 1 Xisanhuan Zhonglu, Beijing 100036, People's Republic of China. TEL 896217-802. (Dist. in US by: China Books & Periodicals, 2929 24th St., San Francisco, CA 94110. TEL 415-282-2994) Ed. Fu Juchuan.

340   CC
FAZHI. (Text in Chinese) m. Y12. (Guangdong Sheng Sifa-ting) Guangdong Fazhi Baokan She, No.26, Qiye Lu, Guangzhou, Guangdong 510030, People's Republic of China. TEL 348264. Ed. Zhong Qiliang.

340   CC   ISSN 1000-3568
FAZHI JIANSHE/LAW & ORDER. (Text in Chinese) 1983. m. $41.30. (Zhonghua Renmin Gongheguo Sifabu - Ministry of Justice) Beijing Falu Chubanshe, Baiguang Lu 1, Xuanwu Qu, Beijing, People's Republic of China. (Dist. in US by: China Books & Periodicals, Inc., 2929 24th St., San Francisco, CA 94110. TEL 415-282-2994)

340   US
FAZHI RIBAO/LEGAL DAILY. (Text in Chinese) d. $244.75. China Books & Periodicals, Inc., 2929 24th St., San Francisco, CA 94110. TEL 415-282-2994. FAX 415-282-0994. **Document type:** newspaper.

340   CC   ISSN 1003-5818
FAZHI TIANDI. (Text in Chinese) m. Jilin Sheng Sifa Ting, 39, Stalin Street, Changchun, Jilin 130051, People's Republic of China. TEL 36095. Ed. Sun Libo.

340   CC
FAZHI YU WENMING/LEGAL SYSTEM AND CIVILIZATION. (Text in Chinese) m. Liaoning Sheng Sifa Ting, 8, Congshan Donglu 1 Duan, Huanggu-qu, Shenyang, Liaoning 110032, People's Republic of China. TEL 461317. Ed. Ba Wen.

340 350   AT
FEDERAL ADMINISTRATIVE LAW. 1985. 6/yr. in 2 vols. Aus.$330 with updates. Law Book Co. Ltd., 44-50 Waterloo Rd., North Ryde, N.S.W. 2113, Australia. TEL 02-887-0177. FAX 02-888-9706. TELEX ASBOOK 27995. Ed. Geoffrey Flick. (looseleaf format)
Description: Contains all relevant legislation with authoritative and up-to-date legislation and annotations.

340   US
FEDERAL APPEALS: JURISDICTION AND PRACTICE. 1987. base vol. (plus a. suppl.). $95. Shepard's - McGraw-Hill, Inc., Box 35300, Colorado Springs, CO 80935-3530. TEL 800-525-2474.
Description: Covers all areas of federal jurisdiction and offers practical tips on how to successfully file, brief and argue an appeal.

FEDERAL BANKING LAW REPORTS. see *BUSINESS AND ECONOMICS — Banking And Finance*

340   US
FEDERAL BANKRUPTCY LAW HANDBOOK. 1989. a. $19. Gould Publications, 1333 N. U.S. Hwy. 17-92, Longwood, FL 32750-3724. TEL 407-695-9500. FAX 407-695-2906. adv.; bk.rev. (looseleaf format)
Description: Contains the complete unannotated code of Title 11.

340   US   ISSN 0279-4691
K6
FEDERAL BAR NEWS & JOURNAL. 1981. 10/yr. $25 to non-members (foreign $35) (effective 1993). Federal Bar Association, 1815 H St., N.W., Ste. 408, Washington, DC 20006-3697. TEL 202-638-0252. FAX 202-775-0295. Ed. Joryn Jenkins. adv.; bk.rev. circ. 14,500. (also avail. in microform from WSH,PMC; reprint service avail.) **Indexed:** Abstr.Bk.Rev.Curr.Leg.Per., Acid Rain Abstr., Acid Rain Ind., Bank.Lit.Ind., C.L.I., Curr.Cont., HR Rep., L.R.I., Leg.Cont., Leg.Per., Pers.Lit., SSCI. **Document type:** trade publication.
●Also available online. Vendor(s): West Services, Inc.
—BLDSC (3901.873200); Faxon; UnCover; UMI.
Formed by the 1981 merger of (1953-1981): Federal Bar News (ISSN 0014-9047); (1931-1981): Federal Bar Journal (ISSN 0014-9039)

340   US   ISSN 0093-2108
FEDERAL CARRIERS CASES. 1937. irreg. $64.50 per no. Commerce Clearing House, Inc., 4025 W. Peterson Ave., Chicago, IL 60646. TEL 312-583-8500. Ed. D. Newquist.

347.73   US   ISSN 1055-8195
K6
FEDERAL CIRCUIT BAR JOURNAL; the national quarterly review of the United States Court of Appeals for the Federal Circuit. 1991. q. Federal Circuit Bar Association, 1300 I St., N.W., Ste. 700, Washington, DC 20005-3315.

340   US   ISSN 0163-7606
K6
FEDERAL COMMUNICATIONS LAW JOURNAL. vol.30, 1977. 3/yr. $18. University of California, Los Angeles, School of Law, 405 Hilgard Ave., Los Angeles, CA 90024. TEL 213-825-3712. (Co-sponsor: Federal Communications Bar Association) Ed. Keith Nichols. adv.; bk.rev. circ. 2,000. (also avail. in microform from UMI,WSH; reprint service avail. from UMI,WSH) **Indexed:** ABI Inform., Abstr.Bk.Rev.Curr.Leg.Per., BPIA, Bus.Ind., C.L.I., CAD CAM Abstr., Commun.Abstr., L.R.I., Leg.Cont., Leg.Per., Tel.Abstr.
—BLDSC (3901.873700); Faxon; UnCover; UMI.
Formerly: Federal Communications Bar Journal.

340 614.7   US
FEDERAL ENVIRONMENTAL LAWS. a. West Publishing Corp., 620 Opperman Dr., Eagan, MN 55123. TEL 612-687-8000; 800-328-9352. FAX 612-687-7302. **Document type:** trade publication.

FEDERAL ENVIRONMENTAL REGULATION. see *ENVIRONMENTAL STUDIES*

340   US
FEDERAL EVIDENCE FOUNDATIONS. 1988. base vol. (plus suppl.). $90. Butterworth Legal Publishers (Salem) (Subsidiary of: Reed Elsevier plc), 8 Industrial Way, Bldg. C, Salem, NH 03079. TEL 800-548-4001. FAX 603-898-9858. Ed. Murl A. Larkin. (looseleaf format)
Description: Identifies and sets out the requirements for admissibility of all types of evidence in federal courts under the Federal Rules and common law.

FEDERAL HEALTH MONITOR. see *PUBLIC HEALTH AND SAFETY*

340 325.1   US
FEDERAL IMMIGRATION LAWS AND REGULATIONS. a. West Publishing Corp., 620 Opperman Dr., Eagan, MN 55123. TEL 612-687-8000; 800-328-9352. FAX 612-687-7302. **Document type:** trade publication.

340   US
FEDERAL INFORMATION DISCLOSURE, 2-E. 1990. 2 base vols. (plus s-a. supplements). $195. Shepard's - McGraw-Hill, Inc., Box 35300, Colorado Springs, CO 80935-3530. TEL 800-525-2474. (looseleaf format)
Description: Covers the disclosure of information from agency files under the Freedom of Information Act, the mechanics of suing the government for mandatory disclosure of this information, the 1974 Privacy Act and its significant impact on gathering information.

340 331   US
FEDERAL LABOR LAWS. 1974. a. West Publishing Corp., 620 Opperman Dr., Eagan, MN 55123. TEL 612-687-8000; 800-328-9352. FAX 612-687-7602. **Document type:** trade publication.

340   CN
FEDERAL LIMITATION PERIODS; a handbook of limitation periods and other statutory time limits. s-a. Can.$85. Butterworths Canada Ltd., Part of the Reed Elsevier group, 75 Clegg Rd., Markham, ON L6G 1A1, Canada. TEL 905-479-2665. FAX 905-479-2826. (looseleaf format)
Description: Tables of time limits.

340   US   ISSN 0886-621X
KF8840.A2
FEDERAL LITIGATOR. 1985. 10/yr. $290. Shepard's - McGraw-Hill, Inc., Box 35300, Colorado Springs, CO 80935-3530. TEL 719-488-3000. Eds. Neil Levy, Jeffrey Brand. s-a. index. (looseleaf format) **Document type:** newsletter.

353   US   ISSN 0097-6326
KF70   CODEN: FEREAC
FEDERAL REGISTER. 1936. d., a. cumulation: Code of Federal Regulations. $490 for print ed. (foreign $612.50); microfiche $403 (foreign $503.75) (includes Federal Register Subject Index). U.S. Office of the Federal Register, National Archives and Records Administration, Washington, DC 20408. TEL 202-523-5230. (Orders to: Superintendent of Documents, U.S. Government Printing Office, Box 371954, Pittsburgh, PA 15250-7954. TEL 202-783-3238. FAX 202-512-2233) index. circ. 50,000. (also avail. in microfiche from UMI; microfilm from BHP; reprint service avail. from UMI) **Indexed:** Acid Rain Abstr., Acid Rain Ind., API Abstr., API Catal., API Hlth.& Environ., API Oil., API Pet.Ref., API Pet.Subst., API Transport., Art & Archaeol.Tech.Abstr., C.I.S. Abstr., CAD CAM Abstr. (until 1993), Chem.Abstr., Food Sci.& Tech.Abstr., I.P.A., Ind.Hyg.Dig., INIS Atomind., Int.Packag.Abstr., Noise Pollut.Publ.Abstr., Ocean.Abstr., Pollut.Abstr., Rehabil.Lit., Sel.Water Res.Abstr., Sugar Ind.Abstr., Telegen, Text.Tech.Dig. **Document type:** government publication.
●Also available online. Vendor(s): BRS Online Products (DIOG), DIALOG Information Services, Inc. (File no.669), Mead Data Central, Inc., West Services, Inc.
Also available on CD-ROM.
—BLDSC (3292.773100); SWETS; UMI; CASDDS.
Description: Provides a uniform system for making available regulations and legal notices issued by federal agencies available to the public.

340   US
FEDERAL REGISTER HIGHLIGHTS NEWSLETTER. fortn. $50. National Clearinghouse for Legal Services, Inc., 205 W. Monroe, 2nd Fl., Chicago, IL 60606. TEL 312-263-3830. FAX 312-263-3846. **Document type:** newsletter.

340   US
FEDERAL REGULATION OF ENERGY. 1983. base vol. (plus a. suppl.). $95. Shepard's - McGraw-Hill, Inc., Box 35300, Colorado Springs, CO 80935-3530. TEL 800-525-2474.
Description: Provides a historical perspective on energy regulation. Covers current Federal Energy Regulatory Commission regulations on controversial topics such as nuclear waste disposal.

340   US   ISSN 1048-0838
▼**FEDERAL RULES CITATIONS.** 1992. 3 base vols. (plus q. supplements). $450. Shepard's - McGraw-Hill, Inc., Box 35300, Colorado Springs, CO 80935. TEL 800-525-2474.
Description: Brings together citations to the Federal Rules and all corresponding state rules from every jurisdiction in the nation.

340   US   ISSN 0364-3581
KF8931.A3F4
FEDERAL RULES OF EVIDENCE NEWS. 1976. m. $187.50. Lawyers Cooperative Publishing (Subsidiary of: Thomson Professional Publishing), Acqueduct Bldg., Rochester, NY 14694. TEL 800-527-0430. Ed. John R. Schmertz, Jr. (looseleaf format) **Document type:** newsletter.
—CCC.

FEDERAL RULES SERVICE. see *PUBLIC ADMINISTRATION*

340 332.6   US   ISSN 0162-1084
FEDERAL SECURITIES LAW REPORTS. 1933. w. $1210. Commerce Clearing House, Inc., 4025 W. Peterson Ave., Chicago, IL 60646. TEL 312-583-8500. Ed. D. Newquist.

FEDERAL SENTENCING GUIDELINES HANDBOOK. see *CRIMINOLOGY AND LAW ENFORCEMENT*

FEDERAL SENTENCING REPORTER. see *CRIMINOLOGY AND LAW ENFORCEMENT*

340   US
FEDERAL STANDARDS OF REVIEW. 2nd ed., 1992. 2 base vols. (plus a. supplement). $190. Butterworth Legal Publishers (Salem) (Subsidiary of: Reed Elsevier plc), 8 Industrial Way, Bldg. C, Salem, NH 03079. TEL 800-548-4001. FAX 603-898-9858. Eds. Steven Alan Childress, Martha S. Davis. (looseleaf format)
Description: Comprehensive analysis of the review process in civil, criminal and administrative cases.

3256 LAW

FEDERAL TAXATION. see *BUSINESS AND ECONOMICS — Public Finance, Taxation*

340 US
FEDERAL TRADE COMMISSION. 1979. 2 base vols. (plus a. suppl.). $190. Shepard's - McGraw-Hill, Inc., Box 35300, Colorado Springs, CO 80935-3530. TEL 800-525-2474. (looseleaf format)
Description: Guide to regulations and procedures of the FTC organized with a topical outline that presents comprehensive information on specific problems.

340 US
FEDERAL TRIAL EVIDENCE. (2nd ed., 1991) 1984. 2 base vols. (plus a. supplement). $175. Butterworth Legal Publishers (Salem) (Subsidiary of: Reed Elsevier plc), 8 Industrial Way, Bldg. C, Salem, NH 03079. TEL 800-548-4001. FAX 603-898-9858. Ed. Charles E. Wagner. (looseleaf format)

340 US ISSN 0739-2109
FEDERAL TRIAL NEWS. irreg. membership only. American Bar Association, National Conference of Federal Trial Judges, 750 N. Lake Shore Dr., Chicago, IL 60611. TEL 312-988-5688. circ. 750.
Description: Information to members on conference activities.

340 CN ISSN 0834-4728
FEDERAL TRIAL REPORTS. 1986. irreg. (approx. 7/yr.). Can.$103 per vol. Maritime Law Book Ltd., P.O. Box 302, Fredericton, NB E3B 4Y9, Canada. TEL 506-453-9921; 800-561-0220. FAX 506-453-9525. (back issues avail.)
Description: Contains judgments of the Trial Division of the Federal Court of Canada.

FEDERATION NATIONALE DE L'IMMOBILIERS. INFORMATIONS F N A I M: JURIDIQUES ET TECHNIQUES. see *REAL ESTATE*

340 305.4 UK ISSN 0966-3622
▼**FEMINIST LEGAL STUDIES.** 1993. s-a. £40 (effective 1994). Deborah Charles Publications, 173 Mather Ave., Liverpool L18 6JZ, England. TEL 44-51-724-2500. FAX 44-51-729-0371. (Dist. in US by: William W. Guant & Sons, Inc., 3011 Gulf Dr., Holmes Beach, FL 34217-2199. TEL 813-778-5211) Ed. B. Meteyard. **Document type:** academic/scholarly publication.
—BLDSC (3905.197350); UnCover.
Description: Concerned with issues relating to gender and legal relations, explored through articles, news and notes on current legal developments.

368 340 US ISSN 0747-6582
FIDELITY AND SURETY NEWS. q. $100. American Bar Association, Tort and Insurance Practice Section, Fidelity and Surety Law Committee, 750 N. Lake Shore Dr., Chicago, IL 60611. TEL 312-988-5555. Ed. Donald B. King. (back issues avail.; reprint service avail.)
Description: Provides a current digest of opinions about construction contract bonds, financial institution and other bonds, court bonds, and surety's rights.

328.96 FJ ISSN 0304-7849
FIJI. OFFICE OF THE OMBUDSMAN. ANNUAL REPORT OF THE OMBUDSMAN. (Text in English) 1973. a. price varies. Office of the Ombudsman, Suva, Fiji. TEL 679-211652. circ. 200 (controlled). **Document type:** government publication.

340 SP
FILOSOFIA DEL DERECHO. ANUARIO. 1953-1977; N.S. 1984. a. 3500 ptas. (foreign 3700 ptas.). Ministerio de Justicia, Centro de Publicaciones, Secretaria General Tecnica, Gran Via, 76-8, 28013 Madrid, Spain. TEL 547-54-22. FAX 559-29-48. Ed. L. Legaz Lacambra. **Document type:** government publication.

FINANCE AND COMMERCE. see *BUSINESS AND ECONOMICS — Banking And Finance*

340 332.7 US
FINANCIAL HANDBOOK FOR BANKRUPTCY PROFESSIONALS. 1991. irreg. West Publishing Corp., 620 Opperman Dr., Eagan, MN 55123. TEL 612-687-8000; 800-328-9352. FAX 612-687-7302. **Document type:** trade publication.

FINANCIAL REVIEW OF ALIEN INSURERS. see *INSURANCE*

346.066 UK
FINANCIAL SERVICES - LAW & PRACTICE. 3 base vols. (plus updates 6/yr and m. bulletin). price varies. Butterworth & Co. (Publishers) Ltd. (Subsidiary of: Reed Elsevier plc), 88 Kingsway, London WC2B 6AB, England. TEL 71-405-6900. FAX 71-405-1332. (US addr.: Butterworth Legal Publishers, 90 Stiles Rd., Salem, NH 03079-9981. TEL 603-898-9664) Ed. Andrew M. Whittaker. (looseleaf format)
Description: Reference source on the laws regulating UK investment business.

THE FINANCIAL SERVICES LAW LETTER. see *BUSINESS AND ECONOMICS — Banking And Finance*

FINANCIAL SERVICES REPORT; strategic information for the financial executive. see *BUSINESS AND ECONOMICS — Banking And Finance*

346.066 US
FINANCIAL VALUATION: BUSINESSES AND BUSINESS INTERESTS. 1990. base vol. (plus supplements). Maxwell Macmillan, Rosenfeld Launer, 910 Sylvan Ave., Englewood Cliffs, NJ 07632-3310. TEL 800-562-0245. FAX 201-816-3569. Ed. James H. Zukin.

FINANZRECHTLICHE ERKENNTNISSE DES VERWALTUNGSGERICHTSHOFES; Beilage zur Oesterreichischen Steuer-Zeitung. see *BUSINESS AND ECONOMICS — Public Finance, Taxation*

340 US
FINE'S WISCONSIN EVIDENCE; a quick guide to courtroom evidence. 1988. base vol. (plus suppl.). $95. Butterworth Legal Publishers (Salem) (Subsidiary of: Reed Elsevier plc), 8 Industrial Way, Bldg. C, Salem, NH 03079. TEL 800-548-4001. FAX 603-898-9858. Ed. Ralph Adam Fine. (looseleaf format)

FIRE AND ARSON INVESTIGATOR. see *CRIMINOLOGY AND LAW ENFORCEMENT*

FIREHOUSE LAWYER MONTHLY NEWSLETTER. see *FIRE PREVENTION*

FISCALE EN ADMINISTRATIEVE PRAKTIJKVRAGEN. see *BUSINESS AND ECONOMICS — Public Finance, Taxation*

FISCALITE QUEBECOISE. see *BUSINESS AND ECONOMICS — Public Finance, Taxation*

328 US ISSN 0090-1520
KFF15
FLORIDA. LEGISLATURE. JOINT LEGISLATIVE MANAGEMENT COMMITTEE. SUMMARY OF GENERAL LEGISLATION. 1955. a. free. Legislature, Joint Legislative Management Committee, The Capitol, Tallahassee, FL 32399. TEL 904-488-2812. FAX 904-488-9879. Ed. B. Gene Baker. circ. 500. (processed) **Document type:** government publication.

340 US ISSN 0194-4800
KFF440
FLORIDA ADMINISTRATIVE LAW REPORTS. 1979. s-m. $425. Florida Administrative Law Reports, Inc., Box 385, Gainesville, FL 32602. TEL 904-375-8036. Ed. James Konish. cum.index. circ. 230. (back issues avail.)
Description: Presents lists of public-access publications and indexes on final legal orders after formal proceedings from Florida state agencies and boards, with catalogues of settlements and non-final orders.

340 350 US
FLORIDA ADMINISTRATIVE PRACTICE. 1979. 3 base vols. (plus suppl. 2-3/yr.). $240. Butterworth Legal Publishers (Salem) (Subsidiary of: Reed Elsevier plc), 8 Industrial Way, Bldg. C, Salem, NH 03079. TEL 800-548-4001. FAX 603-898-9858. Eds. Arthur H. England, Jr., L. Harold Levinson. (looseleaf format)

348 US ISSN 0098-874X
KFF36
FLORIDA ADMINISTRATIVE WEEKLY. 1975. w. $165. Department of State, Bureau of Administrative Code, Elliot Bldg., 401 S. Monroe St., Tallahassee, FL 32399-0250. TEL 904-488-8427. FAX 904-488-7869. Ed. Liz Cloud. adv.; cum.index. **Document type:** government publication.
Description: Informational synopses and data on state administrative procedures as they pertain to regulatory actions, public hearings, petitions, and orders.

340 US
FLORIDA APPELLATE PRACTICE. 1979. 3 base vols. (plus suppl. 2-3/yr.). $240. Butterworth Legal Publishers (Salem) (Subsidiary of: Reed Elsevier plc), 8 Industrial Way, Bldg. C, Salem, NH 03079. TEL 800-548-4001. FAX 603-898-9858. (looseleaf format)

342 US
KF200.F624
FLORIDA BAR. ADMINISTRATIVE LAW SECTION. NEWSLETTER. 1980. irreg. (3-4/yr.). membership. Florida Bar, 650 Apalachee Pkwy., Tallahassee, FL 32399-2300. TEL 904-561-5623. circ. 870.

340 US
FLORIDA BAR. APPELLATE PRACTICE AND ADVOCACY SECTION NEWSLETTER. irreg. (3-4/yr.). membership. Florida Bar, 650 Apalachee Pkwy., Tallahassee, FL 32399-2300. TEL 904-561-5623. circ. 310. **Document type:** newsletter.

340 US
▼**FLORIDA BAR. ELDER LAW SECTION NEWSLETTER.** 1992. 2/yr. membership. Florida Bar, Elder Law Section, 650 Apalachee Pkwy., Tallahassee, FL 32399-2300. TEL 904-561-5625. circ. 990. **Document type:** newsletter.

FLORIDA BAR. ENVIRONMENTAL AND LAND USE LAW SECTION. REPORTER. see *ENVIRONMENTAL STUDIES*

340 US
FLORIDA BAR. GOVERNMENT LAWYER SECTION REPORTER. 1991. 2/yr. membership. Florida Bar, Government Lawyer Section, 650 Apalachee Pkwy., Tallahassee, FL 32399-2300. TEL 904-561-5625. circ. 530. **Document type:** newsletter.

340 362.1 US
FLORIDA BAR. HEALTH LAW SECTION. NEWSLETTER. 1988. irreg. (2-4/yr.). membership. Florida Bar, Health Law Section, 650 Apalachee Pkwy., Tallahassee, FL 32399-2300. TEL 904-561-5630. circ. 1,010. **Document type:** newsletter.

340 US
FLORIDA BAR. PRACTICE MANAGEMENT AND TECHNOLOGY SECTION NEWSLETTER. irreg. (3-4/yr.). membership. Florida Bar, 650 Apalachee Pkwy., Tallahassee, FL 32399-2300. TEL 904-561-5650. circ. 710. **Document type:** newsletter.

340 US
FLORIDA BAR. PUBLIC INTEREST LAW SECTION NEWSLETTER. irreg. (3-4/yr.). membership. Florida Bar, 650 Apalachee Pkwy., Tallahassee, FL 32399-2300. TEL 904-561-5650. circ. 285. **Document type:** newsletter.

340 US ISSN 0015-3915
KF200
FLORIDA BAR JOURNAL; advancing the competence and public responsiblity of lawyers. 1927. m. $30 (including annual directory number). Florida Bar, 650 Apalachee Pkwy., Tallahassee, FL 32399-2300. TEL 904-561-5680. FAX 904-681-3859. Ed. Judson H. Orrick. adv.; bk.rev.; illus.; index. circ. 51,000. (also avail. in microfiche from WSH; microfilm from UMI,WSH,PMC; reprint service avail. from UMI) **Indexed:** C.L.I., HRIS, L.R.I., Law Ofc.Info.Svc., Leg.Per.
●Also available online. Vendor(s): West Services, Inc.
—BLDSC (3955.290000); Faxon; UnCover; UMI.
Description: Practical legal articles from the Florida Bar.

LAW

340.06 US ISSN 0360-0114
KF200
FLORIDA BAR NEWS. s-m. $20. Florida Bar, 650 Apalachee Pkwy., Tallahassee, FL 32399-2300. TEL 904-561-5600. FAX 904-681-3859. Ed. Judson H. Orrick. illus. circ. 55,000. (reprint service avail. from UMI.)
—UMI.
Description: Articles on activities, programs and concerns of the legal profession in Florida.

340 US
FLORIDA COMMERCIAL LANDLORD - TENANT LAW. 1985. base vol. (plus suppl. 2-3/yr.). $80. Butterworth Legal Publishers (Salem) (Subsidiary of: Reed International PLC), 8 Industrial Way, Bldg. C, Salem, NH 03079. TEL 800-548-4001. FAX 603-898-9858. (looseleaf format)

340 US
FLORIDA CONDOMINIUM LAW MANUAL. 1980. 3 base vols. (plus suppl. 2-3/yr.). $240. Butterworth Legal Publishers (Salem) (Subsidiary of: Reed Elsevier plc), 8 Industrial Way, Bldg. C, Salem, NH 03079. TEL 800-548-4001. FAX 603-898-9858. (looseleaf format)

340 640.73 US
FLORIDA CONSUMER LAW MANUAL. 1977. 3 base vols. (plus suppl. 2-3/yr.). $240. Butterworth Legal Publishers (Salem) (Subsidiary of: Reed Elsevier plc), 8 Industrial Way, Bldg. C, Salem, NH 03079. TEL 800-548-4001. FAX 603-898-9858. (looseleaf format)

340 US ISSN 1041-3537
KFF331.A15
FLORIDA EMPLOYMENT LAW LETTER. 1989. m. $117. (Haynsworth, Baldwin, Johnson & Haper) M. Lee Smith Publishers & Printers, 162 Fourth Ave., N., Nashville, TN 37219-8867. TEL 615-242-7395; 800-274-6774. FAX 615-256-6601. Ed. T. Harper. *Document type:* newsletter.
Description: Reports state-specific employment law developments that affect companies in Florida/

340 331.1 US
FLORIDA EMPLOYMENT LAW MANUAL. 1984. a. $63 (typically set in Jan.). (Law Firm of Haynsworth, Baldwin, Johnson and Harper) Florida Chamber of Commerce Management Corp., Inc., Box 11309, Tallahassee, FL 32309-3309. TEL 800-940-3034. FAX 904-425-1260. circ. 1,500.
Description: Provides an overview of state and federal employment laws.

340 613.1 US ISSN 1064-1874
KFF354.A15
FLORIDA ENVIRONMENTAL COMPLIANCE UPDATE. 1990. m. $147. (Florida Chambers Environmental Network) M. Lee Smith Publishers & Printers, 162 Fourth Ave., N., Box 198867, Nashville, TN 37219-8867. TEL 615-242-7395; 800-274-6774. FAX 615-256-6601. Ed. Sidney F. Ansbacher. *Document type:* newsletter.
Formerly (until 1992): Florida Environmental and Land Use Letter (ISSN 1047-4641)
Description: Reports the latest state-specific environmental law developments that affect Florida companies.

340 US
FLORIDA EVIDENCE MANUAL. 1975. 4 base vols. (plus suppl. 5-6/yr.). $280. Butterworth Legal Publishers (Salem) (Subsidiary of: Reed Elsevier plc), 8 Industrial Way, Bldg. C, Salem, NH 03079. TEL 800-548-4001. FAX 603-898-9858. (looseleaf format)

340 663 US
FLORIDA FOOD & BEVERAGE NEWS. 1983. m. $27. Beverage Industry Publications, 29605 US Hwy. 19 N., Ste. 330, Clearwater, FL 34621-2134. TEL 813-786-6369. FAX 813-786-5869. Ed. Dennis J. Regan. adv. circ. 16,000. *Document type:* trade publication.
Description: Covers taxing issues, legal views, state and local government issues, and events pertaining to the hospitality industry in Florida.

340 US
FLORIDA GENERAL PRACTICE JOURNAL. irreg. (3-4/yr.). $15 to non-members. Florida Bar, General Practice Section, 650 Apalachee Pkwy., Tallahassee, FL 32399-2300. TEL 904-561-5631. circ. 1,640.
Document type: newsletter.

340 US
FLORIDA LAND USE RESTRICTIONS. 1976. 3 base vols. (plus suppl. 2-3/yr.). $240. Butterworth Legal Publishers (Salem) (Subsidiary of: Reed Elsevier plc), 8 Industrial Way, Bldg. C, Salem, NH 03079. TEL 800-548-4001. FAX 603-898-9858. (looseleaf format)

340 US
FLORIDA LAW OF SECURED TRANSACTIONS IN PERSONAL PROPERTY. 1979. 3 base vols. (plus a. suppl.). $240. Butterworth Legal Publishers (Salem) (Subsidiary of: Reed Elsevier plc), 8 Industrial Way, Bldg. C, Salem, NH 03079. TEL 800-548-4001. FAX 603-898-9858. (looseleaf format)

340 US ISSN 1045-4241
FLORIDA LAW REVIEW. 1948. 5/yr. $30. University of Florida, College of Law, Gainesville, FL 32611. TEL 904-392-2148. Ed. Duane Daiker. adv.; bk.rev.; index. circ. 1,500. (also avail. in microfiche from WSH; microfilm from WSH) *Indexed:* C.L.I., Crim.Just.Abstr., L.R.I., Leg.Cont., Leg.Per., Sel.Water Res.Abstr. *Document type:* academic/scholarly publication.
●Also available online. Vendor(s): West Services, Inc. —BLDSC (3956.068000); Faxon; UnCover.
Formerly: University of Florida Law Review (ISSN 0041-9583)

340 US ISSN 0274-8533
KFF47.1
FLORIDA LAW WEEKLY. 1976. w. $275. Judicial and Administrative Research Association, Inc., 1327 North Adams St., P.O. Box 4284, Tallahassee, FL 32315. TEL 904-222-3171. Ed. E. Neil Young. circ. 4,000. (back issues avail.)
Description: Includes opinions of Florida Appellate Courts.

340 US
FLORIDA LEGAL RESEARCH & SOURCE BOOK. 1989. base vol. (plus a. suppl.). $35. Butterworth Legal Publishers (Salem) (Subsidiary of: Reed Elsevier plc), 8 Industrial Way, Bldg. C, Salem, NH 03079. TEL 800-548-4001. FAX 603-898-9858. (looseleaf format)

340 US
FLORIDA MECHANICS LEIN MANUAL. 1974. 4 base vols. (plus suppl. 4-5/yr.). $280. Butterworth Legal Publishers (Salem) (Subsidiary of: Reed Elsevier plc), 8 Industrial Way, Bldg. C, Salem, NH 03079. TEL 800-548-4001. FAX 603-898-9858. (looseleaf format)

340 380 US
FLORIDA MOTOR VEHICLE LAWS. 1988. a. $14.95. Gould Publications, 1333 N. U.S. Hwy. 17-92, Longwood, FL 32750-3724. TEL 407-695-9500. FAX 407-695-2906. adv.; bk.rev. (looseleaf format)
Description: Contains the state's motor vehicle statutes.

340 US
FLORIDA MOTOR VEHICLE LIABILITY LAW. 1981. 4 base vols. (plus suppl. 4-5/yr.). $240. Butterworth Legal Publishers (Salem) (Subsidiary of: Reed Elsevier plc), 8 Industrial Way, Bldg. C, Salem, NH 03079. TEL 800-548-4001. FAX 603-898-9858. (looseleaf format)

340 US
FLORIDA NEGLIGENCE LAW MANUAL. 1986. 2 base vols. (plus suppl. 3-4/yr.). $160. Butterworth Legal Publishers (Salem) (Subsidiary of: Reed Elsevier plc), 8 Industrial Way, Bldg. C, Salem, NH 03079. TEL 800-548-4001. FAX 603-898-9858. (looseleaf format)

340 US
FLORIDA NOTARY LAW PRIMER. a. $9.95. National Notary Association, 8236 Remmet Ave., Box 7184, Canoga Park, CA 91309-7184. TEL 818-713-4000. FAX 818-713-9061. Ed. Charles N. Faerber. (reprint service avail. from UMI)
Document type: monographic series.

340 US
FLORIDA PREMISES LIABILITY. 1991. base vol. (plus supplements). $80. Butterworth Legal Publishers (Salem) (Subsidiary of: Reed Elsevier plc), 8 Industrial Way, Bldg. C, Salem, NH 03079. TEL 800-548-4001. FAX 603-898-9858. Ed. Douglas MacGregor.
Description: Practical examination of factors determining premises liability, including occupation and control of premises, extent of alleged unsafe conditions, status of the injured or deceased person and negligence on the part of the injured or deceased.

340 US
FLORIDA PROBATE CODE MANUAL. 1975. 3 base vols. (plus suppl. 2-3/yr.). $240. Butterworth Legal Publishers (Salem) (Subsidiary of: Reed Elsevier plc), 8 Industrial Way, Bldg. C, Salem, NH 03079. TEL 800-548-4001. FAX 603-898-9858. (looseleaf format)

340 US
FLORIDA REAL ESTATE CLOSINGS. 1990. base vol. (plus supplement). $50. Butterworth Legal Publishers (Salem) (Subsidiary of: Reed Elsevier plc), 8 Industrial Way, Bldg. C, Salem, NH 03079. TEL 800-548-4001. FAX 603-898-9858. Ed. Neysa Rich. (looseleaf format)
Description: Covers basic procedure as well as special situations involving estates, delinquent mortgages, assignments of contracts, mail closings, and escrow closings.

FLORIDA REAL ESTATE CONTRACTS. see *REAL ESTATE*

340 333.33 US ISSN 1051-4465
KFF282.R4
FLORIDA REAL ESTATE PRINCIPLES, PRACTICES AND LAW. 1977. a. G & C Learning, 1660 Huron Trail, Maitland, FL 32751.

340 333.33 US ISSN 1051-4473
KFF282.R4
FLORIDA REAL ESTATE PRINCIPLES, PRACTICES AND LAW. INSTRUCTOR'S MANUAL. 1983. a. G & C Learning, 1660 Huron Trail, Maitland, FL 32751.

340 333.33 US ISSN 1051-449X
HD266.F6
FLORIDA REAL ESTATE PRINCIPLES, PRACTICES AND LAW. SALESMAN REVIEW OUTLINE & EXAM GUIDE. a. G & S Learning, 1660 Huron Tr., Maitland, FL 32751. Eds. G. Gaines, D.S. Coleman.
Formerly (until 1986): Florida Real Estate Principles, Practices and Law. Salesman Review Outline (ISSN 1051-4481)

FLORIDA REAL ESTATE TRANSACTIONS. see *REAL ESTATE*

340 333.33 US
FLORIDA RESIDENTIAL LANDLORD - TENANT LAW MANUAL. 1983. 3 base vols. (plus a. suppl.). $120. Butterworth Legal Publishers (Salem) (Subsidiary of: Reed Elsevier plc), 8 Industrial Way, Bldg. C, Salem, NH 03079. TEL 800-548-4001. FAX 603-898-9858. (looseleaf format)

328.759 US ISSN 0093-4089
JK4476
FLORIDA SENATE. 1965. biennial. free. Legislature, Senate, The Capitol, Tallahassee, FL 32399. TEL 904-487-5270. Ed. Joe Brown. illus.; stat. circ. 75,000.

340 US ISSN 0096-3070
K6
FLORIDA STATE UNIVERSITY LAW REVIEW. 1973. q. $27. Florida State University, College of Law, Tallahassee, FL 32306. TEL 904-644-2045. Ed. Edward L. Birk. adv.; bk.rev. circ. 925. (also avail. in microform from WSH,PMC; reprint service avail. from WSH) *Indexed:* C.L.I., Crim.Just.Abstr., L.R.I., Leg.Cont., Leg.Per.
●Also available online. Vendor(s): West Services, Inc. —BLDSC (3956.140000); Faxon; UnCover.

340 US
FLORIDA SUMMARY CLAIMS HANDBOOK. 1978. 2 base vols. (plus suppl. 2-3/yr.). $160. Butterworth Legal Publishers (Salem) (Subsidiary of: Reed Elsevier plc), 8 Industrial Way, Bldg. C, Salem, NH 03079. TEL 800-548-4001. FAX 603-898-9858. (looseleaf format)

3258 LAW

FLORIDA TRAFFIC & D U I PRACTICE. see TRANSPORTATION — Roads And Traffic

FLORIDA WORKERS' COMPENSATION MANUAL. see BUSINESS AND ECONOMICS — Labor And Industrial Relations

340 US
FLORIDA ZONING LAW MANUAL. 1980. 3 base vols. (plus suppl. 2-3/yr.) $240. Butterworth Legal Publishers (Salem) (Subsidiary of: Reed Elsevier plc), 8 Industrial Way, Bldg. C, Salem, NH 03079. TEL 800-548-4001. FAX 603-898-9858. (looseleaf format)

340 II
FOCUS; fortnightly digest for the law maker. (Text in English) 1970. fortn. free. Kerala Legislature, Secretariat, P.O. Box 62, Trivandrum, India. bk.rev.; bibl. circ. 350. **Indexed:** Rehabil.Lit.

340 330 US
▼**FOCUS AMERICAS**; an analytical review of law and business in the western hemisphere. 1993. 8/yr. $255. Transnational Juris Publications, Inc., 1 Bridge St., Irvington, NY 10533. TEL 914-591-4288; 800-914-8186. FAX 914-591-2688. Ed. Andrea Bonime-Blanc.
   Description: Features articles on important developments in law, finance, and economic relations in the Americas.

340 378 US
FOCUS ON LAW STUDIES; teaching about law in the liberal arts. 1985. s-a. free. American Bar Association, Commission on College and University Nonprofessional Legal Studies, 541 N. Fairbanks Ct., Chicago, IL 60611-3314. TEL 312-988-5736. FAX 312-988-5032. Ed. John Paul Ryan. bk.rev. circ. 4,500.
   Description: Offers a forum for ideas, resources, analysis, and opinions on teaching about law in liberal arts and professional programs.

344 SW
FOERMYNDARE, GOD MAN OCH FOERVALTARE; en information jaemte foeraeldrabalken 10 - 17 kap. m.m. a. Kommentus, S-125 88 Aelvsjoe, Sweden.
   Former titles (until 1988): Foermyndare och God Man; (until 1978): Information foer Foermyndare och God Man.

340 SW
FOERTECKNING OEVER ADVOKATER OCH ADVOKATBYRAER. a. SEK 250. Sveriges Advokatsamfund - Swedish Bar Association, P.O. Box 27321, 102 54 Stockholm, Sweden.

349 SW ISSN 0015-8585
FOERVALTNINGSRAETTSLIG TIDSKRIFT. 1938. 6/yr. SEK 175 (effective 1991). Norstedt, P.O. Box 4730, S-116 92 Stockholm, Sweden. Ed. Ole Westerberg. abstr.; bibl.

FONTES RERUM AUSTRIACARUM. REIHE 3. FONTES JURIS. see HISTORY — History Of Europe

658.8 340 UN ISSN 0015-6221
FOOD AND AGRICULTURAL LEGISLATION. Spanish edition: Coleccion Legislativa. Agricultura y Alimentacion (ISSN 0426-7362); French edition: Recueil de Legislation. Alimentation et Agriculture (ISSN 0482-0029) 1952. q. $24. Food and Agriculture Organization of the United Nations (Rome), Legislation Branch, Via delle Terme di Caracalla, 00100 Rome, Italy. TEL 57974350. FAX 57975155. stat.; index. **Indexed:** Dairy Sci.Abstr., Food Sci.& Tech.Abstr., Forest.Abstr., Forest Prod.Abstr., Nutr.Abstr. **Document type:** bibliography.

FOOD AND COSMETICS GUIDANCE MANUAL. see PUBLIC HEALTH AND SAFETY

340 615 US
FOOD AND DRUG ADMINISTRATION. 1979. 2 base vols. (plus a. suppl.). $180. Shepard's - McGraw-Hill, Inc., Box 35300, Colorado Springs, CO 80935-3530. TEL 800-525-2474. (looseleaf format)
   Description: Provides information for handling FDA cases.

340 US ISSN 1064-590X
FOOD AND DRUG LAW JOURNAL. 1946. q. $275 to non-members; members $200. Food and Drug Law Institute, 1000 Vermont Ave., N.W., Ste. 1200, Washington, DC 20005. TEL 202-371-1420. FAX 202-371-0649. Ed. Julia K. Ogden. adv.; charts; index. (reprint service avail. from RRI) **Indexed:** C.L.I., Chem.Abstr., Curr.Cont., Excerp.Med., Food Sci.& Tech.Abstr., Hlth.Ind., I.P.A., L.R.I., Leg.Per., SSCI.
   —BLDSC (3977.032300); UnCover; SWETS. CCC.
   Formerly (until 1991): Food Drug Cosmetic Law Journal (ISSN 0015-6361)

340 US ISSN 1053-9034
KF3866.3
FOOD AND DRUG LAW REPORTS. 1989. m. Food and Drug Law Institute, 1000 Vermont Ave., Ste. 1200, Washington, DC 20005. TEL 202-371-1420. FAX 202-371-0649.

340 615 UK ISSN 0266-9366
FOOD & DRUGS INDUSTRY BULLETIN. 10/yr. £139($278) I B C Publishing, Gilmoora House, 57-61 Mortimer St., London W1N 7TD, England. TEL 071-637-4383. FAX 071-636-6414. (Subscr. in U.S. to: IBC (USA), 290 Eliot St., Box 91004, Ashland, MA 01721-9104. TEL 508-881-2800. FAX 508-881-0982) Ed. Keith Anderson. **Document type:** bulletin.

340 664 610
668.55 US ISSN 1057-2759
KFN5630.A15
FOOD, DRUG, COSMETIC, AND MEDICAL DEVICE LAW DIGEST. 1983. 3/yr. $30 (foreign $40) (effective 1994). New York State Bar Association, Food, Drug and Cosmetic Law Section, One Elk St., Albany, NY 12207. TEL 518-463-3200. FAX 518-487-5695. adv.; bk.rev.; circ. 400 (controlled). **Document type:** academic/scholarly publication, newsletter.
   Formerly: Food, Drug and Cosmetic Law Section. Newsletter (ISSN 0742-4051)
   Description: Articles of interest in the substantive law areas of food, drug, cosmetic and medical device law, including information on federal and state legislation and recent administrative decisions and court decisions.

340 US
FOOD DRUG COSMETIC LAW REPORTS. 1938. w. $1985. Commerce Clearing House, Inc., 4025 W. Peterson Ave., Chicago, IL 60646. TEL 312-583-8500. Ed. D. Newquist.

340 664 UK ISSN 0262-0030
FOOD LAW MONTHLY; the advisory service for the food, drug and cosmetics industries. 1981. m. £147 (foreign £169). Monitor Press, Rectory Rd., Great Waldingfield, Sudbury, Suffolk CO10 OTL, England. TEL 0787-378607. FAX 0787-880201. (back issues avail.) **Document type:** newsletter.
   Description: Covers all aspects of the law relating to food manufacture, processing, distribution and importing.

FOOD LEGISLATION NEW SOUTH WALES. see FOOD AND FOOD INDUSTRIES

FOOD LEGISLATION VICTORIA. see FOOD AND FOOD INDUSTRIES

344 US ISSN 0015-6884
KF8911.A3
FOR THE DEFENSE.* 1960. m. (Sep.-June). $35. Defense Research Institute, Inc., 750 N. Lake Shore Dr., Ste. 5000, Chicago, IL 60611-3006. Ed. Donald J. Hirsch. bk.rev.; bibl.; charts; illus.; index, cum.index every 10 yrs. circ. 14,500. (looseleaf format) **Indexed:** C.L.I., Ind.Hyg.Dig., L.R.I.
   —Faxon; UnCover.

340 US
FOR THE RECORD (LAKE OSWEGO). 1987. m. $45 includes Oregon State Bar Bulletin. Oregon State Bar, Box 1689, Lake Oswego, OR 97035-0889. TEL 503-620-0222. FAX 503-684-1366. Ed. Karen McGlone. adv. (tabloid format) **Document type:** newsletter.

346 608.7 US
K6
FORDHAM INTELLECTUAL PROPERTY, MEDIA & ENTERTAINMENT LAW JOURNAL. 1990. s-a. $20. Fordham Entertainment & Intellectual Property Law Forum, Lincoln Center, 140 W. 62nd St., New York, NY 10023. TEL 212-636-6948. FAX 212-636-6582. Ed. Allison J. Unger. **Document type:** academic/scholarly publication.
   ●Also available online. Vendor(s): West Services, Inc.
   —UnCover.
   Formerly: Fordham Entertainment, Media and Intellectual Property Law Forum (ISSN 1056-4128)

340 US ISSN 0015-704X
FORDHAM LAW REVIEW. 1914. 6/yr. $35 (foreign $45) (effective Oct. 1992). Fordham University, School of Law, Lincoln Center, 140 W. 62nd St., Rm. 118, New York, NY 10023. TEL 212-636-6876. FAX 212-636-6899. adv.; bk.rev.; charts; index. circ. 2,800. (also avail. in microfilm from UMI,WSH; back issues avail.; reprint service avail. from UMI,WSH) **Indexed:** A.B.C.Pol.Sci., Abstr.Bk.Rev.Curr.Leg.Per., Bank.Lit.Ind., C.L.I., Crim.Just.Abstr., Curr.Cont., L.R.I., Lang.& Lang.Behav.Abstr., Leg.Cont., Leg.Per., SSCI.
   ●Also available online. Vendor(s): Mead Data Central, Inc., West Services, Inc.
   —BLDSC (3985.900000); Faxon; UnCover; SWETS.

340 US ISSN 0199-4646
FORDHAM URBAN LAW JOURNAL. 1972. q. $15. Fordham University, School of Law, Lincoln Center, 140 W. 62nd St., New York, NY 10023. TEL 212-636-6881. adv.; bk.rev.; index. circ. 1,700. (back issues avail.; reprint service avail. from RRI) **Indexed:** C.L.I., Crim.Just.Abstr., L.R.I., Leg.Cont., Leg.Per., P.A.I.S.
   ●Also available online. Vendor(s): West Services, Inc.
   —BLDSC (3985.960000); Faxon; UnCover; UMI.

343 336.2 US ISSN 0095-7291
LAW
FOREIGN TAX LAW BI-WEEKLY BULLETIN. 1947. fortn. $125 (foreign $175). Foreign Tax Law Publishers, Box 2189, Ormond Beach, FL 32175. TEL 904-253-5785. FAX 904-257-3003. Ed.Bd. bk.rev.; index. circ. 500.
   —UnCover.

340 052 UK ISSN 1350-1771
▼**FORENSIC LINGUISTICS: THE INTERNATIONAL JOURNAL OF LANGUAGE AND THE LAW.** 1994. 2/yr. £75 (foreign £80). Routledge, 11 New Fetter Ln., London EC4P 4EE, England. TEL 071-583-9855. FAX 071-583-0701. (Subscr. to: ITPS Ltd., Cheriton House, N. Way, Andover, Hants. SP10 5BE, England. TEL 0264-342919. FAX 0264-342807) **Document type:** academic/scholarly publication.

340 IT ISSN 0391-2205
FORO AMMINISTRATIVO. 1925. m. L.240000 (foreign L.360000). Casa Editrice Dott. A. Giuffre, Via Busto Arsizio, 40, 20151 Milan, Italy. TEL 02-38000905. FAX 02-38009582. Eds. Eugenio C. Bartoli, Ricardo Chieppa. adv.; bk.rev. circ. 4,800. **Indexed:** ELLIS.

340 IT
FORO COSENTINO. RIVISTA DI PRASSI GIURIDICA. m. L.40000. Editrice Pellegrini, Via Roma 74, Casella Postale 158, 87100 Cosenza, Italy.

349 IT ISSN 0015-783X
KKH19
FORO ITALIANO. 1876. m. L.325000 (foreign L.390000) (effective Feb. 1992). (Societa Editrice del Foro Italiano) Zanichelli Editore S.p.A., Via Irnerio, 34, 40126 Bologna, Italy. TEL 051-293111. FAX 051-249782. index, cum.index. **Indexed:** ELLIS.
   —SWETS.

349 IT ISSN 0015-7848
FORO NAPOLETANO; rivista di dottrina e di giurisprudenza. 1951. q. L.12000. Societa Editrice Napoletana s.r.l., Corso Umberto I 34, 80138 Naples, Italy. Ed. I. Militerni. bk.rev.; abstr.; index. circ. 1,500.

340 CK ISSN 0040-9502
FORO UNIVERSITARIO. 1963. exchange basis. Universidad de Narino, Facultad de Derecho, Apdo. Aereo 505, Pasto, Narino, Colombia.

LAW

340   US   ISSN 0071-7657
FORSCHUNGEN AUS STAAT UND RECHT. irreg. price varies. Springer-Verlag, 175 Fifth Ave., New York, NY 10010. TEL 212-460-1500.
FAX 212-473-6272. (Also: Berlin, Heidelberg, Tokyo and Vienna) (reprint service avail. from ISI) **Document type:** monographic series.

340   AU
FORSCHUNGEN ZUR EUROPAEISCHEN UND VERGLEICHENDEN RECHTSGESCHICHTE. 1976. irreg., vol.5, 1991. price varies. Boehlau Verlag GmbH & Co.KG., Sachsenplatz 4-6, Postfach 87, A-1201 Vienna, Austria. TEL 0222-3302427-0. FAX 0222-3302432. TELEX 114-506-SPRIW-A. Ed. Berthold Sutter. circ. 600. (back issues avail.) **Document type:** monographic series.

340   SZ
FORSCHUNGEN ZUR RECHTSARCHAEOLOGIE UND RECHTLICHEN VOLKSKUNDE. 1978. irreg., vol.10, 1988. price varies. Schulthess Polygraphischer Verlag AG, Zwingliplatz 2, CH-8022 Zurich, Switzerland. TEL 01-251-9336. FAX 01-2616394. Ed. Louis Carlen. **Document type:** monographic series.

340   PR
FORUM. 1979. q. free. Office of Court Administration, Vela St., Stop 35 1-2, Hato Rey Station, P.O. Box 190917, San Juan, PR 00919-0917. Ed. Gricelle Lugo. bk.rev.; circ. 600 (controlled).

340   US   ISSN 0015-8305
FORUM (WASHINGTON, 1963). 1963. 4/yr. $8. Federal Bar Association, District of Columbia Chapter, 1815 H St., N.W., Washington, DC 20006-3697. TEL 202-659-4068. FAX 202-775-0295. Ed. Gwyn Ann Taylor. adv.; illus. circ. 2,700. **Indexed:** Leg.Per. **Document type:** newsletter.
Description: Presents articles on and analysis of current developments and matters of interest pertaining to the Federal Bar Association, its activities and its members, with a calendar of events.

FORUM KEADILAN/MAJALAH HUKUM DAN DEMOKRASI. see *POLITICAL SCIENCE*

340   PH   ISSN 0015-8968
FOUNDATION LAW REVIEW. vol.6, 1971. q. Foundation University, School of Law, Dumaguete City 6501, Philippines. Ed. Saleto J. Erames. bibl.

FRANCE. DIRECTION GENERALE DES IMPOTS. PRECIS DE FISCALITE. see *BUSINESS AND ECONOMICS — Public Finance, Taxation*

346.066   US   ISSN 8756-7962
KF2023.A15
FRANCHISE LAW JOURNAL. 1980. 4/yr. $31 to non-members. (American Bar Association, Forum Commission on Franchising) A B A Press, 750 N. Lake Shore Dr., Chicago, IL 60611. TEL 312-988-6068. Ed. W. Michael Garner. circ. 1,500. **Indexed:** C.L.I., L.R.I., Leg.Info.Manage.Ind., Leg.Per.
Former titles: American Bar Association. Forum Committee on Franchising. Journal (ISSN 0732-1910); Forum Committee on Franchising. Newsletter.
Description: Legal trends in franchising.

340   US
FRANCHISE LEGAL DIGEST. 1973. q. $195 membership. International Franchise Association, 1350 New York Ave. N.W., Ste. 900, Washington, DC 20005. FAX 202-628-0812. TELEX 323175. Ed. Neil A. Simon. circ. 850. (looseleaf format)
Formerly: Current Legal Digest.
Description: Reviews current domestic and international legal and legislative developments concerning franchising.

340 658   US
FRANCHISING ADVISER. 1987. base vol. (plus a. suppl.). $95. Shepard's - McGraw-Hill, Inc., Box 35300, Colorado Springs, CO 80935-3530. TEL 800-525-2474.
Description: Discusses all the key elements of a successful franchise system: trademark selection and registration, trade secret and copyright licensing, franchise agreements, including state and industry regulations.

340   GW
FRANKFURTER WISSENSCHAFTLICHE BEITRAGE. RECHTS- UND WIRTSCHAFTSWISSENSCHAFTLICHE REIHE. 1939. irreg., no.24, 1971. Vittorio Klostermann, Frauenlobstr. 22, 60487 Frankfurt a.M., Germany. TEL 069-774011. FAX 069-708038. (Subscr. to: Postfach 900601, 60446 Frankfurt a.M., Germany) **Document type:** monographic series.

340   US
FRANKLIN ADVOCATE. 1892. w. $22.50. Box 576 Main St., Meadville, MS 39653. TEL 601-384-2484. FAX 601-384-2276. Ed. David Webb. adv. circ. 3,500. (also avail. in microfilm; back issues avail.; reprint service avail.)

340   US
FRATERNAL LAW. 1982. q. $12. Manley, Burke, Fischer & Lipton, 225 W. Court St., Cincinnati, OH 45202. TEL 513-721-5525. FAX 513-721-4268. Ed. William A. McClain. circ. 11,000. (looseleaf format; back issues avail.) **Document type:** newsletter.

340   US
FRAUD, WINDOW DRESSING AND NEGLIGENCE IN FINANCIAL STATEMENTS. 2 base vols. (plus a. supplement). $165. Shepard's - McGraw-Hill, Inc., Box 35300, Colorado Springs, CO 80935-3530. TEL 800-525-2474.
Formerly (until 1990): How to Find Negligence and Misrepresentations in Financial Statements.
Description: Advice to protect yourself and your clients from being victimized by false or negligently prepared financial statements.

340   AT   ISSN 0817-3532
FREEDOM OF INFORMATION REVIEW. bi-m. Aus.$35 (foreign Aus.$47). Legal Service Bulletin Co., Ltd., c/o Monash University, Faculty of Law, Wellington Rd., Clayton, Vic. 3168, Australia. TEL 643-544-0974. FAX 643-565-5305. **Document type:** academic/scholarly publication.

340   GW   ISSN 0343-835X
FREIE UNIVERSITAET BERLIN. OSTEUROPA-INSTITUT. RECHTSWISSENSCHAFTLICHE VEROEFFENTLICHUNGEN. 1974. irreg. price varies. Freie Universitaet Berlin, Osteuropa-Institut, Garystr. 55, 14195 Berlin, Germany. FAX 030-8383788. Eds. Klaus Westen, Herwig Roggemann. circ. 500. **Document type:** monographic series.

FROM THE GYM TO THE JURY. see *SPORTS AND GAMES*

FUEHRER DURCH DIE BAUNORMUNG. see *TECHNOLOGY: COMPREHENSIVE WORKS*

340   US
FULTON COUNTY DAILY REPORT. 1890. d. $425. American Lawyer Media, L.P. (Atlanta), 190 Pryor St., S.W., Atlanta, GA 30303. TEL 404-521-1227. FAX 404-523-5924. Ed. S. Richard Gard, Jr. adv.; bk.rev. circ. 4,300. (also avail. in microfilm)
Description: Official legal newspaper for Fulton County, Georgia. Covers law and business in Atlanta.

340   US
KF1085.A15
FUTURES INTERNATIONAL LAW LETTER. 1981. m. $285. Commodities Law Press Associates, 40 Broad St., 20th Fl., New York, NY 10004-2315. TEL 212-612-9545. FAX 212-425-0266. Ed. Richard A. Miller. bk.rev. (looseleaf format; back issues avail.) **Indexed:** C.L.I. **Document type:** newsletter.
Formerly: Commodities Law Letter (ISSN 0277-2930)
Description: Covers legal developments affecting commodity futures in U.S. and world-wide.

G M P REGULATIONS OF JAPAN. see *PHARMACY AND PHARMACOLOGY*

340   US
G P GAZETTE. 1989. irreg. membership only. New Jersey State Bar Association, General Practice Section, 1 Constitution Sq., New Brunswick, NJ 08901-1500. TEL 908-249-5000. FAX 908-249-2815. Ed. Brian P. Blatz. circ. 400. (back issues avail.) **Document type:** newsletter.

G P L L A NEWSLETTER. (Greater Philadelphia Law Library Association) see *LIBRARY AND INFORMATION SCIENCES*

340   US
G P NEWS. 1984. irreg. (2-4/yr.). membership. State Bar of Wisconsin, General Practice Section, 402 W. Wilson St., Madison, WI 53703. TEL 608-257-3838. FAX 608-257-5502. circ. 2,100. (back issues avail.) **Document type:** newsletter.

340   SP
GACETA FISCAL. 11/yr. Plaza de las Cortes 4, 1o int., 28014 Madrid, Spain. TEL 1-429-21-69. Ed. J. Manuel Diaz-Arias.

340   MX
GACETA INFORMATIVA DE LEGISLACION. 1985. bi-m. $25. Universidad Nacional Autonoma de Mexico, Instituto de Investigaciones Juridicas, Ciudad Universitaria, Delegacion Coyoacan, 04510 Mexico, DF, Mexico. Ed. Eugenio Hurtado Marquez. bk.rev. circ. 1,000.
Formerly: Gaceta Informativa de Legislacion, Jurisprudencia y Bibliografia (ISSN 0187-5841)

613.1   UK
GARNER'S ENVIRONMENTAL LAW. 3 base vols. (plus updates 3/yr. and bi-m. bulletin). $420. Butterworth & Co. (Publishers) Ltd. (Subsidiary of: Reed Elsevier plc), 88 Kingsway, London WC2B 6AB, England. TEL 71-405-6900. FAX 71-405-1332. (US addr.: Butterworth Legal Publishers, 90 Stiles Rd., Salem, NH 03079-9981. TEL 603-898-9664) Ed. D.J. Harris. (looseleaf format)
Formerly: Control of Pollution Encyclopedia.

340   US   ISSN 1054-4674
KF450.P8
GAUER DISTINGUISHED LECTURE IN LAW AND PUBLIC POLICY. 1991. a. National Legal Center for the Public Interest, 1000 16th St. N.W., Ste. 301, Washington, DC 20036.

349   FR   ISSN 0016-5514
GAZETTE DE LA REGION DU NORD. 1956. 3/w. 495 F. La Gazette, 7 rue Jacquemars-Gielee, B.P. 1380, 59015 Lille Cedex, France. adv.; abstr.; bibl.; mkt.; stat. circ. 19,000.
Description: Directory of commercial and legal enterprises in Northern France.

340   FR   ISSN 0242-6331
GAZETTE DU PALAIS. (Supplements avail.: Announces Judiciaires et Legales (ISSN 0242-6366); Legislation (ISSN 0242-6382); Recueils Bimestriels (ISSN 0242-6390); Gazette Europeene (ISSN 1157-951X)) 1881. 3/w. 1820 F. (foreign 2050 F.). Gazette du Palais, 3 bd. du Palais, 75180 Paris Cedex 04, France. TEL 43-25-97-47. FAX 40-46-03-47. TELEX GAZPAL 200 621. adv.; index. circ. 25,000. **Indexed:** ELLIS.
Formerly (until 1886): Gazette du Palais et de Notariat (ISSN 1160-7696); Incorporates: Gazette des Tribunaux (ISSN 1160-767X); Which incorporates: Droit (ISSN 1160-7653)

340   FR   ISSN 0242-6390
GAZETTE DU PALAIS. RECUEIL BIMESTRIEL. (Supplement to: Gazette du Palais (ISSN 0242-6331)) 1886. bi-m. Gazette du Palais, 3 bd du Palais, 75180 Paris Cedex 04, France. TEL 43-25-97-47. FAX 40-46-03-47. TELEX GAZPAL 200 621.
Former titles (until 1971): Gazette du Palais. Supplement Contenant la Jurisprudence et la Legislation et le Recueil Mensuel des Sommaires (ISSN 1160-8552); (until 1924): Gazette du Palais. Jurisprudence et Legislation (ISSN 0249-4981)

340   FR   ISSN 1157-951X
GAZETTE EUROPEENNE. (Supplement to: Gazette du Palais (ISSN 0242-6331)) 1990. m. Gazette du Palais, 3 bd du Palais, 75180 Paris Cedex 04, France. TEL 43-25-97-47. FAX 40-46-03-47. TELEX GAZPAL 200 621.

340 070   AT   ISSN 0818-0148
GAZETTE OF LAW JOURNALISM. 1987. 10/yr. Aus.$195. Law Press of Australia, G.P.O. Box 3793, Sydney, N.S.W. 2001, Australia. TEL 02-360-7788. FAX 02-360-7838. Ed. Richard Ackland. (back issues avail.)

3260 LAW

340 CN
GAZETTE OFFICIELLE DU QUEBEC: AVIS JURIDIQUES. w. Can.$63. Ministere des Communications, P.O. Box 1005, Quebec, PQ G1K 7B5, Canada. TEL 418-643-5150. (Subscr. to: Service Abonnements, CP 1190, Outremont, PQ H2V 4S7, Canada. TEL 514-948-1222) **Document type:** government publication.

340 CN
GAZETTE OFFICIELLE DU QUEBEC: LOIS ET REGLEMENTS. w. Can.$91. Ministere des Communications, P.O. Box 1005, Quebec, PQ G1K 7B5, Canada. TEL 418-643-5150. (Subscr. to: Service Abonnements, CP 1190, Outremont, PQ H2V 4S7, Canada. TEL 514-948-1222) (also avail. in microfilm from BHP) **Document type:** government publication.

340 US ISSN 1068-3801
K7
GEORGE MASON INDEPENDENT LAW REVIEW. 1976. s-a. $25 (effective fall 1994). George Mason Independent Law Journal Association, 3401 N. Fairfax Dr., Arlington, VA 22201. TEL 703-993-8161. FAX 703-993-8088. Ed. Barry M. Parsons. bk.rev.; circ. 750 (paid). (back issues avail.; reprint service avail. from RRI) **Indexed:** C.L.I., L.R.I., Leg.Cont., Leg.Per. **Document type:** academic/scholarly publication.
●Also available online. Vendor(s): Mead Data Central, Inc., West Services, Inc.
—BLDSC (4158.209130); UnCover; UMI.
Former titles (until 1992): G M U Law Review (ISSN 0741-8736); International School of Law. Law Review.
Description: Publishes both scholarly and student written work on general topics of law.

340 US ISSN 0016-8076
K7
GEORGE WASHINGTON LAW REVIEW. 1932. 5/yr. $25. George Washington University, G W Law Review, 716 20th St. N.W., Burns 4th Fl., Washington, DC 20052. TEL 202-994-6835. FAX 202-994-3090. adv.; bk.rev. circ. 2,000. (also avail. in microfilm from WSH,PMC; back issues avail.; reprint service avail. from WSH) **Indexed:** Abstr.Bk.Rev.Curr.Leg.Per., C.L.I., Curr.Cont., Energy Ind., Energy Info.Abstr., L.R.I., Leg.Cont., Leg.Per., P.A.I.S., Pers.Lit., SSCI.
●Also available online. Vendor(s): Mead Data Central, Inc., West Services, Inc.
—BLDSC (4158.230000); Faxon; UnCover; SWETS.

340 325.1 US ISSN 0891-4370
K7
GEORGETOWN IMMIGRATION LAW JOURNAL. 1985. q. $30 (foreign $35). Georgetown University Law Center, 600 New Jersey Ave., N.W., Washington, DC 20001. TEL 202-662-9468. bk.rev. (back issues avail.; reprint service avail. from WSH)
●Also available online. Vendor(s): West Services, Inc..
—Faxon; UnCover.
Description: Contains commentary on judicial and legislative developments in immigration law.

GEORGETOWN INTERNATIONAL ENVIRONMENTAL LAW REVIEW. see ENVIRONMENTAL STUDIES

340 170 US ISSN 1041-5548
K7
GEORGETOWN JOURNAL OF LEGAL ETHICS. vol.6, 1992. q. $35. Georgetown University Law Center, 600 New Jersey Ave., N.W., Washington, DC 20001. TEL 202-662-9468.
—Faxon; UnCover.
Description: Heightens awareness of ethical issues within the legal community.

340 US ISSN 0016-8092
GEORGETOWN LAW JOURNAL. 1912. 6/yr. $35 (foreign $38). (Georgetown Law Journal Association) Georgetown University Law Center, 600 New Jersey Ave., N.W., Washington, DC 20001. TEL 202-662-9468. adv.; bk.rev.; stat.; index. circ. 1,508. (also avail. in microfiche from RRI,WSH; microfilm from RRI,WSH) **Indexed:** Bank.Lit.Ind., C.L.I., Cath.Ind., Crim.Just.Abstr., Curr.Cont., L.R.I., Leg.Cont., Leg.Per., P.A.I.S., Pers.Lit., So.Pac.Per.Ind., SSCI.
●Also available online. Vendor(s): Mead Data Central, Inc., West Services, Inc.
—BLDSC (4158.270000); Faxon; UnCover; SWETS; UMI.

340 US ISSN 8750-0515
GEORGIA ADVANCE SHEETS. 1984. w. $269. Darby Printing Co., 6215 Puroue Dr., S.W., Atlanta, GA 30336-2827. TEL 404-344-2665. Ed. Karen Ehmer. cum.index. circ. 2,000. (back issues avail.)

343 US
GEORGIA ARREST, SEARCH & SEIZURE. 1987. base vol. (plus a. suppl.). $50. Butterworth Legal Publishers (Salem) (Subsidiary of: Reed Elsevier plc), 8 Industrial Way, Bldg. C, Salem, NH 03079. TEL 800-548-4001. FAX 603-898-9858. (looseleaf format)

GEORGIA CONDOMINIUM LAW MANUAL. see REAL ESTATE

246.066 US
GEORGIA CREDITORS' RIGHTS. 1987. 3 base vols. (plus suppl. 2-3/yr.). $120. Butterworth Legal Publishers (Salem) (Subsidiary of: Reed Elsevier plc), 8 Industrial Way, Bldg. C, Salem, NH 03079. TEL 800-548-4001. FAX 603-898-9858.

340 US ISSN 1040-4813
KFG331.A15
GEORGIA EMPLOYMENT LAW LETTER. 1988. m. $117. (Clark, Paul, Hoover, & Mallard) M. Lee Smith Publishers & Printers, 162 Fourth Ave., N., Box 198867, Nashville, TN 37219-8867. TEL 615-242-7395; 800-274-6774. FAX 615-256-6601. Ed. D. Hagaman. **Document type:** newsletter.
Description: Reports the latest state-specific employment law developments that affect companies in Georgia.

340 613.1 US ISSN 1044-2324
KFG354.A15
GEORGIA ENVIRONMENTAL LAW LETTER. 1989. m. $147. (Arnall Golden & Gregory) M. Lee Smith Publishers & Printers, 162 Fourth Ave., N., Box 198867, Nashville, TN 37219-8867. TEL 615-242-7395; 615-256-6601. FAX 615-256-6601. Ed. A. Jean Tolman. **Document type:** newsletter.
Description: Reports the latest state-specific environmental law developments that affect Georgia companies.

340 US ISSN 1047-9228
K7
GEORGIA JOURNAL OF SOUTHERN LEGAL HISTORY.* 1991. s-a. Georgia Legal History Foundation, c/o Patricia G. Dunleavy, Box 326, Loganville, GA 30249.
—UnCover.

GEORGIA LANDLORD - TENANT LAW. see REAL ESTATE

340 US ISSN 0016-8300
K7
GEORGIA LAW REVIEW. 1966. q. $22.50. University of Georgia Law Review, Athens, GA 30602. TEL 706-542-7286. (Co-sponsor: Georgia Law Review Association, Inc.) Ed. Matthew J. Gilligan. adv.; bk.rev.; bibl.; charts; stat. circ. 2,000. (also avail. in microfilm from RRI,WSH) **Indexed:** C.L.I., L.R.I., Leg.Cont., Leg.Per., P.A.I.S. **Document type:** academic/scholarly publication.
●Also available online. Vendor(s): West Services, Inc.
—BLDSC (4158.430000); Faxon; UnCover; SWETS.

344 US ISSN 0362-5931
KFG15
GEORGIA LEGISLATIVE REVIEW. 1974. irreg. Southern Center for Studies in Public Policy, Clark Atlanta College, Atlanta, GA 30314. TEL 404-880-8085.
Description: Covers law and politics in Georgia and how it affects minorities and the poor.

340 333.33 US ISSN 1040-4805
GEORGIA REAL ESTATE LAW LETTER. 1988. m. $137. (Weissman, Nowack, Curry & Zaleon) M. Lee Smith Publishers & Printers, 162 Fourth Ave., N., Box 198867, Nashville, TN 37219-8867. TEL 615-242-7395; 800-274-6774. FAX 615-256-6601. Eds. Seth Weissman, Linda Curry. **Document type:** newsletter.
Description: Review the most recent real estate laws in Georgia.

340 US ISSN 0016-8416
K7
GEORGIA STATE BAR JOURNAL. 1964. q. $10 to non-members. State Bar of Georgia, 800 The Hurt Bldg., Atlanta, GA 30303. TEL 404-527-8700. FAX 404-527-8717. Ed. Stephanie B. Manis. adv.; bk.rev.; index. circ. 25,000. (also avail. in microfiche from BHP; microfilm from WSH) **Indexed:** C.L.I., L.R.I., Law Ofc.Info.Svc., Leg.Per. **Document type:** trade publication.
—Faxon; UnCover.
Supersedes: Georgia Bar Journal.

340
GEORGIA STATE BAR NEWS. vol.18, 1993. m. membership. State Bar of Georgia, 800 The Hurt Bldg., 50 Hurt Plaza, Atlanta, GA 30303. TEL 404-527-8700. FAX 404-527-8717. Ed. Lynne Carpentier. (tabloid format) **Document type:** newsletter.
Description: News of activities and programs of interest to Georgia attorneys.

340 GW
GERICHTSNOTIZEN. 1978. m. free. Amtsgericht Gross-Gerau, Europaring 11-13, 64518 Gross-Gerau, Germany. TEL 06152-170458. FAX 06152-53536. Ed. Manfred Franz. adv.; bk.rev. circ. 170. (looseleaf format; back issues avail.) **Document type:** corporate report.

340 GW
GESETZ- UND VERORDNUNGSBLATT FUER BERLIN. 1945. irreg. (approx. 60/yr.). DM.104. (Senatsverwaltung fuer Justiz) Kulturbuch Verlag GmbH, Postfach 470449, 12312 Berlin, Germany. TEL 030-6618484. FAX 030-6617828. (back issues avail.) **Indexed:** Dok.Str. **Document type:** government publication.

340 GW ISSN 0174-478X
GESETZBLATT FUER BADEN-WUERTTEMBERG. 1952. s-m. DM.65. Staatsministerium Baden-Wuerttemberg, Richard-Wagner-Str. 15, 70184 Stuttgart, Germany. FAX 02153-470. TELEX 722207-STAMID. Ed.Bd. circ. 7,000. (reprint service avail.) **Indexed:** Dok.Str., INIS Atomind. **Document type:** government publication.

349 GH ISSN 0072-436X
LAW
GHANA LAW REPORTS. 1959. a. $79. Council for Law Reporting, P.O. Box M. 165, Accra, Ghana. Ed. S.Y. Bimpong-Buta. adv. circ. 2,000.

340 US
GILBERT LAW SUMMARIES. ADMINISTRATIVE LAW. irreg., 11th ed., 1988. $14.95. Harcourt Brace Legal & Professional Publications, Inc., 176 W. Adams, Ste. 2100, Chicago, IL 60603. TEL 312-853-3662.

340 US
GILBERT LAW SUMMARIES. CALIFORNIA BAR TEST SKILLS. irreg., 4th ed., 1990. $13.95. Harcourt Brace Legal & Professional Publications, Inc., 176 W. Adams, Ste. 2100, Chciago, IL 60603. TEL 312-853-3662.

340 US
GILBERT LAW SUMMARIES. COMMUNITY PROPERTY. irreg., 14th ed., 1986. $12.95. Harvourt brace Legal & Professional Publications, Inc., 176 W. Adams, Ste. 2100, Chicago, IL 60603. TEL 312-853-3662.

340 US
GILBERT LAW SUMMARIES. CONFLICT OF LAWS. irreg., 16th ed., 1990. $15.95. Harcourt Brace Legal & Professional Publications, Inc., 176 W. Adams, Ste. 2100, Chicago, IL 60603. TEL 312-853-3662.

340 US
GILBERT LAW SUMMARIES. DICTIONARY OF LEGAL TERMS. 1984. irreg. $10.95. Harcourt Brace Legal & Professional Publications, Inc., 176 W. Adams, Ste. 2100, Chicago, IL 60603. TEL 312-853-3662.

340 US
GILBERT LAW SUMMARIES. EVIDENCE. irreg., 16th ed., 1992. $16.95. Harcourt Brace legal & Professional Publications, Inc., 176 W. Adams, Ste. 2100, Chicago, IL 60603. TEL 312-853-3622.

LAW

340 US
GILBERT LAW SUMMARIES. FUTURE INTERESTS. irreg., 3rd ed., 1982. $10.95. Harcourt Brace Legal & Professional Publications, Inc., 176 W. Adams, Ste. 2100, Chicago, IL 60603. TEL 312-853-3662.

340 US
GILBERT LAW SUMMARIES. INCOME TAX 1 (INDIVIDUAL). irreg., 17th ed., 1990. $17.95. Law Distributors (Subsidiary of: H B J Legal & Professional Publications Inc.), 14415 S. Main St., Gardena, CA 90248. TEL 800-421-1893. FAX 213-324-6381.

340 US
GILBERT LAW SUMMARIES. LEGAL ETHICS. irreg., 6th ed., 1987. $12.95. Harcourt Brace Legal & Professional Publications, Inc., 176 W. Adams, Ste. 2100, Chicago, IL 60603. TEL 312-853-3662.

340 US
GILBERT LAW SUMMARIES. LEGAL RESEARCH & WRITING. irreg., 5th ed., 1989. $10.95. Harcourt Brace Legal & Professional Publications, Inc., 176 W. Adams, Ste. 2100, Chicago, IL 60603. TEL 312-853-3662.

340 US
GILBERT LAW SUMMARIES. MULTISTATE. irreg., 2nd ed., 1984. $12.95. Harcourt Brace Legal & Professional Publications, Inc., 176 W. Adams, Ste. 2100, Chicago, IL 60603. TEL 312-853-3662.

340 US
GILBERT LAW SUMMARIES. PERSONAL PROPERTY. irreg., 6th ed., 1980. $8.95. Harcourt Brace Legal & Professional Publications, Inc., 176 W. Adams, Ste. 2100, Chicago, IL 60603. TEL 312-853-3662.

340 US
GILBERT LAW SUMMARIES. PROPERTY. irreg., 13th ed., 1991. $18.95. Harcourt Brace Legal & Professional Publications, Inc., 176 W. Adams, Ste. 2100, Chicago, IL 60603. TEL 312-853-3662.

340 US
GILBERT LAW SUMMARIES. REMEDIES. irreg., 9th ed., 1991. $17.95. Harcourt Brace Legal & Professional Publications, Inc., 176 W. Adams, Ste. 2100, Chicago, IL 60603. TEL 312-853-3662.

340 US
GILBERT LAW SUMMARIES. SALES. irreg., 11th ed., 1992. $15.95. Harcourt Brace Legal & professional Publications, Inc., 176 W. Adams, Ste. 2100, Chicago, IL 60603. TEL 312-853-3662.

346.066 US
GILBERT LAW SUMMARIES. SECURED TRANSACTIONS. irreg., 9th ed., 1992. $14.95. Harcourt Brace Legal & Professional Publications, Inc., 176 W. Adams, Ste. 2100, Chicago, IL 60603. TEL 312-853-3662.

340 US
GILBERT LAW SUMMARIES. SECURITIES REGULATION. irreg., 4th ed., 1987. $17.95. Harcourt Brace Legal & Professional Publications, Inc., 176 W. Adams, Ste. 2100, Chicago, IL 60603. TEL 312-853-3662.

340 US
GILBERT LAW SUMMARIES. TORTS. irreg., 19th ed., 1991. $17.95. Harcourt Brace Legal & Professional Publications, Inc., 176 W. Adams, Ste. 2100, Chicago, IL 60603. TEL 312-853-3662.

GIURISPRUDENZA AGRARIA ITALIANA. see *AGRICULTURE*

346.066 IT
GIURISPRUDENZA DELLE IMPOSTE. 1953. q. L.100000 (foreign L.150000). Casa Editrice Dott. A. Giuffre, Via Busto Arsizio 40, 20151 Milan, Italy. TEL 02-38000905. FAX 02-38009582. Ed. C. Berliri. adv. circ. 5,800.

340 IT
GIURISPRUDENZA DI MERITO. 1969. bi-m. L.110000 (foreign L.165000). Casa Editrice Dott. A. Giuffre, Via Busto Arsizio 40, 20151 Milan, Italy. TEL 02-38000905. FAX 02-38009582. Ed. A. Jannuzzi. adv.; bk.rev. circ. 5,000. **Indexed:** ELLIS.

349 IT ISSN 0017-0623
GIURISPRUDENZA ITALIANA. 1848. m. L.203000. Unione Tipografico Editrice Torinese, Corso Raffaello 28, 10125 Turin, Italy. index. circ. 13,500. **Indexed:** ELLIS.

340 IT
GIUSTIZIA CIVILE. MASSIMARIO ANNOTATO DELLA CASSAZIONE. 1955. m. L.160000 (foreign L.240000). Casa Editrice Dott. A. Giuffre, Via Busto Arsizio 40, 20151 Milan, Italy. TEL 02-38000905. FAX 02-38009582. Eds. Mario Barba, Alfio Finocchiaro. adv. circ. 5,000.

349 IT ISSN 0017-064X
GIUSTIZIA NUOVA. 1960. m. L.5000($7) Edizioni Giustizia Nuova, Via Bozzi 47-A, Bari, Italy. Ed. Alfredo Zallone. adv.; bk.rev.; abstr.; bibl.; tr.lit. circ. 15,000. **Document type:** newspaper.

340 US ISSN 0363-2423
K7
GLENDALE LAW REVIEW. 1976. irreg. $9. Glendale University, College of Law, 220 N. Glendale Ave., Glendale, CA 91206. TEL 818-247-0770. Ed. Robert Cohen. circ. 500. (back issues avail.) **Indexed:** C.L.I., L.R.I., Leg.Per., P.A.I.S.
—BLDSC (4195.130000); Faxon; UnCover.

340 378.002 US
▼**GLOBAL DIRECTORY OF SCHOOLS OF LAW OUTSIDE OF THE UNITED STATES OF AMERICA.** 1992. a. $27.50. Graduate Group, 86 Norwood Rd., West Hartford, CT 06117-2336. TEL 203-232-3100. bk.rev. (back issues avail.) **Document type:** directory.

GLOBAL SHAREHOLDER. see *BUSINESS AND ECONOMICS — Investments*

340 940 US ISSN 0214-669X
GLOSSAE; revista de historia del derecho europeo. (Text in Spanish; abstracts in English, Spanish) 1988. a. Universidad de Murcia, Instituto de Derecho Comun Europeo, Servicio de Publicaciones, Calle Santo Cristo 1, 30001 Murcia, Spain. Dir. Antonio Perez Martin.
Description: Contains studies on the history of European law.

349 GW ISSN 0016-3570
K22
GMBH-RUNDSCHAU. 1908. m. DM.165. Verlag Dr. Otto Schmidt KG, Unter den Ulmen 96-98, 50968 Cologne, Germany. TEL 0221-9373801. FAX 0221-93738941. TELEX 8883381. Ed. B. Tillmann. bk.rev.; abstr.; bibl.; index. circ. 9,000. **Document type:** bulletin.
—SWETS. CCC.

GOETTINGER RECHTSWISSENSCHAFTLICHE STUDIEN. see *LAW — International Law*

340 GW ISSN 0933-3002
GOETTINGER STUDIEN ZUR RECHTSGESCHICHTE. 1969. irreg. price varies. Muster-Schmidt Verlag, Brauweg 36a, 37073 Goettingen, Germany. TEL 0551-71741. FAX 0551-7702774. TELEX 96704-GOFAFI. Eds. Dr. Sellert, Dr. Behrends. **Document type:** academic/scholarly publication.

340 US ISSN 0363-0307
K7
GOLDEN GATE UNIVERSITY LAW REVIEW. 1969. 3/yr. $22. Golden Gate University, School of Law, 536 Mission St., San Francisco, CA 94105. TEL 415-442-6691. adv.; bk.rev. circ. 600. (also avail. in microform from WSH,UMI,PMC; back issues avail.; reprint service avail. from UMI) **Indexed:** BPIA, Bus.Ind., C.L.I., Crim.Just.Abstr., L.R.I., Leg.Cont., Leg.Per. **Document type:** academic/scholarly publication.
●Also available online. Vendor(s): West Services, Inc.
—Faxon; UnCover.
 Formerly (until 1975): Golden Gate Law Review (ISSN 0098-6631)

340 US ISSN 0046-6115
K7
GONZAGA LAW REVIEW. 1966. 3/yr. $25. Gonzaga University School of Law, Spokane, WA 99258-0001. TEL 509-328-4220. FAX 509-484-2810. Ed. Robert D. Stone. adv.; bk.rev.; bibl.; index, cum.index every 10 yrs. circ. 2,000. (also avail. in microfilm from WSH,PMC; microfiche from WSH; back issues avail.) **Indexed:** Abstr.Bk.Rev.Curr.Leg.Per., C.L.I., L.R.I., Leg.Cont., Leg.Per.
—Faxon; UnCover.

340 UK
GOODE'S CONSUMER CREDIT LEGISLATION. 2 base vols. (plus updates 3/yr.). $490. Butterworth & Co. (Publishers) Ltd. (Subsidiary of: Reed Elsevier plc), 88 Kingsway, London WC2B 6AB, England. TEL 71-405-6900. FAX 71-405-1332. (US addr.: Butterworth Legal Publishers, 90 Stiles Rd., Salem, NH 03079-9981. TEL 603-898-9664) Ed. R.M. Goode. (looseleaf format)
 Description: Contains all the legislation relating to consumer credit. Also covers significant changes as a result of recent developments in the field.

340 RU
K23
GOSUDARSTVO I PRAVO. (Text in Russian; contents page in English and French; summaries in English) 1927. m. $103. (Rossiiskaya Akademiya Nauk, Institut Gosudarstva i Prava) Izdatel'stvo Nauka, 90 Profsoyuznaya ul., 117864 Moscow, Russia. TEL 095-336-0266. FAX 095-420-2220. (Dist. by: Mezhdunarodnaya Kniga, B. Yakimanka 39, 117049 Moscow, Russia; Dist. in U.S. by: Victor Kamkin Inc., 4956 Boiling Brook Pkwy., Rockville, MD 20852. TEL 301-881-5973. FAX 301-881-1637) Ed. M.I. Piskotin. bk.rev.; bibl.; index. circ. 52,250. (also avail. in microform) **Indexed:** Amer.Hist.& Life, Curr.Dig.Sov.Press, Hist.Abstr., Rural Recreat.Tour.Abstr., World Agri.Econ.& Rural Sociol.Abstr.
 Formerly: Sovetskoe Gosudarstvo i Pravo (ISSN 0132-0769)

GOTHERMAN'S OHIO MUNICIPAL SERVICE. see *PUBLIC ADMINISTRATION*

342 US
GOVERNMENT AND ADMINISTRATIVE LAW NEWS. irreg. (2-4/yr.). membership. State Bar of Wisconsin, Government and Administrative Law Section, 402 W. Wilson St., Madison, WI 53703. TEL 608-257-3838. FAX 608-257-5502. circ. 500. (back issues avail.) **Document type:** newsletter.

GOVERNMENT CONTRACT COSTS, PRICING & ACCOUNTING REPORT. see *BUSINESS AND ECONOMICS — Economic Situation And Conditions*

GOVERNMENT CONTRACTOR. see *BUSINESS AND ECONOMICS — Production Of Goods And Services*

GOVERNMENT CONTRACTS CITATOR. see *BUSINESS AND ECONOMICS — Economic Situation And Conditions*

350 US
GOVERNMENT CONTRACTS REPORTS. 10 base vols. (plus w. updates). $1795. Commerce Clearing House, Inc., 4025 W. Peterson Ave., Chicago, IL 60646. TEL 312-583-8500.

GOVERNMENT CONTRACTS SERVICE. see *BUSINESS AND ECONOMICS — Management*

GOVERNMENT REPORT. see *ADVERTISING AND PUBLIC RELATIONS*

GOWER FEDERAL SERVICE - MISCELLANEOUS LAND DECISIONS. see *MINES AND MINING INDUSTRY*

GOWER FEDERAL SERVICE - OIL AND GAS. see *PETROLEUM AND GAS*

GOWER FEDERAL SERVICE - OUTER CONTINENTAL SHELF. see *MINES AND MINING INDUSTRY*

GOWER FEDERAL SERVICE - ROYALTY VALUATION AND MANAGEMENT. see *MINES AND MINING INDUSTRY*

GRANTS FOR SCHOOL DISTRICTS MONTHLY HOTLINE. see *EDUCATION — School Organization And Administration*

340 UK
GREAT BRITAIN. OFFICE OF FAIR TRADING. REPORT. 1975. a. £12. H.M.S.O., P.O. Box 276, London SW8 5DT, England. (reprint service avail. from UMI) **Document type:** government publication.

LAW

349   UK   ISSN 0080-7915
KDC320
GREAT BRITAIN. SCOTTISH LAW COMMISSION. ANNUAL REPORT. 1965. a. price varies. Scottish Law Commission, 140 Causewayside, Edinburgh EH9 1PR, Scotland. FAX 031-662-4900. (Dist by: H.M.S.O., 71 Lothian Rd., Edinburgh EH3 9AZ, Scotland) circ. 1,000. **Document type:** government publication.
—CCC.

347.9   UK
GREENS WEEKLY DIGEST. w. £95. W. Green, 21 Alva St., Edinburgh EH2 4PS, Scotland. Ed. P. Nicholson.

GRIEVANCE BULLETIN. see *BUSINESS AND ECONOMICS — Labor And Industrial Relations*

340   AT   ISSN 1038-3441
GRIFFITH LAW REVIEW. 1992. s-a. $40. Griffith Law Review Association, c/o Law School, Griffith University, Brisbane, Qld. 4111, Australia. TEL 07-875-6474. (Dist. in N. America by: Wm. W. Gaunt & Sons Inc., Gaunt Bldg., 3011 Gulf Dr., Holmes Beach, FL 34217-2199. TEL 813-778-5211. FAX 813-778-5252) Ed.Bd. **Indexed:** C.L.I.

340   NE   ISSN 0167-3831
GROTIANA. (Text in English, French, German, Italian, Latin) 1980. a. fl.75($30) (Grotiana Foundation) Van Gorcum en Co. B.V., P.O. Box 43, 9400 AA Assen, Netherlands. TEL 31-5920-46864. FAX 31-5920-72064. Ed. B. Vermeulen. adv.; bk.rev. circ. 800. (back issues avail.) **Document type:** academic/scholarly publication.
Description: Covers history of law.

330 380.5   FR
GUIDE DES COUTS DE TRANSPORT. a. 1445 F. Lamy S.A., 187-189 Quai de Valmy, 75490 Paris Cedex 10, France. TEL 44-72-13-43. FAX 44-72-13-95.

330 380.5   FR
GUIDE DES PROCEDURES DOUANIERES. a. 1030 F. (effective 1993). Lamy S.A., 187-189 Quai de Valmy, 75490 Paris Cedex 10, France. TEL 44-72-13-43. FAX 44-72-13-95.
Description: Covers duties still existing within the EC and between EC countries and the US, Japan, Eastern Europe and developing countries.

340   US   ISSN 1052-8253
KF154
GUIDE TO AMERICAN LAW. 1984. a. West Publishing Corp., 620 Opperman Dr., Eagan, MN 55123. TEL 612-687-8000; 800-328-9352. FAX 612-687-7302.
Formerly (until 1988): Guide to American Law. Yearbook (ISSN 0895-0989)

GUIDE TO COMPUTER LAW. see *COMPUTERS*

340   CN
GUIDE TO ONTARIO PERSONAL PROPERTY SECURITY. q. Can.$250. Carswell, One Corporate Plaza, 2075 Kennedy Rd., Scarborough, ON M1T 3V4, Canada. TEL 416-609-8000. FAX 416-298-5094. Ed. Barry I. Goldberg, Steven G. Golick. (looseleaf format)
Description: Provides a practical, step-by-step guide to protection, preservation and perfection of security under the new Ontario Act.

GUIDEBOOK TO LABOR RELATIONS. see *BUSINESS AND ECONOMICS — Labor And Industrial Relations*

349   II   ISSN 0017-551X
GUJARAT LAW REPORTER; reportable judgements of the Supreme Court and the Gujarat High Court. (Text in English) 1960. m. Rs.350. Chandrakant Chimanlal Vora, 57-2 Gandhi Rd., P.O. Box 163, Ahmedabad 380 001, Gujarat, India. adv.; bk.rev.; index. circ. 3,000. (back issues avail.)

349   II   ISSN 0017-5528
GUJARAT LAW TIMES; law journal publishing short-notes on the cases decided by the High Court of Gujarat (India) as well as those of Supreme Court of India. (Text in English) 1964. fortn. Rs.175. Chandrakant Chimanlal Vora, 57-2 Gandhi Rd., P.O. Box 163, Ahmedabad 380 001, Gujarat, India. Ed. Babubhai A. Soni. adv.; bk.rev.; index. circ. 2,000. (back issues avail.)

349   II   ISSN 0017-5536
GUJARAT REVENUE TRIBUNAL LAW REPORTER; judgements of the Gujarat Revenue Tribunal. (Text in English) 1961. m. Rs.125. Chandrakant Chimanlal Vora, 57-2 Gandhi Rd., P.O. Box 163, Ahmedabad 380 001, Gujarat, India. Ed. N.C. Vakil. adv.; bk.rev.; index. circ. 350. (back issues avail.)

H A L L NEWSLETTER. (Houston Area Law Librarians) see *LIBRARY AND INFORMATION SCIENCES*

340   US   ISSN 0198-7364
K8
HAMLINE LAW REVIEW. 1978. 3/yr. $17. Hamline University School of Law, Hamline Law Review, 1536 Hewitt Ave., St. Paul, MN 55104-1284. TEL 612-641-2350. FAX 612-641-2435. bk.rev.; illus. circ. 1,300. (also avail. in microform from WSH,PMC; reprint service avail. from WSH) **Indexed:** Abstr.Bk.Rev.Curr.Leg.Per., C.L.I., Crim.Just.Abstr., L.R.I., Leg.Cont., Leg.Per. **Document type:** academic/scholarly publication.
●Also available online. Vendor(s): West Services, Inc.
—BLDSC (4241.473000); UnCover; UMI. **CCC.**
Supersedes: Midwestern Advocate (ISSN 0360-5094)

340   GW
HANDBUCH DER JUSTIZ. 1953. biennial. DM.84. (Deutscher Richterbund) R. v. Decker's Verlag, G. Schenck GmbH, Im Weiher 10, 69121 Heidelberg, Germany. TEL 06221-489369. FAX 06221-489-410. TELEX 461727-HUE-HD. Ed. P. Marqua. adv. circ. 4,000. **Document type:** monographic series.

340 614.8   US
HANDGUN CONTROL. SEMI-ANNUAL PROGRESS REPORT. 1974. s-a. free to members. Handgun Control, Inc., 1225 Eye St., N.W., Washington, DC 20005. TEL 202-898-0792. Ed. Cheryl Brolin. **Document type:** newsletter.
Formerly (until 1989): Washington Report (Washington, 1974).
Description: Reports on federal and state legislative efforts toward stronger gun laws. Cites new studies on gun issues.

340   AU
HANS KELSEN - INSTITUT. SCHRIFTENREIHE. 1974. irreg., vol.18, 1992. price varies. Manzsche Verlags- und Universitaetsbuchhandlung, Kohlmarkt 16, A-1014 Vienna, Austria. TEL 0222-531610. FAX 0222-53161-181. **Document type:** monographic series.
Description: Focuses on legal philosophy.

340 323.4   US
HARVARD BLACKLETTER JOURNAL. a. $12 (foreign $14). Harvard University, Law School, Publications Center, Hastings Hall, Cambridge, MA 02138. TEL 617-495-3694. circ. 300. (also avail. in microform from WSH; reprint service avail. from WSH)
Description: Dedicated to the dissemination of legal literature, thought and ideas which have direct impact on the minority community.

340   US   ISSN 0147-8257
K8
HARVARD ENVIRONMENTAL LAW REVIEW. 1976. 2/yr. $24 (Canada $30). Harvard University, Law School, Publications Center, Hastings Hall, Cambridge, MA 02138. TEL 617-495-3694. circ. 1,000. (also avail. in microform from WSH,PMC; back issues avail.; reprint service avail. from WSH) **Indexed:** Acid Pre.Dig., Acid Rain Abstr., Acid Rain Ind., C.L.I., Deep Sea Res.& Oceanogr.Abstr., Energy Info.Abstr., Energy Rev., Environ.Abstr., Environ.Per.Bibl. (1979-), Geo.Abstr., INIS Atomind., L.R.I., Leg.Per., Mar.Aff.Bibl., P.A.I.S., Risk Abstr., Sel.Water Res.Abstr., SSCI, Telegen.
●Also available online. Vendor(s): West Services, Inc.
—BLDSC (4265.944000); CIS; Faxon; UnCover; SWETS.
Description: Provides a forum for in-depth technical and legal analysis of complex environmental problems, ranging from energy and urban land use to hazardous wastes and wilderness preservation.

340   US   ISSN 0193-4872
K8
HARVARD JOURNAL OF LAW AND PUBLIC POLICY. 1978. 3/yr. $32.50 to individuals and institutions; students $17.50; foreign $35. Harvard Society for Law and Public Policy, Inc., Harvard Law School, Cambridge, MA 02138. TEL 617-495-3105. FAX 617-495-1110. adv.; bk.rev. circ. 4,800. (also avail. in microform from WSH,PMC; back issues avail.; reprint service avail. from WSH) **Indexed:** C.L.I., L.R.I., Leg.Per., P.A.I.S., Pers.Lit. **Document type:** academic/scholarly publication.
●Also available online. Vendor(s): West Services, Inc.
—BLDSC (4267.380000); Faxon; UnCover; UMI.
Description: Student-run law journal.

340   US   ISSN 0017-808X
K8
HARVARD JOURNAL ON LEGISLATION. 1964. 2/yr. $24 (Canada $30). Harvard University, Law School, Publications Center, Hastings Hall, Cambridge, MA 02138. TEL 617-495-3694. adv.; bk.rev.; charts. circ. 800. (also avail. in microform from UMI; microfilm from RRI,WSH; reprint service avail. from RRI,UMI) **Indexed:** A.B.C.Pol.Sci., Abstr.Bk.Rev.Curr.Leg.Per., BPIA, Bus.Ind., C.L.I., L.R.I., Leg.Cont., Leg.Per., Mar.Aff.Bibl., P.A.I.S., SSCI.
●Also available online. Vendor(s): West Services, Inc..
—BLDSC (4267.400000); Faxon; UnCover; SWETS.
Description: Examines the current state of the law, trends and the theoretical underpinnings of legislation. Presents detailed statements of how the law should be changed, and proposes specific model acts for adoption by legislatures.

HARVARD LAW BULLETIN. see *COLLEGE AND ALUMNI*

340   US   ISSN 0017-8101
HARVARD LAW RECORD. 1946. 25/yr. $30. Harvard Law Record Corporation, Harvard Law School, Cambridge, MA 02138. TEL 617-495-4418. FAX 617-495-8457. Ed. Lisa Zornberg. adv.; B&W page $800; adv. contact: Johanna Davis. bk.rev.; charts; illus.; stat.; index. circ. 15,000. (tabloid format; also avail. in microform from WSH; reprint service avail. from WSH) **Document type:** newspaper.
Description: Serves the students, faculty and alumni of the school.

340   US   ISSN 0017-811X
K8   CODEN: HALRAF
HARVARD LAW REVIEW. 1887. m. (8/yr.). $40 (foreign $46). Harvard Law Review Association, Gannett House, Cambridge, MA 02138. TEL 617-495-4650. Ed.Bd. adv.; bk.rev.; bibl.; index, cum.index: vols.1-86 (1887-1972). circ. 7,500. (also avail. in microfiche from RRI,WSH; microfilm from RRI,WSH; microform from UMI; reprint service avail. from RRI,UMI) **Indexed:** A.B.C.Pol.Sci., ABI Inform., Abstr.Bk.Rev.Curr.Leg.Per., Account.Ind. (1974-), Bank.Lit.Ind., Bk.Rev.Ind. (1965-), BPIA, Bus.Ind., C.L.I., Child.Bk.Rev.Ind. (1965-), Crim.Just.Abstr., Curr.Cont., L.R.I., Leg.Per., Mar.Aff.Bibl., Mid.East: Abstr.& Ind., P.A.I.S., Pers.Lit., Risk Abstr., SSCI. **Document type:** academic/scholarly publication.
●Also available online. Vendor(s): Mead Data Central, Inc. (Lexis), West Services, Inc.
—BLDSC (4267.500000); Faxon; UnCover; SWETS; UMI.

349.73 305.4   US   ISSN 0270-1456
K8
HARVARD WOMEN'S LAW JOURNAL. 1978. a. $15 (foreign $27). Harvard University, Law School (Women's Law Journal), Publications Center, Hastings Hall, Cambridge, MA 02138. TEL 617-495-3726. FAX 617-495-1110. Ed. Peggy Smith. adv.; bk.rev. circ. 900. (also avail. in microfilm from WSH,PMC; back issues avail.; reprint service avail. from WSH) **Indexed:** Abstr.Bk.Rev.Curr.Leg.Per., Alt.Press Ind., C.L.I., HR Rep., L.R.I., Leg.Per., Mult.Ed.Abstr., P.A.I.S., Stud.Wom.Abstr. **Document type:** academic/scholarly publication.
●Also available online. Vendor(s): West Services, Inc.
—UnCover; SWETS.
Description: Devoted to the development of a feminist jurisprudence, which explores both the impact of the law on women and the impact of women on the law. Legal, political, economical, historical and sociological perspectives are combined in order to clarify legal issues affecting women.

340 001.6 790 US ISSN 1061-6578
K3
HASTINGS COMMUNICATIONS AND ENTERTAINMENT LAW JOURNAL (COMM - ENT). 1977. q. $20 (foreign $22). University of California at San Francisco, Hastings College of the Law, 200 McAllister St., San Francisco, CA 94102-4978. TEL 415-565-4731. FAX 415-565-4814. Ed. Karen Gibbs. adv.; bk.rev.; abstr.; bibl.; cum.index every 5 yrs. circ. 1,200. (tabloid format; also avail. in microfilm from PMC,WSH; back issues avail.; reprint service avail.) Indexed: C.L.I., Commun.Abstr., L.R.I., Leg.Per.
Document type: academic/scholarly publication.
●Also available online. Vendor(s): West Services, Inc. Also available on CD-ROM.
—Faxon; UnCover.
Formerly: Comm-Ent: Hastings Journal of Communications and Entertainment Law (ISSN 0193-8398)
Description: Covers telecommunications, broadcasting, cable and other nonbroadcast video, the print media, defamation, advertising, the arts, entertainment, sports, computers and high-technology information services, copyright, patent, trademark, privacy, film and other First Amendment issues.

340 US ISSN 0017-8322
HASTINGS LAW JOURNAL. 1949. bi-m. $25 (foreign $27). University of California at San Francisco, Hastings College of the Law, 200 McAllister St., San Francisco, CA 94102-4978. TEL 415-565-4727. FAX 415-565-4814. Ed. Erin Morton. adv.; bk.rev.; bibl.; cum.index: 1947-1969, 1970-1979. circ. 1,700. (tabloid format; also avail. in microfilm from UMI,WSH,PMC; back issues avail; reprint service avail. from UMI) Indexed: Abstr.Bk.Rev.Curr.Leg.Per., C.L.I., L.R.I., Leg.Cont., Leg.Per., SSCI. Document type: academic/scholarly publication.
●Also available online. Vendor(s): Mead Data Central, Inc., West Services, Inc.
Also available on CD-ROM.
—BLDSC (4273.050000); Faxon; UnCover; SWETS; UMI.
Description: Contributes to the advancement of knowledge in legal thinking through scholarly articles written by experts in the legal community.

340 US ISSN 1061-0901
K8
HASTINGS WOMEN'S LAW JOURNAL. 1989. s-a. $25. University of California at San Francisco, Hastings College of the Law, 200 McAllister St., San Francisco, CA 94102. TEL 415-565-4870. FAX 415-464-4814. Ed. Ellen Fenichel. adv.; bk.rev. circ. 600. (tabloid format; back issues avail.)
Document type: academic/scholarly publication.
●Also available online. Vendor(s): West Services, Inc. Also available on CD-ROM.
Description: Promotes feminist legal perspectives and scholarship in issues of concern common to all women.

340 GW ISSN 0930-6692
HAUSBESITZER A B C; Recht - Steuern - Finanzierung - Vorsicherung. 1986. q. DM.58. Wirtschaft Recht und Steuern Verlag, Fraunhoferstr. 5, 82152 Planegg, Germany. TEL 089-89517-0. FAX 089-89517250. (Subscr. to: Postfach 1363, 82142 Planegg, Germany) (looseleaf format) Document type: bulletin.
Description: News about finance and law for the homeowner.

347.9 US
HAWAII. COMMISSION ON JUDICIAL CONDUCT. ANNUAL REPORT. 1980. a. Commission on Judicial Conduct, Box 2560, Honolulu, HI 96804. circ. 250.
Formerly: Hawaii. Commission on Judicial Discipline. Annual Report.

HAWAII. STATE COMMISSION ON THE STATUS OF WOMEN. ANNUAL REPORT. see WOMEN'S STUDIES

347.9 US
HAWAII. STATE JUDICIARY. ANNUAL REPORT. 1962. a. Judiciary Department, Box 2560, Honolulu, HI 96804. TEL 808-548-4634. FAX 808-548-6002. (Or: 417 S. King St., Honolulu, HI 96813) illus.; stat. circ. 4,500.
Formerly: Hawaii. Judiciary Department. Annual Report.

340 US ISSN 1063-1585
KF200
HAWAII BAR JOURNAL. 1966. m. $30. Hawaii State Bar Association, 1136 Union Mall, PH1, Honolulu, HI 96813. TEL 808-537-1868. FAX 808-521-7936. Ed. Carole K. Muranaka. adv.; bk.rev. circ. 5,400. (also avail. in microfilm from WSH; back issues avail.) Indexed: C.L.I., L.R.I., Leg.Per.
—UnCover; UMI.
Formerly: Hawaii Bar News (ISSN 1054-8424)

340 US
HAWAII STATE BAR ASSOCIATION. ANNUAL DIRECTORY. a. $24. Hawaii State Bar Association, 1136 Union Mall, PH1, Honolulu, HI 96813. TEL 808-537-1868. FAX 808-521-7936. adv. circ. 6,000. Document type: directory.

HAZARD COMMUNICATION HANDBOOK; a right-to-know compliance guide. see ENVIRONMENTAL STUDIES — Waste Management

340 US ISSN 0275-0244
KF3946.A59
HAZARDOUS WASTE LITIGATION REPORTER; the national journal of record of hazardous waste-related litigation. 1980. s-m. $850. Andrews Publications, 1646 West Chester Pike, Box 1000, Westtown, PA 19395. TEL 215-399-6600; 800-345-1101. FAX 215-399-6610. Ed. Barbara Murphy. bibl.; stat.; s-a. index. (looseleaf format; back issues avail.) Document type: newsletter.

HEALTH ADVOCATE. see PHYSICAL FITNESS AND HYGIENE

HEALTH & SAFETY MONITOR. see OCCUPATIONAL HEALTH AND SAFETY

340 US
HEALTH AND WELFARE BENEFIT PLANS. 1991. base vol. (plus a. supplement). $90. Butterworth Legal Publishers (Salem) (Subsidiary of: Reed Elsevier plc), 8 Industrial Way, Bldg. C, Salem, NH 03079. TEL 800-548-4001. FAX 603-898-9858. Ed. James M. Nelson. (looseleaf format)
Description: Covers all aspects of health and welfare benefits regulations.

340 362.1 US
HEALTH CARE AND THE LAW. 1987. irreg. (3-4/yr.). free. Reed McClure, 3600 Columbia Center, 701 Fifth Ave., Seattle, WA 98104-7081. TEL 206-292-4900. FAX 206-223-0152. Ed. Denise Dee Behrens. circ. 1,600. Document type: newsletter.

340 US ISSN 1060-2909
HEALTH CARE FEDERAL REGISTER ALERT. 1991. w. $325. L R P Publications, 747 Dresher Rd., Horsham, PA 19044. TEL 215-784-0860. FAX 215-784-0870. Ed. Kenneth Kahn. (looseleaf format) Document type: newsletter.

HEALTH CARE LABOR MANUAL. see HOSPITALS

340 US ISSN 0893-6099
HEALTH CARE LAW NEWSLETTER. 1986. 12/yr. $220. Matthew Bender & Co., Inc., 11 Penn Plaza, New York, NY 10001-2006. TEL 212-967-7707. FAX 212-967-1069. (looseleaf format) Document type: newsletter.

340 610 US
HEALTH CARE LAWYER. 1985. q. $14. Illinois State Bar Association, Illinois Bar Center, Springfield, IL 62701. TEL 217-525-1760. FAX 217-525-0712. Eds. W.E. Basanta, Ted LeBlanc. bk.rev. circ. 1,000. (looseleaf format; back issues avail.) Document type: newsletter.

346 US
HEALTH CITY SUN. 1929. w. $10. Health City Sun Inc., 900 Park Ave. S.W., Albuquerque, NM 87102. TEL 505-242-3010. FAX 505-842-5464. Ed. Francisco Collado; Pub. Francisco Collado. adv. circ. 2,000. (tabloid format; back issues avail.) Document type: newspaper.
Former titles (until 1980): Health City Sun and the News Chieftain; Health City Sun and Bernalillo County Legal News; Health City Sun.

HEALTH EMPLOYMENT LAW UPDATE. see BUSINESS AND ECONOMICS — Labor And Industrial Relations

HEALTH LAW BULLETIN. see PUBLIC HEALTH AND SAFETY

342 613.7 US
HEALTH LAW DIGEST.* 1972. m. $195. National Health Lawyers Association, 1120 Connecticut Ave., N.W., Ste. 950, Washington, DC 20036-3921. TEL 202-833-1100. Ed. David Rapoport. circ. 7,200.

340 613.7 CN ISSN 1192-8336
▼**HEALTH LAW JOURNAL.** 1993. a. Can.$25. Health Law Institute, 457 Law Centre, University of Alberta, Edmonton, AB T6G 2H5, Canada. TEL 403-492-8343. FAX 403-492-4924. Ed. Patricia L. James. circ. 1,000.
Description: Medical-legal articles addressing emerging issues and suggesting new directions in law and social policy.
Refereed Serial

340 613.7 US ISSN 1043-6081
KFO360.A15
HEALTH LAW JOURNAL OF OHIO. 1987. bi-m. $155. Banks - Baldwin Law Publishing Co., University Center, Box 1974, Cleveland, OH 44106. TEL 216-721-7373. FAX 216-721-8055. Ed. Peter A. Pavarini.
Formerly (until 1989): Ohio Health Law Insider (ISSN 0893-8466)
Description: Review of state and national trends; practical guidance; digest of current court decisions, agency opinions, legislation and rules.

340 362.1 US
HEALTH LAW NEWS. 1991. irreg. (2-3/yr.). membership. State Bar of Wisconsin, Health Law Section, 402 W. Wilson St., Madison, WI 53703. TEL 608-257-3838. FAX 608-257-5502. circ. 400. (back issues avail.) Document type: newsletter.
Formerly: State Bar of Wisconsin. Health Law Section. Newsletter.

340 610 CN ISSN 1188-8725
HEALTH LAW REVIEW. 1991. 3/yr. Can.$45. Health Law Institute, 457 Law Centre, University of Alberta, Edmonton, AB T6G 2H5, Canada. TEL 403-492-8343. FAX 403-492-4924. Ed. Patricia L. James. circ. 1,000 (controlled). (back issues avail.)
Formerly: Health Law News.
Description: Covers issues of interest to lawyers and health care professionals as well as the general public in connection to the medical - legal field.

340 362.1 US ISSN 1063-4061
▼**HEALTH LAW WEEK.** 1992. w. $647. Strafford Publications, Inc., 590 Dutch Valley Rd., N.E., Drawer 13729, Atlanta, GA 30324-0729. TEL 404-881-1141. FAX 404-881-0074. Ed. Nancy Johnson. cum.index. (looseleaf format; back issues avail.) Document type: newsletter.
Description: Summarizes judicial decisions that concern or affect the health care industry. Provides a concise and comprehensive research tool for attorneys and health care administrators and practitioners concerned about trends in health care law.

340 US ISSN 0736-3443
KF3821.A15
HEALTH LAWYER. irreg. (3-4/yr.). membership only. (American Bar Association, Forum Committee on Health Law) A B A Press, 750 N. Lake Shore Dr., Chicago, IL 60611. TEL 312-988-6067. Ed. Lawrence Manson. circ. 3,220. (also avail. in microform) Document type: newsletter.
Description: Legal trends in health law.

340 614 US
HEALTH LAWYERS NEWS REPORT.* 1971. m. $50. National Health Lawyers Association, 1120 Connecticut Ave., N.W., Ste. 950, Washington, DC 20036-3921. TEL 202-833-1100. Ed. David Rapoport. circ. 7,200. Indexed: Med.Care Rev.
Former titles: N H L A News Report; Health Lawyers News Report (ISSN 0145-4129)

HEALTH LEGISLATION. see MEDICAL SCIENCES

340 610 US
HEALTH MATRIX: JOURNAL OF LAW-MEDICINE. 1983. s-a. $24. Case Western Reserve University, School of Law, 11075 East Blvd., Cleveland, OH 44106-7148. TEL 216-368-3304. FAX 216-368-3310. Ed. Dean Schwartz. adv.: B&W page $150; adv. contact: Carolyn L. Speaker. bk.rev. circ. 550. (also avail. in microform; back issues avail.) **Document type:** academic/scholarly publication.
●Also available on CD-ROM.
—UMI.
 Formerly (until 1990): Health Matrix (ISSN 0748-383X)
 Description: Student-edited law journal with focus on the field of law-medicine.
 Refereed Serial

HEALTH POLICY WEEK. see *PUBLIC HEALTH AND SAFETY*

HEALTHSPAN; the report of health business and law. see *BUSINESS AND ECONOMICS — Management*

340 CN
HEARSAY. 1976. a. Dalhousie University, Faculty of Law, Halifax, NS B3H 4H9, Canada. TEL 902-494-3495. FAX 902-494-1316. Ed. Philip Girard. illus. circ. 4,000.
 Formerly: Hearsay, for Dalhousie Law Graduates (ISSN 0704-4860)

340 US
HEARSAY HANDBOOK. 1991. base vol. (plus a. supplement). $95. Shepard's - McGraw-Hill, Inc., Box 35300, Colorado Springs, CO 80935-3530. TEL 800-525-2474.
 Description: Analyzes the critical contemporary case law generated by the Federal Rules of Evidence. Provides definitions and explanations of the Hearsay Rule and its 40 exceptions as they are currently applied in courts throughout the country.

340 CC ISSN 1002-3933
HEBEI FAXUE. (Text in Chinese) 1982. bi-m. Y9. Hebei Sheng Zhengfa Ganbu Guanli Xueyuan - Hebei Administrative Cadre's Institute of Political Science and Law, Wuqi Lu, Shijiazhuang, Hebei 050061, People's Republic of China. TEL 0311-639286. (Co-sponsor: Hebei Law Society) Ed. Xie Shiwen. adv.: page Y2000; adv. contact: Guo Dengke. circ. 5,000. **Document type:** academic/scholarly publication.
 Description: Covers political science and law issues, researches on legislations, foreign legal systems, case analysis, and legal system history.

340 GW ISSN 0170-320X
HEIDELBERGER RECHTSVERGLEICHENDE UND WIRTSCHAFTSRECHTLICHE STUDIEN. 1967. a. price varies. Universitaetsverlag C. Winter Heidelberg GmbH, Hans-Bunte-Str. 18, 69123 Heidelberg, Germany. **Document type:** academic/scholarly publication.

340 GW ISSN 0073-165X
HEIDELBERGER RECHTSWISSENSCHAFTLICHE ABHANDLUNGEN. NEUE FOLGE. 1957. irreg. price varies. (Universitaet Heidelberg, Juristische Fakultaet) Universitaetsverlag C. Winter Heidelberg GmbH, Hans-Bunte-Str. 18, 69123 Heidelberg, Germany. **Document type:** monographic series.

340 US
HEIN CHECKLIST OF STATUTES. s-a. $27. William S. Hein & Co., Inc., 1285 Main St., Buffalo, NY 14209. TEL 800-828-7571. FAX 716-883-8100. TELEX 91-209 WU 7 HEIN BUF. circ. 300. **Document type:** catalog.
 Formerly: Hein Annual Checklist Statutes (ISSN 0891-6527)

HEMLOCK TIMELINES. see *MEDICAL SCIENCES*

340
HENNEPIN LAWYER. vol.62, 1993. bi-m. $20. Hennepin County Bar Association, 514 Nicollet Mall, Ste. 350, Minneapolis, MN 55402-1021. TEL 612-340-0022. FAX 612-340-9518. Ed. Duane D. Stanley. adv.; circ. 6,800 (paid). **Document type:** trade publication.
 Description: Informs lawyers in Hennepin County about current issues and events relating to the law and lawyers.

340 600 US ISSN 0885-2715
K8
HIGH TECHNOLOGY LAW JOURNAL. 1986. s-a. $48 (effective 1994). University of California Press, Journals Division, 2120 Berkeley Way, Berkeley, CA 94720. TEL 510-643-7154. FAX 510-642-9917. adv.; bk.rev. circ. 500. (also avail. in microfiche from WSH; microform from UMI) **Indexed:** ABI Inform, C.L.I., Leg.Per., P.A.I.S., Tel.Abstr., Telegen. **Document type:** academic/scholarly publication.
—BLDSC (4307.363500); CIS; Faxon; UnCover; UMI. **CCC.**
 Description: Addresses new legal issues posed by developing technologies.
 Refereed Serial

HIGHWAY CODE. see *TRANSPORTATION — Roads And Traffic*

340 JA ISSN 0439-1365
HIKAKU HO KENKYU/COMPARATIVE LAW JOURNAL. (Text in Japanese) 1949. s-a. (Hikaku Ho Gakkai - Japanese Society of Comparative Law) Yuhikaku Publishing Co. Ltd., 2-17 Kanda Jinbo-cho, Chiyoda-ku, Tokyo 101, Japan.

340 US
HILDEBRANDT REPORT; a management and marketing newsletter for law firms. 1985. m. free. Hildebrandt, Inc. (Somerville), 501 P.O. Plaza, 50 Division St., Somerville, NJ 08876-2900. TEL 908-725-1600. FAX 908-725-9764. (And: Box 515, Colville, WA 99114) Ed. David Neal. circ. 5,000. **Document type:** newsletter.

HILL & REDMAN'S LAW OF LANDLORD & TENANT. see *REAL ESTATE*

340 US
HINE'S INSURANCE COUNSEL. 1908. a. $25. Hine's Legal Directory, Inc., Box 280, Glen Ellyn, IL 60138. TEL 708-462-9670. Ed. James R. Collins. adv.; circ. 7,000 (controlled). **Document type:** catalog.
 Description: Lists of law firms handling defense trial cases in the United States and Canada.

HISTORIJSKI ARHIV RIJEKA. VJESNIK. see *HISTORY — History Of Europe*

HISTORY AND LAW SERIES. see *HISTORY — History Of Europe*

320 340 JA ISSN 0073-2796
LAW
HITOTSUBASHI JOURNAL OF LAW AND POLITICS. 1960. a. Hitotsubashi Daigaku, Hitotsubashi Gakkai - Hitotsubashi University, Hitotsubashi Academy, 2-1 Naka, Kunitachi-shi, Tokyo 186, Japan. Ed. O. Ishii. circ. 900. **Indexed:** P.A.I.S. **Document type:** academic/scholarly publication.
—Faxon; UnCover.

349 GW ISSN 0018-3059
HOECHSTRICHTERLICHE FINANZRECHTSPRECHUNG. 1961. m. DM.312. Stollfuss Verlag Bonn, Postfach 2428, 53014 Bonn, Germany. TEL 0228-724-0. FAX 0228-659723. Ed. Guenther Wauer. adv. circ. 4,500. **Document type:** bulletin.
—CCC.

340 US
HOFSTRA LABOR LAW JOURNAL. 1982. s-a. $15. Hofstra School of Law, Hempstead, NY 11550. TEL 516-463-5006. FAX 516-565-0074. Ed. Diane Cornelius. (also avail. in microform; back issues avail.)
●Also available online. Vendor(s): West Services, Inc.

340 US ISSN 0091-4029
K8
HOFSTRA LAW REVIEW. 1973. q. $26. Hofstra University, Hofstra Law Review, Hempstead, NY 11550. TEL 516-463-5910. FAX 516-463-5092. adv.; bk.rev.; index. circ. 2,500. (reprint service avail.) **Indexed:** C.L.I., Crim.Just.Abstr., L.R.I., Leg.Per. **Document type:** academic/scholarly publication.
●Also available online. Vendor(s): Mead Data Central, Inc., West Services, Inc.
—BLDSC (4322.010000); Faxon; UnCover.
 Description: Analyzes topical legal issues and suggests reforms.

340 US
HOFSTRA PROPERTY LAW JOURNAL. 1988. s-a. Hofstra School of Law, Hempsted, NY 11550. TEL 516-463-5926. Ed. William Garcia. circ. 500. (back issues avail.)
●Also available online. Vendor(s): West Services, Inc.

340 320 JA ISSN 0385-5082
HOGAKU/JOURNAL OF LAW AND POLITICAL SCIENCE. (Text in Japanese) 1932. bi-m. 1000 Yen per no. Tohoku Daigaku, Hogakkai - Tohoku University, Faculty of Law, Association of Law and Political Science, Kawauchi, Aoba-ku, Sendai-shi, Miyagi-ken 980, Japan. TEL 022-222-1800. FAX 022-263-2933. bk.rev. circ. 1,500. **Document type:** bulletin.

320 340 301 JA
HOGAKU KENKYU/JOURNAL OF LAW, POLITICS, AND SOCIOLOGY. (Text in Japanese) 1922. m. Keio Gijuku Daigaku, Hogakkai Kenkyukai - Keio University, Association for the Study of Law and Politics, 2-2 Mita, Minato-ku, Tokyo 108, Japan. bk.rev.; bibl. **Indexed:** Amer.Hist.& Life (until 1992), Hist.Abstr. (until 1992), Numis.Lit.

340 AF
HOKOUK. (Text in English or Persian) 1972. q. $10. Kabul University, Faculty of Law and Political Science, Djamal-Mina, Kabul, Afghanistan.

340 UK ISSN 0260-5864
K8
HOLDSWORTH LAW REVIEW. 1974. s-a. £14. University of Birmingham, Faculty of Law, P.O. Box 363, Birmingham B15 2TT, England. TEL 021-472-1301. FAX 021-414-3585. Ed. Jeremy McBride. adv.; bk.rev. circ. 300. (back issues avail.; reprint service avail.)
—BLDSC (4322.294600).
 Description: Covers all fields of law.

HOLZBAU - REPORT. see *BUILDING AND CONSTRUCTION — Carpentry And Woodwork*

HOME SCHOOLING LAWS IN ALL FIFTY STATES. see *EDUCATION*

340 HO ISSN 0016-3791
HONDURAS. CORTE SUPREMA DE JUSTICIA. GACETA JUDICIAL.* 1889. bi-m. L.3($1.50) Corte Suprema de Justicia, Tegucigalpa D.C., Honduras. bk.rev. (tabloid format)

340 HK
HONG KONG LAW DIGEST. (Text in English) 1985. 11/yr. HK.$3500. Longman Asia Ltd., Taikoo Place, 979 King's Rd., Quarry Bay, Hong Kong. TEL 852-856-6335. FAX 852-565-7440. (back issues avail.)
 Description: Contains all legal developments in Hong Kong. Provides digests of all significant cases decided in the territory, together with comprehensive tables of new and amended legislation.

340 HK ISSN 0378-0600
HONG KONG LAW JOURNAL. (Text in English) 1971. 3/yr. HK.$540 (students HK.$240). Hong Kong Law Journal Ltd., 1424 Prince's Bldg., Hong Kong. TEL 5260318. FAX 5371346. adv.; bk.rev.; cum.index. (back issues avail.)
—UnCover.

340 HK
HONG KONG LAW YEARBOOK. (Text in English) 1985. a. HK.$995($125) Longman Asia Ltd., Taikoo Place, 979 King's Rd., Quarry Bay, Hong Kong. TEL 852-856-6335. FAX 852-565-7440. (back issues avail.)
 Description: Contains cases digested throughout the year listed alphabetically under subject areas. Also includes tables of legislation for easy reference.

340 382 AT
HONG KONG REVENUE LEGISLATION. (In 2 vols.) 1989. irreg. (approx. 4-6/yr.) C C H Australia Ltd., P.O. Box 230, North Ryde, N.S.W. 2113, Australia. TEL 02-888-2555. FAX 02-888-7324.
 Description: Includes the Inland Revenue Department Interpretation and Practice notes, case reporting.

LAW

340 US
HOSPITAL LAW MANUAL. ADMINISTRATORS. q. $640 (foreign $780); including Attorneys section $825 (foreign $990). Aspen Publishers, Inc., 200 Orchard Ridge Dr., Gaithersburg, MD 20878. TEL 301-417-7500. FAX 301-417-7550.

340 US
HOSPITAL LAW MANUAL. ATTORNEYS. 1959. q. $750 (foreign $900); including Administrators section $825 (foreign $990). Aspen Publishers, Inc., 200 Orchard Ridge Dr., Gaithersburg, MD 20878. TEL 301-417-7500. FAX 301-417-7550. charts; illus. circ. 450.
Formerly: Hospital Law Manual and Quarterly Service (ISSN 0018-5728)

HOSPITAL LAW NEWSLETTER. see *HOSPITALS*

HOSPITAL LITIGATION REPORTER. see *HOSPITALS*

HOSPITAL RISK CONTROL; an information and consultation system. see *HOSPITALS*

HOSPITALITY LAW; the preventive-law information service for the lodging industry. see *HOTELS AND RESTAURANTS*

HOTLINE (STONY BROOK); news service on the missing children field. see *CRIMINOLOGY AND LAW ENFORCEMENT*

340 UK ISSN 1352-2191
▼**HOUSING LAW MONITOR**. 1993. m. £127 (foreign £149). Monitor Press, Rectory Rd., Great Waldingfield, Sudbury, Suffolk CO10 OTL, England. TEL 0787-378607. FAX 0787-880201. **Document type:** newsletter.

340 UK ISSN 0263-7537
HOUSING LAW REPORTS. 1981. bi-m. £179($312) Sweet & Maxwell, South Quay Plaza, 7th Fl., 183 Marsh Wall, London E14 9FT, England. TEL 071-538-8686. FAX 071-538-8626. Ed. Julie Stott. adv. contact: Jackie Wood. **Document type:** bulletin.
—BLDSC (4335.098950).

340 382 US ISSN 0194-1879
JX1
HOUSTON JOURNAL OF INTERNATIONAL LAW. 1978. 3/yr. $20 (foreign $25). University of Houston, Law Center, 4800 Calhoun Rd., BLB, Ste. 29, Houston, TX 77004-6370. TEL 713-749-3774. Eds. Bill Welch, Tony Visage. adv.; bk.rev.; cum.index. circ. 600. (back issues avail.; reprint service avail. from WSH) **Indexed:** C.L.I., HR Rep, L.R.I., Leg.Per.
●Also available online. Vendor(s): West Services, Inc. —BLDSC (4335.153270); Faxon; UnCover.

340 US ISSN 0018-6694
K8
HOUSTON LAW REVIEW. 1963. 5/yr. $28. (University of Houston, Law Center) Houston Law Review Inc., University of Houston Law Center-University Park, Houston, TX 77004. TEL 713-749-3195. FAX 713-749-4661. Ed. Nicolas Eranoff. adv.; bk.rev.; bibl.; illus.; stat.; index. circ. 1,400. (also avail. in microform from UMI; reprint service avail. from UMI) **Indexed:** C.L.I., Crim.Just.Abstr., Curr.Cont., L.R.I., Leg.Cont., Leg.Per., Ocean.Abstr., Pollut.Abstr., SSCI.
●Also available online. Vendor(s): West Services, Inc. —Faxon; UnCover.

340 US
HOW TO PREPARE WITNESSES FOR TRIAL. 1985. base vol. (plus a. suppl.) $95. Shepard's - McGraw-Hill, Inc., Box 35300, Colorado Springs, CO 80935-3530. TEL 800-525-2474.
Description: Provides practical ideas and insights on evaluating and assessing potential witnesses, educating witnesses and handling expert witnesses.

HOW TO USE THE FEDERAL F O I ACT. see *JOURNALISM*

HOW TO USE THE FREEDOM OF INFORMATION ACT. see *LIBRARY AND INFORMATION SCIENCES*

340 US ISSN 0018-6813
HOWARD LAW JOURNAL. 1955. s-a. $22 (foreign $25). Howard University, School of Law, 2900 Van Ness St., N.W., Washington, DC 20008. TEL 202-806-8084. FAX 202-806-8098. Ed. Alice Thomas. adv.; bk.rev.; index. circ. 1,100. (also avail. in microfilm from WSH,PMC; reprint service avail. from WSH) **Indexed:** C.L.I., L.R.I., Lang.& Lang.Behav.Abstr., Leg.Per., P.A.I.S.
●Also available online. Vendor(s): Mead Data Central, Inc., West Services, Inc.
—BLDSC (4335.247000); Faxon; UnCover.

HSIEN CHENG SSU CH'AO. see *POLITICAL SCIENCE*

340 IO ISSN 0125-9687
HUKUM DAN PEMBANGUNAN. 1972. bi-m. Rps.15000. University of Indonesia, Faculty of Law - Universitas Indonesia, Fakultas Hukum, Jl. Cirebon 5, Jakarta 10310, Indonesia. Eds. Koestantinah Soeparno, Mardjono Reksodiputro. adv.; bk.rev. circ. 3,000. (also avail. in microfiche) **Indexed:** E.I.
Formerly (until vol.7, no.1, 1977): Universitas Indonesia. Fakultas Hukum. Majalah.

HUMAN RESEARCH REPORT; protecting researchers and research subjects. see *MEDICAL SCIENCES — Experimental Medicine, Laboratory Technique*

340 MP
HUUL' DZUYN MEDEELE/LEGAL INFORMATION. (Text in Mongolian) 1990. m. Ulan Bator, Mongolia.

HYRESGAESTEN. see *HOUSING AND URBAN PLANNING*

340 US
I A D C NEWS.* irreg. (3-4/yr.). membership only. International Association of Defense Counsel, 1 N. Franklin St., Ste. 2400, Chicago, IL 60606-3401. TEL 312-368-1494. FAX 312-368-1854. Ed. Richard J. Hayes. circ. 2,500. **Document type:** newsletter.

247 332 US
I B A LAW WATCH. 1986. q. (Illinois Bankers Association, 111 N. Canal, Ste. 1111, Chicago, IL 60606. TEL 312-876-9900. FAX 312-876-3826. Ed. James J. Brennan. circ. 350. (looseleaf format; back issues avail.)
Description: Highlights legal developments affecting the Illinois banking industry and preventative banking law.

I C S I D REVIEW: FOREIGN INVESTMENT LAW JOURNAL. (International Center for Settlement of Investment Disputes) see *BUSINESS AND ECONOMICS — Investments*

I J O NEWSLETTER. (International Juridicial Organization for Environment and Development) see *ENVIRONMENTAL STUDIES*

340 UN ISSN 0378-7362
K1704.23
I L O JUDGEMENTS OF THE ADMINISTRATIVE TRIBUNAL. 2/yr. 65 SFr.($52) (International Labour Office) I L O Publications, CH-1211 Geneva 22, Switzerland. TEL 022-7996-111. FAX 022-798-6358. TELEX 415647-ILO-CH. (Dist. in U.S. by: ILO Publications Center, 49 Sheridan Ave., Albany, NY 12210. TEL 1-518-436-9686) circ. 1,800. (also avail. in microform from ILO) **Document type:** bulletin.

340 US
I O L T A UPDATE. q. free. American Bar Association, Commission on Interest on Lawyers' Trust Accounts, 541 N. Fairbanks Ct., Chicago, IL 60611-3314. TEL 312-988-5750.
Description: Discusses trends in lawyers' trust accounts nationwide.

I O M A'S REPORT ON COMPENSATION & BENEFITS FOR LAW OFFICES. see *BUSINESS AND ECONOMICS — Personnel Management*

I P A - JOURNAL. (International Police Association) see *CRIMINOLOGY AND LAW ENFORCEMENT*

340 US
I P C REPORT. q. $18 to non-members; members $13. (International Procurement Committee) American Bar Association, Public Contract Law Section, 750 N. Lake Shore Dr., Chicago, IL 60611. TEL 312-988-5555. **Document type:** newsletter.
Description: Examines the questions involving public contracts in countries other than the U.S.

340 US ISSN 1059-1729
KF4742
I R & R NEWS REPORT. 1969. 2/yr. $30 to non-members; members $18. (American Bar Association, Section of Individual Rights and Responsibilities) A B A Press, 750 N. Lake Shore, Chicago, IL 60611. TEL 312-988-5000. Ed. Vicki Quade. circ. 6,000. **Document type:** newsletter.
Formerly (until 1989): American Bar Association. Section of Individual Rights and Responsibilities. Newsletter (ISSN 0572-3590)

340 US ISSN 1058-1863
I S B A BAR NEWS. 23/yr. $1.70 to members. Illinois State Bar Association, 20 S. Clark St., Chicago, IL 60603-1802. TEL 312-726-8775. FAX 217-525-0712. Ed. Stephen Anderson. circ. 31,000.

I T LAW TODAY. (Information Technology) see *COMPUTERS*

340 US ISSN 0019-1205
K9
IDAHO LAW REVIEW. 1964. 4/yr. $26.65. University of Idaho, College of Law, Moscow, ID 83843. TEL 208-885-7241. adv.; bk.rev.; cum.index. circ. 750. (also avail. in microfiche from WSH; microfilm from WSH,PMC) **Indexed:** C.L.I., L.R.I., Leg.Cont., Leg.Per., Sel.Water Res.Abstr. **Document type:** academic/scholarly publication.
●Also available online. Vendor(s): West Services, Inc. —Faxon; UnCover; UMI.

435 US
IDAHO LEGISLATIVE REPORT. d. during legislative session. $390. Goller Publishing Corp., Box 2576, Boise, ID 83701. TEL 208-336-4715. Ed. Jane Crosby. (looseleaf format; also avail. in diskette format) **Document type:** newsletter.

340 US
ILLINOIS. LEGISLATIVE REFERENCE BUREAU. LEGISLATIVE SYNOPSIS AND DIGEST. 1913. irreg. (during sessions, approx. Feb.-June). $55. Legislative Reference Bureau, Rm. 112, Statehouse, Springfield, IL 62706. TEL 217-782-6625. Ed. Kathleen H. Kenyon. index. circ. 1,800. **Document type:** government publication.
Description: Includes synopses of bills and resolutions pending in the House of Representatives and the Senate and indices by statute reference, subject matter and sponsor.

340 US
ILLINOIS ATTORNEY GENERAL'S REPORT AND OPINIONS. 1872. irreg., latest 1984. Attorney General, 500 S. Second St., Springfield, IL 62706. TEL 217-782-1090. index. circ. 1,400. (back issues avail.) **Document type:** government publication.

340 US ISSN 0019-1876
K9
ILLINOIS BAR JOURNAL. 1931. m. $60 to non-lawyers; $50 to law libraries. Illinois State Bar Association, Illinois Bar Center, Springfield, IL 62701. TEL 217-525-1760. Ed. Mark S. Mathewson. adv.; charts; illus.; index. circ. 30,000. (also avail. in microfiche from WSH; microfilm from WSH,PMC) **Indexed:** C.L.I., HRIS, L.R.I., Law Ofc.Info.Svc., Leg.Per. —BLDSC (4364.980000); UnCover; UMI.
Description: Articles on new laws, recent court decisions, and developments in the law profession. Includes news of the association's activities.

340 US ISSN 0019-1957
ILLINOIS COURTS BULLETIN. 1955. m. $35 to non-members; members $25. Illinois State Bar Association, Illinois Bar Center, Springfield, IL 62701. TEL 217-525-1760. Ed. Dennis A. Rendleman. bk.rev. circ. 2,700.
Description: Digest of opinions of the Illinois Supreme Court, Apellate Courts, and Courts of Appeal.

340 331 US ISSN 1049-9385
ILLINOIS EMPLOYMENT LAW LETTER. 1990. m. $95. (Matkov, Salzman, Madoff & Gunn) M. Lee Smith Publishers & Printers, 162 Fourth Ave., N., Box 198867, Nashville, TN 37219-8867. TEL 615-242-7395; 800-274-6774. FAX 615-256-6601. Ed. Allan Gunn. **Document type:** newsletter.
Description: Reports the latest Illinois employment law developments that affect Illinois companies.

3266 LAW

340 613.1   US   ISSN 1059-5074
▼ILLINOIS ENVIRONMENTAL LAW LETTER. 1992. m. $137. (Wildman, Harrold, Allen & Dixon) M. Lee Smith Publishers & Printers, 162 Fourth Ave., N., Box 198867, Nashville, TN 37219-8867. TEL 615-242-7385; 800-274-6774. FAX 615-256-6601. Ed. S. Stein. **Document type:** newsletter.
Description: Reports the latest state-specific developments in environmental laws that affect Illinois companies.

ILLINOIS FARMWEEK. see *AGRICULTURE*

340   US   ISSN 1063-3014
K13
ILLINOIS LEGAL TIMES. 1987. m. $48. Giant Steps Publishing Corporation, 222 Merchandise Mart Plaza, Ste. 1513, Chicago, IL 60654. TEL 312-644-4378. FAX 312-644-0765. Ed. Kelly Fox. adv.; bk.rev. circ. 13,500. (tabloid format) **Document type:** trade publication, newspaper.
●Also available online. Vendor(s): Mead Data Central, Inc., West Services, Inc.
Description: Contains news and analysis of law business for Illinois lawyers and other legal professionals.

340   US
ILLINOIS LIMITATIONS MANUAL. 1989. base vol. (plus suppl.), 2nd ed. $50. Butterworth Legal Publishers (Salem) (Subsidiary of: Reed Elsevier plc), 8 Industrial Way, Bldg. C, Salem, NH 03079. TEL 800-548-4001. FAX 603-898-9858. Ed.Bd. (looseleaf format)

340   US
ILLINOIS STATE BAR ASSOCIATION. LEGISLATIVE BULLETIN. irreg. during Assembly session. $20 to non-members; members $10. Illinois State Bar Association, Illinois Bar Center, Springfield, IL 62701. TEL 217-525-1760.
Description: Digests of recent legislative action on bills of interest to lawyers.

340   US
KFI1595.A15I44
ILLINOIS STATE BAR ASSOCIATION. SCHOOL LAW. 1956. q. $12. Illinois State Bar Association, Illinois Bar Center, Springfield, IL 62701. TEL 217-525-1760. FAX 217-525-0712. Ed. Lawrence Weiner. circ. 550. (looseleaf format; back issues avail.) **Document type:** newsletter.

340   US
ILLINOIS TORT LAW. 1986. base vol. (plus suppl.). $120. Butterworth Legal Publishers (Salem) (Subsidiary of: Reed Elsevier plc), 8 Industrial Way, Bldg. C, Salem, NH 03079. TEL 800-548-4001. FAX 603-898-9858. Eds. Bruce L. Ottley, Michael J. Polelle.

340   US
ILLINOIS TRIALS; law and strategy. 1990. base vol. (plus irreg. supplements). $88. Butterworth Legal Publishers (Salem) (Subsidiary of: Reed Elsevier plc), 8 Industrial Way, Bldg. C, Salem, NY 03079. TEL 800-548-4001. FAX 603-898-9858. Ed. Kenneth L. Gillis. (looseleaf format)

340 380   US
ILLINOIS VEHICLE CODE. 1988. a. $16.95. Gould Publications, 1333 N. U.S. Hwy. 17-92, Longwood, FL 32750-3724. TEL 407-695-9500. FAX 407-695-2906. adv.; bk.rev. (looseleaf format)
Description: Contains the complete motor vehicle laws of the state.

340 325.1   US
IMMIGRATION LAW ADVISORY. m. Clark - Boardman - Callaghan Company Ltd., 375 Hudson St., New York, NY 10014. TEL 212-929-7500; 800-221-9428. FAX 212-924-0460.
Description: Reports on significant immigration-related judicial and administrative decisions, and actual proposed legislative and regulatory developments.

340 325.1   CN
IMMIGRATION LAW & PRACTICE. irreg. Can.$300. Butterworths Canada Ltd., Part of the Reed Elsevier group, 75 Clegg Rd., Markham, ON L6G 1A1, Canada. TEL 905-479-2265. FAX 905-479-2826. (looseleaf format)

340 325.1   US
IMMIGRATION PROCEDURES HANDBOOK. a. $135. Clark - Boardman - Callaghan Company Ltd., 375 Hudson St., New York, NY 10014. TEL 212-929-7500; 800-221-9428. FAX 212-924-0460. Ed.Bd.

IMPACT; labour law and management. see *BUSINESS AND ECONOMICS — Labor And Industrial Relations*

IMPACT (WASHINGTON). see *TRANSPORTATION — Automobiles*

347.91   CN
IMPAIRED DRIVING & BREATHALYZER LAW. (Supplement avail.: Monthly Newsletter) s-a. Can.$180. Butterworths Canada Ltd., Part of the Reed Elsevier group, 75 Clegg Rd., Markham, ON L6G 1A1, Canada. TEL 905-479-2665. FAX 905-479-2826. Ed. K.R. Hamilton. (looseleaf format)
Description: Reference to statutes and case law.

340 613.1   US
IN BRIEF (SAN FRANCISCO, 1983); a quarterly newsletter on environmental law. 1983. q. $10. Sierra Club Legal Defense Fund, 180 Montgomery St., Ste. 1400, San Francisco, CA 94104-4230. TEL 415-627-6700. FAX 415-627-6740. circ. 150,000 (paid). **Indexed:** Environ.Abstr. **Document type:** newsletter.

IN DEPTH (WASHINGTON). see *POLITICAL SCIENCE — International Relations*

340   IT
IN IURE PRAESENTIA. 1975. s-a. L.55000 (foreign L.83000). Casa Editrice Dott. A. Giuffre, Via Busto Arsizio 40, 20151 Milan, Italy. TEL 02-38000905. FAX 02-38009582.

INCOME TAXATION OF NATURAL RESOURCES. see *BUSINESS AND ECONOMICS — Public Finance, Taxation*

340   IE
INCORPORATED LAW SOCIETY OF IRELAND GAZETTE. 10/yr. Blackhall Pl., Dublin 7, Ireland. TEL 710711. FAX 770511. Ed. Mary Gaynor. circ. 5,000.

340   CE   ISSN 0073-5728
INCORPORATED LAW SOCIETY OF SRI LANKA. ANNUAL REPORT.* 1960. a. Incorporated Law Society of Sri Lanka, 129-5 Hultsdorf St., Colombo 12, Sri Lanka.

340   CE   ISSN 0073-5736
INCORPORATED LAW SOCIETY OF SRI LANKA. JOURNAL.* irreg. Incorporated Law Society of Sri Lanka, 129-5 Hultsdorf St., Colombo 12, Sri Lanka.

INDEPENDENT ASSOCIATION OF QUESTIONED DOCUMENT EXAMINERS. JOURNAL. see *CRIMINOLOGY AND LAW ENFORCEMENT*

INDEPENDENT POWER REPORT. see *ENERGY*

340   UK   ISSN 0265-2501
INDEPENDENT SOLICITOR.* 1968. s-a. £0.75 per no. to individuals; free to qualified personnel. British Legal Association, 56 Wind St., Swansea SA1 1EG, England. Ed. Stanley Best. adv.; bk.rev.
Formerly: B L A Solicitor.

INDEX - DIGEST BULLETIN. see *BUSINESS AND ECONOMICS — Public Finance, Taxation*

340   IT
INDEX: INTERNATIONAL SURVEY OF ROMAN LAW. (Text in various languages) 1970. a. L.115000 (effective 1993). Casa Editrice Dott. Eugenio Jovene, Via Mezzocannone, 109, 80134 Naples, Italy. TEL 081-5521019. FAX 081-5520687. Ed. Luigi Labruna.

340   CN   ISSN 0701-760X
INDEX OF CURRENT B C REGULATIONS. 1958. 2/yr. Can.$13. Ministry of Attorney General, Parliament Bldgs., Victoria, B.C. V8V 1X4, Canada. TEL 604-387-5818. (Subscr. to: Crown Publications, 546 Yates St., Victoria, B.C. V8W 1K8, Canada. TEL 604-386-4636)

340   UK
INDEX TO LEGAL CITATIONS AND ABBREVIATIONS. 1981. irreg. 2nd ed., 1994. £65($100) Bowker - Saur Ltd., A Reed Reference Publishing Company, Part of the Reed Elsevier group, Maypole House, Maypole Rd., E. Grinstead, W. Sussex RH19 1HH, England. TEL 0342-330100. FAX 0342-330191. (Subscr. to: c/o Butterworths Service Co., Borough Green, Sevenoaks, Kent TN15 8PH, England. TEL 0732-884567) Ed. Donald Raistrick. **Document type:** directory.
Description: Lists 25,000 entries covering the legal literature of the United States, the United Kingdom, the Commonwealth, and Europe.

340   II
INDIA. SUPREME COURT REPORTS. (Text in English) m. Rs.585($210) Government of India, Department of Publications, Civil Lines, Delhi 110 054, India. **Document type:** government publication.

348.54   II
INDIA. SUPREME COURT. UNREPORTED JUDGMENTS. (Text in English) 1969. s-m. Rs.45. Supreme Court, Jodhpur, High Court Rd., Jodhpur, Rajasthan, India. Ed. Dharm Veer Kalia. adv.; index. circ. 3,000.

349   II   ISSN 0019-4301
INDIAN ADVOCATE. (Text in English) 1961. q. Rs.15($5.50) Bar Association of India, Chamber No. 93, Supreme Court Building, Tilak Marg, New Delhi 110001, India. Ed. C. K. Daphtary. adv.; bk.rev. circ. 2,000. **Indexed:** P.A.I.S.

340   II
INDIAN BAR REVIEW. (Text in English) 1974. q. $25. Bar Council of India, AB-21, Lal Bahadur Shastri Marg, Facing Supreme Court Bldg., New Delhi 110001, India. bk.rev. circ. 1,500. **Indexed:** C.L.I., Leg.Per.
Formerly (until Jan. 1983): Bar Council of India. Journal.

349   II   ISSN 0019-5731
INDIAN LAW INSTITUTE. JOURNAL. (Text in English) 1958. q. Rs.300. Indian Law Institute, Bhagwandas Rd., New Delhi 110001, India. Ed. Dr. Upendra Baxi. bk.rev. (also avail. in microform from UMI; reprint service avail. from UMI) **Indexed:** P.A.I.S.
—BLDSC (4766.300000).

340 917.306   US   ISSN 0097-1154
KF8201.A3
INDIAN LAW REPORTER. 1974. m. $396 (effective 1993). American Indian Lawyer Training Program, Inc., 319 MacArthur Blvd., Oakland, CA 94610. TEL 510-834-9333. FAX 510-834-3836. Ed. Patricia M. Zell. abstr.; index. circ. 650. (looseleaf format; also avail. in microform from WSH,PMC; back issues avail.; reprint service avail. from WSH) **Indexed:** C.L.I., HR Rep.
Description: Comprehensive case reporting service that collects, reports and summarizes all current developments in Indian law from federal, tribal, and state courts as well as administrative agencies.

342   II
INDIAN LAW REPORTS. (Text in English) m. Rs.120($43.20) Government of India, Department of Publication, Civil Lines, Delhi 110 054, India. TEL 11-2512527. **Document type:** government publication.

INDIANA CENTER ON GLOBAL CHANGE AND WORLD PEACE. OCCASIONAL PAPER SERIES. see *ENVIRONMENTAL STUDIES*

340 331   US   ISSN 1053-6191
INDIANA EMPLOYMENT LAW LETTER. 1991. m. $95. (Baker & Daniels) M. Lee Smith Publishers & Printers, 162 Fourth Ave., N., Box 198867, Nashville, TN 37219-8867. TEL 615-242-7395; 800-274-6774. FAX 615-256-6601. Eds. John T. Neighbors, Todd M. Nierman. **Document type:** newsletter.
Description: Reports the latest Indiana employment law developments that affect Indiana employers.

340 613.1   US   ISSN 1053-6183
INDIANA ENVIRONMENTAL LAW LETTER. 1991. m. $137. (Baker & Daniels) M. Lee Smith Publishers & Printers, 162 Fourth Ave., N., Box 198867, Nashville, TN 37219-8867. TEL 615-242-7395; 800-274-6774. FAX 615-256-6601. Ed. Lewis D. Beckwith.
  Description: Reports the latest state-specific environmental law developments that affect Indiana companies.

340   US   ISSN 0019-6665
K9
INDIANA LAW JOURNAL. 1926. q. $25 (foreign $29). Indiana University, School of Law, Law Building, Bloomington, IN 47405. TEL 812-855-5175. FAX 812-855-7099. adv.; bk.rev.; bibl.; index. circ. 1,165. (also avail. in microfilm from RRI; microfiche from RRI; reprint service avail. from RRI) **Indexed:** Account.Ind. (1974-), C.L.I., Curr.Cont., L.R.I., Leg.Cont., Leg.Per., SSCI. **Document type:** academic/scholarly publication.
  ●Also available online. Vendor(s): Mead Data Central, Inc., West Services, Inc.
  —BLDSC (4431.750000); Faxon; UnCover; SWETS.
  Description: General interest legal journal.

340   US   ISSN 0090-4198
INDIANA LAW REVIEW. 1967. q. $22. Indiana University, Indianapolis School of Law, 735 W. New York St., Indianapolis, IN 46202. TEL 317-264-4039. Ed. Eric Graninger. adv.; bk.rev.; index. circ. 2,000. (also avail. in microfiche from WSH; microfilm from RRI,WSH; reprint service avail. from RRI) **Indexed:** C.L.I., L.R.I., Lang.& Lang.Behav.Abstr., Leg.Cont., Leg.Per.
  ●Also available online. Vendor(s): West Services, Inc.
  —BLDSC (4431.760000); Faxon; UnCover.
  Formerly: Indiana Legal Forum.

345.01   US   ISSN 1054-3732
THE INDIANA LAWYER. 1990. 26/yr. $19. I B J Corp., 431 N. Pennsylvania, Indianapolis, IN 46204. TEL 317-636-2000. Ed. Chris Banguis. adv. contact: Greg Morris. circ. 4,000. (tabloid format) **Document type:** newspaper.

INDIVIDUALS WITH DISABILITIES EDUCATION LAW REPORTER. see EDUCATION — Special Education And Rehabilitation

340 628.53   US   ISSN 0894-0533
INDOOR POLLUTION LAW REPORT. 1987. m. $190. New York Law Publishing Co., 345 Park Ave. S., New York, NY 10010. TEL 212-545-6170. FAX 212-696-1848. **Document type:** newsletter.
  Description: Covers pollution issues such as preventative measures, latest technologies, government regulations and litigation alternatives. For those involved in real estate and environmental areas.

INDUSTRIAL HEALTH & HAZARDS UPDATE. see OCCUPATIONAL HEALTH AND SAFETY

INDUSTRIAL HEALTH FOUNDATION. LEGAL SERIES BULLETINS. see OCCUPATIONAL HEALTH AND SAFETY

346.066   AT
INDUSTRIAL LAWS NEW SOUTH WALES. base vol. (plus updates 6/yr.). $365. Butterworths, 271-273 Lane Cove Rd., P.O. Box 345, N. Ryde, N.S.W. 2113, Australia. TEL 02-335-4444. FAX 02-335-4655. (looseleaf format)

INDUSTRIAL RELATIONS LAW REPORTS. see BUSINESS AND ECONOMICS — Labor And Industrial Relations

INDUSTRIAL RELATIONS LEGAL INFORMATION BULLETIN. see BUSINESS AND ECONOMICS — Labor And Industrial Relations

INFANCIA Y SOCIEDAD. see CHILDREN AND YOUTH — About

340   GW   ISSN 0930-5483
INFO 7. 1986. s-a. DM.30. Nomos Verlagsgesellschaft mbH und Co. KG, Waldseestr. 3-5, 76530 Baden-Baden, Germany. TEL 07221-21040. FAX 07221-210427. TELEX 781201. (Subscr. to: Postfach 610, 76484 Baden-Baden, Germany) **Document type:** bulletin.

340   CU
INFORMACION JURIDICA. 1975. irreg. Fiscalia General de la Republica, San Rafael 3, Havana, Cuba. illus.

340   NE   ISSN 0920-3745
INFORMATIERECHT. 1977. s-m. fl.85. Uitgeverij Kluwer BV, Postbus 23, 7400 GA Deventer, Netherlands. Ed.Bd. circ. 800. **Indexed:** ELLIS.
  —SWETS.
  Formerly (until 1986): Auteursrecht (ISSN 0165-9235)

340 004   NE   ISSN 0926-9800
INFORMATION LAW SERIES. Constitutes: Institute for Information Law (Proceedings). (Text in English) 1991. irreg., vol.2, 1992. price varies. (Amsterdam University, Institute for Information Law) Kluwer Law and Taxation Publishers (Subsidiary of: Wolters Kluwer N.V.), P.O. Box 23, 7400 GA Deventer, Netherlands. TEL 31-5700-74261. FAX 31-5700-22244. TELEX 49295 KLUDV NL. (Dist. by: Libresso Distribution Centre, P.O. Box 23, 7400 GA Deventer, Netherlands. TEL 31-5700-33155. FAX 31-5700-33834; In N. America: Kluwer Law and Taxation Publishers, 675 Massachusetts Ave., Cambridge, MA 02139. TEL 617-354-0140. FAX 617-354-8595) (back issues avail.) **Document type:** monographic series, proceedings.
  —BLDSC (4493.608300).
  Description: Discusses aspects of international information law as well as relevant developments in information technology.
  Refereed Serial

340 004   UK   ISSN 0950-7388
INFORMATION SECURITY MONITOR. m. £237($474) I B C Publishing, Gilmoora House, 57-61 Mortimer St., London W1N 7TD, England. TEL 071-637-4383. FAX 071-636-6414. (Subscr. in U.S. to: IBC (USA), 290 Eliot St., Box 91004, Ashland, MA 01721-9104. TEL 508-881-2800. FAX 508-881-0982) Ed. Vincent Jones. **Document type:** newsletter.
  —BLDSC (4494.316000).

INFORMATIVO JURIDICO. see INSURANCE

340 323.4   PE
INFORMATIVO LEGAL RODRIGO. 1961. m. $350. Asesores Financieros S.A., Jr. Pachacutec 1133, Jesus Maria, Lima, Peru. FAX 637300. TELEX 25622 PE LUCARO. bk.rev. circ. 570. (back issues avail.)
  Description: Publishes legal rules with summarized ordered references in chronological and thematical order. Also offers sections of judicial reports and comments on judgements.

INFORMATORE GIURIDICO DELL'OPERATORE TURISTICO. see TRAVEL AND TOURISM

INITIAL DECISIONS AND BOARD OPINIONS AND ORDERS IN SAFETY. see TRANSPORTATION — Air Transport

340   US   ISSN 0020-1391
INJURY VALUATION REPORTS AND SPECIAL RESEARCH REPORTS. (Supplement to: Personal Injury Valuation Handbooks) 1959. m. $29.50 per no. L R P Publications, 747 Dresher Rd., Box 980, Horsham, PA 19044. TEL 800-341-7874. charts; pat.; tr.mk. (looseleaf format)
  Description: Articles on injuries and liability in personal damage litigation. Includes diagrams and graphs.

INQUIRY & ANALYSIS. see EDUCATION

340   US   ISSN 0890-7315
KF8911.A3
INSIDE LITIGATION. 1986. m. $295. Prentice Hall Law & Business, 270 Sylvan Ave., Englewood Cliffs, NJ 07632. TEL 201-894-8538. FAX 201-894-8666. Ed. J. Stratton Shartel. index. (back issues avail.)

344.022   US   ISSN 0884-4925
KF1147
INSIGHT (CHATSWORTH). 1985. m. N I L S Publishing Company, 21625 Prairie St., Box 2507, Chatsworth, CA 91311. TEL 818-998-8830. Eds. Barbara Booth, Jon Van Gorder.
  Description: Summarizes insurance legislation in all 50 states.

340   UK   ISSN 0950-2645
INSOLVENCY INTELLIGENCE. 1988. 10/yr. £95($175) Longman Group UK Ltd., 21-27 Lamb's Conduit St., London WC1 3NJ, England. TEL 01-242-2548. FAX 01-831-8119. Eds. Steven Frieze, David Graham.
  —BLDSC (4518.364000); UMI. CCC.

LAW   3267

340   UK   ISSN 0267-0771
KD2142
INSOLVENCY LAW & PRACTICE. 1985. 6/yr. £130. Tolley Publishing Co. Ltd., Tolley House, 2 Addiscombe Rd., Croydon, Surrey CR9 5AF, England. TEL 081-686-9141. FAX 081-686-3155. Eds. Harry Rajak, Shashi Rajani. adv.; bk.rev.; index. (back issues avail.) **Document type:** trade publication.
  —BLDSC (8863.686519).
  Description: Covers all areas of insolvency law and practice.

340   AT   ISSN 1039-3293
▼**INSOLVENCY LAW JOURNAL.** 1993. 4/yr. Aus.$195. Law Book Co. Ltd., 44-50 Waterloo Rd., North Ryde, N.S.W. 2113, Australia. TEL 02-887-0177. FAX 02-888-9706. TELEX AHBOOK 27995. (Dist. overseas by: Wm. W. Gaunt & Sons, Inc., Gaunt Bldg., 3011 Gulf Dr., Holmes Beach, FL 34217-2199. TEL 800-942-8683) Ed. Andrew Keay. bk.rev.
  Description: Covers both the practical and theoretical issues of insolvency, from bankruptcy to liquidation, and to receivership.

340   UK
INSOLVENCY LAWYER. 1991. 3/yr. £90. (Insolvency Lawyers Association) John Wiley & Sons Ltd., Journals, Baffins Ln., Chichester, Sussex PO19 1UD, England. TEL 0243-779777. FAX 0243-775878. TELEX 86290-WIBOOK-G. Ed. Harry Rajak. **Document type:** academic/scholarly publication.

340   FR
INSTITUT DE RECHERCHES JURIDIQUES, POLITIQUES ET SOCIALES DE STRASBOURG. FACULTE DE DROIT ET DE SCIENCE POLITIQUE. ANNALES. a. price varies. Editions Juridiques Associees, 26 rue Vercingetorix, 75014 Paris, France. TEL 1-43-35-01-67. FAX 43-20-07-42. TELEX EJA 203 918 F. (Co-sponsor: Librairie Generale de Droit et de Jurisprudence) (back issues avail.)

INSTITUT FUER FINANZWIRTSCHAFT UND FINANZRECHT. SCHRIFTENREIHE. see BUSINESS AND ECONOMICS — Banking And Finance

340   GW   ISSN 0073-8492
INSTITUT FUER OSTRECHT. STUDIEN. 1958. irreg. price varies. Deutscher Bundes-Verlag, 5300 Bonn, Germany. circ. 1,000.

342   CI   ISSN 0350-0365
INSTITUT ZA JAVNO UPRAVO. VESTNIK. (Text in Slovenian; table of contents in English) 1961. q. 2500 din.($15) Institut za Javno Upravo - Institute of Public Administration, Trg Osvoboditve 11, P.O. Box 469, 61001 Ljubljana, Slovenia. TEL 061 331-855. (Co-sponsor: Republic Secretatiat for Science, Research and Technology) Ed. Rupko Godec. bk.rev.; abstr.; bibl.; charts. circ. 500. (back issues avail.)

INSTITUTE OF PATENT ATTORNEYS OF AUSTRALIA. ANNUAL PROCEEDINGS. see PATENTS, TRADEMARKS AND COPYRIGHTS

INSTITUTE ON ADVANCED TAX PLANNING FOR REAL PROPERTY TRANSACTIONS. see BUSINESS AND ECONOMICS — Public Finance, Taxation

INSTITUTE ON OIL AND GAS LAW AND TAXATION. PROCEEDINGS. see PETROLEUM AND GAS

340 333.33   US   ISSN 0730-3009
KF5692.A5
INSTITUTE ON PLANNING, ZONING AND EMINENT DOMAIN. PROCEEDINGS. 1971. a. $85. Southwestern Legal Foundation, c/o Carol Holgren, Box 830707, Richardson, TX 75083. TEL 214-690-2370. index. (also avail. in microfilm from RRI; back issues avail.; reprint service avail. from RRI) **Indexed:** C.L.I., Leg.Per. **Document type:** proceedings.
  —Faxon.
  Formed by the merger of: Institute on Planning and Zoning. Proceedings; Institute on Eminent Domain. Proceedings.

340   SP
INSTITUTO DE CIENCIAS PARA LA FAMILIA. 1982. irreg., no.5, 1986. price varies. (Universidad de Navarra, Facultad de Derecho) Ediciones Universidad de Navarra, S.A., Apdo. 396, 31080 Pamplona, Spain. TEL 94 825 6850.
  Formerly: Division Interdisciplinar para la Familia.

LAW

349   VE   ISSN 0020-3823
INSTITUTO DE DERECHO PRIVADO. BOLETIN. 1966. s-a. Bs.12 per no. Universidad Central de Venezuela, Instituto de Derecho Privado, Departamento de Distribucion de Publicaciones, Edificio de la Biblioteca Central, Apdo. 47004, Caracas 1041, Venezuela. bk.rev.; abstr.; bibl. circ. 2,000.

340   SP
INSTITUTO DE ESTUDIOS TARRACONENSES RAMON BERENGUER IV. SECCION DE ESTUDIOS JURIDICOS. PUBLICACION. (Text in Catalan or Spanish) 1972. irreg. Instituto de Estudios Tarraconenses Ramon Berenguer IV, Calle Santa Ana 8, Tarragona, Spain.

340 100   VE   ISSN 1315-3269
INSTITUTO DE FILOSOFIA DEL DERECHO DR. JOSE MANUEL DELGADO OCANDO. BOLETIN. 1973. biennial. free. (Universidad del Zulia, Instituto de Filosofia del Derecho) Ediluz, Apdo. 526, Maracaibo, Venezuela. TEL 61-424788. FAX 61-423913. Ed. Ana Ferrer. circ. 500. **Document type:** newsletter.
    Formerly: Instituto de Filosofia del Derecho. Boletin Informativo.

340 100   VE
▼**INSTITUTO DE FILOSOFIA DEL DERECHO DR. JOSE MANUEL DELGADO OCANDO. REVISTA.** 1994. a. (Universidad del Zulia) Ediluz, Apdo. 526, Maracaibo, Venezuela. TEL 61-424788. FAX 61-423913. Ed. Ana Ferrer. circ. 500. **Document type:** academic/scholarly publication.

340 100   VE
INSTITUTO DE FILOSOFIA DEL DERECHO DR. JOSE MANUEL DELGADO OCANDO. COLECCION DE CURSOS Y LECCIONES. 1969. irreg., latest no.11. (Universidad del Zulia, Insituto de Filosofia del Derecho) Ediluz, Apdo. 526, Maracaibo, Venezuela. TEL 61-424788. FAX 61-423913. Ed. Ana Ferrer. circ. 100. **Document type:** academic/scholarly publication.

340 100   VE
INSTITUTO DE FILOSOFIA DEL DERECHO DR. JOSE MANUEL DELGADO OCANDO. COLECCION DE MONOGRAFIAS. 1974. irreg., latest no.11. price varies. (Universidad del Zulia) Ediluz, Apdo. 526, Maracaibo, Venezuela. TEL 61-424788. FAX 61-423913. Ed. Ana Ferrer. circ. 1,000. **Document type:** monographic series.

340 100   VE   ISSN 1315-3072
INSTITUTO DE FILOSOFIA DEL DERECHO DR. JOSE MANUEL DELGADO OCANDO. CUADERNO DE TRABAJO. 1972. a. (Universidad del Zulia, Instituto de Filosofia del Derecho) Ediluz, Apdo. 526, Maracaibo, Venezuela. TEL 61-424788. FAX 61-423913. Ed. Ana Ferrer. circ. 1,000. **Document type:** academic/scholarly publication, monographic series.

340   BL
INSTITUTO DOS ADVOGADOS DE S. PAULO. REVISTA. 1976. s-a. (Instituto dos Advogados de Sao Paulo) Editora Resenha Tributaria, Rue Xavier de Toledo 210, Sao Paulo, Brazil.
    Supersedes (in 1985): Analise Jurisprudencial.

INSTITUTO INTERAMERICANO DEL NINO. JURIDICO SOCIAL. INFORMES TECNICOS. see *SOCIOLOGY*

340   BL
INSTITUTO NACIONAL DE COLONIZACAO E REFORMA AGRARIA. PROCURADORIA GERAL. BOLETIM. PARECERES. 1972. s-a. free. Instituto Nacional de Colonizacao e Reforma Agraria, Procuradoria Geral, Palacio do Desenvolvimento, 21 andar, Setor Bancario Norte, CEP 70437-Brasilia D.F., Brazil. Eds. Agnaldo Jurandyr Silva, Eliene Rodriques da Costa Maia. circ. 800.

INSTITUTO NACIONAL DE MEDICINA LEGAL DE COLOMBIA. REVISTA. see *MEDICAL SCIENCES — Forensic Sciences*

340   CN
INSURANCE CASE LAW DIGEST. q. Can.$560. Butterworths Canada Ltd., Part of the Reed Elsevier group, 75 Clegg Rd., Markham, ON L6G 1A1, Canada. TEL 905-479-2665. FAX 905-479-2826. Ed. John Newcombe. (looseleaf format)
    Description: Complete coverage of automobile and property insurance cases in Canada.

340   US   ISSN 0887-7858
KF1159
INSURANCE INDUSTRY LITIGATION REPORTER; the national journal of record for insurance litigation. 1985. s-m. $825. Andrews Publications, 1646 West Chester Pike, Box 1000, Westtown, PA 19395. TEL 215-399-6600; 800-345-1101. FAX 215-399-6610. Ed. Jay Steinberg. abstr.; bibl.; stat.; s-a. index. (looseleaf format; back issues avail.) **Document type:** newsletter.

340 368   UK   ISSN 0962-1385
K24
INSURANCE LAW & PRACTICE. 1991. 4/yr. £105. Tolley Publishing Co. Ltd., Tolley House, 2 Addiscombe Rd., Croydon, Surrey CR9 5AF, England. TEL 081-686-9141. FAX 081-686-3155. Eds. Andrew McGee, Ray Hodgin. adv.; bk.rev. **Document type:** trade publication.
    Description: Covers all aspects of insurance law and practice.

INSURANCE LAW ANTHOLOGY, see *INSURANCE*

340 368   US   ISSN 1060-7382
INSURANCE LAW CITATIONS. 6 base vols. (plus q. suppl.). $660. Shepard's - McGraw-Hill, Inc., Box 35300, Colorado Springs, CO 80935-3530. TEL 800-525-2474.
    Description: Lists insurance law cases, with citations to cases decided by the U.S. Supreme Court, lower federal courts and state courts.

340 368   AT   ISSN 1030-2379
K9
INSURANCE LAW JOURNAL. 1988. 3/yr. Aus.$125. Butterworths, 271-273 Lane Cove Rd., North Ryde, N.S.W. 2113, Australia. TEL 02-335-4444. FAX 02-335-4678. Ed. A.A. Tarr. bk.rev. **Indexed:** C.L.I. **Document type:** academic/scholarly publication.
    —BLDSC (4531.721000).

INSURANCE LAW REPORTS: FIRE & CASUALTY. see *INSURANCE*

INSURANCE LAW REPORTS: LIFE, HEALTH & ACCIDENT. see *INSURANCE*

368   US   ISSN 0195-1858
KF1159
INSURANCE LITIGATION REPORTER; recent decisions of national significance. 1978. m. $320. (Litigation Research Group) Shepard's - McGraw-Hill, Inc., Box 35300, Colorado Springs, CO 80935-3530. Ed. John K. DiMugno. bibl.; index. (looseleaf format; back issues avail.) **Indexed:** BPIA.
    Description: Analyzes trends and summarizes recent litigation affecting insurance law.

340   PH   ISSN 0115-138X
K9
INTEGRATED BAR OF THE PHILIPPINES. JOURNAL. (Text in English) 1973. q. $32. Integrated Bar of the Philippines, Dona Julia Vargas Ave., Ortigas Office Bldg. Complex, Pasig, Metro Manila, Philippines. FAX 631-3014. Ed. Beda G. Fajardo. adv.; bk.rev. circ. 30,000. **Indexed:** Ind.Phil.Per.
    —BLDSC (4802.062000).

340 608.7   CN   ISSN 0824-7064
K9
INTELLECTUAL PROPERTY JOURNAL. (Text in English, French) 1984. 3/yr. (plus bound vol.). Can.$190. Carswell, One Corporate Plaza, 2075 Kennedy Rd., Scarborough, ON M1T 3V4, Canada. TEL 416-609-8000. FAX 416-298-5094. Ed. David Vaver. adv. contact: M. Lalani. bk.rev. circ. 450. **Indexed:** C.L.I., Ind.Can.L.P.L.
    —BLDSC (4531.823800); UnCover. **CCC**.
    Description: Covers matters of interest relating to patents, trademarks, copyright, designs, trade secrets, and competitive torts.

INTELLECTUAL PROPERTY LAW (NEW YORK). see *PATENTS, TRADEMARKS AND COPYRIGHTS*

INTELLECTUAL PROPERTY LAW (SPRINGFIELD). see *PATENTS, TRADEMARKS AND COPYRIGHTS*

INTELLECTUAL PROPERTY LAW NEWS. see *PATENTS, TRADEMARKS AND COPYRIGHTS*

340   AT   ISSN 0812-2024
INTELLECTUAL PROPERTY REPORTS. 1982. 3/yr. Aus.$130. Butterworths, P.O. Box 345, North Ryde, N.S.W. 2113, Australia. TEL 02-335-4444. FAX 02-335-4678.

340   CN   ISSN 0715-4771
INTER-AMERICAN ARBITRATION. (Text in English, French, Spanish) 1981. q. Can.$10. Canadian Arbitration, Conciliation and Amicable Composition Centre, Inc., c/o Civil Law Section, University of Ottawa, Ottawa, Ont. K1N 6N5, Canada. TEL 613-232-1476. FAX 613-564-9800. TELEX 0533338. Ed. L. Kos Rabcewicz-Zubkowski. bk.rev. circ. 400. (back issues avail.)

340   US
INTER-AMERICAN BAR ASSOCIATION. CONFERENCE PROCEEDINGS. 1941. biennial. $30. Inter-American Bar Association, 815 15th St., N.W., Ste. 921, Washington, DC 20005-2201. TEL 202-393-1217. FAX 202-393-1241. **Document type:** proceedings.
    Description: Papers presented during the biennial conference of the association.

340   US
INTER-AMERICAN BAR ASSOCIATION. LETTER TO MEMBERS. (Text in English and Spanish) 1961. q. $6. Inter-American Bar Association, 815 15th St., N.W., Ste. 921, Washington, DC 20005-2201. TEL 202-393-1217. FAX 202-393-1241. Ed. Jose A. Toro. circ. 3,000. (processed) **Document type:** newsletter.

340   US
INTERNATIONAL ACADEMY OF TRIAL LAWYERS. DEAN'S ADDRESS. a. International Academy of Trial Lawyers, 4 N. Second St., Ste. 175, San Jose, CA 95113. TEL 408-275-6767. FAX 408-275-6874.
    Description: Aimed primarily at attorneys who have been practicing for at least 12 years.

340   US
INTERNATIONAL ACADEMY OF TRIAL LAWYERS. JOURNAL. 1959. 3/yr. free to members. International Academy of Trial Lawyers, 4 N. Second St., No. 175, San Jose, CA 95113. TEL 408-275-6767. FAX 408-275-6874. Ed. Barbara V. Laskin. circ. 700.
    Formerly: International Academy of Trial Lawyers. Bulletin.

340   BE   ISSN 0074-1604
INTERNATIONAL ASSOCIATION OF DEMOCRATIC LAWYERS. CONGRESS REPORT. quadrennial, 12th, 1984, Athens. International Association of Democratic Lawyers, 263 av. Albert, 1180 Brussels, Belgium.

340 539   UN   ISSN 0074-1868
INTERNATIONAL ATOMIC ENERGY AGENCY. LEGAL SERIES. (Text in English) 1959. irreg. price varies. International Atomic Energy Agency, Wagramerstr. 5, P.O. Box 100, A-1400 Vienna, Austria. (Dist. in U.S. by: Unipub, 4611-F Assembly Dr., Lanham, MD 20706-4391)

INTERNATIONAL COMPUTER LAW ADVISER; a monthly research report on the international law of computers, telecommunications & information. see *COMPUTERS*

INTERNATIONAL CONFERENCE OF INSURANCE REGULATORY OFFICIALS. PROCEEDINGS. see *INSURANCE*

340   IS
INTERNATIONAL CONGRESS OF COMPARATIVE LAW. ISRAEL REPORTS. (Text in English) quadrennial. IS.50($35) P.O. Box 24100, Mt. Scopus, Jerusalem, Israel.

INTERNATIONAL DIGEST OF HEALTH LEGISLATION. see *PUBLIC HEALTH AND SAFETY*

340 410   UK   ISSN 0952-8059
INTERNATIONAL JOURNAL FOR THE SEMIOTICS OF LAW/REVUE INTERNATIONALE DE SEMIOTIQUE JURIDIQUE; semiotic, linguistic, discursive approach to law. 1988. 3/yr. £55 (effective 1994). (International Association for the Semiotics of Law) Deborah Charles Publications, 173 Mather Ave., Liverpool L18 6JZ, England. TEL 44-51-724-2500. FAX 44-729-0371. (Dist. in US by: William Gaunt & Sons, Inc., 3011 Gulf Dr., Holmes Beach, FL 34217-2199. TEL 813-778-5211. FAX 813-778-5252) Ed. E. Landowski. adv.; bk.rev. circ. 400. **Indexed:** Bibl.Ling. **Document type:** academic/scholarly publication.
    —BLDSC (4542.544670); UnCover.

341 II ISSN 0020-7098
INTERNATIONAL JOURNAL OF ARBITRATION. 1970. 3/yr. Rs.100($20) K.K. Roy (Private) Ltd., 55 Gariahat Rd., P.O. Box 10210, Calcutta 700 019, India. Ed. K.K. Roy. adv.; bk.rev.; abstr.; bibl.; index. circ. 500. (tabloid format)

340 331 NE ISSN 0952-617X
THE INTERNATIONAL JOURNAL OF COMPARATIVE LABOUR LAW AND INDUSTRIAL RELATIONS. (Text in English) 1985. 4/yr. fl.195($105) (effective 1994). Kluwer Law and Taxation Publishers (Subsidiary of: Wolters Kluwer N.V.), P.O. Box 23, 7400 GA Deventer, Netherlands. TEL 31-5700-47261. FAX 31-5700-22244. TELEX 49295 KLUDV NL. (Dist. by: Libresso Distribution Centre, P.O. Box 23, 7400 GA Deventer, Netherlands. TEL 31-5700-33155. FAX 31-5700-33834; In N. America: Kluwer Law and Taxation Publishers, 675 Massachusetts Ave., Cambridge, MA 02139. TEL 617-354-0140. FAX 617-354-8595) Eds. Lammy Betten, Alan Neal. **Indexed:** ELLIS. **Document type:** academic/scholarly publication.
—BLDSC (4542.172900).
Description: Covers significant international issues in comparative labor law and industrial relations, including legislation, case law and discussions of public policy.
Refereed Serial

340 600 UK ISSN 0967-0769
▼**INTERNATIONAL JOURNAL OF LAW AND INFORMATION TECHNOLOGY.** 1993. 3/yr. £95($185) Oxford University Press, Oxford Journals, Walton St., Oxford OX2 6DP, England. TEL 0865-56767. FAX 0865-56646. TELEX 837330-OXPRES-G. (U.S. subscr. to: Oxford University Press Inc., 2001 Evans Rd., Cary, NC 27513. TEL 919-677-0977) Eds. Christopher Millard, Richard Susskind. adv. contact: Jane Parker. bk.rev. circ. 800. **Document type:** academic/scholarly publication.
—BLDSC (4542.312370). **CCC.**
Description: Provides information about all aspects of the use of information technology in legal practice and of the legal implications of developments in information technology.

340 616.8 UK ISSN 0160-2527
K9
INTERNATIONAL JOURNAL OF LAW AND PSYCHIATRY. 1978. 4/yr. £214($330) (effective 1994). Elsevier Science Ltd., Pergamon, P.O. Box 800, Kidlington, Oxford OX5 1DX, England. TEL 44-865-843000. FAX 44-865-843010. (Subscr. in U.S. and Canada to: Elsevier Science, 660 White Plains Rd., Tarrytown, NY 10591-5153. TEL 914-524-9200. FAX 914-333-2444) Ed. D.N. Weisstub. adv. circ. 1,100. (also avail. in microfilm from UMI; reprint service avail. from UMI) **Indexed:** Adol.Ment.Hlth.Abstr., Amer.Bibl.Slavic & E.Eur.Stud., C.C.L.P., C.L.I., Crim.Just.Abstr., Curr.Cont., Excerp.Med., Ind.Med., L.R.I., Lang.& Lang.Behav.Abstr., Leg.Cont., Leg.Per., Psychol.Abstr., SSCI. **Document type:** academic/scholarly publication.
—BLDSC (4542.312500); Faxon; UnCover; SWETS; UMI. **CCC.**
Refereed Serial

INTERNATIONAL JOURNAL OF LEGAL INFORMATION. see LIBRARY AND INFORMATION SCIENCES

340 UK ISSN 0969-5958
▼**INTERNATIONAL JOURNAL OF THE LEGAL PROFESSION.** 1994. 3/yr. £54 to individuals; institutions £198 (effective 1994). Carfax Publishing Co., P.O. Box 25, Abingdon, Oxon. OX14 3UE, England. TEL 44-235-555335. FAX 44-235-553559. (N. American subscr. to: Carfax Publishing Co., Box 2025, Dunnellon, FL 34430-2025) Ed. Avrom Sherr. adv.; bk.rev.; index. (also avail. in microfiche) **Document type:** academic/scholarly publication.

340 UK ISSN 0194-6595
K9
INTERNATIONAL JOURNAL OF THE SOCIOLOGY OF LAW. 1972. q. £94 (effective 1994). Academic Press Ltd. (Subsidiary of: Harcourt Brace & Company Ltd.), 24-28 Oval Rd., London NW1 7DX, England. TEL 44-71-267-4466. FAX 44-71-482-2293. TELEX 25775-ACPRES-G. (Subscr. to: Harcourt Brace & Company Ltd., Foots Cray High St., Sidcup, Kent DA14 5HP, England. TEL 44-81-300-3322. FAX 44-81-309-0807) Eds. S. Picciotto, C. Smart. bk.rev. (back issues avail.) **Indexed:** ASSIA, C.L.I., CJPI, Crim.Just.Abstr., L.R.I., Lang.& Lang.Behav.Abstr., Leg.Per., Psychol.Abstr., Soc.Sci.Ind., Sociol.Abstr. (1979-), SSCI. **Document type:** academic/scholarly publication.
—BLDSC (4542.574000); Faxon; SWETS. **CCC.**
Formerly (until vol.7, 1979): International Journal of Criminology and Penology (ISSN 0306-3208)
Description: Contains theoretical and empiricl studies of law as a social process from an international perspective.

347.9 NE ISSN 0168-6526
INTERNATIONAL LABOUR LAW REPORTS. 1978. a. price varies. Kluwer Academic Publishers, Postbus 17, 3300 AA Dordrecht, Netherlands. TEL 31-78-334911. FAX 31-78-334254. TELEX 29245 KAPG NL. (Dist. by: Kluwer Academic Publishers Group, P.O. Box 322, 3300 AH Dordrecht, Netherlands. TEL 31-78-524400. FAX 31-78-524474; N. America dist. addr.: Box 358, Accord Sta., Hingham, MA 02018-0358. TEL 617-871-6600. FAX 617-871-6528) Ed.Bd. **Document type:** monographic series.
Refereed Serial

INTERNATIONAL LABOUR OFFICE. LABOUR LAW DOCUMENTS. see BUSINESS AND ECONOMICS — Labor And Industrial Relations

340 CN ISSN 0229-2181
INTERNATIONAL OMBUDSMAN INSTITUTE. NEWSLETTER. 1974. 4/yr. $10. International Ombudsman Institute, Faculty of Law, University of Alberta, Edmonton, AB T6G 2H5, Canada. TEL 403-492-3196. **Indexed:** HR Rep. **Document type:** newsletter.

340 CN
INTERNATIONAL OMBUDSMAN INSTITUTE. OCCASIONAL PAPER SERIES. 3/yr. $8 per no. International Ombudsman Institute, Faculty of Law, University of Alberta, Edmonton, AB T6G 2H5, Canada. TEL 403-492-3196. **Indexed:** HR Rep.

340 BE ISSN 0048-7473
INTERNATIONAL REVIEW OF CONTEMPORARY LAW. French edition: Revue Internationale de Droit Contemporain. (None published 1970-1975) (Editions in English, French) 1954. s-a. 600 Fr.($15) International Association of Democratic Lawyers, 263 av. Albert, 1180 Brussels, Belgium. **Indexed:** HR Rep.

340 330 US ISSN 0144-8188
K9 CODEN: IRLEE8
INTERNATIONAL REVIEW OF LAW AND ECONOMICS. 1981. 4/yr. $80 to individuals (foreign $95); institutions $195 (foreign $225). Butterworth - Heinemann, Part of the Reed Elsevier group, 313 Washington St., Newton, MA 02158. TEL 617-928-2500; 800-366-2665. FAX 617-928-2610. TELEX 880052. Ed.Bd. bk.rev.; index. (also avail. in microform from UMI; back issues avail.) **Indexed:** C.L.I., C.R.E.J., J.of Econ.Lit., L.R.I., Leg.Per., P.A.I.S. **Document type:** academic/scholarly publication.
—BLDSC (4547.330000); Faxon; UnCover; SWETS; UMI. **CCC.**
Description: Research on interface between economics and law including legal institutions, jurisprudence, legal history and political-legal theory.
Refereed Serial

340 US
INTERNATIONAL RIGHT OF WAY. bi-m. International Right of Way Association, 13650 S. Gramercy Place, Gardena, CA 90249-2465. TEL 213-538-0233. FAX 213-538-1471. Ed. David M. Roman. circ. 9,000.

INTERNATIONAL SOCIETY FOR LABOUR AND SOCIAL SECURITY. BULLETIN. see BUSINESS AND ECONOMICS — Labor And Industrial Relations

344.01 TH ISSN 0074-8455
INTERNATIONAL SOCIETY FOR LABOUR LAW AND SOCIAL LEGISLATION. PROCEEDINGS OF CONGRESS. (Proceedings published in host country) 1951. triennial, 13th, Athens, 1991. International Society for Labour Law and Social Legislation - Societe Internationale de Droit du Travail et de la Securite Sociale, c/o Jean-Michel Servais, Sec.-Gen., ILO Office for Asia & the Pacific, P.O. Box 1759, Bangkok 10501, Thailand. **Document type:** proceedings.

INTERNATIONAL STUDIES. see POLITICAL SCIENCE — International Relations

342.085 NE ISSN 0903-9961
JC599.D44
INTERNATIONAL STUDIES. NORDIC SEMINAR ON HUMAN RIGHTS. PROCEEDINGS. (Text in English) irreg., no.4, 1989. (Danish Center for Human Rights, DK) Martinus Nijhoff Publishers, Human Rights and International Law (Subsidiary of: Kluwer Academic Publishers Group), Postbus 163, 3300 AD Dordrecht, Netherlands. TEL 31-78-334911. FAX 31-78-334254. (Dist. by: Kluwer Academic Publishers Group, P.O. Box 322, 3300 AH Dordrecht, Netherlands. TEL 31-78-524400. FAX 31-78-524474; N. America dist. addr.: Box 358, Accord Sta., Hingham, MA 02018-0358. TEL 617-871-6600. FAX 617-871-6528) Eds. Lars Rehof, Claus Gulman. **Document type:** proceedings.
—BLDSC (4336.439200).

340 AU
INTERNATIONALE GESELLSCHAFT FUER URHEBERRECHT. SCHRIFTENREIHE.* 1955. irreg., vol.61, 1984. price varies. (Internationale Gesellschaft fuer Urheberrecht e.V. - International Copyright Society) Nomos Verlagsgesellschaft mbH und Co. KG, Waldseestr. 3-5, Postfach 610, 76530 Baden-Baden, Germany. TEL 07221-20140. FAX 07221-210427. (Subscr. to: Postfach 610, 76484 Baden-Baden, Germany)

INTERPRETER RELEASES; report and analysis of immigration and nationality law. see POPULATION STUDIES

340 US
INTERROGATORIES, DOCUMENTS AND ADMISSIONS. 1989. base vol. (plus a. suppl.). $70. Butterworth Legal Publishers (Salem) (Subsidiary of: Reed Elsevier plc), 8 Industrial Way, Bldg. C, Salem, NH 03079. TEL 800-548-4001. FAX 603-898-9858. Ed. John Hardin Young. (looseleaf format)

INTERSTATE INFORMATION REPORT; a monthly bulletin for motor carrier licensing managers. see TRANSPORTATION — Trucks And Trucking

INTERVENOR. see ENVIRONMENTAL STUDIES

340 US ISSN 0578-6533
KF292.I614
IOWA ADVOCATE. s-a. University of Iowa, College of Law, Iowa City, IA 52242. TEL 319-335-9034. (Co-sponsor: Iowa Law School Foundation) illus. **Document type:** academic/scholarly publication.

340 US ISSN 0021-0552
K9
IOWA LAW REVIEW. 1915. 5/yr. $33. University of Iowa, College of Law, Iowa City, IA 52242. TEL 319-335-9132. FAX 319-335-9019. adv.; bk.rev.; charts; index, cum.index every 10 yrs. circ. 1,800. (also avail. in microfilm from WSH,PMC; reprint service avail. from WSH) **Indexed:** Account.Ind. (1974-), C.L.I., Curr.Cont., L.R.I., Leg.Cont., Leg.Per., P.A.I.S., SSCI. **Document type:** academic/scholarly publication.
●Also available online. Vendor(s): Mead Data Central, Inc., West Services, Inc.
—BLDSC (4566.300000); Faxon; UnCover; SWETS.

340 US ISSN 1052-5327
IOWA LAWYER. 1940. m. $30 to non-members; members $5. Iowa State Bar Association, 521 E. Locust, Des Moines, IA 50309. TEL 515-243-3179. Ed. Carl V. Nielsen. adv. contact: Sue Derscheid. illus.
Formerly (until 1990): Iowa State Bar Association. News Bulletin (ISSN 1043-0482)
Description: Covers state and national news, professional announcements and other items of interest to lawyers in Iowa.

340   US
IOWA PLEADING AND CAUSES OF ACTION. 1989. 2 base vols. (plus suppl.). $160. Butterworth Legal Publishers (Salem) (Subsidiary of: Reed Elsevier plc), 8 Industrial Way, Bldg. C, Salem, NH 03079. TEL 800-548-4001. FAX 603-898-9858. Ed. George A. La Marca. (looseleaf format)

340   IE   ISSN 0791-5403
K9
▼**IRISH JOURNAL OF EUROPEAN LAW.** 1992. a. I£45($70) The Round Hall Press, Kill Lane, Blackrock, Co. Dublin, Ireland. TEL 2892922. FAX 2893072. Eds. James O'Reilly, Anthony Collins. circ. 300 (controlled). **Document type:** bulletin.
—BLDSC (4571.975000).
 Description: Articles, law reports and case references to the leading decisions of the courts on European Law.

340   IE   ISSN 0021-1273
IRISH JURIST. N.S. 1966. s-a. £25. Jurist Publishing Co., University College, Dublin 4, Ireland. Ed. W.N. Osborough. adv.; bk.rev.; index. circ. 700. (also avail. in microfilm from BHP,RRI) **Indexed:** C.L.I., Leg.Per.
—BLDSC (4572.500000); UnCover.

340 340   IE   ISSN 0332-3293
KDK63 1867.A2
IRISH LAW REPORTS MONTHLY. 1981. 12/yr. I£225($330) The Round Hall Press, Kill Lane, Blackrock, Co. Dublin, Ireland. TEL 2892922. FAX 2893072. Ed. Hilary Delany. index. circ. 750. (back issues avail.) **Document type:** bulletin.
 Description: Reports of judgments from the High and Superior Courts in Ireland.

340   IE   ISSN 0021-1281
LAW
IRISH LAW TIMES AND SOLICITORS' JOURNAL. 1867; N.S. 1983. m. I£130($195) The Round Hall Press, Kill Lane, Blackrock, Co. Dublin, Ireland. TEL 2892922. FAX 2893072. Ed. Raymond Byrne. adv.; bk.rev.; cum.index. circ. 1,000. **Indexed:** ELLIS. **Document type:** bulletin.
 Description: Reports on a wide range of legal areas. Includes a digest of cases delivered in the Irish Superior Courts.

340   IE
THE IRISH STUDENT LAW REVIEW. 1991. a. $80 for 2 vol. set. Law Students' Debating Society of Ireland, King's Inns, Dublin 2, Ireland. (Dist. in US by: Wm. W. Gaunt & Sons, Inc., Gaunt Bldg., 3011 Gulf Dr., Holmes Beach, FL 34217-2199. TEL 813-778-5211. FAX 813-778-5252) **Indexed:** C.L.I.
 Description: Consists of articles written by law students from every law faculty in Ireland.

340   US
▼**IRREVOCABLE TRUSTS.** 1989. base vol. (plus a. supplement). $95. Shepard's - McGraw-Hill, Inc., Box 35300, Colorado Springs, CO 80935-3530. TEL 800-525-2474.
 Description: Looks at the types of trusts used for estate planning. Examines the income tax implications of an irrevocable trust, involvement with the IRS, and the problems of calculating assets being transferred to the trustee.

340   UK
IS IT IN FORCE?. a. $46. Butterworth & Co. (Publishers) Ltd. (Subsidiary of: Reed Elsevier plc), 88 Kingsway, London WC2B 6AB, England. TEL 71-405-6900. FAX 71-405-1332. (US addr.: Butterworth Legal Publishers, 90 Stiles Rd., Salem, NH 03079-9981. TEL 603-898-9664)
 Description: A concise guide to the exact commencement dates of all UK Acts of Parliament and General Synod Measures passed over the last quarter century.

349.710   CN   ISSN 0827-441X
ISAAC PITBLADO LECTURES. a. University of Manitoba, Faculty of Law, Winnipeg, MB R3T 2N2, Canada. TEL 204-474-6159. FAX 204-275-5540. (Co-sponsors: Manitoba Bar Association, Law Society of Manitoba) **Indexed:** Ind.Can.L.P.L.
 Formerly (until 1983): Isaac Pitblado Lectures on Continuing Legal Education (ISSN 0578-7726)

ISLAMIC LAW & SOCIETY. see *RELIGIONS AND THEOLOGY — Islamic*

340   IS   ISSN 0021-2237
LAW
ISRAEL LAW REVIEW. (Text in English) 1966. q. IS.100($42) (effective 1994). Israel Law Review Association, c/o Hebrew University, Faculty of Law, P.O. Box 24100, Mount Scopus, Jerusalem 91240, Israel. TEL 972-2-882520. FAX 972-2-823042. Ed.Bd. adv.; bk.rev.; index. circ. 1,500. (also avail. in microfiche from WSH; microfilm from WSH,PMC; back issues avail.) **Indexed:** Curr.Cont., Foreign Leg.Per., Lang.& Lang.Behav.Abstr., Leg.Cont., Leg.Per., Sociol.Abstr., SSCI. **Document type:** academic/scholarly publication.
—BLDSC (4583.820000); Faxon; UnCover.
 Description: Contains articles on contemporary Israeli law, Jewish law, international and comparative law, and digests of major decisions of the Israeli Supreme Court.

ISSUES IN LAW AND MEDICINE. see *HANDICAPPED*

340   IT
ISTITUTO DI DIRITTO ROMANO. BOLLETTINO. (Text in various European Languages) 1888. a. price varies. Casa Editrice Dott. A. Giuffre, Via Busto Arsizio 40, Milan 20151, Italy. TEL 02-38000905. FAX 02-3809582. Ed. Marco Talamanca. adv.; bk.rev.; index. circ. 500.

340   NE
▼**ITALIAN STUDIES IN LAW;** a review of legal problems. (Text in English) 1992. irreg. price varies. (Italian Association of Comparative Law) Kluwer Academic Publishers, Postbus 17, 3300 AA Dordrecht, Netherlands. TEL 31-78-334911. FAX 31-78-334254. TELEX 29245 KAPG NL. (Dist. by: Kluwer Academic Publishers Group, P.O. Box 322, 3300 AH Dordrecht, Netherlands. TEL 31-78-524400; N. America dist. addr.: Box 358, Accord Sta., Hingham, MA 02018-0358. TEL 617-871-6600) Ed. Alessandro Pizzorusso. **Document type:** monographic series.
 Description: Overview of developments and issues in Italian legal scholarship of interest to an international audience.
 Refereed Serial

340   IT   ISSN 0021-3241
IURA; rivista internazionale di diritto romano e antico. (Text in various languages) 1950. irreg. price varies. Casa Editrice Dott. Eugenio Jovene, Via Mezzocannone, 109, 80134 Naples, Italy. TEL 081-5521019. FAX 081-5520687. Ed. Cesare Sanfilippo. bk.rev.
—BLDSC (4589.058000).

340   BE
IURIS SCRIPTA HISTORICA. (Text in Dutch) 1985. irreg., vol.4, 1991. price varies. Koninklijke Academie voor Wetenschappen, Letteren en Schone Kunsten van Belgie, 1 Hertogsstraat, B-1000 Brussels, Belgium. (Dist. by: N.V. Brepols, Steenweg op Tielen, 2300 Turnhout, Belgium. TEL 32-14-4205005. FAX 32-14-428919) **Document type:** monographic series.
 Description: Publishes studies relating to the origins and development of European law from medieval times to the present.

IUS ICCLESIAE; rivista internazionale di diritto canonico. see *RELIGIONS AND THEOLOGY — Roman Catholic*

340   IT   ISSN 0075-2037
IUS ROMANUM MEDII AEVI. (Text in English, French, German, Italian, Spanish) 1961. irreg. price varies. Casa Editrice Dott. A. Giuffre, Via Busto Arsizio 40, 20151 Milan, Italy. TEL 02-38000905. FAX 02-3809582.

349   IT   ISSN 0021-3268
IUSTITIA. 1948. q. L.40000 (foreign L.60000). (Unione Giuristi Cattolici Italiani) Casa Editrice Dott. A. Giuffre, Via Busto Arsizio 40, 20151 Milan, Italy. TEL 02-38000905. FAX 02-38009582. Ed. Sergio Cotta. adv.; bk.rev.; index. circ. 1,300. **Indexed:** CERDIC.
—SWETS.

340   YU
IZVORI SRPSKOG PRAVA/SOURCES DE DROIT SERBE/SERBISCHE RECHTSQUELLEN. (Subseries of: Srpska Akademija Nauka i Umetnosti. Odeljenje Drustvenih Nauka) (Text in Serbian; summaries in English, French, German, Russian) 1967. irreg. Srpska Akademija Nauka i Umetnosti, Odeljenje Drustvenih Nauka, Knez Mihailova 35, 11001 Belgrade, Serbia, Yugoslavia. FAX 38-11-182-825. TELEX 72593 SANU YU. illus.

340   US
J A D NEWS. s-a. free. American Bar Association, Judicial Administration Division, 750 N. Lake Shore Dr., Chicago, IL 60611. TEL 312-988-5000. (tabloid format)

J.C.H.R. NEWS LETTER. (Jamaica Council of Human Rights) see *POLITICAL SCIENCE — Civil Rights*

312   UK
J C W I BULLETIN. 1982. q. membership. Joint Council for the Welfare of Immigrants, 115 Old St., London EC1V 9JR, England. TEL 071-251-8706. FAX 071-253-3832. circ. 1,000. (back issues avail.) **Document type:** bulletin.
 Description: Examines the issues pertaining to immigration and nationality laws.

340 360   SW   ISSN 0281-0883
J K - BESLUT; beslut och yttranden af Justiekanslern vilka har bedoemts vara av allmaent intresse. 1982. a. SEK 194 (effective 1994). (Justitiekanslern) Fritzes, S-106 47 Stockholm, Sweden.

349   SW   ISSN 1100-620X
J U S E K TIDNINGEN. 1951. m. SEK 150. Foerbundet foer Jurister, Samhaellsvetare och Ekonomer (JUSEK) - Swedish Federation of Jurists, Social Scientists and Economists, PO Box 5167, S-102 44 Stockholm, Sweden. FAX 08-6627923. Ed. Ann Marie Bergstroem. adv.; bk.rev.; charts; illus.; index. circ. 32,772.
 Former titles (until vol.4, 1989): J U S E K (ISSN 0349-4055); (until vol.9, 1979): J U S (ISSN 0345-5742); (until 1972): Juristnytt - Samhaellsvetaren (ISSN 0022-6947)

340   II   ISSN 0448-1054
JABALPUR LAW JOURNAL. (Text in English) 1952. m. Rs.140. Law Journal Publications, Jayendraganj, Gwalior 474009, India. Ed. Harihar Nivas Dvivedi. adv.; bk.rev.; bibl. circ. 2,683.

JAHRBUCH DES SOZIALRECHTS DER GEGENWART. see *SOCIAL SERVICES AND WELFARE*

340   GW   ISSN 0722-2181
JAHRBUCH FUER AFRIKANISCHES RECHT/YEARBOOK OF AFRICAN LAW. (Text in English, French and German; summaries in English and French) 1980. a. price varies. C.F. Mueller Juristischer Verlag GmbH, Im Weiher 10, 69121 Heidelberg, Germany. TEL 06221-489281. FAX 06221-489279. bk.rev. **Indexed:** Documentatieblad. **Document type:** bulletin.

340   GW   ISSN 0075-2746
K10
JAHRBUCH FUER OSTRECHT. (Issued in 2 parts) 1960. a. DM.48. (Institut fuer Ostrecht, Munich) Deutscher Bundes-Verlag, 5300 Bonn, Germany. Ed. Erhardt Gralla. circ. 750.

340   GW   ISSN 0944-4610
▼**JAHRBUCH FUER RECHT UND ETHIK/ANNUAL REVIEW OF LAW AND ETHICS.** (Text in English, German) 1993. a. DM.148. Duncker und Humblot GmbH, Postfach 410329, 12113 Berlin, Germany. TEL 030-7900060. FAX 030-79000631. Ed. B. Sharon Byrd. **Document type:** academic/scholarly publication.

JAHRESFACHKATALOG RECHT - WIRTSCHAFT - STEUERN. see *BUSINESS AND ECONOMICS*

340   JM
JAMAICAN BAR ASSOCIATION. ANNUAL REPORT. a. Jamaican Bar Association, 78-80 Harbour St., Kingston, Jamaica, W.I. TEL 922-2319. **Document type:** corporate report, academic/scholarly publication.

340   II
JAMMU AND KASHMIR LAW REPORTER. (Text in English) 1970. m. Rs.30. High Court of Jammu and Kashmir, Srinagar, Jammu, India. Ed. Mufti Salah-Ud-Din Arshad. bibl. circ. 475.

340   JA   ISSN 1340-5349
JAPAN LAW JOURNAL; a bimonthly on legal affairs in Japan and abroad. (Text in English) bi-m. 16000 Yen (Asia $120; Central & N. America, Oceania & Mideast $125; elsewhere £130. Survey Japan, Ste. 603 Ichigaya-mitsuke Heim, Ichigaya-Hachimancho 16, Shinjuku-ku, Tokyo 162, Japan. TEL 03-3235-3421. FAX 03-3235-3422. Ed. Kuni Sadamoto.

JESSUP'S LANDS TITLES OFFICE PRACTICE S.A.. see
REAL ESTATE

349   FR   ISSN 0021-6151
JEUNES AVOCATS.* 1963. 6 F. Union des Jeunes Avocats a la Cour de Paris, Palais de Justice, Paris, France. Ed. Jean-Paul Clement.

340 296   US   ISSN 0276-1432
JEWISH JURISPRUDENCE SERIES. irreg. Harwood Academic Publishers, 820 Town Center Dr., Langhorne, PA 19047. TEL 215-750-2642. FAX 215-750-6343. (U.K. subscr. to: Box 90, Reading, Berkshire RG1 8JL, England. TEL 0734-560-080) Eds. E.B. Quint, N.S. Hecht. (also avail. in microform)
—BLDSC (4668.356000).
Refereed Serial

296   US   ISSN 0169-8354
K10
JEWISH LAW ANNUAL. (Supplement avail.) 1978. a. price varies. Harwood Academic Publishers, 820 Town Center Dr., Langhorne, PA 19047. TEL 215-750-2642. FAX 215-750-6343. (UK subscr. to: Box 90, Reading, Berkshire RG1 8JL, England. TEL 0734-560-080) Ed. Bernard S. Jackson. (also avail. in microform) **Indexed:** Old Test.Abstr. **Document type:** monographic series.
—UnCover.
Description: Presents research on laws in the Old Testament.
Refereed Serial

340 296   US   ISSN 1045-6015
JEWISH LAW IN CONTEXT. irreg. Harwood Academic Publishers, 820 Town Center Dr., Langhorne, PA 19047. TEL 215-750-2642. FAX 215-750-6343. (U.K. subscr. to: Box 90, Reading, Berkshire RG1 8JL, England. TEL 0734-560-080) Ed. N.S. Hecht. (also avail. in microform)
Refereed Serial

340   CC
JIN DUN/GOLDEN SHIELD. (Text in Chinese) m. Jin Dun Zazhishe, No. 25, Dongjiao Minxiang, Beijing 100006, People's Republic of China. TEL 5128871. Ed. Ma Weidong.

340   HU   ISSN 0209-5394
JOGASZ SZOVETSEGI ERTEKEZESEK. 1977. s-a. Magyar Jogasz Szovetseg, Szemere u.10, 1054 Budapest 5, Hungary. TEL 314-575. Ed. Laszlo Nagy.

349   HU   ISSN 0021-7166
JOGTUDOMANYI KOZLONY/LAW SCIENCES REVIEW; tudomanyos folyoirat mellekletekkel. (Text in Hungarian; summaries in English, German) 1866. m. $65. Jogtudomanyi Kozlony, Vaci u. 69-71, 1139 Budapest XIII, Hungary. TEL 36-1-1491-748. FAX 36-1-149-7747. (Subscr. to: Kultura, Box 149, H-1389 Budapest, Hungary) Ed. Imre Voros. bk.rev.; abstr. circ. 2,000.
—BLDSC (4670.400000).

JOHN HOWARD SOCIETY OF ALBERTA REPORTER. see *CRIMINOLOGY AND LAW ENFORCEMENT*

340   US   ISSN 0270-854X
K10
JOHN MARSHALL LAW REVIEW. 1967. a. $18. (John Marshall Law School) Christensen Inc. (Chicago), 315 S. Plymouth Ct., Chicago, IL 60604. TEL 312-987-1415. FAX 312-427-8307. Ed. Lance Peterson. adv.; bk.rev.; bibl.; charts; illus.; index. circ. 2,500. (also avail. in microform from UMI; reprint service avail. from RRI,UMI) **Indexed:** C.L.I., Crim.Just.Abstr., HRIS, L.R.I., Leg.Cont., Leg.Per.
●Also available online. Vendor(s): West Services, Inc.
—BLDSC (4671.117000); Faxon; UnCover; UMI.
Formerly (until 1979): John Marshall Journal of Practice and Procedure (ISSN 0021-7312)

JORNADAS NACIONALES DE DERECHO AERONAUTICO Y ESPACIAL. TRABAJOS. see *TRANSPORTATION — Air Transport*

343   BE   ISSN 0773-3453
JOURNAL DE DROIT FISCAL. 1927. bi-m. 3185 BEF (effective 1992). Maison Ferdiand Larcier S.A., Rue des Minimes 39, 1000 Brussels, Belgium. TEL 32-2-5124712. FAX 32-2-5139009. index. circ. 1,000. **Indexed:** ELLIS.
Formed by the 1974 merger of: Journal Pratique de Droit Fiscal et Financier (ISSN 0022-5495); Revue Fiscale (ISSN 0035-2810); Repertoire Fiscal (ISSN 0773-347X)

340   BE
▼ **JOURNAL DE TRIBUNAUX. DOSSIERS.** 1992. irreg., vol.2, 1992. price varies. Maison Ferdinand Larcier S.A., Rue des Minimes 39, 1000 Brussels, Belgium. TEL 32-2-5139009. FAX 32-2-5124712. **Document type:** monographic series.
Description: Extended monographic studies of specific aspects of Belgian and European law.

340   BE
JOURNAL DES JUGES DE PAIX. (Text in Dutch, French) 1891. m. (except July-Aug.). 4150 BEF (4600 BEF outside the EC) (effective 1994). Union Royale des Juges de Paix, c/o M. Benoit, Rue Fransman, 89, 1020 Brussels, Belgium. FAX 050-39-37-68. adv.; bk.rev.

349   BE   ISSN 0021-812X
JOURNAL DES TRIBUNAUX; hebdomadaire judiciaire. (Text in French) 1882. w. 9500 BEF (effective 1992). Maison Ferdinand Larcier S.A., Rue des Minimes 39, 1000 Brussels, Belgium. TEL 32-2-5124712. FAX 32-2-5139009. Ed. Roger O. Dalcq. bk.rev.; charts. **Indexed:** ELLIS.
Description: Publishes articles contributing to the understanding of legal theory, reports court decisions and jurisprudential issues, and chronicles the activities of the judiciary.
Refereed Serial

340   BE   ISSN 0778-9009
JOURNAL DES TRIBUNAUX DU TRAVAIL. 3/m. 9600 BEF (effective 1992). Maison Ferdinand Larcier S.A., Rue des Minimes 39, 1000 Brussels, Belgium. TEL 32-2-5124712. FAX 32-2-5139009. **Indexed:** ELLIS.
Description: Presents comprehensive information, reviews of doctrine and commentary on European labor law, social and social security law, and significant jurisprudence from the Cour de Cassation, all national jurisdictions, and the European Communities Court of Justice.

340   CN   ISSN 0833-921X
KEQ160
JOURNAL DU BARREAU; le journal de la communaute juridique. (Text in French) 1969. 20/yr. free. Barreau du Quebec, Maison du Barreau, 445 St-Laurent Blvd., Montreal, PQ H2Y 3T8, Canada. TEL 514-954-3440. FAX 514-954-3477. Ed. Leon Bedard. adv. contact: Yves Gougeon. bk.rev.; index; circ. 21,800 (controlled). (tabloid format; back issues avail.) **Document type:** academic/scholarly publication, corporate report.
Formerly: Barreau (ISSN 0381-7016)
Description: Provides the legal community with detailed information on events and subject matter directly related to the profession and the daily practice of law.

340   SA   ISSN 0258-252X
K24
JOURNAL FOR JURIDICAL SCIENCE/TYDSKRIF VIR REGSWETENSKAP. (Text in Afrikaans and English) 1976. s-a. R.20. University of the Orange Free State, P.O. Box 339, Bloemfontein 9300, South Africa. TEL 051-401-2309. Ed. Dirk C. Du Toit. cum.index. circ. 800. (back issues avail.)

340   GW   ISSN 0943-4011
JOURNAL FUER RECHTSPOLITIK. q. DM.140($88) Springer-Verlag, Heidelberger Platz 3, 14197 Berlin, Germany. TEL 030-8207-1. FAX 030-8214091. (Subscr. in N. America to: Springer-Verlag New York, Inc., 44 Hartz Way, Secaucus 07096-2491. TEL 201-348-4033. FAX 201-348-4505) **Document type:** academic/scholarly publication.

JOURNAL OF AFFORDABLE HOUSING AND COMMUNITY DEVELOPMENT LAW. see *HOUSING AND URBAN PLANNING*

LAW   3271

341   UK   ISSN 0021-8553
JOURNAL OF AFRICAN LAW. 1956. 2/yr. £26($50) (University of London, School of Oriental and African Studies) Oxford University Press, Oxford Journals, Walton St., Oxford OX2 6DP, England. TEL 0865-56767. FAX 0865-56646. TELEX 837330-OXPRES-G. (U.S. subscr. to: Oxford University Press Inc., 2001 Evans Rd., Cary, NC 27513. TEL 919-677-0977) Eds. Peter Slinn, Simon Coldham. adv. contact: Jane Parker. bk.rev.; bibl.; index. circ. 500. (also avail. in microfilm from WSH,PMC; reprint service avail. from WSH) **Indexed:** A.I.C.P., C.L.I., Curr.Cont.Africa, Documentatieblad, L.R.I., Leg.Per., P.A.I.S. **Document type:** academic/scholarly publication.
—BLDSC (4919.995000); Faxon; UnCover; SWETS. CCC.
Description: Covers a range of subjects including crime, family law, human rights, and nationality and constitutional law.

341.57   US   ISSN 0021-8642
K10
JOURNAL OF AIR LAW AND COMMERCE. 1930. q. $35 (foreign $42). S M U Law Review Association, Southern Methodist University, School of Law, Dallas, TX 75275. TEL 214-768-8250. FAX 214-768-3946. adv.; bk.rev.; bibl.; index, cum.index every 10 yrs. circ. 2,100. (also avail. in microform from UMI; microfilm from WSH,PMC; reprint service avail. from UMI,WSH) **Indexed:** C.L.I., Int.Aerosp.Abstr., L.R.I., Leg.Cont., Leg.Per., P.A.I.S. **Document type:** academic/scholarly publication.
●Also available online. Vendor(s): West Services, Inc.
—BLDSC (4926.420000); Faxon; UnCover; SWETS; UMI.

JOURNAL OF APPLIED BIOMATERIALS. see *MEDICAL SCIENCES — Experimental Medicine, Laboratory Technique*

349.73 700   US   ISSN 1061-0553
K10
JOURNAL OF ART & ENTERTAINMENT LAW. 1991. s-a. $20 (effective until Mar. 1994). Depaul University, College of Law, 25 E. Jackson Blvd., Chicago, IL 60604. TEL 312-362-5635. Ed. Leslie Morse. (back issues avail.) **Document type:** academic/scholarly publication.
●Also available online.
—UnCover.
Description: Covers intellectual property law, sports law, and art & entertainment law for legal practitioners, law professors and students.

340   US   ISSN 1063-2921
PN2000
JOURNAL OF ARTS MANAGEMENT, LAW, AND SOCIETY. 1969. q. $43 to individuals; institutions $86. (Helen Dwight Reid Educational Foundation) Heldref Publications, 1319 Eighteenth St., N.W., Washington, DC 20036-1802. TEL 202-296-6267. FAX 202-296-5149. Ed. Zell Rosenfelt. adv. contact: Raymond Rallo. bk.rev.; charts; illus.; stat.; index. circ. 700. (also avail. in microform from WSH,PMC; reprint service avail. from WSH) **Indexed:** Abstr.Bk.Rev.Curr.Leg.Per., Arts & Hum.Cit.Ind., Bk.Rev.Ind. (1985-), C.L.I., CHild.Bk.Rev.Ind. (1985-), Commun.Abstr., Curr.Cont., Ind.Bk.Rev.Hum., L.R.I., Leg.Cont., Leg.Per., Music Ind. **Document type:** academic/scholarly publication.
—BLDSC (4947.217500); Faxon; UnCover; UMI. CCC.
Former titles: Journal of Arts Management and Law (ISSN 0733-5113); (until 1982): Performing Arts Review (ISSN 0031-5249)
Refereed Serial

JOURNAL OF ASIA-PACIFIC BUSINESS. see *BUSINESS AND ECONOMICS — International Commerce*

340   US
JOURNAL OF BANKRUPTCY LAW AND PRACTICE. bi-m. $141.50 (overseas $210) (effective 1994). Warren Gorham Lamont, One Penn Plaza, New York, NY 10119. TEL 212-971-5000. (Subscr. to: The Park Square Bldg., 31 St. James St., Boston, MA 02116-4112. TEL 800-950-1207) Ed. Peter A. Alces. **Document type:** trade publication.

JOURNAL OF BUSINESS ETHICS. see *BUSINESS AND ECONOMICS*

LAW

340 951 K10 · US · ISSN 1041-7567
JOURNAL OF CHINESE LAW. 1987. s-a. (Center for Chinese Legal Studies) Columbia University, School of Law, 435 W. 116th St., Box C-10, New York, NY 10027. TEL 212-854-2628. FAX 212-854-7946. bk.rev.
—UnCover.

340 200 K10 · US · ISSN 0741-6075
JOURNAL OF CHRISTIAN JURISPRUDENCE. 1980. a. $9.95. Regent University, College of Law and Government, Virginia Beach, VA 23464. TEL 804-424-7000. Ed. Joseph N. Kickasola. circ. 300. **Indexed:** C.L.I.
—BLDSC (4958.272000); UnCover.

JOURNAL OF CHURCH AND STATE. see RELIGIONS AND THEOLOGY

JOURNAL OF CLINICAL ETHICS. see MEDICAL SCIENCES

340 K10 · US · ISSN 0093-8688
JOURNAL OF COLLEGE AND UNIVERSITY LAW. 1973. q. $40. (National Association of College and University Attorneys) Fred B. Rothman & Co., 10368 W. Centennial Rd., Littleton, CO 80127. TEL 303-979-5657. FAX 303-978-1457. Ed. Laura F. Rothstein. (back issues avail.; reprint service avail. from RRI,UMI) **Indexed:** Abstr.Bk.Rev.Curr.Leg.Per., C.I.J.E., C.L.I., Cont.Pg.Educ., L.R.I., Leg.Cont., Leg.Per. **Document type:** academic/scholarly publication.
—BLDSC (4958.799700); Faxon; UnCover; UMI.

JOURNAL OF CONTEMPORARY HEALTH LAW AND POLICY. see MEDICAL SCIENCES

340 K10 · US · ISSN 0097-9937
JOURNAL OF CONTEMPORARY LAW. 1974. s-a. $10. University of Utah, College of Law, Salt Lake City, UT 84112. TEL 801-581-6833. Ed.Bd. bk.rev.; index. circ. 350. (also avail. in microform from UMI; back issues avail.; reprint service avail. from RRI,UMI) **Indexed:** Abstr.Bk.Rev.Curr.Leg.Per., C.C.L.P., C.L.I., L.R.I., Leg.Cont., Leg.Per. **Document type:** academic/scholarly publication.
—BLDSC (4965.233000); Faxon; UnCover; UMI.

340 K10 · AT · ISSN 1030-7230
JOURNAL OF CONTRACT LAW. 1988. 3/yr. Aus.$135. Butterworths, 271-173 Lane Cove Rd., North Ryde, N.S.W. 2113, Australia. TEL 02-335-4444. FAX 02-335-4678. Ed. J.W. Carter. bk.rev. (back issues avail.) **Document type:** academic/scholarly publication.
Description: Forum, discussion and analysis of issues confronting contract lawyers.

653 Z54 · US · ISSN 1057-5847
JOURNAL OF COURT REPORTING. 1905. m. (Nov.-Aug.). $35. National Court Reporters Association, 8224 Old Courthouse Rd., Vienna, VA 22182-3808. Ed. Benjamin M. Rogner. adv.; index. circ. 32,000. **Indexed:** Bus.Educ.Ind.
Formerly: National Shorthand Reporter (ISSN 0028-0178)

JOURNAL OF CRIME & JUSTICE. see CRIMINOLOGY AND LAW ENFORCEMENT

JOURNAL OF DISABILITY POLICY STUDIES. see HANDICAPPED

340 · US · ISSN 1052-2859
JOURNAL OF DISPUTE RESOLUTION. 1984. s-a. $18. University of Missouri at Columbia, School of Law, 104 Hulston Hall, Columbia, MO 65211. Ed.Bd. adv.; bk.rev. **Document type:** academic/scholarly publication.
—Faxon.
Formerly: Missouri Journal of Dispute Resolution.

340 · US · ISSN 1046-7491
JOURNAL OF EMPLOYEE OWNERSHIP LAW AND FINANCE. 1989. q. $100. National Center for Employee Ownership, Inc., 2201 Broadway, Ste. 807, Oakland, CA 94612. TEL 510-272-9461. FAX 510-272-9510. Ed. Greg Shaw. circ. 300. (back issues avail.)
Description: In-depth articles on all aspects of law and finance relevant to employee ownership.

346.046 333.79 · UK · ISSN 0264-6811
JOURNAL OF ENERGY AND NATURAL RESOURCES LAW. 1984. 4/yr. fl.402($210) (effective 1994). (International Bar Association, Section on Energy and Natural Resources Law) Graham & Trotman Ltd. (Subsidiary of: Kluwer Academic Publishers Group), Sterling House, 66 Wilton Rd., London SW1V 1DE, England. TEL 44-71-821-1123. FAX 44-71-630-5229. (Dist. by: Kluwer Academic Publishers Group, P.O. Box 322, 3300 AH Dordrecht, Netherlands. TEL 31-78-524400. FAX 31-78-524474; N. America dist. addr.: Box 358, Accord Sta., Hingham, MA 02018-0358. TEL 617-871-6600. FAX 617-871-6528) (Co-sponsor: University of Dundee, Centre for Petroleum and Mineral Law Studies, UK) Eds. Thomas Walde, Alan C. Page. (also avail. in microform from UMI; back issues avail.) **Indexed:** ELLIS, Energy Info.Abstr. **Document type:** academic/scholarly publication.
—BLDSC (4978.302000); UnCover; SWETS.
Description: Provides comprehensive coverage of issues and events relevant to the law of energy and natural resources worldwide.
Refereed Serial

JOURNAL OF ENERGY, NATURAL RESOURCES AND ENVIRONMENTAL LAW. see ENERGY

JOURNAL OF ENVIRONMENTAL LAW. see ENVIRONMENTAL STUDIES

344.710 · CN · ISSN 1181-7534
JOURNAL OF ENVIRONMENTAL LAW AND PRACTICE. 1990. irreg. (2-3/yr.). (Environmental Law Centre) Carswell, One Corporate Plaza, 2075 Kennedy Rd., Scarborough, ON M1T 3V4, Canada. TEL 416-609-8000. FAX 416-298-5094. **Indexed:** Ind.Can.L.P.L.
—UnCover.

JOURNAL OF ENVIRONMENTAL REGULATION. see ENVIRONMENTAL STUDIES

JOURNAL OF HALACHA AND CONTEMPORARY SOCIETY. see ETHNIC INTERESTS

JOURNAL OF HAZARDOUS MATERIALS; management - handling - disposal - risk - assessment. see ENVIRONMENTAL STUDIES — Waste Management

JOURNAL OF HEALTH AND HOSPITAL LAW. see MEDICAL SCIENCES

JOURNAL OF HEALTH POLITICS, POLICY AND LAW. see MEDICAL SCIENCES

JOURNAL OF INDIVIDUAL EMPLOYMENT RIGHTS. see BUSINESS AND ECONOMICS — Labor And Industrial Relations

JOURNAL OF INSURANCE REGULATION. see INSURANCE

340 LAW · PL · ISSN 0075-4277
JOURNAL OF JURISTIC PAPYROLOGY. (Text in English, German, Italian and Russian) 1949. irreg., vol.19, 1983. price varies. (Uniwersytet Warszawski, Instytut Papirologii i Prawa Antycznego - Warsaw University, Institute of Papyrology and Ancient Laws) Wydawnictwa Uniwersytetu Warszawskiego, Ul. Obozna 8, 00-032 Warsaw, Poland. Ed. H. Kupiszewski. bk.rev. circ. 510.
—BLDSC (5009.700000).

JOURNAL OF LAND USE AND ENVIRONMENTAL LAW. see ENVIRONMENTAL STUDIES

340 330 LAW · US · ISSN 0022-2186 · CODEN: JLLEA7
JOURNAL OF LAW AND ECONOMICS. 1958. s-a. $27 to individuals; institutions $41; students $16. (University of Chicago Law School) University of Chicago Press, Journals Division, 5720 S. Woodlawn Ave., Chicago, IL 60637. TEL 312-753-3347. FAX 312-753-0811. TELEX 25-4603. (Subscr. to: Box 37005, Chicago, IL 60637) Ed.Bd. adv.; charts; stat.; cum.index: 1958-1972. circ. 3,400. (also avail. in microform from UMI) **Indexed:** A.B.C.Pol.Sci., ABI Inform, Amer.Hist.& Life, Bank.Lit.Ind., BPIA, Bus.Ind., C.L.I., C.R.E.J., Cont.Pg.Manage., Curr.Cont., Deep Sea Res.& Oceanogr.Abstr., ELLIS, Excerp.Med., Hist.Abstr., Int.Lab.Doc., J.of Econ.Lit., L.R.I., Leg.Per., Oper.Res.Manage.Sci., P.A.I.S., Soc.Sci.Ind., SSCI. **Document type:** academic/scholarly publication.
—BLDSC (5010.130000); Faxon; UnCover; SWETS; UMI.
Description: Focuses on the influence of regulation and legal institutions on the operation of economic systems, especially the behavior of markets, and the effect of governmental institutions on markets.
Refereed Serial

340 370 K10 · US · ISSN 0275-6072
JOURNAL OF LAW AND EDUCATION. 1972. q. $42.50 (foreign $51). Anderson Publishing Co., 2035 Reading Rd., Cincinnati, OH 45202. TEL 513-421-4142. FAX 513-562-8116. Eds. Laurence W. Knowles, Eldon D. Wedlock, Jr. adv.; bk.rev. circ. 2,500. (also avail. in microform from UMI; back issues avail.; reprint service avail. from UMI) **Indexed:** Abstr.Bk.Rev.Curr.Leg.Per., C.I.J.E., C.L.I., CJPI, Cont.Pg.Educ., Educ.Admin.Abstr., Educ.Ind., L.R.I., Leg.Cont., Leg.Per., Sp.Ed.Needs Abstr., SSCI. **Document type:** academic/scholarly publication.
—BLDSC (5010.132200); Faxon; UnCover; SWETS.

340 · US
JOURNAL OF LAW AND HEALTH. 1985. s-a. $20. Cleveland State University, Cleveland-Marshall College of Law, Cleveland, OH 44115. TEL 216-687-2336. **Indexed:** C.L.I., Hlth.Ind., Leg.Per.

340 025 · AT · ISSN 0729-1485
JOURNAL OF LAW AND INFORMATION SCIENCE. 1981. a. $85. University of Tasmania, Law Faculty, G.P.O. Box 252X, Hobart, Tas, 7001, Australia. (Dist. in N. America by: Wm. W. Gaunt & Sons, Inc., Gaunt Bldg., 3011 Gulf Dr., Holmes Beach, FL 34217-2199. TEL 813-778-5211. FAX 813-778-5252) **Indexed:** C.L.I.
—BLDSC (5010.132900).

340 610 · AT · ISSN 1044-6419
▼**JOURNAL OF LAW & MEDICINE.** 1993. q. Aus.$180. Law Book Co. Ltd., 44-50 Waterloo Rd., North Ryde, N.S.W. 2113, Australia. TEL 02-887-0177. FAX 02-888-9706. TELEX ASHBOOK 27995. Ed. Ian Freckelton.
—BLDSC (5010.132500); Faxon; UnCover.

320 340 · JA · ISSN 0387-2882
JOURNAL OF LAW AND POLITICS/HO-SEI KENKYU. (Text in Japanese; contents page in English) 1931. q. 1,000 Yen. Kyushu University, Institute of Law and Politics - Kyushu Daigaku Hosei Gakkai, c/o Faculty of Law, Kyushu University, Hakozaki, Higashi-ku, Fukuoka 812, Japan. bk.rev. **Indexed:** C.L.I., Jap.Per.Ind., Leg.Per.
—UnCover.

340 200 K10 · US · ISSN 0748-0814
JOURNAL OF LAW AND RELIGION. 1983. s-a. $15 to individuals (students $10); institutions $25. Hamline University School of Law, Journal of Law and Religion, 1536 Hewitt Ave., St. Paul, MN 55104. bk.rev. (also avail. in microfilm from WSH,PMC; reprint service avail. from WSH) **Indexed:** C.L.I., Rel.& Theol.Abstr. (1988-), Rel.Per. **Document type:** academic/scholarly publication.
—BLDSC (5010.170000); UnCover.

| 340 | UK | ISSN 0263-323X |
K2
JOURNAL OF LAW AND SOCIETY. 1974. 4/yr. £26($55) to individuals; institutions £91($193). Basil Blackwell Ltd., 108 Cowley Rd., Oxford OX4 1JF, England. TEL 0865-791100. FAX 0865-791347. TELEX 837022-OXBOOK-G. Ed. P.A. Thomas. adv.; bk.rev.; index. circ. 900. **Indexed:** A.B.C.Pol.Sci., Abstr.Bk.Rev.Curr.Leg.Per., Amer.Hist.& Life (until 1993), ASSIA, C.L.I., Crim.Just.Abstr., Hist.Abstr. (until 1993), Int.Polit.Sci.Abstr., L.R.I., Lang.& Lang.Behav.Abstr., Leg.Per., Soc.Work Res.& Abstr., Sociol.Abstr., Stud.Wom.Abstr.
—BLDSC (5010.180000); Faxon; UnCover; SWETS; UMI. **CCC.**
Formerly: British Journal of Law and Society (ISSN 0306-3704)

| 340 330.1 | US | ISSN 8756-6222 |
K10
JOURNAL OF LAW, ECONOMICS, AND ORGANIZATION. 1985. 2/yr. $28 to individuals; institutions $43 (effective 1994). Oxford University Press, Journals, 200 Madison Ave., New York, NY 10016. TEL 212-679-7300. FAX 212-689-5312. TELEX 6859654. (Subscr. to: Oxford Journals Fulfillment, 2001 Evans Rd., Cary, NC 25713. TEL 919-677-0977. FAX 919-677-1714) Ed. Alan Schwartz. circ. 1,090. **Indexed:** C.L.I., J.of Econ.Lit. **Document type:** academic/scholarly publication.
—BLDSC (5010.190000); Faxon; UnCover; SWETS; UMI. **CCC.**
Description: Interdisciplinary journal integrating legal-economic scholarship with other social science disciplines. Promotes an understanding of complex social phenomena by examining such matters from a legal, economic, and organizational perspective.
Refereed Serial

THE JOURNAL OF LAW, MEDICINE & ETHICS. see *MEDICAL SCIENCES — Forensic Sciences*

| 340 370 | US | ISSN 0022-2208 |
K10
JOURNAL OF LEGAL EDUCATION. 1937. q. $38 (foreign $42). Association of American Law Schools, Case Western Reserve University, 11075 East Blvd., Cleveland, OH 44106-7148. TEL 216-368-3304. FAX 216-368-3310. Ed.Bd. bk.rev.; index. (also avail. in microform from UMI; reprint service avail. from RRI,UMI) **Indexed:** Abstr.Bk.Rev.Curr.Leg.Per., C.I.J.E., C.L.I., Cont.Pg.Educ., Curr.Cont., High.Educ.Curr.Aware.Bull., L.R.I., Leg.Per., SSCI. **Document type:** academic/scholarly publication.
—BLDSC (5010.250000); Faxon; UnCover; SWETS; UMI.
Formerly (until 1940): National Jounal of Legal Education.
Description: Focuses on study and teaching.

| 340 | UK | ISSN 0144-0365 |
K10
JOURNAL OF LEGAL HISTORY. 1980. 3/yr. £32($48) to individuals; institutions £85 ($135). Frank Cass & Co. Ltd., Gainsborough House, 11 Gainsborough Rd., London E11 1RS, England. TEL 081-530-4226. FAX 081-530-7795. Ed. Andrew Lewis. adv.: B&W page £185; adv. contact: Anne Kidson. bk.rev.; index. (also avail. in microform from UMI; back issues avail.) **Indexed:** C.L.I., L.R.I., Lang.& Lang.Behav.Abstr., Leg.Per. **Document type:** academic/scholarly publication.
—BLDSC (5010.260000); Faxon; UnCover; UMI.
Description: Covers the history of the law of the British Isles as well as all significant developments in the countries of the Commonwealth, the US, and continental Europe.

JOURNAL OF LEGAL MEDICINE. see *MEDICAL SCIENCES*

| 340 | US | ISSN 0732-9113 |
K1
JOURNAL OF LEGAL PLURALISM AND UNOFFICIAL LAW. 1969. a. $20 to individuals; institutions $35. (Foundation for the Journal of Legal Pluralism) Fred B. Rothman & Co., 10368 W. Centennial Rd., Littleton, CO 80127. TEL 303-979-5657. FAX 303-978-1457. (Co-sponsor: University of California, Los Angeles, African Studies Center) Ed. John Griffiths. (back issues avail.; reprint service avail. from RRI) **Indexed:** C.L.I., Curr.Cont.Africa, Documentatieblad, Foreign Leg.Per., Leg.Per. **Document type:** academic/scholarly publication.
—BLDSC (5010.272000); UnCover.
Formerly (until 1981): African Law Studies (ISSN 0002-0060)

| 340 | US | ISSN 0047-2530 |
K10
JOURNAL OF LEGAL STUDIES. 1972. s-a. $27 to individuals; institutions $41; students $16. (University of Chicago Law School) University of Chicago Press, Journals Division, 5720 S. Woodlawn Ave., Chicago, IL 60637. TEL 312-753-3347. FAX 312-753-0811. TELEX 25-4603. (Subscr. to: Box 37005, Chicago, IL 60637) Eds. William M. Landes, Geoffrey P. Miller. adv.; bibl.; charts. circ. 1,500. (also avail. in microform from UMI,WSH; reprint service avail. from UMI,WSH) **Indexed:** A.B.C.Pol.Sci., C.L.I., CJPI, Crim.Just.Abstr., Curr.Cont., J.of Econ.Lit., L.R.I., Lang.& Lang.Behav.Abstr., Leg.Cont., Leg.Per., Risk Abstr., SSCI. **Document type:** academic/scholarly publication.
—BLDSC (5010.275000); Faxon; UnCover; SWETS; UMI.
Description: Presents theoretical and empirical research on law and legal institutions, emphasizing the use of social science research techniques to obtain new information about the actual functioning of legal systems.
Refereed Serial

| 340 | US | ISSN 0146-9584 |
K14
JOURNAL OF LEGISLATION. 1974. 2/yr. $16 in N. America & UK; elsewhere $18. University of Notre Dame, Notre Dame Law School, Notre Dame, IN 46556. TEL 219-631-5819. Ed. Vincent A. Sanchez. adv.; bk.rev.; bibl. circ. 1,500. (also avail. in microform from UMI,WSH; back issues avail.; reprint service avail. from WSH) **Indexed:** A.B.C.Pol.Sci., Abstr.Bk.Rev.Curr.Leg.Per., C.L.I., Energy Abstr., INIS Atomind., L.R.I., Leg.Cont., Leg.Per., P.A.I.S., Sage Fam.Stud.Abstr., Sage Pub.Admin.Abstr., Sage Urb.Stud.Abstr., Sociol.Abstr., Work Rel.Abstr. **Document type:** academic/scholarly publication.
—BLDSC (5010.276000); Faxon; UnCover.
Formerly: Notre Dame Journal of Legislation (ISSN 0360-4209); Which superseded: New Dimensions in Legislation (ISSN 0300-6018)
Description: Studies current public policy issues facing state, national and international legislative bodies.

| 340 341 | MY | ISSN 0126-6322 |
K10
JOURNAL OF MALAYSIAN AND COMPARATIVE LAW/JERNAL UNDANG-UNDANG. (Text in English and Malay) 1974. s-a. M.$30. (University of Malaya, Faculty of Law) University of Malaya Press, c/o University Library, Pantai Valley, 59100 Kuala Lumpur, Malaysia. FAX 03-7573661. TELEX MA-37453. Eds. P. Balan, Wan Arfah. adv.; bk.rev.; index, cum.index: vols. 1-4. circ. 500.

| 340 301.16 | UK | ISSN 0144-0373 |
K10
JOURNAL OF MEDIA LAW AND PRACTICE. 1980. 4/yr. £105. Tolley Publishing Co. Ltd., Tolley House, 2 Addiscombe Rd., Croydon, Surrey CR9 5AF, England. TEL 081-686-9141. FAX 081-686-3155. Eds. David Goldberg, Michael Rudin. adv.; bk.rev. **Indexed:** Commun.Abstr., Lang.& Lang.Behav.Abstr. **Document type:** trade publication.
—UnCover.
Incorporates: Advertising and Marketing Law and Practice; Which was formerly: Advertising Law and Practice (ISSN 0267-0763)
Description: Covers all aspects of law and practice governing the media in the UK and worldwide.

| 340 380.5 | CN | ISSN 0840-7754 |
JOURNAL OF MOTOR VEHICLE LAW. 1989. 3/yr. Can.$135. Carswell, One Corporate Plaza, 2075 Kennedy Rd., Scarborough, ON M1T 3V4, Canada. TEL 416-609-8000. FAX 416-298-5094. Eds. Murray D. Segal, Rick Libman. adv. contact: M. Lalani. bk.rev.; cum.index. **Indexed:** Ind.Can.L.P.L.
Description: Covers issues relating to driving offences arising from both criminal and highway traffic law. Includes an update of the most recent developments in the case law and legislation.

| 347.016 | US |
JOURNAL OF NOTARIAL ACTS AND RECORDKEEPING PRACTICES. 1974. a. $9.95. National Notary Association, 8236 Remmet Ave., Box 7184, Canoga Park, CA 91309-7184. TEL 818-713-4000. FAX 818-713-9061. Ed. Charles N. Faerber. (reprint service avail. from UMI)
Supersedes in part: Customs and Practices of Notaries Public and Digest of Notary Laws in the U.S.

| 340 | UK | ISSN 0307-4870 |
K10
JOURNAL OF PLANNING AND ENVIRONMENT LAW. 1948. m. £96. Sweet & Maxwell, South Quay Plaza, 7th Floor, 183 Marsh Wall, London E14 9FT, England. TEL 071-538-8686. FAX 071-538-9508. Ed. Lyndsay Walker. adv. contact: Jackie Wood. bk.rev.; index. (reprint service avail. from RRI) **Indexed:** ASSIA, Br.Archaeol.Abstr., Br.Tech.Ind., C.L.I., Environ.Abstr., Geo.Abstr., L.R.I., Leg.Cont., Leg.Per., P.A.I.S., RICS, Sage Urb.Stud.Abstr. **Document type:** bulletin.
●Also available online.
—BLDSC (5040.380000); UnCover; SWETS; UMI.
Formerly: Journal of Planning and Property Law (ISSN 0022-376X)

| 340 620 | UK | ISSN 0967-2680 |
K10
| | | CODEN: JPTLEW |
JOURNAL OF PRODUCTS AND TOXICS LIABILITY. 1977. 4/yr. £205($315) (effective 1994). Elsevier Science Ltd., Pergamon, P.O. Box 800, Kidlington, Oxford OX5 1DX, England. TEL 44-865-843000. FAX 44-865-843010. (Subscr. in U.S. and Canada to: Elsevier Science, 660 White Plains Rd., Tarrytown, NY 10591-5153. TEL 914-524-9200. FAX 914-333-2444) Eds. Verne L. Roberts, Kenneth Ross. adv.; charts; illus. circ. 1,000. (also avail. in microfilm from UMI; back issues avail.) **Indexed:** ABI Inform., BPIA, Bus.Ind., C.L.I., Consum.Ind., Curr.Cont., L.R.I., Manage.Cont., Risk Abstr., Tr.& Indus.Ind. **Document type:** academic/scholarly publication.
—BLDSC (5042.665000); EI; Faxon; UnCover; UMI. **CCC.**
Formerly (until vol.14, no.3, 1992): Journal of Products Liability (ISSN 0363-0404)
Description: Publishes original research papers from the legal as well as from technical fields such as engineering and medicine bearing upon issues of product safety and liability.
Refereed Serial

JOURNAL OF PROPRIETARY RIGHTS. see *PATENTS, TRADEMARKS AND COPYRIGHTS*

| 340 616.8 | US | ISSN 0093-1853 |
K10
| | | CODEN: JPSLAN |
JOURNAL OF PSYCHIATRY AND LAW. 1973. q. $45 to individuals; institutions $36. Federal Legal Publications, Inc., 157 Chambers St., New York, NY 10007. TEL 212-619-4949. Ed. Howard Nashel. adv.; bk.rev.; charts; stat. circ. 1,500. (also avail. in microfilm from UMI; back issues avail.; reprint service avail. from UMI) **Indexed:** Abstr.Bk.Rev.Curr.Leg.Per., Adol.Ment.Hlth.Abstr., C.L.I., Crim.Just.Abstr., Curr.Cont., Excerp.Med., Hlth.Ind., Ind.Per.Art.Relat.Law., L.R.I., Leg.Cont., Leg.Per., Mid.East: Abstr.& Ind., Psychol.Abstr., SSCI.
—BLDSC (5043.260000); Faxon; UnCover; UMI.

| 347.7 | US | ISSN 0022-4243 |
K10
JOURNAL OF REPRINTS FOR ANTITRUST LAW & ECONOMICS. 1969. s-a. $55. Federal Legal Publications, Inc., 157 Chambers St., New York, NY 10007. TEL 212-619-4949. Ed. William J. Curran, III. adv.; bk.rev.; mkt.; pat.; tr.mk.; index. circ. 1,500. (back issues avail.; reprint service avail. from UMI) **Indexed:** C.L.I., Leg.Per.
—Faxon.

JOURNAL OF REPRINTS OF DOCUMENTS AFFECTING WOMEN. see *WOMEN'S INTERESTS*

| 343.05 387.2 | II | ISSN 0377-0494 |
LAW
JOURNAL OF SHIPPING, CUSTOMS, AND TRANSPORT LAW. (Text in English) 1974. m. Rs.100. Milan Law Publishers, Box 4591, 15-2 Navjivan, Bombay 400008, India. Ed. A.B. Gandhi. adv.; bk.rev.; bibl. circ. 500.

JOURNAL OF SOIL CONTAMINATION. see *ENVIRONMENTAL STUDIES — Pollution*

| 340 | US | ISSN 0196-7487 |
JOURNAL OF THE LEGAL PROFESSION. 1976. a. $12. University of Alabama, School of Law, Box 870382, University, AL 35487-0382. TEL 205-348-4996. (also avail. in microform from WSH; reprint service avail. from WSH) **Indexed:** Abstr.Bk.Rev.Curr.Leg.Per., C.L.I., L.R.I., Leg.Per.
—BLDSC (5010.274000); UnCover; UMI.

3274 LAW

342 351.713 US ISSN 8756-0801
K25
JOURNAL OF URBAN & CONTEMPORARY LAW. Variant title: Washington University Journal of Urban & Contemporary Law. 1968. 2/yr. $20. Washington University, One Brookings Dr., Campus Box 1120, St. Louis, MO 63130-4899. TEL 314-889-6436. FAX 314-935-6493. adv.; bk.rev.; cum.index: 1968-1984. circ. 1,000. (also avail. in microfiche from WSH,PMC; microfilm WSH,PMC; back issues avail.) **Indexed:** C.L.I., Leg.Cont., Leg.Per.
—Faxon; UnCover.

JOURNAL OF WORLD TRADE. see *LAW — International Law*

JOURNAL RECORD. see *BUSINESS AND ECONOMICS*

340 FR ISSN 0756-3825
JOURNEES DE LA SOCIETE DE LEGISLATION COMPAREE. 1979. a. 350 F. Societe de Legislation Comparee, 28 rue St. Guillaume, 75007 Paris, France. TEL 44-39-86-23. FAX 44-39-86-28. (back issues avail.) **Document type:** proceedings.
Description: Collection of all the papers presented at the society's bilateral international conferences.

340 US ISSN 0022-5789
JUDGE. 1969. 8/yr. $8. Syracuse University College of Law, c/o Paul Mulligan, Ed., E.I. White Hall, Syracuse, NY 13210. TEL 315-443-2524. adv. circ. 300. (processed)

JUGOSLOVENSKA REVIJA ZA KRIMINOLOGIJU I KRIVICNO PRAVO. see *CRIMINOLOGY AND LAW ENFORCEMENT*

340 GW ISSN 0170-1452
K10
JURA; Juristische Ausbildung. 1979. m. DM.194 (students DM.128). Walter de Gruyter und Co., Genthiner Str. 13, 10785 Berlin, Germany. TEL 030-26005-0. FAX 030-26005251. TELEX 184027. (US addr.: Walter de Gruyter, 200 Saw Mill Rd., Hawthorne, NY 10532) Ed.Bd. index. (back issues avail.) **Document type:** trade publication.

340 330.9 MG
JURECO. 1986. m. $50. Immeuble S O M A G I, 120 rue Rainandriamampandry, 101 Antananarivo, Malagasy Republic. TEL 24145. FAX 20397. TELEX 22365. Ed. Mboara Andrianarimanana.

340 MX
JURIDICA. (Published under a different title each year.) 1969. a. $30. Universidad Iberoamericana, Departamento de Derecho, Prol. Paseo de la Reforma 880, Col. Lomas de Santa Fe, 01210 Mexico, D.F., Mexico. TEL 5-570-29-44. FAX 5-726-90-48. Ed. Jorge Diaz Estrada. circ. 1,000. **Document type:** academic/scholarly publication.
Description: Contians articles on topics related to Mexican law and comparative law.

349 UK ISSN 0022-6785
LAW
JURIDICAL REVIEW; law journal of Scottish universities. 1889. 2/yr. £48. W. Green, 21 Alva St., Edinburgh EH2 4PS, Scotland. Ed. J.P. Grant. adv.; bk.rev.; index. (reprint service avail. from RRI) **Indexed:** Abstr.Bk.Rev.Curr.Leg.Per., Br.Hum.Ind., C.L.I., L.R.I., Leg.Per.
—BLDSC (5075.560000); Faxon; UnCover; SWETS.

349 FI ISSN 0040-6953
K24
JURIDISKA FOERENINGEN I FINLAND. TIDSKRIFT. 1865. 6/yr. FIM 230. Juridiska Foereningen i Finland - Finnish Law Association, c/o Christian Wik, Centralgatan 7A, 00100 Helsinki, Finland. Ed. Edward Andersson. bk.rev. circ. 1,400. (reprint service avail.) **Document type:** academic/scholarly publication.

340 001.6 US ISSN 0022-6793
K10 CODEN: JURJAD
JURIMETRICS JOURNAL; journal of law, science and technology. 1959. q. $29 (foreign $33). American Bar Association, Science and Technology Section, 750 N. Lake Shore Dr., Chicago, IL 60611. TEL 312-988-5000. (Co-sponsor: Arizona State University, Center for the Study of Law, Science and Technology) Ed. David Kaye. bk.rev.; abstr.; bibl.; charts; illus.; index, cum.index. circ. 5,000. (also avail. in microfilm from UMI; reprint service avail. from RRI) **Indexed:** C.L.I., CJPI, Comput.Lit.Ind., Comput.Rev., Data Process.Dig., ELLIS, L.R.I., Law Ofc.Info.Svc., Leg.Per., Sci.Abstr. **Document type:** academic/scholarly publication.
—BLDSC (5075.565000); UnCover; SWETS.
Formerly: Modern Uses of Logic in Law (MULL).
Description: Legal issues in science and technology.

340 US ISSN 0022-6807
K10
JURIS. 1967. q. free. Duquesne University, School of Law, 900 Locust St., Pittsburgh, PA 15282. TEL 412-434-6305. adv.; bk.rev. circ. 5,500.

JURISDOCS. see *LIBRARY AND INFORMATION SCIENCES*

346.013 CN ISSN 0835-0892
JURISFEMME. (Editions in English, French) 1975. 3/yr. Can.$30 (effective 1992). National Association of Women & the Law - Association Nationale de la Femme et du Droit, 604 - 1 Nicholas St., Ottawa, ON K1N 7B7, Canada. TEL 613-241-7570. FAX 613-241-4657. Ed. Sandra Sellens. bk.rev.; index. circ. 1,000. (back issues avail.) **Document type:** newsletter.

340 JA ISSN 0022-6815
JURISPRUDENCE ASSOCIATION. JOURNAL/HOGAKU KYOKAI ZASSHI. (Text in Japanese; contents page in English) 1883. m. 15000 Yen. Jurisprudence Association - Hogaku Kyokai, c/o Faculty of Law, University of Tokyo, 7-3-1 Hongo, Bunkyo-ku, Tokyo 113, Japan. TEL 03-3812-2111. FAX 03-3816-7375. Ed. Kazao Sugeno. bk.rev.; index. circ. 1,450. **Document type:** academic/scholarly publication.

342 BE
JURISPRUDENCE DU DROIT SOCIAL. 1985. q. 3000 BEF. Etablissements Emile Bruylant, 67 Rue de Regence, B-1000 Brussels, Belgium. TEL 02-512-9845.
Formerly: Jurisprudence des Jurisdictions du Travail de Bruxelles.

340 CN ISSN 0830-0380
JURISPRUDENCE LOGEMENT. 4/yr. Can.$65. (Regie du Logement et des Tribunaux Civil) S O Q U I J, 715 Square Victoria, Bur. 800, Montreal, PQ H2Y 2H7, Canada. TEL 514-948-1222. (Subscr. to: Service Abonnements, CP 1190, Outremont, PQ H2V 4S7, Canada)

348.46 SP
JURISPRUDENCIA ARAGONESA. 1972. s-a. Colegio de Abogados de Zaragoza, Zaragoza, Spain. Ed. Miguel Monserrat. circ. 1,500.

340 AG ISSN 0326-1190
JURISPRUDENCIA ARGENTINA. (In 5 vols. including an index) 1918. a. $100 per volume. Jurisprudencia Argentina S.A., Talcahuano 650, 1013 Buenos Aires, Argentina. TEL 40-7850. Dir. Ricardo Estevez Boero. circ. 10,000.
Formerly: Anuario de Jurisprudencia Argentina.

349 BL ISSN 0022-684X
JURISPRUDENCIA E DOUTRINA. 1951. q. Cr.$60($12) (Ordem dos Advogados do Brasil, Secao do Ceara) Editora Juridica Ltda., Rua Princesa Isabel 639, Caixa Postal 428, Fortaleza, Ceara, Brazil. (Co-sponsors: Tribunal de Justica do Estado do Ceara; Tribunal de Justica do Estado da Bahia; Tribunal de Justica do Estado de Pernambuca) Ed. Jose Josino Da Costa. bk.rev.; cum.index: nos.1-35, nos.36-75. circ. 7,500.

340 NE ISSN 0924-4824
JURISPRUDENTIE VOOR GEMEENTEN. 1990. 10/yr. fl.120. V N G Uitgeverij, P.O. Box 30435, 2500 GK The Hague, Netherlands. TEL 31-70-3738788. FAX 31-70-3651826. adv. circ. 900. **Document type:** trade publication.

340 US ISSN 0022-6858
JURIST; studies in church order and ministry. 1941. s-a. $35. Catholic University of America, Department of Canon Law, Washington, DC 20064. TEL 202-319-5439. FAX 202-319-4967. Ed. Frederick R. McManus. adv.; bk.rev.; index, cum.index. circ. 2,100. (also avail. in microfilm from UMI; reprint service avail. from UMI) **Indexed:** Abstr.Bk.Rev.Curr.Leg.Per., C.L.I., Canon Law Abstr., Cath.Ind., CERDIC, L.R.I., Leg.Per. **Document type:** academic/scholarly publication.
—Faxon; UnCover; UMI.

340 378 CN ISSN 0829-5476
JURISTE. (Text in French) 1985. s-a. free. University of Moncton Law School, Moncton, NB E1A 3E9, Canada. TEL 506-858-4564. FAX 506-858-4534. bk.rev. circ. 2,400. (back issues avail.) **Document type:** newsletter.

338 DK ISSN 0107-699X
JURISTEN. 1918. s-m. DKK 400. Danmarks Jurist og Oekonomforbund, Gothersgade 133, DK-1123 Copenhagen K, Denmark. TEL 45-33-14-29-20.
Supersedes in part: Juristen og Oekonomen (ISSN 0108-2817); Which was formed by the 1976 merger of: Oekonomen (ISSN 0108-2809); Juristen (ISSN 0022-6874)

349 GW ISSN 0022-6882
LAW
JURISTENZEITUNG. 1951. s-m. DM.266 to individuals; students DM.134. Verlag J.C.B. Mohr (Paul Siebeck), Wilhelmstr. 18, 72074 Tuebingen, Germany. TEL 07071-923-0. FAX 07071-51104. TELEX 7262872-MOHR-D. (Subscr. to: Postfach 2040, 72010 Tuebingen, Germany) Ed.Bd. adv.; bk.rev. **Indexed:** CERDIC, ELLIS, INIS Atomind. **Document type:** bulletin.
—SWETS. **CCC.**
Description: Current aspects of German law, legislation and jurisdiction.

340 GW ISSN 0449-4342
JURISTISCHE ABHANDLUNGEN. 1964. irreg., vol.24, 1993. price varies. Vittorio Klostermann, Frauenlobstr. 22, 60487 Frankfurt a.M., Germany. TEL 069-774011. FAX 069-708038. (Subscr. to: Postfach 900601, 60446 Frankfurt a.M., Germany) **Document type:** monographic series.
—BLDSC (5075.592000).

349 AU ISSN 0022-6912
LAW CODEN: JUBLA7
JURISTISCHE BLAETTER; mit Beilage WBL Wirtschaftsrechtliche Blaetter. (Text in German) 1872. 12/yr. DM.426($266) Springer-Verlag, Sachsenplatz 4-6, Postfach 89, A-1201 Vienna, Austria. TEL 030-8207-1. FAX 030-8214091. (Subscr. in N. America to: Springer-Verlag New York, Inc., 44 Hartz Way, Secaucus, NJ 07096-2491. TEL 201-348-4033. FAX 201-348-4505) Eds. P. Rummel, H.R. Klecatsky. adv.; bk.rev.; illus.; index. (also avail. in microfiche from UMI; reprint service avail. from ISI) **Indexed:** ELLIS **Document type:** academic/scholarly publication.
—BLDSC (5075.595000). **CCC.**
Incorporated: Beilage Wirtschaftsrechtliche Blaetter (ISSN 0930-3855)
Description: Discusses various theoretical and practical problems in Austrian law.

DAS JURISTISCHE BUERO. see *BUSINESS AND ECONOMICS — Production Of Goods And Services*

349 GW ISSN 0022-6920
JURISTISCHE RUNDSCHAU. 1928. m. DM.344 (students DM.140). Walter de Gruyter und Co., Genthiner Str. 13, 10785 Berlin, Germany. TEL 030-26005-0. FAX 030-26005251. TELEX 184027. (US addr.: Walter de Gruyter, Inc., 200 Saw Mill Rd., Hawthorne, NY 10532) Ed. Olzen Troendle. adv.; bk.rev. **Document type:** trade publication.
—SWETS.

349 GW ISSN 0022-6939
LAW
JURISTISCHE SCHULUNG; Zeitschrift fuer Studium und praktische Ausbildung mit JUS-Kartei und JUS-Lernbogen. 1961. m. DM.135.20 (students DM.113.60). C.H. Beck'sche Verlagsbuchhandlung, Wilhelmstr. 9, 80801 Munich, Germany. TEL 089-38189-338. FAX 089-38189-398. TELEX 5215085-BECK-D. Eds. Hermann Weber, K.-P. Schroeder. adv.: B&W page DM.3900; color page DM.7800; trim 260 x 186. bk.rev.; index, cum.index every 5 yrs.; circ. 22,858 (controlled). (back issues avail.) **Document type:** academic/scholarly publication.
—SWETS.

340 NO ISSN 0332-7590
JURISTKONTAKT. 1967. m. (9/yr.). NOK 300. Norges Juristforbund, Juristenes Hus, Kr. Augustgt. 9, 0164 Oslo 1, Norway. TEL 02-11-68-68. FAX 02-11-51-18. Ed. Ulf Ertzaas. adv.: B&W page NOK 7900, color page NOK 12800; trim 190 x 230; adv. contact: Annelise Myreng. circ. 6,600. (back issues avail.) **Description:** News and events affecting the Norwegian legal community.

340 US
JURY SELECTION, 2-E. 1990. base vol. (plus a supplement). $95. Shepard's - McGraw-Hill, Inc., Box 35300, Colorado Springs, CO 80935-3530. TEL 800-525-2474. **Description:** Discusses everyday problems that arise in choosing a jury. Offers practical advice and solutions.

349 IT ISSN 0022-6955
K10
JUS; rivista di scienze giuridiche. 1940. 3/yr. L.95000 (foreign L.146000 ($120)) (effective 1994). (Universita Cattolica del Sacro Cuore) Vita e Pensiero, Largo Gemelli 1, 20123 Milan, Italy. TEL 02-72342310. FAX 02-72342260. TELEX 321033 UCATMI 1. Ed. Giorgio Berti. adv.; bk.rev.; bibl.; index.
—SWETS. **Description:** Covers political issues, looks at the contributions of debate within an institution and how this institution is faced by conflict within itself as well as socially.

340 PE
JUS; revista peruana de derecho. 1974. m. Editorial Jus, Paseo Colon 270, Of. 202, Lima, Peru.

349 NO ISSN 0022-6971
JUSSENS VENNER; a journal on the study of law. 1952. bi-m. NOK 490 in the Nordic countries; elsewhere NOK 550. Scandinavian University Press, P.O. Box 2959-Toeyen, N-0608 Oslo, Norway. TEL 472-67-7600. FAX 472-67-7575. (U.S. addr.: Scandinavian University Press, 200 Meacham Ave., Elmont, NY 11003. TEL 516-352-7300) Ed.Bd. adv. circ. 3,900. **Description:** Focuses on the study of law for law students as well as lawyers.

340 US ISSN 0738-6494
JUST COMPENSATION. 1957. m. $95. Just Compensation, Inc., Box 5133, Sherman Oaks, CA 91403. TEL 818-848-6765. Ed. Gideon Kanner. bk.rev.; index.

340 IS
JUSTICE. (Text in English, French, Spanish) a. International Association of Jewish Lawyers and Jurists, 10 Daniel Frish St., Tel Aviv, Israel. TEL 972-3-6910673. FAX 972-3-6953855. **Document type:** newsletter.
Former titles (until 1994): International Association of Jewish Lawyers and Jurists. newsletter; (until 1990): International Association of Jewish Lawyers and Jurists. Bulletin.

JUSTICE AND THE J.P. see *CRIMINOLOGY AND LAW ENFORCEMENT*

340 US
JUSTICE IN AMERICA SERIES.* 1969. irreg. $9.20 for 6 vols. (Law in American Society Foundation) Houghton Mifflin Co., 222 Berkeley St., Boston, MA 02116-3764. TEL 617-725-5000. FAX 617-227-5409. Ed. Robert H. Ratcliffe. bibl.; illus.
Formerly: Justice in Urban America Series.

JUSTICE INSTITUTE OF BRITISH COLUMBIA. ANNUAL REPORT. see *EDUCATION — Higher Education*

340 UK ISSN 0264-3731
KD291
JUSTICE OF THE PEACE REPORTS. 1838. 26/yr. £110. Justice of the Peace Ltd., Little London, Chichester, W. Sussex PO19 1PG, England. TEL 0243-787841. FAX 0243-779278. Ed. Nicholas Yell. index. (also avail. in microfiche from BHP; back issues avail.) **Document type:** newsletter.
—BLDSC (5075.670000). **Description:** Reports on specialist subjects: coroners law, consumer law, domestic proceedings, licensing law, local government law and road traffic law.

JUSTICE QUARTERLY. see *CRIMINOLOGY AND LAW ENFORCEMENT*

340 SP ISSN 0211-7754
JUSTICIA. 12/yr. Arturo Soria 241, portal 1-4o, 28033 Madrid, Spain. TEL 1-457-42-45. FAX 1-457-95-73. Ed. Fernando Becerra.

340 UY ISSN 0797-2695
JUSTICIA URUGUAYA. 1940. w. 25 de Mayo 555, Montevideo, Uruguay. Ed. Oscar Arias Barbe. circ. 3,000.

340 AT ISSN 0157-5317
JUSTINIAN. 10/yr. Aus.$195. Law Press of Australia, G.P.O. Box 3793, Sydney, N.S.W. 2001, Australia. TEL 02-360-7788. FAX 02-360-7838. Ed. Richard Ackland.

349 GW ISSN 0022-7064
JUSTIZ-MINISTERIAL-BLATT FUER HESSEN. 1949. s-m. DM.34.60. Ministerium der Justiz, Luisenstr. 13, 65189 Wiesbaden, Germany. bk.rev.; index. circ. 2,400. (tabloid format)

340 GW ISSN 0941-6781
JUSTUF; das Juramagazin. 1986. s-a. DM.20($20) Weimann Presse und Verlag, Boellerts Hoefe 3, 45479 Muehlheim, Germany. TEL 0208-426502. FAX 0208-428271. Ed. Tom Weimann. adv.; bk.rev.; bibl. circ. 52,000. (back issues avail.) **Description:** Magazine for young lawyers and law students.

JUVENILE JUSTICE DIGEST. see *CRIMINOLOGY AND LAW ENFORCEMENT*

340 GW ISSN 0943-8106
▼**K G REPORT BERLIN.** 1993. fortn. DM.300. Verlag Dr. Otto Schmidt KG, Unter den Ulmen 96-98, 50968 Cologne, Germany. TEL 0221-9373801. FAX 0221-93738941. TELEX 8883381. Ed.Bd. **Document type:** bulletin.

340 GW
K11
K T S - ZEITSCHRIFT FUER INSOLVENZRECHT, KONKURS, TREUHAND, SANIERUNG. 1939. q. DM.205. Carl Heymanns Verlag KG, Luxemburgerstr. 449, 50939 Cologne, Germany. TEL 0221-46010-0. FAX 0221-4601069. Ed. Juergen Mohrbutter. adv.; bk.rev.; abstr.; index. circ. 1,150. **Document type:** bulletin.
Formerly: Konkurs, Treuhand- und Schiedsgerichtswesen (ISSN 0023-3552)

KANAZAWA UNIVERSITY. FACULTY OF LAW AND LITERATURE. STUDIES AND ESSAYS. see *LITERATURE*

340 US
KANE COUNTY BAR ASSOCIATION BAR BRIEFS. m. Kane County Bar Association, 128 James, Box 571, Geneva, IL 60134. TEL 708-232-6416. Ed. Dan Kleinke. illus. **Document type:** newsletter.

KANO STATE OF NIGERIA GAZETTE. see *PUBLIC ADMINISTRATION*

340 AU ISSN 0259-0727
KANON. 1973. irreg., no.10, 1991. price varies. (Gesellschaft fuer das Recht der Ostkirchen) Verband der Wissenschaftlichen Gesellschaften Oesterreichs, Lindengasse 37, A-1070 Vienna, Austria. TEL 932166. **Indexed:** CERDIC.

340 JA ISSN 0388-886X
K11
KANSAI UNIVERSITY REVIEW OF LAW AND POLITICS. (Text mainly in English) 1980. a. exchange basis. Kansai University, Faculty of Law - Kansai Daigaku Hogakubu, Exchange Department (LP), Kansai University Library, P.O. Box 50, Suita, Osaka 564, Japan. TEL 06-330-1435. Ed. Katsumi Yamakawa. adv.; bk.rev. circ. 750. **Document type:** academic/scholarly publication.
—UnCover. **Description:** Each number examines a current policy issue of interest to the study of law and politics. Thorough discussions on the structure and content of treaties are presented with conclusions.

340 US ISSN 0022-8486
K2
KANSAS BAR ASSOCIATION. JOURNAL. 1932. 10/yr. $45 to non-members. Kansas Bar Association, 1200 Harrison, Box 1037, Topeka, KS 66601. TEL 913-234-5696. FAX 913-234-3813. Ed. Patti Slider. adv. contact: Patti Slider. bk.rev.; illus.; index, cum.index every 10 yrs. circ. 5,800. (also avail. in microform from UMI; reprint service avail. from WSH) **Indexed:** C.L.I., L.R.I., Leg.Per. **Document type:** academic/scholarly publication.
—Faxon; UnCover; UMI.
Incorporates (in Feb. 1986): Barletter.
Description: Covers association news and activities, court digests, practice aid articles.

340 613.1 US ISSN 1057-4174
KANSAS - IOWA ENVIRONMENTAL LAW LETTER. 1990. m. $137. (Armstrong, Teasdale, Schlafly & Davis) M. Lee Smith Publishers & Printers, 162 Fourth Ave., N., Box 198867, Nashville, TN 37219. TEL 615-242-7385; 800-274-6774. FAX 615-256-6601. Eds. George M. von Stamwitz, Norella V. Huggins. **Document type:** newsletter.
Supersedes in part (in 1991): Midwest Environmental Law Letter (ISSN 1049-9350) **Description:** Reports the latest state-specific developments in environmental laws that affect Kansas and Iowa companies.

340 IO ISSN 0215-4757
KEADILAN. 1973. bi-m. Rps.1000 per no. Islamic University of Indonesia, Faculty of Law - Universitas Islam Indonesia, Fakultas Hukum, Jalan Taman Siswa 158, Yogyakarta 55151, Indonesia. TEL 2978. Ed. Sobirin Malian. adv.; bk.rev.; circ. 2,500 (controlled).

340 500 US
KEJI YU FALU/SCIENCE, TECHNOLOGY AND LAW. (Text in Chinese) 1991. a. Y10. Beijing University, Law Department, Beijing Daxue Siyuan, Beijing 100871, People's Republic of China. **Description:** Covers legal applications in science and technology.

340 US ISSN 0164-9345
KENTUCKY BENCH & BAR. 1936. q. $15. Kentucky Bar Association, 514 W. Main St., Frankfort, KY 40601-1883. TEL 502-564-3795. FAX 502-564-3225. Ed. Gerald R. Toner. adv.; bk.rev.; illus.; index. circ. 10,675. (also avail. in microform from UMI; reprint service avail. from UMI) **Indexed:** C.L.I., L.R.I., Law Ofc.Info.Svc., Leg.Per. **Document type:** trade publication.
—Faxon; UnCover; UMI.
Formerly: Kentucky State Bar Journal (ISSN 0023-0367)

340 331 US ISSN 1052-4371
KENTUCKY EMPLOYMENT LAW LETTER. 1990. m. $94. (Greenbaum Doll & McDonald) M. Lee Smith Publishers & Printers, 162 Fourth Ave., N., Box 198867, Nashville, TN 37219-8867. TEL 615-242-7385; 800-274-6774. FAX 615-256-6601. Ed. Richard Cleary. **Document type:** newsletter. **Description:** Reports the latest Kentucky employment law developments that affect Kentucky companies.

LAW

340 US ISSN 0023-026X
LAW
KENTUCKY LAW JOURNAL. 1912. q. $28. University of Kentucky, College of Law, Lexington, KY 40506. TEL 606-257-4747. FAX 606-258-1061. Ed. Michele McCarthy. adv.; bk.rev.; index. circ. 1,000. (also avail. in microfiche from WSH,PMC; microfilm from RRI,WSH; back issues avail.) Indexed: C.L.I., L.R.I., Lang.& Lang.Behav.Abstr., Leg.Cont., Leg.Per., P.A.I.S., SSCI. Document type: academic/scholarly publication.
• Also available online. Vendor(s): West Services, Inc. —BLDSC (5089.645000); Faxon; UnCover; SWETS.

349 II ISSN 0023-0510
LAW
KERALA LAW JOURNAL. (Text in English) vol.15, 1971. w. Rs.20. Mathrubhumi Press, c/o Mr. C.P.M. Sundaram, T. D. Road, "Menons", Cochin 682011, Kerala, India.

349 II ISSN 0023-0529
LAW
KERALA LAW TIMES. (Text in English) 1949. w. Rs.100. High Court Rd., Ernakulam, Cochin 11, Kerala, India. Ed. M.C. Mathew. adv.; bk.rev.; abstr.; index. circ. 5,500.

340 SJ
KHARTOUM LAW REVIEW. 1979. a. (University of Khartoum, Faculty of Law) Khartoum University Press, Box 321, Khartoum, Sudan.

340 UK
KINGS COLLEGE LAW JOURNAL. 1936. a. $20. University of London, Kings College, School of Law, Strand, London WC2R 2LS, England. TEL 071-836-5454. FAX 071-873-2465. (back issues avail.)
Formerly: Kings Counsel.

340 AU ISSN 0259-0735
KIRCHE UND RECHT. irreg., no.19, 1992. price varies. Verband der Wissenschaftlichen Gesellschaften Oesterreichs, Lindengasse 37, A-1070 Vienna, Austria. TEL 932166.

340 690 CN
KIRSH'S CONSTRUCTION LIEN CASE FINDER. irreg. Can.$145. Butterworths Canada Ltd., Part of the Reed Elsevier group, 75 Clegg Rd., Markham, ON L6G 1A1, Canada. TEL 905-479-2265. FAX 905-479-2826. (looseleaf format)

340 388.3 UK ISSN 0308-8987
KITCHIN'S ROAD TRANSPORT LAW.* 1959. biennial. Reed Business Publishing Group (Subsidiary of: Reed Elsevier group), Rm. L431 Quadrant House, the Quadrant, Sutton, Surrey SM2 5AS, England. TEL 081-652-3284. FAX 081-652-3925. Ed. James Duckworth.
—BLDSC (5098.334000).

340 350 UK ISSN 0140-3281
KD4755.A2
KNIGHT'S LOCAL GOVERNMENT REPORTS. 1902. 11/yr. £295. Charles Knight Publishing, Tolley House, 2 Addiscombe Rd., Croydon, Surrey CR9 5AF, England. TEL 01-686-9141. FAX 01-686-3155. Ed. E.M. Wellwood. index. circ. 750. Document type: bulletin.
Formerly (until 1975): Knight's Local Government and Magisterial Reports.

340 JA ISSN 0075-6423
LAW
KOBE UNIVERSITY LAW REVIEW. INTERNATIONAL EDITION. (Text in English, French, German and other languages) 1961. a. Kobe University Law Review Association, Faculty of Law, Kobe University, Rokkodai-cho, Kobe-shi, Hyogo-ken 657, Japan. TEL 078-881-1212. FAX 078-802-3614. Ed. Aritoshi Fukunaga. circ. 460.
—BLDSC (5100.612000); UnCover.
Description: Covers legal issues in an international scope.

340 GR
KODIX NOMIKOU VEMATOS. s-m. Dr.7500. Athens Bar Association, Academia 60, 106 79 Athens, Greece. TEL 361-4289-290. FAX 36-10-537.

340 DK ISSN 0108-9811
KOEBENHAVNS UNIVERSITET. RETSVIDENSKABELIGT INSTITUT B. STUDIER. 1983. irreg. free. Koebenhavns Universitet, Retsvidenskabeligt Institut B, Studiegaarden, Studiestraede 6, 1455 Copenhagen K, Denmark. FAX 339-0552. Ed. Peter Blume. circ. 150.

KOKUGAKUIN UNIVERSITY. FACULTY OF LAW AND POLITICS. JOURNAL/KOKUGAKUIN HOGAKU. see POLITICAL SCIENCE

340 PL ISSN 0023-4478
LAW
KRAKOWSKIE STUDIA PRAWNICZE. (Text in Polish; summaries in English, French, German or Russian) 1968. a. price varies. (Polska Akademia Nauk, Oddzial w Krakowie, Komisja Nauk Prawnych) Ossolineum, Publishing House of the Polish Academy of Sciences, Rynek 9, Wroclaw, Poland. TEL 48-71-386-25. FAX 48-71-448-103. TELEX 0712771 OSS PL. Ed. Joseph Filipek. Document type: academic/scholarly publication.
Description: Theory of all branches of law. Comparative studies.

KRCKI ZBORNIK. see HISTORY — History Of Europe

KRIMINALVAARDSVERKETS FOERFATTNINGSSAMLING. see CRIMINOLOGY AND LAW ENFORCEMENT

KRITISCHE JUSTIZ. see POLITICAL SCIENCE — Civil Rights

340 GW ISSN 0179-2830
KRITISCHE VIERTELJAHRESSCHRIFT FUER GESETZGEBUNG UND RECHTSWISSENSCHAFT. 1917. q. DM.138. Nomos Verlagsgesellschaft mbH und Co. KG, Waldseestr. 3-5, 76530 Baden-Baden, Germany. TEL 07221-21040. FAX 07221-210427. Ed. P.-A. Albrecht. (reprint service avail. from SCH) Document type: academic/scholarly publication.
—CCC.

340 DK ISSN 0108-7878
KROGHS LOVINFORMATION. (Register for: Samling af Bekendtgoerelser, and Cirkulaeresamlingen, Indeholdende Samtlige Gaeldende Lovebestemmelse, Bekendtgoerelser, Anordninger, Cirkulaerer m.m.) 1983. q. DKK 860. Kroghs Forlag A S, Chr. Hansensvej 3, 7100 Vejle, Denmark.
Formerly: Kroghs Register (ISSN 0106-4878)

340 II
KURUKSHETRA LAW JOURNAL. (Text in English) 1971. a. Rs.7.50($2) Kurukshetra University, Faculty of Law, Kurukshetra 132118, Haryana, Punjab, India. Ed. S.C. Srivastava. bk.rev. circ. 700.

340 658 US
L A M A MANAGER. 1984. q. $45. Legal Assistant Management Association, 638 Prospect Ave., Hartford, CT 06105-4298. adv.; bk.rev. circ. 600. Document type: newsletter.
Formerly: Legal Assistant Management Newsletter.

346.013 CN
L E A F LINES. (Text in English, French) 1985. q. Can.$40. Women's Legal Education and Action Fund, 489 College St., Ste. 403, Toronto, Ont. M6G 1A5, Canada. TEL 416-963-9654. FAX 416-963-8455. Ed. Jane Craig. circ. 8,500. (also avail. in audio cassette)
Description: Describes test case litigation undertaken by LEAF based on sexual equality guarantees in Canadian Chartered Rights and Freedoms.

340 US
Z675.L2L53
L H & R B NEWSLETTER. 1991. s-a. free to members. American Association of Law Libraries, Legal History and Rare Books S I S, c/o Janet Snider, Ed., Duke University School of Law Library, Durham, NC 27706. TEL 919-684-6182. FAX 919-684-8770. adv. Document type: newsletter.

L I R S BULLETIN. (Lutheran Immigration and Refugee Service) see RELIGIONS AND THEOLOGY — Protestant

340 US ISSN 0731-9711
KF4208.5.L3
L R E REPORT. (Law-Related Education) 3/yr. free. American Bar Association, Youth Education for Citizenship, 541 N. Fairbanks Ct., 15th Fl., Chicago, IL 60611-3314. TEL 312-988-5735. FAX 312-988-5032. Ed. Paula Nessel. Document type: academic/scholarly publication.
Description: Contains current information on resources, instructional materials, forthcoming conferences, new projects, funding opportunities, and other developments in the field of LRE.

349 IT ISSN 0023-6462
LABEO; rassegna quadrimestrale di diritto romano. 1955. 3/yr. L.115000. Casa Editrice Dott. Eugenio Jovene, Via Mezzocannone 109, 80134 Naples, Italy. TEL 081-5521019. FAX 081-5520687. Ed. Antonio Guarino.

LABOR AND EMPLOYMENT IN CONNECTICUT. see BUSINESS AND ECONOMICS — Labor And Industrial Relations

LABOR & EMPLOYMENT IN MASSACHUSETTS; a guide to employment laws, regulations and practices. see BUSINESS AND ECONOMICS — Labor And Industrial Relations

LABOR AND EMPLOYMENT IN NEW YORK. see BUSINESS AND ECONOMICS — Labor And Industrial Relations

LABOR & EMPLOYMENT LAW. see BUSINESS AND ECONOMICS — Labor And Industrial Relations

347 US ISSN 0892-4449
LABOR AND EMPLOYMENT LAW ANTHOLOGY. 1993. a. $149.95. International Library Law Book Publishers, Inc., 101 Lakeforest Blvd., Ste. 270, Gaithersburg, MD 20877. TEL 301-990-7755. FAX 301-990-7642. Ed. Donald J. Hoyes. bibl.; index. Document type: monographic series.
Description: Selected US review articles on labor and employment, culled from over 900 US law review journals and printed in their entirety.

340 331.8 US
LABOR ARBITRATION ADVOCACY; effective tactics and techniques. 1989. base vol. (plus a. update). $80. Butterworth Legal Publishers (Salem) (Subsidiary of: Reed Elsevier plc), 8 Industrial Way, Bldg. C, Salem, NH 03079. TEL 800-548-4001. FAX 603-898-9858. Eds. Jay E. Grenig, R. Wayne Estes.

LABOR CONTRACT LAW BULLETIN. see BUSINESS AND ECONOMICS — Labor And Industrial Relations

340 331.1 US
LABOR LAW INSTITUTE. 1967. a. $100. Southwestern Legal Foundation, Attn: Carol Holgren, Ed., Box 830707, Richardson, TX 75083. TEL 214-690-2370. (also avail. in microfilm from RRI; reprint service avail. from RRI)
Formerly: Institute on Labor Law. Labor Law Developments. Annual Proceeding.

347.9 US ISSN 0023-6586
K12
LABOR LAW JOURNAL; to promote sound thinking on labor law problems. 1949. m. $120. Commerce Clearing House, Inc., 4025 W. Peterson Ave., Chicago, IL 60646. TEL 312-583-8500. bk.rev.; abstr.; charts; illus.; stat.; cum.index: 1949-1954, vols.1-5. circ. 3,000. (also avail. in microform from UMI; reprint service avail. from RRI) Indexed: B.P.I., BPIA, C.L.I., Curr.Cont., Int.Lab.Doc., L.R.I., Leg.Per., P.A.I.S., Pers.Lit., Risk Abstr., SSCI, Tr.& Indus.Ind., Work Rel.Abstr.
—BLDSC (5137.920000); Faxon; UnCover; SWETS.

LABOR LAW PERSONNEL NOTES. see LABOR UNIONS

340 331.8 US
LABOR LAW REPORTS. 1934. w. $2280. Commerce Clearing House, Inc., 4025 W. Peterson Ave., Chicago, IL 60646. TEL 312-583-8500. Ed. D. Newquist. (looseleaf format)

LABOR LAW REPORTS: SUMMARY. see BUSINESS AND ECONOMICS — Labor And Industrial Relations

LAW

347.9 US ISSN 8756-2995
K12
LABOR LAWYER. 1985. q. $23 (foreign $28). American Bar Association, Labor and Employment Law Section, 750 N. Lake Shore Dr., Chicago, IL 60611. TEL 312-988-6083. Ed. Robert Rabin. circ. 14,240. (back issues avail.) **Indexed:** Leg.Per. —BLDSC (5137.920100); Faxon; UnCover.
Description: Provides discussions of developments in all areas of employment to practitioners, judges, administrators, and public.

LABOR LETTER. see BUSINESS AND ECONOMICS — Labor And Industrial Relations

LABOR RELATIONS CIRCULAR. see BUSINESS AND ECONOMICS — Labor And Industrial Relations

LABOR RELATIONS IN MAINE. see BUSINESS AND ECONOMICS — Labor And Industrial Relations

LABOR RELATIONS LAW. see BUSINESS AND ECONOMICS — Labor And Industrial Relations

LABOR RELATIONS REPORTER. STATE LABOR LAWS. see BUSINESS AND ECONOMICS — Labor And Industrial Relations

LABORATORY REGULATION MANUAL. see MEDICAL SCIENCES — Experimental Medicine, Laboratory Technique

LABORWATCH. see BUSINESS AND ECONOMICS — Labor And Industrial Relations

LABOUR AND INDUSTRIAL CASES. see BUSINESS AND ECONOMICS — Labor And Industrial Relations

347.9 331.8 CN ISSN 0821-2635
KEB404.3
LABOUR ARBITRATION. (Text in English) 1978. a. price varies. Continuing Legal Education Society of British Columbia, 300-845 Cambie St., Vancouver, BC V6B 5T2, Canada. TEL 604-669-3544. FAX 604-669-9260. Ed. Karen Imeson. circ. 300. (looseleaf format; back issues avail.) **Document type:** proceedings.

347.9 331 II ISSN 0023-6977
LABOUR LAW JOURNAL. 1949. m. Rs.300. 18 Daiva Sigamani Rd., Madras 600 014, India. TEL 471621. Ed.Bd. adv.; charts; index every 6 mos. cum.index covering 11 yrs. circ. 5,000. **Indexed:** Bus.Ind.

LABOUR LAW REPORTER; a magazine of decision makers. see BUSINESS AND ECONOMICS — Labor And Industrial Relations

LABOUR LEGISLATION IN NOVA SCOTIA. see BUSINESS AND ECONOMICS — Labor And Industrial Relations

LABOUR TIMES. see BUSINESS AND ECONOMICS — Labor And Industrial Relations

340 US ISSN 0023-7078
LAW
LACKAWANNA JURIST. 1879. w. $35. Lackawanna Bar Association, 205 1 Pyramid Center, Corner Spruce and Wyoming Aves., Scranton, PA 19503. TEL 717-969-9161. FAX 717-969-9150. Ed. Cheryl Watson. adv. circ. 650. (also avail. in microform) **Document type:** newsletter.

LAG & AVTAL; tidningen om arbetsraett i praktiken. see BUSINESS AND ECONOMICS — Labor And Industrial Relations

LAGBOK FOER ARBETSMARKNADEN. see BUSINESS AND ECONOMICS — Labor And Industrial Relations

340 FI ISSN 0023-7353
LAW
LAKIMIES. 8/yr. FIM 55. Suomalainen Lakimiesyhdistys, Bulevardi 32 B, FIN-00120 Helsinki, Finland. bk.rev.; index.

340 FI ISSN 0023-7361
LAKIMIESUUTISET/JURISTNYTT. (Text in Finnish and Swedish) 1945. m. FIM 170. Suomen Lakimiesliitto - Union of Finnish Lawyers, Uudenmaankatu 4-6 B, 00120 Helsinki, Finland. TEL 90-649201. FAX 90-602139. Eds. Liisa Groenroos, Juha Mikkonen. adv.; bk.rev.; stat. circ. 12,112.

LAMBDA UPDATE. see HOMOSEXUALITY

346.066 600 FR
LAMY DROIT DE L'INFORMATIQUE; informatique, telematique, reseaux. (Supplement avail.: Lamy Droit de l'Informatique - Formulaire) a. 2060 F. (effective 1994). Lamy S.A., 187-189 Quai de Valmy, 75490 Paris Cedex 10, France. TEL 44-72-13-43. FAX 44-72-13-95.
Description: Treats questions of law raised by new technologies - expert systems, integrated circuits, video games.

346.066 330 FR
LAMY DROIT ECONOMIQUE; concurrence, distribution, consommation. (Supplement avail.: Lamy Droit Economique - Formulaire) a. 1670 F. (effective 1994). Lamy S.A., 187-189 Quai de Valmy, 75490 Paris, France. TEL 44-72-13-43. FAX 44-72-13-93.
Description: Provides in-depth analysis of the economics of competition, distribution and consumption.

346.066 332 FR
LAMY FISCAL; l'outil pratique pour connaitre et exploiter la reglementation fiscale. a. 1880 F. (effective 1994). Lamy S.A., 187-189 Quai de Valmy, 75490 Paris, France. TEL 44-72-13-43. FAX 44-72-13-95. charts; index.
•Also available on CD-ROM.
Description: Covers corporate, income, state, local and vehicular taxes, Value Added Tax, penal laws and special regulations.

346.066 330 FR
LAMY SOCIAL; droit du travail et de la securite sociale. (Supplement avail.: Lamy Social Formulaire) a. 1590 F. (effective 1994). Lamy S.A., 187-189 Quai de Valmy, 75490 Paris, France. TEL 44-72-13-43. FAX 44-72-13-95. charts; index.
•Also available on CD-ROM.
Description: Aims to evaluate new legislative texts and the fluctuation and evolution of jurisprudence.

340 CC
LAN DUN/BLUE SHIELD. (Text in Chinese) 1985. m. Y30 (effective 1994). (Tianji Shi Faxuehui) Tianji Ribao She, 62 Tangshan Rd., Heping-qu, Tianjin 300040, People's Republic of China. TEL 022-303866. FAX 022-303866. (Subscr. to: Tianjin Publishing Trading Corp., Books Dept., No. 130 Chi Feng Dao, Tianjin, P.R. China. TEL 022-707858) Ed. Zhu Qihua. adv.: page $1500; adv. contact: San Guoying. **Document type:** newsletter.
Description: Contains short stories and novels about the fight against criminal offences. Also discusses relevant social issues.

340 628 AT
▼**LAND AND ENVIRONMENT COURT LAW AND PRACTICE NEW SOUTH WALES.** 1993. irreg.? $275. Law Book Co. Ltd., 44-50 Waterloo Rd., North Ryde, N.S.W. 2113, Australia. TEL 02-887-0177. FAX 02-888-9706. TELEX ASBOOK 27995. (Dist. in N. America by: Wm. W. Gaunt & Sons, Inc., Gaunt Bldg., 3011 Gulf Dr., Holmes Beach, FL 34217-2199. TEL 813-778-5211. FAX 813-778-5252) Ed. Terry Naughton. (looseleaf format)

340 US ISSN 0023-7612
K12
LAND AND WATER LAW REVIEW. 1966. s-a. $18 to non-members. University of Wyoming, College of Law, Box 3035, University Sta., Laramie, WY 82070. TEL 307-766-3359. FAX 307-766-4044. (Co-sponsors: Wyoming State Bar; Water Resources Research Institute) adv.; bk.rev.; cum.index: vols. 1-20. circ. 2,150. (also avail. in microform from UMI,WSH,PMC; reprint service avail. from WSH) **Indexed:** Bibl.& Ind.Geol., C.L.I., Energy Info.Abstr., Environ.Abstr, INIS Atomind., L.R.I., Leg.Per., Ocean.Abstr., Pollut.Abstr., Sel.Water Res.Abstr. **Document type:** academic/scholarly publication.
—BLDSC (5146.790000); CIS; Faxon; UnCover; UMI.
Incorporates: Wyoming Law Journal.

340 CN ISSN 0380-4208
KE5175.A45
LAND COMPENSATION REPORTS. 1971. m. (with q. cumulations). Can.$108. Canada Law Book Inc., 240 Edward St., Aurora, ON L4G 3S9, Canada. TEL 905-841-6472. FAX 905-841-5085. adv. contact: Mary Cull.

340 333.33 US ISSN 1058-7012
LAND USE FORUM; a journal of law, policy, and practice. 1991. 4/yr. $225. Continuing Education of the Bar - California, University of California Extension, 2300 Shattuck Ave., Berkeley, CA 94704. TEL 510-642-2064; 800-924-3924. FAX 510-642-3788. (Co-sponsor: State Bar of California) Ed. Johanna Sherlin. bk.rev. (tabloid format; back issues avail.)
Description: Addresses land use issues at an advanced level from the standpoints of law, policy, and practice. Explores key issues recently developing as they relate to land use process.

LAND USE LAW AND ZONING DIGEST. see REAL ESTATE

LAND USE LAW REPORT. see HOUSING AND URBAN PLANNING

340 US
LANDMARK LITIGATION REPORT. 1976. q. free. Landmark Legal Foundation, 1006 Grand Ave., 8th Fl., Kansas City, MO 64106. TEL 816-474-6600. FAX 816-474-6609. Ed. Jerald L. Hill. circ. 4,500. (back issues avail.) **Document type:** newsletter.

LANSKY: BIBLIOTHEKSRECHTLICHE VORSCHRIFTEN. see LIBRARY AND INFORMATION SCIENCES

LATIN AMERICA SERVICE. see BUSINESS AND ECONOMICS — Investments

LAVORO E DIRITTO. see LABOR UNIONS

340 AU ISSN 0259-0816
K12
LAW & ANTHROPOLOGY; internationales Jahrbuch fuer Rechtsanthropologie. 1986. a. price varies. Verband der Wissenschaftlichen Gesellschaften Oesterreichs, Lindengasse 37, A-1070 Vienna, Austria. TEL 932166. (Co-sponsor: Klaus Renner Verlag) **Indexed:** Anthropol.Lit.
—SWETS.

346.066 US
LAW & BUSINESS DIRECTORY OF BANKRUPTCY ATTORNEYS (YEAR). a. $225. Prentice Hall Law & Business, 270 Sylvan Ave., Englewood Cliffs, NJ 07632-2513. TEL 201-894-8484. FAX 201-894-8666. **Document type:** directory.

340 US ISSN 0023-9186
K12
LAW AND CONTEMPORARY PROBLEMS. 1933. q. $45 (foreign $51). Duke University, School of Law, Box 90364, Durham, NC 27708-0364. TEL 919-684-5966. FAX 919-684-3417. Ed. Theresa N. Glover. adv.; index. circ. 2,100. (also avail. in microfilm from RRI; reprint service avail. from KTO,RRI) **Indexed:** A.B.C.Pol.Sci., Account.Ind. (1974-), ASSIA, C.L.I., Commun.Abstr., Crim.Just.Abstr., Curr.Cont., Energy Ind., Energy Info.Abstr., J.of Econ.Lit., L.R.I., Lang.& Lang Behav.Abstr., Leg.Cont., Leg.Per., Mar.Aff.Bibl., Mid.East: Abstr.& Ind., P.A.I.S., Soc.Sci.Ind., SSCI. —BLDSC (5161.350000); Faxon; UnCover; SWETS.

340 UK ISSN 0957-8536
CODEN: LACREI
LAW AND CRITIQUE; journal of critical legal studies. 1990. 2/yr. £40 (effective 1994). Deborah Charles Publications, 173 Mather Ave., Liverpool LI8 6JZ, England. TEL 44-51-724-2500. FAX 44-51-729-0371. (Dist. in US by: Wm. W. Gaunt & Sons, Inc., Gaunt Bldg., 3011 Gulf Dr., Holmes Beach, FL 34217-2199. TEL 813-778-5211. FAX 813-778-5252) Ed. P. Goodrich. adv.; bk.rev. circ. 400. **Document type:** academic/scholarly publication.
—BLDSC (5161.350700); UnCover.

340 US
LAW AND ETHICS SERIES. (Former name of issuing body: Academy for Contemporary Problems) 1977. irreg. Academy for State and Local Government, 444 N. Capitol St., N.W., Ste. 345, Washington, DC 20001. TEL 202-434-4851. FAX 202-434-4850.

LAW

340 US ISSN 0738-2480
K12
LAW AND HISTORY REVIEW. 1983. s-a. $35 to individuals (foreign $40); institutions $50 (foreign $55). (American Society for Legal History) University of Illinois Press, 1325 S. Oak St., Champaign, IL 61820. TEL 217-244-0626. FAX 217-244-8082. Ed. Michael Grossberg. adv.; bk.rev. circ. 1,350. (also avail. in microform from UMI) **Indexed:** Amer.Hist.& Life, C.L.I., Hist.Abstr., Leg.Per. **Document type:** academic/scholarly publication.
—BLDSC (5161.351500); Faxon; UnCover; UMI. **CCC.**
Refereed Serial

340 150 US ISSN 0147-7307
K12 CODEN: LHBEDM
LAW AND HUMAN BEHAVIOR. 1977. bi-m. $315 (foreign $370) (effective 1994). Plenum Publishing Corp., 233 Spring St., New York, NY 10013-1578. TEL 212-620-8000. FAX 212-463-0742. TELEX 23-421139. Ed. Ronald Roesch. adv. (also avail. in microfilm from JSC; back issues avail.) **Indexed:** Adol.Ment.Hlth.Abstr., Biol.Abstr., C.L.I., Crim.Just.Abstr., Curr.Cont., Excerp.Med., L.R.I., Lang.& Lang.Behav.Abstr., Leg.Per., Psychol.Abstr., Psycscan, Sociol.Abstr., SSCI. **Document type:** academic/scholarly publication.
—BLDSC (5161.352500); Faxon; UnCover; SWETS; UMI. **CCC.**
Refereed Serial

340 US ISSN 0737-089X
K12
LAW & INEQUALITY; a journal of theory and practice. 1983. 2/yr. $15. University of Minnesota, Law School, 229 19th Ave. S., Minneapolis, MN 55455. TEL 612-625-8034. Ed. David P. Swenson. bk.rev. circ. 5,600. (also avail. in microform from WSH; back issues avail.; reprint service avail. from WSH) **Indexed:** C.L.I., Leg.Per.
—BLDSC (5161.352700); Faxon; UnCover.

340 BG
LAW AND INTERNATIONAL AFFAIRS. (Text in English) 1975. s-a. $6. Bangladesh Institute of Law and International Affairs, 501 Dhanmondi Residential Area, Rd. No. 7, Dhaka 5, Bangladesh. (Dist. by: Karim International, 3, Padmalochon Roy Ln., Mahutuly, Dhaka 1, Bangladesh) Ed. Kamruddin Ahmed. bk.rev. circ. 2,000.

340 UK ISSN 0269-817X
LAW & JUSTICE. 1962. s-a. £12.50 (foreign £13.50). Edmund Plowden Trust, 100A Hazellville Rd., London N19 3NA, England. Ed. John Duddington. adv.; bk.rev. bibl. circ. 250. **Indexed:** C.L.I., Canon Law Abstr, CERDIC, L.R.I.
—BLDSC (5161.353000).
Formerly: Quis Custodiet (ISSN 0033-6610)

340 347 US ISSN 0740-090X
KF190
LAW AND LEGAL INFORMATION DIRECTORY. 1980. biennial. $320 (effective Oct. 1992). Gale Research Inc., 835 Penobscot Bldg., Detroit, MI 48226. TEL 313-961-2242. FAX 313-961-6083. TELEX 810-221-7086. Eds. Jacqueline Wasserman O'Brien, Steven Wasserman. **Document type:** directory.
Description: Guide to law enforcement organizations and legal information in the U.S.

340 100 NE ISSN 0167-5249
K12 CODEN: LAWPDG
LAW AND PHILOSOPHY; an international journal for jurisprudence and legal philosophy. 1982. 4/yr. fl.343($179) (effective 1994). Kluwer Academic Publishers, Postbus 17, 3300 AA Dordrecht, Netherlands. TEL 31-78-334911. FAX 31-78-334254. TELEX 29245 KAPG NL. (Dist. by: Kluwer Academic Publishers Group, P.O. Box 322, 3300 AH Dordrecht, Netherlands. TEL 31-78-524400. FAX 31-78-524474; N. America dist. addr.: Box 358, Accord Sta., Hingham, MA 02018-0358. TEL 617-871-6600. FAX 617-871-6528) Eds. A. Mabe, Roxane Fletcher. adv.; bk.rev. (also avail. in microform from UMI; back issues avail.; reprint service avail. from SWZ) **Indexed:** ASCA, C.L.I., Curr.Cont., L.R.I., Lang.& Lang.Behav.Abstr., Leg.Cont., Leg.Per., Phil.Ind., Sociol.Abstr., SSCI. **Document type:** academic/scholarly publication.
—BLDSC (5161.362600); Faxon; UnCover; SWETS; UMI. **CCC.**
Refereed Serial

340 100 NE
LAW AND PHILOSOPHY LIBRARY. 1985. irreg., vol.18, 1993. price varies. Kluwer Academic Publishers, Spuiboulevard 50, Postbus 17, 3300 AA Dordrecht, Netherlands. TEL 31-78-334911. FAX 31-78-334254. TELEX 29245 KAPG NL. (Dist. by: Kluwer Academic Publishers Group, P.O. Box 322, 3300 AH Dordrecht, Netherlands. TEL 31-78-524400. FAX 31-78-524474; N. America dist. addr.: Box 358, Accord Sta., Hingham, MA 02018-0358. TEL 617-871-6600. FAX 617-871-6528) Eds. Alan Mabe, Aulis Aarnio. **Document type:** monographic series.
Refereed Serial

340 320 UK ISSN 0265-8240
K12 CODEN: LAPOE6
LAW & POLICY. 1979. q. £31($45) to individuals; institutions £74($110). Basil Blackwell Ltd., 108 Cowley Rd., Oxford OX4 1JF, England. TEL 0865-791100. FAX 0865-791347. TELEX 837022-OXBOOK-G. Ed.Bd. adv.; bk.rev.; bibl.; charts; stat.; index. circ. 700. (also avail. in microform; reprint service avail. from WSH) **Indexed:** A.B.C.Pol.Sci., Amer.Hist.& Life (until 1993), C.L.I., Crim.Just.Abstr., Hist.Abstr. (until 1993), L.R.I., Mid.East: Abstr.& Ind., Sage Pub.Admin.Abstr.
—BLDSC (5161.362800); Faxon; UnCover; SWETS; UMI. **CCC.**
Formerly: Law and Policy Quarterly (ISSN 0164-0267)

340 320 KO
LAW AND POLITICAL REVIEW. (Text in Korean; table of contents in English) 1958. a. Ewha Women's University, College of Law and Political Science, 11-1 Dai-Hyun-dong, Seodaimoon-ku, Seoul, S. Korea. bibl.

340 II ISSN 0377-0850
LAW AND PROGRESS.* (Text in English) 1974. q. Rs.18. Indian Association of Lawyers, 29-B Maharani Bagh, New Delhi, India. Ed. Harish Chandra. bk.rev.; bibl.

340 300 616.8 US ISSN 0098-5961
K12
LAW AND PSYCHOLOGY REVIEW. 1975. a. $12. University of Alabama, School of Law, Box 870382, Tuscaloosa, AL 35487-0382. TEL 205-348-4527. adv.; bk.rev. circ. 400. (also avail. in microfilm from WSH,PMC; reprint service avail. from WSH) **Indexed:** Adol.Ment.Hlth.Abstr., C.L.I., Crim.Just.Abstr., L.R.I., Leg.Per., Psychol.Abstr., Psycscan.
—BLDSC (5161.363800); UnCover.

340 301.415 US
LAW & SEXUALITY; a review of lesbian and gay legal issues. a. Tulane University, School of Law, New Orleans, LA 70118.

340 US ISSN 0897-6546
K1
LAW AND SOCIAL INQUIRY. 1976. q. $36 to individuals; institutions $59; academic $29. (American Bar Foundation) University of Chicago Press, Journals Division, 5720 S. Woodlawn Ave., Chicago, IL 60637. TEL 312-753-3347. FAX 312-753-0811. TELEX 25-4603. (Subscr. to: Box 37005, Chicago, IL 60637) Ed.Bd. bibl. circ. 6,700. (also avail. in microform from UMI; back issues avail.; reprint service avail. from RRI) **Indexed:** Abstr.Bk.Rev.Curr.Leg.Per., C.L.I., CJPI, Crim.Just.Abstr., Curr.Cont., L.R.I., Law Ofc.Info.Svc., Leg.Cont., Leg.Per., SSCI. **Document type:** academic/scholarly publication.
—BLDSC (5161.364300); Faxon; UnCover; SWETS; UMI. **CCC.**
Formerly: American Bar Foundation Journal (ISSN 0361-9486)
Description: Provides empirical studies on the legal system. Reviews social issues and includes notes annotating recent legal publications in law and social science.
Refereed Serial

340 US ISSN 8755-7088
KF200.L36
LAW & SOCIETY NEWSLETTER. 3/yr. free to members. Law & Society Association, Hampshire House, University of Massachusetts, Amherst, MA 01003. TEL 413-545-4617. FAX 413-545-1640. Ed. Ronald Pipkin. circ. 2,400. **Document type:** newsletter.

340 300 US ISSN 0023-9216
K12
LAW & SOCIETY REVIEW. 1966. 4/yr. $96 (foreign $101) (effective 1994). Law and Society Association, Hampshire House, University of Massachusetts, Amherst, MA 01003. TEL 413-545-4617. FAX 413-545-1640. Ed. Frank Munger. adv.; bk.rev.; bibl.; charts. circ. 2,400. (also avail. in microform from UMI; microfiche from WSH; microfilm from RRI,WSH; back issues avail.; reprint service avail. from ISI) **Indexed:** A.B.C.Pol.Sci., Abstr.Crim.& Pen., Acad.Ind., Adol.Ment.Hlth.Abstr., Amer.Hist.& Life, Anthropol.Lit., ASSIA, C.L.I., Crim.Just.Abstr., Curr.Cont., E.I., Hist.Abstr, HRIS, Int.Bibl.Soc.Sci., L.R.I., Lang.& Lang.Behav.Abstr., Leg.Cont., Leg.Per., P.A.I.S., Psychol.Abstr., Sage Urb.Stud.Abstr., Soc.Sci.Ind., Soc.Work Res.& Abstr., Sociol.Abstr. (1966-), SSCI.
—BLDSC (5161.365000); Faxon; UnCover; SWETS; UMI.
Description: Examines the relationship between society and the legal process. Includes the cultural, economic, political, psychological, and social aspects of law and the legal system.

323.42 US
LAW & WOMEN SERIES.* 1972. irreg. $2 per no. M & O Communications, 120 E. 34th St., 7th Fl., New York, NY 10016. TEL 202-638-0348. Ed. Myra E. Barrer.

LAW AND YOU. see *BUSINESS AND ECONOMICS — Chamber Of Commerce Publications*

340 ZA
LAW ASSOCIATION JOURNAL. vol.9, 1983. a. Law Association of Zambia, P.O. Box 35271, Lusaka, Zambia. **Indexed:** P.L.E.S.A. (1984-).

340 001.535 UK ISSN 0962-9580
▼**LAW, COMPUTERS, AND ARTIFICIAL INTELLIGENCE.** 1992. 3/yr. £36 to individuals; institutions £64. Triangle Journals Ltd., P.O. Box 65, Wallingford, Oxfordshire OX10 0YG, England. TEL 0491-838013. FAX 0491-834968. **Document type:** academic/scholarly publication.
—BLDSC (5161.369050); UnCover.

340 ZA
LAW DEVELOPMENT COMMISSION. ANNUAL REPORT. (Text in English) 1976. a. K.50. (Law Development Commission) Government Printing Department, P.O. Box 30136, Lusaka, Zambia. TEL 01-215-401. circ. 500.

340 US
LAW ENFORCEMENT LEGAL REPORTER. 1977. m. $24.50. Law Enforcement Legal Reporter, Box 1356, Torrance, CA 90505. TEL 213-379-3214. Ed. Elliot E. Alhadeff. circ. 3,000. (back issues avail.) **Document type:** academic/scholarly publication, newsletter.

340 US ISSN 1061-9410
▼**LAW FIRM BENEFITS.** 1992. m. Leader Publications, Inc. (Subsidiary of: New York Law Publishing Co.), 111 Eighth Ave., New York, NY 10011. TEL 212-463-5733. FAX 212-463-5573. Ed. Patricia L. Johnson. index. (back issues avail.) **Document type:** newsletter.

340 658 US
KF316.5.A15
LAW FIRM MARKETING AND PROFIT REPORT. 1981. m. $129 (foreign $144). James Publishing Group, Inc., 3520 Cadillac Ave., Ste. E, Costa Mesa, CA 92626. TEL 714-755-5450. FAX 714-549-8835. Ed. Sarah Pate. **Document type:** newsletter.
—**CCC.**
Formerly: Attorneys Marketing Report (ISSN 0745-1369)
Description: To help law firm marketers design, implement and evaluate effective programs to attract new clients, enhance the firm's image, improve client relations and build a sound practice.

340 US ISSN 1056-2028
LAW FIRM PARTNERSHIP REPORT. 1991. m. $135. Leader Publications, Inc. (Subsidiary of: New York Law Publishing Co.), 111 Eighth Ave., New York, NY 10011. TEL 212-463-5709. FAX 212-463-5523. Ed. Justine Jeffrey. index. (back issues avail.; reprint service avail.)

340 US
LAW FIRM PROFIT REPORT. 1988. m. $139. Newsletter Services, Inc., 1545 New York Ave., N.E., Washington, DC 20002. TEL 202-529-5700. Ed. Nancy Koran. bk.rev.; index.

340 US ISSN 1054-4054
KF190
▼**LAW FIRMS YELLOW BOOK**; who's who in the management of the leading U.S. law firms. 1992. s-a. $170 (foreign $220). Monitor Leadership Directories Inc., 104 Fifth Ave., 2nd Fl., New York, NY 10011. TEL 212-627-4140. FAX 212-645-6931. **Document type:** directory.
—CCC.
   Description: Covers more than 675 American Bar Association member law firms, list more than 14,000 key individuals with a management role, department heads, managing partners of branch office, and administrators of central and branch offices.

340.05 US
THE LAW FORUM. 1970. 3/yr. free. University of Baltimore, School of Law, Managing Editor, 1420 N. Charles St., Baltimore, MD 21202. TEL 410-837-4493. Ed. Karl Chen. circ. 8,000. (also avail. in microform from UMI; reprint service avail. from UMI) **Document type:** academic/scholarly publication.
   Former titles: Forum Law Journal (ISSN 0360-2044); Forum (Baltimore) (ISSN 0094-1848)

340 AT ISSN 0811-5796
K12
LAW IN CONTEXT. 1983. s-a. Aus.$36.50 to institutions (foreign Aus.$39.50). La Trobe University Press, Bundoora, Vic. 3083, Australia. TEL 03-479-1234. Ed. Martyn Chanock. adv.; bk.rev. circ. 500. (back issues avail.)

340 NR ISSN 0458-8592
LAW IN SOCIETY. 1964. irreg. (1-2/yr.). Ahmadu Bello University, Law Society, Zaria, Nigeria.

340 AT ISSN 0023-9267
LAW INSTITUTE JOURNAL. 1927. m. (except Jan.). Aus.$83 (foreign Aus.$128 to individuals; institutions Aus.$114). Law Institute of Victoria, 470 Bourke St, Melbourne, Vic. 3000, Australia. TEL 03-607-9342. FAX 03-607-9451. Ed. M. Schiel. adv.; bk.rev.; index. circ. 10,500. (tabloid format; also avail. in microfiche from WSH,PMC; microfilm from WSH,PMC) **Indexed:** C.L.I., L.R.I., Leg.Per.
—BLDSC (5161.390000); UnCover; UMI. **CCC.**

LAW LIBRARIAN. see *LIBRARY AND INFORMATION SCIENCES*

026 US
LAW LIBRARIAN'S BULLETIN BOARD. 1989. 8/yr. $36 (foreign $44). Legal Information Services, Box 67, Newton Highlands, MA 02161-0067. TEL 508-443-4087. Ed. Elyse H. Fox.
   Description: Provides international coverage of news and developments in law libraries, government information, library organizations, industry news and job listings.

LAW LIBRARY ASSOCIATION OF MARYLAND NEWS. see *LIBRARY AND INFORMATION SCIENCES*

340 US ISSN 0268-8336
LAW LIBRARY INFORMATION REPORTS. 1981. irreg. (3-6/yr.). $100 per report. Glanville Publishers, Inc., 75 Main St., Dobbs Ferry, NY 10522. TEL 914-693-5956. FAX 914-693-0402. Ed. Roy M. Mersky. circ. 250. **Document type:** monographic series.
   Description: Provides information and recommendations which librarians and administrative personnel can apply in making decisions for the law library.

LAW LIBRARY JOURNAL. see *LIBRARY AND INFORMATION SCIENCES*

LAW LIBRARY LIGHTS. see *LIBRARY AND INFORMATION SCIENCES*

LAW LINES. see *LIBRARY AND INFORMATION SCIENCES*

340 US
LAW MARKETING EXCHANGE. 1985. m. free to members. National Law Firm Marketing Association, 60 Revere Dr., Ste. 500, Northbrook, IL 60062. TEL 708-480-9641. FAX 708-480-9282. Ed. Tim Turner. circ. 1,000. **Document type:** newsletter.

340 UK ISSN 0141-5867
LAW NOTES. 1881. m. £1.70 per no. (College of Law) Law Notes Lending Library, 25-26 Chancery Lane, London WC2A 1NB, England. FAX 071-831-5905. Ed. P.J. Hawkins. adv.; bk.rev. circ. 4,750. (also avail. in microfilm from BHP) **Indexed:** C.L.I., L.R.I.

340 659.1 US
THE LAW OF ADVERTISING. (Issued as 4 base vols. with supplements) 1973. irreg. $890. Matthew Bender & Co., Inc., 11 Penn Plaza, New York, NY 10001. TEL 212-967-7707. Eds. George Eric Rosden, Peter E. Rosden. (looseleaf format)
   Description: Covers the rules governing each party to the advertising contract: media, consumers, advertisers, and advertising agencies.

340 361.73 US
LAW OF ASSOCIATIONS: AN OPERATING LEGAL MANUAL FOR EXECUTIVES AND COUNSEL. (Issued as 1 base vol. with supplements) 1971. irreg. $225. Matthew Bender & Co., Inc., 11 Penn Plaza, New York, NY 10001. TEL 212-967-7707. Ed. George D. Webster. (looseleaf format)
   Description: Covers all legal and tax aspects of non-profit associations. Provides specialized information regarding tax exemptions and liabilities, executive compensation plans, political action committees, antitrust liability, public relations, and accounting procedures.

LAW OF BANK DEPOSITS, COLLECTIONS AND CREDIT CARDS (SUPPLEMENT). see *BUSINESS AND ECONOMICS — Banking And Finance*

340 CN
LAW OF COSTS. base vol. (plus a. updates). Can.$110. Canada Law Book Inc., 240 Edward St., Aurora, ON L4G 3S9, Canada. TEL 905-841-6472. FAX 905-841-5085. Ed. Mark M. Orkin. (looseleaf format)
   Description: A guide to the awarding and assessment of costs between party and party and between solicitor and client.

340 AT ISSN 0725-6892
LAW OF STAMP DUTIES IN QUEENSLAND. 1981. 4/yr. Aus.$295 with updates. Law Book Co. Ltd., 44-50 Waterloo Rd., N. Ryde, N.S.W. 2113, Australia. TEL 02-887-0177. FAX 02-888-9706. TELEX ASBOOK 27995. Ed. J.G. Mann. (looseleaf format)

LAW OFFICE GUIDE TO SMALL COMPUTERS. see *COMPUTERS — Microcomputers*

340 US ISSN 0735-4843
LAW OFFICE MANAGEMENT & ADMINISTRATION REPORT. m. $295. Institute of Management and Administration, 29 W. 35th St., 5th Fl., New York, NY 10001-2299. TEL 212-244-0360. FAX 212-564-0465. Ed. Sherrye Henry, Jr. index. (back issues avail.)
—CCC.

340 CN ISSN 0843-7076
LAW OFFICE MANAGEMENT JOURNAL. 1989. 3/yr. Can.$128($102) Carswell, One Corporate Plaza, 2075 Kennedy Rd., Scarborough, ON M1T 3V4, Canada. TEL 416-609-8000. FAX 416-298-5094. Ed. Louis Eisen. adv. contact: M. Lalani. bk.rev.; cum.index.
   Description: Offers practical guidance on how to deal with the crucial management issues facing contemporary law firms. Designed to help increase efficiency and profit potential through the application of sound business techniques and to assist in the implementation and management of technology within the firm.

LAW OFFICE TECHNOLOGY REVIEW. see *LAW — Computer Applications*

338.4 658 US ISSN 1045-9081
KF315.A15 CODEN: LPMAEK
LAW PRACTICE MANAGEMENT; the magazine of law office management. 1975. 8/yr. $48 (foreign $54). American Bar Association, Law Practice Management Section, 750 N. Lake Shore Dr., Chicago, IL 60611. TEL 312-988-5000. Ed. Delmar L. Roberts. adv.; bk.rev.; illus. circ. 23,817. (reprint service avail.) **Indexed:** ABI Inform., Account.Ind. (1987-), C.L.I., L.R.I., Law Ofc.Info.Svc., Leg.Cont., Leg.Info.Manage.Ind., P.A.I.S. **Document type:** trade publication.
●Also available online. Vendor(s): Mead Data Central, Inc., West Services, Inc.
—BLDSC (5161.408800); Faxon; UnCover; UMI.
   Formerly: Legal Economics (ISSN 0360-1439)
   Description: Includes feature articles, reports on technical innovations and announcements of forthcoming events.

LAW QUADRANGLE NOTES. see *COLLEGE AND ALUMNI*

340 PK
LAW QUARTERLY. (Text in English) vol. 3, 1970. q. Rs.12($4) Supreme Court, Lahore, Pakistan.

340 UK ISSN 0023-933X
LAW
LAW QUARTERLY REVIEW. 1885. 4/yr. £65. Sweet & Maxwell, South Quay Plaza, 7th Floor, 183 Marsh Wall, London E14 9FT, England. TEL 071-538-8686. FAX 071-538-9508. Ed. Ruth Chapman. adv. contact: Jackie Wood. bk.rev.; index. (reprint service avail. from RRI) **Indexed:** Abstr.Bk.Rev.Curr.Leg.Per., Br.Hum.Ind., C.L.I., L.R.I., Leg.Cont., Leg.Per., RICS, SSCI. **Document type:** bulletin.
—BLDSC (5161.410000); Faxon; UnCover; SWETS; UMI.

340 II
LAW REFERENCER. (Contains an annotated index to selected Indian legal periodicals) (Text in English) 1958. m. Rs.30($15) 35 Lawyers' Chambers, Supreme Court, New Delhi 110001, India. Ed. S.S. Husain.

350 AT
LAW
LAW REFORM COMMISSION OF WESTERN AUSTRALIA. REPORTS. ANNUAL REPORTS AND DISCUSSION PAPERS. 1968. a. Aus.$25 within Western Australia; interstate Aus.$50; foreign Aus.$85. Law Reform Commission of Western Australia, KPMG House, 214 St. Georges Terrace, Perth, W.A. 6000, Australia. TEL 09-481-3711. FAX 09-481-4197. stat. circ. 500. (also avail. in microfiche) **Document type:** academic/scholarly publication.
   Formerly: Law Reform Commission of Western Australia. Annual Report (ISSN 0311-2276)

340 370 US
LAW-RELATED EDUCATION NEWSLETTER. 1982. s-a. Illinois State Bar Association, Committee on Law-Related Education, Illinois Bar Center, Springfield, IL 62701. TEL 217-525-0712. FAX 213-525-0712. Eds. Frank Kopecky, Donna Schechter. circ. 2,150. (back issues avail.) **Document type:** newsletter.

340 332.1 AT
LAW RELATING TO BANKER AND CUSTOMER IN AUSTRALIA. 1990. 3/yr. Aus.$495 with updates. Law Book Co. Ltd., 44-50 Waterloo Rd., North Ryde, N.S.W. 2113, Australia. TEL 02-887-0177. FAX 02-888-9706. TELEX ASBOOK 27995. Eds. G.A. Weaver, C.R. Craigie. (looseleaf format)
   Description: Includes all major developments in case and statute law, including statutes dealing with cheques and corporations.

347.91 US ISSN 1052-4649
KF294.A8
LAW REPORTER. 1957. m. (10/yr.). $135 includes membership. Association of Trial Lawyers of America, 1050 31st St., N.W., Washington, DC 20007-4499. TEL 202-965-3500. Ed. Liane Leshne. abstr.; index. circ. 60,000. (also avail. in microfilm from UMI) **Indexed:** C.L.I.
—UnCover; UMI. **CCC.**
   Former titles (until 1985): A T L A Law Reporter (ISSN 0364-8125); (until vol.19, no.10, 1976): Association of Trial Lawyers of America. Newsletter (ISSN 0093-1160); American Trial Lawyers Association Newsletter (ISSN 0003-1437)

LAW

340 US
LAW REPORTS. 1973. q. free to attorneys. Catholic Health Association, 4455 Woodson Rd., St. Louis, MO 63134. TEL 314-427-2500. FAX 314-427-0029. Ed. John Miles. circ. 1,200. (back issues avail.)

347.91 UK ISSN 0265-122X
LAW REPORTS: APPEAL CASES. m. £55 (overseas £58) (effective Aug. 1993). Incorporated Council of Law Reporting for England and Wales, 3 Stone Bldgs., Lincoln's Inn, London WC2A 3XN, England. TEL 071-242 6471. FAX 071-831-5247. Ed. M.J. Ellis. (also avail. in microfiche from BHP) —SWETS.

340 US ISSN 1071-1376
K33.L39
LAW REVIEW ACCESS. 1985. w. $150. 8 N. Main St., West Hartford, CT 06107. TEL 203-232-9974. FAX 203-236-8024. Ed. Steve Apsland. circ. 110. (back issues avail.)
Description: Publishes tables of contents of law related periodicals used in research.

340 US ISSN 0734-1938
KF250
LAW REVIEW JOURNAL. 1979. 3/yr. $9.75. Legal Institute, 3250 Wilshire Blvd., Ste. 1000, Los Angeles, CA 90010. TEL 213-487-6268. Ed. Herman B. Lancaster. adv.; bk.rev.; bibl.; charts; illus.; stat.; tr.lit. circ. 200. (back issues avail.) —BLDSC (5161.441000).

340 US ISSN 0741-1170
LAW SCHOOL ADMINISTRATOR'S JOURNAL. 1982. 3/yr. $9.75 per no. Legal Institute, 3250 Wilshire Blvd., Ste. 1000, Los Angeles, CA 90010. TEL 213-487-6268. FAX 213-385-2396. Ed.Bd. circ. 300.

340 US ISSN 0737-2590
KF283
LAW SCHOOL JOURNAL. 1980. 3/yr. $9.75 per no. Legal Institute, 3250 Wilshire Blvd., Ste. 1000, Los Angeles, CA 90010. TEL 213-487-6268. FAX 213-385-2396. Ed.Bd.

340 378 US
LAW SCHOOL RECORD. 1951. s-a. $15 includes Occasional Papers. University of Chicago Law School, 1111 E. 60th St., Chicago, IL 60637. TEL 312-702-9629. FAX 312-702-0730. (Subscr. to: William S. Hein & Co., Inc., 1285 Main St., Buffalo, NY 14209) Ed. Dan McGeehan. circ. 8,700. (also avail. in microfilm from PMC; microfiche from PMC; reprint service avail. from UMI) **Indexed:** C.L.I., L.R.I. **Document type:** academic/scholarly publication.

340 378.002 US
LAW SCHOOL SUMMER SCHOOL PROGRAMS AT HOME AND ABROAD. 1988. a. $27.50. Graduate Group, 86 Norwood Rd., West Hartford, CT 06117. TEL 203-232-3100. bk.rev. circ. 100. (back issues avail.) **Document type:** directory.

340 US
KF285.Z9L2
LAW SERVICES REPORT. 1988. bi-m. free. Law School Admission Services, Inc., Box 63, Newtown, PA 18940. TEL 215-968-1136. FAX 215-968-1169. Ed. Wendy Margolis. circ. 12,500. (back issues avail.)
Former titles: Data and Development; Prelaw Advisor Bulletin.

340 US
LAW, SOCIETY, AND POLICY. 1982. irreg., vol.6, 1992. price varies. Plenum Publishing Corp., 233 Spring St., New York, NY 10013-1578. TEL 212-620-8000. FAX 212-463-0742. TELEX 23-421139. Ed.Bd. **Document type:** monographic series.
Refereed Serial

340 KE
LAW SOCIETY DIGEST. (Text in English) 1975. q. Law Society of Kenya, Nairobi, Kenya.

340 CN ISSN 0023-9364
LAW
LAW SOCIETY GAZETTE. 1967. q. Can.$15 to non-members. Law Society of Upper Canada, Osgoode Hall, Toronto, Ont. M5H 2N6, Canada. TEL 416-366-3726. FAX 416-367-2502. TELEX 065-28013. (Subscr. to: John Honsberger, Rm. 500, 85 Richmond St. W., Toronto, Ont. M5H 2C9, Canada) Ed. John Honsberger. bk.rev.; illus. circ. 19,000. (tabloid format) **Indexed:** C.L.I., Ind.Can.L.P.L., L.R.I., Leg.Per.

340 AT ISSN 0023-9372
LAW
LAW SOCIETY JOURNAL. 1963. 11/yr. Aus.$90 (foreign Aus.$110). Law Society of New South Wales, 170 Phillips St., Sydney, N.S.W. 2000, Australia. FAX 231-5809. TELEX AA73063. Ed. Robert Campbell. adv. contact: John Toltrup. bk.rev.; cum.index. circ. 13,852. (also avail. in microfiche from WSH) **Indexed:** C.L.I., L.R.I. **Document type:** trade publication.

340 HK ISSN 1015-5570
LAW SOCIETY OF HONG KONG GAZETTE. (Text in English) 1987. m. Asia Law and Practice Ltd., 2F, 29 Hollywood Rd., Central, Hong Kong. TEL 852-544-9918. FAX 852-543-7617.

340 UK ISSN 0458-8711
LAW
LAW SOCIETY OF SCOTLAND. JOURNAL (YEAR). 1956. m. £48 (effective 1993). Law Society of Scotland, 26 Drumsheugh Gardens, Edinburgh EH3 7YR, Scotland. adv.; bk.rev.; bibl.; charts; illus.; index. circ. 9,400. **Indexed:** C.L.I., ELLIS, L.R.I. **Document type:** bulletin.
—BLDSC (4812.965000); UnCover.

340 AT
LAW SOCIETY OF SOUTH AUSTRALIA. BULLETIN. 1967. m. Aus.$66 to non-members. Law Society of South Australia, 124 Waymouth St., Adelaide, S.A. 5000, Australia. TEL 61-8-231-9972. FAX 61-8-231-1929. Ed. B.C. Fitzgerald. adv.; bk.rev.; index. circ. 2,000. **Document type:** trade publication.

340 CN ISSN 0316-5310
KE16
LAW SOCIETY OF UPPER CANADA. SPECIAL LECTURES. 1950. a. price varies. Carswell, One Corporate Plaza, 2075 Kennedy Rd., Scarborough, ON M1T 3V4, Canada. TEL 416-609-8000. FAX 416-298-5094. **Indexed:** Ind.Can.L.P.L. **Document type:** monographic series.
—BLDSC (8366.600000).

340 UK ISSN 0262-1495
LAW SOCIETY'S GAZETTE. 1903. w. £70. Law Society of England and Wales, 50 Chancery Lane, London WC2A 1SX, England. Ed. Sheila Pratt. adv.; bk.rev.; illus.; s-a. index. circ. 64,797. **Indexed:** ELLIS, Leg.Per., RICS.

340 UK
LAW SOCIETY'S GUARDIAN GAZETTE. 1965. m. £70. Law Society of England and Wales, 50 Chancery Ln., London WC2A 1SX, England. Ed. Sheila Pratt. adv.; bk.rev.; charts; illus.; play rev. circ. 89,226.
Former titles: Guardian Gazette (ISSN 0306-3348); (until 1973): Law Guardian (ISSN 0023-9259)

340 US ISSN 0160-0265
KFN5664.5.L37A134
LAW STUDIES. 1975. irreg. (2-3/yr.). New York State Bar Association, Law, Youth & Citizenship Program, 1 Elk St., Albany, NY 12207-1460. TEL 518-474-1460. FAX 518-486-1571. Ed. Eric Mondschein.

340 UK ISSN 0306-9400
K12
LAW TEACHER. 1965. 3/yr. £38. (Association of Law Teachers) Sweet & Maxwell, South Quay Plaza, 7th Fl., 183 Marsh Wall, London E14 9FT, England. TEL 071-538-8686. FAX 071-538-9508. Ed. Sarah Lewis. adv. contact: Jackie Wood. bk.rev.; bibl.; charts. **Indexed:** C.L.I., L.R.I. **Document type:** bulletin.
—BLDSC (5161.447000). CCC.
Formerly: Association of Law Teachers. Journal (ISSN 0044-9628)

340 US ISSN 0741-1197
LAW TEACHER'S JOURNAL. 1984. 3/yr. $9.75 per no. Legal Institute, 3250 Wilshire Blvd., Ste. 1000, Los Angeles, CA 90010. TEL 213-487-6268. FAX 213-385-2396. Ed.Bd.

340 II ISSN 0023-9399
K12
LAW THESAURUS. (Text in English) m. Rs.4. University Book House, 15 W.B. Bungalow Rd., Tawehar Nagar, Delhi 7, India. Ed. S.M. Katial. circ. 2,000.

340 CN ISSN 0847-5083
LAW TIMES. 1990. w. (43/yr.). Can.$86 (foreign $135). Canada Law Book, 240 Edward St., Aurora, ON L4G 3S9, Canada. TEL 416-841-6481. FAX 416-841-5078. Ed. Paula Kulig. adv.; bk.rev. circ. 14,000. (tabloid format)
Description: Covers breaking legal stories and news to keep lawyers abreast of the fast pace of change in the legal profession.

340 US
LAW TOOLS, MATERIALS, CONTACTS. 1985. 3/yr. $9.75 per no. Legal Institute, 3250 Wilshire Blvd., Ste. 1000, Los Angeles, CA 90010. TEL 213-487-6268. FAX 213-385-2396. Ed.Bd.

340 II
LAW WEEKLY. (Text in English) vol.86, 1973. w. Vasantha Vilas, No. 3 South Mada St., Mylapore, Madras 600004, India. Ed. K.S. Desikan. bibl.

340 378 AT ISSN 1038-5037
LAWASIA DIRECTORY OF LAW COURSES IN THE ASIA AND WEST PACIFIC REGIONS. irreg., 2nd ed., 1993. $30. Centre for Legal Education, G.P.O. Box 232, Sydney, N.S.W. 2001, Australia. FAX 61-02-221-6180. (Exclusive dist. in N. America: Wm. W. Gaunt & Sons, Inc., Law Book Dealers & Subscription Agents, Gaunt Bldg., 3011 Gulf Dr., Holmes Beach, FL 34217-2199. TEL 813-778-5211) (Co-sponsor: Legal Education Standing Committee of Lawasia) Ed. Christopher Roper.

LAWDOCS. see *LIBRARY AND INFORMATION SCIENCES*

340 US
LAWS OF MEXICO. base vols. plus irreg. supplements. $370 base vols.; renewal $180 (diskettes $296; renewal $144). Foreign Tax Law Publishers, Box 2189, Ormond Beach, FL 32175-2189. TEL 904-253-5785. FAX 904-257-3003. (also avail. in diskette format)

340 US ISSN 0738-2049
JX1974.L15
LAWS QUARTERLY.* 1982. q. $20. Lawyers Alliance for World Security, 1601 Connecticut Ave. NW, Washington, DC 20009-1035. TEL 202-296-6054. FAX 202-296-6049. Ed. Jeanne Rhinelander. circ. 2,000. (back issues avail.) **Document type:** newsletter.
Formerly: Lawyers Alliance for Nuclear Arms Control Newsletter.

LAWTALK. see *LIBRARY AND INFORMATION SCIENCES*

340 NR ISSN 0023-9437
LAWYER. (Text in English) vol.3, 1968. irreg. (2-3/yr.). University of Lagos, Law Society, P.O. Box 12003, Lagos, Nigeria. Ed. Jonah O. Aghimien. bk.rev.; charts. circ. 500. (tabloid format)
Description: For the Nigerian lawyer.

340 II
LAWYER. 1969. m. (Indian Law Institute) University of Madras, Chepauk, Triplicane, Madras 600005, Tamil Nadu, India.

340 UK ISSN 0953-7902
THE LAWYER. 1988. w. £50 (N. America £110). Centaur Communications Ltd., St. Giles House, 49-50 Poland St., London W1V 4AX, England. TEL 071-439-4222. FAX 071-439-0110. Ed. Fennell Betson. circ. 18,300. (back issues avail.) **Document type:** trade publication.
—BLDSC (5161.539800); UMI.
Description: Covers legal news from law practice, commerce and industry, and the public sector. Contains features on various aspects of commercial law as well as management.

658.3　　　　US　　ISSN 0739-1706
KF276.5.A15
LAWYER HIRING & TRAINING REPORT. 1980. m. $280. Prentice Hall Law & Business, 270 Sylvan Ave., Englewood Cliffs, NJ 07632-2513. TEL 201-894-8484. FAX 201-894-8666. Ed. Larry Smith. bk.rev.; charts; stat.; video rev.; index. circ. 1,000. (back issues avail.)
　Incorporates: Henning C L E Reporter.

340　　　　US
LAWYER LIABILITY ALERT. bi-m. $600. Computer Law Reporter, Inc., 1519 Connecticut Ave., N.W., Ste. 200, Washington, DC 20036. TEL 202-462-5755. FAX 202-328-2430. Ed. John Noble. (back issues avail.)

LAWYER-PILOTS BAR ASSOCIATION. JOURNAL. see *AERONAUTICS AND SPACE FLIGHT*

LAWYER - PILOTS BAR ASSOCIATION JOURNAL. see *AERONAUTICS AND SPACE FLIGHT*

340　　　　US　　ISSN 0887-7777
LAWYER REFERRAL NETWORK. q. free. American Bar Association, Standing Committee on Lawyer Referral and Information Service, 750 N. Lake Shore Dr., Chicago, IL 60611. TEL 312-988-5000. FAX 312-988-6281.
　Description: News briefs on activities of the LRIS Committee and state and local lawyer referral services.

340　　　　US
KF299.P8N48
LAWYERS ALLIANCE FOR NEW YORK. NEWSLETTER. 1970. q. free to members. Lawyers Alliance for New York, 99 Hudson St., New York, NY 10013. TEL 212-219-1800. FAX 212-941-7458. Ed. Anne Hoyt. circ. 2,500. (back issues avail.; reprint service avail.) Document type: newsletter.
　Former titles: Council of New York Law Associates. Newsletter (ISSN 0747-0576); C N Y L A News Letter (ISSN 0273-5296)

346.066　　　　US
LAWYERS' AND ACCOUNTANTS' GUIDE TO PURCHASE - SALE OF SMALL BUSINESS. 1989. base vol. (plus supplement). Maxwell Macmillan, Rosenfeld Launer, 910 Sylvan Ave., Englewood Cliffs, NJ 07632-3310. TEL 800-562-0245. FAX 201-816-3569. Ed. Willard D. Horwich.

340　　　　US
LAWYERS' ARBITRATION LETTER. 1973. q. $30 to non-members. American Arbitration Association, 140 W. 51st St., New York, NY 10020-1203. TEL 212-484-4011. FAX 212-541-4841. Ed. Vicki Young. index. cum.index.
　Formerly: Lawyers' Arbitration Letter and the Digest of Court Decisions; Formed by the merger of: Lawyers' Arbitration Letter; Arbitration Law.
　Description: Discusses the case history and developments in a specific area of arbitration law. Looks at arbitration and the common law, the enforceability of partial final awards, consolidation, and international arbitration.

341　　　　US　　ISSN 1059-6585
LAWYERS' COMMITTEE ON NUCLEAR POLICY NEWSLETTER. 1983. 4/yr. donation. Lawyers' Committee on Nuclear Policy, Inc., 666 Broadway, Ste. 625, New York, NY 10012. TEL 212-674-7790. FAX 212-674-6199. Eds. Alyn Ware, Pete Waack. adv.; bk.rev. circ. 2,000. Document type: newsletter.
　Description: Lawyers working for the abolition of nuclear weapons.

349　　　　US
LAWYERS FOR THE ARTS NEWSLETTER. s-a. $10. American Bar Association, Young Lawyers Division, 750 N. Lake Shore Dr., Chicago, IL 60611. TEL 312-988-5000. bk.rev. Document type: newsletter.
　Description: Contains articles by lawyers on issues in art law, summaries of recent cases and legislation in the area..

340　　　　UK
LAWYERS IN EUROPE. bi-m. £40. (Solicitors European Group) Chancery Publishing, 22 Eastcastle St., London W1N 7PA, England. TEL 071-323-3328.
　Formerly: Solicitors' European Group Newsletter.
　Description: Examines European law and professional news.

340　　　　US
LAWYERS JOB BULLETIN BOARD. 1975. m. $30 to non-members; members and law students $20 (effective Aug. 1993). Federal Bar Association, 1815 H St., N.W., Ste. 408, Washington, DC 20006-3697. TEL 202-638-0252. FAX 202-775-0295. Ed. Margaret Simon. circ. 300. Document type: newsletter.

340　　　　US　　ISSN 0740-0519
KF8700.A15
LAWYERS LETTER. 3/yr. $13. (American Bar Association, Judicial Administration Division Lawyers Conference) A B A Press, 750 N. Lake Shore Dr., Chicago, IL 60611. TEL 312-988-5691. Ed. Robert B. Yegge. circ. 2,400.
　Description: Informs lawyers of new developments in court improvement and reports on conference activities.

340　　　　US　　ISSN 0896-7075
KF313.A15L375
LAWYERS' LIABILITY REVIEW. 1986. m. $325. Timeline Publishing Co., Inc., Box 1435, Bellevue, WA 98009. TEL 206-462-7714. FAX 206-462-0411. Ed. Ruth G. Bernhardt. index. (back issues avail.) Document type: trade publication.
　•Also available online.
　Description: Covers issues relating to legal malpractice and professional responsibility.

340　　　　AT
LAWYERS PRACTICE MANUAL N.S.W.. 1983. 5/yr. in 2 vols. Aus.$180 with updates. (Redfern Legal Centre) Law Book Co. Ltd., 44-50 Waterloo Rd., North Ryde, N.S.W. 2113, Australia. TEL 02-887-0177. FAX 02-888-9706. TELEX ASBOOK 27995. (looseleaf format)
　Description: Deals with the everyday practice of law and questions which occupy much of the time of practitioners, especially inexperienced lawyers.

340　　　　AT
LAWYERS PRACTICE MANUAL VICTORIA. 1985. 4/yr. in 2 vols. Aus.$180 with updates. (Springvale Legal Service) Law Book Co. Ltd., 44-50 Waterloo Rd., North Ryde, N.S.W. 2113, Australia. TEL 02-887-0177. FAX 02-888-9706. TELEX ASBOOK 27995. (looseleaf format)
　Description: Deals with the day-to-day practice of law and the questions which occupy much of the time of practitioners, particularly inexperienced lawyers.

340　　　　US
LAWYERS PROFESSIONAL LIABILITY UPDATE. 1981. a. $100 for 2-vol. set; a. supplement $30. American Bar Association, Standing Committee on Lawyers Professional Liability, 541 N. Fairbanks Ct., Chicago, IL 60611-3314. TEL 312-988-5763. FAX 312-988-5032. Ed. Alice L. Hughey. bk.rev. circ. 200. Document type: academic/scholarly publication.
　Description: Presents articles on loss prevention, and information about recent developments in the law concerning professional liability. Includes state-by-state list of legal malpractice insurance carriers.

340　　　　US　　ISSN 1061-7272
KF190
LAWYER'S REGISTER INTERNATIONAL BY SPECIALTIES AND FIELDS OF LAW INCLUDING A DIRECTORY OF CORPORATE COUNSEL. 1978. a. $119.50. Lawyer's Register Publishing Co., 28790 Chagrin Blvd., Ste. 140, Cleveland, OH 44122. TEL 216-591-1492. FAX 216-591-0265. Ed. Roger Perlmuter. circ. 4,000. (also avail. in microform; back issues avail.) Document type: directory.
　Former titles (until 1988): Lawyer's Register by Specialties and Fields of Law Including a Directory of Corporate Counsel (ISSN 0883-2412); (until 1982): Lawyer's Register by Specialties and Fields of Law (ISSN 0163-3147)
　Description: A directory listing lawyer specialists, including corporate counsel, for referral or consultation.

340　　　　UK　　ISSN 0142-7490
LAWYER'S REMEMBRANCER. a. $35. Butterworth & Co. (Publishers) Ltd. (Subsidiary of: Reed Elsevier plc), 88 Kingsway, London WC2B 6AB, England. TEL 71-405-6900. FAX 71-405-1332. (US addr.: Butterworth Legal Publishers, 90 Stiles Rd., Salem, NH 03079-9981. TEL 603-898-9664) Ed. Julian Roskams.
　Description: Provides an up-to-date summary of all major areas of law, commercial terms, fees and costs as well as an essential legal directory of names, addresses and phone numbers.

346　　　　US　　ISSN 0361-3763
KF1234.A15
LAWYERS' TITLE GUARANTY FUNDS NEWSLETTER. irreg., latest 1990. free to qualified personnel. American Bar Association, Standing Committee on Lawyers' Title Guaranty Funds, 750 N. Lake Shore Dr., Chicago, IL 60611. TEL 312-988-5604. circ. 5,000. Indexed: C.L.I., L.R.I. Document type: newsletter.
　Description: Information on Bar-related title insurance funds for Bar groups.

347.9　　　　CN　　ISSN 0830-0151
THE LAWYERS WEEKLY. 1983. w. Can.$170 (US Can.$195, elsewhere Can.$225). Butterworths Canada Ltd., Part of the Reed Elsevier group, 75 Clegg Rd., Markham, ON L6G 1A1, Canada. TEL 905-479-2665. FAX 905-479-2826. Ed. Don Brillinger. adv.; bk.rev.; charts; illus.; stat.; index; circ. 9,000 (paid); 29,000 (controlled). (tabloid format; also avail. in microfilm; back issues avail.)
　Formerly: Ontario Lawyers Weekly (ISSN 0822-5745)

340　　　　US　　ISSN 1069-7837
K12
LAWYER'S WEEKLY U S A. 1981. bi-w. $99. Lawyers Weekly Publications, 41 West St., Boston, MA 02111. TEL 617-451-7300. Ed. Tom Harrison. adv.; bk.rev. circ. 15,000. (back issues avail.) Document type: newspaper.
　Formerly (until 1993): Lawyer's Alert (ISSN 0278-9817)
　Description: Covers breakthrough court cases and vital news for small-firm lawyers.

340 004　　　　US　　ISSN 0738-0186
KF320.A9
LEADER'S LEGAL TECH NEWSLETTER. 1983. m. $175 (effective Sep. 1991). Leader Publications, Inc. (Subsidiary of: New York Law Publishing Company), 111 Eighth Ave., Ste. 900, New York, NY 10011. TEL 800-888-8300. FAX 212-463-5523. Ed. Rodney Piette. index. Document type: newsletter.
　Description: Newsletter detailing new technologies of interest to lawyers and legal firms. Covers industry news, computer information, product reviews for law office automation.

LEADER'S PRODUCT LIABILITY LAW AND STRATEGY. see *BUSINESS AND ECONOMICS — Production Of Goods And Services*

340　　　　US
LEAGUE OF WOMEN VOTERS OF GEORGIA. LEGISLATIVE NEWSLETTER. 1962. irreg. (7-8/yr.). $12.50. League of Women Voters of Georgia, 1776 Peachtree St., N.W., Ste. 233, Atlanta, GA 30309-2307. TEL 404-874-7352. FAX 404-874-7353. circ. 180. (back issues avail.) Document type: newsletter.
　Description: Covers bills in Georgia legislature relating to education, taxes, women's issues, ethics and more.

346.066　　　　US
THE LEASING LETTER.* m. Leader Publications, Inc. (Subsidiary of: New York Law Publishing Co.), 111 Eighth Ave., Ste. 900, New York, NY 10011. TEL 800-888-8300. FAX 212-463-5523. Ed. Emil G. Pesiri.

340 900　　　　AG
LECCIONES DE HISTORIA JURIDICA. irreg. (Universidad de Buenos Aires, Instituto de Historia del Derecho Ricardo Levene) Editorial Perrot, Azcuenaga 1846, Buenos Aires, Argentina.

3282 LAW

342 341   AG
LECCIONES Y ENSAYOS. 1956. 3/yr. L.10. (Universidad de Buenos Aires, Facultad de Derecho y Ciencias Sociales) Editorial Astrea, Av. Figueroa Alcorta 2263, Buenos Aires, Argentina. adv.; bk.rev.; bibl. circ. 1,000.
   Description: Articles and essays on national and international law enforcement, public administration, criminology and philosophy.

341   NE   ISSN 0924-8862
LECTURES ON THE COMMON LAW. (Text in English) 1988. irreg., vol.3, 1991. price varies. Kluwer Law and Taxation Publishers (Subsidiary of: Wolters Kluwer N.V.), P.O Box 23, 7400 GA Deventer, Netherlands. TEL 31-5700-47261. FAX 31-5700-22244. TELEX 49295 KLUDV NL. (Dist. by: Libresso Distribution Centre, P.O. Box 23, 7400 GA Deventer, Netherlands. TEL 31-5700-33155. FAX 31-5700-33834; In N. America: Kluwer Law and Taxation Publishers, 675 Massachusetts Ave., Cambridge, MA 02139. TEL 617-354-0140. FAX 617-354-8595) Eds. B. Markesinis, J.H.M. Willems. (back issues avail.) **Document type:** monographic series.
—BLDSC (5179.871500).
   Description: Studies on issues in English common law.

346 657   UK   ISSN 0960-0647
LEGAL ABACUS. 1990. q. £15. Institute of Legal Cashiers and Administrators, 136 Well Hall Rd., Eltham, London SE9 6SN, England. TEL 44-81-294-2021. FAX 44-81-294-2006. (Co-sponsor: Institute of Legal Accountants of Ireland) Ed. Maria Maloney. adv.: B&W page £440; 180 x 270. bk.rev. circ. 2,070. **Document type:** bulletin, newsletter.

345.01   UK
LEGAL ACTION. 1972. m. £59. Legal Action Group, 242-244 Pentonville Rd., London N1 9UN, England. TEL 071-833-2931. FAX 071-837-6094. Eds. Lesley Exton, Hilary Arnolt. adv.; bk.rev.; cum.index. circ. 5,600. (also avail. in microform from UMI; reprint service avail. from UMI) **Indexed:** C.L.I., L.R.I., RICS. **Document type:** bulletin.
   Formerly (until 1983): L A G Bulletin (ISSN 0306-7963)

340   US
KF3942.H3A135
LEGAL ACTION REPORT. 1990. s-a. free. Center to Prevent Handgun Violence, 1225 Eye St., N.W., Ste. 1100, Washington, DC 20005. TEL 202-289-7319. FAX 202-408-1851. Ed. Gail Robinson. circ. 12,000. (back issues avail.)
   Description: Covers activities of the Center.

LEGAL ADVISORY. see *INSURANCE*

340   UK
LEGAL & GENERAL GAZETTE. 1971. m. free. Legal & General Assurance Society Ltd., Temple Court, 11 Queen Victoria St., London EC4N 4TP, England. Ed. Roy Moore. circ. 7,700.

340 658   US
LEGAL ASSISTANT MANAGEMENT ASSOCIATION. DIRECTORY. 1984. a. membership only. Legal Assistant Management Association, 638 Prospect Ave., Hartford, CT 06105-4298. circ. 550. **Document type:** directory.

340   US   ISSN 1051-3663
KF320.L4
LEGAL ASSISTANT TODAY. 1983. bi-m. $39.98. James Publishing Group, Inc., 3520 Cadillac Ave., Ste. E, Costa Mesa, CA 92626-1419. TEL 714-755-5450. Ed. Don DeBenedictus. adv. contact: Lorraine Thinnes. circ. 16,500. **Indexed:** ABI Inform. **Document type:** trade publication.
—BLDSC (5181.312207); UMI. **CCC.**
   Former titles (until 1990): Legal Professional (ISSN 1045-6686); (until Apr. 1989): Legal Assistant Today (ISSN 0741-7772)
   Description: Provides information on the day-to-day activities of paralegals, practical advice on working with attorneys, how to handle the case load, and how to get ahead in their careers.

340.023   US   ISSN 0272-1961
KF320.L4
LEGAL ASSISTANTS UPDATE. 1980. a. $6. American Bar Association, Standing Committee on Legal Assistants, 750 N. Lake Shore Dr., Chicago, IL 60611. TEL 312-988-5555. FAX 312-988-6281. Ed. Roger Larson. circ. 3,500. **Indexed:** Anbar.

340 658   CK   ISSN 0458-9564
LEGAL BULLETIN. 1963. m. $155. Ediciones Juan Caro & Asociados Ltda., Apdo Aereo 241518, Bogota, Colombia. FAX 57-1-3102606. Ed. Juan Caro. index. **Indexed:** C.L.I.

346.066   UK   ISSN 0958-4609
LEGAL BUSINESS. 1990. 10/yr. £450($495) Legalease, 28-33 Cato St., London W1H 5HS, England. TEL 071-396-9292. FAX 071-396-9300. Ed. John Pritchard. adv.; bk.rev. circ. 8,000. **Document type:** newsletter.
   Description: Covers news of commercial law firms and their clients.

340   US
KF 3781.A15C4
LEGAL COMPASS. 1936. m. $69. American Cemetery Association, 5201 Leesburg Pike, Ste. 1111, Falls Church, VA 22042. TEL 703-379-5838. FAX 703-998-0162. Ed. Robert Fells. index. (back issues avail.)
   Formerly: Cemetery Legal Compass.
   Description: Contains court decisions relating to the liability of cemeteries and funeral homes.

340   US   ISSN 0270-3424
KF195.C6
LEGAL CONNECTION: CORPORATIONS AND LAW FIRMS; a directory of publicly-held corporations and their law firms. 1979. a. Box 801, Menlo Park, CA 94025. Ed. S.P. Harris. **Document type:** directory.

340   AT
LEGAL COSTS N S W. base vol. (plus m. update). $290. Butterworths, 271-273 Lane Cove Rd., P.O. Box 345, North Ryde, N.S.W. 2113, Australia. TEL 02-335-4444. FAX 02-335-4678. (looseleaf format)

340   AT
LEGAL COSTS VICTORIA. base vol. (plus m. update). $295. Butterworths, 271-273 Lane Cove Rd., P.O. Box 345, North Ryde, N.S.W. 2113, Australia. TEL 02-335-4444. FAX 02-335-4655.

340   US   ISSN 1063-9888
THE LEGAL EDGE; the value of strategic market planning. 1987. 6/yr. $145 (effective 1994). Coulter King O'Neil, Ltd., Inc., 2 Oliver St., 8th Fl., Boston, MA 02109-4901. TEL 617-482-1310. FAX 617-482-6528. (And: 1675 Broadway, Ste. 1800, Denver, CO 80202. TEL 303-592-5916. FAX 303-592-5906) Ed. Ms Hollis R. Chase. adv.; bk.rev. circ. 4,999.
   Description: Explores the changing scope of marketing, planning and client development functions in the practice of law.

340 378   AT
LEGAL EDUCATION REVIEW. 1989. s-a. $240. Centre for Legal Education, G.P.O. Box 232, Sydney, N.S.W. 2001, Australia. FAX 61-02-221-6280. (Exclusive dist. in N. America: Wm. W. Gaunt & Sons, Inc., Law Book Dealers & Subscription Agents, Gaunt Bldg., 2011 Gulf Dr., Holmes Beach, FL 34217-2199. TEL 813-778-5211. FAX 813-778-5252) **Indexed:** C.L.I., Leg.Per.
   Description: Deals with theoretical and practical issues relating to legal education, particularly as they arise in the South Pacific region.

340   UK   ISSN 0024-0362
LAW
LEGAL EXECUTIVE. 1963. m. £30 (foreign £46.92). Institute of Legal Executives, Kempston Manor, Kempston, Bedford, England. TEL 0234-840-022. FAX 0234-841-999. Ed. R. Kendrick. adv.; bk.rev.; illus.; index; circ. 19,997 (controlled).

340   RH
LEGAL FORUM. 1988. 4/yr. $20 (effective 1993). Legal Resources Foundation, P.O. Box 918, Harare, Zimbabwe. TEL 263-4-790947. FAX 263-4-728213. (back issues avail.) **Indexed:** P.L.E.S.A. (1990-).
   Supersedes: Public Prosecutors' Association of Zimbabwe. Bulletin.
   Description: Covers human rights matters and all issues related to the administration, function and reform of law in Zimbabwe.

720   US   ISSN 0887-1183
KF902
LEGAL HANDBOOK FOR ARCHITECTS, ENGINEERS AND CONTRACTORS. 1986. a. $75. Clark - Boardman - Callaghan Company Ltd., 375 Hudson St., New York, NY 10014. TEL 212-929-7500. FAX 212-924-0460.

342   II   ISSN 0377-0907
K12
LEGAL HISTORY. (Text in English) 1975. q. Rs.390($50) (Indian Institute of Legal History) K.K. Roy (Private) Ltd., 55 Gariahat Rd., P.O. Box 10210, Calcutta 700 019, India. Ed. K.K. Roy. bk.rev.; abstr.; bibl. circ. 500. (tabloid format) **Indexed:** Amer.Hist.& Life, Hist.Abstr.
—BLDSC (5181.322000).
   Formerly (until 1975): Journal of Constitutional Law (ISSN 0022-0051)

LEGAL INFORMATION ALERT; what's new in legal publications, databases and research techniques. see *LAW — Abstracting, Bibliographies, Statistics*

026   US
LEGAL INFORMATION MANAGEMENT REPORTS. 1989. q. $50 (foreign $55). Legal Information Services, Box 67, Newton Highlands, MA 02161-0067. TEL 508-443-4087. Ed. Elyse H. Fox.
   Description: Each issue deals with a single topic in the field of law librarianship.

346.066   US
LEGAL INSIGHTS FOR MANAGERS. m. $131.40. Bureau of Business Practice, 24 Rope Ferry Rd., Waterford, CT 06386. TEL 800-243-0876. FAX 203-437-3555. Ed. Jim O'Shea.
   Description: Covers all business management legal issues.

347.91   US
LEGAL INTELLIGENCER. 1843. d. (5/w.). $265. Legal Communications, Ltd., 1617 JFK Blvd., Ste. 960, Philadelphia, PA 19103. TEL 215-563-2700. FAX 215-563-4911. Ed. Brian Harris. adv.: B&W page £1495, color page $1895; trim 11 1/4 x 14. circ. 4,817. (tabloid format; back issues avail.) **Document type:** newspaper.
   Description: Legal news, trial lists, legal notices for the Philadelphia court system.

LEGAL - LEGISLATIVE REPORTER. NEWS BULLETIN. see *BUSINESS AND ECONOMICS — Labor And Industrial Relations*

658 340   US   ISSN 1043-7355
KF318.A1   **CODEN: LEMAEB**
LEGAL MANAGEMENT. 1982. bi-m. free. Association of Legal Administrators, 175 E. Hawthorn Pkwy., Ste. 325, Vernon Hills, IL 60061-1428. TEL 708-816-1212. FAX 708-816-1213. (Subscr. to: Box 1347, Elmhurst, IL 60126) Ed. Nancy Blodgett. adv.; bk.rev.; index; circ. 26,000 (controlled).
—UnCover; CASDDS.
   Formerly: Legal Administration (ISSN 0745-0532)
   Description: Provides information relating to management of a law practice, for the education and benefit of administrators, managing partners and others.

340   US
LEGAL NEWS. q. Association of Idaho Cities, 3314 Grace St., Boise, ID 83703. TEL 208-344-8594. FAX 208-244-8677.

344 US ISSN 0093-397X
KF4119.A1
LEGAL NOTES FOR EDUCATION. 1973. m. $108. Data Research, Inc., 4635 Nicols Rd., Ste. 100, Eagan, MN 55122. TEL 612-452-8267. FAX 612-452-8694. (Subscr. to: Box 490, Rosemount, MN 55068. TEL 800-365-4900) cum.index.
Description: Reports court decisions and legislation affecting education.

347 US ISSN 0886-6678
LEGAL PLAN LETTER. 1982. fortn. $95 to libraries (foreign $120). National Resource Center for Consumers of Legal Services, Box 340, Gloucester, VA 23061. TEL 804-693-9330. FAX 804-693-7363. Ed. William A. Bolger. bk.rev.; s-a. index. circ. 1,000. (back issues avail.)
Supersedes: New Directions - Action Line.
Description: News and resources on legal services plans.

340 US
LEGAL PLANNING FOR THE ELDERLY IN MASSACHUSETTS. 1991. base vol. (plus a. supplement). $95. Butterworth Legal Publishers (Salem) (Subsidiary of: Reed Elsevier plc), 8 Industrial Way, Bldg. C, Salem, NH 03079. TEL 800-548-4001. FAX 603-898-9858. Eds. William J. Brisk, William G. Talis. (looseleaf format)

340 015 070 US ISSN 1056-196X
LEGAL PUBLISHER. 1992. m. $149. J K Publishing, Box 71020, Milwaukee, WI 53211. TEL 414-332-1625. FAX 414-964-0843. Ed. John Kenney. adv.; bk.rev. (back issues avail.) **Document type:** newsletter.
●Also available online. Vendor(s): Information Access Co., NewsNet.
Description: Contains information on new legal information books, magazines, newsletters, online services and related material.

LEGAL QUARTERLY DIGEST OF MINE SAFETY AND HEALTH DECISIONS. see *MINES AND MINING INDUSTRY*

LEGAL REFERENCE SERVICES QUARTERLY. see *LIBRARY AND INFORMATION SCIENCES*

LEGAL REFORMER. see *POLITICAL SCIENCE*

345 AT ISSN 0159-2483
LAW
LEGAL REPORTER. 1980. irreg. (approx. 20/yr.). Aus.$345. Scribe Pty. Ltd., G.P.O. Box 1807, Canberra, A.C.T. 2601, Australia. TEL 062-471069. Ed. David Solomon. bk.rev.; index. circ. 650. (back issues avail.)
—CCC.
Description: Reports on the Australian High Court.

340 US ISSN 0146-0382
KF240
LEGAL RESEARCH JOURNAL. 1977. 3/yr. $9.75. Legal Institute, 3250 Wilshire Blvd., No. 1000, Los Angeles, CA 90010. TEL 213-487-6268. Ed. Herman B. Lancaster. bibl.; charts; illus.; stat. circ. 400. (also avail. in microfilm) **Indexed:** Abstr.Bk.Rev.Curr.Leg.Per., C.L.I.

340 US ISSN 1050-3056
Z675.L2
LEGAL RESEARCHER'S DESK REFERENCE. biennial. $54. Infosources Publishing, 140 Norma Rd., Teaneck, NJ 07666. TEL 201-836-7072. Ed. Arlene L. Eis. adv. **Document type:** directory.
Description: Provides all types of information helpful to the legal researcher: directories of law library suppliers, courts, judges, government agencies, law schools.

LEGAL RESOURCES FOR THE MENTALLY DISABLED: A DIRECTORY OF LAWYERS AND OTHER SPECIALISTS. see *MEDICAL SCIENCES — Psychiatry And Neurology*

340 UK ISSN 0261-3875
K12
LEGAL STUDIES. N.S. 1947. 3/yr. $104. (Society of Public Teachers of Law) Butterworth & Co. (Publishers) Ltd. (Subsidiary of: Reed Elsevier plc), 88 Kingsway, London WC2B 6AB, England. TEL 71-405-6900. FAX 71-405-1332. TELEX 95678. (US addr.: Butterworth Legal Publishers, 90 Stiles Rd., Salem, NH 03079-9981. TEL 603-898-9664) Ed. J.S. Bell. bk.rev. **Indexed:** Abstr.Bk.Rev.Curr.Leg.Per., C.L.I., L.R.I., Leg.Per. **Document type:** academic/scholarly publication.
—BLDSC (5181.413000); Faxon; UnCover.
Formerly (until 1981): Society of Public Teachers of Law Journal (ISSN 0038-0016)

340 US ISSN 0894-5993
K1
LEGAL STUDIES FORUM; an interdisciplinary journal. 1975. q. $50 to institutions (foreign $60). American Legal Studies Association, c/o Law, Policy and Society Program, 341 Cushing Hall, Northeastern University, Boston, MA 02114. TEL 617-437-5211. FAX 617-437-4691. Ed. Leonard G. Buckle. adv.; bk.rev.; film rev.; bibl. circ. 500. (also avail. in microfiche from WSH,PMC; microfilm from WSH,PMC; back issues avail.) **Indexed:** C.L.I., L.R.I., Sociol.Abstr. **Document type:** academic/scholarly publication.
—BLDSC (5181.413200).
Formerly (until vol.8, 1984): A L S A Forum (ISSN 0162-7937)
Description: Publishes humanistic, critical and issue-focused articles about law, legal systems and their portrayal in scholarly works, popular media and non-vocational legal education. Emphasis is on contemporary problems in law and its relationship to society - predominantly in common law nations but including both civil and traditional law systems.
Refereed Serial

340 US ISSN 0732-7536
LEGAL TIMES. 1978. w. $195 to individuals; corporations $475. American Lawyer Media, L.P., 1730 M St., N.W., Ste. 802, Washington, DC 20036. TEL 202-457-0686. FAX 202-457-0718. Ed. Eric Effron. circ. 10,000. (also avail. in microfilm; microfiche) **Indexed:** Bank.Lit.Ind., C.L.I., Hlth.Ind., L.R.I., Leg.Info.Manage.Ind. **Document type:** newspaper.
●Also available online. Vendor(s): Mead Data Central, Inc.
—UnCover. **CCC.**
Former titles: Legal Times of Washington (ISSN 0732-7544); (until 1982): Legal Times (ISSN 0162-7295)
Description: Covers law, lobbying, and politics in Washington, D.C.

340 370 US
LEGAL VIDEO REVIEW. 1984. bi-m. $125. Social Law Library, 1200 Courthouse, Boston, MA 02108. TEL 617-523-0018. FAX 617-523-2458. Ed. Ellen J. Miller. circ. 200. (back issues avail.) **Document type:** newsletter.
Description: Focuses on video tapes produced for continuing legal education and law schools. For law practitioners, students and professors.

340 US
LEGAL VIEWPOINTS. 1989. irreg. Schwabe Williamson & Wyatt, 1211 S.W. Fifth Ave., Ste. 1600-1950, Portland, OR 97204. TEL 503-222-9981. FAX 503-796-2900. **Document type:** newsletter.
Description: Discusses legal topics of interest to the firm's regional client base.

340 US ISSN 0732-4529
KF250
LEGAL WRITING JOURNAL. 1981. 3/yr. $9.95 per no. Legal Institute, 3250 Wilshire Blvd., Ste. 1000, Los Angeles, CA 90010. TEL 213-487-6268. FAX 213-385-2396. Ed.Bd.

340 IT
LEGALITA E GIUSTIZIA. 1973. q. L.88000 to individuals; institutions L.110000; foreign L.132000 (effective 1993). Edizioni Scientifiche Italiane S.p.A., Via Chiatamone, 7, 80121 Naples, Italy. TEL 081-7645768. FAX 081-7646477. Ed. Giovanni Giacobbe. adv. circ. 1,000.

349 IT ISSN 0024-0400
LEGGI. 3/m. L.174000 (foreign L.209000) (effective Feb. 1992). Zanichelli Editore S.p.A., Via Irnerio 34, 40126 Bologna, Italy. TEL 051-293111. FAX 051-249782. index, cum.index.

LEGI-SOCIAL. see *BUSINESS AND ECONOMICS — Investments*

340 FR ISSN 0751-9478
LEGIPRESSE. m. (10/yr.). 1950 F. Victoires - Editions, 38 rue Croix des Petits Champs, 75001 Paris, France. TEL 42-60-01-93. FAX 42-60-10-41. TELEX 615 887 F.

340 BL ISSN 0024-158X
LEGISLACAO FEDERAL E MARGINALIA; coletanea de legislacao e jurisprudencia. (Subseries of: Lex-coletanea de Legislacao e Jurisprudencia) 1937. 3/m. Cr.$123690($609.88) Lex Editora S.A., Machado de Assis, Nrs. 47-57-CEP 04106, Caixa Postal 12888, Sao Paulo, Brazil. Ed. Afonso Vitale Sobrinho. bk.rev.; charts; index. circ. 15,000.

340 SP
LEGISLACION COMUNIDADES AUTONOMAS. (In separate vols. for each of the 17 autonomous communities of Spain.) 1982. irreg. (approx. m.). 52000 ptas. for entire series (also avail. separately). Editorial Aranzadi, S.A., Avda. Carlos III, 34, Apdo. 111, 31080 Pamplona, Spain. TEL 948-331212. FAX 948-330919. index.

340 SP
LEGISLACION COMUNIDADES EUROPEAS. (Includes q. bound vols. with indexes.) 1986. m. 36000 ptas. (effective 1991). Editorial Aranzadi, S.A., Avda. Carlos III, 34, Apdo. 111, 31080 Pamplona, Spain. TEL 948-331212. FAX 948-330919. index.

346.066 AG
LEGISLACION ECONOMICA/ECONOMIC LEGISLATION. (Text in English, Spanish) 1970. fortn. (with annual cum.). $700. Consejo Tecnico de Inversiones, S.A., Tucuman 834, 1o, 1049 Buenos Aires, Argentina. FAX 541-322-4887. Ed. Jose Luis Blanco. adv. circ. 180.
Formerly: Legislacion Economica Argentina.
Description: Publishes the principal laws, decrees, resolutions, central bank circulars and other official communications.

340 FR ISSN 0242-6382
LEGISLATION. (Supplement to: Gazette du Palais (ISSN 0242-6331)) 1971. w. Gazette du Palais, 3 bd du Palais, 75180 Paris Cedex 04, France. TEL 43-25-97-47. FAX 40-46-03-47. TELEX GAZPAL 200 621.

340 US
LEGISLATIVE ADVISORY. m. General Merchandise Distributors Council, 1275 Lake Ave., Colorado Springs, CO 80906. TEL 303-576-4260.

LEGISLATIVE AND REGULATORY UPDATE. see *BUSINESS AND ECONOMICS — Banking And Finance*

LEGISLATIVE MEMORANDA. see *HOTELS AND RESTAURANTS*

LEGISLATIVE NETWORK FOR NURSES. see *MEDICAL SCIENCES — Nurses And Nursing*

340 US
LEGISLATIVE NEWSLETTER. 1988. w. $100. Colorado Assessors' Association, 12346 N. Piney Lake Rd., Parker, CO 80134. TEL 303-841-2163. FAX 303-840-2537. Ed. Jane H. Martin. circ. 135. (looseleaf format; back issues avail.) **Document type:** newsletter.

340 US
LEGISLATIVE REPORTING SERVICE. 1959. w. during legislature session. $990. Legislative Reporting Service, Box 1376, Juneau, AK 99802. TEL 907-586-6672. Ed. Kimberly Metcalfe Helmar. circ. 130. (back issues avail.; reprint service avail.)
Formerly (1985-1987): Alaska Legislative Report.

LEGISLATIVE TAX BILL SERVICE. see *BUSINESS AND ECONOMICS — Public Finance, Taxation*

340 US
LEGISLATIVE WATCH (WASHINGTON, 1989). 1989. w. (Jan.-Jun.); bi-w. (Jul.-Dec.). membership only. American Tort Reform Association, 1212 New York Ave., N.W., Ste. 515, Washington, DC 20005. TEL 202-682-1163. FAX 202-682-1022. Ed. Anne Allen. (back issues avail.)

LEGISLAZIONE E NORMATIVA DELLE COSTRUZIONI. see *BUILDING AND CONSTRUCTION*

LAW

340   IT   ISSN 0024-0524
LEGISLAZIONE ITALIANA. 1943. fortn. L.173000 (foreign L.260000). Casa Editrice Dott. A. Giuffre, Via Busto Arsizio 40, 20151 Milan, Italy. TEL 02-38000905. FAX 02-3809582. Ed. Renato Borruso. adv.; index. circ. 3,600.

340   NE   ISSN 0169-8605
LEIDSE JURIDISCHE REEKS. 1954. irreg., vol.15, 1981. price varies. E.J. Brill, P.O. Box 9000, 2300 PA Leiden, Netherlands. TEL 31-71-312624. FAX 31-71-317532. TELEX 39296-BRILL-NL. (N. America dist. addr.: E.J. Brill, 24 Hudson St., Kinderhook, NY 12106. TEL 800-962-4406. FAX 518-758-1959) **Document type:** monographic series.
Refereed Serial

340   US   ISSN 8755-9021
KF4754.5.A15
LESBIAN - GAY LAW NOTES. 1980. m. (except Aug.). $25 (foreign $30). Lesbian & Gay Law Association of Greater New York, 799 Broadway, New York, NY 10003-6811. TEL 212-353-9118. Ed. Arthur S. Leonard. bk.rev.; index. circ. 1,400. (looseleaf format; back issues avail.) **Document type:** newsletter.
Description: Summary of legal developments in the areas of lesbian and gay rights and AIDS.

325   AT
LESLIE AND BRITTS: MOTOR VEHICLE LAW IN N.S.W.. 1982. 6/yr. in 3 vols. Aus.$415 with updates. Law Book Co. Ltd., 44-50 Waterloo Rd., N. Ryde, N.S.W. 2113, Australia. TEL 02-887-0177. FAX 02-888-9706. TELEX ASBOOK 27995. Ed. M.M.G. Britts. (looseleaf format)
Description: Includes legislation, case notes and commentary on all aspects of the law with regard to motor vehicles and traffic.

LESOTHO ENVIRONMENT AND ENVIRONMENT LAW. see *ENVIRONMENTAL STUDIES*

340   LO   ISSN 0255-6472
K12   CODEN: JMSCED
LESOTHO LAW JOURNAL; a journal of law and development. 1985. s-a. R.40($40) National University of Lesotho, Faculty of Law, P.O. Roma 180, Lesotho. TEL 0266-340-601. FAX 0266-340000. Ed. Sam Rugege. adv.; bk.rev. circ. 500. **Indexed:** Documentatieblad. **Document type:** academic/scholarly publication.
—BLDSC (5184.554530); CASDDS.
Description: Addresses the conflict between the need for governments to govern, and the necessity to protect citizens against the power of the state. Also covers current issues including: the democratization process, human rights, the environment.

340 336   US   ISSN 0883-0487
LETTER OF CREDIT UPDATE. (International edition avail. q. from 1989) 1985. m. $495 (foreign $525). (International Chamber of Commerce, FR) Government Information Services, 4301 Fairfax Dr., Ste. 875, Arlington, VA 22203-1627. TEL 703-528-1000. FAX 703-528-6060. Ed. James E. Byrne. index.
—CCC.
Description: For businessmen, bankers and lawyers. Covers legislative and judicial developments concerning letter of credit practices.

340 332.7   US
LETTERS OF CREDIT. 1987. base vol. (plus suppl.). $185. Matthew Bender & Co., Inc., 11 Penn Plaza, New York, NY 10001. TEL 212-967-7707. (looseleaf format)
Description: Illustrates ways to use letters of credit to your client's advantage. Includes case law discussions.

LETTERS OF CREDIT REPORT; bank guaranties and acceptances. see *BUSINESS AND ECONOMICS — Banking And Finance*

340   IT   ISSN 0024-1598
LEX; legislazione Italiana. 1914. q. L.154000. Unione Tipografico Editrice Torinese, Corso Raffaello 28, 10125 Turin, Italy. charts. circ. 33,000.

LEX COLLEGII. see *EDUCATION — Higher Education*

340   US
LEX VITAE; the pro-life legislation and litigation summary. q. $25. Americans United for Life, 343 S. Dearborn St., Ste. 1804, Chicago, IL 60604. TEL 312-786-9494. Ed. Kevin J. Todd. (tabloid format; back issues avail.)
Description: Summary of cases at all levels of the judiciary and state legislation concerning abortion and euthanasia.

340 330.9 336   GW   ISSN 0171-0826
LEXIKON DES STEUER- UND WIRTSCHAFTSRECHTS. 1974. m. DM.98. Wirtschaft Recht und Steuern Verlag, Fraunhoferstr. 5, 82152 Planegg, Germany. TEL 089-89517-0. FAX 089-89517250. (Subscr. to: Postfach 1363, 82142 Planegg, Germany) Ed.Bd. circ. 24,000. (looseleaf format) **Document type:** bulletin.
Description: Reference on tax and law.

349   AG   ISSN 0024-1636
LEY; revista argentina de jurisprudencia. Alternate title: Revista Juridica Argentina: La Ley. (Text in Spanish) 1935. d. (with q. cum. summaries). Arg.$150($600) Ediciones la Ley S.A., 1471 Tucuman, Buenos Aires (R.34), Argentina. adv.; bk.rev.; bibl.; charts; illus.; stat.; index, cum.index; circ. 12,000. (controlled). (tabloid format)

340   NQ
LEYES DE LA REPUBLICA DE NICARAGUA. 1980. s-a. $10. Ministerio de Justicia, Managua, Nicaragua.

LIABILITY OF ATTORNEYS AND ACCOUNTANTS FOR SECURITIES TRANSACTIONS. see *BUSINESS AND ECONOMICS — Investments*

LIABILITY WEEK. see *INSURANCE*

340 332   FR
LIAISONS JURIDIQUES ET FISCALES. d. 1637 F. (typically set in Oct.). Groupe Liaisons, 5 av. de la Republique, 75541 Paris Cedex 11, France. TEL 1-48-05-91-05. FAX 43-55-02-33.

LIBERATOR; male call. see *MEN'S STUDIES*

340   LB
LIBERIA. MINISTRY OF JUSTICE. ANNUAL REPORT TO THE LEGISLATURE.* 1973. a. Ministry of Justice, Monrovia, Liberia.

340   LB   ISSN 0024-1970
K12
LIBERIAN LAW JOURNAL.* 1965. s-a. $30. University of Liberia, Louis Arthur Grimes School of Law, Monrovia, Liberia. Eds. Boakai Dukuly, Ruth Jappah. adv.; bk.rev.; charts. circ. 300.

340   UK   ISSN 0267-7083
LIBERTARIAN ALLIANCE. LEGAL NOTES. 1985. irreg. £10($20) Libertarian Alliance, 25 Chapter Chambers, Esterbrooke St., London SW1P 4NN, England. TEL 071-821-5502. FAX 071-834-2031. Ed.Bd. adv.; bk.rev.; film rev.; bibl. circ. 1,000. (back issues avail.) **Document type:** monographic series.

340   JA   ISSN 0447-7480
LIBERTY & JUSTICE. 1949. m. 7930 Yen (Asia 12000 Yen; elsewhere 13000 Yen) (effective Apr. 1993). Japan Federation of Bar Associations, 1-1, Kasumigaseki 1-chome, Chiyoda-ku, Tokyo 100, Japan. TEL 81-3-3580-9841. FAX 81-3-3580-2866. adv.; bk.rev. **Document type:** bulletin.

LIBRARIAN'S REPORT. see *LIBRARY AND INFORMATION SCIENCES*

340 382 600   US   ISSN 0731-5783
KF3145.A152
LICENSING LAW HANDBOOK. 1979. a. $85. Clark - Boardman - Callaghan Company Ltd., 375 Hudson St., New York, NY 10014. TEL 212-929-7500; 800-221-9428. FAX 212-924-0460. Eds. Howard C. Anawalt, Elizabeth F. Enayati. index.
Description: Valuable source for practicing attorneys and licensing professionals seeking to assist with the development of licensable properties.

340   AT
LICENSING LAWS N S W: LIQUOR ACT & REGULATIONS. base vol. (plus q. update). $265. Butterworths, 271-273 Lane Cove Rd., P.O. Box 345, North Ryde, N.S.W. 2113, Australia. TEL 02-335-4444. FAX 02-335-4678. (looseleaf format)

340   US
LIFE DOCKET. m. free. Americans United for Life, 343 S. Dearborn St., Ste. 1804, Chicago, IL 60604. TEL 312-786-9494. Ed. Melodie Schlenker Gage.
Description: Summary of legal news relating to abortion and euthanasia.

340   AT
LIQUOR LAWS VICTORIA. base vol. (plus updates 3-4/yr.) $155. Butterworths, 271-273 Lane Cove Rd., P.O. Box 345, N. Ryde, N.S.W. 2113, Australia. TEL 02-335-4444. FAX 02-335-4678. (looseleaf format)

340   AT
LIQUOR LICENSING LAW AND PRACTICE N.S.W. 1984. 4/yr. Aus.$295 with updates. Law Book Co. Ltd., 44-50 Waterloo Rd., North Ryde, N.S.W. 2113, Australia. TEL 02-887-0177. FAX 02-888-9706. TELEX ASBOOK 27995. Eds. K.T. Palmer, B.A. Bulford.

340   US
THE LITERATE LAWYER. irreg., 2nd ed., 1991. $25. Butterworth Legal Publishers (Salem) (Subsidiary of: Reed Elsevier plc), 8 Industrial Way, Bldg. C, Salem, NH 03079. TEL 800-548-4001. FAX 603-898-9858. Ed. Robert B. Smith.
Description: Emphasizes legal writing skills and communication techniques.

347.7   US
LITIGATING PRIVATE ANTITRUST ACTIONS. 1984. base vol. (plus a. suppl.). Shepard's - McGraw-Hill, Inc., Box 35300, Colorado Springs, CO 80935-3530. TEL 800-525-2474.
Description: Policy-oriented guidelines to the intricacies of identifying, proving and litigating antitrust violations.

347.73   US   ISSN 0097-9813
K12
LITIGATION. 1975. q. $40 to non-members (foreign $45). American Bar Association, Litigation Section, 750 N. Lake Shore Dr., Chicago, IL 60611. TEL 312-988-5555. Ed. Cie Brown-Armstead. bk.rev.; illus. circ. 63,000. (also avail. in microfiche from WSH,PMC; microfilm from WSH,PMC) **Indexed:** C.L.I., L.R.I., Law Ofc.Info.Svc., Leg.Cont., Leg.Per. **Document type:** newsletter.
●Also available online. Vendor(s): West Services, Inc..
—BLDSC (5277.462030); UnCover.
Description: For trial lawyers and judges. Each issue focuses on a particular topic involving trial practice.

340   UK   ISSN 0263-2160
LITIGATION. 1981. 8/yr. £48. Barry Rose Law Periodicals, Little London, Chichester, W. Sussex PO19 1PG, England. TEL 0243-787841. FAX 0243-779278. Ed. Richard Colbey. **Document type:** academic/scholarly publication.
—BLDSC (5277.462030).
Description: Looks at the litigation business for British lawyers (solicitors and barristers) involving personal injuries, civil practice and procedure, matrimonial law, landlord and tenant, employment law and commercial law.

340   US
LITIGATION COMMITTEE NEWSLETTER. q. $15. American Bar Association, Young Lawyers Division, 750 N. Lake Shore Dr., Chicago, IL 60611. TEL 312-988-5000. bk.rev.

340   UK   ISSN 0268-0653
THE LITIGATION LETTER. 1982. 10/yr. £105($210) l B C Publishing, Gilmoora House, 57-61 Mortimer St., London W1N 7TD, England. TEL 071-637-4383. FAX 071-636-6414. Ed. Anne Sturdy. bk.rev.; bibl.; charts; illus.; stat.; index. (back issues avail.) **Document type:** newsletter.

340   US   ISSN 1059-0250
KF8900
LITIGATION MANAGEMENT SUPERCOURSE. 1990. a. Practising Law Institute, 810 Seventh Ave., New York, NY 10019.

340 US ISSN 0147-9970
KF200
LITIGATION NEWS. 1975. q. membership only. American Bar Association, Litigation Section, 750 N. Lake Shore Dr., Chicago, IL 60611. TEL 312-988-6063. Ed. Cie Brown-Armstead. circ. 63,000. (back issues avail.) **Indexed:** C.L.I., L.R.I. **Document type:** newsletter.
—UnCover.
Description: Newsletter of council and committee activity, upcoming meetings, legislative activities of interest to trial attorneys.

340 US
LITIGATION NEWS (MADISON). q. membership. State Bar of Wisconsin, Litigation Section, 402 W. Wilson St., Madison, WI 53703. TEL 608-257-3838. FAX 608-257-3838. circ. 2,270. (back issues avail.) **Document type:** newsletter.

340 320 US
LITIGATION UNDER THE FEDERAL OPEN GOVERNMENT LAWS. a. $45. American Civil Liberties Union Foundation, 122 Maryland Ave., N.E., Washington, DC 20002. TEL 202-544-1681. FAX 202-546-0738. Ed. Allan Adler. circ. 2,500. **Document type:** bulletin.
Formerly: Litigation Under the Federal Freedom of Information Act and Privacy Act.
Description: Covers all aspects of the Freedom of Information Act, the Privacy Act and other "open government" law such as the Government-in-the-Sunshine Act and the Federal Advisory Committee Act (FACA).

347 BL
LITIS; revista trimestral de direito processual. 1974. q. Rua Sao Salvador, 31, ZC-01 Rio de Janeiro, Brazil.

LIVE & LOVE. see *MATRIMONY*

340 UK ISSN 0144-932X
K12 CODEN: LLAREH
LIVERPOOL LAW REVIEW; a journal of contemporary legal issues. 1979. s-a. £40 (effective 1994). (Liverpool Law Review Association) Deborah Charles Publications, 173 Mather Ave., Liverpool L18 6JZ, England. TEL 44-51-724-2500. FAX 44-51-729-0371. (Dist. in U.S. by: William Gaunt & Sons, Inc., 3011 Gulf Dr., Holmes Beach, FL 34217-2199. TEL 813-778-5211. FAX 813-778-5252) Ed. S. Salako. adv.; bk.rev. circ. 400. **Indexed:** C.L.I., L.R.I., Leg.Per. **Document type:** academic/scholarly publication.
—BLDSC (5281.143000); UMI.

LLOYD'S AVIATION LAW. see *AERONAUTICS AND SPACE FLIGHT*

340 UK ISSN 0024-5488
KD1815.A2
LLOYD'S LAW REPORTS. 1919. m. $588. Lloyd's of London Press Ltd., Sheepen Place, Colchester, Essex CO3 3LP, England. TEL 0206-772277. FAX 0206-46273. TELEX 987321 LLOYDS G. (Subscr. in US to: Lloyd's of London Press Inc., 611 Broadway, Ste. 308, New York, NY 10012. TEL 212-529-9500) Ed. Mavis d'Souza. s-a. index. (tabloid format; back issues avail.) **Indexed:** RICS.
—BLDSC (5287.250000); SWETS.
Formerly: Lloyd's List Law Reports.
Description: Provides reports of judicial decisions affecting both maritime and commercial spheres. Each report contains a summary of the facts and legal issues raised, followed by the verbatim judgment of the court.

LOAN OFFICERS LEGAL ALERT; the commercial lending law letter. see *BUSINESS AND ECONOMICS — Banking And Finance*

340 350 US ISSN 1057-0594
▼**LOBBYING RESOURCE DIRECTORY;** a practical guide to sources of information and assistance for lobbyists, legislative advocates and citizen activists. 1993. a. $75. Government Research Service, 701 Jackson, Ste. 304, Topeka, KS 66603. TEL 913-232-7720. FAX 913-232-1615. Ed. Lynn Hellebust. **Document type:** directory.
Description: Covers sources of strategic planning assistance, grass roots media, phone and direct mail help, handbooks and manuals, bill status information, policy research organizations and bill drafting manuals.

LOCAL GOVERNMENT AND LAW. see *PUBLIC ADMINISTRATION — Municipal Government*

340 UK ISSN 1351-5764
LOCAL GOVERNMENT REVIEW REPORTS. 1837. w. £151.80 (typically set in Sep.). Barry Rose Law Periodicals, Little London, Chichester, W. Sussex PO19 1PG, England. TEL 0243-787841. FAX 0243-779278. adv.; bk.rev.; stat.; index, cum.index. **Indexed:** ASSIA, C.L.I. **Document type:** academic/scholarly publication.
Formerly (until 1993): Local Government Review (ISSN 0262-4303)
Description: Covers all aspects of local government law practice and administration in England and Wales; also covers Lands Tribunal and planning appeal decisions.

340 UK ISSN 0374-3721
LONDON GAZETTE. 1666. 4/w. £365 (effective 1994). H.M.S.O., 51 Nine Elms Ln., London SW8 5DR, England. TEL 071-873-0011. FAX 071-873-8463. (Subscr. to: H.M.S.O., Publications Centre, P.O. Box 276, London SW8 5DT, England. TEL 071-873-9090. FAX 071-873-8200) (also avail. in microform from UMI; microfilm from KTO; reprint service avail. from UMI) **Document type:** government publication.
—BLDSC (5293.370000).

340 UK
LONGMAN DIRECTORY OF LOCAL AUTHORITIES. a. £21.50. Longman Group Ltd., Law, Tax and Finance Division, 21-27 Lambs Conduit St., London WC1N 3NJ, England. TEL 071-242-2548. FAX 071-831-8119. **Document type:** directory.
Description: Reference of names and addresses of all local authorities in England, Wales and Scotland.

340 US ISSN 0362-5575
LOS ANGELES DAILY JOURNAL. 1888. d. (weekdays). $328. Daily Journal Corporation (Los Angeles), 915 E. First St., Los Angeles, CA 90012. TEL 213-229-5300. FAX 213-680-3682. Ed. T. Sumner Robinson. adv.; bk.rev. circ. 16,000. (also avail. in microfilm) **Indexed:** C.L.I., Hlth.Ind., L.R.I. **Document type:** newspaper.

340 US ISSN 0162-2900
KF200
LOS ANGELES LAWYER. 1978. m. $28. (Los Angeles County Bar Association) Susan Pettit, Ed. & Pub., Box 55020, Los Angeles, CA 90055. TEL 213-896-6501. FAX 213-623-2348. adv.; bk.rev.; illus.; index. circ. 24,000. (also avail. in microfilm from WSH) **Indexed:** C.L.I., Cal.Per.Ind. (1984-), L.R.I., Law Ofc.Info.Svc., Leg.Per.
—Faxon; UnCover; UMI.
Formed by the merger of: Barrister Bulletin (ISSN 0094-310X); Los Angeles Bar Journal (ISSN 0362-837X); Which was formerly: Los Angeles Bar Bulletin (ISSN 0024-6530); Bar Bulletin (ISSN 0197-2588)

LOUISIANA ADMINISTRATIVE CODE. see *PUBLIC ADMINISTRATION*

340 US ISSN 0459-8881
KF200
LOUISIANA BAR JOURNAL. 1942. bi-m. $30. Louisiana State Bar Association, 601 St. Charles Ave., New Orleans, LA 70130. TEL 504-566-1600. FAX 504-566-0930. Ed. J. Robert Ates. adv. circ. 16,700. (also avail. in microfilm from WSH; back issues avail.) **Indexed:** C.L.I.
—Faxon; UnCover.
Description: Topics of interest to members of the Louisiana Bar.

340 639.2 US
LOUISIANA COASTAL LAW; coastal zone management, marine resource law, and environmental law related to coastal and marine issues. 1971. irreg. (3-4/yr.). free. Louisiana Sea Grant Legal Program, 170 Law Center, L.S.U., Baton Rouge, LA 70803. TEL 504-388-5931. FAX 504-388-5938. Eds. Michael W. Wascom, James G. Wilkins. bibl. circ. 1,200. **Document type:** newsletter.
Louisiana Coastal Law Report.

340 331 US ISSN 1059-5058
▼**LOUISIANA EMPLOYMENT LAW LETTER.** 1992. m. $95. (Jones, Walker, Waechter, Poitevent, Carrere & Denegre) M. Lee Smith Publishers & Printers, 162 Fourth Ave., N., Box 198867, Nashville, TN 37219-8867. TEL 615-242-7395; 800-274-6774. FAX 615-256-6601. Eds. H. Mark Adams, Mary Ellen Jordan. **Document type:** newsletter.
Description: Reports the latest state-specific employment law developments that affect companies in Louisiana.

340 613.1 US ISSN 1066-1115
▼**LOUISIANA ENVIRONMENTAL COMPLIANCE UPDATE.** 1993. m. $137. (Jones, Walker, Poitevent, Carrere & Denegre) M. Lee Smith Publishers & Printers, 162 Fourth Ave., N., Box 198867, Nashville, TN 37219-8867. TEL 615-242-7395; 800-274-6774. FAX 615-256-6601. Eds. Mike Chernekoff, Stanley A. Millan. **Document type:** newsletter.
Description: Reports the latest state-specific environmental law developments that affect companies in Louisiana.

340 US ISSN 0024-6859
K12
LOUISIANA LAW REVIEW. 1937. 6/yr. $42 (foreign $54). Louisiana State University, Law School, Baton Rouge, LA 70803. TEL 504-388-1683. FAX 504-388-1685. Ed. Daniel Shapiro. adv.; bk.rev., index, cum.index covering 40 yrs. circ. 2,200. (also avail. in microfiche from WSH; microfilm from WSH; reprint service avail. from UMI,WSH) **Indexed:** C.L.I., Curr.Cont., INIS Atomind., L.R.I., Leg.Cont., Leg.Per., Mar.Aff.Bibl., SSCI. **Document type:** academic/scholarly publication.
●Also available online. Vendor(s): Mead Data Central, Inc., West Services, Inc.
—BLDSC (5296.100000); Faxon; UnCover; SWETS; UMI.

340 US
LOUISIANA LEGAL RESEARCH. irreg., 2nd ed., 1990. $50. Butterworth Legal Publishers (Salem) (Subsidiary of: Reed Elsevier plc), 8 Industrial Way, Bldg. C, Salem, NH 03079. TEL 800-548-4001. FAX 603-898-9858. Ed. Win-Shin S. Chiang.
Description: Covers governmental bodies and sources of law in the state - the legislative, executive, and judicial branches of state and local government plus the law schools, the practicing bar, and state document depository program.

340 US
LOUISIANA OIL AND GAS LAW. 1988. base vol. (plus a. supplement). $120. Butterworth Legal Publishers (Salem) (Subsidiary of: Reed Elsevier plc), 8 Industrial Way, Bldg. C, Salem, NH 03079. TEL 800-548-4001. FAX 603-898-9858. Eds. W.R. Irby, Luther L. McDougal, III. (looseleaf format)
Description: Covers mineral servitudes, oil and gas leases, implied obligations in oil and gas leases, oil and gas royalties, and state regulation of development and production.

LOUISIANA REGISTER. see *PUBLIC ADMINISTRATION*

340 US
LOUISIANA SECURITY RIGHTS IN PERSONAL PROPERTY. 1991. base vol. (plus a. suppl.). $85. Butterworth Legal Publishers (Salem) (Subsidiary of: Reed Elsevier plc), 8 Industrial Way, Bldg. C, Salem, NH 03079. TEL 800-548-4001. FAX 603-898-9858. Ed. Henry D. Gabriel. (looseleaf format)
Description: Provides a complete analysis on all aspects of security rights from creation to default.

340 US
LOUISIANA STATE BAR ASSOCIATION. BAR BRIEFS. 1986. 6/yr. Louisiana State Bar Association, 601 St. Charles Ave., New Orleans, LA 70130-3404. TEL 504-566-1600. FAX 504-566-0930. **Document type:** newsletter.
Description: Discusses association news and activities, continuing legal education opportunities and other items of interest to lawyers in Louisiana.

340 US
LOUISIANA WRONGFUL DEATH & SURVIVAL ACTIONS. 1986. base vol. (plus a. suppl.). $120. Butterworth Legal Publishers (Salem) (Subsidiary of: Reed Elsevier plc), 8 Industrial Way, Bldg. C, Salem, NH 03079. TEL 800-548-4001. FAX 603-898-9858. (looseleaf format)

LAW

340   US
LOUISVILLE LAWYER. 1979. q. Louisville Bar Association, 707 W. Main St., Louisville, KY 40202-2668. TEL 502-583-5314.

349   NO   ISSN 0024-6980
LOV OG RETT; norsk juridisk tidsskrift. 1962. m. (10/yr.). NOK 625 in the Nordic countries; elsewhere NOK 730. Scandinavian University Press, P.O. Box 2959-Toeyen, N-0608 Oslo, Norway. TEL 472-67-7600. FAX 472-67-7575. (US addr.: Scandinavian University Press, 200 Meacham Ave., Elmont, NY 11003. TEL 516-352-7300) Ed. Asbjoern Kjoenstad. adv.; bk.rev.; index. circ. 5,000.
Description: Covers law and legal issues in Norway from a professional standpoint.

340   DK   ISSN 0105-8924
LOVBIBLIOTEK.* 1985. 3/yr. (Juristforbundet) Schultz Information, Mondergade 21, DK-1116 Copenhagen K, Denmark.

340   DK   ISSN 0108-9102
LOVE OG BEKENDTGOERELSER M.V. 1979. s-a. DKK 848. Kroghs Forlag A S, Chr. Hansenvej 3, 7100 Vejle, Denmark.
Formerly: Samling af Bekendtgoerelser (ISSN 0415-3693)

340   DK   ISSN 0108-0849
LAW
LOVNOEGLE; register over love og tilhoerende aendringslove, bekendtgoerelser og cirkulaerer m.v. 1982. q. DKK 895. Schultz Information A-S, Ottiliavej 18, DK-2500 Valby, Denmark. circ. 1,100.

340   FA   ISSN 0907-3728
LOVREGISTER FOR FAEROERNE. (Text in Danish) 1966. irreg. DKK 75. Faeroernes Landsstyre, Rigsombudsmanden paa Faeroerne, P.O. Box 12, FR-110 Torshavn, Faeroe Islands. TEL 298-11040. FAX 298-10864. circ. 450.
Formerly (until 1992): Faeroesk Lovregister (ISSN 0108-142X)

340   DK   ISSN 0106-8458
LOVTIDENDE A FOR KONGERIGET DANMARK. 1871. s-w. DKK 800. Justisministeriet, Sekretariatet for Retsinformation, Axeltorv 6, 5. sal, D-1609 Copenhagen V, Denmark. TEL 33-32-52-22. FAX 33-91-28-01. index. circ. 3,950. **Document type:** government publication.
●Also available online.
Description: Official organ for promulgating statutes, laws and departmental orders in accordance with Danish law.

342   US
LOYOLA LAW REVIEW. 1920. q. $20 (foreign $22). Loyola University, School of Law, 7214 St. Charles, New Orleans, LA 70118. TEL 504-861-5558. bk.rev.; index. circ. 11,000. **Indexed:** Abstr.Bk.Rev.Curr.Leg.Per., C.L.I., Crim.Just.Abstr., L.R.I., Leg.Cont., Leg.Per., Mar.Aff.Bibl.
●Also available online. Vendor(s): West Services, Inc.

340   US   ISSN 0277-5417
K12
LOYOLA OF LOS ANGELES INTERNATIONAL AND COMPARATIVE LAW JOURNAL. 1978. 4/yr. $40. Loyola of Los Angeles Law School, 1441 W. Olympic Blvd., Los Angeles, CA 90015-3980. TEL 213-736-1405. FAX 213-380-3769. Ed. Shannon Sullivan. adv.; bk.rev. circ. 300. (also avail. in microform from WSH; back issues avail.; reprint service avail. from WSH) **Indexed:** C.L.I., L.R.I., Leg.Per., Mar.Aff.Bibl., P.A.I.S. **Document type:** academic/scholarly publication.
●Also available online. Vendor(s): West Services, Inc..
—BLDSC (5299.550000); UnCover.
Formerly (until 1983): Loyola of Los Angeles International and Comparative Law Annual.

340   US   ISSN 0024-7081
K12
LOYOLA UNIVERSITY CHICAGO LAW JOURNAL. 1970. q. $18. Loyola University Chicago, Law School, One E. Pearson St., Chicago, IL 60611. TEL 312-915-7183. FAX 312-915-7201. Ed. Thomas Smith. adv.; B&W page $100. bk.rev. circ. 625. (back issues avail.; reprint service avail. from RRI) **Indexed:** C.L.I., Leg.Cont., Leg.Per. **Document type:** academic/scholarly publication.
●Also available online.
—Faxon; UnCover.

340   II   ISSN 0459-9756
LUCKNOW LAW TIMES; acts, ordinances, rules and notifications of the central and U.P. governments. (Text in English) 1960. m. $41. Eastern Book Company, 34 Lalbagh, Lucknow 226 001, India. TEL 91-522-244328. FAX 91-522-244328. Ed. P.L. Malik. adv.; bk.rev.; index. circ. 3,000. (back issues avail.)

340   SW   ISSN 1100-1100
LUND STUDIES IN LAW AND SOCIETY. (Text in English, Swedish) 1988. irreg. price varies. Lund University Press, P.O. Box 141, S-221 00 Lund, Sweden. TEL 46-46-312000. FAX 46-46-395338. Eds. H. Hyden, K. A. Modeer. **Document type:** academic/scholarly publication, monographic series.

340   SW   ISSN 1101-2005
LUND STUDIES IN LEGAL HISTORY. (Text in English, Swedish) 1990. irreg. price varies. Lund University Press, P.O. Box 141, S-221 00 Lund, Sweden. TEL 46-46-312000. FAX 46-46-305338. Ed. K. A. Modeer. **Document type:** academic/scholarly publication, monographic series.

340   CC
LUSHI SHIJIE. (Text in Chinese) m. Hubei Sheng Sifa Ting, No. 16, Hongshan Celu, Wuchang-qu, Wuhan, Hubei 430071, People's Republic of China. TEL 813498. Ed. Chen Hengchu.

340   CC   ISSN 1001-6376
LUSHI YU FAZHI/LAWYERS AND LEGAL SYSTEM. (Text in Chinese) bi-m. Zhejiang Sheng Sifa-ting - Zhejiang Provincial Judiciaries, 1 Shengfu Lu, Hangzhou, Zhejiang 310007, People's Republic of China. TEL 754413. Ed. Li Xin.

340   350   US   ISSN 0884-1667
KF200
M S B A IN BRIEF. 1985. m. $15. Minnesota State Bar Association, 514 Nicollet Ave., Ste. 300, Minneapolis, MN 55402. TEL 612-333-1183. FAX 612-333-4927. Ed. Judson Haverkamp. adv. circ. 13,700. (back issues avail.)
Description: News of the legal profession in Minnesota.

340   US
M S N NEWSLETTER. 1985. 3/yr. $7.50 (foreign $10). Center for Constitutional Rights, Movement Support Network, 666 Broadway, 7th Fl., New York, NY 10012. TEL 212-614-6422. FAX 212-614-6499. circ. 4,000. (back issues avail.) **Document type:** newsletter.
Supersedes: Quash.

340   CN   ISSN 0024-9041
LAW
MCGILL LAW JOURNAL/REVUE DE DROIT DE MCGILL. (Text in English, French) 1952. 4/yr. Can.$43($36.75) McGill Law Journal, Faculty of Law, Chancellor Day Hall, 3644 Peel St., Montreal, PQ H3A 1W9, Canada. TEL 514-398-7397. FAX 514-398-8197. Ed. Erica Stone. adv. contact: Caroline Thomassin. bk.rev.; index, cum.index. circ. 1,500. (also avail. in microfilm from RRI; reprint service avail. from RRI) **Indexed:** C.L.I., Can.Per.Ind., Curr.Cont., Ind.Can.L.P.L., L.R.I., Leg.Cont., Leg.Per., Refug.Abstr., SSCI. **Document type:** academic/scholarly publication.
—BLDSC (5413.428000); Faxon; UnCover; SWETS; UMI.

346.066   US   ISSN 0024-9289
MACOMB COUNTY LEGAL NEWS. 1957. w. $25. Independent Newspapers, Inc., 67 Cass Ave., Mt. Clemens, MI 48043. TEL 313-469-4510. (Subscr. to: Box 707, Mt. Clemens, MI 48046) Ed. Diane Kish. adv. circ. 1,000. (back issues avail.) **Document type:** newspaper.
Description: Covers general, legal and business news in Macomb County.

340   352   US
MCQUILLIN MUNICIPAL LAW REPORT; a monthly review for lawyers, administrators and officials. 1982. m. $195. Clark - Boardman - Callaghan Company Ltd., 375 Hudson St., New York, NY 10014. TEL 212-929-7500; 800-221-9428. FAX 212-924-0460. Ed. Jim Fegen. index. circ. 1,500. (tabloid format) **Document type:** newsletter.
Description: Covers the lates cases in civil rights, licensing, permits, building, zoning, budgets, public utilities, and land use.

340   II   ISSN 0024-9459
MADHYA PRADESH LAW JOURNAL. (Text in English) 1956. m. Rs.265. Journal Publications, Road No. 12, Dhantoli, Nagpur 440 012, India. TEL 0712-522565. Ed. Shri A.G. Dhande. bk.rev. circ. 4,500. **Document type:** newspaper.

342   II
MADRAS LAW JOURNAL. (Text in English) 1891. w. Rs.300 (effective 1991). Madras Law Journal Office, Box 604, Mylapore, Madras 4, India. Ed. S. Venkatraman. bk.rev.

MADRAS LAW JOURNAL (CRIMINAL). see LAW — Criminal Law

340   330   UA
AL-MAGALLAH AL-QANUNIYYAH AL-IQTISADIYYAH. (Text in Arabic) 1986. irreg. Zagazig University, Faculty of Law, Zagazig, Egypt.

340   UA
MAGALLAT AL-DIRASAT AL-QANUNIYYAH. (Text in Arabic) vol.10, 1988. m. Assiut University, Faculty of Law, Assiut, Egypt.

340   SA   ISSN 0024-9971
K12
THE MAGISTRATE/LANDDROS. (Text in Afrikaans, English) 1965. q. R.54 membership (effective 1994). (Magistrates' Association) Digma Publications (Pty) Ltd., 270 Main St., Waterkloof, Pretoria 0181, South Africa. TEL 27-12-346-3840. FAX 27-12-346-3845. TELEX 4-25847 SA. (Subscr. to: P.O. Box 95466, Pretoria 0181, South Africa) Ed. P.J. Theron. adv.; bk.rev.; bibl.; circ. 1,900. (controlled). **Document type:** academic/scholarly publication.
Description: Covers a variety of legal topics from a practitioner's point of view, including laws of evidence, jurisdiction, unreported cases, rules of practice, criminal law, civil and criminal procedure, and sentencing.

340   HU   ISSN 0025-0147
K13
MAGYAR JOG. 1954. m. $38.50. Magyar Jogasz Szovetseg, Szemere u. 10, 1054 Budapest 5, Hungary. TEL 314-574. (Subscr. to: Kultura, Box 149, 1389 Budapest, Hungary) Ed. Peter Boor. adv.; bk.rev.; index. circ. 29,500.
Former titles: Magyar Jog es Kulfoldi Jogi Szemle (ISSN 0034-6829); Magyar Jog.

340   II   ISSN 0025-0465
LAW
MAHARASHTRA LAW JOURNAL. (Text in English) 1963. m. Rs.400. Journal Publications, Road No. 12, Dhantoli, Nagpur 440 012, India. TEL 0712-522565. Ed. Shri J.N. Chandurkar. bk.rev. circ. 5,000. **Document type:** newspaper.
Supersedes: Nagpur Law Journa.

340   US
MAINE BAR DIRECTORY. 1974. a. $41.50. Tower Publishing Co., 34 Diamond St., Box 7220, Portland, ME 04112-7220. TEL 207-774-9813; 800-287-7323. FAX 207-775-1740. Mary Anne Hildreth. adv. contact: Charles Todorich. circ. 1,000 (paid). (looseleaf format; also avail. in diskette format) **Document type:** directory.
●Also available on CD-ROM.
Formerly: Bar Directory of Maine.
Description: Lists lawyers, law firms, and legal services for Maine.

340   US   ISSN 0885-9973
KF200
MAINE BAR JOURNAL. 1986. bi-m. membership. Maine State Bar Association, 124 State St., Box 788, Augusta, ME 04332-0788. TEL 207-622-7523. Ed. Edward M. Bonney. adv.; bk.rev. circ. 2,850. (also avail. in microfiche; back issues avail.; reprint service avail. from Westlaw) **Indexed:** C.L.I., Leg.Per. —UnCover.
Description: Presents articles on substantive areas of the law, Maine legal history, Maine bar and court news and other notices of interest to Maine practicioners.

LAW

340   US
MAINE JURY INSTRUCTION MANUAL. irreg., 2nd ed., 1990. $75. Butterworth Legal Publishers (Salem) (Subsidiary of: Reed Elsevier plc), 8 Industrial Way, Bldg. C, Salem, NH 03079. TEL 800-548-4001. FAX 603-898-9858. Ed. Donald G. Alexander. (looseleaf format)
Description: Covers statutory and judicial developments and offers instructions to assist attorneys and judges in communicating legal issues to jurors.

340   US   ISSN 0025-0651
K13
MAINE LAW REVIEW. 1908. s-a. $25 (Canada $27; Europe $29) (typically set in Feb.). University of Maine, School of Law, 246 Deering Ave., Portland, ME 04102. TEL 207-780-4357. Ed. Larissa Shumway. adv.; bk.rev.; bibl.; index. circ. 1,200. (also avail. in microform from UMI,PMC; microfiche from WSH; microfilm from WSH; back issues avail.) **Indexed:** C.L.I., L.R.I., Leg.Cont., Leg.Per., Mar.Aff.Bibl. **Document type:** academic/scholarly publication.
●Also available online. Vendor(s): Mead Data Central, Inc., West Services, Inc.
—Faxon; UnCover; UMI.

340   US
MAINE MANUAL ON PROFESSIONAL RESPONSIBILITY. (2nd ed., 1992) 1986. 2 base vols. (plus irreg. supplements). $65 per vol. Butterworth Legal Publishers (Salem) (Subsidiary of: Reed Elsevier plc), 8 Industrial Way, Bldg. C, Salem, NH 03079. TEL 800-548-4001. FAX 603-898-9858. (looseleaf format)

MAINE WORKERS' COMPENSATION. see BUSINESS AND ECONOMICS — Labor And Industrial Relations

MAINE WORKERS COMPENSATION COMMISSION: APPELLATE DIVISION DECISIONS. see BUSINESS AND ECONOMICS — Labor And Industrial Relations

340.59 297   TS
MAJALLAT AL-SHARI'AH WAL-QANUN. (Text in Arabic) 1987. a. exchange basis. United Arab Emirates University, Faculty of Law and Islamic Jurisprudence, P.O. Box 15551, Al-Ain, United Arab Emirates. TEL 643998. TELEX 33521 JAMEAH EM. Ed. Moustafa M. El Gammal. bk.rev. circ. 1,000.
Document type: academic/scholarly publication.
Description: Publishes research on topics in Islamic jurisprudence and legal issues in the U.A.E. and the Gulf region.

340   UG
MAKERERE LAW JOURNAL.* 1971. s-a. EAs.250. (Makerere Law Society) Makerere University, Faculty of Law, Box 7062, Kampala, Uganda. Ed.Bd. bk.rev. circ. 1,000.

340   UG   ISSN 0075-4781
MAKERERE UNIVERSITY. FACULTY OF LAW. HANDBOOK. 1970. a. Makerere University, Faculty of Law, Box 7062, Kampala, Uganda.

340   SI   ISSN 0025-1283
LAW
MALAYAN LAW JOURNAL. 1932. fortn. S.$370 for Singapore and Brunei; Malaysia M.$595. Butterworths Asia (Subsidiary of: Reed International (Singapore) Pte Ltd.), 3 Shenton Way, No. 14-03, Shenton House, Singapore 0106, Singapore. TEL 220-3684. FAX 225-2939. Ed. Zarinah Marican. adv.; bk.rev.; s-a. index. circ. 1,450. (back issues avail.)
—BLDSC (5356.006000).

340   SI   ISSN 0961-5563
MALLAL'S MONTHLY DIGEST; Malaysia, Singapore, Brunei. (Text in English) 1987. m. S.$299 in Singapore & Brunei; Malaysia M.$418. Butterworths Asia (Subsidiary of: Reed International (Singapore) Pte. Ltd.), 3 Shenton Way, No. 14-03, Shenton House, Singapore 0106, Singapore. TEL 220-3684. FAX 225-2939. Ed.Bd. adv. circ. 500. (back issues avail.)
Formerly: Butterworths Law Digest (ISSN 0951-5720)
Description: Carries case digests from Malaysia, Singapore and Brunei. Includes summaries of recent Malaysian and Singapore legislation.

MALPRACTICE REPORTER; comprehensive reporting of malpractice issues for the medical, legal, health services, and insurance communities. see MEDICAL SCIENCES

MALPRACTICE REPORTER. HOSPITALS EDITION. see MEDICAL SCIENCES

MALPRACTICE REPORTER. PODIATRY EDITION. see MEDICAL SCIENCES — Orthopedics And Traumatology

346.73 347 617   US   ISSN 0738-1964
MALPRACTICE REPORTER. SURGEON'S. m. $128. Public Reporting Services, Inc., 332 Bleecker St., Ste. 424, New York, NY 10014. TEL 212-989-8303. Ed. Joan Fabricant; Pub. Joan Fabricant.

MANAGED CARE LAW OUTLOOK. see MEDICAL SCIENCES

MANAGEMENT POLICIES & PERSONNEL LAW. see BUSINESS AND ECONOMICS — Management

MANAGERIAL LAW. see BUSINESS AND ECONOMICS — Labor And Industrial Relations

MANAGER'S MANUAL. see BUSINESS AND ECONOMICS — Banking And Finance

340   US   ISSN 1074-3898
MANAGING LITIGATION COSTS. m. $275. Institute of Management and Administration, 29 W. 25th St., 5th Fl., New York, NY 10001-2299. TEL 212-244-0360. FAX 212-564-0465. Ed. Rees Morrison. index.

340   US
MANAGING THE FLORIDA CONDOMINIUM. 1988. base vol. (plus supplements 2-3/yr.). $80. Butterworth Legal Publishers (Salem) (Subsidiary of: Reed Elsevier plc), 8 Industrial Way, Bldg. C, Salem, NH 03079. TEL 800-548-4001. FAX 603-898-9858. Ed. William D. Clark. (looseleaf format)
Description: Comprehensive reference for community association managers, developers, owners and attorneys concerned with the legal duties and responsibilities of condominium management.

MANHATTAN COOP CONDO CONVERSION DIGEST. see REAL ESTATE

340   CN   ISSN 0076-3861
K13
MANITOBA LAW JOURNAL. (Text in English, French) 1962. 3/yr. Can.$30($30) University of Manitoba, Faculty of Law, Winnipeg, MB R3T 2N2, Canada. TEL 204-474-6159. FAX 204-275-5540. Ed. L. Yvette Creft. adv.; bk.rev.; cum.index; circ. 450 (paid). (also avail. in microfilm from WSH,PMC; back issues avail.; reprint service avail. from WSH) **Indexed:** Abstr.Bk.Rev.Curr.Leg.Per., C.C.L.P., C.L.I., Foreign Leg.Per., Ind.Can.L.P.L., L.R.I., Leg.Cont., Leg.Per. **Document type:** academic/scholarly publication.
—BLDSC (5360.630000); UnCover.
Incorporates: Manitoba Bar News.

340   CN   ISSN 0713-7109
MANITOBA REPORTS. irreg. (approx. 6/yr.). Can.$125 per vol. Maritime Law Book Ltd., Box 302, Fredericton, NB E3B 4Y9, Canada. TEL 506-453-9921; 800-561-0220. FAX 506-453-9525. (back issues avail.)
●Also available online. Vendor(s): QL Systems Ltd. **Formerly (until 1891):** Reports of Cases Argued and Determined in the Court of Queen's Bench, Manitoba (ISSN 0713-8784)
Description: Contains all of the judgments of the Manitoba Court of Appeal and selected judgments from other Manitoba courts.

340   US
MANUAL FOR FLORIDA LEGAL SECRETARIES. 1984. 3 base vols. (plus suppl. 3-4/yr.). (Florida Association of Legal Secretaries) Butterworth Legal Publishers (Salem) (Subsidiary of: Reed Elsevier plc), 8 Industrial Way, Bldg. C, Salem, NH 03079. TEL 800-548-4001. FAX 603-898-9858. (looseleaf format)
Description: Practical up-to-date procedural guide providing forms and checklists, plus explanations on everyday use.

330   US   ISSN 0893-7788
MARKETING FOR LAWYERS NEWSLETTER. 1987. m. $175. New York Law Publishing Co., 345 Park Ave. S., New York, NY 10010. TEL 212-545-6170. FAX 212-696-1848. **Document type:** newsletter.
Description: Helps attorneys to expand their practices by covering marketing techniques and strategies such as cross-marketing, using newsletters and seminars, opening branch offices, and servicing existing clients.

340 658 659.1   CN
MARKETING LAW REPORTING SERVICE. 1973. m. Can.$335($295) Businesstek Publishing Inc., P.O. Box 250, Carleton Place, ON K7C 3P4, Canada. TEL 613-253-2833. FAX 613-253-2834. Ed. Shaun McLaughlin. circ. 140. (looseleaf format)
Formerly: Marketing and Advertising Law Reporter (ISSN 0827-2115)
Description: Covers Canadian federal and provincial laws and regulation regarding marketing, packaging, advertising and labelling of consumer products.

340   US   ISSN 0025-3987
MARQUETTE LAW REVIEW. 1916. q. $25. Marquette University, Law School, 1103 W. Wisconsin Ave., Milwaukee, WI 53233. TEL 414-288-5143. Ed. Laurence M. Brooks. adv.; bk.rev.; index, cum.index. circ. 1,800. (also avail. in microfiche from WSH; microfilm from WSH) **Indexed:** C.L.I., Crim.Just.Abstr., L.R.I., Leg.Cont., Leg.Per., P.A.I.S.
●Also available online. Vendor(s): West Services, Inc.
—BLDSC (5382.500000); Faxon; UnCover; UMI.

MARQUETTE SPORTS LAW JOURNAL. see SPORTS AND GAMES

340   AT   ISSN 0728-5981
MARTIN AND MORLEY MOTOR VEHICLE LAW (QUEENSLAND). 1982. 4/yr. in q. with Aus.$330 with updates. Law Book Co. Ltd., 44-50 Waterloo Rd., N. Ryde, N.S.W. 2113, Australia. TEL 02-887-0177. FAX 02-888-9706. TELEX ASBOOK 27995. Ed. M.G. Martin. (looseleaf format)
Description: Covers motor vehicles, negligence, traffic regulation, traffic offenses, and motor vehicle insurance in Queensland.

340   US   ISSN 1051-5518
MARTINDALE-HUBBELL BAR REGISTER OF PREEMINENT LAWYERS. Key Title: Martindale-Hubbell Bar Register. 1917. a., 78th ed., 1994. $145. Martindale-Hubbell, A Reed Reference Publishing Company, Part of the Reed Elsevier group, 121 Chanlon Rd., New Providence, NJ 07974. TEL 800-526-4902. FAX 908-464-3553. TELEX 138755. (Subscr. to: Box 1001, Summit, NJ 07902-1001) **Document type:** directory.
Formerly (until 1990): Bar Register (ISSN 0277-3848)
Description: Lists over 8,000 members of the Bar in the United States and Canada who have been designated by their colleagues as preeminent in their field. Presents complete information on each partnership, including current addresses and telephone numbers, names of members of the firm, and major clients represented. Includes firms in General Practice and over 28 specific fields of law.

340   US
▼**MARTINDALE-HUBBELL CANADIAN LAW DIRECTORY.** 1993. a. $75. Martindale-Hubbell, A Reed Reference Publishing Company, Part of the Reed Elsevier group, 121 Chanlon Rd., New Providence, NJ 07974. TEL 800-526-4902. FAX 908-464-3553. TELEX 138755. (Subscr. to: Box 1001, Summit, NJ 07902-1001) **Document type:** directory, bibliography.
Description: Presents practice profiles for virtually every practicing lawyer, and detailed biographical information for leading lawyers and firms.

340   US   ISSN 0191-0221
KF190
MARTINDALE-HUBBELL LAW DIRECTORY. (In 24 vols.) 1868. a., 126th ed., 1994. $645. Martindale-Hubbell, A Reed Reference Publishing Company, Part of the Reed Elsevier group, 121 Chanlon Rd., New Providence, NJ 07974. TEL 800-526-4902. FAX 908-464-3553. TELEX 138755. (Subscr. to: Box 1001, Summit, NJ 07902-1001) **Document type:** directory, bibliography.
● Also available online. Vendor(s): Mead Data Central, Inc.
Also available on CD-ROM. Producer(s): Bowker - Reed Reference Electronic Publishing.
—CCC.
Description: Lists virtually every lawyer and law firm in the US and Canada, plus leading lawyers and firms in over 130 countries. Consists of three main parts: practice profiles, professional biographies, and services, suppliers and consultants. Includes concise Digests of the laws of the US, Canada and 60 other countries.

340   US
MARTINDALE-HUBBELL LAW DIRECTORY ON C D - R O M. q. $995. Martindale-Hubbell, A Reed Reference Publishing Company, Part of the Reed Elsevier group, 121 Chanlon Rd., New Providence, NJ 07974. TEL 800-526-4902. FAX 908-464-3553. TELEX 138 755. (Subscr. to: Box 1001, Summit, NJ 07902-1001)
● Available only on CD-ROM. Producer(s): Bowker - Reed Reference Electronic Publishing.
Description: Provides rapid access to information on over 80,000 lawyers, law firms, corporate legal departments, banks and services, suppliers, and consultants for lawyers in the US, Canada and the international community.

MARTINDALE-HUBBELL PREMIER ACCOUNT NEWS. see BIOGRAPHY

340   US
MARYLAND. HOUSE OF DELEGATES. JOURNAL OF PROCEEDINGS. REGULAR SESSION. 1826. a. $80. Department of Legislative Reference, Legislative Sales, 90 State Circle, Annapolis, MD 21401. TEL 410-841-3885. **Document type:** government publication.

340   US
MARYLAND. SENATE. JOURNAL OF PROCEEDINGS. REGULAR SESSION. 1826. a. $80. Department of Legislative Reference, Legislative Sales, 90 State Circle, Annapolis, MD 21401. TEL 410-841-3885. **Document type:** government publication.

340   US   ISSN 0025-4177
K13
MARYLAND BAR JOURNAL. 1968. bi-m. $25 to non-members. Maryland State Bar Association, 520 W. Fayette St., Baltimore, MD 21201. TEL 410-685-7878. FAX 410-837-0518. Ed. Janet Stidman Eveleth. adv.; bk.rev.; illus.; index. circ. 16,000. **Indexed:** C.L.I., Law Ofc.Info.Svc., Leg.Per.
—BLDSC (5383.410000); Faxon; UnCover.

340 331   US   ISSN 1049-9377
KFM1534.A15
MARYLAND EMPLOYMENT LAW LETTER. 1990. m. $95. (Venable, Baetjer & Howard) M. Lee Smith Publishers & Printers, 162 Fourth Ave., N., Box 198867, Nashville, TN 37219-8867. TEL 615-242-7395; 800-274-6774. FAX 615-256-6601. Eds. Patrick Clancy, Patrick J. Stewart. **Document type:** newsletter.
Description: Reports the latest state-specific employment law developments that affect Maryland companies.

340 613.1   US   ISSN 1062-7960
▼**MARYLAND ENVIRONMENTAL LAW.** 1992. m. $137. (Piper & Marbury) M. Lee Smith, 162 Fourth Ave., N., Box 198867, Nashville, TN 37219-0678. TEL 615-242-7395; 800-274-6774. FAX 615-256-6601. Ed. Deborah Jennings. **Document type:** academic/scholarly publication.
Description: Reports the latest state-specific environmental law developments that affect companies in Maryland.

340   US
MARYLAND JOURNAL OF CONTEMPORARY LEGAL ISSUES. 1989. 2/yr. $15 ($10 per issue). University of Maryland School of Law, Student Bar Association, 500 W. Baltimore St., Baltimore, MD 21201. TEL 301-328-2115. Ed. Rita Edwards. circ. 600.
Description: Contains current social and political concerns. Explores a separate topic of contemporary significance, and includes pieces from authors prominent in their respective fields.

340   US   ISSN 0025-4282
K13
MARYLAND LAW REVIEW. 1936. q. $20. University of Maryland School of Law, 500 W. Baltimore St., Baltimore, MD 21201. TEL 301-328-7214. Ed. Linda M. Thomas. adv.; bk.rev.; index, cum.index every 10 yrs. circ. 2,200. (also avail. in microform from RRI,UMI; back issues avail.; reprint service avail. from RRI) **Indexed:** C.L.I., L.R.I., Leg.Cont., Leg.Per., P.A.I.S., Refug.Abstr.
● Also available online. Vendor(s): West Services, Inc.
—BLDSC (5383.505000); Faxon; UnCover.

340   US   ISSN 0542-836X
MARYLAND LAWYER'S MANUAL. 1968. a. $63 to non-members. Maryland State Bar Association, 520 W. Fayette St., Baltimore, MD 21201. TEL 301-685-7878. Ed. Arthur S. Gilbert. adv. circ. 18,000.

MARYLAND REGISTER. see PUBLIC ADMINISTRATION

MARYLAND REGISTER CONTRACT WEEKLY. see PUBLIC ADMINISTRATION

340   US
MARYLAND STATE BAR ASSOCIATION. BAR BULLETIN. 1986. m. $12 to non-members. Maryland State Bar Association, 520 W. Fayette St., Baltimore, MD 21201. TEL 410-685-7878. FAX 410-837-0518. Ed. Elise A. Braase. adv. (tabloid format) **Document type:** bulletin.

MARYLAND TAX COURT SERVICE. see BUSINESS AND ECONOMICS — Public Finance, Taxation

340   US
▼**MASSACHUSETTS ATTORNEY CONDUCT MANUAL.** 1992. base vol. (plus supplements). $65. Butterworth Legal Publishers (Salem) (Subsidiary of: Reed Elsevier plc), 8 Industrial Way, Bldg. C, Salem, NH 03079. TEL 800-548-4001. FAX 603-898-9858. Ed. Gilda M. Tuoni. (looseleaf format)
Description: Practical guide to all aspects of the ethics code for Massachusetts attorneys, including a review of topics of professional responsibility and all relevant rules and procedures.

340   US
MASSACHUSETTS ATTORNEY DISCIPLINE REPORTS. (In 4 vols.) 1980. a. $55 per vol. Butterworth Legal Publishers (Salem) (Subsidiary of: Reed Elsevier plc), 8 Industrial Way, Bldg. C, Salem, NH 03079. TEL 800-548-4001. FAX 603-898-9858.

340   US
MASSACHUSETTS BAR ASSOCIATION LAWYERS JOURNAL. vol.33, 1993. m. membership. Massachusetts Bar Association, 20 West St., Boston, MA 02111-1218. TEL 617-542-3602. Ed. Benjamin Fierro III. adv. **Document type:** newspaper.
Formerly: Massachusetts Bar Association Newsletter (ISSN 0465-2029)
Description: Covers legal and professional issues of interest to lawyers in Massachusetts.

344   US
MASSACHUSETTS CIVIL SERVICE REPORTER. 1990. m. $185. New England Legal Publishers, Box 425, Weston, MA 02193. TEL 617-891-6200.
Description: Digests of decisions of the Massachusetts Civil Service Commission and related court decisions.

340   US
MASSACHUSETTS COLLECTIONS MANUAL. irreg., 2nd ed., 1990. $75. Butterworth Legal Publishers (Salem) (Subsidiary of: Reed Elsevier plc), 8 Industrial Way, Bldg. C, Salem, NH 03079. TEL 800-548-4001. FAX 603-898-9858. Ed.Bd. (looseleaf format)
Description: For practitioners of commercial law who collect business debts for clients and all lawyers who are faced with clients who do not pay them.

340 346   US   ISSN 0199-5235
MASSACHUSETTS DISCRIMINATION LAW REPORTER. 1978. m. $260 (effective 1993). New England Legal Publishers, Box 425, Weston, MA 02193-0425. TEL 617-891-6200. Ed. J. Ambash. index. (back issues avail.)
Description: Presents digests of decisions of ther Massachusetts Commission Against Discrimination and Massachusetts court decisions affecting discrimination law, as well as the full text of decisions, applicable rules, regulations, and statutes.

340 331   US   ISSN 1049-2062
KFM2731.A15
MASSACHUSETTS EMPLOYMENT LAW LETTER. 1990. m. $95. (Skoler, Abbot, & Presser) M. Lee Smith Publishers & Printers, 162 Fourth Ave., N., Box 198867, Nashville, TN 37219-8867. TEL 615-242-7395; 800-274-6774. FAX 615-256-6601. Eds. Ralph F. Abbott, Toby G. Hartt. **Document type:** newsletter.
Description: Reports the latest state-specific employment law developments that affect Massachusetts employers.

340 613.1   US   ISSN 1064-2374
▼**MASSACHUSETTS ENVIRONMENTAL COMPLIANCE UPDATE.** 1992. m. $137. (McGregor & Shea) M. Lee Smith Publishers & Printers, 162 Fourth Ave., N., Box 198867, Nashville, TN 37219-8867. TEL 615-242-7395; 800-274-6774. FAX 615-256-6601. Eds. Gregor I. McGregor, John F. Shea. **Document type:** newsletter.
Description: Reports the latest state-specific environmental law developments that affect companies in Massachusetts.

MASSACHUSETTS LABOR CASES. see BUSINESS AND ECONOMICS — Labor And Industrial Relations

MASSACHUSETTS LABOR RELATIONS REPORTER. see BUSINESS AND ECONOMICS — Labor And Industrial Relations

340   US   ISSN 0163-1411
K13
MASSACHUSETTS LAW REVIEW. 1915. q. $48 to non-members. Massachusetts Bar Association, 20 West St., Boston, MA 02111-1218. Ed. Barry Ravech. adv.; bk.rev.; index every 2 yrs. circ. 22,000. (also avail. in microfiche from WSH,PMC; microfilm from UMI,WSH,PMC; reprint service avail.) **Indexed:** C.L.I., L.R.I., Leg.Cont., Leg.Per. **Document type:** academic/scholarly publication.
—Faxon; UnCover; UMI.
Formerly (until vol.60, 1979): Massachusetts Law Quarterly (ISSN 0025-4835)

349.744   US   ISSN 0196-7509
K13
MASSACHUSETTS LAWYER WEEKLY. (Supplement avail.: Lawyers Monthly (ISSN 1044-2731)) 1972. w. $225. Lawyers Weekly Publications, 41 West St., Boston, MA 02111. TEL 617-451-7700. FAX 617-451-7324. Ed. Robert J. Ambrogi. circ. 10,100. **Document type:** newspaper.
● Also available online. Vendor(s): Mead Data Central, Inc.
—UMI.
Description: Contains news about court decisions, laws and lawyers in Massachusetts.

MASSACHUSETTS SALES AND USE TAX MANUAL. see BUSINESS AND ECONOMICS — Public Finance, Taxation

340   IT   ISSN 0025-4932
MASSIMARIO DEL FORO ITALIANO. m. L.142000 (foreign L.170000)(effective Feb. 1992). Zanichelli Editore S.p.A., Via Irnerio, 34, 40126 Bologna, Italy. TEL 081-293111. FAX 051-249782. index, cum.index.

340   IT   ISSN 0025-4940
MASSIMARIO DELLA GIURISPRUDENZA ITALIANA. 1931. m. L.109000. Unione Tipografico Editrice Torinese, Corso Raffaello 28, 10425 Turin, Italy. index. circ. 9,000.

340   IT   ISSN 0025-4959
MASSIMARIO DI GIURISPRUDENZA DEL LAVORO. 1929. bi-m. L.130000 (foreign L.170000). Servizio Italiano Pubblicazioni Internazionali s.r.l., Viale L. Pasteur, 6, 00144 Rome, Italy. TEL 06-5918586. FAX 06-5924819. index, cum.index every 10 yrs. circ. 2,000.

340 GW ISSN 0579-2428
MAX-PLANCK-INSTITUT FUER EUROPAISCHE RECHTSGESCHICHTE. VEROEFFENTLICHUNGEN. IUS COMMUNE. a. price varies. Vittorio Klostermann, Frauenlobstr. 22, 60487 Frankfurt a.M., Germany. TEL 069-774011. FAX 069-708038. (Subscr. to: Postfach 900601, 60446 Frankfurt a.M., Germany) Eds. Dieter Simon, Michael Stolleis. **Document type:** academic/scholarly publication.

340 GW ISSN 0175-6532
MAX-PLANCK-INSTITUT FUER EUROPAISCHE RECHTSGESCHICHTE. VEROEFFENTLICHUNGEN. IUS COMMUNE. SONDERHEFTE. irreg., vol.63, 1993. price varies. Vittorio Klostermann, Frauenlobstr. 22, 60487 Frankfurt a.M., Germany. TEL 069-774011. FAX 069-708038. (Subscr. to: Postfach 900601, 60446 Frankfurt a.M., Germany) **Document type:** monographic series.

340 NZ
MAZENGARB'S INDUSTRIAL LAW SERVICE. 2 base vols. (plus updates 13/yr.). NZ.$450. Butterworths of New Zealand Ltd., 203-207 Victoria St., P.O. Box 472, Wellington, New Zealand. TEL 04-385-1479. FAX 04-385-1598. Ed. Moira Thompson. (looseleaf format)
  Description: Full text of relevant legislation with case notes and commentary.

MEDIATION QUARTERLY. see *PSYCHOLOGY*

340 610 US
MEDICAID FRAUD REPORT. 1981. 10/yr. $150. National Association of Medicaid Fraud Control Units, 444 N. Capitol St., Washington, DC 20001. TEL 202-434-8020. FAX 202-434-8008. Ed. Barbara L. Zelner.

MEDICAL AND RADIOLOGICAL DEVICES GUIDANCE MANUAL. see *PUBLIC HEALTH AND SAFETY*

MEDICAL DEVICE ESTABLISHMENT REGISTRATION MASTER FILE. see *PUBLIC HEALTH AND SAFETY*

MEDICAL DEVICE PROBLEMS REPORT FROM THE D E N: REPORTS FROM MEDICAL DEVICE USERS. see *PUBLIC HEALTH AND SAFETY*

MEDICAL DEVICE REPORTING FROM THE D E N: REPORTS FROM MEDICAL DEVICE MANUFACTURERS. see *PUBLIC HEALTH AND SAFETY*

MEDICAL DEVICE TECHNOLOGY. see *MEDICAL SCIENCES*

MEDICAL DEVICES, DIAGNOSTICS & INSTRUMENTATION REPORTS: THE GRAY SHEET. see *MEDICAL SCIENCES*

MEDICAL ETHICS ADVISOR. see *MEDICAL SCIENCES*

MEDICAL LAW INTERNATIONAL. see *MEDICAL SCIENCES*

340 610 UK ISSN 0967-0742
▼**MEDICAL LAW REVIEW.** 1993. 3/yr. £75($145) (Centre of Medical Law and Ethics) Oxford University Press, Oxford Journals, Walton St., Oxford OX2 6DP, England. TEL 0865-56767. FAX 0865-56646. TELEX 837330-OXPRES-G. (U.S. subscr. to: Oxford University Press Inc., 2001 Evans Rd., Cary, NC 27513. TEL 919-677-0977) Eds. Ian Kennedy, Andrew Grubb. adv. contact: Jane Parker. circ. 850. **Document type:** academic/scholarly publication.
  —BLDSC (5529.480000). **CCC.**
  Description: Provides information for academics, lawyers, legal practitioners and all others interested in health care and the law.

614.19 340 SA ISSN 0723-1393
K13 CODEN: MELADG
MEDICINE AND LAW; an international journal. 1982. 4/yr. University of Bophuthatswana, International Center of Medicine and Law, Mmabatho Campus, Mmabatho 8681, Bophuthatswana, South Africa. Ed. Judge Amnon Carmi. (also avail. in microform from UMI; reprint service avail. from ISI) **Indexed:** BPIA, Ind.Med., Leg.Cont.
  —BLDSC (5534.006300); Faxon; SWETS; UMI. **CCC.**

340 341 AU ISSN 0257-3822
MEDIEN UND RECHT INTERNATIONAL; Zeitschrift fuer das Recht der Medien und der Werbung. 1983. bi-m. S.1300. Verlag Medien und Recht, Danhausergasse 6, A-1041 Vienna, Austria. TEL 01-5052766. FAX 01-505276615. Ed. Dr. Heinz Wittmann. adv.; bk.rev.; index. circ. 1,900. (back issues avail.) **Document type:** bulletin.
  Formerly: Medien und Recht.

340 PP ISSN 0254-0657
K13
MELANESIAN LAW JOURNAL. 1970. a. K.15. University of Papua New Guinea, Faculty of Law, P.O. Box 317, University P.O., Papua New Guinea. TEL 675-267-618. FAX 675-267-187. TELEX NE 22366. (Overseas subscr. to: William Gaunt & Son, Inc., 3011 Gulf Dr., Holmes Beach, FL 34217-2199, USA. TEL 817-778-5211) Ed. John Nonggarr. bk.rev. circ. 1,000. **Indexed:** C.L.I., L.R.I., Leg.Per.
  —UnCover.

340 AT ISSN 0025-8938
K13
MELBOURNE UNIVERSITY LAW REVIEW. 1957. s-a. Aus.$15. University of Melbourne, Law School, Parkville 3052, Victoria, Australia. FAX 02-888-9706. (Subscr. to: Law Book Co. Ltd., 44-50 Waterloo Rd., North Ryde, N.S.W. 2113, Australia; Dist. in US by: Wm. W. Gaunt & Sons, Inc., Gaunt Bldg., 2011 Gulf Dr., Homes Beach, FL 34217-2199. TEL 813-778-5211. FAX 813-778-5252) adv.; bk.rev.; index every 2 yrs. circ. 2,000. (reprint service avail.) **Indexed:** Aus.P.A.I.S., C.L.I., L.R.I., Leg.Per.
  —BLDSC (5536.830000); Faxon; UnCover.

340 US ISSN 0047-6714
K24
MEMPHIS STATE UNIVERSITY LAW REVIEW. 1970. q. $18. Memphis State University, Cecil C. Humphreys School of Law, Memphis, TN 38152. TEL 901-454-2078. adv.; bk.rev.; index. circ. 800. (also avail. in microfilm from UMI; reprint service avail. from RRI,UMI) **Indexed:** Abstr.Bk.Rev.Curr.Leg.Per., C.L.I., L.R.I., Leg.Cont., Leg.Per.
  —Faxon; UnCover; UMI.

MENSILE EUROPEO DI ECONOMIA, FINANZA, FISCO E NORME C E E. see *BUSINESS AND ECONOMICS*

MENTAL HEALTH WEEKLY; news for policy and program decision-makers. see *PSYCHOLOGY*

340 US ISSN 0025-987X
LAW
MERCER LAW REVIEW. 1949. 4/yr. $30. Mercer University, Walter F. George School of Law, Macon, GA 31207. TEL 912-752-2622. Ed. Mary Sullivan. adv.; index, cum.index. circ. 1,800. (also avail. in microform from UMI; reprint service avail. from UMI) **Indexed:** C.L.I., L.R.I., Leg.Cont., Leg.Per., Mar.Aff.Bibl., SSCI.
  ●Also available online. Vendor(s): West Services, Inc.
  —BLDSC (5678.820000); Faxon; UnCover; UMI.

340 296 US ISSN 0094-9701
BM520
HA-MESIVTA. (Text in Hebrew) 1940. a. $4. Yeshivath Torah Vodaath, Inc., 452 E. Ninth St., Brooklyn, NY 11218. TEL 718-462-6087. Ed. Elie Goldberg. adv. circ. 1,000.

340 US ISSN 0164-3576
KF200
MICHIGAN BAR JOURNAL. 1921. m. $35. State Bar of Michigan, 306 Townsend, Lansing, MI 48933. TEL 517-372-9030. Ed. Nancy F. Brown. adv. contact: Mary Stowell. bk.rev.; illus.; index. circ. 27,518. (also avail. in microform from UMI; microfilm from WSH) **Indexed:** C.L.I., HRIS, L.R.I., Law Ofc.Info.Svc., Leg.Per.
  ●Also available online. Vendor(s): West Services, Inc.
  —BLDSC (5753.625000); Faxon; UnCover; UMI.
  Formerly (until Jan. 1979): Michigan State Bar Journal (ISSN 0162-5101)

340 331 US ISSN 1046-9109
MICHIGAN EMPLOYMENT LAW LETTER. 1990. m. $95. (Honigman Miller Schwartz & Cohn) M. Lee Smith Publishers & Printers, 162 Fourth Ave., N., Box 198867, Nashville, TN 37219-8867. TEL 615-242-7395; 800-274-6774. FAX 615-256-6601. Eds. Frank T. Mamat, A. David Mikesell. **Document type:** newsletter.
  Description: Reports the latest state-specific employment law developments that affect Michigan companies.

340 613.1 US ISSN 1073-9459
MICHIGAN ENVIRONMENTAL COMPLIANCE UPDATE. 1990. m. $137. (Honigman Miller Schwartz & Cohn) M. Lee Smith Publishers & Printers, 162 Fourth Ave., N., Box 198867, Nashville, TN 37219-8867. TEL 615-242-7395; 800-274-6774. FAX 615-256-6601. Eds. J. Polito, Sally Churchill. **Document type:** newsletter.
  Formerly: Michigan Environmental Law Letter (ISSN 1046-9192)
  Description: Reports the latest state-specific environmental law developments that affect Michigan companies.

340 US ISSN 0026-2234
K13
MICHIGAN LAW REVIEW. 1902. 8/yr. $40 (foreign $46). Michigan Law Review Association, Ann Arbor, MI 48109-1215. TEL 313-763-5870. FAX 313-764-8309. Ed.Bd. adv.; bk.rev.; index, cum.index. circ. 2,500. (also avail. in microform from UMI,WSH,PMC; reprint service avail. from WSH) **Indexed:** ABI Inform., Account.Ind. (1974-), Bank.Lit.Ind., BPIA, C.L.I., Crim.Just.Abstr., Curr.Cont., J.of Econ.Lit., L.R.I., Leg.Cont., Leg.Per., P.A.I.S., SSCI. **Document type:** academic/scholarly publication.
  ●Also available online. Vendor(s): Mead Data Central, Inc., West Services, Inc.
  —BLDSC (5755.300000); Faxon; UnCover; SWETS; UMI.

340 US ISSN 0897-618X
MICHIGAN LAWYERS WEEKLY. 1986. w. $225. Michigan Lawyers Weekly, 333 S. Washington Sq., No.300, Lansing, MI 48933. TEL 517-374-6200. FAX 517-374-6222. Ed. Darial J. Kim. adv. circ. 4,848. **Document type:** newspaper.
  ●Also available online. Vendor(s): Mead Data Central, Inc.
  Description: Provides summaries of court decisions for all state and federal courts in Michigan. Reports local and state legal news, State Bar news, and includes judicial profiles.

340 380 US
MICHIGAN MOTOR VEHICLE LAWS. 1988. a. $15.95. Gould Publications, 1333 N. U.S. Hwy. 17-92, Longwood, FL 32750-3724. TEL 407-695-9500. FAX 407-695-2906. adv.; bk.rev. (looseleaf format)

340 US
MIDWEST LAW REVIEW. 1981. a. $5. (Midwest Regional Business Law Association) Illinois State University, College of Business, 328 William Hall, Illinois State University, Normal, IL 61761. TEL 309-438-5675. Ed. Dennis Kruse. bk.rev. circ. 200.
  Description: Covers business law, the legal environment, and government regulation.

340 640.73 UK
MILLER'S PRODUCT LIABILITY & SAFETY ENCYCLOPAEDIA. 2 base vols. (plus updates 3/yr. and m. bulletin). $390. Butterworth & Co. (Publishers) Ltd. (Subsidiary of: Reed Elsevier plc), 88 Kingsway, London WC2B 6AB, England. TEL 71-405-6900. FAX 71-405-1332. (US addr.: Butterworth Legal Publishers, 90 Stiles Rd., Salem, NH 03079-9981. TEL 603-898-9664) Ed. C.J. Miller. (looseleaf format)
  Description: Covers liability in contract, liability in tort, criminal law, product safety, European developments, codes of practice and a consumer protection directory.

LAW

340 622 US
MINERAL LAW NEWSLETTER. 1967. 4/yr. $60. Rocky Mountain Mineral Law Foundation, Porter Administration Bldg., 7039 E. 18th Ave., Denver, CO 80220. TEL 303-321-8100. FAX 303-321-7657. Eds. John S. Lowe, Mark J. Squillace. circ. 600. **Document type:** newsletter.
—CCC.
   Formerly (until 1984): Rocky Mountain Mineral Law Newsletter (ISSN 0557-8051)

340 622 AT
MINING AND PETROLEUM LEGISLATION SERVICE. 1990. 18/yr. in 15 vols. Aus.$125 with updates. Law Book Co. Ltd., 44-50 Waterloo Rd., North Ryde, N.S.W. 2113, Australia. TEL 02-887-0177. FAX 02-888-9706. TELEX ASBOOK 27995. (looseleaf format)
   Description: Contains all legislation from the Australian Commonwealth, states, and territories relating to mining and petroleum; up-to-date and annotated.

MINNESOTA ADMINISTRATIVE PROCEDURE. see *PUBLIC ADMINISTRATION*

340 331 US ISSN 1054-6367
MINNESOTA EMPLOYMENT LAW LETTER. 1991. m. $95. (Felhaber, Larson, Fenlon & Vogt, P.A.) M. Lee Smith Publishers & Printers, 162 Fourth Ave., N., Box 198867, Nashville, TN 37219-8867. TEL 615-242-7395; 800-274-6774. FAX 615-256-6601. Eds. Edward J. Bohrer, Stephen J. Burton. **Document type:** newsletter.
   Description: Reports the latest state-specific employment law developments that affect Minnesota companies.

340 613.1 US ISSN 1072-916X
▼**MINNESOTA ENVIRONMENTAL COMPLIANCE UPDATE.** 1994. m. $137. (Oppenheimer, Wolff & Donnelly) M. Lee Smith Publishers & Printers, 162 Fourth Ave., N., Box 198867, Nashville, TN 37219-8867. TEL 615-242-7395; 800-274-6774. FAX 615-256-6601. Eds. Jonathan Bloomberg, Robert Cattanach. **Document type:** newsletter.
   Description: Reports the latest state-specific environmental law developments that affect companies in Minnesota.

340 US ISSN 0026-5535
K13
MINNESOTA LAW REVIEW. 1917. 6/yr. $24. (Minnesota Law Review Foundation) University of Minnesota, Law School, 229 19th Ave. S., Minneapolis, MN 55455. TEL 612-625-8034. adv.; bk.rev.; charts; index, cum.index every 5 yrs. circ. 1,486. (also avail. in microfilm from WSH,PMC; back issues avail.; reprint service avail. from WSH) **Indexed:** A.B.C.Pol.Sci., Abstr.Bk.Rev.Curr.Leg.Per., Bank.Lit.Ind., C.L.I., Crim.Just.Abstr., L.R.I., Leg.Cont., Leg.Per., P.A.I.S., SSCI.
●Also available online. Vendor(s): Mead Data Central, Inc., West Services, Inc.
—BLDSC (5810.390000); Faxon; UnCover; SWETS.

MINNESOTA NO-FAULT AUTOMOBILE INSURANCE. see *INSURANCE*

340 US
MINNESOTA REAL ESTATE LAW JOURNAL. 1981. bi-m. $75. Butterworth Legal Publishers (Subsidiary of: Reed Elsevier plc), 8 Industrial Way, Bldg. C, Salem, NH 03079-2837. TEL 800-333-3839. Ed. Stephen Liebo. (back issues avail.)
   Description: Real estate law articles, case comments and court decisions.

348.776 350 US ISSN 0146-7751
KFM5436
MINNESOTA STATE REGISTER. 1976. 2/w. $150 for Monday edition; with Tuesday, Wednesday, and Friday Contract supplements $275. Department of Administration, Print Communications Division, 117 University Ave., St. Paul, MN 55155. TEL 612-296-0931. Ed. Robin PanLener. index, cum.index. circ. 1,250. (also avail. in microfiche; back issues avail.) **Document type:** government publication.
   Description: Focuses on the administrative rules of state government, official notices, state contracts for commodities, printing, and professional, technical, and consulting services.

MINNESOTA TAX APPEALS. see *BUSINESS AND ECONOMICS — Public Finance, Taxation*

MINZHU YU FAZHI/DEMOCRACY & LEGAL SYSTEMS. see *POLITICAL SCIENCE*

340 IS
MISHPATIM. 1971. 3/yr. IS.60($40) Hebrew University of Jerusalem, Faculty of Law, P.O. Box 24100, Jerusalem, Israel. TEL 02-882550. Eds. A. Aberman, A. Well. bk.rev. circ. 1,500.

MISSET'S MILIEU MAGAZINE. see *ENVIRONMENTAL STUDIES*

340 US ISSN 0277-1152
K13
MISSISSIPPI COLLEGE LAW REVIEW. 1978. s-a. $12. (Mississippi College of Law) Mississippi College Law Review, 151 E. Griffith St., Jackson, MS 39201. TEL 601-944-1950. Ed. Denise Schreiber. adv.; bk.rev.; index, cum.index. circ. 650. (also avail. in microfilm from WSH,PMC; back issues avail.; reprint service avail. from WSH) **Indexed:** Abstr.Bk.Rev.Curr.Leg.Per., C.L.I., L.R.I., Leg.Per.
●Also available online. Vendor(s): West Services, Inc.
—Faxon; UnCover.

340 US ISSN 0026-6280
K13
MISSISSIPPI LAW JOURNAL. 1928. 3/yr. $35. (University of Mississippi Law School) Mississippi Law Journal, Box 849, University, MS 38677. TEL 601-232-7361. FAX 601-232-7731. Ed. John J. Healy. adv.; bk.rev.; index, cum.index every 10 yrs. circ. 1,100. (also avail. in microfilm from RRI; reprint service avail. from RRI) **Indexed:** C.C.L.P., C.L.I., Curr.Cont., L.R.I., Leg.Per., SSCI. **Document type:** academic/scholarly publication.
●Also available online. Vendor(s): West Services, Inc.
—BLDSC (5828.927000); Faxon; UnCover; UMI.

340 US ISSN 0462-8551
THE MISSISSIPPI LAWYER. vol.39, 1993. bi-m. membership. Mississippi Bar, 643 N. State St., Box 2168, Jackson, MS 39225. TEL 601-948-4471. Ed. Pamela Prather. adv.
—UnCover.
   Description: Discusses professional, legal and management issues of interest to lawyers in Mississippi.

340 US ISSN 0026-6485
KF200
MISSOURI BAR. JOURNAL. Key Title: Journal of the Missouri Bar. 1945. 6/yr. membership. Missouri Bar, 326 Monroe St., Box 119, Jefferson City, MO 65102. TEL 314-635-4128. FAX 314-635-2811. Ed. Gary P. Toohey. adv.; index, cum.index: 1958-1972. circ. 13,000. (also avail. in microform from UMI; reprint service avail. from UMI) **Indexed:** C.L.I., L.R.I., Law Ofc.Info.Svc., Leg.Per.
—BLDSC (5020.450000); Faxon; UnCover; UMI.

340 US
KFM7815.L44
MISSOURI BAR. LEGISLATIVE DIGEST. q. free to members. Missouri Bar, Box 119, Jefferson City, MO 65102. TEL 314-635-4128. FAX 314-635-2811. Ed. Catherine Barrie. index.

340 331 US ISSN 1054-6375
MISSOURI EMPLOYMENT LAW LETTER. 1991. m. $94. (Lashly & Baer) M. Lee Smith Publishers & Printers, 162 Fourth Ave., N., Box 198867, Nashville, TN 37219-8867. TEL 615-252-7395; 800-274-6774. FAX 615-256-6601. Eds. Robert A. Kaiser, Vance D. Miller. **Document type:** newsletter.
   Description: Reports the latest state-specific employment law developments that affect Missouri employers.

340 613.1 US ISSN 1057-4166
MISSOURI ENVIRONMENTAL LAW LETTER. 1990. m. $137. (Armstrong, Teasdale, Schlafly & Davis) M. Lee Smith Publishers & Printers, 162 Fourth Ave., N., Box 198867, Nashville, TN 37219-8867. TEL 615-242-7385; 800-274-6774. FAX 615-256-6601. Ed. George M. von Stamwitz. **Document type:** newsletter.
   Supersedes in part (in 1991): Midwest Environmental Law Letter (ISSN 1049-9350)
   Description: Reports the latest state-specific environmental law developments that affect Missouri companies.

340 US ISSN 0026-6604
K13
MISSOURI LAW REVIEW. 1936. q. $30 (foreign $35). University of Missouri at Columbia, School of Law, Box 203, Hulston Hall, Columbia, MO 65211. TEL 314-882-7055. FAX 314-882-9675. adv.; bk.rev.; index, cum.index every 10 yrs. circ. 1,350. (tabloid format; also avail. in microfilm from WSH,PMC; reprint service avail. from WSH) **Indexed:** C.L.I., L.R.I., Leg.Cont., Leg.Per., P.A.I.S. **Document type:** academic/scholarly publication.
●Also available online. Vendor(s): West Services, Inc.
—BLDSC (5829.075000); Faxon; UnCover.

340 US ISSN 0899-5907
MISSOURI LAWYERS; the complete statewide legal newspaper. 1987. w. $195. 223 Madison, Jefferson City, MO 65101. TEL 800-635-5297. FAX 314-634-2287. Ed. Charlie Fraas. adv.: B&W page $1300, color page $1960; trim 10 x 16. bk.rev. circ. 2,455. **Document type:** newspaper, trade publication.
   Description: Provides summaries of all Missouri appellate opinions, federal court opinions, and news stories for lawyers and judges.

340 US
MISSOURI NOTARY LAW PRIMER. a. $9.95. National Notary Association, 8236 Remmet Ave., Box 7184, Canoga Park, CA 91309-7184. TEL 818-713-4000. FAX 818-713-9061. Ed. Charles N. Faerber. (reprint service avail. from UMI) **Document type:** monographic series.

340 GW ISSN 0723-5984
DIE MITBESTIMMUNG. 1954. m. DM.55. (Hans-Boeckler-Stiftung) Nomos Verlagsgesellschaft mbH und Co. KG, Waldseestr. 3-5, 76530 Baden-Baden, Germany. TEL 07221-21040. FAX 07221-210427. (Subscr. to: Postfach 610, 76484 Baden-Baden, Germany) bk.rev. circ. 16,500. **Document type:** bulletin.
—BLDSC (5829.599600); SWETS.

MITTEILUNGEN DER DEUTSCHEN PATENTANWAELTE. see *PATENTS, TRADEMARKS AND COPYRIGHTS*

347.016 GW ISSN 0941-4193
MITTEILUNGEN DES BAYERISCHEN NOTARVEREINS, DER NOTARKASSE UND DER LANDESNOTARKAMMER BAYERN. 1864. bi-m. DM.65. Landesnotarkammer Bayern, Ottostr. 10, 80333 Munich, Germany. TEL 089-55166-0. FAX 089-55166-234. Ed. Oliver Vossius. bk.rev.; index. circ. 2,700. (back issues avail.) **Document type:** academic/scholarly publication.

340 US
MOBILE BAR ASSOCIATION. MONTHLY BULLETIN. vol.27, no.6, 1993. m. membership. Mobile Bar Association, P.O. Drawer 2005, Mobile, AL 36652. TEL 205-433-9790. **Document type:** bulletin.
   Description: News and association activities of interest to lawyers in the Mobile area.

MOBILE HOMES AND MOBILE HOME PARKS. see *HOUSING AND URBAN PLANNING*

340 UK ISSN 0026-7961
K13
MODERN LAW REVIEW. 1937. 6/yr. £45($79.50) Sweet & Maxwell Stevens Journals, 11 New Fetter Ln., London EC4P 4EE, England. Ed. Simon Roberts. adv.; bk.rev.; index. circ. 3,100. **Indexed:** Abstr.Bk.Rev.Curr.Leg.Per., Br.Hum.Ind., C.L.I., L.R.I., Leg.Cont., Leg.Per., RICS, SOMA.
—BLDSC (5887.900000); Faxon; UnCover; SWETS; UMI. CCC.

340 AT ISSN 0311-3140
K13
MONASH UNIVERSITY LAW REVIEW. 1974. s-a. Aus.$30 (effective 1993). Monash University, Faculty of Law, Wellington Rd., Clayton, Vic. 3168, Australia. FAX 03-565-3374. TELEX AA 32961. Ed.Bd. adv.; bk.rev. circ. 1,000. (also avail. in microform from UMI) **Indexed:** Aus.P.A.I.S., C.L.I., L.R.I., Leg.Per. **Document type:** academic/scholarly publication.
—BLDSC (5901.594000); Faxon; UnCover; UMI.
Refereed Serial

340   GW   ISSN 0340-1812
MONATSSCHRIFT FUER DEUTSCHES RECHT. 1947. m. DM.208 (students DM.139). Verlag Dr. Otto Schmidt KG, Unter den Ulmen 96-98, 50968 Cologne, Germany. TEL 0221-9373801. FAX 0221-93738941. TELEX 8883381. Ed. H.J. Below. adv.; bk.rev. circ. 6,500. **Indexed:** Dok.Str., ELLIS. **Document type:** bulletin.
—BLDSC (5906.320000); SWETS. **CCC.**

340   SP   ISSN 0077-0442
MONOGRAFIAS DE FILOSOFIA JURIDICA Y SOCIAL/MONOGRAPHS OF SOCIAL AND LEGAL PHILOSOPHY.* 1967. a. Universidad de Granada, Facultad de Derecho, Granada, Spain. **Document type:** monographic series.

340   US   ISSN 0026-9972
MONTANA LAW REVIEW. 1940. s-a. $25 (foreign $26). University of Montana, Students of School of Law, Missoula, MT 59812. TEL 406-243-2023. adv.; bk.rev.; cum.index: vols. 1-53. circ. 2,300. (also avail. in microform from UMI,PMC; microfiche from WSH; microfilm from WSH) **Indexed:** C.L.I., L.R.I., Leg.Cont., Leg.Per., SSCI. **Document type:** academic/scholarly publication.
—BLDSC (5928.006500); Faxon; UnCover; UMI.

340   US   ISSN 0276-3788
MONTANA LAWYER. 1975. m. (10/yr.). $25 to non-members. State Bar of Montana, 46 N. Last Chance Gulch, Ste. 2, Box 577, Helena, MT 59264. TEL 406-442-7660. FAX 406-442-7763. Ed. Sally K. Hilander. adv. **Document type:** trade publication.
—UnCover.
Description: Discusses legal and professional issues affecting lawyers in the state of Montana.

340   US
MONTEREY COUNTY BAR ASSOCIATION NEWSLETTER. q. membership. Monterey County Bar Association, 411 Pacific St., Ste. 308, Monterey, CA 93940. TEL 408-375-1693. Ed. Susan Goodrich. **Document type:** newsletter.
Description: Discusses legal issues and local and state developments of interest to lawyers in the Monterey area.

MONTHLY PRESCRIBING REFERENCE. see *MEDICAL SCIENCES*

MOREANA; time trieth truth. see *HISTORY — History Of Europe*

349   RU   ISSN 0027-1357
MOSKOVSKII UNIVERSITET. VESTNIK. SERIYA 12: PRAVO. 1960. bi-m. 13.50 Rub. Moskovskii Universitet, Ul. Gertsena 5-7, 103009 Moscow, Russia. (Dist. by: Mezhdunarodnaya Kniga, Moscow, G-200, Russia) bk.rev.; index.

340   AG
MUNDO JUSTICIALISTA. 1983. m. Billinghurst 527, Piso 6, Buenos Aires, Argentina. Dir. Hugo Cesar Luna.

MUNICIPAL AND PLANNING LAW REPORTS (2ND SERIES). see *HOUSING AND URBAN PLANNING*

340   US   ISSN 0027-3449
K13
MUNICIPAL ATTORNEY. 1959. bi-m. membership only. National Institute of Municipal Law Officers, 1000 Connecticut Ave., N.W., Ste. 902, Washington, DC 20036. TEL 202-466-5424. FAX 202-785-0152. Ed. Benjamin L. Brown. circ. 2,500 (controlled). **Indexed:** C.L.I., L.R.I.
Incorporates (1941-1991): Municipal Law Court Decisions (ISSN 0027-3503); (1947-1991): Municipal Ordinance Review (ISSN 0027-3538); Municipal Law Journal; (1985-1991): Municipalities in the United States Supreme Court; (1986-1991): N I M L O'S Congressional News; (1977-1991): Municipal Law Docket (ISSN 0148-3366); Which incorporated: Municipal Attorneys' Opinions (ISSN 0277-6294).
Description: Articles on legal issues affecting cities, case digests, ordinances, summaries of federal and state regulations, opinions and reviews.

MUNICIPAL GOVERNMENT PERMITS AND LICENSES. see *PUBLIC ADMINISTRATION*

MUNICIPAL IMMUNITY LAW BULLETIN. see *PUBLIC ADMINISTRATION — Municipal Government*

340   II   ISSN 0377-757X
LAW
MUNICIPALITIES AND CORPORATION CASES; a monthly law reporter. (Text in English) m. Rs.120. International Law Book Co., Nijhawan Bldg., 1562 Church Rd., Kashmere Gate, Delhi 6, India. Ed. Mrs. Swarn Bhati Nijhawan.

340   SP
MUTUALIDAD DE LA ABOGACIA. 52/yr. Serrano 9, 28001 Madrid, Spain. TEL 1-435-24-86. FAX 1-431-99-15. TELEX 47312 MGPA E. Ed. P. Moreno Lendinez.

N A B TALK. (National Association of Bankruptcy Trustees) see *BUSINESS AND ECONOMICS — Banking And Finance*

340 346.013   US
N A B W A CONVENTION BULLETIN. a. National Association of Black Women Attorneys, 3711 Macomb St., N.W., 2nd Fl., Washington, DC 20016. TEL 202-966-9693. FAX 202-244-6648. **Document type:** bulletin.

340 346.013   US
N A B W A NEWS. q. National Association of Black Women Attorneys, 3711 Macomb St., N.W., 2nd Fl., Washington, DC 20016. TEL 202-966-9693. FAX 202-244-6648.

N A I C NEWSLETTER. (National Association of Insurance Commissioners) see *INSURANCE*

N A J I T NEWS. (National Association of Judiciary Interpreters and Translators) see *LAW — Judicial Systems*

340   US
N A L P BULLETIN. 1971. m. $70 to non-members. National Association for Law Placement, 1666 Connecticut Ave., Ste. 450, Washington, DC 20009. TEL 202-667-1666. Ed. Honora A. Mara. bk.rev.; index. circ. 1,100. (back issues avail.) **Document type:** bulletin, newsletter.
Formerly: N A L P Notes.
Description: Articles on legal career development.

N A P F PENSIONS LEGISLATION SERVICE. see *INSURANCE*

N A R F LEGAL REVIEW. (Native American Rights Fund) see *ETHNIC INTERESTS*

N A S D NOTICES TO MEMBERS. see *BUSINESS AND ECONOMICS — Investments*

N A S D REGULATORY AND COMPLIANCE ALERT. (National Association of Securities Dealers, Inc.) see *BUSINESS AND ECONOMICS — Investments*

N A S F A A NEWSLETTER. (National Association of Student Financial Aid Administrators) see *EDUCATION — Higher Education*

N A S S P LEGAL MEMORANDUM. (National Association of Secondary School Principals) see *EDUCATION — School Organization And Administration*

340 346.013   US
N B A BULLETIN. q. National Bar Association, 1225 11th St., N.W., Washington, DC 20001. TEL 202-842-3900. circ. 12,500. **Document type:** bulletin.
Description: Contains legal information of interest to African-American and other minority attorneys.

340 346.013   US
N B A JOURNAL. s-a. National Bar Association, 1225 11th St., N.W., Washington, DC 20001. TEL 202-842-3900. **Document type:** trade publication.
Description: Contains legal information of interest to African-American and other minority attorneys.

340 346.013   US   ISSN 0741-0115
KF200
N B A MAGAZINE. m. $60 for non-members; members $36. National Bar Association, 1225 11th St., N.W., Washington, DC 20001. TEL 202-842-3900. Ed. John Crump. adv. contact: Harry Carter. circ. 16,000. (back issues avail.) **Document type:** trade publication.
—UnCover.
Description: Contains legal information of interest to minority attorneys.

N C A M P'S TECHNICAL REPORT. (National Coalition Against the Misuse of Pesticides) see *ENVIRONMENTAL STUDIES*

340   US
N C B P BEST PROJECTS. National Conference of Bar Presidents, Division of Bar Services, 541 N. Fairbanks Ct., 4th Fl., Chicago, IL 60611-3314. TEL 312-988-5346. FAX 312-988-5492.

346.066 640.73   US   ISSN 1070-9312
N C L C ENERGY & UTILITY UPDATE. $95 to private-sector individuals and institutions; government and community action agencies $45. National Consumer Law Center, 11 Beacon St., Boston, MA 02108. TEL 617-523-8010. FAX 617-523-8010. circ. 700. **Document type:** newsletter.
Formerly: N C L C Energy Update.
Description: Reports on developments in state and federal programs in public-assistance housing.

346.066 640.73   US   ISSN 1054-3775
KF1507
N C L C REPORTS: BANKRUPTCY & FORECLOSURES. 1982. bi-m. $35. National Consumer Law Center, 11 Beacon St., Ste. 821, Boston, MA 02108. TEL 617-523-8010. FAX 671-523-7398. Ed. Kathleen Keest. index. circ. 4,000. (looseleaf format; back issues avail.)
Formerly: N C L C Reports: Consumer Bankruptcy and Foreclosures Edition (ISSN 0890-2623)
Description: Covers latest developments in the practice of consumer law, with emphasis on bankruptcy and foreclosures.

346.066 640.73   US   ISSN 0890-2615
KF1039.A15
N C L C REPORTS: CONSUMER CREDIT & USURY. 1982. bi-m. $35. National Consumer Law Center, 11 Beacon St., Ste. 821, Boston, MA 02108. TEL 617-523-8010. Ed. Kathleen Keest. index. circ. 4,000. (looseleaf format; back issues avail.)
Description: Covers latest developments and new ideas in the practice of consumer law, with emphasis on consumer credit and usury.

346.066 640.73   US   ISSN 0890-2607
KF1024.A15
N C L C REPORTS: DEBT COLLECTION & REPOSESSIONS. 1982. bi-m. $35. National Consumer Law Center, 11 Beacon St., Ste. 821, Boston, MA 02108. TEL 617-523-8010. Ed. Kathleen Keest. index. circ. 4,000. (looseleaf format; back issues avail.)
Description: Covers latest developments and new ideas in the practice of consumer law, with emphasis on debt collection and repossessions.

346.066 640.73   US   ISSN 0890-0973
KF1602
N C L C REPORTS: DECEPTIVE ACTS & WARRANTIES. 1982. bi-m. $35. National Consumer Law Center, 11 Beacon St., Ste. 821, Boston, MA 02108. TEL 617-523-8010. Ed. Kathleen Keest. index. circ. 4,000. (looseleaf format; back issues avail.)
Description: Covers latest developments and new ideas in the practice of consumer law, with emphasis on deceptive acts and warranties.

340 346.013   US
N C W B A NEWSLETTER. 1981. q. $25 membership. National Conference of Women's Bar Associations, P.O. Box 77, Edenton, NC 27932-0077. TEL 919-482-8202. FAX 919-482-8202. **Document type:** newsletter.

N F R A NEWSLETTER. (National Forest Recreation Association) see *CONSERVATION*

N I A INFORMERAR. (Statens Naemnd foer Internationella Adoptionsfraagor) see *SOCIAL SERVICES AND WELFARE*

346.066   US
N L R B CASE HANDLING MANUAL. 1976. irreg. $260. (U.S. National Labor Relations Board) Commerce Clearing House, Inc., 4925 W. Peterson Ave., Chicago, IL 60646. TEL 312-583-8500. Ed. D. Newquist.

N O L P E NOTES. (National Organization on Legal Problems of Education) see *EDUCATION — School Organization And Administration*

3292 LAW

340 370   US   ISSN 1059-4094
KF4114
N O L P E SCHOOL LAW REPORTER. 1961. m. $95 includes N O L P E Notes (Canada $105; elsewhere $115). National Organization on Legal Problems of Education, 3601 S.W. 29th, Ste. 223, Topeka, KS 66614. TEL 913-273-3550. Eds. Patricia First, Lawrence Rossow. cum.index. circ. 2,800. (looseleaf format) **Indexed:** Educ.Admin.Abstr. **Document type:** newsletter.

799.202 364.4   US
N R A ACTION. 1974. m. $20. National Rifle Association of America, Institute for Legislative Action, 1600 Rhode Island Ave., N.W., Washington, DC 20036. TEL 202-828-6000. FAX 202-833-4323. Ed. T.C. Wyld. circ. 340,000. (tabloid format; back issues avail.)
    Former titles: N R A Monitor; N R A Institute for Legislative Action. Reports from Washington; N R A Unified Sportsmen of America. Reports from Washington.
    Description: Covers legislative initiatives and Second Amendment issues, including relevant discussions of constitutional law and criminology, as well as hunting, wildlife conservation and the animal rights movement.

343   US   ISSN 0362-8833
KF2125.A15
N R E C A - A P P A LEGAL REPORTING SERVICE. 1975. m. $90. National Rural Electric Cooperative Association, Management Services Department, 1800 Massachusetts Ave., N.W., Washington, DC 20036. TEL 202-857-9500. (Co-sponsor: American Public Power Association)
    Formerly: N R E C A Legal Reporting Service (ISSN 0547-8847)

340   US
N S B A NEWS. 1970. 7/yr. $10 (effective 1994). Nebraska State Bar Association, 635 S. 14th St., Box 81809, Lincoln, NE 68501-1809. TEL 402-475-7091. FAX 402-475-7098. Ed. Jennifer Schizas. circ. 7,900. **Document type:** newsletter.
    Description: Covers news, legal issues and professional matters of interest to lawyers in Nebraska.

340 388   AT
▼**N S W MOTOR ACCIDENTS PRACTITIONERS HANDBOOK.** 1992. 3/yr. C C H Australia Ltd., P.O. Box 230, North Ryde, N.S.W. 2113, Australia. TEL 02-888-2555. FAX 02-888-7324. (looseleaf format)

N T S A REPORTER. (National Technical Services Association) see *BUSINESS AND ECONOMICS — Labor And Industrial Relations*

340   GW   ISSN 0934-8603
N V W Z RECHTSPRECHUNGS REPORT VERWALTUNGSRECHT. 1988. m. DM.364 (students DM.320). C.H. Beck'sche Verlagsbuchhandlung, Wilhelmstr. 9, 80801 Munich, Germany. TEL 089-38189-338. FAX 089-38189398. TELEX 5215085-BECK-D. adv.: B&W page DM.2200, color page DM.4400; trim 260 x 186. index. circ. 3,000. (back issues avail.) **Document type:** bulletin.
    ●Also available on CD-ROM.

340   US
N.Y. COUNTY LAWYER. 1970. 10/yr. membership. New York County Lawyers' Association, 14 Vesey St., New York, NY 10007. TEL 212-267-6646. FAX 212-285-4482. Ed. Steve Bookbinder. adv. circ. 10,500.
    Formerly (until 1981): Vesey Street Letter (ISSN 0049-6030)

340   SW   ISSN 0348-4351
NAEMNDEMANNEN. 1978. q. SEK 100 (effective 1991). Naemndemaennens Riksfoerbund (NRF), P.O. Box 8140, S-104 20 Stockholm, Sweden.

340   KE   ISSN 1015-7166
THE NAIROBI LAW MONTHLY. (Text in English) 1987. m. Kaibi Ltd., P.O. Box 53234, Nairobi, Kenya. TEL 728978. Ed. Gitobu I. Imanyara. **Indexed:** P.L.E.S.A. (1990-).

363.2   US   ISSN 0889-7794
NARC OFFICER. 1985. m. $35 (foreign $70). International Narcotic Enforcement Officers Association, 112 State St., Ste. 1200, Albany, NY 12207. TEL 518-463-6232. Ed. Celeste Morga. adv.; illus. circ. 10,000. **Document type:** consumer publication.
    Incorporates (in Sept. 1985): International Narcotic Enforcement Officers Association. Annual Conference Report (ISSN 0538-8821)

349   CI   ISSN 0027-8165
K30
NASA ZAKONITOST; periodical for law theory and practice. (Text in Serbo-Croatian) 1947. m. 2000 din. to individuals; institutions 4000 din. Savez Drustava Pravnika Hrvatske, Savska 41, P.O. Box 684, 41000 Zagreb, Croatia. (Subscr. to: "Mladost" Export Import, Ilica 30, 41000 Zagreb, Croatia) (Co-sponsors: Udruzenje za Upravne Znanosti i Praksu Hrvatske; Republicki Zavod za Javnu Upravu Sr Hrvatske) Ed. Ilija Bekic. adv.; bk.rev. circ. 4,000.

340   US   ISSN 0047-8695
K14
NASSAU LAWYER. 1943. m. $15. (Nassau County Bar Association) Business Technology Communications Inc., 15th and West Sts., Mineola, NY 11501. TEL 516-747-4070. FAX 516-747-4147. Ed.Bd. adv.; bk.rev.; illus.; tr.lit. circ. 7,000.

340   CN   ISSN 0315-2286
LAW
NATIONAL (OTTAWA, 1974). Variant title: Canadian Bar National. (Text in English, French) 1974. 10/yr. Can.$40. (Canadian Bar Association - Association du Barreau Canadien) Maclean-Hunter Ltd., Business Publications Division, 777 Bay St., 5th Fl., Toronto, ON M5W 1A7, Canada. TEL 416-593-3162. (Editorial & membership addr.: Canadian Bar Association, Communications Committee, Ste. 902, 50 O'Connor St., Ottawa, ON K1P 6L2, Canada. TEL 613-237-2925) Ed. J. Stuart Langford. adv.; bk.rev.; bibl.; illus. circ. 38,000. (also avail. in microfilm)
    Incorporates: Ontario Bar News (ISSN 0317-4603); Formed by the 1974 merger of: Canadian Bar Bulletin (ISSN 0045-4443); Canadian Bar Association. Journal (ISSN 0591-0919); Which was formerly: Canadian Bar Journal (ISSN 0008-2996)
    Description: Covers news, technical, management and legal issues of interest to members of the Canadian legal profession.

NATIONAL ADOPTION REPORTS. see *SOCIAL SERVICES AND WELFARE*

NATIONAL ADVERTISING DIVISION CASE REPORT. see *ADVERTISING AND PUBLIC RELATIONS*

340   US
NATIONAL ADVOCATES SOCIETY. BULLETIN. a. National Advocates Society, c/o Chester Cyzio, 600 Ave. of the Arts, Philadelphia, PA 19107. TEL 215-735-5378. **Document type:** bulletin.
    Description: Aimed at US lawyers and physicians of Polish descent.

NATIONAL AND FEDERAL LEGAL EMPLOYMENT REPORT. see *BUSINESS AND ECONOMICS — Personnel Management*

340   US
NATIONAL ASSOCIATION OF BENCH AND BAR SPOUSES. NEWSLETTER. s-a. National Association of Bench and Bar Spouses, 3055 Ludlow Rd., Shaker Heights, OH 70808. TEL 216-752-4986. **Document type:** newsletter.
    Description: Aimed at spouses of attorneys seeking to participate in civic, cultural, and social activities that promote the image of the legal profession.

NATIONAL ASSOCIATION OF INSURANCE COMMISSIONERS. COMPILATION OF REPORTS. see *INSURANCE*

NATIONAL ASSOCIATION OF INSURANCE COMMISSIONERS. LIFE AND HEALTH ACTUARIAL REPORT. see *INSURANCE*

NATIONAL ASSOCIATION OF INSURANCE COMMISSIONERS. LISTING OF COMPANIES. see *INSURANCE*

NATIONAL ASSOCIATION OF INSURANCE COMMISSIONERS. PROCEEDINGS. see *INSURANCE*

340   US
NATIONAL ASSOCIATION OF J D - M B A PROFESSIONALS. JOURNAL. q. National Association of J D - M B A Professionals, c/o B V Capital, 575 Fifth Ave., 17th Fl., New York, NY 10017. TEL 212-808-0990. **Document type:** trade publication.

340   US
NATIONAL ASSOCIATION OF J D - M B A PROFESSIONALS. NEWSLETTER. irreg. National Association of J D - M B A Professionals, c/o B V Capitol, 575 Fifth Ave., 17th Fl., New York, NY 10017. TEL 212-808-0990. **Document type:** newsletter.

NATIONAL ASSOCIATION OF STATE BOARDS OF ACCOUNTANCY. STATE BOARD REPORT. see *BUSINESS AND ECONOMICS — Accounting*

340   US
NATIONAL ASSOCIATION OF WOMEN LAWYERS. PRESIDENT'S NEWSLETTER. q. National Association of Women Lawyers, 750 N. Lake Shore Dr., Chicago, IL 60611. TEL 312-988-6186. FAX 312-988-6821. **Document type:** newsletter.

NATIONAL BANKING LAW REVIEW; banking business and the law. see *BUSINESS AND ECONOMICS — Banking And Finance*

340   US   ISSN 0896-0194
K2
NATIONAL BLACK LAW JOURNAL. 1971. 3/yr. $18 to individuals; institutions $25; students $12.50. University of California, Los Angeles, School of Law, 405 Hilgard Ave., Los Angeles, CA 90024. TEL 310-825-7941. adv.; bk.rev. circ. 650. (tabloid format; also avail. in microform from UMI,WSH,PMC; reprint service avail. from UMI,WSH) **Indexed:** Abstr.Bk.Rev.Curr.Leg.Per., C.L.I., L.R.I., Leg.Per. **Document type:** academic/scholarly publication.
    —BLDSC (6017.370000); UnCover; UMI.
    Formerly (until 1987): Black Law Journal (ISSN 0045-2181)
    Description: Provides a forum for legal solutions and guidelines for action to the age-old problems facing minorities.

NATIONAL CONFERENCE OF APPELLATE COURT CLERKS. NEWSLETTER. see *LAW — Judicial Systems*

340 346.013   US
NATIONAL CONFERENCE OF BLACK LAWYERS. NOTES. q. free to members. National Conference of Black Lawyers, 2 W. 125th St., New York, NY 10027. TEL 212-864-4000. Eds. Mark Fancher, Cheryl Harris. **Document type:** newsletter.
    Description: Covers material of interest to African-American attorneys throughout the US and Canada who seek to use their expertise to serve the poor and communities of color.

NATIONAL COUNCIL FOR CRIME PREVENTION. INFORMATION BULLETIN. see *CRIMINOLOGY AND LAW ENFORCEMENT*

NATIONAL COURT REPORTERS ASSOCIATION. MEMBERSHIP DIRECTORY AND REGISTRY OF PROFESSIONAL REPORTERS. see *LAW — Judicial Systems*

651   US
NATIONAL COURT REPORTERS ASSOCIATION. PROCEEDINGS OF THE ANNUAL CONVENTION. a. National Court Reporters Association, 8224 Old Courthouse Rd., Vienna, VA 22182-3808. circ. 500. **Document type:** proceedings.
    Formerly: National Shorthand Reporters Association. Proceedings of the Annual Convention (ISSN 0077-572X)

NATIONAL CREDITOR - DEBTOR REVIEW; a journal of creditor-debtor relations. see *BUSINESS AND ECONOMICS — Banking And Finance*

340 350   JA   ISSN 0034-2912
H8
NATIONAL DIET LIBRARY. REFERENCE/KOKURITSU KOKKAI TOSHOKAN. REFARENSU. (Text in English, Japanese) 1951. m. 10176 Yen. National Diet Library - Kokuritsu Kokkai Toshokan, 1-10-1 Nagata-cho, Chiyoda-ku, Tokyo 100, Japan. TEL 03-3581-2331. FAX 03-3597-9104. bk.rev.; abstr.; charts; illus.; stat.; index, cum.index; circ. 1,570 (controlled).
—BLDSC (7331.880000).

340   US
NATIONAL DISTRICT ATTORNEYS ASSOCIATION. DIRECTORY OF PROSECUTING ATTORNEYS. biennial. National District Attorneys Association, 99 Canal Center Plaza, Ste. 510, Alexandria, VA 22314. TEL 703-549-9222. FAX 703-836-3195.

NATIONAL FIRE AND ARSON REPORT. see *FIRE PREVENTION*

NATIONAL FUTURES ASSOCIATION MANUAL. see *BUSINESS AND ECONOMICS — Investments*

NATIONAL INSOLVENCY REVIEW. see *BUSINESS AND ECONOMICS — Banking And Finance*

340   US
NATIONAL INSTITUTE FOR TRIAL ADVOCACY. DOCKET. 1977. 4/yr. free. National Institute for Trial Advocacy, Notre Dame Law School, Notre Dame, IN 46556. TEL 219-239-7770. FAX 219-282-1263. adv.; bk.rev. circ. 80,000. **Document type:** newsletter.

344.022   US   ISSN 0743-7927
K14
NATIONAL INSURANCE LAW REVIEW. 1984. q. $90. N I L S Publishing Company, 21625 Prairie St., Box 2507th, Chatworth, CA 91311. TEL 818-998-8830. Ed.Bd. (back issues avail.)
Description: Disseminates articles on insurance from law reviews of schools and universities.

340   US   ISSN 0162-7325
K14
NATIONAL LAW JOURNAL; the weekly newspaper for the profession. 1978. w. $110 (foreign $130) (effective 1994). New York Law Publishing Co., 345 Park Ave. S., New York, NY 10010. TEL 212-779-9200. (Subscr. to: Box 58494, Boulder, CO 80321-8494. TEL 800-274-2893) Ed. Doreen Weisenhaus. adv. circ. 45,000. (tabloid format; also avail. in microfiche from NYL) **Indexed:** Bank.Lit.Ind., C.L.I., CAD CAM Abstr., Environ.Abstr., Hlth.Ind., L.R.I., Law Ofc.Info.Svc., Leg.Info.Manage.Ind., Tel.Abstr., Telegen. **Document type:** newspaper.
●Also available online. Vendor(s): Mead Data Central, Inc.
—BLDSC (6026.164000).
Description: News and analyses of latest trends and developments in all areas of the law.

340   US   ISSN 0148-0588
KF200
NATIONAL LAWYERS GUILD. GUILD NOTES. 1972. q. $50 to institutions; free to members. National Lawyers Guild, 55 Sixth Ave., New York, NY 10013-1601. TEL 212-966-5000. Ed. Rick Best. adv.; bk.rev.; index. 1937-1970. circ. 10,000. (back issues avail.) **Indexed:** Alt.Press Ind., Chic.Per.Ind. **Document type:** newsletter.
—UMI.

340   US   ISSN 0730-532X
NATIONAL LAWYERS GUILD PRACTITIONER. 1937. q. $25 to individuals; institutions $30; students $10 (effective 1993). National Lawyers Guild (Berkeley), 1715 Francisco St., Berkeley, CA 94701. TEL 510-848-0599. FAX 510-848-6008. Ed.Bd. adv.; bk.rev. circ. 700. (also avail. in microfilm from RRI; reprint service avail. from RRI) **Indexed:** C.L.I., HR Rep., L.R.I., Leg.Per., P.A.I.S.
—Faxon; UnCover.
Formerly (until 1981): Guild Practitioner (ISSN 0017-5390); Which was formed by the merger of: Law in Transition; Lawyers Guild Review; Which incorporates (in 1943): International Juridical Association. Monthly Bulletin (ISSN 0098-7700); (in 1940): National Lawyers Guild Quarterly.

340   US
NATIONAL LAWYERS GUILD REFERRAL DIRECTORY. 1986. triennial. $50. National Lawyers Guild, 55 Sixth Ave., New York, NY 10013-1601. TEL 212-966-5000. **Document type:** directory.
Description: Lists guild attorneys by state and city, with their areas of practice.

347.016   US   ISSN 0894-7872
NATIONAL NOTARY. 1957. bi-m. $26. National Notary Association, 8236 Remmet Ave., Box 7184, Canoga Park, CA 91309-7184. TEL 818-713-4000. FAX 818-713-9061. Ed. Charles N. Faerber. adv.; bk.rev.; index. circ. 80,000. (also avail. in microfilm; back issues avail.; reprint service avail. from UMI) **Document type:** trade publication.

347.016   US
NATIONAL NOTARY YEARBOOK. 1977. a. $26 (foreign $30). National Notary Association, 8236 Remmet Ave., Box 7184, Canoga Park, CA 91309-7184. TEL 818-713-4000. FAX 818-713-9061. Ed. Charles N. Faerber. charts; illus.; index. circ. 80,000. (also avail. in microfilm; back issues avail.) **Document type:** trade publication.
Description: Articles, lists and directories of interest to notaries and to government officials regulating notaries.

340 331.1   US
NATIONAL PARALEGAL EMPLOYMENT & SALARY SURVEY. (9 regional editions avail.) 1984. a. $50 to non-members (members $30). National Paralegal Association, Box 406, Solebury, PA 18963. TEL 215-297-8333. FAX 215-297-8358. Ed. H. Jeffrey Valentine.
Description: Regional and national compilation of paralegal jobs, salaries, work environment, and benefits.

340   US
NATIONAL PRODUCTS LIABILITY DATABASE REPORT. 1991. m. $279. M. Lee Smith Publishers & Printers, 162 Fourth Ave. N., Box 2678, Nashville, TN 37219. TEL 615-255-6288. Ed. Lewis Laska. (back issues avail.)
Description: Reports on litigation and regulation of products in the United States. Categorized by product type.

346   US   ISSN 0363-8340
KF567.8
NATIONAL PROPERTY LAW DIGESTS. m. $360. National Property Law Digests, Inc., 7200 Wisconsin Ave., Ste. 314, Bethesda, MD 20814-4811. TEL 301-654-8004. FAX 301-654-8894. circ. 1,000.

NATIONAL PUBLIC EMPLOYMENT REPORTER. see *BUSINESS AND ECONOMICS — Labor And Industrial Relations*

340   CN   ISSN 0317-641X
NATIONAL REPORTER. (Text in English; occasionally in French) 1966. irreg. (approx. 9/yr.). Can.$119 per vol. Maritime Law Book Ltd., Box 302, Fredericton, NB E3B 4Y9, Canada. TEL 506-453-9921; 800-561-0220. FAX 506-453-9525. Ed. Eric B. Appleby. (back issues avail.)
●Also available online. Vendor(s): QL Systems Ltd.
Formerly (until 1969): N.B. Law News (ISSN 0715-4836)
Description: Contains all of the judgments of the Supreme Court of Canada, all of the judgments of the Federal Court of Appeal, judgments from the Court Martial Appeal Court and selected judgments from the British House of Lords and the Judicial Committee of the Privy Council.

340   US
NATIONAL REPORTER ON LEGAL ETHICS AND PROFESSIONAL RESPONSIBILITY. 1982. 10/yr. $730. University Publications of America (Subsidiary of: Congressional Information Service), 4520 East-West Hwy. Ste. 800, Bethesda, MD 20814-3389. TEL 301-657-3200. FAX 301-657-3203. Ed. David Luban. abstr.; bibl.; index. (looseleaf format)
Description: Provides Rules of Professional Conduct, Codes of Jusicial Conduct, and ethics opinions from state bar associations full-text.

NATIONAL RIGHT TO LIFE NEWS. see *SOCIAL SERVICES AND WELFARE*

340   US
KF4850.A15
NATIONAL SECURITY LAW REPORT. 1979. m. free. American Bar Association, Standing Committee on Law and National Security, c/o Holly Stewart McMahon, 1800 M St., N.W., 2nd Fl. S., Washington, DC 20036-5886. TEL 202-466-8463. FAX 202-331-2220. Ed. Robert Turner. bk.rev. circ. 2,600.
Formerly (until 1991): Intelligence Report (Washington) (ISSN 0736-2773)
Description: Cases, articles, legislation, regulations, and other materials concerning law and national security.

340 362.6   US   ISSN 0277-7460
NATIONAL SENIOR CITIZENS LAW CENTER WEEKLY. 1974. w. $150. National Senior Citizens Law Center, 1815 H St., N.W., Ste. 700, Washington, DC 20006. TEL 202-887-5280. FAX 202-785-6702. Ed. Rita E. Johnson. bk.rev. circ. 1,700.

NATIONAL TRADE AND TARIFF SERVICE. see *BUSINESS AND ECONOMICS — Public Finance, Taxation*

340   US
NATIONAL TRIAL AND DEPOSITION DIRECTORY.* 1980. a. $35 to reporters. Richard Tackman, 421 W. Franklin St., Boise, ID 83702-4516. adv. **Document type:** directory.

347.91   US   ISSN 1049-684X
K14
NATIONAL TRIAL LAWYER. 1989. bi-m. $30. Trial Lawyer Publications, Inc., Box 1217, 212 E. Vine St., Millville, NJ 08332-8217. TEL 609-825-9099. FAX 609-825-5959. Ed. Stephen C. Rubino; Pub. James M. Rossi. adv. contact: Pat Haffert. bk.rev. circ. 15,240. **Document type:** trade publication.
—UnCover.
Description: Independent forum for the exchange of professional information, news and opinions.

NATIONAL TRUCK EQUIPMENT ASSOCIATION. LEGISLATIVE REPORT. see *TRANSPORTATION — Trucks And Trucking*

NATIONAL TRUCK EQUIPMENT ASSOCIATION. REGULATIONS REPORT. see *TRANSPORTATION — Trucks And Trucking*

NATIONAL WETLANDS NEWSLETTER. see *ENVIRONMENTAL STUDIES*

NATURAL GAS LAWYER'S JOURNAL. see *ENERGY*

NATURAL GAS POLICY ACT NOTICES OF DETERMINATION (F E R C FORM 121). see *PETROLEUM AND GAS*

NATURAL RESOURCES & ENVIRONMENT. see *CONSERVATION*

THE NATURAL REOURCES JOURNAL. see *CONSERVATION*

NATURAL RESOURCES LAW NEWSLETTER. see *CONSERVATION*

NATURAL RIGHTS. see *ENVIRONMENTAL STUDIES*

NATURAL RIGHTS CENTER ANNUAL REPORT. see *ENVIRONMENTAL STUDIES*

340   US
NEBRASKA CHAMBER OF COMMERCE & INDUSTRY. LEGISLATIVE REPORT. 1960. w. during legislative sessions. free to members. Nebraska Chamber of Commerce & Industry, Box 95128, Lincoln, NE 68509. TEL 402-474-4422. FAX 402-474-2510. Ed. Jack Swartz. index. circ. 200. (back issues avail.)
Formerly: N A C I Legislative Report.
Description: Covers Nebraska business legislation.

LAW

340 US ISSN 0047-9209
K14
NEBRASKA LAW REVIEW. 1922. q. $36. University of Nebraska at Lincoln, College of Law, Nebraska Law Review, Lincoln, NE 68583-0903. TEL 402-472-1267. adv.; bk.rev.; bibl.; index. circ. 1,000. (also avail. in microform from WSH; reprint service avail. from WSH) **Indexed:** C.L.I., Crim.Just.Abstr., L.R.I., Leg.Cont., Leg.Per., Sel.Water Res.Abstr. **Document type:** academic/scholarly publication.
●Also available online. Vendor(s): West Services, Inc.
—BLDSC (6068.250000); Faxon; UnCover.

340 US
NEBRASKA LIMITATIONS MANUAL. 2nd ed., 1990. base vol. (plus suppl.). $50. Butterworth Legal Publishers (Salem) (Subsidiary of: Reed Elsevier plc), 8 Industrial Way, Bldg. C, Salem, NH 03079. TEL 800-548-4001. FAX 603-898-9858. Ed.Bd. (looseleaf format)
Description: Quick reference to Nebraska statutes and rules of court that set time limitations.

NEBRASKA LIVESTOCK BRAND BOOK. see
AGRICULTURE — Poultry And Livestock

340 US
NEBRASKA TRANSCRIPT. 1966. q. free to qualified personnel. University of Nebraska at Lincoln, College of Law, Lincoln, NE 68583-0902. TEL 402-472-2161. Ed. Michelle McDonald. bk.rev.; illus. circ. 4,500. **Document type:** academic/scholarly publication.

NEGOTIATORS HANDBOOK: ASIA & AUSTRALASIA. see
PETROLEUM AND GAS

NEGOTIATORS HANDBOOK: CENTRAL AMERICA & CARIBBEAN. see PETROLEUM AND GAS

NEGOTIATORS HANDBOOK: EUROPE. see PETROLEUM AND GAS

NEGOTIATORS HANDBOOK: MIDDLE EAST. see
PETROLEUM AND GAS

NEGOTIATORS HANDBOOK: NORTH AFRICA. see
PETROLEUM AND GAS

NEGOTIATORS HANDBOOK: SOUTH AMERICA. see
PETROLEUM AND GAS

NEGOTIATORS HANDBOOK: SOUTH & CENTRAL AFRICA.
see PETROLEUM AND GAS

418.02 NP
NEPAL RECORDER. (Text in English) 1957. irreg. (2-3/mo.). Rs.900($50) Nepal Press Digest (Pvt) Ltd., Lazimpat, Kathmandu, Nepal. Ed. Mahesh C. Regmi. index. (also avail. in microfilm from LCP)
Formerly: Nepal Gazette Translation Service (ISSN 0028-2707)

340 NP ISSN 0259-2193
NEPALA KANUNA PARICARCA/NEPAL LAW REVIEW. (Text in English and Nepali) 1977. q. Rs.4. Tribhuvan University, Institute of Law, Box 1247, Kathmandu, Nepal. Ed. Tope Bahadur Singh. bk.rev. circ. 1,000.

347.9 NE
NETHERLANDS. CENTRAAL BUREAU VOOR DE STATISTIEK. CIVIL AND ADMINISTRATIVE JURISDICTION. BURGERLIJKE EN ADMINISTRATIEVE RECHTSPRAAK. (Text in Dutch and English) 1951. a. Centraal Bureau voor de Statistiek, Prinses Beatrixlaan 428, 2270 AZ Voorburg, Netherlands. TEL 070-694341. (Orders to: SDU - Publishers, Christoffel Plantijnstraat, The Hague, Netherlands) **Document type:** government publication.
Formerly: Netherlands. Centraal Bureau voor de Statistiek. Justitiele Statistiek. Judicial Statistics.

340 GW ISSN 0341-1915
NEUE JURISTISCHE WOCHENSCHRIFT. 1947. w. DM.306 (students DM.197.20) (microfiche edition (1947-70) DM.898). (Deutscher Anwaltverein) C.H. Beck'sche Verlagsbuchhandlung, Wilhelmstr. 9, 80801 Munich, Germany. TEL 089-38189-338. FAX 089-38189-398. TELEX 5215085-BECK-D. (Co-sponsor: Bundesrechtsanwaltskammer) Ed.Bd. adv.: B&W page DM.5800, color page DM.11600; trim 260 x 186. cum.index; circ. 55,858 (controlled). (also avail. in microfiche; back issues avail.) **Indexed:** Dok.Str., ELLIS. **Document type:** trade publication.
●Also available on CD-ROM.
—SWETS.

349 GW ISSN 0028-3231
LAW
NEUE JUSTIZ; Zeitschrift fuer Rechtsetzung und Rechtsanwendung. 1947. m. DM.80. Nomos Verlagsgesellschaft mbH und Co. KG, Waldseestr. 3-5, 76530 Baden-Baden, Germany. TEL 07221-21040. FAX 07221-210427. (Subscr. to: Postfach 610, 76484 Baden-Baden, Germany) adv.; bk.rev.; charts; index. circ. 40,000. **Document type:** newsletter.

NEUE WIRTSCHAFTS-BRIEFE; Zeitschrift fuer Steuer- und Wirtschaftsrecht. see BUSINESS AND ECONOMICS — Public Finance, Taxation

340 GW
NEUE ZEITSCHRIFT FUER ARBEITSRECHT; Zweiwochenschrift fuer die betriebliche Praxis. 1981. s-m. DM.320 (students DM.302). C.H. Beck'sche Verlagsbuchhandlung, Wilhelmstr. 9, 80801 Munich, Germany. TEL 089-38189-338. FAX 089-38189-398. TELEX 5215085-BECK-D. Ed.Bd. adv.: B&W page DM.2600, color page DM.5200; trim 260 x 186. circ. 8,000. (back issues avail.) **Document type:** academic/scholarly publication.
Formerly: Neue Zeitschrift fuer Arbeits- und Sozialrecht (ISSN 0176-3814)

340 GW ISSN 0941-7915
▼**NEUE ZEITSCHRIFT FUER SOZIALRECHT;** Monatschrift fuer die betriebliche, behoerdliche und gerichtliche Praxis. 1992. m. DM.324 (students DM.284). C.H. Beck'sche Verlagsbuchhandlung, Wilhelmstr. 9, 80801 Munich, Germany. TEL 089-38189338. FAX 089-38189398. TELEX 5215085-BECK-D. Ed.Bd. adv.: B&W page DM.2000, color page DM.4000; trim 260 x 186. circ. 4,000. (back issues avail.) **Document type:** academic/scholarly publication.

NEUE ZEITSCHRIFT FUER VERKEHRSRECHT. see
TRANSPORTATION

NEUES STEUERRECHT VON A BIS Z; Kommentar-Zeitschrift fuer das gesamte Steuerrecht. see BUSINESS AND ECONOMICS — Public Finance, Taxation

340 US ISSN 1068-882X
K14
NEVADA LAWYER. 1936. m. $40. State Bar of Nevada, 1325 Airmotive Way, Ste. 140, Reno, NV 89502-3239. TEL 702-329-4100. FAX 702-329-0522. Ed. Rosalie A. Small. adv.; bk.rev. circ. 4,100. (also avail. in microfilm from WSH) **Indexed:** C.L.I., L.R.I., Law Ofc.Info.Svc., Leg.Per. **Document type:** trade publication.
●Also available online. Vendor(s): West Services, Inc.
—Faxon; UnCover.
Formed by the 1993 merger of: State Bar of Nevada. Bar Letter (1989-1992) (ISSN 1052-4541); And: Inter Alia (ISSN 0092-6086); Which was formerly (until 1973): Nevada State Bar Journal (ISSN 0028-4092)

340 CN ISSN 0713-8989
LAW
NEW BRUNSWICK REPORTS. (Text in English, French) 1968. irreg., latest vol.131. Can.$118 per vol. Maritime Law Book Ltd., Box 302, Fredericton, NB E3B 4Y9, Canada. TEL 506-453-9921; 800-561-0220. FAX 506-453-9525. (back issues avail.)
●Also available online. Vendor(s): QL Systems Ltd.
Description: Includes all of the judgments of the New Brunswick court of Appeal plus selected trial court judgments.

340 US ISSN 0893-7133
NEW DEVELOPMENTS IN EMPLOYMENT DISCRIMINATION. 1987. q. $65. Butterworth Legal Publishers (Salem), 8 Industrial Way, Bldg. C, Salem, NH 03079. TEL 800-548-4001. FAX 603-898-9858. Ed. Michael Weisberg. (tabloid format)

340 US ISSN 0740-8994
K14
NEW ENGLAND JOURNAL ON CRIMINAL AND CIVIL CONFINEMENT. 1973. s-a. $20 (foreign $22). New England School of Law, 154 Stuart St., Boston, MA 02116-5687. TEL 617-451-0010. FAX 617-482-6634. Ed. Lawrence Elemer. bk.rev. circ. 500. (also avail. in microfilm from RRI; reprint service avail. from RRI) **Indexed:** Abstr.Bk.Rev.Curr.Leg.Per., C.C.L.P., C.L.I., Crim.Just.Abstr., L.R.I., Leg.Cont., Leg.Per. **Document type:** academic/scholarly publication.
—Faxon; UnCover.
Formerly: New England Journal on Prison Law (ISSN 0095-7364)
Description: Covers current trends and future proposals for correctional law and the prison community. Includes criminal, juvenile and civil confinement law and discrimination.

340 US ISSN 0028-4823
NEW ENGLAND LAW REVIEW. 1965. q. $26. New England School of Law, New England Law Review, 154 Stuart St., Boston, MA 02116. TEL 617-422-7294. FAX 617-422-7451. Eds. Monique M. Gousie, Elizabeth Delfs. bk.rev.; cum.index: 1965-1975. circ. 750. (also avail. in microfilm from UMI,WSH,PMC; reprint service avail. from WSH) **Indexed:** C.L.I., L.R.I., Leg.Cont., Leg.Per. **Document type:** academic/scholarly publication.
●Also available online. Vendor(s): West Services, Inc.
—BLDSC (6084.010000); Faxon; UnCover.
Formerly: Portia Law Journal.
Description: Provides the legal community with well-researched, reasoned analyses of important issues. Includes articles by members of the judiciary, legal educators and practicing attorneys.

340 US
NEW ENGLAND LEGAL FOUNDATION. DOCKET. 4/yr. free. New England Legal Foundation, 150 Lincoln St., Boston, MA 02111. TEL 617-695-3660. FAX 617-695-3656. circ. 1,300. (back issues avail.) **Document type:** newsletter.

340 US ISSN 0548-4928
NEW HAMPSHIRE BAR JOURNAL. 1758. q. $40 (foreign $50). New Hampshire Bar Association, 112 Pleasant St., Concord, NH 03301. TEL 603-224-6942. FAX 603-224-2910. Ed. Michael Delucia. adv.: B&W page $700; trim 8 1/2 x 11; adv. contact: Donna J. Parker. circ. 4,500. (back issues avail.)
—Faxon; UnCover.

343 US ISSN 1051-4023
KF200
NEW HAMPSHIRE BAR NEWS. 1974. fortn. $60 to non-members (foreign $70) (effective 1994). New Hampshire Bar Association, 112 Pleasant St., Concord, NH 03301. TEL 603-224-6942. FAX 603-224-2910. Ed. Martin E. Murray. adv.; bk.rev.; abstr.; charts; illus.; stat.; index. circ. 4,500. (back issues avail.) **Indexed:** C.L.I., L.R.I.
Formerly (until 1990): New Hampshire Law Weekly (ISSN 0362-1073)

NEW HAMPSHIRE INSURANCE LAWS (YEAR). see
INSURANCE

NEW HAMPSHIRE PRACTICE SERIES. VOLS. 13 AND 14: LOCAL GOVERNMENT LAW. see PUBLIC ADMINISTRATION — Municipal Government

340 US
NEW HAMPSHIRE REPORTS. irreg. (4-6/yr. in 1-2 vols./yr.). $38 per vol. Butterworth Legal Publishers (Salem) (Subsidiary of: Reed Elsevier plc), 8 Industrial Way, Bldg. C, Salem, NH 03079. TEL 800-548-4001. FAX 603-898-9858.

NEW JERSEY EDUCATION LAW REPORT; the authority on labor relations in New Jersey schools. see EDUCATION

340 331   US   ISSN 1064-2390
▼**NEW JERSEY EMPLOYMENT LAW LETTER.** 1992. m. $94. (Pitney, Hardin, Kipp & Szuch) M. Lee Smith Publishers & Printers, 162 Fourth Ave., N., Box 198867, Nashville, TN 37219-8867. TEL 615-242-7395; 800-274-6774. FAX 615-256-601. Ed.Bd. **Document type:** newsletter.
 Description: Reports on the latest state-specific employment law developments that affect New Jersey companies.

340 613.1   US   ISSN 1060-9954
▼**NEW JERSEY ENVIRONMENTAL LAW LETTER.** 1992. m. $137. (Pitney, Hardin, Kipp & Szuch) M. Lee Smith Publishers & Printers, 162 Fourth Ave., N., Box 198867, Nashville, TN 37219-8867. TEL 615-242-7385; 800-274-6774. FAX 615-256-6601. Ed.Bd. **Document type:** newsletter.
 Description: Reports the latest state-specific environmental law developments that affect companies in New Jersey.

340   US
NEW JERSEY LABOR AND EMPLOYMENT LAW QUARTERLY. 1966. q. $40 to non-members; members $25. New Jersey State Bar Association, 1 Constitution Sq., New Brunswick, NJ 08901-1500. TEL 908-249-5000. FAX 908-249-2815. Ed. Laura A. Schwarzkopf. circ. 800.
 Formerly: New Jersey State Bar Association. Labor and Employment Law Section Newsletter.
 Description: Provides substantive and practical information regarding labor and employment law, arbitration, and agency procedure.

340   US   ISSN 0028-5803
LAW
NEW JERSEY LAW JOURNAL. 1878. w. $272. American Lawyer Media, L.P. (Newark), 238 Mulberry St., Box 20081, Newark, NJ 07101-6081. TEL 201-642-0075. FAX 201-642-0920. Ed. Ronald J. Fleury; Pub. Robert S. Steinbaum. adv.; bk.rev.; abstr.; s-a. index. circ. 10,481. (also avail. in microform) **Indexed:** C.L.I., Hlth.Ind., L.R.I. **Document type:** newspaper.
●Also available online. Vendor(s): West Services, Inc.
 Description: Contains the complete and official text of all state and federal court notices; digest of all published NJ state journal and administrative decisions and all relevant court decisions; independent reporting on state-wide legal issues.

340   US   ISSN 0195-0983
KF200
NEW JERSEY LAWYER. 1957. w. $99 to non-members; NJSBA members $35. (New Jersey State Bar Association) New Jersey Lawyer, Inc., 2825 Woodbridge Ave., Edison, NJ 08817. TEL 908-549-4800. FAX 908-549-9352. (Co-sponsors: Advisory Committee on Professional Ethics; New Jersey Corporate Counsel Association) Ed. Ron Ostroff. adv.: B&W page $1700. bk.rev.; illus.; index. circ. 20,000. (tabloid format; also avail. in microfiche from WSH,PMC; microfilm from WSH,PMC) **Indexed:** C.L.I., L.R.I., Leg.Per. **Document type:** newspaper.
●Also available online. Vendor(s): West Services, Inc.
 —UnCover.
 Former titles: Bar Journal (Trenton) (ISSN 0162-1211); New Jersey State Bar Journal (ISSN 0028-5951)
 Description: Covers news, issues and trends for the New Jersey legal community.

340 380   US
NEW JERSEY MOTOR VEHICLE AND TRAFFIC LAWS. 1988. a. $16.95 (effective May 1992). Gould Publications (Binghamton), 199-300 State St., Binghamton, NY 13201. TEL 607-724-3000. FAX 607-723-4285. adv.; bk.rev. (looseleaf format)
 Description: Contains title 39 and NJ statutes.

340   US
NEW JERSEY STATE BAR ASSOCIATION. CASINO LAW SECTION NEWSLETTER. 1986. irreg. (2-3/yr.) free to members. New Jersey State Bar Association, Casino Law Section, 1 Constitution Sq., New Brunswick, NJ 08901-1500. TEL 908-249-5000. FAX 908-249-2815. Ed. Brian P. Blatz. bk.rev. circ. 200. (back issues avail.) **Document type:** newsletter.

NEW JERSEY STATE BAR ASSOCIATION. CREDITOR AND DEBTOR RELATIONS SECTION NEWSLETTER. see BUSINESS AND ECONOMICS — Banking And Finance

NEW JERSEY STATE BAR ASSOCIATION. ENVIRONMENTAL LAW SECTION. NEWSLETTER. see ENVIRONMENTAL STUDIES

NEW JERSEY STATE BAR ASSOCIATION. HEALTH AND HOSPITAL LAW SECTION. NEWSLETTER. see HOSPITALS

347.91   US
NEW JERSEY TRIAL LAWYER. 1987. bi-m. $30. Trial Lawyer Publications, Inc., Box 1217, 212 E. Vine St., Millville, NJ 08332-8217. TEL 609-825-9099. FAX 609-825-5959. Ed. Stephen C. Rubino; Pub. James M. Rossi. adv. circ. 4,197. **Document type:** trade publication.
 Description: Independent, open forum for the free exchange of information, ideas, and opinions.

340   US   ISSN 0890-2941
KF1
NEW LAW BOOKS REVIEWER.* 1986. bi-m. $90. Huddleston Brown Publishers, Inc., 60 Madison Ave., Ste. 1201, New York, NY 10010. Ed. Gerome Leone. bk.rev. circ. 120.

340   UK   ISSN 0306-6479
K14
NEW LAW JOURNAL. 1980. w. $336. Butterworth & Co. (Publishers) Ltd. (Subsidiary of: Reed Elsevier plc), 88 Kingsway, London WC2B 6AB, England. TEL 71-405-6900. FAX 71-405-1332. (US addr.: Butterworth Legal Publishers, 90 Stiles Rd., Salem, NH 03079-9981. TEL 603-898-9664) Ed. James Morton. adv. circ. 8,500. **Indexed:** ASSIA, C.L.I., ELLIS, L.R.I., Lang.& Lang.Behav.Abstr., Leg.Per.
●Also available online. Vendor(s): Mead Data Central, Inc.
 —BLDSC (6084.350000); Faxon; UnCover; SWETS. CCC.
 Incorporates: Law Times; Law Journal.
 Description: Covers the entire legal spectrum, including the provision of legal services and legal practice.

340   US   ISSN 0028-6214
K14
NEW MEXICO LAW REVIEW. 1971. 3/yr. $26 (foreign $26). University of New Mexico, School of Law, 1117 Stanford, N.E., Albuquerque, NM 87131. TEL 505-277-2146. Ed. Frederick M. Hart. adv.; bk.rev.; index, cum.index every 10 yrs. circ. 1,000. (also avail. in microfiche from WSH,PMC; microfilm from WSH,PMC) **Indexed:** C.L.I., L.R.I., Leg.Cont., Leg.Per. **Document type:** academic/scholarly publication.
 —BLDSC (6084.650000); Faxon; UnCover.

346.043   US   ISSN 0951-547X
NEW MEXICO REAL ESTATE LAW REPORTER. 1987. q. $80. Butterworth Legal Publishers, Austin Division (Subsidiary of: Reed Elsevier plc), Echelon II, Ste. 100, 9430 Research, Austin, TX 78759-6598. TEL 512-346-9686. FAX 512-346-9373. Ed.Bd. (looseleaf format; back issues avail.)

348   US   ISSN 0094-7148
KFN3645
NEW MEXICO REPORTS. Spine title: Report of Cases Determined in the Supreme Court and Court of Appeals of the State of New Mexico. irreg. (Supreme Court) West Publishing Corp., 620 Opperman Dr., Eagan, MN 55123. TEL 612-687-8000; 800-328-9352. FAX 612-687-7302. **Document type:** trade publication.

340.3   AT   ISSN 0085-400X
NEW SOUTH WALES. LAW REFORM COMMISSION. REPORTS. 1966. irreg., no.70, 1993. price varies. Law Reform Commission, G.P.O. Box 5199, Sydney, N.S.W. 2001, Australia. FAX 02-247-1054.

347 336   AT
NEW SOUTH WALES CONVEYANCING LAW AND PRACTICE. (In 4 vols: Vols.1 & 2: Commentary; Vol.3: New Developments, Cases and Index; Vol.4: Legislation) 1980. 10/yr. C C H Australia Ltd., P.O. Box 230, North Ryde, N.S.W. 2113, Australia. TEL 888-2555. FAX 02-888-7324. (looseleaf format)

340   AT
NEW SOUTH WALES STRATA AND COMMUNITY TITLES LAW. (In 2 vols.) 1979. q. C C H Australia Ltd., P.O. Box 230, North Ryde, N.S.W. 2113, Australia. TEL 02-888-2555. FAX 02-888-7324. (looseleaf format)
 Formerly: New South Wales Strata Title Law.

NEW YORK APARTMENT LAW INSIDER. see REAL ESTATE

NEW YORK BANKING LAW. see BUSINESS AND ECONOMICS — Banking And Finance

NEW YORK BUILDING LAWS MANUAL. see BUILDING AND CONSTRUCTION

340 690   US
NEW YORK CITY BUILDING CODE. 1988. a. $49.95. Gould Publications (Binghamton), 199-300 State St., Binghamton, NY 13091. TEL 607-724-3000. FAX 607-723-4285. adv.; bk.rev. (looseleaf format)
 Description: Contains complete laws dealing with buildings in NYC.

340   US
NEW YORK CITY CHARTER: ADMINISTRATIVE CODE. 1948. biennial. price varies. New York Legal Publishing Corp., 6 Charles Park, Guilderland, NY 12084. TEL 800-541-2681. FAX 518-456-0828. index, cum.index. (back issues avail.)
 Description: Certified and recodified charter for New York City.

340 352.3   US
NEW YORK CITY FIRE LAW HANDBOOK. 1988. a. $15.95. Gould Publications (Binghamton), 199-300 State St., Binghamton, NY 13901. TEL 607-724-3000. FAX 607-723-4285. adv.; bk.rev. (looseleaf format)
 Description: Contains title 15 fire prevention and control and chapter 4 of title 27 fire prevention code of NYC.

340 352.7   US
NEW YORK CITY HOUSING MAINTENANCE CODE. 1989. a. $15. Gould Publications (Binghamton), 199-300 State St., Binghamton, NY 13901. TEL 607-724-3000. FAX 607-723-4285. adv.; bk.rev. (looseleaf format)
 Description: Contains the housing maintenance code with rules and regulations for housing maintenance and the multiple dwelling law.

340   US
NEW YORK CITY LAW DIGEST. 1988. a. $9.95. Gould Publications (Binghamton), 199-300 State St., Binghamton, NY 13901. TEL 607-724-3000. FAX 607-723-4285. adv.; bk.rev. (looseleaf format)
 Description: Contains the text of certain laws used by police, peace officers, judges and attorneys. Includes part of NYC Charter, NYC Administrative Code and NYC Health Code.

340 388.31   US
NEW YORK CITY TRAFFIC RULES AND REGULATIONS. 1989. a. $5.95. Gould Publications (Binghamton), 199-300 State St., Binghamton, NY 13901. TEL 607-724-3000. FAX 607-723-4285. adv.; bk.rev. circ. 5.95. (looseleaf format)
 Description: Contains complete regulations relating to NYC traffic.

NEW YORK EDUCATION LAW REPORT. see EDUCATION

NEW YORK EMPLOYER'S ALERT. see BUSINESS AND ECONOMICS — Labor And Industrial Relations

NEW YORK EMPLOYER'S GUIDE. see BUSINESS AND ECONOMICS — Labor And Industrial Relations

340 331   US   ISSN 1072-9178
▼**NEW YORK EMPLOYMENT LAW LETTER.** 1994. m. $95. (O'Melveny & Meyers) M. Lee Smith Publishers & Printers, 162 Fourth Ave., N., Box 198867, Nashville, TN 37219-8867. TEL 615-242-7395; 800-274-6774. FAX 615-256-6601. Ed.Bd. **Document type:** newsletter.
 Description: Reports the latest state-specific employment law developments that affect companies in New York.

340 333.7   US
NEW YORK ENVIRONMENTAL CONSERVATION LAW. 1989. a. $19.95. Gould Publications (Binghamton), 199-300 State St., Binghamton, NY 13901. TEL 607-724-3000. FAX 607-723-4285. adv.; bk.rev. (looseleaf format)
 Description: Contains Chapter 43B of the consolidated laws.

NEW YORK LANDLORD V. TENANT. see REAL ESTATE

LAW

340   US   ISSN 0028-7326
NEW YORK LAW JOURNAL. 1888. d. (5/wk.). $445. New York Law Publishing Co., 345 Park Ave. S., New York, NY 10010. TEL 212-779-9200. Ed. Ruth Hochberger. circ. 15,150. (also avail. in microfilm from NYL) Indexed: C.L.I., Hlth.Ind., L.R.I., Leg.Info.Manage.Ind. **Document type:** newspaper.
● Also available online. Vendor(s): Mead Data Central, Inc., Wilsonline.
    Description: Covers trends in the law and decisions of statewide and national interest. Provides commentary by experts in various specialties.

NEW YORK LAW JOURNAL DIGEST ANNOTATOR. see *LAW — Judicial Systems*

340   US   ISSN 0145-448X
K14
NEW YORK LAW SCHOOL LAW REVIEW. 1955. 4/yr. $30. New York Law School, 57 Worth St., New York, NY 10013-2960. TEL 212-431-2118. Ed. Jeffrey W. Berkman. adv.; bk.rev.; bibl.; charts; illus.; stat.; index, cum.index. circ. 1,500. (also avail. in microform from UMI,WSH; reprint service avail. from UMI,WSH) Indexed: Abstr.Bk.Rev.Curr.Leg.Per., C.L.I., L.R.I., Leg.Cont., Leg.Per., P.A.I.S.
—BLDSC (6089.341000); Faxon; UnCover; SWETS; UMI.
    Formerly: New York Law Forum (ISSN 0028-7318)
    Description: Examines the complete range of topics available to scholars of law, from legal ethics to interpretations of SEC regulations.

NEW YORK LAW SCHOOL REPORTER. see *COLLEGE AND ALUMNI*

340   352.7   US
NEW YORK MULTIPLE DWELLING LAW. 1988. a. $15. Gould Publications (Binghamton), 199-300 State St., Binghamton, NY 13901. TEL 607-724-3000. FAX 607-723-7285. adv.; bk.rev. (looseleaf format)
    Description: Contains Chapter 61A of the consolidated laws, applicable to multiple dwellings.

340   368   US
NEW YORK NO-FAULT ARBITRATION REPORTS. 1977. m. $90. American Arbitration Association, 140 W. 51st St., New York, NY 10020-1203. TEL 212-484-4011. FAX 212-541-4841. Ed. Richard Wentzler. s-a. cum.index. circ. 500. (looseleaf format; back issues avail.)
    Description: Summarizes cases involving personal injuries caused by automobiles.

340   US
NEW YORK NOTARY LAW PRIMER. a. $9.95. National Notary Association, 8236 Remmet Ave., Box 7184, Canoga Park, CA 91309-7184. TEL 818-713-4000. FAX 818-713-9061. Ed. Charles N. Faerber. (reprint service avail. from UMI) **Document type:** monographic series.

346.043   US   ISSN 0894-4903
NEW YORK REAL ESTATE REPORTER. 1986. m. $185. New York Law Publishing Co., 345 Park Ave. S., New York, NY 10010. TEL 212-545-6170. FAX 212-696-1848. **Document type:** newsletter.
    Description: Roundup of New York's real estate cases, with commentary on what impacts real estate practices. Also covers current developments affecting the real estate industry.

340   US
NEW YORK REAL PROPERTY LAWS HANDBOOK. 1989. a. $21.95. Gould Publications (Binghamton), 199-300 State St., Binghamton, NY 13901. TEL 607-724-3000. FAX 607-723-4285. adv.; bk.rev. (looseleaf format)
    Description: Contains all real property laws and tax laws for NYS.

340   330   US   ISSN 1056-4136
NEW YORK STATE BAR ASSOCIATION. ANTITRUST LAW SECTION SYMPOSIUM. Represents: Proceedings of the Antitrust Law Section Annual Meeting. 1989. a. $15 (effective 1993). New York State Bar Association, Antitrust Law Section, 1 Elk St., Albany, NY 12207. TEL 518-463-3200. FAX 518-487-5699. Ed. Mary Beth Martin. circ. 750 (controlled). (reprint service avail. from RRI) **Document type:** proceedings.
    Description: Publishes speeches on various topics in antitrust law, including court cases, legislation and business climate.

NEW YORK STATE BAR ASSOCIATION. ENVIRONMENTAL LAW SECTION. JOURNAL. see *ENVIRONMENTAL STUDIES*

NEW YORK STATE BAR ASSOCIATION. LABOR AND EMPLOYMENT LAW SECTION. NEWSLETTER. see *BUSINESS AND ECONOMICS — Labor And Industrial Relations*

340   US   ISSN 0028-7547
K14
NEW YORK STATE BAR JOURNAL. vol.41, 1969. m. $16. New York State Bar Association, One Marine Midland Plaza, Binghamton, NY 13902. FAX 607-772-6093. (Subscr. to: Records Dept., NYSBA, One Elk St., Albany, NY 12207-1096. TEL 518-463-3200) Ed. Eugene Gerhart. adv.; bk.rev.; charts; illus.; stat.; tr.lit.; circ. 59,000 (controlled). (also avail. in microform from UMI; microfiche from WSH; reprint service avail. from UMI) Indexed: C.L.I., L.R.I., Law Ofc.Info.Svc., Leg.Per., P.A.I.S.
● Also available online. Vendor(s): West Services, Inc. (NYSTBJ).
—Faxon; UnCover; UMI.

340   US
NEW YORK STATE COMMITTEE ON OPEN GOVERNMENT. ANNUAL REPORT. 1978. a. New York State Committee on Open Government, Department of State, 162 Washington Ave., Albany, NY 12231. TEL 518-474-2518. cum.index. circ. 1,000. (back issues avail.)

340   US   ISSN 0028-7636
NEW YORK STATE LAW DIGEST; reporting important opinions of the New York Court of Appeals and of other courts. 1961. m. New York State Bar Association, 1 Elk St., Albany, NY 12207. TEL 518-463-3200. FAX 518-487-5699. Ed. David D. Siegel. circ. 45,000. (looseleaf format; also avail. in microform from UMI; back issues avail.; reprint service avail. from UMI)
—UMI.

340   US
NEW YORK TOWN LAW. 1989. a. $15. Gould Publications (Binghamton), 199-300 State St., Binghamton, NY 13901. TEL 607-724-3000. FAX 607-723-4285. adv.; bk.rev. (looseleaf format)
    Description: Contains Chapter 62 of the consolidated laws of NY, unannotated. Includes uniform rules for justice courts.

NEW YORK UNIVERSITY. INSTITUTE ON FEDERAL TAXATION. CONFERENCE ON CHARITABLE FOUNDATIONS. see *BUSINESS AND ECONOMICS — Public Finance, Taxation*

NEW YORK UNIVERSITY ENVIRONMENTAL LAW JOURNAL. see *ENVIRONMENTAL STUDIES*

340   US   ISSN 0028-7881
K14
NEW YORK UNIVERSITY LAW REVIEW. 1924. 6/yr. $35 (foreign $40). New York University Law Review, 110 W. Third St., New York, NY 10012. TEL 212-998-6350. FAX 212-995-4032. adv.; bk.rev.; index. circ. 2,800. (also avail. in microfiche from RRI,WSH; microfilm from RRI,WSH; reprint service avail. from RRI) Indexed: Abstr.Bk.Rev.Curr.Leg.Per., Account.Ind. (1974-), C.L.I., Crim.Just.Abstr., Curr.Cont., HRIS, L.R.I., Leg.Cont., Leg.Per., P.A.I.S, SSCI. **Document type:** academic/scholarly publication.
● Also available online. Vendor(s): Mead Data Central, Inc., West Services, Inc.
—BLDSC (6089.820000); Faxon; UnCover; SWETS.

340   US   ISSN 0894-3303
NEW YORK UNIVERSITY SCHOOL OF LAW. INGRAM DOCUMENTS IN AMERICAN LEGAL HISTORY. 1986. irreg. price varies. Oceana Publications, Inc., 75 Main St., Dobbs Ferry, NY 10522. TEL 914-693-1320. FAX 914-693-0402. (back issues avail.) **Document type:** monographic series.
    Description: Scholarly discussion of social justice issues in American legal history.

340   US   ISSN 0894-329X
NEW YORK UNIVERSITY SCHOOL OF LAW. LINDEN STUDIES IN LEGAL HISTORY. 1984. irreg., latest 1991. price varies. Oceana Publications, Inc., 75 Main St., Dobbs Ferry, NY 10522. TEL 914-693-1320. FAX 914-693-0402. (back issues avail.) **Document type:** academic/scholarly publication, monographic series.
    Description: Scholarly treatment of issues in American legal history.

340   US
NEW YORK VILLAGE LAW. 1989. a. $12.95. Gould Publications (Binghamton), 199-300 State St., Binghamton, NY 13901. TEL 607-724-3000. FAX 607-723-4285. adv.; bk.rev. (looseleaf format)
    Description: Contains village law, Chapter 64 of the consolidated laws.

342.93   NZ   ISSN 0110-1277
LAW
NEW ZEALAND ADMINISTRATIVE REPORTS. 1976. m. NZ.$624. Butterworths of New Zealand Ltd., P.O. Box 472. 203-207 Victoria St., Wellington, New Zealand. TEL 04-385-1479. FAX 04-385-1598. Ed. John Cottle.
—CCC.
    Description: Reproduces a selection of decisions of most administrative tribunals, especially accident compensation.

NEW ZEALAND BUSINESS BULLETIN. see *BUSINESS AND ECONOMICS*

NEW ZEALAND BUSINESS LAW GUIDE. see *BUSINESS AND ECONOMICS — Public Finance, Taxation*

340   NZ
NEW ZEALAND CONVEYANCING LAW AND PRACTICE. 1989. 8/yr. NZ.$488. C C H New Zealand Limited, P.O. Box 2378, Auckland, New Zealand. TEL 483-9179. FAX 483-4009. (looseleaf format)
    Description: Includes full text of legislation, full text or extracts of cases, and information on new developments. Covers proposed legislation, reports and government statements.

347   336   NZ
NEW ZEALAND DUTIES GUIDE. 1974. 4/yr. NZ.$438. C C H New Zealand Limited, P.O. Box 2378, Auckland, New Zealand. TEL 483-9179. FAX 483-4009.
    Former titles: New Zealand Duties and Sales Tax Guide; (until 1983): New Zealand Estate and Gift Duty Reporter.
    Description: Commentary, text of legislation and other information on duties in New Zealand.

NEW ZEALAND EMPLOYERS HANDBOOK. see *BUSINESS AND ECONOMICS — Personnel Management*

NEW ZEALAND EMPLOYMENT LAW LIBRARY. see *BUSINESS AND ECONOMICS — Personnel Management*

340   NZ
NEW ZEALAND FORMS & PRECEDENTS. 4 base vols. (plus updates 3-4/yr.). Butterworths of New Zealand Ltd., 203-207 Victoria St., P.O. Box 472, Wellington, New Zealand. TEL 04-385-1479. FAX 04-385-1598. Ed. Christine O'Brien. (looseleaf format)
    Description: Modern precedents library written specifically for New Zealand.

NEW ZEALAND GOODS AND SERVICES TAX GUIDE. see *BUSINESS AND ECONOMICS — Public Finance, Taxation*

NEW ZEALAND INCOME TAX LEGISLATION. see *BUSINESS AND ECONOMICS — Public Finance, Taxation*

NEW ZEALAND JOURNAL OF INDUSTRIAL RELATIONS. see *BUSINESS AND ECONOMICS — Labor And Industrial Relations*

340   NZ   ISSN 0028-8373
NEW ZEALAND LAW JOURNAL. 1925; N.S.1962. m. NZ.$360. Butterworths of New Zealand Ltd., P.O. Box 472, 203-207 Victoria St., Wellington, New Zealand. TEL 04-385-1479. FAX 04-385-1598. Ed. P.J. Downey. adv.; bk.rev.; index. circ. 1,750. (also avail. in microfiche from BHP,PMC) Indexed: C.L.I., L.R.I., Leg.Per., P.A.I.S.
—BLDSC (6095.500000); UnCover. **CCC.**
    Description: Current legal news, editorials and articles; comment on recent cases.

346 AT ISSN 0078-0081
LAW
NEW ZEALAND LAW REGISTER. 1950. a. Aus.$49 (NZ.$69). Law Book Co. Ltd., 44-50 Waterloo Rd., North Ryde, N.S.W. 2113, Australia. TEL 02-887-0177. FAX 02-888-9706. TELEX ASBOOK 27995. circ. 3,500.

340 NZ ISSN 0110-148X
NEW ZEALAND LAW REPORTS. 1861. 3 base vols. (plus updates 18/yr.). NZ.$1000. (New Zealand Council of Law Reporting) Butterworths of New Zealand Ltd., P.O. Box 472, 203-207 Victoria St., Wellington, New Zealand. TEL 04-385-1479. FAX 04-385-1598. Ed. Christine O'Brien. index, cum.index.
   Description: The official report series on law in NZ.

340 NZ ISSN 0114-0655
K14
NEW ZEALAND RECENT LAW REVIEW. 1975. q. NZ.$160 (overseas NZ.$170) (effective 1994). Legal Research Foundation, University of Auckland, Private Bag, Auckland, New Zealand. TEL 09-3099540. FAX 09-3737473. (Subscr. to: P.O. Box 741, Auckland, New Zealand; Dist. in N. America by: Wm. W. Gaunt & Sons, Inc., Gaunt Bldg., 3011 Gulf Dr., Holmes Beach, FL 34217-2199. TEL 813-778-5211. FAX 813-778-5252) Ed. Paul Rishworth. adv.; index; circ. 1,000 (paid). (back issues avail.) **Document type:** academic/scholarly publication.
   Formerly (until 1989): New Zealand Recent Law (ISSN 0110-2095)
   Description: Publishes research on recent law and comments on new law.

NEW ZEALAND SUPERANNUATION GUIDE. see BUSINESS AND ECONOMICS — Public Finance, Taxation

NEW ZEALAND TAX CASES. see BUSINESS AND ECONOMICS — Public Finance, Taxation

NEW ZEALAND TAX REPORTS. see BUSINESS AND ECONOMICS — Accounting

340 NZ ISSN 0549-0618
NEW ZEALAND UNIVERSITIES LAW REVIEW. 1963. s-a. NZ.$65($40) Oxford University Press - New Zealand, P.O. Box H-149, Auckland 5, New Zealand. TEL 64-9-523-3134. FAX 64-9-524-6723. adv.; bk.rev.; cum.index. circ. 700. (back issues avail.) **Indexed:** C.L.I., Leg.Per.
—BLDSC (6099.600000); UnCover. CCC.
   Description: Publishes articles on all topics of legal interest, and notes significant new legislation, as well as providing case notes.

340 US
NEWBERG ON CLASS ACTIONS, 2-E. 1985. 5 base vols. (plus s-a. supplements). $475 price varies. Shepard's - McGraw-Hill, Inc., Box 35300, Colorado Springs, CO 80935-3530. TEL 800-525-2474. Ed. Herbert Newberg. cum.index.
   Description: Provides current class action decisions and rules at federal and state levels.

340 CN ISSN 0715-4755
NEWFOUNDLAND & PRINCE EDWARD ISLAND REPORTS. 1970. irreg., latest vol.105. Can.$133 per vol. Maritime Law Book Ltd., Box 302, Fredericton, NB E3B 4Y9, Canada. TEL 506-453-9921; 800-561-0220. FAX 506-453-9525. (back issues avail.)
   ●Also available online. Vendor(s): QL Systems Ltd.
   Description: Includes all of the judgments of the Newfoundland Court of Appeal and the Prince Edward Island Court of Appeal plus selected trial court judgments.

NEWS MEDIA AND THE LAW. see JOURNALISM

340 US
NEWZ LETTER. 1976. q. $20 (effective 1993). Freedom Lawyers of America, Box 309, South Haven, MI 49090-0309. TEL 616-637-6557. FAX 616-637-6557. Ed. Sheldon R. Waxman. circ. 20. (back issues avail.) **Document type:** newsletter.

349 GW ISSN 0028-9787
NIEDERSAECHSISCHER STAATSANZEIGER. 1945. w. DM.65. (Ministerium der Justiz) Schluetersche Verlagsanstalt GmbH and Co., Hans-Boeckler-Allee 7, 30173 Hannover, Germany. TEL 0511-1236-0. (Subscr. to: Postfach 5440, 30054 Hannover, Germany) adv.; bk.rev. circ. 2,095.

340 NR ISSN 0189-207X
K14
NIGERIAN CURRENT LAW REVIEW. (Text in English) 1982. a. $80. Nigerian Institute of Advanced Legal Studies, University of Lagos Campus, P.M.B. 12820, Lagos, Nigeria. FAX 825558. TELEX 27506-NIALS-NG. Ed. M.A. Ajomo. bk.rev. circ. 2,000. (back issues avail.)
   Description: Carries a digest of all the legislation, both Federal and State, throughout the country with reports of important decisions of the Superior Courts with commentary.

340 NR ISSN 0048-0401
NIGERIAN JOURNAL OF CONTEMPORARY LAW. 1970. 3/yr. EAs.21. University of Lagos, Faculty of Law, P.O. Box 12003, Lagos, Nigeria. Ed.Bd. bibl.

370.26 JA
NIHON KYOIKUHO GAKKAI NENPO. Added title: Educational Law Review. 1972. a. 1000 Yen. (Nihon Kyoikuho Gakkai - Japan Society for Education Law) Yuhikaku Publishing Co. Ltd., 2-17 Kanda Jimbocho, Chiyoda-ku, Tokyo 101, Japan. circ. 2,000.

340 NE ISSN 0924-4549
NIJHOFF LAW SPECIALS. (Text in English) 1984. irreg. price varies. Kluwer Academic Publishers, Postbus 17, 3300 AA Dordrecht, Netherlands. TEL 31-78-334911. FAX 31-78-334254. TELEX 29245 KAPG NL. (Dist. by: Kluwer Academic Publishers, P.O. Box 322, 3300 AH Dordrecht, Netherlands. TEL 31-78-524400. FAX 31-78-524474; N. America dist. addr.: Box 358, Accord Sta., Hingham, MA 02018-0358. TEL 617-871-6600. FAX 617-871-6528) **Document type:** monographic series.
   Refereed Serial

340 CE
NITI VIMAMSA. (Text in Sinhalese) a. Rs.12. Sri Lanka Nitivedi Shishya Sanvidhanaya, Sevana, Seeduwa North, Sri Lanka.

340 CE
NITIVIDYA. (Text in Sinhalese) q. Rs.3 per no. Nitividya Study Circle, 80 Sanchi Arachchige Watta, Colombo 12, Sri Lanka.

NOISE REGULATION REPORT. see ENVIRONMENTAL STUDIES — Pollution

340 US ISSN 0890-2208
K14
NOLO NEWS; consumer and legal information for everyone. 1980. q. $12 (foreign $30). Nolo Press, Inc., 950 Parker St., Berkeley, CA 94710. TEL 510-549-1976. FAX 510-548-5902. Ed. Mary Randolph. bk.rev.; software rev. circ. 100,000. (tabloid format) **Document type:** newspaper.
—CCC.
   Description: Self-help articles on wide variety of legal matters, including consumer issues, small business, wills and estate planning, family law, taxes, zoning and more.

340 GR
NOMIKO VEMA. 1953. m. Dr.7500. Athens Bar Association, 60 Odos Academia, 106 79 Athens, Greece. TEL 361-4289-290. FAX 36-10-537. **Indexed:** ELLIS.

340 NO ISSN 0029-1315
NORDISK DOMSSAMLING; a collection of cases from the supreme courts of the Scandinavian countries. (Text in Danish, Norwegian, Swedish) 1958. q. NOK 510 in the Nordic countries; elsewhere NOK 585. Scandinavian University Press, P.O. Box 2959-Toeyen, N-0608 Oslo, Norway. TEL 472-67-7600. FAX 472-67-7575. (U.S. addr.: Scandinavian University Press, 200 Meacham Ave., Elmont, NY 11003. TEL 516-352-7300) Ed.Bd. adv.; index. circ. 1,000.
   Description: Presents a collection of verdicts passed by the Danish, Finnish, Icelandic, Norwegian and Swedish Supreme Courts in areas of legal cooperation within the Nordic countries.

364 NO ISSN 0349-1730
NORDISK KRIMINOLOGI; nyhetsbrev. 1975. irreg. (3-4/yr.) Nordisk Samarbedsraad for Kriminologi - Scandinavian Research Council for Criminology, University of Oslo, Faculty of Law, Department of Criminology, Karl Johans gt. 47, N-0162 Oslo, Norway. TEL 47-22-85-93-28. FAX 47-22-85-93-40. Ed. Annika Snare.

340 SW ISSN 0300-3094
DL1
NORDISK STATUTSAMLING. (Subseries of: Nordisk Utredningsserie) (Text in Danish, Finnish, Icelandic, Norwegian, or Swedish) 1970. a. Nordisk Raad, P.O. Box 19506, S-104 32 Stockholm, Sweden.

340 SW ISSN 0281-319X
NORDISKA RETTSHISTORISKA NYHETER/JOURNAL DE LA SOCIETE NORDIQUE D'HISTOIRE DU DROIT. Variant title: N.R.N. (Text in French, Swedish) 1983. 2/yr. Nordiska Rettshistoriska Nyheter, c/o K.A. Modeer, P.O. Box 1165, S-221 05 Lund, Sweden.

340 NO ISSN 0085-4220
NORDISKE DOMME I SJOEFARTSANLIGGENDER. 1900. irreg. NOK 80. Nordisk Skibsrederforening, Kristinelundvei 22, 0207 Oslo 2, Norway. adv.; index, cum.index every 10 yrs. circ. 900. (tabloid format)

340 GW ISSN 0932-710X
NORDRHEIN-WESTFAELISCHE VERWALTUNGSBLAETTER; Zeitschrift fuer Oeffentliches Recht und Oeffentliche Verwaltung. 1987. m. DM.285.60. Richard Boorberg Verlag (Stuttgart), Scharrstr. 2, 70563 Stuttgart, Germany. TEL 0711-7385-0. bibl.; index. (back issues avail.) **Document type:** bulletin.

340 GW
NORDRHEIN-WESTFALEN. JUSTIZMINISTERIALBLATT. m. DM.60. Karl-Heinz Junge GmbH Druckerei u. Verlag, Sessenbergstr. 2, 45127 Essen, Germany.

349 NO ISSN 0029-2060
NORSK RETSTIDENDE. 1836. 23/yr. NOK 900. Advokatenes Servicekontor - Norwegian Bar Association, Kr. Augustsgt. 0164, 0153 Oslo 1, Norway. Ed. Hans Stenberg-Nilsen. adv.; index, cum.index.

340 331 US ISSN 1054-6359
NORTH CAROLINA EMPLOYMENT LAW LETTER. 1991. m. $95. (Womble, Carlyle, Sandrige & Rice) M. Lee Smith Publishers & Printers, 162 Fourth Ave., N., Box 198867, Nashville, TN 37219-8867. TEL 615-242-7395; 800-274-6774. FAX 615-256-6601. Eds. David A. Irvin, Richard L. Rainey. **Document type:** newsletter.
   Description: Reports the latest state-specific employment law developments that affect North Carolina employers.

340 613.1 US ISSN 1047-4633
NORTH CAROLINA ENVIRONMENTAL LAW LETTER. 1990. m. $137. (Womble, Carlyle, Sandridge & Rice) M. Lee Smith Publishers & Printers, 162 Fourth Ave., N., Box 198867, Nashville, TN 37219-8867. TEL 615-242-7385; 800-274-6774. FAX 615-256-6601. Eds. R. Howard Grubbs, Martin L. Holton, III. **Document type:** newsletter.
   Description: Reports the latest state-specific environmental law developments that affect North Carolina companies.

340 US
NORTH CAROLINA LAWYER. bi-m. North Carolina Bar Association, Box 12806, Raleigh, NC 27605-2806. TEL 919-828-0561. FAX 919-821-2410. Ed. Clifton Barnes. adv. contact: Terri Miller. circ. controlled. (tabloid format) **Document type:** trade publication.
   Formerly: North Carolina Bar Association. Bar Notes.

340 US
NORTH CAROLINA LAWYERS WEEKLY. 1988. w. $195. Lawyers Weekly Publications, Inc., Box 27566, Raleigh, NC 27611-7566. TEL 919-829-9333. FAX 919-829-8088. Ed. Michael Dayton. adv. circ. 3,071.
   Description: Contains recent court opinions from local and state courts. Reports news of the legal community and issues relevant to the state.

340 US
NORTH CAROLINA NOTARY LAW PRIMER. a. $9.95. National Notary Association, 8236 Remmet Ave., Box 7184, Canoga Park, CA 91309-7184. TEL 818-713-4000. FAX 818-713-9061. Ed. Charles N. Faerber. **Document type:** monographic series.

LAW

340 US
NORTH CAROLINA STATE BAR NEWSLETTER. vol.18, 1993. q. $6 to non-members. North Carolina State Bar, Box 25908, Raleigh, NC 27611. TEL 919-828-4620. Ed. Jennifer Eichenberger. **Document type:** newsletter.
Description: Covers news and developments of interest to the legal profession in North Carolina.

340 US ISSN 0164-6850
KF200
NORTH CAROLINA STATE BAR QUARTERLY. 1954. q. $10. North Carolina State Bar, Box 25908, Raleigh, NC 27611. TEL 919-828-4620. Ed. Jennifer Eichenberger. adv.; bk.rev.; illus. circ. 12,500. (also avail. in microform from UMI; reprint service avail. from UMI) **Indexed:** C.L.I., L.R.I., Leg.Per.
—Faxon; UnCover.
Formerly (until 1978): North Carolina Bar (ISSN 0048-0657)

340 US
NORTH DAKOTA. STATE BAR BOARD. DIRECTORY OF LAWYERS AND JUDGES. a. $10. State Bar Board, Judicial Wing, 1st Fl., 600 E. Boulevard Ave., Bismarck, ND 58505-0530. TEL 701-224-4201. **Document type:** directory.
Former titles: North Dakota Directory of Lawyers and Judges; North Dakota Directory of Judges and Attorneys; Directory of North Dakota Lawyers.

340 US ISSN 0029-2745
NORTH DAKOTA LAW REVIEW. 1927. q. $20 (effective Mar. 1994). (State Bar Association of North Dakota) University of North Dakota, School of Law, Grand Forks, ND 58201. TEL 701-777-2941. FAX 701-777-2217. Ed. Tamara Yon. adv.; bk.rev.; index. circ. 2,000. (also avail. in microfiche from WSH,PMC; microfilm from WSH,PMC; reprint service avail. from WSH) **Indexed:** C.L.I., L.R.I., Leg.Cont., Leg.Per., Sel.Water Res.Abstr. **Document type:** academic/scholarly publication.
●Also available online. Vendor(s): West Services, Inc.
—BLDSC (6149.392000); Faxon; UnCover.

340 US ISSN 0734-1490
K14
NORTHERN ILLINOIS UNIVERSITY LAW REVIEW. 1980. 3/yr. $18. Northern Illinois University, College of Law, DeKalb, IL 60115. TEL 815-753-0619. bk.rev. circ. 535. (also avail. in microform from WSH; reprint service avail. from WSH) **Indexed:** C.L.I., Crim.Just.Abstr., L.R.I., Leg.Cont., Leg.Per.
—BLDSC (6151.005900); Faxon; UnCover.

340 UK
NORTHERN IRELAND LAW REPORTS. 1925. q. £40. Incorporated Council of Law Reporting for Northern Ireland, Bar Library, Royal Courts of Justice, Belfast BT1 3JX, N. Ireland. Ed. Gillian Kerr. circ. 700. (back issues avail.)

340 UK ISSN 0029-3105
K14
NORTHERN IRELAND LEGAL QUARTERLY. 1937. q. £47.50. S L S Legal Publications, School of Law, Belfast BT7 1NN, N. Ireland. TEL 0232-245133. FAX 0232-247895. Ed. P. Ingram. adv.; bk.rev.; index, cum.index: vols.1-14. circ. 700. **Indexed:** Abstr.Bk.Rev.Curr.Leg.Per., C.L.I., ELLIS, L.R.I., Leg.Per. **Document type:** bulletin.
—BLDSC (6151.012000); UnCover.

340 US ISSN 0198-8549
K14
NORTHERN KENTUCKY LAW REVIEW. 1973. 3/yr. $15. Northern Kentucky University, Salmon P. Chase College of Law, Highland Heights, KY 41076. TEL 606-572-5444. Ed. Marla Merdinger. adv.; bk.rev. circ. 2,500. (also avail. in microform from UMI; reprint service avail. from UMI) **Indexed:** C.L.I., L.R.I., Leg.Cont., Leg.Per., P.A.I.S.
●Also available online. Vendor(s): West Services, Inc.
—BLDSC (6151.013550); Faxon; UnCover; UMI.
Formerly: Northern Kentucky State Law Forum.

340 CN ISSN 0824-3433
NORTHWEST TERRITORIES REPORTS. 1983. 4/yr. (in 1 vol.). Can.$118. Carswell, One Corporate Plaza, 2075 Kennedy Rd., Scarborough, ON M1T 3V4, Canada. TEL 416-609-8000. FAX 416-298-5094. Ed.Bd. adv. contact: M. Lalani. cum.index. circ. 300.
Description: Provides full-text of all significant decisions of the courts of the Northwest Territories fully headnoted and indexed.

340 US ISSN 0029-3571
K14
NORTHWESTERN UNIVERSITY LAW REVIEW. 1906. q. $30 (foreign $33) (effective 1994). Northwestern University, School of Law - Office of Legal Publications, 357 E. Chicago Ave., Chicago, IL 60611. TEL 312-503-8467. adv.; bk.rev.; charts; index. circ. 1,200. (also avail. in microfiche from RRI,WSH; microfilm from BHP,RRI,UMI,WSH; reprint service avail. from RRI) **Indexed:** A.B.C.Pol.Sci., Abstr.Bk.Rev.Curr.Leg.Per., BPIA, Bus.Ind., C.L.I., Crim.Just.Abstr., Curr.Cont., L.R.I., Lang.& Lang.Behav.Abstr., Leg.Per., P.A.I.S., Sage Pub.Admin.Abstr., SSCI.
●Also available online. Vendor(s): Mead Data Central, Inc., West Services, Inc.
—BLDSC (6152.045000); Faxon; UnCover; SWETS; UMI.
Formerly (until 1952): Illinois Law Review.

349 IT ISSN 0029-3857
NOTARO; periodico quindicinale di libera discussione, organo della classe notarile. 1912. s-m. L.60000 (effective Jan. 1992). Massime, Via Alberico II, 35, 00193 Rome, Italy. TEL 06-5818725. Ed. Massimo Panvini Rosati. bk.rev.; bibl.; index. circ. 3,200. (tabloid format)
Description: Covers civil law, notarial class.

347.016 US
NOTARY PUBLIC PRACTICES & GLOSSARY. 1978. biennial. $17.95. National Notary Association, 8236 Remmet Ave., Box 7184, Canoga Park, CA 91309-7184. TEL 818-713-4000. FAX 818-713-9061. Ed. Charles N. Faerber. (reprint service avail. from UMI) **Document type:** academic/scholarly publication.
Supersedes in part: Customs and Practices of Notaries Public and Digest of Notary Laws in the U.S.

340 US
NOTARY SEAL & CERTIFICATE VERIFICATION MANUAL. a. $49 (effective 1993). National Notary Association, 8236 Remmet Ave., Box 7184, Canoga Park, CA 91309-7184. TEL 818-713-4000. FAX 818-713-9061. Ed. Charles N. Faerber. **Document type:** catalog.

340 US
NOTER UP; an updated service and semi-annual newsletter on legal research and legal bibliography. 1986. s-a. $65. William S. Hein & Co., Inc., 1285 Main St., Buffalo, NY 14209. TEL 800-828-7571. FAX 716-883-8100. TELEX 91-209 WU 7 HEIN BUF. Ed. Donald J. Dunn. illus. **Document type:** newsletter.

NOTRE DAME JOURNAL OF LAW, ETHICS & PUBLIC POLICY. see PUBLIC ADMINISTRATION

340 US ISSN 0745-3515
NOTRE DAME LAW REVIEW. 1925. 5/yr. $28. University of Notre Dame, School of Law, Box 988, Notre Dame, IN 46556. TEL 219-631-7097. FAX 219-631-6371. (Dist. by: Darby Printing Company) Ed. Anthony J. Bellia, Jr. adv.; bk.rev. circ. 1,700. (also avail. in microform from RRI; microfiche from RRI; reprint service avail. from WSH) **Indexed:** Abstr.Bk.Rev.Curr.Leg.Per., C.L.I., Cath.Ind., Curr.Cont., L.R.I., Leg.Cont., Leg.Per., P.A.I.S., SSCI. **Document type:** academic/scholarly publication.
●Also available online. Vendor(s): West Services, Inc.
—BLDSC (6175.409000); Faxon; UnCover; SWETS; UMI.
Formerly (until 1982): Notre Dame Lawyer (ISSN 0029-4535)

340 US
NOTRE DAME STUDIES IN LAW AND CONTEMPORARY ISSUES. 1985. irreg., vol.3, 1990. price varies. University of Notre Dame Press, Notre Dame, IN 46556. TEL 219-631-6346. FAX 219-631-8148. (Orders to: Box 635, South Bend, IN 46624) **Document type:** academic/scholarly publication.

349.41 UK ISSN 0965-0660
K24
NOTTINGHAM LAW JOURNAL. 1977. a. £5. Nottingham Trent University, Nottingham Law School, Burton St., Nottingham NG1 4BU, England. TEL 0602-418418. FAX 0602-486489. (Dist. in N. America by: Wm. W. Gaunt & Sons, Inc., Gaunt Bldg., 2011 Gulf Dr., Homdes Beach, FL 34217-2199) Ed. Janet S. Ulph. adv.; bk.rev. circ. 1,000. **Indexed:** C.L.I., L.R.I., Leg.Per. **Document type:** academic/scholarly publication.
—BLDSC (6175.676000).
Supersedes (in 1991): Trent Law Journal (ISSN 0309-8990)

331 US ISSN 1049-0248
K14
NOVA LAW REVIEW. 1977. 3/yr. $25. Nova Law Review, 3305 College Ave., Fort Lauderdale, FL 33314. TEL 305-522-2300. Ed. Gail E. Ferguson. adv.; bk.rev. circ. 700. (also avail. in microform from WSH,PMC; back issues avail.; reprint service avail. from WSH) **Indexed:** C.L.I., Leg.Per.
●Also available online. Vendor(s): West Services, Inc.
—BLDSC (6179.090000); Faxon; UnCover.
Formerly: Nova Law Journal.

340 CN
NOVA SCOTIA BARRISTERS' SOCIETY. ANNUAL REPORT. a. Nova Scotia Barristers' Society, 1475 Hollis St., Halifax, NS B3J 3M4, Canada. TEL 902-422-1491. **Document type:** corporate report.

340 CN ISSN 0316-6325
KE361.N6
NOVA SCOTIA LAW NEWS. 1974. bi-m. Can.$60. Nova Scotia Barristers' Society, 1475 Hollis St., Halifax, NS B3J 3M4, Canada. TEL 902-422-1491. Ed. Helen MacDonnell. bk.rev.; index. circ. 1,800.
Description: Digests of decisions of Nova Scotia's courts and Nova Scotia legislation, and articles.

340 CN ISSN 0048-0983
LAW
NOVA SCOTIA REPORTS. 1970. irreg., latest vol.120. Can.$112 per vol. Maritime Law Book Ltd., Box 302, Fredericton, NB E3B 4Y9, Canada. TEL 506-453-9921; 800-561-0220. FAX 506-453-9525. Ed.Bd. (back issues avail.)
●Also available online. Vendor(s): QL Systems Ltd.
Description: Includes all of the judgments of the Nova Scotia Court of Appeal plus selected trial court judgments.

NOW HIRING; government jobs for lawyers. see OCCUPATIONS AND CAREERS

340 PL
NOWE PRAWO. 1945. m. $84. Wydawnictwo Prawnicze, Ul. Wisniowa 50, 02-520 Warsaw, Poland. (Dist. by: Ars Polona-Ruch, Krakowskie Przedmiescie 7, Warsaw, Poland)

NUCLEAR LAW BULLETIN. see ENERGY — Nuclear Energy

343 US ISSN 0360-7690
KF2138.A6
NUCLEAR REGULATION REPORTS. 1975. w. $2550. Commerce Clearing House, Inc., 4025 W. Peterson Ave., Chicago, IL 60646. TEL 312-583-8500.
Supersedes: Atomic Energy Law Reports.

341.484 US
NUEVA LEY DE INMIGRACION. (Text in Spanish) s-a. Latin American News and Book Inc., 614 Franklin St., Box 2109, Elizabeth, NJ 07207. TEL 908-355-8835. FAX 908-527-9160. Ed. Jose Tenreiro Napoles. adv.: B&W page $650; 10 x 10. circ. 50,000.
Description: Provides new amendments to immigration laws, information on where to go, what to do and other immigrant status matters.

349 IT ISSN 0029-6368
NUOVO DIRITTO; rassegna giuridica pratica. 1924. m. L.90000 (foreign L.130000) (effective Jan. 1993). Via Antonio Labriola, 64, 00136 Rome, Italy. TEL 06-39736327. FAX 06-85351547. (Subscr. to: Casella Postale 11-171, 00141 Roma-Montesacro, Italy) Ed. Vittoria Maffuccini Visco. adv.; bk.rev. (back issues avail.)

THE NURSE, THE PATIENT AND THE LAW; the journal of nursing law & risk management. see MEDICAL SCIENCES — Nurses And Nursing

NUTRITION LEGISLATION AND REGULATORY NEWS; a twice-monthly report of United States legislative, executive, and regulatory activities. see NUTRITION AND DIETETICS

340 SW ISSN 0282-9525
NYTT JURIDISKT ARKIV. AVD. 1 - RAETTSFALL FRAAN HOEGSTA DOMSTOLEN. 1874. 7/yr. SEK 968. Norstedts Juridik, P.O. Box 6472, S-113 82 Stockholm, Sweden.
●Also available online. Vendor(s): DAFA Data AB.

340 SW ISSN 0345-8792
NYTT JURIDISKT ARKIV. AVD. 2 - TIDSKRIFT FOER LAGSTIFTNING M.M. 1876. 3/yr. SEK 916 (effective 1994). Norstedts Juridik, P.O. Box 6472, S-113 82 Stockholm, Sweden.

340 BL
O A B - R J. REVISTA. 3/yr. Ordem dos Advogados do Brasil - Rio de Janeiro, Av. Mal. Camara, 210-6o, ZC-39 Rio de Janeiro, Brazil.

340 GW ISSN 0945-2176
▼**O L G - RECHTSPRECHUNG NEUE LAENDER**; fuer Brandenburg, Mecklenburg-Vorpommern, Sachsen, Sachsen-Anhalt, Thueringen. 1994. m. DM.198. (Oberlandesgerichte der Neuen Laender) C.H. Beck'sche Verlagsbuchhandlung, Wilhelmstr. 9, 80801 Munich, Germany. TEL 089-38189-338. FAX 089-38189398. TELEX 5215085-BECK-D. adv.: B&W page DM.2200, color page DM.3850; trim 260 x 186. circ. 2,500. Document type: bulletin.

340 GW ISSN 0940-2144
O L G REPORT DUESSELDORF. 1991. fortn. DM.300. Verlag Dr. Otto Schmidt KG, Unter den Ulmen 96-98, 50968 Cologne, Germany. TEL 0221-9373801. FAX 0221-93738941. Eds. H.H. Moehren, H.D. Komanek. Document type: bulletin.

340 GW ISSN 0941-9446
▼**O L G REPORT FRANKFURT.** 1992. fortn. DM.300. Verlag Dr. Otto Schmidt KG, Unter den Ulmen 96-98, 50968 Cologne, Germany. TEL 0221-9373801. FAX 0221-93738941. Ed. Th. Weigel. Document type: bulletin.

340 GW ISSN 0940-2152
O L G REPORT HAMM. 1991. fortn. DM.300. Verlag Dr. Otto Schmidt KG, Unter den Ulmen 96-98, 50968 Cologne, Germany. TEL 0221-9373801. FAX 0221-93738941. TELEX 8883381. Eds. W. Lepsien, M. Rehborn. Document type: bulletin.

340 GW ISSN 0940-2160
O L G REPORT KOELN. 1991. fortn. DM.300. Verlag Dr. Otto Schmidt KG, Unter den Ulmen 96-98, 50968 Cologne, Germany. TEL 0221-9373801. FAX 0221-93738941. TELEX 8883381. Eds. L. Jaeger, L. Schmude. Document type: bulletin.

340 GW ISSN 0941-9438
▼**O L G REPORT MUENCHEN.** 1992. fortn. DM.300. Verlag Dr. Otto Schmidt KG, Unter den Ulmen 96-98, 50968 Cologne, Germany. TEL 0221-9373801. FAX 0221-93738941. TELEX 8883381. Ed. K.M. Groll. Document type: bulletin.

O P A S T C O ROUNDTABLE; the magazine of ideas for small telephone companies. (Organization for the Protection and Advancement of Small Telephone Companies) see COMMUNICATIONS — Telephone And Telegraph

340 NR
OBAFEMI AWOLOWO UNIVERSITY. FACULTY OF LAW. LAW REPORT. 1972. q. $50 per set. Obafemi Awolowo University Press, Ltd., Ile-Ife, Nigeria. Ed. M.A. Owoade. adv. circ. 800.
Formerly: University of Ife. Faculty of Law. Law Report.

340 NR
OBAFEMI AWOLOWO UNIVERSITY LAW JOURNAL. 1987. a. $25. Obafemi Awolowo University Press Ltd., Ile-Ife, Nigeria. Ed. J.O. Fabunmi. circ. 1,000.

340 SA
OBITER. (Text in Afrikaans and English) 1979. s-a. R.60. University of Port Elizabeth, Faculty of Law, P.O. Box 1600, Port Elizabeth 6000, South Africa. TEL 27-41-5042199. FAX 27-41-5042574. Ed. Adriaan van der Walt. adv.; bk.rev. circ. 600. Indexed: Ind.S.A.Per. Document type: academic/scholarly publication.

340 CN ISSN 0029-7585
OBITER DICTA. 1927. 24/yr. Can.$40. (York University, Osgoode Hall Law School) Weller Publishing Co. Ltd., 412 Bloor St. W., Toronto, Ont., Canada. Ed. Stan Grmovsek. adv.; bk.rev.; abstr. circ. 1,500. (tabloid format) Indexed: C.L.I., L.R.I., Leg.Info.Manage.Ind.

340 US
OBJECTIONS AT TRIALS. 1990. irreg. $29.95. Butterworth Legal Publishers (Salem) (Subsidiary of: Reed Elsevier plc), 8 Industrial Way, Bldg. C, Salem, NH 03079. TEL 800-548-4001. FAX 603-898-9858. Eds. Ronald L. Carlson, Myron H. Bright.

950 340 US ISSN 0730-0107
OCCASIONAL PAPERS - REPRINT SERIES IN CONTEMPORARY ASIAN STUDIES. 1977. bi-m. $18 (foreign $24). University of Maryland School of Law, 500 W. Baltimore St., Baltimore, MD 21201. TEL 301-328-7579. Ed. Hungdah Chiu. circ. 800.
—BLDSC (6224.858700).

340 IT
OCCASIONI GIUDIZIARIE. 1978. bi-m. Via Anapo 29, 00199 Rome, Italy.

344.7 614 CN ISSN 0706-5019
OCCUPATIONAL HEALTH AND SAFETY LAW. 1977. m. Can.$340. Business Law Reporting Limited, Box 1762, Kingston, ON K7L 5J6, Canada. TEL 613-546-9163.

340 IS ISSN 0792-3279
OD MEIDA. 1983. bi-m. free to members. Israel Bar Central Committee, 10 Daniel Frish, Tel Aviv 64731, Israel. TEL 972-3-6918691. FAX 972-3-6918696. Ed. Yair Ben-David. adv. circ. 15,000.

O'DWYER'S WASHINGTON REPORT. see ADVERTISING AND PUBLIC RELATIONS

OECUMENE; international bibliography indexed by computer. see RELIGIONS AND THEOLOGY — Abstracting, Bibliographies, Statistics

340 352 GW ISSN 0029-8565
DER OEFFENTLICHE DIENST. 1946. DM.118. Carl Heymanns Verlag KG, Luxemburgerstr. 449, 50939 Cologne, Germany. TEL 0221-46010-0. FAX 0221-4601069. Document type: bulletin.

DIE OEFFENTLICHE VERWALTUNG; Zeitschrift fuer oeffentliches Recht und Verwaltungswissenschaft. see PUBLIC ADMINISTRATION

340 AU ISSN 0029-9251
OESTERREICHISCHE JURISTEN- ZEITUNG. 1946. s-m. S.2170. Manzsche Verlags- und Universitaetsbuchhandlung, Kohlmarkt 16, A-1014 Vienna, Austria. TEL 0222-531610. FAX 0222-53161-181. Ed. Herbert Steininger. adv.; bk.rev.; charts; index. circ. 3,800. (also avail. in microfilm; microfiche) Indexed: CERDIC, ELLIS. Document type: bulletin.
—BLDSC (6307.750000).
Description: For Austrian lawyers on all aspects of law.

340 AU ISSN 0029-9340
OESTERREICHISCHE NOTARIATS-ZEITUNG. 1859. m. S.810. (Oesterreichische Notariatskammer) Manzsche Verlags- und Universitaetsbuchhandlung, Kohlmarkt 16, A-1014 Vienna, Austria. TEL 0222-531610. FAX 0222-53161-181. Ed. Friedrich Stefan. bk.rev.; charts; index, cum.index: 1949-1973. circ. 1,700. (also avail. in microfilm; microfiche) Document type: bulletin.
Description: For the Austrian notary.

340 US ISSN 0173-1718
OESTERREICHISCHE ZEITSCHRIFT FUER OEFFENTLICHES RECHT UND VOELKERRECHT. SUPPLEMENT. 1971. irreg. price varies. Springer-Verlag, 175 Fifth Ave., New York, NY 10010. TEL 212-460-1500. FAX 212-473-6272. (Also: Berlin, Heidelberg, Tokyo and Vienna) (also avail. in microform from UMI; reprint service avail. from ISI) Indexed: ELLIS. Document type: academic/scholarly publication.
—UMI.
Formerly: Oesterreichische Zeitschrift fuer Oeffentliches Recht. Supplement (ISSN 0078-3552)

340 AU ISSN 0378-3073
K15 CODEN: OZORAA
OESTERREICHISCHE ZEITSCHRIFT FUER OEFFENTLICHES RECHT UND VOELKERRECHT/AUSTRIAN JOURNAL OF PUBLIC AND INTERNATIONAL LAW. (Text in English) 1914. 6/yr. (in 2 vols., 3 nos./vol.) DM.632($395) Springer-Verlag, Sachsenplatz 4-6, Postfach 89, A-1201 Vienna, Austria. TEL 0222-3302415. FAX 0222-3302426. (Subscr. in N. America to: Springer-Verlag New York, Inc., 44 Hartz Way, Secaucus, NJ 07096-2491. TEL 201-348-4033. FAX 201-348-4505) Ed.Bd. adv.; bk.rev.; index. (also avail. in microfilm from UMI; back issues avail.; reprint service avail. from ISI) Indexed: ELLIS. Document type: bulletin.
—SWETS. CCC.
Formerly: Oesterreichische Zeitschrift fuer Oeffentliches Recht. Neue Folge (ISSN 0029-9634)

340 AU ISSN 0029-9820
OESTERREICHISCHES ARCHIV FUER KIRCHENRECHT. 1896. 4/yr. $64. Verband der Wissenschaftlichen Gesellschaften Oesterreich, Lindengasse 37, A-1070 Vienna, Austria. TEL 932166. (Co-sponsor: Universitaet Wien, Rechts- und Staatswissenschaftliche Fakultaet, Institut fuer Kirchenrecht) Ed.Bd. circ. 450. Indexed: Amer.Hist.& Life (until 1991), CERDIC, Hist.Abstr. (until 1991).
—BLDSC (6311.700000).

OESTERREICHISCHES RECHT DER WIRTSCHAFT. see BUSINESS AND ECONOMICS

349 AU ISSN 0029-9952
OESTERREICHISCHES STANDESAMT; Fachzeitschrift fuer Personenstands-, Ehe- und Staatsbuergerschaftsrecht. 1947. m. S.300. Fachverband der Oesterreichischen Standesbeamten, Habsburgergasse 5, A-1010 Vienna, Austria. Ed. Ferdinand Deschka. adv.; bk.rev.; index, cum.index. circ. 1,800. (tabloid format)

364.1 362.7 SW ISSN 1101-2927
OEVERGREPP. 1989. q. SEK 60 membership (effective 1989). Riksfoerbundet Mot Sexuella Oevergrepp paa Barn (RMSOe), P.O. Box 19010, S-701 34 Oerebro, Sweden.

340 658 US ISSN 0730-3815
KF300.A1
OF COUNSEL; the monthly legal practice report. s-m. $325. Prentice Hall Law & Business, 270 Sylvan Ave., Englewood Cliffs, NJ 07632-2513. TEL 201-894-8484. FAX 201-894-8666. Eds. Steven Nelson, Larry Smith. adv.; stat.; index. circ. 1,228. (back issues avail.)
Description: Reports on all aspects of running a law office: practice development, technology, salaries.

OFFICE CENTRAL DES TRANSPORTS INTERNATIONAUX FERROVIAIRES. BULLETIN. see TRANSPORTATION — Railroads

OFFICE HEALTH AND SAFETY MONITOR. see OCCUPATIONAL HEALTH AND SAFETY

OFFICE MANAGEMENT NEWS. see BUSINESS AND ECONOMICS — Office Equipment And Services

OFFICIAL GUIDE TO U.S. LAW SCHOOLS. see EDUCATION — Higher Education

OHIO CRIMINAL LAW HANDBOOK. see CRIMINOLOGY AND LAW ENFORCEMENT

3300 LAW

340 331 US ISSN 1046-9206
KFO331.A15
OHIO EMPLOYMENT LAW LETTER. 1990. m. $95. (Denlinger Rosenthal & Greenberg) M. Lee Smith Publishers & Printers, 162 Fourth Ave. N., Box 198867, Nashville, TN 37219-8867. TEL 615-242-7395; 800-274-6774. FAX 615-256-6601. Eds. Dean E. Denlinger, Gary L. Greenberg. **Document type:** newsletter.
  Description: Reports the latest state-specific employment law developments that affect Ohio companies.

340 613.1 US ISSN 1052-4355
OHIO ENVIRONMENTAL LAW LETTER. 1990. m. $137. (Porter, Wright, Morris & Arthur) M. Lee Smith Publishers & Printers, 162 Fourth Ave. N., Box 198867, Nashville, TN 37219-8867. TEL 615-242-7395; 800-274-6774. FAX 615-256-6601. Ed.Bd. **Document type:** newsletter.
  Description: Reports the latest state-specific environmental law developments that affect Ohio companies.

OHIO ENVIRONMENTAL MONTHLY. see *ENVIRONMENTAL STUDIES*

340 US
OHIO LAWYER. 1987. bi-m. $24. Ohio State Bar Association, Box 16562, Columbus, OH 43216-6562. TEL 614-487-2050. Ed. Kate Hagan. circ. 23,000. (back issues avail.)

340 380 US
OHIO MOTOR VEHICLE LAWS. 1988. a. $15.95. Gould Publications, 1333 N. U.S. Hwy. 17-92, Longwood, FL 32750-3724. TEL 407-695-9500. FAX 407-695-2906. adv.; bk.rev. (looseleaf format)
  Description: Presents titles 45 and 55, plus traffic laws.

340 US ISSN 0094-534X
K15
OHIO NORTHERN UNIVERSITY LAW REVIEW. 1973. q. $20. Ohio Northern University, Pettit College of Law, Box 153, Ada, OH 45810. TEL 419-772-2248. adv.; bk.rev. circ. 1,400. (also avail. in microform from UMI,PMC; microfilm from WSH; reprint service avail. from WSH) **Indexed:** C.L.I., L.R.I., Leg.Per.
—BLDSC (6247.146000); Faxon; UnCover.

340 US ISSN 0744-8376
KF200
OHIO STATE BAR ASSOCIATION REPORT. 1928. w. $135. Ohio State Bar Association, Box 16562, Columbus, OH 43216-6562. TEL 614-487-2050. Ed. Kate Hagan. adv.; index. circ. 23,000. **Indexed:** C.L.I., L.R.I.
—UnCover.

340 US
OHIO STATE JOURNAL ON DISPUTE RESOLUTION. 1986. 2/yr. $15 (foreign $18). Ohio State University, College of Law, 1659 N. High St., Columbus, OH 43210-1391. TEL 614-292-7170. adv. circ. 400. **Indexed:** C.L.I., Leg.Per.
• Also available online. Vendor(s): West Services, Inc., Wilsonline.
  Description: A medium for the exchange of information between scholars and law practitioners concerning alternatives to traditional legal redress.

340 US ISSN 0048-1572
K15
OHIO STATE LAW JOURNAL. 1935. 5/yr. $35 (foreign $40). Ohio State University, College of Law, 1659 North High St., Columbus, OH 43210-1391. TEL 614-292-6829. bk.rev. circ. 1,800. (also avail. in microform from UMI; microfiche from WSH; microfilm from WSH; reprint service avail. from WSH) **Indexed:** Abstr.Bk.Rev.Curr.Leg.Per., C.C.L.P., C.L.I., L.R.I., Leg.Per., P.A.I.S., SSCI.
• Also available online. Vendor(s): Mead Data Central, Inc., West Services, Inc., Wilsonline.
Also available on CD-ROM.
—BLDSC (6247.280000); Faxon; UnCover; SWETS.
  Description: General law topics with one issue per year focusing on an annual symposium on banking or insurance law; also includes articles devoted to judges and judging.

OHIO TAVERN NEWS. see *BEVERAGES*

340 US ISSN 0739-0130
OHIO UNITED WAY. LEGISLATIVE BULLETIN. 1941. w. $54 to non-members; members $27. Ohio United Way, 16 E. Broad St., 8th Fl., Columbus, OH 43215. TEL 614-224-8146. FAX 614-224-6597. Ed. Judith Tieman Bird. s-a. index. circ. 800. (back issues avail.) **Document type:** bulletin.
  Description: Covers bills dealing with human service issues.

OIL AND GAS REPORTER. see *PETROLEUM AND GAS*

340 665.5 US ISSN 1055-9175
OIL SPILL U S LAW REPORT; legislation, litigation, regulations & enforcement actions. 1991. m. $927 (foreign $1150). Cutter Information Corp., 37 Broadway, Arlington, MA 02174. TEL 617-648-8700. FAX 617-648-8707. TELEX 650 100 9891 MCI UW. Ed. Amy M. Stolls. charts. (back issues avail.) **Document type:** newsletter.
• Also available online. Vendor(s): NewsNet (EVO6).
—CCC.
  Incorporates: Oil Spill Litigation News.
  Description: Covers developments in law, regulation, and judicial interpretation relating to oil spills in the US and the individual 50 states.

340 UK
O'KEEFE'S LAW OF WEIGHTS & MEASURES. 3/yr. $390. Butterworth & Co. (Publishers) Ltd. (Subsidiary of: Reed Elsevier plc), 88 Kingsway, London WC2B 6AB, England. TEL 71-405-6900. FAX 71-405-1332. (US addr.: Butterworth Legal Publishers, 90 Stiles Rd., Salem, NH 03079-9981. TEL 603-898-9664) Ed. Anthony A. Painter. (looseleaf format)
  Description: Reference source on the complex field of weights and measures law and practice.

340 UK
OKE'S MAGISTERIAL FORMULIST. 2 base vols. (plus updates 3/yr.). $370. Butterworth & Co. (Publishers) Ltd. (Subsidiary of: Reed Elsevier plc), 88 Kingsway, London WC2B 6AB, England. TEL 71-405-6900. FAX 71-405-1332. (US addr.: Butterworth Legal Publishers, 90 Stiles Rd., Salem, NH 03079-9981. TEL 603-898-9664) Ed. Stuart Baker. (looseleaf format)
  Description: Provides access to all the prescribed forms relating to proceedings in magistrates' courts and a comprehensive range of precedents for all statutory offences and many regulatory offences within the jurisdiction of magistrates' courts.

340 US
OKLAHOMA BAR JOURNAL. 1930. w. (except Aug.). $25. Oklahoma Bar Association, c/o Martha M. Snow, Dir. of Public Information, Box 53036, Oklahoma City, OK 73152. TEL 405-524-2365. FAX 405-524-1115. adv.; index, irreg. cum.index. circ. 13,500. (also avail. in microform from UMI,PMC; microfiche from WSH; reprint service avail. from UMI) **Indexed:** C.L.I., L.R.I., Law Ofc.Info.Svc., Leg.Per.
—UnCover; UMI.
  Formerly (until vol.50, Jan. 1979): Oklahoma Bar Association Journal (ISSN 0030-1655)

340 US
OKLAHOMA CITY UNIVERSITY LAW REVIEW. 1976. s-a. $18. Oklahoma City University, School of Law, 2501 N. Blackwelder, Oklahoma City, OK 73106. TEL 405-521-5280. Ed. Cindy Andrews. adv.; bk.rev. circ. 1,000. (also avail. in microform from PMC; microfilm from WSH; back issues avail.; reprint service avail. from WSH) **Indexed:** C.L.I., L.R.I., Leg.Per. **Document type:** academic/scholarly publication.
• Also available online. Vendor(s): West Services, Inc.

340 US
OKLAHOMA DISCOVERY PRACTICE MANUAL. 1987. base vol. (plus a. suppl.). $120. Butterworth Legal Publishers (Salem) (Subsidiary of: Reed Elsevier plc), 8 Industrial Way, Bldg. C, Salem, NH 03079. TEL 800-548-4001. FAX 603-898-9858. Ed. Charles W. Adams. (looseleaf format)
  Description: Contains the text of the Oklahoma Discovery Code and the Federal Rules on which the Code is based, plus analysis of leading cases, practice commentary describing techniques for effective use of the Code.

340 331 US ISSN 1066-1123
▼**OKLAHOMA EMPLOYMENT LAW LETTER.** 1993. m. $95. (Doerner, Stuart, Saunders, Daniel & Anderson) M. Lee Smith Publishers & Printers, 162 Fourth Ave. N., Box 198867, Nashville, TN 37219-8867. TEL 615-242-7395; 800-274-6774. FAX 615-256-6601. Ed.Bd. **Document type:** newsletter.
  Description: Reports the latest state-specific employment law developments that affect employers in Oklahoma.

340 US ISSN 0030-1752
LAW
OKLAHOMA LAW REVIEW. 1948. q. $25. University of Oklahoma, College of Law, 300 Timberdell Rd., Norman, OK 73019. TEL 405-325-5191. Ed. J. Matthew Thompson. adv.; bk.rev.; index. circ. 1,100. (also avail. in microform from MIM,PMC; microfilm from WSH; reprint service avail. from WSH) **Indexed:** Account.Ind. (1974-), C.L.I., Crim.Just.Abstr., L.R.I., Leg.Cont., Leg.Per. **Document type:** academic/scholarly publication.
• Also available online. Vendor(s): West Services, Inc.
—BLDSC (6253.100000); Faxon; UnCover.
  Description: Articles and student notes on all areas of state and federal law.

340 US
OKLAHOMA LIEN LAWS; mechanic's and oil and gas liens and claims against Public Works. base vol. (plus a. suppl.). $120. Butterworth Legal Publishers (Salem) (Subsidiary of: Reed Elsevier plc), 8 Industrial Way, Bldg. C, Salem, NH 03079. TEL 800-549-4001. FAX 603-898-9858. Ed. Charles W. Adams. (looseleaf format)
  Description: Covers all aspects of Oklahoma mechanic's lien laws from the perspective of subcontractors, contractors, property owners, lenders and sureties. Provides advice on how owners and contractors can manage construction projects so mechanic's liens may be avoided.

340 CN ISSN 0710-538X
K15
OMBUDSMAN JOURNAL. a. $40. International Ombudsman Institute, Faculty of Law, University of Alberta, Edmonton, AB T6G 2H5, Canada. TEL 403-492-3196.
  Description: Articles of interest to ombudsmen and students in the area of ombudsmanship.

ON THE LINE (OLYMPIA). see *COMMUNICATIONS — Telephone And Telegraph*

340 CN ISSN 0318-3556
ONTARIO ANNUAL PRACTICE. a. Can.$65. Canada Law Book Inc., 240 Edward St., Aurora, ON L4G 3S9, Canada. TEL 905-841-6472. FAX 905-841-5085.
  Formerly: Chitty's Ontario Annual Practice (ISSN 0084-8751)

340 CN ISSN 0827-3308
ONTARIO APPEAL CASES. 1984. irreg., latest vol.61. Can.$104 per vol. Maritime Law Book Ltd., Box 302, Fredericton, NB E3B 4Y9, Canada. TEL 506-453-9921; 800-561-0220. FAX 506-453-9525.
• Also available online. Vendor(s): QL Systems Ltd.
  Description: Contains all of the judgments of the Ontario Court of Appeal and the Ontario Divisional Court.

340 614 CN
ONTARIO ENVIRONMENTAL PROTECTION ACT ANNOTATED. base vol. (plus s-a. updates). Can.$112. Canada Law Book Inc., 240 Edward St., Aurora, ON L4G 3S9, Canada. TEL 905-841-6472. FAX 905-841-5085. Ed. Dianne Saxe. adv. contact: Mary Cull.
  Description: Explains the intentions and effects of the Act and its regulations.

340 610 CN
ONTARIO HEALTH AND SAFETY LAW; a comprehensive guide to the statute, case-law, policy and procedures. base vol. (plus s-a. updates). Can.$86. Canada Law Book Inc., 240 Edward St., Aurora, ON L4G 3S9, Canada. TEL 905-841-6472. FAX 905-841-5085. Ed. Norman A. Keith. adv. contact: Mary Cull. (looseleaf format)
  Description: Provides updates of statutory amendments, reviews and analyses of the right to refuse to do unsafe work, and of prosecutions under the Act. Also outlines the regulations covering W.H.M.I.S. and appeals of Ministry of Labour orders.

LAW

340   CN   ISSN 0845-4825
ONTARIO LAWYER'S PHONE BOOK (YEAR). a. Can.$37.50. Canada Law Book Inc., 240 Edward St., Aurora, ON L4G 3S9, Canada. TEL 905-841-6472. FAX 905-841-6472. Ed. Patricia Egan. **Document type:** directory.
   Formerly: Lawyer's Phone Book (Year) (ISSN 0317-8668)

340   CN   ISSN 0832-4840
ONTARIO LEGISLATIVE DIGEST SERVICE. 1985. 40/yr. Can.$465. Carswell, One Corporate Plaza, 2075 Kennedy Rd., Scarborough, ON M1T 3V4, Canada. TEL 416-609-8000. FAX 416-298-5094.
   Description: Provides an authoritative summary of all the most recent information regarding the progress of Bills through the Ontario legislature from First Reading to Royal Assent.

340   CN
ONTARIO LIMITATION PERIODS. s-a. Can.$85. Butterworths Canada Ltd., Part of the Reed Elsevier group, 75 Clegg Rd., Markham, ON L6G 1A1, Canada. TEL 905-479-2665. FAX 905-479-2826. (looseleaf format)
   Description: Guide to limitations of action and other statutory time limitations contained in the statutes of Ontario.

340   CN   ISSN 0318-7527
KEO866.4
ONTARIO MUNICIPAL BOARD REPORTS. 1972. bi-m. Can.$108. Canada Law Book Inc., 240 Edward St., Aurora, ON L4G 3S9, Canada. TEL 905-841-6472. FAX 905-841-5085. adv. contact: Mary Cull.

346.043   CN   ISSN 0382-5906
ONTARIO REAL ESTATE LAW GUIDE. m. Can.$540. C C H Canadian Ltd., 6 Garamond Ct., North York, ON M3C 1Z5, Canada. TEL 416-441-2992. FAX 416-444-9011. index.
   Description: Complete coverage of laws governing real estate transactions in Ontario. Texts of over 55 statutes and regulations.

340   CN   ISSN 0030-3089
ONTARIO REPORTS. 1931. w. Can.$105. (Law Society of Upper Canada) Butterworths Canada Ltd., Part of the Reed Elsevier group, 75 Clegg Rd., Markham, ON L6G 1A1, Canada. TEL 905-479-2665. FAX 905-479-2826.
   ●Also available online. Vendor(s): QL Systems Ltd.
   Incorporates: Ontario Weekly Notes.

340   CN   ISSN 0316-6031
ONTARIO SECURITIES LEGISLATION. irreg., 16th ed.; 1994. Can.$39.95. C C H Canadian Ltd, 6 Garamond Court, North York, ON M3C 1Z5, Canada. TEL 416-444-9011. FAX 800-461-4131.

340   CN   ISSN 0030-3127
ONTARIO STATUTE CITATOR. 4/yr. Can.$175. Canada Law Book Inc., 240 Edward St., Aurora, ON L4G 3S9, Canada. TEL 905-841-6472. FAX 905-841-5085. Ed. L.R. MacTavish. adv. contact: Mary Cull. (looseleaf format)

340   CN
ONTARIO STATUTE CITATOR CURRENT BILLS SERVICE. 5/yr. Can.$167. Canada Law Book Inc., 240 Edward St., Aurora, ON L4G 3S9, Canada. TEL 905-841-6472. FAX 905-841-5085. adv. contact: Mary Cull. (looseleaf format)

342   US   ISSN 0030-3429
OPEN FORUM.* 1923. bi-m. $20. American Civil Liberties Union (Southern California), 1616 Beverly Blvd., Los Angeles, CA 90026-5752. TEL 213-487-1720. FAX 213-480-3221. Ed. Rosa Martinez. adv.; illus. circ. 25,000. (tabloid format)

340   US   ISSN 0897-5698
KF200
ORANGE COUNTY LAWYER. 1958. m. Orange County Bar Association, 601 Civic Center Dr. W., Santa Ana, CA 92701-4002. TEL 714-541-6222. adv. contact: Trudy Levindofske.
   Former titles (until 1988): Orange County Bar Association. Bulletin (ISSN 0279-9243); O C B A Bulletin (ISSN 0473-1212)

340   PO   ISSN 0870-8118
ORDEM DOS ADVOGADOS. REVISTA. 1941. 4/yr. Ordem dos Advogados, Lg. S. Domingos 14, Lisbon, Portugal. **Indexed:** ELLIS.

340   US   ISSN 0196-2043
K15
OREGON LAW REVIEW. 1921. 4/yr. $20. University of Oregon, School of Law, Eugene, OR 97403-1221. TEL 503-346-3844. FAX 503-346-1564. Ed. Carson Bowler. adv.; bk.rev.; index. circ. 1,100. (also avail. in microfilm from RRI,WSH; back issues avail.; reprint service avail. from RRI) **Indexed:** C.L.I., L.R.I., Leg.Cont., Leg.Per., Mar.Aff.Bibl., Ocean.Abstr., Pollut.Abstr. **Document type:** academic/scholarly publication.
   ●Also available online. Vendor(s): West Services, Inc.
   —BLDSC (6281.500000); Faxon; UnCover.

340   US
OREGON NOTARY LAW PRIMER. a. $9.95. National Notary Association, 8236 Remmet Ave., Box 7184, Canoga Park, CA 91309-7184. TEL 818-713-4000. FAX 818-713-9061. Ed. Charles N. Faerber. (reprint service avail. from UMI) **Document type:** monographic series.

340   US   ISSN 0030-4816
KF200
OREGON STATE BAR BULLETIN. 1935. m. (10/yr.). $45 includes For the Record. Oregon State Bar, Box 1689, Lake Oswego, OR 97035-0889. TEL 503-620-0222. FAX 503-684-1366. Ed. Paul Nickell. adv.; bk.rev. circ. 11,000. (back issues avail.) **Indexed:** Law Ofc.Info.Svc. **Document type:** trade publication.
   —UnCover.

ORGANISATION; Zeitschrift fuer Leitungs- und Verwaltungsorganisation der sozialistischen Staatsorgans. see *PUBLIC ADMINISTRATION*

340   US
ORGANIZATION OF AMERICAN STATES. LEGAL NEWSLETTER.* 1982. q. $12. Organization of American States, Department of Legal Publications and Informatics, 1889 F St., N.W., Washington, DC 20006. Dir. Christian Garcia-Godoy. circ. 600. **Document type:** newsletter.

ORIENTERING. see *ADVERTISING AND PUBLIC RELATIONS*

340   PL   ISSN 0867-1850
ORZECZNICTWO SADOW POLSKICH. 1957. m. $100. (Polska Akademia Nauk, Instytut Nauk Prawnych) Wydawnictwo Naukowe P W N, Miodowa 10, 00-251 Warsaw, Poland. Ed. W. Czachorski. index. circ. 11,570.
   Formerly (until 1990): Orzecznictwo Sadow Polskich i Komisji Arbitrazowych (ISSN 0030-6061)

340   CN   ISSN 0030-6185
K15
OSGOODE HALL LAW JOURNAL. 1958. 4/yr. Can.$40 to individuals; libraries Can.$60. York University, Osgoode Hall Law School, 4700 Keele St., Rm. 310, North York, ON M3J 1P3, Canada. TEL 416-736-5354. FAX 416-736-5736. adv.; bk.rev.; index. circ. 1,100. (also avail. in microfilm from WSH,PMC; back issues avail.; reprint service avail. from WSH) **Indexed:** C.L.I., Crim.Just.Abstr., Ind.Can.L.P.L., L.R.I., Leg.Cont., Leg.Per. **Document type:** academic/scholarly publication.
   —BLDSC (6300.570000); Faxon; UnCover. **CCC.**

340   IT   ISSN 0030-6290
OSSERVATORE LEGALE;* periodico di informazione giuridico-forense. 1944. s-m. S. Migliarino, Via Canonico Rotolo, 90143 Palermo, Italy.

349   GW   ISSN 0030-6444
LAW
OSTEUROPA-RECHT. (Text in German; occasionally in English) 1955. q. DM.86 (students DM.68). (Deutsche Gesellschaft fuer Osteuropakunde) Deutsche Verlags-Anstalt GmbH, Postfach 106012, 70049 Stuttgart, Germany. TEL 0711-2631-0. FAX 0711-2631-292. Eds. D. Frenzke, A. Uschakow. adv.; bk.rev.; bibl.; index, cum.index. circ. 600. **Document type:** academic/scholarly publication.
   —CCC.

340   NZ   ISSN 0078-6918
K15
OTAGO LAW REVIEW. 1965. a. NZ.$32. Otago Law Review Trust Board, c/o Faculty of Law, University of Otago, P.O. Box 56, Dunedin, New Zealand. TEL 0064-3-479-8854. FAX 0064-3-479-8855. (Dist. in N. America by: Wm. M. Gaunt & Sons, Inc., Gaunt Bldg., 3011 Gulf Dr., Holmes Beach, FL 33510. TEL 813-7778-5211. FAX 813-778-4832) Ed. Michael S. Robertson. adv.; bk.rev. circ. 1,200. **Indexed:** C.L.I., L.R.I., Leg.Per., Manage.Cont. **Document type:** academic/scholarly publication.
   —BLDSC (6313.189400); Faxon; UnCover.
   Description: Articles of general legal interest to the New Zealand law community.

340   CN   ISSN 0048-2331
K15
OTTAWA LAW REVIEW. (Text in English, French) 1967. 3/yr. Can.$30. University of Ottawa, Faculty of Law, Common Law Section, 57 rue Louis Pasteur, Ottawa, ON K1N 6N5, Canada. TEL 613-564-2919. FAX 613-564-9800. adv.; bk.rev.; bibl.; index. circ. 850. (also avail. in microfiche from PMC; microfilm from WSH,PMC; reprint service avail. from WSH) **Indexed:** Abstr.Bk.Rev.Curr.Leg.Per., C.L.I., Ind.Can.L.P.L., L.R.I., Leg.Per., P.A.I.S.
   —BLDSC (6313.890000); Faxon; UnCover.
   Description: Covers all fields of law with particular interest in recent developments in Canadian law.

340   US
OUT-OF-STATE PRACTITIONERS DIVISION NEWSLETTER. irreg. (3-4/yr.). membership. Florida Bar, 650 Apalachee Pkwy., Tallahassee, FL 32399-2300. TEL 904-561-5628. circ. 865. **Document type:** newsletter.

341   UK   ISSN 0143-6503
K15
OXFORD JOURNAL OF LEGAL STUDIES. 1981. 4/yr. £66($130) (effective 1994). Oxford University Press, Oxford Journals, Walton St., Oxford OX2 6DP, England. TEL 0865-56767. FAX 0865-56646. TELEX 837330-OXPRES-G. (U.S. subscr. to: Oxford University Press Inc., 2001 Evans Rd., Cary, NC 27513. TEL 919-677-0977) Ed. J. Eekelaar. adv. contact: Jane Parker. bk.rev.; index. circ. 950. **Indexed:** C.L.I., Leg.Per. **Document type:** academic/scholarly publication.
   —BLDSC (6321.005850); Faxon; UnCover; SWETS; UMI. **CCC.**
   Description: Examines the theory and issues arising from the relationship of law to other disciplines, with an emphasis on legal philosophy and socio-legal matters.

OXY-FUEL NEWS. see *ENERGY*

340   CN   ISSN 0475-1671
OYEZ. 1970. irreg. University of Windsor, Faculty of Law, Student Law Society, Windsor, Ont. N9P 3P4, Canada. TEL 519-253-4232. illus.

340   CN   ISSN 0842-4551
P L I A N NEWS. 1987. irreg. free. Public Legal Information Association of Newfoundland, P.O. Box 1064, Sta. C, St. John's, NF A1C 5M5, Canada. TEL 709-722-2643. FAX 709-722-8902. Ed. Peter Ringrose. circ. 15,000.

P L L PERSPECTIVES. (Private Law Libraries) see *LIBRARY AND INFORMATION SCIENCES*

340 614.7   US   ISSN 0738-6206
K16
PACE ENVIRONMENTAL LAW REVIEW. 1983. s-a. $30. Pace University, School of Law, 78 N. Broadway, White Plains, NY 10603. Ed.Bd. bk.rev. circ. 200. (also avail. in microform from WSH; back issues avail.; reprint service avail. from WSH) **Indexed:** C.L.I., Environ.Abstr., Ind.Per.Art.Relat.Law, Leg.Per.
   —Faxon; UnCover.

340   US   ISSN 0272-2410
K16
PACE LAW REVIEW. 1979. 3/yr. $20. Pace University, School of Law, 78 N. Broadway, White Plains, NY 10603. adv.; bk.rev. circ. 700. (also avail. in microfiche from WSH,PMC; microfilm from WSH,PMC; back issues avail.; reprint service avail. from WSH) **Indexed:** Abstr.Bk.Rev.Curr.Leg.Per., C.L.I., L.R.I., Leg.Cont., Leg.Per.
   —BLDSC (6328.226000); Faxon; UnCover.

3302 LAW

340   US   ISSN 0030-8757
LAW
PACIFIC LAW JOURNAL. 1970. q. $20. (University of the Pacific, McGeorge School of Law) Western Newspaper Publishing, Co., 3200 Fifth Ave., Sacramento, CA 95817. TEL 916-739-7171. adv.; bk.rev. circ. 3,200. (tabloid format; also avail. in microfilm from RRI,WSH; reprint service avail. from RRI) Indexed: C.L.I., Crim.Just.Abstr., L.R.I., Leg.Cont., Leg.Per., Mar.Aff.Bibl. **Document type:** academic/scholarly publication.
 • Also available online. Vendor(s): West Services, Inc. —BLDSC (6330.050000); Faxon; UnCover; UMI.

PAKISTAN. NATIONAL ASSEMBLY. DEBATES. OFFICIAL REPORT. see *PUBLIC ADMINISTRATION*

340   PK   ISSN 0078-785X
LAW
PAKISTAN ANNUAL LAW DIGEST. (Text in English) 1947. a. Rps.750. P.L.D. Publishers, 35 Nabha Rd., Lahore 1, Pakistan. TEL 92-42-213497. (back issues avail.; reprint service avail. from UMI)

340 331   PK   ISSN 0030-994X
LAW
PAKISTAN LABOUR CASES; a monthly law journal containing cases on service laws and labour laws. 1960. m. Rs.1000($55) (effective 1993). P.L.D. Publishers, 35 Nabha Rd., Lahore 1, Pakistan. TEL 92-42-213497. Ed. Malik Muhammad Saeed. (back issues avail.)

340   PK
PAKISTAN LAW JOURNAL. (Text in English, Urdu) 1973. m. Rs.480($30) Punjab Bar Council, 13 Fane Rd., Lahore, Pakistan. Ed. M. Bashir Chaudhri; Pub. Bashir Ahmad. adv. circ. 4,200. **Document type:** proceedings.
 Description: Judgements and decisions of the Superior Courts of Pakistan, and speeches of the judiciary.

PAKISTAN TAX DECISIONS; a comprehensive monthly journal of Pakistan on taxation. see *BUSINESS AND ECONOMICS — Public Finance, Taxation*

340   PL   ISSN 0031-0344
PALESTRA/BAR. m. $78. Wydawnictwo Prawnicze, Ul. Wisniowa 50, 02-520 Warsaw, Poland. (Dist. by: Ars Polona - Ruch, Krakowskie Przedmiescie 7, Warsaw, Poland)

340   II
PANJAB UNIVERSITY LAW REVIEW. (Text in English) 1951. s-a. Rs.50($10) Panjab University, Department of Laws, Chandigarh 160014, Union Territory, India. TEL 22577. Ed.Bd. adv.; bk.rev. circ. 1,000.

340   IO
PANTA-RHEI. 1975. irreg. University of North Sumatra, Faculty of Law - Universitas Sumatera Utara, Fakultas Hukum, Jalan Universitas 4, Medan, Indonesia.

340   US   ISSN 0011-8060
PAPER BOOK. 1913. 4/yr. $1. Delta Theta Phi Law Fraternity, International, 666 High St., Worthington, OH 43085. TEL 614-888-2600; 800-783-2600. FAX 614-888-7680. Ed. Michele Shuster. adv.; bk.rev.; illus.

340   AT
PAPUA NEW GUINEA LABOUR LAW. 1988. irreg. (approx. 2/yr.). C C H Australia Ltd., P.O. Box 230, North Ryde, N.S.W. 2113, Australia. TEL 02-888-2555. FAX 02-888-7324. (looseleaf format)

340   US   ISSN 0739-3601
KF320.L4
PARALEGAL; the publication for the paralegal profession. 1983. irreg., (approx. 6/yr.). $30 (foreign $37.50). National Paralegal Association, Box 406, Solebury, PA 18963. TEL 215-297-8333. FAX 215-297-8358. Ed. William Cameron. adv.; bk.rev. circ. 30,000. (reprint service avail. from WSH)

340 371.0025   US
PARALEGAL SCHOOL DIRECTORY. (State by state listings also avail.) 1983. a. $10. National Paralegal Association, Box 406, Solebury, PA 18963. TEL 215-297-8333. FAX 215-297-8358. Ed. William Cameron. **Document type:** directory.
 Description: Lists over 900 schools, colleges and institutions offering training in paralegal studies.

340   US   ISSN 0738-1247
KF8750.A15
PARASCOPE. 1979. q. $19. (American Bar Association, Committee of Appellate Staff Attorneys) A B A Press, 750 N. Lake Shore Dr., Chicago, IL 60611-4497. TEL 312-988-5700. Ed. Howie Zibel. bk.rev. circ. 500. **Document type:** newsletter.
 Description: Newsletter on matters concerning appellate courts.

PARIS. BULLETIN MUNICIPAL OFFICIEL - BULLETIN DEPARTEMENTAL OFFICIEL. see *PUBLIC ADMINISTRATION*

345   US   ISSN 0196-6138
KF192.C3
PARKER DIRECTORY OF CALIFORNIA ATTORNEYS. 1925. a. $25.45. Parker Publications, Division of Butterwoth Legal Publishers, Box 9040, Carlsbad, CA 92018-9040. Ed. Mary Redondo. adv. circ. 60,000. **Document type:** directory.
 Formerly: Parker Directory of Attorneys (ISSN 0079-0044)

346   UK   ISSN 0079-0095
PARLIAMENT HOUSE BOOK. 1824. 4/yr. (regular updating). W. Green, 21 Alva St., Edinburgh EH2 4PS, Scotland. Ed. P. Nicholson. (looseleaf format)

342 350.086   UK
PARLIAMENTARY HOUSING NEWS. w. £55 (foreign £75). (National Campaign for the Homeless) Shelter Publications, 88 Old St., London EC1V 9HU, England. TEL 071-253-0202. FAX 071-490-8918. **Document type:** newsletter.
 Formerly: Parliamentary News.
 Description: Housing issues in Britain.

340   BE   ISSN 0031-2614
PASICRISIE BELGE. (Text in French) 1814. m. 16500 BEF. Establissements Emile Bruylant, 67 rue de la Regence, B-1000 Brussels, Belgium. TEL 02-512-9845. index. circ. 1,000.
 —SWETS.

349   BE   ISSN 0031-2630
PASINOMIE. (Text in French) 1789. m. 22000 BEF. Establissements Emile Bruylant, 67 rue de la Regence, B-1000 Brussels, Belgium. TEL 02-512-9845. index. circ. 500.
 —SWETS.

340 325.1   US
PATEL'S IMMIGRATION LAW DIGEST. 5 base vols. (plus s-a. updates). $450. Clark - Boardman - Callaghan Company Ltd., 375 Hudston St., New York, NY 10014. TEL 212-929-7500; 800-221-9428. FAX 212-924-0460. Ed. Pravinchandra J. Patel.
 Description: Covers all significant federal judicial and administrative immigration law decisions dating from 1940. Provides a comprehensive research tool for lawyers concerned with the immigration and nationality laws of the United States.

PATENTS AND THE FEDERAL CIRCUIT. see *PATENTS, TRADEMARKS AND COPYRIGHTS*

PATENTS AND THE FEDERAL CIRCUIT. SUPPLEMENT. see *PATENTS, TRADEMARKS AND COPYRIGHTS*

340   UK   ISSN 0269-3658
PATERSON'S LICENSING ACTS. a. $216. Butterworth & Co. (Publishers) Ltd. (Subsidiary of: Reed Elsevier plc), 88 Kingsway, London WC2B 6AB, England. TEL 71-405-6900. FAX 71-405-1332. (US addr.: Butterworth Legal Publishers, 90 Stiles Rd., Salem, NH 03079-9981. TEL 603-898-9664) Ed. Matthew Pink.
 Description: Provides the legislation, regulations, orders and standard froms relating to the licensing of pubs, theatres, cinemas, restaurants, betting offices, competitions and lotteries.

340 658   US
PATIENT CARE LAW. bi-m. $275. Action Kit Publications, 1614 Fifth Ave., Pittsburgh, PA 15213. TEL 800-245-1205. Ed. John Horty. (looseleaf format)
 Description: Serves as a resource for nurse management and provides current legal analyses.

PATIENTS' RIGHTS REPORTER. see *HOSPITALS*

PAY AND BENEFITS BULLETIN. see *BUSINESS AND ECONOMICS — Labor And Industrial Relations*

PAYROLL ADMINISTRATION GUIDE. see *BUSINESS AND ECONOMICS — Labor And Industrial Relations*

PAYROLL ADMINISTRATION GUIDE NEWSLETTER. see *BUSINESS AND ECONOMICS — Labor And Industrial Relations*

PENNSYLVANIA BAR ASSOCIATION. ENVIRONMENTAL, MINERAL & NATURAL RESOURCES LAW SECTION. NEWSLETTER. see *ENVIRONMENTAL STUDIES*

PENNSYLVANIA CHAMBER OF BUSINESS AND INDUSTRY. CHECKLIST. see *PUBLIC HEALTH AND SAFETY*

PENNSYLVANIA CHAMBER OF BUSINESS AND INDUSTRY. TAX BULLETIN. see *BUSINESS AND ECONOMICS — Public Finance, Taxation*

PENNSYLVANIA EDUCATION LAW REPORT. see *EDUCATION*

340 331   US   ISSN 1052-4363
PENNSYLVANIA EMPLOYMENT LAW LETTER. 1990. m. $95. (Morgan, Lewis & Bockius) M. Lee Smith Publishers & Printers, 162 Fourth Ave., N., Box 198867, Nashville, TN 37219-8867. TEL 615-242-7395; 800-274-6774. FAX 615-256-6601. Eds. John E. Krampf, Harry Reagan. **Document type:** newsletter.
 Description: Reports the latest state-specific employment law developments that affect Pennsylvania companies.

340 613.1   US   ISSN 1072-9143
KFP354.A15
PENNSYLVANIA ENVIRONMENTAL COMPLIANCE UPDATE. 1989. m. $137. (Dechert Price & Rhoads) M. Lee Smith Publishers & Printers, 162 Fourth Ave., N., Box 198867, Nashville, TN 37219-8867. TEL 615-242-7395; 800-274-6774. FAX 615-256-6601. Ed. George Miller. bibl.; stat. (looseleaf format; back issues avail.) **Document type:** newsletter.
 Formerly (until 1994): Pennsylvania Environmental Law Letter (ISSN 1046-6568)
 Description: Reports on state-specific environmental law developments that affect companies in Pennsylvania.

340   US   ISSN 1065-0962
K16
PENNSYLVANIA LAW JOURNAL. 1977. w. (48/yr.). $150. Legal Communications, Ltd., 1617 JFK Blvd., Ste. 960, Philadelphia, PA 19103. TEL 215-563-2700. Ed. Fred Maher. adv. contact: David J. Cooper. bk.rev.; charts; stat.; index. circ. 2,500. (tabloid format; also avail. in microfilm; back issues avail.) Indexed: C.L.I., Hlth.Ind., L.R.I. **Document type:** newspaper.
 Former titles (until 1993): Pennsylvania Law Journal Reporter (ISSN 0279-8166); (until 1981): Pennsylvania Law Journal (ISSN 0160-8495)
 Description: Provides coverage of events and significant court decisions.

340   US
PENNSYLVANIA LAWYER. 1978. bi-m. $20. Pennsylvania Bar Association, 100 South St., Harrisburg, PA 17108. TEL 717-238-6715. FAX 717-238-7182. (Subscr. to: Box 186, Harrisburg, PA 17108) Ed. Donald C. Sarvey. adv.; circ. 30,000 (controlled). (back issues avail.) **Document type:** trade publication.
 Description: Covers legal trends of interest to practicing Pennsylvania attorneys.

LAW

340 US
PENNSYLVANIA MECHANICS' LIENS. 1990. base vol. (plus irreg. suppl.). $75. Butterworth Legal Publishers (Salem) (Subsidiary of: Reed Elsevier plc), 8 Industrial Way, Bldg. C, Salem, NH 03079. TEL 800-548-4001. FAX 603-898-9858. Ed. Michael G. Walsh. (looseleaf format)
  Description: Presents detailed account and explanation of every aspect of a lien claim.

340 US
PENNY RESISTANCE; economic and tax resistance to the death penalty. 1984. s-a. free. 8319 Fulham Court, Richmond, VA 23227-1712. TEL 804-266-7400. Ed. Jerome D. Gorman. circ. 200.

340.05 US ISSN 0092-430X
K16
PEPPERDINE LAW REVIEW. 1973. 4/yr. $25. Pepperdine University, School of Law, Malibu, CA 90265. TEL 213-456-4494. FAX 213-456-4266. Ed. Paul Wilkinson. adv.; bk.rev.; index. circ. 600. (also avail. in microfiche from WSH,PMC; microfilm from UMI,WSH,PMC; reprint service avail. from UMI) **Indexed:** C.L.I., Crim.Just.Abstr., L.R.I., Leg.Cont., Leg.Per., Mar.Aff.Bibl. **Document type:** academic/scholarly publication.
  ●Also available online. Vendor(s): West Services, Inc. —BLDSC (6422.953200); Faxon; UnCover; UMI.

340 US
THE PERFECT LAWYER. 1990. m. $110. Shepard's - McGraw-Hill, Inc., Box 35300, Colorado Springs, CO 80935-3530. TEL 719-488-3000. Ed. Robert P. Wilkins.

340 SP ISSN 0211-4526
K16
PERSONA Y DERECHO. 1975. 2/yr. 2800 ptas.($30) (Universidad de Navarra, Facultad de Derecho) Servicio de Publicaciones de la Universidad de Navarra, S.A., Apdo. 177, 31080 Pamplona, Spain. TEL 94 25 2700. Dir. Javier Hervada. bk.rev.

340 GW ISSN 0724-360X
DAS PERSONAL A B C; Arbeitsrecht - Lohnsteuer - Sozialversicherung. 1983. bi-m. DM.78. Wirtschaft Recht und Steuern Verlag, Fraunhoferstr. 5, 82152 Planegg, Germany. TEL 089-89517-0. FAX 089-89517250. (Subscr. to: Postfach 1363, 82142 Planegg, Germany) (looseleaf format) **Document type:** bulletin.

340 610 UK ISSN 0267-3894
PERSONAL AND MEDICAL INJURIES LAW LETTER. 1985. 10/yr. £145(£290) I B C Publishing, Gilmoora House, 57-61 Mortimer St., London W1N 7TD, England. TEL 071-637-4383. FAX 071-636-6414. (Subscr. in U.S. to: IBC (USA), 290 Eliot St., Box 91004, Ashland, MA 01721-9104. TEL 508-881-2800. FAX 508-881-0982) Ed. John Finch. bk.rev.; index. circ. 1,200. (looseleaf format; back issues avail.) **Document type:** newsletter. —BLDSC (6427.852000).

340 GW ISSN 0341-2792
PERSONAL-BUERO IN RECHT UND PRAXIS; Arbeitsrecht - Lohnsteuer - Sozialversicherung - Personalfuehrung - Organisation. 1969. m. DM.128. Rudolf Haufe Verlag GmbH & Co. KG, Hindenburgstr. 64, 79102 Freiburg, Germany. TEL 0761-3683-0. FAX 0761-3683-195. cum.index. (looseleaf format) **Document type:** trade publication.

340 CN
PERSONAL INJURY DAMAGE ASSESSMENTS IN ALBERTA. q. Can.$150. Butterworths Canada Ltd., Part of the Reed Elsevier group, 75 Clegg Rd., Markham, ON L6G 1A1, Canada. TEL 905-479-2665. FAX 905-479-2826. (looseleaf format)
  Description: Catalogues Alberta's judicial awards in motor vehicle accident cases since 1969.

340 CN
PERSONAL INJURY DAMAGE ASSESSMENTS IN BRITISH COLUMBIA. q. Can.$180. Butterworths Canada Ltd., Part of the Reed Elsevier group, 75 Clegg Rd., Markham, ON L6G 1A1, Canada. TEL 905-479-2665. FAX 905-479-2826. (looseleaf format)
  Description: Catalogues British Columbia's judicial awards in motor vehicle accident cases since 1962.

348.73 US
PERSONAL INJURY NEWSLETTER. 1967. fortn. $150. Matthew Bender & Co., 11 Penn Plaza, New York, NY 10001. TEL 212-967-7707. (Subscr. to: 1275 Broadway, Box 989, Albany, NY 12201) Ed. David A. Kaplan. index. circ. 2,315. (looseleaf format; back issues avail.)
  Description: Covers personal injury law, with emphasis on case reports. Includes law review reports and lawyers' medical reports for lawyers and medical professionals.

340 US ISSN 0031-5591
PERSONAL INJURY VALUATION HANDBOOKS; injury valuation & special research reports. 1959. m. $545. L R P Publications, 747 Dresher Rd., Box 980, Horsham, PA 19044. TEL 800-341-7874. (looseleaf format)
  Description: Information aided by the use of graphs and diagrams on injuries and liability in personal damage litigation.

PERSONAL INJURY VERDICT REVIEWS. see INSURANCE

PERSONNEL FORMS AND EMPLOYMENT CHECKLISTS. see BUSINESS AND ECONOMICS — Personnel Management

340 344.73 US ISSN 0888-9732
PERSPECTIVE (MADISON); the campus legal monthly. 1986. m. $147.50. Magna Publications, 2718 Dryden Dr., Madison, WI 53704. TEL 608-246-3580. FAX 608-249-0355. Ed. Dennis Black. circ. 1,300. (back issues avail.) **Document type:** newsletter.
  —CCC.
  Description: Focuses on legal issues for college and university administrators.

340 US ISSN 1062-1083
PERSPECTIVES (CHICAGO); a newsletter for and about women lawyers. 1991. s-a. $14. American Bar Association, Commission on Women in the Profession, 750 N. Lake Shore Dr., Chicago, IL 60611. FAX 312-988-5555. **Document type:** newsletter.

340 150 US ISSN 0160-4422
PERSPECTIVES IN LAW AND PSYCHOLOGY. 1977. irreg., vol.9, 1992. price varies. Plenum Publishing Corp., 233 Spring St., New York, NY 10013. TEL 212-620-8000. FAX 212-463-0742. TELEX 23-421139. Ed. Bruce Dennis Sales. bibl. **Document type:** monographic series.
  Refereed Serial

340 UK ISSN 1353-3541
▼**PERVASIVE TOPICS.** 1993. a. £15. Jordan Publishing Ltd., 21 St. Thomas St., Bristol BS1 6JS, England. TEL 0272-230600. FAX 0272-250486. Ed. Alison Baigent. **Document type:** academic/scholarly publication.

PESTICIDE LITIGATION MANUAL. see ENVIRONMENTAL STUDIES — Toxicology And Environmental Safety

340 364 AT ISSN 0158-2720
PETTY SESSIONS REVIEW. 1967. bi-m. Aus.$35. Petty Publishing Pty. Ltd., c/o Travelaw, 126 Phillip St., Level 7, Sydney, N.S.W., Australia. Ed. R.J. Bartley. adv.; cum.index. circ. 750. (back issues avail.)

PEYRON TAX LETTER & SOCIAL SECURITY REPORT. see BUSINESS AND ECONOMICS — Public Finance, Taxation

PHARMACEUTICAL ADMINISTRATION IN JAPAN. see PHARMACY AND PHARMACOLOGY

PHARMACY LAW DIGEST. see PHARMACY AND PHARMACOLOGY

340 US
PHILADELPHIA BAR ASSOCIATION. LEGAL DIRECTORY. 1880. a. $31. Legal Communications, Ltd., 1617 John F. Kennedy Blvd., Ste. 960, Philadelphia, PA 19103. TEL 215-557-2300. FAX 215-557-2301. Ed. Debra Shain. adv. circ. 27,500. **Document type:** directory.
  Description: Lists attorneys, law firms, and legal associations in the greater Philadelphia area.

340 CN ISSN 0316-3849
THE PHILANTHROPIST. 1972. q. Can.$40. (Canadian Bar Association, Ontario Branch) Agora Foundation, Becker Associates, 36 Bessemer Ct., No.3, Concord, ON L4K 3C9, Canada. TEL 905-669-5373. FAX 905-669-1927. Ed. John Gregory. adv.; bk.rev. circ. 500. (also avail. in microfilm from UMI; reprint service avail. from UMI) **Indexed:** Ind.Can.L.P.L. **Document type:** academic/scholarly publication.

340 PH ISSN 0031-7721
LAW
PHILIPPINE LAW JOURNAL. (Text in English) 1914. 4/yr. P.100($20) University of the Philippines, Law Publishing House, Diliman, Quezon City, Philippines. Ed. Eloisa D. Palazo. bk.rev.; index. circ. 821. (also avail. in microfilm from BHP,WSH,PMC; reprint service avail. from RRI,WSH) **Indexed:** C.L.I., Foreign Leg.Per., HR Rep., Ind.Phil.Per., Leg.Per. —BLDSC (6456.060000); UnCover.

340 PH ISSN 0115-7205
PHILIPPINE LAW REPORT. (Text in English) 1974. m. P.45($12) University of the Philippines, Law Publishing House, Diliman, Quezon City, Philippines.

PHILIPPINES YEARBOOK OF THE FOOKIEN TIMES. see BUSINESS AND ECONOMICS — Banking And Finance

340 US
PIRSIG ON MINNESOTA PLEADING. 1987. 2 base vols. (plus suppl.), latest 5th ed., 1991. $175. Butterworth Legal Publishers (Salem) (Subsidiary of: Reed Elsevier plc), 8 Industrial Way, Bldg. C, Salem, NH 03079. TEL 800-548-4001. FAX 603-898-9858. Ed. Maynard E. Pirsig.
  Description: Guide to pleading under the Minnesota Rules of Civil Procedure.

340 US ISSN 0032-0331
KFP52.P5
PITTSBURGH LEGAL JOURNAL. (Supplement avail.: Allegheny Lawyer) 1963. d. (5/wk.). $70. Allegheny County Bar Association, 436 7th Ave., Ste. 400, Pittsburgh, PA 15219-1818. TEL 412-261-6161. FAX 412-261-3622. Ed.Bd. adv.; bk.rev.; index. circ. 6,300. **Indexed:** Law Ofc.Info.Svc. **Document type:** newspaper.
  Description: Pittsburgh court opinions and announcements of importance to members of the association.

340 SZ
PLAEDOYER; das Magazin fuer Recht und Politik. (Text in French and German) 1976. bi-m. 110 SFr. (students 66 SFr.). Swiss Association of Democratic Lawyers, Postfach 421, CH-8026 Zurich, Switzerland. TEL 01-2423807. FAX 01-2910820. Ed. Catherine Boss. adv.; bk.rev. circ. 4,000. **Document type:** bulletin.
  Formerly (until 1983): Volk und Recht.

340 690 AT ISSN 0727-792X
PLANNING AND DEVELOPMENT SERVICE (NEW SOUTH WALES). 1980. 6/yr. in 2 vols. Aus.$345 with updates. Law Book Co. Ltd., 44-50 Waterloo Rd., N. Ryde, N.S.W. 2113, Australia. TEL 02-887-0177. FAX 02-888-9706. TELEX ASBOOK 27995. Ed. S. White. (looseleaf format)
  Formerly (until 1989): Building, Planning and Development Service (New South Wales) (ISSN 0727-7911)
  Description: Covers land and environment court, land subdivision and building, environmental and planning law.

PLANNING & ENVIRONMENT LAW SERVICE - VICTORIA. see ENVIRONMENTAL STUDIES

340 UK ISSN 1353-3630
▼**PLANNING AND ENVIRONMENTAL LAW.** 1994. a. £17.50. Jordan Publishing Ltd., 21 St. Thomas St., Bristol BS1 6JS, England. TEL 0272-230600. FAX 0272-250486. Ed. Malcolm Maddock. **Document type:** academic/scholarly publication.

347.91 UK ISSN 0268-3644
PLANNING APPEAL DECISIONS. 1985. bi-m. £215. Sweet & Maxwell, South Quay Plaza, 7th Fl., 183 Marsh Wall, London E14 9FT, England. TEL 071-538-8686. FAX 071-538-9508. Eds. Lyndsay Walker, W.G. Nutley. adv. contact: Jackie Wood. (reprint service avail. from RRI) **Document type:** bulletin.

LAW

POLICE MISCONDUCT AND CIVIL RIGHTS LAW REPORT. see *CRIMINOLOGY AND LAW ENFORCEMENT*

340 364 US
POLICE PLAINTIFF.* 1980. q. $35. North Publishing, 701 Warrenville Rd., Ste. 225, Lisle, IL 60532-1376. TEL 312-469-3211. Ed. Kenneth E. North. index. (back issues avail.)
  Description: Covers law suits brought by law enforcement personnel.

POLICIES, PRACTICES, AND EMPLOYEE BENEFITS SURVEY. see *BUSINESS AND ECONOMICS — Labor And Industrial Relations*

340 IT ISSN 0032-3063
POLITICA DEL DIRITTO. 1970. q. L.120000. Societa Editrice Il Mulino, Strada Maggiore, 37, 40125 Bologna, Italy. TEL 051-256011. FAX 051-256034. Ed. Stefano Rodota. adv.; cum.index. circ. 1,700. (tabloid format; back issues avail.) **Indexed:** P.A.I.S.For.Lang.Ind.

340 628.5 CN ISSN 0827-2123
POLLUTION LAW REPORTING SERVICE. 1972. m. Can.$290. Business Law Reporting Limited, Box 1762, Kingston, ON K7L 5J6, Canada. TEL 613-546-9163.

POLLUTION PREVENTION REVIEW. see *ENVIRONMENTAL STUDIES — Waste Management*

347.016 FR
POMPADOUR NOTARIAT 2000; revue independante d'animation et de promotion du notariat francais. 1956. m. 200 F. 19230 Pompadour, France. Ed. Louis Reillier. adv.; bk.rev.; illus.; stat.

340 US ISSN 0739-0203
PONTIAC - OAKLAND AND COUNTY LEGAL NEWS. 1927. w. $45. Pontiac-Oakland County Legal News Publishing Co., Inc., 500 W. Huron, Ste. 102, Box 430238, Pontiac, MI 48343-0238. TEL 313-338-4567. FAX 313-338-4240. Ed. Nancy L. Howarth. adv. contact: Jacqueline Talley. bk.rev. circ. 1,500. (back issues avail.) **Document type:** newspaper.

POPULAR GOVERNMENT. see *POLITICAL SCIENCE*

340 US
PORTAGE COUNTY LEGAL NEWS. 1981. d. (Mon.-Fri.). $50. John L. Burleson, Ed. & Pub., 60 S. Summit St., Akron, OH 44308-1775. TEL 216-747-7777. FAX 216-376-7001. (tabloid format) **Document type:** newspaper.

340 PO
PORTUGAL. MINISTERIO DA JUSTICIA. BOLETIM. no.241, 1974. a. Esc.19,000($120) Ministerio da Justica, Gabinete de Gestao Financeira, Of. Subdirector-Geral, Praca do Comercio, 1194 Lisbon Codex, Portugal. bk.rev.; bibl. circ. 5,500.

340 PL ISSN 0138-0508
PRACE POPULARNONAUKOWE. BIBLIOTECZKA PRAWNICZA. (Subseries of: Prace Popularnonaukowe (ISSN 0079-4805)) 1982. irreg., no.4, 1988. price varies. Towarzystwo Naukowe w Toruniu, Ul. Wysoka 16, 87-100 Torun, Poland. TEL 48-56-23941. TELEX 552388 FSBH PL. circ. 6,500.

340 UK
PRACTICAL CONVEYANCING PRECEDENTS. irreg. £80. Longman Group Ltd., Law, Tax and Finance Division, 21-27 Lambs Conduit St., London WC1N 3NJ, England. TEL 071-242-2548. FAX 071-831-8119. Ed. Trevor Aldridge. (looseleaf format) **Document type:** bulletin.
  Description: Conveyancing forms and precedents.

340 AT ISSN 0048-508X
PRACTICAL FORMS AND PRECEDENTS. 1957-1987; resumed 1990. 4/yr. in 2 vols. Aus.$315 (diskette Aus.$250). Law Book Co. Ltd., 44-50 Waterloo Rd., North Ryde, N.S.W. 2113, Australia. TEL 02-887-0177. FAX 02-888-9706. TELEX ASBOOK 27995. Ed. Ian Salmon. (looseleaf format; also avail. in diskette format)
  Description: Comprises a comprehensive set of precedents covering the entire range of commercial and property matters including revenue notes relevant to N.S.W.

340 610 US
PRACTICAL GUIDE TO PREVENTING LEGAL MALPRACTICE. 1983. base vol. (plus a. suppl.) $95. Shepard's - McGraw-Hill, Inc., Box 35300, Colorado Springs, CO 80935-3530. TEL 800-525-2474.
  Description: Offers practical ideas that can be implemented in everyday practice to reduce and eliminate malpractice risk.

340 US ISSN 0032-6429
K16
THE PRACTICAL LAWYER. 1955. 8/yr. $35. American Law Institute - American Bar Association, Committee on Continuing Professional Education, 4025 Chestnut St., Philadelphia, PA 19104. TEL 215-243-1604. FAX 215-243-1664. Ed. Mark T. Carroll. adv.; bk.rev.; illus.; index, cum.index every 5 yrs. circ. 7,500. (also avail. in microform from UMI; reprint service avail. from UMI) **Indexed:** Account.Ind. (1974-), Bank.Lit.Ind., C.L.I., L.I.I., L.R.I., Law Ofc.Info.Svc., Leg.Cont., Leg.Info.Manage.Ind., Leg.Per. **Document type:** trade publication.
  ●Also available online.
  —BLDSC (6594.700000); Faxon; UnCover; UMI.
  Description: Forms, checklists and practical articles for attorneys.

340 US ISSN 1047-6261
K16
THE PRACTICAL LITIGATOR. 1990. 6/yr. $35. American Law Institute - American Bar Association, Committee on Continuing Professional Education, 4025 Chestnut St., Philadelphia, PA 19104. TEL 215-243-1604. FAX 215-243-1664. Ed. Mark T. Carroll. adv.; illus.; index, cum.index every 5 yrs. circ. 2,000. **Document type:** trade publication.
  —UnCover; UMI.
  Description: Practical articles for litigation attorneys.

346.043 US ISSN 8756-0372
KF566.A3
THE PRACTICAL REAL ESTATE LAWYER. 1985. bi-m. $35. American Law Institute - American Bar Association, Committee on Continuing Professional Education, 4025 Chestnut St., Philadelphia, PA 19104. TEL 215-243-1604. FAX 215-243-1664. Ed. Mark T. Carroll. adv.; cum.index. circ. 5,432. (back issues avail.) **Indexed:** C.L.I., Leg.Per. **Document type:** trade publication.
  —Faxon; UMI.
  Description: Gives practical advice to lawyers in all areas of real estate law.
  Refereed Serial

340 336 US ISSN 0890-4898
THE PRACTICAL TAX LAWYER. 1986. q. $35 to non-members; members $27.50. American Law Institute - American Bar Association, Committee on Continuing Professional Education, 4025 Chestnut St., Philadelphia, PA 19104. TEL 215-243-1604. FAX 215-243-1664. (Co-sponsor: A B A Tax Section) Ed. Mark T. Carroll. adv.; cum.index. circ. 3,643. **Indexed:** Account.Ind. (1986-), C.L.I., Leg.Per. **Document type:** trade publication.
  —Faxon; UnCover; UMI.
  Description: Forms, checklists and practical articles for tax lawyers.

340 US
PRACTITIONER'S GUIDE TO THE OKLAHOMA UNIFORM CONSUMER CREDIT CODE. 1990. base vol. (plus a. suppl.) $89.50. Butterworth Legal Publishers (Salem) (Subsidiary of: Reed Elsevier plc), 8 Industrial Way, Bldg. C, Salem, NH 03079. TEL 800-548-4001. FAX 603-898-9858. Ed.Bd. (looseleaf format)
  Description: Covers credit sales, loans and other consumer finance transactions governed by the UCCC, as well as rent-to-own deals, pawnshop transactions and other special purpose agreements.

PRACTITIONERS 1040 DESKBOOK. see *BUSINESS AND ECONOMICS — Public Finance, Taxation*

349 IS ISSN 0017-7571
PRAKLIT. (Text in Hebrew) 1942. q. IS.0.25 to non-members. Israel Bar Association, Box 14152, Tel-Aviv, Israel. Ed. A. Gabrieli. adv.; bk.rev.; pat.; index. circ. 6,500. **Indexed:** Foreign Leg.Per., Ind.Heb.Per.

347 NE ISSN 0165-0025
PRAKTIJKGIDS. 1939. fortn. fl.0.40 per page. Gouda Quint B.V., P.O. Box 1148, 6801 MK Arnhem, Netherlands. TEL 3185-454762. FAX 3185-514509. adv. (also avail. in looseleaf format) **Indexed:** Key to Econ.Sci.
  —SWETS.
  Description: Decisions of the Dutch Magistrates Courts.

340 BU ISSN 0032-6968
PRAVNA MISAL. (Contents page in French, Russian) 1957. 6/yr. 1.10 lv. per no. (Bulgarska Akademiia na Naukite, Institut za Pravni Nauki) Publishing House of the Bulgarian Academy of Sciences, Acad. G. Bonchev St., Bldg. 6, 1113 Sofia, Bulgaria. (Dist. by: Hemus, 6, Rouski Blvd., 1000 Sofia, Bulgaria) Ed. Stefan Pavlov. bk.rev.; index. circ. 3,600. (reprint service avail. from IRC) **Indexed:** BSL Econ.
  —BLDSC (0131.100000).

340 XR
PRAVNI PRAXE; casopis pro pravni praxi. (Text in Czech or Slovak) 1952. 10/yr. 60 Kcs. Ministerstvo Spravedlnosti Ceske Republiky, Vysehradska 16, 128 10 Prague 2, Czech Republic. TEL 2-294545. FAX 2-531322. (Subscr. to: Artia, Ve Smeckach 30, 111 27 Prague 1, Czech Republic) Ed. Alena Winterova. bk.rev.; bibl. circ. 7,100. **Document type:** newsletter.
  —BLDSC (6603.110000).
  Former titles: Pravo a Zakonnost (ISSN 1210-0900); (until 1990): Socialisticka Zakonnost (ISSN 0037-8305).

340 XO ISSN 0551-9039
PRAVNICKE STUDIE. (Text in Slovak; summaries in German and Russian; contents page in French, German, Russian and Slovak) 1953. a. fl.30 per no. (Slovenska Akademia Vied, Ustav Statu a Prava) Veda, Publishing House of the Slovak Academy of Sciences, Klemensova 19, 814 30 Bratislava, Slovakia. (Dist. in Western countries by: John Benjamins B.V., Amsteldijk 44, Amsterdam (Z.), Netherlands) charts; stat. **Indexed:** Geo.Abstr.

340 XR ISSN 0231-6625
PRAVNIK/LAWYER. (Text in Czech; occasional summaries in English, French, German, Russian) 1861. m. DM.186. (Czechoslovak Academy of Sciences, Institute of State and Law) Academia, Publishing House of the Czechoslovak Academy of Sciences, Vodickova 40, 112 29 Prague 1, Czech Republic. TEL 20-16-20. (Dist. in Western countries by: Kubon & Sagner, P.O. Box 34 01 08, 8000 Munich 34, Germany) Ed. Milan Kindl. bk.rev. circ. 3,200. **Indexed:** CERDIC.

340 XO ISSN 0032-6984
PRAVNY OBZOR/LAW REVIEW. 1917. 10/yr. 120 Kcs.($24) (Slovenska Akademia Vied, Ustav Statu a Prava) Veda, Publishing House of the Slovak Academy of Sciences, Klemensova 19, 814 30 Bratislava, Slovakia. (Dist. in Western countries by: John Benjamins B.V., Amsteldijk 44, Amsterdam (Z.), Netherlands) Ed. Jan Azud. bibl.; index. circ. 2,200. **Indexed:** Geo.Abstr., World Bibl.Soc.Sec.
  Description: Covers actual problems of law theory and practice. Explores questions regarding all areas of law.

340 KR
PRAVO UKRAINY; respublikans'kii yuridichnii zhurnal. (Text in Ukrainian) 1922. m. 8.40 Rub. (Ministerstvo Yustitsii Ukrainy) Pravo Ukrainy, Bul. M. Kotsyubins'kogo, 12, 252601 Kiev 30, Ukraine. TEL 224-1900. (Co-sponsor: Akademiya Nauk Ukrainy, Institut Derzhavy i Prava) Ed. Yu.G. Verbenko.
  Formerly (until 1992): Radyans'ke Pravo (ISSN 0132-1331).

340 PL
PRAWO. (Text in Polish; summaries in English, French or Russian) 1961. irreg., no.149, 1993. price varies. Adam Mickiewicz University Press, Nowowiejskiego 55, 61-734 Poznan, Poland. TEL 527-380. FAX 61-526425. TELEX 413260 UAMPL. Ed.Bd. **Indexed:** Canon Law Abstr. **Document type:** academic/scholarly publication.
  —BLDSC (9120.477000).
  Formerly: Uniwersytet im. Adama Mickiewicza w Poznaniu. Wydzial Prawa. Prace (ISSN 0083-4262)
  Description: Contains current research results of one author in the field of law, including Ph.D. works and monographs.

340   PL   ISSN 0551-9101
PRAWO I ZYCIE. 1956. w. $104. Oferta dla Kazdego, Spolka z o.o., Ul. Wiejska 12, 00-490 Warsaw, Poland. TEL 48-22-272466. FAX 48-22-267585. Ed. Andrzej Dobrzynski. adv.; bk.rev. circ. 120,000. (looseleaf format; back issues avail.)

DIE PRAXIS (BASEL). see *PUBLIC ADMINISTRATION*

340   200   FR   ISSN 0758-802X
PRAXIS JURIDIQUE ET RELIGION. (Text in French; summaries in English, French) 1984. s-a. 250 F. (typically set in Jan.). (Universite de Strasbourg II) CERDIC Publications, 2 Rue Goethe, Palais Universitaire, F-67083 Strasbourg, France. TEL 88-22-97-09. Ed. Marie Zimmermann. adv. circ. 1,000. (back issues avail.) Indexed: Bull.Signal., Cath.Ind., Rel.Ind.One.
—BLDSC (6603.171370).
    Description: Research in the fields of Christian and non-Christian canon, ecclesiastical and religious law and theology.

340   US   ISSN 0741-1162
KF287
PRE LAW JOURNAL. 1983. 3/yr. $9.75. Legal Institute, 3250 Wilshire Blvd., No. 1000, Los Angeles, CA 90010. TEL 213-487-6268. Ed Herman B. Lancaster. circ. 300. **Indexed:** C.L.I.

340   CI
PREGLED SUDSKE PRAKSE. (Issued as Supplement to Nasa Zakonitost, by Ustavni Sud Hrvatske and Other Legislative Bodies) 1972. irreg. (Vrhovni Sud) Narodne Novine, Zagreb, Ratkajev Prolaz 4, Zagreb, Croatia. (Co-sponsors: Croatia. Ustavni Sud; Visi Privredni Sud u Zagrebu) Ed. Ivan Salinovic.

PRESERVATION LAW REPORTER. see *ENVIRONMENTAL STUDIES*

PRESERVING LANDS: LEGAL ISSUES. see *CONSERVATION*

340   CN   ISSN 1192-862X
PRESSE JURIDIQUE. 24/yr. Can.$79. Les Editions Yvon Blais, 430 rue St. Pierre, Bureau 200, Montreal, PQ H2Y 2M5, Canada. TEL 514-842-3937. FAX 514-842-7144. (Subscr. to: C.P. 180, Cowansville, PQ J2K 3H6, Canada. TEL 514-263-1086) adv.; cum.index. **Document type:** newspaper.
    Description: Analyzes recent court decisions in all fields; digests legal news.

340   II
PREVENTION OF FOOD ADULTERATION CASES. (Text in English) 1972. m. Rs.120. International Law Book Co., Nijhawan Bldg., 1562 Church Rd., Kashmere Gate, Delhi 6, India. Ed. Swarn Bhatia Nijhawan. bibl.

PRIMER OF LABOR RELATIONS. see *BUSINESS AND ECONOMICS — Labor And Industrial Relations*

365 340   US
PRISON LEGAL NEWS. 1990. m. $12 to individuals; institutions $35. Box 1684, Lake Worth, FL 33460. TEL 407-547-9716. Eds. Paul Wright, Ed. Mead; Pub. Rollin Wright. adv.; bk.rev.; index. circ. 2,000. **Document type:** newsletter.
    Description: Reports on court decisions to help prisoners vindicate their human rights, both inside and outside the government's judicial system. Assists prisoners and their supporters in organizing themselves to have a voice and be a progressive force in developing a public policy debate around the issue of crime and punishment.

PRIVACY TIMES. see *POLITICAL SCIENCE — Civil Rights*

340   UK   ISSN 1353-3649
▼**PRIVATE CLIENT WORK.** 1994. a. £17.50. Jordan Publishing Ltd., 21 St. Thomas St., Bristol BS1 6JS, England. TEL 0272-230600. FAX 0272-250486. Ed. Robin Riddett. **Document type:** academic/scholarly publication.

PRIVATE LETTER RULINGS. see *BUSINESS AND ECONOMICS — Public Finance, Taxation*

PRIVATE SECURITY CASE LAW REPORTER; the security professional's digest of state & federal court decisions. see *CRIMINOLOGY AND LAW ENFORCEMENT — Security*

340   YU   ISSN 0032-9002
K16
PRIVREDNO PRAVNI PRIRUCNIK; za pravnu opstu i kadrovsku sluzbu privrednih i ostalih radnih organizacija. 1963. m. 5520000 din.($84.50) Skupstina Grada Beograd, Privredni Pravni Prirucnik, Cika Ljubina 16-I, 11000 Belgrade, Yugoslavia. TEL 636-609. Ed. Vojislav Kukoljac. adv. circ. 3,600.

340   BE
PRO JUSTITIA; revue politique de droit. 1973. q. Foulek Ringelheim, Ed. & Pub., 62 rue Emile van Driessche, 1060 Brussels, Belgium.

340   US
PROBATE PRACTICE REPORTER. 1989. m. $235. Shepard's - McGraw-Hill, Inc., Box 35300, Colorado Springs, CO 80935-3530. TEL 719-475-7230. Ed. William Jordan.

PROBLEM ASSET REPORTER. see *REAL ESTATE*

340   IT
PROCESSO LEGISLATIVO NEL PARLAMENTO ITALIANO. no.3, 1974. irreg. (Universita degli Studi di Firenze, Facolta di Scienze Politiche) Casa Editrice Dott. A. Giuffre, Via Busto Arsizio 40, 20151 Milan, Italy. TEL 02-38000905. FAX 02-3809582. Ed. Alberto Predieri.

349   LE   ISSN 0032-9649
K16
PROCHE-ORIENT ETUDES JURIDIQUES. (Text in Arabic, French) 1967. a. $26 (effective 1994). Universite Saint Joseph, Faculte de Droit et des Sciences Politiques, Rue Huvelin, Box 293, Beirut, Lebanon. FAX 961-1-201974. TELEX 44666. (Foreign subscr. addr.: Office du Livre, 14 bis rue Jean Ferrandi, 75006 Paris, France) Ed. I. Najjar. bk.rev. **Indexed:** Refug.Abstr. **Document type:** academic/scholarly publication, monographic series.
    Formerly: Etudes de Droit Libanais.
    Description: Covers topics relating to Lebanese civil law, corporate law, international law, including comparative law, examining French and Middle Eastern legal systems.

340   AT
PROCTOR. 1982. m. (11/yr.). Aus.$60 (foreign Aus.$80). Queensland Law Society, Inc., Law Society House, 179 Ann St., Brisbane, Qld. 4000, Australia. TEL 07-2335888. Ed. Helen Fordham. adv. contact: Gail Baker. index. circ. 4,500. **Document type:** academic/scholarly publication, newsletter.
    Description: Law and legal practice in Queensland and Australia.

340   SP
PROCURADORES. 6/yr. Arturo Soria 241, 28033 Madrid, Spain. TEL 1-457-97-59. FAX 1-457-95-73. Ed. J. Galache Alvarez.

340   US
PRODUCT LIABILITY LAW IN OKLAHOMA. base vol. (plus suppl.). $120. Butterworth Legal Publishers (Salem) (Subsidiary of: Reed Elsevier plc), 8 Industrial Way, Bldg. C, Salem, NH 03079. TEL 800-548-4001. FAX 603-898-9858. Ed. Vicki Lawrence MacDougall. (looseleaf format)
    Description: Analysis of Oklahoma law concerning products liability and related causes of action, highlighting advantages and disadvantages of each theory of recovery.

346.066 368   US   ISSN 0164-9574
K953.A13
PRODUCT LIABILITY TRENDS; a monthly analysis of product liability developments. m. $195. National Legal Research Group, Inc., 2421 Ivy Rd., Box 7187, Charlottesville, VA 22906-7187. TEL 800-446-1870. FAX 804-295-4667. Ed. Jeremy Taylor.
    Description: Analyses of recent cases and reports of legislative developments in product liability trends.

340 338   US
PRODUCTS LIABILITY. 1981. base vol. (plus a. suppl.). $95. Shepard's - McGraw-Hill, Inc., Box 35300, Colorado Springs, CO 80935-3530. TEL 800-525-2474.
    Description: Covers traditional causes of action such as negligence, misrepresentation and warranty under the Uniform Commercial Code. Defines the outer boundaries of strict liability in tort.

340 338   US
PRODUCTS LIABILITY: DESIGN AND MANUFACTURING DEFECTS. 1986. base vol. (plus a. suppl.). $95. Shepard's - McGraw-Hill, Inc., Box 35300, Colorado Springs, CO 80935-3530. TEL 800-525-2474.
    Description: Explores all factors of product liability, including manufacturer's responsibility, advertising material, packaging, instruction manuals, warnings and labels.

340 640.73   US
PRODUCTS LIABILITY LAW JOURNAL. 1989. q. $79.50. Butterworth Legal Publishers (Salem) (Subsidiary of: Reed Elsevier plc), 8 Industrial Way, Bldg. C, Salem, NH 03079. TEL 603-898-9664. FAX 603-898-9858. Ed. Warren W. Eginton.
    Description: Includes articles on current products liability problems and emerging areas of concern.

330 340   US   ISSN 0162-122X
PRODUCTS LIABILITY REPORTER. 1963. fortn. $625. Commerce Clearing House, Inc., 4025 W. Peterson Ave., Chicago, IL 60646. TEL 312-583-8500. Ed. Daniel L. Newquist. circ. 2,414. (looseleaf format; also avail. in microfilm) **Indexed:** I.P.A.
●Also available online.

PROFESSIONAL APARTMENT MANAGEMENT. see *REAL ESTATE*

340   US   ISSN 1042-5675
PROFESSIONAL LAWYER. q. $20. American Bar Association, Center for Professional Responsibility, 541 N. Fairbanks Ct., Chicago, IL 60611-3314. TEL 312-988-5555. **Document type:** newsletter.
—UnCover.
    Description: Provides a forum for the exchange of views and ideas on professional issues for bar leaders, lawyers, law school educators, and others interested in fostering professionalism.

340   US   ISSN 1059-3969
KF1289.A59
PROFESSIONAL LIABILITY LITIGATION REPORTER. 1991. m. $550. Andrews Publications, 1646 West Chester Pike, Box 1000, Westtown, PA 19395. TEL 215-399-6600; 800-345-1101. FAX 215-399-6610. Ed. Edith McFall. bibl.; stat.; s-a. cum.index. (looseleaf format; back issues avail.) **Document type:** newsletter.
    Description: Focuses on lawsuits filed against accountants, attorneys, investment bankers, financial advisors, rating services and other financial professionals.

610 340   US
PROFESSIONAL LIABILITY NEWSLETTER. 1968. m. $45. Professional Liability Newsletter, Inc., Box 834, Berkeley, CA 94701. TEL 510-741-8723. Ed. Dr. David S. Rubsamen. (reprint service avail.) **Document type:** newsletter.
    Description: Analysis of medical malpractice cases for medical doctors and attorneys.

340   US   ISSN 0145-3505
KF1289.A59
PROFESSIONAL LIABILITY REPORTER; recent decisions of national significance. 1976. m. $305. (Litigation Research Group) Shepard's - McGraw-Hill, Inc., Box 35300, Colorado Springs, CO 80935-3530. TEL 719-488-3000. Ed. William Jordan, Esq. bibl.; index. (looseleaf format; back issues avail.)
    Description: Summarizes and analyzes reported and most unreported decisions pertaining to professional liability litigation.

PROFESSIONAL LIABILITY TODAY. see *INSURANCE*

340   US   ISSN 1043-2051
PROFESSIONAL LICENSING REPORT. 1988. m. $168 (effective 1994). Paxton Associates, 9904 Foxborough Cir., Rockville, MD 20850. TEL 301-869-4889. FAX 301-869-8327. Ed. Anne Paxton. circ. 350. **Document type:** newsletter.
    Description: Covers legal and legislative issues affecting the licensing and regulation of professionals in all fields with news on state requirements, relevant court decisions, and discussions of professional ethics.

340   UK   ISSN 0267-078X
KD1978.A13
PROFESSIONAL NEGLIGENCE; a journal of liability, ethics and discipline. 1985. 4/yr. £125. Tolley Publishing Co. Ltd., Tolley House, 2 Addiscombe Rd., Croydon, Surrey CR9 5AF, England. TEL 081-686-9141. FAX 081-686-3155. Ed. David K. Allen. **Indexed:** C.L.I., Hlth.Ind. **Document type:** trade publication.

PROFESSIONAL PURCHASING. see *BUSINESS AND ECONOMICS — Marketing And Purchasing*

PROFESSIONE SERVIZI. see *ADVERTISING AND PUBLIC RELATIONS*

PROFILE OF STATE CHARTERED BANKING. see *BUSINESS AND ECONOMICS — Banking And Finance*

PROFITABILITY BY LINE BY STATE. see *INSURANCE — Abstracting, Bibliographies, Statistics*

340   333.33   UK   ISSN 0955-8659
PROPERTY FINANCE & DEVELOPMENT. m. £159($318) I B C Publishing, Gilmoora House, 57-61 Mortimer St., London W1N 7TD, England. TEL 071-637-4383. (Subscr. in U.S. to: IBC (USA), 290 Eliot St., Box 91004, Ashland, MA 01721-9104. TEL 508-881-2800. FAX 508-881-0982) Ed. Philip Marvin. **Document type:** newsletter.

310   333.33   AT   ISSN 0727-6346
PROPERTY LAW AND PRACTICE IN QUEENSLAND. 1982. 3/yr. Aus.$310 with updates. Law Book Co. Ltd., 44-40 Waterloo Rd., N. Ryde, N.S.W. 2113, Australia. TEL 02-887-0177. Eds. W.D. Duncan, R.J. Vann. (looseleaf format)
    Description: Covers the legal principles of property law and practice in Queensland.

346   UK   ISSN 0144-6517
PROPERTY LAW BULLETIN. 1980. 10/yr. £140($214) Longman Group Ltd., Law, Tax and Finance Division, 21-27 Lamb's Conduit St., London WC1N 3NJ, England. TEL 071-242-2548. FAX 071-831-8119. Ed. John M. Samson. bk.rev. circ. 1,350. **Document type:** bulletin.
—BLDSC (6927.308000). **CCC.**
    Description: Information on all aspects of property law.

347   UK
KD826.A2
PROPERTY, PLANNING AND COMPENSATION REPORTS. 1950. 6/yr. (3 nos./vol., 2 vols./yr.) £160. Sweet & Maxwell, South Quay Plaza, 7th Fl., 183 Marsh Wall, London E14 9FT, England. TEL 071-538-8686. FAX 071-538-9508. Ed. Lyndsay Walker. adv. contact: Jackie Wood. (reprint service avail. from RRI) **Indexed:** C.L.I., Leg.Per., RICS. **Document type:** bulletin.
●Also available online. Vendor(s): Mead Data Central, Inc.
—BLDSC (6927.311200).
    Former titles: Property and Compensation Reports (ISSN 0033-1295); Planning and Compensation Reports.

343   US   ISSN 0027-6383
K16
PROSECUTOR. 1965. 6/yr. membership. National District Attorneys Association, 99 Canal Center Plaza, Ste. 510, Alexandria, VA 22314. TEL 703-549-9222. Ed. Newman Flanagan. adv.; bk.rev.; illus. circ. 7,500. **Indexed:** C.L.I., Crim.Just.Abstr., L.R.I., Leg.Per.
—Faxon; UMI.

340   640.73   US
PROTECTING CONSUMER RIGHTS. 1987. base vol. (plus a. suppl.). $95. Shepard's - McGraw-Hill, Inc., Box 35300, Colorado Springs, CO 80935-3530. TEL 800-525-2474.
    Description: Pragmatic approach to solving consumer problems.

340   CN   ISSN 0709-5139
PROVINCIAL JUDGES JOURNAL/JOURNAL DES JUGES PROVINCIAUX. 1978. q. Canadian Association of Provincial Court Judges, Box 531, Brandon, MB R7A 5Z4, Canada. **Indexed:** Ind.Can.L.P.L.
    Formerly (until 1979): Canadian Provincial Judges Journal (ISSN 0701-1806).

340   GW
PROZESSRECHTLICHE ABHANDLUNGEN. (Text in German) 1952. irreg., no.92, 1993. DM.114. Carl Heymanns Verlag KG, Luxemburgerstr. 449, 50939 Cologne, Germany. TEL 0221-46010-0. Ed. Hanns Pruetting. circ. 500. (back issues avail.) **Document type:** monographic series.

340   150   US
PSYCHIATRIC & PSYCHOLOGICAL EVIDENCE. 1986. base vol. (plus a. suppl.). $95. Shepard's - McGraw-Hill, Inc., Box 35300, Colorado Springs, CO 80935-3530. TEL 800-525-2474.
    Description: Examines and evaluates evidence from psychiatrists and psychologists in civil and criminal proceedings to provide guidelines for admissibility.

PUBLIC AND LOCAL ACTS OF THE LEGISLATURE OF THE STATE OF MICHIGAN. see *PUBLIC ADMINISTRATION — Municipal Government*

340   US   ISSN 0033-3441
K16
PUBLIC CONTRACT LAW JOURNAL. 1967. q. $30 to non-members. American Bar Association, Public Contract Law Section, 750 N. Lake Shore Dr., Chicago, IL 60611. TEL 312-988-5000. Ed. Matthew J. Simchak. (reprint service avail. from RRI) **Indexed:** C.L.I., L.R.I., Leg.Per.
●Also available online. Vendor(s): West Services, Inc.
—BLDSC (6963.100000); UnCover.
    Description: Articles by leading authorities on all phases of federal, state, and local procurement and grant law.

340   US   ISSN 0569-3314
KF849.A1
PUBLIC CONTRACT NEWSLETTER. 1965. q. membership only. American Bar Association, Public Contract Law Section, 750 N. Lake Shore Dr., Chicago, IL 60611. TEL 312-988-5000. Ed. Martin J. Harty. **Indexed:** C.L.I., L.R.I. **Document type:** newsletter.
    Description: Covers current developments in federal grant law, recent developments in state and local public contract law, upcoming educational programs.

PUBLIC EMPLOYEE DISCIPLINE & TERMINATIONS LAW BULLETIN. see *BUSINESS AND ECONOMICS — Labor And Industrial Relations*

PUBLIC EYE (MADISON). see *CONSUMER EDUCATION AND PROTECTION*

330   US   ISSN 1058-384X
K16
PUBLIC INTEREST LAW REVIEW. 1991. a. $32.50. Carolina Academic Press, 700 Kent St., Durham, NC 27701. TEL 919-489-7486. FAX 919-493-5668. Ed. Terry Eastland. bk.rev. **Document type:** monographic series.
—UnCover.
    Description: Aimed at readers with an interest in the making and executing of public policy; discusses and debates issues of consequence for the public interest.

340   US   ISSN 0742-5325
PUBLIC JUSTICE REPORT. 1977. bi-m. $12. Center for Public Justice, Box 48368, Washington, DC 20002-0368. FAX 410-263-3857. Ed. James W. Skillen. bk.rev. circ. 1,500. (looseleaf format; back issues avail.) **Document type:** newsletter.
    Description: Analysis and commentary of domestic and international affairs.

347.2   US   ISSN 0148-6489
K16
PUBLIC LAND & RESOURCES LAW DIGEST. 1962. s-a. $29.50. Rocky Mountain Mineral Law Foundation, Porter Administration Bldg., 7039 E. 18th Ave., Denver, CO 80220. TEL 303-321-8100. FAX 303-321-7657. Ed. Mark H. Holland. index. circ. 500. **Indexed:** Energy Ind., Energy Info.Abstr., Environ.Abstr., GeoRef., Mar.Aff.Bibl., P.A.I.S. —UnCover. **CCC.**
    Formerly (until vol.8): Rocky Mountain Mineral Law Review (ISSN 0035-7618)
    Description: Covers mining, oil, gas and water law.

342   UK   ISSN 0033-3565
K16
PUBLIC LAW; the constitutional and administrative law of the commonwealth. 1956. q. £80. Sweet & Maxwell, South Quay Plaza, 7th Fl., 183 Marsh Wall, London E14 9FT, England. TEL 071-538-8686. FAX 071-538-9508. Ed. Nick O'Dell. adv. contact: Jackie Wood. bk.rev.; index. (reprint service avail. from RRI) **Indexed:** Abstr.Bk.Rev.Curr.Leg.Per., ASSIA, C.L.I., Crim.Just.Abstr., ELLIS, L.R.I., Leg.Cont., Leg.Per. **Document type:** bulletin.
—BLDSC (6967.150000); Faxon; UnCover; SWETS; UMI.

342   JA
PUBLIC LAW REVIEW/KOHO KENKYU. 1949. q. (Japan Public Law Association - Nihon Koho Gakkai) Yuhikaku Publishing Co. Ltd., 2-17 Kanda Jimbo-cho, Chiyoda-ku, Tokyo 101, Japan.

340   AT   ISSN 1034-3024
PUBLIC LAW REVIEW. 1990. q. Aus.$205. Law Book Co. Ltd., 44-50 Waterloo Rd., North Ryde, N.S.W. 2113, Australia. TEL 02-887-0177. FAX 02-388-9706. TELEX ASBOOK 27995. Eds. Cheryl Saunders, Greg Craven.
    Description: Covers new and emerging developments in the law affecting government in Australia and New Zealand.

353
PUBLIC LAWS. irreg. $156 (foreign £195). U.S. Office of the Federal Register, National Archives and Records Administration, Eighth St. & Pennsylvania Ave., N.W., Washington, DC 20408. TEL 202-523-5230. (Subscr. to: Superintendent of Documents, U.S. Government Printing Office, Box 371954, Pittsburgh, PA 15250-7954. TEL 202-783-3238. FAX 202-512-2233) **Document type:** government publication.
    Description: Publishes federal laws once they are enacted.

PUBLIC RADIO LEGAL HANDBOOK. see *COMMUNICATIONS — Radio*

340   363.6   US   ISSN 0095-5086
KF2094.A1
PUBLIC UTILITIES LAW ANTHOLOGY. 1974. s-a. $149.95 per no. International Library Law Book Publishers, Inc., 101 Lakeforest Blvd., Ste. 270, Bethesda, MD 20877. TEL 301-990-7755. FAX 301-990-7642. Ed. Donald J. Hoyes. bibl.; cum.index vols.1-14. **Document type:** monographic series.
    Description: Selected best U.S. law review articles, printed in their entirety, in the field of public utilities culled from over 900 U.S. law review journals.

PUBLIC UTILITIES REPORTS. see *ENERGY*

340   346.013   US
PUERTO RICAN BAR ASSOCIATION. NEWSLETTER.* m. Puerto Rican Bar Association, Box 3554, New York, NY 10008-3554. **Document type:** newsletter.
    Description: Aims to enhance the status of Puerto Rican law students.

PUERTO RICO TAX REPORTS. see *BUSINESS AND ECONOMICS — Public Finance, Taxation*

THE PUNCH LIST. see *BUSINESS AND ECONOMICS — Labor And Industrial Relations*

340   II   ISSN 0033-4332
PUNJAB LAW REPORTER. (Text in English) 1900. fortn. Rs.150. 36 Sector 9-A, Chandigarh 19, India. Eds. Lalit Mohan Suri, Ravinder Mohan Suri. adv.; bk.rev.; index, cum.index every 5 yrs.

340   658   US   ISSN 0898-994X
PURCHASER'S LEGAL ADVISER. 1980. m. $147. Business Laws, Inc., 11630 Chillicothe Rd., Chesterland, OH 44026. TEL 216-729-7996. FAX 216-729-0645. Ed. William A. Hancock. index, cum.index. (back issues avail.) **Document type:** newsletter.
—**CCC.**
    Description: For the purchasing professional. Discusses legal developments affecting purchasing.

340   330   UA
QANOUN WAL IQTISAD/DROIT ET ECONOMIE POLITIQUE. (Text in Arabic, English) 1931. q. P.T.300. University of Cairo, Faculty of Law, Cairo, Egypt. Ed.Bd. bibl.; cum.index: 1931-1960, 1961-1970.

QUADERNI DI DIRITTO E POLITICA ECCLESIASTICA. see *RELIGIONS AND THEOLOGY*

340 900   IT
QUADERNI FIORENTINI PER LA STORIA DEL PENSIERO GIURIDICO MODERNO. (Text in English, French, German, Italian and Spanish) 1972. a. (University of Florence, Centro di Studi per la Storia del Pensiero Giuridico Moderno) Casa Editrice Dott. A. Giuffre, Via Busto Arsizio 40, 20151 Milan, Italy.
TEL 02-38000905. FAX 02-3809582.

340
QUADERNI REGIONALI. 1982. q. L.90000 (foreign L.135000). Casa Editrice Dott. A. Giuffre, Via Busto Arsizio 40, 20151 Milan, Italy. TEL 02-38000905. FAX 02-3809582. Ed. Fausto Cuocolo. adv. circ. 1,500.

340   IT
QUADRIMESTRE - RIVISTA DI DIRITTO PRIVATO. 1984. 3/yr. L.80000 (foreign L.120000). Casa Editrice Dott. A. Giuffre, Via Busto Arsizio 40, 20151 Milan, Italy. TEL 06-38000905. FAX 06-38009582.

QUALITY & RISK MANAGEMENT IN HEALTH CARE; an information service. see *HOSPITALS*

QUALITY ASSURANCE; good practice, regulation, and law. see *BUSINESS AND ECONOMICS — Management*

QUARTERLY LISTING OF ALIEN INSURERS. see *INSURANCE*

340   CN   ISSN 1183-0271
QUEBEC (PROVINCE). COMMISSION DE PROTECTION DU TERRITOIRE AGRICOLE. DECISIONS. 4/yr. Can.$65. (Commission de Protection du Territoire Agricole) S O Q U I J, 715 Square Victoria, Bur. 800, Montreal, PQ H2Y 2H7, Canada. TEL 514-270-7172. (Subscr. to: Service Abonnements, 7 Chemin Bates, Outremont, PQ H2V 1V6, Canada)

354   CN   ISSN 0703-0762
KEQ180.A13
QUEBEC (PROVINCE). COMMISSION DES SERVICES JURIDIQUES. RAPPORT ANNUEL. 1973. a. Commission des Services Juridiques, C.P. 123, Succursale Desjardins, Montreal, PQ H5B 1B3, Canada. TEL 514-873-3562. FAX 514-873-8762. Ed. Jacques Lemaitre-Auger. circ. 800.

340   CN
QUEBEC APPEAL CASES. French edition: Causes en Appel au Quebec. 1987. irreg. (approx. 7/yr.). Can.$113. Maritime Law Book Ltd., P.O. Box 302, Fredericton, NB E3B 4Y9, Canada.
TEL 506-453-9921; 800-561-0220.
FAX 506-453-9525. (back issues avail.)
    Description: Contains judgments of the Quebec Court of Appeal on public law, Canadian law and Quebec civil law cases not reported by SOQUIJ.

QUEBEC CORPORATION AND INCOME TAX LEGISLATION. see *BUSINESS AND ECONOMICS — Public Finance, Taxation*

340   US   ISSN 0048-6302
KF200
QUEENS BAR BULLETIN. 1936. 8/yr. $2.50. Queens County Bar Association, 90-35 148 St., Jamaica, NY 11435. TEL 718-291-4500. adv.; bk.rev.; bibl.; charts; illus.; index. circ. 2,500. **Document type:** newspaper, trade publication.

QUEENS COOP CONDO CONVERSION DIGEST. see *REAL ESTATE*

340   CN   ISSN 0316-778X
QUEEN'S LAW JOURNAL. 1968. s-a. Can.$4 per no. Queen's University, Faculty of Law, Kingston, ON K7L 3N6, Canada. TEL 613-545-2220.
FAX 613-545-6611. Ed. Michael Jones. adv.; bk.rev. circ. 900. **Indexed:** C.L.I., Ind.Can.L.P.L., L.R.I., Leg.Cont., Leg.Per.
—BLDSC (7211.160000); Faxon.
    Formerly: Queen's Intramural Law Journal (ISSN 0048-6310)

340   AT
QUEENSLAND CONVEYANCING LAW AND PRACTICE. (In 3 vols.) 1982. irreg. (approx. 10/yr.). C C H Australia Ltd., P.O. Box 230, North Ryde, N.S.W. 2113, Australia. TEL 02-888-2555.
FAX 02-888-7324. (looseleaf format)
    Description: Reference on conveyancing law for the State of Queensland, Australia.

340
QUEENSLAND DISTRICT COURTS PRACTICE. base vol. (plus updates 3/yr.). $265. Butterworths, 271-273 Lane Cove Rd., P.O. Box 345, North Ryde, N.S.W. 2113, Australia. TEL 02-887-3444. (looseleaf format)

340   AT   ISSN 0726-0784
QUEENSLAND LAW REPORTER. 1908. w. Aus.$125 (effective 1994). Incorporated Council of Law Reporting, c/o Sec. Mrs. J.T. Mengel, P.O. Box 307, 44 Romn St., Qld. 4003, Australia.
TEL 07-236-1855. FAX 07-236-4196. circ. 980.

340   AT   ISSN 0313-4253
K17
QUEENSLAND LAW SOCIETY JOURNAL. 1971. 6/yr. Aus.$80 (foreign Aus.$135). Queensland Law Society, Inc., Law Society House, 179 Ann St., Brisbane, Qld. 4000, Australia. TEL 07-233-5888. FAX 07-233-5999. Ed. J. Kelly. adv. contact: Gail Baker. bk.rev.; index. circ. 4,500. (also avail. in microform from UMI) **Indexed:** C.L.I., L.R.I., Leg.Per. **Document type:** academic/scholarly publication.
    Description: For Australian lawyers covering contract law, business and review law, criminal law and common law. Includes Queensland Law Society news and events.

340   AT   ISSN 0312-1658
LAW
QUEENSLAND LAWYER. 1907. bi-m. Aus.$150. Law Book Co. Ltd., 44-50 Waterloo Rd., N. Ryde, N.S.W. 2113, Australia. TEL 02-887-0177.
FAX 02-888-9706. TELEX ASBOOK 27995. Ed. Bernard Cairns. bk.rev.; cum.index: 1907-1966. (tabloid format)
    Formerly: Queensland Justice of the Peace and Reports (ISSN 0033-6181)
    Description: Presents articles, comments and notes on recent developments and decisions. Reports on cases heard before the various courts of Australia.

340   AT
QUEENSLAND UNIT & GROUP TITLES LAW AND PRACTICE. (In 2 vols.) 1980. irreg. (approx. 10/yr.). C C H Australia Ltd., P.O. Box 230, North Ryde, N.S.W. 2113, Australia. TEL 02-888-2555.
FAX 02-888-7324. (looseleaf format)

340   AT   ISSN 1032-6693
QUEENSLAND UNIVERSITY OF TECHNOLOGY LAW JOURNAL. 1985. a. Aus.$13.50. Queensland University of Technology, Faculty of Law, George St., Brisbane, Qld. 4001, Australia. TEL 8642839. FAX 8641519. (Dist. in N. America by: Wm. W. Gaunt & Sons Inc., 3011 Gulf Dr., Holmes Beach, FL 34217-2199. TEL 813-778-5211. FAX 813-778-5252) adv.; bk.rev. circ. 500. (back issues avail.)
    Formerly (until 1988): Queensland Institute of Technology Law Journal.
    Description: Contains articles on topics of current interest and concern throughout Australia and the common law world.

340   IT
QUESTIONE GIUSTIZIA. 1982. N.S. q. L.95000 (foreign L.120000) (effective 1993). (Magistratura Democratica) Franco Angeli Editore, Viale Monza 106, 20127 Milan, Italy. TEL 02-28-27-651.

340   US
QUESTIONING TECHNIQUES AND TACTICS. 1982. base vol. (plus a. suppl.). $95. Shepard's - McGraw-Hill, Inc., Box 35300, Colorado Springs, CO 80935-3530. TEL 800-525-2474.
    Description: Provides information on new techniques of cross-examination, innovative questioning tactics and proven methods of witness control to help deal with hostile witnesses and opposing counsel at both deposition and trial.

340   GW   ISSN 0942-8283
▼**R A K MITTEILUNGEN.** 1992. q. membership. (Rechtsanwaltskammer Koeln) Verlag Dr. Otto Schmidt KG, Unter den Ulmen 96-98, 50968 Cologne, Germany. TEL 0221-9373801.
FAX 0221-93738941. Ed. K. Knauth. circ. 5,600. **Document type:** bulletin.

R D E - RECHT DER ENERGIEWIRTSCHAFT. see *ENERGY*

340   SW   ISSN 0284-8775
R R; raettsfallsreferat fraan Regeringsraetten - Domstolsvaerket. 1973. irreg. (approx. 10/yr.). SEK 1100 (incl. a.). Domstolsverket, Organistionsenheten, S-551 81 Joenkoeping, Sweden. (Dist. by: Allmaenna Foerlaget AB. S-106 47 Stockholm, Sweden) **Document type:** government publication.
    ●Also available online.
    Formerly (until 1988): Raettsfallsreferat fraan Regeringsraetten och Kammarraetterna.

340 332   BL
R T - INCOLA. (Revista dos Tribunais) 1971. 36/yr. (3/m.). $330. Editora Revista dos Tribunais, Rua Conde do Pinhal 78, 01501 Sao Paulo, Brazil. Ed. Arnaldo Malheiros. adv.; bk.rev.; index. circ. 11,000.
    Formerly (until July 1955): R T - Informa.

RACHEL'S HAZARDOUS WASTE NEWS; providing news and resources for environmental justice. see *ENVIRONMENTAL STUDIES*

RAETTSFALL FRAAN BOSTADSDOMSTOLEN. see *HOUSING AND URBAN PLANNING*

RAETTSFALL FRAAN FOERSAEKRINGSOEVERDOMSTOLEN. see *INSURANCE*

347   SW   ISSN 0349-5272
RAETTSFALL FRAAN HOVRAETTERNA. Cover title: R H. 1980. 3/yr. (plus a. cumulation). SEK 880 (effective 1994). (Domstolsverket) Fritzes, S-106 47 Stockholm, Sweden.

RASSEGNA DELL'EQUO CANONE; locazioni e condominio. see *REAL ESTATE*

340   IT
RASSEGNA DI DIRITTO CIVILE. 1980. q. L.110000 to individuals; institutions L.176000; foreign L.210000 (effective 1993). Edizioni Scientifiche Italiane S.p.A., Via Chiatamone, 7, 80121 Naples, Italy. TEL 081-7645768. FAX 081-7646477. Ed. Pietro Perlingieri. circ. 1,200.

340   IT   ISSN 0300-3485
RASSEGNA DI DIRITTO, LEGISLAZIONE E MEDICINA LEGALE VETERINARIA. (Text in Italian; summaries in English, French and Italian) 1967. q. L.40000 (foreign L.45000). Universita degli Studi di Milano, Istituto di Medicina Legale e Legislazione Veterinaria, Via Celoria 10, 20133 Milan, Italy. TEL 23-62-724. Ed. Pierluigi Canziani. adv.; bk.rev.; index. circ. 1,000.

340   IT   ISSN 0033-9512
RASSEGNA DI DIRITTO PUBBLICO. 1945. q. Via A. Falcone 249, 80127 Naples, Italy. Ed. Alfonso Tesauro. index. circ. 1,000.

340   IT
RASSEGNA FORENSE. 1989. q. L.60000 (foreign L.90000). Casa Editrice Dott. A. Giuffre, Via Busto Arsizio 40, 20151 Milan, Italy. TEL 06-38000905. FAX 06-38009582.

RASSEGNA GIURIDICA DELL'ENERGIA ELETTRICA. see *ENGINEERING — Electrical Engineering*

349
RASSEGNA PARLAMENTARE. (Former name of issuing body: Istituto di Studi Legislativa) 1959. q. L.30000 (foreign L.60000) (effective 1993). Istituto per la Ricerca Normativa, Palazzo Grazioli, Via del Plebiscito 102, Rome 00186, Italy.
TEL 06-6793449. adv.; bk.rev. circ. 2,000.
    Formerly: Rassegna Parlamentare Schedario Legislativo (ISSN 0033-9814)

340   UK   ISSN 0048-6817
RATING AND VALUATION REPORTER. 1924. 11/yr. £155. Rating Publishers Ltd., 4 Breams Bldg., London EC4A 1AQ, England. TEL 0483-233571. FAX 0483-234804. Ed. Christopher Lewsley. adv.; bk.rev.; index. (tabloid format) **Indexed:** RICS.
—BLDSC (7295.350000).

340 100 UK ISSN 0952-1917
K18 CODEN: RAJUEQ
RATIO JURIS; an international journal of jurisprudence and philosophy law. 1988. q. £37.50($70) to individuals; institutions £75($150). Basil Blackwell Ltd., 108 Cowley Rd., Oxford, OX4 1JF, England. TEL 0865-791100. FAX 0865-791347. TELEX 837022-OXBOOK-G. Ed. Enrico Pattaro.
—BLDSC (7295.431000); Faxon; UnCover; UMI. **CCC**.
   Description: International and transcultural forum for philosophical ideas about the legal issues.

340 301.45 US ISSN 8755-8815
LA RAZA LAW JOURNAL. 1987. s-a. $30 (foreign $34) (effective 1994). (University of California at Berkeley, Boalt Hall School of Law) University of California Press, Journals Division, 2120 Berkeley Way, Berkeley, CA 94720. TEL 510-643-7154. FAX 510-642-9917. Ed.Bd. circ. 250. (back issues avail.; reprint service avail. from UMI) **Indexed**: Chic.Per.Ind. **Document type**: academic/scholarly publication.
—UnCover. **CCC**.
   Description: Provides a forum for the analysis of pressing social issues affecting the Latino community.
   Refereed Serial

340 US ISSN 1046-9966
KF1298.A15
REAL ESTATE - ENVIRONMENTAL LIABILITY NEWS; the bi-weekly report on litigation, regulation, and industry practice. 1989. bi-w. $547 (foreign $569). Buraff Publications (Subsidiary of: Millin Publications, Inc.), 1350 Connecticut Ave., N.W., Ste. 1000, Washington, DC 20036. TEL 800-333-1291. FAX 202-862-0999. Ed. Louis LaBrecque. (back issues avail.) **Document type**: newsletter.
—**CCC**.
   Description: Reports and analysis on litigation involving environmental liability in business transactions, innovative solutions to liability problems, changing federal and state requirements, and industry practices.

346.043 US
REAL ESTATE LAW DIGEST (SUPPLEMENT). base vol. (plus s-a. supplement). $115 (foreign $166.95) (effective 1994). Warren Gorham Lamont, One Penn Plaza, New York, NY 10119. TEL 212-971-5000. FAX 212-971-5240. (Subscr. to: The Park Square Bldg., 31 St. James Ave., Boston, MA 02116-4112. TEL 800-950-1207) (also avail. in microform from UMI; reprint service avail. from UMI) **Document type**: trade publication.

346.043 US ISSN 0048-6868
K18
REAL ESTATE LAW JOURNAL. 1972. q. $131.50 (overseas $197.50) (effective 1994). Warren Gorham Lamont, One Penn Plaza, New York, NY 10119. TEL 212-971-5000. FAX 212-971-5240. (Subscr to: The Park Square Bldg., 31 St. James Ave., Boston, MA 02116-4112. TEL 800-950-1207) Ed. R.J. Aalberts. bk.rev.; bibl. (also avail. in microform from UMI; reprint service avail. from RRI,UMI) **Indexed**: ABI Inform., Abstr.Bk.Rev.Curr.Leg.Per., Bank.Lit.Ind., BPIA, Bus.Ind., C.L.I., L.R.I., Leg.Cont., Leg.Per., P.A.I.S., SSCI. **Document type**: trade publication.
—BLDSC (7303.280900); Faxon; UnCover; UMI. **CCC**.
   Description: Draws upon the expertise of leading real estate attorneys, tax specialists, financial experts, and government officials. Covers joint venture agreements, leasebacks, real estate tax shelters, real estate investment trusts, zoning, option agreements, landlords' responsibilities, and new financing methods.
   Refereed Serial

346.043 US ISSN 0162-752X
KF570
REAL ESTATE LAW REPORT. 1971. m. $115.25 (overseas $160.50). Warren Gorham Lamont, One Penn Plaza, New York, NY 10119. TEL 212-971-5000. FAX 212-971-5240. (Subscr. to: The Park Square Bldg., 31 St. James Ave., Boston, MA 02116-4112. TEL 800-950-1207) Ed.Bd. (looseleaf format; also avail. in microform from UMI) **Document type**: newsletter.
—**CCC**.
   Description: Presents case histories in a jargon-free style so that real estate professionals as well as attorneys can keep up with the legal developments in the real estate field. Follows each history with an editorial observation.

333.33 346.043 US
REAL PROPERTY INSTITUTE; troubled projects: workout techniques and litigation strategies. a. $42 softcover. Continuing Education of the Bar - California, University of California Extension, 2300 Shattuck Ave., Berkeley, CA 94704. TEL 510-642-6211; 800-924-3924. FAX 510-642-3788. (Co-sponsor: State Bar of California)

346.043 US ISSN 0898-1698
KFC140.A15
REAL PROPERTY LAW REPORTER. 1977. 8/yr. $175. Continuing Education of the Bar - California, University of California Extension, 2300 Shattuck Ave., Berkeley, CA 94704. TEL 510-642-2064; 800-924-3924. FAX 510-642-3788. (Co-sponsor: State Bar of California) Ed. Jo Sherlin. (tabloid format; back issues avail.)

REAL PROPERTY, PROBATE AND TRUST LAW NEWSLETTER. see *REAL ESTATE*

340 SA ISSN 0250-0329
K18
DE REBUS; the S A attorneys' journal. (Text in English, occasionally in Afrikaans) 1956. m. R.114 (foreign R.150) (effective 1994). Association of Law Societies, P.O. Box 36626 Menlo Park, Pretoria 0102, South Africa. TEL 27-12-3423330. FAX 27-12-3423305. Ed. Philip van der Merwe. adv.: B&W page R.2194.50, color page R.3431.40; trim 297 x 210. bk.rev.; index. circ. 12,200. **Indexed**: Ind.S.A.Per.
   Formerly (until 1979): De Rebus Procuratoriis (ISSN 0045-9755)
   Description: Publishes articles on law and practice, finance and office administration, professional news and practical aids.

340 917.306 US
RECENT ETHICS OPINIONS. irreg. $35. American Bar Association, Center for Professional Responsibility, 541 N. Fairbanks Ct., Chicago, IL 60611-3314. TEL 312-988-5555. (looseleaf format)
   Description: Describes recent opinions on lawyer discipline and professional responsibility.

340 NP ISSN 1017-1452
RECENT LAWS OF NEPAL. (Text in English) 1989. bi-m. $60. Legal Research Associates, P.O. Box 828, Kathmandu, Nepal. TEL 977-1-272-534. FAX 977-1-225-348. Ed. Dhruba Bar Singh Thapa.

RECHERCHES INSTITUTIONNELLES. see *RELIGIONS AND THEOLOGY*

340 SZ ISSN 0253-9810
RECHT; Zeitschrift fuer juristische Ausbildung und Praxis. 1983. 6/yr. 80 SFr. (students 55 SFr.). Staempfli und Cie AG, Hallerstr. 7-9, CH-3001 Bern, Switzerland. TEL 031-276666. FAX 031-3006688. Ed. Wolfgang Wiegand. adv. circ. 2,500. **Document type**: bulletin.
—**CCC**.

RECHT & PSYCHIATRIE. see *PSYCHOLOGY*

340 GW ISSN 0342-1945
RECHT DER ARBEIT; Zeitschrift fuer die Wissenschaft und Praxis des gesamten Arbeitsrechts. 1948. bi-m. DM.226. (Deutscher Arbeitsgerichtsverband e.V.) C.H. Beck'sche Verlagsbuchhandlung, Wilhelmstr. 9, 80801 Munich, Germany. TEL 089-38189-338. FAX 089-38189-398. TELEX 5215085-BECK-D. (Co-sponsor: Institut fuer Arbeits- und Wirtschaftsrecht der Univeristaet zu Koeln) Ed.Bd. adv.: B&W page DM.1800; trim 260 x 186. circ. 1,800. (back issues avail.) **Indexed**: ELLIS. **Document type**: bulletin.
—BLDSC (7309.300000); SWETS.

RECHT DER DATENVERARBEITUNG; Zeitschrift fuer Praxis und Wissenschaft. see *COMPUTERS — Computer Security*

340 330 GW ISSN 0342-8869
DAS RECHT DER WIRTSCHAFT. (Supplement: Schriftenreihe Recht der Wirtschaft) 1948. s-m. DM.288. Richard Boorberg Verlag (Stuttgart), Scharrstr. 2, 70563 Stuttgart, Germany. Ed. Klaus Krohn. adv. **Document type**: bulletin.
   Former titles: Chef; Wichtigste fuer den Chef (ISSN 0043-5236); Rechtsarchiv der Wirtschaft (ISSN 0034-1355)

340 NE ISSN 0165-7607
RECHT EN KRITIEK. 1975. 4/yr. fl.56.25. Stichting Ars Aequi, Postbus 1043, 6501 BA Nijmegen, Netherlands. TEL 31-80-223506. FAX 31-80-241108. adv.; bk.rev. circ. 850.
—SWETS.

340 GW ISSN 0034-1339
RECHT IM AMT; Zeitschrift fuer Behoerden, Verwaltungen und oeffentliche Betriebe. 1954. bi-m. DM.144. Luchterhand Verlag, Heddesdorferstr. 31, 56564 Neuwied, Germany. TEL 02631-801-0. FAX 02631-801210. TELEX 867853-HLVN-D. Ed. Peter Stechele. adv.; bk.rev.; index. circ. 1,200. **Document type**: bulletin.
—**CCC**.

340 GW ISSN 0344-7871
RECHT UND POLITIK; Vierteljahreshefte fuer Rechts- und Verwaltungspolitik. 1965. q. DM.54. Berlin Verlag Arno Spitz GmbH, Pacelliallee 5, 14195 Berlin, Germany. TEL 030-8326232. FAX 030-8316249. Eds. Gerhard Kunze, Rudolf Wassermann. adv.; bk.rev. circ. 1,050. **Document type**: academic/scholarly publication.
—BLDSC (7309.376500).
   Description: Deals with problems and background of administration and jurisdiction in politics and legal practice.

340 AU
RECHT-WIRTSCHAFT-AUSSENHANDEL SCHRIFTENREIHE. 1981. irreg., vol.16, 1992. price varies. Manzsche Verlags-und Universitaetsbuchhandlung, Kohlmarkt 16, A-1014 Vienna, Austria. TEL 0222-531610. FAX 0222-53161-181. Eds. Helmut H. Haschek, Peter Doralt. circ. 1,500. **Document type**: monographic series.

340 GW ISSN 0934-4284
DAS RECHTS A B C. 1988. bi-m. DM.78. Wirtschaft Recht und Steuern Verlag, Fraunhoferstr. 5, 82152 Planegg, Germany. TEL 089-89517-0. FAX 089-89517250. (looseleaf format) **Document type**: consumer publication.

340 320 US ISSN 0080-0163
RECHTS- UND STAATSWISSENSCHAFTEN. 1947. irreg. price varies. Springer-Verlag, 175 Fifth Ave., New York, NY 10010. TEL 212-460-1500. FAX 212-473-6272. (Also: Berlin, Heidelberg, Tokyo and Vienna) (reprint service avail. from ISI) **Document type**: academic/scholarly publication.

340.09 NE ISSN 0169-9032
RECHTSHISTORISCH INSTITUUT LEIDEN. SERIES 1. irreg., vol.6, 1988. price varies. Stichting Rechtshistorisch Instituut Leiden, c/o Mevr. Drs. P.C.M. Scholvinck, Gravensteen, Pieterskerhof 6, 2311 SR Leiden, Netherlands. **Document type**: monographic series.

RECHTSMEDIZIN. see *MEDICAL SCIENCES — Forensic Sciences*

340 610   GW
RECHTSMEDIZINISCHE FORSCHUNGSERGEBNISSE.
1991. irreg., vol.5, 1993. DM.36. Schmidt-Roemhild Verlag, Mengstr. 16, 23552 Luebeck, Germany. TEL 0451-1605-0. FAX 0451-1605253. **Document type:** monographic series.

340   GW   ISSN 0080-018X
RECHTSPFLEGE JAHRBUCH. 1954. a. Gieseking-Verlag, Deckerstr. 2-10, 33617 Bielefeld, Germany.

340   GW   ISSN 0174-0156
RECHTSPFLEGER - STUDIENHEFTE. 1977. bi-m. DM.28. Bund Deutscher Rechtspfleger e.V., Zweibrueckenstr. 2, 80331 Munich, Germany. (Subscr. to: Verlag Ernst und Werner Gieseking GmbH, Postfach 130120, Deckerstr. 30, 4800 Bielefeld 13, Germany) Ed. Hans-Joachim von Schuckmann. adv.; bk.rev.; bibl.; index. circ. 2,000. (back issues avail.)
—CCC.

340   GW   ISSN 0034-1363
RECHTSPFLEGERBLATT. 1953. 6/yr. membership. Bund Deutscher Rechtspfleger, Postfach, D-8000 Munich 35, Germany. Ed. Peter Weber. adv.; bk.rev.; abstr.; stat. circ. 11,000. (tabloid format)

340   GW   ISSN 0931-6183
RECHTSPRECHUNG; Materialen und Studien. 1986. irreg., vol.6, 1993. price varies. (Max-Planck-Institut fuer Europaeische Rechtsgeschichte) Vittorio Klosterman, Frauenlobstr. 22, 60487 Frankfurt a.M., Germany. TEL 069-774011. FAX 069-708038. (Subscr. to: Postfach 900601, 60446 Frankfurt a.M., Germany) **Document type:** monographic series.

RECHTSSTAAT IN DER BEWAEHRUNG. see *LAW — International Law*

340   GW   ISSN 0034-1398
K18
RECHTSTHEORIE; Zeitschrift fuer Logik, Methodenlehre, Kybernetik und Soziologie des Rechts. 1970. q. DM.164. Duncker und Humblot GmbH, Postfach 410329, 12113 Berlin, Germany. TEL 030-7900060. FAX 030-79000631. Ed.Bd. adv.; bk.rev.; index. **Indexed:** Phil.Ind. **Document type:** academic/scholarly publication.
—SWETS. CCC.

340 320   AU
RECHTSWISSENSCHAFT UND SOZIALPOLITIK. 1966. irreg., vol.16, 1991. price varies. Manzsche Verlags- und Universitaetsbuchhandlung, Kohlmarkt 16, A-1014 Vienna, Austria. TEL 0222-531610. FAX 0222-53161-181. Eds. H. Floretta, R. Strasser. **Document type:** monographic series.
 Description: On law and social policy.

RECORDS RETENTION: LAW & PRACTICE. see *BUSINESS AND ECONOMICS*

333.7 340   US   ISSN 0743-5649
KF5638.A59
RECREATION AND PARKS LAW REPORTER. 1984. q. $100 to non-members; members $50. National Recreation and Park Association, 3101 Park Center Dr., Alexandria, VA 22302. TEL 703-820-4940. FAX 703-671-6772. Ed. James C. Kozlowski. index. circ. 1,000. (back issues avail.) **Indexed:** Sportsearch (1987-).
—UnCover; UMI.

342   BE
RECUEIL ANNUEL DE JURISPRUDENCE BELGE. 1950. a. 19500 BEF (for 1992 ed.). Maison Ferdinand Larcier S.A., Rue des Minimes 39, 1000 Brussels, Belgium. TEL 32-2-5124712. FAX 32-2-5139009. (back issues avail.)
 Description: Summarizes the preceding year's jurisprudence, with extensive commentary and supporting reference materials.

340   FR   ISSN 0034-1835
KJV112
RECUEIL DALLOZ-SIREY. (Includes three sections: Chroniques, Jurisprudence, Legislation) 1845. w. 1100 F. (foreign 1300 F.). Editions Dalloz, 11 rue Soufflot, 75240 Paris Cedex 05, France. (Subscr. to: 35, rue Tournefort, 75240 Paris Cedex 05, France. TEL 45-87-37-48) (Co-publisher: Editions Sirey) Ed. Jean Lahille. bk.rev.; bibl.; stat.; index, cum.index every 5 yrs. **Indexed:** ELLIS.
—SWETS. CCC.
 Formerly: Recueil Dalloz.

340   FR   ISSN 0532-3940
RECUEIL DES DECISIONS DU CONSEIL CONSTITUTIONNEL. 1960. a. price varies. Imprimerie Nationale, B.P. 514, 59505 Douai Cedex, France. TEL 27-93-70-70. FAX 27-93-70-96. TELEX 120 389 F. (back issues avail.)

340   FR   ISSN 0249-7271
RECUEIL DES DECISIONS DU CONSEIL D'ETAT. 1821. bi-m. 615 F. (foreign 720 F.). Editions Sirey, 11 rue Soufflot, 75240 Paris Cedex 05, France. TEL 40-51-54-54. FAX 45-87-37-48. TELEX 206 446 F. (Subscr. to: 35, rue Tournefort, 75240 Paris Cedex 05, France. TEL 40-51-54-35. FAX 45-87-37-48) (reprint service avail. from SCH)
—SWETS. CCC.

340   SY
RECUEIL DES LOIS ET DE LA LEGISLATION FINANCIERE DE LA REPUBLIQUE ARABE SYRIENNE. (Text in French) m. $275 (effective 1993). B.P. 539, Damascus, Syria. TEL 237950. Ed. Mouna Michel Seriani. (looseleaf format)
 Description: Publishes translations of all laws and decrees appearing in Syria.

349 368   FR   ISSN 0034-1878
RECUEIL JURIDIQUE DE L'EST SECURITE SOCIALE; doctrine jurisprudence, documents administratifs. 1947. q. 275 F. Association Juridique de l'Est, 25 rue Jean Mieg, 68100 Mulhouse, France. TEL 89-45-82-16. FAX 89-66-33-06. Ed. R. Schwob. bibl. circ. 1,000.

340   FR
RECUEIL PERIODIQUE DES JURIS-CLASSEURS: DROIT CIVIL. q. Editions Techniques, 123, rue d'Alesia, 75014 Paris, France. TEL 45-39-22-91. FAX 45-42-81-55. TELEX EIDTEC 270737.
 Formerly: Juris-Classeurs. Droit Civil.

340 330   US
THE REED MCCLURE LETTER. 1985. 4/yr. free. Reed McClure, 3600 Columbia Center, 701 Fifth Ave., Seattle, WA 98104-7081. TEL 206-292-4900. FAX 206-223-0152. Ed. Denise Dee Behrens. circ. 6,800. **Document type:** newsletter.

340   AT   ISSN 0313-153X
REFORM. 1976. q. Aus.$12. Law Reform Commission, G.P.O. Box 3708, Sydney, N.S.W. 2001, Australia. TEL 02-231-1733. FAX 02-223-1203. Ed. Evelyn McWilliams. bk.rev. circ. 1,800. (also avail. in microform from UMI,PMC; back issues avail.) **Document type:** bulletin.
 Description: Bulletin of law reform news, views and information.

340   US
THE REFORMER. 1986. m. membership. American Tort Reform Association, 1212 New York Ave., N.W., Ste. 515, Washington, DC 20005. TEL 202-682-1163. FAX 202-682-1022. Ed. Martin Connor. (back issues avail.) **Document type:** newsletter.

344.73   US
KF3827.E87
REFUSAL OF TREATMENT LEGISLATION (YEAR). (Supplement avail.) 1975. a. $175 to non-members; members $157.50. Choice in Dying, Inc., 200 Varick St., New York, NY 10014. TEL 212-366-5540; 800-989-WILL. FAX 212-366-5337. Ed. Ann Fade. (back issues avail.)
 Former titles: Handbook of Living Will Laws (ISSN 0886-7402); Society for the Right to Die. Handbook (ISSN 0198-8786); Legislative Manual (ISSN 0193-550X)

340 362   US   ISSN 0034-317X
REGAN REPORT ON HOSPITAL LAW. 1960. m. $48. Medica Press Inc., Westminster Sq. Bldg., Ste. 500, 10 Dorrance St., Providence, RI 02903-2018. TEL 401-421-4747. Ed. A. David Tammelleo, J.D. stat. circ. 5,000. (also avail. in microform from UMI; reprint service avail. from UMI)
—UMI. CCC.
 Description: Reports the latest appellate court decisions on hospital law in a case and comment format.

340 610   US   ISSN 0034-3188
REGAN REPORT ON MEDICAL LAW. 1968. m. $48. Medica Press Inc., Westminster Sq. Bldg., Ste. 500, 10 Dorrance St., Providence, RI 02903-2018. TEL 401-421-4747. Ed. A. David Tammelleo, J.D. stat. circ. 5,000. (also avail. in microform from UMI; reprint service avail. from UMI)
—UMI. CCC.
 Description: Reports the latest appellate court decisions on medical law.

340 610.73   US   ISSN 0034-3196
REGAN REPORT ON NURSING LAW. 1960. m. $48. Medica Press Inc., Westminster Sq. Bldg., Ste. 500, 10 Dorrance St., Providence, RI 02903-2018. TEL 401-421-4747. Ed. A. David Tammelleo, J.D. stat. circ. 10,000. (also avail. in microform from UMI; reprint service avail. from UMI) **Indexed:** C.I.N.L., Int.Nurs.Ind.
—BLDSC (7336.435000); UMI. CCC.
 Description: Reports the latest appellate court decisions on nursing law in a case and comment format.

340   NE   ISSN 0920-8720
REGEL & RECHT NIEUWS. fortn. fl.95. Delwel Uitgeverij B.V., Postbus 19110, 2500 CC The Hague, Netherlands. TEL 31-70-3624800. FAX 31-70-3605606. Ed. J.M. Stevers.

340   US   ISSN 1056-3962
K18
REGENT UNIVERSITY LAW REVIEW. 1991. s-a. $12 per no. Regent University, School of Law, Virginia Beach, VA 23464-9800. TEL 804-523-7439. Ed. Robert H. Woods, Jr. **Document type:** academic/scholarly publication.
—UnCover.

REGERINGSRAETTENS AARSBOK. see *PUBLIC ADMINISTRATION*

REGIMEN LEGAL TRIBUTARIO. see *BUSINESS AND ECONOMICS — Public Finance, Taxation*

340   SA
REGIONAL LEVIES SERVICE. a. R.95. Butterworth Publishers (Pty.) Ltd., P.O. Box 792, Durban 4000, South Africa. TEL 27-31-294247. FAX 27-31-283255. Ed. Trevor Emslie.

340   IT   ISSN 0391-7576
REGIONI; rivista bimestrale di documentazione giuridica. 1973. bi-m. L.150000. (Istituto di Studi Giuridici Regionali) Societa Editrice Il Mulino, Strada Maggiore, 37, 40125 Bologna, Italy. TEL 051-256011. FAX 051-256034. Ed. Umberto Pototschnig. adv.; index. circ. 1,500. (back issues avail.) **Indexed:** ELLIS.

REGULATION OF INVESTMENT ADVISERS. see *BUSINESS AND ECONOMICS — Investments*

340 332.64   US
REGULATION OF THE COMMODITIES FUTURES AND OPTIONS MARKETS. 1983. 2 base vols. (plus a. suppl.). $195. Shepard's - McGraw-Hill, Inc., Box 35300, Colorado Springs, CO 80935-3530. TEL 800-525-2474. (looseleaf format)
 Description: Discusses the Commodity Exchange Act and CFTC regulations. Provides examples of day-to-day issues, in-depth analyses of law and regulations related to exchanges and market participants and off-exchange instruments.

343   SZ
REIHE STRAFRECHT. 1976. irreg., vol.17, 1991. Verlag Rueegger AG, Postfach 1470, CH-8040 Zurich, Switzerland. TEL 01-4912130. FAX 01-4931176. **Document type:** monographic series.

340   PO
RELACAO DOS ADVOGADOS E DAS SOCIEDADES DE ADVOGADOS. (Supplement avail.: Adenda) a. Ordem dos Advogados Portugueses, Largo de S. Domingos, 14 10, 1194 Lisbon, Portugal. TEL 867152. FAX 862403. TELEX 18404 LEXORD.
 Description: Lists lawyers and their societies in Portugal.

3310 LAW

340   US
RELATIVE VALUES: DETERMINING ATTORNEYS' FEES. 1985. base vol. (plus a. suppl.). $95. Shepard's - McGraw-Hill, Inc., Box 35300, Colorado Springs, CO 80935-3530. TEL 800-525-2474. (looseleaf format)
   Description: Guide to legal billing and management procedures.

RELAZIONI INDUSTRIALI. see *BUSINESS AND ECONOMICS — Labor And Industrial Relations*

RELIGION AND LAW REVIEW. see *RELIGIONS AND THEOLOGY — Islamic*

REMEDIATION; the journal of environmental cleanup costs, technologies & techniques. see *ENVIRONMENTAL STUDIES — Waste Management*

340   CC   ISSN 1004-4043
RENMIN JIANCHA/PEOPLE'S PROCURATORIAL WORK. (Text in Chinese) 1953-1960; 1966-1978; resumed 1979. m. Y22.80. Zhongguo Jiancha Baoshe, No. 4A, Jinyuan Rd., Shijinshan District, Beijing 100043, People's Republic of China. TEL 861-8876061. FAX 861-8876068. (Dist. overseas by: China International Book Trading Corp., P.O. Box 399, Beijing, P.R. China) Ed. Yuan Qiguo.
   Formerly (until Jun. 1956): Jiancha Gongzuo Tongxun.

347   II
RENT CASES; a monthly law reporter. m. Rs.48. International Law Book Co., Nijhawan Bldg., Church Rd., Kashmere Gate, Delhi 6, India. Ed. Swarn Bhatia Nkjhawan.

340   FR
REPERTOIRE DU NOTARIAT DEFRENOIS. 1884. 24/yr. 260 F. 83 av. Denfert-Rochereau, 75014 Paris, France. TEL 43-54-80-20. FAX 43-29-63-71. Ed. M. Vion. adv.; bk.rev. circ. 9,500.

340   SP
REPERTORIO ARANZADI DEL TRIBUNAL CONSTITUCIONAL. (Includes q. bound vols. with indexes.) 1981. irreg., (several/wk.). 43450 ptas. (effective 1991). Editorial Aranzadi, S.A., Avda. Carlos III, 34, Apdo. 111, 31080 Pamplona, Spain. TEL 948-331212. FAX 948-330919. bibl.; index, cum.index 1981-1990.

340   SP
REPERTORIO CRONOLOGICO DE LEGISLACION. (Includes bound vols. with indexes.) 1930. irreg., (several/wk.). 44096 ptas. (includes Indice Progresivo de Legislacion)(effective 1991). Editorial Aranzadi, S.A., Avda. Carlos III, 34, Apdo. 111, 31080 Pamplona, Spain. TEL 948-331212. FAX 948-330919. bibl.; index.
● Also available on CD-ROM.

340   SP
REPERTORIO DE JURISPRUDENCIA. (Includes bound vols. and m. Indice Progresivo.) 1930. w. 63000 ptas. (effective 1992). Editorial Aranzadi, S.A., Avda. Carlos III, 34, Apdo. 111, 31080 Pamplona, Spain. TEL 948-331212. FAX 948-330919. index.
● Also available on CD-ROM.

340   IT
REPERTORIO DEL FORO ITALIANO. 1876. a. L.1295000 (price varies). Zanichelli Editore, Via Irnerio 34, 40126 Bologna, Italy. TEL 051-293111. FAX 051-249782. abstr.; bibl.
● Available only on CD-ROM.

342   IT
REPERTORIO DELLE DECISIONI DELLA CORTE COSTITUZIONALE. 1956. biennial. price varies. Casa Editrice Dott. A. Giuffre, Via Busto Arsizio 40, 20151 Milan, Italy. TEL 02-38000905. FAX 02-3809582. Ed. Nicola Lipari.

347.9   IT
REPERTORIO DI GIURISPRUDENZA DEL LAVORO. 1968. biennial. price varies. Casa Editrice Dott. A. Giuffre, Via Busto Arsizio 40, 20151 Milan, Italy. TEL 02-38000905. FAX 02-3809582. Eds. Mario Pacifico, Enrico Pacifico.

340   AG
REPERTORIO GENERAL: LA LEY; fallos de la Corte Suprema Nacional y tribunales provinciales. m. plus s-a. cumulations. Arg.$160($320) Ley, S.A., Tucuman 1471, 1050 Buenos Aires, Argentina.

340 613.62   US   ISSN 1067-0483
KF1256.A75
▼ **REPETITIVE STRESS INJURY LITIGATION REPORTER.** 1992. m. $550. Andrews Publications, 1646 West Chester Pike, Box 1000, Westtown, PA 19395. TEL 215-399-6600; 800-345-1101. FAX 215-399-6610. Ed. Harry Armstrong. bibl.; stat.; cum.index. (looseleaf format; back issues avail.) **Document type:** newsletter.
   Description: Reports information on case developments concerning carpal tunnel injury and accumulative trauma disorders involving product liability and worker compensation issues.

340   GW   ISSN 0941-9195
▼ **REPORT BAYOBLG.** 1992. m. DM.90. Verlag Dr. Otto Schmidt KG, Unter den Ulmen 96-98, 50968 Cologne, Germany. TEL 0221-9373801. FAX 0221-93738941. TELEX 8883381. Ed. K.M. Groll. **Document type:** bulletin.

REPORT FROM STATE CIRCLE. see *PUBLIC ADMINISTRATION*

340 320   US   ISSN 0893-0708
REPORT FROM THE HILL. 6/yr. $10. League of Women Voters of the U S, 1730 M St., N.W., Washington, DC 20036. TEL 202-429-1965. FAX 202-429-0854. Ed. Ellen Weir. circ. 5,000. (tabloid format; back issues avail.) **Document type:** newsletter.
   Description: Legislative newsletter covering the league's issue priorities in Congress.

340   US   ISSN 8756-2057
REPORTER ON HUMAN REPRODUCTION & THE LAW; cases, statutes and materials on law and life sciences. 1971. bi-m. $75. (Legal-Medical Studies, Inc.) Legal-Medical Studies, Inc., Box 8219, Boston, MA 02114. TEL 617-742-7959. bk.rev.; abstr.; bibl.; circ. controlled. (back issues avail.)
   Description: Court decisions and reports on abortion, artificial insemination, in vitro fertilization, surrogate motherhood and genetic planning.

340   US   ISSN 8755-7509
KF300.A1
REPORTER ON THE LEGAL PROFESSION. 1979. a. $120. Legal-Medical Studies, Inc., Box 8219, Boston, MA 02114. TEL 617-742-7959. bk.rev.; abstr.; bibl.; index. (looseleaf format; back issues avail.) **Indexed:** C.L.I., Leg.Per.
   Description: Practical information on lawyer discipline, legal malpractice, fee issues and related subjects in cases in the United States and Canada.

REPRODUCTIVE FREEDOM LEGAL DOCKET. see *POLITICAL SCIENCE — Civil Rights*

REPRODUCTIVE RIGHTS UPDATE. see *POLITICAL SCIENCE — Civil Rights*

340   BE
RES ET JURA IMMOBILIA. q. 2200 Fr. Etablissements Emile Bruylant, 67 rue de la Regence, B-1000 Brussels, Belgium. TEL 02-512-9845.

340   US   ISSN 0557-9295
RES GESTAE. 1956. m. membership only. Indiana State Bar Association, 230 E. Ohio St., Indianapolis, IN 46204. TEL 317-639-5465. FAX 317-266-2588. Ed. Susan J. Ferrer. adv. (also avail. in microfilm from WSH; reprint service avail. from WSH) **Indexed:** C.L.I., L.R.I., Law Ofc.Info.Svc., Leg.Per. —Faxon; UnCover.

340   US
RES IPSA LOQUITUR. 1939. 3/yr. Georgetown University Law Center, Office of Public Relations, 600 New Jersey Ave., N.W., Washington, DC 20001. TEL 202-662-9690. Ed. Adrienne Kuehneman. bk.rev. circ. 19,000. (reprint service avail. from UMI)

RESEARCH IN LAW AND ECONOMICS; a research annual. see *BUSINESS AND ECONOMICS*

340   US
RESEARCH NOTES. * 1991. 4/yr. Trial Behavior Consulting, Inc., 600 Montgomery St., 5th Fl., San Francisco, CA 94111-2702. TEL 415-781-5879. FAX 415-362-8775. Ed. Ronald Beaton. **Document type:** newsletter.

RESEARCH RECOMMENDATIONS; economics, political & tax advisory letter. see *BUSINESS AND ECONOMICS — Small Business*

RESOLUTIONS, BELIEFS & POLICIES, CONSTITUTION AND BYLAWS. see *EDUCATION — School Organization And Administration*

RESOURCE RECYCLING'S BOTTLE - CAN RECYCLING UPDATE; markets, legislation, research, data, technology, economics. see *ENVIRONMENTAL STUDIES — Waste Management*

340 333.8   CN   ISSN 0714-5918
RESOURCES. 1982. q. free. Canadian Institute of Resources Law, Rm. 330, Professional Faculties Bldg., Faculty of Law, University of Calgary, Calgary, AB T2N 1N4, Canada. TEL 403-220-3200. FAX 403-282-6182. Ed. Nancy Money. circ. 6,200. **Document type:** newsletter.
   Description: Comments on current resources legal issues, with information on Institute publications and programs.

340   IT
RESPONSABILITA CIVILE E PREVIDENZA. 1930. bi-m. L.100000 (foreign L.150000). Casa Editrice Dott. A. Giuffre, Via Busto Arsizio 40, 20151 Milan, Italy. TEL 02-38000905. FAX 02-38009852. Eds. Gianguido Scalfi, Ugo Carnevali. adv. circ. 5,500.

RESPONSIBILITIES OF INSURANCE AGENTS AND BROKERS. see *INSURANCE*

340   US
RESTATEMENT IN THE COURTS. POCKET PARTS. 1977. a. price varies. (American Law Institute) American Law Institute Publishers, Box 64526, 50 West Kellogg Blvd., St. Paul, MN 55164-0526. TEL 215-243-1650. (Subscr. to: 4025 Chestnut St., Philadelphia, PA 19104) Ed. Violet Meehan. circ. 2,400.
   Formerly (until 1976): Restatement in the Courts. Supplements.

340   NO   ISSN 0105-1121
RETFAERD. (Text in Scandinavian languages) 1976. q. DKK 320. Scandinavian University Press, P.O. Box 2959 Toeyen, N-0608 Oslo, Norway. (Subscr. to: Akademis Forlag, P.O. Box 54, DK-1002 Copenhagen K, Denmark. TEL 45-33-11-98-26) Ed.Bd. bk.rev. circ. 900. **Document type:** academic/scholarly publication.

RETIREMENT AND BENEFIT PLANNING; strategy and design for businesses and tax-exempt organizations. see *BUSINESS AND ECONOMICS — Personnel Management*

340   NO   ISSN 0034-6187
RETTENS GANG. 1933. 22/yr. NOK 850. Advokatenes Servicekontor - Norwegian Bar Association, Kr.Augustsgt. 9, 0164 Oslo, Norway. Ed. Thor Jensen. index, cum.index.

340 320.531   NE   ISSN 0925-9880
K18   CODEN: RCELEM
REVIEW OF CENTRAL AND EAST EUROPEAN LAW. (Text in English) 1975. 6/yr. fl.515($268.50) (effective 1994). (Rijksuniversiteit te Leiden, Documentation Office for East European Law) Martinus Nijhoff Publishers, Human Rights and International Law (Subsidiary of Kluwer Academic Publishers Group), Postbus 163, 3300 AD Dordrecht, Netherlands. TEL 31-78-334911. FAX 31-78-334254. TELEX 29245 KAPG NL. (Dist. by: Kluwer Academic Publishers Group, P.O. Box 322, 3300 AH Dordrecht, Netherlands. TEL 31-78-524400. FAX 31-78-524474; N. America dist. addr.: Box 358, Accord Sta., Hingham, MA 02018-0358. TEL 617-871-6600. FAX 617-871-6528) (Co-publisher: Graham & Trotman Ltd., UK) Ed. F.J.M Feldbrugge. (also avail. in microform from UMI; back issues avail.) **Indexed:** C.L.I., Foreign Leg.Per., Leg.Per. **Document type:** academic/scholarly publication.
—BLDSC (7788.927000); UnCover; SWETS; UMI. CCC.
   Former titles (until 1992): Review of Socialist Law (ISSN 0165-0300); Communist Law Journal.
   Description: Discusses issues in comparative and international law, with a focus on legal developments in central and eastern Europe, and legal issues relating to increased European integration.
   Refereed Serial

340 616.89 US ISSN 1045-1609
K18
REVIEW OF CLINICAL PSYCHIATRY AND THE LAW. 1990.
a. American Psychiatric Press, Inc., 1400 K St.,
N.W., Washington, DC 20005. TEL 202-682-6240.
FAX 202-789-2648.
—BLDSC (0853.360000).

340 GH ISSN 0034-6578
K18
REVIEW OF GHANA LAW. 1969. a. $46.50. Council for
Law Reporting, Box M.165, Accra, Ghana. Ed. S.Y.
Bimpong-Buta. adv.; bk.rev.; index. circ. 2,000. (also
avail. in microform from UMI; reprint service avail.
from UMI) **Indexed:** Documentatieblad.
—BLDSC (7790.767000).

340 US ISSN 0048-7481
K14.E97
REVIEW OF LAW & SOCIAL CHANGE. 1971. 4/yr. $20
per vol. (foreign $24) (effective 1994). New York
University, Review of Law & Social Change, 110 W.
Third St., New York, NY 10012.
TEL 212-998-6370. FAX 212-995-4032. adv.;
bk.rev. circ. 850. (processed; also avail. in
microform from UMI; microfilm from RRI; reprint
service avail. from RRI,UMI) **Indexed:** C.L.I.,
Crim.Just.Abstr., L.R.I., Leg.Per., Psychol.Abstr.
Document type: academic/scholarly publication.
—BLDSC (6089.820500); UnCover; UMI.

340 US ISSN 0734-4015
K18
REVIEW OF LITIGATION. 1981. 3/yr. $25 (foreign
$28). University of Texas at Austin, School of Law
Publications, Box 149084, Austin, TX 78714-9084.
TEL 512-471-1106. FAX 512-471-6988. bk.rev.
circ. 800. (also avail. in microform from WSH,PMC;
back issues avail.; reprint service avail. from WSH)
—Faxon; UnCover; UMI.
Description: Articles, comments and notes on
current legal topics.

340 CL
REVISTA CHILENA DE DERECHO. 1974. q. $50.
Universidad Catolica de Chile, Facultad de Derecho,
Casilla 114D, Santiago, Chile. Ed. Jose Luis Cea.
bk.rev. circ. 1,000.

340 CU ISSN 0864-165X
REVISTA CUBANA DE DERECHO. (Text in Spanish;
summaries in English, French, Russian) q. $22 in S.
America; N. America $24; elsewhere $28.
(Comision de Estudios Juridicos) Ediciones Cubanas,
Obispo No. 527, Apdo. 605, Havana, Cuba.
—BLDSC (7852.102000).
Description: Covers legal topics of interest to all
members of the legal and judicial community.

340 AG ISSN 0325-0601
REVISTA DE CIENCIAS JURIDICAS SOCIALES. 1922.
irreg. exchange basis. Universidad Nacional del
Litoral, Facultad de Ciencias Juridicas y Sociales,
Candido Pujato 2751, 3000 Santa Fe, Argentina.
bk.rev. circ. 500.

340 BO ISSN 0034-7868
REVISTA DE DERECHO. q. Universidad Boliviana Mayor
de San Andres, Facultad de Economia, Juridica y
Ciencias Sociales, Departamento de Publicaciones,
La Paz, Bolivia. Dir. Dr. Alipio Valencia Vega.

340 HO
REVISTA DE DERECHO. 1969. s-a. $7 per no.
Universidad Nacional Autonoma de Honduras,
Instituto de Investigacion Juridica, Bloque de Aulas,
2, Ciudad Universitaria, Tegucigalpa, D.C., Honduras.
Ed. Jorge Omar Casco. bk.rev.

300 340 CL ISSN 0303-9986
REVISTA DE DERECHO (CONCEPCION). vol.33, 1965.
s-a. exchange basis. Universidad de Concepcion,
Escuela de Derecho, Casilla 26C, Concepcion, Chile.
FAX 222712. (Subscr. to: Biblioteca Central, Canje y
Donacion, Casilla 1807, Concepcion, Chile) Dir.
Hernan Troncoso Larronde. circ. 1,000.
Formerly: Revista de Derecho y Ciencias Sociales
(ISSN 0034-7957)

340 CL
REVISTA DE DERECHO (VALPARAISO). 1976. a. $40.
(Universidad Catolica de Valparaiso, Escuela de
Derecho) Ediciones Universitarias de Valparaiso,
Casilla 1415, Valparaiso, Chile. TEL 032-252900.
FAX 032-272746. TELEX 230389 UCVAL CL. Dir.
Alejandro Guzman Brito. bk.rev. circ. 300. **Document
type:** academic/scholarly publication.

349 UY ISSN 0797-0501
REVISTA DE DERECHO COMERCIAL Y DE LA EMPRESA.
1977. q. $35. Fundacion de Cultura Universitaria,
25 de Mayo 568, Casilla de Correo No. 1155,
Montevideo, Uruguay. TEL 961152. FAX 952549.
Ed. Sagunto F. Perez Fontana. bk.rev.; bibl.; pat.;
index.
Supersedes (1964-1973): Revista de Derecho
Comercial (ISSN 0034-7876)

340 388.31 SP
REVISTA DE DERECHO DE LA CIRCULACION. 6/yr. Santa
Engracia 151, 28003 Madrid, Spain.
TEL 1-533-15-78. FAX 1-533-61-96. Ed. Manuel
Maestro Lopez.

346.066 332 336 SP ISSN 0484-6885
**REVISTA DE DERECHO FINANCIERO Y DE HACIENDA
PUBLICA.** 1951. bi-m. 12500 ptas.($122)
Editoriales de Derecho Reunidas, S.A., Valverde 32,
1o Izqda., 28004 Madrid, Spain. TEL 1-521-0246.
FAX 1-521-0539. Ed. J.L. Perez de Ayala. index.
(back issues avail.)

340 UY ISSN 0034-7906
**REVISTA DE DERECHO, JURISPRUDENCIA Y
ADMINISTRACION.** (Text in Spanish; occasionally in
English, French, Portuguese) 1894. m. $18. c/o
Prof. Horacio Cassinelli Munoz, 18 de Julio 1745,
Montevideo, Uruguay. bk.rev.; bibl.; index, cum.index.
circ. 2,000. (tabloid format)

340 331 AG
REVISTA DE DERECHO LABORAL. m. Calle Uruguay
115, Buenos Aires, Argentina.

343 UY
REVISTA DE DERECHO PENAL. 1981. irreg. $35.
Fundacion de Cultura Universitaria, 25 de Mayo
568, Casilla de Correo No. 1155, 11000
Montevideo, Uruguay. TEL 961152. FAX 952549.

340 SP ISSN 0034-7922
REVISTA DE DERECHO PRIVADO. 1913. 11/yr.
14000 ptas.($137) Editoriales de Derecho
Reunidas, S.A., Valverde 32, 1o, 28004 Madrid,
Spain. TEL 91-5210246. Dir. Manuel Albaladejo.
adv.; bk.rev.; index, cum.index. circ. 4,500.
—BLDSC (7852.480000); SWETS.

340 CL
REVISTA DE DERECHO PROCESAL. 1971. s-a.
(Universidad de Chile, Facultad de Ciencias Juridicas
y Sociales, Departamento de Derecho Procesal)
Editorial Juridica de Chile, Avda. Ricardo Lyon 946,
Casilla 4256, Santiago, Chile.

340 CL
REVISTA DE DERECHO PUBLICO.* 1950. irreg.
Universidad Nacional de Tucuman, Instituto de
Derecho Publico, Ayacucho 491, 4000 San Miguel
de Tucuman, Argentina.

342 VE
REVISTA DE DERECHO PUBLICO. q. Bs.350.00. Editorial
Juridica Venezolana, Apdo. Postal No. 17598,
Caracas, Venezuela.

340 CL ISSN 0716-0267
REVISTA DE DERECHO PUBLICO. 1965. s-a. $15.
Universidad de Chile, Facultad de Derecho, Casilla
94, Correo 22, Santiago, Chile. FAX 562-737-0445.
Dir. Eduardo Soto Kloss.
—BLDSC (7852.483000).

340 PR ISSN 0034-7930
LAW
REVISTA DE DERECHO PUERTORRIQUENO. 1961. q.
$15. Universidad Catolica de Puerto Rico, School of
Law, Ponce, PR 00732. Ed. Edna Santiago. bk.rev.;
bibl. circ. 1,000. **Indexed:** C.L.I., L.R.I., Leg.Per.

340 EC ISSN 0484-6923
REVISTA DE DERECHO SOCIAL ECUATORIANO.
1952-1956; resumed 1958. irreg. Universidad
Central del Ecuador, Box 2349, Quito, Ecuador. Ed.
H. Valencia.

349 PE ISSN 0034-7949
K19
REVISTA DE DERECHO Y CIENCIAS POLITICAS. 1936.
3/yr. S.300($10) Universidad Nacional Mayor de
San Marcos, Facultad de Derecho, Apdo. 524, Lima,
Peru. adv.; bk.rev.; bibl.; index, cum.index every 20
yrs. (1936-1956). circ. 4,500. (tabloid format)

340 630 VE
REVISTA DE DERECHO Y REFORMA AGRARIA. 1969. a.
$7. (Universidad de los Andes, Instituto
Iberoamericano de Derecho Agrario y Reforma
Agraria) Talleres Graficos, Merida, Venezuela.
FAX 074-404644. bk.rev.; bibl. circ. 1,200.

630 340 BL
REVISTA DE DIREITO AGRARIO. 1973. s-a. free. Instituto
Nacional de Colonizacao e Reforma Agraria,
Procurador Geral, Palacio do Desenvolvimento, 21
andar, Setor Bancario Norte CEP 70437, Brasilia,
DF, Brazil. Eds. Agnaldo Silva, Eliene Rodrigues da
Costa Maia.

340 BL
REVISTA DE DIREITO CIVIL; imobiliario, agrario e
empresarial. 1977. q. Cz.$800($80) Editora
Revista dos Tribunais, Rua Conde do Pinhal 78,
01501 Sao Paulo, Brazil. Ed. R. Limongi Franca.
adv.; bk.rev.; abstr.; bibl.; index. circ. 5,000.

340 BL
REVISTA DE DIREITO DO TRABALHO (PETROPOLIS).*
1973. irreg. Industrias Graficas Centrograf Ltd., Rua
Alencar Lima, 35- Grupo 903-7, Petropolis, Brazil.
Indexed: Int.Lab.Doc.

347.9 331 BL
REVISTA DE DIREITO DO TRABALHO (SAO PAULO).
1976. q. $60. Editora Revista dos Tribunais, Rua
Conde do Pinhal 78, 01501 Sao Paulo, Brazil. Ed.
Alvaro Malheiros. adv.; bk.rev.; abstr.; bibl.; index.
circ. 5,000.

340 BL
**REVISTA DE DIREITO MERCANTIL, INDUSTRIAL,
ECONOMICO, E FINANCEIRO.** 1951; N.S. 1971. q.
$40. (Instituto Brasileiro de Direito Comercial
Comparado) Editora Revista dos Tribunais, Rua
Conde do Pinhal, 78-01501 Sao Paulo, SP, Brazil.
(Co-sponsors: Biblioteca Tullio Ascarelli; Instituto de
Direito Economico e Financeiro) Ed. Alvaro
Malheiros. adv.; bk.rev.; bibl.; index. circ. 5,000.

340 BL ISSN 0034-8015
K19
REVISTA DE DIREITO PUBLICO. 1967. q. $80.
(Universidade de Sao Paulo, Instituto de Direito
Publico) Editora Revista dos Tribunais, Rua Conde do
Pinhal, 78, 01501 Sao Paulo, SP, Brazil. Ed. Dr.
Alvaro Malheiros. adv.; bk.rev.; abstr.; bibl.; index.
circ. 6,000.

340 BL
REVISTA DE DIREITO TRIBUTARIO. 1977. 2/yr. $80.
Editora Revista dos Tribunais, Rua Conde do Pinhal
78, 01501 Sao Paulo, Brazil. Ed. Geraldo Ataliba.
adv.; bk.rev.; bibl.; index. circ. 5,000.

340 AG
REVISTA DE ESTUDIOS PROCESALES. 1969. 2/yr. $30.
Centro de Estudios Procesales, Dorrego No. 1748,
2000 Rosario, Argentina. Ed. Adolfo Alvarado
Velloso. bk.rev.; abstr.; bibl.; charts; stat.; index,
cum.index. circ. 1,500.

340 AG
REVISTA DE HISTORIA DE DERECHO. 1973. a. (Instituto
de Investigaciones de Historia del Derecho) Librart
s.r.l., Departamento de Publicaciones Cientificas
Argentinas, Avda. Corrientes 127, Casilla Correo
Central 5047, Buenos Aires, Argentina. Dir. Ricardo
Zorraquin Becu.

340 BL ISSN 0034-835X
CODEN: RINLE7
REVISTA DE INFORMACAO LEGISLATIVA. 1964. q.
Cr.$4500. Senado Federal, Subsecretaria de Edicoes
Tecnicas, Anexo 1, 22 andar, Praca dos Tres
Poderes, 70160 Brasilia, D.F., Brazil. FAX 611156.
TELEX 612025SEFE BR. Dir. Anna Maria Villela.
cum.index: nos.1-100. circ. 5,000. (tabloid format)
Indexed: P.A.I.S.For.Lang.Ind.

340 SP
REVISTA DE LA FACULTAD DE DERECHO. a. Universidad
de Granada, Servicio de Publicaciones, Antiguo
Colegio Maximo, Campus de Cartuja, 18071
Granada, Spain. TEL 243930. Ed. Jose M. Perez
Prendes. **Document type:** academic/scholarly
publication.

LAW

340   PO   ISSN 0870-8487
REVISTA DE LEGISLACAO E DE JURISPRUDENCIA. 1868. m. $14.20. Coimbra Editora Limitada, Rua do Arnado, P.O. Box 101, 3002 Coimbra, Portugal. TEL 25459. index. circ. 3,250.

340   AG   ISSN 0034-8481
LAW
REVISTA DE LEGISLACION ARGENTINA. 1966. a. (in 3 vols.). $100 per volume. Jurisprudencia Argentina S.A., Talcahuano 650, 1013 Buenos Aires, Argentina. TEL 40-0528. Dir. Ricardo Estevez Boero. adv.; charts; illus.; stat.

340   SP
REVISTA DE LEGISLACION DE HACIENDA. 12/yr. Embajadores 55, 28012 Madrid, Spain. TEL 1-230-80-49. Ed. D.F. Gonzalez Ortiz.

340 300   CL
REVISTA DE LEGISLACION Y DOCUMENTACION EN DERECHO Y CIENCIAS SOCIALES. 1976. 4/yr. free. Congreso Nacional, Biblioteca, Compania 1175, Clasificador 1199, Santiago, Chile. Ed. Neville Blanc-Renard. index. circ. 600. (back issues avail.)
Formed by the merger of: Boletin de Legislacion Nacional; Boletin de Autoridades; Boletin de Documentacion en Derecho y Ciencias Sociales.

340   BL
REVISTA DE PROCESSO. 1976. q. $85. Editora Revista dos Tribunais, Rua Conde do Pinhal 78, 01501 Sao Paulo, Brazil. Ed. Arruda Alvim. adv.; bk.rev.; abstr.; bibl.; index. circ. 6,000.

340 330   AG
REVISTA DEL DERECHO INDUSTRIAL. 1979. 3/yr. $80 (effective Jan. 1992). Ediciones Depalma S.r.l., Talcahuano No. 494, Buenos Aires, Argentina. FAX 054-40-6913. Ed. Carlos Correa. bk.rev.
Description: Provides updated information on economic law, intellectual property, communications and computer law, from a Latin American point of view.

349   BL   ISSN 0034-9275
REVISTA DOS TRIBUNAIS. 1912. m. $375. Editora Revista dos Tribunais, Rua Conde do Pinhal, 78, 01501 Sao Paulo SP, Brazil. Ed. Alvaro Malheiros. adv.; bk.rev.; abstr.; bibl.; cum.index. circ. 11,000.

340   BL   ISSN 0034-9739
K19
REVISTA JURIDICA. 1977. irreg. (1-3/yr.). Cr.$30($7.) Av. Paris 72, ZC-24 Bonsucesso, 20000 Rio de Janeiro, Brazil. Eds. Angelito A. Aiquel, Jamil A. Aiquel. illus.; charts.

340   BO
REVISTA JURIDICA. 1938. q. Universidad Boliviana Mayor de "San Simon", Departamento de Derecho, Casilla 658, Cochambamba, Bolivia. bibl.

340   CU
REVISTA JURIDICA. q. $16 in N. America; S. America $18; Europe $21. (Ministerio de Justicia, Departamento de Divulgacion) Ediciones Cubanas, Obispo No. 527, Apdo. 605, Havana, Cuba. (And: O No. 261st 23 y 25, Vedado, Havana, Cuba.)

340   SP   ISSN 0210-4296
REVISTA JURIDICA DE CATALUNA. 1895. q. Academia de Jurisprudencia y Legislacion, Colegio de Abogados de Barcelona, Mallorca 283, 08037 Barcelona, Spain. Ed.Bd. bk.rev.; bibl. circ. 5,500.
Indexed: ELLIS.

340   SP   ISSN 0213-5795
REVISTA JURIDICA DE NAVARRA. 1986. s-a. 1600 ptas. Gobierno de Navarra, Fondo de Publicaciones, Navas de Tolosa, 21, 31002 Pamplona, Spain. TEL 10-71-21. FAX 22-76-73.

340   PE
REVISTA JURIDICA DEL PERU. 1950. q. $100. Julio Ayasta Gonzalez, Ed. & Pub., Lampa 1115, Lima, Peru. TEL 277854. adv.; bk.rev. circ. 2,000.

619 331   CL
REVISTA JURIDICA DEL TRABAJO. 1929. 10/yr. $180. (Sociedad Chilena de Derecho del Trabajo) Editorial Arbi Ltda., Avenida Bulnes 180, ofc. 80, Casilla 9447, Santiago, Chile. TEL 00562-6967474. FAX 00562-6726320. Ed. Veronica Acosta Zavala. bk.rev. circ. 1,100. (back issues avail.)

340   DR
REVISTA JURIDICA DOMINICANA. 1939. q. (some double issues). (Secretaria de Estado de Justicia y Trabajo) Editoria del Caribe, Autopista Duarto Km. 7 1-2, Apdo. 416, Santo Domingo, Dominican Republic.

340   SP   ISSN 0211-2744
REVISTA JURIDICA ESPAÑOLA LA LEY. Variant title: Ley Jurisprudencia. 1980. d. 75600 ptas. Monterrey 1, 28230 Las Rozas, Spain. TEL 6345362. Dir. Jose Manuel Otero Lastres.

340   PE
REVISTA PERUANA DE DERECHO DE LA EMPRESA. 1984. q. $100. Revista Peruana de Derecho de la Empresa y Asesorandina, Av. Salaverry 674, Of. 403 Jesus Maria, Casilla 11-0059, Peru. TEL 237730. adv.; bk.rev.; stat. circ. 1,200.

REVISTA POLITICA COMPARADA. see *POLITICAL SCIENCE*

340   RM   ISSN 0035-0435
REVISTA ROMANA DE DREPT. 1945. m. 200 lei($25) Asociatia Juristilor din Republica Socialista Romania, B-Dul Magheru Nr. 22, Bucharest, Rumania. (Subscr. to: ILEXIM, Str. 13 Decembrie Nr. 3, P.O. Box 136-137, Bucharest, Rumania) Ed. Vasile Patulea. bibl.; index. circ. 8,000.

340   BL
REVISTA TRIMESTRAL DE JURISPRUDENCIA. 1964. q. price varies. Supremo Tribunal Federal, SIG-Quadra 6-Lote 800, 70604 Brasilia, D.F., Brazil. index; circ. 2,000. (controlled). (processed)
Former titles: Tribunal Federal de Recursos. Revista (ISSN 0041-2813); Ter Jurisprudencia.

340   UY
REVISTA URUGUAYA DE DERECHO PROCESAL. 1975. q. $80. Fundacion de Cultura Universitaria, 25 de Mayo no. 568, Casilla de Correo No. 1155, 11000 Montevideo, Uruguay. TEL 961152. FAX 952549.

340   US
REVOCABLE TRUSTS, 2-E. 1991. base vol. (plus a. suppl.) $95. Shepard's - McGraw-Hill, Inc., Box 35300, Colorado Springs, CO 80935-3530. TEL 800-525-2474.
Description: Provides a forum for the analysis of drafting techniques, using specific documents such as revocable trusts, pour-over wills and accompanying transfer documents.

340   BD
REVUE ADMINISTRATIVE ET JURIDIQUE DU BURUNDI. 1967. q. Association d'Etudes Administratives et Juridiques du Burundi, B.P. 1613, Bujumbura, Burundi.

340 320 340   AE
REVUE ALGERIENNE DES SCIENCES JURIDIQUES. 1964. q. 120 din. Universite d'Alger, Institut des Sciences Juridiques et Administratives, 11 Chemin Mokhtar Doudou ITFC, Ben-Aknoun, Algiers, Algeria. TEL 64-69-70. (Dist. in US by: African Imprint Library Service, Box 350, West Falmouth, MA 02574. TEL 508-540-5378) bk.rev.; bibl. **Indexed:** Documentatieblad, P.A.I.S.For.Lang.Ind., Rural Recreat.Tour.Abstr., World Agri.Econ.& Rural Sociol.Abstr.
Former titles: Revue Algerienne des Sciences Juridiques, Economiques et Politiques; (until 1968): Revue Algerienne des Sciences Juridiques, Politiques et Economiques (ISSN 0035-0699).

340   BE   ISSN 0035-0966
REVUE CRITIQUE DE JURISPRUDENCE BELGE. (Text in French) 1947. q. 5200 Fr. Etablissements Emile Bruylant, 67 rue de la Regence, B-1000 Brussels, Belgium. TEL 02-512-9845. index. circ. 1,250.
—SWETS.

347.7   BE   ISSN 0772-8050
REVUE DE DROIT COMMERCIAL BELGE/TIJDSCHRIFT VOOR BELGISCH HANDELSRECHT. (Text in Dutch, French) 1968. 12/yr. 2950 Fr. Palais de Justice, Place Poelaert, B-1000 Brussels, Belgium. TEL 02-508-62-45. FAX 02-358-4597. (Subscr. to: E. Story-Scientia, Bd. E. Bockstael 228, B-1020 Brussels, Belgium. TEL 11-68-68) Ed. I Verougstraete. bk.rev. (also avail. in microfiche)
Formerly: Jurisprudence Commerciale de Belgique.
Refereed Serial

340 341   FR   ISSN 0768-9659
REVUE DE DROIT FRANCAIS COMMERCIAL MARITIME ET FISCAL. (Text in French) 1924. q. 250 Fr. 28 bd. Peytral, F-13006 Marseille, France. TEL 9133-3829. Ed. Louis Scapel. index. circ. 300. (back issues avail.) **Indexed:** World Agri.Econ.& Rural Sociol.Abstr.

340   FR   ISSN 0180-9849
REVUE DE DROIT IMMOBILIER. 1979. q. 590 F. (foreign 720 F.). Editions Sirey, 11 rue Soufflot, 75240 Paris Cedex 05, France. TEL 40-51-54-54. FAX 45-87-37-48. TELEX 206 446 F. (Subscr. to: 35, rue Tournefort, 75240 Paris Cedex 05, France. TEL 45-87-37-48) Ed. Philippe Malinvaud.
—CCC.

340   BE   ISSN 0035-1083
REVUE DE DROIT INTELLECTUEL L'INGENIEUR-CONSEIL. (Text in Dutch, French) 1911. bi-m. 4200 BEF. Bureau Vander Haeghen, 108A Rue Colonel Bourg, B-1040 Brussels, Belgium. TEL 32-2-7363963. FAX 32-2-7339809. Ed. Daniel Grisar. bk.rev.; index. circ. 625. **Indexed:** ELLIS.
Description: Disseminates intellectual property law and practice through discussion of a variety of subjects, including patents, trademarks, copyright and competition.

REVUE DE DROIT INTERNATIONAL DE SCIENCES DIPLOMATIQUES ET POLITIQUES. see *POLITICAL SCIENCE*

REVUE DE DROIT INTERNATIONAL ET DE DROIT COMPARE. see *LAW — International Law*

340   CN
REVUE DE DROIT JUDICIAIRE.* (Text in French) 1898. bi-m. Can.$125. Wilson et Lafleur Ltee., C.P. 24, Place d'Armees, Montreal, Que. H2Y 3L2, Canada. Ed. Mario Du Mesnil. circ. 1,250. **Indexed:** Ind.Can.L.P.L.
Supersedes: Rapports de Pratique de Quebec (ISSN 0384-6970)
Description: Covers law in the Quebec province.

343.710 380   CN   ISSN 1180-4831
REVUE DE DROIT MEDIA ET COMMUNICATIONS/MEDIA AND COMMUNICATIONS LAW REVIEW. 1990. 3/yr. Carswell, One Corporate Plaza, 2075 Kennedy Rd., Scarborough, ON M1T 3V4, Canada. TEL 416-609-8000. FAX 416-298-5094. **Indexed:** Ind.Can.L.P.L.

340   FR
REVUE DE DROIT RURAL. 1971. 10/yr. 770 F. Editions Techniques, 18 rue Seguier, 75006 Paris, France. TEL 46-34-21-30. adv.; bk.rev. **Indexed:** ELLIS, Geo.Abstr.

347.9   BE   ISSN 0035-1113
REVUE DE DROIT SOCIAL/TIJDSCHRIFT VOOR SOCIAAL RECHT. (Text in Dutch, French) 1913. 6/yr. 3200 BEF (effective 1993). Maison Ferdinand Larcier S.A., Rue des Minimes 39, 1000 Brussels, Belgium. TEL 32-2-5124712. FAX 32-2-5139009. Ed. R. Geysen. bk.rev.; index, cum.index every 5 yrs. **Indexed:** ELLIS, P.A.I.S.For.Lang.Ind.
—SWETS.

346   FR   ISSN 0048-7937
REVUE DE JURISPRUDENCE COMMERCIALE; journal des agrees. 1957. m. 850 F. 77 rue Royale, 78000 Versailles, France. TEL 39-50-44-97. FAX 39-49-52-13. adv.; bk.rev. **Indexed:** ELLIS.
—CCC.

REVUE DE JURISPRUDENCE DE DROIT DES AFFAIRES. see *BUSINESS AND ECONOMICS — Management*

REVUE DE JURISPRUDENCE FISCALE. see *PUBLIC ADMINISTRATION*

REVUE DE JURISPRUDENCE SOCIALE. see *BUSINESS AND ECONOMICS — Labor And Industrial Relations*

REVUE DE SCIENCE CRIMINELLE ET DE DROIT PENAL COMPARE. see *CRIMINOLOGY AND LAW ENFORCEMENT*

340   FR
REVUE DES HUISSIERS DE JUSTICE. 1948. 22/yr. 1825 F. 80 rue du Bourg-Voisin, 21140 Semur-en-Auxois, France. TEL 80-97-12-12. FAX 80-97-21-83. Ed. R. Soulard. circ. 3,000.

340   FR
REVUE DES SOCIETES. q. 520 F. (foreign 620 F.). Editions Dalloz, 11 rue Soufflot, 75240 Paris Cedex 05, France. (Subscr. to: 35, rue Tournefort, 75240 Paris Cedex 05, France. TEL 45-87-37-48) (reprint service avail. from SCH) **Indexed:** ELLIS.
    Formerly: Revue des Societes - Journal des Societes; Which incorporates (in 1974): Journal des Societes.

340   CN   ISSN 0383-669X
REVUE DU BARREAU. (Text in English, French) 1941. 5/yr. Can.$30. (Barreau du Quebec) Les Editions Yvon Blais, 445 bd. St-Laurent, Montreal, PQ H2Y 3T8, Canada. TEL 514-954-3400. FAX 514-954-3463. Ed.Bd. adv.; bk.rev.; bibl.; charts; illus.; stat.; index, cum.index. circ. 14,000. **Indexed:** C.L.I., Ind.Can.L.P.L., L.R.I., Leg.Per., Pt.de Rep. (1983-).

340   FR   ISSN 0035-2578
JA11
REVUE DU DROIT PUBLIC ET DE LA SCIENCE POLITIQUE EN FRANCE ET A L'ETRANGER. 1894. bi-m. 610 F. (foreign 640 F.). (Librairie Generale de Droit et de Jurisprudence) Editions Juridiques Associees, 26 rue Vercingetorix, 75014 Paris, France. TEL 1-43-35-01-67. FAX 43-20-07-42. TELEX EJA 203 918 F. Eds. Jacques Robert, J.M. Auby. bk.rev.; abstr.; bibl.; index, cum.index: 1951-1964. circ. 3,800. (reprint service avail. from SCH) **Indexed:** P.A.I.S.For.Lang.Ind.
—BLDSC (7898.550000); SWETS. **CCC.**

340   CN   ISSN 0035-2632
LAW
REVUE DU NOTARIAT. 1898. bi-m. (except July & Aug.). Can.$40. Chambre des Notaires du Quebec, 630 Blvd. Rene Levesque, Ste. 1700, Montreal, PQ H3B 1T6, Canada. TEL 514-879-1793. FAX 514-879-1923. adv.; bk.rev.; index. circ. 3,500. **Indexed:** C.L.I., Ind.Can.L.P.L., L.R.I., Leg.Per., Pt.de Rep. (1983-).

347.016   BE
REVUE DU NOTARIAT BELGE.* q. 2850 Fr. 535 Chaussee de Waterloo, bte 6, 1050 Brussels, Belgium.

346.066 330   FR   ISSN 0775-3209
REVUE EUROPEENNE DE DROIT DE LA CONSOMMATION. English edition: European Consumer Law Journal. Spanish edition: Revista Europea de Derecho del Consumo. q. 1050 F. (effective 1994). Lamy S.A., 187-189 Quai de Valmy, 75490 Paris, France. TEL 44-72-13-43. FAX 44-72-13-95.
    Description: Analyzes the evolution and implications of the communal arrangement and national laws of distribution, competition and consumption in 17 European countries.

340   FR
REVUE FRANCAISE DE DROIT ADMINISTRATIF. 6/yr. 650 F. (foreign 750 F.). Editions Sirey, 11, rue Soufflet, 75240 Paris, France. TEL 40-51-54-54. FAX 45-87-37-48. TELEX 206 446 F. (Subscr. to: 35 rue Tournefort, 75240 Paris Cedex 05, France. TEL 45-87-37-48) **Indexed:** ELLIS.

REVUE FRANCAISE DE DROIT AERIEN. see
AERONAUTICS AND SPACE FLIGHT

340   FR   ISSN 0035-3280
REVUE HISTORIQUE DE DROIT FRANCAIS ET ETRANGER. 1855. 4/yr. 630 F. (foreign 700 F.). Editions Sirey, 22 rue Soufflot, 75005 Paris, France. (Subscr. to: Diffusion Dalloz, 35 rue Tournefort, 75240 Paris Cedex 05, France. TEL 40-51-54-35. FAX 45-87-37-48) Ed.Bd. bk.rev.; bibl.; index. (reprint service avail. from SCH) **Indexed:** Amer.Hist.& Life, CERDIC, Hist.Abstr.
—SWETS. **CCC.**

340   BE
REVUE INTERDISCIPLINAIRE D'ETUDES JURIDIQUES. s-a. 800 BEF to individuals (foreign 900 BEF); institutions 1000 BEF (foreign 1200 BEF). Universite de Saint Louis, Facultes des Seminaire Interdisciplinaire d'Etudes Juridiques, Boulevard du Jardin Botanique, 43, 1000 Brussels, Belgium. TEL 32-2-2117894. FAX 32-2-2117997. **Document type:** academic/scholarly publication.

340 330   BE   ISSN 1010-8831
REVUE INTERNATIONALE DE DROIT ECONOMIQUE. Short title: R.I.D.E. (Text in French) 1986. 3/yr. 3000 BEF (Europe 3250 BEF; elsewhere 3300 BEF) (effective 1994). De Boeck Universite, Fond Jean-Paques 4, B-1348 Louvain-la-Neuve, Belgium. TEL 32-10-482509. FAX 32-10-482519. Ed. A. Pappalardo. **Indexed:** ELLIS. **Document type:** academic/scholarly publication.

340 940   BE   ISSN 0556-7939
REVUE INTERNATIONALE DES DROITS DE L'ANTIQUITE. 1948. a. 1100 BEF (foreign 1200 BEF) (effective 1994). Office International des Periodiques, Kouterveld 14, B-1831 Diegem, Belgium. TEL 32-2-7231111. FAX 32-2-7231413. circ. 500. (back issues avail.) **Document type:** academic/scholarly publication.
—SWETS.

REVUE INTERNATIONALE DU DROIT D'AUTEUR. see
PATENTS, TRADEMARKS AND COPYRIGHTS

340   IV   ISSN 0048-816X
REVUE IVOIRIENNE DE DROIT. 1971. s-a. 120 F. Centre Ivoirien d'Etude et de Recherche Juridique, B.P. 3811, Abidjan, Ivory Coast. Ed.Bd. adv. circ. 1,500.

REVUE JURIDIQUE DE L'ENVIRONNEMENT. see
ENVIRONMENTAL STUDIES

340   BD
REVUE JURIDIQUE DU BURUNDI.* 1980. q. 120 F. Ecole Nationale d'Administration, B.P. 1613, Bujumbura, Burundi.

REVUE JURIDIQUE DU RWANDA. see *LAW — Judicial Systems*

REVUE JURIDIQUE DU ZAIRE. see *LAW — Judicial Systems*

REVUE JURIDIQUE THEMIS. see *LAW — Judicial Systems*

340   CN   ISSN 0035-3604
REVUE LEGALE.* (Text in French) 1952. bi-m. Can.$100. Wilson et Lafleur Ltee., C.P. 24, Place d'Armes, Montreal, Que. H2Y 3L2, Canada. Ed. Mario Du Mesnil. adv. circ. 1,000. **Indexed:** C.L.I., Leg.Per.
    Description: Covers law in the Quebec province.

343   FR   ISSN 0035-3825
REVUE PENITENTIAIRE ET DE DROIT PENAL. 1877. q. 252 F. Societe Generale des Prisons et de Legislation Criminelle, 5 Petit Place, 78000 Versailles, France. Ed. Gilbert Marc. **Indexed:** Excerp.Med.
—SWETS.

340   FR   ISSN 0399-1148
REVUE PRATIQUE DE DROIT SOCIAL. 1944. m. 305 F. Vie Ouvriere, 33 rue Bouret, 75940 Paris cedex 19, France. Ed. Maurice Cohen. circ. 17,500.

301
REVUE PRATIQUE DES SOCIETES CIVILES ET COMMERCIALES. 1889. q. 2700 BEF. Etablissements Emile Bruylant, 67 rue de la Regence, B-1000 Brussels, Belgium. TEL 02-512-9845. **Indexed:** ELLIS.

346   FR   ISSN 0244-9358
K21
REVUE TRIMESTRIELLE DE DROIT COMMERCIAL ET DU DROIT ECONOMIQUE. 1948. q. 535 F. (foreign 640 F.). Editions Sirey, 11 rue Soufflot, 75240 Paris Cedex 05, France. TEL 40-51-54-54. FAX 45-87-37-48. TELEX 206 446 F. (Subscr. to: 35, rue Tournefort, 75240 Paris Cedex 05, France. TEL 40-51-54-35. FAX 45-87-37-48) bk.rev.; bibl. (reprint service avail. from SCH) **Indexed:** ELLIS.
—SWETS. **CCC.**
    Formerly: Revue Trimestrielle de Droit Commercial (ISSN 0048-8208)

340   FR   ISSN 0035-4317
K21
REVUE TRIMESTRIELLE DE DROIT EUROPEEN. 1965. q. 580 F. (foreign 755 F.). Editions Sirey, 11 rue Soufflot, 75240 Paris Cedex 05, France. TEL 40-51-54-54. FAX 45-87-37-48. TELEX 206 446 F. (Subscr. to: 35 rue Tournefort, 75240 Paris Cedex 05, France. TEL 40-51-54-35) bk.rev.; bibl.; index, cum.index. **Indexed:** ELLIS, P.A.I.S.For.Lang.Ind., Rural Recreat.Tour.Abstr., World Agri.Econ.& Rural Sociol.Abstr.
—BLDSC (7956.785000); SWETS. **CCC.**

340   SZ
REVUE VALAISANNE DE JURISPRUDENCE. 1967. q. 70 SFr. Rue Mathieu-Schiner, CH-1951 Sion, Switzerland. TEL 027-229393. Ed. J. Berthouzoz. circ. 500. **Document type:** bulletin.

340   ZR
REVUE ZAIROISE DE DROIT.* 1971. s-a. $6. Office National de la Recherche et du Developpement, B.P. 16706, Kinshasa, Zaire. Ed.Bd. bibl.

340   US   ISSN 0556-8595
LAW
RHODE ISLAND BAR JOURNAL. 1952. m. (Oct.-June). $20. Rhode Island Bar Association, 115 Cedar St., Providence, RI 02903-1035. Ed.Bd. adv. bk.rev.; bibl.; index. circ. 4,200. (also avail. in microfilm from WSH) **Indexed:** Abstr.Bk.Rev.Curr.Leg.Per., C.L.I., L.R.I., Leg.Per. **Document type:** trade publication.
—UnCover.

340   US   ISSN 0279-0882
K22
RHODE ISLAND LAWYERS WEEKLY. 1982. w. $195. Lawyers Weekly Publications, 30 Court Sq., Boston, MA 02108. TEL 617-227-6034. Ed. Danial Hackett. adv. circ. 900.

340   US
RHODE ISLAND RULES OF EVIDENCE. 1990. base vol. (plus a. supplement). $85.50. Butterworth Legal Publishers (Salem) (Subsidiary of: Reed Elsevier plc), 8 Industrial Way, Bldg. C, Salem, NH 03079. TEL 800-548-4001. FAX 603-898-9858. Ed. Eric D. Green. (looseleaf format)

340   SW   ISSN 0280-2007
RIKSAAKLAGARENS FOERFATTNINGSSAMLING. 1977-1985; resumed 1987-1989; resumed 1990. irreg. SEK 3 per page (effective 1991). Riksaaklagarens Kansli, P.O. Box 2108, S-103 13 Stockholm, Sweden.

340   BL   ISSN 0101-1480
RIO GRANDE DO SUL, BRAZIL. PROCURADORIA GERAL DO ESTADO. REVISTA. 1971. irreg. free. (Instituto de Informatica Juridica) Procuradoria Geral do Estado, Av. Borges Medeiros 1501, 13th, Porto Alegre 90060, Brazil. FAX 0512-255496. circ. 1,500 (controlled).
    Formerly (until 1979): Rio Grande do Sul, Brazil. Consultoria-Geral. Revista.
    Description: Contains legal doctrine and procedure and the Attorney General's juridicial reports.

RISK MANAGEMENT FOR EXECUTIVE WOMEN. see
INSURANCE

RISK MANAGER'S LAW ALERT. see *HOSPITALS*

RISK RETENTION REPORTER. see *INSURANCE*

RIVERS; studies in the science, environmental policy and law of instream flow. see *WATER RESOURCES*

340   IT   ISSN 0035-5763
RIVISTA AMMINISTRATIVA DELLA REPUBBLICA ITALIANA. 1850. m. Via Barnaba Tortolini 34, 00197 Rome, Italy. Ed. Leopoldo Piccardi.

340   IT
RIVISTA DEL CONSIGLIO. 1989. q. L.30000 (foreign L.60000). Casa Editrice Dott. A. Giuffre, Via Busto Arsizio 40, 20151 Milan, Italy. TEL 06-38000905. FAX 06-38009582.

340 600   IT   ISSN 0394-6916
RIVISTA DEL CONSULENTE TECNICO. 1985; N.S. 1991. 3/yr. L.124000 (effective 1994). Maggioli Editore, Viale Vespucci 12-n, Casella Postale 290, 47037 Rimini, Italy. TEL 0541-626777. FAX 0541-622020. adv.; B&W page L.1800000, color page L.2800000; trim 115 x 200.

LAW

340   IT   ISSN 0035-5887
RIVISTA DEL DIRITTO COMMERCIALE E DEL DIRITTO GENERALE DELLE OBBLIGAZIONI. 1903. bi-m. L.135000($170) Piccin Editore, Via Altinate 107, 35100 Padua, Italy. TEL 39-49-655566. FAX 39-49-8750693. Ed. Prof. Libonati. adv.; bk.rev.; index. circ. 2,000. **Indexed:** ELLIS.
—SWETS.

340   IT
RIVISTA DEL NOTARIATO. 1947. bi-m. L.110000 (foreign L.165000). Casa Editrice Dott. A. Giuffre, Via Busto Arsizio 40, 20151 Milan, Italy. TEL 02-38000905. FAX 02-38009582. Ed. M. Atlante. adv. circ. 5,100. **Indexed:** ELLIS.

340   IT   ISSN 0394-9028
RIVISTA DELLE CANCELLIERE; rassegna bimestrale dei servizi guidiziari. 1968. bi-m. L.80000($100) Edizioni Bucalo snc, Casella Postale, 51, 04100 Latina, Italy. FAX 773-623226. Dir. Angelo Cardillo. adv.; bk.rev.; bibl.; cum.index. circ. 5,500.

340   IT   ISSN 0035-6018
RIVISTA DELLE SOCIETA. (Text in French, Italian) 1956. bi-m. L.120000 (foreign L.180000). Casa Editrice Dott. A. Giuffre, Via Busto Arsizio 40, 20151 Milan, Italy. TEL 02-38000905. FAX 02-38009582. Ed. Giuseppe Auletta. adv.; bk.rev.; bibl.; charts; index. circ. 5,600. (back issues avail.) **Indexed:** ELLIS.
—SWETS.

340   IT   ISSN 0035-6123
RIVISTA DI DIRITTO EUROPEO. 1961. q. L.160000. Via degli Spagnoli 29, 00186 Rome, Italy. Dir. Curti Gialdino Carlo. adv.; bk.rev.; bibl.; index. circ. 1,000. **Indexed:** ELLIS.
—SWETS.

RIVISTA DI DIRITTO FINANZIARIO E SCIENZA DELLE FINANZE. see *BUSINESS AND ECONOMICS — Banking And Finance*

340   IT   ISSN 0035-614X
RIVISTA DI DIRITTO INDUSTRIALE. 1952. q. L.80000 (foreign L.120000). Casa Editrice Dott. A. Giuffre, Via Busto Arsizio 40, Milan 20151, Italy. TEL 02-38000905. FAX 02-38009582. Ed. Remo Franceschelli. adv.; bk.rev.; abstr. circ. 1,200.
—SWETS.

RIVISTA DI DIRITTO SPORTIVO. see *SPORTS AND GAMES*

340   IT
RIVISTA DI DIRITTO TRIBUTARIO. 1991. m. L.150000 (foreign L.225000). Casa Editrice Dott. A. Giuffre, Via Busto Arsizio 40, 20151 Milan, Italy. TEL 02-38000905. FAX 02-38009582.

RIVISTA GIURIDICA DEL LAVORO E DELLA PREVIDENZA SOCIALE. DOTTRINA. see *LABOR UNIONS*

340   IT   ISSN 1120-9542
RIVISTA GIURIDICA DEL MEZZOGIORNO. 1987. q. L.140000. (Associazione per lo Sviluppo dell'Industria nel Mezzogiorno) Societa Editrice Il Mulino, Strada Maggiore, 37, 40125 Bologna, Italy. TEL 051-256011. FAX 051-256034. Ed. Massimo Annesi. adv. circ. 1,100. (back issues avail.)

340   IT
RIVISTA GIURIDICA DEL MOLISE E DEL SANNIO. 1990. q. L.77000 to individuals; institutions L.88000; foreign L.100000 (effective 1993). Edizioni Scientifiche Italiane S.p.A., Via Chiatamone 7, 80121 Naples, Italy. TEL 081-7645768. FAX 081-7646477.

RIVISTA GIURIDICA DELL'AMBIENTE. see *ARCHITECTURE*

RIVISTA GIURIDICA DELL'EDILIZIA. see *BUILDING AND CONSTRUCTION*

349   IT   ISSN 0035-6700
RIVISTA GIURIDICA DELLA CIRCOLAZIONE E DEI TRASPORTI. 1947. bi-m. L.120000($120) (Automobile Club d'Italia) Editrice dell' Automobile s.r.l., Viale Regina Margherita 290, I-00198 Rome, Italy. TEL (06) 4402061. FAX 06-8840926. Ed. Sabino Cassese. bk.rev.; bibl. circ. 10,000.

340   IT
RIVISTA GIURIDICA SARDA. 1986. 3/yr. L.80000 (foreign L.120000). Casa Editrice Dott. A. Giuffre, Via Busto Arsizio 40, 20151 Milan, Italy. TEL 02-38000902. FAX 02-38009582.

340 323.4   IT   ISSN 0394-6495
RIVISTA INTERNAZIONALE DEI DIRITTI DELL'UOMO. 1988. 3/yr. L.93000 (foreign L.135000 ($111)) (effective 1994). (Universita Cattolica del Sacro Cuore) Vita e Pensiero, Largo Gemelli, 1, 20123 Milan, Italy. TEL 02-72342310. FAX 02-42342260. Dir. Giovanni Maria Umbertazzi. —SWETS.
Description: Covers the doctrine and science of jurisprudence. Covers the activities of organizations concerned with human rights.

341   IT   ISSN 0035-6727
K22
RIVISTA INTERNAZIONALE DI FILOSOFIA DEL DIRITTO. 1921. q. L.70000 (foreign L.105000). (Societa Italiana di Filosofia Giuridica e Politica) Casa Editrice Dott. A. Giuffre, Via Busto Arsizio 40, 20151 Milan, Italy. TEL 02-38000905. FAX 02-38009582. (Co-sponsor: Istituto di Filosofia del Diritto dell'Universita di Roma) Ed. Sergio Cotta. adv.; bk.rev.; bibl.; index. circ. 700.
—SWETS.

340 331   IT   ISSN 0393-2494
K22
RIVISTA ITALIANA DI DIRITTO DEL LAVORO. (Text in Italian; summaries in English, French, German and Spanish) 1982. q. L.140000 (foreign L.210000). Casa Editrice Dott. A. Giuffre, Via Busto Arsizio 40, 20151 Milan, Italy. TEL 02-38000905. FAX 02-38009582. Ed. Giuseppe Pera. adv.; bk.rev.; bibl.; illus.; index. circ. 3,200. **Indexed:** ELLIS.
Supersedes: Rivista di Diritto del Lavoro (ISSN 0035-6107)

340   IT   ISSN 0557-1391
RIVISTA ITALIANA DI DIRITTO E PROCEDURA PENALE. 1958. q. L.130000 (foreign L.195000). Casa Editrice Dott. A. Giuffre, Via Busto Arsizio 40, 20151 Milan, Italy. TEL 02-38000905. FAX 02-38009582. Ed. Cesare Pedrazzi. adv. circ. 3,500. **Indexed:** CERDIC.
—SWETS.
Formed by the merger of: Rivista Italiana di Diritto Penale & Rivista di Diritto Processuale Penale.

340   IT
RIVISTA ITALIANA DI DIRITTO PUBBLICO COMUNITARIO. 1991. q. L.100000 (foreign L.150000). Casa Editrice Dott. A. Giuffre, Via Busto Arsizio 40, 20151 Milan, Italy. TEL 02-38000905. FAX 02-38009582.

340   IT   ISSN 0557-1464
RIVISTA TRIMESTRALE DI DIRITTO PUBBLICO. 1951. q. L.120000 (foreign L.180000). Casa Editrice Dott. A. Giuffre, Via Busto Arsizio 40, 20151 Milan, Italy. TEL 02-38000905. FAX 02-38009582. Eds. Giovanni Miele, Massimo Severo Giannini. adv. circ. 2,200. **Indexed:** ELLIS.
—SWETS.

340   UK   ISSN 1352-0717
ROAD LAW AND ROAD LAW REPORTS. 1985. 8/yr. £47.75. Barry Rose Law Periodicals, Little London, Chichester, W. Sussex PO19 1PG, England. TEL 0243-787841. FAX 0243-779278. Eds. Charles Arnold-Baker, John Spencer. **Document type:** academic/scholarly publication.
—BLDSC (7994.820000).
Supersedes (in 1993): Road Law (ISSN 0951-0028); **Incorporates (in 1993):** Road Law Reports (ISSN 0966-8403)
Description: Topics covered include deregulation, road traffic regulations, competition, tachographs, European Community law, PSV operations and road law reports.

ROAD WORK SAFETY REPORT. see *TRANSPORTATION — Roads And Traffic*

ROCKY MOUNTAIN MINERAL LAW INSTITUTE. PROCEEDINGS. see *MINES AND MINING INDUSTRY*

ROYAL NATIONAL INSTITUTE FOR THE BLIND. LAW NOTES. EXTRACTS. see *HANDICAPPED — Visually Impaired*

340   PL   ISSN 0035-9629
RUCH PRAWNICZY, EKONOMICZNY I SOCJOLOGICZNY. 1921. q. $48. (Akademia Ekonomiczna, Poznan) Adam Mickiewicz University Press, Nowowiejskiego 55, 61-734 Poznan, Poland. (Dist. by: Ars Polona, Krakowskie Przedmiescie 7, 00-068 Warsaw, Poland) Ed. Z. Radwanski. adv.; bk.rev.: charts; index, cum.index. circ. 1,100. **Document type:** academic/scholarly publication.

340   UA
RUH AL-QAWANIN. 1989. a? Jami'at Tanta, Kulliyyat al-Huquq - Tanta University, Faculty of Law, Tanta, Egypt.

346.066   US
LAW
RUSSIA AND COMMONWEALTH BUSINESS LAW REPORT; monthly news and analysis. 1990. bi-w. $970 (foreign $992). Buraff Publications (Subsidiary of: Millin Publications, Inc.), 1350 Connecticut Ave., N.W., Ste. 1000, Washington, DC 20036. TEL 800-333-1291. FAX 202-862-0999. Ed. Ted Stewart. (back issues avail.) **Document type:** newsletter.
●Also available online. Vendor(s): Mead Data Central, Inc.
—CCC.
Formerly: Soviet Business Law Report (ISSN 1050-3730)
Description: Text and analysis of legal and regulatory developments from the former Soviet Republics and the Baltics for Western lawyers and business persons whose companies and clients do (or want to do) business in the former Soviet Union.

349   US   ISSN 1061-1940
K22
RUSSIAN POLITICS AND LAW; a journal of translations. 1962. bi-m. $429 (foreign $472). M.E. Sharpe, Inc., 80 Business Park Dr., Armonk, NY 10504. TEL 914-273-1800. FAX 914-273-2106. Ed. Nils H. Wessell. adv.; index. (also avail. in microfilm from WSH;PMC; reprint service avail. from WSH) **Indexed:** ASCA, C.L.I., Curr.Cont., Leg.Per., SSCI.
—BLDSC (8052.816500); Faxon; UnCover; SWETS; UMI.
Former titles: Russian Politics; Soviet Law and Government (ISSN 0038-5530)
Refereed Serial

340   US   ISSN 0277-318X
K22
RUTGERS LAW JOURNAL. 1969. q. $22.50 (foreign $27.50) (effective 1992). Rutgers University, School of Law, Camden, Rutgers Law Journal, Fifth & Penn Sts., Camden, NJ 08102. TEL 609-757-6177. Ed. D. Matthew Jameson. adv.; B&W page $100. bk.rev.; charts; cum.index. circ. 1,200. (also avail. in microfilm from RRI; back issues avail.; reprint service avail. from RRI) **Indexed:** C.L.I., Crim.Just.Abstr., L.R.I., Leg.Cont., Leg.Per. **Document type:** academic/scholarly publication.
—BLDSC (8053.389000); Faxon; UnCover; UMI.
Formerly (until 1980): Rutgers-Camden Law Journal (ISSN 0036-0449)

340   US   ISSN 0036-0465
LAW
RUTGERS LAW REVIEW. 1936. q. $30 (foreign $35). Rutgers University, School of Law, Law Review, 15 Washington St., Newark, NJ 07102. TEL 201-648-5391. FAX 201-648-1497. adv.; bk.rev. circ. 1,200. (reprint service avail. from RRI) **Indexed:** Abstr.Bk.Rev.Curr.Leg.Per., ASCA, Bank.Lit.Ind., C.L.I., Crim.Just.Abstr., Curr.Cont., L.R.I., Leg.Cont., Leg.Per., Sage Urb.Stud.Abstr., SSCI. **Document type:** academic/scholarly publication.
—BLDSC (8053.390000); Faxon; UnCover; SWETS; UMI.
Formerly (until 1942): University of Newark Law Review.

S A C AWARD REPORTER. (Securities Arbitration Commentator) see *BUSINESS AND ECONOMICS — Investments*

S A E. (Sammlung Arbeitsrechtlicher Entscheidungen) see *BUSINESS AND ECONOMICS — Labor And Industrial Relations*

340 378   US
S A L T EQUALIZER. 1986. q. $50 membership. Society of American Law Teachers, c/o Stuart Filler, Treas., Quinnipiac College, School of Law, Rm.248, 303 University Ave., Bridgeport, CT 06604. TEL 203-576-4442. FAX 203-333-5058. Ed. Michael Rooke-Lee. circ. 650. (back issues avail.) **Document type:** newsletter.

340   SA   ISSN 0258-6568
S A PUBLIEKREG/S A PUBLIC LAW. (Text in Afrikaans, English) 1986. 2/yr. $40 (effective 1994). University of South Africa, VerLoren van Themaat Centre for Public Law Studies, P.O. Box 392, Pretoria 0001, South Africa. TEL 27-12-429-8468. FAX 27-12-429-3321. Ed. D.H. van Wyk. circ. 350. (back issues avail.) **Document type:** academic/scholarly publication.

S A TAX REVIEW. see BUSINESS AND ECONOMICS — Public Finance, Taxation

S C A L L NEWSLETTER. (Southern California Association of Law Libraries) see LIBRARY AND INFORMATION SCIENCES

340   US
S C BAR NEWS. bi-m. membership. South Carolina Bar Association, Box 608, 950 Taylor St., Columbia, SC 29202. Ed. Beth Littlejohn. adv. **Document type:** newsletter.

340 360   UK   ISSN 0264-8717
S C O L A G. 1975. 12/yr. £18 to individuals; institutions £27.50. Scottish Legal Action Group, 13D Hazlehead Court, Dundee DD2 3RN, Scotland. TEL 0382-817474. Ed. J. Black. adv.; bk.rev.; index. circ. 1,100. **Indexed:** ASSIA, C.L.I.
—BLDSC (8205.456000).

S E C COMPLIANCE: FINANCIAL REPORTING AND FORMS. see BUSINESS AND ECONOMICS — Investments

S E C GUIDELINES (YEAR); rules and regulations. (Security Exchange Commission) see BUSINESS AND ECONOMICS — Investments

340   US   ISSN 0894-3486
S E R B OFFICIAL REPORTER. (State Employment Relations Board) 1987. m. $320. Banks - Baldwin Law Publishing Co., University Center, Box 1974, Cleveland, OH 44106. TEL 216-721-7373. FAX 216-721-8055. charts.
Description: Includes the full text of SERB opinions: new court decisions; relevant statutes and rules; official forms, practice outlines; and research aids.

340   NE   ISSN 0165-098X
S E W; tijdschrift voor europees en economisch recht. 1952. m. fl.209.50. W.E.J. Tjeenk Willink B.V., Postbus 25, 8000 AA Zwolle, Netherlands. TEL 31-38-211444. Pub. A.E. van Arkel. adv.; bk.rev.; bibl.; index. circ. 1,200. **Indexed:** ELLIS.
—BLDSC (8253.985000); SWETS.
Supersedes: Sociaal-Economische Wetgeving (ISSN 0037-7597).

S I A WASHINGTON REPORT. (Securities Industry Association (Washington)) see BUSINESS AND ECONOMICS — Investments

340 604.7 333.79   US
S O N R E E L MONOGRAPH SERIES. irreg. price varies. American Bar Association, Section of Natural Resources, Energy, and Environmental Law, 750 N. Lake Shore Dr., Chicago, IL 60611. FAX 312-988-5568. **Document type:** monographic series.
Description: Covers various legal topics in oil and gas drilling, environmental remediation, and land patents.

SACRAMENTO NEWSLETTER. see POLITICAL SCIENCE

340   AT
SAFETY & INDUSTRY LAW SERVICE N S W. (In 2 volumes) q. (plus bulletins). $425. Butterworths, 271-273 Lane Cove Rd., P.O. Box 345, North Ryde, N.S.W. 2113, Australia. TEL 02-335-4444. FAX 02-335-4655. (looseleaf format)

346.066   SZ
ST. GALLER STUDIEN ZUM PRIVAT-, HANDELS- UND WIRTSCHAFTSRECHT. 1982. irreg. vol.34, 1993. price varies. (Hochschule St. Gallen fuer Wirtschafts- und Sozialwissenschaften) Paul Haupt AG, Falkenplatz 14, CH-3001 Bern, Switzerland. TEL 031-3012345. FAX 031-3014669. **Document type:** monographic series.

340   US   ISSN 0036-2905
K23
ST. JOHN'S LAW REVIEW. 1926. q. $24. St. John's University, School of Law, 8000 Utopia Pkwy., Jamaica, NY 11439. TEL 718-990-6654. bk.rev.; charts; stat.; index. circ. 3,000. (also avail. in microfiche from WSH,PMC; microfilm from WSH,PMC) **Indexed:** Account.Ind. (1974-), C.L.I., Cath.Ind., Crim.Just.Abstr., L.R.I., Leg.Cont., Leg.Per. **Document type:** academic/scholarly publication.
—BLDSC (8070.163000); Faxon; UnCover; SWETS; UMI.

340   US   ISSN 0581-3344
ST. LOUIS BAR JOURNAL.* 1950. q. (Bar Association of Metropolitan St. Louis) ADmore, Inc., Box 28830, St. Louis, MO 63123-0030. TEL 800-451-0914. FAX 314-638-3880.
—UnCover.

345.01   US   ISSN 0036-2948
ST. LOUIS COUNTIAN.* 1902. d. (except Sun.& Mon.). $177. Legal Communications Corp., 7777 Bonhomme Ave., Ste. 1205, St. Louis, MO 63105-1911. TEL 314-727-6111. FAX 314-727-7407. Ed. Will Connagham. adv. contact: Rhonda Davis. circ. 1,800. (tabloid format; also avail. in microform) **Document type:** newspaper.

340   US
ST. LOUIS DAILY RECORD.* d. (Tue.-Sat.). Legal Communications Corp., 7777 Bonhomme Ave., Ste. 1205, St. Louis, MO 63105-1911. TEL 314-421-1880. FAX 314-421-0436. Ed. Will Connaghan. adv. contact: Niki Watters. bk.rev. circ. 1,219. (tabloid format) **Document type:** newspaper.

340   US   ISSN 0893-5971
ST. LOUIS LAWYER.* 1987. m. $24. (Bar Association of Metropolitan St. Louis) ADmore, Inc., Bxo 28830, St. Louis, MO 63123-0030. TEL 314-638-4050. FAX 314-638-3880. (One Metropolitan Sq., Ste. 1400, St. Louis, MO 63102-2745. TEL 800-451-0914)

340   US   ISSN 0036-3030
LAW
SAINT LOUIS UNIVERSITY LAW JOURNAL. 1949. q. $25 (foreign $27). St. Louis University School of Law, 3700 Lindell Blvd., St. Louis, MO 63108. TEL 314-658-3933. Ed.Bd. adv.; bk.rev.; charts; index. circ. 1,000. (also avail. in microfiche from PMC; microfilm from WSH,PMC; back issues avail.; reprint service avail. from WSH) **Indexed:** Abstr.Bk.Rev.Curr.Leg.Per., C.L.I., L.R.I., Leg.Cont., Leg.Per. **Document type:** academic/scholarly publication.
●Also available online. Vendor(s): West Services, Inc.
—BLDSC (8070.180000); Faxon; UnCover.

340   US   ISSN 0898-8404
SAINT LOUIS UNIVERSITY PUBLIC LAW REVIEW. 1981. s-a. $20 (foreign $25). Saint Louis University School of Law, 3700 Lindell Blvd., St. Louis, MO 63108. TEL 314-658-3937. Ed.Bd. adv.; bk.rev. circ. 750. (reprint service avail. from WSH) **Indexed:** C.L.I., L.R.I., Leg.Per., P.A.I.S. **Document type:** academic/scholarly publication.
—BLDSC (8070.182000); Faxon; UnCover.
Formerly: Saint Louis University Public Law Forum (ISSN 0738-5390)
Description: Takes a multidisciplinary approach in analyzing topical social and public policy legal issues.

340   US   ISSN 0581-3441
K23
ST. MARY'S LAW JOURNAL. 1969. 4/yr. $25. St. Mary's University School of Law, 1 Camino Santa Maria, San Antonio, TX 78228-8604. TEL 512-436-3439. FAX 512-436-3756. Ed.Bd. adv.; bk.rev. circ. 1,600. (also avail. in microform from MIM; microfilm from RRI,WSH; reprint service avail. from RRI) **Indexed:** C.L.I., L.R.I., Leg.Cont., Leg.Per. **Document type:** academic/scholarly publication.
—Faxon; UnCover.

340   US
ST. PAUL LEGAL LEDGER. 1927. d. $90. Legal Ledger, Inc., 640 Minnesota Bldg., 46 E. 4th St., St. Paul, MN 55101-1163. TEL 612-222-0059. Ed. Samuel E. Lewis, Jr. adv. circ. 600. (tabloid format) **Document type:** newspaper.

340   US   ISSN 1065-318X
K23
ST. THOMAS LAW REVIEW. 1988. q. St. Thomas University, School of Law, 16400 N.W. 32nd Ave., Miami, FL 33054. TEL 305-623-2373. FAX 305-623-2390. **Document type:** academic/scholarly publication.
●Also available online. Vendor(s): West Services, Inc.
—UnCover.
Formerly (until 1991): St. Thomas Law Forum (ISSN 1044-8942)

340   AT   ISSN 0310-6861
ST. THOMAS MORE SOCIETY. JOURNAL. 1971. irreg. St. Thomas More Society, G.P.O. Box 282, Sydney, N.S.W. 2001, Australia. TEL 231-1006. FAX 232-8995. Ed. John McCarthy.

346.066   US
SALES OF A BUSINESS IN MINNESOTA. 1990. base vol. (plus supplement). $88. Butterworth Legal Publishers (Salem) (Subsidiary of: Reed Elsevier plc), 8 Industrial Way, Bldg. C, Salem, NH 03079. TEL 800-548-4001. FAX 603-898-9858. Ed. George Gaffaney. (looseleaf format)
Description: Examines the basic types of sales and discusses related issues such as the tax consequences of a sale, minority interests, and how to investigate both buyers and sellers.

340   GW   ISSN 0558-3624
SAMMELBLATT FUER RECHTSVORSCHRIFTEN DES BUNDES UND DER LAENDER.* 1947. bi-m. DM.248. N.P. Engel Verlag, Gutenbergstr. 29, 77694 Kehl, Germany. TEL 07851-2463. FAX 07851-4234. circ. 2,000.

340   AU
SAMMLUNG ARBEITSRECHTLICHER ENTSCHEIDUNGEN DER GERICHTE UND EINIGUNGSAEMTER. 1932. q. Manzsche Verlags- und Universitaetsbuchhandlung, Kohlmarkt 16, A-1014 Vienna, Austria. TEL 0222-531610. FAX 0222-53161-181. Ed. Helmut Tades. circ. 3,000. **Document type:** bulletin.
Description: Collects cases concerning labor law.

340 664   GW   ISSN 0080-5831
SAMMLUNG LEBENSMITTELRECHTLICHER ENTSCHEIDUNGEN. 1959. irreg., vol.25, 1992. DM.890. Carl Heymanns Verlag KG, Luxemburgerstr. 449, 50939 Cologne, Germany. TEL 0221-46010-0. FAX 0221-4601069. Ed. Heribert Benz. **Document type:** monographic series.

SAMSOM MILIEU & BEDRIJF. see ENVIRONMENTAL STUDIES

SAMSOM NAAMLOZE VENNOOTSCHAPPEN. see BUSINESS AND ECONOMICS

340   US
SAN DIEGO COUNTY BAR ASSOCIATION. BAR BRIEFS. vol.3, 1993. m. membership. San Diego County Bar Association, 1333 Seventh Ave., San Diego, CA 92101. TEL 619-231-0781. Ed. Susan Ferrer. **Document type:** newsletter.
Description: News and activities of the association, including continuing education and volunteer opportunities for area lawyers.

345.01   US
SAN DIEGO DAILY TRANSCRIPT. (Annual supplements avail.: Law Day, Corporate Profiles, Soaring Dimensions) 5/wk. Transcript Publishing Co., 2131 Third Ave., San Diego, CA 92101-2095. TEL 619-232-4381. FAX 619-236-8126. Ed. Gary Shaw. adv. contact: Al Zmolek. circ. 10,000. **Document type:** newspaper.
●Also available online. Vendor(s): Mead Data Central, Inc.

340   US   ISSN 0036-4037
LAW
SAN DIEGO LAW REVIEW. 1964. 5/yr. $25. (San Diego Law Review Association, San Diego Law Review) University of San Diego, School of Law, 5998 Alcala Park, San Diego, CA 92110. TEL 619-260-4531. Ed.Bd. adv.; index. circ. 2,000. (also avail. in microform from WSH; reprint service avail. from WSH) Indexed: ABI Inform., BPIA, C.L.I., Crim.Just.Abstr., Deep Sea Res.& Oceanogr.Abstr., L.R.I., Leg.Cont., Leg.Per., Ocean.Abstr., Pollut.Abstr., PSI, Sel.Water Res.Abstr. **Document type:** academic/scholarly publication.
—BLDSC (8072.870000); Faxon; UnCover; SWETS.

340   US
SAN FRANCISCO ATTORNEY MAGAZINE. 6/yr. $26. Bar Association of San Francisco, 685 Market St., Ste. 700, San Francisco, CA 94105. Ed. James Hargarten. bk.rev. circ. 9,000. Indexed: C.L.I., Leg.Per.
  Former titles: Brief - Case; In Re (ISSN 0046-8754)

340   US
SAN FRANCISCO BAY AREA REGISTER OF EXPERTS AND CONSULTANTS. a. $16.50 to non-members. Bar Association of San Francisco, 685 Market St., Ste. 700, San Francisco, CA 94105. Ed. Nancy McDonald. circ. 15,000.
  Formerly: Forensic Register of Expert Consultants.
  Description: Lists expert witnesses and consultants in over 280 specialties who service the legal community.

340   US
SAN FRANCISCO DAILY JOURNAL. d. (Mon.-Fri.). $234. Daily Journal Corporation (San Francisco), 1390 Market St., Ste. 910, San Francisco, CA 94102-5402. TEL 415-558-9888. FAX 415-558-8469. Ed. Ray Reynolds. adv.; bk.rev. circ. 5,512.

340   630   US   ISSN 1055-422X
K23
SAN JOAQUIN AGRICULTURAL LAW REVIEW. 1991. a. San Joaquin College of Law, 3385 E. Shields Ave., Fresno, CA 93726.
  —UnCover.

340   US   ISSN 0036-4185
SAN JOSE POST-RECORD; daily legal, & commercial real estate & financial news. 1910. d. $95. Daily Journal Corporation (Los Angeles), 915 E. First St., Los Angeles, CA 90012. TEL 213-229-5300. Ed. Opal McLean. adv.; bk.rev.; stat.; circ. 700 (paid). (tabloid format) **Document type:** newspaper.

340   US
SANCTIONS IN FEDERAL LITIGATION. 1991. base vol. (plus a supplement). $95. Butterworth Legal Publishers (Salem) (Subsidiary of: Reed Elsevier plc), 8 Industrial Way, Bldg. C, Salem, NH 03079. TEL 800-548-4001. FAX 603-898-9858. Ed.Bd. (looseleaf format)
  Description: Addresses statutory and case law and strategies for asking for or defending against a motion for sanctions.

340   IO   ISSN 0303-321X
SANGKAKALA PERADILAN. Rps.450. Ikatan Hakim Indonesia, Tjabang Semarang, Jalan Siliwangi 151, Semarang, Indonesia. illus.

340   SZ
ST. GALLER STUDIEN ZUM WETTBEWERBS UND IMMATERIALGUETERRECHT. 1971. irreg. price varies. Verlag Ostschweiz, Oberer Graben 8, Postfach 716, CH-9001 St. Gallen, Switzerland. Ed. Mario M. Pedrazzini.

340   600   US   ISSN 0882-3383
SANTA CLARA COMPUTER AND HIGH-TECHNOLOGY LAW JOURNAL. 1985. s-a. $40. Santa Clara University, School of Law, Santa Clara, CA 95053. TEL 408-554-4197. FAX 408-554-4191. E-mail: SCCHTLJ@scuacc.scu.edu. Ed. Evelyn Peyton. Indexed: C.L.I., Leg.Per. **Document type:** academic/scholarly publication.
  ●Also available online.
  —BLDSC (8075.317000); Faxon; UnCover.
  Formerly: Computer and Technology Law Journal.
  Description: Aimed at lawyers and laypersons interested in current issues and decisions in computer and technology law.

340   US   ISSN 0146-0315
K23
SANTA CLARA LAW REVIEW. 1961. q. $40. Santa Clara University, School of Law, Santa Clara, CA 95053. TEL 408-554-4074. circ. 615. circ. 450 (paid). (also avail. in microform from WSH; microfilm from WSH) Indexed: Abstr.Bk.Rev.Curr.Leg.Per., C.L.I., L.R.I., Leg.Cont., Leg.Per., Sel.Water Res.Abstr. **Document type:** academic/scholarly publication.
  ●Also available online. Vendor(s): West Services, Inc.
  —BLDSC (8075.320000); Faxon; UnCover.
  Formerly (until vol.15, no.4, 1975): Santa Clara Lawyer (ISSN 0581-6106)

SAO PAULO, BRAZIL (STATE). SECRETARIA DA EDUCACAO. ATIVIDADES DESENVOLVIDAS. see EDUCATION

340   CN
SASKATCHEWAN DECISIONS CITATOR. (Includes: Statute Citator, Rules Citator, Regulations Table and Library News) 1981. m. Can.$130. Western Legal Publications, 301-1 Alexander St, Vancouver, BC V6A 1B2, Canada. TEL 604-687-5671. FAX 604-687-2796.
  Formerly: Saskatchewan Decisions - Rules and Statute Citator (ISSN 0824-7285)

340   CN   ISSN 0319-7999
SASKATCHEWAN DECISIONS, CIVIL AND CRIMINAL CASES. 1975. m. Can.$290. Western Legal Publications, 301-1 Alexander St, Vancouver, BC V6A 1B2, Canada. TEL 604-687-5671. FAX 604-687-2796. (looseleaf format)
  ●Also available online.
  Description: Presents all available civil and criminal decisions from the Saskatchewan Court of Appeal, Court of Queen's Bench and selected decisions of the Provincial Court of Saskatchewan.

340   CN   ISSN 0036-4894
                                 CODEN: SAGAEU
SASKATCHEWAN GAZETTE. 1905. w. Can.$115. Queen's Printer, Saskatchewan, 1871 Smith St., Regina, SK S4P 3V7, Canada. TEL 306-787-6894. FAX 306-787-9111. Ed. Marilyn A. Lustig-McEwen. illus. circ. 3,000. (also avail. in microfilm from UMI,KTO; reprint service avail. from UMI) **Document type:** government publication.

340   CN   ISSN 0036-4916
SASKATCHEWAN LAW REVIEW. 1935. s-a. Can.$26. University of Saskatchewan, College of Law, Law Building, Saskatoon, SK S7N 0W0, Canada. TEL 306-966-5869. FAX 306-966-5900. adv.; bk.rev.; index, cum.index; circ. 1,800 (paid). (also avail. in microfiche from WSH,PMC; microfilm from WSH,PMC) Indexed: C.L.I., HR Rep., Ind.Can.L.P.L., L.R.I., Leg.Cont., Leg.Per.
  —BLDSC (8076.537000); Faxon; UnCover.
  Formerly: Saskatchewan Bar Review.
  Refereed Serial

340   CN   ISSN 0713-7095
KES104
SASKATCHEWAN REPORTS. 1979. irreg. latest.vol.106. Can.$125 per vol. Maritime Law Book Ltd., Box 302, Fredericton, NB E3B 4Y9, Canada. TEL 506-453-9921; 800-561-0220. FAX 506-453-9525. (back issues avail.)
  ●Also available online. Vendor(s): QL Systems Ltd.
  Description: Contains all of the judgments of the Saskatchewan Court of Appeal plus selected trial court judgments.

340   GW   ISSN 0323-4045
SAVIGNY-STIFTUNG FUER RECHTSGESCHICHTE. ZEITSCHRIFT. GERMANISTISCHE ABTEILUNG. a., vol.13, 1991. DM.248. Boehlau Verlag GmbH, Theodor-Heuss-Str. 76, 51149 Cologne, Germany. TEL 02203-307021. FAX 02203-307349. adv.; bk.rev.; bibl.; illus.; index. circ. 800. Indexed: Amer.Hist.& Life, Canon Law Abstr., Hist.Abstr. **Document type:** academic/scholarly publication.
  —SWETS.

340   AU   ISSN 0323-4142
SAVIGNY-STIFTUNG FUER RECHTSGESCHICHTE. ZEITSCHRIFT. KANONISTISCHE ABTEILUNG. a., vol.110, 1993. S.1876. Boehlau Verlag GmbH & Co.KG., Sachsenplatz 4-6, A-1201 Vienna, Austria. TEL 0222-3302427. FAX 0222-3302432. Ed.Bd. bk.rev. Indexed: CERDIC. **Document type:** monographic series.
  —SWETS.

340   AU   ISSN 0323-4096
SAVIGNY-STIFTUNG FUER RECHTSGESCHICHTE. ZEITSCHRIFT. ROMANISTISCHE ABTEILUNG. a., vol.110, 1993. DM.352. Boehlau Verlag GmbH & Co.KG., Sachsenplatz 4-6, A-1201 Vienna, Austria. TEL 0222-3302427. FAX 0222-3302432. **Document type:** monographic series.
  —SWETS.

SAVINGS & COMMUNITY BANKERS OF AMERICA. DIRECTORS & TRUSTEES DIGEST. see BUSINESS AND ECONOMICS — Banking And Finance

SAVINGS & COMMUNITY BANKERS OF AMERICA. OPERATIONS ALERT. see BUSINESS AND ECONOMICS — Banking And Finance

SAVINGS & COMMUNITY BANKERS OF AMERICA. REGULATORY REPORT. see BUSINESS AND ECONOMICS — Banking And Finance

340   YU   ISSN 0036-5173
SAVREMENA PRAKSA; list za privredna i pravna pitanja radnih organizacija. 1966. w. 49000 din. Savremena Administracja, Knez Mihajlova 6-V, 11001 Belgrade, Yugoslavia. TEL 623-287. Ed. Stevan Petrovic. circ. 13,000.

340   XR   ISSN 0036-522X
SBIRKA SOUDNICH ROZHODNUTI A STANOVISEK. 1949. 11/yr. 1375 Kcs. (Nejvyssi Soud) O R A C Ltd., Masarykova 31, 602 00 Bron, Czech Republic. index.
  Formerly: Sbirka Rozhodnuti a Sdeleni Soudu C S S R.
  Description: Collection of court decisions.

340   AT   ISSN 0727-7903
SCALES OF COST QUEENSLAND. 1979. 10/yr. in 1 vol. Aus.$260 (renewal Aus.$210). Law Book Co. Ltd., 44-5- Waterloo Rd., North Ryde, N.S.W. 2113, Australia. TEL 02-887-0177. FAX 02-888-9706. TELEX ASBOOK 27995. (looseleaf format)
  Description: Scales of costs are provided from a wide range of services without commentary or precedent. Covers both Queensland and federal jurisdictions.

340   AT   ISSN 0727-7881
SCALES OF COSTS, CHARGES AND FEES N.S.W. 1984. 12/yr in 1 vol. Aus.$270 (rewewal Aus.$220). Law Book Co. Ltd., 44-50 Waterloo Rd., North Ryde, N.S.W. 2113, Australia. TEL 02-887-0177. FAX 02-888-9706. TELEX ASBOOK 27995. (looseleaf format)
  Description: Provides information to assist practitioners in the preparation of bills of costs.

340   SW   ISSN 0085-5944
SCANDINAVIAN STUDIES IN LAW. (Text in English) 1957. a. SEK 210. (Stockholms Universitet) A W I International AB, P.O. Box 4627, S-116 91 Stockholm, Sweden. TEL 468-640-8800. FAX 468-641-1180. Ed. Anders Victorin. circ. 900.

340   323.4 350   GW   ISSN 0945-7097
SCHIEDSAMTSZEITUNG. 1926. m. DM.80. Carl Heymanns Verlag, Hahnenfussweg 70, 44797 Bochum, Germany. TEL 0221-46010-0. FAX 0221-4601069. Ed. Ludwig Hans Serwe. circ. 4,840. **Document type:** bulletin.
  —BLDSC (8088.689900).
  Formerly (until 1993): Schiedsmanns Zeitung (ISSN 0342-7471)

SCHNELLBRIEF FUER PERSONALWIRTSCHAFT UND ARBEITSRECHT; aktuelle Gesetzgebung, neue Rechtsprechung und alle wichtigen Trends fuer die Personalarbeit. see BUSINESS AND ECONOMICS — Personnel Management

SCHOOL LAW BULLETIN (BOSTON). see EDUCATION — School Organization And Administration

340   370   US   ISSN 0886-2508
SCHOOL LAW BULLETIN (CHAPEL HILL). 1970. q. $20. University of North Carolina at Chapel Hill, Institute of Government, CB No. 3330, Knapp Bldg., Chapel Hill, NC 27599-3330. TEL 919-966-4119. FAX 919-962-2707. Ed. Carol Offen. (also avail. in microform from UMI; reprint service avail. from UMI) Indexed: C.I.J.E., C.L.I., L.R.I., P.A.I.S. **Document type:** academic/scholarly publication, bulletin.
  —BLDSC (8092.779000); Faxon; UMI.

340   US   ISSN 0891-5474
KF4102.S36
SCHOOL LAW NEWSLETTER. 1970. 3/yr. $36 for 2 yrs. Box 199, Ranger, TX 76470. TEL 817-647-3300. Ed. Joe Mills. circ. 4,000. (back issues avail.) **Document type:** newsletter.

SCHOOL OFFICIALS AND THE COURTS. see EDUCATION — School Organization And Administration

344.73   US   ISSN 0164-3851
KF4150.A59
SCHOOLS AND THE COURTS; briefs of selected court cases involving secondary and elementary schools. 1975. q. $104.50. College Administration Publications, Inc., Box 15898, Asheville, NC 28813-0898. TEL 704-277-8777. Eds. D. Parker Young, Donald D. Gerhing. index. circ. 1,800.
   Formerly (until vol.5, no.1, Feb. 1979): School Student and the Courts (ISSN 0098-8952)
   Description: Lists of publications on legislative, policy, judicial, and procedural developments pertaining to the managerial activities and responsibilities of faculty and administrators in the field of higher education.

340   SZ
SCHWEIZER ANWALT. 6/yr. Schweizerischer Anwaltsverband, Postfach 8321, CH-3001 Bern, Switzerland. TEL 031-3122505. FAX 031-3123103. circ. 5,000. **Document type:** bulletin.

340   SZ   ISSN 0036-7613
SCHWEIZERISCHE JURISTEN-ZEITUNG/REVUE SUISSE DE JURISPRUDENCE. (Text in French and German) 1904. s-m. 140 SFr. (students 95 SFr.). (Schweizerischer Anwaltsverband - Federation Suisse des Avocats) Schulthess Polygraphischer Verlag AG, Zwingliplatz 2, CH-8022 Zurich, Switzerland. TEL 01-2519336. FAX 01-2616394. Eds. P. Forstmoser, H. Aeppli. adv.; bk.rev.; bibl.; index, cum.index every 10 yrs.: vols.1-65 (1904-1969), vols.66-76 (1970-1979), vols.77-85 (1980-1989). circ. 4,000. **Indexed:** CERDIC. **Document type:** newsletter.
—SWETS.

340   PO   ISSN 0559-1422
SCIENTIA JURIDICA. 1951. bi-m. Esc.750($20) (Associacao Juridica) Livraria Cruz, Rua D. Diogo de Sousa 127-133, Braga, Portugal. Ed. F.J. Velozo.
—BLDSC (8172.500000).

SCIENZA, DIRITTO E ECONOMIA DELL'AMBIENTE. see ENVIRONMENTAL STUDIES

340   UK   ISSN 0036-908X
SCOTS LAW TIMES. 1893. w. £330. W. Green, 21 Alva St., Edinburgh EH2 4PS, Scotland. adv.; bk.rev.; index. (also avail. in microfiche from BHP) **Indexed:** C.L.I., RICS.

340   UK
SCOTS LAW TIMES CHRISTMAS CHARITY. SUPPLEMENT. a. W. Green, 21 Alva St., Edinburgh EH2 4PS, Scotland.

340   UK   ISSN 0265-6159
SCOTTISH CURRENT LAW YEAR BOOK. 1948. a. £320. W. Green, 21 Alva St., Edinburgh EH2 4PS, Scotland.

346   UK   ISSN 0080-8083
SCOTTISH LAW DIRECTORY. 1892. a. £29. T & T Clark, 59 George St., Edinburgh EH2 2LQ, Scotland. TEL 031-225-4703. FAX 031-220-4260. circ. 4,500. **Document type:** directory.

340   UK   ISSN 0036-9314
SCOTTISH LAW GAZETTE. 1933. q. £16 to non-members; students £5. Scottish Law Agents Society, c/o R.M. Sinclair, Secy., 3 Albyn Place, Edinburgh EH2 4NQ, Scotland. TEL 031-225-7515. FAX 031-220-1083. Ed. Enid Marshall. adv.; bk.rev.; index. circ. 2,500. **Document type:** bulletin.
—BLDSC (8210.670000).

340   US   ISSN 1049-5177
K23
SCRIBES JOURNAL OF LEGAL WRITING. 1990. a. $15. American Society of Writers on Legal Subjects, Wake Forest University, School of Law, Box 7206, Winston-Salem, NC 27109. TEL 919-759-5440. FAX 919-759-6077. Ed. Bryan A. Garner. bk.rev.; circ. 3,900 (controlled). (reprint service avail. from RRI)
   ●Also available online. Vendor(s): West Services, Inc. —UnCover.

340   US
SCRIVENER. 1972. q. American Society of Writers on Legal Subjects, Wake Forest University, School of Law, Box 7206, Winston-Salem, NC 27109. TEL 919-759-5440. FAX 919-759-6077. Ed. James Hambleton. bk.rev. circ. 800. (back issues avail.) **Document type:** newsletter.

340   US   ISSN 0746-5254
SECOND CIRCUIT DIGEST. 1974. 10/yr. $7.50. Federal Bar Council, 145 E. 49th St., New York, NY 10017. TEL 212-644-9771. FAX 212-355-0129. Ed. Jay Carlisle. circ. 2,000. (looseleaf format; back issues avail.) **Document type:** newsletter.

SECURITIES ARBITRATION COMMENTOR; covering significant issues & events in securities - commodities arbitration. see BUSINESS AND ECONOMICS — Investments

340   US
SECURITIES ARBITRATION PROCEDURE MANUAL. 1990. base vol. (plus a. suppl.). Butterworth Legal Publishers (Salem) (Subsidiary of: Reed Elsevier plc), 8 Industrial Way, Bldg. C, Salem, NH 03079. TEL 800-548-4001. FAX 603-898-9858. (looseleaf format)
   Description: Discusses issues encountered in a securities arbitration dispute, including evaluation of the merits of a case and its preparation and presentation to arbitration panels anywhere in the country.

340 332.64   US
SECURITIES FRAUD AND COMMODITIES FRAUD. 1980. 7 base vols. (plus a. suppl.). $490. Shepard's - McGraw-Hill, Inc., Box 35300, Colorado Springs, CO 80935-3530. TEL 800-525-2474.
   Description: Covers misrepresentation, non-disclosure, manipulation, churning and insider trading.

340 332.6   US
SECURITIES FRAUD: LITIGATING UNDER RULE 10B-5. 1991. base vol. (plus a. updates). $99. Butterworth Legal Publishers (Salem) (Subsidiary of: Reed Elsevier plc), 8 Industrial Way, Bldg. C, Salem, NH 03079. TEL 800-548-4001. FAX 603-898-9858. Eds. Thomas E. Patton, Terry R. Saunders. (looseleaf format)

340   US   ISSN 1065-2515
SECURITIES INSIDER TRADING LITIGATION REPORTER; the national journal of record reporting litigation concerning insider trading and other securities law abuses which adversely affect market stability. 1987. s-m. $1250. Andrews Publications, 1646 West Chester Pike, Box 1000, Westtown, PA 19395. TEL 215-399-6600; 800-345-1101. FAX 215-399-6610. Ed. Barbara Pizzirani. bibl.; stat.; cum.index every 6 mos. (looseleaf format; back issues avail.) **Document type:** newsletter.

340 332   US
SECURITIES INSTITUTE. a. $35 softcover. Continuing Education of the Bar - California, University of California Extension, 2300 Shattuck Ave., Berkeley, CA 94704. TEL 510-642-6211; 800-924-3924. FAX 510-642-3788. (Co-sponsor: State Bar of California)

SECURITIES LAW HANDBOOK. see BUSINESS AND ECONOMICS — Investments

SECURITIES LAW REVIEW. see BUSINESS AND ECONOMICS — Banking And Finance

SECURITIES REGULATION. see BUSINESS AND ECONOMICS — Investments

340   US   ISSN 0037-0665
KF1439.A1
SECURITIES REGULATION & LAW REPORT. 1969. w. $977. The Bureau of National Affairs, Inc., 1231 25th St., N.W., Washington, DC 20037. TEL 202-452-4200. FAX 202-822-8092. TELEX 285656 BNAI WSH. (Subscr. to: 9435 Key West Ave., Rockville, MD 20850. TEL 800-372-1033) Ed. Susan Raleigh Jenkins. q. index. (looseleaf format; back issues avail.) **Indexed:** Leg.Per.
   ●Also available online. Vendor(s): Bureau of National Affairs, Mead Data Central, Inc. (SECREG), West Services, Inc. (BNA-SRLR).
—CCC.
   Description: Covers the latest securities and commodities activity at the federal and state levels, including developments from Congress, the Administration, SEC, CFTC, banking regulations, FASB, professional associations, the courts and industry. Contains full text of selected regulations, opinions and legislation.

SECURITIES REGULATION LAW JOURNAL. see BUSINESS AND ECONOMICS — Investments

SECURITIZATION: ASSET-BACKED AND MORTGAGE-BACKED SECURITIES. see BUSINESS AND ECONOMICS — Banking And Finance

942   UK
SELDEN SOCIETY, LONDON. HANDBOOK: PUBLICATIONS, LIST OF MEMBERS AND RULES. 1952. irreg. (every 4-5 yrs.). $10 to non-members. Selden Society, Queen Mary College, Faculty of Laws, Mile End Rd., London E1 4NS, England. TEL 071-975-5136. FAX 081-981-8733. TELEX 893750.
   Description: List of publications and members of the Selden Society worldwide.

942   UK
SELDEN SOCIETY, LONDON. LECTURES. 1953. irreg. (every 2-3 yrs.). price varies. Selden Society, Queen Mary College, Faculty of Laws, Mile End Rd., London E1 4NS, England. TEL 071-975-5136. FAX 081-981-8733. TELEX 893750.
   Description: Lectures on English legal history.

942   UK
SELDEN SOCIETY, LONDON. MAIN (ANNUAL) SERIES. (Text in English, French, Latin; summaries in English) 1887. a. $50 to individuals; libraries $65. Selden Society, Queen Mary College, Faculty of Laws, Mile End Road, London E1 4NS, England. TEL 071-975-5136. FAX 081-981-8733. TELEX 893750. bibl.; charts; illus.; cum.index: vols. 1-108. circ. 1,800.
   Description: Source material on the history of English law, legal institutions and the legal profession.

942   UK   ISSN 0582-4788
SELDEN SOCIETY, LONDON. SUPPLEMENTARY SERIES. 1965. irreg. price varies. Selden Society, Queen Mary College, Faculty of Laws, Mile End Rd., London E1 4NS, England. TEL 071-975-5136. FAX 081-981-8733. TELEX 893750.
   Description: Compilations and reference works for the study of English legal history.

174 340   US   ISSN 1054-2469
KF305.A29
SELECTED STATUTES, RULES, AND STANDARDS ON THE LEGAL PROFESSION. 1984. a. West Publishing Corp., 620 Opperman Dr., Eagan, MN 55123. TEL 612-987-8000; 800-328-9352. FAX 612-687-7302. **Document type:** trade publication.

340   SZ
SEMAINE JUDICIAIRE. 1879. w. 90 SFr. (foreign 150 SFr.). Greffe de la Cour de Justice, Case Postale 137, CH-1211 Geneva 3, Switzerland. TEL 022-3191111. Ed. Christian Reymond. adv.; bk.rev. circ. 1,000. **Document type:** newsletter.

340   FR   ISSN 0049-0156
SEMAINE JURIDIQUE; juris-classeur periodique. (In three editions: Commerce et Industrie, Generale and Notariale) 1924. 43/yr. $120 for each edition. Editions Techniques, 18 rue Seguier, 75006 Paris, France. TEL 46-33-15-85. Ed. Jacques Beguin. adv.; bibl.; index. circ. 28,000. **Indexed:** ELLIS.
—CCC.

LAW

340   FR   ISSN 0223-4637
SEMAINE SOCIALE LAMY; l'actualite du droit social, de la gestion et des remunerations. w. 1135 F. (effective 1994). Lamy S.A., 187-189 Quai de Valmy, 75490 Paris, France. TEL 44-72-13-43. FAX 44-72-13-95. (back issues avail.)
—CCC.
Description: Analyzes the diversity of social laws and their impact on the economy.

340   CN
SENTENCES ARBITRALES DE LA FONCTION PUBLIQUE. m. Can.$125. Ministere des Communications, P.O. Box 1005, Quebec, PQ G1K 7B5, Canada. TEL 418-643-5150. (Subscr. to: Service Abonnements, CP 1190, Outremont, PQ H2V 1V6, Canada. TEL 613-948-1222) **Document type:** government publication.

340   SP   ISSN 0210-3427
SENTENCIAS EN APELACION DE LAS AUDIENCIAS PROVINCIALES; en materia civil y penal. 1969. a. 5800 ptas.($34) Ministerio de Justicia, Centro de Publicaciones, Secretaria General Tecnica, Gran Via, 76-8, 28013 Madrid, Spain. TEL 547-54-22. FAX 559-29-48. Ed.Bd. circ. 3,000. (back issues avail.) **Document type:** government publication.

340   US
SENTENCING IN WASHINGTON. 1985. irreg., latest ed. 1991. $120. Butterworth Legal Publishers (Salem) (Subsidiary of: Reed Elsevier plc), 8 Industrial Way, Bldg. C, Salem, NH 03079. TEL 800-548-4001. FAX 603-898-9858. Ed. David Boerner. (looseleaf format)
Description: Covers all aspects of the Sentencing Reform Act of 1981.

347   II   ISSN 0304-100X
LAW
SERVICES LAW CASES; monthly law reporter dealing with law relating to promotion, discharge, dismissals, etc. containing recent judgments of all the high courts in the country and Supreme Court of India. (Text in English) m. Rs.60. International Law Book Co., Nijhawan Bldg., 1562 Church Rd., Kashmere Gate, Delhi 6, India. Ed. Mrs. Swarn Bhati Nijhawan.

340   UK   ISSN 0037-282X
SESSION CASES; the official Law Reports of Scotland. 1904. irreg. (approx. 3-4/yr.) £100. (Scottish Council of Law Reporting) T & T Clark Ltd., 59 George St., Edinburgh EH2 2LQ, Scotland. TEL 031-225-4703. FAX 031-220-4260. Ed. R.J. Hunter. index, cum.index. circ. 1,000.
Description: Official law reports of Scotland.

340   US
SETON HALL LEGISLATIVE JOURNAL. 1975. s-a. $20. (Seton Hall Legislative Bureau) Seton Hall University, Law Center, 1 Newark Center, Newark, NJ 07102. TEL 201-642-8261. bk.rev. circ. 4,000. (also avail. in microform from WSH; reprint service avail. from WSH) **Indexed:** Abstr.Bk.Rev.Curr.Leg.Per., C.L.I., Crim.Just.Abstr., L.R.I., Leg.Cont., Leg.Per. **Document type:** academic/scholarly publication.

340   IT
SETTIMANA GIURIDICA. 1960. w. L.600000. Casa Editrice Italedi, Piazza Cavour 19, 00193 Rome, Italy. TEL 6-321-08-03. Ed. Ignazio Scotto. adv. circ. 5,000.

340   CC
SHANDONG LUSHI/SHANDONG LAWYERS. (Text in Chinese) q. Shandong Lushi Xiehui - Shandong Lawyers Association, No. 9, Jing 10 Lu, Jinan, Shandong 250014, People's Republic of China. TEL 616138. Ed. Wang Weimin.

340   CC
SHANGHAI FAYUAN/SHANGHAI LEGAL WORLD. (Text in Chinese) m. Shanghai Shi Sifaju - Shanghai Municipal Bureau of Justice, No.3. Alley 112, Fenyang Lu, Shanghai 200031, People's Republic of China. TEL 4312801. Ed. Xu Qingzhen.

SHAREHOLDER REMEDIES IN CANADA. see *BUSINESS AND ECONOMICS — Investments*

340   US   ISSN 0730-465X
SHEPARD'S CODE OF FEDERAL REGULATIONS CITATIONS. 1986. supplements 5/yr. plus a. cum. $336. Shepard's - McGraw-Hill, Inc., Box 35300, Colorado Springs, CO 80935-3530.
TEL 800-525-2474.

340 613.1   US   ISSN 1054-4771
KF1298.A59
SHEPARD'S ENVIRONMENTAL LIABILITY IN COMMERCIAL TRANSACTIONS. 1990. m. (typically set in Jan.). Shepard's - McGraw-Hill, Inc., Box 35300, Colorado Springs, CO 80935-3530. TEL 719-488-3000. FAX 719-481-7445. Ed.Bd. abstr.; index. (back issues avail.)
Description: Contains current coverage of liability under federal and state environmental statutes and regulations as they affect real estate transactions, bankruptcy proceedings, insurance, lending, and business contracts.

340   US   ISSN 0730-7039
SHEPARD'S FEDERAL CIRCUIT TABLE. 1981. 4/yr. $250. Shepard's - McGraw-Hill, Inc., Box 35300, Colorado Springs, CO 80935-3530.
TEL 800-525-2474.

340   US   ISSN 0730-4633
SHEPARD'S FEDERAL CITATIONS. 1981. 10/yr. (plus s-a. supplements to 24 base vols.) $2633. Shepard's - McGraw-Hill, Inc., Box 35300, Colorado Springs, CO 80935-3530. TEL 800-525-2474.

340   US   ISSN 0746-312X
SHEPARD'S FEDERAL ENERGY LAW CITATIONS. 1982. 3 base vols. (plus q. suppl.) $435. Shepard's - McGraw-Hill, Inc., Box 35300, Colorado Springs, CO 80935-3530. TEL 800-525-2474.

340   US   ISSN 0730-4684
SHEPARD'S FEDERAL LABOR LAW CITATIONS. 1959. 8 base vols. (plus s-a suppl.). $1305. Shepard's - McGraw-Hill, Inc., Box 35300, Colorado Springs, CO 80935-3530. TEL 800-525-2474.

348.7   US   ISSN 0094-9531
KF105.2
SHEPARD'S FEDERAL LAW CITATIONS IN SELECTED LAW REVIEWS. 1974. 6/yr. $230. Shepard's - McGraw-Hill, Inc., Box 35300, Colorado Springs, CO 80935-3530. TEL 719-475-7230.

SHEPARD'S FEDERAL SECURITIES LAW CITATIONS. see *BUSINESS AND ECONOMICS — Investments*

340   US   ISSN 0746-3138
SHEPARD'S IMMIGRATION AND NATURALIZATION CITATIONS. 1982. base vol. (plus q. suppl.). $240. Shepard's - McGraw-Hill, Inc., Box 35300, Colorado Springs, CO 80935-3530. TEL 800-525-2474.

340   US
SHEPARD'S INSURANCE LAW CITATIONS. 1987. 6 base vols. (plus q. suppl.) $660. Shepard's - McGraw-Hill, Inc., Box 35300, Colorado Springs, CO 80935-3530. TEL 800-525-2474.

340   US   ISSN 0582-9887
SHEPARD'S LAW REVIEW CITATIONS. 1968. 3 base vols. (plus 6/yr suppl.) $430. Shepard's - McGraw-Hill, Inc., Box 35300, Colorado Springs, CO 80935-3530. TEL 800-525-2474.

340   US   ISSN 8750-1112
SHEPARD'S PARTNERSHIP LAW CITATIONS. 1983. base vol. (plus q. suppl.). $210. Shepard's - McGraw-Hill, Inc., Box 35300, Colorado Springs, CO 80935-3530. TEL 800-525-2474.

340   US   ISSN 8750-1139
SHEPARD'S PRODUCTS LIABILITY CITATIONS. 1983. 2 base vols. (plus q. suppl.) $300. Shepard's - McGraw-Hill, Inc., Box 35300, Colorado Springs, CO 80935-3530. TEL 800-525-2474.

340   US   ISSN 0270-529X
KFT1259
SHEPARD'S TEXAS BRIEFCASE. 1979. base vol. (plus q. suppl.). $85. Shepard's - McGraw-Hill, Inc., Box 35300, Colorado Springs, CO 80935-3530.
TEL 800-525-2474.

340   US   ISSN 0745-5925
SHEPARD'S UNIFORM COMMERCIAL CODE CITATIONS. 1982. 2 base vols. (plus suppl. 6/yr) $390. Shepard's - McGraw-Hill, Inc., Box 35300, Colorado Springs, CO 80935-3530. TEL 800-525-2474.

340   US   ISSN 0582-9909
SHEPARD'S UNITED STATES ADMINISTRATIVE CITATIONS. Variant title: Shepard's United States Administrative Law Citations. 1967. 5 base vols. (plus bi-m. suppl.) $540. Shepard's - McGraw-Hill, Inc., Box 35300, Colorado Springs, CO 80935-3530. TEL 800-525-2474.

340   US   ISSN 0582-9917
SHEPARD'S UNITED STATES PATENTS AND TRADEMARKS CITATIONS. 1968. 9 base vols. (6/yr suppl.). $1044. Shepard's - McGraw-Hill, Inc., Box 35300, Colorado Springs, CO 80935-3530. TEL 800-525-2474.

340   CN
SHERIFF SERVICES SELECTED OPERATING PROCEDURES. base vol. (plus irreg. suppl.). Can.$28. Ministry of Attorney General, Parliament Bldgs., Victoria, B.C. V8V 1X4, Canada. TEL 604-387-5818. (Subscr. to: Crown Publications, 546 Yates St., Victoria, B.C. V8W 1K8, Canada. TEL 604-386-4636) (looseleaf format; back issues avail.)
Description: A guide to the protocol, procedure, conduct and practice of the Office of the Sheriff.

340 320   JA   ISSN 0583-0362
SHIMANE LAW REVIEW. (Text in Japanese) 1955. 3/yr. exchange basis. Shimane Daigaku, Hobungakubu - Shimane University, Faculty of Law and Literature, 1060 Nishi-Kawazu-machi, Matsue-shi, Shimane-ken 690, Japan. Eds. Yuzoh Fukao, Hobotake Nike. bk.rev.

340   US   ISSN 0037-444X
SI DE KA MAGAZINE. 1915. q. membership. Sigma Delta Kappa Law Foundation, Inc., Dixie Bldg., No.107, 2060 N. 14th St., Arlington, VA 22201-2519. TEL 703-524-0220. adv.; charts; illus. circ. 5,000.

SINGAPORE ACCOUNTANT. see *BUSINESS AND ECONOMICS — Accounting*

340   SI   ISSN 0218-2173
SINGAPORE JOURNAL OF LEGAL STUDIES. (Text in English) 1959. s-a. $50 (effective 1994) (typically set in Jan.). National University of Singapore, Faculty of Law, 10 Kent Ridge Cres., Singapore 0511, Singapore. TEL 7756666. FAX 779-0979. TELEX RS 33943-UNISPO. Ed. K.L Koh. adv.: page S.$300. bk.rev. circ. 1,850. (back issues avail.)
—BLDSC (8285.463750).
Formerly (until Jul. 1990): Malaya Law Review (ISSN 0542-335X)
Description: Publishes articles and comments on legislation and cases relevant to Singapore. Also covers commercial and foreign investment laws in ASEAN.

340   SI   ISSN 0218-3161
▼**SINGAPORE LAW REPORTS**. 1992. fortn. S.$375 for Singapore and Brunei; Malaysia M.$605. Butterworths Asia (Subsidiary of: Reed International (Singapore) Pte. Ltd.), 3 Shenton Way, No. 14-03, Shenton House, Singapore 0106, Singapore. TEL 2203684. FAX 2255026. circ. 1,200.

349   SI   ISSN 0080-9691
SINGAPORE LAW REVIEW. (Text in English) 1969. a. S.15. National University of Singapore Law Club, c/o Law Faculty, Kent Ridge Campus, Singapore 0511, Singapore. FAX 7790970. (Dist. by: Wm.W. Gaunt & Sons, Inc., Law Book Dealers & Subscription Agents, Gaunt Bldg., 3011 Gulf Dr., Holmes Beach, FL 34217-2199. TEL 813-778-5211. FAX 813-778-5252) Ed. Ngeow Yuen Lian. adv. circ. 1,350. **Indexed:** Foreign Leg.Per.
Supersedes (1958-1969): Me Judice.

SKATTERETT; Tidsskrift for skatt og avgift. see *BUSINESS AND ECONOMICS — Public Finance, Taxation*

340   UK   ISSN 1352-4550
▼**SKILLS**. 1993. a. £15. Jordan Publishing Ltd., 21 St. Thomas St., Bristol BS1 6JS, England. TEL 0272-230600. FAX 0272-250486. Ed. Ian Cross. **Document type:** academic/scholarly publication.

LAW

340   CN
SMALL CLAIM MANUAL. base vol. (plus irreg. suppl.). Ministry of Attorney General, Parliament Bldgs., Victoria, B.C. V8V 1X4, Canada. TEL 604-387-5818. (Subscr. to: Crown Publications, 546 Yates St., Victoria, B.C. V8W 1K8, Canada. TEL 604-386-4636) (looseleaf format)
    Description: Corrects policies, practices and procedures for the small claim clerk.

333   US   ISSN 1068-8994
▼**SNAKE RIVER BASIN ADJUDICATION DIGEST.** 1993. 26/yr. $169. Ridenbaugh Press, Box 2276, Boise, ID 83701. TEL 208-338-9700. FAX 208-338-9769. Ed. Randy Stapilus. index. (looseleaf format; back issues avail.) **Document type:** newsletter.
    ●Also available online.

SOCIAL ACTION AND THE LAW. see *PSYCHOLOGY*

SOCIAL AND LEGAL STUDIES. see *SOCIOLOGY*

SOCIAL RESPONSIBILITY: BUSINESS, JOURNALISM, LAW, MEDICINE. see *PHILOSOPHY*

340   AT   ISSN 0817-3524
SOCIAL SECURITY REPORTER. 1981. bi-m. Aus.$35 (foreign Aus.$47). Legal Service Bulletin Co., Ltd., c/o Monash University, Faculty of Law, Wellington Rd., Clayton, Vic. 3168, Australia. TEL 64-3-544-0974. FAX 643-565-5305. Ed. Peter Hanks. **Document type:** academic/scholarly publication.
    ●Also available online. Vendor(s): Info-One International Pty Ltd.

340   UK
SOCIAL WELFARE LAW. irreg. £130. Longman Group Ltd., Law, Tax and Finance Division, 21-27 Lambs Conduit St., London WC1N 3NJ, England. TEL 071-242-2548. FAX 071-831-8119. Ed. David Pollard. (looseleaf format) **Document type:** bulletin.
    Description: Analysis of laws relating to the welfare system.

SOCIALFOERFATTNINGAR. see *SOCIAL SERVICES AND WELFARE*

340   SP   ISSN 0213-0483
K3
SOCIEDAD DE ESTUDIOS VASCOS. CUADERNOS DE SECCION. DERECHO. 1984. irreg. Eusko Ikaskuntza, Legazpi, 10-1, 20004 Donostia-San Sebastian, Spain. TEL 425 111.

344   PE
SOCIEDAD Y DERECHO. q. Jiron Huancavelica No. 470-Of. 308, Lima, Peru.

SOCIEDADES POR ACOES. see *BUSINESS AND ECONOMICS*

340   IT
▼**SOCIETA E DIRITTO;** mensile di diritto e pratica per le imprese e i professionisti. 1992. m. L.180000 (effective 1993). Pirola Editore S.p.a., Casella Postale 10444, Via Parabiago 19, 20151 Milan, Italy. TEL 02-30-22-635. FAX 02-38-011-205. Ed. Luigi Tondi. **Document type:** consumer publication.

340   FR   ISSN 0081-0843
SOCIETE DES AUTEURS, COMPOSITEURS, EDITEURS POUR LA GERANCE DES DROITS DE REPRODUCTION MECANIQUE. BULLETIN. Variant title: A.C.E. Bulletin. irreg. price varies. Societe des Auteurs, Compositeurs, Editeurs pour la Gerance des Droits de Reproduction Mecanique, 62 rue Blanche, 75009 Paris, France.

SOCIETY OF MARITIME ARBITRATORS. AWARD SERVICE. see *TRANSPORTATION — Ships And Shipping*

340.023   CN   ISSN 1186-284X
SOCIETY RECORD. 1979. 6/yr. membership. Nova Scotia Barristers' Society, 1475 Hollis St., Halifax, NS B3J 3M4, Canada. TEL 902-422-1491. FAX 902-429-4869. **Document type:** newsletter.

340 300   UK   ISSN 0957-7017
SOCIO-LEGAL NEWSLETTER. q. £10 (foreign £13). Socio-Legal Studies Association, Centre for Socio-Legal Studies, Wolfson College, Oxford OX2 6UD, England. TEL 0865-52967. FAX 0865-274125. Ed. Nancy Drucker. **Document type:** newsletter.

344   IT
SOCIOLOGIA DEL DIRITTO. 1974; N.S. 3/yr. L.75000 (foreign L.90000) (effective 1993). (Centro Nazionale di Prevenzione e Difesa Sociale, Commissione Permanente di Sociologia del Diritto) Franco Angeli Editore, Viale Monza 106, 20127 Milan, Italy. TEL 02-28-27-651. Ed. Renato Treves. **Indexed:** Lang.& Lang.Behav.Abstr., Sociol.Abstr.

340   BU   ISSN 0081-1866
K7
SOFIISKI UNIVERSITET. JURIDIHESKI FAKULTET. GODISNIK. (Summaries in English, French, and German) irreg., vol.72, 1979. price varies. Publishing House of the Bulgarian Academy of Sciences, Acad. G. Bonchev St., Bldg. 6, 1113 Sofia, Bulgaria. Ed. G. Boychev. circ. 550. (reprint service avail. from IRC) **Indexed:** BSL Econ.
    —BLDSC (0051.190000).

SOFTWARE LAW BULLETIN; a compendium of current issues and cases involving software. see *COMPUTERS — Software*

SOFTWARE LAW JOURNAL. see *COMPUTERS — Software*

SOFTWARE PROTECTION; a journal on the legal, technical and practical aspects of protecting computer software. see *COMPUTERS — Software*

SOLAR LAW. see *ENERGY — Solar Energy*

340   UK   ISSN 0038-1047
K23
SOLICITORS' JOURNAL. 1857. w. £85($130) Longman Group Ltd., Law, Tax and Finance Division, 21-27 Lamb's Conduit St., London WC1N 3NJ, England. TEL 071-242-2548. FAX 071-831-8119. Ed. Julian Harris. **Indexed:** Abstr.Bk.Rev.Curr.Leg.Per., C.L.I., L.R.I., Leg.Per., RICS. **Document type:** trade publication.
    —BLDSC (8327.270000); UnCover; SWETS; UMI. CCC.
    Description: Information for practicing solicitors.

340   CN
SOLICITOR'S JOURNAL. (Text in English, French) 1985. 3/yr. Can.$20 to non-members. Canadian Bar Association, New Brunswick Branch, 1133 Regent St., Ste. 206, Fredericton, NB E3B 3Z2, Canada. TEL 506-458-8536. FAX 506-451-1421. Ed. Michael Bray. adv. circ. 1,200. (looseleaf format) **Document type:** academic/scholarly publication, newsletter.

SONOMA COUNTY DAILY HERALD-RECORDER. see *BUSINESS AND ECONOMICS*

340   CH   ISSN 0259-3750
SOOCHOW LAW REVIEW. Key Title: Dongwu Falu Xuebao. (Text in Chinese or English) 1976. s-a. $20 per no. Soochow University, Wai Shuang Hsi, Shih Lin, Taipei, Taiwan, Republic of China. FAX 886-02-8812317. (reprint service avail.) **Document type:** academic/scholarly publication.
    Description: Publication of the Soochow University School of Law.

340 610   US
SOURCEBOOK ON ASBESTOS DISEASES. (Supplement avail.: Sourcebook on Asbestos Diseases Case Law Quarterly) 1980. 6 base vols. (plus supplements). $400 for set. Butterworth Legal Publishers (Salem) (Subsidiary of: Reed Elsevier plc), 8 Industrial Way, Bldg. C, Salem, NH 03079. TEL 800-548-4001. FAX 603-898-9858. Eds. George A. Peters, Barbara J. Peters.
    Description: Contains information, insights, and data for trial attorneys and others involved in asbestos litigation or legal research.

340 610   US
SOURCEBOOK ON ASBESTOS DISEASES CASE LAW QUARTERLY. (Supplement to: Sourcebook on Asbestos Diseases) 1989. q. $85. Butterworth Legal Publishers (Salem) (Subsidiary of: Reed Elsevier plc), 8 Industrial Way, Bldg. C, Salem, NH 03079. TEL 800-548-4001. FAX 603-898-9858.
    Description: Provides summaries of recent asbestos cases organized by issue.

340   US
SOURCES OF CONNECTICUT LAW. 1987. base vol. (plus suppl.). $65. Butterworth Legal Publishers (Salem) (Subsidiary of: Reed Elsevier plc), 8 Industrial Way, Bldg. C, Salem, NH 03079. TEL 800-548-4001. FAX 603-898-9858. Ed. Shirley Rassi Bysiewicz.
    Description: Comprehensive citator to all sources of Connecticut law, from historical beginnings to the present.

340   SA
SOUTH AFRICAN HUMAN RIGHTS YEARBOOK. 1972. a. R.60. University of Natal, Howard College School of Law, King George V Ave., Durban, Natal 4001, South Africa. TEL 27-31-2602558. (Dist. by: Oxford University Press Southern Africa, Harrington House, 37 Barrack St., Cape Town 8001, South Africa. TEL 27-21-457266. FAX 27-21-457265) adv.; bk.rev. circ. 700. (back issues avail.) **Indexed:** Documentatieblad, Foreign.Leg.Per., Ind.S.A.Per. **Document type:** academic/scholarly publication.
    Former titles: South African Human Rights and Labour Law Yearbook; (until 1989): Natal University Law and Society Review; Natal University Law Review.

SOUTH AFRICAN JOURNAL OF LABOUR RELATIONS. see *BUSINESS AND ECONOMICS — Labor And Industrial Relations*

SOUTH AFRICAN JOURNAL ON HUMAN RIGHTS. see *POLITICAL SCIENCE — Civil Rights*

340   SA   ISSN 0038-2388
K23
SOUTH AFRICAN LAW JOURNAL. 1884. q. R.115. Juta & Co. Ltd., P.O. Box 14373, Kenwyn 7790, South Africa. TEL 021-797-5101. FAX 021-761-5010. Ed. Ellison Kahn. adv.; bk.rev.; index. (also avail. in microfiche from WSH) **Indexed:** Abstr.Bk.Rev.Curr.Leg.Per., C.L.I., Ind.S.A.Per., Leg.Per.
    —BLDSC (8340.700000); UnCover.
    Description: Articles on Roman, Dutch and modern South African law.

340   SA   ISSN 0038-2396
SOUTH AFRICAN LAW REPORTS. (Text and summaries in Afrikaans, English) 1947. m. R.573.60. Juta & Co. Ltd., P.O. Box 14373, Kenwyn 7790, South Africa. TEL 27-21-7975101. FAX 27-21-7615010. Ed.Bd. index, cum.index. (also avail. in microfiche from BHP)
    Description: For the South African lawyer.

346.066   SA   ISSN 1015-0099
SOUTH AFRICAN MERCANTILE LAW JOURNAL/SUID-AFRIKAANSE TYDSKRIF VIR HANDELSREG. (Text in Afrikaans and English) 1979. 3/yr. R.79. (University of South Africa, Faculty of Law, Department of Mercantile Law) Juta & Co. Ltd., P.O. Box 14373, Kenwyn 7790, South Africa. TEL 021-761-5010. FAX 021-797-5101. (Editorial addr.: P.O. Box 392, Pretoria 0001, South Africa. TEL 012-429-8465) Ed.Bd. adv.; bk.rev. circ. 1,000. **Indexed:** Ind.S.A.Per.
    Supersedes (with vol.11, 1989): Modern Business Law - Moderne Besigheidreg.
    Description: Concerned with the legal aspects of commerce and trade.

340   AT   ISSN 0049-1470
SOUTH AUSTRALIAN STATE REPORTS. 1866. irreg. Law Book Co. Ltd., 44-50 Waterloo Rd., N. Ryde, N.S.W. 2113, Australia. TEL 02-887-0177. FAX 02-888-9706. TELEX ASBOOK 27995. Ed. Elliot Johnston. cum.index. (back issues avail.)
    ●Also available online. Vendor(s): Info-One International Pty Ltd.
    Description: Reports on decisions and appeals of the South Australian Supreme Court.

340   US   ISSN 0743-2453
KFS1857
SOUTH CAROLINA APPELLATE DIGEST; bi-weekly case law review for South Carolina attorneys including up-to-date summaries of State and Federal cases from South Carolina. 1985. bi-w. $85. National Legal Research Group, Inc., 2421 Ivy Rd., Box 7187, Charlottesville, VA 22906-7187. TEL 800-446-1870. FAX 804-295-4667. Ed. Chris Hudson.
    Description: For South Carolina attorneys. Contains summaries of recent opinions from South Carolina Supreme Court and Court of Appeals, U.S. Supreme Court and South Carolina Fourth Circuit.

LAW

340 331 US ISSN 1064-461X
▼SOUTH CAROLINA EMPLOYMENT LAW LETTER. 1992. m. $95. (McNair & Sanford, P.A.) M. Lee Smith Publishers & Printers, 162 Fourth Ave., N., Box 198867, Nashville, TN 37219-8867. TEL 615-242-7395; 800-274-6774. FAX 615-256-6601. Ed.Bd. **Document type:** newsletter.
  Description: Reports the latest state-specific employment law developments that affect companies in South Carolina.

340 613.1 US ISSN 1065-7975
▼SOUTH CAROLINA ENVIRONMENTAL COMPLIANCE UPDATE. 1993. m. $137. (McNair & Sanford) M. Lee Smith Publishers & Printers, 162 Fourth Ave., N., Box 198867, Nashville, TN 37219-8867. TEL 615-242-7395; 800-274-6774. FAX 615-256-6601. Eds. Elizabeth F. Mallin, James W. Porter. **Document type:** newsletter.
  Description: Reports the latest state-specific environmental law developments that affect companies in South Carolina.

340 US ISSN 0038-3104
LAW
SOUTH CAROLINA LAW REVIEW. 1949. 4/yr. $30 to S.C. Bar members; non-members $35. University of South Carolina, School of Law, Columbia, SC 29208. TEL 803-777-5874. FAX 803-777-2368. Ed. David Rothstein. adv.; bk.rev.; index, cum.index every 10 yrs. circ. 3,000. (also avail. in microfiche from WSH,PMC; microfilm from WSH,PMC) **Indexed:** C.L.I., L.R.I., Leg.Cont., Leg.Per. **Document type:** academic/scholarly publication.
  ●Also available online. Vendor(s): West Services, Inc.
  —BLDSC (8350.100000); Faxon; UnCover.
  Formerly: South Carolina Law Quarterly.

340 US ISSN 1044-4238
K23
SOUTH CAROLINA LAWYER. 1989. bi-m. $18. South Carolina Bar, c/o Beth Littlejohn, Man. Ed., Box 608, Columbia, SC 29202. TEL 803-799-6653. FAX 803-799-4118. Ed. Robert Wilkins. adv.; circ. 8,000. (controlled). (also avail. in microform from UMI)
  —UnCover.
  Description: Covers legal issues, court decisions, new rulings and changes in the law. University of South Carolina presents the latest cases and their significance.

SOUTH CAROLINA RULES AND REGULATIONS FOR HUNTING AND FISHING LICENSES. see SPORTS AND GAMES — Outdoor Life

340 US ISSN 0038-3325
K23
SOUTH DAKOTA LAW REVIEW.* 1956. 3/yr. $20. University of South Dakota, School of Law, 414 E. Clark St., Vermilion, SD 57069-2390. TEL 605-677-5646. FAX 605-677-5417. Ed. Bruce Kness. adv.; bk.rev. cum.; c. 1,200. (also avail. in microfiche from WSH,PMC; microfilm from WSH,PMC) **Indexed:** C.L.I., L.R.I., Leg.Per., Sel.Water Res.Abstr. **Document type:** academic/scholarly publication.
  ●Also available online. Vendor(s): West Services, Inc.
  —BLDSC (8351.200000); Faxon; UnCover; UMI.

340 US
SOUTH TEXAS LAW REVIEW.* 1954. 3/yr. $30. (South Texas College of Law) South Texas Law Review, Inc., 1303 San Jacinto St., Houston, TX 77002. Ed. Robert S. Marsel. adv.; bk.rev.; cum.index. circ. 2,200. (also avail. in microfilm from WSH,PMC; reprint service avail. from WSH) **Indexed:** C.L.I., Leg.Cont., Leg.Per., Mar.Aff.Bibl.
  ●Also available online. Vendor(s): West Services, Inc.
  Formerly: South Texas Law Journal (ISSN 0038-3546)

340 US
SOUTHEAST TRANSACTION GUIDE. (Issued in 20 base vols. with supplements) 1976. irreg. $1835. Matthew Bender & Co., Inc., 11 Penn Plaza, New York, NY 10001. TEL 212-967-7707. (looseleaf format)
  Description: For Florida, Georgia and Alabama practitioners. Covers a wide variety of business and legal transactions.

SOUTHEASTERN LAW LIBRARIAN. see LIBRARY AND INFORMATION SCIENCES

340 US ISSN 0038-3910
K23
SOUTHERN CALIFORNIA LAW REVIEW. 1927. bi-m. $36 (foreign $45). University of Southern California, Law Center, Room 330, University Park, Los Angeles, CA 90089-0071. TEL 213-740-8475. FAX 213-740-5502. Ed. Eric Claeys. adv.; bk.rev.; abstr.; index. circ. 1,500. (also avail. in microfilm from WSH,PMC; reprint service avail. from WSH) **Indexed:** ASCA, BPIA, Bus.Ind., C.L.I., Crim.Just.Abstr., L.R.I., Leg.Cont., Leg.Per., Sage Pub.Admin.Abstr., Sage Urb.Stud.Abstr., SSCI.
  —BLDSC (8352.930000); Faxon; UnCover; SWETS.

340 US ISSN 0145-3432
K23
SOUTHERN ILLINOIS UNIVERSITY LAW JOURNAL. 1976. q. $20. Southern Illinois University, Carbondale, School of Law, Lesar Law Bldg., Carbondale, IL 62901. TEL 618-453-8721. FAX 618-453-8769. Ed. Kurt Wagner. adv.; bk.rev.; index. circ. 900. (also avail. in microform from UMI; reprint service avail. from RRI,UMI) **Indexed:** C.L.I., L.R.I., Leg.Per.
  —BLDSC (8354.180000); Faxon; UnCover; UMI.
  Description: Articles analyzing current legal issues with emphasis on topics of interest to Illinois attorneys, judges and legislators.

340 US ISSN 1056-2184
K23
SOUTHERN LAW JOURNAL. 1991. q. $20 (foreign $25) (effective 1992). Abilene Christian University, Southern Academy of Legal Studies in Business, University of Arkansas, 204 Business Administration Bldg., Fayetteville, AR 72701. TEL 501-575-6353. FAX 501-757-7687. (Co-sponsor: Southern Business Law Association) Ed. John M. Norwoood. adv.; bk.rev.; circ. 100 (paid). **Document type:** academic/scholarly publication.
  Description: Contains items of interest to teachers of business law, and managers.

340 US ISSN 0006-9965
SOUTHERN METHODIST UNIVERSITY SCHOOL OF LAW. BRIEF. 1965. a. Southern Methodist University School of Law, Dallas, TX 75275. TEL 214-692-4330. circ. 6,500.
  —UMI.

344 US ISSN 0361-0861
KF4114
SOUTHERN SCHOOL LAW DIGEST.* 1974. m. $55. Louisiana School Boards Association, 7912 Summa Ave., Baton Rouge, LA 70809-3416. TEL 504-769-3191. Ed. Robert Hammomds.

340 US ISSN 0038-4836
K23
SOUTHWESTERN LAW JOURNAL. 1947. 5/yr. $36 (foreign $43). S M U Law Review Association, Southern Methodist University, School of Law, Dallas, TX 75275. TEL 214-768-2594. FAX 214-768-3946. bk.rev.; index, cum.index every 10 yrs. circ. 1,000. (also avail. in microform from WSH; reprint service avail. from WSH) **Indexed:** Abstr.Bk.Rev.Curr.Leg.Per., C.L.I., L.R.I., Leg.Cont., Leg.Per. **Document type:** academic/scholarly publication.
  ●Also available online. Vendor(s): West Services, Inc.
  —Faxon; UnCover.
  Formerly: S M U Law Review.

340 341 US ISSN 0561-1784
SOUTHWESTERN LEGAL FOUNDATION. ANNUAL REPORT. 1955. a. free. Southwestern Legal Foundation, Box 830707, Richardson, TX 75083-0707. TEL 214-690-2370. TELEX 284522 SWLF UR. circ. 2,000. (back issues avail.)

340 RU ISSN 0038-5115
SOVETSKAYA YUSTITSIYA. 1957. s-m. $13.20. Izdatel'stvo Kniga, 50, Gorky St., 125047 Moscow, Russia. bk.rev.; index. **Indexed:** Curr.Dig.Sov.Press.

340 US
SOVIET LAW. irreg., 2nd ed., 1988. $40. Butterworth Legal Publishers (Salem) (Subsidiary of: Reed Elsevier plc), 8 Industrial Way, Bldg. C, Salem, NH 03079. TEL 800-548-4001. FAX 603-898-9858. Ed. W.E. Butler.

340 AU
SOZIALVERSICHERUNGSRECHTLICHE ENTSCHEIDUNGEN. 1953. a. price varies. Manzsche Verlags- und Universitaetsbuchhandlung, Kohlmarkt 16, A-1014 Vienna, Austria. TEL 0222-531610. FAX 0222-53161-181. Ed. Hellmut Teschner. circ. 2,000. **Document type:** bulletin.
  Description: Collects cases on provisions of social welfare law.

370.26 SP
SPAIN. MINISTERIO DE EDUCACION Y CIENCIA. BOLETIN OFICIAL: COLECCION LEGISLATIVA. m. 2500 ptas. (foreign 4215 ptas.). Ministerio de Educacion y Ciencia, Centro de Publicaciones, Ciudad Universitaria, 28040 Madrid, Spain. TEL 549-77-00.

340 SP
SPAIN. MINISTERIO DE JUSTICIA. BOLETIN DE INFORMACION. (Supplements avail.) 34/yr. 4500 ptas. (foreign 5500 ptas.). Ministerio de Justicia, Centro de Publicaciones, Secretaria General Tecnica, Gran Via, 76-8, 28013 Madrid, Spain. TEL 547-54-22. FAX 559-29-48. **Document type:** government publication, bulletin.

340 SP ISSN 0210-1165
KKT496.3
SPAIN. MINISTERIO DE JUSTICIA. DICCIONARIOS INDICE DE JURISPRUDENCIA CIVIL. (Subseries of: Coleccion Legislativa de Espana) 1971. irreg., latest 1988-1990. 13500 ptas. Ministerio de Justicia, Centro de Publicaciones, Secretaria General Tecnica, Gran Via, 76-8, 28013 Madrid, Spain. TEL 547-54-22. FAX 599-29-48. Ed. Urbano Ruiz Gutierrez. **Document type:** government publication.

340 SP ISSN 0210-1157
SPAIN. MINISTERIO DE JUSTICIA. DICCIONARIOS INDICE DE JURISPRUDENCIA PENAL. (Subseries of: Coleccion Legislativa de Espana) 1957. irreg., latest 1983-1988. 37700 ptas. Ministerio de Justicia, Centro de Publicaciones, Gran Via, 76-8, 28013 Madrid, Spain. TEL 547-54-22. FAX 599-29-48. **Document type:** government publication.

340 SP ISSN 0210-3419
SPAIN. MINISTERIO DE JUSTICIA. SECRETARIA GENERAL TECNICA. DOCUMENTACION JURIDICA. 1974. q. 4700 ptas. (foreign 5350 ptas.). Ministerio de Justicia, Centro de Publicaciones, Secretaria General Tecnica, Gran Via, 76-8, 28013 Madrid, Spain. TEL 547-54-22. FAX 559-29-48. Ed.Bd. bk.rev. circ. 1,200. (back issues avail.) **Document type:** government publication.
  Supersedes: Spain. Ministerio de Justicia. Secretaria General Tecnica. Informacion Juridica (ISSN 0303-9927)

347 US ISSN 0275-2913
KF8759.A15S66
SPECIAL COURT NEWS. 1980. q. membership only. American Bar Association, National Conference of Special Court Judges, 750 N. Lake Shore Dr., Chicago, IL 60611. TEL 312-988-5555. FAX 312-988-6281. Ed. Doug Somerlot. **Document type:** newsletter.
  Description: Newsletter reporting current activities and plans of the conference.

SPECIAL EDUCATION UPDATE. see EDUCATION — Special Education And Rehabilitation

THE SPECIAL EDUCATOR. see EDUCATION — Special Education And Rehabilitation

340 US
SPECIALIZATION UPDATE. s-a. free. American Bar Association, Standing Committee on Specialization, 541 N. Fairbanks Ct., Chicago, IL 60611-3314. TEL 312-988-5753. FAX 312-988-5032. Ed. Adrian Hochstadt. **Document type:** newsletter.
  Description: Compilation of current news briefs and articles.

340 US ISSN 0198-8778
KF3821.A59
SPECIALTY LAW DIGEST: HEALTH CARE. 1979. m. $380. Specialty Digest Publications, Inc., 10301 University Ave., N.E., Blaine, MN 55434. TEL 612-780-3157.
  —BLDSC (8406.280000). CCC.

THE SPECTRUM (TOPEKA). see POLITICAL SCIENCE — Civil Rights

SPILL REPORTING PROCEDURES GUIDE. see ENVIRONMENTAL STUDIES — Waste Management

340 617.1 US
SPORTS AND RECREATIONAL INJURIES. 1985. base vol. (plus a. suppl.). $95. Shepard's - McGraw-Hill, Inc., Box 35300, Colorado Springs, CO 80935-3530. TEL 800-525-2474.
Description: Discusses the liability of sporting goods manufacturers and retailers, governments, schools, commercial recreational facilities and insurance carriers in more than 40 different areas of sport.

SPORTS AND THE COURTS; physical education and sports law newsletter. see SPORTS AND GAMES

340 US
SPORTS AND THE LAW. 1986. q. Constitutional Rights Foundation, 601 S. Kingsley Ave., Los Angeles, CA 90005. TEL 213-487-5590. FAX 213-386-0459. Ed. Marshall Croddy. circ. 7,000. (back issues avail.) **Document type:** newsletter.

340 790.1 UK ISSN 0968-6037
SPORTS LAW & FINANCE. bi-m. £99($198) I B C Publishing, Gilmoora House, 57-61 Mortimer St., London W1N 7TD, England. TEL 071-637-4383. FAX 071-636-6414. (Subscr. in U.S. to: IBC (USA), 290 Eliot St., Box 91004, Ashland, MA 01721-9104. TEL 508-881-2800. FAX 508-881-0982) Ed. Stephen Townley. **Document type:** newsletter.

340 617.1 US ISSN 1041-696X
KF2910.S653
SPORTS MEDICINE STANDARDS & MALPRACTICE REPORTER. q. $39.95. Professional Reports Corporation, 4418 Belden Village St., N.W., Canton, OH 44718-2516. TEL 216-492-6063; 800-336-0083. FAX 216-492-6176. (looseleaf format) **Document type:** newsletter.
Description: Covers legal issues of interest to sports medicine professionals, including current trends in liability, professional standards, drug screening, legal aspects of athletic programs, and more.

340 790.1 US ISSN 0893-8210
KF1290.S66
SPORTS, PARKS AND RECREATION LAW REPORTER. 1987. q. $39.95. Professional Reports Corporation, 4418 Belden Village St., N.W., Canton, OH 44718-2516. TEL 216-492-6063; 800-336-0083. FAX 216-492-6176. adv.; bk.rev. circ. 300. (looseleaf format) **Document type:** newsletter.
Description: Covers legal issues of interest to sports, parks and recreation professionals, including liability, releases and waivers, drug testing, professional standards, and more.

340 US
▼**SPOTLIGHT (NEW BRUNSWICK).** 1992. irreg. New Jersey State Bar Association, Entertainment and Arts Law Section, One Constitution Sq., New Brunswick, NJ 08901-1500. TEL 908-249-5000. FAX 908-249-2815. Ed. Brian Blatz. **Document type:** newsletter.

340 790.1 GW
▼**SPURT;** Zeitschrift fuer Sport und Recht. 1994. bi-m. DM.174. C.H. Beck'sche Verlagsbuchhandlung, Wilhelmstr. 9, 80801 Munich, Germany. TEL 089-38189-338. FAX 089-38189-398. TELEX 5215085-BECK-D. Ed.Bd. adv.; bk.rev. circ. 5,000. **Document type:** bulletin.

347.91 II
SRINAGAR LAW JOURNAL; a monthly law reporter. 1979. m. Rs.300. Court Rd., Srinagar, J & K, Kashmir 190001, India. TEL 31065. Ed. Hakim Tshtiag Hussain. adv.; bk.rev.

DER STAAT; Zeitschrift fuer Staatslehre, Oeffentliches Recht und Verfassungsgeschichte. see POLITICAL SCIENCE

340 GW ISSN 0724-7885
STAATSANZEIGER FUER DAS LAND HESSEN. 1946. w. DM.112.40. (Hessisches Ministerium des Innern) Verlag Kultur und Wissen GmbH, Wilhelmstr. 42, 65185 Wiesbaden, Germany. TEL 0611-36098-0. FAX 0611-301303. (back issues avail.)

340 UK
STAIR SOCIETY. 1936. a. £12. Stair Society, 16 Charlotte Sq., Edinburgh EH2 2BB, Scotland. TEL 031-225-8585. FAX 031-225-1110. Ed. William Gordon. circ. 580. **Document type:** academic/scholarly publication.

STAMP DUTIES N.S.W. & A.C.T. see BUSINESS AND ECONOMICS — Public Finance, Taxation

STAMP DUTIES SOUTH AUSTRALIA. see BUSINESS AND ECONOMICS — Public Finance, Taxation

STAMP DUTIES W.A. see BUSINESS AND ECONOMICS — Public Finance, Taxation

STANDARD & POOR'S REVIEW OF SECURITIES, COMMODITIES REGULATION; an analysis of current laws, regulations and court decisions affecting the securities industry. see BUSINESS AND ECONOMICS — Investments

340 GW ISSN 0341-3977
DAS STANDESAMT. 1877. m. DM.196. (Bundesverband der deutschen Standesbeamten e.V) Verlag fuer Standesamtswesen GmbH, Hanauer Landstr. 197, 60314 Frankfurt a.M., Germany. TEL 069-405894-0. FAX 069-405894-99. Ed.Bd. **Document type:** bulletin.
—SWETS.
Incorporated (in Jan. 1979): Bayerische Standesamt (ISSN 0005-7096); Standesbeamte.

344.73 US ISSN 0892-7138
K23
STANFORD ENVIRONMENTAL LAW JOURNAL. 1978. 2/yr (Jan., Jun.). $15. Stanford Environmental Law Society, Stanford Law School, Stanford, CA 94305. TEL 415-723-4421. Ed. Michael Pyle. bk.rev. circ. 500. (also avail. in microform from WSH; reprint service avail. from WSH) **Indexed:** C.L.I., Environ.Per.Bibl., L.R.I., Leg.Per. **Document type:** academic/scholarly publication.
—BLDSC (8431.330000); Faxon; UnCover.
Formerly (until 1985): Stanford Environmental Law Annual (ISSN 0197-7873)

STANFORD LAW ALUM. see COLLEGE AND ALUMNI

340 US ISSN 1044-4386
H97
STANFORD LAW & POLICY REVIEW. 1989. s-a. $15 to individuals; institutions $20. Stanford Law School, Crown Quadrangle, Stanford, CA 94305-8610. TEL 415-725-7297. FAX 415-723-0501. Ed. Shannon Hansen. adv.; abstr. circ. 5,000. (back issues avail.) **Document type:** academic/scholarly publication.
●Also available online. Vendor(s): West Services, Inc.
—BLDSC (8432.150000); Faxon; UnCover.
Description: Contains nonideological publication written for and distributed to the nation's policymakers. Each issue features a symposium on a current policy topic.

340 US ISSN 0038-9765
K23
STANFORD LAW REVIEW. 1948. 6/yr. $35 (foreign $40). Stanford University, Stanford Law School, Crown Quadrangle, Stanford, CA 94305-8610. TEL 415-723-3210. Ed. Sthephen Thau. adv.; bk.rev.; index. cum.index: vols.1-30. (also avail. in microfiche from RRI,WSH; microfilm from RRI,WSH; back issues avail.; reprint service avail. from RRI) **Indexed:** A.B.C.Pol.Sci., Abstr.Bk.Rev.Curr.Leg.Per., Account.Ind. (1974-), ASCA, BPIA, C.L.I., Crim.Just.Abstr., Curr.Cont., L.R.I., Leg.Cont., Leg.Per., P.A.I.S., SSCI. **Document type:** academic/scholarly publication.
●Also available online. Vendor(s): Mead Data Central, Inc., West Services, Inc.
—BLDSC (8432.200000); Faxon; UnCover; SWETS; UMI.
Formerly: Stanford Intramural Law Review.
Description: Articles and notes with conclusions on the interdisciplinary study of law.

340 320 US ISSN 0585-0576
KF292.S7
STANFORD LAWYER. 1966. a. Stanford University, Stanford Law School, Stanford, CA 94305-8610. TEL 415-723-9301. Ed. Constance Hellyer. illus. circ. 9,500. **Indexed:** C.L.I. **Document type:** academic/scholarly publication.
Description: Contains articles on law and legal studies, politics, history and government, along with news of Stanford Law School.

340 US
STARK COUNTY BAR JOURNAL. m. Stark County Bar Association, 309 AmeriTrust Bldg., Canton, OH 44702. TEL 216-453-0685. FAX 216-453-0180. Ed. Mary Z. McNulty. adv.
Description: News and announcements of interest to lawyers in the Canton area.

340 US
STATE BAR ASSOCIATION OF NORTH DAKOTA. NOTE PAD. vol.18, 1993. bi-m. membership. State Bar Association of North Dakota, Box 2136, Bismarck, ND 58502-2136. TEL 701-255-1404. **Document type:** newsletter.
Description: Professional announcements and news of interest to lawyers in North Dakota.

340 US ISSN 0363-0331
STATE BAR NEWS. 1969. 10/yr. membership. New York State Bar Association, Committee on Public Relations, 1 Elk St., Albany, NY 12207. TEL 518-463-3200. Ed. Daniel M. Kittay. adv. (tabloid format) **Document type:** newsletter.
Formerly (until 1975): New York State Bar Association. Newsletter (ISSN 0548-8958)
Description: News and items of interest to lawyers in New York State.

340 US ISSN 1062-6611
KF200
STATE BAR OF NEW MEXICO. BAR BULLETIN; advance opinions of the New Mexico Supreme Court and Court of Appeals. Variant title: New Mexico State Bar Bulletin & Advance Opinions. 1960. w. $55. State Bar of New Mexico, 121 Tijeras N.E., Albuquerque, NM 87102. TEL 505-842-6132. FAX 505-843-8765. (Subscr. to: Box 25883, Albuquerque, NM 87125) Ed. Cheryl Bruce. adv. contact: Lynne M. Luciero. bk.rev.; index; circ. 800 (paid); 4,700 (controlled). (looseleaf format) **Document type:** bulletin.
Former titles: State Bar of New Mexico. Bulletin and Advance Opinions; (until 1986): State Bar of New Mexico. News and Views (ISSN 0279-375X); State Bar of New Mexico. Bar Bulletin and Advance Opinions (ISSN 0039-0038)

340 US
STATE BAR OF SOUTH DAKOTA. NEWSLETTER. m. State Bar of South Dakota, 222 E. Capitol, Pierre, SD 57501-2596. TEL 605-224-7554. **Document type:** newsletter.
Description: Announcements of meetings and other professional news of interest to lawyers in South Dakota.

340 US
STATE BAR OF WISCONSIN. GOVERNMENT LAWYERS DIVISION NEWS. 1988. 2/yr. membership. State Bar of Wisconsin, Government Lawyers Division, 402 W. Wilson St., Madison, WI 53703. TEL 608-257-3838. FAX 608-257-5502. circ. 1,500. (back issues avail.) **Document type:** newsletter.

340 US
STATE BAR OF WISCONSIN. INDIVIDUAL RIGHTS & RESPONSIBILITIES SECTION. irreg. (2-4/yr.). membership. State Bar of Wisconsin, Individual Rights & Responsibilities Section, 402 W. Wilson, Madison, WI 53703. TEL 608-257-3838. FAX 608-257-5502. circ. 280. (back issues avail.) **Document type:** newsletter.

STATE CAPITOL WATCH. see BUSINESS AND ECONOMICS — Marketing And Purchasing

340 US ISSN 0145-3076
KF8732.A15
STATE COURT JOURNAL. 1977. q. $24. National Center for State Courts, 300 Newport Ave., Williamsburg, VA 23187-8798.
TEL 804-253-2000. FAX 804-220-0449. bibl.; illus.; stat. (also avail. in microform from UMI; microfiche from WSH; reprint service avail. from WSH) **Indexed:** C.L.I., CJPI, Crim.Just.Abstr., L.R.I., Law Ofc.Info.Svc., Leg.Per. **Document type:** academic/scholarly publication.
—UnCover.

STATE HAZARDOUS WASTE REGULATION. see ENVIRONMENTAL STUDIES — Waste Management

STATE HEALTH NOTES. see PUBLIC HEALTH AND SAFETY

340
KF3941.Z95 US ISSN 0276-7651
STATE LAWS AND PUBLISHED ORDINANCES, FIREARMS. a. U.S. Department of the Treasury, Bureau of Alcohol, Tobacco and Firearms, 15th and Pennsylvania Ave. N.W., Washington, DC 20224. TEL 202-566-7777.
Formerly: Firearms, State Laws and Published Ordinances.

340 350 US ISSN 0898-7297
JK2495
STATE LEGISLATIVE SOURCEBOOK; a resource guide to legislative information in the fifty states. 1985. a. $140 (effective 1993). Government Research Service, 701 Jackson, Ste. 304, Topeka, KS 66603. TEL 913-232-7720. FAX 913-232-1615. Ed. Lynn Hellebust. Document type: directory.
Description: Contains information on legislation in the 50 states, D.C. and Puerto Rico.

STATE LEGISLATIVE UPDATE. see FOOD AND FOOD INDUSTRIES

347.016
KF8797.A15N68 US ISSN 0744-236X
STATE NOTARY BULLETIN. 1973. bi-m. $26. National Notary Association, 8236 Remmet Ave., Box 7184, Canoga Park, CA 91309-7184. TEL 818-713-4000. FAX 818-713-9061. Ed. Charles N. Faerber. circ. 80,000. (also avail. in microfilm; reprint service avail. from UMI) Document type: newsletter.
Formerly: Notary Viewpoint.

346 AT ISSN 0158-1996
STATE REPORTS W.A. 1899. irreg. (with annual cumulation). price varies. Law Book Co. Ltd., 44-50 Waterloo Rd., N. Ryde, N.S.W. 2113, Australia. TEL 02-887-0177. FAX 02-888-9706. TELEX ASBOOK 27995.
Formerly (until 1984): Western Australian Reports (ISSN 0083-8764)
Description: Reports from Family Court, District Court, Workers Compensation Board, and Town Planning Tribunal of Western Australia.

STATISTICAL PROOF OF DISCRIMINATION. see POLITICAL SCIENCE — Civil Rights

340 UK ISSN 0144-3593
K23
STATUTE LAW REVIEW. 1980. 3/yr. £64($120) (effective 1994). (Statute Law Society) Oxford University Press, Oxford Journals, Walton St., Oxford OX2 6DP, England. TEL 0865-56767. FAX 0865-56646. TELEX 837330-OXPRES-G. (U.S. subscr. to: Oxford University Press Inc., 2001 Evans Rd., Cary, NC 27513. TEL 919-677-0977) Ed. T. St. John Bates. adv. contact: Jane Parker. bk.rev. circ. 500. (reprint service avail. from RRI) Indexed: C.L.I., ELLIS, L.R.I., Leg.Per. Document type: academic/scholarly publication.
—BLDSC (8458.558000); Faxon; SWETS; UMI. CCC.
Description: Provides a forum for the consideration of the legislative process, the use of legislation as an instrument of public policy, and the drafting and interpretation of legislation.

349 US ISSN 1061-0014
K23
STATUTES AND DECISIONS: THE LAWS OF THE USSR & ITS SUCCESSOR STATES; a journal of translations. 1964. bi-m. $485 (foreign $534). M.E. Sharpe, Inc., 80 Business Park Dr., Armonk, NY 10504. TEL 914-273-1800. FAX 914-273-2106. Ed. Serge Levitsky. adv.; index. (also avail. in microfilm from WSH,PMC; back issues avail.) Indexed: C.L.I., Leg.Per., P.A.I.S.
—SWETS; UMI.
Formerly: Soviet Statutes and Decisions (ISSN 0038-5840)
Refereed Serial

340 II ISSN 0039-0763
STATUTES AND NOTIFICATIONS. (Editions in Gujarati, Hamarastra) 1965. m. Rs.40. Chandrakant Chimanlal Vora, 57-2 Gandhi Rd., P.O. Box 163, Ahmedabad 380 001, Gujarat, India. index. circ. 500.

347.9 CN
STATUTES OF ALBERTA - JUDICIALLY CONSIDERED; case annotations. 1980. 3/yr. Can.$135. Carswell, One Corporate Plaza, 2075 Kennedy Rd., Scarborough, ON M1T 3V4, Canada. TEL 403-609-8000. FAX 416-298-5094. Ed. John Leeder.
Former titles: Alberta - Judicially Considered; Alberta Statutes and Rules of Court - Judicially Considered.

340 NZ
STATUTES OF NEW ZEALAND. a. NZ.$60. (Parliamentary Services Commission) Government Printing Office, Private Bag, Wellington, New Zealand. TEL 737-320. index. (back issues avail.)

340 CN
STATUTES OF NEWFOUNDLAND. (Text in English) a. price varies. Office of The Queen's Printer, Confederation Bldg., East Block, St. John's, NF A1B 4J6, Canada. TEL 709-729-3649. FAX 709-729-1900. Ed. David C.B. Dawe. index. circ. 800. (back issues avail.) Document type: government publication.

340 US
STATUTORY TIME LIMITATIONS: COLORADO. 1981. base vol. (plus a. suppl.) $50. Butterworth Legal Publishers (Salem) (Subsidiary of: Reed Elsevier plc), 8 Industrial Way, Bldg. C, Salem, NH 03079. TEL 800-548-4001. FAX 603-898-9858. (looseleaf format)

340 US
STATUTORY TIME LIMITATIONS: WASHINGTON STATE. 1981. base vol. (plus a. suppl.) $55. Butterworth Legal Publishers (Salem) (Subsidiary of: Reed Elsevier plc), 8 Industrial Way, Bldg. C, Salem, NH 03079. TEL 800-548-4001. FAX 603-898-9858. Ed.Bd. (looseleaf format)
Description: Identifies limitation periods as found in the revised code of Washington, including the rules of court.

340 US
STEIN ON PROBATE; administration of decedents' estates under the Uniform Probate Code as enacted in Minnesota. (Second edition) 1986. 2 base vols. (plus suppl.) $225. Butterworth Legal Publishers (Salem) (Subsidiary of: Reed Elsevier plc), 8 Industrial Way, Bldg. C, Salem, NH 03079. TEL 800-548-4001. FAX 603-898-9858. Ed. Robert A. Stein. (looseleaf format)

340 SA ISSN 1016-4359
STELLENBOSCH LAW REVIEW. 1990. 3/yr. $225 for 3 vol. set. University of Stellenbosch, Faculty of Law, University, 7600 Stellenbosch, South Africa. (Dist. in N. America by: Wm. W. Gaunt & Sons, Inc., Gaunt Bldg., 3011 Gulf Dr., Holmes Beach, FL 34217-2199. TEL 813-778-5211. FAX 813-778-5252) Ed. Lourens de Plessis.

340 US
STETSON LAW JOURNAL. 2/yr. Stetson University College of Law, 1401 61st St. S., St. Petersburg, FL 33707. TEL 813-345-1300. FAX 813-345-8973. Ed. Debra A. Lamm. Document type: trade publication.
Description: Introduces a variety of topics for a broad readership, including legal papers, columns from legal updates, and humor.

340 US
STETSON LAW REVIEW. 1970. 3/yr. $25. Stetson University, College of Law, 1401 61 St. S., St. Petersburg, FL 33707. TEL 813-345-1300. FAX 813-345-8973. Ed. Laura Belflower. adv. circ. 9,000. (also avail. in microfilm from RRI; back issues avail.; reprint service avail. from RRI) Indexed: C.L.I., L.R.I., Leg.Per.
•Also available online. Vendor(s): West Services, Inc.

346 GW ISSN 0170-6845
STEUER TRAINING. 1975. m. DM.175.20. Verlag Dr. Peter Deubner GmbH, Wolfgang-Mueller-Str. 14, 50968 Cologne, Germany. TEL 0221-9370180. FAX 0221-93701890. Document type: trade publication.

340 336 GW ISSN 0173-1599
STEUER UND STUDIUM; Zeitschrift fuer die Aus- und Fortbildung im Steuerrecht. 1980. m. DM.130. Neue Wirtschafts Briefe Verlag, Eschstr. 22, 44629 Herne, Germany. TEL 02323-141-0. Ed.Bd. bk.rev.; index. circ. 7,000. (back issues avail.)
—CCC.

340 SZ ISSN 0254-8992
KKW3546.3
DER STEUERENTSCHEID; Sammlung aktueller steuerrechtlicher Entscheidungen. 1983. 10/yr. 285 SFr. (Praxis in der Wissenschaft) Helbing & Lichtenhahn Verlag AG, Freie Str. 84, CH-4051 Basel, Switzerland. TEL 061-2721116. FAX 061-2721150. (Subscr. to: Sauerlaender AG, Laurenzenvorstadt 89, CH-5001 Aarau, Switzerland. TEL 064-268626) adv.: B&W page 773 SFr. index. circ. 1,500. (back issues avail.) Document type: academic/scholarly publication.
—CCC.

STICHTING TOT UITGAAF VAN DE BRONNEN VAN HET OUD-VADERLAANDSE RECHT. 2 SERIES: WERKEN, VERSLAGEN EN MEDEDELINGEN. see HISTORY — History Of Europe

340 UK ISSN 0269-3682
STONE'S JUSTICES' MANUAL. a. $403. Butterworth & Co. (Publishers) Ltd. (Subsidiary of: Reed Elsevier plc), 88 Kingsway, London WC2B 6AB, England. TEL 71-405-6900. FAX 71-405-1332. (US addr.: Butterworth Legal Publishers, 90 Stiles Rd., Salem, NH 03079-9981. TEL 603-898-9664) Eds. S.J. Richman, A.T. Draycott.
—BLDSC (8466.170000).
Description: Compendium of legislation and case law affecting the administration of justice in the magistrates' courts of England and Wales.

343 GW ISSN 0720-1605
K23
STRAFVERTEIDIGER. 1980. m. DM.288. Luchterhand Verlag, Heddesdorferstr. 31, 56564 Neuwied, Germany. TEL 02631-801-0. FAX 02631-801210. (reprint service avail. from SCH) Document type: bulletin.

340 YU ISSN 0039-2138
STRANI PRAVNI ZIVOT. SERIJA D: TEORIJA, ZAKONODAVSTVO, PRAKSA. 1956. q. $30. Institut za Uporedno Pravo, Belgrade, Terazije 41, 11000 Belgrade, Yugoslavia. Ed. Vladimir Jovanovic. circ. 300.
Description: Theory, legislation and practice of foreign law, translations and notes on important foreign statutes, and international regulation.

340 AT
STRATA TITLES (N.S.W.) 1989. 3/yr. Aus.$235. Law Book Co. Ltd., 44-50 Waterloo Rd., North Ryde, N.S.W 2113, Australia. TEL 02-887-0177. FAX 02-888-9706. TELEX ASBOOK 27995. (looseleaf format)
Description: Contains the full text of the Strata Titles Act 1973 and Strata Titles Regulations 1974, with commentary relating to the meaning ambit and application of each section.

STREETWIZE COMICS; youth rights comics. see CHILDREN AND YOUTH — For

340 333.33 NE
STRUCTURING FOREIGN INVESTMENT IN U.S. REAL ESTATE. (Text in English) 1982. 2 base vols. (plus s-a. updates). fl.330($189) (effective 1994). Kluwer Law and Taxation Publishers (Subsidiary of: Wolters Kluwer N.V.), P.O. Box 23, 7400 GA Deventer, Netherlands. TEL 31-5700-47261. FAX 31-5700-22244. TELEX 49295 KLUDV NL. (Dist. by: Libresso Distribution Centre, P.O. Box 23, 7400 GA Deventer, Netherlands. TEL 31-5700-33155. FAX 31-5700-33834; In N. America: Kluwer Law and Taxation Publishers, 675 Massachusetts Ave., Cambridge, MA 02139. TEL 617-354-0140. FAX 617-354-8595) Eds. W. Donald Knight, Richard L. Doernberg. (looseleaf format)
Description: Provides detailed coverage of all major issues of interest to foreign individuals and corporations with US real estate holdings, including all special provisions of US income, gift and estate tax regulations. Also discusses tax and investment protection strategies.

340 GW
STUD.JUR. 8/yr. DM.32. Nomos Verlagsgesellschaft mbH und Co. KG, Waldseestr. 3-5, 76530 Baden-Baden, Germany. TEL 07221-2104-0. FAX 07221-210427. TELEX 781201. (Subscr. to: Postfach 610, 76484 Baden-Baden, Germany) Document type: bulletin.

STUDENT AID NEWS; the independent biweekly news service on student financial assistance programs. see EDUCATION — Higher Education

STUDENT GUIDE TO GRADUATE LAW STUDY PROGRAMS. see EDUCATION — Guides To Schools And Colleges

340.07 US ISSN 0197-6656
KF266
STUDENT GUIDE TO SUMMER LAW STUDY PROGRAMS. 1980. a. $17.50. Joint Committee on Law Study Programs, 154 Stuart St., Boston, MA 02116. TEL 617-451-0010. Eds. Ellen Wayne, Betsy McCombs.
 Formerly: Directory of Summer Law Programs.

340 US ISSN 0039-274X
K23
STUDENT LAWYER (CHICAGO). 1972. m. $21 to non-members. American Bar Association, Law Student Division, 750 N. Lake Shore Dr., Chicago, IL 60611. TEL 312-988-6048. Ed. Sarah Hoban. adv.; bk.rev.; illus.; index. circ. 37,283. (also avail. in microfiche; microfilm; back issues avail.; reprint service avail. from UMI) **Indexed:** C.L.I., L.R.I., Law Ofc.Info.Svc., Leg.Cont.
—Faxon; UnCover.
 Supersedes: Student Lawyer Journal.
 Description: For law students, featuring articles on legal, political and social issues, law school and the profession.

340 US ISSN 0160-3825
KF4165.A15
STUDENT PRESS LAW CENTER REPORT. vol.3, 1979. 3/yr. $15. Student Press Law Center, Inc., 1735 Eye St., N.W., Washington, DC 20006. TEL 202-466-5242. FAX 202-466-6326. circ. 2,700. (back issues avail.) **Indexed:** ERIC. **Document type:** trade publication.
—Faxon.

340 945 IT ISSN 0039-3010
STUDI SENESI. 1884. q. L.55000 (foreign L.90000). Universita degli Studi di Siena, Facolta di Giurisprudenza, Siena, Italy. TEL 0577-298712. FAX 0577-298746. Ed. Paolo Nardi. adv.; bk.rev. circ. 350. **Document type:** academic/scholarly publication.

340 IT ISSN 0039-307X
STUDI URBINATI. SERIE A: DIRITTO. N.S. 1950. s-a. L.7000. (Universita degli Studi di Urbino, Facolta di Giurisprudenza) Armando - Argalia Editore, N. Sauro 1, 61029 Urbino, Italy. Ed. Carlo Bo. bk.rev.; charts; illus.; index. **Indexed:** Chem.Abstr.

STUDIA ET DOCUMENTA AD IURA ORIENTIS ANTIQUI PERTINENTIA. see ORIENTAL STUDIES

STUDIA ET DOCUMENTA HISTORIAE ET IURIS. see HISTORY

340 PL ISSN 0081-6671
STUDIA IURIDICA. (Text in Polish; summaries in English, French, German) 1962. irreg., vol.19, no.1, 1992. price varies. Towarzystwo Naukowe w Toruniu, Ul. Wysoka 16, 87-100 Torun, Poland. TEL 48-56-23941. TELEX 552388 FSBH PL. Ed. Janusz Gilas. circ. 500. **Document type:** academic/scholarly publication.
—BLDSC (8482.954000).

340 HU ISSN 0324-5934
LAW
STUDIA IURIDICA AUCTORIATATE UNIVERSITATIS PECS PUBLICATA. (Text in Hungarian; summaries in English, French, German, Russian) 1958. irreg., no.121, 1992. exchange basis. Janus Pannonius Tudomanyegyetem, Allam- es Jogtudomanyi Kara, 48-as ter 1, 7601 Pecs, Hungary. FAX 72-15-114. TELEX 12301. Ed. Miklos Kengyel. circ. 400. **Document type:** academic/scholarly publication.

347.9 IT ISSN 0081-6698
STUDIA JURIDICA. 1964. irreg., no.85, 1992. price varies. L'Erma di Bretschneider, Via Cassiodoro, 19, 00193 Rome, Italy. TEL 06-687-41-27. FAX 06-687-41-29.

340 PL ISSN 0039-3312
LAW
STUDIA PRAWNICZE. 1962. q. $52. (Polska Akademia Nauk, Instytut Panstwa i Prawa) Ossolineum, Publishing House of the Polish Academy of Sciences, Rynek 9, 50-106 Wroclaw, Poland. TEL 48-71-386-25. FAX 48-71-448-103. TELEX 0712771 OSS PL. Ed. Jan Skupinski. abstr. circ. 600. (cards) **Document type:** academic/scholarly publication.
 Description: Contemporary research on all domains of law.

340 PL ISSN 0081-6841
STUDIA PRAWNO-EKONOMICZNE. (Text in Polish; summaries in English) 1968. irreg. (1-2/yr.). price varies. Lodzkie Towarzystwo Naukowe, Ul. Piotrowska 179, 90-447 Lodz, Poland. TEL 48-42-361026. FAX 48-42-362415. TELEX 884519 PAN PL. (Co-sponsor: Polska Akademia Nauk) Ed. Wladyslaw Welfe. bk.rev. circ. 500. **Document type:** academic/scholarly publication.
—BLDSC (8483.190000).

340 RM ISSN 0578-5464
STUDIA UNIVERSITATIS "BABES-BOLYAI". IURISPRUDENTIA. (Text in Rumanian; summaries in English, French, German) 1958. s-a. exchange basis. Universitatea "Babes-Bolyai", Biblioteca Centrala Universitara, Str. Clinicilor nr. 2, Cluj-Napoca 3400, Rumania. TEL 95-117092. FAX 95-117633. bk.rev.; cum.index: 1956-1963, 1964-1970. **Document type:** academic/scholarly publication.

340 AU
STUDIEN ZU POLITIK UND VERWALTUNG. 1981. irreg., vol.46, 1993. price varies. Boehlau Verlag GmbH & Co.KG, Sachsenplatz 4-6, Postfach 87, A-1201 Vienna, Austria. TEL 0222-3302427-0. FAX 0222-3302432. TELEX 114-506-SPRIW-A. Ed.Bd. **Document type:** monographic series.

900 340 330 AU
STUDIEN ZUR RECHTS-, WIRTSCHAFTS- UND KULTURGESCHICHTE. (Subseries of: Universitaet Innsbruck. Veroeffentlichungen) 1969. irreg., vol.10, 1974. price varies. (Universitaet Innsbruck) Oesterreichische Kommissionsbuchhandlung, Maximilianstr. 17, A-6020 Innsbruck, Austria. Ed. Nikolaus Grass.

STUDIES IN INTERNATIONAL POLITICAL ECONOMY. see POLITICAL SCIENCE

340.1 301 US ISSN 1059-4337
K18 CODEN: SLPSE2
STUDIES IN LAW, POLITICS, AND SOCIETY; a research annual. 1978. a. $63.50 to institutions. J A I Press Inc., 55 Old Post Rd., No. 2, Box 1678, Greenwich, CT 06836-1678. TEL 203-661-7602. (UK addr.: J A I Press Ltd., 3 Henrietta St., London WC2E 8LU, England) Eds. Susan S. Silbey, Austin Sarat. **Indexed:** C.L.I., L.R.I., Lang.& Lang.Behav.Abstr., Leg.Per.
—UnCover.
 Formerly (until 1988): Research in Law, Deviance and Social Control.

340 US
STUDIES IN LEGAL HISTORY. 1973. irreg., latest 1992. price varies. (University of North Carolina at Chapel Hill, Department of English) University of North Carolina Press, Box 2288, Chapel Hill, NC 27515-2288. TEL 919-966-3561. FAX 919-966-3829. (Co-sponsor: American Society for Legal History) Ed. Stanley N. Katz. **Document type:** academic/scholarly publication.
 Refereed Serial

340 RM
STUDII DE DREPT ROMANESC. 1955. 4/yr. $56. (Academia Romana) Editura Academiei Romane, Calea Victoriei 125, 79717 Bucharest, Rumania. (Dist. by: Rompresfilatelia, Calea Grivitei 64-66, P.O. Box 12-201, 78104 Bucharest, Rumania) bk.rev.; index.
 Formerly: Studii si Cercetari Juridice (ISSN 0039-4041)

340 IT
STUDIO LEGALE. 1972. bi-m. Casa Editrice Dott. A. Giuffre, Via Busto Arsizio 40, 20151 Milan, Italy. TEL 02-38000905. FAX 02-38009582. Ed. Gaetano Giuffre. adv. circ. 46,000.

343 US ISSN 0362-2983
KF6450.A7
STUDY OF FEDERAL TAX LAW. INCOME TAX VOLUME: BUSINESS ENTERPRISES. 1975. irreg. $42. Commerce Clearing House, Inc., 4025 W. Peterson Ave., Chicago, IL 60646. TEL 312-583-8500.
 Formerly: Study of Federal Tax Law. Income Tax Materials, Business Enterprises; Supersedes in part: Study of Federal Tax Law. Income Tax Volume.

343 US
STUDY OF FEDERAL TAX LAW. TAXATION OF INCOME. 1976. irreg. $46. Commerce Clearing House, Inc., 4025 W. Peterson Ave., Chicago, IL 60646. TEL 312-583-8500.
 Formerly (until 1993): Study of Federal Tax Law. Income Tax Volume: Individuals; Supersedes in part: Study of Federal Tax Law. Income Tax Volume (ISSN 0362-5230)

340 SJ ISSN 0585-8631
SUDAN LAW JOURNAL AND REPORTS. 1956. a. Judiciary, Khartoum, Sudan.

SUEDDEUTSCHE METALL-BERUFSGENOSSENSCHAFT. MITTEILUNGEN. see OCCUPATIONAL HEALTH AND SAFETY

340 US
K23
SUFFOLK TRANSNATIONAL LAW REVIEW. 1977. 2/yr. $18 (foreign $23). Suffolk University Law School, Suffolk Transnational Law Review, 41 Temple St., Boston, MA 02114-4280. TEL 617-573-8610. bk.rev.; index every 5 yrs. (also avail. in microfilm from RRI,PMC; back issues avail.; reprint service avail. from RRI) **Indexed:** Abstr.Bk.Rev.Curr.Leg.Per., C.L.I., L.R.I., Leg.Cont., Leg.Per., Mar.Aff.Bibl. **Document type:** academic/scholarly publication.
●Also available online. Vendor(s): West Services, Inc.
—Faxon; UnCover.
 Formerly (until 1992): Suffolk Transnational Law Journal (ISSN 0886-2648)
 Description: Covers current topics in international law.

340 US ISSN 0039-4696
SUFFOLK UNIVERSITY LAW REVIEW. 1967. 4/yr. $18. (Suffolk University Law School) Joe Christensen, Inc. (Boston), Beacon Hill, Boston, MA 02114. TEL 617-573-8180. FAX 617-573-8143. Ed. Phyllis Flora. bk.rev.; index, cum.index every 5 yrs. circ. 1,200. (also avail. in microform from MIM; microfilm from RRI,WSH; back issues avail.; reprint service avail. from RRI) **Indexed:** Abstr.Bk.Rev.Curr.Leg.Per., C.L.I., L.R.I., Leg.Cont., Leg.Per. **Document type:** academic/scholarly publication.
●Also available online. Vendor(s): West Services, Inc.
—BLDSC (8509.870000); Faxon; UnCover.

340 US
SUMMARY OF ALASKA LEGISLATION. a. (for qualified personnel only). Legislative Affairs Agency, 130 Seward St., Ste. 313, Juneau, AK 99801-2197. TEL 907-465-4648. **Document type:** government publication.

340 US ISSN 0039-5072
SUMMONS. 1921. q. membership. Tau Epsilon Rho Law Society, c/o Alan M. Tepper, 36 Kresson Rd., Ste.E, Cherry Hill, NJ 08034. adv.; bk.rev. circ. 4,000. (tabloid format)

340 AT
SUPERANNUATION & RETIREMENT BENEFITS IN AUSTRALIA. base vol. (plus bi-m. update). $380. Butterworths, 271-273 Lane Cove Rd., P.O. Box 345, North Ryde, N.S.W. 2113, Australia. TEL 02-335-4444. FAX 02-335-4655. (looseleaf format)

SUPERFUND WEEK. see ENVIRONMENTAL STUDIES

340 CN ISSN 0228-0108
K23
SUPREME COURT LAW REVIEW. (Text in English) 1980. a. Can.$165. Butterworths Canada Ltd., Part of the Reed Elsevier group, 75 Clegg Rd., Markham, ON L6G 1A1, Canada. TEL 905-479-2665. FAX 905-479-2826. Eds. E.P. Belobaba, E. Gertner. **Indexed:** C.L.I., Ind.Can.L.P.L., L.R.I., Leg.Per.
 Description: Offers in-depth analysis of Supreme Court of Canada's key decisions and a critical examination of Court's performance in reaching them.

3324 LAW

340   US   ISSN 0892-810X
KF101
SUPREME COURT RECORD.* 1980. irreg. $96. Hale Ridge Publishing, Box 628, Windham, NH 03087. TEL 603-889-7231. Ed. David Armstrong. adv.; index. circ. 300. (looseleaf format; back issues avail.)

SURVEY OF PHARMACY LAW. see *PHARMACY AND PHARMACOLOGY*

347   SW   ISSN 0346-5845
SVENSK FOERFATTNINGSSAMLING. 1825. irreg. SEK 515 (effective 1990). Fritzes, S-106 47 Stockholm, Sweden.

SVENSKA NARKOTIKAPOLISFOERENINGEN. PUBLIKATION. see *CRIMINOLOGY AND LAW ENFORCEMENT*

340   US
SWEDISH AND INTERNATIONAL ARBITRATION. a. $45. (Stockholm Chamber of Commerce, Arbitration Institute) Transnational Juris Publications, Inc., 1 Bridge St., Irvington, NY 10533.
TEL 914-591-4288; 800-914-8186.
FAX 914-591-2688.

347   AT   ISSN 0082-0512
SYDNEY LAW REVIEW. 1953. q. Aus.$25 per part. Law Book Co. Ltd., 44-50 Waterloo Rd., North Ryde, N.S.W. 2113, Australia. TEL 02-887-01776. FAX 02-888-9706. (U.S. subscr. to: Wm. Gaunt & Sons, Inc., 3011 Gulf Dr., Holmes Beach, FL 33510) adv.; bk.rev.; index. circ. 1,250. (also avail. in microform from UMI; reprint service avail. from UMI) **Indexed:** Aus.Leg.Mon.Dig., Aus.P.A.I.S., C.C.L.P., C.L.I., L.R.I., Leg.Cont., Leg.Per., SSCI.
—BLDSC (8577.200000); Faxon; UnCover; UMI.

340   US
SYLLABUS (CHICAGO). 1981. q. $15. American Bar Association, Legal Education and Admissions to the Bar Section, 750 N. Lake Shore Dr., Chicago, IL 60611. TEL 312-988-5581. FAX 317-988-4664. Ed. Susan K. Boyd. bk.rev. circ. 10,000. (tabloid format) **Indexed:** Anbar, C.L.I., L.R.I.
Formerly: Legal Education Newsletter.
Description: Describes and comments on developments in legal education; also reports on the activities of the Section.

SYNTHESIS (ASHEVILLE); law and policy in higher education. see *EDUCATION — Higher Education*

340   US   ISSN 0039-7938
K23
SYRACUSE LAW REVIEW. 1949. q. $22.50 (foreign $35). Syracuse University College of Law, Syracuse, NY 13210. TEL 315-423-3680.
FAX 315-443-9568. adv. circ. 1,200. (also avail. in microfiche from WSH,PMC; microfilm from WSH,PMC) **Indexed:** ASCA, C.L.I., Crim.Just.Abstr., Curr.Cont., L.R.I., Leg.Cont., Leg.Per., SSCI. **Document type:** academic/scholarly publication.
—BLDSC (8588.800000); Faxon; UnCover; UMI.

T M A GUIDE TO TOBACCO TAXES; summaries of key provisions of tobacco tax laws, all tobacco products, all states. (Tobacco Merchants Association of the United States, Inc.) see *TOBACCO*

T M A LEGISLATIVE BULLETIN. see *TOBACCO*

342   BE
TABLES CHRONOLOGIQUES ET ALPHABETIQUES DU MONITEUR BELGE. (Supplement to: Bulletin Legislatif Belge) m. 2499 BEF (effective 1993). Maison Ferdinand Larcier S.A., Rue des Minimes 39, 1000 Brussels, Belgium. TEL 32-2-5124712.
FAX 32-2-5139009.
Description: Cumulating index to recent Belgian and European Communities legislation.

340   US
TAKING SIDES: CLASHING VIEWS ON CONTROVERSIAL LEGAL ISSUES. irreg., 4th ed., 1990. $12.95. Dushkin Publishing Group, Inc., Sluice Dock, Guilford, CT 06437-9989. TEL 203-453-4351.
FAX 203-453-6000. Ed. M. Ethan Katsh; Pub. Lan Nielsen. illus. **Document type:** academic/scholarly publication.

340   SP   ISSN 1131-656X
TAPIA; publicacion para el mundo del derecho. 1982. 6/yr. free. Campomanes 5-7, 28013 Madrid, Spain. TEL 1-542-23-88. FAX 1-542-28-62. Ed. Carlos Tapia Navarro. adv.; bk.rev. circ. 75,000. **Document type:** newspaper.

340   330   HU   ISSN 0231-2522
H8
TARSADALOMKUTATAS. 1966. q. $12. (Magyar Tudomanyos Akademia) Akademiai Kiado, Publishing House of the Hungarian Academy of Sciences, P.O. Box 245, H-1519, Budapest, Hungary.
TEL 181-2134. FAX 166-6466. TELEX 22-6228 AKNYO H. Ed. K. Kulcsar. adv.; bk.rev. **Indexed:** World Agri.Econ.& Rural Sociol.Abstr.
—BLDSC (8606.355000).
Formerly: Gazdasag es Jogtudomany (ISSN 0580-4795)

TAX ANALYSTS LETTER RULING SERVICE. see *BUSINESS AND ECONOMICS — Public Finance, Taxation*

TAX JOURNAL. see *BUSINESS AND ECONOMICS — Public Finance, Taxation*

346.066 336   US   ISSN 0040-0041
TAX LAW REVIEW. 1945. q. $107.75 (overseas $168.25) (effective 1994). (New York University, School of Law) Warren Gorham Lamont, One Penn Plaza, New York, NY 10119. TEL 212-971-5000. (Subscr. to: The Park Ssquare bldg., 31 St. James Ave., Boston, MA 02116-4112. TEL 800-950-1207) Ed.Bd. bk.rev.; bibl.; index. cum.index. (back issues avail.; reprint service avail. from RRI,UMI) **Indexed:** ABI Inform., Account.Ind. (1974-), Bank.Lit.Ind., BPIA, C.L.I., L.I.I., L.R.I., Leg.Cont., Leg.Per., P.A.I.S. **Document type:** trade publication.
—BLDSC (8611.606000); Faxon; UnCover. **CCC.**

343 336.2   US
TAX LAWS OF THE WORLD. (46 vol. set plus supplements) bi-w. $1300 (diskettes $1040; renewal $900). Foreign Tax Law Publishers, Box 2189, Ormond Beach, FL 32175-2189.
TEL 904-253-5785. FAX 904-257-3003. (looseleaf format; also avail. in diskette format)
Description: Includes laws from over 100 countries translated into English.

345 336.2   US   ISSN 0040-005X
K24
TAX LAWYER. 1947. q. $53. American Bar Association, Taxation Section, 1800 M St., N.W., Washington, DC 20036. TEL 202-331-2231. FAX 202-331-2220. (Alt. addr.: 750 N. Lake Shore Dr., Chicago, IL 60611) Ed. Paul J. Sax. adv.; bk.rev. circ. 32,000. (looseleaf format; also avail. in microform from UMI; microfilm from RRI,WSH; reprint service avail. from RRI) **Indexed:** ABI Inform, Account.Ind. (1974-), Bank.Lit.Ind., BPIA, C.L.I., L.I.I., L.R.I., Leg.Cont., Leg.Per., PSI.
●Also available online. Vendor(s): Mead Data Central, Inc., West Services, Inc.
—BLDSC (8611.606050); Faxon; UnCover.
Description: Scholarly articles with student notes and comments on tax law.

TAX NEWS. see *BUSINESS AND ECONOMICS — Public Finance, Taxation*

TAX NOTES; the weekly tax service. see *BUSINESS AND ECONOMICS — Public Finance, Taxation*

TAXATION FOR LAWYERS. see *BUSINESS AND ECONOMICS — Public Finance, Taxation*

TEAM LICENSING BUSINESS. see *SPORTS AND GAMES*

340   IS
TEL AVIV UNIVERSITY. LAW REVIEW/IYUNEI MISHPAT. (Text in Hebrew; summaries in English) 1971. q. $81 (effective 1994). (Tel Aviv University, Faculty of Law) Ramot, 32 University St., P.O. Box 39296, Ramat Aviv, Tel Aviv 61392, Israel.
TEL 972-3-6408113. FAX 972-3-6429865. Ed. Izhak Hadari. bk.rev.; index. **Indexed:** Ind.Heb.Per. **Document type:** academic/scholarly publication.

TELE-SERVICE NEWS. see *COMMUNICATIONS — Telephone And Telegraph*

TELECOMMUNICATIONS POLICY AND REGULATION. see *COMMUNICATIONS — Telephone And Telegraph*

TELECOMMUNICATIONS REPORTER. see *COMMUNICATIONS — Telephone And Telegraph*

340   SP
TEMAS DE HISTORIA DEL DERECHO. irreg. Universidad de Sevilla, Servicio de Publicaciones, Valparaiso 5, 41013 Seville, Spain. TEL 954-231958.
FAX 954-235976.

340   IT   ISSN 0495-0658
TEMI ROMANA. 1952. s-a. L.50000 (foreign L.75000). Casa Editrice Dott. A. Giuffre, Via Busto Arsizio 40, 20151 Milan, Italy. TEL 02-38000905.
FAX 02-38009582. Ed. M. Rossi. adv. circ. 8,250.

340   LV
TEMIDA. m? 1.50 Rub. per issue. Brivibas Bulv. 35, Riga, Latvia. Ed. Imants Lastovskis.

240 600   US   ISSN 0885-2987
K24
TEMPLE ENVIRONMENT LAW & TECHNOLOGY JOURNAL. 1984. a. Temple University, School of Law, Box 143, Philadelphia, PA 19122. **Document type:** academic/scholarly publication.
—Faxon; UnCover.

340   US   ISSN 0899-8086
K24
TEMPLE LAW REVIEW. 1927. q. $25 (foreign $27.50). Temple University School of Law, Philadelphia, PA 19122. TEL 215-204-4528. adv.; bk.rev.; bibl.; index. circ. 2,300. (also avail. in microfilm from WSH) **Indexed:** ASCA, C.L.I., Curr.Cont., L.R.I., Leg.Cont., Leg.Per., SSCI. **Document type:** academic/scholarly publication.
●Also available online. Vendor(s): West Services, Inc.
—BLDSC (8790.034200); Faxon; UnCover; SWETS.
Formerly (until vol.60, 1988): Temple Law Quarterly (ISSN 0040-2974)

TENDENCIAS ECONOMICAS: LEGISLACION ECONOMICAS ARGENTINA/BUSINESS TRENDS: ARGENTINE ECONOMIC LEGISLATION. see *BUSINESS AND ECONOMICS*

340   US
TENNESSEE ATTORNEYS DIRECTORY AND BUYERS GUIDE. 1982. a. $45. M. Lee Smith Publishers & Printers, 162 Fourth Ave. N., Nashville, TN 37219-8867. TEL 615-242-7395.
FAX 615-256-6601. Ed. Joseph L. White. **Document type:** directory.
Description: Lists Tennessee attorneys and legal secretaries.

340   US   ISSN 0194-1259
TENNESSEE ATTORNEYS MEMO. 1975. w. $262. M. Lee Smith Publishers & Printers, 162 Fourth Ave., N., Box 198867, Nashville, TN 37219-8867. TEL 615-242-7395; 800-274-6774.
FAX 615-256-6601. Ed. Bradford N. Forrister. index. (back issues avail.) **Document type:** newsletter.
Description: Summarizes opinions of Tennessee appellate courts (published and unpublished), new General Assembly acts, and selected opinions of the Tennessee attorney general and of the Sixth Circuit Court of Appeals.

320   US   ISSN 0497-2325
TENNESSEE BAR JOURNAL. 1952. 6/yr. $35. Tennessee Bar Association, c/o Mary M. Tucker, 3622 West End Ave., Nashville, TN 37205-2403. Ed. Suzanne Craig Robertson. adv. circ. 6,800. **Indexed:** C.L.I., L.R.I., Law Ofc.Info.Svc., Leg.Per.
●Also available online. Vendor(s): West Services, Inc.
—Faxon; UnCover.
Supersedes (in 1985): Tennessee Lawyer (ISSN 0495-1328)

340 331   US   ISSN 0886-8557
KFT331.A59
TENNESSEE EMPLOYMENT LAW UPDATE. (Supplement to: Tennessee Employment Law) 1986. m. $90. (Miller & Martin) M. Lee Smith Publishers & Printers, 162 Fourth Ave., N., Nashville, TN 37219-8867. TEL 615-242-7395;
800-274-6774. FAX 615-256-6601. Ed. John B. Phillips, Jr. index. circ. 1,400. (back issues avail.)
Description: Analyzes Tennessee appellate court decisions, laws enacted by the Tennessee legislature concerning employment and labor law, government agencies regulating employment for Tennessee employers.

LAW 3325

340 613.1　US　ISSN 1042-3168
TENNESSEE ENVIRONMENTAL LAW LETTER. 1989. m. $177. (Bass, Berry & Sims) M. Lee Smith Publishers & Printers, 162 Fourth Ave., N., Box 198867, Nashville, TN 37219-8867. TEL 615-242-7395; 800-247-6447. FAX 615-256-6601. Eds. J. Andrew Goddard, G. Scott Thomas. index. **Document type:** newsletter.
　Description: Reports the latest state-specific environmental law developments that affect Tennessee companies.

340　US
TENNESSEE LAW OFFICE DESK BOOK. 1990. a. $34. M. Lee Smith Publishers & Printers, 162 Fourth Ave. N., Nashville, TN 37219-8867. TEL 615-242-7395. FAX 615-256-6601. Ed. Pamela D. Brooks. **Document type:** directory.
　Description: Designed to assist the daily work of a law office by providing attorneys, legal secretaries, paralegals and legal assistants with information that is routinely needed.

340　US　ISSN 0040-3288
K24
TENNESSEE LAW REVIEW. 1923. q. $24 (foreign $26). Tennessee Law Review Association, Inc., 1505 W. Cumberland Ave., Knoxville, TN 37996-1800. Ed.Bd. adv.; bk.rev.; index, cum.index. circ. 1,800. (also avail. in microfiche from BHP; microform from WSH; reprint service avail. from WSH) Indexed: C.L.I., L.R.I., Leg.Cont., Leg.Per. **Document type:** academic/scholarly publication.
　●Also available online. Vendor(s): West Services, Inc.
　—BLDSC (8790.730000); Faxon; UnCover.

340　US
TENNESSEE LITIGATION REPORTER; a summary of Tennessee trial court actions. 1984. bi-m. $180. (Tennessee Trial Lawyers Association) M. Lee Smith Publishers & Printers, 162 Fourth Ave., Box 2678, Nashville, TN 37203. Ed. Lewis Laska. circ. 1,500 (controlled). (back issues avail.) **Document type:** academic/scholarly publication.
　Description: Contains reports of Tennessee court cases, categorized by type of case, including personal injury.

346　US
TENNESSEE MEDICO-LEGAL REPORTER. 1983. m. $180. M. Lee Smith Publishers & Printers, 162 Fourth Ave. N., Nashville, TN 37219-8867. TEL 615-242-7395. FAX 615-256-6601. Ed. Lewis L. Laska.
　Description: Reviews trial and appellate cases and developments of interest to Tennessee health care lawyers and managers.

346.043　US　ISSN 1059-5090
TENNESSEE REAL ESTATE LAW LETTER. 1983. m. $93. M. Lee Smith Publishers & Printers, 162 Fourth Ave., N., Box 198867, Nashville, TN 37219-8867. TEL 615-242-7395; 800-274-6774. FAX 615-256-6601. (Co-sponsor: Bass, Berry & Sims) Ed. C. Dewees Berry, IV. **Document type:** newsletter.
　Description: Surveys Tennessee real estate law developments.

TERMINATION OF EMPLOYMENT; employer and employee rights. see BUSINESS AND ECONOMICS — Personnel Management

340　US
TESTIMONIAL PRIVILEGES. 1983. base vol. (plus a. suppl.). $95. Shepard's - McGraw-Hill, Inc., Box 35300, Colorado Springs, CO 80935-3530. TEL 800-525-2474.
　Description: Provides advice on problems ranging from maintaining the confidentiality of office files to conducting complex intra-corporate investigations. Discussions explain the legal principles and precedents needed for successful assertion of privileges.

340　US　ISSN 0040-4187
K24
TEXAS BAR JOURNAL. 1938. m. (11/yr.). $12. State Bar of Texas, Box 12487, Capitol Sta., Austin, TX 78711. TEL 512-463-1522. Ed. Kelley Jones. adv.; bk.rev.; illus.; index. circ. 62,000. (also avail. in microfiche from UMI,BHP,PMC; microfiche from WSH; microfilm from WSH) Indexed: C.L.I., L.R.I., Law Ofc.Info.Svc., Leg.Per.
　—BLDSC (8798.673000); Faxon; UnCover.

340　US
TEXAS COMMERCIAL COLLECTIONS; forms and procedures for attorneys and legal assistants. 1989. base vol. (plus suppl. 1-2/yr.). $150. Butterworth Legal Publishers (Salem) (Subsidiary of: Reed Elsevier plc), 8 Industrial Way, Bldg. C, Salem, NH 03079. TEL 800-548-4001. FAX 603-898-9858. (looseleaf format)

346.043　US
TEXAS CONDOMINIUM LAW MANUAL. 1983. base vol. (plus supplements 1-2/yr.). $95. Butterworth Legal Publishers (Salem) (Subsidiary of: Reed Elsevier plc), 8 Industrial Way, Bldg. C, Salem, NH 03079. TEL 800-548-4001. FAX 603-898-9858. (looseleaf format)

340 690　US
TEXAS CONSTRUCTION LAW MANUAL. 1981. base vol. (plus a. suppl.). $95. Shepard's - McGraw-Hill, Inc., Box 35300, Colorado Springs, CO 80935-3530. TEL 800-525-2474.
　Description: Designed to guide attorneys and contractors working in Texas through the complexities and the legal considerations of the construction business.

345 388　US　ISSN 1055-1913
TEXAS CRIMINAL LAW & MOTOR VEHICLE HANDBOOK. a. $19.95. Gould Publications, 1333 N. U.S. Hwy. 17-92, Longwood, FL 32750-3724. TEL 407-695-9500. FAX 407-695-2906. (looseleaf format)

340　US
TEXAS DRUNK DRIVING LAW. 2nd ed. 1991. 2 base vols. (plus a. suppl.). $195. Butterworth Legal Publishers (Salem) (Subsidiary of: Reed Elsevier plc), 8 Industrial Way, Bldg. C, Salem, NH 03079. TEL 800-548-4001. FAX 603-898-9858. Eds. J. Gray Trichter, W. Troy McKinney. (looseleaf format)
　Description: Provides a textual discussion and analysis of the current law; includes applicable statutes, codes, Department of Public Safety guidelines and regulations, and case law and literature, as well as pre-trial and courtroom mechanics of DWI prosecution and defense.

340 331　US　ISSN 1046-9214
KFT1531.A15
TEXAS EMPLOYMENT LAW LETTER. 1990. 12/yr. $92. (Clark, West, Keller, Butler & Ellis) M. Lee Smith Publishers & Printers, 162 Fourth Ave., N., Box 198867, Nashville, TN 37219-8867. TEL 615-242-7395; 800-274-6774. FAX 615-256-6601. Eds. David M. Ellis, Michael P. Maslanka. index. (looseleaf format; back issues avail.) **Document type:** newsletter.
　Description: Reports the latest state-specific employment law developments that affect Texas companies.

340 613.1　US　ISSN 1056-7585
TEXAS ENVIRONMENTAL LAW LETTER. 1991. m. $147. (Bickerstaff, Heath & Smiley) M. Lee Smith Publishers & Printers, 162 Fourth Ave., N., Box 198867, Nashville, TN 37219-8867. TEL 615-242-7395; 800-274-6774. FAX 615-256-6601. Ed. Douglas Caroom. **Document type:** newsletter.
　Description: Reports the latest state-specific environmental law developments that affect Texas companies.

340　US　ISSN 0266-0814
KFT1740.A15
TEXAS EVIDENCE REPORTER. 1984. bi-m. $96. Butterworth Legal Publishers, Austin Division (Subsidiary of: Reed Elsevier plc), Echelon II, Ste. 100, 9430 Research, Austin, TX 78759-6598. TEL 512-346-9686. FAX 512-346-9373. Ed. Richard J. Clarkson. index. (looseleaf format; back issues avail.)

340 610　US　ISSN 0266-0806
KFT1560.A15
TEXAS HEALTH LAW REPORTER. 1984. bi-m. $96. Butterworth Legal Publishers, Austin Division (Subsidiary of: Reed Elsevier plc), Echelon II, Ste. 100, 9430 Research, Austin, TX 78759-6598. TEL 512-346-9686. FAX 512-346-9373. Eds. David M. Davis, Brian McElroy. index. (looseleaf format; back issues avail.)

340　US
TEXAS HOSPITAL LAW. 1988. base vol. (plus a. supplement). $115. Butterworth Legal Publishers (Salem) (Subsidiary of: Reed Elsevier plc), 8 Industrial Way, Bldg. C, Salem, NH 03079. TEL 800-548-4001. FAX 603-898-9858. Eds. Richard L. Griffith, Dewey M. Johnston. (looseleaf format)
　Description: Case analysis and examination of legal and administrative issues affecting the medical community in Texas.

340 368　US
KFT1385.A15
TEXAS INSURANCE LAW JOURNAL. 1983. q. $96. Butterworth Legal Publishers, Austin Division (Subsidiary of: Reed Elsevier plc), Echelon II, Ste. 100, 9430 Research, Austin, TX 78759-6598. TEL 512-346-9686. FAX 512-346-9373. Ed.Bd. index. (looseleaf format; back issues avail.)
　Formerly (until 1991): Texas Insurance Law Reporter (ISSN 0264-6307)

340 323.4　US　ISSN 1058-5427
▼**TEXAS JOURNAL OF WOMEN AND THE LAW.** 1992. a. $25 (students $12.50; foreign $27). 727 E. 26th St., Austin, TX 78705. TEL 512-471-3227. FAX 512-471-6988. Eds. Kelle Krull, Paula Tucker. adv.; bk.rev. circ. 473. (reprint service avail. from WSH) **Document type:** academic/scholarly publication.
　●Also available online. Vendor: West Services, Inc.
　—UnCover; UMI.
　Description: Inspires dialogue about legal, social and political issues affecting women - their rights, their bodies, their careers, their families.

340　US
TEXAS LAW OF OIL AND GAS. 1989. 3 base vols. (plus supplement). $350. Butterworth Legal Publishers (Salem) (Subsidiary of: Reed Elsevier plc), 8 Industrial Way, Bldg. C, Salem, NH 03079. TEL 800-548-4001. FAX 603-898-9858. Eds. Ernest E. Smith, Jacqueline Lang Weaver. (looseleaf format)

340　US　ISSN 0040-4411
K24
TEXAS LAW REVIEW. 1922. 6/yr. $32 (foreign $39). University of Texas at Austin, School of Law Publications, Box 149084, Austin, TX 78714-9084. TEL 512-471-3164. FAX 512-471-6988. adv.; bk.rev.; index. circ. 2,100. (also avail. in microfiche from RRI,WSH; microfilm from RRI,WSH; back issues avail.; reprint service avail. from RRI) Indexed: A.B.C.Pol.Sci., ABI Inform, ASCA, C.L.I., Curr.Cont., L.R.I., Leg.Cont., Leg.Per., Mar.Aff.Bibl., SSCI.
　●Also available online. Vendor(s): Mead Data Central, Inc.
　—BLDSC (8799.300000); Faxon; UnCover; SWETS; UMI.
　Description: Examines current legal issues.

340　US　ISSN 0267-8306
K24
TEXAS LAWYER. 1985. w. $159. American Lawyer Media, L.P. (New York), 600 Third Ave., 3rd Fl., New York, NY 10016. TEL 212-973-2800. FAX 214-741-2325. (Subscr. to: 400 S. Record, Ste. 1400, Dallas, TX 75202. TEL 214-744-9300) Ed. Mark Obbie. adv.; index. circ. 10,237. (tabloid format; also avail. in microfiche; back issues avail.)
　●Also available online. Vendor(s): Mead Data Central, Inc.
　—CCC.
　Description: Presents articles on law cases, firms and politics in Texas; includes court summaries.

340　US
TEXAS LEGISLATIVE HANDBOOK. biennial. $4.95. Texas State Directory Press, Box 12186, Austin, TX 78711. TEL 512-477-5698. FAX 512-473-2447. (back issues avail.) **Document type:** directory.
　Description: Lists the members of the Texas Senate and House of Representatives.

340　US
TEXAS LIMITATIONS MANUAL. 1987. biennial. $85. Butterworth Legal Publishers (Salem) (Subsidiary of: Reed Elsevier plc), 8 Industrial Way, Bldg. C, Salem, NH 03079. TEL 800-548-4001. FAX 603-898-9858. Ed. Jennifer Nosler Mellett. (looseleaf format)
　Description: Quick reference to statutes, codes and statewide rules of court that set time limitations.

340 US
TEXAS LITIGATOR'S HANDBOOK. 1989. base vol. (plus suppl.). $95. Butterworth Legal Publishers (Salem) (Subsidiary of: Reed Elsevier plc) 8 Industrial Way, Bldg. C, Salem, NH 03079. TEL 800-548-4001. FAX 603-898-9858. Ed. Edward F. Butler. (looseleaf format)
Description: Trial strategy guide designed for Texas attorneys when handling tort, contract and business litigation or divorce and custody suits.

333.33 US
TEXAS MUNICIPAL ZONING LAW. 1985. base vol. (plus a. supplement). $110. Butterworth Legal Publishers (Salem) (Subsidiary of: Reed Elsevier plc), 8 Industrial Way, Bldg. C, Salem, NH 03079. TEL 800-548-4001. FAX 603-898-9858. Ed. John Mixon. (looseleaf format)
Description: Analysis of Texas case law and procedure governing the creation, enforcement and modification of local zoning.

TEXAS NATURAL RESOURCES REPORTER. see WATER RESOURCES

340 US
TEXAS NOTARY LAW PRIMER. a. $9.95. National Notary Association, 8236 Remmet Ave., Box 7184, Canoga Park, CA 91309-7184. TEL 818-713-4000. FAX 818-713-9061. Ed. Charles N. Faerber. (reprint service avail. from UMI) **Document type:** monographic series.

340 US ISSN 0950-3285
TEXAS OIL AND GAS LAW JOURNAL. 1986. bi-m. $96. Butterworth Legal Publishers, Austin Division (Subsidiary of: Reed Elsevier plc), Echelon II, Ste. 100, 9430 Research, Austin, TX 78759-6598. TEL 512-346-9686. FAX 512-346-9373. Ed. Owen Anderson. (looseleaf format; back issues avail.)

340 US
TEXAS PERSONAL INJURY LAW. (2nd ed., 1991) 1981. 2 base vols. (plus irreg. supplements). $185. Butterworth Legal Publishers (Salem) (Subsidiary of: Reed Elsevier plc), 8 Industrial Way, Bldg. C, Salem, NH 03079. TEL 800-548-4001. FAX 603-898-9858. Ed. Jennifer Nosler Mellett. (looseleaf format)
Description: Analysis of the applicable statutes, rules and case law.

340 US ISSN 0264-4770
KFT1397.P3
TEXAS PERSONAL INJURY LAW REPORTER. 1983. bi-m. $96. Butterworth Legal Publishers, Austin Division (Subsidiary of: Reed Elsevier plc), Echelon II, Ste. 100, 9430 Research, Austin, TX 78759-6598. TEL 512-346-9686. FAX 512-346-9373. Ed. Frank R. Southers. index. (looseleaf format; back issues avail.)

340 US
TEXAS PROBATE CODE MANUAL. 1984. 2 base vols. (plus suppl. 1-2/yr.). $125. Butterworth Legal Publishers (Salem) (Subsidiary of: Reed Elsevier plc), 8 Industrial Way, Bldg. C, Salem, NH 03079. TEL 800-548-4001. FAX 603-898-9858. (looseleaf format)

340 US
TEXAS PRODUCT LIABILITY LAW. 1986. base vol. (plus a. suppl.). $110. Butterworth Legal Publishers (Salem) (Subsidiary of: Reed Elsevier plc), 8 Industrial Way, Bldg. C, Salem, NH 03079. TEL 800-548-4001. FAX 603-898-9858. Ed. William Powers, Jr. (looseleaf format)
Description: Describes and analyzes current Texas products liability law, including all potential theories of recovery, the effects of recent tort reform legislation, and relevent Texas Supreme Court and Court of Appeals decisions through the prior calendar year.

TEXAS PUBLIC UTILITY NEWS. see ENERGY

340 333.33 US ISSN 0267-8896
TEXAS REAL ESTATE LAW REPORTER. 1985. bi-m. $96. Butterworth Legal Publishers, Austin Division (Subsidiary of: Reed Elsevier plc), Echelon II, Ste. 100, 9430 Research, Austin, TX 78759-6598. TEL 512-346-9686. FAX 512-346-9373. Ed. Charles J. Jacobus. index. (looseleaf format; back issues avail.)

348 US ISSN 0362-4781
KFT1236
TEXAS REGISTER. 1976. s-w. $95 (on diskette $90). Secretary of State, Texas Register Division, Box 13824, TX 78711-3824. TEL 512-463-5564. FAX 512-463-5569. Ed. Dan Procter. circ. 4,700. (also avail. in diskette format; back issues avail.) **Document type:** government publication.

TEXAS SCHOOL LAW BULLETIN. see EDUCATION — School Organization And Administration

340 US ISSN 0564-6197
K24
TEXAS TECH LAW REVIEW. 1969. q. $32. Texas Tech University, School of Law, Lubbock, TX 79409. TEL 806-742-3789. FAX 806-742-1629. Ed. Gregory Westfall. adv. circ. 1,300. (also avail. in microfilm from WSH,PMC; reprint service avail. from WSH) **Indexed:** C.L.I., L.R.I., Leg.Cont., Leg.Per., Mar.Aff.Bibl.
●Also available online. Vendor(s): West Services, Inc.
—Faxon; UnCover; UMI.

340 FR
TEXTES D'INTERET GENERAL. irreg. Direction des Journaux Officiels, 26 rue Desaix, 75727 Paris Cedex 15, France. TEL 1-45-78-61-44.

340 PH
THOMASIAN LAW UPDATE. (Text in English) 1985. s-a. P.50. University of Santo Tomas, Faculty of Civil Law, Sampalco St., Espana, Manila, Philippines. circ. 800.

340.05 US
K24
THURGOOD MARSHALL LAW REVIEW. 1975. 2/yr. $20. Texas Southern University, Thurgood Marshall School of Law, 3100 Cleburne, Houston, TX 77004. TEL 713-527-7246. FAX 713-639-1049. Ed. Lateefah Muhammad. adv.; bk.rev. circ. 500. (also avail. in microform from UMI) **Indexed:** C.L.I., Leg.Per.
●Also available online. Vendor(s): West Services, Inc.
Formerly: Texas Southern University Law Review (ISSN 0092-3559)

TIDBITS. see EDUCATION

TIDE. see CONSERVATION

TIDNING FOER KUNGOERELSER OM EFTERNAMN. see GENEALOGY AND HERALDRY

TIDSKRIFT FOER FOLKETS RAETTIGHETER. see POLITICAL SCIENCE — Civil Rights

340 309 SW ISSN 0281-2584
TIDSKRIFT FOER RAETTSSOCIOLOGI. (Text in Danish, English, Swedish; summaries in English) 1983. q. SEK 140($30) Humanistisk-Samhaellsvetenskapliga Forskningsradet, P.O. Box 6712, S-113 85 Stockholm, Sweden. TEL 08-151580. (Subscr. to: Bredgatan 4, S-222 21 Lund, Sweden) Ed. Antoinette Hetzler. adv.; bk.rev.; charts; index. circ. 300. (back issues avail.)

340 SW ISSN 1102-2752
TIDSKRIFT FOER SVERIGES DOMAREFOERBUND. 1940. 3/yr. SEK 200 membership (effective 1991). Sveriges Domarefoerbund, c/o B. Almebaeck, Marieholmsv. 28, S-21763 Malmoe, Sweden.
Former titles (until vol.2, 1991): Sveriges Domarefoerbund. Aarstryck; (until 1974): Foereningen Sveriges Tingsraettsdomare (Domarefoereningen). Aarstryck; (until 1971): Foereningen Sveriges Haeradshoevdingar och Statsdomare. Aarstryck; (until 1968): Foereningen Sveriges Haeradshoevdingar. Aarstryck.

349 DK ISSN 0040-6880
TIDSSKRIFT FOR GROENLANDS RETSVAESEN. 1965. q. DKK 300. Danish Polar Center, Strandgade 100 H, DK-1401 Copenhagen K, Denmark. TEL 45-32-88-01-00. FAX 45-32-88-01-01. Ed. Tinne Thomassen. adv.; bk.rev.; charts; stat.; index. circ. 500.

349 NO ISSN 0040-7143
K24
TIDSSKRIFT FOR RETTSVITENSKAP; Scandinavian journal of law. Short title: T F R. (Text in Danish, Norwegian, Swedish) 1888. 5/yr. NOK 460 575. Scandinavian University Press, P.O. Box 2959-Tooeyen, N-0608 Oslo, Norway. TEL 472-67-7600. FAX 472-67-7575. (U.S. addr.: Scandinavian University Press, 200 Meacham Ave., Elmont, NY 11003. TEL 516-352-7300) Eds. Birger Stuevold Lassen, Magnus Aarbakke. adv.; bk.rev.; bibl.; cum.index. circ. 2,000. (back issues avail.)
—BLDSC (8828.040000).
Description: Scholarly journal of law and legal matters.

349 NA
TIJDSCHRIFT VOOR ANTILLIAANS RECHT - JUSTICIA. Short title: T A R - Justicia. (Text in Dutch) 1965. q. $55. Stichting Tijdschrift voor Antilliaans Recht - Justicia, P.O. Box 4779, Curacao, Netherlands Antilles. TEL 599-9-684422. FAX 599-9-685465. adv.; B&W page $450. bk.rev.; index. circ. 250. **Document type:** academic/scholarly publication.
Formerly (until 1985): Justicia (ISSN 0022-7056)
Description: Juridical review with special emphasis on issues in Netherland Antilles law.

340 NE ISSN 0167-1359
TIJDSCHRIFT VOOR ARBITRAGE. 1980. bi-m. fl.91.50. (Stichting Tijdschrift Arbitrage) Kluwer Law and Taxation Publishers (Subsidiary of: Wolters Kluwer N.V.), P.O. Box 23, 7400 GA Deventer, Netherlands. TEL 31-5700-47261. FAX 31-5700-2224. TELEX 49295 KLUWDV NL. (Dist. by: Libresso Distribution Centre, P.O. Box 23, 7400 GA Deventer, Netherlands. TEL 31-5700-33155. FAX 31-5700-33834; In N. America: Kluwer Law and Taxation Publishers, 675 Massachusetts Ave., Cambridge, MA 02139. TEL 617-354-0140. FAX 617-354-8595) (Co-sponsors: T.M.C. Asser Institut, Instituut voor International Privaat- en Publiekrecht, Internationale Handelsarbitrage en Europees Recht) Ed. A.J. van den Berg. adv.; bk.rev. circ. 900. **Document type:** academic/scholarly publication.
—SWETS.

340 BE ISSN 0040-7437
TIJDSCHRIFT VOOR BESTUURSWETENSCHAPPEN EN PUBLIEKRECHT. Short title: T B P. 1946. m. 3500 BEF. c/o P. Berckx, G. Mercatorlaan 28, B-1780 Wemmel, Belgium. TEL 32-2-2694109. FAX 32-2-2701319. Ed. F. Debaedts. adv. contact: P. Berckx. bk.rev.; index. circ. 2,000. **Indexed:** ELLIS. **Document type:** academic/scholarly publication.
Description: Focuses on Belgian, international and European law concerning public administration, management, social regulations education and environment, with summaries and comments of judgments.

349 BE ISSN 0082-4313
TIJDSCHRIFT VOOR PRIVAATRECHT. Short title: T P R. 1964. q. 4000 BEF. Kluwer Editions Juridiques Belgique, E. Story-Scientia (Subsidiary of: Wolters Kluwer N.V.), 230 bd. Emile Bockstael, B-1020 Brussels, Belgium. TEL 32-2-4223911. FAX 32-2-4223979. Ed. M. Storme. bk.rev. circ. 1,200. **Indexed:** ELLIS.

340 900 NE ISSN 0040-7585
K24 CODEN: TIREES
TIJDSCHRIFT VOOR RECHTSGESCHIEDENIS/REVUE D'HISTOIRE DU DROIT/LEGAL HISTORY REVIEW. (Text in English, French, German, Italian, Latin and Spanish) 1918. 4/yr. fl.324($169.50) (effective 1994). Martinus Nijhoff Publishers, Human Rights and International Law (Subsidiary of: Kluwer Academic Publishers Group), Postbus 163, 3300 AD Dordrecht, Netherlands. TEL 31-78-334911. FAX 31-78-334254. TELEX 29245 KAPG NL. (Dist. by: Kluwer Academic Publishers Group, P.O. Box 322, 3300 AH Dordrecht, Netherlands. TEL 31-78-524400. FAX 31-78-524474; N. America dist. addr.: Box 358, Accord Sta., Hingham, MA 02018-0358. TEL 617-871-6600. FAX 617-871-6528) Ed.Bd. bk.rev. (also avail. in microform from UMI; back issues avail.) **Indexed:** Amer.Hist.& Life (until 1992), Hist.Abstr. (until 1992). **Document type:** academic/scholarly publication.
—BLDSC (5181.325000); SWETS; UMI. **CCC.** *Refereed Serial*

340 IC
TIMARIT LOEGFRAEDINGA. 1951. q. ISK 3534. Loegfraedingafelag Islands, Alftamyri 9, IS-108 Reykjavik, Iceland. TEL 354-1-680887. FAX 354-1-687057. Eds. Fridgeir Bjoernsson, Steingrimur Gautur Kristjansson. circ. 1,100.
Document type: trade publication.
Description: Publishes articles, some of technical nature, on various branches of Icelandic, Scandinavian and European law.

TIME CHARTERS. see TRANSPORTATION — Ships And Shipping

340 UK ISSN 0958-0441
TIMES LAW REPORTS. 1990. m. £75($135) (The Times) T & T Clark, 59 George St., Edinburgh EH2 2LQ, Scotland. TEL 031-225-4703. FAX 031-220-4260. Ed. Iain Sutherland. cum.index. circ. 2,000.
●Also available online. Vendor(s): Context Ltd.
Description: Law cases of England and Wales, European courts.

TITLE AND REGISTRATION BOOK; summary of motor vehicle laws and regulations. see TRANSPORTATION — Automobiles

340 AT
TITLES OFFICE PRACTICE (QUEENSLAND). 1986. 2/yr. Aus.$215 with updates. Law Book Co. Ltd., 44-50 Waterloo Rd., North Ryde, N.S.W. 2113, Australia. TEL 02-887-0177. FAX 02-888-9706. TELEX ASBOOK 27995. Ed. A.J.S. Byrne. (looseleaf format)
Description: Provides information regarding the practices, procedures and requirements of the Titles Office.

340 US ISSN 0887-7831
KF1297.T63
TOBACCO INDUSTRY LITIGATION REPORTER; the national journal of record of litigation affecting the tobacco industry. 1985. m. $675. Andrews Publications, 1646 West Chester Pike, Box 1000, Westtown, PA 19395. TEL 215-399-6600; 800-345-1101. FAX 215-399-6610. Ed. Nick Sullivan. abstr.; bibl.; stat.; cum.index every 6 mos. (looseleaf format; back issues avail.) Document type: newsletter.

657 US
TODAY'S LAWYER. q. C P A Associates International, Inc., Meadows Office Complex, 201 Rte. 17 N., Rutherford, NJ 07070-2574. TEL 212-804-8686.
Description: Provides information on members' services to clients.

340 IT ISSN 0040-8654
TOGA CALABRESE; rassegna di dottrina giurisprudenza-vita e varieta giudiziarie e forensi. 1932. bi-m. L.10000. Corso Mazzini 291, 88100 Catanzaro (Calabria), Italy. TEL 23700. Dir. Domenico Pittelli. adv.; bk.rev.; film rev.; charts; illus. Document type: newspaper.
Description: Covers current events in law, politics and other various topics related to lawyers.

TOILETRIES, FRAGRANCES AND SKIN CARE: THE ROSE SHEET. see BEAUTY CULTURE — Perfumes And Cosmetics

340 US ISSN 0493-4571
TOLEDO BAR ASSOCIATION NEWSLETTER. vol.40, 1993. 10/yr. membership. Toledo Bar Association, 311 N. Superior, Toledo, OH 43604. TEL 419-242-9363. Ed. Andrew J. Ayers. Document type: newsletter.
Description: News and other items of interest to lawyers in the Toledo area.

340 US
TOLEDO LEGAL NEWS. 1895. d. (Mon.-Fri.). $75. Toledo Legal News Inc., 520 Madison Ave., Ste. 218, Toledo, OH 43604. TEL 419-241-3333. adv. circ. 1,000. (tabloid format) Document type: newspaper.

345.1 330 US ISSN 1060-3018
TOPEKA METRO NEWS. 1897. s-w. $34. Hall Publications, Inc., 630 S. Kansas Ave., 630, Topeka, KS 66603. TEL 913-232-8600. FAX 913-235-8707. Ed. Cliff Hall. bk.rev.; circ. 1,500 (paid). (tabloid format) Document type: newspaper.
Formerly (until 1991): Topeka Legal News (ISSN 0889-5295)

TORONTO LEGAL DIRECTORY. see BUSINESS AND ECONOMICS — Trade And Industrial Directories

340 333.33 AT
TORRENS SYSTEM IN N.S.W. 1985. 3/yr. Aus.$310 with updates. Law Book Co. Ltd., 44-50 Waterloo Rd., North Ryde, N.S.W 2113, Australia. TEL 02-887-0177. FAX 02-888-9706. TELEX ASBOOK 27995. Eds. F. Ticehourst, P. Butt. (looseleaf format)
Description: Text provides both annotations and commentary to all provisions of the legislation and the Real Property Act 1990 and the Conveyancing Act, dealing with easements and covenants.

340 FR ISSN 1149-2767
TOUT LYON ET LE MONITEUR JUDICIAIRE REUNIS. 1895. 100/yr. 400 F. 40 rue President Edouard Herriot, B.P. 1511, 69204 Lyon Cedex 01. TEL 78-28-68-18. FAX 78-27-99-23. Ed. Denis Tardy. adv. circ. 10,000.
Formed by the merger of: Tout Lyon (ISSN 1149-2759); Moniteur Judiciaire de l'Arrondissement de Lyon (ISSN 1149-574X)

340 US
KF3958.A59
TOXIC CHEMICALS - INDOOR POLLUTION LITIGATION REPORTER; the national journal of record for litigation involving claims of personal injury and/or property damage from exposure to toxic chemicals. 1983. s-m. $850. Andrews Publications, 1646 West Chester Pike, Box 1000, Westtown, PA 19395. TEL 215-399-6600; 800-345-1101. FAX 215-399-6610. Ed. Edith McFall. bibl.; stat.; cum.index every 6 mos. (looseleaf format; back issues avail.) Document type: newsletter.
Formerly (until 1992): Toxic Chemicals Litigation Reporter (ISSN 0737-8513); Incorporates (1990-1992): Indoor Pollution Litigation Reporter (ISSN 1053-024X)

340 604.7 US
TOXIC TORT LITIGATION. 1989. base vol. (plus s-a. supplement). Maxwell Macmillan, Rosenfeld Launer, 910 Sylvan Ave., Englewood Cliffs, NJ 07632-3310. TEL 800-562-0245. FAX 201-816-3569. Eds. Edward Greer, Warren Freedman.

TOXIC TORT LITIGATION HANDBOOK; a step-by-step guide with forms. see ENVIRONMENTAL STUDIES — Waste Management

TOXICS LAW REPORTER; a weekly review of toxic torts, hazardous waste, and insurance litigation. see ENVIRONMENTAL STUDIES — Waste Management

340 341 US ISSN 0731-5813
KF3176.A32
TRADEMARK LAW HANDBOOK. 1981. a. $65. (United States Trademark Association) Clark - Boardman - Callaghan Company Ltd., 375 Hudson St., New York, NY 10014. TEL 212-929-7500; 800-221-9428. FAX 212-924-0460. Eds. Anthony L. Fletcher, David J. Kera.
Description: Provides a comprehensive overview of the quickly evolving area of United States trademark law and practice.

340 UK
TRADING LAW AND TRADING LAW REPORTS. 1993. 6/yr. £69.75. Barry Rose Law Periodicals, Little London, Chichester, W. Sussex PO19 1PG. England. TEL 0243-787841. FAX 0243-779278. Ed. Susan Singleton. Document type: academic/scholarly publication.
—BLDSC (8881.051300).
Formed by the merger of (1981-1993): Trading Law (ISSN 0262-9240); (1982-1993): Trading Law Reports (ISSN 0268-9510)
Description: Details various aspects of consumer: trading law, competition, monopolies, mergers, international trade, credit trading and fair trading, including important trading law cases.

340 US ISSN 1058-1006
K24
TRANSNATIONAL LAW & CONTEMPORARY PROBLEMS. 1991. 2/yr. (in 1 vol.). $22 (foreign $30). University of Iowa, College of Law, Boyd Law Bldg., Rm. 187, Iowa City, IA 52242. TEL 319-335-9736. FAX 319-335-9019. Document type: academic/scholarly publication.
—BLDSC (9024.975950); UnCover.

TRANSPORT-DE-REGULATION REPORT. see TRANSPORTATION

340 380.5 UK ISSN 0967-2141
TRANSPORT LAW & POLICY. 10/yr. £142($284) I B C Publishing, Gilmoora House, 57-61 Mortimer St., London W1N 7TD, England. TEL 071-637-4383. FAX 071-636-6414. (Subscr. in U.S. to: IBC (USA), 290 Eliot St., Box 91004, Ashland, MA 01721-9104. TEL 508-881-2800. FAX 508-881-0982) Ed. Iain Dale. Document type: newsletter.

340 388.324 US
KF2179.A2
TRANSPORTATION LAW INSTITUTE PAPERS AND PROCEEDINGS. 1971. a. Association of Transportation Practitioners, 19564 Club House Rd., Gaithersburg, MD 20879-3002. TEL 301-670-6733. Document type: proceedings.
Supersedes (in 1988): Eastern Transportation Law Seminar Papers and Proceedings (ISSN 0271-437X); Western Transportation Law Seminar Papers and Proceedings (ISSN 0271-4396); Supersedes in part: Transportation Law Seminar. Papers and Proceedings (ISSN 0164-1689)

343.093 US ISSN 0049-450X
K24
TRANSPORTATION LAW JOURNAL. 1969. s-a. $15 (foreign $20). c/o Paul Stephen Dempsey, Ed., University of Denver, College of Law, 1900 Olive St., Denver, CO 80220. TEL 303-871-6269. FAX 303-871-6411. adv.; bk.rev. circ. 2,000. (also avail. in microform from WSH,PMC; reprint service avail. from WSH) Indexed: BPIA, Bus.Ind., C.L.I., L.R.I., Leg.Cont., Leg.Per.
—Faxon; UnCover; UMI.

347.7 US ISSN 8756-9302
K24
TRANSPORTATION PRACTITIONERS JOURNAL. 1933. q. $55. Association of Transportation Practitioners, 19564 Club House Rd., Gaithersburg, MD 20879-3002. TEL 301-670-6733. Ed. James F. Bromley. bk.rev.; charts; illus.; index. circ. 4,000. (also avail. in microfilm from WSH,PMC; reprint service avail. from WSH) Indexed: C.L.I., Hlth.Ind., L.R.I., Leg.Per. Document type: newsletter.
—Faxon; UnCover.
Formerly: I C C Practitioners' Journal (ISSN 0018-8859)

240 US
TRANSPORTATION SAFETY LAW PRACTICE MANUAL. 1989. 2 base vols. (plus supplements). $165. Butterworth Legal Publishers (Salem) (Subsidiary of: Reed Elsevier plc), 8 Industrial Way, Bldg. C, Salem, NH 03079. TEL 800-548-4001. FAX 603-898-9858. Ed. William E. Kenworthy. (looseleaf format)
Description: Provides information enabling attorneys to establish or improve safety programs in transportation companies, and to ensure compliance with current regulations.

340 US ISSN 0191-7684
TRAWICK'S FLORIDA PRACTICE AND PROCEDURE. a. $59.95. Harrison Company Publishers, 3110 Crossing Park, Norcross, GA 30071. TEL 404-447-9150. circ. 4,450.
Formerly: Florida Practice and Procedure (ISSN 0191-7676)

TREATMENT ISSUES; newsletter of experimental AIDS therapies. see MEDICAL SCIENCES — Communicable Diseases

TRENDS IN HEALTH CARE, LAW & ETHICS; a journal of contemporary issues in health care. see MEDICAL SCIENCES

340 US
TRESPASS TO TRY TITLE. 1988. base vol. (plus a. supplement). $95. Butterworth Legal Publishers (Salem) (Subsidiary of: Reed Elsevier plc), 8 Industrial Way, Bldg. C, Salem, NH 03079. TEL 800-548-4001. FAX 603-898-9858. Ed. Harold F. Thurow. (looseleaf format)
Description: Practitioner's guide to determine who has the right of possession to any interest or title in real estate.

TRIBUNA MEDICA HOSPITALES. see HOSPITALS

LAW

340 SP
TRIBUNAL. (Includes bound vols. with indexes.) m. 46000 ptas. (effective 1991). Editorial Aranzadi, S.A., Avda. Carlos III, 34, Apdo. 111, 31080 Pamplona, Spain. TEL 948-331212. FAX 948-330919.

349 FR ISSN 0071-9129
TRIBUNAL DE COMMERCE, PARIS. ANNUAIRE. 1969. a. price varies. Tribunal de Commerce de Paris, 1 Bd. du Palais, Paris, France.

340 BL ISSN 0041-2805
TRIBUNAL DE JUSTICA DO ESTADO DO RIO GRANDE DO SUL. REVISTA DE JURISPRUDENCIA;* doutrina, jurisprudencia, legislacao. 1966. bi-m. Cr.$90. Tribuna de Justica, Palacio da Justica, Porto Alegre, RS, Brazil. bk.rev.; cum.index.

340 CU
TRIBUNAL SUPREMO POPULAR. BOLETIN. s-a. $12 in S. America; N. America $14; elsewhere $16. Ediciones Cubanas, Obispo No. 527, Adpo. 605, Havana, Cuba.

340 IT
TRIBUNALI AMMINISTRATIVI REGIONALI. 1974. m. L.550000. Casa Editrice Italedi, Piazza Cavour 19, 00193 Rome, Italy. Ed. Ignazio Scotto.

TRINGA PRESS MONOGRAPH SERIES. see *MEDICAL SCIENCES*

TRIUMPH OF HOPE. see *SOCIAL SERVICES AND WELFARE*

340 US
TRUST DEPARTMENT ADMINISTRATION AND OPERATIONS. (Issued in 2 base vols. with supplements) 1981. irreg. $260. Matthew Bender & Co., Inc., 11 Penn Plaza, New York, NY 10001. TEL 212-967-7707. (looseleaf format)
   Description: Covers every aspect of setting up a trust department, day-to-day administration, asset management, operations, marketing, and internal management.

346.066 UK ISSN 0962-2624
KD1480.A13
TRUST LAW INTERNATIONAL. 1986. 4/yr. £110. Tolley Publishing Co. Ltd., Tolley House, 2 Addiscombe Rd., Croydon, Surrey CR9 5AF, England. TEL 081-686-9141. FAX 081-686-3155. Ed.Bd. adv.; bk.rev.; index. (back issues avail.) **Document type:** trade publication.
   Formerly: Trust Law and Practice (ISSN 0269-5782)
   Description: Offers extensive coverage of trust law both within the UK and internationally.

TRUSTS AND ESTATES. see *BUSINESS AND ECONOMICS — Investments*

340 GW ISSN 0082-6731
TUEBINGER RECHTSWISSENSCHAFTLICHE ABHANDLUNGEN. 1961. irreg. price varies. (Universitaet Tuebingen, Rechts- und Wirtschaftswissenschaftliche Fakultaet) Verlag J.C.B. Mohr (Paul Siebeck), Wilhelmstr. 18, 72074 Tuebingen, Germany. TEL 07071-923-0. FAX 07071-51104. TELEX 7262872-MOHR-D. (Subscr. to: Postfach 2040, 72010 Tuebingen, Germany) **Document type:** monographic series.

TULANE ENVIRONMENTAL LAW JOURNAL. see *ENVIRONMENTAL STUDIES*

340 US ISSN 0041-3992
K24
TULANE LAW REVIEW. 1929-30. 6/yr. $35. Tulane Law Review Association, Tulane University Sta., New Orleans, LA 70118. TEL 504-865-5969. Ed. Louis L. Plotkin. adv.; bk.rev.; index, cum.index: vols. 1-15; 16-35; 36-45. circ. 2,954. (also avail. in microform from UMI; microfiche from RRI,WSH; microfilm from RRI,WSH; reprint service avail. from RRI) **Indexed:** A.B.C.Pol.Sci., Amer.Bibl.Slavic & E.Eur.Stud., C.L.I., L.R.I., Leg.Cont., Leg.Per., Mar.Aff.Bibl., Sel.Water Res.Abstr.
   ●Also available online. Vendor(s): Mead Data Central, Inc., West Services, Inc.
   —BLDSC (9070.300000); Faxon; UnCover; SWETS.

340 US ISSN 0041-4050
TULSA LAW JOURNAL. 1964. q. $23 (typically set in Sep.). University of Tulsa, College of Law, 3120 E. Fourth Pl., Tulsa, OK 74104. TEL 918-631-2408. FAX 918-631-3556. adv.; bk.rev.; index, cum.index every 5 yrs. circ. 1,350. (tabloid format; also avail. in microform from UMI; reprint service avail. from RRI) **Indexed:** C.C.L.P., C.L.I., L.R.I., Leg.Per. **Document type:** academic/scholarly publication.
   ●Also available online. Vendor(s): West Services, Inc.
   —BLDSC (9070.450000); Faxon; UnCover; UMI.
   Description: Provides articles on legal subjects of special concern in the Southwest, including oil and gas law, environmental law, and American Indian law, with many articles of broad national interest.

340 US ISSN 0041-4069
TULSA LAWYER. 1961. m. membership. Tulsa County Bar Association, 1446 S. Boston, Tulsa, OK 74119-3612. TEL 918-584-5243. FAX 918-592-0208. Ed. Delores Bedington. adv.; bk.rev.; charts. circ. 2,000.

346.066 US ISSN 0889-1699
TURNAROUNDS & WORKOUTS; news for people tracking distressed companies. 1986. s-m. $354. Beard Group, Inc., Box 9867, Washington, DC 20016. TEL 301-951-6400. FAX 301-951-3621. Ed. Janet Flint.

346.066 US ISSN 1061-4389
TURNAROUNDS & WORKOUTS - SUPPLEMENT; troubled companies data. 1990. m. $48. Beard Group, Inc., Box 9867, Washington, DC 20016. TEL 301-951-6400. FAX 301-951-3621. Ed. Nancy Parks. adv.
   Description: Contains data and statistics for professionals on troubled companies in the US and Canada.

346.066 US ISSN 1061-4184
TURNAROUNDS & WORKOUTS - SURVEY; bankruptcy & insolvency issues. 1991. m. $195. Beard Group, Inc., Box 9867, Washington, DC 20016. TEL 301-951-6400. FAX 301-951-3621. Ed. Janet Flint.

340 BE
TWEETALIGE LOSBLADIGE WETBOEKEN. 1965. irreg. price varies. Kluwer Editions Juridiques Belgique, E. Story-Scientia (Subsidiary of: Wolters Kluwer N.V.), 230 bd. Emile Bockstael, B-1020 Brussels, Belgium. TEL 32-2-4223911. FAX 32-2-4223979. (looseleaf format)

340 SA ISSN 0257-7747
TYDSKRIF VIR DIE SUID-AFRIKAANSE REG/JOURNAL OF SOUTH AFRICAN LAW. (Text in Afrikaans or English; summaries in English) 1976. q. R.100. Juta & Co. Ltd., P.O. Box 14373, Kenwyn 7790, South Africa. TEL 021-797-5101. FAX 021-761-5010. Ed. J.C. Sonnekus. adv.; bk.rev. circ. 1,300. **Indexed:** Ind.S.A.Per.
   Description: Covers all aspects of South African law.

340 SA
TYDSKRIF VIR HEDENDAAGSE ROMEINS-HOLLANDSE REG/JOURNAL OF CONTEMPORARY ROMAN DUTCH LAW. (Text in Afrikaans, English; summaries in English) 1939. q. R.97. Butterworth Publishers (Pty) Ltd., P.O. Box 792, Durban 4000, South Africa. TEL 27-31-294247. FAX 27-31-283255. Ed. J. Neethling. adv.; bk.rev.; index. circ. 2,000. **Document type:** academic/scholarly publication, bulletin.

340 US
TYLER REVIEW. 1980. m. Box 871, Tyler, TX 75710. TEL 903-592-1356. adv. circ. 10,000.

340 368.4 FR
U C A N S S. BULLETIN JURIDIQUE. 1947. w. Union des Caisses Nationales de Securite Sociale, Tour Maine Montparnasse, 33 av. du Maine, Boites 45 & 46, 75755 Paris Cedex 15, France. cum.index.

340 US ISSN 0197-4564
K3
U C DAVIS LAW REVIEW. 1966. q. $30. University of California, Davis, School of Law, Martin Luther King, Jr. Hall, Davis, CA 95616. TEL 916-752-2551. FAX 916-752-4704. adv.; bk.rev. circ. 800. (also avail. in microfilm from RRI; back issues avail.; reprint service avail. from RRI) **Indexed:** C.L.I., Leg.Cont., Leg.Per. **Document type:** academic/scholarly publication.
   ●Also available online. Vendor(s): Mead Data Central, Inc., West Services, Inc.
   Also available on CD-ROM.
   —BLDSC (9104.455000); Faxon; UnCover.
   Description: Explores contemporary legal issues.

340 US ISSN 0733-401X
K25
U C L A JOURNAL OF ENVIRONMENTAL LAW AND POLICY. 1980. s-a. $15. University of California, Los Angeles, School of Law, 405 Hilgard Ave., Los Angeles, CA 90024. TEL 213-825-0314. adv. (back issues avail.) **Indexed:** C.L.I., Energy Rev., Environ.Per.Bibl. (1985-), Leg.Per. **Document type:** academic/scholarly publication.
   —Faxon; UnCover.

340 US ISSN 0041-5650
K25
U C L A LAW REVIEW. 1953. 6/yr. $24. University of California, Los Angeles, School of Law, 405 Hilgard Ave., Los Angeles, CA 90024. TEL 213-825-4841. adv.; bk.rev. circ. 1,660. (also avail. in microfiche from RRI,WSH; microfilm from RRI,WSH; reprint service avail. from RRI) **Indexed:** ABI Inform., BPIA, Bus.Ind., C.C.L.P., C.L.I., Commun.Abstr., Crim.Just.Abstr., Curr.Cont., L.R.I., Leg.Cont., Leg.Per., P.A.I.S., SSCI.
   ●Also available online. Vendor(s): Mead Data Central, Inc.
   —BLDSC (9079.640000); Faxon; UnCover; SWETS.

340 SZ ISSN 0003-9454
U F I T A. (Archiv fuer Urheber-, Film-, Funk- und Theaterrecht) (Text in English, French, German and Italian) 1928. 3/yr. 195 SFr. Staempfli und Cie AG, Hallerstr. 7-9, CH-3001 Bern, Switzerland. TEL 031-276666. FAX 031-3006688. Ed. Manfred Rehbinder. adv.; bk.rev.; charts; index. circ. 500. **Document type:** bulletin.
   —CCC.

340 341 MW
U M A STUDENTS LAW JOURNAL. 1978. a. K.4.00. University of Malawi, Students Law Society, Chancellor College, Box 280, Zomba, Malawi. TELEX 44742. adv.; bk.rev.

340 US ISSN 0047-7575
K11
U M K C LAW REVIEW. 1932. 4/yr. $25. University of Missouri, Kansas City, School of Law, 5100 Rockhill Rd., Kansas City, MO 64110. TEL 816-276-1656. FAX 816-276-5276. Ed.Bd. adv.; bibl. circ. 1,200. (also avail. in microfiche from WSH,PMC; microfilm from WSH,PMC) **Indexed:** C.L.I., L.R.I., Leg.Cont., Leg.Per.
   —Faxon; UnCover.

U P R - UMWELT- UND PLANUNGSRECHT. see *ENVIRONMENTAL STUDIES*

U S AVIATION REPORTS. see *TRANSPORTATION — Air Transport*

U S ENVIRONMENTAL LAWS. see *ENVIRONMENTAL STUDIES*

330 US ISSN 1055-8276
U S IMMIGRATION. (Supplement avail.) 1991. q. $29.99. Publishing & Business Consultants, 951 S. Oxford, No. 109, Los Angeles, CA 90006. TEL 213-732-3477. FAX 213-732-9123. (Subscr. to: Box 75392, Los Angeles, CA 90075) Ed. Andeson Naopleon Atia. adv. circ. 120,000. **Document type:** consumer publication.
   Description: Provides general information on visas and other immigration topics affecting foreign nationals in the US.

U S LABOR AND EMPLOYMENT LAW. see *BUSINESS AND ECONOMICS — Labor And Industrial Relations*

U S MARITIME ALERT. see *TRANSPORTATION — Ships And Shipping*

U S OIL WEEK; inside report on trends in petroleum marketing without the influence of advertising. see PETROLEUM AND GAS

U S P - D I, VOLUME 3. APPROVED DRUG PRODUCTS AND LEGAL REQUIREMENTS. (United States Pharmacopeia) see PHARMACY AND PHARMACOLOGY

340 US ISSN 0899-7446
K25
U W L A LAW REVIEW. 1967. a. $25. University of West Los Angeles, Law Review, 1155 W. Arbor Vitae St., Inglewood, CA 90301-2902. TEL 310-215-3339. FAX 310-670-9331. adv.; bk.rev. circ. 1,000. (also avail. in microfilm from WSH,PMC; reprint service avail. from WSH) **Indexed:** C.L.I., L.R.I., Leg.Cont., Leg.Per.
—UnCover; UMI.
Formerly (until 1981): University of West Los Angeles Law Review (ISSN 0083-4068)

340 657.6 DK
UGESKRIFT FOR RETSVAESEN. w. (Danmarks Jurist- og Oekonomforbund) G.E.C. Gads Forlag, Vimmelskaftet 32, DK-1161 Copenhagen K, Denmark. TEL 45-33-15-05-58. adv. circ. 9,800. **Indexed:** ELLIS.

UKRAINIAN BUSINESS DIGEST; a monthly report on the business environment in Ukraine. see BUSINESS AND ECONOMICS — Domestic Commerce

340 US
UNCLAIMED PROPERTY LAW AND REPORTING FORMS. (Issued in 4 vols. with supplements) 1984. irreg. $965. Matthew Bender & Co., Inc., 11 Penn Plaza, New York, NY 10001. TEL 212-967-7707. Ed.Bd. (looseleaf format)
Description: Comprehensive coverage of the escheat laws and unclaimed property requirements applicable in each state. Includes analysis of the Uniform Unclaimed Property Acts, relevant case law, and state statutes.

UNFAIR LABOR PRACTICES BULLETIN. see BUSINESS AND ECONOMICS — Labor And Industrial Relations

UNIFORM COMMERCIAL CODE LAW LETTER. see BUSINESS AND ECONOMICS — Domestic Commerce

340 US
UNIFORM COMMERCIAL CODE REPORTING SERVICE. 1965. m. $782.50. Callaghan & Co., 155 Pfingsten Rd., Deerfield, IL 60015. TEL 800-323-8067. (back issues avail.)
Description: Official text of the code, focusing on sales of goods, leases, bankruptcy, secured transactions, product liabilities, warranties, consumer loans, debt collections, letters of credit, and damages.

UNION LABOR REPORT. see BUSINESS AND ECONOMICS — Labor And Industrial Relations

665.5 UK
UNITED KINGDOM OFFSHORE LEGISLATION GUIDE. 1980. a. £225. Charles Knight Publications, Tolley House, 2 Addiscombe Rd., Croydon, Surrey CR9 5AF, England. TEL 081-686-9141. FAX 081-686-3155. Ed. Fred Osliff. circ. 500. (looseleaf format) **Document type:** bulletin.

UNITED NATIONS POPULATION FUND. ANNUAL REVIEW OF POPULATION LAW. see POPULATION STUDIES

U.S. CHAMBER OF COMMERCE. ANALYSIS OF WORKERS' COMPENSATION LAWS. see BUSINESS AND ECONOMICS — Labor And Industrial Relations

346.066 US ISSN 0734-4074
U.S. CHAMBER WATCH ON SMALL BUSINESS LEGISLATION & REGULATION; an inside Washington report. 1988. 11/yr. $65 to non-members; members $49.50. U.S. Chamber of Commerce, Small Business Center, 1615 H St., N.W., Washington, DC 20062-2000. TEL 202-463-5503. Ed. Cheryl Nikos. circ. 1,000. (tabloid format; back issues avail.) **Document type:** newsletter.
Formerly: Services Watch.
Description: Reports to the small business community about issues impacting the way they do business. Provides insight into priority small business legislation; includes how-to articles on small business persons on a variety of issues.

345 US ISSN 0082-9943
U.S. DEPARTMENT OF JUSTICE. ANNUAL REPORT OF THE ATTORNEY GENERAL OF THE UNITED STATES. 1870. a. price varies. U.S. Department of Justice, Office of Legal Policy, Constitution Ave. & 10th St., N.W., Washington, DC 20530. TEL 202-633-4601. (Subscr. to: Supt. of Documents, Washington DC 20402.)

340 US
U.S. DEPARTMENT OF JUSTICE. OFFICE OF LEGAL COUNSEL. OPINIONS. 1977. a. $15. U.S. Department of Justice, Office of Legal Counsel, Washington, DC 20530. Ed. Margaret C. Love. circ. 800.

345 US ISSN 0082-9951
U.S. DEPARTMENT OF JUSTICE. OPINIONS OF ATTORNEY GENERAL. 1789. irreg. price varies. U.S. Department of Justice, Office of Legal Counsel, Constitution Ave. & 10th St., N.W., Washington, DC 20530. TEL 202-633-2041. (Subscr. to: Supt. of Documents, Washington DC 20402.) Ed. Margaret C. Love. cum.indexes issued separately. (also avail. in microfiche)
—UMI.

U.S. DEPARTMENT OF THE INTERIOR. A L J DECISIONS. see PUBLIC ADMINISTRATION

U.S. DEPARTMENT OF THE INTERIOR. DECISIONS OF THE DEPARTMENT OF THE INTERIOR. see PUBLIC ADMINISTRATION

U.S. DEPARTMENT OF THE INTERIOR. I B I A CITATOR - DESCRIPTIVE WORD INDEX. see PUBLIC ADMINISTRATION

U.S. DEPARTMENT OF THE INTERIOR. INTERIOR BOARD OF CONTRACT APPEALS. see PUBLIC ADMINISTRATION

U.S. DEPARTMENT OF THE INTERIOR. INTERIOR BOARD OF INDIAN APPEALS. see PUBLIC ADMINISTRATION

U.S. DEPARTMENT OF THE INTERIOR. INTERIOR BOARD OF LAND APPEALS. see PUBLIC ADMINISTRATION

U.S. DEPARTMENT OF THE INTERIOR. LISTING OF APPEALS DOCKETED BY THE BOARD OF LAND APPEALS. see PUBLIC ADMINISTRATION

602.7 US ISSN 0042-1219
U.S. FEDERAL REGISTER. (MICROFICHE EDITION). 1936. w. $530. William S. Hein & Co., Inc., 1285 Main St., Buffalo, NY 14209. TEL 716-882-2600. FAX 716-883-8100. TELEX 91-209 WU 7 HEIN BUF. (microfiche; also avail. in microform from PMC; back issues avail.) **Indexed:** Ocean.Abstr., Pollut.Abstr. **Document type:** government publication.

U.S. FEDERAL TRADE COMMISSION. COURT DECISIONS PERTAINING TO THE FEDERAL TRADE COMMISSION. see BUSINESS AND ECONOMICS — Domestic Commerce

U.S. FEDERAL TRADE COMMISSION. FEDERAL TRADE COMMISSION DECISIONS, FINDINGS, ORDERS AND STIPULATIONS. see BUSINESS AND ECONOMICS — Domestic Commerce

346 US ISSN 0093-4631
KF5640
U.S. FISH AND WILDLIFE SERVICE. SELECTED LIST OF FEDERAL LAWS AND TREATIES RELATING TO SPORT FISH AND WILDLIFE. Key Title: Selected List of Federal Laws and Treaties Relating to Sport Fish and Wildlife. irreg. $1.75. U.S. Fish and Wildlife Service, Dept. of the Interior, Washington, DC 20240. TEL 202-343-1100. (Subscr. to: Supt. of Documents, Washington DC 20402.) (looseleaf format)

340 US
U.S. LIBRARY OF CONGRESS. CONGRESSIONAL RESEARCH SERVICE. DIGEST OF PUBLIC GENERAL BILLS AND RESOLUTIONS. 1936. irreg. U.S. Library of Congress, Congressional Research Service, Washington, DC 20540. TEL 202-707-5000. (Dist. by: Supt. of Documents, Washington DC 20402) Ed. Terry G. Guertin. abstr.; cum.index for session. circ. 5,000. (also avail. in microfiche from BHP)
—UMI.
Former titles: U.S. Library of Congress. Congressional Research Service. Digest of Public Bills and Resolutions (ISSN 0012-2785); U.S. Library of Congress. Legislative Reference Service. Digest of Public General Bills and Selected Resolutions (ISSN 0090-0125); U.S. Library of Congress. Legislative Reference Service. Digest of Public General Bills (ISSN 0090-0117)

U.S. NUCLEAR REGULATORY COMMISSION. INFORMATION REPORT ON STATE LEGISLATION. see ENERGY — Nuclear Energy

U.S. OCCUPATIONAL SAFETY AND HEALTH REVIEW COMMISSION. ADMINISTRATIVE LAW JUDGE AND COMMISSION DECISIONS. see OCCUPATIONAL HEALTH AND SAFETY

340 US ISSN 0566-0785
KF127
UNITED STATES ATTORNEY'S BULLETIN. 1963. m. U.S. Department of Justice, Executive Office for United States Attorneys, Rm. 6419, Patrick Henry Bldg., 601 D St., N.W., Washington, DC 20530. TEL 202-501-6098. Ed. Judith A. Beeman. **Document type:** government publication.

340 US
UNITED STATES CODE UNANNOTATED. a. $445 for 12 vol. set; $39 per vol. Gould Publications, 1333 N. U.S. Hwy. 17-92, Longwood, FL 32750-3724. TEL 407-695-9500. FAX 407-695-9500. (looseleaf format)
●Also available on CD-ROM.
Description: Compiles all 50 titles of the federal statutes.

340 US ISSN 0148-8139
LAW
UNITED STATES LAW WEEK; a national survey of current law. 1933. w. $750. The Bureau of National Affairs, Inc., 1231 25th St., N.W., Washington, DC 20037. TEL 202-452-4200. FAX 202-822-8092. TELEX 285656 BNAI WSH. (Subscr. to: 9435 Key West Ave., Rockville, MD 20850. TEL 800-372-1033) Ed. Gregory R. Pease. bk.rev.; abstr.; bibl.; index. (back issues avail.)
●Also available online. Vendor(s): Mead Data Central, Inc. (USLW), West Services, Inc.
—CCC.
Description: Notification and reference service providing current information about all significant court decisions, rulings, regulations, and interpretations in state and federal law.

340 US ISSN 0190-5252
UNITED STATES LAW WEEK SUMMARY AND ANALYSIS; a national survey of current law. 1933. w. $150. The Bureau of National Affairs, Inc., 1231 25th St., N.W., Washington, DC 20037. TEL 202-452-4200. FAX 202-822-8092. TELEX 285656 BNAI WSH. (Subscr. to: 9435 Key West Ave. Rockville, MD 20850. TEL 800-372-1033) Ed. Gregory R. Pease. index. (back issues avail.)
—CCC.
Description: Summary of current legal developments, with an index and table of cases.

345 US ISSN 0083-3401
UNITED STATES STATUTES AT LARGE. 1873. a. $132. U.S. Office of the Federal Register, National Archives and Records Administration, Eighth St. and Pennsylvania Ave., N.W., Washington, DC 20408. TEL 202-523-5230. (Subscr. to: Superintendent of Documents, U.S. Government Printing Office, Box 371954, Pittsburgh, PA 15250-7954. TEL 202-783-3238. FAX 202-512-2233) (also avail. in microform from UMI,BHP) **Document type:** government publication.
—UMI.
Description: Cumulation of daily slip law prints and annotated pamphlets of public laws enacted by Congress.

UNITED STATES TAX COURT REPORTS. see BUSINESS AND ECONOMICS — Public Finance, Taxation

UNITS. see *HOUSING AND URBAN PLANNING*

340   VE
UNIVERSIDAD CENTRAL DE VENEZUELA. FACULTAD DE CIENCIAS JURIDICAS Y POLITICAS. REVISTA. 1954. q. price varies. Universidad Central de Venezuela, Facultad de Ciencias Juridicas y Politicas, Caracas, Venezuela. Ed.Bd. bk.rev.; bibl.; cum.index: nos. 1-50. circ. 2,000. **Indexed:** Foreign Leg.Per.
    Formerly (until 1981?): Universidad Central de Venezuela. Facultad de Derecho. Revista (ISSN 0041-8293)

340   EC
UNIVERSIDAD CENTRAL DEL ECUADOR. INSTITUTO DE DERECHO COMPARADO. BOLETIN. 1951. s-a. Universidad Central del Ecuador, Instituto de Derecho Comparado, Editorial Universitaria, Quito, Ecuador. bibl.

340   SP   ISSN 0075-773X
UNIVERSIDAD DE LA LAGUNA. FACULTAD DE DERECHO. ANALES. 1963. a. 150 ptas. Universidad de la Laguna, Secretariado de Publicaciones, San Agustin, 30, 38201 La Laguna-Tenerife, Canary Islands, Spain. TEL 922-25-81-27. **Indexed:** Amer.Hist.& Life, Hist.Abstr.

347.9 320   VE
UNIVERSIDAD DE LOS ANDES. FACULTAD DE CIENCIAS JURIDICAS Y POLITICAS. ANUARIO. a. Universidad de Los Andes, Facultad de Ciencias Juridicas y Politicas, Centro de Investigaciones Juridicas, Ed. Admin. de la Ula, 4o piso, Av. Tulio Febres Cordero, Merida 5101, Venezuela. Ed. Manuel Lacruz M. charts; stat.

340   VE   ISSN 0076-6550
UNIVERSIDAD DE LOS ANDES. FACULTAD DE DERECHO. ANUARIO.* 1970. irreg. Universidad de Los Andes, Facultad de Derecho, Centro de Investigaciones Juridicas, Via los Chorras, C.P. 5101, Merida, Venezuela. Ed.Bd. bibl.
    Supersedes (1955-19??): Universidad de Los Andes. Facultad de Derecho. Revista.

340   SP
UNIVERSIDAD DE MURCIA. DEPARTAMENTO DE DERECHO POLITICO. PUBLICACIONES. SERIE MONOGRAFIAS. 1977. irreg. Universidad de Murcia, Secretariado de Publicaciones e Intercambio Cientifico, Santo Cristo, 1, 30001 Murcia, Spain. **Document type:** monographic series.

349   SP
UNIVERSIDAD DE NAVARRA. COLECCION MANUALES DE DERECHO. irreg., no.17, 1989. price varies. (Universidad de Navarra, Facultad de Derecho) Ediciones Universidad de Navarra, S.A., Apdo. 396, 31080 Pamplona, Spain. TEL 94 825 6850.
    Formerly: Universidad de Navarra. Manuales: Derecho Notarial Espanol (ISSN 0078-8767)

340 327   PN
UNIVERSIDAD DE PANAMA. FACULTAD DE DERECHO Y CIENCIAS POLITICAS. CUADERNOS. 1960. irreg. Universidad de Panama, Facultad de Derecho y Ciencias Politicas, Oficina de Informacion y Publicaciones, Panama, Panama.

340 658   SP   ISSN 0582-8929
UNIVERSIDAD DE SEVILLA. INSTITUTO GARCIA OVIEDO. PUBLICACIONES. irreg., latest no.52. price varies. Universidad de Sevilla, Instituto Garcia Oviedo, Servicio de Publicaciones, Valparaiso 5, 41013 Seville, Spain. TEL 954-231958. FAX 954-232245.

340   SP
UNIVERSIDAD DE SEVILLA. SERIE: DERECHO. irreg, latest no.53. price varies. Universidad de Sevilla, Servicio de Publicaciones, Valparaiso 5, 41013 Seville, Spain. TEL 954-231958. FAX 954-232245.
    Formerly (until 1967): Universidad Hispalense. Anales. Serie: Derecho (ISSN 0210-7686)

344.01   SP
UNIVERSIDAD DE VALENCIA. CATEDRA DE DERECHO DEL TRABAJO. CUADERNOS.* 1971. s-a. Universidad de Valencia, Nave 2, Valencia, Spain.

340   VE
UNIVERSIDAD DEL ZULIA. FACULTAD DE DERECHO. REVISTA. (Not published 1976) 1961. irreg. no.49, 1977. Bs.15($3.50) Universidad del Zulia, Facultad de Derecho, Apdo. 526, Maracaibo, Venezuela. Dir. Alice Adrianza Alvarez. circ. 2,500. **Indexed:** P.A.I.S.

340   MX
UNIVERSIDAD NACIONAL AUTONOMA DE MEXICO. FACULTAD DE DERECHO DE MEXICO. REVISTA. (Text mainly in Spanish) 1939. bi-m. Mex.$3000($50) Universidad Nacional Autonoma de Mexico, Facultad de Derecho, Ciudad Universitaria, 04510 Mexico, D.F., Mexico. Ed. Fernando Flores Garcia. abstr.; bibl.; cum.index: 1939-1950. circ. 3,000. (back issues avail.) **Indexed:** Amer.Hist.& Life (until 1988), Hist.Abstr. (until 1988).

340   PE
UNIVERSIDAD NACIONAL FEDERICO VILLAREAL. FACULTAD DE DERECHO. REVISTA.* 1967. s-a. Universidad Nacional Federico Villareal, Facultad de Derecho, Av. Nicolas de Pierota 1128, Lima, Peru.

340   PO
UNIVERSIDADE DE LISBOA. FACULDADE DE DIREITO. REVISTA. 1944. a. Universidade de Lisboa, Faculdade de Direito, Lisbon, Portugal. bk.rev.

340   BL   ISSN 0080-6250
K23.
UNIVERSIDADE DE SAO PAULO. FACULDADE DE DIREITO. REVISTA. 1893. a. Cr.$2000. Universidade de Sao Paulo, Faculdade de Direito, Biblioteca Central, Largo de Sao Francisco, 01 andar, 01005 Sao Paolo, Brazil. Ed. Antonio Augusto Machado de Campos. bk.rev. circ. 1,500.

340   BL   ISSN 0102-1397
UNIVERSIDADE FEDERAL DE UBERLANDIA. CURSO DE DIREITO. REVISTA. 1972. a. free. Universidade Federal de Uberlandia, Curso de Direito, Campus Umuarama-Bloco E, Sala 2E25, 38400 Uberlandia, MG, Brazil. Eds. Jacy de Assis, Dinah Fernandes de Carvalho. bibl. circ. 5,000.
    Formerly (until 1978): Universidade de Uberlandia. Faculdade de Direito. Revista.

340   IT   ISSN 0435-3048
UNIVERSITA DEGLI STUDI DI GENOVA. FACOLTA DI GIURISPRUDENZA. ANNALI. 1962. s-a. price varies. Casa Editrice Dott. A. Giuffre, Via Busto Arsizio 40, 20151 Milan, Italy. TEL 02-38000905. FAX 02-38009582. Ed. Enrico Zanelli.

340   XO
UNIVERSITAS COMENIANA: ACTA FACULTATIS IURIDICAE. (Text in Slovak; summaries in German, Russian) 1980. irreg. exchange basis. Univerzita Komenskeho, Pravnicka Fakulta, c/o Study and Information Center, Safarikovo nam. 6, 818 06 Bratislava, Slovakia. Ed. Jordan Girasek. circ. 500.

340   RM   ISSN 0379-7872
UNIVERSITATEA "AL. I. CUZA" DIN IASI. ANALELE STIINTIFICE. SECTIUNEA 3D: STIINTE JURIDICE. (Text in Rumanian; summaries in foreign languages) 1955. a. 35 lei. Universitatea "Al. I. Cuza" din Iasi, Calea M. Eminescu 11, Jassy, Rumania. (Subscr. to: ILEXIM, Str. 13 Decembrie Nr. 3, P.O. Box 136-137, Bucharest, Rumania) Ed. I. Macovei. bk.rev.; abstr.; charts; illus. circ. 250.
    Description: Theoretical and practical studies in civil law, criminal sciences and international law.

UNIVERSITATEA BUCURESTI. ANALELE. FILOZOFIE. ISTORIE. DREPT. see *PHILOSOPHY*

340   FR   ISSN 0223-5447
UNIVERSITE DE CLERMONT-FERRAND I. FACULTE DE DROIT ET DE SCIENCE POLITIQUE. ANNALES. a. 220 F. (Universite de Clermont-Ferrand I, Faculte de Droit et de Science Politique) Editions Juridiques Associees, 26 rue Vercingetorix, 75014 Paris, France. TEL 1-43-35-01-67. FAX 43-20-07-42. TELEX EJA 203 918 F. (Co-sponsor: Librairie Generale de Droit et de Jurisprudence) (back issues avail.)

340 300   FR   ISSN 0337-839X
UNIVERSITE DE DROIT, ECONOMIE ET DE SCIENCES SOCIALES DE PARIS. TRAVAUX DU SEMINAIRE DE RECHERCHES SUR LES FAITS ELECTORAUX DE MONSIEUR LE PROFESSEUR ROBERT VILLERS. irreg. price varies. (Universite de Droit, Economie et de Sciences Sociales de Paris) Librarie Touzot, 38 rue Saint Sulpice, 75278 Paris Cedex 06, France.

340   CN   ISSN 0317-9656
K21
UNIVERSITE DE SHERBROOKE. REVUE DE DROIT. (Text in English and French) 1970. s-a. Can.$30($31) Universite de Sherbrooke, Faculte de Droit, Sherbrooke, PQ J1K 2R1, Canada. TEL 819-821-7508. FAX 819-821-7578. Ed. Claude Boisclair. adv.; bk.rev. circ. 2,000. (also avail. in microfilm from UMI) **Indexed:** C.L.I., Ind.Can.L.P.L., Leg.Per., Pt.de Rep. (1983-).

340   BE
UNIVERSITE LIBRE DE BRUXELLES. REVUE DE DROIT. Short title: Revue de Droit de l'U L B. 1990. s-a. 1700 Fr. Etablissements Emile Bruylant, 67 rue de la Regence, B-1000 Brussels, Belgium. TEL 02-512-9845.

340   ZR
UNIVERSITE NATIONALE DU ZAIRE, KINSHASA. FACULTE DE DROIT. ANNALES. 1972. a. Universite Nationale du Zaire, Kinshasa, Faculte du Droit, B.P. 125, Kinshasa XI, Zaire.

340   US   ISSN 0162-8372
K25
UNIVERSITY OF ARKANSAS AT LITTLE ROCK LAW JOURNAL. 1978. q. $15. University of Arkansas at Little Rock, School of Law, 1201 McAlmont, Little Rock, AR 72202-5142. TEL 501-324-9918. Ed. April Henley. adv.; bk.rev. circ. 3,800. (also avail. in microform from WHS; reprint service avail. from WSH) **Indexed:** C.L.I., L.R.I., Leg.Cont., Leg.Per. **Document type:** academic/scholarly publication.
—BLDSC (9104.040000); Faxon; UnCover.

340   US   ISSN 0091-5440
K2
UNIVERSITY OF BALTIMORE LAW REVIEW. 1971. 3/yr. $15 per vol. University of Baltimore School of Law, Business Editor, 1420 N. Charles St., Baltimore, MD 21201. TEL 410-837-4490. adv.; bk.rev. circ. 2,000. (also avail. in microfilm from WSH,PMC; reprint service avail. from WSH) **Indexed:** C.L.I., L.R.I., Leg.Cont., Leg.Per. **Document type:** academic/scholarly publication.
●Also available online. Vendor(s): West Services, Inc.
—BLDSC (9104.150000); Faxon; UnCover.

346   CN   ISSN 0068-1849
LAW
UNIVERSITY OF BRITISH COLUMBIA LAW REVIEW. 1959. s-a. Can.$35($40) University of British Columbia Law Review Society, Faculty of Law, Vancouver, BC V6T 1Z1, Canada. TEL 604-822-3066. FAX 604-822-8108. adv.; bk.rev.; index: 1949-81; 1982-90. circ. 900. (also avail. in microform from WSH; back issues avail.; reprint service avail. from WSH) **Indexed:** Abstr.Bk.Rev.Curr.Leg.Per., C.L.I., Ind.Can.L.P.L., L.R.I., Leg.Cont., Leg.Per., P.A.I.S. **Document type:** academic/scholarly publication.
—BLDSC (9104.313000); Faxon; UnCover.
    Description: Promotion of legal scholarship, with articles by judges, professors, practising lawyers.

340   US   ISSN 0041-9494
K25   CODEN: UCLRA2
UNIVERSITY OF CHICAGO LAW REVIEW. 1933. q. $30. University of Chicago Law School, 1111 E. 60th St., Chicago, IL 60637. TEL 312-702-9832. FAX 312-702-0730. adv.; bk.rev.; index. circ. 2,400. (also avail. in microfiche from RRI,WSH,PMC; microfilm from WSH,PMC,RRI; reprint service avail. from RRI) **Indexed:** A.B.C.Pol.Sci., ABI Inform, Bank.Lit.Ind., BPIA, Bus.Ind., C.L.I., Crim.Just.Abstr., Curr.Cont., L.R.I., Leg.Cont., Leg.Per., SSCI. **Document type:** academic/scholarly publication.
●Also available online. Vendor(s): Mead Data Central, Inc.
—BLDSC (9106.500000); Faxon; UnCover; SWETS; UMI.

340   US   ISSN 0892-5593
K25
UNIVERSITY OF CHICAGO LEGAL FORUM. 1986. a. $20. University of Chicago Law School, 1111 E. 60th St., Chicago, IL 60637. TEL 312-702-9832. FAX 312-702-0730. circ. 1,000. **Document type:** academic/scholarly publication.
●Also available online. Vendor(s): West Services, Inc.
—Faxon; UnCover.
    Description: Examines on noteworthy contemporary legal issues.

340   US   ISSN 0041-9516
K25
UNIVERSITY OF COLORADO LAW REVIEW. 1929. 4/yr. $25. University of Colorado Law Review, Inc., c/o Robert Davis, Bus. Sec., 290 Fleming Law Bldg., Campus Box 401, Boulder, CO 80309. TEL 303-492-6145. FAX 303-492-1200. adv.; bk.rev.; index. circ. 875. (also avail. in microfilm from RRI,WSH; reprint service avail.) **Indexed:** Abstr.Bk.Rev.Curr.Leg.Per., C.L.I., L.R.I., Leg.Cont., Leg.Per., Sel.Water Res.Abstr.
—BLDSC (9106.990000); Faxon; UnCover; UMI.
Formerly: Rocky Mountain Law Review.

340   US   ISSN 0162-9174
K4
UNIVERSITY OF DAYTON LAW REVIEW. 1976. 3/yr. $17.50. University of Dayton, Law School, 300 College Park, Dayton, OH 45469. TEL 513-229-3642. Ed. Patrick Edward Beck. adv.; bk.rev. circ. 750. (also avail. in microfiche from WSH,PMC; microfilm from WSH,PMC) **Indexed:** C.L.I., L.R.I., Leg.Cont., Leg.Per., M.L.A.
—BLDSC (9109.357000); UnCover.
Formerly (until vol.2): University of Dayton Intramural Law Review (ISSN 0363-2148)

340   US   ISSN 1058-4323
K25
UNIVERSITY OF DETROIT MERCY LAW REVIEW. 1916. 4/yr. $17. University of Detroit, School of Law, 651 E. Jefferson Ave., Detroit, MI 48226. TEL 313-596-0237. adv.; bk.rev.; index, cum.index for vols.44-50, 1966-1973. circ. 700. (also avail. in microfiche from WSH,PMC; microfilm from WSH,PMC; reprint service avail. from ISI) **Indexed:** C.C.L.P., C.L.I., Cath.Ind., Curr.Cont., L.R.I., Leg.Cont., Leg.Per., Sage Pub.Admin.Abstr., Sage Urb.Stud.Abstr., SSCI.
—BLDSC (9109.370510); Faxon; UnCover.
Former titles (until 1991): University of Detroit Law Review (ISSN 0886-9456); (until vol.61, no.4, 1984): University of Detroit Journal of Urban Law (ISSN 0161-7095); (until 1976): Journal of Urban Law (ISSN 0041-9559); (until 1966): University of Detroit Law Journal (ISSN 8755-2183)

340   BG
UNIVERSITY OF DHAKA. DEPARTMENT OF LAW. JOURNAL. (Text in Bengali or English) 1978. Tk.2.50. University of Dhaka, Department of Law, Dhaka 2, Bangladesh.

340   GH   ISSN 0041-9605
UNIVERSITY OF GHANA LAW JOURNAL. 1964. s-a. $15. University of Ghana, Faculty of Law, Legon, Ghana. Ed.Bd. adv.; bk.rev.; index. circ. 500. **Indexed:** Documentatieblad, Leg.Per.

340   US   ISSN 0271-9835
UNIVERSITY OF HAWAII LAW REVIEW. 1979. s-a. $16. William S. Richardson School of Law, Law Review, 2515 Dole St., Honolulu, HI 96822. FAX 808-956-6402. Ed. Katherine G. Leonard. adv.; bk.rev. circ. 500. (back issues avail.) **Indexed:** C.L.I., Leg.Cont., Leg.Per.
—Faxon; UnCover.
Description: Focuses on cases and legal issues of particular interest in Hawaii and the Pacific region.

340   US   ISSN 0276-9948
K25
UNIVERSITY OF ILLINOIS LAW REVIEW. 1949. q. $30. University of Illinois at Urbana-Champaign, College of Law, Champaign, IL 61820. TEL 217-333-3156. Ed. Dennis Coghlan. adv.; bk.rev.; index, cum.index every 10 yrs. circ. 2,100. (also avail. in microfilm from UMI) **Indexed:** Abstr.Bk.Rev.Curr.Leg.Per., C.L.I., Crim.Just.Abstr., L.R.I., Leg.Cont., Leg.Per., SSCI. **Document type:** academic/scholarly publication.
●Also available online. Vendor(s): West Services, Inc.
—BLDSC (9110.663100); Faxon; UnCover.
Formerly: University of Illinois Law Forum (ISSN 0041-963X)

340   US   ISSN 0083-4025
K25
UNIVERSITY OF KANSAS LAW REVIEW. (Supplement avail. annually: Criminal Procedure Review) 1952. q. $26 (including Criminal Procedure Review $31). University of Kansas, School of Law, Rm. 510, Green Hall, Lawrence, KS 66045. TEL 913-864-3463. FAX 913-864-3680. Ed. Sharon Stallbaumer. adv.; bk.rev.; index, cum.index every 5 yrs. circ. 1,375. (also avail. in microfiche from WSH,PMC; microfilm from WSH,PMC; back issues avail.; reprint service avail. from WSH) **Indexed:** Abstr.Bk.Rev.Curr.Leg.Per., C.C.L.P., C.L.I., L.R.I., Leg.Cont., Leg.Per., Mar.Aff.Bibl. **Document type:** academic/scholarly publication.
●Also available online. Vendor(s): Mead Data Central, Inc., West Services, Inc.
—BLDSC (9110.930000); Faxon; UnCover.
Description: Contains critical and analytical articles written by scholars, practicing lawyers, judges and other public officials focusing on problems and developments in the law.

340   PH   ISSN 0041-9796
UNIVERSITY OF MANILA LAW GAZETTE. 1951. s-a. free to law students. University of Manila, 546 Dr. M. V. de los Santos St., Sampaloc, Manila D-403, Philippines. Ed. Antonio A. Figueras. bk.rev.; abstr.; circ. 500 (controlled).

340   US   ISSN 0041-9818
UNIVERSITY OF MIAMI LAW REVIEW. 1947. 5/yr. $18. University of Miami, School of Law, Coral Gables, FL 33124. TEL 305-284-2523. Ed. Tucker Ronzetti. adv.; index. circ. 1,400. (also avail. in microform from UMI,PMC; microfiche from WSH,PMC; microfilm from WSH) **Indexed:** Abstr.Bk.Rev.Curr.Leg.Per., Account.Ind. (1974-), C.L.I., Crim.Just.Abstr., L.R.I., Lang.& Lang.Behav.Abstr., Leg.Cont., Leg.Per., Mar.Aff.Bibl., P.A.I.S. **Document type:** academic/scholarly publication.
—BLDSC (9113.560000); Faxon; UnCover; SWETS; UMI.

340   US   ISSN 0033-1546
K16
UNIVERSITY OF MICHIGAN JOURNAL OF LAW REFORM. 1968. q. $28 (foreign $31). University of Michigan, S-324 Legal Research Bldg., Ann Arbor, MI 48109. TEL 313-763-2195. Ed. Valerie J. Wald. adv. circ. 1,000. (also avail. in microform from WSH,PMC; reprint service avail. from WSH) **Indexed:** C.L.I., Crim.Just.Abstr., L.R.I., Leg.Cont., Leg.Per., P.A.I.S.
—BLDSC (9113.650000); UnCover.
Formerly: Prospectus.

346   CN   ISSN 0836-6632
UNIVERSITY OF NEW BRUNSWICK LAW JOURNAL. (Text in English, French) 1947. a. Can.$15. University of New Brunswick, Faculty of Law, P.O. Box 4400, Fredericton, NB E3B 5A3, Canada. TEL 506-453-4657. FAX 506-453-5186. (Subscr. to: Carswell, Thomson Professional Publishing, Corporate Plaza, 2075 Kennedy Rd., Scarborough, ON M1T 3V4, Canada) Ed. D. Linehan, S. MacDonald. adv.; bk.rev.; cum.index: 1947-87. circ. 2,200. (also avail. in microform from UMI,PMC; microfiche from WSH; microfilm from WSH; reprint service avail. from UMI) **Indexed:** C.L.I., Ind.Can.L.P.L., L.R.I., Leg.Per. **Document type:** academic/scholarly publication.
●Also available online. Vendor(s): West Services, Inc.

340   AT   ISSN 0811-7632
UNIVERSITY OF NEW SOUTH WALES. FACULTY HANDBOOKS: LAW. a. Aus.$4. University of New South Wales, Kensington, N.S.W. 2052, Australia. TEL 02-697-2840. FAX 02-662-2163.

340   AT   ISSN 0313-0096
K25
UNIVERSITY OF NEW SOUTH WALES LAW JOURNAL. 1975. a. Aus.$50. University of New South Wales, Faculty of Law, P.O. Box 1, Kensington, N.S.W. 2033, Australia. TEL 02-697-2237. FAX 02-313-7209. (Dist. in N. America by: Wm. W. Gaunt & Sons, Inc., Gaunt Bldg., 3011 Gulf Dr., Homes Beach, FL 34217-2199. TEL 813-778-5211. FAX 813-778-5252) Ed.Bd. adv.; bk.rev.; cum.index: 1975-1984. circ. 1,500. (also avail. in microfilm from RRI; back issues avail) **Indexed:** C.L.I., Leg.Cont., Leg.Per. **Document type:** academic/scholarly publication.
—BLDSC (9116.183000); UnCover.
Description: Legal periodical of contemporary issues.

UNIVERSITY OF OSAKA PREFECTURE. BULLETIN. SERIES D: ECONOMICS, BUSINESS ADMINISTRATION AND LAW/OSAKA-FURITSU DAIGAKU KIYO, D. KEIZAIGAKU, KEIEIGAKU, HOGAKU. see BUSINESS AND ECONOMICS

340   US   ISSN 0041-9907
K25
UNIVERSITY OF PENNSYLVANIA LAW REVIEW. 1852. 6/yr. $38 (foreign $44) (effective 1994). (University of Pennsylvania Law School) University of Pennsylvania Law Review, 3400 Chestnut St., Philadelphia, PA 19104-6204. TEL 215-898-7060. FAX 215-573-2005. Ed. Megan Jacobson. adv. contact: Brett Lawrence. bk.rev.; index. circ. 2,150. (also avail. in microfiche from RRI,WSH; microfilm from RRI,WSH; back issues avail.; reprint service avail. from RRI) **Indexed:** A.B.C.Pol.Sci., Abstr.Bk.Rev.Curr.Leg.Per., C.L.I., Crim.Just.Abstr., Curr.Cont., L.R.I., Leg.Cont., Leg.Per., P.A.I.S., SSCI. **Document type:** academic/scholarly publication.
●Also available online. Vendor(s): Mead Data Central, Inc.
Also available on CD-ROM.
—BLDSC (9116.380000); Faxon; UnCover; SWETS.

340   US   ISSN 0041-9915
K25
UNIVERSITY OF PITTSBURGH LAW REVIEW. 1935. q. $25 (foreign $30). University of Pittsburgh, School of Law, Pittsburgh, PA 15260. TEL 412-648-1354. Ed. Richard A. Halloran. adv.; bk.rev.; index, cum.index every 25 yrs. circ. 1,500. (also avail. in microfilm from RRI,WSH; reprint service avail. from WSH) **Indexed:** Abstr.Bk.Rev.Curr.Leg.Per., C.L.I., Curr.Cont., L.R.I., Leg.Per., SSCI.
●Also available online. Vendor(s): Mead Data Central, Inc., West Services, Inc.
—BLDSC (9116.385000); Faxon; UnCover.
Description: Provides scholarly legal articles on all areas and facets of the law.

340   US   ISSN 0161-0708
K24
UNIVERSITY OF PUGET SOUND LAW REVIEW. 1977. 3/yr. $18. University of Puget Sound, School of Law, 950 Broadway Plaza, Tacoma, WA 98402. TEL 206-591-2995. bk.rev.; cum.index. circ. 3,000. (also avail. in microfilm from RRI; back issues avail.; reprint service avail. from RRI) **Indexed:** C.L.I., Leg.Per.
—BLDSC (9116.386700); Faxon; UnCover.

340   AT   ISSN 0083-4041
UNIVERSITY OF QUEENSLAND LAW JOURNAL. 1948. a. Aus.$27.50. University of Queensland Press, P.O. Box 42, St. Lucia, Qld. 4067, Australia. TEL 07-365-2740. FAX 07-365-1988. Eds. R. O'Hair, D. Gifford. adv.; bk.rev. circ. 750. (also avail. in microform from UMI) **Indexed:** Aus.P.A.I.S., C.L.I., L.R.I., Leg.Per.
—BLDSC (9116.387000); UMI.

340   US   ISSN 0566-2389
K25
UNIVERSITY OF RICHMOND LAW REVIEW. 1958. 5/yr. $30. University of Richmond, T C Williams School of Law, Richmond, VA 23173. TEL 804-289-8216. FAX 804-289-8683. Ed. M.E. Blanton III. adv.; bk.rev. circ. 1,200. (also avail. in microform from WSH,PMC; reprint service avail. from WSH) **Indexed:** Abstr.Bk.Rev.Curr.Leg.Per., C.C.L.P., C.L.I., L.R.I., Leg.Cont., Leg.Per. **Document type:** academic/scholarly publication.
●Also available online. Vendor(s): West Services, Inc.
—BLDSC (9116.840000); Faxon; UnCover.
Formerly (until 1968): University of Richmond Law Notes.

340   US   ISSN 0042-0018
LAW
UNIVERSITY OF SAN FRANCISCO LAW REVIEW. 1966. 4/yr. $25 per vol. University of San Francisco, School of Law, Kendrick Hall, 2130 Fulton St., San Francisco, CA 94117. TEL 415-666-6154. FAX 415-666-6433. Ed.Bd. adv.; bk.rev.; index. circ. 1,000. (also avail. in microform from UMI; back issues avail.) **Indexed:** Abstr.Bk.Rev.Curr.Leg.Per., C.L.I., HR Rep., L.R.I., Leg.Cont., Leg.Per., Mar.Aff.Bibl. **Document type:** academic/scholarly publication.
●Also available online. Vendor(s): West Services, Inc.
—BLDSC (9116.950000); Faxon; UnCover; UMI.

LAW

340   AT   ISSN 0082-2108
K25
UNIVERSITY OF TASMANIA LAW REVIEW. Title varies: Tasmanian University Law Review. 1958. s-a. Aus.$20 (foreign Aus.$25) per issue. University of Tasmania, Law Faculty, G.P.O. Box 252C, Hobart, Tas. 7001, Australia. TEL 02-202071. FAX 02-207623. Ed. Michael Tilbury. adv.; bk.rev.; index. circ. 500. (also avail. in microfilm from UMI,PMC; microform from WSH,PMC; reprint service avail. from WSH) **Indexed:** Aus. P.A.I.S., C.C.L.P., C.L.I., L.R.I., Leg.Per. **Document type:** academic/scholarly publication.
—BLDSC (9118.280000); Faxon; UnCover; UMI.
Description: Includes articles on all aspects of law throughout the world, not just in Tasmania and Australia.

340 375   AT   ISSN 1036-0689
UNIVERSITY OF TECHNOLOGY, SYDNEY. FACULTY OF LAW & LEGAL PRACTICE HANDBOOK. 1990. a. Aus.$5 (foreign Aus.$10). University of Technology, Sydney, P.O. Box 123, City Camp, Broadway, N.S.W. 2007, Australia. TEL 02-330-1990. FAX 02-330-1551. circ. 3,000.

340   US   ISSN 0042-0190
K24
UNIVERSITY OF TOLEDO LAW REVIEW. 1969. q. $16. University of Toledo, College of Law, Toledo, OH 43606. TEL 419-537-2962. index. circ. 900. (also avail. in microfilm from WSH,PMC; reprint service avail. from WSH) **Indexed:** C.L.I., L.R.I., Leg.Cont., Leg.Per., SSCI. **Document type:** academic/scholarly publication.
—BLDSC (9118.800000); Faxon; UnCover.

340   CN   ISSN 0381-1638
K24
UNIVERSITY OF TORONTO. FACULTY OF LAW. REVIEW. 1942. 2/yr. Can.$28.50 per no. University of Toronto, Faculty of Law, Toronto, ON M5S 2C5, Canada. TEL 416-978-1075. FAX 416-978-7899. (Dist. by: Carswell Co., Ltd., 2075 Kennedy Rd., Scarborough, ON M4A 2V8, Canada) **Indexed:** Abstr.Bk.Rev.Curr.Leg.Per., C.L.I., Ind.Can.L.P.L., L.R.I., Leg.Cont., Leg.Per. **Document type:** academic/scholarly publication.
—BLDSC (9119.050000); Faxon; UnCover. CCC.

340   CN   ISSN 0042-0220
K25
UNIVERSITY OF TORONTO LAW JOURNAL. (Text in English, French) 1937. q. $35 to individuals; institutions $65; students $25. University of Toronto Press, Journals Department, 5201 Dufferin St., Downsview, ON M3H 5T8, Canada. TEL 416-667-7782. FAX 416-667-7803. Ed. S. Waddams. adv.; bk.rev.; index. circ. 1,000. (also avail. in microform from JAI,UMI,MIM; reprint service avail. from WSH) **Indexed:** Abstr.Bk.Rev.Curr.Leg.Per., C.L.I., Ind.Can.L.P.L., L.R.I., Leg.Per., P.A.I.S., SSCI.
—BLDSC (9119.100000); Faxon; UnCover; UMI. CCC.

340   AT   ISSN 0042-0328
K25
UNIVERSITY OF WESTERN AUSTRALIA LAW REVIEW. 1948. s-a. Aus.$40 (foreign Aus.$45). University of Western Australia, Faculty of Law, Nedlands (Perth), W.A., Australia. TEL 09-380-2478. FAX 09-380-1045. TELEX AA92992. Ed.Bd. adv.; bk.rev.; index. circ. 450. (also avail. in microform from WSH; reprint service avail. from WSH) **Indexed:** Aus.P.A.I.S., C.L.I., L.R.I., Leg.Per. **Document type:** academic/scholarly publication.
—BLDSC (9120.135000); Faxon; UnCover.

349   YU   ISSN 0003-2565
K1
UNIVERZITET U BEOGRADU. PRAVNI FAKULTET. ANALI. (Text in Serbo-Croatian) 1953. bi-m. 72500 din.($15) Univerzitet u Beogradu, Pravni Fakultet, Bulevar Revolucije 67, Belgrade, Yugoslavia. Ed. Obren Stankovic. bk.rev. circ. 1,500.

340 330.1 301   CI   ISSN 0350-2058
UNIVERZITET U ZAGREBU. PRAVNI FAKULTET. ZBORNIK. (Text in English, German, Italian and Serbo-Croatian) 1948. bi-m. 6000 din.($15) Univerzitet u Zagrebu, Pravni Fakultet, Trg Marsala Tita 14, 41000 Zagreb, Croatia. TEL 429-222. Ed. Stanko Petkovic. index. circ. 1,000. (back issues avail.) **Indexed:** Leg.Per.

340   PL   ISSN 1230-6061
UNIWERSYTET GDANSKI. ADMINISTRACJA I ZARZADZANIE. PRACE I MATERIALY. (Text in Polish; summaries in English, Russian) 1976. irreg., latest no.12. price varies. Uniwersytet Gdanski, Wydzial Prawa i Administracji, c/o Biblioteka Glowna, Ul. Armii Krajowej 110, 81-824 Sopot, Poland. TEL 51-0061. TELEX 051 2247 BMOR PL. (Dist. by: Ars Polona-Ruch, Krakowskie Przedmiescie 7, 00-680 Warsaw, Poland) Ed. Eugeniusz Bojanowski. circ. 250. **Document type:** academic/scholarly publication.
Former titles (until 1991): Uniwersytet Gdanski. Wydzial Prawa i Administracji. Zeszyty Naukowe. Prace z Zakresu Administracji i Zarzadzania (ISSN 0867-3365); Uniwersytet Gdanski. Wydzial Prawa i Administracji. Zeszyty Naukowe. Prace Instytutu Administracji i Zarzadzania (ISSN 0208-4929)
Description: Covers problems in the structure of governmental and economic administration and the role of public finances in the state and national economy.

340   PL   ISSN 0208-4910
LAW
UNIWERSYTET GDANSKI. WYDZIAL PRAWA I ADMINISTRACJI. ZESZYTY NAUKOWE. PRAWO. (Text in Polish; summaries in English and Russian) 1972. irreg. price varies. Uniwersytet Gdanski, Wydzial Prawa i Administracji, c/o Biblioteka Glowna, Ul. Armii Krajowej 110, 81-824 Sopot, Poland. TEL 51-0061. TELEX 051-2247 BMOR PL. (Dist. by: Ars Polona-Ruch, Krakowskie Przedmiescie 7, 00-680 Warsaw, Poland) Ed. Marian Cieslak. circ. 250. **Document type:** academic/scholarly publication.
—BLDSC (9512.437000).
Description: Problems of criminal and civil law and procedures, evidence, public law, history of state, law and legal doctrines, chronicle of law.

340   PL   ISSN 0860-3731
UNIWERSYTET GDANSKI. WYDZIAL PRAWA I ADMINISTRACJI. ZESZYTY NAUKOWE. STUDIA PRAWNO-USTROJOWE. 1988. irreg., latest no.3. price varies. Uniwersytet Gdanski, Wydzial Prawa i Administracji, Biblioteka Glowna, Ul. Armii Krajowej 110, 81-824 Sopot, Poland. TEL 51-00-61. (Dist. by: Ars Polona-Ruch, Krakowskie Przedmiescie 7, Warsaw, Poland) Ed. Tomasz Langer. circ. 200. **Document type:** academic/scholarly publication.

349   PL   ISSN 0083-4394
UNIWERSYTET JAGIELLONSKI. ZESZYTY NAUKOWE. PRACE PRAWNICZE. (Text in Polish; summaries in English, Russian) 1955. irreg., no.110, 1984. price varies. Uniwersytet Jagiellonski, Ul. Golegia 24, 31-007 Krakow, Poland. (Dist. by: Ars Polona, Krakowskie Przedmiescie 7, 00-068 Warsaw, Poland) Ed. W. Litewski. circ. 500.

340 622   PL   ISSN 0208-5488
UNIWERSYTET SLASKI W KATOWICACH. PRACE NAUKOWE. PROBLEMY PRAWNE GORNICTWA. (Text in Polish; summaries in German and Russian) 1977. irreg. price varies. Wydawnictwo Uniwersytetu Slaskiego, Ul. Bankowa 12B, 40-007 Katowice, Poland. TEL 48-32-596-915. FAX 48-32-599-605. TELEX 0315584 USKPL. (Dist. by: CHZ Ars Polona, P.O. Box 1001, 00-950 Warsaw, Poland) Ed. Barbara Woznica. **Document type:** academic/scholarly publication.
Description: Legal problems of mining, especially the substance and nature of mining rights and environmental protection related to their exploitation.

347   PL   ISSN 0208-502X
UNIWERSYTET SLASKI W KATOWICACH. PRACE NAUKOWE. STUDIA IURIDICA SILESIANA. (Text in Polish; summaries in French, German, Russian) 1976. irreg. price varies. Wydawnictwo Uniwersytetu Slaskiego, Ul. Bankowa 12B, 40-007 Katowice, Poland. TEL 48-32-596-915. FAX 48-32-599-605. TELEX 0315584 USKPTL. (Dist. by: CHZ Ars Polona, P.O. Box 1001, 00-950 Warsaw, Poland) Ed. Barbara Woznica. **Document type:** academic/scholarly publication.
Description: Covers theoretical, historical and constitutional law.

340   PL   ISSN 0208-5003
UNIWERSYTET SLASKI W KATOWICACH. PRACE NAUKOWE. Z PROBLEMATYKI PRAWA PRACY I POLITYKI SOCJALNEJ. (Text in Polish; summaries in French and Russian) 1977. irreg. Wydawnictwo Uniwersytetu Slaskiego, Ul. Bankowa 12B, 40-007 Katowice, Poland. TEL 48-32-596-915. FAX 48-32-599-605. TELEX 0315584 USKPL. (Dist. by: CHZ Ars Polona, P.O. Box 1001, 00-950 Warsaw, Poland) Ed. Barbara Woznica. **Document type:** academic/scholarly publication.
Description: Covers problems of the labor laws (individual and collective) in the aspect of legal practice, legal legislation and teaching.

UNMARRIED PARENTS TODAY. see *SOCIAL SERVICES AND WELFARE*

340 375   US   ISSN 0147-8648
KF4208.5.L3
UPDATE ON LAW-RELATED EDUCATION. (Student ed. avail.) 3/yr. $18. American Bar Association, Youth Education for Citizenship, 541 N. Fairbanks Ct., 15th Fl., Chicago, IL 60611-3314. TEL 312-988-5735. FAX 312-988-5032. Ed. Jack Wolowiec. adv. **Indexed:** A.D.& D., C.I.J.E., C.L.I., L.R.I. **Document type:** academic/scholarly publication.
—BLDSC (9121.956000); UnCover.
Description: Provides articles on the law in clear, informal language; current legal developments, including Supreme Court previews and decisions; classroom strategies and reviews of current curriculum materials; practical law for teachers and their middle and secondary level students.

340   US   ISSN 0042-0905
K25
URBAN LAWYER; the national quarterly on urban law. 1969. q. $45 (foreign $50). (American Bar Association, Urban, State and Local Government Law Section) A B A Press, 750 N. Lake Shore Dr., Chicago, IL 60611. TEL 312-988-5000. FAX 312-988-6281. Ed. Robert H. Freilich. bk.rev.; index. circ. 7,600. (also avail. in microfiche from WSH,PMC; microfilm from WSH,PMC; back issues avail.) **Indexed:** Abstr.Bk.Rev.Curr.Leg.Per., C.L.I., Curr.Cont., Energy Ind., Energy Info.Abstr., Environ.Per.Bibl. (1975-), L.R.I., Leg.Cont., Leg.Per., Sage Pub.Admin.Abstr., Sage Urb.Stud.Abstr., SSCI. **Document type:** academic/scholarly publication.
—BLDSC (9123.688500); Faxon; UnCover.
Description: Articles on various areas of urban, state, and local government law.

URBAN, STATE, AND LOCAL LAW NEWSLETTER. see *PUBLIC ADMINISTRATION — Municipal Government*

340   US   ISSN 0042-1448
K25
UTAH LAW REVIEW. 1949. q. $25. (Utah Law Review Society) University of Utah College of Law, Salt Lake City, UT 84112. TEL 801-581-6833. Ed.Bd. adv.; bk.rev.; index. circ. 800. (also avail. in microform from UMI,WSH; reprint service avail. from WSH) **Indexed:** C.L.I., Crim.Just.Abstr., L.R.I., Leg.Cont., Leg.Per., Sel.Water Res.Abstr. **Document type:** academic/scholarly publication.
●Also available online. Vendor(s): West Services, Inc.
—BLDSC (9135.180000); Faxon; UnCover; UMI.

340   US
UTAH NOTARY LAW PRIMER. irreg. $9.95. National Notary Association, 8236 Remmet Ave., Box 7184, Canoga Park, CA 91309-7184. TEL 818-713-4000. FAX 818-713-9061. Ed. Charles N. Faerber. (reprint service avail. from UMI) **Document type:** monographic series.

340   US   ISSN 1053-0258
KF2089
UTILITIES INDUSTRY LITIGATION REPORTER; national coverage of the many types of litigation stemming from the transmission and distribution of energy by publicly and privately owned utilities. 1989. s-m. $700. Andrews Publications, 1646 West Chester Pike, Box 1000, Westtown, PA 19395. TEL 215-399-6600; 800-345-1101. FAX 215-399-6610. Ed. Ronald Baker. abstr.; bibl.; stat.; cum.index every 6 mos. (looseleaf format; back issues avail.) **Document type:** newsletter.

340 363.6 UK ISSN 0960-2356
K25 CODEN: ULAWET
UTILITIES LAW REVIEW. 1990. q. £255. John Wiley & Sons Ltd., Journals, Baffins Ln., Chichester, Sussex PO19 1UD, England. TEL 0243-779777. FAX 0243-775878. TELEX 86290-WIBOOK-G. Eds. Leigh Hancher, Cosmo Graham. circ. 140. **Document type:** academic/scholarly publication.
—BLDSC (9135.377200).
Description: Presents a regular and detailed sector-by-sector survey focusing on the main policy and regulatory developments at community and national level for the energy, telecommunications, media and transport sectors.

340 NE ISSN 0924-6231
UTRECHT STUDIES IN AIR AND SPACE LAW. (Text in English) 1987. a. Kluwer Academic Publishers, Postbus 17, 3300 AA Dordrecht, Netherlands. TEL 31-78-334911. FAX 31-78-334254. TELEX 29245 KAPG NL. (Dist. by: Kluwer Academic Publishers, P.O. Box 322, 3300 AH Dordrecht, Netherlands. TEL 31-78-524400; N. America dist. addr.: Box 358, Accord Sta., Hingham, MA 02018-0358. TEL 617-871-6600) **Document type:** monographic series.
—BLDSC (9135.518520).
Refereed Serial

340 FR ISSN 0339-3577
V I P NOTAIRE. 1975. 8/yr. Conseil Superieur du Notariat, 31 rue du General-Foy, 75008 Paris, France. TEL 42-93-06-45. FAX 42-94-28-79. TELEX 640 059 CONSNOT. Ed. Claude Mercier. circ. 9,200.

340 US ISSN 0042-2363
K26
VALPARAISO UNIVERSITY LAW REVIEW. 1966. 3/yr. $20. Valparaiso University, School of Law, Valparaiso, IN 46383. TEL 219-465-7807. FAX 219-465-7872. adv.; bk.rev.; bibl.; index. circ. 750. (also avail. in microfilm from WSH,PMC; reprint service avail. from WSH) **Indexed:** Abstr.Bk.Rev.Curr.Leg.Per., C.L.I., L.R.I., Leg.Per., P.A.I.S. **Document type:** academic/scholarly publication.
● Also available online. Vendor(s): West Services, Inc.
—BLDSC (9141.720000); Faxon; UnCover.

340 US ISSN 0042-2533
K26
VANDERBILT LAW REVIEW. 1947. 6/yr. $28 (foreign $30). Vanderbilt University School of Law, Nashville, TN 37240. TEL 615-322-4766. Ed. Julia Bunting. adv.; bk.rev.; bibl.; index, cum.index every 10 yrs. circ. 1,600. (also avail. in microform from UMI,PMC; microfilm from WSH; reprint service avail. from UMI,WSH) **Indexed:** Abstr.Bk.Rev.Curr.Leg.Per., Account.Ind. (1974-), BPIA, Bus.Ind., C.L.I., Commun.Abstr., Crim.Just.Abstr., Curr.Cont., L.R.I., Leg.Cont., Leg.Per., SSCI. **Document type:** academic/scholarly publication.
● Also available online. Vendor(s): Mead Data Central, Inc., West Services, Inc.
—BLDSC (9144.500000); Faxon; UnCover; SWETS; UMI.

VERBRAUCHER UND RECHT. see *REAL ESTATE*

240 US
VERDICT REVIEW. w. $375. L R P Publications, 747 Dresher Rd., Box 980, Horsham, PA 19044. TEL 800-341-7874. index. (looseleaf format; back issues avail.)
Formerly: Verdict Reports (ISSN 0092-2293)
Description: Analysis of verdict trends.

340 US ISSN 1041-0740
KF1256.A75V47
VERDICTS, SETTLEMENTS & TACTICS. 1988. m. $340. Shepard's - McGraw-Hill, Inc., Box 35300, Colorado Springs, CO 80935-3530. TEL 800-525-2474. FAX 800-525-0053. Ed. William Jordan.

VEREENIGING TOT UITGAAF VAN DE BRONNEN VAN HET OUD-VADERLANDSE RECHT. WERKEN. see *HISTORY*

340 GW ISSN 0506-7286
LAW
VERFASSUNG UND RECHT IN UEBERSEE; law and politics in Africa, Asia, and Latin America. (Text in English, French, German and Spanish; summaries in English) 1968. q. DM.108. (Hamburger Gesellschaft fuer Voelkerrecht und Auswaertige Politik e.V.) Nomos Verlagsgesellschaft mbH und Co. KG, Waldseestr. 3-5, 76530 Baden-Baden, Germany. TEL 07221-21040. FAX 07221-210427. (Subscr. to: Postfach 610, 76484 Baden-Baden, Germany) (Co-sponsor: Universitaet Hamburg. Institut fuer Internationale Angelegenheiten) Ed.Bd. adv.; bk.rev.; abstr.; index. circ. 500. (back issues avail.) **Indexed:** Documentatieblad, Foreign Leg.Per., Int.Polit.Sci.Abstr., P.A.I.S., P.A.I.S.For.Lang.Ind. **Document type:** bulletin.
—BLDSC (9155.900000); SWETS. CCC.

VERFASSUNG UND VERFASSUNGSWIRKLICHKEIT. see *POLITICAL SCIENCE*

340 NE ISSN 0042-398X
VERKEERSRECHT. 1953. m. fl.229 to non-members. Koninklijke Nederlandse Toeristenbond ANWB - Royal Dutch Touring Club, Wassenaarseweg 220, Postbus 93200, 2509 BA The Hague, Netherlands. TEL 31-70-3146119. FAX 31-70-3242509. bk.rev.; index. circ. 2,252. **Document type:** trade publication.
—SWETS.
Description: Covers legal issues relating to road traffic, inluding liability, damage and insurance.

VERKEHRSRECHTLICHE MITTEILUNGEN. see *TRANSPORTATION*

340 RU
VERKHOVNYI SUD S.S.S.R. VESTNIK. 1991. m. 1 Rub. per issue. Verkhovnyi Sud S.S.S.R., Ul. Vorovskogo 15, 121260 Moscow, Russia. TEL 202-66-08. Ed. N.P. Zaikin. circ. 63,000.

340 US ISSN 0748-4925
KF200.V521
VERMONT BAR JOURNAL AND LAW DIGEST. 1960. bi-m. $35 (effective Sep. 1990). Vermont Bar Association, Box 100, Montpelier, VT 05601. TEL 802-223-2020. FAX 802-223-1573. Ed. Phyllis A. Andrews. adv.; bk.rev. circ. 2,000. (back issues avail.)
—UnCover.

340 US
VERMONT FISH AND WILDLIFE REGULATIONS. 1985. base vol. (plus supplements). $10.50. Butterworth Legal Publishers (Salem) (Subsidiary of: Reed Elsevier plc), 8 Industrial Way, Bldg. C, Salem, NH 03079. TEL 800-548-4001. FAX 603-898-9858. Ed.Bd.
Description: Contains recent amended laws and regulations covering Vermont fish and wildlife, together with historical notes, annotations and an index.

VERMONT NATURAL RESOURCES COUNCIL. BULLETIN. see *ENVIRONMENTAL STUDIES*

340 US
VERMONT REPORTS. irreg. (1-2 vols./yr.) $32 per vol. Butterworth Legal Publishers (Salem) (Subsidiary of: Reed Elsevier plc), 8 Industrial Way, Bldg. C, Salem, NH 03079. TEL 800-548-4001. FAX 603-898-9858. Ed.Bd.
Description: Contains current opinions with headnotes, table of cases reported arranged in alpha-county order.

340 US
VERMONT RULES OF EVIDENCE. a. $13. Butterworth Legal Publishers (Salem) (Subsidiary of: Reed Elsevier plc), 8 Industrial Way, Bldg. C, Salem, NH 03079. TEL 800-548-4001. FAX 603-898-9858. Ed.Bd.

340 US
VERMONT STATUTES ANNOTATED. 25 base vols. (plus a. suppl.) $699. Butterworth Legal Publishers (Salem) (Subsidiary of: Reed Elsevier plc), 8 Industrial Way, Bldg. C, Salem, NH 03079. TEL 800-548-4001. FAX 603-898-9858. Ed.Bd.
Description: Official statutes of the state of Vermont, containing all the laws of a general and permanent nature.

340 943 GW
VEROEFFENTLICHUNGEN ZUR VERFASSUNGSGESCHICHTE VON BADEN-WUERTTEMBERG SEIT 1945. 1983. irreg. Kommission fuer Geschichtliche Landeskunde in Baden-Wuerttemberg, Eugenstr. 7, 70182 Stuttgart, Germany. circ. 1,000. **Document type:** monographic series.
Description: Sources of information about the constitutional development of southwest Germany after the Second World War.

340 GW ISSN 0935-1248
VERWALTUNG HEUTE; Zeitschrift fuer Auszubildende und Ausbilder in der oeffentlichen Verwaltung. m. DM.54. Nomos Verlagsgesellschaft mbH und Co. KG, Waldseestr. 3-5, 76530 Baden-Baden, Germany. TEL 07221-2104-0. FAX 07221-210427. TELEX 781201. (Subscr. to: Postfach 610, 76484 Baden-Baden, Germany) **Document type:** bulletin.

340 GW ISSN 0042-4501
VERWALTUNGSARCHIV; Zeitschrift fuer Verwaltungslehre, Verwaltungsrecht und Verwaltungspolitik. 1893. q. DM.120. Carl Heymanns Verlag KG, Luxemburgerstr. 41, 50939 Cologne, Germany. TEL 0221-46010-0. FAX 0221-4601069. Ed. C.H. Ule. adv.; bk.rev.; abstr.; charts; stat.; index. circ. 3,300. (reprint service avail. from SCH) **Indexed:** ELLIS. **Document type:** bulletin.
—SWETS.

340 GW ISSN 0342-5592
VERWALTUNGSRUNDSCHAU; Zeitschrift fuer Verwaltung in Praxis und Wissenschaft. m. DM.188.90. W. Kohlhammer GmbH, Hessbruehlstr. 69, 70565 Stuttgart, Germany. TEL 0711-7863-1. **Document type:** bulletin.
—CCC.

340 GW ISSN 0174-6162
DER VERWALTUNGSWIRT. bi-m. DM.68 (foreign DM.71). R. v. Decker's Verlag, G. Schenck GmbH, Im Weiher 10, 69121 Heidelberg, Germany. TEL 06221-489281. FAX 06221-489279. TELEX 461727-HUEHD-D. **Document type:** academic/scholarly publication.
—CCC.

340 GW
VERZEICHNIS RHEINLAND-PFAELZISCHER RECHT- UND VERWALTUNGSVORSCHRIFTEN. 1981. a. (Ministerium der Justiz) Nomos Verlagsgesellschaft mbH und Co. KG, Waldseestr. 3-5, 76530 Baden-Baden, Germany. TEL 07221-21040. FAX 07221-210427. (Subscr. to: Postfach 610, 76484 Baden-Baden, Germany) **Document type:** government publication.

VETERINARY MEDICINE GUIDANCE MANUAL. see *PUBLIC HEALTH AND SAFETY*

LA VETTA D'ITALIA; mensile di politica e di cultura dell'Alto Adige. see *BIOGRAPHY*

340 NZ ISSN 0042-5117
K26
VICTORIA UNIVERSITY OF WELLINGTON LAW REVIEW. 1955. 4/yr. NZ.$55 (Australia NZ.$65; elsewhere NZ$85). (Victoria University of Wellington, Law Faculty) Victoria University Press, P.O. Box 600, Wellington, New Zealand. (Subscr. in U.S. to: William W. Gaunt & Sons Inc., Gaunt Building, 3011 Gulf Dr., Holmes Beach, FL 33510-2199) Ed. A.H. Angelo. adv.; bk.rev. circ. 600. (also avail. in microfiche; back issues avail.) **Indexed:** C.L.I., L.R.I., Leg.Cont., Leg.Per., Mar.Aff.Bibl. **Document type:** academic/scholarly publication.
—BLDSC (9232.600000); UnCover. CCC.
Description: General Law Faculty review with special issues on treaties, land claims, constitutional, criminal and international issues.

340 331 AT
VICTORIAN ACCIDENT COMPENSATION PRACTICE GUIDE. (In 2 vols.) 1980. 6/yr. C C H Australia Ltd., P.O. Box 230, North Ryde, N.S.W. 2113, Australia. TEL 888-2555. FAX 02-888-7324. (looseleaf format)
Formerly: Victorian Workers Compensation Practice Guide.

LAW

340   350   AT
VICTORIAN ADMINISTRATIVE LAW. 1986. 6/yr. in 2 vols. Aus.$310 with updates. Law Book Co. Ltd., 44-50 Waterloo Rd., North Ryde, N.S.W. 2113, Australia. TEL 02-887-0177. FAX 02-888-9706. TELEX ASBOOK 27995. Ed. Emilios Kyrou. (looseleaf format)
  Incorporates: Victorian Administrative Reports.
  Description: Provides commentary on administrative law remedies and jurisdiction of the Administrative Appeals Tribunal.

340   AT
VICTORIAN BAR COUNCIL. ANNUAL REPORT. 1964. a. members only. Victorian Bar Council, Owen Dixon Chambers, 205 William St., Melbourne, Vic. 3000, Australia. TEL 03-608-7111. FAX 03-670-2959. Ed.Bd. circ. 1,850.

340   AT
VICTORIAN BAR: ITS WORK AND ORGANISATION. 1990. a.? free. Victorian Bar Council, Owen Dixon Chambers, 205 William St., Melbourne, Vic. 3000, Australia. TEL 03-608-7111. FAX 03-670-2959.
  Description: Provides a practical overview of the Victorian Bar for people who want to pursue a career as a barrister.

340   990   AT   ISSN 0159-3285
VICTORIAN BAR NEWS. 1971. q. free. Victorian Bar Council, Owen Dixon Chambers, 205 William St., Melbourne, Vic. 3000, Australia. TEL 03-608-7111. FAX 03-670-2959. Eds. Gerard Nash Q.C., Paul Elliott. bk.rev. circ. 2,000. (back issues avail.) **Document type:** newsletter.
  Description: Journal of the Victorian Bar, reporting law, movement in the profession of barristers, and general interest in the Bar of the State of Victoria, Australia.

340   AT
VICTORIAN CONVEYANCING LAW AND PRACTICE. (In 3 vols.) 10/yr. C C H Australia Ltd., P.O. Box 230, North Ryde, N.S.W. 2113, Australia. TEL 888-2555. (looseleaf format)
  Description: Reference on conveyancing law for the State of Victoria, Australia.

340   AT   ISSN 0042-5214
VICTORIAN REPORTS. 1966. m. Butterworths, 271-273 Lane Cove Rd., North Ryde, N.S.W. 2113, Australia. TEL 02-335-4444. FAX 02-335-4678.
  ●Also available online. Vendor(s): Info-One International Pty Ltd.

368   344   GW   ISSN 0301-2999
K26
VIERTELJAHRESSCHRIFT FUER SOZIALRECHT. (Text in German; summaries in English) 1973. q. DM.150. Carl Heymanns Verlag KG, Luxemburgerstr. 449, 50939 Cologne, Germany. TEL 0221-046010-0. FAX 0221-4601069. Ed.Bd. (reprint service avail. from UMI) **Document type:** bulletin.
  —CCC.

VIEWPOINTS. see *ENVIRONMENTAL STUDIES*

340   US   ISSN 0042-6229
K26
VILLANOVA LAW REVIEW. 1955. 5/yr. $25. Villanova University Law School, Villanova, PA 19085. TEL 215-645-7053. Ed. Christopher Shields. adv.; bk.rev.; index. circ. 1,600. (also avail. in microfiche from WSH,PMC; microfilm from WSH,PMC; back issues avail.) **Indexed:** Abstr.Bk.Rev.Curr.Leg.Per., C.I.J.E., C.L.I., Crim.Just.Abstr., L.R.I., Lang.& Lang.Behav.Abstr., Leg.Cont., Leg.Per., Sociol.Abstr. **Document type:** academic/scholarly publication.
  ●Also available online. Vendor(s): West Services, Inc.
  —BLDSC (9236.500000); Faxon; UnCover.

340   US
VIRGIN ISLANDS CODE ANNOTATED. 14 base vols. (plus supplements). $600. Butterworth Legal Publishers (Salem) (Subsidiary of: Reed Elsevier plc), 8 Industrial Way, Bldg. C, Salem, NH 03079. TEL 800-548-4001. FAX 603-898-9858. Ed.Bd.
  Description: Official statutes for the US Virgin Islands, containing all of the general and permanent laws of the Territory.

340   US
▼**VIRGIN ISLANDS DIGEST.** 1992. 5 base vols. (plus supplements). $50 per vol. Butterworth Legal Publishers (Salem) (Subsidiary of: Reed Elsevier plc), 8 Industrial Way, Bldg. C, Salem, NH 03079. TEL 800-548-4001. FAX 603-898-9858. Ed.Bd. (looseleaf format)
  Description: Complete summary of Virgin Islands jurisprudence.

340   US   ISSN 0360-3857
KF200
THE VIRGINIA BAR ASSOCIATION JOURNAL. 1975. q. $30 (effective Jan. 1992). Virginia Bar Association, 3849 W. Weyburn Rd., Richmond, VA 23235. TEL 804-644-0041. FAX 804-272-4469. (Or: c/o Charles E. Friend, 322 Scotland St., Williamsburg, VA 23185) Ed.Bd. bk.rev.; illus. circ. 3,800. **Indexed:** C.L.I., L.R.I., Leg.Per. **Document type:** academic/scholarly publication.
  —UnCover.

340   US
VIRGINIA CONDOMINIUM LAW. 1987. base vol. (plus supplements 2-3/yr.). $50. Butterworth Legal Publishers (Salem) (Subsidiary of: Reed Elsevier plc), 8 Industrial Way, Bldg. C, Salem, NH 03079. TEL 800-548-4001. FAX 603-898-9858. Ed. Douglas S. MacGregor. (looseleaf format)
  Description: Includes an analysis of the current state Condominium Act and Regulations, the Uniform Act, and relevant federal legislation.

340   331   US   ISSN 1042-461X
KFV2731.A15
VIRGINIA EMPLOYMENT LAW LETTER. 1989. m. $95. (Williams, Mullen, Christian & Dobbins) M. Lee Smith Publishers & Printers, 162 Fourth Ave., N., Box 198867, Nashville, TN 37219-8867. TEL 615-242-7395; 800-274-6774. FAX 615-256-6601. Eds. James V. Meath, Robert L. Musick, Jr. **Document type:** newsletter.
  Description: Reports the latest state-specific employment law developments that affect companies in Virginia.

340   US   ISSN 1045-5183
K26
VIRGINIA ENVIRONMENTAL LAW JOURNAL. 1980. s-a. $32 (foreign $48) (typically set in Nov.). Virginia Environmental Law Journal, University of Virginia, School of Law, Charlottesville, VA 22901. TEL 804-924-3683. FAX 804-924-7536. Ed. John S. Decker. circ. 460. **Indexed:** C.L.I., Environ.Abstr., Leg.Per.
  ●Also available online. Vendor(s): West Services, Inc.
  —BLDSC (9238.460000); CIS; Faxon; UnCover.
  Formerly (until 1988): Virginia Journal of Natural Resources Law (ISSN 0748-8122)

340   US   ISSN 0042-6601
K26   CODEN: VLIBAD
VIRGINIA LAW REVIEW. 1913. 8/yr. $40. Virginia Law Review Association, University of Virginia, School of Law, Charlottesville, VA 22901. TEL 804-924-3079. adv.; bk.rev.; index, cum.index. circ. 2,200. (also avail. in microfiche from RRI,WSH; microfilm from RRI,WSH; back issues avail.; reprint service avail. from RRI) **Indexed:** A.B.C.Pol.Sci., ABI Inform., Abstr.Bk.Rev.Curr.Leg.Per., Account.Ind. (1974-), BPIA, Bus.Ind., C.L.I., Chic.Per.Ind., Crim.Just.Abstr., L.R.I., Leg.Cont., Leg.Per., P.A.I.S., Pers.Lit., SSCI. **Document type:** academic/scholarly publication.
  —BLDSC (9239.300000); Faxon; UnCover; SWETS.
  Description: General law publication.

340   US   ISSN 0042-661X
VIRGINIA LAW WEEKLY. 1948. 28/yr. $25 (typically set in May). University of Virginia, School of Law, Charlottesville, VA 22901. TEL 804-924-3070. FAX 804-924-7536. Ed. William Merone. adv.; bk.rev.; illus.; stat. circ. 1,200. **Document type:** newspaper.
  Description: Student-run newspaper chronicling the events and opinions of the law school and the nation.

340   US
VIRGINIA LAWYER. Variant title: Virginia Lawyer Register. 1953. m. $18. Virginia State Bar, 707 E. Main St., Ste. 1500, Richmond, VA 23219-2803. TEL 804-775-0500. FAX 804-775-0501. Ed. Caroline B. Bolte. adv.; bk.rev.; stat. circ. 26,000. **Indexed:** Law Ofc.Info.Svc. **Document type:** academic/scholarly publication, trade publication.
  Formerly: Virginia Bar News.

340   US
VIRGINIA LAWYER'S WEEKLY. 1986. w. $195. Lawyer's Weekly Publications, 106 N. Eighth St., Richmond, VA 23219. TEL 804-783-0770. FAX 804-343-7365. Ed. Paul E. Fletcher. adv.; index. circ. 3,100. (tabloid format; back issues avail.) **Document type:** newspaper.
  Description: Contains summaries of current precedent setting cases from Virginia state and federal courts.

340   US
VIRGINIA PROBATE LAW. 1987. 2 base vols. (plus supplements 2-3/yr.). $80. Butterworth Legal Publishers (Salem) (Subsidiary of: Reed Elsevier plc), 8 Industrial Way, Bldg. C, Salem, NH 03079. TEL 800-548-4001. FAX 603-898-9858. Ed. Elizabeth Hapner. (looseleaf format)
  Description: Practical analysis of the methods and problems of estate administration in Virginia.

340   333.33   US
VIRGINIA RESIDENTIAL LANDLORD AND TENANT LAW. 1991. base vol. (plus s-a. suppl.). $60. Butterworth Legal Publishers (Salem) (Subsidiary of: Reed Elsevier plc), 8 Industrial Way, Bldg. C, Salem, NH 03079. TEL 800-548-4001. FAX 603-898-9664. Ed. Douglas S. MacGregor. (looseleaf format)

343   US   ISSN 0364-2232
KF9602
VOICE FOR THE DEFENSE.* 1973. m. $36 to non-members; members $10. (Texas Criminal Defense Lawyers Association) Artforms, Inc., Box 1434, Round Rock, TX 78680-1434. TEL 512-451-3588. Ed. Kerry Fitzgerald. adv.; bk.rev.; charts; illus.; stat. circ. 2,000.

W A D E EXCHANGE. (World Association of Document Examiners) see *CRIMINOLOGY AND LAW ENFORCEMENT*

W A D E JOURNAL. (World Association of Document Examiners) see *CRIMINOLOGY AND LAW ENFORCEMENT*

347.9   CN   ISSN 0509-5166
W.C.J. MEREDITH MEMORIAL LECTURES. 1961. a. $65. Les Editions Yvon Blais, 430 rue St. Pierre, Bureau 200, Montreal, PQ H2Y 2M5, Canada. TEL 514-842-3937. FAX 514-842-7144. (Subscr. to: C.P. 180, Cowansville, PQ J2K 3H6, Canada. TEL 514-263-1086) **Indexed:** Ind.Can.L.P.L.
  Formerly: Lectures Bar Extension.

340   GW   ISSN 0042-9678
K27
W G O - MONATSHEFTE FUER OSTEUROPAEISCHES RECHT. 1959. bi-m. DM.184 (foreign DM.196). (Universitaet Hamburg, Seminarabteilung fuer Ostrechtforschung) Verlag C.F. Mueller GmbH, Im Weiher 10, 69121 Heidelberg, Germany. TEL 06221-489281. FAX 06221-489279. Eds. G. Tontsch, B. Bytomski. adv.; bk.rev.; abstr.; bibl.; charts; index. circ. 315.

346.013   US   ISSN 0736-9433
KF477.A15
W L D F NEWS. 1971. 3/yr. free. Women's Legal Defense Fund, 1875 Connecticut Ave N.W. No. 710, Washington, DC 20009-5728. Ed. Debra Ness. (back issues avail.) **Document type:** newsletter.
  Description: Covers activities in the areas of equal employment opportunity for women, women's health, and family income security.

346.066   GW
W M TEIL IV: ZEITSCHRIFT FUER WIRTSCHAFTS- UND BANKRECHT. w. DM.107.60. Herausgebergemeinschaft Wertpapier-Mitteilungen Keppler, Lehmann GmbH & Co., Postfach 110932, 60044 Frankfurt a.M., Germany. TEL 069-2732-0. FAX 069-232264. TELEX 412066-BZFFM. index. (back issues avail.) **Indexed:** ELLIS. **Document type:** bulletin.

347   NE ISSN 0165-8476
W P N R. (Weekblad voor Notariaat en Registratie) 1870. w. fl.195.75. Koninklijke Notariele Broederschap, Postbus 96827, 2509 JE The Hague, Netherlands. TEL 31-70-3307138. FAX 3170-3307180. Ed. A.L. Moussault-Jeswiet. adv.; bk.rev.; index. circ. 4,500. **Indexed:** Key to Econ.Sci.
—BLDSC (9284.660000); SWETS.
 Incorporates: Maandblad voor het Notariaat; **Formerly:** Weekblad voor Privaatrecht, Notariaat en Registratie.

340   NZ
▼**WAIKATO LAW REVIEW**. 1993. a. $20. University of Waikato, School of Law, Private Bag 3105, Hamilton, New Zealand. (Dist. in N. America by: Wm. W. Gaunt & Sons, Inc., Gaunt Bldg., 3011 Gulf Dr., Holmes Beach, FL 34217-2188. TEL 813-778-5211. FAX 813-778-5252)
 Description: Reflects the development of New Zealand jurisprudence.

340 US ISSN 0043-003X
K27
WAKE FOREST LAW REVIEW. vol.7, 1970. 4/yr. $21. Wake Forest Law Review Association, Inc., Wake Forest University, Winston-Salem, NC 27109. TEL 919-761-5439. FAX 919-759-6077. Ed. Steve Gardner. adv.; bk.rev.; cum.index; circ. 1,500 (controlled). (processed; also avail. in microfilm from RRI,WSH; reprint service avail. from RRI) **Indexed:** ABI Inform., C.L.I., L.R.I., Leg.Per., PSI.
—BLDSC (9261.430000); Faxon; UnCover; UMI.
 Formerly: Wake Forest Intramural Law Review.

340   US
WAKE FOREST UNIVERSITY SCHOOL OF LAW. CONTINUING LEGAL EDUCATION. ANNUAL REVIEW, NORTH CAROLINA. a. $80. Wake Forest University School of Law, Continuing Legal Education, Box 7206, Reynolds Sta., Winston-Salem, NC 27109. TEL 919-761-5560.

WALTER EUCKEN INSTITUT. WIRTSCHAFTSWISSENSCHAFTLICHE UND WIRTSCHAFTSRECHTLICHE UNTERSUCHUNGEN. see BUSINESS AND ECONOMICS

340   IQ
WAQAI AL-IRAQIYA; official gazette of the Republic of Iraq. 1924. w. ID.21 for Arabic edition; English edition ID.27. Ministry of Justice, Judicial Relations Department, Baghdad, Iraq. Dr. H.N. Jaafar. circ. 13,000 (12,000 Arabic ed.; 1,000 English ed.). (also avail. in microfilm from BHP)
 Formerly: Iraq. Weekly Gazette of the Republic of Iraq.

340 US ISSN 0043-0420
K27
WASHBURN LAW JOURNAL. 1960. 3/yr. $10. Washburn University, School of Law, Topeka, KS 66621. TEL 913-295-6660. Ed. Denise Anderson. adv.; bk.rev.; charts; illus.; index, cum.index every 5 yrs. circ. 2,100. (also avail. in microfilm from WSH,PMC; reprint service avail. from WSH) **Indexed:** C.L.I., Crim.Just.Abstr., L.R.I., Leg.Cont., Leg.Per.
—BLDSC (9263.125000); Faxon; UnCover; UMI.

WASHINGTON ADMINISTRATIVE LAW PRACTICE MANUAL. see PUBLIC ADMINISTRATION

340 US ISSN 0043-0463
K27
WASHINGTON AND LEE LAW REVIEW. 1939. 4/yr. $32.50 (overseas $36). Washington and Lee University, School of Law, Lewis Hall, Lexington, VA 24450-1799. TEL 703-463-8566. FAX 703-463-8488. adv.; bk.rev.; index. circ. 1,675. (also avail. in microfilm from RRI,WSH; reprint service avail. from RRI) **Indexed:** Account.Ind. (1974-), Bank.Lit.Ind., C.L.I., L.R.I., Leg.Cont., Leg.Per., Mar.Aff.Bibl. **Document type:** academic/scholarly publication.
●Also available online. Vendor(s): Mead Data Central, Inc., West Services, Inc.
—BLDSC (9263.127000); Faxon; UnCover; UMI.
 Description: Provides a forum for discussion of legal problems.

340 331 US ISSN 1072-0588
▼**WASHINGTON EMPLOYMENT LAW LETTER**. 1994. m. $95. (Perkins & Coie) M. Lee Smith Publishers & Printers, 162 Fourth Ave., N., Box 198867, Nashville, TN 37219-8867. TEL 615-242-7395; 800-274-6774. FAX 615-256-6601. Eds. Michael Reynvaan, Nancy Williams. **Document type:** newsletter.
 Description: Reports the latest state-specific employment law developments that affect companies in Washington.

340 613.1 US ISSN 1072-0596
▼**WASHINGTON ENVIRONMENTAL COMPLIANCE UPDATE**. 1994. m. $137. (Perkins & Coie) M. Lee Smith Publishers & Printers, 162 Fourth Ave., N., Box 198867, Nashville, TN 37219-8867. TEL 615-242-7395; 800-274-6774. FAX 615-256-6601. Ed.Bd. **Document type:** newsletter.
 Description: Reports the latest state-specific environmental law developments that affect companies in Washington.

340 368 US ISSN 1064-1378
WASHINGTON INSURANCE LAW LETTER. 1976. q. free to qualified personnel. Reed McClure, 3600 Columbia Center, 701 Fifth Ave., Seattle, WA 98104-7081. TEL 206-292-4900. FAX 206-223-0152. Ed. William R. Hickman. charts; index. circ. 2,366. (looseleaf format; back issues avail.) **Document type:** newsletter.
 Description: Survey of current insurance law and tort law court case decisions.

340   US
WASHINGTON LAND USE AND ENVIRONMENTAL PRACTICE. 1983. irreg., latest 1991. $65. Butterworth Legal Publishers (Salem) (Subsidiary of: Reed Elsevier plc), 8 Industrial Way, Bldg. C, Salem, NH 03079. TEL 800-548-4001. FAX 603-898-9858. Ed. Richard L. Settle.
 Description: Provides a comprehensive description of the law and practical analysis of its application.

340 US ISSN 0043-0617
WASHINGTON LAW REVIEW. 1926. 4/yr. $26 (foreign $30). Washington Law Review Association, University of Washington, School of Law, Condon Hall, JB-20, 1100 N.E. Campus Pkwy., Seattle, WA 98105. TEL 206-543-4069. FAX 206-543-5671. adv.; index. circ. 1,300. (also avail. in microfiche from RRI,WSH; microfilm from RRI) **Indexed:** Account.Ind. (1979-), C.L.I., Curr.Cont., Leg.Per., Mar.Aff.Bibl., Ocean.Abstr., Risk Abstr., Sel.Water Res.Abstr., SSCI. **Document type:** academic/scholarly publication.
●Also available online. Vendor(s): Mead Data Central, Inc., West Services, Inc.
—BLDSC (9263.165000); Faxon; UnCover; SWETS.

340 US ISSN 0890-8761
WASHINGTON LAWYER. 1976. bi-m. $20. District of Columbia Bar, 1707 L St., N.W., Ste. 350, Washington, DC 20036-4201. TEL 202-331-7700. FAX 202-223-7726. Ed. Jane Ottenberg. adv.; illus. circ. 62,000. (also avail. in microfilm from WSH,PMC) **Indexed:** C.L.I., L.R.I., Leg.Per.
—UnCover.
 Formerly: District Lawyer (ISSN 0147-7943)

WASHINGTON MEMO (NEW YORK). see MEDICAL SCIENCES — Obstetrics And Gynecology

340   US
WASHINGTON NOTARY LAW PRIMER. a. $9.95. National Notary Association, 8236 Remmet Ave., Box 7184, Canoga Park, CA 91309-7184. TEL 818-713-4000. FAX 818-713-9061. Ed. Charles N. Faerber. (reprint service avail. from UMI) **Document type:** monographic series.

342   US
WASHINGTON STATE BAR ASSOCIATION. ADMINISTRATIVE LAW SECTION. NEWSLETTER. 1978. q. $15. Washington State Bar Association, Administrative Law Section, 500 Westin Bldg., 2001 Sixth Ave., Seattle, WA 98121. TEL 206-727-8239. FAX 206-727-8320. circ. 440. (looseleaf format) **Document type:** newsletter.

340 330   US
WASHINGTON STATE BAR ASSOCIATION. BUSINESS AND LAW SECTION. NEWSLETTER. 1974. q. $20. Washington State Bar Association, Business and Law Section, 500 Westin Bldg., 2001 Sixth Ave., Seattle, WA 98121. TEL 206-727-8239. FAX 206-727-8320. circ. 1,650. (looseleaf format) **Document type:** newsletter.

WASHINGTON STATE BAR ASSOCIATION. CREDITOR-DEBTOR LAW SECTION NEWSLETTER. see BUSINESS AND ECONOMICS — Banking And Finance

WASHINGTON STATE BAR ASSOCIATION. INTELLECTUAL AND INDUSTRIAL PROPERTY SECTION. NEWSLETTER. see PATENTS, TRADEMARKS AND COPYRIGHTS

340   US
WASHINGTON STATE BAR NEWS. 1947. m. $24. Washington State Bar Association, 500 Westin Bldg., 2001 Sixth Ave., Seattle, WA 98121-2599. TEL 206-727-8215. adv. contact: Jack Young. bk.rev.; index. circ. 20,000. (also avail. in microform from WSH; reprint service avail.) **Indexed:** C.L.I.

340   US
WASHINGTON STATE ENVIRONMENTAL POLICY ACT; a legal and policy analysis. 1987. base vol. (plus supplements). $75. Butterworth Legal Publishers (Salem) (Subsidiary of: Reed Elsevier plc), 8 Industrial Way, Bldg. C, Salem, NH 03079. TEL 800-548-4001. FAX 603-898-9858. Ed. Richard L. Settle. (looseleaf format)

WASHINGTON STATE PATROL. ANNUAL REPORT. see CRIMINOLOGY AND LAW ENFORCEMENT

WASHINGTON TROOPER. see CRIMINOLOGY AND LAW ENFORCEMENT

340 US ISSN 0043-0862
K23
WASHINGTON UNIVERSITY LAW QUARTERLY. 1915. 4/yr. $24. Washington University, School of Law, St. Louis, MO 63130. TEL 314-935-6498. FAX 314-935-6493. Ed. H. Christopher Boehning. adv.; bk.rev.; index. circ. 800. (also avail. in microfiche from WSH,PMC; microfilm from RRI,WSH,PMC) **Indexed:** C.L.I., L.R.I., Leg.Cont., Leg.Per. **Document type:** academic/scholarly publication.
●Also available online. Vendor(s): Mead Data Central, Inc., West Services, Inc.
—BLDSC (9263.450000); Faxon; UnCover.
 Formerly: St. Louis Law Review (ISSN 0271-2849)

WASSERRECHT UND WASSERWIRTSCHAFT. see WATER RESOURCES

WASTE MINIMIZATION & RECYCLING REPORT; hazardous & solid waste. see ENVIRONMENTAL STUDIES — Waste Management

WASTELINE. see ENVIRONMENTAL STUDIES — Waste Management

WATER LAW. see WATER RESOURCES

340 US ISSN 0043-1249
WATER LAW NEWSLETTER. 1965. 3/yr. $20. Rocky Mountain Mineral Law Foundation, Porter Administration Bldg., 7039 E. 18th Ave., Denver, CO 80220. TEL 303-321-8100. FAX 303-321-7657. Ed. George A. Gould. circ. 500. **Document type:** newsletter.
—CCC.

340   UK
WATERLOW'S SOLICITORS' AND BARRISTERS' DIRECTORY. 1844. a. £49. Waterlow Legal Publishing, Paulton House, 8 Shepherdess Walk, London N1 7LB, England. TEL 071-490-0049. FAX 071-253-1308. adv. circ. 8,000. **Document type:** directory.
 Formerly: Solicitors' and Barristers' Directory; Which superseded in part: Solicitors' and Barristers' Directory and Diary; Formerly: Solicitors' Diary and Directory.
 Description: Directory of solicitors and barristers in England and Wales arranged alphabetically, individually, and geographically by firm.

LAW

340 UK
WATERLOW'S SOLICITORS' DIARY AND DIRECTORY. 1843. a. £45. Waterlow Legal Publishing, 8 Shepherdess Walk, London N1 7LB, England. TEL 071-490-0049. FAX 071-253-1308. adv. circ. 3,000. **Document type:** directory.
Supersedes in part: Solicitors' and Barristers' Directory and Diary.

340 US ISSN 0043-1621
LAW
WAYNE LAW REVIEW. 1953. 4/yr. $28. Wayne State University Law School, 468 W. Ferry, Detroit, MI 48202. TEL 313-577-3939. FAX 313-577-5498. Ed. Mike Molitor. adv.; bk.rev.; abstr.; bibl.; charts; illus.; stat.; index, cum.index. circ. 1,200. (also avail. in microfiche from WSH,PMC; microfilm from WSH,PMC) **Indexed:** Abstr.Bk.Rev.Curr.Leg.Per., C.L.I., L.R.I., Leg.Cont., Leg.Per.
—BLDSC (9280.980000); Faxon; UnCover; UMI.

340 NE ISSN 0043-1796
WEEKBLAD VOOR FISCAAL RECHT. 1872. w. fl.175($75) Postbus 30104, 2500 GC The Hague, Netherlands. adv.; bk.rev.; index. circ. 6,800. (looseleaf format) **Indexed:** ELLIS, Key to Econ.Sci.
—SWETS.

340 UK ISSN 0019-3518
WEEKLY LAW REPORTS. 1953. w. £185 (overseas £200) (effective Aug. 1993). Incorporated Council of Law Reporting for England and Wales, 3 Stone Bldgs., Lincoln's Inn, London WC2A 3XN, England. TEL 071-242-6471. FAX 071-831-5247. Managing Ed. R.C. Williams. **Indexed:** RICS.
● Also available online. Vendor(s): Context Ltd. Also available on CD-ROM.

340 JM ISSN 0253-7370
K27
WEST INDIAN LAW JOURNAL. 1977. s-a. $20. Council of Legal Education, P.O. Box 231, Mona, Kingston, Jamaica, W.I. Ed. H. Aubrey Fraser. adv.; bk.rev. circ. 1,000. **Indexed:** C.L.I., L.R.I., Leg.Per., Mar.Aff.Bibl.
—BLDSC (9299.075000).
Supersedes: Jamaica Law Journal.

340 US ISSN 0043-3268
K27
WEST VIRGINIA LAW REVIEW. 1894. 4/yr. $27. West Virginia University Law Center, Morgantown, WV 26506-6130. TEL 304-293-2301. FAX 304-293-6891. Ed. John Douglas Moore. adv.; bk.rev.; abstr.; cum.index. circ. 1,200. (processed; also avail. in microform from UMI; microfiche from WSH; microfilm from WSH) **Indexed:** Abstr.Bk.Rev.Curr.Leg.Per., C.L.I., L.R.I., Leg.Cont., Leg.Per., SSCI. **Document type:** academic/scholarly publication.
—BLDSC (9300.030000); Faxon; UnCover; UMI.

340 US
WEST VIRGINIA LAWYER. vol.6, 1993. m. $25 membership. West Virginia State Bar, 2006 Kanawha Blvd. E., Charleston, WV 25311. TEL 304-558-7990. Ed. Thomas R. Tinder. adv. circ. 5,000. **Document type:** trade publication.
Description: Covers news and current topics concerning the legal profession of interest to lawyers in West Virginia.

340 US ISSN 0049-7274
K27
WESTCHESTER LAW JOURNAL. 1936. w. $40. Westchester Law Journal Inc., 175 Main St., White Plains, NY 10601. TEL 914-948-0715. FAX 914-948-3014. adv. circ. 226. **Document type:** newspaper.

340 CN
▼**WESTERN APPEAL CASES.** 1992. irreg. (approx. 14/yr.). Can.$90. Maritime Law Book Ltd., P.O. Box 302, Fredericton, NB E3B 4Y9, Canada. TEL 506-453-9921; 800-561-0220. FAX 506-453-9525.
Description: Contains all of the decisions of the Courts of Appeal for Saskatchewan, Alberta, Manitoba and British Columbia.

340 AT ISSN 0085-8161
WESTERN AUSTRALIA LAW ALMANAC. 1913. a. Aus.$12.50. Ministry of Justice, Ministry of Justice, Westralia Sq., 141, St. Georges Terr., Perth, W.A. 6000, Australia. TEL 09-264-1711. FAX 09-322-4713. Ed. Ken Suttie. circ. 1,500. (also avail. in diskette format)

347.9 979 US ISSN 0896-2189
K27
WESTERN LEGAL HISTORY. 1988. s-a. $25 (effective 1993). Ninth Judicial Circuit Historical Society, 125 S. Grand Ave., Pasadena, CA 91105. TEL 818-795-0266. FAX 818-405-7018. Ed. Bradley B. Williams. adv.; bk.rev. circ. 2,000. **Indexed:** Amer.Hist.& Life, Hist.Abstr.
—UnCover.
Description: Explores, analyzes, and presents the history of law, the legal profession, and the courts, particularly the federal courts in Alaska, Arizona, California, Hawaii, Idaho, Montana, Nevada, Oregon, Washington, Guam, and the Northern Mariana Islands.

340 US ISSN 0190-6593
K27
WESTERN NEW ENGLAND LAW REVIEW. 1978. s-a. $10 (foreign $12). Western New England College, School of Law, 1215 Wilbraham Rd., Springfield, MA 01119. TEL 413-782-3111. (Subscr. to: William S. Hein & Co., Inc. 1285 Main St. Buffalo, New York 14209.) Ed. Cheryl A. O'Brien. adv.; bk.rev.; index. circ. 2,000. (also avail. in microfiche from WSH,PMC; microfilm from WSH,PMC; back issues avail.) **Indexed:** Abstr.Bk.Rev.Curr.Leg.Per., C.L.I., L.R.I., Leg.Cont., Leg.Per.
—BLDSC (9301.432000); Faxon; UnCover.

340 CN ISSN 0049-7525
WESTERN WEEKLY REPORTS. 1911. 48/yr. (in 6 vols.). Can.$120 per vol. Carswell, One Corporate Plaza, 2075 Kennedy Rd., Scarborough, ON M1T 3V4, Canada. TEL 416-609-8000. FAX 416-298-5094. adv. contact: M. Lalani. cum.index. circ. 1,170.
● Also available online. Vendor(s): QL Systems Ltd.
Description: Offers full-text of leading decisions from the courts of western Canada and appeals to the Supreme Court of Canada fully headnoted and topically indexed.

340 US ISSN 8750-2623
KFC47
WEST'S CALIFORNIA REPORTER. 1960. irreg. West Publishing Co., 620 Opperman Dr., Eagan, MN 55123. TEL 612-687-8000; 800-328-9352. FAX 612-687-7302. **Document type:** trade publication.
● Also available on CD-ROM.

340 344.07 US ISSN 0744-8716
WEST'S EDUCATION LAW REPORTER. 1982. bi-w. West Publishing Corp., 620 Opperman Dr., Eagan, MN 55123. TEL 612-687-8000; 800-328-9352. FAX 612-687-7302. **Document type:** trade publication.
—Faxon.

346.066 GW ISSN 0172-049X
KK6456.A13
WETTBEWERB IN RECHT UND PRAXIS. Short title: W R P. 1955. m. DM.664 (foreign DM.678). Deutscher Fachverlag GmbH, Mainzer Landstr. 251, 60326 Frankfurt a.M., Germany. TEL 069-759501. FAX 069-75952999. (Subscr. to: Postfach 100606, 60006 Frankfurt a.M., Germany) circ. 1,827. (reprint service avail. from SCH) **Indexed:** ELLIS. **Document type:** trade publication.
—SWETS.

340 AT ISSN 0085-820X
WHITEACRE.* 1967. irreg. free. University of Sydney, Law Graduates Association, 173-175 Phillip St., Sydney, N.S.W. 2000, Australia.

340 US ISSN 0162-7880
KF372
WHO'S WHO IN AMERICAN LAW. 1977. biennial, 8th ed. 1994. $249.95. Marquis Who's Who, A Reed Reference Publishing Company, Part of the Reed Elsevier group, 121 Chanlon Rd., New Providence, NJ 07974. TEL 908-464-6800. FAX 908-665-6688. TELEX 138 755. (Subscr. to: Order Dept., Box 31, New Providence, NJ 07974-9903. TEL 800-521-8110) (also avail. in magnetic tape) **Document type:** directory.
● Also available on CD-ROM. Producer(s): Bowker - Reed Reference Electronic Publishing.
—CCC.
Description: Includes more than 29,500 biographical sketches of leading attorneys, judges, educators, and other top professionals in the legal field. Entries contain principal occupation, fields of practice or interest, education, bar(s), civic and political activities, military service, professional memberships, and home, office addresses.

WICKEN'S THE LAW OF LIFE INSURANCE IN AUSTRALIA.
see *INSURANCE*

340 AU ISSN 0084-0025
WIENER RECHTSWISSENSCHAFTLICHE STUDIEN. 1964. irreg., no.21, 1992. price varies. (Universitaet Wien, Institut fuer Rechtsvergleichung) Manzsche Verlags- und Universitaetsbuchhandlung, Kohlmarkt 16, A-1014 Vienna, Austria. TEL 0222-531610. FAX 0222-53161-181. (Co-sponsor: Oesterreichische Gesellschaft fuer Rechtsvergleichung) Ed. Fritz Schwind. **Document type:** monographic series.
Description: Legal doctoral theses.

344 690 US ISSN 1054-9331
KF902
WILEY CONSTRUCTION LAW UPDATE. 1991. irreg. John Wiley & Sons, Inc., 605 Third Ave., New York, NY 10158. TEL 212-850-6000. FAX 212-850-6088.

344 US ISSN 1054-402X
KF3319
WILEY EMPLOYMENT LAW UPDATE (YEAR). 1991. irreg. John Wiley & Sons, Inc., 605 Third Ave., New York, NY 10158. TEL 212-850-6000. FAX 212-850-6088.

340 UK ISSN 0265-7937
KD2617.A13
WILKINSON'S ROAD TRAFFIC LAW BULLETIN. 1984. 10/yr. £89($136) Longman Group Ltd., Law, Tax and Finance Division, 21-27 Lambs Conduit St., London WC1N 3NJ, England. TEL 071-242-2548. FAX 071-831-8119. Ed. Paul Niekirk. **Document type:** bulletin.
—UMI.
Description: Information on all aspects of motoring and traffic law.

340 US ISSN 0043-5589
K27
WILLIAM AND MARY LAW REVIEW. 1957. q. $20. College of William and Mary, Marshall-Wythe School of Law, Williamsburg, VA 23185. TEL 804-221-3845. adv.; bk.rev. circ. 1,200. (also avail. in microfiche from WSH) **Indexed:** C.L.I., Geo.Abstr., L.R.I., Leg.Per., Mar.Aff.Bibl., P.A.I.S.
—BLDSC (9318.909500); Faxon; UnCover.

340 US ISSN 0270-272X
K27
WILLIAM MITCHELL LAW REVIEW. 1974. q. $24. William Mitchell College of Law, 875 Summit Ave., St. Paul, MN 55105. TEL 612-290-6450. FAX 612-290-6450. circ. 2,100. (also avail. in microfiche from WSH,PMC; microfilm from WSH,PMC; reprint service avail. from WSH) **Indexed:** C.L.I., Crim.Just.Abstr., L.R.I., Leg.Cont., Leg.Per.
● Also available online. Vendor(s): Mead Data Central, Inc., West Services, Inc.
—BLDSC (9318.918200); UnCover; UMI.

340 CN
WILLISTON & ROLLS COURT FORMS. q. Can.$590. Butterworths Canada Ltd., Part of the Reed Elsevier group, 75 Clegg Rd., Markham, ON L6G 1A1, Canada. TEL 905-479-2665. FAX 905-479-2826. Ed. R.J. Rolls. (looseleaf format)
Description: Every type of form used in Ontario civil trials.

340 CN ISSN 0838-3596
K3
WINDSOR REVIEW OF LEGAL AND SOCIAL ISSUES/REVUE DES AFFAIRES JURIDIQUES ET SOCIALES. (Text in English and French) 1977. a. University of Windsor, Faculty of Law, Windsor, ON N9B 3P4, Canada. TEL 519-885-1211. **Indexed:** Abstr.Bk.Rev.Curr.Leg.Per., C.L.I., Ind.Can.L.P.L., L.R.I.
Formerly (until 1989): Canadian Community Law Journal (ISSN 0704-0857)

347.91 CN ISSN 0710-0841
K27
WINDSOR YEARBOOK OF ACCESS TO JUSTICE/RECUEIL ANNUEL DE WINDSOR D'ACCES A LA JUSTICE. (Text in English, French) 1981. a. Can.$25. University of Windsor, Faculty of Law, Windsor, ON N9B 3P4, Canada. TEL 519-253-4232. FAX 519-973-7064. Ed.Bd. **Indexed:** C.L.I., Curr.Cont., Ind.Can.L.P.L., Leg.Per., PAIS, SSCI.
—BLDSC (9319.371000); UnCover.

WIRTSCHAFT UND WETTBEWERB; Zeitschrift fuer Kartellrecht, Wettbewerbsrecht und Marktorganisation. see BUSINESS AND ECONOMICS — Production Of Goods And Services

340   GW
WIRTSCHAFTSRECHT; Zeitschrift fuer Theorie und Praxis des sozialistischen Wirtschaftsrechts. 1957. q. DM.24. Staatsverlag der DDR, Otto-Grotewohl-Str. 17, 1086 Berlin, Germany.
   Formerly: Vertragssystem (ISSN 0042-4463)

WIRTSCHAFTSRECHTLICHE BERATUNG (W I B); Zeitschrift fuer Wirtschaftsanwaelte und Unternehmensjuristen. see BUSINESS AND ECONOMICS

340   331   US   ISSN 1059-5066
▼**WISCONSIN EMPLOYMENT LAW LETTER**. 1992. m. $95. (Melli, Walker, Paese & Ruhly) M. Lee Smith Publishers & Printers, 162 Fourth Ave., N., Box 198867, Nashville, TN 37219-8867. TEL 615-242-7395; 800-274-6774. FAX 615-256-6601. Eds. Susan C. Sheeran, Jack D. Walker. **Document type:** newsletter.
   Description: Reports the latest state-specific employment law developments that affect companies in Wisconsin.

340   613.1   US   ISSN 1072-9151
▼**WISCONSIN ENVIRONMENTAL COMPLIANCE UPDATE**. 1994. m. $137. (DeWett, Porter et al.) M. Lee Smith Publishers & Printers, 162 Fourth Ave., N., Box 198867, Nashville, TN 37219-8867. TEL 615-242-7395; 800-274-6774. FAX 615-256-6601. Eds. Paul Kent, Peter Peshek. **Document type:** newsletter.
   Description: Reports on the latest state-specific environmental law developments that affect companies in Wisconsin.

340   US   ISSN 0043-650X
K27
WISCONSIN LAW REVIEW. 1920. bi-m. $30. University of Wisconsin Law School, 975 Bascom Mall, Madison, WI 53706-1399. TEL 608-262-5815. FAX 608-262-5485. Ed. Beth M. Young. adv. contact: Robert L. Striker, Jr. bk.rev.; cum.index. circ. 2,150. (also avail. in microform from UMI; microfiche from WSH; microfilm from WSH; back issues avail.) **Indexed:** BPIA, Bus.Ind., C.L.I., Crim.Just.Abstr., Curr.Cont., L.R.I., Leg.Cont., Leg.Per., P.A.I.S., SSCI. **Document type:** academic/scholarly publication.
   ●Also available online. Vendor(s): Mead Data Central, Inc., West Services, Inc.
   —BLDSC (9325.770000); Faxon; UnCover; SWETS; UMI. **CCC**.
   Description: Forum for analysis and discussions of various subjects related to law.

340   US   ISSN 1043-0490
WISCONSIN LAWYER. 1927. m. $42 to non-members; students $18. State Bar of Wisconsin, 402 W. Wilson St., Madison, WI 53703. TEL 608-257-3838. FAX 608-257-5502. Ed. Joyce R. Hastings. adv.; bk.rev.; index. circ. 18,000. (also avail. in microform from UMI; microfilm from WSH; reprint service avail. from UMI) **Indexed:** C.L.I., HRIS, L.R.I., Law Ofc.Info.Svc., Leg.Per. **Document type:** academic/scholarly publication.
   —UnCover; UMI.
   Formerly (until 1988): Wisconsin Bar Bulletin (ISSN 0043-6380)
   Description: Contains articles and columns on Wisconsin's legal system, including official notices from the Wisconsin Supreme Court.

340   US
WISCONSIN LEGISLATIVE COUNCIL RULES CLEARINGHOUSE. ANNUAL REPORT. 1980. a. free. Wisconsin Legislative Council, Box 2536, Madison, WI 53701-2536. TEL 608-266-1304. Ed. Ronald Sklansky. (back issues avail.) **Document type:** government publication.

340   US
WISCONSIN MISDEMEANORS AND MOVING TRAFFIC VIOLATIONS. irreg., 2nd ed., 1989. $88. Butterworth Legal Publishers (Salem) (Subsidiary of: Reed Elsevier plc), 8 Industrial Way, Bldg. C, Salem, NH 03079. TEL 800-548-4001. FAX 603-898-9858. Ed. Clifford R. Steele. (looseleaf format)
   Description: Guide to prosecution and defense of misdemeanor cases in the circuit and municipal courts of Wisconsin.

340   346.013   US   ISSN 1052-3421
K27
WISCONSIN WOMEN'S LAW JOURNAL. 1985. a. $8 to individuals; institutions $15. University of Wisconsin-Madison, Law School, 975 Bascom Mall, Madison, WI 53706. TEL 608-262-8294. bk.rev. circ. 500. (back issues avail.) **Indexed:** Leg.Per.

340   GW
WISSENSCHAFT UND GEGENWART. JURISTISCHE REIHE. 1970. irreg., no.6, 1973. price varies. Vittorio Klostermann, Frauenlobstr. 22, 60487 Frankfurt a.M., Germany. TEL 069-774011. FAX 069-708038. (Subscr. to: Postfach 900601, 60446 Frankfurt a.M., Germany) **Document type:** monograph series.

301   340   GW   ISSN 0084-0939
WISSENSCHAFTLICHE GESELLSCHAFT FUER PERSONENSTANDSWESEN UND VERWANDTE GEBIETE. SCHRIFTENREIHE. NEUE FOLGE. 1960. irreg., vol.39, 1993. price varies. Verlag fuer Standesamtswesen GmbH, Hanauer Landstr. 197, 60314 Frankfurt a.M., Germany. TEL 069-405894-0. FAX 069-405894-99. Ed.Bd. **Document type:** monograph series.

349   GW   ISSN 0043-6976
WISSENSCHAFTSRECHT, WISSENSCHAFTSVERWALTUNG, WISSENSCHAFTSFOERDERUNG. 1968. 3/yr. DM.165. Verlag J.C.B. Mohr (Paul Siebeck), Wilhelmstr. 18, 72074 Tuebingen, Germany. TEL 07071-923-0. FAX 07071-51104. TELEX 7262872-MOHR-D. (Subscr. to: Postfach 2040, 72010 Tuebingen, Germany) Ed.Bd. adv.; bk.rev.; bibl.; index, cum.index: 1968-1977, 1978-1987. **Document type:** academic/scholarly publication.
   —CCC.
   Description: Studies the legal and administrative problems of modern research and teaching at the university level.

346   GW   ISSN 0721-6890
K27
WISTRA; Zeitschrift fuer Wirtschaft Steuer Strafrecht. 1982. 9/yr. DM.322 (foreign DM.332). C.F. Mueller Juristischer Verlag GmbH, Im Weiher 10, 69121 Heidelberg, Germany. TEL 06221-489281. FAX 06221-489279. (reprint service avail. from SCH) **Document type:** academic/scholarly publication.

340   352.7   AU   ISSN 0933-2766
WOHNRECHTLICHE BLAETTER. 1988. m. DM.200($125) Springer-Verlag, Sachsenplatz 4-6, Postfach 89, A-1201 Vienna, Austria. TEL 0222-3302415. FAX 0222-3302426. (Subscr. in N. America to: Springer-Verlag New York, Inc., 44 Hartz Way, Secaucus, NJ 07096-2491. TEL 201-348-4033. FAX 201-348-4505) **Document type:** academic/scholarly publication.
   —CCC.

DER WOHNUNGSEIGENTUEMER. see BUILDING AND CONSTRUCTION

340   GW
WOHNUNGSWIRTSCHAFT UND MIETRECHT. 1948. m. DM.120. (Deutscher Mieterbund e.V.) Verlagsgesellschaft des Deutschen Mieterbundes mbH, Postfach 410269, 50862 Cologne, Germany. TEL 0221-40083-0. FAX 0221-4008322. Ed. Ulrich von Schoenebeck. adv.; bk.rev.; index. circ. 6,000. **Document type:** consumer publication.

WOMEN & GUNS. see SPORTS AND GAMES

340   US   ISSN 0043-7468
WOMEN LAWYERS JOURNAL. 1911. q. $16. National Association of Women Lawyers, 750 N. Lake Shore Dr., Chicago, IL 60611. TEL 312-988-6186. Ed. Linda Lengyel. adv.; bk.rev.; charts; illus.; index. circ. 1,312. (also avail. in microform from UMI; reprint service avail. from RRI) **Indexed:** C.L.I., L.R.I., Leg.Per.
   —UnCover; UMI.

323.4   305.4   US   ISSN 0085-8269
KF478.A45
WOMEN'S RIGHTS LAW REPORTER. 1970. 3/yr. $20 to individuals; institutions $40. Rutgers University School of Law, 15 Washington St., Newark, NJ 07102. TEL 201-648-5320. Eds. Robert Bomersbach, Lisa Menoli. adv.; bk.rev.; bibl.; illus.; index. circ. 2,000. (tabloid format; also avail. in microform from UMI,PMC; microfilm from WSH; reprint service avail. from UMI,WSH) **Indexed:** Alt.Press Ind., C.C.L.P., C.L.I., Crim.Just.Abstr., L.R.I., Lang.& Lang.Behav.Abstr., Leg.Cont., Leg.Per., P.A.I.S., Sociol.Abstr., Stud.Wom.Abstr., Wom.Stud.Abstr. (1970-). **Document type:** academic/scholarly publication.
   —BLDSC (9343.450000); Faxon; UnCover; UMI.

A WORD ON.... see EDUCATION — School Organization And Administration

347   US   ISSN 0074-0837
WORK ACCOMPLISHED BY THE INTER-AMERICAN JURIDICAL COMMITTEE DURING ITS MEETING. Spanish edition: Trabajos Realizados por el Comite Juridico Interamericano Durante el Periodo Ordinario de Sesiones. (Editions in English, French, Portuguese, Spanish) a. price varies. Organization of American States, Department of Publications, 1889 F St., N.W., Washington, DC 20006. TEL 703-789-3533. circ. 2,000.

WORKERS' COMP ADVISOR; helping doctors, lawyers, and employers cope with the workers' comp system. see BUSINESS AND ECONOMICS — Labor And Industrial Relations

WORKERS' COMPENSATION COST CONTROL. see INSURANCE

WORKERS' COMPENSATION JOURNAL OF OHIO. see PUBLIC ADMINISTRATION

WORKERS' COMPENSATION LAW BULLETIN. see BUSINESS AND ECONOMICS — Labor And Industrial Relations

WORKER'S COMPENSATION LAW REVIEW. see INSURANCE

340   331   US   ISSN 0748-4135
KFC592.A29
WORKERS' COMPENSATION LAWS OF CALIFORNIA. 1961. a. Matthew Bender & Co., Inc., 11 Penn Plaza, New York, NY 10001. TEL 212-967-7707.
   Description: Covers California and federal statutes, administrative rules and regulations, tables and schedules for determining compensation payments and medical fees, and digests of relevant opinions from the California and federal court systems.

WORKERS COMPENSATION N S W. see BUSINESS AND ECONOMICS — Labor And Industrial Relations

340   GW
WORLD COURT DIGEST. 1931. irreg. DM.80. Max-Planck-Institut fuer Auslaendisches Oeffentliches Recht und Voelkerrecht, Berliner Str. 48, 69120 Heidelberg, Germany. FAX 06221-43982. TELEX 461505-MPIMF. (Subscr. to: Springer-Verlag Berlin, Heidelberger Platz 3, 14197 Berlin, Germany) Ed.Bd. adv. circ. 700. **Document type:** monograph series.
   Former titles: Max-Planck-Institut fuer Auslaendisches Oeffentliches Recht und Voelkerrecht. Fontes Iuris Gentium; Max-Planck-Institut fuer Auslaendisches Oeffentliches Recht und Voelkerrecht. Fontes (ISSN 0076-5651)

WORLD FOOD REGULATION REVIEW. see FOOD AND FOOD INDUSTRIES

WORLD PETROLEUM EXPLORATION & EXPLOITATION AGREEMENTS. see PETROLEUM AND GAS

3338 LAW

340 US ISSN 1053-0274
KF3471.A59
WRONGFUL DISCHARGE REPORT. 1987. m. $350. Andrews Publications, 1646 West Chester Pike, Box 1000, Westtown, PA 19395. TEL 215-399-6600; 800-345-1101. FAX 215-399-6610. Ed. Linda Coady. bibl.; stat.; cum.index: 1987-1988. (looseleaf format; back issues avail.) **Document type:** newsletter.
 Formerly (until 1989): Wrongful Discharge Case Law Reporter (ISSN 0893-8458)
 Description: Provides coverage of employment-related litigation for attorneys and human resource executives.

340 658.3 CN
WRONGFUL DISMISSAL. base vol. (plus updates 2/yr.). Can.$175. Carswell, One Corporate Plaza, 2075 Kennedy Rd., Scarborough, ON M1T 3V4, Canada. TEL 416-609-8000. FAX 416-298-5094. (looseleaf format)
 Description: Covers current issues including awards for mental distress, constructive dismissal and punitive and aggravated damages, just cause for dismissal, impact of employment contracts, settlement negotiations.

340 331 CN
WRONGFUL DISMISSAL PRACTICE MANUAL. q. Can.$310. Butterworths Canada Ltd., Part of the Reed Elsevier group, 75 Clegg Rd., Markham, ON L6G 1A1, Canada. TEL 905-479-2665. FAX 905-479-2826. Ed. Ellen E. Mole. (looseleaf format)
 Description: Examines all aspects of wrongful dismissal in Canada.

342 US ISSN 8755-125X
WYOMING LAWYER. 1977. bi-m. $12 to non-members. Wyoming State Bar, 500 Randall Ave., Box 109, Cheyenne, WY 82003-0109. TEL 307-632-9061. Ed. Linda Gosbee. adv.: B&W page $200.
 —UnCover.
 Description: Publishes news and announcements of interest to lawyers in Wyoming.

340 CC ISSN 1001-2397
KNQ6
XIANDÀI FAXUE/MODERN LAW SCIENCE. (Text in Chinese; summaries in English) 1979. bi-m. (Xinan Zhengfa Xueyuan) Xiandai Faxue Zazhishe, Chongqing, Sichuan 630031, People's Republic of China. TEL 661671. Ed. Xu Jingcun. circ. 10,000 (paid); 50,000 (controlled).
 Description: Theoretical law journal.

340 CC
XUEXI YU FUDAO/STUDY AND GUIDANCE. (Text in Chinese) m. Zuigao Renmin Fayuan - Supreme Court, 27, Dongjiao Minxiang, Beijing 100745, People's Republic of China. TEL 548311. Ed. Hui Huming.

340 US
Y L D NEWS. (Young Lawyers Division) irreg. (2-4/yr.). membership. State Bar of Wisconsin, Young Lawyers Division, 402 W. Wilson St., Madison, WI 53703. TEL 608-257-3838. FAX 608-257-5502. circ. 4,500. (back issues avail.) **Document type:** newsletter.

347 305.4 US ISSN 1043-9366
K29
YALE JOURNAL OF LAW AND FEMINISM. 1989. s-a. $12 to individuals; institutions $25. Yale University, School of Law, 401A Yale Sta., New Haven, CT 06520. TEL 203-432-4056. FAX 203-432-2592. circ. 550. (back issues avail.)
 —BLDSC (9370.019000); UnCover.
 Description: Forum for discussion of women's and feminist issues.

YALE JOURNAL OF LAW & THE HUMANITIES. see *HUMANITIES: COMPREHENSIVE WORKS*

346.006 363.6 US ISSN 0741-9457
K29
YALE JOURNAL ON REGULATION. 1983. s-a. $16 to individuals (foreign $26); institutions $25 (foreign $35). Yale University, School of Law, Yale Journal on Regulation Staff, 401A Yale Sta., New Haven, CT 06520. TEL 203-432-4861. FAX 203-432-2592. adv.; bk.rev.; bibl.; charts; stat. circ. 1,300. (also avail. in microfiche; back issues avail.) **Indexed:** Abstr.Health Care Manage.Stud., C.L.I., Energy Info.Abstr., Environ.Abstr., J.of Econ.Lit., Leg.Per., P.A.I.S., Tel.Abstr.
 ●Also available online. Vendor(s): West Services, Inc.
 —BLDSC (9370.040000); CIS; Faxon; UnCover.
 Description: Forum for research and debate on regulatory policy and its impact on the public and private sectors.

340 US
YALE LAW & POLICY REVIEW. 1982. s-a. $16 to individuals; institutions $25. Yale University, School of Law, 401A Yale Sta., New Haven, CT 06520. TEL 203-432-4863. adv.; bk.rev. circ. 500. (also avail. in microform from WSH; reprint service avail. from WSH) **Indexed:** Abstr.Health Care Manage.Stud., C.L.I., Leg.Per.

340 US ISSN 0044-0094
K29
YALE LAW JOURNAL. 1891. 8/yr. $36. (Yale University, School of Law) Yale Law Journal Co., Inc., 401-A Yale Sta., New Haven, CT 06520. TEL 203-432-1666. FAX 203-432-2592. adv.; bk.rev.; index. circ. 4,500. (also avail. in microfiche from RRI,WSH; microfilm from RRI,WSH; reprint service avail. from ISI,RRI) **Indexed:** A.B.C.Pol.Sci., ABI Inform., Abstr.Bk.Rev.Curr.Leg.Per., Account.Ind. (1974-), Bank.Lit.Ind., Bk.Rev.Ind. (1981-), BPIA, C.L.I., Child.Bk.Rev.Ind. (1981-), Crim.Just.Abstr., Curr.Cont., Energy Ind., Energy Info.Abstr., J.of Econ.Lit., L.R.I., Leg.Cont., Leg.Per., P.A.I.S., Pers.lit., Risk Abstr., SSCI.
 ●Also available online. Vendor(s): Mead Data Central, Inc.
 —BLDSC (9370.200000); Faxon; UnCover; SWETS; UMI.

340 US ISSN 1049-0264
YEARBOOK OF EDUCATIONAL LAW. 1972. a. $45.95 to non-members; members $35.95. National Organization on Legal Problems of Education, 3601 S.W. 29th St., Ste. 223, Topeka, KS 66614. TEL 913-273-3550. circ. 3,000. (also avail. in microform from UMI) **Indexed:** Educ.Ind.
 —BLDSC (9411.677000); UMI.
 Formerly: Yearbook of School Law.

YEARBOOK OF EUROPEAN STUDIES/ANNUAIRE D'ETUDES EUROPEENNES. see *POLITICAL SCIENCE — International Relations*

YEARBOOK OF LAW COMPUTERS AND TECHNOLOGY. see *LAW — Computer Applications*

YEARBOOK OF MARYLAND LEGISLATORS. see *POLITICAL SCIENCE*

340 KO
YONSEI LAW JOURNAL. (Text in Korean) 1990. a? Yonsei Association of Legal Research, College of Law, Yonsei University, 134 Sinchon-Dong, Seodaemoon-ku, Seoul, S. Korea. TEL 392-0131.

YOU AND THE LAW; executive guide to legal problems. see *BUSINESS AND ECONOMICS — Small Business*

343 CN
YOUNG OFFENDERS SERVICE. q. Can.$415. Butterworths Canada Ltd., Part of the Reed Elsevier group, 75 Clegg Rd., Markham, ON L6G 1A1, Canada. TEL 905-479-2665. FAX 905-479-2826. Ed. Priscilla Platt. (looseleaf format)
 Description: Updates all judicial and statutory developments pertaining to youthful offenders.

340 US ISSN 0882-8520
KF3731.A3
YOUTH LAW NEWS. 1982. bi-m. $40 to individuals; institutions $95. National Center for Youth Law, 114 Sansome St., Ste. 900, San Francisco, CA 94104. TEL 415-543-3307. FAX 415-956-9024. Ed. Marcia Henry. bk.rev.; cum.index: 1982-1987. circ. 2,500. (back issues avail.)
 Description: Provides current information to attorneys and other youth-serving professionals about legal issues affecting low-income children and youth.

340 YU ISSN 0350-2252
K29
YUGOSLAV LAW/DROIT YOUGOSLAVE. (Text in English and French) 1975. 3/yr. $30. (Union of Jurists Associations of Yugoslavia) Institut za Uporedno Pravo, Belgrade, Terazije 41, 11000 Belgrade, Yugoslavia. Ed. Vladimir Jovanovic. bibl. circ. 900. **Indexed:** P.A.I.S.
 —BLDSC (9421.659600).
 Formerly: New Yugoslav Law (ISSN 0028-7946)
 Description: Contemporary issues, constitutional courts of justice and surveys of legislation in Yugoslavian law.

340 IO ISSN 0215-840X
YURIDIKA; Majalah Fakultas Hukum Universitas Airlangga. (Text in English and Indonesian) 1981. bi-m. Rps.1750. Universitas Airlangga, Fakultas Hukum, Jalan Darmawangsa Dalam Selatan, Surabaya 60286, Indonesia. TEL 031-41228. (Subscr. to: Sari Agung PT, Jl. Tunjungan 5, Surabaya, Indonesia) Ed. S.S. Rangkuti. adv.; bk.rev. circ. 750.
 Formerly: Majalah Fakultas Hukum Universitas Airlangga.

Z F A. (Zeitschrift fuer Arbeitsrecht) see *BUSINESS AND ECONOMICS — Labor And Industrial Relations*

340 640 GW ISSN 0342-3476
K30
Z L R - ZEITSCHRIFT FUER DAS GESAMTE LEBENSMITTELRECHT. 1974. 6/yr. DM.390 (foreign DM.399). Deutscher Fachverlag GmbH, Mainzer Landstr. 251, 60326 Frankfurt a.M., Germany. TEL 069-759501. FAX 069-75952999. (Subscr. to: Postfach 100606, 60006 Frankfurt a.M., Germany) Ed. Sabine Klamroth. circ. 800. **Indexed:** ELLIS. **Document type:** trade publication.
 —SWETS.

328.675 ZR
ZAIRE. CONSEIL LEGISLATIF NATIONAL. COMPTE RENDU ANALYTIQUE. 1972. irreg. Conseil Legislatif National, Kinshasa, Zaire.
 Formerly: Zaire. Assemblee Nationale. Compte Rendu Analytique.

340 RU ISSN 0869-4486
ZAKONNOST'. (Text in Russian) 1922. m. 180000 Rub.($60) (General'naya Prokuratura Rossiiskoi Federacii) Zakonnost', Pushkinskaya ul., d.9, ctr.6, 103868 Moscow, K-9, Russia. TEL 7-095-2290106. (Dist. in U.S. by: Victor Kamkin Inc., 4956 Boiling Brook Pkwy, Rockville, MD 20852. TEL 301-881-5973) (Co-sponsor: Goskomitet po Pechati) Ed. Nikolai Zaikin. adv.; bk.rev.; index. circ. 10,000. **Indexed:** Curr.Dig.Sov.Press, World Bibl.Soc.Sec.
 Formerly (until 1992): Sotsialisticheskaya Zakonnost' (ISSN 0038-1691)

345.01 ZA ISSN 0304-6931
ZAMBIA. DEPARTMENT OF LEGAL AID. ANNUAL REPORT. (Text in English) a. K.300. Zambia Government Printing Department, P.O. Box 30136, Lusaka, Zambia. **Document type:** government publication.
 Description: Covers legal aid for civil cases in the High Courts and Subordinate Courts of Zambia.

340 ZA
ZAMBIA. HIGH COURT. LAW DIRECTORY AND LEGAL CALENDAR. (Text in English) a. Zambia Government Printing Department, P.O. Box 30136, Lusaka, Zambia. **Document type:** government publication.
 Description: Directory of barristers and judges in Zambia.

340 ZA
ZAMBIA LAW JOURNAL. (Text in English) 1969. a. K.780($15) University of Zambia, School of Law, P.O. Box 32379, Lusaka, Zambia. FAX 260-1-254408. TELEX 44370 UNZALU ZA. (Subscr. to: Dr. A. Milner, Law Reports International, Trinity College, Oxford OX1 3BH, England) Ed. Alfred W. Chanda. adv.; bk.rev.; bibl.; circ. 300 (controlled). **Indexed:** Documentatieblad. **Document type:** academic/scholarly publication.
 Description: Articles on legal issues with particular reference to Africa. Occasional legislative and case commentaries.

348 ZA
ZAMBIA LAW REPORTS. 1963. a. K.15. Council of Law Reporting, Box 50067, Lusaka, Zambia. Ed. Margaret S. Sekaggya. cum.index. circ. 500.

340   SZ   ISSN 0044-2127
ZEITSCHRIFT DES BERNISCHEN JURISTENVEREINS.
(Text in French and German) 1865. m. 79 SFr.
Staempfli und Cie AG, Hallerstr. 7-9, CH-3001 Bern,
Switzerland. TEL 031-276666. FAX 031-3006688.
Ed. Heinz Hausheer. adv.; bk.rev.; bibl.; charts; index.
circ. 4,800. **Document type:** bulletin.
—CCC.

347.9   AU   ISSN 0044-2321
ZEITSCHRIFT FUER ARBEITSRECHT UND SOZIALRECHT.
1966. bi-m. S.480. (Bundeskammer der
Gewerblichen Wirtschaft) Manzsche Verlags- und
Universitaetsbuchhandlung, Kohlmarkt 16, A-1014
Vienna, Austria. TEL 0222-531610.
FAX 0222-53161181. Ed. Theodor Tomandl.
bk.rev.; charts; index. circ. 2,700. (also avail. in
microfilm; microfiche) **Document type:** bulletin.
—SWETS.
 Description: Examines labor and social law.

340   GW   ISSN 0721-5746
**ZEITSCHRIFT FUER AUSLAENDERRECHT UND
AUSLAENDERPOLITIK.** Short title: Z A R. q. DM.89.
Nomos Verlagsgesellschaft mbH und Co. KG,
Waldseestr. 3-5, 76530 Baden-Baden, Germany.
TEL 07221-21040. FAX 07221-210427. (Subscr.
to: Postfach 610, 76484 Baden-Baden, Germany)
circ. 2,000. **Indexed:** ELLIS, Refug.Abstr. **Document
type:** newsletter.
—BLDSC (9426.775000). **CCC.**

347.9   GW   ISSN 0930-861X
**ZEITSCHRIFT FUER AUSLAENDISCHES UND
INTERNATIONALES ARBEITS- UND SOZIALRECHT.** q.
DM.314 (foreign DM.322). C.F. Mueller Juristischer
Verlag GmbH, Im Weiher 10, 69121 Heidelberg,
Germany. TEL 06221-489281.
FAX 06221-489279. TELEX 461727-HUEHD-D.
Document type: academic/scholarly publication.

340 351.1   GW   ISSN 0514-2571
ZEITSCHRIFT FUER BEAMTENRECHT. 1953. m.
DM.172. W. Kohlhammer GmbH, Hessbruehlstr. 69,
70565 Stuttgart, Germany. TEL 0711-7863-1.
Document type: trade publication.
—CCC.

340   GW
ZEITSCHRIFT FUER BERGRECHT. 1860. q. DM.128. Carl
Heymanns Verlag KG, Luxemburgerstr. 449, 50939
Cologne, Germany. TEL 0221-46010-0.
FAX 0221-46010-69. **Document type:** bulletin.

340   GW   ISSN 0044-2410
ZEITSCHRIFT FUER DAS GESAMTE FAMILIENRECHT; Ehe
und Familie im privaten und oeffentlichen Recht.
1954. m. DM.106.80. Gieseking-Verlag, Deckerstr.
2, 33617 Bielefeld, Germany. Ed. F.W. Bosch.
bk.rev.; bibl.; index. circ. 2,000. (tabloid format;
reprint service avail. from SCH)
—SWETS. **CCC.**

340   GW   ISSN 0044-2437
**ZEITSCHRIFT FUER DAS GESAMTE HANDELSRECHT UND
WIRTSCHAFTSRECHT.** 1858. bi-m. DM.288. Verlag
Recht und Wirtschaft GmbH, Haeusserstr. 14,
69115 Heidelberg, Germany. TEL 06221-906-1.
(Subscr. to: Postfach 105960, 69049 Heidelberg,
Germany) Eds. K. Schmidt, P. Ulmer. adv.; bk.rev.;
index per vol. circ. 1,750. **Indexed:** ELLIS, SCIMP
(1991-). **Document type:** academic/scholarly
publication.
—SWETS. **CCC.**

347.016   GW
**ZEITSCHRIFT FUER DAS NOTARIAT IN
BADEN-WUERTTEMBERG.** m. Wuertt. Notarverein e.V.,
Kronenstr. 34, 70174 Stuttgart, Germany.

340 336   ISSN 0044-247X
ZEITSCHRIFT FUER DEN LASTENAUSGLEICH. 1953. q.
DM.60. Verlag Otto Schwartz und Co., Annastr. 7,
37075 Goettingen, Germany. TEL 0551-31051.
FAX 0551-372812. adv.; bk.rev.; index. **Document
type:** academic/scholarly publication.

343   GW   ISSN 0084-5310
K30
**ZEITSCHRIFT FUER DIE GESAMTE
STRAFRECHTSWISSENSCHAFT.** 1881. 4/yr. DM.372.
Walter de Gruyter und Co., Genthiner Str. 13,
10785 Berlin, Germany. TEL 030-26005-0.
FAX 030-26005251. TELEX 184027. (U.S. addr.:
Walter de Gruyter, Inc., 200 Saw Mill Rd.,
Hawthorne, NY 10532) Ed.Bd. adv.; bk.rev.; bibl.;
index. **Document type:** academic/scholarly
publication.
—SWETS.

ZEITSCHRIFT FUER EVANGELISCHES KIRCHENRECHT.
see *RELIGIONS AND THEOLOGY — Protestant*

340   GW   ISSN 0179-4051
K30
ZEITSCHRIFT FUER GESETZGEBUNG; Vierteljahresschrift
fuer staatliche und kommunale Rechtsetzung. 1986.
q. DM.218. C.H. Beck'sche Verlagsbuchhandlung,
Wilhelmstr. 9, 80801 Munich, Germany.
TEL 089-38189-338. FAX 089-38189-398. TELEX
5215085-BECK-D. Ed. J. Hensen. adv.; B&W page
DM.1300, color page DM.2600; trim 200 x 120.
circ. 750. (back issues avail.) **Indexed:** ELLIS.
Document type: bulletin.

ZEITSCHRIFT FUER MIET- UND RAUMRECHT. see *REAL
ESTATE*

340   AU   ISSN 0250-6459
K30
ZEITSCHRIFT FUER NEUERE RECHTSGESCHICHTE.
1979. q. S.1160. Manzsche Verlags- und
Universitaetsbuchhandlung, Kohlmarkt 16, A-1014
Vienna, Austria. TEL 0222-531610.
FAX 0222-53161181. Ed. Wilhelm Brauneder. circ.
800. **Document type:** bulletin.
—SWETS.

340   GW   ISSN 0514-6496
ZEITSCHRIFT FUER RECHTSPOLITIK. (Supplement to:
Neue Juristische Wochenschrift) 1968. m. DM.98.
C.H. Beck'sche Verlagsbuchhandlung, Wilhelmstr. 9,
80801 Munich, Germany. TEL 089-38189-338.
FAX 089-38189-398. TELEX 5215085-BECK-D.
Eds. R. Gerhardt, M. Kriele. circ. 59,000. (back
issues avail.) **Indexed:** Refug.Abstr. **Document type:**
bulletin.
—SWETS.

ZEITSCHRIFT FUER RECHTSSOZIOLOGIE. see
SOCIOLOGY

340   AU
**ZEITSCHRIFT FUER RECHTSVERGLEICHUNG,
INTERNATIONALES PRIVATRECHT UND
EUROPARECHT.** 1960. bi-m. S.1540. (Universitaet
Wien, Institut fuer Rechtsvergleichung) Manzsche
Verlags- und Universitaetsbuchhandlung, Kohlmarkt
16, A-1014 Vienna, Austria. TEL 0222-531610.
FAX 0222-53161181. (Co-sponsor:
Oesterreichische Gesellschaft fuer
Rechtsvergleichung) Ed.Bd. bk.rev. circ. 800. (back
issues avail.) **Indexed:** CERDIC, ELLIS. **Document type:**
bulletin.
 Formerly: Zeitschrift fuer Rechtsvergleichung (ISSN
0514-275X)
 Description: Covers comparative law; includes
reports and judgements.

340   GW   ISSN 0173-0568
KK1610.A13
ZEITSCHRIFT FUER SCHADENSRECHT; monatliches
Fachblatt fuer Schadens-, Versicherungs- und
Verkehrsstrafrecht. Short title: Z F S. 1980. m.
DM.198. Deutscher Anwaltverlag GmbH, Bocholder
Str. 259, 45369 Essen, Germany.
TEL 0201-611114. (back issues avail.)

340   SZ   ISSN 0254-945X
**ZEITSCHRIFT FUER SCHWEIZERISCHES RECHT/REVUE
DE DROIT SUISSE.** (Text in German and French)
1860. 11/yr. 185 SFr. Helbing & Lichtenhahn
Verlag AG, Freie Str. 84, CH-4051 Basel,
Switzerland. TEL 061-2721116.
FAX 061-2721150. (Subscr. to: Sauerlaender AG,
Laurenzenvorstadt 89, CH-5001 Aarau, Switzerland.
TEL 064-268626) Ed.Bd. adv.: B&W page 744 SFr.
bk.rev.; index, cum.index every 10 yrs. **Document
type:** academic/scholarly publication.
—SWETS. **CCC.**

**ZEITSCHRIFT FUER STRAFVOLLZUG UND
STRAFFAELLIGENHILFE.** see *CRIMINOLOGY AND LAW
ENFORCEMENT*

340   GW   ISSN 0340-2479
**ZEITSCHRIFT FUER UNTERNEHMENS- UND
GESELLSCHAFTSRECHT.** 1972. 4/yr. DM.306
(bound ed. DM.356). Walter de Gruyter und Co.,
Genthiner Str. 13, 10785 Berlin, Germany.
TEL 030-26005-0. FAX 030-26005251. TELEX
184027. (U.S. addr.: Walter de Gruyter, Inc., 200
Saw Mill Rd., Hawthorne, NY 10532) Ed.Bd. circ.
1,400. (back issues avail.) **Indexed:** ELLIS. **Document
type:** academic/scholarly publication.
—BLDSC (9487.470000); SWETS.

340   GW   ISSN 0177-6762
ZEITSCHRIFT FUER URHEBER- UND MEDIENRECHT.
1957. m. DM.293. (Institut fuer Urheber- und
Medienrecht) Nomos Verlagsgesellschaft mbH und
Co. KG, Waldseestr. 3-5, 76530 Baden-Baden,
Germany. TEL 07221-21040.
FAX 07221-210427. (Subscr. to: Postfach 610,
76484 Baden-Baden, Germany) Ed. Manfred
Rehbinder. adv.; bk.rev.; abstr.; bibl.; index. **Indexed:**
ELLIS. **Document type:** newsletter.
—SWETS. **CCC.**
 Formerly: Film und Recht (ISSN 0015-1440)

340   AU   ISSN 0044-3662
ZEITSCHRIFT FUER VERKEHRSRECHT. (Includes irreg.
supplement: Gesamtregister mit den Rechtssaetzen
und Fundstellen der Zeitschrift fuer Verkehrsrecht)
1956. m. S.1090. Manzsche Verlags- und
Universitaetsbuchhandlung, Kohlmarkt 16, A-1014
Vienna, Austria. TEL 0222-531610.
FAX 0222-53161181. Ed. Robert Dittrich. adv.;
bk.rev.; index. circ. 2,800. (also avail. in microfiche;
microfilm) **Document type:** trade publication.
 Description: Covers traffic law, including treaties
and judgments.

ZEITSCHRIFT FUER WASSERRECHT. see *WATER
RESOURCES*

340 332   GW   ISSN 0723-9416
K9
ZEITSCHRIFT FUER WIRTSCHAFTSRECHT - Z I P. 1980.
s-m. DM.588. Verlag Kommunikationsforum GmbH
Recht Wirtschaft Steuern, Aachener Str. 217,
50931 Cologne, Germany. TEL 0221-40088-0.
FAX 0221-4008828. Ed. Bruno M. Kuebler. adv.;
bk.rev. (back issues avail.) **Indexed:** ELLIS.
—SWETS.

**ZENTRALBLATT FUER SOZIALVERSICHERUNG,
SOZIALHILFE UND VERSORGUNG;** Zeitschrift fuer das
Recht der Sozialen Sicherheit. see *POLITICAL
SCIENCE*

340   CC   ISSN 1000-0208
ZHENGFA LUNTAN/POLITICAL SCIENCE & LAW TRIBUNE;
zhongguo zhengfa daxue xuebao. (Text in Chinese)
bi-m. $30.60. Zhongguo Zhengfa Daxue, Zhengfa
Luntan Bianjibu - China University of Political Science
and Law, 41 Xueyuan Lu, Beijing 100088, People's
Republic of China. TEL 2015577. (Dist. in US by:
China Books & Periodicals, Inc., 2929 24th St., San
Francisco, CA 94110. TEL 415-282-0994) Ed. Gao
Chao.

340 320   CC
ZHENGZHI YU FALU/POLITICS AND LAW. (Text in
Chinese) 1982. bi-m. Y1.75 per no. Shanghai
Shehui Kexueyuan, Faxue Yanjiusuo - Shanghai
Academy of Social Sciences, Institute of Law, No.7,
Alley 622, Huaihai Zhonglu, Shanghai 200020,
People's Republic of China. TEL 3271076. Ed. Qi
Naikuan. adv.; bk.rev.; circ. 15,000 (paid). **Document
type:** academic/scholarly publication.

340   CC
ZHONGGUO FALU NIANJIAN/CHINA LAW YEARBOOK.
(Text in Chinese) a. Zhongguo Faxuehui, Zhongguo
Falu Nianjian Bianjibu, No. 23, Fuxing Lu, Beijing
100036, People's Republic of China. TEL 8317547.
Ed. Gan Zhongdou.

340   CC
ZHONGGUO FAXUE/JURISPRUDENCE IN CHINA. (Text in
Chinese) bi-m. $54. Zhongguo Faxuehui - China
Jurisprudence Society, 23 Fuxing Lu, Haidian Qu,
Beijing 100036, People's Republic of China.
TEL 447471. (Dist. in US by: China Books &
Periodicals, Inc., 2929 24th St., San Francisco, CA
94110. TEL 415-282-2994) Ed. Song Shutao.

LAW — ABSTRACTING, BIBLIOGRAPHIES, STATISTICS

340 US
ZHONGGUO LUSHI/CHINA LAWYERS. (Text in Chinese) bi-m. $28.25. China Books & Periodicals, Inc., 2929 24th St., San Francisco, CA 94110. TEL 415-292-2994. FAX 415-282-0994.

340 US
ZHONGHUA RENMIN GONGHEGUO ZUIGAO RENMIN FAYUAN GONGBAO/CHINA, PEOPLE'S REPUBLIC. PEOPLE'S SUPREME COURT. BULLETIN. (Text in Chinese) irreg. $17.25. (Zuigao Renmin Fayuan, CC) China Books & Periodicals, Inc., 2929 24th St., San Francisco, CA 94110. TEL 415-282-2994. FAX 415-282-0994.

340 CC ISSN 1000-5234
ZHONGNAN ZHENGFA XUEYUAN XUEBAO/SOUTH CENTRAL INSTITUTE OF POLITICAL SCIENCE AND LAW. JOURNAL. (Text in Chinese) 1957-1958; resumed 1986. bi-m. Y8. Zhongnan Zhengfa Xueyuan - South Central Institute of Political Science and Law, No. 1, Zhengyuan Lu, Honshan District, Wuhan, Hubei 430074, People's Republic of China. TEL 27-701620. Ed. Wu Handong. adv.; bk.rev. circ. 2,200. **Document type:** academic/scholarly publication.

340 CC ISSN 1002-4875
ZHONGWAI FAXUE/PEKING UNIVERSITY LAW JOURNAL. (Text in Chinese; summaries in Chinese, English) 1989. bi-m. Y15($60) Beijing University, Law Department, Beijing 100871, People's Republic of China. TEL 2561166. Eds. Xiao Weiyun, Luo Yuzhong. circ. 8,000. (back issues avail.)
Formerly: Peking University Chinese and Comparative Law.
Description: Covers legal science and legislature research in China and abroad.

340 RH
ZIMBABWE LAW REPORTS. (In 2 vols.) a., latest for year 1992. $80 (effective 1993). Legal Resources Foundation, P.O. Box 918, Harare, Zimbabwe. TEL 263-4-790947. FAX 263-4-728213. (Co-sponsor: Ministry of Justice) cum.index: 1984-1991. (back issues avail.)
Supersedes (in 1981): Rhodesian Law Reports.
Description: Compilation of official texts, decisions and documents of Zimbabwe Law.

340 RH ISSN 1016-0523
ZIMBABWE LAW REVIEW. 1985. a. Z.$40. University of Zimbabwe, Department of Law, P.O. Box MP 167, Harare, Zimbabwe. Ed. R.H.F. Austin. adv.; bk.rev. circ. 600. **Indexed:** Documentatieblad, P.L.E.S.A. **Document type:** academic/scholarly publication. —BLDSC (9513.252800).

ZONING BULLETIN. see REAL ESTATE

340 US
44TH STREET NOTES. 1986. 10/yr. $25 to non-members. Association of the Bar of the City of New York, 42 W. 44th St., New York, NY 10036. TEL 212-382-6651. FAX 212-768-8630. Ed. Carla Albergo. circ. 19,000. (back issues avail.) **Document type:** newsletter.

LAW — Abstracting, Bibliographies, Statistics

A B C POL SCI; a bibliography of contents: political science and government. see POLITICAL SCIENCE — Abstracting, Bibliographies, Statistics

ANNUAL DIGEST OF THE PUBLIC UTILITIES REPORTS. see ENERGY — Abstracting, Bibliographies, Statistics

347.788 US ISSN 0094-7504
KFC1871
ANNUAL STATISTICAL REPORT OF THE COLORADO JUDICIARY. 1970. a. $7. State Judicial Department, Office of the Court Administrator, 1301 Pennsylvania St., No.300, Denver, CO 80203-2416. FAX 303-831-1814. Ed.Bd. circ. 1,100.

347.9 CL
ANUARIO DE JUSTICIA. 1987. a. Instituto Nacional de Estadisticas, Av. Bulnes 418, Casilla 498, Correo 3 Santiago, Chile.

340 016 GW ISSN 0300-0990
ARBEITSGEMEINSCHAFT FUER JURISTISCHEN BIBLIOTHEKS- UND DOKUMENTATIONSWESEN. MITTEILUNGEN. Key Title: Mitteilungen der Arbeitsgemeinschaft fuer Juristische Bibliotheks- und Dokumentationswesen. 1971. 3/yr. DM.30. Arbeitsgemeinschaft fuer Juristische Bibliotheks- und Dokumentationswesen, Memmingerstr. 6, 86159 Augsburg, Germany. Ed. Burkard Meyer. adv.; bk.rev.; index. circ. 350.

345 AT ISSN 0819-1158
AUSTRALIA. BUREAU OF STATISTICS. AUSTRALIAN CAPITAL TERRITORY COURTS. 1985. a. Aus.$1.80. Australian Bureau of Statistics, P.O. Box 10, Belconnen, A.C.T. 2616, Australia. **Document type:** government publication.
Description: Contains data on criminal matters finalized in the A.C.T. Supreme Court, the Magistrates Court and the Children's Court.

345 AT ISSN 1035-9915
AUSTRALIA. BUREAU OF STATISTICS. NEW SOUTH WALES OFFICE. CRIME AND SAFETY SURVEY, NEW SOUTH WALES. 1990. a. Aus.$10. Australian Bureau of Statistics, New South Wales Office, St. Andrews House, Sydney Square, George St., Sydney, N.S.W. 2000, Australia. **Document type:** government publication.
Description: Provides summaries on household break-ins and attempted break-ins, and robberies and assaults in the 12 months prior to the survey.

345 AT ISSN 1033-6818
AUSTRALIA. BUREAU OF STATISTICS. TASMANIAN OFFICE. COURT STATISTICS, TASMANIA. 1988. a. Aus.$11. Australian Bureau of Statistics, Tasmanian Office, G.P.O. Box 66A, Hobart, Tas. 7001, Australia. **Document type:** government publication.
Description: Presents criminal offences finalized by type of offense and outcome.

345 AT ISSN 1037-9177
AUSTRALIA. BUREAU OF STATISTICS. WESTERN AUSTRALIAN OFFICE. SUMMARY OF CRIMINAL COURT PROCEEDINGS, WESTERN AUSTRALIA. 1991. a. Aus.$18.40. Australian Bureau of Statistics, Western Australian Office, 30 Terrace Rd., E. Perth, W.A. 6004, Australia. **Document type:** government publication.
Formed by the merger of (1986-1989): Australia. Bureau of Statistics. Western Australian Office. Court Statistics: Courts of Petty Sessions, Western Australia (ISSN 0817-9204); (1986-1989): Australia. Bureau of Statistics. Western Australian Office. Court Statistics: Higher Criminal Courts, Western Australia (ISSN 0816-5882); (1983-1989): Australia. Bureau of Statistics. Western Australian Office. Court Statistics: Children's Courts, Western Australia (ISSN 0817-7155)
Description: Contains data on criminal matters finalized in the Western Australia Higher Courts, Courts of Petty Sessions, and Children's Courts.

340 011 AT ISSN 1321-1269
AUSTRALIAN AND NEW ZEALAND CITATOR TO UK REPORTS. 1973. a. Aus.$149. Butterworths, 271-273 Lane Cove Rd., North Ryde, N.S.W. 2113, Australia. TEL 02-335-4444. FAX 02-335-4655. Ed. M. Healey. (back issues avail.) **Document type:** abstracting/indexing.
Formerly: Australian and New Zealand Citator to UK Reports. Cumulative Supplement (ISSN 0814-5733)
Description: Covers law reports of the United Kingdom.

340 AT ISSN 1036-0425
KU11
AUSTRALIAN CURRENT LAW LEGISLATION. (Annual cumulation avail.) 1963. m. Aus.$565. Butterworths, 271-273 Lane Cove Rd., North Ryde, N.S.W. 2113, Australia. TEL 02-335-4444. FAX 02-335-4655. Ed. F. Smith. bk.rev. **Document type:** abstracting/indexing.
Supersedes in part: Australian Current Law (ISSN 0045-0405)

340 AT ISSN 1036-0417
KU22
AUSTRALIAN CURRENT LAW REPORTER. (Annual cumulation avail.) 1963. fortn. Butterworths, 271-273 Lane Cove Rd., North Ryde, N.S.W. 2113, Australia. TEL 02-335-4444. FAX 02-335-4655. **Document type:** abstracting/indexing.
Supersedes in part: Australian Current Law (ISSN 0045-0405)

346.066 AT
AUSTRALIAN INDUSTRIAL LAW INDEX. (Previously included in: Australian Labour Law Reporter) 1991. q. C C H Australia Ltd., P.O. Box 230, North Ryde, N.S.W. 2113, Australia. TEL 02-888-2555. FAX 02-888-7324. (looseleaf format)
Description: Includes an alphabetical listing of subjects, an inventory of principles, precedents and sources in the field of industrial relations law and practice.

340 AU
AUSTRIA. STATISTISCHES ZENTRALAMT. STATISTIK DER RECHTSPFLEGE. a. S.240. Hintere Zollamtsstr. 2b, A-1033 Vienna, Austria. TEL 0222-71128-0. FAX 0222-7156828. **Document type:** government publication.

340 BE ISSN 0775-311X
BELGIUM. INSTITUT NATIONAL DE STATISTIQUE. STATISTIQUES JUDICIAIRES. Key Title: Statistiques Judiciaires. Dutch edition: Gerechtelijek Statistieken (ISSN 0771-5935) (Text in French) 1955. irreg. (approx 4/yr.). 620 BEF (foreign 775 BEF) (effective 1993). Institut National de Statistique, 44 rue de Louvain, B-1000 Brussels, Belgium. TEL 32-2-5486211. FAX 32-2-5486367. **Indexed:** P.A.I.S.For.Lang.Ind. **Document type:** government publication.
Supersedes (1943-1954): Statistique Criminelle de la Belgique (ISSN 0081-5268)
Description: Provides statistical information on judicial activity in Belgium, including criminal statistics, family law, civil status, and other court matters.

340 016 US ISSN 0360-2745
K38
BIBLIOGRAPHIC GUIDE TO LAW.* 1975. a. $340 cloth (foreign $375). G.K. Hall & Co., c/o MacMillan Publishing Co., 866 Third Ave., 18th fl., New York, NY 10022. TEL 212-702-6789. (Orders to: MacMillan Distribution Center, 100 Front St., Box 500, Riverside, NJ 08075-7500. TEL 800-257-5755) **Document type:** bibliography, abstracting/indexing.
Formerly: Law Book Guide (ISSN 0146-3861)
Description: Covers all aspects of law.

349 016 SZ
BIBLIOGRAPHIE DES SCHWEIZERISCHEN RECHTS. (Text in French, German, Italian) a. price varies. Helbing und Lichtenhahn Verlag AG, Freie Str. 84, CH-4051 Basel, Switzerland. TEL 064-268626. FAX 064-245780. (Subscr. to: Sauerlaender AG, Postfach, CH-5001 Aarau, Switzerland) bibl.; index, cum.index every 5 yrs. **Document type:** bibliography.

340 016 FR ISSN 0067-6985
BIBLIOGRAPHIE EN LANGUE FRANCAISE D'HISTOIRE DU DROIT DE 987 A 1940. N.S. 1961. a. price varies. Centre d'Histoire du Droit de l'Universite de Paris II, c/o Mme. Boulet-Sautel, Universite de Paris II (Universite de Droit d'Economie et des Sciences Social), 12 pl. du Pantheon, 75005 Paris, France. Ed.Bd. **Document type:** bibliography.
Supersedes: Bibliographie en Langue Francaise d'Histoire du Droit de 987 a 1914; (in 1945): Bibliographie en la Langue Francaise d'Histoire du Droit de 987 a 1875.

340 016 GW
BIBLIOGRAPHIE RECHTSWISSENSCHAFT. 1963. s-m. DM.12. Hochschule fuer Recht und Verwaltung, Informationszentrum, August-Bebel-Str. 89, 14482 Potsdam, Germany. circ. 300. **Document type:** bibliography.
Former titles: Bibliographie Staat und Recht; (until 1972): Rechtswissenschaftliche Dokumentation (ISSN 0138-1385).

340 320 US ISSN 0742-6909
BIBLIOGRAPHIES AND INDEXES IN LAW AND POLITICAL SCIENCE. 1984. irreg., no.15, 1992. price varies. Greenwood Press, Inc. (Subsidiary of: Greenwood Publishing Group Inc.), 88 Post Rd. W., Box 5007, Westport, CT 06881-5007. TEL 203-226-3571. FAX 203-222-1502.

LAW — ABSTRACTING, BIBLIOGRAPHIES, STATISTICS

016 US ISSN 0067-7329
K38
BIBLIOGRAPHY ON FOREIGN AND COMPARATIVE LAW: BOOKS AND ARTICLES IN ENGLISH. 1953. a. price varies. (Columbia University, Parker School of Foreign and Comparative Law) Oceana Publications, Inc., Dobbs Ferry, NY 10522. TEL 914-693-1320. FAX 914-693-0402. Ed. Vratislav Pechota. circ. 500. **Document type:** bibliography.
 Description: Bibliography of books and articles in English that focus on foreign and comparative law.

340 011 BL ISSN 0006-1662
BIBLIOTECA DO SEJUR. BOLETIM. (Text in Portuguese; summaries in English, French, Italian, Portuguese and Spanish) 1966. q. free. Petroleo Brasileiro S.A., Servico Juridico, Av. Republica do Chile, 65 S-2056, 20035 Rio de Janeiro, Brazil. (processed)

340 US ISSN 0882-7052
BIO-BIBLIOGRAPHIES IN LAW AND POLITICAL SCIENCE. 1985. irreg. price varies. Greenwood Press, Inc. (Subsidiary of: Greenwood Publishing Group Inc.) 88 Post Rd. W., Box 5007, Westport, CT 06881-5007. TEL 203-226-3571. FAX 203-222-1502.

BIOETHICS LITERATURE REVIEW. see *MEDICAL SCIENCES — Abstracting, Bibliographies, Statistics*

380 340 016 US ISSN 0000-0752
KF1
BOWKER'S LAW BOOKS AND SERIALS IN PRINT; a multimedia sourcebook. Cover title: R.R. Bowker - Martindale Hubbell Law Books and Serials in Print. Variant title: Law Books and Serials in Print. (Issued in 3 vols.) 1982. a. (plus supplement 3/yr.). $650 (includes the Supplements). R.R. Bowker, A Reed Reference Publishing Company, Part of the Reed Elsevier group, 121 Chanlon Rd., New Providence, NJ 07974. TEL 908-464-6800. FAX 908-665-3502. TELEX 138 755. (Subscr. to: Order Dept., Box 31, New Providence, NJ 07974-9903. TEL 800-521-8110) (also avail. in magnetic tape) **Document type:** bibliography, directory.
 ●Also available on CD-ROM.
 —CCC.
 Formerly: Law Information (ISSN 0000-0701)
 Description: Lists print and nonprint materials designed for lawyers and legal researchers. Provides capsule descriptions for major book entries which are indexed by subject, author and title; also includes publisher information directory.

340 016 US ISSN 0000-1031
KF1
BOWKER'S LAW BOOKS AND SERIALS IN PRINT SUPPLEMENT; materials on law and law related topics recently published and to be published. 1983. a. (avail. only with Bowker's Law Books and Serials In Print). R.R. Bowker, A Reed Reference Publishing Company, Part of the Reed Elsevier group, 121 Chanlon Rd., New Providence, NJ 07974. TEL 908-464-6800. FAX 908-665-3502. TELEX 138 755. (Subscr. to: Order Dept., Box 31, New Providence, NJ 07974-9903. TEL 800-521-8110) **Document type:** bibliography, directory.
 Former titles: Bowker's Law Books and Serials in Print Update (ISSN 0000-0760); Law Information Update (ISSN 0000-0728)
 Description: Lists new books and serials information received after publication of base volume. Cumulates previous issues. Books indexed by subject, author and title; includes publisher information.

346 332 US ISSN 0896-906X
KF1396.A27
BOWNE DIGEST FOR CORPORATE & SECURITIES LAWYERS; abstracts of current articles from more than 280 legal periodicals. 1986. m. free. (Bowne & Co.) Brumberg Publications, Inc., 124 Harvard St., Brookline, MA 02146. TEL 617-734-1979. FAX 617-734-1989. Ed. Bruce Brumberg. bk.rev.; index. (back issues avail.; reprint service avail.) **Document type:** abstracting/indexing.
 ●Also available online. Vendor(s): NewsNet (LA11).
 Formerly (until 1987): Abstracts of Legal Periodicals: Corporate and Securities Edition (ISSN 0894-2447)

C A SELECTS. FOOD, DRUGS, & COSMETICS — LEGISLATIVE & REGULATORY ASPECTS. see *FOOD AND FOOD INDUSTRIES — Abstracting, Bibliographies, Statistics*

CANADIAN INCOME TAX RESEARCH INDEX. see *BUSINESS AND ECONOMICS — Abstracting, Bibliographies, Statistics*

340 026 US ISSN 1049-796X
KF4
CATALOG OF CURRENT LAW TITLES; recent acquisitions of major legal libraries. 1984. a. $295. William S. Hein & Co., Inc., 1285 Main St., Buffalo, NY 14209. TEL 800-828-7571. FAX 716-883-8100. TELEX 91-209 WU 7 HEIN BUF. Eds. Margaret A. Goldblatt, Peter D. Ward. circ. 250. **Document type:** catalog, bibliography.
 Formerly: National Legal Bibliography (ISSN 0739-1951)

340 026 US ISSN 1043-4852
K40.C38
CATALOG OF NEW FOREIGN AND INTERNATIONAL LAW TITLES. 1989. 6/yr. $250. Ward and Associates, 317 S. Division, Ste. 66, Ann Arbor, MI 48104. TEL 313-665-3520. FAX 313-665-3924. Eds. Peter Ward, M. Goldblatt. (back issues avail.) **Document type:** bibliography.
 Description: Comprehensive bibliography of new law and law-related titles.

340 US ISSN 0000-1058
KF70.A34
CODE OF FEDERAL REGULATIONS INDEX. 1988. a. $595. R.R. Bowker, A Reed Reference Publishing Company, Part of the Reed Elsevier group, 121 Chanlon Rd., New Providence, NJ 07974. TEL 908-464-6800. FAX 908-665-6688. TELEX 138 755. (Subscr. to: Order Dept., Box 31, New Providence, NJ 07974-9903. TEL 800-521-8110) Ed. Lucille Boorstein. **Document type:** bibliography, directory.
 —CCC.
 Description: Organizes and cross-references CFR subjects by title and by subject.

341 US ISSN 0886-6724
COLLECTION OF BIBLIOGRAPHIC AND RESEARCH RESOURCES. 1984. irreg. price varies. Oceana Publications, Inc., 75 Main St., Dobbs Ferry, NY 10522. TEL 914-693-1320. FAX 914-693-0402. Ed.Bd. circ. 150. (back issues avail.) **Document type:** bibliography.
 Description: A series of bibliographies, primarily in international law and relations.

340 011
COMPREHENSIVE INDEX TO OREGON STATUTES (YEAR). (Suppl. to: Oregon Revised Statutes Annotated) 1991. biennial. $90. Butterworth Legal Publishers (Salem) (Subsidiary of: Reed Elsevier plc), 8 Industrial Way, Bldg. C, Salem, NH 03079. TEL 800-548-4001. FAX 603-898-9858. Ed.Bd. **Document type:** abstracting/indexing.

340
CONGRESSIONAL INDEX. w. during session. $870. Commerce Clearing House, Inc., 4025 W. Peterson Ave., Chicago, IL 60646. TEL 312-583-8500. **Document type:** abstracting/indexing.

340 RH
▼**CONSOLIDATED INDEX TO THE ZIMBABWE LAW REPORTS.** 1993. irreg. $80. Legal Resources Foundation, P.O. Box 918, Harare, Zimbabwe. TEL 263-4-790947. FAX 263-4-728213. **Document type:** abstracting/indexing.
 Description: Indexes official law reports of judicial decisions of Zimbabwe.

690 340 UK ISSN 0263-9751
CONSTRUCTION LAW DIGEST. 1982. 10/yr. £142.50 (overseas £156) (effective Nov. 1993). Blackwell Scientific Publications, Osney Mead, Oxford OX2 0EL, England. TEL 0865-240201. FAX 0865-721205. TELEX 83355-MEDBOK-G. Ed. John Parris. bk.rev.; index. (looseleaf format; back issues avail.) **Document type:** newsletter.
 Description: Digest cases of interest to the U.K. construction industry, including arbitration. Also of interest to other jurisdictions.

340 016 EI
COUNCIL OF EUROPE. DOCUMENTATION SECTION. BIBLIO BULLETIN. SERIES: LEGAL AFFAIRS. 1973. 6/yr. free. Council of Europe, Documentation Section, BP 431 R6, 67006 Strasbourg, France. TEL 88-41-20-00. FAX 88-36-70-57. TELEX EUR 870 943F. (Dist. in U.S. by: Manhattan Publishing Co., 225 Lafayette St., New York, NY 10012) circ. 250. **Document type:** bibliography.
 Former titles: Council of Europe. Central Library. Biblio Bulletin. Series: Legal Affaires; Council of Europe. Documentation Section and Library. Bibliographical Bulletin. Series: Legal Affairs.
 Description: Index of periodical articles on law, lawyers and human rights.

340 US ISSN 0196-1780
K33
CURRENT LAW INDEX; multiple access to legal periodicals in print. m. (plus 3 q. and 1 a. cumulations). $395. Information Access Company, 362 Lakeside Dr., Foster City, CA 94404. TEL 415-378-5200; 800-227-8431. FAX 415-378-5369. (Co-sponsor: American Association of Law Libraries) Ed. Cheryl Ann Toliver. **Document type:** abstracting/indexing.
 ●Also available online. Vendor(s): BRS Online Products, DIALOG Information Services, Inc., Mead Data Central, Inc., West Services, Inc.
 —CCC.
 Description: Timely guide to the legal periodicals of the United States, Canada, the UK, Australia and New Zealand.

340 016 US ISSN 0011-3859
CURRENT PUBLICATIONS IN LEGAL AND RELATED FIELDS. 1953. m. (except June, July & Sep.; plus a. cumulation). $150. (American Association of Law Libraries) Fred B. Rothman & Co., 10368 W. Centennial Rd., Littleton, CO 80127. TEL 303-979-5657. FAX 303-978-1457. index. circ. 500. (back issues avail.; reprint service avail. from RRI) **Document type:** abstracting/indexing.

341.2 US ISSN 0731-8189
JX236.5
CURRENT TREATY INDEX; a cumulative index to the United States slip treaties and agreements. 1982. s-a. $98. William S. Hein & Co., Inc., 1285 Main St., Buffalo, NY 14209. TEL 800-828-7571. FAX 716-883-8100. TELEX 91-209 WU 7 HEIN BUF. Eds. Igor I. Kavass, Adolf Sprudzs. circ. 400. **Document type:** directory, abstracting/indexing.
 Incorporates (in 1990): United States International Treaties Today, Unpublished and unnumbered Treaties Index (ISSN 1050-9445); Which was formerly (until 1989): Unpublished and Unnumbered Treaties Index (ISSN 0894-1564)

340 UK
DAILY LAW REPORTS INDEX. 1988. w. £285. Legal Information Resources Ltd., Elphin House, 1 New Rd., Mytholmroyd, Hebden Bridge, W. Yorkshire HX7 5DZ, England. TEL 0422-886277. FAX 0422-886250. Ed.Bd. cum.index. (also avail. in magnetic tape; back issues avail.) **Document type:** abstracting/indexing.
 Description: Contains abstracts for all law reports published in English and Scottish newspapers.

340 KU
DALIL AL-KUWAIT AL-YAWM. (Text in Arabic) 1975. a. K.5000. Kuwait Information and Microfilm Centre, Ministry of Planning, P.O. Box 15 - Safat, 13001 Safat, Kuwait. TEL 965-2420331. FAX 965-2426797. TELEX 22468 TAKHTEET. Ed. Abdulaziz A. Al-Askar. circ. 1,000. (also avail. in microfiche; back issues avail.) **Document type:** abstracting/indexing.
 Description: An abstracting and indexing service to Kuwait Official Gazette. Provides a brief abstract, publishing and microfilming data of Kuwait laws, decrees and ministerial issues.

LAW — ABSTRACTING, BIBLIOGRAPHIES, STATISTICS

340 UK
THE DIGEST; annotated British, Commonwealth and European cases. 1919. 6/yr. Butterworth & Co. (Publishers) Ltd. (Subsidiary of: Reed Elsevier plc), 88 Kingsway, London WC2B 6AB, England. TEL 71-405-6900. FAX 71-405-1332. TELEX 95678. (US addr.: Butterworth Legal Publishers, 90 Stiles Rd., Salem, NH 03079-9981. TEL 603-898-9664) Ed. Andrew Marshall. index, cum.index. (back issues avail.) **Document type:** abstracting/indexing.
Description: Digested case law with over 350,000 legal cases. All legal subjects covered with full annotations.

347.9 IT ISSN 0419-4632
DIZIONARIO BIBLIOGRAFICO DELLE RIVISTE GIURIDICHE ITALIANE. 1956. a. price varies. Casa Editrice Dott. A. Giuffré, Via B. Arsizio 40, 20151 Milan, Italy. TEL 02-38000905. FAX 02-38009582. Ed. Vincenzo Napoletano.

340 011 NE ISSN 0256-4467
KJE901
ELLIS; a master guide to commentary on European Community law. Key Title: Ellis (English Edition). (Text in English) 1985. irreg., vol.4, 1992 (for the year 1988). price varies. (European Legal Literature Information Service) Kluwer Law and Taxation Publishers (Subsidiary of: Wolters Kluwer N.V.), P.O. Box 23, 7400 GA Deventer, Netherlands. TEL 31-5700-47261. FAX 31-5700-22244. TELEX 49295 KLUDV NL. (Dist. by: Libresso Distribution Center, P.O. Box 23, 7400 GA Deventer, Netherlands. TEL 31-5700-33155. FAX 31-5700-33834; In N. America: Kluwer Law and Taxation Publishers, 675 Massachusetts Ave., Cambridge, MA 02139. TEL 617-354-0140. FAX 617-354-8595) Ed. Richard Hainebach. (back issues avail.) **Document type:** abstracting/indexing.
Description: Bibliographic indexing service providing comprehensive access to important articles, comments and EC legislation, as well as a wide variety of opinions and interpretation concerning the latest developments in EC law.

665.5 016 BL ISSN 0013-662X
EMENTARIO DA LEGISLACAO DO PETROLEO. 1968. s-a. free. Petroleo Brasileiro S.A., Servico Juridico, Setor de Documentacao, Av. Republica do Chile, 65 S-2056, 20035 Rio de Janeiro, Brazil. (processed)

318 PN ISSN 0378-259X
HV7322
ESTADISTICA PANAMENA. SITUACION POLITICA, ADMINISTRATIVA Y JUSTICIA. SECCION 631. JUSTICIA. circa. a. Bl.0.75. Direccion de Estadistica y Censo, Contraloria General, Apartado 5213, Panama 5, Panama. FAX 69-7294. circ. 800. **Document type:** government publication, bulletin.

340 UK
▼**EUROPEAN LEGAL JOURNALS INDEX.** 1993. m. £300. Legal Information Resources Ltd., Elphin House, 1 New Rd., Mytholmroyd, Hebden Bridge, W. Yorkshire HX7 5DZ, England. TEL 0422-886277. FAX 0422-886250. Ed.Bd. cum.index. (also avail. in magnetic tape; back issues avail.) **Document type:** abstracting/indexing.
Description: Includes articles relating to the legal developments concerning the Council of Europe, European Communities and individual European countries - including Central and Eastern Europe - drawn from nearly 300 periodical titles.

353 US
FEDERAL REGISTER SUBJECT INDEX. m. $22 (foreign $27.50) (included with subscr. to Federal Register). U.S. Office of the Federal Register, National Archives and Records Administration, Eighth St. and Pennsylvania Ave., N.W., Washington, DC 20408. TEL 202-523-5230. (Subscr. to: Superintendent of Documents, U.S. Government Printing Office, Box 371954, Pittsburgh, PA 15250-7954. TEL 202-783-3238. FAX 202-512-2233) **Document type:** government publication, abstracting/indexing.
Description: Itemizes the material published in the Federal Register.

FEDERAL STATUTES ANNOTATIONS. see *PUBLIC ADMINISTRATION — Abstracting, Bibliographies, Statistics*

331 340 GW ISSN 0173-1688
FUNDHEFT FUER ARBEITS- UND SOZIALRECHT; systematischer Nachweis der Gesetzgebung, Rechtsprechung, Buecher und Aufsaetze. 1945. a. price varies. C.H. Beck'sche Verlagsbuchhandlung, Wilhelmstr. 9, 80801 Munich, Germany. TEL 089-38189-338. FAX 089-38189-398. TELEX 5215085-BECK-D. Eds. Wolfgang Blomeyer, Walter Knorr. circ. 1,400. **Document type:** bulletin.
Formerly (until 1977): Fundheft fuer Arbeitsrecht (ISSN 0071-9900)

340 011 GW ISSN 0071-9919
FUNDHEFT FUER OEFFENTLICHES RECHT; systematischer Nachweis der Rechtsprechung, Zeitschriftenaufsaetze und selbstaendigen Schriften. 1948. a. price varies. C.H. Beck'sche Verlagsbuchhandlung, Wilhelmstr. 9, 80801 Munich, Germany. TEL 089-38189-338. FAX 089-38189-398. TELEX 5215085-BECK-D. Ed.Bd. circ. 1,800. **Document type:** bulletin.

340 011 GW ISSN 0071-9927
FUNDHEFT FUER ZIVILRECHT; systematischer Nachweis der Rechtsprechung und Zeitschriftenaufsaetze. 1948. a. price varies. C.H. Beck'sche Verlagsbuchhandlung, Wilhelmstr. 9, 80801 Munich, Germany. TEL 089-38189-338. FAX 089-38189-398. TELEX 5215085-BECK-D. Ed.Bd. circ. 2,400. **Document type:** bulletin.

340 314 GW ISSN 0072-1859
GERMANY. STATISTISCHES BUNDESAMT. FACHSERIE 10. RECHTSPFLEGE. (Consists of several subseries) 1959. a. price varies. 65180 Wiesbaden, Germany. TEL 0611-75-1. FAX 0611-724000. TELEX 61186-STBA-D. **Document type:** government publication.

340 AU
GESAMTREGISTER MIT DEN RECHTSSAETZEN UND FUNDSTELLEN DER ENTSCHEIDUNGEN DER ZEITSCHRIFT FUER VERKEHRSRECHT. 1956. irreg. price varies. Manzsche Verlags- und Universitaetsbuchhandlung, Kohlmarkt 16, A-1014 Vienna, Austria. TEL 0222-531610. FAX 0222-53161-181. Ed. Erika Veit. circ. 2,400. **Document type:** abstracting/indexing.
Description: Abstracts on traffic law.

340 RU
K15
GOSUDARSTVO I PRAVO: OTECHESTVENNAYA LITERATURA; referativnyi zhurnal. 1974. q. $44. Rossiiskaya Akademiya Nauk, Institut Nauchnoi Informatsii po Obshchestvennym Naukam, Ul. Krasikova 28-21, 117418 Moscow V-418, Russia. Ed. I.A. Isaev.
Formerly: Obshchestvennye Nauki v S.S.S.R. Gosudarstvo i Pravo (ISSN 0202-2060)

340 RU
GOSUDARSTVO I PRAVO: ZARUBEZHNAYA LITERATURA; referativnyi zhurnal. 1973. q. $32. Rossiiskaya Akademiya Nauk, Institut Nauchnoi Informatsii po Obshchestvennym Naukam, Ul. Krasikova 28-21, 117418 Moscow V-418, Russia. Ed. V.S. Nerseyants.
Formerly: Obshchestvennye Nauki za Rubezhom. Gosudarstvo i Pravo (ISSN 0202-2109)

341.2 US ISSN 0736-5713
JX236.5
GUIDE TO UNITED STATES TREATIES IN FORCE. 1982. s-a. $142.50. William S. Hein & Co., Inc., 1285 Main St., Buffalo, NY 14209. TEL 800-828-7571. FAX 716-883-8100. TELEX 91-209 WU 7 HEIN BUF. Eds. Igor I. Kavass, Adolf Sprudzs. circ. 400. **Document type:** directory, academic/scholarly publication.
Description: Information on current treaties and other international acts published in slip form and not yet bound in the United States treaty index.

I C E L REFERENCES. (International Council of Environmental Law) see *ENVIRONMENTAL STUDIES — Abstracting, Bibliographies, Statistics*

340 AU
INDEX DER RECHTSMITTELENTSCHEIDUNGEN UND DES SCHRIFTTUMS. 1947. a. price varies. Manzsche Verlags- und Universitaetsbuchhandlung, Kohlmarkt 16, A-1014 Vienna, Austria. TEL 0222-531610. FAX 0222-53161-181. Ed. Rudolf Stohanzl. circ. 2,400. **Document type:** abstracting/indexing.
Description: A general index of Austrian law.

340 CN ISSN 0316-8891
LAW
INDEX TO CANADIAN LEGAL PERIODICAL LITERATURE. (Text in English and French) 1960. q. Can.$140. P.O. Box 386, N.D.G. Station, Montreal, PQ H4A 3P7, Canada. TEL 514-288-1893. bk.rev. circ. 450. **Document type:** abstracting/indexing.

340 016 CH ISSN 0259-3793
INDEX TO CHINESE LEGAL PERIODICALS. Key Title: Zhongwen Falu Lunwen Suoyin. 1963-1970; resumed 1972. a. $30. Soochow University, Library - Tung Wu Ta Hsueh T'u Shu Kuan, Wai Shuang Hsi, Taipei, Taiwan, Republic of China. FAX 886-02-8812317. (reprint service avail.) **Document type:** abstracting/indexing.

340 016 US ISSN 0019-400X
LAW
INDEX TO FOREIGN LEGAL PERIODICALS. (Subject headings in English with translation into French, German and Spanish included in a. cumulation) 1960. q. (plus a. cumulations). $490 (foreign $502) (effective 1994). (American Asscociation of Law Libraries, School of Law Library) University of California Press, Journals Division, 2120 Berkeley Way, Berkeley, CA 94720. TEL 510-643-7154. FAX 510-642-9917. Ed. Thomas H. Reynolds. index. circ. 600. (also avail. in microform from UMI; back issues avail.) **Document type:** abstracting/indexing.
●Also available on CD-ROM. Producer(s): SilverPlatter Information, Inc.
—BLDSC (4377.900000).
Description: Indexes more than 400 legal and business periodicals from 59 countries. Includes legal essays.

340 016 II ISSN 0019-4034
INDEX TO INDIAN LEGAL PERIODICALS. 1963. s-a. Rs.60. Indian Law Institute, Bhagwandass Rd., New Delhi 110001, India. **Document type:** abstracting/indexing.

340 016 US ISSN 0019-4077
K9
INDEX TO LEGAL PERIODICALS. 1908. m. (plus q. & a. cumulations). $245. H.W. Wilson Co., 950 University Ave., Bronx, NY 10452. TEL 800-367-6770. FAX 718-590-1617. TELEX 4990003HWILSON. Ed. Joy London. (also avail. in magnetic tape). Indexed: C.L.I., Refug.Abstr. **Document type:** abstracting/indexing.
●Also available online. Vendor(s): BRS Online Products (WILP), Mead Data Central, Inc., West Services, Inc., Wilsonline (File ILP).
Also available on CD-ROM. Producer(s): H.W. Wilson (WILSONDISC).
—BLDSC (4380.800000).
Description: Author and subject index to legal periodicals published in the U.S., Canada, Great Britain, Ireland, Australia, and New Zealand. Includes a table of cases under both the plaintiff's and the defendant's name and a table of statutes by jurisdiction.

340 RH
INDEX TO LEGISLATION IN FORCE IN ZIMBABWE. 1989. a. $80 (effective 1994). Legal Resources Foundation, P.O. Box 918, Harare, Zimbabwe. TEL 263-4-728213. (looseleaf format) **Document type:** abstracting/indexing.
Description: Indexes all legislation currently in force in Zimbabwe.

340 016 US ISSN 0019-4093
INDEX TO PERIODICAL ARTICLES RELATED TO LAW. 1958. q. $65. Glanville Publishers, Inc., 75 Main St., Dobbs Ferry, NY 10522. TEL 914-693-5956. FAX 914-693-0402. Ed.Bd. cum.index: 1958-1988. circ. 600. **Document type:** abstracting/indexing.
Description: Provides bibliographic information on law-related periodical articles not included in Current Law Index, Index to Foreign Legal Periodicals, Index to Legal Periodicals, Legal Resource Index or Legaltrac.

LAW — ABSTRACTING, BIBLIOGRAPHIES, STATISTICS

340   SP   ISSN 0213-4683
INDICE ESPANOL DE CIENCIAS SOCIALES. SERIES C: LAW. 1979. a. 10000 ptas. or exchange basis (effective 1994). Centro de Informacion y Documentacion Cientifica (Cindoc), Pinar, 25, 3, 28006 Madrid, Spain. TEL 1-563-5482. FAX 1-5642644. **Document type:** abstracting/indexing.
●Also available online.
Also available on CD-ROM.
Supersedes in part (in 1982): Indice Espanol de Ciencias Sociales (ISSN 0211-1373)

340 004   NE   ISSN 0925-9872
K87   CODEN: ITLAEA
INFORMATION TECHNOLOGY AND THE LAW; an international bibliography. (Text in English) 1975. 2/yr. fl.284($149.50) (effective 1994). (Consiglio Nazionale delle Ricerche, Istituto per la Documentazione Giuridica, IT) Martinus Nijhoff Publishers, Human Rights and International Law (Subsidiary of: Kluwer Academic Publishers Group), Postbus 163, 3300 AD Dordrecht, Netherlands. TEL 31-78-334911. FAX 31-78-332454. TELEX 29245 KAPG NL. (Dist. by: Kluwer Academic Publishers Group, P.O. Box 322, 3300 AH Dordrecht, Netherlands. TEL 31-78-524400. FAX 31-78-524474; N. America dist. addr.: Box 358, Accord Sta., Hingham, MA 02018-0358. TEL 617-871-6600. FAX 617-871-6528) Ed.Bd. illus. (also avail. in microform from UMI; back issues avail.) **Indexed:** Sci.Abstr. **Document type:** bibliography.
—BLDSC (4496.368702); UMI.
Formerly (until 1992): Informatica e Diritto. Bibliografia Internazionale (ISSN 0390-0975); **Supersedes:** Bollettino Bibliografico d'Informatica Generale e Applicata al Diritto.
Description: Comprehensive international bibliography of significant literature in the field of legal information science and computer law.
Refereed Serial

340 010   SP
INSTITUTO INTERNACIONAL DE HISTORIA DEL DERECHO INDIANO. ACTAS Y ESTUDIOS. a. 1500 ptas. Instituto Nacional de Estudios Juridicos, Duque de Medinaceli St., No. 8, Madrid, Spain.

INSURANCE REGULATORY INFORMATION SYSTEM RATIO RESULTS. see *INSURANCE — Abstracting, Bibliographies, Statistics*

341   UN   ISSN 0085-2139
INTERNATIONAL COURT OF JUSTICE. BIBLIOGRAPHY/COUR INTERNATIONALE DE JUSTICE. BIBLIOGRAPHIE. 1947. a. International Court of Justice, Peace Palace, 2517 KJ The Hague, Netherlands. TEL 31-70-3924441. FAX 31-70-3649928. TELEX 32323. (Dist. by: Distribution and Sales Section Office of the United Nations, 1211 Geneva 10, Switzerland; Dist. in U.S. by: United Nations - Sales Section, New York, NY 10017. TEL 212-963-8300) (also avail. in microfiche) **Document type:** bibliography.

347.9   IS   ISSN 0075-1030
ISRAEL. CENTRAL BUREAU OF STATISTICS. JUDICIAL STATISTICS. (Subseries of its Special Series) (Text in English, Hebrew) 1951. irreg., no.748, 1983. price varies. Central Bureau of Statistics, Box 13015, Jerusalem 91 130, Israel. TEL 02-21 12 11. **Document type:** government publication.

340   IT   ISSN 0392-7571
ISTITUTO PER LA DOCUMENTAZIONE GIURIDICA. BIBLIOGRAFIA. DIRITTO CIVILE. 1979. a. L.23000. Giuffre Editore, Via Busto Arsizio 40, 20151 Milan, Italy. Ed. Mario Ragona. circ. 400. **Document type:** bibliography.

340   IT
ISTITUTO PER LA DOCUMENTAZIONE GIURIDICA. BIBLIOGRAFIA. DIRITTO INTERNAZIONALE; rassegna automatica di dottrina giuridica. a. Istituto per la Documentazione Giuridica, Via Panciatichi, 56-16, 50127 Florence, Italy. (Subscr. to: Casa Editrice Giuffre, Via Statuto, 2, 20121 Milan, Italy) Ed.Bd. **Document type:** bibliography.

340   IT
ITALY. ISTITUTO NAZIONALE DI STATISTICA. STATISTICHE GIUDIZIARIE. 1949. a. L.44000 (effective 1992). Istituto Nazionale di Statistica, Via Cesare Balbo 16, 00100 Rome, Italy. FAX 06-46735198. circ. 1,050. **Document type:** government publication.
Formerly (until 1962): Italy. Istituto Centrale di Statistica. Annuario di Statistiche Giudiziario (ISSN 0075-1715)

347.9   CN   ISSN 0715-271X
JURISTAT. irreg. Can.$78($94) (foreign $109). Statistics Canada, Publications Division, Ottawa, Ont. K1A 0T6, Canada. TEL 613-951-7277. FAX 613-951-1584.
Description: Provides readers with timely and succinct statistical information on a variety of justice related programs.

340 016   GW
JURISTISCHE NEUERSCHEINUNGEN. 1923. bi-m. DM.46.80. Theodor Oppermann Verlag, Im Moore 17, 30167 Hannover, Germany. Ed. Andreas Ullrich. adv.; bibl. circ. 6,800. **Document type:** bibliography.

JUSTITIELE VERKENNINGEN. see *CRIMINOLOGY AND LAW ENFORCEMENT — Abstracting, Bibliographies, Statistics*

340 314   GW
JUSTIZ IN ZAHLEN. 1980. a. Justizministerium NW Duesseldorf, Martin-Luther-Platz 40, 40212 Duesseldorf, Germany. FAX 0211-8792456. TELEX 2114184. circ. 10,000. **Document type:** government publication.
Description: Data and figures on the criminal justice system in the German state of Northrhine-Westfalia.

340 016   GW   ISSN 0453-3283
K11
KARLSRUHER JURISTISCHE BIBLIOGRAPHIE; systematischer Nachweis neuer Buecher und Aufsaetze in monatlicher Folge aus Recht, Staat, Gesellschaft. 1965. m. DM.430. C.H. Beck'sche Verlagsbuchhandlung, Wilhelmstr. 9, 80801 Munich, Germany. TEL 089-38189-338. FAX 089-38189-398. TELEX 5215085-BECK-D. Ed.Bd. circ. 1,200. (reprint service avail. from SCH) **Document type:** bibliography.

340 362.7   US   ISSN 0733-8937
K33
KINDEX; an index to legal periodical literature concerning children. 1976. a. $45. National Center for Juvenile Justice, 701 Forbes Ave., Pittsburgh, PA 15219. TEL 412-227-6950. Ed. Linda Szymanski. index. circ. 300. (back issues avail.) **Document type:** abstracting/indexing.

340   US   ISSN 0075-8221
LAW BOOKS IN PRINT; law books in English published throughout the world. (Supplement 2/yr.: Law Books Published) 1957. triennial, 7th ed., 1994. $750. Glanville Publishers, Inc., 75 Main St., Dobbs Ferry, NY 10522. TEL 914-693-5956. FAX 914-693-0402. Ed. Nicholas Triffin. index. circ. 700. **Document type:** bibliography.
Description: Provides author-title, subject, publisher and series listings of law books and other formats in print throughout the world in the English language.

340 016   US   ISSN 0886-0408
KF1
LAW BOOKS IN REVIEW; a quarterly journal of reviews of current publications in law and related fields. 1974. q. $55. Glanville Publishers, Inc., Dobbs Ferry, NY 10522. TEL 914-693-5956. FAX 914-693-0402. Ed. Alden W. Domizio. cum.index: 1974-1979. circ. 250. (processed; back issues avail.) **Indexed:** Leg.Info.Manage.Ind. **Document type:** abstracting/indexing.
Description: Features timely reviews of legal coretexts, in all legal subject areas.

340 016   US   ISSN 0023-9240
KF1
LAW BOOKS PUBLISHED. (Supplement to: Law Books in Print) 1969. 2/yr. (cumulative each year). $140. Glanville Publishers, Inc., 75 Main St., Dobbs Ferry, NY 10522. TEL 914-693-5956. FAX 914-693-0402. Ed. Nicholas Triffin. circ. 700. (processed; back issues avail.) **Document type:** bibliography.
Description: Provides bibliographic information on law books published in the English language in a given year.

340   US   ISSN 1049-7978
LAWYERS MONTHLY CATALOG. GOVERNMENT DOCUMENTS FROM OFFICIAL AND COMMERCIAL SOURCES. 1986. a. $295. William S. Hein & Co., Inc., 1285 Main St., Buffalo, NY 14209. TEL 800-828-7571. FAX 716-883-8100. TELEX 91-209 WU 7 HEIN BUF. Ed. Peter D. Ward. **Document type:** bibliography.
Formerly: National Legal Bibliography. Part 2. Government Documents from Official and Commercial Sources (ISSN 0887-106X)

340   US   ISSN 0741-1189
LEGAL BIBLIOGRAPHY JOURNAL. 1983. 3/yr. $9.75 per no. Legal Institute, 3250 Wilshire Blvd., Ste. 1000, Los Angeles, CA 90010. TEL 213-487-6268. FAX 213-385-2396. Ed.Bd. circ. 300.

340 011   AT   ISSN 1038-5622
▼**LEGAL EDUCATION DIGEST.** 1992. q. $30. Centre for Legal Education, G.P.O. Box 232, Sydney, N.S.W. 2001, Australia. TEL 61-2-221-3699. FAX 61-2-221-6280. (Exclusive dist. in N. America: Wm. W. Gaunt & Sons, Inc., Law Book Dealers & Subscription Agents, Gaunt Bldg., 3011 Gulf Dr., Holmes Beach, FL 34217-2199. TEL 813-778-5211. FAX 813-778-5252) circ. 150. **Document type:** abstracting/indexing.
Description: Provides up-to-date information, in digested form (under 36 different headings), of what is being published, or being said, about the various aspects of legal education. More than 160 journals are kept under review.

340 016   US   ISSN 0883-1297
KF240
LEGAL INFORMATION ALERT; what's new in legal publications, databases and research techniques. 1981. m. (10/yr.) $149. Alert Publications, Inc., 401 W. Fullerton Pkwy., Ste. 1403E, Chicago, IL 60614-3857. TEL 312-525-7594. FAX 312-525-7015. Ed. Donna Tuke Heroy. bk.rev. (reprint service avail.) **Document type:** newsletter.
—CCC.
Formerly: U S Law Library Alert (ISSN 0278-5854)
Description: Designed to keep law librarians and legal researchers informed of new legal information products and research techniques.

340 020   US   ISSN 0747-9298
Z675.L2
LEGAL INFORMATION MANAGEMENT INDEX. 1984. bi-m. (plus a. cum.) $118 (foreign $140). Legal Information Services, Box 67, Newton Highlands, MA 02161-0067. TEL 508-443-4087. Ed. Elyse H. Fox. (back issues avail.)
Description: Provides broad subject coverage, including legal research and bibliography, law library management, automation, space planning, microforms, budgeting, online databases and many other topics.

340   UK   ISSN 0950-4206
LEGAL JOURNALS INDEX. 1986. m. £560 (typically set in Sep.). Legal Information Resources Ltd., Elphin House, 1 New Rd., Mytholmroyd, Hebden Bridge, W. Yorkshire HX7 5DZ, England. TEL 0422-886277. FAX 0422-886250. Ed.Bd. abstr.; cum.index. (also avail. in magnetic tape; back issues avail.) **Document type:** abstracting/indexing.
—BLDSC (5181.327800).
Description: Covers over 300 legal journals devoted to law. Contains articles on legal topics giving quick access to comprehensive commentary on latest developments in English and Scots law, for solicitors, barristers, law librarians, articled clerks, and law students.

LAW — ABSTRACTING, BIBLIOGRAPHIES, STATISTICS

340   US   ISSN 0275-4088
KF1
LEGAL LOOSELEAFS IN PRINT. 1981. a. $90. Infosources Publishing, 140 Norma Rd., Teaneck, NJ 07666. TEL 201-836-7072. Ed. Arlene L. Eis. adv. circ. 1,000. **Document type:** bibliography, directory.
—CCC.
Description: Bibliography of 3,500 legal looseleafs with subject and publisher indexes.

340 015   US   ISSN 8755-416X
KF1
LEGAL NEWSLETTERS IN PRINT. 1985. a. $85. Infosources Publishing, 140 Norma Rd., Teaneck, NJ 07666. TEL 201-836-7072. Ed. Arlene L. Eis. adv. **Document type:** bibliography, directory.
—CCC.
Description: Bibliography of 2,200 legal newsletters with publisher and subject indexes.

340 016   US
LEGAL PERIODICALS IN ENGLISH. (Set of 5 binders) 1976. a. (released in irreg. sections). $125 per update; whole set $525. Glanville Publishers, Inc., 75 Main St., Dobbs Ferry, NY 10522. TEL 914-693-5956. FAX 914-693-0402. Ed. Eugene M. Wypyski. (looseleaf format) **Document type:** abstracting/indexing.
Description: Catalogs all legal periodical which are published in English.

340   US
LEGALTRAC. m. $3500. Information Access Company, 362 Lakeside Dr., Foster City, CA 94404. TEL 415-378-5200; 800-227-8431. FAX 415-378-5369. (Co-sponsor: American Association of Law Libraries) **Document type:** abstracting/indexing.
● Also available online. Vendor(s): BRS Online Products (LAWS), DIALOG Information Services, Inc. (File no.150), Mead Data Central, Inc. (LGLIND), West Services, Inc. (LRI).
Also available on CD-ROM.
Formerly: Legal Resource Index (ISSN 0272-9296)
Description: Comprehensive guide to over 900 law journals, legal newspapers and articles selected from the general press.

340 350   US   ISSN 0457-3633
KFN5001
LEGISLATIVE TRENDS; recent acquisitions received in the New York State Library. 1971. 9/yr. $9. New York State Library, Cultural Education Center, Empire State Plaza, Albany, NY 12230. TEL 518-474-3940. FAX 518-474-5786. Ed. Robert Allan Carter. index. circ. 900. (back issues avail.) **Document type:** government publication, bibliography.

340   US
LIBRARY BULLETIN. 1968. m. free. Center on Social Welfare Policy and Law, 275 Seventh Ave., 6th Fl., New York, NY 10001-6708. TEL 212-633-6967. FAX 212-633-6371. Ed. Ramon Curva. index. circ. 1,400. (back issues avail.) **Document type:** abstracting/indexing.
Description: Contains summaries of new or revised publications, court decisions, and federal agency policy materials relating to AFDC and general assistance programs.

340 011   NZ
LINX DATABASE. 1987. d. Auckland District Law Society, P.O. Box 58, Auckland, New Zealand. TEL 64-9-3031040. FAX 64-9-3033359. (Co-sponsor: Cantebury District Law Society)
● Available only online. Vendor(s): Kiwinet.
Formerly: Legal Index.
Description: Updated daily database of New Zealand reported and unreported High Court and Court of Appeal judgments since 1983, Family Court since 1991, NZ, Australian, British, Canadian legal journals since 1986.

340 690   AT   ISSN 0727-7989
LOCAL GOVERNMENT INDEX (NEW SOUTH WALES). 1975. 2/yr. Aus.$225 (renewal Aus.$175). Law Book Co. Ltd., 44-50 Waterloo Rd., North Ryde, N.S.W. 2113, Australia. TEL 02-887-0177. FAX 02-888-9706. TELEX ASBOOK 27995. Eds. W.A.C. Dale, S. White. (looseleaf format) **Document type:** abstracting/indexing.
Description: An index to government law, building law, environmental planning and planning law in N.S.W.

340   MH
MACAO. DIRECCAO DOS SERVICOS DE ESTATISTICA E CENSOS. ESTATISTICAS DA JUSTICA E DA CRIMINALIDADE/MACAO. CENSUS AND STATISTICS DEPARTMENT. STATISTICS OF JUSTICE AND CRIMINALITY. (Text in Portuguese) 1981. irreg. free. Direccao dos Servicos de Estatistica e Censos, Rua Inacio Baptista, No. 4-6, P.O. Box 3022, Macao. TEL 399-5311. FAX 307825. **Document type:** government publication.

011 341   US   ISSN 0226-8361
Z6464.M2
MARINE AFFAIRS BIBLIOGRAPHY; a comprehensive index to marine law and policy literature. (Text in French, German, Italian and Spanish) 1980. q. $95. University of Virginia, School of Law Library, Charlottesville, VA 22901. TEL 804-924-3384. FAX 804-982-2232. Eds. Christian L. Wiktor, Larry B. Wenger. circ. 350. **Document type:** abstracting/indexing, bibliography.

343.70   CN   ISSN 1182-8617
MARITIME LAW BOOK LTD. MASTER KEY WORD INDEX. 1990. a. Can.$42 (renewals Can.$12). Maritime Law Book Ltd., P.O. Box 302, Fredericton, NB E3B 4Y9, Canada. TEL 506-453-9921; 800-561-0220. FAX 506-453-9525. (looseleaf format)
Description: Provides cross-references to topical indexes.

340   US
MARYLAND. GENERAL ASSEMBLY. SUBJECT INDEX TO BILLS INTRODUCED IN THE SESSION. 1976. a. $10. Department of Legislative Reference, Legislative Sales, 90 State Circle, Annapolis, MD 21401. TEL 410-841-3885. **Document type:** government publication, abstracting/indexing.

347   US   ISSN 0098-7875
KFM4271
MICHIGAN. STATE COURT ADMINISTRATOR. ANNUAL REPORT. Key Title: Judicial Statistics. (Supplement avail.) 1961. a. $10 for annual report; supplement $25. State Court Administrative Office, Box 30048, Lansing, MI 48909. TEL 517-373-0130. FAX 517-373-8922. circ. 1,500 (controlled).

340   NE   ISSN 0921-819X
NETHERLANDS. CENTRAAL BUREAU VOOR DE STATISTIEK. KWARTAALBERICHT RECHTSBESCHERMING EN VEILIGHEID/NETHERLANDS. CENTRAL BUREAU OF STATISTICS. QUARTERLY BULLETIN ON JUSTICE AND SECURITY STATISTICS. (Text in Dutch and English) q. Centraal Bureau voor de Statistiek, Prinses Beatrixlaan 428, Postbus 959, 2270 AZ Voorburg, Netherlands. TEL 070-694341. (Orders to: SDU - Publishers, Postbus 20014, 2500 EA The Hague, Netherlands) **Document type:** government publication.
Formerly: Netherlands. Centraal Bureau voor de Statistiek. Maandstatistiek Rechtsbescherming en Veiligheid - Monthly Bulletin on Justice and Security Statistics.

340 011   CN
NEW BRUNSWICK STATUTE INDEX. 1971. a. Can.$110. Maritime Law Book Ltd., Box 302, Fredericton, NB E3B 4Y9, Canada. TEL 506-453-9921; 800-561-0220. FAX 506-453-9525. (back issues avail.) **Document type:** abstracting/indexing.
Formerly: Subject Matter Index to Public and Private Statutes of New Brunswick (ISSN 0713-8954)
Description: Arranged by topic or subject matter for both the public and private statutes of New Brunswick. Includes key word index.

347.9   US
NEW JERSEY. ADMINISTRATIVE OFFICE OF THE COURTS. COURT MANAGEMENT REPORT. m. Administrative Office of the Courts, RJH Justice Complex CN-037, Trenton, NJ 08625. TEL 609-292-9580.
Description: Statistical summary of court workload.

340   AT   ISSN 1031-7872
NEW SOUTH WALES STATUTES ANNOTATIONS. 3/yr. $360. Butterworths, 271-273 Lane Cove Rd., P.O. Box 345, N. Ryde, N.S.W. 2113, Australia. TEL 02-335-4444. FAX 02-335-4678. **Document type:** abstracting/indexing.

347   US
NORTH DAKOTA. JUDICIAL SYSTEM. ANNUAL REPORT. 1928. a. free. Judicial System, Office of State Court Administrator, State Capitol, Bismarck, ND 58505. TEL 701-224-4216. FAX 701-224-4480. Ed. Keith E. Nelson. stat.; circ. 1,000 (controlled). **Document type:** government publication.
Former titles: North Dakota. Judicial Conference. Annual Report; North Dakota. Judicial Council. Annual Report; North Dakota. Judicial Council. Statistical Compilation and Report (ISSN 0095-6120)

340   IT
NOSTRA TRIBUNA. 1952. m. L.15000 (Europe L.22500; elsewhere L.30000) (effective 1994). Casa Editrice La Tribuna, Via Don Minzoni 51, 29100 Piacenza, Italy. TEL 0523-759015. FAX 0523-757219. Dir. Mario Vitali.
Description: Anthology of reviews of new books on legislation, economy and agriculture.

340 016   CN
NOVA SCOTIA CURRENT LAW. every 4 wks. Can.$70. Nova Scotia Barristers' Society, 1475 Hollis St., Halifax, NS B3J 3M4, Canada. TEL 902-422-1491. Ed. Helen MacDonnell. **Document type:** abstracting/indexing.
Description: A cumulative index to Nova Scotia court decisions.

340 016   RU
NOVAYA LITERATURA PO SOTSIAL'NYM I GUMANITARNYM NAUKAM. GOSUDARSTVO I PRAVO; bibliograficheskii ukazatel' 1992. m. $114. Rossiiskaya Akademiya Nauk, Institut Nauchnoi Informatsii po Obshchestvennym Naukam, Ul. Krasikova 28-21, 117418 Moscow V-418, Russia. Ed. B.L. Polunin. **Document type:** bibliography.
Formed by the merger of (1973-1992): Novaya Inostrannaya Literatura po Obshchestvennym Naukam. Gosudarstvo i Pravo (ISSN 0134-2843); Which was formerly: Inostrannaya Literatura po Gosudarstvu i Pravu; (1973-1992): Novaya Sovetskaya Literatura po Obshchestvennym Naukam. Gosudarstvo i Pravo (ISSN 0134-2738)

340 016   US
PIMSLEUR'S CHECKLIST OF BASIC AMERICAN LEGAL PUBLICATIONS. irreg., latest 1988 (supplemented 1991). price varies. (American Association of Law Libraries) Fred B. Rothman & Co., 10368 W. Centennial Rd., Littleton, CO 80127. TEL 303-979-5657. FAX 303-978-1457. Ed. Marcia S. Zubrow. (looseleaf format) **Document type:** bibliography.
Formerly: Checklist of Basic American Legal Publications.

343   GW   ISSN 0340-7349
Z6461   CODEN: PILAEA
PUBLIC INTERNATIONAL LAW; a current bibliography of books and articles. (Text in English) 1975. 2/yr. DM.150($94) (Max-Planck Institute for Comparative Public Law and International Law) Springer-Verlag, Heidelberger Platz 3, 14197 Berlin, Germany. TEL 030-8207-1. FAX 030-8214091. (Subscr. in N. America to: Springer-Verlag New York, Inc., 44 Hartz Way, Secaucus, NJ 07096-2491. TEL 201-348-4033. FAX 201-348-4505) Ed.Bd. bibl. (also avail. in microform from UMI; reprint service avail. from ISI) **Indexed:** C.L.I., Leg.Per. **Document type:** bibliography.
—SWETS. **CCC.**
Description: Provides a comprehensive classification of the literature in bibliography form.

016 340   SZ   ISSN 0250-5940
RECHTSBIBLIOGRAPHIE/BIBLIOGRAPHIE JURIDIQUE/LAW BIBLIOGRAPHY. (In 2 vols.: Vol.1 Switzerland; Vol.2 Austria, Liechtenstein) 1978. a. 33 Fr. per vol. Studio Verlag, CH-8023 Zurich, Switzerland. Ed. N. Mario Cerutti. bk.rev. circ. 5,000. (also avail. in microfiche) **Document type:** bibliography.

REFUGEE ABSTRACTS. see *POPULATION STUDIES — Abstracting, Bibliographies, Statistics*

LAW — CIVIL LAW 3345

011 320　　　　EI　　ISSN 0256-3096
Z7165.E
S C A D BULLETIN. (Systeme Communautaire d'Acces a la Documentation) (Text in Danish, Dutch, English, French, German, Italian, Portuguese, Spanish) 1977. w. $138. Commission of the European Communities, 200 rue de la Loi, B-1049 Brussels, Belgium. (Dist. in U.S. by: UNIPUB, 4611-F Assembly Dr., Lanham, MD 20706-4391) Ed.Bd. **Document type:** bibliography.
●Also available online. Vendor(s): Commission of the European Communities.
—BLDSC (8087.449290).
　　Formerly (until 1985): Commission of the European Communities. Documentation Bulletin (ISSN 0378-441X)
　　Description: Analytical bulletin mentioning the bibliographic references of the main Community acts.

340　　　　　　　　　　GW
SCHWEITZER'S VADEMECUM RECHT. 1987. biennial. Schweitzer Sortiment, Lenbachplatz 1, Postfach 370104, 8000 Munich 37, Germany. TEL 089-55134-0.

340　　　　　　　　　　GW
SCHWEITZER'S VADEMECUM STEUERRECHT, JAHRESABSCHLEISS UND WIRTSCHAFTSPRUEFUNG. 1986. biennial. Schweitzer Sortiment, Lenbachplatz 1, Postfach 370104, 80333 Munich, Germany. TEL 089-55134-0.
　　Formerly: Schweitzer's Vademecum Steuerrecht und Wirtschaftspruefung.

345 316.8　　　　　　　SA
SOUTH AFRICA. CENTRAL STATISTICAL SERVICE. CRIMES: PROSECUTIONS AND CONVICTIONS WITH REGARD TO CERTAIN OFFENCES. (Report No. 00-11-01) a., latest for years 1992-1993. R.10 (foreign R.12.50). Central Statistical Service - Sentrale Statistiekdiens, Private Bag X44, Pretoria 0001, South Africa. TEL 27-12-310-8911. FAX 27-12-310-8500. (Orders to: Government Printing Works, Private Bag X85, Pretoria 0001, South Africa) **Document type:** government publication.

340.5 316.8　　　　　　SA
SOUTH AFRICA. CENTRAL STATISTICAL SERVICE. STATISTICAL RELEASE. STATISTICS OF CIVIL CASES FOR DEBT. (No. P0041) m. free. Central Statistical Service - Sentrale Statistiekdiens, Private Bag X44, Pretoria 0001, South Africa. TEL 27-12-310-8911. FAX 27-12-310-8500. **Document type:** government publication.
　　Description: Number and value of civil cases for debt recorded in South Africa.

340.5 316.8　　　　　　SA
SOUTH AFRICA. CENTRAL STATISTICAL SERVICE. STATISTICAL RELEASE. STATISTICS OF LIQUIDATIONS AND INSOLVENCIES. (No. P0043) m. free. Central Statistical Service - Sentrale Statistiekdiens, Private Bag X44, Pretoria 0001, South Africa. TEL 27-12-310-8911. FAX 27-12-310-8500. **Document type:** government publication.

340 016　　　　GW　　ISSN 0081-3680
KKA3
SPEZIALBIBLIOGRAPHIEN ZU FRAGEN DES STAATES UND DES RECHTS. 1963. irreg. price varies. Hochschule fuer Recht und Verwaltung, Informationszentrum, August-Bebel-Str. 89, 14482 Potsdam, Germany.

340 011　　　　US　　ISSN 1057-0586
Z7165.U5
STATE REFERENCE PUBLICATIONS; a bibliographic guide to state blue books, legislative manuals and other general reference sources. 1990. a. $60 (typically set in June). Government Research Service, 701 Jackson, Ste. 304, Topeka, KS 66603. TEL 913-232-7720. FAX 913-232-1615. Ed. Lynn Hellebust. **Document type:** bibliography, directory.
　　Formerly (until 1990): State Blue Books, Legislative Manuals and Reference Publications.
　　Description: Covers all fifty states, D.C., and Puerto Rico. Entries include the book's name, content, author & editor, publication date, frequency, price, address, telephone and fax numbers, plus the 800 number of the publishing agency or firm.

340　　　　　　　　　　US
STATISTICS IN LITIGATION: PRACTICE APPLICATIONS FOR LAWYERS. 1985. base vol. (plus a. suppl.) $95. Shepard's - McGraw-Hill, Inc., Box 35300, Colorado Springs, CO 80935-3530. TEL 800-525-2474.
　　Description: Practice-oriented information on how to strengthen client's cases with statistics.

340　　　　　　GW　　ISSN 0945-4527
STEUERRECHT - FUNDSTELLEN; Rechtsprechung, Verwaltung, Schrifttum. 1949. a. price varies. C.H. Beck'sche Verlagsbuchhandlung, Wilhelmstr. 9, 80801 Munich, Germany. TEL 089-38189-338. FAX 089-38189-398. TELEX 5215085-BECK-D. Ed. Joerg Moessner. circ. 3,300. **Document type:** bulletin.
　　Formerly (until 1990): Fundheft fuer Steuerrecht (ISSN 0532-8632)

340　　　　　　　　　　GW
STUDIENKATALOG-GRUNDKATALOG. RECHTSWISSENSCHAFT. 1953. s-a. DM.4.30. Buchwerbung in Berlin GmbH, Luetzowstr. 105-106, 10785 Berlin, Germany. adv.; bibl. **Document type:** bibliography.
　　Description: A student's bibliography of law.

347　　　　　　　　　　US
SURVEY OF JUDICIAL SALARIES. 1976. s-a. $12. National Center for State Courts, 300 Newport Ave., Williamsburg, VA 23187-8798. TEL 804-253-2000. FAX 804-220-0449. Ed. Janice Fernette. stat. circ. 3,600.
　　Former titles: Survey of Judicial Salaries in State Court Systems (ISSN 0196-7304); Quarterly Survey of Judicial Salaries in State Court Systems (ISSN 0098-9061)

340　　　　　　SW　　ISSN 0082-0318
HV8440
SWEDEN. STATISTISKA CENTRALBYRAAN. STATISTISKA MEDDELANDEN. SERIE R, RAETTSVAESEN. (Text in Swedish; table heads and summaries in English) 1963 N.S. irreg. SEK 700. Statistiska Centralbyraan, Publishing Unit, S-701 89 Oerebro, Sweden. circ. 1,400.

315.61　　　　　　　　　TU
TURKEY. DEVLET ISTATISTIK ENSTITUSU. ADALET ISTATISTIKLERI/TURKEY. STATE INSTITUTE OF STATISTICS. JUDICIAL STATISTICS. (Text in English, Turkish) 1937. a., latest 1991. $45. Devlet Istatistik Enstitusu - State Institute of Statistics, Necatibey Caddesi No. 114, 06100 Ankara, Turkey. TEL 90-312-4185027. FAX 90-312-4170432. circ. 840. **Document type:** government publication.
　　Description: Provides comprehensive statistics on the activities of all branches of government connected with the judiciary, including civil, administrative and criminal courts, the Supreme Court and Constitutional Court, Department of Forensic Medicine, and details of prison populations, sentencing, and prisoners released.

340 016 380　　　US　　ISSN 0041-672X
K25　　　　　　　　　CODEN: UCCLA7
UNIFORM COMMERCIAL CODE LAW JOURNAL. 1968. q. $131.50 (overseas $197.50) (effective 1994). Warren Gorham Lamont, One Penn Plaza, New York, NY 10119. TEL 212-971-5000. FAX 212-971-5240. (Subscr. to: The Park Square Bldg., 31 St. James Ave., Boston, MA 02116-4112. TEL 800-950-1207) Ed. Thomas M. Quinn. (also avail. in microform from UMI; reprint service avail. from RRI) Indexed: ABI Inform., Bank.Lit.Ind., BPIA, Bus.Ind., C.L.I., L.R.I., Leg.Cont., Leg.Per., Manage.Cont., SSCI, Tr.& Indus.Ind. **Document type:** trade publication.
—BLDSC (9090.666400); Faxon; UnCover; UMI. **CCC.**
　　Description: Covers every aspect of business practice affected by the Uniform Commercial Code: commercial lending, secured transactions, consumer credit, and negotiable instruments. Includes truth-in-lending and fair credit reporting.

341.2　　　　　　UN　　ISSN 0252-5321
JX170
UNITED NATIONS. TREATY SERIES. CUMULATIVE INDEX. French edition: Nations Unies. Recueil des Traites. Index Cumulatif (ISSN 0252-5461) 1957. irreg. United Nations Publications, Rm. DC2-0853, New York, NY 10017. TEL 212-963-8302. FAX 212-963-3489. **Document type:** abstracting/indexing.

340　　　　　　　　　　US
UNIVERSITY OF SOUTHERN CALIFORNIA. LAW CENTER. BIBLIOGRAPHY SERIES. irreg. University of Southern California, Law Center, Los Angeles, CA 90089-0071. TEL 213-740-8475. FAX 213-740-5502. **Document type:** bibliography.

016 340　　　　US　　ISSN 0085-7092
UNIVERSITY OF TEXAS AT AUSTIN. TARLTON LAW LIBRARY. LEGAL BIBLIOGRAPHY SERIES. 1970. irreg., no.36, 1993. price varies. University of Texas at Austin, Tarlton Law Library, 727 E. 26 St., Austin, TX 78705-5799. TEL 512-471-7726. FAX 512-471-6988. bibl. (processed) **Document type:** bibliography.

340　　　　　　AT　　ISSN 0816-9799
VICTORIAN STATUTES - ANNOTATIONS. 3/yr. (plus 2 updates). $260. Butterworths, 271-273 Lane Cove Rd., P.O. Box 345, North Ryde, N.S.W. 2113, Australia. TEL 02-335-4444. FAX 02-335-4678. **Document type:** abstracting/indexing.

340　　　　　　US　　ISSN 0886-0807
KF49
WASHINGTON SUMMARY. w. when Congress is in session. $55 to non-members; members $45. American Bar Association, Governmental Affairs Office, 1800 M St., N.W., Washington, DC 20036. TEL 202-331-2606. Ed. Julia C. Ross. circ. 2,000. **Document type:** newsletter.
　　Description: Abstracts from the Congressional Record and Federal Register items pertaining to legislation and federal agency activity of interest to the legal profession.

340　　　　　　UK　　ISSN 0264-3723
WEEKLY LAW DIGEST. 1958. w. £25.20 (typically set in Sep.). Justice of the Peace Ltd., Little London, Chichester, W. Sussex PO19 1PG, England. TEL 0243-783637. FAX 0243-779278. (back issues avail.) **Document type:** abstracting/indexing, academic/scholarly publication.
—BLDSC (9284.940000).
　　Description: Contains abbreviated summaries of cases, sentencing features and miscellaneous information.

362.7 345.01　　　GW　　ISSN 0176-6449
KK1192.A13
ZENTRALBLATT FUER JUGENDRECHT; Jugend und Familie - Jugendhilfe - Jugendgerichtshilfe. 1913. m. DM.136. Carl Heymanns Verlag KG, Luxemburgerstr. 449, 50939 Cologne, Germany. TEL 0221-46010-0. FAX 0221-4601069. Ed. Walter H. Zarbock. adv.; bk.rev. circ. 1,650. (back issues avail.) **Document type:** abstracting/indexing.
—BLDSC (9508.690000).
　　Formerly (until 1983): Zentralblatt fuer Jugendrecht und Jugendwohlfahrt.

LAW — Civil Law

A B I JOURNAL. (American Bankruptcy Institute) see BUSINESS AND ECONOMICS — Banking And Finance

340.5　　　　　　CN　　ISSN 0704-0288
K1
ADVOCATES QUARTERLY; a Canadian journal for practitioners of civil litigation. 1977. q. Can.$105. Canada Law Book Inc., 240 Edward St., Aurora, ON L4G 3S9, Canada. TEL 905-841-6472. FAX 905-841-5085. Ed. P. Theodore Matlow. adv. contact: Mary Cull. bk.rev. Indexed: C.L.I., Ind.Can.L.P.L., L.R.I., Leg.Per.
—BLDSC (0719.560000); Faxon.

340.5　　　　　　GW　　ISSN 0003-8997
ARCHIV FUER DIE CIVILISTISCHE PRAXIS. 1828. bi-m. DM.224. Verlag J.C.B Mohr (Paul Siebeck), Wilhelmstr. 18, 72074 Tuebingen, Germany. TEL 07071-923-0. FAX 07071-51104. TELEX 7262872-MOHR-D. (Subscr. to: Postfach 2040, 72010 Tuebingen, Germany) Ed.Bd. adv.; bk.rev.; index, cum.index. **Document type:** academic/scholarly publication.
—SWETS. **CCC.**
　　Description: Covers all aspects of German civil law.

LAW — CIVIL LAW

340.5   IT
ARCHIVIO CIVILE; revista mensile di dottrina, giurisprudenza e legislazione. 1964. m. L.100000 (Europe L.150000; elsewhere L.200000) (effective 1994). Casa Editrice La Tribuna, Via Don Minzoni 51, 29100 Piacenza, Italy. TEL 0523-759015. FAX 0523-757219. Dir. Alfonso Alibrandi. bibl.
Formerly (until 1975): Archivio della Responsabilita Civile.
Description: Covers doctrine, jurisprudence and legislation.

340.5   US   ISSN 0099-1244
KF8841
B A R - B R I BAR REVIEW. CIVIL PROCEDURE. a. $395. B A R - B R I Bar Review, 3280 Motor Ave., Los Angeles, CA 90034-3710. TEL 213-477-2542.

340.5   US
B N A CIVIL TRIAL MANUAL. (Subseries of: Trial Practice Series) 1985. bi-w. $877. The Bureau of National Affairs, Inc., 1231 25th St., N.W., Washington, DC 20037. TEL 202-452-4200. FAX 202-822-8092. TELEX 285656 BNAI WSH. (Subscr. to: 9435 Key West Ave., Rockville, MD 20037. TEL 800-372-1033) Ed. Robert A. Robbins. (looseleaf format; back issues avail.)
Description: Notification and reference service covering the litigation process from initial client interview through trial. Newsletter covers decisions on civil procedure and evidence, verdicts and settlements, and new procedure and practice techniques.

340.5   US
B N A CIVIL TRIAL MANUAL CURRENT REPORTERS. (Subseries of: Trial Practice Series) 1985. bi-w. $527. The Bureau of National Affairs, Inc., 1231 25th St., N.W., Washington, DC 20037. TEL 202-452-4200. FAX 202-822-8092. TELEX 285656 BNAI WSH. (Subscr. to: 9435 Key West Ave., Rockville, MD 20850. TEL 800-372-1033) Ed. Robert A. Robbins. index. (back issues avail.)
Document type: newsletter.
Description: Covers decisions on civil procedure and evidence, verdicts and settlements, and new procedures and practice techniques.

340.5   GW   ISSN 0522-5140
BAYERISCHES OBERSTES LANDESGERICHT. ENTSCHEIDUNGEN IN ZIVILSACHEN. 1951. q. C.H. Beck'sche Verlagsbuchhandlung, Wilhelmstr. 9, 80801 Munich, Germany. TEL 089-38189338. FAX 089-38189-398. Ed.Bd. (back issues avail.)
Document type: bulletin.

340.5   CN   ISSN 0824-717X
BRITISH COLUMBIA DECISIONS - CIVIL CASES. 1972. fortn. Can.$495. Western Legal Publications, 301-1 Alexander St., Vancouver, BC V6A 1B2, Canada. TEL 604-681-5671. FAX 604-687-2796. m.index. (looseleaf format)
●Also available online.
Description: Allows access to all available civil decisions from the British Columbia Court of Appeal, Supreme Courts of British Columbia and selected decisions of the British Columbia Provinical Courts.

340.5   AT
BRITTS: COMPARABLE VERDICTS IN PERSONAL INJURY CLAIMS. 1975. 6/yr. in 2 vols. Aus.$350 with updates. Law Book Co. Ltd., 44-50 Waterloo Rd., N. Ryde, N.S.W. 2113, Australia. TEL 02-887-0177. FAX 02-888-9706. TELEX ASBOOK 27995. Ed. M.G. Britts. (looseleaf format)
Description: Covers damages, personal injury claims and jurisdiction in Australia.

340.5 345   US   ISSN 0741-5788
KF4742
BULWARK. irreg. (approx. q.). membership only. (N L G Foundation) National Lawyers Guild (Boston), Civil Liberties Committee, 14 Beacon St., Ste. 407, Boston, MA 02108.

BUSINESS LAW IN EUROPE. see *LAW — International Law*

340.5   NZ
BUTTERWORTHS DISTRICT COURTS PRACTICE - CIVIL. base vol. (plus q. update). NZ.$296. Butterworths of New Zealand Ltd., 203-207 Victoria St., P.O. Box 472, Wellington, New Zealand. TEL 04-385-1479. FAX 04-385-1598. Ed. Moira Thompson. (looseleaf format)
Description: Guide to the workings of the District Court in its civil jurisdiction, including the annotated text of the District Courts Act.

340.5   US
C I S LEGISLATIVE HISTORIES ANNUAL. 1984. a. $245. Congressional Information Service, A Reed Reference Publishing Company, Part of the Reed Elsevier group, 4520 East-West Hwy., Bethesda, MD 20814-3389. TEL 301-654-1550; 800-638-8380. FAX 301-654-4033. bibl. (back issues avail.)
Description: Covers every significant law enacted during the year. Provides a summary of major provisions, citations to key publications in the law's history, citations to previous as well as current Congresses.

340.5   US
CALIFORNIA CIVIL ACTIONS: PLEADING AND PRACTICE. 1983. 5 base vols. (plus irreg. suppl.). $800. Matthew Bender & Co., Inc., 11 Penn Plaza, New York, NY 10001. TEL 212-967-7707. (looseleaf format)
Description: Practice guide for handling civil action and proceedings in California. Provides detailed textual analysis of all the important stages before, during and after trial.

340.5   US
KFC995.A1C32
CALIFORNIA CIVIL LAW REPORTER. 1989. 26/yr. $250. La Jolla Legal Publications, Inc., 5580 La Jolla Blvd., Ste. 116, La Jolla, CA 92037. TEL 619-236-0679. Ed. Bruce E. May. **Document type:** newsletter.

340.5   US
CALIFORNIA DEPOSITION AND DISCOVERY PRACTICE. 1958. 3 base vols. (plus irreg. suppl.). $480. Matthew Bender & Co., Inc., 11 Penn Plaza, New York, NY 10001. TEL 212-967-7707. Eds. J.N. DeMeo, John F. DeMeo. (looseleaf format)
Description: Complete guide, with law, text, annotated forms, and procedural checklists to every phase of discovery procedure in civil cases. Provides extensive discussion of privileges, motion procedures, and sanctions, as well as thorough coverage of all methods of obtaining discovery under the Civil Discovery Act of 1986.

340.5   US
CALIFORNIA TORTS. 1985. 6 base vols. (plus irreg. suppl.). $935. Matthew Bender & Co., Inc., 11 Penn Plaza, New York, NY 10001. TEL 212-967-7707. Ed.Bd. (looseleaf format)
Description: Covers the well-established areas of civil tort liability, such as government tort liability, professional malpractice, and motor vehicle cases. Highlights the newly emerging areas as well.

340.5   US
CALIFORNIA TRIAL GUIDE. 1986. 5 base vols. (plus irreg. suppl.). $640. Matthew Bender & Co., Inc., 11 Penn Plaza, New York, NY 10001. TEL 212-967-7707. Ed. Earl Johnson. (looseleaf format)
Description: Practice tool for civil practitioners, providing substantive and procedural guidance to the evidentiary issues encountered throughout the trial process.

340.5 325.1   CN   ISSN 0843-7564
CANADA'S IMMIGRATION AND CITIZENSHIP BULLETIN. 1989. 10/yr. Can.$112. Canada Law Book Inc., 240 Edward St., Aurora, ON L4G 3S9, Canada. TEL 905-841-6472. FAX 905-841-5085. Ed. Frank N. Marrocco. **Document type:** newsletter.

340.5   US
CIVIL ACTIONS AGAINST STATE GOVERNMENT: ITS DIVISIONS, AGENCIES, AND OFFICES. 1982. base vol. (plus a. suppl.). $95. Shepard's - McGraw-Hill, Inc., Box 35300, Colorado Springs, CO 80935-3530. TEL 800-525-2474.
Description: Information on bringing or defending a civil action suit against state or local governments in all 50 states. State and federal cases are examined as well as statutes and constitutional provisions.

CIVIL & MILITARY LAW JOURNAL. see *LAW — Military Law*

340.5   US
CIVIL COMMITMENT IN MINNESOTA. base vol. (plus irreg. suppl.) 2nd ed., 1991. $95. Butterworth Legal Publishers (Salem) (Subsidiary of: Reed Elsevier plc), 8 Industrial Way, Bldg. C, Salem, NH 03079. TEL 800-548-4001. FAX 603-898-9858. Ed. Eric S. Janus. (looseleaf format)
Description: Covers all the procedures from admissions and rights of patients to review and discharge.

340.5   CN
CIVIL DOCUMENT PROCESSING MANUAL. base vol. (plus irreg. suppl.). Can.$28. Ministry of Attorney General, Parliament Bldgs., Victoria, B.C. V8V 1X4, Canada. TEL 604-387-5818. (Subscr. to: Crown Publications, 546 Yates St., Victoria, B.C. V8W 1K8, Canada. TEL 604-386-4636) (looseleaf format; back issues avail.)

340.5   UK   ISSN 0261-9261
CIVIL JUSTICE QUARTERLY. 1982. q. £86. Sweet & Maxwell, South Quay Plaza, 7th Fl., 183 Marsh Wall, London E14 9FT, England. TEL 071-538-8816. FAX 071-538-9508. Ed. Annabel Macris. adv. contact: Jackie Wood. (reprint service avail. from RRI) **Indexed:** C.L.I., Leg.Per. **Document type:** bulletin. —BLDSC (3273.740000); UnCover; SWETS; UMI.

340.5   PK
CIVIL LAW CASES. (Text in English) 1979. m. Rps.640($42) (effective 1993). P.L.D. Publishers, 35 Nabha Rd., Lahore 1, Pakistan. TEL 92-42-213497. Ed. Malik Muhammad Saeed. (also avail. in microfilm from UMI; back issues avail.)

340.5   US   ISSN 0009-7934
CIVIL LIBERTIES REPORTER. vol.5, 1970. q. $20 includes membership. American Civil Liberties Union of New Jersey, 2 Washington Place, Newark, NJ 07102. TEL 201-642-2084. adv.; circ. 6,600 (controlled). **Document type:** newspaper.

340.5   UK   ISSN 1352-4496
▼**CIVIL LITIGATION.** 1993. a. £15. Jordan Publishing Ltd., 21 St. Thomas St., Bristol BS1 6JS, England. TEL 0272-230600. FAX 0272-250486. Ed. Grenville Perry. **Document type:** academic/scholarly publication.

340.5   US   ISSN 0199-0802
KFC995.A1
CIVIL LITIGATION REPORTER. 1979. 8/yr. $175. Continuing Education of the Bar - California, University of California Extension, 2300 Shattuck Ave., Berkeley, CA 94704. TEL 510-642-0306; 800-924-3924. FAX 510-642-3788. (Co-sponsor: State Bar of California) Ed. Michael Woods. index. (tabloid format; back issues avail.)

340.5   AT
CIVIL PROCEDURE VICTORIA. 3 base vols. (plus updates 12/yr.). $565. Butterworths, 271-273 Lane Cove Rd., P.O. Box 345, North Ryde, N.S.W. 2113, Australia. TEL 02-335-4444. FAX 02-335-4655. (looseleaf format)

340.5 364   US
KF9375.A59
CIVIL R I C O LITIGATION REPORTER; the national journal of record of litigation brought under the Federal Racketeer Influenced Corrupt Organizations Act. 1984. m. $800. Andrews Publications, 1646 West Chester Pike, Box 1000, Westtown, PA 19395. TEL 215-399-6600; 800-345-1101. FAX 215-399-6610. Ed. Jay Steinberg. abstr.; bibl.; stat.; s-a. cum.index. (looseleaf format; back issues avail.) **Document type:** newsletter.
Formerly: Racketeering Litigation Reporter (ISSN 0887-7874)

LAW — CIVIL LAW

340.5 US ISSN 0884-0032
KF9375.A15
CIVIL R I C O REPORT; the weekly newsletter on civil litigation under the Racketeer Influenced and Corrupt Organization Act. 1985. w. $795 (foreign $817). Buraff Publications (Subsidiary of: Millin Publications, Inc.), 1350 Connecticut Ave. N.W., Ste. 1000, Washington, DC 20036. TEL 800-333-1291. FAX 202-862-0999. Ed. Robert Latzko. (looseleaf format; back issues avail.) **Document type:** newsletter.
—CCC.
Description: Covers civil litigation under the Racketeer Influenced and Corrupt Organizations Act: case summaries, new RICO suits being filed, practical defense tactics, and legislation. Features advice from leading attorneys on significant trends and new strategies.

340.5 364 US
CIVIL REMEDIES IN DRUG ENFORCEMENT REPORT. 1988. 6/yr. free. National Association of Attorneys General, 444 N. Capitol St., N.W., Ste. 309, Washington, DC 20001. TEL 202-434-8000. FAX 202-434-8008. Ed. Mark Cohen. (looseleaf format; back issues avail.) **Document type:** newsletter.
Formerly: State Civil R I C O Drug Enforcement Newsletter.

340.5 US
CIVIL RIGHTS AND CIVIL LIBERTIES LITIGATION: THE LAW OF SECTION 1983, 3-E. 2 base vols. (plus a. suppl.) $165. Shepard's - McGraw-Hill, Inc., Box 35300, Colorado Springs, CO 80935-3530. TEL 800-525-2474.
Description: Covers Section 1983 issues, from both the plaintiff's and the defendant's perspective. Includes the "new" due process, local government and supervisory liability, immunities, damages and injunctive relief, attorney's fees and advice on whom to sue.

340.5 US ISSN 0887-1191
KF1325.C58
CIVIL RIGHTS LITIGATION AND ATTORNEY FEES ANNUAL HANDBOOK. 1985. a. $75. (National Lawyers Guild) Clark - Boardman - Callaghan Company Ltd., 375 Hudson St., New York, NY 10014. TEL 212-929-7500; 800-221-9428. FAX 212-924-0460. Eds. Steven Saltzman, Barbara Wolvovitz.
—UnCover.
Description: Offers an update and overview of Section 1983 litigation, with emphasis on recent developments, emerging trends, attorney fees and practical aids, all from the perspectives of civil rights experts.

CIVIL SERVICE PERSONNEL NOTES. see *BUSINESS AND ECONOMICS — Personnel Management*

340.5 NE
COMPANIES AND OTHER LEGAL PERSONS UNDER NETHERLANDS LAW AND NETHERLANDS ANTILLES LAW. (Text in English) 1989. base vol. (plus a. update). fl.295($169) (effective 1994). Kluwer Law and Taxation Publishers (Subsidiary of: Wolters Kluwer N.V.), P.O. Box 23, 7400 GA Deventer, Netherlands. TEL 31-5700-47261. FAX 31-5700-22244. TELEX 49295 KLUDV NL. (Dist. by: Libresso Distribution Centre, P.O. Box 23, 7400 GA Deventer, Netherlands. TEL 31-5700-33155. FAX 31-5700-33834; In N. America: Kluwer Law and Taxation Publishers, 675 Massachusetts Ave., Cambridge, MA 02139. TEL 617-354-0140. FAX 617-354-8595) Eds. H.C.S. Warendorf, R.L. Thomas. (looseleaf format)
Description: Authorized translation of the Netherlands Civil Code section covering the law on legal persons, with commentary and references to other relevant points of Dutch law.

340.5 US
CONSUMER FINANCE LAW QUARTERLY REPORT. q. $21 to non-members. Conference on Consumer Finance Law, 2501 N. Blackwelder, Box 117-A, Oklahoma City, OK 73106. TEL 405-521-5198. Ed. Alvin C. Harrell. adv.
Description: Analyzes trends in banking, financial services, and consumer finance and covers developments affecting consumer credit.

340.5 UK ISSN 0967-1978
CONSUMER LAW JOURNAL. bi-m. £125. Sweet & Maxwell, South Quay Plaza, 7th Fl., 183 Marsh Wall, London E14 9FT, England. TEL 071-538-8686. FAX 071-538-9508. Ed. Sally Ann Drever. adv. contact: Jackie Wood. **Document type:** bulletin.
Description: Presents articles covering all areas of consumer law.

CONTRATTO E IMPRESA; dialoghi con la giurisprudenza civile e commerciale. see *LAW — Corporate Law*

345 US ISSN 0895-0016
K9
DEFENSE COUNSEL JOURNAL.* 1934. q. $55. International Association of Defense Counsel, 1 N. Franklin St., Ste. 2400, Chicago, IL 60606-3401. TEL 312-368-1494. FAX 312-368-1854. Ed. Richard B. Allen. bk.rev.; index, cum.index every 5 yrs. circ. 3,700. (also avail. in microform from UMI,WSH; reprint service avail. from UMI,WSH) **Indexed:** ABI Inform., BPIA, Bus.Ind., C.L.I., Geo.Abstr., INIS Atomind., L.R.I., Leg.Cont., Leg.Per., Mar.Aff.Bibl. **Document type:** academic/scholarly publication.
●Also available online. Vendor(s): West Services, Inc. Also available on CD-ROM. Producer(s): University Microfilms International.
—BLDSC (3546.213600); Faxon; UnCover; UMI.
Formerly (until vol. 53, 1987): Insurance Counsel Journal (ISSN 0020-465X)
Description: For lawyers and insurance executives engaged in the defense of major civil litigation, provides commentary, analysis, and developments in insurance and tort and civil procedure law.

340.5 US ISSN 0011-7587
K4
DEFENSE LAW JOURNAL. 1957. 5/yr. $85. Michie Company, Box 7587, Charlottesville, VA 22906-7587. TEL 804-972-7600. FAX 804-972-7666. Ed. Richard M. Patterson. bk.rev.; index, cum.index. (looseleaf format; also avail. in microform from UNM; reprint service avail. from UMI) **Indexed:** C.L.I., Curr.Cont., L.R.I., Leg.Per., SSCI.
—BLDSC (3546.220000); Faxon; UnCover; UMI.

EMPLOYEE RELATIONS GUIDE TO FEDERAL LAWS AND REGULATIONS. see *BUSINESS AND ECONOMICS — Labor And Industrial Relations*

340.5 UK ISSN 0966-193X
ENTERTAINMENT & MEDIA LAW REPORTS. bi-m. £195. Sweet & Maxwell, South Quay Plaza, 7th Fl., 183 Marsh Wall, London E14 9FT, England. TEL 071-538-8686. FAX 071-538-9508. Ed. Nick Gingell. adv. contact: Jackie Wood. **Document type:** bulletin.
Description: Presents decisions of the High Court in the media and entertainment fields.

340.5 GW ISSN 0425-1288
ENTSCHEIDUNGEN DER OBERLANDESGERICHTE IN ZIVILSACHEN. 1965. 5/yr. DM.208. C.H. Beck'sche Verlagsbuchhandlung, Wilhelmstr. 9, 80801 Munich, Germany. TEL 089-38189-338. FAX 089-38189-398. TELEX 521085-BECK-D. Eds. J. Kuntze, M. Maerz. (back issues avail.) **Document type:** bulletin.

340.5 US
FEDERAL CIVIL JUDICIAL PROCEDURE AND RULES. a. West Publishing Corp., 620 Opperman Dr., Eagan, MN 55123. TEL 612-687-8000; 800-328-9352. FAX 612-687-7302. **Document type:** trade publication.

340.5 US
FEDERAL CIVIL PROCEDURE HANDBOOK. 1988. a. $19. Gould Publications, 1333 N. U.S. Hwy. 17-92, Longwood, FL 32750-3724. TEL 407-695-9500. FAX 407-695-2906. adv.; bk.rev. (looseleaf format)
Description: Contains the federal rules of civil procedure, unannotated.

340.5 US
FLORIDA CIVIL DISCOVERY MANUAL. 1979. base vol. (plus suppl. 2-3/yr.). $80. Butterworth Legal Publishers (Salem) (Subsidiary of: Reed Elsevier plc), 8 Industrial Way, Bldg. C, Salem, NH 03079. TEL 800-548-4001. FAX 603-898-9858. (looseleaf format)

340.5 US
FLORIDA CIVIL PROCEDURE. 1990. 3 base vols. (plus irreg. supplements). $120. Butterworth Legal Publishers (Salem) (Subsidiary of: Reed Elsevier plc), 8 Industrial Way, Bldg. C, Salem, NH 03079. TEL 800-548-4001. FAX 603-898-9858. Ed. Elizabeth Hapner. (looseleaf format)
Description: Includes practical analysis of current law and developments, forms, checklists and applicable provisions of all relevant rules and statutes.

FREE SPEECH NEWSLETTER. see *POLITICAL SCIENCE — Civil Rights*

340.5 US ISSN 0363-5783
KFC52.S8
THE GAVEL;* jury verdicts on civil actions in California and Nevada Superior Courts. 1961. s-m. $260. California Jury Verdicts, 5900 Hollis St., No. R2, Emeryville, CA 94608-2008. TEL 916-485-4990. FAX 916-485-4917. Ed. John D. Hartney. adv.; bk.rev. circ. 300. **Indexed:** C.L.I., Leg.Per.

340.5 US
GILBERT LAW SUMMARIES. CIVIL PROCEDURE. irreg., 14th ed., 1989. $15.95. Harcourt Brace Legal & Professional Publications, Inc., 176 W. Adams, Ste. 2100, Chicago, IL 60603. TEL 312-853-3662.

340.5 IT ISSN 0017-0631
GIUSTIZIA CIVILE; rivista mensile di giurisprudenza. 1951. m. L.220000 (foreign L.330000). Casa Editrice Dott. A. Giuffre, Via Busto Arsizio 40, 20151 Milan, Italy. TEL 02-38000905. FAX 02-38009582. Ed. Mario Stella Richter. adv.; bk.rev.; bibl.; index, cum.index. circ. 9,700. (tabloid format) **Indexed:** ELLIS.

340.5 IT
GIUSTIZIA CIVILE. REPERTORIO GENERALE ANNUALE. 1955. a. price varies. Casa Editrice Dott. A. Giuffre, Via Busto Arsizio 40, 20151 Milan, Italy. TEL 02-38000905. FAX 02-38009582. Ed. Angelo Jannuzzi.

340.5 US ISSN 0017-8039
K8
HARVARD CIVIL RIGHTS - CIVIL LIBERTIES LAW REVIEW. 1966. 2/yr. $24 (Canada $30). Harvard University, Law School, Publications Center, Hastings Hall, Cambridge, MA 02138. TEL 617-495-3694. adv.; bk.rev. circ. 1,300. (also avail. in microform from UMI,WSH,PMC; back issues avail.; reprint service avail. from UMI,WSH) **Indexed:** C.I.J.E., C.L.I., Crim.Just.Abstr., Curr.Cont., Human Resour.Abstr., L.R.I., Leg.Cont., Leg.Per., P.A.I.S., Refug.Abstr., Sage Urb.Stud.Abstr., SSCI. **Document type:** academic/scholarly publication.
●Also available online. Vendor(s): West Services, Inc.
—BLDSC (4265.885000); Faxon; UnCover.

HARVARD HUMAN RIGHTS JOURNAL. see *POLITICAL SCIENCE — Civil Rights*

340.5 618 US
KF2905.3.A59
HEALTH LAW LITIGATION REPORTER; the monthly national journal of record reporting general medical malpractice, obstetrical and gynecological litigation. 1985. m. $800. Andrews Publications, 1646 West Chester Pike, Box 1000, Westtown, PA 19395. TEL 215-399-6600; 800-345-1101. FAX 215-399-6610. Ed. Mary Rhoads. abstr.; bibl.; stat.; cum.index every 6 mos. circ. 92. (looseleaf format; back issues avail.) **Document type:** newsletter.
Former titles (until 1993): Medical Malpractice - Ob-Gyn Litigation Reporter (ISSN 1056-4098); (until 1991): Medical Malpractice Litigation Reporter (ISSN 0882-8555)
Description: Covers litigation involving medical negligence, breach of standard of care, as well as women's health concerns such as contraceptive devices and abortion.

HUMAN RIGHTS. see *POLITICAL SCIENCE — Civil Rights*

HUMAN RIGHTS QUARTERLY; a comparative and international journal of the social sciences, humanities and law. see *SOCIOLOGY*

LAW — CIVIL LAW

345   US
I A D C COMMITTEE NEWSLETTER.* m. International Association of Defense Counsel, 1 N. Franklin St., Ste. 2400, Chicago, IL 60606-3401. TEL 312-368-1494. FAX 312-368-1854. **Document type:** newsletter.
    Description: Aimed primarily at defense attorneys in trial law.

340.5   GW   ISSN 0942-8712
▼**I M M - D A T SCHMERZENSGELD DATENBANK**. 1992. q. DM.192. C.H. Beck'sche Verlagsbuchhandlung, Wilhelmstr. 9, 80801 Munich, Germany. TEL 089-38189338. FAX 089-38189398. TELEX 5215085-BECK-D. Eds. Andreas Slizyk, Hermann Schlindwein. **Document type:** bulletin.

IDAHO BANKRUPTCY COURT REPORT. see *LAW — Judicial Systems*

IMMIGRATION BRIEFINGS; practical, tight-knit analysis of U.S. immigration and nationality law. see *POPULATION STUDIES*

IMMIGRATION LAW REPORTER. SECOND SERIES. see *POPULATION STUDIES*

341   NE
▼**INTERNATIONAL ENCYCLOPAEDIA OF LAWS. COMMERCIAL AND ECONOMIC LAW**. (Text in English) 1994. base vol. (plus irreg. updates). Kluwer Law and Taxation Publishers (Subsidiary of: Wolters Kluwer N.V.), P.O. Box 23, 7400 GA Deventer, Netherlands. TEL 31-5700-47261. FAX 31-5700-22244. TELEX 49295 KLUDV NL. (Dist. by: Libresso Distribution Centre, P.O. Box 23, 7400 GA Deventer, Netherlands. TEL 31-5700-33155. FAX 31-5700-33834; In N. America: Kluwer Law and Taxation Publishers, 675 Massachusetts Ave., Cambridge, MA 02139. TEL 617-354-0140. FAX 617-354-8595) Ed. J. Stuyck. (looseleaf format) **Document type:** monographic series.
    Description: Publishes studies of the legal rules of individual countries which directly affect economic relations, from an international, comparative perspective; also discusses international aspects of private and public law, including GATT, and EC economic law and legislation, including case law of the EC Court of Justice.

341   NE
▼**INTERNATIONAL ENCYCLOPAEDIA OF LAWS. CONTRACTS**. (Text in English) 1993. base vol. (plus irreg. updates). fl.200($115) (effective 1994). Kluwer Law and Taxation Publishers (Subsidiary of: Wolters Kluwer N.V.), P.O. Box 23, 7400 GA Deventer, Netherlands. TEL 31-5700-47261. FAX 31-5700-22244. TELEX 49295 KLUDV NL. (Dist. by: Libresso Distribution Centre, P.O. Box 23, 7400 GA Deventer, Netherlands. TEL 31-5700-33155. FAX 31-5700-33834; In N. America: Kluwer Law and Taxation Publishers, 675 Massachusetts Ave., Cambridge, MA 02139. TEL 617-354-0140. FAX 617-354-8595) Ed. Jacques Herbots. (looseleaf format) **Document type:** monographic series.
    Description: Publishes studies of the contract law of individual countries, discussing general principles from an international, comparative perspective, as well as specific contracts and quasi-contracts.

INTERNATIONAL JOURNAL OF REFUGEE LAW. see *POLITICAL SCIENCE — International Relations*

340.5 610   JA
IRYO JIKO JOHO SENTA. SENTA NYUSU/MEDICAL MALPRACTICE INFORMATION CENTER IN JAPAN. NEWS. (Text in Japanese) 1991. m. 3000 Yen. Iryo Jiko Joho Senta, 807, Ofisu Sakae, 16-23, Sakae 4-chome, Naka-ku, Nagoya-shi, Aichiken 460, Japan.

340.5   AT   ISSN 0727-7954
JACKSON AND BYRON LOCAL COURTS (CIVIL CLAIMS) PRACTICE. (Avail. in Premier Series of Standard Series) 1980. 8/yr. in 4 vols. Aus.$460 with updates. Law Book Co. Ltd., 44-50 Waterloo Rd., N. Ryde, N.S.W. 2113, Australia. TEL 02-887-0177. FAX 02-888-9706. TELEX ASBOOK 27995. Eds. M. Morahan, M. Price. (looseleaf format)
    Description: Covers court practice, local courts, civil claims, small debts and jurisdiction in New South Wales.

340.5   JA   ISSN 0075-4188
JOURNAL OF CIVIL PROCEDURE/MINJI SOSHO ZASSHI. (Text in Japanese; summaries in English or German) 1954. a. 1500 Yen. (Japan Association of Civil Procedure - Minji Soshoho Gakkai) Horitsu Bunka Sha, 71 Kamigamo-Iwagu-Kakiuchi-cho, Kita-ku, Kyoto, Japan. adv.; bk.rev. circ. 1,500.

340 301.4157   US
JOURNAL OF SEXUAL LIBERTY. 1985. m. $10. Committee to Preserve Our Sexual & Civil Liberties, Box 422385, San Francisco, CA 94142-2385. Ed. Jerry Jansen. adv.; bk.rev. circ. 100. (back issues avail.)
    Description: Summary of recent happenings in the area of sex and civil liberties.

340.5
JURISDICTION IN CIVIL ACTIONS. 2 base vols. (plus a. suppl.), 2nd ed., 1991. $165. Butterworth Legal Publishers (Salem) (Subsidiary of: Reed Elsevier plc), 8 Industrial Way, Bldg. C, Salem, NH 03079. TEL 800-548-4001. FAX 603-898-9858. Ed. Robert C. Casad.
    Description: Provides treatment of civil jurisdiction in all state and federal courts.

340.5   US   ISSN 0737-8130
KF1266.A15L35
L D R C BULLETIN. 1981. q. $110. Libel Defense Resource Center, 404 Park Ave. S., 16th Fl., New York, NY 10016. TEL 212-889-2306. FAX 212-689-3315. (back issues avail.) **Document type:** bulletin.
    Description: Covers new developments in media libel and privacy law.

346 333.33
LANDLORD REMEDIES IN FLORIDA. 1987. base vol. (plus supplement). $80. Butterworth Legal Publishers (Salem) (Subsidiary of: Reed Elsevier plc), 8 Industrial Way, Bldg. C, Salem, NH 03079. TEL 800-548-4001. FAX 603-898-9858. (looseleaf format)

340.5   US   ISSN 0271-5228
KF587.8.L35
LANDLORD TENANT LAW BULLETIN. 1979. m. $60. Quinlan Publishing Co., Inc., 23 Drydock Ave., Boston, MA 02110. TEL 617-542-0048; 800-229-2084. FAX 617-345-9646. index. (back issues avail.) **Document type:** newsletter. —UMI. CCC.
    Description: For residential and commerical property owners and managers. Contains court decisions on tenancy law.

340.5   US   ISSN 0191-877X
KF1307.A73
LAW ENFORCEMENT LEGAL DEFENSE MANUAL. Key Title: Defense Manual. 1973. q. $98 (effective 1994). (Americans for Effective Law Enforcement, Inc.) Legal Research Publications, Inc., 421 Ridgewood Ave., Ste. 100, Glen Ellyn, IL 60137-4900. TEL 708-858-6392. Ed. James P. Manak. adv.; bk.rev. circ. 1,000. (also avail. in microform from UMI; back issues avail.) **Indexed:** CJPI. **Document type:** trade publication.
    Formerly (until 1978): A.E.L.E. Law Enforcement Legal Defense Manual (ISSN 0092-2552)
    Description: Covers civil litigation involving state, county and municipal law enforcement agencies.

347.91   CN
LAW OF DAMAGES. base vol. (plus irreg. updates). Can.$127. Canada Law Book Inc., 240 Edward St., Aurora, ON L4G 3S9, Canada. TEL 905-841-6472. FAX 905-841-5085. Ed. Stephen M. Waddams. adv. contact: Mary Cull. (looseleaf format)
    Description: Provides an accurate account of the present law in Canadian common law jurisdictions, with reference to English, Commonwealth and American cases where appropriate.

346   US
LAW OF PRODUCTS LIABILITY. 1990. 2 base vols. (plus a. supplement). $185. Butterworth Legal Publishers (Salem) (Subsidiary of: Reed Elsevier plc), 8 Industrial Way, Bldg. C, Salem, NH 03079. TEL 800-548-4001. FAX 603-898-9858. Ed. Marshall S. Shapo.
    Description: Study of issues that occur in products liability litigation.

LAWYERS' COMMITTEE FOR CIVIL RIGHTS UNDER LAW. COMMITTEE REPORT. see *POLITICAL SCIENCE — Civil Rights*

346   US
LAWYER'S GUIDE TO THE TEXAS DECEPTIVE TRADE PRACTICES ACT. base vol. (plus a. supplement). $95. Butterworth Legal Publishers (Salem) (Subsidiary of: Reed Elsevier plc), 8 Industrial Way, Bldg. C, Salem, NH 03079. TEL 800-548-4001. FAX 603-898-9858. Ed. Richard M. Alderman. (looseleaf format)

340.5   UK
LEASEHOLD LAW. irreg. £172. Longman Group Ltd., Law, Tax and Finance Division, 21-27 Lambs Conduit St., London WC1N 3NJ, England. TEL 071-242-2548. FAX 071-831-8119. Ed. Trevor Aldridge. **Document type:** bulletin.
    Description: Analysis of landlord and tenant law.

347.7 658   US
LEGAL ASPECTS OF SELLING AND BUYING. base vol. (plus a. supplement). $70. Shepard's - McGraw-Hill, Inc., Box 35300, Colorado Springs, CO 80935-3530. TEL 800-525-2474. Ed. Philip F. Zeidman.
    Description: Antitrust and distribution law guide for dealing with the relationships between buyers and sellers.

LENDER LIABILITY LITIGATION REPORTER; the national journal of record of lawsuits brought by borrowers against their lending institutions. see *LAW — Corporate Law*

346   US
LETTERS OF INTENT AND OTHER PRECONTRACTUAL DOCUMENTS; comparative analysis and forms. base vol. (plus supplements). $85. Butterworth Legal Publishers (Salem) (Subsidiary of: Reed Elsevier plc), 8 Industrial Way, Bldg. C, Salem, NH 03079. TEL 800-548-4001. FAX 603-898-9858. Ed. Ralph B. Lake.
    Description: Examines the impact of precontractual agreements on subsequently created contracts, comparing civil law and common law countries' practices with regard to the use and enforceability of precontractual documents.

340.5   US
KF4225.A15L48
LEVY'S CITES. 1989. 9/yr. $135. Adolph J. Levy, Ed. & Pub., 518 S. Rampart St., New Orleans, LA 70113. TEL 504-586-9707. (back issues avail.) **Document type:** newsletter.
    Description: Reports plaintiff-favorable personal injury cases.

340   US   ISSN 0271-5481
KF1307.A73
LIABILITY REPORTER. 1973. m. $158. Americans for Effective Law Enforcement, Inc., 5519 N. Cumberland Ave., Ste. 1008, Chicago, IL 60656-1498. TEL 312-763-2800. Ed.Bd. adv.; bk.rev.; bibl.; index. circ. 3,000. (looseleaf format; back issues avail.) **Indexed:** CJPI. —UMI.
    Formerly (until 1979): A E L E Law Enforcement Legal Liability Reporter (ISSN 0092-0940)
    Description: Covers law regarding civil liability issues in law enforcement.

346 368.5   US
LITIGATION AND PREVENTION OF INSURER BAD FAITH. base vol. (plus a. supplement). $95. Shepard's - McGraw-Hill, Inc., Box 35300, Colorado Springs, CO 80935-3530. TEL 800-525-2474.
    Description: Traces the development of damages for breach of contract, claims for foreseeable or consequential damages, claims for emotional distress and punitive damages.

346 333.33   US
LOUISIANA LANDLORD & TENANT LAW. 1987. base vol. (plus a. supplement). $120. Butterworth Legal Publishers (Salem) (Subsidiary of: Reed Elsevier plc), 8 Industrial Way, Bldg. C, Salem, NH 03079. TEL 800-548-4001. FAX 603-898-9858. (looseleaf format)

LAW — CIVIL LAW

340.5   US
LOUISIANA LAW OF UNJUST ENRICHMENT IN QUASI-CONTRACTS. 1991. base vol. (plus supplements). $110. Butterworth Legal Publishers (Salem) (Subsidiary of: Reed Elsevier plc), 8 Industrial Way, Bldg. C, Salem, NH 03079. TEL 800-548-4001. FAX 603-898-9858. Ed. Alain A. Levasseur. (looseleaf format)
   Description: Discusses all aspects of quasi-contracts and the principle of unjust enrichment in the Louisiana Civil Code, including examples, interpretations and case analyses.

346   AT
MCDONALD, HENRY AND MEEK: AUSTRALIAN BANKRUPTCY LAW AND PRACTICE. 1977. 6/yr. in 2 vols. Aus.$410 with updates. Law Book Co. Ltd., 44-50 Waterloo Rd., N. Ryde, N.S.W. 2113, Australia. TEL 02-887-0177. FAX 02-888-9706. TELEX ASBOOK 27995. Ed.Bd. (looseleaf format)
   Description: Covers bankruptcy, court practice and jurisdiction in Australia.

340.5   US
MAINE CIVIL REMEDIES. (2nd ed., 1992) 1988. base vol. (plus supplement). $95. Butterworth Legal Publishers (Salem) (Subsidiary of: Reed Elsevier plc), 8 Industrial Way, Bldg. C, Salem, NH 03079. TEL 800-548-4001. FAX 603-898-9858. Ed.Bd. (looseleaf format)
   Description: Analysis of remedies available to civil litigants in the Maine state courts including damages, injunctions and other equitable remedies, and declaratory judgement.

MANAGERS GUIDE TO THE AMERICANS WITH DISABILITIES ACT. see *BUSINESS AND ECONOMICS — Labor And Industrial Relations*

MANITOBA DECISIONS - CIVIL AND CRIMINAL CASES. see *LAW — Judicial Systems*

340.5   US
MASSACHUSETTS CONDOMINIUM LAW. (2nd ed., 1992) 1985. 2 base vols. (plus irreg. supplements). $160. Butterworth Legal Publishers (Salem) (Subsidiary of: Reed Elsevier plc), 8 Industrial Way, Bldg. C, Salem, NH 03079. TEL 800-548-4001. FAX 603-898-9858. Eds. Barry Brown, Bernard V. Keenan. (looseleaf format)
   Description: Covers condominium law; provides advice on every step of the process, from creating the condominium to ongoing operations.

342   US   ISSN 0742-4647
KF3964.A73
MEALEY'S LITIGATION REPORT: ASBESTOS. 1984. s-m. $925. Mealey Publications, Inc., Box 446, Wayne, PA 19087. TEL 215-688-6566. FAX 215-688-7552. Eds. Scott Jacobs, Sue Sutter. (looseleaf format)
  —CCC.
   Description: Editorial and document coverage of asbestos litigation nationwide, as well as related insurance litigation. Includes commentaries by principles on key subjects of interest.

340.5   US   ISSN 1040-0192
KF3964.A73
MEALEY'S LITIGATION REPORT: ASBESTOS PROPERTY ACTIONS. 1988. s-m. $795. Mealey Publications, Inc., Box 446, Wayne, PA 19087. TEL 215-688-6566. FAX 215-688-7552. Ed. Sue Sutter. (looseleaf format)
  —CCC.
   Description: Covers asbestos in buildings. Includes litigation, insurance coverage, asbestos abatement regulations, training and certification programs.

340.5   340.5   US   ISSN 0893-1011
KF1301.5.I58
MEALEY'S LITIGATION REPORT: BAD FAITH. 1987. s-m. $795. Mealey Publications, Inc., Box 446, Wayne, PA 19087. TEL 215-688-6566. FAX 215-688-7552. Ed. Karen Storey. (looseleaf format)
  —CCC.
   Description: Tracks bad faith insurance law in courts nationwide. Summaries and full texts of opinions, briefs and motions.

340.5   US   ISSN 1067-0246
KF1297.B74
▼**MEALEY'S LITIGATION REPORT: BREAST IMPLANTS.** 1993. s-m. $695. Mealey Publications, Inc., Box 446, Wayne, PA 19807. TEL 215-688-6566. FAX 215-688-7552. Ed. Karen Storey. (looseleaf format)
   Description: Provides detailed coverage of jury verdicts, medical studies, multi-district litigation, discovery coordination, class action updates, insurance coverage disputes and other issues relating to breast implant litigation.

340.5   332   US   ISSN 1068-414X
KF1009.A15
MEALEY'S LITIGATION REPORT: DIRECTORS' AND OFFICERS' LIABILITY. 1990. s-m. $750. Mealey Publications, Inc., Box 446, Wayne, PA 19087. TEL 215-688-6566. FAX 215-688-7552. Ed. John T. Hayes. (looseleaf format)
  —CCC.
   Former titles (until 1992): Mealey's Litigation Report: Banking Insolvency (ISSN 1057-1000); (until 1991): Mealey's Litigation Report: S and L Bailout (ISSN 1047-6385); Mealey's S and L Bailout Report.
   Description: Tracks litigation involving corporate executives in banking and related industries, particularly that arising from bank and thrift failures. Covers topics such as direct and derivative shareholder actions, the extent of D&O coverage, and the increasing scrutiny of regulators.

342   US   ISSN 8755-9005
KF1147
MEALEY'S LITIGATION REPORT: INSURANCE. 1984. 4/m. (48/yr.). $1375. Mealey Publications, Inc., Box 446, Wayne, PA 19087. TEL 215-688-6566. FAX 215-688-7552. Ed. Steven Berstler. (looseleaf format; also avail. in diskette format; back issues avail.)
  —CCC.
   Description: Covers insurance disputes concerning latent property damage or personal injury from asbestos, toxic chemicals, hazardous wastes and pharmaceuticals.

340.5   368   US
▼**MEALEY'S LITIGATION REPORT: INSURANCE FRAUD.** 1994. m. $390. Mealey Publications, Inc., Box 446, Wayne, PA 19087. TEL 215-688-6566. FAX 215-688-7552. Ed. John Hames. (looseleaf format)
   Description: Monitors lawsuits brought by insurers against policyholders for submitting fraudulent claims involving arson, automobile damage, bodily injury and other losses. Also covers litigation initiated by insured parties against their carriers or agents for fraudulent practices.

340   368   US   ISSN 1043-8416
KF1535.I58
MEALEY'S LITIGATION REPORT: INSURANCE INSOLVENCY. 1989. s-m. $795. Mealey Publications, Inc., Box 446, Wayne, PA 19087. TEL 215-688-6566. FAX 215-688-7552. Ed. Teresa Zink. (looseleaf format; also avail. in diskette format; back issues avail.)
  —CCC.
   Description: Covers legal and financial implications of the growing number of insurer insolvencies across the country.

340.5   US   ISSN 1059-4116
MEALEY'S LITIGATION REPORT: LEAD. 1991. s-m. $650. Mealey Publications, Inc., Box 446, Wayne, PA 19087. TEL 215-688-6566. FAX 215-688-7552. Ed. John Hayes. (looseleaf format)
  —CCC.
   Description: Follows litigation and regulation concerning lead abatement and personal injury, including suits brought against the lead industry by government agencies, landlords and workers; litigation brought on behalf of children; environmental cleanup actions, and declaratory judgement actions for and against insurance companies.

340.5   US   ISSN 1055-307X
KF1246.A3
MEALEY'S LITIGATION REPORT: PUNITIVE DAMAGES AND TORT REFORM. 1986. s-m. $695. Mealey Publications, Inc., Box 446, Wayne, PA 19087. TEL 215-688-6566. FAX 215-688-7552. Ed. Pam Craft. (looseleaf format)
  —CCC.
   Former titles (until 1991): Insurance Anti-Trust and Tort Reform Report (ISSN 0898-5170); Mealey's Litigation Report: National Tort Reform (ISSN 0888-3114)
   Description: Covers punitive damages, initiatives to revise tort laws, anti-trust actions brought against the insurance industry, and precedent-setting civil litigation in product liability and personal injury cases.

340.5   368   US   ISSN 1049-5347
KF1236.A15
MEALEY'S LITIGATION REPORT: REINSURANCE. 1990. s-m. $850. Mealey Publications, Inc., Box 446, Wayne, PA 19087. TEL 215-688-6566. FAX 215-688-7552. Ed. Teresa Zink. (looseleaf format)
  —CCC.
   Formerly: Mealey's Reinsurance Report.
   Description: Focuses on the rapidly developing field of reinsurance law, including litigation of reinsurance disputes, regulatory concerns, and issues pertaining to insolvency.

340.5   US   ISSN 0897-3407
KF1299.H39
MEALEY'S LITIGATION REPORT: SUPERFUND. 1988. s-m. $795. Mealey Publications, Inc., Box 446, Wayne, PA 19087. TEL 215-688-6566. FAX 215-688-7552. Ed. Steve Edgecumbe. (looseleaf format)
  —CCC.
   Description: Covers events surrounding all sites on Superfund's national priority list. Includes litigation, insurance disputes, agency actions and awards.

340   US   ISSN 1064-1475
▼**MEALEY'S LITIGATION REPORT: TOXIC TORTS.** 1992. s-m. $695. Mealey Publications, Inc., Box 446, Wayne, PA 19087. TEL 215-688-6566. FAX 215-688-7552. Ed. Steve Edgcumbe. (looseleaf format)
   Description: Provides current information on latent bodily injury claims concerning chemicals, heavy metals, pesticides, electromagnetic fields and environmental factors.

MEALEY'S LITIGATION REPORTS: INTELLECTUAL PROPERTY. see *PATENTS, TRADEMARKS AND COPYRIGHTS*

340.5   US   ISSN 0199-1272
KF2905.3.A15
MEDICAL LIABILITY ADVISORY SERVICE. 1976. m. $201. Business Publishers, Inc., 951 Pershing Dr., Silver Spring, MD 20910-4464. TEL 301-587-6300. FAX 301-587-1081. Ed. Bryan Morris. **Document type:** newsletter.
  —CCC.

340   US   ISSN 0199-1833
KF2905.3.A59
MEDICAL LIABILITY REPORTER; recent decisions of national significance. 1979. m. $295. (Litigation Research Group) Shepard's - McGraw-Hill, Inc., Box 35300, Colorado Springs, CO 80935-3530. TEL 719-488-3000. Ed. Kevin Bushnell. bibl.; index. (looseleaf format; back issues avail.)
   Description: Summarizes and analyzes all reported and most unreported decisions related to health care law.

340.5   630   US
MEDICAL MALPRACTICE: BASES OF LIABILITY. 1985. base vol. (plus a. supplement). $95. Shepard's - McGraw-Hill, Inc., Box 35300, Colorado Springs, CO 80935-3530. TEL 800-525-2474.
   Description: Examines the elements of malpractice and their interpretations in the courts, as well as the frontier issues of constitutional law.

LAW — CIVIL LAW

340 610   US
MEDICAL MALPRACTICE DEFENSE AND HEALTH CARE COUNSEL DIRECTORY. a. $12.45. Professional Reports Corporation, 4418 Belden Village St., N.W., Canton, OH 44718-2516. TEL 216-492-6063; 800-336-0083. FAX 216-492-6176. index.
Document type: directory.
   Formerly: Medical Malpractice Defense Attorney and Health Care Counsel Directory.
   Description: For professionals in the health care fields. Lists medical malpractice defense firms, attorneys, and health care counsel.

340.5 610   US   ISSN 0893-8229
KF2905.3.A15
MEDICAL MALPRACTICE DEFENSE REPORTER. q. $59.95. Professional Reports Corporation, 4418 Belden Village St., N.W., Canton, OH 44718-2516. TEL 216-492-6063; 800-336-0083. FAX 216-492-6176. (looseleaf format) **Document type:** newsletter.
   Description: Provides current information on developments affecting medical malpractice defense attorneys, health care professionals, insurance adjusters and risk management professionals.

340.5 617.6   US
MEDICAL MALPRACTICE: HANDLING DENTAL CASES, 2-E. 1991. 2 base vols. (plus a. supplement). $185. Shepard's - McGraw-Hill, Inc., Box 35300, Colorado Springs, CO 80935-3530. TEL 800-525-2474.
   Description: Covers methods of investigating dental malpractice and provides tips on how to trap the defendant and structure the plaintiff's closing argument. Includes sample complaints and interrogations.

340.5 618   US
MEDICAL MALPRACTICE: HANDLING OBSTETRIC AND NEONATAL CASES. 1986. base vol. (plus a. supplement). $95. Shepard's - McGraw-Hill, Inc., Box 35300, Colorado Springs, CO 80935-3530. TEL 800-525-2474. **Document type:** trade publication.
   Description: Helps to answer questions such as whether to accept a case, how to efficiently win a case, and what a case can be worth to your client and yourself.

340.5 610   US   ISSN 0747-8925
MEDICAL MALPRACTICE LAW & STRATEGY. 1983. m. $185. New York Law Publishing Co., 345 Park Ave. S., New York, NY 10010. TEL 212-545-6170. FAX 212-696-1848.
   Description: Latest court developments, new negotiating techniques, presentation suggestions and changes in the law for malpractice lawyers.

340.5 615   US
MEDICAL MALPRACTICE: PHARMACY LAW. 1986. base vol. (plus a. supplement). $95. Shepard's - McGraw-Hill, Inc., Box 35300, Colorado Springs, CO 80935-3530. TEL 800-525-2474.
   Description: Presents precedent-setting decisions and explains complicated issues in laymen's terms.

340.5 616.8   US
MEDICAL MALPRACTICE: PSYCHIATRIC CARE. 1986. base vol. (plus a. supplement). $105. Shepard's - McGraw-Hill, Inc., Box 35300, Colorado Springs, CO 80935-3530. TEL 800-525-2474.
   Description: Highlights developing trends in the law which have direct impact on the standards of care in psychiatric practice.

340.5   US   ISSN 1045-960X
KF2905.3.A15
MEDICAL MALPRACTICE REPORTS. 1987. m. $210. Matthew Bender & Co., Inc., 11 Penn Plaza, New York, NY 10001. TEL 212-967-7707. Ed. Leonard J. Nelson.
   Description: Provides medical malpractice news, abstracts of cases, including text and analysis of the decision, plus discussions of growing trends.

340.5   US   ISSN 0888-658X
KF2905.3.A59
MEDICAL MALPRACTICE VERDICTS, SETTLEMENTS & EXPERTS. 1985. m. $247. Lewis L. Laska, Ed. & Pub., 901 Church St., Nashville, TN 37203. TEL 615-255-6288. FAX 615-255-6289. index.
Document type: newsletter.
   Description: Looks at the outcome of medical malpractice cases nationally.

MEDICAL RECORD RISKS: CLAIMS & LITIGATION. see INSURANCE

340.5 610   US
MEDICAL STAFF LAW MANUAL. 1984. m. $675. Action Kit Publishers, 4614 Fifth Ave., Pittsburgh, PA 15213. TEL 800-245-1205. FAX 412-687-7692. Ed. John Horty. circ. 500. (looseleaf format)
Document type: newsletter.
   Description: Helps hospital medical staff leaders understand their legal roles and responsibility and limit liability.

340.5 610   US   ISSN 0025-7591
LAW
MEDICAL TRIAL TECHNIQUE QUARTERLY. 1954. q. $180. Clark - Boardman - Callaghan Company, Inc., 155 Pfingston Rd., Deerfield, IL 60015. TEL 800-323-1336. Ed. Jean Maess. bk.rev.; bibl.; charts; index. circ. 2,500. (also avail. in microfiche from WSH; microfilm from WSH) **Indexed:** Abstr.Bk.Rev.Curr.Leg.Per., C.L.I., Hlth.Ind., L.R.I., Leg.Cont., Leg.Per.
—BLDSC (5532.045000); Faxon; UnCover; UMI.
   Description: Presents articles on contemporary medico-legal issues confronting today's practitioner.

340 610   US   ISSN 0899-0255
RA1001
MEDICO-LEGAL ADVISOR. 1985. m. $65. Health Law Research Group, Health-Law Plaza, 140 E. Division Rd., Ste. C3, Oak Ridge, TN 37830. TEL 615-482-6600. FAX 615-481-0264. Ed. Dr. Laurence R. Dry. circ. 1,000.
   Formerly (until Apr. 1988): Attorney's Medical Advisory Letter (ISSN 0887-2015)
   Description: Reviews the latest medico-legal developments in medicine and product liability.

344.041   AT   ISSN 0047-6595
MEDICO-LEGAL SOCIETY OF VICTORIA. PROCEEDINGS. 1931. 5/yr. free. Medico-Legal Society of Victoria, 3 Berkeley St., Hawthorn, Vic. 3122, Australia. Ed. Dr. John Silver. circ. 600 (controlled). **Document type:** proceedings.

340.5 610   US
MEDICO-LEGAL WATCH. 12/yr. $175. Clark - Boardman - Callaghan Company Ltd., 375 Hudson St., New York, NY 10014. TEL 212-929-7500; 800-221-9428. FAX 212-924-0460. Ed. Gary Freed.
   Description: Summarizes articles from medical publications, and offers a view on how recent medical developments may affect personal injury and medical malpractice cases.

340.5 610   GW   ISSN 0340-9511
MEDIZIN IN RECHT UND ETHIK. 1976. irreg., latest vol.27, 1992. price varies. Ferdinand Enke Verlag, Postfach 101254, 70011 Stuttgart, Germany. TEL 0711-135798-0. FAX 0711-135798-30. TELEX 07252275-GTV-D. Eds. A. Eser, E. Seidler. (reprint service avail. from IRC) **Document type:** monographic series.

340.5 150   US   ISSN 0883-7902
KF480.A15
MENTAL AND PHYSICAL DISABILITY LAW REPORTER; covers all aspects of handicapped law. 1976. bi-m. $185 to individuals; institutions $240. American Bar Association, Commission on the Mental & Physical Disability Law, 1800 M St., N.W., Ste. 200 S., Washington, DC 20036. TEL 202-331-2240. FAX 202-331-2220. Ed. John W. Parry. bk.rev.; index. circ. 2,000. (back issues avail.) **Indexed:** Adol.Ment.Hlth.Abstr., C.L.I., Crim.Just.Abstr., Hlth.Ind., L.R.I., Leg.Cont., Leg.Per., Psychol.Abstr.
—BLDSC (5678.559000); UnCover; UMI.
   Formerly (until 1984): Mental Disability Law Reporter (ISSN 0147-3700)
   Description: Articles on subjects of interest to practitioners and consumers. Indexes are available by case name and subject matter.

MENTAL CAPACITY: MEDICAL AND LEGAL ASPECTS OF THE AGING. see GERONTOLOGY AND GERIATRICS

614.58 340   US   ISSN 0889-017X
KF2910.P75
MENTAL HEALTH LAW NEWS. 1986. m. $79. Interwood Publications, 3 E. Interwood Pl., Box 20241, Cincinnati, OH 45220. TEL 513-221-3715. Ed. Frank J. Bardack. (looseleaf format) **Document type:** newsletter.
   Description: Provides case law summaries on mental health malpractice, commitment, appropriate treatment, consent and patient danger to community.

614.58 340   US   ISSN 0741-5141
KF480.A15
MENTAL HEALTH LAW REPORTER. 1983. m. $216. Business Publishers, Inc., 951 Pershing Dr., Silver Spring, MD 20910-4464. TEL 301-587-6300. FAX 301-585-9075. Ed. Bonita Becker. (looseleaf format; back issues avail.) **Document type:** newsletter.
●Also available online. Vendor(s): NewsNet.
—CCC.
   Description: Covers the avoidance of mental health lawsuits for mental health professionals, advice on winning suits that are brought.

MICHIGAN CIVIL RIGHTS COMMISSION NEWSLETTER. see POLITICAL SCIENCE — Civil Rights

MICHIGAN COUNCIL FOR THE ARTS. LEGISLATIVE REPORT. see ART

340.5   AU
MIETRECHTLICHE ENTSCHEIDUNGEN. Abbreviated title: MietSlg. 1951. irreg., vol.42, 1993. price varies. Manzsche Verlags- und Universitaetsbuchhandlung, Kohlmarkt 16, A-1014 Vienna, Austria. TEL 0222-531610. FAX 0222-53161-181. Ed. Helmut Wuerth. (back issues avail.) **Document type:** monographic series.
   Description: Collects decisions on landlord and tenant law.

340.5   US
MINNESOTA CIVIL PRACTICE. 2nd ed., 1990. 4 base vols. (plus a. suppl.). $295. Butterworth Legal Publishers (Salem) (Subsidiary of: Reed Elsevier plc), 8 Industrial Way, Bldg. C, Salem, NH 03079. TEL 800-548-4001. FAX 603-898-9858. Eds. Douglas D. McFarland, William J. Keppel.
   Description: Provides a practical step-by-step guide through all facets of civil practice, from the client interview to final judgement and appeal. Presents an analysis of the rules of civil procedure, with emphasis on pertinent and recent case law, books, journals, articles and statutes.

346.043   US
MINNESOTA RESIDENTIAL REAL ESTATE. 1991. 2 base vols. (plus supplements). $160. Butterworth Legal Publishers (Salem) (Subsidiary of: Reed Elsevier plc), 8 Industrial Way, Bldg. C, Salem, NH 03079. TEL 800-548-4001. FAX 603-898-9858. Ed. James D. Olson. (looseleaf format)
   Description: Complete guide to the law of residential real estate transactions in Minnesota.

MODEL BUSINESS CONTRACTS. see BUSINESS AND ECONOMICS

MONOGRAPHS ON INDUSTRIAL PROPERTY AND COPYRIGHT LAW. see PATENTS, TRADEMARKS AND COPYRIGHTS

340   US
MOTIONS IN FEDERAL COURT: CIVIL PRACTICE, 2-E. 1991. 3 base vols. (plus a. suppl.). $225. Shepard's - McGraw-Hill, Inc., Box 35300, Colorado Springs, CO 80935-3530. TEL 800-515-2474.
   Description: Supplies information on more than 125 of the most frequently used motions as provided by the Federal Rules of Civil Procedure and federal statutes.

340   AT
MOTOR & TRAFFIC LAW SERVICE - VICTORIA. 2 base vols. (plus updates 6/yr.). $395. Butterworths, 271-273 Lane Cove Rd., P.O. Box 345, N. Ryde, N.S.W. 2113, Australia. TEL 02-335-4444. FAX 02-335-4678. (looseleaf format)

340   AT
MOTOR VEHICLE LAW S.A. 1983. 4/yr. Aus.$310 with updates. Law Book Co. Ltd., 44-50 Waterloo Rd., North Ryde, N.S.W. 2113, Australia. TEL 02-887-0177. FAX 02-888-9706. TELEX ASBOOK 87995. Ed. D.W. Bollen. (looseleaf format)
   Description: A manual for motor vehicle and traffic law in South Australia.

MOTOR VEHICLE REPORTS. see TRANSPORTATION

340   AT   ISSN 0813-782X
MOTOR VEHICLE REPORTS. 1983. 4/yr. Aus.$205. Butterworths, P.O. Box 345, North Ryde, N.S.W. 2113, Australia. TEL 02-335-4444. FAX 02-335-4678.

LAW — CIVIL LAW

340.5   GW   ISSN 0179-4043
KK40
N J W - RECHTSPRECHUNGS-REPORT ZIVILRECHT. 1986. s-m. DM.502 (students DM.440). C.H. Beck'sche Verlagsbuchhandlung, Wilhelmstr. 9, 80801 Munich, Germany. TEL 089-38189-338. FAX 089-38189-398. TELEX 5215085-BECK-D. Ed.Bd. adv.: B&W page DM.2400, color page DM.4800; trim 260 x 186. circ. 6,200. **Document type:** bulletin.
●Also available on CD-ROM.
—SWETS.

340.5 333.33   US
NEIGHBORING PROPERTY OWNERS. 1988. base vol. (plus a. supplement). $95. Shepard's - McGraw-Hill, Inc., Box 35300, Colorado Springs, CO 80935-3530. TEL 800-525-2474.
Description: Analyzes the full range of legal principles that define the legal rights and obligations of neighboring landowners.

340.5   US
▼**NEW HAMPSHIRE ACTIONS AND PROCEEDINGS (YEAR).** 1992. a. $35. Butterworth Legal Publishers (Salem) (Subsidiary of: Reed Elsevier plc), 8 Industrial Way, Bldg. C, Salem, NH 03079. TEL 800-548-4001. FAX 603-898-9858. Ed.Bd.
Description: Compilation of relevant provisions of New Hampshire procedural law regulating the form, manner and order of conducting suits or prosecutions.

340   US
NEW HAMPSHIRE CIVIL JURY INSTRUCTIONS. (2nd ed., 1992) 1989. base vol. (plus supplements). $55. Butterworth Legal Publishers (Salem) (Subsidiary of: Reed Elsevier plc), 8 Industrial Way, Bldg. C, Salem, NH 03079. TEL 800-548-4001. FAX 603-898-9858. Eds. Walter C. Murphy, Daniel C. Pope.
Description: Contains suggested instructions for use in drafting jury instructions in a particular case.

340.5   US
NEW HAMPSHIRE PRACTICE SERIES. VOL. 7: WILLS, TRUSTS AND GIFTS. (Series consists of 14 vols.; Vols. 1 and 2: Criminal Practice and Procedure; Vol. 3: Family Law; Vols. 4, 5 and 6: Civil Practice and Procedure; Vol. 7: Wills, Trusts and Gifts; Vols. 8 and 9: Personal Injury - Tort and Insurance; Vols. 10, 11 and 12: Probate Law and Procedure; Vols. 13 and 14: Local Government Law) 1986. base vol. (plus suppl.). $55 (14-vol. set $575). Butterworth Legal Publishers (Salem) (Subsidiary of: Reed Elsevier plc), 8 Industrial Way, Bldg. C, Salem, NH 03079. TEL 800-548-4001. FAX 603-898-9858. Ed. Charles A. DeGrandpre.
Description: Covers the requirements for and manner of execution of wills, trusts, and gifts.

340.5   US
NEW HAMPSHIRE PRACTICE SERIES. VOLS. 4, 5 AND 6: CIVIL PRACTICE AND PROCEDURE. (Series consists of 14 vols.; Vols. 1 and 2: Criminal Practice and Procedure; Vol. 3: Family Law; Vols. 4, 5 and 6: Civil Practice and Procedure; Vol. 7: Wills, Trusts and Gifts; Vols. 8 and 9: Personal Injury - Tort and Insurance Practice; Vols. 10, 11 and 12: Probate Law and Procedure; Vols. 13 and 14: Local Government Law) 1984. 3 base vols. (plus suppl.). $165 (14-vol. set $575). Butterworth Legal Publishers (Salem) (Subsidiary of: Reed Elsevier plc), 8 Industrial Way, Bldg. C, Salem, NH 03079. TEL 800-548-4001. FAX 603-898-9858. Ed. Richard V. Wiebusch.
Description: Provides analysis of arbitration, equity proceedings, and administrative agency proceedings as well as sample forms and pleadings.

349   US
NEW HAMPSHIRE PRACTICE SERIES. VOLS. 8 AND 9: PERSONAL INJURY - TORT AND INSURANCE PRACTICE. (Series consists of 14 vols.; Vols. 1 and 2: Criminal Practice and Procedure; Vol. 3: Family Law; Vols. 4, 5 and 6: Civil Practice and Procedure; Vol. 7: Wills, Trusts and Gifts; Vols. 8 and 9: Personal Injury - Tort and Insurance Practice; Vol. 10, 11 and 12: Probate Law and Procedure; Vol. 13 and 14: Local Government Law) 1988. 2 base vols. (plus supplements). $110 (14-vol. set $575). Butterworth Legal Publishers (Salem) (Subsidiary of: Reed Elsevier plc), 8 Industrial Way, Bldg. C, Salem, NH 03079. TEL 800-548-4001. FAX 603-898-9858. Ed. Richard B. McNamara.
Description: Analysis of the law involved in personal injury actions along with a discussion of the procedural aspects in resolving a claim.

340.5   US
NEW JERSEY CIVIL PRACTICE AND COURT RULES. 1989. a. $16.95. Gould Publications, 1333 N. U.S. Hwy. 17-92, Longwood, FL 32750-3724. TEL 407-695-9500. FAX 407-695-2906. adv.; bk.rev. (looseleaf format)
Description: Presents the rules governing the courts of NJ.

340.5 347   US
NEW JERSEY STATE BAR ASSOCIATION. CIVIL TRIAL BAR SECTION. NEWSLETTER. 1988. 3/yr. free to members. New Jersey State Bar Association, Civil Trial Bar Section, 1 Constitution Sq., New Brunswick, NJ 08901-1500. Ed. Brian P. Blatz. bk.rev. circ. 2,000. (back issues avail.) **Document type:** newsletter.

349.789   US
NEW MEXICO CONSTRUCTION LAW. 1987. base vol. (plus supplements). $120. Butterworth Legal Publishers (Salem) (Subsidiary of: Reed Elsevier plc), 8 Industrial Way, Bldg. C, Salem, NH 03079. TEL 800-548-4001. FAX 603-898-9858. Ed. Timothy M. Sheehan. (looseleaf format)

349.789   US
NEW MEXICO CREDITOR - DEBTOR LAW. 1989. base vol. (plus supplements 1-2/yr.). $115. Butterworth Legal Publishers (Salem) (Subsidiary of: Reed Elsevier plc), 8 Industrial Way, Bldg. C, Salem, NH 03079. TEL 800-548-4001. FAX 603-898-9858. Ed. Marian Matthews. (looseleaf format)
Formerly: New Mexico Collections Manual.
Description: Practical analysis of New Mexico law and procedure governing the most common forms of action to obtain payment in the event of default on various obligations.

349.789   US
NEW MEXICO PROBATE MANUAL. 1978. base vol. (plus supplements). $120. Butterworth Legal Publishers (Salem) (Subsidiary of: Reed Elsevier plc), 8 Industrial Way, Bldg. C, Salem, NH 03079. TEL 800-548-4001. FAX 603-898-9858. Ed. William N. Henderson. (looseleaf format)
Description: Practical guide to New Mexico estate administration that includes attorney's checklists, legal assistant instructions, master information list, Key Probate Code, forms, and a glossary.

NEW MEXICO RULES OF EVIDENCE. see *LAW — Judicial Systems*

340.5   AT
NEW SOUTH WALES LOCAL COURTS CIVIL PRACTICE. 1989. irreg. (approx. q.). C C H Australia Ltd., P.O. Box 230, North Ryde, N.S.W. 2113, Australia. TEL 02-888-2555. FAX 02-888-7324. (looseleaf format)

349   US
NEW YORK ACTIONS AND REMEDIES. 1991. 5 base vols. (plus suppl.). $375. Butterworth Legal Publishers (Salem) (Subsidiary of: Reed Elsevier plc), 8 Industrial Way, Bldg. C, Salem, NH 03079. TEL 800-548-4001. FAX 603-898-9858. Ed. Mark Rhodes. (looseleaf format)
Description: Topics covered include: torts, contracts, marriage, divorce, and real estate.

340.5   US
NEW YORK CIVIL PRACTICE LAW AND RULES HANDBOOK. 1988. a. $19.95. Gould Publications (Binghamton), 199-300 State St., Binghamton, NY 13901. TEL 607-724-3000. FAX 607-723-4285. adv.; bk.rev. (looseleaf format)
Description: Presents Chapter 8 of the consolidated laws, civil practice law and rules, sections of the NY constitution, judiciary law, NYC civil court act and other NYC laws.

346   US
NEW YORK LANDLORD AND TENANT HANDBOOK. 1987. a. $34.95. Gould Publications (Binghamton), 199-300 State St., Binghamton, NY 13901. TEL 607-724-3000. FAX 607-723-4285. adv.; bk.rev. (looseleaf format)
Description: Contains chapters covering history, jurisdiction and venue, non-payment proceedings, pet cases and business use of residential apartments, legal fees and more.

NEW YORK STATE BAR ASSOCIATION. REAL PROPERTY LAW SECTION. NEWSLETTER. see *REAL ESTATE*

346   IT
NUOVA GIURISPRUDENZA CIVILE COMMENTATA. 1985. bi-m. L.210000 (foreign L.300000) (effective 1994). Casa Editrice Dott. Antonio Milani, Via Jappelli 5, 35121 Padua, Italy. TEL 049-656677. FAX 049-8752900. Eds. Paolo Zatti, Guido Alpa. circ. 5,500.

348   IT
NUOVE LEGGI CIVILI COMMENTATE. 1978. bi-m. L.220000 (foreign L.310000) (effective 1994). Casa Editrice Dott. Antonio Milani, Via Jappelli 5, 35121 Padua, Italy. TEL 049-656677. FAX 049-8752900. Ed. Piero Schlesinger. circ. 7,000. **Indexed:** ELLIS.
Description: Present comments on all the new civil laws.

349   US
OREGON DEBTOR - CREDITOR LAW. (2nd ed., 1992) 1986. base vol. (plus supplements). $75. Butterworth Legal Publishers (Salem) (Subsidiary of: Reed Elsevier plc), 8 Industrial Way, Bldg. C, Salem, NH 03079. TEL 800-548-4001. FAX 603-898-9858. Ed. Brian A. Blum.
Description: Covers Oregon law relating to attachment, claim and delivery, restraining orders, receivership, judgement by default and confession, judgement liens, enforcement of foreign judgements, execution, redemption, garnishment, liens and lien foreclosure, foreclosure of mortgages, tax liens, and fraudulent conveyances.

340.5   US   ISSN 1069-0352
KFO2929
OREGON RULES OF CIVIL PROCEDURE ANNOTATED (YEAR). 1991. a. $35. Butterworth Legal Publishers (Salem) (Subsidiary of: Reed Elsevier plc), 8 Industrial Way, Bldg. C, Salem, NH 03079. TEL 800-548-4001. FAX 603-898-9858. Ed.Bd.
Description: Full text of each rule, accompanied by summaries of cases discussing the rules.

340.5   US
OREGON RULES OF CIVIL PROCEDURE HANDBOOK (YEAR). biennial. $29.50. Butterworth Legal Publishers (Salem) (Subsidiary of: Reed Elsevier plc), 8 Industrial Way, Bldg. C, Salem, NH 03079. TEL 800-548-4001. FAX 603-898-9858. Ed. Frederic R. Merrill.

346   US
OREGON UNIFORM COMMERCIAL CODE. 3 base vols. (plus supplements). $225. Butterworth Legal Publishers (Salem) (Subsidiary of: Reed Elsevier plc), 8 Industrial Way, Bldg. C, Salem, NH 03079. TEL 800-548-4001. FAX 603-898-9858. Ed. Henry J. Bailey, III.

340.5   US
PENNSYLVANIA BAR ASSOCIATION. CIVIL LITIGATION LAW SECTION. NEWSLETTER. 9/yr. free to members. Pennsylvania Bar Association, Civil Litigation Law Section, 100 South St., Harrisburg, PA 17108. TEL 717-238-6715. FAX 717-238-7182. **Document type:** newsletter.

340.5 US ISSN 1062-1822
PENNSYLVANIA CIVIL APPELLATE REPORTER. s-m. $350. Andrews Publications, 1646 West Chester Pike, Box 1000, Westtown, PA 19395. TEL 215-399-6600; 800-345-1101. FAX 215-399-6610. **Document type:** newsletter.
  Description: Offers digests of decision regarding Pennsylvania civil law as interpreted by the state's three appellate courts and the Third Circuit U.S. Court of Appeals.

340.5 US
PENNSYLVANIA RULES OF CIVIL PROCEDURE. 1988. a. $16.95. Gould Publications, 1333 N. U.S. Hwy. 17-92, Longwood, FL 32750. TEL 407-695-9500. FAX 407-695-2906. adv.; bk.rev. (looseleaf format)
  Description: Presents title 231 of the PA code, rules of civil procedure and orphan's court rules.

340.5 UK ISSN 1353-3622
▼**PERSONAL INJURY LITIGATION.** 1994. a. £17.50. Jordan Publishing Ltd., 21 St. Thomas St., Bristol BS1 6JS, England. TEL 0272-230600. FAX 0272-250486. Ed. Paul White. **Document type:** academic/scholarly publication.

349 US ISSN 0887-7815
KF1297.D7
PHARMACEUTICAL LITIGATION REPORTER; the national journal of record of pharmaceutical litigation. 1985. m. $750. Andrews Publications, 1646 West Chester Pike, Box 1000, Westtown, PA 19395. TEL 215-399-6600; 800-345-1101. FAX 215-399-6610. Ed. Robert Sullivan. abstr.; bibl.; stat.; cum.index every 6 mos. (looseleaf format; back issues avail.) **Document type:** newsletter.

340.5 UK ISSN 1353-3665
▼**RESIDENTIAL LANDLORD AND TENANT.** 1994. a. £17.50. Jordan Publishing Ltd., 21 St. Thomas St., Bristol BS1 6JS, England. TEL 0272-230600. FAX 0272-250486. Ed. Paul Butt. **Document type:** trade publication.

340.5 FR ISSN 0397-9873
K21
REVUE TRIMESTRIELLE DE DROIT CIVIL. 1902. q. 510 F. (foreign 625 F.). Editions Sirey, 11 rue Soufflot, 75240 Paris Cedex 05, France. TEL 40-51-54-54. FAX 45-87-37-48. TELEX 206 446 F. (Subscr. to: 35 rue Tournefort, 75240 Paris Cedex 05, France. TEL 40-51-54-35. FAX 45-87-37-48) (back issues avail.) **Indexed:** ELLIS. —BLDSC (7956.770000); SWETS. CCC.

340.5 US
RIGHTS AND LIABILITIES OF PUBLISHERS, BROADCASTERS, AND REPORTERS. 1982. 2 base vols. (plus a. suppl.). $195. Shepard's - McGraw-Hill, Inc., Box 35300, Colorado Springs, CO 80935-3530. TEL 800-525-2474. (looseleaf format)
  Description: Covers entire spectrum of media litigation: libel, privacy, compelled disclosure, media access, prior restraint, anti-trust law and commercial speech and advertising.

RIGHTS OF PHYSICALLY HANDICAPPED PERSONS. see HANDICAPPED — Physically Impaired

340.5 IT ISSN 0035-6093
K22
RIVISTA DI DIRITTO CIVILE. (Text in French, Italian; summaries in Italian) 1955. bi-m. L.170000 (foreign L.240000) (effective 1994). Casa Editrice Dott. Antonio Milani, Via Jappelli 5, 35121 Padua, Italy. TEL 049-656677. FAX 049-8752900. Ed. Alberto Trabucchi. index, cum.index: 1955-1974. circ. 3,500. (back issues avail.) **Indexed:** ELLIS, World Agri.Econ.& Rural Sociol.Abstr. —SWETS.

340.5 IT ISSN 0035-6182
RIVISTA DI DIRITTO PROCESSUALE. 1924. q. L.160000 (foreign L.220000) (effective 1994). Casa Editrice Dott. Antonio Milani, Via Jappelli 5, 35121 Padua, Italy. TEL 049-656677. FAX 049-8752900. Ed. Giuseppe Tarzia. bk.rev.; bibl.; index, cum.index: 1946-1965. circ. 2,200.
  —SWETS.
  Formerly (until 1943): Rivista di Diritto Processuale Civile.

340.5 IT
RIVISTA TRIMESTRALE DI DIRITTO E PROCEDURA CIVILE. 1947. q. L.110000 (foreign L.165000). Casa Editrice Dott. A. Giuffre, Via Busto Arsizio 40, 20151 Milan, Italy. TEL 02-38000905. FAX 02-38009582. Eds. Umberto Romagnoli, Federico Carpi. adv. circ. 3,150. **Indexed:** ELLIS.

340.5 AU ISSN 0379-4423
K22
RUNDFUNKRECHT. 1977. q. Manzsche Verlags- und Universitaetsbuchhandlung, Kohlmarkt 16, A-1014 Vienna, Austria. TEL 0222-531610. FAX 0222-53161181. Ed. Robert Dittrich. circ. 900. **Document type:** trade publication.
  Description: Concerns law on radio and television broadcasting.

340.5 UK ISSN 0951-0443
SCOTTISH CIVIL LAW REPORTS. 1987. a. £90 (effective 1993). Law Society of Scotland, 26 Drumsheugh Gardens, Edinburgh EH3 7YR, Scotland. Ed. Sheriff Alastair L. Stewart. **Document type:** bulletin.

340 US
SHEPARD'S MEDICAL MALPRACTICE CITATIONS. 1987. base vol. (plus q. suppl.). $230. Shepard's - McGraw-Hill, Inc., Box 35300, Colorado Springs, CO 80935-3530. TEL 800-525-2474.

SOUTH AFRICA. CENTRAL STATISTICAL SERVICE. STATISTICAL RELEASE. STATISTICS OF CIVIL CASES FOR DEBT. see LAW — Abstracting, Bibliographies, Statistics

SOUTH AFRICA. CENTRAL STATISTICAL SERVICE. STATISTICAL RELEASE. STATISTICS OF LIQUIDATIONS AND INSOLVENCIES. see LAW — Abstracting, Bibliographies, Statistics

340.5 US
TEXAS RESIDENTIAL LANDLORD - TENANT LAW. 1986. 2 base vols. (plus supplemenets 2-3/yr.). $125. Butterworth Legal Publishers (Salem) (Subsidiary of: Reed Elsevier plc), 8 Industrial Way, Bldg. C, Salem, NH 03079. TEL 800-548-4001. FAX 603-898-9858. Ed.Bd. (looseleaf format)
  Description: Practical guide to using Texas statutes, rules and court decisions in handling landlord-tenant disputes.

340.5 US
TEXAS RULES OF CIVIL PROCEDURE. 1984. base vol. (plus supplements). $38.50. Butterworth Legal Publishers (Salem) (Subsidiary of: Reed Elsevier plc), 8 Industrial Way, Bldg. C, Salem, NH 03079. TEL 800-548-4001. FAX 603-898-9858. Ed.Bd. (looseleaf format)

340.5 US ISSN 0885-856X
K6
TORT & INSURANCE LAW JOURNAL. 1965. q. $23 (foreign $28). American Bar Association, Tort and Insurance Practice Section, 750 N. Lake Shore Dr., Chicago, IL 60611. TEL 312-988-5000. Ed. Jeffery Anne Tatum. abstr.; charts; illus.; stat.; tr.lit.; index. circ. 35,000. (also avail. in microform from UMI; microfilm from WSH; reprint service avail.) **Indexed:** C.L.I., INIS Atomind., L.R.I., Leg.Per., Risk Abstr.
  ●Also available online. Vendor(s): Mead Data Central, Inc., West Services, Inc.
  —BLDSC (8869.702000); Faxon; UnCover.
  Formerly: Forum (Chicago, 1965) (ISSN 0015-8356)
  Description: Scholarly journal on current or emerging issues of national scope in the fields of tort and insurance law.

340.5 US
TORT LAW AND PERSONAL INJURY PRACTICE (RHODE ISLAND). 1990. 2 base vols. (plus a. suppl.). $145. Butterworth Legal Publishers (Salem) (Subsidiary of: Reed Elsevier plc), 8 Industrial Way, Bldg. C, Salem, NH 03079. TEL 800-548-4001. FAX 603-898-9858. Ed. Ronald J. Resmini.
  Description: Analyzes the statutes, common law and case law pertaining to torts, motor vehicles, insurance and arbitration.

340.5 AT ISSN 1039-3285
▼**TORT LAW REVIEW.** 1993. 3/yr. Aus.$175. Law Book Co. Ltd., 44-50 Waterloo Rd., North Ryde, N.S.W. 2113, Australia. TEL 02-887-0177. FAX 02-888-9706. TELEX AHBOOK 27995. Ed. Nicholas Mullany.
  Description: Discusses all significant developments in tort law, both in Australia and overseas.

340.5 US
TORT TRENDS NEWSLETTER. 1955. q. $38 to non-profit institutions, excluding libraries; profit institutions $68. Illinois State Bar Association, 424 S. Second St., Springfield, IL 62701. TEL 217-525-1760. Eds. Lester Foreman, Joseph R. Marconi. circ. 5,750.
  Formerly: Illinois State Bar Association. Tort Trends (ISSN 0040-9626)

340 US
TULANE EUROPEAN AND CIVIL LAW FORUM. 1973. a. $20 (foreign $25). Tulane University School of Law, New Orleans, LA 70118. TEL 504-865-5978. FAX 504-865-6748. Ed.Bd. circ. 250. (also avail. in microform from UMI,WSH; back issues avail.; reprint service avail. from WSH) **Indexed:** Leg.Per.
  Formerly (until 1987): Tulane Civil Law Forum.

340.5 PH ISSN 0047-5734
K25
UNIVERSITY OF SANTO TOMAS. FACULTY OF CIVIL LAW. LAW REVIEW. (Text in English) 1950. s-a. P.60($7) University of Santo Tomas, Faculty of Civil Law, Espana St., Sampaloc, Metro Manila, Philippines. Ed. Liza A. Lopez. adv.; bk.rev.

340.5 CN ISSN 0827-4266
WEEKLY DIGEST OF CIVIL PROCEDURE (2ND SERIES). 1987. 40/yr. Can.$350. Carswell, One Corporate Plaza, 2075 Kennedy Rd., Scarborough, ON M1T 3V4, Canada. TEL 416-609-8000. FAX 416-298-5094. (looseleaf format) **Document type:** newsletter.
  Description: Remains a conspectus of relevant civil procedure issues in recent unreported cases from the Supreme Court of Canada, the Federal Court of Canada, the Tax Court of Canada and the Ontario Courts.

348.73 347 US ISSN 1048-3888
KF105
WEST'S FEDERAL REPORTER. 1925, N.S. 1988. irreg. West Publishing Corp., 620 Opperman Dr., Eagan, MN 55123. TEL 612-687-8000; 800-328-9352. FAX 612-687-7302. **Document type:** trade publication.

340.5 336 GW
▼**ZEITSCHRIFT FUER ERBRECHT UND VERMOEGENSNACHFOLGE (Z E V);** Erbrecht - Gesellschaftsrecht - Steuerrecht. 1994. bi-m. DM.360. C.H. Beck'sche Verlagsbuchhandlung, Wilhelmstr. 9, 80801 Munich, Germany. TEL 089-38189-338. FAX 089-38189-398. TELEX 5215085-BECK-D. Ed.Bd. adv.; B&W page DM.2000, color page DM.3500; trim 260 x 186. bk.rev. circ. 2,000. **Document type:** bulletin.

340.5 GW ISSN 0342-3468
ZEITSCHRIFT FUER ZIVILPROZESS. q. DM.198. Carl Heymanns Verlag KG, Luxemburgerstr. 449, 50939 Cologne, Germany. TEL 0221-46010-0. FAX 0221-46010-69. adv.; bk.rev. (back issues avail.) **Document type:** bulletin.
  —SWETS.

LAW — Computer Applications

340 001.642 US ISSN 1055-4017
A B A - UNIX - GROUP NEWSLETTER. 1987. q. $53. American Bar Association, Law Practice Management Section, 750 N. Lake Shore Dr., Chicago, IL 60611. TEL 312-988-5555. FAX 312-988-6281. bk.rev. **Document type:** newsletter.
  Description: Provides readers with updates on the use of UNIX system computers, articles on hardware and software, software reviews, tips and tricks, and information on the UNIX User Group.

340 US
A M S ADVISOR. (Acquisition Management Service) 1981. m. $495. I D C Government, 3110 Fariview Park Dr., Ste. 1100, Falls Church, VA 22042-4503. TEL 703-876-5055. FAX 703-356-3111. Ed. Alvin Young. circ. 250. (back issues avail.)
  Formerly (until Jan. 1990): P I M S Advisor.
  Description: Covers developments affecting the world of federal procurements and ADP acquisition policies.

LAW — COMPUTER APPLICATIONS

340 US ISSN 0191-863X
KF318.A1
ALTMAN WEIL PENSA REPORT TO LEGAL MANAGEMENT. 1974. m. Can.$245($195) (foreign $220). Altman Weil Pensa Publications, Inc., Box 625, Newtown Sq., PA 19073. TEL 215-359-9900. FAX 215-359-0467. Ed. James Wilber. bk.rev.; index. circ. 1,000. (back issues avail.) **Document type:** newsletter.
—CCC.
Description: Geared to the legal profession.

340 US
AUTO-CITE INSIGHTS. 1983. q. free. Lawyers Cooperative Publishing (Subsidiary of: Thomson Professional Publishing), c/o Rob Tyler, Marketing Dept., Aqueduct Bldg., Rochester, NY 14694. TEL 800-828-6373. Ed. Nora A. Uehlein. (back issues avail.) **Document type:** newsletter.
Formerly: Auto-Cite Update.

340 US ISSN 1065-1772
AUTOMATOME. 1980. q. membership. American Association of Law Libraries, Automation & Scientific Developments S I S, c/o Vanderbilt Law Library, Nashville, TN 37203. TEL 615-322-0023. Ed. Anna Belle Leiserson. bk.rev. (back issues avail.) **Indexed:** Leg.Info.Manage.Ind. **Document type:** newsletter.

340 US ISSN 1055-4009
KF320.A9
BUSINESS LAWYER'S COMPUTER NEWS. 1989. q. $50. American Bar Association, Law Practice Management Section, 750 N. Lake Shore Dr., Chicago, IL 60611. TEL 312-988-5555. FAX 312-988-6281. **Document type:** newsletter.

340 371.394 US ISSN 0897-1226
K4.A4
C A L I REPORT. 1983. q. free. Center for Computer-Assisted Legal Instruction, 229 19th Ave. S., Minneapolis, MN 55455. TEL 612-625-3419. Ed. LaVonne K. Molde. (back issues avail.) **Document type:** newsletter.

340 US
COMPUTER LAW ASSOCIATION BULLETIN. q. free to members only. Computer Law Association Inc., 3028 Javier Rd., Ste. 500 E, Fairfax, VA 22031. TEL 703-560-7747. FAX 703-207-7028. Ed. William Tanenbaum. circ. 1,300 (controlled). **Document type:** newsletter, bulletin.

340 US
COMPUTER LAW FORMS HANDBOOK; a legal guide to drafting and negotiating. a. $85. Clark - Boardman - Callaghan Company Ltd., 375 Hudson St., New York, NY 10014. TEL 212-929-7500; 800-221-9428. FAX 212-924-0460. Ed. Laurens R. Schwartz.
Description: Explains the applicable technology needed in drafting and negotiating contracts.

340 340 GW ISSN 0934-8778
COMPUTERREPORT DER NEUE JURISTISCHEN WOCHENSCHRIFT; Informationsmanagement und Bueroorganisation in der juristischen Praxis. Short title: N J W - Co R. (Supplement to: Neue Juristische Wochenschrift) 1988. bi-m. DM.64. C.H. Beck'sche Verlagsbuchhandlung, Wilhelmstr. 9, 80801 Munich, Germany. TEL 089-38189-338. FAX 089-38189-398. adv.: B&W page DM.5800, color page DM.10150; trim 260 x 186. bk.rev.; index. circ. 56,217. (back issues avail.) **Document type:** bulletin.
—SWETS.

340 026 EI
COUNCIL OF EUROPE. SYMPOSIUM ON LEGAL PROCESSING. PROCEEDINGS. no.5, 1979. irreg. price varies. Council of Europe, Publishing and Documentation Service, 67075 Strasbourg, France. (Dist. in U.S. by: Manhattan Publishing Co., 225 Lafayette St., New York, NY 10012) **Document type:** proceedings.

340 US
▼**COUNSEL CONNECT;** the user's guide to Counsel Connect's electronic highway. 1993. m. Counsel Connect, Inc., 600 Third Ave., New York, NY 10016. TEL 800-955-5291. FAX 212-973-6797. Ed. Joseph Lamport. **Document type:** newsletter.
Description: Discusses issues relating to new and developing applications of e-mail and on-line technology in the legal profession, and reports on the Counsel Connect electronic service.

340 US ISSN 1063-0643
Z699.4.D18D53
DIALOG DOCKET. 1990. 3/yr. free to Dialog subscribers. Dialog Information Services, Inc., 3460 Hillview Ave., Palo Alto, CA 94304. TEL 415-858-3785. FAX 415-858-7069. Ed. Margot Carrington. **Document type:** newsletter.

340 US ISSN 1065-0334
K87
▼**DIRECTORY OF LAW-RELATED C D - R O MS.** (Supplement avail.: Law-Related C D - R O M Update (ISSN 1065-9285)) 1992. a. $49. Infosources Publishing, 140 Norma Rd., Teaneck, NJ 07666. TEL 201-836-7072. Ed. Arlene L. Eis. adv. **Document type:** directory.
Description: Provides detailed information on 450 CD-ROM products in the areas of law, legislation and regulation. Includes publisher, search software and subject indexes.

340 301 001.2 FR ISSN 1157-3813
F R A N C I S. 603: INFORMATIQUE ET SCIENCES JURIDIQUES. (Text in English, French, German) 1974. 2/yr. 195 F. (outside EEC 205 F.). Centre National de la Recherche Scientifique, Institut de l'Information Scientifique et Technique, 2 allee du Parc de Brabois, 54514 Vandoeuvre-les-Nancy Cedex, France. TEL 83-50-46-00. FAX 83-50-46-50. adv. contact: Veronique Guinvarc'h. **Document type:** bibliography.
●Also available online. Vendor(s): Telesystemes - Questel.
Also available on CD-ROM.
Formerly: Informatique et Sciences Juridiques (ISSN 0181-110X)

INFORMATION TECHNOLOGY AND THE LAW; an international bibliography. see *LAW — Abstracting, Bibliographies, Statistics*

340 US
INTERNATIONAL UPDATE NEWSLETTER. q. Computer Law Association, Inc., 3028 Javier Rd., Ste. 500 E, Fairfax, VA 22031. TEL 703-560-7747. FAX 703-207-7028. **Document type:** newsletter.

340 US ISSN 1055-128X
LAW OFFICE COMPUTING. 1991. bi-m. $54.99. James Publishing Group, Inc., 3520 Cadillac Ave., Costa Mesa, CA 92626. TEL 714-755-5450. Ed. Wendi Webb. adv. contact: Lorraine Thinnes. circ. 8,000. **Document type:** trade publication.
—UMI. CCC.
Description: Contains practical solutions to law office computer problems, practical applications for small firms and how-to advice for both experienced users and beginners.

340 US ISSN 0458-8630
K12
LAW OFFICE ECONOMICS & MANAGEMENT. 1960. q. $115. Clark - Boardman - Callaghan Company, Inc., 155 Pfingsten Rd., Deerfield, IL 60015. TEL 800-323-1336. Ed. Paul Hoffman. bk.rev.; illus.; index. circ. 1,850. (also avail. in microfiche from UMI) **Indexed:** Account.Ind. (1974-), C.L.I., L.R.I., Law Ofc.Info.Svc., Leg.Cont., Leg.Per.
—UnCover; UMI.
Former titles: Law Office Economics and Management Manual (ISSN 0023-9313); Law Office Economics and Management.
Description: For lawyers and office managers. Covers client relations, personnel, strategic planning and computers in the office.

340 US ISSN 1047-6482
KF320.A9
LAW OFFICE TECHNOLOGY REVIEW. 1989. m. $99.50. 2640 W. 183 St., Box 2577, Homewood, IL 60430. TEL 708-957-3322. FAX 708-957-3337. Ed.Bd. bk.rev.
●Also available online. Vendor(s): DIALOG Information Services, Inc., NewsNet (LA15), West Services, Inc.
Description: Features hands-on reviews of computer software, add-ons, and systems for law office computer users.

340 US ISSN 1065-9285
▼**LAW-RELATED C D - R O M UPDATE.** (Supplement to: Directory of Law-Related C D - R O Ms (ISSN 1065-0334)) 1993. 3/yr. $39 in US and Canada; elsewhere $49. Infosources Publishing, 140 Norma Rd., Teaneck, NJ 07666. TEL 201-836-7072. Ed. Arlene L. Eis. adv. **Document type:** newsletter.

340 510.78 US ISSN 0278-3916
K87 CODEN: LATEDT
LAW - TECHNOLOGY. 1968. q. $85. World Jurist Association, Section on Law & Computer Technology, 1000 Connecticut Ave., Ste. 202, Washington, DC 20036. TEL 202-466-5428. FAX 202-452-8540. TELEX 440456. bk.rev.; bibl.; charts. circ. 800. (processed; also avail. in microform from UMI) **Indexed:** C.L.I., Comput.Cont., Comput.Lit.Ind., L.R.I., Leg.Per., Sci.Abstr. **Document type:** academic/scholarly publication.
—BLDSC (5161.447500); Faxon; UnCover; SWETS; UMI.
Formerly: Law and Computer Technology (ISSN 0023-9178)

340 UK ISSN 0961-6209
LAW TECHNOLOGY JOURNAL. £60. University of Warwick, CTI Law Technology Centre, Coventry CV4 7AL, England. TEL 0203-523294. FAX 0203-524105. (Co-sponsor: British & Irish Legal Education Technology Association) Ed. A. Paliwala. adv.; bk.rev.; bibl.; circ. 400 (controlled). (back issues avail.) **Document type:** newsletter.
—BLDSC (5161.448400).
Formerly: Law Technology Centre and B I L E T A Newsletter.

340 US
LAWYERS' MICRO USERS GROUP NEWSLETTER. 1983. m. Paul Bernstein, Ed. & Pub. (Chicago), 333 E. Ontario St., Ste. 2102-B, Chicago, IL 60611. TEL 312-951-8451. **Document type:** newsletter.
●Available only online. Vendor(s): NewsNet (LA05).

340 621.381 US ISSN 0740-0942
KF320.A9
LAWYER'S P C. 1983. bi-m. $105. Shepard's - McGraw-Hill, Inc., Box 35300, Colorado Springs, CO 80935-3530. TEL 719-488-3000. Ed. Robert P. Wilkins. adv.; bk.rev. **Indexed:** Comput.Cont., Comput.Lit.Ind., Leg.Cont.
—UMI.
Incorporates: Lawyer's Microcomputer (ISSN 0732-0922)
Description: For lawyers using personal computers. Features articles about hardware and software--advances and applications. Also contains product and service announcements of interest in the legal field.

LEADER'S LEGAL TECH NEWSLETTER. see *LAW*

340.0285 US ISSN 1055-4084
KF320.A9
LITIGATION APPLICATIONS. 1989. q. $50. American Bar Association, Law Practice Management Section, 750 N. Lake Shore Dr., Chicago, IL 60611. TEL 312-988-5000. **Document type:** newsletter.
Formerly: Litigation User Group News.
Description: Includes updates on computer use in litigation practice and news about the activities of the user group.

340 011 FR ISSN 0296-8908
REPERTOIRE INTERNATIONAL DES BANQUES DE DONNEES JURIDIQUE. 1985. irreg. 470 F. (Association pour le Developpement de l'Information Juridique) Editions F L A Consultants, 27 rue de la Vistule, 75013 Paris, France. TEL 1-45-82-75-75. FAX 1-45-82-46-04. Ed. Clotilde Scemama. adv. contact: Beatrice Riou. **Document type:** directory.
Description: A tool to better understand and use French and foreign law data bases.

340 330 US ISSN 0735-8938
K22 CODEN: RCTJDM
RUTGERS COMPUTER & TECHNOLOGY LAW JOURNAL. 1970. s-a. $34 (effective 1993). Rutgers University, School of Law - Newark, 15 Washington St., Newark, NJ 07102. TEL 201-648-5549. FAX 201-648-1447. Ed. Christopher W. Hager. adv.; bk.rev.; bibl.; charts; cum.index: vols.1-16 in vol.16. circ. 1,500. (also avail. in microfilm from UMI,WSH) reprint service avail. from UMI,WSH) **Indexed:** C.L.I., Comput.Cont., Comput.Lit.Ind., L.R.I., Leg.Per., Sci.Abstr. **Document type:** academic/scholarly publication.
—BLDSC (8053.360000); Faxon; UnCover.
Former titles (until 1981): Rutgers Journal of Computers, Technology, and the Law (ISSN 0278-5633); (until 1978): Rutgers Journal of Computers and the Law (ISSN 0048-8844)

SANTA CLARA COMPUTER AND HIGH-TECHNOLOGY LAW JOURNAL. see *LAW*

3354 LAW — CONSTITUTIONAL LAW

TRENDS IN THE LAW LIBRARY MANAGEMENT AND TECHNOLOGY. see *LIBRARY AND INFORMATION SCIENCES*

340   US
WORD PROGRESS. q. $50. American Bar Association, Law Practice Management Section, 750 N. Lake Shore Dr., Chicago, IL 60611. TEL 312-988-5000. **Document type:** newsletter.
   Description: Includes updates on word processing in the law office, "how to" articles on hardware and software, and news about the activities of the Word Processing User Group.

340 005.3   US   ISSN 1070-3896
WORDPERFECT FOR THE LAW OFFICE. 1992. bi-m. $59.95 (foreign $74.95). James Publishing Inc., 3520 Cadillac Ave., Ste. E, Costa Mesa, CA 92626. TEL 714-755-5450. FAX 714-549-8835. Ed. Wendi Webb. adv. contact: Lorraine Thinnes. circ. 8,000. **Document type:** trade publication.

340 510.78
K29   UK   ISSN 0965-528X
YEARBOOK OF LAW COMPUTERS AND TECHNOLOGY. 1984. a. $88 to individuals; institutions $176 (effective 1994). Carfax Publishing Co., P.O. Box 25, Abingdon, Oxon. OX14 3UE, England. TEL 44-235-555335. FAX 44-235-553559. (N. American subscr. to: Carfax Publishing Co., Box 2025, Dunnellon, FL 34430-2025) Ed.Bd. adv.; bk.rev.; index. (also avail. in microfiche; back issues avail.) **Document type:** academic/scholarly publication.
—BLDSC (9414.450000). **CCC.**
   Formerly: Yearbook of Law Computers and Technology (ISSN 0269-3712)

LAW — Constitutional Law

342   US
KFA2431.A75
ARIZONA LEGISLATIVE REPORT. d. during regular session. Arizona News Service, 14 N. 18th Ave., Phoenix, AZ 85007. TEL 602-258-7026. FAX 602-258-2504. Ed. Ned Creighton. **Document type:** newsletter.
●Also available online.

342   US
ARKANSAS CAPITOL REPORT. w. during session. membership. Arkansas State Chamber of Commerce and Associated Industries of Arkansas, Box 3645, Little Rock, AR 72203-3645. TEL 501-374-9225. FAX 501-372-2722. circ. 2,000. **Document type:** newsletter.

342   US
ARKANSAS DAILY LEGISLATIVE DIGEST. 1941. d. (during legislative sessions). $560. Arkansas Legislative Digest, Inc., 1401 W. Sixth St., Little Rock, AR 72201. TEL 501-376-2843. FAX 501-374-9256. Ed. Roger Potts. **Document type:** newsletter.

342   US
JK1571.073
ARKANSAS LEGISLATIVE REPORT.* 1983. d. during session. $525. Legislative Reports, Inc., Box 7345, Little Rock, AR 72217-7345. TEL 501-663-5081. FAX 501-375-3163. Ed. Ken Parker. **Document type:** newsletter.

ARKANSAS POLITICAL REPORT. see *PUBLIC ADMINISTRATION*

342   AT
▼**AUSTRALIAN JOURNAL OF ADMINISTRATIVE LAW.** 1993. q. Aus.$195. Law Book Co. Ltd., 44-50 Waterloo Rd., North Ryde, N.S.W. 2113, Australia. TEL 02-887-0177. FAX 02-888-9806. TELEX ASBOOK 27995. (Dist. in US by: Wm. W. Gaunt & Sons, Inc., Gaunt Bldg., 3011 Gulf Dr., Holmes Beach, FL 34217-2199) Ed. Richard Tracey.
   Description: Contains articles and specialist contributions in areas including immigration, corporate regulation, freedom of information, customs and excise, broadcasting, and social security.

342   US   ISSN 0098-7638
KF4550.Z9
B A R - B R I BAR REVIEW. CONSTITUTIONAL LAW. a. $395. B A R - B R I Bar Review, 3280 Motor Ave., Los Angeles, CA 90034-3710. TEL 213-477-2542.

342   US   ISSN 0743-0310
KF4546.A3
BENCHMARK (RICHMOND);* a quarterly review of the constitution and the courts. 1984. q. $18 to individuals; institutions $20. Center for Judicial Studies, Box 113, Hampden-Sydney, VA 23943-0113. TEL 804-282-1798. Ed. James McClellan. adv.; bk.rev. circ. 5,000. (also avail. in microform from WSH; back issues avail.; reprint service avail. from WSH)
—Faxon; UnCover.
   Description: Articles on the Constitution and the role of the courts.

342   US   ISSN 0160-7731
KF4742
BILL OF RIGHTS IN ACTION. Short title: B R I A. 1971. q. free. Constitutional Rights Foundation, 601 S. Kingsley Dr., Los Angeles, CA 90005. TEL 213-487-5590. FAX 213-386-0459. Ed. Marshall Croddy. bk.rev. circ. 40,000. (also avail. in microform from UMI; back issues avail.; reprint service avail. from UMI)
—UMI.
   Formerly: Bill of Rights Newsletter (ISSN 0006-2502)
   Description: Contains educational materials for grades 7-12.

342 365   US   ISSN 0884-0075
THE CALIFORNIA PRISONER. 1972. q. $30 to individuals; institutions $35; $5 to California prisoners. Prisoners Rights Union, Box 1019, Sacramento, CA 95812-1019. TEL 916-441-4214. FAX 916-442-2073. adv.: B&W page $600. bk.rev.; illus. circ. 8,700. (tabloid format) **Indexed:** Alt.Press Ind. **Document type:** newspaper.
   Former titles (until 1982): Prisoners Union Journal; (until 1980): Outlaw.
   Description: Reports on the current status of legislative and judicial decisions affecting the lives of prisoners and their families in California, with coverage of aspects of prison life, from prisoners' and professionals' viewpoints.

342 350   IT
CAMERA DEI DEPUTATI. BOLLETTINO DI INFORMAZIONI COSTITUZIONALI E PARLAMENTARI. 1981. q. L.40000. Camera dei Deputati, Palazzo Montecitorio, Rome, Italy. TEL 06-67179328. FAX 06-6783082. Ed. Anton Paolo Tanda. circ. 200. (back issues avail.)
   Description: Examines original documents of parliamentary procedure and constitutional law.

342   US
CASES AND MATERIALS ON CONSTITUTIONAL LAW. irreg. price varies. Foundation Press, Inc., 615 Merrick Ave., Westbury, NY 11590-6607.

342   CN
CHARTER OF RIGHTS IN LITIGATION; direction from the Supreme Court of Canada. base vol. (plus updates 3/yr.). Can.$177. Canada Law Book Inc., 240 Edward St., Aurora, ON L4G 3S9, Canada. TEL 905-841-6472. FAX 905-841-5085. Ed. David Stratas. (looseleaf format)
   Description: Provides issue-by-issue, case-by-case Charter decisions of the Supreme Court of Canada.

342   CN   ISSN 0838-4843
CHARTER OF RIGHTS NEWSLETTER. 1988. 10/yr. Can.$104. Canada Law Book Inc., 240 Edward St., Aurora, ON L4G 3S9, Canada. TEL 905-841-6472. FAX 905-841-5085. Ed. David J. Martin. **Document type:** newsletter.
   Description: Provides current analysis of Charter issues and trends as they occur.

342   US
CONSTITUTIONAL COMMENTARIES.* 1984. irreg. (approx. 2/yr.). $6. Center for Judicial Studies, Box 113, Hampden-Sydney, VA 23943-0113. TEL 804-282-1798. Ed. James McClellan. circ. 1,500. (back issues avail.) **Indexed:** C.L.I. **Document type:** academic/scholarly publication.
   Description: Scholarly studies on the Constitution, constitutional law and the courts.

342   CN   ISSN 0847-3889
CONSTITUTIONAL FORUM/FORUM CONSTITUTIONNEL. 1989. q. Centre for Constitutional Studies, University of Alberta, Edmonton, AB T6G 2H5, Canada. **Indexed:** Ind.Can.L.P.L.

342   US
CONSTITUTIONAL LAW AND LIBERTY. 1974. 6/yr. $12 to members. Illinois State Bar Association, Individual Rights & Responsibilities Section, Illinois Bar Center, Springfield, IL 62701. TEL 217-525-1760. FAX 217-525-0712. Ed. Patrick J. Hughes, Jr. (looseleaf format; back issues avail.) **Document type:** newsletter.

342 320   US   ISSN 1043-4062
CONSTITUTIONAL POLITICAL ECONOMY. 1990. 3/yr. $27 to individuals (foreign $33); institutions $65 (foreign $71) (typically set in Jan.). George Mason University, Center for Study of Public Choice, George's Hall, Fairfax, VA 22030-4444. TEL 703-993-2329. FAX 703-993-2323. Eds. Viktor J. Vanberg, Richard E. Wagner. adv.; bk.rev. circ. 615. **Indexed:** Int.Polit.Sci.Abstr., J.of Econ.Lit.
   Description: Provides a forum for papers in the broad area of constitutional analysis. Integrates the institutional dimension (the study of legal, political and moral institutions) into economic analysis.

CORPORATE CRIMINAL AND CONSTITUTIONAL LAW REPORTER. see *LAW — Corporate Law*

342   US
FIRST AMENDMENT LAW HANDBOOK. a. $75. Clark - Boardman - Callaghan Company Ltd., 375 Hudson St., New York, NY 10014. TEL 212-929-7500; 800-221-9428. FAX 212-924-0460. Ed. James L. Swanson.
   Description: Provides law review articles, legal briefs, letters, and short, practical articles on subjects whose issues and legal confrontations change dramatically from year to year.

342   US
FIRST AMENDMENT LAWYERS ASSOCIATION. BULLETIN. bi-m. 125 S. Wacker Dr., Ste. 2700, Chicago, IL 60606. TEL 312-236-0606. **Document type:** bulletin.

342 345   US
FORUM (VALPARAISO). 1969. m. $8. Valparaiso University, School of Law, Wesemann Hall, Valparaiso, IN 46383. TEL 219-465-7831. FAX 219-465-7921. Ed. Mike English. adv.; bk.rev. circ. 1,000. (tabloid format; back issues avail.) **Document type:** academic/scholarly publication.
   Description: Discusses constitutional and criminal law.

342   US
GILBERT LAW SUMMARIES. CONSTITUTIONAL LAW. irreg., 26th ed., 1991. $19.95. Harcourt Brace Legal & Professional Publications, Inc., 176 W. Adams, Ste. 2100, Chicago, IL 60603. TEL 312-853-3662.

342   IT
GIURISPRUDENZA COSTITUZIONALE. 1956. bi-m. L.220000 (foreign L.330000). Casa Editrice Dott. A. Giuffre, Via Busto Arsizio 40, 20151 Milan, Italy. TEL 02-38000905. FAX 02-38009582. Ed. Leopoldo Elia. adv.; bk.rev. circ. 2,400.

342   US   ISSN 0094-5617
K8
HASTINGS CONSTITUTIONAL LAW QUARTERLY. 1974. q. $20 (foreign $22). University of California at San Francisco, Hastings College of the Law, 200 McAllister St., San Francisco, CA 94102-4978. TEL 415-565-4726. FAX 415-565-4814. Ed. Tracey Letteau. adv.; bk.rev. circ. 1,200. (tabloid format; also avail. in microform from WSH,PMC; back issues avail.; reprint service avail.) **Indexed:** C.C.L.P., C.L.I., Crim.Just.Abstr., L.R.I., Leg.Cont., Leg.Per. **Document type:** academic/scholarly publication.
●Also available online. Vendor(s): West Services, Inc. Also available on CD-ROM.
—BLDSC (4273.030000); Faxon; UnCover.
   Description: Legal scholarship on topics significant to current developments in constitutional law.

340 341 US ISSN 1064-4016
HUMAN RIGHTS & PEACE LAW DOCKET. biennial. $55 to individuals; institutions $66. Meiklejohn Civil Liberties Institute, Box 673, Berkeley, CA 94701-0673. TEL 510-848-0599. FAX 510-848-6008. (Subscr. to: Box 673, Berkeley, CA 94701) Eds. Ann Fagan Ginger, Frank Cialone. (looseleaf format)
  Former titles (until 1992): Peace Law Docket (ISSN 0894-9956); (until 1987): Studies in Law and Social Change.
  Description: Publishes digests of hundreds of national and international court cases, treatises and legislative actions.

342 GW ISSN 0174-4704
K8
HUMAN RIGHTS LAW JOURNAL. (Text in English) 1980. m. DM.314($208) N.P. Engel Verlag, Gutenbergstr. 29, 77694 Kehl, Germany. TEL 07851-2463. FAX 07851-4234. (U.S. addr.: N.P. Engel, Publisher, 3608 S. 12th St., Arlington, VA 22204. TEL 703-920-3126. FAX 703-920-3127) Ed. Erika Engel. adv.; cum.index: 1980-1988. **Indexed:** C.L.I., HR Rep., L.R.I., Leg.Per. **Document type:** bulletin. —BLDSC (4336.440500); UnCover; SWETS.
  Incorporates: Human Rights Review.
  Description: Articles, reports and documentation on constitutional and Supreme Court decisions. Includes information on pending proceedings.

341 NE
▼**INTERNATIONAL ENCYCLOPAEDIA OF LAWS. CONSTITUTIONAL LAW.** (Text in English) 1992. base vol. (plus irreg. updates). fl.300($162) (effective 1994). Kluwer Law and Taxation Publishers (Subsidiary of: Wolters Kluwer N.V.), P.O. Box 23, 7400 GA Deventer, Netherlands. TEL 31-5700-47261. FAX 31-5700-22244. TELEX 49295. (Dist. by: Libresso Distribution Centre, P.O. Box 23, 7400 GA Deventer, Netherlands. TEL 31-5700-33155. FAX 31-5700-33834; In N. America: Kluwer Law and Taxation Publishers, 675 Massachusetts Ave., Cambridge, MA 02139. TEL 617-354-0140. FAX 617-354-8595) Ed. Andre Alen. (looseleaf format) **Document type:** monographic series.
  Description: Publishes studies of the constitutional law of individual countries, from an international, comparative perspective, with discussion of general principles, sources of constitutional law, and historical background, as well as the form of government and issues such as citizenship, taxation, foreign relations and the constitutional relations between church and state.

342 II
INTRODUCTION TO THE CONSTITUTION OF INDIA. (Text in English) irreg., 15th ed., 1993. $75. (National Research Professor of Constitutional Law) Prentice - Hall of India Pvt., Ltd., M-97, Connaught Circus, New Delhi 110 001, India. TEL 011-332-1779. FAX 011-371-7179. TELEX 031-61808 PH IN.

342 GW ISSN 0075-2517
JF13
JAHRBUCH DES OEFFENTLICHEN RECHTS DER GEGENWART. N.S. 1951. a. price varies. Verlag J.C.B. Mohr (Paul Siebeck), Wilhelmstr. 18, 72074 Tuebingen, Germany. TEL 07071-923-0. FAX 07071-51104. TELEX 7262872-MOHR-D. (Subscr. to: Postfach 2040, 72010 Tuebingen, Germany) Ed. Peter Haeberle. **Indexed:** CERDIC. **Document type:** bulletin.
  Description: Developments in constitutional law in Europe and elsewhere.

342 SP
JURISPRUDENCIA CONSTITUCIONAL. 1980. 3/yr. price varies per no. (Tribunal Constitucional) Boletin Oficial del Estado, Trafalgar 27-29, 28071 Madrid, Spain.

342 US
LANDMARK BRIEFS AND ARGUMENTS OF THE SUPREME COURT OF THE UNITED STATES: CONSTITUTIONAL LAW. (Issued as 80 vol.set covering 1793-1973; annual supplements in several vols. cover each court term thereafter) 1974. a. price varies. University Publications of America (Subsidiary of: Congressional Information Service), 4520 East-West Hwy., Ste. 800, Bethesda, MD 20814-3389. TEL 301-657-3200. FAX 301-657-3203. Eds. Philip B. Kurland, Gerhard Casper. (back issues avail.)

342 UK ISSN 0951-0699
LAW REPORTS OF THE COMMONWEALTH. CONSTITUTIONAL AND ADMINISTRATIVE LAW REPORTS. 1985. a. Butterworth & Co. (Publishers) Ltd. (Subsidiary of: Reed Elsevier plc), 88 Kingsway, London WC2B 6AB, England. TEL 071-405-6900. FAX 071-405-1332. TELEX 95678. (US addr.: Butterworth Legal Publishers, 90 Stiles Rd., Salem, NH 03079) Ed.Bd.

342 IT
LEGGI DELLO STATO E DELLE REGIONI; le decisioni della corte costituzionale. 1972. every 10 days. L.100000 (Europe L.150000; elsewhere L.200000) (effective 1994). Casa Editrice La Tribuna, Via Don Minzoni 51, 29100 Piacenza, Italy. TEL 0523-75915. FAX 0523-757219. Ed. Mario Vitali. (back issues avail.)

LOUISIANA INDUSTRY ENVIRONMENTAL ALERT. see ENVIRONMENTAL STUDIES

342 350 US
MAJOR LEGISLATION OF THE CONGRESS. 1979. irreg. $19. U.S. Library of Congress, Congressional Research Service, Washington, DC 20540. Ed. Sully K. Craig.

342.710 CN ISSN 1181-9340
NATIONAL JOURNAL OF CONSTITUTIONAL LAW/REVUE NATIONALE DE DROIT CONSTITUTIONNEL. 1991. 3/yr. Carswell, One Corporate Plaza, 2075 Kennedy Rd., Scarborough, ON M1T 3V4, Canada. TEL 416-609-8000. FAX 416-298-5094. **Indexed:** Ind.Can.L.P.L.

NATIONAL SECOND MORTGAGE ASSOCIATION. LEGISLATIVE REPORT. see BUSINESS AND ECONOMICS — Banking And Finance

342 US
▼**NATIONAL SURVEY OF STATE LAWS.** 1992. a. $49.95 (effective Aug. 1993). Gale Research Inc., 835 Penobscot Bldg., Detroit, MI 48266. TEL 313-961-2242; 800-877-4253. FAX 313-961-6083. Ed. Richard A. Leiter.

342 323.4 NZ
▼**NEW ZEALAND BILL OF RIGHTS REPORTS.** 1992. irreg. NZ.$250($130) Oxford University Press - New Zealand, P.O. Box 11-149, Auckland 5, New Zealand. TEL 64-9-523-3134. FAX 64-0-524-6723. Eds. Antony Shaw, Andrew Butler. (back issues avail.)
  Description: Provides comprehensive coverage of the New Zealand Bill of Rights jurisprudence; contains decisions of courts, tribunals, and administrative bodies at all levels.

342 IT ISSN 0392-6664
QUADERNI COSTITUZIONALI. 1981. 3/yr. L.110000. Societa Editrice Il Mulino, Strada Maggiore, 37, 40125 Bologna, Italy. TEL 051-256011. FAX 051-256034. Ed. Livio Paladin. adv.; index. circ. 1,700. (back issues avail.) **Indexed:** P.A.I.S.For.Lang.Ind.
—SWETS.

RELIGIOUS FREEDOM REPORTER. see POLITICAL SCIENCE — Civil Rights

342 AG ISSN 0326-8594
REVISTA DE DERECHO PUBLICO Y TEORIA DEL ESTADO. 1986. s-a. Instituto de Derecho Publico y Teoria del Estado Dr. Arturo Enrique Sampay, Carlos Pellegrini 961, 1er piso, Buenos Aires, Argentina. TEL 313-6836. Ed.Bd.

342 SP
REVISTA ESPANOLA DE DERECHO CONSTITUCIONAL. 3/yr. $40. (Centro de Estudios Constitucionales) Edisa, Lopez de Hoyos, 141, 28002 Madrid, Spain. TEL 415-97-12. **Indexed:** ELLIS.

342 FR ISSN 1151-2385
REVUE FRANCAISE DE DROIT CONSTITUTIONNEL. 1990. 4/yr. 495 F. (foreign 555 F.). Presses Universitaires de France, Departement des Revues, 14 av. du Bois-de-l'Epine, B.P. 90, 91003 Evry Cedex, France. TEL 1-60-77-82-05. FAX 1-60-79-20-45. TELEX PUF 600 474 F. Eds. Louis Favoreu, Didier Maus.
—SWETS.

342 GW ISSN 0937-714X
LA REVUE UNIVERSELLE DES DROITS DE L'HOMME. (Text in French) 1989. m. DM.314. N.P. Engel Verlag, Gutenbergstr. 29, 77694 Kehl, Germany. TEL 07851-2463. FAX 07851-4234. (Dist. in U.S by: N.P. Engel, Publisher, 3608 S. 12th St., Arlington, VA 22204. TEL 703-920-3126. FAX 703-920-3127) Ed. Erika Engel. **Document type:** bulletin.

342 US
KF4550.Z95S68
STATE CONSTITUTIONAL LAW BULLETIN. 1987. 10/yr. $50. National Association of Attorneys General, 444 N. Capitol St., N.W., Ste. 339, Washington, DC 20001. TEL 202-434-8000. FAX 202-434-8008. Ed. Eleni Constantine. (looseleaf format) **Document type:** bulletin.

TEXAS INDUSTRY ENVIRONMENTAL ALERT. see ENVIRONMENTAL STUDIES

342 PN
UNIVERSIDAD DE PANAMA. CENTRO DE INVESTIGACION JURIDICA. JURISPRUDENCIA CONSTITUCIONAL. 1968. irreg. price varies. Universidad de Panama, Centro de Investigacion Juridica, Estafeta Universitaria, Panama, Panama. Ed. Aura G. de Villalaz.

UNIWERSYTET SLASKI W KATOWICACH. PRACE NAUKOWE. STUDIA IURIDICA SILESIANA. see LAW

342 AT ISSN 0314-5204
VICTORIAN STATUTES CUMULATIVE SUPPLEMENT. 1962. a. Law Book Co. Ltd., 44-50 Waterloo Rd., North Ryde, N.S.W. 2113, Australia. TEL 02-887-0177. FAX 02-888-9706. TELEX ASBOOK 27995.
  Description: Provides a legislative history of principal acts since the 1958 consolidation. Includes notes on administration of acts and references to relevant journals and periodicals.

342 US
WE THE PEOPLE (DENVER). 1991. q. membership. American Constitutional Law Foundation, Inc., 601 S. Broadway, Ste. U, Denver, CO 80209. TEL 303-744-6449. Ed. Chuck Beck.

342 UK
WEST INDIAN REPORTS. s-a. Butterworth & Co. (Publishers) Ltd. (Subsidiary of: Reed Elsevier plc), 88 Kingsway, London WC2B 6AB, England. TEL 071-405-6900. FAX 071-405-1332. TELEX 95678. (US addr.: Butterworth Legal Publishers, 90 Stiles Rd., Salem, NH 03079. TEL 603-898-9664) Ed.Bd.
  Description: Provides a vital service to the leagal profession, both in the West indies and internationally.

342 US ISSN 1065-8254
K27
WILLIAM AND MARY BILL OF RIGHTS JOURNAL. s-a. $20. College of William and Mary, Marshall-Wythe School of Law, Box 8795, Williamsburg, VA 23187-8795. TEL 804-221-3706. FAX 804-221-3775. adv.; bk.rev. circ. 1,500. (back issues avail.)
—UnCover.
  Formerly (until 1992): Colonial Lawyer (ISSN 0884-4429)

LAW — Corporate Law

346 657 AT ISSN 1036-4803
A A S B ACCOUNTING STANDARDS. 1991. irreg. Aus.$5 per issue. Australian Accounting Standards Board, 211 Hawthorn Rd., Caulfield, Vic. 3162, Australia. TEL 61-3-523-8111. FAX 61-3-523-5499. circ. 2,000.

A B I JOURNAL. (American Bankruptcy Institute) see BUSINESS AND ECONOMICS — Banking And Finance

346 US
A C C A ALERT. bi-m. American Corporate Counsel Association, 1225 Connecticut Ave., N.W., Ste. 302, Washington, DC 20036-2604. TEL 202-296-4522. **Document type:** newsletter.
  Description: Covers association activities.

LAW — CORPORATE LAW

346 330 US ISSN 0895-9544
A C C A DOCKET. q. American Corporate Counsel Association, 1225 Connecticut Ave., N.W., Ste. 302, Washington, DC 20036-2604. TEL 202-296-4522. Ed. Susan J. Hackett. circ. 10,000. **Document type:** newsletter.
—UMI.

346 US
▼**A C C A NEWS.** 1992. bi-m. membership. American Corporate Counsel Association, 1225 Connecticut Ave., N.W., Ste. 302, Washington, DC 20036-2604. TEL 202-296-4522. FAX 202-331-7454. Ed. Cecilia B. Sepp. circ. 8,000. **Document type:** newsletter.

346 US
A L S B NEWSLETTER. 3/yr. $50 includes membership. (American Business Law Association, Inc.) Academy of Legal Studies in Business (Oxford), Department of Finance, 120 Upham Hall, Miami University, Oxford, OH 45056. circ. 1,200. **Document type:** newsletter.
Formerly (until 1991): A B L A Newsletter.

346 UK ISSN 1353-355X
▼**ACQUISITIONS AND GROUP STRUCTURES.** 1994. a. £17.50. Jordan Publishing Ltd., 21 St. Thomas St., Bristol BS1 6JS, England. TEL 0272-230600. FAX 0272-250486. Ed. Denis Heshon. **Document type:** academic/scholarly publication.

ADMINISTRATOR. see BUSINESS AND ECONOMICS — Management

346 CN
ALBERTA CORPORATION MANUAL. q. Can.$380. Carswell, One Corporate Plaza, 2075 Kennedy Rd., Scarborough, ON M1T 3V4, Canada. TEL 416-609-8000. FAX 416-298-5094. Ed. Macleod Dixon. (looseleaf format)
Description: Includes authoritative commentary on corporate law, departmental practice and procedure notes, a comprehensive collection of forms and precedents and relevant statutes and regulations.

AMERICAN BANKER'S WASHINGTON WATCH. see BUSINESS AND ECONOMICS — Banking And Finance

346 US ISSN 0002-7766
K1 CODEN: ABLJAN
AMERICAN BUSINESS LAW JOURNAL. 1963. 4/yr. $24 (foreign $27). Academy of Legal Studies in Business, c/o Daniel J. Herron, Dept. of Finance, 120 Upham Hall, Miami University, Oxford, OH 45056. TEL 513-529-2945. FAX 513-529-6992. Ed. Johm Gergaczrer. adv.; bk.rev.; charts; illus.; index, cum.index. circ. 2,000. (also avail. in microform from UMI; reprint service avail. from RRI) **Indexed:** ABI Inform., Abstr.Bk.Rev.Curr.Leg.Per., Account.Ind. (1974-), B.P.I., BPIA, Bus.Ind., C.C.L.P., C.L.I., Curr.Cont., L.R.I., Leg.Cont., Leg.Per., SSCI, Tr.& Indus.Ind.
—BLDSC (0811.500000); Faxon; UnCover; SWETS; UMI.
Refereed Serial

346 CN
ANNOTATED ONTARIO BUSINESS CORPORATIONS ACT. base vol. (plus s-a. updates). Can.$140. Canada Law Book Inc., 240 Edward St., Aurora, ON L4G 3S9, Canada. TEL 905-841-6472. FAX 905-841-5085. Ed. Stephen N. Adams. (looseleaf format)

346 US ISSN 1051-1539
KF975
ANNUAL INSTITUTE, SECURITIES ACTIVITIES OF BANKS. a. Prentice Hall Law & Business, 270 Sylvan Ave., Engelwood Cliffs, NJ 07632.
Former titles: Annual Seminar, Securities Activities of Banks (ISSN 1047-0603); (until 1984): Annual Securities Activities of Banks (ISSN 0742-0358); (until 1983): Annual Seminar, Securities Activities of Banks (ISSN 0743-1295)

346 US ISSN 0162-7996
KF1632
ANTITRUST. 1986. 3/yr. $30 (foreign $35). American Bar Association, Antitrust Law Section, 750 N. Lake Shore Dr., Chicago, IL 60611. TEL 312-988-5605. Ed. Tina Miller. **Indexed:** C.L.I., ELLIS.
●Also available online. Vendor(s): West Services, Inc. (ANTITR).
—UnCover.
Description: Publishes articles on developments in antitrust law.

346 US
ANTITRUST ADVISER, 3-E. irreg. $95. Shepard's - McGraw-Hill, Inc., Box 35300, Colorado Springs, CO 80935-3530. TEL 800-525-2474.
Description: Pragmatic discussions of the Sherman Act, the Clayton Act, the Robinson-Patman Act and the Federal Trade Commission Act.

346 US
ANTITRUST AND AMERICAN BUSINESS ABROAD, 2-E. 1981. 2 base vols. (plus a. suppl.). $210. Shepard's - McGraw-Hill, Inc., Box 35300, Colorado Springs, CO 80935-3530. TEL 800-525-2474.
Description: For litigants, counselors and scholars. Reflects the sweeping changes taking place in American law related to the worldwide issues of antitrust.

346 US
ANTITRUST & COMMERCE REPORT. 1974. 10/yr. $145. National Association of Attorneys General, 444 N. Capitol St., N.W., Ste. 403, Washington, DC 20001. TEL 202-628-0435. Ed. Elena Boisuert. index. circ. 250. (back issues avail.)

346 US ISSN 0003-603X
K1 CODEN: ATBUAU
ANTITRUST BULLETIN. 1955. q. $85 to individuals; academic & government personnel $52. Federal Legal Publications, Inc., 157 Chambers St., New York, NY 10007. TEL 212-619-4949. Ed. William J. Curran, III. adv.; bk.rev.; bibl.; charts; cum.index: 1955-1977. circ. 2,000. (also avail. in microfilm from UMI; back issues avail.; reprint service avail. from UMI) **Indexed:** ABI Inform., Abstr.Bk.Rev.Curr.Leg.Per., BPIA, Bus.Ind., C.L.I., C.R.E.J., ELLIS, J.of Econ.Lit., L.R.I., Leg.Per., P.A.I.S., SCIMP, Tr.& Indus.Ind. **Document type:** bulletin.
—BLDSC (1552.400000); Faxon; UnCover; SWETS; UMI.

346 US
ANTITRUST COUNSELING AND LITIGATION TECHNIQUES. 1984. 4 base vols., with a. supplements. $650. Matthew Bender & Co., Inc., 11 Penn Plaza, New York, NY 10001. TEL 212-967-7707. (looseleaf format)
Description: Practical guide to corporate antitrust counseling and successful antitrust litigation, complementing von Kalinowski's treatise on antitrust.

346 338.8 US ISSN 0003-6048
K1.
ANTITRUST LAW AND ECONOMICS REVIEW. 1967. q. $98.50. Antitrust Law and Economics Review, Inc., Beach P.O. Box 3532, Vero Beach, FL 32964-9990. Ed. Charles E. Mueller. bk.rev. **Indexed:** ABI Inform., B.P.I., BPIA, Bus.Ind., C.L.I., C.R.E.J., L.R.I., Leg.Per., P.A.I.S.
—BLDSC (1552.700000); Faxon; UnCover; SWETS.

346 US ISSN 0738-5919
KF1632.5
ANTITRUST LAW HANDBOOK. 1984. a. $79.50. Clark - Boardman - Callaghan Company Ltd., 375 Hudson St., New York, NY 10014. TEL 212-929-7500; 800-221-9428. FAX 212-924-0460. Ed. Robert Bouchard.
Description: Presents a comprehensive overview and update of American antitrust law and practice, featuring governing theory, substantive issues, procedural aspects, significant developments and trends and key cases.

346 US ISSN 0003-6056
K1
ANTITRUST LAW JOURNAL. 1931. 3/yr. $30 (foreign $35). American Bar Association, Antitrust Law Section, 750 N. Lake Shore Dr., Chicago, IL 60611. TEL 312-988-5606. Ed. Tina Miller. cum.index: 1960-1967, 1968-1980. circ. 12,000. (also avail. in microfilm from RRI; reprint service avail. from RRI) **Indexed:** C.L.I., ELLIS, L.R.I., Leg.Cont., Leg.Per., Tr.& Indus.Ind.
●Also available online. Vendor(s): Mead Data Central, Inc., West Services, Inc. (ANTITRLJ).
—BLDSC (1552.800000); Faxon; UnCover; SWETS.
Description: Publishes articles on antitrust law; covers meeting proceedings, section reports and positions on legislation.
Refereed Serial

346 US
ANTITRUST LAW SOURCEBOOK. a. $79.50. Clark - Boardman - Callaghan Company Ltd., 375 Hudson St., New York, NY 10014. TEL 212-929-7500; 800-221-9428. FAX 212-924-0460. Eds. William C. Holmes, Dawn E. Holmes.
Description: Offers a compilation of federal and state statutory and administrative materials regularly used by antitrust practitioners, and a plethora of information on antitrust enforcement in domestic and international arenas.

346 US
ANTITRUST LAWS AND TRADE REGULATION. (Issued with Antitrust Laws and Trade Regulation Newsletter) 1969. 4/yr. Matthew Bender & Co., Inc., 11 Penn Plaza, New York, NY 10001. TEL 212-967-7707. (looseleaf format)
Description: Detailed treatise on antitrust.

346 US
ANTITRUST LAWS AND TRADE REGULATION: DESK EDITION. 1981. 2 base vols. (plus irreg. supplements). $530. Matthew Bender & Co., Inc., 11 Penn Plaza, New York, NY 10001. TEL 212-967-7707. (looseleaf format)
Description: Examines the essence of von Kalinowski's master treatise.

340 US ISSN 0733-6160
ARBITRATION & THE LAW. 1981. a. fl.110($65) (effective 1992). American Arbitration Association, Office of the General Counsel, 140 W. 51st St., New York, NY 10020-1203. TEL 212-484-4110. FAX 212-765-4874. (Dist. outside U.S. by: Kluwer LAw and Taxation Publishers, P.O. Box 23, 7400 GA Deventer, Netherlands. TEL 31-5700-47261) Ed. Michael F. Hoellering. abstr.; index. circ. 600.
Description: Covers rules, cases, statutes, commentaries and recent developments in commercial and international arbitration, including specialized sections on securities, textiles, labor, insurance and medical malpractice arbitration.

346 330 340 US ISSN 0571-8279
KF297.A1
ATTORNEY - C P A. 1966. 5/yr. $30 to non-members; foreign $40. American Association of Attorney-Certified Public Accountants, Inc., 24196 Alicia Pkwy., Ste. K, Mission Viejo, CA 92691. TEL 714-768-0336. Ed. Ronald M. DeVore. adv.; bk.rev. circ. 1,600. (back issues avail.) **Indexed:** Account.Ind. (1974-). **Document type:** newsletter.
—UMI.
Description: Technical information and updates on dual license regulation. Includes association news.

346 657 US
ATTORNEY'S HANDBOOK OF ACCOUNTING. 1965. base vol. (plus irreg. suppl.). $170. Matthew Bender & Co., Inc., 11 Penn Plaza, New York, NY 10001. TEL 212-967-7007.
Formerly: Attorney's Practical Guide to Accounting.
Description: Covers accounting principles and practices, from financial statement analysis to accounting procedures for businesses and nonprofit organizations.

346 AT ISSN 0310-1053
K1 CODEN: ABRVDO
AUSTRALIAN BUSINESS LAW REVIEW. 1973. bi-m. Aus.$205. Law Book Co. Ltd., 44-50 Waterloo Rd., N. Ryde, N.S.W. 2113, Australia. TEL 02-887-0177. FAX 02-888-9706. TELEX ASBOOK 27995. bk.rev.; illus. **Indexed:** ABI Inform., Abstr.Bk.Rev.Curr.Leg.Per., Aus.P.A.I.S., BPIA, C.L.I., L.R.I., Leg.Cont.
—BLDSC (1798.095000); UMI.
Description: Contains leading articles on matters of topical interest and comments by regular contributors on legislative and case law developments affecting banking and investment.

346 AT
AUSTRALIAN COMPANY LAW CASES. 1971. 16/yr. (every 3 wks.). C C H Australia Ltd., P.O. Box 230, North Ryde, N.S.W. 2113, Australia. TEL 888-2555. FAX 02-888-7324. (looseleaf format)

346 330 AT
AUSTRALIAN COMPANY SECRETARY'S BUSINESS LAW MANUAL 1987. s-a. C C H Australia Ltd., P.O. Box 230, North Ryde, N.S.W. 2113, Australia. TEL 02-888-2555. FAX 02-888-7324. (looseleaf format)

LAW — CORPORATE LAW

346 336 AT ISSN 0729-1221
AUSTRALIAN COMPANY SECRETARY'S LETTER; a practical business review for corporate administrators. 1982. irreg. (approx. 3/w.). C C H Australia Ltd., P.O. Box 230, North Ryde, N.S.W. 2113, Australia. TEL 02-888-2555. FAX 02-888-7324. (looseleaf format)

346 AT
AUSTRALIAN CORPORATIONS & SECURITIES LAW REPORTER. (In 3 vols.) 1990. every 3 wks. C C H Australia Ltd., P.O. Box 230, North Ryde, N.S.W. 2113, Australia. TEL 02-888-2555. FAX 02-888-7324. (looseleaf format)

346 AT
AUSTRALIAN CORPORATIONS AND SECURITIES LEGISLATION. (In 2 vols.) 1982. irreg. (as required for all legislative changes). C C H Australia Ltd., P.O. Box 230, North Ryde, N.S.W. 2113, Australia. TEL 02-888-2555. FAX 02-888-7324. (looseleaf format)
 Formerly: C C H Australian Companies and Securities Legislation.

346 AT ISSN 1033-7466
LAW
AUSTRALIAN CORPORATIONS AND SECURITIES REPORTS; reports of leading cases in company law in Australia. 1977. 2/yr. (plus updates every 3 wks.). Aus.$218 per vol. Butterworths, 271-273 Lane Cove Rd., North Ryde, N.S.W. 2113, Australia. TEL 02-335-4444. FAX 02-335-4655. circ. 1,608. (back issues avail.)
 Formerly (until 1990): Australian Company Law Reports (ISSN 0313-8445)

346 347 AT
▼**AUSTRALIAN CORPORATIONS COURT RULES**. 1992. irreg. (as required for legislative changes). C C H Australia Ltd., P.O. Box 230, North Ryde, N.S.W. 2113, Australia. TEL 02-888-2555. FAX 02-888-7324. (looseleaf format)

346 331 AT
AUSTRALIAN EMPLOYMENT LAW GUIDE. 1984. 10/yr. C C H Australia Ltd., P.O. Box 230, North Ryde, N.S.W. 2113, Australia. TEL 02-888-2555. FAX 02-888-7324. (looseleaf format)

346 331 AT
AUSTRALIAN EMPLOYMENT LEGISLATION. (In 3 vols.) 1984. m. C C H Australia Ltd., P.O. Box 230, North Ryde, N.S.W. 2113, Australia. TEL 02-888-2555. FAX 02-888-7324. (looseleaf format)

346 336 AT
AUSTRALIAN FRINGE BENEFITS TAX GUIDE FOR EMPLOYERS. 1986. bi-m. C C H Australia Ltd., P.O. Box 230, North Ryde, N.S.W. 2113, Australia. TEL 02-888-2555. FAX 02-888-7324. (looseleaf format)
 Description: Provides practical commentary and full text legislation.

346 AT ISSN 0726-5883
AUSTRALIAN INDUSTRIAL LAW REVIEW. 1976. fortn. C C H Australia Ltd., P.O. Box 230, North Ryde, N.S.W. 2113, Australia. TEL 888-2555. FAX 02-888-7324. (looseleaf format)

346 331 AT ISSN 1030-7222
AUSTRALIAN JOURNAL OF LABOUR LAW. 1988. 3/yr. Aus.$130. Butterworths, 271-273 Lane Cove Rd., North Ryde, N.S.W. 2113, Australia. TEL 02-335-4444. FAX 02-335-4655. Ed. Richard Mitchell. bk.rev. circ. 1,000. **Document type:** academic/scholarly publication.
 Description: Articles, notes, comments and commentaries on recent cases, legislation on labor law and labor relations suited for academics and practitioners.

346 331 AT
AUSTRALIAN LABOUR LAW REPORTER. (In 3 vols.) 1977. m. C C H Australia Ltd., P.O. Box 230, North Ryde, N.S.W. 2113, Australia. TEL 888-2555. FAX 02-888-7324. charts. (looseleaf format)

346 AT
AUSTRALIAN SECURITIES COMMISSION RELEASES. 1991. fortn. C C H Australia Ltd., P.O. Box 230, North Ryde, N.S.W. 2113, Australia. TEL 02-888-2555. FAX 02-888-7324. (looseleaf format)

346 US ISSN 0099-1236
KF1414.3
B A R - B R I BAR REVIEW. CORPORATIONS. a. $395. B A R - B R I Bar Review, 3280 Motor Ave., Los Angeles, CA 90034-3710. TEL 213-477-2542.

346 US
▼**B N A - A C C A COMPLIANCE MANUAL: PREVENTION OF CORPORATE LIABILITY**. 1993. m. $540. The Bureau of National Affairs, Inc., 1231 25th St., N.W., Washington, DC 20037. TEL 202-452-4200. FAX 202-822-8092. TELEX 285656 BNAI WSH. (Subscr. to: 9435 Key West Ave., Rockville, MD 20850. TEL 800-372-1033) Ed. Larry Lempert. s-a. index. (looseleaf format; back issues avail.)
 Description: Covers judicial decisions, pre-decisional developments in criminal prosecutions, enforcement trends, state and federal legislation, company activity, and Sentencing Commission activity.

B N A'S EASTERN EUROPE REPORTER. see BUSINESS AND ECONOMICS — Economic Situation And Conditions

346 US
BALLANTINE AND STERLING CALIFORNIA CORPORATION LAWS. 1932. 6 base vols. (plus irreg. suppl.). $1160. Matthew Bender & Co., Inc., 11 Penn Plaza, New York, NY 10001. TEL 212-967-7707. (Co-publisher: Parker & Son)
 Description: Provides detailed analysis of both the general and non-profit corporation law of California, combined with procedural guides from incorporation to dissolution.

346 US
BANK AND CORPORATE GOVERNANCE. 1988. m. $1450. Computer Law Reporter, Inc., 1519 Connecticut Ave., N.W., Ste. 200, Washington, DC 20036. TEL 202-462-5755. FAX 202-328-2430. Ed. Neil J. Cohen. (back issues avail.)
 Formerly: Mergers and Acquisitions Law Reporter.

346 US ISSN 0098-7336
KF1519
BANKRUPTCY COURT DECISIONS. 1974. w. $770. L R P Publications, 747 Dresher Rd., Box 980, Horsham, PA 19044. TEL 215-784-0860. Ed. Joanne E. Fiore. bk.rev. circ. 2,000. (back issues avail.)
 —CCC.

346 US ISSN 0005-5530
BANKRUPTCY LAW REPORTS. fortn. $770. Commerce Clearing House, Inc., 4025 W. Peterson Ave., Chicago, IL 60646. TEL 312-583-8500. Ed. Martin Bernstein. bibl.; charts; stat.; index. (looseleaf format)

346 657 US ISSN 1043-0547
K6
BANKRUPTCY LAW REVIEW. 1989. q. $125. Faulkner & Gray, Inc. (New York), 11 Penn Plaza, 17th Fl., New York, NY 10001. TEL 212-967-7000. FAX 212-967-7155. Ed. Bob Murdich. **Indexed:** Account.Ind. (1989-).
 Description: Presents interpretations, analysis and news.

246 US
BANKRUPTCY LOCAL COURT RULES SERVICE. base vol. (plus q. updates). $455. (Pike & Fischer, Inc.) Clark - Boardman - Callaghan Company, Ltd., 375 Hudson St., New York, NY 10014. TEL 212-929-7500; 800-221-9428. FAX 212-924-0460. (looseleaf format)
 Description: Provides up-to-date information on local bankruptcy court rules changes in all 94 bankruptcy jurisdictions.

346 US
BANKRUPTCY PRACTICE DESKBOOK. 3 base vols. (plus a. suppl.). $285. Butterworth Legal Publishers (Salem) (Subsidiary of: Reed Elsevier plc), 8 Industrial Way, Bldg. C, Salem, NH 03079. TEL 800-548-4001. FAX 603-898-9858. Eds. David D. Bird, Richard H.W. Maloy. (looseleaf format)
 Formerly: Bankruptcy Practice Manual.
 Description: Incorporates the ongoing changes in the Bankruptcy Code, Rules, and case law developments in all states.

346 US
BANKRUPTCY PRACTICE FOR THE GENERAL PRACTITIONER. 1980. 2 base vols. (plus s-a. suppl.). $195. Shepard's - McGraw-Hill, Inc., Box 35300, Colorado Springs, CO 80935-3530. TEL 800-525-2474. (looseleaf format)
 Description: Focuses on the procedural and substantive aspects of the Bankruptcy Code.

346 330 US
KF1520.B264
BANKRUPTCY SERVICE CURRENT AWARENESS ALERT. 1980. 12/yr. $175. Clark - Boardman - Callaghan (Rochester), 50 Broad St., E., Rochester, NY 14694. TEL 716-546-1490. FAX 716-258-3768. Ed. David M. Holliday. (looseleaf format)
 Description: Places in context recent rulings and developments in bankruptcy law and practice.

346 330 US
BANKRUPTCY SERVICE LAWYERS EDITION. 1979. base vol. (plus q. updates). $1225. Clark - Boardman - Callaghan Company Ltd., 375 Hudson St., New York, NY 10014. TEL 212-929-7500; 800-221-9428. FAX 212-924-0460.
 Description: Features an analysis of bankruptcy law and practice from a topical perspective.

346 US
BAR ASSOCIATION RESEARCH PROJECT REPORT. irreg. American Corporate Counsel Institute, c/o American Corporate Counsel Association, 1225 Connecticut Ave., N.W., Ste. 302, Washington, DC 20036-2604. TEL 202-296-4522. FAX 202-331-7454.

346 US
BASIC PATTERNS IN UNION CONTRACTS. irreg., 13th ed., 1992. $30. B N A Books (Subsidiary of: The Bureau of National Affairs, Inc.), 1231 25th St., N.W., Washington, DC 20037. TEL 202-833-7470. FAX 202-833-7490. (Subscr.to: BNA Books Distribution Center, 300 Raritan Center Parkway, Box 7816, Edison, NJ 08818-7816. TEL 800-372-1033) Ed.Bd; Pub. Richard H. Cornfield.

BERKELEY JOURNAL OF EMPLOYMENT AND LABOR LAW. see BUSINESS AND ECONOMICS — Labor And Industrial Relations

346 GW ISSN 0005-9935
DER BETRIEB; Wochenzeitschrift fuer Betriebswirtschaft, Steuerrecht, Wirtschaftsrecht, Arbeitsrecht. 1948. w. DM.447. Verlagsgruppe Handelsblatt GmbH, Kasernenstr. 67, 40213 Duesseldorf, Germany. TEL 0211-8870. (Subscr. to: Postfach 102717, 40018 Duesseldorf, Germany) Ed. G. Ackermann. adv.; bk.rev.; charts; illus.; stat.; index, cum.index. circ. 32,000. (reprint service avail. from UMI) **Indexed:** CERDIC, Dok.Arbeitsmed., ELLIS, INIS Atomind., SSCI. **Document type:** newspaper.
 —SWETS. CCC.

346 US
▼**BIZ LAW UPDATE**. 1992. m. $125. Biz Law Association, Inc., Box 247, Springdale, UT 84767. TEL 801-635-9817. FAX 801-772-3433. **Document type:** newsletter.

BOWNE DIGEST FOR CORPORATE & SECURITIES LAWYERS; abstracts of current articles from more than 280 legal periodicals. see LAW — Abstracting, Bibliographies, Statistics

346 CN
BRITISH COLUMBIA CORPORATION MANUAL. bi-m. Can.$380. Carswell, One Corporate Plaza, 2075 Kennedy Rd., Scarborough, ON M1T 3V4, Canada. TEL 416-609-8000. FAX 416-298-5094. circ. 400. (looseleaf format)

346 CN
BRITISH COLUMBIA CORPORATIONS LAW GUIDE. m. Can.$485. C C H Canadian Ltd., 6 Garamond Ct., North York, ON M3C 1Z5, Canada. TEL 416-441-2992. FAX 416-444-9011. index.
 Description: Covers British Columbia company act and regulations.

BRITISH COLUMBIA DECISIONS - LABOUR RELATIONS BOARD DIGESTS. see BUSINESS AND ECONOMICS — Labor And Industrial Relations

LAW — CORPORATE LAW

346   CN   ISSN 1180-5617
BULLETIN DU LIBRE - ECHANGE/FREE-TRADE UPDATE. (Text in English, French) 4/yr. Can.$125. Les Editions Yvon Blais, 430 rue St-Pierre, Ste. 200, Montreal, PQ H2Y 2M5, Canada. TEL 514-842-3937. FAX 514-842-7144. (Subscr. to: C.P. 180, Cowansville, PQ J2K 3H6, Canada. TEL 514-263-1086) Eds. Ivan Bernier, Sophie Dufoure.

346 332   US   ISSN 1067-618X
▼**BURAFF'S LITIGATION REPORT: BANK LAWYER LIABILITY NEWS.** 1992. bi-w. $745 (foreign $767). Buraff Publications (Subsidiary of: Millin Publications, Inc.), 1350 Connecticut Ave., N.W., Washington, DC 20036. FAX 202-862-0999.
—CCC.
Description: Text and analysis of RTC, FDIC, OTS, and related actions against bank lawyers. Emphasizes full-text copies of complaints, pleadings and opinions.

346 640.73   CN   ISSN 1193-1264
BUSINESS & EMPLOYMENT LAW NEWS. 1979. bi-m. Can.$115. Dunhill Publishing Company, 6389 Coburg Rd., Halifax, NS B3H 2A5, Canada. TEL 902-429-7272. FAX 902-452-2191. **Document type:** newsletter.
Former titles: Business Law News; Dunhill Products Liability Law Report.

346   CN   ISSN 0825-4982
BUSINESS & THE LAW. 1984. m. Can.$175. Carswell, One Corporate Plaza, 2075 Kennedy Rd., Scarborough, ON M1T 3V4, Canada. TEL 416-609-8000. FAX 416-298-5094. s-a. index. **Indexed:** Ind.Can.L.P.L. **Document type:** newsletter.
Description: Topical coverage and analysis of critical legal issues affecting business in Canada with contributions from leading legal authorities in the country.

346   US
BUSINESS COUNSEL; a quarterly update of the litigation activities of the U.S. Chambers of Commerce. 1979. q. $15 to non-member legal libraries. National Chamber Litigation Center (NCLC), 1615 H St., N.W., Washington, DC 20062. TEL 202-463-5337. FAX 202-463-5346. Ed. Cam Esser. illus.; tr.lit. circ. 1,000. **Document type:** newsletter.
Formerly: Business Advocate (ISSN 0193-4414); Supersedes (1979-1983): Washington Report (Washington, 1979) (ISSN 0043-0714)

346   UK   ISSN 1352-4488
▼**BUSINESS LAW AND PRACTICE.** 1993. a. £17.50. Jordan Publishing Ltd., 21 St. Thomas St., Bristol BS1 6JS, England. TEL 0272-230600. FAX 0272-250486. Ed. Alison Harvey. **Document type:** academic/scholarly publication.

346   UK   ISSN 0266-7630
BUSINESS LAW BRIEF. 1972. m. £328($557) (overseas £348) (effective 1993). Financial Times Business Information Ltd., 126 Jermyn St., London SW1Y 4UJ, England. TEL 071-411-4414. FAX 071-411-4415. Ed. A.H. Hermann. bk.rev.; index. **Document type:** newsletter.
●Also available online. Vendor(s): Data-Star, Mead Data Central, Inc.
Formed by the merger of (in Dec. 1983): Commercial Law Reports (ISSN 0262-8872); Eurolaw Commercial Intelligence (ISSN 0305-9561); European Law Letter (ISSN 0954-3910); Which was formerly (until 1976): European Law Newsletter (ISSN 0300-2233)
Description: Provides the latest information on judicial developments and judgments.

346   GW
BUSINESS LAW EUROPE. (Text in English, German) fortn. DM.888. Verlagsgruppe Jehle - Rehm, Einsteinstr. 172, 81675 Munich, Germany. TEL 089-416006-0. FAX 089-4706998. **Document type:** trade publication.

346 330   US
BUSINESS LAW MONOGRAPHS. 1984. 26 base vols. (plus q. updates). $2000. Matthew Bender & Co., Inc., 11 Penn Plaza, New York, NY 10001. TEL 212-967-7707. (looseleaf format)
Description: Each monograph concentrates on a particular subject of interest to corporate counsel, explaining what the law requires and how counsel can handle common transactions and prevent or resolve common problems.

346   US
BUSINESS LAW NEWS (MADISON). q. membership. State Bar of Wisconsin, Business Law Section, 402 W. Wilson St., Madison, WI 53703. TEL 608-257-3838. FAX 608-257-5502. circ. 1,620. **Document type:** newsletter.

346   US
KFC225.A1S7
BUSINESS LAW NEWS (SAN FRANCISCO). q. membership. State Bar of California, Business Law Section, 555 Franklin St., San Francisco, CA 94102. TEL 415-561-8264. FAX 415-561-8228. **Document type:** newsletter.

346   CN   ISSN 0703-5551
KE915.8
BUSINESS LAW REPORTS (2ND SERIES). 1977. m. (4 vols./yr.) Can.$120. Carswell, One Corporate Plaza, 2075 Kennedy Rd., Scarborough, ON M1T 3V4, Canada. TEL 416-609-8000. FAX 416-298-5094. Ed. George C. Glover, Jr. adv. contact: M. Lalani. (looseleaf format) **Indexed:** C.L.I., Ind.Can.L.P.L., L.R.I.
Description: Features important decisions in corporate, commercial and business law from Canadian jurisdictions. Includes cases under the federal and provincial corporation statutes, prosecution under the Competition Act, cases on shareholders' rights, partnerships, rights of debtors and creditors, bills of exchange.

346 330   UK   ISSN 0143-6295
BUSINESS LAW REVIEW. 1980. 11/yr. £242($410) (effective 1994). Graham & Trotman Ltd. (Subsidiary of: Kluwer Academic Publishers Group), Sterling House, 66 Wilton Rd., London SW1V 1DE, England. TEL 44-71-821-1123. (Dist. by: Kluwer Academic Publishers Group, P.O. Box 322, 3300 AH Dordrecht, Netherlands. TEL 31-78-524400. FAX 31-78-524474; N. America dist. addr.: Box 358, Accord Station, Hingham, MA 02018-0358. TEL 617-871-6600. FAX 617-871-6528) Ed. Susan Nicholas. adv. **Indexed:** Bus.Ind., ELLIS, L.R.I. **Document type:** academic/scholarly publication.
—BLDSC (2934.122000); UnCover; SWETS; UMI.
Description: Provides practical news for business lawyers in all branches.

346 381   UK
BUSINESS LAWS OF EGYPT. a. £690($1195) Graham & Trotman Ltd. (Subsidiary of: Kluwer Academic Publishers Group), Sterling House, 66 Wilton Rd., London SW1V 1DE, England. TEL 44-71-821-1123. FAX 44-71-630-5229. (Dist. by: Kluwer Academic Publishers Group, P.O. Box 322, 3300 AH Dordrecht, Netherlands. TEL 31-78-524400. FAX 31-78-524474; N. America dist. addr.: Box 358, Accord Sta., Hingham, MA 02018-0358. TEL 617-871-6600. FAX 617-871-6528) Ed. N.H. Karam. (looseleaf format) **Document type:** trade publication.

346 381   UK
BUSINESS LAWS OF IRAQ. a. £550($1100) Graham & Trotman Ltd. (Subsidiary of: Kluwer Academic Publishers Group), Sterling House, 66 Wilton Rd., London SW1V 1DE, England. TEL 44-71-821-1123. FAX 44-71-630-5229. (Dist by: Kluwer Academic Publishers Group, P.O. Box 322, 3300 AH Dordrecht, Netherlands. TEL 31-78-521174; N. America dist. addr.: Box 358, Accord Sta., Hingham, MA 02018-0358. TEL 617-871-6600. FAX 617-871-6528) Ed. N.H. Karam. (looseleaf format) **Document type:** trade publication.

346 381   UK   ISSN 0144-2546
BUSINESS LAWS OF KUWAIT. 1979. a. (plus q. supplements). £895($1835) for basic work; supplement service £399 ($840). Graham & Trotman Ltd. (Subsidiary of: Kluwer Academic Publishers Group), Sterling House, 66 Wilton Rd., London SW1V 1DE, England. TEL 44-71-821-1123. FAX 44-71-630-5229. (Dist. by: Kluwer Academic Publishers Group, P.O. Box 322, 3300 AH Dordrecht, Netherlands. TEL 31-78-524400. FAX 31-78-524474; N. America dist. addr.: Box 358, Accord Sta., Hingham, MA 02018-0358. TEL 617-871-6600. FAX 617-871-6528) Ed. N.H. Karam. (looseleaf format) **Document type:** trade publication.

346 381   UK   ISSN 0141-6642
BUSINESS LAWS OF SAUDI ARABIA. 1979. a. (plus bi-m. supplements). £750($1500) for basic work; supplement service £385 ($810). Graham & Trotman Ltd. (Subsidiary of: Kluwer Academic Publishers Group), Sterling House, 66 Wilton Rd., London SW1V 1DE, England. TEL 44-71-821-1123. FAX 44-71-630-5229. (Dist. by: Kluwer Academic Publishers Group, P.O. Box 322, 3300 AH Dordrecht, Netherlands. TEL 31-78-524400. FAX 31-78-524474; N. America dist. addr.: Box 358, Accord Sta., Hingham, MA 02018-0358. TEL 617-871-6600. FAX 617-871-6528) Ed. N.H. Karam. (looseleaf format) **Document type:** trade publication.

346 381   UK   ISSN 0144-2724
BUSINESS LAWS OF UNITED ARAB EMIRATES. 1979. a. (plus s-a. supplements). £740($1500) for basic work; supplement service £370 ($715). Graham & Trotman Ltd. (Subsidiary of: Kluwer Academic Publishers Group), Sterling House, 66 Wilton Rd., London SW1V 1DE, England. TEL 44-71-821-1123. FAX 44-71-630-5229. (Dist. by: Kluwer Academic Publishers Group, P.O. Box 322, 3300 AH Dordrecht, Netherlands. TEL 31-78-524400. FAX 31-78-524474; N. America dist. addr.: Box 358, Accord Sta., Hingham, MA 02018-0358. TEL 617-871-6600. FAX 617-871-6528) Ed. M.J. Hall. **Document type:** trade publication.
—BLDSC (2934.160000).

346   US   ISSN 0007-6899
LAW
BUSINESS LAWYER. 1946. q. $28 to non-members (foreign $33). American Bar Association, Business Law Section, 750 N. Lake Shore Dr., Chicago, IL 60611. TEL 312-988-5588. Ed. George Freeman. adv.; bk.rev. circ. 55,000. (also avail. in microfilm from MIM,RRI; reprint service avail. from RRI) **Indexed:** AAR, ABI Inform., Account.Ind. (1974-), BPIA, Bus.Ind., C.L.I., Curr.Cont., L.R.I., Law Ofc.Info.Svc., Leg.Per., P.A.I.S., SSCI, Tr.& Indus.Ind.
●Also available online. Vendor(s): Mead Data Central, Inc. (BUSLAW), West Services, Inc. (BUSLAW).
—BLDSC (2934.170000); Faxon; UnCover; SWETS.
Description: Covers business and financial law, with articles on current legal topics and substantive section programs.

346   US   ISSN 0884-1977
KF872
BUSINESS LAWYER UPDATE. 1980. bi-m. membership only. American Bar Association, Business Law Section, 750 N. Lake Shore Dr., Chicago, IL 60611. TEL 312-988-5588. Ed. Larry Scriggins. circ. 50,000. **Document type:** newsletter.
Formerly: Business Law Memo (ISSN 0271-9045)
Description: Newsletter on Section activities and recent developments in business or banking law.

346 330   US
BUSINESS ORGANIZATIONS: CORPORATE ACQUISITIONS AND MERGERS. 1968. 4 base vols. (plus irreg. supplements). $945. Matthew Bender & Co., Inc., 11 Penn Plaza, New York, NY 10001. TEL 212-967-7707. Eds. Byron E. Fox, Eleanor M. Fox.
Description: Guide to the anti-trust, tax, corporate, securities and financial aspects of business combinations.

346 331   US
BUSINESS ORGANIZATIONS: PENSION AND PROFIT-SHARING PLANS. 1977. 5 base vols. (plus irreg. supplements). $1125. Matthew Bender & Co., Inc., 11 Penn Plaza, New York, NY 10001. TEL 212-967-7707. Ed. Sheldon Mike Young.
Description: Covers the whole field of pension and profit-sharing plans. Provides detailed treatment of attributes, benefits, special plans, rights of participants, processing plan through the IRS and other agencies, integration with Social Security benefits, union negotiated plans and terminations.

BUSINESS ORGANIZATIONS: PROFESSIONAL CORPORATIONS AND ASSOCIATIONS. see *BUSINESS AND ECONOMICS*

346   US
BUSINESS TORT OF FRAUD & MISREPRESENTATION. 1989. 2 base vols. (plus suppl.). $180. Butterworth Legal Publishers (Salem) (Subsidiary of: Reed Elsevier plc), 8 Industrial Way, Bldg. C, Salem, NH 03079. TEL 800-548-4001. FAX 603-898-9858. Ed. Warren Freedman. (looseleaf format)

LAW — CORPORATE LAW

346 330 US
BUSINESS TORTS. 1989. 4 base vols. (plus irreg. supplements). $495. Matthew Bender & Co., Inc., 11 Penn Plaza, New York, NY 10001. TEL 212-967-7707. Ed. Joseph D. Zamore.
   Description: Covers a variety of important business torts.

346 US
KF1301.A213B87
BUSINESS TORTS REPORTER. 1988. m. $250. Business Torts Research, Inc., Box 20818, Shaker Sta., Cleveland, OH 44120. TEL 216-283-2300. FAX 216-283-2326. Ed. Matthew B. Cockley. index. (looseleaf format) **Document type:** newsletter.

346 SA ISSN 0045-3668
BUSINESSMAN'S LAW. 1971. 8/yr. R.150. Juta & Co. Ltd., P.O. Box 14373, Kenwyn 7790, South Africa. TEL 021-797-5101. FAX 021-761-5010. Ed. M. Dendy. adv. circ. 3,000. **Indexed:** Ind.S.A.Per.

346 UK
BUTTERWORTHS CENTRAL AND EAST EUROPEAN BUSINESS LAW BULLETIN. q. $385. Butterworth & Co. (Publishers) Ltd. (Subsidiary of: Reed Elsevier plc), 88 Kingsway, London WC2B 6AB, England. TEL 071-405-6900. FAX 071-405-1332. Ed.Bd.
Document type: newsletter.
   Description: Provides expert, practical advice on international transactions issues that confront counsel and client alike.

346 UK
BUTTERWORTHS CENTRAL AND EASTERN EUROPEAN BUSINESS LAW BULLETIN. 1990. q. $425. Butterworth & Co. (Publishers) Ltd. (Subsidiary of: Reed Elsevier plc), 55 Kingsway, London WC2B 6AB, England. TEL 071-405-6900. FAX 071-405-1332. TELEX 95678. (US addr.: Butterworth Legal Publishers, 90 Stiles Rd., Salem, NH 03079. TEL 603-898-9664)
   Formerly: Butterworths Soviet and Eastern European Business Law Bulletin (ISSN 0961-3676)
   Description: Keeps solicitors and professional advisers informed of legal developments affecting business in the region.

346 NZ
BUTTERWORTHS COMMERCIAL SERVICE. 2 base vols. (plus updates 3/yr.) NZ.$296. Butterworths of New Zealand Ltd., 203-207 Victoria St., P.O. Box 472, Wellington, New Zealand. TEL 04-385-1479. FAX 04-385-1598. Ed. Michael Midgley. (looseleaf format)
   Description: Full text of acts, regulations, orders and notices most frequently consulted in commercial practice.

346 UK ISSN 0267-145X
BUTTERWORTHS COMPANY LAW CASES. 1983. bi-m. (plus a. bound vol.). $334. Butterworth & Co. (Publishers) Ltd. (Subsidiary of: Reed Elsevier plc), 88 Kingsway, London WC2B 6AB, England. TEL 071-405-6900. FAX 071-405-1332. (US addr.: Butterworth Legal Publishers, 90 Stiles Rd., Salem, NH 03079-9981. TEL 603-898-9664) Eds. D.D. Prentice, M. Stokes. (looseleaf format; back issues avail.)
   Description: Covers all company law and financial services cases which are of relevance and practical importance to company law specialists.

346 UK
BUTTERWORTHS COMPANY LAW HANDBOOK (YEAR). irreg., no.9, 1993. Butterworth & Co. (Publishers) Ltd. (Subsidiary of: Reed Elsevier plc), 88 Kingsway, London WC2B 6AB, England. TEL 071-405-6900. FAX 071-405-1332. (US addr.: Butterworth Legal Publishers, 90 Stiles Rd., Salem, NH 03079-9981. TEL 603-898-9664) Ed. Keith Walmsky.
   Description: Provides reference for lawyers coping with company legislations.

346 UK
BUTTERWORTHS COMPANY LAW SERVICE. 2 base vols. (plus bi-m. bulletin & updates). $440. Butterworth & Co. (Publishers) Ltd. (Subsidiary of: Reed Elsevier plc), 88 Kingsway, London WC2B 6AB, England. TEL 71-405-6900. FAX 71-405-1332. (US addr.: Butterworth Legal Publishers, 90 Stiles Rd., Salem, NH 03079-9981. TEL 603-898-9664) Ed. Philip L.R. Mitchell. (looseleaf format)
   Description: Geared to the needs of solicitors and accountants in the mainstream of general practice.

346 331 NZ ISSN 0969-1669
BUTTERWORTHS EMPLOYMENT LAW BULLETIN. 1981. 3/yr. NZ.$192. Butterworths of New Zealand Ltd., P.O. Box 472, 203-207 Victoria St., Wellington, New Zealand. TEL 04-385-1479. FAX 04-385-1598. Ed. Moira Thompson. **Document type:** bulletin.
   —CCC.
   Formerly: Mazengarb's Industrial Law Bulletin (ISSN 0111-6770)
   Description: Articles plus notes on all developments of relevance to industrial law in New Zealand.

BUTTERWORTHS WORKERS' COMPENSATION IN ONTARIO SERVICE. see INSURANCE

346 UK ISSN 0953-4423
C M L R ANTITRUST REPORTS. m. £222. Sweet & Maxwell, South Quay Plaza, 7th Fl., 183 Marsh Wall, London E14 9FT, England. TEL 071-538-8686. FAX 071-538-9508. Ed. Joe McDonald Hill. adv. contact: Jackie Wood. **Document type:** bulletin.
   —UnCover; SWETS.

C S C P A NEWSLETTER. (Connecticut Society of Certified Public Accountants) see BUSINESS AND ECONOMICS — Accounting

346 US ISSN 0892-2349
CALIFORNIA BUSINESS LAW PRACTITIONER. 1986. 4/yr. $175. Continuing Education of the Bar - California, University of California Extension, 2300 Shattuck Ave., Berkeley, CA 94704. TEL 510-642-2040; 800-924-3924. FAX 510-642-3788. (Co-sponsor: State Bar of California) Ed. Hale Kronenberg. (tabloid format; back issues avail.)

346 US ISSN 0199-669X
KFC337.A15
CALIFORNIA BUSINESS LAW REPORTER. 1980. 8/yr. $175. Continuing Education of the Bar - California, University of California Extension, 2300 Shattuck Ave., Berkeley, CA 94704. TEL 510-642-2040; 800-924-3924. FAX 510-642-3788. (Co-sponsor: State Bar of California) Ed. Hale Kronenberg. (tabloid format; back issues avail.)

346 381 US
CALIFORNIA CORPORATIONS CODE AND CORPORATE SECURITIES RULES. 1972. a. $33. Matthew Bender & Co., Inc., 11 Penn Plaza, New York, NY 10001. TEL 212-967-7707. Ed.Bd.

346 CN ISSN 0317-6649
CANADA BUSINESS CORPORATIONS ACT WITH REGULATIONS. vol.5, 1983. irreg. Can.$19.95. C C H Canadian Ltd., 6 Garamond Ct., North York, ON M3C 1Z5, Canada. TEL 416-441-2992. FAX 416-445-9011. index.

346 CN
CANADA CORPORATIONS LAW REPORTER. m. Can.$545. C C H Canadian Ltd., 6 Garamond Ct., North York, ON M3C 1Z5, Canada. TEL 416-441-2992. FAX 416-444-9011. index.
   Formerly: Dominion Companies Law Reports (ISSN 0046-0559)
   Description: Reports on federal legislation governing companies under federal charter.

346 CN
K18
CANADA - U S BUSINESS LAW REVIEW. 1988. base vol. (plus supplements 3/yr.). Can.$118. Carswell, One Corporate Plaza, 2075 Kennedy Rd., Scarborough, ON M1T 3V4, Canada. TEL 416-609-8000. FAX 416-298-5094. Ed. Errol P. Mendes. adv. contact: M. Lalani. bk.rev. (also avail. in microform from WSH; reprint service avail. from WSH) **Indexed:** Ind.Can.L.P.L.
   Formerly: Review of International Business Law (ISSN 0835-2399)
   Description: Analysis and discussion of Canada - U S trade, securities and banking law, dispute settlement, foreign investment and taxation questions. Articles, updates on current issues, and case comments on significant decisions.

346 CN ISSN 0319-3322
K3
CANADIAN BUSINESS LAW JOURNAL. 1976. q. Can.$119. Canada Law Book Inc., 240 Edward St., Aurora, ON L4G 3S9, Canada. TEL 905-841-6472. FAX 905-841-5085. **Indexed:** ABI Inform., Abstr.Bk.Rev.Curr.Leg.Per., BPIA, Bus.Ind., C.L.I., Can.B.P.I., Ind.Can.L.P.L., L.R.I., Leg.Cont., Leg.Per.
   —BLDSC (3018.255000).

346 CN
CANADIAN COMMERCIAL LAW GUIDE. 1967. m. Can.$550. C C H Canadian Ltd., 6 Garamond Ct., North York, ON M3C 1Z5, Canada. TEL 416-441-2992. FAX 416-444-9011. index.
   Formerly: Canadian Sales and Credit Law Guide (ISSN 0045-5318)
   Description: Full texts of federal and provincial laws relating to sales contracts, conditional sales, installment sales, chattel mortgages and bills of sale.

346 336 US
CHAPTER 11: REORGANIZATIONS. 1983. base vol. (plus a. suppl.). $95. Shepard's - McGraw-Hill, Inc., Box 35300, Colorado Springs, CO 80935-3530. TEL 800-525-2474.
   Description: Explains reorganization law from the pragmatic viewpoint of a long-time practitioner, emphasizing examples of how the law works.

346 US ISSN 1055-9477
CHAPTER 11 UPDATE; monitors all major developments in today's corporate bankruptcies and examines pertinent court decisions related to Chapter 11 filings. 1991. s-m. $450. Andrews Publications, 1646 West Chester Pike, Box 1000, Westtown, PA 19395. TEL 215-399-6600; 800-345-1101. FAX 215-399-6610. Ed. Mary Rhoads. bibl.; stat. (looseleaf format; back issues avail.) **Document type:** newsletter.

346 331 US
CHECKOFF (TALLAHASSEE). irreg. (3-4/yr.). membership. Florida Bar, Labor and Employment Law Section, 650 Apalachee Pkwy., Tallahassee, FL 32399-3200. TEL 904-561-5631. circ. 1,000. **Document type:** newsletter.

346 AT
CHINA BUSINESS LAW GUIDE. 1991. q. C C H Australia Ltd., P.O. Box 230, North Ryde, N.S.W. 2113, Australia. TEL 02-888-2555. FAX 02-888-7324. (looseleaf format)
   Description: Contains information of immediate importance to business people on every major area of China's business laws. Companion publication to CCH's China Laws for Foreign Business.

346 341 332.6 AT
CHINA LAWS FOR FOREIGN BUSINESS - BUSINESS REGULATION. (In 3 vols.) (Text in Chinese, English) 1985. q. C C H Australia Ltd., P.O. Box 230, North Ryde, N.S.W. 2113, Australia. TEL 02-888-2555. FAX 02-888-7324. (looseleaf format)
   Supersedes in part (in 1993): China Laws for Foreign Business.

346 341 AT
CHINA LAWS FOR FOREIGN BUSINESS - SPECIAL ZONES & CITIES. (In 2 vols.) (Text in Chinese, English) 1985. 3/yr. C C H Australia Ltd., P.O. Box 230, North Ryde, N.S.W. 2113, Australia. TEL 02-888-2555. FAX 02-888-7324. (looseleaf format)
   Supersedes in part (in 1993): China Laws for Foreign Business.

346 341 332.6 AT
CHINA LAWS FOR FOREIGN BUSINESS - TAXATION & CUSTOMS. (In 2 vols.) (Text in Chinese, English) 1985. 3/yr. C C H Australia Ltd., P.O. Box 230, North Ryde, N.S.W. 2113, Australia. TEL 02-888-2555. FAX 02-888-7324. (looseleaf format)
   Supersedes in part (in 1993): China Laws for Foreign Business.

346 AT
COMMERCIAL ARBITRATION LAW AND PRACTICE. 1990. 4/yr. Aus.$495 with updates. Law Book Co. Ltd., 44-50 Waterloo Rd., North Ryde, N.S.W. 2113, Australia. TEL 02-887-0177. FAX 02-888-9706. TELEX ASHBOOK 27995. Ed. M. Jacobs. (looseleaf format)

LAW — CORPORATE LAW

346 US ISSN 1052-2980
KF1507
COMMERCIAL LAW ADVISER. 1988. m. $233. Business Laws, Inc., 11630 Chillicothe Rd., Chesterland, OH 44026. TEL 216-729-7996. FAX 216-729-0645. Ed. William A. Hancock. index, cum.index. (back issues avail.) **Document type:** newsletter.
—CCC.
Formerly (until 1989): Bankruptcy and Commercial Law Adviser (ISSN 0898-9893)
Description: Reports on developments pertaining to commercial law.

346 UK ISSN 1353-3568
▼**COMMERCIAL LAW AND PRACTICE.** 1994. a. £17.50. Jordan Publishing Ltd., 21 St. Thomas St., Bristol BS1 6JS, England. TEL 0272-230600. Ed. Stephen Hildreth. **Document type:** academic/scholarly publication.

346 US
COMMERCIAL LAW ANNUAL. a. $95. Clark - Boardman - Callaghan Company Ltd., 375 Hudson St., New York, NY 10014. TEL 212-929-7500; 800-221-9428. FAX 212-924-0460. Eds. Louis F. Del Duca, Patrick L. Del Duca.
Description: Highlights significant developments in the law of sales, leasing, bulk transfers, secured transactions, and other UCC topics.

346 US
COMMERCIAL LAW HANDBOOK. 1988. a. $19.95. Gould Publications, 1333 N. U.S. Hwy. 17-92, Longwood, FL 32750-3724. TEL 407-695-9500. FAX 407-695-2906. adv.; bk.rev. (looseleaf format)
Description: Contains the complete uniform commercial code with official comments.

346 UK ISSN 1353-3576
▼**COMMERCIAL LITIGATION.** 1994. a. £17.50. Jordan Publishing Ltd., 21 St. Thomas St., Bristol BS1 6JS, England. TEL 0272-230600. FAX 0272-250486. Ed. Nick Adlem. **Document type:** academic/scholarly publication.

346 UK ISSN 1353-3584
▼**COMMERCIAL PROPERTY AND BUSINESS LEASES.** 1994. a. £17.50. Jordan Publishing Ltd., 21 St. Thomas St., Bristol BS1 6JS, England. TEL 0272-230600. FAX 0272-250486. Ed. Alan Riley. **Document type:** academic/scholarly publication.

346 IT ISSN 1121-340X
▼**COMMERCIO E SERVIZI;** rivista trimestrale di dottrina e pratica professionale per gli operatori del settore. 1992. q. L.160000 (effective 1994). Maggioli Editore, Viale Vespucci 12-n, 47037 Rimini, Italy. TEL 0541-626777. FAX 0541-622020. adv.: B&W page L.1600000, color page L.2700000; trim 115 x 195. bk.rev.; index. circ. 4,000. (back issues avail.)
●Also available on CD-ROM.

346 AT ISSN 0729-2775
COMPANIES AND SECURITIES LAW JOURNAL. 1982. 8/yr. Aus.$290. Law Book Co. Ltd., 44-50 Waterloo Rd., North Ryde, N.S.W. 2113, Australia. TEL 02-887-0177. FAX 02-888-9706. TELEX ASBOOK 27995. Ed. S. Sievers. bk.rev.; index. circ. 509. (back issues avail.) **Indexed:** Leg.Per.
—BLDSC (3363.734700).
Description: Examines a range of subjects including company law, takeovers and public securities, proprietary companies and insolvency.

346 UK
COMPANY LAW (YEAR). a. £24.95. Blackstone Press, Aldine St., London W12 8AW, England. TEL 081-740-1173. FAX 081-743-2292. Ed.Bd.

346 II ISSN 0045-7787
COMPANY LAW INSTITUTE OF INDIA. REPORTS OF COMPANY CASES INCLUDING BANKING & INSURANCE. (Text in English) 1931. fortn. Rs.405. Company Law Institute of India Pvt. Ltd., 88 Thayagaraya Rd., Madras 600017, India. Ed.Bd. index. circ. 5,000.

346 UK ISSN 0969-3831
COMPANY LAW MONITOR. 1977. m. £160 (foreign £182). Monitor Press, Rectory Rd., Great Waldingfield, Sudbury, Suffolk CO10 OTL, England. TEL 0787-378607. FAX 0787-880201. (back issues avail.) **Document type:** newsletter.
Formerly (until 1993): Corporate Legal Letter (ISSN 0141-4852)
Description: Addresses the practical implications of all the major relevant cases, statutes and regulations, including those from the European Economic Community for company lawyers and senior management.

346 UK ISSN 0144-1027
K3
COMPANY LAWYER. 1980. m. £180($275) Longman Group Ltd., Law, Tax and Finance Division, 21-27 Lamb's Conduit St., London WC1N 3NJ, England. TEL 071-242-2548. FAX 071-831-8119. Eds. B. Rider, M. Khan. **Indexed:** C.L.I., L.R.I. **Document type:** trade publication.
—BLDSC (3363.739500); SWETS. **CCC.**
Description: Information on changes and developments in business and company law.

346 AT
▼**COMPANY RECEIVERS & MANAGERS.** 1992. base vol. (plus updates 3/yr.). Aus.$295. Law Book Co. Ltd., 44-50 Waterloo Rd., North Ryde, N.S.W. 2113, Australia. TEL 02-887-0177. FAX 02-888-9706. TELEX AHBOOK 27995. Ed. J. O'Donovan. (looseleaf format)
Description: Devoted to company receivership and official management and voluntary administration.

346 UK ISSN 0309-703X
KD2072
COMPANY SECRETARY'S REVIEW. 1977. fortn. £119. Tolley Publishing Co. Ltd., Tolley House, 2 Addiscombe Rd., Croydon, Surrey CR9 5AF, England. TEL 081-686-9141. FAX 081-686-3155. Ed. Nick Parmee. **Indexed:** RICS. **Document type:** trade publication.
—BLDSC (3363.740500).

346 CN
COMPETITION LAW SERVICE. base vol. (plus s-a. updates). Can.$149. Canada Law Book Inc., 240 Edward St., Aurora, ON L4G 3S9, Canada. TEL 905-841-6472. FAX 905-841-5085. Eds. George N. Addy, William L. Vanveen. adv. contact: Mary Cull. bibl.; index. (looseleaf format)
Description: Includes statutes and commentary, case digests, information bulletins, regulations and forms, sentence dispositions specifically noted.

346 UK ISSN 0953-9239
COMPLIANCE MONITOR. 1988. m. £275. Tolley Publishing Co. Ltd., Tolley House, 2 Addiscombe Rd., Croydon, Surrey CR9 5AF, England. TEL 081-686-9141. FAX 081-686-3155. Ed. Stephen Harris. **Document type:** trade publication.

346.066 US
CONNECTICUT CORPORATION STATUTES AND FORMS. a. $25. Connecticut Law Book Company, Box 575, Guilford, CT 06437. TEL 203-458-8000.
Description: Compilation of the current statutes of this state that deal with corporations and of the official forms utilized by the office of the Connecticut Secretary of the State.

CONSULENZA AMBIENTE. see BUSINESS AND ECONOMICS

346 658 UK ISSN 0952-2956
CONSUMER AND MARKETING LAW. 1982. 10/yr. £142($284) I B C Publishing, Gilmoora House, 57-61 Mortimer St., London W1N 7TD, England. TEL 071-637-4383. FAX 071-636-6414. Ed. Roland Rowell. index. (back issues avail.) **Document type:** newsletter.
Formerly (until 1987): Advertising and Marketing Law Letter (ISSN 0267-3045)
Description: For lawyers, advertising executives, marketing-sales managers. Keeps them up-to-date on all the new laws and regulations that could affect the sale and marketing of their company's products.

346 340.5 IT
CONTRATTO E IMPRESA; dialoghi con la giurisprudenza civile e commerciale. 1985. 3/yr. L.160000 (foreign L.220000) (effective 1994). Casa Editrice Dott. Antonio Milani, Via Jappelli 5, 35121 Padua, Italy. TEL 049-656677. FAX 049-8752900. Ed. Francesco Galgano. cum.index: 1985-1992. circ. 4,500. (back issues avail.) **Indexed:** ELLIS.

346.066 US
CORPORATE ACQUISITIONS, MERGERS AND DIVESTITURES. base vol. (plus m. Ideas Letter and updates). Warren Gorham Lamont, One Penn Plaza, New York, NY 10119. TEL 800-950-1201. FAX 212-971-5240. Ed. Lewis D. Solomon. (looseleaf format)

346 AT ISSN 1033-2405
CORPORATE AND BUSINESS LAW JOURNAL. 1988. s-a. $40. Corporate & Business Law Centre, c/o Department of Law, University of Adelaide, N. Terr., Adelaide, S.A. 5000, Australia. TEL 08-228-5063. FAX 08-232-4679. (Dist. in U.S. by: William S. Hein & Co., 1285 Main St., Buffalo, NY 14209)

346 UK ISSN 0950-6209
CORPORATE BRIEFING. 10/yr. £145($290) I B C Publishing, Gilmoora House, 57-61 Mortimer St., London W1N 7TD, England. TEL 071-637-4383. FAX 071-636-6414. (Subscr. in U.S. to: IBC (USA), 290 Eliot St., Box 91004, Ashland, MA 01721-9104. TEL 508-881-2800. FAX 508-881-0982) **Document type:** newsletter.
—BLDSC (3472.060650).

346 US
CORPORATE COMMUNICATIONS HANDBOOK; a guide for managing unstructured public disclosure in today's corporate environment. a. $105. Clark - Boardman - Callaghan Company Ltd., 375 Hudson St., New York, NY 10014. TEL 212-929-7500; 800-221-9428. FAX 212-929-0460. Ed. Wesley S. Walton.

CORPORATE CONDUCT QUARTERLY; a practical guide for corporate ethics & compliance. see BUSINESS AND ECONOMICS

346 US ISSN 0743-0272
KF1477.A15
CORPORATE CONTROL ALERT; a report on current changes in corporate control. 1984. m. $1495. American Lawyer Media, L.P. (New York), 600 Third Ave., New York, NY 10016. TEL 212-986-0088. FAX 212-972-6258. Ed. Martha Sellers Klein. charts. (back issues avail.)
Description: News on mergers and acquisitions.

346 US
CORPORATE CONTROL NEWSLETTER. 4/yr. free. Sachnoff & Weaver, Ltd., 30 S. Wacker Dr., Ste. 2900, Chicago, IL 60606. TEL 312-207-1000. FAX 312-207-6400. Ed. Thomas J. Bamonte. circ. 500. (back issues avail.) **Document type:** newsletter.

346 658 US
KF1397.C65
CORPORATE COUNSEL. 1975. 6/yr. $395. Executive Press, Box 3895, San Francisco, CA 94119. TEL 510-685-5111. Ed. Jesse M. Brill. index. (back issues avail.) **Document type:** newsletter.

346 658 US ISSN 0888-5877
KF1425.A15C67
CORPORATE COUNSELLOR. 1986. m. $220. New York Law Publishing Co., 345 Park Ave. S., New York, NY 10010. TEL 212-545-6170. FAX 212-696-1848. **Document type:** newsletter.
Description: Provides reports on legal and regulatory issues faced in an in-house practice, as well as administrative, recruitment and financial issues involved in running an in-house firm.

346 US ISSN 0898-9923
KF1397.C653
CORPORATE COUNSEL'S MONITOR. 1986. m. $275. Business Laws, Inc., 11630 Chillicothe Rd., Chesterland, OH 44026. TEL 216-729-7996. FAX 216-729-0645. Ed. William A. Hancock. (looseleaf format; back issues avail.) **Document type:** newsletter.
—CCC.
Description: Developments in US federal laws that are pertinent information to corporate attorneys.

CORPORATE CRIME REPORTER. see CRIMINOLOGY AND LAW ENFORCEMENT — Security

LAW — CORPORATE LAW

346 342 345   US
CORPORATE CRIMINAL AND CONSTITUTIONAL LAW REPORTER. 1989. 15/yr. $295. Lexline Publishing Co., 233 Broadway, Ste. 944, New York, NY 10279. TEL 212-964-6173. Ed. Norman A. Olch. bk.rev.; s-a. index. (looseleaf format) **Document type:** newsletter.

CORPORATE ENVIRONMENTAL DATA CLEARINGHOUSE REPORTS. see ENVIRONMENTAL STUDIES — Waste Management

346   UK   ISSN 0964-8410
▼**CORPORATE GOVERNANCE;** an international review. 1992. q. $140. Basil Blackwell Ltd., 108 Cowley Rd., Oxford OX4 1JF, England. TEL 0865-791100. FAX 0865-791347. TELEX 837022-OXBOOK-G. **Document type:** academic/scholarly publication.
—BLDSC (3472.066100); UMI. **CCC.**

346   US   ISSN 1053-5489
HD2745
CORPORATE GOVERNANCE BULLETIN. 1981. bi-m. $275 (effective 1992). Investor Responsibility Research Center, Inc., 1755 Massachusetts Ave., N.W., Ste. 600, Washington, DC 20036-2102. TEL 202-234-7500. FAX 202-332-8570. Ed. Robert Walters. circ. 1,200. (looseleaf format) **Document type:** bulletin.
—UnCover.

346   US
HG4028.M4
CORPORATE GROWTH REPORT. 1992. w. $895. Quality Services Company, 5290 Overpass Rd., Ste.126, Santa Barbara, CA 93111-9950. TEL 805-964-7841. Ed. Carmen Lodise. adv. circ. 800. (also avail. in microform from UMI) **Indexed:** BPIA, P.A.I.S.
Formed by merger of (1981-1992): Acquisition - Divestiture Weekly Report (ISSN 0279-4160); (1982-1992): Corporate Growth Magazine (ISSN 0898-8390); Which was formerly: Buyouts and Acquisitions Magazine; Journal of Buyouts and Acquisitions (ISSN 0736-5527)
Description: Provides legal and financial details on current mergers and acquisitions, as well as joint ventures, restructurings and methods of increasing shareholder value.

346   US
KFI1413.A15I4
CORPORATE LAWYER. 1964. 4/yr. $14 to members. Illinois State Bar Association, Section on Corporate Law Departments, Illinois Bar Center, Springfield, IL 62701. TEL 217-525-1760. FAX 217-525-0712. circ. 1,000. (looseleaf format; back issues avail.) **Document type:** newsletter.

346 330   US   ISSN 1063-3006
KF1425.A15
CORPORATE LEGAL TIMES; the national monthly on managing in-house corporate legal departments. 1991. m. $95 (effective 1992). Corporate Legal Times Corporation, 222 Merchandise Mart Plaza, Ste. 1513, Chicago, IL 60654. TEL 312-644-4378. FAX 312-644-0765. Ed. Bruce Rubenstein. adv.; bk.rev. circ. 40,000. (tabloid format; back issues avail.)
●Also available online. Vendor(s): Mead Data Central, Inc.
Description: Contains news and analysis for general counsel and other in-house lawyers.

346   US   ISSN 0887-7793
KF1423.A59
CORPORATE OFFICERS AND DIRECTORS LIABILITY LITIGATION REPORTER; the twice-monthly national journal of record of litigation based on fiduciary responsibility. 1985. s-m. $850. Andrews Publications, 1646 West Chester Pike, Box 1000, Westtown, PA 19395. TEL 215-399-6600; 800-345-1101. FAX 215-399-6610. Ed. Frank Reynolds. abstr.; bibl.; stat.; cum.index every 6 mos. (looseleaf format; back issues avail.) **Document type:** newsletter.

346   US   ISSN 0010-8995
K3
CORPORATE PRACTICE COMMENTATOR. 1959. q. $180. Clark - Boardman - Callaghan Company, Inc., 155 Pfingsten Rd., Deerfield, IL 60015. TEL 800-323-1336. Ed. Jim Fegen. bk.rev.; abstr.; index. Indexed: Account.Ind. (1986-), C.L.I., L.R.I., Leg.Cont., Leg.Per., Tr.& Indus.Ind.
—UMI.

346   US   ISSN 0162-5691
KF1397
CORPORATE PRACTICE SERIES. (Includes BNA's Corporate Counsel Weekly) 1978. w. $1336. The Bureau of National Affairs, Inc., 1231 25th St., N.W., Washington, DC 20037. TEL 202-452-4200. FAX 202-822-8092. TELEX 285656 BNAI WSH. (Subscr. to: 9435 Key West Ave., Rockville, MD 20850. TEL 800-372-1033) Ed. Larry Lempert. bibl.; charts; stat. (looseleaf format; back issues avail.)
—CCC.
Description: Corporate law reference service organized into a series of portfolios written by legal experts. Each portfolio covers a different legal subject with detailed analyses, working papers and a bibliography.

342.37   US
CORPORATE SECRETARY. 1957. irreg. (6-8/yr.). $125 to non-members. American Society of Corporate Secretaries, Inc., 1270 Ave. of the Americas, New York, NY 10020. TEL 212-765-2620. FAX 212-765-8349. Ed. Michael E. Goodman. (looseleaf format) **Document type:** newsletter.

346 332   US
KFI1413.A15C67
CORPORATION AND SECURITIES. 1956. 4/yr. $16 to members. Illinois State Bar Association, Illinois Bar Center, Springfield, IL 62701. TEL 217-525-1760. FAX 217-525-0712. Ed. John Doyle. circ. 2,000. (looseleaf format) **Document type:** newsletter.

346 332   US
CORPORATION, BANKING & BUSINESS LAW NEWSLETTER. 3/yr. membership. Pennsylvania Bar Association, 100 South St., Harrisburg, PA 17108. TEL 717-238-6715. FAX 717-238-7182. **Document type:** newsletter.

346   US
CREDITORS' RIGHTS HANDBOOK; a guide to the debtor-creditor relationship. a. $78. Clark - Boardman - Callaghan Company Ltd., 375 Hudson St., New York, NY 10014. TEL 212-929-7500; 800-221-9428. FAX 212-924-0460. Ed.Bd.
Description: Provides attorneys, corporate creditors, institutional lenders, and other finance professionals with a clear explanation of the laws, procedures, and strategies controlling the creditor-debtor relationship.

346   US
D & O LIABILITY LITIGATION NEWS. 1991. s-m. $797. Litigation Reporting Service, Box 248, Chalfont, PA 18914. TEL 215-822-9158. FAX 215-822-9158. Ed. William T. Keough; Pub. William T. Keough. bk.rev.; s-a index. (looseleaf format; back issues avail.) **Document type:** newsletter.

346   US   ISSN 0740-1949
DAILY COURT REVIEW. 1889. d. (Mon.-Fri.). $195. Daily Court Review, Inc., Box 1889, Houston, TX 77251. TEL 713-869-5434. FAX 713-869-8887. Ed. E. Milton Morin, Jr. adv. contact: Jeanne Blaylock. bk.rev. circ. 2,430. **Document type:** newspaper.
●Also available on CD-ROM.
Description: Contains law opinions, legal notices, real estate listings, construction and financial reports.

DAILY REPORT FOR EXECUTIVES. see BUSINESS AND ECONOMICS — Management

346   US
DE PAUL BUSINESS LAW JOURNAL. s-a $42.50. William S. Hein & Co., Inc., 1285 Main St., Buffalo, NY 14209-1987.

346   CN
DEBT COLLECTION; a step-by-step legal guide. base vol. (plus irreg. updates). Can.$63. Canada Law Book Inc., 240 Edward St., Aurora, ON L4G 3S9, Canada. TEL 905-841-6472. FAX 905-841-5085. Ed. Marcia J. Fraser. adv. contact: Mary Cull. (looseleaf format)

346   CN
DEBT RESTRUCTURING; principles and practice. base vol. (plus irreg. updates). Can.$86. Canada Law Book Inc., 240 Edward St., Aurora, ON L4G 3S9, Canada. TEL 905-841-6472. FAX 905-841-5085. Ed. John D. Honsberger. adv. contact: Mary Cull. (looseleaf format)
Description: For lawyers, trustees, receivers, accountants, corporate managers and executive officers.

346.066   US   ISSN 1042-5756
KFD213.A59
DELAWARE CORPORATE LITIGATION REPORTER; the journal reporting service of litigation concerning record of law in Delaware. s-m. $825. Andrews Publications, 1646 West Chester Pike, Box 1000, Westtown, PA 19395. TEL 215-399-6600; 800-345-1101. FAX 215-399-6610. Ed. Frank Reynolds. abstr.; bibl.; stat.; cum.index every 6 mos. (looseleaf format; back issues avail.) **Document type:** newsletter.

346.066   US   ISSN 0888-434X
KFD213.A59
DELAWARE CORPORATION LAW UPDATE. 1985. m. $475. Andrews Publications, 1646 West Chester Pike, Box 1000, Westtown, PA 19395. TEL 215-399-6600; 800-345-1101. FAX 215-399-6610. Ed. Frank Reynolds. bibl.; stat.; cum.index every 6 mos. (looseleaf format; back issues avail.) **Document type:** newsletter.
Description: Analysis of every opinion, reported and unreported, issued by Delaware's courts involving corporate law issues. Also reports new suits filed in DE Chancery Court.

346.066   US   ISSN 0364-9490
K4
DELAWARE JOURNAL OF CORPORATE LAW. 1976. 2/yr. $50 for 2 vols. Widener University, School of Law, Box 7286, Wilmington, DE 19803. TEL 302-477-2145. Ed. Blaine T. Phillips, Jr. adv.; bk.rev. circ. 2,100. (also avail. in microform from UMI,WSH; microfilm from RRI; reprint service avail. from UMI,WSH) **Indexed:** BPIA, Bus.Ind., C.L.I., L.R.I., Leg.Cont., Leg.Per.
●Also available online. Vendor(s): Mead Data Central, Inc., West Services, Inc.
—Faxon; UnCover; UMI.

346   AT
▼**THE DIRECTORS MANUAL.** 1993. s-a. C C H Australia Ltd., P.O. Box 230, North Ryde, N.S.W. 2113, Australia. TEL 02-888-2555. FAX 02-888-7324.

346 368   US
DIRECTORY OF WORKERS' COMPENSATION MANAGED CARE ORGANIZATIONS. a. $129. Business Information Services, Inc. (Laurel), 12811 N. Point Ln., Laurel, MD 20708. TEL 301-604-4001. FAX 301-604-5126. Ed. Jim Gutman; Pub. James H. Gutman. **Document type:** directory.
Description: Provides alphabetical listing of organizations involved in workers' compensation managed care; state-by-state listings of the same organizations; service-by-service listings of 17 categories of activity.

346   IT
DIRITTO DELL'ECONOMIA. 3/yr. L.100000. Mucchi Editore s.r.l., Via Emilia Est. 1527, 41100 Modena, Italy. (Co-sponsors: Unione Italiana Camere di Commercio; Associazione Bancaria Italiana) Ed.Bd.

346   IT
DIRITTO E PRATICA DEL LAVORO. 51/yr. Strada 1, Palazzo F6, 20090 Assago Milanofiori (MI), Italy. TEL 2-82-47-61. FAX 2-82-47-66-09. Ed. Massimiliano Galioni. circ. 13,873.

LAW — CORPORATE LAW

346 336   NE
DUTCH BUSINESS LAW. (Text in English) 1989. base vol. (plus s-a. updates). fl.435($235) (effective 1994). Kluwer Law and Taxation Publishers (Subsidiary of: Wolters Kluwer N.V.), P.O. Box 23, 7400 GA Deventer, Netherlands. TEL 31-5700-47261. FAX 31-5700-22244. TELEX 49295 KLUDV NL. (Dist. by: Libresso Distribution Centre, P.O. Box 23, 7400 GA Deventer, Netherlands. TEL 31-5700-33155. FAX 31-5700-33834; In N. America: Kluwer Law and Taxation Publishers, 675 Massachusetts Ave., Cambridge, MA 02139. TEL 617-354-0140. FAX 617-354-0140) Ed.Bd. (looseleaf format)
    Description: Contains comprehensive, up-to-date guide to legal, accounting and tax aspects of doing business in the Netherlands.

346 341   NE
E E C MERGER CONTROL REPORTER. (Includes s-a. bibliographic supplement) (Text in English, occasionally in other European languages) 1991. 2 base vols. (plus irreg. updates, approx. 10/yr.). fl.1500($858) (effective 1994). Kluwer Law and Taxation Publishers (Subsidiary of: Wolters Kluwer N.V.), P.O. Box 23, 7400 GA Deventer, Netherlands. TEL 31-5700-47261. FAX 31-5700-22244. TELEX 49295 KLUDV NL. (Dist. by: Libresso Distribution Centre, P.O. Box 23, 7400 GA Deventer, Netherlands. TEL 31-5700-33155. FAX 31-5700-33834; In N. America: Kluwer Law and Taxation Publishers, 675 Massachusetts Ave., Cambridge, MA 02139. TEL 617-354-0140. FAX 617-354-8595) Ed. G. van Gerven. (looseleaf format)
    Description: Publishes all EC merger control decisions in the original language and in English translation. Also includes the basic EC merger-control legislation, coverage of other relevant decisions, and case notes.

E G WIRTSCHAFTSRECHT AUSSENWIRTSCHAFT. see *BUSINESS AND ECONOMICS — International Commerce*

346   UK   ISSN 0965-7355
EAST EUROPEAN BUSINESS LAW. 1991. m. £390($691) (foreign £432) (effective 1993). Financial Times Business Information Ltd., 126 Jermyn St., London SW1Y 4UJ, England. TEL 071-411-4414. FAX 071-411-4415. **Document type:** newsletter.
    Description: Provides news and analysis of legal developments in central and eastern Europe.

346   UK   ISSN 1353-3606
▼**EMPLOYMENT LAW.** 1994. a. £17.50. Jordan Publishing Ltd., 21 St. Thomas St., Bristol BS1 6JS, England. TEL 0272-230600. FAX 0272-250486. Ed. Peter Rumbelow. **Document type:** academic/scholarly publication.

EMPLOYMENT LAW BRIEFING. see *BUSINESS AND ECONOMICS — Labor And Industrial Relations*

EMPLOYMENT LAW COUNSELOR. see *BUSINESS AND ECONOMICS — Labor And Industrial Relations*

EMPLOYMENT LAW NEWS. see *BUSINESS AND ECONOMICS — Labor And Industrial Relations*

EMPLOYMENT LAW REPORT. see *BUSINESS AND ECONOMICS — Labor And Industrial Relations*

ENVIRONMENT WATCH: EAST EUROPE, RUSSIA & EURASIA; news and analysis for business and policy professionals. see *ENVIRONMENTAL STUDIES*

ENVIRONMENT WATCH: LATIN AMERICA; news and analysis for business and policy professionals. see *ENVIRONMENTAL STUDIES*

ENVIRONMENT WATCH: WEST EUROPE. see *ENVIRONMENTAL STUDIES*

ENVIRONMENTAL COUNSELOR. see *ENVIRONMENTAL STUDIES*

346   GW   ISSN 0937-7204
KJE6411.3
EUROPAEISCHE ZEITSCHRIFT FUER WIRTSCHAFTSRECHT. 1990. s-m. DM.470 (students DM.396). C.H. Beck'sche Verlagsbuchhandlung, Wilhelmstr. 9, 80801 Munich, Germany. TEL 089-38189-338. FAX 089-38189-398. TELEX 5215085-BECK-D. Ed.Bd. adv.: B&W page DM.2200, color page DM.4400; trim 260 x 186. circ. 2,600. (back issues avail.) **Document type:** trade publication.
    —SWETS.

346   CN
▼**EXECUTIVE EMPLOYMENT LAW.** 1993. irreg. Can.$175. Butterworths Canada Ltd., Part of the Reed Elsevier group, 75 Clegg Rd., Markham, ON L6G 1A1, Canada. TEL 905-479-2265. FAX 905-479-2826. (looseleaf format)

346   US   ISSN 0747-9700
KF846.3
FEDERAL CONTRACT DISPUTES. 1984. m. $279. Business Publishers, Inc., 951 Pershing Dr., Silver Spring, MD 20910-4464. TEL 301-587-6300. FAX 301-585-9075. Ed. Bruce M. Jervis. index. (looseleaf format; back issues avail.) **Document type:** newsletter.
    ●Also available online. Vendor(s): NewsNet.
    —CCC.
    Description: Studies cases and provides advice for contractors with the federal government who find themselves in disputes over contract terms or payments.

340 540
FEDERAL REGULATION OF THE CHEMICAL INDUSTRY. 1980. base vol. (plus biennial supplements). $195. Shepard's - McGraw-Hill, Inc., Box 35300, Colorado Springs, CO 80935-3530. TEL 800-525-2474. (looseleaf format)
    Description: Addresses problems and methods of dealing with plant personnel, regulatory compliance officers, company managers, investment or consultant service executives and recent governmental restraints on the chemical industry.

346 368   US   ISSN 0887-0942
K6
FEDERATION OF INSURANCE AND CORPORATE COUNSEL QUARTERLY. 1950. q. $26 (law college libraries $20). Federation of Insurance and Corporate Counsel, Law School, Marquette Univ., 1103 W. Wisconsin Ave., Milwaukee, WI 53233. TEL 414-288-7095. FAX 414-288-5914. (Subscr. to: c/o Joseph Olshan, Admin. Secy., Box 111, Walpole, MA 02081-0111. TEL 508-668-6859. FAX 508-668-6892) Ed. John J. Kircher. cum.index: 1950-1970. circ. 2,200. (also avail. in microform from UMI; reprint service avail. from RRI,UMI) **Indexed:** ABI Inform, C.L.I., L.R.I., Leg.Per., Mar.Aff.Bibl. **Document type:** academic/scholarly publication.
    —BLDSC (7169.616500); UnCover; UMI.
    Formerly (until Oct. 1985): Federation of Insurance Counsel Quarterly (ISSN 0430-2583)

346   US
FIDUCIARY RESPONSIBILITY UNDER E R I S A. 1991. base vol. (plus a. supplement). $90. Butterworth Legal Publishers (Salem) (Subsidiary of: Reed Elsevier plc), 8 Industrial Way, Bldg. C, Salem, NH 03079. TEL 800-548-4001. FAX 603-898-9858. Ed. Daniel C. Knickerbocker, Jr. (looseleaf format)
    Description: Practical in-depth history and analysis of the Employee Retirement Income Security Act.

FINANCIAL FORUM. see *BUSINESS AND ECONOMICS — Accounting*

346   US
FLETCHER CORPORATION LAW ADVISER. 1982. m. $295. Clark - Boardman - Callaghan Company Ltd., 375 Hudson St., New York, NY 10014. TEL 212-929-7500; 800-221-9428. FAX 212-924-0460. Eds. Timothy P. Bjur, James Perkwitz-Solheim. index.
    Description: Analyzes recent cases of interest to business lawyers.

346   US
KFF213.A16C67
FLORIDA BAR. BUSINESS LAW SECTION. QUARTERLY REPORT. 1976. irreg. (3-4/yr.). membership. Florida Bar, Business Law Section, 650 Apalachee Pkwy., Tallahassee, FL 32399-2300. TEL 904-561-5626. circ. 3,950. **Document type:** newsletter.

346 690   US
FLORIDA CONSTRUCTION LAW MANUAL, 2-E. 1988. base vol. (plus a. supplement). $95. Shepard's - McGraw-Hill, Inc., Box 35300, Colorado Springs, CO 80935-3530. TEL 800-525-2474.
    Description: Explains the principles of the law of contracts, mechanics' liens, bid disputes and surety bonds.

346   US
FLORIDA CORPORATIONS MANUAL. 1977. 5 base vols. (plus suppl. 2-3/yr.). $320. Butterworth Legal Publishers (Salem) (Subsidiary of: Reed Elsevier plc), 8 Industrial Way, Bldg. C, Salem, NH 03079. TEL 800-548-4001. FAX 603-898-9858. (looseleaf format)

346   US
FLORIDA CREDITORS' RIGHTS MANUAL. 1975. 4 base vols. (plus suppl. 4-5/yr.). Butterworth Legal Publishers (Salem) (Subsidiary of: Reed Elsevier plc), 8 Industrial Way, Bldg. C, Salem, NH 03079. TEL 800-548-4001. FAX 603-898-9858. (looseleaf format)

346   US
FLORIDA SECURITIES LAW. 1989. base vol. (plus a. suppl.). $60. Butterworth Legal Publishers (Salem) (Subsidiary of: Reed Elsevier plc), 8 Industrial Way, Bldg. C, Salem, NH 03079. TEL 800-548-4001. FAX 603-898-9858. (looseleaf format)

346   NE   ISSN 1052-9756
FORDHAM CORPORATE LAW INSTITUTE (PROCEEDINGS). (Text in English) 1977. a. fl.210($123) (effective 1994). (Fordham University, School of Law, US) Kluwer Law and Taxation Publishers (Subsidiary of: Wolters Kluwer N.V.), P.O. Box 23, 7400 GA Deventer, Netherlands. TEL 31-5700-47261. FAX 31-5700-22244. TELEX 49295 KLUDV NL. (Dist. by: Libresso Distribution Centre, P.O. Box 23, 7400 GA Deventer, Netherlands. TEL 31-5700-33155. FAX 31-5700-33834; In N. America: Kluwer Law and Taxation Publishers, 675 Massachusetts Ave., Cambridge, MA 02139. TEL 617-354-0140. FAX 617-354-8595) Ed. Barry Hawk. cum.index: 1980-1991. (back issues avail.) **Document type:** proceedings.
    Supersedes (1974-1977): Fordham Corporate Law Institute. Annual Proceedings (1974) (ISSN 0363-8871)
    Description: Discusses aspects of U.S. and EC antitrust and trade law, including legislation, policy, practice and theory.

346 331.1 658.3   US   ISSN 0733-0324
FORDYCE LETTER; commentary and information provided exclusively for those involved in the personnel, search, employment, recruiting and outplacement professions. 1969. m. $126. Kimberly Organization, Box 31011, Des Peres, MO 63131. TEL 314-965-3883. FAX 314-965-8177. Ed. Paul A. Hawkinson. bk.rev. circ. 8,500. **Document type:** newsletter.

FOREIGN INVESTMENTS IN BRAZIL. LEGISLATION. see *BUSINESS AND ECONOMICS — International Commerce*

FORUM INTERNATIONALE; lectures on commercial law and arbitration. see *LAW — International Law*

GABLERS - MAGAZIN; Zeitschrift fuer innovative Fuehrungskraefte. see *BUSINESS AND ECONOMICS — Management*

346   AU   ISSN 0250-6440
DER GESELLSCHAFTER. 1972. q. S.610. Manzsche Verlags- und Universitaetsbuchhandlung, Kohlmarkt 16, A-1014 Vienna, Austria. TEL 0222-531610. FAX 0222-53161-181. Ed. Rudolf Jahn. adv. circ. 1,500. **Document type:** trade publication.
    Description: Covers corporate and partnership law.

346 658.3   GW
GEWERBEARCHIV; Zeitschrift fuer Gewerbe- und Wirtschaftsverwaltungsrecht. 1955. m. DM.360 (foreign DM.376.50). Gildefachverlag GmbH & Co. KG, Postfach 1351, 31043 Alfeld, Germany. TEL 05181-80040. Ed. Ludwig Froehler. circ. 1,900. (back issues avail.; reprint service avail. from SCH) **Indexed:** INIS Atomind. **Document type:** trade publication.

LAW — CORPORATE LAW

346 US
GILBERT LAW SUMMARIES. AGENCY AND PARTNERSHIP. irreg., 4th ed., 1982. $11.95. Harcourt Brace Legal & Professional Publications, Inc., 176 W. Adams, Ste. 2100, Chicago, IL 60603. TEL 312-853-3662.

346 US
GILBERT LAW SUMMARIES. ANTITRUST. irreg., 8th ed., 1983. $11.95. Harcourt Brace Legal & Professional Publications, Inc., 176 W. Adams, Ste. 2100, Chicago, IL 60603. TEL 312-853-3662.

346 US
GILBERT LAW SUMMARIES. BANKRUPTCY. 1989. irreg. $18.95. Harcourt Brace Legal & Professional Publications, Inc., 176 W. Adams, Ste. 2100, Chicago, IL 60603. TEL 312-853-3662.

346 657 US
GILBERT LAW SUMMARIES. BASIC ACCOUNTING FOR LAWYERS. 1984. irreg. $10.95. Harcourt Brace Legal Publications, Inc., 176 W. Adams, Ste. 2100, Chicago, IL 60603. TEL 312-853-3662.

346 US
GILBERT LAW SUMMARIES. BUSINESS LAW. irreg., 2nd ed., 1984. $10.95. Harcourt Brace legla & Professional Publications, Inc., 176 W. Adams, Ste. 2100, Chicago, IL 60603. TEL 312-853-3662.

346 US
GILBERT LAW SUMMARIES. COMMERCIAL PAPER AND PAYMENT LAW. irreg., 14th ed., 1992. $15.95. Harcourt Brace Legal & Professional Publications, Inc., 176 W. Adams, Ste. 2100, Chicago, IL 60603. TEL 312-853-3662.
    Formerly: Gilbert Law Summaries. Commercial Paper.

346 US
GILBERT LAW SUMMARIES. CONTRACTS. irreg., 11th ed., 1984. $14.95. Harcourt Brace Legal & Professional Publications, Inc., 176 W. Adams, Ste. 2100, Chicago, IL 60603. TEL 312-853-3662.

346 US
GILBERT LAW SUMMARIES. CORPORATIONS. irreg., 13th ed., 1989. $15.95. Harcourt Brace Legal & Professional Publications, Inc., 176 W. Adams, Ste. 2100, Chicago, IL 60603. TEL 312-853-3662.

346 US
GILBERT LAW SUMMARIES. INCOME TAX 2 (CORPORATE). irreg., 11th ed., 1990. $14.95. Harcourt Brace Legal & Professional Publications, Inc., 176 W. Adams, Ste. 2100, Chicago, IL 60603. TEL 312-853-3662.

347.9 US
GILBERT LAW SUMMARIES. LABOR LAW. irreg., 10th ed., 1989. $14.95. Harcourt Brace legal & Professional Publications, Inc., 176 W. Adams, Ste. 2100, Chicago, IL 60603. TEL 312-853-3662.

346 IT
GIURISPRUDENZA ANNOTATA DI DIRITTO INDUSTRIALE. (Issued in pts.) 1972. a. price varies. Casa Editrice Dott. A. Giuffre, Via B. Arsizio 40, 20151 Milan, Italy. TEL 02-38000905. FAX 02-38009582.

346 332 IT
GIURISPRUDENZA COMMERCIALE. 1974. bi-m. L.160000 (foreign L.240000). Casa Editrice Dott. A. Giuffre, Via Busto Arsizio 40, 20151 Milan, Italy. TEL 02-38000905. FAX 02-38009582. Ed. Pier Giusto Jaeger. adv.; bk.rev.; bibl. circ. 5,800.
    Indexed: ELLIS.
    Formerly: Giurisprudenza Commerciale - Societa e Fallimento.

346 380.5 US
GOODS IN TRANSIT. 1976. 3 base vols. (plus supplements). $685. Matthew Bender & Co., Inc., 11 Penn Plaza, New York, NY 10001. TEL 212-967-7707. Ed. Saul Sorkin. (looseleaf format)
    Description: Provides information on how to recover or avoid liability for lost, damaged or delayed goods shipped by air, sea, rail or truck anywhere in the world; plus practical coverage of the rights, obligations and remedies for losses, damages and delays.

346 GW ISSN 0533-3407
GRUNDLAGEN UND PRAXIS DES WIRTSCHAFTSRECHTS. 1964. irreg., vol.11, 1992. Erich Schmidt Verlag GmbH & Co. (Berlin), Genthiner Str. 30G, 10785 Berlin, Germany. TEL 030-2500850. FAX 030-25008521. (back issues avail.) *Document type:* monographic series.

GUIDE TO TEXAS WORKERS' COMPENSATION REFORM. see BUSINESS AND ECONOMICS — Personnel Management

GUIDEBOOK TO FAIR EMPLOYMENT PRACTICES. see BUSINESS AND ECONOMICS — Labor And Industrial Relations

346 331 US ISSN 1059-0277
KF3455.Z9
H C E P. 1990. a. Practising Law Institute, 810 Seventh Ave., New York, NY 10019. TEL 212-765-5700.
    Formerly (until 1991): Handling Corporate Employment Law Problems (ISSN 1059-0269)

346.066 US
HANDBOOK OF CONNECTICUT CORPORATION STATUTES. a. $25. Connecticut Law Book Company, Box 575, Guilford, CT 06437. TEL 203-458-8000.

346 AU
HANDELSRECHTLICHE ENTSCHEIDUNGEN. 1961. a. price varies. Manzsche Verlags- und Universitaetsbuchhandlung, Kohlmarkt 16, A-1014 Vienna, Austria. TEL 0222-531610. FAX 0222-53161-181. Ed. Johannes Wolfgang Steiner. circ. 2,000. *Document type:* trade publication.
    Description: Collection of decisions on commercial law.

HARVEY ON INDUSTRIAL RELATIONS & EMPLOYMENT LAW. see BUSINESS AND ECONOMICS — Labor And Industrial Relations

HUMAN RESOURCES MANAGEMENT IN CANADA. see BUSINESS AND ECONOMICS — Personnel Management

346 NE
I C C A CONGRESS SERIES. 1983. irreg., no.5, 1992. price varies. (International Council for Commercial Arbitration) Kluwer Law and Taxation Publishers (Subsidiary of: Wolters Kluwer N.V.), P.O. Box 23, 7400 GA Deventer, Netherlands. TEL 31-5700-47261. FAX 31-5700-22244. TELEX 49295 KLUDV NL. (Dist. by: Libresso Distribution Centre, P.O. Box 23, 7400 GA Deventer, Netherlands. TEL 31-5700-33155. FAX 31-5700-33834; In N. America: Kluwer Law and Taxation Publishers, 675 Massachusetts Ave., Cambridge, MA 02139. TEL 617-354-0140. FAX 617-354-8595) (Co-sponsor: T.M.C. Asser Institute for International and European Law) Ed. P. Sanders. *Document type:* monographic series, proceedings.

346 US ISSN 1060-5924
▼**I O M A'S REPORT ON CONTROLLING LAW FIRMS COSTS.** 1992. m. $175. Institute of Management and Administration, 29 W. 35th St., 5th Fl., New York, NY 10001-2299. TEL 212-244-0360. FAX 212-564-0465. Ed. Ann Podolske. *Document type:* newsletter.
    —CCC.
    Description: Covers staffing, equipment, production, record-keeping and other management techniques to get the most productivity.

I O M A'S REPORT ON MANAGING 401K PLANS. (Institute of Management and Administration) see BUSINESS AND ECONOMICS — Banking And Finance

346 US ISSN 1058-5443
KFI3331.A29
INDIANA EMPLOYMENT LAW. 1990. biennial. Indiana Chamber of Commerce, 1 N. Capitol, Ste. 200, Indianapolis, IN 46204-2248.

346 UK ISSN 0306-2163
KD3040.A38
INDUSTRIAL CASES REPORTS. 1972. m. £168 (overseas £182) (Effective Aug. 1993). Incorporated Council of Law Reporting for England and Wales, 3 Stone Bldgs., Lincoln's Inn, London WC2A 3XN, England. TEL 071-242 6471. FAX 071-831-5247. Eds. C.J. Ellis, C. Noon.
    ●Also available online. Vendor(s): Mead Data Central, Inc.
    Incorporates: Restrictive Practices Reports (ISSN 0073-571X)

INDUSTRIAL COURT REPORTER. see BUSINESS AND ECONOMICS — Labor And Industrial Relations

346 AT
INDUSTRIAL LAW: FEDERAL. base vol. (plus updates 8/yr.). $405. Butterworths, 271-273 Lane Cove Rd., P.O. Box 345, North Ryde, N.S.W. 2113, Australia. TEL 02-335-4444. FAX 02-335-4655. (looseleaf format)
    Formerly: Federal Industrial Law.

INDUSTRIAL LAW JOURNAL. see BUSINESS AND ECONOMICS — Labor And Industrial Relations

346 SA ISSN 0258-249X
INDUSTRIAL LAW JOURNAL. (Text in English) 1980. bi-m. R.300. Juta & Co. Ltd., P.O. Box 14373, Kenwyn 7790, South Africa. TEL 021-797-5101. FAX 021-761-5010. Ed.Bd. cum.index. circ. 2,200. (back issues avail.)

346 AT ISSN 0728-8417
KU1216.3
INDUSTRIAL REPORTS. 1948. irreg. Law Book Co. Ltd., 44-50 Waterloo Rd., North Ryde, N.S.W. 2113, Australia. TEL 02-887-0177. FAX 02-888-9706. TELEX ASBOOK 27995. Ed.Bd.
    ●Also available online. Vendor(s): Info-One International Pty Ltd.
    Supersedes (in 1981): Industrial Arbitration Service (ISSN 0312-4029)

346 GW
INDUSTRIEGESELLSCHAFT UND RECHT.* 1974. irreg., vol.5, 1975. price varies. Gieseking-Verlag, Deckerstr. 2, Postfach 42, 4813 Bielefeld-Bethel, Germany. Eds. Manfred Rehbinder, Bernd Rebe.

346 US ISSN 0736-0150
INSIDE (ALBANY). 1982. 3/yr. $25 to non-members. New York State Bar Association, Corporate Counsel Section, 1 Elk St., Albany, NY 12207-1096. TEL 518-463-3200. FAX 518-487-5699. Ed. Terence J. Gallagher. adv. (back issues avail.) *Document type:* newsletter.

INTERNATIONAL BANKING REGULATOR. see BUSINESS AND ECONOMICS — Banking And Finance

346 341 AT
▼**INTERNATIONAL COMMERCIAL ARBITRATION IN AUSTRALIA.** 1992. 2 base vols. (plus updates 2/yr.). Aus.$490. Law Book Co. Ltd., 44-50 Waterloo Rd., North Ryde, N.S.W. 2113, Australia. TEL 20-887-0177. FAX 02-888-9706. TELEX AHBOOK 27995. Ed. Marcus Jacobs. (looseleaf format)
    Description: Covers the entire field of international commercial arbitration in Australia, with detailed references to the major arbitration agreements and commentary.

346 UK ISSN 0961-5326
CODEN: ICRLEM
INTERNATIONAL CORPORATE LAW. m. $333. Euromoney Publications PLC, Nestor House, Playhouse Yard, London EC4V 5EX, England. TEL 071-779-8660. FAX 071-779-8667. (Subscr. to: Quadrant Subscription Services, Oakfield House, Perrymount Rd., Haywards Heath, RH16 2DH, England)
    —BLDSC (4539.469390); UMI.

3364 LAW — CORPORATE LAW

341 NE
▼**INTERNATIONAL ENCYCLOPAEDIA OF LAWS. CORPORATIONS AND PARTNERSHIPS.** (Text in English) 1992. 2 base vols. (plus irreg. updates). fl.325($176) (effective 1994). Kluwer Law and Taxation Publishers (Subsiciary of: Wolters Kluwer N.V.), P.O. Box 23, 7400 GA Deventer, Netherlands. TEL 31-5700-47261. FAX 31-5700-22244. TELEX 49295 KLUDV NL. (Dist. by: Libresso Distribution Centre, P.O. Box 23, 7400 GA Deventer, Netherlands. TEL 31-5700-33155. FAX 31-5700-33834; In N. America: Kluwer Law and Taxation Publishers, 675 Massachusetts Ave., Cambridge, MA 02139. TEL 617-354-0140. FAX 617-354-8595) Ed. K. Geens. (looseleaf format)
Document type: monographic series.
Description: Publishes studies of the law of public and private companies and partnerships in individual countries, from an international, comparative perspective, with discussion of EC company law and decisions of the European Court of Justice.

346 341 US ISSN 1041-3855
INTERNATIONAL QUARTERLY (CHESTERLAND). 1989. q. $135. Business Laws, Inc., 11630 Chillicothe Rd., Chesterland, OH 44026. TEL 216-729-7996. FAX 216-729-0645. Ed. William A. Hancock.
Document type: newsletter.
—UnCover. **CCC.**

INTERNATIONAL SECURITIES REGULATION REPORT. see *BUSINESS AND ECONOMICS — Investments*

INTERNATIONALE WIRTSCHAFTS-BRIEFE; Zeitschrift fuer internationales Steuer- und Wirtschaftsrecht, Euratom, OECD, Steuern und Zoelle im gemeinsamen Markt. see *BUSINESS AND ECONOMICS — Public Finance, Taxation*

INVESTMENT LIMITED PARTNERSHIPS HANDBOOK. see *BUSINESS AND ECONOMICS — Investments*

346 336 US ISSN 0893-1364
KF6415.A15
INVESTMENT LIMITED PARTNERSHIPS LAW REPORT. 1981. 10/yr. $185. Clark - Bordman - Callaghan Company, Inc., 375 Hudson St., New York, NY 10014. TEL 800-323-1336. FAX 212-924-0460. Eds. Robert J. Haft, Peter M. Fass. index. (looseleaf format; back issues avail.) **Document type:** newsletter.
Formerly: Tax Sheltered Investments Law Report (ISSN 0731-5759)

346 US
IOWA BANKRUPTCY. 1984. base vol. (plus suppl.). $55. Butterworth Legal Publishers (Salem) (Subsidiary of: Reed Elsevier plc), 8 Industrial Way, Bldg. C, Salem, NH 03079. TEL 800-548-4001. FAX 603-898-9858. Ed. Robert S. Oppold. (looseleaf format)
Description: Covers chapter 7 liquidation cases in Iowa.

346 CC
JINGJI FAZHI. (Text in Chinese) m. Zhongguo Jingjifa Yanjiuhui - China Economic Law Research Society, No. 11, Wenjin Jie, Xicheng-qu, Beijing 100017, People's Republic of China. TEL 6016633. Ed. Gu Ming.

346 330 US
JOINT VENTURES: STRUCTURING ALTERNATIVES. 1988. base vol. (plus a. suppl.). $95. Shepard's - McGraw-Hill, Inc., Box 35300, Colorado Springs, CO 80935-3530. TEL 800-525-2474. (looseleaf format)
Description: Gives lawyers, accountants and anyone involved in business transactions more creative alternatives to reaching financial goals.

JOURNAL OF BANKING AND FINANCE - LAW AND PRACTICE. see *BUSINESS AND ECONOMICS — Banking And Finance*

346 UK ISSN 0021-9460
K10
JOURNAL OF BUSINESS LAW. 1957. 6/yr. £80. Sweet & Maxwell, South Quay Plaza, 7th Fl., 183 Marsh Wall, London E14 9FT, England. TEL 071-538-8686. FAX 071-538-9508. Ed. Caroline Vandridge-Ames. adv. contact: Jackie Wood. bk.rev.; index. (reprint service avail. from RRI) **Indexed:** BPIA, Bus.Ind., C.L.I., C.R.E.J., Cont.Pg.Manage., ELLIS, L.R.I., Leg.Cont., Leg.Per., Mar.Aff.Bibl., SCIMP (1979-), SSCI. **Document type:** bulletin.
—BLDSC (4954.700000); Faxon; UnCover; SWETS; UMI. **CCC.**

346 330 US
JOURNAL OF CORPORATE DISCLOSURE AND CONFIDENTIALITY. q. $95. Shepard's - McGraw-Hill, Inc., Box 35300, Colorado Springs, CO 80935-3530.

346 US ISSN 0360-795X
K10
JOURNAL OF CORPORATION LAW. 4/yr. $30. University of Iowa, College of Law, Iowa City, IA 52242. TEL 319-335-9061. FAX 319-335-9019. bk.rev.; cum.index every 10 yrs. (also avail. in microfilm from RRI; reprint service avail. from WSH) **Indexed:** Account.Ind. (1975-), Bank.Lit.Ind., BPIA, Bus.Ind., C.L.I., Curr.Cont., L.R.I., Leg.Per., P.A.I.S. **Document type:** academic/scholarly publication.
●Also available online. Vendor(s): West Services, Inc. Also available on CD-ROM.
—BLDSC (4965.340000); Faxon; UnCover; SWETS; UMI.

346 UK ISSN 0267-937X
K10
JOURNAL OF INTERNATIONAL BANKING LAW. 1986. m. £295. (E S C Publishing Ltd.) Sweet & Maxwell, South Quay Plaza, 7th Fl., 183 Marsh Wall; London E14 9FT, England. TEL 071-538-8686. FAX 071-538-8625. Ed. Cheri Evans. adv. contact: Jackie Wood. bk.rev.; index. (back issues avail.) **Document type:** bulletin.
—BLDSC (5007.583000); SWETS. **CCC.**
Description: Legal information service on case law, new legislation and developments in the globalization of the banking regulatory system.

346.066 US ISSN 0733-2491
K10
JOURNAL OF LAW & COMMERCE. 1980. 2/yr. $20. University of Pittsburgh, School of Law, 3900 Forbes Ave., Pittsburgh, PA 15260. TEL 412-648-1361. FAX 412-648-2649. adv.; bk.rev. circ. 500. (also avail. in microform from WSH; back issues avail.; reprint service avail. from WSH) **Indexed:** C.L.I., Leg.Cont., Leg.Per.
●Also available online. Vendor(s): West Services, Inc.
—BLDSC (5010.118000); Faxon; UnCover.
Description: Focuses on commercial law, providing scholarly and practical articles written by scholars, practitioners, and students that are of immediate interest to practitioners, academicians, and leaders in the legal and business community.

346 US ISSN 1054-3023
K10 CODEN: JLECE4
JOURNAL OF LEGAL ECONOMICS. 1991. 3/yr. $60. American Academy of Economic and Financial Experts, University of North Alabama, Box 5077, Florence, AL 35630. TEL 205-760-4100. Ed. Michael Butler. **Document type:** bulletin.
—BLDSC (5010.249000); UnCover; UMI.

346 US
L A M A NEWSLETTER: WASHINGTON NOTES. 1980. bi-m. free to members. Latin-American Management Association, 419 New Jersey Ave., S.E., Washington, DC 20003. TEL 202-546-3803. FAX 202-546-3807. Ed. Kathleen Braun. circ. 5,000. (back issues avail.) **Document type:** newsletter.
Description: Covers current legislations on minority and small business.

346.066 330 FR
LAMY DROIT COMMERCIAL. (Supplement avail.: Lamy Droit Commercial - Formulaire) a. 1700 F. (effective 1994). Lamy S.A., 187-189 Quai de Valmy, 75490 Paris, France. TEL 44-72-13-43. FAX 44-72-12-12. index.

346.066 330 FR
LAMY PROTECTION SOCIALE; regime general de securite sociale - salaires, regimes des non-salaries, retraites complementaires, regimes de retraite d'entreprise, prevoyance, aide sociale et action sociale. a. 1450 F. (effective 1994). Lamy S.A., 187-189 Quai de Valmy, 75490 Paris, France. TEL 44-72-13-43. FAX 44-72-13-95. charts; index.
Description: Answers the daily questions faced by those who manage the benefits of a company.

346.066 332 FR
LAMY SOCIETE COMMERCIALES. (Supplements avail.: Lamy Societes Commerciales - Formulaire S.A. a Conseil d'Adiministration; Lamy Societes Commerciales - Formulaire S.A. a Directiore; Lamy Societes Commerciales - Formulaire S.A.R.L.; Lamy Societes Commerciales - Formulaire Societes Autres que S.A.R.L. et S.A. Regroupements de Societes) a. 1630 F. (effective 1994). Lamy S.A., 187-189 Quai de Valmy, 75490 Paris, France. TEL 44-72-13-43. FAX 44-72-13-95. charts; index.
Description: Analyzes the constitution, management, finances and benefits, competition and dissolution of commercial companies.

310 US
LAW & BUSINESS DIRECTORY OF CORPORATE COUNSEL. Short title: Directory of Corporate Counsel. a. $275. Law & Business, Inc. (Subsidiary of: Prentice Hall), 270 Sylvan Ave., Englewood Cliffs, NJ 07632. TEL 201-894-8484.
●Also available online. Vendor(s): West Services, Inc.

346 US ISSN 1052-2972
LAW DEPARTMENT MANAGEMENT ADVISER. 1984. m. $147. Business Laws, Inc., 11630 Chillicothe Rd., Chesterland, OH 44026. TEL 216-729-7996. FAX 216-729-0645. Ed. William A. Hancock. (back issues avail.) **Document type:** newsletter.
—CCC.
Formerly (until 1989): Corporate Counsel's Adviser (ISSN 0898-9915)
Description: For corporate law departments. Covers ways of increasing productivity, cost-effectiveness and management skills.

346.066 UK ISSN 0954-2809
LAW FOR BUSINESS. 1988. 10/yr. £189($300) Wallace Publishing Ltd., 161 Chertsey Road, Twickenham, Mddx. TW1 1EP, England. TEL 01-891-3575. Ed. Jean Campbell. index. circ. 1,000. (back issues avail.)

LAW RELATING TO BANKER AND CUSTOMER IN AUSTRALIA. see *LAW*

346 UK ISSN 0952-1046
LAW REPORTS OF THE COMMONWEALTH. COMMERCIAL LAW REPORTS. 1985. a. Butterworth & Co. (Publishers) Ltd. (Subsidiary of: Reed Elsevier plc), 88 Kingsway, London WC2B 6AB, England. TEL 071-405-6900. FAX 071-405-1332. TELEX 95678. (US addr.: Butterworth Legal Publishers, 90 Stiles Rd., Salem, NH 03079, USA. TEL 603-898-9664) Ed.Bd.

346 US ISSN 0898-9966
LAWYER'S BRIEF. 1970. s-m. $398. Business Laws, Inc., 11630 Chillicothe Rd., Chesterland, OH 44026. TEL 216-729-7996. FAX 216-729-0645. Ed. William Hancock. index, cum.index: 1980-1992. (back issues avail.) **Document type:** newsletter.
—CCC.

LEGAL CONNECTION: CORPORATIONS AND LAW FIRMS; a directory of publicly-held corporations and their law firms. see *LAW*

LEGAL INSIGHTS FOR MANAGERS. see *LAW*

346 657 AT ISSN 1037-5562
LEGISLATIVE POLICY DISCUSSION PAPER. 1991. irreg. price varies. Australian Accounting Research Foundation, 211 Hawthorn Rd., Caulfield, Vic. 3162, Australia. TEL 61-3-523-8111. FAX 61-3-523-5499. (Co-sponsors: Australian Society of Certified Practising Accountants; Institute of Chartered Accountants in Australia) circ. 1,000. **Document type:** monographic series.

LAW — CORPORATE LAW

346 332   US
LENDER LIABILITY LAW AND LITIGATION. (Issued in 1 base vol. with supplements) 1989. irreg. $165. Matthew Bender & Co., Inc., 11 Penn Plaza, New York, NY 10001. TEL 212-967-7707. (looseleaf format)
Description: Complete guide to the theory and practice of lender liability cases. Includes discussions of causes of action and defenses, as well as information on how to litigate these often complex disputes.

346 332.3   US
LENDER LIABILITY LAW REPORT. 1987. m. $173 (overseas $232). Warren Gorham Lamont, 1 Penn Plaza, New York, NY 10019. TEL 212-971-5000. FAX 212-971-5240. (Subscr. to: The Park Square Bldg., 31 St. James Ave., Boston, MA 02116-4112. TEL 800-950-1207) Ed. Helen Davis Chaitman. **Document type:** newsletter.
Description: Analyzes recent court decisions and new legislation. Provides suggestions for developing protective mechanisms for lenders and the means of defending borrowers' suits.

346 332   US   ISSN 1042-5764
KF1301.5.B36
LENDER LIABILITY LITIGATION REPORTER; the national journal of record of lawsuits brought by borrowers against their lending institutions. 1988. m. $329. Andrews Publications, 1646 West Chester Pike, Box 1000, Westtown, PA 19395. TEL 215-399-6600; 800-345-1101. FAX 215-399-6610. Ed. Mary Rhoads. abstr.; bibl.; stat.; s-a. cum.index. (looseleaf format; back issues avail.) **Document type:** newsletter.

346 332.3   US   ISSN 0898-7645
KF1035.A15
LENDER LIABILITY NEWS. 1988. bi-w. $597 (foreign $619). Buraff Publications (Subsidiary of: Millin Publications, Inc.), 1350 Connecticut Ave. N.W., Ste. 1000, Washington, DC 20036. TEL 800-333-1291. FAX 202-862-0999. Ed. Linda Jespereny. (back issues avail.) **Document type:** newsletter.
—CCC.
Description: Covers liability claims - policies and procedures, strategies for winning cases, trend-setting court decisions and jury verdicts.

346 658   FR
LETTRE DES ASSOCIATIONS. fortn. 515 F. Lamy S.A., 187-189 Quai de Valmy, 75490 Paris Cedex 10, France. TEL 44-72-13-43. FAX 44-72-13-95.
Description: Provides judicial, fiscal and social news of interest to managers.

346   US
KF3145.L5
LICENSING ECONOMICS REVIEW. 1990. m. $295. Box 650, Moorestown, NJ 08057-0650. TEL 609-234-1199. Ed. Russell L. Parr.

346.066   US   ISSN 0162-5764
KF3145.A15   CODEN: LLBRDL
LICENSING LAW AND BUSINESS REPORT. 1978. bi-m. $195. Clark - Boardman - Callaghan Company Ltd., 375 Hudson St., New York, NY 10014. TEL 212-929-7500; 800-221-9428. FAX 212-924-0460. index. (looseleaf format; back issues avail.) Indexed: C.L.I., L.R.I.
—CASDDS.
Description: Provides articles on recent cases and developments, detailed analysis, and practical strategies in the field of licensing law.

LLOYD'S LAW REPORTS. see *LAW*

MCDONALD, HENRY AND MEEK: AUSTRALIAN BANKRUPTCY LAW AND PRACTICE. see *LAW — Civil Law*

MANAGER'S LEGAL BULLETIN. see *BUSINESS AND ECONOMICS — Labor And Industrial Relations*

346   CN
MANUEL DES CORPORATIONS DU QUEBEC. q. Can.$460. Carswell, One Corporate Plaza, 2075 Kennedy Rd., Scarborough, ON M1T 3V4, Canada. TEL 416-609-8000. FAX 416-298-5094. (looseleaf format)
Description: Includes authoratative commentary on corporate law, departmental practice and procedure notes, a collection of forms and precedents and relevant statutes and regulations.

346 658   US
▼**MARKETER'S LEGAL GUIDE.** 1993. biennial. $39.95 (softcover $17.95). Gale Research Inc., 835 Penobscot Bldg., Detroit, MI 48226. TEL 313-961-2242. FAX 313-961-6083. Ed. Steven Meyerowitz.
Description: Provides a basic understanding of marketing law for small business owners and lawyers.

MASSACHUSETTS CORPORATE TAX MANUAL. see *BUSINESS AND ECONOMICS — Public Finance, Taxation*

MASSACHUSETTS DISCRIMINATION LAW REPORTER. see *LAW*

340   US
MASSACHUSETTS WORKERS' COMPENSATION PRACTICE MANUAL. 1988. base vol. (plus a. supplement), 2nd ed. $115. Butterworth Legal Publishers (Salem) (Subsidiary of: Reed Elsevier plc), 8 Industrial Way, Bldg. C, Salem, NH 03079. TEL 800-548-4001. FAX 603-898-9858. Ed. Paul A. Gargano. (looseleaf format)

346   US
MASSACHUSETTS WORKERS' COMPENSATION REPORTS. 1988. 3 base vols. (plus a. supplement). $75. Butterworth Legal Publishers (Salem) (Subsidiary of: Reed Elsevier plc), 8 Industrial Way, Bldg. C, Salem, NH 03079. TEL 800-548-4001. FAX 603-898-9858. Ed. Paul A. Gargano.

346   US
▼**MEALEY'S LITIGATION REPORT: PREMISES LIABILITY.** 1993. s-m. $650. Mealey Publications, Inc., Box 446, Wayne, PA 19087. TEL 215-688-6566. FAX 215-688-7552. Ed. Scott Jacobs. (looseleaf format)
Description: Provides exhaustive coverage of premises liability for the criminal acts of third parties, such as theft, assault and rape. Tracks litigation topics including foreseeability, security adequacy, negligence, duty of care, causation and insurance.

346   US   ISSN 0897-2281
METROPOLITAN NEWS - ENTERPRISE. d. (Mon.-Fri.). $139. Grace Communications, Inc., 210 S. Spring St., Los Angeles, CA 90012. TEL 213-628-4384. Ed. Roger M. Grace. circ. 2,500. (tabloid format) **Document type:** newspaper.
Incorporates (in 1987): Metropolitan News (ISSN 0893-9071)

346   US
MINNESOTA CORPORATIONS PRACTICE MANUAL. 1986. base vol. (plus suppl.). $78. Butterworth Legal Publishers (Salem) (Subsidiary of: Reed Elsevier plc), 8 Industrial Way, Bldg. C, Salem, NH 03079. TEL 800-548-4001. FAX 603-898-9858. Ed. Bert Black. (looseleaf format)
Description: Provides a complete analysis of corporate law in Minnesota by tracking the chronological "life" of a corporation from creation to dissolution.

346   US
▼**MISSOURI BAR. COMMERCIAL LAW COMMITTEE. NEWSLETTER.** 1992. 4/yr. free to members. Missouri Bar, Commercial Law Committee, Box 119, Jefferson City, MO 65102. TEL 314-635-4128. FAX 314-625-2811. Ed. Francis X. Buckley, Jr. **Document type:** newsletter.

346   US
MONTANA CHAMBER OF COMMERCE. LEGISLATIVE BULLETIN. w. free to members. Montana Chamber of Commerce, 2030 11th Ave., Helena, MT 59601. TEL 406-442-2405. FAX 406-442-2409. circ. 1,200. (back issues avail.) **Document type:** bulletin.

340   NZ
MORISON'S COMPANY LAW IN NEW ZEALAND. 2 base vols. (plus update 8/yr.). NZ.$296 includes subscr. to Morison's Company Law Reports. Butterworths of New Zealand Ltd., 203-207 Victoria St., P.O. Box 472, Wellington, New Zealand. TEL 04-385-1479. FAX 04-385-1598. Ed. John Cottle. (looseleaf format)
Description: Statutes and regulations followed by a treatise on company law and discussion on cases.

346   NZ   ISSN 0962-4961
MORISON'S COMPANY LAW REPORTS. 1985. m. NZ.$440. Butterworths of New Zealand Ltd., 203-207 Victoria St., P.O. Box 472, Wellington, New Zealand. TEL 04-385-1479. FAX 04-385-1598. Ed. John Cottle.
Formerly (until June 1991): Butterworths Company Reports.
Description: Detailed coverage of High Court, Court of Appeal and Privy Council decisions pertaining to company law.

MUNICIPALITIES AND CORPORATION CASES; a monthly law reporter. see *LAW*

N C U A WATCH. (National Credit Union Administration) see *BUSINESS AND ECONOMICS — Banking And Finance*

NATURAL GAS FUELS. see *TRANSPORTATION*

NEW HAMPSHIRE CORPORATIONS, PARTNERSHIPS AND ASSOCIATIONS. see *BUSINESS AND ECONOMICS*

346   US
NEW HAMPSHIRE WORKERS' COMPENSATION MANUAL. base vol. (plus supplement). $45. Butterworth Legal Publishers (Salem) (Subsidiary of: Reed Elsevier plc), 8 Industrial Way, Bldg. C, Salem, NH 03079. TEL 800-548-4001. FAX 603-898-9858. Ed. Richard Galway.
Description: Covers the history, statutory requirements, judicial interpretation, and procedure of workers' compensation law in New Hampshire.

346   US
NEW JERSEY STATE BAR ASSOCIATION. CORPORATE AND BUSINESS LAW SECTION. NEWSLETTER. 1967. irreg. free to members. New Jersey State Bar Association, Corporate and Business Law Section, 1 Constitution Sq., New Brunswick, NJ 08901-1500. TEL 908-249-5000. FAX 908-249-2815. Ed. Brian P. Blatz. bk.rev.; circ. 1,300 (controlled). (back issues avail.) **Document type:** newsletter.

346   US   ISSN 1054-0326
NEW YORK STATE BAR ASSOCIATION. BUSINESS LAW SECTION. NEWSLETTER. 1975. 3/yr. $15 to non-members. New York State Bar Association, Business Law Section, One Elk St., Albany, NY 12207-1096. TEL 518-463-3200. FAX 518-487-5699. Ed. Janet Geldzahler. adv. circ. 4,600. **Document type:** newsletter.

346   US   ISSN 1060-4081
KFN5225.A75
NEW YORK STATE BAR ASSOCIATION. BUSINESS LAW SECTION. PROCEEDINGS OF THE ANNUAL MEETING. 1989. a. $15 (effective 1993). New York State Bar Association, Business Law Section, One Elk St., Albany, NY 12207. TEL 518-463-3200. circ. 5,000 (controlled). (back issues avail.) **Document type:** proceedings.

346   NZ
NEW ZEALAND COMPANY LAW AND PRACTICE. 1979. 10/yr. NZ.$1370. C C H New Zealand Limited, P.O. Box 2378, Auckland, New Zealand. TEL 483-9179. FAX 483-4009. (looseleaf format)
Formerly: New Zealand Company Secretary's Practice Manual and Company Law Service.
Description: Provides analysis of new developments in companies and securities law and their impact on professional and corporate practice. Includes full text legislation, and cases, and new developments covering legislative proposals, government reports and statements.

346 657   NZ
NEW ZEALAND COMPANY LAW GUIDE. 1987. 4/yr. NZ.$398. C C H New Zealand Ltd., P.O. Box 2378, Auckland, New Zealand. TEL 483-9179. FAX 483-4009. (looseleaf format)
Formerly: New Zealand Company Secretary's Guide.
Description: Provides information on company law matters for company secretaries, accountants and business executives in commerce, and legal and accounting practitioners.

346.066   US   ISSN 1058-4552
KF1388.A65
NONPROFIT CORPORATION FORMS HANDBOOK. 1990. a. $105. Clark - Boardman - Callaghan Company Ltd., 375 Hudson St., New York, NY 10014. TEL 212-929-7500. FAX 212-924-0460. Ed. Barbara L. Kirschten.

LAW — CORPORATE LAW

NORMATIVA TECNICA AGGIORNAMENTI. see *BUILDING AND CONSTRUCTION*

346 US
NORTON BANKRUPTCY CODE AND RULES PAMPHLETS. a. $85. Clark - Boardman - Callaghan Company, Inc., 155 Pfingsten Rd., Deerfield, IL 60015. TEL 800-323-1336. Ed. William L. Norton Jr.
Description: Contains federal rules of bankruptcy procedure and official bankruptcy forms.

346 US
NORTON BANKRUPTCY LAW ADVISER. 1983. m. $225. Clark - Boardman - Callaghan Company, Inc., 155 Pfingsten Rd., Deerfield, IL 60015. TEL 800-323-1336. Ed. Jean Maess. (looseleaf format)
Description: Information on current court and legislative activity. Includes a practice guide.

346 368.4 IT
NOTIZIARIO DEL LAVORO E PREVIDENZA. 33/yr. De Lillo Editore s.r.l., Via Mecerate 76-3, 20138 Milan, Italy. TEL 2-50-64-741. FAX 2-506-48-18. Ed. Pietro de Lillo. circ. 17,500.

O S H A FASTSEARCH; Occupational Safety and Health Administration regulations. see *BUSINESS AND ECONOMICS — Labor And Industrial Relations*

346 CN
ONTARIO CORPORATIONS LAW GUIDE. m. Can.$470. C H Canadian Ltd., 6 Garamond Ct., North York, ON M3C 1Z5, Canada. TEL 416-441-2992. FAX 416-444-9011. index.
Formerly: Ontario Companies Law Guide (ISSN 0048-1750)
Description: Relevant Ontario statutes dealing with company law, editorial commentary, forms and precedents.

346 331 CN
ONTARIO PAY & EMPLOYMENT EQUITY GUIDE. bi-m. Can.$195. C C H Canadian Ltd., 6 Garamond Ct., North York, ON M3C 1Z5, Canada. TEL 416-441-0086; 800-268-4522. FAX 416-444-9011.
Description: Reference for the implementation and administration of pay equity and employment equity in Ontario.

340 330 US
ORGANIZING CORPORATE AND OTHER BUSINESS ENTERPRISES. 1949. irreg. $210. Matthew Bender & Co., Inc., 11 Penn Plaza, New York, NY 10001. TEL 212-967-7707.
Description: For the attorney who is advising proposed or existing small businesses. Acts as a guide to the legal and tax factors to be considered in selecting a form of business organization.

346 AT
PAPUA NEW GUINEA COMPANIES LEGISLATION. 1980. irreg., as required for legislative changes. C C H Australia Ltd., P.O. Box 230, N. Ryde, N.S.W. 2113, Australia. TEL 888-2555. FAX 02-888-7324. (looseleaf format)

346 US ISSN 0892-4805
PARTNER'S REPORT, A MONTHLY BRIEF FOR LAW FIRM OWNERS. m. $245. Institute of Management and Administration, 29 W. 35th St., 5th Fl., New York, NY 10001-2299. TEL 212-244-0360. FAX 212-564-0465. Ed. Sherrye Henry Jr. index. (back issues avail.)
—CCC.

340 KF3512 US ISSN 1052-9640
PENSION FUND LITIGATION REPORTER. 1990. m. $650. Andrews Publications, 1646 West Chester Pike, Box 1000, Westtown, PA 19395. TEL 215-399-6600; 800-345-1101. FAX 215-399-6610. Ed. Barbara Pizzirani. bibl.; stat.; cum index every 6 mos. (looseleaf format; back issues avail.) Document type: newsletter.
Description: Presents record of lawsuits involving benefit plan fiduciaries.

THE PERSONNEL ALERT (RAMSEY). see *BUSINESS AND ECONOMICS — Personnel Management*

346 US
PERTINENT COMMERCIAL STATUTES. 1988. a. $11.95. Gould Publications, 1333 N. U.S. Hwy. 17-92, Longwood, FL 32750-3724. TEL 407-695-9500. FAX 407-695-2906. adv.; bk.rev. (looseleaf format)
Description: Contains uniform consumer code, consumer credit protection, truth in lending regulations, consumer leasing, Magnuson-Moss warranty, FTC improvement act and more.

346 UK ISSN 0959-9940
PRACTICAL LAW FOR COMPANIES. Abbreviated title: P L C. 1990. 11/yr. £240. Legal & Commercial Publishing, Unit 90 - Buttersea Business Centre, Lavender Hill, London SW11 5QL, England. TEL 071-738-2303. FAX 071-978-5452. Eds. R.J. Dow, C.J. Millerchip. adv.; bk.rev. circ. 4,000. Document type: trade publication.
—BLDSC (6594.680000).
Description: Corporate and commercial law journal concentrating on practical developments for lawyers and businesses in the United Kingdom and Europe.

346.092 US
PRACTICE UNDER THE CALIFORNIA CORPORATE SECURITIES LAWS. 1972. 3 base vols. (plus supplements). $500. Matthew Bender & Co., Inc., 11 Penn Plaza, New York, NY 10001. TEL 212-967-7707. Ed.Bd. (looseleaf format)

346 US ISSN 1067-6104
▼**PREVENTION OF CORPORATE LIABILITY: CURRENT REPORT.** (Subseries of: B N A - A C C A Compliance Manual: Prevention of Corporate Liability) 1993. m. $270. The Bureau of National Affairs, Inc., 1231 25th St., N.W., Washington, DC 20037. TEL 202-452-4200. FAX 202-822-8092. TELEX 285656 BNAI WSH. (Subscr. to: 9435 Key West Ave., Rockville, MD 20850. TEL 800-372-1033) Ed. Larry Lempert. s-a. index. (back issues avail.) Document type: newsletter.
—CCC.
Description: Covers judicial decisions, pre-decisional developments in criminal prosecutions, enforcement trends, state and federal legislation, company activity, and Sentencing Commission activity.

PRIMER ON EMPLOYEE RETIREMENT INCOME SECURITY ACT. see *BUSINESS AND ECONOMICS — Labor And Industrial Relations*

346 KF1296.A15 US ISSN 1053-0029
PRODUCTS LIABILITY LAW REPORTER. 1982. m. $195 to non-members; memebers $110. Association of Trial Lawyers of America, Education Fund, 1050 31st St., N.W., Washington, DC 20007. Ed. Liane Leshne. index.
—UnCover. CCC.
Formerly (until 1986): A T L A Products Liability Law Reporter (ISSN 0745-2926)

346 UK ISSN 1353-3657
▼**PUBLIC COMPANIES AND THE CITY.** 1994. a. £17.50. Jordan Publishing Ltd., 21 St. Thomas St., Bristol BS1 6JS, England. TEL 0272-230600. FAX 0272-250486. Ed. Nick Olley. Document type: academic/scholarly publication.

PUBLIC EMPLOYMENT LAW REPORT. see *BUSINESS AND ECONOMICS — Labor And Industrial Relations*

PUBLIC LAW; the constitutional and administrative law of the commonwealth. see *LAW*

001.6 340 US ISSN 0889-0641
R I C O LAW REPORTER. (Racketeer Influenced and Corrupt Organizations) 1985. m. $1200. Computer Law Reporter, Inc., 1519 Connecticut Ave., N.W., Ste. 200, Washington, DC 20036. TEL 202-462-5755. FAX 202-328-2430. Ed. Mary L. Lyons. (back issues avail.)

RASSEGNA DI STATISTICHE DEL LAVORO. see *BUSINESS AND ECONOMICS — Abstracting, Bibliographies, Statistics*

346 368 US
RISK MANAGER LAW BULLETIN. 1986. m. $60. Quinlan Publishing Co., Inc., 23 Drydock Ave., Boston, MA 02110. TEL 617-542-0048; 800-229-2084. FAX 617-345-9646. index. (looseleaf format; back issues avail.) Document type: newsletter.
Formed by the 1992 merger of: Business Risk Management Law Bulletin (ISSN 1043-0911) & Corporate Insurance Law Bulletin (ISSN 1040-3132); Which was formerly (until 1988): Business Liability Insurance Bulletin (ISSN 0889-924X)
Description: Discusses issues and concerns relating to insurance coverage of interest to company directors, financial officers, insurance executives and insurance purchasers.

346 IT
RIVISTA DI DIRITTO DELL'IMPRESA. 1982. 3/yr. L.83000 to individuals; institutions L.105000; foreign L.120000 (effective 1993). Edizioni Scientifiche Italiane S.p.A., Via Chiatamone, 7, I-80121 Naples, Italy. Eds. Giuseppe Guarino, Natalino Irti. adv.; bk.rev. circ. 5,000.

346 IT
RIVISTA PENALE DELL'ECONOMIA. 1988. q. L.122000 to individuals; institutions L.145000; foreign L.176000 (effective 1993). Edizioni Scientifiche Italiane S.p.A., Via Chiatamone, 7, 80121 Naples, Italy. TEL 081-7645768. FAX 081-7646477.

690 340 330 IT ISSN 0394-8374
RIVISTA TRIMESTRALE DEGLI APPALTI; rivista di dottrina-legislazione-giurisprudenza. 1986. q. L.180000 (effective 1992). (Publica S.r.l.) Edicerisop. S.r.l., Via E. Tazzoli, 2, 00195 Rome, Italy. TEL 06-382313. (Subscr. to: Maggioli Editore S.p.a. Via Crimea, 1, 47037 Rimini, Italy. TEL 0541-626777) adv.: B&W page L.2300000, color page L.3400000; trim 115 x 195. circ. 4,062. (back issues avail.)

346 IT
RIVISTA TRIMESTRALE DI DIRITTO PENALE DELL'ECONOMIA. 1988. q. L.170000 (foreign L.230000) (effective 1993). Casa Editrice Dott. Antonio Milani, Via Jappelli 5, 35121 Padua, Italy. TEL 049-656677. FAX 049-8752900. Ed. Giuseppe Zuccala. circ. 1,200.

346 SZ
SCHWEIZERISCHE ZEITSCHRIFT FUER WIRTSCHAFTSRECHT. 6/yr. 148 SFr. (students 85 SFr.). Schulthess Polygraphischer Verlag AG, Zwingliplatz 2, CH-8022 Zurich, Switzerland. TEL 01-2519336. FAX 01-2616394. circ. 2,053. Document type: bulletin.

346 KF1073.I5A137 US
SECTION 16 UPDATES. 1991. q. $295. Executive Press, Box 3895, San Francisco, CA 94119. TEL 510-685-5111. FAX 510-685-4802. Eds. Peter Romeo, Alan Dye. Document type: newsletter.

345 346.066 KF1432 US ISSN 0273-0685
SECURITIES AND FEDERAL CORPORATE LAW REPORT. 1979. 11/yr. $595. Clark - Boardman - Callaghan Company, Ltd., 375 Hudson St., New York, NY 10014. TEL 212-929-7500; 800-221-9428. FAX 212-924-0460. Ed. Harold S. Bloomenthal. index. (looseleaf format; back issues avail.) Indexed: C.L.I., L.R.I. Document type: newsletter.
Description: Features timely articles on topics of major concern in the securities and corporate law field.

SERIES ON INTERNATIONAL CORPORATE LAW. see *LAW — International Law*

346 US ISSN 8750-1104
SHEPARD'S CORPORATION LAW CITATIONS. 1983. 3 base vols. (plus q. suppl.). $480. Shepard's - McGraw-Hill, Inc., Box 35300, Colorado Springs, CO 80935-3530. TEL 800-525-2474.

346.066 US
SOVIET BUSINESS LAW; institutions, principles and processes. 1991. 2 base vols. (plus a. supplement). $180. Butterworth Legal Publishers (Salem) (Subsidiary of: Reed Elsevier plc), 8 Industrial Way, Bldg. C, Salem, NH 03079. TEL 800-548-4001. FAX 603-898-9664. Ed. Christopher Osakwe. (looseleaf format)

STOCKHOLDERS AND CREDITORS NEWS SERVICE CONCERNING L T V CORPORATION, ET AL; the national journal of record reporting details of the L T V bankruptcy. see *BUSINESS AND ECONOMICS — Investments*

TAX PLANNING FOR CORPORATE ACQUISITIONS. see *BUSINESS AND ECONOMICS — Public Finance, Taxation*

TAXATION AND ECONOMY. see *BUSINESS AND ECONOMICS — Banking And Finance*

346   US
TEXAS CORPORATION LAW. 1981. 3 base vols. (plus a. suppl.) $175. Butterworth Legal Publishers (Salem) (Subsidiary of: Reed Elsevier plc), 8 Industrial Way, Bldg. C, Salem, NH 03079. TEL 800-548-4001. FAX 603-898-9858. (looseleaf format)

346 332.04
TEXAS FORECLOSURE: LAW AND PRACTICE. 1984. base vol. (plus biennial suppl.). $95. Shepard's - McGraw-Hill, Inc., Box 35300, Colorado Springs, CO 80935-3530. TEL 800-525-2474.
Description: Covers issues such as bankruptcy considerations, sequestration, receivership, federal tax considerations, setoff, garnishment, sheriff's sales, landlord's liens, injunctions and property exemptions.

TRADE PRACTICES COMMISSION BULLETIN. see *BUSINESS AND ECONOMICS*

346   AT
TRADE PRACTICES LAW. 1989. 5/yr. in 3 vols. Aus.$435 with updates. Law Book Co. Ltd., 44-50 Waterloo Rd., North Ryde, N.S.W. 2113, Australia. TEL 02-887-0177. FAX 02-888-9706. TELEX ASBOOK 27995. Ed. J.D. Heydon. (looseleaf format)
Description: Examines restrictive trade practices, deceptive conduct and consumer protection with enforcement and remedies, with a full reproduction of the 1974 Trade Practices Act.

346   AT
▼**TRADE PRACTICES LAW JOURNAL**. 1993. 4/yr. Aus.$195. Law Book Co. Ltd., 44-50 Waterloo Rd., North Ryde, N.S.W. 2113, Australia. TEL 02-887-0177. FAX 02-888-9706. TELEX AHBOOK 27995. Ed. Ronald Desiatnik.
Formerly: Australasian Trade Practices Journal (ISSN 1039-3277)
Description: Exchanges ideas and information on the whole area of trade practices law.

346.066   US
U C GUIDE (YEAR). (Unemployment Compensation) a. $70 to non-members; members $35. Pennsylvania Chamber of Business and Industry, 417 Walnut St., Harrisburg, PA 17101. TEL 717-255-3252. FAX 717-255-3298.
Description: Provides employers with information on unemployment compensation, including analysis of methods of cost reduction.

346   US
UNIFORM COMMERCIAL CODE (LONGWOOD). 1988. a. $16. Gould Publications, 1333 N. U.S. Hwy. 17-92, Longwood, FL 32750-3724. TEL 407-695-9500. FAX 407-695-2906.
Description: Presents the complete Uniform Commerical Code with official comments and new articles, 4A funds transfers and 6-bulk sale.

346   US
UNIFORM COMMERCIAL CODE FILING GUIDE. 5 base vols. (plus q. updates). $593. U C C Guide Inc., Rte. 9W, Perrine Bldg., Box 338, Ravena, NY 12143. TEL 518-156-3366; 800-345-3822. FAX 800-822-0703. Eds. Jacqueline Lee, Glenn C. Relyea. (looseleaf format)

346   US
UNIFORM COMMERCIAL CODE: STATE VARIATIONS SERVICE. 3 base vols. (plus q. updates). (Pike & Fischer, Inc.) Clark - Boardman - Callaghan Company Ltd., 375 Hudson St., New York, NY 10014. TEL 212-929-7500; 800-221-9428. FAX 212-924-0460.
Description: Contains the full text of the UCC, official comments, and the variations between the official Code text and the version enacted in each state.

346   US
UNIFORM COMMERICAL CODE PAMPHLET. irreg. West Publishing Corp., 620 Opperman Dr., Eagan, MN 55123. TEL 612-687-8000; 612-687-8000. FAX 612-687-7302. Document type: trade publication.

346   UK   ISSN 1353-1247
U.S. BUSINESS LAW; a fortnightly digest of U.S. business law. 1994. s-a. B N A International, Inc. (Subsidiary of: The Bureau of National Affairs, Inc.), Heron House, 6th Fl., 10 Dean Farrar St., London SW1H 0DX, England. TEL 44-71-222-8831. FAX 44-71-222-5550. Ed. S. Joel Kolko. (back issues avail.)

346   US
U.S. DEPARTMENT OF JUSTICE. ANTITRUST DIVISION MANUAL. base vol., plus irreg. updates. $40 (foreign $50). U.S. Department of Justice, Antitrust Division, 10th St. & Constitution Ave., N.W., Washington, DC 20530. (Subscr. to: Superintendent of Documents, U.S. Government Printing Office, Box 317954, Pittsburgh, PA 15250-7954. TEL 202-783-3238. FAX 202-512-2233) (looseleaf format; back issues avail.) Document type: government publication.
Description: Describes the operating policies and procedures of the Antitrust Division.

346.73 347   US   ISSN 1045-3180
HD2743
VOTING BY INSTITUTIONAL INVESTORS ON CORPORATE GOVERNANCE ISSUES. 1987. a. Investor Responsibility Research Center, Inc., 1755 Massachusetts Ave., N.W., Washington, DC 20036.

346   US
WARREN'S FORMS OF AGREEMENTS. 1954. 3/yr. $810. Matthew Bender & Co., Inc., 11 Penn Plaza, New York, NY 10001. TEL 212-967-7707. FAX 212-244-3188. (Subscr. to: International Dept., 1275 Broadway, Albany, NY 12204) Ed. Martin D. Fern. circ. 4,000. (looseleaf format)
Description: Contains business forms with complete and alternative clauses for any transaction.

346   US
WASHINGTON STATE BAR ASSOCIATION. CORPORATE LAW DEPARTMENT NEWSLETTER. q. $15. Washington State Bar Association, Corporate Law Department, 500 Westin Bldg., 2001 Sixth Ave., Seattle, WA 98121. TEL 206-727-8239. FAX 206-727-8320. Document type: newsletter.

WASHINGTON TAXES; a taxpayer's manual for practice before the Department of Revenue. see *BUSINESS AND ECONOMICS — Public Finance, Taxation*

346   GW   ISSN 0935-6886
WIRTSCHAFT HEUTE; Zeitschrift fuer Auszubildende und Ausbilder im kaufmaennischen Bereich. m. DM.54. Nomos Verlagsgesellschaft mbH und Co. KG, Waldseestr. 3-5, 76530 Baden-Baden, Germany. TEL 07221-2104-0. FAX 07221-210427. TELEX 781201. (Subscr. to: Postfach 610, 76484 Baden-Baden, Germany) Document type: bulletin.

346 331
WORKERS' COMPENSATION NEWS AND FOUR-FORTY REPORT. irreg. (3-4/yr.). $27.50 to non-members. Florida Bar, 650 Apalachee Pkwy., Tallahassee, FL 32399-2300. TEL 904-561-5626. circ. 1,430. Document type: newsletter.

WORLD ARBITRATION & MEDIATION REPORT. see *LAW — International Law*

YEARBOOK COMMERCIAL ARBITRATION. see *LAW — International Law*

LAW — Criminal Law

see also Criminology and Law Enforcement

A C J S EMPLOYMENT BULLETIN. (Academy of Criminal Justice Sciences) see *BUSINESS AND ECONOMICS — Personnel Management*

A C J S PROGRAM BOOK. (Academy of Criminal Justice Sciences) see *EDUCATION — Higher Education*

ACTA CRIMINOLOGICA. see *CRIMINOLOGY AND LAW ENFORCEMENT*

345 365   FI   ISSN 0357-542X
ALIBI. m. FIM 225. Yhtyneet Kuvalehdet Oy, Maistraatinportti 1, FIN-00240 Helsinki, Finland. TEL 358-0-156-6524. FAX 358-0-156-6505. TELEX 121364. Ed. Antero Maunula. adv.: B&W page FIM 6700, color page FIM 9800. circ. 55,679.
Description: Focuses on criminal cases and legal issues.

345   US   ISSN 0066-0051
AMERICAN SERIES OF FOREIGN PENAL CODES. 1960. irreg., latest no.29. price varies. (Wayne State University Law School, Comparative Criminal Law Project) Fred B. Rothman & Co., 10368 W. Centennial Rd., Littleton, CO 80127. TEL 303-979-5657. FAX 303-978-1457. Ed. Edward M. Wise. (back issues avail.)
—BLDSC (0857.050000).

345   CN   ISSN 0821-7912
ANNUAL REVIEW OF CRIMINAL LAW (YEAR). 1982. a. Can.$90. Carswell, One Corporate Plaza, 2075 Kennedy Rd., Scarborough, ON M1T 3V4, Canada. TEL 416-609-8000. FAX 416-298-5094. Ed. Alan D. Gold.
Description: Key developments over the past year in the context of criminal law, criminal procedure, criminal evidence as well as the interaction of the Charter with the criminal process are highlighted and analyzed.

345   IT   ISSN 1120-687X
ARCHIVIO DELLA NUOVA PROCEDURA PENALE. 1990. bi-m. L.100000 (Europe L.150000; elsewhere L.200000) (effective 1994). Casa Editrice La Tribuna, Via Don Minzoni, 51, 29100 Piacenza, Italy. TEL 0523-759015. FAX 0523-757219.
Description: Covers doctrine, jurisprudence and legislation.

345   IT   ISSN 0004-0304
ARCHIVIO PENALE. 1945. q. L.110000 to individuals; institutions L.155000; foreign L.198000 (effective 1993). Edizioni Scientifiche Italiane S.p.A., Via Chiatamone 7, 80121 Naples, Italy. TEL 081-7645768. FAX 081-7646477.

AUSTRALIA. BUREAU OF STATISTICS. AUSTRALIAN CAPITAL TERRITORY COURTS. see *LAW — Abstracting, Bibliographies, Statistics*

AUSTRALIA. BUREAU OF STATISTICS. NEW SOUTH WALES OFFICE. CRIME AND SAFETY SURVEY, NEW SOUTH WALES. see *LAW — Abstracting, Bibliographies, Statistics*

AUSTRALIA. BUREAU OF STATISTICS. TASMANIAN OFFICE. COURT STATISTICS, TASMANIA. see *LAW — Abstracting, Bibliographies, Statistics*

AUSTRALIA. BUREAU OF STATISTICS. WESTERN AUSTRALIAN OFFICE. SUMMARY OF CRIMINAL COURT PROCEEDINGS, WESTERN AUSTRALIA. see *LAW — Abstracting, Bibliographies, Statistics*

345   US   ISSN 0889-9312
B N A CRIMINAL PRACTICE MANUAL. (Subseries of: Trial Practice Series) 1987. bi-w. $585. The Bureau of National Affairs, Inc., 1231 25th St., N.W., Washington, DC 20037. TEL 202-452-4200. FAX 202-822-8092. TELEX 285656 BNAI WSH. (Subscr. to: 9435 Key West Ave., Rockville, MD 20850. TEL 800-372-1033) Ed. Judith C. Mroczka. index. (looseleaf format; back issues avail.)
—CCC.
Description: Notification and reference service covering the entire court process from arrest through sentencing, and a newsletter covering developments in criminal law, evidence and procedures, and practice techniques.

345   GW   ISSN 0405-0517
BAYERISCHES OBERSTES LANDESGERICHT. ENTSCHEIDUNGEN IN STRAFSACHEN. 1951. irreg. C.H. Beck'sche Verlagsbuchhandlung, Wilhelmstr. 9, 80801 Munich, Germany. TEL 089-38189338. FAX 089-38189-398. (back issues avail.) Document type: monographic series.

LAW — CRIMINAL LAW

345   CN
BRITISH COLUMBIA DECISIONS - CRIMINAL CONVICTION AND SENTENCE CASES. 1972. m. Can.$280. Western Legal Publications. 301-1 Alexander St., Vancouver, BC V6A 1B2, Canada. TEL 604-687-5671. FAX 604-687-2796. (looseleaf format)
● Also available online.
Formerly: British Columbia Decisions - Criminal Cases (ISSN 0824-7242)
Description: Digests all available criminal decisions from the British Columbia Court of Appeal, Supreme Courts of British Columbia, as well as selected decisions from its Provincial Courts.

BRITISH PSYCHOLOGICAL SOCIETY. DIVISION OF CRIMINOLOGICAL & LEGAL PSYCHOLOGY. OCCASIONAL PAPERS. see *PSYCHOLOGY*

BUERGERRECHTE & POLIZEI. see *CRIMINOLOGY AND LAW ENFORCEMENT*

BULWARK. see *LAW — Civil Law*

345 364   US
CALIFORNIA CRIMINAL DEFENSE PRACTICE. 1981. 6 base vols. (plus irreg. supplements). $1200. Matthew Bender & Co., Inc., 11 Penn Plaza, New York, NY 10001. TEL 212-967-7707. Ed.Bd. (looseleaf format)
Description: Comprehensive exposition of California criminal law and procedure. Chapters are arranged chronologically, in topical order of criminal action, with discussion of substantive law and strategy and procedures available.

345 364   US   ISSN 0731-8820
CALIFORNIA CRIMINAL DEFENSE PRACTICE REPORTER. (Complements California Criminal Defense Practice) 1981. base vol. (plus m. updates). $240. Matthew Bender & Co., Inc., 11 Penn Plaza, New York, NY 10001. TEL 212-967-7707; 800-833-9844. (looseleaf format)
Description: Summarizes all important new criminal cases and statutes each month.

345   US   ISSN 0898-3623
KFC1155.A53C35
CALIFORNIA CRIMINAL LAW REPORTER. 1983. 26/yr. $327.50 for new subscr.; renewal $215. La Jolla Legal Publications, Inc., 5580 La Jolla Blvd., Ste. 116, La Jolla, CA 92037. TEL 619-236-0679. Ed. Patrick M. Ford. **Document type:** newsletter.

345   US
CALIFORNIA PENAL CODE. 1988. a. $19.95. Gould Publications, 1333 N. U.S. Hwy. 17-92, Longwood, FL 32750-3724. TEL 407-695-9500. FAX 407-695-2906. adv.; bk.rev. (looseleaf format)
Description: Contains laws governing crime and punishment, criminal procedure, imprisonment and the death penalty.

345   CN   ISSN 0008-3348
LAW
CANADIAN CRIMINAL CASES. 1898. w. Can.$119. Canada Law Book Inc., 240 Edward St., Aurora, ON L4G 3S9, Canada. TEL 905-841-6472. FAX 905-841-6472. Ed. E.L. Greenspan. index.
● Also available online.

345   CN
CANADIAN CRIMINAL EVIDENCE. base vol. (plus s-a. updates). Can.$182. Canada Law Book Inc., 240 Edward St., Aurora, ON L4G 3S9, Canada. TEL 905-841-6472. FAX 905-841-5085. Ed. Peter K. McWilliams. (looseleaf format)
Formerly: Canadian Criminal Law.

345   AT
CARTER'S CRIMINAL LAW OF QUEENSLAND. 2 base vols. (plus updates 3-4/yr.). $355. Butterworths, 271-273 Lane Cove Rd., P.O. Box 345, North Ryde, N.S.W. 2113, Australia. TEL 02-335-4444. FAX 02-335-4655. (looseleaf format)

345   US   ISSN 0744-9488
KF9602
CHAMPION. 1975. m. (10/yr.). $25. National Association of Criminal Defense Lawyers, 1627 K St., N.W., Ste. 12F, Washington, DC 20006-1702. FAX 202-331-8269. Ed. Richard Bing. adv. contact: Cathy Ziomek. bk.rev. circ. 5,000. **Document type:** trade publication.

345   US
CHECKLISTS FOR SEARCHES AND SEIZURES IN PUBLIC SCHOOLS. a. $49.50. Clark - Boardman - Callaghan Company Ltd., 375 Hudson St., New York, NY 10014. TEL 212-929-7500; 800-221-9428. FAX 212-924-0460. Eds. Jon M. Van Dyke, Melvin M. Sakurai.
Description: Explores the constitutional framework regulating how public school officials must conduct searches of students and seizures of contraband.

COALITION FOR PRISONERS' RIGHTS NEWSLETTER. see *CRIMINOLOGY AND LAW ENFORCEMENT*

CORPORATE CRIMINAL AND CONSTITUTIONAL LAW REPORTER. see *LAW — Corporate Law*

345 301   II
CRIME & SOCIETY. (Text in English) 1974. m. Rs.12($8) 305a, Hans Bhavan, Bahadur Shah Zafar Marg, New Delhi 110002, India. Ed. P.J. Koshy. adv. circ. 5,000.
Formerly: Path.
Description: News and current affairs.

345   UK   ISSN 0144-3321
CRIMINAL APPEAL REPORTS (SENTENCING). 1979. 4/yr. £140. Sweet & Maxwell, South Quay Plaza, 7th Fl., 183 Marsh Wall, London E14 9FT, England. TEL 071-538-8686. FAX 071-538-9508. Ed. Rebecca Hough. adv. contact: Jackie Wood.
Document type: bulletin.
—BLDSC (3487.346100).

345   US   ISSN 0887-7785
KF9602
CRIMINAL JUSTICE (CHICAGO). 1986. q. $33 (foreign $38). (American Bar Association, Criminal Justice Section) A B A Press, 750 N. Lake Shore Dr., Chicago, IL 60611-4497. TEL 312-988-6076. FAX 312-988-6281. Ed. Carole Smith. adv.; bk.rev. circ. 11,500. (also avail. in microform from UMI)
Document type: academic/scholarly publication, trade publication.
—BLDSC (3487.347000); Faxon; UnCover.
Description: Provides practical treatment of aspects of the criminal justice system and reports on legislative, policy-making and educational activities of the section.
Refereed Serial

CRIMINAL JUSTICE (SPRINGFIELD). see *CRIMINOLOGY AND LAW ENFORCEMENT*

345   US   ISSN 1043-7436
KFN6155.A15C75
CRIMINAL JUSTICE JOURNAL. 1989. 3/yr. $25 to non-members. New York State Bar Association, One Elk St., Albany, NY 12207-1096. TEL 518-463-3200. FAX 518-487-5699. adv.; bk.rev. circ. 1,600. (back issues avail.) **Document type:** newsletter.

345   US   ISSN 0734-0168
K3   CODEN: CJURE4
CRIMINAL JUSTICE REVIEW. 1976. s-a. $25 to individuals; institutions $30. Georgia State University, College of Public and Urban Affairs, Box 4018, Atlanta, GA 30302-4018. TEL 404-651-3515. adv.; bk.rev.; bibl. circ. 1,200. (also avail. in microfiche from UMI; microfilm from UMI; reprint service avail. from UMI) **Indexed:** Abstr.Bk.Rev.Curr.Leg.Per., C.L.I., CJPI, Crim.Just.Abstr., Leg.Per., Sage Pub.Admin.Abstr., Sage Urb.Stud.Abstr., SSCI.
—BLDSC (3487.351000); Faxon; UnCover; SWETS; UMI.
Description: Dedicated to presenting a broad perspective of criminal justice issues, institutions, and processes. Articles focus on trends, problems, and research on the regional and national levels.

345   US   ISSN 1047-1189
KF9215.C71
CRIMINAL LAW ADVOCACY REPORTER. 1982. 12/yr. $250. Matthew Bender & Co., Inc., 11 Penn Plaza, New York, NY 10001. TEL 212-967-7707. FAX 212-967-1069. index. (looseleaf format)

345   US   ISSN 0011-1317
K3
CRIMINAL LAW BULLETIN. 1964. 6/yr. $1331.50 (overseas $197.50) (effective 1994). Warren Gorham Lamont, One Penn Plaza, New York, NY 10119. TEL 212-971-5000. (Subscr. to: Warren Gorham Lamont, The Park Square Bldg., 31 St. James Ave., Boston, MA 02116-4112. TEL 800-950-1207) Ed. Fred Cohen. abstr.; index. (also avail. in microform from UMI,MIM; reprint service avail. from RRI,UMI) **Indexed:** C.L.I., CJPI, Crim.Just.Abstr., L.R.I., Leg.Cont., Leg.Per. **Document type:** trade publication.
—BLDSC (3487.352000); Faxon; UnCover; SWETS; UMI. **CCC.**
Description: Provides authoritative guidance and insights with current information about state, federal and Supreme Court decisions.
Refereed Serial

343 341   US   ISSN 1046-8374
K3
CRIMINAL LAW FORUM; an international journal. 1990. 3/yr. $45 (foreign $50) (effective 1993). Rutgers University, School of Law, Camden, 5th & Penn Streets, Camden, NJ 08102. TEL 609-757-6352. FAX 609-757-6487. (Co-sponsor: Society for the Reform of Criminal Law, CN) Ed. Roger S. Clark. adv.: B&W page $250; 6 x 9; adv. contact: Madeleine Sann. bk.rev.; bibl.; index. circ. 850. (back issues avail.) **Indexed:** Abstr.Crim.& Pen., Amer.Bibl.Slavic & E.Eur.Stud., ASSIA, C.C.L.P., C.L.I., CJPI, Crim.Just.Abstr., L.R.I., Leg.Per., P.A.I.S. **Document type:** academic/scholarly publication.
—BLDSC (3487.352500); Faxon; UnCover.
Description: Promotes criminal law theory, practice and reform, and the establishment of sound criminal justice principles throughout the world. Disseminates original articles, conference papers and reviews noteworthy documents prepared by governmental and public interest agencies.
Refereed Serial

345   AT   ISSN 0705-7377
HD9696.C63
CRIMINAL LAW IN NEW SOUTH WALES. VOLUME 1: INDICTABLE OFFENCES. 1971. 6/yr. in 2 vols. Aus.$395 with updates. Law Book Co. Ltd., 44-50 Waterloo Rd., North Ryde, N.S.W. 2113, Australia. TEL 02-887-0177. FAX 02-888-9706. TELEX ASBOOK 27995. Eds. R. Watson, H. Purnell. circ. 2,100. (looseleaf format)
Description: Standard practical reference on criminal law serious offences in New South Wales.

345   AT   ISSN 0705-7385
CRIMINAL LAW IN NEW SOUTH WALES. VOLUME 2: SUMMARY OFFENCES. 1978. 6/yr. in 3 vols. Aus.$494 with updates. Law Book Co. Ltd., 44-50 Waterloo Rd., North Ryde, N.S.W. 2113, Australia. TEL 02-887-0177. FAX 02-888-9706. TELEX ASBOOK 27995. Eds. R. Watson, R. Bartley. (looseleaf format; back issues avail.)
Description: Contains every summary offence created by statutes or regulation in New South Wales.

345   II   ISSN 0011-1325
CRIMINAL LAW JOURNAL; full reports of all reportable criminal cases of the High courts and the Supreme Court of India. 1904. m. Rs.288($96) All India Reporter Ltd., P.O. Box 209, Nagpur 440012, India. Ed. V.R. Manohar. adv.; bk.rev.; index. circ. 16,800. **Indexed:** C.L.I., L.R.I., Leg.Per.

345   AT   ISSN 0314-1160
K3
CRIMINAL LAW JOURNAL. 1977. bi-m. Aus.$195. Law Book Co. Ltd., 44-50 Waterloo Rd., North Ryde, N.S.W. 2112, Australia. TEL 02-887-0177. FAX 02-888-9706. TELEX ASBOOK 27995. **Indexed:** Aus.P.A.I.S., Leg.Cont.
—BLDSC (3487.354500); Faxon.
Description: Caters to all those who have an interest in criminal law - whether as legal practitioners, police or academics. Features cases, comments and legislation reviews.

345   US
CRIMINAL LAW NEWS (MADISON). 1985. irreg. (2-4/yr.). membership. State Bar of Wisconsin, Criminal Law Section, 402 W. Wilson St., Madison, WI 53703. TEL 608-257-3838. FAX 608-257-5502. circ. 700. (back issues avail.) **Document type:** newsletter.

LAW — CRIMINAL LAW

345 US
KFC1100.A1C7
CRIMINAL LAW NEWS (SAN FRANCISCO). 1977. q. membership. State Bar of California, Criminal Law Section, 555 Franklin St., San Francisco, CA 94102. TEL 415-561-8290. FAX 415-561-8228. (looseleaf format) **Document type:** newsletter.

345 US
CRIMINAL LAW NEWSLETTER (EUGENE). 1986. s-m. $65. Oregon Criminal Defense Lawyers Association, 44 W. Broadway, Ste. 403, Eugene, OR 97401. TEL 503-686-8716. Ed. Robert C. Homan. s-a. index. circ. 340. (back issues avail.) **Document type:** newsletter.

345 US ISSN 0888-7012
CRIMINAL LAW NEWSLETTER (LA JOLLA). 1968. 20/yr. $95. La Jolla Legal Publications, Inc., 5580 La Jolla Blvd., Ste. 116, La Jolla, CA 92037. TEL 619-236-0679. Ed. Sheldon Portman. index. (back issues avail.) **Document type:** newsletter.

345 US ISSN 0145-7322
KF9210.3
CRIMINAL LAW OUTLINE. 1966. a. $18 (diskette $29.95) (effective 1993). National Judicial College, Judicial College Bldg., University of Nevada, Reno, NV 89557. TEL 702-784-6747. FAX 702-784-4234. Ed. William A. Grimes. circ. 5,000. (also avail. in diskette format)
Description: Guide to U.S. Supreme Court decisions on the Fourth, Fifth, Sixth and Eighth Amendments of the Constitution and on miscellaneous problems relating to criminal law and procedure.

345 CN ISSN 0011-1333
CRIMINAL LAW QUARTERLY; a Canadian journal of criminal law for judges, magistrates, lawyers and police officers. 1958. q. Can.$110. Canada Law Book Inc., 240 Edward St., Aurora, ON L4G 3S9, Canada. TEL 905-841-6472. FAX 905-841-5085. Ed. A.W. Mewett. bk.rev.; charts; illus.; index. **Indexed:** C.L.I., CJPI, Crim.Just.Abstr., Curr.Cont., Ind.Can.L.P.L., L.R.I., Leg.Per., SSCI.
—BLDSC (3487.356000); Faxon; UnCover.

345 US ISSN 0011-1341
KF9615
CRIMINAL LAW REPORTER. 1967. w. $636. The Bureau of National Affairs, Inc., 1231 25th St., N.W., Washington, DC 20037. TEL 202-452-4200. FAX 202-822-8092. TELEX 285656 BNAI WSH. (Subscr. to: 9435 Key West Ave., Rockville, MD 20850. TEL 800-372-1033) Ed. Robert L. Goebes. bk.rev.; index. (also avail. in microform; back issues avail.) **Indexed:** C.L.I., Chic.Per.Ind., L.R.I.
—CCC.
Description: Notification service covering court decisions, federal legislative activities, and administrative developments in the field of criminal law.

345 UK ISSN 0011-135X
K3
CRIMINAL LAW REVIEW. 1954. m. £92. Sweet & Maxwell, South Quay Plaza, 7th Fl., 183 Marsh Wall, London E14 9FT, England. TEL 071-538-8686. FAX 071-538-9508. Ed. Rebecca Hough. adv. contact: Jackie Wood. bk.rev.; abstr.; bibl. **Indexed:** Br.Hum.Ind., C.L.I., CJPI, Crim.Just.Abstr., Curr.Cont., L.R.I., Leg.Cont., Leg.Per., SSCI. **Document type:** bulletin.
—BLDSC (3487.358000); Faxon; UnCover; SWETS; UMI. **CCC.**

345 AT
CRIMINAL LAW VICTORIA. base vol. (plus updates 6/yr.). $315. Butterworths, 271-273 Lane Cove Rd., P.O. Box 345, North Ryde, N.S.W. 2113, Australia. TEL 02-335-4444. FAX 02-335-4655. (looseleaf format)

345 CN
CRIMINAL LAWYERS COMMONPLACE BOOK. s-a. Can.$165. Butterworths Canada Ltd., Part of the Reed Elsevier group, 75 Clegg Rd., Markham, ON L6G 1A1, Canada. TEL 905-479-2665. FAX 905-479-2826. Ed. Paul Richard Meyers. (looseleaf format)
Description: For reference on criminal practice.

345 UK ISSN 1352-4542
▼**CRIMINAL LITIGATION.** 1993. a. £15. Jordan Publishing Ltd., 21 St. Thomas St., Bristol BS1 6JS, England. TEL 0272-230600. FAX 0272-250486. Ed. John Clegg. **Document type:** academic/scholarly publication.

345 CN
CRIMINAL PLEADINGS AND PRACTICE IN CANADA. base vol. (plus s-a. updates). Can.$182. Canada Law Book Inc., 240 Edward St., Aurora, ON L4G 3S9, Canada. TEL 905-841-6472. FAX 905-841-5085. Ed. E.G. Ewaschuk. (looseleaf format)

345 AT
CRIMINAL PRACTICE & PROCEDURE N S W. 3 base vols. (plus updates 6/yr.). $390. Butterworths, 271-273 Lane Cove Rd., P.O. Box 345, North Ryde, N.S.W. 2113, Australia. TEL 02-335-4444. FAX 02-335-4655. (looseleaf format)
Formerly: Justices Act and Summary Offences N S W.

345 US ISSN 1044-3770
K3.R562
CRIMINAL PRACTICE LAW REVIEW. 1988. q. $80. Michie Company, Box 7587, Charlottesville, VA 22906-7587. TEL 804-972-7600. FAX 804-972-7666. (looseleaf format; back issues avail.) **Document type:** newsletter.

345 CN
CRIMINAL PROCEDURE; Canadian law and practice. a. Can.$220. Butterworths Canada Ltd., Part of the Reed Elsevier group, 75 Clegg Rd., Markham, ON L6G 1A1, Canada. TEL 905-479-2665. FAX 905-479-2826. Ed.Bd. (looseleaf format)
Description: Comprehensive review on all aspects of criminal law and criminal practice.

345 US
CRIMINAL PROCEDURE CHECKLISTS. a. $75. Clark - Boardman - Callaghan Company Ltd., 375 Hudson St., New York, NY 10014. TEL 212-929-7500; 800-221-9428. FAX 212-924-0460. Eds. Michele G. Hermann, Barbara Bergman.
Description: Contains major doctrines and cases for criminal and civil rights lawyers and law enforcement professionals involved in all phases of criminal work.

345 US
CRIMINAL PROCEDURE HANDBOOK. a. $80. Clark - Boardman - Callaghan Company Ltd., 375 Hudson St., New York, NY 10014. TEL 212-929-7500; 800-221-9428. FAX 212-924-0460. Ed. James G. Carr.
Description: Covers the latest developments and trends in criminal procedure.

345 CN ISSN 0383-9494
CRIMINAL REPORTS (4TH SERIES). 1967. 8 vols./yr. Can.$110. Carswell, One Corporate Plaza, 2075 Kennedy Rd., Scarborough, ON M1T 3V4, Canada. TEL 416-609-8000. FAX 416-298-5094. Ed. Don Stuart. adv. contact: M. Lalani. cum.index. **Indexed:** C.L.I., Ind.Can.L.P.L., L.R.I.
Description: Features reporting of judgments covering criminal offences from every court level. Includes annotations and articles by leading authorities in the field.

345 CN
▼**CRIMINAL SENTENCING DIGEST.** 1993. irreg. Can.$150. Butterworths Canada Ltd., Part of the Reed Elsevier group, 75 Clegg Rd., Markham, ON L6G 1A1, Canada. TEL 905-479-2265. FAX 905-479-2826.

345 CN
DEFENCE LAWYERS TRIAL BOOK. q. Can.$175. Butterworths Canada Ltd., Part of the Reed Elsevier group, 75 Clegg Rd., Markham, ON L6G 1A1, Canada. TEL 905-479-2665. FAX 905-479-2826. (looseleaf format)
Description: Digest of recent leading cases reflecting the structure of the criminal code on issues affecting the defense of an action at both the trial and appellate court stages.

345 US
DEFENDING D W IS IN WASHINGTON. 1987. base vol. (plus suppl.). $115. Butterworth Legal Publishers (Salem) (Subsidiary of: Reed Elsevier plc), 8 Industrial Way, Bldg. C, Salem, NH 03079. TEL 800-548-4001. FAX 603-898-9858. Eds. Douglas L. Cowan, Stephen W. Hayne. (looseleaf format)

345 US ISSN 1047-1758
KF851.A3D44
DEFENSE CONTRACT LITIGATION REPORTER; covers defense procurement fraud litigation as well as False Claim Acts (Qui Tam) litigation. 1988. s-m. $800. Andrews Publications, 1646 West Chester Pike, Box 1000, Westtown, PA 19395. TEL 215-399-6600; 800-345-1101. FAX 215-399-6610. Ed. Donna Higgins. bibl.; stat.; cum.index every 6 mos. (looseleaf format; back issues avail.) **Document type:** newsletter.

364 NE ISSN 0045-9879
DELIKT EN DELINKWENT; tijdschrift voor strafrecht. 1970. 10/yr. fl.0.275 per page. Gouda Quint B.V., P.O. Box 1148, 6801 MK Arnhem, Netherlands. TEL 3185-454762. FAX 3185-514509. Ed.Bd. bk.rev.; abstr.; bibl. (also avail. in looseleaf format)
—SWETS.
Description: Criminal law journal of the Netherlands with abstracts of important decisions of the Dutch High Court.

345 NE ISSN 0928-9569
▼**EUROPEAN JOURNAL OF CRIME, CRIMINAL LAW AND CRIMINAL JUSTICE.** (Text in English) 1993. 4/yr. fl.265($143) (effective 1994). Kluwer Law and Taxation Publishers (Subsidiary of: Wolters Kluwer N.V.), P.O. Box 23, 7400 GA Deventer, Netherlands. TEL 31-5700-47261. FAX 31-5700-22244. TELEX 49295 KLUDV NL. (Dist. by: Libresso Distribution Centre, P.O. Box 23, 7400 GA Deventer, Netherlands. TEL 31-5700-33155. FAX 31-5700-33834; In N. America: Kluwer Law and Taxation Publishers, 675 Massachusetts Ave., Cambridge, MA 02139. TEL 617-354-0140. FAX 617-354-8595) Eds. C.J.C.F. Fijnaut, G. Kaiser. **Document type:** academic/scholarly publication.
—BLDSC (3829.728242).
Description: Provides an international forum for the discussion of policy and research relating to crime, criminal law and criminal justice in a European context, including coverage of European institutions, case law of the European Court and European Commission on Human Rights, European Communities policies and activities.

EUROPEAN JOURNAL ON CRIMINAL POLICY AND RESEARCH. see *CRIMINOLOGY AND LAW ENFORCEMENT*

345 US
FEDERAL CRIMINAL CODE AND RULES. 1946. a. West Publishing Corp., 620 Opperman Dr., Eagan, MN 55123. TEL 612-687-7302; 800-328-9352. FAX 612-687-7302. **Document type:** trade publication.

345 US
FEDERAL CRIMINAL LAW HANDBOOK. 1989. a. $19. Gould Publications, 1333 N. U.S. Hwy. 17-92, Longwood, FL 32750-3724. TEL 407-695-9500. FAX 407-695-2906. adv.; bk.rev. (looseleaf format)
Description: Contains the complete federal rules of criminal procedure, crimes and criminal procedure, drug abuse prevention and control.

345 364 US
FEDERAL DRUG ENFORCEMENT LAW BULLETIN. 1991. 9/yr. $195. Paks Publishing Group, Box 134, Pitman, NJ 08071. TEL 609-582-3940. FAX 609-582-3940. Ed. Matthew Christopher. index. (looseleaf format; back issues avail.) **Document type:** newsletter.
Description: Reports on critical federal appellate court drug law rulings, for defense attorneys, prosecutors and others handling drug trafficking criminal cases.

345 US
FEDERAL SENTENCING GUIDELINES MANUAL. 1988. a. West Publishing Corp., 620 Opperman Dr., Eagan, MN 55123. TEL 612-687-8000; 800-328-9352. FAX 612-687-7302. **Document type:** trade publication.

LAW — CRIMINAL LAW

345 **US**
KF200.F637
FLORIDA BAR. CRIMINAL LAW SECTION NEWSLETTER. 1979. irreg. (3-4/yr.) membership. Florida Bar, Criminal Law Section, 650 Apalachee Pkwy., Tallahassee, FL 32399-2300. TEL 904-561-5628. circ. 2,190. **Document type:** newsletter.

345 **US**
FLORIDA CRIMINAL DEFENSE TRIAL MANUAL. 1972. 5 base vols. (plus suppl. 5-6/yr.). $320. Butterworth Legal Publishers (Salem) (Subsidiary of: Reed Elsevier plc), 8 Industrial Way, Bldg. C, Salem, NH 03079. TEL 800-548-4001. FAX 603-898-9858. (looseleaf format)

345 **US**
FLORIDA CRIMINAL DISCOVERY & PRETRIAL MOTIONS. 1979. base vol. (plus suppl. 2-3/yr.). $80. Butterworth Legal Publishers (Salem) (Subsidiary of: Reed Elsevier plc), 8 Industrial Way, Bldg. C, Salem, NH 03079. TEL 800-548-4001. FAX 603-898-9858. (looseleaf format)

345 **US**
FLORIDA CRIMINAL PROCEDURE SERVICE. 1980. base vol. (plus a. suppl.). $80. Butterworth Legal Publishers (Salem) (Subsidiary of: Reed Elsevier plc), 8 Industrial Way, Bldg. C, Salem, NH 03079. TEL 800-548-4001. FAX 603-898-9858. (looseleaf format)

345 **US**
FLORIDA CRIMINAL SENTENCING LAW. 1984. 2 base vols. (plus suppl. 2-3/yr.). $160. Butterworth Legal Publishers (Salem) (Subsidiary of: Reed Elsevier plc), 8 Industrial Way, Bldg. C, Salem, NH 03079. TEL 800-548-4001. FAX 603-898-9858. (looseleaf format)

345 **IT** **ISSN 0015-7864**
FORO PENALE. * 1945. q. L.7000. Libreria Scientifica Editrice, Corso Umberto I 38-40, Naples, Italy. Ed.Bd. index. circ. 800.

345 **GW**
FORSCHUNGSREIHE KRIMINAL-WISSENSCHAFTEN. 1980. irreg., vol.16, 1993. DM.98. Schmidt-Roemhild Verlag, Mengstr. 16, 23552 Luebeck, Germany. TEL 0451-1605-0. FAX 0451-1605253. Ed. Friedrich Geerds. **Document type:** monographic series.

FORUM (VALPARAISO). see LAW — Constitutional Law

345 **US**
GILBERT LAW SUMMARIES. CRIMINAL LAW. irreg., 14th ed., 1988. $13.95. Harcourt Brace Legal & Professional Publications, Inc., 176 W. Adams, Ste. 2100, Chicago, IL 60603. TEL 312-853-3662.

345 **US** **ISSN 0193-8010**
KF9619.3
GILBERT LAW SUMMARIES. CRIMINAL PROCEDURE. 1968. irreg., 13th ed., 1991. $14.95. Harcourt Brace Legal & Professional Publications, Inc., 176 W. Adams, Ste. 2100, Chicago, IL 60603. TEL 312-853-3662.
    Formerly: Criminal Practices (ISSN 0193-922X)

345 **IT** **ISSN 0017-0658**
GIUSTIZIA PENALE. 1895. m. L.70000. Giustizia Penale s.r.l. Via Giovanni Nicotera 10, Rome, Italy. charts; stat.

345 **NE** **ISSN 0928-9313**
▼**GLOBAL JOURNAL ON CRIME AND CRIMINAL LAW.** 1993. 2/yr. $75 (effective 1994). Tilburg University, Tilburg Foreign Law Review Institute, P.O. Box 91053, 5000 LE Tilburg, Netherlands. TEL 31-13-669111. (Dist. in N. America by: Wm. W. Gaunt & Sons, Inc, 3011 Gulf Dr., Holmes Beach, FL 34217. TEL 800-942-8683. FAX 813-778-5252)
    Description: Covers issues pertaining to international criminal law, including conventions, treaties, and new developments within the UN and the EC.

GUIDE TO S E C CRIMINAL CASES. see BUSINESS AND ECONOMICS — Investments

345 **US**
ILLINOIS CRIMINAL LAW; a survey of crimes and defenses. 1986. base vol. (plus suppl.). $110. Butterworth Legal Publishers (Salem) (Subsidiary of: Reed Elsevier plc), 8 Industrial Way, Bldg. C, Salem, NH 03079. TEL 800-548-4001. FAX 603-898-9858. Ed. John F. Decker.

345 **US** **ISSN 1049-5002**
ILLINOIS CRIMINAL LAW AND PROCEDURE. Key Title: Criminal Law & Procedure of Illinois. 1988. a. $16.95. Gould Publications, 1333 N. U.S. Hwy. 17-92, Longwood, FL 32750-3724. TEL 407-695-9500. FAX 407-695-2906. adv.; bk.rev. (looseleaf format)
    Description: Presents Chapter 38 complete and unannotated, and important parts of Chapters 23, 37, 56 1/2, 70, 110, 110A, and 111 1/2.

345 **US**
ILLINOIS CRIMINAL PROCEDURE. 1987. base vol. (plus suppl.). $95. Butterworth Legal Publishers (Salem) (Subsidiary of: Reed Elsevier plc), 8 Industrial Way, Bldg. C, Salem, NH 03079. TEL 800-548-4001. FAX 603-898-9858. Ed. Ralph Ruebner.
    Description: Analyzes procedural rules and studies the effect of state statutes, rules and case law on criminal procedure.

345 **US**
ILLINOIS CRIMINAL TRIAL EVIDENCE. (2nd ed., 1992) 1986. base vol. (plus irreg. supplements). $75. Butterworth Legal Publishers (Salem) (Subsidiary of: Reed Elsevier plc), 8 Industrial Way, Bldg. C, Salem, NH 03079. TEL 800-548-4001. FAX 603-898-9858. Ed. Ralph Ruebner.
    Description: Practical, analytical guide to the evidentiary rules applicable in Illinois criminal trials.

345 **II**
INDIAN JOURNAL OF CRIMINOLOGY & CRIMINALISTICS. (Text in English) q. Rs.50($18) Government of India, Department of Publications, Civil Lines, Delhi 110 054, India. **Document type:** government publication.

345 **NE**
▼**INTERNATIONAL ENCYCLOPAEDIA OF LAWS. CRIMINAL LAW.** (Text in English) 1993. base vol. (plus irreg. updates). fl.200($115) (effective 1994). Kluwer Law and Taxation Publishers (Subsidiary of: Wolters Kluwer N.V.), P.O. Box 23, 7400 GA Deventer, Netherlands. TEL 31-5700-47261. FAX 31-5700-22244. TELEX 49295 KLUDV NL. (Dist. by: Libresso Distribution Centre, P.O. Box 23, 7400 GA Deventer, Netherlands. TEL 31-5700-33155. FAX 31-5700-33834; In N. America: Kluwer Law and Taxation Publishers, 675 Massachusetts Ave., Cambridge, MA 02139. TEL 617-354-0140. FAX 617-354-8595) Eds. Lieven Dupont, Cyrillus Fijnaut. (looseleaf format) **Document type:** monographic series.
    Description: Presents studies of the principles of substantive criminal law, criminal procedure and sanctions in individual countries, from an international, comparative perspective; also discusses European Economic Community criminal law, mutual assistance, and jurisprudence of the European Court and European Commission of Human Rights.

INTERNATIONAL TRADE: AVOIDING CRIMINAL RISKS. see LAW — International Law

IOWA CRIMINAL LAW BULLETIN. see CRIMINOLOGY AND LAW ENFORCEMENT

345 **IE** **ISSN 0791-539X**
IRISH CRIMINAL LAW JOURNAL. 1991. s.a. I£32($60) The Round Hall Press, Kill Lane, Blackrock, Co. Dublin, Ireland. TEL 2892922. FAX 2893072. Ed. Shane Murphy. circ. 350 (controlled). **Document type:** bulletin.
    —BLDSC (4571.273500).
    Description: Articles, law reports and case references to the leading decisions in this area.

ISSUES IN CHILD ABUSE ACCUSATIONS. see CHILDREN AND YOUTH — About

ISSUES IN CRIMINOLOGICAL AND LEGAL PSYCHOLOGY. see PSYCHOLOGY

JAIL AND PRISONER LAW BULLETIN. see CRIMINOLOGY AND LAW ENFORCEMENT

345 **UK** **ISSN 0047-2352**
HV7231 CODEN: JCJUDJ
JOURNAL OF CRIMINAL JUSTICE; an international journal. 1973. 6/yr. £250($385) (effective 1994). Elsevier Science Ltd., Pergamon, P.O. Box 800, Kidlington, Oxford, OX5 1DX, England. TEL 44-865-843000. FAX 44-865-843010. (Subscr. in U.S. and Canada to: Elsevier Science, 660 White Plaisn Rd., Tarrytown, NY 10591-5153. TEL 914-524-9200. FAX 914-333-2444) Ed. Kent B. Joscelyn. adv.; bk.rev.; charts; illus.; index. circ. 3,000. (also avail. in microform from UMI; reprint service avail. from UMI) **Indexed:** Abstr.Bk.Rev.Curr.Leg.Per., ASSIA, C.L.I., CJPI, Crim.Just.Abstr., Curr.Cont., L.R.I., Leg.Per., Mid.East Abstr.& Ind., P.A.I.S., Psychol.Abstr., SSCI. **Document type:** academic/scholarly publication.
    —BLDSC (4965.530000); Faxon; UnCover; SWETS; UMI. **CCC.**
    Description: Concerned with all aspects of the criminal justice system, and the relationships of individual elements to the entire process. For both legal practitioners and academicians.
    Refereed Serial

345 **JA** **ISSN 0022-0191**
JOURNAL OF CRIMINAL LAW/KEIHO ZASSHI. (Text in Japanese; title and contents page in English) 1950. q. $28.75. Criminal Law Society of Japan - Nihon Keiho Gakkai, c/o Faculty of Law, University of Tokyo, Motofuji-cho, Bunkyo-ku, Tokyo, Japan. adv.; index. circ. 1,000. **Indexed:** C.L.I.

345 **UK** **ISSN 0022-0183**
LAW
JOURNAL OF CRIMINAL LAW. 1937. q. £75($140) Pageant Publishing, 5 Turners Wood, London NW11 6DT, England. TEL 081-455-3703. FAX 081-209-0726. (Dist. by: Baileys Management Services, 127 Sandgate Rd., Folkestone, Kent CT20 2BL, England) Ed. Neil McKittrick. adv.; bk.rev.; index. circ. 600. (reprint service avail. from KTO) **Indexed:** ASSIA, C.L.I., L.R.I. **Document type:** academic/scholarly publication.
    —BLDSC (4965.580000); Faxon; SWETS. **CCC.**
    Description: Notes and comments on recent cases dealing with the practice of criminal law.

JOURNAL OF CRIMINAL LAW & CRIMINOLOGY. see CRIMINOLOGY AND LAW ENFORCEMENT

345 **CN**
JUDICIAL INTERIM RELEASE: BAIL MANUAL. a. Can.$180. Butterworths Canada Ltd., Part of the Reed Elsevier group, 75 Clegg Rd., Markham, ON L6G 1A1, Canada. TEL 905-479-2665. FAX 905-479-2826. Ed. K.R. Hamilton. (looseleaf format)
    Description: Complete coverage of bail in Canadian law; organized by section and subsection of the Criminal Code.

345 **CN**
THE JURY; a handbook of law and procedure. 1989. a. Can.$95. Butterworths Canada Ltd., Part of the Reed Elsevier group, 75 Clegg Rd., Markham, ON L6G 1A1, Canada. TEL 905-479-2665. FAX 905-479-2826. Ed. Balfour Q.H. Der. (looseleaf format)
    Description: Examines the role of the jury in a criminal trial.

345 **UK** **ISSN 1351-5756**
K10
JUSTICE OF THE PEACE AND LOCAL GOVERNMENT LAW. 1837. w. £125 (typically set in Sep.). Justice of the Peace Ltd., Little London, Chichester, W. Sussex PO19 1PG, England. TEL 0243-787841. FAX 0243-779278. Ed. F. Davies. adv.; bk.rev.; stat.; index. (also avail. in microform from UMI; reprint service avail. from UMI) **Indexed:** ASSIA. **Document type:** newsletter.
    —BLDSC (5075.648000); UnCover; UMI.
    Formerly: Justice of the Peace (ISSN 0141-5859)
    Description: Presents commentary on magisterial and criminal law.

345 346.01 **US** **ISSN 0276-9603**
JUVENILE LAW REPORTS. 1979. m. $115. Knehans-Miller Publications, Box 88, Warrensburg, MO 64093. TEL 816-429-1102. Ed. Dane C. Miller. index. (looseleaf format; back issues avail.) **Document type:** trade publication.
    Description: Summaries and verbatim excerpts of all Federal and State Appellate Court decisions involving juveniles. Indexed by subject and jurisdiction.

LAW — CRIMINAL LAW

345   US   ISSN 1071-7412
LAW ENFORCEMENT PERSONNEL NOTES. m. $70. Nyper Publications, Box 662, Latham, NY 12110. TEL 800-281-8582. FAX 518-456-8582. Ed. Harvey Randall. (back issues avail.) **Document type:** newsletter.
    Description: Discusses legal developments concerning police and corrections personnel.

345   US
LAW OF PROBATION AND PAROLE. 1983. base vol. (plus a. suppl.). $95. Shepard's - McGraw-Hill, Inc., Box 35300, Colorado Springs, CO 80935-3530. TEL 800-525-2474.
    Description: Covers legal issues such as parole granting, rescission, modification and revocation proceedings.

345   UK   ISSN 0952-1038
LAW REPORTS OF THE COMMONWEALTH. CRIMINAL LAW REPORTS. 1985. a. Butterworth & Co. (Publishers) Ltd. (Subsidiary of: Reed Elsevier plc), 88 Kingsway, London WC2B 6AB, England. TEL 071-405-6900. FAX 071-405-1332. TELEX 95678. (US addr.: Butterworth Legal Publishers, 90 Stiles Rd., Salem, NH 03079. TEL 603-898-9664) Ed.Bd.

THE MCGRUFFLETTER; the nation's crime prevention newsletter. see *CRIMINOLOGY AND LAW ENFORCEMENT*

343   II
MADRAS LAW JOURNAL (CRIMINAL). (Text in English) 1957. fortn. Rs.200 (effective 1991). Madras Law Journal Office, Box 604, Mylapore, Madras 4, India. Ed. R. Narayanaswamy. bibl.

345   AT
MAGISTRATES' COURT PRACTICE SOUTH AUSTRALIA. 1979. base vol. (plus updates 4/yr.). Aus.$195. Law Book Co. Ltd., 44-50 Waterloo Rd., North Ryde, N.S.W. 2113, Australia. TEL 02-887-0177. FAX 02-888-9706. TELEX ASBOOK-27995. Eds. A. Cannon, G. Hiskey. (looseleaf format)
    Formerly (until Aug. 1992): Hannan's Local and District Criminal Courts Practice (ISSN 0727-7938)
    Description: Contains all essential legislation and practical material for practice in the civil jurisdiction of the Magistrates Court in South Australia.

345   US
MAINE CRIMINAL PRACTICE. (2nd ed., 1992) 1985. 3 base vols. (plus irreg. supplements). $165. Butterworth Legal Publishers (Salem) (Subsidiary of: Reed Elsevier plc), 8 Industrial Way, Bldg. C, Salem, NH 03079. TEL 800-548-4001. FAX 603-898-9858. (looseleaf format)

MANITOBA DECISIONS - CIVIL AND CRIMINAL CASES. see *LAW — Judicial Systems*

345   CN   ISSN 0527-7892
MARTIN'S ANNUAL CRIMINAL CODE. a. Can.$62. Canada Law Book Inc., 240 Edward St., Aurora, ON L4G 3S9, Canada. TEL 905-841-6472. FAX 905-841-5085. Ed. Edward L. Greenspan. adv. contact: Mary Cull.

345   CN
MARTIN'S CRIMINAL CODE, COUNSEL EDITION. base vol. (plus q. updates). Can.$112. Canada Law Book Inc., 240 Edward St., Aurora, ON L4G 3S9, Canada. TEL 905-841-6472. FAX 905-841-5085. Ed. Edward L. Greenspan. adv. contact: Mary Cull. (looseleaf format)
    Description: Provides access to the latest cases and statute amendments.

345 364   CN   ISSN 0710-1805
MARTIN'S RELATED CRIMINAL STATUTES. biennial. Can.$57. Canada Law Book Inc., 240 Edward St., Aurora, ON L4G 3S9, Canada. TEL 905-841-6472. FAX 905-841-5085. Ed. Edward L. Greenspan. adv. contact: Mary Cull.

345 364   US
MASSACHUSETTS CRIMINAL DEFENSE. 1990. 2 base vols. (plus a. suppl.). $130. Butterworth Legal Publishers (Salem) (Subsidiary of: Reed Elsevier plc), 8 Industrial Way, Bldg. C, Salem, NH 03079. TEL 800-548-4001. FAX 603-898-9858. Ed. Eric D. Blumenson.

345   US
MINNESOTA CRIMES AND DEFENSES. 1991. 3 base vols. (plus supplements). $225. Butterworth Legal Publishers (Salem) (Subsidiary of: Reed Elsevier plc), 8 Industrial Way, Bldg. C, Salem, NH 03079. TEL 800-548-4001. FAX 603-898-9858. Ed.Bd. (looseleaf format) **Document type:** academic/scholarly publication.
    Description: Provides comprehensive current analysis of Minnesota criminal law, including discussion of substantive criminal offenses under the Minnesota Criminal Code, and relevant statutes pertaining to DWI, controlled substances, pornography, taxes and the environment. Lists applicable defenses, including general defenses of common law, statutory basis, and constitutional origin.

345   US
MINNESOTA CRIMINAL LAW DIGEST. 1982. 3 base vols. (plus suppl. 6/yr.). $190. Butterworth Legal Publishers (Salem) (Subsidiary of: Reed Elsevier plc), 8 Industrial Way, Bldg. C, Salem, NH 03079. TEL 800-548-4001. FAX 603-898-9858. Ed.Bd. (looseleaf format)
    Description: Covers state statutes, rules of criminal procedure and case law as well as federal court decisions.

NARCOTICS LAW BULLETIN. see *CRIMINOLOGY AND LAW ENFORCEMENT*

NATIONAL BULLETIN ON POLICE MISCONDUCT. see *CRIMINOLOGY AND LAW ENFORCEMENT*

345   GW   ISSN 0720-1753
NEUE ZEITSCHRIFT FUER STRAFRECHT. 1981. m. DM.238 (students DM.214). C.H. Beck'sche Verlagsbuchhandlung, Wilhelmstr. 9, 80801 Munich, Germany. TEL 089-38189-338. FAX 089-38189-398. TELEX 5215085-BECK-D. Ed.Bd. adv.: B&W page DM.2350, color page DM.4700; trim 260 x 186. circ. 5,100. (back issues avail.) **Document type:** bulletin.
—SWETS.

340   US
NEW HAMPSHIRE CRIMINAL CODE. a. $20. Butterworth Legal Publishers (Salem) (Subsidiary of: Reed Elsevier plc), 8 Industrial Way, Bldg. C, Salem, NH 03079. TEL 800-548-4001. FAX 603-898-9858. Ed.Bd.

195
NEW HAMPSHIRE PRACTICE SERIES. CRIMINAL PRACTICE AND PROCEDURE. (2nd ed., 1991) 1981. 3 base vols. (plus irreg. supplements). $195. Butterworth Legal Publishers (Salem) (Subsidiary of: Reed Elsevier plc), 8 Industrial Way, Bldg. C, Salem, NH 03079. TEL 800-548-4001. FAX 603-898-9858. Ed.Bd.
    Description: Covers pre-arrest investigation, identification procedure, criminal proceedings, trial and sentencing approaches, and appeal and parole practices.

345   US
NEW JERSEY CRIMINAL JUSTICE CODE. 1988. a. $16.95. Gould Publications, 1333 N. U.S. Hwy. 17-92, Longwood, FL 32750-3724. TEL 407-695-9500. FAX 607-695-2906. adv.; bk.rev. (looseleaf format)
    Description: Contains NJ criminal laws.

345   US
NEW JERSEY STATE BAR ASSOCIATION. CRIMINAL LAW SECTION NEWSLETTER. 1966. irreg. New Jersey State Bar Association, Criminal Law Section, One Constitution Sq., New Brunswick, NJ 08901-1500. TEL 908-249-5000. FAX 908-249-2815. Ed. Brian P. Blatz. bk.rev. circ. 600. (back issues avail.) **Document type:** newsletter.

345 364.6   US
NEW YORK (STATE). DIVISION OF CRIMINAL JUSTICE SERVICES. FELONY PROCESSING QUARTERLY REPORT. 1974. q. free. Division of Criminal Justice Services, Executive Park Tower, Stuyvesant Plaza, Albany, NY 12203.

345   US
NEW YORK CORRECTION LAW. 1989. a. $10.95. Gould Publications (Binghamton), 199-300 State St., Binghamton, NY 13901. TEL 607-724-3000. FAX 607-723-7285.
    Description: Presents the correction law chapter 43 of the consolidated laws of New York, plus extracts of other NY laws for correction, probation and parole officers.

345   US   ISSN 1045-1625
KFN6100.A29
NEW YORK CRIMINAL LAW HANDBOOK. Key Title: Gould's Criminal Law Handbook of New York. 1988. a. $21.95. Gould Publications (Binghamton), 199-300 State St., Binghamton, NY 13901. TEL 607-724-3000. FAX 607-723-4285. adv.; bk.rev. (looseleaf format)
    Description: Contains the complete penal law, criminal procedure law, correction law and more.

345   US
NEW YORK CRIMINAL PROCEDURE LAW. 1988. a. $5.95. Gould Publications (Binghamton), 199-300 State St., Binghamton, NY 13901. TEL 607-724-3000. FAX 607-723-4285. adv.; bk.rev. (looseleaf format)
    Description: Presents criminal procedure law, Chapter 11-A of the consolidated laws of NY.

345   US
NEW YORK CRIMINAL PROCEDURE LAW QUESTIONS AND ANSWERS. 1988. a. $8.95. Gould Publications (Binghamton), 199-300 State St., Binghamton, NY 13901. TEL 607-724-3000. FAX 607-723-4285. adv.; bk.rev. (looseleaf format)
    Description: Lists Q and A covering the complete criminal procedure law.

345   US
NEW YORK PENAL LAW AND CRIMINAL PROCEDURE LAW. 1988. a. $8.95. Gould Publications (Binghamton), 199-300 State St., Binghamton, NY 13901. TEL 607-724-3000. FAX 607-723-4285.
    Description: Contains complete penal law and criminal procedure law with the controlled substance schedule, definition and comprehensive indices.

345   US
NEW YORK PENAL LAW QUESTIONS AND ANSWERS. 1988. a. $8.95. Gould Publications (Binghamton), 199-300 State St., Binghamton, NY 13201. TEL 607-724-3000. FAX 607-723-4285. adv.; bk.rev. (looseleaf format)
    Description: Contains Q and A covering the complete penal law.

343   US   ISSN 0271-6283
KFN6155.A59
NEW YORK STATE CRIMINAL LAW REVIEW. 1976. m. Division of Criminal Justice Services, Bureau of Prosecution Services, Executive Park Tower, Stuyvesant Plaza, Albany, NY 12203. TEL 518-457-8413. FAX 518-457-2416. Eds. Valerie Friedlander, Darlene Van Sickle. adv. circ. 10,000.
    Description: Notes on various criminal cases recently before the New York courts and the United States Supreme Court.

345   US   ISSN 0195-1696
KF9444.A15
OBSCENITY LAW BULLETIN. 1977. bi-m. $15. (National Obscenity Law Center) Morality in Media, Inc., 475 Riverside Dr., New York, NY 10115. TEL 212-870-3232. FAX 212-870-2765. Ed. Paul J. McGeady. circ. 800.
    Description: Report and commentary on current court decisions and legislation pertaining to obscenity and related matters.

345   US
OHIO CRIMINAL CODE. 1988. a. $15.95. Gould Publications, 1333 N. U.S. Hwy. 17-92, Longwood, FL 32750-3724. TEL 407-695-9500. FAX 407-695-2906. adv.; bk.rev. (looseleaf format)
    Description: Contains the state's criminal laws.

LAW — CRIMINAL LAW

345 — US
OKLAHOMA CRIMINAL PRACTICE MANUAL. 1987. base vol. (plus a. suppl.). $120. Butterworth Legal Publishers (Salem) (Subsidiary of: Reed Elsevier plc), 8 Industrial Way, Bldg. C, Salem, NH 03079. TEL 800-548-4001. FAX 603-898-9858. Eds. Chris Blair, Charles L. Cantrell. (looseleaf format)
  Description: Covers all the procedural steps in a criminal trial, from initial appearance and preliminary matters to post-conviction proceedings, arranged in chronological sequence.

343 — CN
ONTARIO DECISIONS - CRIMINAL CONVICTION AND SENTENCE CASES. 1980. m. Can.$290. Western Legal Publications, 301-1 Alexander St., Vancouver, BC V6A 1B2, Canada. TEL 604-687-5671. FAX 604-687-2796. m.index. (looseleaf format)
  Formerly: Ontarion Decisions - Criminal Cases (ISSN 0824-7269)
  Description: Digests all available criminal decisions in conviction and sentence matters from the Ontario Court of Appeal, Ontario Courts of Justice as well as all decisions of the Supreme Court of Canada regarding Ontario criminal cases.

345 — PK
PAKISTAN CRIMINAL LAW JOURNAL; a monthly journal of criminal cases. (Text in English) 1968. m. Rs.640($42) (effective 1993). P.L.D. Publishers, 35 Nabha Rd., Lahore 1, Pakistan. TEL 92-42-213497. Ed. Malik Muhammed Saeed. (back issues avail.; reprint service avail. from UMI)

345 — AT
PAUL'S SUMMARY AND TRAFFIC OFFENCES. 1981. 2 base vols. (plus updates 5/yr.). Aus.$315. Law Book Co. Ltd., 44-50 Waterloo Rd., N. Ryde, N.S.W. 2113, Australia. TEL 02-887-0177. FAX 02-888-9706. TELEX ASBOOK 27995. circ. 574. (looseleaf format)
  Formerly: Paul's Police Offences (ISSN 0728-3210)
  Description: Covers summary criminal matters in the Magistrates' Court of Victoria.

345 — US
PENNSYLVANIA BAR ASSOCIATION. CRIMINAL LAW SECTION NEWSLETTER. 1990. 4/yr. membership. Pennsylvania Bar Association, Criminal Law Section, 100 South St., Harrisburg, PA 17108. TEL 717-238-6715. FAX 717-238-7182. Document type: newsletter.

345 — US
PENNSYLVANIA CRIMES CODE. 1988. a. $19.95. Gould Publications, 1333 N. U.S. Hwy. 17-92, Longwood, FL 32750-3724. TEL 407-695-9500. FAX 407-695-2906. adv.; bk.rev. (looseleaf format)
  Description: Contains title 18 of the PA consolidated statutes.

345 — US
PENNSYLVANIA CRIMINAL LAW DIGEST. 1988. a. $19.95. Gould Publications, 1333 N. U.S. Hwy. 17-92, Longwood, FL 32750-3724. TEL 407-695-9500. FAX 407-695-2906. adv.; bk.rev. (looseleaf format)
  Description: Contains selected sections of various PA laws which are used by personnel in the criminal justice system.

PRECINCT REPORTER. see *LABOR UNIONS*

PROBATION AND PAROLE LAW REPORTS. see *LAW — Judicial Systems*

345 — PL — ISSN 0860-8903
PRZEGLAD PRAWA KARNEGO. 1990. m. (Towarzystwo Naukowe Prawa Karnego) Ossolineum, Publishing House of the Polish Academy of Sciences, Rynek 9, 50-106 Wroclaw, Poland. TEL 48-71-386-25. FAX 48-71-448-103. Ed. Janina Wojciechowska. circ. 1,000.

345 — US
READINGS FROM CRIMINAL JUSTICE HISTORY. 1990. irreg. price varies. Praeger Publishers (Subsidiary of: Greenwood Publishing Group Inc.), 88 Post Rd. W., Box 5007, Westport, CT 06881-5007. TEL 203-226-3571. FAX 203-222-1502. Document type: monographic series.

345 — CN
RESUMES DES JURISPRUDENCE PENALE DU QUEBEC. 24/yr. Can.$150. Les Editions Yvon Blais, 430 rue St-Pierre, Ste. 200, Montreal, PQ H2Y 2M5, Canada. TEL 514-842-3937. FAX 514-842-7144. (Subscr. to: C.P. 180, Cowansville, PQ J2K 3H6, Canada. TEL 514-263-1086) (back issues avail.) Document type: bulletin.

345 — BE — ISSN 0035-4384
REVUE DE DROIT PENAL ET DE CRIMINOLOGIE. (Supplements avail.) 1920. m. (10/yr.). 3780 BEF to non-members (foreign 5200 BEF); members 3180 BEF; students 2980 BEF. La Charte - Die Keure, Oude Gentweg 108, B-8000 Brugge, Belgium. FAX 32-50-34-37-68. bk.rev.; abstr.; bibl.; charts; index. circ. 1,050. (back issues avail.)
  Indexed: Refug.Abstr.
  —BLDSC (7898.540000); SWETS.
  Description: Discusses criminology and penal law.

345 — US
RHODE ISLAND CRIMINAL PROCEDURE. 1988. base vol. (plus suppl.). $125. Butterworth Legal Publishers (Salem) (Subsidiary of: Reed Elsevier plc), 8 Industrial Way, Bldg. C, Salem, NH 03079. TEL 800-548-4001. FAX 603-898-9858. Eds. Barbara Hurst, John A. MacFadyen. (looseleaf format)
  Description: Covers the mechanics of criminal litigation, including discussion of pleas at arraignment, discovery, the filing and grounds for pretrial motions, voir dire, objections to evidence, mid-trial motions, jury instructions and verdicts.

340 — US
RHODE ISLAND SUPREME COURT AND THE LAW OF CRIMES. 1983. base vol. (plus suppl.). $60. Butterworth Legal Publishers (Salem) (Subsidiary of: Reed Elsevier plc), 8 Industrial Way, Bldg. C, Salem, NH 03079. TEL 800-548-4001. FAX 603-898-9858. Ed. Bruce G. Pollock. (looseleaf format)
  Description: Covers cases pertaining to homicide, assault, robbery and other offenses; includes evidence issues, exclusions and privileges.

455 364 — US
RIGHTS OF PRISONERS. 1981. base vol. (plus a. suppl.). $95. Shepard's - McGraw-Hill, Inc., Box 35300, Colorado Springs, CO 80935-3530. TEL 800-525-2474.
  Description: Analysis of appropriate caveats, qualifications and indications of potential or emerging trends. Covers both statutory and constitutional development.

345 — IT — ISSN 0035-7022
RIVISTA PENALE. 1874. m. L.100000 (Europe L.150000; elsewhere L.200000) (effective 1994). Casa Editrice la Tribuna, Via Don Minzoni 51, 29100 Piacenza, Italy. TEL 0523-759015. FAX 0523-757219. Ed. Paolo Appella. bk.rev.; index. (back issues avail.)
  Description: Covers doctrine, jurisprudence, and legislation.

345 — US — ISSN 1073-676X
SAN DIEGO JUSTICE JOURNAL. 1976. s-a. $18. Western State University, College of Law, 2121 San Diego Ave., San Diego, CA 92110. TEL 619-298-3111. bk.rev. (also avail. in microform from WSH,PMC; back issues avail.; reprint service avail. from WSH) Indexed: C.L.I., Leg.Per.
  Formerly (until 1993): Criminal Justice Journal (San Diego).
  Description: Covers a wide variety of civil, criminal, and international law topics.

345 — US — ISSN 1043-4224
KF9214.S35
SCIENTIFIC SLEUTHING REVIEW; forensic science in criminal law. 1976. q. $20 (foreign $25). c/o J.E. Starrs, Ed., George Washington University, National Law Center, Washington, DC 20052. TEL 202-994-6770. FAX 202-994-9446. Ed. Sherrie S. Hardwick. adv.; bk.rev. circ. 800. (looseleaf format; back issues avail.) Document type: academic/scholarly publication.
  Former titles: Scientific Sleuthing Newsletter (ISSN 0749-1395); Science in Criminal Law Newsletter; Scientific Sleuthing Newsletter.

345 — UK — ISSN 0263-2381
SCOTTISH CRIMINAL CASE REPORTS. a. £108. Law Society of Scotland, 26 Drumsheugh Gardens, Edinburgh EH3 7YR, Scotland. Ed. Sheriff Gerald H. Gordon. Document type: bulletin.

SEARCH AND SEIZURE BULLETIN. see *CRIMINOLOGY AND LAW ENFORCEMENT*

345.73 347 — US — ISSN 1045-8719
KF9630.Z9
SEARCH AND SEIZURE CHECKLISTS. 1979. a. $69.50. Clark - Boardman - Callaghan Company Ltd., 375 Hudson St., New York, NY 10014. TEL 212-929-7500; 800-221-9428. FAX 212-924-0460. Ed. Michele G. Hermann.
  Description: Provides attorneys and law enforcement professionals with the crucial fundamentals of search and seizure principles, and the black-letter rule of law concerning all elements that must be proven in order to justify a search.

345 — US — ISSN 0095-1005
KF9630.A73
SEARCH AND SEIZURE LAW REPORT. 1973. 11/yr. $150. Clark - Boardman - Callaghan Company Ltd., 375 Hudson St., New York, NY 10014. TEL 212-929-7500; 800-221-9428. FAX 212-924-0460. Ed. John M. Burkoff. index. (looseleaf format; back issues avail.) Indexed: C.L.I., CJPI, L.R.I.
  —UMI.
  Description: Provides detailed, current coverage of the law, procedure, trends, and developments evolving in search and seizure law.

SECURITY AND SPECIAL POLICE LEGAL UPDATE. see *CRIMINOLOGY AND LAW ENFORCEMENT — Security*

SECURITY LAW NEWSLETTER. see *CRIMINOLOGY AND LAW ENFORCEMENT — Security*

345 — US — ISSN 0363-0978
KF9610.5
SHEPARD'S CRIMINAL JUSTICE CITATIONS. 1975. 4/yr. $144. Shepard's - McGraw-Hill, Inc., Box 35300, Colorado Springs, CO 80935-3530. TEL 800-525-2474.

345 — SA — ISSN 1011-8527
K23
SOUTH AFRICAN JOURNAL OF CRIMINAL JUSTICE/SUID-AFRIKAANSE TYDSKRIF VIR STRAFREGSPLEGING. 1988. 3/yr. Juta & Co. Ltd., P.O. Box 14373, Kenwyn 7790, South Africa. TEL 27-21-797-5101. FAX 27-21-761-5010.

345 — II — ISSN 0253-6544
SUPREME COURT CASES (CRIMINAL). (Text in English) 1970. m. $41. Eastern Book Company, 34 Lalbagh, Lucknow 226 001, India. TEL 91-522-244328. FAX 91-522-244328. Ed. Surendra Malik. adv.; bk.rev. circ. 3,000. (back issues avail.)

TEXAS CRIMINAL LAW & MOTOR VEHICLE HANDBOOK. see *LAW*

345 — UK
▼**TEXTBOOK ON CRIMINAL LAW.** 1992. irreg., 2nd ed., 1993. £16.95($38) Blackstone Press, Aldine St., London W12 8AW, England. TEL 081-740-1173. FAX 081-743-2292. (Dist. by: Wm. W. Gaunt & Sons, Inc., Law Book Dealers & Subscription Agents, Gaunt Bldg., 3011 Gulf Dr., Holmes Beach, FL 34217-2199. TEL 813-778-5211)

345 — PL — ISSN 0208-5577
UNIWERSYTET SLASKI W KATOWICACH. PRACE NUKOWE. PROBLEMY PRAWA KARNEGO. (Text in Polish; summaries in German, Russian) 1975. irreg. price varies. Wydawnictwo Uniwersytetu Slaskiego, Ul. Bankowa 12B, 40-007 Katowice, Poland. TEL 48-32-596-915. FAX 48-32-599-605. TELEX 0315584 USKPL. (Dist. by: CHS Ars Polona, P.O. Box 1001, 00-950 Warsaw, Poland) Ed. Barbara Woznica. Document type: academic/scholarly publication.
  Description: Covers criminal law, the law of criminal court proceedings, executive criminal law, criminology, crime detection law.

340 345   CN   ISSN 1180-0453
VICTIMS OF VIOLENCE REPORT. 1990. 5/yr. Can.$25($25) (effective 1991). Victims of Violence International, B150 151 Slater St., Ottawa, Ont. K1P 5H3, Canada. TEL 613-233-0052. FAX 613-233-2712. (Subscr. in US to: Box 1305, Ogdensburg, NY 13669) Ed. Gary Rosenfeldt. adv. circ. 21,000. (back issues avail.)
    Description: Covers crime victimization, child abuse, crime and punishment.

345   US
WASHINGTON STATE BAR ASSOCIATION. CRIMINAL LAW SECTION NEWSLETTER. irreg. $12.50. Washington State Bar Association, Criminal Law Section, 500 Westin Bldg., 2001 Sixth Ave., Seattle, WA 98121. TEL 206-727-8239. FAX 206-727-8320. **Document type:** newsletter.

345   US
WAYNE STATE UNIVERSITY LAW SCHOOL. COMPARATIVE CRIMINAL LAW PROJECT. PUBLICATIONS SERIES. 1961. irreg., latest vol.17. price varies. Fred B. Rothman & Co., 10368 W. Centennial Rd., Littleton, CO 80127. TEL 303-979-5657. FAX 303-978-1457. Ed. Edward M. Wise. (back issues avail.) **Document type:** monographic series.
    Formerly (until 1983): New York University. Comparative Criminal Law Project. Publications (ISSN 0077-944X)

345   CN
WEAPONS OFFENCES MANUAL. base vol. (plus s-a. updates). Can.$92. Canada Law Book Inc., 240 Edward St., Aurora, ON L4G 3S9, Canada. TEL 905-841-6472. FAX 905-841-5085. Ed. Peter Harris. adv. contact: Mary Cull. (looseleaf format)
    Description: Provides a detailed survey of all Criminal Code weapons sections, regulations and amendments along with an in-depth analysis of case-law and policy.

345   CN   ISSN 0703-1319
WEEKLY CRIMINAL BULLETIN. 1977. w. Can.$172. Canada Law Book Inc., 240 Edward St., Aurora, ON L4G 3S9, Canada. TEL 905-841-6472. FAX 905-941-5085. adv. contact: Mary Cull. **Document type:** bulletin.
●Also available online.

345 305.4   US   ISSN 0897-4454
HV7231   CODEN: WCJUER
WOMEN & CRIMINAL JUSTICE. 1989. s-a. $28 to individuals; institutions $36; libraries $60. Haworth Press, Inc., 10 Alice St., Binghamton, NY 13904. TEL 607-722-5857; 800-342-9678. FAX 607-722-1424. TELEX 4932599. Ed. Clarice Feinman. adv. bk.rev. (also avail. in microfiche from UMI; reprint service avail. from HAW) **Indexed:** Wom.Stud.Abstr. (1989-).
    —BLDSC (9343.241000); Faxon; UnCover.
    Description: Devoted specifically to interdisciplinary scholarly research dealing with all areas of women and criminal justice.
    Refereed Serial

345   CN
YOUNG OFFENDERS ACT MANUAL. base vol. (plus irreg. updates). Can.$135. Canada Law Book Inc., 240 Edward St., Aurora, ON L4G 3S9, Canada. TEL 905-841-6472. FAX 905-841-5085. Ed. Peter J. Harris. adv. contact: Mary Cull.
    Description: An in-court reference manual providing the principles and procedures of the Act and monitoring the changing issues that arise.

LAW — Estate Planning

332.04   US
KF765.A15P762
A C T E C NOTES. 1975. q. $60 to non-members. American College of Trust and Estate Counsel, 3415 S. Sepulveda Blvd., Ste. 460, Los Angeles, CA 90034. TEL 310-398-1888. FAX 310-572-7280. Ed. William Weinsheiner. index, cum.index every 5 yrs. circ. 2,600. (looseleaf format; back issues avail.)
    Formerly: Probate Notes.

332.04   US
KF200.F674
ACTION-LINE (TALLAHASSEE). 1969. irreg. (6-12/yr.). $15 to non-members. Florida Bar, Real Property, Probate and Trust Law Section, 650 Apalachee Pkwy., Tallahassee, FL 32399-2300. TEL 904-561-5619. circ. 7,400. **Document type:** newsletter.
    Formerly: Florida Bar. Real Property, Probate and Trust Law Section. Review.

AGRICULTURAL ESTATE, TAX & BUSINESS PLANNING.
    see *BUSINESS AND ECONOMICS — Banking And Finance*

332.04 333.33   US
AUDIO ESTATE PLANNER. 4/yr. $75. American Law Institute - American Bar Association, Committee on Continuing Professional Education, 4025 Chestnut St., Philadelphia, PA 19104. TEL 215-243-1697. FAX 215-243-1664. Ed. William S. Stevens. circ. 350. (audio cassette) **Document type:** trade publication.
    Description: Articles of practical interest to the attorney specializing in estate planning and administration.

346   US
B A R - B R I BAR REVIEW. COMMUNITY PROPERTY. a. $395. B A R - B R I Bar Review, 3280 Motor Ave., Los Angeles, CA 90034-3710. TEL 213-477-2542.

332.04   US
B A R - B R I BAR REVIEW. TRUSTS. a. $395. B A R - B R I Bar Review, 3280 Motor Ave., Los Angeles, CA 90034-3710. TEL 213-477-2542.

332.04   US
B A R - B R I BAR REVIEW. WILLS. a. $395. B A R - B R I Bar Review, 3280 Motor Ave., Los Angeles, CA 90034-3710. TEL 213-477-2542.

343.05   CN
CANADIAN ESTATE PLANNING AND ADMINISTRATION REPORTER. 1979. m. Can.$475. C C H Canadian Ltd., 6 Garamond Ct., North York, ON M3C 1Z5, Canada. TEL 416-441-2992. FAX 416-444-9011. index.
    Supersedes: Provincial Inheritance and Gift Tax Reports; Which was formerly: Canadian Estate and Gift Tax Reports (ISSN 0008-3488)
    Description: Detailed commentary on estate planning and administration in Canada including co-ownership of property inter-vivos transfers, estate freezing and will planning.

CHASE REVIEW. see *BUSINESS AND ECONOMICS — Banking And Finance*

332.040   US
DRAFTING WILLS AND TRUST AGREEMENTS. 1980. base vol. (plus m. supplements). $220. Shepard's - McGraw-Hill, Inc., Box 35300, Colorado Springs, CO 80935-3530. TEL 800-525-2474. (Co-sponsor: R.P.W. Publishing Corp.) Ed. Robert P. Wilkins. (looseleaf format)

332.04   US
ESTATE ADMINISTRATION; a handbook with forms. 1985. base vol. (plus suppl.). $85. Butterworth Legal Publishers (Salem) (Subsidiary of: Reed Elsevier plc), 8 Industrial Way, Bldg. C, Salem, NH 03079. TEL 800-548-4001. FAX 603-898-9858. Ed. Michael H. Riley. (looseleaf format)

332   US   ISSN 1044-7911
KF6352.R47
ESTATE AND FINANCIAL PLANNERS ALERT. 1976. m. $125. Research Institute of America, Inc., 90 Fifth Ave., New York, NY 10011. TEL 212-645-4800. FAX 212-337-4279. (Subscr. to: 117 E. Stevens Ave., Valhalla, NY 10595) **Indexed:** L.I.I. **Document type:** newsletter.
    ●Also available online. Vendor(s): Mead Data Central, Inc.
    —CCC.
    Formerly: Research Institute of America. Estate Planners Alert (ISSN 0163-9986)
    Description: Reports on key developments in estate and financial planning.

343.05   US   ISSN 0014-1216
ESTATE PLANNING (ENGLEWOOD CLIFFS). 1958. base vol. (plus m. updates and Estate Planning Ideas newsletter). $264. Maxwell Macmillan, Professional and Business Reference Publishing, 910 Sylvan Ave., Englewood Cliffs, NJ 07632-3310. TEL 800-562-0245. FAX 201-816-3569. adv.; bk.rev. (looseleaf format) **Indexed:** C.L.I., L.R.I., PSI, Tr.& Indus.Ind.

332.04   US   ISSN 0094-1794
KF750.A1
ESTATE PLANNING (NEW YORK). 1973. bi-m. $136.50 (overseas $204) (effective 1994). Warren Gorham Lamont, 1 Penn Plaza, New York, NY 10119. TEL 212-971-5000. (Subscr. to: The Park Square Bldg., 31 St. James Ave., Boston, MA 02116-4112. TEL 800-950-1207) Ed. Charis Emley. adv.; bk.rev.; index. (also avail. in microform from UMI; reprint service avail. from RRI,UMI) **Indexed:** Account.Ind. (1974-), BPIA, Bus.Ind, C.L.I., L.R.I., Leg.Cont., Leg.Per., Tr.& Indus.Ind. **Document type:** trade publication.
    —BLDSC (3812.537500); Faxon; UnCover; UMI. CCC.
    Description: Provides a current picture of opportunities in estate planning and family asset management.
    Refereed Serial

332.04   US   ISSN 0273-7027
KFC195.A15
ESTATE PLANNING AND CALIFORNIA PROBATE REPORTER. 1980. 6/yr. $125. Continuing Education of the Bar - California, University of California Extension, 2300 Shattuck Ave., Berkeley, CA 94704. TEL 510-642-8317; 800-924-3924. FAX 510-642-3788. (Co-sponsor: State Bar of California) Ed. Jeffrey Strathmeyer. (tabloid format; back issues avail.)

343.05   US
ESTATE PLANNING & TAXATION COORDINATOR. 9 base vols. (bi-w. supplements). $760. Research Institute of America, Inc., 90 Fifth Ave., New York, NY 10011. TEL 212-645-4800. (Subscr. to: 117 E. Stevens Ave., Valhalla, NY 10595) Ed.Bd. (looseleaf format)
    Description: Provides analysis of federal tax laws affecting estates, gifts and trusts, as well as planning startegies and implementation tools.

332.04   US   ISSN 0014-1224
ESTATE PLANNING CHECKLISTS AND FORMS. base vol. (plus q. updates). $264. Maxwell Macmillan, Professional and Business Reference Publishing, 910 Sylvan Ave., Englewood Cliffs, NJ 07632-3310. TEL 800-562-0245. FAX 201-816-3569. adv.; bk.rev.; charts. (looseleaf format)

332.04 630   US
ESTATE PLANNING FOR FARMERS AND RANCHERS, 2-E. 1986. 2 base vols. (plus a. supplement). $210. Shepard's - McGraw-Hill, Inc., Box 35300, Colorado Springs, CO 80935-3500. TEL 800-525-2474. (looseleaf format)
    Description: Covers tax laws, rulings and cases.

343.05   US
ESTATE PLANNING PROBATE AND TRUST. 1954. 6/yr. $16 to members. Illinois State Bar Association, Section on Estate Planning, Probate & Trust, Illinois Bar Center, Springfield, IL 62701. TEL 217-525-1760. FAX 217-525-0712. Ed. C. Glennon Rau. index. circ. 5,100. (looseleaf format; back issues avail.) **Document type:** newsletter.

332.04   US   ISSN 0098-2873
KF746.A3
ESTATE PLANNING REVIEW. 1974. m. $150. Commerce Clearing House, Inc., 4025 W. Peterson Ave., Chicago, IL 60646. TEL 312-583-8500. index. (also avail. in microform from UMI) **Indexed:** L.I.I.

343.05   US
ESTATE PLANNING, TRUST & PROBATE NEWS. 4/yr. membership. State Bar of California, 555 Franklin St., San Francisco, CA 94102. TEL 415-561-8264. FAX 415-561-8228. **Document type:** newsletter.

LAW — ESTATE PLANNING

346.01 US
ESTATE PLANNING: WILLS AND TRUSTS. (Number of base vols. varies depending on number of states) base vol. (plus m. Report Bulletins and updates). Maxwell Macmillan, 910 Sylvan Ave., Englewood Cliffs, NJ 07632-3310. FAX 201-816-3569. (looseleaf format)

346.01 US
ESTATE PLANNING: WILLS, TRUSTS AND FORMS. base vol. (plus bi-m. Report Bulletins and updates). Maxwell Macmillan, 910 Sylvan Ave., Englewood Cliffs, NJ 07632-3310. TEL 800-562-0245. FAX 201-816-3569. (looseleaf format)

332.04 CN ISSN 0840-7886
ESTATES AND TRUSTS JOURNAL. 1974. q. Can.$99. Canada Law Book Inc., 240 Edward St., Aurora, ON L4G 3S9, Canada. TEL 905-841-6472. FAX 905-841-5085. Ed. Robert C. Dick. **Indexed:** BPIA, Bus.Ind., C.L.I., Ind.Can.L.P.L., L.R.I. —BLDSC (3812.537800).
Formerly (until 1988): Estates and Trusts Quarterly (ISSN 0381-8888)

332.04 CN ISSN 0706-5655
ESTATES & TRUSTS REPORTS. 1977. 12/yr. (in 4 vols.). Can.$125. Carswell, One Corporate Plaza, 2075 Kennedy Rd., Scarborough, ON M1T 3V4, Canada. TEL 416-609-8000. FAX 416-298-5094. Ed. T.G. Youdan. adv. contact: M. Lalani. **Indexed:** C.L.I., Ind.Can.L.P.L., L.R.I.
Description: Features all important decisions in estates and trusts law from all Canadian jurisdictions selected by experts in the field. Includes cases on all aspects of wills, estate administration, devolution of estate, dependents' relief, tax matters relating to trusts.

ESTATES GAZETTE; devoted to land, commercial, industrial, residential and agricultural properties. see *REAL ESTATE*

ESTATES GAZETTE LAW REPORTS. see *REAL ESTATE*

332.04 US
ESTATES, POWERS & TRUSTS LAW OF NEW YORK. 1988. a. $8.95 (effective 1992). Gould Publications (Binghamton), 199-300 State St., Binghamton, NY 13901. TEL 607-724-3000. FAX 607-723-4285. (looseleaf format)

343.05 336 US ISSN 0162-1114
FEDERAL ESTATE AND GIFT TAX REPORTS. 1913. w. $445. Commerce Clearing House, Inc., 4025 W. Peterson Ave., Chicago, IL 60646. TEL 312-583-8500. Ed. J. Rooney.

FEDERAL ESTATE AND GIFT TAXATION (SUPPLEMENT). see *BUSINESS AND ECONOMICS — Public Finance, Taxation*

343.05 US
FEDERAL ESTATE AND GIFT TAXES. 1925. 2 base vols. (plus bi-w. Report Bulletins and updates). $365. Maxwell Macmillan, Professional and Business Reference Publishing, 910 Sylvan Ave., Englewood Cliffs, NJ 07632-3310. TEL 800-562-0245. (looseleaf format)
● Also available online. Vendor(s): Research Institute of America.
Description: Comprehensive reference for all aspects of estate planning, including the impact of related transfer taxes. Simplifies complex estate planning decisions.

343.05 US ISSN 0092-6531
KF6572.Z9
FEDERAL ESTATE AND GIFT TAXES EXPLAINED, INCLUDING ESTATE PLANNING. Key Title: Federal Estate and Gift Taxes Explained. irreg., latest 1993. $23. Commerce Clearing House, Inc., 4025 W. Peterson Ave., Chicago, IL 60646. TEL 312-583-8500.

343.05 CN
FIDUCIARY DUTIES IN CANADA. base vol. (plus irreg. updates). Can.$185. Carswell, One Corporate Plaza, 2075 Kennedy Rd., Scarborough, ON M1T 3V4, Canada. TEL 416-609-8000. FAX 416-298-5094. (looseleaf format)
Description: Provides a basis to assess when a fiduciary duty exists, what is required to fill that duty and resulting remedies if that duty is not satisfied.

332.04 US
FIDUCIARY STANDARDS IN PENSION AND TRUST FUND MANAGEMENT. 1989. base vol. (plus suppl.). $65. Butterworth Legal Publishers (Salem) (Subsidiary of: Reed Elsevier plc), 8 Industrial Way, Bldg. C, Salem, NH 03079. TEL 800-548-4001.
FAX 603-898-9858. Ed. Betty L. Krikorian.
Description: Provides an explanation of the complex legal and business environment in which today's pension and trust fund fiduciaries work.

FIELD GUIDE TO ESTATE PLANNING, BUSINESS PLANNING & EMPLOYEE BENEFITS. see *INSURANCE*

FINANCIAL AND ESTATE PLANNING. see *BUSINESS AND ECONOMICS — Banking And Finance*

332.04 US ISSN 0423-4596
FINANCIAL ESTATE PLANNERS QUARTERLY. 1956. q. $175 for 2 vol. set. Dearborn - R & R Newkirk, 520 N. Dearborn, Chicago, IL 60610-4901. TEL 312-836-4400. Ed. Georgia Mann. index. circ. 1,000. (looseleaf format; back issues avail.)
Formerly: Estate Planners Quarterly.

340
FLORIDA PARALEGAL SERIES: WILLS, TRUSTS, ESTATES. 1982. base vol. (plus a. suppl.). $60. Butterworth Legal Publishers (Salem) (Subsidiary of: Reed Elsevier plc), 8 Industrial Way, Bldg. C, Salem, NH 03079. TEL 800-548-4001. FAX 603-898-9858. (looseleaf format)

343.05 US
GEORGIA PROBATE MANUAL. 1985. 2 base vols. (plus supplements 2-3/yr.). $80. Butterworth Legal Publishers (Salem) (Subsidiary of: Reed Elsevier plc), 8 Industrial Way, Bldg. C, Salem, NH 03079. TEL 800-548-4001. FAX 603-898-9858. (looseleaf format)

332.04 US
GILBERT LAW SUMMARIES. ESTATE AND GIFT. irreg., 14th ed., 1988. $15.95. Harcourt Brace Legal & Professional Publications, Inc., 176 W. Adams, Ste. 2100, Chicago, IL 60603. TEL 312-853-3662.

343.05 US
GILBERT LAW SUMMARIES. TRUSTS. irreg., 11th ed., 1990. $14.95. Harcourt Brace legal & Professional Publications, Inc., 176 W. Adams, Ste. 2100, Chicago, IL 60603. TEL 312-853-3662.

332.04 US
GILBERT LAW SUMMARIES. WILLS. irreg., 10th ed., 1986. $15.95. Harcourt Brace Legal & Professional Publications, Inc., 176 W. Adams, Ste. 2100, Chicago, IL 60603. TEL 312-853-3662.

332.04 US
GUARDIANSHIP AND CONSERVATORSHIP IN MASSACHUSETTS. 1991. base vol. (plus irreg. supplements). $85. Butterworth Legal Publishers (Salem) (Subsidiary of: Reed Elsevier plc), 8 Industrial Way, Bldg. C, Salem, NH 03079. TEL 800-548-4001. FAX 603-898-9858. Eds. John H. Cross, Robert D. Fleischner. (looseleaf format)
Description: Provides information concerning procedures for the appointment of guardians and conservators for individuals with mental and physical disabilities.

INTERNAL REVENUE SERVICE. BULLETIN INDEX - DIGEST SYSTEM: PART 2. ESTATE AND GIFT TAXES. see *BUSINESS AND ECONOMICS — Public Finance, Taxation*

332.6 US
INTERNATIONAL ESTATE PLANNING. 1981. 2 base vols. (plus a. supplements). $195. Shepard's - McGraw-Hill, Inc., Box 35300, Colorado Springs, CO 80935-3500. TEL 800-525-2474. (looseleaf format)
Description: Covers changes in rulings, case law, regulations and legislation which affect both foreigners with investments in the U.S. and Americans with investments abroad.

332.04 US
MAINE PROBATE LAW. 2nd ed., 1991. base vol. (plus supplements). $95. Butterworth Legal Publishers (Salem) (Subsidiary of: Reed Elsevier plc), 8 Industrial Way, Bldg. C, Salem, NH 03079. TEL 800-548-4001. FAX 603-898-9858. Ed. Philip C. Hunt. (looseleaf format)
Description: Complete text, with commentary, for all statutes and rules governing probate practice in the State of Maine, including administration of estates, conservatorships and trusts, with discussion of probate matters not covered by the codes and rules.

332.04 US
MAINE PROBATE MANUAL. 1988. base vol. (plus suppl.). $95. Butterworth Legal Publishers (Salem) (Subsidiary of: Reed Elsevier plc), 8 Industrial Way, Bldg. C, Salem, NH 03079. TEL 800-548-4001. FAX 603-898-9858. Ed. James E. Mitchell. (looseleaf format)
Description: Contains the Maine Rules of Probate Procedure with notes and commentary.

332.04 US
MAINE PROBATE PROCEDURE. 2nd ed., 1992. base vol. (plus supplement). $95. Butterworth Legal Publishers (Salem) (Subsidiary of: Reed Elsevier plc), 8 Industrial Way, Bldg. C, Salem, NH 03079. TEL 800-548-4001. FAX 603-898-9858. Eds. James E. Mitchell, Philip C. Hunt. (looseleaf format)
Description: Covers selecting and completing the correct official and recommended forms for probate filings in the State of Maine.

343.05 US
MICHIGAN PROBATE CODE. 1988. a. $14. Gould Publications, 1333 N. U.S. Hwy. 17-92, Longwood, FL 32750-3724. TEL 407-695-9500. FAX 407-695-2906. adv.; bk.rev. (looseleaf format)
Description: Presents the probate code of Michigan, chapter 700 of the Compiled laws.

343.05 US
NEW HAMPSHIRE PRACTICE SERIES. VOLS. 10, 11 AND 12: PROBATE LAW AND PROCEDURE. (Series consists of 14 vols.; Vols. 1 and 2: Criminal Practice and Procedure; Vol. 3: Family Law; Vols. 4, 5 and 6: Civil Practice and Procedure; Vol. 7: Wills, Trusts and Gifts; Vols. 8 and 9: Personal Injury - Tort and Insurance Practice; Vols. 10, 11 and 12: Probate Law and Procedure; Vols. 13 and 14: Local Government Law) 1990. 3 base vols. (plus a. supplement). $165 (14-vol. set $525). Butterworth Legal Publishers (Salem) (Subsidiary of: Reed Elsevier plc), 8 Industrial Way, Bldg. C, Salem, NH 03079. TEL 800-548-4001. FAX 603-898-9858. Eds. Charles A. DeGrandpre, Kathleen M. Robinson. (looseleaf format)
Description: Contains practical advice, analysis of current law, checklists and completed forms used in probate proceedings.

332.04 US
NEW JERSEY STATE BAR ASSOCIATION. LAND USE LAW SECTION. NEWSLETTER. 1982. irreg. free to members. New Jersey State Bar Association, Land Use Law Section, One Constitution Sq., New Brunswick, NJ 08901-1500. TEL 908-249-2815. FAX 908-249-2815. Ed. Brian P. Blatz. bk.rev. circ. 750. (back issues avail.) Document type: newsletter.

332.04 US
NEW YORK E.P.T.L. AND S.C.P.A. 1988. a. $19.95. Gould Publications (Binghamton), 199-300 State St., Binghamton, NY 13901. TEL 607-724-3000. FAX 607-723-4285. adv.; bk.rev. (looseleaf format)
Description: Contains the estates, powers, and trust laws and the Surrogate's Court Procedure Act with official forms.

349 US
NEW YORK ESTATES - WILLS - TRUSTS. m. $980. Commerce Clearing House, Inc., 4025 W. Peterson Ave., Chicago, IL 60646. TEL 312-583-8500. (looseleaf format)

346 US
OKLAHOMA WILLS AND INTESTATE SUCCESSION. 1987. base vol. (plus supplements). $95. Butterworth Legal Publishers (Salem) (Subsidiary of: Reed Elsevier plc), 8 Industrial Way, Bldg. C, Salem, NH 03079. TEL 800-548-4001. FAX 603-898-9858. Ed. Nancy I. Kenderdine. (looseleaf format)

LAW — FAMILY AND MATRIMONIAL LAW

OREGON DEPARTMENT OF REVENUE. INCOME AND INHERITANCE TAX LAW ABSTRACTS. see *BUSINESS AND ECONOMICS* — *Abstracting, Bibliographies, Statistics*

346   US   ISSN 0164-0372
KF325.187
PROBATE & PROPERTY. 1959. 6/yr. $40 (foreign $52). American Bar Association, Real Property, Probate and Trust Law Section, 750 N. Lake Shore Dr., Chicago, IL 60611. TEL 312-988-5591. Ed. Ann E. Houle. adv.; bk.rev.; charts; illus. circ. 37,500. Indexed: Account.Ind. (1988-), C.L.I., L.R.I., Leg.Per.
● Also available online. Vendor(s): West Services, Inc.
—Faxon; UnCover.
     Former titles (until 1987): Probate and Property Newsletter; American Bar Association. Section of Real Property, Probate and Trust Law. Newsletter (ISSN 0569-3357)
     Description: Recent developments in estate, trust, and real property law.

346   US   ISSN 0737-3112
K16
PROBATE LAW JOURNAL. 1982. 3/yr. $25. (National College of Probate Judges) Boston University, School of Law, Probate Law Journal, 765 Commonwealth Ave., Boston, MA 02215. TEL 617-353-4797. Dir. Faye G. Yoffa Stone. adv. circ. 1,000. Indexed: Leg.Per. **Document type:** academic/scholarly publication.
—Faxon; UnCover.

346   US   ISSN 1050-5342
KFO144.A15
PROBATE LAW JOURNAL OF OHIO. 1990. bi-m. $150. Banks - Baldwin Law Publishing Co., University Center, Box 1974, Cleveland, OH 44106. TEL 216-721-7373. FAX 216-721-8055. Ed. Robert M. Brucken.
     Description: Analysis of new legislation, rules, court decisions, developments in Ohio probate, estate planning, and juvenile law and practice.

343.05   US
R I A ANALYSIS OF FEDERAL TAXES: ESTATE AND GIFT. 1991. 2 base vols. (plus bi-w. supplements). $300. Research Institute of America, Inc., 90 Fifth Ave., New York, NY 10011. TEL 212-645-4800. FAX 212-337-4279. (Subscr. to: 117 E. Stevens Ave., Valhalla, NY 10595) (looseleaf format)
     Description: Provides analaysis of the tax laws affecting estates and gifts.

332.04   US
R P P T NEWS. (Real Property, Probate and Trust) 1985. 4/yr. State Bar of Wisconsin, 402 W. Wilson St., Madison, WI 53703. TEL 608-257-3838. FAX 608-257-5502. circ. 1,680. (back issues avail.) **Document type:** newsletter.

332.04   US   ISSN 0034-0855
K18
REAL PROPERTY, PROBATE AND TRUST JOURNAL. 1966. q. $22 (foreign $27). American Bar Association, Real Property, Probate and Trust Law Section, 750 N. Lake Shore Dr., Chicago, IL 60611. TEL 312-988-6083. Ed. S. Alan Medlin. bk.rev. circ. 37,970. (also avail. in microform from UMI; microfilm from RRI; reprint service avail. from RRI,UMI) Indexed: Abstr.Bk.Rev.Curr.Leg.Per., Account.Ind. (1974-), BPIA, Bus.Ind., C.L.I., Curr.Cont., L.I.I., L.R.I., Leg.Cont., Leg.Per., SSCI.
● Also available online. Vendor(s): West Services, Inc.
—BLDSC (7303.282570); Faxon; UnCover; UMI.
     Description: Scholarly articles in the fields of estate planning, trust law, and real property law.

332.04 352.7   UK   ISSN 0144-8196
KDC446.A13
SCOTTISH PLANNING LAW & PRACTICE. 1980. 3/yr. £25 (foreign £35). Planning Exchange, 186 Bath St., Glasgow G2 4HG, Scotland. TEL 041-332-8541. FAX 041-332-8277. Ed.Bd. (back issues avail.) Indexed: Geo.Abstr. **Document type:** consumer publication.
     Description: For planners, surveyors, lawyers, architects, councillors and others: all aspects of planning law in Scotland.

332.04   US
SUCCESSFUL ESTATE PLANNING: IDEAS AND METHODS. 2 base vols. (plus s-m. updates). Maxwell Macmillan, Professional and Business Reference Publishing, 910 Sylvan Ave., Englewood Cliffs, NJ 07632-3310. TEL 800-562-0245. FAX 201-816-3569. (looseleaf format)

TEXAS FORECLOSURE: LAW AND PRACTICE. see *LAW — Corporate Law*

332.04   UK   ISSN 0269-9087
TRUSTS & ESTATES. 10/yr. £147($294) I B C Publishing, Gilmoora House, 57-61 Mortimer St., London W1N 7TD, England. TEL 071-637-4383. FAX 071-636-6414. (Subscr. in U.S. to: IBC (USA), 290 Eliot St., Box 91004, Ashland, MA 01721-9104. TEL 508-881-2800. FAX 508-881-0982) Ed. Richard Williams. **Document type:** newsletter.

332.04   US
UNIFORM PROBATE CODE. irreg. West Publishing Corp., 620 Opperman Dr., Eagan, MN 55123. TEL 612-687-8000; 800-328-9352. FAX 612-687-7302. **Document type:** trade publication.

332.04   UK   ISSN 1352-4569
▼**WILLS, PROBATE AND ADMINISTRATION.** 1993. a. £17.50. Jordan Publishing Ltd., 21 St. Thomas St., Bristol BS1 6JS, England. TEL 0272-230600. FAX 0272-250486. Ed. Robin Riddett. **Document type:** academic/scholarly publication.

332.04   AT
WILLS, PROBATE & ADMINISTRATION SERVICE N S W. base vol. (plus q. update). $385. Butterworths, 271-273 Lane Cove Rd., P.O. Box 345, North Ryde, N.S.W. 2113, Australia. TEL 02-335-4444. FAX 02-335-4678. (looseleaf format)

332.04   US
WILLS, TRUSTS AND GIFTS - RHODE ISLAND. 1991. base vol. (plus a. suppl.). $90. Butterworth Legal Publishers (Salem) (Subsidiary of: Reed Elsevier plc), 8 Industrial Way, Bldg. C, Salem, NH 03079. TEL 800-548-4001. FAX 603-898-9858. Ed. David T. Riedel.
     Description: Contains the cases and statutes in Rhode Island relating to wills, trusts and gifts complete with summaries and analysis.

LAW — Family And Matrimonial Law

346.01   CN
ALBERTA FAMILY LAW. 4/yr. Can.$205. Butterworths Canada Ltd., Part of the Reed Elsevier group, 75 Clegg Rd., Markham, ON L6G 1A1, Canada. TEL 905-479-2665. FAX 905-479-2826. (looseleaf format)
     Description: All federal and provincial statutes, rules and regulations pertaining to family law practice in Alberta.

346.01   US   ISSN 1052-5106
KF505.Z9
AMERICAN BAR ASSOCIATION. FAMILY LAW SECTION. ANNUAL MEETING COMPENDIUM. a. American Bar Association, Family Law Section, 750 N. Lake Shore Dr., Chicago, IL 60611.

346.01   US   ISSN 0891-6330
K1
AMERICAN JOURNAL OF FAMILY LAW. 1987. q. $120 (foreign $136). John Wiley & Sons, Inc., Journals, 605 Third Ave., New York, NY 10158-0012. TEL 212-850-6000. FAX 212-850-6088. cum.index. circ. 800. (back issues avail.) Indexed: C.L.I.
—UnCover.
     Description: Provides in-depth, relevant commentary on current issues in practice; includes sample forms, checklists, and useful guidelines for day-to-day use for family law practitioners, paralegals, or judges.

346.01 301   AT   ISSN 1038-0507
▼**AUSTRALIAN FAMILY BRIEFINGS.** 1992. irreg. Aus.$5 per no. Australian Institute of Family Studies, 300 Queen St., Melbourne, Vic. 3000, Australia. TEL 03-608-6888. FAX 03-600-0886. stat. **Document type:** bulletin.
     Description: Every issue focuses on one family-related topic.

346.01   AT
AUSTRALIAN FAMILY LAW & PRACTICE. (In 3 vols.) 1975. every 3 weeks. C C H Australia Ltd., P.O. Box 230, North Ryde, N.S.W. 2113, Australia. TEL 888-2555. charts. (looseleaf format)
     Description: Includes family law cases.

346.01   AT
AUSTRALIAN FAMILY LAW - COURT HANDBOOK. 1989. bi-m. C C H Australia Ltd., P.O. Box 230, North Ryde, N.S.W. 2113, Australia. TEL 02-888-2555. FAX 02-888-7324. (looseleaf format)

346.01   AT
AUSTRALIAN FAMILY LAW SERVICE. base vols. (plus m. updates). $715. Butterworths, 271-273 Lane Cove Rd., P.O. Box 345, North Ryde, N.S.W. 2113, Australia. TEL 02-335-4444. FAX 02-335-4655.

346.01   AT   ISSN 0817-623X
K1
AUSTRALIAN JOURNAL OF FAMILY LAW. 1986. 3/yr. Aus.$130. Butterworths, P.O. Box 345, North Ryde, N.S.W. 2113, Australia. TEL 02-335-4444. FAX 02-335-4655. **Document type:** academic/scholarly publication.

346.01   CN   ISSN 0824-7196
BRITISH COLUMBIA DECISIONS - FAMILY LAW CASES. 1980. m. Can.$140. Western Legal Publications, 301-1 Alexander St., Vancouver, BC V6A 1B2, Canada. TEL 604-687-5671. FAX 604-687-2796. m.index. (looseleaf format)
● Also available online.

346.01   CN   ISSN 0824-7781
BRITISH COLUMBIA FAMILY LAW. m. Can.$350. Butterworths Canada Ltd., Part of the Reed Elsevier group, 75 Clegg Rd., Markham, ON L6G 1A1, Canada. TEL 905-479-2665. FAX 905-479-2826.
     Description: Provides family lawyers with a guide to the legislation and case law on family law practice in British Columbia.

346.01   NZ
BUTTERWORTHS FAMILY LAW BULLETIN. 1985. 8/yr. NZ.$108. Butterworths of New Zealand Ltd., P.O. Box 472, 203-207 Victoria St., Wellington, New Zealand. TEL 04-385-1479. FAX 04-385-1598. Ed. Christine O'Brie. **Document type:** bulletin.
—CCC.
     Formerly: New Zealand Family Law Bulletin (ISSN 0112-6261)
     Description: Articles plus notes on all developments of relevance to family law in New Zealand.

346.01   NZ
BUTTERWORTHS FAMILY LAW REPORTS. 1981. 18/yr. Butterworths of New Zealand Ltd., P.O. Box 472, 203-207 Victoria St., Wellington, New Zealand. TEL 04-385-1479. FAX 04-385-1598. Ed. Christine O'Brie.
—CCC.
     Formerly: New Zealand Family Law Reports (ISSN 0111-8358)
     Description: Full text of latest decisions from Family Courts, the High Court and Court of Appeal.

346.01   NZ
BUTTERWORTHS FAMILY LAW SERVICE; for New Zealand use. 2 base vols. (plus q. update). NZ.$296. Butterworths of New Zealand Ltd., 203-207 Victoria St., P.O. Box 472, Wellington, New Zealand. TEL 04-385-1479. FAX 04-385-1598. Ed. Christine O'Brien. (looseleaf format)
     Description: Legislation and commentary for those involved in proceedings before the Family Court and in matters concerning the family generally.

346.01   UK
BUTTERWORTHS FAMILY LAW SERVICE; for UK use. 3 base vols. (plus updates 6/yr. and bulletin). $520. Butterworth & Co. (Publishers) Ltd. (Subsidiary of: Reed Elsevier plc), 88 Kingsway, London WC2B 6AB, England. TEL 71-405-6900. FAX 71-405-1332. (US addr.: Butterworth Legal Publishers, 90 Stiles Rd., Salem, NH 03079-9981. TEL 603-898-9664) Ed. P.M. Bromley. (looseleaf format)
     Description: Covers divorce petition for family law practitioners. Focuses on the consequences of divorce such as custody of the children, the distribution of family assets and the associated tax problems.

LAW — FAMILY AND MATRIMONIAL LAW

343.05   US
CALIFORNIA COMMUNITY PROPERTY WITH TAX ANALYSIS. 1985. base vol. with irreg. supplements. $140. Matthew Bender & Co., Inc., 11 Penn Plaza, New York, NY 10001. TEL 212-967-7707. Ed.Bd. (looseleaf format)
    Description: Practical, research-oriented treatise providing detailed coverage of the California Community Property System, and other family law matters affecting property ownership of married and unmarried couples and their tax consequences.

346.01   US
CALIFORNIA FAMILY LAW FIRST ALERT. 1982. 48/yr. $250. California Family Law Report, Inc., Box 5917, Sausalito, CA 94966. TEL 415-332-9000. Ed. Stephen Adams. (looseleaf format; back issues avail.) **Document type:** newsletter.

346.01 360   US   ISSN 0882-7842
KFC115.A15C35
CALIFORNIA FAMILY LAW MONTHLY. 1984. m. $265. Matthew Bender & Co., Inc., 11 Penn Plaza, New York, NY 10001. TEL 212-967-7707. FAX 212-967-1069. Ed.Bd.

346.01   US
CALIFORNIA FAMILY LAW: PRACTICE AND PROCEDURE. 1978. 7 base vols. (plus irreg. supplements). $1140. Matthew Bender & Co., Inc., 11 Penn Plaza, New York, NY 10001. TEL 212-967-7707. Ed. Hon. Christian E. Markey, Jr. (looseleaf format)
    Description: Covers law and procedure for contemporary family law problems, on issues arising in cases of dissolution, as well as those related to ongoing family situations.

346.01   US   ISSN 0164-7040
CALIFORNIA FAMILY LAW REPORT. 1977. m. $280. California Family Law Report, Inc., Box 5917, Sausalito, CA 94966. TEL 415-332-9000. Ed. Stephen Adams. (looseleaf format; back issues avail.) **Document type:** newsletter.

346.01   US
KFC115.C36
CALIFORNIA FAMILY LAW SERVICE NEWSALERT. 1986. bi-m. $180. Bancroft-Whitney Company, Box 7005, San Francisco, CA 94120-7005. TEL 800-848-4000. Ed. Alan Stephens. (looseleaf format) **Document type:** newsletter.

346.01   CN
CANADIAN FAMILY LAW GUIDE. 1976. m. Can.$570. C C H Canadian Ltd., 6 Garamond Ct., North York, ON M3C 1Z5, Canada. TEL 416-441-2992. FAX 416-444-9011.
    Description: Text of more than 175 federal, provincial and territorrial statutes on family law in Canada, commentary and court decisions concerning marriage and annulment of marriage, custody and access to children, status of children, guardianship, adoption and children in need of protection.

346.01   CN   ISSN 0832-6983
K3
CANADIAN FAMILY LAW QUARTERLY; a journal for practitioners. 1986. 3/yr. (plus bound vol.). Can.$135. Carswell, One Corporate Plaza, 2075 Kennedy Rd., Scarborough, ON M1T 3V4, Canada. TEL 416-609-8000. FAX 416-298-5094. Ed. James G. McLeod. adv. contact: M. Lalani. bk.rev. **Indexed:** C.L.I., Ind.Can.L.P.L.
    Description: Focuses on topics of practical interest to family law practitioners. Deals with current and emerging issues including "casual connection" in spousal support; mobility rights in child custody matters and other family issues.

346.01 362.7   US
CHILD FIND NEWS. 1985. q. free. Child Find of America, Inc., 7 Innis Ave., Box 277, New Paltz, NY 12561. TEL 914-255-1848. FAX 914-255-5706. Ed. Michael Messnen. circ. 16,000. **Document type:** newsletter.
    Description: Missing children and organizational news.

346.01   US   ISSN 1048-8669
KF549.A15C47
CHILD SUPPORT PROSECUTORS' BULLETIN. 1990. 6/yr. free. American Bar Association, 750 N. Lake Shore Dr., Chicago, IL 60611. TEL 312-988-5555. FAX 312-988-6281. **Document type:** newsletter.

346.01   US
▼**CHILDREN'S LAW NEWS.** 1992. irreg. (2-3/yr.) membership. State Bar of Wisconsin, Children's Law Section, 402 W. Wilson St., Madison, WI 53703. TEL 608-257-5502. FAX 608-257-5502. circ. 370. (back issues avail.) **Document type:** newsletter.

340   US   ISSN 0278-7210
KF479.A15
CHILDREN'S LEGAL RIGHTS JOURNAL. 1979. q. $55. William S. Hein & Co., Inc., 1285 Main St., Buffalo, NY 14209. TEL 716-883-8100. TELEX 91-209 WU 7 HEIN BUF. Ed. Robert Horowitz. (also avail. in microform from WSH; back issues avail.; reprint service avail. from WSH) **Indexed:** C.I.J.E., C.L.I., Child Devel.Abstr., Except.Child Educ.Abstr., Leg.Cont. **Document type:** academic/scholarly publication.
    —BLDSC (3172.990340); Faxon; UnCover.
    Description: Focuses on the relationship between the legal professional and children.
Refereed Serial

346.01   US
HV741.C5377X
CHILDREN'S MONITOR. 1988. m. free to members. Child Welfare League of America, Inc., 440 First St., N.W., Ste. 310, Washington, DC 20001. TEL 202-638-2952. FAX 202-638-4004. Ed. Mary Bourdette. circ. controlled. **Document type:** newsletter.
    Description: Presents the latest information on children's policy decisions at the federal level.

346.01   US
CONNECTICUT FAMILY LAW CITATIONS. 1980. s-a. $25 per no. Butterworth Legal Publishers (Salem) (Subsidiary of: Reed Elsevier plc), 8 Industrial Way, Bldg. C, Salem, NH 03079. TEL 800-548-4001. FAX 603-603-898-9858. Ed. Cynthia C. George.
    Description: Contains case names and citations accumulated from all reported and unreported cases from 1979 to date.

346.01 301.42   US
DISSOLUTION OF MARRIAGE. 1986. base vol. (plus a. suppl.). $70. Shepard's - McGraw-Hill, Inc., Box 35300, Colorado Springs, CO 80935-3530. TEL 800-525-2474.
    Description: Reviews current national trends in family law and their historical roots. Focuses on significant changes in state legislation, federal legislation and case law with complete documentation.

346.01   US   ISSN 1042-5934
KFO94.A15D66
DOMESTIC RELATIONS JOURNAL OF OHIO. 1989. bi-m. $125. Banks - Baldwin Law Publishing Co., University Center, Box 1974, Cleveland, OH 44106. TEL 216-721-7373. FAX 216-721-8055. Ed. Stanley Morganstern. (looseleaf format)
    Description: Commentary on developments in domestic relations law and practice on topics such as marital asset valuation and visitation rights. Includes current case analysis, recent legislative actions, and court rule changes.

346.01   US
DOMESTIC RELATIONS: THE SUBSTANTIVE LAW. 1984. base vol. (plus suppl.). $50. Butterworth Legal Publishers (Salem) (Subsidiary of: Reed Elsevier plc), 8 Industrial Way, Bldg. C, Salem, NH 03079. TEL 800-548-4001. FAX 603-898-9858. Ed. Ernest I. Rotenberg. (looseleaf format)

346.01   US   ISSN 0273-3560
KF506.A3
FAIRSHARE; the matrimonial law monthly. m. $145. Prentice Hall Law & Business, 270 Sylvan Ave., Englewood Cliffs, NJ 07632-2513. TEL 201-894-8484. FAX 201-894-8666. Ed. Ronald L. Brown.
    Description: Information on approaches, techniques, and precedents used by lawyers to solve the financial and economic questions of equitable distribution divorce practice.

346.01   GW   ISSN 0937-2180
FAMILIE UND RECHT. bi-m. DM.150. Luchterhand Verlag, Heddesdorferstr. 31, 56564 Neuwied, Germany. TEL 02631-801-0. FAX 02631-801210. **Document type:** bulletin.

346.01   US   ISSN 0163-710X
KF501.A3
FAMILY ADVOCATE. 1978. q. $39.50 (foreign $44.50. American Bar Association, Family Law Section, 750 N. Lake Shore Dr., Chicago, IL 60611. TEL 312-988-6069. Ed. Deborah Eisel. adv.; bk.rev. circ. 17,000. (also avail. in microfilm from WSH) **Indexed:** Adol.Ment.Hlth.Abstr., C.L.I., L.R.I., Leg.Per.
●Also available online. Vendor(s): West Services, Inc. (FAMADVO).
    —BLDSC (3865.557000); Faxon; UnCover.
    Formerly: Family Law Newsletter (ISSN 0427-9638)
    Description: Pratical advice for attorneys practicing family law.

346.01 360   US   ISSN 1047-5699
K3   CODEN: FCCREY
FAMILY AND CONCILIATION COURTS REVIEW. 1963. q. $47 to individuals; institutions $110 (effective 1994). (Association of Family and Conciliation Courts) Sage Publications, Inc., 2455 Teller Rd., Thousand Oaks, CA 91320. TEL 805-499-0721. FAX 805-499-0871. (Subscr. to: Sage Publications, Inc., Box 5084, Thousand Oaks, CA 91359; Overseas subscr. to: Sage Publications, Ltd., 6 Bonhill St., London EC2A 4PU, England; Sage Publications India Pvt. Ltd., P.O. Box 4215, New Delhi 110 048, India) Ed. Hugh McIsaac. index. circ. 2,200. (back issues avail.) **Indexed:** Psychol.Abstr. **Document type:** academic/scholarly publication.
    —BLDSC (3865.558700); UnCover.
    Formerly: Conciliation Courts Review.
    Description: Provides an international communication forum to develop and improve the practice of conciliation counseling as a complement to judicial procedures.

346.01   UK   ISSN 1350-1860
▼**FAMILY COURT PRACTICE.** 1993. a. Jordan Publishing Ltd., 21 St. Thomas St., Bristol BS1 6JS, England. TEL 0272-230600. FAX 0272-250486. **Document type:** trade publication.

346.01   UK   ISSN 0952-8199
KD750
FAMILY COURT REPORTER. 1987. w. £75 (typically set in Sep.). Justice of the Peace Ltd., Little London, Chichester, W. Sussex PO19 1PG, England. TEL 0243-787841. FAX 0243-779278. Ed. C.T. Latham. (back issues avail.) **Document type:** newsletter.
    Description: Provides family law report news and commentary.

346.01   UK   ISSN 0014-7281
K6
FAMILY LAW; every development in UK family law. 1971. 12/yr. £75. Jordan Publishing Ltd., 21 St. Thomas St., Bristol BS1 6JS, England. TEL 0272-230600. FAX 0272-250486. TELEX 449119. Ed. Elizabeth Walsh. bk.rev.; stat.; index. circ. 5,000. **Indexed:** Adol.Ment.Hlth.Abstr., ASSIA, C.L.I., L.R.I., Stud.Wom.Abstr. **Document type:** bulletin.
    —BLDSC (3865.565100); UnCover; SWETS.

346.01   UK   ISSN 1353-3614
▼**FAMILY LAW AND PRACTICE.** 1994. a. £17.50. Jordan Publishing Ltd., 21 St. Thomas St., Bristol BS1 6JS, England. TEL 0272-230600. FAX 0272-250486. Ed. Imogen Burton. **Document type:** academic/scholarly publication.

346.01   US
FAMILY LAW COMMENTATOR. 1975. 4/yr. membership only. Florida Bar, 650 Apalachee Pkwy., Tallahassee, FL 32399-2300. TEL 904-561-5650. circ. 2,950. **Document type:** newsletter.
    Incorporates (1991-1993): Family Law Recent Decisions.

346.01   UK   ISSN 1350-9438
▼**FAMILY LAW DIRECTORY.** 1993. a. Jordan Publishing Ltd., 21 St. Thomas St., Bristol BS1 6JS, England. TEL 0272-230600. FAX 0272-250486. Ed. Elizabeth Walsh. **Document type:** directory.

346.01   US
FAMILY LAW GUIDEBOOK; a handbook with forms. 1985. base vol. (plus suppl.). $50. Butterworth Legal Publishers (Salem) (Subsidiary of: Reed Elsevier plc), 8 Industrial Way, Bldg. C, Salem, NH 03079. TEL 800-548-4001. FAX 603-898-9858. Ed. Edward M. Ginsburg. (looseleaf format)

LAW — FAMILY AND MATRIMONIAL LAW

346.01   CN
FAMILY LAW IN ONTARIO; a practical guide for lawyers and law clerks. base vol. (plus irreg. updates). Can.$75. Canada Law Book Inc., 240 Edward St., Aurora, ON L4G 3S9, Canada. TEL 905-841-6472. FAX 905-841-5085. Ed. Michael G. Cochrane. adv. contact: Mary Cull.
    Description: For law clerks, paralegals and secretaries as well as lawyers seeking an up-to-date, practical look at family law in Ontario.

346.01   US
KFC115.A1F3
FAMILY LAW NEWS. 1977. 4/yr. membership. State Bar of California, Family Law Section, 555 Franklin St., San Francisco, CA 94102. TEL 415-561-8225. FAX 415-561-8228. (looseleaf format) **Document type:** newsletter.

346.01   US   ISSN 0014-729X
K6
FAMILY LAW QUARTERLY. 1967. q. $39.50 to non-members. American Bar Association, Family Law Section, 750 N. Lake Shore Dr., Chicago, IL 60611. TEL 312-988-6068. Ed. Linda D. Elrod. adv.; bk.rev.; abstr.; charts; index. circ. 16,000. (also avail. in microfiche from WSH; microfilm from UMI,WSH,PMC) **Indexed:** Adol.Ment.Hlth.Abstr., C.L.I., Crim.Just.Abstr., Curr.Cont., L.R.I., Leg.Cont., Leg.Per., SSCI, SSCI.
•Also available online. Vendor(s): West Services, Inc. (FAMLQ).
—BLDSC (3865.566000); Faxon; UnCover; SWETS.
    Description: Scholarly journal on judicial decisions, legislation, taxation, and summaries of state and local bar association projects.

346.01   US   ISSN 0148-7922
KF501.A3
FAMILY LAW REPORTER. 1974. w. $581. The Bureau of National Affairs, Inc., 1231 25th St., N.W., Washington, DC 20037. TEL 202-452-4200. FAX 202-822-8092. TELEX 285656 BNAI WSH. (Subscr. to: 9435 Key West Ave., Rockville, MD 20850. TEL 800-372-1033) Ed. David B. Jackson. (looseleaf format; back issues avail.) **Indexed:** CJPI.
—CCC.
    Description: Notification and reference service dealing with all significant state and federal developments in the field of family law.

345.05   UK   ISSN 0261-4375
FAMILY LAW REPORTS. 1980. 12/yr. £132. Jordan Publishing Ltd., 21 St. Thomas St., Bristol BS1 6JS, England. TEL 0272-230600. FAX 0272-250486. TELEX 449119. Eds. Nigel Lowe, Elizabeth Walsh. circ. 1,500. **Document type:** bulletin.
•Also available online. Vendor(s): Mead Data Central, Inc.

346.05   AT   ISSN 0726-5824
F1086
FAMILY LAW REPORTS. 1976. m. Aus.$125. Butterworths, P.O. Box 345, North Ryde, N.S.W. 2113, Australia. TEL 02-335-4444. FAX 02-335-4678. circ. 800. (back issues avail.)

346.01   US   ISSN 0149-1431
FAMILY LAW REVIEW. 1968. 4/yr. $35 to non-members. New York State Bar Association, Family Law Section, 1 Elk St., Albany, NY 12207-1096. TEL 518-463-3200. FAX 518-487-5699. Ed. Elliot Samuelson. (looseleaf format; back issues avail.) **Document type:** newsletter.

346.05   SA
FAMILY LAW SERVICE. s-a. R.300. Butterworth Publishers (Pty.) Ltd., P.O. Box 792, Durban 4000, South Africa. TEL 27-31-294247. FAX 27-31-283255. (looseleaf format) **Document type:** proceedings.

346.05   US
FAMILY LAW TAX GUIDE. 1985. m. $485. Commerce Clearing House, Inc., 4025 W. Peterson Ave., Chicago, IL 60646. TEL 312-583-8500.

346.01 336   UK   ISSN 1350-9446
▼**FAMILY LAW TAX GUIDE.** 1993. a. Jordan Publishing Ltd., 21 St. Thomas St., Bristol BS1 6JS, England. TEL 0272-230600. FAX 0272-250486. **Document type:** bulletin.

346.01   UK   ISSN 0968-8846
▼**FAMILY LAW TODAY.** 1992. m. £127 (foreign £149). Monitor Press, Rectory Rd., Great Waldingfield, Sudbury, Suffolk CO10 OTL, England. TEL 0787-378607. FAX 0787-880201. (back issues avail.) **Document type:** newsletter.

346.05   US
FAMILY MATTERS. 1989. q. $20. Center for Law and Social Policy, 1616 P St., N.W., Ste. 450, Washington, DC 20036. TEL 202-328-5140. FAX 202-328-5195. circ. 400. (back issues avail.)

346.01   US
FLORIDA FAMILY LAW PRACTICE. 1976. 4 base vols. (plus suppl. 4-5/yr.). $280. Butterworth Legal Publishers (Salem) (Subsidiary of: Reed Elsevier plc), 8 Industrial Way, Bldg. C, Salem, NH 03079. TEL 800-548-4001. FAX 603-898-9858. (looseleaf format)

346.01   US
FLORIDA JUVENILE PROCEDURE. 1985. base vol. (plus suppl. 2-3/yr.). $80. Butterworth Legal Publishers (Salem) (Subsidiary of: Reed Elsevier plc), 8 Industrial Way, Bldg. C, Salem, NH 03079. TEL 800-548-4001. FAX 603-898-9858. (looseleaf format)

346.01   US
GEORGIA FAMILY LAW MANUAL. 1985. 2 base vols. (plus suppl. 2-3/yr.). $80. Butterworth Legal Publishers (Salem) (Subsidiary of: Reed Elsevier plc), 8 Industrial Way, Bldg. C, Salem, NH 03079. TEL 800-548-4001. FAX 603-898-9858. (looseleaf format)

346.01   US
GITLIN ON DIVORCE; a guide to Illinois matrimonial law. 1991. 2 base vols. (plus a. supplement). $160. Butterworth Legal Publishers (Salem) (Subsidiary of: Reed Elsevier plc), 8 Industrial Way, Bldg. C, Salem, NH 03079. TEL 800-548-4001. FAX 603-898-9858. Ed. H. Joseph Gitlin. (looseleaf format)
    Description: Analyzes all areas of Illinois law from jurisdiction and venue to grounds and post-judgement proceedings.

346.01 301.4
HANDLING CHILD CUSTODY CASES. 1983. base vol. (plus a. suppl.). $70. Shepard's - McGraw-Hill, Inc., Box 35300, Colorado Springs, CO 80935-3530. TEL 800-525-2474.
    Description: Covers representation of parents, grandparents, adopting parents and children, as well as the intricacies of state and federal child custody laws.

346.01 613.9   US
HANDLING PREGNANCY AND BIRTH CASES. 1983. base vol. (plus a. suppl.). $70. Shepard's - McGraw-Hill, Inc., Box 35300, Colorado Springs, CO 80935-3530. TEL 800-525-2474.
    Description: Discusses surgical sterilizations, wrongful conception, wrongful pregnancy, artificial insemination, in vitro fertilization, surrogate motherhood, abortion, and prenatal injury actions.

346.01   US
ILLINOIS FAMILY LAWS AND COURT RULES. a. West Publishing Corp., 620 Opperman Dr., Eagan, MN 55123. TEL 612-687-8000; 800-328-9352. FAX 612-687-7302.

347.6   US   ISSN 0073-5019
ILLINOIS STATE BAR ASSOCIATION. FAMILY LAW BULLETIN. 1957. 4/yr. $16 to members. Illinois State Bar Association, Section of Family Law, Illinois Bar Center, Springfield, IL 62701. TEL 217-525-1760. FAX 217-525-0712. Ed. Harry M. Schaffner.

INCOME TAX AND FAMILY LAW HANDBOOK. see BUSINESS AND ECONOMICS — Public Finance, Taxation

346.01 362.7   PO   ISSN 0870-6565
INFANCIA E JUVENTUDE. 1955. q. Esc.1900 (effective 1994). Direccao Geral dos Servicos Tutelares de Menores, Av. Almirante Reis, No. 101, 5 Andar, 1197 Lisbon Codex, Portugal. TEL 352-47-09. FAX 52-69-85. Dir. Maria Manuela Baptista Lopes. bk.rev.; charts; illus.; stat. circ. 1,000.

INTERNATIONAL ENFORCEMENT LAW REPORTER. see LAW — International Law

THE INTERNATIONAL JOURNAL OF CHILDREN'S RIGHTS. see POLITICAL SCIENCE — Civil Rights

346.01   UK   ISSN 0950-4109
K9   CODEN: IJLFEN
INTERNATIONAL JOURNAL OF LAW AND THE FAMILY. 1987. 3/yr. £58($112) (effective 1994). Oxford University Press, Oxford Journals, Walton St., Oxford OX2 6DP, England. TEL 0865-56767. FAX 0865-56646. TELEX 837330-OXPRES-G. (U.S. subscr. to: Oxford University Press Inc., 2001 Evans Rd., Cary, NC 27513. TEL 919-677-0977) Eds. Robert Dingwall, John Eekelaar. adv. contact: Jane Parker. bk.rev. circ. 600. **Indexed:** ASSIA, Br.Hum.Ind., P.A.I.S., Sage Fam.Stud.Abstr., Sociol.Abstr. **Document type:** academic/scholarly publication.
—BLDSC (4542.312350); UnCover; SWETS; UMI. CCC.
    Description: Theoretical analyses of family law.

346.01   US
IOWA MATRIMONIAL LAW. 1986. base vol. (plus suppl.). $88. Butterworth Legal Publishers (Salem) (Subsidiary of: Reed Elsevier plc), 8 Industrial Way, Bldg. C, Salem, NH 03079. TEL 800-548-4001. FAX 603-898-9858. Ed. Daniel L. Bray. (looseleaf format)

346.01   UK   ISSN 0955-4475
K24
JOURNAL OF CHILD LAW. 1988. 4/yr. £75. Tolley Publishing Co. Ltd., Tolley House, 2 Addiscombe Rd., Croydon, Surrey CR9 5AF, England. TEL 081-686-9141. FAX 081-686-3155. Ed. Jane Fortin. adv.; bk.rev.; index. (back issues avail.) **Document type:** bulletin.
    Description: Aimed at practitioners in child law.

346.01   US   ISSN 0022-1066
K10
JOURNAL OF FAMILY LAW. 1961. q. $30. University of Louisville, School of Law, Louisville, KY 40292. TEL 502-588-6396. adv.; bk.rev.; abstr. circ. 1,200. (also avail. in microform from UMI; reprint service avail. from RRI) **Indexed:** Abstr.Soc.Work., Adol.Ment.Hlth.Abstr., C.L.I., Crim.Just.Abstr., Curr.Cont., L.R.I., Leg.Cont., Leg.Per., Psychol.Abstr., Soc.Work Res.& Abstr., Sociol.Abstr., SSCI. **Document type:** academic/scholarly publication.
—BLDSC (4983.700000); Faxon; UnCover; SWETS.

346.01   US   ISSN 0160-2098
K10
JOURNAL OF JUVENILE LAW. 1977. a. $12. (University of La Verne, College of Law) La Verne Law Review, Inc., 1950 Third St., La Verne, CA 91750. TEL 714-596-1848. Ed. Nancy I. Kellner. adv.; bk.rev. circ. 2,000. (also avail. in microform from WSH; back issues avail.; reprint service avail. from WSH) **Indexed:** Adol.Ment.Hlth.Abstr., C.L.I., Crim.Just.Abstr., L.R.I., Leg.Per. **Document type:** academic/scholarly publication.
—UnCover.

346.01   US   ISSN 0161-7109
K10   CODEN: JFCJD6
JUVENILE AND FAMILY COURT JOURNAL. 1949. q. $40 (foreign $46). National Council of Juvenile and Family Court Judges, Box 8978, University of Nevada, Reno, NV 89507. TEL 702-784-6012. Ed. Marie Mildon. bk.rev.; cum.index: 1974-1984. circ. 2,700. (also avail. in microform from UMI; back issues avail.; reprint service avail. from RRI,UMI) **Indexed:** Adol.Ment.Hlth.Abstr., C.L.I., CJPI, Crim.Just.Abstr., Curr.Cont., L.R.I., Leg.Per., Soc.Work Res.& Abstr., SSCI. **Document type:** academic/scholarly publication.
—BLDSC (5077.290000); Faxon; UnCover; UMI.
    Former titles: Journal of Juvenile and Family Courts (ISSN 0162-0525); Juvenile Justice (ISSN 0093-7231); (until 1972): Juvenile Court Judges Journal (ISSN 0022-7153)
    Description: Compendium of articles centering on a variety of juvenile justice issues, occasionally exploring a single topic of current interest to juvenile justice professionals.

LAW — FAMILY AND MATRIMONIAL LAW

346.09 US ISSN 1062-2926
KF9772
JUVENILE AND FAMILY JUSTICE TODAY. 6/yr. $16. National Council of Juvenile and Family Court Judges, Box 8970, University of Nevada, Reno, NV 89507. TEL 702-784-6012. Ed. Verita Black. circ. 2,500. **Document type:** newsletter.
—UnCover.
Formerly: Juvenile and Family Court Newsletter (ISSN 0162-9859)
Description: News for members of the council's officers, educational programs, and results of studies in the field of juvenile justice.

364.36 US ISSN 0279-2257
KF9776.3
JUVENILE AND FAMILY LAW DIGEST. 1967. m. $120 (foreign $130). National Council of Juvenile and Family Court Judges, Box 8978, University of Nevada, Reno, NV 89507. TEL 702-784-6012. Ed. Lindsay G. Arthur. circ. 2,700. (also avail. in microform from UMI; back issues avail.; reprint service avail. from RRI,UMI) **Indexed:** Abstr.Crim.& Pen., C.L.I., CJPI, Leg.Per.
—Faxon; UnCover; UMI.
Former titles: Juvenile Law Digest (ISSN 0162-5055); Juvenile Court Digest (ISSN 0085-2430)
Description: Digest of current juvenile and family law court cases from state level to Supreme Court.

JUVENILE LAW REPORTS. see LAW — Criminal Law

346.01 UK ISSN 0265-1211
LAW REPORTS: CHANCERY AND FAMILY DIVISION. m. £55 (overseas £58) (effective Aug. 1993). Incorporated Council of Law Reporting for England and Wales, 3 Stone Bldgs., Lincoln's Inn, London WC2A 3XN, England. TEL 071-242 6471. FAX 07-831-5247. Ed. C.J. Ellis. (also avail. in microfiche from BHP)

346.01 301.42 US
MARRIAGE AND FAMILY LAW AGREEMENTS. 1984. base vol. (plus a. suppl.). $70. Shepard's - McGraw-Hill, Inc., Box 35300, Colorado Springs, CO 80935-3530. TEL 800-525-2474.
Description: Covers antenuptial agreements, nonmarital cohabitation agreements, separation and property settlement agreements and surrogate motherhood contracts.

346.01 US
MASSACHUSETTS ACTIONS AND REMEDIES: FAMILY LAW. 1991. base vol. (plus supplements). $75. Butterworth Legal Publishers (Salem) (Subsidiary of: Reed Elsevier plc), 8 Industrial Way, Bldg. C, Salem, NH 03079. TEL 800-548-4001. FAX 603-898-9858. Eds. Marc G. Perlin, Assunta DiBiase Perez. (looseleaf format)
Description: Surveys the applicable laws, rules, statutes and relevant cases pertaining to family law for Massachusetts practitioners, with particular emphasis on new and developing legal doctrines concerning children, parents, marriage and dissolution of marriage.

346.01 US
MASSACHUSETTS FAMILY LAW JOURNAL. 1983. 6/yr. $75. Butterworth Legal Publishers (Salem) (Subsidiary of: Reed Elsevier plc), 8 Industrial Way, Bldg. C, Salem, NH 03079. TEL 800-548-4001. FAX 603-898-9858. cum.index. (looseleaf format; back issues avail.)
Description: Family law articles, case comments, and Massachusetts Probate Court decisions.

346.01 II
MATRIMONIAL LAW REPORTER. (Text in English) 1977. m. Rs.70. G.R. Arora, 33-34 Gokhale Market, Delhi 110054, India. Ed. Shiv Narayan. adv.; bk.rev. circ. 3,000.

346.01 US ISSN 0736-4881
MATRIMONIAL STRATEGIST. 1983. m. $155. New York Law Publishing Co., 345 Park Ave. S., New York, NY 10010. TEL 212-545-6170. FAX 212-696-1848.
Description: Reports on taxation, valuation, discovery, trial, appeal, ethical dilemmas, fee arrangements and other topics for matrimonial lawyers.

346.01 US
MINNESOTA FAMILY LAW JOURNAL. 1981. bi-m. $75. Butterworth Legal Publishers (Subsidiary of: Reed Elsevier plc), 8 Industrial Way, Bldg. C, Salem, NH 03079-2837. TEL 800-333-3839. Ed. Stephen Liebo. (back issues avail.)
Description: Family law articles, case comments and court decisions.

346.01 US
MINNESOTA FAMILY LAW PRACTICE MANUAL. base vol. (plus suppl. 6/yr.). $95. Butterworth Legal Publishers (Salem) (Subsidiary of: Reed Elsevier plc), 8 Industrial Way, Bldg. C, Salem, NH 03079. TEL 800-548-4001. FAX 603-898-9858. Ed. Cathy E. Gorlin. (looseleaf format)

346.01 US
MISSOURI BAR. FAMILY LAW SECTION. NEWSLETTER. 3/yr. membership. Missouri Bar, Family Law Section, 326 Monroe St., Box 119, Jefferson City, MO 65102. TEL 314-635-4128. FAX 314-635-2811. Ed. Anita I. Rodarte. circ. 750. **Document type:** newsletter.

NATIONAL COUNCIL FOR ADOPTION. LEGAL NOTES. see SOCIAL SERVICES AND WELFARE

NATIONAL COUNCIL FOR ADOPTION. MEMO. see SOCIAL SERVICES AND WELFARE

346.01 US
▼**NEW HAMPSHIRE JUVENILE LAWS (YEAR).** 1992. a. $30. Butterworth Legal Publishers (Salem) (Subsidiary of: Reed Elsevier plc), 8 Industrial Way, Bldg. C, Salem, NH 03079. TEL 800-548-4001. FAX 603-898-9858. Ed.Bd. (looseleaf format)
Description: Compendium of statutes and laws pertaining to paternity, custody and child support, adoption, surrogacy, termination of parental rights, and the statutes governing human services for children.

340 US
NEW HAMPSHIRE PRACTICE SERIES: FAMILY LAW. (2nd ed., 1992) 1982. 2 base vols. (plus irreg. supplements). $130. Butterworth Legal Publishers (Salem) (Subsidiary of: Reed Elsevier plc), 8 Industrial Way, Bldg. C, Salem, NH 03079. TEL 800-548-4001. FAX 603-898-9858. Ed. Charles D. Douglas, III.
Description: Detailed treatment of all aspects of family law from premarital issues through marriage, separation and divorce.

346.01 364 US
NEW YORK (CITY). DEPARTMENT OF JUVENILE JUSTICE. ANNUAL REPORT. a. Department of Juvenile Justice, 365 Broadway, New York, NY 10013-3991. TEL 212-925-7779. Ed.Bd. **Document type:** government publication.

NEW YORK ACTIONS AND REMEDIES. see LAW — Civil Law

346.01 US ISSN 1045-2842
NEW YORK FAMILY LAW HANDBOOK. Key Title: Gould's Family Law Handbook of New York. 1988. a. $19.95. Gould Publications (Binghamton), 199-300 State St., Binghamton, NY 13901. TEL 607-724-3000. FAX 607-723-4285.
Description: Presents the complete text of the Family Court Act, domestic relations law, uniform family court rules and the social service law.

346.01 US ISSN 1049-6319
NEW YORK FAMILY LAW UPDATE. 1990. 48/yr. $249 (effective 1992). New York Family Law Institute, Inc., 32 S. Monsey Rd., Monsey, NY 10952. TEL 914-426-3930. FAX 914-426-3930. (Subscr. to: Box 774, Monsey, NY 10952-0774) Ed. David A. Blumberg. s-a. cum.index. (looseleaf format; back issues avail.) **Document type:** newsletter.
Description: Provides timely reports of developments in matrimonial and family law, for New York lawyers, judges and related professionals.

346.01 US
NEW YORK GITLITZ ON DIVORCES AND ANNULMENTS. 1988. a. $34.95. Gould Publications (Binghamton), 199-300 State St., Binghamton, NY 13901. TEL 607-724-3000. FAX 1-607-725-4285. adv.; bk.rev. (looseleaf format)
Formerly: New York Uncontested Divorces and Annulments.
Description: Guide to legal rules and requirements applicable to uncontested divorces and annulments in NYS.

346.01 CN
ONTARIO ANNOTATED FAMILY LAW SERVICE. q. Can.$350. Butterworths Canada Ltd., Part of the Reed Elsevier group, 75 Clegg Rd., Markham, ON L6G 1A1, Canada. TEL 905-479-2665. FAX 905-479-2826. (looseleaf format)
Description: Practical reference for the practitioner of Ontario family law.

346.01 CN
ONTARIO FAMILY LAW ACT MANUAL. 5/yr. Can.$132. Canada Law Book Inc., 240 Edward St., Aurora, ON L4G 3S9, Canada. TEL 905-841-6472. FAX 905-841-5085. adv. contact: Mary Cull. (looseleaf format)
Formerly: Ontario Family Law Reform Act Manual.

346.01 301.4 CN
ONTARIO FAMILY LAW QUANTUM SERVICE. q. Can.$190. Butterworths Canada Ltd., Part of the Reed Elsevier group, 75 Clegg Rd., Markham, ON L6G 1A1, Canada. TEL 905-479-2665. FAX 905-479-2826.
Description: Reference on facts relevant to the support amounts awarded in family law cases in Ontario.

346.01 CN ISSN 0835-636X
ONTARIO FAMILY LAW REPORTER. 1987. m. Can.$250. Butterworths Canada Ltd., Part of the Reed Elsevier group, 75 Clegg Rd., Markham, ON L6G 1A1, Canada. TEL 905-479-2665. FAX 905-479-2826. Eds. Malcolm C. Kronby, Jeffery Wilson. cum.index. circ. 330. (back issues avail.)
Description: Summarizes and analyzes unreported cases and family law developments.

PANEL NEWS; a quarterly journal for guardians ad litem, reporting officers and other child care law professionals. see SOCIAL SERVICES AND WELFARE

346.01 US
PIED PIPER. 1980. q. donation. Organization for the Enforcement of Child Support, Inc., 1712 Deer Park Rd., Finksburg, MD 21048. TEL 410-876-1826. Eds. William & Elaine Fromm. (looseleaf format) **Document type:** newsletter.
Description: Covers child support enforcement procedures at federal and state levels.

346.01 UK ISSN 0954-6421
PRACTITIONERS' CHILD LAW BULLETIN. 10/yr. £85. Longman Law, Tax and Finance, 21-27 Lamb's Conduit St., London WC1N 3NJ, England. TEL 0279-429655. (Subscr. to: Longman Group UK Ltd., Fourth Ave., Pinnacles, Harlow, Essex CM19 5AA, England) bk.rev.
Formerly: Practitioners' Child Law Journal.

346.01 UK
RAYDEN & JACKSON ON DIVORCE & FAMILY MATTERS. 2 base vols. (plus updates). $790. Butterworth & Co. (Publishers) Ltd. (Subsidiary of: Reed Elsevier plc), 80 Kingsway, London WC2B 6AB, England. TEL 71-409-6900. FAX 71-405-1332. (US addr.: Butterworth Legal Publishers, 90 Stiles Rd., Salem, NH 03079-9981. TEL 603-898-9664)

346.01 CN ISSN 0317-4859
LAW
REPORTS OF FAMILY LAW (3RD SERIES). 1970. 24/yr. (in 6 vols.). Can.$118. Carswell, One Corporate Plaza, 2075 Kennedy Rd., Scarborough, ON M1T 3V4, Canada. TEL 416-609-8000. FAX 416-298-5094. Ed. James G. McLeod. adv. contact: M. Lalani. cum.index. **Indexed:** C.L.I., Ind.Can.L.P.L., L.R.I.

LAW — International Law

346   BE   ISSN 0779-4711
REVUE TRIMESTRIELLE DE DROIT FAMILIAL. Short title: R.T.D.F. (Text in French) q. 3000 BEF (outside Europe 3800 BEF) (effective 1993). Maison Ferdinand Larcier S.A., Rue des Minimes 39, B-1000 Brussels, Belgium. TEL 32-2-5124712. FAX 32-2-5139009. Ed. J.L. Renchon. **Document type:** academic/scholarly publication.
   Former titles (until 1993): Revue de Droit Familial (ISSN 0482-7678); (until 1978): Cahiers de Droit Familial (ISSN 0772-1994)

STATE REPRODUCTIVE HEALTH MONITOR; legislative proposals and actions. see *MEDICAL SCIENCES — Obstetrics And Gynecology*

346.01   US   ISSN 0890-5355
KFT94.A59
TENNESSEE FAMILY LAW LETTER. 1986. m. $80. M. Lee Smith Publishers & Printers, 162 Fourth Ave. N., Nashville, TN 37219-8867. TEL 615-242-7395. FAX 615-256-6601. Ed. W. Walton Garrett. **Document type:** newsletter.
   Description: Digest of Tennessee family law developments.

346.01 305.31   US   ISSN 1062-1768
TODAY'S DADS; Wisconsin's voice for equal justice. 1988. m. $20 membership (foreign $25). Wisconsin Fathers for Equal Justice, Inc., Box 1742, Madison, WI 53701-1741. TEL 608-255-3237. Ed. William N. Fetzner. adv.; bk.rev. circ. 800. **Document type:** newsletter.
   Description: Offers information regarding father's relationship with children, custody, child support, divorce, paternity, and equal rights.

UTAH. JUVENILE COURT. ANNUAL REPORT. see *LAW — Judicial Systems*

346.01   US
▼**VERMONT FAMILY LAW (YEAR).** 1992. a. $35. Butterworth Legal Publishers (Salem) (Subsidiary of: Reed Elsevier plc), 8 Industrial Way, Bldg. C, Salem, NH 03079. TEL 800-548-4001. FAX 603-898-9858. Ed.Bd. (looseleaf format)
   Description: Single volume reference for all aspects of Vermont family law, including all relevant statutes, rules of practice and family court rules.

346.01   US
VIRGINIA FAMILY LAW. 1991. base vol. (plus s-a. suppl.). $80. Butterworth Legal Publishers (Salem) (Subsidiary of: Reed Elsevier plc), 8 Industrial Way, Bldg. C, Salem, NH 03079. TEL 800-548-4001. FAX 603-898-9858. Ed. Anita Butler. (looseleaf format)
   Description: Addresses issues which practitioners need to be aware of in handling family law cases in Virginia.

346.01   US
WASHINGTON STATE BAR ASSOCIATION. FAMILY LAW SECTION. NEWSLETTER. 1974. irreg. $20. Washington State Bar Association, Family Law Section, 500 Westin Bldg., 2001 Sixth Ave., Seattle, WA 98121. TEL 206-727-8239. FAX 206-727-8320. circ. 750. (looseleaf format) **Document type:** newsletter.

346.01   CN   ISSN 0713-7907
WEEKLY DIGEST OF FAMILY LAW. 1982. w. (50/yr.). Can.$375. Carswell, One Corporate Plaza, 2075 Kennedy Rd., Scarborough, ON M1T 3V4, Canada. TEL 416-609-8000. FAX 416-298-5094. adv.; cum.index. circ. 240. (back issues avail.)
   Description: Pre-reporting service consisting of digests of all available family law judgments from courts across Canada. Includes decisions of young offenders.

346.01   US
WISCONSIN JOURNAL OF FAMILY LAW. q. membership. State Bar of Wisconsin, Family Law Section, 402 W. Wilson St., Madison, WI 53703. TEL 608-257-3838. FAX 608-257-5502. (back issues avail.) **Document type:** newsletter.
   Description: Covers issues pertaining to Wisconsin family law.

ZENTRALBLATT FUER JUGENDRECHT; Jugend und Familie - Jugendhilfe - Jugendgerichtshilfe. see *LAW — Abstracting, Bibliographies, Statistics*

LAW — International Law

341   GW   ISSN 0581-9792
A D A C HANDBUCH: SCHMERZENSGELD-BETRAEGE. biennial. DM.58. (Allgemeiner Deutscher Automobil-Club e.V.) A D A C Verlag GmbH, Am Westpark 8, 81373 Munich, Germany. TEL 089-7676-0.
   Formerly: Schmerzensgeld-Betraege.

A P T I R C BULLETIN. (Asian-Pacific Tax and Investment Research Centre) see *BUSINESS AND ECONOMICS — Public Finance, Taxation*

341   US   ISSN 1049-7803
KF200
A S I L NEWSLETTER. 1961. 5/yr. American Society of International Law, 2223 Massachusetts Ave. N.W., Washington, DC 20008-2864. TEL 202-939-6000. FAX 202-797-7133. **Document type:** newsletter.
   Former titles: American Society of International Law. Newsletter (ISSN 0066-0639); American Society of International Law. Letter to Members.
   Description: Newsletter for society members.

341   NE   ISSN 0001-401X
JX74
ACADEMIE DE DROIT INTERNATIONAL DE LA HAYE. RECUEIL DES COURS/HAGUE ACADEMY OF INTERNATIONAL LAW. COLLECTED COURSES. (Text in English, French) 1923. 5/yr. $120 per no. Kluwer Academic Publishers, Postbus 17, 3300 AA Dordrecht, Netherlands. TEL 31-78-334911. FAX 31-78-334254. TELEX 29245 KAPG NL. (Dist. by: Kluwer Academic Publishers Group, P.O. Box 322, 3300 AH Dordrecht, Netherlands. TEL 31-78-524400. FAX 31-78-524474; N. America dist. addr.: Box 358, Accord Sta., Hingham, MA 02018-0358. TEL 617-871-6600. FAX 617-871-6528) index, cum.index. **Indexed:** Foreign Leg.Per. **Document type:** monographic series.
   Refereed Serial

AIR & SPACE LAW. see *TRANSPORTATION — Air Transport*

ALLIANCE ENVIRONMENTAL LAW NEWSLETTER. see *ENVIRONMENTAL STUDIES*

341.57   NE
ALLIANCE EUROPEAN COMMUNITY LAW NEWS; review of current legal developments in the E E C. (Text in English) 1990. 5/yr. fl.200($108) (effective 1994). Kluwer Law and Taxation Publishers (Subsidiary of: Wolters Kluwer N.V.), P.O. Box 23, 7400 GA Deventer, Netherlands. TEL 31-5700-47261. FAX 31-5700-22244. (Dist. by: Librosso Distribution Center, P.O. Box 23, 7400 GA Deventer, Netherlands. TEL 31-5700-33155. FAX 31-5700-33834; In N. America: Kluwer Law and Taxation Publishers, 675 Massachusetts Ave., Cambridge, MA 02139. TEL 617-354-0140. FAX 617-354-8595) Ed.Bd. **Document type:** newsletter.
   Formerly (until 1993): E E C Newsletter (ISSN 0925-4641)
   Description: Highlights developments in European case law, legislation and administrative decisions.

ALMANAC OF CHINA'S FOREIGN ECONOMIC RELATIONS AND TRADE. see *BUSINESS AND ECONOMICS — International Development And Assistance*

341   US
AMERICAN FOREIGN LAW ASSOCIATION NEWSLETTER. no.24, 1974. 3/yr. $20. American Foreign Law Association, c/o James R. Maxeiner, Ed., 111 White Plains Post Rd., Bronxville, NY 10708. circ. 550 (controlled). (processed) **Document type:** newsletter.
   Description: Reports on programs sponsored by the Association and on other activities related to foreign, international and comparative law and international affairs of interest to Association members and practitioners.

340.5   US   ISSN 0002-919X
K1
AMERICAN JOURNAL OF COMPARATIVE LAW. 1952. q. $20. American Association for the Comparative Study of Law, 394 Boalt Hall, University of California, Berkeley, CA 94720. FAX 415-643-6171. Ed. Richard M Buxbaum. adv.; bk.rev.; bibl.; index, cum.index: 1952-1961, 1962-1967, 1968-1977. circ. 2,100. (also avail. in microform from UMI; reprint service avail. from ISI,RRI,UMI) **Indexed:** A.B.C.Pol.Sci., Abstr.Bk.Rev.Curr.Leg.Per., Amer.Bibl.Slavic & E.Eur.Stud., Bibl.Ind., C.L.I., Crim.Just.Abstr., Curr.Cont., ELLIS, Foreign Leg.Per., Int.Lab.Doc., L.R.I., Leg.Cont., Leg.Per., P.A.I.S., SSCI.
   —BLDSC (0824.100000); Faxon; UnCover; SWETS; UMI.

341   US   ISSN 0002-9300
JX1
AMERICAN JOURNAL OF INTERNATIONAL LAW. 1907. 4/yr. $110 (foreign $125). American Society of International Law, 2223 Massachusetts Ave., N.W., Washington, DC 20008-2864. TEL 202-939-6000. FAX 202-797-7133. Ed.Bd. adv. contact: Sandra Liebel. bk.rev.; bibl.; index, cum.index thru vol.84, 1990. circ. 7,000. (also avail. in microfilm from UMI,WSH; microfiche from IDC; back issues avail.) **Indexed:** A.B.C.Pol.Sci., Amer.Bibl.Slavic & E.Eur.Stud., Amer.Hist.& Life (until 1993), C.L.I., Curr.Cont., Deep Sea Res.& Oceanogr.Abstr., Hist.Abstr. (until 1993), HR Rep., Int.Lab.Doc., L.R.I., Leg.Cont., Leg.Info.Manage.Ind., Leg.Per., Mar.Aff.Bibl., Mid.East: Abstr.& Ind., P.A.I.S., Peace Res.Abstr., Refug.Abstr., Sel.Water Res.Abstr., So.Pac.Per.Ind., Soc.Sci.Ind., SSCI. **Document type:** academic/scholarly publication.
   ●Also available online. Vendor(s): Mead Data Central, Inc.
   Also available on CD-ROM. Producer(s): University Microfilms International.
   —BLDSC (0826.800000); Faxon; UnCover; SWETS; UMI. **CCC.**
   Description: Articles and commentary on developments and judicial decisions in international law.

341 382   US   ISSN 1050-4109
AMERICAN REVIEW OF INTERNATIONAL ARBITRATION. 1990. 4/yr. fl.230($120) (effective 1993). (Columbia University, Parker School of Foreign and Comparative Law) Transnational Juris Publications, Inc., 1 Bridge St., Irvington-on-Hudson, NY 10533. TEL 914-591-4288. FAX 914-591-2688. (Dist. outside N. America by: Kluwer Law and Taxation Publishers, Librosso Distribution Centre, P.O. Box 23, 7400 GA Deventer, Netherlands. TEL 31-5700-33155) Ed.Bd; Pub. Heike Fenton. bk.rev.; bibl.
   —UnCover.
   Description: Provides comprehensive coverage of developments in international commercial arbitration, including analysis of recent cases and arbitration awards.

341   US   ISSN 0272-5037
AMERICAN SOCIETY OF INTERNATIONAL LAW. PROCEEDINGS OF THE ANNUAL MEETING. 1907. a. $60 (foreign $70). American Society of International Law, 2223 Massachusetts Ave. N.W., Washington, DC 20008-2864. TEL 202-265-4313. FAX 202-797-7133. Ed. John Lawrence Hargrove. adv. contact: Sandra Liebel. circ. 2,000. (also avail. in microform from UMI,WSH; back issues avail.; reprint service avail. from WSH) **Indexed:** Amer.Hist.& Life (until 1988), C.L.I., Deep Sea Res.& Oceanogr.Abstr., Hist.Abstr. (until 1988), L.R.I., Leg.Per., Mar.Aff.Bibl. **Document type:** proceedings.
   —BLDSC (6841.279500); UnCover; UMI. **CCC.**
   Formerly (until 1974): American Society of International Law. Proceedings (ISSN 0066-0647)
   Description: Digest of the annual meeting.

LAW — INTERNATIONAL LAW

341 — NE
AMSTERDAM FINANCIAL SERIES. (In 4 sections: Financial Services and E E C Law; Banking and E E C Law: Commentary; Insurance and E E C Law: Commentary; Stock Exchange and E E C Law: Commentary) (Text in English) 1991. base vols. (plus irreg. updates). price varies. Kluwer Law and Taxation Publishers (Subsidiary of: Wolters Kluwer N.V.), P.O. Box 23, 7400 GA Deventer, Netherlands. TEL 31-5700-47261. FAX 31-5700-22244. TELEX 49295 KLUDV NL. (Dist. by: Libresso Distribution Centre, P.O. Box 23, 7400 GA Deventer, Netherlands. TEL 31-5700-33155. FAX 31-5700-33834; In N. America: Kluwer Law and Taxation Publishers, 675 Massachusetts Ave., Cambridge, MA 02139. TEL 617-354-0140. FAX 617-354-8595) Ed. Martijn van Empel. (looseleaf format)
Description: Comprehensive guide to the impact of European Communities regulations on the financial services sector.

AMSTERDAM FINANCIAL SERIES. BANKING AND E E C LAW: COMMENTARY. see *BUSINESS AND ECONOMICS — Banking And Finance*

AMSTERDAM FINANCIAL SERIES. FINANCIAL SERVICES AND E E C LAW: MATERIALS AND CASES. see *BUSINESS AND ECONOMICS — Banking And Finance*

AMSTERDAM FINANCIAL SERIES. INSURANCE AND E E C LAW: COMMENTARY. see *INSURANCE*

AMSTERDAM FINANCIAL SERIES. STOCK EXCHANGE AND E E C LAW: COMMENTARY. see *BUSINESS AND ECONOMICS — Investments*

341 K1 — BE — ISSN 0770-6472
ANNALES DE DROIT DE LOUVAIN; revue trimestrielle. 1930. q. 3100 BEF (foreign 3600 BEF) (effective 1993). (Universite Catholique de Louvain, Association des Diplomes en Droit) Maison Ferdinand Larcier S.A., Rue des Minimes 39, 1000 Brussels, Belgium. TEL 32-2-5124712. FAX 32-2-5139009. Eds. Jacques van Compernolle, Gilberte Closset-Marechal. adv.; bk.rev.; bibl. **Indexed:** ELLIS. **Document type:** academic/scholarly publication.
Formerly (until 1981): Annales de Droit (ISSN 0303-9595)
Description: Discusses significant current questions pertaining to Belgian, European and international law, with particular emphasis on the evolution of the law.
Refereed Serial

341 323.4 DT30 — FR — ISSN 0570-1937
ANNEE AFRICAINE. 1963. a. price varies. Editions A. Pedone, 13 rue Soufflot, 75005 Paris, France. Ed. A. Pedone. **Indexed:** Documentatieblad.

341 JX21 — FR — ISSN 0066-3085
ANNUAIRE FRANCAIS DE DROIT INTERNATIONAL. 1955. a. price varies. (Academie de Droit International de la Haye, Groupe Francais des Anciens Auditeurs, NE) C N R S Editions, 20-22 rue St. Amand, 75015 Paris, France. TEL 45-33-16-00. FAX 45-33-92-13. TELEX 200 356 F. adv.; bk.rev.; index; circ. 1,500 (controlled). **Indexed:** Int.Lab.Doc.
—BLDSC (1069.500000); SWETS.

ANNUAL ON TERRORISM (YEAR). see *CRIMINOLOGY AND LAW ENFORCEMENT*

341 — SP — ISSN 0212-0747
ANUARIO DE DERECHO INTERNACIONAL. 1975. a. 3000 ptas.($36) (foreign 5000 ptas.). (Universidad de Navarra, Departamento de Derecho Internacional Publico) Servicio de Publicaciones de la Universidad de Navarra, S.A., Apdo. 177, 31080 Pamplona, Spain. TEL 94-25-2700. Dir. Romualdo Bermejo Garcia. bk.rev.
—BLDSC (1563.455000).

341 — EC — ISSN 0570-4251
ANUARIO ECUATORIANO DE DERECHO INTERNACIONAL. 1964. a. $24. Universidad Central del Ecuador, Instituto de Investigaciones Internationales, Apdo. 17-07-9078, Quito, Ecuador. FAX 5932-234392. Ed. Mario A. Gomez de la Torre. bk.rev. circ. 2,000.

341 — US — ISSN 0920-7775
ANUARIO INTERAMERICANO DE DERECHOS HUMANOS/INTER-AMERICAN YEARBOOK ON HUMAN RIGHTS. (Text in English and Spanish) 1987. a., vol.5, 1993 (for the year 1989). fl.520 (effective 1993). (Organization of American States, Inter-American Commission on Human Rights) Martinus Nijhoff Publishers, Human Rights and International Law (Subsidiary of: Kluwer Academic Publishers Group), Postbus 163, 3300 AD Dordrecht, Netherlands. TEL 31-78-334911. FAX 31-78-334254. TELEX 29245 KAPG NL. (Dist. by: Kluwer Academic Publishers Group, P.O. Box 322, 3300 AH Dordrecht, Netherlands. TEL 31-78-524400; N. America dist. addr.: Box 358, Accord Sta., Hingham, MA 02018-0358. TEL 617-871-6600) **Indexed:** Refug.Abstr.

341 K1 — UK — ISSN 0268-0556 CODEN: ALQUEJ
ARAB LAW QUARTERLY. 1986. 4/yr. fl.564($294) (effective 1994). (Society of Arab Comparative and International Law) Graham & Trotman Ltd. (Subsidiary of: Kluwer Academic Publishers Group), Sterling House, 66 Wilton Rd., London SW1V 1DE, England. (Dist. by: Kluwer Academic Publishers Group, P.O. Box 322, 3300 AH Dordrecht, Netherlands. TEL 31-78-524400. FAX 31-78-524474; N. America dist. addr.: Box 358, Accord Station, Hingham, MA 02018-0358. TEL 617-871-6600. FAX 617-871-6528) Ed. Mark S.W. Hoyle. **Indexed:** Foreign Leg.Per., Per.Islam. (1991-). **Document type:** academic/scholarly publication.
—BLDSC (1583.239850); SWETS.
Description: Articles on legal developments throughout the Arab world, covering secular and Shari'a law, transnational affairs, commercial law and international comparative law.

340 K1 — UK — ISSN 0957-0411
ARBITRATION INTERNATIONAL. 1985. q. fl.394($205) (effective 1994). (London Court of International Arbitration) Graham and Trotman Ltd. (Subsidiary of: Kluwer Academic Publishers Group), Sterling House, 66 Wilton Rd., London SW1V 1DE, England. (Dist. by: Kluwer Academic Publishers Group, P.O. Box 322, 3300 AH Dordrecht, Netherlands. TEL 31-78-524400. FAX 31-78-524474; N. America dist. addr.: Box 358, Accord Station, Hingham, MA 02018-0358. TEL 617-871-6600. FAX 617-871-6528) Ed. Jan Paulsson. circ. 1,000. (looseleaf format) **Document type:** academic/scholarly publication.
—BLDSC (1588.340000); UnCover; SWETS.
Description: Publishes articles relating to the development and application of international arbitration as a means of international business dispute resolution.

ARBITRATION MATERIALS. see *BUSINESS AND ECONOMICS — International Commerce*

341 — US — ISSN 0743-6963
ARIZONA JOURNAL OF INTERNATIONAL & COMPARATIVE LAW. 1982. a. University of Arizona, College of Law, Tucson, AZ 85721. TEL 602-621-5593. FAX 602-621-9140. Ed. Kristine Fox. adv.; bk.rev.; index. circ. 400. (also avail. in microform from UMI; reprint service avail. from RRI,UMI) **Document type:** academic/scholarly publication.
—BLDSC (1668.438200); UnCover.

341 — NE — ISSN 0928-432X
▼**ASIAN YEARBOOK OF INTERNATIONAL LAW.** 1993. a. fl.250. Martinus Nijhoff Publishers, Human Rights and International Law (Subsidiary of: Kluwer Academic Publishers Group), Postbus 163, 3300 AD Dordrecht, Netherlands. TEL 31-78-334911. FAX 31-78-334254. TELEX 29245 KAPG NL. (Dist. by: Kluwer Academic Publishers Group, P.O. Box 322, 3300 AH Dordrecht, Netherlands. TEL 31-78-524400. FAX 31-78-524474; N. America dist. addr.: Box 358, Accord Sta., Hingham, MA 02018-0358. TEL 617-871-6600. FAX 617-871-6528) Ed.Bd. **Document type:** academic/scholarly publication.
—UnCover.
Description: Discusses international law from an Asian perspective, including articles by experts from the region. Provides an insight into Asian views and practices.
Refereed Serial

341.18 JN94 — FR
ASSEMBLEE DE L'UNION DE L'EUROPE OCCIDENTALE. LETTRE DE L'ASSEMBLEE. English edition: Assembly of Western European Union. Letter from the Assembly. 1955. 4/yr. free. Assemblee de l'Union de l'Europe Occidentale - Assembly of Western European Union, 43 av. du President Wilson, 75775 Paris Cedex 16, France. TEL 47-23-54-32. FAX 47-20-45-43. (Dist. in the U.S. by: Manhattan Publishing Co., P.O. Box 650, Croton on Hudson, NY 10520. TEL 914-271-5194)
Formerly: Assembly of Western European Union. Proceedings (ISSN 0083-8853)
Description: Contains news about the activities of the Assembly, press releases and summaries of reports.

341 — NE — ISSN 0066-8923
ASSOCIATION OF ATTENDERS AND ALUMNI OF THE HAGUE ACADEMY OF INTERNATIONAL LAW. YEARBOOK. 1925. a. price varies. Kluwer Academic Publishers, Postbus 17, 3300 AA Dordrecht, Netherlands. TEL 31-78-334911. FAX 31-78-334254. TELEX 29245 KAPG NL. (Dist. by: Kluwer Academic Publishers Group, P.O. Box 322, 3300 AH Dordrecht, Netherlands. TEL 31-78-524400; N. America dist. addr.: Box 358, Accord Sta., Hingham, MA 02018-0358. TEL 617-871-6600)
Refereed Serial

341 — SZ
ASYL; Schweizerische Zeitschrift fuer Asylrecht und -praxis. (Supplement avail.) (Text in French and German) 1986. q. 40 SFr. (foreign 45 SFr.). Schweizerische Fluechtlingshilfe, Kinkelstr. 2, Postfach 279, CH-8035 Zurich, Switzerland. TEL 01-3619640. FAX 01-3628710. adv.; bk.rev.; stat. circ. 1,600. **Indexed:** Refug.Abstr. **Document type:** newsletter.
Description: Articles on asylum law and policy and administrative decisions concerning refugees in Switzerland. Includes list of events and new publications.

ATMA JAYA RESEARCH CENTRE. INTERNATIONAL CONTRACT LABOUR. see *BUSINESS AND ECONOMICS — Labor And Industrial Relations*

341 — AT — ISSN 0811-9260
AUSTRALIAN INTERNATIONAL LAW NEWS. 1984. s-a. Aus.$20. University of Technology, Sydney, Faculty of Law and Legal Practice, P.O. Box 123, Broadway, N.S.W. 2007, Australia. (Dist. in N. America by: Wm. W. Gaunt & Sons, Inc., Law Book Dealers & Subscription Agents, Gaunt Bldg., 3011 Gulf Dr., Holmes Beach, FL 34217-2199. TEL 813-778-5211) (Co-sponsor: International Law Association, Australian Branch) Eds. D. Flint, A. Goh. circ. 500. **Document type:** academic/scholarly publication.
Description: Updates recent developments of legal interest in the international scene.

341.2 — AT — ISSN 1036-3467
AUSTRALIAN TREATY SERIES. 1955. irreg. price varies. (Department of Foreign Affairs and Trade) Australian Government Publishing Service, G.P.O. Box 84, Canberra, A.C.T. 2601, Australia. TEL 61-6-295-4612. FAX 61-295-4500. **Document type:** government publication.
Former titles (until 1989): Treaty Series (ISSN 0729-6525); Australian Treaty List.

BAILRIGG MEMORANDA. see *POLITICAL SCIENCE — International Relations*

BAILRIGG PAPERS ON INTERNATIONAL SECURITY. see *POLITICAL SCIENCE — International Relations*

340 — BG
BANGLADESH IN INTERNATIONAL AFFAIRS. (Text in English) 1978. m. $6.50. Bangladesh Institute of Law and International Affairs, 501 Dhanmondi Residential Area, Rd. No. 7, Dhaka 5, Bangladesh. (Dist. by: Karim International, 3 Padmalochon Roy Lane, Mahttuly, Dhaka 1, Bangladesh) Ed.Bd. circ. 3,000.

LAW — INTERNATIONAL LAW

341   NE
BASIC LEGAL DOCUMENTS ON REGIONAL ENVIRONMENTAL COOPERATION. 1991. irreg. price varies. Martinus Nijhoff Publishers, Human Rights and International Law (Subsidiary of: Kluwer Academic Publishers Group), Postbus 163, 3300 AD Dordrecht, Netherlands. TEL 31-78-334911. FAX 31-78-334254. TELEX 29245 KAPG NL. (Dist. by: Kluwer Academic Publishers Group, P.O. Box 322, 3300 AH Dordrecht, Netherlands. TEL 31-78-524400. FAX 31-78-524474; N. America dist. addr.: Box 358, Accord Sta., Hingham, MA 02018-0358. TEL 617-871-6600. FAX 617-871-6528) (Co-publisher: Graham & Trotman Ltd., UK) Eds. D. Freestone, T. Ijlstra. Document type: monographic series.
Refereed Serial

341 338.47   US
BASIC OIL LAWS & CONCESSION CONTRACTS: ASIA & AUSTRALASIA. q. $6350 (renewal $1550). Barrows Co., Inc., 116 E. 66th St., New York, NY 10021. TEL 212-772-1199. FAX 212-288-7242. TELEX 4971238 BARROWS. Eds. Gordon H. Barrow, Marta Guerra.
Formerly: Far East Oil Laws and Concession Contracts.
Description: Contains the complete texts, in English translation, of oil laws, contracts and concessions in Asian and Australasian countries.

341 338.47   US
BASIC OIL LAWS & CONCESSION CONTRACTS: CENTRAL AMERICA & CARIBBEAN. q. $6350 (renewal $1550). Barrows Co., Inc., 116 E. 66th St., New York, NY 10021. TEL 212-772-1199. FAX 212-288-7242. TELEX 4971238 BARROWS. Eds. Gordon H. Barrows, Marta Guerra.
Description: Contains the complete texts, in English translation, of oil laws, contracts, and concessions in all Central American and Caribbean countries.

341 338.47   US   ISSN 0093-5018
LAW
BASIC OIL LAWS & CONCESSION CONTRACTS: EUROPE. q. $6350 (renewal $1550). Barrows Co., Inc., 116 E. 66th St., New York, NY 10021. TEL 212-772-1199. FAX 212-288-7242. TELEX 4971238 BARROWS. Eds. Gordon H. Barrows, Marta Guerra.
Description: Contains the complete texts, in English translation, of oil laws, contracts, and concessions in all European countries.

341 338.47   US
BASIC OIL LAWS & CONCESSION CONTRACTS: MIDDLE EAST. q. $6350 (renewal $1550). Barrows Co., Inc., 116 E. 66th St., New York, NY 10021. TEL 212-772-1199. FAX 212-288-7242. TELEX 4971238 BARROWS.
Description: Contains the complete texts, in English translation, of oil laws, contracts and concessions in all Middle Eastern countries.

341 338.47   US
BASIC OIL LAWS & CONCESSION CONTRACTS: NORTH AFRICA. q. $6350 (renewal $1550). Barrows Co., Inc., 116 E. 66th St., New York, NY 10021. TEL 212-772-1199. FAX 212-288-7242. TELEX 4971238 BARROWS. Eds. Gordon H. Barrows, Marta Guerra.
Description: Contains the complete texts, in English translation, of oil laws, contracts and concessions in all North African countries.

341 338.47   US
BASIC OIL LAWS & CONCESSION CONTRACTS: RUSSIA & NIS. (Newly Independent States) q. $3000 (renewal $1200). Barrows Co., Inc., 116 E. 66th St., New York, NY 10021. TEL 212-772-1199. FAX 212-772-1199. TELEX 4971238 BARROWS.
Description: Contains the complete texts, in English translation, of oil laws, contracts and concessions in Russia and newly independent states.

341 338.47   US
BASIC OIL LAWS & CONCESSION CONTRACTS: SOUTH AMERICA. q. $6350 (renewal $1550). Barrows Co., Inc., 116 E. 66th St., New York, NY 10021. TEL 212-772-1199. FAX 212-288-7242. TELEX 4971238 BARROWS. Eds. Gordon H. Barrows, Marta Guerra.
Description: Contains the complete texts, in English translation, of oil laws, contracts, and concessions in all South American countries.

341 338.47   US
BASIC OIL LAWS & CONCESSION CONTRACTS: SOUTH & CENTRAL AFRICA. q. $6350 (renewal $1550). Barrows Co., Inc., 116 E. 66th St., New York, NY 10021. TEL 212-772-1199. FAX 212-288-7242. TELEX 4971238 BARROWS. Eds. Gordon H. Barrows, Marta Guerra.
Description: Contains the complete texts, in English translation, of oil laws, contracts, and concessions in all South and Central African countries.

341   US   ISSN 0172-4770
BEITRAEGE ZUM AUSLAENDISCHEN OEFFENTLICHEN RECHT UND VOELKERRECHT. (Text mainly in German) vol.86, 1984. irreg., vol.99 1989. price varies. Springer-Verlag, 175 Fifth Ave., New York, NY 10010. TEL 212-460-1500. FAX 212-473-6272. (Also: Berlin, Heidelberg, Tokyo and Vienna) (reprint service avail. from ISI) Document type: academic/scholarly publication.

341   SP
BOLETIN DE LEGISLACION EXTRANJERA. q. 8600 ptas. Congreso de los Diputados, C. Floridablanca s-n., 28014 Madrid, Spain.

341   US   ISSN 0277-5778
K2
BOSTON COLLEGE INTERNATIONAL AND COMPARATIVE LAW REVIEW. 1977. s-a. $10. Boston College, School of Law, 885 Centre St., Newton, MA 02159. TEL 617-552-8554. circ. 400. (also avail. in microfilm from WSH,PMC; reprint service avail. from WSH) **Indexed:** A.B.C.Pol.Sci., Abstr.Bk.Rev.Curr.Leg.Per., Amer.Bibl.Slavic & E.Eur.Stud., C.L.I., ELLIS, L.R.I., Leg.Cont., Leg.Per., Mar.Aff.Bibl., P.A.I.S. Document type: academic/scholarly publication.
—BLDSC (2251.812200); UnCover; SWETS; UMI.
Formerly: Boston College International and Comparative Law Journal (ISSN 0161-2832)
Description: Indexed journal covering international law.

341 950   US   ISSN 0276-3583
K2
BOSTON THIRD WORLD LAW JOURNAL. 1980. s-a. $10 (foreign $13). Boston College, School of Law, 885 Centre St., Newton, MA 02159. TEL 617-552-8569. bk.rev. circ. 350. (also avail. in microfilm from WSH,PMC; back issues avail.; reprint service avail. from WSH) Document type: academic/scholarly publication.
—BLDSC (2251.813400); Faxon; UnCover; SWETS.
Description: Covers legal issues in Third World countries, and civil, human and minority rights issues throughout the world.

341   US   ISSN 0737-8947
K2
BOSTON UNIVERSITY INTERNATIONAL LAW JOURNAL. 1981. s-a. $25 (foreign $28). Boston University, School of Law, International Law Journal, 765 Commonwealth Ave., Boston, MA 02215. TEL 617-353-3157. FAX 617-353-7400. Ed. Laurance R. Moon. circ. 450. (back issues avail.) **Indexed:** C.L.I., Leg.Per. Document type: academic/scholarly publication.
●Also available online. Vendor(s): West Services, Inc.
—BLDSC (2251.838000); UnCover.

340   US   ISSN 0162-1726
KF1987.A15
BOYCOTT LAW BULLETIN. 1977. m. $495. Nu-Tec Publishing, Inc., 4715 Strack Rd., Ste. 211, Houston, TX 77069-1617. TEL 713-444-6562. FAX 713-444-6564. (Subscr. to: Box 73326, Houston, TX 77273-3326) Ed. Joe Kamalick. Document type: newsletter.
Formerly (until 1978): Anti-Boycott Bulletin (ISSN 0149-3310)
Description: News and analysis of U.S. federal and state antiboycott laws, regulations, enforcement and litigation; also covers boycott policies and practices of some 40 Arab and Islamic countries which participate in the boycott of Israel. For non-attorney executives as well as their in-house or outside counsel.

341 382   US
▼**BREACH AND ADAPTATION OF INTERNATIONAL BUSINESS CONTRACTS;** an introduction to Lex Mercatoria. 1992. base vol. (plus a. updates). $100. Butterworth Legal Publishers (Salem) (Subsidiary of: Reed Elsevier plc), 8 Industrial Way, Bldg. C, Salem, NH 03079. TEL 800-548-4001. FAX 603-898-9858. Ed.Bd.
Description: Examines the ways various legal systems treat international business contracts.

BRITISH INSTITUTE OF INTERNATIONAL AND COMPARATIVE LAW. COMPARATIVE LAW AND PRIVATE INTERNATIONAL LAW SERIES. see *LAW*

341   UK
BRITISH INSTITUTE OF INTERNATIONAL AND COMPARATIVE LAW. PUBLIC INTERNATIONAL LAW. irreg., 1993. price varies. British Institute of International and Comparative Law, Charles Clore House, 17 Russell Sq., London WC1B 5DR, England. TEL 071-636-5802. FAX 071-323-2016. Document type: monographic series.

341   UK
BRITISH INSTITUTE OF INTERNATIONAL AND COMPARATIVE LAW. QUARTERLY NEWSLETTER. 1973. q. free with International and Comparative Law Quarterly (ISSN 0020-5893). British Institute of International and Comparative Law, Charles Clare House, 17 Russell Sq., London WC1B 5DR, England. TEL 071-636-5802. FAX 071-323-2016. Document type: newsletter.
Description: Contains information about the institute activities and programs.

341.058   UK   ISSN 0068-2691
JX21
BRITISH YEAR BOOK OF INTERNATIONAL LAW. 1920? a. varies. (Royal Institute of International Affairs) Oxford University Press, Oxford Journals, Walton St., Oxford OX2 6DP, England. TEL 0865-56767. FAX 0865-267773. TELEX 837330-OXPRES-G. (U.S. subscr. to: Oxford University Press Inc., 2001 Evans Rd., Cary, NC 27513. TEL 919-677-0977) Eds. D.W. Bowett, I. Brownlie. adv.; bk.rev.; index. (also avail. in microfilm from RRI; reprint service avail. from RRI) **Indexed:** C.L.I., L.R.I., Leg.Per. Document type: academic/scholarly publication.
—BLDSC (2348.200000); UnCover; SWETS.
Description: Contains surveys of decisions of the British courts, the Court of Justice of the EC and the European Convention on Human Rights.

341.05   US   ISSN 0740-4824
JX1
BROOKLYN JOURNAL OF INTERNATIONAL LAW. 1975. 3/yr. $15. Brooklyn Law School, 250 Joralemon, Brooklyn, NY 11201. TEL 718-780-7971. bk.rev.; index. (also avail. in microfilm from WSH,PMC; back issues avail.; reprint service avail. from WSH) **Indexed:** Abstr.Bk.Rev.Curr.Leg.Per., C.C.L.P., C.L.I., L.R.I., Leg.Cont., Leg.Per., So.Pac.Per.Ind. Document type: academic/scholarly publication.
●Also available online. Vendor(s): West Services, Inc.
—BLDSC (2350.140000); Faxon; UnCover.

341   NE
BUSINESS LAW IN EUROPE. (Text in English) 1990. base vol. (plus a. update). fl.360($206) (effective 1994). Kluwer Law and Taxation Publishers (Subsidiary of: Wolters Kluwer N.V.), P.O. Box 23, 7400 GA Deventer, Netherlands. TEL 31-5700-47261. FAX 31-5700-22244. TELEX 49295 KLUDV NL. (Dist. by: Libresso Distribution Centre, P.O. Box 23, 7400 GA Deventer, Netherlands. TEL 31-5700-33155. FAX 31-5700-33834; In N. America: Kluwer Law and Taxation Publishers, 675 Massachusetts Ave., Cambridge, MA 02139. TEL 617-354-0140. FAX 617-354-8595) Eds. Paul Storm, Maarten Ellis. (looseleaf format)
Description: Provides comprehensive, up-to-date information on significant aspects of company, tax and labor law affecting business and investment decisions in the EC member states and Switzerland.

341 382   UK
BUTTERWORTHS EUROPEAN COMMUNITIES BRIEF. w. $563. Butterworth & Co. (Publishers) Ltd. (Subsidiary of: Reed Elsevier plc), 88 Kingsway, London WC2B 6AB, England. TEL 071-405-6900. FAX 071-405-1332.
Description: Covers in summary for all proposed and enacted EC legislation, and all UK legislation implementing it, as well as decisions of the European Court, COM Docs and other official reports.

LAW — INTERNATIONAL LAW

BUYER. see *BUSINESS AND ECONOMICS — International Commerce*

341   SZ
▼ **C D - I H L.** (International Humanitarian Law) (Text in English, French) 1993. a. 480 SFr. International Committee of the Red Cross, Public Information Division, 19 avenue de la Paix, CH-1202 Geneva, Switzerland. TEL 022-7302885. FAX 022-7332057. **Document type:** bulletin.
●Available only on CD-ROM.

341   FR
C E E INTERNATIONAL. DROIT ET AFFAIRES.* a. Communaute Economique Europeenne - European Communities, 2 Rue Dufrenoy, 75116 Paris, France.

341 332.6   US
C I T B A NEWSLETTER. 1985. 6/yr. free to members. Customs and International Trade Bar Association, c/o Brian S. Goldstein, Siegel, Mandell & Davidson, 1515 Broadway, 43rd Fl, New York, NY 10016. TEL 212-944-7900. FAX 212-944-8497. Ed. Edward B. Ackerman. circ. 400. (back issues avail.) **Document type:** newsletter.

341 382   US
C I T RULES. (Court of International Trade) 1991. a. (plus irreg. updates). $75 (outside N. America $90). International Business Reports, Box 1009, Falls Church, VA 22041. TEL 703-998-2927. FAX 703-998-0019. Ed. Edward P. Kemp. (looseleaf format)
   Description: Annotated, fully indexed version of the Rules of the US Court of International Trade; Appendix of Forms; supplementary rules governing judicial misconduct or disability.

341 332.6   US   ISSN 1065-9684
C I T TEST CASE RECORD. (Court of International Trade) 1990. 3/yr. $60 (outside N. America $80). International Business Reports, Box 1009, Falls Church, VA 22041-0009. TEL 703-998-2927. FAX 703-998-0019. Ed. Edward P. Kemp. **Document type:** newsletter.
   Description: Compilation of Test Cases, fully indexed by plaintiff, attorney and judicial assignment; annotation of suspended cases.

341   BE   ISSN 0007-9758
CAHIERS DE DROIT EUROPEEN. 1965. 6/yr. 4900 BEF (students 2450 BEF) (effective 1992). Maison Ferdinand Larcier S.A., Rue des Minimes 39, 1000 Brussels, Belgium. TEL 32-2-5124712. FAX 32-2-5139009. Ed. Leon Goffin. adv.; bk.rev.; index, cum.index. circ. 1,000. **Indexed:** ELLIS. **Document type:** academic/scholarly publication.
—BLDSC (2948.855000); SWETS.
   Description: Publishes legal and jurisprudential commentary on the application of European law, reports of significant cases before the Court of Justice of the European Communities, the Human Rights Court, the Courts of Belgium, Luxembourg and the Netherlands, and in addition provides coverage of legislative developments.
   Refereed Serial

341.7   NE   ISSN 0168-0455
CAHIERS DE DROIT FISCAL INTERNATIONAL. 1939. a. (2 nos./vol.). price varies. (International Fiscal Association) Kluwer Law and Taxation Publishers (Subsidiary of: Wolters Kluwer N.V.), P.O. Box 23, 7400 GA Deventer, Netherlands. TEL 31-5700-47261. FAX 31-5700-22244. TELEX 49295 KLUDV NL. (Dist. by: Libresso Distribution Centre, P.O. Box 23, 7400 GA Deventer, Netherlands. TEL 31-5700-33155. FAX 31-5700-33834; In N. America: Kluwer Law and Taxation Publishers, 675 Massachusetts Ave., Cambridge, MA 02139. TEL 617-354-0140. FAX 617-354-8595) (reprint service avail. from SWZ) **Document type:** monographic series.
   Description: In-depth analysis of international tax law, practice and theory.

341   US
CALIFORNIA INTERNATIONAL LAW SECTION NEWSLETTER. 6/yr. $40 membership. State Bar of California, International Law Section, 555 Franklin St., San Francisco, CA 94102. (Subscr. to: Orrick, Herrington & Sutcliffe, Old Federal Reserve Bank Bldg., 400 Sansome St., San Francisco, CA 90071-2005. TEL 213-485-1234) Ed. Frederick Brown. **Document type:** newsletter.

341   US
CALIFORNIA INTERNATIONAL PRACTITIONER. 2/yr. $40 membership. State Bar of California, International Law Section, 555 Franklin St., San Francisco, CA 94102. Ed. John B. Houck. charts. (looseleaf format)

341   US   ISSN 0886-3210
JX1
CALIFORNIA WESTERN INTERNATIONAL LAW JOURNAL. 1970. 2/yr. $20 (foreign $25). California Western School of Law, 350 Cedar St., San Diego, CA 92101. TEL 619-239-0391. FAX 619-696-9999. Ed.Bd. adv.; bk.rev.; bibl. circ. 1,300. (also avail. in microfilm from RRI; back issues avail.; reprint service avail. from RRI) **Indexed:** Abstr.Bk.Rev.Curr.Leg.Per., Amer.Bibl.Slavic & E.Eur.Stud., C.L.I., L.R.I., Leg.Per., Mar.Aff.Bibl., Peace Res.Abstr.
—BLDSC (3015.359000); Faxon; UnCover.

341 323.4   CN   ISSN 0826-9904
CANADA. INFORMATION COMMISSIONER. ANNUAL REPORT. (Text in English, French) 1983. a. free. Information Commissioner, 112 Kent St., Ottawa, ON K1A 1H3, Canada. TEL 613-995-2410. FAX 613-995-1501. stat. circ. 5,000. (back issues avail.) **Document type:** government publication.

CANADA. PRIVACY COMMISSIONER. ANNUAL REPORT.
see *COMPUTERS — Computer Security*

CANADA - U.S. BUSINESS IMMIGRATION HANDBOOK.
see *BUSINESS AND ECONOMICS — Personnel Management*

341   US   ISSN 0163-6391
K3
CANADA - UNITED STATES LAW JOURNAL. (Text in English and French) 1978. a. $15. Case Western Reserve University, School of Law, 11075 East Blvd., Cleveland, OH 44106-7148. TEL 216-368-3304. FAX 216-368-6144. adv.; bk.rev. circ. 650. (also avail. in microfilm from WSH,PMC) **Indexed:** Abstr.Bk.Rev.Curr.Leg.Per., C.L.I., Foreign Leg.Per., Ind.Can.L.P.L., L.R.I., Leg.Cont., Leg.Per., P.A.I.S. **Document type:** academic/scholarly publication.
—Faxon; UnCover.

341   CN   ISSN 0317-9087
CANADIAN COUNCIL ON INTERNATIONAL LAW. PROCEEDINGS OF THE ANNUAL CONFERENCE. (Text in English and French) 1972. a. Can.$10. Canadian Council on International Law, 236 Metcalfe St., Ottawa, ON K2P 1R3, Canada. TEL 613-235-0442. **Indexed:** Ind.Can.L.P.L.
—BLDSC (6840.263900).

CANADIAN R & D DIRECTORY. see *BUSINESS AND ECONOMICS — Trade And Industrial Directories*

341   CN   ISSN 0382-8662
CANADIAN WORLD FEDERALIST/FEDERALISTE MONDIAL DU CANADA. (Text in English, French) 1961. 5/yr. Can.$8. World Federalist Foundation, 145 Spruce St., Ste. 207, Ottawa, Ont. K1R 6P1, Canada. TEL 613-232-0647. FAX 613-563-0017. Ed. Fergus Watt. bk.rev. circ. 3,000. (tabloid format; back issues avail.)

341   CN   ISSN 0069-0058
JX21
CANADIAN YEARBOOK OF INTERNATIONAL LAW/ANNUAIRE CANADIEN DE DROIT INTERNATIONAL. (Editions in English and French) 1963. a. price varies. University of British Columbia Press, 6344 Memorial Rd., Vancouver, BC V6T 1Z2, Canada. TEL 604-822-3259. FAX 604-822-6083. Ed. C.B. Bourne. bk.rev. (also avail. in microfilm from RRI) **Indexed:** Amer.Bibl.Slavic & E.Eur.Stud., C.L.I., Can.Per.Ind., Foreign Leg.Per., Ind.Can.L.P.L., L.R.I., Leg.Per., Mar.Aff.Bibl. **Document type:** monographic series.
—BLDSC (3046.180000); UnCover.
   Description: Articles on international law, Canadian practice in international law, and a digest of Canadian cases in public international law and conflict of law.

341   US   ISSN 0008-7254
JX1
CASE WESTERN RESERVE JOURNAL OF INTERNATIONAL LAW. 1968. 3/yr. $20. Case Western Reserve University, School of Law, 11075 East Blvd., Cleveland, OH 44106-7148. TEL 216-368-3304. FAX 216-368-6144. bk.rev.; abstr.; index. circ. 800. (also avail. in microfilm from RRI) **Indexed:** ABI Inform., Amer.Bibl.Slavic & E.Eur.Stud., C.C.L.P., C.L.I., Curr.Cont., Foreign Leg.Per., HR Rep., L.R.I., Leg.Per., Mar.Aff.Bibl., P.A.I.S., Sel.Water Res.Abstr., SSCI.
—BLDSC (3058.239000); Faxon; UnCover; UMI.

341   US
CASES AND MATERIALS ON THE LAW OF THE EUROPEAN COMMUNITIES. irreg., 2nd ed., 1990. $54. Butterworth Legal Publishers (Salem) (Subsidiary of: Reed Elsevier plc), 8 Industrial Way, Bldg. C. Salem, NH 03079. TEL 800-548-4001. FAX 603-898-9858. Ed. Richard Plender.

341 382   US
CENTRAL AND EASTERN EUROPEAN LEGAL MATERIALS. 1990. 7 base vols. (plus bi-m. supplements). $595 for base vols.; supplement price varies. (Columbia University, Parker School of Foreign and Comparative Law) Transnational Juris Publications, Inc., 1 Bridge St., Irvington-on-Hudson, NY 10533. TEL 914-591-4288. FAX 914-591-2688. (Dist. outside N. America by: Kluwer Academic Publishers Group, P.O. Box 322, 3300 AH Dordrecht, Netherlands. TEL 31-78-524400. FAX 31-78-524474) Ed. Vratislav Pechota. (looseleaf format)
   Description: Consists of English translations of Central and Eastern European business and investment laws.

341   US
CHINA LAW REPORTER. 1983. q. $43 (foreign $53). American Bar Association, International Law and Practice Section, 750 N. Lake Shore Dr., Chicago, IL 60611. TEL 312-988-5555. Eds. James V. Feinerman, Stephanie J. Mitchell. **Indexed:** C.L.I., L.R.I., Leg.Per.
   Description: Issues facing lawyers and scholars who deal with business law in the People's Republic of China.

CHINA LAWS FOR FOREIGN BUSINESS - BUSINESS REGULATION. see *LAW — Corporate Law*

CHINA LAWS FOR FOREIGN BUSINESS - SPECIAL ZONES & CITIES. see *LAW — Corporate Law*

CHINA LAWS FOR FOREIGN BUSINESS - TAXATION & CUSTOMS. see *LAW — Corporate Law*

COLLECTION OF BIBLIOGRAPHIC AND RESEARCH RESOURCES. see *LAW — Abstracting, Bibliographies, Statistics*

341.11   BE   ISSN 0503-2407
COLLECTION OF DOCUMENTS FOR THE STUDY OF INTERNATIONAL NON-GOVERNMENTAL RELATIONS. Alternate title: Union of International Associations. Documents. (Text in English or French) 1956. irreg., latest vol.20. Union of International Associations, c/o Jacques Raeymaeckers, Sec.-Gen., Rue Washington 40, 1050 Brussels, Belgium. TEL 32-2-6401808. FAX 32-2-6460525. **Document type:** monographic series.

COLLOQUIUM ON THE LAW OF OUTER SPACE. PROCEEDINGS. see *AERONAUTICS AND SPACE FLIGHT*

341 614.7   US   ISSN 1050-0391
K3
COLORADO JOURNAL OF INTERNATIONAL ENVIRONMENTAL LAW AND POLICY. 1990. s-a. $20 to individuals (foreign $26); institutions $35 (foreign $41). (University of Colorado, School of Law) University Press of Colorado, Box 849, Niwot, CO 80544. TEL 303-530-5337. FAX 303-530-5306. Ed.Bd. **Indexed:** Environ.Abstr. **Document type:** academic/scholarly publication.
—BLDSC (3321.390000); UnCover.
   Description: Examines environmental issues with international implications, such as global climate change, and the legal and policy ramifications of international environmental concerns.

341 US ISSN 0010-1931
LAW
COLUMBIA JOURNAL OF TRANSNATIONAL LAW. 1961. 3/yr. $30 (foreign $33). (Columbia University, School of Law) Columbia Journal of Transnational Law Association, 435 W. 116th St., Box D25, Columbia University, New York, NY 10027. TEL 212-663-8709. Ed. Glenn Butterton. adv.; bk.rev.; cum.index. circ. 1,000. (also avail. in microfilm from PMC,WSH; back issues avail.; reprint service avail. from WSH) Indexed: A.B.C.Pol.Sci., Abstr.Bk.Rev.Curr.Leg.Per., Amer.Bibl.Slavic & E.Eur.Stud., Amer.Hist.& Life, C.L.I., Curr.Cont., ELLIS, Hist.Abstr., L.R.I., Leg.Cont., Leg.Per., SSCI. **Document type:** academic/scholarly publication.
●Also available online. Vendor(s): West Services, Inc.
—BLDSC (3323.100000); Faxon; UnCover; SWETS.
Description: Covers issues in public and private international law, comparative and foreign law, for legal practitioners and scholars of the law.

341.57 II
COMMERCIAL LAW GAZETTE. (Text in English) 1978. fortn. Rs.75. Commercial Law Publications, E-157, Kamla Nagar, Delhi 110007, India. Ed. S.N. Gupta. adv.; bk.rev.; index. circ. 5,000.

341.57 382 US
COMMERCIAL LAWS OF THE WORLD. (33 vol. set plus supplements) bi-w. $1050 (diskette $840; renewal $400). Foreign Tax Law Publishers, Box 2189, Ormond Beach, FL 32175. TEL 904-253-5785. FAX 904-257-3003. (looseleaf format; also avail. in diskette format)
Description: Includes laws from more than 100 countries translated into English.

COMMISSION OF THE EUROPEAN COMMUNITIES. COLLECTION OF AGREEMENTS. see BUSINESS AND ECONOMICS — International Commerce

341.18 EI ISSN 0590-6563
COMMISSION OF THE EUROPEAN COMMUNITIES. COMMUNITY LAW. (Editions also in Dutch, French, German, Italian) 1968. a. free. Commission of the European Communities, Service de Renseignement et de Diffusion des Documents, 200 rue de la Loi, B-1049 Brussels, Belgium.
Description: Reports on activities of the EEC.

341.11 EI ISSN 0591-1745
HC240.A1
COMMISSION OF THE EUROPEAN COMMUNITIES. DIRECTORY. (Text in English, French) 1968. a. $10. Office for Official Publications of the European Communities, L-2985 Luxembourg, Luxembourg. (Dist. in the U.S. by: Unipub, 4611-F Assembly Dr., Lanham, MD 20706-4391. TEL 800-274-4888. FAX 301-459-0056) **Document type:** directory.

341 NE ISSN 0165-0750
LAW CODEN: CMLRDD
COMMON MARKET LAW REVIEW. (Text in English) 1963. 6/yr. fl.779($406) (effective 1994). (British Institute of International and Comparative Law, UK) Martinus Nijhoff Publishers, Human Rights and International Law (Subsidiary of: Kluwer Academic Publishers Group), Postbus 163, 3300 AD Dordrecht, Netherlands. TEL 31-78-334911. FAX 31-78-334254. (Dist. by: Kluwer Academic Publishers Group, P.O. Box 322, 3300 AH Dordrecht, Netherlands. TEL 31-78-524400. FAX 31-78-524474; N. America dist. addr.: Box 358, Accord Sta., Hingham, MA 02018-0358. TEL 617-871-6600. FAX 617-871-6528) (Co-publisher: Graham & Trotman Ltd., UK) (Co-sponsor: University of Leiden, Europa Institute) Ed. Henry G. Schermers. adv.; bk.rev.; index. (also avail. in microform from UMI; back issues avail.) Indexed: Abstr.Bk.Rev.Curr.Leg.Per., C.L.I., C.R.E.J., Curr.Cont., ELLIS, Foreign Leg.Per., Int.Lab.Doc., L.R.I., Leg.Per., Mar.Aff.Bibl., RICS, SCIMP, SSCI, World Bank.Abstr. **Document type:** academic/scholarly publication.
—BLDSC (3339.270000); Faxon; UnCover; SWETS; UMI. **CCC.**
Description: Covers the theory and practice of law in the EC, including commentary on decisions of the EC Court of Justice and national courts in matters of Community law.
Refereed Serial

341 US
COMMONWEALTH INTERNATIONAL LAW CASES. 1964. irreg., vol.17, 1994. price varies. (International Law Fund) Oceana Publications, Inc., Dobbs Ferry, NY 10522. TEL 914-693-1320. FAX 914-693-0402. (Co-sponsor: British Institute of Foreign and Comparative Law) Eds. C. Parry, J.A. Hopkins. (back issues avail.) **Document type:** abstracting/indexing.
Supersedes (in 1974): British International Law Cases (ISSN 0068-2195)
Description: Annotated decisions of British and Commonwealth courts on points of international law.

341 SA ISSN 0010-4051
K3
COMPARATIVE AND INTERNATIONAL LAW JOURNAL OF SOUTHERN AFRICA. (Text in English; occasionally in Afrikaans, French, German, Portuguese; summaries in English) 1968. 3/yr. R.30($30.) University of South Africa, Institute of Foreign and Comparative Law, P.O. Box 392, Pretoria 0001, South Africa. FAX 012-4292925. TELEX 9-350068. Ed. J.J. Joubert Ball. adv.; bk.rev.; index. circ. 900. (also avail. in microform from PMC,WSH; back issues avail.) Indexed: Abstr.Bk.Rev.Curr.Leg.Per., C.L.I., Curr.Cont.Africa, Documentatieblad, Ind.S.A.Per., Leg.Per., Mar.Aff.Bibl. **Document type:** academic/scholarly publication.
—BLDSC (3363.746000); UnCover; SWETS.
Description: Comprehensive coverage of international law and comparative law contributions in South Africa.

341 UK ISSN 0141-769X
COMPETITION LAW IN THE EUROPEAN COMMUNITIES. 1977. 12/yr. £290 (foreign £312). Monitor Press, Rectory Rd., Great Waldingfield, Sudbury, Suffolk CO10 0TL, England. TEL 0787-378607. FAX 0787-880201. index. (back issues avail.) **Document type:** newsletter.
—BLDSC (3363.993000).
Description: For the specialist lawyer or legal advisor in companies or organizations needing to be informed about the complex decisions and regulations emanating from the common market.

341.57 NE
COMPETITION LAW IN WESTERN EUROPE AND THE U S A. (Text in English) 1974. 16 base vols. (plus updates 8/yr.). fl.1500($858) (effective 1994). Kluwer Law and Taxation Publishers (Subsidiary of: Wolters Kluwer N.V.), P.O. Box 23, 7400 GA Deventer, Netherlands. TEL 31-5700-47261. FAX 31-5700-22244. TELEX 48285 KLUDV VL. (Dist. by: Libresso Distribution Centre, P.O. Box 23, 7400 GA Deventer, Netherlands. TEL 31-5700-33155. FAX 31-5700-33834; In N. America: Kluwer Law and Taxation Publishers, 675 Massachusetts Ave., Cambridge, MA 02139. TEL 617-354-0140. FAX 617-354-8595) Ed. D.J. Gijlstra. (looseleaf format)
Formerly: Competition Law.
Description: Covers all aspects of antitrust law or competition law, including full texts of all legislation, case law and regulations, with expert commentaries, as well as relevant EEC treaties, regulations, notices and announcements.

341 UK
COMPLETING THE INTERNAL MARKET OF THE EUROPEAN COMMUNITY: 1992 LEGISLATION - BUSINESS. (Complete set consists of 6 sectors in 14 vols.) 1989. a. (plus q. supplement). £395($798) for basic work; supplement service £210 ($399). (Commission of the European Communities, EI) Graham & Trotman Ltd. (Subsidiary of: Kluwer Academic Publishers Group), Sterling House, 66 Wilton Rd., London SW1V 1DE, England. TEL 44-71-821-1123. FAX 44-71-630-5229. (Dist. by: Kluwer Academic Publishers Group, P.O. Box 322, 3300 AH Dordrecht, Netherlands. TEL 31-78-524400. FAX 31-78-524474; N. America dist. addr.: Box 358, Accord Sta., Hingham, MA 02018-0358. TEL 617-871-6600. FAX 617-871-6528) Eds. Mark Brealey, Conor Quigley. (looseleaf format) **Document type:** trade publication.
Description: Covers legislation as it affects various sectors of business, commerce, and industry.

341 UK
COMPLETING THE INTERNAL MARKET OF THE EUROPEAN COMMUNITY: 1992 LEGISLATION - FINANCIAL SERVICES AND CAPITAL MOVEMENTS. (Complete set consists of 6 sectors in 14 vols.) a. (plus q. supplement). £295($610) for basic work; supplement service £195 ($370). (Commission of the European Communities, EI) Graham & Trotman Ltd. (Subsidiary of: Kluwer Academic Publishers Group), Sterling House, 66 Wilton Rd., London SW1V 1DE, England. TEL 44-71-821-1123. FAX 44-71-630-5229. (Dist. by: Kluwer Academic Publishers Group, P.O. Box 322, 3300 AH Dordrecht, Netherlands. TEL 31-78-524400. FAX 31-78-524474; N. America dist. addr.: Box 358, Accord Sta., Hingham, MA 02018-0358. TEL 617-871-6600. FAX 617-871-6528) Eds. Mark Brealey, Conor Quigley. (looseleaf format) **Document type:** trade publication.
Description: Covers the legislation as it affects financial services and capital movements.

341 UK ISSN 0958-9139
COMPLETING THE INTERNAL MARKET OF THE EUROPEAN COMMUNITY: 1992 LEGISLATION. (Complete set consists of 6 sectors in 14 vols.) 1989. a. (plus q. supplement). £795($1650) for basic work; supplement service £300 ($580) (vol.1-8). (Commission of the European Communities, EI) Graham & Trotman Ltd. (Subsidiary of: Kluwer Academic Publishers Group), Sterling House, 66 Wilton Rd., London SW1V 1DE, England. TEL 44-71-821-1123. FAX 44-71-630-5229. (Dist. by: Kluwer Academic Publishers Group, P.O. Box 322, 3300 Dordrecht, Netherlands. TEL 31-78-524400. FAX 31-78-524474; N. America dist. addr.: Box 358, Accord Sta., Hingham, MA 02018-0358. TEL 617-871-6600. FAX 617-871-6528) Eds. Mark Brealey, Conor Quigley. (looseleaf format) **Document type:** trade publication.
Description: Covers the European Economic Community laws and proposals that form the 1992 legislative program.

341 UK
COMPLETING THE INTERNAL MARKET OF THE EUROPEAN COMMUNITY: 1992 LEGISLATION - TRANSPORT, CUSTOMS & TRAVEL. (Complete set consists of 6 sectors in 14 vols.) a. (plus q. supplement). £295($610) for basic work; supplement service £195 ($370). (Commission of the European Communities, EI) Graham & Trotman Ltd. (Subsidiary of: Kluwer Academic Publishers Group), Sterling House, 66 Wilton Rd., London SW1V 1DE, England. TEL 44-71-821-1123. FAX 44-71-630-5229. (Dist. by: Kluwer Academic Publishers Group, P.O. Box 322, 3300 AH Dordrecht, Netherlands. TEL 31-78-524400. FAX 31-78-524474; N. America dist. addr.: Box 358, Accord Sta., Hingham, MA 02018-0358. FAX 617-871-6528) Eds. Mark Brealey, Conor Quigley. (looseleaf format) **Document type:** trade publication.
Description: Covers the legislation as it affects transport, customs, and travel.

341 UK
COMPLETING THE INTERNAL MARKET OF THE EUROPEAN COMMUNITY: 1992 LEGISLATION - TECHNICAL STANDARDS. (Complete set consists of 6 sectors in 14 vols.) a. (plus q. supplement). £395($798) for basic work; supplement service £210 ($399). (Commission of the European Communities, EI) Graham & Trotman Ltd. (Subsidiary of: Kluwer Academic Publishers Group), Sterling House, 66 Wilton Rd., London SW1V 1DE, England. TEL 44-71-821-1123. FAX 44-71-630-5229. (Dist. by: Kluwer Academic Publishers Group, P.O. Box 322, 3300 AH Dordrecht, Netherlands. TEL 31-78-524400. FAX 31-78-824474; N. America dist. addr.: Box 358, Accord Sta., Hingham, MA 02018-0358. TEL 617-871-6600. FAX 617-871-6528) Eds. Mark Brealey, Conor Quigley. (looseleaf format) **Document type:** trade publication.
Description: Covers legislation as it affects technical standards.

LAW — INTERNATIONAL LAW

341 636.089   UK
COMPLETING THE INTERNAL MARKET OF THE EUROPEAN COMMUNITY: 1992 LEGISLATION - VETERINARY & PHYTOSANITARY CONTROLS. (Complete set consists of 6 sectors in 14 vols.) a. (plus q. supplement) £395($798) for basic work; supplement service £210 ($399). (Commission of the European Communities, EI) Graham & Trotman Ltd. (Subsidiary of: Kluwer Academic Publishers Group), Sterling House, 66 Wilton Rd., London SW1V 1DE, England. TEL 44-71-821-1123. FAX 44-71-630-5229. (Dist. by: Kluwer Academic Publishers Group, P.O. Box 322, 3300 AH Dordrecht, Netherlands. TEL 31-78-524400. FAX 31-78-524474; N. America dist. addr.: Box 358, Accord Sta., Hingham, MA 02018-0358. TEL 617-871-6600. FAX 617-871-6528) Eds. Mark Brealey, Conor Quigley. (looseleaf format) **Document type:** trade publication.
    Description: Covers the legislation as it affects veterinary and phytosanitary controls.

COMUNITA INTERNAZIONALE see *POLITICAL SCIENCE — International Relations*

341   NE   ISSN 0072-9272
CONFERENCE DE LA HAYE DE DROIT INTERNATIONAL PRIVE. ACTES ET DOCUMENTS/HAGUE CONFERENCE ON PRIVATE INTERNATIONAL LAW. PROCEEDINGS. (Text in English and French) 1893. quadrennial, latest 1993. price varies. Hague Conference on Private International Law, Permanent Bureau, Scheveningseweg 6, 2517 KT The Hague, Netherlands. FAX 31-70-3604867. circ. 1,000. (also avail. in microfiche) **Document type:** proceedings.

341.2   US   ISSN 1053-9905
JX236 1990
CONSOLIDATED TREATIES & INTERNATIONAL AGREEMENTS: UNITED STATES CURRENT DOCUMENT SERVICE. 1990. 4/yr. $125 per issue. Oceana Publications, Inc., 75 Main St., Dobbs Ferry, NY 10522. TEL 914-693-8100. FAX 914-693-0402. Ed. Erwin C. Surrency. (back issues avail.)
● Also available on CD-ROM.
    Description: Full text of all current international agreements to which the U.S. is signatory, with subject index and cross-references to treaties cited.

341   US   ISSN 0010-8812
JX1
CORNELL INTERNATIONAL LAW JOURNAL. 1968. 3/yr. $25 (foreign $28). Cornell University, Law School, Myron Taylor Hall, Ithaca, NY 14853. TEL 607-255-9666. Ed.Bd. adv.; bk.rev.; bibl.; index. circ. 1,000. (also avail. in microform from MIM; microfilm from RRI; back issues avail.; reprint service avail. from RRI,UMI) **Indexed:** Abstr.Bk.Rev.Curr.Leg.Per., C.L.I., Foreign Leg.Per., L.R.I., Leg.Cont., Leg.Per., P.A.I.S., SSCI.
● Also available online. Vendor(s): West Services, Inc.
—BLDSC (3470.950500); Faxon; UnCover; SWETS.

CORPORATE COUNSEL'S INTERNATIONAL ADVISER. see *BUSINESS AND ECONOMICS — International Commerce*

341.18   EI   ISSN 0070-105X
JX626 1954
COUNCIL OF EUROPE. EUROPEAN TREATY SERIES. (Text in English, French) 1949. irreg., no.150, 1993. $4. Council of Europe, Publishing and Documentation Service, 67075 Strasbourg Cedex, France. (Dist. in U.S. by: Manhattan Publishing Co., One Croton Point Ave., Box 650, Croton-on-Hudson, NY 10520)
—BLDSC (3830.330000).

341.18   EI   ISSN 0252-0656
JN22
COUNCIL OF EUROPE. PARLIAMENTARY ASSEMBLY. DOCUMENTS: WORKING PAPERS. (Text in English, French) 1949. a. $17 per vol. Council of Europe, Parliamentary Assembly, Publications Section, F 67075 Strasbourg Cedex, France. (Dist. in U.S. by: Manhattan Publishing Co., Box 650, Croton-on-Hudson, NY 10520) (also avail. in microfiche from BHF)
—BLDSC (3608.805000).
    Supersedes (since vol.26, pt.3, 1974): Council of Europe. Consultative Assembly. Documents: Working Papers (ISSN 0070-1009)

341.8   EI   ISSN 0252-0664
JN22
COUNCIL OF EUROPE. PARLIAMENTARY ASSEMBLY. OFFICIAL REPORT OF DEBATES. (Text in English or French) 1949. a. (in 3 vols.). $17 per vol. Council of Europe, Parliamentary Assembly, Publications Section, 67075 Strasbourg Cedex, France. (Dist. in U.S. by: Manhattan Publishing Co., Box 650, Croton-on-Hudson, NY 10520)

341.18   EI   ISSN 0377-1962
JN22
COUNCIL OF EUROPE. PARLIAMENTARY ASSEMBLY. ORDERS OF THE DAY, MINUTES OF PROCEEDINGS. (Text in English, French) 1949. a. 3/yr. $7. Council of Europe, Publishing and Documentation Service, 67075 Strasbourg Cedex, France. (Dist. in U.S. by: Manhattan Publishing Co., One Croton Point Ave., Box 650, Croton-on-Hudson, NY 10520) **Document type:** proceedings.
    Supersedes (in 1974): Council of Europe. Consultative Assembly. Orders of the Day, Minutes of Proceedings (ISSN 0070-1017)

341.18   EI   ISSN 0377-6093
JN22
COUNCIL OF EUROPE. PARLIAMENTARY ASSEMBLY. TEXTS ADOPTED BY THE ASSEMBLY. (Text in English, French) 1949. a. (in 3 vols.). $7 per vol. Council of Europe, Parliamentary Assembly, Publications Section, 67075 Strasbourg Cedex, France. (Dist. in U.S. by: Manhattan Publishing Co., 80 Brook St., Box 650, Croton-on-Hudson, NY 10520)
—BLDSC (8813.777000).
    Supersedes (in 1974): Council of Europe. Consultative Assembly. Texts Adopted by the Assembly (ISSN 0070-1033)

CRIMINAL LAW FORUM; an international journal. see *LAW — Criminal Law*

341   NE
CROSS-BORDER PRACTICE COMPENDIUM. (Text in English) 1991. base vol. (plus a. update). fl.210($114) (effective 1994). (Conseil des Barreaux de la Communaute Europeenne - CCBE - Council of European Bars and Law Societies) Kluwer Law and Taxation Publishers (Subsidiary of: Wolters Kluwer N.V.), P.O. Box 23, 7400 GA Deventer, Netherlands. TEL 31-5700-47261. FAX 31-5700-22244. TELEX 49295 KLUDV NL. (Dist. by: Libresso Distribution Centre, P.O. Box 23, 7400 GA Deventer, Netherlands. TEL 31-5700-33155. FAX 31-5700-33834; In N. America: Kluwer Law and Taxation Publishers, 675 Massachusetts Ave., Cambridge, MA 02139. TEL 617-354-0140. FAX 617-354-8595) Ed. Dorothy Little. (looseleaf format)
    Description: Describes the rules, guidelines, codes, statutes, professional rules and customs governing the legal profession in the EC, including CBCE observer states.

341   UY
CUADERNOS DE DERECHO INTERNACIONAL PRIVADO. 1975. irreg. Fundacion de Cultura Universitaria, 25 de Mayo no. 568, Casilla de Correo No. 1155, Montevideo, Uruguay. TEL 961152. FAX 952549.

341   NE   ISSN 0772-1668
CURRENT LEGAL THEORY; international journal for the theory of law and its documentation. (Text in English) 1983. q. Tilburg University, Tilburg Foreign Law Review Institute, P.O. Box 91053, 5000 LE Tilburg, Netherlands. (Dist. in N. America by: Wm. W. Gaunt & Sons, Inc., 3011 Gulf Dr., Holmes Beach, FL 34217. TEL 800-942-8683. FAX 813-778-5252) (Co-sponsor: Centrum voor Grondslagenonderzoek van het Recht) (back issues avail.) **Document type:** academic/scholarly publication, bibliography.
    Description: Publishes surveys, reviews and critical discussion of legal theory and jurisprudence.

CURRENT TREATY INDEX; a cumulative index to the United States slip treaties and agreements. see *LAW — Abstracting, Bibliographies, Statistics*

341   US
CUSTOMS LAW HANDBOOK. 1989. a. $28. Gould Publications, 1333 N. U.S. Hwy. 17-92, Longwood, FL 32750-3724. TEL 407-695-9500. FAX 407-695-2906. adv.; bk.rev. (looseleaf format)
    Description: Contains title 18 crimes and criminal procedure, title 19 customs duties, and title 21 drug abuse, prevention and control.

341   GW
D A J V - NEWSLETTER. (Text in English and German) 1975. q. DM.90 membership to individuals; law libraries DM.50. Deutsch-Amerikanische Juristen-Vereinigung e.V., Alte Bonnhofstr. 10, 53173 Bonn, Germany. TEL 0228-361376. FAX 0228-357972. bk.rev. circ. 2,700. **Document type:** newsletter.
    Description: Comparative studies of American and European law.

341.18 330   EI   ISSN 0378-5041
DEBATES OF THE EUROPEAN PARLIAMENT. French edition: Debats du Parlement Europeen (ISSN 0378-5017); German edition: Verhanlungen des Europischen Parlaments (ISSN 0378-5009); Italian edition: Discussioni del Parlamento Europeo (ISSN 0378-5114); Dutch edition: Handelingen van Het Europese Parlament (ISSN 0378-5025); Danish edition: Forhandlinger i Europa Parlamentet (ISSN 0378-5033) Greek edition: Episeme Efemerida ton Europaikon Koinoteton (EI ISSN 0251-2009) Spanish edition: Debates del Parlamento Europeo (EI ISSN 1011-2472) Portuguese edition: Debates do Parlamento Europen (EI ISSN 1011-2480) 1958. a. $260. (European Parliament) Office for Official Publications of the European Communities, L-2985 Luxembourg, Luxembourg. (Dist. in the U.S. by: Unipub. 4611-F Assembly Dr., Lanham, MD 20706-4391. TEL 800-274-4888. FAX 301-459-0056) (microfiche) **Document type:** proceedings.
—BLDSC (6239.823000).

341   US   ISSN 0196-2035
JX1
DENVER JOURNAL OF INTERNATIONAL LAW AND POLICY. 1971. 3/yr. $27. University of Denver, College of Law, 7039 E. 18th Ave., Ste. 235, Denver, CO 80220. TEL 303-871-6170. Ed. Debra Asimus. bk.rev.; cum.index every 10 yrs. circ. 700. (also avail. in microform from UMI; microfiche from WSH; microfilm from WSH,PMC; back issues avail.; reprint service avail. from UMI) **Indexed:** Abstr.Bk.Rev.Curr.Leg.Per., Amer.Bibl.Slavic & E.Eur.Stud., C.L.I., Environ.Abstr., Environ.Ind., Foreign Leg.Per., Int.Polit.Sci.Abstr., L.R.I., Leg.Cont., Leg.Per., P.A.I.S., Sel.Water Res.Abstr., So.Pac.Per.Ind.
● Also available online. Vendor(s): West Services, Inc.
—BLDSC (3553.564000); Faxon; UnCover; SWETS; UMI.

341   UY
DERECHO INTERNACIONAL PUBLICO. 1987. irreg. $20. Fundacion de Cultura Universitaria, 25 de Mayo 568, Casilla de Correo 1155, Montevideo, Uruguay. TEL 961152. FAX 952549.
    Formerly (until 1993): Documentacion Internacional.

341   NE   ISSN 0924-5332
DEVELOPMENTS IN INTERNATIONAL LAW. (Text in English) 1979. irreg., vol.15, 1993. price varies. Martinus Nijhoff Publishers, Human Rights and International Law (Subsidiary of: Kluwer Academic Publishers Group), Postbus 163, 3300 AD Dordrecht, Netherlands. TEL 31-78-334911. FAX 31-78-334254. TELEX 29245 KAPG NL. (Dist. by: Kluwer Academic Publishers Group, P.O. Box 322, 3300 AH Dordrecht, Netherlands. TEL 31-78-524400. FAX 31-78-524474; N. America dist. addr.: Box 358, Accord Sta., Hingham, MA 02018-0358. TEL 617-871-6600. FAX 617-871-6528) **Document type:** monographic series.
—BLDSC (3579.082800).
Refereed Serial

341 327   US   ISSN 0887-283X
K4
DICKINSON JOURNAL OF INTERNATIONAL LAW. 1982. 3/yr. $25. Dickinson School of Law, 150 S. College St., Carlisle, PA 17013. TEL 717-243-4611. FAX 717-243-4443. Ed. Andrew L. Stern. circ. 250. (also avail. in microform from WSH,PMC; back issues avail.; reprint service avail. from WSH) **Indexed:** C.L.I., Leg.Per. **Document type:** academic/scholarly publication.
● Also available online. Vendor(s): West Services, Inc.
—BLDSC (3580.260000); Faxon; UnCover.
    Formerly: Dickinson International Law Annual.

DICTIONNAIRE JOLY PRATIQUE DES CONTRATS INTERNATIONAUX. see *BUSINESS AND ECONOMICS — International Commerce*

LAW — INTERNATIONAL LAW

341   FR
DICTIONNAIRE PERMANENT DROIT EUROPEEN DES AFFAIRES. m. 1700 F. base vols. (m. updates 450 F.). Editions Legislatives et Administratives, 80, ave. de la Marne, 92546 Montrouge Cedex, France. TEL 1-40-92-68-68. FAX 1-46-56-00-15. TELEX 632 855 F. (looseleaf format)
   Description: Addresses the evolution of European common law, and studies how it will affect France in particular.

341.57 382   US   ISSN 0419-1285
DIGEST OF COMMERCIAL LAWS OF THE WORLD. 1968. irreg. $1100 (includes forms of commercial agreements and state variations). (National Association of Credit Management) Oceana Publications, Inc., Dobbs Ferry, NY 10522. TEL 914-693-1320. FAX 914-693-0402. Ed. Lester Nelson. bibl. circ. 500. (looseleaf format)
   Description: Compilation of commercial laws for countries of the world.

347   US   ISSN 0070-4857
DIGEST OF LEGAL ACTIVITIES OF INTERNATIONAL ORGANIZATIONS AND OTHER INSTITUTIONS. 1969. irreg. $150. (Unidroit - International Institute for the Unification of Private Law) Oceana Publications, Inc., Dobbs Ferry, NY 10522. TEL 914-696-1320. FAX 914-693-0402. Ed.Bd. circ. 300. (looseleaf format)
   Description: Provides a comprehensive view of the variety of legal activities conducted in numerous international and inter-federal organizations.

341.2   FR   ISSN 0338-4454
DOCUMENTS D'ACTUALITE INTERNATIONALE. 1972. 24/yr. 400 F. (Europe 500 F., elsewhere 650 F.). (Ministere des Affaires Etrangeres) Documentation Francaise, 29-31 Quai Voltaire, 75340 Paris Cedex 07, France. TEL 1-40-15-70-00. FAX 40-15-72-30. TELEX 215 666 DOCFRAN. (Subscr. to: 124 rue Henri Barbusse, 93308 Aubervilliers Cedex, France. TEL 48-39-56-00. FAX 48-39-56-01) bibl. (also avail. in microfiche from DFR) **Indexed:** ELLIS. **Document type:** government publication.
   —SWETS.
   Description: Lists treaty agreements.

341   FR   ISSN 0335-5047
K4
DROIT ET PRATIQUE DU COMMERCE INTERNATIONAL/INTERNATIONAL TRADE LAW AND PRACTICE. (Text in English, French) 1975. q. $264 (typically set in Jan.). Masson - Periodiqeus, Villa Laromiguiere, 75005 Paris, France. TEL 1-40-46-62-00. FAX 1-40-46-62-01. Ed. P. Juillard. adv.; bk.rev.; index. circ. 1,600. (also avail. in microform from UMI; reprint service avail. from ISI,SCH) **Indexed:** P.A.I.S.For.Lang.Ind., P.A.I.S. **Document type:** academic/scholarly publication.
   —BLDSC (3627.359300); SWETS; UMI. **CCC.**

341   FR
DROIT INTERNATIONAL PRIVE. a. price varies. C N R S Editions, 20-22 rue St. Amand, 75015 Paris, France. TEL 45-33-16-00. FAX 45-33-92-13. TELEX 200 356 F. adv.; bk.rev.; index; circ. 1,500 (controlled).

E C CORPORATE TAX LAW. see BUSINESS AND ECONOMICS — Public Finance, Taxation

341 338.1   UK   ISSN 0965-0717
E C FOOD LAW. (European Community) m. £260 in the UK; elsewhere £275. Agra Europe (London) Ltd., 25 Frant Rd., Tunbridge Wells, Kent TN2 5JT, England. TEL 44-892-533813. FAX 44-892-544895. TELEX 95114 AGRATW G. **Document type:** trade publication.
   —SWETS.
   Description: Monitors EC and national legislation affecting the production, processing, and distribution of food and food products.

E E C MERGER CONTROL REPORTER. see LAW — Corporate Law

E I P R: EUROPEAN INTELLECTUAL PROPERTY REVIEW.
   see PATENTS, TRADEMARKS AND COPYRIGHTS

E L L I S; a master guide to commentary on European Community law. (European Legal Literature Information Service) see LAW — Abstracting, Bibliographies, Statistics

341.18   EI   ISSN 0250-5754
E P NEWS. (Issued in relation to Parliament's sessions.) (Editions in Danish, Dutch, French, German, Greek, Italian, Portuguese, Spanish) 1967. m. (except Aug.). free. European Parliament, Secretariat, Centre Europeen, Case Postale 1601, L-2929 Luxembourg, Luxembourg. FAX 43-70-09. Ed. R. Worsley. bk.rev. circ. 150,000.
   —BLDSC (3793.200000).
   Formerly (until 1979): European Parliament News (ISSN 0531-4321)

341   UK
EASTERN EUROPEAN FORUM NEWSLETTER. 1991. 2/yr. £60. International Bar Association, 2 Harewood Pl., Hanover Sq., London W1R 9HB, England. TEL 44-71-629-1206. FAX 44-71-409-0456. Ed. Ruth Eldon. adv.; bk.rev.; index. circ. 1,000. **Document type:** academic/scholarly publication.

341.4   UA   ISSN 0080-259X
JX3
EGYPTIAN REVIEW OF INTERNATIONAL LAW/REVUE EGYPTIENNE DE DROIT INTERNATIONAL. (Text in Arabic, English, French) 1945. a. $45. Egyptian Society of International Law, 16 Rameses St., Cairo, Egypt. Ed. Salah Amer. bk.rev.; cum.index: 1945-49. **Indexed:** A.B.C.Pol.Sci., Mar.Aff.Bibl.

ELECTION ARCHIVES AND INTERNATIONAL POLITICS.
   see POLITICAL SCIENCE

340   US   ISSN 1052-2840
K5
EMORY INTERNATIONAL LAW REVIEW. 1986. s-a. $18 (foreign $20). Emory University, School of Law, 1722 North Decatur Rd., Atlanta, GA 30322. Ed. Julia J. Yoffee. bk.rev. (back issues avail.) **Document type:** academic/scholarly publication.
   ●Also available online. Vendor(s): West Services, Inc.
   —BLDSC (3733.553000); UnCover.
   Formerly (until 1990): Emory Journal of International Dispute Resolution.
   Description: Dedicated to fostering an awareness for the problems that arise among nations, between peoples, or in the course of international trade. Provides a voice for peaceful resolution of international disputes.

EUROFOOD MONITOR. see FOOD AND FOOD INDUSTRIES

341.7   US   ISSN 1050-8236
EUROMEDIA REGULATION. 1990. m. $525. Kagan World Media, Ltd., 126 Clock Tower Place, Carmel, CA 93923. TEL 408-624-1536. FAX 408-625-3225. Ed. John Mansell.
   Description: Follows government oversight of public and private media throughout Europe, including new regulations, programming quotas and recent lobbying efforts.

341   IT
L'EUROPA DELLA C E E. (Comunita Europea Economica) 1988. m. L.150000($95) Pirola Editore S.p.A., Via Parabiago 19, Casella Postale 10444, 20110 Milan, Italy. TEL 2-30-221. FAX 2-380-11-205. Ed.Bd. bk.rev. circ. 1,200.

341   GW   ISSN 0531-2485
EUROPARECHT. 1966. q. DM.125. (Wissenschaftliche Gesellschaft fuer Europarecht) Nomos Verlagsgesellschaft mbH und Co. KG, Waldseestr. 3-5, 76530 Baden-Baden, Germany. TEL 07221-21040. FAX 07221-210427. (Subscr. to: Postfach 610, 76484 Baden-Baden, Germany) **Indexed:** ELLIS, INIS Atomind. **Document type:** academic/scholarly publication.
   —SWETS. **CCC.**

344   US   ISSN 1047-2827
KJE6411.3
EUROPE 1992: LAW & STRATEGY. 1989. m. $295. Leader Publications, Inc. (Subsidiary of: New York Law Publishing Co.), 111 Eighth Ave., New York, NY 10011. TEL 212-463-5709. FAX 212-463-5523. Ed. John Sarna. (back issues avail.) **Document type:** newsletter.

EUROPEAN AIR LAW; texts and documents. see TRANSPORTATION — Air Transport

EUROPEAN AIR LAW ASSOCIATION CONFERENCE PAPERS. see TRANSPORTATION — Air Transport

341.1   EI   ISSN 0589-9575
EUROPEAN CO-OPERATION. irreg. Council of Europe, Publishing and Documentation Service, 67075 Strasbourg Cedex, France. (Dist. in U.S. by: Manhattan Publishing Co., Box 650, Croton-on-Hudson, NY 10520)

EUROPEAN COMMUNITIES. COURT OF JUSTICE AND COURT OF FIRST INSTANCE. PROCEEDINGS. see LAW — Judicial Systems

341   EI   ISSN 0378-7591
KJE924.5
EUROPEAN COMMUNITIES. COURT OF JUSTICE. REPORTS OF CASES BEFORE THE COURT. Key Title: Reports of Cases Before the Court. Court of Justice of the European Communities. (Editions in Danish, Dutch, English, French, German, Greek, Italian, Portuguese, Spanish) 1954. irreg. (10-12/yr.). $235. Office for Official Publications of the European Communities, L-2985 Luxembourg, Luxembourg. (Dist. in the U.S. by: Unipub, 4611-F Assembly Dr., Lanham, MD 20706-4391. TEL 800-274-4888. FAX 301-459-0056)

341   UK
EUROPEAN COMMUNITY LAW SERIES. 1990. irreg. (approx. 1-2/yr.). £45. Athlone Press Ltd., 1 Park Dr., London NW11 7SG, England. TEL 081-458-0888. FAX 081-201-8115. (Dist in U.S. by: Athelone Press, 165 Fifth Ave., Atlantic Highlands, NJ 07781. TEL 908-872-1441) Ed. D. Lasok. bk.rev.; bibl.; index. (back issues avail.) **Document type:** monographic series.
   Description: Examines copyright and company law in the UK and EC, taxation, public procurement, mergers and joint ventures, transport laws and the legalities of drug control in the EC and other legal EC issues.

EUROPEAN FINANCIAL SERVICES LAW. see BUSINESS AND ECONOMICS — Banking And Finance

341   NE   ISSN 0938-5428
K5
EUROPEAN JOURNAL OF INTERNATIONAL LAW/JOURNAL EUROPEEN DE DROIT INTERNATIONAL. 1990. 4/yr. fl.220 (effective 1994). (Law Books in Europe) Kluwer Law and Taxation Publishers (Subsidiary of: Wolters Kluwer N.V.), P.O. Box 23, 7400 GA Deventer, Netherlands. TEL 31-5700-47261. FAX 31-5700-22244. (Dist. by: Libresso Distribution Centre, P.O. Box 23, 7400 GA Deventer, Netherlands. TEL 31-5700-33155. FAX 31-5700-33834; N. America dist. addr.: 6 Bigelow St., Cambridge, MA 02139. TEL 617-354-0140. FAX 617-354-8595) (Co-publisher: C.H. Beck'sche Verlagsbuchhandlung, GW) Ed.Bd. adv.: B&W page DM.2200; trim 200 x 120. circ. 2,200. **Document type:** academic/scholarly publication.
   —BLDSC (3829.730850); UnCover; SWETS.
   Description: Publishes international contributions on the theory and practice of international law, including recent developments in general international law, legal issues relating to the EC's role in world affairs and international trade, East-West and North-South issues affecting Europe, as well as legislative, judicial and international trade measures affecting the EC.

341 320   NE
▼**EUROPEAN MONOGRAPHS.** (Text in English) 1992. irreg., vol.6, 1994. price varies. Kluwer Law and Taxation Publishers (Subsidiary of: Wolters Kluwer N.V.), P.O. Box 23, 7400 GA Deventer, Netherlands. TEL 31-5700-47261. FAX 31-5700-22244. TELEX 49295 KLUDV NL. (Dist. by: Libresso Distribution Centre, P.O. Box 23, 7400 GA Deventer, Netherlands. TEL 31-5700-33155. FAX 31-5700-33834; In N. America: Kluwer Law and Taxation Publishers, 675 Massachusetts Ave., Cambridge, MA 02139. TEL 617-354-0140. FAX 617-354-8595) Ed. Lammy Betten. (back issues avail.) **Document type:** monographic series.
   Description: Provides information about the future of Europe from a variety of legal and public policy perspectives, with particular emphasis on European integration.

EUROPEAN PATENT OFFICE REPORTS. see PATENTS, TRADEMARKS AND COPYRIGHTS

LAW — INTERNATIONAL LAW

341   NE   ISSN 0928-9801
▼**EUROPEAN REVIEW OF PRIVATE LAW/REVUE EUROPEENNE DE DROIT PRIVE/EUROPAEISCHE ZEITSCHRIFT FUER PRIVATRECHT.** (Text in English, French, German) 1993. 4/yr. fl.402($210) (effective 1994). Martinus Nijhoff Publishers, Human Rights and International Law (Subsidiary of: Kluwer Academic Publishers Group), Postbus 163, 3300 AD Dordrecht, Netherlands. TEL 31-78-334911. FAX 31-78-334254. TELEX 29245 KAPG NL. (Dist. by: Kluwer Academic Publishers Group, P.O. Box 322, 3300 AH Dordrecht, Netherlands. TEL 31-78-524400. FAX 31-78-524474; N. America dist. addr.: Box 358, Accord Sta., Hingham, MA 02018-0358. TEL 617-871-6600. FAX 617-871-6528) Eds. E.H. Hondius, M.E. Storme. **Document type:** academic/scholarly publication.
   Description: Focuses on practical and academic discussions of legal developments relating to national private law, within a broad European perspective. Provides a forum for debate on issues involving unified private law for the EC.
   Refereed Serial

EUROPEAN TAX HANDBOOK. see *BUSINESS AND ECONOMICS — Public Finance, Taxation*

EUROPEAN TAXATION. see *BUSINESS AND ECONOMICS — Public Finance, Taxation*

EUROPEAN TRANSPORT LAW/DROIT EUROPEEN DES TRANSPORTS/EUROPAEISCHES TRANSPORTRECHT/DIRITTO EUROPEO DEI TRASPORTI/EUROPEES VERVOERRECHT. see *TRANSPORTATION*

341   US   ISSN 1060-9105
EUROSCOPE; providing access to information necessary to do business in the European Union. 1992. m. $200 (effective 1994). EuroScope, Inc., 46679 Winchester Dr., Sterling, VA 22170. TEL 703-430-5417. Ed. John Baird. index. (looseleaf format; back issues avail.) **Document type:** newsletter.
   Description: Summarizes recent European Union legislation and judgements of the European Court of Justice and Court of First Instance in the single market, economic and social arena, European Union external relations, European Union institutions, as well as noteworthy questions from members of the European parliament. Source is The Official Journal of the European Communities.

F C I L NEWSLETTER. (Foreign, Comparative and International Law S I S) see *LIBRARY AND INFORMATION SCIENCES*

FLETCHER FORUM OF WORLD AFFAIRS. see *POLITICAL SCIENCE — International Relations*

341   US   ISSN 0882-6420
K6
FLORIDA INTERNATIONAL LAW JOURNAL. 1984. 3/yr. $21 (foreign $25). University of Florida, College of Law, Holland Law Center, Gainesville, FL 32611. TEL 904-392-4980. Ed. Andrea Fisher. circ. 250. (reprint service avail. from WSH) Indexed: C.L.I., Leg.Per. **Document type:** academic/scholarly publication.
—UnCover.

341   US   ISSN 0426-7230
FONTES IURIS GENTIUM. SECTION 2. (Text in English, French and German) irreg. price varies. Springer-Verlag, 175 Fifth Ave., New York, NY 10010. TEL 212-460-1500. FAX 212-473-6272. (Also: Berlin, Heidelberg, Tokyo and Vienna) Eds. H. Mosler, R. Bernhardt. (reprint service avail. from ISI) **Document type:** monographic series.
   Supersedes in part: Fontes Iuris Gentium (ISSN 0428-903X)

FOOD POLICY INTERNATIONAL. see *AGRICULTURE — Agricultural Economics*

FORDHAM CORPORATE LAW INSTITUTE (PROCEEDINGS). see *LAW — Corporate Law*

341   US   ISSN 0747-9395
JX1
FORDHAM INTERNATIONAL LAW JOURNAL. 1977. 4/yr. $30 (foreign $35) (effective Sep. 1993). Fordham University, School of Law, 140 W. 62nd St., Rm. 015, New York, NY 10023-7477. TEL 212-636-6931. FAX 212-636-6932. adv.; bk.rev.; index. circ. 900. (also avail. in microform from WSH; back issues avail.; reprint service avail. from WSH) Indexed: ELLIS, Leg.Cont., Leg.Per.
●Also available online. Vendor(s): West Services, Inc.
—BLDSC (3985.850000); Faxon; UnCover; SWETS.
Formerly: Fordham International Law Forum.

FOREIGN INVESTMENT IN CANADA. see *BUSINESS AND ECONOMICS — Investments*

341 382   US
FOREIGN INVESTMENT IN CENTRAL AND EASTERN EUROPE. 1990. irreg. $125. (Columbia University, Parker School of Foreign and Comparative Law) Transnational Juris Publications, Inc., 1 Bridge St., Irvington-on-Hudson, NY 10533. TEL 914-591-4288. FAX 914-591-2688. (Dist. outside N. America by: Kluwer Academic Publishers Group, P.O. Box 322, 3300 AH Dordrecht, Netherlands. TEL 31-78-524400. FAX 31-78-524474) Ed. Vratislav Pechota. (looseleaf format)
   Description: Presents comprehensive information on doing business in Central and Eastern Europe.

FOREIGN POLICY BULLETIN; the documentary record of United States foreign policy. see *POLITICAL SCIENCE — International Relations*

341   US
FOREIGN STATE IMMUNITY IN COMMERCIAL TRANSACTIONS. 1991. base vol. (plus a. supplement) $100. Butterworth Legal Publishers (Salem) (Subsidiary of: Reed Elsevier plc), 8 Industrial Way, Bldg. C, Salem, NH 03079. TEL 800-548-4001. FAX 603-898-9858. Ed. Michael Wallace Gordon. (looseleaf format)
   Description: Covers the Foreign Sovereign Immunities Act of 1976 (US) and the State Immunity Act of 1978 (UK).

346.066   US
FOREIGN TRADE AND INVESTMENT. 2nd ed., 1991. base vol. (plus a. supplement). $95. Butterworth Legal Publishers (Salem) (Subsidiary of: Reed Elsevier plc), 8 Industrial Way, Bldg. C, Salem, NH 03079. TEL 800-548-4001. FAX 603-898-9858. Ed. Thomas F. Clasen. (looseleaf format)
   Description: Guide to foreign trade and investment principles of international law.

341   NE   ISSN 0924-8153
FORUM INTERNATIONALE; lectures on commercial law and arbitration. 1983. irreg., no.18, 1993. fl.43($24) per no. (effective 1994). (Stichting Forum Internationale) Kluwer Law and Taxation Publishers (Subsidiary of: Wolters Kluwer N.V.), P.O. Box 23, 7400 GA Deventer, Netherlands. TEL 31-5700-47261. FAX 31-5700-22244. TELEX 49295 KLUDV NL. (Dist. by: Libresso Distribution Centre, P.O. Box 23, 7400 GA Deventer, Netherlands. TEL 31-5700-33155. FAX 31-5700-33834; In N. America: Kluwer Law and Taxation Publishers, 675 Massachusetts Ave., Cambridge, MA 02139. TEL 617-354-0140. FAX 617-354-8595) (looseleaf format) **Document type:** monographic series.
—BLDSC (4024.086250).
   Description: Publishes lectures given at the Peace Palace in The Hague on topics relating to commercial law and commercial arbitration in specific European countries as well at an international level.

341   FR   ISSN 0071-8971
FRANCE. SECRETARIAT D'ETAT AUX AFFAIRES ETRANGERES CHARGE DE LA COOPERATION. RECUEIL DES TRAITES ET ACCORDS DE LA FRANCE. 1961. a. price varies. Secretariat d'Etat aux Affaires Etrangeres Charge de la Cooperation, Direction de l'Aide au Developpement, 37, Quai d'Orsay, 75700 Paris, France.

341   GW   ISSN 0340-0255
JX1903
DIE FRIEDENS - WARTE; Blaetter fuer internationale Verstaendigung und zwischenstaatliche Organisation. 1899. s-a. DM.50. Berlin Verlag Arno Spitz GmbH, Pacelliallee 5, 14195 Berlin, Germany. TEL 030-8326232. FAX 030-8316249. Ed. Ferenc Majoros. adv.; bk.rev. circ. 500. **Document type:** academic/scholarly publication.
   Description: Forum for the discussion of contemporary theoretical and practical problems of international law and peace studies.

FRONTIER-FREE EUROPE. see *BUSINESS AND ECONOMICS — International Commerce*

341 382   US
G A T T LEGAL SYSTEM AND WORLD TRADE DIPLOMACY. (General Agreement on Tariffs and Trade) irreg., 2nd ed., 1990. $85. Butterworth Legal Publishers (Salem) (Subsidiary of: Reed Elsevier plc), 8 Industrial Way, Bldg. C, Salem, NH 03079. TEL 800-548-4001. FAX 603-898-9858. Eds. Robert E. Hudec, Melvin C. Steen.
   Description: Examines the historical development of the GATT legal system, from the negotiation of the GATT Agreement in 1946-1948 to the beginning of the Tokyo Round in 1975.

341   GW
DAS GELTENDE SEEVOELKERRECHT IN EINZELDARSTELLUNGEN. 1970. irreg., vol.11, 1979. price varies. (Universitaet Hamburg, Institut fuer Internationale Angelegenheiten) Nomos Verlagsgesellschaft mbH und Co. KG, Waldseestr. 3-5, 76530 Baden-Baden, Germany. TEL 07221-21040. FAX 07221-210427. (Subscr. to: Postfach 610, 76484 Baden-Baden, Germany) **Document type:** monographic series.
   Formerly: Geltende Seekriegsrecht in Einzeldarstellungen (ISSN 0435-1924)

341   US   ISSN 0748-4305
GEORGE WASHINGTON JOURNAL OF INTERNATIONAL LAW AND ECONOMICS. 1966. 3/yr. $23 (foreign $25) (effective Mar. 1994). George Washington University, National Law Center, 2008 G St., N.W., Washington, DC 20052. TEL 202-676-3847. Ed.Bd. adv.; bk.rev. circ. 1,250. (also avail. in microform from UMI,WSH,PMC; reprint service avail. from UMI,WSH) Indexed: ABI Inform., Abstr.Bk.Rev.Curr.Leg.Per., Amer.Bibl.Slavic & E.Eur.Stud., BPIA, Bus.Ind., C.L.I., Curr.Cont., Foreign Leg.Per., L.R.I., Leg.Cont., Leg.Per., Mar.Aff.Bibl., P.A.I.S., SSCI. **Document type:** academic/scholarly publication.
●Also available online. Vendor(s): Mead Data Central, Inc., West Services, Inc.
—BLDSC (4158.228000); Faxon; UnCover; SWETS; UMI.
   Formerly: Journal of International Law and Economics (ISSN 0022-2003)

341 340.2   US   ISSN 0046-578X
K7
GEORGIA JOURNAL OF INTERNATIONAL AND COMPARATIVE LAW. 1970. 3/yr. $15. Georgia Journal of International and Comparative Law, Inc., University of Georgia, School of Law, Athens, GA 30602. TEL 706-542-5205. Ed.Bd. adv.; bk.rev.; index. circ. 900. (also avail. in microfilm from UMI; microfiche from UMI; reprint service avail. from RRI,UMI) Indexed: Abstr.Bk.Rev.Curr.Leg.Per., C.C.L.P., C.L.I., Foreign Leg.Per., L.R.I., Leg.Cont., Leg.Per., P.A.I.S. **Document type:** academic/scholarly publication.
●Also available online. Vendor(s): Mead Data Central, Inc., West Services, Inc.
—BLDSC (4158.420000); Faxon; UnCover; SWETS; UMI.

341   GW   ISSN 0344-3094
JX21
GERMAN YEARBOOK OF INTERNATIONAL LAW. 1948. a. price varies. (Universitaet Kiel, Institut fuer Internationales Recht) Duncker und Humblot GmbH, Postfach 410329, 12113 Berlin, Germany. TEL 030-7900060. FAX 030-79000631. Indexed: Amer.Hist.& Life (until 1989), Hist.Abstr. (until 1989). **Document type:** academic/scholarly publication.
—BLDSC (4162.158600). CCC.
   Formerly: Jahrbuch fuer Internationales Recht (ISSN 0021-3993)

GLOBAL JOURNAL ON CRIME AND CRIMINAL LAW. see *LAW — Criminal Law*

LAW — INTERNATIONAL LAW

341 340 GW
GOETTINGER RECHTSWISSENSCHAFTLICHE STUDIEN. 1951. irreg., vol. 146, 1993. price varies. Verlag Otto Schwartz und Co., Annastr. 7, 37075 Goettingen, Germany. TEL 0551-31051. FAX 0551-372812. **Document type:** monographic series.

341 382 323.4 US ISSN 1058-1049
KF1976.Z95
GUIDE TO AMERICAN STATE AND LOCAL LAWS ON SOUTH AFRICA. 1990. a. Investor Responsibility Research Center, Inc., 1755 Massachusetts Ave. N.W., Ste. 600, Washington, DC 20036-2102. TEL 202-234-7500. FAX 202-332-8570.

341 382 US ISSN 1050-3900
K2400.A13
GUIDE TO INTERNATIONAL ARBITRATION AND ARBITRATORS (YEAR). 1989. a., latest 2nd ed. 1992. $245. (Columbia University, Parker School of Foreign and Comparative Law) Transnational Juris Publications, Inc., 1 Bridge St., Irvington-on-Hudson, NY 10533. TEL 914-591-4288. FAX 914-591-2688. Ed.Bd; Pub. Heike Fenton. **Document type:** directory.
Description: Includes data on more than 500 commercial arbitrators, including nationality, qualifications, specializations, addresses.

341.57 382 US
GUIDE TO INTERNATIONAL COMMERCE LAW. 1982. 2 base vols. (plus a. suppl.) $195. Shepard's - McGraw-Hill, Inc., Box 35300, Colorado Springs, CO 80935-3530. TEL 800-525-2474. (looseleaf format)
Description: Discusses laws relating to import and export of products and technology, distribution in the U.S. and abroad and foreign investment, with emphasis on transactions and contracts between U.S. and foreign firms.

GUIDE TO THE EUROPEAN V A T DIRECTIVES; commentary on the value added tax of the European Community. see *BUSINESS AND ECONOMICS — Public Finance, Taxation*

GUIDE TO UNITED STATES TREATIES IN FORCE. see *LAW — Abstracting, Bibliographies, Statistics*

341 332.6 NE
HANDBOOK OF G A T T DISPUTE SETTLEMENT. (General Agreement of Tariffs and Trade) 1991. base vol. (plus a. update). fl.410($235) (effective 1993). Transnational Juris Publications, Inc., 1 Bridge St., 7400 GA Deventer, Netherlands. TEL 914-591-4288. FAX 914-591-2688. (Dist. outside N. America by: Libresso Distribution Service, P.O. Box 23, 7400 GA Deventer, Netherlands. TEL 31-5700-33155) (Co-publisher: Kluwer Law and Taxation Publishers, NE) Ed. William E. Davey, Andreas Loewenfeld. (looseleaf format)
Description: Comprehensive reference to GATT proceedings, including discussions of the principles of GATT, its dispute resolution system, summaries of dispute settlements, citations of pertinent articles and clauses of the General Agreement, and comparison to standard commercial arbitration.

HANDBOOK ON EUROPEAN EMPLOYEE CO-MANAGEMENT. see *BUSINESS AND ECONOMICS — Labor And Industrial Relations*

HANDBOOK ON THE 1989 DOUBLE TAXATION CONVENTION BETWEEN THE FEDERAL REPUBLIC OF GERMANY AND THE UNITED STATES OF AMERICA. see *BUSINESS AND ECONOMICS — Public Finance, Taxation*

341 US ISSN 0017-8063
JX1
HARVARD INTERNATIONAL LAW JOURNAL. 1959. 2/yr. $24 (Canada $30). Harvard University, Law School, Publications Center, Hastings Hall, Cambridge, MA 02138. TEL 617-495-3694. bk.rev.; cum.index. circ. 1,200. (also avail. in microform from RRI,UMI; back issues avail.; reprint service avail. from RRI,UMI) **Indexed:** A.B.C.Pol.Sci., Abstr.Bk.Rev.Curr.Leg.Per., Amer.Bibl.Slavic & E.Eur.Stud., C.L.I., ELLIS, HR Rep., L.R.I., Leg.Cont., Leg.Per., P.A.I.S., So.Pac.Per.Ind.
●Also available online. Vendor(s): West Services, Inc.
—BLDSC (4267.200000); Faxon; UnCover; SWETS.
Formerly: Harvard International Law Club Journal.
Description: Publishes articles and comments on varied topics of interest to international lawyers and scholars.

HARVARD INTERNATIONAL REVIEW. see *POLITICAL SCIENCE — International Relations*

341 US ISSN 0149-9246
K8
HASTINGS INTERNATIONAL AND COMPARATIVE LAW REVIEW. 1977. q. $20 (foreign $22). University of California at San Francisco, Hastings College of the Law, 200 McAllister St., San Francisco, CA 94102-4978. TEL 415-565-4730. FAX 415-565-4814. Ed. Peter Gal. adv.; bk.rev.; cum.index every 5 yrs. circ. 1,100. (tabloid format; also avail. in microfilm from RRI; back issues avail.; reprint service avail.) **Indexed:** A.B.C.Pol.Sci., Abstr.Bk.Rev.Curr.Leg.Per., Amer.Bibl.Slavic & E.Eur.Stud., C.L.I., L.R.I., Leg.Per., P.A.I.S., Peace Res.Abstr. **Document type:** academic/scholarly publication.
●Also available online. Vendor(s): West Services, Inc. Also available on CD-ROM.
—BLDSC (4273.040000); Faxon; UnCover; SWETS.
Description: Publishes articles by law professors and practitioners addressing timely issues in public and private international law.

341 GR ISSN 0251-6535
HELLINIKI EPITHEORISSIS EVROPAIKOU DIKAIOU/GREEK REVIEW OF EUROPEAN LAW/REVUE HELLENIQUE DE DROIT EUROPEEN. 1981. 3/yr. Dr.5500($50) Centre of International and European Economic Law, Bar of Thessaloniki, P.O. Box 14, 551 02 Kalamaria, Thessaloniki, Greece. TEL 30-31-473403. FAX 30-31-434100. Ed. S. Menglidou. adv.; index, cum.index. (back issues avail.) **Document type:** academic/scholarly publication.
Description: Covers European Community law, international and economic law, and human rights law for lawyers and postgraduate students.

HUMAN RIGHTS & PEACE LAW DOCKET. see *LAW — Constitutional Law*

I C C A CONGRESS SERIES. (International Council for Commercial Arbitration) see *LAW — Corporate Law*

I F A CONGRESS SEMINAR SERIES. (International Fiscal Association) see *BUSINESS AND ECONOMICS — Public Finance, Taxation*

341 US ISSN 0190-5821
I L A NEWSLETTER. 1974. bi-m. membership. International Law Association, American Branch, c/o P. Nicholas Kourides, Chase Manhattan Bank, N.A., One Chase Manhattan Plaza, 29th Fl., New York, NY 10081. circ. 700.

341 US
I L A PRACTITIONER'S NOTEBOOK. 1978. q. $20 to non-members. International Law Association, American Branch, c/o P. Nicholas Kourides, Chase Manhattan Bank, N.A., One Chase Manhattan Plaza, 29th Fl., New York, NY 10081. Eds. Howard Hill, Ved Nanda. circ. 850.

341 US
I L S A JOURNAL OF INTERNATIONAL LAW. 1977. a. $9. International Law Students Association, Tillar House, 2223 Massachusetts Ave., N.W., Washington, DC 20008. FAX 202-797-7133. Ed. Denise M. Hodge. adv.; bk.rev. circ. 500. **Indexed:** C.L.I., L.R.I., Leg.Per., Peace Res.Abstr.
Formerly: A S I L S International Law Journal (ISSN 0161-1402)

341.4 UK ISSN 0269-5774
IMMIGRATION AND NATIONALITY LAW & PRACTICE. 1986. 4/yr. £95. Tolley Publishing Co. Ltd., Tolley House, 2 Addiscombe Rd., Croydon, Surrey CR9 5AF, England. TEL 081-686-9141. FAX 081-686-3155. Eds. Lawrence Grant, David Pearl. adv.; bk.rev.; index. (back issues avail.) **Indexed:** Refug.Abstr. **Document type:** trade publication.
Description: Covers immigration and nationality law and practice in the UK and overseas.

341.4 325.1 US ISSN 0149-9807
K9
IMMIGRATION AND NATIONALITY LAW REVIEW. 1986. a. $75. William S. Hein & Co., Inc., 1285 Main St., Buffalo, NY 14209. TEL 716-882-2600. FAX 716-883-8100. TELEX 91-209 WU 7 HEIN BUF. Ed. Maurice A. Roberts. (reprint service avail. from WSH)
Refereed Serial

341.4 US ISSN 0731-5767
KF4802
IMMIGRATION LAW REPORT. 1981. 11/yr. $150. (Fragomen, Del Rey & Bernsen) Clark - Boardman - Callaghan Company Ltd., 375 Hudson St., New York, NY 10014. TEL 212-929-7500; 800-221-9428. FAX 212-924-0460. index. (looseleaf format; back issues avail.) **Indexed:** HR Rep.
Description: Comments on current case law, developments, and emerging trends in immigration law.

341 US ISSN 0145-3416
JV6001.A1
IMMIGRATION NEWSLETTER. 1972. q. $50 to individuals; institutions and libraries $75. National Lawyers Guild (Boston), National Immigration Project, 14 Beacon St., Ste. 506, Boston, MA 02108. TEL 617-227-9727. FAX 617-227-5495. Ed. Dan Kesselbrenner. bk.rev. circ. 600. **Indexed:** HR Rep., Refug.Abstr. **Document type:** newsletter.
Description: Includes legal analysis and political comment of interest to immigration practitioners.

341.4 US ISSN 1067-3377
JV6001.F3
IMMIGRATION REPORT. 1979. m. $25. Federation for American Immigration Reform (FAIR), 1666 Connecticut Ave., N.W., Ste. 400, Washington, DC 20009. TEL 202-328-7004. FAX 202-387-3447. Ed. Louisa Parker. bk.rev. circ. 45,000. (back issues avail.) **Document type:** newsletter.
Formerly (until 1990): F A I R Immigration Report (ISSN 0737-867X)
Description: Presents news articles and reports dealing with the impact of legal and illegal immigration on the U.S.; also tracks immigration-related legislation.

341 II ISSN 0019-5294
JX18
INDIAN JOURNAL OF INTERNATIONAL LAW. (Text in English) 1960. q. $35. Indian Society of International Law, 7-8 Scindia House, Kasturba Gandhi Marg, New Delhi 110001, India. Ed. Rahmatullah Khan. adv.; bk.rev.; bibl. circ. 1,500. **Indexed:** C.L.I., HR Rep., Leg.Per., Refug.Abstr. —UnCover; SWETS.

341 II ISSN 0073-6678
INDIAN SOCIETY OF INTERNATIONAL LAW. PUBLICATIONS. 1960. q. $35. Indian Society of International Law, 7-8 Scindia House, Kasturba Gandhi Marg, New Delhi 110001, India. Ed. Rahmatullah Khan. adv.; bk.rev. circ. 1,500.

341 GW ISSN 0174-2108
KK6050.A13
INFORMATIONSBRIEF AUSLAENDERRECHT. 1979. m. DM.198. Luchterhand Verlag, Heddesdorferstr. 31, 56564 Neuwied, Germany. TEL 02631-801-0. TELEX 02631-801210. Ed.Bd; adv.; bk.rev. circ. 2,600. **Indexed:** Refug.Abstr. **Document type:** bulletin.

341 SZ
INSTITUT FUER INTERNATIONALES RECHT UND INTERNATIONALE BEZIEHUNGEN. SCHRIFTENREIHE. (Text mainly in German; occasionally in English or French) 1939. irreg. price varies. Helbing und Lichtenhahn Verlag AG, Freie Str. 84, CH-4051 Basel, Switzerland. TEL 064-268626. FAX 064-245780. (Subscr. to: Sauerlaender AG, Postfach, CH-5001 Aarau, Switzerland) **Document type:** monographic series.

341 CI ISSN 0351-2800
INSTITUTE OF INTERNATIONAL LAW AND INTERNATIONAL RELATIONS. CONTRIBUTIONS TO THE STUDY OF COMPARATIVE AND INTERNATIONAL LAW/PRINOSI ZA POREDBENO PROUCAVANJE PRAVA I MEDUNARODNO PRAVO. (Text in English, German and Serbo-Croatian; summaries English, French, German and Serbo-Croatian) 1968. s-a. free. University of Zagreb, Faculty of Law, Institute of International Law and International Relations, Cirilometodska 4, 41000 Zagreb, Croatia. Ed. Kresimir Sajko. bk.rev. circ. 500. (back issues avail.)

INTELLECTUAL PROPERTY DECISIONS. see *BUSINESS AND ECONOMICS — International Commerce*

LAW — INTERNATIONAL LAW

341.57 UK ISSN 0955-2197
INTELLECTUAL PROPERTY IN BUSINESS (BRIEFING AND REVIEW); the European review of the law relating to technological innovation & product development. 1989. 10/yr.(Briefing); bi-m.(Review). £180 (foreign £200). Eclipse Publications Ltd., 18-20 Highbury Place, London N5 1QP, England. TEL 071-354-5858. FAX 071-359-4000. Ed. Anthony Korn. circ. 400. (back issues avail.)
 Description: Covers national and international intellectual property law: legal, commercial and regulatory developments affecting the management, protection and marketing of innovation.

INTELLECTUAL PROPERTY NEWSLETTER. see *BUSINESS AND ECONOMICS — International Commerce*

341 US
INTELLECTUAL PROPERTY PROTECTION IN ASIA. 1991. base vol. (plus a. supplement). $125. Butterworth Legal Publishers (Salem) (Subsidiary of: Reed Elsevier plc), 8 Industrial Way, Bldg. C, Salem, NH 03079. TEL 800-548-4001. FAX 603-898-9858. Ed. Arthur Wineburg. (looseleaf format)
 Description: Provides attorneys and their clients with information and methods to determine where, when, and how to establish and exercise the right to their intellectual property.

INTELLECTUAL PROPERTY WORLD DESK REFERENCE; a guide to practice by country, state and province. see *PATENTS, TRADEMARKS AND COPYRIGHTS*

341 US ISSN 0884-1756
INTER-AMERICAN LAW REVIEW. 1969. 3/yr. $22. University of Miami, School of Law, Box 248087, Coral Gables, FL 33124. TEL 305-284-5562. (Co-sponsor: Inter-American Bar Association) adv.; bk.rev.; index. circ. 800. (tabloid format; also avail. in microfilm from WSH,PMC; reprint service avail. from RRI,WSH) **Indexed:** C.L.I., L.R.I., Leg.Per., Ocean.Abstr., Pollut.Abstr. **Document type:** academic/scholarly publication.
 ●Also available online. Vendor(s): West Services, Inc.
 —Faxon; UnCover.
 Formerly (until 1984): Lawyer of the Americas (ISSN 0023-9445)

341 US ISSN 0886-7747
INTER-AMERICAN LEGAL MATERIALS. 1983. q. $71 (foreign $81). American Bar Association, International Law and Practice Section, 750 N. Lake Shore Dr., Chicago, IL 60611. TEL 312-988-5000.
 —UnCover.
 Description: Designed to increase understanding and communication between US lawyers and their collegues in Latin America and the Caribbean.

346.066 US
INTERNATIONAL AGENCY AND DISTRIBUTION AGREEMENTS. (Vol.1: Analysis and Forms; Vol.2: Europe; Vol.3: Middle East, Africa, Asia, Pacific; Vol.4: North America, South America) 1991. 4 base vols. (plus a. supplements). $425 for set. Butterworth Legal Publishers (Salem) (Subsidiary of: Reed Elsevier plc), 8 Industrial Way, Bldg. C, Salem, NH 03079. TEL 800-548-4001. FAX 603-898-9858. Ed. Thomas F. Clasen. (looseleaf format)
 Description: Provides US and foreign practitioners with information needed to prepare and review foreign sales agency and distribution agreements.

341 UK ISSN 0020-5893
LAW
INTERNATIONAL AND COMPARATIVE LAW QUARTERLY. 1952. q. £65($125) (students £65 ($125)) (effective 1994). British Institute of International and Comparative Law, Charles Clore House, 17 Russell Sq., London WC1B 5DR, England. TEL 071-636-5802. FAX 071-323-2016. Ed. Hazel Fox. adv.; bk.rev.; bibl.; index; cum. 1952-1976; 1977-1992. circ. 2,500. (reprint service avail. from KTO) **Indexed:** A.B.C.Pol.Sci., Abstr.Bk.Rev.Curr.Leg.Per., C.L.I., ELLIS, Foreign Leg.Per., HRIS, Int.Lab.Doc., L.R.I., Leg.Info.Manage.Ind., Leg.Per., Mar.Aff.Bibl., P.A.I.S., SSCI. **Document type:** academic/scholarly publication.
 —BLDSC (4535.700000); Faxon; UnCover; SWETS.
 Description: Covers public and private international law, human rights, European Commonwealth and comparative law

341 382 US ISSN 0886-0114
K2400.A13
INTERNATIONAL ARBITRATION REPORT. 1986. m. $600. Mealey Publications, Inc., Box 446, Wayne, PA 19087. TEL 215-688-6566. FAX 215-688-7552. Ed. Edie Scott. (looseleaf format)
 —CCC.
 Description: Covers court and arbitration panel opinions worldwide concerning international arbitration.

341 UK ISSN 0143-7453
K110.I47
INTERNATIONAL BAR NEWS. 1970. q. membership only. International Bar Association, 2 Harewood Pl., Hanover Sq., London W1R 9HB, England. TEL 44-71-629-1206. FAX 44-71-409-0456. Ed. Ruth Eldon. adv.; bk.rev.; bibl.; circ. 16,000 (controlled). **Indexed:** C.L.I., Leg.Per. **Document type:** academic/scholarly publication.
 Formerly (until 1980): International Bar Journal (ISSN 0047-0589)

INTERNATIONAL BOUNDARY STUDY. see *GEOGRAPHY*

346.07 UK ISSN 0309-7676
K9
INTERNATIONAL BUSINESS LAWYER. 1973. 11/yr. £130. International Bar Association, 2 Harewood Pl., Hanover Sq., London W1R 9HB, England. TEL 44-71-629-1206. FAX 44-71-409-0456. Ed. Ruth Eldon. adv.; bk.rev.; cum.index. circ. 12,000. **Indexed:** C.L.I., ELLIS, L.R.I., Leg.Per.
 —BLDSC (4538.370000); Faxon; UnCover; SWETS.

341 332.6 NE
INTERNATIONAL BUSINESS SERIES. VOLUME 1: LEGAL ASPECTS OF DOING BUSINESS IN EUROPE. (Text in English) base vol. (plus a. update). fl.455($260) (effective 1994). Kluwer Law and Taxation Publishers (Subsidiary of: Wolters Kluwer N.V.), P.O. Box 23, 7400 GA Deventer, Netherlands. TEL 31-5700-47261. FAX 31-5700-22244. TELEX 49295 KLUDV NL. (Dist. by: Libresso Distribution Centre, P.O. Box 23, 7400 GA Deventer, Netherlands. TEL 31-5700-33155. FAX 31-5700-33834; In N. America: Kluwer Law and Taxation Publishers, 675 Massachusetts Ave., Cambridge, MA 02139. TEL 617-354-0140. FAX 617-354-8595) Ed. Dennis Campbell. (looseleaf format)
 Description: Provides up-to-date references to the laws and regulations of countries in Western and Central Europe, including tax and labor laws, and regulations governing imports, investment and expatriation of profits.

341 332.6 NE
INTERNATIONAL BUSINESS SERIES. VOLUME 2: LEGAL ASPECTS OF DOING BUSINESS IN LATIN AMERICA. (Text in English) base vol. (plus a. update). fl.370($212) (effective 1994). Kluwer Law and Taxation Publishers (Subsidiary of: Wolters Kluwer N.V.), P.O. Box 23, 7400 GA Deventer, Netherlands. TEL 31-5700-47261. FAX 31-5700-22244. TELEX 49295 KLUDV NL. (Dist. by: Libresso Distribution Centre, P.O. Box 23, 7400 GA Deventer, Netherlands. TEL 31-5700-33155. FAX 31-5700-33834; In N. America: Kluwer Law and Taxation Publishers, 675 Massachusetts Ave., Cambridge, MA 02139. TEL 617-354-0140. FAX 617-354-8595) Ed. Dennis Campbell. (looseleaf format)
 Description: Provides up-to-date references to the laws and regulations of Central and Latin American and Caribbean countries, including tax and labor laws, regulations governing investment, imports and the expatriation of profits.

341 332.6 NE
INTERNATIONAL BUSINESS SERIES. VOLUME 3: LEGAL ASPECTS OF DOING BUSINESS IN ASIA AND THE PACIFIC. (Text in English) base vol. (plus a. update). fl.355($203) (effective 1994). Kluwer Law and Taxation Publishers (Subsidiary of: Wolters Kluwer N.V.), P.O. Box 23, 7400 GA Deventer, Netherlands. TEL 31-5700-47261. FAX 31-5700-22244. TELEX 49295 KLUDV NL. (Dist. by: Libresso Distribution Centre, P.O. Box 23, 7400 GA Deventer, Netherlands. TEL 31-5700-33155. FAX 31-5700-33834; In N. America: Kluwer Law and Taxation Publishers, 675 Massachusetts Ave., Cambridge, MA 02139. TEL 617-354-0140. FAX 617-354-8595) Ed. Dennis Campbell. (looseleaf format)
 Description: Provides up-to-date references to laws and regulations of countries in South and East Asia and the Pacific Island nations, including tax and labor laws and regulations concerning investment, imports and the expatriation of profits.

341 332.6 NE
INTERNATIONAL BUSINESS SERIES. VOLUME 4: LEGAL ASPECTS OF DOING BUSINESS IN AFRICA. (Text in English) base vol. (plus a. update). fl.255($146) (effective 1994). Kluwer Law and Taxation Publishers (Subsidiary of: Wolters Kluwer N.V.), P.O. Box 23, 7400 GA Deventer, Netherlands. TEL 31-5700-47261. FAX 31-5700-22244. TELEX 49295 KLUDV NL. (Dist. by: Libresso Distribution Centre, P.O. Box 23, 7400 GA Deventer, Netherlands. TEL 31-5700-33155. FAX 31-5700-33834; In N. America: Kluwer Law and Taxation Publishers, 675 Massachusetts Ave., Cambridge, MA 02139. TEL 617-354-0140. FAX 617-354-8595) Ed. Dennis Campbell. (looseleaf format)
 Description: Provides up-to-date references to laws and regulations of countries in sub-Saharan Africa, including tax and labor laws, and regulations governing investment, imports and the expatriation of profits.

341 332.6 NE
INTERNATIONAL BUSINESS SERIES. VOLUME 5: LEGAL ASPECTS OF DOING BUSINESS IN THE MIDDLE EAST. (Text in English) base vol. (plus a. update). fl.255($146) (effective 1994). Kluwer Law and Taxation Publishers (Subsidiary of: Wolters Kluwer N.V.), P.O. Box 23, 7400 GA Deventer, Netherlands. TEL 31-5700-47261. FAX 31-5700-22244. TELEX 49295 KLUDV NL. (Dist. by: Libresso Distribution Centre, P.O. Box 23, 7400 GA Deventer, Netherlands. TEL 31-5700-33155. FAX 31-5700-33834; In N. America: Kluwer Law and Taxation Publishers, 675 Massachusetts Ave., Cambridge, MA 02139. TEL 617-354-0140. FAX 617-354-8595) Ed. Dennis Campbell. (looseleaf format)
 Description: Provides up-to-date references on the laws and regulations of countries in the Middle East and North Africa, including tax and labor laws and regulations governing investment, imports and the expatriation of profits.

341 332.6 NE
INTERNATIONAL BUSINESS SERIES. VOLUME 6-7: LEGAL ASPECTS OF DOING BUSINESS IN NORTH AMERICA. (Text in English) base vol. (plus a. update). fl.359($206) (effective 1994). Kluwer Law and Taxation Publishers (Subsidiary of: Wolters Kluwer N.V.), P.O. Box 23, 7400 GA Deventer, Netherlands. TEL 31-5700-47261. FAX 31-5700-22244. TELEX 49295 KLUDV NL. (Dist. by: Libresso Distribution Centre, P.O. Box 23, 7400 GA Deventer, Netherlands. TEL 31-5700-33155. FAX 31-5700-33834; In N. America: Kluwer Law and Taxation Publishers, 675 Massachusetts Ave., Cambridge, MA 02139. TEL 617-354-0140. FAX 617-354-8595) Ed. Dennis Campbell. (looseleaf format)
 Description: Provides up-to-date references to the laws and regulations of each of the 9 provinces of Canada, the 50 states of the US and Puerto Rico, including tax and labor laws and regulations governing investments, imports and the expatriation of profits.

LAW — INTERNATIONAL LAW

341 332.6   NE
INTERNATIONAL BUSINESS TRANSACTIONS; commercial forms and documents including wordprocessing software. (Text in English) 1989. 2 base vols. (plus a. update). fl.595($340) (effective 1994). Kluwer Law and Taxation Publishers (Subsidiary of: Wolters Kluwer N.V.), P.O. Box 23, 7400 GA Deventer, Netherlands. TEL 31-5700-47261. FAX 31-5700-22244. TELEX 49295 KLUDV NL. (Dist. by: Libresso Distribution Centre, P.O. Box 23, 7400 GA Deventer, Netherlands. TEL 31-5700-33155. FAX 31-5700-33834; In N. America: Kluwer Law and Taxation Publishers, 675 Massachusetts Ave., Cambridge, MA 02139. TEL 617-354-0140. FAX 617-354-8595) Eds. Dennis Campbell, Reinhard Proksch. (looseleaf format; software avail. in DOS and Macintosh versions)
    Description: Provides all major contracts and forms of agreement used in international business, including licensing agreements, joint ventures, letters of credit, arbitration clauses. Each form is accompanied by an introduction and commentary.

INTERNATIONAL CENTRE FOR SETTLEMENT OF INVESTMENT DISPUTES. ANNUAL REPORT. see BUSINESS AND ECONOMICS — Investments

INTERNATIONAL COMMERCIAL ARBITRATION IN AUSTRALIA. see LAW — Corporate Law

341   SZ   ISSN 0020-6393
K9
INTERNATIONAL COMMISSION OF JURISTS. REVIEW. 1969. s-a. 33 SFr. International Commission of Jurists, 26 Chemin de Joinville, CH-1216 Cointrin - Geneva, Switzerland. TEL 022-7884747. FAX 022-7884880. Ed. Adama Dieng. bk.rev.; bibl. circ. 7,000. (also avail. in microform from JAI,MIM; back issues avail.) Indexed: C.L.I., Documentatieblad, L.R.I., Mid.East: Abstr.& Ind., P.A.I.S., Refug.Abstr. **Document type:** academic/scholarly publication.
—BLDSC (7786.180000); Faxon; UnCover; SWETS.
    Formed by the merger of: International Commission of Jurists. Bulletin (ISSN 0534-8242); International Commission of Jurists. Journal (ISSN 0047-0678)
    Description: Non-governmental organization concerned with the legal protection of human rights.

341   UK   ISSN 0958-5214
INTERNATIONAL COMPANY AND COMMERCIAL LAW REVIEW. 1990. m. £295 (effective 1994). Sweet & Maxwell, South Quay Plaza, 183 Marsh Wall, London, England. **Document type:** academic/scholarly publication.
—BLDSC (4538.724100).
    Description: Provides insight into worldwide developments in case law and changes in legislation that affect company and commercial lawyers.

341 690   UK   ISSN 0265-1416
K9
INTERNATIONAL CONSTRUCTION LAW REVIEW. 1983. q. $308. Lloyd's of London Press Ltd., Sheepen Place, Colchester, Essex CO3 3LP, England. TEL 0206-772277. FAX 0260-46273. (In US, subscr. to: 611 Broadway, Ste. 308, New York, NY 10012. TEL 212-529-9500) Eds. Humphrey Lloyd, David Wightman. bk.rev.; index. circ. 400.
—BLDSC (4539.410000); SWETS.
    Description: Covers legal and commercial aspects on international construction. Contains case notes from all parts of the world, correspondents' reports on current developments and articles on a wide range of topics.

341   US   ISSN 0899-7799
INTERNATIONAL CONTRACT ADVISER; the newsletter for global business. 1988. 12/yr. $250 (effective 1993). Kluwer Law and Taxation Publishers, 675 Massachusetts Ave., Cambridge, MA 02139. TEL 617-354-0140. FAX 617-354-8595. (Dist. outside U.S. by: Libresso Distribution Centre, P.O. Box 23, 7400 GA Deventer, Netherlands. TEL 31-5700-33155) Eds. Martin F. Klingenberg, Joseph E. Pattison. **Document type:** newsletter.
    Description: Provides concise and practical information regarding international business, including analysis of international contract clauses, reports on arbitration and litigation developments affecting global business, negotiation strategies.

341 332.6   NE
INTERNATIONAL CONTRACT MANUAL. (Consists of: Guide to Practical Applications of the U.N. Convention on Contracts for International Sale of Goods; Contract Checklists; Country Handbooks; Compliance Checklists) (Text in English) 1990. 4 base vols. (plus updates 8/yr.). price varies. Kluwer Law and Taxation Publishers (Subsidiary of: Wolters Kluwer N.V.), P.O. Box 23, 7400 GA Deventer, Netherlands. TEL 31-5700-47261. FAX 31-5700-22244. TELEX 49295 KLUDV NL. (Dist. by: Libresso Distribution Centre, P.O. Box 23, 7400 GA Deventer, Netherlands. TEL 31-5700-33155. FAX 31-5700-33834; In N. America: Kluwer Law and Taxation Publishers, 675 Massachusetts Ave., Cambridge, MA 02139. TEL 617-354-0140. FAX 617-354-8595) Ed. Andreas Kritzer. (looseleaf format)
    Description: Practical information for negotiating contracts with overseas customers, including information on competitive practices and government requirements.

INTERNATIONAL COURT OF JUSTICE. BIBLIOGRAPHY/COUR INTERNATIONALE DE JUSTICE. BIBLIOGRAPHIE. (International Court of Justice) see LAW — Abstracting, Bibliographies, Statistics

341   UN   ISSN 0074-445X
JX1971.6
INTERNATIONAL COURT OF JUSTICE. YEARBOOK. French edition: Cour Internationale de Justice. Annuaire (ISSN 0251-0669) (Editions in English and French) 1946. a. price varies. United Nations Publications, Room DC2-853, New York, NY 10017. TEL 212-963-8300. FAX 212-963-3489. TELEX 32323. (And: Peace Palace, 2517 KJ The Hague, Netherlands; Distribution and Sales Section, Palais des Nations, CH-12 Geneva, Switzerland) Ed.Bd. circ. 2,000.

341   NE
INTERNATIONAL ENCYCLOPAEDIA OF LAWS. (Consists of 12 sections: Civil Procedure; Commercial and Economic Law; Constitutional Law; Contracts; Corporations and Partnerships; Criminal Law; Environmental Law; Insurance Law; Labour Law and Industrial Relations; Medical Law; Social Security Law; Transport Law) (Text in English) 1991. base vols. (plus irreg. supplements). Kluwer Law and Taxation Publishers (Subsidiary of: Wolters Kluwer N.V.), P.O. Box 23, 7400 GA Deventer, Netherlands. TEL 31-5700-47261. FAX 31-5700-22244. TELEX 49295 KLUDV NL. (Dist. by: Libresso Distribution Centre, P.O. Box 23, 7400 GA Deventer, Netherlands. TEL 31-5700-33155. FAX 31-5700-33834; In N. America: Kluwer Law and Taxation Publishers, 675 Massachusetts Ave., Cambridge, MA 02139. TEL 617-354-0140. FAX 617-354-8595) Ed. Roger Blanpain. (looseleaf format) **Document type:** monographic series.
    Description: Discusses specific aspects of the law of individual countries throughout the world from an international, comparative perspective. Includes commentary on the principles of law, case law, practice, and relevant legislation in each field.

INTERNATIONAL ENCYCLOPAEDIA OF LAWS. CIVIL PROCEDURE. see LAW — Judicial Systems

INTERNATIONAL ENCYCLOPAEDIA OF LAWS. COMMERCIAL AND ECONOMIC LAW. see LAW — Civil Law

INTERNATIONAL ENCYCLOPAEDIA OF LAWS. CONSTITUTIONAL LAW. see LAW — Constitutional Law

INTERNATIONAL ENCYCLOPAEDIA OF LAWS. CONTRACTS. see LAW — Civil Law

INTERNATIONAL ENCYCLOPAEDIA OF LAWS. CORPORATIONS AND PARTNERSHIPS. see LAW — Corporate Law

INTERNATIONAL ENCYCLOPAEDIA OF LAWS. CRIMINAL LAW. see LAW — Criminal Law

INTERNATIONAL ENCYCLOPAEDIA OF LAWS. ENVIRONMENTAL LAW. see ENVIRONMENTAL STUDIES

INTERNATIONAL ENCYCLOPAEDIA OF LAWS. INSURANCE LAW. see INSURANCE

INTERNATIONAL ENCYCLOPAEDIA OF LAWS. LABOUR LAW AND INDUSTRIAL RELATIONS. see BUSINESS AND ECONOMICS — Labor And Industrial Relations

INTERNATIONAL ENCYCLOPAEDIA OF LAWS. MEDICAL LAW. see MEDICAL SCIENCES

INTERNATIONAL ENCYCLOPAEDIA OF LAWS. SOCIAL SECURITY LAW. see INSURANCE

INTERNATIONAL ENCYCLOPAEDIA OF LAWS. TRANSPORT LAW. see TRANSPORTATION

341   US   ISSN 1063-083X
INTERNATIONAL ENFORCEMENT LAW REPORTER. 1985. m. $305 (foreign $315). 818 Connecticut Ave., N.W., Ste. 700, Washington, DC 20006. TEL 202-293-4690. FAX 202-293-1877. Ed. Bruce Zagaris. adv. contact: Erika Barnes. bk.rev. circ. 125. (looseleaf format; back issues avail.) **Document type:** newsletter, academic/scholarly publication.
    Description: Summarizes key developments in international criminal law and policy, and related enforcement areas.

INTERNATIONAL ENVIRONMENTAL LAW AND POLICY. see ENVIRONMENTAL STUDIES

341   US
INTERNATIONAL ENVIRONMENTAL LAW AND REGULATION; a practical guide. 1991. base vol. (plus a. supplement). $125. Butterworth Legal Publishers (Salem) (Subsidiary of: Reed Elsevier plc), 8 Industrial Way, Bldg. C, Salem, NH 03079. TEL 800-548-4001. FAX 603-898-9858. Ed.Bd. (looseleaf format)
    Description: Summary overview and commentary on environmental compliance in the EC and 15 countries, considering both national laws and regulatory structures for environmental protection, and the developing body of transnational law on international environmental issues.

341 332.4   UK   ISSN 0262-6969
K9
INTERNATIONAL FINANCIAL LAW REVIEW. 1982. m. Euromoney Publications PLC, Nestor House, Playhouse Yard, London EC4V 5EX, England. Ed. Josephine Carr. Indexed: ABI Inform., Bank.Lit.Ind., BPIA, Cont.Pg.Manage., ELLIS, Leg.Cont., World Bank.Abstr.
—BLDSC (4540.189700); Faxon; UMI.

341.7   NE
INTERNATIONAL FISCAL ASSOCIATION. YEARBOOK. a. membership only. International Fiscal Association, World Trade Center, Beursplein 37, Postbus 30215, 3001 DE Rotterdam, Netherlands. TEL 31-10-4052990. FAX 31-10-4055031. TELEX 23229 BEURS NL.

INTERNATIONAL GENEVA YEARBOOK. see POLITICAL SCIENCE — International Relations

INTERNATIONAL GUIDE TO MERGERS AND ACQUISITIONS. see BUSINESS AND ECONOMICS — Public Finance, Taxation

341.57   NE
INTERNATIONAL HANDBOOK ON COMMERCIAL ARBITRATION; national reports and basic legal texts. (Text in English) 1984. 3 base vols. (plus s-a. updates). fl.525($300) (International Council for Commercial Arbitration) Kluwer Law and Taxation Publishers (Subsidiary of: Wolters Kluwer N.V.), P.O. Box 23, 7400 GA Deventer, Netherlands. TEL 31-5700-47261. FAX 31-5700-22244. TELEX 49295 KLUDV NL. (Dist. by: Libresso Distribution Centre, P.O. Box 23, 7400 GA Deventer, Netherlands. TEL 31-5700-33155. FAX 31-5700-33834; In N. America: Kluwer Law and Taxation Publishers, 675 Massachusetts Ave., Cambridge, MA 02139. TEL 617-354-0140. FAX 617-354-8595) Ed. Albert Jan van den Berg. (looseleaf format)
    Formerly: Handbook Commercial Law.
    Description: Provides the text of national Arbitration Acts and other relevant provisions, with comprehensive information and commentary on the arbitration law and practice current in virtually every country of the world.

INTERNATIONAL HANDBOOK ON CONTRACTS OF EMPLOYMENT. see BUSINESS AND ECONOMICS — Labor And Industrial Relations

3390 LAW — INTERNATIONAL LAW

INTERNATIONAL HUMAN RIGHTS REPORTS. see
POLITICAL SCIENCE — Civil Rights

INTERNATIONAL INCOME TAX RULES OF THE UNITED STATES. see BUSINESS AND ECONOMICS — Public Finance, Taxation

INTERNATIONAL JOURNAL ON GROUP RIGHTS. see
POLITICAL SCIENCE — Civil Rights

340   US
INTERNATIONAL LAW AND TRADE PERSPECTIVE. 1975. m. $150. 604 S. King St., Ste. 100 B, Leesburg, VA 22075. TEL 202-429-2098. Ed.Bd. bk.rev.; abstr. circ. 250.
  Formed by the July 1987 merger of: International Law Perspective & International Trade Perspective (ISSN 0098-7719)
  Description: Reviews and summarizes significant and interesting developments in the Congress, the courts, the legal periodicals, as well as other sources, pertaining to international law and trade.

341   US
INTERNATIONAL LAW ASSOCIATION. AMERICAN BRANCH. PROCEEDINGS. biennial. $35. International Law Association, American Branch, c/o P. Nicholas Kourides, Chase Manhattan Bank, N.A., One Chase Manhattan Plaza, 29th Fl., New York, NY 10081. Ed. Theordore Giuttari. bibl. circ. 650. **Document type:** proceedings.

341   UK   ISSN 0074-6738
INTERNATIONAL LAW ASSOCIATION. REPORTS OF CONFERENCES. (Text in English; some papers in French) 1875. biennial; 63rd, 1988, Warsaw. price varies. International Law Association, 3 Paper Bldgs., The Temple, London EC4Y 7EU, England. TEL 01-353-2904. cum.index: 1873-1972. circ. 4,000. **Indexed:** C.L.I., Leg.Per.
  Formerly: Association Internationale du Droit Commercial. Et du Droit Affaires. Groupe Francais. Travaux (ISSN 0571-5873)

341   US   ISSN 0047-0813
JX1
INTERNATIONAL LAW NEWS. 1972. q. membership only. American Bar Association, International Law and Practice Section, 750 N. Lake Shore Dr., Chicago, IL 60611. TEL 312-988-5555. Ed. Beth Van Hanswyk. circ. 17,000. **Indexed:** C.L.I., L.R.I. **Document type:** newsletter.
  Description: Newsletter reports on committee activities and other current matters of interest to Section members.

341   US   ISSN 1041-3405
K1001.2
INTERNATIONAL LAW PRACTICUM; practicing the law of the world from New York. 1988. s-a. $65 (foreign $75) includes New York International Law Review (free to qualified personnel). New York State Bar Association, International Law and Practice Section, 1 Elk St., Albany, NY 12207-1096. TEL 518-463-3200. FAX 518-487-5699. Ed. Ingrid Sapona. circ. 1 900 (controlled). **Document type:** academic/scholarly publication.
  Description: Articles relating to the practical needs of attorneys in an international setting, emphasizing clinical matters as opposed to academic, exploring the application of the law for the generalist rather than theoretical discussions for the expert.
  Refereed Serial

341   US
KF200.F568
INTERNATIONAL LAW QUARTERLY. 1982. irreg. (3-4/yr.). $25 to non-members. Florida Bar, 650 Apalachee Pkwy., Tallahasee, FL 32399-2300. TEL 904-561-5625. circ. 875. **Document type:** newsletter.

341   II   ISSN 0300-4058
INTERNATIONAL LAW REPORTER. (Text in English) 1970. m. Rs.45($15) Intlaw Publishers Corporation, P.O. Box 3528, New Delhi 110024, India. Ed. R.S. Butalia. adv.; bk.rev.; index.

341 327   UK
INTERNATIONAL LAW REPORTS. 1932. q. $127 per no. (University of Cambridge, Research Centre for International Law) Grotius Publications Ltd., P.O. Box 115, Cambridge CB3 9BP, England. FAX 0223-313545. Ed. E. Lauterpacht. cum.index. (back issues avail.)

341   US   ISSN 0020-7810
JX1
INTERNATIONAL LAWYER. 1966. q. $31 to non-members. American Bar Association, International Law and Practice Section, 750 N. Lake Shore Dr., Chicago, IL 60611. TEL 312-988-6067. Ed. Joseph J. Norton. adv.; bk.rev.; abstr.; bibl.; charts; index. circ. 18,000. (also avail. in microfilm from RRI,WSH; reprint service avail. from RRI) **Indexed:** Abstr.Bk.Rev.Curr.Leg.Per., Amer.Bibl.Slavic & E.Eur.Stud., C.L.I., ELLIS, Int.Lab.Doc., L.R.I., Leg.Per., Mar.Aff.Bibl., Sel.Water Res.Abstr., SSCI.
  ●Also available online. Vendor(s): Mead Data Central, Inc., West Services, Inc.
  —BLDSC (4542.840000); Faxon; UnCover; SWETS.
  Formerly: American Bar Association. Section of International and Comparative Law. Journal and Proceedings.
  Description: Articles directed at lawyers with an interest in the fields of international business transactions, public international law and comparative law.

341   US   ISSN 0738-9728
K120.A2
INTERNATIONAL LAWYERS' NEWSLETTER; a private network of practical international news. 1979. bi-m. $100 (effective 1994). Kluwer Law and Taxation Publishers, 675 Massachusetts Ave., Cambridge, MA 02139. TEL 617-354-0140. FAX 617-354-8595. (Dist. outside the U.S. by: Libresso Distribution Centre, P.O. Box 23, 7400 GA Deventer, Netherlands. TEL 31-5700-33155) Eds. Carol A. Emory, Arthur G. Kroos. bk.rev. circ. 1,000. **Document type:** newsletter.
  —CCC.
  Description: Contains timely legal news and information from around the globe, including coverage of recent political, legal and social developments, important statutes and rulings with an impact on international transactions, and other matters of interest to members of the international legal profession.

INTERNATIONAL LEGAL BOOKS IN PRINT. see
BIBLIOGRAPHIES

341   US   ISSN 0020-7829
JX68
INTERNATIONAL LEGAL MATERIALS. 1962. bi-m. $160 (foreign $180). American Society of International Law, 2223 Massachusetts Ave., N.W., Washington, DC 20008-2864. TEL 202-939-6000. FAX 202-797-7133. Ed. Marilou M. Righini. adv. contact: Sandra Liebel. index, cum.index: 1962-1969, 1970-1979, 1980-1989. circ. 2,600. (also avail. in microfiche from WSH; back issues avail.) **Indexed:** A.B.C.Pol.Sci., C.L.I., Deep Sea Res.& Oceanogr.Abstr., L.R.I., Leg.Per., Mar.Aff.Bibl., Mid.East: Abstr.& Ind., P.A.I.S. **Document type:** academic/scholarly publication.
  ●Also available online. Vendor(s): Mead Data Central, Inc.
  —Faxon; UnCover; SWETS. **CCC.**

341   UK   ISSN 0309-7684
K110.I47
INTERNATIONAL LEGAL PRACTITIONER. 1976. q. £80. International Bar Association, 2 Harewood Pl., Hanover Sq., London W1R 9HB, England. TEL 44-71-629-1206. FAX 44-71-409-0456. Ed. Ruth Eldon. adv.; bk.rev.; index. circ. 3,000. **Indexed:** ELLIS. **Document type:** academic/scholarly publication.
  —BLDSC (4542.870000); UnCover.

341   UK   ISSN 0958-9767
INTERNATIONAL LITIGATION PROCEDURE. 1990. m. £265. (European Law Centre) Sweet & Maxwell, South Quay Plaza, 7th floor, 183 Marsh Wall, London E14 9FT, England. TEL 071-538-8686. FAX 071-538-9508. Ed. Marina Milmo. adv. contact: Jackie Wood. (back issues avail.) **Document type:** bulletin.

341   UK   ISSN 0263-6395
INTERNATIONAL MEDIA LAW; bulletin on rights, clearances and legal practice. 1982. m. £199($304) Longman Group Ltd., Law, Tax and Finance Division, 21-27 Lamb's Conduit St., London WC1N 3NJ, England. TEL 071-242-2548. FAX 071-831-8119. Ed. Clive Fisher. **Document type:** bulletin.
  —BLDSC (4544.008300). **CCC.**
  Description: Analysis of laws relating to broadcasting, publishing, film, video, music and live performance.

341   US
INTERNATIONAL PRACTICE LAW NEWSLETTER. irreg. $20. Washington State Bar Association, International Practice Law Section, 500 Westin Bldg., 2001 Sixth Ave., Seattle, WA 98121. TEL 206-727-8239. FAX 206-727-8320. circ. 300. (looseleaf format; back issues avail.) **Document type:** newsletter.

341   US
INTERNATIONAL PRACTICE NEWS. irreg. (2-4/yr.). membership. State Bar of Wisconsin, International Practice Section, 402 W. Wilson St., Madison, WI 53703. TEL 608-257-3838. FAX 608-257-5502. circ. 250. (back issues avail.) **Document type:** newsletter.

INTERNATIONAL PROBLEMS; society and politics. see
POLITICAL SCIENCE — International Relations

INTERNATIONAL QUARTERLY (CHESTERLAND). see
LAW — Corporate Law

341 361.77   SZ   ISSN 0020-8604
INTERNATIONAL REVIEW OF THE RED CROSS. French edition: Revue Internationale de la Croix Rouge (ISSN 0035-3361); Spanish edition: Revista Internacional de la Cruz Roja (ISSN 0250-569X); German edition: Auszuege der Revue Internationale de la Croix-Rouge (ISSN 0250-5681) 1961 (English ed.); 1869 (French ed.); 1976 (Spanish ed.); 1988 (Arabic ed.); 1950 (German ed.). bi-m. 30 SFr.($18) International Committee of the Red Cross, 19 Avenue de la Paix, CH-1202 Geneva, Switzerland. TEL 022-7346001. FAX 022-7348280. Ed. Dr. J. Meurant. stat. **Indexed:** HR Rep., Refug.Abstr. **Document type:** bulletin.
  —BLDSC (4545.840000); UnCover.

341 336   US   ISSN 0741-4269
K9
INTERNATIONAL TAX AND BUSINESS LAWYER. 1983. s-a. $43 (effective 1994). (University of California at Berkeley, Boalt Hall School of Law) University of California Press, Journals Division, 2120 Berkeley Way, Berkeley, CA 94720. TEL 510-643-7154. FAX 510-642-9917. Ed.Bd. adv.; index. circ. 500. (also avail. in microfiche from WSH; microform from UMI; back issues avail.) **Indexed:** C.L.I., Foreign Leg.Per., L.R.I., Leg.Cont., Leg.Per., P.A.I.S. **Document type:** academic/scholarly publication.
  —BLDSC (4550.392000); Faxon; UnCover; UMI. **CCC.**
  Description: Contains information on all legal aspects of international tax and business transactions.
  Refereed Serial

INTERNATIONAL TAX HANDBOOK. see BUSINESS AND ECONOMICS — Public Finance, Taxation

341 336   US   ISSN 0892-1032
K4473
INTERNATIONAL TAX TREATIES OF ALL NATIONS. SERIES A. 1975. irreg., vol.14, 1992. $50 per vol. Oceana Publications, Inc., 75 Main St., Dobbs Ferry, NY 10522. TEL 914-693-1320. FAX 914-693-0402. Eds. Walter H. Diamond, Dorothy B. Diamond. cum.index. circ. 300. (back issues avail.)
  Description: Provides English language texts of all tax treaties in force between two or more nations.

341 336   US   ISSN 0892-1040
K4473
INTERNATIONAL TAX TREATIES OF ALL NATIONS. SERIES B. 1975. irreg., vol.25, 1992. price varies. Oceana Publications, Inc., 75 Main St., Dobbs Ferry, NY 10522. TEL 914-693-1320. FAX 914-693-0402. Eds. Walter H. Diamond, Dorothy B. Diamond. cum.index. circ. 300. (back issues avail.)
  Description: Tax treaties in force between two or more nations not yet published by the U.N.

INTERNATIONAL TAXATION SERIES. see BUSINESS AND ECONOMICS — Public Finance, Taxation

345 US
INTERNATIONAL TRADE: AVOIDING CRIMINAL RISKS.
1991. base vol. (plus a. supplements). $110. Butterworth Legal Publishers (Salem) (Subsidiary of: Reed Elsevier plc), 8 Industrial Way, Bldg. C, Salem, NH 03079. TEL 800-548-4001. FAX 603-898-9858. Ed. William M. Hannay. (looseleaf format)
  Description: Practical, comprehensive advice on identifying, avoiding and coping with potentially criminal risks faced by US companies doing business overseas, including applications of US criminal laws relevant to the conduct of American businesses and executives.

INTERNATIONAL TRADE REPORTER DECISIONS. see BUSINESS AND ECONOMICS — International Commerce

INTERNATIONAL V A T MONITOR. see BUSINESS AND ECONOMICS — Public Finance, Taxation

341 338.91 NE ISSN 0020-9317
D839 CODEN: ISPCET
INTERNATIONALE SPECTATOR; maandblad voor internationale politiek. (Text in Dutch; occasionally in English; summaries in English) 1947. m. fl.89.50 in Netherlands (students fl.75); elsewhere fl.125 (students fl.110.50). (Nederlands Instituut voor Internationale Betrekkingen - Netherlands Institute of International Relations) Van Gorcum en Co. B.V., P.O. Box 43, 6400 AA Assen, Netherlands. TEL 31-5920-46846. FAX 31-5920-72064. Ed. J.J. Voorhoeve. adv.; bk.rev.; index. circ. 4,500. **Indexed:** Amer.Hist.& Life, Documentatieblad, ELLIS, Hist.Abstr., Key to Econ.Sci., Rural Recreat.Tour.Abstr., World Agri.Econ.& Rural Sociol.Abstr.
—BLDSC (4554.700000); SWETS.
  Description: Examines developments in international relations, politics and international law.

INTO THE NIGHT; a newsletter for freedom for political prisoners held in the U.S. see POLITICAL SCIENCE — Civil Rights

341 US ISSN 0277-2922
JX238.I7
IRANIAN ASSETS LITIGATION REPORTER. 1980. m. $2300. Andrews Publications, 1646 West Chester Pike, Box 1000, PA 19395. TEL 215-399-6600; 800-345-1101. FAX 215-399-6610. Ed. Edith F. McFall. abstr.; bibl.; stat.; s-a. index. (looseleaf format; back issues avail.) **Document type:** newsletter.
  Description: Covers events in the U.S. and foreign countries regarding the attachment of Iranian assets and the complicated litigation and international arbitration that has resulted.

ISRAEL YEARBOOK ON HUMAN RIGHTS. see POLITICAL SCIENCE — Civil Rights

341 IT
ITALIA E L'EUROPA. no.28, 1991. s-a. L.90000 (effective 1994). (Istituto Italiano di Studi Legislativi) Maggioli Editore, Viale Vespucci 12-n, 47037 Rimini, Italy. TEL 0541-625777. FAX 0541-522020. adv.; B&W page L.2500000; trim 115 x 195. circ. 5,000.

341 IT
ITALIAN YEARBOOK OF INTERNATIONAL LAW. 1975. a. $25. Casa Editrice Dott. A. Guiffre, Via Busto Arsizio 40, 20151 Milan, Italy. **Indexed:** Mar.Aff.Bibl.

JAPAN BUSINESS LAW GUIDE. see BUSINESS AND ECONOMICS — International Commerce

341 382 US
JOINT VENTURES IN THE SOVIET UNION; a legal treatise with forms and commentary. (Supplements avail.) irreg. $165. (Columbia University, Parker School of Foreign and Comparative Law) Transnational Juris Publications, Inc., 1 Bridge St., Irvington-on-Hudson, NY 10533. TEL 914-591-4288. FAX 914-591-2688. Ed. Kaj Hober. (looseleaf format)
  Description: Provides comprehensive discussion of legal aspects of doing business in the former Soviet Union, including foreign exchange laws, property rights, dispute resolution, and negotiating techniques.

341 382 US
JOINT VENTURES WITH INTERNATIONAL PARTNERS.
1989. 2 base vols. (plus a. supplement). $200 (effective 1992). Butterworth Legal Publishers (Salem) (Subsidiary of: Reed Elsevier plc), 8 Industrial Way, Bldg. C, Salem, NH 03079. TEL 800-548-4001. FAX 603-898-9644. Eds. Jeffrey A. Burt, James A. Dobkin. (looseleaf format)
  Description: Technical and legal examination of joint venture laws and practices; provides the "ins" and "outs" of forming joint ventures with overseas business entities.

346.066 US
JOINT VENTURES WITH THE SOVIET REPUBLICS; law and practice. 1990. base vol. (plus a. supplement). $125. Butterworth Legal Publishers (Salem) (Subsidiary of: Reed Elsevier plc), 8 Industrial Way, Bldg. C, Salem, NH 03079. TEL 800-548-4001. FAX 603-898-9858. Ed. Christopher Osakwe. (looseleaf format)
  Formerly: Joint Ventures with the Soviet Union.

341 FR ISSN 0021-8170
JX6002
JOURNAL DU DROIT INTERNATIONAL. 1874. q. $110. Editions Techniques, 123 rue d'Alesia, 75014 Paris Cedex 14, France. TEL 45-39-22-91. FAX 45-42-81-55. TELEX EDITEC 270737 F. bk.rev.; abstr.; charts; index, cum.index. circ. 2,000. (reprint service avail. from SCH) **Indexed:** ELLIS, Mar.Aff.Bibl., P.A.I.S.For.Lang.Ind., P.A.I.S.
—BLDSC (4970.500000); SWETS. **CCC.**

341 US ISSN 1053-6736
K4
JOURNAL OF COMPARATIVE AND INTERNATIONAL LAW.
1991. s-a. $20 (foreign $23). Duke University, School of Law, Box 90364, Durham, NC 27708-0364. TEL 919-684-5966. FAX 919-684-3417. **Document type:** academic/scholarly publication.
—UnCover.

341 SZ ISSN 0255-8106
K10
JOURNAL OF INTERNATIONAL ARBITRATION. 1984. q. 330 SFr.($235) Werner Publishing Co. Ltd., 5 place de la Fusterie, CH-1211 Geneva 11, Switzerland. **Indexed:** Leg.Per. **Document type:** bulletin.
—BLDSC (5007.581500); Faxon; UnCover; SWETS. **CCC.**

341 UK ISSN 0950-365X
JOURNAL OF INTERNATIONAL FRANCHISING AND DISTRIBUTION LAW. 1986. 4/yr. £100. Tolley Publishing Co. Ltd., Tolley House, 2 Addiscombe Rd., Croydon, Surrey CR9 5AF, England. TEL 081-686-9141. FAX 081-686-3155. Ed. Martin Mendelsohn. adv.; bk.rev. **Document type:** trade publication.
  Description: Covers all aspects of international franchising and distribution law.

341 332.6 IT ISSN 0394-3933
HC307.S69
JOURNAL OF REGIONAL POLICY; mezzogiorno d'Europa. (Text in English) 1981. q. Institute for the Economic Development of Southern Italy, Via Alcide De Gasperi, 71, 801333 Naples, Italy. TEL 081-7853640. (Subscr. to: Via San Giacomo, 19, 80133 Naples, Italy) index. (back issues avail.) **Indexed:** ELLIS, World Agri.Econ.& Rural Sociol.Abstr.
—BLDSC (5048.680000).
  Formerly: Mezzogiorno d'Europa.
  Description: Covers regional and European economics and law.

629.1 340 US ISSN 0095-7577
JX1
JOURNAL OF SPACE LAW. 1973. s-a. $69.50 (foreign $75)(typically set in Oct.; effective Jan.). Journal of Space Law, Inc., Box 308, University, MS 38677. TEL 601-234-2391. FAX 601-232-7010. Ed.Bd. adv.; bk.rev.; index. circ. 900. (also avail. in microform from MIM,PMC; microfilm from WSH; back issues avail. (vols.1-16); reprint service avail. from WSH) **Indexed:** C.L.I., Int.Aerosp.Abstr., L.R.I., Leg.Cont., Leg.Per. **Document type:** academic/scholarly publication.
—BLDSC (5066.090000); Faxon; UnCover.
  Description: Covers legal problems arising out of human activities in outer space.

341.57 382 SZ ISSN 0022-5444
K10
JOURNAL OF WORLD TRADE. 1967. bi-m. 430 SFr.($315) Werner Publishing Co. Ltd., 5 place de la Fusterie, CH-1211 Geneva 11, Switzerland. Ed. Jacques Werner. adv.; bk.rev.; index. **Indexed:** ABI Inform., Abstr.Bk.Rev.Curr.Leg.Per., Amer.Hist.& Life, Asian-Pac.Econ.Lit., BPIA, Br.Hum.Ind., Bus.Ind., C.L.I., C.R.E.J., Cont.Pg.Manage., Curr.Cont., Hist.Abstr., Int.Lab.Doc., J.of Econ.Lit., Key to Econ.Sci., L.R.I., Leg.Per., Mar.Aff.Bibl., P.A.I.S., Risk Abstr., Rural Recreat.Tour.Abstr., SCIMP (1978-), SSCI, Tr.& Indus.Ind., World Agri.Econ.& Rural Sociol.Abstr., World Bank.Abstr. **Document type:** bulletin.
—CCC.

341 YU ISSN 0022-6084
JX18
JUGOSLOVENSKA REVIJA ZA MEDJUNARODNO PRAVO. (Text in Serbo-Croatian; summaries in English and French) 1954. 3/yr. Jugoslovensko Udruzenje za Medjunarodno Pravo, Makedonska 25, Belgrade, Yugoslavia. Ed. B. Babovic. bk.rev.; bibl.; index. circ. 1,200.

341 327 IT ISSN 0022-6963
JUS GENTIUM; diritto delle relazioni internazionali. (Consists of two issues not available separately: Part A, Theoretical Elaborations (Ratio and Lectio); Part B, Positive Applications (Ars and Jura).) (Text in English, French and Italian) 1950. s-a. L.100000. Corso Vittorio Emanuele 142, 00186 Rome, Italy. TEL 6869012. (Subscr. to: Casella Postale 410 (Centro), 00100 Rome, Italy) Ed. Giovanni Scarangella. bk.rev.; index. circ. 1,000.

341 JA ISSN 0023-2866
KOKUSAIHO GAIKO ZASSHI/JOURNAL OF INTERNATIONAL LAW AND DIPLOMACY. (Text in Japanese; table of contents and summaries in English) 1903. bi-m. 7200 Yen to non-members (effective 1993). Kokusaiho Gakkai - Japanese Association of International Law, c/o Faculty of Law, University of Tokyo, 3-1, Hongo 7-chome, Bunkyo-ku, Tokyo, Japan. TEL 03-3812-2111. (Subscr. to: Yuhikaku, 2-17 Jinbo-cho, Kanda, Chiyoda-ku, Tokyo, Japan) Ed. Nisuke Ando. bk.rev.; circ. 800 (controlled). **Indexed:** Amer.Hist.& Life, Hist.Abstr.
  Description: Public and private international law and diplomacy.

341 KO ISSN 0023-3994
KOREAN JOURNAL OF INTERNATIONAL LAW. (Text in Korean; summaries in English or other languages) 1956. 2/yr. $50. Korean Association of International Law, 37 Suhsomoon-Dong, Suhdaimoon-Ky, Seoul, S. Korea. TEL 02-752-9605. FAX 02-752-4646. adv.; bk.rev.; cum.index. circ. 400. (back issues avail.) **Document type:** academic/scholarly publication.

LAMY CONTRATS INTERNATIONAUX. see BUSINESS AND ECONOMICS — International Commerce

341.57 380.5 FR
LAMY TRANSPORT TOME 1; route. a. 915 F. Lamy S.A., 187-189 Quai de Valmy, 75490 Paris, France. TEL 44-72-13-43. FAX 44-72-13-95. index.
  Description: Covers responsibilities and obligations of the transporter, contract types, legislation, insurance, regulations.

341.57 380.5 FR
LAMY TRANSPORT TOME 2; douane, commissionnaires de transport, transports maritime, transports par chemin de fer, transports aeriens, lexique. a. 710 F. (effective 1994). Lamy S.A., 187-189 Quai de Valmy, 75490 Paris, France. TEL 44-72-13-43. FAX 44-72-13-95. index.
  Description: Covers regulations, responsibilities and privileges of the transporter, customs regulations, international sales, air and sea insurance.

341.57 380.5 FR
LAMY TRANSPORT TOME 3; marchandises dangereuses. (Includes supplement: Nomenclatures des matieres) a. 990 F. (effective 1994). Lamy S.A., 187-189 Quai de Valmy, 75490 Paris, France. TEL 44-72-13-43. FAX 44-72-13-95. index.
  Description: Covers regulations concerning the national and international transport of hazardous materials.

LAW — INTERNATIONAL LAW

LATIN AMERICAN TAXATION DATA BASE ON CD-ROM. see *BUSINESS AND ECONOMICS — Public Finance, Taxation*

341 US ISSN 0023-9208
K12
LAW AND POLICY IN INTERNATIONAL BUSINESS. 1969. 4/yr. $30 (foreign $35). Georgetown University Law Center, 600 New Jersey Ave., N.W., Washington, DC 20001. TEL 202-662-9468. Ed. Gil Bonwitt. adv.; bk.rev.; index. circ. 1,183. (also avail. in microform from UMI; microfiche from WSH; reprint service avail. from UMI) **Indexed:** ABI Inform, Abstr.Bk.Rev.Curr.Leg.Per., Amer.Bibl.Slavic & E.Eur.Stud, BPIA, Bus.Ind., C.L.I., Foreign Leg.Per., Geo.Abstr., L.R.I., Leg.Cont., Leg.Per., P.A.I.S., Tr.& Indus.Ind.
●Also available online. Vendor(s): West Services, Inc.
—BLDSC (5161.363000); Faxon; UnCover; SWETS; UMI.

341 GW ISSN 0341-6151
K12
LAW AND STATE; a biannual collection of recent German contributions to these fields. 1970. s-a. DM.40 per no. Institute for Scientific Co-operation with Developing Countries, Landhausstr. 18, 72074 Tuebingen, Germany. TEL 07071-5066. Ed. K.-H.W. Bechtold. circ. 3,000. **Indexed:** HR Rep., Refug.Abstr. **Document type:** academic/scholarly publication.
—BLDSC (5161.366050).

LAW GROUP DOCKET. see *POLITICAL SCIENCE — Civil Rights*

340 NE ISSN 0075-823X
KJC510.A15
LAW IN EASTERN EUROPE. (Text in English) 1958. irreg., no.45, 1993. price varies. (Rijksuniversiteit te Leiden, Institute for East European Law and Russian Studies) Martinus Nijhoff Publishers, Human Rights and International Law, Postbus 163, 3300 AD Dordrecht, Netherlands. TEL 31-78-334228. FAX 31-78-334254. TELEX 29245 KAPG NL. (Dist. by: Kluwer Academic Publishers Group, P.O. Box 322, 3300 AH Dordrecht, Netherlands. TEL 31-78-524400. FAX 31-78-524474; N. America dist. addr.: Box 358, Accord Sta., Hingham, MA 02018-0358. TEL 617-871-6600. FAX 617-871-6528) Ed. F.J. Feldbrugge. index. circ. 900. **Document type:** monograph series.
Refereed Serial

341 US
LAW OF THE EUROPEAN ECONOMIC COMMUNITY. 1976. s-a. $865. Matthew Bender & Co., Inc., 11 Penn Plaza, New York, NY 10001. TEL 212-967-7707. FAX 212-244-3188. (Subscr. to: International Dept., 1275 Broadway, Albany, NY 12204) Eds. Peter Herzog, Dennis Campbell. bibl.; index. (looseleaf format)
Description: Covers the history and development of the EEC on an article-by-article basis.

LAW REPRINTS: TRADE REGULATION SERIES. see *BUSINESS AND ECONOMICS — International Commerce*

340 AT ISSN 0047-4207
LAWASIA. 1969. a. Aus.$22. (Law Association for Asia and the Western Pacific) University of Technology, Sydney, Faculty of Law and Legal Practice, P.O. Box 123, City Campus, Broadway, N.S.W. 2007, Australia. TEL 02-330-3412. FAX 02-330-3421. Ed. G.F. Payne. adv.; bk.rev.; bibl. circ. 2,000. **Indexed:** Abstr.Bk.Rev.Curr.Leg.Per., C.L.I., Leg.Per., So.Pac.Per.Inc.
Description: Covers legal issues and developments which have a bearing on countries in the Asian and Pacific regions.

341 IE ISSN 0791-7481
▼**LAWYER INTERNATIONAL.** 1992. 10/yr. I£499. Lafferty Publications Ltd., The Tower, IDA Enterprise Centre, Pearse St., Dublin 2, Ireland. TEL 01-6718022. FAX 01-6718520. (U.S. subscr. to: 2970 Clairmount Rd., Ste. 800, Atlanta, GA 30329. TEL 404-636-6610) Ed. Sandra Burke. **Document type:** trade publication.
Description: Business briefing for internationally minded lawyers.

LECCIONES Y ENSAYOS. see *LAW*

341 NE ISSN 0924-4883
LEGAL ASPECTS OF INTERNATIONAL ORGANIZATION. 1983. irreg., vol.14, 1993. Martinus Nijhoff Publishers, Human Rights and International Law (Subsidiary of: Kluwer Academic Publishers Group), Postbus 17, 3300 AA Dordrecht, Netherlands. TEL 31-78-334911. FAX 31-78-334254. TELEX 29245 KAPG NL. (Dist. by: Kluwer Academic Publishers Group, P.O. Box 322, 3300 AH Dordrecht, Netherlands. TEL 31-78-524400. FAX 31-78-524474; N. America dist. addr.: Box 358, Accord Sta., Hingham, MA 02018-0358. TEL 617-871-6600. FAX 617-871-6528) **Document type:** monograph series.
Refereed Serial

341.57 NE ISSN 0377-0915
LEGAL ISSUES OF EUROPEAN INTEGRATION. (Text in English) 1974. s-a. price varies. (Universiteit van Amsterdam, Europa Instituut) Kluwer Law and Taxation Publishers (Subsidiary of: Wolters Kluwer N.V.), P.O. Box 23, 7400 GA Deventer, Netherlands. TEL 31-5700-47261. FAX 31-5700-22244. TELEX 49295 KLUDV NL. (Dist. by: Libresso Distribution Centre, P.O. Box 23, 7400 GA Deventer, Netherlands. TEL 31-5700-33155. FAX 31-5700-33834; In N. America: Kluwer Law and Taxation Publishers, 675 Massachusetts Ave., Cambridge, MA 02139. TEL 617-354-0140. FAX 617-354-8595) Ed.Bd. (back issues avail.) **Indexed:** ELLIS, Key to Econ.Sci. **Document type:** academic/scholarly publication.
—BLDSC (5181.327000); UnCover.
Formerly: *Legal Issues*.

341.05 NE ISSN 0922-1565
LEIDEN JOURNAL OF INTERNATIONAL LAW. (Text in English) 1988. s-a. fl.80($50) Leiden University, Faculty of Law, P.O. Box 9520, 2300 RA Leiden, Netherlands. TEL 31-71-272727. (Dist. by: Wm. W. Gaunt & Sons, Inc., Gaunt Bldg., 3011 Gulf Dr., Homes Beach, FL 34217-2199. TEL 813-778-5211. FAX 813-778-5252) bk.rev. **Indexed:** C.L.I., ELLIS. **Document type:** academic/scholarly publication.
—BLDSC (5181.985200); UnCover; SWETS.
Description: Promotes the understanding of the priniciples and purposes of international law and to describe current developments.

341 DK ISSN 0106-8474
LOVTIDENDE C FOR KONGERIGET DANMARK. 1936. irreg. DKK 325. Justitsministeriet, Sekretariatet for Retsinformation, Axeltorv 6, 5. sal, D-1609 Copenhagen V, Denmark. TEL 45-33-32-52-22. FAX 45-33-91-28-01. index. circ. 760. **Document type:** government publication.
●Also available online.
Description: Official organ for promulgating international treaties and agreements in accordance with Danish law.

LOW INTENSITY CONFLICT & LAW ENFORCEMENT. see *POLITICAL SCIENCE — International Relations*

MAGHREB, MACHREK, MONDE ARABE. see *POLITICAL SCIENCE*

341.2 MW ISSN 0076-3357
MALAWI TREATY SERIES. (Text in English) a. K.0.60. Government Printer, P.O. Box 37, Zomba, Malawi. Ed. James S. Friedlander. cum.index 1964-1969.

341 332.6 NE
MANUAL FOR THE PRACTICE OF UNITED STATES IMPORT LAW. (Text in English) 1990. base vol. (plus a. update). fl.355($203) (effective 1994). (Federal Bar Association, US) Kluwer Law and Taxation Publishers (Subsidiary of: Wolters Kluwer N.V.), P.O. Box 23, 7400 GA Deventer, Netherlands. TEL 31-5700-47261. FAX 31-5700-22244. TELEX 49295 KLUDV NL. (Dist. by: Libresso Distribution Centre, P.O. Box 23, 7400 GA Deventer, Netherlands. TEL 31-5700-33155. FAX 31-5700-33834; In N. America: Kluwer Law and Taxation Publishers, 675 Massachusetts Ave., Cambridge, MA 02139. TEL 617-354-0140. FAX 617-354-8595) Eds. William K. Ince, Leslie A. Glick. (looseleaf format)
Description: Comprehensive, up-to-date to the substance and procedures of the U.S. laws that regulate imports of both goods and services. Includes complete statutes and administrative regulations concerning matters such as anti-dumping, unfair trade actions, special duty exemptions, as well as commentary on current practice.

MARITIME LAW HANDBOOK. see *LAW — Maritime Law*

341 AT ISSN 0728-7445
MARTIN PLACE PAPERS. 1982. irreg. price varies. International Law Association, Australian Branch, Garfield Barwick Chambers, 53 Martin Place, Sydney, N.S.W. 2000, Australia. (Dist. outside Australia and New Zealand by: Wm. W. Gaunt & Sons, Inc., Gaunt Bldg., 3011 Gulf Dr., Holmes Beach, FL 34217-2199. TEL 813-778-5211. FAX 813-778-5252)

341 382 US
MARYLAND JOURNAL OF INTERNATIONAL LAW AND TRADE. 1975. s-a. $12 (foreign $14). University of Maryland School of Law, 500 W. Baltimore St., Baltimore, MD 21201. Ed. Peggy A. Rodgers. circ. 500. (also avail. in microfilm from RRI; back issues avail.; reprint service avail. from RRI) **Indexed:** C.L.I., Leg.Per.

MEALEY'S LITIGATION REPORTS: INTELLECTUAL PROPERTY. see *PATENTS, TRADEMARKS AND COPYRIGHTS*

341 610 US
MEDICOLEGAL LIBRARY. 1984. irreg. price varies. Springer-Verlag, 175 Fifth Ave., New York, NY 10010. TEL 212-460-1500. FAX 212-473-6272. (Also: Berlin, Heidelberg, Tokyo and Vienna) (reprint service avail. from ISI) **Document type:** monographic series.

MEDIEN UND RECHT INTERNATIONAL; Zeitschrift fuer das Recht der Medien und der Werbung. see *LAW*

341 SZ
MENSCH UND RECHT. 1981. q. 18.50 SFr. Schweizerische Gesellschaft fuer die Europaeische Menschenrechtskonvention, Postfach 10, CH-8127 Forch, Switzerland. TEL 0411-9800454. TELEX 817585159-COM-CH. Ed. Ludwig A. Minelli. circ. 11,500. (back issues avail.) **Document type:** bulletin.
Description: Provides information on human rights in Europe.

340 364 US ISSN 1052-2867
K13
MICHIGAN JOURNAL OF INTERNATIONAL LAW. 1979. q. $30 (foreign $35). University of Michigan, Hutchins Hall, Ann Arbor, MI 48109-1215. TEL 313-763-2050. FAX 313-764-8309. bk.rev.; bibl.; index. circ. 500. (reprint service avail. from WSH) **Indexed:** C.L.I., L.R.I., Leg.Per.
—BLDSC (5755.283000); Faxon; UnCover; SWETS.
Formerly (until 1988): *Michigan Yearbook of International Legal Studies* (ISSN 8756-0615)

341.57 622 US
MINING LEGISLATION: WORLD (BY COUNTRY). base vols. (plus q. supplements). $3600 (renewal $1500) per country. Barrows Co., Inc., 116 E. 66th St., New York, NY 10021. TEL 212-772-1199. FAX 212-288-7242. TELEX 4971238 BARROWS. Eds. G.H. Barrows, Marta Guerra.
Description: Contains the complete text, in English translation, of mining laws.

MONTHLY IMPORT DETENTION LIST. see *PUBLIC HEALTH AND SAFETY*

LAW — INTERNATIONAL LAW

341 NE ISSN 0165-070X
JX18 CODEN: NILRE5
NETHERLANDS INTERNATIONAL LAW REVIEW. (Text in English) 1953. 4/yr. fl.412($215) (effective 1994). (T.M.C. Asser Institute) Martinus Nijhoff Publishers, Human Rights and International Law (Subsidiary of: Kluwer Academic Publishers Group), Postbus 163, 3300 AD Dordrecht, Netherlands. TEL 31-78-334911. FAX 31-78-334254. TELEX 29245 KAPG NL. (Dist. by: Kluwer Academic Publishers Group, P.O. Box 322, 3300 AH Dordrecht, Netherlands. TEL 31-78-524400. FAX 31-78-524474; N. America dist. addr.: Box 358, Accord Sta., Hingham, MA 02018-0358. TEL 617-871-6600. FAX 617-871-6528) Ed. P. Morris. adv.; bk.rev.; index. (also avail. in microform from UMI; reprint service avail. from SWZ) **Indexed:** Foreign Leg.Per., Int.Lab.Doc., Key to Econ.Sci., Mar.Aff.Bibl. **Document type:** academic/scholarly publication.
—BLDSC (6076.700000); UnCover; SWETS. **CCC.**
 Formerly: Nederlands Tijdschrift voor Internationaal Recht - Netherlands International Law Review (ISSN 0028-2138)
 Description: Forum for the publication of articles in the field of private and public international law and comparative law.
 Refereed Serial

342.085 NE ISSN 0924-0519
NETHERLANDS QUARTERLY OF HUMAN RIGHTS. (Text in English) 1983. q. fl.105($57) (effective 1994). (Studie- en Informatiecentrum Mensenrechten - Netherlands Institute of Human Rights) Kluwer Law and Taxation Publishers (Subsidiary of: Wolters Kluwer N.V.), P.O. Box 23, 7400 GA Deventer, Netherlands. TEL 31-5700-27461. FAX 31-5700-22244. (Dist. by: Libresso Distribution Centre, P.O. Box 23, 7400 GA Deventer, Netherlands. TEL 31-5700-33155. FAX 31-5700-33834; In N. America: Kluwer Law and Taxation Publishers, 675 Massachusetts Ave., Cambridge, MA 02139. TEL 617-354-0140. FAX 617-354-8595) Ed.Bd. index. circ. 700. **Indexed:** Refug.Abstr. **Document type:** academic/scholarly publication.
—BLDSC (6077.101600).
 Formerly (until 1988): S I M Newsletter (ISSN 0169-3441)
 Description: Covers the theory and practice of international and European human rights protection, recent developments, human rights news and important documents from around the world.
 Refereed Serial

341 NE ISSN 0167-6768
NETHERLANDS YEARBOOK OF INTERNATIONAL LAW. (Text in English) 1970. a. fl.412($215) includes Netherlands Review of International Law (effective 1994). (T.M.C. Asser Institute) Martinus Nijhoff Publishers, Human Rights and International Law (Subsidiary of: Kluwer Academic Publishers Group), Postbus 163, 3300 AD Dordrecht, Netherlands. TEL 31-78-334267. FAX 31-78-334254. TELEX 29245 KAPG NL. (Dist. by: Kluwer Academic Publishers Group, P.O. Box 322, 3300 AH Dordrecht, Netherlands. TEL 31-78-524400; N. America dist. addr.: Box 358, Accord Sta., Hingham, MA 02018-0358) Ed. Ko Swan Sik. bk.rev.; bibl. circ. 750. (also avail. in microform from UMI; reprint service avail. from SWZ) **Indexed:** Foreign Leg.Per., Mar.Aff.Bibl. **Document type:** academic/scholarly publication.
—SWETS.
 Refereed Serial

341 NE ISSN 0738-2812
NEW HAVEN STUDIES IN INTERNATIONAL LAW AND WORLD PUBLIC ORDER. (Text in English) 1987. irreg. price varies. Kluwer Academic Publishers, Postbus 17, 3300 AA Dordrecht, Netherlands. TEL 31-78-334911. FAX 31-78-334254. TELEX 29245 KAPG NL. (Dist. by: Kluwer Academic Publishers, P.O. Box 322, 3300 AH Dordrecht, Netherlands. TEL 31-78-524400; N. America dist. addr.: Box 358, Accord Sta., Hingham, MA 02018-0358. TEL 617-871-6600) **Document type:** monographic series.
 Refereed Serial

341 US
NEW JERSEY STATE BAR ASSOCIATION. INTERNATIONAL LAW AND ORGANIZATIONS SECTION. NEWSLETTER. 1966. irreg. membership only. New Jersey State Bar Association, International Law and Organizations Section, 1 Constitution Sq., New Brunswick, NJ 08901-1500. TEL 908-249-5000.
FAX 908-249-2815. Ed. Brian P. Blatz. bk.rev. (back issues avail.) **Document type:** newsletter.

341 US ISSN 1050-9453
K14
NEW YORK INTERNATIONAL LAW REVIEW; views of the law of the world from New York. 1988. s-a. $65 (foreign $75) includes International Law Practicum (free to qualified personnel). New York State Bar Association, International Law and Practice Section, 1 Elk St., Albany, NY 12207-1096. TEL 518-463-3200. FAX 518-487-5699. Ed. Lester Nelson. circ. 1,900 (controlled). **Document type:** academic/scholarly publication.
 Refereed Serial

341 US ISSN 0736-4075
K14
NEW YORK LAW SCHOOL JOURNAL OF INTERNATIONAL AND COMPARATIVE LAW. vol.12, 1991. 3/yr. $22 (foreign $27). New York Law School, 57 Worth St., New York, NY 10013-2960. TEL 212-431-2113. adv. circ. 1,000. (reprint service avail. from RRI)
—BLDSC (6089.340900); UnCover; SWETS.

341 US ISSN 0028-7873
JX1
NEW YORK UNIVERSITY JOURNAL OF INTERNATIONAL LAW AND POLITICS. 1968. 4/yr. $25 (foreign $29) (effective 1994). New York University, Law Publications, 110 W. Third St., New York, NY 10012. TEL 212-998-6520. FAX 212-995-4032. Ed.Bd. adv.; bk.rev.; abstr.; bibl.; index. circ. 800. (also avail. in microfilm from RRI; back issues avail.; reprint service avail. from RRI) **Indexed:** A.B.C.Pol.Sci., Abstr.Bk.Rev.Curr.Leg.Per., Amer.Bibl.Slavic & E.Eur.Stud., Amer.Hist.& Life (until 1993), C.L.I., Foreign Leg.Per., Hist.Abstr. (until 1993), L.R.I., Leg.Cont., Leg.Per., P.A.I.S. **Document type:** academic/scholarly publication.
—BLDSC (6089.810000); Faxon; UnCover; SWETS; UMI.
 Description: Addresses current international topics that impinge upon the legal and non-legal communities.

341 DK ISSN 0902-7351
JX18
NORDIC JOURNAL OF INTERNATIONAL LAW/ACTA SCANDINAVICA JURIS GENTIUM. (Text in English) 1930. q. DKK 320. (Koebenhavns Universitet, Institut for International Ret og Europaret) Akademisk Forlag, Store Kanikestraede i, P.O. Box 54, DK-1002 Copenhagen K, Denmark. adv.; bk.rev.; bibl.; charts; illus.; index. circ. 600. **Indexed:** ELLIS, Mar.Aff.Bibl.
—BLDSC (6117.926300); SWETS.
 Formerly (until 1986): Nordisk Tidsskrift for International Ret (ISSN 0029-151X)

341 US ISSN 0743-1759
K10
NORTH CAROLINA JOURNAL OF INTERNATIONAL LAW AND COMMERCIAL REGULATION. 1976. 3/yr. $21 (foreign $25). University of North Carolina at Chapel Hill, School of Law, Chapel Hill, NC 27599-3380. TEL 919-962-4402. FAX 919-962-1193. Ed. Julia Reinhart. circ. 400 (paid). (back issues avail.) **Indexed:** Abstr.Bk.Rev.Curr.Leg.Per., C.L.I., L.R.I., Leg.Per. **Document type:** academic/scholarly publication.
●Also available online. Vendor(s): Mead Data Central, Inc., West Services, Inc.
—BLDSC (6149.045000); Faxon; UnCover.
 Description: Focuses on business, trade, and other international issues.

NORTHERN IRELAND NEWS SERVICE; NINS NewsBreak. see POLITICAL SCIENCE

341 US ISSN 0196-3228
K14
NORTHWESTERN JOURNAL OF INTERNATIONAL LAW & BUSINESS. Short title: J I L B. 1979. 3/yr. $30 (foreign $33) (effective 1994). Northwestern University, School of Law - Office of Legal Publications, 357 E. Chicago Ave., Chicago, IL 60611. TEL 312-503-8467. circ. 500. (also avail. in microfilm from RRI,UMI; reprint service avail. from RRI) **Indexed:** C.L.I., Chic.Per.Ind., ELLIS, L.R.I., Leg.Per., P.A.I.S.
●Also available online. Vendor(s): West Services, Inc.
—BLDSC (6152.025000); Faxon; UnCover; SWETS; UMI.

OCEAN DEVELOPMENT AND INTERNATIONAL LAW; the journal of marine affairs. see EARTH SCIENCES — Oceanography

OESTERREICHISCHE ZEITSCHRIFT FUER OEFFENTLICHES RECHT UND VOELKERRECHT/AUSTRIAN JOURNAL OF PUBLIC AND INTERNATIONAL LAW. see LAW

OESTERREICHISCHE ZEITSCHRIFT FUER WIRTSCHAFTSRECHT. see BUSINESS AND ECONOMICS — Public Finance, Taxation

ORGANIZATION OF AMERICAN STATES. PERMANENT COUNCIL. DECISIONS TAKEN AT MEETINGS (CUMULATED EDITION). see HISTORY — History Of North And South America

341 CY
PALESTINE YEARBOOK OF INTERNATIONAL LAW. (Text in English) 1984. a. $55. Al-Shaybani Society of International Law Ltd., P.O. Box 4247, Nicosia, Cyprus. Ed. Anis F. Kassim. bk.rev. circ. 500. (back issues avail.)
 Description: Dedicated to the rule of law, justice and equality in Palestine.

341.484 NE
PASSPORT HANDBOOK/REPERTOIRE DES PASSEPORTS. (Editions in English, French) base vol. (plus a. update). fl.950($543) (effective 1994). Kluwer Law and Taxation Publishers (Subsidiary of: Wolters Kluwer N.V.), P.O. Box 23, 7400 GA Deventer, Netherlands. TEL 31-5700-47261.
FAX 31-5700-22244. TELEX 49295 KLUDV NL. (Dist. by: Libresso Distribution Centre, P.O. Box 23, 7400 GA Deventer, Netherlands. TEL 31-5700-33155. FAX 31-5700-33834; In N. America: Kluwer Law and Taxation Publishers, 675 Massachusetts Ave., Cambridge, MA 02139. TEL 617-354-0140. FAX 617-354-8595) Ed. David Henny. (looseleaf format)
 Description: Provides authorized color reproductions of 240 passports, travel and identity documents from 103 countries, with discussion of security characteristics, watermarks and printing characteristics, to enable the user to authenticate passports.

341.57 665.5 US
PETROLEUM CONCESSION HANDBOOK. base vols. (plus q. supplements). $4400 (renewal $1550). Barrows Co., Inc., 116 E. 66th St., New York, NY 10021. TEL 212-772-1199. FAX 212-288-7242. TELEX 4971238 BARROWS. Eds. G.H. Barrows, Marta Guerra.
 Description: Contains a summary of concession contracts worldwide.

341.57 665.5 US
PETROLEUM LEGISLATION. base vols. (plus q. supplements). $4800 (renewal $1400). Barrows Co., Inc., 116 E. 66th St., New York, NY 10021. TEL 212-772-1199. FAX 212-288-7242. TELEX 4971238 BARROWS.
 Description: Presents an overview of oil and gas regulation, with a summary and analysis by country.

341 PH ISSN 0115-8805
PHILIPPINE YEARBOOK OF INTERNATIONAL LAW. 1972. a. P.100 (foreign $30). Philippine Society of International Law, University of the Philippines, College of Law, Diliman, Quezon City, Philippines. (Co-sponsor: U.P. Law Complex) Ed. Myrna S. Feliciano. bibl.; stat. **Indexed:** C.L.I., Ind.Phil.Per., Leg.Per., Mar.Aff.Bibl.

LAW — INTERNATIONAL LAW

341 338.1   UK   ISSN 0967-7836
POLICY IMPACT ANALYSIS. irreg. £750. Agra Europe (London) Ltd., 25 Frant Rd., Tunbridge Wells, Kent TN2 5JT, England. TEL 44-892-533813. FAX 44-892-544895. TELEX 95114 AGRATW G. **Document type:** trade publication.
   Description: Studies the effects of policy change on European agriculture and agribusiness in depth; forecasts how such legislation affects producer prices, productivity, gross margins, and farm incomes.

341 347   NE
PRACTITIONER'S HANDBOOKS ON THE WORLD COURT. (Text in English, French) 1991. irreg. price varies. Martinus Nijhoff Publishers, Human Rights and International Law (Subsidiary of: Kluwer Academic Publishers Group), Postbus 163, 3300 AD Dordrecht, Netherlands. TEL 31-78-334911. FAX 31-78-334254. TELEX 29245 KAPG NL. (Dist. by: Kluwer Academic Publishers Group, P.O. Box 322, 3300 AH Dordrecht, Netherlands. TEL 31-78-524400. FAX 31-78-524474; N. America dist. addr.: Box 358, Accord Sta., Hingham, MA 02018-0358. TEL 617-871-6600. FAX 617-871-6528) Ed. Shabtai Rosenne.
   Refereed Serial

PRINCETON UNIVERSITY. CENTER OF INTERNATIONAL STUDIES. MONOGRAPH SERIES. see *POLITICAL SCIENCE — International Relations*

PRINCETON UNIVERSITY. CENTER OF INTERNATIONAL STUDIES. PROGRAM ON U S - JAPAN RELATIONS. MONOGRAPH SERIES. see *POLITICAL SCIENCE — International Relations*

PRIVATE INVESTMENTS ABROAD; problems and solutions in international business. see *BUSINESS AND ECONOMICS — Investments*

341   NE
PROBLEMS IN PRIVATE INTERNATIONAL LAW. 1977. irreg., vol.3, 1982. price varies. Elsevier Science B.V., Books Division, P.O. Box 211, 1000 AE Amsterdam, Netherlands. TEL 31-20-5803911. FAX 31-20-5803705. TELEX 18582 ESPA NL. (Subscr. in U.S. and Canada to: Elsevier Science Inc., Box 882, Madison Sq. Sta., New York, NY 10159. TEL 212-989-5800) **Document type:** monographic series.
   Refereed Serial

PUBLIC INTERNATIONAL LAW; a current bibliography of books and articles. see *LAW — Abstracting, Bibliographies, Statistics*

341   NE
PUBLIC POLICY IN TRANSNATIONAL RELATIONSHIPS. (Text in English) 1991. base vol. (plus a. update). fl.170($97) (effective 1994). Kluwer Law and Taxation Publishers (Subsidiary of: Wolters Kluwer N.V.), P.O. Box 23, 7400 GA Deventer, Netherlands. TEL 31-5700-47261. FAX 31-5700-22244. TELEX 49295 KLUDV NL. (Dist. by: Libresso Distribution Centre, P.O. Box 23, 7400 GA Deventer, Netherlands. TEL 31-5700-33155. FAX 31-5700-33834; In N. America: Kluwer Law and Taxation Publishers, 675 Massachusetts Ave., Cambridge, MA 02139. TEL 617-354-0140. FAX 617-354-8595) Eds. M. Rubino-Sammartano, C.G.J. Morse. (looseleaf format)
   Description: Provides country by country analysis of differences in interpretation of legislation resulting from public policy rules in the different branches of law.

PUBLICATIONS ON OCEAN DEVELOPMENT; a series of studies on the international, legal, institutional and policy aspects of the ocean development. see *EARTH SCIENCES — Oceanography*

341   GW   ISSN 0033-7250
K1
RABELS ZEITSCHRIFT FUER AUSLAENDISCHES UND INTERNATIONALES PRIVATRECHT. (Text in English and German) 1927. q. DM.234. (Max-Planck-Institut fuer Auslaendisches und Internationales Privatrecht) Verlag J.C.B. Mohr (Paul Siebeck), Wilhelmstr. 18, 72074 Tuebingen, Germany. TEL 07071-923-0. FAX 07071-51104. TELEX 7262872-MOHR-D. (Subscr. to: Postfach 2040, 72010 Tuebingen, Germany) Ed.Bd. adv.; bk.rev.; charts; cum.index: vols.1-44 (1927-1980). **Indexed:** ELLIS. **Document type:** bulletin.
   —BLDSC (7225.815000); UnCover; SWETS. **CCC**.
   Description: Studies comparative law and foreign law, law of international transactions and the unification of law, including the law of the European Community.

382 341   GW   ISSN 0340-7926
K1
RECHT DER INTERNATIONALEN WIRTSCHAFT; Betriebs-Berater International. 1954. m. DM.612. Verlag Recht und Wirtschaft GmbH, Haeussterstr. 14, 69115 Heidelberg, Germany. TEL 06221-906-1. FAX 06221-906-259. (Subscr. to: Postfach 105960, 69049 Heidelberg, Germany) Ed.Bd. adv.; bk.rev.; abstr.; tr.lit.; index. circ. 3,000. **Indexed:** Dairy Sci.Abstr., ELLIS, Key to Econ.Sci. **Document type:** academic/scholarly publication.
   —BLDSC (7309.330000); SWETS. **CCC**.
   Formerly: Aussenwirtschaftsdienst des Betriebs-Berater (ISSN 0004-8232)

341   GW   ISSN 0486-1485
K18
RECHT IN OST UND WEST; Zeitschrift fuer Ostrecht und Rechtsvergleichung. 1957. m. DM.128. Berlin Verlag Arno Spitz GmbH, Pacelliallee 5, 14195 Berlin, Germany. TEL 030-8326232. FAX 030-8316249. Ed. Horst-Dieter Kittke. adv.; bk.rev. circ. 1,000. **Indexed:** Amer.Hist.& Life, Hist.Abstr. **Document type:** academic/scholarly publication.
   Description: Analyzes and comments on legal development and jurisdiction in Middle East and East European countries in the fields of public law, civil and criminal law, economic law and property regulations.

341.57   GW   ISSN 0343-9771
K18
RECHT UND SCHADEN; Monatliche Informationsschrift fuer Schadenversicherung und Schadenersatz. 1974. m. DM.198. Verlag Information Ambs GmbH, Postfach 208, 77968 Kippenheim, Germany. TEL 07825-7114. adv.; bk.rev. circ. 2,600. **Document type:** bulletin.

340 341   GW
RECHTSSTAAT IN DER BEWAEHRUNG. 1975. irreg. price varies. C.F. Mueller Juristischer Verlag GmbH, Im Weiher 10, 69121 Heidelberg, Germany. TEL 06221-489281. FAX 06221-489279. **Document type:** monographic series.

341   UK
REGISTER OF LAWS OF THE ARABIAN GULF. 1986. a. (plus q. supplements). £1285($2670) for basic work; supplement service £670 ($1365). Graham & Trotman Ltd. (Subsidiary of: Kluwer Academic Publishers Group), Sterling House, 66 Wilton Rd., London SW1V 1DE, England. TEL 44-71-821-1123. FAX 44-71-530-5229. (Dist. by: Kluwer Academic Publishers Group, P.O. Box 322, 3300 AH Dordrecht, Netherlands. TEL 31-78-524400. FAX 31-78-524474; N. America dist. addr.: Box 358, Accord Sta., Hingham, MA 02018-0358. TEL 617-871-6600. FAX 617-871-6528) Ed. W. Ballantyne. (looseleaf format) **Document type:** trade publication.

346.066   US
REGULATION OF FOREIGN BANKS; United States and international. 1991. base vol. (plus a. supplement). $125. Butterworth Legal Publishers (Salem) (Subsidiary of: Reed Elsevier plc), 8 Industrial Way, Bldg. C, Salem, NH 03079. TEL 800-548-4001. FAX 603-898-9858. Eds. Micheal Gruson, Ralph Reisner.
   Description: Provides a comprehensive and practical resource for banking law practitioners, managers of internationally orientated financial institutions, and bank regulators. Details analysis of the laws governing the regulation of foreign banks in the US and in other money center countries.

REVIEW OF EUROPEAN COMMUNITY AND INTERNATIONAL ENVIRONMENTAL LAW. see *ENVIRONMENTAL STUDIES*

341   AG   ISSN 0034-7892
REVISTA DE DERECHO INTERNACIONAL Y CIENCIAS DIPLOMATICAS.* 1949. s-a. Arg.$14($3.50) Universidad Nacional de Rosario, Instituto de Derecho Internacional, Cordoba 1814, 2000 Rosario, Argentina. Ed. Prof. Dr. Werner Goldschmidt. adv.; bk.rev.; abstr.; bibl. circ. 1,750. **Indexed:** Geo.Abstr.

341   SP   ISSN 0034-9380
JX9
REVISTA ESPANOLA DE DERECHO INTERNACIONAL. 1948-1978; resumed 1985. s-a. 3300 ptas. (foreign 4950 ptas.). Consejo Superior de Investigaciones Cientificas (C.S.I.C.), Departamento de Derecho Internacional "Francisco de Vitoria", Vitruvio, 8, 28006 Madrid, Spain. bk.rev.; bibl.; index.
   —BLDSC (7853.935000); SWETS.
   Description: Covers international law, both public and private, Spanish jurisprudence and law practice in Spain.

341   PE   ISSN 0035-0370
REVISTA PERUANA DE DERECHO INTERNACIONAL. 1941. s-a. $4 per. no. Sociedad Peruana de Derecho Internacional, Box 686, Lima, Peru. Ed.Bd. bk.rev.; index. circ. 600. **Indexed:** P.A.I.S.For.Lang.Ind.

341   BE   ISSN 0035-0788
JX3
REVUE BELGE DE DROIT INTERNATIONAL/BELGIAN REVIEW OF INTERNATIONAL LAW. (Text in Dutch, English and French) 1965. s-a. 3042 Fr. (Societe Belge de Droit International) Etablissements Emile Bruylant, 67 rue de la Regence, B-1000 Brussels, Belgium. TEL 02-512-9845. Dir. J.A. Salmon. bk.rev.; index. **Indexed:** ELLIS, Mar.Aff.Bibl., P.A.I.S., P.A.I.S.For.Lang.Ind.
   —BLDSC (7891.700000); SWETS.

341   FR   ISSN 0035-0958
K21
REVUE CRITIQUE DE DROIT INTERNATIONAL PRIVE. 1905. q. 655 F. (foreign 745 F.). Editions Sirey, 22 rue Soufflot, 75240 Paris Cedex 05, France. TEL 40-51-54-54. FAX 45-87-37-48. TELEX 206446F. (Subscr. to: Dalloz, 35 rue Tournefort, 75240 Paris Cedex 05, France. TEL 1-40-51-54-54) Ed. Paul Lagarde. bk.rev.; abstr.; index, cum.index every 25 yrs. (reprint service avail. from SCH) **Indexed:** ELLIS.
   —BLDSC (7897.700000); SWETS. **CCC**.

341   NE   ISSN 0295-5830
REVUE DE DROIT DES AFFAIRES INTERNATIONALES/INTERNATIONAL BUSINESS LAW JOURNAL. (Text in English, French) 8/yr. fl.735($397) (effective 1994). Kluwer Law and Taxation Publishers (Subsidiary of: Wolters Kluwer N.V.), P.O. Box 23, 7400 GA Deventer, Netherlands. TEL 31-5700-47261. FAX 31-5700-22244. TELEX 49295 KLUDV NL. (Dist. by: Libresso Distribution Centre, P.O. Box 23, 7400 GA Deventer, Netherlands. TEL 31-5700-33155. FAX 31-5700-33834; In N. America: Kluwer Law and Taxation Publishers, 675 Massachusetts Ave., Cambridge, MA 02139. TEL 617-354-0140. FAX 617-354-8595) Ed. Henry Lesguillons. **Indexed:** ELLIS. **Document type:** academic/scholarly publication.
   —BLDSC (4538.360000); SWETS.
   Formerly: Journal de Droit des Affaires Internationales (ISSN 0753-275X)
   Description: Provides up-to-date information in the fields of international business law, international finance and international taxation, including recent rulings and decisions, research, theory and practice.

REVUE DE DROIT FRANCAIS COMMERCIAL MARITIME ET FISCAL. see *LAW*

REVUE DE DROIT INTERNATIONAL DE SCIENCES DIPLOMATIQUES ET POLITIQUES. see *POLITICAL SCIENCE*

341   BE   ISSN 0035-1105
K21
REVUE DE DROIT INTERNATIONAL ET DE DROIT COMPARE. 1908. q. 3425 Fr. (Institut Belge de Droit Compare) Etablissements Emile Bruylant, 67 rue de la Regence, B-1000 Brussels, Belgium. TEL 02-512-9845. index.

341   FR   ISSN 1152-9172
REVUE DES AFFAIRES EUROPEENNES. q. 920 F. (foreign 940 F.). (Librairie Generale de Droit et de Jurisprudence) Editions Juridiques Associees, 26 rue Vercingertorix, 75014 Paris, France. TEL 1-43-35-01-67. FAX 43-20-07-42. TELEX EJA 203 918 F. Ed. Charles-Etienne Gudin. bibl.
—BLDSC (7882.928000).

341   FR   ISSN 0035-3094
REVUE GENERALE DE DROIT INTERNATIONAL PUBLIC; droit des gens, histoire diplomatique, droit penal, droit fiscal, droit administratif. 1894. q. 800 F. Editions A. Pedone, 13 rue Soufflot, 75005 Paris, France. Eds. P.M. Dupuy, J.P. Queneudec. adv.; bk.rev.; bibl.; index. circ. 1,200. (reprint service avail. from SCH) **Indexed:** CERDIC, ELLIS, Int.Lab.Doc., Mar.Aff.Bibl.
—Faxon. CCC.

341   GR   ISSN 0035-3256
REVUE HELLENIQUE DE DROIT INTERNATIONAL. (Text in English, French, German, Italian) 1948. q. $35. Hellenic Institute of International and Foreign Law - Institut Hellenique de Droit International et Etranger, 73 Solonos St., Athens, Greece. TEL 30-1-3615646. FAX 30-1-3619777. bk.rev.; bibl.; index. circ. 2,000. (reprint service avail. from SCH)
—UnCover; SWETS.

341   FR   ISSN 0035-3337
K21
REVUE INTERNATIONALE DE DROIT COMPARE. 1949. q. 645 F. Societe de Legislation Comparee, 28 rue Saint Guillaume, 75007 Paris, France. TEL 44-39-86-23. FAX 44-39-86-28. adv.; bk.rev.; bibl.; cum.index: 1949-1973, 1974-1988. circ. 1,600. **Indexed:** A.B.C.Pol.Sci., Foreign Leg.Per.
—SWETS.
Description: Sole review of comparative law published in France.

341   CN   ISSN 0828-9999
K21
REVUE QUEBECOIS DE DROIT INTERNATIONAL. 1984. a. Can.$48($35) Societe Quebecoise de Droit International, University of Montreal, Faculte de Droit, C.P. 6128, Succ. A, Montreal, Que. H3C 3J7. TEL 514-343-6124. cum.index every 5 yrs. circ. 500. (back issues avail.) **Indexed:** Ind.Can.L.P.L., Leg.Per.

REVUE ROUMAINE D'ETUDES INTERNATIONALES. see POLITICAL SCIENCE — International Relations

341   IT   ISSN 0035-6158
RIVISTA DI DIRITTO INTERNAZIONALE. (Text in English, French and Italian) 1906. q. L.90000 (foreign L.135000). Casa Editrice Dott. A. Giuffre, Via Busto Arsizio 40, 20151 Milan, Italy. TEL 02-38000905. FAX 02-38009582. Ed. Giorgio Gaja. adv.; bk.rev.; abstr.; bibl.; index. circ. 900. **Indexed:** ELLIS, Mar.Aff.Bibl.

341   IT   ISSN 0035-6174
RIVISTA DI DIRITTO INTERNAZIONALE PRIVATO E PROCESSUALE. (Text in English, French, Italian and Spanish) 1965. q. L.160000 (foreign L.240000) (effective 1994). Casa Editrice Dott. Antonio Milani, Via Jappelli 5, 35121 Padua, Italy. TEL 049-656677. FAX 049-8752900. Ed. Fausto Pocar. bk.rev.; bibl.; cum.index: 1965-1974. circ. 1,200. **Indexed:** ELLIS.
—SWETS.

340 382   IT   ISSN 0392-8748
RIVISTA DI DIRITTO VALUTARIO E DI ECONOMIA INTERNAZIONALE/REVIEW OF CURRENCY LAW AND INTERNATIONAL ECONOMICS; legislazione internazionale - ricerche - giurisprudenza - documenti. 1979. q. L.270000. Edizioni Giuridico Scientifiche s.r.l., Via Dondotte 37, 20122 Milan, Italy. TEL 02-795700. FAX 76110744. TELEX 323319 EGS MIZ I. Ed. Ennio Alessio Mizzau. adv.; bk.rev. circ. 3,500.
Formerly: Rivista di Diritto ed Economia Valutaria.

341 382   US
RUSSIA AND THE REPUBLICS LEGAL MATERIALS. 5 base vols. (plus bi-m. supplements). $395 for base vols.; supplement price varies. (Columbia University, Parker School of Foreign and Comparative Law) Transnational Juris Publications, Inc., 1 Bridge St., Irvington-on-Hudson, NY 10533. TEL 914-591-4288. FAX 914-591-2688. (Dist. outside N. America by: Kluwer Academic Publishers Group, P.O. Box 322, 3300 AH Dordrecht, Netherlands. TEL 31-78-524400. FAX 31-78-524474) Ed. Vratislav Pechota. (looseleaf format)
Formerly (until no.4): U S S R Legal Materials.
Description: Consists of English translations of Russian and former Soviet Republic business and investment laws.

341   GW   ISSN 0172-7796
SCHRIFTEN ZUM STAATS- UND VOELKERRECHT. 1975. irreg., vol.54, 1993. Peter Lang GmbH Europaeischer Verlag der Wissenschaften, Eschborner Landstr. 42-50, 60489 Frankfurt a.M, Germany. TEL 069-7807050. FAX 069-785893. Ed. Dieter Blumenwitz. **Document type:** monographic series.
Formerly: Augsburger Schriften zum Staats- und Voelkerrecht.

341   SZ
SCHWEIZERISCHE ZEITSCHRIFT FUER INTERNATIONALES UND EUROPAEISCHES RECHT/REVUE SUISSE DE DROIT INTERNATIONAL ET DE DROIT EUROPEEN. (Text in French, German) 4/yr. 175 SFr. (foreign 190 SFr.). (Schweizerische Vereinigung fuer Internationales Recht) Schulthess Polygraphischer Verlag AG, Zwingliplatz 2, CH-8022 Zurich, Switzerland. TEL 01-2519336. FAX 01-2616394. Ed.Bd. **Document type:** bulletin.
Formerly (until 1991): Schweizerisches Jahrbuch fuer Internationales Recht.

341   NE   ISSN 0924-4638
SERIES ON INTERNATIONAL CORPORATE LAW. 1985. irreg., vol.3, 1992. price varies. Kluwer Law and Taxation Publishers (Subsidiary of: Wolters Kluwer N.V.), P.O. Box 23, 7400 GA Deventer, Netherlands. TEL 31-5700-47261. FAX 31-5700-22244. TELEX 49295 KLUDV NL. (Dist. by: Libresso Distribution Centre, P.O. Box 23, 7400 GA Deventer, Netherlands. TEL 31-5700-33155. FAX 31-5700-33834; In N. America: Kluwer Law and Taxation Publishers, 675 Massachusetts Ave., Cambridge, MA 02139. TEL 617-354-0140. FAX 617-354-8595) (back issues avail.) **Document type:** monographic series.
Description: Provides a parallel language edition of articles on selected European countries' corporate law systems, with English translation, and commentary on the country's corporate law system.

SERIES ON INTERNATIONAL TAXATION. see BUSINESS AND ECONOMICS — Public Finance, Taxation

341   NE
SINGLE EUROPEAN MARKET REPORTER. (Text in English) 1991. base vol. (plus q. updates). fl.350($200) (effective 1994). (Baker & McKenzie) Kluwer Law and Taxation Publishers (Subsidiary of: Wolters Kluwer N.V.), P.O. Box 23, 7400 GA Deventer, Netherlands. TEL 31-5700-47261. FAX 31-5700-22244. TELEX 49295 KLUDV NL. (Dist. by: Libresso Distribution Centre, P.O. Box 23, 7400 GA Deventer, Netherlands. TEL 31-5700-33155. FAX 31-5700-33834; In N. America: Kluwer Law and Taxation Publishers, 675 Massachusetts Ave., Cambridge, MA 02139. TEL 617-354-0140. FAX 617-354-8595) (looseleaf format)
Description: Comprehensive practical guide to changes in European legislation as a result of the European Commission's Single European Market programme, including an overview of likely future developments, and discussion of strategic implications.

341 382   US
▼**SLIP OPINION SERVICES.** 1994. w. $595. International Business Reports, Box 1009, Falls Church, VA 22041. TEL 703-998-2927. FAX 703-998-0019. Ed. Edward P. Kemp.
Description: Full, original text of all slip opinions issued by the US Court of International Trade, US Court of Appeals for the Federal Circuit and-or Supreme Court.

341   BL
SOCIEDADE BRASILEIRA DE DIREITO INTERNACIONAL. BOLETIM. 1945. 2/yr. Sociedade Brasileira de Direito Internacional, Palacio Itamaraty, Rio de Janeiro, Brazil.

341   SA   ISSN 0379-8895
JX21
SOUTH AFRICAN YEARBOOK OF INTERNATIONAL LAW/SUID-AFRIKAANSE JAARBOEK VIR VOLKEREG. 1975. a. $55. University of South Africa, VerLoren van Themaat Centre for Public Law Studies, P.O. Box 392, Pretoria 0001, South Africa. TEL 27-12-429-8468. FAX 27-12-429-3321. (Dist. in N. America by: Wm. W. Gaunt & Sons, Inc., Gaunt Bldg., 3011 Gulf Dr., Holmes Beach, FL 34217-2199. TEL 813-778-5211. FAX 813-778-5252) Ed. N.J. Botha. adv.; bk.rev. circ. 500. **Indexed:** Documentatieblad, Ind.S.A.Per. **Document type:** academic/scholarly publication.

SOUTHWESTERN LEGAL FOUNDATION. ANNUAL REPORT. see LAW

SOVIET & EASTERN EUROPEAN REPORT; the monthly newsletter on developments in business, law & finance. see BUSINESS AND ECONOMICS — International Development And Assistance

341   US   ISSN 0731-5082
JX1
STANFORD JOURNAL OF INTERNATIONAL LAW. 1966. s-a. $22 (foreign $28). Stanford University, Stanford Law School, Stanford, CA 94305-8610. TEL 415-723-1375. adv.; bk.rev. circ. 600. (reprint service avail. from RRI) **Indexed:** A.B.C.Pol.Sci., ASCA, C.L.I., Ind.Per.Art.Relat.Law, L.R.I., Leg.Cont., Leg.Per., Mar.Aff.Bibl., Mid.East: Abstr.& Ind., P.A.I.S., SSCI. **Document type:** academic/scholarly publication.
●Also available online. Vendor(s): West Services, Inc.
—BLDSC (8432.080000); Faxon; UnCover; SWETS.
Formerly: Stanford Journal of International Studies (ISSN 0081-4326)

341.7   NE
STUDIES IN TRANSNATIONAL ECONOMIC LAW. 1980. irreg., no.9, 1993. price varies. Kluwer Law and Taxation Publishers (Subsidiary of: Wolters Kluwer N.V.), P.O. Box 23, 7400 GA Deventer, Netherlands. TEL 31-5700-47261. FAX 31-5700-22244. TELEX 49295 KLUDV NL. (Dist. by: Libresso Distribution Centre, P.O. Box 23, 7400 GA Deventer, Netherlands. TEL 31-5700-33155. FAX 31-5700-33834; In N. America: Kluwer Law and Taxation Publishers, 675 Massachusetts Ave., Cambridge, MA 02139. TEL 617-354-0140. FAX 617-354-8595) Ed. Norbert Horn. bibl. (back issues avail.) **Document type:** monographic series.
Description: International forum for the analysis of legal problems affecting international business and economic cooperation.

340   US   ISSN 1057-0551
STUDIES IN TRANSNATIONAL LEGAL POLICY. Variant title: American Society of International Law. Occasional Papers. irreg., latest no.26. price varies. American Society of International Law, 2223 Massachusetts Ave, N.W., Washington, DC 20008-2864. TEL 202-939-6000. FAX 202-797-7133. **Indexed:** Deep Sea Res.& Oceanogr.Abstr. **Document type:** monographic series.
—CCC.

341 382   US   ISSN 1070-9185
SURVEY OF EAST EUROPEAN LAW. Short title: S E E L. 1990. 12/yr. $295. Transnational Juris Publications, Inc., 1 Bridge St., Irvington-on-Hudson, NY 10533. TEL 914-591-4288. FAX 914-591-2688. Ed. Kaj Hober.
Formerly: Soviet and East European Law (ISSN 1049-8753)
Description: Covers new developments affecting investment and trade in the Russian Federation and Eastern Europe, with analysis of legislative changes.

341.57   SW   ISSN 1101-3540
SVENSK HANDELSTIDNING JUSTITA - KVARTAL. (Supplement avail.) 1979. q. SEK 1395 (effective 1990). Svensk Handelstidning Justitia A-B, P.O. Box 1508, 171 29 Solna, Sweden. Ed. Thomas Aroseniusg. adv.; bk.rev. circ. 13,500.
Formerly (until vol. 2, 1990): Justitia Kreditregister (ISSN 0349-974X); (until 1981): Svensk Handelstidning Justitia - Aarsbok (ISSN 0349-9316)

LAW — INTERNATIONAL LAW

341 332.6   US
SYMPOSIUM ON PRIVATE INVESTMENTS ABROAD.
1967. a. $90. Southwestern Legal Foundation, Box 830707, Richardson, TX 75083-0707. TEL 214-690-2370. Ed. Carol Holgren.

341 382   US   ISSN 0093-0709
JX1
SYRACUSE JOURNAL OF INTERNATIONAL LAW & COMMERCE. 1972. a. $10 (foreign $13). (Syracuse University, College of Law) Joe Christensen, Inc. (Syracuse), E I White Hall, Ste. 0041, Syracuse, NY 13244-1030. TEL 315-443-2056. adv.; bk.rev. circ. 500. (reprint service avail. from RRI) Indexed: ABI Inform, BPIA, C.L.I., L.R.I., Leg.Cont., Leg.Per., Mar.Aff.Bibl., Refug.Abstr., Sel.Water Res.Abstr., Sel.Water Res.Abstr.
● Also available online. Vendor(s): West Services, Inc.
—BLDSC (8588.750000); Faxon; UnCover; SWETS; UMI.
Description: Publishes articles prepared by scholars and practitioners in the field of public and private international law.

TAXATION LAWS OF INDONESIA. see BUSINESS AND ECONOMICS — Public Finance, Taxation

TAXATION OF PERMANENT ESTABLISHMENTS. see BUSINESS AND ECONOMICS — Public Finance, Taxation

341 327   US   ISSN 1062-4007
TERRORISM: DOCUMENTS OF INTERNATIONAL AND LOCAL CONTROL. 1979. irreg., vol.6, 1992. price varies. Oceana Publications, Inc., 75 Main St., Dobbs Ferry, NY 10522. TEL 914-693-8100. FAX 914-693-0402. Ed. Robert A. Friedlander. (back issues avail.)
Description: Compilation of documents focusing on the U.S. role in the terrorist dilemma, including legal responses to international terrorism.

341 327   US   ISSN 1064-9352
▼**TERRORISM: DOCUMENTS OF INTERNATIONAL AND LOCAL CONTROL. SECOND SERIES.** 1992. irreg. price varies. Oceana Publications, Inc., 75 Main St., Dobbs Ferry, NY 10522. TEL 914-693-8100. FAX 914-693-0402. Ed. Robert A. Friedlander. **Document type:** monographic series.
Description: Provides commentary and analysis of world terrorism.

341   US   ISSN 0163-7479
JX1
TEXAS INTERNATIONAL LAW JOURNAL. 1964. 3/yr. $25 (foreign $28). University of Texas at Austin, School of Law Publications, Box 149084, Austin, TX 78714-9084. TEL 512-471-1106. FAX 512-471-6988. adv.; bk.rev.; index, cum.index every 5 yrs. circ. 850. (also avail. in microform from UMI,PMC; microfilm from WSH; back issues avail.; reprint service avail. from WSH) **Indexed:** Amer.Bibl.Slavic & E.Eur.Stud., C.L.I., L.R.I., Leg.Cont., Leg.Per., Mar.Aff.Bibl.
—BLDSC (8798.892000); UnCover; SWETS; UMI.
Formerly: Texas International Law Forum (ISSN 0040-4381)

341 338.91   US   ISSN 0895-5018
THIRD WORLD LEGAL STUDIES (YEAR). 1982. a. $20. International Third World Legal Studies Association, c/o Valparaiso University, School of Law, Valparaiso, IN 46383. TEL 219-465-7829. FAX 219-465-7872. Ed. Samuel O. Gyandoh Jr. circ. 800. **Indexed:** C.L.I. **Document type:** academic/scholarly publication.
Description: Examines legal problems in the development of Third World countries.

THIRD WORLD WITHOUT SUPERPOWERS: COLLECTED DOCUMENTS OF THE GROUP OF 77. see POLITICAL SCIENCE — International Relations

341   NE   ISSN 0926-874X
K24
TILBURG FOREIGN LAW REVIEW; journal on foreign & comparative law. (Text mainly in English) 1991. q. Katholieke Universiteit Brabant, Faculteit der Rechtsgeleerdheid - Tilburg University, Faculty of Law, Postbus 90153, 5000 LE Tilburg, Netherlands. (Dist. in U.S. and Canada by: Wm. W. Gaunt & Sons Inc., 3011 Gulf Dr., Holmes Beach, FL 34217-2199. TEL 800-942-8683. FAX 813-778-5252) (back issues avail.) **Document type:** academic/scholarly publication.
—BLDSC (8845.555000); UnCover.

TRADEMARK LAW HANDBOOK. see LAW

TRANSPORT: INTERNATIONAL TRANSPORT TREATIES. see TRANSPORTATION

341   US   ISSN 1061-4176
TURNAROUNDS & WORKOUTS - EUROPE. 1991. q. $195. Beard Group, Inc., Box 9867, Washington, DC 20016. TEL 301-951-6400. FAX 301-951-3621. Ed. Nadine Granoff. adv.
Description: Covers current developments in bankruptcy and insolvency in Europe.

U M A STUDENTS LAW JOURNAL. (University of Malawi) see LAW

U N I D I R NEWSLETTER/LETTRE DE L'U N I D I R. (United Nations Institute for Disarmament Research) see POLITICAL SCIENCE — International Relations

341 382   US
U S INTERNATIONAL TRADE LAWS. 1988. irreg., latest 1989 ed. $48. B N A Books, 1231 25th St., N.W., Washington, DC 20037. TEL 202-833-7470; 800-372-1033. FAX 202-833-7490. (Subscr. to: BNA Books Distribution Center, 300 Raritan Center Parkway, Box 7816, Edison, NJ 08818-7816. TEL 908-225-1900. FAX 908-417-0482) Ed. Alan M. Stowell.

341   US   ISSN 0390-3761
UNIFORM LAW REVIEW/REVUE DE DROIT UNIFORME. 1973. s-a. $25. (Unidroit - International Institute for the Unification of Private Law) Oceana Publications, Inc., 75 Main St., Dobbs Ferry, NY 10522. TEL 914-693-1320. FAX 914-693-0402. circ. 150. **Indexed:** ELLIS.
Formed by the merger of: Uniform Law Cases; Unidroit Yearbook.

341   UN   ISSN 0082-8289
JX1261
UNITED NATIONS. INTERNATIONAL LAW COMMISSION YEARBOOK. French edition: Nations Unies. Commission de Droit International. Annuaire (ISSN 0497-9877); Russian edition: Organizatsiya Ob'edinennykh Natsii. Komissiya Mezhdunarodnogo Prava. Ezhegodnik (ISSN 0251-771X); Spanish edition: Naciones Unidas. Comision de Derecho Internacional. Anuario (ISSN 0497-9885) (Issued in 2 vols.) (Text in English) 1949. a. price varies. United Nations Publications, Room DC2-853, New York, NY 10017. TEL 212-963-8302. FAX 212-963-3489. (And: Distribution and Sales Section, Palais des Nations, CH-1211 Geneva 10, Switzerland) (also avail. in microfiche; reprint service avail. from KTO)
—BLDSC (9388.550000).

341.2   UN   ISSN 0255-724X
UNITED NATIONS. MULTILATERAL TREATIES DEPOSITED WITH THE SECRETARY-GENERAL. French edition: Nations Unies. Traites Mulitnationaux Deposes aupres de Secretaire General (ISSN 0255-7258) (Text in English and French) 1967. irreg. $70. United Nations Publications, Room DC2-853, New York, NY 10017. TEL 212-963-8302. FAX 212-963-3489. (And: Distribution and Sales Section, Palais des Nations, CH-1211 Geneva 10, Switzerland) (also avail. in microfiche)
Formerly (until 1980): United Nations. Multilateral Treaties in Respect of Which the Secretary-General Performs Depository Functions (ISSN 0082-8319)

341.2   UN   ISSN 0379-8267
JX170
UNITED NATIONS. TREATY SERIES. (Text in English and French) 1947. irreg. United Nations Publications, Rm. DC2-853, New York, NY 10017. TEL 212-963-8302. FAX 212-963-3489.

UNITED NATIONS. TREATY SERIES. CUMULATIVE INDEX. see LAW — Abstracting, Bibliographies, Statistics

UNITED NATIONS ASSOCIATION IN CANADA. QUARTERLY BULLETIN. see POLITICAL SCIENCE — International Relations

341.7   UN   ISSN 0251-9127
UNITED NATIONS COMMISSION ON INTERNATIONAL TRADE LAW. REPORT ON THE WORK OF ITS SESSION. Arabic edition: Al-Umam al-Muttahidaho Lajnahj lil-Qanun al-Tijari al-Duwali. Taqrir 'an 'Amal Dawratiha (ISSN 0251-9178); Chinese edition: Lianhegu Guoji Maoyifa Weiyuanhui Huiyi Gongzuo Baogao (ISSN 0251-916X); French edition: Commission des Nations Unies pour le Droit Commercial International. Rapport des Travaux de sa Session (ISSN 0251-9151); Spanish edition: Comision de las Naciones Unidas para el Derecho Mercantil Internacional. Informe sobre la Labor Realizada en su Periodo de Sesiones (ISSN 0251-9143); Russian edition (ISSN 0251-9135) (Subseries of: United Nations. General Assembly. Official Records. Supplement no.17) 1968. a. United Nations Commission on International Trade Law (UNCITRAL), Vienna International Centre, P.O. Box 500, A-1400 Vienna, Austria. TEL 2631-4060. FAX 431-237485. (Dist. by: Distribution and Sales Section, Palais des Nations, CH-1211 Geneva 10, Switzerland; and United Nations Publications, Room DC2-853, New York, N.Y. 10017, U.S.A.) Sec. Gerold Herrmann. **Document type:** corporate report.

341 382   UN   ISSN 0251-4265
K1004.5
UNITED NATIONS COMMISSION ON INTERNATIONAL TRADE LAW. YEARBOOK. French edition: Commission des Nations Unies pour le Droit Commercial International. Annuaire (ISSN 0251-4257); Spanish edition: Comision de las Naciones Unidas para el Derecho Mercantil Internacional. Anuario (ISSN 0251-4273); Russian edition: Komissiya Organizatsii Ob'edinnykh Natsii po Pravu Mezhdunarodnoi Torgovli. Ezegodnik (ISSN 0251-4281) irreg. (approx. a.), vol.22, 1991. price varies. United Nations Commission on International Trade Law (UNCITRAL), Vienna International Centre, P.O. Box 500, A-1400 Vienna, Austria. TEL 2631-4060. FAX 431-237485. (Dist. by: Distribution and Sales Section, Palais des Nations, CH-1211 Geneva 10, Switzerland; and United Nations Publications, Rm. DC2-853, New York, N.Y. 10017) Sec. Gerold Herrmann. bibl.

341   UN   ISSN 0082-8297
JX1977.A1
UNITED NATIONS JURIDICAL YEARBOOK. French edition: Nations Unies Annuaire Juridique (ISSN 0251-7558); Russian edition: Organizatsiya Ob'edinennykh Natsii. Yuridicheskiy Ezhegodnik (ISSN 0251-7574); Spanish edition: Naciones Unidas Anuario Juridico (ISSN 0251-7566) 1962. a. price varies. United Nations Publications, Room DC2-853, New York, NY 10017. TEL 212-963-8302. FAX 212-963-3489. (Or: Distribution and Sales Section, CH-1211 Geneva 10, Switzerland) (also avail. in microfiche) **Indexed:** Refug.Abstr.
—BLDSC (9097.010000).

341   US   ISSN 0886-6686
JX1977.A3155
UNITED NATIONS RESOLUTIONS. SERIES 1. RESOLUTIONS ADOPTED BY THE GENERAL ASSEMBLY. 1972. irreg., vol.24, 1988. price varies. (United Nations, General Assembly) Oceana Publications, Inc., 75 Main St., Dobbs Ferry, NY 10522. TEL 914-693-1320. FAX 914-693-0402. Ed. Dusan Djonovich. cum.index. circ. 375. (back issues avail.)
Description: Compilation of documents pertaining to resolutions of the United Nations for the General Assembly.

341   US   ISSN 0898-2929
JX1977
UNITED NATIONS RESOLUTIONS. SERIES 2. RESOLUTIONS AND DECISIONS OF THE SECURITY COUNCIL. (Text in English, French) 1988. irreg., vol.11, 1992. price varies. (United Nations, General Assembly) Oceana Publications, Inc., 75 Main St., Dobbs Ferry, NY 10522. TEL 914-693-1320. FAX 914-693-0402. Ed. Dusan J. Djonovich. circ. 400.
Description: Contains resolutions and decisions of the United Nations Security Council, with a topical index, clarifying documents, and country-by-country voting records.

UNITED NATIONS REVIEW. see POLITICAL SCIENCE — International Relations

LAW — INTERNATIONAL LAW

327 341.2   US   ISSN 0083-0186
JX235.9
U.S. DEPARTMENT OF STATE. TREATIES AND OTHER INTERNATIONAL ACTS SERIES. (Texts of individual treaties collected and issued in bound form as United States Treaties and Other International Agreements: ISSN 0083-3487) 1946. irreg., vol.32, pt.5, 1979-80. $9 price varies. U.S. Department of State, Office of the Legal Adviser, 2201 C St., N.W., Washington, DC 20520. TEL 202-647-2044. (Dist. by Supt. of Documents, Washington, DC 20402-9371) **Document type:** government publication.

341.2   US   ISSN 0083-0194
U.S. DEPARTMENT OF STATE. TREATIES IN FORCE. 1956. a. price varies. U.S. Department of State, Office of the Legal Adviser, 2201 C St., N.W., Washington, DC 20520. TEL 202-647-2044. (Dist. by: Supt. of Documents, Washington, DC 20402) **Document type:** government publication.

341 332.6   US
▼**UNITED STATES IMPORT TRADE LAW.** 1992. 2 base vols. (plus supplements). $200. Butterworth Legal Publishers (Salem) (Subsidiary of: Reed Elsevier plc), 8 Industrial Way, Bldg. C, Salem, NH 03079. TEL 800-548-4001. FAX 603-898-9858. Eds. Eugene T. Rossides, Alexandra Maravel. (looseleaf format)
Description: Annotated examination of all current laws, regulations, international agreements and legal processes governing the import trade in the US.

UNITED STATES INCOME TAX TREATIES. see *BUSINESS AND ECONOMICS — Public Finance, Taxation*

UNITED STATES INTERNAL REVENUE SERVICE INTERNATIONAL TAX COMPLIANCE INFORMATION. see *BUSINESS AND ECONOMICS — Public Finance, Taxation*

327 341.2   US   ISSN 0083-3487
JX231
UNITED STATES TREATIES AND OTHER INTERNATIONAL AGREEMENTS. 1950. a. price varies. U.S. Department of State, Office of the Legal Adviser, 2201 C St., N.W., Washington, DC 20520. TEL 202-647-2044. (Dist. by: Supt. of Documents, Washington, DC 20402) (also avail. in microform from PMC) **Document type:** government publication.

341   PO   ISSN 0303-9773
UNIVERSIDADE DE COIMBRA. FACULDADE DE DIREITO. BOLETIM. 1914. a. $20. Coimbra Editora Lda., Rua do Arnado, Apdo. 101, 3002 Coimbra Codex, Portugal. TEL 039-25459. FAX 039-37531. bk.rev.; bibl. circ. 1,200.

341 327   GW   ISSN 0341-3241
UNIVERSITAET HAMBURG. INSTITUT FUER INTERNATIONALE ANGELEGENHEITEN. WERKHEFTE. 1965. irreg., vol.38, 1982. price varies. Nomos Verlagsgesellschaft mbH und Co. KG, Waldseestr. 3-5, 76530 Baden-Baden, Germany. TEL 07221-21040. FAX 07221-210427. (Subscr. to: Postfach 610, 76484 Baden-Baden, Germany) (Co-sponsor: Deutscher Verein fuer Internationales Seerecht) **Document type:** monographic series.
Formerly: Forschungstelle fuer Voelkerrecht und Auslaendisches Oeffentliches Recht. Werkhefte (ISSN 0072-9493)

341.57   US   ISSN 0891-9895
K10
UNIVERSITY OF PENNSYLVANIA JOURNAL OF INTERNATIONAL BUSINESS LAW. (Continues numbering of Journal of Comparative Business and Capital Market Law) (Text in English) 1978. q. $87.50 (foreign $38.50). University of Pennsylvania, Law School, 3400 Chestnut St., Philadelphia, PA 19104-6204. TEL 215-898-6869. FAX 215-573-2304. Ed. Michael Kelsen. adv.; bk.rev.; index. circ. 500. (also avail. in microform from UMI; reprint service avail. from UMI, WSH; back issues avail.) **Indexed:** BPIA, C.L.I., L.R.I., Leg.Per. **Document type:** academic/scholarly publication.
●Also available online. Vendor(s): Mead Data Central, Inc., West Services, Inc.
—BLDSC (9116.375000); Faxon; UnCover; SWETS; UMI. **CCC.**
Supersedes (as of vol.9, 1987): Journal of Comparative Business and Capital Market Law; (until 1983): Journal of Comparative Corporate Law and Securities Regulation (ISSN 0165-0165)
Description: Covers all areas of international business law, including securities, taxation, corporate and tort issues.

341   PL   ISSN 0208-5496
UNIWERSYTET SLASKI W KATOWICACH. PRACE NAUKOWE. PROBLEMY PRAWNE HANDLU ZAGRANICZNEGO. (Text in Polish; summaries in English and Russian or French) 1977. irreg. price varies. Wydawnictwo Uniwersytetu Slaskiego, Ul. Bankowa 12B, 40-007 Katowice, Poland. TEL 48-32-596-915. FAX 48-32-599-605. TELEX 0315584 USKPL. (Dist. by: CHZ Ars Polona, P.O. Box 1001, 00-950 Warsaw, Poland) Ed. Barbara Woznica. **Document type:** academic/scholarly publication.
Description: Covers international private and commercial law and international procedure, international arbitration and comparative law of obligations.

UTRECHT STUDIES IN AIR AND SPACE LAW. see *LAW*

341   US   ISSN 0090-2594
JX1
VANDERBILT JOURNAL OF TRANSNATIONAL LAW. 1967. 5/yr. $23 (foreign $24). Vanderbilt University School of Law, Nashville, TN 37240. TEL 615-322-2284. Ed. Anne Hilbert. adv.; bk.rev. circ. 1,100. (also avail. in microform from UMI,WSH,PMC; reprint service avail. from WSH) **Indexed:** Abstr.Bk.Rev.Curr.Leg.Per., Amer.Bibl.Slavic & E.Eur.Stud., C.L.I., ELLIS, L.R.I., Leg.Cont., Leg.Per., Mar.Aff.Bibl., P.A.I.S., Refug.Abstr. **Document type:** academic/scholarly publication.
●Also available online. Vendor(s): West Services, Inc.
—BLDSC (9144.300000); UnCover; SWETS; UMI.
Formerly: Vanderbilt International (ISSN 0042-2525)

341   US   ISSN 0042-6571
JX1
VIRGINIA JOURNAL OF INTERNATIONAL LAW. 1960. q. $30 (foreign $40). Virginia Journal of International Law Association, University of Virginia, School of Law, Charlottesville, VA 22901. TEL 804-924-3415. adv.; bk.rev.; stat.; index, cum.index. circ. 1,000. (also avail. in microfilm from RRI,WSH; back issues avail.; reprint service avail. from RRI) **Indexed:** A.B.C.Pol.Sci., Abstr.Bk.Rev.Curr.Leg.Per., Amer.Bibl.Slavic & E.Eur.Stud., C.L.I., Deep Sea Res.& Oceanogr.Abstr., ELLIS, L.R.I., Leg.Cont., Leg.Per., Mar.Aff.Bibl., Mid.East: Abstr.& Ind., Refug.Abstr., Sel.Water Res.Abstr., So.Pac.Per.Ind., SSCI. **Document type:** academic/scholarly publication.
●Also available online. Vendor(s): West Services, Inc.
—BLDSC (9238.950000); Faxon; UnCover; SWETS; UMI.

WARSAW CONVENTION; international transport law - commentary. see *TRANSPORTATION*

341.57 382   US   ISSN 0276-8255
WASHINGTON TARIFF & TRADE LETTER; a weekly report for business executives on U.S. international trade policies, legislation, opportunities and restrictions. 1981. 50/yr. $487 (foreign $517) (effective 1994). Gilston Communications Group, Box 467, Washington, DC 20044. TEL 301-570-4544. FAX 301-570-4545. Ed. Samuel M. Gilston. (back issues avail.) **Document type:** newsletter.

WIENER RECHTSWISSENSCHAFTLICHE STUDIEN. see *LAW*

341   GW   ISSN 0941-6293
▼**WIRTSCHAFT UND RECHT IN OSTEUROPA;** Zeitschrift zur Rechts- und Wirtschaftsentwicklung in den Staaten Mittel- und Osteuropas. 1992. m. DM.392. C.H. Beck'sche Verlagsbuchhandlung, Wilhelmstr. 9, 80801 Munich, Germany. TEL 089-38189338. FAX 089-38189398. TELEX 5215085-BECK-D. Ed.Bd. adv.: B&W page DM.2200, color page DM.4400; trim 260 x 186. circ. 2,800. (back issues avail.) **Document type:** academic/scholarly publication.

382   GW   ISSN 0938-3050
WIRTSCHAFTS- UND STEUERRECHT. 1990. m. DM.426. Verlag Recht und Wirtschaft GmbH, Haeusserstr. 14, 69115 Heidelberg, Germany. TEL 06221-906-1. **Document type:** academic/scholarly publication.

341   US   ISSN 0743-7951
K27
WISCONSIN INTERNATIONAL LAW JOURNAL. 1983. 2/yr. $18. University of Wisconsin-Madison, Law School, 975 Bascom Mall, Madison, WI 53706. TEL 608-262-3877. Ed. Heather E. Gange. circ. 1,000. (back issues avail.) **Indexed:** C.L.I., Leg.Per. **Document type:** academic/scholarly publication.
—BLDSC (9325.735000); Faxon; UnCover.
Description: Forum for analysis and discussion of international law.

346.066   US   ISSN 0960-0949
WORLD ARBITRATION & MEDIATION REPORT. 1990. 12/yr. fl.800($455) (effective 1993). Transnational Juris Publications, Inc., 1 Bridge St., Irvington-on-Hudson, NY 10533. TEL 914-591-4288. FAX 914-591-2688. (Dist. outside N. America by: Kluwer Law and Taxation Publishers, Libresso Distribution Center, P.O. Box 23, 7400 GA Deventer, Netherlands. TEL 31-5700-33155) Ed. S. Gale Dick. (back issues avail.) **Document type:** newsletter.
—**CCC.**
Description: Covers arbitration and other alternatives to litigation in international commercial disputes.

341 327   US   ISSN 1062-676X
WORLD CITIZEN NEWS. 1975. 10/yr. $20. (World Service Authority) N W O Publications, 113 Church St., Burlington, VT 05401. TEL 802-864-4656. FAX 802-864-6878. Ed. Kevin Kelley; Pub. S. Gareth Davis. bk.rev. circ. 17,000. (back issues avail.) **Document type:** newsletter.
Description: Covers world citizenship news, world government news, world law news, world economic news, world ecological news human rights news, and world service authority news.

341   SZ   ISSN 1011-4548
K21
WORLD COMPETITION; law and economics review. (Text in English) 4/yr. 280 SFr.($215) Werner Publishing Co. Ltd., 5 place de la Fusterie, CH-1211 Geneva 11, Switzerland. **Indexed:** ELLIS, P.A.I.S. **Document type:** bulletin.
—BLDSC (9353.255500); SWETS. **CCC.**
Formerly: Swiss Review of International Competition Law (ISSN 0255-8246)

341   US
WORLD DIRECTORY OF RESEARCH AND TRAINING INSTITUTIONS IN INTERNATIONAL LAW. irreg., 3rd ed., 1994. $49.95. (Unesco) Basil Blackwell Inc., 238 Main St., Cambridge, MA 02142. TEL 617-547-7110. **Document type:** directory.

341   US
WORLD JURIST. 1964. bi-m. $75. World Jurist Association, 1000 Connecticut Ave., N.W., Ste. 202, Washington, DC 20036. TEL 202-466-5428; 202-466-5428. FAX 202-4528540. TELEX 440456. bibl. circ. 6,000. **Document type:** academic/scholarly publication.

341.57 665.5   US
WORLD L N G - GAS CONTRACTS. base vols. (plus q. supplements). $2100 (renewal $1300). Barrows Co., Inc., 116 E. 66th St., New York, NY 10021. TEL 212-772-1199. FAX 212-288-7242. TELEX 4971238 BARROWS.
Description: Contains text, in English translations, of contracts for production, liquefaction, and transport of liquefied natural gas (LNG) in all countries.

LAW — JUDICIAL SYSTEMS

241.57 665.5 US
WORLD NATIONAL OIL COMPANY STATUTES. base vols. (plus q. supplements). $1750 (renewal $900). Barrows Co., Inc., 116 E. 65th St., New York, NY 10021. TEL 212-772-1199. FAX 212-288-7242. TELEX 4971238 BARROWS.
  Description: Contains texts, in English translation, of statutes, by-laws, and related statutes of national oil companies for over 85 countries.

WORLD TRADE NEWS. see *BUSINESS AND ECONOMICS*

WORLD TRADE UPDATE. see *BUSINESS AND ECONOMICS*

320 US ISSN 0889-7743
YALE JOURNAL OF WORLD PUBLIC ORDER. 1974. s-a. $25 (foreign $35). Yale Journal of International Law, Inc., Yale Law School, Box 208215, New Haven, CT 06520-8215. TEL 203-432-4884. FAX 203-432-2592. adv.; bk.rev.; bibl. circ. 1,000. (also avail. in microform from WSH; reprint service avail. from WSH) **Indexed:** Amer.Bibl.Slavic & E.Eur.Stud., C.L.I., L.R.I., Leg.Per.
  ●Also available online.
  —BLDSC (9370.010000); Faxon; UnCover; SWETS.
  Former titles: Yale Journal of World Public Order; Yale Studies in World Public Order.
  Description: Discusses current topics relating to international law.

341.57 NE ISSN 0169-0981
YEARBOOK COMMERCIAL ARBITRATION. (Supplemet avail.: Yearbook Key (ISSN 0923-7038)) (Text in English) 1976. a. fl.225($120) (effective 1994). (International Council for Commercial Arbitration) Kluwer Law and Taxation Publishers (Subsidiary of: Wolters Kluwer N.V.), P.O. Box 23, 7400 GA Deventer, Netherlands. TEL 31-5700-47261. FAX 31-5700-22244. TELEX 49295 KLUDV NL. (Dist. by: Libresso Distribution Centre, P.O. Box 23, 7400 GA Deventer, Netherlands. TEL 31-5700-33155. FAX 31-5700-33834; In N. America: Kluwer Law and Taxation Publishers, 675 Massachusetts Ave., Cambridge, MA 02139. TEL 617-354-0140. FAX 617-354-8595) (Co-sponsor: T.M.C. Asser Institute for International and European Law) Ed. A.J. van den Berg. cum.index: vols.1-15, 1976-1990, in vol.15. (back issues avail.)
  Description: Provides comprehensive and up-to-date information on worldwide developments in international arbitration, including arbitral awards, court decisions, arbitration rules, and recent amendment of arbitration statutes and changes in arbitration law and practice.

341 UK ISSN 0266-7223
YEARBOOK OF EUROPEAN LAW. 1981. a. price varies. Oxford University Press, Oxford Journals, Walton St., Oxford OX2 6DP, England. TEL 0865-56767. FAX 0865-56646. TELEX 837330-OXPRES-G. (U.S. subscr. to: Oxford University Press Inc., 2001 Evans Rd., Cary, NC 27513. TEL 919-677-0977) Ed. F. Jacobs. **Indexed:** ELLIS (1987).
  —SWETS.

341 GW ISSN 0044-2348
K30
ZEITSCHRIFT FUER AUSLAENDISCHES OEFFENTLICHES RECHT UND VOELKERRECHT. (Text in English, French or German; summaries in English) 1929. q. DM.289. (Max-Planck-Institut fuer Voelkerrecht) W. Kohlhammer GmbH, Hessbruehlstr. 69, 70565 Stuttgart, Germany. TEL 0711-7863-1. adv.; bk.rev.; abstr.; bibl. index. circ. 1,000. **Indexed:** A.B.C.Pol.Sci., ELLIS, Mar.Aff.Bibl., P.A.I.S.For.Lang.Ind. **Document type:** bulletin.
  —UnCover; SWETS. **CCC.**

341 GW ISSN 0943-3929
▼**ZEITSCHRIFT FUER EUROPAEISCHES PRIVATRECHT (Z EU P)**. 1993. q. DM.198 (students DM.98). C.H. Beck'sche Verlagsbuchhandlung, Wilhelmstr. 9, 80801 Munich, Germany. TEL 089-38189-338. FAX 089-38189-398. TELEX 5215085-BECK-D. Ed.Bd. adv.: B&W page DM.2200, color page DM.3850; trim 200 x 120. bk.rev. circ. 2,000. (back issues avail.) **Document type:** bulletin.

341.57 GW ISSN 0340-8329
K30
ZEITSCHRIFT FUER LUFT- UND WELTRAUMRECHT. 1952. q. DM.228. (Universitaet zu Koeln, Institut fuer Luft- und Weltraumrecht) Carl Heymanns Verlag KG, Luxemburgerstr. 449, 50939 Cologne, Germany. TEL 0221-46010-0. FAX 0221-4601069. Ed. Prof. Dr. Alex Meyer. adv.; bk.rev.; bibl.; tr.lit. circ. 600. **Indexed:** ELLIS, Int.Aerosp.Abstr. **Document type:** bulletin.
  —BLDSC (9469.540000); SWETS. **CCC.**
  Formerly: Zeitschrift fuer Luftrecht und Weltraumrechtsfragen (ISSN 0044-3034)

341 GW ISSN 0044-3638
K30
ZEITSCHRIFT FUER VERGLEICHENDE RECHTSWISSENSCHAFT; Archiv fuer Internationales Wirtschaftsrecht. 1878. q. DM.210. Verlag Recht und Wirtschaft GmbH, Haeusserstr. 14, 69115 Heidelberg, Germany. TEL 06221-906-1. (Subscr. to: Postfach 105960, 69049 Heidelberg, Germany) adv.; bk.rev. circ. 400. **Indexed:** A.I.C.P., ELLIS. **Document type:** academic/scholarly publication.
  —SWETS. **CCC.**

LAW — Judicial Systems

347 US
ALASKA COURT RULES, STATE AND FEDERAL. a. West Publishing Corp., 620 Opperman Dr., Eagan, MN 55123. TEL 612-687-8000; 800-328-9352. FAX 612-387-7302.

347 UK ISSN 0002-5569
ALL ENGLAND LAW REPORTS. 1936. w. (plus 4 bound vols./yr.). Butterworth & Co. (Publishers) Ltd. (Subsidiary of: Reed Elsevier plc), 88 Kingsway, London WC2B 6AB, England. TEL 71-405-6900. FAX 71-405-1332. (US addr.: Butterworth Legal Publishers, 90 Stiles Rd., Salem, NH 03079-9981. TEL 603-898-9664) Ed. Peter Hutchesson. cum.index: 1936-1981. circ. 15,000. (back issues avail.) **Indexed:** RICS.
  ●Also available online. Vendor(s): Mead Data Central, Inc.
  —SWETS. **CCC.**
  Supersedes: Law Times Reports; Law Journal Reports.
  Description: Provides a series of reports of leading cases form the English courts.

347 UK ISSN 0265-766X
ALL ENGLAND LAW REPORTS. ANNUAL REVIEW. 1983. a. Butterworth & Co. (Publishers) Ltd. (Subsidiary of: Reed Elsevier plc), 88 Kingsway, London WC2B 6AB, England. TEL 71-405-6900. FAX 71-405-1332. (US addr.: Butterworth Legal Publishers, 90 Stiles Rd., Salem, NH 03079-9981. TEL 603-898-9664) (back issues avail.)
  —BLDSC (0788.642000).
  Description: Survey of developments in English law during the year, including analyses of decisions handed down by the higher courts.

347 UK ISSN 0262-3234
ANTHONY AND BERRYMAN'S MAGISTRATES' COURT GUIDE. a. $41. Butterworth & Co. (Publishers) Ltd. (Subsidiary of: Reed Elsevier plc), 88 Kingsway, London WC2B 6AB, England. TEL 71-405-6900. FAX 71-405-1332. (US addr.: Butterworth Legal Publishers, 90 Stiles Rd., Salem, NH 03079-9981. TEL 603-898-9664) Ed. T.G. Moore.
  —BLDSC (1542.399500).
  Description: Reference guide for magistrates, court clerks, the police, and probation officers.

347 US
KFA2940.A971
ARIZONA COURTROOM EVIDENCE MANUAL REPORTER. 1991. bi-m. $75. State Bar of Arizona, 363 N. First Ave., Phoenix, AZ 85003. TEL 602-252-4804. FAX 602-271-4930. Ed. Crane McClennen. (looseleaf format) **Document type:** newsletter.

347 AT
AUSTRALIAN CASE CITATOR. 1983. 5/yr. Aus.$320. Law Book Co. Ltd., 44-50 Waterloo Rd., North Ryde, N.S.W. 2113, Australia. TEL 02-887-0177. FAX 02-888-9707. TELEX ASBOOK 27995. Ed.Bd.
  Description: Contains the most recent case citations, covering almost the entire length of Australian reporting.

AUSTRALIAN CORPORATIONS COURT RULES. see *LAW — Corporate Law*

347 AT ISSN 0004-9611
LAW
AUSTRALIAN LAW JOURNAL. 1927. m. Aus.$305. Law Book Co. Ltd., 44-50 Waterloo Rd., North Ryde, N.S.W. 2113, Australia. TEL 02-887-0177. FAX 02-888-9706. TELEX ASBOOK 27995. bk.rev.; index, cum.index. circ. 7,400. **Indexed:** Aus.P.A.I.S., C.L.I., Curr.Aus.N.Z.Leg.Lit.Ind., L.R.I., Leg.Cont., Leg.Per., Refug.Abstr.
  —BLDSC (1813.300000); Faxon; UnCover; UMI.
  Description: Contains advance reports of High Court cases, including headnotes and the full text of reasons for decisions.

347 AT ISSN 0004-9646
AUSTRALIAN LEGAL MONTHLY DIGEST. 1967. m. Aus.$455. Law Book Co. Ltd., 44-50 Waterloo Rd., North Ryde, N.S.W. 2113, Australia. TEL 02-887-0177. FAX 02-888-9706. TELEX ASBOOK 27995. Ed.Bd. adv.; bk.rev.; illus.; index. circ. 3,500.
  Description: Covers Australian case law and legislation.

347 US
BERKS COUNTY LAW JOURNAL. w. $30. Berks County Bar Association, 544 Court St., Box 1058, Reading, PA 19603. TEL 215-375-4593. FAX 215-373-0256. Ed. Marcia A. Binder. adv. circ. 750. (also avail. in microfiche; back issues avail.)
  Description: Opinions of county court judges, legal news, notices from appellate courts.

347 FR ISSN 0995-2330
CAHIERS D'EXPERTISE JUDICIAIRE. 4/yr. 232 F. to individuals (foreign 294 F.); institutions 279 F. (foreign 329 F.). Editions Alexandre Lacassagne, 162 av. Lacassagne, 69424 Lyon Cedex 03, France. TEL 72-33-40-40. FAX 72-34-16-74. Ed. J. Melin; Pub. Serge Kebabtchieff.

CALIFORNIA PENAL CODE. see *LAW — Criminal Law*

347 UK
CAMBRIDGE STUDIES IN ENGLISH LEGAL HISTORY. irreg. price varies. Cambridge University Press, Edinburgh Bldg., Shaftesbury Rd., Cambridge CB2 2RU, England. TEL 0223-312393. FAX 0223-315052. TELEX 851817256. (N. American addr.: Cambridge Univeristy Press, Journals Dept., 40 W. 20th St., New York, NY 10011. TEL 212-924-3900. FAX 212-691-3239) Ed. J.H. Baker. **Document type:** monographic series, academic/scholarly publication.

347 US
CHILDREN BEFORE THE COURT; reflections on legal issues affecting minors. irreg., 2nd ed. 1991. $45. Butterworth Legal Publishers (Salem) (Subsidiary of: Reed Elsevier plc), 8 Industrial Way, Bldg. C, Salem, NH 03079. TEL 800-548-4001. FAX 603-898-9664. Ed. Paul R. Kfoury.
  Description: Examines the role of the court in protecting and advocating children's rights; challenges the juvenile justice system to expand its approaches to guarantee the rights of privacy, confidentiality and permanency.

347 BL ISSN 0530-0657
COLECAO DE ESTUDOS JURIDICOS. 1956. irreg., latest 1982. Fundacao Casa de Rui Barbosa, Rua Sao Clemente 134, Botafogo 22260, Rio de Janeiro, RJ, Brazil. FAX 5371114. Dir. Agnello Uchoa Bittencourt.

347 SP ISSN 0069-5122
COLECCION JURIDICA. 1954. irreg., no.101, 1990. price varies. (Universidad de Navarra, Facultad de Derecho) Ediciones Universidad de Navarra, S.A., Apdo. 396, 31080 Pamplona, Spain. TEL 94 825 6850. cum.index: vols.1-6.

347 SP
COLECCION JURISPRUDENCIA Y TEXTOS LEGALES. 1973. irreg., no.6, 1984. price varies. (Universidad de Navarra, Facultad de Derecho) Ediciones Universidad de Navarra, S.A., Apdo. 396, 31080 Pamplona, Spain. TEL 94 825 6850.

347
COLLEAGUE. 1988. 4/yr. free. Michigan Judicial Institute, Box 30205, Lansing, MI 48909. TEL 517-334-7805. Ed. Leonard J. Kowalski. circ. controlled. (looseleaf format) **Document type:** newsletter.

LAW — JUDICIAL SYSTEMS

347   US
COLORADO COURT RULES, STATE AND FEDERAL. a. West Publishing Corp., 620 Opperman Dr., Eagan, MN 55123. TEL 612-687-8000; 800-241-0214. FAX 612-687-7302.

347   AT
COMMONWEALTH STATUTES ANNOTATIONS. a. Law Book Co. Ltd., 44-50 Waterloo Rd., North Ryde, N.S.W. 2113, Australia. TEL 02-887-0177. FAX 02-888-9706. TELEX ASBOOK 27995.
Formerly: Commonwealth Statutes Cumulative Supplement.

347   US
THE CONNECTICUT LAW REPORTER; reporting Connecticut Superior Court decisions. 1990. w. $290. Connecticut Law Book Company, Box 575, Guilford, CT 06437. TEL 203-458-8000.

347   US
THE CONNECTICUT LAW REPORTER, BOUND SERIES. s-a. $95. Connecticut Law Book Company, Box 575, Guilford, CT 06437. TEL 203-458-8000.

347   US
CONNECTICUT RULES OF COURT, STATE AND FEDERAL. a. West Publishing Corp., 620 Opperman Dr., Eagan, MN 55123. TEL 612-687-8000; 800-241-0214. FAX 612-687-7302.

347   US
COOK COUNTY FINANCIAL MALPRACTICE SUIT FILING LIST. 1974. m. $75. Cook County Jury Verdict Reporter, 415 North State St., Chicago, IL 60610. TEL 312-644-7800. Ed. John Kirkton. index. (looseleaf format) **Document type:** newsletter.

347   US
KF11799.C6A42
COOK COUNTY JURY VERDICT REPORTER. 1959. w. $285. Cook County Jury Verdict Reporter, 415 North State St., Chicago, IL 60610. TEL 213-644-7800. Ed. John Kirkton. index. (looseleaf format; back issues avail.) **Document type:** newsletter.

347   US
COOK COUNTY MEDICAL MALPRACTICE SUIT FILING LIST. 1972. m. $250. Cook County Jury Verdict Reporter, 415 North State St., Chicago, IL 60610. TEL 312-644-7800. Ed. John Kirkton. index. (looseleaf format) **Document type:** newsletter.

347   US
COOK COUNTY PRODUCTS LIABILITY SUIT FILING LIST. 1973. m. $150. Cook County Jury Verdict Reporter, 415 North State St., Chicago, IL 60610. TEL 312-644-7800. Ed. John Kirkton. index. (looseleaf format) **Document type:** newsletter.

347   CN
COUR SUPREME EN BREF/SUPREME COURT NEWS. irreg. Can.$185. Les Editions Yvon Blais, 430 rue St-Pierre, Ste. 200, Montreal, PQ H2Y 2M5, Canada. TEL 514-842-3937. FAX 514-842-7144. (Subscr. to: C.P. 180, Cowansville, PQ J2K 3H6, Canada. TEL 514-263-1086) Eds. Simon Noel, Sylvie Roussel.
Description: Contains digests of the most recent Supreme Court judgments.

347   US
COURT EXCELLENCE. 1987. 3/yr. $50. Council for Court Excellence, 1800 M St., N.W., Ste. 750-S, Washington, DC 20036-5802. TEL 202-785-5917. FAX 202-785-5922. Ed. Samuel F. Harahan. circ. 2,000. (back issues avail.)
Description: News of civic public interest group working to improve the administration of justice.

347   AT
COURT FORMS, PRECEDENTS & PLEADINGS - N S W. 3 base vols. (plus q. updates). Aus.$475. Butterworths, 271-273 Lane Cove Rd., P.O. Box 345, North Ryde, N.S.W. 2113, Australia. TEL 02-335-4444. FAX 02-335-4655.

347   AT
COURT FORMS, PRECEDENTS & PLEADINGS - QUEENSLAND. 3 base vols. (plus q. updates). Aus.$335. Butterworths, 271-273 Lane Cove Rd., P.O. Box 345, North Ryde, N.S.W. 2113, Australia. TEL 02-335-4444. FAX 02-335-4655.

347   US
COURT INDEX. 1890. d. (Mon.-Fri.). $65. 215 Ninth St., Cincinnati, OH 45202. TEL 513-241-1450. FAX 513-241-5902. Ed. Harry Gilligan. circ. 1,800. **Document type:** newspaper.

347   US   ISSN 1063-0821
KF8732.A15
COURT MANAGEMENT & ADMINISTRATIVE REPORT; newsletter for professionals in justice systems management. 1990. 11/yr. $145. G P Subscription Publications (Subsidiary of: Greenwood Publishing Group Inc.), 88 Post Rd., W., Box 5007, Westport, CT 06881-5007. TEL 203-226-3571. FAX 203-222-1502. Ed. Clifford Kirsch. (looseleaf format; reprint service avail.) **Document type:** newsletter.

347   US   ISSN 1046-249X
KF8732.A15C685
COURT MANAGER. 1973. q. $25. National Association for Court Management, National Center for State Courts, Box 8798, Williamsburg, VA 23187. TEL 804-259-1841. FAX 804-229-7899. Ed. Thomas J. Ralston. adv. contact: Anne Kelly. illus. circ. 2,000. **Document type:** trade publication.
Formerly: Court Crier (ISSN 0098-8871)

347   US
COURT NEWS. 1927. bi-m. free. Judicial Council of California, Administrative Office of the California Courts, 303 Second St., S. Twr., San Francisco, CA 94107-1366. FAX 415-396-9349. Dir. William C. Vickey. circ. 3,600. **Document type:** government publication.
Formerly (until 1990): A O C Newsletter.

347   US   ISSN 0011-0647
K3
COURT REVIEW. 1961. q. $25 to non-members. (American Judges Association) National Center for State Courts, 300 Newport Ave., Williamsburg, VA 23187-8798. TEL 804-253-2000. FAX 804-220-0449. Ed. Martin Kravarik. adv.; bk.rev.; illus. circ. 2,800. Indexed: Crim.Just.Abstr. —UnCover.
Formerly: Municipal Court Review.

340 600
KF8736.A5C8
COURT TECHNOLOGY BULLETIN. 1989. 6/yr. free. National Center for State Courts, 300 Newport Ave., Williamsburg, VA 23187-8798. TEL 804-253-2000. FAX 804-220-0449. Ed. Lawrence Webster. circ. 3,500. **Document type:** newsletter, bulletin.

347   US   ISSN 0544-4993
KF200.C69
COURTS AND C L E BULLETIN. 1965. m. membership. Missouri Bar, 326 Monroe St., Box 119, Jefferson City, MO 65102. TEL 314-635-4128. FAX 314-635-2811. Ed. Catherine J. Barrie. **Document type:** newsletter, bulletin.

347   US
KFT1742.A75C69
COURT'S CHARGE REPORTER. 1973. a. $175. Butterworth Legal Publishers, Austin Division (Subsidiary of: Reed Elsevier plc), Echelon II, Ste. 100, 9430 Research Blvd., Austin, TX 78759. TEL 512-346-9686. FAX 512-346-9373. Ed. Will G. Barber. (looseleaf format) **Document type:** newsletter.
Description: Contains condensed transcripts of actual charges from Texas civil jury cases.

347   US   ISSN 1056-2230
KF5106.A15
D O J ALERT. (Department of Justice) 1991. m. $225. Prentice Hall Law & Business (Subsidiary of: Simon & Schuster), 270 Sylvan Ave., Englewood Cliffs, NJ 07632. TEL 800-223-0231. FAX 201-894-8666. index. (looseleaf format; back issues avail.) **Document type:** newsletter.

347   AT
DISTRICT COURT PRACTICE. 1974. 6/yr. Aus.$310 with updates. Law Book Co. Ltd., 44-50 Waterloo Rd., North Ryde, N.S.W. 2113, Australia. TEL 02-887-0177. FAX 02-888-9706. TELEX ASBOOK 27995. Ed. E.J. O'Grady. (looseleaf format)
Description: An annotated reproduction of the District Court Act 1973, the District Court Rules 1973 and other relevant acts, plus the approved forms and fees, costs and practice notes.

347   US   ISSN 0889-3179
KF8700.A19
ELECTED AND APPOINTED BLACK JUDGES IN THE UNITED STATES. biennial. $10. Joint Center for Political Studies, Inc., 1090 Vermont Ave., N.W., Ste. 1100, Washington, DC 20005-4905. (Co-sponsor: Judicial Council of the National Bar Association) **Document type:** directory.

348   US
ELEVENTH CIRCUIT REVIEW. 1991. 24/yr. $215. Barclays Law Publishers, 400 Oyster Point Blvd., Ste. 500, South San Francisco, CA 94080. TEL 415-588-1155. FAX 415-244-6619. Ed. Frank Gomez. (looseleaf format) **Document type:** newsletter.

347   EI   ISSN 1018-5933
EUROPEAN COMMUNITIES. COURT OF JUSTICE AND COURT OF FIRST INSTANCE. PROCEEDINGS. Key Title: Proceedings of the Court of Justice and of the Court of First Instance of the European Communities. 1973. w. free. European Communities, Court of Justice, Information Service, L-2925 Luxembourg, Luxembourg. (Co-sponsor: European Communities, Court of First Instance) **Document type:** proceedings, bulletin.
—BLDSC (6685.750000).
Formerly: European Communities. Court of Justice. Proceedings (ISSN 1016-5843)

347   US
EVIDENCE LAWS OF NEW YORK. 1989. a. $34.95 (effective May 1992). Gould Publications (Binghamton), 199-300 State St., Binghamton, NY 13901. TEL 607-724-3000. FAX 607-723-4285. adv.; bk.rev. (looseleaf format)
Description: Covers burden of proof, judicial notice, presumptions, admissions, confessions, witnesses on the stand, competency, parole, evidence and more.

347   US   ISSN 0882-5041
FEDERAL AND STATE JUDICIAL CLERKSHIP DIRECTORY. a. $100. National Association for Law Placement, 1666 Connecticut Ave., Ste.450, Washington, DC 20009. TEL 202-667-1666. circ. 300. (looseleaf format) **Document type:** directory.

347   US   ISSN 1059-6828
▼**FEDERAL COURT APPOINTMENTS REPORT.** 1992. 6/yr. $125. Want Publishing Co., 1511 K St., N.W., Washington, DC 20005. TEL 202-783-1887. FAX 202-393-5106. Ed. Robert Want. (looseleaf format; back issues avail.) **Document type:** newsletter.

347 350   US
FEDERAL COURT CLERKS' NEWS. bi-m. Federal Court Clerks Association, c/o Candice Clark Quinn, 120 Oriole Ln., La Plata, MD 20646.

347   CN   ISSN 0227-0390
FEDERAL COURT OF APPEAL DECISIONS. 1981. m. Can.$165. Western Legal Publications, 301-1 Alexander St., Vancouver, BC V6A 1B2, Canada. TEL 604-687-5671. FAX 604-687-2796. index, cum.index. (looseleaf format)
●Also available online.
Description: Digests of all current Federal Court of Appeal decisions.

347   CN
FEDERAL COURT OF CANADA SERVICE. q. Can.$430. Butterworths Canada Ltd., Part of the Reed Elsevier group, 75 Clegg Rd., Markham, ON L6G 1A1, Canada. TEL 905-479-2665. FAX 905-479-2826. Ed. Roger T. Hughes. (looseleaf format)
Description: Coverage of the Federal Court Act and Regulations, and includes courtroom procedure and digests of cases.

347   AT
FEDERAL COURT PRACTICE. 1989. 7/yr. Aus.$310 with updates. Law Book Co. Ltd., 44-50 Waterloo Rd., North Ryde, N.S.W. 2113, Australia. TEL 02-887-0177. FAX 02-888-9706. TELEX ASBOOK 27995. Ed. Geoffrey Flick. (looseleaf format)
Description: Comprehensive guide to practice in the Federal Court of Australia.

330.9   US   ISSN 0734-9513
KF845.A2
FEDERAL COURT PROCUREMENT DECISIONS. m. $788. Federal Publications Inc., 1120 20th St., N.W., Ste. 500 S., Washington, DC 20036. TEL 202-377-7000. FAX 202-659-2233.
Description: Reports on government contracts.

LAW — JUDICIAL SYSTEMS

347   AT   ISSN 0728-6082
FEDERAL COURT REPORTER (SYDNEY). 1982. 20/yr. Aus.$295. Law Press of Australia, G.P.O. Box 3793, Sydney, N.S.W. 2001, Australia. TEL 02-360-7788. FAX 02-360-7838. Ed. Richard Ackland. bk.rev. (back issues avail.)

347   AT   ISSN 0813-7803
FEDERAL COURT REPORTS (NORTH RYDE). 1984. irreg. Law Book Co. Ltd., 44-50 Waterloo Rd., North Ryde, N.S.W. 2113, Australia. TEL 02-887-0177. FAX 02-888-9706. TELEX ASBOOK 27995. Ed. V. Kline. cum.index. (back issues avail.)
    Description: Contains full text of all reportable decisions of the Full Court of single judges.

347   AT   ISSN 0085-0462
FEDERAL LAW REPORTS. 1956. irreg. Law Book Co. Ltd., 44-50 Waterloo Rd., North Ryde, N.S.W. 2113, Australia. TEL 02-887-0177. FAX 02-888-9706. TELEX ASBOOK 27995. **Indexed:** C.L.I., Curr.Aus.N.Z.Leg.Lit.Ind.
    Description: Reports all decisions on federal law, includes important rulings in the State and Territory Supreme Courts, Family Court and in the federal tribunals.

347   US   ISSN 0745-2306
FEDERAL LOCAL COURT RULES. 1964. bi-m. $261. Lawyers Cooperative Publishing (Subsidiary of: Thomson Professional Publishing), Acqueduct Bldg., Rochester, NY 14694. TEL 800-527-0430.
    Description: Compilation of U.S. federal district court and court of appeals local rules pertaining to civil procedures in all U.S. jurisdictions, for the legal practitioner.

347   US
KF8840.F42
FEDERAL PRACTICE ADVISORY. 1984. 6/yr. $60. Lawyers Cooperative Publishing (Subsidiary of: Thomson Professional Publishing), Acqueduct Bldg., Rochester, NY 14694. TEL 800-527-0430. Ed. Wayne Foster. (looseleaf format; back issues avail.) **Document type:** newsletter.

347   US
FEDERAL RULES OF EVIDENCE. 1988. a. $12. Gould Publications, 1333 N. U.S. Hwy. 17-92, Longwood, FL 32750-3724. TEL 407-695-9500. FAX 407-695-2906. adv.; bk.rev. (looseleaf format)
    Description: Complete text of federal rules of evidence with official advisory committee notes and forms.

347   US
FLORIDA RULES OF COURT SERVICE. 1972. 2 base vols. (plus supplements) $80. Butterworth Legal Publishers (Salem) (Subsidiary of: Reed Elsevier plc), 8 Industrial Way, Bldg. C, Salem, NH 03079. TEL 800-548-4001. FAX 603-898-9858. (looseleaf format)

348   US   ISSN 0889-3578
KF1124TH.1.F684
FOURTH CIRCUIT REVIEW (LOUISVILLE). 1985. 24/yr. $245. Appellate Review, 500 Country Ln., Louisville, KY 40207. TEL 502-897-5079. Ed. Laura Haller. index. (looseleaf format; back issues avail.) **Document type:** newsletter.

348   US
FOURTH CIRCUIT REVIEW (SOUTH SAN FRANCISCO). 1990. 26/yr. $215. Barclays Law Publishers, 400 Oyster Point Blvd., Ste. 500, San Francisco, CA 94080. TEL 415-588-1155. FAX 415-244-6619. Ed. Frank Gomez. (looseleaf format) **Document type:** newsletter.

347   US
FRIENDS OF THE COURT. 1982. bi-m. free. Administrative Office of the Courts, Justice Bldg., 625 Marshall, State Capitol Grounds, Little Rock, AR 72201. TEL 501-376-6655. Ed. Karolyn Bond. bk.rev.; bibl. circ. 1,500.
    Formerly (until 1982): Amicus Curiae (ISSN 0360-7739)

347   US
GENERAL LAWS OF MASSACHUSETTS. OFFICIAL EDITION (YEAR). a. West Publishing Corp., 620 Opperman Dr., Eagan, MN 55123. TEL 612-687-8000; 800-328-9352. FAX 612-687-7302.

347   US
GEORGIA COURT RULES AND PROCEDURE, STATE AND FEDERAL. a. West Publishing Corp., 620 Opperman Dr., Eagan, MN 55123. TEL 612-687-8000; 800-241-0214. FAX 612-687-7602.

347   US
GEORGIA COURTS JOURNAL. 1974. bi-m. (Judicial Council of Georgia) Administrative Office of the Courts, 244 Washington St., S.W., Ste. 550, Atlanta, GA 30334. TEL 404-656-5171. FAX 404-651-6449. Ed. Nancy Kahnt. circ. 3,000 (controlled). (looseleaf format; back issues avail.) **Document type:** government publication, newsletter.
    Description: Keeps Georgia's judges and court employees informed regarding state and local court-related issues, trends and plans.

347   US
GEORGIA STATE RULES OF COURT. 1986. base vol. (plus suppl.). $50. Butterworth Legal Publishers (Salem) (Subsidiary of: Reed Elsevier plc), 8 Industrial Way, Bldg. C, Salem, NH 03079. TEL 800-548-4001. FAX 603-898-9858. Ed.Bd. (looseleaf format)
    Description: Tracks all the latest changes in the uniform rules for the probate, juvenile and magistrate, superior and state courts as well as the Rules of the Supreme Court and the Court of Appeals of Georgia.

347   US
GILBERT LAW SUMMARIES. FEDERAL COURTS. 1987. irreg. 2nd ed., 1991. $15.95. Harcourt Brace Legal & Professional Publications, Inc., 176 W. Adams, Ste. 2100, Chicago, IL 60603. TEL 312-853-3662.

347   UK   ISSN 0308-4388
KD310
HALSBURY'S LAWS OF ENGLAND ANNUAL ABRIDGMENT. Short title: Laws of England Annual Abridgment. 1974. a. Butterworth & Co. (Publishers) Ltd. (Subsidiary of: Reed Elsevier plc), 88 Kingsway, London WC2B 6AB, England. TEL 71-405-6900. FAX 71-405-1332. (US addr.: Butterworth Legal Publishers, 90 Stiles Rd., Salem, NH 03079-9981. TEL 603-898-9664) (back issues avail.)

347   UK   ISSN 0307-9821
HALSBURY'S LAWS OF ENGLAND MONTHLY REVIEW. 1973. m. avail. only with subscr. to Halsbury's Laws of England. Butterworth & Co. (Publishers) Ltd. (Subsidiary of: Reed Elsevier plc), 88 Kingsway, London WC2B 6AB, England. TEL 71-405-6900. FAX 71-405-1332. (US addr.: Butterworth Legal Publishers, 90 Stiles Rd., Salem, NH 03079-9981. TEL 603-898-9664) circ. 10,000.

347   UK
HALSBURY'S STATUTES OF ENGLAND AND WALES. irreg. 4th ed., 1993. price varies. Butterworth & Co. (Publishers) Ltd. (Subsidiary of: Reed Elsevier plc), 88 Kingsway, London WC2B 6AB, England. TEL 071-405-6900. FAX 071-405-1332. TELEX 95678. (US addr.: Butterworth Legal Publishers, 90 Stiles Rd., Salem, NH 03079, USA. TEL 603-898-9664) Ed.Bd. (looseleaf format)

347 297   TS
AL-HAQQ - SHARI'AH WA QANUN. (Text in Arabic) 1982. a. exchange basis. Jam'iyat al-Huquqiyyin - Jurisprudents' Society, P.O. Box 2233, Sharjah, United Arab Emirates. TEL 371166. circ. 1,000.
    Description: Focuses on Islamic jurisprudence and legal research, court rulings, and society activities.

347   UK
HAZELL'S GUIDE TO THE JUDICIARY & THE COURTS WITH THE HOLBORN LAW SOCIETY'S BAR LIST. 1985. a. £26($45) Court & Judicial Publishing Co. Ltd., P.O. Box 39, Henley-on-Thames, Oxon. RG9 5UA, England. (Co-publisher: R. Hazell & Co.) Ed. C.G.A. Parker. adv.; index. **Document type:** directory.
    Former titles: Hazell's Guide to the Judiciary and the Courts with the Holborn Law Society's Bar List by Chambers; Hazell's Guide to the Judiciary and the Courts with the Holborn Law Society's List of Barristers by Chambers (ISSN 0266-3597)
    Description: Lists all the judiciary, courts, and advocates of the U.K.

347   HK
HONG KONG. LAW REFORM COMMISSION. REPORT. (Editions in Chinese, English) irreg., latest no.17. price varies. Government Publication Centre, G.P.O. Bldg., Ground Fl., Connaught Place, Hong Kong, Hong Kong. TEL 842-8801. (Subscr. to: Director of Information Services, Information Services Dept., 1 Battery Path, G-F, Central, Hong Kong) Ed.Bd.

348   US
IDAHO BANKRUPTCY COURT REPORT. 1980. m. $120. Goller Publishing Corp., Box 2576, Boise, ID 83701. TEL 208-336-4715. Ed. Jane Crosby. index. (looseleaf format) **Document type:** newsletter.

348 350   US
IDAHO GOVERNMENT DIGEST. 1990. 26/yr. $169. Ridenbaugh Press, Box 2276, Boise, ID 83701. TEL 208-344-9700. FAX 208-338-9769. Ed. Randy Stapilus. index. (looseleaf format; back issues avail.) **Document type:** newsletter.
    ●Also available online.
    Formerly (until 1993): Idaho Regulatory Letter (ISSN 1050-9666)

348   US   ISSN 1057-4050
IDAHO SUPREME COURT REPORT AND IDAHO COURT OF APPEALS REPORT. 1990. 26/yr. $199. Goller Publishing Corp., Box 2576, Boise, ID 83701. TEL 208-336-4715. Ed. Jane Crosby. index. circ. 350. (looseleaf format) **Document type:** newsletter.
    Formed by the merger of: Idaho Court of Appeals Report & Idaho Supreme Court Report.
    Description: Contains case summaries and full text of all opinions issued during previous two weeks.

347   US   ISSN 0536-3713
KFI1708
ILLINOIS. ADMINISTRATIVE OFFICE OF ILLINOIS COURTS. ANNUAL REPORT TO THE SUPREME COURT OF ILLINOIS. Key Title: Annual Report to the Supreme Court of Illinois. 1959. a. free. Administrative Office of Illinois Courts, Supreme Court Bldg., Springfield, IL 62706. TEL 217-782-7770. FAX 217-785-9114. stat. circ. 1,500. (also avail. in microfiche from CIS) **Indexed:** SRI. **Document type:** government publication.
    Description: Provides narrative and statistical summaries of what happened in the Illinois judicial system during the calendar year.

341   NE
▼**INTERNATIONAL ENCYCLOPAEDIA OF LAWS. CIVIL PROCEDURE.** (Text in English) 1994. base vol. (plus irreg. updates). Kluwer Law and Taxation Publishers (Subsidiary of: Wolters Kluwer N.V.), P.O. Box 23, 7400 GA Deventer, Netherlands. TEL 31-5700-47261. FAX 31-5700-22244. TELEX 49295 KLUDV NL. (Dist. by: Libresso Distribution Centre, P.O. Box 23, 7400 GA Deventer, Netherlands. TEL 31-5700-33155. FAX 31-5700-3834; In N. America: Kluwer Law and Taxation Publishers, 675 Massachusetts Ave., Cambridge, MA 02139. TEL 617-354-0140. FAX 617-354-8595) Ed. P. Lemmens, S. Raes. (looseleaf format) **Document type:** monographic series.
    Description: Publishes studies of the rules and principles of judicial organization in individual countries, with an international, comparative perspective; also covers international multilateral agreements and EEC agreements on jurisdiction.

347   US
IOWA LIMITATIONS MANUAL. 1989. base vol. (plus suppl.). $50. Butterworth Legal Publishers (Salem) (Subsidiary of: Reed Elsevier plc), 8 Industrial Way, Bldg. C, Salem, NH 03079. TEL 800-548-4001. FAX 603-898-9858. Ed.Bd. (looseleaf format)
    Description: Reference to Iowa statutes and rules of court that set time limitations within which certain actions must or should be taken.

347   US
IOWA RULES OF COURT, STATE AND FEDERAL. a. West Publishing Corp., 620 Opperman Dr., Eagan, MN 55123. TEL 612-687-8000; 800-241-0214. FAX 612-687-7302.

LAW — JUDICIAL SYSTEMS 3401

347 AT ISSN 1036-7918
K10
JOURNAL OF JUDICIAL ADMINISTRATION. 1991. a. in 4 parts. Aus.$195. (Australian Institute of Judicial Administration) Law Book Co. Ltd., 44-50 Waterloo Rd., North Ryde, N.S.W. 2113, Australia. TEL 02-887-1077. FAX 02-888-9706. TELEX ASHBOOK 27995. (Dist. in N. America by: Wm. W. Gaunt & Sons, Inc., Law Book Dealers & Subscription Agents, Gaunt Bldg., 3011 Gulf Dr., Holmes Beach, FL 34217-2199. TEL 813-778-5211) Ed. Peter Sallmann.

347 US ISSN 1059-4329
KF8741.A15
JOURNAL OF SUPREME COURT HISTORY. 1976. a. $20 hardcover; softcover $15. Supreme Court Historical Society, 111 Second St., N.E., Washington, DC 20002. TEL 202-543-0400. FAX 202-547-7730. Ed. Mel Urofsky. illus. circ. 5,000. **Indexed:** Amer.Hist.& Life, C.L.I., Hist.Abstr., L.R.I., Leg.Per.
—BLDSC (9403.850000); UnCover.
Formerly (until 1989): Supreme Court Historical Society. Yearbook (ISSN 0362-5249)

347 US ISSN 0047-2972
K10
JUDGES' JOURNAL. vol.10, 1971. q. $25 to non-members. American Bar Association, Judicial Administration Division, 750 N. Lake Shore Dr., Chicago, IL 60611. TEL 312-988-6077. Ed. Frederic G. Melcher. bk.rev.; illus.; index. circ. 8,600. **Indexed:** C.L.I., Crim.Just.Abstr., L.R.I., Leg.Per. **Document type:** trade publication.
—BLDSC (5073.829400); Faxon; UnCover.
Formerly: Trial Judges Journal.
Description: Created to help judges and lawyers improve the administration of justice. Includes articles on successful court innovations and major jurisprudential issues.

347 300 US ISSN 0022-5800
K10
JUDICATURE. 1917. bi-m. $48. American Judicature Society, 25 E. Washington, Ste. 1600, Chicago, IL 60602-1805. Ed. David Richert. adv.; bk.rev.; charts; illus.; index, cum.index every 20 yrs. circ. 15,000. (also avail. in microform from UMI; reprint service avail. from ISI,RRI,UMI) **Indexed:** C.L.I., CJPI, Crim.Just.Abstr., Curr.Cont., L.R.I., Law Ofc.Info.Svc., Leg.Cont., Leg.Per., P.A.I.S., SSCI. **Document type:** academic/scholarly publication.
●Also available online. Vendor(s): West Services, Inc.
—BLDSC (5073.830000); Faxon; UnCover; UMI.
Formerly: American Judicature Society Journal.
Description: Discusses all aspects of the administration of justice and its improvement.
Refereed Serial

347.91 US ISSN 0193-7367
KF8779.A15
JUDICIAL CONDUCT REPORTER. 1979. q. $20. American Judicature Society, Center for Judicial Conduct Organizations, 25 E. Washington, Ste. 1600, Chicago, IL 60602. TEL 312-558-6900. FAX 312-558-9175. Ed. Cynthia Gray; Pub. David Richert. adv.; bk.rev.; index. circ. 63,000. **Document type:** newsletter.
●Also available online. Vendor(s): West Services, Inc.
Description: Developments in judicial discipline and disability law.

347.9 US
JUDICIAL COUNCIL REPORT TO THE GOVERNOR AND LEGISLATURE. 1962. a. free. Judicial Council of California, Administrative Office of the Courts, South Tower, Ste. 400, 303 Second St., San Francisco, CA 94107-1366. Dir. Robert W. Page Jr. circ. 4,000.
Formerly: California. Administrative Office of the Courts. Annual Report (ISSN 0068-5488); Incorporates: Judicial Council of California. Annual Report.

347 350 US
JUDICIAL STAFF DIRECTORY. 1986. a. $69. Staff Directories Ltd., Box 62, Mount Vernon, VA 22121. TEL 703-739-0900. FAX 703-739-0234. Ed. Anna L. Brownson. index. **Document type:** directory.
●Also available on CD-ROM.
Description: Lists 13,000 federal court personnel - judges, magistrate judges, secretaries, and law clerks. Includes the Supreme Court, circuit courts, district courts, bankruptcy courts, U.S. marshals and U.S. attorneys, and more than 1,400 biograpies.

340 BL
JURISCIVEL DO S T F. Cover title: Revista Juriscivel do S.T.F. 1972. irreg. (Supremo Tribunal Federal) Cultural Distribuidora de Livros, Praca dos Tres Poderes, Brasilia, D.F., Brazil.

347.9 US ISSN 0098-261X
K10
JUSTICE SYSTEM JOURNAL. 1974. 3/yr. $30. National Center for State Courts, 300 Newport Ave., Williamsburg, VA 23187-8798. TEL 804-253-2000. FAX 804-220-0449. Ed. Keith Boyum. bk.rev. circ. 1,000. (also avail. in microform from UMI,WSH; reprint service avail. from UMI,WSH) **Indexed:** C.L.I., CJPI, Crim.Just.Abstr., Curr.Cont., L.R.I., Leg.Per., SSCI.
—BLDSC (5075.678000); Faxon; UnCover; UMI.

347 UK
JUSTICES' CLERK. 1943. 3/yr. £12. Justices' Clerks' Society, The Magistrates' Court, N. Parade Rd., Bath, Avon BA1 5AF, England. FAX 0225-420255. Ed. N.J. Stevens. adv.; bk.rev. circ. 800. **Document type:** proceedings.

348 US ISSN 0748-9005
KENTUCKY ATTORNEY GENERAL OPINIONS. 1964. q. $90. Banks - Baldwin Law Publishing Co., University Center, Box 1974, Cleveland, OH 44106. TEL 216-721-7373. FAX 216-721-8055. (back issues avail.)
Description: Contains all formal opinions of the Attorney General, in either full text or synopsis treatment, with cumulative research aids.

347 US
KENTUCKY RULES OF COURT, STATE AND FEDERAL. a. West Publishing Corp., 620 Opperman Dr., Eagan, MN 55123. TEL 612-687-8000; 800-241-0214. FAX 612-687-7302.

348 KE
KENYA. COURT OF APPEAL. DIGEST OF DECISIONS OF THE COURT. (Text in English) 1968. m. Court of Appeal, Box 30187, Nairobi, Kenya.
Formerly: Court of Appeal for East Africa. Digest of Decisions of the Court.

347 BE ISSN 0778-8983
▼**LARCIER CASSATION.** 1992. w. 2300 BEF (effective 1993). Maison Ferdinand Larcier S.A., Rue des Minimes 39, 1000 Brussels, Belgium. TEL 32-2-5124712. FAX 32-2-5139009. Ed. Annik Bouche.
Description: Publishes summaries of the latest decisions of the Cour de Cassation, classed by subject, with detailed references to the complete legislation.

348 US
LAW OF EVIDENCE IN WASHINGTON. 1986. base vol. (plus a. supplement). $65. Butterworth Legal Publishers (Salem) (Subsidiary of: Reed Elsevier plc), 8 Industrial Way, Bldg. C, Salem, NH 03079. TEL 800-548-4001. FAX 603-898-9858. Ed. Robert H. Aronson. (looseleaf format)
Description: Contains the full text of the Code plus legislative commentary, applicable Federal Advisory Committee commentary, analysis of the rules and recent court interpretations.

347 CN ISSN 0839-4539
KES168.A72
LAW REFORM COMMISSION OF SASKATCHEWAN. ANNUAL REPORT AND REVIEW. 1980. a. free. Law Reform Commission of Saskatchewan, 122 Third Ave., North Saskatoon, Sask. S7K 2H6, Canada. TEL 306-933-6127. FAX 306-933-6999. index. circ. 400. (back issues avail.)
Supersedes: Law Reform Commission of Saskatchewan. Yearly Review (ISSN 0711-0751)
Description: Contains objectives of the commission, description of the programs and activities carried out, plans for the upcoming year and financial information.

348 TZ
LAW REPORTS OF TANZANIA. 1973. s-a. EAs.140. University of Dar es Salaam, Faculty of Law, Box 35093, Dar es Salaam, Tanzania. Ed. B.A. Rwezaura. circ. 500. (back issues avail.)
Formerly: Tanzania High Court Digest.

347 UK ISSN 0264-1127
LAW REPORTS: QUEEN'S BENCH DIVISION. 1865. m. £55 (overseas £58) (effective Aug. 1993). Incorporated Council of Law Reporting for England and Wales, 3 Stone Bldgs., Lincoln's Inn, London WC2A 3XN, England. TEL 071-242 6471. FAX 071-831-5247. Ed. C.J. Ellis. (also avail. in microfiche from BHP)

348 KE
LAWS OF KENYA. SUPPLEMENT. (Text in English) 1963. a. KShs.653. Government Press, Haile Selaissie Ave., P.O Box 30128, Nairobi, Kenya. TEL 254-2-334075-9. **Document type:** government publication.

348 CC
LAWS OF THE PEOPLE'S REPUBLIC OF CHINA. (Editions in Chinese and English) 1987. irreg., vol.3, 1989. $60. (Quanguo Renmin Daibiao Dahui, Changwu Weiyuanhui, Lifa Shiwu Weiyuanhui - National People's Congress, Standing Committee, Legislative Affairs Commission) Kexue Chubanshe, Qikan Bu - Science Press, 16 Donghuangchenggen Beijie, Beijing 100707, People's Republic of China. TEL 4010642. FAX 4012180. TELEX 210247-SPBJ-CN. (US office: Science Press New York, Ltd., 63-117 Alderton St., Rego Park, NY 11374. TEL 718-459-4638)
Description: Compiles new laws enacted by the NPC and its standing committee.

347 620.85 AT ISSN 1039-7213
LAW
LOCAL GOVERNMENT AND ENVIRONMENTAL REPORTS OF AUSTRALIA. 1956. irreg. Aus.$195. Law Book Co. Ltd., 44-50 Waterloo Rd., North Ryde, N.S.W. 2113, Australia. TEL 02-887-0177. FAX 02-888-9706. TELEX ASBOOK 27995. Eds. T.F.M. Naughton, N.J. Haxton.
●Also available online. Vendor(s): Info-One International Pty Ltd.
Formerly: Local Government Reports of Australia (ISSN 0076-0242)
Description: Reports cases relating to environmental control, local government, valuation of land, compensation, town planning and powers and duties of statutory authorities from the the High Court and supreme courts of the states and territories.

347 AT ISSN 0727-7830
LOCAL GOVERNMENT LAW & PRACTICE (NEW SOUTH WALES). 1987. 8/yr. in 3 vols. Aus.$415 (renewal Aus.$345). Law Book Co. Ltd., 44-50 Waterloo Rd., N. Ryde, N.S.W. 2113, Australia. TEL 02-887-0177. FAX 02-888-9706. TELEX ASBOOK 27995. Ed. S. White. (looseleaf format)
Description: Includes the fully annotated Local Government Act 1993 (NSW) and a wide range of related legislation.

348 AT
LOCAL GOVERNMENT REGULATIONS SERVICES (NEW SOUTH WALES). 1945. 4/yr. in 1 vol. Aus.$195 (renewal Aus.$145). Law Book Co. Ltd., 45-50 Waterloo Rd., N. Ryde, N.S.W. 2113, Australia. TEL 02-887-0177. FAX 02-888-9706. TELEX ASBOOK 27995. (looseleaf format)
Formerly: Local Government Ordinances Services (New South Wales) (ISSN 0727-8004)
Description: Includes all the regulations made under the Local Government Act 1993 (NSW).

348 US
LOCAL RULES OF THE DISTRICT COURTS IN TEXAS. 1981. base vol. (plus s-a. supplements). $135. Butterworth Legal Publishers (Salem) (Subsidiary of: Reed Elsevier plc), 8 Industrial Way, Bldg. C, Salem, NH 03079. TEL 800-548-4001. FAX 603-898-9858. Ed. Sterling W. Steves. (looseleaf format)
Description: Contains the complete local rules of the district courts in Texas' 254 counties, along with a schedule of court costs, names, addresses and phone numbers of the district judges, court reporters, and other personnel.

348 US
LOCAL RULES OF THE SUPERIOR COURT: WASHINGTON STATE. 1981. 2 base vols. (plus supplements 4-5/yr.). $70. Butterworth Legal Publishers (Salem) (Subsidiary of: Reed Elsevier plc), 8 Industrial Way, Bldg. C, Salem, NH 03079. TEL 800-548-4001. FAX 603-898-9858. Ed.Bd. (looseleaf format)

LAW — JUDICIAL SYSTEMS

347   US
LOS ANGELES COUNTY COURT RULES - SUPERIOR, MUNICIPAL, AND JUSTICE COURTS. a. West Publishing Corp., 620 Opperman Dr., Eagan, MN 55123. TEL 612-687-8000; 800-328-9352. FAX 612-687-7302.

347   UK   ISSN 0024-9920
THE MAGISTRATE. 1921. 10/yr. £35. The Magistrates' Association, 28 Fitzroy Sq., London W1P 6DD, England. TEL 037-975-5190. FAX 037-975-8173. Ed. Caroline Ball. adv.; bk.rev. circ. 28,000. (also avail. in microform from UMI) **Document type:** academic/scholarly publication.
—BLDSC (5334.830000); UMI.
    Description: For lay magistrates and all professionals working in the magistrates' courts and other parts of the criminal justice and child care systems.

347   US
MAGISTRATES DESK BOOK. 1984? biennial. $34.95. (New York State Magistrates Association) Gould Publications (Binghamton), 199-300 State St., Binghamton, NY 13901-2782. TEL 607-724-3000. FAX 607-723-4285.

347 350   US
MAINE ADMINISTRATIVE PROCEDURE. 1985. base vol. (plus a. supplement). $65. Butterworth Legal Publishers (Salem) (Subsidiary of: Reed Elsevier plc), 8 Industrial Way, Bldg. C. Salem, NH 03079. TEL 800-548-4001. FAX 603-898-9858. Ed. John N. Ferdico. (looseleaf format)
    Description: Covers the Maine Administrative Procedure Act, Maine Freedom of Access Law, selected Maine Rules of Civil Procedure and Maine Administrative Court Rules, plus attorney general opinions.

348   US
MAINE EVIDENCE. 1987. base vol. (plus supplement). $85. Butterworth Legal Publishers (Salem) (Subsidiary of: Reed Elsevier plc), 8 Industrial Way, Bldg. C, Salem, NH 03079. TEL 800-548-4001. FAX 603-898-9858. Ed. Peter L. Murray. (looseleaf format)
    Description: Contains the complete text of the Rules of Evidence with advisor's notes and commentary which explains each rule.

347   US
MAINE RULES OF COURT, STATE AND FEDERAL. a. West Publishing Corp., 620 Opperman Dr., Eagan, MN 55123. TEL 612-687-8000; 800-328-9352. FAX 612-687-7302.

347.9   MW   ISSN 0076-3160
LAW
MALAWI. MINISTRY OF JUSTICE. ANNUAL REPORT. a., latest 1969. K.0.50. Government Printer, Box 37, Zomba, Malawi.

348   MW
MALAWI. MINISTRY OF JUSTICE. LAWS AMENDMENTS. (Text in English) 1969. a. Government Printer, Box 37, Zomba, Malawi. **Document type:** government publication.

348   MW
MALAWI LAW REPORTS. a., vol.7, 1988 (for years 1973-1974). Government Printer, Box 37, Zomba, Malawi. Ed. James 3. Kalaile. **Document type:** government publication.
    Formerly (until 1973): African Law Reports: Malawi Series.

347   CN   ISSN 0380-0008
MANITOBA DECISIONS - CIVIL AND CRIMINAL CASES. 1975. m. Can.$290. Western Legal Publications, 301-1 Alexander St., Vancouver, BC V6A 1B2, Canada. TEL 604-687-5671. FAX 604-687-2796. (looseleaf format)
●Also available on ine.
    Description: Provides summaries of both civil and criminal decisions from the Manitoba Court of Appeal, Court of Queen's Bench and selected decisions of the Provicial Court of Manitoba.

347   CN   ISSN 0824-7293
MANITOBA DECISIONS - RULES AND STATUTE CITATOR. 1981. m. Can.$130. Western Legal Publications, 301-1 Alexander St, Vancouver, BC V6A 1B2, Canada. TEL 604-687-5671. FAX 604-687-2796.
    Description: Provides notes on all current judgments of the Supreme Court of Canada and the Manitoba Courts, case citations for all decisions of the Manitoba Courts in which a Manitoba Rule of Court was cited.

348.752   US   ISSN 0093-0520
KFM1238
MARYLAND. STATE DEPARTMENT OF LEGISLATIVE REFERENCE. SYNOPSIS OF LAWS ENACTED BY THE STATE OF MARYLAND. Key Title: Synopsis of Laws Enacted by the State of Maryland. 1916. a. $25. Department of Legislative Reference, Legislative Sales, 90 State Circle, Annapolis, MD 21401. TEL 410-841-3885. **Document type:** government publication, abstracting/indexing.

347   IT   ISSN 0076-5163
MATERIALI PER UNA STORIA DELLA CULTURA GIURIDICA. 1979. 2/yr. L.110000. (Universita degli Studi di Genova, Istituto di Filosofia del Diritto) Societa Editrice Il Mulino, Strada Maggiore, 37, 40125 Bologna, Italy. TEL 051-256011. FAX 051-256034. Ed.Bd. adv.; index. circ. 800. (back issues avail.)

347   MF
MAURITIUS. JUDICIAL DEPARTMENT. ANNUAL REPORT. (Text in English) a., latest 1989. Government Printing Office, Elizabeth II Ave., Port Louis, Mauritius. (Subscr. to: La Tour Koenig, Pointe aux Sables, Port Louis, Mauritius. TEL 3245294. FAX 2084011)

340.5   US
▼**MEALEY'S LITIGATION REPORT: AMERICANS WITH DISABILITIES ACT.** 1993. m. $450. Mealey Publications, Inc., Box 446, Wayne, PA 19087. TEL 800-553-6397. FAX 215-688-7552. Ed. Maureen McGuire. (looseleaf format)
    Description: Covers recent legal developments, including pending court cases, judicial decisions, awards and settlements arising from recently enacted Federal legislation.

349.776   US
MINNESOTA CONDEMNATION LAW AND PRACTICE. 1990. base vol. (plus a. supplement). $95. Butterworth Legal Publishers (Salem) (Subsidiary of: Reed Elsevier plc), 8 Industrial Way, Bldg. C, Salem, NH 03079. TEL 800-548-4001. FAX 603-898-9858. Ed.Bd. (looseleaf format)
    Description: For attorneys representing both the condemning authorities or the property owners.

349.776   US
MINNESOTA EVIDENCE TRAILBOOK. 1987. base vol. (plus supplements). $54. Butterworth Legal Publishers (Salem) (Subsidiary of: Reed Elsevier plc), 8 Industrial Way, Bldg. C, Salem, NH 03079. TEL 800-548-4001. FAX 603-898-9858. Ed. Bertrand Poritsky. (looseleaf format)

349.776   US
MINNESOTA LEGAL REGISTER: MINNESOTA TAX COURT DECISIONS. 1985. a. $48. Philip G. Bradley, Ed. & Pub., Box 3645, Duluth, MN 55803. TEL 218-724-0401. index. circ. 140. (looseleaf format)
    Description: Complete text of all decisions.

349.776   US   ISSN 0026-5543
MINNESOTA LEGAL REGISTER: OPINIONS OF THE MINNESOTA ATTORNEY GENERAL. 1968. m. $42 for 2 yrs. Philip G. Bradley, Ed. & Pub., Box 3645, Duluth, MN 55803. TEL 218-724-0401. index. circ. 260. (looseleaf format)
    Description: Complete text of all opinions.

349.776   US
MINNESOTA LEGISLATIVE MANUAL. 1865. biennial. free. Secretary of State, 180 State Office Bldg, St. Paul, MN 55155. TEL 612-296-2805. Ed. Joseph Mansky. circ. 15,000. **Document type:** government publication.

349.776   US
MINNESOTA LIMITATIONS MANUAL. 1989. base vol. (plus a. supplement), 2nd ed. 1990. $50. Butterworth Legal Publishers (Salem) (Subsidiary of: Reed Elsevier plc), 8 Industrial Way, Bldg. C, Salem, NH 03079. TEL 800-548-4001. FAX 603-898-9858. Ed.Bd. (looseleaf format)

349.776   US
MINNESOTA MECHANICS' LIENS PRACTICE MANUAL. 1987. base vol. (plus supplements). $78. Butterworth Legal Publishers (Salem) (Subsidiary of: Reed Elsevier plc), 8 Industrial Way, Bldg. C, Salem, NH 03079. TEL 800-548-4001. FAX 603-898-9858. Ed. James E. Snoxell. (looseleaf format)
    Description: Covers all aspects of a liens claim and includes over 30 forms as well as the complete text of the state statute.

349.776   US
MINNESOTA MISDEMEANORS AND MOVING TRAFFIC VIOLATIONS. 2nd ed., 1990. 2 base vols. (plus supplements). $160. Butterworth Legal Publishers (Salem) (Subsidiary of: Reed Elsevier plc), 8 Industrial Way, Bldg. C, Salem, NH 03079. TEL 800-548-4001. FAX 603-898-9858. Ed.Bd. (looseleaf format)
    Description: Guide to the prosecution and defense of misdemeanor, gross, and petty misdemeanor cases in the district courts on Minnesota.

349.776   US
MINNESOTA PROBATE LAW DIGEST. 1982. 3 base vols. (plus a. supplement). $185. Butterworth Legal Publishers (Salem) (Subsidiary of: Reed Elsevier plc), 8 Industrial Way, Bldg. C, Salem, NH 03079. TEL 800-548-4001. FAX 603-898-9858. Ed.Bd. (looseleaf format)

348.776   US
MINNESOTA RULES. 1983. biennial. $200. Office of Revisor of Statutes, 700 State Office Bldg., St. Paul, MN 55155. TEL 612-296-2868. circ. 1,000. **Document type:** government publication.

348.776   US
MINNESOTA RULES. SUPPLEMENT. 1984. biennial (2/yr. in even-numbered years). Office of Revisor of Statutes, 700 State Office Bldg., St. Paul, MN 55155. TEL 612-296-2868. **Document type:** government publication.

348.776   US   ISSN 0191-1562
KFM5429
MINNESOTA STATUTES. 1941. biennial. $165. Office of Revisor of Statutes, 700 State Office Bldg., St. Paul, MN 55155. TEL 612-296-2868. circ. 4,500. **Document type:** government publication.
●Also available on CD-ROM.

348.776   US   ISSN 0094-1727
KFM5431
MINNESOTA STATUTES. SUPPLEMENT. 1973. biennial. Office of Revisor of Statutes, 700 State Office Bldg., St. Paul, MN 55155. TEL 612-296-2868. circ. 2,800. **Document type:** government publication.

348.776   US
MINNESOTA STATUTES ON C D - R O M. 1989. a. $205. Office of Revisor of Statutes, 700 State Office Bldg., St. Paul, MN 55155. TEL 612-296-2868. circ. 100. **Document type:** government publication.
●Available only on CD-ROM.

348.778   US
MISSOURI COURT RULES HANDBOOK; local rules of the forty-four Judicial Circuit Courts in Missouri. 1989. base vol. (plus q. supplements). $135. Butterworth Legal Publishers (Salem) (Subsidiary of: Reed Elsevier plc), 8 Industrial Way, Bldg. C, Salem, NH 03079. TEL 800-548-4001. FAX 603-898-9858. Ed.Bd. (looseleaf format)

347   US
MODERN COURTS. 1984. q. free. Fund for Modern Courts, Inc., 36 W. 44th St., Ste. 310, New York, NY 10036-8181. TEL 212-575-1577. FAX 212-869-1133. Ed. Robert M. Fabricant. bk.rev. circ. 10,000. (back issues avail.)
    Description: Covers judicial issues, court reform, merit selection of judges, court merger, and jury service.

LAW — JUDICIAL SYSTEMS

348   CE
MODERN LAW REPORTS, EMBODYING CASES DECIDED BY THE SUPREME COURT OF THE REPUBLIC OF SRI LANKA.* (Text in English or Sinhalese) 1975. w. Rs.2.50. (Sresthadikaranaya) C.L. Perera, c/o Ministry of Justice, Hulftsdrop, Colombo 12, Sri Landa.

347   CN   ISSN 0828-4989
K13
MONDE JURIDIQUE. 1984. 6/yr. $34 (effective Jan. 1991). Agence Quebec Nouvelles Inc., 381 Richelieu Bvd., Saint-Basile-le-Grand, PQ J3N 1M4, Canada. TEL 514-658-5983. FAX 514-658-3398. Ed. Andre Gagnon. adv.; bk.rev. circ. 10,000. **Indexed:** Ind.Can.L.P.L. **Document type:** trade publication.
    Description: Information about lawyers, their professional life, profiles and trends in French Canada.

347   IT
MONDO GIUDIZIARIO. 1946. w. L.460000. (Associazione del Mondo Giudiziario) Edizioni del Mondo Giudiziario, Viale Angelico 90, 00195 Rome, Italy. TEL 6-37-21-071. FAX 6-32-50-961. Ed. Federico Brusca. adv. circ. 4,800.

MONITOR (ATLANTA). see *POLITICAL SCIENCE — Civil Rights*

348.5491   PK
MONTHLY LEGAL DIGEST; containing civil, criminal and revenue cases decided by High Courts of Pakistan & Azad Jammu and Kashmir. 1984. m. Rs.640 (foreign $42) (effective 1993). P.L.D. Publishers, 35 Nabha Rd., Lahore 1, Pakistan. TEL 92-42-213497. (back issues avail.)

347 340   US
N A J I T NEWS. q. National Association of Judiciary Interpreters and Translators, 12298 W. Connecticut Dr., Lakewood, CO 80228-3633. **Document type:** bulletin.

351.26   US
N A W J COUNTERBALANCE. 1980. 3/yr. $10. National Association of Women Judges, 1020 19th St., N.W., Ste. LL01, Washington, DC 20036. TEL 202-872-0963. FAX 202-872-0965. Ed. Mary Kay LeFevour. circ. 1,200. **Document type:** newsletter.
    Formerly: N A W J News and Announcements.

347   AT   ISSN 0705-3886
NASH ON MAGISTRATES' COURTS - VICTORIA. 1975. 8/yr. in 3 vols. Aus.$500 (renewal Aus.$400). Law Book Co. Ltd., 44-50 Waterloo Rd., N. Ryde, N.S.W. 2113, Australia. TEL 02-887-0177. FAX 02-888-9706. TELEX ASBOOK 27995. Ed. G. Nash. (looseleaf format)
    Description: Covers civil and criminal court practice, magistrates courts, juvenile courts and coroners jurisdiction in Victoria.

347   US
NATIONAL CENTER FOR STATE COURTS. PUBLICATIONS. irreg. National Center for State Courts, 300 Newport Ave., Williamsburg, VA 23187-8798. TEL 804-253-2000. FAX 804-220-0449.

347   US   ISSN 0195-5241
KF8736.A15
NATIONAL CENTER FOR STATE COURTS. REPORT. 1974. m. $12 (includes Master Calendar). National Center for State Courts, 300 Newport Ave., Williamsburg, VA 23187-8798. TEL 804-253-2000. FAX 804-220-0449. circ. 3,500. (looseleaf format; back issues avail.) **Document type:** newsletter.

347 340   US
NATIONAL CONFERENCE OF APPELLATE COURT CLERKS. NEWSLETTER. bi-m. National Conference of Appellate Court Clerks, National Center for State Courts, 300 Newport Ave., Williamsburg, VA 23187-8798. TEL 804-253-2000. **Document type:** newsletter.
    Description: Seeks to enhance judicial administration of appellate courts by means of education.

348   US
NATIONAL CONFERENCE OF COMMISSIONERS ON UNIFORM STATE LAWS. HANDBOOK AND PROCEEDINGS. 1982. a. price varies. (National Conference of Commissioners on Uniform State Laws) William S. Hein & Co., Inc., 1285 Main St., Buffalo, NY 14209. TEL 800-828-7571. FAX 617-883-8100. TELEX 91-209 WU 7 HEIN BUF. Ed. Edith Davies. circ. 800. (also avail. in microfiche from WSH,PMC; reprint service avail. from RRI) **Indexed:** C.L.I., Leg.Per. **Document type:** proceedings.

347 340   US
NATIONAL COURT REPORTERS ASSOCIATION. MEMBERSHIP DIRECTORY AND REGISTRY OF PROFESSIONAL REPORTERS. Variant title: National Shorthand Reporters Association. Membership Directory and Registry of Professional Reporters. a. $50 to non-members; members $15. National Court Reporters Association, 8224 Old Courthouse Rd., Vienna, VA 22182. TEL 703-556-6272. adv. circ. 3,500. **Document type:** directory.
    Description: Lists shorthand reporters by name and geographic region both in the U.S. and abroad.

347 380 020   US   ISSN 1054-9471
KF8700.A19
NATIONAL DIRECTORY OF COURTS OF LAW. 1991. biennial. $90 (effective Mar.1991). Information Resources Press, 1110 N. Glebe Rd., Ste. 550, Arlington, VA 22201. TEL 703-558-8270. FAX 703-558-4979. Ed. Mark A, Yannone. (back issues avail.) **Document type:** directory.
    Description: Encompasses every identifiable U.S. federal, state, county, local, territorial, tribal and specialized agency officially designated or functioning as a court of law. Contains 20,130 entries.

348.5496   NP
NEPAL MISCELLANEOUS SERIES. (Text in English) 1964. irreg. Rs.900($50) Regmi Research (Pvt.) Ltd., Lazimpat, Kathmandu, Nepal. TEL 4-11927. Ed. Mahesh C. Regmi. (also avail. in microfilm from LCP)
    Formerly: Nepal Law Translation Series (ISSN 0077-6572)
    Description: Texts of laws and regulations, periodically revised to incorporate amendments and additions.

342   GW   ISSN 0721-880X
KK5571.2
NEUE ZEITSCHRIFT FUER VERWALTUNGSRECHT. 1949. m. DM.338 (students DM.304). C.H. Beck'sche Verlagsbuchhandlung, Wilhelmstr. 9, 80801 Munich, Germany. TEL 089-38189-338. FAX 089-38189-398. TELEX 5215085-BECK-D. Ed.Bd. adv.: B&W page DM.2400, color page DM.4800; trim 260 x 186. circ. 6,700. (back issues avail.) **Indexed:** ELLIS. **Document type:** bulletin.
● Also available on CD-ROM.
—BLDSC (6077.827750); SWETS.
    Formerly (until Dec. 1981): Verwaltungsrechsprechung in Deutschland (ISSN 0342-2534).

348.742   US
NEW HAMPSHIRE CODE OF ADMINISTRATIVE RULES ANNOTATED. 1984. 6 base vols. (plus supplements 1-2/yr.). $300. Butterworth Legal Publishers (Salem) (Subsidiary of: Reed Elsevier plc), 8 Industrial Way, Bldg. C, Salem, NH 03079. TEL 800-548-4001. FAX 603-898-9858. Ed.Bd. (looseleaf format)
    Description: Codification of the administrative rules of 24 selected agencies and departments.

348.742   US
NEW HAMPSHIRE COURT RULES ANNOTATED. 1979. 2 base vols. (plus a. supplement). $98. Butterworth Legal Publishers (Salem) (Subsidiary of: Reed Elsevier plc), 8 Industrial Way, Bldg. C, Salem, NH 03079. TEL 800-548-4001. FAX 603-898-9858. Ed.Bd. (looseleaf format)
    Description: Contains the rules for the New Hampshire courts plus those for the US Court of Appeals and the US District Court.

348.742   US
NEW HAMPSHIRE EVIDENCE MANUAL. (2nd ed., 1992) 1986. base vol. (plus supplements). $55. Butterworth Legal Publishers (Salem) (Subsidiary of: Reed Elsevier plc), 8 Industrial Way, Bldg. C, Salem, NH 03079. TEL 800-548-4001. FAX 603-898-9858. Ed. Charles G. Douglas, III. (looseleaf format)
    Formerly (until 1992): New Hampshire Rules of Evidence Manual.

348.742   US
NEW HAMPSHIRE FISH AND GAME LAWS. a. $19. Butterworth Legal Publishers (Salem) (Subsidiary of: Reed Elsevier plc), 8 Industrial Way, Bldg. C, Salem, NH 03079. TEL 800-548-4001. FAX 603-898-9858. Ed.Bd.
    Description: For attorneys, law enforcement agencies, environmentalists, sportsmen and students.

348.742   US
NEW HAMPSHIRE MOTOR VEHICLE AND BOATING LAWS. (In 2 vols.) q. $30. Butterworth Legal Publishers (Salem) (Subsidiary of: Reed Elsevier plc), 8 Industrial Way, Bldg. C, Salem, NH 03079. TEL 800-548-4001. FAX 603-898-9858. Ed.Bd. charts.

348.742   US
NEW HAMPSHIRE REVISED STATUTES ANNOTATED. 23 base vols. (plus a. suppl.). $928. Butterworth Legal Publishers (Salem) (Subsidiary of: Reed Elsevier plc), 8 Industrial Way, Bldg. C, Salem, NH 03079. TEL 800-548-4001. FAX 603-898-9858. Ed.Bd.

348.742   US
NEW HAMPSHIRE RULES OF EVIDENCE. a. $13. Butterworth Legal Publishers (Salem) (Subsidiary of: Reed Elsevier plc), 8 Industrial Way, Bldg. C, Salem, NH 03079. TEL 800-548-4001. FAX 603-898-9858. Ed.Bd.

348.742   US
NEW HAMPSHIRE STATUTES RELATING TO SURVEYING AND BOUNDARIES. a. $19.50. Butterworth Legal Publishers (Salem) (Subsidiary of: Reed Elsevier plc), 8 Industrial Way, Bldg. C, Salem, NH 03079. TEL 800-548-4001. FAX 603-898-9858. Ed.Bd.

347   US
NEW JERSEY. ADMINISTRATIVE OFFICE OF THE COURTS. ANNUAL REPORT OF THE NEW JERSEY JUDICIARY. 1949. a. free. Administrative Office of the Courts, RJH Justice Complex CN-037, Trenton, NJ 08625. TEL 609-292-9580. illus. circ. 2,000.
    Formerly: New Jersey. Administrative Office of the Courts. Annual Report of the Administrative Director of the Courts.
    Description: Annual compendium of statistical and programmatic information on the operation of the courts.

NEW JERSEY PRACTICE SERIES. LOCAL GOVERNMENT LAW. see *PUBLIC ADMINISTRATION — Municipal Government*

347   US
NEW JERSEY RULES OF COURT, STATE AND FEDERAL. a. West Publishing Corp., 620 Opperman Dr., Eagan, MN 55123. TEL 612-687-8000; 800-241-0214. FAX 612-687-7302.

347.91   US
NEW JERSEY STATE BAR ASSOCIATION. CERTIFIED TRIAL ATTORNEYS SECTION. NEWSLETTER. 1989. irreg. free to members. New Jersey State Bar Association, Certified Trial Attorneys Section, 1 Constitution Sq., New Brunswick, NJ 08901-1500. TEL 908-249-5000. FAX 908-249-2815. Ed. Brian P. Blatz. bk.rev.; circ. 400 (controlled). (back issues avail.) **Document type:** newsletter.

NEW JERSEY STATE BAR ASSOCIATION. CIVIL TRIAL BAR SECTION. NEWSLETTER. see *LAW — Civil Law*

348.789   US
NEW MEXICO APPELLATE PRACTICE MANUAL. 1978. base vol. (plus a. supplement). $115. Butterworth Legal Publishers (Salem) (Subsidiary of: Reed Elsevier plc), 8 Industrial Way, Bldg. C, Salem, NH 03079. TEL 800-548-4001. FAX 603-898-9858. Ed. Michael Schwarz. (looseleaf format)

LAW — JUDICIAL SYSTEMS

348.789 US
NEW MEXICO LOCAL AND FEDERAL RULES HANDBOOK. 1976. 2 base vols. (plus q. supplement). $135. Butterworth Legal Publishers (Salem) (Subsidiary of: Reed Elsevier plc), 8 Industrial Way, Bldg. C, Salem, NH 03079. TEL 800-548-4001. FAX 603-898-9858. Ed.Bd. (looseleaf format)
  Description: Complete and current compilation of rules applicable to New Mexico practice.

348.789 US
NEW MEXICO RULES OF EVIDENCE. (Revised ed., 1991) 1983. base vol. (plus supplements). $125. Butterworth Legal Publishers (Salem) (Subsidiary of: Reed Elsevier plc), 8 Industrial Way, Bldg. C, Salem, NH 03079. TEL 800-548-4001. FAX 603-898-9858. Ed. Murl A. Larkin. (looseleaf format)
  Description: Contains current case law and commentary on the construction and interpretation of the rules.

347 AT ISSN 0312-1674
LAW
NEW SOUTH WALES LAW REPORTS. 1971. irreg. (6-8/yr.). (Council of Law Reporting for New South Wales) Law Book Co. Ltd., 44-50 Waterloo Rd., North Ryde, N.S.W. 2113, Australia. TEL 02-887-0177. FAX 02-888-9706. TELEX ASBOOK 27995. index.
  ●Also available online. Vendor(s): Info-One International Pty Ltd.
  Supersedes: New South Wales Weekly Notes (ISSN 0023-9232); New South Wales State Reports (ISSN 0085-6703)
  Description: Authorized reports of state and federal cases decided in the Supreme Court.

348 US
NEW YORK (STATE). OPINIONS OF THE ATTORNEY GENERAL. 1890. a. (plus bi-m. supplements). $66. (Department of Law, Office of the Attorney General) Lenz & Riecker, Inc., Legal Publishing Division, 1 Columbia Pl., Albany, NY 12207. TEL 518-436-8647. FAX 518-436-0939. (looseleaf format; back issues avail.) **Document type:** academic/scholarly publication.
  Description: Formal and informal opinions on legal questions concerning state and local government. Includes subject index, statutory reference table, and concise descriptions of recent judicial opinions.

NEW YORK (STATE). OPINIONS OF THE COMPTROLLER.
see PUBLIC ADMINISTRATION

348.747 US ISSN 1045-4659
KFN5029
NEW YORK CONSOLIDATED LAWS. Key Title: Gould's Consolidated Laws of New York. 1989. a. $179 for 9 vol. set. Gould Publications (Binghamton), 199-300 State St., Binghamton, NY 13901. TEL 607-724-3000. FAX 607-723-4285. adv.; bk.rev. (looseleaf format)
  Description: Contains the complete laws of NY.

347 US
NEW YORK COURT FORMS. 1988. a. $34.95. Gould Publications (Binghamton), 199-300 State St., Binghamton, NY 13901. TEL 607-724-3000. FAX 607-723-4285. adv.; bk.rev. (looseleaf format)
  Description: Contains forms necessary for courts and law enforcement agencies in NYS along with instruction materials.

347 US
NEW YORK COURTS MANUAL OF PROCEDURE. 1989. a. $28. Gould Publications (Binghamton), 199-300 State St., Binghamton, NY 13901. TEL 607-724-3000. FAX 607-723-4285.
  Description: Reviews general provisions of criminal procedure law, arraignment, securing defendant's attorney, bail, uniform rules for trial courts, Uniform Justice Court Act.

347 US ISSN 0748-3430
NEW YORK JURY VERDICT REPORTER. 1981. w. $300. Box 310, Islip, NY 11751. TEL 516-581-1930. FAX 516-581-8937. Ed. Russell F. Moran. adv. circ. 1,000. (looseleaf format; back issues avail.) **Document type:** academic/scholarly publication.
  Description: Covers both city and state civil jury verdicts.

348.747 US ISSN 0745-4406
NEW YORK LAW JOURNAL DIGEST ANNOTATOR. 12/yr. (plus a. cumulation). $395. New York Law Publishing Co., 345 Park Ave. S., New York, NY 10010. TEL 212-779-8200. **Document type:** abstracting/indexing.
  Description: A guide to Lower Court opinions in New York's First and Second Judicial Departments, and an index to the New York Law Journal.

347 US
NEW YORK SURROGATE'S COURT PROCEDURE ACT. 1988. a. $9.95. Gould Publications (Binghamton), 199-300 State St., Binghamton, NY 13901. TEL 607-724-3000. FAX 607-723-4285. adv.; bk.rev. (looseleaf format)
  Description: Contains Chapter 59A, Surrogate's Court Procedure Act uniform rules for surrogate's court of NY. Includes forms.

347.7 NQ
NICARAGUA. CORTE SUPREMA DE JUSTICIA. BOLETIN JUDICIAL. irreg. Corte Suprema de Justicia, Managua, Nicaragua.

348 AT ISSN 1038-9237
▼**NORTHERN TERRITORY LAW REPORTS.** 1992. 3/yr. Aus.$186. Law Book Co. Ltd., 44-50 Waterloo Rd., North Ryde, N.S.W. 2113, Australia. TEL 02-887-0177. FAX 02-888-9706. TELEX AHBOOK 27995. Ed. Tom Pauling. (looseleaf format)
  Description: Contains the authorized reports of the Supreme Court of the Northern Territory.

348 CN
NOTARY'S COMPENDIUM. B.C. statutes and regulations. base vol. (plus irreg. supplement). Can.$135.50. Ministry of Attorney General, Parliament Bldgs., Victoria, B.C. V8V 1X4, Canada. TEL 604-387-5818. (Subscr. to: Crown Publications, 546 Yates St., Victoria, B.C. V8W 1K8, Canada. TEL 604-386-4636) (looseleaf format; back issues avail.) **Document type:** government publication.
  Description: Contains statutes and regulations required by Notaries for their respective provincees.

347 IT
NOTIZIARIO GIURIDICO. m. L.70000 (foreign L.140000) (effective 1993). Ediesse s.r.l., Via dei Frentani, 4-A, 00185 Rome, Italy. TEL 06-448701. FAX 06-44481260.

347 FR ISSN 0338-1552
NOUVEAU POUVOIR JUDICIAIRE. 1975. q. 170 F. Union Syndicale des Magistrats, 33 rue du Four, 75006 Paris, France. TEL 43-54-21-26. FAX 43-29-96-20. Ed. Paquerette Girard-Thuilier; Pub. Claude Pernollet. adv.; illus. **Document type:** trade publication.
  Supersedes: Pouvoir Judiciaire.

348 US ISSN 0748-6170
LAW
OHIO ATTORNEY GENERAL OPINIONS. 1963. q. $100. (Office of the Attorney General) Banks - Baldwin Law Publishing Co., University Center, Box 1974, Cleveland, OH 44106. TEL 216-721-7373. FAX 216-721-8055.

347 US
OHIO COURTS. 1957. q. Supreme Court of Ohio, Office of the Administrative Director, 30 E. Broad St., Columbus, OH 43215-3431. TEL 614-466-3456. Ed. Brenda English.

348 US ISSN 0274-7294
KF128.036
OHIO DISTRICT COURT REVIEW. 1980. m. $225. Anadem Publishing, Inc., 3620 N. High St., Columbus, OH 43214. TEL 614-262-2539. index.
  Description: Summaries of unreported Court of Appeals cases in Ohio.

347 US
OHIO RULES OF COURT, STATE AND FEDERAL. a. West Publishing Corp., 620 Opperman Dr., Eagan, MN 55123. TEL 612-687-8000; 800-328-9352. FAX 612-687-7302.

348 US ISSN 0475-0926
KFO1640
OKLAHOMA. ATTORNEY GENERAL'S OFFICE. OPINIONS OF THE ATTORNEY GENERAL. 1968. a. price varies. Attorney General's Office, Rm. 112, State Capitol, Oklahoma City, OK 73105. TEL 405-521-3921. FAX 405-521-6246. circ. 1,000. (back issues avail.) **Document type:** government publication.

348 US ISSN 0030-1728
J1
OKLAHOMA REGISTER (OKLAHOMA CITY). 1962. s-m. $150. Secretary of State, Office of Administrative Rules, 4118 Will Rogers Bldg., Box 53571, Oklahoma City, OK 73152. TEL 405-521-4911. Ed. Peggy Coe. circ. 280. **Document type:** government publication.
  Description: State administrative rules, notification of rulemaking actions, and local project funding contract announcements by state entities.

349 US
OREGON APPELLATE MANUAL. 1986. base vol. (plus supplements). $60. Butterworth Legal Publishers (Salem) (Subsidiary of: Reed Elsevier plc), 8 Industrial Way, Bldg. C, Salem, NH 03079. TEL 800-548-4001. FAX 603-898-9858. Ed. George Kelly. (looseleaf format)
  Description: Follows an imaginary case through the appellate process to illustrate the application of the hundred-plus rules that apply to appeals under Oregon law.

348 US
OREGON EVIDENCE. 1989. base vol. (plus a. supplement). $80. Butterworth Legal Publishers (Salem) (Subsidiary of: Reed Elsevier plc), 8 Industrial Way, Bldg. C, Salem, NH 03079. TEL 800-548-4001. FAX 603-898-9858. Ed. Laird C. Kirkpatrick.
  Description: Contains current statutory amendments and current case law and provides thorough analysis of the rules of Oregon and federal cases interpreting them.

348 US
OREGON REVISED STATUTES ANNOTATED. (Supplement avail.: Comprehensive Index to Oregon Statutes (Year)) 1983. 52 base vols. (plus a. supplement). $2400. Butterworth Legal Publishers (Salem) (Subsidiary of: Reed Elsevier plc), 8 Industrial Way, Bldg. C, Salem, NH 03079. TEL 800-548-4001. FAX 603-898-9858. Ed.Bd.

347 US
OREGON UNIFORM TRIAL COURT RULES AND SUPPLEMENTARY LOCAL RULES. 1985. base vol. (plus suppl.). $50. Butterworth Legal Publishers (Salem) (Subsidiary of: Reed Elsevier plc), 8 Industrial Way, Bldg. C, Salem, NH 03079. TEL 800-548-4001. FAX 603-898-9858. Ed.Bd. (looseleaf format)

348.5491 PK
PAKISTAN SUPREME COURT CASES. (Text in English) 1982. m. R.120($20) Supreme Court, 1 Turner Rd., Lahore, Pakistan. Ed. Malik Muhammad Qayyum. index. circ. 2,000. (back issues avail.)

348 AT ISSN 0085-4689
PAPUA AND NEW GUINEA LAW REPORTS. 1963. a. Law Book Co. Ltd., 44-50 Waterloo Rd., North Ryde, N.S.W. 2113, Australia. TEL 02-887-0177. FAX 02-888-9706. TELEX ASBOOK 27995. Ed. Naida J. Haxton. index. (back issues avail.)
  Description: Reports of the Supreme Court of Justice and National Court of Justice of Papua New Guinea.

347 US
PENNSYLVANIA RULES OF COURT, STATE AND FEDERAL. a. West Publishing Corp., 620 Opperman Dr., Eagan, MN 55123. TEL 612-687-8000; 800-328-9352. FAX 612-687-7302.

PRACTITIONER'S HANDBOOKS ON THE WORLD COURT.
see LAW — International Law

348 US ISSN 0363-0048
KF4547.8
PREVIEW OF UNITED STATES SUPREME COURT CASES. 1963-1973; resumed 1982. irreg. (10-12/yr.) $95. American Bar Association, Public Education Division, 750 N. Lake Shore Dr., Chicago, IL 60611. TEL 312-988-5728. FAX 312-988-5494. Ed. L. Anita Richardson. index. circ. 3,000.
●Also available online. Vendor(s): West Services, Inc. —UnCover.
Description: Offers analysis of every case orally argued before the Supreme Court.

347 BL
PRINCIPIOS DE JUSTICIA E PAZ. s-a.? Comissao Justica e Paz de Sao Paulo, Av. Higienopolis 890, salas 21-23, 01238 Sao Paulo SP, Brazil. TEL 826-0133.

345 US ISSN 0276-6965
KF9750.A59
PROBATION AND PAROLE LAW REPORTS. 1979. m. $115. Knehans-Miller Publications, Box 88, Warrensburg, MO 64093. TEL 816-429-1102. Ed. Dane C. Miller. index. (looseleaf format; back issues avail.) **Document type:** trade publication.
Formerly: Probation and Parole Law Summaries.
Description: Summaries and verbatim excerpts of all Federal and State Appellate Court decisions relating to probation and parole. Indexed by subject and jurisdiction.

347 AT ISSN 0727-8063
QUEENSLAND MAGISTRATES COURTS. 1982. 5/yr. in 2 vols. Aus.$330 with updates. Law Book Co. Ltd., 44-50 Waterloo Rd., N. Ryde, N.S.W. 2113, Australia. TEL 02-887-0177. FAX 02-888-9706. TELEX ASBOOK 27995. Eds. M.G. Morley, G. Marth. (looseleaf format; back issues avail.)
Description: Covers magistrate, land and environment courts, industrial tribunals, and court practice. Includes summary jurisdiction.

347 AT ISSN 0726-3759
QUEENSLAND REPORTS. 1908. m. Aus.$255. Incorporated Council of Law Reporting, c/o Mrs. J.T. Mengel, Sec., P.O. Box 307, 44 Romn St., Qld. 4003, Australia. TEL 07-236-1855. FAX 07-236-4196. adv. circ. 1,700.
Description: Reports of the Supreme Court of Queensland; includes Full and Appeal Courts.

347 AT
QUEENSLAND SUPREME COURT PRACTICE. 2 base vols. (plus q. update). $445. Butterworths, 271-273 Lane Cove Rd., P.O. Box 345, North Ryde, N.S.W. 2113, Australia. TEL 02-335-4444. FAX 02-335-4678. (looseleaf format)

347 CL
REVISTA DE ESTUDIOS HISTORICO JURIDICO. 1976. a. $42. (Universidad Catolica de Valparaiso, Escuela de Derecho) Ediciones Universitarias de Valparaiso, Casilla 1415, Valparaiso, Chile. TEL 032-252900. FAX 032-212746. TELEX 230389 UCVAL CL. Dir. Alejandro Guzman B. bk.rev. circ. 300. **Indexed:** Amer.Hist.& Life, Hist.Abstr. **Document type:** academic/scholarly publication.

347 340 RW ISSN 1010-8238
REVUE JURIDIQUE DU RWANDA. (Text in French, Kinyarwanda) 1977. q. $50. Ministere de la Justice, Faculte de Droit, B.P. 1690, Kigali, Rwanda. TEL 250-73142. Ed. Charles Ntampaka. bk.rev. (back issues avail.) **Indexed:** Documentatieblad.

347 ZR
REVUE JURIDIQUE DU ZAIRE. 1924. 3/yr. $1000. (Societe d'Etudes Juridiques du Zaire) Universite de Lubumbashi, B.P. 510, Lubumbashi, Zaire. **Indexed:** Documentatieblad.
Supersedes: Revue Juridique du Congo.

347 CN ISSN 0556-7963
K21
REVUE JURIDIQUE THEMIS. Running title: Themis. (Text in English and French) 1953. a. Can.$36. Editions Themis, C.P. 6128, Succ. A, Montreal, PQ H3C 3J7, Canada. TEL 514-739-9945. FAX 514-739-2910. Ed. Monique Ouellette. adv. contact: Christiane Dubreuil. bk.rev.; bibl.; index; circ. 1,700 (paid). (also avail. in microfilm from WSH,PMC; reprint service avail. from WSH) **Indexed:** C.L.I., Ind.Can.L.P.L., L.R.I., Leg.Cont., Leg.Per., Mar.Aff.Bibl., Pt.de Rep. (1982-).
—UMI.
Supersedes: Revue Juridique Themis de l'Universite de Montreal.

347 RM ISSN 1220-5435
REVUE ROUMAINE DE SCIENCES JURIDIQUES. 1956. 2/yr. 80 lei($45) (Academia Romana) Editura Academiei Romane, Calea Victoriei 125, 79717 Bucharest, Rumania. TEL 50-76-80. (Dist. by: Rompresfilatelia, Calea Grivitei 64-66, P.O. Box 12-201, 78104 Bucharest, Rumania) **Indexed:** P.A.I.S.For.Lang.Ind.
—BLDSC (7946.520000).
Formerly (until 1990): Revue Roumaine des Sciences Sociales. Serie de Sciences Juridiques (ISSN 0035-4023); Which superseded in part (in 1964): Revue des Sciences Sociales (ISSN 0484-8640).

347 US
RHODE ISLAND APPELLATE PRACTICE. 1985. base vol. (plus suppl.). $50. Butterworth Legal Publishers (Salem) (Subsidiary of: Reed Elsevier plc), 8 Industrial Way, Bldg. C, Salem, NH 03079. TEL 800-548-4001. FAX 603-898-9858. Ed. Joseph R. Weisberger. (looseleaf format)
Description: Rules and statutes affecting appellate practice and procedure with commentary.

347 CN
RULES OF COURT AND RELATED ENACTMENTS. base vol. (plus irreg. suppl.). Can.$58. Ministry of Attorney General, Parliament Bldgs., Victoria, B.C. V8V 1X4, Canada. TEL 604-387-5818. (Subscr. to: Crown Publications, 546 Yates St., Victoria, B.C. V8W 1K8, Canada. TEL 604-386-4636) (looseleaf format; back issues avail.)
Description: Consists of the procedural rules by which the affairs of the BC Supreme and County Courts and the Court of Appeal are conducted.

348 US ISSN 1046-1337
KF112
SECOND CIRCUIT REVIEW. 1988. 26/yr. $215. Barclays Law Publishers, 400 Oyster Point Blvd., Ste. 500, San Francisco, CA 94080. TEL 415-588-1155. FAX 415-244-6619. Ed. Frank Gomez. (looseleaf format) **Document type:** newsletter.

348 US ISSN 1045-9006
KF1127TH.1.B37
SEVENTH CIRCUIT REVIEW. 1988. 26/yr. $215. Barclays Law Publishers, 400 Oyster Point Blvd., Ste. 500, San Francisco, CA 94080. TEL 415-588-1155. FAX 415-244-6619. Ed. Frank Gomez. (looseleaf format) **Document type:** newsletter.

347 UK ISSN 0264-312X
SHAW'S DIRECTORY OF COURTS IN THE UNITED KINGDOM. 1970. a. £27. Shaw & Sons Ltd., Shaway House, 21 Bourne Park, Bourne Rd., Crayford, Kent DA1 4BZ, England. TEL 0322-550676. FAX 0322-550553. Ed. Gordon Morris. adv.; bk.rev. circ. 3,000. **Document type:** directory.
Former titles (until 1983): Shaw's Directory of Courts in England and Wales (ISSN 0085-6061); Shaw's Directory of Magistrates' Courts and Crown Courts; Directory of Magistrates Courts.

347 US ISSN 0730-6229
KF308.A535
SHEPARD'S PROFESSIONAL AND JUDICIAL CONDUCT CITATIONS. 1980. base vol. (plus q. suppl.). $100. Shepard's - McGraw-Hill, Inc., Box 35300, Colorado Springs, CO 80935-3530. TEL 800-525-2474.

347 NZ
SIM & CAIN: PRACTICE & PROCEDURE OF THE HIGH COURT & COURT OF APPEAL OF NEW ZEALAND. (12th ed.) base vol. (plus updates 5/yr.). NZ.$296. Butterworths of New Zealand Ltd., 203-207 Victoria St., P.O. Box 472, Wellington, New Zealand. TEL 04-385-1479. FAX 04-385-1598. Ed. Moira Thompson. (looseleaf format)
Former title: Sim & Cain: Practice & Procedure of the High Court of Appeal of New Zealand.
Description: Full text of statutes and rules plus commentary on law relating to the practice of the High Court and Court of Appeal.

348 US ISSN 0889-356X
KF112.S52X
SIXTH CIRCUIT REVIEW (LOUISVILLE). 1971. 24/yr. $245. Appellate Review, 500 Country Ln., Louisville, KY 40207. TEL 502-897-5079. Ed. Sue Simon. (looseleaf format; back issues avail.) **Document type:** newsletter.

348 US ISSN 0894-5241
KF112 6th .1
SIXTH CIRCUIT REVIEW (SAN FRANCISCO). 1987. 26/yr. $215. Barclays Law Publishers, 400 Oyster Point Blvd., Ste. 500, San Francisco, CA 94080. TEL 415-588-1155. FAX 415-244-6619. Ed. Frank Gomez. (looseleaf format) **Document type:** newsletter.

347 US
SOUTH CAROLINA RULES OF COURT, STATE AND FEDERAL. a. West Publishing Corp., 620 Opperman Dr., Eagan, MN 55123. TEL 612-687-8000; 800-241-0214. FAX 612-687-7302.

347 US
STARE DECISIS FOR THE SECOND CIRCUIT. 1983. 52/yr. $6080. Stare Decisis, Three Mile Bay, NY 13693. TEL 800-332-7547. Ed. Seth Buchman. (looseleaf format; back issues avail.) **Document type:** newsletter.

347 US
KF122.N484S73
STARE DECISIS FOR THE SOUTHERN DISTRICT OF NEW YORK. 1983. 52/yr. $6080. Stare Decisis, Three Mile Bay, NY 13693. TEL 800-332-7547. Ed. Seth Buchman. (looseleaf format; back issues avail.) **Document type:** newsletter.

347 US ISSN 0199-5030
SUPREME COURT BULLETIN.* 1979. w. during U.S. Supreme Court session. $29. Hale Ridge Publishing, Box 628, Windham, NH 03087. TEL 603-889-7231. adv.; index. circ. 2,500. (looseleaf format; back issues avail.)

347 II ISSN 0039-5951
SUPREME COURT CASES. (Text in English) 1969. fortn. $126. Eastern Book Company, 34 Lalbagh, Lucknow 226 001, India. TEL 91-522-244328. FAX 91-522-244328. Ed. Surendra Malik. adv.; bk.rev.; index. circ. 10,000. (back issues avail.)

SUPREME COURT CASES (CRIMINAL). see *LAW — Criminal Law*

347 II ISSN 0253-6552
SUPREME COURT CASES (LABOUR AND SERVICES). (Text in English) 1973. m. $41. Eastern Book Company, 34 Lalbagh, Lucknow 226 001, India. TEL 91-522-244328. FAX 91-522-244328. Ed. Surendra Malik. adv.; bk.rev.; index. circ. 2,200. (back issues avail.)

349 PK ISSN 0585-9794
SUPREME COURT MONTHLY REVIEW; a monthly journal comprising Supreme Court cases. (Text in English) 1968. m. Rs.640($42) (effective 1993). P.L.D. Publishers, 35 Nabha Rd., Lahore 1, Pakistan. TEL 92-42-213497. Ed. Malik Muhammad Saeed. (back issues avail.; reprint service avail. from UMI)

340 II ISSN 0039-596X
LAW
SUPREME COURT NOTES. (Text in English) 1959. fortn. Rs.60. Supreme Court, New Delhi, D-8 Nizamuddin East, New Delhi 13, India. Ed. Saroja Gopalakrishnan. circ. 1,200. (back issues avail.)

LAW — JUDICIAL SYSTEMS

347   CN
SUPREME COURT OF CANADA DECISIONS. 1978. m. Can.$125. Western Legal Publications, 301-1 Alexander St., Vancouver, BC V6A 1B2, Canada. TEL 604-687-5671. FAX 604-687-2796. index. (looseleaf format)
● Also available online.
Formerly: Supreme Court of Canada Decisions. Civil and Criminal (ISSN 0709-5600)

347   CN
SUPREME COURT OF CANADA REPORTS SERVICE. 5/yr. Can.$315. Butterworths Canada Ltd., Part of the Reed Elsevier group, 75 Clegg Rd., Markham, ON L6G 1A1, Canada. TEL 905-479-2665. FAX 905-479-2826. (looseleaf format)
Description: Indexes and digests recent judgments of the Canadian Supreme Court.

347   AT
SUPREME COURT PROCEDURE N S W. 2 base vols. (plus m. update) $465. Butterworths, 271-273 Lane Cove Rd., P.O. Box 345, North Ryde, N.S.W. 2113, Australia. TEL 02-335-4444. FAX 02-335-4655. (looseleaf format)

347   US   ISSN 0081-9557
KF4546
SUPREME COURT REVIEW. 1960. a. University of Chicago Press, Journals Division, 5720 S. Woodlawn Ave., Chicago, IL 60637. TEL 312-753-3347. FAX 312-753-0811. TELEX 25-4603. (Subscr. to: Box 37005, Chicago, IL 60637) Ed.Bd. (also avail. in microform from UMI,PMC; reprint service avail. from UMI,ISI) **Indexed:** A.B.C.Pol.Sci., ASCA, C.L.I., L.R.I., Leg.Per., SSCI. **Document type:** academic/scholarly publication.
—BLDSC (8547.650000); Faxon; UnCover; UMI.
Description: Comprises essays by scholars with a wide range of expertise, presenting informed analyses of court opinions and examining important legal issues that have come under the court's consideration.
Refereed Serial

347   US   ISSN 1054-2701
KF8741.A152
SUPREME COURT YEARBOOK. 1990. a. Congressional Quarterly Inc., 1414 22nd St. N.W., Washington, DC 20037.

SURVEY OF JUDICIAL SALARIES. see *LAW — Abstracting, Bibliographies, Statistics*

347   SW   ISSN 0039-6591
SVENSK JURISTTIDNING.* 1916. 10/yr. SEK 350 (effective 1990). Norstedts Juridikfoerlag, P.O. Box, 106 47 Stockholm, Sweden. Ed. Hans Danelius. adv.; bk.rev.; index, cum.index every 10 yrs. circ. 6,000. **Indexed:** ELLIS.
—BLDSC (8560.200000).

347   AT   ISSN 0085-7106
LAW
TASMANIAN REPORTS. 1897. a. Law Book Co. Ltd., 44-50 Waterloo Rd., North Ryde, N.S.W. 2113, Australia. TEL 02-887-0177. FAX 02-888-9706. TELEX ASBOOK 27995.
● Also available online. Vendor(s): Info-One International Pty Ltd.
Description: Contains cases determined in the Supreme Court of Tasmania and other Superior Courts in the Island.

347   US
TENNESSEE RULES OF COURT, STATE AND FEDERAL. a. West Publishing Corp., 620 Opperman Dr., Eagan, MN 55123. TEL 612-687-8000; 800-328-9352. FAX 612-687-7302.

347   US
TEXAS RULES OF APPELLATE PROCEDURE. 1986. base vol. (plus supplements). $40. Butterworth Legal Publishers (Salem) (Subsidiary of: Reed Elsevier plc), 8 Industrial Way, Bldg. C, Salem, NH 03079. TEL 800-548-4001. FAX 603-898-9858. Ed.Bd. (looseleaf format)
Description: Compilation of the complete text of the new rules governing appellate procedure in civil cases and posttrial, appellate and review procedures in criminal cases, promulgated by the Texas Supreme Court and the Texas Court of Criminal Appeals.

347   US   ISSN 0040-6120
KF8700.A16
THIRD BRANCH; a newsletter of the federal courts. 1968. m. free. United States Courts, Administrative Office, One Columbus Circle, Washington, DC 20544. TEL 202-273-1120. FAX 202-273-1139. Eds. Karen Redmond, David Sellers. illus.; index. circ. 13,000. **Indexed:** C.L.I., Leg.Per.
—UnCover.

348   US   ISSN 1043-1470
THIRD CIRCUIT DIGEST (LOUISVILLE). 1986. 24/yr. $255. Appellate Review, 500 Country Ln., Louisville, KY 40207. TEL 502-897-5079. Ed. Ruth Coleman. **Document type:** newsletter.

347   US
THIS WEEK IN COURT; summaries of Mississippi Supreme Court opinions. 1977. w. $30. Mississippi College Law Review, 151 E. Griffith, Jackson, MS 39201. TEL 601-944-1950. Ed. Denise Schreiber. circ. 225. (tabloid format)

347.91   US   ISSN 0041-2538
KF8911.A3
TRIAL. 1965. m. $48. Association of Trial Lawyers of America, 1050 31st St., N.W., Washington, DC 20007. TEL 202-965-3500. Ed. Elizabeth Yeary. adv.; bk.rev.; abstr. circ. 60,000. (also avail. in microfilm from UMI) **Indexed:** Abstr.Bk.Rev.Curr.Leg.Per., ASCA, C.L.I., Chic.Per.Ind., CJPI, Crim.Just.Abstr., Curr.Cont., Hlth.Ind., HRIS, L.R.I., Law Ofc.Info.Svc., Leg.Info.Manage.Ind., Leg.Per., Risk Abstr., Soc.Sci.Ind., SSCI. **Document type:** trade publication.
—BLDSC (9050.050000); Faxon; UnCover; UMI. CCC.
Formerly: National Legal Magazine (ISSN 0027-9625)

347   US   ISSN 0743-412X
KFF538.A1
TRIAL ADVOCATE QUARTERLY. 1981. q. $35. (Florida Defense Lawyers Association) Fred B. Rothman & Co., 10368 W. Centennial Rd., Littleton, CO 80127. TEL 303-979-5657. FAX 303-978-1457. Ed. Michael L. Richmond. (back issues avail.; reprint service avail. from RRI) **Indexed:** C.L.I.

347   US
TRIAL COMMUNICATION SKILLS. 1986. base vol. (plus a. suppl.). $95. Shepard's - McGraw-Hill, Inc., Box 35300, Colorado Springs, CO 80935-3530. TEL 800-525-2474. **Document type:** trade publication.
Description: Covers the art of persuasion and effective communication and its specific applications in the courtroom.

347.91   US   ISSN 0160-7308
KF8911.A3
TRIAL DIPLOMACY JOURNAL. 1978. bi-m. $108 (foreign $132). John Wiley & Sons, Inc., 605 Third Ave., New York, NY 10158-0012. TEL 212-850-6000. FAX 212-850-6088. Eds. J. Romano, R. Romano. adv.; bk.rev.; illus. circ. 3,000. (reprint service avail. from UMI) **Indexed:** C.L.I., CJPI, L.R.I., Leg.Per. **Document type:** trade publication.
—BLDSC (9050.055000); Faxon; UnCover; UMI.
Description: Articles and interviews targeted to trial attorneys.

347   US
TRIAL JUDGES NEWS. 1981. q. $13. American Bar Association, National Conference of State Trial Judges, 750 N. Lake Shore Dr., Chicago, IL 60611. TEL 312-988-5691. FAX 312-988-6281. Ed. Jon R. Kerian. circ. 2,250. **Document type:** newsletter.
Description: Reports activities and programs of the conference.

347.91   US   ISSN 0041-2546
K24.R46
TRIAL LAWYER'S GUIDE. 1957. q. $100. Callaghan & Co., 155 Pfingsten Rd., Deerfield, IL 60015. TEL 800-323-1336. Ed. John J. Kennelly. bk.rev.; index. (also avail. in microfiche from WSH; microfilm from WSH) **Indexed:** C.L.I., L.R.I., Leg.Per. **Document type:** trade publication.
—Faxon; UMI.

347   US
TRIAL LAWYERS MARKETING BRIEFS. m. Trial Lawyers Marketing Association, One Boston Pl., Boston, MA 02108-4401. TEL 617-742-0696. Ed. Fran Senner-Hurley.

347.91   US   ISSN 0041-2554
K24
TRIAL LAWYERS QUARTERLY. 1959. q. $25. New York State Trial Lawyers Association, 132 Nassau St., Ste. 200, New York, NY 10038. TEL 212-349-5890. FAX 212-608-2310. Ed.Bd. adv.; bk.rev. circ. 5,000. (reprint service avail. from UMI) **Indexed:** C.L.I., L.R.I., Leg.Per.
—BLDSC (9050.070000); UMI.

347   US
U S SUPREME COURT BULLETIN. 1936. w. $615. Commerce Clearing House, Inc., 4025 W. Peterson Ave., Chicago, IL 60646. TEL 312-583-8500. Ed. J. Rooney. (looseleaf format) **Document type:** government publication, bulletin.

347   US   ISSN 0097-7977
KF9670
U.S. ADMINISTRATIVE OFFICE OF THE UNITED STATES COURTS. REPORT ON APPLICATIONS FOR ORDERS AUTHORIZING OR APPROVING THE INTERCEPTION OF WIRE OR ORAL COMMUNICATIONS. Key Title: Report on Applications for Orders Authorizing or Approving the Interception of Wire or Oral Communications. 1972. a. free. Administrative Office of the United States Courts, Washington, DC 20544. TEL 202-633-6036. **Document type:** government publication.

347   US   ISSN 0083-1239
U.S. IMMIGRATION AND NATURALIZATION SERVICE. ADMINISTRATIVE DECISIONS UNDER IMMIGRATION AND NATIONALITY LAWS. INTERIM DECISIONS OF THE DEPARTMENT OF JUSTICE. irreg. $63. U.S. Immigration and Naturalization Service, Department of Justice, Office of Information, 425 I St., N.W., Washington, DC 20536. TEL 202-724-7796. (Orders to: Supt. of Documents, Washington, DC 20402) **Document type:** government publication.

347   US   ISSN 0094-2553
KF105.1
UNITED STATES JUDICIAL REPORTER. m. $35. Box 541, Harrisburg, PA 17108.

347   PN
UNIVERSIDAD DE PANAMA. CENTRO DE INVESTIGACION JURIDICA. ANUARIO. a. price varies. Universidad de Panama, Centro de Investigacion Juridica, Estafeta Universitaria, Panama, Panama.

347   PN
UNIVERSIDAD DE PANAMA. CENTRO DE INVESTIGACION JURIDICA. BOLETIN DE INFORMACION JURIDICA. s-a. $1. Universidad de Panama, Centro de Investigacion Juridica, Estafeta Universitaria, Panama, Panama. Dir. Aura G. de Villalaz.

347   PN
UNIVERSIDAD DE PANAMA. CENTRO DE INVESTIGACION JURIDICA. LEGISLACION PANAMENA. INDICES CRONOLOGICOS Y ANALITICO DE LEYES (O DECRETOS EJECUTIVOS). 1958. quinquennial. price varies. Universidad de Panama, Centro de Investigacion Juridica, Estafeta Universitaria, Panama, Panama. Dir. Aura G. de Villalaz.

347   PR
LAW
UNIVERSIDAD DE PUERTO RICO. REVISTA JURIDICA. (Text in English, Spanish) 1932. 4/yr. $34 (effective 1994). Universidad de Puerto Rico, Escuela de Derecho, Apdo. 23349, San Juan, PR 00931-3349. TEL 809-764-0000. Ed. Anibelle Sloan. adv.; bk.rev.; index, cum.index: vols.1-30, vols.31-48. circ. 900. (also avail. in microform from WSH; back issues avail.) **Indexed:** C.L.I., L.R.I., Leg.Per. **Document type:** academic/scholarly publication.
—BLDSC (7862.300000).
Formerly: Universidad de Puerto Rico. Escuela de Derecho. Revista Juridica (ISSN 0041-851X)
Description: Puerto Rican juridical problems and solutions.

347   CK   ISSN 0041-9060
AS82
UNIVERSITAS; ciencias juridicas y socio-economicas. 1951. s-a. Col.$80($12) Pontificia Universidad Javeriana, Facultad de Ciencias Juridicas y Socioeconomicas, Departamento de Publicaciones, Carrera 7, No. 40-62, Bogota DE, Colombia. Ed. Gabriel Giraldo, S.J. adv.; bk.rev.; abstr.; index. circ. 1,500. **Indexed:** Int.Lab.Doc.
—BLDSC (9101.341000).

LAW — LEGAL AID

347　　　　　　CN　　ISSN 0845-9401
UNIVERSITE LAVAL. REVUE JURIDIQUE DES ETUDIANTS ET ETUDIANTES. 1987. a. Wilson et Lafleur Ltee., C.P. 24, Place d'Armes, Montreal, PQ H2Y 3L2, Canada. **Indexed:** Ind.Can.L.P.L.
　　Formerly (until 1989): Universite Laval. Revue Juridiques des Etudiants (ISSN 0832-848X)

345　　　　　　US　　ISSN 0566-4152
HV9093.U8
UTAH. JUVENILE COURT. ANNUAL REPORT.* Key Title: Annual Report - Utah Juvenile Court. a. Juvenile Court, 3522 S. 700 W., Salt Lake City, UT 84119. TEL 801-265-5900. illus. **Document type:** government publication.
　　Formerly: Utah. Juvenile Court. Annual Administrative Report.

347　　　　　　US
VERMONT COURT RULES ANNOTATED. 1981. 2 base vols. (plus a. supplements). $85. Butterworth Legal Publishers (Salem) (Subsidiary of: Reed Elsevier plc), 8 Industrial Way, Bldg. C, Salem, NH 03079. TEL 800-548-4001. FAX 603-898-9858. Ed.Bd. (looseleaf format)
　　Description: Contains the rules of procedure for all civil and criminal trial and appellate courts in Vermont.

347　　　　　　AT
VICTORIA COURT PRACTICE. (In 2 vols.) 1987. q. C C H Australia Ltd., P.O. Box 230, North Ryde, N.S.W. 2113, Australia. TEL 02-888-2555. FAX 02-888-7324. (looseleaf format)

347　　　　　　FR　　ISSN 0042-5567
VIE JUDICIAIRE; informations judiciaires et juridiques. 1901. w. 200 F. Vie Judicaire, 41 rue de Richelieu, 75001 Paris, France. TEL 42-96-23-54. FAX 42-96-91-39. Ed. Roland Ferrari. adv.; bk.rev.; bibl.; illus. circ. 16,000.
　　Description: News for professionals on law history, judicial cases, professions, schedules of events, summaries of legal information and reflections of law and justice.

347　　　　　　US
VIRGINIA COURT RULES AND PROCEDURE, STATE AND FEDERAL. a. West Publishing Corp., 620 Opperman Dr., Eagan, MN 55123. TEL 612-687-7302; 800-241-0214. FAX 612-687-7302.

WANT'S FEDERAL - STATE COURT DIRECTORY (YEAR).
　　see BUSINESS AND ECONOMICS — Trade And Industrial Directories

347　　　　　　US
WASHINGTON COURT RULES, STATE AND FEDERAL. a. West Publishing Corp., 620 Opperman Dr., Eagan, MN 55123. TEL 621-687-8000; 800-241-0214. FAX 612-687-7302.

347　　　　　　US
WASHINGTON GUARDIANSHIP LAW; administration and litigation. 1988. base vol. (plus supplements). $75. Butterworth Legal Publishers (Salem) (Subsidiary of: Reed Elsevier plc), 8 Industrial Way, Bldg. C, Salem, NH 03079. TEL 800-548-4001. FAX 603-898-9858. Ed. Gerald B. Treacy, Jr. (looseleaf format)
　　Description: Describes the law of guardianship and related issues; explains how the law is applied and what to do.

347　　　　　　AT
WESTERN AUSTRALIA REPORTS. 1960. bi-m. Law Book Co. Ltd., 44-50 Waterloo Rd., North Ryde, N.S.W. 2113, Australia. TEL 02-887-0177. FAX 02-888-9706. TELEX ASBOOK 27995.
　　●Also available online. Vendor(s): Info-One International Pty Ltd.
　　Formerly (until 1983): West Australian Reports.
　　Description: Authorized law reports of the Supreme Court of Western Australia.

347　　　　　　US
WEST'S CALIFORNIA CODE FORMS WITH PRACTICE COMMENTARIES, CORPORATIONS. irreg, no.2, 1993. West Publishing Corp., 620 Opperman Dr., Eagan, MN 55123. TEL 612-687-8000; 800-241-0214. FAX 612-687-7302. Ed. Janet E. Kerr.
　　Description: Discusses changes in all areas of corporate law, securities law, and tax law, as they affect corporations.

347　　　　　　US　　ISSN 0162-2005
WEST'S FEDERAL CASE NEWS. (Includes: Summary of Congressional and Administrative Highlights) w. West Publishing Corp., 620 Opperman Dr., Eagan, MN 55123. TEL 612-687-8000; 800-328-9352. FAX 612-687-7302. (back issues avail.) **Document type:** trade publication.
　　Description: Summarizes important cases recently decided in the U.S. Supreme Court, Courts of Appeals, District Courts, Court of Federal Claims, Bankruptcy Courts, Court of International Trade, and current cases of interest from state courts.

347　　　　　　US　　ISSN 1052-9837
KLF529
WEST'S LOUISIANA RULES OF COURT, STATE. 1988. a. West Publishing Corp., 620 Opperman Dr., Eagan, MN 55123. TEL 612-687-8000; 800-241-0214. FAX 612-687-7302.

347　　　　　　US
WISCONSIN COURT RULES AND PROCEDURE, STATE AND FEDERAL. a. West Publishing Corp., 620 Opperman Dr., Eagan, MN 55123. TEL 612-687-8000; 800-241-0214. FAX 612-687-7302.

LAW — Legal Aid

A D A FASTSEARCH; Americans with Disabilities Act reference guide. see HANDICAPPED

A D A POLICY & LAW. (Americans with Disabilities Act) see HANDICAPPED

362.5　　　　　　US
AIDS LEGAL BIBLIOGRAPHY. (Acquired Immune Deficiency Syndrome) irreg., no.2, 1993. $40. University of Texas at Austin, Tarlton Law Library, 727 E. 26th St., Austin, TX 78705-3224. TEL 512-471-7726. FAX 512-471-0243. **Document type:** bibliography, abstracting/indexing.
　　Description: Identifies articles from the popular and academic presses that deal with the social, political, and legal ramifications of AIDS.

347　　　　　　US
KF337.T4L4
ALERT (AUSTIN). 1978. m. Texas Legal Services Center, 815 Brazos, Ste. 1100, Austin, TX 78701. TEL 512-477-4562. FAX 512-477-6576. Ed. Penny Ferrell. bk.rev. circ. 1,000. **Document type:** newsletter.
　　●Also available online.

AMERICANS WITH DISABILITIES ACT UPDATE. see HANDICAPPED

362.5 368.4　　　　US
ATTORNEY'S GUIDE TO SOCIAL SECURITY DISABILITY CLAIMS. 1986. base vol. (plus a. suppl.). $95. Shepard's - McGraw-Hill, Inc., Box 35300, Colorado Springs, CO 80935-3530. TEL 800-525-2474.
　　Description: Discusses the Disability Reform Act of 1984, its ramifications and the mental impairment regulations. Provides a listing of impairments now in effect.

362.5　　　　　　AU
AUSTRIA. ENTSCHEIDUNGEN DES OBERSTEN GERICHTSHOFES IN SOZIALRECHTSSACHEN (SSV-NF). 1961. a. price varies. Manzsche Verlags- und Universitaetsbuchhandlung, Kohlmarkt 16, A-1014 Vienna, Austria. TEL 0222-531610. FAX 0222-53161-181. Eds. Wilhelm Resch, Peter Bauer. circ. 2,000. **Document type:** government publication.
　　Formerly (until 1988): Austria. Oberlandesgericht Wien im Leistungsstreitverfahren Zweiter Instanz der Sozialversicherung (SSV). Entscheidungen.
　　Description: Collects decisions on legal aspects of social welfare.

362.5　　　　　　US
▼**B N A'S AMERICANS WITH DISABILITIES ACT MANUAL**. 1992. m. $670. The Bureau of National Affairs, Inc., 1231 25th St., N.W., Washington, DC 20037. TEL 202-452-4200. FAX 202-822-8092. TELEX 285656 BANI WSH. (Subscr. to: 9435 Key West Ave., Rockville, MD 20850. TEL 800-372-1033) Ed. Jeff Day. (looseleaf format; back issues avail.) **Document type:** newsletter.
　　●Also available online. Vendor(s): Human Resources Information Network (File ADAM).
　　Description: Reference service providing guidance on the provisions of the Americans with Disabilities Act that concern employers, employment and public accommodations.

362.5 362.4　　　US　　ISSN 1063-3111
▼**B N A'S AMERICANS WITH DISABILITIES ACT MANUAL NEWSLETTER**. 1992. m. $101. The Bureau of National Affairs, Inc., 1231 25th St., N.W., Washington, DC 20037. TEL 202-452-4200. FAX 202-822-8092. TELEX 285656 BANI WSH. (Subscr. to: 9435 Key West Ave., Rockville, MD 20850. TEL 800-372-1033) Ed. Jeff Day. s-a. index. (back issues avail.) **Document type:** newsletter.
　　—CCC.
　　Description: Covers discrimination against the handicapped, law and legislation.

362.5 658.3　　　US　　ISSN 0897-7992
K2
BENEFITS LAW JOURNAL. 1988. 4/yr. $198 (foreign $248). Executive Enterprises Publications Co., Inc., 22 W. 21st St., New York, NY 10010-6904. TEL 212-645-7880. FAX 212-645-117-. Ed. Isabelle Cohen. (also avail. in microform from WSH; reprint service avail. from UMI,WSH) **Indexed:** Account.Ind. (1988-).
　　—Faxon; UMI. **CCC.**
　　Description: Reviews existing state and federal laws for their effect on benefits, evaluates pending proposals, presents informed explanations of pending changes in federal tax and labor law.

345.01　　　　　US
KF336
DIRECTORY OF LEGAL AID AND DEFENDER OFFICES IN THE UNITED STATES AND TERRITORIES. biennial. $30. National Legal Aid & Defender Association, 1625 K St., N.W., 8th Fl., Washington, DC 20006. TEL 202-452-0620. FAX 202-872-1031. **Document type:** directory.
　　Former titles: Directory of Legal Aid and Defender Offices in the United States (ISSN 0276-5365) & National Legal Aid and Defender Association Directory.
　　Description: Lists legal aid and defender offices by state and territory.

362.5 362.4　　　US
▼**DISABILITIES IN THE WORKPLACE ALERT**. 1993. m. $104.98 (overseas $146.20). Warren Gorham Lamont, One Penn Plaza, New York, NY 10119. TEL 212-971-5000. (Subscr. to: The Park Square Bldg., 31 St. James Ave., Boston, MA 02116-4112. TEL 800-950-1207) **Document type:** newsletter.
　　Description: Reports on legal developments affecting the employment of persons with disabilities and offers advice on how to comply with the Americans with Disabilities Act.

362.5　　　　　　US
▼**FAMILY AND MEDICAL LEAVE ACT**. 1993. a. West Publishing Corp., 620 Opperman Dr., Eagan, MN 55123. TEL 612-687-8000; 800-241-0214. FAX 612-687-7302.
　　Description: Provides an in-depth, up-to-date analysis of the 1993 legislation.

347　　　　　　AT
HEARSAY. 1980. q. free. Legal Aid Commission of Western Australia, 105 St. George's Terrace, Perth, W.A. 6000, Australia. FAX 09-321-8785. Ed. J.R. Armitage. circ. 3,000.
　　Description: Legal aid newsletter for the community.

362.5　　　　　　US　　ISSN 0730-7624
KF3675.Z95
HIGHLIGHTS OF STATE UNEMPLOYMENT COMPENSATIONS LAWS.* 1981. a. $15. National Foundation for Unemployment Compensation & Workers' Compensation, 1331 Pennsylvania Ave., N.W., Ste. 1500, Washington, DC 20004-1703. TEL 202-484-3346. circ. 3,000.

LAW — MARITIME LAW

362.5   US
INDIAN LAW NEWS. irreg. (2-4/yr.). membership. State Bar of Wisconsin, Indian Law Section, 402 W. Wilson St., Madison, WI 53703. TEL 608-257-3838. FAX 608-257-5502. circ. 150. (back issues avail.) **Document type:** newsletter.
Description: Covers American Indian legal matters in Wisconsin.

347   CN   ISSN 0829-3929
JOURNAL OF LAW AND SOCIAL POLICY. (Text in English, French) 1985. a. Can.$15. Ontario Legal Aid Plan, Clinic Funding Staff, 375 University Ave., Ste. 810, Toronto, ON M5G 2G1, Canada. TEL 416-979-1446. FAX 416-979-7146. adv. contact: Gwen Cortis. circ. 400. **Indexed:** Ind.Can.L.P.L. **Document type:** academic/scholarly publication.

LAW AND LEGAL INFORMATION DIRECTORY. see *LAW*

347.01   CN   ISSN 0381-2049
LAW
LEGAL AID NEW BRUNSWICK ANNUAL REPORT/AIDE JURIDIQUE NOUVEAU BRUNSWICK RAPPORT ANNUEL. (Text in English and French) 1972. a. Law Society of New Brunswick, 1133 Regent St., Ste. 206, Fredericton, NB E3B 3Z2, Canada. TEL 506-458-8540. FAX 506-458-1076. circ. 1,500.
Description: Reports on the activities of New Brunswick's legal aid program.

362.5 350   US
LEGAL ISSUES, GOVERNMENT PROGRAMS & THE ELDERLY (FLORIDA); a handbook for the advocates. 1987. base vol. (plus suppl.) $50. (Center for Governmental Responsibility, Gainesville) Butterworth Legal Publishers (Salem) (Subsidiary of: Reed Elsevier plc), 8 Industrial Way, Bldg. C, Salem, NH 03079. TEL 800-548-4001. FAX 603-898-9858. (looseleaf format) **Document type:** trade publication.
Description: Designed to help Florida attorneys, social workers and other professionals who act as advocates, conduct research and prepare for litigation, recognize problems for which legal assistance should be sought, recognize services or benefits available under various government programs and know where to obtain further assistance and information.

340   US   ISSN 0739-9111
N L A D A CORNERSTONE. 1980. 4/yr. $20. National Legal Aid and Defender Association, 1625 K St. N.W., 8th Fl., Washington, DC 20006. TEL 202-452-0620. FAX 202-872-1031. tr.lit. circ. 4,000. (back issues avail.; reprint service avail. from UMI) **Document type:** newsletter.
Formerly: N L A D A Washington Memo (ISSN 0196-1624)
Description: Technical information for public defenders, legal services attorneys, pro bono attorneys and clients.

347   US
OHIO LEGAL RIGHTS SERVICE. ANNUAL REPORT. 1976. a. $1. Ohio Legal Rights Service, Atlas Bldg., 8 E. Long St., Columbus, OH 43215. TEL 614-466-7264. Ed. David E. Merry. circ. 300.

347   US   ISSN 0737-7630
KF298
PASSPORT TO LEGAL UNDERSTANDING; the newsletter on public education programs and materials. 1983. 3/yr. free. American Bar Association, Commission on Public Understanding About the Law, 541 N. Fairbanks, Chicago, IL 60611. TEL 312-988-5726. FAX 312-988-5032. Ed. Cynthia Canary. adv.; bk.rev. circ. 10,000. (back issues avail.) **Document type:** newsletter.

PHILADELPHIA BAR ASSOCIATION. LEGAL DIRECTORY. see *LAW*

362.5 614.7 350   US
PUBLIC INTEREST BRIEFS. 1971. 2/yr. membership. Center for Law in the Public Interest, 5750 Wilshire Blvd., Ste. 561, Los Angeles, CA 90036-3697. TEL 213-470-3000. FAX 213-474-7083. Ed. Marian Samuels. bk.rev. circ. 2,000.
Description: Provides free legal services on a broad range of important issues: civil rights, free speech, affordable housing, the homeless, fair elections, environmental protection, land use, corporate and governmental accountability.

347   US
KFC77.5.S72
STATE BAR OF CALIFORNIA. LEGAL SERVICES SECTION. NEWSLETTER. 3/yr. free to members. State Bar of California, Legal Services Section, 555 Franklin St., San Francisco, CA 94102. TEL 415-561-8280. **Document type:** newsletter.
Description: Covers trends and new developments in legal services.

362.5   UK   ISSN 1353-3673
▼**WELFARE LAW AND IMMIGRATION.** 1994. a. £17.50. Jordan Publishing Ltd., 21 St. Thomas St., Bristol BS1 6JS, England. TEL 0272-230600. FAX 0272-250486. Ed. Brigid Campbell. **Document type:** academic/scholarly publication.

LAW — Maritime Law

343.09   US
ADMIRALTY LAW NEWSLETTER. s-a. $15. American Bar Association, Young Lawyers Division, 750 N. Lake Shore Dr., Chicago, IL 60611. TEL 312-988-5000. **Document type:** newsletter.
Description: Focuses on summaries of recent case law developments, CLE programs in maritime law area, and information and articles on programs and projects.

343.09   US   ISSN 0002-9874
AMERICAN MARITIME CASES. 1923. m. (except Aug.). $685. American Maritime Cases, Inc., 28 E. 21st St., Baltimore, MD 21218. TEL 410-752-2939. FAX 410-625-1174. Eds. Graydon S. Staring, Donald C. Greenman. index. circ. 1,064. (back issues avail.) **Document type:** trade publication.
●Also available online. Vendor(s): Mead Data Central, Inc.

343.09 387   US
BENEDICT ON ADMIRALTY. (Issued in 25 base vols. with supplements) irreg. $2295. Matthew Bender & Co., Inc., 11 Penn Plaza, New York, NY 10001. TEL 212-967-7707. (looseleaf format)
Description: Covers all aspects of the American law of the sea and shipping.

C I B DAILY MARITIME NEWSLETTER. (Congressional Information Bureau, Inc.) see *TRANSPORTATION — Ships And Shipping*

C I B DAILY MARITIME NEWSLETTER INDEX. (Congressional Information Bureau, Inc.) see *TRANSPORTATION — Ships And Shipping*

COASTAL MANAGEMENT; an international journal of marine environment, resources, law and society. see *EARTH SCIENCES — Oceanography*

347   AT   ISSN 0069-7133
LAW
COMMONWEALTH LAW REPORTS. 1901. irreg. (approx. 10/yr.). Law Book Co. Ltd., 44-50 Waterloo Rd., North Ryde, N.S.W. 2112, Australia. TEL 02-887-0177. FAX 02-888-9706. TELEX ASBOOK 27995. index, cum.index: vols.1-150, 151-171. **Indexed:** C.L.I., Curr.Aus.N.Z.Leg.Lit.Ind., Leg.Per.
●Also available online.
Description: Contains authorized reports of the High Court of Australia.

341.7 340   US
COURT CASE DIGEST. 1981. m. $440. Maritime Advisory Services Inc., 10 Signal Rd., Stamford, CT 06902. TEL 203-975-7070. FAX 203-975-7002. circ. 185. (back issues avail.) **Document type:** newsletter.
Description: Reviews all major American and Canadian court decisions.

343.09   FR   ISSN 0012-642X
DROIT MARITIME FRANCAIS. 1923. m. 1450 F. (foreign 1830 F.). Moreux, 190 bd. Haussmann, 75008 Paris, France. TEL 44-95-99-50. TELEX 290 131. bk.rev.; bibl.; charts; stat. circ. 12,000. **Indexed:** Mar.Aff.Bibl.
—SWETS.

343.09 387   US
FEDERAL MARITIME COMMISSION SERVICE. 1970. irreg. (10-12/yr.). $300. Hawkins Publishing Co., Inc., Box 480, Mayo, MD 21106-0480. TEL 301-798-1677. Ed. Carl R. Eyler. (looseleaf format) **Document type:** abstracting/indexing.

INTERNATIONAL ENCYCLOPAEDIA OF LAWS. TRANSPORT LAW. see *TRANSPORTATION*

341.7   UK   ISSN 0927-3522
K9
INTERNATIONAL JOURNAL OF MARINE AND COASTAL LAW. 1986. q. fl.589($307) (effective 1994). Graham & Trotman Ltd. (Subsidiary of: Kluwer Academic Publishers Group), Sterling House, 66 Wilton Rd., London SW1V 1DE, England. TEL 44-71-821-1123. FAX 44-71-630-5229. (Dist. by: Kluwer Academic Publishers Group, P.O. Box 322, 3300 AH Dordrecht, Netherlands. TEL 31-78-524400. FAX 31-78-524474; N. America dist. addr.: Box 358, Accord Station, Hingham, MA 02018-0358. TEL 617-871-6600. FAX 617-871-6528) (Co-publisher: Martinus Nijhoff Publishers, Human Rights and International Law, NE) Eds. David Freestone, Gerald J. Mangone. adv. (also avail. in microform from UMI; back issues avail.) **Indexed:** C.L.I., Deep Sea Res.& Oceanogr.Abstr., ELLIS, Environ.Per.Bibl. **Document type:** academic/scholarly publication.
—BLDSC (4542.329300); SWETS; UMI.
Formerly (until 1993): International Journal of Estuarine and Coastal Law (ISSN 0268-0106)
Refereed Serial

341.7   NE   ISSN 0920-7767
INTERNATIONAL ORGANIZATIONS AND THE LAW OF THE SEA (YEAR); documentary yearbook. (Text in English) 1987. a., vol.7, 1993 (for the year 1991). $2550 (effective 1993). (Netherlands Institute for the Law of the Sea (NILOS)) Kluwer Academic Publishers, Postbus 17, 3300 AA Dordrecht, Netherlands. TEL 31-78-334911. FAX 31-78-334254. TELEX 29245 KAPG NL. (Dist. by: Kluwer Academic Publishers Group, P.O. Box 322, 3300 AH Dordrecht, Netherlands. TEL 31-78-524400; N. America dist. addr.: Box 358, Accord Sta., Hingham, MA 02018-0358. TEL 617-871-6600. FAX 617-871-524474) (back issues avail.) **Document type:** academic/scholarly publication.
Refereed Serial

INTERNATIONAL STRAITS OF THE WORLD. see *POLITICAL SCIENCE — International Relations*

341.7 387   US   ISSN 0022-2410
K10
JOURNAL OF MARITIME LAW AND COMMERCE. 1969. q. $85 (foreign $95). Anderson Publishing Co., 2035 Reading Rd., Cincinnati, OH 45202. TEL 513-421-4142. FAX 513-562-8116. Ed. Nicholas J. Healy. adv.; bk.rev.; bibl. circ. 2,500. (back issues avail.; reprint service avail. from UMI) **Indexed:** Abstr.Bk.Rev.Curr.Leg.Per., BMT, C.L.I., C.R.E.J., Deep Sea Res.& Oceanogr.Abstr., L.R.I., Leg.Cont., Leg.Per., Mar.Aff.Bibl., Ocean.Abstr., P.A.I.S., Pollut.Abstr., Sel.Water Res.Abstr., SSCI. **Document type:** academic/scholarly publication.
—BLDSC (5012.070000); Faxon; UnCover; SWETS.

343.09   BE   ISSN 0022-6831
JURISPRUDENCE DU PORT D'ANVERS. (Text in Dutch, French) 1856. bi-m. 4500 BEF. Lloyd Anversois S.A., Eiermarkt 23, B-2000 Antwerp, Belgium. TEL 32-3-2340550. FAX 32-3-2340850. TELEX 31446. Ed. G. Dubois. index. circ. 750.
Description: Verbatim reports of important judicial decisions affecting maritime cases.

LAMY TRANSPORT TOME 1; route. see *LAW — International Law*

LAMY TRANSPORT TOME 2; douane, commissionnaires de transport, transports maritime, transports par chemin de fer, transports aeriens, lexique. see *LAW — International Law*

LAMY TRANSPORT TOME 3; marchandises dangereuses. see *LAW — International Law*

LAND AND WATER LAW REVIEW. see *LAW*

341.7   US   ISSN 0080-2808
                             CODEN: OLURDD
LAW OF THE SEA INSTITUTE. OCCASIONAL PAPER. 1969. irreg, no.37, 1991. Law of the Sea Institute, University of Hawaii - Manoa, Richardson School of Law, 2515 Dole St., Honolulu, HI 96822. TEL 808-956-6750. FAX 808-956-6402. TELEX 7431895. circ. 250 (controlled). **Indexed:** Deep Sea Res.& Oceanogr.Abstr.
—BLDSC (6217.490000).

341.7   US
LAW OF THE SEA INSTITUTE. PROCEEDINGS OF THE ANNUAL CONFERENCE. no.3, 1968. a. price varies. Law of the Sea Institute, University of Hawaii, Richardson School of Law, 2515 Dole St., Honolulu, HI 96822. TEL 808-956-6750. FAX 808-956-6402. TELEX 7431895. **Document type:** proceedings.

341.44   US   ISSN 0092-6426
JX4131
LIMITS IN THE SEAS. irreg., no.101, 1984. free. U.S. Department of State, Office of Ocean Law and Policy, c/o Bureau of Oceans and Environmental Science, 2201 C St., N.W., Washington, DC 20520. TEL 202-647-2250.

LLOYD'S LAW REPORTS. see *LAW*

340 341.7   UK   ISSN 0306-2945
K12
LLOYD'S MARITIME & COMMERCIAL LAW QUARTERLY. 1974. q. $205. Lloyd's of London Press Ltd., Sheepen Place, Colchester, Essex CO3 3LP, England. TEL 0206-772277. FAX 0206-46273. TELEX 987321 LLOYDS G. (US subscr. to: 611 Broadway, Ste. 308, New York, NY 10012. TEL 212-529-9500) bk.rev. (also avail. in microfilm from WSH,PMC; reprint service avail. from WSH) Indexed: Abstr.Bk.Rev.Curr.Leg.Per., C.L.I., ELLIS, L.R.I., Leg.Per., Mar.Aff.Bibl.
—BLDSC (5287.270000); Faxon; SWETS; UMI.
  Description: Covers commercial and shipping law on an international scale. Provides general information noting international developments in the law, notable meetings and seminars.

340   UK   ISSN 0268-0696
LLOYD'S MARITIME LAW NEWSLETTER. 1979. fortn. $548. Lloyd's of London Press Ltd., Sheepen Place, Colchester, Essex CO3 3LP, England. TEL 0206-772277. FAX 0206-46273. TELEX 987321 LLOYDS G. (US subscr. to: 611 Broadway, Ste. 308, New York, NY 10012. TEL 212-529-9500) Ed. Joseph Sweeney.

LOUISIANA COASTAL LAW; coastal zone management, marine resource law, and environmental law related to coastal and marine issues. see *LAW*

343.09 551.46   US
MARINE LAWS; navigation and safety. 1985. 3 base vols. (plus a. supplement), 3rd ed. $135. Butterworth Legal Publishers (Salem) (Subsidiary of: Reed Elsevier plc), 8 Industrial Way, Bldg. C, Salem, NH 03079. TEL 800-548-4001. FAX 603-898-9858.
  Description: Contains the principal laws relating to navigational and safety aspects of commercial shipping, supplemented by selected laws and international agreements and conventions on related subjects.

MARINE POLICY. see *EARTH SCIENCES — Oceanography*

MARITIME ADVISOR ARBITRATION AWARD DIGEST. see *TRANSPORTATION — Ships And Shipping*

MARITIME ADVISOR MARINE OPERATIONS REPORTER. see *TRANSPORTATION — Ships And Shipping*

341.7   NE
MARITIME LAW HANDBOOK. (Text in English) 1984. 2 base vols. (plus s-a. updates). fl.425($243) (effective 1994). Kluwer Law and Taxation Publishers (Subsidiary of: Wolters Kluwer N.V.), P.O. Box 23, 7400 GA Deventer, Netherlands. TEL 31-5700-47261. FAX 31-5700-22244. TELEX 49295 KLUDV NL. (Dist. by: Libresso Distribution Centre, P.O. Box 23, 7400 GA Deventer, Netherlands. TEL 31-5700-33155. FAX 31-5700-33834; In N. America: Kluwer Law and Taxation Publishers, 675 Massachusetts Ave., Cambridge, MA 02139. TEL 617-354-0140. FAX 617-354-8595) Eds. Roger Heward, Hans-Christian Albrecht. (looseleaf format)
  Description: Provides a country-by-country overview of registration of vessels, arrest or enforced sale of vessels, and mortgages on vessels, with texts of relevant maritime law conventions.

347.75   US
MARITIME LAW REPORTER. 1987. bi-m. $185. Butterworth Legal Publishers (Salem) (Subsidiary of: Reed Elsevier plc), 8 Industrial Way, Bldg. C, Salem, NH 03079. TEL 800-548-4001. FAX 603-898-9858. (looseleaf format)

387 343.09   ISSN 0894-5713
KF1107.A59
MARITIME PERSONAL INJURY REPORT. 1986. m. $195. Maritime Advisory Services Inc., 10 Signal Rd., Stamford, CT 06902-7909. TEL 203-975-7070. FAX 203-975-7002. Ed. Chris Dupin. circ. 150. (back issues avail.) **Document type:** newsletter.
  Description: Covers court cases, insurance reviews and maintenance care.

MEDITERRANEAN SHIPPING DIRECTORY. see *TRANSPORTATION — Ships And Shipping*

343.09   US
NEW YORK NAVIGATION LAWS. 1989. a. $6. Gould Publications (Binghamton), 199-300 State St., Binghamton, NY 13901. TEL 607-724-3000. FAX 607-723-4285. adv.; bk.rev. (looseleaf format)
  Description: Contains Chapter 37 of the consolidated laws.

343.09   US   ISSN 1073-8843
K24
OCEAN & COASTAL LAW JOURNAL; legal and policy journal on U.S. ocean and coastal law. 1990. s-a. $35 to individuals; institutions $50. (University of Maine, School of Law) Marine Law Institute, 246 Deering Ave., Portland, ME 04102. TEL 207-780-4474. FAX 207-780-4913. Ed. Alison Rieser. bk.rev. circ. 300. **Document type:** academic/scholarly publication.
—UnCover.
  Former titles (until 1994): Territorial Sea Journal (ISSN 1046-9680); (until 1990): Territorial Sea (ISSN 0890-0647)

343.09   US   ISSN 1052-6730
JX4419
OCEAN AND COASTAL LAW MEMO. 1973. irreg., no.39, 1993. free. University of Oregon, School of Law, Ocean and Coastal Law Center, Eugene, OR 97403-1221. TEL 503-346-3845. FAX 503-346-1564. Eds. Richard G. Hildreth, Jon L. Jacobson. circ. 1,500. (back issues avail.) **Document type:** newsletter.
  Formerly (until no.32, 1989): Ocean Law Memo (ISSN 0361-2473)
  Description: Analyzes a current issue in ocean and coastal law in each number.

343.09   US   ISSN 1059-5376
OCEANA'S LEGAL ALMANACS, SECOND SERIES. 1952; N.S. 1991. irreg. price varies. Oceana Publications Inc., Dobbs Ferry, NY 10522. TEL 914-693-1320. FAX 914-693-0402. Ed. Irving J. Sloan. (back issues avail.) **Document type:** monographic series.
—BLDSC (5181.312000).
  Supersedes (in 1991): Legal Almanac Series (ISSN 0075-8582)
  Description: Monographs on popular legal matters for a non-specialist audience.

341 614.7   US
OCEANS POLICY NEWS. 1983. 6/yr. $50 membership. Council on Ocean Law, 1600 H St. N.W., 2nd Fl., Washington, DC 20006-4407. circ. 1,000. (back issues avail.)
  Description: For ocean law and policy specialists.

SMALL CRAFT ADVISORY. see *SPORTS AND GAMES — Boats And Boating*

343.09   US
SOUNDINGS (SPRINGFIELD). 1965. 5/yr. $12. Illinois State Bar Association, Admiralty and Maritime Law Section, Illinois Bar Center, Springfield, IL 62701. TEL 217-525-1760. FAX 217-525-0712. Eds. Steven Belgrade, Dennis Minichello. circ. 200. (looseleaf format; back issues avail.) **Document type:** newsletter.

STUDI MARITTIMI; economia, diritto e tecnica della navigazione dei porti. see *TRANSPORTATION — Ships And Shipping*

343.09   PL   ISSN 1230-6037
STUDIA IURIDICA MARITIMA. 1989. irreg., latest no.3. price varies. Uniwersytet Gdanski, Wydzial Prawa i Administracji, c/o Biblioteka Glowna, Ul. Armii Krajowej 110, 81-824 Sopot, Poland. TEL 51-00-61. (Dist. by: Ars Polona-Ruch, Krakowskie Przedmiescie 7, Warsaw, Poland) Ed. Zdzislaw Brodecki. circ. 200. **Document type:** academic/scholarly publication.
  Formerly (until 1990): Uniwersytet Gdanski. Wydzial Prawa i Administracji. Zeszyty Naukowe. Studia Iuridica Maritima (ISSN 0860-374X)

343.09   US   ISSN 1048-3748
K13   CODEN: TMLJE7
TULANE MARITIME LAW JOURNAL. 1975. s-a. $20 (foreign $25) (effective Dec. 1993). Tulane University, School of Law, New Orleans, LA 70118. TEL 504-865-5959. FAX 504-865-6748. Ed. Michelle O'Daniels. adv.; bk.rev. circ. 1,000. (also avail. in microfilm from RRI; reprint service avail. from RRI) Indexed: C.L.I., L.R.I., Leg.Per., Mar.Aff.Bibl.
●Also available online. Vendor(s): Mead Data Central, Inc., West Services, Inc.
—BLDSC (9070.330000); Faxon; UnCover.
  Formerly: Maritime Lawyer.

U.S. COAST GUARD MARINE SAFETY COUNCIL. PROCEEDINGS. see *TRANSPORTATION — Ships And Shipping*

LAW — Military Law

343   US   ISSN 0094-8381
K25
AIR FORCE LAW REVIEW. 1959. s-a. $10 (foreign $12.50). U.S. Air Force, Judge Advocate General School, CPD-JAL, Maxwell AFB, AL 36112-5712. TEL 205-953-2802. (Subscr. to: Superintendent of Documents, U.S. Government Printing Office, Box 371954, Pittsburgh, PA 15250-7954. TEL 202-783-3238. FAX 202-512-2233) Ed. Mark G. Jackson. bk.rev.; charts; index. circ. 1,800. (also avail. in microform from UMI; back issues avail.) Indexed: Abstr.Bk.Rev.Curr.Leg.Per., Air Un.Lib.Ind., C.C.L.P., C.L.I., Ind.U.S.Gov.Per., L.R.I., Leg.Cont., Leg.Per., PROMT. **Document type:** academic/scholarly publication, government publication.
—Faxon; UnCover; UMI.
  Former titles: J A G Law Review; J A G Bulletin (ISSN 0021-3527)
  Description: Contains articles of interest to Air Force judge advocates, civilian attorneys and other military lawyers.

355.133   MX   ISSN 0006-6419
BOLETIN JURIDICO MILITAR. 1935. bi-m. Secretaria de la Defensa Nacional y de la Procuraduria General de Justicia Militar, Mexico, D.F., Mexico.

343   II   ISSN 0045-7043
CIVIL & MILITARY LAW JOURNAL. (Text in English) 1965. q. Rs.150($40) Defence Employees Welfare Council, New Delhi, D-1-24, Rajouri Garden, New Delhi 110 027, India. TEL 504498. Ed. H.S. Bhatin. adv.; bk.rev. circ. 1,050.
  Description: Covers Indian rule of law, military jurisprudence and legal aid for defense personnel.

342   US   ISSN 0928-964X
▼**JOURNAL OF CONSTITUTIONAL LAW IN EASTERN AND CENTRAL EUROPE.** 1993. s-a. $125. Wm. W. Gaunt & Sons, Inc., Gaunt Bldg., 3011 Gulf Dr., Holmes Beach, FL 34217-2199. TEL 813-778-5211; 800-942-8683. FAX 813-778-5252.

343   UK
MANUAL OF AIR FORCE LAW - AMENDMENTS. irreg. price varies. H.M.S.O., P.O. Box 276, London SW8 5DT, England. circ. 4,650. **Document type:** government publication.

343   UK
MANUAL OF MILITARY LAW - AMENDMENTS. irreg. price varies. H.M.S.O., P.O. Box 276, London SW8 5DT, England. circ. 13,000. **Document type:** government publication.

LEATHER AND FUR INDUSTRIES

343
KF7606.5 US ISSN 0193-3906
MILITARY LAW REPORTER. 1973. 6/yr. $350 (effective 1992). Public Law Education Institute, 1601 Connecticut Ave. N.W., Ste. 450, Washington, DC 20009-1035. TEL 202-232-1400. Eds. Thomas Alder, Lawrence Baskir. bk.rev.; abstr.; bibl. circ. 1,000. (looseleaf format)
  Supersedes (in 1974): Selective Service Law Reporter (ISSN 0049-0113)

343
K13 US ISSN 0026-4040
MILITARY LAW REVIEW. 1958. q. $12 (foreign $15). U.S. Army, Judge Advocate Generals School, Charlottesville, VA 22903-1781. TEL 804-293-4382. (Subscr. to: Superintendent of Documents, U.S. Government Printing Office, Box 371954, Pittsburgh, PA 15250-7954. TEL 202-783-3238. FAX 202-512-2233) Ed. Daniel P. Shaver. bk.rev.; bibl.; index. circ. 8,000. (also avail. in microform from MIM,UMI; back issues avail.) **Indexed:** A.B.C.Pol.Sci., Abstr.Bk.Rev.Curr.Leg.Per., C.I.I., Curr.Cont., Ind.U.S.Gov.Per., L.R.I., Leg.Cont., Leg.Per., Mid.East: Abstr.& Ind., P.A.I.S., Pers.Lit., SSCI. **Document type:** government publication.
  ●Also available online. Vendor(s): Mead Data Central, Inc.
  —BLDSC (5768.100000); Faxon; UnCover; SWETS; UMI.
  Description: Provides a forum for military lawyers, both active and reserve, within the U.S. Army.

343 GW ISSN 0028-3525
NEUE ZEITSCHRIFT FUER WEHRRECHT. 1959. 6/yr. DM.144. J. Schweitzer Verlag, Heddesdorfer Str. 31, 56564 Neuwid, Germany. TEL 02631-8010. FAX 02631-801210. Ed. Klaus Dau. adv.; bk.rev.; index. (reprint service avail. from UMI)
  —CCC.

343 SP ISSN 0034-9399
REVISTA ESPANOLA DE DERECHO MILITAR. 1956. s-a. 1600 ptas. per no. Escuela Militar de Estudios Juridicos, Calle Tambre No. 35, 28071 Madrid, Spain. TEL 4117463. FAX 4113964. bk.rev.; bibl.; index, cum.index: nos.1-24 (1956-1968). circ. 800. **Document type:** government publication.

ROYAL MILITARY POLICE JOURNAL. see *MILITARY*

343 US ISSN 0163-1101
SHEPARD'S MILITARY JUSTICE CITATIONS. 1978. base vol. (plus bi-m. supplements). $220. Shepard's - McGraw-Hill, Inc., Box 35300, Colorado Springs, CO 80935-3530. TEL 800-525-2474.

U.S. ARMS CONTROL AND DISARMAMENT AGENCY. ANNUAL REPORT. see *MILITARY*

U.S. ARMY. ENVIRONMENTAL COMPLIANCE ASSESSMENT SYSTEM (ECAS). ANNUAL REPORT. see *ENVIRONMENTAL STUDIES — Pollution*

LEATHER AND FUR INDUSTRIES

see also *Clothing Trade; Shoes and Boots*

685 639.9 US
AMERICAN FUR INDUSTRY. NEWSLETTER.* q. membership only. American Fur Industry, 101 W. 30th St., Ste. 512, New York, NY 10001-4105. TEL 212-564-5133. circ. 3,000.
  Description: Covers association and industry developments. Promotes fur and the conservation of fur-bearing animals.

675.2 660 US ISSN 0002-9726
TS940 CODEN: JALCAQ
AMERICAN LEATHER CHEMISTS ASSOCIATION. JOURNAL. 1906. m. $90 to non-members (effective 1993). American Leather Chemists Association, Campus Sta., Location 14, Cincinnati, OH 45221. TEL 513-556-1197. Ed. Stephen Feairheller. adv. contact: Velma Becker. bk.rev.; abstr.; bibl.; charts; illus.; pat.; index; circ. 1,066 (paid). (also avail. in microform from UMI,PMC; reprint service avail. from UMI) **Indexed:** Biol.Abstr., C.I.S. Abstr., Chem.Abstr., Curr.Cont., Curr.Leather Lit., Eng.Ind., Ind.Vet., Soils & Fert., Vet.Bull.
  —BLDSC (4688.000000); SWETS; UMI; CASDDS.
  Description: Publishes original research reports on technological advancements in the leather and tanning industry, as well as patents issues and research articles from other publications are covered in abstract form.
  Refereed Serial

AMERICAN SHOEMAKING. see *SHOES AND BOOTS*

639.1 US
AMERICAN TRAPPER. bi-m. National Trappers Association, P.O. Box 513, Riverton, WY 82501-0513. TEL 307-856-3830. FAX 307-856-4000. Ed. Tom Krause. bk.rev. circ. 20,000.

685 FR ISSN 0066-2526
ANNUAIRE DE LA CHAUSSURE ET DES CUIRS. 1905. a. 570 F. Editions Louis Johanet, 68 rue Boursault, 75017 Paris, France.

685 IT ISSN 1120-2777
ARPEL; fashion review on Italian and international leathergoods, luggage, leather garments. (Text in English, French, German, Italian and Spanish) 1964. 4/yr. $282. Editrice Arpel s.r.l., Via I. Nievo 33, 20145 Milan, Italy. TEL 2-315-951. FAX 2-3491097. circ. 50,000.

685.2 659.152 IT ISSN 1120-3501
ARPEL FUR; fashion review on Italian and international furs and leather garments. (Text in English, French, German, Italian, Spanish) 1982. 3/yr. $169. Editrice Arpel S.r.l., Via I. Nievo 33, 20145 Milan, Italy. TEL 2-315-951. FAX 2-349-10-97. Ed. Laura Muggiani.

685 646.3 IT ISSN 1120-2785
ARS WEEK; fashion and economy news on footwear and leather field. (Text in English, Italian) w. $220. Editrice Arpel S.r.l., Via I. Nievo 33, 20145 Milan, Italy. TEL 2-315-951. FAX 2-349-1097. adv.

685 SP
ARTEPIEL; moda y comercio de la piel en Espana. 4/yr. 4000 ptas. Pedeca Sociedad Cooperativa Ltda., Maria Auxiliadora 5, 28040 Madrid, Spain. TEL 1-450-88-37. FAX 1-450-94-29. Ed. Leandro Alarco.

675.2 NE ISSN 0067-4834
BEDRIJFSCHAP VOOR DE LEDERWARENINDUSTRIE. JAARVERSLAG. 1957. a. fl.35($18) Bedrijfschap voor de Lederwarenindustrie, Postbus 90154, 5000 LG Tilburg, Netherlands. TEL 31-13-654390. FAX 31-13-686872. Ed. M.T. Adema. circ. 400.
  Description: Includes complete statistics of turnover, number of workers, imports, and exports.

636.088 US
BLUE BOOK OF FUR FARMING. 1943. a. $20. Communications Marketing, Inc., 9995 W. 69th St., Eden Prairie, MN 55344-3408. TEL 612-941-5820. FAX 612-941-1708. adv. circ. 2,100.

675 685 HU ISSN 0006-7652
CODEN: BOPCAM
BOR- ES CIPOTECHNIKA. (Text in Hungarian; contents page in English, German, Russian) 1951. m. $40.50. (Bor- es Cipoipari Tarsasag) Lapkiado Vallalat, Lenin korut 9-11, 1073 Budapest 7, Hungary. TEL 222-408. (Subscr. to: Kultura, P.O. Box 149, H-1389 Budapest, Hungary) Ed. E. Vermes. adv.; bk.rev.; charts; illus.; stat. circ. 690. **Indexed:** Chem.Abstr.
  —CASDDS.

675.3 GW ISSN 0007-2664
CODEN: BRULDU
BRUEHL; Fachzeitschrift fuer Rauchwarenhandel, Pelzkleidung, Rauchwarenveredlung und Pelztierzucht. (Text in German; summaries in English, French, Russian) 1960. 6/yr. DM.36 (foreign DM.46.20). Rundschau-Verlag Otto G. Koeniger GmbH und Co., Ohmstr. 15, Postfach 401568, 80802 Munich, Germany. TEL 089-381605-0. FAX 089-331731. adv.; bk.rev.; charts; illus.; tr.lit.; index. **Indexed:** Chem.Abstr., Nutr.Abstr. **Document type:** trade publication.
  Description: Trade publication for the fur industry. Covers fur trade, market, farming, and fashions, reports and announcements of events, auctions. Includes new publications, bibliographies.

CANADIAN FOOTWEAR & LEATHER DIRECTORY. see *BUSINESS AND ECONOMICS — Trade And Industrial Directories*

CANADIAN FOOTWEAR JOURNAL. see *SHOES AND BOOTS*

CANADIAN LEATHERCRAFT. see *ARTS AND HANDICRAFTS*

636 338.1 US ISSN 0009-3521
CHICAGO DAILY HIDE AND TALLOW BULLETIN; the first daily hide market service established in America. d. $328 (foreign $479). Jacobsen Publishing Co., 300 W. Adams St., Chicago, IL 60606. TEL 312-726-6600. FAX 312-726-6654. TELEX 190053. adv.; charts; mkt.; stat. (processed) **Document type:** bulletin.
  Description: Updates daily comparative price guides, targets packer, render and processor hide trading.

685 AG ISSN 0009-8728
CLEO EN LA MODA. English edition: Cleo Internacional. 1966. bi-m. Arg.$4000($10) Ediciones Ariadna, 472 Suipacha, Buenos Aires, Argentina. Ed. Alvaro D'Elia. adv.; tr.lit. circ. 5,000. (tabloid format)

675.2 685 IT
CONCERIA. 26/yr. Via Brisa 3, 20123 Milan, Italy. TEL 2-80-10-20. FAX 2-86-00-32. Ed. S. Mercogliano.

675.2 FR ISSN 0011-2690
LE CUIR PARIS. 1908. w. 814 F. (foreign 995 F.). Societe des Publications le Cuir, 1 rue Garnier, 92200 Neuilly Seine, France. TEL 47-38-11-07. FAX 46-24-99-24. Ed. Frederic Taddei. adv. contact: J. Verry. stat. **Document type:** trade publication.

675.2 685.31 IT ISSN 0011-3034
CODEN: CPMAAJ
CUOIO PELLI MATERIE CONCIANTI. (Special issues avail.) 1923. bi-m. L.71400 (foreign L.120000) (effective 1993). Stazione Sperimentale per l'Industria delle Pelli e delle Materie Concianti, Via Poggioreale 39, 80143 Naples, Italy. TEL 081-5536019. FAX 081-265574. TELEX STSPNA 721160 I. adv.; bk.rev.; abstr.; bibl.; charts; illus. circ. 2,000. **Indexed:** C.I.S. Abstr., Chem.Abstr., Curr.Leather Lit.
  —BLDSC (3493.000000); CASDDS.

675.3 DK ISSN 0011-6424
DANSK PELSDYRAVL. 1938. m. DKK 300 to non-members. Dansk Pelsdyravlerforening - Danish Fur Breeders Association, Langagervej 60, DK-2600 Glostrup, Denmark. TEL 43-434400. FAX 42-452546. TELEX 33171. Ed. Peter Hjorth. adv.; bk.rev. circ. 6,000. **Indexed:** Anim.Breed.Abstr., Chem.Abstr., Nutr.Abstr.
  Formerly: Dansk Pelsdyrblad (ISSN 0105-0834)

636.088 US ISSN 0013-6905
SF405.C45
EMPRESS CHINCHILLA BREEDER. 1945. m. $25 (foreign $30). Empress Chinchilla Breeders Cooperative, Inc., Box 318, Sixes, OR 97476. TEL 503-332-ECBC. FAX 503-332-4704. Ed. Wendell Bird. adv.; bk.rev.; charts; illus.; stat. circ. 400. **Document type:** trade publication.

FASHION EXTRAS. see *CLOTHING TRADE — Fashions*

| 636.088 | FI | ISSN 0430-5817
FINSK PALSTIDSKRIFT. 1928. m. FIM 340. Finlands Palsdjursuppfodares Forbund r.f. - Finnish Fur Breeders' Association, P.O. Box 5, FIN-01601 Vanda 60, Finland. FAX 358-90-8498217. TELEX 124786 FUR. Ed. Maj-Britt Johansson. adv. circ. 1,200. **Indexed:** Anim.Breed.Abstr., Nutr.Abstr. **Document type:** trade publication.
   Description: Trade magazine for fur farmers.

FOOTWEAR INDUSTRIES OF AMERICA. EXECUTIVE DIGEST. see SHOES AND BOOTS

| 685 | FR | ISSN 0764-0048
FOURRURE ET CUIR. 193. 11/yr. 850 F. 37 passage du Desir, 75010 Paris, France. TEL 48-24-74-94. FAX 48-00-08-67. Ed. Brigitte Bouhana. adv. **Document type:** directory, corporate report.
   Formerly: Courrier de la Fourrure (ISSN 0764-003X)

| 675.3 | US | ISSN 0016-2884
FUR AGE WEEKLY. 1918. w. $68. Fur Vogue Publishing Co. Inc., Box 868, Glenwood Landing, NY 11547-0703. TEL 516-484-0631. Ed. Marc L. Rubman. adv.; bk.rev.; circ. 2,000 (paid). (tabloid format) **Document type:** newspaper.
   Incorporates: Fur Age Monthly.
   Description: Covers all aspects of the fur industry.

| 636.088 | US | ISSN 0744-7701
FUR RANCHER. 1922. q. $20 (includes Blue Book of Fur Farming). Communications Marketing, Inc., 9995 W. 69th St., Eden Prairie, MN 55344-3408. TEL 612-941-5820. FAX 612-941-1708. Ed. Frank Zaworski. adv.; bk.rev.; charts; illus.; mkt.; stat.; tr.lit.; index. circ. 2,100. **Indexed:** Agri.Ind.
   —UnCover.
   Formerly (until 1978): U S Fur Rancher (ISSN 0041-7653)

| 636.088 | US | ISSN 0016-2965
FUR TAKER JOURNAL. 1968. m. $15. Fur Takers of America, Inc., 1541 Shannon Dr., New Haven, IN 46774-2318. FAX 319-927-4945. adv. contact: Bernie Barringer. bk.rev.; charts; illus. circ. 3,000. (also avail. in diskette format)

| 675.3 | UK | ISSN 0016-2981
FUR WEEKLY NEWS. 1933. w. L.3. Fur Weekly News Ltd., 122 Lea Bride Rd., London E5 9RB, England. Ed. A. Coster. adv.; bk.rev.

| 685 685.31 | IE | ISSN 0016-3252
FUTURA.* 1965-19??; resumed. m. $50. Futura Communications Ltd., Sandyford Office Park, Unit 9, Sandyford, Dublin 18, Ireland. Ed. Pat Lehane. adv.; illus.; tr.lit.; index. circ. 2,387.
   Incorporates: Leather and Footwear Journal.

| 675.2 | FR | ISSN 0399-5461
HEBDOCUIR. 1977. w. 446 F. (foreign 590 F.). Promotion Press Internationale, 7 ter, Cour des Petites-Ecuries, 75010 Paris, France. TEL 42-47-12-05. FAX 47-70-33-94. Ed. Philippe Gilles. circ. 7,000.
   Formed by the merger of: Independant Chaussure; Halle aux Cuirs.

| 685.31 | US | ISSN 0018-1293
HIDE AND LEATHER BULLETIN; for the tanning and shoe manufacturing industry. d. $288 (foreign $448). Jacobsen Publishing Co., 300 W. Adams St., Chicago, IL 60606. TEL 312-726-6600. FAX 312-726-6654. TELEX 190053. adv.; stat. (processed) **Document type:** bulletin.
   Description: Reports daily on hide trading.

| 685 | HK
▼**HONG KONG LEATHER GOODS AND BAGS.** (Text in English) 1993. a. $40 (free to qualified personnel). Hong Kong Trade Development Council, 38th Fl., Office Tower, Convention Plaza, 1 Harbour Rd., Wanchai, Hong Kong. TEL 852-584-4333. FAX 852-824-0249. Ed. Saul Lockhart. circ. 30,000.

| 685 | IT
IDEA PELLE; rivista di moda, della pelletteria, coordinati e abbigliamento in pelle. 3/yr. L.10000($120) (effective 1992). Editoriale di Foto Shoe s.r.l., Via Leonardo da Vinci, 43, 20090 Trezzano s-n (MI), Italy. TEL 4459191. FAX 48402959. TELEX 320606 FOSHOE I.
   Description: Covers leather fashions and products, companies and trade fairs, and personalities in the field.

| 675.2 | GW | ISSN 0178-5052
IN LEDER. 1922. m. DM.159. Umschau Zeitschriftenverlag Breidenstein GmbH, Stuttgarter Str. 18-24, 60329 Frankfurt a.M., Germany. TEL 069-2600-0. FAX 069-2600-609. TELEX 411964. Ed. Christiane Knauthe. adv.; bk.rev.; illus.; pat.; stat.; tr.lit. circ. 6,600. **Indexed:** Key to Econ.Sci. **Document type:** trade publication.
   Formerly: Lederwaren-Zeitung (ISSN 0047-4312)

| 675.2 | II | ISSN 0019-574X
INDIAN LEATHER. (Text in English) 1967. m. $100. Indian Leather, 120 Vepery High Rd., Periamet, Madras 600 003, India. TEL 586566. Ed. S. Sankaran. adv.; bk.rev. circ. 1,000. **Indexed:** Curr.Leather Lit. **Document type:** trade publication.

| 675.2 | II | ISSN 0019-5758
CODEN: JILTAV
INDIAN LEATHER TECHNOLOGISTS' ASSOCIATION. JOURNAL. (Text in English) 1952. m. Rs.200($45) Indian Leather Technologists' Association, Mercantile Bldgs., 1st Fl., E. Gate, Lalbazar St., Calcutta 700 001, India. TEL 20-7472. Ed. Sushil Ranjan Sarkar. adv.; bk.rev.; charts; illus.; index. circ. 1,500. **Indexed:** Chem.Abstr. **Document type:** trade publication.
   —CASDDS.
   Description: Serves the leather and footwear industry with up-to-date information on technological developments.

| 685.2 | FR | ISSN 0980-1367
CODEN: INCUEH
INDUSTRIE DU CUIR. Short title: I D C. (Text in English, French) m. (10/yr.). 690 F. (foreign 920 F.). Societe de Publications le Cuir, 1 rue Garnier, 92200 Neuilly Seine, France. TEL 47-38-11-07. FAX 46-24-99-24. adv. contact: J. Verry. **Document type:** trade publication.
   —CASDDS.
   Formerly: Revue Technique des Industries du Cuir (ISSN 0004-5462)

INSTITUTUL POLITEHNIC DIN IASI. BULETINUL. SECTIA VIII: TEXTILE, PIELARIE. see TEXTILE INDUSTRIES AND FABRICS

| 675.2 | UK | ISSN 0955-5080
TS945
INTERNATIONAL LEATHER GUIDE. (Includes a five-language glossary) 1968. a. £89 (overseas £104). Benn Business Information Services Ltd. (Subsidiary of: Morgan-Grampian plc), Riverbank House, Angel Ln., Tonbridge, Kent TN9 1SE, England. TEL 0732-362666. FAX 0732-367301. TELEX 957829 BENTON G. Ed.Bd. adv.; index. circ. 1,850. **Document type:** directory.
   Former titles: Leather Guide (ISSN 0140-413X); European Leather Guide (ISSN 0071-2906)
   Description: Contains data of interest to tanners and merchants, hide and skin suppliers, machinery manufacturers, and chemical suppliers.

| 685 | II | ISSN 0047-0988
INTERNATIONAL PRESS CUTTING SERVICE: LEATHER - HIDES - SKIN - FOOTWEAR. 1967. w. $65. International Press Cutting Service, P.O. Box 63, Allahabad 211001, India. Ed. N. Khanna. bk.rev.; index. circ. 1,200. (processed)

| 685 685.31 | JA
KAWA TO HAKIMONO/LEATHER & FOOTWEARS. (Text in Japanese) 1972. q. free. Tokyo-to Sangyo Rodo Kaikan - Tokyo Industrial and Vocational Center, 1-6 Hashiba 1-chome, Taito-ku, Tokyo, Japan. TEL 03-3876-2961. charts; illus.; stat. circ. 3,000.

| 675.2 | XR | ISSN 0023-4338
TS940 CODEN: KOZAAT
KOZARSTVI/LEATHER INDUSTRY; odborny casopis pro prumysl kozedelny, obuvnicky a gumove obuvi. (Text in Czech; summaries in English, German, Russian) 1950. m. $44. Nakladatelstvi Technicke Literatury, Spalena 51, 113 02 Prague 1, Czech Republic. (Dist. by: Artia, Ve Smeckach 30, 111 27 Prague 1, Czech Republic) Ed. Josef Cundrle. **Indexed:** Art & Archaeol.Tech.Abstr., C.I.S. Abstr., Chem.Abstr.
   —CASDDS.

| 675 685.3 | BU
KOZHARSKA I OBUVNA PROMISHLENOST.* (Text in Bulgarian; summaries in English, German and Russian) 1960. 8/yr. $7. Ministry of Industry, Trade and Services, Ul. Slavyanska 8, Sofia, Bulgaria. (Dist. by: Hemus, 6, Rouski Blvd., 1000 Sofia, Bulgaria) circ. 1,588. **Indexed:** Chem.Abstr.

KOZHEVENNO-OBUVNAYA PROMYSHLENNOST'. see SHOES AND BOOTS

| 675.2 | SA
L I R I QUARTERLY REVIEW. 1941. q. (Rhodes University, Leather Industries Research Institute) L I R I Technologies, P.O. Box 185, Grahamstown 6140, South Africa. FAX 0461-26517. illus.; stat.; index. circ. 1,200.
   Formerly: L I R I Monthly Circular (ISSN 0023-9755)

| 675 | SA | ISSN 0085-2724
L I R I RESEARCH BULLETIN. 1942. irreg. (approx. 20/yr.). price varies. (Rhodes University, Leather Industries Research Institute) L I R I Technologies, P.O. Box 185, Grahamstown 6140, South Africa. FAX 0461-26517. charts; illus. **Document type:** bulletin.

| 675 | SA
L I R I TECHNICAL BULLETIN. 1975. irreg. (approx. 10/yr.). (Rhodes University, Leather Industries Research Institute) L I R I Technologies, P.O. Box 185, Grahamstown 6140, South Africa. FAX 0461-26517. **Document type:** bulletin.

| 675.3 | GW | ISSN 0941-9136
L P T JOURNAL. (Leder Pelz Textil) 1905. m. DM.150. C B Verlag Carl Boldt, Baseler Str. 80, 12205 Berlin, Germany. TEL 030-8337087. FAX 030-8339125. Ed. J. Sartorius. adv.; bk.rev. circ. 5,500. **Document type:** trade publication.
   —CCC.
   Formerly: Pelzwirtschaft (ISSN 0048-3176); Which incorporated (1948-1989): Pelzspiegel.

| 675.2 | UK | ISSN 0023-9739
TS940
LEATHER. 1867. m. £53 (foreign £71). Benn Publications Ltd. (Subsidiary of: Morgan-Grampian plc), Benn House, Sovereign Way, Tonbridge, Kent TN9 1RW, England. TEL 0732-364422. FAX 0732-361534. Ed. Shelagh Davy. adv. contact: Graham Bond. bk.rev.; illus.; mkt.; tr.lit. circ. 4,000. (also avail. in microform from UMI) **Indexed:** Key to Econ.Sci. **Document type:** trade publication.
   —BLDSC (5179.332000); SWETS.

| 675.2 | JA | ISSN 0018-1811
CODEN: HIKAAF
LEATHER CHEMISTRY/HIKAKU KAGAKU. (Text in Japanese; summaries in English) 1955. q. 2500 Yen. Japanese Association of Leather Technology - Nihon Hikaku Gijutsu Kyokai, c/o Scleroprotein and Leather Research Institute, Tokyo Noko University, 3-5-8 Saiwai-cho, Fuchu-shi, Tokyo 183, Japan. Ed.Bd. adv.; abstr.; index. circ. 900. **Indexed:** Chem.Abstr., Curr.Leather Lit.
   —BLDSC (4312.500000); CASDDS.

LEATHER CONSERVATION NEWS. see MUSEUMS AND ART GALLERIES

LEATHER CRAFTERS JOURNAL. see ARTS AND HANDICRAFTS

| 685 | PK
LEATHER GOODS INTERNATIONAL. (Text in English) 1991. m. $4 per no. Press Corporation of Pakistan, P.O. Box 3138, Karachi 75400, Pakistan. TEL 21-455-3703. FAX 21-7736198. Ed. Saeed Hafeez. circ. 5,000.

| 675.23 | US
LEATHER INDUSTRIES OF AMERICA. NEWSBREAK. 1933. every 3 wks. membership. Leather Industries of America, 1000 Thomas Jefferson St., N.W., Ste. 515, Washington, DC 20007. TEL 202-342-8086. FAX 202-342-9063. Ed. Jean Ann Firestone. stat. circ. 1,000.
   Former titles: Tanner's Council of America. Newsbreak; Tanners' Council of America. Council News (ISSN 0010-9932)
   Description: Information on government regulation, leather statistics, environmental concerns, business productivity.

| 685 | US
LEATHER: LATIN AMERICAN INDUSTRIAL REPORT. (Avail. for each of 22 Latin American countries) 1985. a. $435 per country report. Aquino Productions, Box 15760, Stamford, CT 06901. TEL 203-325-3138. Ed. Andres C. Aquino.

LEATHER AND FUR INDUSTRIES

675.23   US   ISSN 0023-9763
CODEN: LEMAA7
LEATHER MANUFACTURER. 1883. m. $43. Shoe Trades Publishing Co., Box 198, Cambridge, MA 02140. TEL 617-648-8160. Ed. J.D. Sutton. adv.; illus.; mkt.; stat.; index. Indexed: Chem.Abstr. **Document type:** trade publication.
—UMI; CASDDS.

LEATHER MANUFACTURER DIRECTORY. see *BUSINESS AND ECONOMICS — Trade And Industrial Directories*

675.2   II   ISSN 0023-9771
TS940
LEATHER SCIENCE. 1954. m. Rs.50($25) Central Leather Research Institute, Adyar, Madras 600020, India. TEL 412616. (Affiliate: Council of Scientific and Industrial Research) Ed. G. Thyagarajn. adv.; bk.rev.; abstr.; charts; illus.; pat.; tr.mk.; index. circ. 500. Indexed: Chem.Abstr., Irr.& Drain.Abstr., Soils & Fert., Sorghum & Millets Abstr.
—BLDSC (5179.398000).

675.2   JA   ISSN 0018-1803
CODEN: HIKGAX
LEATHER TECHNOLOGY/HIKAKU GIJUTSU. (Text in Japanese) 1960. s-a. 3000 Yen. Japanese Association of Leather Technology - Nihon Hikaku Gijutsu Kyokai, c/o Scleroprotein and Leather Research Institute, Tokyo Noko University, 3-5-8 Saiwai-cho, Fuchu-shi, Tokyo 183, Japan. Ed.Bd. adv.; illus. circ. 900. Indexed: Chem.Abstr.
—CASDDS.

675.2 382   II   ISSN 0023-9828
HD9780.I62
LEATHERS. (Text in English) 1957. bi-m. Rs.100($40) Council for Leather Exports, 53 Sydenhams Rd., Periamet, Madras 600 003, India. TEL 589098. TELEX 41-7354 CLE IN. Ed. S. Manoharan. adv.; bk.rev.; charts; mkt.; stat. circ. 4,000. **Document type:** trade publication.
Description: Covers the leather industry.

675.2   GW   ISSN 0024-0176
TS940   CODEN: LEDEA8
DAS LEDER; Fachzeitschrift fuer die Chemie und Technologie der Lederherstellung. (Text in German; summaries in English, French and Spanish) 1950. m. DM.125. (Verein fuer Gerberei-Chemie und Technik e.V.) Eduard Roether Verlag, Berliner Allee 56, 64295 Darmstadt, Germany. TEL 06151-3001-17. Ed. E. Heidemann. adv.; bk.rev.; abstr.; bibl.; charts; illus.; pat. circ. 2,500. (also avail. in microform from UMI) Indexed: Biol.Abstr., Chem.Abstr. **Document type:** trade publication.
—SWETS; UMI; CASDDS.

675.2   GW   ISSN 0024-0184
LEDER ECHO. 1949. m. DM.10 to non-members. Gewerkschaft Leder, Will-Bleicher-Str. 20, 70174 Stuttgart, Germany. FAX 0711-293345. Ed. Doerte Hautmann. adv.; bk.rev.; film rev.; play rev.; bibl.; illus.; stat.; circ. 42,000 (controlled).

685   GW   ISSN 0342-7641
CODEN: LHGPDC
LEDER- UND HAEUTEMARKT. 36/yr. DM.295.20. Umschau Zeitschriftenverlag Breidenstein GmbH, Stuttgarterstr. 18-24, 60329 Frankfurt a.M., Germany. TEL 069-2600-0. FAX 069-2600-609. illus. **Document type:** trade publication.
—CASDDS. **CCC.**

685   GW   ISSN 0024-0214
LEDERWAREN-REPORT. 1958. m. DM.250. Verlag Otto Sternefeld GmbH, Postfach 111249, 40512 Duesseldorf, Germany. TEL 0211-575096. FAX 0211-578852. Ed. J. Sternefeld. circ. 6,100. (processed) **Document type:** trade publication.

685   II
LEXPORT. vol.11, 1974. a. Export Promotion Council for Finished Leather & Leather Manufacturers, 15-46 Civil Lines, P.O. Box 198, Kanpur 208001, India.

675.2 685   IT
LINEAPELLE. 3/yr. Via Brisa 3, 20123 Milan, Italy. TEL 2-80-10-20. FAX 2-86-00-32. Ed. S. Mercogliano.

LIVING AMONG NATURE DARINGLY!; how to for trappers, farmers, and homesteaders. see *GARDENING AND HORTICULTURE*

685   CN   ISSN 0836-3862
LUGGAGE, LEATHERGOODS & ACCESSORIES. Short title: L L A. 5/yr. Can.$32.10($48) Laurentian Media Inc., 501 Oakdale Rd., Downsview, ON M3N 1W7, Canada. TEL 613-475-3217; 800-565-8148. FAX 416-746-1421. Ed. Virginia Hutton. adv. circ. 5,200. **Document type:** trade publication.
Formerly (until Dec. 1987): Luggage and Leathergoods News.
Description: Covering the luggage and leathergoods industries.

636.088   CC   ISSN 1000-7407
MAOPI DONGWU SIYANG/BREEDING OF FUR-BEARING ANIMALS. (Text in Chinese) q. Jilin Nongye Daxue - Jilin University of Agriculture, Donghuan Lunan, Changchun, Jilin 130118, People's Republic of China. TEL 42112. Ed. Chen Qiren.

685   SP
MARROQUINERIA ESPANOLA. 1972. s-a. 2400 ptas. Prensa Tecnica, S.A., Caspe 118-120, 6o, 08013 Barcelona, Spain. TEL 3-24-55-190. FAX 3-232-27-33. Ed. F. Canet Tomas. adv.; illus. circ. 10,000.

685   SP
MECANIPEL; revista de informacion general y tecnica de la piel y sus manufacturas. 12/yr. 5000 ptas. Pedeca Sociedad Cooperativa Ltda., Maria Auxiliadora 5, 28040 Madrid, Spain. TEL 1-450-88-37. FAX 1-450-94-29. Ed. Leandro Alarcon. circ. 6,000.

MUSEUM OF THE FUR TRADE QUARTERLY. see *HISTORY — History Of North And South America*

636.088   CN   ISSN 0027-8963
NATIONAL CHINCHILLA BREEDERS OF CANADA. BULLETIN. (Text in English and French) 1946. m. $30. National Chinchilla Breeders of Canada, R.R. 10, Brampton, ON L6V 3N2, Canada. TEL 905-451-8736. FAX 905-457-5326. Ed. T. Riedstra. adv.; stat. circ. 600. (processed) **Document type:** bulletin, trade publication.
Description: Technically oriented trade magazine providing education for the chinchilla rancher.

636.088   NO   ISSN 0369-5255
NORSK PELSDYRBLAD. 1926. m. NOK 250. Norges Pelsdyralslag, P.O. Box 145, Okern, N-0509 Oslo, Norway. TEL 47-22-64-41-50. FAX 47-22-64-35-91. TELEX 76724 OSKIN. Ed. Einar Storsul. adv. circ. 3,000. Indexed: Anim.Breed.Abstr., Nutr.Abstr. **Document type:** trade publication.
—BLDSC (6144.500000).

685 333.7   CN   ISSN 0705-4831
NOVA SCOTIA TRAPPERS NEWSLETTER. 1964. a. free. Nova Scotia Natural Resources, P.O. Box 68, Truro, NS B2N 5B8, Canada. TEL 902-893-5660. FAX 902-893-6102. bk.rev. circ. 6,800. **Document type:** newsletter.
Description: Conservation, management and trapping statistics for trappers and managers.

685   FR
OFFICIEL DES METIERS DE LA CHAUSSURE.* 6/yr. 60 F. 21 rue Jean Poulmarch, 75010 Paris, France. TEL 42-08-47-50. Ed. Michel Juignet. adv. circ. 5,000.

675   PK
PAKISTAN LEATHER TRADE JOURNAL. (Text in English) 1974. q. $35. (Pakistan Society of Leather Technologists) Alam Ara Jamil, 132-A Block 2, P.E.C.H.S., P.O. Box 7187, Mahmood Ghaznavi Road, Karachi 75400, Pakistan. TEL 431900. TELEX 23364 KHLIL PK. Ed. M. Jamil Khan. adv.; bk.rev. circ. 1,000. **Document type:** trade publication.

PARFYME OG PORTEFOELJE. see *BEAUTY CULTURE — Perfumes And Cosmetics*

685.1   IT
PELLICE MODA. 6/yr. Galleria Unione 1, 20123 Milan, Italy. TEL 2-87-21-14. Ed. Anna Maria Lancellotti.

PLASTICS, RUBBER AND LEATHER INDUSTRIES JOURNAL. see *PLASTICS*

PREVISIONS GLISSANTES DETAILLEES EN PERSPECTIVES SECTORIELLES (VOL.3): TEXTILE - HABILLEMENT - CUIR. see *BUSINESS AND ECONOMICS — Economic Situation And Conditions*

685   PL   ISSN 0370-1743
TS940   CODEN: PRZKAX
PRZEGLAD SKORZANY. (Text in Polish; summaries in English, German, Russian) 1946. bi-m. $61. (Polska Izba Przemyslu Skorzanego) Wydawnictwo Czasopism i Ksiazek Technicznych SIGMA - NOT, Ul. Ratuszowa 11, P.O. Box 1004, 00-950 Warsaw, Poland. TEL 48-22-180918. FAX 48-22-192187. TELEX 814550 SIGMA PL. (Dist. by: SIGMA NOT Ltd., Ul. Bartycka 20, 00-716 Warsaw, Poland) adv.; bk.rev. circ. 930. Indexed: Chem.Abstr.
—CASDDS.

338.7   II   ISSN 0302-4881
TS959.I4
RAJASTHAN STATE TANNERIES LIMITED. ANNUAL REPORT. Key Title: Annual Report - Rajasthan State Tanneries Limited. (Text in English) 1973. a. Rajasthan State Tanneries Limited, P-6 Tilak Marg, C Scheme, Jaipur, India. **Document type:** corporate report.

636   US   ISSN 1064-0029
SANDY PARKER REPORTS; weekly international fur news. 1977. w. $125. Sandford Advertising, Inc., 363 Seventh Ave., New York, NY 10001. TEL 212-947-1144. FAX 516-791-4751. Ed. Sandy Parker. charts; illus.; tr.lit.; circ. 800 (paid). (back issues avail.)
Description: Provides information about supply, demand, price trends, government actions, and the general development of the international fur trade.

639.11   CN
SASKATCHEWAN, ALBERTA, YUKON TRAPPER. 1986. q. Can.$10. McIntosh Publishing Co. Ltd., P.O. Box 430, N. Battleford, Sask. S9A 2Y5, Canada. TEL 306-445-4401. Ed. C. Irwin McIntosh. circ. 9,800.
Formerly: Saskatchewan Trapper.

SCHOENWERELD. see *SHOES AND BOOTS*

SCHUH-ZEITUNG. see *SHOES AND BOOTS*

SCHUHMARKT. see *SHOES AND BOOTS*

SHOE AND LEATHER NEWS. see *SHOES AND BOOTS*

SHOW REPORTER. see *SHOES AND BOOTS*

675.2 660   UK   ISSN 0144-0322
CODEN: JSLTBY
SOCIETY OF LEATHER TECHNOLOGISTS AND CHEMISTS. JOURNAL. 1917. bi-m. £39 to non-members. Society of Leather Technologists and Chemists, 1 Edges Court, Moulton, Northampton NN3 7UJ, England. TEL 0604-647318. Ed. M.K. Leafe. adv.; bk.rev.; abstr.; bibl.; charts; illus.; pat.; index. circ. 900. Indexed: Anal.Abstr., Br.Tech.Ind., Chem.Abstr., Chem.Eng.Abstr., Curr.Cont., Curr.Leather Lit., W.R.C.Inf. **Document type:** academic/scholarly publication.
—BLDSC (4889.900000); SWETS; CASDDS.
Formerly: Society of Leather Trades' Chemists. Journal (ISSN 0037-9921)

SOUTH AFRICAN SHOEMAKER AND LEATHER REVIEW. see *SHOES AND BOOTS*

675.23   II   ISSN 0039-9442
TANNER.* (Text in English) 1946. m. Rs.21($6) S. Raja, 32-2 Aga Abbas Ali Rd., 3rd Cross, Bangalore 560 042, India. Ed. Mrs. L.S. Raja. adv.; bk.rev.; charts; illus.; mkt.; tr.lit. (reprint service avail. from UMI) Indexed: Chem.Abstr.

685   BL   ISSN 0101-1138
TECNICOURO. (Text in Portuguese; abstracts in English and Portuguese) 1979. 8/yr. Cz.$2085($65) Centro Tecnologico do Couro, Calcados e Afins, Rua Araxa, 750, Caixa Postal 450, 93334-000 Novo Hamburgo, RS, Brazil. TEL 051-593-2922. FAX 051-5932102. TELEX 522101 TNCT BR. Ed. Mauro Heitor Klein. adv.; bk.rev. circ. 7,500.

639.11   CN
TRAPPER. 1986. 6/yr. Can.$12.50($18) McIntosh Publishing Co. Ltd., P.O. Box 430, 1132 - 98 St., North Battleford, Sask. S9A 2Y5, Canada. TEL 306-445-4401. FAX 306-445-1977. Ed. Becky McIntosh-McDonald. adv.

685.5　US
TRAVELWARE. 9/yr. $32. Business Journals, 50 Day St., Box 5550, Norwalk, CT 06856. TEL 203-853-6015. Ed. Villia Morgan. **Indexed:** Key to Econ.Sci.
　Former titles: Luggage and Travelware (ISSN 0193-0559); Luggage and Leather Goods.

TRAVELWARE RESOURCES DIRECTORY. see *BUSINESS AND ECONOMICS — Trade And Industrial Directories*

685.1　IT
ULTIMISSIME PELLICCERIA. 11/yr. Editrice S A E s.r.l., Via Cagnola 3, 20154 Milan, Italy. TEL 2-331-1003. FAX 2-33-11-320. Ed. Alessandra Dagnino. circ. 6,500.

V W D - TEXTIL, BEKLEIDUNG, LEDER. see *BUSINESS AND ECONOMICS — Investments*

636.088　SW　ISSN 0042-2703
VAARA PAELSDJUR/OUR FURRED ANIMALS. 1930. 8/yr. SEK 200 (typically set in Jan.). Sveriges Paelsdjursuppfoedares Riksfoerbund - Swedish Fur Breeders' Association, P.O. Box 8124, S-163 08 Spaanga, Sweden. TEL 46-8-36-27-70. FAX 46-8-7618169. Ed. Berit Skenbaeck. adv.; charts; illus.; index. circ. 900. **Indexed:** Vet.Bull. **Document type:** trade publication.

VOGUE PELLE. see *CLOTHING TRADE — Fashions*

WIADOMOSCI PRODUKCYJNE: WLOKNO, ODZIEZ, SKORA. see *CLOTHING TRADE*

675.3　GW
WINCKELMANN PELZMARKET. 1969. w. DM.95. Winckelmann Verlag GmbH, Savignystr. 49, 60325 Frankfurt, Germany.

WINCKELMANN SALES REPORT. see *CLOTHING TRADE*

675.2　US　ISSN 0894-3087
WORLD LEATHER. 1987. 6/yr. $55. 61 Massachusetts, Arlington, MA 02174. TEL 617-648-8160. FAX 617-492-0126. Ed. David Buirsti. adv. circ. 10,000. (back issues avail.) **Document type:** trade publication.
　Description: Covers the leather tanning industry worldwide.

LEATHER AND FUR INDUSTRIES — Abstracting, Bibliographies, Statistics

636.088　CN　ISSN 0318-7888
CANADA. STATISTICS CANADA. REPORT ON FUR FARMS. (Catalogue 23-208) (Text in English and French) 1919. a. Can.$34($41) (foreign $48). Statistics Canada, Publications and Services, Ottawa, Ont. K1A 0T6, Canada. TEL 613-951-7277. FAX 613-951-1584. (also avail. in microform from MML)
　Description: Contains supply and disposition of fox and mink on fur farms, by province, the number of farms classified by number and reported by province, number and value of mink pelts by color, type and province.

675 016　II
TS940
LEATHER SCIENCE ABSTRACTS. (Text in English) 1968. m. Rs.100($50) Central Leather Research Institute, Adyar, Madras 600020, India. TEL 412616. (Affiliate: Council of Scientific and Industrial Research) Ed. R. Vengan. index. circ. 500. **Document type:** abstracting/indexing.
　Formerly (until 1988): Current Leather Literature (ISSN 0011-3638)

LEGAL AID

see *Law–Legal Aid*

LEISURE AND RECREATION

see also *Hobbies; Sports and Games*

790.1　UK
ALL SPORT & LEISURE MONTHLY. 1990. m. £15($32) Graphic House, 3 High Rd., Ickenham, Mddx. UB10 8LE. TEL 0895-679333. FAX 0895-677830. Ed. Tony Potts. adv.: page £1638; adv. contact: Julian Davies. bk.rev.; circ. 50,000 (paid). (tabloid format; also avail. in magnetic tape; large print edition avail.; back issues avail.) **Document type:** newspaper.
　Formerly (until 1993): All Sport Weekly.
　Description: Covers local and national sports around the London area.

790.1 700　US
ARTS & LEISURE TIMES. 1972. w. $35. Kenneth Brown, Ed. & Pub., 275 Bay 37th St., Brooklyn, NY 11214. TEL 718-996-5406. FAX 718-373-1352. adv. contact: Adrienne Knoll. circ. 186,000 (controlled). **Document type:** newspaper.
　Description: Covers all facets of leisure and entertainment activities.

791.068　US　ISSN 1048-9118
AT THE PARK; a journal for the amusement park industry. 1989. bi-m. $24.95 (foreign $32.95). Yellow Dot Publishing, Box 597783, Chicago, IL 60659-7783. TEL 312-465-4880. Ed. Allen Ambrosini. adv.; bk.rev.; illus. **Document type:** trade publication.
　Description: Covers all aspects of the amusement industry.

BARE IN MIND. see *PHYSICAL FITNESS AND HYGIENE*

790.1　US
BETTER HOMES AND GARDENS LEISURE AND OUTDOOR PRODUCT GUIDE. a. Meredith Corporation, Special Interest Publications, 1716 Locust St., Des Moines, IA 50336. TEL 515-284-3000. Pub. Steve Levinson. adv.: B&W page $20025, color page $28775; adv. contact: Pat Tomlinson. circ. 400,000.

790.1　UK
BRIEF. 1988. q. (Lawyer's Club) National Press Publishers, Peel House, 5 Balfour Rd., Weybridge, Surrey KT13 8HE, England. TEL 0932-859155. FAX 0932-859661. Ed. Chris Locke. adv.; bk.rev.; play rev.

BRITAIN'S LEISURE INDUSTRY. see *BUSINESS AND ECONOMICS — Trade And Industrial Directories*

BRITISH LEISURE & SWIMMING POOL DIRECTORY. see *BUSINESS AND ECONOMICS — Trade And Industrial Directories*

BRITISH LEISURE CENTRE DIRECTORY. see *BUSINESS AND ECONOMICS — Trade And Industrial Directories*

C P L - CHASSE, PECHE ET LOISIRS. see *SPORTS AND GAMES — Outdoor Life*

790.1 333.78　US
CALIFORNIA PARKS & RECREATION. vol.28, 1972. q. membership. California Park & Recreation Society Inc., 3031 F St., Ste. 202, Box 161118, Sacramento, CA 95816. TEL 916-446-2777. Ed. Anna Poole. adv.; cum.index; circ. 4,000 (controlled). **Indexed:** Cal.Per.Ind. (1990-).

790.1 331.1　US
CALIFORNIA PARKS AND RECREATION JOBMARKET. m. California Park and Recreation Inc., Box 161118, Sacramento, CA 95816-1118. Ed. Stephanie Beavers.

CANADIAN ALPINE JOURNAL. see *SPORTS AND GAMES — Outdoor Life*

790.1 630　IT　ISSN 1120-6381
CASA SUI CAMPI. 1990. 11/yr. L.40000 (effective 1993). Edagricole S.p.A., Via Emilia Levante 31-2, 40139 Bologna, Italy. TEL 051-492211. FAX 051-493660. Ed. Roberto Bartolini. adv.: B&W page L.2300000, color page L.3700000; trim 188 x 260. circ. 58,700.
　Description: For people who live in and/or own houses in the country.

796 917.1　CN
CATALOGUE OF CANADIAN RECREATION AND LEISURE RESEARCH. 1973. irreg. (every 2-3/yrs.). price varies. (Ontario Research Council on Leisure) O R C O L Publications, c/o Department of Recreation and Leisure Studies, University of Waterloo, Waterloo, Ont. N2L 3G1, Canada. TEL 519-888-4823. Ed. Bryan Smale. circ. 5,000. **Document type:** catalog.

790.1　US
CENTER; the magazine of Rockefeller Center. q. free. Rockefeller Center Management Corp., 1230 Ave. of the Americas, 7th Fl., New York, NY 10020-1579. TEL 212-698-8979. Ed. Adrian Fanning; Pub. James V. Reed. adv. **Document type:** consumer publication.
　Description: Discusses activities taking place at the world-famous New York City landmark.

CHARTERED INSTITUTE OF PUBLIC FINANCE AND ACCOUNTANCY. CHARGES FOR LEISURE SERVICES. ACTUALS. see *SPORTS AND GAMES — Abstracting, Bibliographies, Statistics*

CHARTERED INSTITUTE OF PUBLIC FINANCE AND ACCOUNTANCY. LEISURE AND RECREATION STATISTICS. ESTIMATES. see *SPORTS AND GAMES — Abstracting, Bibliographies, Statistics*

790.1　US
COAST TO COAST RECREATIONAL LIFE. m.? Aqua-Field Publishing Co., Inc., 66 W. Gilbert St., Shrewsbury, NJ 07702. TEL 908-842-8300.

CONGRESS FOR RECREATION AND PARKS. SYMPOSIUM FOR LEISURE RESEARCH. ABSTRACTS. see *SPORTS AND GAMES — Abstracting, Bibliographies, Statistics*

051
DISNEY NEWS. 1965. q. $15.95 for 8 nos. Box 3310, Anaheim, CA 92803. Ed. Anne Okey. adv. circ. 290,000. **Document type:** consumer publication.
　Description: Provides articles about Disneyland, Walt Disney World, Tokyo Disneyland, Euro Disney, new program offerings from the Disney Channel, network TV and syndicated television and latest movies from Walt Disney Pictures and Touchstone Films.

790.1 910.5　US　ISSN 0363-4825
DIVERSION (NEW YORK); for physicians at leisure. 1973. m. $54. Hearst Professional Magazines, Inc., 60 E. 42nd St., New York, NY 10065. TEL 212-297-9600. FAX 212-808-9079. Ed. Tom Passavant. adv.: B&W page $8695, color page $12385; trim 8 1/8 x 10 7/8. bk.rev.; illus.; circ. 176,000 (controlled). **Document type:** trade publication.
　Description: Covers topics of interest to physicians at leisure: travel, investing, gourmet cooking and food, gardening, photography, sports and conventions.

DIVIDENDS. see *SPORTS AND GAMES — Outdoor Life*

306.7 790.1　US
EMERGE PLAYCOUPLE. 1970. bi-m. $15. Lifestyles Press, Box 5366, Buena Park, CA 90622. TEL 714-821-9953. FAX 714-821-1465. Ed. Robert L. McGinley. adv.; bk.rev. circ. 3,000.
　Description: For those unique couples who have romance and adventure in their hearts and seek excitement and freedom in their sexual and intimate life and erotic relationship.

790.1　UK
ENGLISH BRIDGE. 1984. bi-m. free to members. English Bridge Union Ltd., Broadfields Rd., Bicester Rd., Aylesbury, Bucks. HP19 3BG, England. FAX 0296-392464. (Dist. by Andover Press, West Pathway, Andover, Hants. SP10 3SF, England. TEL 0264-355111) Ed. K. Rowe. adv.; bk.rev. circ. 30,000. (back issues avail.) **Document type:** consumer publication.
　Description: Covers all aspects of tournament bridge.

3414 LEISURE AND RECREATION

790 US
ENTERTAINMENT: AN INDUSTRY OVERVIEW. 1991. a. $395. Dun & Bradstreet Information Services (Murray Hill) (Subsidiary of: Dun & Bradstreet, Inc.), One Diamond Hill Rd., Murray Hill, NJ 07974. TEL 908-665-5224. FAX 908-771-7599. Ed. Paulette Roberts.
  Description: Covers film production, distribution and exhibition, prerecorded music, cable and network television, radio broadcasting. Examines trends toward vertical integration and globalization and the struggle of smaller firms for survival in the face of industry giants.

790.1 658.8 UK
ENTERTAINMENT SOFTWARE: THE INTERNATIONAL MARKET. a. £1375($2750) Euromonitor, 87-88 Turnmill St., London EC1M 5QU, England. TEL 071-251-8024. FAX 071-608-3149. (Addr. in N. America: Euromonitor International, 111 W. Washington St., Ste. 920, Chicago, IL 60602. TEL 312-541-8024. FAX 312-541-1567) (looseleaf format) Document type: trade publication.
●Also available online. Vendor(s): Data-Star, DIALOG Information Services, Inc.
  Description: Analyzes the entertainment audio, video, and software markets for France, Germany, Italy, Spain, the U.K., the U.S., and Japan.

790.1 658.8 UK ISSN 1352-0024
▼**EUROPEAN LEISURE AND ENTERTAINMENT MARKETING DIRECTORY.** 1993. irreg. £160($335) Euromonitor, 87-88 Turnmill St., London EC1M 5QU, England. TEL 071-251-8024. FAX 071-608-3149. (Addr. in N. America: Euromonitor International, 111 W. Washington St., Ste. 920, Chicago, IL 60602. TEL 312-541-8024. FAX 312-541-1567) Document type: directory.
  Description: Lists the names and addresses of all the major European leisure and entertainment operators and compiles details on every aspect of the industry.

790.1 GW
EXTRABLATT; die frische Zeitung. 1982. m. Agentur A & W, Hermann-Sack-Str. 2, 80331 Munich, Germany. TEL 089-268511. FAX 089-2609098. Ed. Victor Roeder. adv.; bk.rev.; film rev.; play rev.; illus. circ. 125,000. (looseleaf format; back issues avail.)

790.01 340 US
F R V T A NEWS. 1986. m. membership. Florida Recreational Vehicle Trade Association, 401 N. Parsons Ave., No. 107, Brandon, FL 33510-4538. TEL 813-684-7882. FAX 813-653-0211. Ed. David Kelly. charts. circ. 500. (looseleaf format)
  Description: Covers legislative issues dealing with Florida's RV industry.

790.1 071.1 US
FAMILY LEISURE TIMES. m. $12; newsstand price: 1. 31 Valencia Isle, Lake Hopatcong, NJ 07849. TEL 201-663-4649. Ed. Marlene Genaud. cols./p.: 2; pp./issue: 12. (tabloid format; back issues avail.) Document type: newspaper.
  Description: Reports on leisure-time and educational opportunities in the Morris County, NJ, area.

THE FOOTPRINT. see SPORTS AND GAMES — Outdoor Life

791.068 US
FUNWORLD. 1983. m. $40 to non-members; members $20. International Association of Amusement Parks & Attractions, 1448 Duke St., Alexandria, VA 22314-3403. TEL 703-836-4800. FAX 703-836-4801. Ed. Rick Henderson. adv.: B&W page $1000, color page $1450. bk.rev.; stat. circ. 6,800. (back issues avail.) Document type: trade publication.
  Formerly: Actionews.
  Description: Statistical and analytical information for members of the association on the amusement industry.

GAP SPORT. see SPORTS AND GAMES

790.01 UK
GOOD TIMES. 1990. w. £20. Scam Publishing Ltd., The Elephant House, Hawley Crescent, London NW1 8NP, England. TEL 071-911-6010. FAX 071-911-0599. Ed. Amanda Lipman. adv.; bk.rev.; film rev.; play rev. circ. 44,136. (tabloid format; back issues avail.)

790.068 US
▼**GREEN INDUSTRY.** 1993. bi-m. Madisen Publishing Division, Box 1936, Appleton, WI 54913. TEL 414-733-2301. Ed. Erik Madsen, Jr. adv.: B&W page $750, color page $1250; trim 8 1/4 x 10 7/8. circ. 3,616. Document type: trade publication.

HARPERS SPORTS & LEISURE. see SPORTS AND GAMES — Outdoor Life

790.1 US
F394.H8
HOUSTON LIFE. 1974. m. distributed in The Houston Post newspaper. Travel & Life Publishing, 5615 Kirby Dr., Ste. 600, Houston, TX 77005. TEL 713-524-3000. FAX 713-524-8213. Ed. David Walker. adv. contact: Roger Tremblay. bk.rev.; illus. circ. 337,656. Indexed: Access (1976-). Document type: consumer publication.
  Former titles (until 1994): Houston Metropolitan (ISSN 1057-8579); (until 1988): Houston Home and Garden (ISSN 0360-2087)
  Description: Covers local consumer home, family activities, gardening, food, health, and travel interests.

791.068 IT
▼**IMMAGINIFICO**; trimestrale di spettacolo popolare - culture materiali - mestieri - nomadismi. 1992. q. Pretini & C. s.r.l. - Trapezio Libri, Morena Torre 2, Reana del Rojale (Udine), Italy. TEL 0432-852202.

790.01 FR
INTER AUTOMATIQUE. m. 2 place de l'Amirande, B.P. 52, 84000 Avignon, France. TEL 90-82-54-03. FAX 90-86-29-88. TELEX 432 770. Ed. F. Pey. circ. 3,200.
  Description: Dedicated to games and leisure.

790.1 333.7 US
IOWA PARKS & RECREATION. q. Iowa Parks & Recreation Association, 203 Field House, University of Iowa, Iowa City, IA 52242. TEL 319-335-9351.

796 917.1 CN ISSN 0843-9117
JOURNAL OF APPLIED RECREATION RESEARCH. 1971. q. $35 membership. University of Waterloo Press, Waterloo, Ont. N2L 3G1, Canada. TEL 519-885-1211. FAX 519-747-4606. Ed. Bryan J.A. Smale. bk.rev. Indexed: Rural Recreat.Tour.Abstr., Sportsearch (1989-), World Agri.Econ.& Rural Sociol.Abstr.
  Formerly (until vol.14, no.4, 1989): Recreation Research Review (ISSN 0702-9284)

JOURNAL OF HOSPITALITY & LEISURE MARKETING. see HOTELS AND RESTAURANTS

371.9 CN ISSN 0711-222X
JOURNAL OF LEISURABILITY. 1974. 4/yr. Can.$28 to individuals; libraries Can.$38. Leisurability Publications Inc., 36 Bessemer Ct., Unit 3, Concord, ON L4K 3C9, Canada. TEL 416-669-5373. FAX 416-669-1927. Ed. Judith McGill. adv.; bk.rev. circ. 800. (also avail. in microfilm from UMI; back issues avail; reprint service avail. from UMI) Indexed: Phys.Ed.Ind., Psychol.Abstr., Rehabil.Lit., Rural Recreat.Tour.Abstr., Sportsearch (1980-), World Agri.Econ.& Rural Sociol.Abstr. Document type: academic/scholarly publication.
  —BLDSC (5010.277000); Faxon; UnCover; UMI. CCC.

333.78 US ISSN 0022-2216
GV1 CODEN: JLERA
JOURNAL OF LEISURE RESEARCH. 1968. q. $30 to non-members; members $20; institutions $50. National Recreation and Park Association, 3101 Park Center Dr., Alexandria, VA 22302. TEL 703-820-4940. FAX 703-671-6772. (Co-sponsor: University of North Texas) Ed. Peter A. Witt. adv.; bk.rev.; bibl.; charts; illus.; stat.; index. (also avail. in microfilm from UMI; reprint service avail. from UMI) Indexed: Art.Hosp.& Tour., ASSIA, C.I.J.E., Commun.Abstr., Curr.Cont., Geo.Abstr., Lang.& Lang.Behav.Abstr., Mag.Ind., Phys.Ed.Ind., Psychol.Abstr., Rural Recreat.Tour.Abstr., Soc.Sci.Ind., Sportsearch (1974-), SSCI, World Agri.Econ.& Rural Sociol.Abstr.
  —BLDSC (5010.280000); Faxon; UnCover; SWETS; UMI.

K A H P E R D JOURNAL. (Kentucky Association for Health, Physical Education, Recreation and Dance) see EDUCATION

790.1 UK
L S A NEWSLETTER. (Supplement avail.) 1980. 3/yr. £23 to members; institutions £48. Leisure Studies Association, Chelsea School Research Centre, University of Brighton, Eastbourne BN20 7SP, England. TEL 0273-643747. FAX 0273-643704. Ed. Alan Tomlinson. adv.; bk.rev. circ. 500. Indexed: Rural Recreat.Tour.Abstr., World Agri.Econ.& Rural Sociol.Abstr. Document type: newsletter.
  Formerly: L S A Quarterly (ISSN 0260-6364)

LA VERNE MAGAZINE. see COLLEGE AND ALUMNI

LEISURE ARTS. see HOBBIES

332 UK ISSN 0263-7774
LEISURE FUTURES. 1976. q. £1125. Henley Centre for Forecasting Ltd., 2 Tudor St., Blackfriars, London EC4Y 0AA, England. TEL 071-3535-9961. Ed. Richard Woods. charts; stat. (back issues avail.) Indexed: Art.Hosp.& Tour.
●Also available online.
  —BLDSC (5182.240000).
  Description: Analysis of free time activity patterns and associated spending in the UK.

790.1 US
LEISURE INDUSTRY REPORT. 1981. 10/yr. $65. Leisure Industry - Recreation News, Box 43563, Washington, DC 20010. TEL 202-232-7107. Ed. Marj Jensen. adv.; bk.rev. (back issues avail.) Document type: newsletter.
  Formerly: Leisure Industry Digest (ISSN 0276-0916)
  Description: Compiles news reports from a wide range of sources into summary reviews of trends and developments on leisure and discretionary spending.

301 US
LEISURE INFORMATION QUARTERLY.* 1972. q. $14 to individuals (foreign $20); institutions $24 (foreign $30). New York University, School of Education, Health, Nursing and Arts Profession, 635 East Bldg., Washington Square, New York, NY 10003. Ed. Arnold Grossman. bk.rev.; bibl. circ. 300. (back issues avail.) Indexed: Rural Recreat.Tour.Abstr., Sportsearch (1983-), World Agri.Econ.& Rural Sociol.Abstr.
  Formerly: Leisure Information Newsletter.

052 UK
LEISURE INTELLIGENCE. 1983. q. £995. Mintel International Group Ltd., 18-19 Long Lane, London EC1A 9HE, England. TEL 071-606-4533. FAX 071-606-5932. Ed. Pat Neiran. (back issues avail.) Indexed: Art.Hosp.& Tour. Document type: trade publication.
●Also available online.

333.78 US
LEISURE LINES; a monthly action report. vol.6, 1980. 8/yr. membership. California Park and Recreation Society, Inc., 3031 F St., Ste. 202, Box 161118, Sacramento, CA 95816. TEL 919-446-2777.

790.1 790.13 UK ISSN 0266-9102
LEISURE MANAGEMENT. 1981. m. £36($120) (Europe £45; elsewhere £60). Dicestar Ltd., 40 Bancroft, Hitchin, Herts. S95 1LA, England. TEL 0462-431385. FAX 0462-433909. Ed. Liz Terry. adv.; bk.rev. circ. 16,500. (back issues avail.) Indexed: Art.Hosp.& Tour. Document type: trade publication.
  —BLDSC (5182.266000).
  Description: Documents and analyzes the leisure markets for policy makers, managers, developers and investors in and of leisure facilities.

790.1 658 NZ ISSN 1171-2317
LEISURE MANAGEMENT. 1991. 4/yr. NZ.$27. Associated Group Media Ltd., Private Bag 99-915, Newmarket, Auckland, New Zealand. TEL 09-379-5393. FAX 09-308-9523. Ed. Eion Scott. adv.; charts; illus. tr.lit. Document type: trade publication.
  Description: Embraces the full range of activities adopted by people in their free time and addresses the role-development of the professional managers and administrators behind this growing sector.

LEISURE AND RECREATION

333.78 790.1   UK   ISSN 0267-3754
LEISURE MANAGER. 1936. m. £35. (Institute of Leisure and Amenity Management) John S. Turner & Associates Ltd., Victoria House, 25 High St., Over, Cambridge CB4 5NB, England. TEL 0954-30940. FAX 0954-31886. Ed. Judy Richardson. adv.; bk.rev.; illus.; index. circ. 7,500. **Indexed:** Art.Hosp.& Tour., Curr.Adv.Ecol.Sci., Rural Recreat.Tour.Abstr., Sportsearch (1985-), World Agri.Econ.& Rural Sociol.Abstr. **Document type:** trade publication.
—BLDSC (5182.266200); UnCover.
 Former titles (until Dec. 1984): I L A M Journal (ISSN 0265-6000); (until Jan. 1983): I L A M; Parks and Recreation (ISSN 0031-2223); Park Administration.

306.4   UK   ISSN 0952-8210
LEISURE OPPORTUNITIES. m. Dicestar Ltd., 40 Bancroft, Hitchin, Herts SG5 1LA, England. TEL 0462-431385. FAX 0462-433909. Ed. W. Terry. circ. 16,500. **Document type:** consumer publication.

LEISURE, RECREATION AND TOURISM ABSTRACTS. see TRAVEL AND TOURISM — Abstracting, Bibliographies, Statistics

150   US   ISSN 0149-0400
GV1   CODEN: LESCDC
LEISURE SCIENCES; an interdisciplinary journal. 1977. q. $60 to individuals; institutions $110. Taylor & Francis, 1900 Frost Rd., Ste. 101, Bristol, PA 19007. TEL 215-785-5800. FAX 215-785-5515. Ed. T. Goodale. adv.; bk.rev.; abstr.; index. **Indexed:** Art.Hosp.& Tour., Commun.Abstr., Environ.Per.Bibl. (1992-), Forest.Abstr., Geo.Abstr., Human Resour.Abstr., P.A.I.S., Psychol.Abstr., Rural Recreat.Tour.Abstr., Sage Pub.Admin.Abstr., Sage Urb.Stud.Abstr., Sportsearch (1977-).
—BLDSC (5182.270000); Faxon; UnCover; SWETS. **CCC.**
 Description: Presents scientific inquiries into the study of leisure, recreation, travel and their impact on the physical and social environment.
 Refereed Serial

301 790.1   UK   ISSN 0261-4367
LEISURE STUDIES. 1982. 3/yr. £80 (foreign £90). (Leisure Studies Association) E. & F.N. Spon, 2-6 Boundary Row, London SE1 8HN, England. TEL 071-865-0066. FAX 071-522-9623. (Dist. by: International Thomson Publishing Services, Ltd., N. Way, Andover, Hampshire SP10 5BE, England. TEL 0264-342919; U.S. addr.: Chapman & Hall, One Penn Plaza, 41st Fl., New York, NY 10119. TEL 212-564-1060. FAX 212-564-1505) Ed. Jonathan Long. bk.rev. (reprint service avail. from SWZ) **Indexed:** Art.Hosp.& Tour., I D A, Psychol.Abstr., Sportsearch (1983-), Stud.Wom.Abstr. **Document type:** academic/scholarly publication.
—BLDSC (5182.272000); Faxon; UnCover; SWETS; UMI. **CCC.**
 Description: Covers all aspects of leisure and recreation: leisure behaviour in the arts, sports, cultural and informal activities, tourism, and urban and rural recreation.

306   UK
LEISURE WEEK. w. 50 Poland St., London W1V 4AX, England. TEL 071-494-0300. FAX 071-734-2741. Ed. R. Cohen. circ. 15,000.

910.202   CN   ISSN 1184-146X
LEISURE WORLD. 1988. bi-m. Can.$15. Ontario Motorist Publishing Co. Ltd., 1253 Ouellette Ave., Windsor, ON N8X 1J3, Canada.
TEL 519-971-3208. FAX 519-977-1197. Ed. Douglas O'Neil. adv.; bk.rev.; film rev.; illus.; tr.lit. circ. 316,000. (back issues avail.)
 Formerly: Leisure Ontario (ISSN 0838-2913)
 Description: Covers Canadian and international travel, destinations, automobiles and leisure time activities.

301 790.1   CN   ISSN 0705-3436
GV14.45
LOISIR ET SOCIETE/SOCIETY AND LEISURE. (Text in English and French) 1978. s-a. Can.$20 to individuals; institutions Can.$35. Presses de l'Universite du Quebec, C.P. 250, Sillery, Que. G1T 2R1, Canada. TEL 418-657-3551. (In Europe subscr. to: Editions ESKA, 30 de Domremy, 75013 Paris, France) (Co-sponsor: International Sociological Association) Ed. Max D'Amours. bk.rev. (reprint service avail.) **Indexed:** Lang.& Lang.Behav.Abstr., Pt.de Rep. (1982-), Sportsearch (1978-). **Document type:** academic/scholarly publication.
—BLDSC (8319.191700); Faxon; UnCover.
 Description: Humanities and social sciences journal devoted to the academic study of leisure in various societies.

MATRA; Majalan Trend Pria. see MEN'S INTERESTS

790.1   US
MAZAMA. 1896. m. $12. The Mazamas, 909 N.W. 19th Ave., Portland, OR 97209. illus.

MOTORING & LEISURE. see TRANSPORTATION — Automobiles

MOVES. see HISTORY

790.1 333.78   US   ISSN 0276-8186
SB482.A4
NATIONAL PARKS. 1919. bi-m. $25. National Parks and Conservation Association, 1776 Massachusetts Ave., N.W., Washington, DC 20036.
TEL 202-223-6722. FAX 202-629-0650. Ed. Sue Dodge. adv. contact: Carol Cummins. bk.rev.; illus.; index. circ. 350,000. (also avail. in microform from UMI; reprint service avail. from UMI) **Indexed:** Acad.Ind., Amer.Hist.& Life, Biol.Abstr., Biol.Dig., Bk.Rev.Ind. (1965-), Child.Bk.Rev.Ind. (1965-), Environ.Abstr., Environ.Ind., Environ.Per.Bibl. (1977-), Geo.Abstr., GeoRef., Hist.Abstr., Mag.Ind., PMR, R.G., Sportsearch. **Document type:** trade publication.
—Faxon; UnCover; SWETS; UMI.
 Former titles (until 1981): National Parks and Conservation Magazine (ISSN 0027-9870); National Parks.

NEGOZIANTE GARDEN & GRILL. see GARDENING AND HORTICULTURE

790.1   US   ISSN 0896-1506
NEW ENGLAND ENTERTAINMENT DIGEST. 1978. m. $15; newsstand price: 1.50. Taylor Publishing, Box 313, 2 Freestone Ave., Portland, CT 06480. TEL 203-342-4730. FAX 203-342-5368. Ed. Bob Taylor. adv.: page $450. bk.rev.; film rev.; play rev.; circ. 3,000 (paid). cols./p.: 4; pp./issue: 16. (tabloid format; back issues avail.) **Document type:** newspaper.
 Description: Provides arts and entertainment news for persons involved in the performing arts and for serious arts patrons. Contains casting notices.

OFF-SEASON TRAVELING. see TRAVEL AND TOURISM

790.1   US
ON THE SCENE; Albuquerque's entertainment & lifestyles magazine. 1979. m. $18. Unicorn Publications, Inc., 3507 Wyoming N.E., Albuquerque, NM 87111. TEL 505-299-4401. Ed. Gail P. Skinner. adv. contact: Jay Butler. bk.rev. circ. 30,000. (tabloid format; back issues avail.) **Document type:** consumer publication.
 Formed by the 1987 merger of: Albuquerque's Senior Scene; Albuquerque's Singles Scene.
 Description: Covers local entertainment for all ages.

790.1   CN   ISSN 0827-2352
ONTARIO OUTDOOR GUIDE & CALENDAR. a. 296 Glen Rd., Toronto, Ont. N4W 2X3, Canada.
TEL 416-960-9997. Ed. David Crandall. circ. 60,000.

790.1   US
OUT YOUR BACKDOOR; a global magazine of informal adventure. 1989. q. $8. 4686 Meridian Rd., Williamston, MI 48895. TEL 517-347-1689. FAX 517-339-4455. Ed. Jeff Potter. adv.; bk.rev. circ. 5,000. (back issues avail.) **Document type:** consumer publication.
 Description: Specializes in alternative approaches to outdoor and physical culture activities such as bicycling, boating and travel.

790.1   CN   ISSN 0826-3019
OUTDOOR REPORT. 1977. q. Can.$10. Outdoor Recreation Council of B.C., 334-1367 W. Broadway, Vancouver, BC V6H 4A9, Canada.
TEL 604-737-3058. FAX 604-737-3666. **Document type:** newsletter, bulletin.
 Description: Contains informative accounts of developments in outdoor recreation of interest to the Council's members as well as elected officials, recreation managers, media and public libraries.

OUTDOOR TRADE AND INDUSTRY. see SPORTS AND GAMES — Outdoor Life

OUTDOORS, RECREATION & LEISURE. see SPORTS AND GAMES — Outdoor Life

658 910.202   UK   ISSN 0960-6629
PAPERS IN LEISURE AND TOURISM STUDIES. 1990. irreg., no.3, 1991. (Centre for Leisure and Tourism Studies) U N L Press, 166-220 Holloway Rd., London N7 8DB, England. TEL 071-753-5065. FAX 071-753-5051. **Document type:** monographic series.
—BLDSC (6396.952200).

790.068   US   ISSN 1057-204X
SB481.A1
PARK & GROUNDS MANAGEMENT. 1948. m. $20. Madisen Publishing Division, Box 1936, Appleton, WI 54913. TEL 414-733-2301. FAX 414-733-2301. Ed. Erik Madisen, Jr. adv.: B&W page $1400; 8 1/4 x 10 7/8. bk.rev.; illus.; tr.lit.; index. circ. 15,000. **Indexed:** Sportsearch. **Document type:** trade publication.
—UnCover.
 Former titles: Park Maintenance and Grounds Management (ISSN 0192-2505); Park Maintenance (ISSN 0031-2134); Incorporates: Concessions and Vending.
 Description: Provides technical information relative to the management of large outdoor grounds areas.

PARQUES Y JARDINES. see GARDENING AND HORTICULTURE

790.1   US   ISSN 0899-6008
PARTY & PAPER RETAILER. 1986. m. $33. 4Ward Corporation, 70 New Canaan Ave., Norwalk, CT 06850-2600. TEL 203-845-8020.
FAX 203-845-8022. (Subscr. to: P.O. Box 925, Darien, CT 06820) Ed. Trisha McMahon Drain; Pub. Russell Ward. adv.; bk.rev. circ. 22,000. (also avail. in microfilm; back issues avail.) **Document type:** trade publication.
 Description: Covers the retailing of party supplies including balloons, plastics and paper tableware, gift wrap, and greeting cards.

PROGRAMMING TRENDS IN THERAPEUTIC RECREATION. see EDUCATION — Special Education And Rehabilitation

790.01   UK   ISSN 0964-5160
THE PUNTER. 1984. m. £12. Devonshire Mansions, Devonshire Pl., Brighton BN2 1QH, England.
TEL 0273-692960. FAX 0273-738473. Ed. Kathryn Holliday. adv.; bk.rev. circ. 10,000. (back issues avail.)

R A NEWS. (Recreation Association of the Public Service of Canada) see CLUBS

R VERS GUIDE TO FLORIDA. see BUSINESS AND ECONOMICS — Trade And Industrial Directories

790.1   US
RANGER (MORRISTOWN). bi-m. Park Commission, Box 1295, Morristown, NJ 07962-1295.
TEL 201-326-7600. Ed. Denise Lanza. adv. **Document type:** bulletin.
 Description: Lists and describes outdoor activities sponsored by the Morris County Park Commission.

790   US
RECREATION ADVISOR. 1984. bi-m. $15 include membership. (International Family Recreation Association) Recreational World Services, Inc., P.O. Drawer 17148, Pensacola, FL 32522.
TEL 904-477-2123. Ed. K.W. Stephens. adv.: B&W page $490; 9 1/2 x 12 1/2; adv. contact: David Dykes. bk.rev.; charts; illus.; stat.; tr.lit. circ. 15,000. (tabloid format) **Document type:** newsletter.
 Description: Covers the recreation, leisure and travel industry, with association news, legislative updates, membership profiles, recreational opportunities.

LIBRARY AND INFORMATION SCIENCES

790.1 613.7   CN   ISSN 0031-2231
RECREATION CANADA. 1952. 5/yr. Can.$45($50) (typically set Oct.). Canadian Parks - Recreation Association, c/o Diana M. Smith, Exec.Dir., 1600 James Naismith Dr., Gloucester, ON K1B 5N4, Canada. TEL 613-748-5651. FAX 613-748-5854. adv.: B&W page $965, color page $1565; 8 1/4 x 11 3/8. bk.rev.; charts; illus.; index. circ. 3,000. (also avail. in microform from UMI) **Indexed:** Sportsearch (1972-). **Document type:** consumer publication.
—UnCover; UMI.
   Incorporates (in 1992): Recreation Newsletter.
   Description: Covers current research and trends, innovative leisure programs and facilities, arts and culture, wellness - fitness for those who are interested in the parks - recreation - leisure industry.

790   US   ISSN 0890-2194
RECREATION EXECUTIVE REPORT. 1973. 10/yr. $65. Leisure Industry - Recreation News, Box 43563, Washington, DC 20010. TEL 202-232-7107. Ed. Marj Jensen. adv.; index. circ. 600. **Document type:** newsletter.
   Supersedes: Leisure Information Service. Fund Development and Revenue Source Report; Which was formerly: Leisure Information Service. Fund Development and Technical Assistance Report.
   Description: Presents coverage of recreation issues, directed primarily to those involved in public recreation.

790.1   US
RECREATION RESOURCES; new products and services for professional recreation managers in parks, schools, clubs, resorts and other fitness and leisure facilities. 1981. 9/yr. $24 (Canada $27; elsewhere $50). Lakewood Publications (Subsidiary of: Maclean Hunter Publishing Company), 50 S. Ninth St., Minneapolis, MN 55402. TEL 612-333-0471. FAX 612-333-6526. Ed. Galynn Nordstrom. circ. 51,000. (tabloid format; back issues avail.) **Document type:** trade publication.
   Formerly: Recreation Sports and Leisure (ISSN 0277-707X)
   Description: Product information for the managed recreation industry.

S B/SPORTS FACILITIES AND SWIMMING POOLS/EQUIPEMENT SPORTIF ET PISCINES/CONSTRUCCION DE INSTALLACIONES DEPORTIVAS Y PISCINAS. (Sportstaettenbau und Baederanlagen) see BUILDING AND CONSTRUCTION

059.927   LE
AL-SHABAKAH. Variant title: Achabaka. (Text in Arabic) 1976. w. $300. Dar Assayad S.A.L., P.O. Box 1038, Hazmieh, Beirut, Lebanon. FAX 961-1-456373. TELEX 44224 SAYYAD LE. (UK addr.: c/o Contact PR & Mgt (UK) Ltd., 3 Park Pl., 12 Lawn Ln., London SW8, England. TEL 071-582-2220) Ed. Georges Ibrahim El Khoury. circ. 102,000. **Document type:** consumer publication.

790.1 051   US
SKINNYDIPPING; if God had wanted us to be naked, we would have been born that way. 1990. q. $20 membership. The Skinnydippers, 41-04 39th Ave., Woodside, NY 11377-3145. TEL 718-651-4689. FAX 718-424-1883. Ed. Peter Kacalanos. adv.: full page $130. bk.rev.; film rev.; play rev, illus.; circ. 3,000. (paid). (back issues avail.) **Document type:** newsletter.
   Description: Describes places and nonsexual events of interest to nudists. Fosters unencumbered relaxation in a variety of activities.

SKYLINER. see SPORTS AND GAMES — Outdoor Life

SOPHISTICATED LEISURE TRAVEL DIRECTORY. see TRAVEL AND TOURISM

SPORT & LEISURE (CARDIFF). see SPORTS AND GAMES

SPORT AND LEISURE (LONDON). see SPORTS AND GAMES

790.1   FR
SPORT ECO. 24/yr. Canal Sport, 73 rue Orfila, B.P. 202, 75020 Paris, France. TEL 46-36-22-77. FAX 43-66-77-53. Ed. Philippe Cazeel. circ. 3,500.
   Description: News and information on the sports and leisure market.

SPORT PREMIERE MAGAZINE. see SPORTS AND GAMES

790.1 910.202   FR   ISSN 0769-4830
SPORTS LOISIRS TOURISME; la lettre de l'economie des equipements. (Supplement avail.: L'Observatoire des Sports Loisirs Tourisme) bi-m. 3000 F. L'Agence Innovapresse, 29 rue du Faubourg Poissoniere, 75009 Paris, France. TEL 48-24-08-97. FAX 42-47-00-76. Ed. Marie-Christine Vatov.

790.1   UK
STREET. 1988. m. £10. Street Magazine Ltd., P.O. Box 67, Darlington, County Durham DL3 7UR, England. TEL 0325-380623. FAX 0325-369964. Ed. Peter Bulloch. film rev. circ. 40,000. (back issues avail.)

SUID-AFRIKAANSE TYDSKRIF VIR NAVORSING IN SPORT, LIGGAAMLIKE OPVOEDKUNDE EN ONTSPANNING/SOUTH AFRICAN JOURNAL FOR RESEARCH IN SPORT, PHYSICAL EDUCATION AND RECREATION. see PHYSICAL FITNESS AND HYGIENE

790.1 910.09   US
SUMMER WEEK. 1972. w. (during summer). Mountain Media, 111 Main St., Plymouth, NH 03264. Ed. Patricia Cowley.

790.01   IT
TECHNICS & LEISURE. 6/yr. Sinopia s.r.l., Via G. Murat 84, 20159 Milan, Italy. TEL 2-688-36-41. FAX 2-688-02-971. Ed. Pietro Chianchiano. circ. 11,500.

790.1   UK
TEE TO GREEN. q. (Golf Foundation) Custom Publishing Company Ltd. (Subsidiary of: Glendower Holdings Ltd.), 45 Station Rd., Redhill, Surrey RH1 1QU, England. TEL 0737-767213. FAX 0737-771662. Ed. Chris Plumridge. adv.: B&W page £950; color page £1195; adv. contact: John Bailey. circ. 11,100 (controlled). **Document type:** consumer publication.
   Description: Covers all golfing activities.

790.01 352   CN
TIDINGS. 1979. q. Can.$15($20) (typically set in Jan.). Recreation Association of Nova Scotia, P.O. Box 3010 S., Halifax, NS B3J 3G6, Canada. TEL 902-425-1128. FAX 902-425-5606. Ed. Linda Atkinson. adv. contact: Brenda MacDonald. bk.rev. circ. 1,500. (back issues avail.) **Document type:** trade publication.
   Description: Deals with a broad range of leisure services, developments, issues and trends.

791.068 658   US
TOURIST ATTRACTIONS AND PARKS. 1972. 7/yr. $25. Kane Communications, Inc., 7000 Terminal Square, Ste. 210, Upper Darby, PA 19082. TEL 215-734-2420. Ed. Sandy Meschkow. adv.: B&W page $2050, color page $2550; 8 1/4 x 10 7/8. circ. 27,000.
   Incorporates: American Showman.
   Description: For the management personnel of theme, water, and amusement parks, zoos, museums and arcades.

TOURIST MAGAZINE. see TRAVEL AND TOURISM

790.1   US
TRAILHEAD. 1974. bi-m. $10 to individuals; institutions $20. Idaho Trails Council, Inc., Box 1629, Sun Valley, ID 83353. TEL 208-622-3046. Ed. Bernice E. Paige. circ. 200. (tabloid format) **Document type:** newsletter.

TRAVEL & LEISURE. see TRAVEL AND TOURISM

790.068 333.78   US
TRENDS (ALEXANDRIA). vol.5, 1968. q. $25. National Recreation and Park Association, Park Practice Program, 3101 Park Center Dr., Alexandria, VA 22302. TEL 703-820-4940. FAX 703-671-6772. Ed. Kathleen Pleasant. charts; illus.; index. circ. 1,500. **Indexed:** Ind.U.S.Gov.Per., Rehabil.Lit., Sportsearch (1976-).
   Incorporates: Guideline; Formerly: Trends in Parks and Recreation (ISSN 0041-2414)

790.1   US
U.S. DEPARTMENT OF THE INTERIOR. NATIONAL PARK SERVICE. REPORT TO CONGRESS. a. U.S. Department of the Interior, National Park Service, Interior Bldg., Washington, DC 20240.

790.01   CN   ISSN 0828-4253
F1060.A1
UP HERE; life in Canada's North. 1984. bi-m. Can.$21 (foreign Can.$30). Outcrop Ltd., P.O. Box 1350, Yellowknife, NT X1A 2N9, Canada. TEL 403-920-4652. FAX 403-873-2844. Ed. Rosemary Allerston; Pub. Marion Lavigne. adv.: B&W page $1995, color page $2493; adv. contact: Joy Watt. bk.rev.; film rev.; play rev. circ. 35,000. (also avail. in microfiche from MML) **Indexed:** Can.Per.Ind. **Document type:** consumer publication.
   Description: Lifestyles, travel and issues in Canada's Northwest Territories and the Yukon.

VACATION INDUSTRY REVIEW. see TRAVEL AND TOURISM

790.01 028.5   CN   ISSN 0380-9552
VANCOUVER MAGAZINE. 1968. m. Can.$18. Telemedia West, 300 Southeast Twr., 555 W. 12th Ave., Vancouver, BC V5Z 4L4, Canada. TEL 604-877-7732. FAX 604-877-4849. Ed. Jim Suterland. adv.; bk.rev.; film rev.; play rev.; illus. circ. 70,000.
   Former titles: Vancouver's Leisure Magazine (ISSN 0380-9544); Dick Maclean's Leisure Magazine; Maclean's Leisure Magazine; Maclean's Guide (ISSN 0024-9254)

THE WEEKLY FARCE; Ohio's funniest newspaper. see LITERARY AND POLITICAL REVIEWS

790.01   CC   ISSN 1000-2928
WENHUA YULE/CULTURE & RECREATION. (Text in Chinese) 1980. m. Y12($36.80) (Zhejiang Sheng Qunzhong Yishu-guan - Zhejiang Provincial Popular Art Center) Wenhua Yule Bianjibu, 51 Wulin Lu, Hangzhou, Zhejiang 310006, People's Republic of China. TEL 778991. (Subscr. to: Nanjing City Post, Nanjing, Jiangsu, P.R.C.; Dist. in US by: China Books & Periodicals, Inc., 2929 24th St., San Francisco, CA 94110) Ed. Guo Jinkang. circ. 210,000.
   Description: Contains popular literature, folklore, art, and information on recreation and culture.

WESTWORLD ALBERTA MAGAZINE. see TRANSPORTATION — Automobiles

790.01   CN
WORLD LEISURE AND RECREATION. 1958. q. $35 to individuals; institutions $60; students $15. World Leisure and Recreation Association, Box 309, Sharbot Lake, ON K0H 2P0, Canada. TEL 613-279-3172. FAX 613-279-3372. adv.; bk.rev.; abstr.; bibl.; illus. circ. 3,000. **Indexed:** Art.Hosp.& Tour., Rural Recreat.Tour.Abstr., Sportsearch (1984-), World Agri.Econ.& Rural Sociol.Abstr.
   Former titles: World Leisure Review; (until 1984): W L R A Journal; W L R A Bulletin; International Recreation Association. Bulletin (ISSN 0441-9057)

LIBRARY AND INFORMATION SCIENCES

see also Bibliographies

020.6   CN
A A B C NEWSLETTER. 1981. q. membership. Archives Association of British Columbia, P.O. Box 78530, University Post Office, Vancouver, B.C. V6T 2E7, Canada. TEL 604-683-8588. FAX 604-683-8568. Ed. Anne Maclean. adv. circ. 1,300. **Document type:** newsletter.
   Former titles: A I B C Newsletter (ISSN 0835-3859); Architectural Institute of British Columbia. News, Views and Reviews.
   Description: Association news, news on members, industry news.

A A L L DIRECTORY AND HANDBOOK. (American Association of Law Libraries) see LAW

A A L L PUBLICATIONS SERIES. (American Association of Law Libraries) see LAW

LIBRARY AND INFORMATION SCIENCES

020 GW ISSN 0720-6763
Z678.9.A1
A B I TECHNIK; Zeitschrift fuer Automation, Bau und Technik im Archiv, Bibliotheks- und Informationswesen. 1981. q. DM.153.50 (foreign DM.162). Verlag Karlheinz Holz, Aarstr. 24, 65195 Wiesbaden, Germany. TEL 0611-9450751. FAX 0611-9450074. Ed. Berndt Dugall. adv.; bk.rev.; index. circ. 2,000. (back issues avail.) **Indexed:** LISA. **Document type:** academic/scholarly publication.
—BLDSC (0549.396000); SWETS.
 Description: Covers information on automation, building and technology of libraries and information centers. Includes reports of events and exhibitions and new products.

020 AT ISSN 1039-348X
Z674.83.A82
A B N NEWS WITH OZLINE NEWS. (Australian Bibliographic Network) 1993. bi-m. Aus.$40. National Library of Australia, Services to Libraries Division, Canberra, A.C.T. 2600, Australia. TEL 06-262-1111. FAX 06-257-1703. **Indexed:** AESIS.
 Formed by the merger of (1982-1993): A B N News (ISSN 0726-0644) & OZLINE News.
 Description: Contains articles of interest to users of the ABN and the OZLINE Databases.

020 FR ISSN 1163-4979
A C B INFOS. q. 150 F. Association des Conservateurs de Bibliotheque, 16 rue Claude Bernard, 75231 Paris Cedex 05, France. **Document type:** bulletin.
 Formerly: Association de l'Ecole Nationale Superieure des Bibliothecaires. Infos (ISSN 0992-6801)

020 UK ISSN 0969-4625
A C L A I I R NEWSLETTER. 1980. s-a. £15. Institute of Latin American Studies, Advisory Council for Latin American and Iberian Information Resources, 31 Tavistock Sq., London WC1H 9HA, England. TEL 071-387-4055. FAX 071-388-2233. Ed. A. Biggins. circ. 50. (back issues avail.) **Document type:** newsletter.
 Formerly (until 1992): A C O L A M Newsletter (ISSN 0263-6832)
 Description: Reports Committee activities and news of library and information matters relating to Latin American and Iberian studies in the UK and elsewhere.

A F V A EVALUATIONS. (American Film & Video Association, Inc.) see EDUCATION — Teaching Methods And Curriculum

020 011 IT ISSN 1120-2521
A I B NOTIZIE. 1988. m. L.65000. Associazione Italiana Biblioteche, Casella Postale 2461, 00100 Rome, Italy. TEL 06-4463532. Dir. Aurelio Aghemo. circ. 3,000.

020 296 US ISSN 0747-6175
A J L NEWSLETTER. 4/yr. $25 includes Judaica Librarianship. Association of Jewish Libraries, c/o National Foundation for Jewish Culture, 330 7th Ave., 21st Fl., New York, NY 10001-5010. TEL 215-238-1290. FAX 215-238-1540. (Subscr. to: c/o Aviva Astrinsky, AJL Vice Pres. for membership, Annenberg Research Institute Library, 420 Walnot St., Philadelphia, PA 19106) Eds. Hazel Karp, Irene Levin. circ. 1,200. (back issues avail.) **Document type:** newsletter.
 Description: Focuses on Judaica library-related activities. Includes media reviews, and job listings.

020.6 US ISSN 8755-9277
A L A BLACK CAUCUS NEWSLETTER. 1972. bi-m. $8.50 to non-members (effective July 1992). (American Library Association, Black Caucus) Four-G Publishers, Inc., Rollins College, No. 2654, 1000 Holt Ave., Winter Park, FL 32789. TEL 407-646-2676. FAX 407-646-1515. Ed. George C. Grant. adv.; bk.rev. circ. 1,500. **Document type:** newsletter.

020.622 US ISSN 0084-6406
Z673.A5
A L A HANDBOOK OF ORGANIZATION. a. $20 to non-members. American Library Association, 50 E. Huron St., Chicago, IL 60611. TEL 800-545-2433. FAX 312-440-9374. (reprint service avail. from UMI)
 Description: Information on staff, officers and committees of the American Library Association.

020 US ISSN 0001-1746
Z671   CODEN: AWNEEX
A L A WASHINGTON NEWSLETTER. 1949. 12/yr. $25 (foreign $30). American Library Association, Washington Office, 110 Maryland Ave., N.E., Washington, DC 20002. TEL 202-547-4440. Eds. Eileen D. Cooke, Carol C. Henderson. circ. 2,500. (processed; back issues avail.) **Indexed:** Lib.Lit. **Document type:** newsletter.
—CASDDS.
 Description: Informs librarians and educators of the current status of all federal legislation that concerns libraries and librarians.

020.6 US ISSN 1047-949X
Z688.5 CODEN: ALNWEA
A L C T S NEWSLETTER. 1976. 6/yr. $25 to non-members (foreign $35). American Library Association, Association for Library Collections & Technical Services, 50 E. Huron St., Chicago, IL 60611-2795. TEL 312-280-5035. FAX 312-280-3257. Ed. Edward Swanson. circ. 8,200. (also avail. in microform from UMI; back issues avail.; reprint service avail. from UMI) **Indexed:** LHTN, Lib.Lit. **Document type:** newsletter.
—BLDSC (0786.804300); UnCover; UMI; CASDDS.
 Formerly: R T S D Newsletter (Resources and Technical Services Division) (ISSN 0360-5906)

020 PN
A L E B C I; BOLETIN INFORMATIVO. 1972. s-a. membership. Asociacion Latinoamericana de Escuelas de Bibliotecologia y Ciencias de la Informacion, Escuela de Bibliotecologia, Centro Regional de Veraguas, Santiago de Veraguas, Panama. FAX 984056. (Subscr. to: c/o Estela Morales Campos, Torre II de Humanidades, pisos 12 y 13, Ciudad Universitario, 04510 Mexico D.F., Mexico. TEL 550-5931) Ed. Carlos Ceballos Sosa. circ. 500 (controlled). (back issues avail.)

020 340 US
A L L A NEWSLETTER. 1980. q. $10 to non-members. Atlanta Law Libraries Association, Box 56632, Atlanta, GA 30342. Ed. Pamela E. Deener. adv. contact: Roger Glenn. bk.rev. **Indexed:** Leg.Info.Manage.Ind. **Document type:** newsletter.
 Description: Articles concerning law librarianship and law information providers, announcements form ALLA and other law library associations and law libraries.

020 340 US
A L L - S I S NEWSLETTER. 1979. q. membership. American Association of Law Libraries, Academic Law Libraries S I S, c/o Univ. of Puget Sound Law Library, 950 Broadway Plaza, Tacoma, WA 94802-4470. TEL 206-591-2977. FAX 206-591-6313. Ed. Marilyn Harhai. **Document type:** newsletter.

020 US ISSN 0162-6612
A L S C NEWSLETTER. vol.5, 1973. 4/yr. membership. American Library Association, Association for Library Service to Children, 50 E. Huron St., Chicago, IL 60611. TEL 800-545-2433. FAX 312-280-3257. Ed. Anitra T. Steele. circ. 4,000. **Document type:** newsletter.
—UMI.
 Description: Contains ALSC news items, conference information, awards, election slate, etc.

027.4 US ISSN 0734-8991
A L T A NEWSLETTER. 1958-1974; resumed 1981. bi-m. membership. (American Library Trustee Association) American Library Association, 50 E. Huron St., Chicago, IL 60611. TEL 312-280-2161. FAX 312-280-3257. Ed. Robert Faherty. illus. (also avail. in microform from UMI; reprint service avail. from UMI) **Indexed:** Lib.Lit. **Document type:** newsletter.
 Former titles (until 1982): A L T A President's Newsletter (ISSN 0734-8649); (until 1974): Public Library Trustee (ISSN 0033-3581)
 Description: Covers association events and activities and discusses the responsibilities of public library trustees.

020 CN ISSN 0827-0074
A M A NEWSLETTER.* (Text in English, French) 1980. 4/yr. membership. Association of Manitoba Archivists, c/o Jerry Burkowski, 200 Vaughn St., Winnipeg, MB R3C 1T5, Canada. TEL 204-945-3971. bk.rev. (back issues avail.) **Document type:** newsletter.
 Description: Articles related to archives in Manitoba and issues of interest to individuals working on Manitoba's archival community.

020 MX ISSN 0001-186X
A M B A C NOTICIERO. 1966. q. $25 to non-members (effective 1994). Asociacion Mexicana de Bibliotecarios, A.C., Apdo. 27-651, 06760 Mexico, D.F., Mexico. TEL 575-11-35. Ed. Jose Orozco-Tenorio. adv.; bk.rev.; illus. circ. 1,000.

020 US ISSN 1040-5631
A M S STUDIES IN LIBRARY AND INFORMATION SCIENCE. 1989. irreg., no.3, 1994. A M S Press, Inc., 56 E. 13th St., New York, NY 10003. TEL 212-777-4700. FAX 212-995-5413. **Document type:** monographic series.
 Description: Numbered monographic series of library science information.

023 SP ISSN 0210-4164
A N A B A D BOLETIN. 1950. q. 10600 ptas.($102) (effective 1993). Asociacion Espanola de Archiveros Bibliotecarios, Museologos y Documentalistas, C. Recoletos 5, 28001 Madrid, Spain. TEL 5751727. (Dist. by: Arco-Libros, S.L., Juan Bautista de Toledo 28, 28002 Madrid, Spain. TEL 415-36-87) Ed.Bd. bk.rev.; bibl.; stat. circ. 3,000. **Indexed:** Amer.Hist.& Life, Hist.Abstr.
 Formerly (until 1977): A N A B A Boletin (ISSN 0044-9288)

029.7 CN ISSN 0821-7157
A N L A BULLETIN. 1983. q. Can.$10. Association of Newfoundland Labrador Archivists, c/o Colonial Bldg., Military Rd., St. John's, NF A1C 2C9, Canada. TEL 709-737-7475. FAX 709-737-3118. Ed. Mary Bridson. bk.rev.; bibl.; charts; illus. circ. 150. **Document type:** bulletin.
 Description: Outlines the activities of the archives and archivists in the province.

020 CN ISSN 0001-2203
A P L A BULLETIN. (Text in English, French) 1936. 6/yr. Can.$25. Atlantic Provinces Library Association, c/o School of Library and Information Studies, Dalhousie University, Halifax, NS B3H 4H8, Canada. TEL 902-542-2201. FAX 902-542-2128. Ed. Edith Haliburton. adv.; bk.rev.; illus. circ. 550. (also avail. in microform from MIM,UMI; reprint service avail. from UMI) **Indexed:** Can.Per.Ind., CMI, Lib.Sci.Abstr., LISA. **Document type:** bulletin.
—UMI.
 Supersedes (in 1958, vol.23): M L A Bulletin.

020 312 US ISSN 0891-0847
A P L I C COMMUNICATOR. q. $25. Association for Population - Family Planning Library & Information Center International, c/o A V S C, 79 Madison Ave., New York, NY 10016. circ. 200 (paid). **Document type:** newsletter.

020 US ISSN 1050-6098
Z671
A R L; a bimonthly newsletter of research library issues and actions. 1965. 6/yr. $50 to non-members (foreign $55). Association of Research Libraries, 21 Dupont Circle, Ste. 800, Washington, DC 20036. TEL 202-296-2296. Ed. Jaia Barrett. circ. 1,000. (back issues avail.) **Document type:** newsletter.
 Formerly (until 1990): A R L Newsletter (ISSN 0066-9652)

020.6 US ISSN 0361-5669
Z682.3
A R L ANNUAL SALARY SURVEY. 1968. a. $65. Association of Research Libraries, 21 Dupont circle, Ste. 800, Washington, DC 20036. TEL 202-296-2296. Ed. Gordon Fretwell. circ. 500. (also avail. in microfiche from CIS; back issues avail.) **Indexed:** SRI.

026 700 UK ISSN 0308-809X
A R L I S NEWS - SHEET. 1976. 6/yr. £16 to individuals; institutions £38. Art Libraries Society (UK & Eire), 18 College Rd., Bromsgrove, Worcs B60 2NE, England. Eds. E. Kerr, H. Pye-Smith. circ. 400. (back issues avail.)
 Description: Contains details of the Society's activities, information about new books, journals and audiovisual materials, reports of meetings, conferences and forthcoming events.

LIBRARY AND INFORMATION SCIENCES

020   US   ISSN 0044-9652
Z673   CODEN: ARLPDK
A R L MINUTES. Variant title: Minutes of the Meetings. 1932. s-a. $70 to non-members. Association of Research Libraries, 21 Dupont Circle, Ste. 800, Washington, DC 20036. TEL 202-296-2296. Ed. Sarah E. Mooney. cum.index: 1932-1954, 1954-1969. circ. 500. (back issues avail.)
—BLDSC (5810.740000); CASDDS.

A R S C JOURNAL. (Association for Recorded Sound Collections, Inc.) see *SOUND RECORDING AND REPRODUCTION*

A R S C NEWSLETTER. (Association for Recorded Sound Collections, Inc.) see *SOUND RECORDING AND REPRODUCTION*

027   CN   ISSN 0835-8672
A RAYONS OUVERTS. 1967. q. free. Bibliotheque Nationale du Quebec, 1700 rue Saint-Denis, Montreal, PQ H2X 3K6, Canada. TEL 514-873-1100. FAX 514-873-9932. bibl. circ. 1,200. (back issues avail.)
Description: Information about the library, its documents and services, and news about exhibitions.

020   US   ISSN 0887-9915
A S I D I C NEWSLETTER. 1969. s-a. $50. Association of Information and Dissemination Centers, Box 8105, Athens, GA 30603. TEL 706-542-6820. Ed. Donald T. Hawkins. circ. 125. (also avail. in looseleaf format; back issues avail.) **Document type:** newsletter.

029.7   US   ISSN 0066-0124
CODEN: AIHDC2
A S I S HANDBOOK AND DIRECTORY. a. $100 to non-members; members $25. American Society for Information Science, 8720 Georgia Ave., Ste. 501, Silver Spring, MD 20910. TEL 301-495-0900. FAX 301-495-0810. adv. **Document type:** directory.

020   US
A S I S KEY PAPERS SERIES. irreg., latest 1983. price varies. (American Society for Information Science) Greenwood Press, Inc. (Subsidiary of: Greenwood Publishing Group Inc.), 88 Post Rd. W., Box 5007, Westport, CT 06881-5007. TEL 203-226-3571. FAX 203-222-1502. **Indexed:** C.I.J.E.

020.6   US   ISSN 0515-0272
A S L A NEWSLETTER. 1961. 10/yr. membership. Arizona State Library Association, 13832 N. 32nd St., D-1, Phoenix, AZ 85032. TEL 602-971-3885. FAX 602-482-1011. Ed. Louis Howley. adv.: B&W page $250; adv. contact: Chris Millson Martula. circ. 1,300. **Document type:** newsletter.
Description: Contains news about the association and its activities, Arizona libraries, and pertinent national news relating to Arizona libraries.

026   PH   ISSN 0001-2548
Z671
A S L P BULLETIN. 1954. q. 30p.($15) membership. Association of Special Libraries of the Philippines, National Library Bldg., Rm. 301, T.M. Kalaw St., Manila 2801, Philippines. Ed. Angelica A. Cabanero. adv.; bk.rev.; illus.; index, cum.index. circ. 500.

027.4   CN   ISSN 0827-2735
A S P L O NEWSLETTER. 1982. s-a. Can.$5. Association of Small Public Libraries of Ontario, 2 Library La., Tillsonburg, ON N4G 4S7, Canada. TEL 519-842-5571. Ed. Matthew Scholtz. circ. 110. (looseleaf format; back issues avail.) **Document type:** newsletter.

020 340   US
A - V & MICROGRAPHICS S I S NEWSLETTER. (Audio - Visual) 1980. 3/yr. membership. American Association of Law Libraries, A-V & Micrographics S I S, c/o Columbus Law Library Assn., 369 S. High St., 10th Fl., Columbus, OH 43215. TEL 614-221-4181. FAX 614-221-2115. Ed. Andrew Brann. cum.index. **Document type:** newsletter.
Formerly: A V M News.

020   US   ISSN 0276-8291
ABBEY NEWSLETTER; bookbinding and conservation. 1975. 8/yr. $40 to individuals; institutions $49. Abbey Publications, Inc., 7105 Geneva Dr., Austin, TX 78723-1510. TEL 512-929-3992. FAX 512-929-3995. Ed. Ellen R. McCrady. bk.rev.; bibl.; charts; illus.; stat.; tr.lit.; index. circ. 1,300. (back issues avail.) **Indexed:** Abstr.Bull.Inst.Pap.Chem., Art & Archaeol.Tech.Abstr., Graph.Arts Lit.Abstr. **Document type:** newsletter.
—BLDSC (0537.724860).
Description: Covers bookbinding and conservation of book and paper materials, world wide. Includes current news and events.

020   US   ISSN 0278-2820
Z668
ABSTRACTS STRENGTHENING RESEARCH LIBRARY RESOURCES PROGRAM. 1978. a. free. U.S. Department of Education, Library Programs, Washington, DC 20208-5571. Ed. Louise Sutherland. circ. 1,000. (back issues avail.) **Document type:** abstracting/indexing.
Description: Information on grants funded by Title II-C of the Higher Education Act under the Research Library Resources Program.

ACADEMIA; a monthly magazine of academic titles and information. see *PUBLISHING AND BOOK TRADE*

020   US   ISSN 0894-993X
ACADEMIC LIBRARY BOOK REVIEW. 1985. bi-m. $36 (foreign $44). 290 Broadway, Ste. 354, Lynbrook, NY 11563. FAX 516-596-2911. Ed. Hannah Merker. adv.; bk.rev. circ. 5,000.

020   IT   ISSN 0001-4451
ACCADEMIE E BIBLIOTECHE D'ITALIA. 1927. q. L.80000. (Ministero per i Beni Culturali e Ambientali) Casa Editrice Fratelli Palombi, Via dei Gracchi 181-185, 00192 Rome, Italy. TEL 06-354456. FAX 06-319806. Dir. Renzo Frattarolo. illus.; index. **Indexed:** Lib.Lit., Lib.Sci.Abstr., LISA, M.L.A.
—BLDSC (0570.805000).
Description: Forum features bibliographies, initiatives and activities promoting cultural institutes.

020   AT   ISSN 1030-0155
ACCESS (ELIZABETH). 1964. q. Aus.$40 (foreign Aus.$48) (effective 1994). Australian School Library Association, Inc., P.O. Box 140, Elizabeth, S.A. 5112, Australia. TEL 08-282-2100. FAX 08-282-2142. Ed. Andrew Perry. adv.; bk.rev. circ. 3,000. (back issues avail.)
—BLDSC (0570.819750).
Supersedes (in 1987): Australian School Librarian (ISSN 0005-0199)
Description: Provides a focus for those teachers and teacher-librarians concerned with co-operative planning and teaching.

020   US   ISSN 0896-3576
Z689.A15   CODEN: AQLIER
ACQUISITIONS LIBRARIAN. 1989. s-a. $34 to individuals; institutions and libraries $90. Haworth Press, Inc., 10 Alice St., Binghamton, NY 13904. TEL 607-722-5857; 800-342-9678. FAX 607-722-1424. Ed. Bill Katz. adv.; bk.rev. circ. 396. (also avail. in microfiche from HAW; reprint service avail. from HAW) **Indexed:** Chem.Abstr., LISA. **Document type:** trade publication.
—BLDSC (0578.881170); Faxon; SWETS; CASDDS.
Description: Devoted to a single, broad, but well-defined and practical issue or topic of immediate concern to librarians and information professionals.
Refereed Serial

020   SW   ISSN 0065-1060
ACTA BIBLIOTHECAE REGIAE STOCKHOLMIENSIS. 1961. irreg. price varies. Kungliga Biblioteket, Box 5039, 102 41 Stockholm, Sweden. FAX 08-6116956. TELEX 19640-KBS-S. **Document type:** monographic series.

020   SW   ISSN 0065-1079
ACTA BIBLIOTHECAE UNIVERSITATIS GOTHOBURGENSIS. 1941. irreg., no.25, 1991. price varies; also exchange basis. Goeteborgs Universitet, Universitetsbibliotek, Centralbiblioteket, P.O. Box 5096, S-402 22 Goeteborg, Sweden. **Document type:** monographic series.
—BLDSC (0580.575000).
Formerly: Acta Bibliothecae Gothoburgensis.

010 020   HU   ISSN 0001-7175
ACTA UNIVERSITATIS SZEGEDIENSIS DE ATTILA JOZSEF NOMINATAE. ACTA BIBLIOTHECARIA. (Text in English, German or Hungarian; summaries in English, French, German or Russian) 1955. irreg. exchange basis. Attila Jozsef University, c/o E. Szabo, Exchange Librarian, Dugonics ter 13, P.O.B. 393, Szeged H-6701, Hungary. TEL 62-24-022. TELEX 82605 JATCK H. (Subscr. to: Kultura, Box 149, H-1389 Budapest, Hungary) Ed. Bela Karacsonyi. charts. circ. 500. **Document type:** academic/scholarly publication.
Description: Library science and cultural history with publishing history as secondary concern.

027   PL   ISSN 0524-4471
Z671
ACTA UNIVERSITATIS WRATISLAVIENSIS. BIBLIOTEKOZNAWSTWO. (Text in Polish; summaries in English, German or Russian) 1955. irreg. price varies. (Uniwersytet Wroclawski) Wydawnictwo Uniwersytetu Wroclawskiego, Pl. Uniwersytecki 9-13, 50-137 Wroclaw, Poland. TEL 44-10-06. (Dist. by: Ksiegarnia Uniwersytetu Wroclawskiego, Pl. Uniwersytecki 9-13, 50-137 Wroclaw, Poland) Ed. Anna Zbikowska-Migon. circ. 200. **Document type:** academic/scholarly publication.

025   US   ISSN 0363-0250
ACTION FOR LIBRARIES. 1975. m. $10 to foreign libraries (free to US libraries). Bibliographical Center for Research, Rocky Mountain Region, Inc., 14394 E. Evans Ave., Aurora, CO 80014. TEL 303-751-6277. Ed. Joyce Hillshafer. adv.; bk.rev. circ. 2,000. **Document type:** newsletter.
—BLDSC (0675.625000).

020   CN
ACTUALITES S D M. (Text and summaries in French) 1972. irreg. free. Services Documentaires Multimedia Inc., 75 Port Royal E., No. 300, Montreal, Que H3L 3T1, Canada. TEL 514-382-0895. FAX 514-384-9139. Ed. Francoise Bray. circ. 7,000. (looseleaf format)
Former titles: Actualites C B; (until 1987): Information C.B. (ISSN 0704-2728)

027.7   ET   ISSN 0017-6680
ADDIS ABABA UNIVERSITY. COLLEGE OF TECHNOLOGY. LIBRARY BULLETIN. (Name of issuing body varies: Haile Sellassie I University, University of Addis Ababa, National University) vol.10, 1977. q. free. Addis Ababa University, College of Technology, P.O. Box 518, Addis Ababa, Ethiopia. Ed. Befekadu Debela. bibl. (looseleaf format) **Document type:** bulletin.

ADDRESS LIST, REGIONAL AND SUBREGIONAL LIBRARIES FOR THE BLIND AND PHYSICALLY HANDICAPPED. see *HANDICAPPED — Visually Impaired*

020   GW   ISSN 0939-5032
Z801.A1
ADRESSBUCH DEUTSCHER BIBLIOTHEKEN. 1990. biennial. DM.24. Deutsches Bibliotheksinstitut, Abt. 1 - Publikationen, Bundesallee 184-185, 10717 Berlin, Germany. TEL 030-8505-0. FAX 030-8505100. **Document type:** directory.

ADVANCE FOR HEALTH INFORMATION PROFESSIONALS. see *MEDICAL SCIENCES*

029   US   ISSN 0044-636X
Z671   CODEN: ATLBAN
ADVANCED TECHNOLOGY LIBRARIES. Variant title: A T - L Newsletter. 1971. m. $89 (effective 1992). Macmillan Publishing Company, Macmillan Reference, 866 Third Ave., New York, NY 10022. TEL 212-702-4301. FAX 212-605-9368. adv.; bibl.; index. (also avail. in microform from UMI) **Indexed:** Info.Media & Tech., Leg.Info.Manage.Ind., Pers.Lit., PROMT, Tr.& Indus.Ind.
—BLDSC (0696.935000); UnCover; SWETS; UMI; CASDDS.
Description: Covers technical advances in library science: optical publishing, hardware and software, library services, bibliographic utilities, legislation and results of meetings.

LIBRARY AND INFORMATION SCIENCES

020   US   ISSN 0065-2830
Z674   CODEN: AVLSA
ADVANCES IN LIBRARIANSHIP. 1970. irreg., vol.16, 1992. Academic Press, Inc., 525 B St., Ste. 1900, San Diego, CA 92101-4495. TEL 619-231-0926. FAX 619-699-6715. (Subscr. to: Order Dept., 6277 Sea Harbor Dr., 4th Fl., Orlando, FL 32887. TEL 800-321-5068) Ed. Melvin J. Voigt. (reprint service avail. from ISI)
—BLDSC (0709.260000); UnCover. **CCC.**

025   US   ISSN 0732-0671
Z678
ADVANCES IN LIBRARY ADMINISTRATION AND ORGANIZATION. 1982. a. $63.50 to institutions. J A I Press Inc., 55 Old Post Rd. No. 2, Box 1678, Greenwich, CT 06836-1678. TEL 203-661-7602. Ed.Bd. **Document type:** trade publication.
—Faxon.

020   II
ADVANCES IN LIBRARY AND INFORMATION SCIENCE. (Text and summaries in English) 1990. a. Rs.270($50) Scientific Publishers, P.O. Box 91, 5A, New Pali Rd., Jodhpur 342 001, India. TEL 33323. FAX 91-291-32085. Ed. D.C. Ojha. circ. 300.

020   US   ISSN 0899-1227
ADVANCES IN LIBRARY INFORMATION TECHNOLOGY. 1988. irreg. U.S. Library of Congress, Cataloging Distribution Service, Washington, DC 20541-5017. TEL 202-707-6100. FAX 202-707-1334. **Document type:** government publication.
—BLDSC (0709.275000).

020   US   ISSN 1052-262X
Z731
ADVANCES IN LIBRARY RESOURCE SHARING. 1990. a. Meckler Publishing Corporation, 11 Ferry Lane W., Westport, CT 06880. TEL 203-226-6967.
—BLDSC (0709.277000). **CCC.**

020   US   ISSN 1040-4384
Z692.S5
ADVANCES IN SERIALS MANAGEMENT. 1986. irreg. $58.50 to institutions. J A I Press Inc., 55 Old Post Rd., Box 1678, Greenwich, CT 06836-1678. TEL 203-661-7602. Eds. Marcia Tuttle, Jean Cook.
—BLDSC (0711.383500).

020.6   NR   ISSN 0189-6709
AFRICAN JOURNAL OF ACADEMIC LIBRARIANSHIP. (Text in English; summaries in French) 1983. s-a. £N25($50) Standing Conference of African University Libraries (SCAUL), P.O. Box 46, University of Lagos, Akoka, Yaba, Lagos, Nigeria. TEL 524968. Ed. E.B. Bankole. adv.; bk.rev. circ. 200. **Indexed:** LISA. **Document type:** academic/scholarly publication.
—BLDSC (0732.514000).
Supersedes: S C A U L Newsletter (ISSN 0563-0924)

021   SA
AFRICAN LIBRARY ASSOCIATION OF S.A. NEWSLETTER.* (Text mainly in English; occasionally in Afrikaans) 1967. q. R 0.50. African Library Association of South Africa, c/o Mamelodi Branch Library, P.O. Mamelodi, Pretoria, South Africa.
Formerly: B L A S A Newsletter (ISSN 0006-4580)

AFRICANA JOURNAL; a bibliographic library journal and review annual. see *BIBLIOGRAPHIES*

026   US
     CODEN: ALNWD9
AFRICANA LIBRARIES NEWSLETTER. 1975. q. free. c/o Joseph J. Lauer, Ed., Africana Bibliographer, Michigan State University Libraries, E. Lansing, MI 48824-1048. TEL 517-355-2366. FAX 517-336-1445. bibl.; circ. 600 (controlled). (looseleaf format; back issues avail.) **Document type:** newsletter.
—BLDSC (0735.169000); CASDDS.
Former titles: Boston University Africana Libraries. Newsletter; Africana Libraries Newsletter (ISSN 0148-7868)
Description: News, minutes and other information of interest to librarians involved with African studies and others.

020   US   ISSN 1043-2094
Z689.5.U6
AGAINST THE GRAIN. 1989. 5/yr. $25 (foreign $35). Katina Strauch, Ed. & Pub., Citadel Sta., Charleston, SC 29409. TEL 803-953-8020. FAX 803-723-8019. adv.; bk.rev.; abstr. circ. 1,100. **Document type:** academic/scholarly publication, trade publication.
—UnCover.
Description: Covers library-vendor and publisher-library relations, acquisition business, publisher profiles, prices, studies, and collection development.

026 630   US
AGRICULTURAL INFORMATION RESOURCE CENTERS (YEAR); a world directory. 1991. every 5 yrs. $140. International Association of Agricultural Librarians and Documentalists, 1347 Maple Ave., Twin Falls, ID 83301. TEL 208-734-9349. Ed. Carol Boast. **Document type:** directory.
Description: Provides a subject index to collections and specialists in all areas of agricultural information. Detailed descriptions of libraries and information centers throughout the world.

020 630   US   ISSN 0095-2699
Z675.A8   CODEN: ALINDP
AGRICULTURAL LIBRARIES INFORMATION NOTES. 1975. m. free. U.S. Department of Agriculture, National Agricultural Library, 10301 Baltimore Blvd., Beltsville, MD 20705. TEL 301-344-3937. FAX 301-344-5472. Ed. Joseph N. Swab. adv.; bk.rev.; charts; stat. circ. 4,500.
—BLDSC (0750.240000); CASDDS.

020   PL
AKADEMIA EKONOMICZNA, KRAKOW. BIBLIOTEKA GLOWNA. BIULETYN INFORMACYJNY. irreg. price varies. Akademia Ekonomiczna, Krakow, Biblioteka Glowna, Ul. Rakowicka 27, 31-510 Krakow, Poland. TEL 48-12-210099. circ. 250. **Document type:** bulletin.

027.4   US
ALABAMA. PUBLIC LIBRARY SERVICE. ANNUAL REPORT. 1956. a. free to Alabama libraries. Public Library Service, 6030 Monticello Dr., Montgomery, AL 36130. TEL 205-277-7330. circ. 1,200. (also avail. in microform from EDR; microfiche from CIS) **Indexed:** SRI. **Document type:** corporate report.
Supersedes: Alabama. Public Library Service. Basic State Plan and Annual Program (ISSN 0095-361X)

027.7   US
ALABAMA JUNIOR COLLEGE LIBRARY ASSOCIATION NEWSLETTER. 1965. 3/yr. membership. (Alabama Junior College Library Association) George C. Wallace State Community College, Drawer 1049, Salem, AL 36702-1049. Ed. Ann B. Mobbs. cum.index: 1965-1975. circ. 200. **Document type:** newsletter.
Formerly (until 1973): Alabama Junior College Librarian (ISSN 0002-4260)

020   US   ISSN 0002-4295
Z671
ALABAMA LIBRARIAN. 1949. q. $25 (foreign $55). Alabama Library Association, Inc., 400 S. Union St., Ste. 255, Montgomery, AL 36104. TEL 205-262-5210. Ed. Sheila Delacroix. adv.; illus.; cum.index: vols. 1-7. circ. 1,400. (also avail. in microform from UMI) **Indexed:** Lib.Lit., Lib.Sci.Abstr. **Document type:** bulletin.
—UMI.

070   US
ALABAMA PRESS ASSOCIATION. RATE AND DATA GUIDE. (Cover title: Alabama Rate and Data) a. $20. Alabama Press Association, Commerce Center, Ste. 1100, 2027 1st Ave., N., Birmingham, AL 35203. TEL 205-322-0380. FAX 205-322-0389. Ed. Mike Ryland. adv. circ. 2,000.
Formerly: A P A Newspaper Directory (ISSN 0065-5643)

021   US
ALASKA LIBRARY DIRECTORY. 1973. a. $20 to non-members; members $10. Alaska Library Association (Fairbanks), c/o Betty Calbraith, Treas., Box 81084, Fairbanks, AK 99708. TEL 907-479-5196. circ. controlled. **Document type:** directory.
Formerly: Alaska Libraries and Library Personnel Directory.
Description: Lists names and addresses of Alaskan libraries and their staffs.

027.7   CN   ISSN 0829-4321
ALBERTA ASSOCIATION OF COLLEGE LIBRARIANS. NEWSLETTER. 1978. 2/yr. Can.$20. Alberta Association of College Librarians, Canadian Union College Library, Box 460, College Heights, AB T0C 0Z0, Canada. FAX 403-782-3977. Ed. Joyce Van Scheik. adv.; bk.rev.; circ. 100 (controlled). **Document type:** newsletter.
Formerly: Alberta Council of College Librarians. Newsletter (ISSN 0707-7327)

020   CN   ISSN 0707-0306
ALBERTA GOVERNMENT LIBRARIES' NEWSLETTER. 1974. m. (11/yr.) Can.$14.25. Alberta Legislature Library, Cooperative Government Library Service Section, 902 Legislature Annex, 9718-107 St., Edmonton, AB T5K 1E4, Canada. TEL 403-427-3837. FAX 403-427-1623. Ed. Karen Powell. circ. 145. **Document type:** newsletter.

020   IS   ISSN 0334-4754
ALEI SEFER. (Text in Hebrew) s-a. $15 per no. Bar-Ilan University Press, Ramat Gan 52900, Israel. TEL 03-5318401. Ed. S.Z. Havlin. (back issues avail.) **Document type:** academic/scholarly publication.
Description: Innovative comprehensive journal devoted to the scientific examinations of bibliographies and to the study of the Hebrew book.

020   UK   ISSN 0955-7490
     CODEN: ALEXE2
ALEXANDRIA: JOURNAL OF NATIONAL & INTERNATIONAL LIBRARY & INFORMATION ISSUES. 1989. 3/yr. £84 (foreign £106). Ashgate Publishing Ltd. (Subsidiary of: Gower Publishing Co. Ltd.), Gower House, Croft Rd., Aldershot, Hants. GU11 3HR, England. TEL 0252-331551. FAX 0252-344405. **Indexed:** LISA.
—BLDSC (0786.938600); SWETS.
Description: National library and international policy issues of interest to all in the library and information world.

020   US   ISSN 8756-4173
Z673.W3
ALKI. 1985. 3/yr. $18 to non-members; members free (effective 1994). Washington Library Association, 1232 143rd Ave., S.E., Bellevue, WA 98007. TEL 206-747-6917. E-mail: WlIF@wln.com. Ed. John Sheller. adv.; index. circ. 1,350. (also avail. in microform from UMI) **Document type:** academic/scholarly publication.
Description: Philosophical and substantive analyses of current and enduring issues for and about Washington State libraries.

020 800   SW   ISSN 0280-2260
ALLT OM BOECKER. 1987. bi-m. SEK 310 in Sweden; other Nordic countries SEK 340; elsewhere SEK 350. PROGEK, P.O. Box 31003, S-400 32 Goeteborg, Sweden. TEL 46-31-24-34-25. FAX 46-31-24-38-10. adv.; bk.rev.

020 808.8   CN
ALTERNATIVE ARCHIVIST. 1979. q. Can.$5. Federation of Alternative Libraries, Box 1294, Kitchener, Ont. N2G 4G8, Canada. adv.; bk.rev.; abstr.; bibl. circ. 75. (looseleaf format)

020   US   ISSN 0749-6885
Z716.4
ALTERNATIVE LIBRARY LITERATURE. 1984. biennial. $35. McFarland & Company, Inc., Box 611, Jefferson, NC 28640. Eds. Sanford Berman, James P. Danky.
—BLDSC (0803.587500).
Description: Anthology on library issues and current topics. Includes essays and cartoons.

070.5 970   US   ISSN 0569-2229
E172
AMERICAN ANTIQUARIAN SOCIETY. NEWS-LETTER. 1968. s-a. included in subscr. to its proceedings. American Antiquarian Society, 185 Salisbury St., Worcester, MA 01609. TEL 508-755-5221. Ed. Lynnette P. Sodha. illus. circ. 1,525. (also avail. in microform from UMI; reprint service avail. from UMI) **Document type:** newsletter.
—UMI.
Description: Contains information about programs, grants, and members and staff of the Society.

LIBRARY AND INFORMATION SCIENCES

970   US   ISSN 0044-751X
E172
AMERICAN ANTIQUARIAN SOCIETY. PROCEEDINGS.
1812. s-a. $45 (foreign $53). American Antiquarian Society, 185 Salisbury St., Worcester, MA 01609. TEL 508-755-5221. Ed. John B. Hench. bibl.; illus. circ. 1,000. (also avail. in microfilm from UMI; reprint service avail. from KTO) **Indexed:** Amer.Hist.& Life, Art & Archaeol.Tech.Abstr., Arts & Hum.Cit.Ind., Bibl.Ind., Curr.Cont., Hist.Abstr., RILA. **Document type:** proceedings.
—Faxon; UnCover.
Description: Focuses on tools for scholarship-bibliographies, finding aids, and edited primary documents concerning American history and culture through 1876.

026   US   ISSN 0572-4953
Z675.L2
AMERICAN ASSOCIATION OF LAW LIBRARIES. NEWSLETTER. (Supersedes the association's President's Newsletter) 1972. 10/yr. $50. American Association of Law Libraries, 53 W. Jackson Blvd., Ste. 940, Chicago, IL 60604. TEL 312-939-4764. FAX 312-431-1097. Ed. Peter Beck. circ. 4,700. **Indexed:** Leg.Info.Manage.Ind. **Document type:** newsletter.

AMERICAN CHEMICAL SOCIETY PUBLICATIONS QUARTERLY; a newsletter for librarians and information specialists. see *CHEMISTRY*

AMERICAN INDIAN LIBRARIES NEWSLETTER. see *ETHNIC INTERESTS*

020   US   ISSN 0002-9769
Z673.A5   CODEN: AMLRBN
AMERICAN LIBRARIES. 1907. m. (11/yr.). $60 (foreign $70) to institutions and libraries only. American Library Association, 50 E. Huron St., Chicago, IL 60611-2795. TEL 800-545-2433. FAX 312-440-0901. Ed. Thomas Gaughan. adv.; bk.rev.; illus.; index. circ. 53,300. (also avail. in microfilm from UMI,PMC; back issues avail.; reprint service avail. from UMI) **Indexed:** Access (1975-), Bk.Rev.Ind. (1969-), C.I.J.E., Child.Bk.Rev.Ind. (1969-), Educ.Ind., Inform.Sci.Abstr., Leg.Info.Manage.Ind., LHTN, Lib.Lit., LISA, Mag.Ind., Media Rev.Dig., P.A.I.S., Pers.Lit., PROMT, R.G., Resour.Ctr.Ind. **Document type:** trade publication.
●Also available online. Vendor(s): DIALOG Information Services, Inc.
—BLDSC (0840.730000); Faxon; UnCover; SWETS; UMI; CASDDS. **CCC**.
Formerly: A L A Bulletin (ISSN 0364-4006)
Description: Provides current news and information concerning the library industry.

020   US
AMERICAN LIBRARY ASSOCIATION. ANNUAL CONFERENCE PROGRAM. a. $12. American Library Association, Conference Arrangements Office, 50 E. Huron St., Chicago, IL 60611. TEL 312-280-3218. FAX 312-280-3224. Ed. Pier A. London. adv. circ. 16,000. **Document type:** proceedings.

020   US   ISSN 0065-910X
Z731   CODEN: ALDIDJ
AMERICAN LIBRARY DIRECTORY. (Issued in 2 vols.) 1908. a., 47th ed., 1994. $239.95. R.R. Bowker, A Reed Reference Publishing Company, Part of the Reed Elsevier group, 121 Chanlon Rd., New Providence, NJ 07974. TEL 908-464-6800. FAX 908-665-6638. TELEX 138 755. (Subscr. to: Order Dept., Box 31, New Providence, NJ 07974-9903. TEL 800-521-8110) (also avail. in magnetic tape) **Document type:** directory.
●Also available online. Vendor(s): DIALOG Information Services, Inc. (File no.460).
Also available on CD-ROM. Producer(s): Bowker - Reed Reference Electronic Publishing.
—BLDSC (0840.750000); CASDDS. **CCC**.
Description: Lists all types of libraries and library-related organizations in US and Canada.

026   US
AMERICAN MERCHANT MARINE LIBRARY ASSOCIATION. ANNUAL REPORT. 1921. a. free. American Merchant Marine Library Association, One World Trade Center, Ste. 2161, New York, NY 10048. TEL 212-775-1038. FAX 212-432-5492. TELEX 222146 UNS UR. Ed. C. Elizabeth Leach. circ. 2,500.
Formerly: American Merchant Marine Library Association. Report (ISSN 0065-938X)

AMERICAN PETROLEUM INSTITUTE. CENTRAL ABSTRACTING & INFORMATION SERVICES. THESAURUS. see *PETROLEUM AND GAS — Abstracting, Bibliographies, Statistics*

020   US   ISSN 0160-0044
Z1008   CODEN: PAISDQ
AMERICAN SOCIETY FOR INFORMATION SCIENCE. ANNUAL MEETING. PROCEEDINGS. 1964. a. $45 to non-members; members $36. (American Society for Information Science) Learned Information, Inc., 143 Old Marlton Pike, Medford, NJ 08055-8750. TEL 609-654-6266. FAX 609-654-4309. Ed. Jose-Marie Griffiths. illus.; index. (back issues avail.) **Indexed:** Biol.Abstr., C.I.J.E., Compumath, SSCI. **Document type:** proceedings.
—BLDSC (6841.279000); Faxon; UnCover; CASDDS. **CCC**.
Formerly: American Society for Information Science. Proceedings (ISSN 0044-7870)

029.7   US   ISSN 0095-4403
Z699.A1   CODEN: BASICR
AMERICAN SOCIETY FOR INFORMATION SCIENCE. BULLETIN. 1974. bi-m. $60 to non-members (foreign $70). American Society for Information Science, 8720 Georgia Ave, Ste. 501, Silver Spring, MD 20910. TEL 301-495-0900. FAX 301-495-0810. Ed. Richard Hill. adv.; bibl. circ. 4,500. (also avail. in microform from UMI; back issues avail.; reprint service avail. from UMI) **Indexed:** C.I.J.E., Curr.Cont., GeoRef., Inform.Sci.Abstr., Leg.Info.Manage.Ind., LHTN, Lib.Lit., LISA, Mag.Ind., Sci.Abstr., Soc.Work Res.& Abstr., SSCI. **Document type:** bulletin.
—BLDSC (2392.805000); Faxon; UnCover; SWETS; UMI; CASDDS. **CCC**.
Supersedes: A S I S Newsletter (ISSN 0001-2513); Former titles: American Documentation Institute. Newsletter; American Society for Information Science. Newsletter (ISSN 0190-5201).
Description: Offers news, opinions and analysis of happenings in the world of information.

029.7 016   US   ISSN 0002-8231
Z1007   CODEN: AISJB6
AMERICAN SOCIETY FOR INFORMATION SCIENCE. JOURNAL. Abbreviated title: J A S I S. 1950. 10/yr. $395 to individuals (foreign $532.50). John Wiley & Sons, Inc., Journals, 605 Third Ave., New York, NY 10158-0012. TEL 212-850-6000. FAX 212-850-6088. Ed. Donald H. Kraft. adv.; bk.rev.; charts; illus.; index. circ. 5,200. (also avail. in microform; back issues avail.; reprint service avail. from KTO,RPI) **Indexed:** ABI Inform, Abstr.Bull.Inst.Pap.Chem., Amer.Hist.& Life, BPIA, Bus.Ind., Chem.Abstr., Compumath, Comput.Cont., Comput.Rev., Curr.Cont., Excerp.Med., GeoRef., Hist.Abstr., Inform.Sci.Abstr., Key to Econ.Sci., Lang.& Lang.Behav.Abstr., Leg.Info.Manage.Ind., LHTN, Lib.Lit., LISA, P.A.I.S., Sci.Abstr., Sci.Cit.Ind., Soc.Work Res.& Abstr., SSCI. **Document type:** trade publication.
—BLDSC (4692.870000); EI; Faxon; UnCover; SWETS; UMI; CASDDS. **CCC**.
Formerly: American Documentation.
Description: Forum for discussion and experimentation in the theory and practice of communicating information. Articles cover operations research, automation applications, communications and computer technology.

020   UK   ISSN 0265-3389
AMERICAN STUDIES LIBRARY NEWSLETTER. 1978. 2/yr. free to qualified personnel. S.C.O.N.U.L. Advisory Committee on American Studies, c/o Liverpool School of Tropical Medicine, School Library, Pembroke Place, Liverpool L3 5QA, England. TEL 051-708-9393. FAX 051-708-8733. Ed. C.M. Deering. adv.; bk.rev. circ. 400. **Indexed:** LISA. **Document type:** newsletter.
—BLDSC (0857.677000).
Formerly (until no.15, 1984): A.S.L.G. Newsletter (ISSN 0141-6383)

025   US   ISSN 0066-0868
Z673
AMERICAN THEOLOGICAL LIBRARY ASSOCIATION. CONFERENCE. SUMMARY OF PROCEEDINGS. 1947. a. $20 (foreign $22). American Theological Library Association, Director of Member Services, 820 Church St., Ste. 300, Evanston, IL 60201. TEL 708-869-7788. Dir. Madeline D. Gray. cum.index every 40 yrs. circ. 700. (also avail. in microfilm) **Indexed:** Rel.Ind.One. **Document type:** proceedings.
—BLDSC (8531.140000).

027.67   US   ISSN 0003-1399
Z675.T4
AMERICAN THEOLOGICAL LIBRARY ASSOCIATION. NEWSLETTER. 1953. q. $15. American Theological Library Association, Director of Member Services, 820 Church St., Ste. 300, Evanston, IL 60201. TEL 708-869-7788. Dir. Madeline D. Gray. cum.index every 5 yrs. circ. 700. (processed) **Indexed:** Lib.Lit. **Document type:** newsletter.
—BLDSC (6106.338150).

020   UK   ISSN 0260-3667
AMERICAN TRUST FOR THE BRITISH LIBRARY. NEWSLETTER. 1980. 3/yr. British Library, Humanities and Social Sciences, Great Russell St., London WC1B 3DG, England. TEL 071-323-7704. FAX 071-323-7736. TELEX 21462. Ed. Andrea Polden. illus.; circ. controlled. **Document type:** newsletter.
—BLDSC (6106.338200).
Description: Covers details of exhibitions, acquisitions and other interesting and important developments.

AMERIKAI MAGYAR LEVELESTAR/HUNGARIAN ARCHIVES OF AMERICA. see *HISTORY — History Of Europe*

AMICI. see *RELIGIONS AND THEOLOGY — Roman Catholic*

027.4 021.7   US   ISSN 0003-195X
Z671
AMONG FRIENDS. 1945. s-a. $2 to non-members. Friends of the Detroit Public Library, Inc., 5201 Woodward Ave., Detroit, MI 48202. TEL 313-833-4048. Ed. Paul T. Scupholm. bk.rev.; illus. circ. 4,500.

027.4   US
ANALYSES OF NEW JERSEY PUBLIC LIBRARY STATISTICS FOR (YEAR). 1981. a. free. New Jersey State Library, CN-520, Trenton, NJ 08625-0520. TEL 609-292-6294. Ed. Robert K. Fortenbaugh. circ. 675. **Indexed:** SRI. **Document type:** government publication.

ANDREWS ADVISOR; quarterly newsletter for law librarians. see *LAW*

020 001.539   II   ISSN 0003-4835
Z671   CODEN: ALSDA8
ANNALS OF LIBRARY SCIENCE AND DOCUMENTATION. (Text in English) 1954. q. Rs.100($50) Indian National Scientific Documentation Centre, 14 Satsang Vihar Mag, Off SJS Sansanwal Marg, New Delhi 110 067, India. Ed. B. Guha. adv.; bk.rev.; bibl.; index. circ. 650. **Indexed:** Chem.Abstr., Lib.Lit., LISA.
—BLDSC (1041.810000); SWETS; CASDDS.

ANNOTATED BIBLIOGRAPHIES OF SERIALS: A SUBJECT APPROACH. see *BIBLIOGRAPHIES*

ANNOTATION. see *HISTORY — History Of North And South America*

LIBRARY AND INFORMATION SCIENCES

001.5 US ISSN 0066-4200
Z699.A1 CODEN: ARISBC
ANNUAL REVIEW OF INFORMATION SCIENCE AND TECHNOLOGY. 1966. a., latest, vol.28, 1993. $92.50 to non-members; members $74. (American Society for Information Science, Information & Business Division) Learned Information, Inc., 143 Old Marlton Pike, Medford, NJ 08055. TEL 609-654-6266. FAX 609-654-4309. Ed. Martha E. Williams. bibl.; index, cum.index: vols.1-10. (back issues avail.) **Indexed:** Biol.Abstr., Compumath, Curr.Cont., Sci.Abstr., SSCI. **Document type:** monographic series.
—BLDSC (1522.570000); Faxon; UnCover; SWETS; UMI; CASDDS. **CCC.**
 Description: Current reviews and analyses of the year's most important trends, innovations, and advances in the field of information science.
 Refereed Serial

026 282 IT
ANNUARIO DELLE BIBLIOTECHE ECCLESIATICHE ITALIANE. irreg. (Asociazione Bibliotecari Ecclesiastici Italiani) Editrice Bibliografica s.r.l., Viale Veneto 24, 20124 Milan, Italy. TEL 02-29006965. FAX 02-654624. Eds. Sergio Bigatton, Piergiorgio Figini.

020 US
ANSWERS; the information access digest. 1977. m. (except Jul. and Aug.). $45. Data and Research Technology Corp., 1102 McNeilly Ave., Pittsburgh, PA 15216. TEL 412-563-2212. Ed. K.K. McNulty, Sr. adv.; bk.rev.; bibl.; index. circ. 5,000. (also avail. in microfiche) **Document type:** abstracting/indexing, consumer publication.
 Former titles: Information Access Digest & Information Access.

ANTHROPOS; revista de documentacion cientifica de la cultura. see *HUMANITIES: COMPREHENSIVE WORKS*

ANTHROPOS. DOCUMENTOS A; genealogia cientifica de la cultura. see *HUMANITIES: COMPREHENSIVE WORKS*

ANTHROPOS. SUPLEMENTOS. see *HUMANITIES: COMPREHENSIVE WORKS*

020 SW ISSN 0283-1333
ANTIKVARIATET; tidning & katalog foer laesare och samlare. 1985. 5/yr. SEK 95 (effective 1990). Antikvariatet, P.O. Box 32065, S-126 11 Stockholm, Sweden. **Document type:** catalog.

ANUARIO INTERAMERICANO DE ARCHIVOS. see *HISTORY — History Of North And South America*

020 410 053 GW
ARBEITSGEMEINSCHAFT DER BIBLIOTHEKEN UND DOKUMENTATIONSSTELLEN DER OST-, OSTMITTEL- UND SUEDOSTEUROPAFORSCHUNG. MITTEILUNGEN. (Text in English, German, Russian) 1981. q. free. Arbeitsgemeinschaft der Bibliotheken und Dokumentationsstellen der Ost-, Ostmittel- und Suedosteuropaforschung, c/o Martin-Opitz-Bibliothek, Berliner Platz 11, 44623 Herne, Germany. TEL 23230162805. Ed. W. Kessler. adv.; bk.rev.; abstr.; bibl. circ. 400. (back issues avail.) **Document type:** newsletter.
 Formerly: Arbeitsgemeinschaft der Bibliotheken und Dokumentationsstellen der Osteuropa-, Suedosteuropa- und DDR-Forschung. Mitteilungen (ISSN 0721-9105)
 Description: Information on libraries and documentation centersconcerned with Eastern, East Central and Southeastern Europe. Includes annual reports, events and statistics.

020 GW ISSN 0518-2220
ARBEITSGEMEINSCHAFT DER PARLAMENTS- UND BEHOERDENBIBLIOTHEKEN. ARBEITSHEFTE. 1958. a. DM.32. Arbeitsgemeinschaft der Parlaments- und Behoerdenbibliotheken, c/o Abt. Informationsdienste des Deutschen Patentamtes, Zweibrueckenstr. 12, 80297 Munich, Germany. TEL 089-2195-2448. FAX 089-2195-2221. circ. 600. **Document type:** government publication.

020 GW ISSN 0170-5598
ARBEITSGEMEINSCHAFT DER PARLAMENTS- UND BEHOERDENBIBLIOTHEKEN. MITTEILUNGEN. 1958. s-a. DM.32. Arbeitsgemeinschaft der Parlaments- und Behoerdenbibliotheken, c/o Abt. Informationsdienste des Deutschen Patentamts, Zweibrueckenstr. 12, 80297 Munich, Germany. TEL 089-2195-2448. FAX 089-2195-2221. circ. 600. **Document type:** government publication.

027.7 GW ISSN 0177-8358
ARBEITSGEMEINSCHAFT KATHOLISCH-THEOLOGISCHER BIBLIOTHEKEN. MITTEILUNGSBLATT. 1952. a. DM.20. Arbeitsgemeinschaft Katholisch-Theologischer Bibliotheken (AKThB), Bibliothek des Priester Seminars, Jesuitenstr. 13, 54290 Trier, Germany. Ed. Michael Embrach. adv.; bk.rev.; cum.index. circ. 250. **Document type:** newsletter.

020 SZ ISSN 0258-0764
Z673.V43
ARBIDO-B; offizielles Mitteilungsorgan - bulletin d'information officiel - bollettino d'informazioni officiale. (Text in French, German and Italian) 1925. 8/yr. 30 SFr. Vereinigung Schweizerischer Archivare - Association des Bibliotheques et des Bibliothecaires Suisses - Associazione delle Biblioteche e dei Bibliotecari Svizzeri, c/o Sekretariat REBUS, Sprengliweg 6, CH-3360 Herzogenbuchsee, Switzerland. TEL 063-615543. FAX 063-614995. (Co-sponsor: Association Suisse de Documentation - Associazione Svizzera di Documentazione) Ed. C. Staudenmann. adv.; bk.rev.; charts; illus.; index. circ. 3,200. **Indexed:** Lib.Lit. **Document type:** bulletin.
—SWETS.
 Formerly (until 1984): Nachrichten V S B - S V D (ISSN 0042-3807)
 Description: Covers association news, information and reports. Includes budgets, reports and lists of events, and positions available.

020 SZ ISSN 0258-0772
Z837.A1
ARBIDO-R; Fachorgan - revue professionnelle - rivista professionale. (Text in French, German and Italian) 1986. 4/yr. 25 SFr. Association des Archivistes Suisses, c/o Institut d'Etudes Sociales, Ecole Superieure d'Information Documentaire, Case Postale, CH-1211 Geneva 4, Switzerland. TEL 022-3209311. FAX 022-3207246. (Co-sponsors: Association des Bibliotheques et Bibliothecaires Suisses; Association Suisse de Documentation) Ed. Michel Gorin. adv.; bk.rev. circ. 2,500. **Indexed:** Lib.Lit. **Document type:** academic/scholarly publication.
—SWETS.
 Description: Provides information specialists with articles and reports in the fields of archives, library and documentation sciences.

027 NZ ISSN 0303-7940
CD2560
ARCHIFACTS. 1974. q. NZ.$19 to individuals, institutions NZ$28. Archives and Records Association of New Zealand, Maori Studies Library, University of Auckland, Private Bag, Auckland, New Zealand. adv.; bk.rev.; illus. circ. 550. **Indexed:** LISA.
—BLDSC (1597.450000). **CCC.**

029.7 FR ISSN 0769-0975
ARCHIMAG; le magazine des nouvelles technologies de l'information. 1986. m. 75 F. per no. Editions N T D A, 9 rue Bleue, 75009 Paris, France. TEL 47-70-41-41. FAX 48-00-03-42. Ed. Isabelle Perriault. adv. contact: Gwenaelle Joffre. circ. 3,500.
—BLDSC (1597.480000).
 Description: Covers documentation and archives.

ARCHIVAL ISSUES. see *HISTORY*

026 974.4 CN ISSN 0044-9423
ARCHIVES. 1969. q. Can.$50 (US Can.$75, elsewhere Can.$90). Association des Archivistes du Quebec, C.P. 423, Sillery, PQ G1T 2R8, Canada. TEL 514-343-2244. FAX 514-343-5753. Ed. Florence Ares. adv.; bk.rev.; bibl.; illus. circ. 500. (also avail. in microfiche) **Indexed:** Arts & Hum.Cit.Ind., Curr.Cont., Pt.de Rep. (1982-), SSCI. **Document type:** consumer publication.

ARCHIVES; journal of the British Records Association. see *HISTORY — History Of Europe*

025.17 UK ISSN 0066-653X
ARCHIVES AND THE USER. 1970. irreg. price varies. British Records Association, 18 Padbury Court, London E2 7EH, England. TEL 071-729-1415. **Document type:** academic/scholarly publication, monographic series.
—BLDSC (1631.200000).

ARCHIVES ET BIBLIOTHEQUES DE BELGIQUE/ARCHIEF- EN BIBLIOTHEEKWEZEN IN BELGIE. see *HISTORY — History Of Europe*

025.17 CN
ARCHIVES SOCIETY OF ALBERTA. NEWSLETTER. 4/yr. Can.$20. Archives Society of Alberta, P.O. Box 21080, Dominion Postal Outlet, Calgary, AB T2P 4H5, Canada. Eds. Donna Kynaston, Jill Clayton. circ. 300. **Document type:** newsletter.
 Formerly: Alberta Society of Archivists. Newsletter (ISSN 1180-162X)

025.17 GW ISSN 0004-038X
CD1373.A2
ARCHIVMITTEILUNGEN; Zeitschrift fuer Theorie und Praxis des Archivwesens. 1951. bi-m. DM.36. (Staatliche Archivverwaltung) Staatsverlag der DDR, Otto-Grotewohl-Str. 17, 10117 Berlin, Germany. adv.; bk.rev.; charts; illus.; index, cum.index. circ. 5,000. **Indexed:** Amer.Hist.& Life, Hist.Abstr.

025 XR ISSN 0004-0398
CD15
ARCHIVNI CASOPIS. (Text in Czech; summaries in German) 1951. q. 32 Kcs.($27.10) Sekce Archivni Spravy MV, Milady Horakove 133, 166 21 Prague 6, Czech Republic. TEL 422-3121049. (Dist. by: Artia, Ve Smeckach 30, 111 27 Prague 1, Czech Republic) Ed. Jana Prazakova. adv.; bk.rev.; cum.index: 1951-1965, 1966-1980. **Indexed:** Amer.Hist.& Life, Hist.Abstr.

930.25 AG ISSN 0325-2868
CD4020
ARCHIVO GENERAL DE LA NACION. REVISTA. 1971-1975; resumed 1976. a. Archivo General de la Nacion, Fundacion Amigos, Av Leandro N. Alem 246, 1003 Buenos Aires, Argentina. Ed. Eugenio Rom. bk.rev.; bibl. circ. 1,000. **Indexed:** Amer.Hist.& Life, Hist.Abstr.

020 982 AG
▼**ARCHIVO HISTORICO ALBERTO Y FERNANDO VALVERDE. REVISTA.** 1992. irreg. Archivo Historico Alberto y Fernando Valverde, Olavarria, Argentina. Ed. Aurora Alonso de Rocha.

020 972 UY ISSN 0797-0129
Z907.U83
ARCHIVOS DE LA BIBLIOTECA NACIONAL. 1987. irreg. exchange basis. Biblioteca Nacional del Libro, Av. 18 de Julio, 1790, Casilla de Correo 452, Montevideo, Uruguay.

020 GW ISSN 0066-6793
CD1
ARCHIVUM; international review on archives-revue internationale des archives. Every 4th year includes: International Congress on Archives. Proceedings. (Text in English, French, German, Italian, Spanish) 1951. irreg., vol.38, 1992. price varies. (Conseil International des Archives, FR - International Council on Archives) K.G. Saur Verlag KG, A Reed Reference Publishing Company, Part of the Reed Elsevier group, Ortlerstr. 8, 81373 Munich, Germany. TEL 089-76902-0. FAX 089-76902150. TELEX 5212067-SAUR-D. (Subscr. to: Postfach 701620, 81316 Munich, Germany) Ed. Andre Vanrie. circ. 2,000. **Indexed:** A.B.C.Pol.Sci., Amer.Hist.& Life, Hist.Abstr. **Document type:** monographic series.
—BLDSC (1658.400000); SWETS.
 Description: Monographs and studies on archive administration.

027.8 370 FR
ARGOS; revue des B C D et C D I. 3/yr. 110 F. Centre Regional de Documentation Pedagogique (Creteil), 20 rue D. Casanova, 94170 Le Perreux, France.

LIBRARY AND INFORMATION SCIENCES

020   CN   ISSN 0315-9930
Z673.C9533
ARGUS (MONTREAL). (Text in English, French) 1971. 3/yr. Can.$35($35) Corporation des Bibliothecaires Professionnels du Quebec - Corporation of Professional Librarians of Quebec, 307 rue Ste-Catherine Ouest, Ste.320, Montreal, PQ H2X 2A3, Canada. TEL 514-845-3327. FAX 514-845-1618. Ed. Patrick Delobel. adv.; bk.rev. circ. 1,200. **Indexed:** Bull.Signal., Inform.Sci.Abstr., Lib.Lit., LISA, Pt.de Rep. (1983-), RADAR.
—BLDSC (1664.359000).

020   US   ISSN 0004-184X
Z732
ARKANSAS LIBRARIES. 1930. bi-m. membership. Arkansas Library Association, 1100 N. University, Ste. 109, Little Rock, AR 72207. TEL 501-661-1127. FAX 501-663-1218. Eds. Patti Zabel, Crata Castleberry. adv.; bk.rev.; illus. circ. 900. (also avail. in microfilm; reprint service avail. from UMI) **Indexed:** Lib.Lit.
—UMI.

ARKHIVY UKRAINY. see HISTORY — History Of Europe

ARKIV; tidsskrift for arkivforskning. see HISTORY

020   SW   ISSN 0349-0505
CD1830
ARKIV, SAMHAELLE OCH FORSKNING. 1953. a. SEK 100. Svenska Arkivsamfundet - Swedish Archival Association, R ksarkivet, P.O. Box 12541, S-10229 Stockholm, Sweden. Ed. Britta Jonell-Ericsson. bk.rev. circ. 500.
Formerly: Svenska Arkivsamfundets Skrifterie (ISSN 0562-7451)

700 020   US   ISSN 0743-040X
Z675.A85
ARLIS - N A UPDATE. 1984. bi-m. membership only. Art Libraries Society of North America, 3900 E. Timrod St., Tucson, AZ 85711. TEL 602-881-8479. FAX 602-322-6778. Eds. Pamela J. Parry, Judy Dyki. adv. circ. 1,300. (back issues avail.) **Document type:** newsletter.
Description: Covers professional and society news for art librarians and visual resources curators; includes job ads.

020   US
▼**ARMED FORCES LIBRARIES ROUNDTABLE OF A L A NEWSLETTER**; air force, army, navy, marine corps. 1992. q. membership. American Library Association, Armed Forces Libraries Roundtable, 110 Maryland Ave., N.E., Washington, DC 20002. TEL 202-547-4440. Ed. Karen E. Pollok. **Document type:** newsletter.
Description: News and information on Army, Air Force, Navy and Marine Corps libraries and librarians.

700 020   US   ISSN 0730-7187
Z5937
ART DOCUMENTATION. 1972. 4/yr. $55 to individuals; institutions $75. Art Libraries Society of North America, 3900 E. Timrod St., Tucson, AZ 85711. TEL 602-881-8479. FAX 602-322-6778. Eds. Beryl K. Smith, Judy Dyki. adv.; bk.rev. circ. 1,300. (also avail. in microfilm from UMI; back issues avail.) **Indexed:** Artbibl.Mod., CALL, Curr.Cont., Lib.Lit., LISA, RILA. **Document type:** academic/scholarly publication.
—BLDSC (1733.395800); Faxon; UnCover; SWETS; UMI.
Supersedes (in 1981): A R L I S - N A Newsletter (ISSN 0090-3515)
Description: Articles relevant to art librarianship and visual resources curatorship.
Refereed Serial

026 700   UK   ISSN 0307-4722
Z675.A85
ART LIBRARIES JOURNAL. 1976. q. £45. Art Libraries Society (UK & Eire), 18 College Rd., Bromsgrove, Worcs B60 2NE, England. Ed. Philip Pacey. adv.; bk.rev.; bibl.; index. circ. 725. (also avail. in microfiche; back issues avail.) **Indexed:** Artbibl.Mod., Avery Ind.Archit.Per., Br.Tech.Ind., Lib.Lit., LISA, RILA.
—BLDSC (1733.461500); UnCover; SWETS.
Formerly: A R L I S Newsletter (ISSN 0044-9032)
Description: Publishes articles on art librarianship and documentation, including conference papers.

700 020   US   ISSN 0730-7160
ART LIBRARIES SOCIETY OF NORTH AMERICA. OCCASIONAL PAPERS. 1982. irreg. price varies. Art Libraries Society of North America, 3900 E. Timrod St., Tucson, AZ 85711. TEL 602-881-8479. FAX 602-322-6778. bibl.; charts; illus. (back issues avail.) **Document type:** monographic series.
Description: Professional monographs on a variety of topics of interest to art librarians and visual resources curators.

020   US   ISSN 1063-6196
▼**ART LIBRARIES SOCIETY OF NORTH AMERICA. TOPICAL PAPERS.** 1992. irreg. price varies. Art Libraries Society of North America, 3900 E. Timrod St., Tucson, AZ 85711. TEL 602-881-8479. FAX 602-322-6778. **Document type:** monographic series.
Description: Professional monographs on a variety of topics of interest to the art librarians and visual resources curators.

020   SA   ISSN 1011-8012
ARTES NATALES. (Text in Afrikaans, English) 1971. 6/yr. free to libraries in South Africa. Provincial Library Service, Private Bag 9016, Pietermaritzburg 3200, South Africa. TEL 27-331-940241. TELEX 643030. Ed. J.R. Hart. bk.rev.; bibl. circ. 600. (processed)
Formerly (until 1982): Libri Natales.
Description: Disseminates local news for non-urban librarians in Natal and acts as a medium for in-service training and information.

020   HK   ISSN 1017-6748
Z665.2.A78
ASIAN LIBRARIES; the library & information services journal. (Text in English) 1991. 4/yr. $72 (effective 1993). Library Marketing Services Ltd., 11th Fl., Hophing Centre, 8 Hennessy Road, Hong Kong. (Subscr. to: GPO Box 701, Bangkok 10501, Thailand. TEL 66-2-247-1032. FAX 66-2-247-1033) Eds. Y.F.J. Yee, James Pruess. adv. circ. 1,000. (back issues avail.) **Document type:** academic/scholarly publication.
—BLDSC (1742.623000); UnCover.
Description: Covers Asian information technology trends, information industry and products.
Refereed Serial

020   US   ISSN 1040-8517
ASIAN - PACIFIC AMERICAN LIBRARIANS ASSOCIATION NEWSLETTER. 1980. q. membership. Asian - Pacific American Librarians Association, c/o Wilfred W. Fong, Ed., School of Library and Information Science, University of Wisconsin, Milwaukee, Box 413, Milwaukee, WI 53201. TEL 414-229-5421. FAX 414-229-4848. adv.; bk.rev. circ. 300. (looseleaf format; back issues avail.) **Document type:** newsletter.
Description: Designed specifically to meet the needs of Association members, professional growth, collection development, and needs of Asian communities.

020   UK
ASLIB ANNUAL REPORT. a. free. Aslib, Association for Information Management, Publications Department, Information House, 20-24 Old St., London EC1V 9AP, England. TEL 071-253-4488. FAX 071-430-0514. **Document type:** corporate report.
Formerly: Work of Aslib: Annual Report (ISSN 0084-1285)

020   UK   ISSN 0001-253X
Z673   CODEN: ASLPAO
ASLIB PROCEEDINGS. 1949. 10/yr. £110($220) to non-members; members £75. Aslib, Association for Information Management, Publications Department, Information House, 20-24 Old St., London EC1V 9AP, England. TEL 071-253-4488. FAX 071-430-0514. (Dist. in N. America by: Learned Informaton, Inc., 143 Old Marlton Pike, Medford, NJ 08055-8750. TEL 609-654-6266) Ed. Moira Duncan. adv.; charts; illus.; index. circ. 3,500. **Indexed:** Abstr.Hum.Comp.Inter., Account.& Data Proc.Abstr., Br.Ceram.Abstr., Build.Manage.Abstr., Chem.Abstr., Compumath, Curr.Cont., Dairy Sci.Abstr., Excerp.Med., Forest.Abstr., Forest Prod.Abstr., Int.Lab.Doc., Key to Econ.Sci., LHTN, Lib.Lit., LISA, Res.High.Educ.Abstr., Sci.Abstr., SSCI, World Surf.Coat. **Document type:** proceedings.
—BLDSC (1745.000000); Faxon; UnCover; SWETS; CASDDS.
Description: Published papers from the Association's meetings and conferences with articles on new equipment, techniques and services for the information industry.

ASOCIACION ARCHIVISTICA ARGENTINA BOLETIN. see HISTORY — History Of North And South America

020   CR   ISSN 0004-4784
ASOCIACION COSTARRICENSE DE BIBLIOTECARIOS. BOLETIN. 1955. irreg. free. Asociacion Costarricense de Bibliotecarios, Apdo. 3308, San Jose, Costa Rica. circ. 500. **Indexed:** Lib.Sci.Abstr.

020.6   MX
ASOCIACION DE BIBLIOTECARIOS DE INSTITUCIONES DE ENSENANZA SUPERIOR E INVESTIGACION. ARCHIVOS. 1976. irreg. $15. Asociacion de Bibliotecarios de Instituciones de Ensenanza Superior e Investigacion, Apartado Postal 70462, 04511 Mexico D.F., Mexico. **Document type:** monographic series.

020.7   AG   ISSN 0004-4806
ASOCIACION DE EX-ALUMNOS DE LA ESCUELA NACIONAL DE BIBLIOTECARIOS. BOLETIN. 1965. q. free. Asociacion de Ex-Alumnos de la Escuela Nacional de Bibliotecarios, Mexico 564, Buenos Aires, Argentina. adv.; bk.rev.; bibl.; index, cum.index. circ. 1,000.

ASOCIACION INTERAMERICANA DE BIBLIOTECARIOS Y DOCUMENTALISTAS AGRICOLAS. BOLETIN ESPECIAL. see AGRICULTURE

020   CR   ISSN 0001-1495
ASOCIACION INTERAMERICANA DE BIBLIOTECARIOS Y DOCUMENTALISTAS AGRICOLAS. BOLETIN INFORMATIVO. 1966. 3/yr. $12 to non-members. Asociacion Interamericana de Bibliotecarios y Documentalistas Agricolas, Apdo. Postal 55, 2200 Coronado, Costa Rica. TEL 29-0222. FAX 506-294741. TELEX 2144 IICA. Ed. Ghislaine Poitevien. bk.rev.; illus. circ. 900. **Document type:** bulletin.
Description: Covers association activities, current news on library and information sciences, conferences and new publications.

020   VE   ISSN 0066-8591
ASOCIACION VENEZOLANA DE ARCHIVEROS. COLECCION DOCTRINA.* 1970. irreg. Asociacion Venezolana de Archiveros, Archivo General de la Nacion, Santa Capilla a Carmelitas 15, Av. Urdaneta, Caracas 100, Venezuela.

ASSISTANT EDITOR; original short articles, fillers, and clip art for library newsletter. see LITERATURE

023   UK   ISSN 0004-5152
Z671
ASSISTANT LIBRARIAN. 1898. m. £29($90) (overseas £40). Association of Assistant Librarians, Toxleth Library, Windsor St., Liverpool L8 1XF, England. TEL 0602-606680. FAX 0602-504207. (Subscr. to: c/o Tony Protchard, Library HQ, 32 York Rd., Leeds LS9 8TD England) Ed. Phil Taylor. adv.: B&W page £205; adv. contact: V. Halton. bk.rev.; bibl.; illus.; index; circ. 14,500 (paid); 10,500 (controlled). (also avail. in microfilm from UMI) **Indexed:** Lib.Lit., Lib.Sci.Abstr., LISA. **Document type:** trade publication.
—BLDSC (1746.661500); SWETS; UMI.

LIBRARY AND INFORMATION SCIENCES

029.7   **BE**   **ISSN 0007-9804**
Z1008
ASSOCIATION BELGE DE DOCUMENTATION. CAHIERS DE LA DOCUMENTATION. (Text in Dutch, English and French) 1947. q. 1500 BEF includes special no. (effective 1994). Association Belge de Documentation, Boulevard L. Schmidt 119, B3, B-1040 Brussels, Belgium. TEL 32-2-6729748. FAX 32-2-5188306. Ed. G. Delcol. adv.; bk.rev. circ. 360.
—BLDSC (2948.830000).

020   **FR**   **ISSN 0066-8958**
ASSOCIATION DES BIBLIOTHEQUES ECCLESIASTIQUES DE FRANCE. BULLETIN DE LIAISON. 1971. q. 120 F. Association des Bibliotheques Ecclesiastiques de France, 6 rue du Regard, 75006 Paris, France. Ed. M. Francoise Dupuy. bk.rev. circ. 220. **Document type:** bulletin.

020   **FR**
ASSOCIATION DES CONSERVATUERS DE BIBLIOTHEQUE. ANNUAIRE. 1969. irreg. 180 F. Association des Conservateurs de Bibliotheque, 16 rue Claude Bernard, 75231 Paris Cedex 05, France. adv. circ. 1,200.
Formerly: Association de l'Ecole Nationale Superieure des Bibliothecaires. Annuaire (ISSN 0066-8877)

026.95   **US**   **ISSN 0148-6225**
Z688.E25
ASSOCIATION FOR ASIAN STUDIES. COMMITTEE ON EAST ASIAN LIBRARIES. BULLETIN. 3/yr. $15 to individuals; institutions $25. Association for Asian Studies, Inc., Committee on East Asian Libraries, c/o Maureen H. Donovan, Main Library, Rm.310, Ohio State University Libraries, 1858 Neil Ave. Mall, Columbus, OH 43210-1286. TEL 614-292-3502. FAX 614-292-7859. Ed. Edward Martinique. bk.rev.; illus. circ. 300. **Document type:** bulletin.
—UnCover.
Formerly: Association for Asian Studies. Committee on East Asian Libraries. Newsletter (ISSN 0571-5520)

020   **US**   **ISSN 0748-5786**
ASSOCIATION FOR LIBRARY AND INFORMATION SCIENCE EDUCATION. DIRECTORY. a. $30. Association for Library and Information Science Education, 4101 Lake Boone Tr., Ste. 201, Raleigh, NC 27607. TEL 919-787-5181. circ. 4,700. (also avail. in microfilm from UMI) **Document type:** directory.
Formerly: Association of American Library Schools Directory.

029.7 378   **GH**
ASSOCIATION OF AFRICAN UNIVERSITIES. NEW ACQUISITIONS LIST. irreg. free. Association of African Universities, Box 5744, Accra, Ghana.

020 200 100   **UK**   **ISSN 0305-781X**
Z675.T4
ASSOCIATION OF BRITISH THEOLOGICAL AND PHILOSOPHICAL LIBRARIES. BULLETIN. N.S. 1974. 3/yr. £12($20) Association of British Theological and Philosophical Libraries, c/o Rev. Alan F. Jesson, Cambridge University Library, West Rd., Cambridge CB3 9OR, England. TEL 44-223-333000. FAX 44-223-333160. TELEX 81395 CUL G. (Subscr. to: M.J. Walsh, Heythrop College Library, Kensington Sq., London W1M 0AN, England) adv.; bk.rev.; abstr.; bibl. circ. 300. (back issues avail.) **Indexed:** LISA. **Document type:** bulletin.
—BLDSC (2396.810000).
Description: Provides a forum for professional discussion and development, with special emphasis on international aspects of theological and philosophical librarianship.

020.6   **PR**
ASSOCIATION OF CARIBBEAN UNIVERSITY RESEARCH AND INSTITUTIONAL LIBRARIES. CARTA INFORMATIVA DE A C U R I L / A C U R I L NEWSLETTER. (Text in English, Spanish) 1973. q. $10 to non-members. Association of Caribbean University Research and Institutional Libraries, Box 23317, Estacion de la Universidad, San Juan, PR 00931. TEL 809-764-1000. FAX 809-765-5685. Ed.Bd. bk.rev.; bibl.; illus.; circ. controlled. (back issues avail.)
Formerly: Association of Caribbean University and Research Libraries. Carta Informativa de ACURIL.

020   **US**   **ISSN 0897-6465**
ASSOCIATION OF COLLEGE AND RESEARCH LIBRARIES. SLAVIC AND EASTERN EUROPEAN SECTION NEWSLETTER. 1985. a. $6 to non-members (foreign $8). American Library Association, 50 E. Huron St., Chicago, IL 60611. TEL 312-944-6780. (Subscr. to: SEES Newsletter, c/o Allan Urbanic, The Library, Rm. 346, University of California, Berkeley, CA 94720. TEL 800-545-2433) Ed. Harold M. Leich.
—BLDSC (6106.355410).

027.7   **US**   **ISSN 0734-4503**
ASSOCIATION OF COLLEGE AND RESEARCH LIBRARIES. WESTERN EUROPEAN SPECIALISTS SECTION NEWSLETTER. q. American Library Association, 50 E. Huron St., Chicago, IL 60611-2795. TEL 800-545-2433. FAX 312-440-9374. **Document type:** newsletter.

ASSOCIATION OF LAW LIBRARIES OF UPSTATE NEW YORK. NEWSLETTER. see *LAW*

020   **CN**   **ISSN 0316-0963**
ASSOCIATION POUR L'AVANCEMENT DES SCIENCES ET DES TECHNIQUES DE LA DOCUMENTATION. NOUVELLES DE L'ASTED. 1974. 5/yr. membership. Association pour l'Avancement des Sciences et des Techniques de la Documentation, 1030 rue Cherrier, Bureau 505, Montreal, PQ H2L 1H9, Canada. TEL 514-522-7833. bk.rev. circ. 700. **Indexed:** Can.Per.Ind.
Formerly (until 1974): Association Canadienne des Bibliothecaires de Langue Francaise. Nouvelles de l'ACBLF (ISSN 0044-9407)

020   **CN**   **ISSN 0316-0955**
ASSOCIATION POUR L'AVANCEMENT DES SCIENCES ET DES TECHNIQUES DE LA DOCUMENTATION. RAPPORT ANNUEL. 1945. a. Association pour l'Avancement des Sciences et des Techniques de la Documentation, 1030 rue Cherrier, Bureau 505, Montreal, PQ H2L 1H9, Canada. TEL 514-522-7833. FAX 514-521-9561. circ. 2,000.
Formerly: Association Canadienne des Bibliothecaires de Langue Francaise. Rapport (ISSN 0066-8826)

020   **IT**   **ISSN 1121-1490**
Z671
ASSOCIAZIONE ITALIANA BIBLIOTECHE. BOLLETTINO; rivista italiana di biblioteconomia e scienze dell'informazione. (Text in Italian; summaries in English) 1961. q. L.100000 (foreign L.150000) (effective 1992). Associazione Italiana Biblioteche, Casella Postale 2461, 00100 Rome, Italy. TEL 06-4463532. Dir. Alberto Petrucciani. adv.; bk.rev.; abstr.; bibl.; illus. circ. 3,300. (also avail. in microform from UMI; back issues avail.) **Indexed:** Bull.Signal., Lib.Lit., LISA. **Document type:** bulletin.
—BLDSC (2234.270000); SWETS; UMI.
Formerly (until 1991): Associazione Italiana Biblioteche. Bollettino d'Informazioni (ISSN 0004-5934)

027.4   **US**
AT THE LIBRARY. 1965. q. $3. Public Library of Youngstown and Mahoning County, 305 Wick Ave., Youngstown, OH 44503. TEL 216-744-8636. FAX 216-744-2258. Ed. Janet S. Loew. bk.rev.; illus.; stat. circ. 2,000. (processed) **Document type:** trade publication.
Formerly (until 1991): Biblio-Files; Supersedes (in 1980): Public Library of Youngstown and Mahoning County. Staff Bulletin (ISSN 0033-3573)

020   **IO**   **ISSN 0126-1630**
ATMA JAYA RESEARCH CENTRE. LIBRARY BULLETIN. (Text in Indonesian) 1978. m. Atma Jaya Research Centre - Pusat Penelitian Atma Jaya, Jalan Jenderal Sudirman 51, P.O. Box 2639, Jakarta 10001, Indonesia. **Document type:** bulletin.

AUCHMUTY LIBRARY PUBLICATION. see *BIBLIOGRAPHIES*

020   **UK**   **ISSN 0302-3451**
Z717
AUDIOVISUAL LIBRARIAN; the multimedia information journal. 1973. q. £41 in the UK and other EC nations; elsewhere £45 (effective 1994). c/o A.H. Thompson, Ed., Coach House Frongog, Llanbadarn Fawr, Aberystwyth SY23 3HN, Wales. TEL 0970-617322. FAX 0947-298513. (Subscr. to: Bailey Management Services, 127 Sandgate Rd., Folkestone, Kent CT20 2BL, England) Ed. A.H. Thompson. adv.: B&W page £120; trim 187 x 130; adv. contact: Frances Thorpe. bk.rev.; bibl.; index. circ. 3,000. (also avail. in microform from UMI) **Indexed:** CINAHL, Educ.Tech.Abstr., Lib.Lit., LISA.
—BLDSC (1789.020000); SWETS; UMI.
Former titles: Library Association. Audiovisual Group. Bulletin; Aslib Audio-Visual Group Newsletter; Aslib Sound Recordings Group Newsletter.
Description: Covers multimedia developments of interest to librarians, information specialists, archivists, and educators.

025   **CN**   **ISSN 0714-7058**
AURORA. 1981. irreg. (4-5/yr.) free. Northern Lights Library System, Postal Bag 8, Elk Point, AB T0A 1A0, Canada. TEL 403-724-2596. FAX 403-724-2597. Ed. K. Taber. bk.rev.; circ. 700 (controlled). (also avail. in microfilm from MML; back issues avail.) **Document type:** newsletter.
Description: Provides information about local, regional and provincial public library activities and offers articles for rural public library staff and trustees.

020   **AT**   **ISSN 1030-5033**
Z870.A1
AUSTRALASIAN PUBLIC LIBRARIES AND INFORMATION SERVICES. 1988. q. Aus.$42 to individuals; institutions Aus.$40. Auslib Press, P.O. Box 622, Blackwood, S.A. 5051, Australia. TEL 08-278-4363. FAX 08-270-4000. TELEX AA88420. Ed. Alan Bundy. circ. 900. (back issues avail.) **Indexed:** Aus.Educ.Ind., LISA. **Document type:** academic/scholarly publication.
—BLDSC (1796.150000).
Description: Publishes articles and shorter items on public libraries and other publicly accessible information services in Australia, New Zealand and the South Pacific.

027.7   **AT**   **ISSN 0004-8623**
Z675.U5
AUSTRALIAN ACADEMIC AND RESEARCH LIBRARIES. 1970. q. Aus.$40 (foreign Aus.$50)(effective 1992). Australian Library and Information Association, University College & Research Libraries Section, P.O. Box E411, Queen Victoria Terrace, A.C.T. 2600, Australia. TEL 06-285-1877. FAX 06-282-2249. Ed. J.I. Horacek. adv.; bk.rev.; bibl.; stat.; index. circ. 1,100. (also avail. in microform) **Indexed:** AESIS, Aus.P.A.I.S., Inform.Sci.Abstr., Lib.Lit., Lib.Sci.Abstr., Ref.Sour.
—BLDSC (1796.660000); Faxon.
Supersedes: New Sheet.

020   **US**   **ISSN 0898-3283**
Z692.S5   **CODEN: ANZLEH**
AUSTRALIAN & NEW ZEALAND JOURNAL OF SERIALS LIBRARIANSHIP; the serials journal of Australasia. 1990. q. $28 to individuals; institutions and libraries $36. Haworth Press, Inc., 10 Alice St., Binghamton, NY 13904. TEL 607-722-5857; 800-342-9678. FAX 607-722-1424. Ed. Toby Burrows. adv.; bk.rev. (also avail. in microfiche from HAW; reprint service avail. from HAW) **Indexed:** LISA. **Document type:** trade publication.
—BLDSC (1796.895000).
Description: Presents reviews and news of serials in the area, in order to provide collection development tools for librarians interested in Australasian serials, and to deal with practical aspects of collection management.
Refereed Serial

AUSTRALIAN EDUCATION INDEX. see *EDUCATION — Abstracting, Bibliographies, Statistics*

LIBRARY AND INFORMATION SCIENCES

020　　　　　　　AT　ISSN 1039-6616
AUSTRALIAN LAW LIBRARIAN. 1973. bi-m. Aus.$48 (foreign Aus.$50) (effective 1994). Australian Law Librarians' Group, P.O. Box E40, Queen Victoria Terrace, Canberra, A.C.T. 2600, Australia. TEL 06-270-6922. FAX 06-273-2110. Ed. Jacqueline Elliott. adv. contact: Julia Bueler. bk.rev. circ. 485. (back issues avail.) **Indexed:** Leg.Info.Manage.Ind. **Document type:** trade publication.
　　Formerly (until Jan. 1993): Australian Law Librarians' Group. Newsletter (ISSN 0311-5984)
　　Description: Details developments law librarianship and legal bibliography.

020　　　　　　　AT　ISSN 1031-5187
Z870.A1
AUSTRALIAN LIBRARIES: THE ESSENTIAL DIRECTORY. biennial. Aus.$30 plus Aus.$6 postage. Auslib Press, P.O. Box 622, Blackwood, S.A. 5051, Australia. TEL 08-2784363. FAX 08-278-4000. TELEX AA88420. Eds. Alan and Judith Bundy. adv. circ. 2,500. **Document type:** directory.
　　Incorporates (in 1988): W A T Acronyms and Initialisms in Australian Library and Information Science.
　　Description: Contains brief details of all Australian academic, public and special libraries, publishers, consultants etc.

020　　　　　　　AT　ISSN 0004-9670
Z671
AUSTRALIAN LIBRARY JOURNAL. 1951. 4/yr. Aus.$40 (foreign Aus.$50)(effective 1992). Australian Library and Information Association, P.O. Box E411, Queen Victoria Terrace, A.C.T. 2600, Australia. TEL 06-285-1877. FAX 06-282-2249. adv.; bk.rev.; illus.; index, cum.index: 1951-1965, 1966-1970. circ. 7,000. **Indexed:** AESIS, Aus.P.A.I.S., GdIns, LHTN, Lib.Lit., Lib.Sci.Abstr., LISA, Ref.Sour.
　　—BLDSC (1813.800000); Faxon; UnCover; SWETS; UMI.
　　Description: Presents articles of interest to people working in library and information management.

020　　　　　　　AT　ISSN 1034-8042
AUSTRALIAN LIBRARY REVIEW. vol.7, 1990. 4/yr. Aus.$35. Charles Sturt University - Riverina, Centre for Information Studies, Locked Bag 660, Wagga Wagga, N.S.W. 2678, Australia. TEL 069-222-325. FAX 069-222-733. Ed. G.E. Gorman. adv.; bk.rev. circ. 1,000. **Indexed:** Aus.Educ.Ind., Aus.P.A.I.S., Lib.Lit., LISA. **Document type:** academic/scholarly publication.
　　—BLDSC (1813.832000).
　　Former titles: Riverina Library Review (ISSN 0812-7352) & Riv Lib File (ISSN 0157-650X)
　　Description: Covers current issues of importance to the information professions and includes an extensive book reviewing section on library and information science, and general reference literature.

026　　　　　　　AT　ISSN 0005-027X
Z675.A2
AUSTRALIAN SPECIAL LIBRARY NEWS. 1967. q. Aus.$36 (foreign Aus.$42)(effective 1992). Australian Library and Information Association, P.O. Box E411, Queen Victoria Terrace, A.C.T. 2600, Australia. TEL 06-285-1877. FAX 06-282-2249. adv.; bk.rev.; bibl. circ. 1,000. **Indexed:** AESIS, Aus. P.A.I.S., LISA.
　　Description: Covers a wide variety of articles of interest to special librarians.

029.7 510 400　　　US　ISSN 0005-1055
Z699.A1　　　　　　　　　CODEN: ADMLAE
AUTOMATIC DOCUMENTATION AND MATHEMATICAL LINGUISTICS. English Translation of: Nauchno-Tekhnicheskaya Informatsyia. Seriya 2. 1967. bi-m. $840. (Vsesoyuznyi Institut Nauchno-Tekhnicheskoi Informatsii (VINITI), RU) Allerton Press, Inc., 150 Fifth Ave., New York, NY 10011. TEL 212-924-3950. FAX 212-463-9684. Ed. R.S. Gilyarevskii. charts. **Indexed:** Chem.Abstr., M.L.A., Math.R. **Document type:** academic/scholarly publication.
　　—BLDSC (0404.850000); UnCover. **CCC.**
　　Description: Reports on the most recent advancements in the field of science concerned with the relationship between studies in linguistics and verbal behavior, and computer engineering and artificial intelligence.

020 070.5　　　UK　ISSN 0261-0302
AVERAGE PRICES OF BRITISH ACADEMIC BOOKS. 1974. s-a. £9. Loughborough University, Library and Information Statistics Unit, Loughborough, Leicestershire LE11 3TU, England. TEL 0509-223071. FAX 0509-223072. (Co-sponsor: British Library) Ed. John Sumsion. circ. 300. **Document type:** catalog.
　　—BLDSC (5276.223000).

020 070.5　　　UK　ISSN 0951-8975
AVERAGE PRICES OF U S A ACADEMIC BOOKS. 1986. s-a. £9. Loughborough University, Library and Information Statistics Unit, Department of Library and Information Studies, Loughborough, Leicestershire LE11 3TU, England. TEL 0509-223071. FAX 0509-223072. (Co-sponsor: British Library) Ed. John Sumsion. **Document type:** catalog.
　　—BLDSC (5276.227000).

020　　　　　　　CN　ISSN 0005-2876
B C L A REPORTER. 1957. 5/yr. Can.$25 to non-members. British Columbia Library Association, 6545 Bonsor Ave., Ste. 110, Burnaby, BC V5H 1H3, Canada. TEL 604-430-9633. FAX 604-430-8595. Ed. Jim Herrington. adv.; bk.rev.; bibl. circ. 810. (reprint service avail. from UMI) **Indexed:** Lib.Lit. **Document type:** newsletter.
　　Description: Reports on activities of BCLA, policy and news pertaining to libraries in BC. Includes features on information retrieval and technology, library architecture, literacy, management, finance.

020　　　　　　　US　ISSN 0897-5167
B N A'S REVIEW OF WHAT'S NEW. 1988. q. free. The Bureau of National Affairs, Inc., 1231 25th St., N.W., Washington, DC 20850. TEL 202-452-4200. FAX 202-822-8092. TELEX 285656 BNAI WSH. (Subscr to: 1231 25th St., N.W., Rm. 3-466, Washington, DC 20037) Ed. Sarita Cabrera. (back issues avail.) **Document type:** newsletter.
　　Description: For librarians featuring new BNA information resources: books, looseleafs, newsletters, conferences, reports, videos, software, info-paks and online products.

020　　　　　　　DK　ISSN 0905-4650
Z671
B 70. Variant title: B Halvfjerds. 1970. 22/yr. DKK 295 (typically set in Jan.). (Bibliotekarforbundet - Union of Danish Librarians) Bibliotek 70, Lindevangs Alle 2, DK-2000 Frederiksberg, Denmark. TEL 38-88-17-70. FAX 38-88-31-01. Eds. Per Nyeng, Joergen Nielsen. adv.; bk.rev.; illus.; index; circ. 6,000 (controlled). **Indexed:** Lib.Lit., Lib.Sci.Abstr., LISA. **Document type:** trade publication.
　　—BLDSC (2942.910000); SWETS.
　　Formerly: Bibliotek 70 (ISSN 0006-1824);
Supersedes: Bibliotekaren.

020　　　　　　　IO　ISSN 0125-9008
BACA/READ; brief communication for information workers and information users in science and technology. 1974. q. Rps.10000($10) Indonesian Institute of Sciences, Centre for Scientific Documentation and Information - Lembaga Ilmu Pengetahuan Indonesia, Pusat Dokumentasi dan Informasi Ilmiah, P.O. Box 4298, Jakarta 12042, Indonesia. TEL 021-5733465. FAX 021-5733467. TELEX 62875 IA. (Subscr. to: Yayasan Memajukan Jasa Informasi (YASMIN), Jln. Widya Chandra XI/3, Kompleks LIPI, P.O. Box 4509, Jakarta 12045, Indonesia) Ed. Antari Wahyuning Maharani. bk.rev. circ. 300. **Indexed:** E.I., Ind.Child.Mag., LISA.

020　　　　　　　US
BAKKEN LIBRARY AND MUSEUM. 1979. 3/yr. $35 includes membership. Bakken, 3537 Zenith Ave. S., Minneapolis, MN 55416. TEL 612-927-6508. FAX 612-927-7265. Ed. David Rhees. circ. 1,300. (back issues avail.) **Document type:** newsletter.
　　Formerly: Electric Quarterly.
　　Description: Covers the Bakken library activities, announcements, calendar of events (including music concerts), and news of recent acquisitions.

027　　　　　　　US　ISSN 0067-3412
Z881.C1522
BANCROFTIANA. 1950. 3/yr. membership. Friends of the Bancroft Library, University of California, Berkeley, Bancroft Library, Berkeley, CA 94720. TEL 510-642-3781. Ed. Anthony S. Bliss. cum.index: 1950-1966. circ. 1,500.

020　　　　　　　BG
BANGLADESH LIBRARY SCIENCE NEWS BULLETIN. Running title: B L S News Bulletin. (Text in English) 1975. bi-m. exchange basis. University of Dhaka, Department of Library Science, Ramna, Dhaka 2, Bangladesh. Ed. A.K.M. Shamsul Alam. (processed) **Indexed:** Lib.Lit., LISA. **Document type:** bulletin.

020　　　　　　　FR　ISSN 0067-3951
PC2689　　　　　　　　　CODEN: BAMOEH
BANQUE DES MOTS. 2/yr. 260 F. Conseil International de la Langue Francaise, 11 rue de Navarin, 75009 Paris, France. TEL 48-78-73-95. FAX 48-78-49-28. (reprint service avail. from KTO) **Indexed:** Bibl.Ling., Pt.de Rep. (1979-).
　　—SWETS.

027.8　　　　　　　SW　ISSN 0037-6477
Z671
BARN OCH KULTUR/CHILDREN AND CULTURE. 1955. 6/yr. SEK 280. Bibliotekstjaenst AB, Box 200, 221 00 Lund, Sweden. TEL 46-180-000. Ed. Charlotte Brattstroem. adv.; bk.rev.; illus.; index, cum.index: 1955-1957, 1958-1960. circ. 2,400. **Indexed:** Child.Lit.Abstr., Lib.Lit.
　　Formerly: Skolbiblioteket.

BASE DE DONNEES P A S C A L. PLAN DE CLASSEMENT. see *LIBRARY AND INFORMATION SCIENCES — Computer Applications*

BASE LINE. see *GEOGRAPHY*

020　　　　　　　US　ISSN 0005-6944
Z673.M4
BAY STATE LIBRARIAN. 1910. q. $50. Massachusetts Library Association, Country Side Offices, 707 Turnpike St., N. Andover, MA 01845. TEL 508-686-8543. adv. circ. 2,000. (also avail. in microfilm from UMI) **Indexed:** Lib.Lit. **Document type:** newsletter.
　　—UMI.
　　Formerly: Bay State Letter.

020　　　　　　　GW　ISSN 0342-0221
BAYERISCHE STAATSBIBLIOTHEK. JAHRESBERICHT. 1972. a. Bayerische Staatsbibliothek, Ludwigstr. 16, 80539 Munich, Germany. TEL 089-28638-0. FAX 089-28638-293. **Document type:** government publication.

029.7　　　　　　　UK　ISSN 0308-8537
BECTIS BULLETIN. 1976. 10/yr. £50 (effective Apr. 1993). Bell College of Technology, Almada St., Hamilton ML3 OJB, Scotland. FAX 44-698-282131. Ed. J. O'Brien. adv.; bk.rev. circ. 200. **Document type:** bulletin.
　　Description: Covers courses, news items, film and government publication reviews, periodical abstracts, and British Standards.

020　　　　　　　US　ISSN 0163-9269
Z675.S6　　　　　　　　　CODEN: BSSLDR
BEHAVIORAL & SOCIAL SCIENCES LIBRARIAN. 1979. s-a. $38 to individuals; institutions and libraries $80. Haworth Press, Inc., 10 Alice St., Binghamton, NY 13904. TEL 607-722-5857; 800-342-9678. FAX 607-722-1424. Ed. David Longergan. adv.; bk.rev.; bibl. circ. 314. (also avail. in microfiche from HAW; back issues avail.; reprint service avail. from HAW) **Indexed:** ASSIA, C.I.J.E., CINAHL, Comput.& Info.Sys., Curr.Cont., Excerp.Med., Inform.Sci.Abstr., Lib.Lit., LISA, P.A.I.S., Psychol.Abstr., Ref.Zh., Sci.Abstr., Soc.Work Res.& Abstr., SSCI, Stud.Wom.Abstr. **Document type:** trade publication.
　　—BLDSC (1877.296000); Faxon; UnCover; SWETS.
　　Description: Presents current research by librarians in the field. Focuses in detail on the day-to-day basics of the practice, from networking, on both formal and informal levels, to the pleasures and perils of automation.
　　Refereed Serial

020　　　　　　　GW　ISSN 0408-8107
BEITRAEGE ZUM BUCH- UND BIBLIOTHEKSWESEN. 1965. irreg., vol.33, 1993. price varies. Harrassowitz Verlag, Taunusstr. 14, 65183 Wiesbaden, Germany. TEL 0611-530-0. FAX 0611-530570. TELEX 4186135. (Subscr. to: Postfach 2929, 65019 Wiesbaden, Germany) Ed. Max Pauer. **Document type:** monographic series.

BEITRAEGE ZUR INKUNABELKUNDE. DRITTE FOLGE. see *PUBLISHING AND BOOK TRADE*

BENTLEY HISTORICAL LIBRARY. see *HISTORY — History Of North And South America*

LIBRARY AND INFORMATION SCIENCES

027.7 US ISSN 0362-6881
Z733.B476
BENTLEY HISTORICAL LIBRARY ANNUAL REPORT. 1935. a. free. University of Michigan, Bentley Historical Library, 1150 Beal Ave., Ann Arbor, MI 48109-2113. TEL 313-764-1817. Ed. William K. Wallach. circ. 500.
 Description: Reports on annual accessions, processing activities, reference work, special projects, grants and essays on a variety of historical topics.

020 016 GW
BERGAKADEMIE FREIBERG. BIBLIOTHEK "GEORGIUS AGRICOLA". VEROEFFENTLICHUNGEN. 1964. irreg., no.120, 1990. exchange basis. Bergakademie Freiberg, Hochschulbibliothek, Agricolastr. 10, 09599 Freiberg, Germany. Ed. Hans-Henning Walter. Indexed: LISA.
 Formerly: Bergakademie Freiberg. Wissenschaftliches Informationszentrum. Veroeffentlichungen.

020 IT ISSN 0409-1132
LA BERIO; rivista semestrale di storia locale e di informazioni bibliografiche. 1961. s-a. free. Servizio Biblioteche del Comune di Genova, Largo Pertini, 4, 16121 Genova, Italy. TEL 010-587314. FAX 010-566717. Ed. Laura Malfatto. bk.rev. circ. 1,000. **Document type**: academic/scholarly publication.

025 US ISSN 0897-5728
BERNAN ASSOCIATES' GOVERNMENT PUBLICATIONS NEWS. 1988. 10/yr. free. Bernan Associates, 461-F Assembly Dr., Lanham, MD 20706-5728. TEL 301-459-7666. FAX 301-459-0056. Ed. Blake Buckingham. circ. 8,000 (controlled). (looseleaf format) **Document type**: newsletter.
 Formerly (until 1988): Government Publications News (ISSN 0897-571X)

020 HU
BERZSENYI DANIEL MEGYEI KONYVTAR. EVKONYVE. 1962. irreg. free. (Vas Megye Tanacsa) Berzsenyi Daniel Megyei Konyvtar, Petofi Sandor u. 43, 9700 Szombathely, Hungary. TEL 94-311-366. FAX 94-312-179. Ed. Miklos Takacs. abstr.; bibl.; illus.; stat. circ. 600. (back issues avail.) **Document type**: academic/scholarly publication.

020 GW ISSN 0724-8164
Z1035.A1
BESPRECHUNGEN ANNOTATIONEN. 1949. m. DM.600. Einkaufszentrale fuer Oeffentliche Bibliotheken, Bismarckstr. 3, 72764 Reutlingen, Germany. Ed. Erich H. Wurster. index, cum.index. circ. 1,700.

BEST RATED C DS - CLASSICAL. see *MUSIC —*
 Abstracting, Bibliographies, Statistics

BEST RATED C DS - JAZZ, POPULAR ETC.. see *MUSIC —*
 Abstracting, Bibliographies, Statistics

020 US ISSN 1041-2751
BETA PHI MU MONOGRAPH SERIES. 1987. irreg. Greenwood Press, Inc. (Subsidiary of: Greenwood Publishing Group Inc.), 88 Post Rd. W., Box 5007, Westport, CT 06881-5007. TEL 203-226-3571. FAX 203-22-1502. Ed. Wayne A. Wiegand. **Document type**: monographic series.

020.7 US ISSN 1059-0757
BETA PHI MU NEWSLETTER. 1954. s-a. membership. Beta Phi Mu, International Library and Information Science Honor Society, c/o University of Pittsburgh, School of Library and Information Science, 135 N. Bellefield, Pittsburgh, PA 15260. TEL 412-624-9435. (processed) **Document type**: newsletter.

011 VE ISSN 0006-1085
Z1911
BIBLIOGRAFIA VENEZOLANA. 1970. s-a. Bs.650($20) Instituto Autonomo Biblioteca Nacional y de Servicios de Bibliotecas, Oficina de Information, Apdo. 6525, Caracas 1010A, Venezuela. TEL 5723623. FAX 9415219. bibl.; circ. 1,500 (controlled). (processed) **Document type**: bibliography.
 ●Also available online.
 Formerly (until 1982): Bibliografia Venezuela Anuario.

020 949.7 YU ISSN 0409-3739
BIBLIOGRAFSKI VJESNIK. 1961. 3/yr. 800 din. Centralna Narodna Biblioteka SR Crne Gore Djurdje Crnojevic Cetinje, Bulevar Lenjina 163, Cetinje, Montenegro, Yugoslavia. Ed. Dusan Martinovic. adv.; bibl. **Document type**: bibliography.

BIBLIOGRAPHICAL SOCIETY OF AMERICA. PAPERS. see *PUBLISHING AND BOOK TRADE*

011 020 US ISSN 0145-3084
Z1219
BIBLIOGRAPHY NEWSLETTER. Abbreviated title: BiN. 1973. q. $20. Walrus Press, 32 Trimountain Ave., P.O. Box 280, South Rage, MI 49963. Ed. Bryan R. Johnson. bk.rev.; illus.; index. circ. 800. (back issues avail.)
 Description: Publishes articles, news and reviews on the history of books and printing.

020 001.3 US ISSN 1064-301X
Z881
BIBLION. 1897-1986 (vol.87, no.4); resumed 1992. 2/yr. $60 (effective 1993). (New York Public Library) Greenwood Press, Inc. (Subsidiary of: Greenwood Publishing Group Inc.), 88 Post Rd. W., Box 5007, Westport, CT 06881. TEL 203-226-3571. FAX 203-222-1502. Ed. Anne Skillion. bibl.; illus.; index, cum.index: nos.1-65 (1897-1962) in 3 vols. **Indexed**: Abstr.Engl.Stud., Amer.Hist.& Life (1992-), Amer.Hum.Ind., Arts & Hum.Cit.Ind., Bibl.Ind., Biog.Ind., Curr.Cont., Hist.Abstr. (1992-), Hum.Ind., Lib.Lit., M.L.A., P.A.I.S. **Document type**: academic/scholarly publication.
 —UnCover.
 Supersedes: Bulletin of Research in the Humanities (ISSN 0160-0168); Which was formerly (until vol.81, 1978): New York Public Library. Bulletin (ISSN 0028-7466)
 Description: Covers the collections, services, history, and staff of the library.
 Refereed Serial

BIBLIOTECA "JOSE ARTIGAS". BOLETIN - JUNTA DE VECINOS. see *BIBLIOGRAPHIES*

020 IT
BIBLIOTECA MUNICIPALE A. PANIZZI. CONTRIBUTI. 1977. s-a. L.30000. Biblioteca Municipale "A. Panizzi", Via Farini 3, 42100 Reggio Emilia, Italy. Ed.Bd. adv.; bk.rev. circ. 1,000.

020 BL ISSN 0100-1922
BIBLIOTECA NACIONAL DE BRASIL. ANAIS. 1876. a. Biblioteca Nacional do Brasil, Av. Rio Branco 219, 20042 Rio de Janeiro, Brazil. TEL 021-262-8255. FAX 021-220-4173. TELEX 21-22941. circ. 1,000.

020 PO ISSN 0251-1711
Z946.L72
BIBLIOTECA NACIONAL DE PORTUGAL. REVISTA. 1981. s-a. Esc.360($10) Biblioteca Nacional de Portugal, Campo Grande 83, 1751 Lisbon, Portugal. TEL 01-7950130. circ. 2,500.

020 UY ISSN 0544-9189
Z907
BIBLIOTECA NACIONAL DE URUGUAY. REVISTA. 1966. irreg. donation or exchange basis. Biblioteca Nacional de Uruguay, Av. 18 de Julio, 1790, Casilla de Correo 452, Montevideo, Uruguay. Ed. Alvaro Miranda. adv.; bk.rev. circ. 750. **Indexed:** Hisp.Amer.Per.Ind.

020 PE ISSN 0031-6067
Z907
BIBLIOTECA NACIONAL DEL PERU. BOLETIN. 1943. a. $20. Biblioteca Nacional del Peru, Digbine, Apdo. 2335, Lima, Peru. Ed. Isabel Miranda M. bk.rev.; abstr.; bibl.; illus. circ. 500. **Indexed:** A.I.C.P.

020 IT
IL BIBLIOTECARIO. 1984. q. L.55000. Bulzoni Editore, Via dei Liburni n.14, 00185 Rome, Italy. TEL 06-4455207. FAX 06-4450355. Ed. Alfredo Serrai. **Indexed:** LISA.

021 CU ISSN 0006-176X
BIBLIOTECAS. 1963. s-a. free or exchange basis. Biblioteca Nacional Jose Marti, Plaza de la Revolucion, Havana, Cuba. Ed.Bd. bk.rev.; bibl.; charts. circ. 500. **Indexed:** Amer.Hist.& Life, Hist.Abstr.

027.7 NQ
BIBLIOTECAS UNIVERSITARIAS. 1981. 1/yr. free to universities. Universidad Nacional Autonoma de Nicaragua, Biblioteca Central, Apartado 68, Leon CA, Nicaragua. Ed. Walterio Lopez Adaros.

027 IT ISSN 0392-8586
Z809.A1
BIBLIOTECHE OGGI; mensile di informazione, dibattito. 1983. m. L.112000 (foreign L.170000) (effective 1994). Editrice Bibliografica s.r.l., Viale Vittorio Veneto 24, 20124 Milan, Italy. TEL 02-29006965. FAX 02-654624. Ed. Massimo Belotti. adv.; bk.rev. circ. 3,000. **Indexed:** LISA. **Document type**: trade publication.
 —BLDSC (2016.567400).
 Description: Library science review.

020 PY ISSN 0258-6436
BIBLIOTECOLOGIA Y DOCUMENTACION PARAGUAYA. 1972. irreg. $5. Asociacion de Bibliotecarios del Paraguay, Casilla de Correo 1505, Asuncion, Paraguay. Eds. Sofia Mareski, Margarita Kallsen. circ. 200. (processed; also avail. in microform)

026.61 610 DK ISSN 0006-1786
BIBLIOTEK FOR LAEGER. 1809. 4/yr. DKK 130. Almindelige Danske Laegeforening - Danish Medical Association, Trondhjemsgade 9, 2100 Copenhagen, Denmark. TEL 31 38 55 00. FAX 31-15-28-58. (Subscr. to: Laegeforeningens Forlag, Esplanaden 8A, DK-1263 Copenhagen K, Denmark) Eds. Povl Riis, Eskil Hohwy. adv. circ. 1,100. **Indexed:** Biol.Abstr., Chem.Abstr., Excerp.Med.

020 BU ISSN 0861-847X
Z665.2.B8
BIBLIOTEKA; spisanie za bibliotechno delo. (Text in Bulgarian; contents page in Bulgarian, English) 1954. m. 180 lv.($62) Narodna Biblioteka Sv.sv. Kiril i Metodii, 88, V. Levski Blvd., 1504 Sofia, Bulgaria. TEL 00359-2-882811. FAX 00359-2-881600. (Dist. by: Hemus, 6, Rouski Blvd., 1000 Sofia, Bulgaria) Ed. Ju. Baicheva. bk.rev.; bibl.; charts; illus.; index. circ. 2,000. **Indexed:** Lib.Sci.Abstr., LISA.
 —BLDSC (0016.268900).
 Formerly (until 1993): Bibliotekar (ISSN 0204-7438)

020 UK ISSN 1011-2340
BIBLIOTEKA BULTENO. (Text in Esperanto) 3/yr. £5.50. Tutmonda Esperantista Biblioteka Asocio, 228 Capworth St., London E10 7HL, England. TEL 081-556-0984. Ed. Douglas Portmann. bk.rev. **Document type**: bulletin.
 Description: Covers the application of Esperanto in library work, comparative librarianship, and the use of library terminology in Esperanto.

020 RU ISSN 0006-1808
Z671
BIBLIOTEKAR'. 1923. m. $69. Tovarishchestvo Libedeya, Prospekt Marksa 11-1, 121019 Moscow, G-19, Russia. TEL 095-202-6308. (Subscr. to: Mezhdunarodnaya Kniga, Moscow G-200, Russia; Dist. in U.S. by: Victor Kamkin Inc., 4956 Boiling Brook Pkwy, Rockville, MD 20852. TEL 301-881-5973) (Co-sponsor: Ministerstvo Kultury) Ed. G.I. Samsonov. index. circ. 169,609. **Indexed:** Lib.Lit.

020 YU ISSN 0006-1816
Z671
BIBLIOTEKAR. 1948. bi-m. 60 din.($4.58) Drustvo Bibliotekara Srbije - Society of Librarians of Serbia, Skerliceva 1, 11000 Belgrade, Yugoslavia. Ed. Vlarimir Jokanovic. adv.; bk.rev. circ. 1,000. **Indexed:** Lib.Lit., Lib.Sci.Abstr.
 —BLDSC (0017.030000).

020 SW ISSN 0345-1097
BIBLIOTEKARIESAMFUNDET MEDDELAR. 1971. 3/yr. SEK 200. Svenska Bibliotekariesamfundet, c/o Kerstin Assarsson-Rizzi, Vitterhetsakademiens Bibliotek, Box 5405, S-114 84 Stockholm, Sweden. FAX 46-8-663-3528. Ed. Kerstin Assarsson-Rizzi. adv.; bk.rev. circ. 1,300. **Document type**: bulletin.

020 BN ISSN 0006-1832
BIBLIOTEKARSTVO/LIBRARIANSHIP. (Text in Serbo-Croatian; summaries in English, German) 1956. a. 100 din.($6.25) Drustvo Bibliotekara Bosne i Hercegovine - Library Association of Bosnia and Hercegovina, Vojvode Stepe Obala 42, 71000 Sarajevo, Bosnia Hercegovine. Ed. Tatjana Prastalo. adv.; bk.rev. circ. 750.

LIBRARY AND INFORMATION SCIENCES

020   PL   ISSN 0208-4333
Z671
BIBLIOTEKARZ. 1934. m. $36. Stowarzyszenie Bibliotekarzy Polskich, Konopczynskiego 5-7, 00-953 Warsaw, Poland. TEL 27 52 96. (Dist. by: Ars Polona-Ruch, Krakowskie Przedmiescie 7, 00-068 Warsaw, Poland) Ed. Jan Wolosz. bk.rev.; bibl. circ. 6,600. **Indexed:** Lib.Lit., LISA.
—BLDSC (2017.000000).

020   PL   ISSN 0406-1578
BIBLIOTEKARZ ZACHODNIOPOMORSKI/LIBRARIAN OF WEST POMERANIA. 1959. q. price varies. Wojewodzka i Miejska Biblioteka Publiczna, Ksiaznica Szczecinska im. Stanislawa Staszica, Podgorna 15, 70-952 Szczecin, Poland. TEL 341-662. TELEX 422335. Ed. Stanislaw Krzywicki. bk.rev.; bibl.; illus.; stat. circ. 500. (also avail. in microfilm)
Description: For librarians and library management students.

020   RU
BIBLIOTEKOVEDENIE, BIBLIOGRAFIYA I INFORMATIKA. 1974. irreg. 0.60 Rub. Moskovskii Gosudarstvennyi Institut Kul'tury, Moscow, Russia.

020   RU   ISSN 0320-7838
BIBLIOTEKOVEDENIE I BIBLIOGRAFIYA ZA RUBEZHOM. 1958. 4/yr. price varies. Gosudarstvennaya Biblioteka Rosii - Russian State Library, Ul. Vozdizhenka, 3, 101000 Moscow, Russia. Ed. N.P. Igumnova. cum.index: nos.1-100 (1958-1984). circ. 2,000. (also avail. in microfilm) **Indexed:** Lib.Sci.Abstr. **Document type:** academic/scholarly publication.

020   BU   ISSN 0861-4881
BIBLIOTEKOZNANIE, BIBLIOGRAFIA, KNIGOZNANIE. 1991. a. 20 lv.($35) Narodna Biblioteka Sv.sv. Kiril i Metodii, 88, V. Levski Blvd., 1504 Sofia, Bulgaria. TEL 00359-2-882811. FAX 00359-2-881600. Ed. B. Hristova. circ. 350.

020 016   BU   ISSN 0324-1858
BIBLIOTEKOZNANIE, BIBLIOGRAFIIA, KNIGOZNANIE, NAUCHNA INFORMATSIIA. 1969. a. $18. Narodna Biblioteka Sv.sv. Kiril i Metodii, 88, V. Levski Blvd., 1504 Sofia, Bulgaria. TEL 00359-2-882811. FAX 00359-2-881600. circ. 350. **Indexed:** LISA.

027   DK   ISSN 0084-957X
BIBLIOTEKSAARBOG. (In three parts: Statistik for Folke- og Skolebibliotekerne; Statistik for Forskningsbibliotekerne; Beretning for Folke- og Forskningsbibliotekerne) 1939. a. DKK 255.60 each Statistik; DKK 455 for Beretning. Dansk BiblioteksCenter as, Tempovej 7-11, DK-2750 Ballerup, Denmark. TEL 44-97-40-00. FAX 44-68-24-42. (Co-sponsor: Statens Bibliotekstjeneste) Ed. Inge Holm Pedersen. circ. 4,800.
Description: Contains information from research libraries, public libraries, institutions and associations concerning libraries.

020 011   SW   ISSN 0006-1867
Z671
BIBLIOTEKSBLADET/LIBRARY JOURNAL. Key Title: BBL. Biblioteksbladet. (Text in Scandinavian languages) 1916. 10/yr. SEK 320. Sveriges Allmaenna Biblioteksfoerening - Swedish Library Association, Box 3127, 103 62 Stockholm, Sweden. TEL 46-8-7230082. FAX 46-8-7230038. Ed. Ylva Mannerheim. adv. contact: Lena Sjoelin. bk.rev.; bibl.; illus.; circ. 4,918 (controlled). (also avail. in microform from UMI; reprint service avail. from UMI) **Indexed:** Lib.Lit., Lib.Sci.Abstr., Tr.& Indus.Ind. **Document type:** trade publication.
—SWETS.

020   DK   ISSN 0109-923X
BIBLIOTEKSHISTORIE. a. DKK 175. (Dansk Bibliotekhistorisk Selskab) Dansk BiblioteksCenter as, Tempovej 7-11, DK-2750 Ballerup, Denmark. TEL 45-44-97-40-00. FAX 45-44-68-24-42.
●Also available online.
Also available on CD-ROM.

027   DK   ISSN 0420-1108
BIBLIOTEKSVEJVISER/GUIDE TO DANISH LIBRARIES. (Subtitles and index in English) 1970. a. DKK 335($50) Danmarks Biblioteksforening - Danish Library Association, Telegrafvej 5, DK-2750 Ballerup, Denmark. FAX 45-44-68-11-03. Ed. Hanne Klemmed. circ. 2,200. **Document type:** directory.

026   CN   ISSN 0707-3674
BIBLIOTHECA MEDICA CANADIANA. (Text in English, French) 1979. q. Can.$65 to non-members; members Can.$55; institutions Can.$85. Canadian Health Libraries Association - Association des Bibliotheques de la Sante du Canada, P.O. Box 94038, 3332 Yonge St., Toronto, ON M4N 3R1. TEL 416-485-0377. FAX 416-485-0377. Ed. Sandra Shores. index. circ. 450. **Indexed:** CINAHL, LISA.
—BLDSC (2019.129420).
Description: Vehicle to increase communication among health libraries and health science librarians in Canada.

020   BE   ISSN 0772-7003
BIBLIOTHEEK- EN ARCHIEFGIDS. 1922. 5/yr. 1600 BEF. Vlaamse Vereniging voor Bibliotheek-, Archief- en Documentatiewezen v.z.w., Goudbloemstraat 10-12, B-2060 Antwerp, Belgium. FAX 32-3-232-42-94. Ed. Peter Van den Broeck. adv.; bk.rev.; bibl.; illus.; index. circ. 1,450. **Indexed:** Bull.Signal., Inform.Sci.Abstr., Lib.Lit., Lib.Sci.Abstr., LISA, Ref.Zh.
—BLDSC (2019.875000); SWETS.
Formerly (until 1983): Bibliotheekgids (ISSN 0006-1956)

020   NE   ISSN 0165-1048
Z671
BIBLIOTHEEK EN SAMENLEVING. 1973. 11/yr. fl.50.35. Nederlands Bibliotheek en Lektuur Centrum, Postbus 93054, 2509 AB The Hague, Netherlands. Ed.Bd. adv.; bk.rev.; illus.; index. circ. 5,000. **Indexed:** Key to Econ.Sci., LISA. **Document type:** trade publication.
—BLDSC (2019.900000); SWETS.
Description: Professional journal for public librarians.

070   GW   ISSN 0340-8051
BIBLIOTHEK DES BUCHWESENS (B B) 1972. irreg., vol.10, 1993. price varies. Anton Hiersemann Verlag, Rosenbergstr. 113, 70193 Stuttgart, Germany. TEL 0711-638265. FAX 0711-6369010. (Subscr. to: Postfach 140155, 70071 Stuttgart, Germany) **Document type:** bibliography.

020   GW   ISSN 0341-4183
Z671
BIBLIOTHEK FORSCHUNG UND PRAXIS. 1977. 3/yr. DM.228. K.G. Saur Verlag KG, A Reed Reference Publishing Company, Part of the Reed Elsevier group, Ortlerstr. 8, 81373 Munich, Germany. TEL 089-76902-0. FAX 089-76902150. TELEX 5212067-SAUR-D. (Subscr. to: Postfach 701620, 81316 Munich, Germany) Ed.Bd. bk.rev.; bibl. **Indexed:** LISA. **Document type:** academic/scholarly publication.
—BLDSC (2020.162000); SWETS. **CCC.**

026   GW   ISSN 0176-2397
BIBLIOTHEK FUER ALLE; Informationen ueber soziale Bibliotheksarbeit. 1984. q. DM.20. Deutsches Bibliotheksinstitut, Abt. 1 - Publikationen, Bundesallee 184-185, 10717 Berlin, Germany. TEL 030-8505-0. FAX 030-8505100. bibl.; stat. circ. 800. (back issues avail.) **Document type:** bulletin.

020   GW   ISSN 0067-8236
BIBLIOTHEK UND WISSENSCHAFT. (Text in English, French, German and Italian) 1964. a., vol.26, 1993. price varies. Harrassowitz Verlag, Taunusstr. 14, 65183 Wiesbaden, Germany. TEL 0611-530-0. FAX 0611-530570. TELEX 4186135. (Subscr. to: Postfach 2929, 65019 Wiesbaden, Germany) Ed.Bd. adv. circ. 400. (back issues avail.) **Document type:** academic/scholarly publication.

020   GW   ISSN 0175-6796
BIBLIOTHEKEN DER BUNDESREPUBLIK DEUTSCHLAND. DATIERTE HANDSCHRIFTEN. 1984. irreg., vol.4, 1994. price varies. Anton Hiersemann Verlag, Rosenbergstr. 113, 70193 Stuttgart, Germany. TEL 0711-638265. FAX 0711-6369010. (Subscr. to: Postfach 140155, 70071 Stuttgart, Germany) Ed. J. Autenrieth. **Document type:** catalog.

020   GW   ISSN 0720-4310
BIBLIOTHEKS TASCHENBUCH. 1980. a. DM.9.80. Bock und Herchen Verlag, Postfach 1145, 53581 Bad Honnef, Germany. TEL 02224-5443. FAX 02224-78310. **Document type:** bulletin.

020   GW   ISSN 0006-1972
Z801.A1
BIBLIOTHEKSDIENST. 1966. m. DM.60. Deutsches Bibliotheksinstitut, Abt. 1 - Publikationen, Bundesallee 184-185, 10717 Berlin, Germany. TEL 030-8505-0. FAX 030-8505-100. adv.; bk.rev. circ. 4,400. **Document type:** bulletin.
—BLDSC (2020.198000); SWETS.
Formerly: Buechereidienst.

020   GW   ISSN 0340-000X
Z801.B3
BIBLIOTHEKSFORUM BAYERN. Abbreviated title: B F B. 1973. 3/yr. DM.60. (Bayerischen Staatliche Bibliotheken, Munchen) K.G. Saur Verlag KG, A Reed Reference Publishing Company, Part of the Reed Elsevier group, Ortlerstr. 8, 81373 Munich, Germany. TEL 089-76902-0. FAX 089-76902150. TELEX 5212067-SAUR-D. (Subscr. to: Postfach 702620, 81316 Munich, Germany; Dist. in North America by: R.R. Bowker, 121 Chanlon Rd., New Providence, NJ 07974, USA) Ed.Bd. adv.; bk.rev.; bibl.; charts; illus. circ. 2,000. **Document type:** bibliography.
—BLDSC (2020.240000); SWETS. **CCC.**

020   GW   ISSN 0940-7944
BIBLIOTHEKSINFO. 1991. m. DM.40. Deutsches Bibliotheksinstitut, Abt. 1 - Publikationen, Bundesallee 184-185, 10717 Berlin, Germany. TEL 030-8505-0. FAX 030-8505100. **Document type:** bulletin.

020   GW   ISSN 0300-287X
BIBLIOTHEKSPRAXIS. irreg., vol.31, 1992. price varies. K.G. Saur Verlag KG, A Reed Reference Publishing Company, Part of the Reed Elsevier group, Ortlerstr. 8, 81373 Munich, Germany. TEL 089-76902-0. FAX 089-76902150. TELEX 5212067-SAUR-D. (Subscr. to: Postfach 701620, 81316 Munich, Germany) Ed.Bd. **Document type:** bibliography.

020   FR   ISSN 0249-7344
Z927.P22
BIBLIOTHEQUE NATIONALE. REVUE. 1976. q. 380 F.($98) Bibliotheque Nationale, 58 rue Richelieu, 75084 Paris Cedex 02, France. TEL 47-03-81-07. FAX 42-96-84-47. (Dist. by: Armand Colin, B.P. 22, 41353 Vineuil Cedex, France) Ed. A. Fauve-Chamoux. adv.; bk.rev.; illus. circ. 2,000.
—SWETS.
Formerly: Bibliotheque Nationale Bulletin (ISSN 0338-4446)

020   BE   ISSN 0770-4372
BIBLIOTHEQUE ROYAL ALBERT 1ER. BULLETIN TRIMESTRIEL D'INFORMATION. Dutch edition: Koninklijke Bibliotheek Albert I. Driemaandelijks Informatie Bulletin (ISSN 0770-4429) bi-m. free to institutions. Bibliotheque Royale Albert 1er, 4 bd. de l'Empereur, 1000 Brussels, Belgium. illus. **Document type:** bulletin.
Former titles: Bibliotheque Royal Albert 1er. Bulletin Bimestriel d'Information; Bibliotheque Royal Albert 1er. Bulletin; Bibliotheque Royale de Belgique. Bulletin (ISSN 0524-7632)

020   BE   ISSN 0772-3776
BIBLIOTHEQUE ROYALE ALBERT 1ER. PUBLICATIONS ANNONCEES/KONINKLIJKE BIBLIOTHEEK ALBERT I. AANGEKONDIGDE PUBLIKATIES. 1983. 24/yr. 1000 BEF. Bibliotheque Royale Albert 1er - Koninklijke Bibliotheek Albert I, 4 bd. de l'Empereur, B-1000 Brussels, Belgium. **Document type:** bibliography.

020   BE   ISSN 0770-4526
BIBLIOTHEQUE ROYALE ALBERT 1ER. RAPPORT ANNUEL. Dutch edition: Koninklijke Bibliotheek Albert I. Jaarverslag (ISSN 0770-447X) a. free to institutions. Bibliotheque Royale Albert 1er - Koninklijke Bibliotheek Albert I, 4 bd. de l'Empereur, B-1000 Brussels, Belgium. stat. **Document type:** corporate report.
Formerly: Bibliotheque Royale de Belgique. Rapport Annuel.

015 026   JA   ISSN 0006-2030
Z675.A2
BIBLOS/BIBUROSU; monthly magazine for branch libraries, executive, judicial, and other special libraries. (Text in Japanese) 1950. m. 4404 Yen. National Diet Library - Kokuritsu Kokkai Toshokan, 1-10-1 Nagata-cho, Chiyoda-ku, Tokyo 100, Japan. TEL 03-3581-2331. FAX 03-3597-9104. bibl.; charts; illus. circ. 1,470. **Indexed**: LISA.
—BLDSC (2021.970000).

020   SW   ISSN 1100-3847
BIBSAMNYTT. (Text in Swedish) 1989. irreg. (3-4/yr.). free. BIBSAM - the Royal Library's Office for National Planning and Co-ordination, Royal Library, P.O. Box 5039, S-102 41 Stockholm, Sweden. TEL 468-679-5040. FAX 468-611-2570. TELEX 19640 KBS S. Ed. Inger Klondiras. circ. 800.

020   BE   ISSN 0067-8538
BIJDRAGEN TOT DE BIBLIOTHEEKWETENSCHAP/CONTRIBUTIONS TO LIBRARY SCIENCE. 1961. irreg. price varies. Universiteit te Gent, Centrale Bibliotheek, Rozier 9, B-9000 Gent, Belgium. TEL 32-91-643851. FAX 32-91-644196. **Document type**: academic/scholarly publication.

020 012   YU   ISSN 0352-6437
BILTEN DOKUMENTACIJE. SERIJA I1. INFORMATIKA/BULLETIN OF DOCUMENTATION. SERIES I1. INFORMATICS. 1972. bi-m. $198. Jugoslovenski Centar za Tehnicku i Naucnu Dokumentaciju - Yugoslav Center for Technical and Scientific Documentation (YCTSD), Sl. Penezica-Krcuna 29-31, Box 724, 11000 Belgrade, Yugoslavia. Ed. Ljiljana Kojic-Bogdanovic.
Former titles (until 1985): Bilten Dokumentacije. Serija I1, 1. Informatika (ISSN 0351-4056); (until 1980): Bilten Dokumentacije. Serija I1. Informatika (ISSN 0350-0357)

BIMONTHLY REVIEW OF LAW BOOKS. see LAW

BIOFEEDBACK (SAN FRANCISCO). see BIOLOGY

021   PL   ISSN 0006-3983
BIULETYN INFORMACYJNY BIBLIOTEKI NARODOWEJ. (Text in Polish; contents page in English) 1956. q. 5000 Zl. Biblioteka Narodowa, Al. Niepodleglosci 213, 00-973 Warsaw, Poland. TEL 48-22-259271. FAX 48-22-255251. TELEX 813702 BN PL. (Dist. by: P.P. CHZ Ars Polona, ul. Krakowskie Przedmiescie 7, 00-068 Warsaw, Poland) Ed. Waclaw Sznee. adv.; bibl.; illus.; index, cum.index. circ. 500. **Document type**: bulletin.
Description: Presents the library's activities, collections and cooperation with domestic and foreign libraries.

020   UK   ISSN 0959-2725
BLAISE - LINE NEWSLETTER. 1990. £15. British Library, National Bibliograhic Service, Boston Spa, Wetherby, W. Yorks. LS23 7BQ, England. TEL 0937-546585. FAX 0935-546586. circ. 1,100. (back issues avail.) **Document type**: academic/scholarly publication, newsletter.
—BLDSC (2108.236800).
Former titles: Blaise Link; Blaise Services Newsletter.
Description: Contains information about the bibliograhic database service provided by the British Library. Includes all subjects.
Refereed Serial

029   UK   ISSN 0520-2795
Z696.B59
BLISS CLASSIFICATION BULLETIN. 1954. a. £10 to individuals; institutions £15. Bliss Classification Association, c/o Library, Fitzwilliam College, Huntingdon Rd., Cambridge CB3 0DG, England. FAX 0223-464162. Ed. A.G. Curwen. bk.rev. circ. 200. **Document type**: bulletin.

020   UK   ISSN 0067-9488
Z792.094
BODLEIAN LIBRARY RECORD. 1938. s-a. £7 per no. Bodleian Library, Oxford OX1 3BG, England. FAX 0865-277182. Ed. D.S. Porter. index. circ. 1,500. (also avail. in microform from UMI; reprint service avail. from UMI,KTO) **Indexed**: Abstr.Engl.Stud., Amer.Hist.& Life, Br.Hum.Ind., Hist.Abstr., M.L.A. **Document type**: academic/scholarly publication.
—BLDSC (2117.000000).
Description: Articles based on Bodleian holdings, news of acquisitions.

BOERN OG BOEGER. see PUBLISHING AND BOOK TRADE

028   DK   ISSN 0006-5692
Z671
BOGENS VERDEN; tidsskrift for dansk biblioteksvaesen. 1918. 8/yr. DKK 400($58) for non-members. Danmarks Biblioteksforening - Danish Library Association, Telegrafvej 5, DK-2750 Ballerup, Denmark. FAX 45-44-68-11-03. Ed. Flemming Ettrup. circ. 2,700. (also avail. in microform from UMI; reprint service avail. from UMI) **Indexed**: Lib.Lit, Lib.Sci.Abstr., LISA.
—SWETS; UMI.
Description: Information of Danish literature and libraries.

021   NO   ISSN 0006-5811
Z671
BOK OG BIBLIOTEK. 1934. 8/yr. NOK 125. Statens Bibliotektilsyn, Postboks 8145, DEP 0033 Oslo 1, Norway. TEL 02-832585. FAX 02-83-1552. Ed. Mar't Boedtker. adv.; bk.rev.; charts; illus.; stat.; index. circ. 11,000. **Indexed**: Lib.Lit., M.L.A.
—BLDSC (2121.450000); SWETS. **CCC**.

020   IC
BOKASAFNID. (Text in Icelandic; summaries in English) 1974. a. ISK 550($10) (Felag Bokasafnsfraedinga) Bokafulltrui Rikisins, Soelvholsgata 4, IS-150 Reykjavik, Iceland. TEL 354-1-609529. FAX 354-1-623068. Ed. Regina Eiriksdottir. adv.; bk.rev.; abstr.; bibl. circ. 900. (back issues avail.) **Indexed**: LISA. **Document type**: trade publication.

020   GW   ISSN 0068-0028
BONNER BEITRAEGE ZUR BIBLIOTHEKS- UND BUECHERKUNDE. 1954. irreg., vol.30, 1985. price varies. Bouvier Verlag Herbert Grundmann, Am Hof 28, 53113 Bonn, Germany. TEL 0228-7290124. FAX 0228-7290179. Eds. Hartwig Lohse, Irmgard Ooms. **Document type**: monographic series.

020   US
BOOK MARKS. 1949. 6/yr. non-members $15. South Dakota Library Association, 610 Quincy, Rapid City, SD 57701-0045. TEL 605-394-4171. FAX 605-394-6626. Ed. Susan Braunstein. adv.; bk.rev. circ. 800.
Formerly: Catalyst (ISSN 0045-5954)
Description: Covers regional library issues and provides features on library services.

027.8 028.1   SA   ISSN 0258-7149
BOOK PARADE/BOEKPARADE. (Text in Afrikaans, English) 1976. q. free. Transvaal Provincial Library Service - Transvaalse Provinsiale Biblioteekdiens, Private Bag X288, Pretoria 0001, South Africa. TEL 012-201-3349. FAX 012-201-2445. Ed. Karin Kriel. bk.rev.; film rev. circ. 1,100. **Document type**: government publication.
Description: Contains general information on the Transvaal Provincial Library Service, as well as reviews of newly acquired books.

027.8   US   ISSN 0731-4388
Z675.S3
BOOK REPORT; journal for junior and senior high school librarians. 1982. bi-m. (during school yr.) $39. Linworth Publishing, Inc., 480 E. Wilson Bridge Rd., Ste. L, Worthington, OH 43085. TEL 614-436-7107. FAX 614-436-9490. Ed. Carolyn Hamilton. adv.; bk.rev. circ. 11,900. (also avail. in microfilm; microfiche from UMI; back issues avail.; reprint service avail. from UMI) **Indexed**: Bk.Rev.Ind. (1983-), Child.Bk.Rev.Ind. (1983-), Ind.Child.Mag., Jun.High.Mag.Abstr. **Document type**: trade publication.
—BLDSC (2248.187800); UMI.
Description: Provides articles, tips and ideas for day-to-day school library management, as well as reviews of audio-visuals and software, all written by school librarians.

202 051   US   ISSN 0893-6471
Z732.P42
BOOKENDS. 1982. 6/yr. membership. Friends of the Reading-Berks Public Libraries, Box 227, Wernersville, PA 19565. TEL 215-678-6480. Ed. Chet Hagan. bk.rev.; circ. 2,000. (controlled). **Document type**: newsletter.
Description: News and informational articles on the activities, events, and holdings of the Reading-Berks (Pennsylvania) public libraries, with profiles of resident authors and publishing executives.

BOOKLEGGER. see PUBLISHING AND BOOK TRADE

BOOKMARK. see EDUCATION

020   US   ISSN 0006-7407
CODEN: BOKMA
BOOKMARK (ALBANY); news about library services. 1949. q. $15 (foreign $20); or exchange basis. New York State Library, Albany, NY 12230. FAX 518-474-5786. Ed. Joseph F. Shubert. bibl. circ. 5,000. (also avail. in microform from UMI; reprint service avail. from UMI) **Indexed**: LHTN, Lib.Lit., P.A.I.S.
—BLDSC (2250.099500); Faxon; UMI.
Formerly: J P S Bookmark (ISSN 0275-8539)
Description: Articles on professional library issues with emphasis on New York State.

021.7   US   ISSN 0006-7393
BOOKMARK (CHAPEL HILL). 1944. irreg. membership. (Friends of the University of North Carolina Library) University of North Carolina, Academic Affairs Library, Rare Book Collection, CB 3936 Wilson Library, Chapel Hill, NC 27514-8890. TEL 919-962-1143. Ed. Charles B. McNamara. circ. 600. **Document type**: bulletin.

027.7   US   ISSN 0735-0295
BOOKMARK (MOSCOW); a newsletter about the library for the University of Idaho community. 1948. q. $25 to members. University of Idaho Library, Moscow, ID 83843. TEL 208-885-6584. FAX 208-885-6817. Ed. R. Force, M. Pollastro. bk.rev.; circ. 1,100 (controlled). (also avail. in microfilm) **Indexed**: Lib.Lit. **Document type**: newsletter.
—UMI.

027.7   US   ISSN 0006-7458
BOOKS AND LIBRARIES AT THE UNIVERSITY OF KANSAS. 1952. irreg. free. University of Kansas Libraries, Lawrence, KS 66045. TEL 913-864-4334. Ed. James Helyar. bibl.; illus.; circ. controlled. **Document type**: bibliography.

021.7   US   ISSN 0006-7474
Z881 .I644
BOOKS AT IOWA. 1964. s-a. $25 membership. Friends of the University of Iowa Libraries, University of Iowa, Iowa City, IA 52242. TEL 319-335-5921. FAX 319-335-5830. Ed. Robert A. McCown. illus.; cum.index every 5 yrs. circ. 1,130. **Indexed**: Abstr.Engl.Stud., M.L.A. **Document type**: academic/scholarly publication.

020   US   ISSN 0891-9615
BORGO CATALOGING GUIDES. 1987. irreg., no.4, 1993. price varies. Borgo Press, Box 2845, San Bernardino, CA 92406. TEL 909-884-5813. FAX 909-888-4942. Ed. Michael Burgess.
Description: Provides current surveys of cataloging practice and science in the Library of Congress classification scheme.

BOSTON SPA SERIALS ON C D - R O M. see BIBLIOGRAPHIES

026   BS
BOTSWANA. NATIONAL ARCHIVES. REPORT ON THE NATIONAL ARCHIVES. 1975. a. free. National Archives, c/o T. Masisi Lekaukau, Director, Box 239, Gaborone, Botswana. FAX 313584. TELEX 2994 HOMES BD. circ. 200. **Document type**: government publication.
Description: Records the activities of a given year for the information of the relevant authorities in the country, as well as the users.

021   BS
BOTSWANA. NATIONAL LIBRARY SERVICE. REPORT. (Text in English) irreg. National Library Service, Private Bag 0036, Gaborone, Botswana. illus. **Document type**: government publication, corporate report.
Description: A report of activities of the Botswana National Library Service over a specified period.

LIBRARY AND INFORMATION SCIENCES

332 020 US ISSN 0888-045X
Z683 CODEN: BOLIEO
BOTTOM LINE (NEW YORK); a financial magazine for librarians. q. $49.95 (Canada $60; elsewhere $65). Neal-Schuman Publishers, Inc., 100 Varick St., New York, NY 10013. TEL 212-925-8650. FAX 212-219-8916. **Document type:** trade publication.
—BLDSC (2264.020100).
 Description: Aimed at managers in all types of libraries. Provides practical information on planning, budgeting, managing cash, purchasing, investment, cost analysis, new technology, and other financial tools and techniques.

020 070.5 US ISSN 0068-0540
Z731
THE BOWKER ANNUAL LIBRARY AND BOOK TRADE ALMANAC; facts, figures and reports. Short title: Bowker Annual. 1955. a., 39th ed., 1994. $155. R.R. Bowker, A Reed Reference Publishing Company, Part of the Reed Elsevier group, 121 Chanlon Rd., New Providence, NJ 07974. TEL 908-464-6800. FAX 908-665-6688. TELEX 138 755. (Subscr. to: Order Dept., Box 31, New Providence, NJ 07974-9903. TEL 800-521-8110) stat.; cum.index: 1972-1976 n 1976 ed. (also avail. in magnetic tape; microfiche from CIS) **Indexed:** SRI. **Document type:** directory.
●Also available online. Vendor(s): BRS Online Products (BBIP), DIALOG Information Services, Inc., European Space Agency Orbit Search Service. Also available on CD-ROM. Producer(s): Bowker - Reed Reference Electronic Publishing.
—BLDSC (2265.049000). **CCC**.
 Description: Essays and reports reviewing book industry and library developments, with statistical information on pricing and expenditures, and funding and legislative changes.

BRAILLE BOOK REVIEW (LARGE PRINT EDITION). see HANDICAPPED — Visually Impaired

020 US
BRANCHING OUT. 1963. m. free. Baltimore County Public Library, 320 York Rd., Towson, MD 21204. TEL 301-296-8500. FAX 301-296-3139. Ed. Kenna Forsyth. circ. 1,000 (controlled). (looseleaf format)

020 BL
BRAZIL. INSTITUTO NACIONAL DO LIVRO. RELATORIO DE ATIVIDADES. 1974-1985. a. Instituto Nacional do Livro, Brasilia, D.F., Brazil. **Document type:** government publication.

026.78 UK ISSN 0007-0173
BRIO. 1964. s-a. £22.50($48) International Association of Music Libraries, Archives & Documentation Centres (U.K. Branch), Faculty of Music Lib., St. Aldate's, Oxford OX1 1DB, England. (Subscr. to: Susi Wocdhouse, 47 Berriedale Ave., Hove, E. Sussex BN3 4JG, England. TEL 0273-779129. FAX 0273-779129) Ed. John Wagstaff. adv.; bk.rev.; music rev. circ. 500. (reprint service avail. from UMI) **Indexed:** Lib.Lit., Lib.Sci.Abstr., LISA, Music Ind., RILM. **Document type:** academic/scholarly publication.
—BLDSC (2284.400000); Faxon; UnCover; UMI.
 Description: Contains articles on music librarianship, music bibliography, and news from music libraries.

020 UK ISSN 0269-0497
Z675.U5
BRITISH JOURNAL OF ACADEMIC LIBRARIANSHIP. 1986. 3/yr. £60($117) Taylor Graham Publishing, 500 Chesham House, 150 Regent St., London W1R 5FA, England. Ed. Colin Harris. adv.; bk.rev. (back issues avail.) **Indexed:** Lib.Lit., LISA. **Document type:** academic/scholarly publication.
—BLDSC (2303.760000); UnCover; SWETS.

020 UK
BRITISH LIBRARIANSHIP & INFORMATION WORK. (In two volumes) 1972. quinquennial. price varies. Library Association Publishing Ltd., 7 Ridgmount St., London WC1E 7AE, England. TEL 071-636-7543. FAX 071-636-3627. TELEX 9312134504-LAG. (Dist. in U.S by: UNIPUB, 4611-F Assembly Dr., Lanham, MD 20706-4391) Eds. D. Bromley, A. Allott. index. **Document type:** trade publication.
 Former titles: British Librarianship and Information Science (ISSN 0071-5662); Five Years Work in Librarianship.

027 UK ISSN 0305-7887
Z792 CODEN: ARBLDQ
BRITISH LIBRARY. ANNUAL REPORT (YEAR). 1973. a. £8.50. British Library, Document Supply Centre, Publications Sales Unit, Boston Spa, Wetherby. W. Yorks. LS23 7BQ, England. TEL 0937-546061. FAX 0937-546286. Ed. A. Arthur. circ. 4,000. **Indexed:** Apic.Abstr. **Document type:** corporate report.
—BLDSC (1125.900000).
 Description: Reports on the developments of the British Library over the previous year.

020 UK ISSN 0952-892X
CODEN: DSNEE4
BRITISH LIBRARY. DOCUMENT SUPPLY CENTRE. DOCUMENT SUPPLY NEWS. 1985. q. free. British Library, Document Supply Centre, Boston Spa, Wetherby, W. Yorks. LS23 7BQ, England. TEL 0937-546061. FAX 0937-546333. TELEX 557381. Ed. Katy King. circ. 15,000. **Indexed:** AESIS. **Document type:** newsletter.
—BLDSC (3609.193900); CASDDS.
 Former titles: British Library. Document Supply Centre. Newsletter (ISSN 0269-1175); (until 1986): British Library. Lending Division Newsletter (ISSN 0267-064X)
 Description: Follows the activities of the British Library Document Supply Centre (BLDSC).

BRITISH LIBRARY. DOCUMENT SUPPLY CENTRE. SCIENCE REFERENCE AND INFORMATION SERVICE. CURRENT SERIALS RECEIVED. see BIBLIOGRAPHIES

026 UK ISSN 0144-9958
BRITISH LIBRARY. NEWSPAPER LIBRARY. NEWSLETTER. 1980. s-a. free. British Library, Newspaper Library, Colindale Ave., London NW9 5HE, England. TEL 071-323-7357. FAX 071-323-7379. TELEX 21462. Ed. Jill Allbrooke. bk.rev. circ. 2,000. **Document type:** newsletter.
—BLDSC (2327.679700).
 Formerly: British Library. Reference Division Newspaper Library. Newsletter (ISSN 0144-9958)
 Description: Reports developments in the Library and in newspaper services in the UK and worldwide.

020 UK ISSN 0305-5167
Z921.B854
BRITISH LIBRARY JOURNAL. 1975. s-a. £35 (foreign £40). British Library, Humanities and Social Sciences, Great Russell St., London WC1B 3DG, England. TEL 071-323-7704. FAX 071-323-7736. TELEX 21462. Ed. C. Wright. illus.; cum.index. circ. 900. **Indexed:** Amer.Hist.& Life, Arts & Hum.Cit.Ind., Br.Hum.Ind., Curr.Cont., Hist.Abstr., M.L.A., RILA. **Document type:** trade publication.
—BLDSC (2327.679000); Faxon; UnCover; SWETS.

020.6 UK ISSN 0307-9481
CODEN: BLNEDY
BRITISH LIBRARY NEWS. 1976. m. free. British Library, 96 Euston Rd., London NW1 2DB, England. (Subscr. to: British Library, Publications Sales Unit, Boston Spa, Wetherby, W. Yorkshire LS23 7BQ, England) bk.rev. circ. 8,000. **Indexed:** Apic.Abstr, Br.Ceram.Abstr. **Document type:** trade publication.
—BLDSC (2327.679500); CASDDS.

020 UK ISSN 0952-2832
Z921.B854 CODEN: RBBDEA
BRITISH LIBRARY RESEARCH AND DEVELOPMENT DEPARTMENT RESEARCH BULLETIN. 1981. irreg. free. British Library, Research and Development Department, 2 Sheraton St., London W1V 4BH, England. TEL 44-71-323-7054. FAX 44-71-323-7251. TELEX 21462. (Dist. in the U.S. by: ALA Publishing Services, 50 E. Huron St., Chicago, IL 60611) **Document type:** bulletin.
—BLDSC (7719.305000); CASDDS.
 Formerly (until 1987): British Library Research Reviews (ISSN 0261-2178)
 Description: Describes the research funding and dissemination activities of the department. Also covers international activities, new publications, attendance at meetings, study visits overseas, assistance to other libraries, the BNB Research Fund, andsome activities funded by the U.K. Department of National Heritage.

021 US ISSN 0007-2397
BROOKLYN PUBLIC LIBRARY BULLETIN. 1952. q. free. Brooklyn Public Library, Grand Army Plaza, Brooklyn, NY 11238. TEL 718-780-7700. Ed. Ellen Rudley. charts; illus. circ. 10,000.

027.4 US
BROOME COUNTY PUBLIC LIBRARY. ANNUAL REPORT. 6000. (Former name of issuing body: Binghamton Public Library) a. Broome County Public Library, 78 Exchange St., Binghamton, NY 13901-3489. TEL 607-778-6400. FAX 607-778-1441. **Document type:** newsletter.
 Formerly: Binghamton Public Library. Annual Report.

020 GW ISSN 0340-0301
BUCH UND BIBLIOTHEK. Abbreviated title: B u B. 1948. m. DM.130 (foreign DM.145). (Verein der Bibliothekare an Oeffentlichen Bibliotheken e.V.) Bock and Herchen Verlag, Postfach 1145, 53581 Bad Honnef, Germany. TEL 02224-5443. FAX 02224-78310. Ed.Bd. adv.; bk.rev.; illus.; index; circ. 7,200 (controlled). **Indexed:** Lib.Lit., Lib.Sci.Abstr., LISA, Rural Ext.Educ.& Tr.Abstr. **Document type:** bulletin.
—BLDSC (2354.780000); SWETS.
 Formerly (until 1971): Buecherei und Bildung (ISSN 0007-3024)

655 AU ISSN 0007-3040
BUECHERSCHAU; Zeitschrift fuer Betriebs- und Gewerkschaftsbibliotheken. 1962. q. free. Oesterreichischer Gewerkschaftsbund, Hohenstaufengasse 10-12, A-1010 Vienna, Austria. Ed. Martina Tichy. bk.rev.; mkt. circ. 2,500. **Document type:** trade publication.

021 US ISSN 0020-966X
BUFFALO AND ERIE COUNTY PUBLIC LIBRARY BULLETIN. 1969. m. (except Jul.-Aug.). free. Buffalo and Erie County Public Library, Lafayette Sq., Buffalo, NY 14203. TEL 716-858-7181. FAX 716-858-6211. Ed. Michael C. Mahaney. bk.rev. circ. 750. **Indexed:** Lib.Lit. **Document type:** bulletin.
 Supersedes: Interpreter.

020 FR ISSN 0006-2006
Z671
BULLETIN DES BIBLIOTHEQUES DE FRANCE. 1956. 6/yr. 450 F. Ecole Nationale Superieure des Sciences de l'Information et des Bibliotheques, 17-21 bd. du 11 Novembre 1918, 69623 Villeurbanne Cedex, France. TEL 72-44-43-16. FAX 72-44-27-88. Ed.Bd. adv.; bk.rev.; abstr.; bibl.; charts; illus.; index. circ. 2,200. (back issues avail.) **Indexed:** Curr.Cont., Int.Lab.Doc., Lib.Lit., Lib.Sci.Abstr., LISA.
—BLDSC (2411.480000); SWETS.

028.5 GW ISSN 0045-351X
BULLETIN JUGEND UND LITERATUR. 1969. m. DM.125. (Eulenhof Institut) Eulenhof-Verlag, Hallerplatz 5, 20146 Hamburg, Germany. TEL 040-45011013. FAX 040-445282. Ed. Ehrhardt Heinold. adv.; bk.rev.; film rev.; play rev.; bibl.; illus. circ. 1,500. **Indexed:** Child.Lit.Abstr. **Document type:** bibliography. —CCC.
 Description: Contains critical reviews of newly published children's and young adult books. Also includes literary information, articles about writers and library practice, events, readers' comments, and title index.

BULLETIN OF BIBLIOGRAPHY. see BIBLIOGRAPHIES

020 US
Z674.5.U5
BURWELL DIRECTORY OF INFORMATION BROKERS. 1978. a. $59.50. Burwell Enterprises, 3724 F.M. 1960 W., Ste. 214, Houston, TX 77068. TEL 713-537-9051. FAX 713-537-8332. Ed. Helen P. Burwell. **Document type:** directory.
 Formerly: Directory of Fee-Based Information Services (ISSN 0147-1678)
 Description: Directory of companies and individuals worldwide who provide information for a fee.

020 330 UK
BUSINESS AND GOVERNMENT: A MONTHLY SURVEY OF OFFICIAL PUBLICATIONS FOR BUSINESS AND GOVERNMENT. 1981. m. £31.50. Key Facts, The Old Rectory, Northill, Bedfordshire SG18 9AH, England. **Indexed:** Br.Ceram.Abstr.

BUSINESS ARCHIVES; sources and history. see BUSINESS AND ECONOMICS

BUSINESS ARCHIVES COUNCIL. PRINCIPLES AND PRACTICE. see BUSINESS AND ECONOMICS

LIBRARY AND INFORMATION SCIENCES

020 330   US   ISSN 1042-0746
BUSINESS INFORMATION ALERT; what's new in business publications, databases and research techniques. 1988. m. (10/yr.) $142. Alert Publications, Inc., 401 W. Fullerton Pkwy., Ste. 1403E, Chicago, IL 60614-3857. TEL 312-525-7594. FAX 312-525-7015. Ed. Donna Tuke Heroy. bk.rev. (reprint service avail.) **Document type**: trade publication, bibliography.
—CCC.
   Description: Designed to keep librarians and related information professionals informed of new literature, information services and research techniques in the field of business.

020   US   ISSN 0892-6034
BUSINESS INFORMATION FROM YOUR PUBLIC LIBRARY. 1973. 3/yr. $54 (minimum order: 100 copies). Administrator's Digest, Inc., Box 993, South San Francisco, CA 94080. TEL 415-573-5474. Ed. Robert S. Alvarez. circ. 34,000. **Document type**: newsletter.

026   US   ISSN 0191-4006
BUSINESS LIBRARY NEWSLETTER. 1978. m. $52. Business Library Newsletter, Inc., 427-3 Amherst St., Ste. 305, Nashua, NH 03063. TEL 603-672-0705. Ed. Raymond T. Hubbard. adv.; bk.rev.; index. circ. 500. (back issues avail.)
   Description: Publishes a review of 12-15 of the latest titles in business and related areas.

BUY BOOKS WHERE, SELL BOOKS WHERE; a directory of out of print booksellers and collectors and their author and subject specialties. see *PUBLISHING AND BOOK TRADE*

027.8   CN   ISSN 0829-254X
C A A T TRACKS. 1986. q. Can.$20. Ontario Colleges of Applied Arts and Technology, Committee on Learning Resources, St. Lawrence College, King and Portsmouth Avenues, Kingston, ON K7L 5A6, Canada. TEL 613-544-5400. FAX 613-545-3920. Eds. Barbara Carr, Barbara Love. bk.rev. circ. 60. (back issues avail.)
   Formerly: Com-O-Lib.
   Description: Newsletter for and about Ontario Community Colleges libraries.

020   IT
▼ **C A B NEWSLETTER**. (Conservazione negli Archivi e nelle Biblioteche) 1992. bi-m. L.30000 to individuals; institutions L.50000. (Biblioconsult s.r.l.) Editrice Bibliografica s.r.l., Viale Vittorio Veneto 24, 20124 Milan, Italy. TEL 02-29006965. FAX 06-654624. Dir. Carlo Federici. adv. **Document type**: newsletter, trade publication.

020   US   ISSN 0091-5270
Z666
C A L L. (Current Awareness - Library Literature) 1972. bi-m. $25. Goldstein Associates, 35 Whittemore Rd., Framingham, MA 01701. Ed. Samuel Goldstein. bk.rev.; abstr.; index.

026 340   US
C A L L BULLETIN. 1957. 5/yr. free to members. Chicago Association of Law Libraries, Box 1767, Chicago, IL 60690. TEL 312-915-6434. adv.; index. circ. 400. (back issues avail.) **Indexed**: Leg.Info.Manage.Ind. **Document type**: newsletter.

C A M L NEWSLETTER/A C B M NOUVELLES. (Canadian Association of Music Libraries) see *MUSIC*

020   CN
C A N B GAZETTE. 6/yr. Council of Archives of New Brunswick, Provincial Archives of New Brunswick, P.O. Box 6000, Fredericton, N.B. E3B 5H1, Canada. Ed. Louise Charlebois. **Document type**: newspaper.

026   CN   ISSN 0821-3127
C A S L I S, CALGARY CHAPTER. NEWSLETTER. 1976. bi-m. Can.$20 (effective Jan. 1991). Canadian Library Association, Canadian Association of Special Libraries and Information Services, 401 9th Ave. S.W., P.O. Box 22152, Calgary, AB T2P 4J5, Canada. Ed. Jean Peterson. circ. 210. (back issues avail.) **Document type**: newsletter.
   Description: News of interest to regional professional librarians.

C & L APPLICATIONS; monthly information for libraries and information services. see *LIBRARY AND INFORMATION SCIENCES — Computer Applications*

C D M A R C BIBLIOGRAPHIC. see *BIBLIOGRAPHIES*

C D - M A R C NAMES. see *BIBLIOGRAPHIES*

C D - M A R C SERIALS. see *BIBLIOGRAPHIES*

020   JA   ISSN 0914-6601
C D N L A O NEWSLETTER. (Conference of Directors of National Libraries on Resource Sharing in Asia and Oceania) 3/yr. National Diet Library, International Cooperation Division - Kokuritsu Kokkai Toshokan, 1-10-1, Nagata-cho, Chiyoda-ku, Tokyo 100, Japan. TEL 03-3581-2331. FAX 03-3597-9104. circ. 1,100 (controlled). **Document type**: newsletter.
   Formerly: A O Newsletter.
   Description: Forum for the exchange of information, views, and experiences among librarians in Asia and Oceania.

621.38   US   ISSN 1066-274X
Z681.3.O67   CODEN: CDWOEV
C D - R O M WORLD; the magazine and review for CD-ROM users. 1986. m. (except July-Aug., Nov.-Dec. combined). $29. Meckler Publishing Corporation, 11 Ferry Lane W., Westport, CT 06880-5808. TEL 203-226-6967. Ed. Todd Harris. circ. 28,000. **Indexed**: Compumath, Info.Media & Tech., Lib.Lit., LISA, Tr.& Indus.Ind.
   ●Also available online. Vendor(s): DIALOG Information Services, Inc., NewsNet.
—BLDSC (3096.305700); Faxon; UnCover; SWETS; UMI. CCC.
   Former titles: C D - R O M Librarian (ISSN 0893-9934); (until 1987): Optical Information Systems Update: Library and Information Center Applications (ISSN 0886-019X)

020   US   ISSN 0895-2485
C D S CONNECTION. 1988. s-a. free. U.S. Library of Congress, Cataloging Distribution Service, Customer Services Section, Washington, DC 20541-5017. TEL 202-707-6100. FAX 202-707-1334. Ed. Terry Erb. circ. 7,000. **Document type**: newsletter.
   Description: Reports on news, developments, and ideas for new products that will affect library professionals.

020   CN   ISSN 1183-9120
C D THEQUE FRANCOPHONIE. (Not avail. in printed format) 1991. irreg. Can.$150 (600 F.). Banque Internationale d'Information sur les Etats Francophones, c/o Patrimoine Canadien, Ottawa, ON K1A 0M5, Canada. TEL 819-997-3857. FAX 819-953-8439. TELEX SEC 053-3384.
   ●Also available online.
Also available on CD-ROM.

021   US
C E F TRAILBLAZER. 1974. q. free. Clinton - Essex - Franklin Library System, 17 Oak St., Plattsburgh, NY 12901. TEL 518-563-5190. Ed. Mary Shaw Hopkins. bk.rev. circ. 860.
   Supersedes: C E F News (ISSN 0007-8212)

C E R L A L C: EL LIBRO EN AMERICA LATINA Y EL CARIBE. see *PUBLISHING AND BOOK TRADE*

C H R A PROGRESS NOTES. (Canadian Health Record Association) see *MEDICAL SCIENCES*

020   AT   ISSN 1038-5355
C I S RESEARCH REPORTS. 1991. irreg. Centre for Information Studies, Charles Sturt University - Riverina, Locked Bag 660, Wagga Wagga, N.S.W. 2678, Australia. **Document type**: academic/scholarly publication.

020   CN
C L A DIRECTORY. 1950. irreg., latest 1990-1991. $25 to non-members. Canadian Library Association, 200 Elgin St., Ste. 602, Ottawa, ON K2P 1L5, Canada. TEL 613-232-9625. FAX 613-563-9895. **Document type**: directory.
   Former titles: C L A Organization Handbook and Membership List (ISSN 0068-9130); Canadian Library Directory.

020   US
C L E N EXCHANGE. 1984. q. $20 (foreign $25). (Continuing Library Education Network and Exchange Round Table) American Library Association, 50 E. Huron St., Chicago, IL 60611. TEL 312-944-6780. FAX 312-440-9374. Ed. Marie E. Bryan. circ. 450. **Document type**: newsletter.

020   II   ISSN 0970-0943
Z665.2.I4
C L I S OBSERVER. 1984. q. Rs.300($40) Centre for Library and Information Study, C-30, Lajpat Nagar III, New Delhi 110 024, India. TEL 11-6836119. Ed. D.R. Kalia. adv.; bk.rev. circ. 1,000.
   Description: Research and development in library and information sciences.

020   US   ISSN 0892-0605
Z671   CODEN: CLRRE3
C L R REPORTS. 1957. irreg. free to qualified personnel. Council on Library Resources, Inc., 1400 16th St., N.W., Ste. 510, Washington, DC 20036. TEL 202-483-7474. FAX 202-483-6410. Ed. Ellen Timmer. circ. 4,000.
—BLDSC (7304.100000); CASDDS.
   Supersedes (in 1986, vol.14, no.2): C L R Recent Developments (ISSN 0034-1169)

020   US   ISSN 0887-3550
C L S NEWSLETTER. s-a. (Association of College and Research Libraries, College Libraries Section) American Library Association, 50 E. Huron St., Chicago, IL 60611-2795. Ed. Damon D. Hickey.

027.8 370   US   ISSN 0196-3309
Z675.S3
C M L E A JOURNAL. 1977. 2/yr. $15 to non-members. California Media and Library Educators Association, 1499 Old Bayshore Hwy., No. 142, Burlingame, CA 94010. TEL 415-692-2350. Ed. Barbara Jeffus. illus. circ. 2,000. (also avail. in microform from UMI; reprint service avail. from UMI) **Indexed**: Cal.Per.Ind. (1980-), Lib.Lit.
—UnCover; UMI.
   Former titles: Journal of Media and Technology; California School Libraries (ISSN 0008-1523)
   Description: Addresses current issues of interest to school library media personnel.

020   JM   ISSN 0378-1070
C O M L A NEWSLETTER. (Text in English) 1973. q. $35. Commonwealth Library Association, P.O. Box 144, Kingston 7, Jamaica, W.I. TEL 809-927-2123. FAX 809-927-1926. Eds. Norma Y. Amenu-Kpodo, H. Brown. adv.; bk.rev.; bibl. circ. 500. (back issues avail.) **Indexed**: LISA. **Document type**: newsletter.
—BLDSC (3331.270000).

023   ISSN 1052-0112
Z678.3
C O S L A DIRECTORY. a. $25. Council of State Governments, Chief Officers of State Library Agencies, Box 11910, Lexington, KY 40578-1910. **Document type**: government publication, directory.

C P L DIRECTORY OF PLANNING AND URBAN AFFAIRS. (Council of Planning Librarians) see *HOUSING AND URBAN PLANNING*

C P L NEWSLETTER. (Council of Planning Librarians) see *HOUSING AND URBAN PLANNING*

025   US   ISSN 0882-6846
C R I A R L NEWSLETTER. 1982. 3/yr. free to libraries. Consortium of Rhode Island Academic and Research Libraries, c/o Helena F. Rodrigues, Ed., Library, Roger Williams University, One Old Ferry Rd., Bristol, RI 02809-2921. TEL 401-254-3053. circ. 500. **Document type**: newsletter.

026 340   US
C R I V SHEET. 1978. 3/yr. American Association of Law Libraries, Committee on Relations with Information Vendors, 53 W. Jackson Blvd., Chicago, IL 60604. TEL 312-939-4764. FAX 312-431-1097. Ed. Kendall Svengalis. bk.rev. (back issues avail.) **Document type**: newsletter.
   Formerly: Publications Clearing House Bulletin (ISSN 0734-9106)

026 340   US
Z675.L2A37
C S P NEWSLETTER. 3/yr. membership. American Association of Law Libraries, Contemporary Social Problems Special Interest Section, c/o Ruth Parlin, Ed., Univ. of Miami Law Library, Box 248087, Coral Gables, FL 33124. TEL 305-284-2250. FAX 305-284-3554. **Document type**: newsletter.

LIBRARY AND INFORMATION SCIENCES

020   PO   ISSN 0007-9421
Z671
CADERNOS DE BIBLIOTECONOMIA, ARQUIVISTICA E DOCUMENTACAO. Short title: Cadernos B A D. 1963. q. Esc.1500 ($45 to individuals; institutions $84). Associacao Portuguesa de Bibliotecarios, Arquivistas e Documentalistas, Edificio da Biblioteca Nacional, Campo Grande 83, 1751 Lisbon, Portugal. FAX 8134697. Ed. Maria Luisa Cabral. adv.; bk.rev.; abstr.; bibl.; charts. circ. 1,000. **Indexed:** Bull.Signal.

001 020   FR   ISSN 0339-3097
CODEN: CADODG
CAHIERS DE L'ANALYSE DES DONNEES. (Text in French; summaries in Arabic, English, French) 1975. q. 650 F. (Association pour le Developpement et la Diffusion de l'Analyse des Donnees) Dunod, 15 rue Gossin, 92543 Montrouge Cedex, France. TEL 33-1-40-92-65-00. FAX 33-1-40-92-65-97. TELEX 634 916 F. (Subscr. to: Centrale des Revues, 11 rue Gossin, 92543 Montrouge Cedex, France. TEL 33-1-46-56-52-66) Ed. J.P. Benzecri. adv. circ. 800. (also avail. in microform) **Indexed:** Br.Archaeol.Abstr., INIS Atomind.
—BLDSC (2948.618500); SWETS. **CCC.**
   Description: Features articles on statistics and data processing from a teacher's point of view, listings, programs of computation designed for techniques of data analysis.

020   US   ISSN 1056-1528
Z673.C16
CALIFORNIA LIBRARIES. 1967. m. membership. California Library Association, 717 K St., Ste. 300, Sacramento, CA 95814. TEL 916-447-8541. FAX 914-447-8394. Ed. Mary Sue Ferrell. adv.; bk.rev. circ. 3,600. (also avail. in microfilm) **Document type:** newsletter.
   Formerly: C L A Newsletter (ISSN 0007-8557)

020   US   ISSN 0740-7688
CALIFORNIA LIBRARY DIRECTORY. 1976. a. California State Library, Box 942837, Sacramento, CA 94237-0001. TEL 916-654-0174. FAX 916-654-0064. **Document type:** directory.
   Supersedes in part (in 1983): California Library Statistics and Directory (ISSN 0148-4583)

979 020   US   ISSN 0741-0344
Z733.C13
CALIFORNIA STATE LIBRARY FOUNDATION BULLETIN. 1982. q. $20. California State Library Foundation, 1225 8th St., Ste. 345, Sacramento, CA 95814. TEL 916-447-6331. Ed. Gary E. Strong. cum.index: 1982-1988. circ. 1,200. (back issues avail.) **Indexed:** Lib.Lit. **Document type:** bulletin.
   Description: Provides a combination of library-related news and information, as well as coverage of topics relevant to California history and library services.

020   US   ISSN 0276-6973
CALIFORNIA STATE LIBRARY NEWSLETTER. bi-m. California State Library, Box 942837, Sacramento, CA 94237-0001. TEL 916-654-0174. FAX 916-654-0064. circ. 2,300. **Document type:** newsletter.

020   US   ISSN 0008-1744
CALL NUMBER. 1939. 3/yr. free to qualified personnel. University of North Texas, School of Library and Information Sciences, NT Box 13796, Denton, TX 76203. TEL 817-565-2445. FAX 817-565-3101. Ed. Jane Hicks. circ. 3,000 (controlled). **Document type:** newsletter.

029   BL   ISSN 0101-6903
CAMARA BRASILEIRA DO LIVRO. CENTRO DE CATALOGACAO NA FONTE. OFICINA DE LIVROS; novidades catalogadas na fonte. Key Title: Oficina de Livros. 1974. a. free. Camara Brasileira do Livro, Centro de Catalogacao na Fonte, Av. Ipiranga, 1267, 10 andar, 01039-907 Sao Paulo SP, Brazil. TEL 11-225-8277. FAX 11-229-7463. TELEX 24788 VRLI. Ed. Zanizer Zeila Castelo Chaves. bk.rev.; bibl. circ. 1,000. **Document type:** bibliography.

020   UK
CAMBRIDGE UNIVERSITY LIBRARY LIBRARIANSHIP SERIES. irreg. price varies. Cambridge University Press, Edinburgh Bldg., Shaftesbury Rd., Cambridge CB2 2RU, England. TEL 0223-312393. FAX 0223-315052. TELEX 851817256. (N. American ed.: Cambridge University Press, Journals Dept., 40 W. 20th St., New York, NY 10011. TEL 212-924-3900. FAX 212-691-3239) **Document type:** monographic series.

026   UK
CAMBRIDGE UNIVERSITY MEDICAL LIBRARY BULLETIN. 1980. 4/yr. free. Cambridge University, Medical Library, Addenbrooke's Hospital, Hills Rd., Cambridge CB2 2QQ, England. TEL 0223-336750. FAX 0223-336709. circ. 380. **Document type:** trade publication.
   Former titles: Cambridge Medical Library Bulletin; Medical Library Bulletin.
   Description: Library accession list plus library news.

027.7   CN   ISSN 0831-4497
CANADIAN ARCHIVAL INVENTORY SERIES. 1986. irreg. price varies. University of Calgary Press, 2500 University Dr. N.W., Calgary, AB T2N 1N4, Canada. TEL 403-220-7578. FAX 403-282-0085. TELEX 03-821545. (Subscr. to: UBC Press, 6344 Memorial Rd., Vancouver, BC V6T 1Z2, Canada. TEL 604-822-5959. FAX 604-822-6083)

020   CN
Z1007   CODEN: CJISDE
CANADIAN JOURNAL OF INFORMATION AND LIBRARY SCIENCE/REVUE CANADIENNE DES SCIENCES DE L'INFORMATION ET DES BIBLIOTHECONOMIE. (Text in English and French) 1976. q. Can.$95 (foreign Can.$110). (Canadian Association for Information Science) University of Toronto Press, Journals Department, 5201 Dufferin St., Downsview, ON M3H 5T8, Canada. TEL 416-667-7781. Ed. Joan Cherry. bk.rev.; illus. **Indexed:** Can.Per.Ind., CMI, Compumath, Comput.Cont., Curr.Cont., Lib.Lit., LISA, Sci.Abstr., SSCI.
—UnCover; SWETS. **CCC.**
   Formerly (until 1993): Canadian Journal of Information Science (ISSN 0380-9218); Incorporates (as of 1986): Canadian Conference on Information Science. Proceedings (ISSN 0703-3249)
   Description: Aims to contribute to the advancement of information and library science in Canada.

020.6 340   CN   ISSN 1180-176X
CANADIAN LAW LIBRARIES/BIBLIOTHEQUES DE DROIT CANADIENNES. 1970. 5/yr. Can.$60. Canadian Association of Law Libraries - Association Canadienne des Bibliotheques de Droit, P.O. Box 1570, 190 Railway St., Kingston, ON K7L 5C8, Canada. adv.; bk.rev.; bibl.; index. circ. 500. **Indexed:** Ind.Can.L.P.L. **Document type:** trade publication.
—BLDSC (3037.315000).
   Formerly: Canadian Association of Law Libraries. Newsletter (ISSN 0319-5376)
   Description: Publishes news, developments, articles, reports of interest to its members.

020   CN   ISSN 0225-1574
CANADIANA AUTHORITIES; a microfiche publication that provides libraries with an up-to-date list of standardized name headings of Canadian origin. (Text in English, French) 1976. q. base vol. plus bi-w. supplements. National Library of Canada, Canadiana Editorial Division, Aquisitions and Bibliographic Services Branch, 395 Wellington St., Ottawa, ON K1A 0N4, Canada. TEL 819-994-6912. FAX 819-953-0291. (also avail. in magnetic tape)

020   SA   ISSN 0008-5790
Z671
CAPE LIBRARIAN/KAAPSE BIBLIOTEKARIS. (Text in Afrikaans, English) 1957. m. (except July & Dec.). R.50 free to affiliated public libraries or on exchange basis. Cape Provincial Library Service, Box 2108, Cape Town, South Africa. TEL 27-21-4102446. FAX 27-21-419-7541. Ed. Grizell Acar-Luxton. bk.rev.; index. circ. 1,200. (also avail. in microfilm from UMI; reprint service avail. from UMI) **Indexed:** Lib.Lit., Lib.Sci.Abstr., LISA.
—BLDSC (3050.647000); UMI.
   Description: Promotes the information function of the Cape Provincial library.

CARIBBEAN ARCHIVES/ARCHIVES ANTILLAISES/ARCHIVOS DEL CARIBE. see HISTORY — History Of North And South America

021.7   US   ISSN 0008-6894
Z881
CARRELL. 1960. a. $5. (Friends of the University of Miami Library) University of Miami Library, Box 248214, Coral Gables, FL 33124. TEL 305-284-4585. FAX 305-665-7352. Eds. Ronald P. Naylor, Laurence Donovan. bibl.; illus.; cum.index: vol.1-13, 1972. circ. 500. **Indexed:** Bibl.Engl.Lang.& Lit., M.L.A., Numis.Lit.
   Description: Poetry, literature, criticism and art by the university's faculty and students.

CARTA DE ARCHIVO. see HISTORY — History Of North And South America

CASSETTE BOOKS. see HANDICAPPED — Abstracting, Bibliographies, Statistics

CATALEG AUTOMATITZAT DE PUBLICACIONS EN SERIE. see BIBLIOGRAPHIES

020   US   ISSN 0163-9374
Z693.A15   CODEN: CCQUDB
CATALOGING & CLASSIFICATION QUARTERLY. 1980. q. $45 to individuals; institutions $115. Haworth Press, Inc., 10 Alice St., Binghamton, NY 13904. TEL 607-722-5857; 800-342-9678. FAX 607-722-1424. TELEX 4932599 HAWORTH. Ed. Ruth Carter. adv.; bk.rev. circ. 997. (also avail. in microfiche from HAW; back issues avail.; reprint service avail. from HAW) **Indexed:** Bull.Signal., C.I.J.E., Comput.& Info.Sys., Excerp.Med., Inform.Sci.Abstr., Lib.Lit., LISA, Ref.Zh., Sci.Abstr. **Document type:** academic/scholarly publication.
—BLDSC (3074.275000); Faxon; UnCover; SWETS; CASDDS.
   Description: Presents theoretical and applied articles in the field of cataloging and classification.
   Refereed Serial

020   AT   ISSN 0312-4371
Z693.5.A8
CATALOGUING AUSTRALIA. q. Aus.$28 (foreign Aus.$36)(effective 1992). Australian Library and Information Association, P.O. Box E411, Queen Victoria Terrace, A.C.T. 2600, Australia. TEL 06-285-1877. FAX 06-282-2249. **Indexed:** LISA. **Document type:** trade publication.
—BLDSC (3090.414000).
   Description: Materials of professional interest to catalogers.

020   US   ISSN 0730-711X
Z673
CATALYST (DES MOINES). 1948. bi-m. $25 to non-members. Iowa Library Association, 823 Insurance Exchange Bldg., Des Moines, IA 50309. TEL 515-243-2172. FAX 515-243-0614. Ed. Naomi Stovall. adv.; bk.rev. circ. 1,800. **Document type:** newsletter.
   Formerly: I L A Catalyst (ISSN 0018-9944)

020   UK   ISSN 0144-9931
CATALYST (LONDON); information from the University of London Shared Automated Library Services. 1980; N.S. 1985. irreg. free. University of London, Library Resources Co-ordinating Committee, Senate House, Malet St., London WC1E 7HU, England. Ed. Paul McLaughlin. **Indexed:** LISA. **Document type:** trade publication.

020 282   US   ISSN 0008-8161
CATHOLIC LIBRARY ASSOCIATION. NORTHERN ILLINOIS CHAPTER. NEWSLETTER. 1957. 4/yr. $8. Catholic Library Association, Northern Illinois Chapter, c/o Sr. Lauretta McCusker, Oak Lawn Public Library, 9427 S. Raymond, Oak Laun, IL 60653. Ed. Kathleen O'Learyr. bk.rev. circ. 450. (processed) **Document type:** newsletter.

020 282   US   ISSN 0008-820X
Z671
CATHOLIC LIBRARY WORLD. 1929. 4/yr. $45. Catholic Library Association, 9009 Carta, Allen Park, MI 48101. TEL 215-649-5250. Ed. Allen Gruenke. adv.; bk.rev.; bibl.; index. circ. 3,000. (also avail. in microfilm from UMI) **Indexed:** Bk.Rev.Ind. (1965-), C.I.J.E., Cath.Ind., Child.Bk.Rev.Ind. (1965-), Lib.Lit., Lib.Sci.Abstr., Ref.Sour.
—BLDSC (3093.077000); UnCover; SWETS; UMI.

LIBRARY AND INFORMATION SCIENCES

020   US   ISSN 0887-1116
CENTENNIAL STATE LIBRARIES. 1968. bi-m. free to Colorado institutions. State Library, Department of Education, 201 E. Colfax Ave., Rm. 309, Denver, CO 80203. TEL 303-866-6881. FAX 303-830-6940. Ed. Barbara Padgett. bk.rev.; circ. 3,500 (controlled). **Document type:** newsletter.
    Formerly: Colorado State Library Newsletter (ISSN 0010-1761); **Supersedes:** Capitol Hill Library Crier.
    Description: Includes current library news, editorials, items of interest, bibliographies, and calendar of events.

020   US
CENTER FOR RESEARCH LIBRARIES. HANDBOOK. irreg. $15 to non-members. Center for Research Libraries, 6050 S. Kenwood Ave., Chicago, IL 60637-2804. TEL 312-955-4545. index.
    Description: Descriptions of collections and access to them.

020   AT   ISSN 1038-0140
CENTRE FOR INFORMATION STUDIES. OCCASIONAL MONOGRAPHS. 1983. irreg. Centre for Information Studies, Charles Sturt University - Riverina, Locked Bag 660, Wagga Wagga, N.S.W. 2678, Australia. TEL 069-222325. FAX 069-222733. **Document type:** monographic series.
    —BLDSC (6209.690000).
    Former titles (until 1990): Riverina - Murray Institute of Higher Education. Centre for Information Studies. Occasional Monographs (ISSN 1033-5889); (until 1989): Riverina - Murray Institute of Higher Education. Centre for Library Studies. Occasional Monographs (ISSN 0815-0400); Riverina College of Advanced Education. Centre for Library Studies. Occasional Monographs (ISSN 0814-0901)

020   MX
CENTRO DE BIBLIOTECOLOGIA, ARCHIVOLOGIA E INFORMACION. ANUARIO. 1961. a. Universidad Nacional Autonoma de Mexico, Centro de Bibliotecologia, Archivologia e Informacion, Villa Obregon, Ciudad Universitaria, Mexico 20, D.F., Mexico. Ed. Alicia Perales de Mercado. bk.rev.; cum.index. circ. 1,000. (back issues avail.)
    Formerly: Anuario de Bibliotecologia, Archivologia e Informatica.

020   SP   ISSN 0210-9492
Z5140
CENTRO DE INFORMACION DOCUMENTAL DE ARCHIVOS. BOLETIN DE INFORMACION. 1980. q. free. Centro de Informacion Documental de Archivos, Avda. Juan de Herrera 2, planta 4a, 28040 Madrid, Spain. TEL 543-70-48. **Document type:** bulletin.

020 001.3   IT
CENTRO DI RICERCHE INFORMATICHE PER I BENI CULTURALI. QUADERNI. 1980. s-a. Scuola Normale Superiore Pisa, Centro di Richerche Informatiche per i Beni Culturali, Via C. Cattaneo 64, Pisa, Italy. TEL 050-502783. Ed. Paola Barocchi.
    Formerly (until 1991): Centro di Elaborazione Automatica di Dati e Documenti Storico Artistici. Bollettino d'Informazione (ISSN 0392-9957)

CENTRO INTERNAZIONALE DI RICERCA SUI PERIODICI MUSICALI. BOLLETTINO. see *MUSIC*

CERCLE BELGE DE LA LIBRAIRIE. ANNUAIRE. see *PUBLISHING AND BOOK TRADE*

020   XR
CESKOSLOVENSKA AKADEMIE VED. USTREDNI ARCHIV. ARCHIVNI ZPRAVY. 1970. 1-2/yr. free. Academia, Publishing House of the Czechoslovak Academy of Sciences, Vodickova 40, 112 29 Prague 1, Czech Republic. TEL 23-63-065. Ed. Jindrich Schwippel. bk.rev.; bibl. circ. 500.

020   US   ISSN 0146-1095
CHANNEL D L S. 1966. m. (combined Jul.-Aug.). free. Department of Public Instruction, Division for Library Services, 125 S. Webster St., 5th Fl., Box 7841, Madison, WI 53707. TEL 608-266-9679. FAX 608-267-1052. Ed. Telise E.M. Johnsen. circ. 3,600 (controlled). (reprint service avail. from UMI) **Document type:** government publication.

020.4   US
CHAUTAUQUA - CATTARAUGUS LIBRARY SYSTEM NEWSLETTER. q. Chautauqua - Cattaraugus Library System, 106 W. Fifth St., Jamestown, NY 14701. FAX 716-483-6880. circ. 500. **Document type:** newsletter.

020   CN
CHECK IT OUT!. 1972. bi-m. free. Mississauga Library System, 301 Burnhamthorpe Rd. W., Mississauga, Ont. L5B 3Y3, Canada. TEL 416-615-3611. FAX 416-615-3615. Ed. Kelly Smith. adv.; bk.rev. circ. 15,000.
    Formerly (until vol.19, no.2, 1991): Link (Mississauga) (ISSN 0703-7007)
    Description: Calendar of library events and services for the public.

020   US
CHICORY (BATON ROUGE). 1980. 3/yr. membership. Louisiana Library Association, Box 3058, Baton Rouge, LA 70821. TEL 504-342-4928. Ed. Carlos Colon. circ. 450. (back issues avail.; reprint service avail. from UMI)

CHILDREN'S BOOK REVIEW SERVICE. see *PUBLISHING AND BOOK TRADE*

028.5   US   ISSN 0885-0429
PN1008.2
CHILDREN'S LITERATURE ASSOCIATION QUARTERLY. 1976. q. membership. Children's Literature Association, Box 138, Battle Creek, MI 49016-0138. TEL 616-965-8180. Ed. Gillian Adams. adv.; bk.rev. circ. 750. **Indexed:** Bk.Rev.Ind. (1986-), Child.Bk.Rev.Ind. (1986-), Child.Lit.Abstr., M.L.A. **Document type:** academic/scholarly publication.
    —BLDSC (7169.587000); Faxon; UnCover.
    Description: Editorials, articles, and announcements pertaining to scholarship and research in the field.

020   CH   ISSN 0034-5016
Z846.K864
CHINA, REPUBLIC. NATIONAL CENTRAL LIBRARY. NEWSLETTER. 1969. q. free. National Central Library, Bureau of International Exchange of Publications - Kuo Li Chung Yang T'u Shu Kuan, 20 Chung Shan S. Rd., Taipei, Taiwan 10040, Republic of China. FAX 02-311-0155. bibl. **Document type:** newsletter.
    —BLDSC (6021.511320).

026 280   US   ISSN 0412-3131
Z665   CODEN: CHLIDJ
CHRISTIAN LIBRARIAN. 1957. q. $20 (foreign $24). Association of Christian Librarians Inc., Box 4, Cedarville, OH 45314. TEL 513-766-7842. FAX 513-766-2337. Ed. Ron Jordahl. adv.; bk.rev.; illus.; bibl. circ. 450. (back issues avail.; reprint service avail. from UMI) **Indexed:** Child Lit.Abstr., Chr.Per.Ind., Inform.Sci.Abstr., Sci.Abstr. **Document type:** trade publication.
    —BLDSC (3181.831000); UMI.
    Description: Vehicle for Christian interpretation of library science in institutions of higher learning.

020 266 200   UK   ISSN 0309-4170
CHRISTIAN LIBRARIAN. 1976. a. £2. Librarians' Christian Fellowship, c/o Graham Hedges, Ed., 34 Thurlestone Ave., Seven Kings, Ilford, Essex IG3 9DU, England. TEL 081-599-1310. adv.; bk.rev.; abstr. circ. 500. (back issues avail.) **Indexed:** Chr.Per.Ind., Lib.Sci.Abstr. **Document type:** bulletin.
    Description: Articles on librarianship issues written from a Christian perspective.

026   US   ISSN 0009-6342
Z675.C5
CHURCH AND SYNAGOGUE LIBRARIES. 1967. bi-m. $18. Church & Synagogue Library Association, Box 19357, Portland, OR 97280-0357. TEL 503-244-6919. Ed. Sarah Moore. adv.: B&W page $250; trim 8 1/2 x 11. bk.rev.; charts; illus.; index. circ. 3,400. (back issues avail.; reprint service avail. from UMI) **Indexed:** CERDIC, Chr.Per.Ind. **Document type:** newsletter.
    —UMI.
    Formerly: Church and Synagogue Library Association. News Bulletin.
    Description: News articles, announcements, and book reviews pertaining to the members and activities of the association.

020 286   US   ISSN 0884-6197
CHURCH MEDIA LIBRARY MAGAZINE. 1970. q. $13.10. Southern Baptist Convention, Sunday School Board, 127 Ninth Ave., N., Nashville, TN 37234. TEL 800-458-2772. bk.rev./ rec.rev.; bibl.; charts; illus.; index, cum.index. circ. 20,000. **Indexed:** South.Bap.Per.Ind.
    Formerly: Media: Library Services Journal (ISSN 0009-6423); **Supersedes:** Church Library Magazine.

020   BL   ISSN 0100-1965
Z1007
CIENCIA DA INFORMACAO. (Text in Portuguese; summaries in English and Portuguese) 1972. 3/yr. $17.70. Instituto Brasileiro de Informacao em Ciencia e Tecnologia, SAS Quadra 2, Lote 6, Bloco H, 70070-000 Brasilia, D.F., Brazil. TEL 2176161. FAX 2262677. Ed. Noris A. Bethonico Foresti. adv.; bk.rev.; abstr.; bibl.; charts; illus. **Indexed:** Bull.Signal., Inform.Sci.Abstr., Lib.Lit., LISA, P.A.I.S.For.Lang.Ind., P.A.I.S., Ref.Zh.
    —BLDSC (3196.400000).

020   CU   ISSN 0864-4659
Z1007
CIENCIAS DE LA INFORMACION. (Text in Spanish; summaries in English, Spanish) 1968. q. $50 (effective 1994). (Academia de Ciencias de Cuba, Instituto de Documentacion e Informacion Cientifica y Tecnologica) Centro de Estudios y Desarrollo Professional en Ciencias de la Informacion (ProInfo), Apdo. 2035, 10200 Havana, Cuba. TEL 537-62-6501. FAX 537-33-8237. TELEX 028-512321. (Co-sponsor: Sociedad Cubana de Informacion Cientifica y Technica) Ed. Ana E. Maza Varela. adv.: B&W page $760. bk.rev. circ. 500. **Indexed:** LISA.
    —BLDSC (3198.203900); EI; SWETS.
    Formerly (until 1990): Actualidades de la Informacion Cientifica y Tecnica (ISSN 0138-7324)
    Description: Covers information and library systems, technology, economics, and management. Includes classification, indexing, statistical analysis, bibliometrics, research methodology and general theory.

027   US   ISSN 0069-4215
CIRCUM-SPICE. 1965. s-a. free. City College of New York, Library, Convent Ave. & W. 138 St., New York, NY 10031. TEL 212-650-7271. FAX 212-650-7604. Ed. Judy Connorton. circ. 2,000. **Document type:** newsletter.
    Description: Newsletter reporting library news.

020   US
CODE NAMES DICTIONARY. 1963. irreg. $55. Gale Research Inc., 835 Penobscot Bldg., Detroit, MI 48226. TEL 313-961-2242. FAX 313-961-6083. TELEX 810-221-7086. Eds. Frederick G. Ruffner, Robert C. Thomas.

090   AU   ISSN 0379-3621
CODICES MANUSCRIPTI; Zeitschrift fuer Handschriftenkunde. 1975. 4/yr. S.1200. Verlagsbuchhandlung Brueder Hollinek und Co. GmbH, Feldgasse 13, A-1238 Vienna, Austria. TEL 0222-885646. FAX 0222-889364724. Eds. Otto Mazal, Eva Irblich. bk.rev. (reprint service avail. from ISI) **Document type:** academic/scholarly publication.

020   US   ISSN 0738-4319
COGNOTES. q. $5 (free to qualified personnel). America Library Association, New Members Round Table, 50 E. Huron St., Chicago, IL 60611. TEL 312-280-3218. FAX 312-280-3224. Ed. Deb Tuma. adv. contact: Pier A. London. **Document type:** newspaper.
    Description: Daily newspaper published during the ALA annual conference and midwinter meetings.

027.7   CK
COLEGIO MAYOR DE NUESTRA SENORA DEL ROSARIO. BIBLIOTECA. BOLETIN INFORMACION. 1975. m. Colegio Mayor de Nuestra Senora del Rosario, Biblioteca, Calle 14 no. 6-25, Bogota, Colombia.

027   IT   ISSN 0069-5181
COLLANA DI MONOGRAFIE DELLE BIBLIOTECHE D'ITALIA. 1954. irreg., no.8, 1983. price varies. Casa Editrice Leo S. Olschki, Casella Postale 66, 50100 Florence, Italy. TEL 055-6530684. FAX 055-6530214. **Document type:** monographic series.

025.21   US   ISSN 0160-4953
Z689
COLLECTION BUILDING. 1978. 4/yr. $58.50 (Canada $63.50; elsewhere $65.50). Neal-Schuman Publishers, Inc., 100 Varick St., New York, NY 10013. TEL 212-925-8650. FAX 212-219-8916. Ed. Kay Ann Cassell. **Indexed:** Leg.Info.Manage.Ind., Lib.Lit., LISA. **Document type:** trade publication.
    —BLDSC (3310.477400); Faxon; UnCover; SWETS.

LIBRARY AND INFORMATION SCIENCES

020 US ISSN 0146-2679
Z703.6 CODEN: COMADF
COLLECTION MANAGEMENT; a quarterly journal devoted to the management of library collections. 1975. q. $45 to individuals; institutions $120. Haworth Press, Inc., 10 Alice St., Birghamton, NY 13904. TEL 607-722-5857; 800-342-9678. FAX 607-722-1424. Ed. Peter Gellatly. adv.; bk.rev.; abstr. circ. 576. (also avail. in microfiche from HAW; reprint service avail. from HAW) **Indexed:** Behav.Abstr., Bull.Signal., CALL, Ind.Per.Art.Relat.Law, Inform.Sci.Abstr., Leg.Info.Manage.Ind., LHTN, Lib.Lit., LISA, Ref.Zh. **Document type:** trade publication.
—BLDSC (3310.588500); Faxon; UnCover; SWETS.
Formerly (until 1978): De-Acquisitions Librarian (ISSN 0098-2121)
Description: Focuses on all aspects of collection management and development that affect college, university, and research libraries of all types.
Refereed Serial

027.7 026 US ISSN 0010-0870
Z671 CODEN: CRLIAI
COLLEGE & RESEARCH LIBRARIES. Short title: C R L (Supplement avail.: C & R L News) 1939. bi-m. $50 (Canada, Spain and other PUAS countries $55; elsewhere $60). (Association of College and Research Libraries) American Library Association, 50 E. Huron St., Chicago, IL 60611-2795. TEL 312-944-6780. FAX 312-440-9374. Ed. Gloriana St. Clair. adv.; bk.rev.; charts; index, cum.index every 5 yrs. circ. 13,000. (also avail. in microfilm from UMI; back issues avail.; reprint service avail. from UMI,KTO) **Indexed:** Amer.Bibl.Slavic & E.Eur.Stud., Amer.Hist.& Life, Bk.Rev.Dig., Bk.Rev.Ind. (1965-), C.I.J.E., Chem.Abstr., Child.Bk.Rev.Ind. (1965-), Cont.Pg.Educ., Curr.Bk.Rev.Cit., Curr.Cont., Educ.Ind., High.Educ.Curr.Aware.Bull., Hist.Abstr., Inform.Sci.Abstr., Lib.Lit., Lib.Sci.Abstr., LISA, P.A.I.S., Pers.Lit., Ref.Sour., Sci.Cit.Ind., SSCI. **Document type:** academic/scholarly publication, trade publication.
—BLDSC (3311.000000); Faxon; UnCover; SWETS; UMI; CASDDS. **CCC.**
Description: Articles of interest to college and research libraries.

027.7 US ISSN 0099-0086
Z671 CODEN: CRLND2
COLLEGE & RESEARCH LIBRARIES NEWS. (Supplement to: College & Research Libraries) 1966. m. (11/yr.). $25 in US, Canada, Mexico; Spain $30; elsewhere $35. (Association of College and Research Libraries) American Library Association, 50 E. Huron St., Chicago, IL 60611-2795. TEL 800-545-2433. FAX 312-280-2520. Ed. Mary Ellen Kyger Davis. adv. circ. 10,500. (back issues avail.; reprint service avail. from UMI) **Indexed:** Art & Archaeol.Tech.Abstr., C.I.J.E., Curr.Cont., Inform.Sci.Abstr., LHTN, Lib.Lit, LISA, Sci.Cit.Ind. **Document type:** academic/scholarly publication, trade publication.
—BLDSC (3311.008000); Faxon; UnCover; SWETS; UMI; CASDDS. **CCC.**

020 US
▼**COLLEGE & UNDERGRADUATE LIBRARIES**. 1994. q. Haworth Press, Inc., 10 Alice St., Binghamton, NY 13904. TEL 800-342-9678. FAX 607-722-1424. Ed. Alice Harrison Bahr. adv.: page $300. bk.rev. (also avail. in microfiche)
Description: Deals with all aspects of practice for the four-year college library, as well as undergraduate libraries housed in larger university settings.
Refereed Serial

COLLEGE CATALOG COLLECTION ON MICROFICHE. see *EDUCATION*

020 US
Z732.C6
COLORADO EDUCATION & LIBRARY DIRECTORY. a. $15. Department of Education, Communications Center, 201 E. Colfax Ave., Denver, CO 80203. TEL 303-866-6937. FAX 303-866-6938. adv. circ. 8,000. **Document type:** directory.
Formed by the 1990 merger of: Directory of Colorado Libraries (ISSN 0094-8403) & Colorado Education Directory.
Description: Lists the Dept. of Ed. offices, school districts, and libraries throughout the state.

020 US ISSN 0147-9733
COLORADO LIBRARIES. 1975. q. $25 to non-members; foreign $35. Colorado Library Association, Box 489, Pinecliffe, CO 80471-0489. TEL 303-642-0203. FAX 303-642-0201. Ed. Nancy Carter. adv.; bk.rev.; bibl.; stat. circ. 1,000. (also avail. in microfiche; back issues avail.) **Indexed:** Lib.Lit.
—BLDSC (3321.550000); UnCover.

020 US ISSN 0084-8905
COLORADO STATE UNIVERSITY LIBRARIES. PUBLICATION. 1966. irreg. no.22, 1979. free. Colorado State University, University Library, Fort Collins, CO 80523. TEL 303-491-5911. circ. 300.

021.7 US ISSN 0010-1966
Z671
COLUMBIA LIBRARY COLUMNS. 1951. 3/yr. $12. (Friends of Columbia Libraries, Butler Library) Columbia University Libraries, New York, NY 10027. TEL 212-854-2231. FAX 212-222-0331. Ed. Rudolph Ellenbogen. illus. circ. 800. **Indexed:** Lib.Lit., M.L.A. **Document type:** bibliography.
—UnCover.

020 US ISSN 0192-5881
PN6700
COMIC ART COLLECTION. 1979. q. exchange basis. (Russel B. Nye Popular Culture Collection) Michigan State University Libraries, Special Collections Division, East Lansing, MI 48824-1048. TEL 517-355-3770. Ed. Randall W. Scott. circ. 400. (back issues avail.)
Description: Newsletter to facilitate communication about holdings at the Michigan State University Library and about public-comics collecting in general, with inventories.

025 US
COMMISSION ON PRESERVATION AND ACCESS ANNUAL REPORT. 1988. a. free. Commission on Preservation & Access, 1400 16th St., N.W., Ste. 740, Washington, DC 20036-2217. TEL 202-939-3400. FAX 202-939-3407. Ed. Maxine Sitts. circ. 2,500 (controlled). (back issues avail.) **Document type:** corporate report.

025 US ISSN 1045-1919
Z700.9
COMMISSION ON PRESERVATION AND ACCESS NEWSLETTER; providing access to the accumulated human record as far into the future as possible. 1988. m. free. Commission on Preservation and Access, 1400 16th St., N.W., Ste. 740, Washington, DC 20036-2217. TEL 202-939-3400. FAX 202-939-3407. Ed. Sonny Koerner. circ. 2,500 (controlled). **Document type:** newsletter.
Description: Twenty-year Brittle Book Program for the preservation of books and information in all forms.

026 959 US ISSN 1067-0580
Z3001
COMMITTEE ON EAST ASIAN LIBRARIES DIRECTORY. irreg. $10 per no. Association for Asian Studies, Inc., Committee on East Asian Libraries, c/o Maureen H. Donovan, Main Library, Rm.310, Ohio State University Libraries, 1858 Neil Ave. Mall, Columbus, OH 43210-1286. TEL 614-292-3502. FAX 614-292-7859. **Document type:** directory.
Former titles: C E A L Directory; Directory of East Asian Collections in North American Libraries (ISSN 0148-0065)

020 US
COMMUNICATOR (LOS ANGELES). irreg. $10 to non-members. The Librarians' Guild, AFSCME Local 2626, Box 71568, Los Angeles, CA 90071. Ed. Helene Mochedlover.

027.7 US ISSN 0276-3915
Z675.J8 CODEN: CJCLDV
COMMUNITY & JUNIOR COLLEGE LIBRARIES; the journal for learning resources centers. 1982. s-a. $34 to individuals; institutions $60. Haworth Press, Inc., 10 Alice St., Binghamton, NY 13904. TEL 607-722-5857; 800-342-9678. FAX 607-722-1424. Ed. Kathy Rutz. adv.; bk.rev. circ. 449. (also avail. in microfiche from HAW; reprint service avail. from HAW) **Indexed:** C.I.J.E., Excerp.Med., Lib.Lit., LISA, Ref.Zh., Sci.Abstr.
—BLDSC (3363.588200); Faxon; UnCover.
Description: Presents current profiles of LRCs around the country, news of special relevance, such as legislation, systems and development, and pertinent reviews.
Refereed Serial

020 025 II
CONCEPTS IN COMMUNICATION INFORMATICS AND LIBRARIANSHIP. (Text in English) 1988. irreg. (approx. 4-5/yr.). price varies. Concept Publishing Company, A 15-16, Commercial Block, Mohan Garden, New Delhi 110 059, India. TEL 11-5554-042. Ed. Shri S.P. Agrawal. bibl.; stat.; index. **Document type:** monographic series.
Description: Covers communication, information technology, and librarianship for academics and professionals in related fields. Includes computer applications.

347 SI
CONFERENCE OF SOUTHEAST ASIAN LIBRARIANS. PROCEEDINGS. 1970. irreg. price varies. Chopmen Publishers, Katong Shopping Centre, Mountbatten Rd., No. 05-28, Singapore 1543, Singapore. TEL 3441495. FAX 340180. **Document type:** proceedings.

020 US ISSN 0010-5821
Z881
CONGREGATIONAL LIBRARY. BULLETIN. 1949. 3/yr. $5. (American Congregational Association) Congregational Library, 14 Beacon St., Boston, MA 02108. TEL 617-523-0470. FAX 617-523-0491. Ed. Harold F. Worthley. bk.rev.; bibl.; illus. circ. 1,000. **Document type:** bulletin.
—UMI.

021 US ISSN 0010-616X
CONNECTICUT LIBRARIES. 1958. 11/yr. $35 (foreign $40). Connecticut Library Association, Inc., 638 Prospect Ave., Hartford, CT 06105. TEL 203-232-4825. FAX 203-232-0819. Ed. David L. Kapp. circ. controlled. (also avail. in microform from UMI; reprint service avail. from UMI)
—UMI.
Formerly: C L A News and Views.
Description: News items and feature articles relating to Connecticut libraries and librarians.

020 US ISSN 0192-2912
CONSERVATION ADMINISTRATION NEWS; library and archival preservation. 1979. q. $30. University of Texas at Austin, Graduate School of Library and Information Science, Preservation and Conservation Studies, EDB 564, Austin, TX 78712-1276. TEL 512-471-8289. FAX 512-471-8285. Eds. Paul Barks, Roberta Austin. adv.; bk.rev.; bibl. circ. 648. (also avail. in microfiche; back issues avail.) **Indexed:** Art & Archaeol.Tech.Abstr., Biodet.Abstr., Graph.Arts Lit.Abstr., LHTN, Lib.Lit., LISA. **Document type:** trade publication.
—BLDSC (3417.960000); Faxon.

CONTINUO. see *MUSIC*

029.7 US ISSN 0084-9243
CONTRIBUTIONS IN LIBRARIANSHIP AND INFORMATION SCIENCE. 1972. irreg., no.72, 1992. price varies. Greenwood Press, Inc. (Subsidiary of: Greenwood Publishing Group Inc.), 88 Post Rd. W., Box 5007, Westport, CT 06881-5007. TEL 203-226-3571. FAX 203-222-1502. Ed. Paul Wasserman. **Document type:** academic/scholarly publication, trade publication.
—BLDSC (3458.890000).

027 US ISSN 1041-343X
CORN BELT LIBRARY SYSTEM. SUM AND SUBSTANCE.* 1967. m. free. Corn Belt Library System, Box 1744, Bloomington, IL 61702-1744. Ed.Bd. bk.rev. circ. 550. (processed) **Document type:** newsletter.
Description: For the Corn Belt Library System members and interested individuals and organizations. Provides information and stories of interest which relate to CBLS and its members.

020 CN ISSN 0843-140X
CORPO CLIP. 1975. 5/yr. Can.$6. Corporation des Bibliotecaires Professionnels du Quebec - Corporation of Professional Librarians of Quebec, 307 Ste-Catherine W., Ste. 320, Montreal, PQ H2X 2A3, Canada. TEL 514-845-3327. FAX 514-845-1618. Ed. Josee Saint-Marseille. circ. 1,000. (also avail. in microfiche from BNQ; back issues avail.)
Formerly: Bulletin Argus.
Description: News about events in the field and information about the Corporation.

LIBRARY AND INFORMATION SCIENCES

020 US ISSN 1061-5288
▼**CORPORATE LIBRARY UPDATE**; news for information managers and special librarians. 1992. s-m. $69 (foreign $76). Cahners Publishing Company (New York), Printing and Publishing Division, Division of Reed Elsevier Inc., 249 W. 17th St., New York, NY 10011. TEL 212-645-0067. (Subscr. to: Box 718, Brewster, NY 10509-0718. TEL 800-722-2346) Ed. Susan DiMattia. (looseleaf format) **Document type:** trade publication.
—CCC.
Description: Covers library and information technology and trends for corporate and specialized libraries.

020 US ISSN 0196-8238
COTTONBOLL. 1979. q. Public Library Service, 6030 Monticello Dr., Montgomery, AL 36130. TEL 205-277-7330. Ed. Julie Hare. circ. 400.

020 CN ISSN 0829-7142
COUNCIL OF NOVA SCOTIA ARCHIVES NEWSLETTER. 1981. s-a. Can.$25. Council of Nova Scotia Archives, Public Archives of Nova Scotia, 6016 University Ave., Halifax, NS B3H 1W4, Canada. TEL 902-424-6070. FAX 902-424-0628. Ed. Margaret McBride. bk.rev. circ. 200. **Document type:** newsletter.

020 US
COUNCIL ON LIBRARY - MEDIA TECHNICAL ASSISTANTS. NEWSLETTER.* 1968. m. membership. Council on Library - Media Technical Assistants, c/o Margaret Barron, Cuyahoga Community College, 2900 Community College Ave., Cleveland, OH 44115. TEL 216-987-4621. Ed. Shirley Daniels. illus. circ. 600. **Document type:** newsletter.
Formerly: Council of Library Technology. Newsletter (ISSN 0010-9983)

025 US
COUNCIL ON LIBRARY RESOURCES ANNUAL REPORT. 1957. a. free. Council on Library Resources, Inc., 1400 16th St., N.W., Ste. 510, Washington, DC 20036. TEL 202-483-7474. FAX 202-483-6410. circ. 4,000. (also avail. in microform from EDR) **Indexed:** ERIC. **Document type:** corporate report.
—BLDSC (1157.980000).
Formerly: Council on Library Resources Report (ISSN 0070-1181)

COUNTY LAW LIBRARY PROGRAM BULLETIN. see LAW

020 US ISSN 0300-7561
Z673.M393
CRAB. 1971. q. $15. Maryland Library Association, 400 Cathedral St., 3rd Fl., Baltimore, MD 21201. TEL 301-727-7422. Eds. Kathleen Reif, Lynne Degen. adv.; bk.rev. circ. 1,300. (also avail. in microform from UMI; reprint service avail. from UMI) **Indexed:** Lib.Lit.
—UMI.
Supersedes: Maryland Libraries.
Description: Covers issues, information and personalities of interest to Maryland librarians.

020 800 XR ISSN 0011-2321
CTENAR; mesicnik pro praci s knihou. (Supplement avail.: Knihovnictvi a Bibliografie) (Text in Czech; contents page also in English, German and Russian) vol.19, 1967. m. 42 Kcs.($36) (Ministerstvo Kultury Ceske Republiky) Panorama, Halkova ul. 1, 120 72 Prague 2, Czech Republic. (Dist. by: Artia, Ve Smeckach 30, 111 27 Prague 1, Czech Republic) Ed. Vladimir Voznicka. bk.rev.; film rev.; bibl.; charts; illus. circ. 7,300. **Indexed:** Lib.Sci.Abstr.
—BLDSC (3490.503000).

020 UK
CURRENT AWARENESS ABSTRACTS; a review of information management literature. 1973. 10/yr. £90($160) to non-members; members £80. Aslib, Association for Information Management, Publications Department, Information House, 20-24 Old St., London EC1V 9AP, England. TEL 071-253-4488. FAX 071-430-0514. (Dist. in N. America by: Learned Information, Inc., 143 Old Marlton Pike, Medford, NJ 08055-8750. TEL 609-654-6266) Ed. Monty Hyams. adv.; bibl. circ. 700. **Indexed:** Print.Abstr. **Document type:** abstracting/indexing.
Formerly (until 1992): Current Awareness Bulletin (ISSN 0265-9271)
Description: Abstracts of professional literature in the library and information fields.

020 UK ISSN 0263-9254
Z669.7
CURRENT RESEARCH IN LIBRARY & INFORMATION SCIENCE. 1974. q. £125($255) Bowker - Saur Ltd., A Reed Reference Publishing Company, Part of the Reed Elsevier group, Maypole House, Maypole Rd., E. Grinstead, W. Sussex RH19 1HH, England. TEL 0342-330-100. FAX 0342-330-191. (Subscr. to: c/o Butterworths Service Co., Borough Green, Sevenoaks, Kent TN15 8PH, England. TEL 0732-884567) Ed. N. L. Moore. adv.; index. (also avail. in magnetic tape) **Document type:** abstracting/indexing.
●Also available online. Vendor(s): BRS Online Products (LISA), DIALOG Information Services, Inc. (File no.61).
Also available on CD-ROM. Producer(s): Bowker - Saur Ltd.
—BLDSC (3501.963000).
Formerly: R A D I A L S Bulletin (ISSN 0302-2706)
Description: Covers current research in library and information science and related subjects.

025 US ISSN 0742-8227
CURRENT STUDIES IN LIBRARIANSHIP. 1977. irreg. (1-2/yr.). $10. Clarion University, Department of Library Science, Clarion, PA 16214. TEL 814-226-2314. FAX 814-226-2150. Ed. Rashelle S. Karp. circ. 600. **Indexed:** Lib.Lit., LISA. **Document type:** academic/scholarly publication.
—BLDSC (3504.043100).

010 AT
CURTIN UNIVERSITY OF TECHNOLOGY. LIBRARY. MONOGRAPH FICHE CATALOGUE. 1980. q. Aus.$138. Curtin University of Technology, Library, Kent St., Bentley, W.A. 6102, Australia. (microfiche) **Document type:** catalog.
Formerly: Western Australian Institute of Technology. Library. Monograph Fiche Catalogue.

020 AT
CURTIN UNIVERSITY OF TECHNOLOGY. LIBRARY. WESTERN LIBRARY STUDIES. 1983. irreg. price varies. Curtin University of Technology, Library, Kent St., Bentley, W.A. 6102, Australia. **Document type:** monographic series.
—BLDSC (9300.910000).
Formerly: Western Australian Institute of Technology. Library. Western Library Studies (ISSN 0810-5030)

021 UK ISSN 0011-4421
CYLCHGRAWN LLYFRGELL GENEDLAETHOL CYMRU/NATIONAL LIBRARY OF WALES JOURNAL. (Text in English, Welsh) 1939. s-a. £8. National Library of Wales, Aberystwyth, Dyfed SY23 3BU, Wales. Ed. Lionel Madden. charts; illus. circ. 500. **Indexed:** Amer.Hist.& Life, Br.Archaeol.Abstr., Br.Hum.Ind., Hist.Abstr., M.L.A., RILA. **Document type:** trade publication.
—BLDSC (6026.640000).

020 340 US
Z675.L2A25
D A L L ADVANCE SHEET. m. $10. Dallas Association of Law Librarians, Box 50545, Dallas, TX 75250. TEL 214-744-3700. Ed. Katherine Foster. bk.rev. circ. 250. **Document type:** newsletter.
Formerly: Advance Sheet.

020 GW ISSN 0175-6893
D B I - PRESSESPIEGEL. 1981. m. DM.36. Deutsches Bibliotheksinstitut, Abt. 1 - Publikationen, Bundesallee 184-185, 10717 Berlin, Germany. TEL 030-8505-0. FAX 030-8505-100. circ. 300. **Document type:** bulletin.

020 II ISSN 0971-4383
D E S I D O C BULLETIN OF INFORMATION TECHNOLOGY. 1980. bi-m. (Ministry of Defence, Defence Scientific Information & Documentation Centre) Defence Research & Development Organization, Metcalfe House, Delhi-110 054, India. FAX 011-2919151. TELEX 031-78030. Ed. S.S. Murthy. bk.rev.; abstr. circ. 1,000. **Document type:** government publication, bulletin.
Formerly (until 1990): D E S I D O C Bulletin.
Description: Covers the latest developments in different fields of information science, and activities of D R D O information centres.

029 GW ISSN 0344-5372
D G D SCHRIFTENREIHE. irreg., no.9, 1990. DM.248. (Deutsche Gesellschaft fuer Dokumentation e.V.) K.G. Saur Verlag KG, A Reed Reference Publishing Company, Part of the Reed Elsevier group, Ortlerstr. 8, 81373 Munich, Germany. TEL 089-76902-0. FAX 089-76902150. TELEX 5212067-SAUR-D. (Subscr. to: Postfach 701620, 81316 Munich, Germany) **Document type:** monographic series.

020 SW ISSN 0281-6873
D I K - FORUM; facklig tidskrift foer anstaellda inom dokumentation, information och kultur. 1973. 20/yr. SEK 325 (effective 1994). D I K - Forum, P.O. Box 760, S-131 24 Nacka, Sweden. Ed. Karin Almegaard. **Document type:** trade publication.

020 410 US
D S N A NEWSLETTER. 1977. 2/yr. $6. Dictionary Society of North America, Cleveland State University, RT-967, 1983 E. 24th St., Cleveland, OH 44115. TEL 216-687-4830. FAX 216-687-9366. Ed. Louis T. Milic. adv.; bk.rev.; bibl. circ. 600. (tabloid format; back issues avail.) **Document type:** newsletter.
Description: Information on dictionaries and other word reference books.

020 US
DAILY DEPOSITORY SHIPPING LIST. d. (weekdays only). $297 (foreign $371.25). U.S. Government Printing Office, Library Programs Service, Washington, DC 20402. (Subscr. to: Superintendent of Documents, U.S. Government Printing Office, Box 371954, Pittsburgh, PA 15250-7954. TEL 202-783-3238. FAX 202-512-2233) **Document type:** bibliography, government publication.
Description: Lists all the publications mailed each day to depository libraries.

020 CN
DALHOUSIE UNIVERSITY. SCHOOL OF LIBRARY AND INFORMATION STUDIES. NEWSLETTER. 1971. a. Dalhousie University, School of Library and Information Studies, Halifax, NS B3H 4H8, Canada. TEL 902-494-3656. FAX 902-494-2451. TELEX 019-21863. Ed. Mary Dykstra. circ. 1,000. **Document type:** newsletter.
Formerly: Dalhousie University. School of Library Service. Newsletter (ISSN 0315-0054)

020 CN
DALHOUSIE UNIVERSITY. SCHOOL OF LIBRARY AND INFORMATION STUDIES. OCCASIONAL PAPERS. irreg. price varies. Dalhousie University, School of Library and Information Studies, Halifax, NS B3H 4H8, Canada. TEL 902-494-3656. FAX 902-494-2451. TELEX 019-21863. Ed. Mary Dykstra. **Indexed:** LISA. **Document type:** academic/scholarly publication, bibliography, directory.
Former titles: Dalhousie University. University Libraries and School of Library Service. Occasional Papers; Dalhousie University. School of Library Service. Occasional Papers (ISSN 0318-7403)
Description: Forum for the dissemination of refereed scholarly papers, bibliographies, checklists and symposia proceedings on topics of interest to librarians and other information professionals.
Refereed Serial

020 CN
DALHOUSIE UNIVERSITY. SCHOOL OF LIBRARY AND INFORMATION STUDIES. Y-A HOTLINE; an alert to matters concerning young adults. 1977. irreg. Can.$10($12) for 4 nos. Dalhousie University, School of Library and Information Studies, Halifax, NS B3H 4H8, Canada. TEL 902-494-3656. FAX 902-494-2451. TELEX 019-21863. Ed. L.J. Amey. bk.rev. circ. 310.
Formerly: Dalhousie University. School of Library Service. Y-A Hotline (ISSN 0701-8894)
Description: Devoted to library services for junior and senior high school-aged youth in schools, public libraries and institutions.

029.7 CC
DANG'AN XUE YANJIU. (Text in Chinese) q. Zhongguo Dang'an Xuehui, 21, Fengsheng Hutong, Beijing 100032, People's Republic of China. TEL 6013970. Ed. Pei Tong.

LIBRARY AND INFORMATION SCIENCES

025.171 900   CC   ISSN 1001-201X
DANG'ANXUE TONGXUN/ARCHIVES SCIENCE BULLETIN. (Text in Chinese; table of contents in English) 1978. bi-m. $6. Zhongguo Renmin Daxue - People's University of China, 3, Zhang Zizhong Lu, Beijing 100007, People's Republic of China. TEL 4035109. (Subscr. to: China International Book Trading Corporation, 21 Chegongzhuang Xilu, P.O. Box 399, Beijing, P.R. China. TEL 8413063. FAX 8412023) Ed. Chen Zhaowu. bk.rev. circ. 27,000. **Document type:** academic/scholarly publication.
—BLDSC (1641.700000).
    Description: Covers the theory and practice of archives science.

DANMARKS BIBLIOTEKSSKOLE. BIBLIOTEKET. D B I ACCESSION. see *BIBLIOGRAPHIES*

020   DK   ISSN 0069-9861
DANMARKS BIBLIOTEKSSKOLE. SKRIFTER. 1965. a. price varies. Danmarks Biblioteksskole, 6 Birketinget, 2300 Copenhagen S, Denmark. FAX 45-32-84-02-01. bk.rev.

020   DK   ISSN 0900-4645
DANMARKS TEKNISKE BIBLIOTEK. KATALOG. a. DKK 50 (foreign DKK 250). Danmarks Tekniske Bibliotek, Anker Engelunds Vej 1, DK-2800 Lungby, Denmark. **Document type:** catalog.
● Available only online.

027.7   US   ISSN 0011-6750
DARTMOUTH COLLEGE LIBRARY BULLETIN. N.S. 1957. s-a. free to educational institutions & other libraries. Dartmouth College, Library, Hanover, NH 03755. TEL 603-646-2235. Ed.Bd. charts; illus.; index every 3 yrs. circ. 1,000. (also avail. in microfilm) **Indexed:** Lib.Lit. **Document type:** academic/scholarly publication, bulletin.
—Faxon; UnCover.

020   CC
DAXUE TUSHUGUAN XUEBAO/JOURNAL OF UNIVERSITY LIBRARIES. (Text in Chinese) bi-m. Quanguo Gaodeng Xuexiao Tushu Qingbao Gongzuo Weiyuanhui - National Committee on Higher Education Institution Library Affairs, Beijing Daxue, Hadian, Beijing 100871, People's Republic of China. TEL 2561166. Ed. Li Xiaoming.

020   US   ISSN 0011-7773
DELAWARE LIBRARY ASSOCIATION BULLETIN.* 1947. 3/yr. $25 includes membership. Delaware Library Association, Box 816, Dover, DE 19903-0816. adv.; bk.rev. circ. 650.

027.5489   DK   ISSN 0069-9896
Z941
DENMARK. KONGELIGE BIBLIOTEK. FUND OG FORSKNING. Key Title: Fund og Forskning i Det Kongelige Biblioteks samlinger. Cover title: Fund og Forskning. (Text in Danish; summaries in English) 1954. a. price varies. Kongelige Bibliotek, Christians Brygge 8, DK-1219 Copenhagen K, Denmark. cum.index: 1954-73. **Document type:** government publication, academic/scholarly publication.
    Description: Findings and research in the collections of the Royal Library.

020   DK   ISSN 0905-555X
DENMARK. STATENS BIBLIOTEKSTJENESTE. RETNINGSLINIER. 1987. irreg. free. Statens Bibliotekstjeneste, Nyhavn 31 E, DK-1051 Copenhagen K, Denmark. TEL 45-33-93-46-93. FAX 45-33-93-60-93. **Document type:** government publication.
    Formerly (until 1988): Rigsbibliotekarembedet. Retningslinier (ISSN 0903-8302)

020   US   ISSN 0011-9156
DES MOINES. PUBLIC LIBRARY. MONTHLY MEMO; current business materials available at the Public Library of Des Moines. 1955. m. free. Public Library of Des Moines, 100 Locust St., Des Moines, IA 50309. TEL 515-283-4152. FAX 515-283-4503. Dir. Elaine G. Estes. bk.rev.; illus.; circ. 1,000 (controlled). (looseleaf format) **Document type:** bibliography.

020   UY   ISSN 0797-6402
Z907
▼**DESLINDES.** 1992. bi-m. (Biblioteca Nacional de Uruguay) Impresora Cordon, Uruguay 1573, Montevideo, Uruguay. **Document type:** academic/scholarly publication.

025.4   US   ISSN 0191-3646
Z696.D5
DEWEY DECIMAL CLASSIFICATION ADDITIONS, NOTES AND DECISIONS. 1959. a. free to qualified personnel. (Online Computer Library Center, Inc.) Forest Press, 85 Watervliet Ave., Albany, NY 12206. TEL 518-489-8549. FAX 518-489-7804. **Document type:** bulletin.
    Formerly: Decimal Classification Additions, Notes and Decisions (ISSN 0083-1573)

020 410   US   ISSN 0197-6745
P327   CODEN: DICTEQ
DICTIONARIES. (Text in English, French) 1979. a. $20 (foreign $25). Dictionary Society of North America, Cleveland State University, RT-936, 1983 E. 24th St., Cleveland, OH 44115. TEL 216-687-4830. FAX 216-687-9366. Ed. William S. Chisholm; Pub. Louis T. Milie. bk.rev. circ. 500. (back issues avail.) **Indexed:** Bibl.Ling. **Document type:** academic/scholarly publication, monographic series.
—BLDSC (3580.285000).
    Description: Dictionary making, collection, use; dissemination of information and ideas on lexicography to editors, scholars and users.

020   US   ISSN 0363-5414
Z711.92.P5
DIKTA. 1976. s-a. $8. Southern Conference of Librarians for the Blind and Physically Handicapped, 420 Platt St., Daytona Beach, FL 32114-2804. TEL 904-239-6050. FAX 904-239-6069. (Subscr. to: c/o Joyce Smith, Box 443, Huntsville, AL 35804) Ed. Michael Gunde. bk.rev.; illus.; index. circ. 200. (back issues avail.)
—BLDSC (3588.397950).

020   US   ISSN 0899-5877
DIRECTIONS FOR UTAH LIBRARIES. 1959. m. (except June-July, Nov.-Dec., combined) free to qualified personnel. Department of Community and Economic Development, State Library Division, 2150 S. 300 W., Ste. 16, Salt Lake City, UT 84115. TEL 801-466-5888. FAX 801-533-4657. Ed. Chip Ward. bk.rev.; circ. 2,000 (controlled). (processed) **Document type:** government publication, newsletter.
    Formerly (until vol.23, no.6, 1988): Horsefeathers (ISSN 0018-5205)
    Description: Focuses on statewide library service developments, news, and issues. Includes calender of events.

020   SP
DIRECTORIO DE ESPECIALISTAS IBEROAMERICANOS EN INFORMACION Y DOCUMENTACION/DIRECTORIO DE ESPECIALISTAS IBERO-AMERICANOS EM INFORMACAO E DOCUMENTACAO; area educacion - area educacao. (Text in Portuguese, Spanish) 1989. biennial. 2500 ptas.($25) Organizacion de Estados IberoAmericanos para la Educacion, la Ciencia y la Cultura (OEI), C. Bravo Murillo 38a, 28015 Madrid, Spain. TEL 594-43-82. FAX 594-32-86. **Document type:** directory.
    Description: Lists education specialists in order to set up collaboration between schools and between specialists

027.7   AT
Z870.A1
DIRECTORY OF AUSTRALIAN ACADEMIC AND RESEARCH LIBRARIES. 1978. irreg. (approx. 3/yr.). Aus.$44. Auslib Press, P.O. Box 622, Blackwood, S.A. 5051, Australia. TEL 08-2784363. FAX 08-278-4000. TELEX AA88420. Ed. Alan and Judith Bundy. adv. circ. 1,200. **Document type:** directory.
    Formerly (until 1989): Directory of Australian Academic Libraries (ISSN 0155-1027)

020   AT   ISSN 0729-4271
Z870.A1
DIRECTORY OF AUSTRALIAN PUBLIC LIBRARIES. 1982. irreg. (every 2-3 yrs.). Aus.$44. Auslib Press, P.O. Box 622, Blackwood, S.A. 5051, Australia. TEL 08-278-4363. FAX 08-370-4000. Eds. Alan and Judith Bundy. circ. 1,000. **Indexed:** LISA. **Document type:** directory.
    Description: Comprehensive directory of Australian public lending libraries and state reference libraries.

DIRECTORY OF CANADIAN MAP COLLECTIONS. see *GEOGRAPHY*

023   US
DIRECTORY OF CHINESE AMERICAN LIBRARIANS. (Text in Chinese, English) 1977. irreg. latest ed., 1986. $6. Chinese Culture Service, Box 444, Oak Park, IL 60303. TEL 708-848-2235. FAX 708-848-2218. Ed. Tze-chung Li. circ. 500. **Document type:** directory.

027   US   ISSN 0070-5276
DIRECTORY OF COLLEGE AND UNIVERSITY LIBRARIES IN NEW YORK STATE. 1965. irreg. free to libraries in New York State; libraries elsewhere on exchange basis. New York State Library, Library Development, Albany, NY 12230. circ. 1,000. **Document type:** academic/scholarly publication.

380 027.4   US
DIRECTORY OF CONNECTICUT LIBRARIES AND MEDIA CENTERS. 1980. a. $69.95. L D A Publishers, 42-36 209 St., Bayside, NY 11361-2747. TEL 718-224-9484. FAX 718-224-9487. adv. circ. 1,000. **Document type:** directory.
    Former titles (until 1991): Directory of Connecticut Libraries and Media Centers Including Finding; Directory of Connecticut Libraries and Media Centers and Buyers' Guide (ISSN 0748-2574)
    Description: Lists academic, special, public and school libraries and media centers by geographic region and CLSU with extensive indexing. Includes library associations and CLSU information and membership.

DIRECTORY OF GAY AND LESBIAN LIBRARY WORKERS. see *HOMOSEXUALITY*

020   US   ISSN 0276-959X
Z1223.Z7
DIRECTORY OF GOVERNMENT DOCUMENT COLLECTIONS AND LIBRARIANS. 1974. triennial. $57.50. Congressional Information Service, A Reed Reference Publishing Company, Part of the Reed Elsevier group, 4520 East-West Hwy., Bethesda, MD 20814. TEL 301-654-1550; 800-638-8380. FAX 301-654-4033. Ed. Judy Horn. circ. 1,500. **Document type:** directory.
    Description: Guide to federal, state, local, foreign and international documents collections in US, including collection specialties and contact names.

020   US   ISSN 1051-9416
Z672
DIRECTORY OF INTERNATIONAL LIBRARY EDUCATION EXPERIENCE. 1990. a.? American Library Association, 50 E. Huron St., Chicago, IL 60611. (Co-sponsor: International Library Education Subcommittee) **Document type:** directory.

027   US
DIRECTORY OF LIBRARIES AND LIBRARY SYSTEMS IN THE SOUTH CENTRAL RESEARCH LIBRARY COUNCIL REGION. 1969. a. $25. South Central Research Library Council, DeWitt Bldg., 215 N. Cayuga St., Ithaca, NY 14850. TEL 607-273-9106. FAX 607-272-0740. Ed. Janet E. Steiner. circ. 1,100. **Document type:** directory.
    Former titles: Directory of Libraries and Library Resources in the South Central Research Library Council Region; South Central Research Library Council. Library Directory (ISSN 0081-2722)
    Description: Information on all types of libraries in a fourteen county region.

020   CN
DIRECTORY OF LIBRARIES IN CANADA. a. Can.$150. Micromedia Ltd., 20 Victoria St., Toronto, ON M5C 2N8, Canada. TEL 416-362-5211. FAX 416-362-6161. Ed. Lynn Fraser. (also avail. in microform) **Document type:** directory.
    Formerly (until 1991): Canadian Library Yearbook (ISSN 0827-3715); **Supersedes:** Canadian Library Handbook (ISSN 0707-9680)

021   CN   ISSN 0317-8536
Z735.M3
DIRECTORY OF LIBRARIES IN MANITOBA. 1973. irreg. Public Library Services, 1525 1st St., Unit 200, Brandon, MB R7A 7A1, Canada. TEL 204-726-6590. FAX 204-726-6868. **Document type:** directory.

LIBRARY AND INFORMATION SCIENCES

020   US
DIRECTORY OF LIBRARY & INFORMATION PROFESSIONALS. 1988. irreg. $365. Gale Research Inc., 835 Penobscot Bldg., Detroit, MI 48226. TEL 800-223-4153. FAX 313-961-6815. TELEX 810-221-7086. **Document type:** directory.
 Description: Lists over 43,000 library and information specialists currently working in North America.

027   US
DIRECTORY OF LIBRARY SYSTEMS IN NEW YORK STATE. 1976. a. $8 (one copy free to libraries in New York State). New York State Library, Library Development, Albany, NY 12230. (Co-sponsor: New York State Education Department) circ. 1,250. **Document type:** directory.
 Formed by the merger of (1960-1975): Directory of New York State Public Library Systems (ISSN 0070-5950); (1967-1975): Directory of Reference and Research Library Resource Systems in New York State (ISSN 0070-6183)

027   US   ISSN 0070-5810
Z675.M4
DIRECTORY OF MEDICAL LIBRARIES IN NEW YORK STATE. 1967. irreg. 8th ed., 1985. free to libraries in New York State; libraries elsewhere on exchange basis. New York State Library, Library Development, Albany, NY 12230. FAX 518-474-5786. circ. 800. **Document type:** directory.

027   US   ISSN 0092-4067
Z732.M82
DIRECTORY OF MISSOURI LIBRARIES; public, college, university & special libraries. 1965. a. free. State Library, Box 387, Jefferson City, MO 65102. TEL 314-751-3615. FAX 314-751-3612. stat. circ. 750. (reprint service avail. from UMI) **Indexed:** SRI. **Document type:** directory.
 Description: Statistics and information about Missouri libraries.

026   GH
DIRECTORY OF RESEARCH AND SPECIAL LIBRARIES IN GHANA. 1974. irreg. Council for Scientific and Industrial Research, Box M32, Accra, Ghana. Ed. L. Agyei-Gyane. circ. 500. **Document type:** directory.
 Formerly: Directory of Special Libraries in Ghana.

DIRECTORY OF RESEARCH INSTITUTES IN ISRAEL. see SCIENCES: COMPREHENSIVE WORKS

026   TH   ISSN 0858-1630
DIRECTORY OF SCIENTIFIC AND TECHNICAL LIBRARIES IN THAILAND. 1973. irreg. Thailand Institute of Scientific and Technological Research, 196 Phahonyothin Rd., Chatuchak, Bangkok 10900, Thailand. TEL 579-8594. FAX 662-579-8594. **Document type:** directory.
 Formerly: Directory of Scientific Libraries in Thailand.
 Description: Information on facilities and services of 119 libraries in Thailand.

DIRECTORY OF SOUTH AFRICAN PUBLISHERS; with addresses and ISBN identifiers. see PUBLISHING AND BOOK TRADE

020   HK   ISSN 1019-7516
Z845.A1
DIRECTORY OF SOUTHEAST ASIAN ACADEMIC & SPECIAL LIBRARIES. a? $150. Library Marketing Services Ltd., 11th Fl., Hophing Centre, 8 Hennessy Rd., Hong Kong. (Subscr. to: GPO Box 701, Bangkok 10501, Thailand. TEL 66-2-2471032) **Document type:** directory.
 Description: Lists of Southeast Asia's major academic, medical, special, research and corporate libraries, including names, addresses, phone and fax numbers, personnels, services, publications, databases, computerization status and classifications.

027.4   SA
DIRECTORY OF SOUTHERN AFRICAN LIBRARIES. irreg., latest 1990. State Library, P.O. Box 397, Pretoria 0001, South Africa. TEL 27-12-21-8931. FAX 27-12-325-5984. TELEX 3-22171 SA. **Document type:** directory.

020   UK
▼**DIRECTORY OF SPECIAL COLLECTIONS IN WESTERN EUROPE.** 1992. irreg. £45($75) Bowker - Saur Ltd., A Reed Reference Publishing Company, Part of the Reed Elsevier group, Maypole House, Maypole Rd., E. Grinstead. W. Sussex RH19 1HH, England. TEL 0342-330100. FAX 0342-330191. (Subscr. to: c/o Butterworths Service Co., Borough Green, Sevenoaks, Kent TN15 8PH, England. TEL 0732-884567) Ed. Alison Gallico. **Document type:** directory.
 Description: Provides information on over 700 special collections held by major libraries throughout Western Europe. Each entry includes details on the institution, subject matter, time period covered, language, size, formats, and accessibility.

026   US
DIRECTORY OF SPECIAL LIBRARIES AND INFORMATION CENTERS. (In 3 vols.) 1963. a. $399 for vol.1; vol.2 $340; vol.3 $335. Gale Research Inc., 835 Penobscot Bldg., Detroit, MI 48226. TEL 313-961-2242. FAX 313-961-6083. TELEX 810-221-7086. Ed. Janice DeMaggio. **Document type:** directory.
 —BLDSC (3595.242000).
 Formerly: Directory of Special Libraries and Information Centers in the U S and Canada (ISSN 0731-633X)
 Description: Directory of libraries for specialized purposes in the U.S.

026   IO   ISSN 0216-2164
Z845.I6
DIRECTORY OF SPECIAL LIBRARIES AND INFORMATION SOURCES IN INDONESIA (YEAR). (Text in Indonesian, English) 1961. irreg., latest 1990. $15 per no. Indonesian Centre for Scientific Documentation and Information - Pusat Dokumentasi dan Informasi Ilmiah, Jalan Jenderal Gatot Subroto, Box 4298, Jakarta 12042, Indonesia. TEL 021-5733465. FAX 021-5733465. TELEX 62875 IA. Eds. R. Boediardjo, Antari Mawarni. circ. 1,000. (also avail. in microfiche) **Document type:** directory.
 Former titles: Directory of Special Libraries and Information Sources (Year); Directory of Special Libraries in Indonesia (ISSN 0376-8600)

020   CN   ISSN 0319-2563
DIRECTORY OF SPECIAL LIBRARIES IN THE MONTREAL AREA/REPERTOIRE DES BIBLIOTHEQUES SPECIALISEES DE LA REGION DE MONTREAL. (Text in English and French) biennial. Can.$75. Special Libraries Association, Eastern Canada Chapter, Box 1538, Sta. B, Montreal, PQ H3B 3L2, Canada. Ed. Anne M. Galler. circ. 350. **Document type:** directory.
 Formerly: Directory of Special Libraries in Montreal (ISSN 0070-6396)
 Description: Includes keyword description of each library's specializations.

020   US   ISSN 0070-6663
DISCOURSE UNITS IN HUMAN COMMUNICATION FOR LIBRARIANS. 1969. irreg., no.27, 1983. price varies. University of Pittsburgh, Communications Media Research Center, c/o Patrick R. Penland, Graduate School of Library and Information Science, 135 No. Bellefield, Pittsburgh, PA 15260. TEL 412-624-4469. Ed. Patrick R. Penland. (back issues avail.) **Indexed:** ERIC, Lib.Lit.

621.38   US   ISSN 1054-9692
TK5105   CODEN: DIATEG
DOCUMENT & IMAGE AUTOMATION. 1981. bi-m. $125. Meckler Publishing Corporation, 11 Ferry Lane W., Westport, CT 06880-5808. TEL 203-226-6967. Ed. Judith Paris Roth. adv.; bk.rev. (also avail. in microform from UMI) **Indexed:** ABI Inform., C.I.J.E., Cab.Vid.Ind., Compumath, Comput.Cont., Comput.Dtbs., Educ.Tech.Abstr., Info.Media & Tech., Leg.Info.Manage.Ind., LHTN, Lib.Lit., LISA, Resour.Ctr.Ind., Sci.Abstr.
 —Faxon; UnCover; SWETS; UMI; CASDDS. **CCC.**
 Former titles: Optical Information Systems (ISSN 0886-5809); Videodisc and Optical Disk (ISSN 0742-5740); (until 1984): Videodisc - Videotex (ISSN 0278-9183); (until vol.1, no.3): Videodisc - Teletext (ISSN 0198-9656)

DOCUMENT & IMAGE AUTOMATION UPDATE. see COMMUNICATIONS — Television And Cable

029   SP
DOCUMENTACION. 12/yr. Arenal 22, 50 Dcha., Apto. 1058, 28011 Madrid, Spain. TEL 1-531-63-74. Ed. F. Javier de Castro. circ. 25,000.

029   020   FR   ISSN 0012-4508
Z1007   CODEN: DSINE6
DOCUMENTALISTE - SCIENCES DE L'INFORMATION. (Text in French; summaries in English) 1964. 5/yr. 520 F. (foreign 580 F.). Association Francaise des Documentalistes et des Bibliothecaires Specialises, 25 rue Claude Tillier, 75012 Paris, France. TEL 43-72-25-25. FAX 43-72-30-41. Ed. J.M. Rauzier. adv.; bk.rev.; abstr.; bibl.; charts; illus.; index. circ. 5,000. **Indexed:** Bull.Signal., Chem.Abstr., Inform.Sci.Abstr., Lib.Lit., LISA, Ref.Zh., Sci.Abstr.
 —BLDSC (3609.900000); Faxon; SWETS.
 Incorporates: Sciences de l'Information (ISSN 0395-3858)
 Description: Devoted to techniques, professions, services and policies in the information and library fields, and to research in information sciences; with particular focus on European and French-speaking countries.

020   CN   ISSN 0315-2340
Z735.A1   CODEN: DCBBO
DOCUMENTATION ET BIBLIOTHEQUES. 1955. q. Can.$42. Association pour l'Avancement des Sciences et des Techniques de la Documentation, 1030 rue Cherrier, Bureau 505, Montreal, PQ H2L 1H9, Canada. TEL 514-522-7833. FAX 514-521-9561. Ed. Jean-Remi Brault. adv.; bk.rev.; bibl.; charts; illus.; index, cum.index: 1955-1962. circ. 1,100. (also avail. in microfilm from BNQ) **Indexed:** Bull.Signal., Can.Per.Ind., Lib.Lit., LISA, Pt.de Rep. (1983-), Sci.Abstr.
 —BLDSC (3610.710000); SWETS.
 Formerly (until 1973): Association Canadienne des Bibliothecaires de Langue Francaise. Bulletin (ISSN 0004-5314)

020   UN
DOCUMENTATION, LIBRARIES AND ARCHIVES: STUDIES AND RESEARCH. (Editions in English, French and Spanish) 1951. irreg. price varies. Unesco Press, 7 Place de Fontenoy, F-75700 Paris, France. (Dist. in U.S. by: Unipub, 4611-F Assembly Drive, Lanham MD, 20706-4391)
 Formerly (until 1972): Unesco Manuals for Libraries (ISSN 0082-7495)

020   US   ISSN 0091-2085
DOCUMENTS TO THE PEOPLE. Short title: D t t P. 1972. q. $20 (foreign $25). American Library Association, Government Documents Round Table, 50 E. Huron St., Chicago, IL 60611. TEL 312-944-6780. Ed. Jim Walsh. adv. circ. 2,000. (also avail. in microfilm; back issues avail. from UMI) **Indexed:** Leg.Info.Manage.Ind. **Document type:** newsletter.
 —BLDSC (3630.517000).
 Description: Information on librarianship, government publications and other information products on related governmental activities.

350   US   ISSN 0749-0356
DOCUMENTS TO THE PEOPLE OF NEW YORK STATE. 1980. q. membership. New York State Library Association, Government Information Roundtable, 252 Hudson Ave., Albany, NY 12210-1802. Ed. Jyoti Pandit. adv.; bk.rev. circ. 85. **Document type:** newsletter.
 Description: Covers news pertaining to federal and New York State documents of interest to member librarians.

DOKUMENTATION ZUR GERMANISTISCHEN SPRACHWISSENSCHAFT. see LINGUISTICS

020   GW   ISSN 0176-781X
Z666
DOKUMENTATIONSDIENST BIBLIOTHEKSWESEN. Short title: D O B I. 1984. q. DM.120. Deutsches Bibliotheksinstitut, Abt. 1 - Publikationen, Bundesallee 184-185, 10717 Berlin, Germany. TEL 030-8505-0. FAX 030-8505-100. circ. 400. **Document type:** bulletin.
 Incorporates (in 1992): Informationsdienst Bibliothekswesen (ISSN 0044-1457)

027   IE   ISSN 0332-0006
DUBLIN. NATIONAL LIBRARY OF IRELAND. COUNCIL OF TRUSTEES REPORT. 1901. a. Stationery Office, Dublin, Ireland. (Avail. from: Government Publications Postal Sales Office, St. Martin's House, Waterloo Rd., Dublin 4, Ireland) illus. circ. 500. **Document type:** government publication.

LIBRARY AND INFORMATION SCIENCES

020 370   US   ISSN 0895-4909
Z733
DUKE UNIVERSITY LIBRARIES. 1987. 3/yr. $15. Duke University, Library, 220 Perkins Library, Durham, NC 27708-0193. TEL 919-684-2034. FAX 919-684-2855. Ed. Joline R. Ezzell. illus. circ. 2,800. (back issues avail.) **Document type:** newsletter.
    Description: Descriptions of library collections, programs, and activities.

025   BA
DUNYA AL-MAKTABAT. (Text in Arabic) m. Ministry of Education, Manama Central Library, P.O. Box 43, Manama, Bahrain. TEL 258550. TELEX 9094.

027.4   SA
DURBAN MUNICIPAL LIBRARY. ANNUAL REPORT. (Text in English) 1854. a. free Durban Municipal Library, P.O. Box 917, Durban 4000, South Africa. FAX 27-31-3006301. circ. 75. **Document type:** corporate report.

020   UK   ISSN 0968-2856
▼**E I A REVIEW.** 1993. s-a. European Information Association, Central Library, St. Peter's Sq., Manchester M2 5PD, England. TEL 061-228-3691.

029 015   UK   ISSN 0968-2848
E I A UPDATE. 1980. m. membership. European Information Association, Central Library, St. Peter's Sq., Manchester Ms 5PD, England. TEL 061-228-3691. bk.rev.; bibl. circ. 400. **Indexed:** World Bank.Abstr.
    Former titles (until 1992): E I A News (ISSN 0962-1482); (until 1991): E D C Newsletter (European Documentation Centers) (ISSN 0262-9216); (until 1980): Northern E D C Newsletter.

027.7   UK   ISSN 0267-3614
E L G NEWS. 1971. 3/yr. membership. Library Association, Education Librarians Group, The Education Library, University of Birmingham, Edgbaston, Birmingham B15 2TT, England. Ed. H. Medcalf. adv.; bk.rev. circ. 1,100. **Document type:** newsletter.
    —BLDSC (3730.559000).
    Supersedes (in 1981): C I S E Newsletter.

027.5967   RH   ISSN 0376-4753
E S A R B I C A JOURNAL. 1973. a. $5.50 to non-members. International Council on Archives, Eastern and Southern Africa Regional Branch, c/o TechTop (pvt), Ltd., P.O. Box 4555, Harare, Zimbabwe. TEL 735607. TELEX 6444 ZW. (Subscr. to: c/o Mrs. M. Lekaukau, Treasurer, National Archives of Botswana, P.O. Box 239, Gaborone, Botswana) Ed. Peter C. Mazikana. circ. 100. (back issues avail.)
    —BLDSC (3647.287000).
    Description: Articles on various aspects of information science.

020   BG   ISSN 1021-3651
Z671
EASTERN LIBRARIAN. (Text in English) 1966. s-a. $30 (effective 1993). Library Association of Bangladesh, c/o Library Training Institute, Bangladesh Central Public Library Bldg., Shahbagh, Dhaka 1000, Bangladesh. TEL 880-2-504269. Ed. M. Shamsul Islam Khan. adv.; bk.rev.; index. circ. 300. **Indexed:** Lib.Sci.Abstr. **Document type:** academic/scholarly publication.
    Description: Contains research articles, case studies, and short reports on library and information science, and documentation.

020   US   ISSN 0012-8899
EASTERN MASSACHUSETTS REGIONAL LIBRARY SYSTEM. EASTERN REGION NEWS. 1966. 4/yr. free to qualified personnel. Eastern Massachusetts Regional Library System, Boston Public Library, Copley Square, Boston, MA 02117. TEL 617-536-4010. Ed. Edward J. Montana, Jr. bk.rev.; illus.; stat.; circ. 2,400 (controlled). (looseleaf format) **Document type:** newsletter.

020   UK
EASTERNER. 1960. 4/yr. free. East Anglian Librarian's Consultative Committee, Central Library, St. Andrews St. North, Bury St. Edmunds IP33 1TZ, England. TEL 0284-701611. FAX 0284-705875. Ed. B. King. adv.; bk.rev. circ. controlled. (processed) **Document type:** newsletter.
    Description: Newsletter to the East Anglians Librarians' Consultative Committee, which represents all members of the Library Association in East Anglia.

016.05 020   US   ISSN 0360-0637
Z6941
EBSCO BULLETIN OF SERIALS CHANGES. 1975. bi-m. $20. EBSCO Industries, Inc., Title Information Department, 5724 Hwy. 280 East, Birmingham, AL 35242. TEL 205-991-6600. FAX 205-995-1518. (Subscr. to: EBSCO Subscription Services, Box 2543, Birmingham, AL 35201. TEL 800-826-3024) adv.; illus. circ. 8,000.
    —BLDSC (3647.168000).

027.4   CN   ISSN 0706-5205
L'ECHANGE. 1977. bi-m. Can.$20 (typically set in Jan.). Bibliotheque Centrale de Pret de l'Abitibi-Temiscamingue, 20 boul. Quebec, Rouyn-Noranda, Que. J9X 2E6, Canada. TEL 819-762-4305. FAX 819-797-5309. Ed. Norman Fink. adv.; bk.rev. circ. 350.
    Description: A brief survey of activities within the library system. Informative articles on library technologies, management, marketing. For library boards in small rural communities.

020   CN   ISSN 0840-9471
ECLUSE. 1989. q. free. Banque Internationale d'Information sur les Etats Francophones, c/o Patrimoine Canadien, Ottawa, ON K1A 0M5, Canada. TEL 819-997-3857. FAX 819-953-8439. TELEX 053-3384. Ed. Suzanne Richer. bk.rev. circ. 2,500. **Document type:** bulletin.
    Description: Serves as an administrative, technical and professional information bulletin for BIEF partners.

027.4   CN   ISSN 1195-3381
EDMONTON PUBLIC LIBRARY. CALENDAR. 3/yr. free. Edmonton Public Library, 7 Sir Winston Churchill Sq., Edmonton, AB T5J 2V4, Canada. TEL 403-423-2331. FAX 403-429-9825. Ed. Iolani Domingo. circ. 20,000. **Document type:** newsletter.
    Description: Lists programs and activities of the Library.

020   NE   ISSN 0167-8329
EDUCATION FOR INFORMATION. (Text in English) 1983. q. fl.379($202) (effective 1994). I O S Press, Van Diemenstraat 94, 1013 CN Amsterdam, Netherlands. TEL 31-20-6382189. FAX 31-20-6203419. (In N. America: Box 10558, Burke, VA 22009-0558. TEL 703-323-5554. FAX 703-250-4705) Eds. R.F. Guy, J.A. Large. **Indexed:** ASCA, Cont.Pg.Educ., Educ.Tech.Abstr., Lib.Lit., LISA. **Document type:** academic/scholarly publication.
    —BLDSC (3661.286500); EI; SWETS. **CCC.**
    Description: For educators, librarians and information managers. Articles cover new technology and procedures utilized in the library and information science fields.

378   AT   ISSN 0813-4235
EDUCATION FOR LIBRARIANSHIP: AUSTRALIA. 1984. 3/yr. Aus.$30 (foreign Aus.$38). Australian Library and Information Association, Education for Librarianship and Information Services Section, P.O. Box E441, Queen Victoria Terrace, A.C.T. 2600, Australia. TEL 06-285-1877. FAX 06-282-2249. Eds. Kate Beattie, Pam Naylor. adv.; bk.rev.; cum.index. circ. 350. (back issues avail.) **Indexed:** LISA.
    Description: Information about education for librarianship and information management, library schools, training and current developments in the field.
Refereed Serial

027.8   CN   ISSN 0148-1061
Z675.P3
EDUCATION LIBRARIES. 1976. 3/yr. $15 to individuals; libraries $20; foreign $25 (effective 1992). Special Library Association, Education Division, c/o Concordia University, 7141 Sherbrooke St. W., TA 7079, Montreal, PQ H4B 1R6, Canada. TEL 514-848-2543. FAX 514-848-3492. Ed. Anne M. Galler. adv.; bk.rev.; bibl. circ. 400. (also avail. in microform from UMI) **Indexed:** C.I.J.E.
    —BLDSC (3661.291300); UMI.
    Description: Provides a forum for new and challenging ideas in the education field to be presented in a scholarly fashion and introduces and reviews new and forthcoming reference publications.
Refereed Serial

026   UK   ISSN 0076-079X
EDUCATION LIBRARIES BULLETIN SUPPLEMENTS. 1958. irreg., no.25, 1993. price varies. University of London, Institute of Education Library, 20 Bedford Way, London WC1H 0AL, England. TEL 071-612-6060. FAX 071-612-6126. Ed. Claire E. Drinkwater. adv. circ. 500. **Indexed:** Br.Educ.Ind., Lib.Sci.Abstr. **Document type:** monographic series.
    Description: Covers all aspects of libraries in education.

026   UK   ISSN 0957-9575
EDUCATION LIBRARIES JOURNAL. 1958. 3/yr. £12. University of London, Institute of Education Library, 20 Bedford Way, London WC1H 0AL, England. TEL 071-612-6060. FAX 071-612-6126. Ed. Claire E. Drinkwaker. bk.rev.; bibl.; index. circ. 400. (processed; also avail. in microfilm from UMI; reprint service avail. from UMI) **Indexed:** Br.Educ.Ind., Cont.Pg.Educ., Lib.Sci.Abstr., LISA. **Document type:** academic/scholarly publication.
    —BLDSC (3661.296300); SWETS; UMI.
    Formerly: Education Libraries Bulletin (ISSN 0013-1407)
    Description: Covers all aspects of libraries in education.

020   UA   ISSN 0531-6723
EGYPTIAN LIBRARY JOURNAL/SAHIFAT AL-MAKTABAH. (Text in Arabic; summaries in English) 1969. q. P.T.300($9) Egyptian School Library Association, 35 al-Galaa St., Cairo, Egypt. TEL 753 001. Ed. Medhat Kazem. adv.; bk.rev.; bibl.

027.8 372.21   US
ELEMENTARY SCHOOL LIBRARY COLLECTION. 1965. biennial. $99.95. Brodart Co., 500 Arch St., Williamsport, PA 17705. TEL 800-233-8467. FAX 717-326-6769. Ed. Lauren Lee. bk.rev.; bibl. circ. 10,000. **Document type:** bibliography.
●Also available on CD-ROM.
    Description: Lists titles for core collections in elementary school libraries. Includes books, periodicals, audiovisuals, and microcomputer software.

ELSEVIER SCIENCE. DISPATCH LIST FOR JOURNALS, BOOK SERIES AND PROCEEDINGS. see *SCIENCES: COMPREHENSIVE WORKS*

ELSEVIER SCIENCE. NEW AND FORTHCOMING PUBLICATIONS. see *SCIENCES: COMPREHENSIVE WORKS*

020 301.412   CN   ISSN 0315-8888
EMERGENCY LIBRARIAN. (Text in English) 1973. 5/yr. Can.$47. Ken Hancock & Associates, Inc., 284 - 810 W. Broadway, Vancouver, BC V5Z 4C9, Canada. TEL 604-925-0266. FAX 604-925-0566. (U.S. subscr. to: Department 284, Box C34069, Seattle, WA 98124-1069) Ed. Ken Haycock. adv.; bk.rev.; bibl. circ. 10,000. (processed; also avail. in microfiche from UMI; back issues avail.; reprint service avail. from UMI) **Indexed:** Bk.Rev.Ind. (1981-), Can.Per.Ind., Chic.Per.Ind., Child.Bk.Rev.Ind. (1981-), Child.Lit.Abstr., CMI, Ind.Child.Mag., Lib.Lit., LISA, New Per.Ind.
    —BLDSC (3733.184000); UnCover; UMI. **CCC.**
Refereed Serial

EMPLOYMENT NEWS. see *LABOR UNIONS*

021   US   ISSN 0013-8495
ENOCH PRATT FREE LIBRARY. STAFF REPORTER. 1933. m. $3 (foreign $6). Enoch Pratt Free Library, 400 Cathedral St., Baltimore, MD 21201-4484. TEL 410-396-5494. FAX 410-837-0582. Ed. Averil Jordan Kadis. circ. 500. (processed) **Document type:** newsletter.

LIBRARY AND INFORMATION SCIENCES

ENVIRONMENTAL N G O'S IN INDIA; a directory. see *ENVIRONMENTAL STUDIES*

020   ET   ISSN 0014-1747
Z673.E85
ETHIOPIAN LIBRARY ASSOCIATION. BULLETIN. (Text in Amharic and English) 1969. 2/yr. $10. Ethiopian Library Association, Box 30530, Addis Ababa, Ethiopia. Ed. Kebreab W. Giorgis. bk.rev. circ. 200.

778.5   US
ETIN. 1974. 8/yr. membership. National Association of Regional Media Centers, Grant Wood AEA, 4401 Sixth St., S.W., Cedar Rapids, IA 52404. TEL 319-399-6741. FAX 319-399-6457. Ed. Jerry Cochrane. adv. circ. 400. **Document type:** newsletter.
Description: Informs members of current activities in the film and video world.

020.6   UK   ISSN 0261-2747
EUROPEAN INFORMATION SERVICE. 1978. 10/yr. £100 to individuals; institutions £200. Local Government International Bureau, 35 Gt. Smith St., London SW1P 3BJ, England. TEL 071-222-1636. FAX 071-233-2179. TELEX 21879-ATT-IUL. Ed. Judith Barton. bk.rev. circ. 1,500. **Document type:** bulletin.
—BLDSC (3829.720740).

020   GW
Z675.R45
EUROPEAN RESEARCH LIBRARY COOPERATION. 1978. q. DM.240. Akademische Druck- und Verlagsanstalt, c/o Prof. H.-A. Koch, Sec., Staats- und Universitaetsbibliothek, Postfach 330160, 28331 Bremen, Germany. (Co-sponsor: Ligue des Bibliotheques Europeenes de Recherche) Ed. Heiner Schnelling. adv.; bk.rev. (back issues avail.) **Indexed:** LISA. **Document type:** academic/scholarly publication.
Formerly: L I B E R News Sheet (ISSN 0721-6858); Incorporates: L I B E R Bulletin (ISSN 0304-0224)
Description: Promotes cooperation of European research libraries.

020   US   ISSN 1069-4641
EUROSERIALS. 1989. q. $28 to individuals; institutions $36. Haworth Press, Inc., 10 Alice St., Binghamton, NY 13904. TEL 607-722-5857; 800-342-9678. FAX 607-722-1424. Ed. Jim E. Cole. adv.; B&W page $300. bk.rev. (also avail. in microform from UMI; reprint service avail. from HAW) **Indexed:** LISA.
Former titles: European Journal of Serials Librarianship (ISSN 1048-5287); (until 1991); British Journal of Serials Librarianship (ISSN 0896-0844)
Description: Deals with emerging issues of European serials acquisitions, collection management, networking, bibliographic control and culture and history.
Refereed Serial

027.4   US
EVANSVILLE - VANDERBURGH COUNTY PUBLIC LIBRARIES. STAFF NEWS BULLETIN. 1952. s-m. $3.50. Evansville - Vanderburgh County Public Libraries, 22 S.E. Fifth St., Evansville, IN 47708. TEL 812-428-8200. FAX 812-428-8215. Ed. Carol Young. cum.index: 1952-1990. circ. 60.
Former titles: Evansville - Vanderburgh County Public Library. Staff News Bulletin; Evansville Public Library and Vanderburgh County Public Library. Staff News Bulletin (ISSN 0014-3669)
Description: Contains calendar of events, minutes from staff meetings, departmental and agency news, and Library-related articles.

020   SW   ISSN 0282-4906
EXLIBRISCIRKULAERET. 1947. q. SEK 120 membership (effective 1991). Svenska Exlibrisfoereningen, c/o Bengt Rur, Kometvaegen 19, S-183 33 Taeby, Sweden.

029   NE   ISSN 0014-5424
EXTENSIONS AND CORRECTIONS TO THE U D C. (Text in English, French, German) 1950. a. fl.290. Federation Internationale d'Information et de Documentation - International Federation for Information and Documentation, Postbus 90402, 2509 LK The Hague, Netherlands. TEL 31-70-3140671. FAX 31-70-3140667. TELEX 34402 KB GV NL. circ. 500.
—BLDSC (3853.000000).

026.34   US
F C I L NEWSLETTER. 1986. 3/yr. membership. American Association of Law Libraries, Foreign, Comparative and International Law S I S, c/o Yale Law School Library, Box 401A, Yale Sta., New Haven, CT 06520. TEL 203-432-1615. FAX 203-432-4604. Ed. Dan Wade. index, cum.index. **Document type:** newsletter.

029   GW
F I D - C R NEWS. (Included in: Knowledge Organization) 1973. 4/yr. (Federation Internationale d'Information et de Documentation - International Federation for Documentation) Indeks Verlag, Woogstr. 36a, 60431 Frankfurt a.M., Germany. TEL 069-523690. FAX 069-520566. Ed. Nancy Williamson. circ. 900. **Document type:** trade publication.
Formerly: F I D - C R Newsletter.

029.7   NE   ISSN 0379-3680
Z1008   CODEN: FIDIDJ
F I D DIRECTORY. 1958. biennial. fl.100. Federation Internationale d'Information et de Documentation - International Federation for Information and Documentation, Postbus 90402, 2509 LK The Hague, Netherlands. TEL 31-70-3140671. FAX 31-70-3140667. TELEX 34402 KB GV NL. circ. 1,000. **Document type:** directory.
—CASDDS.
Formerly: F I D Yearbook (ISSN 0074-5839)

029   NE   ISSN 0014-5874
Z699.A1   CODEN: FDNBAA
F I D NEWS BULLETIN. (Includes Quarterly Document Delivery Survey & Newsletter on Education and Training Programmes for Information Personnel) (Text in English) 1951. 11/yr. fl.160 (effective 1994). Federation Internationale d'Information et de Documentation - International Federation for Information and Documentation, Postbus 90402, 2509 LK The Hague, Netherlands. TEL 31-70-3140671. FAX 31-70-3140667. TELEX 34402 KB GV NL. Ed. Theresa Stanton. adv.; bk.rev.; bibl.; index, cum.index every 3 yrs. circ. 2,000. (also avail. in microfilm from SWZ,UMI; reprint service avail. from UMI) **Indexed:** CALL, Info.Media & Tech., Inform.Sci.Abstr., Key to Econ.Sci., Lib.Lit., LISA, Ref.Zh.
—BLDSC (3918.800000); EI; SWETS; UMI; CASDDS.
Description: Covers members' news, meeting and publications announcements, committees and special interest groups, articles on new developments in information management, industrial, business and financial news and marketing of systems and services.

020   US   ISSN 0882-908X
Z675.G7   CODEN: FLNEEB
F L I C C NEWSLETTER. 1965. q. free. U.S. Library of Congress, Federal Library and Information Center Committee, Washington, DC 20540. TEL 202-707-4828. FAX 202-707-4818. Ed. Darlene Dolan. bk.rev.; stat.; circ. controlled. (processed) **Document type:** government publication.
—CASDDS.
Formerly: F L C Newsletter (ISSN 0014-5939)

020   GW   ISSN 0724-0775
FACHHOCHSCHULE FUER BIBLIOTHEKS- UND DOKUMENTATIONSWESEN IN KOELN. AMTLICHE MITTEILUNGEN. 1983. irreg. free. Fachhochschule fuer Bibliotheks- und Dokumentation in Koeln, Claudiusstr. 1, 50678 Cologne, Germany. TEL 0221-8275-3376. FAX 0221-3318583. index. (back issues avail.) **Document type:** newsletter.
Description: Legal regulations of library and information education.

070.5   GW   ISSN 0071-3627
FACHLITERATUR ZUM BUCH- UND BIBLIOTHEKSWESEN/INTERNATIONAL BIBLIOGRAPHY OF THE BOOK TRADE AND LIBRARIANSHIP. 1961. irreg. latest 1981. DM.168. K.G. Saur Verlag KG (Subsidiary of: Reed Reference Publishing), Ortlerstr. 8, 81373 Munich, Germany. TEL 089-76902-0. FAX 089-76902150. TELEX 5212067-SAUR-D. (Subscr. to: Postfach 701620, 81316 Munich, Germany) Ed. Gitta Hausen. adv.
Formerly: Literature about the Book and Librarianship.

026 686.2   UK   ISSN 0141-3635
Z699.4.E17
FACTOTUM. 1978. 2/yr. free. British Library, Humanities and Social Sciences, Great Russell St., London WC1B 3DG, England. TEL 071-323-7607. FAX 071-323-7782. TELEX 21462. Ed. J.L. Wood. bibl.; cum.index. circ. 2,000. (back issues avail.)
—BLDSC (3864.106000).
Description: News of the progress of the Eighteenth Century Short Title Catalogue.

020   IR
FASLNAME-YI KETAB. (Text in Persian) 1990. q. $20 per no. National Library of Iran, 30 Tir St., 11364 Tehran, Iran. TEL 98-21-673315. FAX 98-21-662040. **Document type:** academic/scholarly publication.
Description: Library sciences journal of the National Library of Iran.

023   US   ISSN 0273-1061
FEDERAL LIBRARIAN. 1972. q. $20 to non-members. American Library Association, Federal Librarians Round Table, c/o Patricia Muir, 110 Maryland Ave., N.E., Washington, DC 20002. Ed. Gail Kohlhorst. adv. contact: Barbara Busch. circ. 500. **Document type:** newsletter.
Supersedes (in 1986): F L I R T Newsletter (ISSN 0090-9661)

020   HU   ISSN 0139-2115
FEJER MEGYEI KONYVTAROS. 1961. s-a. 200 Ft. Vorosmarty Mihaly Megyei Konyvtar, Bartok Bala ter 1, 8000 Szekesfehervar, Hungary. TEL 36-22-312-684. FAX 36-22-311-634. Ed. Eva Hegedus. abstr.; bibl.; illus. circ. 300. (looseleaf format; back issues avail.) **Indexed:** Hung.Lib.& Info.Sci.Abstr. (1991). **Document type:** trade publication.
Description: Informs and provides colleagues in the country with up-to-date information.

020   CN   ISSN 0014-9802
FELICITER. Variant title: C.L.A. Feliciter. 1956. 10/yr. Can.$95 or membership. Canadian Library Association, 200 Elgin St., Ste. 602, Ottawa, ON K2P 1L5, Canada. TEL 613-232-9625. FAX 613-563-9895. Ed. Mary Moore. adv. circ. 4,000. (tabloid format; also avail. in microfilm from CLA) **Indexed:** Can.Per.Ind., CMI, Lib.Lit., LISA. **Document type:** newspaper.
—BLDSC (3905.113000).
Description: Contains news and opinions on issues in the Canadian library community, as well as association positions and proceedings.

028   PE   ISSN 0015-0002
Z671
FENIX. 1944. a. $30. Biblioteca Nacional del Peru, Digbine, Apartado 2335, Lima, Peru. Ed. Isabel Miranda M. bk.rev.; music rev.; bibl.; cum.index. circ. 500. **Indexed:** Amer.Hist.& Life, Hist.Abstr.

020   FJ   ISSN 1016-9989
FIJI LIBRARY ASSOCIATION. JOURNAL. (Text in English) 1979. s-a. F.$7 per no. Fiji Library Association, c/o Editor, Government Bldgs., Box 2292, Suva, Fiji. circ. 150. **Indexed:** LISA, So.Pac.Per.Ind.
Description: Articles and reviews relating to librarianship in Fiji and the South Pacific.

025   FJ   ISSN 1016-9997
FIJI LIBRARY ASSOCIATION. NEWSLETTER. (Text in English) 1973. m. F.$0.50 per no. plus postage. Fiji Library Association, c/o Editor, FLA Newsletter, Government Buildings, Box 2292, Suva, Fiji. circ. 150. **Indexed:** So.Pac.Per.Ind. **Document type:** newsletter.
Description: Brief articles and reviews regarding the activities of the Fiji Library Association.

020   FJ   ISSN 0376-933X
FIJI LIBRARY DIRECTORY. irreg. latest 1991. F.$10 to non-members (foreign F.$20); members F.$5 (foreign F.$15). Fiji Library Association, Government Buildings, Box 2292, Suva, Fiji. circ. 55. **Document type:** directory.
Description: Lists of school, public, governmental, special and academic libraries in Fiji.

FINANCIAL ASSISTANCE FOR LIBRARY AND INFORMATION STUDIES. see *EDUCATION — Higher Education*

LIBRARY AND INFORMATION SCIENCES

020 651   US   ISSN 0892-7367
Z684
FINDING. 1986. a. $34.95. L D A Publishers, 42-36 209 St., Bayside, NY 11361-2747. TEL 718-224-9484. FAX 718-224-9487. Ed. Margaret Riconda. adv. circ. 12,500. **Document type:** directory.
   Description: Buyers guide to products and services for information and media specialists, librarians, record managers, information brokers, archivists, consultants and purchasing agents.

020   US   ISSN 0195-4016
FINGER LAKES LIBRARY SYSTEM. NEWSLETTER. 1979. bi-m. free. Finger Lakes Library System, 314 N. Cayuga St., Ithaca, NY 14850. TEL 607-273-4074. FAX 607-273-3618. Ed. Loretta Heimbuch. bk.rev.; film rev.; illus.; stat.; tr.lit. circ. 450. (back issues avail.) **Document type:** newsletter.
   Description: For member librarians, trustees, friends and local politicians. Covers news of the system and its members and general interest in the library community.

020   US   ISSN 1068-5383
FLICKERTALE NEWSLETTER. 1969. bi-m. $12. North Dakota State Library, Capitol Grounds, 604 E. Boulevard Ave., Bismarck, ND 58505-0800. TEL 701-224-4622. FAX 701-224-2040. bk.rev.; bibl. circ. 1,600. **Document type:** newsletter.

020   US
FLORIDA STATE UNIVERSITY. SCHOOL OF LIBRARY AND INFORMATION STUDIES. ALUMNI NEWSLETTER. 1954. q. membership. Florida State University, School of Library and Information Studies Alumni Association, Shores Bldg., Tallahassee, FL 32306. TEL 904-644-2761. FAX 904-644-9763. Ed. Mary Alice Hunt. circ. 4,000. (back issues avail.)

020 301.435
027.663   US   ISSN 0740-4956
FOCUS: LIBRARY SERVICE TO OLDER ADULTS, PEOPLE WITH DISABILITIES. 1983. m. $16 (Canada $18; elsewhere $20) (effective 1994). Michael G. Gunde, Ed. & Pub., 216 N. Frederick Avenue, Daytona Beach, FL 32114-3408. TEL 904-257-4259. FAX 904-239-6069. bk.rev.; index. circ. 300. (back issues avail.) **Document type:** newsletter.
   Description: Newsletter of library resources and services pertaining to elderly persons and persons with disabilities.

020   US   ISSN 0015-5152
Z732.I4
FOCUS ON INDIANA LIBRARIES. 1946. m. $15 for non-members. Indiana Library Federation, 6408 Carrollton Ave., Indianapolis, IN 46220-1615. TEL 317-257-2040. (Co-sponsor: State Library) Ed. Racquel Ravinet. adv. contact: Racquel Ravinet. bk.rev.; illus.; index. circ. 3,500. (also avail. in microfilm from UMI; reprint service avail. from UMI) **Indexed:** Lib.Lit. **Document type:** newspaper.
—UMI.

020   UK   ISSN 0305-8468
FOCUS ON INTERNATIONAL AND COMPARATIVE LIBRARIANSHIP. 1967. 3/yr. £15. International Group of the Library Association, 25 Bromford Gardens, Westfield Rd., Edgbaston, Birmingham B15 3XD, England. TEL 021-454-0935. Ed. Michael Wise. adv.; bk.rev.; bibl.; charts; cum.index; circ. 1,800 (paid). (tabloid format) **Indexed:** Inform.Sci.Abstr., LISA, Ref.Zh. **Document type:** newsletter.
—BLDSC (3964.216000); SWETS.

020   US   ISSN 0275-4924
Z675.R45
FOCUS: ON THE CENTER FOR RESEARCH LIBRARIES. 1949. 6/yr. free. Center for Research Libraries, 6050 S. Kenwood, Chicago, IL 60637. TEL 312-955-4545. Ed. Linda Naru. bibl. circ. 4,000. (tabloid format; back issues avail.)
—BLDSC (3964.186000).
   Supersedes (in 1980): Center for Research Libraries. Newsletter (ISSN 0008-9087); **And (in 1964):** Midwest Inter-Library Center. Newsletter.
   Description: News and feature articles on Center for Research Libraries activities and programs.

020   SW   ISSN 1100-5327
FOERENINGSARKIVEN. 1979. q. SEK 50 (effective 1991). Folkroerelsernas Arkivfoerbund, P.O. Box 317, S-101 26 Stockholm, Sweden. Ed. Owe Norberg. adv.; bk.rev. circ. 500.

026   US
FOLGER NEWS. 1969. 3/yr. membership only. Folger Shakespeare Library, 201 E. Capitol St., S.E., Washington, DC 20003. TEL 202-544-4600. Ed. Ann Greer. circ. 3,000. (also avail. in microfilm from UMI)
   Formerly: Folger Library Newsletter (ISSN 0015-5438)

026 664   US   ISSN 0198-0246
FOOD FOR THOUGHT (LOS ANGELES). vol.7, 1975. bi-m. $10. Special Libraries Association, Food & Nutrition Division, c/o Lawry's Foods Inc., 570 W. Avenue 26, Los Angeles, CA 90065. Ed. Susan N. Newcomer. bk.rev.; bibl. circ. 250.

020   US   ISSN 0736-8879
Z673.A52
FOOTNOTES (CHICAGO). 1970. q. membership. American Library Association, New Members Round Table, 50 E. Huron St., Chicago, IL 60611. TEL 312-944-6780. Ed. Marilynn Green. adv.; bk.rev. circ. 1,400. **Indexed:** Sportsearch. **Document type:** newsletter.
   Formerly: Junior Members Round Table. News Notes (ISSN 0022-6661)
   Description: News, information and issues of interest to NMRT members, including state and regional events, conferences and activities.

020   US   ISSN 0015-685X
FOR REFERENCE. 1966. m. $10. New York Metropolitan Reference & Research Library Agency (METRO), 57 E. 11th St., New York, NY 10003-4605. TEL 212-228-2320. circ. 2,000. (processed)

FOR THE RECORD (SPRINGFIELD). see HISTORY — History Of North And South America

023   US
FOR YOUR INFORMATION (BUFFALO). 1972. bi-m. free. Western New York Library Resources Council, 180 Oak St., Buffalo, NY 14203. TEL 716-852-3844. FAX 716-852-0276. Ed. Mary Ghikas. circ. 1,050. (back issues avail.)
   Formerly: Western New York Library Resources Council Newsletter.

FORECAST (BRIDGEWATER); a prepublication announcement journal of hardcover and trade-paper titles (adult and children's) for public libraries. see PUBLISHING AND BOOK TRADE

029   GW   ISSN 0942-0347
▼**FORTSCHRITTE IN DER WISSENSORGANISATION.** 1992. irreg., vol.2, 1992. (Internationale Gesellschaft fuer Wissensorganisation) Indeks Verlag, Woogstr. 36a, 60431 Frankfurt a.M., Germany. TEL 069-523690. FAX 069-520566. circ. 500. **Document type:** monographic series.

020 378   US
FORUM (WASHINGTON, 1970). 1970. 2/yr. Catholic University of America, School of Library & Information Science, 620 Michigan Ave., N.E., Marist Hall, Rm. 228, Washington, DC 20064. TEL 202-319-5085. FAX 202-319-5574. Ed. Michelle Peterson. circ. 2,600. **Document type:** newsletter.
   Description: Alumni magazine circulated to school of library and information science alumni only.

020   US
FOUNDATIONS IN LIBRARY AND INFORMATION SCIENCE; a series of monographs, texts and treatises. 1980. irreg., vol.23, 1986. $58.50 to institutions. J A I Press Inc., 55 Old Post Rd., No. 2, Box 1678, Greenwich, CT 06836-1678. TEL 203-661-7602. Ed. Thomas Leonhart.
   Description: Readings on information technology and information services.

FREE MAGAZINES FOR LIBRARIES. see PUBLISHING AND BOOK TRADE

020   SA   ISSN 0016-0458
FREE STATE LIBRARIES/VRYSTAATSE BIBLIOTEKE. (Text in Afrikaans, English) 1958. q. exchange basis. Provincial Library Service, Private Bag X20606, Bloemfontein 9300, South Africa. TEL 27-51-4054680. FAX 27-51-304958. Ed.Bd. bk.rev.; bibl. circ. 500.

028.9   US   ISSN 0046-5038
KF4774.A16
FREEDOM TO READ FOUNDATION NEWS. 1971. q. membership. Freedom to Read Foundation, 50 E. Huron St., Chicago, IL 60611. TEL 312-280-4223. FAX 312-440-9374. Ed. Judith F. Krug. circ. controlled.
   Description: Covers legislative cases and judicial decisions that affect censorship in the United States. Provides information on the activities of the foundation.

020   US
FRIENDS OF LIBRARIES U S A NEWS UPDATE. 1978. q. membership. American Library Association, Friends of Library U S A, 50 E. Huron St., Chicago, IL 60611. Ed. James A. Houck. circ. 1,500. **Document type:** newsletter.
   Former titles: Friends of Libraries U S A National Notebook; Friends of the Library National Notebook (ISSN 0195-3419)

020   US
FRIENDS OF THE AMHERST COLLEGE LIBRARY. NEWSLETTER. 1972. a. free. Friends of the Amherst College Library, Box 2256, Amherst, MA 01002. TEL 413-542-2212. Eds. Richard Cody, Alan Powers. bk.rev.
   Description: Presents articles of literary interest, and news of the Friends of the Amherst College Library.

020   US
FRIENDS OF THE DARTMOUTH LIBRARY NEWSLETTER. 1976. s-a. Friends of the Dartmouth Library, Dartmouth College, 115 Baker Library, Hanover, NH 03755. TEL 603-646-2236. FAX 603-646-3702. circ. 1,000. **Document type:** newsletter.

020 070   UK
FRIENDS OF THE NATIONAL LIBRARIES. ANNUAL REPORT. 1932. a. £15($40) to individuals; institutions £30 ($70) (effective Jan. 1994). Friends of the National Libraries, British Library, Great Russell St., London WC1B 3DG, England. TEL 071-323-7559. Ed. A. Payne. circ. 900. **Document type:** corporate report.

020   US   ISSN 0192-5539
FRIENDSCRIPT. 1979. q. membership. University of Illinois at Urbana-Champaign, Library Friends, 227 Library, 1408 W. Gregory, Urbana, IL 61801. TEL 217-333-5682. Ed. Terry Maher. illus. circ. 7,000. (looseleaf format) **Document type:** newsletter.
   Description: Information on new purchases, existing collections, services, and programs at the university library.

G L T F NEWSLETTER. (Gay and Lesbian Task Force of the Social Responsibilities Round Table) see HOMOSEXUALITY

025 340   US   ISSN 1061-3072
Z675.L2G6
G P L L A NEWSLETTER. 1977. 4/yr. membership. Greater Philadelphia Law Library Association, c/o Susan G. Alford, Dechert Price & Rhoads, 4000 Bell Atlantic Tower, 1717 Arch St., Philadelphia, PA 19103-3793. adv. contact: Denise Mines. bibl. circ. 240. **Document type:** newsletter.

020   US
G P O. (Government Publications for Oklahoma) 1987. bi-m. free. Oklahoma Department of Libraries, 200 N.E. 18th St., Oklahoma City, OK 73105-3298. TEL 405-521-2502. FAX 405-525-7804. Ed. Steve Beleu. circ. 225. **Document type:** government publication, newsletter.

020   PE   ISSN 0433-0730
GACETA BIBLIOTECARIA DEL PERU. 1963. irreg. Biblioteca Nacional del Peru, Direccion General de Bibliotecas Publicas, Apdo. 2335, Lima, Peru. Ed. Carlos Puntriano. illus. circ. 1,000.

GANZTAGSSCHULE. see EDUCATION — School Organization And Administration

LIBRARY AND INFORMATION SCIENCES

025 US
GEAC - C L S I LIBRARY NEWS. 1976. irreg. free. C L S I, Inc., 320 Nevada St., Newtonville, MA 02160. TEL 617-965-6310. FAX 617-969-1928. Ed. Lisa Bologna. index. circ. 5,000. **Document type:** newsletter.
Former titles: C L S I Newsletter of Library Automation; C L S I Newsletter (ISSN 0363-9479)
Description: Yearly articles about CLSI and Geac, its customers' automation activities, and the company's latest developments in product, personnel and technology.

020 GW ISSN 0724-6358
GEMEINSAME KOERPERSCHAFTSDATEI. 1980. a. DM.298. Harrassowitz Verlag, Taunusstr. 14, 65183 Wiesbaden, Germany. TEL 0611-530-0. FAX 0611-530570. TELEX 4186135. (Subscr. to: Postfach 2929, 65019 Wiesbaden, Germany) Ed.Bd. (microfiche)

020 UN ISSN 0379-2218
Q223 CODEN: GIPND3
GENERAL INFORMATION PROGRAM - U N I S I S T NEWSLETTER. (Unesco Programme of International Cooperation in Scientific and Technological Information) French edition: Programme General d'Information - Bulletin de l'U N I S I S T (ISSN 0379-2226); Spanish edition: Programa General de Informacion - Boletin del U N I S I S T (ISSN 0379-2242); Arabic edition: Al-Barnamaj al-Amm lil-Ma'lumat - Al-Nasrah al-I'lamiyyah lil-Yunisist (ISSN 1011-5226); Russian edition: Obshchaya Programa po Informatsii - Byulleten' J U N I S I S T (ISSN 0379-2234) 1973, Spanish edition 1975. 3/yr. free. Unesco, Division of the General Information Programme, 7-9 Place de Fontenoy, 75352 Paris 07 SP, France. TEL 45-68-45-00. FAX 43-06-16-40. circ. 7,150 (3,500 English ed., 1,500 French ed., 1,000 Spanish ed., 300 Arabic ed., 850 Russian ed.) (also avail. in microfiche) **Indexed:** Field Crop Abstr., Herb.Abstr., Nutr.Abstr. **Document type:** newsletter.
—BLDSC (9090.784000); CASDDS.
Formerly: U N I S I S T Newsletter (ISSN 0300-2519)

GEOACTIVE. see *GEOGRAPHY*

020 US ISSN 0016-8319
Z732.G4
GEORGIA LIBRARIAN. 1964. q. $12.50 (foreign $20). Georgia Library Association, Box 39, Young Harris, GA 30582-0039. TEL 404-827-8725. FAX 404-669-2705. Ed. Joanne Lincoln. adv.; bk.rev. circ. 1,400. (also avail. in microform from UMI; reprint service avail. from UMI) **Indexed:** Lib.Lit. —UMI.
Description: Features news and information of interest to Georgia librarians as well as articles of both state-wide or general interest in the field of librarianship.

027.4 CN ISSN 0380-8068
GEORGIAN BAY REGIONAL LIBRARY SYSTEM. DIRECTORY - MEMBER LIBRARIES. 1968. irreg. Georgian Bay Regional Library System, 30 Morrow Rd., Barrie, Ont. L4N 3V8, Canada. TEL 705-726-8251. circ. 100. **Document type:** directory.

020 069 US
GERALD R. FORD FOUNDATION. NEWSLETTER. 1982. s-a. free. Gerald R. Ford Foundation, 1000 Beal Ave., Ann Arbor, MI 48109. TEL 313-741-2218. FAX 313-741-2341. Ed. Nancy Mirshah. circ. 3,000. **Document type:** newsletter.
Description: Covers activities of the Foundation, the Ford Library, and the Ford Museum, which sponsor programs to improve understanding of the challenges confronting government and the presidency today.

020 UK ISSN 0951-2616
GERMAN STUDIES LIBRARY GROUP NEWSLETTER. 1987. 2/yr. free to members. German Studies Library Group, c/o Janet Wharton, Institute of German, Austrian & Swiss Affairs, University of Nottingham, Nottingham NG7 2RD, England. TEL 0602-514666. FAX 0602-513666. circ. 100. **Document type:** newsletter.
—BLDSC (4162.157380).
Description: Matters relating to library provision for the study of German-speaking countries and their cultures.

020 US ISSN 0891-0553
Z733.G47
GEST LIBRARY JOURNAL. 1986. s-a. $25 to individuals and institutions; students and scholars $15. c/o Friends of the Gest Library, Jones Hall 211, Princeton University, Princeton, NJ 08544. Ed. H.L. Goodman. bk.rev. circ. 200.
Description: Forum for scholarship, news, notes and reviews on East Asian libraries, particularly Princeton's Gest Oriental Library.

GETTING THE LOWDOWN ON EMPLOYERS AND A LEG UP ON THE JOB MARKET. see *OCCUPATIONS AND CAREERS*

020.6 MM
GHAQDA BIBLJOTEKARJI/LIBRARY ASSOCIATION NEWSLETTER. (Text in English) 1969. q. membership. Library Association, c/o Public Library, Floriana, Malta. Ed. Anita Ragonesi. bk.rev.; circ. 170 (controlled). **Document type:** newsletter.
Formerly (until no.30, 1978): Malta Library Association Newsletter.
Description: Contains news items and coverage of association activities and local and international library and information developments.

GLOWNA BIBLIOTEKA LEKARSKA. BIULETYN. see *MEDICAL SCIENCES*

020 US
GOLDA MEIR LIBRARY NEWSLETTER. 1974. irreg. free. University of Wisconsin-Milwaukee, Golda Meir Library, 2311 E. Hartford Ave., Box 604, Milwaukee, WI 53201. TEL 414-229-4786. FAX 414-229-4380. Ed. Jeane Knapp. circ. 4,000 (controlled). **Document type:** newsletter.
Formerly: U W M Library Newsletter.
Description: Contains news of library activities, collections and services.

020 US ISSN 0882-4746
GOOD STUFF. 1971. q. $25 to non-members. North Dakota Library Association, c/o Chester Fritz Library, University of North Dakota, Box 9000, Grand Forks, ND 58202. TEL 701-777-4645. FAX 701-777-3319. Ed. Ellen Kotrba. adv.; bk.rev. circ. 500.
Description: Covers association activities, local and regional events and concerns.

020 US ISSN 0890-3360
GOSSAGE REGAN MANAGER'S MEMO; trends & events in management & personnel for libraries/information centers. 1986. q. $25. (Gossage Regan Associates) Gordon Associates, 118 W. 74th St., Ste. 2B, New York, NY 10023. TEL 212-787-8930. Ed. Lucille Gordon. bk.rev. circ. 1,200. (back issues avail.)
Description: Brief articles, and announcements on issues of interest to management and personnel in libraries and information centers.

020 US ISSN 0740-624X
Z688.G6 CODEN: GIQUEU
GOVERNMENT INFORMATION QUARTERLY; an international journal of resources, services, policies, and practices. 1984. q. $55 to individuals (foreign $65); institutions $135 (foreign $155). J A I Press Inc., 55 Old Post Rd., No. 2, Box 1678, Greenwich, CT 06836-1678. TEL 203-661-7602. FAX 203-661-0792. (Addr. in Europe: J A I Press Ltd., The Courtyard, 28 High St., Hampton Hill, Mddx. TW12 1PD, England. TEL 44-81-943-9296. FAX 44-81-943-9317) Ed. Peter Hernon. (back issues avail.) **Indexed:** ASCA, Lib.Lit., LISA, P.A.I.S. —BLDSC (4204.235000); Faxon; UnCover. **CCC**.

020 US ISSN 0046-6301
GRANITE STATE LIBRARIES. 1965. bi-m. free to New Hampshire libraries, library organizations and qualified personnel. State Library, Department of Cultural Affairs, 20 Park St., Concord, NH 03301. TEL 603-271-2425. FAX 603-271-2205. Ed. Matthew J. Higgins. adv.; bk.rev.; bibl.; illus.; circ. 2,500 (controlled).
Formerly: Books and Libraries.
Description: Reports on matters of importance to all types of libraries.

020 II ISSN 0017-324X
GRANTHAGAR. (Text in Bengali; summaries in English) 1937. m. Rs.36($8) Indian Association of Special Libraries and Information Centre, Bengal Library Association, P134 C.I.T. Scheme No. 52., Calcutta 700014, India. Ed. Ramkrishna Saha. adv.; bk.rev.; bibl.; charts; index. circ. 2,500. **Indexed:** LISA.

020 II ISSN 0971-2941
GRANTHALAYA VIJNANA. (Text in Hindi) 1970. s-a. Rs.165($35) P. Kaula Endowment for Library and Information Science, C-239 Indira Nagar, Lucknow 226 016, India. Ed. P.N. Kaula. adv.; bk.rev.; charts; illus.; index. **Indexed:** Indian Lib.Sci.Abstr. **Document type:** academic/scholarly publication.
Description: Covers library science in the Hindi language. Each issue has a specific theme.

GREATER NEW ORLEANS ARCHIVISTS NEWSLETTER. see *HISTORY — History Of North And South America*

GREEN LIBRARY JOURNAL; environmental topics in the information world. see *ENVIRONMENTAL STUDIES*

020 US ISSN 0894-2986
GREENWOOD LIBRARY MANAGEMENT COLLECTION. 1988. irreg. price varies. Greenwood Press, Inc. (Subsidiary of: Greenwood Publishing Group Inc.), 88 Post Rd. W., Box 5007, Westport, CT 06881-5007. TEL 203-226-3571. FAX 203-222-1502.

GROWING POINT. see *PUBLISHING AND BOOK TRADE*

GUIDE TO MICROFORMS IN PRINT. AUTHOR - TITLE. see *BIBLIOGRAPHIES*

027.5 UN ISSN 0072-8608
GUIDE TO NATIONAL BIBLIOGRAPHICAL INFORMATION CENTRES. (Text in English, French) 1962. irreg., 3rd ed., 1970. 23 F. Unesco, 7-9 Place de Fontenoy, 75700 Paris, France.

020 US ISSN 0271-6461
GUIDE TO RECORD RETENTION REQUIREMENTS IN THE CODE OF FEDERAL REGULATIONS. 1955. irreg., latest Jan. 1992. National Archives and Records Administration, Office of the Federal Register, Seventh St. and Pennsylvania Ave., N.W., Washington, DC 20408. TEL 202-724-0087. (Dist. by: U.S. Government Printing Office, Supt. of Docs., Washington, DC 20402-9328)

020 CC
GUJI ZHENGLI YANJIU XUEKAN. (Text in Chinese) bi-m. Dongbei Shifan Daxue - Northeast Normal University, 110, Stalin Street, Changchun, Jilin 130024, People's Republic of China. TEL 882320. Ed. Gao Zhenfeng.

020 GY
GUYANA LIBRARY ASSOCIATION BULLETIN. 1970. s-a. $20. Guyana Library Association, c/o National Library, Box 10240, 76-77 Main St., Georgetown, Guyana. Ed. Karen Sills. adv. circ. 75. **Indexed:** LISA.
Description: Aimed at keeping interested persons informed on developments in library and information science in Guyana.

025 340 US
H A L L NEWSLETTER. 1982. 10/yr. $20. Houston Area Law Librarians, Box 61643, Houston, TX 77208. adv.; bk.rev. **Document type:** newsletter.

020 US
H C L AUTHORITY FILE (MICROFICHE EDITION). 1977. q. $7.50. Hennepin County Library, Technical Services Division, 12601 Ridgedale Dr., Minnetonka, MN 55305. TEL 612-541-8565. FAX 612-541-7986.
Description: Contains personal and corporate authors, added name entries (e.g., for joint authors, illustrators, translators, editors, government agencies, small presses) uniform title headings, author-title added entries, series forms, subject headings, and cross-references.

029 GW ISSN 0340-1332
HANDBUCH DER INTERNATIONALEN DOKUMENTATION UND INFORMATION/HANDBOOK OF INTERNATIONAL DOCUMENTATION AND INFORMATION. irreg. price varies. K.G. Saur Verlag KG (Subsidiary of: Reed Reference Publishing), Ortlerstr. 8, 81373 Munich, Germany. TEL 089-76902-0. FAX 089-76902150. TELEX 5212067-SAUR-D. (Subscr. to: Postfach 701620, 81316 Munich, Germany)
Formerly: Handbuch der Technischen Dokumentation und Bibliographie.
Description: Consists of a series of bibliographies, directories and guides to various aspects of documentation and information science.

HANGKONG DANG'AN/AERONAUTICS ARCHIVES. see *AERONAUTICS AND SPACE FLIGHT*

LIBRARY AND INFORMATION SCIENCES

020   CN   ISSN 0844-5753
HAPPENINGS. 1979. 3/yr. Calgary Public Library, 616 Macleod Tr. S.E., Calgary, AB T2G 2M2, Canada. TEL 403-260-2640. FAX 403-234-8763. Ed. Maryann Bredin. adv. circ. 60,000. (back issues avail.)
    Description: Covers children's, young adult, adult programs.

027
Z881   US   ISSN 0073-0564
HARVARD LIBRARIAN. 1957. 4/yr. free. Harvard University Library, Publications Office, Wadsworth House, Cambridge, MA 02138. TEL 617-495-7793. FAX 617-495-0370. Ed. Timothy Hanke. circ. 4,000. (reprint service avail. from UMI) **Indexed:** CALL. **Document type:** newsletter.

027.7
Z881   US   ISSN 0017-8136
HARVARD LIBRARY BULLETIN. 1920-1988; N.S. 1990. q. $35. Harvard University Library, 25 Mount Auburn St., Cambridge, MA 02138. TEL 617-495-8596. FAX 617-496-8344. Ed. Kenneth E. Carpenter. bibl.; illus. circ. 1,500. (also avail. in microform from JAI,MIM,UMI; reprint service avail. from UMI) **Indexed:** Abstr.Engl.Stud., Amer.Bibl.Slavic & E.Eur.Stud., Amer.Hist.& Life, Arts & Hum.Cit.Ind., CERDIC, Curr.Cont., Hist.Abstr., Lib.Lit., M.L.A., Mid.East: Abstr.& Ind. **Document type:** academic/scholarly publication.
—Faxon; UnCover; SWETS; UMI.
    Former titles (until 1942): Harvard University Library Notes (ISSN 1052-3685); (until 1940): Harvard Library Notes (ISSN 0363-7107)

027.7   US   ISSN 1050-2408
HARVARD UNIVERSITY LIBRARY NOTES. 1968. w. Harvard University Library, Wadsworth House, Cambridge, MA 02138. TEL 617-495-7793. FAX 617-495-0370. **Document type:** newsletter.
    Formerly (until 1990): H U L Notes (ISSN 0098-0919)

026   UK   ISSN 0305-9340
HEALTH AND WELFARE LIBRARIES QUARTERLY. 1965. q. L.3. Library Association, Hospital Libraries and Handicapped Readers Group, 50 Canadian Ave., Catford, London S.E.6., England. Ed. Antonia Bunch. adv. **Indexed:** Hosp.Abstr., LISA.
    Formerly: Book Trolley (ISSN 0045-2513)

026
Z675.M4   HU   ISSN 0864-991X
HEALTH INFORMATION AND LIBRARIES; international journal for medical, health and welfare librarians and information officers. (Text in English) 1990. q. $45 to individuals; institutions $55; students $25 (effective Jan. 1992). Orszagos Orvostudomanyi Informacios Intezet es Konyvtar - National Institute for Medical Information and Libraries, Szentkiralyi u. 21, Box 278, 1444 Budapest, Hungary. TEL 361-117-6352. FAX 361-266-9710. (Subscr. to: O.M.I.K.K., Technoinform, P.O. Box 12, H-1428 Budapest, Hungary) Ed. Dr. Tibor Koltay. bk.rev. **Indexed:** LISA. **Document type:** academic/scholarly publication.
—BLDSC (4275.016900).
    Description: Attempts to help librarians and information specialists publish their scientific work based on their practical experience in the health field.

020 610
Z675.M4   UK   ISSN 0265-6647
HEALTH LIBRARIES REVIEW. Issued with: Medical, Health and Welfare Libraries Group. Newsletter (ISSN 0266-853X) 1984. q. £79 in Europe; elsewhere £87 ($129) (effective 1994). (Library Association, Medical Health & Welfare Libraries Group) Blackwell Scientific Publications Ltd., Osney Mead, Oxford OX2 OEL, England. TEL 0865-240201. FAX 0865-721205. TELEX 83355-MEDBOK-G. Ed. S. Godbolt. adv.; bk.rev.; abstr.; bibl.; illus.; index. circ. 650. (also avail. in microform from UMI; back issues avail.) **Indexed:** CINAHL, LISA. **Document type:** academic/scholarly publication.
—BLDSC (4275.050650); Faxon; SWETS; UMI. CCC.

HEALTH LITERATURE REPORTS. see *MEDICAL SCIENCES*

020   US
HEALTHDOCS. 1986. bi-m. free. Oklahoma Department of Libraries, 200 N.E. 18th St., Oklahoma City, OK 73105-3298. TEL 405-521-2502. FAX 405-525-7804. Ed. Steve Beleu. circ. 61. **Document type:** government publication, directory.

027   FI   ISSN 0355-1350
HELSINGIN YLIOPISTON KIRJASTON. JULKAISUJA/HELSINGFORS UNIVERSITETS BIBLIOTEKS SKRIFTER/HELSINKI UNIVERSITY LIBRARY. PUBLICATIONS. 1918. irreg., no.55, 1993. price varies. Helsingin Yliopiston Kirjasto - Helsinki University Library, Box 15, Unioninkatu 36, SF-00014, University of Helsinki, Finland. bibl.
    Description: Includes special bibliographies, studies on library and information science.

025.305   US   ISSN 0732-894X
Z693.A15
HENNEPIN COUNTY LIBRARY CATALOGING BULLETIN. Key Title: Cataloging Bulletin (Edina). 1973. bi-m. $12. Hennepin County Library, Technical Services Division, 12601 Ridgedale Dr., Minnetonka, MN 55305. TEL 612-541-8565. FAX 612-541-7986. circ. 200.
    Description: Reports new or altered cross-references, DCC-numbers, and subject descriptors, citing authorities, precedents and applications.

HENRY MILLER MEMORIAL LIBRARY. REVIEW. see *LITERATURE*

020
Z671   II   ISSN 0018-0521
                                         CODEN: HLBSAB
HERALD OF LIBRARY SCIENCE. (Special Numbers issued irregularly) 1962. q. Rs.295($72) P. Kaula Endowment for Library and Information Science, C-239 Indira Nagar, Lucknow 226 016, India. Ed. P.N. Kaula. adv.; bk.rev.; charts; illus.; index. (also avail. in microform from UMI; reprint service avail. from UMI) **Indexed:** Indian Lib.Sci.Abstr., Lib.Lit., LISA, Sci.Abstr. **Document type:** academic/scholarly publication.
—BLDSC (4296.100000); UMI.
    Description: Features articles, technical and information notes, as well as reports on library science.

020   US   ISSN 0197-6044
HIGH ROLLER. 1964. q. $20 to non-members. Nevada Library Association, c/o UNLV Library, 4505 S. Maryland Pkwy., Las Vegas, NV 89154-7001. TEL 702-895-3061. FAX 702-895-3050. Ed. Lauralee Nelson. adv.; bk.rev.; illus.; stat.; circ. 400 (paid). (processed)
    Former titles (until 1977): Nevada Libraries Highroller (ISSN 0148-5946); (until 1974): Nevada Libraries (ISSN 0028-4068)

027.4   US
HITCHHIKER; for librarians in New Mexico. 1972. w. free to qualified personnel. New Mexico State Library, 325 Don Gaspar, Santa Fe, NM 87503. TEL 505-827-3813. FAX 505-827-3888. (Co-sponsor: Office of Cultural Affairs) Ed. Robert Upton. circ. 1,200. **Document type:** newsletter.
    Description: Covers news and events of New Mexico libraries. Includes information on job openings and workshops.

020   JA   ISSN 0018-3431
HOKKAIDO TOSHOKAN KENKYUKAI. KAIHO/HOKKAIDO LIBRARIANS STUDY CIRCLE. BULLETIN. (Text in Japanese) 1954. a. 1000 Yen. Hokkaido Toshokan Kenkyukai - Hokkaido Librarians Study Circle, c/o Sapporo Ika Daigaku Fuzoku Toshokan, Nishi-17-chome, Minami 1-jo, Sapporo, Japan. adv. circ. 300.

020   HK   ISSN 0073-3237
Z845.H6
HONG KONG LIBRARY ASSOCIATION. JOURNAL. (Text in Chinese, English) 1969. a. $20. Hong Kong Library Association, G.P.O. Box 10095, Hong Kong. TEL 3581443. Eds. E. Spodick, I. Shieh. adv.; bk.rev.; abstr. circ. 500. **Indexed:** LISA. **Document type:** academic/scholarly publication.
—BLDSC (4758.567000).

HORIZONT; veszprem megyei kozmuvelodesi tajekoztato. see *CLUBS*

HORN BOOK GUIDE TO CHILDREN'S AND YOUNG ADULT BOOKS. see *PUBLISHING AND BOOK TRADE*

025   US
HOW TO DO IT MANUALS FOR LIBRARIANS. 1989. irreg. (approx 12/yr.). price varies. Neal-Schuman Publishers, Inc., 100 Varick St., New York, NY 10013. TEL 212-925-8650. FAX 212-219-8916. **Document type:** monographic series.
    Description: Focuses on specific technological, administrative and service-oriented aspects of librarianship, from computers and cataloguing to personnel, fundraising and community issues.

025   US
▼**HOW TO DO IT MANUALS FOR SCHOOL AND PUBLIC LIBRARIANS.** (Subseries of: How To Do It Manuals for Librarians) 1992. irreg. (approx. 10/yr.). price varies. Neal-Schuman Publishers, Inc., 100 Varick St., New York, NY 10013. TEL 212-925-8650. FAX 212-219-8916. Ed. Barbara Stein. **Document type:** monographic series.
    Description: For professionals working in public and school libraries, with children and young adults.

HOW TO FIND BUSINESS INTELLIGENCE IN WASHINGTON. see *BUSINESS AND ECONOMICS*

HOW TO FIND COMPANY INTELLIGENCE IN FEDERAL DOCUMENTS. see *BUSINESS AND ECONOMICS*

020 330   US   ISSN 1041-8040
HOW TO FIND COMPANY INTELLIGENCE IN LIBRARIES. 1986. biennial. Washington Researchers Publishing (Subsidiary of: Washington Researchers, Ltd.), 2612 P St., N.W., Washington, DC 20007-3062. TEL 202-333-3499. FAX 202-625-0656. **Document type:** directory.

HOW TO FIND INFORMATION ABOUT ACQUISITION CANDIDATES. see *BUSINESS AND ECONOMICS*

HOW TO FIND INFORMATION ABOUT DIVISIONS, SUBSIDIARIES, & PRODUCTS. see *BUSINESS AND ECONOMICS*

020   US   ISSN 1044-9299
HOW TO FIND INFORMATION ABOUT EXECUTIVES. irreg. $115. Washington Researchers Publishing (Subsidiary of: Washington Researchers, Ltd.), 2612 P St., N.W., Washington, DC 20007-3062. TEL 202-333-3499. FAX 202-625-0656. Ed. Walt Seager. **Document type:** directory.

020   US   ISSN 1044-3606
HD2771
HOW TO FIND INFORMATION ABOUT FOREIGN FIRMS. irreg. $145. Washington Researchers Publishing, 2612 P St., N.W., Washington, DC 20007-3062. TEL 202-333-3499. FAX 202-625-0656. (Washington Researchers, Ltd.) Ed. Walt Seager. **Document type:** directory.

020   US   ISSN 1044-9329
HD2771
HOW TO FIND INFORMATION ABOUT PRIVATE COMPANIES. every 18 mos. $145. Washington Researchers Publishing (Subsidiary of: Washington Researchers, Ltd.), 2612 P St., N.W., Washington, DC 20007-3062. TEL 202-333-3499. FAX 202-625-0656. Ed. Walt Seager. **Document type:** directory.

HOW TO FIND INFORMATION ABOUT SERVICE COMPANIES. see *BUSINESS AND ECONOMICS*

020 340   US   ISSN 1041-8067
HOW TO USE THE FREEDOM OF INFORMATION ACT. 1986. biennial. Washington Researchers Publishing (Subsidiary of: Washington Researchers, Ltd.), 2612 P St., N.W., Washington, DC 20007-3062. TEL 202-333-3499. FAX 202-625-0656. **Document type:** directory.

020   GW   ISSN 0522-9898
HUMBOLDT-UNIVERSITAET ZU BERLIN. UNIVERSITAETSBIBLIOTHEK. SCHRIFTENREIHE. 1967. irreg., no.56, 1993. price varies. Humboldt-Universitaet zu Berlin, Universitaetsbibliothek, Clara-Zetkin-Str. 27, 10117 Berlin, Germany. TEL 030-20378705. FAX 030-20378707. Ed. Milan Bulaty. **Document type:** monographic series.

LIBRARY AND INFORMATION SCIENCES

020 600   XR   ISSN 0862-9382
Z665
I'(YEAR). (Informatika) (Text in Czech or Slovak; summaries in English and Russian) 1957. m. $76. (Ministry for Economic Politics and Development of the Czech Republic) Narodni Informacni Stredisko Ceske Republiky - National Information Centre of the Czech Republic, Havelkova 22, 130 57 Prague 1, Czech Republic. TEL 02-235-9788. FAX 02-236-06203. Ed. Jelena Hankova. adv.; bk.rev.; stat.; index. **Indexed:** Bibl.Ling., LISA, Sci.Abstr.
—BLDSC (8732.540000).
    Formed by the 1990 merger of: Ceskoslovenska Informatika (ISSN 0322-8509) & Technicka Knihovna (ISSN 0049-3171)
    Description: Presents original papers on all aspects of librarianship and information science.

020   US   ISSN 0257-3229
Z675.S3
I A S L CONFERENCE PROCEEDINGS.* 1972. a. $25. International Association of School Librarianship, c/o Secretariate, Box 19586, Kalamazoo, MI 49019-0586. TEL 616-343-5728. Ed. J. Lowrie. circ. 250. (looseleaf format; back issues avail.) **Indexed:** ERIC. **Document type:** proceedings.

026   II   ISSN 0018-8441
Z671   CODEN: IASLA9
I A S L I C BULLETIN. (Text in English) 1956. q. Rs.300($50) Indian Association of Special Libraries and Information Centres, P-291 C.I.T. Scheme No. 6M, Kankurgachi, Calcutta 700 054, India. TEL 34-9651. adv.; bk.rev.; index. circ. 1,300. **Indexed:** Biol.Abstr., Lib.Lit., Lib.Sci.Abstr., LISA. **Document type:** bulletin.
—BLDSC (4359.543000).

026   II   ISSN 0018-845X
I A S L I C NEWSLETTER. 1966. m. membership. Indian Association of Special Libraries and Information Centres, P-291 C.I.T. Scheme No. 6M, Kankurgachi, Calcutta 700 054, India. TEL 34-9651. circ. 1,300. **Document type:** newsletter.

026   II   ISSN 0073-6279
I A S L I C SPECIAL PUBLICATION; working papers of seminars and conferences. (Text in English) 1960. a. price varies. Indian Association of Special Libraries and Information Centres, P-291 C.I.T. Scheme No. 6M, Kankurgachi, Calcutta 700 054, India. TEL 34-9651.

026   II   ISSN 0073-6260
I A S L I C TECHNICAL PAMPHLETS. 1964. a. price varies. Indian Association of Special Libraries and Information Centres, P-291 C.I.T. Scheme No. 6M, Kankurgachi, Calcutta 700 054, India. TEL 34-9651.

020   US   ISSN 0085-2015
I A S L NEWSLETTER.* 1971. q. $20. International Association of School Librarianship, c/o Secretariate, Box 19586, Kalamazoo, MI 49019-0586. TEL 616-327-1390. Ed. Peter Genco. bk.rev. circ. 950. (processed; back issues avail.) **Document type:** newsletter.
    Description: Covers international programs in school library centers to publicize activities in the field.

020 310 025   US   ISSN 0739-1137
I A S S I S T QUARTERLY. 1974. q. $70 to non-members; members $40; students $20. International Association for Social Science Information Services and Technology, c/o Martin Pawlocki, Treas., ISSR, Rm. 303, GSLIS Bldg., University of Calif., Los Angeles, Los Angeles, CA 90024-1484. TEL 310-825-0716. Ed. E. W. Piovesan. adv.; bk.rev. circ. 400. **Document type:** newsletter.
    Formerly: I A S S I S T Newsletter.
    Description: Articles relating to the production, acquisition, preservation, processing, distribution and utilization of machine readable data in the international social science community.

020   UK   ISSN 0950-4117
Z675.T3   CODEN: IATQEX
I A T U L QUARTERLY. (International Association of Technological Universities Libraries) 1963. q. £40($83) Oxford University Press, Oxford Journals, Walton St., Oxford OX2 6DP, England. TEL 0865-56767. FAX 0865-56646. TELEX 837330-OXPRES-G. (U.S. subscr. to: Oxford University Press Inc., 2001 Evans Rd., Cary, NC 27513. TEL 919-677-0977) Ed. Joan Hardy. adv.; bk.rev.; bibl.; illus. circ. 600. **Indexed:** Inform.Sci.Abstr., Lib.Lit., LISA, Sci.Abstr. **Document type:** academic/scholarly publication.
—Faxon; UnCover. **CCC.**
    Supersedes: I A T U L Proceedings (ISSN 0018-8476); I A T U L Newsletter.
    Description: Forum for the exchange of views and ideas on common problems for librarians.

I B B Y CONGRESS PROCEEDINGS. (International Board on Books for Young People) see PUBLISHING AND BOOK TRADE

020   FR   ISSN 1018-9580
I C S T I FORUM. (Text in English) 1990. q. free. International Council for Scientific and Technical Information - Conseil International pour l'Information Scientifique et Technique, 51 bd. de Montmorency, 75016 Paris, France. TEL 45-25-65-92. FAX 42-15-12-62. TELEX ICSU 645 554 F. bk.rev. circ. 600.
    Description: Aims at increasing accessibility to, and awareness of, scientific and technical information.

I D. (Information Display) see LIBRARY AND INFORMATION SCIENCES — Computer Applications

020   GW   ISSN 0074-5987
I F L A ANNUAL; proceedings of the General Council Meetings. (Text in English) 1927. a. DM.78. (International Federation of Library Associations and Institutions) K.G. Saur Verlag KG (Subsidiary of: Reed Reference Publishing), Ortlerstr. 8, 81373 Munich, Germany. TEL 089-76902-0. FAX 089-76902150. TELEX 5212067-SAUR-D. (Subscr. to: Postfach 701620, 81316 Munich, Germany) Eds. Willem R.H. Koops, Carol Henry. **Document type:** proceedings.
    Description: Detailed summary of activities for the year and plans for the future. Lists conference participants and papers presented.

020   NE   ISSN 0074-6002
Z673
I F L A DIRECTORY. 1969. biennial. fl.75 to non-members; members free. International Federation of Library Associations and Institutions, I F L A Headquarters, P.O. Box 95312, 2509 CH The Hague, Netherlands. TEL 31-70-3140884. FAX 31-70-3834827. TELEX 34402 KB NL. Ed.Bd. circ. 2,000. **Document type:** directory.

020   GW   ISSN 0340-0352
Z672
I F L A JOURNAL. (Includes annual: I F L A Progress Report) (Text in English, French and German) 1975. q. DM.178. (International Federation of Library Associations and Institutions) K.G. Saur Verlag KG, A Reed Reference Publishing Company, Part of the Reed Elsevier group, Ortlerstr. 8, 81373 Munich, Germany. TEL 089-76902-0. FAX 089-76902150. TELEX 5212067-SAUR-D. (Subscr. to: Postfach 701620, 81316 Munich, Germany) Ed.Bd. adv.; bk.rev. circ. 1,500. **Indexed:** Curr.Cont., Lib.Lit., LISA, So.Pac.Per.Ind., SSCI. **Document type:** bulletin.
—BLDSC (4363.301400); Faxon; UnCover; SWETS; UMI. **CCC.**
    Supersedes: I F L A News (ISSN 0018-9685)

025   GW   ISSN 0344-6891
I F L A PUBLICATIONS. (Text in English and French) 1974. irreg., vol.60, 1992. DM.68. (International Federation of Library Associations and Institutions) K.G. Saur Verlag KG (Subsidiary of: Reed Reference Publishing), Ortlerstr. 8, 81373 Munich, Germany. TEL 089-76902-0. FAX 089-76902150. TELEX 5212067-SAUR-D. (Subscr. to: Postfach 701620, 81316 Munich, Germany) Eds. Willem R. Koops, P. Havard-Williams. bibl.
—BLDSC (4363.315500).
    Description: Consists of papers presented at various symposia, bibliographies, studies and monographs on aspects of library science.

020   US
I F R T REPORT. 1973. s-a. membership only. American Library Association, Intellectual Freedom Round Table, 50 E. Huron St., Chicago, IL 60611. TEL 312-280-4224. Ed. Sue Kamm. circ. 2,000. (back issues avail.) **Document type:** newsletter.
    Description: Includes news about current censorship controversies, ALA conferences and the activities of the round table.

020   US   ISSN 0018-9979
I L A REPORTER. 1962. 10/yr. $25 membership. Illinois Library Association, 33 W. Grand Ave No. 301, Chicago, IL 60610. TEL 312-644-1896. FAX 312-644-1899. adv.; illus.; circ. 4,400 (controlled). **Document type:** newsletter.
    Description: Professional association publication containing news about or of interest to all types of Illinois libraries, staff and trustees, including a statewide calendar of Illinois library events.

010   UN   ISSN 0047-0856
I N I S NEWSLETTER. 1972. irreg. free. International Atomic Energy Agency, Wagramerstr. 5, P.O. Box 100, A-1400 Vienna, Austria. **Document type:** newsletter.
—BLDSC (4513.930000).

539   UN   ISSN 1014-1561
Z699.5.A85
I N I S REFERENCE SERIES. 1969. irreg. price varies. International Atomic Energy Agency, Wagramerstr. 5, P.O. Box 100, A-1400 Vienna, Austria. (also avail. in microfiche)

020   CI   ISSN 0351-0123
                         CODEN: IRBUD5
I R C I H E BULLETIN. (Text in English) 1975. q. 250 din.($24) International Referral Centre for Information Handling Equipment, c/o Institute for Information Sciences, P.O. Box 327, Trg. Marsala Tita 3, 41001 Zagreb, Croatia. TEL 38-41-427-866. FAX 38-41-427-903. TELEX 22486 RCSZ26 YU. Ed.Bd. adv. circ. 600. (back issues avail.)
—BLDSC (4567.643000); CASDDS.

I S B N NEWSLETTER. (International Standard Book Number) see PUBLISHING AND BOOK TRADE

I S B N REVIEW. (International Standard Book Number) see PUBLISHING AND BOOK TRADE

I S C A QUARTERLY. (International Society of Copier Artists) see ART

I S O BULLETIN (ENGLISH EDITION). (International Organization for Standardization) see METROLOGY AND STANDARDIZATION

020   US
I U L FACULTY NEWSLETTER. 1989. irreg. Indiana University Libraries, c/o Jennifer Paustenbaugh, Ed., Library Administration, Library C-2, Bloomington, IN 47405. FAX 812-855-2576. circ. 2,500.
    Description: Focuses on library issues of current concern to teaching faculty and administrators. News of new and noteworthy materials and exhibitions as well as research interests of library faculty are included.

021.7   US   ISSN 0360-8409
Z881.C25
ICARBS. 1973. irreg. $5 per vol. (2 issues). Friends of Morris Library, Southern Illinois University, Morris Library, Carbondale, IL 62901. TEL 618-453-2516. Eds. David V. Koch, Alan M. Cohn. adv. circ. 600. (back issues avail.) **Indexed:** Abstr.Engl.Stud., Amer.Hum.Ind., M.L.A.
—BLDSC (4360.249000).
    Description: Publishes research emanating from the special research collection of Morris Library.

027   IC
ICELAND. LANDSBOKASAFN ISLANDS. ARBOK. NYR FLOKKUR/ICELAND. NATIONAL LIBRARY. YEARBOOK. NEW SERIES. 1944. a. ISK 900($14) Landsbokasafn Islands - National Library of Iceland, Safnahusinu, Hverfisgoetu 15, 101 Reykjavik, Iceland. TEL 354-1-68-64. Dir. Finnbogi Gudmundsson.
    Supersedes in part (in 1975): Iceland. Landsbokasafn Islands. Arbok (ISSN 0254-1335)

LIBRARY AND INFORMATION SCIENCES

020　　　　US　ISSN 0019-1213
IDAHO LIBRARIAN. 1945. q. $15 to non-members. Idaho Library Association, Library, Univ. of Idaho, Moscow, ID 83843. TEL 208-885-7737. FAX 208-858-6817. Ed. Mary K. Bolin. adv. contact: Diane Prorak. bk.rev.; bibl.; illus.; index. circ. 600. (also avail. in microform from UMI; microfiche from CIS; reprint service avail. from UMI) **Indexed:** Lib.Lit., SRI. **Document type:** academic/scholarly publication.
—UMI.

610 026　　　　JA　ISSN 0445-2429
　　　　　　　　CODEN: IGTODY
IGAKU TOSHOKAN/JAPAN MEDICAL LIBRARY ASSOCIATION. JOURNAL. (Text in Japanese) 1954. q. 7000 Yen. Nihon Igaku Toshokan Kyokai - Japan Medical Library Association, 5-F, Gakkai Center Bldg., 2-4-16 Yayoi, Bunkyo-ku, Tokyo 113, Japan. FAX 03-3815-1608. Ed. Shigeaki Yamazaki. adv.; bk.rev. circ. 1,650. **Document type:** academic/scholarly publication.
—CASDDS.

025 380　　　　TS
AL-I'LAMIYYAH/INFORMATION. (Text in Arabic) 1985. q. exchange basis. United Arab Emirates University, Information Department, P.O. Box 15551, Al-Ain, United Arab Emirates. TEL 678333. TELEX 33521 JAMEAH EM. Ed. Tawfiq Yaqub. circ. 1,000.
Description: Social and cultural examination of the role of information and television in development.

020　　　　US　ISSN 0019-2104
Z732.I2
ILLINOIS LIBRARIES. 1919. 6/yr. free. State Library, 300 S. Second St., Springfield, IL 62701. TEL 217-782-2994. FAX 217-785-4326. bibl.; illus.; stat. circ. 9,000. (also avail. in microfilm from UMI; reprint service avail. from UMI) **Indexed:** Lib.Lit., Rehabil.Lit.
—BLDSC (4365.380000); Faxon; UnCover; UMI.

020　　　　US　ISSN 0732-2402
IMPULSE. 1913. w. $7. Fresno County Public Library, 2420 Mariposa St., Fresno, CA 93721. TEL 209-488-3223. FAX 209-488-1971. Ed. John Freitas. circ. 280.
Description: Staff newsletter of the Fresno County Public Library.

IN TOUCH (AUSTIN). see HANDICAPPED — Visually Impaired

020　　　　AT　ISSN 0158-0876
Z673
INCITE. 1980. 20/yr. Aus.$80 (foreign Aus.$100) (effective 1992). Australian Library and Information Association, P.O. Box E411, Queen Victoria Terrace, A.C.T. 2600, Australia. TEL 06-285-1877. FAX 06-282-2249. adv.
—BLDSC (4374.970000).
Description: Information in the field of library and information management.

020　　　　UK　ISSN 0073-6066
Z5055.G69
INDEX TO THESES ACCEPTED FOR HIGHER DEGREES IN THE UNIVERSITIES OF GREAT BRITAIN AND IRELAND. s-a. £165. Aslib, Association for Information Management, Publications Department, Information House, 20-24 Old St., London EC1V 9AP, England. TEL 071-253-4488. FAX 071-430-0514. (Dist. in N. America by: Learned Information, Inc., 143 Old Marlton Pike, Medford, NJ 08055-8750. TEL 609-654-6266) Eds. G.M. Paterson, Joan Hardy. (reprint service avail. from KTO) **Indexed:** Agri.Eng.Abstr., Anim.Breed.Abstr., Bio-Contr.News & Info., Cott.& Trop.Fibr.Abstr., Crop Physiol.Abstr., Dairy Sci.Abstr., Field Crop Abstr., Herb.Abstr., Ind.Vet., Pig News & Info., Plant Grow.Reg.Abstr., Poult.Abstr., Protozool.Abstr., Rev.Med.& Vet.Mycol., Rural Devel.Abstr., Seed Abstr., Small Anim.Abstr., Sugar Ind.Abstr., Triticale Abstr., Vet.Bull., Weed Abstr.
Description: Lists and abstracts all theses accepted for higher degrees in the universities of Great Britain and Ireland.

029.7　　　　II　ISSN 0046-8975
INDIAN ARCHIVES. (Text in English) 1947. s-a. Rs.19($6.84) National Archives of India, Janpath, New Delhi 110001, India. Ed. R.K. Perti. bk.rev. circ. 300. **Indexed:** Amer.Hist.& Life, Chem.Abstr., Hist.Abstr.
Description: Examines archival studies and the preservation of manuscripts. Features technical as well as general information on records administration, preparation and preservation of reference media as well as various documents and records of various bodies and institutions. Includes microfilming as well as other forms of documentary reproduction.

INDIAN BOOK REVIEW SUPPLEMENT. see PUBLISHING AND BOOK TRADE

020　　　　II　ISSN 0019-5782
Z671
INDIAN LIBRARY ASSOCIATION. BULLETIN. (Text in English) 1965. q. Rs.400($40) to non-members. Indian Library Association, A-40-41 Flat No.201, Ansal Bldg., Dr. Mukerjee Nagar, Delhi 110009, India. Ed. S. Ansari. adv.; bk.rev.; bibl.; illus. circ. 2,000. (also avail. in microfilm from UMI) **Indexed:** Lib.Lit., Lib.Sci.Abstr.
Supersedes: Indian Library Association. Journal.

020　　　　II　ISSN 0377-7367
Z845.I4
INDIAN LIBRARY MOVEMENT. (Text in Hindi) 1974. q. Rs.200($100) Model Town, Ambala City 134003, India. Ed. N.K. Bhagi. adv.; bk.rev.; bibl. circ. 500.

020　　　　II　ISSN 0067-3439
INDIAN STATISTICAL INSTITUTE. DOCUMENTATION RESEARCH AND TRAINING CENTRE. D R T C ANNUAL SEMINAR. 1963. a. price varies. Indian Statistical Institute, Documentation Research and Training Centre, 8th Mile, Mysore Road, Bangalore 560 059, India. TELEX 845-8376 ISIB IN. circ. 500. (also avail. in microfilm; microfiche) **Indexed:** Inform.Sci.Abstr., LISA.

020　　　　II
INDIAN STATISTICAL INSTITUTE. DOCUMENTATION RESEARCH AND TRAINING CENTRE. D R T C REFRESHER SEMINAR. 1969. a. price varies. Indian Statistical Institute, Documentation Research and Training Centre, 8th Mile, Mysore Road, Bangalore 560 059, India. TELEX 845-8376 ISIB IN. circ. 500. (also avail. in microform) **Indexed:** Inform.Sci.Abstr., LISA.

020　　　　US　ISSN 0275-777X
INDIANA LIBRARIES. 1906. irreg. (2-4/yr.). $10. Indiana Library Association, 6408 Carrollton Ave., Indianapolis, IN 46220-1615. TEL 317-636-6613. (Co-sponsors: Indiana State Library; Indiana Library Trustee Association) Ed. Dan Callison. bibl.; charts; illus. circ. 2,000. (also avail. in microform from UMI; back issues avail.) **Indexed:** Lib.Lit.
Supersedes (in 1981): Library Occurrent (ISSN 0024-2454)

020　　　　US
INDIANA UNIVERSITY. SCHOOL OF LIBRARY & INFORMATION SCIENCES. ALUMNI NEWSLETTER. 1968. s-a. Indiana University, Alumni Association, Fountain Sq., No.219, Bloomington, IN 47402-4822. TEL 812-855-5844. Ed. Mary Krutulis. illus.; circ. 3,800 (controlled).
Former titles: Vibrations; Indiana University. School of Library and Information Science. Alumni Newsletter; Indiana University. Graduate Library School Alumni Newsletter (ISSN 0019-6827)

020　　　　IT　ISSN 0394-0810
L'INDICIZZAZIONE; rivista per archivi, biblioteche, musei, banche dati e centri di documentazione. (Text in Italian; summaries in English, Italian) 1986. s-a. L.65000 to non-members (foreign L.85000) (effective 1992). (Centro di Informazione e Documentazione Automatizzata) Proxima Scientific Press S.r.l., Via San Francesco, 24, 34100 Trieste, Italy. (Edit. addr.: Biblioteca Statale del Popolo, Via del Teatro Romano, 17, 34121 Trieste, Italy. TEL 040-631679) Ed. Benedetto Aschero. bk.rev.; abstr.; bibl.

INFO OUTLOOK (YEAR); a guide to trends and sources for the information community. see BUSINESS AND ECONOMICS — Management

020　　　　US
INFOCUS (EMPORIA). 1973. s-a. free. (Emporia State University, School of Library and Information Management) Emporia State University Press, 1200 Commercial, Emporia, KS 66801-5087. TEL 316-341-5203. FAX 316-341-5997. Ed. Martha Hale. illus.; stat. circ. 2,500. **Indexed:** Amer.Hist.& Life, Hist.Abstr. **Document type:** newsletter.
Former titles (until 1987): Gleanings (Emporia); Library School Review Newsletter (ISSN 0277-8939); E S U Library School Newsletter.

020　　　　UK　ISSN 0306-0756
INFORM. 10/yr. £35 (to non-members) (effective 1994). Institute of Information Scientists, 44 Museum St., London WC1A 1LY, England. TEL 071-831-8003. FAX 071-430-1270. Sheila Webber. circ. 2,900. **Document type:** newsletter.
—BLDSC (4478.886000).
Description: Covers recent developments in the information world. Includes association news for members.

027.4　　　　SA　ISSN 1018-3310
INFORMAT (INTERNATIONAL EDITION). National edition (ISSN 0256-4106) (Text in English) 1990. bi-m. free. State Library - Staatsbiblioteek, P.O. Box 397, Pretoria 0001, South Africa. TEL 27-12-21-8931. FAX 27-12-325-5984. TELEX 3-22171 SA. Ed. Hester van der Walt. bk.rev.; illus. circ. 535. **Document type:** newsletter.

027.4　　　　SA　ISSN 0256-4106
INFORMAT (NATIONAL EDITION). International edition (ISSN 1018-3310) (Text in Afrikaans, English) 1985. bi-m. free. State Library - Staatsbiblioteek, P.O. Box 397, Pretoria 0001, South Africa. TEL 27-12-21-8931. FAX 27-12-325-5984. TELEX 3-22171-SA. Ed. Hester van der Walt. bk.rev.; illus. circ. 937. **Document type:** newsletter.
Description: Discusses international and national conferences, quality control, board appointments and activities.

029 004　　　　YU　ISSN 0019-9923
INFORMATIKA. (Text in Serbo-Croatian; summaries in English, Russian, Serbo-Croatian) 1967. q. $214. Jugoslovenski Centar za Tehnicku i Naucnu Dokumentaciju - Yugoslav Center for Technical and Scientific Documentation (YCTSD), Sl. Penezica-Krcuna 29-31, Box 724, 11000 Belgrade, Yugoslavia. Ed. Ljiljana Kojic-Bogdanovic.

020 500　　　　HU　ISSN 0230-4619
INFORMATIKA ES TUDOMANYELEMZES. (Text in English, Hungarian) 1981. irreg. price varies or exchange basis. Magyar Tudomanyos Akademia Konyvtara, Aranyjanos u.1, P.O. Box 7, 1361 Budapest 5, Hungary. Ed. T. Braun. **Document type:** monographic series.
Description: Contains studies on information science and scientometrics, quantitative aspects of the science of science and science policy.

026　　　　IS
INFORMATION & LIBRARIANSHIP. (Text in Hebrew; summaries in English) 1966. 2/yr. $80. Israel Society of Special Libraries and Information Centers, P.O. Box 43074, Tel Aviv 61430, Israel. TEL 972-3-492064. Ed. Moshe Grundman. adv.; bk.rev.; bibl.; index. circ. 1,000. (processed) **Indexed:** Ind.Heb.Per., LISA, Sci.Abstr.
—BLDSC (2593.470000).
Formerly (until vol.20): I S L I C Bulletin (ISSN 0021-2318)

020　　　　US　ISSN 0895-9927
INFORMATION BROKER. 1978. 6/yr. $35. Burwell Enterprises, Houston, TX 77068. TEL 713-537-9051. FAX 713-537-8332. Ed. Helen P. Burwell. **Document type:** newsletter.
—BLDSC (4481.958000).
Formerly: Journal Fee-Based Information Services (ISSN 0190-2261)
Description: Newsletter for, by, and about the companies which offer information for a fee.

LIBRARY AND INFORMATION SCIENCES

020   AT   ISSN 1037-6399
INFORMATION CENTRES IN THE NORTHERN TERRITORY. LIST. 1980. a. Aus.$10 to non-members (typically set in Dec.). Library Association of Australia, Northern Territory, G.P.O. Box 2786, Darwin, N.T. 0891, Australia. TEL 089-895279. FAX 089-814806. Ed. Murray Maynard. circ. 80. (back issues avail.).
   Formerly: Libraries and Resources Centres in the Northern Territory. List (ISSN 0728-7429)

020   UK   ISSN 0266-6669
Z672   CODEN: INDEE8
INFORMATION DEVELOPMENT; the international journal for librarians, archivists and information specialists. (Text in English, French, Portuguese, Spanish; summaries in English) 1985. q. £75($58.50) to individuals; institutions £65($117). Bowker - Saur Ltd., A Reed Reference Publishing Company, Part of Reed Elsevier plc, Maypole House, Maypole Rd., E. Grinstead, W. Sussex RH19 1HH, England. TEL 0342-330-100. FAX 0342-330-191. (Subscr. to: c/o Baileys, 127 Sandgate Rd., Folkestone, Kent CT20 2BL, England. TEL 0303-850801) Ed. J. Stephen Parker. adv.; bk.rev. circ. 500. (also avail. in microfiche; back issues avail.). Indexed: Info.Media & Tech., Lib.Lit., LISA, Rural Ext.Educ.& Tr.Abstr., World Agri.Econ.& Rural Sociol.Abstr.
—BLDSC (4493.538200); UnCover; SWETS.
   Description: Contains articles, news, book reviews on current issues, problems and trends in information work throughout the world, with particular emphasis in the needs and concerns of developing countries.

INFORMATION DISPLAY. see *LIBRARY AND INFORMATION SCIENCES — Computer Applications*

020   365.34   US
▼**INFORMATION GATHERER NEWSLETTER**; a quarterly publication for information professionals. 1994. q. $20. Worldwide Consultants, 2421 W. Pratt Blvd., Ste. 971, Chicago, IL 60645. E-mail: worldwid@uunet.uu.net. Ed. David Johnson.
   Description: Presents topics of interest to information professionals - investigators, journalists, information brokers, records researchers, intelligence analysts, librarians.

029.7   US   ISSN 0360-5817
Q223   CODEN: INHODN
INFORMATION HOTLINE. 1969. 10/yr. $150 (foreign $175). Science Associates International, Inc., 465 West End Ave., New York, NY 10024. TEL 212-873-0656. FAX 212-873-5587. Ed. Ivan Lyons. bk.rev.; bibl. (also avail. in microfilm from UMI; back issues avail.; reprint service avail. from UMI) Indexed: Comput.& Info.Sys., Inform.Sci.Abstr., Leg.Info.Manage.Ind., Lib.Lit., Lib.Sci.Abstr., PROMT, Resour.Ctr.Ind. Document type: trade publication.
—BLDSC (4493.607300); UnCover; UMI; CASDDS.
   Former titles: Information News and Sources (ISSN 0360-5809); Information-Part 1-News, Sources, Profiles (ISSN 0036-8776); Scientific Information Notes.
   Description: Enables librarians to understand new technologies and the ins and outs of governmental influence on information science and libraries.

INFORMATION MANAGEMENT & COMPUTER SECURITY. see *BUSINESS AND ECONOMICS — Management*

020   US
INFORMATION MANAGEMENT, POLICIES AND SERVICES. 1988. irreg. price varies. Ablex Publishing Corporation, 355 Chestnut St., Norwood, NJ 07648. TEL 201-767-8450. FAX 201-767-6717. TELEX 135-393. Eds. Charles R. McClure, Peter Hernon.

INFORMATION MANAGEMENT REPORT. see *LIBRARY AND INFORMATION SCIENCES — Computer Applications*

020   US   ISSN 0897-3199
INFORMATION MANAGEMENT SOURCEBOOK. 1987. a. $79 (free to new members, $39 thereafter). Association for Information & Image Management, 1100 Wayne Ave., Ste. 1100, Silver Spring, MD 20910. TEL 301-587-8202. adv. circ. 10,000. Document type: directory.
   Description: Annual directory of products, services, vendors and manufacturers of information and image management technologies and systems.

029.7   UK   ISSN 0306-4573
Z699.A1   CODEN: IPMADK
INFORMATION PROCESSING & MANAGEMENT; an international journal. (Text in English, French, German, Italian) 1963. 6/yr. £341($525) (effective 1994). Elsevier Science Ltd., Pergamon, P.O. Box 800, Kidlington, Oxford OX5 1DX, England. TEL 44-865-843000. FAX 44-865-843010. (Subscr. in U.S. and Canada to: Elsevier Science, 660 White plains Rd., Tarrytown, NY 10591-5153. TEL 914-524-9200. FAX 914-333-2444) Ed. Tefko Saracevic. adv.; bk.rev.; charts; illus.; index. circ. 2,000. (also avail. in microfilm from UMI; reprint service avail. from UMI) Indexed: ABI Inform., Biol.Abstr., BPIA, CLOSS, Commun.Abstr., Compumath, Comput.Abstr., Comput.Cont., Comput.Rev., Curr.Cont., Excerp.Med., Key to Econ.Sci., Leg.Info.Manage.Ind., LHTN, Lib.Lit., LISA, Math.R., Sci.Abstr., Soft.Abstr.Eng., SSCI, Tr.& Indus.Ind. Document type: academic/scholarly publication.
—BLDSC (4493.893000); Faxon; UnCover; SWETS; UMI; CASDDS. CCC.
   Formerly: Information Storage and Retrieval (ISSN 0020-0271)
   Description: For library and information scientists, managers of information systems and communication networks, and researchers. Provides papers on research and development of non-traditional approaches to information management, electronic publishing, library and information systems and related fields.
Refereed Serial

020   UK   ISSN 0959-8928
INFORMATION RESEARCH NEWS. 1976. 3/yr. £16 (foreign £20). University of Sheffield, Department of Information Studies, Western Bank, Sheffield S10 2TN, England. TEL 0742-768555. FAX 0742-739826. TELEX 547216-UGSHEF-G. adv.; bk.rev. circ. 1,100. Indexed: Curr.Cont., Lib.Sci.Abstr., LISA. Document type: academic/scholarly publication.
—BLDSC (4494.141000).
   Formerly: C R U S News (ISSN 0140-4253)
   Description: Disseminates findings in library and information studies resulting from recent research.

INFORMATION RESOURCES MANAGEMENT JOURNAL. see *BUSINESS AND ECONOMICS — Management*

020   US
INFORMATION RESOURCES MANAGEMENT PROGRAM. every 5 yrs. (plus a. update). U.S. Department of Veterans Affairs, 810 Vermont Ave., N.W. (008B3), Washington, DC 20420. TEL 202-233-3557. Document type: government publication.
   Description: Aims to improve management of information resources by strengthening and integrating the information resources management program planning, programming, and budgeting activities.

029.7   JA   ISSN 0913-3801
Z671   CODEN: JKGIEP
INFORMATION SCIENCE AND TECHNOLOGY ASSOCIATION. JOURNAL/JOHO NO KAGAKU TO GIJUTSU. 1950. m. 20517 Yen. Information Science and Technology Association, Sasaki Bldg., 5-7 Koisikawa 2-chome, Bunkyo-ku, Tokyo 112, Japan. TEL 813-3813-3791. FAX 813-3813-3793. Ed. Gen Masuda. adv.; bk.rev. circ. 3,000. Indexed: INIS Atomind., LISA.
—BLDSC (4769.700000); CASDDS.
   Formerly: Dokumenteysyon Kenkyu - Documentation Study (ISSN 0012-5180)

020   NE   ISSN 0167-5265
Z699.A1   CODEN: ISUDX8
INFORMATION SERVICES & USE; an international journal. (Text in English) 1981. 4/yr. fl.391($214) (effective 1994). I O S Press, Van Diemenstraat 94, 1013 CN Amsterdam, Netherlands. TEL 31-20-6382189. FAX 31-20-6203419. (Subscr. in U.S. and Canada to: Box 10558, Burke, VA 22009-0558. TEL 703-323-5554. FAX 703-250-4705) Ed. A.W. Elias, T. Cawkell. adv.; bk.rev. (also avail. in microform from UMI) Indexed: AESIS, BPIA, Bus.Ind., Comput.Abstr., Comput.Cont., Comput.Lit.Ind., Fluidex, Key to Econ.Sci., Leg.Info.Manage.Ind., LHTN, LISA, Manage.Cont., Mgmt.& Market.Abstr., Sci.Abstr., Tr.& Indus.Ind. Document type: academic/scholarly publication.
—BLDSC (4495.950000); EI; Faxon; SWETS; CASDDS. CCC.
   Incorporates (1987-1993): Infomediary (ISSN 0169-2763)
   Description: Contains data on international developments in information management and its applications. Articles cover on-line systems, library automation, word processing, micrographics, videotex and telecommunications.
Refereed Serial

INFORMATION SOLUTIONS; a newsletter of ideas and techniques about how to profit from information. see *BUSINESS AND ECONOMICS — Management*

INFORMATION STANDARDS QUARTERLY. see *PUBLISHING AND BOOK TRADE*

020   UK   ISSN 0266-8513
INFORMATION TECHNOLOGY AND PUBLIC POLICY. 1982. 3/yr. £35($68) (foreign £40). (Parliamentary Information Technology Committee) Philip Virgo, 2. Eastbourne Ave., Acton, London W3 6JN, England. TEL 081-993-8716. FAX 081-992-3575. Ed. K. Norman. adv. circ. 500. Indexed: Abstr.Hum.Comp.Inter., CAD CAM Abstr., Cont.Pg.Manage., Sci.Abstr. Document type: proceedings.
—BLDSC (4496.368740).
   Formerly: P I T C O M (ISSN 0263-614X)

020   BS
INFORMATION TRENDS - NEWS MAGAZINE; review of developments in information studies in the Eastern & Southern African region. (Text in English) 1988. 3/yr. University of Botswana, Department of Library & Information Studies, P.O. Box 0022, Gaborone, Botswana. (Co-sponsors: German Foundation for International Development; Education, Science and Documentation Centre) Eds. K.J. Mchombu, J.R. Neill. Indexed: P.L.E.S.A. (1989-).

020   GW   ISSN 0944-1867
▼**INFORMATIONSMITTEL FUER BIBLIOTHEKEN**. 1993. q. DM.64. Deutsches Bibliotheksinstitut, Abt. 1 - Publikationen, Bundesallee 184-185, 10717 Berlin, Germany. TEL 030-8505-0. FAX 030-8505100. Document type: bulletin.

020   CI   ISSN 0354-2874
INFORMATOLOGIA. (Text and summaries in Croatian, English) 1969. s-a. $60 1000 CRD (effective 1992). Institut Informacijskih Znanosti - Institute for Information Sciences, Trg Marsala Tita 3, Box 327, 41001 Zagreb, Croatia. TEL 38-41-427-878. FAX 38-41-427-903. TELEX 22486 RCSZGH. Ed. Mario Plenkovic. bk.rev.; abstr.; charts; index. circ. 600. (back issues avail.) Indexed: Lib.Sci.Abstr., Ref.Zh., Sci.Abstr. Document type: academic/scholarly publication.
   Formerly (until vol.23, 1991): Informatologia Yugoslavica (ISSN 0046-9483)
   Description: Publishes original scientific papers, professional papers, short notes, preliminary communications, reports, recommendations and reviews in the field of librarianship and the documentation and information sciences.

INFOTERM SERIES. (International Information Centre for Terminology, Vienna) see *LINGUISTICS*

LIBRARY AND INFORMATION SCIENCES

027.4　　　　　US　　ISSN 0020-1308
Z689.8.P82
INGLEWOOD PUBLIC LIBRARY QUARTERLY REPORT. 1962. q. free. Inglewood Public Library, 101 W. Manchester Blvd., Inglewood, CA 90301-1771. TEL 310-412-5397. FAX 310-412-8848. Ed. Miguel J.C. Alaniz. stat. circ. 200. (processed; also avail. in microfiche.) **Indexed:** Ind.Curr.Urb.Doc. **Document type:** newsletter.
Description: Events and performance indicators during the quarter at the library.

020 011　　　　EI　　ISSN 0255-0806
　　　　　　　　　　　CODEN: ITETEW
INNOVATION AND TECHNOLOGY TRANSFER. (Text in English) 1980. irreg., 5-6/yr. free. Commission of the European Communities, Directorate XIII-D-2, DG XIII-D-2, JMO B4-082, 2920 Luxembourg, Luxembourg. TEL 342-4301-2916. FAX 352-430132084. TELEX 3423 COMEUR LU. bk.rev. circ. 48,000. (back issues avail.) **Document type:** newsletter.
—BLDSC (4515.480370).
Former titles: New Technologies and Innovation Policy; New Technologies; D S T C Newsletter (ISSN 0251-2645)
Description: Provides information on research and research-related activities of the commission, with particular emphasis on exploitation of research results.

INSIDE CONFERENCES ON C D - R O M. see BIBLIOGRAPHIES

020 001.539　　UK　　ISSN 0952-9527
INSIDE INFORMATION. 1989. biennial. £35. T F P L Publishing, 17-18 Britton St., London EC1M 5NQ, England. TEL 071-251-5522. FAX 071-251-8318. **Document type:** trade publication.
—BLDSC (4518.152200).

INSIDE INFORMATION ON C D - R O M. see BIBLIOGRAPHIES

020　　　　　　　CN　　ISSN 0832-9605
INSIDE O L A. bi-m. Can.$36. Ontario Library Association, 100 Lombard St., Ste. 303, Toronto, ON M5C 1M3, Canada. TEL 416-363-3388. FAX 416-941-9581. Ed. Jefferson A.R. Gilbert. adv.: page Can.$500. circ. 4,200. **Document type:** newsletter.

027.4　　　　　　US
INSIGHT (AKRON). 1960. bi-m. $2 (free to libraries). Akron - Summit County Public Library, 55 S. Main St., Akron, OH 44326. TEL 216-762-7621. Ed. Patricia H. Latshaw. illus.; circ. 2,000. (controlled). (processed) **Document type:** newsletter.
Formerly (until 1986): Owlet (ISSN 0030-7602)
Description: Aims to keep Summit County residents informed of library resources and services.

020　　　　　　　US
INSIGHT (SPRINGFIELD); a newsletter from the Illinois State Library. 1972. bi-m. free. State Library, 300 S. Second St., Springfield, IL 62701. TEL 217-785-6925. FAX 217-785-4324. Ed. Jan Grimes. circ. 3,900. (controlled). (back issues avail.) **Document type:** newsletter.
Formerly (until 1991): Illinois Notes.

020　　　　　　　US
Z733
INSIGHTS (WASHINGTON, 1988). 1969. bi-m. membership. Library of Congress Professional Association, Library of Congress, Washington, DC 20540. TEL 202-707-3635. Eds. Tim Carlton, Sarah Rouse. adv.; bk.rev.; circ. 2,200 (controlled). (processed) **Document type:** newsletter.
Formerly (until 1988): Library of Congress Professional Asscciation. Newsletter (ISSN 0098-1648)

026　　　　　　　GW　　ISSN 0019-0217
Z675.A2　　　　　　　　CODEN: INPLBI
INSPEL. (Text in English, French) 1975. q. DM.80. Technische Universitaet Berlin, Universitaetsbibliothek, Str. des 17. Juni 135, 10623 Berlin, Germany. TEL 030-31423980. FAX 030-31424743. (Co-sponsor: International Federation of Library Associations) Ed. Ekkehart Seusing. bk.rev.; index. circ. 300. **Indexed:** LHTN, Lib.Lit., LISA, Sci.Abstr. **Document type:** academic/scholarly publication.
—BLDSC (4518.660000); SWETS. **CCC**.

INSTITUT PROVINCIAL D'ETUDES ET RECHERCHES BIBLIOTHECONOMIQUES. MEMOIRES. see BIBLIOGRAPHIES

020 300　　　　JA　　ISSN 0020-2827
INSTITUTE OF DEVELOPING ECONOMIES. LIBRARY BULLETIN/AJIA KEIZAI SHIRYO-GEPPO. (Text in English and Japanese) 1959. m. 7200 Yen. Institute of Developing Economies - Ajia Keizai Kenkyusho, 42 Ichigaya-Hommura-cho, Shinjuku-ku, Tokyo 162, Japan. bibl. circ. 1,000. (also avail. in microform)

INTER DOCUMENTATION COMPANY. CATALOGUE OF CATALOGUES. see BIBLIOGRAPHIES

020　　　　　　　US　　ISSN 0047-0414
Z732.D62
INTERCOM (WASHINGTON, 1971). 1971. m. (11/yr.). membership. District of Columbia Library Association, Box 14177, Benjamin Franklin Sta., Washington, DC 20044. Eds. Ann Benson, Jacque-Lynne Schulman. adv. circ. 1,000. (processed)
Supersedes: D.C. Libraries.
Description: Lists courses, seminars and job opportunities.

026　　　　　　　US　　ISSN 0270-6717
Z672
INTERFACE (CHICAGO, 1978). 1978. q. $15 (foreign $25). American Library Association, Association of Specialized and Cooperative Library Agencies, 50 E. Huron St., Chicago, IL 60611-2795. TEL 312-944-6780. Ed. Thomas Dorst. adv.; bk.rev. circ. 2,000. (also avail. in microform from UMI; back issues avail.; reprint service avail. from UMI) **Indexed:** API Abstr., Lib.Lit. **Document type:** bulletin.
—UMI.
Supersedes: A S L A President's Newsletter; H R L S D Journal; Which was formerly (nos.1-2, 1975): Health and Rehabilitative Library Services News (ISSN 0098-3462); Which superseded: Association of Hospital and Institution Libraries. Quarterly (ISSN 0090-3116) & A H I L Quarterly (ISSN 0001-1428)

020　　　　　　　UK　　ISSN 0264-1615
Z921.B854　　　　　　　CODEN: IDSUDQ
INTERLENDING AND DOCUMENT SUPPLY. 1971. q. $259.95. M C B University Press Ltd., 60-62 Toller Ln., Bradford, W. Yorks BD8 9BY, England. TEL 0274-499821. FAX 0274-547143. TELEX 51317-MCBUNI-G. Ed. David Wood. bibl.; index, cum.index: 1971-1975. (back issues avail.) **Indexed:** Br.Ceram.Abstr., Curr.Cont., Dairy Sci.Abstr., Field Crop Abstr., Herb.Abstr., Inform.Sci.Abstr., LHTN, Lib.Lit., LISA, Nutr.Abstr., Ref.Zh., Sci.Abstr., SSCI. **Document type:** academic/scholarly publication.
—BLDSC (4534.463000); Faxon; UnCover; SWETS; CASDDS.
Former titles (until 1983): Interlending Review: Journal of the British Library Lending Division (ISSN 0140-2773); (until 1978): B L L Review (ISSN 0305-6503); N L L Review (ISSN 0027-6790)

026　　　　　　　US
INTERNATIONAL ASSOCIATION OF LAW LIBRARIES. DIRECTORY. 1977. irreg., latest ed. 1988. $55 to individuals; institutions $80. International Association of Law Libraries, c/o Dr. Ivan Sipkov, Box 5709, Washington, DC 20016-1309. FAX 202-778-6652. adv.; bk.rev. circ. 500. **Indexed:** C.L.I., Leg.Per. **Document type:** directory.

INTERNATIONAL ASSOCIATION OF ORIENTALIST LIBRARIANS. BULLETIN. see ORIENTAL STUDIES

INTERNATIONAL ASSOCIATION OF PERFORMING ARTS LIBRARIES AND MUSEUMS. CONGRESS PROCEEDINGS. see ART

INTERNATIONAL BULLETIN OF MISSIONARY RESEARCH. see RELIGIONS AND THEOLOGY — Protestant

029　　　　　　　GW　　ISSN 1011-8829
Z693.A15　　　　　　　CODEN: ICBCEH
INTERNATIONAL CATALOGUING AND BIBLIOGRAPHIC CONTROL. 1972. q. £32($55) International Federation of Library Associations, UBCIM Programme, c/o Deutsche Bibliothek, 4-8 Zeppelinallee, 60325 Frankfurt a.M., Germany. TEL 069-7410906. FAX 069-7566224. (Subscr. to: Bailey Management Services, 127 Sandgate Rd., Folkestone, Kent CT20 2BL, England) Ed. Marie-France Plassard. bk.rev.; bibl. **Indexed:** Lib.Lit., LISA. **Document type:** trade publication.
—BLDSC (4538.411000); Faxon; UnCover; SWETS.
Formerly: International Cataloguing (ISSN 0047-0635)
Refereed Serial

020　　　　　　　US　　ISSN 0364-3670
　　　　　　　　　　　CODEN: ICDIDA
INTERNATIONAL CODEN DIRECTORY. every 5 yrs. (plus a. supplements). $900 for base vol.; $270 for each supplement (effective Jan. 1994). Chemical Abstracts Service (Subsidiary of: American Chemical Society), 2540 Olentagy River Rd., Box 3012, Columbus, OH 43210-0012. TEL 614-447-3600. FAX 614-447-3713. TELEX 6842086. (microfiche) **Document type:** directory.
—BLDSC (4538.703000).

026　　　　　　　BS
INTERNATIONAL COUNCIL ON ARCHIVES. EASTERN AND SOUTHERN AFRICA REGIONAL BRANCH. GENERAL CONFERENCE PROCEEDINGS. 1969. a. $30. International Council on Archives, Eastern and Southern Africa Regional Branch, c/o Botswana National Archives and Records Services, Government Enclave, Khama Crescent, P.O. Box 239, Gaborone, Botswana. TEL 3601000. FAX 313584. TELEX 2994 BD. Ed. R.J. Kukubo. **Document type:** proceedings.
Description: Covers biennial conference proceedings of ESARBICA - various themes and subthemes.

025　　　　　　　US
INTERNATIONAL DIRECTORY OF NEWS LIBRARIES AND NEWSPAPER BANNERS. 1985. irreg. $99.95. (Special Libraries Association, News Division) L D A Publishers, 42-36 209 St., Bayside, NY 11361. TEL 718-224-9484. FAX 718-224-9487. index. circ. 350. **Document type:** directory.
Former titles: International Directory of News Libraries Including Finding (ISSN 1048-1087) & International Directory of News Libraries Including Buyers' Guide (Year); International Directory of News Libraries and Buyers' Guide (Year) (ISSN 0889-0919)
Description: Alphabetical listings by country, state and city of major news libraries worldwide. Includes banners from major daily newspapers.

029.7　　　　　　NE
INTERNATIONAL FEDERATION FOR INFORMATION AND DOCUMENTATION. PROCEEDINGS OF CONGRESS. 1895. biennial, latest 1989. price varies. Elsevier Science B.V., Books Division, P.O. Box 211, 1000 AE Amsterdam, Netherlands. TEL 31-20-5803911. FAX 31-20-5803705. TELEX 18582 ESPA NL. (Subscr. in U.S. and Canada to: Elsevier Science Inc., Box 882, Madison Sq. Sta., New York, NY 10159. TEL 212-989-5800) **Document type:** proceedings.
Formerly: International Federation for Documentation. Proceedings of Congress (ISSN 0074-5812)
Refereed Serial

020 700　　　　JA　　ISSN 0261-152X
Z675.A85
INTERNATIONAL FEDERATION OF LIBRARY ASSOCIATIONS AND INSTITUTIONS. SECTION OF ART LIBRARIES. NEWSLETTER. 1981. 3/yr. membership. International Federation of Library Associations and Institutions, Section of Art Libraries, c/o Hiroyuki Hatano, Ed., National Museum of Modern Art, 7-7 Veno Koen, Taito-ku, Tokyo, Japan. circ. 900. **Document type:** newsletter.
—BLDSC (6107.449000).
Formerly: Round Table of Art Librarians. Newsheet.
Description: News about upcoming conferences and new art library literature.

020 029   RU   ISSN 0304-9701
Z1007   CODEN: IFIDD7
INTERNATIONAL FORUM ON INFORMATION AND DOCUMENTATION. (Editions in English, Russian) 1975. q. fl.100. Vsesoyuznyi Institut Nauchno-Tekhnicheskoi Informatsii (VINITI), Ul. Baltiiskaya 14, 125219 Moscow, Russia. (Subscr. to: F I D General Secretariat, P.O. Box 90402, 2509 LK The Hague, Netherlands) (Co-sponsor: International Federation for Documentation) Ed. A.I. Mikhailov. adv. circ. 6,000. **Indexed:** Curr.Cont., Lib.Lit., LISA, Sci.Abstr., SSCI.
—BLDSC (4540.340000); Faxon; UnCover; SWETS; CASDDS. **CCC.**

020   II   ISSN 0970-1850
Z671
INTERNATIONAL INFORMATION, COMMUNICATION AND EDUCATION. 1982. s-a. Rs.340($70) P. Kaula Endowment for Library and Information Science, C-239, Indira Nagar, Lucknow 226 016, India. Ed. P.N. Kaula. adv.; bk.rev.; charts; index. (also avail. in microform from UMI) **Indexed:** Curr.Cont., Inform.Sci.Abstr., LISA. **Document type:** academic/scholarly publication.
—BLDSC (4541.274000).
  Description: Multidisciplinary journal on communication and information sciences within developing nations. Includes relevant computer applications, digests, notes and viewpoints from several countries.

020   UK   ISSN 0953-556X
Z671
INTERNATIONAL JOURNAL OF INFORMATION AND LIBRARY RESEARCH. 1989. 3/yr. £58($110) Taylor Graham Publishing, 500 Chesham House, 150 Regent St., London W1R 5FA, England. Ed. Stephen Roberts. adv.; bk.rev. **Indexed:** LISA. **Document type:** academic/scholarly publication.
—BLDSC (4542.304800); SWETS.
  Description: Current research and development in information management and information technology.

INTERNATIONAL JOURNAL OF INFORMATION MANAGEMENT. see *COMPUTERS — Information Science And Information Theory*

026.34 340   US   ISSN 0731-1265
Z675.L2
INTERNATIONAL JOURNAL OF LEGAL INFORMATION. (Text in English) 1973. 3/yr. $55 to individuals; institutions $80. International Institute for Legal Information, Box 5709, Washington, DC 20016-1309. TEL 202-244-3386. FAX 202-662-6291. adv.; bk.rev.; index. circ. 1,000. **Indexed:** C.L.I., ELLIS, Foreign Leg.Per., Int.Lab.Doc., L.R.I., Leg.Info.Manage.Ind., Leg.Per., LISA. **Document type:** academic/scholarly publication.
—BLDSC (4542.315000); Faxon; UnCover; SWETS.
  Formerly: International Journal of Law Libraries (ISSN 0340-045X); Which supersedes in part: International Association of Law Libraries. Bulletin (ISSN 0538-4524)

020 327   US   ISSN 0892-4546
Z672
INTERNATIONAL LEADS. 1957. q. $12. American Library Association, International Relations Round Table, 50 E. Huron St., Chicago, IL 60611. TEL 312-280-3200. FAX 312-944-3897. TELEX 4909992000 ALA Ul. Ed. Robert P. Doyle. bk.rev.; bibl.; circ. 900 (controlled). **Indexed:** Lib.Lit., LISA. **Document type:** trade publication.
—SWETS.
  Former titles: Leads (ISSN 0458-8983); Leads: A Fact Sheet.

020   UK   ISSN 1057-2317
Z671
THE INTERNATIONAL LIBRARY AND INFORMATION REVIEW. 1969. q. £115 (effective 1994). Academic Press Ltd. (Subsidiary of: Harcourt Brace & Company Ltd.), 24-28 Oval Rd., London NW1 7DX, England. TEL 44-71-267-4466.
FAX 44-71-482-2293. TELEX 25775-ACPRES-G. (Subscr. to: Harcourt Brace & Company Ltd., Foots Cray High St., Sidcup, Kent DA14 5HP, England. TEL 44-81-300-3322. FAX 44-81-309-0807) Eds. N. Moore, T. Carbo Bearman. **Indexed:** Amer.Hist.& Life, C.I.J.E., Comput.Rev., Curr.Cont., Hist.Abstr., Lib.Lit., LISA, So.Pac.Per.Ind., SSCI. **Document type:** academic/scholarly publication.
—BLDSC (4541.266000); Faxon; UnCover; SWETS. **CCC.**
  Formerly: International Library Review (ISSN 0020-7837)
  Description: Addresses progress and research in international and comparative librarianship, documentation, and information retrieval for librarians worldwide.

025   II   ISSN 0970-0048
Z671
INTERNATIONAL LIBRARY MOVEMENT. (Text in English) 1974. q. Rs.350($120) Post Box No. 1, (G.P.O.), Model Town, Ambala City 134 003, India. Ed. N.K. Bhagi. adv.; bk.rev.; abstr.; bibl.; stat. circ. 1,000.
—BLDSC (4542.930000).
  Description: Examines the theory and practice of librarianship and information science with emphasis on the needs and problems of developing countries.

020   UK   ISSN 0269-0500
INTERNATIONAL REVIEW OF CHILDREN'S LITERATURE AND LIBRARIANSHIP. 1986. 3/yr. £452($100) Taylor Graham Publishing, 500 Chesham House, 150 Regent St., London W1R 5FA, England. Ed. Margaret Kinnell. adv.; bk.rev. (back issues avail.) **Indexed:** Lib.Lit., LISA, Mult.Ed.Abstr. **Document type:** academic/scholarly publication.
—BLDSC (4546.343000).

020 025   US
INTERNATIONAL YEARBOOK OF SERIALS LIBRARIANSHIP. 1988. a. $34.95. Haworth Press, Inc., 10 Alice St., Binghamton, NY 13904.
TEL 607-722-5857; 800-342-9678.
FAX 607-722-1424. Ed. David P. Woodworth.
  Refereed Serial

020   MX   ISSN 0187-358X
INVESTIGACION BIBLIOTECOLOGICA; archivonomia, bibliotecologia, e informacion. (Text in Spanish; abstracts in English) 1986. s-a. $15. Universidad Nacional Autonoma de Mexico, Centro Universitario de Investigaciones Bibliotecologicas, Torre II de Humanidades, pisos 12 y 13, Ciudad Universitaria, 04510 Mexico, D.F., Mexico. TEL 623-03-34. FAX 550-74-61. Ed. Carlos Ceballos Sosa. adv.; bk.rev.; abstr.; bibl.; circ. 1,000 (controlled). **Indexed:** Inform.Sci.Abstr., Lib.Lit., LISA. **Document type:** academic/scholarly publication.
  Refereed Serial

027.8   US
IOWA MEDIA MESSAGE. (Former name of issuing body: Audiovisual Education Association of Iowa) 1972. 4/yr. membership. Iowa Educational Media Association, 2306 Sixth St., Harlan, IA 51537. adv.; bk.rev. circ. 650.
  Formerly: Iowa Association of School Librarians. Library Lines (ISSN 0021-0447)

029   SP   ISSN 1130-9008
IRARGI; artxibistika aldizkaria - revista de archivistica. (Text in Gallegan) 1988. q. (Kultura Saila - Departamento de Cultura) Eusko Jaurlaritzaren Argitalpen Zerbitzu Nagusia - Servicio Central de Publicaciones del Gobierno Vasco, Duque de Wellington 2, 01011 Vitoria-Gasteiz, Spain. circ. 2,000.

026 025   IE
IRISH ARCHIVES. (Text in English, Gaelic) 1971. irreg. £4.50. Irish Society for Archives, c/o Mr. Brian Donnelly, National Archives, Four Courts, Dublin 7, Ireland. Ed. Ailsa C. Holland. bk.rev. circ. 200. (back issues avail.)
  Formerly: Irish Archives Bulletin.
  Description: Contains material on archival practices and development inland and overseas.

020   AT   ISSN 0814-303X
ISSUES; for serials librarians. 1984. irreg. (2-3/yr.) free. I S A Australia, 2nd Fl., 41 Sherwood Rd., Toowong, Qld. 4066, Australia. TEL 07-371-7500. FAX 61-7-371-5566. (Subscr. to: P.O. Box 709, Toowong, Qld. 4066, Australia) Ed. Alfred J Gans. adv.; bk.rev. circ. 2,000. (back issues avail.) **Document type:** newsletter.
  Description: Discusses issues relating to subscription agents and serials librarians. Also covers news and activities of ISA Australia.

016   IT
ITALY. ISTITUTO DI STUDI SULLA RICERCA E DOCUMENTAZIONE SCIENTIFICA. NOTE DI BIBLIOGRAFIA E DOCUMENTAZIONE SCIENTIFICA. 1955. irreg., vol.52, 1989. price varies. Istituto di Studi sulla Ricerca e Documentazione Scientifica, Centro di Riferimento Italiano Diane, Via Cesare do Lollis 12, 00185 Rome, Italy. FAX 06-493836. TELEX 610076 CORICERC. Ed. Maria Pia Carosella. circ. 1,000.
  Former titles: Italy. Laboratorio di Studi sulla Ricerca e sulla Documentazione. Note di Bibliografia e Documentazione Scientifica; Italy. Consiglio Nazionale delle Ricerche. Nota di Bibliografia e di Documentazione Scientifica (ISSN 0085-2309)

026   IT   ISSN 0036-9845
ITALY. SCUOLA DI GUERRA. BIBLIOTECA. BOLLETTINO. 1952. bi-m. Scuola di Guerra, Biblioteca, Civitavecchia, Italy.

020   SP   ISSN 0214-0349
ITEM; revista de biblioteconomia i documentacio. (Text in Catalan) 1987. s-a. 1600 ptas. (effective 1992). Col.legi Oficial de Bibliotecaris-documentalistes de Catalunya, Gran Via 600, 08007 Barcelona, Spain. TEL 3-317-25-99. FAX 3-412-59-68. Ed. C. Espelt. adv.; bk.rev.; abstr.; bibl.; illus. circ. 1,500.
—BLDSC (4588.578000).
  Description: Deals with all aspects of library and information work in Catalonia and Spain.

ITIHAS; journal of the Andhra Pradesh archives. see *HISTORY — History Of Asia*

020.6   JM
J L A NEWS. q. Jamaica Library Association, P.O. Box 58, Kingston 5, Jamaica, W.I.
  Description: News of current events in the libraries of Jamaica.

JAHRBUCH DER AUKTIONSPREISE FUER BUECHER, HANDSCHRIFTEN UND AUTOGRAPHEN; Ergebnisse der Auktionen in Deutschland, den Niederlanden, Oesterreich und der Schweiz. see *MUSEUMS AND ART GALLERIES*

020   GW   ISSN 0075-2223
Z801
JAHRBUCH DER DEUTSCHEN BIBLIOTHEKEN. 1902. biennial, no.55, 1993. price varies. (Verein Deutscher Bibliothekare) Harrassowitz Verlag, Taunusstr. 14, 65183 Wiesbaden, Germany. TEL 0611-530-0. FAX 0611-530570. TELEX 4186135. (Subscr. to: Postfach 2929, 65019 Wiesbaden, Germany) adv. circ. 2,600. **Document type:** monographic series.

020.6   JM
JAMAICA LIBRARY ASSOCIATION. BULLETIN. 1950. a. Jamaica Library Association, P.O. Box 58, Kingston 5, Jamaica, W.I.
  Formerly: Jamaica Library Association. Annual Bulletin (ISSN 0448-2174)
  Description: Reports on developments and issues affecting the library and information profession in Jamaica.

020   JA   ISSN 0040-9650
JAPAN SOCIETY OF LIBRARY SCIENCE. ANNALS/TOSHOKAN GAKKAI NENPO. (Text in Japanese; summaries in English) 1954. q. (plus a. supplement). 8000 Yen. Japan Society of Library Science - Nippon Toshokan Gakkai, c/o Office of Library and Information Science, Faculty of Sociology, Tokyo University, 28-20 Hakusan 5-chome, Bunkyo-ku, Tokyo 112, Japan. Ed. Shojiro Maruyama. adv.; bk.rev.; charts; index. circ. 900. **Indexed:** LISA.
—BLDSC (1028.380000); UnCover.

LIBRARY AND INFORMATION SCIENCES

020   CC   ISSN 1001-9618
JIANGSU TUSHUGUAN XUEBAO/JIANGSU LIBRARY JOURNAL. (Text in Chinese) 1980. bi-m. Y13.8 (foreign $3). Jiangsu Tushuguan Xuehui - Jiangsu Library Association, Nanjing Tushuguan, 66 Chengxian Jie, Nanjing, Jiangsu 210018, People's Republic of China. TEL 025-6-637654. Ed. Lu Zibo. adv.; bk.rev. circ. 2,500. **Document type:** academic/scholarly publication.
   Formerly (until 1984): Jiangsu Library Works.

JIANGXI TUSHUGUAN XUEKAN/JIANGXI LIBRARY JOURNAL. (Text in Chinese) q. Jiangxi Sheng Tushuguan - Jiangxi Provincial Library, No. 65, Zhongshan Lu, Nanchang, Jiangxi 330008, People's Republic of China. TEL 62269. Ed. Zheng Jinhui.

020   CC   ISSN 1004-1680
JINTU XUEKAN. (Text in Chinese) 1985. q. $2 per no. Shanxi Sheng Tushuguan Xuehui, Shanxi Daxue Tushuguan, Wucheng Lu, Taiyuan, Shanxi 030006, People's Republic of China. TEL 7710444. Ed. Feng Jinsheng. bk.rev. **Document type:** academic/scholarly publication.

027.4   SA
JOHANNESBURG PUBLIC LIBRARY. ANNUAL REPORT. (Text in English) 1891. a. free. Johannesburg Public Library, Market Square, Johannesburg 2001, South Africa. TEL 27-11-836-3787. FAX 27-11-836-6607. (back issues avail.) **Document type:** corporate report.

JOHN RYLANDS UNIVERSITY LIBRARY OF MANCHESTER. BULLETIN. see *HUMANITIES: COMPREHENSIVE WORKS*

JOKESMITH. see *LITERARY AND POLITICAL REVIEWS*

020   BE
JOURNAL DE LA LIBRAIRIE.* 1883. bi-m. 1325 Fr. Cercle Belge de la Librairie (CBL), 140 Blvd. Lanbermont, 1030 Brussels, Belgium. Ed. N. Mertens. adv.; bk.rev.

020   US   ISSN 0099-1333
Z671
JOURNAL OF ACADEMIC LIBRARIANSHIP; articles, features, and book reviews for the academic library professional. 1975. bi-m. $29 to individuals (foreign $37); institutions $65 (foreign $73). J A I Press, Inc., 55 Old Post Rd. No. 2, Box 1678, Greenwich, CT 06836-1678. TEL 203-661-7602. FAX 203-661-0792. Ed. Richard M. Dougherty. adv.; bk.rev.; abstr.; bibl.; charts; illus.; index. circ. 3,000. (also avail. in microform from UMI; back issues avail.; reprint service avail. from UMI) **Indexed:** Bk.Rev.Ind. (1975-), C.I.J.E., CALL, Child.Bk.Rev.Ind. (1975-), Curr.Cont., Educ.Ind., Leg.Info.Manage.Ind., LHTN, Lib.Lit., LISA, PSI, Ref.Sour., SSCI. **Document type:** academic/scholarly publication.
—BLDSC (4918.858000); Faxon; UnCover; SWETS. **CCC.**
   Description: Covers all aspects of academic librarianship plus offers an extensive review of the literature through its "Guide to the Professional Literature."
   Refereed Serial

020 330   US   ISSN 0896-3568
Z675.B8   CODEN: JBFLEY
JOURNAL OF BUSINESS & FINANCE LIBRARIANSHIP. 1989. q. $34 to individuals; institutions $40. Haworth Press, Inc., 10 Alice St., Binghamton, NY 13904. TEL 607-722-5857; 800-342-9678. FAX 607-722-1424. Ed. Catherine Friedman. adv.; bk.rev. (also avail. in microfiche from HAW; reprint service avail. from HAW) **Indexed:** LISA. **Document type:** academic/scholarly publication.
—BLDSC (4954.661057); UnCover.
   Description: Prov des articles to information professionals who are involved with, or have an interest in, the creation, organization, dissemination, retrieval, and use of business information.
   Refereed Serial

JOURNAL OF CHEMICAL INFORMATION AND COMPUTER SCIENCES. see *CHEMISTRY — Computer Applications*

JOURNAL OF CLASSIFICATION. see *MATHEMATICS*

JOURNAL OF DOCUMENT AND TEXT MANAGEMENT. see *COMPUTERS — Data Base Management*

029   UK   ISSN 0022-0418
Z1007   CODEN: JDOCAS
JOURNAL OF DOCUMENTATION; devoted to the recording, organization and dissemination of specialized knowledge. 1945. q. £90($180) to non-members; members £60. Aslib, Association for Information Management, Publications Department, Information House, 20-24 Old St., London EC1V 9AP, England. TEL 071-253-4488. FAX 071-430-0514. (Dist. in N. America by: Learned Information Inc., 143 Old Marlton Pike, Medford, NJ 08055-8750. TEL 609-654-6266) Ed. R.T. Kimber. adv.; bk.rev.; abstr.; bibl.; index. circ. 3,500. (reprint service avail. from KTO) **Indexed:** Abstr.Bull.Inst.Pap.Chem., Abstr.Hum.Comp.Inter., Biol.Abstr., Br.Ceram.Abstr., C.I.J.E., Chem.Abstr., Compumath, Comput.Cont., Curr.Cont., Dairy Sci.Abstr., Deep Sea Res.& Oceanogr.Abstr., Excerp.Med., Fluidex, Ind.Sci.Rev., Ind.Vet., Int.Lab.Doc., Key to Econ.Sci., Lib.Lit., LISA, M.L.A., Mid.East: Abstr.& Ind., Sci.Abstr., Sci.Cit.Ind., SSCI, Vet.Bull., World Surf.Coat.
—BLDSC (4970.000000); Faxon; UnCover; SWETS; CASDDS.
   Description: Articles on documentation, librarianship and information science, both theoretical and practical.

020.7   US   ISSN 0748-5786
Z671
JOURNAL OF EDUCATION FOR LIBRARY AND INFORMATION SCIENCE. 1960. 4/yr. $60 (foreign $70). Association for Library and Information Science Education, 4101 Lake Boone Tr., Ste. 201, Raleigh, NC 27607. TEL 919-787-5181. Ed. Rosemary DuMont. bk.rev.; charts; cum.index: 1960-1975, 1975-1980. circ. 1,700. (also avail. in microfilm from UMI,ISI; back issues avail.; reprint service avail. from UMI) **Indexed:** C.I.J.E., Cont.Pg.Educ., Curr.Cont., Educ.Ind., Lib.Lit., Lib.Sci.Abstr., LISA, Res.High.Educ.Abstr., Sci.Abstr., SSCI.
—BLDSC (4973.150100); Faxon; UnCover; SWETS; UMI.
   Formerly (until 1984): Journal of Education for Librarianship (ISSN 0022-0604)
   Refereed Serial

370 020   CH   ISSN 1013-090X
CODEN: CYTHD5
JOURNAL OF EDUCATIONAL MEDIA AND LIBRARY SCIENCES. Key Title: Jiaoyu Ziliao yu Tushuguan Xue. (Text in Chinese and English; summaries in English) 1970. q. NT.$360($30) Tamkang University, Graduate Institute of Educational Media and Library Sciences, Tamsui, Taipei, Taiwan 25137, Republic of China. FAX 02-622-6149. (Co-sponsor: Chueh Sheng Memorial Library) Ed. Shih-hsion Huang. adv.; bk.rev.; index. circ. 1,200. (back issues avail.; reprint service avail. from UMI) **Indexed:** C.I.J.E., Educ.Ind., Inform.Sci.Abstr., Lib.Lit., LISA, P.A.I.S.
—BLDSC (4973.157500).
   Formerly (until 1982): Journal of Educational Media Sciences (ISSN 0377-9890)

JOURNAL OF GOVERNMENT INFORMATION; an international journal of issues and information resources. see *PUBLIC ADMINISTRATION*

020 170   US   ISSN 1061-9321
Z682.35.P75
▼**JOURNAL OF INFORMATION ETHICS.** 1992. s-a. $38 (foreign $44) (effective 1992). McFarland & Company, Inc., Box 611, Jefferson, NC 28640. TEL 910-246-4460. FAX 910-246-5018. Ed. Robert Hauptman. adv. contact: Steve Wilson. bk.rev.; abstr.; bibl. (back issues avail.) **Document type:** academic/scholarly publication.
—BLDSC (5006.747000); UnCover.
   Description: Deals with ethical issues in all of the information sciences, from library acquisitions to database management, with a multidisciplinary approach.

029.7   JA   ISSN 0021-7298
CODEN: JOKAAB
JOURNAL OF INFORMATION PROCESSING AND MANAGEMENT/JOHO KANRI. (Text in Japanese, summaries in English) 1958. m. $175. Japan Information Center of Science and Technology - Nihon Kagaku Gijutsu Joho Senta, 5-2 Nagata-cho, 2-chome, Chiyoda-ku, Tokyo 100, Japan. TEL 03-3581-6411. FAX 03-3581-6446. adv.; bk.rev.; abstr.; charts; illus.; index. circ. 5,000. **Indexed:** Chem.Abstr., INIS Atomind., JTA, Math.R., Sci.Abstr.
—BLDSC (5006.772200); UnCover; CASDDS.
   Formerly: Information and Documentation.

020 025   UK   ISSN 0165-5515
Z1007   CODEN: JISCDI
JOURNAL OF INFORMATION SCIENCE; principles and practice. 1979. 6/yr. £105($175) (Institute of Information Scientists) Bowker - Saur Ltd., A Reed Reference Publishing Company, Part of the Reed Elsevier group, Maypole House, Maypole Rd., E. Grinstead, W. Sussex RH19 1HH, England. TEL 0342-330100. FAX 0342-330192. (Subscr. to: Bailey Management Services Ltd., 127 Sandgate Rd., Folkestone, Kent CT20 2BL, England. TEL 0303-850501. FAX 0303-850162) Ed. A. Gilchrist. adv.; illus.; index, cum.index. circ. 3,800. (also avail. in microform from UMI; back issues avail.; reprint service avail.) **Indexed:** AESIS, Bus.Ind., Chem.Abstr., Compumath, Comput.Abstr., Comput.Cont., Comput.Lit.Ind., Comput.Rev., Curr.Cont., Eng.Ind., ERIC, Fluidex, Inform.Sci.Abstr., INSPEC, Intl.Civil Eng.Abstr., LHTN, Lib.Lit., LISA, Manage.Cont., Ref.Zh., Sci.Abstr., Sci.Cit.Ind., Soft.Abstr.Eng., SSCI, Tr.& Indus.Ind., World Text.Abstr. **Document type:** academic/scholarly publication.
—BLDSC (5006.772800); EI; Faxon; UnCover; UMI; CASDDS. **CCC.**
   Supersedes: Information Scientist (ISSN 0020-0263)
   Description: Offers information scientists a theoretical and practical outlook on current developments and work being carried out.
   Refereed Serial

020   UK   ISSN 0268-3962
CODEN: JINTEB
JOURNAL OF INFORMATION TECHNOLOGY. Abbreviated title: J I T. q. £45 to institutions in EC nations (North America $83) (effective 1993). (Association for Information Technology) Chapman & Hall, 2-6 Boundary Row, London SE1 8HN, England. TEL 071-865-0066. FAX 071-522-9623. TELEX 290164-CHAPMAG. (Dist. by: International Thomson Publishing Serices, Ltd., N. Way, Andover, Hants. SP10 5BE, England. TEL 0264-332919; U.S. addr.: Chapman & Hall, Journals Promotion Department, One Penn Plaza, 41st Fl., New York, NY 10019. TEL 212-564-1060. FAX 212-564-1505) Ed. Anne Leeming. adv.; abstr. (back issues avail.) **Indexed:** Abstr.Hum.Comp.Inter., Cont.Pg.Manage. **Document type:** academic/scholarly publication.
—BLDSC (5006.790000); Faxon; SWETS. **CCC.**
   Description: Contains views and opinions from the information technology community in Britain, Europe, the US, and Japan.

020   US
Z713
JOURNAL OF INTERLIBRARY LOAN, DOCUMENT DELIVERY & INFORMATION SUPPLY. 1990. q. $24 to individuals; institutions and libraries $28. Haworth Press, Inc., 10 Alice St., Binghamton, NY 13904. TEL 607-722-5857; 800-342-9678. FAX 607-722-1424. Ed. Leslie R. Morris. (also avail. in microfiche from UMI; reprint service avail. from HAW) **Indexed:** Ind.Per.Art.Relat.Law, Lib.Lit., LISA, Ref.Zh.
—UnCover.
   Formerly (until vol.4, no.1, 1993): Journal of Interlibrary Loan and Information Supply (ISSN 1042-4458)
   Description: Devoted to practice-oriented interlibrary loan problems and the basic expanding roles of interlibrary loan librarians.
   Refereed Serial

LIBRARY AND INFORMATION SCIENCES 3447

020   UK   ISSN 0961-0006
Z671   CODEN: JLSCE6
JOURNAL OF LIBRARIANSHIP AND INFORMATION SCIENCE. 1969. q. £70($125) Bowker - Saur Ltd., A Reed Reference Publishing Company, Part of the Reed Elsevier group, Maypole House, Maypole Rd., E. Grinstead, W. Sussex RH19 1HH, England. TEL 0342-330100. FAX 0342-330192. (Subscr. to: Bailey Management Services Ltd., 127 Sandgate Rd., Folestone, Kent CT20 2BL, England. TEL 0303-850501. FAX 0303-850162) Ed. David Stoker. bk.rev.; index. circ. 1,400. **Indexed:** Curr.Cont., Lib.Lit., LISA, Sci.Abstr., SSCI. **Document type:** academic/scholarly publication.
—BLDSC (5010.330100); Faxon; UnCover; SWETS; UMI.
Formerly (until 1991): Journal of Librarianship (ISSN 0022-2232)
Description: Reports and reflects significant work and developments in all aspects of library and information science worldwide. Includes articles and critical reviews of new publications.

025   US   ISSN 0193-0826
Z678   CODEN: JLADEL
JOURNAL OF LIBRARY ADMINISTRATION. 1980. q. $35 to individuals; institutions $95. Haworth Press, Inc., 10 Alice St., Binghamton, NY 13904. TEL 607-722-5857; 800-342-9678. FAX 607-722-1424. TELEX 4932599. Ed. Sul Lee. adv.; bk.rev.; charts; illus.; stat. circ. 910. (also avail. in microfiche from HAW) **Indexed:** BPIA, Bull.Signal., C.I.J.E., Comput.& Info.Sys., Excerp.Med., Inform.Sci.Abstr., Leg.Info.Manage.Ind., Lib.Lit., LISA, Manage.Cont., P.A.I.S., Pers.Lit., Ref.Zh., Tr.& Indus.Ind.
—BLDSC (5010.333000); Faxon; UnCover; SWETS.
Description: Provides information on all aspects of the effective management of libraries, with emphasis on practical applications.
Refereed Serial

020   CH   ISSN 0363-3640
Z671   CODEN: TSKHE4
JOURNAL OF LIBRARY & INFORMATION SCIENCE/TUSHUGUANXUE YU ZIXUN KEXUE. 1975. s-a. NT.$300($20) National Taiwan Normal University, Department of Adult and Continuing Education - Tai-wan Shih Fan Ta Hsueh, 162 Ho-ping E. Rd. Sec.1, Taipei, Taiwan 10610, Republic of China. TEL 02-393-6798. FAX 02-394-6506. (Subscr. to: Student Book Co. Ltd., 198 Ho-ping E. Rd. Sec.1, Taipei, Taiwan 10610, Republic of China. TEL 02-363-1097. FAX 02-363-6334) (Co-sponsor: Chinese American Librarians Association) Ed.Bd. bk.rev. circ. 1,000. **Indexed:** Inform.Sci.Abstr., Lib.Lit., LISA, P.A.I.S.
—BLDSC (5010.340000).
Description: Aims to serve as a forum for discussion of problems common to librarians and information scientists, to introduce new concepts, systems, and technology, to report leading events worldwide, and to promote the development of Chinese library and information services.

020   II   ISSN 0970-714X
Z671
JOURNAL OF LIBRARY AND INFORMATION SCIENCE. Variant title: J L I S. (Text in English) 1976. s-a. Rs.80($14) (typically set in Jan.). University of Delhi, Department of Library and Information Science, Delhi 110 007, India. Ed. P. B. Mangla. adv.; bk.rev. circ. 350. **Indexed:** Curr.Cont., Ind.Per.Lit., Inform.Sci.Abstr., LISA, P.A.I.S.
—BLDSC (5010.335000).
Description: Research journal with the objective to keep users informed about the latest developments in the field and to encourage research programs.

JOURNAL OF NEWSPAPER AND PERIODICAL HISTORY. see *PUBLISHING AND BOOK TRADE*

020   PH   ISSN 0022-359X
JOURNAL OF PHILIPPINE LIBRARIANSHIP. (Text in English) 1968-1971; resumed 1981. s-a. P.100($20) (effective 1992). University of the Philippines, Institute of Library Science, c/o Ursula G. Picache, U.P. Diliman, Quezon City 1101, Philippines. TEL 98-24-71-6249. Ed. Rosa M. Vallejo. **Indexed:** Ind.Phil.Per., LISA. **Document type:** academic/scholarly publication.
—BLDSC (5034.200000).
Description: Contains articles and theses on special problems relating to Philippine libraries and librarianship.

028.1   US   ISSN 0894-2498
Z718.1.A1
JOURNAL OF YOUTH SERVICES IN LIBRARIES. 1946. q. $40 (foreign $50). American Library Association, Association for Library Service to Children, and Young Adult, 50 E. Huron St., Chicago, IL 60611-2795. TEL 800-545-2433. FAX 312-440-9374. Eds. Donald J. Kenney, Linda J. Wilson. adv.; bk.rev.; bibl.; illus.; index, cum.index: 1942-1963. circ. 9,500. (also avail. in microform from UMI; back issues avail.; reprint service avail. from UMI) **Indexed:** Bk.Rev.Ind. (1967-), C.I.J.E., Chic.Per.Ind., Child.Bk.Rev.Ind. (1967-), Child.Lit.Abstr., LHTN, Lib.Lit., LISA, Media Rev.Dig.
—BLDSC (5072.722000); Faxon; UnCover; SWETS; UMI. **CCC.**
Formerly (until 1987): Top of the News (ISSN 0040-9286)
Description: News and articles of interest to children and young adult librarians.

026 296   US   ISSN 0739-5086
Z675.J4
JUDAICA LIBRARIANSHIP. 1983. s-a. $25 to individuals and institutions; students $18. Includes A J L Newsletter. Association of Jewish Libraries, c/o National Foundation for Jewish Culture, 330 7th Ave., 21st Fl., New York, NY 10001-5010. TEL 215-238-1290. FAX 215-238-1540. (Subscr. to: Aviva Astrinsky, AJL Vice Pres. for Membership, Annenberg Research Institute Library, 420 Walnut St., Philadelphia, PA 19106) Ed. Bella Hass Weinberg. adv.: Page $200. bk.rev.; bibl.; charts; illus.; index. circ. 1,300. (also avail. in microform; reprint service avail.; back issues avail.) **Indexed:** Geneal.Per.Ind., Ind.Artic.Jew.Stud., Ind.Jew.Per., Inform.Sci.Abstr., Lib.Lit., Lib.Sci.Abstr., LISA, M.L.A., Ref.Sour. **Document type:** academic/scholarly publication.
—UMI.
Supersedes: Association of Jewish Libraries Bulletin.
Description: Covers the full spectrum of functions and types of Judaica libraries.
Refereed Serial

610 020   IR
JUNDI SHAPUR UNIVERSITY. FACULTY OF MEDICINE. LIBRARY BULLETIN/DANESHGAH-E JONDISHAPUR. DANESHKADE-YE PEZESAKI. BULTAN-E KETABKHANEH. (Text in Persian) 1972. q. free. Jundi Shapur University, Faculty of Medicine, Box 339, Ahvaz, Iran.

JUNIOR BOOKSHELF; a review of children's books. see *PUBLISHING AND BOOK TRADE*

020   US
JUNIOR HIGH SCHOOL LIBRARY CATALOG. 1965. quinquennial (plus a. supplement). $105. H.W. Wilson Co., 950 University Ave., Bronx, NY 10452. TEL 800-367-6770. FAX 718-590-1617. TELEX 4990003HWILSON. Ed. Juliette Yaakov. **Document type:** catalog.
Description: Classified list of books recommended for young people (grades 7-9), including fiction and story collections; with author, title, subject, and analytical index.

025 340   US   ISSN 0162-3079
JURISDOCS. 1978. 3/yr. $5 to non-members. American Association of Law Libraries, Government Documents Special Interest Section, c/o Keith Buckley, Indiana Univ. Law Library, Bloomington, IN 47405. **Document type:** newsletter.

JUVENILE MISCELLANY. see *CHILDREN AND YOUTH — About*

020   SW   ISSN 0283-4081
K K S MEDDELANDEN; information om katalogiserings- och klassifikationsfraagor fraan S A B's kommitte foer katalogisering och klassifikation. 1978-1983; resumed 1985. q. SEK 88 (effective 1991). Bibliotekstjaenst AB, P.O. Box 200, S-221 Lund, Sweden.
Former titles (until 1986): K R S - Meddelanden; (until 1983): S K R - Meddelanden.

020   KO   ISSN 0022-7358
K L A BULLETIN. 1960. 6/yr. $20. Korean Library Association, C.P.O. Box 2041, 100-177, 1-KA, Hoehyun-Dong, Choong-ku, Seoul, S. Korea. Ed. Dae Kwon Park. adv.; bk.rev. circ. 5,000.

020.6   US
K L A NEWSLETTER. vol.10, 1983. 4/yr. membership. Kansas Library Association, c/o South Central Kansas Library System, 901 N. Main St., Hutchinson, KS 67501. TEL 316-663-2501. FAX 316-662-1215. Ed. Paul Hawkins. adv. circ. 1,100. **Document type:** newsletter.
Description: Covers association sponsored activities and news of interest to the Kansas library community.

020   US
KA RI WEH HA WI. 1971. m. free. Akwesasne Library, R.R. 1, Box 14C, Hogansburg, NY 13655. TEL 518-358-2240. FAX 518-358-2649. Ed. Susan Rourke. circ. 1,135. (looseleaf format; back issues avail.) **Document type:** newsletter.
Description: Includes news for the general public of the St. Regis Mohawk Reservation.

020   US   ISSN 0889-2709
KANSAS LIBRARIES. 1984. m. free. Kansas State Library, 300 W. 10th St., Rm.343, State Capitol, Topeka, KS 66612-1593. TEL 913-296-3296. FAX 913-296-6650. Ed. Roy Bird. bk.rev. circ. 1,800. (back issues avail.) **Document type:** newsletter.
Description: Serves as an official print bulletin board to all libraries in Kansas from the Kansas State Library.

020   II   ISSN 0022-9083
KARNATAK GRANTHALAYA. (Text in Kannada; contents page in English and Kannada) 1969. q. Rs.25. S. R. Gunjal, Ed. & Pub., Granthalaya Vijnana Prakashana, Gulbarga University, Gulbarga 585106, Karnatak, India. adv.; bk.rev.; bibl.; illus.

020.6 282   GW   ISSN 0931-4458
KATHOLISCHE OEFFENTLICHE BUECHEREI; Vierteljahreszeitschrift fuer Mitarbeiter der Katholische Oeffentlichen Buechereien. Short title: K Oe B. 1957. q. DM.20. Erzbistum Koeln, Fachstelle fuer Buechereien, Marzellenstr. 32, 50668 Cologne, Germany. TEL 0221-1642630. FAX 0221-1642-700. Ed. Siegmund Schramm. cum.index every 5 yrs. circ. 5,500. **Document type:** newsletter.
Formerly (until 1987): Unsere Sammlung.
Description: Covers library and literary subjects.

020   CC   ISSN 1000-4467
KEJI QINGBAO GONGZUO/SCIENCE AND TECHNOLOGY INFORMATION. (Text in Chinese) m. Zhongguo Kexue Jishu Qingbao Yanjiusuo - China Science and Technology Information Institute, 15 Fuxing Lu, Beijing 100038, People's Republic of China. TEL 8015544. Ed. Li Wenyun.

020   CC
KEJI QINGBAO SHICHANG/INFORMATION MARKET OF SCIENCE AND TECHNOLOGY. (Text in Chinese) m. Sichuansheng Kexue Jishu Qingbao Yanjiusuo - Sichuan Science and Technology Information Research Institute, 32 Dongfeng Lu Yiduan (Sec. 1), Chengdu, Sichuan 610016, People's Republic of China. TEL 22946-36.

020   US   ISSN 0732-5452
Z732.K37
KENTUCKY LIBRARIES. 1933. q. $18 for non-members (foreign $50). Kentucky Library Association, 1501 Twilight Trail, Frankfort, KY 40601. TEL 502-223-5322. adv.; bk.rev. circ. 1,800. (also avail. in microform from UMI; reprint service avail. from UMI) **Indexed:** Lib.Lit.
—UMI.
Formerly: K L A Bulletin (ISSN 0022-734X)
Description: Keeps readers and members of the profession informed of new developments and thinking in the broad areas of librarianship and information science.

020   KE   ISSN 0075-5923
KENYA NATIONAL LIBRARY SERVICE BOARD. ANNUAL AND AUDIT REPORT. 1967. a. exchange basis. Kenya National Library Services, P.O. Box 30573, Nairobi, Kenya. FAX 254-2-721749. TELEX KENLIB. circ. 1,000. **Document type:** corporate report.

KEYWORD INDEX TO SERIAL TITLES. see *LIBRARY AND INFORMATION SCIENCES — Abstracting, Bibliographies, Statistics*

KIDSTUFF. see *CHILDREN AND YOUTH — For*

LIBRARY AND INFORMATION SCIENCES

020   US
KING COUNTY LIBRARY SYSTEM. NEWS. 1973-1975; resumed 1978. m. free. King County Library System, 300 Eighth Ave., N., Seattle, WA 98109. TEL 206-684-6606. FAX 206-684-6690. Ed. Jeanne Thorsen. illus. circ. 5,000. (also avail. in microform from UMI; reprint service avail. from UMI) **Indexed:** Arts & Hum.Cit.Ind., Curr.Cont., Hum.Ind. **Document type:** newsletter.
   Formerly: Etc.

020   FI   ISSN 0023-1843
Z673
KIRJASTOLEHTI. (Text in Finnish; summaries in English and Swedish) 1908. m. FIM 250. Suomen Kirjastoseura - Finnish Library Association, Museokatu 18 A 5, SF-00100 Helsinki, Finland. TEL 358-0-441-986. FAX 358-0-441-345. Ed. Jari Paavonheimo. adv.: B&W page FIM 7150, color page FIM 12000; trim 210 x 297; adv. contact: Tuula Blafield. bk.rev.; bibl.; illus.; stat.; index; circ. 6,748 (controlled). **Indexed:** Lib.Lit., LISA.

020   GW   ISSN 0937-9835
KLEINE HISTORISCHE REIHE. a. Laurentius, Koertingstr. 8, 30161 Hannover, Germany. TEL 0511-621045. FAX 0511-5323346. (Subscr. to: Laurentius Vertrieb, Bonhoefferstr. 19, 30926 Seelze, Germany. TEL 05137-5653) Ed. Raimund Dehmlow. **Document type:** bulletin.

020   XO
Z671   CODEN: KVIFA8
KNIZNICE A INFORMACIE. (Text in Czech or Slovak; summaries in English, German, Russian) 1968. m. price varies. Matica Slovenska, Ul. Mudronova 26, 036 52 Martin, Slovak a. TEL 42-842-38706. FAX 42-842-32454. (Subscr. to: Slovart, Gottwaldovo nam. 48, 805 32 Bratislava, Slovakia) Ed. Andrej Risko. illus.; index. **Indexed:** LISA, Sci.Abstr. **Document type:** academic/scholarly publication.
   Formerly (until 1992): Kniznice a Vedecke Informacie (ISSN 0322-807X)

020   XO   ISSN 0075-6369
Z671
KNIZNICNY ZBORNIK. (Text in Slovak; summaries in English, German, Russian) 1957. a. price varies. Matica Slovenska, Slovenska Narodna Kniznica, Ul. L. Novomeskeho 32, 036 52 Martin, Slovakia. TEL 42-842-32454. FAX 42-842-33160. TELEX 075 331. Ed. Margita Buocikova. bk.rev.; circ. 600 (paid). **Document type:** proceedings.

020 010   XV   ISSN 0023-2424
Z671
KNJIZNICA; glasilo Zveze Bibliotekarskih Drustev Slovenije. (Text in Slovenian; summaries in English) 1957. q. $20. Zveza Bibliotekarskih Drustev Slovenije, Turjaska 1, Ljubljana, Slovenia. TEL 061-150-131. (Co-sponsors: Ministrstvo za Kulturo; Ministrstvo za Znanost in Tehnologijo) Ed. Jelka Gazvoda. adv.; bk.rev.; bibl. circ. 1,300. **Indexed:** LISA.
   ●Also available on CD-ROM.

020   XV   ISSN 0353-9237
KNJIZNICARSKE NOVICE. 1975. m. Narodna in Univerzitetna Knjiznica, Turjaska 1, 61001 Ljubljana, Slovenia. TEL 061-150-141. FAX 38-611-150-134. TELEX 32285 NUK-LJB-SLO.
   Former titles (until 1991): Obvesila Republiske Maticne Sluzbe (ISSN 0350-3577); (until 1975): Obvestila Republiske Maticne Knniznice.

020   GW   ISSN 0943-7444
Z696   CODEN: KNOREM
KNOWLEDGE ORGANIZATION; international journal devoted to concept theory, classification, indexing, and knowledge representation. (Text in English, French, German) 1974. 4/yr. DM.120 to institutions. (International Society for Knowledge Organization) Indeks Verlag, Woogstr. 36a, 60431 Frankfurt a.M., Germany. TEL 069-523690. FAX 069-520566. adv.; bk.rev.; abstr.; bibl. circ. 1,000. (reprint service avail. from UMI, ISI) **Indexed:** Bull.Signal., Curr.Cont., Lib.Lit., LISA, Sci.Abstr., SSCI.
   —BLDSC (5100.453000); Faxon; SWETS.
   Formerly (until 1992): International Classification (ISSN 0340-0050)
   Refereed Serial

020   JA   ISSN 0919-2557
KOCHI UNIVERSITY. FACULTY OF SCIENCE. MEMOIRS. SERIES F, INFORMATION SCIENCE. (Text in English) 1980. a. Kochi University, Faculty of Science - Kochi Dagaiku Rigakubu, 5-1, Akebono-cho 2-chome, Kochi-shi, Kochi-ken 780, Japan. **Document type:** academic/scholarly publication.
   —BLDSC (5597.838500).

027   JA   ISSN 0027-9153
Z955.T585   CODEN: KKTGDQ
KOKURITSU KOKKAI TOSHOKAN GEPPO/NATIONAL DIET LIBRARY. MONTHLY BULLETIN. (Text in Japanese; contents page in English) 1961. m. 3660 Yen. National Diet Library - Kokuritsu Kokkai Toshokan, 1-10-1 Nagata-cho, Chiyoda-ku, Tokyo 100, Japan. TEL 03-3581-2331. FAX 03-3597-9104. bk.rev.; bibl.; charts; illus.; circ. 3,889 (controlled). **Document type:** bulletin.
   —CASDDS.

027   JA   ISSN 0385-325X
KOKURITSU KOKKAI TOSHOKAN NENPO/NATIONAL DIET LIBRARY. ANNUAL REPORT. (Text in Japanese) 1948. a. 3770 Yen. National Diet Library - Kokuritsu Kokkai Toshokan, 1-10-1 Nagata-cho, Chiyoda-ku, Tokyo 100, Japan. TEL 03-3581-2331. FAX 03-3597-9104. circ. 1,910.

020   JA   ISSN 0385-3306
KOKUTRITSU KOKKAI TOSHOKAN. SANKO SHOSI KENKYU/NATIONAL DIET LIBRARY. REFERENCE SERVICE AND BIBLIOGRAPHY. (Text in Japanese) 1970. s-a. price varies. National Diet Library - Kokutritsu Kokkai Toshokan, 1-10-1 Nagata-cho, Chiyoda-ku, Tokyo 100, Japan. TEL 03-3581-2331. FAX 03-3597-9104. circ. 921. **Document type:** bibliography.
   —UnCover.

020   DK   ISSN 0905-5533
Z824.K65
KONGELIGE BIBLIOTEK. MAGASIN. Key Title: Magasin fra Det Kongelige Bibliotek. 1948. q. free. Kongelige Bibliotek, Christians Brygge 8, 1219 Copenhagen K, Denmark. Ed. Lotte Philipson. circ. 3,000.
   Former titles (until 1990): Kongelige Bibliotek og Universitetsbiblioteket. Magasin (ISSN 0901-7496); (until 1986): Rigsbibliotekaren. Meddelelser (ISSN 0461-5298)

020   DK   ISSN 0105-3167
KONGELIGE BIBLIOTEK. PUBLIKUMSORIENTERINGER. 1974. irreg., latest no.21, 1990. Kongelige Bibliotek - Royal Library, Christians Brygge 8, DK-1219 Copenhagen K, Denmark.

020   HU   ISSN 0139-1305
KONYV ES KONYVTAR/BOOK AND LIBRARY. (Text in Hungarian; summaries in English, French, German and Russian) 1958. irreg., vol.16, 1991. $5 (effective 1991). Kossuth Lajos Tudomanyegyetem, Konyvtara, Egyetem ter 1, 4010 Debrecen, Hungary. TEL 36-52-16-666. FAX 36-52-16-835. TELEX 72200. Ed. Olga Gomba. bk.rev.; illus. circ. 400. (back issues avail.)
   Description: Concerned with the history of manuscripts, books, literature, libraries and printing offices. Includes articles on bibliography, reading habits and bibliophilism.

023   HU   ISSN 1216-6804
KONYV, KONYVTAR, KONYVTAROS.* 1951. m. $25. Vaci ut 19, 1134 Budapest, Hungary. TEL 111-3279. Ed. Laszlo Berecky. circ. 6,000. **Indexed:** Hung.Lib.& Info.Sci.Abstr. (1972-).
   —BLDSC (5113.250000).
   Former titles (until 1992): Konyvtaros (ISSN 0450-7886); (until 1952): Konyvbarat (ISSN 0200-1012)

020   HU   ISSN 0865-0276
KONYVTARI FIGYELO. UJ FOLYAM/LIBRARY REVIEW. NEW SERIES. (Text in Hungarian; summaries in English, German) 1955. q. 700 Ft.($35) or exchange basis. Orszagos Szechenyi Konyvtar, Konyvtartudomanyi es Modszertani Kozpont - Centre for Library and Information Science at the National Szechenyi Library, Budavari Palota F epulet, 1827 Budapest, Hungary. TEL 1750-686. TELEX 224226 BIBLN H. Ed. Emoke Kovacs. bk.rev.; index. circ. 1,350. **Indexed:** Hung.Lib.& Info.Sci.Abstr. (1972-), Lib.Sci.Abstr., LISA, Ref.Zh. **Document type:** academic/scholarly publication.
   —BLDSC (5113.240000).
   Former titles (until 1990): Konyvtari Figyelo (ISSN 0023-3773); (until 1957): Konyvtari Tajekoztato (ISSN 0200-0202)
   Description: Contains essays related to the theory of librarianship and information science, a rich abstracting feature and review articles.

020   HU   ISSN 0865-1329
KONYVTARI LEVELEZO/LIBRARY POSTCARD. m. 300 Ft. or exchange basis. Orszagos Szechenyi Konyvtar, Konyvtartudomanyi es Modszertani Kozpont - National Szechenyi Library, Center for Library and Information Science, Budavari Palota F. Epulet, 1827 Budapest, Hungary. TEL 175-7533. TELEX 224226 BIBLN H. Ed. Gyula Gero. adv.; bk.rev. circ. 900. **Indexed:** Hung.Lib.& Info.Sci.Abstr. (1992-). **Document type:** newsletter.
   —BLDSC (5113.242000).
   Supersedes (in 1989): Konyvtari Expressz (ISSN 0239-1333)
   Description: Contains general interest items for librarians.

020   DK   ISSN 0902-7270
KORT SAGT. 1987. 10/yr. DKK 420($55) Danmarks Biblioteksforenings Forlag - Danish Library Association Publishing, Telegrafvej 5, 2. sal, DK-2750 Ballerup, Denmark. TEL 45-44-68-14-66. FAX 45-44-68-11-03. Ed.Bd. adv. circ. 2,100. **Document type:** newsletter.
   Description: Newsletter on library and information work, mainly in Denmark.

020   PL   ISSN 0208-5798
KSIAZNICA SLASKA. 1956. irreg., vol.23, 1988. free. Biblioteka Slaska, Dzial Katalogow i Informacji, Ul. Francuska 12, 40-956 Katowicw, Poland. TEL 48-32-155-43-05. Ed.Bd. bk.rev.; bibl.; cum.index every 5 yrs. circ. 300. **Document type:** bulletin.
   Formerly (until 1980): Biblioteka Slaska. Biuletyn Informacyjny.
   Description: Provides information on the Silesian Library's activities and articles on the history of Silesian books.

026   KO   ISSN 0027-8572
KUKHOE TOSOGWANBO/NATIONAL ASSEMBLY LIBRARY REVIEW. Variant spelling: Kuk Hoe Do So Kwan Bo. (Text in Korean) 1964. bi-m. free. National Assembly Library - Kukhoe Tosogwan, 1 Yoido-dong, Seoul, S. Korea. FAX 02-788-4194. bk.rev.; bibl.; charts; illus.; stat.; index. circ. 1,700. (processed)

026   UK
L A I G NEWS. bi-m. membership. Library Association, Industrial Group, 7 Ridgmount St., London WC1E 7AE, England. TEL 081-943-7572. FAX 081-943-2767. Ed. Helen Page. bk.rev. circ. 1,550. **Document type:** newsletter.
   Formerly (until 1988): Library Association. Industrial Group Newsletter.

020   US
L A S L NEWSLETTER. 1980. 3/yr. membership. (Louisiana Association of School Librarians) Louisiana Library Association, Box 3058, Baton Rouge, LA 70821. TEL 504-342-4928. Ed. Terry Thibodeaux. circ. 500. (back issues avail.; back issues avail. from UMI)

020 398   US   ISSN 0736-4903
ML156.4.F5
L C FOLK ARCHIVE FINDING AID. (Library of Congress) 1983. irreg. free. U.S. Library of Congress, Archive of Folk Culture, American Folklife Center, 10 First St., S.E., Washington, DC 20540-8100. TEL 202-707-5510. Ed. Joseph C. Hickerson. circ. 3,000.

LIBRARY AND INFORMATION SCIENCES 3449

020 398   US   ISSN 0736-4911
Z5982
L C FOLK ARCHIVE REFERENCE AID. (Library of Congress) irreg. free. U.S. Library of Congress, Archive of Folk Culture, 10 First St., S.E., Washington, DC 20540-8100. TEL 202-707-5510. Ed. Joseph C. Hickerson. circ. 3,000.

020 011   US   ISSN 1052-1437
L C PERIOD SUBDIVISIONS UNDER NAMES OF PLACES. irreg. U.S. Library of Congress, Cataloging Distribution Service, Washington, DC 20541-5017. TEL 202-707-6100. FAX 202-707-1334. **Document type:** government publication.

020   US   ISSN 8755-366X
L.C. SUBJECT HEADINGS WEEKLY LISTS: A WORKING CUMULATION. 3/yr. $425. Gale Research Inc., 835 Penobscot Bldg., Detroit, MI 48226. TEL 313-961-2242. FAX 313-961-6083.

900 020   US   ISSN 0737-4984
L H R T NEWSLETTER. 1979. s-a. membership. American Library Association, Library History Round Table, 50 E. Huron St., Chicago, IL 60611. TEL 312-280-2156. FAX 312-440-9374. circ. 390. **Document type:** newsletter.
    Formerly: A L H R T Newsletter.

020   US   ISSN 0024-6867
Z673
L L A BULLETIN. 1937. q. $15 for out-of-state non-members. Louisiana Library Association, Box 3058, Baton Rouge, LA 70821. Ed. Florence Jumonville. adv.; bk.rev.; illus.; cum.index: 1937-1968. circ. 1,600. (also avail. in microfilm from UMI; reprint service avail. from UMI) **Indexed:** Lib.Lit.
    —BLDSC (5285.548000).
    Description: Articles concerning libraries, poetry, reviews and Association news.

LABORATORY INFORMATION MANAGEMENT. see MEDICAL SCIENCES — Experimental Medicine, Laboratory Technique

023   NR   ISSN 0047-3901
LAGOS LIBRARIAN. 1966. irreg., vol.12, no.1 & 2, 1985. $20. Nigerian Library Association, Lagos Division, c/o University Library, University of Lagos, Yaba, Lagos, Nigeria. Ed. S.O. Olanlokun. adv.; bk.rev. circ. 400.

020 340   GW   ISSN 0175-6524
LANSKY: BIBLIOTHEKSRECHTLICHE VORSCHRIFTEN. a. DM.50. Vittorio Klostermann, Frauenlobstr. 22, 60487 Frankfurt a.M., Germany. TEL 069-774011. FAX 069-708038. (Subscr. to: Postfach 900601, 60446 Frankfurt a.M., Germany) **Document type:** monographic series.

027.7   US   ISSN 0047-4053
LANTERN'S CORE. 1970. m. free. Northwestern University Library, Staff Association, 1935 Sheridan Rd., Evanston, IL 60208. TEL 312-491-7633. FAX 312-491-5685. Ed.Bd. bk.rev.; bibl.; stat.; circ. 650 (controlled). **Document type:** newsletter.

LATIN AMERICAN MARKETS. see BUSINESS AND ECONOMICS — International Commerce

020   GW   ISSN 0175-8152
LAURENTIUS. 1983. 3/yr. DM.20. Laurentius, Koertingstr. 8, 30161 Hannover, Germany. TEL 0511-621045. FAX 0511-5323346. (Subscr. to: Laurentius Vertrieb, Bonhoefferstr. 19, 30926 Seelze, Germany. TEL 05137-5653) Ed. Raimund Dehmlow. **Document type:** bulletin.

020 020   GW   ISSN 0930-9950
LAURENTIUS SONDERHEFTE. a. Laurentius, Koertingstr. 8, 30161 Hannover, Germany. TEL 0511-621045. FAX 0511-5323346. (Subscr. to: Laurentius Vertrieb, Bonhoefferstr. 19, 30926 Seelze, Germany. TEL 05137-5653) Ed. Raimund Dehmlow. adv.; bk.rev. **Document type:** bulletin.

026 340   UK   ISSN 0023-9275
Z675.L2   CODEN: LALIE2
LAW LIBRARIAN. 1970. 4/yr. £38 to non-members. Sweet & Maxwell, South Quay Plaza, 7th Fl., 183 Marsh Wall, London E14 9FT, England. TEL 071-538-8686. FAX 071-538-9508. Ed. Sarah Lewis. adv. contact: Jackie Wood. bk.rev.; bibl.; cum.index. **Indexed:** C.L.I., L.R.I., Leg.Cont., Leg.Per., LHTN, Lib.Lit., LISA. **Document type:** bulletin.
    —BLDSC (5161.395000); UnCover. **CCC.**

LAW LIBRARIAN'S BULLETIN BOARD. see LAW

026   US
LAW LIBRARY ASSOCIATION OF MARYLAND NEWS. 1981. q. membership. Law Library Association of Maryland, c/o Baltimore Bar Library, 618 Mitchell Courthouse, Baltimore, MD 21202. FAX 301-685-4791. (Subscr. to: Sally Miles, c/o Weinberg & Green, 100 S. Charles St., 15th Fl., Baltimore, MD 21201) Ed. Maxine Grosshans. adv. circ. 130.
    Description: Announcements of events and publication information pertaining to legal research management and documentation in the state.

LAW LIBRARY INFORMATION REPORTS. see LAW

026 340   US   ISSN 0023-9283
K12
LAW LIBRARY JOURNAL. 1908. q. $50 (foreign $55). American Association of Law Libraries, 53 W. Jackson Blvd., Ste. 940, Chicago, IL 60604. TEL 312-939-4764. FAX 312-431-1097. Ed. Richard A. Danner. adv.; bk.rev.; bibl.; stat.; index, cum.index: vols.1-72 (1908-1967). circ. 5,000. (also avail. in microform from PMC; reprint service avail. from RRI) **Indexed:** C.I.S. Abstr., C.L.I., Curr.Cont., L.R.I., Leg.Info.Manage.Ind., Leg.Per., LHTN, Lib.Lit., LISA, SSCI.
    —BLDSC (5161.400000); Faxon; UnCover; SWETS.

020 340   US   ISSN 0457-2483
LAW LIBRARY LIGHTS. 1957. 5/yr. $35 to non-members. Law Librarians' Society of Washington, D.C., 669 S. Washington St., Alexandria, VA 22914-4109. TEL 703-683-5107. FAX 703-519-7732. adv.; bibl.; index. (back issues avail.) **Document type:** newsletter.

026.34   US   ISSN 0148-0553
LAW LINES. Variant title: L L A G N Y Law Lines. 1976. 6/yr. membership. Law Library Association of Greater New York, c/o Deborah G. Cinque, Ed., Weil, Gotshal & Manges, 767 Fifth Ave., New York, NY 10153. TEL 212-310-8626. FAX 212-310-8786. (Subscr. to: Elizabeth M. Evans, New York University School of Law, Rm. 108, 40 Washington Sq. S., New York, NY 10012. TEL 212-998-6319) adv. circ. 800. **Document type:** newsletter.
    Description: Discusses association news and activities, professional issues, and other concerns relevant to law librarianship.

020   US
LAWDOCS. 1986. q. free. Oklahoma Department of Libraries, 200 N.E. 18th St., Oklahoma City, OK 73105-3298. TEL 405-521-2502. FAX 405-525-7804. Ed. Steve Beleu. circ. 40. **Document type:** government publication, newsletter.

026.34   US
LAWTALK. 1972. q. free to law librarians. Lawyers Cooperative Publishing (Subsidiary of: Thomson Professional Publishing), Acqueduct Bldg., Rochester, NY 14694. TEL 800-527-0430. Ed. George Gabel. **Document type:** newsletter.
    Description: Covers issues of interest to law librarians, including research and library management tips, new technology, and how-to articles.

020   UK   ISSN 0023-9542
Z671
AN LEABHARLANN/IRISH LIBRARY. 1972. q. £12. Library Association of Ireland and the Library Association, Northern Ireland Branch, c/o Main Library, Queen's University of Belfast, Belfast BT7 1NN, N. Ireland. TEL 0232-323340. FAX 0232-247895. Eds. N. Butterwick, L. Ronayne. adv.; bk.rev.; charts; illus.; index. circ. 1,000. **Indexed:** Lib.Lit., Lib.Sci.Abstr., LISA, So.Pac.Per.Ind.
    —BLDSC (4572.840000).
    Supersedes: Northern Ireland Libraries (ISSN 0029-3113)

020   US   ISSN 0170-8643
LECTURE NOTES IN CONTROL AND INFORMATION SCIENCES. 1978. irreg. price varies. Springer-Verlag, 175 Fifth Ave., New York, NY 10010. TEL 212-460-1500. FAX 212-473-6272. (Also: Berlin, Heidelberg, Tokyo and Vienna) Eds. A.V. Balakrishnan, M. Thoma. (reprint service avail. from ISI) **Indexed:** CAD CAM Abstr. (until 1993), Compumath. **Document type:** monographic series.
    —BLDSC (5180.187000). **CCC.**

LEGAL INFORMATION ALERT; what's new in legal publications, databases and research techniques. see LAW — Abstracting, Bibliographies, Statistics

LEGAL INFORMATION MANAGEMENT INDEX. see LAW — Abstracting, Bibliographies, Statistics

LEGAL INFORMATION MANAGEMENT REPORTS. see LAW

020 340   US   ISSN 0270-319X
K12   CODEN: LRSQD9
LEGAL REFERENCE SERVICES QUARTERLY. 1981. q. $36 to individuals; institutions $105. Haworth Press, Inc., 10 Alice St., Binghamton, NY 13904. TEL 607-722-5857; 800-342-9678. FAX 607-722-1424. TELEX 4932599. Ed. Robert C. Berring. adv.; bk.rev.; bibl.; charts; illus. circ. 978. (also avail. in microfiche from UMI; back issues avail.; reprint service avail. from HAW) **Indexed:** C.I.J.E., C.L.I., Comput.& Info.Sys., Educ.Ind., Ind.Per.Art.Relat.Law, INSPEC, Leg.Info.Manage.Ind., Leg.Per., Lib.Lit., LISA, P.A.I.S., Sci.Abstr.
    —BLDSC (5181.377000); Faxon; UnCover; SWETS.
    Description: Directed towards the working reference librarian involved with legal research materials.
    Refereed Serial

020   JA   ISSN 0914-2045
LEGIS-MATE/REJISUMEITO. (Text in Japanese) 1987. irreg. National Diet Library - Kokuritsu Kokkai Toshokan, 1-10-1 Nagata-cho, Chiyoda-ku, Tokyo 100, Japan. TEL 03-3581-2331. FAX 03-3597-9104. circ. 1,800 (controlled).
    Description: Intended for Diet members, their staff and people working closely with them. Each issue carries a variety of current information to help readers better utilize the services provided by the library.

020.6   CN   ISSN 0705-4890
LETTER OF THE L A A. 5/yr. membership. Library Association of Alberta, Box 64197, 5512-4 St. N.W., Calgary, AB T2K 6J1, Canada. TEL 403-284-5818. FAX 403-282-6646. Ed. Karen Labuik. circ. 500. **Document type:** newsletter.

020   CN
LETTER OF THE L A A. NEWSLETTER. 1969. 5/yr. membership. Library Association of Alberta, Box 64197, 5512-4 St. N.W., Calgary, AB T2K 6J1, Canada. TEL 403-284-5818. FAX 403-282-6646. Ed. Karen Labuik. bk.rev. circ. 700. **Document type:** newsletter.
    Former titles: Library Association of Alberta. Newsletter; Library Association of Alberta. Occasional Papers (ISSN 0075-904X)

020   UK   ISSN 0968-0810
Z668.5
▼**LIBRARIAN CAREER DEVELOPMENT.** 1993. 4/yr. $199.95. M C B University Press Ltd., 60-62 Toller Ln., Bradford, W. Yorks BD8 9BY, England. TEL 0274-499821. FAX 0274-547143. TELEX 51317-MCBUNI-G. (N. American subscr. to: M C B University Press Limited, Box 1943, Birmingham, AL 35201) Ed. Beryl Morris. **Document type:** academic/scholarly publication.
    —BLDSC (5186.855400); SWETS.

020   US   ISSN 1069-0832
▼**LIBRARIANS AT LIBERTY;** an interactive newsletter. 1993. s-a. $10 (foreign $15). C R I S E S Press, Inc., 1716 S.W. Williston Rd., Gainesville, FL 32608. TEL 904-335-2200. Ed. Charles Willett. **Document type:** academic/scholarly publication, newsletter.
    Description: Aims to give people working in libraries and related fields an unconstrained opportunity to express professional concerns.

020 266 200   UK   ISSN 0308-5473
LIBRARIANS' CHRISTIAN FELLOWSHIP NEWSLETTER. 1974. 3/yr. £7. Librarians' Christian Fellowship, 34 Thurlestone Ave., Seven Kings, Ilford, Essex IG3 9DU, England. TEL 081-599-1310. Ed. Graham Hedges. adv.; bk.rev.; abstr. circ. 500. (back issues avail.) **Document type:** newsletter.
    Description: Covers issues in librarianship from a Christian perspective.

020 340   US
LIBRARIAN'S REPORT. q.? free. Warren Gorham Lamont, One Penn Plaza, New York, NY 10119-4098. TEL 800-950-1201. circ. 2,000.

LIBRARY AND INFORMATION SCIENCES

020 070.5   US   ISSN 0739-0297
LIBRARIAN'S WORLD. 1970. q. $15 (foreign $20). Evangelical Church Library Association, Box 353, Glen Ellyn, IL 60138. TEL 312-668-0519. Ed. Nancy Dick. adv.; bk.rev. circ. 689. (back issues avail.)
Description: Presents promotional ideas for church librarians.

020   UK   ISSN 0968-0780
LIBRARIANSHIP AND INFORMATION WORK WORLDWIDE; an annual survey. 1991. a. £65($110) Bowker-Saur Ltd., A Reed Reference Publishing Company, Part of the Reed Elsevier group, Maypole House, Maypole Rd., E. Grinstead. W. Sussex RH19 1HH, England. TEL 0342-330-100. FAX 0342-330-191. (Subscr. to: Butterworths Service Co., Borough Green, Sevenoaks, Kent TN15 8PH, England. TEL 0732-884567) Ed.Bd. **Document type:** directory.
Description: Review of developments in library and information science around the world. Emphasizes issues and events in Europe, Australia, Japan, US, and Canada.

020 970   US   ISSN 0894-8631
Z671
LIBRARIES & CULTURE. 1966. q. $24 to individuals; institutions $40. University of Texas Press, Box 7819, Austin, TX 78713. TEL 512-471-3821. FAX 512-320-0668. Ed. Donald G. Davis, Jr. adv.; bk.rev.; abstr.; bibl.; charts; illus.; stat.; index, cum.index: 1966-1976. circ. 800. (also avail. in microfilm from UMI; reprint service avail. from UMI.) **Indexed:** Amer.Bibl.Slavic & E.Eur.Stud., Amer.Hist.& Life, Bk.Rev.Ind. (1966-), CALL, Child.Bk.Rev.Ind. (1966-), Hist.Abstr., Lib.Lit., LISA, M.L.A., SSCI.
—BLDSC (5186.892520); Faxon; UnCover; SWETS; UMI. **CCC.**
Former titles: Journal of Library History, Philosophy and Comparative Librarianship (ISSN 0275-3650); Journal of Library History. State Library History Bibliography Series.
Description: Explores collections of graphic records and their creators and users in the context of cultural history.

027   US   ISSN 1055-3665
Z731   CODEN: LITDEF
LIBRARIES AND INFORMATION SERVICES TODAY. 1991. a. American Library Association, 50 E. Huron St., Chicago, IL 60611.
—BLDSC (5186.893000).

020   UK   ISSN 0961-4575
LIBRARIES DIRECTORY. 1897. biennial. £80($150) James Clarke & Co. Ltd., P.O. Box 60, Cambridge CB1 2NT, England. TEL 0223-350865. FAX 0223-66951. (Dist. in U.S. by: Gale Research Inc., Box 33477, Detroit, MI 48232-5477) Ed. Akiko Kimura. adv.; index. circ. 3,500. **Document type:** directory.
—BLDSC (5186.901800).
Former titles: Libraries Yearbook (ISSN 0955-4645); Libraries, Museums and Art Galleries Year Book (ISSN 0075-899X)

020   UK
LIBRARIES IN THE UNITED KINGDOM & THE REPUBLIC OF IRELAND. 1960. a. price varies. Library Association Publishing Ltd., 7 Ridgmount St., London WC1E 7AE, England. TEL 071-636-7543. FAX 071-636-3627. TELEX 9312134504-LAG. (Dist. in U.S. by: UNIPUB, 4611-F Assembly Dr., Lanham, MD 20706-4391) Ed. Ann Harrold. **Document type:** directory.
Description: An annual listing, with addresses and telephone numbers, of over 700 major libraries and library authorities.

020   JA
LIBRARIES TODAY/GENDAI NO TOSHOKAN. (Text in Japanese) 1963. q. 6000 Yen. Japan Library Association - Nihon Toshokan Kyokai, 1-1-10 Taishido, Setagaya-ku, Tokyo 154, Japan. FAX 81-3-3421-7588. Ed. Yoshitomi Okazaki. bk.rev.; abstr.; charts. circ. 5,000.
Formerly: Contemporary Library Trends (ISSN 0016-6332)

027.4
LIBRARIES UNLIMITED NEWSLETTER. 1964. irreg. membership. Gloucester City Library, Gloucester City, NJ 08030. TEL 609-456-4181. Ed. Elizabeth Egan. bk.rev. circ. 150. **Document type:** newsletter.
Description: Serves South Jersey libraries. Provides information for library development and innovation.

020   UK   ISSN 0024-2160
Z671
THE LIBRARY; The transactions of the Bibliographical Society. 1899. q. £21($43) (effective 1994). (Bibliographical Society) Oxford University Press, Oxford Journals, Walton St., Oxford OX2 6DP, England. TEL 0865-56767. FAX 0865-56646. TELEX 837330-OXPRES-G. (U.S. subscr. to: Oxford University Press Inc., 2001 Evans Rd., Cary, NC 27513. TEL 919-677-0977) Ed. M.C. Davies. adv.; bk.rev.; bibl.; illus.; index. circ. 1,200. (also avail. in microform from UMI) **Indexed:** Amer.Hist.& Life, Artbibl.Mod., Bk.Rev.Ind. (1967-), Child.Bk.Rev.Ind. (1967-), Curr.Cont., Hist.Abstr., Ind.Bk.Rev.Hum., Lib.Lit., Lib.Sci.Abstr., M.L.A., RILA. **Document type:** academic/scholarly publication.
—BLDSC (5186.950000); Faxon; UnCover; SWETS; UMI. **CCC.**
Description: Official journal of the Bibliographical Society for the history of books, both manuscript and printed, covering the role of books in history.

020   UK   ISSN 0364-6408
Z689   CODEN: LAPTDK
LIBRARY ACQUISITIONS: PRACTICE AND THEORY. 1977. 4/yr. £90($140) (effective 1994). Elsevier Science Ltd., Pergamon, P.O. Box 800, Kidlington, Oxford OX5 1DX, England. TEL 44-865-843000. FAX 44-865-843010. (Subscr. in U.S. and Canada to: Elsevier Science, 660 White Plains Rd., Tarrytown, NY 10591-5153. TEL 914-524-9200. FAX 914-333-2444) Ed. Carol Pitts Hawks. adv. circ. 5,300. (also avail. in microform from UMI; back issues avail.) **Indexed:** Comput.& Info.Sys., Curr.Cont., Leg.Info.Manage.Ind., LHTN, Lib.Lit., LISA, Sci.Abstr., SSCI. **Document type:** academic/scholarly publication.
—BLDSC (5188.130000); Faxon; UnCover; SWETS; UMI; CASDDS. **CCC.**
Description: A forum for the exchange of ideas and experiences among members of library acquisitions, collections management and bookselling communities worldwide. Emphasizes practical experience as well as theoretical foundations of the profession.
Refereed Serial

020   US   ISSN 0888-4463
Z678
LIBRARY ADMINISTRATION AND MANAGEMENT. 1975. q. $50 in US, Canada, Mexico; elsewhere $60. American Library Association, Library Administration and Management Association, 50 E. Huron St., Chicago, IL 60611-2795. TEL 312-944-6780. FAX 312-440-9374. Ed. Diane Graves. adv. circ. 6,000. (also avail. in microform from UMI; back issues avail.; reprint service avail. from UMI) **Indexed:** C.I.J.E., Lib.Lit. **Document type:** trade publication.
—BLDSC (5188.158000); Faxon; UnCover; SWETS; UMI. **CCC.**
Former titles (until 1986): L A M A Newsletter (Library Administration and Management Association) (ISSN 0193-0451); L A D Newsletter (Library Administration Division) (ISSN 0098-7972)

020   US   ISSN 0746-6129
LIBRARY ADMINISTRATOR'S DIGEST. 1965. m. (except Jul. & Aug.). $36. Administrator's Digest, Inc., Box 993, S. San Francisco, CA 94080. TEL 415-573-5474. Ed. Robert S. Alvarez. (also avail. in microfilm from UMI; reprint service avail. from UMI) **Document type:** newsletter.
—UMI.
Formerly (until 1983): Administrator's Digest (ISSN 0001-8422)

020   US   ISSN 0196-0075
Z679.6
LIBRARY & ARCHIVAL SECURITY. 1975. s-a. $36 to individuals; institutions $95. Haworth Press, Inc., 10 Alice St., Binghamton, NY 13904. TEL 607-722-5857; 800-342-9678. FAX 607-722-1424. TELEX 4932599. Ed. Bruce A. Shuman. adv.; bk.rev.; abstr.; bibl.; index. (also avail. in microfiche from UMI; back issues avail.; reprint service avail. from HAW) **Indexed:** Comput.& Info.Sys., Inform.Sci.Abstr., Leg.Info.Manage.Ind., Lib.Lit., LISA.
—BLDSC (5188.250000); Faxon; SWETS.
Formerly (until 1979): Library Security Newsletter (ISSN 0094-0216)
Description: Provides information to librarians, scholars, and researchers concerned with security planning, policies, procedures, and strategies for libraries and archives.
Refereed Serial

020   UK
LIBRARY AND INFORMATION ACTIVISTS RECORD. 1987. 4/yr. £5. Hector & Ruffle Ltd., 11 Eaton Court, Eaton Road, Sutton, Surrey SM2 5DZ, England. circ. 750.
Description: Covers library administration and operation, information science, and computer applications.

020.6   UK   ISSN 0957-7912
LIBRARY AND INFORMATION ASSISTANT. 1988. s-a. £7.50. Association for the Education and Training of Library Technicians and Assistants, c/o Donald Steele, Ed., Telford College, Crewe Toll, Edinburgh EH4 2NZ, Scotland. FAX 031-343-1218. adv.; bk.rev. circ. 400.
Description: Articles and news columns cover items of interest to junior library staff, with an emphasis on education, training and career enhancement.

020   UK   ISSN 0963-0236
LIBRARY AND INFORMATION NEWS. 1972. m. £50. Dawson U K Ltd., Cannon House, Park Farm Rd., Folkestone, Kent CT19 5EE, England. TEL 0303-850101. FAX 0303-850440. TELEX 96392. Ed. John Cowley. adv.; bk.rev. circ. 1,500. **Document type:** newsletter.
—BLDSC (5188.535000); SWETS.
Description: News and articles about library and information service developments as well as those organizations who supply libraries with goods or services.

020   UK   ISSN 0141-6561
LIBRARY AND INFORMATION RESEARCH NEWS. 1978. 3/yr. £15 to individuals; institutions £35 (foreign £40). Library and Information Research Group, c/o British Library, Research and Development Dept., 2 Sheraton St., London W1V 4BH, England. TEL 071-323-7049. FAX 071-323-7251. (Dist. by: Library Document Supply Centre, Boston Spa, Wetherby, W. Yorkshire LS23 7BQ, England; Subscr. to: Christine Abbott, Library Information Services, Aston University, Aston Triangle, Birmingham B4 7ET, England. TEL 021-359-3611. FAX 021-359-7358) Ed. Ros Cotton. adv.; bk.rev. circ. 350. **Indexed:** LISA. **Document type:** academic/scholarly publication.
—BLDSC (5188.550000); UnCover.
Description: Contains articles, news and reviews relating to research in librarianship and information science.

020   JA   ISSN 0373-4447
Z671   CODEN: LIFSBL
LIBRARY AND INFORMATION SCIENCE. (Text in English and Japanese) 1963. a. $20. Mita Society for Library and Information Science - Mita Toshokan Joho Gakkai, c/o Keio University, 2-15-45 Mita, Minato-ku, Tokyo 108, Japan. TEL 03-3453-3920. FAX 03-3798-7480. Ed. Shuichi Ueda. bk.rev. circ. 1,650. **Indexed:** Curr.Cont., Lib.Lit., Lib.Sci.Abstr., SSCI. **Document type:** academic/scholarly publication.
—BLDSC (5188.600000).

020   US   ISSN 0740-8188
Z671   CODEN: LISRDH
LIBRARY & INFORMATION SCIENCE RESEARCH; an international journal. 1979. q. $45 to individuals; institutions $95. Ablex Publishing Corporation, 355 Chestnut St., Norwood, NJ 07648. TEL 201-767-8450. FAX 201-767-6717. TELEX 135-393. Ed. Jane Robbins. adv.; bk.rev. circ. 650. (back issues avail.; reprint service avail. from ISI) **Indexed:** ASCA, C.I.J.E., Curr.Cont., Lang.& Lang.Behav.Abstr., Lib.Lit., LISA, Res.High.Educ.Abstr., Sociol.Abstr.
—BLDSC (5188.730000); Faxon; UnCover; SWETS. **CCC.**
Formerly (until 1983): Library Research (ISSN 0164-0763)

020   AT
LIBRARY AND INFORMATION SERVICE OF WESTERN AUSTRALIA. NEWSLETTER. 1955. m. Aus.$20. Library and Information Service of Western Australia, Alexander Library Building, Perth Cultural Centre, Perth, W.A. 6000, Australia. circ. 700. (back issues avail.)
Formerly: Library Service of Western Australia. Newsletter (ISSN 0159-7477)
Description: Library service news from public libraries throughout Western Australia.

LIBRARY AND INFORMATION SCIENCES

027.7   UK   ISSN 0144-056X
LIBRARY ASSOCIATION. UNIVERSITY, COLLEGE AND RESEARCH GROUP. NEWSLETTER. 1980. 3/yr. free to qualified personnel. Library Association, University College and Research Section, c/o Mrs. M.A. Watson, Dept. Information & Library Management, University of Northumbria at Newcastle, Newcastle-upon-Tyne NE1 8ST, England. TEL 091-232-6002. FAX 091-235-8572. adv./ bk.rev. circ. 4,000.
Document type: newsletter.
—BLDSC (6108.423400).

020   UK   ISSN 0075-9066
LIBRARY ASSOCIATION. YEARBOOK. 1892. a. price varies. Library Association Publishing Ltd., 7 Ridgmount St., London WC1E 7AE, England. TEL 071-636-7543. FAX 071-636-3627. TELEX 9312134504-LAG. (Dist. in U.S. by: UNIPUB, 4611-F Assembly Dr., Lanham, MD 20706-4391)
Document type: corporate report.
—BLDSC (9389.000000).

020.6   BB
LIBRARY ASSOCIATION OF BARBADOS. BULLETIN. 1968. irreg., no.12, 1985. $5. Library Association of Barbados, P.O. Box 827E, Bridgetown, Barbados, W.I.

020   CH   ISSN 0254-4784
Z673
LIBRARY ASSOCIATION OF CHINA. NEWSLETTER. Key Title: Zhongguo Tushuguan Xuehui Huiwu Tongxun. 1954. a. NT.$400($15) Library Association of China, c/o National Central Library, 20 Chung Shan S. Rd., Taipei, Taiwan 10040, Republic of China. FAX 02-311-0155. Ed. Teresa Wang Chang. adv.; bk.rev. circ. 2,000.
Description: Aims to improve the overall effectiveness of libraries and library management. Covers issues in data collection, library automation, cataloging, history and more.

020   TR   ISSN 0521-9590
LIBRARY ASSOCIATION OF TRINIDAD AND TOBAGO. BULLETIN. 1964. a. T.T.$20. Library Association of Trinidad and Tobago, P.O. Box 1275, Port-of-Spain, Trinidad & Tobago, W.I. Ed.Bd. adv. circ. 200.
Document type: bulletin.

020   UK   ISSN 0024-2195
Z671
LIBRARY ASSOCIATION RECORD. 1899. 12/yr. £75($170) (foreign £92.50). Library Association, 7 Ridgmount St., London WC1E 7AE, England. TEL 071-636-7543. FAX 071-436-7218. Ed. Christine Brockhurst. adv. contact: Andrew Nelson-Cole. bk.rev.; bibl.; index; circ. 28,000 (controlled). (also avail. in microfilm from UMI; reprint service avail. from KTO) **Indexed:** Bk.Rev.Ind. (1991-), Child.Bk.Rev.Ind. (1991-), Child.Lit.Abstr., LHTN, Lib.Lit., LISA, Ref.Sour. **Document type:** trade publication.
—BLDSC (5189.000000); Faxon; UnCover; SWETS.
Description: News briefs on current regulatory developments, profiles and feature articles pertaining to the administrative and operational aspects of library and information management, with announcements of conferences and seminars.

020   US   ISSN 0024-2241
Z881
LIBRARY CHRONICLE (AUSTIN). 1944; N.S. 1970. q. $30 (overseas $50). University of Texas at Austin, Harry Ransom Humanities Research Center, Box 7219, Austin, TX 78713. TEL 512-471-8944. FAX 512-471-9646. Ed. Dave Oliphant. illus. circ. 350. (also avail. in microform from UMI; back issues avail.; reprint service avail. from UMI) **Indexed:** Abstr.Engl.Stud., Amer.Hist.& Life, Amer.Hum.Ind., Arts & Hum.Cit.Ind., Curr.Cont., Hist.Abstr. **Document type:** academic/scholarly publication.
—BLDSC (5194.700000); Faxon; UMI.
Description: Covers the library's collection and features articles on poetry, fiction, cultural studies, and texts.

020.6   US   ISSN 0160-922X
Z733
LIBRARY COMPANY OF PHILADELPHIA. ANNUAL REPORT. 1874. a. free. Library Company of Philadelphia, 1314 Locust St., Philadelphia, PA 19107. Ed. John C. Van Horn. bibl.; illus.; stat. **Document type:** corporate report.

LIBRARY COMPANY OF PHILADELPHIA. OCCASIONAL MISCELLANY. see HISTORY — History Of North And South America

LIBRARY CONSERVATION NEWS. see CONSERVATION

020   US   ISSN 0741-4188
LIBRARY CURRENTS; your source for current library information. 1984. m. $45. Practical Perspectives, Inc., Box 202108, Austin, TX 78720-2108. TEL 512-218-8038. Ed. Edward Seidenberg. bk.rev. circ. 1,000.

020   US   ISSN 0145-5397
Z732.T25
LIBRARY DEVELOPMENTS. 1974. bi-m. free. Texas State Library, Library Development Division, Box 12927, Austin, TX 78711. TEL 512-463-5465. FAX 512-463-5436. Ed. Jeanette Larson. circ. 1,000 (controlled).

LIBRARY EDITIONS. see BIBLIOGRAPHIES

020   UK   ISSN 0269-963X
LIBRARY EQUIPMENT REPORT. 1986. 6/yr. £119($239) Headland Press, One Henry Smith's Terrace, Headland, Cleveland TS24 OPD, England. TEL 0429-231902. FAX 0429-860674.
—BLDSC (5198.685000).
Description: Provides advice on all categories of library equipment, from microcomputers to rubber stamps.

020   II   ISSN 0024-2292
Z671
LIBRARY HERALD. (Text in English) 1958. q. Rs.70($25) Delhi Library Association, Box 1270, c/o Hardinge Public Library, Queen's Garden, Delhi 110006, India. Ed.Bd. adv.; abstr.; index. circ. 800. **Indexed:** Lib.Lit., Lib.Sci.Abstr., LISA.
—BLDSC (5198.800000); UnCover; UMI.

020   UK   ISSN 0024-2306
Z721
LIBRARY HISTORY. 1967. s-a. £11($20) Library Association, Library History Group, 7 Ridgmount St., London WC1E 7AE, England. Ed. K.A. Manley. adv.; bk.rev.; bibl.illus. circ. 1,200. **Indexed:** Amer.Hist.& Life, Br.Hum.Ind., Hist.Abstr., Lib.Lit., LISA. **Document type:** academic/scholarly publication.
—UnCover; SWETS.

020   II   ISSN 0378-7508
LIBRARY HISTORY REVIEW. (Text in English) 1974. q. Rs.360($45) (International Agency for Research in Library History) K.K. Roy (Private) Ltd., 55 Gariahat Rd., P.O. Box 10210, Calcutta 700 019, India. Ed. K.K. Roy. adv.; bk.rev.; index. circ. 1,650. **Indexed:** Amer.Hist.& Life, Hist.Abstr.
—BLDSC (5198.920000).

020   US   ISSN 0740-736X
Z671   CODEN: LIHODL
LIBRARY HOTLINE. 1972. w. (except last 2 weeks of yr.) $74 (foreign $91). Cahners Publishing Company (New York), Printing and Publishing Division, Division of Reed Elsevier Inc., 249 W. 17th St., New York, NY 10011. TEL 800-722-2346. FAX 212-242-7216. (Subscr. to: Box 713, Brewster, NY 10509-0713) Ed. Susan S. DiMattia. adv. (looseleaf format; reprint service avail. from UMI) **Document type:** trade publication.
—BLDSC (5198.933000); CASDDS. **CCC.**
Formerly (until 1983): L J - S L J Hot Line (Library Journal - School Library Journal) (ISSN 0000-0078)
Description: Newsletter summarizing developments affecting libraries and librarians. Includes job postings.

027   US   ISSN 0197-5587
LIBRARY IMAGINATION PAPER. 1979. q. $30 (foreign $34). Carol Bryan Imagines, 1000 Byus Dr., Charleston, WV 25311. TEL 304-345-2378. Ed. Carol Bryan. circ. 2,400. (tabloid format; back issues avail.) **Document type:** newsletter.
Description: Library promotional clip art, articles, tips and help on public relations topics by field experts.

027   US   ISSN 0734-3035
Z675.U5
LIBRARY ISSUES; briefings for faculty and administrators. bi-m. $40. Mountainside Publishing, Inc., 321 S. Main St., Box 8330, Ann Arbor, MI 48107. TEL 313-662-3925. FAX 313-662-4450. Ed. Richard M. Dougherty. **Document type:** newsletter.
—CCC.
Description: In layman's terms, explains academic library problems as they relate to faculty, administrators and the parent institution.

020   US   ISSN 0363-0277
Z671
LIBRARY JOURNAL. 1876. 21/yr. $87.50 (Canada $109; elsewhere $149) (effective 1994). Cahners Publishing Company (New York), Printing and Publishing Division, Division of Reed Elsevier Inc., 249 W. 17th St., New York, NY 10011. TEL 212-463-6819. FAX 212-463-6734. (Subscr. to: Box 59690, Boulder, CO 80322-9690. TEL 800-677-6694) Ed. Francine Fialkoff. adv.; bk.rev.; bibl.; illus.; index. circ. 24,145. (also avail. in microfilm from RPI,PMC; microfiche from CIS; reprint service avail. from UMI) **Indexed:** Acad.Ind., Access (1980-), Bk.Rev.Dig., Bk.Rev.Ind. (1965-), Bus.Ind., C.I.J.E., Chic.Per.Ind., Child.Bk.Rev.Ind. (1965-), CINAHL, Curr.Cont., Educ.Ind., Gard.Lit. (1992-), Hlth.Ind., Leg.Info.Manage.Ind., LHTN, Lib.Lit., Lib.Sci.Abstr., Mag.Ind, Mid.East: Abstr.& Ind., P.A.I.S., Peace Res.Abstr., Pers.Lit., PMR, PROMT, Ref.Sour., Rehabil.Lit., So.Pac.Per.Ind., SRI, SSCI, Tel.Abstr., Tr.& Indus.Ind. **Document type:** academic/scholarly publication, trade publication.
—BLDSC (5199.000000); Faxon; UnCover; SWETS; UMI. **CCC.**
Description: News and events, articles identifying trends, and reviews of books, magazines and audiovisual materials.

020.6   JA   ISSN 0385-4000
Z671
LIBRARY JOURNAL/TOSHOKAN ZASSHI. (Text in Japanese) 1907. m. 12000 Yen. Japan Library Association - Nihon Toshokan Kyokai, 1-1-10 Taishido, Setagaya-ku, Tokyo 154, Japan. FAX 81-3-3421-7588. **Indexed:** LISA.
—BLDSC (5199.200000); UnCover.

020   NZ
Z673.N683
LIBRARY LIFE TE RAU ORA. 1956. 11/yr. NZ.$55 (effective 1992). New Zealand Library and Information Association, P.O. Box 12-212, Wellington 1, New Zealand. TEL 04-473-5834. FAX 04-499-1480. adv. circ. 2,200.
—CCC.
Formerly: Library Life (ISSN 0110-4373); Supersedes (in 1977): N Z L A Newsletter (ISSN 0027-7215)

026   CN
LIBRARY LINES. 1975. 3/yr. membership. Church Library Association of Ontario, 877 Yonge St., Ste. 504B, Toronto, ON M4W 3M2, Canada. TEL 416-966-9186. Ed. Emma Austin. bk.rev. circ. 225.
Description: News for church librarians.

020   II
LIBRARY LITERATURE IN INDIA SERIES. no.2, 1975. irreg. price varies. Library Literature House, Chandigarh, India. illus.

020   UK   ISSN 0143-5124
Z678
LIBRARY MANAGEMENT. 1976. 8/yr. $2639.95. M C B University Press Ltd., 60-62 Toller Ln., Bradford, W. Yorks BD8 9BY, England. TEL 0274-499821. FAX 0274-547143. TELEX 51317-MCBUNI-G. Ed. Ken Bakewell. (reprint service avail. from SWZ) **Indexed:** ABI Inform., Anbar, Curr.Cont., LISA. **Document type:** academic/scholarly publication.
—BLDSC (5200.415000); Faxon; SWETS; UMI. **CCC.**
Formerly: Library Research Occasional Paper (ISSN 0309-2232)
Description: Monitors the dynamic new techniques which are pushing forward the frontiers of the profession.

025   US   ISSN 0271-3306
Z675.A2
LIBRARY MANAGEMENT QUARTERLY. 1977. q. $25 (foreign $35). Special Libraries Association, Library Management Division, c/o Susan Warner, Ed., Wang Laboratories, One Industrial Ave, Lowell, MA 01851. TEL 508-967-6366. (Subscr. to: Jean Scanlan, Price Waterhouse, 160 Federal St., Boston, MA 02110. TEL 617-439-7412) adv.; bk.rev. circ. 1,800. **Indexed:** LISA.
—BLDSC (5200.430000).
Formerly (until 1985): Library Management Bulletin.

LIBRARY AND INFORMATION SCIENCES

020   US
LIBRARY MATERIALS GUIDE. s-a. $27.50 per no. Christian Schools International, 3350 E. Paris Ave., S.E., Grand Rapids, MI 49512. TEL 616-957-1070. bk.rev. circ. 400.
  Description: Includes reviews of approximately 500 new books for school libraries.

027.4
LIBRARY MATTERS. 1969. q. free. Queens Borough Public Library, 89-11 Merrick Blvd., Jamaica, NY 11432. TEL 718-990-0705. FAX 718-291-8936. Ed. Himi Koren. charts; illus.; circ. 20,000 (controlled). **Document type:** newsletter.
  Formerly (until 1985): Queens Borough Public Library News.
  Description: Includes photos, news stories about Queens Library collections, services, and events.

020   US   ISSN 1054-9676
Z671
LIBRARY MOSAICS. 1989. bi-m. $20. Yenor, Inc., P.O. Box 5171, Culver City, CA 90231. TEL 310-410-1573. Ed. Ed Martinez. adv.; bk.rev.; circ. 4,000 (paid). **Indexed:** Lib.Lit.
  —Faxon; UnCover.
  Description: Focuses on library, media and information center support staff issues, trends and developments.

021.7
LIBRARY NEWS (ATLANTA). m. Atlanta Public Library, One Margaret Mitchell Square, Atlanta, GA 30303. **Indexed:** Bibl.Cart.

020 579   US
LIBRARY NEWS FOR ZOOS AND AQUARIUMS. 1982. s-a. free. Indianapolis Zoological Society, Inc., 1200 W. Washington St., Indianapolis, IN 46222. TEL 317-630-5110. FAX 317-630-5114. Ed. Suzanne K. Braun. bk.rev. circ. 350. (back issues avail.)
  Description: Provides information for operation of zoo or aquarium library.

LIBRARY OF CONGRESS. COMPLETE CATALOG OF BIBLIOGRAPHIC PRODUCTS AND SERVICES. see *BIBLIOGRAPHIES*

020   US   ISSN 0895-1179
Z711.92.A32
LIBRARY OUTREACH REPORTER. 1987. 6/yr. $21. Library Outreach Reporter, 148 Liberty St., Fords, NJ 08863-2042. TEL 908-738-5183. Ed. Allan M. Kleiman. adv.; bk.rev. index. circ. 1,000. (back issues avail.)
  Description: Professional publication that provides information, analysis and evaluation of issues in Outreach special services.

025   US   ISSN 0164-9566
LIBRARY P R NEWS. 1978. bi-m. $29.95 in U.S.; Canada $31.95; elsewhere $40.95. (Library Educational Institute. Inc.) L E I, Inc., Rd. 1, Box 219, New Albany, PA 18833. TEL 717-746-1842. FAX 717-746-1114. Ed. Phillip J. Bradbury. bk.rev. circ. 5,000. **Document type:** newsletter.
  Incorporates: Tips from C.L.I.P. (Coordinated Library Information Program).
  Description: For public, school, and academic libraries. Devoted to library public relations, programming, promotion exhibits and graphic arts.

023   US   ISSN 0891-2742
Z681.5
LIBRARY PERSONNEL NEWS. 1987. 6/yr. $20. American Library Association, Office for Library Personnel Resources, 50 E. Huron St., Chicago, IL 60611-2795. TEL 312-280-4279. FAX 312-280-3526. Eds. Margaret Myers, Jeniece Guy. circ. 800 (paid). (back issues avail.) **Indexed:** Lib.Lit. **Document type:** newsletter.
  —UMI.
  Description: Provides information on general personnel, administration, trends, practices, and employment legislative news.

020   US
LIBRARY POINTES. 1982. q. free. Grosse Pointe Public Library, 10 Kercheval Ave., Grosse Pointe, MI 48236. TEL 313-343-2074. Eds. Helen Leonard, Carol Evans.
  Formerly (until 1984): Word.

020   II   ISSN 0970-1052
Z730
LIBRARY PROGRESS. 1981. 2/yr. Rs.40($8) to individuals; institutions Rs.80($12). Dr. A.K. Sharma, Ed. & Pub., P.O. Box 38, Modinagar 201 204, India. adv.; bk.rev. circ. 300. **Document type:** academic/scholarly publication.
  —CCC.

020   US   ISSN 0024-2519
Z671   CODEN: LIBQAS
LIBRARY QUARTERLY; a journal of investigation and discussion in the field of library science. 1931. q. $29 to individuals; institutions $46; students $23. (University of Chicago Graduate Library School) University of Chicago Press, Journals Division, 5720 S. Woodlawn Ave., Chicago, IL 60637. TEL 312-753-3347. FAX 712-753-0811. TELEX 25-4603. (Subscr. to: Box 37005, Chicago, IL 60637) Ed. Stephen P. Harter. adv.; bk.rev.; charts; stat.; index. circ. 2,200. (also avail. in microform from MIM,UMI,PMC; reprint service avail. from UMI,ISI) **Indexed:** Amer.Bibl.Slavic & E.Eur.Stud., Amer.Hist.& Life, Bk.Rev.Dig., Bk.Rev.Ind. (1965-), C.I.J.E., Chem.Abstr., Child.Bk.Rev.Ind. (1965-), Child.Lit.Abstr., Curr.Cont., Hist.Abstr., Lib.Lit., Lib.Sci.Abstr., LISA, Mag.Ind., Mid.East: Abstr.& Ind., P.A.I.S., Ref.Sour., Res.High.Educ.Abstr., Sci.Abstr., SSCI. **Document type:** academic/scholarly publication.
  —BLDSC (5202.000000); Faxon; UnCover; SWETS; UMI; CASDDS. **CCC.**
  Description: A general interest journal for scholars and professionals, covering a wide range of topics.
  Refereed Serial

020 011   US   ISSN 1067-8166
Z716.6
LIBRARY REFERENCE PLUS; complete reference information about US libraries, bookstores, publishers, distributors, wholesalers and statistical data on library and book trade activities. a. $795. R.R. Bowker, A Reed Reference Publishing Company, Part of the Reed Elsevier group, 121 Chanlon Rd., New Providence, NJ 07974. TEL 908-464-6800. FAX 908-665-6688. TELEX 138-755. (Subscr. to: Order Dept., Box 31, New Providence, NJ 07974-9903. TEL 800-323-3288) (avail. for MS-DOS version)
  ●Available only on CD-ROM. Producer(s): Bowker - Reed Reference Electronic Publishing.
  Description: Contains facts, statistics, contact names, addresses, activities and support services relating to the library world, publishing and book trades.

020 950   AT
LIBRARY RESEARCH IN ASIA, AFRICA & AUSTRALIA. 1990. a. Aus.$156. Noyce Publishing, G.P.O. Box 2222T, Melbourne, Vic. 3001, Australia. bibl. (back issues avail.)

025   US   ISSN 0024-2527
Z671   CODEN: LRTSAH
LIBRARY RESOURCES & TECHNICAL SERVICES. 1957. q. $45 in US, Canada, Mexico; elsewhere $55. American Library Association, Association for Library Collections and Technical Services, 50 E. Huron St., Chicago, IL 60611-2795. TEL 312-280-5035. FAX 312-280-3257. Ed. Richard Smiraglia. adv.; bk.rev.; bibl.; charts; index. circ. 9,600. (also avail. in microform from UMI; back issues avail.) **Indexed:** ASCA, Bk.Rev.Ind. (1965-), C.I.J.E., Child.Bk.Rev.Ind. (1965-), Curr.Cont., LHTN, Lib.Lit., LISA, Pers.Lit., Resour.Ctr.Ind., Sci.Abstr., SSCI, Tr.& Indus.Ind. **Document type:** academic/scholarly publication.
  —BLDSC (5204.400000); Faxon; UnCover; SWETS; UMI; CASDDS. **CCC.**
  Formed by the merger of: Serial Slants (ISSN 0559-5258); Journal of Cataloging and Classification.
  Description: Scholarly papers on bibliographic access and control, preservation, conservation and reproduction of library materials.

027 362.4   US   ISSN 0364-1236
Z675.B6
LIBRARY RESOURCES FOR THE BLIND AND PHYSICALLY HANDICAPPED (PRINT EDITION). 1968. a. free to qualified individuals. U.S. Library of Congress, National Library Service for the Blind and Physically Handicapped, Washington, DC 20542. TEL 202-707-5100. FAX 202-707-0712. **Indexed:** ERIC. **Document type:** directory, government publication.
  Formerly: Directory of Library Resources for the Blind and Physically Handicapped (ISSN 0278-7857)

020   UK   ISSN 0024-2535
Z671
LIBRARY REVIEW; a journal devoted to information transfer, conservation and exploitation. 1927. 8/yr. $1229.95. M C B University Press Ltd., 60-62 Toller Ln., Bradford, W. Yorks BD8 9BY, England. TEL 0274-499821. FAX 0274-547143. TELEX 51317-MCBUNI-G. Ed. Stuart James. bk.rev.; index. (back issues avail.; reprint service avail. from SWZ) **Indexed:** Abstr.Engl.Stud., Amer.Hist.& Life, Bk.Rev.Ind. (1965-), Child.Bk.Rev.Ind. (1965-), Hist.Abstr., Lib.Lit., LISA, Ref.Sour. **Document type:** academic/scholarly publication.
  —BLDSC (5204.450000); Faxon; SWETS; UMI.
  Description: Covers all topics of concern to librarians and information professionals combining scholarly and technical analysis with discussions of and opinion on current and future trends.

027.7   US   ISSN 0041-9788
Z881 .L898
LIBRARY REVIEW. 1960. s-a. $15 includes membership. University of Louisville, Library Associates, University of Louisville Library, Louisville, KY 40292. TEL 502-588-6762. FAX 502-588-8753. Ed. William F. Axton. circ. 500. **Indexed:** Amer.Hum.Ind.

027.8   US   ISSN 1043-237X
LIBRARY TALK; the magazine for elementary school libraries. 1988. bi-m. $39. Linworth Publishing, Inc., 480 E. Wilson Bridge Rd., Ste. L, Worthing, OH 43085. TEL 614-436-7107. FAX 614-436-9490. Ed. Carolyn Hamilton. adv.; bk.rev. circ. 8,244. (also avail. in microform; back issues avail.; reprint service avail. from UMI) **Indexed:** Bk.Rev.Ind. (1989-), Child.Bk.Rev.Ind. (1989-). **Document type:** trade publication.
  Description: Provides articles, tips, and ideas for elementary school librarians, as well as reviews of audio-visuals and software, written by school librarians.

020   US   ISSN 0024-2586
Z684
LIBRARY TECHNOLOGY REPORTS; evaluative information on library systems, equipment and supplies. 1965. bi-m. $185 (foreign $215). American Library Association, 50 E. Huron St., Chicago, IL 60611-2795. TEL 800-545-2433. FAX 312-440-9374. Ed. Howard S. White. abstr.; charts; illus.; cum.index. circ. 1,900. (looseleaf format; back issues avail.; reprint service avail. from UMI) **Indexed:** Consum.Ind., Info.Media & Tech., Leg.Info.Manage.Ind., LHTN, Lib.Lit., LISA, Mag.Ind., Resour.Ctr.Ind. **Document type:** academic/scholarly publication.
  —BLDSC (5205.700000); Faxon; UnCover; SWETS. **CCC.**
  Description: Evaluative information on library systems, equipment and supplies.

020   US   ISSN 0743-4839
   CODEN: LTINEX
LIBRARY TIMES INTERNATIONAL; world news digest of library and information science. 1984. q. $18 to individuals (foreign $24); institutions $25 (foreign $31). Future World Publishing Company of Canada, India and the United States, Box 15661, Evansville, IN 47716. TEL 812-473-2420. Ed. R.N. Sharma. adv. contact: V. Joshi. bk.rev. **Indexed:** LISA. **Document type:** newsletter.
  —BLDSC (5205.770000); CASDDS.
  Description: Aimed at librarians, library educators, information scientists. Includes: pertinent world news, information science update, special reports on conferences, calendar of national and international conferences, and more.

020   US   ISSN 0024-2594
Z671   CODEN: LIBTA3
LIBRARY TRENDS. 1952. q. $75 (foreign $82). University of Illinois at Urbana-Champaign, Graduate School of Library and Information Science, Publication Office, 501 E. Daniel St., Champaign, IL 61820-6211. TEL 217-333-1359. FAX 217-244-7329. (Subscr. to: University of Illinois Press, Journals Dept., 1325 S. Oak St., Champaign, IL 61820) Ed. F.W. Lancaster. index. circ. 3,000. (also avail. in microform from MIM,UMI) **Indexed:** C.I.J.E., Curr.Cont., Leg.Info.Manage.Ind., Lib.Lit., LISA, Mag.Ind., Mid.East: Abstr.& Ind., P.A.I.S., Pers.Lit., Sci.Abstr., Sci.Cit.Ind., SSCI. **Document type:** academic/scholarly publication.
  —BLDSC (5207.150000); Faxon; UnCover; SWETS; UMI; CASDDS. **CCC.**

020.6   JA
LIBRARY YEARBOOK/TOSHOKAN NENKAN. 1982. a. 12360 Yen. Japan Library Association - Nihon Toshokan Kyokai, 1-1-10 Taishido, Setagaya-ku, Tokyo 154, Japan. FAX 81-3-3421-7588.

020   DK   ISSN 0024-2667
Z671
LIBRI; international library review. (Text in English, French and German) 1951. q. DKK 1050. Munksgaard International Publishers Ltd., 35 Noerre Soegade, P.O. Box 2148, DK-1016 Copenhagen K, Denmark. TEL 33-127030. FAX 33-129387. Ed.Bd. adv.; bk.rev.; charts; index. circ. 900. (also avail. in microform from SWZ; reprint service avail. from ISI,SWZ) **Indexed:** Curr.Cont., Lib.Lit., LISA, P.A.I.S., P.A.I.S.For.Lang.Ind., SSCI.
—BLDSC (5207.300000); Faxon; UnCover; SWETS. **CCC.**
   Refereed Serial

020   CN   ISSN 0712-6115
LIBSAT. 1982. 2/yr. Can.$4($3) for four nos. Gananoque Public Library Board, 100 Park St., Gananoque, Ont. K7G 2Y5, Canada. Ed. John Love. circ. 50. (back issues avail.)

020   FR
LIEN INFORMATIQUE; magazine de detente de l'informaticien. 1977. m. 100 F. Manifestation S.A.R.L., 61 rue Falguiere, 75015 Paris, France. Ed. Joelle Daireaux Chapon. adv.

026   US   ISSN 0024-3698
LINCOLN LIBRARY BULLETIN. 1942. m. (Sep.-June). free. Lincoln Library, 326 S. Seventh St., Springfield, IL 62701. TEL 217-753-4925. Ed. Corrine Frisch. adv.; bk.rev. circ. 7,000. **Document type:** newsletter.

LINK-UP. see HANDICAPPED

027.4   US
LINKING LIBRARIES. 1981. bi-m. membership. Rochester Regional Library Council, Box 66160, Fairport, NY 14450-6160. Dir. Janet M. Welch. circ. 1,050 (controlled). **Document type:** newsletter.
   Formerly (until 1986): Local Data Record.

LISHI DANG'AN/HISTORICAL ARCHIVES. see HISTORY — History Of Asia

020   US
THE LITERARIAN. bi-m. Mercantile Library Association of the City of New York, 17 E. 47th St., New York, NY 10017. TEL 212-755-6711. Ed. Harold Augenbraum. circ. 600. **Document type:** newsletter.

021   UK   ISSN 0269-1361
LLYFRGELL GENEDLAETHOL CYMRU. ADRODDIAD BLYNYDDOL/NATIONAL LIBRARY OF WALES. ANNUAL REPORT. (Text in English, Welsh) a. Llyfrgell Genedlaethol Cymru - National Library of Wales, Aberystwyth, Dyfed SY23 3BU, Wales. **Document type:** government publication.
—BLDSC (1365.000000).

LOCAL GOVERNMENT LIBRARY BULLETIN/BULLETIN VAN DIE PLAASLIKE REGERINGSBIBLIOTEEK. see PUBLIC ADMINISTRATION — Municipal Government

020   UK   ISSN 0263-0273
LOCAL STUDIES LIBRARIAN. 1977. 3/yr. Library Association, Local Studies Group, University of Northumbria School of Librarianship, Lipman Bldg., Newcastle-upon-Tyne NE1 8ST, England. **Indexed:** LISA.
—BLDSC (5290.048600).
   Formerly (until 1982): Library Association. Local Studies Group. Newsletter (ISSN 0261-9970)

020   UK   ISSN 0957-6053
HF5415.6   CODEN: LINMEC
LOGISTICS INFORMATION MANAGEMENT. 1981. 6/yr. $999.95. M C B University Press Ltd., 60-62 Toller Ln., Bradford, W. Yorks BD8 9BY, England. TEL 0274-499821. FAX 0274-547143. TELEX 51317-MCBUNI-G. (Dist. in N. America by: M C B University Press Ltd., Box 10812, Birmingham, AL 35201-0812. TEL 800-633-4931) Ed. Abby Day. bk.rev. (reprint service avail. from SWZ) **Indexed:** ERIC, Leg.Info.Manage.Ind., LISA. **Document type:** academic/scholarly publication.
—BLDSC (5292.316000); UnCover; SWETS; UMI. **CCC.**
   Former titles (until 1991): Information and Library Manager (ISSN 0260-6879); (until 1989): Logistics World (ISSN 0953-2137)
   Description: Aims to increase awareness and understanding of the information professional's role. Presents a number of articles concerned with the changing face of the profession. Technology and systems are covered.

LOGOS; the professional journal of the book world. see PUBLISHING AND BOOK TRADE

029.7 976 929   US
LOUISIANA ARCHIVES AND MANUSCRIPTS ASSOCIATION. NEWSLETTER. 1978. s-a. $10. Louisiana Archives and Manuscripts Association, Box 51213, Main Post Office, New Orleans, LA 70151. Ed. Sally Power. bibl. circ. 400. **Document type:** newsletter.
   Formerly (until 1990): Friends of the Archives of Louisiana. Newsletter.
   Description: Lists events, exhibits, publications and acquisitions of state manuscript and archival repositories. Features a topical article each issue and a biographical sketch of a Louisiana archivist.

027   US   ISSN 0085-2759
Z671
LOUISIANA STATE UNIVERSITY. LIBRARY LECTURES. 1965. irreg. (free to qualified personnel). Louisiana State University, Library, Baton Rouge, LA 70803-7507. TEL 504-388-2217. FAX 504-388-6825. circ. controlled. (also avail. in microform from EDR) **Indexed:** Inform.Sci.Abstr., Lib.Lit., LISA.
   Description: Series of lectures sponsored by Louisiana State University pertaining to library management, facilities, technology and employment.

020   II   ISSN 0024-7219
Z671
LUCKNOW LIBRARIAN. (Text in English) 1962. q. Rs.150($30) (£20). Uttar Pradesh Library Association, Lucknow Branch, U.P. Library Association, P.O. Box 446, Lucknow 226 001, India. Ed. S.N. Agarwal. adv.; bk.rev.; bibl.; charts; illus.; index. circ. 1,000. **Indexed:** Art & Archaeol.Tech.Abstr., G.Indian Per.Lit., Indian Lib.Sci.Abstr., Lib.Lit., LISA.
● Also available on CD-ROM.
—BLDSC (5303.150000).

027.4   ZA
LUSAKA CITY LIBRARY. ANNUAL REPORT. 1977. a. free. Lusaka City Library, P.O. Box 31304, Katondo Rd., Lusaka, Zambia. TEL 227282. circ. 150. (processed)

020 284   US   ISSN 0024-7472
LUTHERAN LIBRARIES. 1958. q. $15 to individuals; institution price varies. Lutheran Church Library Association, 122 W. Franklin Ave., Minneapolis, MN 55404. TEL 612-870-3623. FAX 612-870-0170. Ed. Felicity Hanson. adv.; bk.rev.; video rev.; illus.; tr.lit. circ. 5,000. (back issues avail.) **Indexed:** CERDIC.
   Description: Provides news and promotional ideas for church librarians.

020   US   ISSN 0741-0379
M A C NEWSLETTER. 1973. q. $16 to individuals; institutions $32. Midwest Archives Conference, c/o Becky Haglund Tousey, Kraft General Foods Inc., Archives Dept., 6370 Kirk St., Morton Grove, IL 60053. (Subscr. to: Stephen McShane, Calumet Regional Archives, 3400 Broadway, Gary, IN 46408) Ed. Kenn Thomas. bibl. circ. 1,100. (also avail. in microfilm) **Document type:** newsletter.
—UMI.

025   MW
M A L A BULLETIN. (Text in English) 1978. s-a. K.25($20) (effective through 1995). Malawi Library Association, Attn.: The University Librarian, P.O. Box 429, Zomba, Malawi. TEL 265-50-522-222. FAX 265-50-523-225. Ed. D.B. Vuwa Phiri. bk.rev. **Indexed:** P.L.E.S.A. **Document type:** bulletin.
   Description: Discusses trends in librarianship, such as automation and networking exercises and features conference reports and news on training in library science.

025   CN   ISSN 0710-3417
M A L T NEWSLETTER. 1976. q. Can.$25 to individuals; students Can.$12.50. Manitoba Association of Library Technicians, P.O. Box 1872, Winnipeg, MB R3C 3R1, Canada. circ. 100. **Document type:** newsletter.

020   US   ISSN 0364-2410
M E L A NOTES. 1973. 3/yr. $10 (foreign $15). Middle East Librarians Association, c/o Andras J. Riedlmayer, Fine Arts Library, Harvard University, Cambridge, MA 02138. TEL 617-495-3372. FAX 617-436-4889. Ed. John A. Eilts. bibl. circ. 200. (back issues avail.)

026   CN   ISSN 0848-9009
M H L A NEWS. 1979. 3/yr. membership. Manitoba Health Libraries Association, Box 232, Winnipeg, MB R3M 3S7, Canada. FAX 204-787-2765. bk.rev. circ. 75.
   Formerly (until 1989): M H L A Newsletter (ISSN 0821-1310)

023   US   ISSN 1049-0760
M H L S NEWS. 1974. q. free. Mid-Hudson Library System, 103 Market St., Poughkeepsie, NY 12601. TEL 914-471-6060. FAX 914-454-5940. Eds. Deborah Begley, Joshua Cohen. adv.; bk.rev.; circ. 1,100 (controlled). **Document type:** newsletter.
   Former titles: Mid-Hudson News; Mid-Hudson Library Systems Newsletter.
   Description: News and announcements on issues of interest to trustees of public libraries throughout the New York State region.

M L A NEWS (CHICAGO). (Medical Library Association) see MEDICAL SCIENCES

020.6   US
M L A NEWSLETTER (MINNEAPOLIS). 1974. 10/yr. $20. Minnesota Library Association, 1315 Lowry Ave. N., Minneapolis, MN 55411. TEL 612-521-1735. Eds. Kristi Gibson, Janet Urbanowicz. circ. 1,000. **Document type:** newsletter.

020 658   US   ISSN 0896-3908
                    CODEN: MLISE3
M L S. (Marketing Library Services) 1987. 8/yr. $59 (foreign $70)(effective 1992). Learned Information, Inc., 143 Old Marlton Pike, Medford, NJ 08055-8750. TEL 609-654-6266. FAX 609-654-4309. Ed. Sharon La Rosa. bk.rev. circ. 1,200.
—BLDSC (5381.648200); SWETS; CASDDS.
   Supersedes (1986-1987): P C Free.
   Description: Provides information on designing and presenting plans for new services and acquiring new products.

020   US   ISSN 0145-6180
Z671
M P L A NEWSLETTER. 1956. bi-m. $22. Mountain Plains Library Association, c/o University of South Dakota Libraries, 414 E. Clark St., Vermillion, SD 57069-2390. TEL 605-677-6082. Ed. Jim Dertien. adv.; bk.rev.; bibl.; charts; illus. circ. 1,200. (also avail. in microform from UMI; back issues avail.) **Indexed:** Lib.Lit. **Document type:** newsletter.
—UMI.
   Incorporates (in 1965): Mountain-Plains in Books (ISSN 0580-0714); Which was formerly: Mountain-Plains Library Quarterly (ISSN 0027-2582)

020   US
M P L NOW!. 1970. m. free. Muncie Public Library, 301 E. Jackson St., Muncie, IN 47305. TEL 317-747-8200. FAX 317-747-8221. Ed. John Drumm. bk.rev. circ. 500. **Document type:** newsletter.

M S L A V A JOURNAL. (Manitoba School Library Audio Visual Association) see EDUCATION — Teaching Methods And Curriculum

LIBRARY AND INFORMATION SCIENCES

020   US
M S R R T NEWSLETTER. (Minnesota Social Responsibilities Round Table) 1988. 10/yr. $15. Minnesota Library Association, 4645 Columbus Ave., S., Minneapolis, MN 55407. TEL 612-823-1214. Eds. Christopher Dodge, Jan DeSirey. bk.rev.; index. circ. 225. **Document type:** newsletter.
   Description: Provides news and opinions about a wide range of domestic and international issues covered by small press.

MAGAZINES FOR LIBRARIES; for the general reader and school, junior college, university and public libraries. see *BIBLIOGRAPHIES*

MAGAZINES FOR YOUNG PEOPLE; a Children's Magazine Guide companion volume. see *BIBLIOGRAPHIES*

026.025   US   ISSN 0091-0759
Z732.M2
MAINE. STATE LIBRARY. SPECIAL SUBJECT RESOURCES IN MAINE. Key Title: Special Subject Resources in Maine. irreg. latest 1972. State Library, State House Sta. 64, Augusta, ME 04333. TEL 207-289-5600.

020   US
MAINE ENTRY. 1974. 4/yr. $25. Maine Library Association, c/o Maine Municipal Association, Community Dr., Augusta, ME 04330. TEL 207-623-1634. (Co-sponsor: Maine State Library) Ed.Bd. circ. 1,200.
   Formerly: Downeast Libraries; Formed by the merger of: Downeast Newsletter; Maine Library Association. Bulletin.

380 021   US   ISSN 0092-833X
MAINE LIBRARY DIRECTORY. 1966. a. free. State Library, State House Sta. 64, Augusta, ME 04333. TEL 207-289-5620. stat. **Document type:** government publication, directory.

020   US
MAINE MEMO. 1979. m. $25. Maine Library Association, Maine Municipal Association, Community Dr., Augusta, ME 04330. TEL 207-623-1634. (Co-sponsor: Maine State Library) Ed. Laura Juraska. circ. 1,500.
   Formerly: Maine Library Association. Monthly Memo.

020   MY   ISSN 0126-7809
Z845.M3
MAJALLAH PERPUSTAKAAN MALAYSIA. (Text in English and Malay) 1972. a. M.8. Persatuan Perpustakaan Malaysia, Box 2545, Kuala Lumpur, Malaysia. Ed. Lim Hucktee. adv ; bk.rev. circ. 500. **Indexed:** LISA.

025   XN   ISSN 0350-1728
MAKEDONSKI ARHIVIST. (Text in Macedonian; summaries in English, French, Russian) 1972. a. 350 din.($1.50) Sojuz na Drustvata na Arhivskite Rabotnici i Arhivite na R. Makedonija, Gligor Prlicev 3, P.O. Box 496, Skopje 91001, Macedonia. TEL 091-234-451. Ed. Violeta Gerasimova. bk.rev.; illus.

020   UG   ISSN 0075-4854
MAKERERE UNIVERSITY. LIBRARY. MAKERERE LIBRARY PUBLICATIONS. Short title: Makerere Library Publications. 1961. irreg. free. Makerere University, Library, Box 16002, Kampala, Uganda.

020   KE   ISSN 0070-7988
MAKTABA. (Text in English, Swahili) 1962. s-a. $25. Kenya Library Association, Box 46031, Nairobi, Kenya. Ed. Symphrose Ouma. adv.; bk.rev. **Indexed:** LISA.
   Incorporates: Kenya Library Association Chairman's Annual Report; **Formerly:** East African Library Association. Bulletin.

027.5689   MW
MALAWI. NATIONAL LIBRARY SERVICE BOARD. ANNUAL REPORT. 1969. a. free. National Library Service Board, Box 30314, Lilongwe 3, Malawi. FAX 783560. Ed. R.S. Mabomba. circ. controlled. **Document type:** government publication.
   Formerly: Malawi. National Library. Annual Report (ISSN 0581-0906)

023   MW
MALAWI. NATIONAL LIBRARY SERVICE BOARD. STAFF NEWSLETTER. 1982. biennial. free. National Library Service Board, P.O. Box 30314, Lilongwe 3, Malawi. TEL 365-783700. FAX 365-783560. Dir. R.S. Mabomba. circ. 400 (controlled). **Document type:** newsletter.
   Description: Provides a forum for staff expression on various library themes and topics of general interest.

027.4   MW
MALAWI. NATIONAL LIBRARY SERVICE. BULLETIN. (Text in English) no.10, 1970. s-a. free. National Library Service, Box 30314, Lilongwe 3, Malawi. TEL 783700. FAX 783560. Ed. Anne Kulemeka. circ. 700. **Document type:** bulletin, government publication.

020   UK   ISSN 1352-0229
Z674.2   CODEN: ASIFDG
MANAGING INFORMATION. 1973. 10/yr. £59. Aslib, Association for Information Management, Publications Department, Information House, 20-24 Old St., London EC1V 9AP, England. TEL 071-253-4488. FAX 071-430-0514. (Dist. in N. America by: Learned Information, Inc., 143 Old Marlton Pike, Medford, NJ 08055-8750) Ed. Moira Duncan. adv.; bibl. circ. 2,700. **Indexed:** Abstr.Hum.Comp.Inter., Br.Ceram.Abstr., Key to Econ.Sci., LISA. **Document type:** trade publication.
—BLDSC (5359.287600); UnCover; SWETS; CASDDS.
   Formerly (until 1994): Aslib Information (ISSN 0305-0033)
   Description: News and articles about the information profession and Aslib's activities.

020   UK
MANCHESTER METROPOLITAN UNIVERSITY. DEPARTMENT OF LIBRARY AND INFORMATION STUDIES. OCCASIONAL PAPERS. 1980. irreg. price varies. Manchester Metropolitan University, Department of Library and Information Studies, All Saints, Manchester M15 6BH, England. TEL 061-247-6151. FAX 061-236-7383. circ. 200.
   Formerly: Manchester Polytechnic. Department of Library and Information Studies. Occasional Papers (ISSN 0260-8502)

021   CN   ISSN 0706-7798
MANITOBA. PUBLIC LIBRARY SERVICES. NEWSLETTER. 1978. 5/yr. free. Public Library Services, 1525 First St., Unit 200, Brandon, MB R7A 7A1, Canada. TEL 204-726-6590. FAX 204-726-6868. circ. 250. **Document type:** newsletter.

020   CN   ISSN 0700-3684
MANITOBA LIBRARY ASSOCIATION. NEWSLINE. 12/yr. membership. Manitoba Library Association, 208 - 100 Arthur St., Winnipeg, MB R3B 1H3, Canada. TEL 204-943-4567. Ed. Norma Godavari. **Document type:** newsletter.
   Incorporates (in 1991): Manitoba Library Association Bulletin.

MARIAN LIBRARY STUDIES. NEW SERIES. see *RELIGIONS AND THEOLOGY — Roman Catholic*

020   UK
MARITIME INFORMATION ASSOCIATION NEWSLETTER. 1970. 4/yr. membership. Maritime Information Association, 202 Lambeth Rd., London SE1 7JW, England. (Co-sponsor: Marine Society) **Document type:** newsletter.
   Formerly: Marine Librarians' Association Newsletter.
   Description: Covers matters relating to members of the association.

020   US   ISSN 0895-1799
    CODEN: MRKTEQ
MARKETING TREASURES. 1987. bi-m. $54 (Canada $59; elsewhere $66). Chris Olson & Associates, 857 Twin Harbor Dr., Arnold, MD 21012. TEL 410-647-6708. FAX 410-647-0415. Ed. Christine Olson. adv.; bk.rev.; index. circ. 1,000. (back issues avail.)
—CASDDS.
   Description: Designed to help librarians promote the services of their libraries. Provides creative ideas, helpful hints and insights on how other libraries promote their services.

MARTIN & OSA JOHNSON SAFARI MUSEUM WAIT-A-BIT NEWS. see *MUSEUMS AND ART GALLERIES*

021   UK
MARX MEMORIAL LIBRARY BULLETIN. 1957. irreg. (2-3/yr.) £5.50 to non-members (Europe £9.50; America £10.50). Marx Memorial Library, 37a Clerkenwell Green, London EC1R 0DU, England. TEL 071-253-1485. Ed. Mary Rosser. bk.rev. circ. 1,000. **Document type:** bulletin.
   Formerly: Marx Memorial Library. Quarterly Bulletin (ISSN 0025-410X)

020   IT
MASS MEDIA. 1981. m. L.44000 (foreign L.88000). Capone Editore s.r.l., Via Capraricca 35, 73020 Cavallino (LE), Italy. TEL 0832-611877. FAX 0832-612618. Ed. Gino Agnese.

025   US
MASTER'S PROGRAMS IN LIBRARY AND INFORMATION STUDIES; accredited by the American Library Association. s-a. American Library Association, Committee on Accreditation, 50 E. Huron St., Chicago, IL 60611. TEL 312-280-2432. FAX 312-280-2433. **Document type:** directory.
   Former titles: Graduate Library Education Programs; Graduate Library School Programs.

020   MF   ISSN 0076-5481
MAURITIUS. ARCHIVES DEPARTMENT. ANNUAL REPORT. (Includes yearly supplement Bibliography of Mauritius) (Text in English; bibliographical supplement in English, French) 1950. a. Rs.15. Archives Department, Development Bank of Mauritius Complex, Petite Riviere, Beau-Bassin, Mauritius. (Subscr. to: Government Printing Office, La Tour Koenig G.R.N.W., Port Louis, Mauritius) **Document type:** government publication.

027.8   SA   ISSN 1016-8206
MEDIA FOCUS/MEDIAFOKUS. (Text in Afrikaans, English) 1969. s-a. R.30 to non-members (effective 1992). Transvaal School Media Association, c/o Transvaal Education Media Service, Private Bag X290, Pretoria 0001, South Africa. FAX 27-12-3227699. Ed.Bd. adv.; bk.rev. circ. 2,300. **Indexed:** Child.Lit.Abstr., LISA.
   Former titles (until 1988): School Media Centre; (until 1980): School Library (ISSN 0036-6617)
   Description: Aims to heighten media awareness in South African schools.

MEDIAFILE. see *EDUCATION — Teaching Methods And Curriculum*

020   FR   ISSN 0153-4270
MEDIATHEQUES PUBLIQUES. 1967. q. 45 F.($15) Association pour la Mediatheque Publique, 37 rue St. Georges, 59409 Cambrai, France. Ed. Michel Bouvy. adv.; bk.rev. **Indexed:** LISA.
   Formerly: Lecture et Bibliotheques.

020 610   UK   ISSN 0266-853X
MEDICAL, HEALTH AND WELFARE LIBRARIES GROUP. NEWSLETTER. Issued with: Health Libraries Review (ISSN 0265-6647) 1978. q. free to members. Blackwell Scientific Publications Ltd., Osney Mead, Oxford OX2 0EL, England. TEL 0865-241201. FAX 0865-721205. TELEX 83355-MEDBOK-G. Ed. S. Godbolt. **Document type:** newsletter.
—BLDSC (6107.526000).
   Former titles (until 1984): Library Association. Medical, Health and Welfare Libraries Group. Newsletter (ISSN 0263-2365); (until 1981): Medical, Health and Welfare Libraries Newsletter (ISSN 0141-6955).

MEDICAL LIBRARY ASSOCIATION. BULLETIN. see *MEDICAL SCIENCES*

020   US   ISSN 0276-3869
R118.2   CODEN: MRSQDK
MEDICAL REFERENCE SERVICES QUARTERLY. 1982. q. $36 to individuals; institutions $95. Haworth Press, Inc., 10 Alice St., Binghamton, NY 13904. TEL 607-722-5857; 800-342-9678. FAX 607-722-1424. TELEX 4932599. Ed. M. Sandra Wood. adv.; bk.rev.; abstr.; bibl. circ. 1,006. (also avail. in microfiche from UMI; back issues avail.; reprint service avail. from HAW) **Indexed:** Abstr.Health Care Manage.Stud., Biol.Abstr., CINAHL, Excerp.Med., Hosp.Lit.Ind., Inform.Sci.Abstr., Leg.Info.Manage.Ind., Lib.Lit., LISA, Sci.Abstr.
—BLDSC (5531.593000); Faxon; UnCover; SWETS.
   Description: Specializes in practice-oriented articles relating to medical reference services, with an emphasis on online search services.
Refereed Serial

LIBRARY AND INFORMATION SCIENCES

020   CN
MEDIUM. vol.18, 1977. irreg. Can.$36. (Saskatchewan Association of Educational Media Specialists) Saskatchewan Teachers' Federation, Box 1108, Saskatoon, SK S7K 3N3, Canada. TEL 306-525-0368. Ed. Susan McCutcheon. adv.; bk.rev.; bibl.; circ. 400 (controlled). (processed) **Indexed:** Can.Educ.Ind., Lang.Teach.& Ling.Abstr., Pt.de Rep.
    Formerly: Saskatchewan Association of Media Specialists. Medium (ISSN 0025-8377)

020   NE
MEDIUM-TERM PROGRAMME (YEARS). (Editions in English, French, German, Russian, Spanish) 1981. quinquennial. fl.40($20) International Federation of Library Associations and Institutions, I F L A Headquarters, P.O. Box 95312, 2509 CH The Hague, Netherlands. TEL 31-70-3140884. FAX 31-70-3834827. TELEX 34402 KB NL. Ed.Bd. charts; illus.; stat. circ. 2,000.

020   US   ISSN 1040-7421
Z692.M3
MERIDIAN. 1989. 2/yr. $20 to individuals (foreign $25); institutions $25 (foreign $30). Map and Geography Round Table, American Library Association, c/o Charles A. Seavey, Ed., School of Library Science, 1515 E. First St., Tucson, AZ 85719. TEL 602-621-3957. FAX 609-621-3279. (Subscr. to: Christine Kollen, Main Library, University of Arizona, Tucson, AZ 85721) Ed. Charles A. Seavey. adv.; bk.rev.; bibl.; charts; illus. circ. 600. (back issues avail.) **Document type:** academic/scholarly publication.
    —UnCover.
    Description: Contains articles in map librarianship, history of cartography, trends and issues in organization and dissemination of cartographic, geographic and remote sensing collections and information.
    Refereed Serial

020   JO   ISSN 0257-7739
MESSAGE OF THE LIBRARY/RISALAT AL-MAKTABA. (Text in Arabic; summaries in English) 1965. q. $20. Jordan Library Association, P.O. Box 6289, Amman, Jordan. TEL 629-412. adv.; bk.rev.; index. circ. 1,200. **Indexed:** LISA.
    Description: Focuses on research and technology in the areas of library and information science.

026   US   ISSN 0076-7018
METRO; NEW YORK METROPOLITAN REFERENCE AND RESEARCH LIBRARY AGENCY. METRO MISCELLANEOUS PUBLICATIONS SERIES. 1968. irreg., latest no.40. New York Metropolitan Reference & Research Library Agency (METRO), 57 E. 11th St., New York, NY 10003-4605. TEL 212-228-2320.

025   CN   ISSN 0700-4532
METROPOLITAN TORONTO LIBRARY BOARD. ANNUAL REPORT. 1968. a. free. Metropolitan Toronto Library Board, Public Relations Office, 789 Yonge St., Toronto, ON M4W 2G8, Canada. TEL 416-393-7133. FAX 416-393-7229. TELEX 06-22232. Ed. Mario Bernardi. illus. circ. 3,000.

023   CN   ISSN 0842-9707
METROPOLITAN TORONTO REFERENCE LIBRARY. NEWS. 4/yr. Metropolitan Toronto Library Board, 789 Yonge St., Toronto, ON M4W 2G8, Canada. TEL 416-393-7134. Ed. Jytte Birnbaum. **Document type:** newsletter.
    Formerly: Metropolitan Toronto Library Board. News (ISSN 0318-9244)

027   US
MICHIE LIBRARY QUARTERLY. 1982. q. free. Michie Company, Box 7587, Charlottesville, VA 22906-7587. TEL 804-972-7600. Ed. Gretchen Notermann.

020   US
MICHIGAN LIBRARIAN. 1935. 10/yr. $40 (foreign $50). Michigan Library Association, 1000 Long Blvd., Ste. 1, Lansing, MI 48911-6857. TEL 517-694-6615. FAX 517-694-4330. Ed. Marianne Hartzell. adv. circ. 1,800. (also avail. in microform from UMI; reprint service avail. from UMI) **Indexed:** Lib.Lit. **Document type:** newsletter.
    Former titles: Michigan Librarian Newsletter (ISSN 0149-435X); (until 1980): Michigan Librarian (ISSN 0026-2242)
    Description: Covers the history of the Association. Provides information on the Association's fund raising activities and other administrative matters.

380 021
MICHIGAN LIBRARY DIRECTORY. 1967. a. free. Library of Michigan, Box 30007, Lansing, MI 48909. TEL 517-373-1580. Ed. John Rummel. circ. 2,000. **Document type:** directory.
    Continues in part: Michigan Library Directory and Statistics (ISSN 0076-8081); **Formerly:** Michigan Library News.
    Description: Directory of academic, public, special and state agency libraries, as well as library cooperative, multitype groups, document depositories, library associations and library schools.

020 010   KO   ISSN 0026-2536
MICRO-LIBRARY BULLETIN.* 1963. m. Won100($2.) Korean Micro-Library Association, C/o Central National Library, San 60-1, Panpo-Dong, Socho-Gu, Seoul, S. Korea. Ed. Dae-Sup Ohm. bk.rev.; bibl.; illus. (processed)

778.1   GW   ISSN 0362-0999
Z286.M5
MICROFORM MARKET PLACE; an international directory of micropublishing. Short title: M M P. 1974. biennial. DM.115($75) K.G. Saur Verlag KG, A Reed Reference Publishing Company, Part of the Reed Elsevier group, Ortlerstr. 8, 81373 Munich, Germany. TEL 089-76902-0. FAX 089-76902150. TELEX 5212067-SAUR-D. (Subscr. to: Postfach 701620, 81316 Munich, Germany; N. America subscr. to: K.G. Saur, A Reed Reference Publishing Company, 121 Chanlon Rd., Box 31, New Providence, NJ 07974-9903, USA. TEL 908-665-3576) Ed. Barbara Hopkinson. adv. **Document type:** directory.
    Description: Provides information on the specialized world of microform publishing. Main entries furnish publisher name, address, telephone, fax and telex numbers, ISBN prefix, key personnel, major microform programs and micro-formats offered.

778.315   GW   ISSN 0002-6530
Z265   CODEN: MFRVA
MICROFORM REVIEW. 1972. q. DM.248($140) K.G. Saur Verlag KG, A Reed Reference Publishing Company, Part of the Reed Elsevier group, Ortlerstr. 8, 81373 Munich, Germany. TEL 089-76902-0. FAX 089-76902150. TELEX 5212067-SAUR-D. (Subscr. to: Postfach 701620, 81316 Munich, Germany; Dist. in US by: R.R. Bowker, 121 Chanlon Rd., New Providence, NJ 07974. TEL 908-665-6719) Ed. Susan Szasz. adv.; bk.rev.; index. (also avail. in microform) **Indexed:** C.I.J.E., Info.Media & Tech., Inform.Sci.Abstr., Leg.Info.Manage.Ind., LHTN, Lib.Lit., LISA., Resour.Ctr.Ind., Sci.Abstr. **Document type:** academic/scholarly publication.
    —BLDSC (5759.120000); Faxon; UnCover; SWETS; UMI. **CCC.**

020   US   ISSN 0738-9396
MID-ATLANTIC ARCHIVIST. 1972. 4/yr. $10. Mid-Atlantic Regional Archives Conference, University Archives, Gelman Library, George Washington University, Washington, DC 20052. TEL 202-994-7549. FAX 202-994-1340. (Subscr. to: Marsha Trimble, University of Virginia Law Library, Charlottesville, VA 22901. TEL 804-924-3023) Ed. G. David Anderson. adv.; bk.rev. circ. 1,000. (processed)
    Description: Promotes the professional welfare of its members and cooperation among individuals concerned with the documentation of the human experience.

MIDDLE ATLANTIC PERSPECTIVE. see *MEDICAL SCIENCES*

MINGUO DANG'AN/ARCHIVES OF THE REPUBLIC OF CHINA. see *HISTORY* — History Of Asia

027.4   US   ISSN 0026-5438
MINNESOTA. DEPARTMENT OF EDUCATION. PUBLIC LIBRARY NEWSLETTER. 1970. m. free to public libraries in Minnesota. Department of Education, Office of Library Development and Services, 440 Capitol Square Bldg., 550 Cedar St., St. Paul, MN 55101. TEL 612-296-2821. Ed. Darlene M. Arnold. circ. 750. (processed; reprint service avail. from UMI) **Document type:** newsletter.
    Description: Includes brief summaries of library news and events.

020   US   ISSN 0026-5551
Z732
MINNESOTA LIBRARIES. 1904. q. free to libraries in Minnesota; on exchange basis to out-of-state and -nation libraries. Department of Education, Office of Library Development and Services, 440 Capitol Square Bldg., 550 Cedar St., St. Paul, MN 55101. TEL 612-296-2821. Ed. William G. Asp. stat.; index. circ. 1,968. (also avail. in microform from UMI; microfiche from CIS; reprint service avail. from UMI) **Indexed:** Lib.Lit., Lib.Sci.Abstr., SRI.
    Description: Covers state long range plan, and library development and services. Includes library statistics.

026   IT   ISSN 0394-7866
MISCELLANEA MARCIANA. 1986. a. exchange basis. Ministero per i Beni Culturali e Ambientali, Biblioteca Nazionale Marciana, S. Marco 7, Venice, Italy. TEL 041-5208788. FAX 041-5238803. Ed.Bd. bk.rev. circ. 300. **Document type:** academic/scholarly publication.
    Description: Covers the history of the library, its collections and related matters.

020   US   ISSN 0194-388X
Z671
MISSISSIPPI LIBRARIES. 1936. q. $16 to non-members (foreign $24). Mississippi Library Association, Box 20448, Jackson, MS 39289-1448. TEL 601-352-3917. FAX 601-352-4240. Ed. Casey R. Phillips. adv.; bk.rev.; bibl.; stat.; index. circ. 1,500. (also avail. in microfilm from UMI; reprint service avail. from UMI) **Indexed:** Lib.Lit.
    —BLDSC (5810.393000); UMI.
    Formerly (until vol.43, 1979): Mississippi Library News (ISSN 0026-6302)
    Description: News, articles, book reviews, and announcements of interest to members of the Mississippi Library Association.

020   US   ISSN 0899-6458
MISSOURI LIBRARIES. 1988. bi-m. free. State Library, Box 387, Jefferson City, MO 65102-0387. TEL 314-751-3615. FAX 314-751-3612. Ed. Madeline Matson. circ. 4,250 (controlled). **Document type:** newsletter.
    Description: News about the State Library and Missouri libraries.

MITTEILUNGEN FUER DIE ARCHIVPFLEGE IN BAYERN. see *HISTORY*

020   US   ISSN 0884-2205
Z673
MO INFO.* 1970. 6/yr. $6 to non-members. Missouri Library Association, 1306 Business 63 S., NO 8, Columbia, MO 65201-8409. TEL 314-449-4627. Ed. J. McCartney. adv.; bk.rev. circ. 1,500. (also avail. in microform from UMI; reprint service avail. from UMI) **Document type:** newsletter.
    Former titles (until 1985): M L A Newsletter (ISSN 0581-0205); M L A Quarterly.
    Description: News, announcements, and issues of interest to members of the Missouri Library Association.

027.4   US
MOBILE PUBLIC LIBRARY TODAY. 1984. bi-m. free. Mobile Public Library, 701 Government St., Mobile, AL 36602. FAX 205-434-7571. Ed. C. Bowersox. bk.rev. circ. 11,000.
    Description: News of the library, articles about library users and coverage of the organizational meetings.

LIBRARY AND INFORMATION SCIENCES

021   US
Z732.M9
MONTANA LIBRARY DIRECTORY. a. State Library, 1515 E. Sixth Ave., Helena, MT 59620. TEL 406-444-3115. FAX 406-444-5612. stat. **Indexed:** SRI. **Document type:** directory.
    Formerly: Montana Library Directory, with Statistics of Montana Public Libraries (ISSN 0094-873X)
    Description: Contains names, addresses, phone and fax numbers of over 600 public, school, academic, institutional and special libraries in the State of Montana.

020   US
MONTANA STATE LIBRARY NEWS. bi-m. free. Montana State Library, 1515 E. 6th Ave., Helena, MT 59620. TEL 406-444-5353. FAX 406-444-5612. Ed. Richard T. Miller. bk.rev. circ. 1,800. (back issues avail.) **Document type:** newsletter.
    Description: Covers news on the State Library and all libraries in Montana.

020   US
MONTANA STATE LIBRARY NEWS UPDATE. 1988. bi-m. free. Montana State Library, 1515 E. 6th Ave., Helena, MT 59620. TEL 406-444-3115. FAX 406-444-5612. Ed. Richard T. Miller. circ. 1,200 (controlled). (looseleaf format; back issues avail.) **Document type:** newsletter.
    Description: Presents an update of library-related news, construction projects, conferences, personnel changes, policy announcements, calendar.

020   SA   ISSN 0027-2639
Z857.S7
MOUSAION; library science contributions. (Text in Afrikaans, English) 1955. 2/yr. R.13.20 (overseas $16.50) (effective 1994). University of South Africa, P.O. Box 392, Pretoria 0001, South Africa. FAX 27-12-429-2533. (Co-sponsor: University Library) illus. circ. 1,000. (reprint service avail. from UMI) **Indexed:** Ind.S.A.Per., LHTN, Lib.Lit., Lib.Sci.Abstr., LISA. **Document type:** academic/scholarly publication.
—BLDSC (5980.C00000).

020 060   AU   ISSN 0077-2208
MUSEION. 1957. irreg. price varies. (Oesterreichische Nationalbibliothek) Verlagsbuchhandlung Brueder Hollinek und Co. GmbH, Feldgasse 13, A-1238 Vienna, Austria. TEL 0222-885646. FAX 0222-889364724. (reprint service avail. from ISI) **Document type:** academic/scholarly publication.

026 780   US   ISSN 0027-4283
ML111
MUSIC CATALOGING BULLETIN. 1970. m. $25 (foreign $35). Music Library Association, Box 487, Canton, MA 02021. TEL 617-828-8450. Ed. Catherine Gerhart. circ. 850.
—UnCover.

MUSIC FILE. see *EDUCATION — Teaching Methods And Curriculum*

026 780   US   ISSN 0027-4380
ML27.U5
MUSIC LIBRARY ASSOCIATION. NOTES. 1942. q. $60 to individuals; institutions $65. Music Library Association, P.O. Box 487, Canton, MA 02021. TEL 617-828-8450. Ed. Daniel Zager. adv.; bk.rev.; music rev.; bibl.; tr.lit.; index. circ. 2,900. (also avail. in microform from UMI) **Indexed:** Bk.Rev.Dig., Bk.Rev.Ind. (1966-), Child.Bk.Rev.Ind. (1966-), G.Perf.Arts, Hum.Ind., Lib.Lit., Lib.Sci.Abstr., Music Artic.Guide, Music Ind., Ref.Sour., RILM.
—BLDSC (6155.860000); Faxon; UnCover; SWETS.

026   US   ISSN 0094-5099
MUSIC LIBRARY ASSOCIATION. TECHNICAL REPORTS; information for music media specialists. 1973. irreg. price varies. Music Library Association, Box 487, Canton, MA 02021. TEL 617-828-8450. Ed. Richard Smiraglia. circ. 150. **Indexed:** RILM.
—BLDSC (5879.716300).

020   US   ISSN 0161-1704
MUSIC O C L C USERS GROUP. NEWSLETTER. (Includes membership directories) 1977. irreg. $10 to individuals; institutions $15; foreign $25. Music O C L C Users Group, c/o Christine Grandy, Treas., Knight Library, University of Oregon, Eugene, OR 97403-1299. TEL 503-346-1850. Ed. Sue Weiland. circ. 570. (back issues avail.) **Document type:** newsletter.
    Description: Contains summaries of annual meeting presentations, articles, and news relating to OCLC, Inc., its products, and the music library community.

020 780.7   US   ISSN 1058-8167
ML110
▼**MUSIC REFERENCE SERVICES QUARTERLY.** 1993. q. $24 to individuals; institutions & libraries $36. Haworth Press, Inc., 10 Alice St., Binghamton, NY 13904. TEL 607-722-5857; 800-342-9678. FAX 607-722-1424. TELEX 4932599. Ed. William Studwell. adv.; bk.rev. (also avail. in microfiche from UMI; reprint service avail. from HAW)
—BLDSC (5990.401520).
    Description: Covers administration, collection development, cataloguing, online services, and bibliographies.
Refereed Serial

020   HU   ISSN 0027-3015
MUSZAKI EGYETEMI KONYVTAROS/TECHNICAL UNIVERSITY LIBRARIAN. 1964. s-a. exchange basis. Budapesti Muszaki Egyetem, Konyvtar es Tajekoztatasi Kozpont - Technical University of Budapest, Information Center and Library, Budafoki ut 4-6, 1111 Budapest XI, Hungary. TEL 166-4305. FAX 181-2753. Ed. Pal Vasarhelyi. bk.rev.; bibl.; charts. circ. 300. (also avail. in microfilm) **Document type:** academic/scholarly publication.

020   GW   ISSN 0340-9090
N A B D - MITTEILUNGEN. 1976. irreg. (approx 3/yr.). free. Normenausschuss Bibliotheks- und Dokumentationswesen (NABD) im D I N, Burggrafenstr. 6, 10787 Berlin, Germany. TEL 030-26012791. FAX 030-26011231. TELEX 184273-DIN-D. Ed. Edith Lechner. circ. 460. (looseleaf format; back issues avail.) **Document type:** newsletter.

778.5   US
N A R M C HIGHLIGHTS. 8/yr. membership. National Association of Regional Media Centers, Grant-Woods AEA, 4401 Sixth St., S.W., Cedar Rapids, IA 52404. TEL 319-399-6741. FAX 319-399-6457. Ed. Jerry Cochrane. **Document type:** newsletter.
    Description: Provides coverage of current activities in different states' centers.

027.7   US   ISSN 0892-1733
                          CODEN: NASNE6
N A S I G NEWSLETTER. 1986. 5/yr. $20 (outside N. America $30). North American Serials Interest Group, M I T Libraries, Rm. 14E-210, Cambridge, MA 02139. TEL 617-253-7028. FAX 617-253-2464. Ed. Ellen Finnie Duranceau. circ. 1,100. **Document type:** newsletter.
—BLDSC (6015.602300); CASDDS.
    Description: Covers NASIG meetings and conferences. Includes pertinent news items and announcements.

025   II
N A S S D O C RESEARCH INFORMATION SERIES. ACQUISITION UPDATE. (Text in English) s-a. Rs.20. Indian Council of Social Science Research, National Social Science Documentation Centre, 35 Ferozshah Rd., New Delhi 110 001, India. TEL 91-11-384353. FAX 91-11-388037. TELEX 31-61083-ISSR-IN. Eds. Sudha Gambhir, Kusum A. Parihar. circ. 100. **Description:** Classified list of books, theses, and research reports acquired in NASSSOC.

020   UN
N A T I S - NEWS. (National Information System) French edition: N A T I S-Nouvelles. Spanish edition: N A T I S Noticias. (Text in English) 1975. irreg. free. Unesco, 7-9 Place de Fontenoy, 75700 Paris, France. TEL 45-77-16-10.
    Description: Covers efforts by Unesco member states to implement a national information system.

020   US
N C S U LIBRARIES FOCUS. 1964. 3/yr. free. North Carolina State University, Libraries, Box 7111, Raleigh, NC 27695-7111. TEL 919-515-2843. FAX 919-515-3628. Ed. Terrell A. Crow. circ. 4,300. (processed) **Document type:** newsletter.
    Formerly: D.H. Hill Library Focus.

025   US   ISSN 0027-6448
Z673
N E L A NEWSLETTER. 1968. bi-m. $35. New England Library Association, Inc., 707 Turnpike St., N. Andover, MA 01845-6120. TEL 617-438-7179. Ed. Cara Barlow. circ. 1,500. **Document type:** newsletter.
    Description: Covers Association news and events.

020   US   ISSN 0028-5269
N H L A NEWSLETTER. vol.31, 1977. 6/yr. $4. New Hampshire Library Association, c/o Conway Public Library, Box 2100, Conway, NH 03818-2100. Ed. Betty Parker. circ. 700. (processed) **Document type:** newsletter.

020   TH   ISSN 0125-5606
N I D A BULLETIN. (Text in English, Thai) 1969. bi-m. $16. National Institute of Development Administration, Library and Information Center, Publication and Dissemination of Information Division, Klongjan, Bangkapi, Bangkok 10240, Thailand. Ed. Prapassorn Moraruang. **Document type:** bulletin.

020   US
N M R T NEWSLETTER. (New Members Round Table) 1980. 3/yr. membership. Louisiana Library Association, Box 3058, Baton Rouge, LA 70821. TEL 504-342-4928. Ed. Lois Grant. circ. 125. (back issues avail.) **Document type:** newsletter.

020   FI   ISSN 0358-7045
N O R D I N F O PUBLIKATION. 1981. irreg., no.25, 1993. price varies. Nordiska Samarbetsorganet for Vetenskaplig Information - Nordic Council for Scientific Information, c/o Helsinki University of Technology Library, Otnaesvaegen 9, SF-02150 Esbo, Finland. TEL 358-0-455-2633. FAX 358-0-455-2576. Ed. Marianne Heikell. circ. 1,500. **Document type:** monographic series.
—BLDSC (6117.938000).
    Description: Information about the project activities of Nordinfo.

600   US
N T I S DIGEST. 1984. irreg. free. U.S. National Technical Information Service, 5285 Port Royal Rd., Springfield, VA 22161. TEL 703-487-4679. FAX 703-321-8547. TELEX 64617. **Indexed:** Concr.Abstr.

020   US   ISSN 0027-7134
Z671
N Y L A BULLETIN. 1953. m. (Sep.-June). membership. New York Library Association, 252 Hudson Ave., Albany, NY 12210-1802. TEL 518-432-6952. FAX 518-427-1697. Ed. Gail Sacco. adv.; bk.rev.; illus. circ. 3,500. (also avail. in microform from UMI; reprint service avail. from UMI) **Indexed:** ERIC, Lib.Lit.
—UMI.

029   GW   ISSN 0027-7436
Z1007   CODEN: NADOAW
NACHRICHTEN FUER DOKUMENTATION; Zeitschrift fuer Information und Dokumentation mit Schrifttum zu den Informationswissenschaften. (Summaries in English, German) 1950. 6/yr. DM.234. (Deutsche Gesellschaft fuer Dokumentation (D G D) e.V.) Verlag Hoppenstedt GmbH, Havelstr. 9, 64295 Darmstadt, Germany. TEL 06151-380-0. FAX 06151-380360. (Co-sponsors: Normenausschuss Bibliotheks- und Dokumentationswesen im Deutschen Institut fuer Normung (D I N) e.V.; Arbeitsgemeinschaft der Spezialbibliotheken (A Sp B); Verein Deutscher Dokumentare (V D D)) Ed. Dr. Hansjoachim Samulowitz. adv.; bk.rev.; abstr.; bibl.; charts; illus.; index, cum.index every 20 yrs. circ. 23,668. (reprint service avail. from UMI, ISI) **Indexed:** Curr.Cont., Key to Econ.Sci., Lib.Lit., Lib.Sci.Abstr., LISA, P.A.I.S.For.Lang.Ind., Sci.Abstr., SSCI. **Document type:** trade publication.
—BLDSC (6006.600000); Faxon; SWETS; CASDDS. CCC.

LIBRARY AND INFORMATION SCIENCES

020   BU   ISSN 0204-6091
NARODNA BIBLIOTEKA SV.SV. KIRIL I METODII. IZVESTIYA. (Table of contents in English and Russian) 1953. irreg. 40 lv.($45) Narodna Biblioteka Sv.sv. Kiril i Metodii, 88, V. Levski Blvd., 1504 Sofia, Bulgaria. TEL 00359-2-882811. FAX 00395-2-881600. bk.rev.; bibl.; charts; illus. **Indexed:** Amer.Hist.& Life, Hist.Abstr.
   Formerly (1959-1965): Izvestiya na Narodnata Biblioteka Kiril i Metodii i na Bibliotekata na Sofiiskiya Universitet Kliment Okhridski.

020   XV   ISSN 0350-3569
NARODNA IN UNIVERZITETNA KNJIZNICA. ZBORNIK. (Text in Slovenian; summaries in French and German) 1974. irreg. Narodna in Univerzitetna Knjiznica, Turjaska 1, 61001 Ljubljana, Slovenia. TEL 061-150-141. FAX 38-611-150-134. TELEX 32285 NUK-LJB-SLO. illus.

020   XR   ISSN 0862-7487
Z795.A1
NARODNI KNIHOVNA. 6/yr. 60 Kcs. per issue. Narodni Knihovna v Praze, Klementium 190, 110 01 Prague 1, Czech Republic. TEL 24229500. FAX 24227796. (Dist. by: Narodni Knihovna v Praze, Odd. Prodeje a Expedice, Liliova 5, 110 01 Prague 1, Czech Republic. TEL 262058) Ed. Milena Redinova. circ. 300.
   Formerly (until 1990): Statni Knihovna C S R. Zpravodaj (ISSN 0139-6129)
   Description: Covers theory and practice of librarianship.

020   XR   ISSN 0036-5351
PG5000
NARODNI MUZEUM V PRAZE. SBORNIK. RADA C: LITERARNI HISTORIE/ACTA MUSEI NATIONALIS PRAGAE. SERIES C: HISTORIA LITTERARUM. (Text in Czech; summaries in English, French, German, Russian) 1955. q. 20 Kcs. Narodni Muzeum, Vaclavske nam. 68, 115 79 Prague 1, Czech Republic. TEL 269-451. (Dist. by: PNS - Ustredni Expedice a Dovoz Tisku Praha, Zavod 01, Administrace Vyvozu Tisku, Kafkova 19, 160 00 Prague 6, Czech Republic) Ed. Helga Turkova. bibl.; illus. **Indexed:** Hist.Abstr.
—BLDSC (8083.100000).
   Formerly: Narodni Muzeum v Praze. Sbornik: Literarni Historie.

020   UK   ISSN 0950-5326
NATIONAL ACQUISITIONS GROUP. NEWSLETTER. 1986. 4/yr. free. National Acquisitions Group, Westfield House, North Rd., Horsforth, Leeds LS18 5HG, England. TEL 0532-591447. adv. circ. 450. **Document type:** newsletter.
   Description: Covers the acquisition of library materials from book trade suppliers, topics in library collection development, bookselling and publishing.

025.17   ZA   ISSN 0084-4942
NATIONAL ARCHIVES OF ZAMBIA. ANNUAL REPORT. 1964. a. K.500. National Archives, P.O. Box RW 50010, Ridgeway, Lusaka, Zambia. **Document type:** government publication.

020   CH
NATIONAL CENTRAL LIBRARY BULLETIN. (Text in Chinese) 1967. s-a. free. National Central Library, 20 Chung Shan S. Rd., Taipei, Taiwan 10040, Republic of China. FAX 02-311-0155. adv.; bk.rev.; bibl. circ. 700.
   Formerly: National Central Library News Bulletin (ISSN 0251-4796)
   Description: Covers the affairs of the Library, theory and practice of library science. Includes the history of books and printing as well as other areas of history and literature.

020   NP
NATIONAL COUNCIL FOR SCIENCE & TECHNOLOGY. DIRECTORY; scientists and technologists of Nepal. (Text in English) 1977. a. $20. National Council for Science & Technology, Kirtipur, Kathmandu, Nepal. circ. 500.

027   JA   ISSN 0027-9161
Z955.T585   CODEN: NDLNDP
NATIONAL DIET LIBRARY. NEWSLETTER. (Supplement avail. 3/yr.: National Diet Library. Books on Japan in Western Languages Recently Acquired) (Text in English) 1958. 3/yr. National Diet Library, Library Cooperation Department - Kokuritsu Kokkai Toshokan, 1-10-1 Nagata-cho, Chiyoda-ku, Tokyo 100, Japan. TEL 03-3581-2331. FAX 03-3597-9104. bk.rev.; bibl.; charts; illus.; stat.; circ. 1,050 (controlled). **Document type:** newsletter.
—BLDSC (6021.875000); CASDDS.
   Description: Focuses on innovations in library science, staff activities and foreign language book acquisitions.

NATIONAL DIRECTORY OF BULLETIN BOARD SYSTEMS.
see BUSINESS AND ECONOMICS — Trade And Industrial Directories

NATIONAL INFORMATION CENTER FOR CHILDREN AND YOUTH WITH DISABILITIES. TRANSITION SUMMARY.
see HANDICAPPED

020   US   ISSN 1041-5653
NATIONAL INFORMATION STANDARDS SERIES. irreg. National Information Standards Organization (NISO), Box 1056, Bethesda, MD 20827. TEL 301-975-2814. FAX 301-869-8071.
   Description: Develops and promotes voluntary standards for information science, libraries, and related publishing practices.

020   US   ISSN 0191-359X
NATIONAL LIBRARIAN; the N L A newsletter. 1976. q. $15. National Librarians Association, Box 486, Alma, MI 48801. TEL 517-463-7227. FAX 517-463-8694. Ed. Peter Dollard. adv.; bk.rev.; abstr.; bibl.; circ. 500 (paid). (back issues avail.) **Document type:** newsletter.
—CCC.
   Formerly: N L A Newsletter.

020   RH
NATIONAL LIBRARY AND DOCUMENTATION SERVICE. ANNUAL REPORT. 1961. a. exchange basis. National Library and Documentation Service, P.O. Box 1773, Bulawayo, Zimbabwe. circ. 450. **Document type:** corporate report.
   Former titles (until 1989): National Free Library of Zimbabwe. Annual Report; National Free Library Service. Annual Report; National Free Library of Rhodesia. Annual Report (ISSN 0068-3612)

020   CN   ISSN 0027-9633
Z883.O76   CODEN: NLNBBJ
NATIONAL LIBRARY NEWS/BIBLIOTHEQUE NATIONALE. NOUVELLES. (Text in English and French) 1969. 10/yr. free. National Library of Canada, Publication and Marketing Services, 395 Wellington St., Ottawa, Ont. K1A 0N4, Canada. TEL 613-995-7969. FAX 613-991-9871. Ed.Bd. bibl.; illus. circ. 5,000. **Indexed:** Can.Per.Ind., CMI.
●Also available online.
—BLDSC (6026.610000); CASDDS.
   Incorporates: Accessible (ISSN 0315-0003)
   Description: Information, news, and updates on activities and services of the National Library of Canada.

020   AT   ISSN 0313-1971
NATIONAL LIBRARY OF AUSTRALIA. ANNUAL REPORT. 1961. a. Aus.$12.50. National Library of Australia, Publications Section, Cultural and Educational Services Division, Canberra, A.C.T. 2600, Australia. TEL 06-262-1365. FAX 06-273-4493. (reprint service avail. from ISI/UMI)
   Formerly: National Library of Australia. Annual Report of the Council (ISSN 0069-0082)

020   AT   ISSN 1039-3498
Z870.A1
NATIONAL LIBRARY OF AUSTRALIA GATEWAYS. 1979. bi-m. Aus.$40. National Library of Australia, Services to Libraries, Canberra, A.C.T. 2600, Australia. TEL 06-262-1580. FAX 06-273-1180. Ed.Bd. circ. 865. (back issues avail.) **Document type:** newsletter.
   Supersedes (in 1993): Acquisition, Bibliography, Cataloguing News (ISSN 0725-0037); Which was formerly (until 1981): R O D News.

020   AT   ISSN 1035-753X
NATIONAL LIBRARY OF AUSTRALIA NEWS. 1990. m. National Library of Australia, Publications Section, Cultural and Educational Serivces Division, Canberra, A.C.T. 2600, Australia. TEL 06-262-1365. FAX 06-273-4493. Ed. Paul Hetherington. circ. 5,000. (reprint service avail. from ISI,UMI)
   Description: Informative guide to library services.

027.571   CN   ISSN 0078-7000
NATIONAL LIBRARY OF CANADA. ANNUAL REPORT. (Text in English and French) 1953. a. free. National Library of Canada, Publications and Marketing Services, 395 Wellington St., Ottawa, Ont. K1A 0N4, Canada. TEL 613-995-7969. FAX 613-991-9871. circ. 4,500. **Document type:** corporate report.

020   US   ISSN 0093-0393
Z733
NATIONAL LIBRARY OF MEDICINE. PROGRAMS AND SERVICES. a. price varies. U.S. National Library of Medicine, 8600 Rockville Pike, Bethesda, MD 20894. (Back issues avail. from: National Technical Information Service, 5285 Port Royal Rd., Springfield, VA 22161 (Current report avail. from National Library of Medicine). TEL 703-487-4650. FAX 703-321-8547) (reprint service avail. from UMI) **Document type:** corporate report, government publication.
   Formerly (until 1972): U.S. National Library of Medicine. Annual Report (ISSN 0083-2243)

026 610   US   ISSN 0027-965X
    CODEN: NLMNAF
NATIONAL LIBRARY OF MEDICINE NEWS. 1945. m. free. (U.S. National Library of Medicine, Office of Public Information) University Microfilms International, 330 N. Zeeb St., Ann Arbor, MI 48106. TEL 800-521-0600. Ed. Roger L. Gilkeson. illus. circ. 6,000. (also avail. in microfilm from UMI; back issues avail.; reprint service avail. from UMI) **Indexed:** CINAHL, MEDOC.
—BLDSC (6102.600000); UMI; CASDDS.
   Description: Provides ongoing information about the world's largest medical library's people, programs, projects, and publications.

020   UK   ISSN 0950-7086
NATIONAL LIBRARY OF SCOTLAND NEWS. 1986. 3/yr. free. National Library of Scotland, George IV Bridge, Edinburgh EH1 1EW, Scotland. TEL 031-226-4531. FAX 031-220-6662. Eds. Pauline Scott, Jackie Cromarty. circ. 4,500. **Document type:** newsletter.
—BLDSC (6102.601000).
   Description: Discusses current activities and policies of the National Library of Scotland and the library community in Scotland.

NATIONAL ONLINE MEETING. PROCEEDINGS. see MEETINGS AND CONGRESSES

NATIONAL PRESERVATION OFFICE SEMINAR PAPERS. see CONSERVATION

020   RU   ISSN 0548-0019
Z699.A1   CODEN: NTOMAA
NAUCHNO-TEKHNICHESKAYA INFORMATSIYA. SERIYA 1. ORGANIZATSIYA I METODIKA INFORMATSIONNOI RABOTY. English translation: Scientific and Technical Information Processing (US ISSN 0147-6882) 1967. m. 15.6 Rub.($24) Vsesoyuznyi Institut Nauchno-Tekhnicheskoi Informatsii (VINITI), Baltiiskaya Ul., 14, Moscow A-219, Russia. bk.rev.; charts. **Indexed:** Chem.Abstr., Compumath, Curr.Cont., Lib.Lit., LISA, Sci.Abstr., SSCI.
—CASDDS.
   Formerly: Nauchno-Tekhnicheskaya Informatsiya (ISSN 0028-1131)

021   US
NEBRASKA LIBRARIES: A DIRECTORY. a. Nebraska Library Commission, 1200 N St., No. 120, Lincoln, NE 68508-2023. TEL 402-471-2045. circ. 1,200. **Document type:** directory.
   Former titles: Nebraska Library Commission. Library Directory; Nebraska Library Commission Biennial Report; Nebraska Library Commission. Annual Report (ISSN 0099-0299)
   Description: Listing of all public, academic, special and institutional libraries in the state of Nebraska.

LIBRARY AND INFORMATION SCIENCES

020 US ISSN 0028-1883
NEBRASKA LIBRARY ASSOCIATION QUARTERLY. 1970. q. $10 to non-members. Nebraska Library Association, c/o R. B. Means, Creighton University, 2500 California St., Omaha. NE 68178. TEL 402-280-2217. FAX 402-280-2435. Ed. Ron Norman. adv.; bk.rev. circ. 900. **Indexed:** Lib.Lit.
—UnCover.
Supersedes: Nebraska Library Association. Newsletter.

027 NE ISSN 0165-2583
NEDERLANDS BIBLIOTHEK EN LEKTUUR CENTRUM. INFO BULLETIN. Key Title: Info Bulletin. 1973. w. Nederlands Bibliotheek en Lektuur Centrum, Postbus 93054, 2509 AB The Hague, Netherlands. Ed. F. Stein.
—SWETS.
Incorporates (1979-1985): Infomedia (ISSN 0168-7042); (1972-1982): N I A M Mediatiek (ISSN 0165-6988)
Description: Information on the activities of the NBLC, including news from local public libraries.

020 NE
NEDERLANDSE BIBLIOTHEEK- EN DOCUMENATIEGIDS; adresboek van in Nederland gevestigde bibliotheken en documentatieinstellingen. 1984. triennial. fl.125. (Federatie van Organistie op gebied van Bibliotheek-, Informatie-, en Documentatiewezen) Nederlands Bibliotheek en Lektuur Centrum, Postbus 93054, 2509 AB the Hague, Netherlands. adv. **Document type:** directory.
Formerly: Venadam Bibliotheekgids.

020.6 UK
NEMCON. 1966. s-a. membership. Library Association, East Midlands Branch, Skegness Library, 23 Roman Bank, Skegness, Lincolnshire PE25 25A, England. Ed. Debbie Fossey. bk.rev. circ. 1,350. **Document type:** newsletter.

020 011 GW ISSN 0028-3126
Z801
DIE NEUE BUECHEREI; Zeitschrift fuer die oeffentlichen Buechereien in Bayern. 1964. 5/yr. DM.35. Generaldirektion der Bayerischen Staatlichen Bibliotheken, Ludwigstr. 16, 80539 Munich, Germany. TEL 089-28638247. FAX 089-28638630. Eds. Helga Unger, Franz Kaessl. bk.rev.; charts, illus.; index, cum.index. circ. 1,500. **Document type:** government publication.

380 020 310 US
NEVADA LIBRARY DIRECTORY AND STATISTICS. 1975. a. free. Nevada State Library and Archives, Capitol Complex, Carson City, NV 89710. TEL 702-687-8313. (also avail. in microfiche from CIS) **Indexed:** SRI. **Document type:** government publication, directory.
Description: Annual directory of libraries Nevada, their hours, directors and staff.

025 US ISSN 0887-3844
NEW DIRECTIONS IN INFORMATION MANAGEMENT. 1978. irreg., no.29, 1992. price varies. Greenwood Press, Inc. (Subsidiary of: Greenwood Publishing Group Inc.), 88 Post Rd. W., Box 5007, Westport, CT 06881-5007. TEL 203-226-3571. FAX 203-222-1502. Ed. Michael Buckland.
—BLDSC (6083.377000).
Formerly: New Directions in Librarianship (ISSN 0147-1090)

NEW ENGLAND SOUNDING LINE. see *MEDICAL SCIENCES — Abstracting, Bibliographies, Statistics*

020 US ISSN 0028-5811
Z732.N6
NEW JERSEY LIBRARIES. 1966; N.S. 1968. 4/yr. $12 to non-members. New Jersey Library Association, Box 1534, Trenton, NJ 08607. Ed. Eleanor Clarke. adv.; bibl. circ. 1,900. (also avail. in microform from UMI; reprint service avail. from UMI) **Indexed:** Lib.Lit.
—UnCover; UMI.

027.4 US
NEW JERSEY LIBRARIES NEWSLETTER. 1982. 10/yr. membership. New Jersey Library Association, Box 1534, Trenton, NJ 08607. Ed. Patricia A. Tumulty. circ. 1,900. **Document type:** newsletter.

020 AT ISSN 1320-5609
▼**NEW LIBRARIAN.** 1994. m. (11/yr.). Aus.$49. D.W. Thorpe, A Reed Reference Publishing Company, Part of the Reed Elsevier group, 18 Salmon St., Port Melbourne, Vic. 3207, Australia. TEL 03-245-7370. FAX 03-245-7395. Ed. Virginia Maxwell; Pub. Michael Webster. adv. contact: Judy Hille.
Description: Serves the Australian and New Zealand library communities.

025.7 655 US ISSN 0735-8571
Z671
NEW LIBRARY SCENE. 1953. bi-m. $18. Library Binding Institute, 7401 Metro Blvd., No. 325, Edina, MN 55439-3031. TEL 612-835-4707. FAX 612-835-4780. Ed. Sally Grauer. adv.; bk.rev.; charts; illus. circ. 3,000. (also avail. in microfilm; back issues avail.; reprint service avail. from UMI) **Indexed:** Abstr.Engl.Stud., Graph.Arts Lit.Abstr., Leg.Info.Manage.Ind., LHTN, Lib.Lit.
—BLDSC (6084.454700); Faxon; UnCover; UMI.
Former titles (until 1982): Library Scene (ISSN 0090-8746); Library Binder (ISSN 0024-2209)
Description: Covers the library, binding preservation and conservation fields. Also addresses new technology, profiling individuals and achievements in the library binding fields.

020 UK ISSN 0307-4803
Z671
NEW LIBRARY WORLD. 1898. 13/yr. $1199.95. M C B University Press Ltd., 60-62 Toller Ln., Bradford, W. Yorks BD8 9BY, England. TEL 0274-499821. FAX 0274-547143. TELEX 51317-MCBUNI-G. Ed. Ian Pettman. bk.rev.; bibl.; illus.; index. (also avail. in microform from UMI; reprint service avail. from SWZ,UMI) **Indexed:** BMT, Educ.Tech.Abstr., LISA. **Document type:** academic/scholarly publication.
—BLDSC (6084.455000); UnCover; SWETS; UMI.
Formerly: Library World (ISSN 0024-2616)
Description: Covers news from America, commercial and technical news, research, community information, cuts and alerts.

020 US
NEW MEDIA. 1991. m. $48 (free to qualified personnel). HyperMedia Communications, 901 Mariner's Island Blvd., Ste. 365, San Mateo, CA 94404. Ed. David Bunnell. adv.; illus.; circ. controlled.
Description: Covers new media, such as interactive CD-ROM and touchscreen technology.

020.6 US ISSN 0893-2956
NEW MEXICO LIBRARY ASSOCIATION NEWSLETTER. 1972. 4/yr. membership. New Mexico Library Association, 11200 Montgomery N.E., Ste. 8, Eldorado Sq., Albuquerque, NM 87111. TEL 505-646-6926. Ed. Donnelyn Curtis. adv.; bk.rev. circ. 700. **Document type:** newsletter.

026 US ISSN 0193-4287
NEW SPECIAL LIBRARIES. (Supplement to: Directory of Special Libraries and Information Centers) no.4, 1973. 2/yr. $335. Gale Research Inc., 835 Penobscot Bldg., Detroit, MI 48226. TEL 313-961-2242. FAX 313-961-6083. TELEX 810-221-7086. Ed. Janice A. DeMaggio.

027.4 US
NEW YORK PUBLIC LIBRARY NEWS. 1983. 5/yr. $35 membership. New York Public Library, Fifth Ave. at 42nd St., New York, NY 10018. TEL 212-704-8600. FAX 212-768-7439. Ed. Esther Harriott. circ. 20,000. **Document type:** newsletter.
Formerly: Library Lines.
Description: Reports on activities of the New York Public Library for its donors.

027 US ISSN 0077-930X
KFN5675.A29
NEW YORK STATE LIBRARY, ALBANY. LIBRARY DEVELOPMENT. EXCERPTS FROM NEW YORK STATE EDUCATION LAW, RULES OF THE BOARD OF REGENTS, AND REGULATIONS OF THE COMMISSIONER OF EDUCATION PERTAINING TO PUBLIC AND FREE ASSOCIATION LIBRARIES, LIBRARY SYSTEMS, TRUSTEES AND LIBRARIANS. 1959. irreg. free to libraries in New York State; libraries elsewhere on exchange basis. New York State Library, Library Development, Albany, NY 12230. circ. 1,500.

020 NZ ISSN 0028-8381
Z671
NEW ZEALAND LIBRARIES. 1937. q. NZ.$55 (effective 1992). New Zealand Library and Information Association, P.O. Box 12-212, Wellington 1, New Zealand. TEL 04-473-5834. FAX 04-499-1480. Ed. P. Calvert. adv.; bk.rev.; illus.; index, cum.index: vols. 1-20; 21-33. circ. 2,220. (also avail. in microfilm from UMI; reprint service avail. from UMI) **Indexed:** Lib.Lit., Lib.Sci.Abstr., LISA.
—BLDSC (6096.000000). **CCC.**

020 070.5 US
A NEWBERRY NEWSLETTER. 1973. 4/yr. membership only. Newberry Library, 60 W. Walton St., Chicago, IL 60610. TEL 312-943-9090. illus. circ. 5,500.
Document type: newsletter.

NEWS ABOUT LIBRARY SERVICES FOR THE BLIND AND PHYSICALLY HANDICAPPED. see *HANDICAPPED*

020 US ISSN 0730-1618
NEWS & CLUES. 1959. m. $35. San Joaquin Valley Library System, 2420 Mariposa St., Fresno, CA 93721. TEL 209-488-3229. FAX 209-488-2965. Ed. David DeLaurant. bk.rev. circ. 275. **Document type:** newsletter.
Description: Newsletter for cooperative library system.

020 US ISSN 0146-1842
Z732.S72
NEWS FOR SOUTH CAROLINA LIBRARIES. 1957. q. free. South Carolina State Library, 1500 Senate St., Box 11469, Columbia, SC 29211. TEL 803-734-8666. FAX 803-734-8676. Ed. Angela Cook. bibl.; circ. 1,800 (controlled). (processed) **Document type:** newsletter.

020 US ISSN 1047-417X
NEWS LIBRARY NEWS. 1978. q. $30. Special Libraries Association, News Division, c/o Advocate Library, Box 588, Baton Rouge, LA 70821. TEL 504-388-0327. Ed. Mona Hatfield. adv.; bk.rev.; index; circ. 820 (paid). **Document type:** newsletter.
●Also available online. Vendor(s): VU/TEXT Information Services, Inc.
Description: Provides information and technology services for news researchers and professionals.

020 323.4 US ISSN 0028-9485
Z671
NEWSLETTER ON INTELLECTUAL FREEDOM. 1952. bi-m. $40 (foreign $50). American Library Association, Intellectual Freedom Committee, 50 E. Huron St., Chicago, IL 60611-2795. TEL 800-545-2433. FAX 312-440-9374. Ed. Judith F. Krug. bk.rev.; bibl.; index, cum.index: 1952-65 (in 2 vols.), 1966-72 (in 7 vols.), 1973-84 (in 4 vols.). circ. 3,200. (also avail. in microform from UMI; back issues avail.; reprint service avail. from UMI) **Indexed:** Curr.Lit.Fam.Plan., Lib.Lit. **Document type:** academic/scholarly publication, newsletter.
—Faxon; UMI. **CCC.**
Description: Report on threats to First Amendment rights.

020 US ISSN 1046-3410
Z692.S5 CODEN: NSPIEY
NEWSLETTER ON SERIALS PRICING ISSUES. 1989; N.S. 1991. irreg. free. Marcia Tuttle, Ed. & Pub., Serials Department, C.B. 3938, Davis Library, University of North Carolina, Chapel Hill, NC 27514-8890. TEL 919-962-1067. FAX 919-962-0484. circ. 800. (back issues avail)
●Available only online.
Description: Scope includes trends in pricing for library serials, specific examples of price increases - decreases, libraries' strategies for coping with increasing prices of serials. Audience includes librarians, publishers, subscription agents, faculty members, and other scholars.

025 GW ISSN 0072-4866
NIEDERSAECHSISCHE STAATS- UND UNIVERSITAETSBIBLIOTHEK, GOETTINGEN. ARBEITEN. 1954. irreg. price varies. (Niedersaechsische Staats- und Universitaetsbibliothek) Vandenhoeck und Ruprecht, Robert-Bosch-Breite 6, 37079 Goettingen, Germany. TEL 0551-6959-0. FAX 0551-695917. (Subscr. to: 37070 Goettingen, Germany) **Document type:** monographic series.

LIBRARY AND INFORMATION SCIENCES

020   NR   ISSN 0794-3865
NIGERIA PERIODICALS REVIEW. 1986. q. Abic Books & Equipment Ltd., 18 Kenyatta St., P.O. Box 13740, Enugu, Nigeria. TEL 042-331827. Ed. C.N.C. Asomugha. bk.rev.; abstr.; bibl. (back issues avail.)
—BLDSC (6112.147000).

020 655   NR   ISSN 0029-0122
Z673.N698
NIGERIAN LIBRARIES. (Text in English) 1963. 3/yr. $6. (Nigerian Library Association) Ibadan University Press, University of Ibadan, Dept. of Library Studies, Ibadan, Nigeria. (Orders to: Business Manager, c/o University of Ibadan Library, Ibadan, Nigeria or P.M.B. 12655, Lagos, Nigeria) Ed. E. Bejide Bankole. adv.; bk.rev.; charts; illus.; stat.; index. circ. 500. (tabloid format) **Indexed:** Lib.Lit., Lib.Sci.Abstr.

020   NR   ISSN 0189-4412
Z857.N5
NIGERIAN LIBRARY AND INFORMATION SCIENCE REVIEW. 1983. s-w. £N50($35) Nigerian Library Association, Oyo State Chapter, P.O. Box 20672, U.I. Post Office, Ibadan, Nigeria. Ed. B.C. Nzotta. adv.; bk.rev. circ. 1,000. (back issues avail.) **Document type:** academic/scholarly publication.
Description: Publishes results of empirical research in library and information science, especially in Nigeria and Africa.

020 070.5   CC   ISSN 1002-1248
NONGYE TUSHU QINGBAO XUEKAN/JOURNAL OF LIBRARY AND INFORMATION SCIENCES IN AGRICULTURE. (Text in Chinese) 1989. bi-m. Y18. Zhongguo Nongye Kexueyuan, Zhongguo Nongye Tushuguan Xiehui - Chinese Academy of Agricultural Sciences, Scientech Documentation and Information Centre, 30 Baishiqiao Lu, Beijing 100081, People's Republic of China. TEL 8314433. FAX 8323577. Ed. Wang Yonghou. bk.rev. circ. 1,000. **Document type:** academic/scholarly publication.
—BLDSC (5010.341000).

020   FI   ISSN 0356-9624
NORDINFO-NYTT. (Text in Danish, English, Norwegian, Swedish) 1978. 4/yr. free. Nordiska Samarbetsorganet for Vetenskaplig Information - Nordic Council for Scientific Inormation, c/o Helsinki University of Technology Library, Otnaesvaegen 9, SF-02150 Esbo, Finland. TEL 358-0-455-2633. FAX 358-0-455-2576. Ed. Marianne Heikell.
Description: Information about the project activities and working program of Nordinfo.

NORDISK TIDSKRIFT FOER BOK- OCH BIBLIOTEKSVAESEN/SCANDINAVIAN JOURNAL OF LIBRARIES. see *PUBLISHING AND BOOK TRADE*

026   NO
NORSKE VITENSKAPELIGE OG FAGLIGE BIBLIOTEKER; en haandbok. (Text in Norwegian; contents and subject index in English) 1963. irreg., no.7, 1991. price varies. Riksbibliotektjenesten, Box 2439, Solli, 0201 Oslo, Norway. TEL 22-430880. FAX 22-560981. (Dist. by: A-L Biblioteksentralen, Malerhaugveien 20, 0661 Oslo, Norway) Ed. Libena Vokac. bk.rev. **Document type:** directory.
Description: Detailed information about 380 academic and special libraries.

020   US   ISSN 0029-2540
Z671
NORTH CAROLINA LIBRARIES. 1942. q. $32 to non-members; foreign $50. North Carolina Library Association, Department of Public Instruction, 301 N. Wilmington St., Raleigh, NC 27601-2825. Ed. Frances Bryant Bradburn. adv.; bk.rev.; index. circ. 2,000. (also avail. in microform from UMI; reprint service avail. from UMI) **Indexed:** Lib.Lit., Lib.Sci.Abstr. **Document type:** academic/scholarly publication.
—BLDSC (6149.055000); UMI.

027.7   CN   ISSN 0048-0754
NORTHERN AIR. 1969. s-a. free. Wapiti Regional Library, 145-12 St. E., Prince Albert, Sask. S6V 0K7, Canada. Ed. Karen Labuik. bk.rev. circ. 200.

020   UK
NORTHERN EASTERN EDUCATION LIBRARY BOARD. LIBRARY BULLETIN. 1974. 3/yr. free. Northern Eastern Education Library Board, Area Library, Demesne Ave., Ballymena, Co. Antrim BT43 7BG, N. Ireland. TEL 0266-41531. **Document type:** bulletin.
Formerly: Antrim County Library Quarterly Newssheet.

020   UK
NORTHERN LIBRARIAN. 1979. 6/yr. free. c/o Dorothy Procter, Denton Park Library, West Denton Way, Newscastle Upon Tyne NE5 2QZ, England. TEL 091-267-7922. circ. 1,300.
Formerly: East Libraries Bulletin.
Description: Information and comments about professional activities in the Library Association's northern branch area.

020   NO   ISSN 0800-4153
NORWAY. RIKSBIBLIOTEKTJENESTEN. AARSMELDING. a. free. Riksbibliotektjenesten, Box 2439, Solli, 0201 Oslo, Norway. TEL 22-430880. FAX 22-560981. **Document type:** monographic series.
Description: National Office for Research and Special Libraries' annual report.

020   NO   ISSN 0800-4129
NORWAY. RIKSBIBLIOTEKTJENESTEN. SKRIFTER. (Text in Norwegian) irreg. free. Riksbibliotektjenesten, Box 2439, Solli, 0201 Oslo, Norway. TEL 22-430880. FAX 22-560981. **Document type:** monographic series.
—BLDSC (8306.600000).
Description: Committee reports and library studies.

NOTES AND QUERIES; for readers and writers, collectors and librarians. see *LITERATURE*

020   US
NOTES AND TRACINGS. 1980. 3/yr. membership. Louisiana Library Association, Box 3058, Baton Rouge, LA 70821. TEL 504-342-4928. Ed. Paul Haschak. circ. 450. (back issues avail.)

020.6   PO   ISSN 0870-0680
NOTICIA B A D. 1975. bi-m. free. Associacao Portuguesa de Bibliotecarios Arquivistas e Documentalistas, Edificio da Biblioteca Nacional, Campo Grande 83, 1751 Lisbon, Portugal. FAX 8134697. adv.; bk.rev.; bibl. circ. 2,000. **Indexed:** Bull.Signal., LISA.
Formerly (until 1983): Associacao Portuguesa de Bibliotecarios Arquivistas e Documentalistas. Noticia (ISSN 0251-4141)

020   FR
NOUVELLES DE L'I S S N. English edition: News from I S S N (ISSN 1021-9749) 1984. irreg., latest Oct. 1993. International Serials Data System International Center, 20 Rue Bachaumont, 75002 Paris, France. FAX 40-26-32-43. (In U.S.: National Serials Data Program, Library of Congress, Washington, DC 20540. TEL 202-707-6452) **Document type:** newsletter.
Formerly (until 1993): Nouvelles de l'I S D S (ISSN 0256-999X)
Description: Contains news in the serials field.

020   NR   ISSN 0331-1481
Z858.U465
NSUKKA LIBRARY NOTES. 1975. a. £N20($10) University of Nigeria, Library, Nsukka, Nigeria. TELEX ULIONS 51496. Ed. M.W. Anyakoha. adv. circ. 400. (back issues avail.) **Indexed:** Lib.Lit. **Document type:** academic/scholarly publication.

020   DK   ISSN 0903-6342
NYT FRA NYHAVN. 1968. 4/yr. free. Statens Bibliotekstjeneste, Nyhavn 31E, DK-1051 Copenhagen K, Denmark. FAX 45-33-93-60-93. Ed. Peter Heise.
Formerly (until 1988): Information for Forskningsbiblioteker (ISSN 0105-2616)
Description: Official news and information from the Danish National Library Authority.

021.6   US   ISSN 1044-3800
Z732.O5
O C L C ANNUAL REPORT. a. free. Online Computer Library Center, Inc., 6565 Frantz Rd., Dublin, OH 43017. TEL 614-764-6000. FAX 614-764-6096.
—BLDSC (1382.160000).
Former titles: Ohio College Library Center. Annual Report (1978) (ISSN 0730-5125); Ohio College Library Center. Annual Report (1968) (ISSN 0090-8673)

020 378   US   ISSN 0163-898X
Z674.82.O15   CODEN: OCLNDT
O C L C NEWSLETTER. 1967. bi-m. free to qualified persons. Online Computer Library Center, Inc., 6565 Frantz Rd., Dublin, OH 43017. TEL 614-764-6000. Ed. Nita Dean. bibl. circ. 15,000. **Indexed:** LISA. **Document type:** newsletter.
—BLDSC (6235.137000); Faxon; SWETS; CASDDS.

352   NE   ISSN 0923-6600
O D. 1947. m. fl.56. (Vereniging voor Documentaire Informatievoorziening en Administratieve Organisatie) V N G Uitgeverij, P.O. Box 30435, 2500 GK The Hague, Netherlands. TEL 31-70-3738888. FAX 31-70-3651826. Ed.Bd. adv.; bk.rev.; illus.; index. circ. 4,000. **Indexed:** Key to Econ.Sci. **Document type:** trade publication.
—SWETS.
Formerly (untiI 1989): Overheidsdocumentatie (ISSN 0166-9028)

020   US
O D L RECORD. 1982. 4/yr. free. Oklahoma Department of Libraries, 200 N.E. 18th St., Oklahoma City, OK 73105-3298. TEL 405-521-2502. FAX 405-525-7804. Eds. Linda Raulston, Robert Rankin. circ. 400. **Document type:** government publication, newsletter.
Description: Information to Oklahoma State Government Agencies on records management issues, workshops, helpful tips and more.

020   US   ISSN 0193-3086
O D L SOURCE. 1976. m. free. Oklahoma Department of Libraries, 200 N.E. 18th St., Oklahoma City, OK 73105. TEL 405-521-2502. FAX 405-525-7804. Eds. William O. Petrie, William R. Young. circ. 3,800. **Document type:** government publication, newsletter.
Description: Agency newsletter on news and events for Oklahoma's library community.

026   CN   ISSN 0843-5901
O H L A NEWSLINE. 1986. q. Can.$50. Ontario Hospital Libraries Association, c/o Library, Ontario Hospital Assoc., 150 Ferrand Dr., Don Mills, ON M3C 1H6, Canada. TEL 416-429-2661. FAX 416-429-1363. Ed. John Tagg. bk.rev. circ. 200. (back issues avail.)
Formerly: O H L A Newsletter.

020   US
O I F MEMORANDUM. 1968. m. $20. American Library Association, Office for Intellectual Freedom, 50 E. Huron St., Chicago, IL 60611. FAX 312-440-9374. Eds. Judith F. Krug, Anne L. Penway. bk.rev. circ. 700.
Formerly: American Library Association. Memorandum (ISSN 0734-3086)
Description: Communication link between ALA Office for Intellectual Freedom and Intellectual Freedom Committees of the state library associations. Includes information on legislation, trends in censorship, and suggestions for programs through which librarians and the public can understand the importance of protecting intellectual freedom.

O I O C NEWSLETTER. (Oriental and India Office Collections) see *ORIENTAL STUDIES*

020   US   ISSN 0739-1153
O L A C NEWSLETTER. 1981. q. $10 to individuals; institutions $16 (foreign $18). Online Audiovisual Catalogers, Inc., c/o Susan M. Neumeister, Ed., State University of New York at Buffalo, Central Technical Services, Lockwood Library Bldg., Buffalo, NY 14260-2200. FAX 716-645-5955. (Subscr. to: Johanne LaGrange, Treas., Health Sciences Library, Columbia University, 701 W. 168th St., New York, NY 10032) bk.rev.; cum.index: 1981-1990. circ. 705. **Document type:** newsletter.
Description: For catalogers of audiovisual media in an online environment.

026 016   AU
OESTERREICHISCHES STAATSARCHIV. PUBLIKATIONEN; Inventare oesterreichischer staatlicher Archive. 1909. irreg., vol.36, 1984. price varies. Verlag Ferdinand Berger und Soehne GmbH, Wienerstr. 21-23, A-3580 Horn, Austria. TEL 02982-2317-0. **Document type:** monographic series.

LIBRARY AND INFORMATION SCIENCES

380 027.4 US
Z732.N6
OFFICIAL DIRECTORY OF NEW JERSEY LIBRARIES AND MEDIA CENTERS. 1983. a. $69.95. (New Jersey State Library) L D A Publishers, 42-36 209 St., Bayside, NY 11361-2747. TEL 718-224-9484. FAX 718-224-9487. adv. circ. 1,000. **Document type:** directory.
  Former titles (until 1991): Official Directory of New Jersey Libraries and Media Centers Including Finding; Official Directory of New Jersey Libraries and Media Centers Including Buyer's Guide (ISSN 0748-2469); Official Directory of New Jersey Libraries and Media Centers.
  Description: Lists academic, special, public and school libraries and media centers geographically with extnesive indexing. Indludes state library organization and access information to public, academic and state libraries.

027 US ISSN 0164-1794
OHIO. STATE LIBRARY. ANNUAL REPORT. 1972. a. free. State Library Board, 65 S. Front St., Columbus, OH 43266-0334. TEL 614-644-6875. FAX 614-466-3584. Ed. Jane M. Byrnes. charts; illus.; stat. **Document type:** government publication.
  Formerly: Ohio. State Library. State Library Review.

029 US ISSN 1047-5400
OHIO ARCHIVIST. 1970. s-a. $10 to individuals; institutions $15; students $5. Society of Ohio Archivists, c/o Cleveland Clinic Archives, P-22, 9500 Euclid Ave., Cleveland, OH 44195. TEL 216-444-2929. FAX 216-445-6868. Ed. Frederick Lautzenheiser. adv.; bk.rev.; charts; illus. circ. 500. **Document type:** academic/scholarly publication, newsletter.
  Formerly: Society of Ohio Archivists Newsletter (ISSN 0030-0780)
  Description: Includes articles of interest to archives and manuscripts collections, news from Ohio archival and manuscripts collections and announcements and reports of meetings.

020 US ISSN 1046-4336
Z671 CODEN: OHLIEG
OHIO LIBRARIES.* 1988. 4/yr. $30. Ohio Library Association, c/o Ohio Library Council, 35 E. Gay St., No. 305, Columbus, OH 43215-3138. TEL 614-221-9057. FAX 614-221-6234. Ed. Lynda Murray. adv. circ. 5,000. (also avail. in microform from UMI; reprint service avail. from UMI) **Indexed:** Lib.Lit.
  —UMI.
  Formed by the 1988 merger of: O L A Bulletin (ISSN 0029-7135); Ohio Libraries Newsletter; Ohio Library Trustee (ISSN 0030-0977).
  Description: Contains articles of current interest, historical significance, or literary value concerning all aspects of librarianship, especially items pertinent to Ohio, and includes official statements of the Association.

027.8 US ISSN 0192-6942
Z675.S3
OHIO MEDIA SPECTRUM.* 1976. q. $30. Ohio Educational Library Media Association, c/o Ohio Library Council, 35 E. Gay St., No. 305, Columbus, OH 43215-3840. TEL 614-221-9057. Ed. Edward F. Newren. adv.; bk.rev.; cum.index. circ. 1,300. (also avail. in microfilm from UMI; reprint service avail. from UMI) **Indexed:** Lib.Lit.
  —BLDSC (6247.105000); Faxon; UMI.
  Formed by the 1976 merger of: Ohio Association of School Librarians' Bulletin (ISSN 0030-0799); Educational Media in Ohio.
  Description: Provides news of Association activities and discussions of issues in librarianship.

OHIOANA QUARTERLY. see LITERATURE

020 JA
OKINAWA TOSHOKAN KYOKAI SHI/OKINAWA LIBRARY ASSOCIATION. ANNALS. 1964. a. 500 Yen. Okinawa Toshokan Kyokai - Okinawa Library Association, c/o Okinawa Prefectural Library, 2-16 Yorimiya 1-chome, Naha, Okinawa, Japan. adv.; bk.rev. circ. 1,000.

OKLAHOMA GOVERNMENT PUBLICATIONS; a checklist. see PUBLIC ADMINISTRATION

020 US ISSN 0030-1760
Z732
OKLAHOMA LIBRARIAN. 1950. bi-m. $15 (foreign $20). Oklahoma Library Association, 300 Hardy Dr., Edmond, OK 73013. TEL 405-348-0506. Eds. Karen Morris, Jennifer Paustenbaugh. adv.; bk.rev.; bibl.; illus.; cum.index: 1950-1965. circ. 1,100. (also avail. in microform from UMI; reprint service avail. from UMI)
  —UMI.

OMNIBUS (SEATTLE). see BIBLIOGRAPHIES

023 US ISSN 0748-8831
ONE-PERSON LIBRARY; a newsletter for librarians & management. 1984. m. $75 (Canada $80; elsewhere $85). O P L Resources, Ltd., Murray Hill Sta., Box 948, New York, NY 10156-0614. TEL 212-683-6285. Ed. Guy St. Clair. bk.rev.; index. circ. 2,000. (looseleaf format; back issues avail.) **Document type:** newsletter.
  —BLDSC (6260.243300). **CCC.**

ONLINE BUSINESS SOURCEBOOK. see BUSINESS AND ECONOMICS

026 CN ISSN 0826-7871
ONTARIO GOVERNMENT LIBRARIES COUNCIL. EXCHANGE. 1971. q. free. Ontario Government Libraries Council, 77 Wellesley St., W., 4th Fl., Ferguson Block, Toronto, ON M7A 1N3, Canada. TEL 416-327-2535. FAX 416-327-2530. circ. 110. (looseleaf format) **Document type:** newsletter.
  Description: News and issues of interest to Ontario government libraries.

020 NE ISSN 0030-3372
CODEN: OPNNBQ
OPEN; vaktijdschrift voor bibliothecarissen, literatuuronderzoekers en documentalisten. (Text mainly in Dutch; occasionally in English; summaries in English) 1969. 11/yr. fl.100 (effective 1994). c/o C. Van Schendel, Keizersgracht 802III, 1017 ED Amsterdam, Netherlands. TEL 31-20-6224322. FAX 31-20-6384860. (Subscr. to: Stichting Vaktydschrift, Postbus 572, 2600 AN Delft, Netherlands) adv.; bk.rev.; abstr.; bibl.; charts; illus.; index; circ. 4,500. (paid). (also avail. in microform from UMI; reprint service avail. from UMI) **Indexed:** Key to Econ.Sci., Lib.Lit., LISA, Sci.Abstr.
  —BLDSC (6265.945000); SWETS.

023 UK ISSN 0048-1904
OPEN ACCESS; a magazine for West Midland librarians. vol.22, 1978. 2/yr. £7. Library Association, West Midland Branch, c/o Book Purchase Dept., Birmingham Central Library, Chamberlain Square, Birmingham B3 3HQ, England. FAX 021-233-4458. Ed. Martin Underwood. adv. circ. 1,650.
  —BLDSC (6265.950000).

027.625 AT
ORANA; journal for school and children's librarians. 1965. q. Aus.$25 (foreign Aus.$32)(effective 1992). Australian Library and Information Association, P.O. Box E411, Queen Victoria Terrace, A.C.T. 2600, Australia. TEL 06-285-1877. FAX 06-282-2249. Ed. Mrs. Val Watson. adv.; bk.rev. circ. 3,700. **Indexed:** Aus.Educ.Ind., Aus.P.A.I.S., Child.Lit.Abstr.
  —BLDSC (6277.813000).
  Formerly: Children's Libraries Newsletter (ISSN 0045-6705)

020 US
ORANGE SEED TECHNICAL BULLETIN. 1973. m. free to qualified personnel. Department of State, Division of Library and Information Services, R.A. Gray Bldg., Tallahassee, FL 32399-0250. TEL 904-487-2651. FAX 904-488-2746. Ed. Lawrence Webster. bk.rev.; film rev.; circ. 1,200 (controlled).
  Formerly: Orange Seed; Incorporates (1970-1989): Intercom Technical Bulletin (ISSN 0741-9171); (1968-1988): Keystone (ISSN 0741-918X)
  Description: News from the State Library on all library related news, resources, new publications, events, and fundraising throughout the state. Includes information on the activities of Friends of Libraries groups throughout the state, and articles for librarians in special libraries.

020 US ISSN 0030-4735
OREGON LIBRARY NEWS. 1952. m. $15 Oregon Library Association, c/o Carolyn Peake, Pres., 6 Adams Ct., Lake Oswego, OR 97034. Ed. Wayne L. Suggs. adv. circ. 750. (processed)

020 US ISSN 0078-6381
ORGANIZATION OF AMERICAN STATES. DEPARTMENT OF CULTURAL AFFAIRS. MANUALES DEL BIBLIOTECARIO. 1961. irreg., latest no.9. $15. Organization of American States, 1889 F St., N.W., Washington, DC 20006. TEL 703-941-1617. circ. 2,000.

ORO MADRE. see LITERATURE

020 HU ISSN 0524-8868
ORSZAGOS SZECHENYI KONYVTAR EVKONYVE. (Text in Hungarian; summaries in English, French, German, Russian) 1958. a. price varies. Orszagos Szechenyi Konyvtar - National Szechenyi Library, Budavari Palota F epulet, 1827 Budapest, Hungary. TEL 175-7533. FAX 202-0804. TELEX 224226 BIBLN H. Ed. Ilona Kovacs. circ. 800.
  Description: Yearbook containing reports and essays on the history and activity of the National Szechenyi Library, as well as studies on the history of bibliography and culture.

026 HU ISSN 0030-6010
Z675.M4
ORVOSI KONYVTAROS/MEDICAL LIBRARIAN. (Text in Hungarian; summaries in English) 1961. q. 240 Ft.($17.50) Orszagos Orvostudomanyi Informacios Intezet es Konyvtar - National Institute for Medical Information and Library of Medicine, Szentkiralyi u. 21, 1088 Budapest, Hungary. TEL 361-117-6352. FAX 361-266-9710. Ed. Dr. Tibor Koltay. bk.rev.; index. circ. 350. **Indexed:** LISA. **Document type:** academic/scholarly publication.
  —BLDSC (6296.504000).
  Description: Directed at continuing education of medical librarians.

026 610 CN ISSN 0085-4557
OSLER LIBRARY NEWSLETTER. 1969. 3/yr. free. McGill University, Osler Library, 3655 Drummond St., Montreal, Que. H3G 1Y6, Canada. TEL 514-398-4720. FAX 514-398-5747. Ed. F.E. Wallis. circ. 1,400. **Document type:** newsletter.

020 US ISSN 0030-7319
OUTRIDER. 1968. m. free. Wyoming State Library, Supreme Court Bldg., Cheyenne, WY 82002. TEL 307-777-7281. FAX 307-777-6289. Ed. Linn Rounds. bk.rev. circ. 1,550. (processed) **Document type:** newsletter.
  Description: Covers news of the state library as well as other state and national libraray items.

020 DK ISSN 0904-3853
OVER BROEN. 1970. m. DKK 40. Danmarks Biblioteksskole, Birketinget 6, 2300 Copenhagen S, Denmark. Ed.Bd. bibl.; illus. circ. 500.
  Formerly (until 1988): Biblioten.

020 US ISSN 0161-1828
HV1571
OVERSEAS OUTLOOK (LARGE-PRINT EDITION). 1977. s-a. free to qualified personnel. U.S. Library of Congress, National Library Service for the Blind and Physically Handicapped, Washington, DC 20542. TEL 202-707-5100. FAX 202-707-0712. (large print in 18 pt.) **Document type:** newsletter, government publication.

020 FJ ISSN 1011-5080
P I C NEWSLETTER. 1980. q. free. Pacific Information Centre, University of the South Pacific, G.P.O. Box 1168, Suva, Fiji. TEL 313900. FAX 300830. **Document type:** newsletter.
  Supersedes: R B C Newsletter.

020 PK ISSN 0048-2714
P L A NEWSLETTER.* (Text in English) 1970. m. Rs.12. Pakistan Library Association, c/o Pakistan Institute of Development Economics, P.O.B. 1091, Islamabad, Pakistan. Ed. Syed Mubarak Ali. adv.; charts. circ. 1,000. (processed; also avail. in microform from UMI; reprint service avail. from UMI) **Indexed:** Lib.Lit.

025 340 US ISSN 1068-9346
P L L PERSPECTIVES. (Private Law Libraries) 1989. 4/yr. $25 (effective 1993). Sabrina I. Pacifici, Ed. & Pub., 1722 Eye St., N.W., Washington, DC 20006. TEL 202-736-8510. FAX 202-736-8711. adv.; B&W page $600; adv. contact: Jeff Bosh. circ. 1,600.
  Description: For the private law firm and corporate law librarian. Covers professional issues including management, technology, online research, legal and nonlegal research, cataloguing, technical services, and other relevant topics.

LIBRARY AND INFORMATION SCIENCES

027.4   **PP**
P N G L A NIUS. 1980. s-a. (included in subscr. to: Tok Tok Bilong Haus Buk) Papua New Guinea Library Association, c/o National Library Service, Boroko 5770, Boroko, N.S.C., Papua New Guinea. Ed.Bd.

020   **US**   **ISSN 0030-8188**
Z673.P11
P N L A QUARTERLY. 1936. q. $20 (foreign $25). Pacific Northwest Library Association, 1631 E. 24th Ave., Eugene, OR 97403-1718. TEL 503-344-2027. FAX 503-341-5898. Ed. Katherine G. Eaton. adv.: B&W page $150. bk.rev.; bibl.; illus.; index. circ. 1,000. (also avail. in microform from UMI; reprint service avail. from UMI) **Indexed:** Curr.Cont., Lib.Lit., Lib.Sci.Abstr.
—BLDSC (6541.130000); UnCover; UMI.

P R ACTIVITY REPORT. see *ADVERTISING AND PUBLIC RELATIONS*

020   **US**   **ISSN 0195-9646**
THE PACKET. 1968. m. free. Mississippi Library Commission, Box 10700, Jackson, MS 39289-0700. TEL 601-359-1036. FAX 601-354-4181. Ed. Lisa W. Ruble. adv.; bk.rev. circ. 2,700. (reprint service avail. from UMI) **Document type:** newsletter.

020   **CR**   **ISSN 0257-0114**
PAGINAS DE CONTENIDO: CIENCIAS DE LA INFORMACION. 1979. 3/yr. $12 to non-members. Asociacion Interamericana de Bibliotecarios y Documentalistas Agricolas, Apdo. Postal 55, 2200 Coronado, Costa Rica. TEL 29-0222. FAX 506-294741. TELEX 2144 IICA. Ed. Ghislaine Poitevien.
Description: Reproduction of table of contents of library and information science journals available at cooperating libraries.

020   **PK**   **ISSN 0030-9966**
Z845.P28
PAKISTAN LIBRARY BULLETIN. (International ed. in English; domestic ed. in English and Urdu) 1966. q. Rs.80($80) per no. Library Promotion Bureau, P.O. Box 8421, University of Karachi, Karachi 75270, Pakistan. Ed.Bd. adv.; bk.rev.; charts; index. circ. 500. **Indexed:** Amer.Hist.& Life, Hist.Abstr., Lib.Lit., LISA, R.G. **Document type:** bulletin.
—BLDSC (6343.029000).

PAKISTAN'S BOOKS & LIBRARIES; the only monthly magazine of its kind. see *PUBLISHING AND BOOK TRADE*

020.6   **DR**
PAPIRO. 1976. q. $5. Asociacion Dominicana de Bibliotecarios, Biblioteca Nacional, Plaza de la Cultura, Santo Domingo, Dominican Republic. Dir. Miriam Michel de Campusano. adv.; bk.rev.; bibl. circ. 500.

020   **AT**
PARAPHERNALIA. 1978. a. Aus.$15 to non-members. Australian Library and Information Association, Norther Territory Branch, P.O. Box 41303, Casuarina, N.T. 0811, Australia. FAX 089-228208. Eds. Ann Alderslade, Lucinda Steuart. adv. circ. 120.
Formerly (until 1989): N T Newsletter (ISSN 0157-2229)
Description: Information for and about libraries in the Northern Territory.

020 282   **US**
PARISH AND COMMUNITY LIBRARIES NEWS. 1960. bi-m. membership. Catholic Library Association, Parish Section, Box 16321, St. Paul, MN 55116. FAX 612-690-2131. Ed. Betty Hammargren. adv.; bk.rev.; bibl.; circ. 350 (controlled). (processed) **Document type:** bulletin, newsletter.
Formerly: Parish and Lending Library News (ISSN 0008-8188)

PASSING THE WORD. see *EDUCATION*

020   **US**   **ISSN 0197-9299**
Z673.P395
PENNSYLVANIA LIBRARY ASSOCIATION. BULLETIN. Short title: P L A Bulletin. 1945. 12/yr. $40 to non-members. Pennsylvania Library Association, 1919 N. Front St., Harrisburg, PA 17102-2214. FAX 717-233-3121. Ed. Margaret Bauer. adv.; bk.rev.; illus.; stat.; index, cum.index: 1945-1958. circ. 2,000. (looseleaf format; also avail. in microfilm from UMI; back issues avail.; reprint service avail. from UMI) **Indexed:** Lib.Lit, Lib.Sci.Abstr, LISA.
Document type: bulletin, newsletter.

020   **US**   **ISSN 0079-0656**
PENNSYLVANIA STATE UNIVERSITY. LIBRARIES. BIBLIOGRAPHICAL SERIES. 1969. irreg., latest no.12. price varies. Pennsylvania State University, University Libraries, University Park, PA 16802. TEL 814-865-0401. FAX 814-865-3665. Ed. Jillian Stevenson. circ. 500. **Document type:** bibliography.

PERIOSCOPE. see *EDUCATION*

020   **UK**
PERSONNEL, TRAINING AND EDUCATION; a journal for library and information workers. 1983. 3/yr. £40. Library Association, Personnel, Training and Education Group, c/o George Edwards Library, University of Surrey, Guildford GU2 5XH, England. FAX 0483-259500. Ed. G.M. Davies. adv.; bk.rev. circ. 1,400. **Indexed:** C.I.J.E., Cont.Pg.Educ., Inform.Sci.Abstr., Lib.Lit., LISA, Ref.Zh. **Document type:** academic/scholarly publication.
Formerly: Training and Education (ISSN 0264-8466)

027.4   **MY**
PERUTUSAN RATU DARUL EHSAN. 1989. a. Selangor Public Library Corporation, Perpustakaan Raja Tun Uda, Persiaran Perdagangan, 40572 Shah Alam, Malaysia. FAX 03-559-6045. circ. 1,000.
Description: Newsletter of the library.

020   **HU**   **ISSN 0209-6145**
PEST MEGYEI KONYVTAROS. 1955. q. free. Pest Megyei Konyvtar, Patriarka u. 7, 2000 Szentendre, Hungary. TEL 310-870. FAX 310-320. Ed. Peter Biczak. bk.rev. circ. 500. (back issues avail.)

026   **JA**   **ISSN 0386-2062**
Z675.P48   **CODEN: YATODW**
PHARMACEUTICAL LIBRARY BULLETIN/YAKUGAKU TOSHOKAN. (Text in Japanese) 1956. q. 1500 Yen per no. Japan Pharmaceutical Library Association - Nihon Yakugaku Toshokan Kyogikai, 3-1, Hongo 7-chome, Bunkyo-ku, Tokyo 113, Japan. Ed. S. Takada. adv.; bk.rev. circ. 1,200. **Indexed:** Chem.Abstr., LISA.
—BLDSC (6444.007000); CASDDS.

020   **PH**
PHILIPPINE LIBRARY ASSOCIATION. BULLETIN. (Text in English) vol.8, 1973. a. P.10($6) Philippine Library Association, c/o National Library, T.M. Kalaw St., Manila, Philippines. Ed. Angelica A. Cabanero. adv.; bk.rev. circ. 1,000. (back issues avail.) **Indexed:** Ind.Phil.Per.

020   **PH**   **ISSN 0115-7167**
PHILIPPINES. NATIONAL LIBRARY. T N L NEWS. (The National Library) q. National Library, T.M. Kalaw St., Manila, Philippines. **Document type:** newsletter.
Description: Official newsletter of the Philippine National Library.

PHILIPPINES. NATIONAL PRINTING OFFICE. ITEMIZATION OF PERSONAL SERVICES AND ORGANIZATIONAL CHARTS. see *PUBLIC ADMINISTRATION*

027   **US**   **ISSN 0196-6707**
PITTSBURGH REGIONAL LIBRARY CENTER. NEWSLETTER. 1967. irreg. $25 (foreign $50). Pittsburgh Regional Library Center, 103 Yost Blvd., Pittsburgh, PA 15221. TEL 412-825-0600. FAX 412-825-0762. adv. circ. 600. **Document type:** newsletter.

020   **CN**   **ISSN 0704-0628**
PLUG-IN. 1977. irreg. free. Ontario Library Services Center, 141 Dearborn Place, Waterloo, Ont. N2J 4N5, Canada. TEL 519-746-4420. FAX 519-746-4425. Ed. Marilyn Cranford. circ. 250.

020   **US**
POINTS NORTH. 1968. 10/yr. membership. North Country Reference & Research Resources Council, Box 568, Canton, NY 13617. TEL 315-386-4569. FAX 315-379-9553. Ed. Bridget Doyle. stat.; circ. 200. (controlled). (processed) **Document type:** newsletter.
Formerly (until 1988): North Country Reference and Research Resources Council. Newsletter (ISSN 0029-2699)

020   **US**
POINTS NORTHWEST. 1972. 4/yr. membership. American Society for Information Science, Pacific Northwest Chapter, c/o Jane E. Starnes, Ed., 2572 Glen Eagles Pl., Lake Oswego, OR 97034. adv.; bk.rev. circ. 120.
Description: Includes references to articles of current interest, information about the Society, the PNW Chapter and its meetings.

026 060   **PL**   **ISSN 0079-3140**
Z818.P62
POLSKA AKADEMIA NAUK. BIBLIOTEKA, KRAKOW. ROCZNIK. (Text in Polish; summaries in English and Russian) 1955. a. price varies. Ossolineum, Publishing House of the Polish Academy of Sciences, Rynek 9, 50-106 Wroclaw, Poland. TEL 48-71-386-25. FAX 48-71-448-103. TELEX 0712771 OSS PL. Ed. Krystyna Stachowska. index. **Document type:** academic/scholarly publication.
Description: Articles and source materials related to the history of science, culture and recordmaking of the library collection in Krakow and Krakow region.

020   **CN**   **ISSN 1183-0824**
LE PONT. 1984. 6/yr. Can.$25. Biblio-Regions de Quebec et Chaudiere-Appalaches, 3189 Rue Albert-Demers, Charny, PQ G6X 3A1, Canada. FAX 418-832-6168. Ed. Denis Gravel. adv. circ. 550. **Document type:** newsletter, bulletin.
Formerly (until 1990): L'Agent 03 (ISSN 0829-0938)

020   **US**   **ISSN 1053-8747**
Z688.P64   **CODEN: PCLIEQ**
▼**POPULAR CULTURE IN LIBRARIES.** 1993. q. $24 to individuals; institutions & libraries $28. Haworth Press, Inc., 10 Alice St., Binghamton, NY 13904-1580. TEL 607-722-5857; 800-342-9678. FAX 607-722-1424. TELEX 4932599. Ed. Frank Hoffmann. (also avail. in microfiche from UMI; reprint service avail. from HAW) **Indexed:** Human Resour.Abstr., Ind.Per.Art.Relat.Law, LISA, Sociol.Abstr.
—UnCover.
Description: Deals with the selection, acquisition, evaluation, organization, and utilization of popular culture materials and concepts for libraries, special collections, and archives.
Refereed Serial

020   **PL**   **ISSN 0032-4752**
Z671
PORADNIK BIBLIOTEKARZA. 1949. m. $45. Stowarzyszenie Bibliotekarzy Polskich, Konopczynskiego 5-7, 00-950 Warsaw, Poland. TEL 27 52 96. (Dist. by: Ars Polona-Ruch, Krakowskie Przedmiescie 7, 00-068 Warsaw, Poland) Ed. Wladyslawa Wasilewska. bk.rev.; bibl.; illus.; index. circ. 23,341. **Indexed:** LISA.
—BLDSC (6553.800000).

020   **CN**   **ISSN 1184-1125**
PREFACE. 1966. bi-m. free. Saskatoon Public Library, 311 - 23rd St. E., Saskatoon, SK S7K 0J6, Canada. TEL 306-975-7530. FAX 306-975-7766. Ed. Lise Henderson. adv.; bk.rev. circ. 6,000. **Document type:** newsletter.
Description: Guide to Library programs and services.

025.8 370   **US**   **ISSN 1049-619X**
Z701.3.E38
PRESERVATION EDUCATION DIRECTORY. 1981. a.? American Library Association, Resources and Technical Services Division, 50 E. Huron St., Chicago, IL 60611-2795. **Document type:** directory.

LIBRARY AND INFORMATION SCIENCES

029.7 976 333.7 US ISSN 0741-6563
THE PRIMARY SOURCE. 1979. q. $7.50 to individuals. Society of Mississippi Archivists, Box 1151, Jackson, MS 39215-1151. TEL 601-359-6873. FAX 601-359-6905. Ed. Mattie Sink. bk.rev. circ. 200. (looseleaf format; back issues avail.) **Document type:** newsletter.
Description: Compilation of meeting reports and publications, accessions from state repositories, and news for those interested in archives and history.

020 US ISSN 1042-8216
Z688.A2
PRIMARY SOURCES & ORIGINAL WORKS. 1981. q. $34 to individuals; institutions and libraries $45. Haworth Press, Inc., 10 Alice St., Binghamton, NY 13904. TEL 607-722-5857; 800-342-9678. FAX 607-722-1424. TELEX 4932599. Ed. Lawrence J. McCrank. acv.; bk.rev.; bibl. circ. 240. (also avail. in microfiche from HAW; back issues avail.; reprint service avail. from HAW) **Indexed:** Inform.Sci.Abstr., Lib.Lit. LISA, Sci.Abstr.
—BLDSC (6612.913130); UnCover.
Formerly (until vol.4, no.2, 1990): Special Collections (ISSN 0270-3157)
Description: Provides guide to and description of collections in a specific subject field.
Refereed Serial

027.1 UK ISSN 0032-8898
Z990
PRIVATE LIBRARY. 1957. q. £25($40) Private Libraries Association, Ravelston, South View Rd., Pinner, Middlesex HA5 3YD, England. (US address: c/o William A. Klutts, 145 East Jackson, Box 289, Ripley, TN 38063) Ed. David Chambers. adv.; bk.rev.; illus. circ. 1,500. **Indexed:** Abstr.Engl.Stud., Artbibl.Mod., Ind.Bk.Rev.Hum., Lib.Lit., Lib.Sci.Abstr. **Document type:** academic/scholarly publication.
—BLDSC (6617.066000).
Description: Essays concerned with book collecting.

029.7 RM ISSN 0018-9111
PROBLEME DE INFORMARE SI DOCUMENTARE. (Text in English, Rumanian) 1967. q. $111 or exchange basis. Institutul National de Informare si Documentare, Str. George Enescu 27-29, 70141 Bucharest, Rumania. TEL 6134010. TELEX 11247 INIDR. bk.rev.; bibl.; charts; illus. circ. 1,500. **Indexed:** Chem.Abstr., LISA, Ref.Zh., Sci.Abstr.
—BLDSC (6617.560000).
Formerly: Probleme de Documentare si Informare.
Description: Contains studies, news, and technical notes in the field of information science and librarianship.

PROGRESS IN COMMUNICATION SCIENCES. see *COMMUNICATIONS*

020 US ISSN 1052-5726
Z716.4
PROGRESSIVE LIBRARIAN. 1990. 3/yr. $15 to individuals; institutions $30. Progressive Librarians Guild, c/o Elaine Harger, Empire State College, SUNY School of Labor Studies Library, 330 W. 32nd St., 4th Fl., New York, NY 10036. **Indexed:** Alt.Press Ind.
Description: Provides a forum for the open exchange of radical views on library issues.

PROVENANCE. see *HISTORY — History Of North And South America*

020 PL ISSN 0033-202X
Z671
PRZEGLAD BIBLIOTECZNY. (Supplement avail.: Bibliografia Analityczna Bibliotekoznawstwa i Informacji Naukowej) (Text in Polish; summaries in English) 1927. q. $32. Polska Akademia Nauk, Biblioteka (Warsaw), Palac Kultury i Nauki, 4th Fl., 00-901 Warsaw, Poland. (Dist. by: Ars Polona-Ruch, Krakowskie Przedmiescie 7, Warsaw, Poland) (Co-sponsor: Stowarzyszenie Bibliotekarzy Polskich) Ed. Barbara Sordylowa. bk.rev.; charts; illus.; index, cum.index: 1927-1976. circ. 5,000. (also avail. in microform from UMI; reprint service avail. from UMI) **Indexed:** Lib.Lit., Lib.Sci.Abstr., LISA.
—BLDSC (6939.000000); UMI.

020 US ISSN 1056-4942
▼**PUBLIC & ACCESS SERVICES QUARTERLY.** 1993. q. $24. Haworth Press, Inc., 10 Alice St., Binghamton, NY 13904-1580. TEL 607-722-5857; 800-342-9678. FAX 607-722-1424. TELEX 4932599. Ed. Virgil Blake. adv.; B&W page $300. bk.rev. (also avail. in microform from UMI)
Description: Addresses the rapidly growing areas that involve direct interaction of librarians and patrons.
Refereed Serial

020 659.1 UK ISSN 0268-0149
PUBLIC EYE. 1984. 4/yr. £8. Library Association, Publicity and P R Group, c/o Princes Risborough Library, Bell St., Princes Risborough, Buckinghamshire, England. TEL 08444-3559. Ed. Alec Kennedy. bk.rev.; illus. circ. 1,350. (back issues avail.)
Description: Covers library publicity and promotion, PR, marketing, design and print.

027.4 US ISSN 0163-5506
Z731
PUBLIC LIBRARIES. 1970. 6/yr. $50 (foreign $60). (Public Library Association) American Library Association, 50 E. Huron St., Chicago, IL 60611-2795. TEL 800-545-2433. FAX 312-440-9374. Ed. Sandra Garrison. adv. circ. 5,781. (also avail. in microform from UMI; back issues avail.; reprint service avail. from UMI) **Indexed:** Lib.Lit., LISA.
—BLDSC (6967.185000); Faxon; UnCover; SWETS; UMI. **CCC.**
Former titles: P L A Newsletter (ISSN 0022-6998); Just Between Ourselves.
Description: News and articles of interest to public libraries.

020 UG
PUBLIC LIBRARIES BOARD. NEWSLETTER. 2/yr. Public Libraries Board, P.O. Box 4262, Kampala, Uganda. **Document type:** newsletter.
Description: Contains news of events happening on the library scene at the Public Libraries Board and in Uganda; includes feature articles.

025 UK ISSN 0268-893X
 CODEN: PLJOET
PUBLIC LIBRARY JOURNAL. 1986. bi-m. £36. Library Association - Public Library Group, 7 Ridgmount St., London WC1E 7AE, England. FAX 0278-452787. (Subscr. to: Woodspring Central Library, Blvd. Weston-S-Mare, Avon BS23 1PL, England) Ed. Rob Froud. adv.; bk.rev.; illus.; bibl.; index. circ. 7,000. (back issues avail.) **Indexed:** Lib.Lit., Lib.Sci.Abstr., LISA. **Document type:** trade publication.
—BLDSC (6967.241800).

020 US ISSN 0967-4888
PUBLIC LIBRARY MATERIALS FUND AND BUDGET SURVEY. a. £22.50. Loughborough University, Library and Information Statistics Unit, Loughborough, Leicestershire LE11 3TU, England. TEL 0509-223071. FAX 0509-610361. **Document type:** corporate report.

020 US ISSN 0161-6846
Z671
PUBLIC LIBRARY QUARTERLY. 1979. q. $36 to individuals; institutions $75. Haworth Press, Inc., 10 Alice St., Binghamton, NY 13904. TEL 607-722-5857; 800-342-9678. FAX 607-722-1424. TELEX 4932599. Ed. Richard L. Waters. adv.; bk.rev. circ. 580. (also avail. in microfiche from UMI; back issues avail.; reprint service avail. from HAW) Comput.& Info.Sys., Excerp.Med., Inform.Sci.Abstr., LHTN, Lib.Lit., LISA.
—BLDSC (6967.242000); UnCover; SWETS.
Description: Addresses the major administrative challenges and opportunities that face the nation's public libraries.
Refereed Serial

PUBLISHERS' CATALOGS ANNUAL. see *BIBLIOGRAPHIES*

025 CE ISSN 1391-0000
PUSTAKALA PRAVRTTI. (Text in Sinhalese) 1973. q. Rs.25. National Library of Sri Lanka, P.O. Box 1764, Independence Ave., Colombo 07, Sri Lanka. TEL 94-1-698847. FAX 94-1-685201. Ed.Bd. adv.; bk.rev. circ. 1,000. **Document type:** newsletter.

020 II ISSN 0033-4693
PUSTAKALAYA. (Text in Gujarati) 1925. m. Rs.45. Gujarat Pustakalaya Sahayak Sahakari Mandal Ltd., Raopura, Box 10, Baroda, Gujarat 390 001, India. Ed. Manubhai B. Bhatt. adv.; bk.rev.; abstr.; illus. circ. 2,500.

020 CN ISSN 0380-7150
Q L A BULLETIN/BULLETIN A B Q. (Text in English and French) 3/yr. membership. Quebec Library Association, P.O. Box 1095, Pte. Claire, PQ H9S 4H9, Canada. TEL 514-630-4875. Ed. Margaret Monks. adv.; bk.rev. circ. 300. (also avail. in microfilm from BNQ) **Indexed:** LISA.
Description: Articles cover developments in local library services, new library technology, upcoming provincial events and workshops.

QINGBAO KEXUE/INFORMATION SCIENCE. see *COMPUTERS — Information Science And Information Theory*

020 CC ISSN 1000-7490
QINGBAO LILUN YU SHIJIAN/INFORMATION SCIENCE: THEORY AND APPLICATION. (Text mainly in Chinese, sometimes in English) 1964. bi-m. $40. Qingbao Lilun yu Shijian Zazhishe, P.O. Box 2413, Beijing 100081, People's Republic of China. TEL 8414477. FAX 8413642. TELEX 22558 NISTI CN. Ed. Zhang Lizhi. bk.rev.; bibl.; illus.; index. **Document type:** academic/scholarly publication.
—BLDSC (4494.224000).

020 CC ISSN 1000-0135
Z671
QINGBAO XUEBAO/CHINA SOCIETY FOR SCIENTIFIC AND TECHNICAL INFORMATION. JOURNAL. (Text in Chinese; abstracts in English) bi-m. Y2.80 per no. (Zhongguo Kexue Jishu Qingbao Xuehui - China Society for Scientific and Technical Information) Kexue Jishu Wenxian Chubanshe - Scientific and Technical Documents Publishing House, 15 Fuxing Lu, Beijing 100038, People's Republic of China. TEL 8514025. FAX 8514025. TELEX 20079 ISTIC CN. (Dist. outside China by: Guoji Shudian - China International Book Trading Corp., P.O. Box 399, Beijing, P.R.C.. TEL 8413036) Ed.Bd. **Document type:** academic/scholarly publication.
Description: Discusses information and document acquisition, information classification, storage, retrieval, dissemination and utilization.

020 CC
QINGBAO XUEKAN. (Text in Chinese) bi-m. Sichuansheng Kexue Jishu Qingbao Yanjiusuo - Sichuan Science and Technology Information Research Institute, 32 Dongfeng Lu Yiduan (Sec. 1), Chengdu, Sichuan 610016, People's Republic of China. TEL 22946-93.

020 CC
QINGBAO ZILIAO GONGZUO. (Text in Chinese) bi-m. Zhongguo Shehui Kexue Qingbao Xuehui - China Social Science Information Society, No. 3, Zhangzizhong Lu, Beijing 100007, People's Republic of China. TEL 4014455. (Co-sponsor: Zhongguo Renmin Daxue) Ed. Kou Entian.

QUAERENDO; a quarterly journal from the Low Countries devoted to manuscripts and printed books. see *PUBLISHING AND BOOK TRADE*

QUARTERLY INDEX TO PERIODICAL LITERATURE, EASTERN AND SOUTHERN AFRICA. see *ABSTRACTING AND INDEXING SERVICES*

020 CN
QUEBEC (PROVINCE). SERVICES DOCUMENTATION MULTIMEDIA. CHOIX JEUNESSE: DOCUMENTATION IMPRIMEE. (Text in French) 1978. 10/yr. Can.$41($51) Services Documentaires Multimedia Inc., 75 Port-Royal E., No. 300, Montreal, Que. H3L 3T1, Canada. TEL 514-382-0895. FAX 514-384-9139. (also avail. in microfiche)
●Also available online.
Also available on CD-ROM.
Formerly: Quebec (Province). Centrale des Bibliotheques. Choix Jeunesse: Documentation Imprimee (ISSN 0706-2265)

020 SW ISSN 0284-0103
R A RAPPORTER. 1981. irreg. price varies. Riksarkivet, Box 12541, S-102 29 Stockholm, Sweden. TEL 08-737-63-50. FAX 08-737-64-74. **Document type:** bulletin.
Formerly (until 1987): Riksarkivets Rapporter (ISSN 0280-3046)

LIBRARY AND INFORMATION SCIENCES

020 374   US   ISSN 0198-8344
Z711
R A S D UPDATE. 1980. q. $15 to non-members (foreign $25). American Library Association, Reference and Adult Services Division, 50 E. Huron St., Chicago, IL 60611-2795. TEL 312-280-4398. FAX 312-944-8085. Ed. Jane Kleiner. circ. 5,500. (also avail. in microform from UMI; back issues avail.) Document type: newsletter.
—UMI.
  Description: News about RASD committee, section and discussion group activities, RASD conference programs, RASD Board actions, state and regional events.

R I C S LIBRARY INFORMATION SERVICE. WEEKLY BRIEFING; a digest of news selected from the press. (Royal Institution of Chartered Surveyors) see ENGINEERING — Civil Engineering

020   II   ISSN 0970-7131
R I L I S A R BULLETIN. 1982. q. Rs.100($30) Ranganathan Institute of Library and Information Science for Applied Research, 59-12, IV Main Road, Gandhi Nagar, Adyar, Madras 600 020, India. TEL 412074. Ed. Abbas Ibrahim. adv.; bk.rev. Document type: academic/scholarly publication.
  Description: A multidisciplinary journal for information technology, interacting with information, computers and communication sciences.

020.6   US   ISSN 1068-1507
R L IN FOCUS. q. Research Libraries Group, Inc., 1200 Villa St., Mountain View, CA 94041-1100. TEL 415-691-2207. FAX 415-964-0943.
  Formerly: Operations Update.

026   CN   ISSN 0824-5665
R M S NEWS. (Regional Multilanguage Services) 1981. 10/yr. Can.$8.56. Metropolitan Toronto Reference Library, Language & Literature Department, 789 Yonge Street, Toronto, ON M4W 2G8, Canada. TEL 416-393-7007. FAX 416-393-7229. TELEX 06-22232. Ed. Ted Uranowski. bk.rev.; bibl. circ. 720. Document type: newsletter.
  Description: Aimed at ethnic groups; provides information on multicultural literature, ESL classes, programs and library services.

020   US   ISSN 0884-450X
Z688.R3
RARE BOOKS AND MANUSCRIPTS LIBRARIANSHIP. 1986. 2/yr. $35 (foreign $40). American Library Association, 50 E. Huron St., Chicago, IL 60611-2795. TEL 800-545-2433. FAX 312-440-9374. (Co-sponsor: Association of College and Research Libraries) Ed. Alice D. Schreyer. circ. 450. (back issues avail.; reprint service avail. from UMI) Indexed: LISA. Document type: academic/scholarly publication.
—BLDSC (7291.797270); Faxon; UnCover.
  Description: News and articles on rare books librarianship and archives management.

025.171   UK   ISSN 0959-1656
Z1029
RARE BOOKS NEWSLETTER. 1974. 3/yr. £11 (foreign £15; free to members). Library Association, Rare Books Group, c/o Richard Ovenden, Ed., George IV Bridge, Edinburgh EH1 1EW, Scotland. TEL 031-226-4531. (Subscr. to: Dr. M.C. Simpson, New College Library, Mound Pl., Edinburgh EH1 2LU, Scotland) adv.; bk.rev. circ. 1,500. Document type: academic/scholarly publication.
—BLDSC (7291.797270).
  Formerly (until no.34, 1989): Library Association. Rare Books Group. Newsletter (ISSN 0307-5826)

READ, AMERICA!; a quarterly newsletter for reading coordinators. see EDUCATION — Teaching Methods And Curriculum

370 020   US
READ, SEE AND HEAR. 1950. bi-m. Newark Board of Education, Office of Educational Media Services, 2 Cedar St., Newark, NJ 07102. Ed. Binnie B. McIntosh. circ. 180.
  Description: News of educational materials acquired by the library of the Newark Board of Education.

020   US
READING IN INDIANAPOLIS. 1973. bi-m. free to library patrons. Indianapolis - Marion County Public Library, Box 211, Indianapolis, IN 46206. TEL 317-269-1732. FAX 317-269-1768. Ed.Bd. bk.rev.; film rev. circ. 23,000. Document type: newsletter.

020   US
THE READMORE NEWSLETTER. 1982. q. free. Readmore Publications, Inc., 22 Cortlandt St., New York, NY 10007-3194. TEL 212-349-5540; 800-221-3306. FAX 212-571-7328. TELEX 9102400489. Ed. Lisa Bogutz. adv.: B&W page $500; trim 8 1/2 x 11; adv. contact: Lisa Bogutz. circ. 2,100 (controlled). Document type: newsletter.
  Description: Covers developments in international periodical publishing, for libraries, publishers and CD-ROM manufacturers.

020   US   ISSN 1060-5673
▼**READMORE REPORTER.** 1993. q. free to qualified personnel. Readmore Publications, Inc., 22 Cortlandt St., New York, NY 10007-3194. TEL 212-349-5540; 800-221-3306. FAX 212-571-7328. Ed. Lisa Bogutz. adv. Document type: newsletter.

025   US   ISSN 0277-5948
Z1035.1
RECOMMENDED REFERENCE BOOKS FOR SMALL & MEDIUM-SIZED LIBRARIES AND MEDIA CENTERS. 1981. a. $45. Libraries Unlimited, Inc., Box 6633, Englewood, CO 80155-6633. TEL 800-237-6124. FAX 303-220-8843. Ed. Bohdan S. Wynar. bk.rev.
  Description: Contains price, scope, and coverage of reference books in any subject area. Arranged by subject and coded for application to college, public, or school libraries.

RECORDS & RETRIEVAL REPORT; the newsletter for professional information managers. see BUSINESS AND ECONOMICS — Office Equipment And Services

020   US   ISSN 1050-2343
HF5736   CODEN: RMAQEJ
RECORDS MANAGEMENT QUARTERLY. (Association formed by 1975 merger of American Records Management Association and Association of Records Executives and Administrators) 1967. q. $60 to non-members (foreign $70); libraries and institutions $53. Association of Records Managers and Administrators, 4200 Somerset Dr., Ste. 215, Box 8540, Prairie Village, KS 66208. TEL 913-341-3808. Ed. Ira A. Penn. adv.; bk.rev.; bibl.; charts; illus.; stat.; cum.index. circ. 10,500. (also avail. in microform from UMI; back issues avail., reprint service avail. from UMI) Indexed: ABI Inform., Account.& Data Proc.Abstr., B.P.I., BPIA, Bus.Educ.Ind., Bus.Educ.Ind., Comput.Cont., Manage.Cont., PSI, Sci.Abstr, Tr.& Indus.Ind.
—BLDSC (7325.795000); UnCover; UMI.
  Formerly (until Jan. 1990): A R M A Records Management Quarterly (ISSN 0191-1503)
  Description: Technical methods on all levels for those interested in records and information management.

020   UK   ISSN 0144-2384
Z711
REFER; journal of the I S G. 1980. 3/yr. £14 (foreign £16). Library Association, Information Services Group, School of Information Studies, University of Central England, Perry Barr, Birmingham B42 2SU, England. TEL 021-331-5624. (Subscr. to: ISG Sales Agent, 32 Beachcroft Rd., Kingswinford, W. Midlands DY6 OHX. TEL 0384-833884) Ed. David Butcher. adv. contact: Valerie Nurcombe. bk.rev. circ. 5,200. Indexed: LISA. Document type: academic/scholarly publication.
—BLDSC (7331.570000).
  Description: Covers all aspects of reference and information work, with reviews of new reference works, news from the standing committee on business information, and news of official British and European Communities publications.

REFERENCE AND RESEARCH BOOK NEWS; annotations and reviews of new books for libraries. see BIBLIOGRAPHIES

023   US   ISSN 0276-3877
Z711   CODEN: RELBD6
REFERENCE LIBRARIAN. 1981. s-a. $40 to individuals; institutions and libraries $95. Haworth Press, Inc., 10 Alice St., Binghamton, NY 13904. TEL 607-722-5857; 800-342-9678. FAX 607-722-1424. TELEX 4932599. Ed. Bill Katz. adv.; bk.rev. circ. 768. (also avail. in microfiche from UMI; back issues avail.; reprint service avail. from HAW) Indexed: C.I.J.E., Comput.& Info.Sys., Excerp.Med., Inform.Sci.Abstr., Leg.Info.Manage.Ind., Lib.Lit., LISA, Ref.Zh., Sci.Abstr.
—BLDSC (7331.913700); Faxon; UnCover; SWETS.
  Description: Each issue focuses on a topic of current concern, interest, or practical value to the reference librarian.
  Refereed Serial

020   US
REFERENCE POINT; a newsletter published for Dun's Business Reference library customers. 1987. q. Dun's Marketing Services (Subsidiary of: Dun & Bradstreet, Inc.), 3 Sylvan Way, Parsippany, NJ 07054. TEL 800-526-0651. Ed. Dawn Adams. Document type: newsletter.

020   UK   ISSN 0950-4125
Z1035.1
REFERENCE REVIEWS. 1986. 8/yr. £1299.95. M C B University Press Ltd., 60-62 Toller Ln., Bradford, W. Yorks BD8 9BY, England. TEL 0274-499821. FAX 0274-547143. TELEX 51317-MCBUNI-G. Ed. Stuart James. adv.; bk.rev. circ. 100. Document type: academic/scholarly publication.
—BLDSC (7331.919030); SWETS; UMI.
  Description: Presents independent critiques of new reference works, all written by librarians.

020   CN   ISSN 0384-0697
REFLECTIONS (NORTH BATTLEFORD). 1973. a. free. Lakeland Library Region, 10023 Thatcher Ave., P.O. Box 813, North Battleford, SK S9A 2Z3, Canada. TEL 306-445-6108. FAX 306-445-5717. Ed. Harinder Kaur. bk.rev. circ. 170.

026   US   ISSN 0891-8880
REFORMA NEWSLETTER. 1971. q. $20 (effective Dec. 1991). Reforma: National Association to Promote Library Services to the Spanish Speaking, Box 9441, Washington, DC 20016. TEL 202-473-4050. (Subscr. to: Box 3887, Santa Fe Springs, CA 90670. TEL 714-773-2975) Ed. Francisco Garcia-Ayvens. adv.; bk.rev.; bibl. circ. 1,000. (back issues avail.) Document type: newsletter.
  Description: News and information of interest to librarians, including discussion of minority recruitment issues and local chapter items.

029   US   ISSN 0149-4694
Z695.94.U5
REGISTER OF INDEXERS. 1974. a. $15 to non-members; members $10. American Society of Indexers, Inc., Box 386, Port Aransas, TX 78373. TEL 512-749-4052. circ. 1,000.

029 370   SP   ISSN 1010-2973
REPERTORIO DE SERVICIOS IBEROAMERICANOS DE DOCUMENTACION E INFORMACION EDUCATIVAS/REPERTORIO DE SERVICOS IBERO-AMERICANOS DE DOCUMENTACAO E INFORMACAO EDUCATIVAS. (Text in Portuguese and Spanish) 1982. biennial. 3500 ptas.($35) Organizacion de Estados IberoAmericanos para la Educacion, la Ciencia y la Cultura (OEI), C. Bravo Murillo 38, 28015 Madrid, Spain. TEL 594-43-82. FAX 594-32-86. Document type: directory.
  Formerly: Repertorio de Servicios de Documentacion e Informacion Educativa IberoAmericanos.
  Description: For education specialists, lists services and groups interested in collaboration between institutions.

LIBRARY AND INFORMATION SCIENCES

020.6 US ISSN 0196-173X
Z674.82.R47 CODEN: RLGNDW
RESEARCH LIBRARIES GROUP NEWS. 1980. 3/yr. free. Research Libraries Group, Inc., 1200 Villa St., Mountain View, CA 94041-1100. TEL 415-691-2207. FAX 415-964-0943. illus. **Document type:** newsletter.
—BLDSC (7741.855000); CASDDS.
  Supersedes (in 1991): R G L in (Year); Which was formerly (1975-1983): Research Libraries Group. Annual Report (ISSN 0270-5311); Supersedes (1977-1979): Research Libraries Group. Newsletter (ISSN 0147-3158); Which was formed by the merger of: Ballots Newsletter (ISSN 0360-1579); R L I N Newsletter (Research Libraries Information Network) (ISSN 0163-2388).
  Description: Provides an overview of the activities of the Research Libraries Group.

020 US ISSN 0734-3310
Z675.U5
RESEARCH STRATEGIES; a journal of library concepts and instruction. 1983. q. $28 to individuals (foreign $33); institutions $42 (foreign $47). Mountainside Publishing, Inc., 321 S. Main St., Box 8330, Ann Arbor, MI 48107. TEL 313-662-3925. FAX 313-662-4450. Ed. Barbara Wittkopf. adv.; bk.rev. circ. 900. (also avail. in microfilm from UMI; back issues avail.; reprint service avail. from UMI) **Indexed:** C.I.J.E., LHTN, Lib.Lit., LISA. **Document type:** academic/scholarly publication.
—BLDSC (7770.950000); UnCover; SWETS; UMI. CCC.
  Description: Covers all aspects of bibliographic instruction, teaching library use, and how to research a topic in the library.

020 US
RESEARCH UPDATE. 1985. s-a. University Microfilms International, Research Information Services, 300 N. Zeeb Rd., Ann Arbor, MI 48106-1346. TEL 313-761-4700; 800-521-0600. FAX 313-973-7044. Ed. Mary Kay Murray.
  Formerly: Addendum (Ann Arbor).
  Description: Keeps librarians informed of new collections, dissertation titles and library issues.

RESEARCHING MARKETS, INDUSTRIES, AND BUSINESS OPPORTUNITIES. see BUSINESS AND ECONOMICS

020 US ISSN 0737-7797
Z672
RESOURCE SHARING & INFORMATION NETWORKS. 1981. s-a. $35 to individuals; institutions $90. Haworth Press, Inc., 10 Alice St., Binghamton, NY 13904. TEL 607-722-5857; 800-342-9678. FAX 607-722-1424. TELEX 4932599. Ed. Robert P. Holley. adv.; bk.rev. circ. 337. (also avail. in microfiche from UMI; back issues avail.; reprint service avail. from HAW) **Indexed:** Biol.Abstr., Comput.& Info.Sys., Excerp.Med., Inform.Sci.Abstr., Leg.Info.Manage.Ind., LHTN, Lib.Lit., LISA, Sci.Abstr.
—BLDSC (7777.605430); Faxon; UnCover; SWETS.
  Former titles (until 1983): Resource Sharing and Library Networks (ISSN 0270-3173); Network Librarian.
  Description: Provides a forum for ideas on the basic theoretical and practical problems faced by planners, practitioners, and users of network services.
  Refereed Serial

020 DK ISSN 0034-5806
Z701 CODEN: RESTBP
RESTAURATOR; international journal for the preservation of library and archival material. (Text in English, French, German) 1969. 4/yr. DKK 700. Munksgaard International Publishers Ltd., 35 Noerre Soegade, P.O. Box 2148, DK-1016 Copenhagen K, Denmark. TEL 33-127030. FAX 33-129387. Ed. Helmut Bansa. adv.; illus.; index. circ 800. (reprint service avail. from ISI) **Indexed:** Abstr.Bull.Inst.Pap.Chem., Art & Archaeol.Tech.Abstr., Br.Archaeol.Abstr., C.I.J.E., Chem.Abstr., Curr.Cont., Lib.Lit., LISA, Sci.Cit.Ind., SSCI.
—BLDSC (7777.800000); Faxon; UnCover; SWETS; CASDDS. **CCC.**
  Refereed Serial

020 630 CR ISSN 0250-3190
CODEN: REVADJ
REVISTA A I B D A. (Text in English, Portuguese or Spanish) 1980. s-a. $20 to non-members; institutions $30; members $12. Asociacion Interamericana de Bibliotecarios y Documentalistas Agricolas, Apdo. Postal 55, 2200 Coronado, Costa Rica. TEL 29-0222. FAX 506-294741. TELEX 2144 IICA. Ed. Ghislaine Poitevien. bk.rev. circ. 800.
Indexed: LISA, Sci.Abstr.
—BLDSC (7802.500000).
  Description: Articles on library and information sciences, documents presented to technical conferences and meetings, case studies, and current awareness notes.

REVISTA ARHIVELOR. see HISTORY — History Of Europe

020 BL
REVISTA BRASILEIRA DE BIBLIOTECONOMIA E DOCUMENTACAO. 1973. s-a. $35. Federacao Brasileira de Associacoes de Bibliotecarios, 40 Rua Avanhandava, Conj. 110, CEP 01306 Sao Paulo, Brazil. Ed. Carminda Nogueira de Castro Ferreira. adv.; bk.rev. circ. 2,000. **Indexed:** Lib.Lit., LISA.

020 CK ISSN 0121-0203
Z673.A629
REVISTA DE ASCOLBI; publicacion oficial de la asociacion colombiana de bibliotecologos y documentalistas. q. Col.$3,000 to individuals (foreign $40); institutions Col.$4,000 (foreign $40). (Asociacion Colombiana de Bibliotecologos y Documentalistas (ASCOLBI) Rojas Eberhard Editores, Ltda., Carrera 6 No. 51-21, Apdo. Aereo 34270, Bogota, D.E., Colombia. TEL 285 17 79. FAX 274-44-60. TELEX 44305. (Alt. Addr.: Apdo. aereo 55674, Bogota, Colombia) Ed. Isabel Forero de Moreno. illus.; charts.

020 BL ISSN 0100-7157
Z769.A1
REVISTA DE BIBLIOTECONOMIA DE BRASILIA. (Text in Portuguese; occasionally in Spanish; summaries in English) 1973-1993; resumed 1994. s-a. $25. Universidade de Brasilia, Departamento de Biblioteconomia, Caixa Postal 15-3011, Brasilia, Brazil. (Co-sponsor: Associacao dos Bibliotecarios do Distrito Federal) Ed. Suzana P.M. Mueller. adv.; bk.rev. circ. 2,000. **Indexed:** Bull.Signal., Lib.Lit., Lib.Sci.Abstr., LISA, Ref.Zh.

REVISTA DE LIBRERIA ANTIQUARIA. see HISTORY — History Of Europe

020 SP ISSN 0210-0614
Z695.1.S3 CODEN: REDCD3
REVISTA ESPANOLA DE DOCUMENTACION CIENTIFICA. 1977. q. 4000 ptas. Centro de Informacion y Documentacion Cientifica (Cindoc), Joaquin Costa 22, 28002 Madrid, Spain. TEL 1-5635482. FAX 1-5642644. TELEX 22628 CIDMD E. adv.; abstr.; charts; stat. circ. 2,000. **Indexed:** LISA, Sci.Abstr.
—BLDSC (7853.945000); SWETS.
  Formerly (until 1976, no.451): Ciencia y Tecnica en el Mundo.

020 CK ISSN 0120-0976
Z738.A1
REVISTA INTERAMERICANA DE BIBLIOTECOLOGIA. (Text in Spanish; summaries in English and Spanish) 1978. 2/yr. Col.5000 ($50 in Latin America; U.S. and Europe $65) (effective 1994). Universidad de Antioquia, Escuela Interamericana de Bibliotecologia, Apdo. Aereo 1307, Medellin, Colombia. TEL 210-5930. FAX 263-8282. Ed. Martha Alicia Perez. adv.; bk.rev.; abstr.; charts; stat. circ. 500. **Indexed:** Lib.Lit., LISA, Ref.Zh. **Document type:** academic/scholarly publication.
—BLDSC (7861.450000); SWETS.
  Description: Presents findings and knowledge in the fields of library studies and information sciences that support their progress and enrichment.

REVUE DES LIVRES POUR ENFANTS. see PUBLISHING AND BOOK TRADE

020 FR ISSN 0037-9212
Z119
REVUE FRANCAISE D'HISTOIRE DU LIVRE. 1971. 2/yr. 250 F. to non-members; members 125 F. Societe des Bibliophiles de Guyenne, c/o Bibliotheque de Bordeaux, 7 rue du Corps-Franc-Pommies, 33075 Bordeaux Cedex, France. FAX 56-52-50-73. Ed. Charles Teisseyre. adv.; bk.rev.; bibl.; charts; illus.
—Faxon.

020 US ISSN 0035-4597
RHODE ISLAND. DEPARTMENT OF STATE LIBRARY SERVICES. NEWSLETTER. 1964. bi-m. free. Department of State Library Services, 300 Richmond St., Providence, RI 02903-4222. TEL 401-277-2726. FAX 401-831-1131. Ed. Frank P. Iacono. circ. 800 (controlled). (processed) **Document type:** government publication, newsletter.
  Description: News pertaining to Rhode Island libraries and librarianship.

020 US ISSN 0146-8685
RHODE ISLAND LIBRARY ASSOCIATION. BULLETIN. 1907. bi-m. $15 (foreign $20). Rhode Island Library Association, c/o Mattie Gustafson, Man. Ed., DSLS - 300 Richmond St., Providence, RI 02903-4222. TEL 401-277-2726. adv. circ. 500. (back issues avail.) **Document type:** newsletter, bulletin.
  Description: Covers library activities, personalities and issues for the state.

020 BL
RIO DE JANEIRO, BRAZIL (CITY). ARQUIVO GERAL DA CIDADE DO RIO DE JANEIRO. BOLETIM INFORMATIVO. 1979. 3/yr. Arquivo Geral da Cidade do Rio de Janeiro, Rio de Janeiro, Brazil. bk.rev. circ. 2,000.

027 US ISSN 0080-3227
RIVER BEND LIBRARY SYSTEM. REPORT OF THE DIRECTOR. Variant Title--Annual Report. 1966. a. free. River Bend Library System, Box 125, Coal Valley, IL 61240. TEL 309-799-3155. Ed. Robert W. McKay. (back issues avail.) **Indexed:** Lib.Lit.

020 US
RIVER CITY LIBRARY TIMES. 1977. m. free. Evansville - Vanderburgh County Public Libraries, 22 S.E. Fifth St., Evansville, IN 47708. TEL 812-428-8204. FAX 812-428-8215. Ed. Nancy Allee. circ. 1,500. (back issues avail.)

020 US
ROCKEFELLER COLLEGE. SCHOOL OF INFORMATION SCIENCE AND POLICY. BULLETIN. 1967. biennial. free. Rockefeller College, School of Information Science and Policy, 135 Western Ave., Albany, NY 12222. TEL 518-455-6288. FAX 212-251-3003. Ed. Richard S. Halsey. illus. circ. 3,000. **Document type:** bulletin.
  Formerly: State University of New York at Albany. School of Library and Information Science. Bulletin.

020 PL ISSN 0083-7261
Z674
ROCZNIK BIBLIOTEKI NARODOWEJ/NATIONAL LIBRARY YEAR-BOOK. (List of contents in English, French, German, Russian; summaries in English) 1964. a. 50000 Zl.($20) Biblioteka Narodowa, Al. Niepodleglosci 213, 00-973 Warsaw, Poland. FAX 48-22-255251. TELEX 813702 BN PL. (Dist. by: P.P. CHZ Ars Polona, ul. Krakowskie Przedmiescie 7, 00-068 Warsaw, Poland) Ed. Stanislaw Czajka. bk.rev. circ. 600.

026 PL ISSN 0080-3626
ROCZNIKI BIBLIOTECZNE. (Text in Polish; summaries in English, French, German and Russian) 1957. s-a. price varies. (Ministerstwo Edukacji Narodowey) Wydawnictwo Naukwe P W N, Miodowa 10, 00-251 Warsaw, Poland. Ed. K. Maleczynska. bk.rev. circ. 670.
—BLDSC (8008.600000).

020 DK ISSN 0105-564X
ROSKILDE UNIVERSITETSBIBLIOTEK. SKRIFTSERIE. 1977. irreg., latest no.23. free. Roskilde Universitetsbibliotek - Roskilde University Library, P.O. Box 258, DK-4000 Roskilde, Denmark. FAX 45-46756102. TELEX 43158. circ. 500. (back issues avail.) **Document type:** monographic series.

LIBRARY AND INFORMATION SCIENCES

027   US
ROSTER AND STATISTICS OF OKLAHOMA PUBLIC AND INSTITUTIONAL LIBRARIES. 1984. a. free. Oklahoma Department of Libraries, 200 N.E. 18th St., Oklahoma City, OK 73105. TEL 405-521-2502. FAX 405-525-7804. circ. 400. (also avail. in microfiche from CIS) **Document type:** government publication, directory.
    Supersedes (1984-1991): Annual Directory of Oklahoma Libraries; (1984-1991): Oklahoma Department of Libraries. Annual Report; Which superseded (1955-1984): Oklahoma. Department of Libraries. Annual Report and Directory of Libraries in Oklahoma (ISSN 0066-4065)
    Description: Oklahoma library statistics.

020   US   ISSN 0033-7072
Z671
RQ. 1960. q. $42 (foreign $52) (effective Fall 1991). American Library Association, 50 E. Huron St., Chicago, IL 60611-2795. TEL 800-545-2433. FAX 312-440-9374. Eds. Connie Van Fleet, Danny P. Wallace. adv.; bk.rev.; index, cum.index: 1960-1965. circ. 6,000. (also avail. in microform from UMI; back issues avail.; reprint service avail. from UMI) **Indexed:** Amer.Hist.& Life, Bibl.Ind., Bk.Rev.Ind., C.I.J.E., Chic.Per.Ind., Child.Bk.Rev.Ind. (1969-), Curr.Cont., Hist.Abstr., Inform.Sci.Abstr., Leg.Info.Manage.Ind., Lib.Lit., LISA, Mag.Ind., P.A.I.S., PMR, Ref.Sour., Tr.& Indus.Ind. —BLDSC (8036.500000); Faxon; UnCover; SWETS; UMI. **CCC.**
    Refereed Serial

027.7   GW
RUNDSCHREIBEN. 1951. q. membership. Verein der Diplom-Bibliothekare an Wissenschaftlichen Bibliotheken e.V., Universitaetsstr. 31, Postfach 101043, 93010 Regensburg, Germany. TEL 0941-9433952. FAX 0941-9433285. Ed. Werner Tussing. adv.; bk.rev.; circ. 4,500. **Document type:** newsletter.

020   US   ISSN 0276-2048
Z675.V7
RURAL LIBRARIES; a forum for rural library service. 1980. s-a. $10. Center for the Study of Rural Librarianship, College of Library Science, Clarion University of Pennsylvania, Clarion, PA 16214. TEL 814-226-2383. FAX 814-226-2392. Ed. Mary Lou Pratt.
    •Also available online. Vendor(s): DIALOG Information Services, Inc., Wilsonline.
    —BLDSC (8052.485000); Faxon.

RUSSELL: THE JOURNAL OF THE BERTRAND RUSSELL ARCHIVES. see *PHILOSOPHY*

027.7   US   ISSN 0036-0473
Z733
RUTGERS UNIVERSITY. LIBRARIES. JOURNAL. 1937. s-a. $25 or membership. Rutgers University Libraries, Alexander Library, New Brunswick, NJ 08903. TEL 201-932-7509. FAX 908-932-6916. Ed. Pamela Spence Richards. bk.rev.; illus.; cum.index every 5 yrs.: vols.1-33, Dec.1937-1970. circ. 750. **Indexed:** Amer.Hist.& Life, Bibl.Engl.Lang.& Lit., Hist.Abstr., M.L.A. **Document type:** academic/scholarly publication.
    —UnCover.
    Description: Covers topics pertaining to the history of libraries, Rutgers University history, and New Jerseyana.

020   SA   ISSN 0256-6710
S A I L I S NEWSLETTER/S A I B I NUUSBRIEF. (Text in Afrikaans, English) 1981. m. R.50 (foreign R.70) (effective 1993). South African Institute for Librarianship and Information Science, P.O. Box 36575, Menlo Park, Pretoria 0102, South Africa. TEL 27-12-429-3211. FAX 27-12-429-2925. TELEX 350068. Ed. Gerhard van der Linde. adv.; bk.rev.circ. 2,900. **Document type:** newsletter.
    Supersedes (1947-1981): S A L A Newsletter - S A B V Nuusbrief (ISSN 0036-0783)
    Description: Current news on South African libraries, librarians, information work and workers and products.

S A L A L M NEWSLETTER. (Seminar on the Acquisition of Latin American Library Materials) see *BIBLIOGRAPHIES*

020 616.86   US
S A L I S DIRECTORY. 1981. triennial. $35 in US, Canada & Mexico; elsewhere $38. Substance Abuse Librarians and Information Specialists, Alcohol Research Group, Box 9513, Berkeley, CA 94709-0513. TEL 510-642-5208. FAX 510-642-7175. Ed. A.L. Mitchell. **Document type:** directory.
    Description: International listing of nearly 200 alcohol and other drug-specific libraries, clearing houses, resource and information centers.

020 157.6   US
S A L I S NEWS. 1981. q. $20 in U.S., Can. & Mex; elsewhere $25. Substance Abuse Librarians and Information Specialists, Box 9513, Berkeley, CA 94709-0513. TEL 510-642-5208. FAX 510-642-7175. Ed. A. L. Mitchell. bk.rev. circ. 300. (back issues avail.) **Document type:** newsletter.
    Description: Linkage and networking of relevant information sources.

020   US
S A L S IN BRIEF. 1960. q. free. Southern Adirondack Library System, 22 Whitney Place, Saratoga Springs, NY 12866. TEL 518-584-7300. circ. 425 (controlled). (processed; reprint service avail. from UMI)
    Formerly: Proof Sheet (ISSN 0033-1228)

020 340   US
Z675.L2S642
S C A L L NEWSLETTER. 5/yr. $13.50. Southern California Association of Law Libraries, 8391 Beverly Blvd., Ste. 300, Los Angeles, CA 90048. TEL 213-743-6487. adv.; bk.rev. circ. 550. **Document type:** newsletter.

020   US
S C A N - INFO. 1988. m. free to qualified personnel. State of California Answering Network, Los Angeles Public Library, 630 W. Fifth St., Los Angeles, CA 90071. TEL 213-228-7520. FAX 213-228-7522. Ed. Judy Ann Hermann. bk.rev.; index. circ. 1,480. (back issues avail.) **Document type:** newsletter.
    Description: Focuses on California library reference news, information, updates on public officials, lists of prestigious awards, a who's-who obituary, facts and figures, and movie tie-ins.

020   GW
S C O L M A DIRECTORY OF LIBRARIES AND SPECIAL COLLECTIONS ON AFRICA IN THE UNITED KINGDOM AND WESTERN EUROPE. irreg., 5th ed., 1992. $75. (Standing Conference on Library Materials on Africa) K.G. Saur Verlag KG, Ortlerstr. 8, 81373 Munich, Germany. TEL 089-769020. FAX 089-76902150. (Subscr. to: Postfach 701620, 81316 Munich, Germany; N. American subscr. to: K.G. Saur, A Reed Reference Publishing Company, 121 Chanlon Rd., New Providence, NJ 07974-9903. TEL 908-665-3576) Ed. Tom French. **Document type:** directory.
    Description: Identifies and describes book, periodical and audiovisual holdings on African material in more than 300 libraries of United Kingdom and Western Europe.

620 025.33   US
S H E. (Subject Headings for Engineering) 1972. irreg., latest 1987. $45. Engineering Information, Inc., Castle Point on the Hudson, Hoboken, NJ 07030. TEL 201-216-8500. FAX 202-216-8532. (U.K. and Western Europe subscr. to: Thompson, Henry Ltd., London Rd., Sunningdale, Berks. SL5 OEP, England)
    Description: Alphabetical listing of the controlled vocabulary subject terms used in the indexing of El's products.

020   US   ISSN 0885-3959
S I S A C NEWS. 1985. s-a. Book Industry Study Group, Serials Industry Systems Advisory Committee, c/o Western N Y Library Resources Council, 180 Oak St., Buffalo, NY 14203-1610. TEL 716-852-3844. FAX 716-852-0276. Ed. Mary W. Ghikes. **Document type:** newsletter.
    —BLDSC (8286.375000).
    Description: Contains announcements, news, reviews, and articles of interest to members.

020   SL
S L A A L I S BULLETIN. (Text in English) 1987. q. Le.1.50. Sierra Leone Association of Archivists, Librarians and Information Scientists, c/o S.K. Woode, Ed., British Council Library, Tower Hill, Freetown, Sierra Leone. adv.; bk.rev.; bibl. circ. 200. **Indexed:** Lib.Sci.Abstr. **Document type:** bulletin.
    Supersedes (1974-1981): Sierra Leone Library Journal (ISSN 0377-5275)

026 023   US
S L A BIENNIAL SALARY SURVEY. 1964. biennial. $37.50 to non-members; members $30. Special Libraries Association, 1700 18th St., N.W., Washington, DC 20009. TEL 202-234-4700. FAX 202-265-9317. (also avail. in microfiche from CIS; reprint service avail. from UMI) **Indexed:** SRI.
    Formerly (until 1991): S L A Triennial Salary Survey.

020   GW   ISSN 0863-0682
Z803.S23
S L B KURIER; Nachrichten aus der Saechsischen Landesbibliothek. 1987. 4/yr. DM.3. Saechsische Landesbibliothek, Marienalle 12, 01099 Dresden, Germany. Ed. L. Koch. **Document type:** newspaper.

020   US
S O R T BULLETIN. 1938. s-a. membership. American Library Association, Staff Organizations Round Table, 50 E. Huron St., Chicago, IL 60611. Ed. Yvonne Beever. bk.rev.; circ. 550 (controlled). (looseleaf format) **Document type:** newsletter.

025   US   ISSN 0160-3582
      CODEN: SPKIE9
S P E C KIT. 1973. 10/yr. $250 (foreign $380) to non-members; members $165. (Systems and Procedures Exchange Center) Association of Research Libraries, Office of Management Services, 21 Dupont Circle, Ste. 800, Washington, DC 20036. TEL 202-296-8656. FAX 202-872-0884. Ed. C. Brigid Welch. circ. 475. (back issues avail.) **Indexed:** ERIC. **Document type:** trade publication. —BLDSC (8361.875200).
    Formerly: S P E C Flyer (ISSN 0160-3574)
    Description: Promotes experimentation, innovation, and improved performance in the field of library management.

020 070.5   UK   ISSN 0951-4635
S R IS NEWSLETTER. 1977. irreg. (3-4/yr.). free. Science Reference and Information Service, 25 Southampton Bldgs., Chancery Lane WC2A 1AW, England. TEL 071-323-7959. FAX 071-323-7947. TELEX 266959-SCIFREF-G. Ed. Christine Wise. adv. circ. 8,500. **Document type:** newsletter.
    —BLDSC (6108.282000).
    Formerly (until 1986): S R L News (ISSN 0306-428X)

S R R T NEWSLETTER. (Social Responsibilities Round Table) see *LITERARY AND POLITICAL REVIEWS*

020   US   ISSN 0731-7883
S U N Y L A NEWSLETTER. 1968. 4/yr. membership. State University of New York Librarians Association, c/o James M. Milne Library, State University of New York at Oneonta, Oneonta, NY 13820-4041. TEL 607-436-2453. FAX 607-436-3081. Eds. Kay Benjamin, Kathryn Franco. bibl. circ. 400. **Document type:** newsletter.

020   US
SAN BERNARDINO COUNTY LIBRARY. NEWSLETTER. 1962. bi-m. free in the U.S.; elsewhere $5. San Bernardino County Library, 104 W. Fourth St., San Bernardino, CA 92415. TEL 909-387-5729. FAX 909-387-5724. Ed. John Grimm. bk.rev. circ. 1,500. **Document type:** newsletter.

020   CN   ISSN 0831-3016
SASKATCHEWAN LIBRARY ASSOCIATION. FORUM. 5/yr. Can.$25 (free to members). Saskatchewan Library Association, Box 3388, Regina, Sask. S4P 3H1, Canada. TEL 306-586-3089. FAX 306-347-7500. adv.; bk.rev. circ. 200.

LIBRARY AND INFORMATION SCIENCES

025 943.7 XR ISSN 0036-5246
CD1150
SBORNIK ARCHIVNICH PRACI. (Text in Czech; summaries in German) 1951. s-a. 64 Kcs.($30.90) Sekce Archivni Spravy MV, Milady Horakove 133, 166 21 Prague 6, Czech Republic. TEL 42-2-3121049. (Dist. by: Artia, Ve Smeckach 30, 111 27 Prague 1, Czech Republic) Ed. Rostislav Novy. cum.index: 1951-1970. **Indexed:** Amer.Hist.& Life, CERDIC, Hist.Abstr., Numis.Lit.
—BLDSC (8086.900000).

027.4 SW ISSN 0036-5602
Z822
SCANDINAVIAN PUBLIC LIBRARY QUARTERLY. 1968. q. SEK 200 in Sweden; other Nordic countries SEK 230; elsewhere SEK 250. National Council for Cultural Affairs, P.O. Box 7843, S-10398 Stockholm, Sweden. TEL 46-8-247260. FAX 46-8-211349. (Subscr. to: PROGEK, P.O. Box 31003, S-400 32 Goeteborg, Sweden. TEL 46-31-24-34-25) Ed. Elisabeth Nilsson. circ. 1,000. **Indexed:** Lib.Lit., LISA.
—BLDSC (8087.573000); SWETS.
Formerly: Reol.

025 US
SCARECROW LIBRARY ADMINISTRATION SERIES. irreg., latest no.2. Scarecrow Press, Inc., 52 Library St., Box 4167, Metuchen, NJ 08840. TEL 800-537-7107. **Document type:** trade publication.

020 BE
SCHATTEN VAN DE UNIVERSITEITSBIBLIOTHEEK TE GENT. 1967. irreg. price varies. Universiteit te Gent, Centrale Bibliotheek, Rozier 9, B-9000 Gent, Belgium. TEL 32-91-643851. FAX 32-91-644196. **Document type:** academic/scholarly publication.

027.8 UK ISSN 0036-6595
Z675.S3
SCHOOL LIBRARIAN. 1937. 4/yr. £45 to non-members. School Library Association, Liden Library, Barrington Close Liden, Swindon, Wiltshire SN3 6HF, England. TEL 0793-617838. (Subscr. to: Bailey Management Services, 127 Sandgate Rd., Folkestone, Kent CT20 2BL, England) Ed. Sheila Ray. adv.; bk.rev.; bibl.; index. circ. 4,000. **Indexed:** Bk.Rev.Ind. (1979-), Br.Educ.Ind., Child.Bk.Rev.Ind. (1979-), Child.Lit.Abstr., Cont.Pg.Educ., Lib.Lit., LISA. **Document type:** academic/scholarly publication.
—BLDSC (8092.790000); UnCover; SWETS.
Formerly: School Librarian and School Library Review.
Description: Developments, book reviews and other information for school librarians in primary and secondary schools.

020 US ISSN 0271-3667
SCHOOL LIBRARIAN'S WORKSHOP. 1980. m. (except Jul.-Aug.). $42.99. Library Learning Resources, Inc., 61 Greenbriar Dr., Box 87, Berkeley Heights, NJ 07922. TEL 201-635-1833. FAX 201-635-2614. Eds. Ruth Toor, Hilda K. Weisburg. bk.rev.; bibl.; index. circ. 7,800. (back issues avail.) **Document type:** newsletter.
Description: For school librarians grades K-12. Contains resource based teaching units, literature based learning, professional development concerns, technology updates, activity sheets, annotated thematic bibliographies and bulletin boards.

027.8 NR ISSN 0331-8109
SCHOOL LIBRARIES BULLETIN. 1965. s-a. $20. Anambra State School Libraries Association, c/o Enugu Campus Library, University of Nigeria, Enugu, Nigeria. Eds. Virginia W. Dike, Dorothy S. Obi. adv.; bk.rev.; circ. 250 (controlled). (processed) **Indexed:** Child.Lit.Abstr., Lib.Lit.
Former titles (until 1976): E C S School Libraries Bulletin; Eastern Nigerian School Libraries Association. Bulletin (ISSN 0424-1851)
Description: Scientific journal intended to heighten the standard of education and awareness of resources available in Nigerian libraries. For teacher-librarians.

020 UK ISSN 0261-1678
SCHOOL LIBRARIES GROUP NEWS. 1980. s-a. £2 to non-members. Library Association, School Libraries Group, c/o The Librarian, Solihull Vlth Form College, Widney Manor Rd., Solihull, W. Midlands B91 3JG, England. TEL 021-704-2581. circ. 2,300.
—BLDSC (6102.559000).
Description: Covers school librarianship. Examines the professional aspects, including management, computers, and education.

020 CN ISSN 0227-3780
SCHOOL LIBRARIES IN CANADA. vol.17, 1974. 3/yr. Can.$35($35) Canadian School Library Association, Canadian Library Association, 602-200 Elgin St., Ottawa, Ont. K2P 1L5, Canada. TEL 613-232-9625. FAX 604-321-2153. Ed. Leslie Aitken. adv.; bk.rev. circ. 1,000. (also avail. in microfilm) **Indexed:** Can.Educ.Ind., Can.Per.Ind., Child.Lit.Abstr., CMI, Lib.Lit., LISA.
—BLDSC (8092.805200).
Formerly (until 1980): Moccasin Telegraph (ISSN 0076-9878)
Description: Covers recent developments in the field of school librarianship. Includes information on the activities and news of the Association.

027.8 US ISSN 0362-8930
Z675.S3
SCHOOL LIBRARY JOURNAL; the magazine of children, young adults & school librarians. Key Title: S L J, School Library Journal. (Supplement avail.: Star Track) 1954. 12/yr. $67 (Canada $91; elsewhere $110). Cahners Publishing Company (New York), Printing and Publishing Division, Division of Reed Elsevier Inc., 249 W. 17th St., New York, NY 10011. TEL 800-456-9409. FAX 212-463-6734. (Subscr. to: Box 1978, Marion, OH 43305-1978) Ed. Lillian N. Gerhardt. adv.; bk.rev.; bibl.; charts; illus.; stat.; tr.lit. circ. 42,210. (also avail. in microfilm from UMI; reprint service avail. from UMI) **Indexed:** Access (1989-), Bk.Rev.Dig., Bk.Rev.Ind. (1975-), Bus.Ind., C.I.J.E., Child.Bk.Rev.Ind. (1975-), Child.Lit.Abstr., Cont.Pg.Educ., Educ.Ind., Ind.Child.Mag., Jun.High.Mag.Abstr., LHTN, Lib.Lit., LISA, Mag.Ind., PMR, Tr.& Indus.Ind. **Document type:** trade publication.
—BLDSC (8092.810000); UnCover; SWETS. **CCC.**
Description: For librarians serving children and young adults in schools and public libraries.

020 371.3 US ISSN 0889-9371
Z675.S3
SCHOOL LIBRARY MEDIA ACTIVITIES MONTHLY. 1984. m. (10/yr.). $44. L M S Associates, 17 E. Henrietta St., Baltimore, MD 21230. TEL 410-685-8621. Eds. Paula Montgomery, H. Thomas Walker. adv.; bk.rev.; index. circ. 15,000. (back issues avail.) **Document type:** trade publication.
—BLDSC (8092.812000).
Description: For school library media specialists (K-8), focusing on teaching library media skills.

020 US ISSN 0739-7712
Z675.S3
SCHOOL LIBRARY MEDIA ANNUAL. 1982. a. $42.50. Libraries Unlimited, Inc., Box 6633, Englewood, CO 80155-6633. TEL 800-237-6124. FAX 303-220-8843. Ed. Carol Collier Kuhlthau.
—BLDSC (8092.813000).
Description: Provides fundamental background and current professional information at every level. Covers new materials, equipment, development practices, as well as implications of legal decisions.

027.8 371.3 US ISSN 1042-4245
Z675.S3
SCHOOL LIBRARY MEDIA FOLDERS OF IDEAS FOR LIBRARY EXCELLENCE. 1989. irreg. $27.50. Hi Willow Research and Publications, Box 6633, Englewood, CO 80155-6633. TEL 800-237-6124. FAX 303-220-8843. Ed. David V. Loertscher.

027.8 US ISSN 0278-4823
Z675.S3
SCHOOL LIBRARY MEDIA QUARTERLY. 1952. 4/yr. $40 to non-members (foreign $50). (American Association of School Librarians) American Library Association, 50 E. Huron St., Chicago, IL 60611-2795. TEL 800-545-2433. FAX 312-440-9374. Ed.Bd. adv.; bk.rev.; illus.; cum.index every 5 yrs. circ. 7,400. (also avail. in microform from UMI; back issues avail.; reprint service avail. from UMI) **Indexed:** Bk.Rev.Ind. (1965-), C.I.J.E., Child.Bk.Rev.Ind. (1965-), Child.Lit.Abstr., Curr.Cont., Educ.Ind., Except.Child.Educ.Abstr., Lib.Lit., LISA, Ref.Sour. **Document type:** academic/scholarly publication.
—BLDSC (8092.813500); Faxon; UnCover; SWETS; UMI. **CCC.**
Former titles (until 1981): School Media Quarterly (ISSN 0361-1647); School Libraries (ISSN 0036-6609)
Description: News and articles of interest to school library media specialists from kindergarten to twelfth grade.

020 US ISSN 1050-8147
Z665
SCHOOL OF LIBRARY AND INFORMATION SCIENCE. OCCASIONAL PAPERS SERIES. 1989. irreg., approx. 4/yr. $23. University of Wisconsin - Milwaukee, Enderis Hall, Box 413, Milwaukee, WI 53201. TEL 414-229-4704. FAX 414-229-4848. TELEX 4909991372-ALAUI-G. Ed. Mohammed M. Aman. circ. 600. (back issues avail.)
—BLDSC (6224.967750).
Description: Includes timely papers of interest to librarians and information professionals.

020 GW ISSN 0341-471X
SCHULBIBLIOTHEK AKTUELL. 1975. q. DM.38. Deutsches Bibliotheksinstitut, Abt. 1 - Publikationen, Bundesallee 184-185, 10717 Berlin, Germany. TEL 030-8505-0. FAX 030-8505-100. adv.; bk.rev.; abstr. circ. 750. (back issues avail.) **Indexed:** LISA. **Document type:** bulletin.

020 SZ
SCHWEIZERISCHE BIBLIOTHEKEN/BIBLIOTHEQUES SUISSES. (Text in French and German) 1959. a. 3.50 SFr. Bundesamt fuer Statistik, Schwarztorstr. 96, CH-3003 Bern, Switzerland. TEL 031-3236011. FAX 031-3236061. **Document type:** government publication.

026 US ISSN 0194-262X
Z675.T3 CODEN: STELDF
SCIENCE & TECHNOLOGY LIBRARIES. 1980. q. $40 to individuals; institutions $120. Haworth Press, Inc., 10 Alice St., Binghamton, NY 13904. TEL 607-722-5857; 800-342-9678. FAX 607-722-1424. TELEX 4932599. Ed. Cynthia Steinke. adv.; bk.rev. circ. 812. (also avail. in microfiche from UMI; back issues avail.; reprint service avail. from HAW) **Indexed:** Biol.Abstr., Bull.Signal., Chem.Abstr., Comput.& Info.Sys., Eng.Ind., Excerp.Med., Inform.Sci.Abstr., Lib.Lit., LISA, P.A.I.S., Ref.Zh., Sci.Abstr.
—BLDSC (8134.275000); EI; Faxon; UnCover; SWETS; CASDDS.
Description: Provides a variety of instructive material prepared specifically for the science and technology librarian.
Refereed Serial

020 US ISSN 0147-6882
Z699.A1 CODEN: STIPDD
SCIENTIFIC AND TECHNICAL INFORMATION PROCESSING. English translation of: Nauchno-Tekhnicheskaya Informatsiya. Seriya 1. Organizatsiya i Metodika Informatsionnoi Raboty (RU ISSN 0548-0019) 1974. bi-m. $750. (Vsesoyuznyi Institut Nauchno Teknicheskoi Informatsii (VINITI), RU) Allerton Press, Inc., 150 Fifth Ave., New York, NY 10011. TEL 212-924-3950. FAX 212-463-9684. Ed. R.S. Gilyarevskii. charts. **Indexed:** Biol.Abstr., Excerp.Med. **Document type:** academic/scholarly publication.
—BLDSC (0420.793500); Faxon. **CCC.**
Description: For librarians and professionals involved with information processing. Presents reports on developments in manual and machine methods for storing and retrieving data.

SCIENTIFIC MEETINGS. see *MEETINGS AND CONGRESSES*

020 UK
SCOTTISH ACADEMIC LIBRARIES NEWSLETTER. 1988. 6/yr. £5. c/o David Scott, Ed., Dundee College of Further Education Library, Old Glamis Rd., Dundee DD3 8LE, Scotland. TEL 0382-21125. **Document type:** newsletter.
Description: Short items of interest to Scottish academic librarians.

SCOTTISH BOOK COLLECTOR. see *PUBLISHING AND BOOK TRADE*

020 UK ISSN 0950-0189
SCOTTISH LIBRARIES. 1950. bi-m. £25 to non-members (foreign £27). Scottish Library Association, Motherwell Business Centre, Coursington Rd., Motherwell ML1 1PW, Scotland. TEL 0698-252526. FAX 0698-252057. Ed. A.M. Hamilton. adv.; bk.rev. circ. 2,500. (also avail. in microform from UMI; back issues avail.; reprint service avail. from UMI) **Indexed:** Lib.Lit., Lib.Sci.Abstr., LISA. **Document type:** bulletin.
—BLDSC (8210.676200); UMI.
Formerly: S L A News (ISSN 0048-9786)

021 UK ISSN 0267-1425
SCOTTISH LIBRARY AND INFORMATION RESOURCES. 1984. irreg. £25. Scottish Library Association, Motherwell Business Centre, Coursington Rd., Motherwell ML1 1PW, Scotland. TEL 0698-252526. FAX 0698-252057. **Document type:** bulletin.
Formerly: Library Resources in Scotland.

020 AU
SCRINIUM. 1969. s-a. S.300. Verband Oesterreichischer Archivare, Postfach 164, A-1014 Vienna, Austria. Ed.Bd. adv.; circ. controlled. (back issues avail.) **Indexed:** Amer.Hist.& Life, Hist.Abstr.

020 IT ISSN 1122-0775
SCUOLA SPECIALE PER ARCHIVISTI E BIBLIOTECARI. NUOVI ANNALI. 1986. a. L.68000 (foreign L.75000) (effecte 1994). Casa Editrice Leo S. Olschki, Casella Postale 66, 50100 Florence, Italy. TEL 055-5630684. FAX 055-6530214. Ed. Marco Santoro. **Document type:** academic/scholarly publication.

020 US
SEARCH TOOLS: THE GUIDE TO U M I ONLINE. 1983. biennial. $75. University Microfilms International, 300 N. Zeeb Rd., Ann Arbor, MI 48106. TEL 313-761-4700; 800-521-0600. FAX 313-761-1203.
Former titles (until 1992): Search Tools: The Guide to U M I - Data Courier Online; (until 1991): Search Inform.

020 US
SEARCHING DIALOG: THE COMPLETE GUIDE. 1987. irreg. $90. Dialog Information Services, Inc. (Palo Alto), 3460 Hillview Ave., Palo Alto, CA 94304. TEL 415-858-3785. FAX 415-858-7069. (looseleaf format)
●Also available online.
Also available on CD-ROM.
Formerly: Guide to Dialog Searching.
Description: Reference manual for using the DIALOG systems. Contains detailed explanation on how to access DIALOG and on every commands and features.

027.4 MY
SELANGOR PUBLIC LIBRARY CORPORATION. ANNUAL REPORT/PERBADANAN PERPUSTAKAAN AWAM SELANGOR. LAPURAN TAHUNAN. 1972. a. Selangor Public Library Corporation, Perpustakaan Raja Tun Uda, Persiaran Perdagangan, 40572 Shah Alam, Malaysia. FAX 03-559-6045. stat. circ. 1,000.
Formerly: Selangor Public Library. Annual Report.

020 UK ISSN 0960-1570
CODEN: SELEER
SELECT: NATIONAL BIBLIOGRAPHIC SERVICE NEWSLETTER. 1976. 3/yr. free. British Library, National Bibliographic Service, Boston Spa, Wetherby, W. Yorks. LS23 7BQ, England. TEL 0937-546585. Ed. Jonathan Purday. circ. 4,000. **Indexed:** LISA. **Document type:** newsletter.
—BLDSC (8230.495510).
Former titles: British Library. Bibliographic Services. Newsletter (ISSN 0268-9707); British Library. Bibliographic Services Division. Newsletter (ISSN 0308-230X)
Description: Contains articles of interest to all users of the division's products and services and details of plans and policy.

070 980 US ISSN 0080-8857
SEMINAR ON THE ACQUISITION OF LATIN AMERICAN LIBRARY MATERIALS. MICROFILMING PROJECTS NEWSLETTER. 1964. a. $5. Seminar on the Acquisition of Latin American Library Materials, General Library, University of New Mexico, Albuquerque, NM 87131. TEL 505-277-5102. FAX 505-277-0646. Ed. Basil Malish. cum.index: nos.1-20. circ. 325. (processed; back issues avail.) **Indexed:** Lib.Lit. **Document type:** newsletter.
Description: Lists original microrepoduction projects in Latin American or Iberian subjects.

025 US
SEMINAR ON THE ACQUISITION OF LATIN AMERICAN LIBRARY MATERIALS. PAPERS. (Text in English, Portuguese, Spanish; summaries in English, Spanish) 1956. a. membership; price varies for individual nos. Seminar on the Acquisition of Latin American Library Materials, General Library, University of New Mexico, Albuquerque, NM 87131. TEL 505-277-5702. FAX 505-277-0646. bibl.; charts; stat.; cum.index: nos.1-29. (also avail. in microfiche from BHP; back issues avail.) **Indexed:** Lib.Lit. **Document type:** monographic series.
Former titles: Seminar on the Acquisition of Latin American Library Materials. Final Report and Working Papers (ISSN 0080-8849); Seminar on the Acquistion of Latin American Library Materials. Working Papers.

026 SG ISSN 0850-010X
SENEGAL. ARCHIVES DU SENEGAL. RAPPORT ANNUEL. 1976. a. exchange basis. Archives du Senegal, Immeuble Administratif, Av. Roume, Dakar, Senegal. Ed. Saliou Mbaye.

020 US
SENIOR HIGH SCHOOL LIBRARY CATALOG. quinquennial (with a. supplement). price varies. H.W. Wilson Co., 950 University Ave., Bronx, New York, NY 10452-9978. TEL 800-367-6770. FAX 718-590-1617. TELEX 4990003HWILSON. Ed. Juliette Yaakov. bk.rev. **Document type:** catalog.
Description: Classified list of books recommended for secondary school students (grades 9-12), including fiction and story collection; with author, title, subject, and analytical index.

026 JA ISSN 0385-0188
SENMON TOSHOKAN/JAPAN SPECIAL LIBRARIES ASSOCIATION. BULLETIN. (Text in Japanese; summaries in English) 1960. 5/yr. 10000 Yen. Senmon Toshokan Kyogikai - Japan Special Libraries Association, c/o National Diet Library, 10-1 Nagata-cho 1-chome, Chiyoda-ku, Tokyo 100, Japan. Ed. Kuniko Takeda. adv.; bk.rev. circ. 2,000. **Indexed:** Comput.Cont., Jap.Per.Ind., LISA, Mag.Ind. **Document type:** bulletin.
—BLDSC (2593.872000).
Formerly: Senmon Toshokan Kyogikai Kaiho.

020 UK ISSN 0953-0460
Z692.S5 CODEN: SERIEZ
SERIALS; the journal of the UK Serials Group. 1988. 3/yr. £52.62. United Kingdom Serials Group, c/o Mrs. Jill Tolson, Administrator, 114 Woodstock Rd., Witney, Oxon OX8 6DY, England. TEL 0993-703466. FAX 0993-778879. Ed. John Merriman. adv.: B&W page £100; trim 270 x 182; adv. contact: Stella Pilling. bk.rev. **Indexed:** LISA. **Document type:** bulletin.
—BLDSC (8242.737300); UnCover; SWETS; CASDDS.
Description: Provides a forum for the interchange of information, ideas, suggestions and solution of problems concerning serials and associated areas.

SERIALS IN THE BRITISH LIBRARY. see *BIBLIOGRAPHIES*

SERIALS IN WESTERN LANGUAGES; research collections on microfiche. see *BIBLIOGRAPHIES*

020 US ISSN 0361-526X
Z692.S5 CODEN: SELID4
SERIALS LIBRARIAN; the international quarterly journal of serials management. 1976. q. $38 to individuals; institutions and libraries $105. Haworth Press, Inc., 10 Alice St., Binghamton, NY 13904. TEL 607-722-5857; 800-342-9678. FAX 607-722-1424. TELEX 4932599. Ed. Peter Gellatly. adv.; bk.rev.; index. circ. 1,255. (also avail. in microfiche from HAW; back issues avail.; reprint service avail. from HAW) **Indexed:** Amer.Hist.& Life, ASCA, Bull.Signal., Chem.Abstr., CINAHL, Comput.& Info.Sys., Curr.Cont., Excerp.Med., Hist.Abstr., Ind.Per.Art.Relat.Law, Inform.Sci.Abstr., Leg.Info.Manage.Ind., LHTN, Lib.Lit., LISA, Ref.Zh., SSCI.
—BLDSC (8242.740000); Faxon; SWETS; CASDDS.
Description: Serials management for librarians. Coverage includes serials selection and acquisition, bibliographic control, cataloging, staffing and department management, serials control systems, subscription agencies, publishers, and computerization problems.
Refereed Serial

020 US ISSN 0747-5411
SERIALS PERSPECTIVE. 1984. s-a. free. University Microfilms International, 300 N. Zeeb Rd., Ann Arbor, MI 48106. TEL 313-761-4700; 800-521-0600. FAX 313-761-1203. Ed. Steven Koch. circ. 15,000. **Document type:** trade publication.
Description: Comprises special-interest articles and University Microfilms International product information for serials librarians.

020 US ISSN 0098-7913
PN4832 CODEN: SERRDR
SERIALS REVIEW. 1975. q. $45 to individuals; institutions $75. Pierian Press, Box 1808, Ann Arbor, MI 48106. TEL 313-434-5530. FAX 313-434-6409. Ed. Cindy Hepfer. adv. (back issues avail.) **Indexed:** Bibl.Ind., Bk.Rev.Ind. (1977-), Child.Bk.Rev.Ind. (1977-), Inform.Sci.Abstr., Leg.Info.Manage.Ind., LHTN, Lib.Lit., LISA.
—BLDSC (8242.760000); Faxon; UnCover; SWETS; UMI; CASDDS.
Description: Contains practical information on the management and administration of serial publications.
Refereed Serial

025 UK ISSN 0306-0942
SERVICE POINT. 1972. q. £20 (foreign £30). Library Association, Branch and Mobile Libraries Group, 176 Haigh Moor Rd., Tingley, Wakefield WF3 1EJ, England. TEL 0532-533856. Ed. Ian Stringer. adv.; bk.rev. circ. 1,550. **Indexed:** LISA. **Document type:** bulletin.
—BLDSC (8251.870000).
Description: Presents articles on branch and mobile library service, library group meetings, and library sponsored courses.

025.171 900 US ISSN 1003-9023
SHANGHAI DANG'AN GONGZUO/SHANGHAI ARCHIVAL WORK. (Text in Chinese) 1985. bi-m. $15.50. 684 Gubei Rd., Shanghai 200335, People's Republic of China. TEL 2751700. (Dist. outside China by: China International Book Trading Corporation, P.O. Box 399, P.R. China; Dist. in U.S. by: China Books & Periodicals, Inc., 2929 24th St., San Francisco, CA 94110. TEL 415-282-2994) Ed. Zhang Xetao. **Indexed:** Amer.Hist. & Life (1992), Hist.Abstr. (1992).
—BLDSC (1625.681600).
Formerly: Dang'an yu Lishi - Archives and History (ISSN 1000-4165)

SHIJIE TUSHU/WORLD BOOKS. see *PUBLISHING AND BOOK TRADE*

SHIXUE JIKAN/COLLECTION OF HISTORICAL MATERIALS. see *HISTORY*

020 US ISSN 0037-4326
Z671
SHOW-ME LIBRARIES. 1949. q. $10 (foreign $20). State Library, Box 387, Jefferson City, MO 65102. TEL 314-751-3615. FAX 314-751-3612. Ed. Madeline Matson. bk.rev.; bibl.; charts; illus.; stat. circ. 2,350. (processed; also avail. in microform from UMI; back issues avail.; reprint service avail. from UMI) **Indexed:** CALL, LHTN, Lib.Lit.
—BLDSC (8270.094900); UMI.
Description: Articles pertaining to Missouri libraries and librarians.

LIBRARY AND INFORMATION SCIENCES

020   CC
SHU PIN/BOOK REVIEWS. (Text in Chinese) q. Zhonghua Shuju, No. 36, Wangfujing Dajie, Beijing 100710, People's Republic of China. TEL 554504. Ed. Zhao Shouyan.

SICHUAN DANG'AN/SICHUAN ARCHIVES. see HISTORY — History Of Asia

020   CC
SICHUAN TUSHUGUAN XUEBAO/SICHUAN JOURNAL OF LIBRARY SCIENCE. (Text in Chinese) bi-m. Sichuan Tushuguan Xuehui - Sichuan Libraries Society, 31 Banbianqiao Beijie, Chengdu, Sichuan 610015, People's Republic of China. TEL 667333. Ed. Wang Enlai. **Document type:** academic/scholarly publication.

020   SL   ISSN 0583-2268
SIERRA LEONE. LIBRARY BOARD. REPORT. 1961. a. Library Board, Box 326, Freetown, Sierra Leone. (back issues avail.)

020   GW   ISSN 0724-2530
SIGELVERZEICHNIS FUER DIE BIBLIOTHEKEN DER BUNDESREPUBLIK DEUTSCHLAND. 1982. biennial. DM.36. Deutsches Bibliotheksinstitut, Abt. 1 - Publikationen, Bundesallee 184-185, 10717 Berlin, Germany. TEL 030-8505-0. FAX 030-8505100. (Co-sponsor: Staatsbibliothek zu Berlin) **Document type:** directory.

020   FI   ISSN 0355-0036
SIGNUM. (Text in Finnish and Swedish) 1968. 8/yr. FIM 250. Suomen Tieteellinen Kirjastoseura - Finnish Research Library Association, Koulukatu 116 A 18, Fin-33200 Tampere, Finland. TEL 358-31-534400. FAX 358-31-534-534434. Ed. Liisa Niinikangas. adv.; bk.rev.; abstr.; bibl. circ. 1,200. **Indexed:** CERDIC, LISA. **Document type:** academic/scholarly publication, newsletter.
—BLDSC (8276.326500).

020 366   US
SIMMONS LIBRARIAN. 1970. 2/yr. free. Simmons College, Graduate School of Library and Information Science, Attn: Em Claire Knowles, Asst. Dean, 300 The Fenway, Boston, MA 02115-5898. TEL 617-521-2798. Eds. Judy Blaine, Cara Barlow. circ. 7,000. **Document type:** newsletter.
Description: Directed to alumni to apprise them of alumni and faculty accomplishments and activities.

020   SI   ISSN 0217-1546
Z846
SINGAPORE. NATIONAL LIBRARY. ANNUAL REPORT. 1963. a. exchange basis. National Library, Stamford Rd., Singapore 0617, Singapore. TEL 3323660. FAX 3371470. circ. 1,500.

027   SI   ISSN 0085-6118
Z845.S5
SINGAPORE LIBRARIES. (Text in English) 1971. a. S.$18 in Asia; elsewhere $15. Library Association of Singapore, Bukit Merah Central, P.O. Box 0693, Singapore 9115, Singapore. TEL 4555133. FAX 4583320. Ed. Idris Rashid. adv.; bk.rev. circ. 600. **Indexed:** Lib.Lit., LISA.
—BLDSC (8285.470000); UnCover.
Description: Contains issues pertaining to libraries, librarianship and information services in Singapore.

020   US   ISSN 0037-5837
SIPAPU. 1970. 2/yr. $8. Noel Peattie, Ed. & Pub., 23311 County Rd. 88, Winters, CA 95694-9008. TEL 916-662-3364. bk.rev.; illus.; cum.index every 5 yrs. circ. 350. (processed) **Indexed:** Alt.Press Ind. **Document type:** newsletter.
Description: Newsletter for librarians, collectors and others interested in the alternative press, which includes small and "underground" presses, Third World, dissent, feminist, peace, and other types of publishing.

027.8   DK   ISSN 0105-9556
SKOLEBIBLIOTEKET. 1972. 9/yr. DKK 280. Danmarks Skolebibliotekarforening, Mariavej 1, Sdr. Bjert, DK-6091 Bjert, Denmark. TEL 75-57-71-01. Ed. Bent Rasmussen. adv.; bk.rev. circ. 3,000.

020   SW   ISSN 0346-8488
SKRIFTER UTGIVNA AV SVENSKA RIKSARKIVET. 1931. irreg. price varies. Riksarkivet, Box 12541, S-102 29 Stockholm, Sweden. TEL 08-737-63-50. FAX 08-737-64-74. **Document type:** monographic series.

020   AT
SOCIAL CHANGE AND INFORMATION SYSTEMS. 1972. 3/yr. Aus.$198. Noyce Publishing, G.P.O. Box 2222T, Melbourne, Vic. 3001, Australia. bk.rev.; bibl.; cum.index. (back issues avail.) **Indexed:** LISA.
Formerly (until 1985): Librarians for Social Change (ISSN 0305-165X)

SOCIETY FOR INFORMATION DISPLAY. SEMINAR LECTURE NOTES. see LIBRARY AND INFORMATION SCIENCES — Computer Applications

025.17   UK   ISSN 0037-9816
CD23.S6
SOCIETY OF ARCHIVISTS. JOURNAL. Key Title: Journal of the Society of Archivists. 1955. 2/yr. $38 to individuals; institutions $76 (effective 1994). (Society of Archivists) Carfax Publishing Co., P.O. Box 25, Abingdon, Oxon. OX14 3UE, England. TEL 44-235-555335. FAX 44-235-553559. (U.S. subscr. to: Carfax Publishing Co., Box 2025, Dunnelon, FL 34430-2025) Ed. Christoper Webb. adv.; bk.rev.; cum.index. circ. 1,600. (also avail. in microfilm from UMI; reprint service avail. from UMI (vols.1-3)) **Indexed:** Amer.Hist.& Life, Arts & Hum.Cit.Ind., Br.Archaeol.Abstr., Br.Hum.Ind., Curr.Cont., Hist.Abstr., LISA. **Document type:** academic/scholarly publication.
—BLDSC (4880.780000); Faxon; UnCover. **CCC.** Refereed Serial

027   US
SOCIETY OF MAINE ARCHIVISTS. NEWSLETTER. 1991. q. $10 membership. Society of Maine Archivists, c/o Edmund S. Muskie Archives, Bates College, Lewiston, ME 04240. TEL 207-786-6354. FAX 207-786-6035. Ed. Judy Franke. **Document type:** newsletter.
Description: Publishes news items and announcements of interest to archivists in Maine.

891.8 070.5   UK   ISSN 0038-0903
DJK36.G7
SOLANUS. 1966; N.S 1987. a. £10. University of London, School of Slavonic and East European Studies, c/o Dr. Christine Thomas, Ed., The British Library, Great Russell St., London WC1B 3DG, England. TEL 071-323-7587. FAX 071-323-7554. adv.; bk.rev.; illus. circ. 150. (back issues avail.) **Indexed:** A.I.C.P., LISA. **Document type:** academic/scholarly publication.
—BLDSC (8327.170000).
Description: Presents bibliographic, library and publishing studies in the USSR, and Eastern Europe. Includes research papers, documentary material, reference lists.

020.6   US
SOLINET. ANNUAL REPORT. 1973. a. free. Southeastern Library Network, Inc., 1438 W. Peachtree St., N.W., Atlanta, GA 30309-2955. TEL 404-892-0943. FAX 404-892-7879. Ed. Liz Hornsby. charts; stat. circ. 1,500. **Document type:** corporate report.
Formerly: Southeastern Library Network. Annual Report (ISSN 0099-085X)

020   US   ISSN 0038-1853
Z881.C1579
SOUNDINGS (SANTA BARBARA); collections of the University Library. 1969. a. $4 to non-members. University of California, Santa Barbara, University Library, Santa Barbara, CA 93106. TEL 805-893-3014. FAX 805-961-4676. Ed. Donald E. Fitch. bibl.; illus. circ. 650. **Indexed:** Amer.Hist.& Life, Hist.Abstr., M.L.A.

027.568   SA
SOUTH AFRICA. STATE LIBRARY COUNCIL. ANNUAL REPORT. (Text in Afrikaans, English) 1910. a. free. State Library, P.O. Box 397, Pretoria 0001, South Africa. TEL 27-12-218931. FAX 27-12-325-5984. TELEX 3-22171 SA. illus. circ. 857.
Description: Reports on the activities, finances and publications of the State Library, and outlines prospects for the future.

020   SA   ISSN 0256-8861
Z671   CODEN: SALSE7
SOUTH AFRICAN JOURNAL OF LIBRARY AND INFORMATION SCIENCE. (Text in Afrikaans, English) 1933. q. R.110. (South African Institute for Librarianship and Information Science) Foundation for Education, Science & Technology, P.O. Box 1758, Pretoria 0001, South Africa. TEL 27-12-322-6422. Ed. M. Bester. bk.rev.; illus. circ. 2,500. **Indexed:** Comput.& Contr.Abstr., Ind.S.A.Per., Lib.Lit., LISA, Sci.Abstr. **Document type:** academic/scholarly publication.
—BLDSC (8338.954000); UnCover; SWETS; UMI. **CCC.**
Former titles (until 1983): South African Journal for Librarianship and Information Science; South African Libraries - Suid-Afrikaanse Biblioteke (ISSN 0038-240X)

900   SA   ISSN 0038-2418
Z965
SOUTH AFRICAN LIBRARY. QUARTERLY BULLETIN/SUID-AFRIKAANSE BIBLIOTEEK. KWARTAALBLAD. (Text mainly in English occasionally in Afrikaans; summaries in English) 1946. q. $57. South African Library, P.O. Box 496, Cape Town 8000, South Africa. TEL 27-21-246320. FAX 27-21-244848. Ed. P.E. Westra. adv.; bibl.; illus.; index. circ. 1,000. (also avail. in microform from UMI) **Indexed:** Amer.Hist.& Life, Hist.Abstr., Ind.S.A.Per., Lib.Lit., LISA. **Document type:** bulletin.
—UMI.
Description: Publishes articles on the collections of the Library, and on historical and socio-cultural subjects of Southern African interest.

025   AT   ISSN 0081-2633
SOUTH AUSTRALIA. LIBRARIES BOARD. ANNUAL REPORT. 1940. a. free. Libraries Board of South Australia, Box 419 G.P.O., Adelaide 5001, Australia. circ. 350. **Document type:** government publication.

027   US   ISSN 0361-6479
Z733
SOUTH CAROLINA STATE LIBRARY. ANNUAL REPORT. 1943. a. free. South Carolina State Library, 1500 Senate St., Box 11469, Columbia, SC 29211. TEL 803-734-8666. FAX 803-734-8676. Ed. James B. Johnson, Jr. circ. 500 (controlled). (also avail. in microfiche from CIS) **Indexed:** ERIC, SRI.

027   US   ISSN 0361-7122
SOUTH CENTRAL RESEARCH LIBRARY COUNCIL. REPORTS. Short title: S C R L C Reports. 1968. bi-m. $25. South Central Research Library Council, DeWitt Bldg., 215 N. Cayuga St., Ithaca, NY 14850. TEL 607-273-9106. FAX 607-272-0740. circ. 1,100. **Document type:** newsletter.
Description: Newsletter of a library network serving 82 libraries.

020 950   UK   ISSN 0308-4035
SOUTH EAST ASIA LIBRARY GROUP NEWSLETTER. 1968. irreg. (approx. 2/yr.). £7.50($15) for 2 nos. South East Asia Library Group, c/o Annabel Gallop, Oriental and India Office Collections, The British Library, 197 Blackfriars Rd., London SE1 8NG, England. FAX 071-412-7858. TELEX 83656. Ed. P. Herbert. adv.; bk.rev.; bibl. circ. 200. **Indexed:** A.I.C.P., E.I. **Document type:** newsletter.
—BLDSC (6108.380000).
Description: Newsletter of a West European group of libraries concerned with Southeast Asia.

020 340   US   ISSN 0272-7560
SOUTHEASTERN LAW LIBRARIAN. 1975. q. $20. American Association of Law Libraries, Southeastern Chapter, c/o Legal Information Center, University of Florida, Holland Hall, Gainesville, FL 32611. TEL 904-392-0425. FAX 904-392-5093. Ed. Jim Gates. adv.; bk.rev. circ. 550. (back issues avail.) **Document type:** newsletter.

020   US   ISSN 0038-3686
Z673
SOUTHEASTERN LIBRARIAN. 1951. q. $35 to non-members. Southeastern Library Association, Inc., Box 987, Tucker, GA 30085-0987. TEL 404-939-5080. Ed. Theresa Johnson. adv.; index. circ. 2,200. (also avail. in microform from UMI; reprint service avail. from UMI) **Indexed:** Lib.Lit., LISA. **Document type:** academic/scholarly publication, newsletter.
—BLDSC (8352.460000); UMI.
Description: Includes articles that address professional concerns of the library community, announcements, and news of professional interest to librarians in the Southeast.

020   US
SOUTHEASTERN NEWSLINE. 1982. fortn. $20 to non-members. Southeastern New York Library Resources Council, Box 879, Highland, NY 12528-0879. TEL 914-691-2734. FAX 914-691-6987. Ed. John Shaloiko. bk.rev. circ. 500. **Document type:** newsletter.
Formerly (until 1986): S E News.
Description: Contians library news for members of the Southern New York Library Resources Council.

020   US
SOUTHERN EXPOSURE (CARBONDALE); the newsletter of library affairs. 1955. w. Southern Illinois University at Carbondale, Library Affairs, Carbondale, IL 62901. TEL 618-453-2516. Ed. Jean Stricklin. circ. 404 (controlled). (processed) **Document type:** newsletter.
Formerly: Southern Exposure Library Staff Bulletin (ISSN 0038-4089)

SOUTHWEST BOOK REVIEW. see *LITERARY AND POLITICAL REVIEWS*

026   US   ISSN 0038-6723
Z671   CODEN: SPLBAN
SPECIAL LIBRARIES. 1910. 4/yr. $60 (foreign $65 (subscr. includes m. SpeciaList newsletter). Special Libraries Association, 1700 18th St., N.W., Washington, DC 20009. TEL 202-234-4700. FAX 202-265-9317. Ed. Gail Repsher. adv.; bk.rev.; bibl.; charts; illus.; index, cum.index. circ. 16,000. (also avail. in microform from UMI; reprint service avail. from UMI) **Indexed:** Amer.Hist.& Life, ASCA, B.P.I., Bibl.Cart., Bk.Rev.Ind. (1965-), Bus.Ind., C.I.J.E., Child.Bk.Rev.Ind. (1965-), CINAHL, Comput.Cont., Comput.Lit.Ind., Curr.Cont., Hist.Abstr., Hosp.Lit.Ind., Inform.Sci.Abstr., Intl.Civil Eng.Abstr., Key to Econ.Sci., Leg.Info.Manage.Ind., LHTN, Lib.Lit., LISA, Mag.Ind., P.A.I.S., Sci.Abstr., Sci.Cit.Ind., Soft.Abstr.Eng., SSCI.
—BLDSC (8367.000000); Faxon; UnCover; SWETS; UMI; CASDDS.
Description: Discusses administration, organization and operations. Includes reports on research, technology and professional standards.

020 330   US   ISSN 1048-5376
Z675.A2
SPECIAL LIBRARIES ASSOCIATION. BUSINESS AND FINANCE DIVISION. BULLETIN. 1958. 3/yr. $25 to non-members; members free. Special Libraries Association, Business and Finance Division, 1700 18th St., N.W., Washington, DC 20009-2508. TEL 202-234-4700. FAX 202-265-9317. (Alt addr.: Arthur Andersen & Co., 69 W. Washington, Chicago, IL 60602. TEL 312-507-2710) index. circ. 3,300. (also avail. in diskette format) **Indexed:** Lib.Lit. **Document type:** bulletin.
Description: Covers business and finance topics of interest to business information professionals.

020   CN   ISSN 0824-7749
SPECIAL LIBRARIES ASSOCIATION. EASTERN CANADA CHAPTER. BULLETIN. 1956. q. membership. Special Libraries Association, Eastern Canada Chapter, Box 1538, Sta. B, Montreal, PQ H3B 3L2, Canada. Ed. Melinda Reinhart. adv.; bk.rev.; circ. 335 (controlled).
Former titles: Special Libraries Association. Montreal Chapter. Bulletin (ISSN 0381-9833); Montreal Special Libraries Association. Bulletin (ISSN 0381-9825)
Description: Provides members with information on activities.

026 900   US   ISSN 0036-1607
Z673   CODEN: SGBUB2
SPECIAL LIBRARIES ASSOCIATION. GEOGRAPHY AND MAP DIVISION. BULLETIN. 1947. q. $25 (foreign $30) (effective 1994). Special Libraries Association, Geography and Map Division, c/o Anita T. Sprankle, Bus. Mgr., 406 E. Smith St., Topton, PA 19562-1121. TEL 215-683-4480. FAX 215-683-4483. (Alt. ed. addr.: Kerr Library - 121, Oregon State University, Corvallis, OR 97331-4501. TEL 503-737-2971) Ed. Joanne Perry. bk.rev.; bibl.; illus.; index, cum.index: nos.1-70, 1947-1967; nos. 71-102, 1968-1975. circ. 950. (also avail. in microform from UMI; reprint service avail. from KTO,UMI) **Indexed:** Bibl.& Ind.Geol., Bibl.Cart., Geo.Abstr., LHTN, Lib.Lit., LISA, Ref.Sour. **Document type:** academic/scholarly publication.
—BLDSC (2763.094000); UnCover; SWETS; UMI.

020.6   US
SPECIAL LIBRARIES ASSOCIATION. SOCIAL SCIENCE DIVISION. BULLETIN. 3/yr. membership only. Special Libraries Association, Social Science Division, 2000 15th St., N., Ste. 701, Arlington, VA 22201-2617. TEL 703-524-7802. FAX 708-524-9335. Ed. Olivia Pickett. adv.; bk.rev.; circ. 800 (controlled). **Indexed:** Lib.Lit. **Document type:** bulletin.
Description: Covers the division's activities and news on health and human services, international and urban affairs, international dispute, municipal reference libraries, independent sector, law, and public policy.

020   US
SPECIAL LIBRARIES ASSOCIATION. UPSTATE NEW YORK CHAPTER. BULLETIN. vol.42, 1986. 4/yr. $20 to non-members. Special Libraries Association, Upstate New York Chapter, Library Division, c/o Rensselaer Polytechnic Institute, Folsom Library, Troy, NY 12180. TEL 518-276-8323. Ed. Elizabeth Irish. adv.; bk.rev.; tr.lit. circ. 315. **Document type:** bulletin.

026   US   ISSN 0739-7097
SPECIAL LIBRARIES ASSOCIATION. WASHINGTON D.C. CHAPTER. CHAPTER NOTES. 1968. 10/yr. $10 to non-members. Special Libraries Association, Washington D.C. Chapter, Box 287, Benjamin Franklin Sta., Washington, DC 20044. TEL 202-707-2814. FAX 202-707-2615. Eds. Mary Nell Bryant, Penny Heavner. adv. circ. 1,200. **Document type:** newsletter.
Description: Communicates chapter business, chapter sponsored professional activities and provides notice of other events and opportunities of interest to professional librarians in the Washington DC area.

020 070 051   US   ISSN 0883-282X
D839
SPECTRUM (OLATHE); a guide to the independent press and informative organizations. 1973. a. $19.95 per no. Laird Wilcox, Box 2047, Olathe, KS 66061. TEL 913-829-0609. FAX 913-829-0609. circ. 5,000. **Indexed:** Amer.Hist.& Life, Hist.Abstr. **Document type:** directory, bibliography.
Former titles: Censored (ISSN 0163-2280); Some Hard-to-Locate Sources of Information on Current Affairs.
Description: Provides a listing of 1,000 little-known sources of news, factual background and analysis of current affairs, and controversial issues.

SPORT AND RECREATION INFORMATION GROUP BULLETIN. see *SPORTS AND GAMES*

027.4   US
SPOTLIGHT ON YOUR LIBRARY. 1955. bi-m. free. Dayton & Montgomery County Public Library, 215 E. Third St., Dayton, OH 45402. TEL 513-227-9500. Ed. Mark Willis. circ. 8,000. (processed)
Formerly: This Month in Your Library (ISSN 0040-6252)
Description: Record and promotion of library activities, community involvement and new services.

020   US   ISSN 0720-678X
SPRINGER SERIES IN INFORMATION SCIENCES. 1980. irreg. price varies. Springer-Verlag, 175 Fifth Ave., New York, NY 10010. TEL 212-460-1500. FAX 212-473-6272. (Also: Berlin, Heidelberg, Tokyo and Vienna) Eds. K.S. Fu, T.S. Huang. (reprint service avail. from ISI) **Indexed:** Sci.Abstr. **Document type:** monographic series.
—BLDSC (8424.765000). CCC.

020   CE
Z845.C4
SRI LANKA LIBRARY REVIEW. (Text in English or Sinhalese) 1967. biennial. Rs.100($15) per no. Sri Lanka Library Association, 275-75 Bauddhaloka Mawatha, Colombo 7, Sri Lanka. TEL 01094-1-589103. Ed. Deepall Talagala. adv.; bk.rev. circ. 300. **Document type:** academic/scholarly publication.
Formerly (1973): Ceylon Library Review (ISSN 0009-0867)

026   GW
STAATSBIBLIOTHEK ZU BERLIN. AUSSTELLUNGSKATALOGE. N.F. 1970. irreg. price varies. Staatsbibliothek zu Berlin, Preussischer Kulturbesitz, 10772 Berlin, Germany. TEL 030-266-2338. FAX 030-2662378. TELEX 183160-STAAB-D. **Document type:** monographic series.
Formerly (until 1991): Staatsbibliothek Preussischer Kulturbesitz. Ausstellungskataloge (ISSN 0340-0700)
Description: Exhibition catalogues of important items from the holdings of the Staatsbibliothek.

026   GW
STAATSBIBLIOTHEK ZU BERLIN. JAHRESBERICHT. 1950. irreg. Staatsbibliothek zu Berlin, Preussischer Kulturbesitz, 10772 Berlin, Germany. TEL 030-2662338. FAX 030-2662378. TELEX 183160-STAAB-D. stat. (back issues avail.) **Document type:** corporate report.
Formerly (until 1991): Staatsbibliothek Preussischer Kulturbesitz. Jahresbericht (ISSN 0340-2274)
Description: Bulletin on the work of the Staatsbibliothek and its departments.

026   GW
Z929.B625
STAATSBIBLIOTHEK ZU BERLIN. MITTEILUNGEN N.F.. 1969. 3/yr. Staatsbibliothek zu Berlin, Preussischer Kulturbesitz, 10772 Berlin, Germany. TEL 030-2662338. FAX 030-2662378. TELEX 183160-STAAB-D. Ed. Siegfried Detemple. **Document type:** academic/scholarly publication.
Formerly (until 1991): Staatsbibliothek Preussischer Kulturbesitz. Mitteilungen (ISSN 0038-8866)
Description: Bulletin reporting on the current work of the Staatsbibliothek with articles on subjects relating to the work and collections of the library.

026   UK
STANDARDS AND TECHNOLOGY UPDATE. (Former name of issuing body: Machine Tool Industry Research Association) 1968. m. £75. Advanced Manufacturing Technology Research Institute, Hulley Rd., Macclesfield, Cheshire SK10 2NE, England. TEL 0625-25421. FAX 0625-34964. Eds. K. Gowing, A.B. Whiteley. circ. 250.
Former titles: Standards and Technology Bulletin; (until 1991): A M T R I Library Bulletin; (until 1986): M T I R A Library Bulletin.
Description: Lists articles from journals, reports, proceedings and translations relevant to the manufacturing industry. Includes news on standards and safety topics.

027.7   US
STANFORD UNIVERSITY LIBRARIES. NEWS NOTES. 1948. w. free. Stanford University Libraries, Green Library, Stanford, CA 94305. TEL 415-723-2018. E-mail: CN.LLB@FORSYTHE.STANFORD.EDU. Ed. Lisa Brown. circ. 625.
●Available only online.
Formerly: Stanford University Libraries. Library Bulletin.
Description: Information for and by the staff of the libraries.

027.8   US
STAR TRACK. (Supplement to: School Library Journal) 1990. s-a. free with subscr. to: School Library Journal. Cahners Publishing Company (New York), Bowker Magazine Group, Cahners Magazine Division, Division of Reed Elsevier Inc., 249 W. 17th St., New York, NY 10011. TEL 800-669-1002. FAX 212-242-7216. TELEX 138 755. (Subscr. to: Box 1978, Marion, OH 43305-1978) **Document type:** trade publication.
Description: Reviews all starred titles in School Library Journal.

LIBRARY AND INFORMATION SCIENCES

020 UK ISSN 0305-9189
Z675.G7
STATE LIBRARIAN. 1948. 3/yr. £6.95 per no. to non-members. H.M.S.O., c/o Lewis Forman, F W Library, WO29, King Charles St., London SW1A 2AH, England. TEL 071-2703683. adv.; bk.rev. circ. 700. Indexed: Lib.Lit., LISA.
—BLDSC (8438.260000).
  Formerly: Circle of State Librarians. Bulletin.

020 US ISSN 0889-8812
STORY BAG NEWSLETTER. 1981. bi-m. $15 (effective 1994). 5361 Javier St., San Diego, CA 92117-3215. TEL 619-569-9399. Ed. Harlynne Geisler. adv.; bk.rev.; illus.; cum.index: 1981-1991. circ. 300. (looseleaf format; back issues avail.) **Document type:** newsletter.
  Description: Practical tips for any adult, teacher or librarian about using storytelling for children or adults. Includes stories, reviews, and a listing of storytelling events.

020 IT
STRUMENTI BIBLIOGRAFICI. 1974. irregr., latest no.7. price varies. Angelo Longo Editore, Via Paolo Costa 33, P.O. Box 431, 48100 Ravenna, Italy. TEL 0544-217026. Ed. Enzo Esposito. circ. 2,000. **Document type:** monographic series.

020 AU
STUDIEN ZUR BIBLIOTHEKSGESCHICHTE. 1973. irreg. price varies. Akademische Druck- und Verlagsanstalt Dr. Paul Struzl, Schoenaugasse 6, A-8010 Graz, Austria. TEL 0316-813460. FAX 0316-81346024. **Document type:** academic/scholarly publication.

026 US ISSN 0732-927X
Z675.A2
SUBJECT DIRECTORY OF SPECIAL LIBRARIES AND INFORMATION CENTERS. 1975. a. $695 for 3-vol. set; $250 per vol. Gale Research Inc., 835 Penobscot Bldg., Detroit, MI 48226. TEL 800-877-4253. FAX 313-961-6083. TELEX 810-221-7086. Ed. Janice DeMaggio. **Document type:** directory.
  Description: Lists non-general libraries in the U.S.

020 US ISSN 1048-3977
Z671
SUBJECT INDEX TO S P E C KITS IN PRINT. a. Association of Research Libraries, Systems and Procedures Exchange Center, Dept. 0692, Washington, DC 20073-0692. TEL 202-296-8656.

020 US
SUBJECT SPECIALISTS SECTION NEWSLETTER. 1980. irreg. membership. Louisiana Library Association, Box 3058, Baton Rouge, LA 70821. TEL 504-342-4928. circ. 100. (back issues avail.) **Document type:** newsletter.

027 SJ
SUDAN. NATIONAL COUNCIL FOR RESEARCH. NATIONAL DOCUMENTATION CENTRE. LIBRARY INFORMATION BULLETIN. (Text in English) m. National Council for Research, National Documentation Centre, Box 2404, Khartoum, Sudan.

020 SA ISSN 1012-2796
SUID-AFRIKAANSE ARGIEFBLAD/SOUTH AFRICAN ARCHIVES JOURNAL. (Text and summaries in Afrikaans, English) 1959. a. R.35 to individuals; institutions R.40; outside South Africa R.45). South African Society of Archivists, Private Bag X236, Pretoria 0001, South Africa. TEL 27-12-323-5300. FAX 27-12-323-5287. Eds. A. Nel, V.S. Harris. adv.; bk.rev.; bibl.; cum.index. circ. 300. (back issues avail.) Indexed: LISA. **Document type:** academic/scholarly publication.
  Description: Articles on archival and records management matters, reviews, society notices, select list of publications.

020 UK ISSN 0967-4896
SURVEY OF LIBRARY SERVICES TO SCHOOLS AND CHILDREN IN THE UK. a. £19.50. Loughborough University, Library and Information Statistics Unit, Loughborough, Leicestershire LE11 3TU, England. TEL 0509-223071. FAX 0509-610361. **Document type:** corporate report.
—BLDSC (8550.350000).

SWARBICA JOURNAL. see HISTORY — History Of Asia

020 US ISSN 0095-0874
Z881.U49 CODEN: SALIDA
SYMBOLS OF AMERICAN LIBRARIES. 1932. irreg. $13. U.S. Library of Congress, Enhanced Cataloging Division, Washington, DC 20540. TEL 202-707-6100. (Subscr. to: Cataloging Distribution Service, Washington, DC 20541) Ed. William W. Palmer. circ. 2,500.
—CASDDS.

020 NO ISSN 0332-656X
Z671
SYNOPSIS; informasjon om informasjon. (Text in Norwegian; summaries in English) 1970. bi-m. free. Riksbibliotektjenesten, Bygdoe Alle 21, P.O. Box 2439, Solli, 0201 Oslo, Norway. TEL 22-43-08-80. FAX 22-56-09-81. Ed. Kjellaug Scheie. abstr.; bibl.; index. (back issues avail.) **Document type:** monographic series.
—BLDSC (8586.109000).
  Description: News reports and articles of interest to professional librarians.

020 JA ISSN 0918-404X
▼**T P & D FORUM (YEAR).** (Technical Processing and Documentation) (Text in Japanese; summaries in English) 1992. a. 1500 Yen. (Technical Processing Research Group, Nippon Association for Librarianship) Biblion, 11-804, 1-7 Shinmori, Asahi-ku, Osaka City, Japan. adv.; bk.rev. **Document type:** academic/scholarly publication.

020 CN ISSN 0039-8470
T.P.L. NEWS. 1971. m. free. Toronto Public Library, 281 Front St.E., Toronto, Ont. M5A 4L2, Canada. TEL 416-393-7565. FAX 416-393-7782. Ed. Dora Avramis. bk.rev.; film rev.; circ. 900 (controlled).

025.233 UK ISSN 0966-6745
▼**TAKING STOCK; libraries and the book trade.** 1992. s-a. £20 to non-members. National Acquisitions Group, Westfield House, North Rd., Horsforth, Leeds LS18 5HG, England. TEL 0532-591447. Ed. Lindsay Thomas. **Document type:** trade publication.
—BLDSC (8601.079100).

TALKING BOOK TOPICS (LARGE-PRINT EDITION). see HANDICAPPED — Visually Impaired

020 CN ISSN 0380-2973
TALKING BOOKS IN THE PUBLIC LIBRARY SYSTEMS OF METROPOLITAN TORONTO. 1974. a. Can.$35. Metropolitan Toronto Library Board, 789 Yonge St., Toronto, ON M4W 2G8, Canada. TEL 416-393-7160. bibl. **Document type:** catalog.

020 TZ ISSN 0856-1621
TANZANIA LIBRARY SERVICE. OCCASIONAL PAPER. irreg. price varies. Library Services Board, Box 9283, Dar es Salaam, Tanzania.

TANZANIA NATIONAL BIBLIOGRAPHY. see BIBLIOGRAPHIES

020 US ISSN 0193-4309
TAR HEEL LIBRARIES. 1977. bi-m. membership. Department of Cultural Resources, Division of State Library, 109 E. Jones St., Raleigh, NC 27611. TEL 919-733-2570. FAX 919-733-8748. Ed. Diana D. Young. illus.; stat.; circ. 5,000 (controlled). **Document type:** newsletter.
  Former titles (until 1976): Library Reporter; North Carolina State Library Newsletter (ISSN 0549-7728)

027.8 AT ISSN 0049-3090
TEACHER AND LIBRARIAN. 1965. q. Aus.$30. School Library Association of New South Wales, P.O. Box 1336, Parramatta, N.S.W. 2124, Australia. circ. 900. Indexed: Aus.Educ.Ind. **Document type:** bulletin.

020 CN ISSN 1188-679X
Z675.S3
TEACHING LIBRARIAN. 1974. 3/yr. Can.$36. (Ontario School Library Association) Ontario Library Association, 100 Lombard St., Ste. 303, Toronto, ON M5C 1M3, Canada. TEL 416-363-3388. FAX 416-941-9581. Ed. Judy Tye. adv.; bk.rev.; illus.; index. circ. 1,300. **Document type:** academic/scholarly publication.
  Formerly: Reviewing Librarian (ISSN 0318-0948)
  Description: Articles and reviews of new materials for teachers and librarians with emphasis on applications to learning, teaching styles and curriculum.

020 US ISSN 0731-7131
Z688.5
TECHNICAL SERVICES QUARTERLY. 1983. q. $32 to individuals; institutions and libraries $115. Haworth Press, Inc., 10 Alice St., Binghamton, NY 13904. TEL 607-722-5857; 800-342-9678. FAX 607-722-1424. TELEX 4932599. Ed. Gary Pitkin. adv.; bk.rev. circ. 712. (also avail. in microfiche from UMI; back issues avail.; reprint service avail. from HAW) Indexed: C.I.J.E., Comput.Cont., Inform.Sci.Abstr., Leg.Info.Manage.Ind., Lib.Lit., LISA, Ref.Zh., Sci.Abstr.
—BLDSC (8726.665000); UnCover; SWETS; Faxon; UnCover; SWETS.
  Description: Devoted to new trends in computer automation and advanced technologies in the technical operation of libraries and information centers.
  Refereed Serial

020.5 US ISSN 0272-0884
Z671 CODEN: TCNCDR
TECHNICALITIES. 1980. m. $47. Media Periodicals, Div. of Westport Publishers, 4050 Pennsylvania Ave., Ste. 310, Kansas City, MO 64111-3051. TEL 816-756-1490. FAX 816-756-0159. Ed. Brian Alley. adv.; bk.rev.; index. circ. 750. (also avail. in microfilm from UMI; microfiche; back issues avail.) Indexed: LHTN, Lib.Lit., LISA.
—BLDSC (8732.405000); UnCover; SWETS; UMI; CASDDS.
  Description: Aims at the library technical services practitioners. Emphasizes on computer applications, including online public access catalogs, library budges, collection building, library automation and marketplace trends.

TECHNISCHE UNIVERSITAET BRAUNSCHWEIG. UNIVERSITAETSBIBLIOTHEK. VEROEFFENTLICHUNGEN. see EDUCATION — Higher Education

020 370 US
▼**TECHNOLOGY CONNECTION; the newsletter for school library media specialists.** 1994. m. (exc. July & Aug.). $22. Linworth Publishing, Inc., 480 E. Wilson Bridge Rd., Ste. L, Worthington, OH 43085. **Document type:** newsletter.

020 US ISSN 0162-1564
Z671
TENNESSEE LIBRARIAN. N.S. 1948. q. $10. Tennessee Library Association, Box 158417, Nashville, TN 37215-8417. TEL 615-297-8316. FAX 615-269-1807. Ed. Marie Garrett. adv.; bk.rev.; illus. circ. 1,600. (also avail. in microform from UMI; reprint service avail. from UMI) Indexed: Lib.Lit.
—UMI.
  Formerly: T L - Tennessee Librarian (ISSN 0040-3296)
  Description: Covers subjects of interest to librarians and para-professionals who work in libraries, as well as public library theory.

027.7 US ISSN 0040-4136
TEXAS A & M UNIVERSITY LIBRARY NOTES. 1965. q. free. Texas A & M University Library, College Sta., TX 77843. TEL 409-845-5741. Ed. Roberta Pitts. circ. 3,000.
  Description: Covers current events about Texas A&M libraries.

020 US ISSN 0040-4438
Z671
TEXAS LIBRARIES. 1906. q. free upon written request. Texas State Library and Archives Commission, Box 12927, Austin, TX 78711. TEL 512-463-5493. FAX 512-463-5436. Ed. Michael Clark. bk.rev.; bibl.; illus.; index; circ. 1,400 (controlled). (also avail. in microform from UMI) Indexed: Amer.Hist.& Life (until 1992), Child.Lit.Abstr., Hist.Abstr. (until 1992), Lib.Lit. **Document type:** government publication.
—UMI.
  Description: Features articles of interest to librarians, patrons, and educators in Texas.

020 US ISSN 0040-4446
TEXAS LIBRARY JOURNAL. 1924. q. $20 (foreign $25). Texas Library Association, 3355 Beecave Rd., Ste. 401, Austin, TX 78746. TEL 512-328-1518. FAX 512-328-8852. Ed. Josette Lyders. adv.; illus.; index. circ. 5,500. (also avail. in microfilm) Indexed: Lib.Lit. **Document type:** academic/scholarly publication.
—BLDSC (8799.450000); UMI.

TEXAS WOMAN'S UNIVERSITY. SCHOOL OF LIBRARY AND INFORMATION STUDIES. ALUMNAE NEWSLETTER. see *COLLEGE AND ALUMNI*

020   GW
▼**TEXTBOOKS FOR KNOWLEDGE ORGANIZATION.** 1993. irreg., no.1, 1993. DM.42.80. (International Society for Knowledge Organization) Indeks Verlag, Woogstr. 36a, 60431 Frankfurt a.M., Germany. TEL 069-523690. FAX 069-520566. Ed. Robert Fugmann. **Document type:** monographic series.

020   US
THIRD INDICATOR. 1985. bi-m. $25 (free to qualified personnel). Bibliographical Center for Research, 14394 E. Evans Ave., Aurora, CO 80014-1478. TEL 303-751-6277. Ed. Rosario Garza. circ. 500. (looseleaf format; back issues avail.) **Document type:** newsletter.

020 338.91   US   ISSN 1052-3049
Z730
THIRD WORLD LIBRARIES; an international journal focusing on libraries and socio-economic development. 1990. s-a. $15 in developing countries ($35 to N. America, Europe, Japan, Australia, New Zealand). Rosary College, Graduate School of Library and Information Science, 7900 W. Division, River Forest, IL 60305. TEL 708-524-6866. FAX 703-366-5360. Ed. Guy A. Marco. bk.rev.; index. circ. 500. **Indexed:** LISA. **Document type:** academic/scholarly publication.
—BLDSC (8820.145190); SWETS.
   Description: Covers issues pertaining to libraries and their role in development.
   Refereed Serial

029   SW   ISSN 0040-6872
         CODEN: TDDKA5
TIDSKRIFT FOER DOKUMENTATION/NORDIC JOURNAL OF DOCUMENTATION. Abbreviated title: T D. (Text in the Nordic languages; occasionally in English; summaries in English) 1945. q. SEK 200. Tekniska Litteratursaellskapet, c/o Ingenjoersvetenskapsakademien, P.O. Box 5073, S-102 42 Stockholm, Sweden. TEL 46-8-791-30-35. FAX 46-8-678-23-01. Eds. Gunnar Lager, Birgitta Levin. adv.; bk.rev.; bibl.; illus.; index. circ. 1,000. **Indexed:** Biol.Abstr., Lib.Lit., LISA, Sci.Abstr.
—BLDSC (8821.000000); SWETS; CASDDS.
   Formerly (until 1949): Teknisk Dokumentation.

020   II   ISSN 0563-5489
TIMELESS FELLOWSHIP; annual journal of comparative librarianship. (Text in English) 1964. a. Rs.40($9) Karnatak University Library Association, Karnatak University, Pavat Nagar, Dharwad 580 003, Karnataka, India. Eds. K.S. Deshpande, M.R. Kumbhar. adv.; bk.rev. circ. 500. **Indexed:** LISA.

027.4   PP   ISSN 0310-463X
TOK TOK BILONG HAUS BUK. 1972. s-a. 20 n.($23) Papua New Guinea Library Association, c/o National Library Service, Box 5770, Boroko, N.C.D., Papua New Guinea. Ed.Bd. adv.; bk.rev. circ. 500. **Indexed:** LISA, So.Pac.Per.Ind.

020   HU   ISSN 0133-8358
TOLNAI KONYVTAROS. 1970. s-a. free. Tolna Megyei Konyvtar - Public Library of the County Tolna, Szechenyi ut 51, H-7100 Szekszard, Hungary. TEL 11-834. Ed. Maria Elekes. adv.; bk.rev.; bibl.; illus.; stat.; cum.index: 1970-1985. circ. 300. (back issues avail.)

020   UK   ISSN 0268-9928
TOP 3,000 DIRECTORIES AND ANNUALS: A GUIDE TO THE MAJOR TITLES USED IN BRITISH LIBRARIES. 1980. a. £60. Dawson U K Ltd., Book Division, Crane Close, Dennington Rd., Wellingborough, Northants. NN8 2QG, England. TEL 0933-274444. FAX 0933-225993. TELEX 96292.
   Formerly: Top 2,000 Directories and Annuals: A Guide to the Major Titles Used in British Libraries (ISSN 0262-0219)

020   AT   ISSN 1030-5009
TOPICS IN AUSTRALASIAN LIBRARY AND INFORMATION STUDIES. 1988. irreg. Centre for Information Studies, Charles Sturt University - Riverina, Locked Bag 660, Wagga Wagga, N.S.W. 2678, Australia. TEL 069-222325. FAX 069-222733. Ed. G.E. Gorman. **Document type:** academic/scholarly publication.

020   JA   ISSN 0454-1960
TOSHOKAN KENKYU SIRIZU/N.D.L. LIBRARY SCIENCE SERIES. (Text in Japanese) 1960. a. price varies. National Diet Library - Kokuritsu Kokkai Toshokan, 1-10-1 Nagata-cho, Chiyada-ku, Tokyo 100, Japan. TEL 03-3581-2331. FAX 03-3597-9104. circ. 400.
—BLDSC (6067.848000).

020   JA   ISSN 0913-8005
TOSHOKAN KYORYOKU TSUSHIN/LIBRARY COOPERATION NEWS. (Text in Japanese) 1987. bi-m. National Diet Library - Kokuritsu Kokkai Toshokan, 1-10-1 Nagata-cho, Chiyoda-ku, Tokyo 100, Japan. TEL 03-3581-2331. FAX 03-3597-9104. circ. 4,100 (controlled).
   Description: Provides information about interlibrary loans, photocopying, and reference services that will be of interest to user libraries. Also reports on seminars and workshops organized by the NDL.

020   KO
TOSOGUAN HAK. 1970. a. 400 Won($1) Korean Library Science Society, Yonsei University Library, 134 Sinchon-Dong, Seodaemoon-Ku, Seoul 120, S. Korea.

029   UK   ISSN 0963-0325
TREND MONITOR REPORTS; computing, communications, media and socio-technology. 6/yr. (in 2 vols., 3 nos./vol.) £105 per no. Aslib, Association for Information Management, Publications Department, Information House, 20-24 Old St., London EC1V 9AP, England. TEL 071-253-4488. FAX 071-430-0574. Ed. Jan Wyllie.
—BLDSC (9049.130000).
   Formerly: Trend Monitor (ISSN 0954-7479)

340 025   US   ISSN 0893-6773
Z675.L2T74
TRENDS IN THE LAW LIBRARY MANAGEMENT AND TECHNOLOGY. 1987. 10/yr. $75. Fred B. Rothman & Co., 10368 W. Centennial Rd., Littleton, CO 80127. TEL 303-979-5657. FAX 303-978-1457. Ed. Mark E. Estes. (back issues avail.; reprint service avail. from RRI) **Document type:** newsletter.
—BLDSC (9049.643000).

020   IE   ISSN 0790-388X
TRINITY COLLEGE. FRIENDS OF THE LIBRARY. NEWSLETTER. 1984. 3/yr. £15. Trinity College, Friends of the Library, College St., Dublin 2, Ireland. TEL 01-7022087. FAX 01-6719003. TELEX 93782. Ed. Paul Ferguson. circ. 500. (back issues avail.) **Document type:** newsletter.

027.7   AT
LA TROBE UNIVERSITY LIBRARY NEWS. irreg. (2-4/yr). free. La Trobe University, University Library, Bundoora, Vic. 3085, Australia. TEL 479-1934. FAX 03-479-3018. **Document type:** newsletter.
   Description: News sheet directed at academic staff of the University. Covers library developments.

027.4   US   ISSN 0897-6945
TRUSTEE DIGEST. a. American Library Trustee Association, 50 E. Huron St., Chicago, IL 60611. TEL 312-280-2161. FAX 312-280-3257.
—UMI.

TURNBULL LIBRARY RECORD. see *HISTORY — History Of Australasia And Other Areas*

020 060   FI   ISSN 0082-7010
TURUN YLIOPISTO. KIRJASTO. JULKAISUJA. (Text in English, Finnish, French; summaries in English, French, German) 1948. irreg., no.12, 1983. price varies. Turun Yliopisto, Kirjasto - Turku University Library, Kirjasto, SF-20500 Turku 50, Finland. FAX 358-21-6335050. TELEX 62123 TYK SF. circ. 300.

020   CC   ISSN 0252-3116
Z671   CODEN: TQGOEP
TUSHU QINGBAO GONGZUO/LIBRARY AND INFORMATION SERVICE. (Text in Chinese) 1980. bi-m. $52.80. (Chinese Academy of Sciences, Documentation and Information Center) Science Press, Marketing and Sales Department, 16 Donghuangchenggen Beijie, Beijing 100707, People's Republic of China. TEL 4010642. FAX 4012180. TELEX 210247-SPBJ-CN. Ed. Xin Ximeng. adv. circ. 32,000.
—UnCover; CASDDS.
   Description: Devoted to the study and exploration of library and information work, as well as the theories and methods helpful to the modernization of these services. Reports and comments on the development of these services in China and abroad.

020   CC   ISSN 1003-2797
TUSHU QINGBAO ZHISHI/KNOWLEDGE OF LIBRARY AND INFORMATION SCIENCE. (Text in Chinese) 1980. q. $20. Wuhan Daxue - Wuhan University, Luojiashan, Wuchang-qu, Wuhan, Hubei 430072, People's Republic of China. TEL 027-7822712. Ed. Huang Zongzhong. bk.rev. circ. 16,000. **Document type:** academic/scholarly publication.

020   CC
TUSHUGUAN GONGZUO YU YANJIU. (Text in Chinese) q. Tianjin Tushuguan - Tianjin Library, 12 Chengde Dao, Heping Qu, Tianjin, People's Republic of China. TEL 393561. Ed. Dong Changxu.

020   CC
TUSHUGUAN JIANSHE/LIBRARY DEVELOPMENT. (Text in Chinese) 1976. bi-m. Heilongjiang Sheng Tushuguan - Heilongjiang Provincial Library, 22, Wenchang Jie, Nangang-qu, Harbin, Heilongjiang 150001, People's Republic of China. TEL 2624594. Ed. Wang Kezheng. **Document type:** academic/scholarly publication.
   Formerly (until 1992): Heilongjiang Tushuguan - Heilongjiang Library (ISSN 1001-5604)

020   CC
TUSHUGUAN JIE/LIBRARY WORLD. (Text in Chinese) q. Y1.05 per no. Guangxi Tushuguan Xuehui - Guangxi Library Society, 61 Minzhu Dadao, Nanning, Guangxi 530022, People's Republic of China. TEL 568138. Ed. He Shanxiang. **Document type:** trade publication.

020   CC
TUSHUGUAN XUEBAO/JOURNAL OF LIBRARY SCIENCE IN CHINA. (Text in Chinese) bi-m. $24.30. Zhongguo Tushuguan Xuehui - China Society for Library Science, 39, Baishiqiao Rd., Beijing 100081, People's Republic of China. TEL 8415566. (Dist. in US by: China Books & Periodicals, Inc., 2929 24th St., San Francisco, CA 94110. TEL 415-282-2994) Ed. Qiu Dongjiang. bk.rev. circ. 2,000. **Document type:** academic/scholarly publication.

020   CC
TUSHUGUAN XUEKAN/LIBRARY JOURNAL. (Text in Chinese) bi-m. Liaoning Sheng Tushuguan - Liaoning Provicial Library, 48 Shaoshuaifu Xiang, Chaoyang Jie, Shenyang, Liaoning 110011, People's Republic of China. TEL 443150. Ed. Zhu Yupei.

020   CC
TUSHUGUAN YUAN/LIBRARIANS. (Text in Chinese) 1980. bi-m. Y9 (effective 1994). Sichuan Sheng Tushuguan - Sichuan Provincial Library, 6 Zongfu Jie, Chengdu, Sichuan 610016, People's Republic of China. TEL 028-6629132. (Co-sponsor: Committee of Sichuan Central Libraries) Ed. Hao Chunyang. **Document type:** trade publication.

020   CC   ISSN 0494-1225
TUSHUGUANXUE TONGXUN/BULLETIN OF LIBRARY SCIENCE. (Text in Chinese) bi-m. $24.30. Society of Library Science, 7 Wenjing Jie, Beijing 100802, People's Republic of China. TEL 6016633. (Dist. in US by: China Books & Periodicals, Inc., 2929 24th St., San Francisco, CA 94110. TEL 415-282-2994) Ed. Huang Jungui.

020   UK   ISSN 0264-2441
U A P NEWSLETTER. (Universal Availability of Publications) 1983. irreg. free. International Federation of Library Association and Institutions, International Programme for UAP, c/o British Library Document Supply Centre, Boston Spa, Wetherby, W. Yorks. LS23 7BQ, England. TEL 0937-546123. FAX 0937-546478. TELEX 557381. Ed. Graham Cornish. bk.rev. circ. 800. **Document type:** newsletter.

LIBRARY AND INFORMATION SCIENCES

027.7   CN   ISSN 0382-0661
U B C LIBRARY NEWS. 1968. q. free. University of British Columbia, Main Library, Vancouver, B.C. V6T 1Y3, Canada. Ed. Julie Stevens. circ. 3,200.

020   CN   ISSN 1010-9501
U D T NEWSLETTER. French edition: Universal Dataflow and Telecommunications. Bulletin (ISSN 1011-1301) (Text in English) 1987. 3/yr. free. (International Federation of Library Associations and Institutions, Universal Dataflow and Telecommunications - Federation Internationale des Associations de Bibliothecaires et des Bibliotheques, Flux Universel des Donnees et les Telecommunications) National Library of Canada, 395 Wellington St., Ottawa, Ont. K1A 0N4, Canada. TEL 819-994-6963. FAX 819-994-6833. Ed. Paula Tallim. circ. 800. **Document type:** newsletter.
—BLDSC (9079.712000).
Description: Discusses advances in information and telecommunications technology and their applications for the international library community.

027.7   UK   ISSN 0963-7354
U K O L N NEWSLETTER. 1979-1989; resumed 1991. 2/yr. free. University of Bath, Office for Library and Information Networking, Claverton Down, Bath BA2 7AY, England. TEL 0225-826580. FAX 0225-826229. TELEX 449097. Ed. Philip Bryant. circ. 700. **Document type:** newsletter.
—BLDSC (6107.115000).
Former titles (until 1991): University of Bath. Centre for Bibliographic Management. Newsletter (ISSN 0953-5144); (until 1987): University of Bath. Centre for Catalogue Research. Newsletter (ISSN 0144-5073)

020   US
U L C EXCHANGE. 1984. m. $50. Urban Libraries Council, 1800 Ridge Ave., Ste. 208, Evanston, IL 60201. TEL 708-866-9999. Ed. Kathleen Reif. circ. 230. (back issues avail.) **Document type:** newsletter.
Formerly: Urban Libraries Exchange.
Description: Provides information of interest to large urban public libraries.

020   MX
U N A M DIRECTORIO DE BIBLIOTECAS. 1976. biennial. $8 (or exchange). Universidad Nacional Autonoma de Mexico, Direccion General de Bibliotecas, Ciudad Universitaria, Mexico 20, D.F., Mexico.

020   US   ISSN 0364-5215
Z690
U S B E NEWS.* 1949. m. $75 to non-members. United States Book Exchange, Periodicals and Serials Division, 2969 W. 25th St., Cleveland, OH 44113. Ed. Mary W. Ghikas. circ. 1,800. (processed)
Formerly (until 1976): United States Book Exchange Newsletter (ISSN 0041-753X)

UMBRELLA. see *ART*

020   US   ISSN 0049-514X
Z671
UNABASHED LIBRARIAN; the "how I run my library good" letter. 1971. 4/yr. $30 (foreign $36). Box 2631, New York, NY 10116. Ed. Marvin H. Scilken. bk.rev.; bibl. (back issues avail.) **Indexed:** Lib.Lit.
—BLDSC (9083.900000).

U.S. FEDERAL RESERVE SYSTEM. RESEARCH LIBRARY - RECENT ACQUISITIONS. see *BIBLIOGRAPHIES*

020   KE   ISSN 0145-8736
Z3516
U.S. LIBRARY OF CONGRESS. ANNUAL PUBLISHERS' DIRECTORY, MONOGRAPHS AND SERIALS. (Is supplement to: U.S. Library of Congress. Accessions List: Eastern and Southern Africa (ISSN 1070-2717)) 1976. a. free. U.S. Library of Congress Office, P.O. Box 30598, Nairobi, Kenya. TEL 254-2-225484. FAX 254-2-217646. **Document type:** directory, government publication.

020 025   US   ISSN 0083-1565
Z733   **CODEN:** ARLCDF
U.S. LIBRARY OF CONGRESS. ANNUAL REPORT OF THE LIBRARIAN OF CONGRESS. 1866-1923; N.S. 1938. a. price varies; free to libraries upon request to L.C. Office Systems Services. U.S. Library of Congress, Washington, DC 20540. TEL 202-707-5590. (Subscr. to: Superintendent of Documents, U.S. Government Printing Office, Box 317954, Pittsburgh, PA 15250-7954. TEL 202-783-3238. FAX 202-512-2233) **Document type:** corporate report, government publication.
—CASDDS.
Formerly (until 1923): U.S. Library of Congress. Report of the Librarian of Congress (ISSN 0894-0142)

025.3   US   ISSN 0160-8029
Z693.A15   **CODEN:** CSBUDE
U.S. LIBRARY OF CONGRESS. CATALOGING SERVICE BULLETIN. Key Title: Cataloging Service Bulletin. 1978. q. $21 (foreign $23). U.S. Library of Congress, Distribution Service, Customer Service Section, Washington, DC 20540. TEL 202-707-6100. FAX 202-707-1334. (Also avail. from: Superintendent of Documents, U.S. Government Printing Office, Box 317954, Pittsburgh, PA 15250-7954. TEL 202-783-2233. FAX 202-512-2233) **Document type:** bulletin, government publication.
—BLDSC (3074.300000); SWETS; CASDDS.
Supersedes (1945-1978): U.S. Library of Congress. Cataloging Service (ISSN 0041-7890)

020   US   ISSN 0041-7904
Z733.U57   **CODEN:** LCIBAA
U.S. LIBRARY OF CONGRESS. INFORMATION BULLETIN. Key Title: Information Bulletin - Library of Congress. 1942. fortn. free to libraries, the media and institutions. U.S. Library of Congress, Office of Public affairs, Washington, DC 20540-8610. illus.; index, cum.index 1985-1992. circ. 14,000. (also avail. in microform from LCP) **Indexed:** Amer.Bibl.Slavic & E.Eur.Stud.; Art & Archaeol.Tech.Abstr.; Ind.U.S.Gov.Per., Lib.Lit., LISA. **Document type:** bulletin, government publication.
—BLDSC (5198.200000); UMI; CASDDS.
Description: News and infromation about the Library of Congress, including special exhibits and collections, features on interesting items in the Library's holdings, projects associated with the Library, personnel notes, seminars, conferences and exchanges.

025.3   US   ISSN 0041-7912
Z696   **CODEN:** LCCCAH
U.S. LIBRARY OF CONGRESS. L.C. CLASSIFICATION - ADDITIONS AND CHANGES. 1928. q. $85 (foreign $95). U.S. Library of Congress, Cataloging Distribution Service, Customer Service Section, Washington, DC 20540. TEL 202-707-6100. FAX 202-707-1334. (Also avail. from: Superintendent of Documents, U.S. Government Printing Office, Box 317954, Pittsburgh, PA 15250-7954. TEL 202-783-3238. FAX 202-512-2233) circ. 1,500. **Document type:** government publication.
—CASDDS.

020   US   ISSN 0275-9616
Z733.L735
U.S. LIBRARY OF CONGRESS. MANUSCRIPT DIVISION. ACQUISITIONS. 1979. a. free to libraries. U.S. Library of Congress, Washington, DC 20540. TEL 202-707-5383. FAX 202-707-6336. circ. 1,500. **Document type:** bibliography, government publication.

U.S. LIBRARY OF CONGRESS. NATIONAL LIBRARY SERVICE FOR THE BLIND AND PHYSICALLY HANDICAPPED. NEWS. see *HANDICAPPED — Visually Impaired*

020   US   ISSN 1048-9711
Z695.Z8   **CODEN:** LCSHEE
U.S. LIBRARY OF CONGRESS SUBJECT HEADINGS. (In 4 vols., 16th ed., 1993) a. $185 (foreign $225). U.S. Library of Congress, Cataloging Distribution Service, Customer Service Section, Washington, DC 20541-5017. TEL 202-707-6100. FAX 202-707-1334. (Avail. from: Superintendent of Documents, U.S. Government Printing Office, Box 317954, Pittsburgh, PA 15250-7954. TEL 202-783-3238. FAX 202-512-2233) **Document type:** government publication.
—CASDDS.

020   US   ISSN 0361-5243
U.S. LIBRARY OF CONGRESS SUBJECT HEADINGS CUMULATIVE MICROFORM EDITION. q. $85 (foreign $90). U.S. Library of Congress, Cataloging Distribution Service, Customer Service Section, Washington, DC 20541-5017. TEL 202-707-6100. FAX 202-707-1334. (Subscr. to: Superintendent of Documents, U.S. Government Printing Office, Box 317954, Pittsburgh, PA 15250-7954. TEL 202-783-3238. FAX 202-512-2233) **Document type:** government publication.

020   US   ISSN 8755-6146
Z695
U.S. LIBRARY OF CONGRESS SUBJECT HEADINGS WEEKLY LISTS. w. $400 (foreign $430). U.S. Library of Congress, Cataloging Distribution Service, Customer Service Section, Washington, DC 20541-5017. TEL 202-707-6100. FAX 202-707-1334. (Also avail. from: Superintendent of Documents, U.S. Government Printing Office, Box 317954, Pittsburgh, PA 15250-7954. TEL 202-783-3238. FAX 202-512-2233) **Document type:** government publication.

UNITED STATES BOARD ON BOOKS FOR YOUNG PEOPLE. NEWSLETTER. see *PUBLISHING AND BOOK TRADE*

020   SP   ISSN 0078-8740
UNIVERSIDAD DE NAVARRA. ESCUELA DE BIBLIOTECARIAS. COLECCION BIBLIOTECARIAS. 1969. irreg., no.4, 1977. price varies. Ediciones Universidad de Navarra, S.A., Apdo. 396, 31080 Pamplona, Spain. TEL 94 825 6850.
Formerly: Universidad de Navarra. Escuela de Bibliotecarias. Manuales: Bibliotecarias.

020.7   PN
UNIVERSIDAD DE PANAMA. DEPARTAMENTO DE BIBLIOTECOLOGIA. BOLETIN. 1968. q. Bl.12. Universidad de Panama, Departamento de Bibliotecologia, Estafeta Universitaria, Panama, Panama. adv.; bk.rev.; bibl. circ. 350.
Formerly: Universidad de Panama. Escuela de Bibliotecologia. Boletin (ISSN 0014-0422)

020   MX   ISSN 0185-0067
UNIVERSIDAD NACIONAL AUTONOMA DE MEXICO. INSTITUTO DE INVESTIGACIONES BIBLIOGRAFICA. INSTRUMENTA BIBLIOGRAPHICA; catalogo de seudonimos, anagramas, iniciales otros alias usados por escritores Mexicanos y extranjeros que han publicado en Mexico. 1973. irreg., latest 1985. $10. Universidad Nacional Autonoma de Mexico, Instituto de Investigaciones Bibliograficas, Ciudad Universitaria, Coyoacan, Mexico 04510, D.F., Mexico. (Co-sponsor: Biblioteca Nacional) Ed. Jose G. Moreno de Alba. (back issues avail.) **Document type:** monographic series.

020   PY
UNIVERSIDAD NACIONAL DE ASUNCION. ESCUELA DE BIBLIOTECOLOGIA. INFORMACIONES. 1972. a. $5. Universidad Nacional de Asuncion, Escuela de Bibliotecologia, Espana 1098, Casilla de Correo 1408, Asuncion, Paraguay. Ed.Bd. bk.rev. circ. 200.

020   PO   ISSN 0872-5632
UNIVERSIDADE DE COIMBRA. ARQUIVO. BOLETIM. 1973. a. Esc.3000. Universidade de Coimbra, Arquivo, R.S. Pedro, 2, Coimbra, Portugal. TEL 039-25422. FAX 039-20987. Ed. Manuel Augusto Rodrigues. circ. 3,000. **Document type:** academic/scholarly publication.

020   BL   ISSN 0100-0829
Z671
UNIVERSIDADE FEDERAL DE MINAS GERAIS. ESCOLA DE BIBLIOTECONOMIA. REVISTA. (Text in Portuguese; summaries in English) 1972. s-a. $40 (effective Oct. 1992). Universidade Federal de Minas Gerais, Escola de Biblioteconomia, Caixa Postal 1606, 30161-970 Belo Horizonte MG, Brazil. TEL 448-5227. FAX 031-448-5200. Ed. Eduardo Jose Wense Dias. adv.; bk.rev.; abstr.; bibl.; charts; stat.; cum.index: 1972-1986; circ. 800 (controlled). (back issues avail.) **Indexed:** Inform.Sci.Abstr., Lib.Lit., LISA. **Document type:** academic/scholarly publication.
—BLDSC (7805.520000).
Description: Devoted to research and other contributions in library and information science.

LIBRARY AND INFORMATION SCIENCES

020 GW ISSN 0438-4415
UNIVERSITAETS- UND LANDESBIBLIOTHEK SACHSEN-ANHALT. ARBEITEN. 1952. irreg., vol.39, 1992. price varies. Universitaets- und Landesbibliothek Sachsen-Anhalt, August-Bebel-Str. 13, 06098 Halle, Germany. TEL 0345-8950. FAX 0345-895257. **Document type:** monographic series.

027 GW ISSN 0072-4483
UNIVERSITAETSBIBLIOTHEK GIESSEN. BERICHTE UND ARBEITEN. 1962. irreg. price varies. Universitaetsbibliothek Giessen, Otto-Behaghel-Str. 8, 35394 Giessen, Germany. TEL 0641-702-2330. FAX 0641-46406. circ. 500. **Document type:** academic/scholarly publication, monographic series.
  Description: Bibliographies and studies about the library, the history of the University and the history of printing in Giessen.

020 SP
UNIVERSITAT DE BARCELONA. BIBLIOTECA. MEMORIA ANUAL. 1969. a. free. Universitat de Barcelona, Biblioteca, Gran via de les Corts Catalanes, 585, 08007 Barcelona, Spain. illus.; circ. controlled.

027.7 NO ISSN 0802-2836
UNIVERSITETSBIBLIOTEKET I TRONDHEIM. RAPPORT. 1971. irreg. exchange basis. Universitetsbibliotek i Trondheim, Erling Skakkes gt. 47C, N-7013 Trondheim, Norway. FAX 07-592100. TELEX 55384 BIBL. circ. 200. (also avail. in microfilm) **Indexed:** LISA. **Document type:** corporate report.
  Former titles (until 1985): Universitetsbiblioteket i Trondheim. Biblioteket. Avdeling B. Rapport (ISSN 0800-1383); (until 1974): Universitetet i Trondheim. Kongelige Norske Videnskabers Selskab. Biblioteket. Rapport (ISSN 0801-7565)

027 NR
UNIVERSITY OF BENIN. LIBRARY. ANNUAL REPORT. (Title varies slightly) 1970. a. University of Benin, Library, P.M.B. 1154, Eken Wan Rd., Benin City, Nigeria. stat.

020 US ISSN 0069-3375
UNIVERSITY OF CHICAGO STUDIES IN LIBRARY SCIENCE. 1939. irreg., latest 1984. price varies. University of Chicago Press, 5801 S. Ellis Ave., Chicago, IL 60637. TEL 312-702-7899. Ed. Don R. Swanson. (back issues avail.; reprint service avail. from UMI,ISI)
  Refereed Serial

025 TZ ISSN 0856-1818
UNIVERSITY OF DAR ES SALAAM LIBRARY JOURNAL. 1989. 2/yr.? University of Dar es Salaam, Library, P.O. Box 35092, Dar es Salaam, Tanzania. **Indexed:** P.L.E.S.A.

027.4 CN ISSN 0226-3300
UNIVERSITY OF GUELPH LIBRARY. COLLECTION UPDATE. 1979. a. Can.$6.50 per no. University of Guelph Library, Guelph, ON N1G 2W1, Canada. TEL 519-824-4120. FAX 519-824-6931. Ed. Pat Eaves. bibl.; illus.; cum.index: 1979-1989. circ. 200. (back issues avail.)
  Description: Aims to increase awareness within the University community and among the public, of the diverse materials available at the University Library.

027 NR ISSN 0073-4322
Z858
UNIVERSITY OF IBADAN. LIBRARY. ANNUAL REPORT. 1948. a. free. University of Ibadan, Library, Ibadan, Nigeria. bk.rev. circ. 500.

027.7 NR ISSN 0046-8436
UNIVERSITY OF IBADAN. LIBRARY. LIBRARY RECORD. 1949. m. free. University of Ibadan, Library, Ibadan, Nigeria. bk.rev.; bibl. circ. 80. (processed; back issues avail.)

025 US ISSN 0069-4789
Z678.9.A1
UNIVERSITY OF ILLINOIS AT URBANA-CHAMPAIGN. CLINIC ON LIBRARY APPLICATIONS OF DATA PROCESSING. PROCEEDINGS. 1963. a. price varies. University of Illinois at Urbana-Champaign, Graduate School of Library and Information Science, Publications Office, 501 E. Daniel St., Champaign, IL 61820-6211. TEL 217-333-1359. FAX 217-244-7329. (Orders to: University of Illinois Press, Journals Dept., 1325 S. Oak St., Champaign, IL 61820) index. (also avail. in microfiche; back issues avail.) **Document type:** academic/scholarly publication, proceedings.
  —CCC.

020 US
UNIVERSITY OF ILLINOIS AT URBANA-CHAMPAIGN. GRADUATE SCHOOL OF LIBRARY AND INFORMATION SCIENCE. ALLERTON PARK INSTITUTE. PAPERS. 1954. a. $20. University of Illinois at Urbana-Champaign, Graduate School of Library and Information Science, Publications Office, 501 E. Daniel St., Champaign, IL 61820-6211. TEL 217-333-1359. FAX 217-244-7329. (Subscr. to: University of Illinois Press, Journals Dept., 1325 S. Oak St., Champaign, IL 61820) index. **Document type:** academic/scholarly publication.
  —CCC.
  Formerly: University of Illinois at Urbana-Champaign. Graduate School of Library Science. Allerton Park Institute. Papers (ISSN 0536-4604)

020 US
UNIVERSITY OF ILLINOIS AT URBANA-CHAMPAIGN. GRADUATE SCHOOL OF LIBRARY AND INFORMATION SCIENCE. MONOGRAPH SERIES. 1963. irreg. price varies. University of Illinois at Urbana-Champaign, Graduate School of Library and Information Science, Publications Office, 501 E. Daniel St., Champaign, IL 61820-6211. TEL 217-333-1359. FAX 217-244-7329. (Orders to: University of Illinois Press, Journals Dept., 1325 S. Oak St., Champaign, IL 61820) **Document type:** academic/scholarly publication, monographic series.
  Formerly: University of Illinois at Urbana-Champaign. Graduate School of Library Science. Monograph Series. (ISSN 0073-5302)

020 US
UNIVERSITY OF ILLINOIS AT URBANA-CHAMPAIGN. GRADUATE SCHOOL OF LIBRARY & INFORMATION SCIENCE. NEWSLETTER. 1987. s-a. University of Illinois at Urbana-Champaign, Graduate School of Library & Information Science, Publications Office, 501 E. Daniel St., Champaign, IL 61820-6211. TEL 217-333-1359. FAX 217-244-3302. circ. 5,400. (back issues avail.) **Document type:** academic/scholarly publication, newsletter.
  Description: Provides news about the department and its alumni.

020 US ISSN 0276-1769
UNIVERSITY OF ILLINOIS AT URBANA-CHAMPAIGN. GRADUATE SCHOOL OF LIBRARY AND INFORMATION SCIENCE. OCCASIONAL PAPERS. 1949. irreg. price varies. University of Illinois at Urbana-Champaign, Graduate School of Library and Information Science, Publications Office, 501 E. Daniel St., Champaing, IL 61820-6621. TEL 217-333-1359. FAX 217-244-7329. Ed. Marcella Genz. circ. 500. (back issues avail.) **Indexed:** Biol.Abstr. **Document type:** academic/scholarly publication, monographic series.
  —BLDSC (6223.870000); Faxon; UnCover. CCC.
  Formerly: University of Illinois at Urbana-Champaign. Graduate School of Library Science. Occasional Papers.

027.7 US ISSN 0047-1402
UNIVERSITY OF IOWA. LIBRARIES. NEWSLETTER. 1972. 2/yr. free. (Friends of the University of Iowa Libraries) University of Iowa Libraries, Iowa City, IA 52242. TEL 319-335-5871. Ed. Jeffrey Dodd. bibl. circ. 2,500. **Document type:** newsletter.

020 US
UNIVERSITY OF IOWA. SCHOOL OF LIBRARY AND INFORMATION SCIENCE. NEWSLETTER. 1966. a. free. University of Iowa, School of Library and Information Science, 3087 Library, Iowa City, IA 52242. TEL 319-335-5707. Ed. Ethel Bloesch. bibl. circ. 3,000. (back issues avail.) **Document type:** newsletter.
  Formerly: University of Iowa. School of Library Science. Newsletter (ISSN 0041-9648)

020 US ISSN 0075-5001
UNIVERSITY OF KANSAS LIBRARIES. LIBRARY SERIES. 1935. irreg. price varies. University of Kansas Libraries, Lawrence, KS 66045. TEL 913-864-4334. Ed. James Helyar. **Document type:** monographic series.

020 US ISSN 0743-8915
UNIVERSITY OF KENTUCKY LIBRARIES. OCCASIONAL PAPERS. 1980. irreg. no.4, 1983. price varies. University of Kentucky Library, University of Kentucky, Lexington, KY 40506. Ed. Terry L. Birdwhistell. circ. 300.

027.7 SJ
UNIVERSITY OF KHARTOUM. LIBRARY BULLETIN. (Text in Arabic or English) 1977. a. University of Khartoum, Library, Box 321, Khartoum, Sudan.

020 NR ISSN 0075-7705
UNIVERSITY OF LAGOS. LIBRARY. ANNUAL REPORT. 1962. a. free. (University of Lagos, Library) Lagos University Press, P.O. Box 132, Akoka, Yaba, Lagos, Nigeria. Ed. E.B. Bankole. circ. 1,000.

UNIVERSITY OF LONDON. SCHOOL OF SLAVONIC AND EAST EUROPEAN STUDIES. LIBRARY. BIBLIOGRAPHICAL GUIDES. see BIBLIOGRAPHIES

027.7 MW
UNIVERSITY OF MALAWI. LIBRARY. BULLETIN. (Text in English) 1977. 2/yr. free. University of Malawi, Library, Box 280, Zomba, Malawi. Ed. Foster G. Howse. circ. 200.

027 MW ISSN 0085-3038
UNIVERSITY OF MALAWI LIBRARIES. REPORT TO THE SENATE ON THE UNIVERSITY LIBRARIES. 1965. a. free. University of Malawi Libraries, Central Library Services, Box 280, Zomba, Malawi. TEL 265-522-222-135. FAX 265-523-225. TELEX 4742-CHANCOL-MI. Ed. Steve S. Mwiyeriwa. circ. 200. (processed)
  Description: Report on the activities and progress of five units of the University of Malawi Library System.

020 US ISSN 0076-4841
UNIVERSITY OF MARYLAND. COLLEGE OF LIBRARY AND INFORMATION SERVICES. STUDENT CONTRIBUTION SERIES. 1967. irreg., no.10, 1977. price varies. University of Maryland, College of Library and Information Services, c/o Marilyn Williams, Director of Publications, College Park, MD 20742. TEL 301-405-2032. FAX 301-314-9145. **Indexed:** Lib.Lit. **Document type:** monographic series.

020 US
▼**UNIVERSITY OF MARYLAND. COLLEGE OF LIBRARY AND INFORMATION SERVICES. TECHNICAL REPORT SERIES.** 1994. irreg. price varies. University of Maryland, College of Library and Information Services, c/o Marilyn Williams, College Park, MD 20742. TEL 301-405-2032. FAX 301-314-9145. **Document type:** monographic series.

020 AT ISSN 0313-427X
UNIVERSITY OF NEW SOUTH WALES. LIBRARY. ANNUAL REPORT. 1975. a. free. University of New South Wales, Library, Box 1, Kensington, N.S.W. 2033, Australia. circ. 500. **Document type:** corporate report.

020 US
UNIVERSITY OF RHODE ISLAND. LIBRARY. LIBRARY LETTER. 1967. a. free to qualified personnel. University of Rhode Island, Association of Friends of the Library, Kingston, RI 02881. Ed. Kevin Logan. bk.rev.; circ. (controlled).

027.7 US ISSN 0041-9974
UNIVERSITY OF ROCHESTER LIBRARY BULLETIN. 1945. irreg. (approx. 1-2/yr.) membership. University of Rochester, Rush Rhees Library, Rochester, NY 14627-0055. TEL 716-275-4437. Ed. Margaret Becket. illus. circ. 1,000. (back issues avail.) **Indexed:** Lib.Lit. **Document type:** academic/scholarly publication, bulletin.
  Description: Contains articles of literary, bibliographic and historical interest based on the Libraries' own collections and those of other collectors in the area and beyond.

LIBRARY AND INFORMATION SCIENCES

020 IR ISSN 0497-1000
UNIVERSITY OF TEHERAN. CENTRAL LIBRARY. LIBRARY BULLETIN/DANESHGAH-E TEHRAN. KETABKHANE-YE MARKAZI. NASHRIYE-YE KETABKHANEH. (Text in Persian) 1966. irreg. price varies. University of Teheran, Central Library, Enghelabi Ave., Teheran, Iran. Ed. Iraj Afshar. bk.rev.

610 020 IR
UNIVERSITY OF TEHERAN. FACULTY OF MEDICINE. LIBRARY BULLETIN/DANESHGAH-E TEHRAN. DANESHKADE-YE PEZESHKI. NASHRIYE-YE KETABKHANEH. (Text in Persian) 1971. m. University of Teheran, Faculty of Medicine, Enghelab Ave., Teheran, Iran. bk.rev.

020 US ISSN 0277-450X
UNIVERSITY OF TEXAS AT AUSTIN. GENERAL LIBRARIES. LIBRARY BULLETIN. 1972. w. free. University of Texas at Austin, General Libraries, Box P, Austin, TX 78713-7330. TEL 512-495-4350. FAX 512-495-4347. Ed. Carole Cable. circ. 970.
   Description: Staff communication newsletter.

020 US ISSN 0362-854X
UNIVERSITY OF TEXAS AT AUSTIN. GENERAL LIBRARIES. NEWSLETTER. 1974. irreg. free. University of Texas at Austin, General Libraries, Austin, TX 78713-7330. TEL 512-495-4350. FAX 512-495-4347. Ed. Carole Cable. bibl. circ. 3,500.
   Description: Focuses on the work programs of the General Libraries of the University.

020 378 US
UNIVERSITY OF TEXAS AT AUSTIN. GRADUATE SCHOOL OF LIBRARY AND INFORMATION SCIENCE. ALUMNI NEWS. 1969. s-a. free. University of Texas at Austin, Graduate School of Library and Information Science, EDB 564, Austin, TX 78712-1276. TEL 512-471-8806. FAX 512-471-3971. Ed. Mel Boggins. circ. 2,500. (back issues avail.) **Document type:** newsletter.

020 PH ISSN 0300-3612
UNIVERSITY OF THE PHILIPPINES. INSTITUTE OF LIBRARY SCIENCE. NEWSLETTER. (Text in English) 1965. q. free. University of the Philippines, Institute of Library Science, c/o Ursula G. Picache, U.P. Diliman, Quezon City 1101, Philippines. TEL 98-24-71-6249. Ed. Rosa M. Vallejo. circ. 900 (controlled). **Document type:** newsletter.

027.7 SA
UNIVERSITY OF THE WITWATERSRAND, JOHANNESBURG. LIBRARY. AFRICANA SERIES. 1985. irreg. price varies. University of the Witwatersrand, Johannesburg, Library, Private Bag XI, Wits 2050, South Africa. TEL 27-11-716-2330. FAX 27-11-403-1421. Ed. H.M. Edwards. **Document type:** monographic series.
   Description: Focuses on the unique Africana collections of the University Library.

027 SA ISSN 0075-3807
UNIVERSITY OF THE WITWATERSRAND, JOHANNESBURG. LIBRARY. ANNUAL REPORT OF THE UNIVERSITY LIBRARIAN. (Not published 1984-1992) 1932. a. free. University of the Witwatersrand, Johannesburg, Library, Private Bag XI, Wits 2050, South Africa. TEL 27-11-716-2330. FAX 27-11-403-1421. **Document type:** corporate report.

027.7 SA
UNIVERSITY OF THE WITWATERSRAND, JOHANNESBURG. LIBRARY. ARCHIVAL SERIES. irreg., no.14, 1987. University of the Witwatersrand, Johannesburg, Library, Private Bag XI, Wits 2050, South Africa. TEL 27-11-716-2330. FAX 27-11-403-1421. **Document type:** bibliography.

027.7 SA
UNIVERSITY OF THE WITWATERSRAND, JOHANNESBURG. LIBRARY. OCCASIONAL PUBLICATIONS. 1976. irreg., no.12, 1986. University of the Witwatersrand, Johannesburg, Library, Private Bag XI, Wits 2050, South Africa. TEL 27-11-716-2330. FAX 27-11-403-1421. **Document type:** monographic series.

020 UK
UNIVERSITY OF WARWICK LIBRARY. OCCASIONAL PUBLICATIONS.. 1971. irreg., no.18, 1992. price varies. University of Warwick Library, Coventry, Warwickshire CV4 7AL, England. FAX 0203-524211. TELEX 31406-COVLIB-G. Ed. Dr. J.A. Henshall. circ. controlled. (processed) **Document type:** monographic series.

020 XO
UNIVERZITA KOMENSKEHO. FILOZOFICKA FAKULTA. ZBORNIK: INFORMATIKA. (Text in Slovak; summaries in English, German and Russian) 1973. irreg. exchange basis. Univerzita Komenskeho, Filozoficka Fakulta, c/o Ustredna Kniznica Filozofickej Fakulty, Gondova 2, 818 01 Bratislava, Slovakia. Ed. Anna Cabrunova. circ. 600. **Document type:** academic/scholarly publication.

020.6 BB
UPDATE (BRIDGETOWN); occasional newsletter of the Library Association of Barbados. 1974. irreg., no.9, 1986. membership. Library Association of Barbados, Box 827E, Bridgetown, Barbados, W.I. **Document type:** newsletter.
   Formerly: Library Association of Barbados. Occasional Newsletter.

UPDATE (WASHINGTON). see *HANDICAPPED — Visually Impaired*

020 US
UPDATE C S L. 1988. bi-m. Connecticut State Library, 231 Capitol Ave., Hartford, CT 06106. TEL 203-566-2441. FAX 203-566-8940. Ed. Mike Beringer. circ. 2,500.

020 US ISSN 0276-9298
Z668
URBAN ACADEMIC LIBRARIAN. 1972. s-a. $10 to individuals; institutions $12; (foreign $15). Library Association of the City University of New York, Hunter College Library, 695 Park Ave., New York, NY 10021. TEL 212-772-4168. Ed. Mark Rosenzwig. adv.; bk.rev.; bibl.; illus. circ. 500. **Indexed:** LHTN, Lib.Lit.
—Faxon; UnCover. **CCC.**
   Supersedes (after vol.5, no.2): L A C U N Y Journal (ISSN 0094-615X)
   Description: Focuses on academic libraries and institutions in the urban setting.

UT DE SMIDTE FAN DE FRYSKE AKADEMY. see *PUBLISHING AND BOOK TRADE*

020.6 US
UTAH LIBRARY - NEWS. 1981. bi-m. $8. Utah Library Association, 2150 S. 300 W., Salt Lake City, UT 84115. Ed. Betty Dance. adv.; bk.rev. circ. 650. **Document type:** newsletter.

020 RU ISSN 0042-188X
V MIRE KNIG. 1961. m. 22.20 Rub. (Komitet po Pechati Soveta Ministrov) Izdatel'stvo Kniga, 50, Gorky St., 125047 Moscow, Russia. Ed. P.I. Fedotov. adv.; charts; index, cum.index. (also avail. in microform)

020.6 026 BE ISSN 0777-6306
V R B - INFORMATIE. (Text in Flemish, French) 1971. q. 250 BEF. Vereniging van Religieus - Wetenschappelijke Bibliothecarissen - Association of Scientific - Religious Librarians, Minderbroedersstraat 5, 3800 Sint-Truiden, Belgium. Ed. K. van de Casteele. bk.rev.; bibl. circ. 100.

027.4 CN ISSN 0380-1691
VANCOUVER ISLAND REGIONAL LIBRARY NEWSLETTER. 1960. q. free. Vancouver Island Regional Library, Box 3333, 6250 Hammond Bay Road, Namaimo, BC V9R 5N3, Canada. TEL 604-758-4697. FAX 604-758-2482. Ed. Laurene Miller. circ. 389 (controlled). (looseleaf format; back issues avail.) **Document type:** newsletter.
   Description: In-house publication: activities, developments in the Regional Library.

020 HU ISSN 0133-7351
VAS MEGYEI KONYVTARAK ERTESITOJE. 1971. 3/yr. free. (Vas Megyei Pedagogiai Intezet) Berzsenyi Daniel Megyei Konyvtar, Petofi Sandor u. 43, 9700 Szombathely, Hungary. TEL 94-311-366. FAX 94-312-179. adv.; bk.rev.; bibl.; illus.; stat. circ. 500. **Document type:** bulletin.

027.4 DK ISSN 0902-6533
VEJVISER OVER FOLKEBIBLIOTEKER I STORKOEBENHAVN. 1973. a. DKK 100 (effective 1994). Biblioteksfaglige Samarbejde i Storkoebenhavn (B F S), Ahlmanns alle 6, DK-2900 Hellerup, Denmark. TEL 45-31-62-75-00. FAX 45-31-62-73-99-305. **Document type:** directory.
   Formerly (until 1987): Biblioteksvejviser over Storkoebenhavns Folkebiblioteker (ISSN 0108-8238)

020.6 AU ISSN 1022-2588
VEREINIGUNG OESTERREICHISCHER BIBLIOTHEKARINNEN UND BIBLIOTHEKARE. MITTEILUNGEN. 1948. q. S.350. Vereinigung Oesterreichischer Bibliothekarinnen und Bibliothekare, Innrain 50, A-6010 Innsbruck, Austria. FAX 0512-5072307. Ed. Karin Heller. adv.; bk.rev. circ. 1,400. **Indexed:** LISA. **Document type:** bulletin.
   Formerly: Vereinigung Oesterreichischer Bibliothekare. Mitteilungen (ISSN 0042-3793)

010 US
VERMONT DEPARTMENT OF LIBRARIES NEWS. 1977. q. Department of Libraries, Pavillion Office Bldg., 109 State St., Montpellier, VT 05609. circ. 2,000 (controlled).
   Description: Focuses on information of interest to the public librarians and trustees in Vermont with state agency news.

020 US
VERY OCCASIONAL PAPERS. irreg. membership. Louisiana Library Association, Box 3058, Baton Rouge, LA 70821. TEL 504-342-4928. circ. 100.

VETERAN CAR. see *TRANSPORTATION — Automobiles*

020 US ISSN 0887-6851
Z692.V52
VIDEO LIBRARIAN. 1986. bi-m. $47 (Canada $52; elsewhere $69). Video Librarian, Box 2725, Bremerton, WA 98310. TEL 206-377-2231. FAX 206-373-6805. Ed. Randy Pitman. bk.rev.; film rev. circ. 784. (back issues avail.) **Document type:** newsletter.
   Description: Contains editorials and news and reviews nearly 100 videos for public, school, and university libraries.

020 384.554 US ISSN 1045-3393
Z692.V52
VIDEO RATING GUIDE FOR LIBRARIES. 1990. q. $126. A B C-Clio, 130 Cremona, Box 1911, Santa Barbara, CA 93116-1911. TEL 805-968-1911. FAX 805-685-9685. Ed. Timothy O'Donnell; Pub. Heather Cameron. adv. contact: Laura Wilson. **Document type:** directory.
   Description: Provides evaluative reviews of special-interest, nontheatrical videos. Includes information on how to obtain the individual video.

020 US
VIRGINIA LIBRARIAN. 1953. q. Virginia Library Association, Box 298, Alexandria, VA 22313. TEL 703-370-6020. FAX 703-370-3371. Ed. Jennilou Groutevant. adv.; illus. circ. 1,500. (also avail. in microform from UMI) **Indexed:** Lib.Lit. —UMI.
   Former titles: Virginia Librarian Newsletter (ISSN 0273-3951); Virginia Librarian.

VISUAL RESOURCES ASSOCIATION BULLETIN. see *ART*

020 GR ISSN 0302-1181
VIVLIOGRAPHIKA. Key Title: Bibliografika. 1972. irreg. Vivliographike Hetaireia tes Hellados, 3, Vamva St., T. T. 138, Athens, Greece.

020 CI ISSN 0507-1925
Z671
VJESNIK BIBLIOTEKARA HRVATSKE. (Text in Serbo-Croatian) 1950. q. $30. Hrvatsko Bibliotekarsko Drustvo, Nacionalna i Sveucilisna Biblioteka, Marulicev trg. 21, 41000 Zagreb, Croatia. Ed. Dubravka Kunstek. adv.; bk.rev.; bibl. circ. 1,000. **Indexed:** Bull.Signal., LISA.

VOICE OF YOUTH ADVOCATES. see *CHILDREN AND YOUTH — About*

LIBRARY AND INFORMATION SCIENCES

020   AT   ISSN 1036-1561
Z871.N35
VOICES. 1991. q. Aus.$48 (foreign Aus.$56). National Library of Australia, Publications Section, Cultural and Educational Services Division, Canberra, A.C.T. 2600, Australia. TEL 06-262-1365. FAX 06-273-4493. (Subscr. to: A G P S Subscription Section, G.P.O. Box 84, Canberra, A.C.T. 2601, Australia) Ed. P. Hetherington. circ. 1,000. (reprint service avail from ISI,UMI) **Document type**: government publication.
   Description: Presents information on special collections, library activities, and collections of the nation's network of libraries.

027.1   US
THE VOLUNTEER LIBRARIAN. 1975. irreg. Association of Private Libraries, c/o Mitrisin - Libraries, 66 Frankfort St., Apt. 2G, New York, NY 10038-1622. TEL 212-732-4461. adv.; bk.rev.; circ. controlled. (looseleaf format) **Document type**: newsletter.
   Formerly (until Oct. 1989): T L C Gossip (The Library Club).

020   US   ISSN 0043-6518
W L A NEWSLETTER. 1945. bi-m. $20. Wisconsin Library Association, 4785 Hayes Rd., Madison, WI 53704-7364. TEL 608-242-2040. FAX 608-242-2050. Ed. James A. Gollata. circ. 2,200. **Document type**: newsletter.
   Formerly: Wisconsin Library Association. President's Newsletter (ISSN 0032-7778)
   Description: Reflects the purposes and responsibilities of the Association and reports the activities and developments of the library profession.

020   US   ISSN 0278-4858
Z732.W28
WASHINGTON STATE LIBRARY NEWS. 1982. q. free. Washington State Library, Olympia, WA 98504. TEL 206-586-7010. FAX 206-586-7575. Ed. Grace T. Eubanks. circ. 1,500. **Document type**: newsletter.
   Description: Contains news, features, and photos about the Washington State Library's external and internal work, with emphasis on its support of other libraries in the state.

020 610   US
THE WATERMARK. 1976. q. $10. Archivists and Librarians in the History of the Health Sciences, c/o Susan Tishworth, Sec. & Treas., American College of Obstetricians and Gynecologists, 409 12th St., S.W., Washington, DC 20024. TEL 202-863-2578. Eds. Joan Echtenkamp Klein, Jodi Koste. adv.; bk.rev.; bibl. circ. 200. **Document type**: newsletter.
   Description: Features material of interest to persons working with history of the health sciences collections.

WENXIAN/DOCUMENTS. see *BIBLIOGRAPHIES*

020   US   ISSN 0043-3276
Z673
WEST VIRGINIA LIBRARIES. 1947. bi-m. $15. West Virginia Library Association, Box 884, Morgantown, WV 26507-0884. TEL 304-255-0511. FAX 302-722-4245. Ed. Yvonne Farley. adv.; bk.rev. circ. 1,000. (also avail. in microform from UMI)
—BLDSC (9300.040000).

020   US
WEST VIRGINIA LIBRARY COMMISSION. NEWSLETTER. 1972. irreg., latest 1988. free. West Virginia Library Commission, Cultural Center, Charleston, WV 25305. TEL 304-348-2041. FAX 304-248-2044. Ed. Shirley A. Smith. circ. 1,500. **Document type**: newsletter.

526.8   US   ISSN 0049-7282
WESTERN ASSOCIATION OF MAP LIBRARIES. INFORMATION BULLETIN. 1969. 3/yr. $25 (Canada $28; elsewhere $30). Western Association of Map Libraries, c/o Richard E. Soares, Bus. Mgr., Box 1667, Provo, UT 84603-1667. TEL 801-378-6179. E-mail: LIBRES@BYUVM. Ed. Mary Larsgaard. bk.rev.; bibl.; index, cum.index: vols. 1-10. circ. 425. (processed) **Indexed**: Bibl.Cart., Geo.Abstr., Lib.Lit., LISA.
—BLDSC (4485.342000); UnCover.

020   US
WESTERN ASSOCIATION OF MAP LIBRARIES. OCCASIONAL PAPERS. 1973. irreg., no.14, 1993. price varies. Western Association of Map Libraries, c/o Richard Soares, Bus. Mgr., Box 1667, Provo, UT 84603-1667. TEL 801-378-6179. E-mail: LIBRES@BYUVM. **Indexed**: Geo.Abstr., GeoRef. **Document type**: monographic series.

020   US   ISSN 0043-4051
WESTERN PLAINS LIBRARY SYSTEM NEWSLETTER. 1966. 4/yr. free (US only). Western Plains Library System, Service Center, 605 Avant-Box 1027, Clinton, OK 73601. TEL 405-323-0974. Ed. Dee Ann Ray. bk.rev. circ. 1,700. (processed) **Document type**: newsletter.
   Formerly: Custer-Washita Newsletter.
   Description: Contains timely announcements of coming library events, news from libraries that are part of the system, and information on services available.

027.4   US
WHAT'S LINE. 1979. q. Public Library Service, Division for the Blind & Physically Handicapped, 6030 Monticello Dr., Montgomery, AL 36130. TEL 205-277-7330. circ. 6,500.

020   CN   ISSN 0847-2149
WHAT'S UP DOC. irreg. free. Canada Communication Group, Publishing Division, Ottawa, ON K1A 0S9, Canada. TEL 819-997-5365. FAX 819-956-6341. Ed. Louise Tousignant. **Document type**: government publication, newsletter.
   Formerly (until 1990): Canadian Government Publishing Centre. Newsletter (ISSN 0846-8079)
   Description: Intended to help depository libraries and provide a forum for them.

027.7   US   ISSN 0363-1028
Z990
WHISTLE STOP; Harry S. Truman Library Institute newsletter. 1973. q. membership. Harry S. Truman Library Institute for National and International Affairs, Harry S. Truman Library, US Hwy. 24 and Delaware St., Independence, MO 64050. TEL 816-833-1400. FAX 816-833-4368. Ed. Benedict K. Zobrist. bibl. circ. 2,500. (processed) **Document type**: newsletter.
   Formerly: Harry S. Truman Library Institute Research Newsletter (ISSN 0017-7954)

WHO KNOWS: A GUIDE TO WASHINGTON EXPERTS. see *SCIENCES: COMPREHENSIVE WORKS*

WHO KNOWS ABOUT FOREIGN INDUSTRIES AND MARKETS. see *BUSINESS AND ECONOMICS*

026   US   ISSN 0278-842X
Z673
WHO'S WHO IN SPECIAL LIBRARIES. 1981. a. $40 non-members $60. Special Libraries Association, 1700 18th St., N.W., Washington, DC 20009. TEL 202-234-4700. FAX 202-265-9317. Ed. Gail Repsher. adv. contact: Alisa N. Cooper. circ. 13,500. **Document type**: directory.
—BLDSC (9312.546600).
   Description: Provides a complete alphabetical listing of members, their addresses, and their telephone and fax numbers. Includes indexes for chapters and divisions, a business index, and membership and leadership information.

001.539   UK
▼**WHO'S WHO IN THE EUROPEAN INFORMATION WORLD**. 1993. a. £125. T F P L Publishing, 17-18 Britton St., London EC1M 5NQ, England. TEL 071-251-5522. FAX 071-251-5318. (Subscr. in U.S. to: TFPL Publishing, 1301 20th St., N.W., Ste. 702, Washington, DC 20036. TEL 202-296-6009. FAX 202-296-6343) Ed. Nathalie Dick. **Document type**: directory.

020 920   UK
WHO'S WHO IN THE U K INFORMATION WORLD. 1991. a. £80. T F P L Publishing, 17-18 Britton St., London EC1M 5NQ, England. TEL 071-251-5522. FAX 071-251-5318. (Subscr. in U.S. to: TFPL Publishing, 1301 20th St., N.W., Ste. 702, Washington, DC 20036. TEL 202-296-6009. FAX 202-296-6343) **Document type**: directory.

020   US   ISSN 0043-5651
Z1217   CODEN: WLBUAC
WILSON LIBRARY BULLETIN. 1914. m. (Sept.-June). $52 (foreign $58). H.W. Wilson Co., 950 University Ave., Bronx, NY 10452. TEL 800-367-6770. FAX 718-590-1617. TELEX 4990003HWILSON. Ed. GraceAnne DeCandido. adv.; bk.rev.; bibl.; illus. (also avail. in microform from UMI,PMC) **Indexed**: Acad.Ind., Access (1980-), Amer.Hist.& Life, Bk.Rev.Ind. (1965-), C.I.J.E., Child.Bk.Rev.Ind. (1965-), Child.Lit.Abstr., CINAHL, Curr.Bk.Rev.Cit., Curr.Cont., Educ.Ind., Gard.Lit. (1992-), Hist.Abstr., Leg.Info.Manage.Ind., LHTN, Lib.Lit., LISA, Mag.Ind., PMR, Pop.Per.Ind., PSI, SSCI, TOM. **Document type**: bulletin.
   ●Also available online. Vendor(s): BRS Online Products, DIALOG Information Services, Inc., Wilsonline.
—BLDSC (9319.080000); Faxon; UnCover; UMI; CASDDS. CCC.

025.5   US   ISSN 0361-2848
L216
WISCONSIN LIBRARY SERVICE RECORD. (Subseries of: Wisconsin. Department of Public Instruction. Bulletin) 1973. a. free. Department of Public Instruction, Division for Library Services, 125 S. Webster St., 3rd Fl., Box 7841, Madison, WI 53707. TEL 608-266-2205. FAX 608-267-1052. (also avail. in microfiche from CIS; reprint service avail. from UMI) **Indexed**: SRI. **Document type**: government publication.

027.7   SA
WITS JOURNAL OF LIBRARIANSHIP AND INFORMATION SCIENCE. 1982. a., latest 1988. R.10. University of the Witwatersrand, Johannesburg, Library, Private Bag XI, Wits 2050, South Africa. TEL 27-11-716-2330. FAX 27-11-403-1421. Ed. Reuben Musiker. **Indexed**: Ind.S.A.Per., Lib.Lit., LISA. **Document type**: academic/scholarly publication.

WOLFENBUETTELER BIBLIOTHEKS - INFORMATIONEN. see *HISTORY*

020   GW   ISSN 0300-2012
WOLFENBUETTLER BEITRAEGE. 1972. irreg., vol.10, 1993. price varies. (Herzog-August-Bibliothek, Wolfenbuettel) Vittorio Klostermann, Frauenlobstr. 22, 60487 Frankfurt a.M., Germany. TEL 069-774011. FAX 069-708038. (Subscr. to: Postfach 900601, 60446 Frankfurt a.M., Germany) Ed. Paul Raabe. cum.index. (back issues avail.) **Document type**: monographic series.

020.6 301.412   US
WOMEN IN LIBRARIES. 1971. 5/yr. $5 to individuals; institutions $8. American Library Association, Social Responsibilities Round Table, Feminist Task Force, 50 E. Huron St., Chicago, IL 60611. TEL 312-944-6780. FAX 312-440-9374. Ed. Madeleine Tainton. bk.rev.; cum.index. circ. 400. (processed; back issues avail.)

WOMEN'S COLLECTION NEWSLETTER. see *WOMEN'S INTERESTS*

WOMEN'S INFORMATION UPDATES. see *WOMEN'S INTERESTS*

025   US
WORCESTER PUBLIC LIBRARY STAFF NEWSLETTER. 1941. m. Worcester Public Library, Salem Sq., Worcester, MA 01608. TEL 508-799-1655. Ed. E. Glenn Musser, Jr. circ. 130. (looseleaf format) **Document type**: newsletter.
   Description: For the staff of the Worcester Public Library.

510.78   SZ   ISSN 0074-3127
QA76
WORLD CONGRESSES ON INFORMATION PROCESSING. PROCEEDINGS. Title varies: Triennial World Computer Congress. Proceedings. 1959. triennial, 12th 1992, Madrid. International Federation for Information Processing, 16 place Longemalle, CH-1204 Geneva, Switzerland. TEL 022-3102649. FAX 022-7812322. **Document type**: proceedings.
—CCC.
   Formerly: International Conference on Information Processing. Proceedings.

LIBRARY AND INFORMATION SCIENCES — ABSTRACTING, BIBLIOGRAPHIES, STATISTICS

029 US
WORLD GUIDE TO ABBREVIATIONS OF ORGANIZATIONS. 5th ed., 1974. triennial. $155. Gale Research Inc., 835 Penobscot Bldg., Detroit, MI 48226. TEL 313-961-2242; 800-377-4253. FAX 313-961-6083. TELEX 810-221-7086. Ed. F.A. Buttress.
Description: Guide to organizational title abbreviations.

020 GW ISSN 0000-0221
Z721
WORLD GUIDE TO LIBRARIES. (Text in English and German) 1966. irreg., 11th ed., 1993. DM.498($350) K.G. Saur Verlag KG, A Reed Reference Publishing Company, Part of the Reed Elsevier group, Ortlerstr. 8, 81373 Munich, Germany. TEL 089-76902-0. FAX 089-76902150. TELEX 5212067-SAUR-D. (Subscr. to: Postfach 701620, 81316 Munich, Germany; N. America subscr. to: K.G. Saur, A Reed Reference Publishing Company, 121 Chanlon Rd., Box 31, New Providence, NJ 07974-9903, USA. TEL 908-665-3576) Ed.Bd. adv. **Document type:** directory.
—BLDSC (9356.032000).
Description: Lists libraries in 167 countries, including national, federal, regional, academic, large public, and special libraries. Arranged by continent and country, plus an alphabetical index.

020 011 GW ISSN 0724-8717
WORLD GUIDE TO SPECIAL LIBRARIES. 1983. irreg., 3rd ed., 1994. $325. K.G. Saur Verlag KG, A Reed Reference Publishing Company, Part of the Reed Elsevier group, Ortlerstr. 8, 81373 Munich, Germany. TEL 089-769020. FAX 089-76902150. TELEX 5212067-SARR-D. (Subscr. to: Postfach 701620, 81316 Munich, Germany; N. America subscr. to: K.G. Saur, A Reed Reference Publishing Company, 121 Chanlon Rd., Box 31, New Providence, NJ 07974-9903, USA. TEL 908-665-3576) **Document type:** directory.
—BLDSC (9356.034500).
Description: Includes entries for more than 32,000 libraries in 160 countries; they are divided into 5 major categories: General, Humanities, Social Sciences, Medicine and Life Sciences, and Science and Technology.

WORLD JEWISH DIRECTORY. see RELIGIONS AND THEOLOGY — Judaic

020 PL
WYZSZA SZKOLA PEDAGOGICZNA IM. KOMISJI EDUKACJI NARODOWEJ W KRAKOWIE. ROCZNIK NAUKOWO-DYDAKTYCZNY. PRACE BIBLIOTEKOZNAWCZE. 1982. irreg., no.6, 1991. price varies. Wydawnictwo Naukowe W S P, Ul. Karmelicka 41, 31-128 Krakow, Poland. TEL 33-78-20. (Co-sponsor: Ministerstwo Edukacji Narodowej)

020 IS ISSN 0334-200X
YAD LAKORE/READER'S AID; Israel journal for libraries and archives. (Text in Hebrew; summaries in English) 1946. q. $30. Center for Public Libraries, P.O. Box 242, Jerusalem 91002, Israel. TEL 972-2-247392. FAX 972-2-250620. Ed. Carol Pfeffer. bk.rev. circ. 1,200. (back issues avail.) **Indexed:** Ind.Heb.Per., LISA.
Description: Covers all aspects of library, archive and information studies throughout the world, with emphasis on Israel and Judaica.

027.7 US ISSN 0044-0175
Z733
YALE UNIVERSITY LIBRARY GAZETTE. 1926. s-a. $20. Yale University Library, New Haven, CT 06520. TEL 203-432-2967. FAX 203-432-4047. Ed. Stephen Parks. bibl.; index, cum.index: vols.1-45. circ. 1,500. **Indexed:** Amer.Hist.& Life, Curr.Cont., Hist.Abstr., Lib.Lit., M.L.A., Mid.East: Abstr.& Ind.
—Faxon; UnCover.

020 UK ISSN 0307-2509
YORKSHIRE LIBRARY NEWS. 1974. 4/yr. free to members. Library Association, Yorkshire and Humberside Branch, c/o Ray Prytherch, Ed., Lomond, Scotland Ln., Horsforth, Leeds LS18 5SE, England. TEL 0532-580681. circ. 1,500. **Document type:** newsletter.
—BLDSC (9421.235300).
Formerly: Yorkshire Librarian.

027.7 JA ISSN 0917-3684
YUIN. (Text in Japanese) 1967. q. free. Hokkaido University Library - Hokkaido Daigaku Toshokan, Kita-8, Nishi-5, Kita-ku, Sapporo-shi, Hokkaido 060, Japan. FAX 011-747-2855. Ed. Ikuo Yamamoto. bk.rev. circ. 3,000. **Document type:** bulletin.

026 PL ISSN 0137-5172
Z817.A1
Z BADAN NAD POLSKIMI KSIEGOZBIORAMI HISTORYCZNYMI. 1975. irreg., vol.15, 1992. 35000 Zl. per no. Uniwersytet Warszawski, Instytut Bibliotekoznawstwa i Informacji Naukowej, Krakowskie Przedmiescie 26-28, 00-325 Warsaw, Poland. FAX 48-22-267520. TELEX 815439 UWPL. Ed. Juze3f Wojakowski. index. circ. 350.
Description: Devoted to the history and research of rare book collections.

029.7 PL ISSN 0324-8194
ZAGADNIENIA INFORMACJI NAUKOWEJ. (Text in Polish; summaries in English and Russian) 1962. s-a. $22. (Polska Akademia Nauk, Osrodek Informacji Naukowej - Polish Academy of Sciences, Center of Scientific Information) Ossolineum, Publishing House of the Polish Academy of Sciences, Rynek 9, 50-106 Wroclaw, Poland. TEL 47-71-386-25. FAX 48-71-448-103. TELEX 0712771 OSS PL. Ed. Bronislaw Lugowski. bk.rev.; bibl.; charts. circ. 700. (also avail. in microform) **Indexed:** LISA. **Document type:** academic/scholarly publication.
Formerly: Polska Akademia Nauk. Osrodek Dokumentacji i Informacji Naukowej. Biuletyn (ISSN 0030-6282)
Description: Papers on various practical aspects and theories of the development of modern information sciences.

ZAMBIA. MINISTRY OF LEGAL AFFAIRS. ANNUAL REPORT. see BUSINESS AND ECONOMICS

020 ZA ISSN 0049-853X
Z857.Z3
ZAMBIA LIBRARY ASSOCIATION. JOURNAL. 1969. q. K.10 to institutions. Zambia Library Association, P.O. Box 2839, Lusaka, Zambia. Ed. W.D. Sweeney. adv.; bk.rev.; bibl.; index, cum.index: vols.1-4. circ. 200. (also avail. in microfilm) **Indexed:** LISA.

020.6 ZA
ZAMBIA LIBRARY ASSOCIATION. NEWSLETTER. (Text in English) 1979. bi-m. Zambia Library Association, P.O. Box 32839, Lusaka, Zambia.

020 GW ISSN 0044-2380
Z671
ZEITSCHRIFT FUER BIBLIOTHEKSWESEN UND BIBLIOGRAPHIE. 1953. bi-m. DM.104. (Verein Deutscher Bibliothekare) Vittorio Klostermann, Frauenlobstr. 22, 60487 Frankfurt a.M., Germany. TEL 069-774011. FAX 069-708038. (Subscr. to: Postfach 900601, 60446 Frankfurt a.M., Germany) Ed. Klaus-Dieter Lehmann. adv.; bk.rev.; bibl.; charts; stat.; in. circ. 2,200. (reprint service avail. from KTO) **Indexed:** Curr.Cont., Lib.Lit., LISA, P.A.I.S.For.Lang.Ind., SSCI. **Document type:** academic/scholarly publication.
—BLDSC (9454.000000); Faxon; SWETS. CCC.
Incorporates (in 1991): Zentralblatt fuer Bibliothekswesen (ISSN 0044-4081)

020 ISSN 0514-6364
ZEITSCHRIFT FUER BIBLIOTHEKSWESEN UND BIBLIOGRAPHIE. SONDERHEFTE. 1963. irreg., vol.57, 1994. price varies. Vittorio Klostermann, Frauenlobstr. 22, 60487 Frankfurt a.M., Germany. TEL 069-774011. FAX 069-708038. (Subscr. to: Postfach 900601, 60446 Frankfurt a.M., Germany) **Document type:** monographic series.

020 GW ISSN 0171-8932
ZEITSCHRIFTEN - DATENBANK (Z D B). 1973. s-a. DM.380. Deutsches Bibliotheksinstitut, Abt. 1 - Publikationen, Bundesallee 184-185, 10717 Berlin, Germany. TEL 030-8505-0. FAX 030-8505100. Eds. G. Franzmeier, P. Gruber. circ. 400. (microfiche) **Document type:** catalog.
●Also available online.
Also available on CD-ROM.
—BLDSC (9497.193000).
Supersedes (in 1979): Gesamtverzeichnis der Zeitschriften und Serien in Bibliotheken der Bundesrepublik Deutschland Einschliesslich Berlin (West) (ISSN 0302-0657)

020 CC ISSN 1003-9082
ZHONGWEN XINXI/CHINESE INFORMATION PROCESSING. (Text in Chinese; abstracts in English) 1984. bi-m. $24. Zhongguo Zhongwen Xinxi Xuehui - Chinese Information Processing Society of China, P.O. Box 263, Chendu Keji Daxue - Chengdu University of Science and Technology, Chengdu, Sichuan Province, People's Republic of China. TEL 028-581554. TELEX 606166 CUST CN. Ed. Li Shuo. adv.: page $800; adv. contact: Deng Hegang. circ. 5,000 (controlled).
Description: Covers the Chinese information processing techniques and theories, operating systems, and computer-based applications.
Refereed Serial

020 RH
THE ZIMBABWE LIBRARIAN. 1969. 2/yr. Z.$20($20) to non-members. Zimbabwe Library Association, P.O. Box 3133, Harare, Zimbabwe. TEL 263-4-882017. FAX 263-4-795019. Ed. Sabelo Mapasure. adv.; bk.rev.; index. circ. 450. **Indexed:** Ind.S.A.Per., LISA. **Document type:** newsletter.
—BLDSC (9513.253000); UnCover.
Former titles: Rhodesian Librarian (ISSN 0035-4848); Rhodesia and Nyasaland Library Association. Newsletter.

020 791.43 US
ZOOPRAXOGRAPHIC. 1976. q. $5. West Virginia Library Commission, Cultural Center, Charleston, WV 25305. TEL 304-558-3976. FAX 304-558-2044. Ed. S.L. Fesenmaier. bk.rev.; film rev. circ. 500. **Document type:** newsletter.
Description: Contains information related to the visual arts, including some literary aspects, but emphasizes film and television.

LIBRARY AND INFORMATION SCIENCES — Abstracting, Bibliographies, Statistics

011 RM ISSN 1220-3092
A B S I - ABSTRACTE IN BIBLIOLOGIE SI STIINTA INFORMARII. 1960. m. 2724 lei (effective 1994). Biblioteca Nationala a Romaniei, Str. Ion Ghica 4, 79708 Bucharest, Rumania. abstr.; circ. 1,500. **Document type:** abstracting/indexing.
Formerly: Buletin de Informare in Bibliologie (ISSN 0007-3784)

020 029.7 AT ISSN 0810-9265
A L I S A. (Australian Library and Information Science Abstracts) 1982. a. Aus.$60. Australian Clearing House for Library & Information Science, Library, Lorne Ave., Magill, S. Aust. 5072, Australia. TEL 08-302-4457. FAX 61-8-302-4695. (Co-sponsor: University of South Australia) Ed. Barbara Blacoe. circ. 150. (back issues avail.) **Document type:** abstracting/indexing.
●Also available online. Vendor(s): AUSINET.
Also available on CD-ROM.

020 US ISSN 1050-7442
Z701.4.U6
A R L PRESERVATION STATISTICS. 1988. a. Association of Research Libraries, 1527 New Hampshire Ave. N.W., Washington, DC 20036. TEL 202-232-8656. FAX 202-462-7849.

027 US ISSN 0147-2135
Z675.U5
A R L STATISTICS. 1964. a. $65. Association of Research Libraries, 21 Dupont Circle, Ste. 800, Washington, DC 20036. TEL 202-232-2466. Ed. Nicola Daval. circ. 500. (also avail. in microfiche from CIS; back issues avail.) **Indexed:** SRI.
—BLDSC (1682.110000).
Formerly: Academic Library Statistics (ISSN 0571-6519)

020 CN ISSN 0080-1569
ALBERTA RESEARCH COUNCIL. LIST OF PUBLICATIONS. 1968. a. free. Alberta Research Council, Publications Dept., P.O. Box 8330, Sta. F, Edmonton, Alta. T6H 5X2, Canada. TEL 403-450-5390. FAX 403-461-2651. TELEX 037-2147. **Document type:** bibliography.
Description: Bibliography of reports by the Alberta Research Council.

LIBRARY AND INFORMATION SCIENCES — ABSTRACTING, BIBLIOGRAPHIES, STATISTICS

973 015   US   ISSN 0003-6625
APPALACHIAN OUTLOOK; new sources of regional information. (Supplement to: Appalachian Bibliography) 1964. 3/yr. $6 to individuals; institutions $10 (effective 1992). West Virginia University Library, Main Office, Box 6069, Morgantown, WV 26506-6069. TEL 304-293-3640. Ed. Jo Baily Brown. circ. 130. (processed)

ARCHITECTURAL PERIODICALS INDEX. see ARCHITECTURE — Abstracting, Bibliographies, Statistics

011 020 070.5   AT   ISSN 0314-3767
AUSTRALIAN SOCIETY OF INDEXERS NEWSLETTER. 1977. 11/yr. (except Jan.) Aus.$30 (Metropolitan Aus.$35; foreign Aus.$35). Australian Society of Indexers, G.P.O. Box 1251L, Melbourne, Vic. 3001, Australia. TEL 61-03-418-7201. FAX 61-03-329-6185. Ed. Steve Sunter. adv.; bk.rev. circ. 270. (back issues avail.) Document type: newsletter.

BECTIS BULLETIN. see LIBRARY AND INFORMATION SCIENCES

020 011   JA   ISSN 0006-0860
BIBLIA. (Text in Japanese) 1949. 2/yr. 3500 Yen($25) per no. Tenri University Press, Tenri Central Library, Tenri-shi, Nara 632, Japan. TEL 07436-3-1515. FAX 07436-3-7723. Ed. Teruaki Iida. bk.rev.; bibl. circ. 1,000. (also avail. in microform; back issues avail.)
—UnCover.

020 011   PL   ISSN 0033-233X
BIBLIOGRAFIA ANALITYCZNA BIBLIOTEKOZNAWSTWA I INFORMACJI NAUKOWEJ. (Supplement to: Przeglad Biblioteczny) 1951. q. 60000 Zl. (price changes every quarter). Biblioteka Narodowa, Al. Niepodleglosci 213, 00-973 Warsaw, Poland. TEL 48-22-259271. FAX 48-22-255251. (Dist. by: P.P. CHZ Ars Polona, Krakowskie Przedmiescie 7, 00-068 Warsaw, Poland) Ed. Barbara Eychler. bk.rev.; abstr.; index. circ. 2,250. Document type: academic/scholarly publication, bibliography.
Formerly: Przeglad Pismiennictwa o Ksiazce.

020 016   AG   ISSN 0067-656X
BIBLIOGRAFIA BIBLIOTECOLOGICA ARGENTINA. 1963. irreg. price varies. (Universidad Nacional del Sur) Centro de Documentacion e Informacion Educativa, Paraguay 1657-ler. piso, 1062-Capital Federal, Argentina. bk.rev.; index. circ. 300. Document type: bibliography.
Description: Argentine bibliography on library science.

015   BL   ISSN 0102-3144
BIBLIOGRAFIA BRASILEIRA. 1918. q. Biblioteca Nacional do Brasil, Av. Rio Branco, 219, 20042 Rio de Janeiro, Brazil. TEL 021-262-8255. FAX 021-220-4173. TELEX 21-22941. circ. 2,000. (also avail. in microfiche)
●Also available online.
—BLDSC (1948.070000).
Formerly: Biblioteca Nacional de Brasil. Boletim Bibliografico (ISSN 0100-1876)

BIBLIOGRAPHICAL SOCIETY OF AUSTRALIA AND NEW ZEALAND. BULLETIN. see PUBLISHING AND BOOK TRADE

BIBLIOGRAPHIE DER ANTIQUARIATS-, AUKTIONS- UND KUNSTKATALOGE. see ART — Abstracting, Bibliographies, Statistics

020   GW   ISSN 0723-3590
BIBLIOGRAPHIE DER BUCH- UND BIBLIOTHEKSGESCHICHTE. 1982. a. DM.127. Bibliographischer Verlag Dr. Horst Meyer, Muehlenstr. 47, 49186 Bad Iburg, Germany. TEL 05403-2527. circ. 800. (back issues avail.) Document type: bibliography.

020   US   ISSN 0742-6879
BIBLIOGRAPHIES AND INDEXES IN LIBRARY AND INFORMATION SCIENCE. 1987. irreg. price varies. Greenwood Press, Inc. (Subsidiary of: Greenwood Publishing Group Inc.), 88 Post Rd. W., Box 5007, Westport, CT 06881-5007. TEL 203-226-3571. FAX 203-222-1502. Document type: monographic series, bibliography.

BIBLIOGRAPHY OF EDUCATION THESES IN AUSTRALIA. see EDUCATION — Abstracting, Bibliographies, Statistics

BIBLIOTECA DO SEJUR. BOLETIM. see LAW — Abstracting, Bibliographies, Statistics

020 011   RM   ISSN 1220-3076
BIBLIOTECONOMIE. CULEGERE DE TRADUCERI PRELUCRATE. 1965. q. 1568 lei. Biblioteca Nationala a Romaniei, Str. Ion Ghica 4, 79708 Bucharest, Rumania. abstr.; bibl. circ. 620.
—BLDSC (2016.587000).
Formerly: Revista de Referate in Bibliologie (ISSN 0034-8783)

BIBLOS; oesterreichische Zeitschrift fuer Buch- und Bibliothekswesen, Dokumentation, Bibliographie und Bibliophilie. see PUBLISHING AND BOOK TRADE — Abstracting, Bibliographies, Statistics

020   PO   ISSN 0253-343X
BOLETIM DE BIBLIOGRAFIA PORTUGUESA. DOCUMENTOS NAO TEXTUAIS. 1981. a. Biblioteca Nacional de Portugal, Campo Grande 83, 1751 Lisbon Codex, Portugal. TEL 01-7950130. FAX 01-7933807. index. circ. 500.
Supersedes in part (1935-1980): Boletim de Bibliografia Portuguesa (ISSN 0006-5897)

015   PO   ISSN 0253-3413
Z2715
BOLETIM DE BIBLIOGRAFIA PORTUGUESA. MONOGRAFIAS. 1981. q. Biblioteca Nacional de Portugal, Campo Grande 83, 1751 Lisbon Codex, Portugal. TEL 01-7950130. FAX 01-7933607. index. circ. 500.
Supersedes in part (1935-1980): Boletim de Bibliografia Portuguesa (ISSN 0006-5897)

020   PO   ISSN 0253-3421
Z6956.P8   CODEN: BBPSEH
BOLETIM DE BIBLIOGRAFIA PORTUGUESA. PUBLICACOES EM SERIE. 1981. a. Biblioteca Nacional de Portugal, Campo Grande 83, 1751 Lisbon Codex, Portugal. TEL 01-7950130. FAX 01-7933607. Ed. Fernanda Maria Campos. index. circ. 500. Document type: bulletin.
Supersedes in part (1935-1980): Boletim de Bibliografia Portuguesa (ISSN 0006-5897)

028.5   US   ISSN 0068-0192
Z1037
BOOKS FOR THE TEEN AGE. 1929. a. $7. New York Public Library, Office of Young Adult Services, 455 Fifth Ave., New York, NY 10016. TEL 212-340-0907. Ed. Marilee Foglesong. index. circ. 10,000.
Description: Lists approximately 1,250 titles on subjects of special interest and appeal to adolescents.

020   US
BOOKS IN LIBRARY AND INFORMATION SCIENCE SERIES. 1973. irreg., vol.55, 1993. price varies. Marcel Dekker, Inc., 270 Madison Ave., New York, NY 10016. TEL 212-696-9000. FAX 212-685-4540. TELEX 421419. Ed. A. Kent.
Refereed Serial

027   CN
BRITISH COLUMBIA PUBLIC LIBRARIES. STATISTICS. 1965. a. free. Ministry of Municipal Affairs, Recreation and Housing, Library Services Branch, Parliament Bldgs., Victoria, B.C. V8V 1X4, Canada. FAX 604-387-4048. stat. circ. 750.
Formerly: British Columbia. Library Development Commission. Public Libraries, Statistics (ISSN 0084-8034)

020   UK
BRITISH LIBRARY. NAME AUTHORITY LIST. 1981. m. £205 (foreign £250). British Library, National Bibliographic Service, Boston Spa, Wetherby, W. Yorks. LS23 7BQ, England. TEL 0937-546585. (microfiche) Document type: bibliography.

C P L BIBLIOGRAPHIES. (Council of Planning Librarians) see HOUSING AND URBAN PLANNING — Abstracting, Bibliographies, Statistics

020   US   ISSN 0741-031X
CALIFORNIA LIBRARY STATISTICS. 1976. a. $8. California State Library, Box 942837, Sacramento, CA 94237-0001. TEL 916-654-0174. FAX 916-654-0064. Indexed: Lib.Lit., Lib.Sci.Abstr., SRI.
Supersedes in part (in 1983): California Library Statistics and Directory (ISSN 0148-4583)

CANADIAN NURSES ASSOCIATION. HELEN K. MUSSALLEM LIBRARY. PERIODICAL HOLDINGS. see MEDICAL SCIENCES — Abstracting, Bibliographies, Statistics

016.051 020   CN   ISSN 0000-0345
Z6954.C2
CANADIAN SERIALS DIRECTORY/REPERTOIRE DES PUBLICATIONS SERIEES CANADIENNES. (Text in English and French) 1976. biennial. $45. Reference Press, P.O. Box 70, Teeswater, ON N0G 2S0, Canada. TEL 519-392-6634. Ed. Gordon Ripley; Pub. Gordon Ripley. bibl. circ. 1,000. Document type: directory.
Description: Lists magazines, newsletters, daily newspapers, annuals, yearbooks and journals presently being published in Canada.

CATALOG OF CURRENT LAW TITLES; recent acquisitions of major legal libraries. see LAW — Abstracting, Bibliographies, Statistics

CATALOG OF NEW FOREIGN AND INTERNATIONAL LAW TITLES. see LAW — Abstracting, Bibliographies, Statistics

020   MX
CATALOGO DE PROGRAMAS DE FORMACION DE RECURSOS HUMANOS EN INFORMATICA. 1983. irreg., latest 1987 ed. Instituto Nacional de Estadistica, Geografia e Informatica, Secretaria de Programacion y Presupuesto, Prol. Heroe de Nacozari 2301 Sur, Puerta 11, Acceso, 20270 Aguascalientes, Ags., Mexico. TEL 49-18-19-48. FAX 491-807-39.

020   UK   ISSN 0008-7629
Z695
CATALOGUE & INDEX. 1966. q. £10($12) to non-members. Library Association, Cataloguing and Indexing Group, c/o C.J. Koster, 18 Apple Grove, Enfield, Middx. EN1 3DD, England. Ed. R. Brunt. bk.rev.; cum.index: 1966-67, 1968-69. circ. 3,500. (also avail. in microfilm) Indexed: Lib.Lit., Lib.Sci.Abstr., LISA.
—BLDSC (3086.028000); SWETS; UMI.

020   US   ISSN 0084-6902
CENTER FOR CHINESE RESEARCH MATERIALS. BIBLIOGRAPHICAL SERIES. 1968. irreg. price varies. Center for Chinese Research Materials, Box 3090, Oakton, VA 22124. TEL 703-281-7731. FAX 703-281-1825. Ed. Pingfeng Chi.

020   AT   ISSN 1038-5878
▼**CENTRE FOR INFORMATION STUDIES. BIBLIOGRAPHIES AND INDEXES.** 1992. irreg. Centre for Information Studies, Charles Sturt University - Riverina, Locked Bag 660, Wagga Wagga, N.S.W. 2678, Australia. TEL 069-222325. FAX 069-222733. Ed. Stuart Ferguson. Document type: bibliography, abstracting/indexing.

310   UK   ISSN 0309-6629
Z791.A1
CHARTERED INSTITUTE OF PUBLIC FINANCE AND ACCOUNTANCY. PUBLIC LIBRARIES STATISTICS. ACTUALS. 1957. a. £60. Chartered Institute of Public Finance and Accountancy, 3 Robert St., London WC2N 6BH, England. stat. (back issues avail.)

310   UK   ISSN 0307-0522
Z791.A1
CHARTERED INSTITUTE OF PUBLIC FINANCE AND ACCOUNTANCY. PUBLIC LIBRARIES STATISTICS. ESTIMATES. 1974. a. £32. Chartered Institute of Public Finance and Accountancy, 3 Robert St., London WC2N 6BH, England. TEL 071-895-8823. FAX 071-895-8825. (back issues avail.)

LIBRARY AND INFORMATION SCIENCES — ABSTRACTING, BIBLIOGRAPHIES, STATISTICS

020 016   CH   ISSN 0301-5165
Z3111
CHINESE NATIONAL BIBLIOGRAPHY. Key Title: Zhonghua Minguo Chuban Tushumulu. (Text mainly in Chinese; occasionally in English) 1960. a. $7. National Central Library, Bureau of International Exchange of Publications, 20 Chung Shan S. Rd., Taipei, Taiwan 10040, Republic of China. FAX 02-311-0155. bibl.
● Available only on CD-ROM.
   Formerly (until 1970): Hsin Shu Chien Pao.

011 020   US
COLLEGE READING ASSOCIATION. MONOGRAPHS. irreg. College Reading Association, c/o Dr. E. Sutton Flynt, Dept. Curriculum and Instruction, Pittsburg State University, Pittsburg, KS 56762. TEL 316-235-4494. (reprint service avail. from UMI) **Document type:** monographic series.

025 011   US
COMPUTER LIBRARY'S COMPUTER PERIODICALS DATABASE. 1988. m. $765. Ziff Communications, One Park Ave., New York, NY 10016. TEL 212-503-4400. FAX 212-503-4414. bk.rev.
● Also available online.
Also available on CD-ROM.
   Formerly: Computer Library.
   Description: For information center managers, PC coordinators, MIS directors, product planners, developers and marketers, purchasing agents, systems integrators, journalists and industry analysts. Serves as a comprehensive desktop reference for anyone needing to access and manage large amounts of timely information about the computer industry.

020   UK
COUNCIL OF POLYTECHNIC LIBRARIANS. ANNUAL STATISTICS. a. £30 (effective 1994). Council of Polytechnic Librarians, c/o Christine Moon, Brighton Polytechnic, Watts Bldg., Moulsecoomb, Brighton, Sussex BN2 4GJ, England. stat.

CURRENT RESEARCH IN BRITAIN. BIOLOGICAL SCIENCES. see BIOLOGY — Abstracting, Bibliographies, Statistics

CURRENT RESEARCH IN BRITAIN. PHYSICAL SCIENCES. see SCIENCES: COMPREHENSIVE WORKS — Abstracting, Bibliographies, Statistics

CURRENT RESEARCH IN BRITAIN. SOCIAL SCIENCES. see SOCIAL SCIENCES: COMPREHENSIVE WORKS — Abstracting, Bibliographies, Statistics

020   DK
D T L - DANSK FORENING FOR INFORMATION OG DOKUMENTATION. SKRIFTSERIE. 1960. a. DKK 100. (Dansk Teknisk Litteraturselskab) D T L, c/o D T B, Anker Engelunds Vej 1, DK-2800 Lyngby, Denmark.
   Formerly: Dansk Teknisk Litteraturselskab. Skriftserie (ISSN 0416-6981)

310   GW   ISSN 0720-9681
DEUTSCHE BIBLIOTHEKSSTATISTIK TEIL A: OEFFENTLICHE BIBLIOTHEKEN. 1979. a. DM.36. Deutsches Bibliotheksinstitut, Abt. 1 - Publikationen, Bundesallee 184-185, 10717 Berlin, Germany. TEL 030-8505-0. FAX 030-8505-100. circ. 630. **Document type:** bulletin.

310   GW   ISSN 0720-969X
DEUTSCHE BIBLIOTHEKSSTATISTIK TEIL B: WISSENSCHAFTLICHE BIBLIOTHEKEN. 1979. a. DM.36. Deutsches Bibliotheksinstitut, Abt. 1 - Publikationen, Bundesallee 184-185, 10717 Berlin, Germany. TEL 030-8505-0. FAX 030-8505-100. circ. 450. **Document type:** bulletin.

310   GW   ISSN 0722-639X
DEUTSCHE BIBLIOTHEKSSTATISTIK TEIL C: WISSENSCHAFTLICHE SPEZIALBIBLIOTHEKEN. 1981. a. DM.30. Deutsches Bibliotheksinstitut, Abt. 1 - Publikationen, Bundesallee 184-185, 10717 Berlin, Germany. TEL 030-8505-0. FAX 030-8505-100. (also avail. in diskette format) **Document type:** directory.

310   GW   ISSN 0177-1396
DEUTSCHE BIBLIOTHEKSSTATISTIK TEIL D: GESAMTSTATISTIK. 1982. a. DM.30. Deutsches Bibliotheksinstitut, Abt. 1 - Publikationen, Bundesallee 184-185, 10717 Berlin, Germany. TEL 030-8505-0. FAX 030-8505-100. (also avail. in diskette format) **Document type:** bulletin.

020   US   ISSN 0162-0290
Z732.O8
DIRECTORY AND STATISTICS OF OREGON LIBRARIES. 1913. a. $14. Oregon State Library, Salem, OR 97310-0640. TEL 503-378-2112. FAX 503-588-7119. circ. 650. **Document type:** directory.
   Formerly: Directory of Oregon Libraries.
   Description: Provides directory and statistical information for public, academic and special libraries in Oregon.

010 020   UN
DOCUMENTATION, LIBRARIES AND ARCHIVES: BIBLIOGRAPHIES AND REFERENCE WORKS. Spanish edition: Documentacion, Bibliotecas, y Archivos: Bibliografias y Obras de Referencia (ISSN 0252-5364); French edition: Documentation, Bibliotheques et Archives: Bibliographies et Ouvrages de Reference (ISSN 0251-432X) 1972. irreg. price varies. Unesco, 7-9 Place de Fontenoy, 75700 Paris, France.
   Formerly: Unesco Bibliographical Handbooks (ISSN 0082-7460)

020   SZ   ISSN 0514-0668
EIDGENOESSISCHE TECHNISCHE HOCHSCHULE ZUERICH. BIBLIOTHEK. SCHRIFTENREIHE. 1948. irreg. price varies. E T H - Bibliothek (Eidgenoessische Technische Hochschule), CH-8092 Zurich, Switzerland. circ. 100. **Document type:** bibliography.

550 910   US   ISSN 0743-7250
GOLDTHWAIT POLAR LIBRARY ACCESSIONS LIST. irreg. free. Ohio State University, Byrd Polar Research Center, Goldthwait Polar Library, 125 S. Oval Mall, Columbus, OH 43210-1308. TEL 614-292-6715. FAX 614-292-4697. TELEX 4945696 OSUPOLAR. (looseleaf format; back issues avail.)
   Formerly (until 1977): I P S Accessions List.
   Description: Listings of new acquisitions in the Goldthwait Polar Library.

029 011   SA
GREY BIBLIOGRAPHIES. 1946. irreg., no.19, 1991. price varies. South African Library, P.O. Box 496, Cape Town 8000, South Africa. TEL 27-21-246320. FAX 27-21-244848. TELEX 5-22604 SA. **Document type:** bibliography.
   Description: Bibliographies of subjects of South African interest.

028.1 011   US   ISSN 0017-5269
Z881.C57
GUIDE POST. 1926. 10/yr. $15 to non-members; members free. Public Library of Cincinnati and Hamilton County, 800 Vine St., Cincinnati, OH 45202. TEL 513-369-6960. FAX 513-396-6067. Ed. Amy Banister. bk.rev.; circ. 3,000 (controlled). **Document type:** consumer publication.
   Description: Notes and comments about new materials in the collections of the Public Library at Cincinnati and Hamilton County.

027.8   US
GUIDE TO REFERENCE BOOKS FOR SCHOOL MEDIA CENTERS. irreg. $38.50. Libraries Unlimited, Inc., Box 6633, Englewood, CO 80155-6633. TEL 800-237-6124. FAX 303-220-8843. Ed. Margaret Irby Nichols.
   Description: Comprehensive guide to current reference materials for school media centers; covers a wide range of subjects, of age and reading levels, depths of information and prices.

011   AT   ISSN 0156-6717
GUIDELINES; a subject guide for Australian libraries. 1969. 9/yr. (plus a. cumulation). Aus.$90. Bibliographic Services, P.O. Box 2, Mount Waverley, Vic. 3149, Australia. Ed. Keith S. Darling. adv. circ. 1,800. (also avail. in microfiche; diskette format) **Document type:** abstracting/indexing.
● Also available on CD-ROM.
   Description: Subject index to Australian and selected overseas periodicals chosen for secondary schools.

026 610.73   CN
HELEN K. MUSSALLEM LIBRARY SELECTED ACQUISITIONS LIST. (Text in English, French) bi-m. Can.$20. Canadian Nurses Association - Association des Infirmieres et Infirmiers du Canada, 50 Driveway, Ottawa, ON K2P 1E2, Canada. TEL 613-237-2133. FAX 613-237-3520. **Document type:** catalog.
   Description: Partial catalogs of the library's collection highlighting some of its holdings. Listed according to subject.

020   AT
HOW AND WHERE DIRECTORY; an index to sources of information. irreg. Aus.$18. School Library Association of New South Wales, P.O. Box 1336, Parramatta, N.S.W. 2124, Australia. circ. 1,000. **Document type:** directory.
   Description: Lists sources of school library materials.

020 016   HU   ISSN 0046-8304
Z671
HUNGARIAN LIBRARY AND INFORMATION SCIENCE ABSTRACTS. (Text in English) 1971. s-a. $10 or exchange basis. Orszagos Szechenyi Konyvtar, Konyvtartudomanyi es Modszertani Kozpont - Centre for Library and Information Science at the National Szechenyi Library, Budavari Palota F epulet, 1827 Budapest, Hungary. TEL 1750-686. TELEX 224226 BIBLN H. Ed. Agnes Feimer. circ. 350. (back issues avail.) **Document type:** abstracting/indexing.
—BLDSC (4337.032300).
   Description: Lists and abstracts books and periodical articles in the field that may be of interest to foreign colleagues.

020.6   NE   ISSN 0109-5366
Z666
I F L A COMMUNICATIONS; bibliography of IFLA conference papers. 1984. a. fl.22. International Federation of Library Associations and Institutions - Federation Internationale des Associations de Bibliothecaires et des Bibliotheques, P.O.B. 95312, 2509 CH The Hague, Netherlands. TEL 31-70-3140884. FAX 31-70-3834827. TELEX 34402 KB NL. circ. 100. **Document type:** bibliography.

600 016   US   ISSN 0019-0136
I N F O. 1965. bi-m. free. Tulsa City-County Library System, Business and Technology Dept., 400 Civic Center, Tulsa, OK 74103. TEL 918-596-7988. FAX 918-596-7895. Ed. Karen S. Curtis. adv.; bk.rev.; bibl.; circ. 1,400 (controlled). (processed) **Document type:** newsletter.
   Description: Informs the community about government documents, on-line data bases, books, plus programs and services available at the library.

015   BL   ISSN 0019-0276
I P A S E BIBLIOTECA INFORMA.* 1965. q. free. Instituto de Previdencia e Assistencia dos Servidores do Estado, Divisao de Relacoes Publicas, Biblioteca, Rua Pedro Lessa 36, 13 Andar, Rio de Janeiro, G B, Brazil. circ. 400 (controlled). (microform)

020   UK
INDEX LIBRARY. 1888. irreg. £15 to individuals; institutions £25. British Record Society, Stone Barn Farm, Sutherland Rd., Longsdon, Stoke-On-Trent ST9 9QD, England. TEL 0538-385024. TELEX 0782-613847. (also avail. in microfiche from CHL; reprint service avail. from KTO)
   Description: Indexes to testamentary material.

020   UN   ISSN 0073-6074
Z6514.T7
INDEX TRANSLATIONUM. (Text in English and French) 1950. a. $80. Unesco, 7-9 Place de Fontenoy, 75700 Paris, France. TEL 45-77-16-10. (Dist. in U.S. by: Unipub, 4611-F Assembly Dr., Lanham, MD 20706-4391) (also avail. in microfilm; reprint service avail. from KTO)

020   II
INDIAN LIBRARY AND INFORMATION SCIENCE INDEXES SERIES. irreg. Gina House Publishers, 71 Sector 27-A, Chandigarh 160019, India.

LIBRARY AND INFORMATION SCIENCES — ABSTRACTING, BIBLIOGRAPHIES, STATISTICS

020 016   II   ISSN 0019-5790
INDIAN LIBRARY SCIENCE ABSTRACTS. (Text in English) 1967. a. Rs.200($35) Indian Association of Special Libraries and Information Centres, P-291 C.I.T. Scheme No. 6M, Kankurgachi, Calcutta 700 054, India. TEL 34-9651. Ed.Bd. **Document type:** abstracting/indexing.
—BLDSC (4422.270000).

020   AG   ISSN 0327-2915
INDICE DE CONTENIDOS - SERIE 1: CIENCIAS DE LA INFORMACION. (Text in English, French, Spanish) 1991. m. $15. Centro Argentino de Informacion Cientifica y Tecnologica, Moreno 431-33, piso 3, 1091 Buenos Aires, Argentina. TEL 34-1777. **Document type:** abstracting/indexing.

INDICE ESPANOL DE CIENCIAS SOCIALES. SERIES D: SCIENCE AND SCIENTIFIC INFORMATION. see *SCIENCES: COMPREHENSIVE WORKS — Abstracting, Bibliographies, Statistics*

011 020   US   ISSN 0738-1522
Z674.5.U5
INFORMATION AMERICA. 1977-1990; resumed 1993. 3/yr. $80. Neal-Schuman Publishers, Inc., 100 Varick St., New York, NY 10013. TEL 212-925-8650. Ed. Tracy Davis. **Document type:** bibliography.
—BLDSC (4481.755000).
Formerly (until vol.6, 1983): Sources: A Guide to Print and Nonprint Materials Available from Organizations, Industry, Government Agencies, and Specialized Publishers (ISSN 0145-2355)

020   US   ISSN 0360-0971
Z699.A1   CODEN: INRBDY
INFORMATION REPORTS AND BIBLIOGRAPHIES. 1972. 6/yr. $95 (foreign $125). Science Associates International, Inc., 465 West End Ave., New York, NY 10024. TEL 212-873-0656. FAX 212-873-5587. Ed. Ivan Lyons. (reprint service avail. from UMI) **Indexed:** LHTN, Lib.Lit.
—BLDSC (4494.130000); Faxon; SWETS; CASDDS.
Formerly: Information-Part 2-Reports - Bibliographies (ISSN 0046-9378)

029.7 651.8 016   US   ISSN 0020-0239
Z699.A1
INFORMATION SCIENCE ABSTRACTS. 1965. m. $515 (foreign $605) (effective 1993). (American Society for Information Science) I F I - Plenum (Subsidiary of: Plenum Publishing Corp.), 233 Spring St., New York, NY 10013. TEL 212-620-8000. FAX 212-463-0742. TELEX 23-421139. (Co-sponsors: Special Libraries Association; American Chemical Society, Division of Chemical Information; American Society of Indexers; Medical Library Association; Association of Library and Information Science Education) Eds. Harry Allcock, Anne Meagher. adv.; bk.rev.; index. (also avail. in microfilm from JSC; back issues avail.) **Document type:** abstracting/indexing.
●Also available online. Vendor(s): DIALOG Information Services, Inc. (File no.202).
—BLDSC (4494.230000); UMI. **CCC.**
Formerly: Documentation Abstracts.

020   UK
INFORMATION SOURCES IN GREY LITERATURE. irreg., 3rd ed. 1994. $60. Bowker - Saur Ltd., A Reed Reference Publishing Company, Part of the Reed Elsevier group, Maypole House, Maypole Rd., E. Grinstead, W. Sussex RH19 1HH, England. TEL 0342-330100. FAX 0342-330191. (Subscr. to: c/o Butterworths Service Co., Borough Green, Sevenoaks, Kent TN15 8PH, England. TEL 0732-884567) Ed. C.P. Auger.
Description: Assists in locating publications with little or no general distribution; such as government reports, conference proceedings, corporate research papers, speeches.

023   US   ISSN 1061-3609
▼**INFORMED LIBRARIAN: PROFESSIONAL READING FOR THE INFORMATION PROFESSIONAL.** 1992. m. $99. Infosources Publishing, 140 Norma Rd., Teaneck, NJ 07666. TEL 201-836-7072. Ed. Arlene L. Eis. (back issues avail.) **Document type:** abstracting/indexing.
Description: Compilation of tables of contents of over 130 library and information science-related journals - domestic and foreign.

020   SI   ISSN 0217-0914
INSTITUTE OF SOUTHEAST ASIAN STUDIES. LIBRARY SERIES. (Text in English) 1971. irreg., no.19, 1992. price varies. Institute of Southeast Asian Studies, Heng Mui Keng Terrace, Pasir Panjang, Singapore 0511, Singapore. TEL 7780955. FAX 7781735. TELEX RS 37068 ISEAS. (Subscr. in U.S. to: Ashgate, Old Post Rd., Brookfield, VT 05036. TEL 802-276-3162) **Document type:** bibliography.
Formerly: Institute of Southeast Asian Studies. Library Bulletin (ISSN 0217-0914)
Description: Bibliographies on Southeast Asia.

INTERNATIONAL ASSOCIATION OF AGRICULTURAL INFORMATION SPECIALISTS. QUARTERLY BULLETIN. see *AGRICULTURE — Abstracting, Bibliographies, Statistics*

020   US   ISSN 1053-8291
TR835
INTERNATIONAL IMAGING SOURCE BOOK. 1972. biennial. $99.50. Microfilm Publishing, Inc., Box 950, Larchmont, NY 10538-0950. TEL 914-834-3044. FAX 914-834-3993. Ed. Mitchell M. Badler. adv.; bk.rev.; illus.; stat. circ. 3,500. **Document type:** directory.
—BLDSC (4541.038860).
Former titles: International Micrographics Source Book (ISSN 0272-0310); International Microfilm Source Book (ISSN 0362-4498); Microfilm Source Book (ISSN 0090-2861)
Description: Gives sources of supply for products and services in twenty areas related to business imaging.

020 016   IT   ISSN 0075-0026
INVENTARI DEI MANOSCRITTI DELLE BIBLIOTECHE D'ITALIA. 1890. irreg., vol.108, 1993. price varies. Casa Editrice Leo S. Olschki, Casella Postale 66, 50100 Florence, Italy. TEL 055-6530684. FAX 055-6530214. circ. 1,000. **Document type:** monographic series.

020 011   IC   ISSN 0254-1378
Z2590.A3
ISLENSK BOKASKRA/ICELANDIC NATIONAL BIBLIOGRAPHY. (Supplement avail.: Islensk Hljodritaskra) 1944. a. ISK 1500($27) (incl. supplement). Landsbokasafn Islands - National Library of Iceland, Safnahusinu, Hverfisgoetu 15, P.O. Box 1210, 121 Reykjavik, Iceland. TEL 354-1-68-64. Ed. Hildur G. Eythorsdottir. **Document type:** bibliography.
Supersedes in part (in 1975): Iceland. Landsbokasafn Islands. Arbok (ISSN 0254-1335)

050   US   ISSN 0893-5386
Z6945
JOURNAL HOLDINGS IN THE NATIONAL CAPITAL AREA. 1969. biennial. $190. Interlibrary Users Association, c/o Macron Systems, Inc., 212 Elmhurst Circle, Evans City, PA 16033. TEL 412-538-5044. Ed. Mary Lynn Kingston. charts; circ. 250 (controlled). (processed) **Document type:** catalog, directory.
Formerly: Journal Holdings in the Washington - Baltimore Area (ISSN 0362-4544)

050 015   II
JOURNAL OF INDEXING & REFERENCE WORK. (Text in English) 1966. m. Rs.15($6) Mukherjee Library, 1 Gopi Mohan Dutta Lane, Calcutta 700003, India. Ed. Amitabha Chatterjee. adv.; bk.rev.; bibl.; index. circ. 200.
Formerly: Indian Periodicals Record (ISSN 0019-6088)

KAGAKU GIJUTSU BUNKEN TOYAMA/TOYAMA SCIENCE AND TECHNICAL DOCUMENTS. see *TECHNOLOGY: COMPREHENSIVE WORKS — Abstracting, Bibliographies, Statistics*

500 016   PL   ISSN 0022-9172
KARTY DOKUMENTACYJNE/DOCUMENTATION CARDS.* 1956-19?? s-m. price varies. Centrum Informacji Naukowej, Technicznej i Ekonomicznej, Al. Niepodleglosci 188, 00-931 Warsaw, Poland. (cards)

020   KE
KENYA NATIONAL LIBRARY SERVICES. BIBLIOGRAPHY. (Text in English) 1980. a. EAs.95($15.50) Kenya National Library Services, P.O. Box 30573, Nairobi, Kenya. FAX 254-2-721749. TELEX KENLIB. Ed. Larissa Oboyo. circ. 500. (back issues avail.) **Document type:** bibliography.

020   KE
KENYA NATIONAL LIBRARY SERVICES. CLASSIFIED ACCESSION LIST OF BOOKS ADDED TO STOCK. (Text in English) q. free. Kenya National Library Services, P.O. Box 30573, Nairobi, Kenya. FAX 254-2-721749. TELEX KENLIB. circ. 50. **Document type:** bibliography.
Supersedes (in 1975): Kenya National Library Services. A Brief Selection of Recent Additions.

020   KE
KENYAN PERIODICALS DIRECTORY. (Text in English) 1984. biennial. EAs.75($9.50) Kenya National Library Services, National Reference and Bibliographic Department, P.O. Box 30573, Nairobi, Kenya. FAX 254-2-721749. TELEX KENLIB. Ed. Larissa Ondoyo. circ. 1,000. **Document type:** directory.

029 011 020   UK   ISSN 0143-9553
   CODEN: KISDDW
KEYWORD INDEX TO SERIAL TITLES. 1980. a. (plus q. updates). £306 (overseas £311). British Library, Document Supply Centre, Publishing Section, Boston Spa, Wetherby, W. Yorks. LS23 7BQ, England. TEL 0937-546080. FAX 0937-546286. (Subscr. to: Turpin Distribution Services Ltd., Blackhorse Rd., Letchworth, Herts. SG6 1HN, England. TEL 0462-672555. FAX 0462-480947) (microfiche) **Document type:** abstracting/indexing.
—CASDDS.

020   US   ISSN 1064-1211
   CODEN: KEYWEO
THE KEYWORDS (PORT ARANSAS). 1970. 6/yr. $30 to non-members. American Society of Indexers, Inc., Box 386, Port Aransas, TX 78373. TEL 805-434-2330. FAX 512-749-6334. Ed. Anne Leach. cum.index: 1970-1983. circ. 1,000. (back issues avail.) **Document type:** newsletter.
Formerly (until Jul. 1992): American Society of Indexers Newsletter (ISSN 0733-3048)

KNJIZNICA; glasilo Zveze Bibliotekarskih Drustev Slovenije. see *LIBRARY AND INFORMATION SCIENCES*

020   GW   ISSN 0721-7587
KOELNER ARBEITEN ZUM BIBLIOTHEKS- UND DOKUMENTATIONSWESEN. 1981. irreg., no.17, 1992. price varies. (Fachhochschule fuer Bibliotheks- und Dokumentationswesen in Koeln) Greven Verlag Koeln GmbH, Neue Weyerstr. 1-3, 50676 Cologne, Germany. TEL 0221-2033-0. FAX 0221-2033-162. circ. 700. **Document type:** bibliography.
Continues: Bibliothekar-Lehrinstitut des Landes Nordrhein-Westfalen. Arbeiten aus dem B L I (ISSN 0069-5858) & Bibliothekar-Lehrinstitut des Landes Nordrhein-Westfalen. Bibliographische Hefte (ISSN 0069-5866)

020 029.7 016   UK   ISSN 0024-2179
Z671
L I S A: LIBRARY & INFORMATION SCIENCE ABSTRACTS. Key Title: Library & Information Science Abstracts. 1969. m. (plus a. cum. index). £325($630) Bowker - Saur Ltd., A Reed Reference Publishing Company, Part of the Reed Elsevier group, Maypole House, Maypole Rd., E. Grinstead, W. Sussex RH19 1HH, England. TEL 0342-330-100. FAX 0342-330-191. (Subscr. to: c/o Butterworths Service Co., Borough Green, Sevenoaks, Kent TN15 8PH, England. TEL 0732-884567) Ed. N. Moore. index, cum.index. circ. 2,500. (also avail. in magnetic tape) **Indexed:** AESIS, Info.Media & Tech. **Document type:** abstracting/indexing.
●Also available online. Vendor(s): BRS Online Products (LISA), DIALOG Information Services, Inc. (File no.61/LISA), Orbit Search Service (LISA). Also available on CD-ROM. Producer(s): Bowker - Saur Ltd..
—BLDSC (5188.700000); UMI.
Supersedes: Library Science Abstracts.

LIBRARY AND INFORMATION SCIENCES — ABSTRACTING, BIBLIOGRAPHIES, STATISTICS

020 029.7 UK ISSN 0966-8799
▼ **L I S A PLUS.** (Library and Information Science Abstracts) 1992. q. £875($1575) Bowker - Saur Ltd., A Reed Reference Publishing Company, Part of the Reed Elsevier group, Maypole House, Maypole Rd., E. Grinstead, W. Sussex, England. TEL 0342-330100. FAX 0342-330191. (Subscr. to: Butterworths Service Cc., Borough Green, Sevenoaks, Kent TN15 8PH, England. TEL 0732-884567) (avail. for MS-DOS version) **Document type:** abstracting/indexing.
● Available only on CD-ROM. Producer(s): Bowker - Saur Ltd.

020 UK ISSN 0967-487X
L I S U ANNUAL LIBRARY STATISTICS; a ten year trend analysis. 1985. a. £24. Loughborough University, Library and Information Statistics Unit, Loughborough, Leics. LE11 3TU, England. TEL 0509-223071. FAX 0509-223072. (Co-sponsor: British Library) Ed. John Sumsion. circ. 240. **Document type:** trade publication.
—BLDSC (5276.225000).
Formerly (until 1993): Public Library Statistics (ISSN 0951-8983)

LEGAL INFORMATION MANAGEMENT INDEX. see *LAW — Abstracting, Bibliographies, Statistics*

020 US ISSN 0093-1888
LIBRARIANS' HANDBOOK. 1971. a. free to qualified personnel. EBSCO Industries, Inc., Title Informtion Department, 5724 Hwy. 280 East, Birmingham, AL 35242. TEL 205-991-6600. FAX 205-995-1518. TELEX 78-2661. (Subscr. to: EBSCO Subscription Services, Box 2543, Birmingham, AL 35201. TEL 800-826-3024) Ed. Mary Beth Vanderpoorten. adv. circ. 25,000. **Document type:** catalog.
—BLDSC (5186.856750).

020 US
LIBRARY AND INFORMATION SCIENCE EDUCATION STATISTICAL REPORT. a. $34. Association for Library and Information Science Education, 4101 Lake Boone Tr., Ste. 201, Raleigh, NC 27607. TEL 919-787-5181. Ed. Timothy W. Sineath. (back issues avail.)
Formerly: A L I S E Statistics Report (ISSN 0739-506X)

020 CN ISSN 0820-0521
LIBRARY AND INFORMATION SCIENCE UPDATE. 1976. m. Can.$24($43) University of Toronto, Library and Information Science Library, 140 St. George Street, Toronto, ON M5S 1A1, Canada. TEL 416-978-7060. FAX 416-978-5762. Ed. K. Lavin. circ. 200. (back issues avail.)
Description: Geared to the needs of information professionals: abstracts of current periodical articles in the fields of library and information science.

020 US ISSN 0085-2767
Z671
LIBRARY LIT. 1971. a. price varies. Scarecrow Press, Inc., 52 Liberty St., Metuchen, NJ 08840. TEL 800-537-7107. Ed. Jane Anne Hannigan. circ. 1,500.

020 029 016 US ISSN 0024-2373
Z666
LIBRARY LITERATURE; an index to library and information science publications. 1921. bi-m. (a. cumulations). service basis. H.W. Wilson Co., 950 University Ave., Bronx, NY 10452. TEL 800-367-6770. FAX 718-590-1617. TELEX 4990003HWILSON. Ed. Cathy Rentschler. (also avail. in magnetic tape)
● Also available online. Vendor(s): BRS Online Products (WILB), Wilsonline (File LIB).
Also available on CD-ROM. Producer(s): H.W. Wilson (WILSONDISC).
—BLDSC (5200.250000).

020 US
LIBRARY OF CONGRESS CLASSIFICATION SCHEDULES: A CUMULATION OF ADDITIONS AND CHANGES. 1971. irreg., latest 1992. $2925 (microfiche ed. $1780). Gale Research Inc., 835 Penobscot Bldg., Detroit, MI 48226. TEL 313-961-2242. FAX 313-961-6083. TELEX 810-221-7086. Eds. Kathy Droste, Rita Runchock. (also avail. in microfiche)
Description: Lists changes in Library of Congress classification schedules.

025 US ISSN 1071-3409
▼ **LIBRARY PERIODICALS: AN ANNUAL GUIDE FOR SUBSCRIBERS, AUTHORS AND PUBLICISTS.** 1993. a. $22 (effective 1994). Periodical Guides Publishing Company, 1633 Pearl St., Alameda, CA 94501. TEL 510-865-7439. Ed. Molly Skeen. **Document type:** directory, bibliography.
Description: Annotated guide to more than 150 periodicals in the library and information sciences fields. Serves as an author's reference, selection tool, and publicist's guide.

LIST OF CANADIAN NURSING-RELATED PERIODICALS. see *MEDICAL SCIENCES — Abstracting, Bibliographies, Statistics*

020 011 IE ISSN 0024-631X
LONG ROOM. 1970. a. a. Ir£10. Trinity College, Friends of the Library, College St., Dublin 2, Ireland. TEL 01-7022087. FAX 01-6719003. TELEX 93782. Ed. V.S. Kinane. adv.; bibl.; illus. circ. 700. (back issues avail.) Indexed: Br.Hum.Ind. **Document type:** academic/scholarly publication.
—BLDSC (5294.225000).

020 016 HU ISSN 0133-736X
MAGYAR KONYVTARI SZAKIRODALOM BIBLIOGRAFIAJA/HUNGARIAN LIBRARY LITERATURE. 1965. q. $30. Orszagos Szechenyi Konyvtar, Konyvtartudomanyi es Modszertani Kozpont - Centre for Library and Information Science at the National Szechenyi Library, Budavari Palota F epulet, 1827 Budapest, Hungary. TEL 1750-686. TELEX 224226 BIBLN H. Ed. Ferencne Javori. circ. 700. (back issues avail.) **Document type:** bibliography.
Formerly: Gyorstajekoztato a Magyar Konyvtartudomanyi Irodalomrol (ISSN 0017-6052)

MAGYAR TUDOMANYOS AKADEMIA KONYVTARANAK KOZLEMENYEI/PUBLICATIONES BIBLIOTHECAE ACADEMIAE SCIENTIARUM HUNGARICAE. see *SCIENCES: COMPREHENSIVE WORKS — Abstracting, Bibliographies, Statistics*

020 610 UG
MAKERERE UNIVERSITY. ALBERT COOK LIBRARY. LIBRARY BULLETIN AND ACCESSION LIST. irreg., no.2, 1977. free. Makerere University, Albert Cook Library, Makerere Medical School, Box 7072, Kampala, Uganda. Ed. Maria Gioretti Musoke. circ. controlled. (processed; back issues avail.)
Description: Each issue consists of hundreds of bibliographic entries pertaining to monographs only.

020 CN
MANITOBA PUBLIC LIBRARY STATISTICS. 1975. biennial. free. Public Library Services, 1525 1st St., Unit 200, Brandon, MB R7A 7A1, Canada. TEL 204-726-6590. FAX 204-726-6868. circ. 450.

020 UK ISSN 0266-4879
MICROINDEXER. 1983. irreg. membership. Society of Indexers, 38 Rochester Rd., London NW1 9JJ, England. TEL 071-916-7809. Ed. P. McLean. adv.; bk.rev. circ. 1,000. **Document type:** newsletter.
—BLDSC (5759.148000).
Description: Information on indexing by micro-computers and word processors.

021 US
MONTANA PUBLIC LIBRARY. ANNUAL REPORT OF STATISTICS. 1989. a. State Library, 1515 E. Sixth Ave., Helena, MT 59620. TEL 406-444-3115. FAX 406-444-5612. (also avail. in microfiche from CIS) Indexed: SRI.
Description: Contains statistics on library income and expenditures, library collections, staff information, library service and resource sharing.

020 II
N A S S D O C RESEARCH INFORMATION SERIES. CURRENT CONTENTS OF INDIAN SOCIAL JOURNALS. (Text in English) 1986. bi-m. Indian Council of Social Science Research, National Social Science Documentation Centre, 35, Ferozshah Rd., New Delhi 110 001, India. TEL 91-11-385959. FAX 91-11-388037. TELEX 31-61083-ISSR-IN. Eds. S.C. Garkoti, Meena Walia. **Document type:** abstracting/indexing.
Formerly: N A S S D O C Research Information Series. Paging Periodical.
Description: Reproduces content pages of Indian social science journals, and author and subject index.

020 016 US
N T I S ALERTS: LIBRARY & INFORMATION SCIENCES. w. $135 (foreign $195). U.S. National Technical Information Service, 5285 Port Royal Rd., Springfield, VA 22161. TEL 703-487-4630. FAX 703-321-8547. TELEX 64617. index. (back issues avail.) **Document type:** abstracting/indexing.
—BLDSC (6180.600580).
Former titles: Abstract Newsletter: Library and Information Sciences; Weekly Abstract Newsletter: Library and Information Sciences; Weekly Government Abstracts. Library and Information Sciences (ISSN 0364-6467)

NATIONAL UNION CATALOG. AUDIOVISUAL MATERIALS. see *MOTION PICTURES — Abstracting, Bibliographies, Statistics*

020 655 011 US ISSN 0734-7650
NATIONAL UNION CATALOG. BOOKS. 1956. m. $660 to N. American libraries; foreign libraries $765. (U.S. Library of Congress) Advanced Library Systems, Inc., 100 Brickstone Sq., Box 246, Andover, MA 01810. TEL 508-470-0610. FAX 508-475-1072. circ. 2,093. (also avail. in microfiche from ADL) **Document type:** catalog.
Formerly (until 1983): National Union Catalog (ISSN 0028-0348)

027.4 NE ISSN 0168-3462
Z815.A1
NETHERLANDS. CENTRAAL BUREAU VOOR DE STATISTIEK. STATISTIEK VAN DE OPENBARE BIBLIOTHEKEN. a. Centraal Bureau voor de Statistiek, Prinses Beatrixlaan 428, Voorburg, Netherlands. (Dist. by: SDU - Publishers, Christoffel Plantijnstraat, The Hague, Netherlands) **Document type:** government publication.

020 310 US
NEW JERSEY PUBLIC LIBRARY STATISTICS FOR (YEAR). 1958. a. free. New Jersey State Library, CN-520, Trenton, NJ 08625-0520. TEL 609-292-7854. Ed. Robert K. Fortenbaugh. circ. 675. Indexed: SRI. **Document type:** government publication.
Formerly: New Jersey Public Libraries. Statistics (ISSN 0093-1098)

027 US ISSN 0077-9318
NEW YORK STATE LIBRARY, ALBANY. LIBRARY DEVELOPMENT. INSTITUTION LIBRARIES STATISTICS. 1954. a. free to libraries in New York State; libraries elsewhere on exchange basis. New York State Library, Library Development, Albany, NY 12230. circ. 1,000.

027 US ISSN 0077-9326
Z732.N7
NEW YORK STATE LIBRARY, ALBANY. LIBRARY DEVELOPMENT. PUBLIC AND ASSOCIATION LIBRARIES STATISTICS. Title varies: 1950-1955: Statistics of Public and Association Libraries. 1950. a. $8 (one copy free to libraries in New York State). New York State Library, Library Development, Albany, NY 12230. circ. 1,250.

021 027.7 US
NORTH DAKOTA LIBRARY STATISTICS. a. $5. North Dakota State Library, Capitol Grounds, 604 E. Boulevard Ave., Bismarck, ND 58505-0800. TEL 701-224-4622. FAX 701-224-2040. (also avail. in microfiche from CIS) Indexed: SRI.
Formerly: North Dakota Academic Library Statistics (ISSN 0094-5455)

020 AT ISSN 0816-956X
 CODEN: ONCUEF
ONLINE CURRENTS. 1986. 10/yr. Aus.$138 (overseas Aus.$156) (typically set Aug.-Sep.). Enterprise Information Management Pty. Ltd., 6-217 Eastern Valley Way, Willoughby, N.S.W. 2068, Australia. TEL 02-958-7099. FAX 02-958-0699. Ed. Katie Blake. adv.; bk.rev.; index. circ. 450. (back issues avail.) **Document type:** abstracting/indexing.
—CASDDS.
Description: Information about the online industry and optical publishing industry. Contains both Australian and overseas news.

LIBRARY AND INFORMATION SCIENCES — ABSTRACTING, BIBLIOGRAPHIES, STATISTICS

500 600 016   FR   ISSN 1146-5026
Z699.2
P A S C A L. T 205: SCIENCES DE L'INFORMATION. DOCUMENTATION. (Text in English, French) 1984. 10/yr. 1020 F. (outside EC 1075 F.). Centre National de la Recherche Scientifique, Institut de l'Information Scientifique et Technique, 2 allee du Parc de Brabois, 54514 Vandoeuvre-les-Nancy Cedex, France. TEL 83-50-46-00.
FAX 83-50-46-50. Ed. L. Vichniakoff. adv. contact: Veronique Guinvarc'h. index, cum.index. (also avail. in microfiche) **Document type:** bibliography.
●Also available online. Vendor(s): DIALOG Information Services, Inc. (File no.144), European Space Agency (File no.14), Telesystemes - Questel. Also available on CD-ROM.
    Former titles: P A S C A L Thema. T 205: Sciences de l'Information. Documentation (ISSN 0761-1641); P A S C A L Thema. Part 205: Sciences de l'Information. Documentation; Which supersedes (in 1984): Bulletin Signaletique. Part 101: Sciences de l'Information. Documentation (ISSN 0301-0309); Bulletin Signaletique. Part 101: Information Scientifique et Technique (ISSN 0007-5310)
    Description: Contains bibliographic references of publications covering all aspects of information science.

PSYCINFO NEWS. see *PSYCHOLOGY — Abstracting, Bibliographies, Statistics*

020   AT   ISSN 0729-199X
PUBLIC LIBRARIES IN WESTERN AUSTRALIA. STATISTICAL BULLETIN. 1981. a. Aus.$12. Library & Information Service of Western Australia, Alexander Library Bldg., Perth Cultural Center, Perth, W.A. 6000, Australia. TEL 09-427-3111. circ. 350. (back issues avail.)
    Description: Compares statistics of all public library operations and stock holdings in Western Australia.

020   US
PUBLIC LIBRARY CATALOG. quinquennial (with a. supplements). price varies. H.W. Wilson Co., 950 University Ave., Bronx, NY 10452.
TEL 800-367-6770. FAX 718-590-1617. TELEX 4990003HWILSON. Ed. Juliette Yaakov. bk.rev.
    Formerly: Standard Catalog for Public Libraries.
    Description: Classified list of nonfiction English-language books recommended for adults; with author, title, subject, and analytical index.

020   CN   ISSN 0075-6113
QUEEN'S UNIVERSITY AT KINGSTON. DOUGLAS LIBRARY. OCCASIONAL PAPERS. 1969. irreg., latest 1987. price varies. Queen's University, Douglas Library, Kingston, ON K7L 5C4, Canada.
TEL 613-545-2528. FAX 613-545-6819. circ. 300. (also avail. in microfilm)

020 016   RU   ISSN 0486-235X
Z699.A1   CODEN: RZNTAA
REFERATIVNYI ZHURNAL. INFORMATIKA. English edition: Informatics Abstracts (ISSN 0203-3054) (English edition without index available) 1963. m. 65 Rub. Vsesoyuznyi Institut Nauchno-Tekhnicheskoi Informatsii (VINITI), Baltiiskaya ul., 14, Moscow A-219, Russia. (Subscr. to: Mezhdunarodnaya Kniga, Dimitrova ul. 39, 113095 Moscow, Russia) **Document type:** abstracting/indexing.

020   SA
REPERTORY OF ARTICLES IN THE SOUTH AFRICAN ARCHIVES JOURNAL. a. R.1.80. South African Society of Archivists, Private Bag X236, Pretoria 0001, South Africa. TEL 27-12-323-5300.
FAX 27-12-323-5287. **Document type:** abstracting/indexing.

011 020   SA
S A JOINT CATALOGUE OF MONOGRAPHS ON MICROFICHE, SERIES 3, UNICAT. Short title: S A UNICAT. 1971. 2/yr. R.210. State Library, P.O. Box 397, Pretoria 0001, South Africa. index.
    Supersedes in part: S A Joint Catalogue of Monographs.
    Description: Listing of monographs in Southern African libraries by ISBN number.

026   US
S A L A L M BIBLIOGRAPHY AND REFERENCE SERIES. (Text in English, French, Portuguese, Spanish) 1969. irreg. (approx. s-a.). price varies. Seminar on the Acquisition of Latin American Library Materials, General Library, University of New Mexico, Albuquerque, NM 87131. TEL 505-277-5102. FAX 505-277-0646. **Document type:** monographic series.
    Incorporates: Seminar on the Acquisition of Latin American Library Materials. Report on Bibliographical Activities; **Formerly:** S A L A L M Bibliography Series (ISSN 0586-9781)

020 011   UK   ISSN 0307-1456
S A L G NEWSLETTER. 1973. a. £4. South Asia Library Group, c/o Oriental and India Office Collections, The British Library, 197 Blackfriars Rd., London SE1 8NG, England. TEL 071-412-7834.
FAX 071-412-7858. Ed. John Sims. circ. 70. (back issues avail.) **Indexed:** LISA. **Document type:** newsletter.
—BLDSC (8070.790000).

020   UK   ISSN 1352-1020
S C O N U L ANNUAL STATISTICS. 1981. a. £30. Standing Conference of National & University Libraries, 102 Euston St., London NW1 2HA, England. TEL 071-387-0317. FAX 071-383-3197. stat. circ. 250. (looseleaf format) **Document type:** corporate report.
—BLDSC (9111.819550).
    Formerly (until 1993): University Library Expenditure Statistics (ISSN 0268-3539)

011   CH   ISSN 0006-1581
SHU MO CHI KAN/BIBLIOGRAPHY QUARTERLY. (Text in Chinese) 1966. q. $32. Student Book Co., Ltd., 198 Ho-Ping E. Rd., Sec. 1, Taipei, Taiwan, Republic of China. FAX 02-3636334. Ed. Ting Wen-Tsu. adv.; bk.rev.; abstr.; bibl. circ. 2,500.

011 029   SL
SIERRA LEONE PUBLICATIONS. 1964. q. $6. Library Board, Box 326, Freetown, Sierra Leone. (back issues avail.)

027   US   ISSN 0081-5152
Z732.I6
STATISTICS OF INDIANA LIBRARIES. 1890. a. $3. Indiana Library Association, 6408 Carrollton Ave., Indianapolis, IN 46220-1615. TEL 317-232-3697. (Co-sponsor: Indiana State Library) circ. 300.
    Description: Contains tables of statistics representing a compilation and analysis of date reported by public, academic, institutional and special libraries.

020   US
STATISTICS OF SOUTHERN COLLEGE AND UNIVERSITY LIBRARIES. 1929. a. free. Middleton Library, Louisiana State University, Baton Rouge, LA 70803. TEL 504-388-2217. FAX 504-388-6825. Ed. D.W. Schneider. circ. 300 (controlled). **Indexed:** SRI.
    Description: Lists broken down by number of volumes, periodicals, and microfilm units; expenditures by library and institution, staff positions, and enrollment figures.

010   US   ISSN 0081-7600
STUDIES IN BIBLIOGRAPHY. 1948. a. $35. (Bibliographical Society of the University of Virginia) University Press of Virginia, Box 3608 University Station, Charlottesville, VA 22903.
TEL 804-924-3468. FAX 804-982-2655. Ed. D. Vander Meulen. circ. 200. **Indexed:** M.L.A. **Document type:** academic/scholarly publication, bibliography.
—BLDSC (8489.650000); Faxon.
    Description: Scholarly articles on bibliographic studies.

026   US   ISSN 0000-0140
SUBJECT COLLECTIONS; a guide to special book collections and subject emphasis in libraries. 1958. irreg., 7th ed., 1992. $275. R.R. Bowker, A Reed Reference Publishing Company, Part of the Reed Elsevier group, 121 Chanlon Rd., New Providence, NJ 07974. TEL 908-464-6800.
FAX 908-665-6688. TELEX 138 755. (Subscr. to: Order Dept., Box 31, New Providence, NJ 07974-9903. TEL 800-521-8110) Eds. Lee Ash, William G. Miller. index. **Document type:** bibliography, directory.
    Description: Locates significant US and Canadian library collections on any subject. Entries for more than 18,000 collections in over 11,000 academic, public, special libraries and museums are indexed and cross-referenced under 37,000 LC subject headings; and provides full contact and descriptive information.

SUGGESTED LIST OF PERIODICALS FOR NURSES FOR THE CANADIAN HEALTH SCIENCE LIBRARY. see *MEDICAL SCIENCES — Abstracting, Bibliographies, Statistics*

027.4   US
Z732.T18
TENNESSEE PUBLIC LIBRARY DIRECTORY AND STATISTICS (YEAR). 1965. a. free. Tennessee State Library and Archives, Planning and Development Section, Office of Secretary of State, Nashville, TN 37243-0312. TEL 615-741-3158.
FAX 615-741-6471. circ. 1,500. **Document type:** directory.
    Formerly (until 1990): Tennessee Public Library Statistics (ISSN 0363-7158)

027   US   ISSN 0082-3120
Z732.T25
TEXAS PUBLIC LIBRARY STATISTICS. 1965. a. free. Texas State Library, Library Development Division, Box 12927, Austin, TX 78711.
TEL 512-463-5465. Ed. Edward Seidenber6. stat.; circ. 1,650 (controlled). (also avail. in microfiche from CIS) **Indexed:** SRI.

029   HU   ISSN 0041-3917
Q4   CODEN: TMTAAG
TUDOMANYOS ES MUSZAKI TAJEKOZTATAS/SCIENTIFIC AND TECHNICAL INFORMATION. (Text in Hungarian; summaries in English, German and Russian) 1953. m. 1680 Ft.($41) Orszagos Muszaki Informacios Kozpont es Konyvtar (O.M.I.K.K.) - National Technical Information Centre and Library, Muzeum u. 17, Box 12, 1428 Budapest, Hungary. TEL 0138-2300. (Subscr. to: OMIKK Technoinform, Box 12, H-1428 Budapest, Hungary) Ed. P. Szanto. bk.rev.; abstr.; bibl.; index. circ. 1,200. **Indexed:** AESIS, Bull.Signal., Chem.Abstr., Hung.Lib.& Info.Sci.Abstr. (1972-), Inform.Sci.Abstr., LISA, Ref.Zh., Sci.Abstr.
—BLDSC (9068.500000).
    Formerly (until 1962): Muszaki Konyvtarosok Tajekoztatoja.

026 011   US
U.S. DEPARTMENT OF STATE. LIBRARY. COMMERCIAL LIBRARY PROGRAM. PUBLICATIONS LIST. 1978. irreg. U.S. Department of State, 2201 C St., N.W., Washington, DC 20520. (Orders to: Supt. of Documents, Washington, DC 20402)

020 016   US   ISSN 0083-1603
Z733.U57
U.S. LIBRARY OF CONGRESS. LIBRARY OF CONGRESS PUBLICATIONS IN PRINT. 1935. a. free. U.S. Library of Congress, Washington, DC 20540.
TEL 202-707-5093. circ. 10,000. **Document type:** bibliography, government publication.

U.S. LIBRARY OF CONGRESS. MUSIC CATALOG. see *MUSIC — Abstracting, Bibliographies, Statistics*

027.7   SA   ISSN 0576-6885
UNIVERSITY OF CAPE TOWN. LIBRARIES. STATISTICAL REPORT. a. free. University of Cape Town, Libraries, Rondebosch 7700, South Africa.
TEL 27-21-650-3097. FAX 27-21-650-3127. TELEX 52-0327.
    Description: Statistical record of both Technical Services and User Services divisions of UCT Libraries.

027.7 011   SU
UNIVERSITY OF RIYADH. CENTRAL LIBRARY. ACCESSION LIST. (Text in English and Arabic) q. University of Riyadh, Central Library, Riyadh, Saudi Arabia.

LIBRARY AND INFORMATION SCIENCES — COMPUTER APPLICATIONS

020 CN ISSN 0829-948X
UNIVERSITY OF WATERLOO BIBLIOGRAPHY SERIES.
1978. irreg. price varies. University of Waterloo, Library, Waterloo, ON N2L 3G1, Canada. TEL 519-885-1211. FAX 519-746-5151. Ed. Bruce MacNeil. (back issues avail.) **Document type:** bibliography.

027 US ISSN 1055-4173
Z1033.U64
UNIVERSITY PRESS BOOKS FOR PUBLIC AND SECONDARY SCHOOL LIBRARIES. 1991. a. Association of American University Presses, 584 Broadway, Ste. 410, New York, NY 10012. TEL 212-941-6610. bk.rev. circ. 20,000.
Formed by the merger of: University Press Books for Public School Libraries (ISSN 0731-2857) & University Press Books for Secondary School Libraries (ISSN 0887-1345)

020 AT ISSN 1035-4832
Z870.V5
VICTORIAN PUBLIC LIBRARIES. ANNUAL SURVEY. 1969. a. Aus.$15. Department of Arts, Sport and Tourism, Office of Library Services, Level 3, 176 Wellington Parade, E. Melbourne, Vic. 3002, Australia. TEL 03-651-7585. FAX 03-651-7177. Ed. Ross Gibbs. circ. 500.
●Also available online.
Supersedes (in 1989): Public Libraries of Victoria. Annual Statistical Bulletin (ISSN 0156-4374)
Description: List of key statistical data relating to operations of Victorian public libraries.

027.4 US
Z732.V8
VIRGINIA PUBLIC LIBRARIES AND ARCHIVES. STATISTICS. 1923. a. free. Virginia State Library and Archives, Public Library Development and Networking Division, Richmond, VA 23219. TEL 804-225-3892. FAX 804-225-4608. Ed. Peggy D. Rudd. circ. 1,500. (also avail. in microfiche from CIS) **Indexed:** SRI. **Document type:** government publication.
Former titles: Virginia Public Libraries and Institutional Libraries. Statistics (ISSN 0731-8464); Virginia Public Libraries. Statistics (ISSN 0095-3490)

700 015 US ISSN 0733-2149
YEAR'S WORK IN COMIC INDEXING. 1978. a. exchange basis. (Amateur Press Alliance for Indexing) Michigan State University Libraries, Special Collections Division, East Lansing, MI 48824-1048. Ed. Randall W. Scott. circ. 75.
Description: Annual index of all contributions to the Amateur Press Alliance in Indexing by mailing number, item number, name of indexer, and title of work.

LIBRARY AND INFORMATION SCIENCES — Computer Applications

025 US ISSN 1056-6694
A L C T S NETWORK NEWS. 1990. irreg. free. American Library Association, Association for Library Collections & Technical Services, 50 E. Huron St., Chicago, IL 60611-2759. TEL 312-280-5035. FAX 312-280-3257. Ed. Karen Muller. **Document type:** newsletter.
●Available only online.

025 621.381 US ISSN 1057-1159
Z678.93.A65
APPLE LIBRARY USERS GROUP NEWSLETTER. 1983. q. free. Apple Computer, Inc., 10381 Bandley Dr., Cupertino, CA 95014. TEL 408-974-2552. Ed. Monica Ertel. bk.rev. circ. 16,000. (back issues avail.)
—Faxon; UnCover.
Formerly: Apple Library Users Group (ISSN 0887-2716)
Description: For people interested in using Apple and Macintosh computers in libraries and information centers.

025 IT ISSN 1121-2462
ARCHIVI & COMPUTER. 1991. q. L.50000 (foreign L.60000). Regione Toscana, Comune di San Miniato, c/o Archivio Storico Comunale, 56027 San Miniato (PI), Italy. TEL 0571-42210. FAX 0571-400262. Ed. Roberto Cerri.

B R S BULLETIN. see COMPUTERS — Information Science And Information Theory

025 029 FR ISSN 1142-3463
BASE DE DONNEES P A S C A L. PLAN DE CLASSEMENT. (Programme Applique a la Selection et la Compilation Automatique de la Literature) 1973. a. free. Centre National de la Recherche Scientifique, Institut de l'Information Scientifique et Technique, 2 allee du Parc de Brabois, 54514 Vandoeuvre-les-Nancy Cedex, France. TEL 83-50-46-00. FAX 83-50-46-83. Ed. Claude Patou. adv. contact: Veronique Guinvarc'h. (also avail. in magnetic tape)
Former titles (until 1989): P A S C A L. Plan de Classement (ISSN 0992-5996); (until 1988): P A S C A L. M et S. Plan de Classement (ISSN 0761-1064); (until 1984): Bulletin Signaletique: Plan de Classement P A S C A L (ISSN 0154-0165); (until 1979): Bulletin Signaletique: P A S C A L. Plan de Classement (ISSN 0301-8016)

350 BE ISSN 0250-9725
BIBLIOTHEEK VOOR HEDENDAAGSE DOKUMENTATIE. BULLETIN. (Text in English) 1973. m. $20. Biblioteek voor Hedendaagse Dokumentatie, Parklaan 2, B-9100 St. Niklaas Waas, Belgium. TEL 32-3-776-5063. FAX 32-3-778-0785. Ed. Yvan van Garsse. circ. 500. (also avail. in microfiche) **Document type:** bulletin.

BIOSIS EVOLUTIONS. see BIOLOGY — Abstracting, Bibliographies, Statistics

020 UK ISSN 0957-4085
CODEN: CLAPEE
C & L APPLICATIONS; monthly information for libraries and information services. 1987. 10/yr. £40 (overseas £45). Information Partnership, 140 Tabernacle St., Ste. 4-2, London EC2A 4SD, England. TEL 071-253-0575. FAX 071-253-0607. Ed. Peter Gillman. adv.; bk.rev. circ. 200. **Indexed:** Abstr.Hum.Comp.Inter. **Document type:** newsletter.
—BLDSC (2943.175130).
Formerly: Computers and Libraries (ISSN 0950-8392)
Description: Covers such computer applications as expert systems, desktop publishing, and databases. Also discussses file conversion, text and data capture, communications software, CD-ROMs, scanning and digitizing, and thesaurus management.

025 US ISSN 0897-3296
C D - R O M DATABASES. (Compact Disc - Read Only Memory) 1988. m. $150 (foreign $190). Worldwide Videotex, Box 3273, Boynton Beach, FL 33424-3273. TEL 407-738-2276. Ed. Mark Wright. bk.rev. **Document type:** directory.
●Also available online. Vendor(s): DIALOG Information Services, Inc., NewsNet (EC71).
—CCC.
Description: Lists all databases currently being marketed on CD-ROMs. Provides titles, prices, categories, and vendors of CD-ROMs and whether they are for use on Macintosh or IBM computers.

025 US ISSN 1049-0833
TA1635 CODEN: CRPFEX
C D - R O M PROFESSIONAL. (Includes supplement: C D - R O M News Extra) 1988. 6/yr. $55 to individuals & school libraries (foreign $90); institutions $98 (foreign $133) (effective 1993). Pemberton Press Inc., 462 Danbury Rd., Wilton, CT 06897. TEL 203-761-1466. FAX 203-761-1444. (Subscr. in Japan to: Kinokuniya Co. Ltd., Subscription Dept., P.O. Box 55, Chitose, Tokyo 156, Japan) Ed. Nancy K. Herther. adv.: B&W page $1260, color page $1855. bk.rev.; circ. 10,800 (paid). (also avail. in microform from UMI) **Indexed:** ABI Inform., CINAHL, Info.Media & Tech., Lib.Lit., LISA, Tr.& Indus.Ind.
●Also available online. Vendor(s): DIALOG Information Services, Inc. (File no.170).
—BLDSC (3096.303980); EI; Faxon; UnCover; SWETS; UMI; CASDDS. **CCC.**
Formerly (until May 1990): Laserdisk Professional.
Description: Assists publishers, librarians and other information professionals in the selection, evaluation, purchase, and operation of CD-ROM systems and titles.

025 US
C D - R O M SOURCEBOOK.* (In 3 vols.; vol 1: Search Software, vol 2: producers, vol 3: consumers) 1986. a. $495 (foreign $595) per vol. Disc Company, 7 Cottonwood Ln., Hilton Head Island, SC 27726-1760. TEL 703-237-0682. FAX 703-532-5447.
●Also available on CD-ROM.
Description: Contains detailed proudct and service specifications and information in 16 sections in three volumes.

025 384.3 US ISSN 0738-8845
C M C NEWS. (Computers and the Media Center) 1979. 4/yr. $13 (foreign $20). C M C News, 515 Oak St., N., Cannon Falls, MN 55009. TEL 507-263-3711. Ed. Jim Deacon. adv.; bk.rev. circ. 1,700. (back issues avail.) **Indexed:** ERIC, Sci.Abstr. **Document type:** newsletter.
Description: Provides information on the application of microcomputers in library media centers, with CD-ROM coverage.

CINFOLINK; directory of information services in China. see BUSINESS AND ECONOMICS — Trade And Industrial Directories

COMPUTER LIBRARY'S COMPUTER PERIODICALS DATABASE. see LIBRARY AND INFORMATION SCIENCES — Abstracting, Bibliographies, Statistics

COMPUTERS IN LIBRARIES. see COMPUTERS — Microcomputers

COMPUTERS IN LIBRARIES: BUYERS GUIDE & CONSULTANT DIRECTORY. see COMPUTERS — Personal Computers

025 AT
CONCATENATION. q. free. Ferntree Information, P.O. Box 42, Clayton, Vic. 3168, Australia. TEL 03-541-5600. Ed. Robert Grundy. circ. 1,500. **Document type:** newsletter.
Formerly (until Aug. 1990): Ausinet Newsletter.
Description: Newsletter to clients of the Ferntree Information. Covers computer applications to online databases and library and information sciences.

CONCEPTS IN COMMUNICATION INFORMATICS AND LIBRARIANSHIP. see LIBRARY AND INFORMATION SCIENCES

025 US ISSN 0272-037X
D L A BULLETIN. 1981. irreg. (2-3/yr.). free. University of California, Division of Library Automation, 300 Lakeside Dr., 8th Fl., Oakland, CA 94612-3550. TEL 510-987-0564. Ed. Mary Jean Moore. bk.rev. circ. 2,500. **Indexed:** LISA. **Document type:** bulletin.
●Also available online.
—BLDSC (3605.635000).
Description: Library automation and library telecommunication networking news from the University of California.

340 US ISSN 1042-2595
CODEN: DARVEH
DATABASE REVIEW. 1989. bi-m. $120 (foreign $135). DataBase Associates, Box 215, Morgan Hill, CA 95038-0215. TEL 408-779-0436. FAX 408-779-3274. Ed. Colin J. White. (back issues avail.) **Document type:** newsletter.
—BLDSC (3535.803575).
Description: Looks at key developments in the database marketplace.

025 JA ISSN 0917-4168
Z674.5.J3
DENSHI RAIBURARI. (Text in Japanese) 1991. bi-m. Denshi Raiburari Konsoshiamu - Electronic Library Consortium, 3-1-401, 1-Chome, Higashiyama, Meguro-ku, Tokyo 153, Japan.

DIRECTORY OF ELECTRONIC JOURNALS, NEWSLETTERS AND ACADEMIC DISCUSSION LISTS. see BIBLIOGRAPHIES

025 US ISSN 8756-2294
DYNIX DATALINE. 1984. q. free. Dynix, Inc., 151 East 1700 South, Provo, UT 84606. TEL 801-375-2770. FAX 801-373-1889. circ. 4,700.

LIBRARY AND INFORMATION SCIENCES — COMPUTER APPLICATIONS 3483

020 600   US
E R I C - I R UPDATE. (Educational Resources Information Center - Information Resources) 1977. 2/yr. free. E R I C Clearinghouse on Information and Technology, 4-194 Center for Science & Technology, Syracuse University, Syracuse, NY 13244-4100. TEL 315-443-3640. FAX 315-443-5732. Ed. Jane K. Janis. bk.rev. circ. 4,200. **Document type:** newsletter.
  Description: Includes publications, practitioner information, and trends and issues in the area of library and information science and education technology.

025 629.13   NE   ISSN 1013-6479
E S A - I R S NEWS & VIEWS. (Information Retrieval Systems) Key Title: News & Views - E S A - I R S. 1976. q. free. European Space Agency, Publications Division, Keplerlaan 1, 22000 AG Noordwijk, Netherlands. TEL 31-1719-86555. FAX 31-1719-85433. TELEX 39098. Ed. N. Longdon. illus. circ. 12,000.

EDUCATIONAL I R M QUARTERLY. see *EDUCATION — Teaching Methods And Curriculum*

025   US   ISSN 0264-0473
Z678.9   CODEN: ELLIDZ
ELECTRONIC LIBRARY. 1983. bi-m. $99. Learned Information, Inc., 143 Old Marlton Pike, Medford, NJ 08055-8750. TEL 609-654-4888. FAX 609-654-4309. (And: Managing Editor, Learned Information Ltd., Woodside, Hinksey Hill, Oxford OX1 5AV, England) Ed. David Raitt. adv.; bk.rev.; bibl. circ. 2,000. **Indexed:** ASCA, CINAHL, Comput.Abstr., Comput.Cont., Curr.Cont., Info.Media & Tech., Leg.Info.Manage.Ind., Lib.Lit., LISA, SSCI, Tr.& Indus.Ind.
  —BLDSC (3702.580500); EI; Faxon; UnCover; SWETS; UMI; CASDDS. **CCC.**
  Description: For librarians and information center managers interested in microcomputers and library automation. Features include industry news and product announcements.

025   US   ISSN 1057-834X
JK468.P76
ELECTRONIC PUBLIC INFORMATION NEWSLETTER. 1991. 24/yr. $249 to individuals; libraries $130. E P I N Publishing, Box 21001, Washington, DC 20009. TEL 301-365-3621. Ed. James McDonough. bk.rev.; q. index. circ. 60. (back issues avail.) **Document type:** newsletter.
  Description: Covers transformation of public information into electronic form, policy issues and practice; for information resource management personnel, information science specialist, librarians, and the information industry.

ELSEVIER SCIENCE. CATALOGUE ON C D - R O M. see *SCIENCES: COMPREHENSIVE WORKS*

ESPIAL CANADIAN DATA BASE DIRECTORY; a guide to current Canadian information contained in national and international databases and data banks. see *BUSINESS AND ECONOMICS — Trade And Industrial Directories*

025   US   ISSN 1055-1743
F Y I - I M. (For Your Information - Image Management); the A I I M newsletter. 1985. s-m. membership only. Association for Information & Image Management, 1100 Wayne Ave., Ste. 1100, Silver Spring, MD 20910-5699. TEL 301-587-8202. FAX 301-587-2711. Ed. Beth S. Rosenberg. adv. circ. 9,000. (looseleaf format; back issues avail.) **Indexed:** Info.Media & Tech. **Document type:** newsletter.
  Description: Designed for end users of systems and manufacturers, consultants, and service companies. Covers news of the information and image management industry, including association news, business news, industry trends, and technology.

025   US   ISSN 1053-6396
Z681.3.067   CODEN: FACDEC
FAXON GUIDE TO C D - R O M. 1988. a. $12 (free to qualified personnel). Faxon Company, Inc., 15 Southwest Park, Westwood, MA 02090. TEL 617-329-3350. FAX 617-461-1862. TELEX 681-7238. Ed. Dolores Fallon. adv. circ. 12,000. **Document type:** catalog.
  —BLDSC (3901.002200).
  Formerly (until 1990): Access Faxon (ISSN 0897-6139)
  Description: Directory of CD-ROM information. Includes a comprehensive listing of CD-ROM discs available through Faxon.

025   US   ISSN 0737-4178
Z674.82.F43   CODEN: FTENDE
FEDLINK TECHNICAL NOTES. 1983. m. free. U.S. Library of Congress, Federal Library and Information Center Committee, Washington, DC 20540. TEL 202-707-4828. FAX 202-707-4818. Ed. Darlene Dolan. **Document type:** government publication.
  —CASDDS.
  Description: Covers the technology and microcomputers, both hardware and software for the library and information sciences.

025 610   CN   ISSN 0826-0125
H L A B C FORUM. 1976. q. Can.$20. Health Libraries Association of British Columbia, 1383 W. 8th Ave., Vancouver, BC V6H 4C4, Canada. TEL 604-733-6671. FAX 604-737-8582. circ. 80. (looseleaf format) **Document type:** newsletter.

I A S S I S T QUARTERLY. (International Association for Social Science Information Services and Technology) see *LIBRARY AND INFORMATION SCIENCES*

651.8 004   US
I D. (Information Display) a. $70 (foreign $75). (Society for Information Display) Palisades Institute for Research Services, Attn: Jay Morreale, 201 Varick St., 11th Fl., New York, NY 10014. TEL 212-305-1502.

025   US   ISSN 0019-0012
TR835   CODEN: IMGCB7
I M C JOURNAL.* 1967. 6/yr. $90 (foreign $115). International Information Management Congress, 1650 38th St., Boulder, CO 80301-2623. TEL 716-383-8330. FAX 716-383-8442. Ed. William McArthur. adv.: B&W page $2925, color page $3965; 8 1/4 x 10 7/8. bk.rev.; abstr.; bibl.; charts; illus.; stat. circ. 30,000. (also avail. in microform from UMI; reprint service avail. from UMI) **Indexed:** ABI Inform., Account.& Data Proc.Abstr., Bus.Educ.Ind., Bus.Ind., Comput.Cont., Comput.Lit.Ind., Info.Media & Tech., Info.Media & Tech., Leg.Info.Manage.Ind., LHTN, Resour.Ctr.Ind., Sci.Abstr.
  —BLDSC (4369.070000); Faxon; SWETS; UMI.
  Formerly: I M C Newsletter (ISSN 0739-4268)
  Description: Covers electronic information and records management trends, computer-assisted retrieval and indexing, micrographics, microfilms, office automation and word processing.

001.6 621.381   FR   ISSN 0754-1996
INDUSTRIE DE L'INFORMATION; quotidien des nouvelles technologies de l'information. (Text in French) 1982. d. 7000 F. A Jour, 11 rue du Marche St. Honore, 75001 Paris, France. TEL 42-96-67-22. FAX 40-20-07-75. TELEX TELEXEL 615887. Ed. Dominique Le Cleach.
  —CCC.

004   CL
INFORMATIA. 1979. m. $100. Publicacions en Computacion Ltda., Avda. Pedro de Valdivia 2103, Santiago, Chile. TEL 2048257. Ed. Jorge Gaticaabar Matte.
  Formerly: Computacion Personal (ISSN 0716-4858)

004   US
INFORMATICA. (Text in Spanish) m. Publicaciones en Computacion, c/o C W Communications, 375 Cochituate Rd., Framingham, MA 01701. TEL 617-879-0700. adv. circ. 1,000.

004   CL   ISSN 0716-0658
INFORMATICA; revista de computacion y sistemas. 1980. m. $82. C I I S A, Avda. Pedro de Valdivia 2103, Santiago, Chile. TEL 2232616. FAX 562-223-1066. Ed. Oscar Barros. adv. circ. 2,000.

001.6 621.381   IT   ISSN 0393-0572
INFORMATICA 70. 1972. m. (10/yr.) L.30000. Editrice il Crogiolo S.r.l., Viale Papiniano 44, 20123 Milan, Italy. TEL 2-58-11-12-83. Ed. Rodolfo Grigolato. adv. circ. 15,000.

025 330   US   ISSN 1050-1576
HF5548.125
INFORMATION ADVISOR.* 1988. m. $130. Information Advisory Services, 300 McLeod Ave., Missoula, MT 59801-4302. Ed. Robert Berkman. bk.rev.; index. circ. 550. (back issues avail.) **Document type:** newsletter.
  ●Also available online. Vendor(s): Information Access Co. (Trade & Industry Index).
  —BLDSC (4481.724000). **CCC.**
  Description: Compares and evaluates business information sources, both print and online, for business researchers. Focuses on data quality, international services and finding the best sources of expertise.

004   US   ISSN 0020-0042
TK7882.I6   CODEN: INFDAB
INFORMATION DISPLAY. 1963. m. $36 (foreign $72). (Society for Information Display) Palisades Institute for Research Services, Attn.: Jay Morreale, 201 Varick St., 11th Fl., New York, NY 10014. Ed. Joseph A. MacDonald. adv.; bk.rev.; charts; illus.; tr.lit. circ. 10,000. (reprint service avail. UMI) **Indexed:** Comput.Cont., Sci.Abstr.
  Formerly: S I D Journal.

025 380.3   UK   ISSN 0961-7612
   CODEN: IMRPE2
INFORMATION MANAGEMENT REPORT. 1991. m. £208($320) (effective 1994). Elsevier Science Ltd., Oxford Fulfilment Centre, P.O. Box 800, Kidlington, Oxford OX5 1DX, England. TEL 44-865-843000. FAX 44-865-843010. (Subscr. in U.S. and Canada to: Elsevier Science, 660 White Plains Rd., Tarrytown, NY 10591-5153. TEL 914-524-9200. FAX 914-333-2444) Eds. R. Prytherch, J. Meyer. bk.rev.; charts; illus.; stat. (back issues avail.) **Indexed:** Comput.Lit.Ind., Info.Media & Tech., LISA, Print.Abstr., PROMT. **Document type:** newsletter.
  ●Also available online. Vendor(s): Data-Star (PTBN), DIALOG Information Services, Inc. (File no.636).
  —BLDSC (4493.687155); SWETS; CASDDS. **CCC.**
  Incorporates (1979-1991): Outlook on Research Libraries (ISSN 0165-2818); **(1979-1991):** Advanced Information Report (ISSN 0953-8712); Which was formerly: Communication Technology Impact (ISSN 0142-5854)
  Description: Provides comprehensive coverage of new developments in the information world, with analysis of the implications of new technology, and other news for information professionals and librarians.

INFORMATION PROCESSING ASSOCIATION OF ISRAEL. NATIONAL CONFERENCE ON DATA PROCESSING. PROCEEDINGS. see *COMPUTERS — Information Science And Information Theory*

029   US   ISSN 0020-0220
   CODEN: IRLAAQ
INFORMATION RETRIEVAL & LIBRARY AUTOMATION. 1965. m. $66 (foreign $79.50). Lomond Publications, Inc., Box 88, Mt. Airy, MD 21771. TEL 301-829-1496. Ed. Susan W. Johnson. bk.rev.; index. circ. 1,160. (also avail. in microfiche from UMI; back issues avail.; reprint service avail. from UMI) **Indexed:** Bk.Rev.Ind. (1981-), Child.Bk.Rev.Ind. (1981-), Comput.Cont., Comput.Lit.Ind., Graph.Arts Lit.Abstr., Intl.Civil Eng.Abstr., Leg.Info.Manage.Ind., LISA, Pers.Lit., Soft.Abstr.Eng.
  —BLDSC (4494.149000); SWETS; UMI; CASDDS.
  Former titles: Information Retrieval and Library Automation Newsletter; Information Retrieval Letter.
  Description: News, articles, and announcements on new techniques, equipment, and software in information services for both the public and private sectors.

INFORMATION SEARCHER. see *EDUCATION — Computer Applications*

INFORMATION SOCIETY; an international journal. see *COMPUTERS — Information Science And Information Theory*

LIBRARY AND INFORMATION SCIENCES — COMPUTER APPLICATIONS

029 005.74   UK   ISSN 0306-4379
QA76.9.D3   CODEN: INSYD6
INFORMATION SYSTEMS; data base: their creation, management and utilization. 1975. 8/yr. £436($670) (effective 1994). Elsevier Science Ltd., Pergamon, P.O. Box 800, Kidlington, Oxford OX5 1DX, England. TEL 44-865-843000. FAX 44-865-843010. (Subscr. in U.S. and Canada to: Elsevier Science, 660 White Plains Rd., Tarrytown, NY 10591-5153. TEL 914-524-9200. FAX 914-333-2444) Ed. Hans Jochen Schneider. adv.; bk.rev. circ. 1,200. (also avail. in microfilm from UMI; reprint service avail. from UMI) **Indexed**: Biol.Abstr., Compumath, Comput.Abstr., Comput.Cont., Comput.Lit.Ind., Comput.Rev., Curr.Cont., Excerp.Med., Sci.Abstr. **Document type**: academic/scholarly publication.
—BLDSC (4496.367300); Faxon; UnCover; SWETS; UMI. **CCC**.
   Incorporates (1988-1992): Database Technology (ISSN 0951-9327)
Refereed Serial

025   US   ISSN 1058-0530
T58.6   CODEN: ISYME2
INFORMATION SYSTEMS MANAGEMENT. 1984. q. $140.50 (overseas $209) (effective 1994). Warren Gorham Lamont, One Penn Plaza, New York, NY 10119. TEL 212-971-5000. (Subscr. to: The Park Square Bldg., 31 St. James Ave., Boston, MA 02116-4112. TEL 800-950-1207) Ed. Robert E. Umbaugh. adv.; B&W page $1105. circ. 5,155. (reprint service avail. from SCH) **Indexed**: ABI Inform., Account.Ind. (1984-), B.P.I., Comput.Lit.Ind., Cont.Pg.Manage., Mgmt.& Market.Abstr. **Document type**: trade publication.
—BLDSC (4496.368400); Faxon; UnCover; SWETS; UMI. **CCC**.
   Formerly (until 1991): Journal of Information Systems Management (ISSN 0739-9014)
   Description: Provides MIS and DP managers with information in the following areas: consultants' experiences, corporate issues, data center operations, data communications, data management, economic and financial issues, and end-user computing.

025 020   II   ISSN 0971-233X
INFORMATION TECHNOLOGY. Short title: I.T. (Text in English) 1991. m. $36. E F Y Enterprises Pvt. Ltd., D-87-1, Okhla Industrial Area, Phase I, New Delhi 110020, India. TEL 11-681-7563. FAX 11-681-7563. TELEX 31 63449 FORU IN. adv.: B&W page $350, color page $500; trim 23 x 17. circ. 30,000.
   Description: Covers the whole gamut of information technology, including computers, communications and telecommunications, satellite and cable TV.

029.7   US   ISSN 0730-9295
Z678.9.A1   CODEN: ITLBDC
INFORMATION TECHNOLOGY AND LIBRARIES. 1968. q. $45 (Canada and Mexico $50; elsewhere $55). (Library and Information Technology Association) American Library Association, 50 E. Huron St, Chicago, IL 60611-2795. TEL 312-944-6780. FAX 312-440-9374. Ed. Thomas W. Leonhardt. adv.; bk.rev.; charts; illus.; index. circ. 6,800. (also avail. in microform from UMI; back issues avail.; reprint service avail. from UMI) **Indexed**: A.I.Abstr., ABI Inform., Bus.Ind., C.I.J.E., Chem.Abstr., Compumath, Comput.Cont., Comput.Lit.Ind., Comput.Rev., Curr.Cont., Educ.Ind., Inform.Sci.Abstr., Leg.Info.Manage.Ind., LHTN, Lib.Lit., LISA, Mag.Ind., Pers.Lit., PMR, Ref.Sour., Ref.Zh., Sci.Abstr., Soft.Abstr.Eng., Tr.& Indus.Ind. **Document type**: academic/scholarly publication.
—BLDSC (4496.368710); EI; Faxon; UnCover; SWETS; UMI; CASDDS. **CCC**.
   Formerly (until 1982): Journal of Library Automation (ISSN 0022-2240)
   Description: Articles on library automation, communication technology, cable systems, computerized information processing and video technologies.
Refereed Serial

025   US   ISSN 0959-3845
INFORMATION TECHNOLOGY AND PEOPLE. 1982-1989; resumed 1992. q. $135 (foreign $155) (effective 1992). Box 500, 19363 Willamette Dr., W. Linn, OR 97068. TEL 503-656-7108. Ed. Eleanor H. Wynn. adv. **Indexed**: Abstr.Hum.Comp.Inter., Account.& Data Proc.Abstr., BPIA, Comput.Cont., Cont.Pg.Manage., Mgmt.& Market.Abstr., Sci.Abstr.
—BLDSC (4496.368733); UnCover; UMI. **CCC**.
   Former titles (until vol.6, no.1, 1992): Technology and People (ISSN 0956-5388); Office - Technology and People (ISSN 0167-5710)
   Description: Provides interdisciplinary international coverage of social and organizational issues in the design and use of information technology. For academics and practitioners in the fields of information system management and computer systems design and management.

001.6 301.16 070.5
340   US   ISSN 8756-0941
INFORMATION TIMES. 1974. q. membership. Information Industry Association, 555 New Jersey Ave., N.W., Ste. 800, Washington, DC 20001. TEL 202-639-8262. Ed. Kevin A. Siegel. adv.; bibl.; illus. **Indexed**: Comput.Lit.Ind., PROMT, Tel.Abstr., Telegen.
—UMI.
   Former titles (until 1983): Information World (ISSN 0163-0067); Information Times (ISSN 0161-9209); Information Action (ISSN 0161-9217); Information Times (ISSN 0095-8131)

004.6   US   ISSN 8755-6286
   CODEN: INTDDG
INFORMATION TODAY; the newspaper for users and producers of electronic information services. 1983. 11/yr. $39.95. Learned Information, Inc., 143 Old Marlton Pike, Medford, NJ 08055. TEL 609-654-6266. FAX 609-654-4309. Ed. Patricia Lane. bk.rev. (also avail. in microform from UMI) **Indexed**: ABI Inform., CAD CAM Abstr., Comput.Bus., Leg.Info.Manage.Ind., LISA, Microcomp.Ind., PCR2, PROMT, PSI, Tr.& Indus.Ind.
● Also available online. Vendor(s): Mead Data Central, Inc.
—BLDSC (4496.373700); SWETS; UMI; CASDDS. **CCC**.
   Description: Geared toward users and producers of electronic information services. Offers articles and news about the industry, calendar of events and product information.

025 004.6   US
INTEGRATED ONLINE LIBRARY SYSTEMS. MEETING PROCEEDINGS. 1983. a. $30. Learned Information, Inc., 143 Old Marlton Pike, Medford, NJ 08055-8750. TEL 609-654-4888. FAX 609-654-4309. Ed. David C. Genaway. **Document type**: proceedings.

025   US
INTERACTION. q. free. Brodart Co., 500 Arch St., Williamsport, PA 17701. TEL 717-326-2461. FAX 717-326-6769. illus.

020 070.5
Z265   UK   ISSN 0958-9961
   CODEN: IMOTEX
INTERNATIONAL JOURNAL OF MICROGRAPHICS & OPTICAL TECHNOLOGY; including all aspects of electronic information transfer. 1982. 4/yr. £135($210) (effective 1994). Elsevier Science Ltd., Pergamon, P.O. Box 800, Kidlington, Oxford OX5 1DX, England. TEL 44-865-843000. FAX 44-865-843010. (Subscr. in U.S. and Canada to: Elsevier Science, 660 White Plains Rd., Tarrytown, NY 10591-5153. TEL 914-524-9200. FAX 914-333-2444) Ed. Don M. Avedon. adv. circ. 1,000. (also avail. in microfilm from UMI; reprint service avil. from UMI) **Indexed**: Account.& Data Proc.Abstr., Br.Archaeol.Abstr., Comput.Cont., Deep Sea Res.& Oceanogr.Abstr., Leg.Info.Manage.Ind., LISA, Sci.Abstr. **Document type**: academic/scholarly publication.
—BLDSC (4542.354300); EI; Faxon; UnCover; UMI. **CCC**.
   Formerly: International Journal of Micrographics and Video Technology (ISSN 0743-9636); Incorporates: Microdoc; Which was formerly (until 1982): Micropublishing of Current Periodicals (ISSN 0364-3999)
Refereed Serial

INTERNATIONAL YEARBOOK OF SERIALS LIBRARIANSHIP. see *LIBRARY AND INFORMATION SCIENCES*

JOURNAL OF INFORMATION SCIENCE; principles and practice. see *LIBRARY AND INFORMATION SCIENCES*

JOURNAL OF LAW AND INFORMATION SCIENCE. see *LAW*

029.7   US   ISSN 0196-1799
Z678.9.A1
L I T A NEWSLETTER. 1980. q. $30 (foreign $40). (Library and Information Technology Association) American Library Association, 50 E. Huron St., Chicago, IL 60611-2795. TEL 312-280-4270. FAX 312-280-3257. Ed. Walt Crawford. illus. circ. 5,000. (back issues avail.) **Document type**: newsletter.
—UnCover.

025   US   ISSN 1059-3195
LETTER TO LIBRARIES ONLINE. Short title: L T L O. 1991. 12/yr. free. Oregon State Library, Salem, OR 97310-0640. TEL 503-378-2112. FAX 503-588-7119. circ. 1,000. **Document type**: newsletter.
● Available only online.
   Description: Provides information on the State Library and statewide library issues and activities.

025   US   ISSN 1040-4333
Z666
LIBRARY HI TECH BIBLIOGRAPHY. 1986. a. $45. Pierian Press, Box 1808, Ann Arbor, MI 48106. TEL 313-434-5530. FAX 313-434-6409. **Document type**: bibliography.
—BLDSC (5198.880000).

025   US   ISSN 0737-8831
Z671   CODEN: LIHTD2
LIBRARY HI TECH JOURNAL. 1983. q. $45 to individuals; institutions $75. Pierian Press, Box 1808, Ann Arbor, MI 48106. TEL 313-434-5530. FAX 313-434-6409. Ed. C. Edward Wall. adv.; bk.rev. circ. 5,000. (also avail. in microform from UMI; back issues avail.) **Indexed**: Bibl.Ind., Bk.Rev.Ind. (1984-), Bus.Educ.Ind., C.I.J.E., Child.Bk.Rev.Ind. (1984-), Comput.Abstr., Comput.Cont., Comput.Lit.Ind., Consum.Ind., Int.Lab.Doc., Leg.Info.Manage.Ind., LHTN, Lib.Lit., LISA, Microcomp.Ind., Pers.Lit., Ref.Zh.
—BLDSC (5198.870000); Faxon; UnCover; SWETS; UMI; CASDDS.
   Description: A comprehensive guide to forthcoming and available technologies applicable to libraries and information centers. Concentrates on reporting on the selection, installation, maintenance and integration of systems and hardware.
Refereed Serial

025   US   ISSN 0741-9058
Z678.9.A1   CODEN: LHTNE4
LIBRARY HI TECH NEWS. 1984. 10/yr. $70 to individuals; institutions $95. Pierian Press, Box 1808, Ann Arbor, MI 48106. TEL 313-434-5530. FAX 313-434-6409. Ed. C. Edward Wall. adv. circ. 5,000. **Indexed**: Bk.Rev.Ind. (1984-), Child.Bk.Rev.Ind. (1984-), Comput.Dtbs., Comput.Lit.Ind., LHTN, LISA. **Document type**: newsletter.
—BLDSC (5198.875000); Faxon; UnCover; SWETS; UMI; CASDDS.
   Description: News about all aspects of technology related to library operations for professionals in the information management-sciences field.

020 029   II   ISSN 0024-2543
Z671   CODEN: LSSDA8
LIBRARY SCIENCE WITH A SLANT TO DOCUMENTATION AND INFORMATION STUDIES. (Text in English) 1964. q. Rs.400($75) Sarada Ranganathan Endowment for Library Science, Bangalore, 432, 10th Cross, 18th Main Rd., Second Phase, J.P. Nagar, Bangalore 560 078, India. Ed. A. Neelameghan. bk.rev.; charts; illus.; index. circ. 500. **Indexed**: Chem.Abstr., Comput.Cont., Curr.Cont., Inform.Sci.Abstr., Lib.Lit., Lib.Sci.Abstr., LISA.
—Faxon; UMI.
   Formerly (until 1988): Library Science with a Slant to Documentation.

LIBRARY SOFTWARE REVIEW. see *COMPUTERS — Software*

020　　　　US　　ISSN 0277-0288
LIBRARY SYSTEMS NEWSLETTER. 1981. m. $40 (foreign $50). American Library Association, Library Technology Reports, 50 E. Huron St., Chicago, IL 60611-2795. TEL 312-944-6780. FAX 312-440-9374. Ed. Howard S. White. circ. 1,500. (tabloid format; back issues avail.) **Indexed:** Leg.Info.Manage.Ind., LHTN, LISA. **Document type:** newsletter.
—BLDSC (5205.660000); SWETS. **CCC.**
   Description: Features articles and news briefs covering all aspects of library automation and the application of information technologies in libraries.

025   004　　　UK　　ISSN 0964-7627
Z678.9.A1　　　　　　CODEN: LTNEEV
LIBRARY TECHNOLOGY NEWS. 1984. 5/yr. £40 (foreign £45). Library Information Technology Centre, South Bank Technopark, 90 London Rd., London SE1 6LN, England. TEL 071-815-7872. FAX 071-815-6699. adv.: B&W page £100. circ. 500. **Indexed:** Info.Media & Tech., LISA, Sci.Abstr. **Document type:** newsletter.
—BLDSC (5205.690000).
   Formerly (until 1991): Library Micromation News (ISSN 0262-7841)
   Description: News of library automation developments in Europe.

004.16　　　　　　US
MICROCOMPUTERS FOR INFORMATION MANAGEMENT; an international journal for library and information services. 1984. q. $39.50 to individuals; institutions $100. Ablex Publishing Corporation, 355 Chestnut St., Norwood, NJ 07648. TEL 201-767-8450. FAX 201-767-6717. TELEX 135-393. Ed. Ching-chih Chen. adv.; abstr.; bibl.; illus. circ. 850. (back issues avail.; reprint service avail.) **Indexed:** C.I.J.E., Comput.Abstr., Curr.Cont., ERIC, Lib.Lit., LISA, Microcomp.Ind., Sci.Abstr.
   Description: For librarians and information specialists. Features articles on the applications of microcomputers in information processing, organization and dissemination as well as information on microcomputer hardware and software.

MULTECHS; technology analyzed for the information community. see COMPUTERS — Information Science And Information Theory

500　　　　　GW　　ISSN 0172-732X
O L B G - INFO; Mitteilungsblatt der Online-Benutzergruppe in der D G D. irreg. (approx. 4/yr.). DM.60 to non-members. Deutsche Gesellschaft fuer Dokumentation e.V., Hanauerlandstr. 126-128, 60314 Frankfurt, Germany. TEL 069-740805. (back issues avail.)
   Formerly: Online Info.
   Description: News on all areas of available online information, including new technologies in the field of information and documentation, calendar of events, and seminars.

025　　　　　UK　　ISSN 0967-6090
ONLINE FILES: COMPARATIVE COST ANALYSIS; a unique guide to the costs of searching the world's major online databases. 1989. q. Effective Technology Marketing Ltd., Enterprise House, Wilton Rd., Humberston, Great Grimsby DB36 4AS, England. TEL 0472-210707. FAX 0472-21304.
—BLDSC (6260.762250).
   Formerly (until 1992): Clover Comparative Cost Chart for Online Files (ISSN 0959-5619)

025　　　　　　US
Z678.9.A1　　　　　　CODEN: IIOMEI
ONLINE LIBRARIES AND MICROCOMPUTERS. 1983. 10/yr. $43.75 to individuals; institutions $62.50; students $25 (combined rates avail.). Information Intelligence, Inc., Box 31098, Phoenix, AZ 85046. TEL 800-228-9982. Ed. George S. Machovec. bk.rev.; index. (looseleaf format; back issues avail.) **Indexed:** LISA, Microcomp.Ind., Ref.Zh. **Document type:** newsletter.
   ●Also available online. Vendor(s): Data-Star, DIALOG Information Services, Inc., Dow Jones News Retrieval, European Space Agency, NewsNet (PB42). Also available on CD-ROM.
—BLDSC (6260.762550); UnCover. **CCC.**
   Formerly: Information Intelligence Online Libraries and Microcomputers (ISSN 0737-7770)
   Description: Aimed at library and information center developments and applications throughout North America. Features articles covering new online library and automation applications using a wide variety of microcomputers and software.

025　　　　　　US
ORBIT ONLINE. 1978. bi-m. free. Orbit Online Service, 8000 Westpark Dr., McLean, VA 22102. TEL 703-442-0900. FAX 703-893-4632. Ed. Carrie Garfield. adv.; index. circ. 11,000. (back issues avail.)
   Formerly (until 1993): Orbit Searchlight.
   Description: To acquaint Orbit Online Service users with new databases available, changes in current database files, price changes, online information searching, tips, techniques and announcements.

025　　　　　US　　ISSN 0278-9469
PALINET NEWS. 1974. m. $25 to non-members; members free. PALINET, 3401 Market St., Ste. 262, Philadelphia, PA 19104. TEL 215-382-7031. FAX 215-382-0022. E-mail: PALEXEC@HLSC.ORG. Ed. Marion W. Andrews. circ. 1,200. (back issues avail.) **Document type:** newsletter.
   Description: Contains information about services, training programs, workshops and products available through the Network. Focuses on library technology and its applications.

020   029　　　UK　　ISSN 0033-0337
Z678.9.A1　　　　　　CODEN: PRGRDU
PROGRAM; automated library and information systems. 1966. q. £95($190) to non-members; members £75. Aslib, Association for Information Management, Publications Department, Information House, 20-24 Old St., London EC1V 9AP, England. TEL 071-253-4488. FAX 071-430-0514. (Dist. in N. America by: Learned Information, Inc., 143 Old Marlton Pike, Medford, NJ 08055-8750. TEL 609-654-6266) Ed. Lucy Tedd. adv.; bk.rev.; index. circ. 1,000. **Indexed:** Abstr.Hum.Comp.Inter., Account.& Data Proc.Abstr., Anbar, Comput.Abstr., Comput.Cont., Curr.Cont., Fluidex, Intl.Civil Eng.Abstr., Lib.Lit., LISA, Sci.Abstr., Soft.Abstr.Eng.
—BLDSC (6864.320000); Faxon; UnCover; SWETS; CASDDS.
   Description: Computer applications to library and information services.

025　　　　　US　　ISSN 0193-273X
S O L I N E W S. 1973. bi-m. free. Southeastern Library Network, Inc., 1438 W. Peachtree St., N.W., Atlanta, GA 30309-2955. TEL 404-892-0943. FAX 404-892-7879. Ed. Liz Hornsby. circ. 1,500. (back issues avail.) **Document type:** newsletter.

651.8   001.53　　　US
SOCIETY FOR INFORMATION DISPLAY. SEMINAR LECTURE NOTES. a. $50 (foreign $55). (Society for Information Display) Palisades Institute for Research Services, Attn: Jay Morreale, 201 Varick St., 11th Fl., New York, NY 10014. TEL 213-305-1502.

020   001.6　　　　US　　ISSN 0273-9399
SPECIALIST. 1978. m. $60 (foreign $65) (subscr. includes Special Libraries). Special Libraries Association, 1700 18th St., N.W., Washington, DC 20009. TEL 202-234-4700. FAX 202-265-9317. Ed. Gail Repsher. adv. circ. 15,000. (back issues avail.; reprint service avail. from UMI) **Indexed:** Fluidex, PROMT. **Document type:** newsletter.
—BLDSC (8404.764000).
   Description: Examines current activities in the library and information sciences and among the S.L.A. membership.

TRENDS IN THE LAW LIBRARY MANAGEMENT AND TECHNOLOGY. see LIBRARY AND INFORMATION SCIENCES

025　　　　　　　US
UNIVERSITY OF CALIFORNIA. DIVISION OF LIBRARY AUTOMATION. TECHNICAL REPORTS. irreg. free. University of California, Division of Library Automation, 300 Lakeside Dr., 8th Fl., Oakland, CA 94612-3550. **Document type:** monographic series.
   ●Also available online.
   Description: Features the development efforts for the MELVYL system, as well as policies or technical issues raised during system development.

025　　　　　UK　　ISSN 0305-5728
Z678.9.A1　　　　　　CODEN: VINEDT
VINE. 1971. 4/yr. £65 (foreign £80). Library Information Technology Centre, South Bank Technopark, 90 London Rd., London SE1 6LN, England. TEL 071-815-7872. FAX 071-815-6699. circ. 800. **Indexed:** LISA. **Document type:** academic/scholarly publication.
—BLDSC (9236.855000); SWETS.
   Description: Covers the application of technology in libraries across Europe, including evaluations of new products.

025　　　　　US　　ISSN 0884-593X
WIRED LIBRARIAN'S NEWSLETTER. 1983. irreg. (approx. m.). $15. c/o Eric Anderson, Ed., 292 Hammertown Rd., Jackson, OH 45640-2058. bk.rev.; software rev. circ. 800. **Document type:** newsletter.

LINGUISTICS

see also Classical Studies; Oriental Studies

A A B'S GUIDE TO ITALIAN PRIVATE ENGLISH LANGUAGE SCHOOLS & ITALIAN LANGUAGE SCHOOLS FOR OVERSEAS & ITALY. see EDUCATION — Guides To Schools And Colleges

A A B'S GUIDE TO PRIVATE ENGLISH LANGUAGE SCHOOLS IN THE U.K. FOR OVERSEAS STUDENTS. see EDUCATION — Guides To Schools And Colleges

A A T A NEWSLETTER. (American Association of Teachers of Arabic) see EDUCATION — Teaching Methods And Curriculum

440   375.4　　　US　　ISSN 0883-6795
A A T F NATIONAL BULLETIN. (Text in English, French) 1975. q. membership. American Association of Teachers of French, c/o Fred M. Jenkins, Exec. Dir., University of Illinois, 57 E. Armory Ave., Champaign, IL 61820. TEL 217-333-2842. Ed. Jane B. Goepper. bk.rev.; bibl.; illus.; stat.; tr.lit. circ. 10,500. (back issues avail.) **Document type:** bulletin.
   Description: Information for U.S. teachers and professors of French; calendar of forthcoming meetings.

430.07   370　　　US　　ISSN 0001-0243
A A T G NEWSLETTER. 1970. 4/yr. $10 to non-members. American Association of Teachers of German, Inc., 112 Haddontowne Ct., Ste. 104, Cherry Hill, NJ 08034. TEL 609-795-5553. FAX 609-795-9398. Ed. Helene Zimmer-Loew. circ. 7,500. **Document type:** newsletter.
   Description: Includes announcements and articles of current interest to members.

450　　　　　　　US
A A T I NEWSLETTER. (Text in English, Italian) 1980. s-a. $40 to institutions; members $30. American Association of Teachers of Italian (Columbus), c/o Albert N. Mancini, Pres., Department of French and Italian, Ohio State University, Columbus, OH 43210-1229. TEL 614-292-4938. FAX 614-292-3927. (Subscr. to: c/o Prof. Louis Kibler, Dept. of Romance Languages, Wayne State University, Detroit, MI 48202) Ed. Salvatore "Rino" Cappelletti. adv.; bk.rev. circ. 1,200. (back issues avail.) **Document type:** newsletter.
   Description: Seeks to inform teachers of Italian at all levels and to stimulate dialogue. Publishes articles on pedagogy, opinion pieces on the status of the Italian teaching profession and reviews of teaching materials.

491   370　　　　　US　　ISSN 0001-0251
A A T S E E L NEWSLETTER. (Text in English and Russian) 1958. 6/yr. $15 to non-members. American Association of Teachers of Slavic and East European Languages, c/o Prof. George Gutsche, Russian - Modern Languages 340, University of Arizona, Tucson, AZ 85721. TEL 602-621-9765. adv.; bk.rev.; abstr.; bibl.; illus. circ. 2,000. (also avail. in microfilm from UMI) **Document type:** newsletter.

A A T T NEWSLETTER. (American Association of Teachers of Turkish) see EDUCATION — International Education Programs

LINGUISTICS

410 371.3   US   ISSN 1043-9560
A C T F L NEWSLETTER. 4/yr. American Council on the Teaching of Foreign Languages, Inc., 6 Executive Plaza, Yonkers, NY 10701-6801. TEL 914-963-8830. FAX 914-963-1275. adv.: page $300. **Document type:** newsletter.
   Formerly (until 1988): A C T F L Public Awareness Network Newsletter (ISSN 1043-9552)

407   US   ISSN 0148-7639
P57.U7
A D F L BULLETIN. 1969. 3/yr. $21 to individuals; libraries $30. Association of Departments of Foreign Languages, 10 Astor Pl., New York, NY 10003. TEL 212-614-6319. FAX 212-477-9863. (Affiliate: Modern Language Association) adv.; bk.rev.; bibl.; tr.lit. circ. 2,100. (also avail. in microfilm from UMI; microfiche from EDR; reprint service avail. from UMI) **Indexed:** C.I.J.E., ERIC, M.L.A., PSI.
   —BLDSC (0680.470000); Faxon; UMI.
   Formerly: Association of Departments of Foreign Languages. Bulletin (ISSN 0148-8066)

410   FI   ISSN 0356-8156
A FIN L A YEARBOOK. (Text in English) 1977. a. Association Finlandaise de Linguistique Appliquee, Language Centre for Finnish Universities, University of Jyvaeskylae, SF-40351 Jyvaeskylae, Finland. TEL 358-41-603535. Ed. Minna-Riitta Luvkka. circ. 600. **Document type:** academic/scholarly publication.

418   IT   ISSN 0044-9490
A I L A BULLETIN. (Text in English, French, German, Spanish) 1970. q. membership. Association Internationale de Linguistique Appliquee, 27 via Cuppari, I-56100 Pisa, Italy. Ed. Antonio Zampolli. adv. **Indexed:** Lang.Teach.& Ling.Abstr.

418.02   US
A L T A NEWSLETTER. 1979. irreg. (3-4/yr.). $30 includes membership. American Literary Translators Association, University of Texas at Dallas, Box 830688, Richardson, TX 75083-0688. TEL 214-690-2093. Ed. Elizabeth Gamble Miller. circ. 1,000. **Document type:** newsletter.

400   US
A N S BULLETIN. 1954. irreg. (2-3/yr.). American Name Society, c/o Wayne F. Finke, Department of Modern Languages, Baruch College, Box 340, 17 Lexington Ave., New York, NY 10010. (Alt. addr.: c/o Edward Callary, Department of English, Northern Illinois University, DeKalb, IL 60115) circ. 900. **Document type:** academic/scholarly publication, bulletin.

410   DK   ISSN 0106-441X
A R K; sproginstitutternes arbejdspapirer. (Text in English, French, German, Italian, Spanish) 1979. 5/yr. DKK 150 to students and employees at the school; others DKK 200. Copenhagen Business School, Faculty of Modern Languages, Dalgas Have 15, DK-2000 Frederiksberg, Denmark. TEL 45-38-15-32-91. FAX 45-31-86-11-88. TELEX 45-31-19-19-19. Ed. Lita Lundquist. circ. 50.
   Description: Contains articles on language use in business as well as general linguistics.

418.02   US
A T A CHRONICLE. 1972. m. $35. American Translators Association, 1735 Jefferson Davis Hwy., Ste. 903, Arlington, VA 22202-3413. TEL 703-412-1500. FAX 703-412-1501. Eds. Lee Curtis, Derick Fajardo. adv.; bk.rev. circ. 5,800.
   Description: Contains association news, short articles of interest to linguists, and dictionary reviews.

418.02   US   ISSN 0890-4111
A T A SCHOLARLY MONOGRAPH SERIES. irreg., latest vol.6. $45 (members $25). (American Translators Association) John Benjamins Publishing Co., Bethlehem Pike, Philadelphia, PA 19118. TEL 215-836-1200; 800-562-5666. FAX 215-836-1204. Ed. Marilyn Gaddis Rose. **Document type:** monographic series, academic/scholarly publication.
   —BLDSC (0857.974500).

410 800   AT
A U L L A; journal of literary criticism, philology & linguistics. (Text in English, French and German) 1951. s-a. Aus.$18($16) Australian Universities Language and Literature Association, University of Sydney, Dept. of French, Sydney, NSW 2006, Australia. Ed. J. Hay. adv.; bk.rev.; cum.index. circ. 950. (back issues avail.)

410   DK   ISSN 0902-9958
AALBORG UNIVERSITETSCENTER. INSTITUT FOR SPROG OG INTERNATIONALE KULTURSTUDIER. ARBEIJDSPAPIRER. English edition: Aalborg University. Papers on Language and Intercultural Studies (ISSN 0903-8892); German edition: Universitaet Aalborg. Arbeitspapiere des Instituts fuer Sprache und Interkulturelle Studien. 1987. irreg. $7 per no. Aalborg University, Department of Languages and Cultural Studies, P.O. Box 159, DK-9100 Aalborg, Denmark. TEL 45-98158522. FAX 45-98157303.
   Formerly (until 1985): Serie om Fremmedsprog (ISSN 0106-1992)

460   DK   ISSN 0107-6531
CB226
AARHUS UNIVERSITET. ROMANSK INSTITUT. SPANSK AFDELINGEN. INFORMATION. 1975. irreg., no.36, 1983. price varies. Aarhus University, Niels Juels Gade 84, DK-8200 Aarhus N, Denmark. TEL 89421111. FAX 86163861. illus.

800   AG   ISSN 0001-3757
AS78
ACADEMIA ARGENTINA DE LETRAS. BOLETIN. 1932. 2/yr. Arg.$20($25) Academia Argentina de Letras, Sanchez de Bustamante 2663, Buenos Aires 1425, Argentina. **Indexed:** Amer.Hist.& Life, Hist.Abstr.

460   BO
ACADEMIA BOLIVIANA DE LA LENGUA. ANALES. 1985. a. Academia Boliviana de la Lengua, Casilla de Correos 4154, La Paz, Bolivia. Dir. Carlos Castanon Barrientos. bk.rev. circ. 400.

400   CK   ISSN 0001-3773
AS82
ACADEMIA COLOMBIANA. BOLETIN. 1936; N.S. 1956. q. $20. Academia Colombiana de la Lengua, Carrera 3-A, Numero 17-34, Bogota, Colombia. Ed. Manuel Jose Forero. bk.rev.; bibl.; index, cum.index. circ. 1,000. **Indexed:** Amer.Hist.& Life, Hist.Abstr., Lang.& Lang.Behav.Abstr., M.L.A.

400 060   HO   ISSN 0065-0471
AS64.A3
ACADEMIA HONDURENA DE LA LENGUA. BOLETIN. 1957. a. $10. Academia Hondurena de la Lengua, Apdo. Postal 38. Tegucigalpa, Honduras. Ed. Jorge Fidel Duron. bk.rev. circ. 500. (back issues avail.)

ACADEMIA PAULISTA DE LETRAS. REVISTA. see LITERATURE

ACADEMIA SCIENTIARUM HUNGARICA. ACTA ANTIQUA. see CLASSICAL STUDIES

ACADEMIA SINICA. INSTITUTE OF HISTORY AND PHILOLOGY. BULLETIN. see HISTORY — History Of Asia

460 375.4   VE   ISSN 1012-960X
ACADEMIA VENEZOLANA DE LA LENGUA. BOLETIN.* vol.39, 1971. a. Academia Venezolana de la Lengua, Bolsa a San Francisco, Caracas 1010, Venezuela. TEL 02-41-17-95. Ed.Bd. adv.; bk.rev.; bibl. **Indexed:** Amer.Hist.& Life, Hist.Abstr.
   Formerly: Academia Venezolana Correspondiente de la Espanola (ISSN 1011-7334)

400 840   FR   ISSN 0065-0544
ACADEMIE DES INSCRIPTIONS ET BELLES-LETTRES. ETUDES ET COMMENTAIRES. 1946. irreg. price varies. Editions Klincksieck, 11 rue de Lille, 75007 Paris, France. (also avail. in microfiche)

840   BE   ISSN 0567-6584
ACADEMIE ROYALE DE LANGUE ET DE LITTERATURE FRANCAISES. ANNUAIRES. a. price changes. Academie Royale de Langue et de Litterature Francaises, Palais des Academies, 1 rue Ducale, Brussels, Belgium. Ed. Thomas Owen. bibl.

440 840   BE   ISSN 0770-7061
ACADEMIE ROYALE DE LANGUE ET DE LITTERATURE FRANCAISES. BULLETIN. 1922. 3/yr. Academie Royale de Langue et de Litterature Francaises, Palais des Academies, 1 rue Ducale, Brussels, Belgium. Ed. Thomas Owen. **Indexed:** Bibl.Ling., M.L.A.

492.4   IS   ISSN 0065-0692
ACADEMY OF THE HEBREW LANGUAGE. SPECIALIZED DICTIONARIES. irreg. Academy of the Hebrew Language, P.O. Box 3449, 91034 Jerusalem, Israel. **Document type:** academic/scholarly publication.

492.4   IS
ACADEMY OF THE HEBREW LANGUAGE. TEXTS & STUDIES. irreg. Academy of the Hebrew Language, P.O. Box 3449, Jerusalem 91034, Israel. **Document type:** academic/scholarly publication.
   Formerly: Academy of the Hebrew Language. Linguistic Studies (ISSN 0075-9643)

423.1   US   ISSN 0270-4404
P365   CODEN: AIADD2
ACRONYMS, INITIALISMS AND ABBREVIATIONS DICTIONARY; a guide to alphabetic designations, contractions, acronyms, initialisms, and similar condensed appellations. 1960. a. $245 (effective June 1994). Gale Research Inc., 835 Penobscot Bldg., Detroit, MI 48226. TEL 313-961-2242; 800-877-4253. FAX 313-961-6083. TELEX 810-221-7086. Ed. Jennifer Mossman.
   —BLDSC (0578.886800); CASDDS.
   Formerly (until 1976): Acronyms and Initialisms Dictionary (ISSN 0065-0889)
   Description: Over 520,000 acronyms, initialisms and abbreviations, and the words and phrases they represent.

480   BE
ACTA COLLOQUII DIDACTICI CLASSICI; didactica classica gandensia. (Text in Dutch, English, French, German and Latin) 1963. a. 350 BEF. International Bureau for the Study of the Problems in the Teaching of Greek and Latin, Blandijnberg 2, B-9000 Ghent, Belgium. Eds. J. Veremans, F. Decreus.

430   GW   ISSN 0065-1273
PF3010
ACTA GERMANICA. (Text in English, French and German) 1966. a. (Suedafrikanischer Germanistenverband, SA - Association for German Studies in Southern Africa) Peter Lang GmbH Europaeischer Verlag der Wissenschaften, Eschborner Landstr. 42-50, 60489 Frankfurt a.M., Germany. TEL 069-7807050. FAX 069-785893. Ed. Walter Koeppe. bk.rev. circ. 200. (back issues avail.) **Indexed:** M.L.A. **Document type:** academic/scholarly publication.

430   GW   ISSN 0938-278X
ACTA GERMANICA. BEIHEFT; Jahrbuch des Germanistenverbandes im suedlichen Afrika. 1990. irreg. (Suedafrikanischer Germanistenverband, SA - Association for German Studies in Southern Africa) Verlag Peter Lang GmbH, Eschborner Landstr. 42-50, 60489 Frankfurt a.M., Germany. TEL 069-7807050. FAX 069-785893. **Document type:** academic/scholarly publication.

410   DK   ISSN 0374-0463
P2
ACTA LINGUISTICA HAFNIENSIA; international journal of general linguistics. (Text in English, French or German) 1939. irreg., vol.19, no.1-2, 1985. DKK 250. (Institute of Linguistics) C A Reitzel A-S, Noerregade 20, 1165 Copenhagen K, Denmark. Ed.Bd. bk.rev.; bibl. circ. 600. (reprint service avail. from ISI) **Indexed:** Bibl.Ling., Curr.Cont., Lang.& Lang.Behav.Abstr. (1973-), M.L.A., Mid.East: Abstr.& Ind.
   —Faxon; UnCover; SWETS.
   Formerly: Acta Linguistica (ISSN 0105-001X)

410   HU   ISSN 1216-8076
P25   CODEN: ALHUE8
ACTA LINGUISTICA HUNGARICA. (Text in English, French, German) 1951. q. $80 (effective 1992). (Magyar Tudomanyos Akademia) Akademiai Kiado, Publishing House of the Hungarian Academy of Sciences, P.O. Box 245, H-1519 Budapest, Hungary. TEL 181-2134. FAX 166-6466. TELEX 22-6228 AKNYO H. Ed. Ferenc Kiefer. adv.; bk.rev.; charts; illus.; index. **Indexed:** Arts & Hum.Cit.Ind., Bibl.Ling., Curr.Cont., Lang.& Lang.Behav.Abstr. (1972-), Lang.Teach.& Ling.Abstr., M.L.A. **Document type:** academic/scholarly publication.
   —CCC.
   Formerly (until 1988): Academia Scientiarum Hungarica. Acta Linguistica (ISSN 0001-5946)
   Description: Presents papers on the subjects of Finno-Ugric, Slavic, Germanic, Oriental and Romance linguistics, as well as on general linguistics.

057 XV ISSN 0567-784X
PN1
ACTA NEOPHILOLOGICA. (Text in various languages) 1968. a. $6. Univerza v Ljubljani, Filozofska Fakulteta, Askerceva 12, 61000 Ljubljana, Slovenia. TEL 061-150-001. FAX 061-159-337. Ed. Janez Stanonik. bk.rev.; bibl. circ. 400. **Indexed:** Bibl.Ling., M.L.A.

410 PL ISSN 0065-1524
ACTA PHILOLOGICA. (Text in English, French, German and Polish) 1968. irreg., vol.17, 1989. price varies. (Uniwersytet Warszawski, Wydzial Neofilologii) Wydawnictwa Uniwersytetu Warszawskiego, Ul. Obozna 8, 00-032 Warsaw, Poland. (Dist. by: Ars Polona-Ruch, Krakowskie Przedmiescie 7, 00-068 Warsaw, Poland) Eds. J. Reychman, Witold Tyloch. circ. 400. **Indexed:** Bibl.Ling.

ACTA REGIAE SOCIETATITIS HUMANIORUM LITTERATUM LUNDENSIS. see ARCHAEOLOGY

440 840 HU ISSN 0567-8099
ACTA UNIVERSITATIS DE ATTILA JOZSEF NOMINATAE. ACTA ROMANICA. (Text in French and Italian) 1964; N.S. 1972. a. exchange basis. Attila Jozsef University, c/o E. Szabo, Exchange Librarian, Dugonics ter 13, P.O.B. 393, Szeged H-6701, Hungary. (Subscr. to: Kultura, P.O. Box 149, H-1389 Budapest, Hungary) Ed. Bd. circ. 250.
Description: Journal of French and Italian studies focusing on language, literature and the history of civilization.

420 810 820 HU ISSN 0230-2780
PE9
ACTA UNIVERSITATIS DE ATTILA JOZSEF NOMINATAE. PAPERS IN ENGLISH AND AMERICAN STUDIES. (Text in English) 1980. irreg. exchange basis. Attila Jozsef University, c/o E. Szabo, Exchange Librarian, Dugonics ter 13, P.O.B. 393, Szeged H-6701, Hungary. (Subscr. to: Kultura, Box 149, H-1389 Budapest, Hungary) Ed. B. Rozsnyai. circ. 400. **Indexed:** M.L.A.
Description: English and American studies with special attention paid to literary studies, generative grammar and teaching English as a foreign language.

410 370 PL ISSN 0208-6077
P1.A1
ACTA UNIVERSITATIS LODZIENSIS: FOLIA LINGUISTICA. (Text in Polish; summaries in various languages) 1955-1974; N.S. 1981. irreg. Wydawnictwo Uniwersytetu Lodzkiego, Ul. Jaracza 34, Lodz, Poland. TEL 331671. (Dist. by: Ars Polona-Ruch, Krakowskie Przedmiescie 7, Warsaw, Poland) **Indexed:** Bibl.Ling. **Document type:** academic/scholarly publication.
—BLDSC (0585.207350).
Supersedes in part: Uniwersytet Lodzki. Zeszyty Naukowe. Seria 1: Nauki Humanistyczno-Spoleczne (ISSN 0076-0358)
Description: Devoted to linguistics, mainly Polish, but also English, German, French and Russian.

430 PL ISSN 0208-5259
ACTA UNIVERSITATIS NICOLAI COPERNICI. FILOLOGIA GERMANSKA. 1974. irreg. price varies. Uniwersytet Mikolaja Kopernika, Katedra Filologii Germanskiej, Biblioteka Uniwersytecka, Ul. Gagarina 13, 87-100 Torun, Poland. TEL 233-52. TELEX 552382. (Dist. by: Osrodek Rozpowszechniania Wydawnictw Naukowych PAN, Palac Kultury i Nauki, 00-901 Warsaw, Poland)

491.85 PL ISSN 0208-5321
PG6014
ACTA UNIVERSITATIS NICOLAI COPERNICI. FILOLOGIA POLSKA. 1959. irreg. price varies. Uniwersytet Mikolaja Kopernika, Biblioteka Uniwersytecka, Ul. Gagarina 13, 87-100 Torun, Poland. TEL 233-52. TELEX 552382. (Dist. by: Osrodek Rozpowszechniania Wydawnictw Naukowych PAN, Palac Kultury i Nauki, 00-901 Warsaw, Poland)
Formerly: Uniwersytet Mikolaja Kopernika, Torun. Nauki Humanistyczno-Spoleczne. Filologia Polska (ISSN 0083-4483)

430 375.4 HU ISSN 0238-079X
PF3009
ACTA UNIVERSITATIS SZEGEDIENSIS DE ATTILA JOZSEF NOMINATAE. ACTA GERMANISTICA. (Text in German) 1961-1972; resumed 1987. biennial. exchange basis. Attila Jozsef University, c/o E. Szabo, Exchange Librarian, Dugonics ter 13, P.O. Box 393, H-6701 Szeged, Hungary. (Subscr. to: Kultura, P.O. Box 149, H-1389 Budapest, Hungary) Eds. Janos Marvany, Miklos Salyamossy. circ. 350.
Supersedes (until 1971): Acta Universitatis Szegediensis de Attila Jozsef Nominatae. Acta Germanica et Romanica; (until 1966): Acta Universitatis Szegediensis de Attila Jozsef Nominatae. Acta Romanica et Germanica; (until 1964): Acta Universitatis Szegedeinsis. Section Scientiarum Philologiae Germanicae.
Description: A journal on the history of German literature and language.

491.7 891.7 HU ISSN 0237-9554
ACTA UNIVERSITATIS SZEGEDIENSIS DE ATTILA JOZSEF NOMINATAE. DISSERTATIONES SLAVICAE. SECTIO LINGUISTICA. Key Title: Dissertationes Slavicae. Sectio Linguistica. (Supplement avail. at irreg. intervals) (Text in Russian) 1962. a. exchange basis. Attila Jozsef University, c/o E. Szabo, Exchange Librarian, Dugonics ter 13, P.O. Box 393, Szeged H-6701, Hungary. (Subscr. to: Kultura, P.O. Box 149, H-1389 Budapest, Hungary) Ed. Imre H. Toth. bk.rev. circ. 350. **Document type:** academic/scholarly publication.
Supersedes in part (in 1982): Acta Universitatis Szegediensis de Attila Jozsef Nominatae. Dissertationes Slavicae (ISSN 0586-3732)
Description: Journal of Russian descriptive linguistics and of Old Slavonic historical and comparative studies.

494.511 HU ISSN 0209-9543
ACTA UNIVERSITATIS SZEGEDIENSIS DE ATTILA JOZSEF NOMINATAE. SECTIO ETHNOGRAPHICA ET LINGUISTICA/NEPRAJZ ES NYELVTUDOMANY. (Summaries in English, French, German and Russian) 1957. a. exchange basis. Attila Jozsef University, c/o E. Szabo, Exchange Librarian, Dugonics ter 13, P.O.B. 393, Szeged H-6701, Hungary. (Subscr. to: Kultura, Box 149, H-1389 Budapest, Hungary) Ed.Bd. bk.rev. circ. 500. **Indexed:** Bibl.Ling., M.L.A.
Description: Hungarian, Finno-Ugrian and universal linguistics and ethnographic studies.

420 810 PL ISSN 0301-7966
ACTA UNIVERSITATIS WRATISLAVIENSIS. ANGLICA WRATISLAVIENSIA. (Text and summaries in English or Polish) 1971. irreg. price varies. (Uniwersytet Wroclawski) Wydawnictwo Uniwersytetu Wroclawskiego, Pl. Uniwersytecki 9-13, 50-137 Wroclaw, Poland. TEL 44-10-06. (Dist. by: Ksiegarnia Uniwersytetu Wroclawskiego, Pl. Uniwersytecki 9-13, 50-137 Wroclaw, Poland) Ed. Jan Cygan. circ. 300. **Document type:** academic/scholarly publication.

430 PL ISSN 0435-5865
ACTA UNIVERSITATIS WRATISLAVIENSIS. GERMANICA WRATISLAVIENSIA. (Text in German, occasionally in Polish; summaries in German) 1957. irreg. price varies. (Uniwersytet Wroclawski) Wydawnictwo Uniwersytetu Wroclawskiego, Pl. Uniwersytecki 9-13, 50-137 Wroclaw, Poland. TEL 44-10-06. (Dist. by: Ksiegarnia Uniwersytetu Wroclawskiego, Pl. Uniwersytecki 9-13, 50-137 Wroclaw, Poland) Ed. Norbert Honsza. circ. 400. **Document type:** academic/scholarly publication.

439.31 PL ISSN 0860-0716
ACTA UNIVERSITATIS WRATISLAVIENSIS. NEERLANDICA WRATISLAVIENSIA. (Text in Dutch, English, German) 1983. irreg. price varies. (Uniwersytet Wroclawski) Wydawnictwo Uniwersytetu Wroclawskiego, Pl. Uniwersytecki 9-13, 50-137 Wroclaw, Poland. TEL 44-10-06. (Dist. by: Ksiegarnia Uniwersytetu Wroclawskiego, Pl. Uniwersytecki 9-13, 50-137 Wroclaw, Poland) Ed. Stanislaw Predota. circ. 250. **Document type:** academic/scholarly publication.

440 PL ISSN 0557-2665
ACTA UNIVERSITATIS WRATISLAVIENSIS. ROMANICA WRATISLAVIENSIA. (Text in French, Polish; summaries in French) 1968. irreg. price varies. (Uniwersytet Wroclawski) Wydawnictwo Uniwersytetu Wroclawskiego, Pl. Uniwersytecki 9-13, 50-137 Wroclaw, Poland. TEL 44-10-06. (Dist. by: Ksiegarnia Uniwersytetu Wroclawskiego, Pl. Uniwersytecki 9-13, 50-137 Wroclaw, Poland) Ed. Jozef Heistein. circ. 350. **Document type:** academic/scholarly publication.

491.8 PL ISSN 0137-1150
ACTA UNIVERSITATIS WRATISLAVIENSIS. SLAVICA WRATISLAVIENSIA. (Text in Polish; occasionally in Russian) 1969. irreg. price varies. (Uniwersytet Wroclawski) Wydawnictwo Uniwersytetu Wroclawskiego, Pl. Uniwersytecki 9-13, 50-137 Wroclaw, Poland. TEL 44-10-06. (Dist. by: Ksiegarnia Uniwersytetu Wroclawskiego, Pl. Uniwersytecki 9-13, 50-137 Wroclaw, Poland) Ed. Franciszek Sielicki. circ. 300. **Document type:** academic/scholarly publication.

410 PL ISSN 0137-1169
ACTA UNIVERSITATIS WRATISLAVIENSIS. STUDIA LINGUISTICA. (Text in Polish, occasionally in French; summaries in English or German) 1974. irreg. price varies. (Uniwersytet Wroclawski) Wydawnictwo Uniwersytetu Wroclawskiego, Pl. Uniwersytecki 9-13, 50-137 Wroclaw, Poland. TEL 44-10-06. (Dist. by: Ksiegarnia Uniwersytetu Wroclawskiego, Pl. Uniwersytecki 9-13, 50-137 Wroclaw, Poland) Ed. Zdzislaw Wasik. circ. 300. **Indexed:** Bibl.Ling. **Document type:** academic/scholarly publication.

410 US ISSN 0761-022X
ACTES SEMIOTIQUES. (Text and summaries in French) 1985. irreg., vol.6, 1988. price varies. John Benjamins Publishing Co. (Subsidiary of: John Benjamins Publishing Co.), 821 Bethlehem Pike, Philadelphia, PA 19118. TEL 215-836-1200. FAX 215-836-1204. (And: Amsteldijk 44, P.O. Box 75577, 1007 AN Amsterdam, Netherlands. TEL 020-6762325) Ed.Bd. **Document type:** monographic series.

440 370 BE ISSN 0775-9045
ACTUA PRESS (EDITION FRANCAISE). Dutch edition (ISSN 0775-9029); English edition (ISSN 0775-9037) (Text in French) 1985. s-m. 1600 BEF. Centre d'Animation en Langues, Chaussee Houtart 2, B-7110 La Louviere, Belgium. TEL 32-624-262045. FAX 32-64-262138. Ed. Eric Cornu. adv.; film rev. (back issues avail.)
Formerly: Actua (Edition Francaise) (ISSN 0775-1761)
Description: Publishes articles on current events and news to allow language students to practice their French skills.

420 370 BE ISSN 0775-9037
ACTUA PRESS (ENGLISH EDITION). Dutch edition (ISSN 0775-9029); French edition (ISSN 0775-9045) 1985. s-m. 1600 BEF. Centre d'Animation en Langues, Chaussee Houtart 2, B-7110 La Louviere, Belgium. TEL 32-64-262045. FAX 32-64-262138. Ed. Eric Cornu. adv.; film rev. circ. 25,000. (back issues avail.)
Formerly: Actua (English Edition) (ISSN 0774-7284)
Description: Publishes articles on current events and news for language students to practice their English skills.

439.31 370 BE ISSN 0775-9029
ACTUA PRESS (NEDERLANDS EDITIE). English edition (ISSN 0775-9037); French edition (ISSN 0775-9045) (Text in Dutch) 1985. s-m. 1600 BEF. Centre d'Animation en Langues, Chaussee Houtart 2, B-7110 La Louviere, Belgium. TEL 32-64-262045. FAX 32-64-262138. Ed. Eric Cornu. adv.; film rev. circ. 25,000. (back issues avail.)
Formerly: Actua (Nederlands Editie).
Description: Publishes articles on current events and news to allow language students to practice their Dutch skills.

LINGUISTICS

499.993   DK   ISSN 0901-2273
ACTUALITATES DE INTERLINGUA. (Text in Danish, Interlingua, Norwegian, Swedish) 1960. 4/yr. DKK 25. Dansk Interlingua Union, Ellegaardspark 79, DK-3520 Farum, Denmark. TEL 45-42-95-41-32. (Subscr. to: Union Danese pro Interlingua, Juvelvej 25, DK-5210 Odense NV, Denmark) (Co-sponsors: Norsk Interlingua Union; Svenska Saellskapet foer Interlingua) Ed. Joergen Kofod-Jensen. bk.rev. **Document type:** newsletter.
    Formerly: Actualitates (ISSN 0106-4819)

418.02   CN   ISSN 0001-7779
ACTUALITE TERMINOLOGIQUE/TERMINOLOGY UPDATE. (Catalog no. S52-1) 1968. 6/yr. Can.$14.95 (foreign $17.95). Canada Communication Group, Publishing Division, Ottawa, Ont. K1A 0S9, Canada. TEL 819-997-2560.

410   US   ISSN 0896-470X
ADVANCES IN DISCOURSE PROCESSES. 1977. irreg., vol.42, 1990. price varies. Ablex Publishing Corporation, 355 Chestnut St., Norwood, NJ 07648. TEL 201-767-8450. FAX 201-767-6717. TELEX 135-393. Ed. Roy O. Freedle. (reprint service avail. from ISI) **Indexed:** Bibl.Ling.
    —BLDSC (0704.245000).
    Formerly (until 1979): Discourse Processes, Advances in Research and Theory (ISSN 0164-0224)

410   US   ISSN 0963-5580
TK7882.S65
ADVANCES IN SPEECH, HEARING, AND LANGUAGE PROCESSING. 1990. a. J A I Press Inc., 55 Old Post Rd., No. 2, Box 1678, Greenwich, CT 06836. TEL 203-661-7602.

400   IT   ISSN 0001-9593
AP37
AEVUM; rassegna di scienze storiche, linguistiche e filologiche. 1927. 3/yr. L.102000 (foreign L.156000 ($128)) (effective 1994). (Universita Cattolica del Sacro Cuore) Vita e Pensiero, Largo Gemelli 1, 20123 Milan, Italy. TEL 02-72342310. FAX 02-72342260. TELEX 321033 UCTMI 1. Ed. Mirella Ferrari. adv.; bk.rev.; bibl.; index. **Indexed:** Amer.Hist.& Life, Bibl.Ling., Hist.Abstr., M.L.A., Old Test.Abstr.
    —Faxon.
    Description: Covers historic, literary, philosophical and linguistic areas on the national, as well as the international level.

AFGHANISTAN. see HISTORY — History Of Asia

496   UK   ISSN 0954-416X
PL8000   CODEN: ALCUEH
AFRICAN LANGUAGES AND CULTURES. 1988. s-a. £16($30) (University of London, School of Oriental and African Studies) Oxford University Press, Oxford Journals, Walton St., Oxford OX2 6DP, England. TEL 0865-56767. FAX 0865-56646. (U.S. subscr. to: Oxford University Press Inc., 2001 Evans Rd., Cary, NC 27513. TEL 919-677-0977) Ed. E.D. Elderkin. adv. contact: Jane Parker. bk.rev.; bibl. circ. 500. **Indexed:** Bibl.Ling., Documentatieblad.
Document type: academic/scholarly publication.
    —BLDSC (0732.596300); UnCover. **CCC.**
    Description: Publishes work on African linguistics and cultural studies, including art and music, and African literature in both African and Western languages.

AFRICAN STUDIES; a biannual journal devoted to the study of African anthropology, history, sociology, literature and languages. see ANTHROPOLOGY

AFRICANA MARBURGENSIA. see HISTORY — History Of Africa

496 896   GW   ISSN 0002-0427
PL8000
AFRIKA UND UEBERSEE; Sprachen, Kulturen. (Text in English, French and German) 1910. 2/yr. DM.148. (Universitaet Hamburg) Dietrich Reimer Verlag, Unter den Eichen 57, 12203 Berlin, Germany. TEL 030-8314081. FAX 030-8316323. Ed. J. Zwernemann. bk.rev.; abstr.; bibl.; index. (reprint service avail. from KTO) **Indexed:** A.I.C.P., Bibl.Ling., Curr.Cont.Africa, Documentatieblad, M.L.A. **Document type:** academic/scholarly publication.
    —UnCover. **CCC.**

492   US   ISSN 0732-6416
AFROASIATIC DIALECTS. 1977. irreg., no.4, 1983. price varies. Undena Publications, Box 97, Malibu, CA 90265. TEL 805-746-5870. FAX 805-746-2728. (Dist. by: Crescent Academic Services, 29528 Madera Ave., Shafter, CA 93263) Ed. Thomas Penchoen. bibl.; charts; illus. (back issues avail.) **Indexed:** Lang.& Lang.Behav.Abstr.
    Description: Data-oriented series which seeks to provide concise descriptions of individual languages which belong to the Afroasiatic language family.

492   US   ISSN 0362-3637
PJ991
AFROASIATIC LINGUISTICS. (Subseries of: Monographic Journals of the Near East) 1974. irreg., latest vol.9, no.3. price varies. Undena Publications, Box 97, Malibu, CA 90265. TEL 805-746-5870. FAX 805-746-2728. (Dist. by: Crescent Academic Services, 29528 Madera Ave., Shafter, CA 93263) Ed. Russell Schuh. bibl.; charts; illus. (back issues avail.) **Indexed:** Bibl.Ling., Curr.Cont.Africa, Lang.& Lang.Behav.Abstr., M.L.A., Old Test.Abstr.
    Description: Articles of general, theoretical interest using Afroasiatic material. Includes descriptive, historical and comparative studies in Afroasiatic (Hamito-Semitic) languages.

460   UK   ISSN 0961-8481
AHORA. (Text in Spanish) 6/yr. (during school year). Mary Glasgow Magazines (Subsidiary of: Scholastic Publications Ltd.), 140 Freston Rd., London W10 6TR, England. TEL 071-792-3644. FAX 071-792-3172. TELEX 311890-MGPUBS. (U.S. subscr. to: Delta Systems, 1400 Pkwy., McHenry, IL 60050-7030. TEL 800-823-8270) charts; illus.
    Description: Spanish-language magazine for intermediate-level students.

420 910   UK   ISSN 0953-461X
AINM. 1986. irreg. (approx. a.). $9. Ulster Place-Name Society, Department of Celtic, Queen's University of Belfast, Belfast BT7 1NN, N. Ireland. TEL 245133. Ed. Ruairi O hUiginn. bk.rev.; maps. circ. 350. **Indexed:** Bibl.Ling. **Document type:** bulletin.
    —BLDSC (0773.304000).
    Supersedes: Ulster Place-Name Society. Bulletin. *Refereed Serial*

400 900   GW   ISSN 0065-5287
P3
AKADEMIE DER WISSENSCHAFTEN IN GOETTINGEN. NACHRICHTEN 1. PHILOLOGISCH-HISTORISCHE KLASSE. (Text in English, German, occasionally French) 1893. irreg. price varies. Vandenhoeck und Ruprecht, Robert-Bosch-Breite 6, 37079 Goettingen, Germany. TEL 0551-6959-0. FAX 0551-695917. (Subscr. to: 37070 Goettingen, Germany) index. (reprint service avail. from KTO) **Indexed:** Amer.Hist.& Life, Bibl.Ling., Hist.Abstr. **Document type:** monographic series.

AKADEMIJA NAUKA I UMJETNOSTI BOSNE I HERCEGOVINE. ODJELJENJE DRUSTVENIH NAUKA. DJELA. see HISTORY — History Of Europe

400 800   AJ
PL311
AKADEMIYA NAUK AZERBAIJANA. IZVESTIYA. SERIYA YAZYKOZNANIE, LITERATURA I ISKUSSTVO. 1967. q. 15 Rub. Izdatel'stvo Elm, Ul. Narimanova, 37, 370073 Baku, Azerbaijan. bk.rev.; index.
    Formerly: Akademiya Nauk Azerbaidzhanskoi S.S.R. Izvestiya. Seriya Yazykoznanie, Literatura i Iskusstvo (ISSN 0002-3132)

400   KZ
AKADEMIYA NAUK KAZAKHSTANA. IZVESTIYA. SERIYA FILOLOGICHESKAYA. 1974. q. 2.40 Rub. Gylym, Ul. Pushkina 111-113, 480100 Alma-Ata, Kazakhstan. TEL 3272-611877.
    Formerly: Akademiya Nauk Kazakhskoi S.S.R. Izvestiya. Seriya Filologicheskaya.

430.07   UK   ISSN 0959-5740
AKTUELL. (Text in German) 1963. 6/yr. (during school year). Mary Glasgow Magazines (Subsidiary of: Scholastic Publications Ltd.), 140 Freston Rd., London W10 6TR, England. TEL 071-792-3644. FAX 071-792-3172. TELEX 311890-MGPUBS. (U.S. subscr. to: Delta Systems, 1400 Miller Pkwy., McHenry IL 60050-7030. TEL 800-823-8270) Ed. Corinna Schicker. charts; illus. (also avail. in microform from UMI; reprint service avail. from UMI)
    Former titles: Aktuell auf Deutsch; Roller (ISSN 0035-7901)
    Description: German-language magazine for advanced-level students.

410   CC
ALABO SHIJIE/ARAB WORLD. (Text in Chinese) q. Shanghai Waiguoyu Xueyuan, Alabo Yu Xi - Shanghai Foreign Language Institute, Arabic Department, 1550 Dalian Xilu, Shanghai 200083, People's Republic of China. TEL 5420900. Ed. Li Qilie.

497 572   US   ISSN 0883-8526
    CODEN: ANLPER
ALASKA NATIVE LANGUAGE CENTER RESEARCH PAPERS. 1979. irreg., no.8, 1990. price varies. University of Alaska, Alaska Native Language Center, Fairbanks, AK 99775-0120. TEL 907-474-7874. FAX 907-474-6586. Ed. Michael Krauss. circ. 200. **Indexed:** Lang.& Lang.Behav.Abstr. (1979-). **Document type:** academic/scholarly publication, monographic series.

410   GW   ISSN 0722-0332
ALEMANNISCH DUNKT UES GUET. (Text in Alemannisch and German) 1967. s-a. membership. Muettersproch - Gesellschaft, Am Hofacker 15, 79256 Buchenbach - Unteribental, Germany. TEL 07661-1236. Ed. Klaus Poppen. bk.rev. circ. 4,300. **Document type:** bulletin.
    Description: Promotes use of Alemannisch, the dialect of south-west Germany.

400 800   BL   ISSN 0002-5216
PN9   CODEN: ALFA.D5
ALFA; revista de linguistica. (Text in Portuguese; summaries in English and Portuguese) 1962-1977; resumed 1980. a. $30 or exchange basis. Universidade Estadual Paulista, Av. Vicente Ferreira, 1278, Caixa Postal 603, 17515-901 Marilia, SP, Brazil. TEL 0144-33-1844. FAX 0144-22-2504. TELEX 111-9016 UJME BR. Ed.Bd. bk.rev.; bibl.; index. circ. 1,000. **Indexed:** Lang.& Lang.Behav.Abstr. (1980-), M.L.A., Sociol.Abstr. **Document type:** academic/scholarly publication.
    —BLDSC (0786.960000).

497.3   CN   ISSN 0711-382X
    CODEN: AIRLEA
ALGONQUIAN AND IROQUOIAN LINGUISTICS. 1972. q. Can.$12($12) c/o J.D. Nichols, Ed., Native Languages Programme, 532 Fletcher Argue University of Manitoba, Winnipeg, MB R3T 2N2, Canada. bk.rev.; bibl. circ. 300. **Indexed:** Anthropol.Lit., Bibl.Ling., M.L.A.
    Description: Research papers and news relating to the languages and literatures of the Algonquian and Iroquoian families.

ALGONQUIAN CONFERENCE. PAPERS. see ANTHROPOLOGY

400   II
ALL-INDIA CONFERENCE OF LINGUISTS. SOUVENIR. 1970. irreg. $2. Linguistic Society of India, c/o Deccan College Postgraduate and Research Institute, Poona 411006, India. Ed. Suresh Kumar. adv.

440.370   UK   ISSN 0957-6215
ALLONS. (Text in French) 1966. 6/yr. (during school year). Mary Glasgow Magazines (Subsidiary of: Scholastic Publications Ltd.), 140 Freston Rd., London W10 6TR, England. TEL 071-792-3644. FAX 071-792-3172. TELEX 311890-MGPUBS. (U.S. subscr. to: Delta Systems, 1400 Miller Pkwy., McHenry IL 60050-7030. TEL 800-823-8270) illus.
    —**CCC.**
    Formerly: Boum (ISSN 0032-0471)
    Description: French language magazine for beginners.

410 GW ISSN 0179-387X
DIE ALTEN SPRACHEN IM UNTERRICHT. 1953. q. DM.21.80. (Altphilologische Fachgruppe im Bayerischen Philologenverband) C.C. Buchners Verlag, Laubanger 8, 96052 Bamberg, Germany. TEL 0951-65202. FAX 0951-61774. adv.; bk.rev. circ. 1,700. **Document type:** academic/scholarly publication.

430 GW
ALTHOCHDEUTSCHES WOERTERBUCH. 1952. a. (Saechsische Akademie der Wissenschaften zu Leipzig) Akademie Verlag GmbH, Muehlenstr. 33-34, 13187 Berlin, Germany. TEL 030-47889348. FAX 030-47889357. Ed. Rudolf Grosse. **Document type:** academic/scholarly publication.
Description: Dictionary of Old High German.

489 371 GW ISSN 0002-6670
DER ALTSPRACHLICHE UNTERRICHT; Arbeitshefte zu seiner wissenschaftlichen Begruendung und praktischen Gestalt. 1958. 6/yr. DM.119.70. Erhard Friedrich Verlag GmbH, Im Brande 17, 30926 Seelze, Germany. TEL 0511-40004-0. (Subscr. to: Postfach 100150, 30917 Seelze, Germany) index: vols. 1-15. circ. 4,800. **Document type:** academic/scholarly publication.
—CCC.

499.992 CN ISSN 0823-2539
ALUMETO. (Not published 1987-1991) (Text in Esperanto) 1984. 3/yr. Can.$8 to non-members. Canadian Esperanto Association, P.O. Box 2159, Sidney, BC V8L 3S6, Canada. Ed. Paul Hopkins. circ. 250 (controlled). (also avail. in diskette format; back issues avail.) **Document type:** newsletter.
Description: Serves to connect Canadian speakers of the international language, Esperanto, and inform them of the activities of the Canadian Esperanto Association and regional Esperanto associations in Canada.

400 US
AMERICAN ASSOCIATION OF LANGUAGE SPECIALISTS. YEARBOOK. a. American Association of Language Specialists, 1000 Connecticut Ave., N.W., Washington, DC 20036. TEL 301-986-1542. Ed. H. Coulter. circ. 750.

AMERICAN ASSOCIATION OF TEACHERS OF ESPERANTO QUARTERLY BULLETIN/AMERIKA ASOCIO DE INSTRUISTOJ DE ESPERANTO KVARONJARA BULTENO. see EDUCATION — Teaching Methods And Curriculum

480 US ISSN 0278-5943
AMERICAN CLASSICAL STUDIES. no.18, 1988. irreg. (American Philological Association) Scholars Press, Box 15399, Atlanta, GA 30333-0399. TEL 404-727-2320. FAX 404-727-2348. Ed. Jim Clauss. **Document type:** monographic series.
—BLDSC (0812.575000).

427 US ISSN 0002-8193
PE2801
AMERICAN DIALECT SOCIETY. NEWSLETTER. 1969. 3/yr. $25 (includes subscr. to P A D S and American Speech). American Dialect Society, c/o Allan Metcalf, Ed., English Department, MacMurray College, Jacksonville, IL 62650. TEL 217-479-7049. FAX 217-245-5214. adv.; bk.rev.; abstr.; bibl. circ. 925. (back issues avail.) **Indexed:** Lang.& Lang.Behav.Abstr., Res.Educ. **Document type:** newsletter.
—BLDSC (6106.329000).
Description: Contains news of American Dialect Society meetings, committees, and publications.

427 US ISSN 0002-8207
PE1702
AMERICAN DIALECT SOCIETY. PUBLICATIONS. Abbreviated title: P A D S. 1944. irreg. price varies. (American Dialect Society) University of Alabama Press, Box 870380, Tuscaloosa, AL 35487-0380. TEL 205-348-5180. circ. 800. **Indexed:** Bibl.Ling., Lang.& Lang.Behav.Abstr. **Document type:** academic/scholarly publication.

430 375.4 US ISSN 1040-8207
CODEN: AJGLL
AMERICAN JOURNAL OF GERMANIC LINGUISTICS AND LITERATURES. 1989. s-a. $25 to members; students & retired $15; institutions & libraries $40. Society for Germanic Philology, Box 020225, Brooklyn, NY 11202-0005. TEL 212-986-6477. Ed. Richard K. Seymour. bk.rev. circ. 250. **Document type:** academic/scholarly publication.
—Faxon; UnCover.
Description: Directed to professionals who study Germanic linguistics and literature, such as early German, Dutch, English, and Scandanavian.
Refereed Serial

420 US ISSN 0002-9475
P1
AMERICAN JOURNAL OF PHILOLOGY. 1880. q. $28 to individuals (foreign $36.50); institutions $69 (foreign $77.50). Johns Hopkins University Press, Journals Publishing Division, 2715 N. Charles St., Baltimore, MD 21218. TEL 410-516-6987. FAX 410-516-6968. Ed. George Kennedy. adv.; bk.rev.; index. circ. 1,407. (also avail. in microform from UMI,PMC; microfiche from IDC; back issues avail.; reprint service avail. from SWZ,UMI) **Indexed:** Arts & Hum.Cit.Ind., Bibl.Ling., Bk.Rev.Ind. (1965-), Child.Bk.Rev.Ind. (1965-), Curr.Cont., Hum.Ind., Ind.Bk.Rev.Hum., Lang.& Lang.Behav.Abstr., Numis.Lit, Phil.Ind., Soc.Sci.Ind. **Document type:** academic/scholarly publication.
—BLDSC (0831.500000); Faxon; UnCover; SWETS. CCC.
Description: Presents articles concerned with literary interpretation and history, textual criticism, historical investigation, epigraphy, religion, linguistics, and philosophy.

480 478 US ISSN 0065-9703
AMERICAN PHILOLOGICAL ASSOCIATION. SPECIAL PUBLICATIONS. 1946. irreg. price varies. American Philological Association, Department of Classics, Holy Cross College, Worcester, MA 01610. TEL 508-793-2203. FAX 508-793-3428.

406 US ISSN 0360-5949
P11 CODEN: TAPAEI
AMERICAN PHILOLOGICAL ASSOCIATION. TRANSACTIONS. 1870. a. $55. (American Philological Association) Scholars Press, Box 15399, Atlanta, GA 30333-0399. TEL 404-727-2320. FAX 404-727-2348. Ed. Sander M. Goldberg. cum.index: 1869-1969. circ. 3,000. (also avail. in microfilm from PMC) **Indexed:** Bibl.Ling., Curr.Cont. **Document type:** proceedings.
—UnCover; SWETS. CCC.
Supersedes in part: American Philological Association. Transactions and Proceedings (ISSN 0065-9711)
Description: Academic papers on Greek, Roman and classical literature and civilizations.

410 US ISSN 0190-4671
AMERICAN SOCIETY OF GEOLINGUISTICS. JOURNAL. (Text in English, French) 1974. a. $25 (students $18). American Society of Geolinguistics, 485 Brooklawn Ave., Fairfield, CT 06432-1805. TEL 203-333-8920. (Subscr. to: Box 6337, FDR Sta., New York, NY 10150) Ed. Jesse Levitt. adv.; bk.rev.; cum.index: 1974-1985. circ. 125. (back issues avail.) **Document type:** academic/scholarly publication.
—BLDSC (4129.950000).
Description: Deals with linguistic geography in terms of ethnic groups, sociolinguistics, language planning, and politics, language education and languages in contact and conflict.

428 US ISSN 0003-1283
PE2801
AMERICAN SPEECH; a quarterly of linguistic usage. 1926. q. $20 to individuals; institutions $25. (American Dialect Society) University of Alabama Press, Box 870380, Tuscaloosa, AL 35487-0380. TEL 205-348-5180. FAX 205-348-9201. Ed. Ronald Butters. adv.; bk.rev.; bibl.; index. circ. 1,800. (also avail. in microform from UMI,SCH) **Indexed:** Abstr.Engl.Stud., Amer.Hist.& Life, Bibl.Ling., Curr.Cont., Hist.Abstr., Hum.Ind., Ind.Bk.Rev.Hum., Lang.& Lang.Behav.Abstr. (1968-), Lang.Teach.& Ling.Abstr., M.L.A. **Document type:** academic/scholarly publication.
—BLDSC (0857.550000); Faxon; UnCover; SWETS; UMI. CCC.

418.02 US
AMERICAN TRANSLATORS ASSOCIATION. ANNUAL CONFERENCE PROCEEDINGS. a. $50. Learned Information, Inc., 143 Marlton Pike, Medford, NJ 08055-8750. TEL 609-654-4888. FAX 609-654-4309. Ed. A. Leslie Willson. **Document type:** proceedings.
Description: Explores new areas of the language-oriented professions.

430 374.4 833.91 US ISSN 0721-1392
AMERICAN UNIVERSITY STUDIES. SERIES 1. GERMANIC LANGUAGES AND LITERATURE. 1981. irreg. Peter Lang Publishing, Inc., 62 W. 45th St., 4th Fl., New York, NY 10036. TEL 212-302-6740. Ed. Michael Flamini. **Indexed:** Bibl.Ling. **Document type:** academic/scholarly publication.

410 495.1 US ISSN 0739-6406
AMERICAN UNIVERSITY STUDIES. SERIES 6. FOREIGN LANGUAGE INSTRUCTION. 1983. irreg. Peter Lang Publishing, Inc., 62 W. 45th St., 4th Fl., New York, NY 10036. TEL 212-302-6740. Ed. Kathryn Earle. **Indexed:** Bibl.Ling. **Document type:** academic/scholarly publication.

891.733 US ISSN 0740-0497
AMERICAN UNIVERSITY STUDIES. SERIES 12. SLAVIC LANGUAGES AND LITERATURE. 1983. irreg. Peter Lang Publishing, Inc., 62 W. 45th St., 4th Fl., New York, NY 10036. TEL 212-302-6740. Ed. Kathryn Earle. **Indexed:** Bibl.Ling. **Document type:** academic/scholarly publication.

447 US ISSN 0740-4557
AMERICAN UNIVERSITY STUDIES. SERIES 13. LINGUISTICS. 1984. irreg. Peter Lang Publishing, Inc., 62 W. 45th St., 4th Fl., New York, NY 10036. TEL 212-302-6740. Ed. Michael Flamini. **Indexed:** Bibl.Ling. **Document type:** academic/scholarly publication.

420 440 375.4 XO
L'AMITIE/FRIENDSHIP. (Text in English and French) 1967. 10/yr. 30 Kcs. (Ministerstvo Skolstvo Slovenskej Republiky) Slovenske Pedagogicke Nakladatelstvo - Slovak Pedagogical Publishing House, Sasinkova 5, 815 60 Bratislava, Slovakia. (Subscr. to: Slovart, Gottwaldovo nam. 6, 805-32 Bratislava, Slovakia) Ed. Jozef Blaho. circ. 55,000.
Description: English and French study and teaching.

880 938 NE
AMSTERDAM STUDIES IN CLASSICAL PHILOLOGY. (Text in English) 1990. irreg., vol.3, 1994. price varies. J.C. Gieben, Nieuwe Herengracht 35, 1011 RM Amsterdam, Netherlands. TEL 31-20-6275170. FAX 31-20-6275170. (back issues avail.) **Document type:** monographic series.

410 150 US ISSN 0165-716X
AMSTERDAM STUDIES IN THE THEORY AND HISTORY OF LINGUISTIC SCIENCE. SERIES 2: CLASSICS IN PSYCHOLINGUISTICS. Short title: C I P L. (Text in English and German) 1978. irreg., vol.5, 1991. price varies. John Benjamins Publishing Co., 821 Bethlehem Pike, Philadelphia, PA 19118. TEL 215-836-1200. FAX 215-836-1204. (And: Amsteldijk 44, P.O. Box 75577, 1070 AN Amsterdam, Netherlands. TEL 020-6762325) Ed. E.F.Konard Koerner. **Indexed:** M.L.A. **Document type:** monographic series.
Description: New editions of seminal works from the nineteenth and twentieth century in the area of psycholinguistics.

410 US ISSN 0304-0720
AMSTERDAM STUDIES IN THE THEORY AND HISTORY OF LINGUISTIC SCIENCE. SERIES 3: STUDIES IN THE HISTORY OF THE LANGUAGE SCIENCES. Variant title: Amsterdam Studies in the Theory and History of the Linguistic Science. Series 3: Studies in the History of Linguistics. Short title: S I H O L S. 1973. irreg., vol.68, 1992. price varies. John Benjamins Publishing Co., 821 Bethlehem Pike, Philadelphia, PA 19118. TEL 215-836-1200. FAX 215-836-1204. (And: Amsteldijk 44, P.O. Box 75577, 1070 AN Amsterdam, Netherlands. TEL 020-6762325) Ed. E.F.K. Koerner. **Indexed:** M.L.A. **Document type:** monographic series.
—BLDSC (0859.603000).
Description: Information concerning the heritage of linguistic ideas of more than two millennia.

LINGUISTICS

410 US ISSN 0304-0763
AMSTERDAM STUDIES IN THE THEORY AND HISTORY OF LINGUISTIC SCIENCE. SERIES 4: CURRENT ISSUES IN LINGUISTIC THEORY. Abbreviated title: C I L T. (Text in English) 1975. irreg., vol.106, 1993. price varies. John Benjamins Publishing Co., 821 Bethlehem Pike, Philadelphia, PA 19118. TEL 215-836-1200. FAX 215-836-1204. (And: Amsteldijk 44, P.O. Box 75577, 1070 AN Amsterdam, Netherlands. TEL 020-6762325) Ed. E.F.K. Koerner. **Indexed:** M.L.A. **Document type:** monographic series.
—BLDSC (0859.604000).
   Description: Forum for discussion of unorthodox ideas in the field of linguistics.

430 NE ISSN 0169-0221
AMSTERDAMER PUBLIKATIONEN ZUR SPRACHE UND LITERATUR. 1972. irreg., vol.105, 1993. price varies. Editions Rodopi B.V., Keizersgracht 302-304, 1016 EX Amsterdam, Netherlands. TEL 31-20-6227507. FAX 31-20-6380948. (In N. America: 233 Peachtree St. N.E., Ste. 404, Atlanta GA 30303-1504. TEL 800-225-3998. FAX 404-522-7116) Ed. A. Quak. circ. 700. **Indexed:** M.L.A. **Document type:** monographic series.
   Description: Covers Germanic languages and literature.

440 840 GW ISSN 0569-986X
ANALECTA ROMANICA. (Beihefte zu den Romanischen Forschungen) 1955. irreg., vol.52. price varies. Vittorio Klostermann, Frauenlobstr. 22, 60487 Frankfurt a.M., Germany. TEL 069-774011. FAX 069-708038. (Subscr. to: Postfach 900601, 60446 Frankfurt a.M., Germany) Ed. Wido Hempel. **Document type:** monographic series.

460 375.4 SP ISSN 0569-9878
ANALES CERVANTINOS. a. 2000 ptas. (foreign 3000 ptas.). Consejo Superior de Investigaciones Cientificas (C.S.I.C.), Instituto de Filologia, Duque de Medinaceli, 6, 28014 Madrid, Spain. Dir. Alberto Sanchez Sanchez. (reprint service avail. from SWZ)

ANCHOR POINT MAGAZINE; the international magazine for effective neuro-linguistic communication. see PSYCHOLOGY

ANCIENT NEAR EAST: HISTORY AND PHILOLOGY. see ORIENTAL STUDIES

420 820.9 DK ISSN 0903-1723
ANGLES. (Text in English) 1986. a. price varies. University of Copenhagen, Department of English, Njalsgade 84, DK-2300 Copenhagen S, Denmark. TEL 45-31-54-22-11. FAX 45-32-96-37-77. Ed.Bd. **Document type:** academic/scholarly publication.

420 GW ISSN 0003-3251
ANGLIA; Zeitschrift fuer englische Philologie. (Text in English and German) 1878. s-a. DM.186. Max Niemeyer Verlag, Postfach 2140, 72011 Tuebingen, Germany. TEL 07071-98940. FAX 07071-989450. Ed.Bd. adv.; bk.rev.; charts; index. circ. 800. (back issues avail.; reprint service avail. from SCH) **Indexed:** Abstr.Engl.Stud., Arts & Hum.Cit.Ind., Bibl.Ling., Can.Rev.Comp.Lit, Curr.Cont., Ind.Bk.Rev.Hum., Lang.& Lang.Behav.Abstr., M.L.A. **Document type:** academic/scholarly publication.
—BLDSC (0902.760000); UnCover; SWETS.
   Description: Essays and reviews of English and American language and literature.

420 JA ISSN 0003-326X
ANGLICA; journal of English philology. (Text in English and Japanese) 1951. s-a. 360 Yen($1) Meicho Fukyukai, 1-16-6 Taira-cho Meguroku, Tokyo 152, Japan. Ed. Tadao Yamamoto. bibl. circ. 900.

430 792 UK
ANGLICA GERMANICA: SERIES 2. irreg. price varies. Cambridge University Press, Edinburgh Bldg., Shaftesbury Rd., Cambridge CB2 2RU, England. TEL 0223-312393. FAX 0223-315052. TELEX 851817256. (N. American addr.: Cambridge University Press, Journals Dept., 40 W. 20th St., New York, NY 10011. TEL 212-924-3900. FAX 212-691-3239) Ed.Bd. **Document type:** monographic series.

ANGLO-AMERICAN FORUM. see LITERATURE

420 820 HU ISSN 0570-0973
ANGOL FILOLOGIAI TANULMANYOK/HUNGARIAN STUDIES IN ENGLISH. (Text in English) 1963. irreg., vol.22, 1991. Kossuth Lajos Tudomanyegyetem, Angol Tanszek, Egyetem Ter 1, Debrecen 4010, Hungary. TEL 36-52-16-666. bibl.; illus. **Indexed:** Bibl.Ling., M.L.A.

ANNALES AEQUATORIA. see ANTHROPOLOGY

ANNALES DU MIDI; revue de la France Meridionale. see ARCHAEOLOGY

400 PL ISSN 0239-426X
PB5
ANNALES UNIVERSITATIS MARIAE CURIE-SKLODOWSKA. SECTIO FF. PHILOLOGIAE. (Text in English, French, German, Polish; summaries in English, French, Polish) 1983. a. price varies. Uniwersytet Marii Curie-Sklodowskiej, Wydawnictwo, Pl. M. Curie-Sklodowskiej 5, 20-031 Lublin, Poland. TEL 48-81-375304. FAX 48-81-336699. TELEX 0643223. Ed. Alina Aleksandrowicz. circ. 550. **Indexed:** Bibl.Ling. **Document type:** academic/scholarly publication.
—BLDSC (0962.150000).

470 FR ISSN 0066-2348
ANNEE EPIGRAPHIQUE; REVUE DES PUBLICATIONS EPIGRAPHIQUES RELATIVES A L'ANTIQUITE ROMAINE. 1962. a. 360 F. (foreign 420 F.). Presses Universitaires de France, Departement des Revues, 14 Avenue du Bois-de-l'Epine, B.P. 90, 91003 Evry Cedex, France. TEL 1-60-77-82-05. FAX 1-60-79-50-45. TELEX PUF 600 474 F. (reprint service avail. from KTO) **Indexed:** Br.Archaeol.Abstr.
—SWETS. CCC.

491.992 US ISSN 0271-9800
PK8001
ANNUAL OF ARMENIAN LINGUISTICS. (Text in English, French, German, Italian) 1980. a. $20 to individuals; institutions $30 (for 2 yrs.). c/o John A.C. Greppin, Ed., Cleveland State University, Cleveland, OH 44115. TEL 216-687-3967. FAX 216-687-9214. adv.; bk.rev.; bibl. circ. 225. (back issues avail.) **Indexed:** Amer.Bibl.Slavic & E.Eur.Stud, Bibl.Ling., Lang.& Lang.Behav.Abstr. (1986-), M.L.A.

418 UK ISSN 0267-1905
P129
ANNUAL REVIEW OF APPLIED LINGUISTICS. a. £19($28) to individuals (overseas £24.50); institutions £38 (overseas £43.50 ($52)). (British Association for Applied Linguistics) Cambridge University Press, Edinburgh Bldg., Shaftesbury Rd., Cambridge CB2 2RU, England. TEL 0223-312393. FAX 0223-315052. TELEX 851817256. (N. American addr.: Cambridge University Press, 40th W. 20th St., New York, NY 10011. TEL 212-924-3900. FAX 212-691-3239) (Co-sponsors: Association Internationale de Linguistique Applique; Australian Association for Applied Linguistics) Ed. William Grabe. adv.; bk.rev. (also avail. in microform from UMI; back issues avail.) **Indexed:** Bibl.Ling., Lang.& Lang.Behav.Abstr. (1984-). **Document type:** academic/scholarly publication.
—BLDSC (1520.474500); UMI. CCC.
   Description: Covers bilingualism, psycholinguistics, computer-assisted instruction, sociolinguistics and lexicography.

410 BE
ANTHROPO-LOGIQUES. (Subseries of: Bibliotheque des Cahier de l'Institut Linguistique de Louvain) (Text in French) 1988. irreg., vol.4, 1992. 540 BEF. (Universite Catholique de Louvain, Institut de Linguistique de Louvain) Editions Peeters s.p.r.l., Bondgenotenlaan 153, B-3000 Louvain, Belgium. TEL 32-16-235170. FAX 32-16-228500. (back issues avail.) **Indexed:** Bibl.Ling. **Document type:** academic/scholarly publication.
   Description: Presents clinical studies illuminating the human sciences, with particular emphasis on the impact of these studies on language and linguistics.

410 306.4 US ISSN 0003-5483
ANTHROPOLOGICAL LINGUISTICS. 1959. 4/yr. $25 to individuals (foreign $33); institutions $35 (foreign $45) (effective 1992). Indiana University, Anthropology Department, Student Services Bldg. Rm. 346, Bloomington, IN 47405. TEL 812-855-1475. FAX 812-855-4358. (Co-sponsor: American Indian Studies Research Institute) Ed. Douglas R. Parks. adv.; bk.rev.; charts; cum.index: 1959-1988. circ. 1,200. (also avail. in microform from JAI,KTO) **Indexed:** A.I.C.P., Abstr.Anthropol., Anthropol.Lit., Bibl.Ling., Curr.Cont., E.I., Lang.& Lang.Behav.Abstr. (1972-), M.L.A., Mid.East: Abstr.& Ind., SSCI. **Document type:** academic/scholarly publication.
—BLDSC (1542.880000); Faxon; UnCover; SWETS.
   Description: Provides a forum for the full range of scholarly study of the languages and cultures of the peoples of the world.

ANTHROPOS; revue internationale d'ethnologie et de linguistique. see ANTHROPOLOGY

ANTICHITA CLASSICA E CRISTIANA. see HISTORY

420 430 SP ISSN 1131-6861
P1.A1
ANUARI DE FILOLOGIA. SECCIO A, FILOLOGIA ANGLESA I ALEMANA. (Text in various European languages) 1975-1986; N.S. 1990. a. $20. Universidad de Barcelona, Facultad de Filologia, Gran Via de les Corts Catalanes 585, 08007 Barcelona, Spain. TEL 318-42-66. FAX 318-81-63. Ed. Javier Orduna. adv.; bk.rev.; cum.index. circ. 600. (back issues avail.) **Indexed:** Old Test.Abstr. **Document type:** academic/scholarly publication.
   Supersedes in part (in 1990): Anuario de Filologia (ISSN 0210-1343); Which was formerly: Universidad de Barcelona. Facultad de Filologia. Anuario.

499.27 SP ISSN 1131-687X
ANUARI DE FILOLOGIA. SECCIO B, ESTUDIS ARABS. (Text in various languages) 1975-1986; N.S. 1990. a. $20. Universidad de Barcelona, Facultad de Filologia, Gran Via de les Cortes Catalanes 585, 08007 Barcelona, Spain. TEL 318-42-66. FAX 318-81-63. Ed. Julio Samso. adv.; bk.rev. circ. 600. (back issues avail.) **Indexed:** Old Test.Abstr. **Document type:** academic/scholarly publication.
   Supersedes in part (in 1990): Anuario de Filologia (ISSN 0210-1343); Which was formerly: Universidad de Barcelona. Facultad de Filologia. Anuario.

449.9 849.9 SP ISSN 1131-6888
ANUARI DE FILOLOGIA. SECCIO C, LLENGUA I LITERATURA CATALANES. (Text in Catalan) 1975-1986; N.S. 1990. a. $20. Universidad de Barcelona, Facultad de Filologia, Gran Via de les Corts Catalanes 585, 08007 Barcelona, Spain. TEL 318-42-66. FAX 318-81-63. Ed. Lidia Pons. adv.; bk.rev. circ. 600. (back issues avail.) **Document type:** academic/scholarly publication.
   Supersedes in part (in 1990): Anuario de Filologia (ISSN 0210-1343); Which was formerly: Universidad de Barcelona. Facultad de Filologia. Anuario.

480 470 SP ISSN 1131-6896
ANUARI DE FILOLOGIA. SECCIO D, STUDIA GRAECA ET LATINA. (Text in various languages) 1975-1986; N.S. 1990. a. $20. Universidad de Barcelona, Facultad de Filologia, Gran Via de les Corts Catalanes 585, 08007 Barcelona, Spain. TEL 318-42-66. FAX 318-81-63. Ed. Carmen Gonzalez. adv.; bk.rev. circ. 600. (back issues avail.) **Indexed:** Old Test.Abstr. **Document type:** academic/scholarly publication.
   Supersedes in part (in 1990): Anuario de Filologia (ISSN 0210-1343); Which was formerly: Universidad de Barcelona. Facultad de Filologia. Anuario.

499.2   SP   ISSN 1131-8597
ANUARI DE FILOLOGIA. SECCIO E, ESTUDIS HEBREUS I ARAMEUS. (Text in various languages) 1975-1986; N.S. 1990. a. $20. Universidad de Barcelona, Facultad de Filologia, Gran Via de les Corts Catalanes 585, 08007 Barcelona, Spain. TEL 318-42-66. FAX 318-81-63. Ed. Josep Ribera. adv.; bk.rev. circ. 600. (back issues avail.) **Indexed:** Old Test.Abstr. Document type: academic/scholarly publication.
 Supersedes in part (in 1990): Anuario de Filologia (ISSN 0210-1343); Which was formerly: Universidad de Barcelona. Facultad de Filologia. Anuario.

460 860   SP   ISSN 1131-690X
ANUARI DE FILOLOGIA. SECCIO F, ESTUDIOS DE LENGUA Y LITERATURA ESPANOLA. (Text in various languages) 1975-1986; N.S. 1990. a. $20. Universidad de Barcelona, Facultad de Filologia, Gran Via de les Corts Catalanes 585, 08007 Barcelona, Spain. TEL 318-42-66. FAX 318-81-63. Ed. Teresa Espanol Giralt. adv.; bk.rev. circ. 600. (back issues avail.) Document type: academic/scholarly publication.
 Supersedes in part (in 1990): Anuario de Filologia (ISSN 0210-1343); Which was formerly: Universidad de Barcelona. Facultad de Filologia. Anuario.

440   SP   ISSN 1131-6918
ANUARI DE FILOLOGIA. SECCIO G, FILOLOGIA ROMANICA. (Text in various European lanugages) 1975-1986; N.S. 1990. a. $20. Universidad de Barcelona, Facultad de Filologia, Gran Via de les Corts Catalanes 585, 08007 Barcelona, Spain. TEL 318-42-66. FAX 318-81-63. Ed. Francisco Lafarga. adv.; bk.rev. circ. 600. (back issues avail.) Document type: academic/scholarly publication.
 Supersedes in part (in 1990): Anuario de Filologia (ISSN 0210-1343); Which was formerly: Universidad de Barcelona. Facultad de Filologia. Anuario.

460 375.4   SP   ISSN 0213-053X
PC4008
ANUARIO DE LINGUISTICA HISPANICA. 1985. irreg., vol.8, 1992. 3000 ptas. Universidad de Valladolid, Secretariado de Publicaciones, C. Juan Mambrilla, 14, 47003 Valladolid, Spain. TEL 983-423000. FAX 34-83-290300. **Indexed:** Bibl.Ling. Document type: academic/scholarly publication.

410   CU
ANUARIO L L ESTUDIOS LINGUISTICOS. (Literatura Linguistica) 1967. a. $12 in S. America; N. America $14; elsewhere $16. (Academia de Ciencias de Cuba, Instituto de Literatura y Linguistica) Ediciones Cubanas, Obispo No. 527, Apdo. 605, Havana, Cuba. TEL 32-556-60.
 Supersedes in part : Anuario L - L (ISSN 1015-0978); Which was formerly: L - L (ISSN 0023-6209)

418.02   II   ISSN 0003-6218
ANUVAD/TRANSLATION; a quarterly on theoretical and practical aspects of translation. (Text in English and Hindi) 1964. q. Rs.35. Translators' Association of India, 203 Asha Deep, 9 Hailey Rd., New Delhi 110 001, India. TEL 11-3714838. FAX 6823217. Ed. Gargi Gupta. adv. contact: Sh. Krishna Kant. bk.rev.; charts; illus.; index. circ. 1,500. Document type: academic/scholarly publication.

491.8   AU   ISSN 0066-5282
ANZEIGER FUER SLAVISCHE PHILOLOGIE. 1966. irreg., vol.20, 1991. Akademische Druck- und Verlagsanstalt Dr. Paul Struzl, Schoenaugasse 6, A-8010 Graz, Austria. TEL 0316-813460. **Indexed:** Bibl.Ling. Document type: academic/scholarly publication.

410 572   FR   ISSN 0755-9291
APPLICATIONS ET TRANSFERTS DE LA S E L A F. (Subseries of: Bibliotheque de la S E L A F) 1982. irreg. price varies. Societe d'Etudes Linguistiques et Anthropologiques de France (SELAF), 52 bd. St. Michel, 75006 Paris, France. (Dist. by Editions Peeters s.p.r.l., Bondgenotenlaan 153, B-3000 Louvain, Belgium. TEL 32-16-235170. FAX 32-16-228500) Document type: academic/scholarly publication.

418   UK   ISSN 0142-6001
P129
APPLIED LINGUISTICS. 1980. 4/yr. £65($125) (effective 1994). Oxford University Press, Oxford Journals, Walton St., Oxford OX2 6DP, England. TEL 0865-56767. FAX 0865-56646. TELEX 837330-OXPRES-G. (U.S. subscr. to: Oxford University Press Inc., 2001 Evans Rd., Cary, NC 27513. TEL 919-677-0977) Eds. Craig Chandron, Rosamond Mitchell. adv. contact: Jane Parker. bk.rev. circ. 1,800. (also avail. in microform) **Indexed:** Bibl.Ling., Cont.Pg.Educ., Lang.& Lang.Behav.Abstr. (1980-), Lang.Teach.& Ling.Abstr., Mult.Ed.Abstr., Sp.Ed.Needs Abstr., SSCI. Document type: academic/scholarly publication.
 —BLDSC (1573.260000); Faxon; UnCover; SWETS; UMI. **CCC.**
 Description: Studies the relationship between theoretical and practical aspects of language education.

418 401 616.8   UK   ISSN 0142-7164
P37   CODEN: APPSDZ
APPLIED PSYCHOLINGUISTICS; psychological studies of language processes. 1980. q. £35($49) to individuals (overseas £48); institutions £73 (overseas £86 ($99)). (American Psychological Association) Cambridge University Press, Edinburgh Bldg. Shaftesbury Rd., Cambridge CB2 2RU, England. TEL 0223-312393. FAX 0223-315052. TELEX 851817256. (N. American addr.: Cambridge University Press, 40 W. 20th St., New York, NY 10011. TEL 212-924-3900. FAX 212-691-3239) (Co-sponsors: American Psychological Society, American Speech-Language-Hearing Association) Eds. Catherine E. Snow, John L. Locke. adv.; bk.rev.; cum.index. (also avail. in microform from UMI; back issues avail.) **Indexed:** ASCA, Bibl.Ling., C.I.J.E., Child Devel.Abstr., Curr.Cont., Lang.& Lang.Behav.Abstr. (1980-), Lang.Teach.& Ling.Abstr., M.L.A., Mult.Ed.Abstr., Psychol.Abstr., Sociol.Abstr., Sp.Ed.Needs Abstr., SSCI. Document type: academic/scholarly publication.
 —BLDSC (1576.545000); Faxon; UnCover; SWETS; UMI. **CCC.**
 Description: Presents papers on the psychological processes in language. Articles address the nature, acquisition and impairments of language expression and comprehension, including writing and reading.

401 150   US
APPLIED PSYCHOLINGUISTICS AND COMMUNICATION DISORDERS. 1979. irreg., latest 1991. price varies. Plenum Publishing Corp., 233 Spring St., New York, NY 10013-1578. TEL 212-620-8000. FAX 212-463-0742. TELEX 23-421139. Ed. R.W. Rieber. **Indexed:** SSCI. Document type: monographic series.
 Formerly: Studies in Applied Psycholinguistics. *Refereed Serial*

401   NE   ISSN 0169-0523
APPROACHES TO TRANSLATION STUDIES. (Text in English) 1970. irreg., vol.11, 1993. price varies. Editions Rodopi B.V., Keizersgracht 302-304, 1016 EX Amsterdam, Netherlands. TEL 31-20-6227507. FAX 31-20-6380948. (In N. America: 233 Peachtree St., N.E., Ste. 404, Atlanta, GA 30303-1504. TEL 800-225-3998) Document type: monographic series.

492.7   SJ
ARAB JOURNAL OF LANGUAGE STUDIES/AL-MAJALLAH AL-'ARABIYYAH LIL-DIRASAT AL-LUGHAWIYYAH. (Text in Arabic, English) 1982. s-a. £30($25) (Arab League Educational, Cultural and Scientific Organization) Khartoum International Institute for Arabic Language, P.O. Box 26, Eastern Deims, Khartoum, Sudan. Ed. Awan Asharif Qasim. **Indexed:** Bibl.Ling. Document type: academic/scholarly publication.
 Description: Focuses on the teaching of Arabic to non-native speakers.

492.7 370   US   ISSN 0889-8731
PJ6001
AL-ARABIYYA. (Text in Arabic and English) 1967. a. (in 2 vols.) $25. American Association of Teachers of Arabic, 280 HRCB, Brigham Young University, Provo, UT 84602. TEL 801-378-6528. FAX 801-378-7075. Ed. Mushira Eid. adv.: Page $50; adv. contact: Mushira Eid. bk.rev.; bibl. circ. 300. (processed; back issues avail.) **Indexed:** Bibl.Ling., C.I.J.E., ERIC, Ind.Islam., M.L.A., Per.Islam. (1991-), Sociol.Abstr. Document type: academic/scholarly publication.
 —BLDSC (1583.375900); SWETS.
 Formerly (until vol. 8): Al-Nashra (ISSN 0003-2387)
 Description: Publishes scholarly, pedagogical articles and reviews which contribute to the advancement of study, research, criticism, and teaching in the fields of Arabic language, literature and linguistics.

ARBEITEN AUS ANGLISTIK UND AMERIKANISTIK. see *LITERATURE*

491.7   GW   ISSN 0173-2307
ARBEITEN UND TEXT ZUR SLAVISTIK. (Text mainly in Russian) 1973. irreg. price varies. Verlag Otto Sagner, Postfach 340108, 80328 Munich, Germany. TEL 089-54218-0. FAX 089-54218218. TELEX 5216711-KUSAD. Ed. Wolfgang Kasack. circ. 200. (back issues avail.) Document type: academic/scholarly publication.

ARBEITSGEMEINSCHAFT DER BIBLIOTHEKEN UND DOKUMENTATIONSSTELLEN DER OST-, OSTMITTEL- UND SUEDOSTEUROPAFORSCHUNG. MITTEILUNGEN. see *LIBRARY AND INFORMATION SCIENCES*

400 800   GW   ISSN 0003-8970
ARCHIV FUER DAS STUDIUM DER NEUEREN SPRACHEN UND LITERATUREN. (Text in English, French, German, Italian or Spanish) 1846. 2/yr. DM.120. Erich Schmidt Verlag GmbH & Co. (Berlin), Genthiner Str. 30G, 10785 Berlin, Germany. TEL 030-2500850. FAX 030-25008521. Ed.Bd. bk.rev.; index. circ. 800. (also avail. in microfiche from IDC; reprint service avail. from SCH,KTO) **Indexed:** Arts & Hum.Cit.Ind., Bibl.Ling., Can.Rev.Comp.Lit, Curr.Cont., Ind.Bk.Rev.Hum., Lang.& Lang.Behav.Abstr., M.L.A. Document type: academic/scholarly publication.
 —BLDSC (1623.970000); Faxon; UnCover; SWETS. **CCC.**

450   IT   ISSN 0004-0207
PC4
ARCHIVIO GLOTTOLOGICO ITALIANO. 1873. s-a. L.98000 (effective 1993). Editoriale e Finanziaria Le Monnier, S.p.a., Via A. Meucci 2, Casella Postale 202, 50100 Florence, Italy. Dir. C.A. Mastrelli. adv.; bk.rev.; bibl.; index. (also avail. in microfiche from BHP) **Indexed:** Bibl.Ling., Lang.& Lang.Behav.Abstr., M.L.A. Document type: academic/scholarly publication.
 —SWETS.
 Description: Looks at general methological and historical research in Indo-European, Romance and Italian linguistics.

450   IT   ISSN 0066-6696
ARCHIVIO LINGUISTICO VENETO. QUADERNI. 1962. irreg., no.5, 1969. price varies. (Fondazione Giorgio Cini) Casa Editrice Leo S. Olschki, Casella Postale 66, 50100 Florence, Italy. TEL 055 6530684. FAX 055-6530214. circ. 1,000. Document type: monographic series.

410 709 880   IT   ISSN 0392-1050
ARCHIVIO PER L'ALTO ADIGE; rivista di studi alpini. 1906. a. L.50000. Istituto di Studi per l'Alto Adige, Via Cesare Battisti 4, 50122 Florence, Italy. circ. 150. **Indexed:** Bibl.Ling., M.L.A.

450   GW
▼**ARCHIVO DELLE SIMILITUDINI.** 1993. irreg., no.1, 1993. DM.98. Georg Olms Verlag, Hagentorwall 7, 31134 Hildesheim, Germany. TEL 05121-1501-0. FAX 05121-150150. (U.S. subscr. to: 111 W. 57th St., New York, NY 10019. TEL 212-757-5237) Ed.Bd. Document type: monographic series.

LINGUISTICS

450   IT   ISSN 0066-6815
ARCHIVUM ROMANICUM. BIBLIOTECA. SERIE 2: LINGUISTICA. (Text in English, French, German or Italian) 1921. irreg., no.48, 1990. price varies. Casa Editrice Leo S. Olschki, Casella Postale 66, 50100 Florence, Italy. TEL 055-6530684. FAX 055-6530214. circ. 1,500. (also avail. in microfiche from BHP) **Document type:** academic/scholarly publication.

499 306   FR
ARCTIQUE. (Subseries of: Bibliotheque de la S E L A F) 1987. irreg., vol.2, 1989. price varies. Societe d'Etudes Linguistiques et Anthropologiques de France (SELAF), 52 bd St. Michel, 75006 Paris, France. (Dist. by: Editions Peeters s.p.r.l., Bondgenotenlaan 153, B-3000 Louvain, Belgium. TEL 32-16-235170. FAX 32-16-228500) (back issues avail.) **Document type:** monographic series.

ARCTOS; ACTA PHILOLOGICA FENNICA. see *CLASSICAL STUDIES*

ARGUMENTATION; an international journal on reasoning. see *PHILOSOPHY*

400   GR
ARISTOTLE UNIVERSITY OF THESSALONIKI. SCHOOL OF PHILOSOPHY. PHILOLOGY DEPARTMENT. SCIENTIFIC YEARBOOK. resumed 1990. a. Aristotle University of Thessaloniki, School of Philosophy, Philology Department, 540 06 Thessaloniki, Greece. TEL 031-9911. FAX 206138. TELEX 041-2181. Ed. A.-Ph. Christides.

ARIZONA ENGLISH BULLETIN. see *EDUCATION — Teaching Methods And Curriculum*

410   US   ISSN 0160-3124
ARKANSAS PHILOLOGICAL ASSOCIATION. PUBLICATIONS. 1974. s-a. $25. University of Central Arkansas Press, Box 4933, Conway, AR 72035. TEL 501-45C-5118. Ed. Bob Lowrey. bk.rev. (also avail. in microfilm)
—BLDSC (7024.822800).

439   SW   ISSN 0066-7668
PD1503
ARKIV FOR NORDISK FILOLOGI/ARCHIVES FOR SCANDINAVIAN PHILOLOGY. (Text in Danish, English, French, German, Norwegian, Swedish) 1882. a. price varies. Lund University Press, P.O. Box 141, S-221 00 Lund, Sweden. TEL 46-46-312000. FAX 46-305338. Eds. Bengt Pamp, Christer Platzack. bk.rev. circ. 470. **Indexed:** Bibl.Ling., M.L.A., NAA. **Document type:** academic/scholarly publication.

ARNAMAGNAEAN INSTITUTE AND DICTIONARY. BULLETIN. see *LITERATURE*

ARS LYRICA: JOURNAL OF LYRICA. see *MUSIC*

ARYANA. see *HISTORY — History Of Asia*

400   KO
ASIAN AND PACIFIC QUARTERLY; of cultural and social affairs. (Text in English) 1969. q. free. Cultural and Social Centre for the Asian and Pacific Region, C.P.O. Box 3129, Seoul, S. Korea. TEL 02-679-5651. FAX 02-679-5653. Ed. Lien-Kong Tsai. bk.rev.; illus. circ. 500. (reprint service avail. from UMI) **Indexed:** Amer.Hist.& Life, Hist.Abstr.
Former titles: Asian Pacific Quarterly of Cultural and Social Affairs; A S P A C Quarterly of Cultural and Social Affairs (ISSN 0001-2599)
Description: Emphasizes language, history, and literature of Korea and China.

410   FR   ISSN 1147-5161
ASIE ET MONDE INSULINDIEN. (Subseries of: Bibliotheque de la S E L A F) 1976. irreg., latest 1992. price varies. Societe d'Etudes Linguistiques et Anthropologiques de France (SELAF), 52 bd. St. Michel, 75006 Paris, France. TEL 42-08-83-93. (Dist. by: Editions Peeters s.p.r.l., Bondgenotenlaan 153, B-3000 Louvain, Belgium. TEL 32-16-235170. FAX 32-16-228500) **Indexed:** Anthropol.Lit., Bibl.Ling., E.I. **Document type:** monographic series.
Supersedes (in 1989): Langues et Civilisations de l'Asie du Sud-Est et du Monde Insulindien (ISSN 0224-2680)

ASOCIACION DE HISPANISTAS DE LAS AMERICAS. PUBLICACIONES. COLECCION MONOGRAFIAS. see *LITERATURE — Poetry*

100   CN   ISSN 0381-5781
ASSOCIATION DES TRADUCTEURS ET INTERPRETES DE L'ONTARIO. INFORMATIO/ASSOCIATION OF TRANSLATORS AND INTERPRETERS OF ONTARIO. INFORMATIO. (Text in English and French) 1971. 6/yr. Can.$20. Association des Traducteurs et Interpretes de l'Ontario, 1 Nicholas, Ste. 1402, Ottawa, ON K1N 7B7, Canada. TEL 613-233-6395. FAX 613-233-7473. circ. 1,200.

400   CN   ISSN 0066-9016
ASSOCIATION DES TRADUCTEURS ET INTERPRETES DE L'ONTARIO. REPERTOIRE/ASSOCIATION OF TRANSLATORS AND INTERPRETERS OF ONTARIO. DIRECTORY. (Text in English, French) 1970. a. free. Association des Traducteurs et Interpretes de l'Ontario, 1 Nicholas, Ste. 1402, Ottawa, ON K1N 7B7, Canada. TEL 613-233-6395. FAX 613-233-7473. Ed.Bd. adv. circ. 5,000. **Document type:** directory.

ASSOCIATION FOR COMMONWEALTH LITERATURE AND LANGUAGE STUDIES. BULLETIN. see *LITERATURE*

840   FR   ISSN 0004-5527
ASSOCIATION GUILLAUME BUDE. BULLETIN. 1923. q. 120 F. Societe d'Edition les Belles Lettres, 95 Bd. Raspail, 75006 Paris, France. Ed. M. Michel. adv.; bk.rev. **Indexed:** Bibl.Ling., M.L.A.
—Faxon.

495.6 370   US   ISSN 0885-9884
PL501
ASSOCIATION OF TEACHERS OF JAPANESE. JOURNAL. 1963. s-a. $25. Association of Teachers of Japanese, c/o University of Pittsburgh, East Asian Languages & Literatures, Pittsburgh, PA 15260. TEL 412-624-5568. FAX 412-624-4419. (Alt. addr.: c/o Japanese Program, Middlebury College, Middlebury, VT 05753. TEL 802-388-3711) Ed.Bd. adv.; bk.rev.; ind.; index. circ. 1,300. (tabloid format; also avail. in microform from UMI; back issues avail., reprint service avail. from UMI) **Indexed:** Bibl.Ling., C.I.J.E. **Document type:** academic/scholarly publication.
—UnCover; SWETS; UMI.
Formerly: Association of Teachers of Japanese. Journal-Newsletter (ISSN 0004-5810)
Description: Explores Japanese literature, linguistics and language pedagogy.
Refereed Serial

491.7 375.4   UK   ISSN 0306-7432
ASSOCIATION OF TEACHERS OF RUSSIAN. NEWSLETTER. 1975. s-a. Association of Teachers of Russian, c/o Philip Hood, 7 Bringhurst, Orton, Goldhay, Peterborough PE20 ORS, England. bk.rev.; bibl. **Document type:** newsletter.
Description: For teachers of Russian in schools, colleges and universities.

410   US   ISSN 0066-9903
ASSYRIOLOGICAL STUDIES. 1931. irreg., vol.25, 1991. price varies. University of Chicago, Oriental Institute, 1155 E. 58th St., Chicago, IL 60637. TEL 312-702-9508. FAX 312-702-9853. **Document type:** monographic series.
Description: Publishes philological researches dealing chiefly with cuneiform grammatical and lexicographical material.

ASTRADO; revue bilingue de Provence. see *LITERATURE*

ATHENA. see *CLASSICAL STUDIES*

480   GW   ISSN 0938-3549
ATHENAEUMS MONOGRAFIEN. ALTERTUMSWISSENSCHAFT. 1960. irreg. price varies. Verlag Anton Hain GmbH, Savignystr. 53, 60325 Frankfurt a.M., Germany. Ed.Bd. **Document type:** monographic series.
Formerly (until 1988): Beitraege zur Klassischen Philologie (ISSN 0522-6821)

ATHENIAN; Greece's English language monthly. see *TRAVEL AND TOURISM*

410   CN   ISSN 0820-8204
ATLANTIC PROVINCES LINGUISTIC ASSOCIATION. ANNUAL MEETING. PAPERS. (Text in English, French) 1977. a. Can.$15 (includes Linguistica Atlantica). Atlantic Provinces Linguistic Association, Linguistics Department, Memorial University, St. John's, NF A1B 3X9, Canada. TEL 709-737-8134. circ. 150.

AUSTRALIAN AND NEW ZEALAND STUDIES IN GERMAN LANGUAGE AND LITERATURE. see *LITERATURE*

AUSTRALIAN JOURNAL OF FRENCH STUDIES. see *LITERATURE*

410   AT   ISSN 0726-8602
P1
AUSTRALIAN JOURNAL OF LINGUISTICS. 1981. s-a. $53. (Australian Linguistic Society) La Trobe University Press, Bundoora, Vic. 3085, Australia. TELEX 851817256. Eds. David Bradley, Roland Sussex. **Indexed:** Bibl.Ling., Lang.& Lang.Behav.Abstr. (1981-). **Document type:** academic/scholarly publication.
—BLDSC (1809.160000); Faxon; SWETS; UMI.

AUTOMATIC DOCUMENTATION AND MATHEMATICAL LINGUISTICS. see *LIBRARY AND INFORMATION SCIENCES*

052   UK   ISSN 0263-550X
B B C ENGLISH. 1968. m. £20 (Europe £22; elsewhere £26) (effective 1994). (British Broadcasting Corporation) B B C World Service, P.O. Box 76, Bush House, Strand, London WC2B 4PH, England. TEL 071-257-2857. FAX 071-240-4769. Ed. Lesley Clark. adv. contact: Ann Curtis. bk.rev. (also avail. in audio cassette; back issues avail.) **Document type:** academic/scholarly publication.
—SWETS.

BABEL. see *EDUCATION — Teaching Methods And Curriculum*

400 800   NE   ISSN 0521-9744
PN241.A1
BABEL; revue internationale de la traduction - international journal of translation. (Text in English and French, occasionally in other languages) 1955. q. fl.130($75) (effective 1994). (International Federation of Translators, BE - Federation Internationale des Traducteurs) John Benjamins Publishing Co., Amsteldijk 44, P.O. Box 75577, 1070 AN Amsterdam, Netherlands. TEL 31-20-6738156. FAX 31-20-6792956. (In N. America: 821 Bethlehem Pike, Philadelphia, PA 19118. TEL 215-836-1200) (Co-sponsor: Unesco) Ed. Rene Haeseryn. (reprint service avail. from SWZ) **Indexed:** Bibl.Ling., C.I.J.E., Lang.Teach.& Ling.Abstr. **Document type:** academic/scholarly publication.
—BLDSC (1854.500000); Faxon; SWETS.
Description: Covers news and events related to the Federation.

BAHANA. see *LITERATURE*

491.9   LI   ISSN 0132-6503
PG8001
BALTISTIKA; studies in Baltic linguistics. (Text in English, French, German, Latvian, Lithuanian and Russian) 1965. 2/yr. price varies. Vilniaus Universitetas, Baltu Filologijos Katedra, c/o Prof. A. Rosinas, Universiteto 3, 2734 Vilnius, Lithuania. TEL 45-85-25. TELEX 261240 TLG SU. Ed. Vytautas Mazuilis. bk.rev.; abstr.; charts; illus. circ. 500. **Indexed:** Bibl.Ling., M.L.A. **Document type:** academic/scholarly publication.
—BLDSC (1861.400000).
Description: Traces the history of Baltic languages and considers the relations between Baltic and Slavonic languages and other problems of comparative linguistics.

BAMLA EKADEMI GABESHANA PATRIKA. see *LITERATURE*

430 375.4   GW   ISSN 0342-8036
BARGFELDER BOTE; Materialien zum Werk Arno Schmidts. 1972. irreg. DM.46 for 6 nos. Edition Text und Kritik GmbH, Levelingstr. 6a, 81673 Munich, Germany. TEL 089-432929. FAX 089-433997. **Document type:** academic/scholarly publication.

410   US   ISSN 0736-1122
PE1630
BARNHART DICTIONARY COMPANION; a quarterly to update general dictionaries. 1982. q. $75 to individuals (overseas $90); academic institutions and libraries $52.50 (overseas $67.50) (effective 1994). Lexik House Publishers, Box 247, Cold Spring, NY 10516. TEL 914-265-2822. Ed. David K. Barnhart. bk.rev.; index. circ. 1,000. **Document type:** academic/scholarly publication.
—CCC.
Description: Updates general dictionaries by providing definitions of new and unrecorded words and meanings that reflect changes occurring in the English language.

BASLER STUDIEN ZUR DEUTSCHEN SPRACHE UND LITERATUR. see *LITERATURE*

430   GW   ISSN 0067-463X
BAUSTEINE ZUR SPRACHGESCHICHTE DES NEUHOCHDEUTSCHEN. 1964. irreg., vol.67, 1992. price varies. Akademie Verlag GmbH, Muehlenstr. 33-34, 13187 Berlin, Germany. TEL 030-47889348. FAX 030-47889357. (U.S. subscr. to: VCH Publishers Inc., 303 N.W. 12th Ave., Deerfield Beach, FL 33442-1788) **Document type:** monographic series.
   Formerly (until 1970): Bausteine zur Geschichte des Neuhochdeutschen.

BAYERISCHE STAATSBIBLIOTHEK. NEW CONTENTS SLAVISTICS. see *BIBLIOGRAPHIES*

BAZMAVEP. see *HISTORY — History Of The Near East*

420 370   GW   ISSN 0005-7347
BEACON; the English student's own magazine. (Text in English and German) 1949. 11/yr. DM.16.50. Beacon-Verlag Koerber oHG, Birkenlal 13, Postfach 1420, 67098 Bad Duerkheim, Germany. Ed. Ortrun Scheumann. adv. circ. 6,000. (tabloid format)

BEACON (GEORGIA). see *EDUCATION*

420 370   GW   ISSN 0005-7363
BEACONETTE; the beginner's English magazine. (Text in English and German) 1952. 11/yr. DM.7.70. Beacon-Verlag Koerber oHG, Birkenlal 13, Postfach 1420, 67098 Bad Duerkheim, Germany. Ed. Ortrun Scheumann. illus. circ. 5,000. (tabloid format)

439.2   NE   ISSN 0005-738X
AS243
BEAKEN. (Text in Dutch, English, French, Frisian and German) 1938. q. fl.42.50. Fryske Akademy, Doelestrjitte 8, 8911 DX Ljouwert-Leeuwarden, Netherlands. TEL 31-58-131414. FAX 31-58-131409. Ed.Bd. bk.rev.; charts; illus.; stat.; index, cum.index. circ. 2,500. **Indexed:** Bibl.Ling., M.L.A.
—SWETS.
   Description: Studies on Frisian language and culture.

430 375.4   GW   ISSN 0522-6341
BEITRAEGE ZUR DEUTSCHEN PHILOLOGIE. 1962. irreg., vol.67, 1990. DM.68. Wilhelm Schmitz Verlag, Staufenbergerweg 22, 35457 Lollar, Germany. TEL 06406-2324. Ed.Bd. circ. 100. **Indexed:** M.L.A. **Document type:** monographic series.

430 830   GW   ISSN 0005-8076
BEITRAEGE ZUR GESCHICHTE DER DEUTSCHEN SPRACHE UND LITERATUR. (Text in English, French or German) 1874. 3/yr. DM.178. Max Niemeyer Verlag, Postfach 2140, 72011 Tuebingen, Germany. TEL 07071-98940. FAX 07071-989450. Ed.Bd. adv.; bk.rev.; charts. circ. 700. (also avail. in microfiche from IDC; back issues avail.; reprint service avail. from SCH) **Indexed:** Arts & Hum.Cit.Ind., Bibl.Ling., Curr.Cont., M.L.A. **Document type:** academic/scholarly publication.
—SWETS.
   Incorporates: Beitraege zur Erforschung der Deutschen Sprache (ISSN 0232-2714)
   Description: Essays and reviews on Old High German and Middle High German language and literature up to 1500.

400   GW   ISSN 0005-8114
P769
BEITRAEGE ZUR NAMENFORSCHUNG. (Neue Folge) 1950; N.S. 1966. 4/yr. DM.160 (students DM.120). Universitaetsverlag C. Winter Heidelberg GmbH, Hans-Bunte-Str. 18, 69213 Heidelberg, Germany. Ed.Bd. adv.; bk.rev.; index. circ. 550. (reprint service avail. from KTO) **Indexed:** Amer.Hist.& Life, Bibl.Ling., Bull.Signal., Hist.Abstr., Lang.& Lang.Behav.Abstr., M.L.A. **Document type:** academic/scholarly publication.
—SWETS.
   Refereed Serial

BEITRAEGE ZUR ROMANISCHEN PHILOLOGIE DES MITTELALTERS. see *LITERATURE*

430 375.4   AU   ISSN 0259-0662
BEITRAEGE ZUR SPRACHINSELFORSCHUNG. 1981. irreg., no.10, 1992. price varies. Verband der Wissenschaftlichen Gesellschaften Oesterreichs, Lindengasse 37, A-1070 Vienna, Austria. TEL 932166. Ed. Maria Hornung.

430 375.4   GW   ISSN 0935-6487
BEITRAEGE ZUR SPRACHWISSENSCHAFT. 1978. irreg., vol.5, 1991. price varies. Helmut Buske Verlag GmbH, Richardstr. 47, 22081 Hamburg, Germany. TEL 040-296842. FAX 040-2993614. Eds. Hans-Werner Eroms, Ludwig Eichinger. **Indexed:** Bibl.Ling. **Document type:** monographic series.
   Formerly: Bayreuther Beitraege zur Sprachwissenschaft (ISSN 0721-4383)

491.799   BW   ISSN 0320-7552
PG2831
BELARUSSKAYA LINGVISTIKA. (Text in Byelorussian; contents in English) 1972. s-a. 1 Rub. (Akademiya Navuk Belarusi, Instytut Movaznaustva im. Yakuba Kolasa) Vydavetstvo Navuka Tekhnika, Zhodzinskaya, 18, 220067 Minsk 67, Belarus. TEL 39-55-17. FAX 252494. TELEX 252277 NAUKA. Ed. A.J. Padluzhnyy. adv.; bk.rev. circ. 700. (also avail. in microform) **Indexed:** Bibl.Ling
—BLDSC (0015.118000).

BELMONDA LETERO. see *RELIGIONS AND THEOLOGY — Other Denominations And Sects*

410   PO
BEM LINGUA PORTUGUESA. no. 25, 1974. bi-m. Esc.300. Sociedade de Lingua Portuguesa, Rua de S. Jose 41, 20 Lisbon, Portugal. Eds. Guilherme Matos, Aldina de Araujo Oliveira. adv.; bk.rev.

BERGOMUM; studi di letteratura, storia ed arte. see *HISTORY — History Of Europe*

410   US   ISSN 0893-6935
BERKELEY INSIGHTS IN LINGUISTICS AND SEMIOTICS. (Text in English and other European languages.) 1988. irreg. Peter Lang Publishing, Inc., 62 W. 45th St., 4th Fl., New York, NY 10036. TEL 212-302-6740. Ed. Irmengard Rauch. **Document type:** academic/scholarly publication.

BEYOND WORDS. see *RELIGIONS AND THEOLOGY*

491.1 294.1   II
BHAU VISHNU ASHETAR VEDIC RESEARCH SERIES. (Text in English, Sanskrit) 1965. irreg. price varies. University of Poona, Centre of Advanced Study in Sanskrit, Ganeshkhind, Poona 411 007, India. TEL 334220. FAX 0212333899. (Subscr. to: Section Officer, Publication Branch, University of Poona, Poona 411 007, India) Ed. V.N. Jha. **Document type:** monographic series.

407   GW   ISSN 0342-5576
BIBLIOGRAPHIE MODERNER FREMDSPRACHENUNTERRICHT.. (Text in various languages) 1970. q. DM.80. (Informationszentrum fuer Fremdsprachenforschung Marburg) Max Hueber Verlag, Max-Hueber-Str. 4, 85737 Ismaning, Germany. TEL 089-9602-0. FAX 089-9602-358. TELEX 523613-HUEBD. abstr.; bibl. **Document type:** bibliography.

BIBLIOGRAPHY OF MEDIAEVAL LATIN LEXICOLOGY. see *BIBLIOGRAPHIES*

460 375.4   SP
BIBLIOTECA DE LINGUISTICA. irreg., no.5, 1983. Editorial Anagrama, S.A., Calle Pedro de la Creu, 58, 08034 Barcelona, Spain.

499.94   IT   ISSN 0067-7450
BIBLIOTECA DI STUDI ETRUSCHI. 1963. irreg., vol.25, 1993. price varies. (Istituto di Studi Etruschi, Florence) Casa Editrice Leo S. Olschki, Casella Postale 66, 50100 Florence, Italy. TEL 055-6530684. FAX 055-6530214. circ. 1,000. **Document type:** monographic series.

410   SP
BIBLIOTECA FILOLOGICA. ENSAYOS. irreg. Editorial Bello, Barcas 5, Valencia, Spain.

410   SP
BIBLIOTECA FILOLOGICA. MANUALES. no.4, 1977. irreg. Editorial Bello, Barcas 5, Valencia, Spain.

BIBLIOTEKA BULTENO. see *LIBRARY AND INFORMATION SCIENCES*

493   US   ISSN 0742-1117
BIBLIOTHECA AFROASIATICA. 1982. irreg., no.3, 1986. price varies. Undena Publications, Box 97, Malibu, CA 90265. TEL 805-746-5870. FAX 805-746-2728. (Dist. in U.S. by: Crescent Academic Services, 29528 Madera Ave., Shafter, CA 93263) Ed.Bd. **Indexed:** M.L.A.

439.6 839.6   DK   ISSN 0067-7841
PT7113
BIBLIOTHECA ARNAMAGNAEANA; a Jon Helgason condita, auspiciis praesidii Arnamagnaeani. (Text in Danish, English, German, Icelandic, Norwegian, and Swedish) 1941. irreg. price varies. Arnamagnaean Commission, Njalsgade 76, DK-2300 Copenhagen S, Denmark. TEL 31-542211. (Dist. by: C.A. Reitzels Boghandel A-S, Noerregade 20, DK-1165 Copenhagen K, Denmark) **Indexed:** M.L.A. **Document type:** monographic series.
—BLDSC (2017.932000).
   Description: Presents editions, articles and monographs primarily in the area of Old Norse-Icelandic philology and literature.

439.6 439.6   DK   ISSN 0067-785X
BIBLIOTHECA ARNAMAGNAEANA. SUPPLEMENTUM. 1956. irreg. price varies. Arnamagnaean Commission, Njalsgade 76, DK-2300 Copenhagen S, Denmark. TEL 31-542211. (Dist. by: C.A. Reitzels Boghandel A-S, Noerregade 20, DK-1165 Copenhagen K, Denmark) **Document type:** monographic series.
   Description: Presents editions, articles and monographs primarily in the area of Old Norse-Icelandic philology and literature.

430 324   GW   ISSN 0067-7477
BIBLIOTHECA GERMANICA. HANDBUECHER, TEXTE UND MONOGRAPHIEN AUS DEM GEBIETE DER GERMANISCHEN PHILOLOGIE. 1969. irreg., vol.34, 1994. price varies. Francke Verlag GmbH, Postfach 2560, 72015 Tuebingen. TEL 07071-78091. FAX 07071-75288. Ed.Bd. **Document type:** monographic series.

410   US   ISSN 0342-4871
BIBLIOTHECA NOSTRATICA. 1977. irreg. price varies. Eurolingua, Box 101, Bloomington, IN 47402-0101. TEL 812-332-8918. **Document type:** monographic series.
   Description: Monographs on interphyletic linguistics, language origins, preproto-linguistics, global and intercontinental language studies.

491 943   FR   ISSN 0067-8325
BIBLIOTHEQUE D'ETUDES BALKANIQUES. 1925. irreg., vol.8, 1965. price varies. Institut d'Etudes Slaves, 9 rue Michelet, F 75006 Paris, France. **Document type:** academic/scholarly publication.

BIBLIOTHEQUE D'ETUDES COPTES. see *RELIGIONS AND THEOLOGY*

BIBLIOTHEQUE DE L'ECOLE DES CHARTES; revue d'erudition. see *HISTORY*

410   BE
BIBLIOTHEQUE DE L'INFORMATION GRAMMATICALE. 1984. irreg., vol.24, 1993. price varies. (Societe pour l'Information Grammaticale, FR) Editions Peeters s.p.r.l., Bondgenotenlaan 153, B-3000 Louvain, Belgium. TEL 32-16-235170. FAX 32-16-228500. (back issues avail.) **Indexed:** Bibl.Ling. **Document type:** monographic series.

496   FR   ISSN 0249-7050
BIBLIOTHEQUE DE LA S E L A F. Key Title: Societe d'Etudes Linguistiques et Anthropologiques de France. 1967. 6/yr. 160 F. Societe d'Etudes Linguistiques et Anthropologiques de France (SELAF), 52 bd. St. Michel, 75006 Paris, France. (Dist. by: Editions Peeters s.p.r.l., Bondgenotenlaan 153, B-3000 Louvain, Belgium. TEL 32-16-235170. FAX 32-16-228500) **Indexed:** Bibl.Ling. **Document type:** academic/scholarly publication, monographic series.
   Former titles (until 1972): Societe pour l'Etude des Langues Africaines (ISSN 0081-1238); **(until 1969):** Societe pour l'Etude des Langues Africaines. Bulletin.

LINGUISTICS

440   FR   ISSN 0067-8341
BIBLIOTHEQUE FRANCAISE ET ROMANE. SERIE A: MANUELS ET ETUDES LINGUISTIQUES. 1960. irreg. price varies. (Universite de Strasbourg II, Centre de Philologie et de Litteratures Romanes) Editions Klincksieck, 11 rue de Lille, 75007 Paris, France. Ed. Georges Straka.

800 479   FR   ISSN 0067-8384
BIBLIOTHEQUE FRANCAISE ET ROMANE. SERIE E: LANGUE ET LITTERATURE FRANCAISES AU CANADA. 1966. irreg., no.8, 1973. price varies. (Universite de Strasbourg II, Centre de Philologie et de Litteratures Romanes) Editions Klincksieck, 11 rue de Lille, 75005 Paris, France. Ed. Georges Straka.

BIBLOS. see *LITERATURE*

430 375.4   GW   ISSN 0172-3510
P51
BIELEFELDER BEITRAEGE ZUR SPRACHLEHRFORSCHUNG. (Text in English, French and German) 1980. s-a. DM.58($10) E. Keimer Verlag, Postfach 1463, 53604 Bad Honnef am Rhein, Germany. Ed. Manfred Sprissler. adv.; bk.rev. **Indexed:** Lang.Teach.& Ling.Abstr.

BIJDRAGEN TOT DE TAAL-, LAND- EN VOLKENKUNDE. see *ANTHROPOLOGY*

410 914.2   UK
BILINGUAL FAMILY NEWSLETTER. 1984. q. £7($14) Multilingual Matters Ltc., Frankfurt Lodge, Clevedon Hall, Victoria Rd., Clevedon, Avon BS21 7SJ, England. TEL 0275-876519. FAX 0275-343096. adv.; bk.rev. (back issues avail.) **Document type:** newsletter.
Description: Features articles on language, learning, linguistics, and biculturalism. A communication liaison between bilingual families throughout the world.

460   US   ISSN 0094-5366
P115
BILINGUAL REVIEW/REVISTA BILINGUE. 1974. 3/yr. $16 to individuals; institutions $28. Bilingual Review Press, Hispanic Research Center, Arizona State University, Tempe, AZ 85287-2702. TEL 602-965-3867. FAX 602-965-8309. Ed. Gary D. Keller. adv.; bk.rev. circ. 1,500. (also avail. in microform from UMI: reprint service avail. from UMI) **Indexed:** Arts & Hum.Cit.Ind., C.I.J.E., Chic.Per.Ind., Curr.Cont., Educ.Ind., Hisp.Amer.Per.Ind., Lang.& Lang.Behav.Abstr., M.L.A., Mid.East: Abstr.& Ind. **Document type:** academic/scholarly publication.
●Also available online.
—BLDSC (2059.900000); UnCover; UMI.
Description: Devoted to the linguistics and literature of bilingualism and bilingual education, primarily Spanish-English, in the United States.

410   US   ISSN 1045-4365
BILINGUALISM TODAY. irreg. Peter Lang Publishing, Inc., 62 W. 45th St., 4th Fl., New York, NY 10036. TEL 212-302-6740. FAX 212-302-7574. Ed. Dennis J. Bixler-Marquez. **Document type:** academic/scholarly publication.
Description: Encompasses theoretical and applied research on societal and cognitive aspects of bilingualism and biculturalism.

410 070   CN   ISSN 1192-1145
BILL PALMER'S WORD WATCHING. 1976. q. Can.$11. 220 Olivier, Ste. 302, Westmount, PQ H3Z 2C5, Canada. TEL 514-932-6370. Ed. Bill Palmer. bk.rev. circ. 350. (tabloid format) **Document type:** newsletter.
Description: Forum for readers to attack or honor the English language.

375.4   IS   ISSN 0334-9985
BITON LEMORIM LE'ARAVIT. (Text in Arabic, Hebrew) 1987. 3/yr. free. Institute for Arabic Studies, Givat Haviva, M.P. Menasche 37 850, Israel. TEL 972-6-373336. FAX 972-6-373335. Eds. Hanna Amit-Kohavi, Sarah Ozacky-Lazar. bk.rev. circ. 1,300. **Document type:** academic/scholarly publication.
Description: Covers the teaching of Arabic as a foreign language.

400 800   PL   ISSN 0067-902X
BIULETYN POLONISTYCZNY. 1958. q. $25. Polska Akademia Nauk, Instytut Badan Literackich, Nowy Swiat 72, Palac Staszica, pok. 128, 00-330 Warsaw, Poland. Ed. Krystyna Sierocka. abstr. circ. 1,500. **Document type:** academic/scholarly publication.
Description: A survey of research results and activities of the Polish philologists in Poland and in the world.

491.8   PL   ISSN 0137-5431
BIULETYN SLAWISTYCZNY. vol.4, 1979. irreg., vol.7, 1983. Polska Akademia Nauk, Instytut Slowianoznawstwa, Palac Kultury i Nauki, P.O. Box 24, 00-901 Warsaw, Poland. (Dist. by: Ars Polona, Krakowskie Przedmiescie 7, 00-068 Warsaw, Poland) Ed. M. Basaj. circ. 320. **Indexed:** Bibl.Ling. **Document type:** academic/scholarly publication.

420 910   GW   ISSN 0172-0872
BLAETTER FUER OBERDEUTSCHE NAMENFORSCHUNG. (Text mainly in German; occasionally in English, Greek, Italian and Latin) 1973. a. DM.30. Verband fuer Orts- und Flurnamenforschung in Bayern (V O F B) e.V., Leonrodstr. 57, 80636 Munich, Germany. Ed. Wolf-Armin von Reitzenstein. circ. 700. **Indexed:** Bibl.Ling., Br.Archaeol.Abstr., Geo.Abstr., NAA. **Document type:** academic/scholarly publication.

407 371.3   US
BLUEGRASS BULLETIN.* 1973. s-a. Kentucky Council on the Teaching of Foreign Languages, c/o Dr. David R. Hume, Ed., Department of Modern Languages, University of Louisville, Louisville, KY 40208. bk.rev.

BOARD OF CELTIC STUDIES. BULLETIN. see *LITERATURE*

400   PO
BOLETIM DE FILOLOGIA.* vol. 23, 1974. q. Centro de Estudos Filologicos, Av. Cinco de Octubro 85, 50 Lisbon 2, Portugal. Ed.Bd. bk.rev. **Indexed:** Bibl.Ling., M.L.A.

400   CL   ISSN 0067-9674
P25
BOLETIN DE FILOLOGIA. (Text in English, French, German, Spanish) 1934. a. $14. Universidad de Chile, Departamento de Linguistica, Facultad de Filosofia, Humanidades y Educacion, Casilla 10136, Correo Central, Santiago, Chile. Ed. Luis Prieto Vera. adv.; bk.rev.; cum.index. circ. 1,000. **Indexed:** Amer.Hist.& Life, Bibl.Ling., Hist.Abstr., M.L.A.

410   IT
BOLLETTINO DELL'ATLANTE LINGUISTICO ITALIANO. 1976. a. L.10000. Istituto dell' Atlante Linguistico Italiano, Via Sant' Ottavio, 20, 10124 Turin, Italy. TEL 011-874848. Ed.Bd. bk.rev. circ. 250. (back issues avail.) **Indexed:** Bibl.Ling., M.L.A.

499.992   SA   ISSN 0006-7024
BONA ESPERO. (Text in Esperanto) 1964. s-a. R.15. Esperanto Association of Southern Africa, 75 Bronkhorst St., Groenkloof, Pretoria 0181, South Africa. Ed. H. von Blottnitz. bk.rev. circ. 120.

440   UK   ISSN 0006-7121
BONJOUR. (Text in French) 1963. 6/yr. (during school year). Mary Glasgow Magazines (Subsidiary of: Scholastic Publications Ltd.), 140 Freston Rd., London W10 6TR, England. TEL 071-792-3644. FAX 071-792-3172. TELEX 311890-MGPUBS. (U.S. subscr. to: Delta Systems, 1400 Miller Pkwy., McHenry IL 60050-7030. TEL 800-823-8270) illus. (also avail. in microform from UMI; reprint service avail. from UMI)
—UMI.
Description: French language magazine for older beginners.

400   GW   ISSN 0170-821X
BONNER ROMANISTISCHE ARBEITEN. 1977. irreg. Universitaet Bonn, Romanisches Seminar, Am Hof 1, 53113 Bonn, Germany. Ed.Bd. (back issues avail.) **Indexed:** M.L.A. **Document type:** monographic series.

BORE DA. see *CHILDREN AND YOUTH — For*

BRAIN AND LANGUAGE. see *PSYCHOLOGY*

437   GW
BRANDENBURG - BERLINISCHES WOERTERBUCH. 1968. a. (Saechsische Akademie der Wissenschaften zu Leipzig) Akademie Verlag GmbH, Muehlenstr. 33-34, 13187 Berlin, Germany. TEL 030-47889348. FAX 030-47889357. **Document type:** academic/scholarly publication.
Description: Dictionary of regional German from the Brandenburg-Berlin area.

BRAZIL. MUSEU DO INDIO. BOLETIM. DOCUMENTACAO. see *ANTHROPOLOGY*

BRILL'S JAPANESE STUDIES LIBRARY. see *ORIENTAL STUDIES*

499.992   UK   ISSN 0007-067X
LA BRITA ESPERANTISTO. (Text in English and Esperanto) 1905. bi-m. 14 membership. Esperanto-Asocio de Britio, 140 Holland Park Ave., London W11 4UF, England. TEL 071-727-7821. Ed. William Auld. adv.; bk.rev.; illus.; index. circ. 1,300. **Document type:** academic/scholarly publication.
Incorporates: Esperanto News (ISSN 0306-5693)
Description: The organ of the British Esperanto movement, with literary items and news of British and international interest to Esperanto speakers.

BRITISH COLUMBIA ENGLISH TEACHERS' ASSOCIATION. JOURNAL. see *EDUCATION — Teaching Methods And Curriculum*

499.27   HU
BUDAPEST STUDIES IN ARABIC. irreg. Eotvos Lorand University, Chair for Arabic Studies, 1364 Budapest, Hungary. (Co-sponsor: Csoma de Koros Society, Section of Islamic Studies) **Document type:** academic/scholarly publication.

491.81   BU   ISSN 0068-3787
BULGARSKA AKADEMIIA NA NAUKITE. INSTITUT ZA BULGARSKI EZIK. IZVESTIIA. (Text in Bulgarian; summaries in various languages) vol.19, 1970. irreg. 4.68 lv. per no. Publishing House of the Bulgarian Academy of Sciences, Acad. G. Bonchev St., Bldg. 6, 1113 Sofia, Bulgaria. (Dist. by: Hemus, 6, Rouski Blvd., 1000 Sofia, Bulgaria) circ. 577. (reprint service avail. from IRC)

491.81   BU   ISSN 0005-4283
PG801
BULGARSKI EZIK. 1951. 6/yr. 1.20 lv. per no. (Bulgarska Akademiia na Naukite, Institut za Bulgarski Ezik) Publishing House of the Bulgarian Academy of Sciences, Acad. G. Bonchev St., Bldg. 6, 1113 Sofia, Bulgaria. (Dist. by: Hemus: 6, Rouski Blvd., 1000 Sofia, Bulgaria) Ed. L. Andreichin. circ. 2,200. (reprint service avail. from IRC) **Indexed:** M.L.A.
—BLDSC (0018.632000).

440 375.4   FR   ISSN 0007-408X
BULLETIN ANALYTIQUE DE LINGUISTIQUE FRANCAISE. 1969. 2/yr. 335 F. Editions Klincksieck, 8 rue de la Sorbonne, 75005 Paris, France. Ed. Annie Becquer. circ. 600. (also avail. in microform from UMI) **Document type:** bulletin.
—SWETS; UMI.
Supersedes: Bulletin Analytique de Lexicologie.
Description: French language study and teaching.

418   SZ   ISSN 0251-7256
P51
BULLETIN C I L A. (Text in English, French, German, Italian) 1966. s-a. 30 SFr. to individuals (foreign 35 SFr.); institutions 50 SFr. (foreign 55 SFr.). Commission Interuniversitaire Suisse de Linguistique Appliquee, Universite de Neuchatel, Institut de Linguistique, CH-2000 Neuchatel, Switzerland. TEL 038-208894. FAX 038-213760. Ed. Gerard Merkt. bk.rev. circ. 750. (also avail. in microfiche) **Indexed:** Bibl.Ling., ERIC, Lang. & Lang.Behav.Abstr. (1971-), Lang.Teach.& Ling.Abstr., M.L.A. **Document type:** bulletin.
—BLDSC (2838.485000).

414   FR   ISSN 1163-7641
BULLETIN DE LA COMMUNICATION PARLEE. (Text in French, ocassionally in English) 1991. a. 100 F. Institut de la Communication Parlee, Universite Stendhal, B.P. 25 X, 38040 Grenoble Cedex, France. TEL 76-82-43-37. FAX 76-82-43-35. Ed.Bd.
Description: Publishes papers on all aspects of speech sciences.
Refereed Serial

BULLETIN HISPANIQUE. see HISTORY — History Of Europe

BULLETIN OF HISPANIC STUDIES. see LITERATURE

BULLETIN OF JUDAEO-GREEK STUDIES. see RELIGIONS AND THEOLOGY — Judaic

400 800   PL   ISSN 0068-4570
BYDGOSKIE TOWARZYSTWO NAUKOWE. WYDZIAL NAUK HUMANISTYCZNYCH. PRACE. SERIA B (JEZYK I LITERATURA). 1965. irreg. price varies. Bydgoskie Towarzystwo Naukowe, Jezuicka 4, Bydgoszcz, Poland. (Dist. by: Ars Polona-Ruch, Krakowskie Przedmiescie 7, Warsaw, Poland)

BYZANTION NEA HELLAS. see HUMANITIES: COMPREHENSIVE WORKS

C E C T A L BIBLIOGRAPHICAL AND SPECIAL SERIES. (Centre for English Cultural Tradition and Language) see SOCIAL SCIENCES: COMPREHENSIVE WORKS

410 800   UK   ISSN 0261-314X
C E C T A L CONFERENCE PAPERS SERIES. 1981. irreg., no.6. price varies. University of Sheffield, Centre for English Cultural Tradition and Language, Sheffield S10 2TN, England. TEL 0742-768555. FAX 0742-768251. Ed. J.D.A. Widdowson. **Document type:** academic/scholarly publication.
—BLDSC (3096.946000).

C E C T A L OCCASIONAL PUBLICATIONS. (Centre for English Cultural Tradition and Language) see SOCIAL SCIENCES: COMPREHENSIVE WORKS

410   TI   ISSN 0564-7975
P2
C E R E S CAHIERS. SERIE LINGUISTIQUE.* 1970. q. Universite de Tunis, Centre d'Etudes et de Recherches Economiques et Sociales, 23 rue d'Espagne, Tunis, Tunisia. bibl.; charts; illus.

491.1 375.4   II
C I I L BILINGUAL EDUCATION SERIES. 1976. irreg., latest 1987. price varies. Ministry of Human Resource Development, Central Institute of Indian Languages, Manasagangotri, Mysore 570 006, India. Ed.Bd.

491.1 375.4   II
C I I L BILINGUAL HINDI SERIES. (Text in English, Hindi) 1976. irreg. Ministry of Human Resource Development, Central Institute of Indian Languages, Manasagangotri, Mysore 570 006, India. bibl.

491.1 375.4   II
C I I L COMMON VOCABULARY SERIES. 1975. irreg., latest 1980. price varies. Ministry of Human Resource Development, Central Institute of Indian Languages, Manasagangotri, Mysore 570 006, India. Ed.Bd.

491.1 375.4   II
C I I L DOCUMENTATION SERIES. 1972. irreg., latest 1984. price varies. Ministry of Human Resource Development, Central Institute of Indian Languages, Manasagangotri, Mysore 570 006, India. Ed.Bd.

491.1 375.4   II
C I I L GRAMMAR SERIES. 1975. irreg., latest 1987. Rs.10. Ministry of Human Resource Development, Central Institute of Indian Languages, Manasagangotri, Mysore 570 006, India. bibl.

491.1 375.4   II
C I I L INTENSIVE COURSE SERIES. 1979. irreg., latest 1987. price varies. Ministry of Human Resource Development, Central Institute of Indian Languages, Manasagangotri, Mysore 570 006, India. Ed.Bd.

491.1 375.4   II
C I I L - K V S. MOTHER TONGUE SERIES - APNI BOLI. 1969. irreg. Ministry of Human Resource Development, Central Institute of Indian Languages, Manasagangotri, Mysore 570 006, India. Ed.Bd.

491.1 375.4   II
C I I L OCCASIONAL BULLETIN SERIES. 1979. irreg., latest 1985. price varies. Ministry of Human Resource Development, Central Institute of Indian Languages, Manasagangotri, Mysore 570 006, India. Ed.Bd.

491.1 375.4   II
C I I L OCCASIONAL MONOGRAPH SERIES. 1971. irreg., latest 1987. price varies. Ministry of Human Resource Development, Central Institute of Indian Languages, Manasagangotri, Mysore 570 006, India. **Document type:** monographic series.

491.1 375.4   II
C I I L PHONETIC READER SERIES. 1972. irreg., latest 1986. price varies. Ministry of Human Resource Development, Central Institute of Indian Languages, Manasagangotri, Mysore 570 006, India. Ed.Bd.

491.1 375.4   II
C I I L PICTORIAL GLOSSARY SERIES. 1986. irreg., latest 1987. price varies. Ministry of Human Resource Development, Central Institute of Indian Languages, Manasagangotri, Mysore 570 006, India. Ed.Bd.

491.1 375.5   II
C I I L READING SERIES. 1974. irreg., latest 1978. price varies. Ministry of Human Resource Development, Central Institute of Indian Languages, Manasagangotri, Mysore 570 006, India. Ed.Bd.

491.1 375.4   II
C I I L SECOND LANGUAGE TEXTBOOK SERIES. 1973. irreg., latest 1986. price varies. Ministry of Human Resource Development, Central Institute of Indian Languages, Manasagangotri, Mysore 570 006, India. Ed.Bd.

491.1 375.4   II
C I I L SOCIOLINGUISTICS SERIES. 1974. irreg., latest 1986. price varies. Ministry of Human Resource Development, Central Institute of Indian Languages, Manasagangotri, Mysore 570 006, India. Ed.Bd.

C I V I C I M A. (Comite International du Vocabulaire des Institutions et de la Communication Intellectuelles au Moyen Age) see HISTORY — History Of Europe

406   US   ISSN 0007-8549
P1.A1
C L A JOURNAL. (Text in various languages) 1957. q. $35 (foreign $40.50). College Language Association, c/o Cason L. Hill, Ed., Morehouse College, Atlanta, GA 30314. TEL 404-681-2800. adv.; bk.rev.; index. circ. 1,500. **Indexed:** Abstr.Engl.Stud., Amer.Bibl.Slavic & E.Eur.Stud., Arts & Hum.Cit.Ind., Curr.Cont., Hum.Ind., Ind.Bk.Rev.Hum., M.L.A. **Document type:** academic/scholarly publication.
—BLDSC (3274.280000); Faxon; UnCover; SWETS.
Description: Scholarly articles on language and literature.

407   FR   ISSN 0765-1937
C R E D I F BULLETIN BIBLIOGRAPHIQUE. 1972. bi-m. 180 F. (outside Europe 240 F.). Ecole Normale Superieure de Fontenay Saint Cloud, Centre de Recherche et d'Etude pour la Diffusion du Francais, Parc de St. Cloud, Grille d'Honneur, 92211 St. Cloud Cedex, France. TEL 47-71-91-11. FAX 46-02-39-11. TELEX ENSCLOU 206937 F. Eds. Rosine Adda, Catherine Robine. **Indexed:** M.L.A.
Description: Reviews recent publications on the art of teaching languages, particularly French as a foreign language.

410   US
C U N Y FORUM; working papers in linguistics. 1976. a. $7.50. City University of New York, Ph.D. Program in Linguistics, Graduate Center, 33 W. 42nd St., New York, NY 10036-8099. TEL 212-642-2154. Ed. Robert Hollander. circ. 125. **Indexed:** ERIC.

440   UK   ISSN 0007-9243
CA VA. (Text in French) 1963. 6/yr. (during school year). Mary Glasgow Magazines (Subsidiary of: Scholastic Publications Ltd.), 140 Freston Rd., London W10 6TR, England. TEL 071-792-3644. FAX 071-792-3172. TELEX 311890-MGPUBS. (U.S. subscr. to: Delta Systems, 1400 Miller Pkwy., McHenry IL 60050-7030. TEL 800-823-8270) charts; illus. (also avail. in microform from UMI; reprint service avail. from UMI)
—UMI.
Description: French-language magazine for intermediate-level students.

410   BL   ISSN 0102-5767
CADERNOS DE ESTUDOS LINGUISTICOS. 1978. s-a. exchange basis. Universidade Estadual de Campinas, Instituto de Estudos da Linguagem, Departamento de Linguistica, Caixa Postal 6045, 13081-970 Campinas SP, Brazil. FAX 55-192-391501. bibl.; charts. **Indexed:** Bibl.Ling., Lang.& Lang.Behav.Abstr. (1981-). **Document type:** academic/scholarly publication.
—BLDSC (2947.120000).
Description: Presents studies in linguistics.

469.794   SP
CADERNOS DE LINGUA. (Text in Gallegan) 1990. s-a. Real Academia Galega, R. Tabernas, 11, 15001 A Coruna, Spain.

487   FR   ISSN 0290-7402
CAHIERS BALKANIQUES. 1981. 2/yr. price varies. Institut National des Langues et Civilisations Orientales, Centre d'Etudes Balkaniques, 2 rue de Lille, 75343 Paris Cedex 07, France. TEL 49-26-42-00. FAX 49-26-42-99. **Indexed:** Bibl.Ling.
Description: Publishes research works by members.

492.7 910   FR   ISSN 0247-2775
CAHIERS D'ONOMASTIQUE ARABE. (Text in Arabic, English, French) 1979. irreg., latest 1993 (for years 1989-1992). price varies. (Centre National de Recherche Scientifique, Institut de Recherche et d'Histoire des Textes) C N R S Editions, 20-2 bd St. Amand, 75015 Paris, France. TEL 45-33-16-00. FAX 45-33-92-13. (Dist. outside France by: N.V. Brepols, Steenweg op Tielen 68, 2300 Turnhout, Belgium. TEL 32-14-402500. FAX 32-14-428919) (Co-sponsor: Onomasticon Arabicum) (back issues avail.) **Document type:** monographic series.
Description: Publishes studies, documents and notes concerning Arabic onomastics, anthroponyms and biographical research.

CAHIERS DE L'ASIE DU SUD-EST. see ORIENTAL STUDIES

428 375.4   FR   ISSN 0759-8661
CAHIERS DE L'I L S E R. s-a. Universite de Montpellier III (Paul Valery), Institut de Langues de Specialite Enseignement et Recherche, B.P. 5043, 34032 Montpellier Cedex 1, France. TEL 67-14-20-00. Dir. Tony Lattes.
Description: Situated on the wide and as yet undefined boundary between English for Specific Purposes (E.S.P.) and linguistic studies.

CAHIERS DE L'INSTITUT D'ETUDES GERMANIQUES. see LITERATURE

418.005   FR   ISSN 0007-9871
CAHIERS DE LEXICOLOGIE. 1960. s-a. $28. Didier Erudition, 6 rue de la Sorbonne, 75005 Paris, France. (U.S. Subscr. to: Didier Erudition, N. American Fullfillment Office, Box 830350, Birmingham, AL 35283-0350) Ed. D.B. Quemada. **Indexed:** Bibl.Ling., Lang.& Lang.Behav.Abstr. (1972-), Lang.Teach.& Ling.Abstr., M.L.A.
—BLDSC (2949.620000); SWETS.

495.1   FR   ISSN 0153-3320
CAHIERS DE LINGUISTIQUE ASIE ORIENTALE. 1977. s-a. 180 F. Centre de Recherches Linguistiques sur l'Asie Orientale, 54 bd. Raspail, 75006 Paris, France. adv.; bk.rev. circ. 300. **Indexed:** Lang.& Lang.Behav.Abstr. (1986-), M.L.A.
—UnCover.

440 375.4   SZ
CAHIERS DE LINGUISTIQUE FRANCAISE. (Text in French) no. 11, 1990. irreg. price varies. (Universite de Geneva, Unite de Linguistique Francaise) Librairie Droz S.A., 11, rue Massot, CH-1211 Geneva 12, Switzerland. TEL 022-3466666. FAX 022-472391. (Subscr. to: Case Postale 389, CH-1211 Geneva 12, Switzerland) Ed.Bd. **Indexed:** Bibl.Ling. **Document type:** academic/scholarly publication.

410   FR
CAHIERS DE LINGUISTIQUE HISPANIQUE MEDIEVALE. 1976. irreg., no.8, 1983. (Universite de Paris XIII) Editions Klincksieck, 11 rue de Lille, 75005 Paris, France. **Indexed:** Bibl.Ling.

418   RM
CAHIERS DE LINGUISTIQUE THEORIQUE ET APPLIQUEE.
(Subseries of: Revue Roumaine de Linguistique) 1963. 2/yr. 70 lei($48) (Academia Romana) Editura Academiei Romane, Calea Victoriei 125, 79717 Bucharest, Rumania. (Dist. by: Rompresfilatelia, Calea Grivitei 64-66, P.O. Box 12-201, 78104 Bucharest, Rumania) **Indexed:** Bibl.Ling., M.L.A.

419   FR   ISSN 0396-891X
CAHIERS DE LITTERATURE ORALE. 2/yr. 160 F. Institut National des Langues et Civilisations Orientales, Centre de Recherche sur l'Oralite, 2 rue de Lille, 75343 Paris Cedex 07, France. TEL 49-26-42-74. FAX 49-26-42-99. Ed. Genevieve Calame-Griaule. (back issues avail.) **Document type:** academic/scholarly publication.
Description: Studies texts transmitted orally.

400   FR   ISSN 0153-5048
CAHIERS DE PHILOLOGIE. (Includes supplements) 1976. irreg. (Universite de Lille III, Centre de Recherche Philologique) Presses Universitaires de Lille, Rue du Barreau, B.P. 199, 59654 Villeneuve d'Ascq Cedex, France. TEL 20-91-65-35. FAX 20-91-03-95. Dir. Jean Bollack. **Document type:** academic/scholarly publication.

440 301   FR   ISSN 0765-4944
CAHIERS DE PRAXEMATIQUE. s.a. Universite de Montpellier (Universite Paul Valery), B.P. 5043, 34032 Montpellier Cedex 1, France. TEL 67-14-20-00. Ed. M. Paul Siblot. **Document type:** academic/scholarly publication.
Description: Contains both theoretical studies and analyses of discursive practices using a linguistic model that accounts for the conditions governing the production and circulation of meaning.

400   CN   ISSN 0068-5070
CAHIERS DE PSYCHOMECANIQUE DE LANGAGE. irreg. price varies. (Universite Laval, Department de Langues et Linguistique) Presses de l'Universite Laval, Cite Universitaire, Quebec, PQ G1K 7P4, Canada. TEL 418-656-5106. FAX 418-656-2600. **Document type:** monographic series.
Formerly: Cahiers de Linguistique Structurale.

410   FR   ISSN 0045-3773
CAHIERS DU BILINGUISME/LAND UN SPROCH. (Text in French, German) 1971. q. 80 F. Cercle Rene Schickele, 31 rue Oberlin, 67000 Strasbourg, France. Ed. R. Greib. adv.; bk.rev.; bibl. circ. 3,000.

410   SZ   ISSN 0068-516X
P25
CAHIERS FERDINAND DE SAUSSURE. review de linguistique generai. 1941. irreg., no.46, 1992. 50 SFr. (Cercle Ferdinand de Saussure) Librairie Droz S.A., 11, rue Massot, CH-1211 Geneva 12, Switzerland. TEL 022-3466666. FAX 022-3472391. bk.rev. circ. 1,000. (back issues avail.) **Indexed:** Bibl.Ling., Lang.Teach.& Ling.Abstr., M.L.A. **Document type:** academic/scholarly publication.
—CCC.

410   CN   ISSN 0315-3967
P1.A1
CAHIERS LINGUISTIQUES D'OTTAWA. (Text in English and French) 1972. s-a. Can.$8 per no. University of Ottawa, Department of Linguistics, Ottawa, ON K1N 6N5, Canada. TEL 613-564-4207. FAX 613-564-9067. Ed. Louise Manga. bk.rev. circ. 200. **Indexed:** Bibl.Ling., Lang.& Lang.Behav.Abstr. (1973-), Lang.Teach.& Ling.Abstr., M.L.A., Sociol.Abstr. **Document type:** academic/scholarly publication.
—BLDSC (2949.675000).

CALIFORNIA ENGLISH. see EDUCATION — Teaching Methods And Curriculum

CAMBRIAN MEDIEVAL CELTIC STUDIES. see HISTORY — History Of Europe

470 870   UK
CAMBRIDGE LATIN TEXTS. irreg. price varies. Cambridge University Press, Edinburgh Bldg., Shaftesbury Rd., Cambridge CB2 2RU, England. TEL 0223-312393. FAX 0223-315052. TELEX 851817256. (N. American addr.: Cambridge University Press, Journals Dept., 40 W. 20th St., New York, NY 10011. TEL 212-924-3900. FAX 212-691-3239) **Document type:** academic/scholarly publication.

CAMBRIDGE PHILOLOGICAL SOCIETY. PROCEEDINGS. see CLASSICAL STUDIES

CAMBRIDGE PHILOLOGICAL SOCIETY. PROCEEDINGS. SUPPLEMENT. see CLASSICAL STUDIES

400   UK   ISSN 0068-676X
CAMBRIDGE STUDIES IN LINGUISTICS. 1969. irreg., no.48, 1987. price varies. Cambridge University Press, Edinburgh Bldg., Shaftesbury Rd., Cambridge CB2 2RU, England. TEL 0223-312393. FAX 0223-315052. TELEX 851817256. (N. American addr.: Cambridge University Press, Journals Dept., 40 W. 20th St., New York, NY 10011. TEL 212-924-3900. FAX 212-691-3239) Ed.Bd. **Indexed:** M.L.A. **Document type:** monographic series.
—BLDSC (3015.994000).

CANADIAN ASSOCIATION OF SLAVISTS NEWSLETTER. see HUMANITIES: COMPREHENSIVE WORKS

CANADIAN COUNCIL OF TEACHERS OF ENGLISH. NEWSLETTER. see EDUCATION — Teaching Methods And Curriculum

400   CN   ISSN 0008-4131
P1
CANADIAN JOURNAL OF LINGUISTICS/REVUE CANADIENNE DE LINGUISTIQUE. (Text in English and French) 1954. q. Can.$40. Association Canadienne de Linguistique, University of Toronto, University College, Rm. 322, Toronto, Ont. M5S 1A1, Canada. TEL 416-599-0973. Ed. William Cowan. adv.; bk.rev.; cum.index: 1954-1980. circ. 750. (also avail. in microfilm from UMI; back issues avail.; reprint service avail. from SWZ,UMI) **Indexed:** Abstr.Anthropol., Arts & Hum.Cit.Ind., Bibl.Ling., Curr.Cont., Ind.Bk.Rev.Hum., Lang.& Lang.Behav.Abstr. (1972-), Lang.Teach.& Ling.Abstr., M.L.A., SSCI. **Document type:** academic/scholarly publication.
—BLDSC (3031.800000); Faxon; UnCover; SWETS; UMI.

400   CN   ISSN 0008-4506
PB5
CANADIAN MODERN LANGUAGE REVIEW/REVUE CANADIENNE DES LANGUES VIVANTES. (Text in English, French, German, Italian, Spanish) 1944. q. Can.$25($25) to individuals; institutions Can.$35($35); foreign $45. 237 Hellems Ave., Welland, ON L3B 3B8, Canada. TEL 905-734-3640. FAX 905-734-3640. Eds. Sally Rehorick, Viviane Edwards. adv. contact: Linda Picard. bk.rev.; charts; illus.; index. circ. 2,400. (also avail. in microform from UMI,MML; reprint service avail. from UMI) **Indexed:** Amer.Bibl.Slavic & E.Eur.Stud., C.I.J.E., Can.Educ.Ind., Can.Per.Ind., Chic.Per.Ind., Curr.Cont., Educ.Ind., Lang.& Lang.Behav.Abstr., Lang.Teach.& Ling.Abstr., M.L.A., Mult.Ed.Abstr., Sp.Ed.Needs Abstr., SSCI. **Document type:** academic/scholarly publication.
—BLDSC (3042.600000); Faxon; UnCover; SWETS; UMI. CCC.
Description: Presents linguistic and pedagogical articles of interest to teachers of French, German, Italian, Russian, Spanish and English as a second language.
Refereed Serial

CANADIAN SLAVONIC PAPERS/REVUE CANADIENNE DES SLAVISTES. see HUMANITIES: COMPREHENSIVE WORKS

420 375.4   AT   ISSN 0311-4627
CANBERRA LINGUIST. (Text in English, French, German and Asian languages; summaries in English) 1974. s-a. Aus.$20. Modern Language Teachers Association of the A.C.T., G.P.O. Box 989, Canberra, A.C.T. 2601, Australia. FAX 069-880073. Ed. Gerda Smith. bk.rev. circ. 150. (back issues avail.)

CANOMA. see GEOGRAPHY

400   SP
CAPLLETRA. s-a. 1600 ptas. per no. (Institut de Filologia Valenciana) Publicacions de l' Abadia de Montserrat, Ausias March 92-98, 08013 Barcelona, Spain.

491.66   UK   ISSN 0263-0362
PB2101
CARDIFF WORKING PAPERS IN WELSH LINGUISTICS/PAPURAU GWAITH IEITHYDDOL CYMRAEG CAERDYDD. (Text in English or Welsh; summary in English) 1981. biennial. £2.75. Department of Welsh, University of Wales College of Cardiff, Cathays Park, Cardiff CF1 3NP, Wales. charts; illus. (back issues avail.)
—BLDSC (3051.175000).

407   CN   ISSN 0824-7714
PB35
CARLETON PAPERS IN APPLIED LANGUAGE STUDIES. 1984. a. Can.$10($10) Carleton University, Centre for Applied Language Studies, Ottawa, ON K1S 5B6, Canada. TEL 613-788-6612. FAX 613-788-6641. TELEX 053-4232. Ed. Lynne Young. circ. 200. (also avail. in microfilm from UMI; reprint service avail. from UMI) **Document type:** academic/scholarly publication.
—BLDSC (3053.416600).
Description: A collection of recent work in the field of applied language studies with particular reference to ESL and first language development. Topics include classroom centered reserach, process writing, discourse analysis, testing and assessment.

410   US   ISSN 0739-3474
PM7801
CARRIER PIDGIN. 1973. 3/yr. $7.50 to individuals; institutions $15 (effective Jan. 1992). c/o Department of Linguistics, University of Hawaii, Manoa, 1890 East-West Rd., Honolulu, HI 96822. TEL 808-956-3239. FAX 808-956-9166. adv.; bk.rev.; bibl. circ. 500. **Document type:** newsletter.
—BLDSC (3055.464000).
Description: Studies Creole and Pidgin languages.

491.7 891.7   NE   ISSN 0862-8459
PB5
CASOPIS PRO MODERNI FILOLOGII. (Previously issued (until 1991) as sub-section of: Philologia Pragensia) (Text in Czech and Russian; summaries in Russian) vol.73, 1991. 2/yr. fl.95($57) (effective 1994). (Czech Academy of Sciences, Institute for Czech Language, XR) John Benjamins Publishing Co., Amsteldijk 44, P.O. Box 75577, 1070 AN Amsterdam, Netherlands. TEL 31-20-6738156. FAX 31-20-6792956. (In N. America: 821 Bethlehem Pike, Philadelphia, PA 19118. TEL 215-836-1200. FAX 215-836-1204) Ed. Jaromir Povejsil. bk.rev.; illus.; index. circ. 1,350. (back issues avail.) **Indexed:** Bibl.Ling., M.L.A. **Document type:** academic/scholarly publication.
Supersedes in part (1956-1991): Ceskoslovenska Rusistika (ISSN 0009-0638)

450 375.4   IT
CE FASTU?. (Text in Friulian, Italian) 1919. s-a. L.50000($33) (Regione Friuli - Venezia - Giulia) GEAP Pordenone, Via Malignani 41, 33080 Fiume Veneto, Italy. TEL 0432-501598. FAX 0432-511766. (Subscr. to: Societa Filologica Friulana, Via Manin 18, 33100 Udine, Italy) bk.rev. circ. 3,800. (back issues avail.) **Indexed:** Bibl.Ling.

407   DK
CEBAL. (Text and summaries in English, French, German) 1970. biennial. price varies. Handelshoejskolens Forlag, Nansensgade 19, DK-1366 Copenhagen K, Denmark. Ed. Niels Davidsen-Nielsen. bk.rev. circ. 500. (back issues avail.)

491.6   IE   ISSN 0069-1399
PB1001
CELTICA. 1946. irreg., vol.22, 1990. price varies. Dublin Institute for Advanced Studies, School of Celtic Studies, 10 Burlington Rd., Dublin 4, Ireland. TEL 01-6680748. FAX 01-6680561. Ed.Bd. bk.rev. circ. 212. **Indexed:** Bibl.Ling., Br.Archaeol.Abstr., Ind.Bk.Rev.Hum., M.L.A.

CENTRAL ASIATIC JOURNAL; international periodical for the languages, literatures, history and archaeology of Central Asia. see ORIENTAL STUDIES

407   US
CENTRAL STATES CONFERENCE ON THE TEACHING OF FOREIGN LANGUAGES. EDUCATION SERIES. 1972. a. $11.95. (Central States Conference on the Teaching of Foreign Languages) National Textbook Co., 4255 W. Touhy Ave., Lincolnwood, IL 60646. TEL 708-679-5500. Ed. Keith Fry. **Document type:** academic/scholarly publication.

410 306.4 ZR
CENTRE D'ETUDES ETHNOLOGIQUES. PUBLICATIONS. SERIE 3: TRAVAUX LINGUISTIQUES. 1972. irreg., no.16, 1989. C E E B A Publications, B.P. 246, Bandundu, Zaire. circ. 700.

410 FR
CENTRE INTERNATIONAL DE DOCUMENTATION OCCITANE. BIBLIOTHEQUE. CATALOGUE. (Text in French and Occitan) 1976. irreg. Centre International de Documentation Occitane, Boite Postale 4202, 34544 Beziers Cedex, France.

492.7 960 NR ISSN 0331-5177
CENTRE OF ARABIC DOCUMENTATION. RESEARCH BULLETIN. irreg. Center of Arabic Documentation, c/o Institute for African Studies, University of Ibadan, Ibadan, Nigeria. **Indexed:** Documentatieblad. **Document type:** academic/scholarly publication.

410 RM
CERCETARI DE LINGVISTICA. (Text in Rumanian; summaries in English, French) 1956. 2/yr. 70 lei($45) (Academia Romana) Editura Academiei Romane, Calea Victoriei 125, 79717 Bucharest, Rumania. (Subscr. to: Rompresfilatelia, Calea Grivitei 64-66, P.O. Box 12-201, 78104 Bucharest, Rumania) Ed. Ioan Patrut. bk.rev.; bibl.; illus. **Indexed:** Bibl.Ling., Lang.& Lang.Behav.Abstr., M.L.A.

CESKOSLOVENSKA AKADEMIE VED. USTAV PRO JAZYK CESKY. ONOMASTICKY ZPRAVODAJ. see HISTORY — History Of Europe

CESKY JAZYK A LITERATURA; casopis pro metodiku. see EDUCATION

407 FR ISSN 1157-4860
CHAMPS DU SIGNE; cahiers de stylistique. 1991. a. 80 F. (effective 1994). (Universite de Toulouse II (le Mirail)) Presses Universitaires du Mirail, 56 rue du Taur, 31000 Toulouse, France. TEL 61-22-58-31. FAX 61-21-84-20. Ed. Francois-Charles Gaudard. **Document type:** academic/scholarly publication.

CHASQUI. see LITERATURE

080 BE ISSN 0577-6570
CHESTER BEATTY MONOGRAPHS. (Text in English) 1951. irreg. price varies. (Chester Beatty Library) Editions Peeters s.p.r.l., Bondgenotenlaan 153, 3000 Leuven, Belgium. TEL 32-16-235170. FAX 32-16-228500. (back issues avail.) **Document type:** monographic series.

440 UK ISSN 0009-3424
CHEZ NOUS. (Text in French) 1963. 6/yr. (during school year). Mary Glasgow Magazines (Subsidiary of: Scholastic Publications Ltd.), 140 Freston Rd., London W10 6TR, England. TEL 071-792-3644. FAX 071-792-3172. TELEX 311890-MGPUBS. (U.S. subscr. to: Delta Systems, 1400 Miller Pkwy., McHenry IL 60050-7030. TEL 800-823-8270) illus.; play rev. (tabloid format; also avail. in microform from UMI; reprint service avail. from BLH, UMI)
—UMI.
Description: French-language magazine for advanced-level students.

410 US ISSN 0577-7240
P21
CHICAGO LINGUISTIC SOCIETY. PAPERS FROM THE REGIONAL MEETINGS. 1965. a. price varies. Chicago Linguistic Society, University of Chicago, Classics 314A, 1050 E. 59th St., Chicago, IL 60637. Ed.Bd. circ. 1,500. (back issues avail.) **Indexed:** Lang.& Lang.Behav.Abstr. (1974-).
—BLDSC (3287.026000); UnCover.
Former titles: Parasession: Non-Declarative Sentences; Parasession: Interplay of Phonology, Morphology and Syntax.

410 US
CHILD LANGUAGE RESEARCH FORUM. 1970. a. $15. University of Chicago Press, Journals Division, 5720 S. Woodlawn Ave., Chicago, IL 60637. TEL 415-723-4284. FAX 415-723-1442. (Subscr. to: E R I C, National Institute of Education, U.S. Dept. of H.H.S., Washington DC 20208) Ed. E.V. Clark. circ. 200. **Indexed:** Lang.& Lang.Behav.Abstr. (1974-), Lang.Teach.& Ling.Abstr. **Document type:** proceedings.
Formerly (until 1991): Papers and Reports on Child Language Development.

410 US ISSN 0163-2809
P118
CHILDREN'S LANGUAGE. 1978. irreg., vol.7, 1990. $59.95. Lawrence Erlbaum Associates, Inc., 365 Broadway, Hillsdale, NJ 07642. TEL 201-666-4110. FAX 201-666-2394. Eds. G. Conti-Ramsden, C.E. Snow. (back issues avail.) **Document type:** monographic series.
—BLDSC (3172.990300).
Refereed Serial

495.1 370 US ISSN 0009-4595
PL1065
CHINESE LANGUAGE TEACHERS ASSOCIATION. JOURNAL. (Text in Chinese and English) 1966. 3/yr. $40. Chinese Language Teachers Association, c/o Kalamazoo College, 1200 Academy St., Kalamazoo, MI 49006. TEL 616-337-7001. FAX 616-337-7251. Ed. James Tai. adv. contact: Madeline Chu. bk.rev. circ. 525. (also avail. in microform from UMI; reprint service avail. from UMI) **Indexed:** Bk.Rev.Ind., C.I.J.E., ERIC, Hum.Ind., Lang.& Lang.Behav.Abstr., Sociol.Abstr. **Document type:** academic/scholarly publication, newsletter.
—BLDSC (4729.320000); Faxon; UnCover; UMI.

495.1 370 US
CHINESE LANGUAGE TEACHERS ASSOCIATION. MONOGRAPH SERIES. irreg. $15. Chinese Language Teachers Association, c/o Kalamazoo College, 1200 Academy St., Kalamazoo, MI 49006. TEL 616-337-7001. FAX 616-337-7251. Ed. James Tai. adv. contact: Madeline Chu. **Document type:** academic/scholarly publication, monographic series.

495.13 CC ISSN 1000-6125
CISHU YANJIU/JOURNAL OF LEXICOGRAPHICAL STUDIES. (Text in Chinese) 1979. bi-m. $12.80 (effective 1994). Shanghai Cishu Chubanshe, 457 Shaanxi Beilu, Shanghai 200040, People's Republic of China. TEL 2472088. FAX 2475370. (Overseas subscr. to: Guoji Shudian - China International Book Trading Corp., P.O. Box 399, P.R.C.) Ed. Chao Feng.
Description: Covers the theory and practice of compiling dictionaries in China.

450 IT ISSN 0069-4339
CIVILTA VENEZIANA. DIZIONARI DIALETTALI E STUDI LINGUISTICI. 1960. irreg., no.5, 1976. price varies. (Fondazione Giorgio Cini) Casa Editrice Leo S. Olschki, Casella Postale 66, 50100 Florence, Italy. TEL 055-6530684. FAX 055-6530214. circ. 1,000. **Document type:** monographic series.

CIZI JAZYKY; casopis pro vyucovani cizim jazykum - zejmena anglictine, nemcine, francouzstine, spanelstine, rustine a latine. see EDUCATION

410 GW
CLASSICA MONACENSIA; Muenchener Studien zur Klassischen Philologie. irreg., vol.8, 1994. DM.68. Gunter Narr Verlag, Postfach 2567, 72015 Tuebingen, Germany. TEL 07071-78091. FAX 07071-75288. **Document type:** monographic series.

CLASSICAL PHILOLOGY; devoted to research in the languages, literatures, history and life of classical antiquity. see CLASSICAL STUDIES

CLASSICUM. see CLASSICAL STUDIES

375.4 UK ISSN 0142-1042
CLICK. 6/yr. (during school year). Mary Glasgow Magazines (Subsidiary of: Scholastic Publications Ltd.), 140 Freston Rd., London W10 6TR, England. TEL 071-792-3644. FAX 071-792-3172. TELEX 311890-MGPUBS. (U.S. subscr. to: Delta Systems, 1400 Miller Pkwy., McHenry IL 60080-7030. TEL 800-823-8270) illus. circ. 75,100.
Description: Directed to beginners learning English.

CLINICAL LINGUISTICS & PHONETICS. see MEDICAL SCIENCES — Psychiatry And Neurology

CLUB DES HEBRAISANTS. see RELIGIONS AND THEOLOGY — Judaic

401 US
COGNITION AND LANGUAGE; a series in psycholinguistics. 1979. irreg., latest 1993. price varies. Plenum Publishing Corp., 233 Spring St., New York, NY 10013-1578. TEL 212-620-8000. FAX 212-463-0742. TELEX 23-421139. Ed. R.W. Rieber. (back issues avail.) **Document type:** monographic series.
Refereed Serial

410 GW ISSN 0936-5907
P165 CODEN: COGLEJ
COGNITIVE LINGUISTICS. 1990. 4/yr. $95. Walter de Gruyter and Co., Mouton de Guyter, Genthiner Str. 13, 10785 Berlin, Germany. TEL 030-26005-0. FAX 030-26005-251. (U.S. addr.: 200 Saw Mill River Rd., Hawthorne, NY 10532) Ed. Dirk Geeraerts. **Indexed:** Bibl.Ling. **Document type:** academic/scholarly publication.
—BLDSC (3292.878000); Faxon; UnCover; SWETS. CCC.
Description: Covers high-quality research on language from a cognitive perspective: as an instrument for organizing, processing, and conveying information.
Refereed Serial

COGNITIVE SCIENCE; a multidisciplinary journal of artificial intelligence, psychology, and language. see PSYCHOLOGY

COGNITIVE SYSTEMS. see PSYCHOLOGY

400 BL ISSN 0587-6435
COLECAO DE ESTUDOS FILOLOGICOS. 1956. irreg. Fundacao Casa de Rui Barbosa, Rua Sao Clemente 134, Botafogo 22260, Rio de Janeiro, RJ, Brazil. FAX 5371114. Dir. Agnello Uchoa Bittencourt.

410 FR ISSN 0220-746X
COLLECTION ORALITES-DOCUMENTS. 1978. irreg. Societe d'Etudes Linguistiques et Anthropologiques de France (SELAF), 52 bd. St. Michel, 75006 Paris, France. TEL 42-08-83-93. (Dist. by: Editions Peeters s.p.r.l., Bondgenotenlaan 153, B-3000 Louvain, Belgium. TEL 32-16-235170) **Document type:** monographic series.

430 GW ISSN 0010-1338
PF3001
COLLOQUIA GERMANICA; an international journal for Germanic philology and literary criticism. (Text in English and German) 1967. 4/yr. DM.138. (University of Kentucky, Department of Germanic and Classical Languages, US) Francke Verlag GmbH, Postfach 2560, 72015 Tuebingen, Germany. TEL 07071-78091. FAX 07071-75288. Ed. Bernd Kratz. adv.; bk.rev.; index. circ. 1,000. **Indexed:** Arts & Hum.Cit.Ind., Bibl.Ling., Can.Rev.Comp.Lit., Curr.Cont., Ind.Bk.Rev.Hum., M.L.A. **Document type:** academic/scholarly publication.
—BLDSC (3315.230000); Faxon; SWETS. CCC.

400 JA ISSN 0069-598X
F2510
COLOQUIO DE ESTUDOS LUSO BRASILEIROS. ANAIS. (Text in Portuguese) 1967. a. 3500 Yen. Associacao Japonesa de Estudos Luso-Brasileiros, c/o Prof. Mineo Ikegami, Tokyo University of Foreign Studies, Nishigahara 4-51-21, Kita-ku, Tokyo 114, Japan. Ed. Vendelino Lorschieter. bk.rev.; bibl.; index. circ. 220. (back issues avail.)

420 375.4 US
COLUMBIA UNIVERSITY. AMERICAN LANGUAGE PROGRAM. BULLETIN; instruction in English as a foreign language. 1953. biennial. free. Columbia University, School of General Studies, American Language Program, 505 Lewisohn Hall, New York, NY 10027. TEL 212-280-3768. Ed. Louis Levi. circ. 6,000.

LINGUISTICS

400   BE   ISSN 0774-8396
COMMISSION ROYALE DE TOPONYMIE ET DIALECTOLOGIE. BULLETIN/KONINKLIJKE COMMISSIE VOOR TOPONYMIE EN DIALECTOLOGIE. HANDELINGEN. (Text in Dutch, French) 1927. a. 500 BEF. Commission Royale de Toponymie et Dialectologie - Koninklijke Commissie voor Toponymie en Dialectologie, c/o Frans Debrabandere, Sec., Keizer Karelstraat 83, B-8000 Bruges, Belgium. TEL 32-50-31-73-66. (Orders to: N.V. Drukkerij G. Michiels, Corverstraat 13, 3700 Tongeren, Belgium) circ. 500. (also avail. in microfiche from IDC) **Indexed:** Bibl.Ling. **Document type:** academic/scholarly publication, bulletin.
   Description: Publishes original contributions on onomastics and the study of French and Dutch dialects in Belgium, and the commissions' annual report.

COMMUNICATION & COGNITION. see *COMMUNICATIONS*

COMMUNICATION MONOGRAPHS. see *EDUCATION*

410   US   ISSN 1050-3293
P87   CODEN: CNTHEV
COMMUNICATION THEORY. 1991. q. $30 to individuals (foreign $47.50); institutions $72 (foreign $89.50) (effective 1994). (International Communication Association) Guilford Publications, Inc., 72 Spring St., 4th Fl., New York, NY 10012. TEL 212-431-9800. FAX 212-966-6708. Ed. Donald Ellis. adv.; bk.rev. (reprint service avail. from UMI) **Document type:** academic/scholarly publication.
—BLDSC (3363.459000); Faxon; UnCover; SWETS; UMI. **CCC.**
   Description: Contributes to the theoretical development and integration of communications. Covers transcending methodological provinces, geographical boundaries and media specializations.
Refereed Serial

COMMUNITY STUDIES SERIES. see *SOCIAL SCIENCES: COMPREHENSIVE WORKS*

COMPARATIVE LITERATURE. see *LITERATURE*

COMPARATIVE LITERATURE STUDIES. see *LITERATURE*

440   US   ISSN 0010-4167
PC1
COMPARATIVE ROMANCE LINGUISTICS NEWSLETTER. 1951. 2/yr. $8 to individuals; institutions $10. Modern Language Association of America, Comparative Romance Linguistics Section, University of Virginia, Department of Spanish, Italian and Portuguese, Charlottesville, VA 22903. Ed. Joel Rini. bk.rev.; bibl. circ. 120. (processed) **Indexed:** M.L.A.

410 370   SP   ISSN 0214-7033
LB1139.L3
COMUNICACION, LENGUAJE Y EDUCACION; metodos y tecnicas para el educador en las areas del curriculum. 1989. q. Aprendizaje, S.L., Crta. de Canillas, 138, 28043 Madrid, Spain. TEL 388-38-74. FAX 300-35-27. Ed.Bd. adv. circ. 2,000.
   Description: Covers topics on all language and representational systems, and their educational treatment.
Refereed Serial

CONNECTICUT ENGLISH JOURNAL. see *EDUCATION*

410 380   US
CONNECTIONS (HATTIESBURG). 1980. 3/yr. $25 (free with subscription to Southern Communication Journal). Southern States Communication Association, c/o Susan A. Siltanen, S.S. Box 5131, Hattiesburg, MS 39406-5131. TEL 601-266-4263. FAX 601-266-4263. Susan A. Siltanen. adv.; film rev. circ. 1,500. (back issues avail.) **Document type:** newsletter.

410.5   BL
CONSTRUCTURA. (Text in Portuguese; summaries in English) 1973. q. $6. (Universidade Catolica do Parana, Departamento de Letras) Editora F T D, C.P. 30402, Rua do Lavapes 1023, Sao Paulo, Brazil. bibl.

492.4   NE   ISSN 0169-7846
CONTRIBUTIONS TO THE SOCIOLOGY OF JEWISH LANGUAGES. (Text in English) 1985. irreg., vol.3, 1988. price varies. E.J. Brill, P.O. Box 9000, 2300 PA Leiden, Netherlands. TEL 31-71-312624. FAX 31-71-317532. TELEX 39296 BRILL NL. (In N. America: E.J. Brill, 24 Hudson St., Kinderhook, NY 12106. TEL 800-962-4406. FAX 518-758-1959) Ed. J.A. Fishman. (back issues avail.) **Document type:** monographic series.
Refereed Serial

440 430   SZ   ISSN 0010-8170
CONVERSATION ET TRADUCTION; franzoesisch-deutsche Sprach- und Unterhaltungszeitschrift. (Text in French and German) 1948. m. 45 SFr. Emmentaler Druck AG, Dorfstr. 5, CH-3550 Langnau, Switzerland. adv.; bk.rev.; illus. circ. 4,500.
—CCC.

054.1   US   ISSN 1055-1220
COPAINS. 6/yr. (during school term). $25. Scholastic Inc., 555 Broadway, New York, NY 10012-3999. TEL 212-343-6100. Ed. Jacqueline Hall. illus. **Document type:** trade publication.

418   DK   ISSN 0907-7901
▼**COPENHAGEN STUDIES IN TRANSLATION.** (Text in English) 1992. a. $28.50. Museum Tusculanum Press, University of Copenhagen, Njalsgade 92, DK-2300 Copenhagen S, Denmark. TEL 45-35-32-91-09. FAX 45-35-32-91-13. (Dist. in U.S. and Canada by: Paul & Co., c/o P C S Data Processing, Inc., 360 W. 31st St., New York, NY 10001. TEL 212-564-3730. FAX 212-971-7200) Ed. Joergen Erik Nielsen. **Document type:** academic/scholarly publication.
   Description: Directed to linguists, translators and English philologists.

410   NE   ISSN 0169-779X
CORNELL LINGUISTIC CONTRIBUTIONS. (Text in English) 1977. irreg., vol.5, 1986. price varies. (Cornell University, US) E.J. Brill, P.O. Box 9000, 2300 PA Leiden, Netherlands. TEL 31-71-312624. FAX 31-71-317532. TELEX 39296 BRILL NL. (In N. America: E.J. Brill, 24 Hudson St., Kinderhook, NY 12106. TEL 800-962-4406. FAX 518-758-1959) Eds. Frans van Coetsem, Linda R. Waugh. (back issues avail.) **Document type:** monographic series.
Refereed Serial

860   US   ISSN 0193-3892
PC4001
CORONICA;* Spanish medieval language and literature newsletter. (Text and summaries in English and Spanish) 1972. s-a. $10 to individuals; institutions $25. Modern Language Association of America, Division of Spanish Medieval Language and Literature, c/o Maier, Phillips Acad., 180 Main St., Andover, MA 01810-4166. Eds. Constance and Heanon Wilkins. bk.rev.; abstr.; bibl.; charts; illus. circ. 300. (back issues avail.) **Indexed:** M.L.A.
—Faxon; UnCover; SWETS.

470 282   BE   ISSN 0777-1673
CORPUS CHRISTIANORUM. LINGUA PATRUM. 1989. irreg. (Abbey of Steenbrugge) N.V. Brepols, Steenweg op Tielen 68, 2300 Turnhout, Belgium. TEL 32-14-415463. FAX 32-14-428919. **Document type:** monographic series.
   Description: Publishes detailed critical studies of the linguistic peculiarities of individual authors and groups of writings from the early and medieval Christian periods.

419   CN   ISSN 0318-0220
COURIER (EDMONTON). (Text in French, English, German) 1962. 10/yr. Can.$20 membership. Alberta Teachers' Association, Modern Language Council, 11010 142nd St., Edmonton, Alta. T5N 2R1, Canada. TEL 403-453-2411. FAX 403-455-6481. Ed. Carolyn King. circ. 650. (looseleaf format; back issues avail.) **Indexed:** Can.Educ.Ind.
   Formerly: Modern and Classical Languages Council. Newsletter.
   Description: Provides classroom methods, curriculum updates, news of innovations in methodology, teaching of second language and culture.

410   US   ISSN 0920-9026
CREOLE LANGUAGE LIBRARY. Abbreviated title: C L L. 1986. irreg., vol.12, 1993. price varies. John Benjamins Publishing Co., 821 Bethlehem Pike, Philadelphia, PA 19118. TEL 215-836-1200. FAX 215-836-1204. (And: Amsteldijk 44, P.O. Box 75577, 1070 AN Amsterdam, Netherlands. TEL 020-6762325) Eds. Pieter Muysken, John Singler. **Indexed:** Bibl.Ling. **Document type:** monographic series.
—BLDSC (3487.299500).
   Description: Descriptive and theoretical studies on Pidgin and Creole languages.

410   US   ISSN 0920-3060
CRITICAL THEORY. Abbreviated title: C T. 1985. irreg., vol.11, 1993. price varies. John Benjamins Publishing Co., 821 Bethlehem Pike, Philadelphia, PA 19118. TEL 215-836-1200. FAX 215-836-1204. (And: Amsteldijk 44, P.O. Box 75577, 1070 AN Amsterdam, Netherlands. TEL 31-20-6762325) Eds. Miriam Diaz-Diocaretz, Iris Zavala. **Document type:** monographic series.
—BLDSC (3487.488640).
   Description: Addresses the interdisciplinary approach to language discourse and ideology.

CROSS CURRENTS; a journal of language teaching and cross-cultural communication. see *EDUCATION — Teaching Methods And Curriculum*

352   UK   ISSN 0045-9127
CROWN. 6/yr. (Sep.-Jun.). Mary Glasgow Magazines (Subsidiary of: Scholastic Publications Ltd.), 140 Freston Rd., London W10 6TR, England. TEL 071-792-3644. FAX 071-792-3172. TELEX 311890-MGPUBS. (U.S. subscr. to: Delta Systems, 1400 Miller Pkwy., McHenry IL 60050-7030. TEL 800-823-8270) illus. circ. 70,000.
   Description: English-language magazine for elementary-level students.

400   SP
CUADERNOS DE FILOLOGIA. (Text in French, German or Spanish) 1971. s-a. Universidad de Valencia, Departamento Literatura Espanola, Avda. Blasco Ibanez, 2, Valencia-10, Spain. bk.rev.; bibl.; illus. **Indexed:** M.L.A.

489   SP   ISSN 0210-0746
CUADERNOS DE FILOLOGIA CLASICA. (Text in Spanish and other languages) 1971. s-a. 500 ptas. Universidad Complutense de Madrid, Facultad de Filologia, Ciudad Universitaria, Madrid 3, Spain. Ed. Antonio Ruiz De Elvira. bk.rev. circ. 700. **Indexed:** Bibl.Ling.

460 800   SP   ISSN 0211-0547
P1.A1
CUADERNOS DE INVESTIGACION FILOLOGICA. 1975. s-a. 1800 ptas. (foreign 2000 ptas.). Universidad de la Rioja, Servicio de Publicaciones, C. Magisterio, s-n, 26004 Logrono, Spain. TEL 34-41-231699. Ed. Ma. Jesus Salinero Cascante. circ. 500. (also avail. in microform; reprint service avail.) **Indexed:** M.L.A., Sociol.Abstr. **Document type:** academic/scholarly publication.
   Description: Includes essays on general linguistics theory of literature and critism applied to classical and modern philological fields such as Greek, Latin, English, French and Spanish.

410   MX
CUADERNOS DE LINGUISTICA. 1975. irreg. price varies. Universidad Nacional Autonoma de Mexico, Instituto de Investigaciones Filologicas, Circuito Mano de la Cueva, Villa Obregau, Ciudad Universitaria, 04510 Mexico 20, D.F., Mexico. Ed. Juan M. Lope Blanch.

460 375.4   SP   ISSN 0212-0550
P306.A1
CUADERNOS DE TRADUCCION E INTERPRETACION. (Monographic supplements avail.) 1982. 2/yr. $14 price varies. Universitat Autonoma de Barcelona, Escola Universitaria de Traductors i d'Intprets, Servicio de Publicaciones e Intercambios, Apartat Postal 20, 08193 Bellaterra (Barcelona), Spain. TEL 3-581-10-22. FAX 3-581-10-22. Ed. Fernando Valls. adv.; bk.rev. circ. 1,000.
—BLDSC (3490.807000).

407   UK   ISSN 0142-1050
AP4
CURRENT. 5/yr. (during school year). Mary Glasgow Magazines (Subsidiary of: Scholastic Publications Ltd.), 140 Freston Rd., London W10 6TR, England, England. TEL 071-792-3644. FAX 071-792-3172. TELEX 311890-MGPUBS. (U.S. subscr. to: Delta Systems, 1400 Miller Pkwy., McHenry IL 60050-7030. TEL 800-823-8270) circ. 59,000. **Indexed:** G.Soc.Sci.& Rel.Per.Lit.
   Description: English-language magazine for advanced-level students.

CURRENTS IN COMPARATIVE ROMANCE LANGUAGES AND LITERATURES. see *LITERATURE*

D S L'S PRAESENTATIONSHAEFTE. (Danske Sprog- og Litteraturselskab) see *LITERATURE*

D S N A NEWSLETTER. (Dictionary Society of North America) see *LIBRARY AND INFORMATION SCIENCES*

840 440   GW
DACOROMANIA; Jahrbuch fuer oestliche Latinitaet. 1973. a. Karl Alber GmbH, Hermann-Herder-Str. 4, 79104 Freiburg, Germany. Ed. Paul Miron. **Indexed:** Bibl.Ling.

DANCE NOTATION BUREAU NEWSLETTER. see *DANCE*

410   DK
DANSKE FOLKEMAAL.* 1927. a. DKK 20. (Institut for Dansk Dialektforskning) C.A. Reitzel AS, Noerregade 20, 1165 Copenhagen K, Denmark. Eds. Poul Andersen, Christian Lisse. bk.rev.; bibl. circ. 500. **Indexed:** Bibl.Ling., M.L.A.

407   PH   ISSN 0117-3561
▼**DE LA SALLE UNIVERSITY. DEPARTMENT OF FILIPINO. JOURNAL.** 1992. a. P.30($3.20) De La Salle University Press, 2401 Taft Ave., Manila, Philippines. TEL 632-259-4831. FAX 632-521-9094. adv.; bk.rev. circ. 350. **Document type:** academic/scholarly publication.
   Description: Publishes scholarly articles reflecting significant quantitative researches.

DECCAN COLLEGE. POSTGRADUATE & RESEARCH INSTITUTE. BULLETIN. see *SOCIAL SCIENCES: COMPREHENSIVE WORKS*

400 100   BE   ISSN 0770-8378
DEGRES; revue de synthese a orientation semiologique. 1973. q. 1250 BEF. A.S.B.L. Degres, 2 Place Constantin Meunier, Bte. 13, 1180 Brussels, Belgium. Ed. Andre Helbo. adv.; bk.rev. **Indexed:** Can.Rev.Comp.Lit, Curr.Cont., Lang.& Lang.Behav.Abstr., M.L.A.

407   US
DELAWARE SYMPOSIUM ON LANGUAGE STUDIES SERIES. 1985. irreg., vol.7, 1990. price varies. Ablex Publishing Corporation, 355 Chestnut St., Norwood, NJ 07648. TEL 201-767-8450. FAX 201-767-6717. TELEX 135-393. Ed. Robert Di Pietro. **Document type:** academic/scholarly publication, proceedings.
   Formerly: Delaware Symposia Series.

430 370   GW   ISSN 0011-9741
PF3003
DEUTSCH ALS FREMDSPRACHE; Zeitschrift fuer Theorie und Praxis des Deutschunterrichts fuer Auslaender. 1964. 4/yr. DM.38. (Universitaet Leipzig, Herder Institut) Verlag Langenscheidt KG, Postfach 401120, 80171 Munich, Germany. TEL 089-36096-0. FAX 089-36096258. bk.rev.; bibl.; charts; illus.; index. (also avail. in microform from UMI; reprint service avail. from UMI) **Indexed:** Bibl.Ling., M.L.A. **Document type:** academic/scholarly publication.
   —BLDSC (3561.650000); Faxon; SWETS.

430 375.4   GW   ISSN 0178-0417
DEUTSCH - BETRIFFT UNS. 1985. 6/yr. DM.63. Bergmoser und Hoeller Verlag GmbH, Karl-Friedrich Str. 76, 52072 Aachen, Germany. TEL 0241-1730925. FAX 0241-1730934. circ. 2,900. (looseleaf format; back issues avail.) **Document type:** academic/scholarly publication.

DEUTSCH LERNEN; Zeitschrift fuer den Sprachunterricht mit auslaendischen Arbeitnehmern. see *EDUCATION — Adult Education*

DEUTSCH-SLAWISCHE FORSCHUNGEN ZUR NAMENKUNDE UND SIEDLUNGSGESCHICHTE. see *HISTORY — History Of Europe*

410   GW   ISSN 0070-3923
PF3013
DEUTSCHE AKADEMIE FUER SPRACHE UND DICHTUNG. JAHRBUCH. 1953. a. DM.26. Luchterhand Literaturverlag, Donnersbergring 18A, 64295 Darmstadt, Germany. Ed. Marieluise Huebscher-Bitter. **Indexed:** M.L.A.

410   GW   ISSN 0179-3233
PF5003
DEUTSCHE DIALEKTGEOGRAPHIE. (Text in English, German) 1908. irreg. price varies. N.G. Elwert Verlag, Reitgasse 7-9, 35037 Marburg, Germany. Ed. Reiner Hildebrandt. **Indexed:** Bibl.Ling., M.L.A. **Document type:** monographic series.

430 375.4   GW   ISSN 0418-8802
DER DEUTSCHE LEHRER IM AUSLAND. 1953. 9/yr. DM.52. Schroedel Schulbuchverlag GmbH, Hildesheimer Str. 202-206, 30519 Hannover, Germany. TEL 0511-8388-0. TELEX 9-23527-HSVHAD. (Subscr. to: Oeding Druck GmbH, Wilhelmstr. 1, 3300 Braunschweig, Germany) Ed.Bd. adv.; bk.rev. circ. 2,600.
   —BLDSC (3572.100000).
   Incorporates: Mitteilungen Meinungen Materialien.

410   GW   ISSN 0340-9341
PF3003
DEUTSCHE SPRACHE; Zeitschrift fuer Theorie, Praxis und Dokumentation. 1972. q. DM.119.60 (students DM.103). (Institut fuer Deutsche Sprache) Erich Schmidt Verlag GmbH & Co. (Bielefeld), Viktoriastr. 44A, 33602 Bielefeld, Germany. (Subscr. to: Postfach 102451, 33524 Bielefeld, Germany) Ed. Siegfried Grosse. adv.; bibl. **Indexed:** Bibl.Ling., Lang.& Lang.Behav.Abstr., Lang.Teach.& Ling.Abstr., M.L.A. **Document type:** academic/scholarly publication.
   —BLDSC (3573.630000); Faxon; SWETS. **CCC.**

DEUTSCHER ALTPHILOLOGEN-VERBAND. MITTEILUNGSBLATT. see *CLASSICAL STUDIES*

430   GW   ISSN 0418-9426
DEUTSCHER GERMANISTEN-VERBAND. MITTEILUNGEN. 1954. q. DM.48. Verlag Moritz Diesterweg GmbH, Waechtersbacher Str. 89, 60386 Frankfurt a.M., Germany. TEL 069-42081-0. FAX 069-1301-100. TELEX 413234-MDD. Ed. Dr. Franz R. Franke. adv.; bk.rev.; bibl. circ. 3,250. **Document type:** bulletin.
   —SWETS. **CCC.**

430 370   SA   ISSN 1016-4367
DEUTSCHUNTERRICHT IM SUEDLICHEN AFRIKA. (Text mainly in German) 1970. s-a. R.10. Sudafrikanischer Germanistenverband - South African Association for German Studies, University of the Western Cape, German Department, Private Bag X17, Bellville 7535, South Africa. FAX 27-21-9592376. Ed. Klaus Menck. adv.; bk.rev. circ. 450. **Document type:** academic/scholarly publication.
   Formerly (until 1990): Deutschunterricht in Suedafrika (ISSN 0012-1487)
   Description: Presents German language study and teaching.

430 375.4   CC
DEYU XUEXI/LEARNING GERMAN. (Text in Chinese and German) bi-m. $14.40. Beijing Foreign Language Institute, German Department, Suzhou Jie, Haidian Qu, Beijing 100081, People's Republic of China. TEL 899791. (Dist. in US by: China Books & Periodicals, Inc., 2929 24th St., San Francisco, CA 94110. TEL 415-282-2994) Ed. Zhu Yan.

DIA REGNO/DIVINE KINGDOM: CHRISTIAN ESPERANTO MAGAZINE; Kristana Esperanto-Gazeto. see *RELIGIONS AND THEOLOGY*

LINGUISTICS 3499

410   NE   ISSN 0176-4225
P140
DIACHRONICA; international journal for historical linguistics. (Text in English, French, German) 1984. 2/yr. fl.164($95) (effective 1994). John Benjamins Publishing Co., Amsteldijk 44, P.O. Box 75577, 1070 AN Amsterdam, Netherlands. TEL 31-20-6738156. FAX 31-20-6792956. (In N. America: 821 Bethlehem Pike, Philadelphia, PA 19118. TEL 215-836-1200. FAX 215-836-1204) Ed.Bd. bk.rev.; bibl. (back issues avail.) **Indexed:** Bibl.Ling., Lang.& Lang.Behav.Abstr. (1984-). **Document type:** academic/scholarly publication.
   —BLDSC (3579.615850); Faxon; UnCover; SWETS.
   Description: Provides a forum for exchanging and synthsizing information concernig historical linguistics in all language families.

447.9   BE   ISSN 0773-7688
PC3041
DIALECTES DE WALLONIE. Spine title: D W. (Text in French) 1972. a. 500 BEF. Societe de Langue et de Litterature Wallonnes, Place du Vingt-Aout 7, B-4000 Liege, Belgium. TEL 041-231960. Ed. Jean Lechanteur. bk.rev.; bibl.; illus. circ. 600. **Indexed:** M.L.A. **Document type:** academic/scholarly publication.
   Description: Covers dialectology, onomastics and ethnography.

DIALETTI D'ITALIA. see *LITERATURE*

460   NE   ISSN 0167-8744
DIALOGOS HISPANICOS DE AMSTERDAM. (Text in Spanish) 1980. irreg. price varies. (Universiteit van Amsterdam, Spaans Seminarium) Editions Rodopi B.V., Keizersgracht 302-304, 1016 EX Amsterdam, Netherlands. TEL 31-20-6227507. FAX 31-20-6380948. (In N. America: 233 Peachtree St. N.E., Ste. 404, Atlanta GA 30303-1504. TEL 800-225-3998. FAX 404-522-7116) Ed.Bd. circ. 750. (back issues avail.) **Indexed:** Bibl.Ling., M.L.A. **Document type:** monographic series.

440 375.4   FR   ISSN 0226-6881
DIALOGUES ET CULTURES. 1970. a. 80 F. Federation Internationale des Professeurs de Francais, 1 av. Leon Journault, 92310 Sevres, France. TEL 46-26-53-16. FAX 46-26-81-69. adv.; bk.rev. circ. 1,500. **Indexed:** Lang.Teach.& Ling.Abstr. **Document type:** academic/scholarly publication.
   —BLDSC (3579.775730).
   Former titles: Dialogues; Federation Internationale des Professeurs de Francais. Bulletin.
   Description: Contains selected acts of congresses, symposiums and meetings of teachers of French worldwide.

440   FR   ISSN 0399-7081
DICO - PLUS. Variant title: Cahiers des Amis du Lexique Francais. 1977. 4/yr. 72 F. Amis du Lexique Francais, 81 bis rue Lauriston, 75016 Paris, France. Dir. Albert Doillon. bk.rev. circ. 160. (processed)

DICTIONARIES. see *LIBRARY AND INFORMATION SCIENCES*

DICTIONARY OF CONTEMPORARY QUOTATIONS. see *LITERATURE*

429.3   CN   ISSN 0826-8134
DICTIONARY OF OLD ENGLISH. PUBLICATIONS. 1980. irreg., vol.4, 1989. price varies. (Dictionary of Old English) Pontifical Institute of Mediaeval Studies, 59 Queen's Park Cres. E., Toronto, ON M5S 2C4, Canada. TEL 416-926-7144. FAX 416-926-7258. (Dist. outside N. America and UK by: N.V. Brepols, Steenweg op Tielen 68, 2300 Turnhout, Belgium. TEL 32-14-415463. FAX 32-14-428919) (back issues avail.) **Document type:** academic/scholarly publication, monographic series.

401   TU
DIL DERGISI/LANGUAGE JOURNAL. (Text in Turkish) no.11, 1993. q. Ankara Universitesi, Dil Ogretim Merkezi - TOMER - Ankara University, Language Instruction Center, Dil Dergisi Mudurlugu, Ziya Golkap Cad. 18-1, 06650 Kizilay - Ankara, Turkey. TEL 90-4-4318292. FAX 90-4-4338190. Ed. Gulcin Ersen. bibl.; illus. **Document type:** academic/scholarly publication.
   Description: Covers news and topics of interest to instructors of Turkish, with news of branch activities and cultural exchanges with Central Asian Republics.

LINGUISTICS

DIMENSION: LANGUAGES (YEAR); proceedings of the Southern Conference on Language Teaching. see EDUCATION — Teaching Methods And Curriculum

DIPOSITIO. see ETHNIC INTERESTS

410 US
DIRECTORY OF PROGRAMS IN LINGUISTICS; in the United States and Canada. 1962. triennial. Linguistic Society of America, 1325 18th St., N.W., Ste. 211, Washington, DC 20036-6501. TEL 202-835-1714. adv. **Document type:** directory.
Former titles: Guide to Programs in Linguistics; University Resources in the United States and Canada for the Study of Linguistics; University Resources in the United States for Linguistics and the Teaching of English as a Foreign Language (ISSN 0511-3040)

DIRECTORY OF TRANSLATORS AND TRANSLATING AGENCIES IN THE UNITED KINGDOM. see BIBLIOGRAPHIES

428 UK ISSN 0307-1006
DISCOURSE ANALYSIS MONOGRAPHS. 1976. irreg., no.16, 1990. £8. University of Birmingham, School of English, Edgbaston, Birmingham B15 2TT, England. TEL 021-414-5669. FAX 021-414-5668. TELEX 333762-UOBHAM-G. Ed.Bd. circ. 400. **Document type:** academic/scholarly publication, monographic series.
—BLDSC (3595.800000).

150 JS ISSN 0163-853X
P302 CODEN: DIPRDG
DISCOURSE PROCESSES; a multidisciplinary journal. 1978. q. $45 to individuals; institutions $110. Ablex Publishing Corporation, 355 Chestnut St., Norwood, NJ 07648. TEL 201-767-8450. FAX 201-767-6717. TELEX 135-393. Ed. Roy O. Freedle. bk.rev.; index. circ. 700. (back issues avail.; reprint service avail. from ISI) **Indexed:** Biol.Abstr., C.I.J.E., Curr.Cont., ERIC, Lang.& Lang.Behav.Abstr. (1978-), Lang.Teach.& Lang.Abstr., M.L.A., Psychol.Abstr., Sociol.Abstr., SSCI.
—BLDSC (3595.860000); Faxon; UnCover; SWETS. **CCC.**

430 375.4 GW ISSN 0342-1589
DISKUSSION DEUTSCH; Zeitschrift fuer Deutschlehrer aller Schulformen in Ausbildung und Praxis. 1970. bi-m. DM.54. Verlag Moritz Diesterweg GmbH, Waechtersbacher Str. 89, 60386 Frankfurt a.M., Germany. TEL 069-42081-0. FAX 069-1301-100. TELEX 413234-MDD. index. circ. 9,000. **Document type:** academic/scholarly publication.
—BLDSC (3598.430000); Faxon. **CCC.**

DISTRIBUTED LANGUAGE TRANSLATION. see LINGUISTICS — Computer Applications

410 BL ISSN 0102-4450
P1.A1
DOCUMENTACAO DE ESTUDOS EM LINGUISTICA TEORICA E APLICADA. Short title: D.E.L.T.A. (Text in Portuguese, English, French) 1985. s-a. $15 to individuals; institutions $30. (Asociacao Brasileira de Linguistica) Editora da Pontificia Universidade Catolica de Sao Paulo, Departamento de Linguistica, Rua Monte Alegre, 984, 05014 Sao Paulo S.P., Brazil. TEL 62-0280. Ed. Mary Aizawa Kato. bk.rev. circ. 1,000. (back issues avail.)

DOITSU BUNGAKU. see LITERATURE

410 378 020 GW ISSN 0933-1484
DOKUMENTATION ZUR GERMANISTISCHEN SPRACHWISSENSCHAFT. 1983. biennial. DM.30. Institut fuer Deutsche Sprache, Postfach 101621, 68016 Mannheim, Germany. TEL 0621-1581-0. FAX 0621-1581200. Ed. Konrad Plastwich. cum.index. circ. 300. (back issues avail.) **Document type:** monographic series.
Formerly (until 1985): Dokumentation Sprachwissenschaftliche Forschungsvorhaben (ISSN 0724-4320)

DOSHISHA LITERATURE; journal of English literature and philology. see LITERATURE

410 XO
DRUZBA. (Text in Russian) 1951. 10/yr. 10 Kcs. (Ministerstvo Skolstvo Slovenskej Republiky) Slovenske Pedagogicke Nakladatelstvo, Sasinkova 5, 815 60 Bratislava, Slovakia. (Subscr. to: Slovart, Gottwaldovo nam. 6, 805-32 Bratislava, Slovakia) Ed. Viera Labuzova. circ. 240,000.

499.992 AU
LA DUA JARCENTO. INFORMILO. (Text in Esperanto) 1950. q. membership. Internacia Esperanto-Muzeo en Wien - Internationales Esperanto-Museum in Wien, Hofburg, A-1015 Vienna, Austria. Ed. Herbert Mayer. bk.rev.; abstr.; bibl. circ. 500.
Formerly: Internacia Esperanto-Muzeo en Wien. Informilo (ISSN 0020-5710)

400 800 US
DUQUESNE STUDIES. LANGUAGE AND LITERATURE SERIES. 1960. irreg. price varies. Duquesne University Press, 600 Forbes Ave., Pittsburgh, PA 15282. TEL 412-396-6610. FAX 412-396-5984. Ed. Albert Labriola. **Indexed:** M.L.A. **Document type:** monographic series.
Formerly (until vol.17): Duquesne Studies. Philological Series (ISSN 0070-7694)

DUTCH STUDIES IN ARMENIAN LANGUAGE AND LITERATURE. see LITERATURE

496 419 TZ
E A C R O T A N A L INFORMATION. (Text in English and French) 1979. a. $3.50 per no. Eastern African Centre for Research on Oral Traditions and African National Languages, P.O. Box 600, Zanzibar, Tanzania. Ed. Didier Rapanoel. bk.rev.; bibl. (back issues avail.)

496 419 TZ
E A C R O T A N A L STUDIES & DOCUMENTS. (Text in English, French) 1980. a. $4. Eastern African Centre for Research on Oral Traditions and African National Languages, Box 600, Zanzibar, Tanzania. Ed. Didier Rapanoel. (back issues avail)

420 US
E S C O L PROCEEDINGS. (Eastern States Conference on Linguistics) 1984. a. $10 to individuals; institutions $15. Ohio State University, Department of Linguistics, 222 Oxley Hall, 1712 Neil Ave., Columbus, OH 43210-1298. TEL 614-292-4052. FAX 614-292-4273. **Document type:** proceedings.

491.6 340 IE ISSN 0790-4657
EARLY IRISH LAW SERIES. 1983. irreg., vol.3, 1988. I£16. Dublin Institute for Advanced Studies, School of Celtic Studies, 10 Burlington Rd., Dublin 4, Ireland. TEL 01-6680748. FAX 01-6680561. **Document type:** academic/scholarly publication.
—BLDSC (3642.984200).

430 NE ISSN 0925-4161
▼**EARLY STUDIES IN GERMANIC PHILOLOGY.** 1992. irreg. price varies. Editions Rodopi B.V., Keizersgracht 302-304, 1016 EX Amsterdam, Netherlands. TEL 31-20-6227507. FAX 31-20-6380948. (In N. America: 233 Peachtree St., N.E., Ste. 404, Atlanta, GA 30303-1504. TEL 800-225-3998. FAX 404-522-7116) Ed. Rolf Bremmer Jr. (back issues avail.) **Document type:** monographic series.

EDITIONES ARNAMAGNAEANAE. SERIES A. see LITERATURE

EDITIONES ARNAMAGNAEANAE. SERIES B. see LITERATURE

EDITOR'S REVENGE. see JOURNALISM

410 US ISSN 0163-3848
EDWARD SAPIR MONOGRAPH SERIES IN LANGUAGE, CULTURE, AND COGNITION. (Supplement to: Forum Linguisticum) 1977. irreg. (approx. 2/yr.) price varies. (Linguistic Association of Canada and the United States) Jupiter Press, Box 101, Lake Bluff, IL 60044. TEL 312-234-3997. Ed. Adam Makkai. circ. 1,000. (back issues avail.) **Indexed:** M.L.A. **Document type:** monographic series.

439.829 NO ISSN 0803-4842
EG; meldingsblad for Norsk Maalungdom. Key Title: Eg (Oslo). 1972. 6/yr. NOK 120. Norsk Maalungdom, Nordahl Brunsgt. 22, N-0165 Oslo 1, Sweden.
Former titles (until **1986**): Folkemaal (ISSN 0803-4850); (until 1980): Maalfront (ISSN 0803-4869)

491.62 891.62 IE ISSN 0013-2608
EIGSE; a journal of Irish studies. 1939. a. (in one vol.). I£10. National University of Ireland, 49 Merrion Sq., Dublin 2, Ireland. TEL 6767246. FAX 6619665. Ed. Padraig Breatnach. bk.rev. circ. 400. **Indexed:** Arts & Hum.Cit.Ind., Bibl.Ling., Curr.Cont., M.L.A. **Document type:** academic/scholarly publication.

ELEMENTA; journal of Slavic studies and comparative cultural semiotics. see HUMANITIES: COMPREHENSIVE WORKS

400 SP ISSN 0013-6662
PA9
EMERITA; revista de linguistica y filologia clasica. (Text in Spanish; summaries in English) 1933. s-a. 3300 ptas. (foreign 4950 ptas.). Consejo Superior de Investigaciones Cientificas (C.S.I.C.), Instituto de Filologia, Duque de Medinaceli, 6, 28014 Madrid, Spain. bk.rev.; charts; illus.; index, cum.index. circ. 400. (reprint service avail. from SCH) **Indexed:** Bibl.Ling., M.L.A. **Document type:** academic/scholarly publication.

493.1 GW ISSN 0340-627X
ENCHORIA; Zeitschrift fuer Demotistik und Koptologie. (Text in English, French, German and Italian) 1971. a. DM.138. Harrassowitz Verlag, Taunusstr. 14, 65183 Wiesbaden, Germany. TEL 0611-530-0. FAX 0611-530570. TELEX 4186135. (Subscr. to: Postfach 2929, 65019 Wiesbaden, Germany) Ed.Bd. bk.rev. circ. 400. (back issues avail.) **Indexed:** Bibl.Ling. **Document type:** academic/scholarly publication.
—BLDSC (3738.480000).

420 370 GW ISSN 0013-8185
ENGLISCH; eine Zeitschrift fuer Englischlehrerinnen und Englischlehrer. (Supplement avail.) (Text mainly in German; occasionally in English) 1966. q. DM.26.80. Cornelsen Verlagskontor GmbH und Co. KG, Kammerratsheide 6, 33598 Bielefeld, Germany. TEL 0521-9719-0. Ed.Bd. adv.; bk.rev.; illus.; tr.lit.; index. circ. 8,500. **Indexed:** Lang.& Lang.Behav.Abstr., Lang.Teach.& Ling.Abstr. **Document type:** academic/scholarly publication.
—CCC.

400 GW ISSN 0071-0490
ENGLISH AND AMERICAN STUDIES IN GERMAN; summaries of theses and monographs. (Supplement to: Anglia - Zeitschrift fuer Englische Philologie) (Text in English) 1969. a. price varies. (German Congress of Scholars of English) Max Niemeyer Verlag, Postfach 2140, 72011 Tuebingen, Germany. TEL 07071-98940. FAX 07071-989450. Ed. Horst Weinstock. (back issues avail.) **Document type:** academic/scholarly publication.
Description: Summaries of theses and monographs on English and American language and literature, (originally written in German).

ENGLISH EDUCATION. see EDUCATION

420 371.3 UK ISSN 0889-4906
PE1128.A2
ENGLISH FOR SPECIFIC PURPOSES; an international journal of English for specific purposes. 1980. 3/yr. £112($170) (effective 1994). Elsevier Science Ltd., Pergamon, P.O. Box 800, Kidlington, Oxford OX5 1DX, England. TEL 44-865-843000. FAX 44-865-843010. (Subscr. in U.S. and Canada to: Elsevier Science, 660 White Plains Rd., Tarrytown, NY 10591-5153. TEL 914-524-9200. FAX 914-333-2444) Eds. John Swales, Ann M. Johns. adv.; bk.rev. (also avail. in microfilm from UMI) **Indexed:** C.I.J.E., Cont.Pg.Educ., Lang.& Lang.Behav.Abstr. (1980-), Lang.Teach.& Ling.Abstr., Mult.Ed.Abstr/ **Document type:** academic/scholarly publication.
—BLDSC (3775.116580); Faxon; UnCover; SWETS. UMI. **CCC.**
Formerly: E S P Journal (ISSN 0272-2380)
Description: Discusses linguistic aspects of the specialized varieties of English in use throughout the world, and the application of linguistic research to specific methodological concerns, language teaching and acquisition, and teacher training or retraining. *Refereed Serial*

420 820 AT ISSN 0046-208X
ENGLISH IN AUSTRALIA. 1965. 4/yr. Aus.$16. Australian Association for the Teaching of English, P.O. Box 3203, Norwood, S.A. 5067, Australia. Ed. W. Corcoran. bk.rev. circ. 5,600. **Indexed:** Aus.Educ.Ind., Aus.P.A.I.S., C.I.J.E., Child.Lit.Abstr.
Incorporates (1970-1994): A.A.T.E. Guide to English Books and Resources.
Description: Contains articles of academic interest, and teacher resource materials in the field of English. Includes reviews of new textbooks and fiction relevant to teachers and librarians.

ENGLISH IN EDUCATION. see EDUCATION — Teaching Methods And Curriculum

LINGUISTICS

420   AG
ENGLISH LANGUAGE JOURNAL/REVISTA DE LA LENGUA INGLESA; for the Latin American teacher of English. (Text in English & Spanish) 1970. q. $30. c/o Aldo O. Blanco, 224 Parana, 1st Fl., 1017 Buenos Aires, Argentina. adv.; bk.rev.; bibl. circ. 500. **Indexed:** Lang.& Lang.Behav.Abstr., Lang.Teach.& Ling.Abstr.

420.07 370   UK   ISSN 0307-8337
PE1128.A2   CODEN: ELTJEB
ENGLISH LANGUAGE TEACHING JOURNAL. 1946. q. £37($69) (effective 1994). (British Council) Oxford University Press, Oxford Journals, Walton St., Oxford OX2 6DP, England. TEL 0865-56767. FAX 0865-56646. TELEX 837330-OXPRES-G. (U.S. subscr. to: Oxford University Press Inc., 2001 Evans Rd., Cary, NC 27513. TEL 919-677-0977) Ed. Tricia Hedge. adv. contact: Jane Parker. bk.rev.; cum.index every 2 yrs. circ. 5,500. (also avail. in microform from UMI; reprint service avail. from UMI) **Indexed:** Br.Educ.Ind., C.I.J.E., Educ.Ind., Lang.& Lang.Behav.Abstr., Lang.Teach.& Ling.Abstr. **Document type:** academic/scholarly publication.
—BLDSC (3732.462000); Faxon; UnCover; SWETS; UMI. **CCC.**
    Formerly: English Language Teaching (ISSN 0013-8290)
    Description: Directed to teachers of English as second language. Includes practical help on procedure and techniques; discusses methods of teaching; reports on new ideas and systems of teaching; covers different uses of the English language.

ENGLISH LEADERSHIP QUARTERLY. see *EDUCATION — Teaching Methods And Curriculum*

420 910   UK   ISSN 0071-0636
ENGLISH PLACE-NAME SOCIETY. 1922. a. $50 (non-members $70). English Place-Name Society, c/o Prof. Christine Fell, Department of English Studies, University of Nottingham, Nottingham NG7 2RD, England. TEL 0602-515914. FAX 0602-515924. Ed. Victor Watts. index. circ. 740. (also avail. in microfiche from IDC) **Indexed:** Br.Archaeol.Abstr., Geo.Abstr., NAA. **Document type:** academic/scholarly publication.

420 375.4   UK   ISSN 0955-8950
ENGLISH REVIEW. 1990. q. £18.50 (foreign £21). Philip Allan Publishers Ltd., Deddington, Oxfordshire OX15 0SE, England. TEL 0869-38652. FAX 0869-38803. (also avail. in microfilm from KTO) **Document type:** academic/scholarly publication.
—BLDSC (3775.115160).

420 820   NE   ISSN 0013-838X
PE1
ENGLISH STUDIES; a journal of English language and literature. 1919. bi-m. $161 to individuals; institutions $216. Swets & Zeitlinger bv, Heereweg 347, 2161 CA Lisse, Netherlands. TEL 31-2521-35111. FAX 31-2521-15888. TELEX 41325. (Dist. in N. America by: Swets & Zeitlinger, 440 Creamery Way, Ste. A, Exton, PA 19341. TEL 800-447-9387. FAX 610-524-5366) Ed. J.M. Blom. adv.; bk.rev.; index, cum.index: vols.1-40, 1919-1959. circ. 2,000. (also avail. in microform from SWZ; reprint service avail. from SWZ) **Indexed:** Abstr.Engl.Stud., Acad.Ind., Arts & Hum.Cit.Ind., Bibl.Ling., Curr.Cont., Hum.Ind., Ind.Bk.Rev.Hum., Lang.& Lang.Behav.Abstr., Lang.Teach.& Ling.Abstr., M.L.A., Soc.Sci.Ind. **Document type:** academic/scholarly publication.
—BLDSC (3775.117000); Faxon; UnCover; SWETS. **CCC.**

410   UK   ISSN 0266-0784
PE1001
ENGLISH TODAY; the international review of the English language. q. £22($36) to individuals (overseas £32); institutions £46 (overseas £56 ($77)). Cambridge University Press, Edinburgh Bldg., Shaftesbury Rd., Cambridge CB2 2RU, England. TEL 0223-312393. FAX 0223-315052. TELEX 851817256. (N. American addr.: Cambridge University Press, Journals Dept., 40 W. 20th St., New York, NY 10011. TEL 212-924-3900. FAX 212-691-3239) Ed. Tom McArthur. adv. (also avail. in microform from UMI; back issues avail.) **Indexed:** Lang.Teach.& Ling.Abstr. **Document type:** academic/scholarly publication.
—BLDSC (3775.155800); Faxon; UnCover; SWETS; UMI. **CCC.**
    Description: Focuses on the usage and teaching of English worldwide.

420 375.4   NE   ISSN 0172-8865
ENGLISH WORLD WIDE; a journal of varieties of English. Short title: E W W. 1980. 2/yr. fl.242($140) (effective 1994). John Benjamins Publishing Co., Amsteldijk 44, P.O. Box 75577, 1070 AN Amsterdam, Netherlands. TEL 31-20-6738156. FAX 31-20-6792956. (In N. America: 821 Bethlehem Pike, Philadelphia, PA 19118. TEL 215-836-1200. FAX 215-836-1204) Ed. Manfred Goerlach. adv.; bk.rev. circ. 600. (back issues avail.) **Indexed:** Bibl.Ling., Lang.& Lang.Behav.Abstr. (1980-), M.L.A. **Document type:** academic/scholarly publication.
—BLDSC (3775.161500); UnCover; SWETS.
    Description: Studies regional and social variations of English around the world.

410   BL
ENSAIOS LINGUISTICOS. 1978. irreg. price varies. Summer Institute of Linguistics, Departamento de Estudos Tecnicos, SAI-NO Lote D, Bloco 3, 70770-730 Brasilia DF, Brazil. **Document type:** academic/scholarly publication.
    Description: Contains sketches of grammar, lexicon and phonology concerning the indigenous languages of Brazil.

400   PL   ISSN 0012-7825
P1.A1
EOS; commentarii societatis philologae polonorum. (Text in English, French, German, Latin and Polish) 1894. s-a. $32. Uniwersytet im. Adama Mickiewicza, Instytut Filologii Klasycznej, Al. Niepodleglosci 4, 61-874 Poznan, Poland. TEL 48-61-521191. FAX 48-61-536-536. (Dist. by: Ars Polona-Ruch, Krakowskie Przedmiescie 7, Warsaw, Poland) Ed. Sylwester Dworacki. bk.rev.; bibl.; charts; illus.; index, cum.index: 1894-1959. circ. 450. **Indexed:** Bibl.Ling., M.L.A. **Document type:** academic/scholarly publication.
    Description: Contains papers on ancient philology, history, philosophy and classical culture (Latin-Greek) in later centuries.

EPIGRAPHIC SOCIETY. OCCASIONAL PAPERS. see *ARCHAEOLOGY*

EPIGRAPHICA BOEOTICA. see *ARCHAEOLOGY*

418.02   BE
EQUIVALENCES. (Text mainly in French; occasionally in Dutch, English, German, Italian, Spanish) 1970. 2/yr. 500 BEF. Institut Superieur de Traducteurs et Interpretes de la Communaute Francaise de Belgique, 34, rue Hazard, 1180 Brussels, Belgium. TEL 02-3440080. (Co-sponsor: Association pour la Promotion de l'Etude des Langues Modernes) Ed. J.M. van der Meerschen. adv.; bk.rev. circ. 500. **Indexed:** Bibl.Ling., M.L.A. **Document type:** academic/scholarly publication.

400   NO   ISSN 0013-9947
PA9
ERANOS; acta philologica Suecana. (Text in English, French, German, Latin) 1896. q. NOK 430 in the Nordic countries; elsewhere NOK 445. Scandinavian University Press, P.O. Box 2959-Toeyen, N-0608 Oslo, Norway. TEL 472-67-7600. FAX 417-67-7575. (U.S. addr.: Scandinavian University Press, 200 Meacham Ave., Elmont, NY 11003. TEL 516-352-7300) Ed Sten Eklund. adv.; index, cum.index every 50 yrs. circ. 850. **Indexed:** M.L.A., Rel.Ind.Two.
—UnCover; SWETS.
    Description: Presents original papers on Greek and Latin philology, including Byzantine and Medieval Latin, and on antiquity and Byzantine studies in general.

460 375.4   SP   ISSN 0425-2772
PC4008
ESPANOL ACTUAL. 1963. s-a. 3700 ptas.($37) (effective 1993). Instituto de Cooperacion Iberoamericana, Avenida los Reyes Catolicos, 4, 28040 Madrid, Spain. TEL 415-36-87. FAX 415-36-07. (Dist. by: Arco-Libros, S.L., Juan Bautista de Toledo 28, 28002 Madrid, Spain. TEL 415-36-87) **Indexed:** Lang.Teach.& Ling.Abstr., M.L.A.

469 375.4   BL   ISSN 0102-7077
ESPECIALIST. (Text in English, French, Portuguese, Spanish) 1981. 2/yr. $20 (effective 1992). (Centro de Pesquisas, Recursos e Informacao em Leitura) Editora da Pontificia Universidade Catolica de Sao Paulo, Rua Monte Alegre 984, 05014 Sao Paulo, SP, Brazil. TEL 62-0280. FAX 62-4920. (Co-sponsor: Conselho Nacional de Pesquisa) Ed. Maria Antonieta Alba Celani. bk.rev.

499.992   NE   ISSN 0014-0635
ESPERANTO. (Text in Esperanto) 1905. m. fl.60($32) Universala Esperanto-Asocio, Nieuwe Binnenweg 176, 3015 BJ Rotterdam, Netherlands. TEL 31-10-4361044. FAX 31-10-4361751. Ed. Istvan Ertl. adv. contact: Osmo Buller. bk.rev.; illus.; index. circ. 6,000. (back issues avail.) **Indexed:** M.L.A.

410   US   ISSN 0165-2575
ESPERANTO DOCUMENTS. N.S. 1976. irreg. (approx. 10/yr.) $27. Esperanto League for North America, Box 1129, El Cerrito, CA 94530. TEL 510-653-0998. FAX 510-653-1468. (European addr.: Universala Esperanto-Asocio, Nieuwe Binnenweg 176, 3015 BJ Rotterdam, Netherlands) (Co-sponsor: Center for Research and Documentation of the World Language Problem) Ed.Bd. adv. **Indexed:** Lang.& Lang.Behav.Abstr. **Document type:** academic/scholarly publication.

410   NE   ISSN 0165-2524
ESPERANTO-DOKUMENTOJ. NOVA SERIO. English edition: Esperanto Documents. New Series (ISSN 0165-2575); French edition: Documents sur l'Esperanto. Nouvelle Serie (ISSN 0165-2621) (Text in Esperanto) 1976. irreg. fl.50($27) for 10 nos. Universala Esperanto-Asocio - Universal Esperanto Association, Nieuwe Binnenweg 176, 3015 BJ Rotterdam, Netherlands. TEL 31-10-4361044. FAX 31-10-4361751. Ed. Thomas Bormann. circ. 550.

499.992   UK   ISSN 0014-0643
ESPERANTO EN SKOTLANDO. (Text in Esperanto) 1947. q. £2. Skota Federacio Esperantista - Scottish Esperanto Federation, 16 Woodlands Dr., Coatbridge ML5 1LE, Scotland. TEL 0236-421636. Ed. Dr. Albert Goodheir. bk.rev. circ. 250. **Document type:** academic/scholarly publication.

499.992   FR   ISSN 0046-2500
ESPERANTO - INTERLANGUE UNIVERSELLE. (Text in Esperanto and French) q. 5 F. Editions Nova, 24 Ave de Riedisheim, F-68 Mulhouse, France.

499.992   FR   ISSN 0014-066X
ESPERANTO - LINGVO INTERNACIA. (Text in Esperanto and French) 1925. q. 4 F.($1) Esperanto-Editions, 24 Ave de Riedisheim, F-68100 Mulhouse, France. TEL 89-44-75-21. Ed. Albert Lienhardt. bk.rev.; bibl.
    Formerly: Tribune de l'Esperanto.

410 371.3   NO   ISSN 0802-0442
ESPERANTO - NYTT. 1959. 3/yr. NOK 20. Norvega - Esperantista Ligo - Norsk Esperanto - Forbund, Olaf Schous vei 18, 0572 Oslo 5, Norway. circ. 2,000. **Document type:** bulletin.

410   UK   ISSN 0046-2527
ESPERANTO TEACHER. (Text in English and Esperanto) 1939. 3/yr. £7.50. Esperanto Teachers Association, 140 Holland Park Ave., London W11 4UF, England. Ed. Arnold Pitt. adv.; play rev.; bibl.; illus. circ. 500. (processed) **Document type:** academic/scholarly publication.

499.992   US   ISSN 1056-0297
ESPERANTO - U S A; news of the language problem and Esperanto as a solution. (Text in English, Esperanto) 1952. bi-m. (plus occasional supplements). $30. Esperanto League for North America, Box 1129, El Cerrito, CA 94530. TEL 510-653-0998; 800-828-5944. FAX 510-653-1468. Ed. D. Harlow. adv.; bk.rev.; illus. circ. 1,200. **Document type:** newsletter.
    Formerly: E L N A Newsletter (ISSN 0030-5065); Incorporates: E L N A Bulteno (ISSN 0012-771X); J E N - Bulteno (Junularo Esperantista de Nord-Amerikio) (ISSN 0021-5848); Supersedes: Organization of Esperanto-Speaking Young Americans. Newsletter.

LINGUISTICS

400   CN   ISSN 1195-6186
▼**ESPERANTO UPDATE.** (Text in English) 1993. 4/yr. $8 to non-member individuals; $3 to members and institutions. Canadian Esperanto Association, Box 2159, Sidney, BC V8L 3S6, Canada. Ed. Paul Hopkins. circ. 300 (paid). (also avail. in diskette format; back issues avail.) **Document type:** newsletter.
Description: Provides current information on the world language problem, the progress of the Esperanto movement and educational materials for learning Esperanto.

499.992   SW   ISSN 0014-0694
ESPERO; Svenska Esperantotidningen. (Text in Esperanto & Swedish) 1913. 6/yr. SEK 150. Svenska Esperantofoerbundet, Vikingagatan 24, S-113 42 Stockholm, Sweden. Ed. Per Aarne Fritzon. adv.; bk.rev. circ. 1,500.
Former titles (until 1957): Svenska Esperanto-Tidningen La Espero; (until 1956): La Espero.
Description: Provides information about the Swedish Esperanto movement; presents readings in Esperanto.

ESTRENO; journal on the contemporary Spanish theater. see *THEATER*

400 800   CL   ISSN 0071-1713
P25
ESTUDIOS FILOLOGICOS. 1965. a. Esc.2000($15) in Latin America; elsewhere $20. Universidad Austral de Chile, Facultad de Filosofia y Humanidades, Casilla 142, Valdivia, Chile. FAX 5663-212589. Ed. Claudio Wagner. adv.; bk.rev. circ. 700. **Indexed:** Amer.Hist.& Life, Arts & Hum.Cit.Ind., Bibl.Ling., Curr.Cont., Hist.Abstr., M.L.A.

469 869   BL
ESTUDOS LINGUISTICOS E LITERARIOS. no.11, Aug. 1991. s-a. Universidade Federal da Bahia, Instituto de Letras, Campus de Ondina, 40210 Salvador, Bahia, Brazil. Ed. Celina Scheinowitz. **Document type:** academic/scholarly publication.

412   US   ISSN 0014-164X
B840
ETC; a review of general semantics. Cover title: Et Cetera. 1943. q. $30. International Society for General Semantics, Box 728, Concord, CA 94522. TEL 510-798-0311. Ed. Jeremy Klein. adv.; bk.rev.; circ. 2,500. (paid). (also avail. in microform from MIM,UMI) **Indexed:** Amer.Hist.& Life, Hist.Abstr., Hum.Ind., M.L.A., Mid.East: Abstr.& Ind., Psychol.Abstr., SSCI.
—BLDSC (3814.185000); Faxon; UnCover; SWETS; UMI.
Description: Reviews general semantics; devoted to how symbols influence human behavior; how uses of language and other media share thought, direct actions and determine the success or failure of communication.

ETHNOSCIENCES. see *ANTHROPOLOGY*

ETUDES AEQUATORIA. see *ANTHROPOLOGY*

ETUDES BALKANIQUES. see *HISTORY — History Of Europe*

491.6   FR   ISSN 0373-1928
ETUDES CELTIQUES. (Text in English and French) a. price varies. (Centre National de la Recherche Scientifique) C N R S Editions, 20-22 rue St. Amand, 75015 Paris, France. TEL 45-33-16-00. FAX 45-33-92-13. TELEX 200 356 F. Ed. Edward Bachellery. adv.; bk.rev.; bibl.; illus.; cum.index; circ. 1,250 (controlled). (reprint service avail. from KTO) **Indexed:** Bibl.Ling., Br.Archaeol.Abstr., M.L.A. **Document type:** academic/scholarly publication.
—UnCover; SWETS.
Description: Presents studies on archaeology and linguistics, especially the ancient and modern Celtic languages. Contains original research.

447   FR   ISSN 0708-2398
PM7851
ETUDES CREOLES; culture, langue, societe. 1978. s-a. 180 F. (outside Europe 210 F.). Institut d'Etudes Ceroles et Francophones, Comite International des Etudes Creoles, Universite de Provence, 29 av. R. Schuman, 13621 Aix-en-Provence, France. TEL 42-64-39-90. FAX 42-59-00-19. (Subscr. to: Didier Erudition, Box 830350, Birmingham, AL 35283-0350) (Co-sponsor: Comite International des Etudes Creoles) Ed. Marie-Christine Hazael-Massieux. bk.rev. circ. 600. **Indexed:** M.L.A. **Document type:** academic/scholarly publication.
—BLDSC (3817.300000).
Description: Promotes and serves Creole culture, languages and society through scholarly understanding.

418.005   FR   ISSN 0071-190X
P1.A1
ETUDES DE LINGUISTIQUE APPLIQUEE. 1962. q. $64. Didier Erudition, 6 rue de la Sorbonne, 75005 Paris, France. (U.S. Subscr. to: Didier Erudition, N. American Fullfillment Office, Box 830350, Birmingham, AL 35283-0350) Ed. R. Galisson. illus. **Indexed:** Lang.& Lang.Behav.Abstr. (1972-), Lang.Teach.& Ling.Abstr., M.L.A. **Document type:** academic/scholarly publication.
—Faxon; SWETS.

400 930.1   BE   ISSN 0071-1926
ETUDES DE PHILOLOGIE, D'ARCHEOLOGIE ET D'HISTOIRE ANCIENNE. 1934. irreg., vol.30, 1993. price varies. (Institut Historique Belge de Rome - Belgische Historisch Instituut te Rome) N.V. Brepols, Steenweg op Tielen 68, 2300 Turnhout, Belgium. TEL 32-14-41-54-63. FAX 32-14-42-89-19. TELEX 34 182. circ. controlled. (back issues avail.) **Document type:** monographic series.
Description: Studies classical philology and art history emphasizing excavation reports of Belgian missions in Italy.

410   GW   ISSN 0176-7879
ETUDES DE PHONOLOGIE, PHONETIQUE ET LINGUISTIQUE DESCRIPTIVE DU FRANCAIS/STUDIEN ZUR PHONOLOGIE, PHONETIK UND LINGUISTIK DES FRANZOESISCHEN. 1984. irreg., vol.6, 1990. price varies. Helmut Buske Verlag GmbH, Richardstr. 47, 22081 Hamburg, Germany. TEL 040-296842. FAX 040-2993614. **Document type:** monographic series.

492.7 306.4   FR   ISSN 0757-7699
ETUDES ETHNO-LINGUISTIQUES MAGHREB-SAHARA. (Subseries of: Bibliotheque de la S E L A F) 1982. irreg., no.7, 1987. price varies. Societe d'Etudes Linguistiques et Anthropologiques de France (SELAF), 52 bd. St. Michel, 75006 Paris, France. TEL 42-08-83-93. (Dist. by: Editions Peeters s.p.r.l., Bondgenotenlaan 153, B-3000 Louvain, Belgium. TEL 32-16-235170. FAX 32-16-228500) **Document type:** academic/scholarly publication.

494.5 894.5   FR   ISSN 0071-2051
ETUDES FINNO-OUGRIENNES. 1964. irreg. price varies. (Centre d'Etudes Finno-Ougriennes) Editions Klincksieck, 11 rue de Lille, 75005 Paris, France. bk.rev. **Indexed:** Bibl.Ling.

400   FR   ISSN 0071-2124
ETUDES LINGUISTIQUES. 1962. irreg. price varies. Editions Klincksieck, 11 rue de Lille, 75005 Paris, France. **Indexed:** Bibl.Ling., Lang.& Lang.Behav.Abstr., M.L.A.

ETUDES MONGOLES ET SIBERIENNES. see *ANTHROPOLOGY*

499.3 306.4   FR   ISSN 0246-0092
ETUDES OCEAN INDIEN. 1982. irreg., latest no.15. price varies. Institut National des Langues et Civilisations Orientales, Centre de Recherche de l'Ocean Indien Occidental, 2 rue de Lille, 75343 Paris Cedex 07, France. TEL 49-26-42-74. **Indexed:** Bibl.Ling., Documentatieblad. **Document type:** academic/scholarly publication.
Description: Studies the linguistics, ethnology and archeology of the Indian Ocean countries.

414   CN
ETUDES PHONETIQUES/STUDIES IN PHONETICS. irreg. (Universite de Toronto) Canadian Scholars Press, 39 Bloor St. W., Ste. 222, Toronto, ON M5S 1W7, Canada. Ed. Pierre Leon. bibl.
Formerly: Studia Phonetica.

410   SW   ISSN 0347-0822
ETUDES ROMANES DE LUND. (Text in French) 1940. irreg. price varies. Lund University Press, P.O. Box 141, S-221 00 Lund, Sweden. TEL 46-46-31-20-00. FAX 46-46-30-53-38. Ed. S. Schlyter. **Document type:** academic/scholarly publication.

491   US   ISSN 0898-0454
EURASIAN LANGUAGE ARCHIVES. 1988. irreg. Eurolingua, Box 101, Bloomington, IN 47402-0101. TEL 812-332-8918.
Description: Focuses on synchronic and diachronic description concerning languages in Northern Eurasia between Japan and Germany.

410   IT
EUROASIATICA; journal of neohistorical linguistics. (Text in various European languages) 1970. irreg., vol.4, 1978. price varies. Giardini Editori e Stampatori, Via Santa Bibbiana 28, 56100 Pisa, Italy. TEL 050 502531. Ed. Nullo Minissi.

053.1   GW
▼**EUROGERMANISTIK.** 1992. irreg., no.4, 1994. DM.68. Gunter Narr Verlag, Postfach 2567, 72015 Tuebingen, Germany. TEL 07071-78091. FAX 07071-75288. Eds. Irmtraud Behr, Herve Quintin. **Document type:** monographic series.

410 572   FR   ISSN 0755-9313
EUROPE DE TRADITION ORALE. (Subseries of: Biblotheque de la S E L A F) 1982. irreg., no.8, 1992. price varies. Societe d'Etudes Linguistiques et Anthropologiques de France (SELAF), 52 bd. St. Michel, 75006 Paris, France. TEL 42-08-83-93. (Dist. by: Editions Peeters s.p.r.l., Bondgenotenlaan 153, B-3000 Louvain, Belgium. TEL 32-16-235170. FAX 32-16-228500) Ed. Fanny de Sivers. adv.; bk.rev. circ. 250. **Document type:** monographic series.

306.4 400   NE   ISSN 0926-6461
EUROPEAN STUDIES ON MULTILINGUALISM. (Text in English) 1991. irreg. fl.48.50($36) Swets & Zeitlinger bv, Heereweg 347, 2161 CA Lisse, Netherlands. TEL 31-2521-35111. FAX 31-2521-15888. TELEX 41325. (Dist. in N. America by: Swets & Zeitlinger, 440 Creamery Way, Ste. A, Exton, PA 19341. TEL 800-447-9387. FAX 610-524-5366) **Document type:** monographic series. *Refereed Serial*

460 375.4   MX
LA EVOLUCION FONOLOGICA DEL PROTOVALTUAT. irreg., no.2, 1982. Universidad Nacional Autonoma de Mexico, Instituto de Investigaciones Filologicas, Ciudad Universitaria, Coyoacan 04510, Mexico, D.F., Mexico.
Formerly: Coleccion Linguistica Indigena.

410 499   AT   ISSN 1039-9380
EXPERANTO SUB LA SUDA KRUCO. (Text in Esperanto) 1940. bi-m. Aus.$30. Australian Esperanto Association, 46 Great Eastern Hwy., Bakers Hill, W.A. 6562, Australia. TEL 09-574-1307. FAX 09-574-1530. (Subscr. to: c/o Owen Loneragan, 16 Deverell Way, S. Bentley, W.A. 6102, Australia) Ed. Donald Broadribb. bk.rev. circ. 350. **Document type:** consumer publication.
Former titles (until 1993): Australian Esperantist; Rondo.
Description: Includes short stories, poems, basic Esperanto news events, columns on language usage.

420   PK   ISSN 0014-4975
P1
EXPLORATIONS. (Text in English) 1969. s-a. Rs.50($6) per no. Government College, Department of English Language and Literature, Lahore, Pakistan. Ed. A. R. Anjum. bk.rev. circ. 900. **Indexed:** M.L.A.

491.7 375.4   CC
EYU XUEXI/LEARNING RUSSIAN. (Text in Chinese and Russian) bi-m. $14.40. Beijing Foreign Language Institute, Russian Department, Suzhou Jie, Haidian Qu, Beijing 100081, People's Republic of China. TEL 890351. (Dist. in US by: China Books & Periodicals, Inc., 2929 24th St., San Francisco, CA 94110. TEL 415-282-2994) Ed. Jiang Xiuwen.

LINGUISTICS

372   **UK**
F C E CLUB. 1971. 6/yr. (during school year). Mary Glasgow Magazines (Subsidiary of: Scholastic Publications Ltd.), 140 Freston Rd., London WC10 6TR, England. TEL 071-792-3644. FAX 071-792-3172. TELEX 311890-MGPUBS. (U.S. subscr. to: Delta Systems, 1400 Miller Pkwy., McHenry IL 60080-7030. TEL 800-823-8270) bk.rev.; film rev.; play rev.; illus.
    Formerly: Club (ISSN 0307-4382)
    Description: English-language magazine for upper intermediate-level students.

F I P L V WORLD NEWS. (Federation Internationale des Professeurs de Langues Vivantes) see *EDUCATION*

418.02   **BE**
F I T NEWSLETTER/NOUVELLES DE LA F.I.T. (Text in various languages) 1968. q. 700 BEF (outside Europe 900 BEF). Federation Internationale des Traducteurs - International Federation of Translators, Heiveldstraat 245, B-9040 Gent, St. Amandsberg, Belgium. TEL 32-9-2283971. FAX 32-9-2283971. (Co-sponsor: Unesco) Ed. R. Haeseryn. adv.; bk.rev. circ. 1,100. Document type: newsletter.
    Description: Reports on activities of the International Federation of Translators as well as general news of interest to those in the field. Includes articles on translation, interpretation, and comparative linguistics.

407   **AU**   **ISSN 0256-2510**
FACHSPRACHE; international journal of LSP. (Text in English, French, German) 1979. s-a. S.650. Wilhelm Braumueller, Universitaets-Verlagsbuchhandlung GmbH, Servitengasse 5, A-1092 Vienna, Austria. TEL 0222-3191159. FAX 0222-3102805. Ed.Bd. adv.; bk.rev.; abstr.; bibl.; charts; illus. (back issues avail.) **Indexed:** Bibl.Ling. **Document type:** academic/scholarly publication.
    Description: Contains didactics and research for teachers, translators, journalists.

FAGUO YANJIU/ETUDES FRANCAISES. see *SOCIAL SCIENCES: COMPREHENSIVE WORKS*

410   **FR**   **ISSN 1244-5460**
▼**FAITS DE LANGUES**; revue de linguistique. 1993. s-a. 275 F. (foreign 325 F.). Presses Universitaires de France, Departement des Revues, 14 av. du Bois-de-l'Epine, 91003 Evry Cedex, France. TEL 60-77-82-05. FAX 60-79-20-45. TELEX PUF 600 474 F. Ed.Bd. **Document type:** academic/scholarly publication.

495.1   **CC**   **ISSN 0257-0203**
FANGYAN/DIALECT. (Text in Chinese; table of contents in English) 1979. q. Y6.80($21.90) Shehui Kexue Zazhishe, A-158 Gulou Xidajie, Beijing 100720, People's Republic of China. TEL 441531. **Indexed:** Bibl.Ling.
    Description: Contains linguistic studies on Chinese dialects.

450   **GW**   **ISSN 0014-8555**
IL FARO; Eine Monatszeitschrift zur Weiterbildung im Italienischen. (Text in German, Italian) 1955. 6/yr. DM.13.20. Beacon-Verlag Koerber oHG, Birkental 13, Postfach 1161, 67098 Bad Duerkheim, Germany. illus. circ. 2,000. (tabloid format)

430 375.4   **AU**
FAUSTCHEN. 1973. irreg. Oesterreichische Hochschuelerschaft, S T R V Germanistik, Universitaetsstr. 7, A-1010 Vienna, Austria. Ed.Bd. bk.rev.; bibl. circ. 1,000.
    Formerly (until 1980): Beitraege zum Deutschstudium.

440 375.4   **CC**   **ISSN 1002-1434**
FAYU XUEXI/LEARNING FRENCH/APPRENONS LE FRANCAIS. (Text in Chinese, French) 1980. q. $9.90. Beijing Foreign Language Institute, French Department, 2 Xisanhuan Beilu, Haidian Qu, Beijing 100081, People's Republic of China. TEL 8422277. (Dist. in U.S. by: China Books & Periodicals, Inc., 2929 24th St., San Francisco, CA 94110. TEL 415-282-2994) Ed. Chen Zhenyao. **Document type:** academic/scholarly publication.

LA FENICE. see *HISTORY*

499.992   **NE**   **ISSN 0921-2302**
FENOMENO. (Text in Dutch, Esperanto) 1969. m. fl.30. Federatie van Esperanto-Organisaties in Nederland - Federacio de Esperanto-Organizoj en Nederlando, c/o D. Ederveen, Populierendreef 7, 2272 RA Voorburg, Netherlands. TEL 31-70-3866653. Ed. S.P. Smits. adv.; bk.rev. circ. 1,200. (also avail. in Braille) **Document type:** newsletter.
    Former titles: Komuna Esperanto-Gazeto (ISSN 0023-317X); Nederlanda Esperantisto; Laborista Esperanto.
    Description: Covers language issues, cultural information, meetings and other items of interest to Esperanto organizations in the Netherlands.

400 860   **AG**   **ISSN 0071-495X**
PC5
FILOLOGIA. 1949. a. $35 or exchange basis. Instituto de Filologia y Literaturas Hispanicas "Dr. Amado Alonso", 25 de Mayo 217, Buenos Aires 1002, Argentina. TEL 302733. (Subscr. to: Oficina de Venta de Publicaciones de la Facultad de Filosofia y Letras, Puan 470, Buenos Aires 1406, Argentina) Ed. Ana Maria Barrenechea. adv.; bk.rev. circ. 1,000. **Indexed:** Amer.Hist.& Life, Hist.Abstr., M.L.A.

420   **PL**   **ISSN 0554-8144**
FILOLOGIA ANGIELSKA. (Text in English, Polish; summaries in English) 1972. irreg., no.24, 1993. price varies. Adam Mickiewicz University Press, Nowowiejskigo 55, 61-734 Poznan, Poland. TEL 527-380. FAX 61-526425. TELEX 413260 UAMPL. Ed.Bd. **Document type:** academic/scholarly publication.
    Formerly: Uniwersytet im. Adama Mickiewicza w Poznaniu. Wydzial Filologiczny. Seria Filologia Angielska.
    Description: Contains current research results of the university's students and professors of English, their Ph.D. works and monographs. Each volume contains monographs (thesis) of one author.

410   **IT**
FILOLOGIA ANTICA E MODERNA. irreg. Universita degli Studi della Calabria, Dipartimento di Filologia, 87036 Arcavacata di Rende (Cosenza), Italy. Ed. Nicola Merola.

480 880   **PL**   **ISSN 0554-8160**
FILOLOGIA KLASYCZNA. (Text in Polish; summaries in various languages) 1966. irreg., no.17, 1994. price varies. Adam Mickiewicz University Press, Nowowiejskiego 55, 61-734 Poznan, Poland. TEL 527-380. FAX 61-526425. TELEX 413260 UAMPL. **Document type:** academic/scholarly publication.
—BLDSC (9120.455000).
    Formerly: Uniwersytet im. Adama Mickiewicza w Poznaniu. Wydzial Filologiczny. Seria Filologia Klasyczna.
    Description: Contains current research results of the university's scholars, their Ph.D. thesis and monographs. Each volume contains the work of one author.

400   **SP**
FILOLOGIA MODERNA. (Text in English, French, German, Italian, and Spanish) 1960. 150 ptas.($5) Universidad Complutense de Madrid, Facultad de Filologia, Cuidad Universitaria, Madrid-3, Spain. Ed. Hans Juretschke. (processed) **Indexed:** Bibl.Ling., Ind.Bk.Rev.Hum.
    Formerly: Revista Filologia Moderna (ISSN 0046-3841)

400   **IT**   **ISSN 0391-2485**
FILOLOGIA MODERNA. 1978. a. L.65000 (effective 1994). Pacini Editore s.r.l., Via A. Gherardesca 1, 56014 Ospedaletto (Pisa), Italy. TEL 050-982439. FAX 050-983906. Ed.Bd. **Indexed:** Bibl.Ling.

491.85   **PL**   **ISSN 0554-8179**
FILOLOGIA POLSKA. (Text in Polish; summaries in English) 1961. irreg., vol.56, 1994. prices varies. (Adam Mickiewicz University) Adam Mickiewicz University Press, Nowowiejskigo 55, 61-734 Poznan, Poland. TEL 527-380. TELEX 413260 UAM PL. Ed.Bd. circ. 600. **Indexed:** Bibl.Ling. **Document type:** academic/scholarly publication.
—BLDSC (9120.456000).

400   **HU**   **ISSN 0015-1785**
FILOLOGIAI KOZLONY/PHILOLOGICAL REVIEW. 1955. q. 400 Ft. (Magyar Tudomanyos Akademia) Akademiai Kiado, Publishing House of the Hungarian Academy of Sciences, P.O. Box 245, H-1519 Budapest, Hungary. TEL 181-2134. FAX 166-6466. TELEX 22-6228 AKNYO H. Ed. M. Horanyi. adv.; bk.rev.; illus.; index. **Indexed:** M.L.A.

400   **RU**   **ISSN 0028-1212**
FILOLOGICHESKIE NAUKI. 1958. bi-m. $15. Izdatel'stvo Vysshaya Shkola, Prospekt Marksa 18, 103009 Moscow K-9, Russia. (Co-sponsor: Ministerstvo Vysshego i Spetsial'nogo Obrazovaniya) index. circ. 1,915. **Indexed:** Lang.& Lang.Behav.Abstr., M.L.A.

400   **CK**   **ISSN 0071-4976**
FILOLOGOS COLOMBIANOS. 1954. irreg., no.9, 1979. price varies. Instituto Caro y Cuervo, Seccion de Publicaciones, Apdo. Aereo 51502, Bogota, Colombia.

491   **XN**   **ISSN 0352-3055**
FILOLOSKI FAKULTET. KATEDRA ZA ISTOCNOSLOVENSKI I ZAPADNOSLOVENSKI JAZICI I KNIZEUNOSTI. SLAVISTICKI STUDII. (Text in all Slavic languages; summaries in English) 1976. biennial. 100 din. Filoloski Fakultet, Katedra za Istocnoslovenski i Zapadnoslovenski Jazici i Knizeunosti, 91000 Skopje, Macedonia. Eds. Boris Markov, Milan Gjurchinov. bk.rev. circ. 300.

410 800   **CI**   **ISSN 0350-3623**
DR1202   CODEN: RFFZEM
FILOZOFSKI FAKULTET - ZADAR. RAZDIO FILOLOSKIH ZNANOSTI. RADOVI. (Text in Croatian, English, French, German, Italian) 1960. a. $20. Filozofski Fakultet u Zadru, Obala Marsala Tita, 2, 57000 Zadar, Croatia. TEL 057-436-623. TELEX 25-882. (Co-sponsor: Samoupravna Interesna Zajednica Znanosti SR Hrvatske) Ed. Vjekoslav Cosic. index, cum.index: nos.1-15. circ. 800. (back issues avail.)

494 305.8   **FI**   **ISSN 0355-1253**
PH1
FINNISCH-UGRISCHE FORSCHUNGEN; Zeitschrift fuer Finnisch-Ugrische Sprach- und Volkskunde. (Text in English, French and German) 1902. irreg. FIM 140 per no. Suomalais-Ugrilainen Seura, PL 320, 00171 Helsinki 17, Finland. (Dist. by: Tiedekirja, Kirkkokatu 14, 00170 Helsinki, Finland) bk.rev.; index. circ. 350. (back issues avail.) **Indexed:** Bibl.Ling., M.L.A. **Document type:** academic/scholarly publication.

494 894   **GW**   **ISSN 0341-7816**
PH1
FINNISCH-UGRISCHE MITTEILUNGEN. (Text in English, French, German) 1977. a. price varies. Helmut Buske Verlag GmbH, Richardstr. 47, 22081 Hamburg, Germany. TEL 040-296842. FAX 040-2993614. Eds. Istvan Futaky, Wolfgang Veenker. index. circ. 400. **Indexed:** Bibl.Ling., Lang.& Lang.Behav.Abstr. **Document type:** academic/scholarly publication.

410   **UK**   **ISSN 0142-7237**
FIRST LANGUAGE. 1980. 3/yr. £46 (U.S. & Japan $99; elsewhere £49). Alpha Academic (Subsidiary of: Richard Sadler Ltd.), Halfpenny Furze, Mill Ln., Chalfont St. Giles, Bucks. HP8 4NR, England. TEL 0494-872509. Ed. Kevin Durkin. adv.; bk.rev.; index. (back issues avail.) **Indexed:** Bibl.Ling., Child Devel.Abstr., Lang.& Lang.Behav.Abstr. (1983-), Lang.Teach.& Ling.Abstr., Mult.Ed.Abstr., Psychol.Abstr., Sp.Ed.Needs Abstr., SSCI. **Document type:** academic/scholarly publication.
—BLDSC (3934.465000); Faxon; UnCover; SWETS. CCC.
    Description: Contains empirical, theoretical, and review papers on all areas of child language development.

420 375.4   **NE**   **ISSN 0925-0700**
FLYER. 1973. 5/yr. WoltersgroepGroningen b.v., Postbus 58, 9700 MB Groningen, Netherlands. TEL 31-50-226922. FAX 31-50-264866.
    Formerly (until 1989): Quads (ISSN 0165-0696)

FOCUS: TEACHING ENGLISH LANGUAGE ARTS. see *EDUCATION — Teaching Methods And Curriculum*

FODOR'S THREE-IN-ONE: FRANCE; guidebook, language cassette and phrase book. see *TRAVEL AND TOURISM*

FODOR'S THREE-IN-ONE: GERMANY; guidebook, language cassette and phrase book. see *TRAVEL AND TOURISM*

FODOR'S THREE-IN-ONE: ITALY; guidebook, language cassette and phrase book. see *TRAVEL AND TOURISM*

FODOR'S THREE-IN-ONE: MEXICO; guidebook, language cassette and phrase book. see *TRAVEL AND TOURISM*

FODOR'S THREE-IN-ONE: SPAIN; guidebook, language cassette and phrase book. see *TRAVEL AND TOURISM*

400   GW   ISSN 0165-4004
FOLIA LINGUISTICA; acta societatis linguisticae Europaeae. (Supplement: Folia Linguistica Historica (ISSN 0168-647X)) 1957. 4/yr. DM.256. (European Society of Linguistics) Walter de Gruyter und Co., Mouton de Gruyter, Genthiner Str. 13, 10785 Berlin, Germany. TEL 030-260050. FAX 030-62005251. Ed. Wolfgang Dressler. circ. 1,500. **Indexed:** Amer.Bibl.Slavic & E.Eur.Stud., Amer.Hist.& Life, Bibl.Ling., Hist.Abstr., Lang.& Lang.Behav.Abstr. (1971-), Lang.Teach.& Ling.Abstr., M.L.A., Mid.East: Abstr.& Ind. **Document type:** academic/scholarly publication.
—BLDSC (3971.200000); Faxon; UnCover; SWETS. **CCC.**
   Description: Treats the scientific study of language in all its aspects.

499.92   SP   ISSN 0046-435X
PH5001
FONTES LINGUAE VASCONUM; studia et documenta. 1969. 3/yr. 2700 ptas. Gobierno de Navarra, Fondo de Publicaciones, Navas de Tolosa, 21, 31002 Pamplona, Spain. TEL 10-71-21. FAX 22-76-73. bk.rev.; bibl.; charts; cum.index: 1969-1985. **Indexed:** Bibl.Ling.

407 370   US   ISSN 0015-718X
PB1
FOREIGN LANGUAGE ANNALS. 1967. q. $60 (foreign $70). American Council on the Teaching of Foreign Languages, Inc., 6 Executive Plaza, Yonkers, NY 10701-6801. TEL 914-963-8830. FAX 914-963-1275. Ed. Frank Grittner. abstr.; charts; index. circ. 7,000. (also avail. in microform from MIM,UMI; reprint service avail. from KTO) **Indexed:** C.I.J.E., Ccnt.Pg.Educ., Curr.Cont., Educ.Ind., Lang.& Lang.Behav.Abstr., Lang.Teach.& Ling.Abstr., Mid.East: Abstr.& Ind., Mult.Ed.Abstr., SSCI. **Document type:** academic/scholarly publication.
—BLDSC (3987.038000); Faxon; UnCover; SWETS; UMI.
   Incorporates (after 1975, vol.5, no.4): Accent on A C T F L.
   Description: Presents study and teaching methods.

FORENSIC LINGUISTICS: THE INTERNATIONAL JOURNAL OF LANGUAGE AND THE LAW. see *LAW*

400   CK   ISSN 0120-338X
P9   CODEN: FOFUE6
FORMA Y FUNCION. 1981. s-a. Universidad Nacional de Colombia, Facultad de Ciencias Humanas, Departamento de Filologia e Idiomas, Ciudad Universitaria, Bogota, Colombia. **Indexed:** Lang.& Lang.Behav.Abstr. (1988-).

410   NE   ISSN 0071-7592
FORMAL LINGUISTICS SERIES. 1970. irreg. price varies. Kluwer Academic Publishers, Postbus 17, 3300 AA Dordrecht, Netherlands. TEL 31-78-334911. FAX 31-78-334254. TELEX 29245 KAPG NL. (Dist. by: Kluwer Academic Publishers Group, P.O. Box 322, 3300 AH Dordrecht, Netherlands. TEL 31-78-524400; N. America dist. addr.: Box 358, Accord Sta., Hingham, MA 02018-0358. TEL 617-871-6600) Eds. Henry Hiz, Henry M. Hoenigswald, and Zellig S. Harris. **Document type:** monographic series.
   Refereed Serial

400   IT   ISSN 1121-2276
LE FORME E LA STORIA; rivista di filologia moderna. 1989. s-a. L.80000. Rubbettino Editore, Viale dei Pini, 88049 Soveria Mannelli, Italy. Eds. Nicolo Mineo, Sergio Romangnoli. circ. 1,000. (back issues avail.)

FORUM (WASHINGTON, 1978). see *EDUCATION — Teaching Methods And Curriculum*

420 375.4   US
FORUM (WASHINGTON, 1980). 1963-1978; resumed 1980? q. $14. U.S. Information Agency, 301 4th St., S.W., Washington, DC 20547. TEL 202-619-4196. FAX 202-619-4173. (Orders to: Supt. of Documents, U.S. Government Printing Office, Washington, DC 20402. TEL 202-783-3238. FAX 202-512-2233) Ed. Anne C. Newton. illus.; index. circ. 110,000. **Indexed:** Cont.Pg.Educ., Ind.U.S.Gov.Per., Lang.Teach.& Ling.Abstr. **Document type:** government publication.
   Formerly: English Teaching Forum.

FORUM DER LETTEREN; tijdschrift voor taal- en letterkunde. see *LITERATURE*

430 375.4   CN   ISSN 0843-929X
FORUM DEUTSCH. (Text in English, French, German) 1989. s-a. Canadian Council of Teachers of German, University of Calgary, Germanic, Slavic & East Asian Studies, Calgary, AB T2N 1N4, Canada. TEL 403-220-3990. FAX 403-284-3810. Ed. Juergen Jahn. adv.; bk.rev. circ. 1,500.

400 800   UK   ISSN 0015-8518
PB1   CODEN: FMLSEG
FORUM FOR MODERN LANGUAGE STUDIES. 1965. q. £54($104) (effective 1994). (University of St. Andrews) Oxford University Press, Oxford Journals, Walton St., Oxford OX2 6DP, England. TEL 0865-56767. FAX 0865-56646. TELEX 837330-OXPRES-G. (U.S. subscr. to: Oxford University Press Inc., 2001 Evans Rd., Cary, NC 27513. TEL 919-677-0977) Ed.Bd. adv. contact: Jane Parker. bk.rev.; index. circ. 650. (back issues avail.) **Indexed:** Arts & Hum.Cit.Ind., Bibl.Ling., Can.Rev.Comp.Lit., Curr.Cont., M.L.A., Mid.East: Abstr.& Ind. **Document type:** academic/scholarly publication.
—BLDSC (4024.093000); Faxon; UnCover; SWETS; UMI. **CCC.**
   Description: Studies in the field of European language and literature, including English and American, from the Middle Ages to the present.

410   GW
FORUM FUER FACHSPRACHEN-FORSCHUNG. irreg., no.24, 1994. DM.96. Gunter Narr Verlag, Postfach 2567, 72015 Tuebingen, Germany. TEL 07071-78091. FAX 07071-75288. Ed. Hartwig Kalverkaemper. **Document type:** monographic series.

410   US   ISSN 0163-0768
FORUM LINGUISTICUM. (Supplement avail.: Edward Sapir Monograph Series in Language, Culture, and Cognition) 1976. 3/yr. $20 to individuals; students $16; institutions $30. (Linguistic Association of Canada and the United States) Jupiter Press, Box 101, Lake Bluff, IL 60044. TEL 312-234-3997. Ed. Adam Makkai. adv.; bk.rev. circ. 1,000. (back issues avail.) **Indexed:** Bibl.Ling., Lang.Teach.& Ling.Abstr., M.L.A.

410   GW   ISSN 0170-8171
FORUM LINGUISTICUM. (Text in English and German; summaries in English) 1974. irreg., no.33, 1991. price varies. Peter Lang GmbH Europaeischer Verlag der Wissenschaften, Eschborner Landstr. 42-50, 60489 Frankfurt a.M., Germany. TEL 069-7807050. FAX 069-785893. Ed. Christoph Gutknecht. bk.rev.; abstr.; bibl. (back issues avail.) **Indexed:** Bibl.Ling., M.L.A. **Document type:** monographic series.

401   US   ISSN 0168-2555
FOUNDATIONS OF SEMIOTICS. Abbreviated title: F O S. (Text in English, French, German; summaries in English, French) 1983. irreg., vol.25, 1990. price varies. John Benjamins Publishing Co., 821 Bethlehem Pike, Philadelphia, PA 19118. TEL 215-836-1200. FAX 215-836-1204. (And: Amsteldijk 44, P.O. Box 75577, 1070 AN Amsterdam, Netherlands. TEL 020-6762325) Ed. Achim Eschbach. **Indexed:** Bibl.Ling. **Document type:** monographic series.
   Description: Provides fundamental research in semiotics with contributions to the theory of signs.

400 800   SL
FOURAH BAY STUDIES IN LANGUAGE AND LITERATURE. (Text in English) 1980. a. L.30. University of Sierra Leone, Fourah Bay College, Freetown, Sierra Leone. Ed.Bd. circ. 150.

440 370   NR   ISSN 0015-9387
FRANCAIS AU NIGERIA. (Text in English and French) 1965. q. £N3. Nigerian Association of French Teachers, c/o A. Iwara, Ed., Department of Modern Languages, University of Ibadan, Ibadan, Nigeria. adv.; bk.rev.; cum.index every 2 yrs. circ. 500. (back issues avail) **Indexed:** M.L.A.
   Description: Presents language study and teaching methods.

440   FR   ISSN 0015-9409
PC2002   CODEN: FRMOEA
FRANCAIS MODERNE; revue de linguistique francaise. 1933. q. 250 F. Conseil International de la Langue Francaise, 11 rue de Navarin, 75009 Paris, France. TEL 48-78-73-95. FAX 48-78-49-28. adv.; bk.rev.; abstr.; bibl.; index. **Indexed:** Arts & Hum.Cit.Ind., Bibl.Ling., Curr.Cont., Ind.Bk.Rev.Hum., Lang.& Lang.Behav.Abstr., Lang.Teach.& Ling.Abstr., M.L.A.
—BLDSC (4032.155000); SWETS.

440 375.4 840   US
FRANCITE. (Text in French) 1973. s-a. $2 per copy. c/o Anne-Marie de Moret, Ed., 221 Northgrand St., St. Louis, MO 63103. bk.rev.; bibl. circ. 750.
   Description: Contains articles about French language and literature.

FRANCOFONIA; studi e ricerche sulle letterature di lingua francese. see *LITERATURE*

440 375.4   UK   ISSN 0957-1744
FRANCOPHONIE. 1990. s-a. £20($40) (overseas £21). Association for Language Learning, 16 Regent Pl., Rugby, Warks. CV21 2PN, England. TEL 44-788-546443. FAX 44-788-544149. Ed. Alan Smalley. adv.; bk.rev.; film rev.; play rev.; abstr.; bibl.; charts; illus.; stat.; index. circ. 5,500. **Document type:** academic/scholarly publication.
—BLDSC (4032.791950).
   Description: Contains articles and information of interest to teachers and students of French.

491.7   GW   ISSN 0473-5277
FRANKFURTER ABHANDLUNGEN ZUR SLAVISTIK. irreg., vol.28, 1979. price varies. Wilhelm Schmitz Verlag, Staufenbergerweg 22, 35457 Lollar, Germany. TEL 06406-2324. Ed. G. Langer. **Document type:** monographic series.

FRANKFURTER BEITRAEGE ZUR GERMANISTIK. see *LITERATURE*

FRANZOESISCH HEUTE; Informationsblaetter fuer Franzoesischlehrer in Schule und Hochschule. see *EDUCATION — Teaching Methods And Curriculum*

491.8 914.96   GW   ISSN 0170-1533
FREIE UNIVERSITAET BERLIN. OSTEUROPA-INSTITUT. BALKANOLOGISCHE VEROEFFENTLICHUNGEN. 1979. irreg., vol.21, 1993. price varies. (Freie Universitaet Berlin, Osteuropa-Institut) Harrassowitz Verlag, Taunusstr. 14, 65183 Wiesbaden, Germany. TEL 0611-530-0. FAX 0611-530570. TELEX 4186135. (Subscr. to: Postfach 2929, 65019 Wiesbaden, Germany) Ed. Norbert Reiter. **Document type:** monographic series.

FREIE UNIVERSITAET BERLIN. OSTEUROPA-INSTITUT. SLAVISTISCHE VEROEFFENTLICHUNGEN. see *LITERATURE*

400   GW   ISSN 0016-0970
FREMDSPRACHEN; Zeitschrift fuer Theorie und Praxis der Sprachmittlung. (Text in English, French, German, Russian and Spanish) 1957. 4/yr. DM.48. Verlag Alexandre Hatier GmbH, Oranienburgerstr. 13-14, 1020 Berlin, Germany. Ed.Bd. adv.; bk.rev. circ. 5,000. **Indexed:** Lang.& Lang.Behav.Abstr., M.L.A.
   Description: Devoted to the translation of German into Russian, English, French, and Spanish.

407   GW   ISSN 0932-6936
FREMDSPRACHEN LEHREN UND LERNEN. 1971. a. DM.58 to individuals; institutions DM.78. Gunter Narr Verlag, Postfach 2567, 72015 Tuebingen, Germany. TEL 07071-78091. FAX 07071-78091. **Document type:** academic/scholarly publication.
—BLDSC (4033.682000).

370 GW
FREMDSPRACHENUNTERRICHT. 1957. 6/yr. DM.54. Paedagogischer Zeitschriftenverlag, Postfach 269, 10107 Berlin, Germany. TEL 030-20343431. FAX 030-20343432. Indexed: Lang.Teach.& Ling.Abstr. **Document type:** academic/scholarly publication.

407 371 GW ISSN 0340-2207
PB35
DER FREMDSPRACHLICHE UNTERRICHT; textarbeit, landeskunde, sprachpraxis und methodenfragen. (Editions in English and French) 1967. 4/yr. DM.75.10. Erhard Friedrich Verlag GmbH, Im Brande 17, 30926 Seelze, Germany. TEL 0511-40004-0. (Subscr. to: Postfach 100150, 30917 Seelze, Germany) cum.index: 1967-1981. circ. 5,600. Indexed: Lang.Teach.& Ling.Abstr. **Document type:** academic/scholarly publication.
—CCC.

FRENCH FORUM. see *LITERARY AND POLITICAL REVIEWS*

440.07 370 US ISSN 0016-111X
PC2001
FRENCH REVIEW. (Text in English, French) 1927. 6/yr. $35 (foreign $38). American Association of Teachers of French, 57 E. Armory Ave., Champaign, IL 61820. TEL 217-333-2842. Ed. Ronald Tobin. adv.; bk.rev.; index. circ. 15,500. (also avail. in microform from JAI,UMI,PMC; back issues avail.; reprint service avail. from UMI,SCH) Indexed: Arts & Hum.Cit.Ind., Bibl.Ling., Bk.Rev.Ind. (1975-), C.I.J.E., Child.Bk.Rev.Ind. (1975-), Educ.Ind., Ind.Bk.Rev.Hum., Lang.& Lang.Behav.Abstr., Lang.Teach.& Ling.Abstr., M.L.A. **Document type:** academic/scholarly publication.
—BLDSC (4034.450000); Faxon; UnCover; SWETS; UMI.
Description: Contains articles and reviews on francophone culture, including literature, language, linguistics, film and software.

439.2 NE
FRYSKE NAMMEN. (Text in Frisian) 1978. irreg. Fryske Akademy, Doelestrjitte 8, 8911 DX Ljouwert-Leeuwarden, Netherlands. TEL 31-58-131414. FAX 31-58-131409. Ed.Bd.

FU JEN STUDIES; literature & linguistics. see *LITERATURE*

420 375.4 CC
FUJIAN WAIYU/FOREIGN LANGUAGES IN FUJIAN. (Text in Chinese) 1984. q. Y4. Fujian Normal University, School of Foreign Languages, Fuzhou, Fujian 350007, People's Republic of China. FAX 591-542840. TELEX 92269 FTUFO CN. (Dist. overseas by: Jiangsu Publications Import & Export Corp., 56 Gao Yun Ling, Nanjing, Jiangsu, P.R.C.) Ed. Xu Chongxin. bk.rev. **Document type:** academic/scholarly publication.
Description: Discusses issues in the teaching of foreign languages, with a focus on English. Also covers Russian, Japanese and other foreign languages.

410 US
FUNCTIONAL GRAMMAR SERIES.* (Text in English) 1985. irreg., no.13, 1990. Walter de Gruyter, Inc., 200 Saw Mill River Rd., Hawthorne, NY 10532. TEL 914-747-0110. FAX 914-747-1326. Ed.Bd. Indexed: Bibl.Ling. **Document type:** monographic series.

401 NE
▼**FUNCTIONS OF LANGUAGE.** (Text in English) 1994. 2/yr. fl.75($45) to individuals; institutions fl.140($85) (effective 1994). John Benjamins Publishing Co., Amsteldijk 44, P.O. Box 75577, 1070 AN Amsterdam, Netherlands. TEL 31-20-6738156. FAX 31-20-6792956. (In N. America: 821 Bethlehem Pike, Philadelphia, PA 19118. TEL 215-836-1200. FAX 215-836-1204) Ed.Bd. **Document type:** academic/scholarly publication.
Description: Discusses language-as-system and texts-in-context from a functional perspective, including theoretical issues, linguistic description, and applied research.

410 GW ISSN 0175-2103
G A L - BULLETIN. (Text in English and German) 1983. s-a. DM.10($6) Gesellschaft fuer Angewandte Linguistik e.V., Universitaet Duisburg, 47048 Duisburg, Germany. TEL 0203-379-2064. TELEX 855793-UNI-DU-D. Ed. Bernd Spillner. adv.; bk.rev.; bibl. circ. 1,500. **Document type:** bulletin.

499.992 370.196 GW ISSN 0942-0576
G E J - GAZETO. (Text in Esperanto and German) 1979. bi-m. DM.20. Deutsche Esperanto-Jugend, Rheinweg 15, 53111 Bonn, Germany. TEL 0228-235898. FAX 0228-232764. Ed. Ulrich Goertz. adv. circ. 2,000.
Description: Information on Esperanto meetings and international youth activities.

410 DK ISSN 0106-0872
PF3025
G I P. (Germansk Instituts Publikationer) 1977. irreg., no.58, 1992. free. Odense Universitet, Center for Tyske Studier, Campusvej 55, DK-5230 Odense M, Denmark. TEL 45-66-15-86-00. FAX 66-15-84-28. Eds. Flemming Talbo Stubkjaer, Helge Nielsen. circ. 200.
Description: Presents the teaching and research activity at the institute.

491.6 375.4 UK
GAELIC SOCIETY OF INVERNESS. TRANSACTIONS. (Text in English, Gaelic) 1872. biennial. Gaelic Society of Inverness, The Granary, Ness-side, Dores Rd., Inverness, Scotland. TEL 0463-236440. circ. 500. Indexed: Bibl.Ling. **Document type:** proceedings.

410 SP ISSN 0213-4403
GAVAGAI. 1985. s-a. $30 to individuals; libraries and institutions $35. Universidad de La Laguna, Asociacion Canaria de Filosofia del Lenguaje y de la Ciencia, Secretariado de Publicaciones, San Agustin, 30, 38201 La Laguna-Tenerife, Islas Canarias, Spain. TEL 922-25-81-27. adv.
Description: Devoted to the philosophy of language and science.

410 PL ISSN 0860-3456
PG6004
GDANSKIE STUDIA JEZYKOZNAWCZE. 1975. irreg., vol.3, 1983. price varies. (Gdansk Scientific Society) Ossolineum, Publishing House of the Polish Academy of Sciences, Rynek 9, 50-106 Wroclaw, Poland. TEL 48-71386-25. FAX 71-48-448-103. TELEX 0712771 OSS PL. Ed. Boguslaw Kreja. Indexed: Bibl.Ling. **Document type:** academic/scholarly publication.
Description: Linguistic studies by authors from the region of Gdansk Pomerania.

423.1 UK ISSN 0072-0542
GEIRIADUR PRIFYSGOL CYMRU. (Text in English and Welsh) 1953. a. £3 per part. (Board of Celtic Studies) University of Wales Press, 6 Gwennyth St., Cathays, Cardiff CF2 4YD, Wales. TEL 0222-31919. FAX 0222-230908. Ed. G. A. Bevan. circ. 1,500. **Document type:** academic/scholarly publication.
Description: Dictionary of the Welsh language.

400 300 US ISSN 0016-6553
GENERAL LINGUISTICS. 1955. q. $22 to individuals (foreign $28); institutions $38 (foreign $45). Medieval & Renaissance Texts and Studies, LNG 99, SUNY - Binghamton, Binghamton, NY 13902-6000. TEL 607-777-6758. Ed.Bd. adv.; bk.rev.; bibl. circ. 800. (tabloid format; also avail. in microform from UMI; back issues avail.; reprint service avail. from UMI) Indexed: Abstr.Anthropol., Amer.Bibl.Slavic & E.Eur.Stud., Arts & Hum.Cit.Ind., Bibl.Ling., Curr.Cont., Ind.Bk.Rev.Hum., Lang.& Lang.Behav.Abstr. (1972-), Lang.Teach.& Ling.Abstr., M.L.A., Mid.East: Abstr.& Ind., SSCI. **Document type:** academic/scholarly publication.
—Faxon; UnCover; SWETS.

412 US ISSN 0072-0771
B820
GENERAL SEMANTICS BULLETIN. 1950. a. $15. Institute of General Semantics, 163 Engle St., Englewood, NJ 07631. TEL 201-568-0551. Ed. Stuart Mayper. adv.; bk.rev.; cum.index: vols.1-37. circ. 600. (also avail. in microform from UMI; reprint service avail. from UMI) Indexed: Lang.& Lang.Behav.Abstr., Sociol.Abstr.
—BLDSC (4111.200000); UnCover.

GENGO TO KYOIKU NO KENKYU. see *EDUCATION — Teaching Methods And Curriculum*

GENRE (NORMAN); forms of discourse and culture. see *LITERATURE*

400 US ISSN 1048-4205
GEORGETOWN JOURNAL OF LANGUAGE AND LINGUISTICS. 1990. q. $15. Georgetown University, School of Languages and Linguistics, Washington, DC 20057. (Orders to: Georgetown University Press, Box 4866, Hampden Sta., baltimore, MD 21211-4866. TEL 410-516-6995. FAX 410-516-6998) Ed. Helen Karn. **Document type:** academic/scholarly publication.
—BLDSC (4158.269800); Faxon; UnCover.

400 US ISSN 0196-7207
P53
GEORGETOWN UNIVERSITY ROUND TABLE ON LANGUAGES AND LINGUISTICS. 1951. a. price varies. Georgetown University, School of Languages and Linguistics, Washington, DC 20007. TEL 202-687-6063. FAX 202-687-6340. (Orders to: Georgetown University Press, Box 4866, Hampden Sta., Baltimore, MD 21211-4866. TEL 410-516-6995. FAX 410-516-6998) circ. 2,000. Indexed: Bibl.Ling., Lang.& Lang.Behav.Abstr. (1972-), M.L.A. **Document type:** proceedings.
—UnCover.
Former titles: Georgetown University. Institute of Languages and Linguistics. Report of the Annual Round Table Meeting on Linguistics and Language Studies (ISSN 0072-1212); Monograph Series on Languages and Linguistics (ISSN 0077-0612)
Description: Provides a forum for internationally known scholars to focus on different aspects of linguistics and language teaching.

GERMAN MONITOR. see *LITERARY AND POLITICAL REVIEWS*

430.07 370 US ISSN 0016-8831
PF3001
GERMAN QUARTERLY. (Text in English and German) 1928. 4/yr. $45 (foreign $55). American Association of Teachers of German, Inc., 112 Haddontowne Ct., Ste. 104, Cherry Hill, NJ 08034. TEL 609-795-5553. FAX 609-795-9398. Ed. Reinhold Grimm. adv.; bk.rev.; index. circ. 5,000. (also avail. in microform from UMI,PMC; reprint service avail. from UMI) Indexed: Amer.Bibl.Slavic & E.Eur.Stud., Arts & Hum.Cit.Ind., Bk.Rev.Ind. (1975-), Child.Bk.Rev.Ind. (1975-), Curr.Cont., Educ.Ind., Ind.Bk.Rev.Hum., Lang.& Lang.Behav.Abstr., Lang.Teach.& Ling.Abstr., M.L.A. **Document type:** academic/scholarly publication.
—BLDSC (4162.151000); Faxon; UnCover; SWETS; UMI.
Description: Presents literary and philological articles.

GERMAN STUDIES LIBRARY GROUP NEWSLETTER. see *LIBRARY AND INFORMATION SCIENCES*

430 375 UK ISSN 0953-4822
GERMAN TEACHING. (Text in English and German) 1969. s-a. £20($40) in the UK; elsewhere £21. Association for Language Learning, 16 Regent Pl., Rugby, Warks. CV21 2PN, England. TEL 44-788-546443. FAX 44-788-544149. Ed. Allan Jones. adv.; bk.rev.; abstr.; bibl.; charts; film rev.; illus.; mkt.; play rev.; record rev.; stat.; index. circ. 3,500. Indexed: Cont.Pg.Educ., Lang.Teach.& Ling.Abstr. **Document type:** academic/scholarly publication.
Formerly: Treffpunkt.
Description: Contains articles and information of interest to teachers and students of German.

430 375.4 US
PD1
GERMANIC NOTES AND REVIEWS. (Text in English, German) 1970. q. $10 (effective 1992). Department of Modern and Classical Languages, Bemidji State University, Bemidji, MN 56601. TEL 218-751-6265. Ed. Richard F. Krummel. adv.; bk.rev.; abstr.; bibl. circ. 500. (also avail. in microform from GMC; reprint servie avail. from GMC; back issues avail.) Indexed: Arts & Hum.Cit.Ind., Curr.Cont., M.L.A. **Document type:** academic/scholarly publication.
—Faxon.
Formerly (until vol.23, Jan. 1992): Germanic Notes (ISSN 0016-8882)

430 US ISSN 0016-8890
PD1
GERMANIC REVIEW; devoted to studies dealing with the Germanic languages and literatures. 1926. q. $32 to individuals; institutions $64. (Helen Dwight Reid Educational Foundation) Heldref Publications, 1319 Eighteenth St., N.W., Washington, DC 20036-1802. TEL 202-296-6267. FAX 202-296-5149. Ed. Heidi Whitesell. adv. contact: Raymond Rallo. bk.rev.; bibl.; index. circ. 1,000. (also avail. in microform from PMC; reprint service avail. from KTO) **Indexed:** Acad.Ind., Amer.Bibl.Slavic & E.Eur.Stud, Arts & Hum.Cit.Ind., Can.Rev.Comp.Lit., Curr.Cont., Hum.Ind., Int.Z.Bibelwiss, Lang.& Lang.Behav.Abstr., M.L.A. **Document type:** academic/scholarly publication.
—Faxon; UnCover; SWETS; UMI. **CCC**.
Refereed Serial

053.1 GW ISSN 0524-8418
GERMANISTIK (BERLIN). (Text in English, French, German) 1959. s-a. DM.18.60. Buchwerbung in Berlin GmbH, Luetzowstr. 105-106, 10785 Berlin, Germany. circ. 4,000. **Document type:** academic/scholarly publication.

430 GW ISSN 0072-1492
PF3025
GERMANISTISCHE LINGUISTIK. 1969. irreg.(4-6 /yr.). price varies. (Forschunginstitut fuer Deutsche Sprache, Marburg) Georg Olms Verlag, Hagentorwall 7, 31134 Hildesheim, Germany. FAX 05121-32007. TELEX 927454-OLMS-D. (Dist. in U.S. by: Hy Cohen, Literary Agency Ltd., 111 West 57 St., New York, NY 10019) Ed.Bd. adv.; bk.rev.; index. circ. 700. **Indexed:** Bibl.Ling., Lang.Teach.& Ling.Abstr. **Document type:** academic/scholarly publication.
—Faxon. **CCC**.

430 375.4 BE ISSN 0344-5909
GERMANISTISCHE MITTEILUNGEN; Zeitschrift fuer deutsche Sprache, Literatur und Kultur in Wissenschaft und Praxis. 1975. s-a. DM.27. Belgischer Germanisten- und Deutschlehrerverband, Vrijheidslaan 17, B-1000 Brussels, Belgium. FAX 32-2-4124200. (Subscr. to: F. Duemmler Verlag, Postfach 1480, D-5200 Bonn, Germany) Eds. Peter Nelde, Rudolf Kern. adv.; bk.rev.; illus.; index. circ. 1,200. (back issues avail.) **Indexed:** Lang.& Lang.Behav.Abstr., M.L.A. **Document type:** academic/scholarly publication.

430 GW
GERMANISTISCHE TEXTE UND STUDIEN. irreg., vol.43, 1994. DM.39.80. Georg Olms Verlag, Hagentorwall 7, 31134 Hildesheim, Germany. TEL 05121-1501-0. FAX 05121-150150. (U.S. subscr. to: 111 W. 57th St., New York, NY 10019. TEL 212-757-5237) **Document type:** monographic series.

410 GW
GIESSENER BEITRAEGE ZUR FREMDSPRACHENDIDAKTIK. a. DM.78. Gunter Narr Verlag, Postfach 2567, 72015 Tuebingen, Germany. TEL 07071-78091. FAX 07071-75288. Ed. Jean Antoine Caravolas. **Document type:** academic/scholarly publication.

450 100 IT ISSN 0017-0461
GIORNALE ITALIANO DI FILOLOGIA; rivista di cultura. 1948. s-a. L.86000. Herder Editrice e Libreria s.r.l., Piazza Montecitorio 120, 00186 Rome, Italy. TEL 67-94-628. FAX 678-47-51. TELEX 621427 NATEL. Ed. N. Scivoletto. bk.rev.; abstr.; index. circ. 800. (back issues avail.) **Indexed:** Bibl.Ling., M.L.A. **Document type:** academic/scholarly publication.

410 AA
GJUHA JONE. 3/yr. Akademia e Shkencave e RPSSH, Instituti i Gjuhesise dhe i Letersise, Tirana, Albania. Ed. Ali Dhiro. **Indexed:** Bibl.Ling.

GLOS NAUCZYCIELA; kwartalnik. see *EDUCATION*

418 PL ISSN 0072-4769
GLOTTODIDACTICA; an international journal of applied liguistics. (Text in English, French, German, and Russian) 1966. irreg., vol.22, 1994. price varies. Adam Mickiewicz University Press, Nowowiejskiego 55, 61-734 Poznan, Poland. TEL 527-380. FAX 61-526425. TELEX 413260 UAMPL. Ed. Waldemar Pfeiffer. bk.rev. circ. 1,500. **Indexed:** Bibl.Ling., Lang.& Lang.Behav.Abstr. (1972-), Lang.Teach.& Ling.Abstr., M.L.A. **Document type:** academic/scholarly publication.
—BLDSC (4195.860000).
Description: Contains current research results done by university students and professors of English, German, French, Russian and other languages, with emphasis on theoretical issues in the field of applied linguistics related to language learning and language teaching.

430 830 SW ISSN 0072-4793
GOETEBORGER GERMANISTISCHE FORSCHUNGEN. (Subseries of Acta Universitatis Gothoburgensis) (Text in German) 1955. irreg., no.32, 1991. price varies; also exchange basis. Acta Universitatis Gothoburgensis, P.O. Box 5096, S-402 22 Goeteborg, Sweden. Ed. Sven-Gunnar Andersson. **Indexed:** Bibl.Ling. **Document type:** monographic series.

430 GW
GOETHE-INSTITUT ZUR PFLEGE DER DEUTSCHEN SPRACHE IM AUSLAND UND ZUR FOERDERUNG DER INTERNATIONALEN KULTURELLEN ZUSAMMENARBEIT. JAHRBUCH. 1965. a. DM.11. Goethe-Institut zur Pflege der Deutschen Sprache im Ausland und zur Foederung der Internationalen Kulturellen Zusammenarbeit, Helene-Weber-Allee 1, 80604 Munich, Germany. TEL 089-15921-0. FAX 089-15921450. Ed. Stephan Wackwitz. circ. 7,000. **Document type:** academic/scholarly publication.
Formerly: Goethe-Institut zur Pflege Deutscher Sprache und Kultur im Ausland. Jahrbuch (ISSN 0072-4858)

400 800 GW ISSN 0017-1549
GOETTINGISCHE GELEHRTE ANZEIGEN. 1739. s-a. DM.80. (Akademie der Wissenschaften, Goettingen) Vandenhoeck und Ruprecht, Robert-Bosch-Breite 6, 37079 Goettingen, Germany. TEL 0551-6959-26. FAX 0551-695917. (Subscr. to: 37070 Goettingen, Germany) Eds. U. Schindel, H. Boockmann. adv.; bk.rev.; index. circ. 600. **Document type:** academic/scholarly publication.
—**CCC**.

400 830 SW ISSN 0072-503X
GOTHENBURG STUDIES IN ENGLISH. (Subseries of Acta Universitatis Gothoburgensis) 1952. irreg., no.63, 1991. price varies; also exchange basis. Acta Universitatis Gothoburgensis, PO Box 5096, S-402 22 Goeteborg, Sweden. **Indexed:** M.L.A. **Document type:** monographic series.
—BLDSC (4203.170000).

410 NE ISSN 0927-3255
GRAMMA - T T T; tijdschrift voor taalwetenschap. 1981. 3/yr. fl.81 to individuals; institutions fl.122.60. I C G Publications, P.O. Box 509, 3300 AM Dordrecht, Netherlands. TEL 31-78-510454. FAX 31-78-510972. adv.; bk.rev. circ. 2,000. **Indexed:** Bibl.Ling. **Document type:** academic/scholarly publication.
—BLDSC (4208.429700). **CCC**.
Formerly (until 1992): T T T - Interdisciplinair Tijdschrift voor Taal en Tekstwetenschap (ISSN 0167-4773)
Description: Discusses linguistics, argumentation, phonetics, semantics, pragmatics, language philosophy and communication.

410 AU
GRAZER LINGUISTISCHE STUDIEN. (Text in English, French, German, Italian and Spanish) 1975. 2/yr. S.700. Universitaet Graz, Institut fuer Allgemeine und Angewandte Sprachwissenschaft, Mozartgasse 8, A-8010 Graz, Austria. FAX 0316-382130. Ed.Bd. adv.; bk.rev. circ. 200. **Indexed:** Bibl.Ling., Lang.& Lang.Behav.Abstr. (1983-), M.L.A. **Document type:** academic/scholarly publication.

GRIECHISCHEN CHRISTLICHEN SCHRIFTSTELLER DER ERSTEN JAHRHUNDERTE. see *RELIGIONS AND THEOLOGY*

GRIPLA. see *LITERATURE*

410 US
GRONINGEN - AMSTERDAM STUDIES IN SEMANTICS. * (Text in English) 1983. irreg., no.12, 1990. Walter de Gruyter, Inc., 200 Saw Mill River Rd., Hawthorne, NY 10532. TEL 914-747-0110. FAX 914-747-1326. Ed.Bd. **Indexed:** Bibl.Ling. **Description:** Contains monographs and collections on the semantics of natural languages.

492 FR
GROUPE LINGUISTIQUE D'ETUDES CHAMITO-SEMITIQUES. COMPTES RENDUS. (Suspended publication 1940-1945) 1934. irreg. (Groupe Linguistique d'Etudes Chamito-Semitiques) Librarie Orientaliste Paul Geuthner, 12 rue Vavin, 75006 Paris, France. TEL 33-1-46-34-71-30. FAX 33-1-43-29-75-64. TELEX 250 303 PUBLIC PARIS. **Indexed:** Bibl.Ling.

430 GW
GRUNDLAGEN DER GERMANISTIK. irreg., vol.31, 1991. Erich Schmidt Verlag GmbH & Co. (Bielefeld), Viktoriastr. 44a, 33602 Bielefeld, Germany. TEL 0521-583080. (Subscr. to: Postfach 102451, 33524 Bielefeld, Germany) Eds. Werner Besch, Hartmut Steinecke. (back issues avail.) **Indexed:** M.L.A. **Document type:** monographic series.

420 375.4 US
GUIDE TO GRANTS AND FELLOWSHIPS IN LINGUISTICS. 1982. triennial. $6.50. Linguistic Society of America, 1325 18th St., N.W., Ste. 211, Washington, DC 20036-6501. TEL 202-835-1714. **Document type:** directory.

410 GW ISSN 0344-242X
AS181
GULLIVER; German-English Yearbook. (Text in English, German; summaries in English) 1976. s-a. DM.38. Argument-Verlag GmbH, Rentzelstr. 1, 20146 Hamburg, Germany. TEL 040-456018. FAX 040-445189. (back issues avail.) **Document type:** academic/scholarly publication.

410 378 US
GUOWAI YUYANXUE. (Text in Chinese) q. $17. China Books & Periodicals, Inc., 2929 24th St., San Francisco, CA 94110. TEL 415-282-2994. FAX 415-282-0994.
Description: Covers the field of linguistics outside of China.

GYPSY LORE SOCIETY. NEWSLETTER. see *ANTHROPOLOGY*

480 GW ISSN 0072-9191
HABELTS DISSERTATIONSDRUCKE. REIHE KLASSISCHE PHILOLOGIE. 1953. irreg., no.39, 1992. price varies. Dr. Rudolf Habelt GmbH, Am Buchenhang 1, 53115 Bonn, Germany. TEL 0228-232016. FAX 0228-232017. Eds. W. Schetter, W. Schmid. **Document type:** monographic series.

491.7 GW ISSN 0072-9515
HAMBURGER BEITRAEGE FUER RUSSISCHLEHRER. 1964. irreg., no.39, 1992. price varies. Helmut Buske Verlag GmbH, Richardstr. 47, 22081 Hamburg, Germany. TEL 040-296842. FAX 040-2993614. Ed. Irene Nowikowa. **Document type:** monographic series.

HANDBUCH DER ORIENTALISTIK. 8. ABTEILUNG. HANDBOOK OF URALIC STUDIES. see *ORIENTAL STUDIES*

491.54 AU ISSN 0017-7377
HANDES AMSORYA; Zeitschrift fuer Armenische Philologie. (Text in Armenian; index in Armenian and German) 1887. a. $100. Mechitharisten-Congregation in Wien, Mechitharistengasse 4, A-1070 Vienna, Austria. TEL 01-5236417. FAX 01-5224565. Ed. P. Kodjanian. bk.rev.; charts. circ. 400. **Indexed:** Bibl.Ling., Numis.Lit. **Document type:** academic/scholarly publication.

LINGUISTICS

495.1 375.4   CC   ISSN 1003-7365
HANYU XUEXI/CHINESE LANGUAGE LEARNING. (Text in Chinese) 1980. bi-m. $7.02. Yanbian Daxue Chubanshe - Yanbian University Press, 105 Gongyuan St., Yanji, Jilin 133002, People's Republic of China. TEL 86-433-515921.
FAX 86-433-519618. (Dist. overseas by: China International Book Trading Corp., P.O. Box 399, Beijing, P.R. China. TEL 861-8413063) Ed. Liu Minzhang. adv.; bk.rev. **Document type:** academic/scholarly publication.
Description: Covers the achievements of scientific researches in linguistics and language teaching in China.

496   NR
HARSUNAN NIJERIYA. (Text in English and Hausa) 1971. a. $3. Bayero University, Kano, Centre for the Study of Nigerian Languages, P.M.B. 3011, Kano, Nigeria. Ed. Horahim Yaro Yahayh. circ. 500. (processed) **Indexed:** Bibl.Ling.

410 890 940   US
HARVARD CELTIC COLLOQUIUM. PROCEEDINGS. 1981. biennial. $18.50 to individuals; institutions $22.50 (clothbound $32.50). (Harvard University, Department of Celtic Languages and Literature) Pangur Publishers, Box 9183, Cambridge, MA 02139. TEL 617-868-8209. FAX 617-628-6173. Eds. Paul Jefferiss, William Mahon. circ. 250. **Indexed:** Bibl.Ling. **Document type:** proceedings, academic/scholarly publication.
Description: Highlights articles of scholarly and general interest on the literature, language, and history of the Celtic-speaking regions worldwide.

HARVARD ENGLISH STUDIES. see LITERATURE

492 220   US   ISSN 0073-0637
HARVARD SEMITIC MONOGRAPHS. 1968. irreg., no.6, 1973. price varies. Scholars Press, Box 15399, Atlanta, GA 30333-0399. TEL 404-727-2320. FAX 404-727-2348. **Document type:** monographic series.
Description: Publishes papers on Semitic language and civilization.

489   US   ISSN 0073-0688
PA25
HARVARD STUDIES IN CLASSICAL PHILOLOGY. 1890. a., latest vol.94, 1992. price varies. Harvard University, Department of the Classics, Boylston 320, Cambridge, MA 02138. TEL 617-495-4027. (reprint service avail. from SCH) **Indexed:** Bibl.Ling. **Document type:** academic/scholarly publication.
—BLDSC (4270.200000); UnCover; SWETS.
Refereed Serial

HARVARD - YENCHING INSTITUTE. MONOGRAPH SERIES. see HISTORY — History Of Asia

HAUTES ETUDES DU MONDE GRECO-ROMAIN. see CLASSICAL STUDIES

492 296   US   ISSN 0146-4094
PJ4501
HEBREW STUDIES; a journal devoted to Hebrew language and literature of all periods. vol.16, 1975. a. $25. National Association of Professors of Hebrew, 1346 Van Hise Hall, 1220 Linden Dr., University of Wisconsin-Madison, Madison, WI 53706. TEL 608-262-2997. Ed. Michael V. Fox. adv.; bk.rev. circ. 600. (also avail. in microform from UMI) **Indexed:** Mid.East: Abstr.& Ind., Old Test.Abstr., Rel.& Theol.Abstr. (1988-), Rel.Ind.One. **Document type:** academic/scholarly publication.
—BLDSC (4282.320000); UMI.
Formerly (until vol. 17, 1976): Hebrew Abstracts (ISSN 0438-895X)
Refereed Serial

HEFTE FUER OSTASIATISCHE LITERATUR. see LITERATURE

400 100   IT
HENOCH. (Text in English, French, German and Italian) 1979. 3/yr. $100. Herder Editrice e Libreria s.r.l., Piazza Montecitorio 120, 00186 Rome, Italy. TEL 67-94-628. FAX 678-47-51. TELEX 621427 NATEL. Ed. Paolo Sacchi. **Indexed:** Bibl.Ling., New Test.Abstr., Old Test.Abstr. **Document type:** academic/scholarly publication.

480   GW   ISSN 0018-0777
PA3
HERMES; Zeitschrift fuer klassische Philologie. (Text in English, French, German and Italian) 1866. q. DM.198 (supplements priced individually). Franz Steiner Verlag Stuttgart GmbH, Birkenwaldstr. 44, 70191 Stuttgart, Germany. TEL 0711-2582-0. FAX 0711-2582290. TELEX 723636-DAZ-D. (Subscr. to: Postfach 101061, 70009 Stuttgart, Germany) Ed.Bd. adv.; index. circ. 900. (also avail. in microfiche from IDC; back issues avail.; reprint service avail. from KTO) **Indexed:** Arts & Hum.Cit.Ind., Bibl.Ling., Curr.Cont., M.L.A. **Document type:** academic/scholarly publication.
—Faxon; UnCover; SWETS. **CCC.**

480   GW   ISSN 0341-0064
HERMES - EINZELSCHRIFTEN. (Supplement to: Hermes) (Text in English and German) irreg., vol.66, 1993. price varies. Franz Steiner Verlag Wiesbaden GmbH, Birkenwaldstr. 44, 70191 Stuttgart, Germany. TEL 0711-2582-0. FAX 0711-2582290. TELEX 723636-DAZ-D. (Subscr. to: Postfach 101061, 70009 Stuttgart, Germany) Ed.Bd. **Document type:** monographic series.
—BLDSC (4300.079200).

HERON; essays on language & literature. see LITERATURE

440   GW   ISSN 0863-436X
HI HELLO SALUT. (Text in English, French, Spanish) 1990. 6/yr. DM.23.40. Paedagogischer Zeitschriftenverlag, Postfach 269, 10107 Berlin, Germany. TEL 030-20343431.
FAX 030-20343432. circ. 21,000. **Document type:** academic/scholarly publication.

HIAKA KHRONIKA. see HISTORY — History Of Europe

460 469 370   US   ISSN 0018-2133
PC4001
HISPANIA; a journal devoted to the interests of the teaching of Spanish and Portuguese. (Text in English, Portuguese, Spanish) 1918. q. $30. American Association of Teachers of Spanish and Portuguese, Inc., Georgetown University, Spanish Dept., Washington, DC 20057-0989.
TEL 617-832-3779. Ed. Estelle Irizarry. adv. contact: Walter C. Oliver. bk.rev.; film rev.; charts; tr.lit.; index, cum.index. circ. 13,000. (also avail. in microform from UMI,PMC; reprint service avail. from UMI,KTO) **Indexed:** Arts & Hum.Cit.Ind., Bibl.Ling., Bk.Rev.Ind. (1965-), C.I.J.E., Child.Bk.Rev.Ind. (1965-), Educ.Ind., Hisp.Amer.Per.Ind., Ind.Bk.Rev.Hum., Lang.& Lang.Behav.Abstr., Lang.Teach.& Ling.Abstr., M.L.A. **Document type:** academic/scholarly publication.
—BLDSC (4315.760000); Faxon; UnCover; SWETS; UMI.

HISPANIC HORIZON. see LITERATURE

460 375.4   US
HISPANIC RESEARCH CENTER. RESEARCH BULLETIN. q. free. Hispanic Research Center, Thebaud Hall, Fordham University, New York, NY 10458. Ed. Stasia Madrigal.

460   US   ISSN 0018-2176
PQ6001
HISPANIC REVIEW; a quarterly journal devoted to research in the Hispanic languages and literatures. (Text in English and Spanish) 1933. q. $25 to individuals (foreign $28); institutions $35 (foreign $38). University of Pennsylvania, Romance Languages Department, Philadelphia, PA 19104-6305. TEL 215-898-7420.
FAX 215-898-0933. Ed. Russell P. Sebold. adv.: Full page $275. bk.rev.; index. circ. 1,600. (also avail. in microform; reprint service avail. from SCH) back issues avail.) **Indexed:** Amer.Hist.& Life, Arts & Hum.Cit.Ind., Bibl.Ling., Curr.Cont., Hisp.Amer.Per.Ind., Hist.Abstr., Hum.Ind., Ind.Bk.Rev.Hum., Lang.& Lang.Behav.Abstr., M.L.A. **Document type:** academic/scholarly publication.
—Faxon; UnCover; SWETS; UMI.

460 375.4   UK
HISPANIC TEXTS. 1957. irreg. price varies. Manchester University Press, Oxford Rd., Manchester M13 9PL, England. TEL 061-273-5539. FAX 061-274-3346. TELEX 666517-UNIMAN. Ed. Herbert Ramsden. **Document type:** monographic series.
Formerly: Spanish Texts.

HISPANORAMA. see LITERATURE

410 900   NE   ISSN 0302-5160
P61
HISTORIOGRAPHIA LINGUISTICA; international journal for the history of the language sciences. (Text in English, French, German, Italian, Spanish) 1974. 3/yr. fl.325($189) (effective 1994). John Benjamins Publishing Co., Amsteldijk 44, P.O. Box 75577, 1070 AN Amsterdam.
TEL 31-20-6738156. FAX 31-20-6792956. (In N. America: 821 Bethlehem Pike, Philadelphia, PA 19118. TEL 215-836-1200. FAX 215-836-1204) Ed. E.F. Konrad Koerner. bk.rev.; bibl.; index, cum.index. circ. 600. (back issues avail.) **Indexed:** Arts & Hum.Cit.Ind., Bibl.Ling., Curr.Cont., Lang.& Lang.Behav.Abstr. (1974-), Lang.Teach.& Ling.Abstr., M.L.A. **Document type:** academic/scholarly publication.
—BLDSC (4317.320000); Faxon; UnCover; SWETS.
Description: Discussion of the epistemological and methodological foundations of a historiography of linguistic thought.

418   GW   ISSN 0935-3518
P501   CODEN: HISPE2
HISTORISCHE SPRACHFORSCHUNG/HISTORICAL LINGUISTICS. (Text partly in English and French) 1852. s-a. DM.102. Vandenhoeck und Ruprecht, Robert-Bosch-Breite 6, 37079 Goettingen, Germany. TEL 0551-6959-26. FAX 0551-695917. (Subscr. to: 37070 Goettingen, Germany) Eds. A. Bammesberger, Guenter Neumann. adv. circ. 420. (also avail. in microfiche from IDC; reprint service avail. from SCH) **Indexed:** Bibl.Ling., Lang.& Lang.Behav.Abstr. (1988-), M.L.A. **Document type:** academic/scholarly publication.
—Faxon; SWETS. **CCC.**
Formerly: Zeitschrift fuer Vergleichende Sprachforschung (ISSN 0044-3646)

HISTORY AND APPLIED LINGUISTICS. see HISTORY

495.1   CH   ISSN 1017-0855
PL1004
HUAWEN SHIJIE/WORLD OF CHINESE LANGUAGE. 1974. q. World Chinese Language Association, 8F, 77 Roosevelt Rd., Sec. 3, Taipei, Taiwan, Republic of China.

HUMAN COMMUNICATION AND ITS DISORDERS; a review. see EDUCATION — Special Education And Rehabilitation

HUMAN COMMUNICATION RESEARCH. see COMMUNICATIONS

410 800   US   ISSN 0194-164X
DB901
HUNGARIAN STUDIES NEWSLETTER. 1973. 3/yr. $10 (effective June 1992). American Hungarian Foundation, Box 1084, New Brunswick, NJ 08903. TEL 908-846-5777. FAX 908-249-7033. Ed. August J. Molnar. adv.; bk.rev. circ. 2,500. **Indexed:** Amer.Bibl.Slavic & E.Eur.Stud. **Document type:** newsletter.

370 407   ISSN 1050-0049
PB36   CODEN: IJLTEV
THE I A L L JOURNAL OF LANGUAGE LEARNING TECHNOLOGIES. (Text in English, French, German) 1968. 3/yr. $25. International Association of Learning Laboratories, c/o Language Laboratories, 304C Moore College Bldg., University of Georgia, Athens, GA 30602. TEL 404-542-5143. Ed. Suzanne E. Lindenau. adv.; bk.rev.; bibl.; illus. circ. 2,000. (reprint service avail.) **Indexed:** C.I.J.E., ERIC, Lang.& Lang.Behav.Abstr., Lang.Teach.& Ling.Abstr.
—BLDSC (4359.522670); UnCover; SWETS; UMI.
Former titles (until 1990): Journal of Educational Techniques and Technologies (ISSN 0891-2521); (until 1986): N A L L D Journal (ISSN 0027-5905)

I F E F, AUSTRIA SEKCIO. BULTENO. (Federacio Esperantista Fervojista) see TRANSPORTATION — Railroads

I LOVE ENGLISH. see CHILDREN AND YOUTH — For

LINGUISTICS

410   NE   ISSN 0921-2566
I P O ANNUAL PROGRESS REPORT. (Text in English) 1966. a. free. Instituut voor Perceptie Onderzoek - Institute for Perception Research, P.O. Box 513, Eindhoven 5600 MB, Netherlands. TEL 31-40-773873. FAX 31-40-773876. Ed.Bd. circ. 1,500 (controlled). **Indexed:** Ergon.Abstr., Lang.& Lang. Behav.Abstr., Psychol.Abstr. **Document type:** academic/scholarly publication, bulletin.

418 370   GW   ISSN 0019-042X
P1.A1   CODEN: IRALA4
I R A L. (International Review of Applied Linguistics in Language Teaching) (Text in English, French and German) 1963. q. DM.110 to individuals; institutions DM.176. Julius Groos Verlag, Hertzstr. 6, 69126 Heidelberg, Germany. TEL 06221-303621. FAX 06221-301993. (Dist. by: Oxford University Press, Walton St., Oxford OX2 6DP, England) Eds. B. Pottier, G. Nickel. adv.; bk.rev.; bibl.; index. circ. 900. (also avail. in microform from UMI; microfiche from UMI; reprint service avail. from UMI) **Indexed:** Bibl.Ling., C.I.J.E., Cont.Pg.Educ., Curr.Cont., Educ.Ind., Ind.Bk.Rev.Hum., Lang.& Lang.Behav.Abstr. (1972-), Lang.Teach.& Ling.Abstr., M.L.A., Mid.East: Abstr.& Ind., Mult.Ed.Abstr., Psychol.Abstr., SSCI. **Document type:** academic/scholarly publication.
—BLDSC (4567.522000); Faxon; UnCover; SWETS; UMI. **CCC.**

418   BE   ISSN 0019-0829
P123
I T L REVIEW OF APPLIED LINGUISTICS. (Text in Dutch, English, French, German, Spanish) 1968. 2/yr. 1300 BEF (foreign 1500 BEF). Katholieke Universiteit Leuven, Afdeling Toegepaste Linguistiek - Universite Catholique de Louvain, Institut de Linguistique Appliquee, Blijde Inkomstraat 21, B-3000 Leuven, Belgium. TEL 32-16-284769. FAX 32-16-285025. Ed. N. Delbecque. bk.rev.; bibl.; charts; illus.; stat. circ. 600. (back issues avail.) **Indexed:** Ind.Bk.Rev.Hum., Lang.& Lang.Behav.Abstr. (1972-), Lang.Teach.& Ling.Abstr., M.L.A. **Document type:** academic/scholarly publication.
—BLDSC (4588.670000); UnCover; SWETS.

479 879   GW   ISSN 0019-0993
PC4001   CODEN: IBERE2
IBERO-ROMANIA; Zeitschrift fuer die iberoromanischen Sprachen und Literaturen in Europa und Amerika. (Text in English, German and Spanish) 1973. s-a. DM.86. Max Niemeyer Verlag, Postfach 2140, 72011 Tuebingen, Germany. TEL 07071-98940. FAX 07071-989450. Ed.Bd. adv.; bk.rev. **Indexed:** Arts & Hum.Cit.Ind., Bibl.Ling. **Document type:** academic/scholarly publication.
—Faxon; SWETS.

IBEROAMERICANA; Lateinamerika-Spanien-Portugal. see *LITERARY AND POLITICAL REVIEWS*

IDIOM. see *EDUCATION — Teaching Methods And Curriculum*

410   US
IDIOMS AND PHRASES INDEX. 1983. irreg. $230. Gale Research Inc., 835 Penobscot Bldg., Detroit, MI 48226. TEL 800-877-4253. FAX 313-961-6083. TELEX 810-221-7086. Ed. Laurence Urdang.
Description: Guide to idioms and phrases in English.

410   UK
IDO-VIVO. 1930. 3/yr. $12. International Language (Ido) Society of Great Britain, 24 Nunn St., Leek, Staffs. ST13 8EA, England. TEL 0538-381491. Ed. niclas ap Glyn. bk.rev. circ. 150. **Document type:** newsletter.
Formerly (until Jan. 1983): Ido-Letro.
Description: Official magazine of the International Language (IDO) Society of Great Britain. Contains articles, puzzles, short stories in English and Ido.

420 375.4   US
ILLINOIS T E S O L - B E NEWSLETTER. vol.7, 1979. 5/yr. membership. Illinois Teachers of English to Speakers of Other Languages - Bilingual Education, c/o G. Henllan-Jones, Amundsen High School, 5110 N. Damen, Chicago, IL 60625. TEL 312-989-3520. Ed. G. Henllan-Jones. adv.; bk.rev. circ. 600.
Description: Includes articles and announcements for teachers of ESL and bilingual education.

IN OTHER WORDS. see *RELIGIONS AND THEOLOGY*

410   IT
INCONTRI LINGUISTICI. 1974. a. L.12000($14) (Universita degli Studi di Udine e Trieste) Editori e Stampatori Giardini, Via di Santa Bibbiana 28, 56100 Pisa, Italy. Ed.Bd. adv.; bk.rev. circ. 3,000. **Indexed:** Bibl.Ling., Lang.& Lang.Behav.Abstr., M.L.A.

418   II   ISSN 0379-0037
PK101
INDIAN JOURNAL OF APPLIED LINGUISTICS. (Text in English) 1975. s-a. Rs.200($50) Bahri Publications, 997-A St., No. 9, Gobindpuri, Kalkaji, New Delhi 110 019, India. TEL 644-8606. Ed. Ujjal Singh Bahri. adv.; bk.rev.; bibl. **Indexed:** Lang.& Lang.Behav.Abstr. (1987-), Lang.Teach.& Ling.Abstr. **Document type:** academic/scholarly publication.
—BLDSC (4410.220000).
Description: Research and theoretical work in applied linguistics.

410   II   ISSN 0378-0759
PK1501
INDIAN LINGUISTICS; journal of the Linguistic Society of India. (Supplement avail.) (Text in English) 1931. q. Rs.120($25) Linguistic Society of India, c/o Deccan College Postgraduate and Research Institute, Poona 411006, India. Ed. Shuresh Kumar. adv.; bk.rev. circ. 800. **Indexed:** Bibl.Ling., Ind.Bk.Rev.Hum., Lang.& Lang.Behav.Abstr. (1972-), M.L.A.

491   II   ISSN 0073-6589
INDIAN LINGUISTICS MONOGRAPH SERIES. (Text in English) 1958. irreg. price varies. Linguistic Society of India, c/o Deccan College Postgraduate and Research Institute, Poona 411006, India. Ed. Suresh Kumar. **Document type:** monographic series.

INDIANA ENGLISH. see *LITERATURE*

494   US   ISSN 0073-7097
INDIANA UNIVERSITY. RESEARCH INSTITUTE FOR INNER ASIAN STUDIES. URALIC AND ALTAIC SERIES.. Short title: Uralic and Altaic Series. (Text in English unless reprint) 1960. irreg., no.156, 1993. price varies. Indiana University, Research Institute for Inner Asian Studies, Goodbody Hall 344, Bloomington, IN 47405. TEL 812-885-1605. FAX 812-855-7500. TELEX 272279 INDIANA U BLOM. Ed. Denis Sinor. **Indexed:** M.L.A. **Document type:** monographic series.

494.2 951.7   HU   ISSN 0073-7194
INDICES VERBORUM LINGUAE MONGOLIAE MONUMENTIS TRADITORUM. (Text in Mongolian with romanization; introduction in French) 1970. irreg. price varies. (Magyar Tudomanyos Akademia) Akademiai Kiado, Publishing House of the Hungarian Academy of Sciences, P.O. Box 245, H-1519 Budapest, Hungary. TEL 181-2134. FAX 166-6466. TELEX 22-6228 AKNYO H. Ed. L. Ligeti.

INDO-IRANIAN JOURNAL. see *ORIENTAL STUDIES*

430   GW   ISSN 0019-7262
INDOGERMANISCHE FORSCHUNGEN; Zeitschrift fuer Indogermanistik und allgemeine Sprachwissenschaft. (Text in English, French, German and Italian) 1891. a. DM.226. Walter de Gruyter und Co., Genthiner Str. 13, 10785 Berlin, Germany. TEL 030-26005-0. FAX 030-26005-251. TELEX 184027. (U.S. addr.: Walter de Gruyter, Inc., 200 Saw Mill Rd., Hawthorne, NY 10532) Ed. Wolfgang P. Schmid. adv.; bk.rev.; charts; illus.; index. (also avail. in microform from PMC) **Indexed:** Arts & Hum.Cit.Ind., Bibl.Ling., Curr.Cont., Ind.Bk.Rev.Hum., Lang.& Lang.Behav.Abstr., M.L.A. **Document type:** academic/scholarly publication.
—SWETS. **CCC.**

INDOLOGICA TAURINENSIA. see *ORIENTAL STUDIES*

INDOLOGICAL STUDIES. see *LITERATURE*

375.4 440   CN   ISSN 0822-5109
INFORM-ACTION; educateurs franco-manitobains. (Text in French) 1968. 3/yr. Can.$5 to non-members (typically set in Sep.). Manitoba Teachers Society, 191 Harcourt St., Winnipeg, MB R3J 3H2, Canada. TEL 204-888-7961. FAX 204-831-0877. Ed. Paul Shurwood. circ. 2,050 (controlled).
Description: Professional journal for teachers of French and French immersion schools.

INFORMATIONEN DEUTSCH ALS FREMDSPRACHE. see *EDUCATION — Higher Education*

INFORMATIONEN ZUR DEUTSCHDIDAKTIK; Zeitschrift fuer den Deutschunterricht in Wissenschaft und Schule. see *EDUCATION*

418 025   GW   ISSN 0941-1313
INFOTERM SERIES. irreg. price varies. (International Information Centre for Terminology, Vienna, AU) K.G. Saur Verlag KG (Subsidiary of: Reed Reference Publishing), Ortlerstr. 8, 81373 Munich, Germany. TEL 089-76902-0. FAX 089-76902150. TELEX 5212067-SAUR-D. (Subscr. to: Postfach 701620, 81316 Munich, Germany).
Description: Consists of bibliographies, guides, and conference proceedings discussing theoretical and practical problems in terminology.

400   FR   ISSN 0073-8018
INITIATION A LA LINGUISTIQUE. SERIE A. LECTURES. 1970. irreg. price varies. Editions Klincksieck, 11 rue de Lille, 75005 Paris, France. Eds. Pierre Guiraud, Alain Rey. **Indexed:** M.L.A.

400   FR   ISSN 0073-8026
INITIATION A LA LINGUISTIQUE. SERIE B. PROBLEMES ET METHODES. 1970. irreg. price varies. Editions Klincksieck, 11 rue de Lille, 75005 Paris, France. Eds. Pierre Guiraud, Alain Rey.

410   KR   ISSN 0320-2372
P9
INOZEMNA FILOLOHIJA. (Text in Ukrainian; summaries in English, French, German, Russian, Spanish) 1964. q. Izdatel'stvo Vysshaya Shkola, L'vovskoe Otdelenie, Ul. Universitetska 1, 290 000 Lvov, Ukraine. (Co-sponsor: Ministerstvo Vysshego i Srednego Spetsial'nogo Obrazovaniya) Ed. B.M. Zadorozhny. circ. 1,000. **Indexed:** Bibl.Ling.

INSTITUT D'ETUDES SLAVES, PARIS. BIBLIOTHEQUE RUSSE. see *LITERATURE*

491   FR   ISSN 0078-9984
INSTITUT D'ETUDES SLAVES, PARIS. COLLECTION DE GRAMMAIRES. 1921. irreg., vol.7, 1980. price varies. Institut d'Etudes Slaves, 9 rue Michelet, 75006 Paris, France. **Document type:** academic/scholarly publication.

491 943   FR   ISSN 0078-9992
INSTITUT D'ETUDES SLAVES, PARIS. COLLECTION DE MANUELS. 1923. irreg., vol.8, 1991. price varies. Institut d'Etudes Slaves, 9 rue Michelet, 75006 Paris, France. **Document type:** academic/scholarly publication.

375.4   FR   ISSN 0300-2594
INSTITUT D'ETUDES SLAVES, PARIS. DOCUMENTS PEDAGOGIQUES. 1970. irreg., vol.36, 1993. price varies. Institut d'Etudes Slaves, 9 rue Michelet, 75006 Paris, France. **Document type:** academic/scholarly publication.
—BLDSC (3609.125000).

410   FR   ISSN 0154-0157
INSTITUT D'ETUDES SLAVES, PARIS. LEXIQUES. 1978. irreg., vol.11, 1993. price varies. Institut d'Etudes Slaves, 9 rue Michelet, 75006 Paris, France. **Document type:** academic/scholarly publication.

INSTITUT D'ETUDES SLAVES, PARIS. TRAVAUX. see *LITERATURE*

414   FR   ISSN 1163-765X
INSTITUT DE LA COMMUNICATION PARLEE. RAPPORT DE RECHERCHE. 1991. a. 100 F. Institut de la Communication Parlee, Universite Stendhal, B.P. 25 X, 38040 Grenoble Cedex 9, France. TEL 76-82-43-37. FAX 76-82-43-35. Ed.Bd.
Description: Brings together all important papers published by members of the laboratory in the major French or international journals.

400   BE
INSTITUT DE LINGUISTIQUE DE LOUVAIN. BIBLIOTHEQUE DES C I L L. (Supplement to: Cahiers de l'Institut de Linguistique de Louvain) (Text in English, French, German, Italian) 1976. irreg. Editions Peeters s.p.r.l., Bondgenotenlaan 153, B-3000 Louvain, Belgium. TEL 32-16-235170. FAX 32-16-228500. TELEX 65981 PULB. **Indexed:** Bibl.Ling. **Document type:** monographic series.

LINGUISTICS

400   BE   ISSN 0771-6524
INSTITUT DE LINGUISTIQUE DE LOUVAIN. CAHIERS. Key Title: Cahiers de l'Institut de Linguistique de Louvain. Short title: C I L L. (Supplements avail.: Institut de Linguistique de Louvain. Bibliotheque des C I L L; Serie Pedagogique) (Text in Dutch, English, French, German, Spanish) 1972. s-a. 1600 BEF (effective 1994). Editions Peeters s.p.r.l., Bondgenotenlaan 153, B-3000 Louvain, Belgium. TEL 32-16-235170. FAX 32-16-228500. Eds. Y. Duhoux, G. Jucquois. adv.; bk.rev.; abstr.; bibl.; illus. circ. 500. (back issues avail.) **Indexed:** Bibl.Ling., Bull.Signal., Lang.Teach.& Ling.Abstr., M.L.A., Sociol.Abstr. **Document type:** academic/scholarly publication.
     Formerly (until 1975): Universite Catholique de Louvain. Institut de Linguistique. Cahiers (ISSN 0303-3880)

410   SW
INSTITUT DE LINGUISTIQUE DE LUND. TRAVAUX. (Text in English, French or German) 1959. irreg., no.19, 1983. price varies. Liber Forlag, S-205 10, Malmo, Sweden. Eds. Eva Gaarding, Bengt Sigurd.

430   GW
INSTITUT FUER DEUTSCHE SPRACHE. FORSCHUNGSBERICHTE. irreg., no.73, 1994. DM.58. Gunter Narr Verlag, Postfach 2567, 72015 Tuebingen, Germany. TEL 07071-78091. FAX 07071-75288. Ed.Bd. **Document type:** monographic series.

430   GW
INSTITUT FUER DEUTSCHE SPRACHE. JAHRBUCH. a. Walter de Gruyter und Co., Genthiner Str. 13, 10785 Berlin, Germany. TEL 030-26005-0. FAX 030-26005251. TELEX 184027. (U.S. addr.: Walter de Gruyter, Inc., 200 Saw Mill Rd., Hawthorne, NY 10532) **Document type:** academic/scholarly publication.

401   BE   ISSN 0777-8600
INSTITUT LINGUISTIQUE DE LOUVAIN. SERIE PEDAGOGIQUE. Key Title: S P I L L. (Text in English, French) 1978. irreg., vol.17, 1992. price varies. Editions Peeters s.p.r.l., Bondgenotenlaan 153, B-3000 Louvain, Belgium. TEL 32-16-235170. FAX 32-16-228500. (back issues avail.) **Document type:** monographic series.

496   FR   ISSN 0249-728X
INSTITUT NATIONAL DES LANGUES ET CIVILISATIONS ORIENTALES. BULLETIN DES ETUDES AFRICAINES. s-a. price varies. Institut National des Langues et Civilisations Orientales, Centre d'Etudes et de Recherche Africaines, 2 rue de Lille, 75343 Paris Cedex 07, France. TEL 49-26-42-74. **Indexed:** Bibl.Ling., Documentatieblad. **Document type:** bulletin.
—BLDSC (2853.655000).
     Description: Studies African languages and cultures.

440   UK   ISSN 0967-1129
PC6
▼**INSTITUTE OF ROMANCE STUDIES. JOURNAL.** 1992. a. £48($80) Institute of Romance Studies, Publications Office, Senate House, Malet St., London WC1E 7HU, England. FAX 071-436-4533. **Document type:** academic/scholarly publication.
—BLDSC (4786.750000).

410   CK
INSTITUTO CARO Y CUERVO. SEMINARIO ANDRES BELLO. CUADERNOS. 1978. irreg., no.5, 1991. Instituto Caro y Cuervo, Seccion de Publicaciones, Apdo. Aereo 51502, Bogota, Colombia. **Document type:** monographic series.

INSTITUTO CARO Y CUERVO. SERIE MINOR. see LITERATURE

INSTITUTO DE ESTUDIOS ASTURIANOS. BOLETIN. see HISTORY — History Of Europe

460 306.4   PE   ISSN 1022-1522
INSTITUTO LINGUISTICO DE VERANO. DOCUMENTOS DE TRABAJO. 1973. irreg., no.24, 1992. price varies. Instituto Linguistico de Verano, Departamento de Estudios Etno-Linguisticos, Casilla 2492, Lima 100, Peru. FAX 5114-629-629. (Subscr. to: E. Iturriaga y Cia., Jiron Ica 441, Ofc. 202-203, Casilla 4640, Lima 100, Peru) Ed. Mary Ruth Wise. (also avail. in microfiche; back issues avail.) **Document type:** academic/scholarly publication.

498   PE
INSTITUTO LINGUISTICO DE VERANO. INFORME ANUAL. a. Instituto Linguistico de Verano, Casilla 2492, Lima 100, Peru. FAX 51-14-629-929. (Subscr. to: E. Iturriaga y Cia., Jiron Ica 441, Ofc. 202-203, Casilla 4640, Lima 100, Peru)

460 375.4   PO
INSTITUTO NACIONAL DE INVESTIGACAO CIENTIFICA. TEXTOS DE LINGUISTICA. 1980. irreg., no.6, 1982. (Instituto Nacional de Investigacao Cientifica, Centro de Linguistica) Universidad de Coimbra, Centro de Estudos Classicos y Humanisticos, Faculdade de Letras, Coimbra, Portugal. circ. 25,000.

410   RM
INSTITUTUL DE SUBINGINERI ORADEA. LUCRARI STIINTIFICE: SERIA LINGVISTICA. (Text in Rumanian, occasionally in English or French; summaries in English, French, German or Rumanian) a. Institutul de Subingineri Oradea, Calea Armatei Rosii Nr. 5, 3700 Oradea, Rumania.
     Formerly: Institutul Pedagogic Oradea. Lucrari Stiintifice: Seria Lingvistica; Which continues in part (in 1973): Institutul Pedagogic Oradea. Lucrari Stiintifice: Seria Filologie; Which superseded in part (in 1971): Institutul Pedagogic Oradea. Lucrari Stiintifice: Seria A and Seria B; Which was formerly (until 1969): Institutul Pedagogic Oradea. Lucrari Stiintifice.

420 370.15 610
300   US
INTERFACES: LINGUISTICS, PSYCHOLOGY AND HEALTH THERAPEUTICS; an international journal of research, notes and commentary. 1973. 3/yr. $10. Providence College Press, Providence, RI 02918. Eds. Robert E. Haskell, Elaine Chiaka. bk.rev.; abstr.; bibl.; charts; stat.; tr.lit. circ. 500. (back issues avail.) **Indexed:** ERIC, Lang.& Lang.Behav.Abstr., Psychol.Abstr., Sociol.Educ.Abstr.
Refereed Serial

410 301   US
INTERLINGUA INSTITUTE REPORT. (Text in English, Interlingua) 1990. irreg. $25. Interlingua Institute, 332 Bleeker St., New York, NY 10014. TEL 212-691-4773. Ed. Frank Esterhill. bk.rev. circ. 500. (looseleaf format; back issues avail.) **Document type:** newsletter.

400   US   ISSN 0743-0523
P365   CODEN: IAIDE7
INTERNATIONAL ACRONYMS, INITIALISMS AND ABBREVIATIONS DIRECTORY. (Supplement avail.: Vol.2 New International Acronyms, Initialisms and Abbreviations) irreg., 3rd ed., 1993. $495 (vol.1 $165, vol.2 $150, vol.3 $180). Gale Research Inc., 835 Penobscot Bldg., Detroit, MI 48266. TEL 313-961-2242. FAX 313-961-6083. Eds. Julie E. Towell, Helen E. Sheppard. (also avail. in magnetic tape; diskette format) **Document type:** directory.
—BLDSC (4535.597800); CASDDS.

410.5   JA
P1.A1
INTERNATIONAL CHRISTIAN UNIVERSITY. LANGUAGE RESEARCH BULLETIN. (Subseries of the university's publication 6-A) (Text in English) 1961. a. 2000 Yen. International Christian University, Division of Languages - Kokusai Kirisutokyo Daigaku, 3-10-2 Osawa, Mitaka, Tokyo 181, Japan. Ed.Bd. bibl. circ. 500. **Indexed:** Lang.& Lang.Behav.Abstr. (1986-).
—BLDSC (5155.711400).
     Formerly: Descriptive and Applied Linguistics. Annual Reports; **Supersedes:** Summer Institute in Linguistics. Studies in Descriptive and Applied Linguistics (ISSN 0385-8960)

410   NE   ISSN 0074-3755
INTERNATIONAL CONGRESS OF LINGUISTS. PROCEEDINGS. (Published in host country) 1928. quinquennial, 14th, 1987, Berlin; 15th, 1992, Quebec. price varies. Permanent International Committee of Linguists, c/o E. M. Uhlenbeck, Dr. Kuyperlaan 11, 2215 NE Voorhout, Netherlands. circ. 1,700. **Indexed:** Bibl.Ling.

410   BE
INTERNATIONAL COUNCIL OF ONOMASTIC SCIENCES. CONGRESS PROCEEDINGS. (Former name of issuing body: International Committee of Onomastic Sciences) 1938. triennial, 18th, 1993, Trier, Germany. (International Council of Onomastic Sciences) International Centre of Onomastics, Blijde-Inkomststr. 21, P.O. Box 33, B-3000 Leuven, Belgium. FAX 32-16-285025. **Document type:** proceedings.
     Formerly (until 1993): International Committee of Onomastic Sciences. Congress Proceedings (ISSN 0074-2791)

INTERNATIONAL JOURNAL FOR THE SEMIOTICS OF LAW/REVUE INTERNATIONALE DE SEMIOTIQUE JURIDIQUE; semiotic, linguistic, discursive approach to law. see LAW

497   US   ISSN 0020-7071
PM101
INTERNATIONAL JOURNAL OF AMERICAN LINGUISTICS. 1917. q. $38 to individuals; institutions $86; students $28. University of Chicago Press, Journals Division, 5720 S. Woodlawn Ave., Chicago, IL 60637. TEL 312-753-3347. FAX 312-753-0811. (Subscr. to: Box 37005, Chicago, IL 60637) Ed. David S. Rood. adv.; bk.rev.; abstr.; index, cum.index: vols. 1-32 (1917-1966). circ. 1,400. (also avail. in microform from UMI,PMC; reprint service avail. from UMI,ISI,KTO) **Indexed:** A.I.C.P., Abstr.Anthropol., Anthropol.Lit., Bibl.Ling., C.I.J.E., Curr.Cont., Hisp.Amer.Per.Ind., Hum.Ind., Ind.Bk.Rev.Hum., Lang.& Lang.Behav.Abstr. (1972-), Lang.Teach.& Ling.Abstr., M.L.A., Mid.East: Abstr.& Ind., SSCI. **Document type:** academic/scholarly publication.
—BLDSC (4542.050000); Faxon; UnCover; SWETS; UMI. **CCC.**
     Description: Scholarly journal devoted to the native languages of the Americas.
Refereed Serial

410   NO   ISSN 0802-6106
P129   CODEN: IJLNED
INTERNATIONAL JOURNAL OF APPLIED LINGUISTICS. 1991. s-a. $82. Novus Press, P.O. Box 748, Sentrum, N-0106 Oslo, Norway. TEL 47-22-71-74-50. FAX 47-22-71-81-07. **Indexed:** Bibl.Ling.
—BLDSC (4542.088000).
     Description: Covers all areas of applied linguistics represented by the various commissions of AILA (L'Association Internationale de Linguistique Appliquee), as well as encourages the development of new fields of applied language study.

410   UK   ISSN 0950-3846
P327
INTERNATIONAL JOURNAL OF LEXICOGRAPHY. 1988. q. £53($97) (effective 1994). Oxford University Press, Oxford Journals, Walton St., Oxford OX2 6DP, England. TEL 0865-56767. FAX 0865-56646. TELEX 837330-OXPRES-G. (U.S. subscr. to: Oxford University Press Inc., 2001 Evans Rd., Cary, NC 27513. TEL 919-677-0977) Ed. Robert Ilson. adv. contact: Jane Parker. bk.rev.; illus. circ. 950. **Indexed:** Bibl.Ling., Lang.& Lang.Behav.Abstr. (1988-). **Document type:** academic/scholarly publication.
—BLDSC (4542.319500); Faxon; UnCover; SWETS; UMI. **CCC.**
     Description: Covers theoretical, practical, diachronic and synchronic aspects of lexicography. Related disciplines such as lexicology, terminology, semantics, pragmatics, are also included.

410 150   JA   ISSN 0165-4055
INTERNATIONAL JOURNAL OF PSYCHOLINGUISTICS. 3/yr. $120. Center for Academic Societies Osaka, Senri Life Science Center Bldg., 14th Fl., 1-4-2 Shinsenrihigashi-machi, Toyonaka 565, Japan. TEL 06-873-2301. FAX 06-873-2300. **Document type:** academic/scholarly publication.
—**CCC.**

LINGUISTICS

491 891 US ISSN 0538-8228
PG1
INTERNATIONAL JOURNAL OF SLAVIC LINGUISTICS AND POETICS. (Text in English, French, German, and all Slavic languages) 1959-1976; resumed 1981. s-a. $20 to individuals; institutions and libraries $40. Slavica Publishers, Inc., Box 14388, Columbus, OH 43214. TEL 614-268-4002. Ed.Bd. bk.rev.; charts; illus. circ. 400. **Indexed:** Bibl.Ling., Ind.Bk.Rev.Hum., M.L.A. **Document type:** academic/scholarly publication.
—SWETS.
Description: Covers the linguistic and poetic traditions of Slavic cultures.
Refereed Serial

410 301 GW ISSN 0165-2516
P40 CODEN: ISLGAH
INTERNATIONAL JOURNAL OF THE SOCIOLOGY OF LANGUAGE. (Text in English) 1974. bi-m. DM.108 to individuals; institutions DM.370. Walter de Gruyter und Co., Mouton de Gruyter, Genthiner Str. 13, 10785 Berlin, Germany. TEL 030-26005-0. FAX 030-26005251. (U.S. subscr. to: Walter de Gruyter Inc., 200 Saw Mill River Rd., Hawthorne, NY 10532) Ed. Joshua Fishman. adv.; bk.rev.; bibl.; circ. 900 (controlled). (back issues avail.) **Indexed:** Anthropol.Lit., Bibl.Ling., Curr.Cont., E.I., Lang.& Lang.Behav.Abstr. (1974-), Lang.Teach.& Ling.Abstr., M.L.A., Mid.East: Abstr.& Ind., Psychol.Abstr., Sociol.Abstr. (1974-), SSCI. **Document type:** academic/scholarly publication.
—BLDSC (4542.573000); Faxon; UnCover; SWETS. **CCC.**

418.02 II ISSN 0970-9819
INTERNATIONAL JOURNAL OF TRANSLATION. (Text in English, French) 1989. s-a. Rs.150($50) Bahri Publications, 997-A St., No. 9, Gobindpuri, Kalkaji, New Delhi 110 019, India. TEL 644-8606. Ed. R.K. Agnihotri. adv.; bk.rev. **Document type:** academic/scholarly publication.
—BLDSC (4542.695950).

400 US ISSN 0074-6797
INTERNATIONAL LINGUISTIC ASSOCIATION. MONOGRAPH. (Supplement to: Word) 1951. irreg. International Linguistic Association, c/o Dr. Theodore S. Beardsley, Jr., Treas., Hispanic Society of America, 613 W. 155th St., New York, NY 10032. (reprint service avail. from UMI) **Document type:** monographic series.

400 US ISSN 0074-6800
INTERNATIONAL LINGUISTIC ASSOCIATION. SPECIAL PUBLICATIONS. 1964. irreg. price varies. International Linguistic Association, c/o Dr. Theodore S. Beardsley, Jr., Treas., Hispanic Society of America, 613 W. 155th St., New York, NY 10032. (reprint service avail. from UMI)

414 UK ISSN 0025-1003
P215
INTERNATIONAL PHONETIC ASSOCIATION. JOURNAL. 1886. s-a. £25($45) International Phonetic Association, Dept. of Linguistics & Phonetics, University of Leeds, Leeds LS2 9JT, England. TEL 0532-333563. FAX 0532-333566. Ed. Ian Maddieson. adv.; bk.rev.; charts. circ. 800. (also avail. in microform from UMI; reprint service avail. from SWZ,UMI) **Indexed:** Bibl.Ling., Lang.& Lang.Behav.Abstr. (1972-), Lang.Teach.& Ling.Abstr., Mid.East: Abstr.& Ind., Sociol.Abstr. **Document type:** academic/scholarly publication.
—BLDSC (4802.350000); UnCover; SWETS; UMI.
Formerly: Maitre Phonetique.
Description: Concerned with all aspects of the theory, description and use of phonetics and phonology.

418.02 SZ ISSN 0047-1291
L'INTERPRETE. 1945. q. 26 SFr. (effective 1993). Association d'Interpretes et de Traducteurs, Case Stand 388, 1211 Geneva 11, Switzerland. Ed. M. Wanstall-Sauty. adv.; bk.rev.; abstr. circ. 600.

418.02 IT
INTERPRETER'S NEWSLETTER. irreg. Universita degli Studi di Trieste, Scuola Superiore di Lingue Moderne per Interpreti e Traduttori, Via B. D'Alviano, 15-1, 34144 Trieste, Italy. Eds. Laura Gran, John Dodds.

IRIAN: BULLETIN OF IRIAN JAYA. see *ANTHROPOLOGY*

410 US ISSN 1050-4273
ISSUES IN APPLIED LINGUISTICS. 1990. s-a. $35. University of California at Los Angeles, Department of TESL and Applied Linguistics, 3300 Rolfe Hall, 405 Hilgard Ave., Los Angeles, CA 90024-1531. Ed. Joseph R. Plummer. **Document type:** academic/scholarly publication.
—BLDSC (4584.137000); UnCover.
Description: Covers studies in the areas of language acquisition, analysis, education, testing, use, and research methodology
Refereed Serial

410 370 US
ISSUES IN LANGUAGE EDUCATION. 1988. irreg., no.7, 1991. $4 per no. Boston University, African Studies Center, 270 Bay State Rd., Boston, MA 02215. TEL 617-353-7306. FAX 617-353-4975. TELEX 9103501947 BUASC.

480 375.4 IT
ISTITUTO DI FILOLOGIA GRECA. BOLLETTINO. 1974. irreg., vol.5, 1980. L.50000. L'Erma di Bretschneider, Via Cassiodoro 19, 00193 Rome, Italy. TEL 06-687-41-27. FAX 06-687-41-29. Dir. Oddone Longo. circ. 500.

480 375.4 IT
ISTITUTO DI FILOLOGIA GRECA. BOLLETTINO. SUPPLEMENTI. 1977. irreg., no.10, 1990. price varies. L'Erma di Bretschneider, Via Cassiodoro 19, 00193 Rome, Italy. TEL 06-687-41-27. FAX 06-687-41-29. Dir. Oddone Longo.

430 IT ISSN 0392-6540
PN5
ISTITUTO UNIVERSITARIO ORIENTALE. ANNALI. SEZIONE GERMANICA. FILOLOGIA GERMANICA. (Text in Dutch, English, French, German, Italian) 1958. N.S. 1991. a. L.20000. Istituto Universitario Orientale, Piazza San Giovanni, Maggiore 30, 80134 Naples, Italy. TEL 081-5517609. FAX 081-5518550. (Dist. by: Herder Editrice e Libreria,. Piazza Montecitorio, 120, 00186 Rome, Italy) Ed.Bd. bk.rev.; bibl. circ. 1,000. **Indexed:** Bibl.Ling.
Supersedes in part (in 1975): Istituto Universitario Orientale. Annali. Sezione Germanica (ISSN 0077-2763)

ISTITUTO UNIVERSITARIO ORIENTALE. ANNALI. SEZIONE GERMANICA. STUDI NORDICI, STUDI NEDERLANDESI. see *LITERATURE*

ISTITUTO UNIVERSITARIO ORIENTALE. ANNALI. SEZIONE GERMANICA. STUDI TEDESCHI. see *LITERATURE*

ISTITUTO UNIVERSITARIO ORIENTALE DI NAPOLI. ANNALI. SEZIONE ROMANZA. see *LITERATURE*

ISTITUTO UNIVERSITARIO ORIENTALE DI NAPOLI. DIPARTIMENTO DI STUDI LETTERARI E LINGUISTICI DELL'OCCIDENTE. ANNUALI: STUDI DI ANGLISTICA. see *LITERATURE*

457 IT ISSN 0085-2295
L'ITALIA DIALETTALE; rivista di Dialettologia Italiana. 1925. a. L.95000. (Universita degli Studi di Pisa, Istituto di Glottologia) Giardini Editori e Stampatori, Via Santa Bibbiana 28, 56100 Pisa, Italy. TEL 050 502531. Ed. Tristano Bolelli. bk.rev. **Indexed:** Bibl.Ling., M.L.A.

ITALIAN QUARTERLY. see *LITERATURE*

ITALICA (MADISON). see *LITERATURE*

450 375.4 GW ISSN 0171-4996
ITALIENISCH; Zeitschrift fuer Italienische Sprache und Literatur in Wissenschaft und Unterricht. 1979. 2/yr. (May, Nov.). DM.25. Verlag Moritz Diesterweg GmbH, Waechsterbacher Str. 89, 60386 Frankfurt a.M., Germany. TEL 069-42081-0. FAX 069-1301-100. TELEX 413234-MDD. **Indexed:** Bibl.Ling., M.L.A. **Document type:** academic/scholarly publication.
—SWETS. **CCC.**

ITALIENISCHE STUDIEN. see *LITERATURE*

420 430 US ISSN 0363-6941
PD1
J E G P: JOURNAL OF ENGLISH AND GERMANIC PHILOLOGY. 1897. q. $24 to individuals (foreign $31); institutions $48 (foreign $55). (University of Illinois at Urbana-Champaign) University of Illinois Press, 1325 S. Oak St., Champaign, IL 61820. TEL 217-333-0950. FAX 217-244-8082. Eds. D. Kramer, M. Kalinke. adv.: B&W page $160; adv. contact: Cat Warren. bk.rev. circ. 1,600. (also avail. in microform from MIM,UMI,PMC; microfiche from IDC; reprint service avail. from UMI,SCH) **Indexed:** Abstr.Engl.Stud., Arts & Hum.Cit.Ind., Bk.Rev.Ind. (1965-), Child.Bk.Rev.Ind. (1965-), Curr.Cont., Hum.Ind., Ind.Bk.Rev.Hum., M.L.A. **Document type:** academic/scholarly publication.
—BLDSC (4979.250000); Faxon; UnCover; SWETS; UMI. **CCC.**
Former titles: Journal of English and Germanic Philology (ISSN 0022-0868); Journal of Germanic Philology (ISSN 0364-2968)
Refereed Serial

418.02 II ISSN 0253-8776
J I S T A. (Journal of the Indian Scientific Translators Association) (Text in English and other languages) 1972. a. Rs.50 (foreign $15). Indian Scientific Translators Association, c/o Indian National Scientific Documentation Centre, 14 Satsang Vihar Marg, New Delhi 110067, India. TEL 91-11-660141. Ed. Chetan Sampat. adv.; bk.rev.; bibl.; charts. circ. 400. **Document type:** academic/scholarly publication.

JAHRBUCH DER DEUTSCHDIDAKTIK. see *LITERATURE*

430 375.4 GW ISSN 0083-5617
PF5601
JAHRBUCH DES VEREINS FUER NIEDERDEUTSCHE SPRACHFORSCHUNG. (Text in English, German) 1875. a. DM.40. Wachholtz Verlag GmbH, Rungestr. 4, 24537 Neumuenster, Germany. TEL 04321-906270. FAX 04321-906275. Ed. Hermann Niebaum. circ. 800. (back issues avail.) **Document type:** bulletin.

JAHRBUCH DEUTSCH ALS FREMDSPRACHE. see *EDUCATION.— Higher Education*

492.7 UA
JAMI'AT AL-AZHAR. KULLIYYAT AL-LUGHAH AL-ARABIYYAH BIL-MANSURAH. MAJALLAH/AL-AZHAR UNIVERSITY. ARABIC LANGUAGE FACULTY IN MANSOURA. JOURNAL. (Text in Arabic) irreg., no.8, 1987. Al-Azhar University, Arabic Language Faculty in Mansoura, Mansoura, Egypt.

492.7 UA
JAMI'AT AL-AZHAR. KULLIYYAT AL-LUGHAH AL-ARABIYYAH BIL-MANUFIYYAH. MAJALLAH/AL-AZHAR UNIVERSITY. ARABIC LANGUAGE FACULTY IN MENOUFIA. JOURNAL. (Text in Arabic) 1982. a. free. Al-Azhar University, Arabic Language Faculty in Menoufia, Menoufia, Egypt. circ. 300. **Document type:** academic/scholarly publication.
Description: Reviews Arabic linguistics, literature, literary criticism and Islamic studies.

492.7 UA
JAMI'AT AL-AZHAR. KULLIYYAT AL-LUGHAH AL-ARABIYYAH BIL-ZAGAZIG. MAJALLAH/AL-AZHAR UNIVERSITY. ARABIC LANGUAGE FACULTY IN ZAGAZIG. JOURNAL. (Text in Arabic) 1983. q. exchange basis. Jami'at al-Azhar, Kulliyyat al-Lughah al-Arabiyyah bil-Zagazig - Al-Azhar University, Arabic Language Faculty in Zagazig, Zagazig, Egypt. TEL 02-055-324114. FAX 02-055-330204. Ed. Dr. Abd al-Rahman Abd al-Hamid Ali. circ. controlled. **Document type:** academic/scholarly publication.
Former titles (until 1992): Majallat Jami'at al-Azhar lil-Dirasat al-Islamiyyah wal-Arabiyyah bil-Zagazig; (until 1991): Jami'at al-Azhar. Kulliyyat al-Lughah al-Arabiyyah bil-Zagazig. Majallah.
Description: Publishes research on topics in Arabic language and linguistics and related matters.

492.7 SU
JAMI'AT UMM AL-QURA. KULLIYYAT AL-LUGHAH AL-ARABIYYAH. MUHADARAT AL-MAWSIM AL-THAQAFI. Cover title: Muhadarat al-Mawsim al-Thaqafi li-Kulliyyat al-Lughah al-Arabiyyah. (Text in Arabic) 1983. a. Umm al-Qura University, Arabic Language Faculty - Jami'at Umm al-Qura, Kulliyat al-Lughah al-Arabiyyah, P.O. Box 407-715, Mecca, Saudi Arabia. TEL 02-5564770. TELEX 440026.

LINGUISTICS

410   JA   ISSN 0389-1186
DJK1
JAPANESE SLAVIC & EAST EUROPEAN STUDIES. a. Japanese Society for Slavic & East European Studies, Sakyo-ku, Kyoto 606, Japan. TEL 075-753-6726. (Subscr. to: Lavis Marketing, 73 Lime Walk, Headington, Oxford OX3 7AD, England) Ed. Wakio Fujimoto.

JAPANESE STUDIES IN GERMAN LANGUAGE AND LITERATURE/JAPANISCHE STUDIEN ZUR DEUTSCHEN SPRACHE UND LITERATUR. see *LITERATURE*

499.992   NE   ISSN 0075-3491
JARLIBRO. (Text in Esperanto) 1908. a. fl.38($22) Universala Esperanto Asocio, Nieuwe Binnenweg 176, 3015 BJ Rotterdam, Netherlands. TEL 31-10-4361044. FAX 31-10-4361751. Ed. Francisco L. Veuthey. adv. contact: Osmo Buller. index. circ. 8,000. (back issues avail.)
Description: Includes specialist organizations and a network of 2300 representatives of the Esperanto movement in 90 countries.

430 800   II   ISSN 0377-0648
P1
JAWAHARLAL NEHRU UNIVERSITY. SCHOOL OF LANGUAGES. JOURNAL. Abbreviated title: J S L. (Text in English) 1973. s-a. $30. (Jawaharal Nehru University, School of Languages) Wiley Eastern Ltd., 4835-24 Ansari Rd., Darya Ganj, New Delhi - 110 002, India. FAX 91-11-3267437. TELEX 03166507 WEL IN. Ed.Bd. adv.; bk.rev. circ. 1,000. Document type: academic/scholarly publication.

400 491.87   XO   ISSN 0448-9241
PG5201
JAZYKOVEDNE STUDIE. (Text in Slovak; summaries in German and Russian) irreg., vol.13, 1976. fl.25 per no. (Slovenska Akademia Vied, Jazykovedny Ustav L. Stura) Veda, Publishing House of the Slovak Academy of Sciences, Klemensova 19, 814 30 Bratislava, Slovakia. (Dist. in Western countries by: John Benjamins B.V., Amsteldijk 44, P.O. Box 75577, 1070 AN Amsterdam, Netherlands) TEL 020-6762325) **Indexed:** Bibl.Ling.

400   XO   ISSN 0021-5597
P9
JAZYKOVEDNY CASOPIS. (Text in Slovak; summaries in English, German, Russian) 1946. s-a. 30 Kcs.($13) (Slovenska Akademia Vied, Jazykovedny Ustav L. Stura) Veda, Publishing House of the Slovak Academy of Sciences, Klemensova 19, 814 30 Bratislava, Slovakia. (Dist. in Western countries by: John Benjamins B.V., Amsteldijk 44, P.O. Box 75577, 1070 AN Amsterdam, Netherlands) TEL 020-6762325) Ed. Jan Horecky. bk.rev.; abstr.; charts; index. circ. 1,000. **Indexed:** Bibl.Ling., Lang.& Lang.Behav.Abstr. (1972-).

JERUSALEM STUDIES IN ARABIC AND ISLAM. see *RELIGIONS AND THEOLOGY — Islamic*

492.4 296   US   ISSN 0792-559X
PJ5061
JEWISH LINGUISTIC STUDIES. (Text mainly in English, occasionally in French and Hebrew) 1981. a. price varies. Association for the Study of Jewish Languages, 67-07 215th St., Oakland Gardens, NY 11364-2523. Ed. David L. Gold. adv.; bk.rev.; bibl. (back issues avail.) **Indexed:** Arts & Hum.Cit.Ind., Bull.Signal., Curr.Cont., Lang.& Lang.Behav.Abstr., M.L.A., Sociol.Abstr.
—CCC.
Formerly (until vol.7, 1987): Jewish Language Review (ISSN 0333-8347)
Description: Devoted to all aspects of the inner and outer linguistic history of the Jewish people and related groups.

491.82   CI   ISSN 0021-6925
PG1201
JEZIK; casopis za kulturu hrvatskoga knjizevnog jezika. (Text in Croatian) 1952. bi-m. DM.25. Hrvatsko Filolosko Drustvo, Djure Salaja 3, 41000 Zagreb, Croatia. TEL 041 513-155. Ed. Stjepan Babic. **Indexed:** Bibl.Ling., M.L.A.

491.84 890   XV   ISSN 0021-6933
PG1801
JEZIK IN SLOVSTVO. (Text in Slovenian) 1955. 8/yr. $12. Slavisticno Drustvo Slovenije, Askerceva 12, 61000 Ljubljana, Slovenia. TEL 061-150-001. FAX 061-159-337. Ed. Alenka Sivic-Dular. bk.rev.; bibl.; charts; index. circ. 2,400. **Indexed:** Bibl.Ling., Lang.& Lang.Behav.Abstr., M.L.A.

491.85   PL   ISSN 0021-6941
PG6001
JEZYK POLSKI. 1913-1939; resumed 1945. 5/yr. 75000 Zl.($28) Towarzystwo Milosnikow Jezyka Polskiego, Straszewskiego 27, 31-113 Krakow, Poland. TEL 22-26-99. (Dist. by: Ars Polona- Ruch, Krakowskie Przedmiescie 7, Warsaw, Poland) Ed. Stanislaw Urbanczyk. adv.; bk.rev.; index. **Indexed:** Bibl.Ling., M.L.A. **Document type:** academic/scholarly publication.
Description: Focuses mainly on the history, and dialectology of the Polish language.

JEZYKI OBCE W SZKOLE. see *EDUCATION*

418   PL   ISSN 0137-1444
JEZYKOZNAWSTWO STOSOWANE/APPLIED LINGUISTICS. 1975. irreg. price varies. Adam Mickiewica University Press, Marchlewskiego 128, 61-874 Poznan, Poland. **Document type:** monographic series.

437.897   GW   ISSN 0720-6666
JIDISCHE SCHTUDIES. 1981. irreg. price varies. Helmut Buske Verlag GmbH, Richardstr. 47, 22081 Hamburg, Germany. TEL 040-296842. FAX 040-2993614. Ed. Walter Roll. **Document type:** monographic series.

496   GW   ISSN 0167-6164
PL8000
JOURNAL OF AFRICAN LANGUAGES AND LINGUISTICS. (Text in English) 1979. 2/yr. DM.72 to individuals; institutions DM.143. Walter de Gruyter und Co., Mouton de Gruyter, Genthiner Str. 13, 10785 Berlin, Germany. TEL 030-26005-0. FAX 030-26005-251. (U.S. addr.: Walter de Gruyter, Inc., 200 Saw Mill Rd., Hawthorne, NY 10532) Ed. Gerrit Dimmendaal. bk.rev. (back issues avail.; reprint service avail. from SWZ) **Indexed:** Anthropol.Lit., Bibl.Ling., Documentatieblad, Lang.& Lang.Behav.Abstr. (1979-), M.L.A. **Document type:** academic/scholarly publication.
—BLDSC (4919.993000); Faxon; UnCover; UMI. CCC.
Description: International academic journal in the African language field.

JOURNAL OF ASIAN PACIFIC COMMUNICATION. see *COMMUNICATIONS*

491.66   UK   ISSN 0962-1377
                                 CODEN: JCLNE9
JOURNAL OF CELTIC LINGUISTICS. 1991. a. £10. University of Wales Press, 6 Gwennyth St., Cathays, Cardiff CF2 4YD, Wales. TEL 0222-231919. FAX 0222-230908. Ed. Martin Ball. adv.; bk.rev. circ. 750. **Document type:** academic/scholarly publication.
—BLDSC (4955.053000).

JOURNAL OF CHILD LANGUAGE. see *CHILDREN AND YOUTH — About*

495.1   US   ISSN 0091-3723
PL1001
JOURNAL OF CHINESE LINGUISTICS. 1973. s-a. $25 to individuals; institutions $35. Project on Linguistic Analysis, 2222 Piedmont Ave., Berkeley, CA 94720. TEL 510-642-5939. Ed. William S.-Y. Wang. adv.; bk.rev.; bibl.; cum.index every 5 yrs. circ. 450. **Indexed:** Bibl.Ling., C.I.J.E., Curr.Cont., Lang.& Lang.Behav.Abstr. (1973-), M.L.A. **Document type:** academic/scholarly publication.
—BLDSC (4958.100000); Faxon; UnCover.
Description: Publishes articles on all aspects of the Chinese language, including relevant contributions on neighboring languages.
Refereed Serial

495.1   US
JOURNAL OF CHINESE LINGUISTICS MONOGRAPH SERIES. 1982. irreg., no.4, 1991. price varies. Project on Linguistic Analysis, 2222 Piedmont Ave., Berkeley, CA 94720. TEL 510-642-5939. Ed. William S.-Y. Wang. (back issues avail.) **Document type:** academic/scholarly publication, monographic series.
Description: Contributions on all aspects of Chinese, including related and neighboring languages.
Refereed Serial

495   NE   ISSN 0925-8558
PJ2
▼**JOURNAL OF EAST ASIAN LINGUISTICS.** (Text in English) 1992. 3/yr. fl.303($158.50) (effective 1994). Kluwer Academic Publishers, Postbus 17, 3300 AA Dordrecht, Netherlands. TEL 31-78-334911. FAX 31-78-334254. TELEX 29245 KAPG NL. (Dist. by: Kluwer Academic Publishers Group, P.O. Box 322, 3300 AH Dordrecht, Netherlands. TEL 31-78-524400. FAX 31-78-524474; N. America dist. addr.: Box 358, Accord Sta., Hingham, MA 02018-0358. TEL 617-871-6600. FAX 617-871-6528) Eds. C.-T. James Huang, S.-Y. Kuroda. bk.rev. (also avail. in microform from UMI; back issues avail.) **Indexed:** Arts & Hum Cit.Ind., Curr.Cont., Sociol.Abstr. **Document type:** academic/scholarly publication.
—BLDSC (4971.460000); UnCover; SWETS; UMI.
Description: Examines original research papers and review articles on theoretical work in East Asian language syntax, semantics, phonology, and morphology. Particular emphasis is on Chinese, Korean, and Japanese. Includes relevant contributions from cognate disciplines and comparative studies.
Refereed Serial

410 420 371.1   II   ISSN 0970-8332
JOURNAL OF ENGLISH AND FOREIGN LANGUAGES. (Text in English) 1988. s-a. Rs.25 (foreign $12 or £6). Central Institute of English and Foreign Languages, Hyderabad 500 007, India. Ed. R. Lalitha Eapen.
—BLDSC (4979.249000).
Description: Serves as a forum for the sharing of experiences and the discussion of problems related to the theory and practice of language and literature teaching.

420   US   ISSN 0075-4242
PE1001
JOURNAL OF ENGLISH LINGUISTICS. 1967. s-a. $15 to individuals; institutions $20. c/o University of Georgia, Athens, GA 30602. TEL 706-542-2246. Ed. William A. Kretzschmar, Jr. adv.; bk.rev. circ. 600. (back issues avail.) **Indexed:** Arts & Hum.Cit.Ind., Bibl.Ling., Curr.Cont., Ind.Bk.Rev.Hum., Lang.& Lang.Behav.Abstr. (1973-), M.L.A.
—UnCover; SWETS. CCC.
Description: Articles on the modern and historical periods of the English language.

420 375.4   NR   ISSN 0189-6652
PE1066
JOURNAL OF ENGLISH STUDIES. 1984. a. £N15($10) (Ademiya College of Education, Department of English) Ife Oluwa Ent. (Nigeria) Ltd., Ife Oluwa St., Ondo - Ore Ring Rd., P.O. Box 304, Ondo, Nigeria. TEL 034-610677. (Subscr. to: Adeyemi College of Education, c/o Business Mngr., P.M.B. 520, Ondo, Ondo State, Nigeria) Ed. Yemi Aboderin. adv.; bk.rev.; abstr. circ. 1,000. (back issues avail.)
Description: Disseminates empirical and non-empirical research reports in the field of English studies.

440 375.4   UK   ISSN 0959-2695
PC2001   CODEN: JFSLEP
JOURNAL OF FRENCH LANGUAGE STUDIES. 1991. s-a. £28($49) to individuals (overseas £37); institutions £44 (overseas £53 ($76)). Cambridge University Press, Edinburgh Bldg., Shaftesbury Rd., Cambridge CB2 2RU, England. TEL 0223-312393. FAX 0223-315052. (N. American addr.: Cambridge University Press, Journals Dept., 40 W. 20th St., New York, NY 10011. TEL 212-924-3900. FAX 212-691-3239) Ed.Bd. adv.; bk.rev. (back issues avail.) **Document type:** academic/scholarly publication.
—BLDSC (4986.535000); Faxon; SWETS.
Description: Covers the French language and linguistics, including sociolinguistics and discourse studies.

JOURNAL OF HELLENIC STUDIES. see *CLASSICAL STUDIES*

JOURNAL OF HISPANIC PHILOLOGY. see *LITERATURE*

LINGUISTICS

420 375.4   US   ISSN 0899-885X
PE1128.A2   CODEN: JENGEC
JOURNAL OF INTENSIVE ENGLISH STUDIES. 1982. a. $15 (foreign $20). University of Arizona, Center for English as a Second Language, CESL 100, Tuscon, AZ 85721. TEL 602-621-1362. FAX 602-621-9180. Ed. Frank Pialorsi. adv. circ. 500. (also avail. in microform from UMI; back issues avail.) **Indexed:** Lang.& Lang.Behav.Abstr.
—UnCover.
  Formerly: American Language Journal (ISSN 0734-7545)

495.6 375.4   JA
JOURNAL OF JAPANESE LINGUISTICS. (Text in English) 1972. a. 4,650 Yen. Nanzan University, J J L Office, Showa-ku, Nagoya 466, Japan. TEL 52-832-3111. FAX 52-832-5490. Eds. Yasuaki Abe, Yoko Sugioka. bk.rev. circ. 500. **Document type:** academic/scholarly publication.
  Formerly: Papers in Japanese Linguistics.
  Description: Publishes articles in various fields of linguistics, and on topics related to the Japanese language.

JOURNAL OF LINGUISTIC ANTHROPOLOGY. see ANTHROPOLOGY

400   UK   ISSN 0022-2267
P1
JOURNAL OF LINGUISTICS. (Text mainly in English, French, German, Russian; Cyrillic, IPA and Greek types where necessary) 1965. s-a. £49($93) to institutions (overseas $60). (Linguistics Association of Great Britain) Cambridge University Press, Edinburgh Bldg., Shaftesbury Rd., Cambridge CB2 2RU, England. TEL 0223-312393. FAX 0223-315052. TELEX 851817256. (N. American addr.: Cambridge University Press, Journals Dept., 40 W. 20th St., New York, NY 10011. TEL 212-924-3900. FAX 212-691-3239) Eds. Robert Borsley, Ian Roberts. adv.; bk.rev.; index. (also avail. in microform from UMI; back issues avail.; reprint service avail. from SWZ) **Indexed:** Abstr.Anthropol., Arts & Hum.Cit.Ind., Bibl.Ling., C.I.J.E., Curr.Cont., Hum.Ind., Ind.Bk.Rev.Hum., Lang.& Lang.Behav.Abstr. (1972-), Lang.Teach.& Ling.Abstr., M.L.A., Mass Spectr.Bull., Mid.East: Abstr.& Ind., Sociol.Abstr., SSCI. **Document type:** academic/scholarly publication.
—BLDSC (5010.480000); Faxon; UnCover; SWETS; UMI. CCC.
  Description: Features studies all branches of theoretical linguistics, including phonetics.

410 800   GW   ISSN 0341-7638
PN54
JOURNAL OF LITERARY SEMANTICS. 1972. 3/yr. DM.72 to individuals; institutions DM.96. Julius Groos Verlag, Hertzstr. 6, 69126 Heidelberg, Germany. TEL 06221-303621. FAX 06221-301993. Ed. Trevor Eaton. adv.; bk.rev. circ. 800. **Indexed:** Arts & Hum.Cit.Ind., Bibl.Ling., Curr.Cont., Ind.Bk.Rev.Hum., Lang.& Lang.Behav.Abstr. (1974-), Lang.Teach.& Ling.Abstr., M.L.A. **Document type:** academic/scholarly publication.
—BLDSC (5010.520000); Faxon; UnCover; SWETS. CCC.

401   NE   ISSN 0925-8531
P39   CODEN: JLLIEN
▼**JOURNAL OF LOGIC, LANGUAGE AND INFORMATION.** (Text in English) 1992. 4/yr. fl.353($184.50) (effective 1994). (European Foundation for Logic, Language and Information) Kluwer Academic Publishers, Postbus 17, 3300 AA Dordrecht, Netherlands. TEL 31-78-334911. FAX 31-78-334254. TELEX 29245 KAPG NL. (Dist. by: Kluwer Academic Publishers Group, P.O. Box 322, 3300 AH Dordrecht, Netherlands. TEL 31-78-524400. FAX 31-78-524474; N. America dist. addr.: Box 358, Accord Sta., Hingham, MA 02018-0358. TEL 617-871-6600. FAX 617-871-6528) Ed. Peter Gardenfors. bk.rev. (also avail. in microform from UMI; back issues avail.) **Indexed:** Sociol.Abstr., Zent.Math. **Document type:** academic/scholarly publication.
—BLDSC (5010.552270); SWETS; UMI.
  Description: Focuses on the logical and computational foundations of natural, formal and programming languages, including both theoretical foundations and interdisciplinary connections.
  Refereed Serial

410   US   ISSN 0195-475X
PM3961
JOURNAL OF MAYAN LINGUISTICS. (Text in English, Mayan) 1978. irreg. price varies. (Louisiana State University, Department of Geography and Anthropology) Geoscience Publications, Box 16010, Baton Rouge, LA 70893-6010. TEL 504-388-6245. FAX 504-388-2912. Ed. M. Jill Brody. adv.; bk.rev. circ. 125. **Indexed:** Anthropol.Lit., Bibl.Ling., Lang.& Lang.Behav.Abstr. (1984-). **Document type:** academic/scholarly publication.
  Description: Covers Mayan linguistics, language and culture, and linguistics in the Mayan heiroglyphs.

471 940.1   BE   ISSN 0778-9750
JOURNAL OF MEDIEVAL LATIN. 1991. a. 1650 BEF (effective 1994). N.V. Brepols, Steenweg op Tielen 68, 2300 Turnhout, Belgium. TEL 32-14-415463. FAX 32-14-428919. (back issues avail.) **Document type:** academic/scholarly publication.

410 301   UK   ISSN 0143-4632
P115
JOURNAL OF MULTILINGUAL & MULTICULTURAL DEVELOPMENT. 1980. bi-m. £29($57) to individuals; libraries £79($157); students £17($34). Multilingual Matters Ltd., Frankfurt Lodge, Clevedon Hall, Victoria Rd., Clevedon, Avon BS21 7SJ, England. TEL 0275-876519. FAX 0275-343096. Ed. John Edwards. adv.; bk.rev.; index. circ. 800. (back issues avail.) **Indexed:** Bibl.Ling., C.I.J.E., Chic.Per.Ind., Cont.Pg.Educ., Lang.& Lang.Behav.Abstr., Lang.Teach.& Ling.Abstr., M.L.A., Sp.Ed.Needs Abstr. **Document type:** academic/scholarly publication.
—BLDSC (5021.060000); Faxon; UnCover; SWETS. CCC.
  Description: Publishes research studies about mulitculturalism and multilingualism in education, psychology, sociology, second language learning, and bilingualism.

JOURNAL OF NEAR EASTERN STUDIES. see ARCHAEOLOGY

JOURNAL OF NEUROLINGUISTICS. see MEDICAL SCIENCES — Psychiatry And Neurology

492   SA   ISSN 0259-0131
PJ3001
JOURNAL OF NORTHWEST SEMITIC LANGUAGES. 1971. a. $37 (effective 1993). University of Stellenbosch, Department of Ancient Near Eastern Studies - Universiteit van Stellenbosch, Departement Ou Nabye Oosterse Studie, University, 7600 Stellenbosch, South Africa. TEL 27-2231-773203. Ed. Ferdinand E. Deist. **Indexed:** Bibl.Ling., M.L.A., Mid.East: Abstr.& Ind., New Test.Abstr., Old Test.Abstr., Rel.& Theol.Abstr. (1973-). **Document type:** academic/scholarly publication.
—BLDSC (5022.845000).
  Supersedes: Journal of North-West Semitic Languages (ISSN 0085-2414)

JOURNAL OF ONE-NAME STUDIES. see GENEALOGY AND HERALDRY

410   UK   ISSN 0095-4470
P221   CODEN: JPHNB9
JOURNAL OF PHONETICS. 1973. q. £135 (effective 1994). Academic Press Ltd. (Subsidiary of: Harcourt Brace & Company Ltd.), 24-28 Oval Rd., London NW1 7DX, England. TEL 44-71-267-4466. FAX 44-71-482-2293. TELEX 25775-ACPRES-G. (Subscr. to: Harcourt Brace & Company Ltd., Foots Cray High St., Sidcup, Kent DA14 5HP, England. TEL 44-81-300-3322) Ed. M.E. Beckman. bk.rev.; index. charts; index. **Indexed:** Abstr.Anthropol., Bibl.Ling., Curr.Cont., Lang.& Lang.Behav.Abstr. (1982-), Lang.Teach.& Ling.Abstr., M.L.A., Psychol.Abstr., SSCI. **Document type:** academic/scholarly publication.
—BLDSC (5034.550000); Faxon; UnCover; SWETS. CCC.
  Description: Contains papers of an experimental or theoretical nature that deal with phonetic aspects of language and linguistic communication processes.

410   NE   ISSN 0920-9034
PM7831
JOURNAL OF PIDGIN AND CREOLE LANGUAGES. (Text in English) 1986. 2/yr. fl.205($119) (effective 1994). John Benjamins Publishing Co., Amsteldijk 44, P.O. Box 75577, 1070 AN Amsterdam, Netherlands. TEL 31-20-6738156. FAX 31-20-6792956. (In N. America: 821 Bethlehem Pike, Philadelphia, PA 19118. TEL 215-836-1200. FAX 215-836-1204) Ed. Glenn Gilbert. bk.rev. circ. 650. (back issues avail.) **Indexed:** Bibl.Ling., Lang.& Lang.Behav.Abstr. (1986-). **Document type:** academic/scholarly publication.
—BLDSC (5040.323000); Faxon; UnCover.
  Description: Presents descriptive and theoretical research into pidgin and creole languages, and its application to language planning, education, and social reform.

407   US   ISSN 1066-2545
JOURNAL OF PLANNED LANGUAGES. (Text in English, Esperanto) 1991. 3/yr. $10. R.K. Harrison & Co., Box 547014, Orlando, FL 32854-7014. TEL 407-645-3031. Ed. Rick Harrison. bk.rev.; bibl. (back issues avail.) **Document type:** academic/scholarly publication.
  Formerly: Vidpuni.
  Description: Covers a variety of "universal languages" (languages invented for global communication and other purposes). Frequently includes samples of text in various languages.

410   NE   ISSN 0378-2166
P99.4.P72
JOURNAL OF PRAGMATICS; an interdisciplinary monthly of language studies. (Text in English, French, German) 1977. 12/yr. (in 2 vols./ 6 nos./vol.). fl.762($412) (effective 1994). North-Holland (Subsidiary of: Elsevier Science B.V.), P.O. Box 211, 1000 AE Amsterdam, Netherlands. TEL 31-20-5803911. FAX 31-20-5803598. TELEX 18582 ESPA NL. (Subscr. in U.S. and Canada to: Elsevier Science Inc., Box 882, Madison Sq. Sta., New York, NY 10159. TEL 212-989-5800. FAX 212-633-3990) Ed. Jacob L. Mey. adv.; bk.rev.; bibl.; index. (also avail. in microform from UMI; back issues avail., reprint service avail. SWZ) **Indexed:** Art.Int.Abstr., Bibl.Ling., Curr.Cont., Lang.& Lang.Behav.Abstr. (1977-), Lang.Teach.& Ling.Abstr., M.L.A., Phil.Ind., Psychol.Abstr., Sociol.Abstr., SSCI. **Document type:** academic/scholarly publication.
—BLDSC (5041.900000); Faxon; UnCover; SWETS. CCC.
  Description: Directed to linguists, sociologists, psychologists, anthropologists and artificial intelligence professionals; covers all aspects of pragmatic studies of language; includes applications in the information sciences, artificial intelligence, person-machine interaction and psychiatry.
  Refereed Serial

401   US   ISSN 0090-6905
P106   CODEN: JPLRB7
JOURNAL OF PSYCHOLINGUISTIC RESEARCH. 1971. bi-m. $385 (foreign $450) (effective 1994). Plenum Publishing Corp., 233 Spring St., New York, NY 10013-1578. TEL 212-620-8000. FAX 212-463-0742. TELEX 23-421139. Ed. R.W. Rieber. adv.; bibl.; charts; illus.; stat. (also avail. in microfilm from JSC; back issues avail.) **Indexed:** Abstr.Anthropol., Bibl.Ling., Biol.Abstr., Child Devel.Abstr., Commun.Abstr., Curr.Cont., Ind.Med., Lang.& Lang.Behav.Abstr. (1973-), Lang.Teach.& Ling.Abstr., M.L.A., Mid.East: Abstr.& Ind., Psychol.Abstr., Ref.Zh., Sociol.Abstr., SSCI, Stud.Wom.Abstr. **Document type:** academic/scholarly publication.
—BLDSC (5043.285000); Faxon; SWETS; UMI. CCC.
  Refereed Serial

375.4 420   US   ISSN 0022-4111
LB1050   CODEN: JRBEAX
JOURNAL OF READING BEHAVIOR. 1969. q. $60 (foreign $70). National Reading Conference, Inc., 200 N. Michigan Ave., 3rd Fl, Chicago, IL 60601-5909. TEL 312-541-1272. Ed. Leslie Morrow. adv.; bk.rev.; index. circ. 2,000. (also avail. in microform from UMI; reprint service avail. from UMI) **Indexed:** C.I.J.E., Commun.Abstr., Cont.Pg.Educ., Curr.Cont., Educ.Ind., ERIC, Lang.& Lang.Behav.Abstr., Psychol.Abstr., SSCI. **Document type:** academic/scholarly publication.
—BLDSC (5047.600000); Faxon; UnCover; SWETS; UMI.

400   US   ISSN 1060-3743
PE1128
▼JOURNAL OF SECOND LANGUAGE WRITING. 1992. 3/yr. $40 to individuals; institutions $80. Ablex Publishing Corporation, 355 Chestnut St., Norwood, NJ 07648. TEL 201-767-8450. FAX 201-767-6717. TELEX 135-393.
—BLDSC (5062.490000).

410   UK   ISSN 0167-5133
P325   CODEN: JOSEEX
JOURNAL OF SEMANTICS. 1982. 4/yr. £62($119) (effective 1994). Oxford University Press, Oxford Journals, Walton St., Oxford OX2 6DP, England. TEL 0865-56767. FAX 0865-56646. TELEX 837330-OXPRES-G. (U.S. subscr. to: Oxford University Press Inc., 2001 Evans Rd., Cary, NC 27513. TEL 919-667-0977) Ed. Peter Bosch. adv. contact: Jane Parker. bk.rev. circ. 500. (reprint service avail. from SWZ) **Indexed:** Bibl.Ling., Lang.& Lang.Behav.Abstr. (1984-), Lang.Teach.& Ling.Abstr. **Document type:** academic/scholarly publication.
—BLDSC (5063.380000); Faxon; UnCover; SWETS; UMI. **CCC.**
Description: Aims at an integration of philosophical, psychological and linguistic semantics as well as work done in artificial intelligence.

410   UK   ISSN 0022-4480
PJ3001
JOURNAL OF SEMITIC STUDIES. 1955. s-a. £57($107) (effective 1994). (University of Manchester, Department of Near Eastern Studies) Oxford University Press, Oxford Journals, Walton St., Oxford OX2 6DP, England. TEL 0865-56767. FAX 0865-56646. TELEX 837330-OXPRES-G. (U.S. subscr. to: Oxford University Press Inc., 2001 Evans Rd., Cary, NC 27513. TEL 919-677-0977) Ed.Bd. adv. contact: Jane Parker. bk.rev.; bibl.; index. circ. 800. (also avail. in microform from UMI; reprint service avail. from SWZ,UMI) **Indexed:** Amer.Hist.& Life, Arts & Hum.Cit.Ind., Bibl.Ling., Br.Hum.Ind., Curr.Cont., Hist.Abstr., M.L.A., Mid.East: Abstr.& Ind., New Test.Abstr., Old Test.Abstr., Rel.& Theol.Abstr. (1967-), Rel.Ind.One, Rel.Per. **Document type:** academic/scholarly publication.
—BLDSC (5063.500000); Faxon; UnCover; SWETS; UMI. **CCC.**
Description: Addresses the modern and ancient Near East, with emphasis on research into the languages and literatures of the area.

JOURNAL OF SPEECH LANGUAGE PATHOLOGY AND AUDIOLOGY/REVUE D'ORTHOPHONIE ET D'AUDIOLOGIE. see EDUCATION — Special Education And Rehabilitation

494 894   II   ISSN 0022-4855
PL4758.A2
JOURNAL OF TAMIL STUDIES. (Text in English, Tamil) 1969. s-a. Rs.40($12) International Institute of Tamil Studies, C.P.T. Campus, T.T.T.I. Post, Madras 600113, Tamil Nadu, India. Ed. A.N. Perumal. adv.; bk.rev.; bibl.; charts; stat. circ. 2,000. **Indexed:** Bibl.Ling., M.L.A. **Document type:** academic/scholarly publication.
Description: Features objective writing covering areas such as literature, music, dance, history, culture, sculpture, folklore, linguistics and philosophy.

407 220 378   US   ISSN 1055-4513
JOURNAL OF TRANSLATION AND TEXTLINGUISTICS. Abbreviated title: J O T T. 1987. 4/yr. price varies. Summer Institute of Linguistics, Inc., Academic Publications, 7500 W. Camp Wisdom Rd., Dallas, TX 75236. TEL 214-709-2403. Ed. Robert L. Longacre. **Document type:** academic/scholarly publication.
—BLDSC (5069.864000).
Formerly (until 1991): Translation and Textlinguistics. Occasional Papers (ISSN 0890-7749).

496   US   ISSN 0022-5401
PL8017
JOURNAL OF WEST AFRICAN LANGUAGES. (Text in English and French) 1964. s-a. $18 to individuals; institutions $30. West African Linguistic Society, 7500 W. Camp Wisdom Rd., Dallas, TX 75236. TEL 214-709-2427. FAX 214-709-2433. Ed. John Bendor-Samuel. adv.; bk.rev.; bibl.; charts; illus. circ. 160. (also avail. in microform; back issues avail.) **Indexed:** Abstr.Anthropol., Bibl.Ling., Lang.& Lang.Behav.Abstr. (1985-), M.L.A., Sociol.Abstr. **Document type:** academic/scholarly publication.
—Faxon; UnCover.

499.992   YU   ISSN 0022-6025
JUGOSLAVIA FERVOJISTO. (Text in Esperanto) vol.11, 1956. bi-m. 200 din. Savez Zeleznicara Esperantista Jugoslavije, Nemanjina 6, Belgrade, Serbia, Yugoslavia. TEL 38-681-286. FAX 641-352. TELEX 11166. Ed. Gvozden Sredic. adv.; bk.rev.

407   YU   ISSN 0350-185X
PG1
JUZNOSLOVENSKI FILOLOG. (Text in Slavic languages, English, French, German) 1913. a. 500 din.($17) Srpska Akademija Nauka i Umetnosti, Institut za Srpskohrvatski Jezik - Serbian Academy of Science and Arts, Knez Mihailova 35, 11000 Belgrade, Serbia, Yugoslavia. TEL 011-635-590. Ed. Milka Ivic. bk.rev. circ. 800. (back issues avail.) **Indexed:** Bibl.Ling.
Description: Contains papers about Serbo-Croatian language, Slavic linguistics and general linguistics.

375.4   GW   ISSN 0939-9275
K L A G E. (Koelner Linguistische Arbeiten - Germanistik) 1979. irreg. price varies. Gabel Verlag, Juelichstr. 7, 50354 Huerth-Efferen, Germany. TEL 02233-63550. FAX 02233-65866. Ed. Heinz Vater. circ. 300. **Indexed:** Bibl.Ling. **Document type:** monographic series.

491.92   LI   ISSN 0130-2795
KALBOS KULTURA. 1961. a. exchange basis. Lietuvos Mokslu Akademija, Lietuviu Kalbos Institutas - Lithuanian Academy of Sciences, Institute of Lithuanian Language, Antakalnio g., 6, Vilnius, Lithuania. TEL 22-60-53. Ed. P. Kniuksta. bk.rev.; bibl. **Document type:** academic/scholarly publication.
—BLDSC (5081.950000).

KATOLICKI UNIWERSYTET LUBELSKI. WYDZIAL HISTORYCZNO-FILOLOGICZNY. ROZPRAWY. see HISTORY

400 800   ER   ISSN 0131-1441
PH601
KEEL JA KIRJANDUS. 1958. m. $48 (effective 1993). (Estonian Academy of Sciences) Kirjastus Perioodika, Parnu mnt. 8, 0090 Tallinn, Estonia. TEL 0142-441-262. FAX 0142-442-484. (U.S. subscr. addr.: Imported Publications, Inc., 320 W. Ohio St., Chicago, IL 60610) Ed. Axel Tamm. bk.rev.; bibl.; charts; illus. circ. 1,500. **Indexed:** Bibl.Ling., M.L.A.
—BLDSC (5088.330000).

KEILSCHRIFTTEXTE AUS BOGHAZKOI. see ARCHAEOLOGY

410 511   JA   ISSN 0453-4611
KEIRYO KOKUGOGAKU/MATHEMATICAL LINGUISTICS. (Text mainly in Japanese; occasionally in English, French, German) 1957. q. 4400 Yen. Keiryo Kokugo Gakkai - Mathematical Linguistic Society of Japan, c/o Tokyo Joshi Daigaku, 6-1, Zenpukuji 2-chome, Suginami-ku, Tokyo 167, Japan. TEL 03-3395-1211. Ed. Sin-ichi Tsuchiya. bk.rev.; index. circ. 600. **Indexed:** M.L.A. **Document type:** academic/scholarly publication.
—BLDSC (5402.400000).
Description: Covers quantitative, mathematical and computational linguistics.

420 375.4 500   CC
KEJI YINGYU XUEXI/LEARNING ENGLISH FOR SCIENCE & TECHNOLOGY. (Text in Chinese and English) m. $19.70. Shanghai Jiaotong Daxue, Keji Yingyu Xuexi Bianjibu, 1954, Huashan Lu, Shanghai 200030. TEL 310310. (Dist. in US by: China Books & Periodicals, Inc., 2929 24th San Francisco, CA 94110. TEL 415-282-2994) Ed. Wu Yingeng.

420 820   US   ISSN 0023-0197
KENTUCKY ENGLISH BULLETIN. 1951. 3/yr. $10 (foreign $12). Kentucky Council of Teachers of English - Language Arts, Western Kentucky University, Dept. of English, Bowling Green, KY 42101. TEL 502-745-3043. FAX 502-745-5760. Ed. John Hagaman. bk.rev. circ. 850. (also avail. in microform) **Indexed:** Lang.& Lang.Behav.Abstr. **Document type:** bulletin.
Description: Articles and essays. Each issue focuses on a single topic relevant to English grammar, composition, writing, linguistics, curricula, or literature.

491   KR
KHAR'KOVSKII GOSUDARSTVENNYI UNIVERSITET. FILOLOGIYA. (Subseries of: Khar'kovskii Gosudarstvennyi Universitet. Vestnik) 1964. a. 1.30 Rub. (Khar'kovskii Gosudarstvennyi Universitet) Izdatel'stvo Vysshaya Shkola, Khar'kovskoe Otdelenie, Ul. Universitetskaya 16, Khar'kov 310003, Ukraine. circ. 500.

418   FI   ISSN 1236-1771
KIELIKESKUSTELVA. m. FIM 70 (foreign FIM 100). Language Centre for Finnish Universities, University of Jyvaeskylae, SF-40351 Jyvaeskylae, Finland. TEL 358-41-60-35-35. FAX 358-41-60-35-21. Kannele Dufva. circ. 1,200. **Document type:** newsletter.
Formerly: Kielikeskusuutisia.

496.392 896.392   TZ   ISSN 0856-048X
PL8701
KISWAHILI. (Text in English, Swahili) a. $15. University of Dar es Salaam, Institute of Kiswahili Research, P.O. Box 35110, Dar es Salaam, Tanzania. FAX 010-255-5148274. Eds. E. Wesana-Chemi, H.J. Mwansoke. **Indexed:** Bibl.Ling., Documentatieblad, M.L.A. **Document type:** academic/scholarly publication.

KLASK. see LITERATURE

410 800   GW   ISSN 0453-9842
PT4848.G7
KLAUS GROTH GESELLSCHAFT. JAHRESGABEN. 1964. a. price varies. Westholsteinische Verlagsanstalt Boyens und Co., Am Wulf-Isebrand-Platz, 25746 Heide, Germany. TEL 0481-691-0. Ed.Bd. illus. **Indexed:** M.L.A.

491 891   YU
KNJIZEVNOST I JEZIK. (Text in Serbo-Croatian) 1954. q. 30 din. Drustvo za Srpskohrvatski Jezik i Knjizevnost Srbije, Knez Mihailova 35, Belgrade, Serbia, Yugoslavia. (Co-sponsor: Drustvo za Srpskohrvatski Jezik i Knjizevnost Crne Gore) Ed. Radoje Simic. **Indexed:** Bibl.Ling., M.L.A.
Formerly: Knjizevnost i Jezik u Skoli.

410 510   DK   ISSN 0106-8563
KOEBENHAVNS UNIVERSITET. INSTITUT FOR ANVENDT OG MATEMATISK LINGVISTIK. SKRIFTER. 1974. irreg. free. Koebenhavns Universitet, Institut for Anvendt og Matematisk Lingvistik, Njalsgade 96, Copenhagen S, Denmark. Ed.Bd. circ. 300.

410   DK   ISSN 0107-3265
KOEBENHAVNS UNIVERSITETS SLAVISKE INSTITUT. RAPPORTER. 1984. a. DKK 45.75. Koebenhavns Universitet, Norregade 10, DK-1165 Copenhagen K, Denmark.

410 800   BE   ISSN 0770-7762
KONINKLIJKE ACADEMIE VOOR NEDERLANDSE TAAL- EN LETTERKUNDE. JAARBOEK. 1887. a. price varies. Koninklijke Academie voor Nederlandse Taal- en Letterkunde, Koningstraat 18, B-9000 Ghent, Belgium. FAX 32-9-3232718.
Supersedes (in 1972): Koninklijke Vlaamse Academie voor Taal- en Letterkunde. Jaarboek (ISSN 0770-7711).

KONINKLIJKE ACADEMIE VOOR NEDERLANDSE TAAL- EN LETTERKUNDE. VERSLAGEN EN MEDEDELINGEN. see LITERATURE

KONTAKTO. see CHILDREN AND YOUTH — For

LINGUISTICS

410 800 GW ISSN 0941-5173
▼**KONTUREN**; Magazin fuer Sprache, Literatur und Landschaft. 1992. 4/yr. DM.51.20. Max Hueber Verlag, Max-Hueber-Str. 4, 85737 Ismaning, Germany. TEL 089-9602-0. FAX 089-9602-358. Ed. Stefan Zarges. adv. circ. 20,000. **Document type:** academic/scholarly publication.
 Description: The multiplicity of culture in Germany and other countries from the point of view of language, literature, landscape and history.

KOROSI CSOMA KISKONYVTAR. see *HISTORY — History Of Asia*

430 GW ISSN 0023-4567
P501
KRATYLOS; kritisches Berichts- und Rezensionsorgan fuer indogermanische und allgemeine Sprachwissenschaft. (Text in English, French, German and Italian) 1956. a. DM.74. Dr. Ludwig Reichert Verlag, Tauernstr. 11, 65199 Wiesbaden, Germany. FAX 0611-468613. Ed. Ruediger Schmitt. adv.; bk.rev. circ. 700. **Indexed:** Bibl.Ling. **Document type:** academic/scholarly publication.
—SWETS. CCC.

430 375.4 GW ISSN 0720-9983
KREOLISCHE BIBLIOTHEK. 1981. irreg., vol.12, 1988. price varies. Helmut Buske Verlag GmbH, Richardstr. 47, 22081 Hamburg, Germany. TEL 040-296842. FAX 040-2993614. Ed. Annegret Bollee. **Document type:** monographic series.

430 800 LU ISSN 0340-9767
KRITIKON LITTERARUM; international book review for American, English, Romance and Slavic studies and for linguistics. (Text in English, German, French or Spanish) 1972. s-a. DM.340. Thesen Verlag, 3, Place de la Gare, L-6674 Mertert, Luxembourg. TEL 00352-748715. Ed.Bd. adv.; bk.rev.; bibl.; index. **Indexed:** Bibl.Ling. **Document type:** academic/scholarly publication.
—SWETS.

491.86 491.87 XO ISSN 0023-5202
PG5201
KULTURA SLOVA/CULTURE OF THE WORD. (Text in Slovak) 1966. 10/yr. 30 Kcs.($14) (Linguistic Institute of L'udovit Stur) Veda, Publishing House of the Slovak Academy of Sciences, Klemensova 19, 814 30 Bratislava, Slovakia. (Dist. in Western countries by: John Benjamins B.V., Amsteldijk 44, P.O. Box 75577, 1070 AN Amsterdam, Netherlands. TEL 020-6762325) Ed. Jan Kacala. bk.rev.; bibl.; illus.; index. **Indexed:** Bibl.Ling.
 Formerly: Ceskoslovensky Terminologicky Casopis.
 Description: Covers the theoretical problems of language culture as well as practical problems of language practice and stylistical appropriateness.

KUNAPIPI. see *LITERATURE*

400 SW ISSN 0083-6745
P17
KUNGLIGA VITTERHETS HISTORIE OCH ANTIKVITETS AKADEMIEN. FILOLOGISKT ARKIV. (Text in English, French, German, Spanish or Swedish) 1955. irreg., no.37, 1993. price varies. Kungliga Vitterhets Historie och Antikvitets Akademien - Royal Academy of Letters, History and Antiquities, P.O. Box 5622, S-114 86 Stockholm, Sweden. (Dist. by: Almqvist & Wiksell International, P.O. Box 4627, S-116 91 Stockholm, Sweden) index.

400 100 SW ISSN 0083-677X
AS284
KUNGLIGA VITTERHETS HISTORIE OCH ANTIKVITETS AKADEMIEN. HANDLINGAR. FILOLOGISK-FILOSOFISKA SERIEN/ROYAL ACADEMY OF LETTERS, HISTORY AND ANTIQUITIES. PROCEEDINGS. PHILOLOGICAL-PHILOSOPHICAL SERIES. (Text in English, French, German and Swedish) 1954. irreg., no.20, 1983. price varies. Kungliga Vitterhets Historie, och Antikvitets Akademien, P.O. Box 5622, S-114 86 Stockholm, Sweden. (Dist. by: Almqvist & Wiksell International, P.O. Box 4627, S-11691, Stockholm, Sweden) index.

410 GW ISSN 0721-4340
KUSCHITISCHE SPRACHSTUDIEN/CUSHITIC LANGUAGE STUDIES. 1982. irreg., vol.9, 1991. price varies. Helmut Buske Verlag GmbH, Richardstr. 47, 22081 Hamburg, Germany. TEL 040-296842. FAX 040-2993614. Ed. H.-J. Sasse. **Document type:** monographic series.

400 PL ISSN 0023-5911
PB5
KWARTALNIK NEOFILOLOGICZNY. (Text in various languages) 1954. q. $48. (Polska Akademia Nauk, Komitet Neofilologiczny) Wydawnictwo Naukowe P W N, Ul. Miodowa 10, 00-251 Warsaw, Poland. Ed. F. Grucza. bk.rev.; charts; index. circ. 600. **Indexed:** Abstr.Engl.Stud., Bibl.Ling., Lang.& Lang.Behav.Abstr., M.L.A.
—SWETS.

KYOIKU KENKYU/EDUCATIONAL STUDIES. see *EDUCATION*

410 572 FR ISSN 0754-2445
L A C I T O DOCUMENTS AFRIQUE. (Subseries of: Bibliotheque de la S E L A F) 1978. irreg., no.10, 1987. price varies. (Laboratoire de Langues et Civilisations a Tradition Orale) Societe d'Etudes Linguistiques et Anthropologiques de France (SELAF), 52 bd. St. Michel, 75006 Paris, France. TEL 42-08-83-93. (Dist. by: Editions Peeters s.p.r.l., Bondgenotenlaan 153, B-3000 Louvain, Belgium. TEL 32-16-235170. FAX 32-16-228500) **Document type:** academic/scholarly publication.

410 572 FR ISSN 0751-4875
L A C I T O DOCUMENTS ASIE - AUSTRONESIE. (Subseries of: Bibliotheque de la S E L A F) 1977. irreg., no.4, 1982. price varies. (Laboratoire de Langues et Civilisations a Tradition Orale) Societe d'Etudes Linguistiques et Anthropologiques de France (SELAF), 52 bd. St. Michel, 75006 Paris, France. TEL 42-08-83-93. (Dist. by: Editions Peeters s.p.r.l., Bondgenotenlaan 153, B-3000 Louvain, Belgium. TEL 32-16-235170. FAX 32-16-228500) **Document type:** academic/scholarly publication.

410 572 FR ISSN 0751-4883
L A C I T O DOCUMENTS EURASIE. (Subseries of: Bibliotheque de la S E L A F) 1978. irreg., no.7, 1984. price varies. (Laboratoire de Langues et Civilisations a Tradition Orale) Societe d'Etudes Linguistiques et Anthropologiques de France (SELAF), 52 bd. St. Michel, 75006 Paris, France. TEL 42-08-83-93. (Dist. by: Editions Peeters s.p.r.l., Bondgenotenlaan 153, B-3000 Louvain, Belgium. TEL 32-16-235170. FAX 32-16-228500) **Document type:** academic/scholarly publication.

410 US ISSN 0195-377X
P21
L A C U S FORUM. 1974. a. $30. (Linguistic Association of Canada and the United States) L A C U S, PO Box 101, Lake Bluff, IL 60044. TEL 708-234-3997. Ed. Valerie Makkai. circ. 1,000. **Indexed:** Bibl.Ling. **Document type:** proceedings.
 Description: Contains proceedings of the annual meeting of the association, along with the Presidents' Prize papers and the Robert J. Di Pietro Memorial Award paper.

L AE S. see *LITERATURE*

400 370 SW ISSN 0023-6330
L M S - LINGUA. (Supplement avail.: Spraakpedagogik) 1955. q. SEK 160. Riksfoereningen foer Laerarna i Moderna Spraak - Modern Language Teachers Association of Sweden, P.O. Box 41, S-425 02 Hisings-Kaerra, Sweden. Ed. Sverker Bengtsson. adv. circ. 4,800.
 Formerly (until 1967): Lingua; **(until 1966):** Spraaklaerarnas Medlemsblad.
 Description: Contains articles on languages and language teaching.

406 US ISSN 0023-6365
P11
L S A BULLETIN. no.43, 1970. q. membership. Linguistic Society of America, 1325 18th St., N.W., Ste. 211, Washington, DC 20036-6501. TEL 202-835-1714. Ed.Bd. adv.; bibl. circ. 7,000. **Document type:** newsletter.
—BLDSC (5300.390000); UMI.

492.4 296 US
LA-MATHIL (AMERICAN EDITION); a voweled Hebrew newspaper. 1954. fortn. $12. World Zionist Organization - American Section Inc., 110 E. 59th St., New York, NY 10022. TEL 212-339-6020. FAX 212-318-6176. Ed. Sam E. Bloch. illus. circ. 5,000. **Document type:** newspaper.

413.028 IT
LABORATORIO THESAURI. QUADERNI. 1990. irreg., no.3, 1994. IFNIA Laboratorio Thesauri, Borgo San Frediano 83, 50124 Florence, Italy. TEL 55-2298377.

427 UK
LAKELAND DIALECT. 1939. a. £3. Lakeland Dialect Society, c/o James T. Relph, Holly Cottage, Crosby Ravensworth, Penrith, Cumbria, CA10 3JP, England. TEL 09315-359. Ed. Ted Relph. bk.rev. circ. 600.
 Formerly: Lakeland Dialect Society. Journal (ISSN 0307-9341)
 Description: Contains stories, poems and articles by members, in the dialects of the former counties of Cumberland, Westmoreland and "Lancashire North of the Sands". Includes news of the society's activities.

491 UK
LALLANS; magazine for writing in Scots. (Text in Scots) 1973. s-a. £7. Scots Language Society, Sandeman Library, Kinnoull St., Perth PH1 5ET, Scotland. TEL 031-339-7929. (Subscr. to: John Mackay, 6 Cairn Walk, Aberdeen AB1 9TF, Scotland) Ed. David Purves. adv.; bk.rev. circ. 1,000. **Document type:** academic/scholarly publication.

492.4 IS ISSN 0333-9688
LAMED LESHONKHA. bi-m. $7. Academy of the Hebrew Language, PO Box 3449, 91 034 Jerusalem, Israel. circ. 15,000. **Document type:** academic/scholarly publication.

296.68 US ISSN 0894-9816
LAMISHPAHA. 1963. m. $15. Histadruth Ivrith of America, Inc., 47 W. 34th St., Rm. 609, New York, NY 10001-3012. TEL 212-629-9443. FAX 212-629-9472. Ed. Vered Raphaeli. adv. contact: Harold Galanter. bk.rev. circ. 6,500. (back issues avail.) **Document type:** newspaper.

410 BE ISSN 0458-7251
LE LANGAGE ET L'HOMME. (Text in English, French) 1966. q. 1450 BEF (Europe 1700 BEF; elsewhere 1750 BEF) (effective 1994). De Boeck Universite, Fond Jean-Paques 4, B-1348 Louvain-la-Neuve, Belgium. TEL 32-10-482509. FAX 32-10-482519. Ed. B. Devlamminck. **Indexed:** Bibl.Ling. **Document type:** academic/scholarly publication.
—BLDSC (5155.668000).
 Description: Publishes original studies in linguistics and philology.

301 410 FR ISSN 0181-4095
P40
LANGAGE ET SOCIETE. 1977. q. 180 F. to individuals (foreign 250 F.); institutions 220 F. (foreign 290 F.). Maison des Sciences de l'Homme, 54 bd. Raspail, 75270 Paris Cedex 06, France. TEL 45-48-83-53. FAX 45-44-05-13. TELEX MSH 203 104 F. (Dist. by: C.I.D., 131 bd. St-Michel, 75005 Paris, France. TEL 43-54-47-15) (Co-Sponsor: Centre National de la Recherche Scientifique) Ed. Pierre Achard. bk.rev. circ. 500. (back issues avail.) **Indexed:** Bibl.Ling.
—BLDSC (5155.669000).
 Description: Concerned with studies of sociolinguistics, sociology of language, discourse, history of language.

400 FR
LANGAGES; semiotiques textuelles. 1966. q. 310 F. Larousse, 17, rue du Montparnasse, 75280 Paris Cedex 06, France. (Dist. by: Gauthier-Villars, Centrale des Revues, 11 rue Gossin, 92543 Montrouge Cedex, France. TEL 1-46-56-52-66) circ. 4,000. (reprint service avail. from SWZ) **Indexed:** Bibl.Ling., Lang.& Lang.Behav.Abstr, Lang.Teach.& Ling.Abstr., M.L.A.

370 GW ISSN 0023-8252
LANGENSCHEIDTS SPRACH-ILLUSTRIERTE; a German language journal. (Text in German; summaries in English, French, Spanish) 1954. 4/yr. DM.14. Verlag Langenscheidt KG, Postfach 401120, 80711 Munich, Germany. TEL 089-36096-0. FAX 089-36096258. illus. circ. 11,500. **Document type:** academic/scholarly publication.

400 US ISSN 0097-8507
P1
LANGUAGE (WASHINGTON). 1925. q. $55 to individuals; students $25; institutions $75. Linguistic Society of America, 1325 18th St., N.W., Ste. 211, Washington, DC 20036-6501. Ed Sarah Thomason. adv.; bk.rev.; charts; illus.; index. circ. 6,500. (also avail. in microfilm; back issues avail.; reprint service avail. from KTO) **Indexed:** A.I.C.P., Anthropol.Lit., Chic.Per.Ind., Hum.Ind., Ind.Bk.Rev.Hum., Lang.& Lang.Behav.Abstr. (1972-), Lang.Teach.& Ling.Abstr., Psychol.Abstr., SSCI. **Document type:** academic/scholarly publication.
—BLDSC (5155.690000); Faxon; UnCover; SWETS; UMI.

410 US ISSN 1048-9223
P118 CODEN: LAACEV
LANGUAGE ACQUISITION; a journal of developmental linguistics. 1990. q. $30 to individuals (foreign $55); institutions $100 (foreign $125). Lawrence Erlbaum Associates, Inc., 365 Broadway, Hillsdale, NJ 07642. TEL 201-666-4110. FAX 201-666-2394. Ed.Bd. **Indexed:** Bibl.Ling. **Document type:** academic/scholarly publication.
—BLDSC (5155.692000); UnCover; SWETS.
Description: Provides a forum for the integration of studies over a wide range of topics related to fundamental questions about how language is learned.
Refereed Serial

410 UK ISSN 0169-0965
CODEN: LCPRET
LANGUAGE AND COGNITIVE PROCESSES. 1985? 4/yr. £44($86) to individuals; institutions £132 ($264). Lawrence Erlbaum Associates Ltd., 27 Palmeira Mansions, Church Rd., Hove, E. Sussex BN3 2FA, England. TEL 0273-207411. FAX 0273-205612. (Co-publisher: V.S.P.) Ed. Lorraine K. Tyler. adv. **Indexed:** Bibl.Ling., Lang.& Lang.Behav.Abstr., Psychol.Abstr. **Document type:** academic/scholarly publication.
—BLDSC (5155.693600); Faxon; UnCover; SWETS.
Description: Provides an international forum for the publication of theoretical and experimental research into the mental processes and representations involved in language use.
Refereed Serial

410 301.16 UK ISSN 0271-5309
P87 CODEN: LACOD8
LANGUAGE & COMMUNICATION. 1981. 4/yr. £152($235) (effective 1994). Elsevier Science Ltd., Pergamon, P.O. Box 800, Kidlington, Oxford OX5 1DX, England. TEL 44-865-843000. FAX 44-865-843010. (Subscr. in U.S. and Canada to: Elsevier Science, 660 White Plains Rd., Tarrytown, NY 10591-5153. TEL 914-524-9200. FAX 914-333-2444) Eds. R. Harris, T. Taylor. (also avail. in microfilm from UMI) **Indexed:** Art.Int.Abstr., Bibl.Ling., Lang.& Lang.Behav.Abstr. (1981-), Lang.Teach.& Ling.Abstr., M.L.A., Psychol.Abstr., Sci.Abstr., SSCI. **Document type:** academic/scholarly publication.
—Faxon; UnCover; SWETS; UMI. **CCC**.
Refereed Serial

408 301.2 JA
LANGUAGE AND CULTURE. (Text in English, French, German, or Japanese) 1982. s-a. Hokkaido University, Institute of Language and Culture Studies, Nishi 8, Kita 17, Kita-ku, Sapporo 060, Japan. circ. 200. **Indexed:** M.L.A.
Supersedes: Essays in Foreign Languages and Literature.

407 UK ISSN 0950-0782
LANGUAGE AND EDUCATION; an international journal. 1987. q. £27($53) to individuals; libraries £77($147); students £16($32). Multilingual Matters Ltd., Frankfurt Lodge, Clevedon Hall, Victoria Rd., Clevedon, Avon BS21 7SJ, England. TEL 0275-876519. FAX 0275-343096. Eds. David Corson, Viv Edwards. **Document type:** academic/scholarly publication.
—BLDSC (5155.694450); SWETS.
Description: Studies the educational implications of research in all aspects of linguistics.

LANGUAGE AND EDUCATIONAL PROCESSES. see EDUCATION — Teaching Methods And Curriculum

LANGUAGE AND IDEOLOGY. see POLITICAL SCIENCE

410 800 US ISSN 1057-6037
PB1
LANGUAGE AND LITERATURE. 1975. a. $25 to individuals; institutions $30. (Trinity University) Pitman Press, P.O. Box 791786, San Antonio, TX 78279-1786. TEL 210-736-7369. FAX 210-736-8512. Ed. Bates L. Hoffer. bk.rev.; bibl.; illus. circ. 150. **Indexed:** M.L.A. **Document type:** academic/scholarly publication.
—BLDSC (5155.696240).
Formerly: Linguistics in Literature (ISSN 0147-0906)

410 UK ISSN 0963-9470
▼**LANGUAGE AND LITERATURE**. 1992. 3/yr. £29($54) to individuals; institutions £48($89). Longman Group UK Ltd., Longman House, Burnt Mill, Harlow, Essex CM20 2JE, England. TEL 0279-426721. FAX 0279-431059. Ed.Bd. adv.; bk.rev. (back issues avail.) **Document type:** academic/scholarly publication.
—UnCover.

410 UK ISSN 0023-8309
P1
LANGUAGE AND SPEECH. 1958. q. £120($220) Kingston Press Services Ltd., 43 Derwent Rd., Whitton, Twickenham, Middlesex TW2 7HQ, England. TEL 081-893-3015. Ed. Bruno H. Repp. adv.; bk.rev.; bibl.; charts; illus.; index. circ. 1,000. (also avail. in microform; reprint service avail. from SCH) **Indexed:** Bibl.Ling., C.I.J.E., Commun.Abstr., Curr.Cont., Dent.Ind., DSH Abstr., Ind.Med., Lang.& Lang.Behav.Abstr. (1972-), Lang.Teach.& Ling.Abstr., M.L.A., Mid.East: Abstr.& Ind., Psychol.Abstr., SSCI. **Document type:** academic/scholarly publication.
—BLDSC (5155.700000); Faxon; UnCover; SWETS; UMI.
Description: Speech transmission and reception.

400 US ISSN 0023-8317
PN203
LANGUAGE AND STYLE; an international journal. (Text in English, French, German) 1968. q. $16 to individuals (foreign $18); institutions $22 (foreign $25). (City University of New York, Queens College, Department of English) Queens College Press, c/o John Cassidy, Kiely 1309, Flushing, NY 11367. TEL 718-520-7773. Ed. Edmund L. Epstein. bk.rev.; charts; stat.; index. circ. 700. (back issues avail.) **Indexed:** Abstr.Engl.Stud., Amer.Hum.Ind., Arts & Hum.Cit.Ind., Can.Rev.Comp.Lit., Curr.Cont., Ind.Bk.Rev.Hum., Lang.& Lang.Behav.Abstr., M.L.A., Mid.East: Abstr.& Ind. **Document type:** academic/scholarly publication.
—Faxon; UnCover; SWETS.

054.1 KE
LANGUAGE ASSOCIATION OF EASTERN AFRICA. JOURNAL. 2/yr. (Language Association of Eastern Africa) Ministry of Information & Broadcasting, P.O. Box 30571, Nairobi, Kenya. TEL 28411. TELEX 22244. Ed. T.P. Gorman.

410 UK ISSN 0965-8416
▼**LANGUAGE AWARENESS**. 1992. q. £27($53) to individuals; libraries £74($147). Multilingual Matters Ltd., Frankfurt Lodge, Clevedon Hall, Victoria Rd., Clevedon, Avon BS21 7SJ, England. TEL 0275-876519. FAX 0275-343096. Ed. Peter Garrett. **Document type:** academic/scholarly publication.
—BLDSC (5155.708367). **CCC**.
Description: Disseminates work that explores the role of explicit knowledge about language in the process of language learning; the role that such explicit knowledge about language plays in language teaching; and, the role of explicit knowledge about language in language use.

407 UK ISSN 0790-8318
LANGUAGE, CULTURE AND CURRICULUM. 1988. 3/yr. £21($43) to individuals; libraries £59($117); students £13($26). (Linguistic Institute of Ireland) Multilingual Matters Ltd., Frankfurt Lodge, Clevedon Hall, Victoria Rd., Clevedon, Avon BS21 7SJ, England. TEL 0275-876519. FAX 0275-343096. Ed. Eoghan MacAogain. circ. 400. **Indexed:** Bibl.Ling., Lang.& Lang.Behav.Abstr. (1988-). **Document type:** academic/scholarly publication.
—BLDSC (5155.708370); UnCover; SWETS.
Description: Covers bilingualism, multiculturalism, language contact, lesser-used languages, cultural studies.
Refereed Serial

491.1 II ISSN 0253-9071
P1.A1
LANGUAGE FORUM. (Text in English) 1975. s-a. Rs.200($50) Bahri Publications, 997-A St., No. 9, Gobindpuri, Kalkaji, New Delhi 110 019, India. TEL 644-8606. Ed. Ujjal Singh Bahri. adv.; bk.rev. **Document type:** academic/scholarly publication.
Description: Contians articles on current trends in Indian literature; emphasizes curriculum planning, linguistic analyses of Indian languages, dialects and comparative literature.

410 UK ISSN 1351-024X
LANGUAGE FORUM. 1976. 2/yr. £8 to individuals; institutions £12. University of East Anglia, Centre for Research in Linguistics and in Language Learning, Norwich NR4 7TJ, England. TEL 0603-56161. FAX 0603-259490. Ed. John Hutchins. circ. 200. (back issues avail.) **Indexed:** Lang.& Lang.Behav.Abstr. (1961-), Lang.Teach.& Ling.Abstr. **Document type:** academic/scholarly publication.
Formerly (until 1992): U E A Papers in Linguistics (ISSN 0951-2292)

410 II ISSN 0254-0207
LANGUAGE FORUM MONOGRAPH SERIES. 1978. irreg. price varies. Bahri Publications, 997-A, Street No.9, Gobindpuri, Kalkaji, New Delhi 110 019, India. TEL 644-8606. Ed. Ujjal Singh Bahri. **Document type:** monographic series.
Description: Focuses on a single theme connected to language, linguistics or literature in each issue.

410 GW
LANGUAGE IN PERFORMANCE. irreg., no.10, 1994. DM.78. Gunter Narr Verlag, Postfach 2567, 72015 Tuebingen, Germany. TEL 07071-78091. FAX 07071-75288. Ed. Franz Poechhacker. **Document type:** monographic series.

400 UK ISSN 0047-4045
P41 CODEN: LGSCBO
LANGUAGE IN SOCIETY. 1972. q. £29($49) to individuals (overseas £43.50); institutions £75 (overseas £89.50 ($103)). Cambridge University Press, Edinburgh Bldg., Shaftesbury Rd., Cambridge CB2 2RU, England. TEL 0223-312393. FAX 0223-315052. TELEX 851817256. (N. American addr.: Cambridge University Press, Journals Dept., 40 W. 20th St., New York, NY 10011. TEL 212-924-3900. FAX 212-691-3239) Ed. William Bright. adv.; bk.rev. (also avail. in microform from UMI; back issues avail.; reprint service avail. from SWZ) **Indexed:** Abstr.Anthropol., Anthropol.Lit., ASSIA, Bibl.Ling., Bk.Rev.Ind. (1984-), C.I.J.E., Chic.Per.Ind., Child.Bk.Rev.Ind. (1984-), Commun.Abstr., Curr.Cont., E.I., Ind.Bk.Rev.Hum., Lang.& Lang.Behav.Abstr. (1972-), Lang.Teach.& Ling.Abstr., M.L.A., Mid.East: Abstr.& Ind., Psychol.Abstr., Sociol.Abstr., Sp.Ed.Needs Abstr., SSCI. **Document type:** academic/scholarly publication.
—BLDSC (5155.711800); Faxon; UnCover; SWETS; UMI. **CCC**.
Description: Covers sociolinguistics (i.e., speech and language as aspects of social life).

410 NE ISSN 0923-182X
P106 CODEN: LAINE2
LANGUAGE INTERNATIONAL; the magazine for language professionals. 1989. bi-m. fl.177($103) (effective 1994). John Benjamins Publishing Co., Amsteldijk 44, P.O. Box 75577, 1070 AN Amsterdam, Netherlands. TEL 31-20-6738156. FAX 31-20-6792956. (In N. America: 821 Bethlehem Pike, Philadelphia, PA 19118. TEL 215-836-1200. FAX 215-836-1204) Ed. Geoffrey Kingscott. index. circ. 2,500. **Indexed:** Bibl.Ling. **Document type:** academic/scholarly publication.
—BLDSC (5155.709680); UnCover; SWETS.
Description: Provides an international forum in which language professionals can exchange the latest information related to their work and research.
Refereed Serial

LINGUISTICS

418 370   US   ISSN 0023-8333
P1
LANGUAGE LEARNING; a journal of research in language studies. 1948. q. $42 to individuals; institutions $68. Research Club in Language Learning, 178 Henry S. Frieze Bldg., 105 S. State St., Ann Arbor, MI 48109-1285. TEL 313-763-9216. Ed. Alister H. Cumming. bk.rev.; charts; stat. circ. 2,000. (also avail. in microform from UMI) **Indexed:** C.I.J.E., Cont.Pg.Educ., Curr.Cont., E.I., Educ.Ind., Ind.Bk.Rev.Hum., Lang.& Lang.Behav.Abstr. (1972-), Lang.Teach.& Ling.Abstr., M.L.A., SSCI. **Document type:** academic/scholarly publication.
—BLDSC (5155.710000); Faxon; UnCover; SWETS; UMI.

400 371.33   UK   ISSN 0957-1736
P51   CODEN: LLEJED
LANGUAGE LEARNING JOURNAL. (Text mainly in English; occasionally in French, German, Russian, Spanish) 1962. s-a. £30($60) (overseas £33). Association for Language Learning, 16 Regent Pl., Rugby, Warks. CV21 2NP, England. TEL 44-788-546443. FAX 44-788-544149. Ed. C.A. Wringe. adv.; bk.rev.; film rev.; play rev.; abstr.; bibl.; charts; illus.; mkt.; stat.; index. circ. 6,000. (reprint service avail. from SWZ) **Indexed:** C.I.J.E., Cont.Pg.Educ., Curr.Cont., Educ.Tech.Abstr., Lang.& Lang.Behav.Abstr., Lang.Teach.& Ling.Abstr., Media Rev.Dig., Sp.Ed.Needs Abstr. **Document type:** academic/scholarly publication.
—BLDSC (5155.710200); Faxon; UnCover; SWETS.
Formed by the merger of: Modern Languages (ISSN 0026-7945) & British Journal of Language Teaching (ISSN 0144-0888); Which was formerly: Audio-Visual Language Journal (ISSN 0004-7589)
Description: Contains articles about teaching and learning languages; applied linguistics, language policy, and current issues; and ideas for practical classroom teaching.

418   US
LANGUAGE MAINTENANCE; a word user's manual. 1990. bi-m. $16. Language Maintenance, 2745 Winnetka Ave., New Hope, MN 55427. TEL 612-533-2427. Ed. Patricia Maynard. circ. 181.
Description: Focuses on the use and misuse of the English language.

428   SA
PE3452.S64
LANGUAGE MATTERS. 1970. a. R.15.73 (overseas $10.50) (effective 1994). University of South Africa, Department of English, P.O. Box 392, Pretoria 0001, South Africa. FAX 27-12-429-3221. TELEX 350068. Ed.Bd. bk.rev.; abstr. circ. 400. **Indexed:** Ind.S.A.Per. **Document type:** academic/scholarly publication.
Formerly (until 1993): English Usage in Southern Africa (ISSN 0256-5986)

499.992   NE   ISSN 0272-2690
P40.5.L35
LANGUAGE PROBLEMS AND LANGUAGE PLANNING. 1969. 3/yr. fl.138($80) (effective 1994). (Center for Research and Documentation on World Language Problems) John Benjamins Publishing Co., Amsteldijk 44, P.O. Box 75577, 1070 AN Amsterdam, Netherlands. TEL 31-20-6738156. FAX 31-20-6792956. (In N. America: 821 Bethlehem Pike, Philadelphia, PA 19118. TEL 215-836-1200. FAX 215-836-1204) Ed. Humphrey Tonkin. adv.; bk.rev.; bibl.; index. circ. 750. (also avail. in microform from UMI; back issues avail.) **Indexed:** Amer.Bibl.Slavic & E.Eur.Stud., Bibl.Ling., C.I.J.E., ERIC, Int.Polit.Sci.Abstr., Lang.& Lang.Behav.Abstr. (1977-), Lang.Teach.& Ling.Abstr., M.L.A. **Document type:** academic/scholarly publication.
—BLDSC (5155.710700); Faxon; UnCover; SWETS; UMI.
Former titles: Lingvaj Problemoj Kaj Lingvo-Planado (ISSN 0165-2672); Mondo Lingvo Problemo (ISSN 0026-9344)
Description: Examines political, social, economic and cultural policies related to language and language use.

400 370 800   US   ISSN 0732-3042
P1.A1
LANGUAGE QUARTERLY. (In 2 double nos. per yr.) 1962. s-a. $15 to individuals; institutions $30. University of South Florida, College of Arts & Sciences, 4202 E. Fowler Ave., CPR 107, Tampa, FL 33620-5550. TEL 813-974-5618. FAX 813-974-5618. Ed. Roger W. Cole. adv.; bk.rev.; charts; cum.index every 5 yrs.; circ. 500 (controlled). (also avail. in microform from UMI; reprint service avail. from UMI) **Indexed:** ERIC, Lang.& Lang.Behav.Abstr., M.L.A. **Document type:** academic/scholarly publication.
—BLDSC (5155.711000); Faxon.
Formerly: University of South Florida Language Quarterly (ISSN 0042-0077)
Description: Concentrates on the study of linguistics and language teaching.
Refereed Serial

410   KO   ISSN 0254-4474
P9
LANGUAGE RESEARCH/OHAK YON'GU. Key Title: Nehag Nyengu. (Text in English and Korean; summaries in English) 1965. q. $25. Language Research Institute, Seoul National University, San 56-1, Sinlim-dong, Kwanak-ku, Seoul 151-742, S. Korea. TEL 82-2-880-5485. FAX 82-2-871-6907. Ed. Un-Kyung Kim. adv.; bk.rev. circ. 1,000. **Indexed:** Lang.& Lang.Behav.Abstr., M.L.A., Sociol.Abstr. **Document type:** academic/scholarly publication.
—BLDSC (5155.711300).

410   UK   ISSN 0388-0001
P1
LANGUAGE SCIENCES; a world journal of the sciences of language. (Includes supplements) (Text in English) 1978. 4/yr. £143($220) (effective 1994). Elsevier Science Ltd., Pergamon, P.O. Box 800, Kidlington, Oxford OX5 1DX, England. TEL 44-865-843000. FAX 44-865-843010. (Subscr. in U.S. and Canada to: Elsevier Science, 660 White Plains Rd., Tarrytown, NY 10591-5153. TEL 914-524-9200. FAX 914-333-2444) Ed. Paul Hopper. adv.; bk.rev.; abstr.; bibl.; charts; illus.; stat.; index. circ. 500. (also avail. in microfilm from UMI; back issues avail.) **Indexed:** Anthropol.Lit., Bibl.Ling., Lang.& Lang.Behav.Abstr., Sociol.Abstr. **Document type:** academic/scholarly publication.
—BLDSC (5155.711700); Faxon; UnCover; SWETS; UMI. CCC.
Description: Emphasizes the investigation of language from extralinguistic perspectives in a broad sense, reflecting interest in language among scholars in a variety of fields.
Refereed Serial

410   UK   ISSN 0265-5322
P53.4
LANGUAGE TESTING. 1984. 3/yr. £44($75) to individuals; institutions £80 ($127) (effective 1994). Edward Arnold (Subsidiary of: Hodder Headline plc), Mill Rd., Dunton Green, Sevenoaks, Kent TN13 2YA, England. TEL 0732-450111. FAX 0732-461321. (Subscr. to: Turpin Distribution Services Ltd., Blackhorse Rd., Letchworth, Herts. SG6 1HN, England) adv.; bk.rev. **Indexed:** Lang.& Lang.Behav.Abstr. (1985-), Lang.Teach.& Ling.Abstr. **Document type:** academic/scholarly publication.
—BLDSC (5155.712910); Faxon; UnCover; SWETS; UMI. CCC.
Description: Provides a forum for work in the field of linguistic testing and assessment.

410   UK   ISSN 0954-3945
P120.V37   CODEN: LVCHEX
LANGUAGE VARIATION AND CHANGE. 3/yr. £19($30) to individuals (overseas £28.50); institutions £39 (overseas £48.50 ($59)). Cambridge University Press, Edinburgh Bldg., Shaftesbury Rd., Cambridge CB2 2RU, England. (N. American addr.: Cambridge University Press, Journals Dept., 40 W. 20th St., New York, NY 10011. TEL 212-924-3900. FAX 212-691-3239) Ed.Bd. adv. (also avail. in microform from UMI; back issues avail.) **Indexed:** Anthropol.Lit., Bibl.Ling., Lang.& Lang.Behav.Abstr. (1989-). **Document type:** academic/scholarly publication.
—BLDSC (5155.712975); Faxon; UnCover; SWETS; UMI.
Description: Studies linguistic variations, with emphasis on sytematic and inherent variation in synchronic and diachronic linguistics.

410   SZ   ISSN 0085-2678
LANGUE ET CULTURES; etudes et documents. (Text and summaries in English and French) 1971. irreg. no.27, 1992. price varies. Librairie Droz S.A., 11, rue Massot, CH-1211 Geneva 12, Switzerland. TEL 022-3466666. FAX 022-3472391. circ. 800. **Document type:** monographic series.
—CCC.
Description: Presents works of contemporary linguistics and classic texts plus philosophies relating to the nature and function of language. Includes the writings of Descartes, Liebnitz, Bopp and Saussure.

440   FR   ISSN 0023-8368
PC2002
LANGUE FRANCAISE. 1969. q. 270 F. Larousse, 17 rue du Montparnasse, 75280 Paris Cedex 06, France. (Dist. by: Gauthier-Villars, Centrale des Revues, 11 rue Gossin, 92543 Montrouge Cedex, France. TEL 1-46-56-52-66) Ed. JCl. Chevalier. adv.; bk.rev.; bibl. circ. 5,000. (also avail. in microform from SWZ; reprint service avail. from SWZ) **Indexed:** Arts & Hum.Cit.Ind., Bibl.Ling., Curr.Cont., Lang.& Lang.Behav.Abstr., Lang.Teach.& Ling.Abstr., M.L.A.
—BLDSC (5155.714000); Faxon; SWETS. CCC.

410   CM
LANGUES DU CAMEROUN. irreg., no.5, 1976. B.P. 5351, Douala, Cameroun.

410 301.2   FR   ISSN 0240-2041
LANGUES ET CIVILISATIONS A TRADITION ORALE. (Subseries of: Bibliotheque de la S E L A F) 1972. irreg., vol.50, no.4, 1992. Societe d'Etudes Linguistiques et Anthropologiques de France (SELAF), 52 bd. St. Michel, 75006 Paris, France. TEL 42-08-83-93. (Dist. by: Editions Peeters s.p.r.l., Bondgenotenlaan 153, B-3000 Louvain, Belgium. TEL 32-16-235170. FAX 32-16-228500) **Document type:** monographic series.
Incorporates: Etudes Pygmees (ISSN 0246-4616)

496 572   FR   ISSN 0755-9305
LANGUES ET CULTURES AFRICAINES. (Subseries of: Bibliotheque de la S E L A F) 1982. irreg., no.16, 1991. price varies. Societe d'Etudes Linguistiques et Anthropologiques de France (SELAF), 52 bd. St. Michel, 75006 Paris, France. TEL 42-08-83-93. (Dist. by: Editions Peeters s.p.r.l., Bondgenotenlaan 153, B-3000 Louvain, Belgium. TEL 32-16-235170. FAX 32-16-228500) **Document type:** academic/scholarly publication.

499 572   FR   ISSN 0750-2036
LANGUES ET CULTURES DU PACIFIQUE. 1982. irreg., no.7, 1990. price varies. Societe d'Etudes Linguistiques et Anthropologiques de France (SELAF), 52 bd. St. Michel, 75006 Paris, France. TEL 42-08-83-93. (Dist. by: Editions Peeters s.p.r.l., Bondgenotenlaan 153, B-3000 Louvain, Belgium. TEL 32-16-235170. FAX 32-16-228500) adv.; bk.rev. circ. 250. **Indexed:** Bibl.Ling. **Document type:** academic/scholarly publication.

410 306   FR
LANGUES ET SOCIETES D'AMERIQUE TRADITIONNELLE. (Subseries of: Bibliotheque de la S E L A F) 1988. irreg., no.3, 1991. price varies. Societe d'Etudes Linguistiques et Anthropologiques de France (SELAF), 52 bd. St. Michel, 75006 Paris, France. (Dist. by: Editions Peeters s.p.r.l., Bondgenotenlaan 153, B-3000 Louvain, Belgium. TEL 32-16-235170. FAX 32-16-228500) (back issues avail.) **Document type:** monographic series.

LANGUES ET STYLES. see LITERATURE

400   FR   ISSN 0023-8376
PB2
LANGUES MODERNES. (Text in French) 1903. 4/yr. 290 F. Association des Professeurs de Langues Vivantes de l'Enseignement Public, 19 rue de la Glaciere, 75013 Paris, France. Ed. Christian Puren. adv.; bk.rev.; charts; index. circ. 5,000. (also avail. in microfiche from IDC) **Indexed:** Lang.& Lang.Behav.Abstr., Lang.Teach.& Ling.Abstr.
—BLDSC (5155.715000); SWETS.
Description: Deals with foreign language teaching; research, experiments and institutional changes.

LINGUISTICS

490   BE   ISSN 0987-7738
LANGUES ORIENTALES ANCIENNES PHILOLOGIE ET LINGUISTIQUE. Short title: L O A P L. 1988. a. 1500 BEF (effective 1994). Editions Peeters s.p.r.l., Bondgenotenlaan 153, B-3000 Louvain, Belgium. TEL 32-16-235170. FAX 32-16-228500. Eds. G. Bohas, G. Roquet. bk.rev. (back issues avail.) **Indexed:** Bibl.Ling. **Document type:** academic/scholarly publication.

470 870   VC   ISSN 0023-883X
PA2009
LATINITAS; commentarii linguae latinae excolendae. (Text in Latin) 1953. q. L.45000($40) (Fondazione Latinitas) Libreria Editrice Vaticana, 00120 Vatican City (Rome), State of the Vatican City. TEL 0039-6-698-3532. FAX 0039-6-698-4716. adv.; bk.rev.; index. circ. 1,500.
Description: Periodical of cultural actuality and classical linguistics.

418.02   SP   ISSN 1131-9151
▼**LAZARILLO;** revista cultural. 1992. s-a. 1000 ptas. in Spain and Portugal; Europe 1200 ptas.; elsewhere 1300 ptas. (effective 1993). Asociacion Internacional de Traductores, Interpretes y Profesores de Espanol, Apdo. de Correos 470, 37008 Salamanca, Spain. TEL 923-21-47-88. FAX 923-21-87-91. Ed. Carmen Perez Sanz. adv.: B&W page 45000 ptas.; 215 x 315. circ. 3,000.
Description: Sections on Spanish and Latin American literature and linguistics.

420.07 370   US   ISSN 0023-964X
LB1631
LEAFLET (LEXINGTON). 1902. 3/yr. (during school year). $30 (includes N E A T E Newsletter). New England Association of Teachers of English, Box 234, Lexington, MA 02173. TEL 617-646-2575. adv.; cum.index: 1969-1980. circ. 950. (back issues avail.) **Indexed:** Rev.Appl.Entomol. **Document type:** academic/scholarly publication.
Formerly: English Leaflet.
Description: Presents study and teaching methods.

400   GW   ISSN 0023-9909
PB5
LEBENDE SPRACHEN; Zeitschrift fuer fremde Sprachen in Wissenschaft und Praxis. (Text in English, French, German, Italian, Spanish) 1956. 4/yr. DM.86. Verlag Langenscheidt KG, Postfach 401120, 80711 Munich, Germany. TEL 089-36096-0. FAX 089-36096258. adv.; bk.rev.; bibl.; tr.lit.; cum.index every 2 yrs. circ. 3,250. **Indexed:** Key to Econ.Sci., Lang.& Lang.Behav.Abstr., Lang.Teach.& Ling.Abstr., M.L.A. **Document type:** academic/scholarly publication.
—BLDSC (5179.622000); Faxon; SWETS.

LECTOR. see *PUBLISHING AND BOOK TRADE*

410 378 371.3   US   ISSN 0325-8637
LB1049.9   CODEN: LVIDDG
LECTURA Y VIDA; revista latinoamericana de lectura. (Text in Spanish) 1980. q. $38 in developed countries; developing countries $19. International Reading Association, Inc., 800 Barksdale Rd., Box 8139, Newark, DE 19714-8139. TEL 302-731-1600. FAX 302-731-1057. TELEX 5106002813READING. Ed. Maria Elena Rodriguez. adv.; bk.rev.; bibl.; index. circ. 1,500. (also avail. in microform from UMI; reprint service avail. from UMI) **Document type:** academic/scholarly publication.
—UMI. **CCC.**
Description: Covers the teaching and learning of reading comprehension among Spanish speakers.
Refereed Serial

LEEDS STUDIES IN ENGLISH. see *LITERATURE*

LEEDS TEXTS AND MONOGRAPHS. NEW SERIES. see *LITERATURE*

410   NE   ISSN 0926-5856
▼**LEIDEN STUDIES IN INDO-EUROPEAN.** 1992. irreg. price varies. Editions Rodopi B.V., Keizersgracht 302-304, 1016 EX Amsterdam, Netherlands. TEL 31-20-6227507. FAX 31-20-6380948. (In N. America: 233 Peachtree St., N.E., Ste. 404, Atlanta, GA 30303-1504. TEL 800-225-3998. FAX 404-522-7116) Eds. Z. Lubotsky, J.J.S. Weitenberg. **Document type:** academic/scholarly publication, monographic series.

479 879   NE   ISSN 0169-8656
LEIDSE ROMANISTISCHE REEKS. (Text in French, Italian and Spanish) 1954. irreg., vol.24, 1990. price varies. E.J. Brill, P.O. Box 9000, 2300 PA Leiden, Netherlands. TEL 31-71-312624. FAX 31-71-317532. TELEX 39296 BRILL NL. (N. America dist. addr.: E.J. Brill, 24 Hudson St., Kinderhook, NY 12106. TEL 800-962-4406. FAX 518-758-1959) (Co-publisher: Leiden University Press) **Document type:** monographic series.
Refereed Serial

LEMOUZI; revue franco-limousine. see *HISTORY — History Of Europe*

401   FR   ISSN 0153-0313
PC3371
LENGAS; revue de sociolinguistique. s-a. 85 F. Universite de Montpellier (Universite Paul Valery), B.P. 5043, 34032 Montpellier Cedex 1, France. TEL 67-14-20-00. **Indexed:** Bibl.Ling.
Description: Examines the socio-linguistics of the Occitan public and individuals or groups involved with the Occitan culture. Includes critical studies of research in the field as well as theoretical articles on the problems and methods of sociolinguistics.

460 375.4   PE   ISSN 1019-4495
LENGUA Y SOCIEDAD. 1974. irreg., no.12, 1990. price varies. (Instituto de Estudios Peruanos) I E P Ediciones, Horacio Urteaga 694, Lima 11, Peru. TEL 32-3070. FAX 324981. (back issues avail.)

410   CK   ISSN 0120-3479
LENGUAJE. 1972. irreg. Col.$110($5) Universidad del Valle, Division de Humanidades, Departamento de Idiomas, Apdo. Aereo 25360, Cali, Colombia. Ed. Samuel Estrada. circ. 1,000. **Indexed:** Lang.& Lang.Behav.Abstr. (1973-), M.L.A.

400 500   PE   ISSN 0024-0796
P1.A1
LENGUAJE Y CIENCIAS. (Text in English, French, German, Spanish; summaries in English) 1961. s-a. $15. Universidad Nacional de Trujillo, Departamento de Idiomas y Linguistica, Trujillo, Peru. Ed. Ernesto Zierer. adv.; bk.rev.; charts; illus. circ. 800. **Indexed:** Bibl.Ling., ERIC, Hisp.Amer.Per.Ind., Lang.& Lang.Behav.Abstr. (1972-), Lang.Teach.& Ling.Abstr., M.L.A.

410   AG
LENGUAJES;* revista de linguistica y semiologia. 1974. 3/yr. Asociacion Argentina de Semiotica, Tucuman 3748, Buenos Aires, Argentina. Ed. Juan Carlos Indart. bk.rev.; bibl.

492.4   IS   ISSN 0334-3626
LESHONENU. (Text in Hebrew) q. $35. Academy of the Hebrew Language, P.O. Box 3449, 91034 Jerusalem, Israel. **Indexed:** Ind.Heb.Per., Rel.& Theol.Abstr. (1969-). **Document type:** academic/scholarly publication.

492.4   IS   ISSN 0024-1091
LESHONENU LA'AM. (Text in Hebrew) q. $25. Academy of the Hebrew Language, P.O. Box 3449, 91034 Jerusalem, Israel. circ. 3,000. **Indexed:** Ind.Heb.Per., M.L.A., Rel.& Theol.Abstr. **Document type:** academic/scholarly publication.

410   VE
LETRAS (CARACAS). 1958. s-a. Bs.200($10) Instituto Universitario Pedagogico de Caracas, Centro de Investigaciones Linguisticas y Literarias Andres Bello, Avda. J.A. Paez, El Paraiso, Caracas, Venezuela. (Subscr. to: Venezuelan Book Service, Apdo. postal 25092, Caracas 1023-A, Venezuela) Dir. Luis Alvarez. bk.rev.; bibl. circ. 2,000. (back issues avail.) **Indexed:** M.L.A.

469   BL   ISSN 0047-4428
P25
LETRAS DE HOJE; estudo e debate de assuntos da lingua Portuguesa. 1967. 4/yr. Cz.$800($10) (Pontificia Universidade Catolica do Rio Grande do Sul, Centro de Estudos de Lingua Portuguesa) Editora de P U C R S, c/o Antoninho M. Naime, Caixa Postal 12001, 90620 Porto Alegre RS, Brazil. Ed. Elvo Clemente. bk.rev. circ. 1,000. **Indexed:** Lang.& Lang.Behav.Abstr.

430   BE   ISSN 0024-1482
PF4
LEUVENSE BIJDRAGEN; tijdschrift voor Germaanse Filologie. (Text in Dutch, English, French, German) 1896. q. 1000 BEF (foreign 1300 BEF). Katholieke Universiteit te Leuven, Linguistiek, Blijde-Inkomststraat 21, B-3000 Leuven, Belgium. TEL 32-16-285030. Ed. G. Geerts. adv.; bk.rev.; charts, illus.; index, cum.index. circ. 594. (reprint service avail. from SWZ) **Indexed:** Bing.Ling., Lang.& Lang.Behav.Abstr., M.L.A. **Document type:** academic/scholarly publication.
—SWETS.
Description: Covers general linguistics, Germanic linguistics and philosophy, and the philological study of the older literary traditions of the Germanic languages (up to the 18th century).

407   NE   ISSN 0024-1539
PB5
LEVENDE TALEN. (Text in Dutch, English, French, German, Italian, Russian and Spanish) 1912. m. (10/yr). fl.98.50. (Vereniging van Leraren in Levende Talen - Association of Teachers in Modern Languages) Wolters-Noordhoff B.V., Postbus 58, 9700 MB Groningen, Netherlands. TEL 31-50-226922. FAX 31-50-264866. Ed. P.J. Slagter. adv.; bk.rev.; bibl.; index. circ. 8,500. **Indexed:** Bibl.Ling., Lang.& Lang.Behav.Abstr., Lang.Teach.& Ling.Abstr., M.L.A. **Document type:** academic/scholarly publication.
—BLDSC (5185.530000).

410   GW   ISSN 0175-6206
LEXICOGRAPHICA; international annual for lexicography. (Text and summaries in English, French, German) 1985. a. DM.164. Max Niemeyer Verlag, Postfach 2140, 72011 Tuebingen, Germany. TEL 07071-98940. FAX 07071-989450. Ed. Antonin Kucera. (back issues avail.) **Indexed:** Bibl.Ling. **Document type:** academic/scholarly publication.
Description: Essays and reviews on lexicography/lexicology (German, English, French, etc., bi- and monolingual dictionaries).

410 860   PE   ISSN 0254-9239
P9
LEXIS; revista de linguistica y literatura. 1977. s-a. $12. Pontificia Universidad Catolica del Peru, Departamento de Humanidades, Fondo Editorial, Apdo. 1761, Lima 100, Peru. TEL 626390. FAX 5114-611785. Ed. Jose L. Rivarola Rubio. **Indexed:** Bing.Ling.
—BLDSC (5185.770000).

LIBRARY OF RHETORICS. see *PHILOSOPHY*

410   FR   ISSN 1146-6480
LIDIL. 1989. 2/yr. 150 F. (Laboratoire de Linguistique et Didactique des Langues Etrangeres et Maternelles) Presses Universitaires de Grenoble, Grenoble, France. TEL 76-82-56-51. FAX 76-82-56-54. Ed. Louise Dabene. **Document type:** academic/scholarly publication.

491.92   LI   ISSN 0130-0172
PG8501
LIETUVIU KALBOTYROS KLAUSIMAI/PROBLEMS OF LITHUANIAN LINGUISTICS. (Text in Lithuanian or Russian; summaries in English, German, Lithuanian or Russian) 1957. a. price varies. (Lithuanian Academy of Sciences, Institute of Lithuanian Language) Mokslo ir Enciklopediju Leidykla, Zvaigzdziu 23, Vilnius 2050, Lithuania. TEL 45-85-25. TELEX 261240 TLG SU. Ed. K. Gaivenis. **Indexed:** Bibl.Ling., M.L.A.
—BLDSC (5208.530000).
Description: Treats problems of Lithuanian linguistics, terminology, and social linguistics.

491.92   LI   ISSN 0235-716X
DK505
LIETUVOS MOKSLU AKADEMIJA. LITUANISTICA. (Text in Lithuanian; summaries in English) 1955. 4/yr. Leidykla Academia, A. Gostauto 12, 2600 Vilnius, Lithuania. TEL 626-851. adv.; bk.rev. circ. 700. **Document type:** academic/scholarly publication.
—BLDSC (5208.806800).

LINGUISTICS

400 800 — GW — ISSN 0049-8653
P3
LILI. (Zeitschrift fuer Literaturwissenschaft und Linguistik) 1971. q. DM.88. Vandenhoeck und Ruprecht, Robert-Bosch-Breite 6, 37079 Goettingen, Germany. TEL 0551-6959-26. FAX 0551-695917. (Subscr. to: 37070 Goettingen, Germany) Ed. Helmut Kreuzer. adv.; bk.rev.; bibl.; charts. circ. 680. **Indexed:** Arts & Hum.Cit.Ind., Bibl.Ling., Curr.Cont., Lang.Teach.& Ling.Abstr., M.L.A. **Document type:** academic/scholarly publication.
—Faxon; UnCover; SWETS. **CCC.**

400 800 — GW
LILI. BEIHEFTE. (Zeitschrift fuer Literaturwissenschaft und Linguistik) 1975. irreg. price varies. Vandenhoeck und Ruprecht, Robert-Bosch-Breite 6, 37079 Goettingen, Germany. TEL 0551-6959-0. FAX 0551-695917. (Subscr. to: 37070 Goettingen, Germany) **Indexed:** Can.Rev.Comp.Lit. **Document type:** monographic series.

459 — RM — ISSN 0024-3523
PC601
LIMBA ROMANA/ROMANIAN LANGUAGE. 1952. 6/yr. 120 lei($48) (Academia Romana) Editura Academiei Romane, Calea Victoriei 125, 79717 Bucharest, Rumania. (Dist. by: Rompresfilatelia, Calea Grivitei 64-66, P.O. Box 12-201, 78104 Bucharest, Rumania) Ed. I. Coteanu. bk.rev.; bibl.; charts; index. circ. 5,000. (back issues avail) **Indexed:** Bibl.Ling., Lang.& Lang.Behav.Abstr. (1973-), M.L.A.

400 — RM — ISSN 0583-8045
LIMBA SI LITERATURA. 1955. 4/yr. $40 (effective Jan. 1991). Societatea de Stiinte Filologice din Romania, Bd. Schitul Magureanu nr.1, Bucharest, cod 79664, sector 5, Rumania. TEL 615-171-92. Ed. Ion Hangiu. bk.rev.; bibl. circ. 3,000. **Indexed:** Bibl.Ling. **Document type:** academic/scholarly publication.
—BLDSC (5219.230000).
Supersedes: Societatea de Stiinte Istorice si Filologice din R.P.R. Limba si Literatura.
Description: Covers linguistics, stylistics, literary history, criticism and theory, texts and documents, text analysis, folklore, didactics and education history.

400 — NE — ISSN 0024-3841
P9   CODEN: LINGAO
LINGUA; international review of general linguistics. (Text in English, French, German) 1947. 12/yr. (in 3 vols.; 4 nos./vol.). fl.1047($566) (effective 1994). North-Holland (Subsidiary of: Elsevier Science B.V.), P.O. Box 211, 1000 AE Amsterdam, Netherlands. TEL 31-20-5803911. FAX 31-20-5803598. TELEX 18582 ESPA NL. (Subscr. in U.S. and Canada to: Elsevier Science Inc., Box 882, Madison Sq. Sta., New York, NY 10159. TEL 212-989-5800. FAX 212-633-3990) Ed. T. Hoekstra. adv.; bk.rev.; bibl.; index. cum.index. circ. 1,078. (also avail. in microform from UMI; back issues avail.; reprint service avail. from SWZ) **Indexed:** Abstr.Anthropol., Arts & Hum.Cit.Ind., Bibl.Ling., Chic.Per.Ind., Curr.Cont., DSH Abstr., E.I., Ind.Bk.Rev.Hum., Lang.& Lang.Behav.Abstr. (1971-), Lang.Teach.& Ling.Abstr., M.L.A., Mid.East: Abstr.& Ind., Sociol.Abstr., SSCI. **Document type:** academic/scholarly publication.
—BLDSC (5221.155000); Faxon; UnCover; SWETS. **CCC.**
Description: Directed to people who are involved in linguistic studies.
Refereed Serial

056.9 — PO — ISSN 0047-4703
P9
LINGUA E CULTURA. 1971. 3/yr. Esc.200. Sociedade de Lingua Portuguesa, Rua de S. Jose 41, 2 Lisbon, Portugal. Ed. Jose Neves Henriques. adv.; bk.rev. circ. 1,000.

400 800 — BL — ISSN 0047-4711
LINGUA E LITERATURA. (Text in various languages) 1972. a. $15. Universidade de Sao Paulo, Faculdade de Filosofia, Letras e Ciencias Humanas, Secao de Publicacoes, C.P. 8105, CEP 05508, Sao Paulo, Brazil. TEL 011-813-3222. Ed.Bd. bk.rev.; charts; illus.; bibl. circ. 1,000. **Indexed:** Hisp.Amer.Per.Ind.

400 810 — IT — ISSN 0024-385X
P9
LINGUA E STILE. (Text in French and Italian; summaries in English) 1966. 4/yr. L.125000. Societa Editrice Il Mulino, Strada Maggiore, 37, 40125 Bologna, Italy. TEL 051-256011. FAX 051-256034. Ed. S. Scalise. adv.; bk.rev.; bibl.; index. circ. 1,600. (back issues avail.) **Indexed:** Arts & Hum.Cit.Ind., Bibl.Ling., Can.Rev.Comp.Lit., Curr.Cont., Lang.Teach.& Ling.Abstr., M.L.A.
—SWETS.

499.99 — UK
LINGUA E VITA. 1969. 3/yr. £3.50. British Interlingua Society, 14 Ventnor Court, Wostenholm Rd., Sheffield S7 1LB, England. TEL 0742-582931. (Subscr. to: c/o P. Berwick, 15 Barnton Park Gardens, Edinburgh EH4 6HL, Scotland; In US subscr. to: Interlingua Institute, 496a Hudson St., G.34, New York 10014) Ed. B.C. Sexton. adv.; bk.rev. circ. 180.
Incorporates: Interlingua Institute Newsletter.

410 — GW
LINGUA ET TRADITIO. irreg., no.12, 1994. DM.68. Gunter Narr Verlag, Postfach 2567, 72015 Tuebingen, Germany. TEL 07071-78091. FAX 07071-75288. Ed. Jean-Alexis Borrelly. **Document type:** monographic series.

450 — IT — ISSN 0024-3868
PC1001
LINGUA NOSTRA. 1939. q. L.110000. Casa Ed. Le Lettere, Costa S. Giorgio 28, Florence, Italy. (Dist. by: Licosa, Via Duca di Calabria 1-1, 50125 Florence, Italy) Eds. G. Folena, G. Ghinassi. bk.rev.; abstr.; index. circ. 1,500. **Indexed:** Arts & Hum.Cit.Ind., Bibl.Ling., Curr.Cont., Lang.& Lang.Behav.Abstr., Lang.Teach.& Ling.Abstr., M.L.A.
—Faxon; SWETS.

491.85 — PL — ISSN 0079-4740
P25
LINGUA POSNANIENSIS. (Text in various languages) 1949. a. price varies. Poznanskie Towarzystwo Przyjaciol Nauk, Ul. Mielzynskiego 27-29, 61-725 Poznan, Poland. Ed. Jerry Banczerowski. **Indexed:** Bibl.Ling., Ind.Bk.Rev.Hum., Lang.& Lang.Behav.Abstr. (1972-), M.L.A.

410 900 — GW — ISSN 0341-3225
LINGUARUM MINORUM DOCUMENTA HISTORIOGRAPHICA. 1977-1990 (no.6). irreg. price varies. Helmut Buske Verlag GmbH, Richardstr. 47, 22081 Hamburg, Germany. TEL 040-296842. FAX 040-2993614. Ed. H. Haarmann. **Document type:** monographic series.

400 — IT — ISSN 0024-3876
LINGUE DEL MONDO. unica rivista Italiana di cultura linguistica. (Text in English, French, German, Italian, Rumanian, Russian, Spanish; summaries in Italian) 1934. bi-m. L.42000($35) Valmartina Editore, Via L. Dottesio, 1, 335138 Padua, Italy. Ed. Gabriele Pasquinelli. adv.; bk.rev.; bibl.; illus.; index. circ. 27,000. **Indexed:** Lang.& Lang.Behav.Abstr. (1985-).

400 — IT — ISSN 1122-0791
LINGUE E ISCRIZIONI DELL'ITALIA ANTICA. 1977. irreg., no.5, 1985. Casa Editrice Leo S. Olschki, Viuzzo del Pozzetto, Casella Postale 66, 50100 Florence, Italy. TEL 055-6530684. FAX 055-6530214. Dir. Aldo Prosdocimi. circ. 1,000. **Document type:** monographic series.

410 — IT — ISSN 0391-3228
LE LINGUE E LE CIVILTA STRANIERE MODERNE. 1981. irreg., no.8, 1989. price varies. Liguori Editore s.r.l., Via Mezzocanone 19, 80134 Naples, Italy. TEL 081-5527139. Ed. Elio Chinol. **Document type:** monographic series.

400 — UK — ISSN 0268-5965
P1
LINGUIST. 1962. bi-m. £25 (rest of Europe £30-£32.50; elsewhere £35). Institute of Linguists, 24a Highbury Grove, London N5 2EA, England. TEL 071-359 7445. FAX 071-354-0202. Ed. J.L. Kettle-Williams. adv.: Page £600. bk.rev. circ. 6,500. **Indexed:** Bibl.Ling., BMT, Lang.& Lang.Behav.Abstr., Lang.Teach.& Ling.Abstr., M.L.A., Mid.East: Abstr.& Ind., Sociol.Abstr.
—BLDSC (5221.220000); UnCover; SWETS.
Formerly (until 1986): Incorporated Linguist (ISSN 0019-3534).

400 — BE
LINGUISTE/TAALKUNDIGE. (Text in Dutch, French) 1955. q. 500 BEF. (Chambre Belge des Traducteurs, Interpretes et Philologues - Belgische Kamer van Vertalers Tolken en Filologen) F. Lepeer, Ed. & Pub., 110 ave. De Heyn, B-1090 Brussels, Belgium. adv.; bk.rev. circ. 1,000.

410 — US — ISSN 0098-9053
P123
LINGUISTIC ANALYSIS. 1975-1986; resumed 1988. 4/yr. $52.50 to individuals; institutions $105 (effective 1993). c/o Michael K. Brame, Ed., University of Washington, Department of Linguistics GN-40, Seattle, WA 98195. TEL 206-463-3451. FAX 206-463-3451. (Subscr. to: Linguistic Analysis, Box 95679, Seattle, WA 98145-2679) adv.; bk.rev. circ. 1,000. **Indexed:** Abstr.Anthropol., Amer.Bibl.Slavic & E.Eur.Stud., Arts & Hum.Cit.Ind., Bibl.Ling., Comput.Rev., Curr.Cont., Lang.& Lang.Behav.Abstr., Lang.Teach.& Ling.Abstr., M.L.A., Mid.East: Abstr.& Ind., SSCI. **Document type:** academic/scholarly publication.
—Faxon; UnCover; SWETS. **CCC.**
Description: Focuses on formal syntax, morphology, semantics, and phonology.

410 800 — US — ISSN 0165-7712
LINGUISTIC & LITERARY STUDIES IN EASTERN EUROPE. Short title: L L S E E. 1979. irreg., vol.39, 1992. price varies. John Benjamins Publishing Co., 821 Bethlehem Pike, Philadelphia, PA 19118. TEL 215-836-1200. FAX 215-836-1204. (And: Amsteldijk 44, P.O. Box 75577, 1070 AN Amsterdam, Netherlands. TEL 020-6762325) Ed. John Odmark. **Indexed:** Bibl.Ling., M.L.A., Math.R. **Document type:** monographic series.
—BLDSC (5221.250000).
Description: Contains recent developments in linguistic and literary research in Eastern Europe.

400 — NE — ISSN 0924-4891
LINGUISTIC CALCULATION. (Text in English, French and German) 1961. a. price varies. Kluwer Academic Publishers, Postbus 17, 3300 AA Dordrecht, Netherlands. TEL 31-78-334911. FAX 31-78-334254. TELEX 29245 KAPG NL. (Dist. by: Kluwer Academic Publishers Group, P.O. Box 322, 3300 AH Dordrecht, Netherlands. TEL 31-78-524400. FAX 31-78-524474; N. America dist. addr.: Box 358, Accord Sta., Hingham, MA 02018-0358. TEL 617-871-6600. FAX 617-871-6528) Ed. Hans Karlgren. **Indexed:** M.L.A., SSCI. **Document type:** monographic series.
Former titles (until 1983): S M I L Quarterly Journal of Linguistic Calculus; (until 1977): Statistical Methods in Linguistics (ISSN 0039-0437)
Refereed Serial

410 — US — ISSN 0075-9597
LINGUISTIC CIRCLE OF MANITOBA AND NORTH DAKOTA. PROCEEDINGS. 1959. a. $10. University of North Dakota, Department of Philosophy and Religion, Box 7128, Grand Forks, ND 58202-7128. FAX 701-777-3650. (Co-sponsors: University of Winnipeg; University of Manitoba; Minot State University; North Dakota State University) Ed. Theodore Messenger. adv.; circ. 500 (controlled).

400 — US — ISSN 0024-3892
P1
LINGUISTIC INQUIRY. 1970. q. $50 to individuals (foreign $61); institutions $100 (foreign $114); students or retired $32 (foreign $46). M I T Press, 55 Hayward St., Cambridge, MA 02142. TEL 617-253-2889. FAX 617-258-6779. TELEX 921473. E-mail: mit.edu. (Editorial addr.: M I T Bldg. 20D-213, Cambridge, MA 02139) Ed. Samuel Jay Keyser. adv.; bk.rev.; index. circ. 3,000. (also avail. in microform from MIM,UMI; back issues avail.; reprint service avail. from ISI,SCH,UMI) **Indexed:** Abstr.Anthropol., Amer.Bibl.Slavic & E.Eur.Stud., Arts & Hum.Cit.Ind., Bibl.Ling., Curr.Cont., Lang.& Lang.Behav.Abstr. (1972-), Lang.Teach.& Ling.Abstr., M.L.A., Mid.East: Abstr.& Ind., SSCI.
●Also available online.
—BLDSC (5221.280000); Faxon; UnCover; SWETS; UMI. **CCC.**
Description: Provides information about new theoretical developments in phonology, syntax, semantics and morphology.
Refereed Serial

410 US
LINGUISTIC MODELS.* (Text in English) 1982. irreg., no.14, 1989. Walter de Gruyter, Inc., 200 Saw Mill River Rd., Hawthorne, NY 10532. TEL 914-747-0110. FAX 914-747-1326. Eds. Teun Hoekstra, Harry van der Hulst. **Indexed:** Bibl.Ling.
 Description: Addresses the development of formal methods in the study of language.

410 US ISSN 0737-4720
CODEN: LNLJES
LINGUISTIC NOTES FROM LA JOLLA. no.5, 1973. irreg. $7 to individuals (foreign $8); institutions $9 (foreign $10). University of California at San Diego, Department of Linguistics, C-0108, La Jolla, CA 92093. TEL 619-452-3600. E-mail: LNLJ@BEND.VCSD.EDU. charts. circ. 75. **Indexed:** Bibl.Ling., Lang.& Lang.Behav.Abstr. (1988-). **Document type:** academic/scholarly publication.

410 GW ISSN 0167-6318
THE LINGUISTIC REVIEW. 1981. 4/yr. DM.111 to individuals; institutions DM.225. Walter de Gruyter und Co., Mouton de Gruyter, Genthiner Str. 13, 10785 Berlin, Germany. TEL 030-26005-0. FAX 030-26005-251. (U.S. addr.: Walter de Gruyter, Inc., 200 Saw Mill Rd., Hawthorne, NY 10532) Ed.Bd. (back issues avail.; reprint service avail. from SWZ) **Indexed:** Bibl.Ling., Curr.Cont., Lang.& Lang.Behav.Abstr. (1981-), Lang.Teach.& Ling.Abstr. **Document type:** academic/scholarly publication.
 —BLDSC (5221.298000); Faxon; UnCover; SWETS; UMI. **CCC.**
 Description: Contributes original insights to the theory of formal grammar within the framework of generative grammar or related approaches.

400 US ISSN 0075-9600
LINGUISTIC SOCIETY OF AMERICA. MEETING HANDBOOKS. 1965. a. $8.50 per vol. (free to meeting attendees). Linguistic Society of America, 1325 18th St., N.W., Ste. 211, Washington, DC 20036-6501. adv. circ. 1,000. (back issues avail.)

491 II ISSN 0075-9627
LINGUISTIC SOCIETY OF INDIA. BULLETIN. 1958. irreg., no.3, 1970. included with subscription to Indian Linguistics. Linguistic Society of India, c/o Deccan College Postgraduate and Research Institute, Poona 411006, India. Ed. Suresh Kumar. **Document type:** bulletin.

400 JA ISSN 0024-3914
LINGUISTIC SOCIETY OF JAPAN. JOURNAL/GENGO KENKYU. (Text in English and Japanese) 1939. s-a. 4000 Yen. Linguistic Society of Japan - Nihon Gengogakkai, c/o Sanseido Co., Ltd., 2-22-14 Misaki-cho, Chiyoda-ku, Tokyo 101, Japan. Ed. Katsumi Matsumoto. bk.rev. circ. 1,000. **Indexed:** Bibl.Ling., Lang.& Lang.Behav.Abstr., M.L.A.
 —UnCover.

400 XV ISSN 0024-3922
P25
LINGUISTICA. (Text in various languages) 1955. a. $10. Univerza v Ljubljani, Filozofska Fakulteta, Askerceva 12, 61000 Ljubljana, Slovenia. TEL 061-150-001. FAX 061-159-337. Ed. Mitja Skubic. circ. 600. **Indexed:** Bibl.Ling., Lang.& Lang.Behav.Abstr. (1972-), M.L.A.

460 SP
LINGUISTICA. 1989. a. 3750 ptas.($36) (ALFAL) Arco Libros, S.A., Juan Bautista de Toledo, 28, 28002 Madrid, Spain. TEL 415-36-87.

410 CN
P1
LINGUISTICA ATLANTICA. 1978. a. Can.$15($15) Atlantic Provinces Linguistic Association, c/o J. Black, Memorial University, Linguistics Department, St. John's, NF A1B 3X9, Canada. TEL 709-737-8134. FAX 709-737-4000. TELEX 016-4101. bk.rev. circ. 200. **Indexed:** Bibl.Ling., Lang.& Lang.Behav.Abstr. (1985-), Sociol.Abstr.
 Formerly (until 1992): Atlantic Provinces Linguistic Association Journal (ISSN 0706-6910)
 Description: Covers all areas of descriptive and theoretical linguistics.

220 400 GW ISSN 0342-0884
BL65.L2
LINGUISTICA BIBLICA; Interdisziplinaere Zeitschrift fuer Theologie, Semiotik und Linguistik. (Text in German, English, French; summaries in English) 1970. 2/yr. DM.46. Verlag Linguistica Biblica, Postfach 130154, 53003 Bonn, Germany. FAX 02225-18474. Ed. Erhardt Guettgemanns. adv.; bk.rev.; abstr.; bibl.; illus.; index. circ. 500. **Indexed:** Arts & Hum.Cit.Ind., Bibl.Ling., CERDIC, Curr.Cont., Lang.& Lang.Behav.Abstr. (1972-), M.L.A., New Test.Abstr., Old Test.Abstr., Rel.& Theol.Abstr. (1973-).
 —SWETS.

410 850 IT
LINGUISTICA E LETTERATURA. s-a. L.130000. Giardini Editori e Stampatori, Via Santa Bibbiana 28, 56100 Pisa, Italy. TEL 050 502531. Ed.Bd. **Indexed:** Bibl.Ling.

410 SP
LINGUISTICA ESPANOLA ACTUAL. 1979. s-a. 4100 ptas.($41) (effective 1993). Instituto de Cooperacion Iberoamericana, Avenida de los Reyes Catolicos, 4, 28040 Madrid, Spain. TEL 415-36-87. FAX 415-36-07. (Subscr. to: Arco-Libros, S.L., Juan Bautista de Toledo 28, 28002 Madrid, Spain. TEL 415-36-87) **Indexed:** Bibl.Ling.

400 800 NE ISSN 0862-8432
P1.A1
LINGUISTICA PRAGENSIA. (Text in English, French, German, Spanish) 1958. 2/yr. fl.98($59) (effective 1994). (Czech Academy of Sciences, Institute for Czech and World Literature, XR) John Benjamins Publishing Co., Amsteldijk 44, P.O. Box 75577, 1070 AN Amsterdam, Netherlands. TEL 31-20-6738156. FAX 31-20-6792956. (In N. America: 821 Bethlehem Pike, Philadelphia, PA 19118. TEL 215-836-1200. FAX 215-836-1204) Ed. Libuse Duskova. bk.rev.; index. circ. 1,000. (back issues avail.) **Indexed:** Bibl.Ling., Lang.& Lang.Behav.Abstr., Lang.Teach.& Ling.Abstr., M.L.A. **Document type:** academic/scholarly publication.
 Supersedes in part (in 1991): Philologica Pragensia (ISSN 0048-3885)
 Description: Covers modern philology, linguistics, and literature.

410 PL ISSN 0208-4228
P9
LINGUISTICA SILESIANA. (Text in English, French, German, Italian, Russian) 1975. a. price varies. Polska Akademia Nauk, Oddzial w Katowicach - Polish Academy of Sciences, Katowice Branch, Ul. Graniczna 32, 40-018 Katowice, Poland. (Dist. by: Wydawnictwo Energeia, ul. Szturmowa 1, 02-678 Warsaw, Poland. TEL 48-22-470053) Ed. Kazimierz Polanski. bk.rev. circ. 1,000. **Indexed:** Bibl.Ling.

491 ER ISSN 0868-4731
LINGUISTICA URALICA. (Text in German, English, French, Russian) 1964. q. $40 (effective 1993). (Eesti Teaduste Akadeemia) Teaduste Akadeemia Kirjastus, Estonia pst.7, 0100 Tallinn, Estonia. TEL 0142-454504. (Subscr. to: Akateeminen Kirjakauppa, 128 SF 00101, Helsinki, Finland; or to: Bibliotekstjanst AB 200, S 22100 Lund, Sweden) Ed. P. Kokla. bk.rev.; bibl.; index. circ. 400.
 Formerly (until 1990): Sovetskoe Finnougrovedenie (ISSN 0132-0777)

410 CK ISSN 0120-5587
P9
LINGUISTICA Y LITERATURA. 1979. s-a. Col.$3000($30) (effective 1992). Universidad de Antioquia, Departamento de Linguistica y Literatura, Facultad de Comunicaciones, Apdo. Aereo 1226, Medellin, Colombia. TEL 574-2630011. FAX 574-2638282. Ed. Oscar Castro Garcia. bk.rev.; film rev. circ. 280.
 Description: Publishes works in linguistics and literature by the department.

400 GW ISSN 0024-3949
P1.A1
LINGUISTICS; an interdisciplinary journal of the language sciences. (Text in English) 1963. bi-m. DM.180 to individuals; institutions DM.592. Walter de Gruyter und Co., Mouton de Gruyter, Genthiner Str. 13, 10785 Berlin, Germany. TEL 030-26005-0. FAX 030-26005251. TELEX 184027. Ed. Wolfgang Klein. adv.; bk.rev.; charts; illus. circ. 1,200. **Indexed:** Abstr.Anthropol., Arts & Hum.Cit.Ind., Bibl.Ling., Curr.Cont., Hum.Ind., Ind.Bk.Rev.Hum., Lang.& Lang.Behav.Abstr. (1972-), Mid.East: Abstr.& Ind., SSCI. **Document type:** academic/scholarly publication.
 —BLDSC (5221.375000); Faxon; UnCover; SWETS; UMI. **CCC.**

410 370 US ISSN 0898-5898
P40.8
LINGUISTICS AND EDUCATION; an international research journal. 1988. 3/yr. $39.50 to individuals; institutions $85. Ablex Publishing Corporation, 355 Chestnut St., Norwood, NJ 07648. TEL 201-767-8450. FAX 201-767-6717. TELEX 1350393. Ed. David Bloome. index. circ. 400. (back issues avail.) **Indexed:** Lang.& Lang.Behav.Abstr. (1988-).
 —BLDSC (5221.375600); Faxon; UnCover; SWETS. **CCC.**
 Description: Provides a forum for researchers from linguistic perspectives to share and discuss their inquiries into educational processes both in and outside of school.

401 NE ISSN 0165-0157
P1.A1 CODEN: LIPHD6
LINGUISTICS AND PHILOSOPHY; a journal of natural language syntax, semantics, logic, pragmatics, and processing. (Text in English) 1977. 6/yr. fl.448($233.50) (effective 1994). Kluwer Academic Publishers, Postbus 17, 3300 AA Dordrecht, Netherlands. TEL 31-78-334911. FAX 31-78-334254. TELEX 29245 KAPG NL. (Dist. by: Kluwer Academic Publishers Group, P.O. Box 322, 3300 AH Dordrecht, Netherlands. TEL 31-78-524400. FAX 31-78-524400; N. America dist. addr.: Box 358, Accord Sta., Hingham, MA 02018-0358. TEL 617-871-6600. FAX 617-871-6528) Ed. Gregory N. Carlson. adv.; bk.rev.; index. (also avail. in microform from UMI; back issues avail.; reprint service avail. from SWZ) **Indexed:** Arts & Hum.Cit.Ind., ASCA, Bibl.Ling., Bull.Signal., Curr.Cont., IBR, IBZ, Lang.& Lang.Behav.Abstr. (1977-), Lang.Teach.& Ling.Abstr., M.L.A., Phil.Ind., Sociol.Abstr., Zent.Math.
 —BLDSC (5221.377000); Faxon; UnCover; SWETS; UMI. **CCC.**
 Refereed Serial

495.4 US ISSN 0731-3500
PL3551
LINGUISTICS OF THE TIBETO - BURMAN AREA. 1974. s-a. $30 (through 1995). University of California, Berkeley, Department of Linguistics, 2337 Dwinelle Hall, Berkeley, CA 94720. TEL 510-643-9910. FAX 510-643-9911. Ed. James A. Matisoff. bk.rev. circ. 150. **Indexed:** M.L.A. **Document type:** academic/scholarly publication.
 Description: Devoted to the synchronic and diachronic study of languages of the Southeast Asian area, especially the Tibeto-Burman family, a proven linguistic relative of Chinese.

410 US ISSN 0166-0829
LINGUISTIK AKTUELL; Amsterdamer Arbeiten zur theoretischen und angewandten Linguistik. Abbreviated title: L.A. 1980. irreg., vol.6, 1989. price varies. John Benjamins Publishing Co., 821 Bethlehem Pike, Philadelphia, PA 19118. TEL 215-836-1200. FAX 215-836-1204. (And: Amsteldijk 44, P.O. Box 75577, 1070 AN Amsterdam, Netherlands. TEL 020-6762325) Ed. Werner Abraham. **Indexed:** M.L.A. **Document type:** monographic series.
 Description: Contains interdisciplinary studies in linguistics and communication sciences, concentrating on studies in Germanic languages.

3520 LINGUISTICS

400   FR   ISSN 0024-3957
P2
LINGUISTIQUE. 1965. s-a. 300 F. (foreign 365 F.) (Societe Internationale de Linguistique Fonctionnelle) Presses Universitaires de France, Departement des Revues, 14 Avenue du Bois-de-l'Epine, B.P.90, 91003 Evry Cedex, France. TEL 1-60-77-82-05. FAX 1-60-79-20-45. TELEX PUF 600 474 F. Dir. Andre Martinet. (reprint service avail. from KTO) **Indexed:** Arts & Hum.Cit.Ind., Bibl.Ling., Curr.Cont., Lang.& Lang.Behav.Abstr. (1972-), Lang.Teach.& Ling.Abstr., M.L.A.
—UnCover; UMI. **CCC.**
    Description: Covers general linguistics, pure and applied.

491.8   BU   ISSN 0324-1653
P381.B3
LINGUISTIQUE BALKANIQUE/BALKANSKO IZIKOZNANIE. (Text in English, French, German, Russian) 1975. q. 7 lv. (Bulgarska Akademiia na Naukite) Publishing House of the Bulgarian Academy of Sciences, Acad. G. Bonchev St., Bldg. 6, 1113 Sofia, Bulgaria. (Dist. by: Hemus, 6, Rouski Blvd., 1000 Sofia, Bulgaria) Ed. Vladimir Georgiev. circ. 530. (back issues avail.; reprint service avail. from IRC) **Indexed:** Bibl.Ling., Lang.& Lang.Behav.Abstr. (1985-), M.L.A.
—BLDSC (0014.400000).

410 375.4   MG
LINGUISTIQUE ET ENSEIGNEMENT. (Text in French or Malagasy) 1971. irreg. (approx. s-a). Universite de Madagascar, Institut de Linguistique Appliquee, B.P. 4099, Antananarivo, Malagasy Republic.

401   FR   ISSN 0298-461X
LINGUISTIQUE GENERALE. (Subseries of: Bibliotheque de la S E L A F) 1985. irreg. price varies. Societe d'Etudes Linguistiques et Anthropologiques de France (SELAF), 52 bd St. Michel, 75006 Paris, France. (Dist. by: Editions Peeters s.p.r.l., Bondgenotenlaan 153, B-3000 Louvain, Belgium. TEL 32-16-235170. FAX 32-16-228500) **Document type:** academic/scholarly publication.

410   GW   ISSN 0344-6727
LINGUISTISCHE ARBEITEN. 1973. irreg., no.306, 1993. price varies. Max Niemeyer Verlag, Postfach 2140, 72011 Tuebingen, Germany. TEL 07071-989440. FAX 07071-989450. (back issues avail.) **Indexed:** Bibl.Ling. **Document type:** monographic series.
    Description: Monographs and collections of essays in all fields of linguistics, especially theoretical linguistics.

400   GW   ISSN 0024-3930
P1.A1
LINGUISTISCHE BERICHTE. (Text in English, French and German; abstracts in English) 1968. bi-m. DM.139 (students DM.79). Westdeutscher Verlag GmbH, Postfach 5829, 65048 Wiesbaden, Germany. TEL 0611-160230. FAX 0611-160229. Eds. H.G Grewendorf, A. Von Stechow. adv.; bk.rev.; index. (back issues avail.; reprint service avail. from SWZ) **Indexed:** Bibl.Ling., Lang.& Lang.Behav.Abstr. **Document type:** academic/scholarly publication.
—BLDSC (5221.460000); Faxon; UnCover; SWETS. **CCC.**

410 440   NE   ISSN 0378-4169
P1.A1
LINGVISTICAE INVESTIGATIONES; revue internationale de linguistique francaise et de linguistique generale. (Supplement avail.) (Text in English, French) 1977. 2/yr. fl.325($189) (effective 1994). (Universite de Paris VIII (Paris-Vincennes), Departement de Linguistique, FR) John Benjamins Publishing Co., Amsteldijk 44, P.O. Box 75577, 1070 AN Amsterdam, Netherlands. TEL 31-20-6738156. FAX 31-20-6792956. (In N. America: 821 Bethlehem Pike, Philadelphia, PA 19118. TEL 215-836-1200. FAX 215-836-1204) (Co-sponsor: Centre National de la Recherche Scientifique, Laboratoire d'Automatique Documentaire et Linguistique) Ed.Bd. adv.; bk.rev.; bibl.; index. circ. 600. (back issues avail.) **Indexed:** Bibl.Ling., Lang.& Lang.Behav.Abstr. (1979-), Lang.Teach.& Ling.Abstr., M.L.A. **Document type:** academic/scholarly publication.
—Faxon; UnCover; SWETS.
    Description: Contans articles on all languages, with emphasis on French.

410 440   US   ISSN 0165-7569
LINGVISTICAE INVESTIGATIONES: SUPPLEMENTA; studies in French and general linguistics/etudes en linguistique francaise et generale. Abbreviated title: L.I.S. 1979. irreg., vol.16, 1988. price varies. (Universite de Paris VIII (Paris-Vincennes), Departement de Linguistique, FR) John Benjamins Publishing Co., 821 Bethlehem Pike, Philadelphia, PA 19118. TEL 215-836-1200. FAX 215-836-1204. (And: John Benjamins B.V., P.O. Box 75577, Amsteldijk 44, 1070 AN Amsterdam, Netherlands. TEL 020-738156) (Co-sponsor: Centre National de la Recherche Scientifique, Laboratoire d'Automatique Documentaire et Linguistique) Ed.Bd. **Indexed:** Bibl.Ling., M.L.A. **Document type:** monographic series.
    Description: Contains French and general linguistics, modern linguistic theory and fundamental descriptive studies.

410   RU   ISSN 0301-6900
P25
LINGVISTICHESKIE ISSLEDOVANIYA. irreg. 0.96 Rub. (Akademiya Nauk S.S.S.R., Institut Yazykoznaniya) Izdatel'stvo Nauka, 90 Profsoyuznaya ul., 117864 Moscow, Russia. TEL 234-05-84.

410   XR
LINGVISTICKE CITANKY/READINGS IN LINGUISTICS. 1970. irreg. 10 Kcs. Universita Karlova, Filosoficka Fakulta, Nam. Krasnoarmejcu 1, 116 38 Prague 1, Czech Republic. Ed. Bohumil Palek. circ. 500.

400   NE   ISSN 0024-4457
PA9
LISTY FILOLOGICKE/JOURNAL OF PHILOLOGY. (Text and summaries in Czech, English, French, German, Latin, Russian, Slovak) 1874. q. fl.205($124) (effective 1994). (Czech Academy of Sciences, Institute of Greek, Roman and Latin Studies, XR) John Benjamins Publishing Co., Amsteldijk 44, P.O. Box 75577, 1070 AN Amsterdam, Netherlands. TEL 31-20-6738156. FAX 31-20-6792956. (In N. America: 821 Bethlehem Pike, Philadelphia, PA 19118. TEL 215-836-1200. FAX 215-836-1204) Ed. Helena Kurzova. bk.rev.; abstr.; bibl.; charts; illus.; index. circ. 700. (also avail. in microfilm from PMC) **Indexed:** Amer.Hist.& Life, Bibl.Ling., Hist.Abstr., M.L.A., Numis.Lit. **Document type:** academic/scholarly publication.
    Description: Focuses on classical philology, archeology, medieval Latin and humanistic studies, and Old Czech language and literature.

410 800   SA   ISSN 0258-2279
PN1
LITERATOR; journal of literary criticism and linguistics. (Text in Afrikaans, English, French, German; summaries in English) 1980. 3/yr. R.30 (effective 1993). (Literator Society - Literatorvereniging van Suid-Afrika) Buro vir Wetenskaplike Tydskrifte - Bureau for Scholarly Journals, Private Bag X6001, Potchefstroom 2520, South Africa. TEL 27-148-991769. FAX 27-148-991562. TELEX 346019 SA. Ed. D.H. Steenberg. adv.; bk.rev. circ. 500. **Document type:** academic/scholarly publication.
    Description: Studies of criticism, linguistics and comparative literature.

LITERATUR IN BAYERN. see *LITERATURE*

LITERATURA KAJERO; monata kultura kajero en esperanto. see *LITERATURE*

LITTERARIA PRAGENSIA. see *LITERATURE*

491   FR
LO GAI SABER. (Text in Catalan, French, Occitan) 1919. q. 80 F. (foreign 90 F.). Escola Occitana, Les Dames, Aureville, 31320 Castanet-Tolosan, France. TEL 61-73-08-70. Ed. Philippe Carbonne. bk.rev. circ. 600. **Indexed:** M.L.A.
    Former titles (until 1985): Gai Saber; (until 1973): Lo Gai Saber (ISSN 0047-4916)

400   PL   ISSN 0076-0390
P19.L6
LODZKIE TOWARZYSTWO NAUKOWE. ROZPRAWY KOMISJI JEZYKOWEJ. 1954. a. price varies. Lodzkie Towarzystwo Naukowe, Ul. Piotrowska 179, 90-447 Lodz, Poland. TEL 48-42-361026. FAX 48-42-362415. TELEX 884519 PAN PL. (Dist. by: Ars Polona, Krakowskie Przedmiescie 7, 00-068 Warsaw, Poland) (Co-sponsor: Polska Akademia Nauk) Ed. Maria Kaminska. circ. 500. **Indexed:** Bibl.Ling. **Document type:** academic/scholarly publication.

400   NE
LONDON STUDIES IN CLASSICAL PHILOLOGY. 1975; N.S. 1981. irreg., vol.25, 1993. price varies. J.C. Gieben, Nieuwe Herengracht 35, 1011 RM Amsterdam, Netherlands. TEL 31-20-6275170. FAX 31-20-6275170. (Dist. in N. America by: John Benjamins Publishing Co., 821 Bethlehem Pike, Philadelphia, PA 19118. TEL 215-836-1200. FAX 215-836-1204) (Back issues avail.) **Indexed:** Bibl.Ling. **Document type:** monographic series.
    Supersedes (in 1981): Museum Philologum Londiniense.

410 398 572   UK   ISSN 0307-7144
GR140
LORE AND LANGUAGE. 1969. s-a. £16.50($27.50) to individuals; institutions £50($80). (Centre for English Cultural Tradition and Language) Sheffield Academic Press, 343 Fulwood Rd., Sheffield S10 3BP, England. TEL 0742-670044. FAX 0742-660291. Ed. J.D.A. Widdowson. adv.; bk.rev.; charts; illus.; cum.index. circ. 700. (back issues avail.) **Indexed:** Bibl.Ling., Lang.& Lang.Behav.Abstr., M.L.A., Sociol.Abstr. **Document type:** academic/scholarly publication.
—BLDSC (5294.586000); UnCover.
    Description: Addresses interdisciplinary issues regarding all aspects of language and cultural tradition.

420 375.4   US   ISSN 0456-7463
PE1065
LOUISIANA ENGLISH JOURNAL. 1960. s-a. $20 membership. Louisiana Council of Teachers of English, c/o Olivia Pass & Susan LeJeune, Louisiana State University, P.O. Box 1129, Eunice, LA 70535. TEL 318-457-7311. FAX 318-546-6620. Eds. Olivia Pass, Susan LeJeune. circ. 400.

400   IT
LUDUS PHILOLOGIAE. 1989. irreg., no.4, 1991. price varies. Edizioni Quattroventi, Via Dini 16, Casella Postale 156, 61029 Urbino, Italy. TEL 0722-2588. FAX 0722-320998. Eds. Cesare Questa, Renato Raffaelli.

496   TZ   ISSN 0047-5165
LUGHA YETU. (Text in Swahili) 1969. 2/yr. Sh.25 per. no. National Swahili Council, P.O. Box 4766, Dar es Salaam, Tanzania. Ed. M. M. Kumbuka. adv.; bk.rev. circ. 5,000.

499.992   CN   ISSN 0827-3154
LUMO; Kanada Esperanto-Revuo. (Text in Esperanto) 1957. 4/yr. Can.$8 to non-members. Canadian Esperanto Association, P.O. Box 2159, Sidney, BC V8L 3S6, Canada. Ed. Jean Smythe. adv.; bk.rev.; illus. circ. 300. **Document type:** newsletter.
    Description: Provides information on the activities of the Esperanto speakers in Canada and throughout the world. Includes the annual report of the CEA, essays, reviews and original literature as well as reports.

420   SW   ISSN 0076-1451
                             CODEN: LSENE6
LUND STUDIES IN ENGLISH. 1933. irreg., no.73, 1985. price varies. Liber Forlag, S-205 10, Maimo, Sweden. Eds. Claes Schaar, Jan Svartvik. (reprint service avail. from KTO) **Indexed:** Bibl.Ling., M.L.A.
—BLDSC (5304.980000).

LUOJI YU YUYAN XUEXI/LOGIC AND LANGUAGE STUDIES. see *PHILOSOPHY*

M L A JOB INFORMATION LISTS. (Modern Language Association of America) see *OCCUPATIONS AND CAREERS*

400   US   ISSN 0026-7910
PB1
M L N. (Modern Language Notes) (Text in English, French, German, Italian, Spanish) 1886. 5/yr. $30 to individuals (foreign $44.80); institutions $78 (foreign $92.80). Johns Hopkins University Press, Journals Publishing Division, 2715 N. Charles St., Baltimore, MD 21218. TEL 410-516-6987. FAX 410-516-6968. Ed. Eduardo Saccone. adv.; bk.rev.; index, cum.index: vols.1-50, vols.51-60. circ. 1,637. (also avail. in microform from UMI,PMC; microfiche from IDC; reprint service avail. from UMI,SCH,KTO) Indexed: Abstr.Engl.Stud., Acad.Ind., Amer.Bibl.Slavic & E.Eur.Stud., Arts & Hum.Cit.Ind., Bibl.Ling., Bk.Rev.Ind. (1986-), Child.Bk.Rev.Ind. (1986-), Curr.Cont., Hum.Ind., Ind.Bk.Rev.Hum., Lang.& Lang.Behav.Abstr., Mid.East: Abstr.& Ind. Document type: academic/scholarly publication. —BLDSC (5879.750000); Faxon; UnCover; SWETS. CCC.
   Description: Presents articles and notes on the theory, interpretation, and history of languages.

407   AT   ISSN 0310-9674
M L T A NEWS. 1973. irreg. Modern Language Teachers' Association of New South Wales, c/o School of Modern Languages, Macquarie University, N. Ryde, NSW 2113, Australia. Ed. K.A.B. Strong. circ. 650 (controlled).

407   AT
M L T A V NEWSLETTER. 1965. 7/yr. Aus.$30 to individuals; schools Aus.$60; students Aus.$10. Modern Language Teachers' Association of Victoria, Statewide Resources Centre, 217 Church St., Richmond, Vic. 3121, Australia. TEL 61-4280248. FAX 61-428-0313. Ed. Barbara Imberger-Sonntag. adv.; bk.rev. circ. 600. Document type: newsletter.
   Formerly: M L Newsletter.

406   US
MA F L A NEWSLETTER. 1956. 5/yr. $20 to non-members. Massachusetts Foreign Language Association, 41 Glenn Dr., Wilbraham, MA 01095-1439. TEL 413-596-9284. (Subscr. to: Patrick Loconto, 182 Marcy St., Southbridge, MA 01550) Ed. Ronie Webster. adv.; bk.rev. circ. 2,000. (processed)
   Supersedes (in 1979): Massachusetts Foreign Language Bulletin; Formerly: Bay State F L Bulletin (ISSN 0005-6936)

410 940   DK
MAL & MAELE. 1974. q. DKK 128. C.B.L. Tryk, P.O. Box 3072, DK-6710 Esbjerg V, Denmark. FAX 32-96-34-74. Ed.Bd. adv.; bk.rev.; bibl.; charts. circ. 2,000.

439 839   NO   ISSN 0024-855X
PD2601
MAAL OG MINNE. 1909. s-a. NOK 150 to individuals; institutions NOK 240. (Norges Almenvitenskapelige Forskningsraad - Norwegian Research Council for Science and the Humanities) Norske Samlaget, Boks 4672 Sofiendrg, 0506 Oslo, Norway. TEL 47-22-68-76-00. FAX 47-22-68-75-02. Eds. Einar Lundeby, Bjarne Fidjestoel. bk.rev.; index. circ. 550. Indexed: Bibl.Ling., M.L.A. Document type: academic/scholarly publication.
   Description: Scholarly publication on linguistics, mostly Scandinavian languages.

492 892   US   ISSN 0149-5712
PJ3001
MAARAV; a journal for the study of the northwest semitic languages and literatures. 1978. a. $23 (Canada $25; elsewhere $27) (effective 1993). Western Academic Press, 12 Empty Saddle Rd., Rolling Hills Estates, CA 90274. TEL 310-541-4573. FAX 310-541-2361. Ed. Bruce Zuckerman. adv.; bk.rev. circ. 600. (back issues avail.) Indexed: Bibl.Ling., Curr.Cont., New Test.Abstr., Old Test.Abstr., Rel.& Theol.Abstr. (1981-), Rel.Ind.One. Document type: academic/scholarly publication.
—Faxon.

440 370   AT   ISSN 0815-7138
MACQUARIE UNIVERSITY FRENCH MONOGRAPHS. 1967-1972; N.S. 1973. irreg. Aus.$3 per no. Macquarie University, School of Modern Languages, North Ryde, N.S.W. 2109, Australia. Eds. Angus Martin, K.R. Dutton. circ. 250. Document type: monographic series.
   Supersedes: Monographs for Teachers of French (ISSN 0047-7907)

494.51   HU   ISSN 0025-0228
PH2001
MAGYAR NYELV/HUNGARIAN LANGUAGE. 1904. q. $9. Magyar Nyelvtudomanyi Tarsasag, Pesti Barnabas u. 1, 1052 Budapest, Hungary. TEL 1376-819. Ed. Lovand Benko. adv.; bk.rev.; index. circ. 800. Indexed: Bibl.Ling., Lang.& Lang.Behav.Abstr., M.L.A. Document type: academic/scholarly publication.
   Description: Provides scientific information on Hungarian linguistics.

410   HU   ISSN 0541-9298
PH2701
MAGYAR NYELVJARASOK. (Text in Hungarian; summaries in German and Russian) 1951. irreg., vol.31, 1993. Kossuth Lajos Tudomanyegyetem, Egyetem Ter 1, 4010 Debrecen, Hungary. bibl. Indexed: M.L.A.

494.51   HU   ISSN 0025-0236
MAGYAR NYELVOR/HUNGARIAN PURIST. 1872. q. $18.50. Magyar Tudomanyos Akademia, Nyelvtudomanyi Intezet, Szinhaz u. 5-9, 1014 Budapest, Hungary. Ed. L. Lorincze. adv.; bk.rev.; index. Indexed: Bibl.Ling., Lang.& Lang.Behav.Abstr., M.L.A.

MAINZER STUDIEN ZUR AMERIKANISTIK. see LITERATURE

400   GW   ISSN 0170-3560
MAINZER STUDIEN ZUR SPRACH- UND VOLKSFORSCHUNG. irreg., vol.18, 1992. price varies. (Universitaet Mainz, Institut fuer Geschichtliche Landeskunde) Franz Steiner Verlag Wiesbaden GmbH, Birkenwaldstr. 44, 70191 Stuttgart, Germany. TEL 0711-2582-0. FAX 0711-2582290. TELEX 723636-DAZ-D. (Subscr. to: Postfach 101061, 70009 Stuttgart, Germany) Ed.Bd. Document type: monographic series.

400   TI
AL-MAJALLAH AL-TUNISIYYAH LIL-LUGHAT AL-HAYYAH/REVUE TUNISIENNE DES LANGUES VIVANTES. (Text in Arabic, French) 1986. a. Faculte des Lettres et Sciences Humaines de Tunis, 94 Bd. du 9 Avril, Tunis, Tunisia. Document type: academic/scholarly publication.

491.55   IR   ISSN 0259-9082
PK6201
MAJALLE-YE ZABANSHENASI/IRANIAN JOURNAL OF LINGUISTICS. (Text in Persian) 1984. s-a. Rs.750 per no. Markaz-i Nashr-i Danishgahi - Iran University Press, 85 Park Ave., Dr. Bihishti Ave., P.O. Box 15875-4748, Tehran, Iran. TEL 98-21-623232. FAX 98-21-8861749. TELEX 213636-8-D5300. Ed. A.A. Sadeghi. bk.rev.; bibl. Indexed: Bibl.Ling. Document type: academic/scholarly publication.
   Description: Articles and comparative studies dealing with linguistics in general and linguistic topics directly related to Persian and its dialects.

MAJMA' AL-LUGHAH AL-ARABIYYAH. MAJALLAH/ACADEMIE ARABE DE DAMAS. REVUE. see LITERATURE

MAKEDONIKA. see HISTORY — History Of Europe

410 890   XN   ISSN 0350-1914
MAKEDONSKA AKADEMIJA NA NAUKITE I UMETNOSTITE. ODDELENIE ZA LINGVISTIKA I LITERATURNA NAUKA. PRILOZI/MACEDONIAN ACADEMY OF SCIENCES AND ARTS. SECTION OF LINGUISTICS AND LITERARY SCIENCES. CONTRIBUTIONS. 1976. s-a. Makedonska Akademija na Naukite i Umetnostite, Oddelenie za Lingvistika i Literaturna Nauka, Bulevar Krste Misrkov bb, P.O. Box 428, 91000 Skopje, Macedonia. TEL 235-506. Ed. Bozidar Videoski.
   Description: Linguistics and literary science topics, concentrating on Southern Slavic languages.

491.81   XN   ISSN 0025-1089
PG1161
MAKEDONSKI JAZIK. (Text in Macedonian and other languages) 1950. a. Institut za Makedonski Jazik, Skopje - Institute of Macedonian Language, P.O. Box 434, 91000 Skopje, Macedonia. (Co-sponsor: Republicka Zaednica za Naucni Dejnosti) Ed. Bozidar Videoski. bk.rev./ circ. 1,000 (controlled). Indexed: Bibl.Ling., M.L.A.
—BLDSC (0098.500000).

418.02   US   ISSN 0363-3659
P409
MALEDICTA; the international journal of verbal aggression. 1977. biennial. $22 to individuals; institutions $26. (International Maledicta Society) Maledicta Press, Box 14123, Santa Rosa, CA 95402-6123. Ed. Reinhold Aman. bk.rev.; bibl.; index. circ. 4,000. (back issues avail.) Indexed: Lang.& Lang.Behav.Abstr., M.L.A., Sociol.Abstr. Document type: academic/scholarly publication. —SWETS.
   Description: Contains essays and glossaries of verbal abuse, insults, curses, slurs, blasphemies, and obscenities in many languages.

418.02   US   ISSN 0363-9037
MALEDICTA PRESS PUBLICATIONS. 1976. irreg., vol.5, 1979. price varies. Maledicta Press, Box 14123, Santa Rosa, CA 95402-6123. Ed. Reinhold Aman. circ. 4,000. Document type: monographic series.
   Description: Dictionaries and glossaries of verbal abuse of any kind and in many languages. Contains originals and reprints.

439.69   IC   ISSN 1011-5889
MALFREGNIR. 1987. s-a. ISK 600. Islensk Malnefnd, Aragoetu 9, IS-101 Reykjavik, Iceland. TEL 354-1-28530. FAX 354-1-622699. Ed. Baldur Jonsson. bk.rev.; bibl. circ. 450. (back issues avail.) Document type: academic/scholarly publication.
   Description: Publishes articles and news on Icelandic language planning and neologism.

410 800   GW
MANNHEIMER BEITRAEGE ZUR SPRACH- UND LITERATURWISSENSCHAFT. irreg., no.24, 1993. DM.168. Gunter Narr Verlag, Postfach 2567, 72015 Tuebingen, Germany. TEL 07071-78091. FAX 07071-75288. Ed. Hartmut Laufhuette. Document type: monographic series.

479.1   BE   ISSN 0542-6669
PC2
MARCHE ROMANE. 1951. q. 1000 BEF. Universite de Liege, Association des Romanistes, 3 Place Cockerill, 4000 Liege, Belgium. bk.rev. circ. 500. Indexed: M.L.A.
—BLDSC (5369.740000).

MARI ANNALES DE RECHERCHES INTERDISCIPLINAIRES. see ARCHAEOLOGY

410 491.8   XR
P19
MASARYKOVA UNIVERSITA. FILOZOFICKA FAKULTA. SBORNIK PRACI. A: RADA JAZYKOVEDNA. 1952. irreg. (approx. a.). price varies. Masarykova Universita, Filozoficka Fakulta, A. Novaka 1, 660 88 Brno, Czech Republic. FAX 41-211241. bk.rev. Document type: proceedings.
   Formerly: Universita J.E. Purkyne. Filozoficka Fakulta. Sbornik Praci. A: Rada Jazykovedna (ISSN 0231-7567)
   Description: Covers problems of general linguistics, as well as Indo-European linguistics and phonetics, Slavonic languages syntax with focus on Czech and Russian languages.

420 430   XR
MASARYKOVA UNIVERSITA. FILOZOFICKA FAKULTA. SBORNIK PRACI. K: RADA GERMANISTICKO - ANGLISTICKA. (Text in English or German) 1959. irreg. (approx. a.). price varies. Masarykova Universita, Filozoficka Fakulta, A. Novaka 1, 660 88 Brno, Czech Republic. FAX 41-211241. bk.rev. Document type: proceedings.
   Formerly: Universita J.E. Purkyne. Filozoficka Fakulta. Sbornik Praci. K: Rada Germanisticko - Anglisticka (ISSN 0231-5351)
   Description: Covers English and German linguistics and literature.

440 809.02   XR
MASARYKOVA UNIVERSITA. FILOZOFICKA FAKULTA. SBORNIK PRACI. L: RADA ROMANISTICKA. 1965. irreg. (approx. a.). price varies. Masarykova Universita, Filozoficka Fakulta, A. Novaka 1, 660 88 Brno, Czech Republic. FAX 41-211241. bk.rev. Document type: proceedings.
   Formerly: Universita J.E. Purkyne. Filozoficka Fakulta. Sbornik Praci. L: Rada Romanisticka (ISSN 0231-7532)
   Description: Romanistic Series publishes studies and reviews concerning Romance linguistics (including phonetics) and literature.

LINGUISTICS

410   AT   ISSN 0811-0069
MATERIALS IN LANGUAGES OF INDONESIA. (Subseries of: Pacific Linguistics. Series D: Special Publications (ISSN 0078-7566)) 1980. irreg. price varies. Australian National University, Research School of Pacific Studies, Pacific Linguistics, Canberra, A.C.T. 0200, Australia. Ed. W.A.L. Stokhof.

491.7   RU
MATERIALY I ISSLEDOVANIYA PO SIBIRSKOI DIALEKTOLOGII. 1974. a. 1.10 Rub. Krasnoyarskii Gosudarstvennyi Pedagogicheskii Institut, Krasnoyarsk, Russia. Ed. N. Tsomakion. circ. 1,000. (reprint service avail. from KTO)

410   FR   ISSN 0293-7107
MATERIAUX POUR L'ETUDE DE L'ASIE ORIENTALE MODERNE ET CONTEMPORAINE. 1966. irreg., latest 1991. price varies. Editions de l' Ecole des Hautes Etudes en Sciences Sociales, 131 bd. St-Michel, 75005 Paris, France. TEL 43-54-47-15. FAX 43-54-80-73. (Dist. by: Centre Interinstitutionnel pour la Diffusion de Publications en Sciences Humaines, 131 bd. St-Michel, 75005 Paris, France).

MEANDER; miesiecznik poswiecony kulturze swiata starozytnego. see CLASSICAL STUDIES

941.6 410   IE   ISSN 0332-4222
MEDIAEVAL AND MODERN BRETON SERIES. 1962. irreg. Dublin Institute for Advanced Studies, School of Celtic Studies, 10 Burlington Rd., Dublin 4, Ireland. TEL 01-6680748. FAX 01-6680561. **Document type:** monographic series.

400   IT   ISSN 0390-0711
PC4
MEDIOEVO ROMANZO. 1974. 3/yr. L.130000. Societa Editrice Il Mulino, Strada Maggiore, 37, 40125 Bologna, Italy. TEL 051-2560111. FAX 051-256034. Ed.Bd. adv.; bibl.; index. circ. 600. (back issues avail.) **Indexed:** Bibl.Ling., Ind.Bk.Rev.Hum., M.L.A.
—BLDSC (5534.350000); SWETS.

MEDITERRANEAN LANGUAGE AND CULTURE MONOGRAPH SERIES. see CLASSICAL STUDIES

MEDITERRANEAN LANGUAGE REVIEW. see CLASSICAL STUDIES

MEDIUM AEVUM. see LITERATURE

410   SW   ISSN 0348-7741
PD5571
MEIJERBERGS ARKIV FOR SVENSK ORDFORSKNING. 1937. irreg. price varies. Meijerbergs Institut, Institutionen for Nordiska Spraak, S-412 98 Gothenburg, Sweden. TEL 031-634-662. Ed. Bo Ralph. (back issues avail.)

450   IT
MESSANA; rassegna di studi filologici linguistici e storici. N.S. 1990. irreg., no.11, 1992. L.32000. (Universita degli Studi di Messina, Facolta di Lettere e Filosofia) Editrice Sicania, Via Catania 62, Messina, Italy. Ed. Gianvito Resta.

418.02   CN   ISSN 0026-0452
P306.A1
META. (Text in English, French) 1956. q. Can.$29 to individuals; institutions Can.$50. Presses de l'Universite de Montreal, C.P. 6128, Succ. A, Montreal, PQ H3C 3J7, Canada. TEL 514-343-6933. Dir. M. Andre Clas. adv.; bk.rev.; bibl.; cum.index: 1955-1980. circ. 3,700. (also avail. in microform from UMI; reprint service avail. from UMI) **Indexed:** Bibl.Ling., Lang.& Lang.Behav.Abstr., NAA, Pt.de Rep. (1983-).
—BLDSC (5683.130000); UnCover; SWETS; UMI.
Formerly: Journal des Traducteurs.

375.4 800   US   ISSN 0885-7253
PN228.M4
METAPHOR AND SYMBOLIC ACTIVITY. 1986. q. $37.50 to individuals (foreign $62.50); institutions $160 (foreign $190). Lawrence Erlbaum Associates, Inc., 365 Broadway, Hillside, NJ 07642. TEL 201-666-4110. FAX 201-666-2394. Ed. Howard R. Pollio. (back volumes avail.) **Indexed:** Psychol.Abstr. **Document type:** academic/scholarly publication.
—BLDSC (5701.650000); Faxon; UnCover; SWETS.
Description: Covers the study of figurative language from a wide variety of perspectives.
Refereed Serial

410   VC
METERIALEN ZUM SUMERISCHEN LEXIKON/MATERIALS FOR THE SUMERIAN LEXICON. (Supplementary series avail., latest no.1, 1986) 1951. irreg., no.17, 1985. price varies. (Pontifico Instituto Biblico) Biblical Institute Press, Piazza della Pilotta 35, 00187 Rome, Italy. TEL 06-687-15-67. FAX 06-687-05-88.
Description: Reconstructs Sumerian and Akkadian lexical texts.

450 156   IT   ISSN 1120-3854
METHODOLOGIA; pensiero linguaggio modelli - thought language models. (Text in English, French, Italian) q. L.100000($150) to individuals; institutions L.150000($250). (Societa di Cultura Metodologica - Operativa - Society of Methodological - Operative Culture) Espansione s.r.l., Via Guinizelli 56, 00152 Rome, Italy. TEL 02-55-181630. FAX 02-5451692. (Editorial addr.: Via Senato 45, 20121 Milan, Italy) Ed. Felice Accame. bk.rev.; abstr.; bibl.

430 830   US   ISSN 0098-8030
PD1
MICHIGAN GERMANIC STUDIES. (Text in English, German) 1975. s-a. $15 to individuals (foreign $16); institutions $30 (foreign $32). University of Michigan, Department of Germanic Languages & Literatures, Ann Arbor, MI 48109-1275. TEL 313-763-6557. FAX 313-764-3521. Ed. Roy C. Cowen. adv.; bk.rev. circ. 300. (also avail. in microfilm from UMI; back issues avail.) **Indexed:** Arts & Hum.Cit.Ind., Bibl.Ling., Curr.Cont., Lang.& Lang.Behav.Abstr., M.L.A., Sociol.Abstr. **Document type:** academic/scholarly publication.
—Faxon; UnCover; SWETS; UMI.
Description: Takes an interdisciplinary approach in bringing together scholarly studies of the histories, cultures, languages, and literatures of the peoples of Central Europe.

MICHIGAN SLAVIC MATERIALS. see LITERATURE

419.7 800   US   ISSN 0888-8752
MIDDLEBURY STUDIES IN RUSSIAN LANGUAGE AND LITERATURE. irreg. Peter Lang Publishing, Inc., 62 W. 45th St., 4th Fl., New York, NY 10036. TEL 212-302-6740. FAX 212-302-7574. Ed. Thomas R. Beyer, Jr. **Document type:** academic/scholarly publication.
Description: Covers the latest developments in linguistics, literary and pedagogical scholarship devoted to Russian language and literature. Includes analyses of texts and authors, translations of literary and scholarly works, and writings on theoretical and applied linguistics with special attention to new methods for the teaching of Russian language and literature.

480   SP   ISSN 0213-9634
PA9
MINERVA: REVISTA DE FILOLOGIA CLASICA. 1987. a. 3000 ptas. Universidad de Valladolid, Secretariado de Publicaciones, C. Juan Mambrilla, 14, 47003 Valladolid, Spain. TEL 983-423000. FAX 34-83-290300. TELEX 26357. **Document type:** academic/scholarly publication.

480   SP   ISSN 0544-3733
P1035   CODEN: MNOSED
MINOS; revista de filologia egea. (Text in English, French, Italian, Spanish) 1951. a. 6000 ptas. Ediciones Universidad de Salamanca, Apdo. 325, 37080 Salamanca, Spain. TEL 923-26-14-54. (Co-sponsor: Universidad del Pais Vasco) Ed. J.L. Melena. **Indexed:** Bibl.Ling. **Document type:** academic/scholarly publication.
Description: Includes studies on Greek philology.

400 809.4   CC   ISSN 0257-5779
MINZU YUWEN/LINGUISTICS - NATIONAL MINORITIES. (Text mainly in Chinese) 1980. bi-m. $22.50. Zhongguo Shehui Kexueyuan, Minzu Yanjiusuo - Chinese Academy of Social Science, National Minorities Institute, 22 Baishiqiao Lu, Beijing 100081, People's Republic of China. TEL 8022288. (Dist. in US by: China Books & Periodicals, Inc., 2929 24th St., San Francisco, CA 94110. TEL 415-282-2994) Ed. Zhao Na Si Tu. **Indexed:** Bibl.Ling.
—UnCover.
Description: Covers the languages of China's national minorities.

400 800   US   ISSN 0026-6272
MISSISSIPPI LANGUAGE CRUSADER. 1953. 3/yr. $10. Mississippi Foreign Language Association, Univ. of Mississippi, Modern Languages Dept., University, MS 38677. TEL 601-232-7298. FAX 601-232-5918. Eds. Hans-Juergen Gaycken, Donald L. Dyer. adv.; bk.rev. circ. 350. **Indexed:** ERIC. **Document type:** bulletin.

491.2   II   ISSN 0026-6787
MITHILA INSTITUTE OF POST GRADUATE STUDIES AND RESEARCH IN SANSKRIT LEARNING. BULLETIN.* (Text in English and Sanskrit) vol.3, 1967. s-a. Rs.10. Mithila Research Institute, Darbhanga, Bihar, India. Ed. S. Bagchi. bk.rev.; bibl.

410   FR   ISSN 0249-6267
MODELES LINGUISTIQUES. 1979. s-a. 160 F. (foreign 130 F.). Universite de Lille III, Rue du Barreau, B.P. 143, 59653 Villeneuve d'Ascq Cedex, France. Dirs. Andre Joly, Richard Lilly. **Indexed:** Bibl.Ling., M.L.A.
—Faxon; SWETS.

410   US   ISSN 0736-5268
MODELS OF SCIENTIFIC THOUGHT; a series of monographs and tracts. price varies. irreg., latest vol.4, 1987. Harwood Academic Publishers, 820 Town Center Dr., Langhorne, PA 19047. TEL 215-750-2642. FAX 215-750-6343. (UK subscr. to: Box 90, Reading, Berkshire RG1 8JL, England. TEL 0734-560-080) (also avail. in microform) **Document type:** monographic series.
—BLDSC (5883.541000).
Refereed Serial

420 375.4   UK   ISSN 0308-0587
PE1128.A2
MODERN ENGLISH TEACHER;* a magazine of practical suggestions for improving the teaching of English as a foreign language. 1973. q. £8.50. Modern English Publications Ltd., Brunel Rd., Houndsmills, Basingstoke, Hants. RG21 2XS, England. Ed. Susan Holden. adv.; bk.rev.; illus.; index. circ. 6,000. **Indexed:** Cont.Pg.Educ., Lang.Teach.& Ling.Abstr.
—BLDSC (5886.440000); SWETS.
Description: Presents study and teaching methods.

410   HU   ISSN 0076-9967
MODERN FILOLOGIAI FUZETEK. 1966. irreg., vol.50, 1992. price varies. (Magyar Tudomanyos Akademia) Akademiai Kiado, Publishing House of the Hungarian Academy of Sciences, P.O. Box 245, H-1519 Budapest, Hungary. TEL 181-2134. FAX 166-6466. TELEX 22-6228 AKNYO H.

MODERN GREEK STUDIES ASSOCIATION BULLETIN. see HISTORY — History Of Europe

400 371.3   US   ISSN 0026-7902
PB1   CODEN: MOLJA8
MODERN LANGUAGE JOURNAL. (Text in various languages) 1916. q. $21 to individuals; institutions $43. (National Federation of Modern Language Teachers Associations) University of Wisconsin Press, Journal Division, 114 N. Murray St., Madison, WI 53715. TEL 608-262-4925. FAX 608-262-7560. Ed. Sally Sieloff Magnan. adv.; bk.rev.; abstr.; charts; film rev.; illus.; stat.; index. circ. 7,000. (also avail. in microform from UMI,PMC; back issues avail.; reprint service avail. from UMI) **Indexed:** Amer.Bibl.Slavic & E.Eur.Stud., Bk.Rev.Ind. (1965-), C.I.J.E., Chic.Per.Ind., Child.Bk.Rev.Ind. (1965-), Cont.Pg.Educ., Curr.Cont., Educ.Ind., Ind.Bk.Rev.Hum., Lang.& Lang.Behav.Abstr., Lang.Teach.& Ling.Abstr., M.L.A., Media Rev.Dig., Mid.East: Abstr.& Ind., Psychol.Abstr., SSCI. **Document type:** academic/scholarly publication.
—BLDSC (5887.500000); Faxon; UnCover; SWETS; UMI. **CCC.**

MODERN LANGUAGE QUARTERLY; a journal of literary history. see LITERATURE

MODERN LANGUAGE REVIEW. see LITERATURE

MODERN LANGUAGE STUDIES. see LITERATURE

| 400 | | US | ISSN 0026-8232 |

PB1
MODERN PHILOLOGY; a journal devoted to research in medieval and modern literature. 1903. q. $28 to individuals; institutions $54; students $18. University of Chicago Press, Journals Division, 5720 S. Woodlawn Ave., Chicago, IL 60637. TEL 312-753-3347. FAX 312-753-0811. TELEX 25-4603. (Subscr. to: Box 37005, Chicago, IL 60637) Ed. Janel Mueller. adv.; bk.rev.; index. circ. 1,800. (also avail. in microform from UMI, PMC; microfiche from IDC; reprint service avail. from UMI,ISI,SCH) **Indexed:** Abstr.Engl.Stud., Acad.Ind., Arts & Hum.Cit.Ind., Bibl.Ling., Bk.Rev.Dig., Bk.Rev.Ind. (1965-), Child.Bk.Rev.Ind. (1965-), Curr.Cont., Hum.Ind., Ind.Bk.Rev.Hum., LCR, M.L.A. **Document type:** academic/scholarly publication.
—BLDSC (5890.780000); Faxon; UnCover; SWETS; UMI. **CCC**.
Refereed Serial

| 400 370 | | SW | ISSN 0026-8577 |

PB5
MODERNA SPRAAK. (Text in several languages) 1906. q. SEK 185. Riksfoereningen foer Laerarna i Moderna Spraak - Modern Language Teachers' Association of Sweden, Aengen, S-560 34 Visingsoe, Sweden. Ed. Claus Ohrt. adv.; bk.rev.; index. circ. 2,000. **Indexed:** Arts & Hum.Cit.Ind., Bibl.Ling., Curr.Cont., Lang.& Lang.Behav.Abstr., Lang.Teach.& Ling.Abstr., M.L.A.
—BLDSC (5900.027000); UnCover; SWETS.

MOKO. see *LITERATURE*

| 430 371.3 | | US | ISSN 0026-9271 |

MONATSHEFTE. (Text in English, German) 1899. q. $26 to individuals; institutions $63. (University of Wisconsin, Department of German) University of Wisconsin Press, Journal Division, 114 N. Murray St., Madison, WI 53715. TEL 608-262-4952. FAX 608-262-7560. Ed. Valters Nollendorfs. adv.; bk.rev.; bibl.; index. circ. 1,350. (also avail. in microform from UMI,PMC; back issues avail.; reprint service avail. from UMI) **Indexed:** Ind.Bk.Rev.Hum., M.L.A. **Document type:** academic/scholarly publication.
—BLDSC (5904.100000); Faxon; UnCover; SWETS; UMI. **CCC**.
Formerly: Monatshefte fuer Deutschen Unterricht.
Description: Presents study and teaching methods.

| 410 800 | | UK | |

MONOGRAPHS IN MODERN LANGUAGES. (Text in all modern languages except English) 1966. irreg. price varies. University of Hull Press, Hull HU6 7RX, England. TEL 0482-46311. FAX 0482-465936. TELEX 592592-KHMAIL-G FAO HULIB 375. Ed. P.A. Holmes. **Indexed:** M.L.A. **Document type:** monographic series.
Formerly: Occasional Papers in Modern Languages (ISSN 0078-3099)

| 420 | | UK | |

MONOGRAPHS IN SYSTEM LINGUISTICS. 1989. irreg. £22.65. University of Nottingham, Department of English Studies, Nottingham NG7 2RD, England. Ed. K.N. Nwogu. **Document type:** monographic series.

| 894.2 494.2 | | HU | ISSN 0230-8452 |

MONUMENTA LINGUAE MONGOLICAE COLLECTA. (Text in Mongolian with transcriptions in Roman letters and introduction in French) 1971. irreg. price varies. (Magyar Tudomanyos Akademia) Akademiai Kiado, Publishing House of the Hungarian Academy of Sciences, P.O. Box 245, H-1519 Budapest, Hungary. TEL 181-2134. FAX 166-6466. TELEX 22-6228 AKNYO H. Ed. L. Ligeti.
Supersedes (1963-1969): Mongol Nyelvemlektar (ISSN 0540-6471)

| 410 | | RU | |

MOSKOVSKII UNIVERSITET. VESTNIK. SERIYA 10: FILOLOGIYA. (Text in Russian; contents page in English) bi-m. 13.50 Rub. Moskovskii Universitet, Ul. Gertsena 5-7, 103009 Moscow, Russia. bk.rev.; bibl.; index. **Indexed:** Bibl.Ling.

| 418 800 | | YU | ISSN 0350-6525 |

MOSTOVI. (Text in Serbian in Cyrillic alphabet) 1970. q. $60. Udruzenje Knjizevnih Prevodilaca Srbije, Francuska 7, Belgrade, Serbia, Yugolsavia. Ed. Jovan Janicijevic. circ. 1,000. **Indexed:** M.L.A.

| 400 | | KR | ISSN 0027-2833 |

MOVOZNAVSTVO; naukovo-teoretychny zhurnal. 1967. bi-m. 3.30 Rub.($7.20) (Akademiya Nauk Ukrainy) Vidavnitstvo Naukova Dumka, Vul. Tereshchenkivska 3, 252601 Kiev, Ukraine. TEL 044-224-4068. FAX 044-224-7060. Ed. V.M. Rusanivs'kii. bk.rev.; bibl. **Indexed:** Bibl.Ling., Lang.& Lang.Behav.Abstr. (1972-), M.L.A.

LE MOYEN AGE. see *HISTORY — History Of Europe*

| 400 | | GW | ISSN 0077-1910 |

P25
MUENCHENER STUDIEN ZUR SPRACHWISSENSCHAFT. (Text in English, French and German) 1954. a. price varies. J.H. Roell, Wuerzburgerstr. 16, 97337 Dettelbach, Germany. TEL 09324-1429. Eds. Heinrich Hettrich, Klaus Strunk. **Indexed:** Bibl.Ling., Lang.& Lang.Behav.Abstr. (1973-). **Document type:** academic/scholarly publication.

MUENCHNER GERMANISTISCHE BEITRAEGE. see *LITERATURE*

| 496.396 896.396 | | TZ | ISSN 0856-0129 |

MULIKA. 1971. a. $5. University of Dar es Salaam, Institute of Kiswahili Research, P.O. Box 35110, Dar es Salaam, Tanzania. Eds. A.M. Khamisi, S.D. Kiange.

| 410 | | GW | ISSN 0167-8507 |
| | | | CODEN: MULTDF |

MULTILINGUA; journal of cross-cultural and interlanguage communication. (Text in English) 1982. 4/yr. DM.84 to individuals; institutions DM.210. Walter de Gruyter und Co., Mouton de Gruyter, Genthiner Str. 13, 10785 Berlin, Germany. TEL 030-26005-0. FAX 030-26005251. TELEX 184027-WDG-D. (U.S. addr.: Walter de Gruyter Inc., 200 Saw Mill River Rd., Hawthorne, NY 10532) Ed. Richard J. Watts. adv.; bk.rev. circ. 550. **Indexed:** Lang.Teach.& Ling.Abstr., M.L.A., Sci.Abstr. **Document type:** academic/scholarly publication.
—BLDSC (5983.136000); SWETS. **CCC**.

| 406 | | AU | ISSN 0027-3228 |

MUNDARTFREUNDE OESTERREICHS. MITTEILUNGEN. 1947. s-a. membership. Mundartfreunde Oesterreichs, Postgasse 7-9, A-1010 Vienna, Austria. Ed. Dr. Isolde Hausner. circ. 1,000. **Document type:** newsletter.

| 407 | | KN | |

MUNHWAO HAKSUP/STUDY OF KOREAN LANGUAGE. (Text in Korean) q. Publishing House of the Academy of Social Sciences, Pyongyang, N. Korea.

MUSEE ROYAL DE L'AFRIQUE CENTRALE. ANNALES - SCIENCES HUMAINES. SERIE IN 8/KONINKLIJK MUSEUM VOOR MIDDEN-AFRIKA. ANNALEN - MENSELIJKE WETENSCHAPPEN. SERIE IN 8. see *HUMANITIES: COMPREHENSIVE WORKS*

MUSEUM HELVETICUM; Schweizerische Zeitschrift fuer klassische Altertumswissenschaft. see *CLASSICAL STUDIES*

| 430 | | GW | ISSN 0027-514X |

PF3003
MUTTERSPRACHE; Zeitschrift zur Pflege und Erforschung der deutschen Sprache. 1886. q. DM.132 (students DM.82.50). Gesellschaft fuer Deutsche Sprache e.V., Taunusstr. 11, 65183 Wiesbaden, Germany. TEL 0611-520031. FAX 0611-51313. Ed. Gerhard Mueller. adv.; bk.rev.; bibl.; index. circ. 1,400. (reprint service avail. from SCH) **Indexed:** Arts & Hum.Cit.Ind., Bibl.Ling., Curr.Cont., Lang.& Lang.Behav.Abstr., M.L.A. **Document type:** academic/scholarly publication.
—BLDSC (5992.130000); Faxon; SWETS.

MYND. see *CHILDREN AND YOUTH — For*

| 480 | | SP | ISSN 0213-7674 |

MYRTIA: REVISTA DE FILOLOGIA CLASICA. 1986. irreg. Universidad de Murcia, Secretariado de Publicaciones e Intercambio Cientifico, Santo Cristo 1, 30001 Murcia, Spain. TEL 968-239450. FAX 968-247936.

| 407 370 | | US | ISSN 0885-5072 |

N A B E JOURNAL.* 1975. 3/yr. $125. National Association for Bilingual Education, 1220 L St., N.W., Ste. 605, Washington, DC 20005-4018. Ed. Reynaldo F. Macias. adv.
—UnCover.
Refereed Serial

| 407 370 | | US | ISSN 0896-8349 |

N A B E NEWS.* 8/yr. $125. National Association for Bilingual Education, 1220 L St., N.W., Ste. 605, Washington, DC 20005-4018. Ed. Nancy Zelasco. adv.; illus.
—UnCover.

| 410 200 | | US | ISSN 0889-342X |

N A O S; notes and materials for the linguistic study of the sacred. (Text in English) 1985. 3/yr. $10 to individuals; institutions $20. University of Pittsburgh, Department of Hispanic Languages and Literatures, Names of the Sacred Project, 1309 Cathedral of Learning, Pittsburgh, PA 15260. TEL 412-624-5225. Ed. Juan Adolfo Vazquez. bk.rev. circ. 500. (back issues avail.) **Indexed:** Bibl.Ling. **Document type:** academic/scholarly publication.

| 663 | | US | |

N E A T E NEWSLETTER. 4/yr. $30 (includes Leaflet). New England Association of Teachers of English, Box 234, Lexington, MA 02173. TEL 617-646-2575. **Document type:** academic/scholarly publication, newsletter.

| 400 | | UK | ISSN 0143-859X |

PB1
N I M L A. 1978. a. £10. Modern Language Association of Northern Ireland, Larne Grammar School, Department of Modern Languages, Larne BT40 1PQ, N. Ireland. TEL 0574-272791. Ed. Roy Blair. adv.: page £60. bk.rev. circ. 500. **Indexed:** ERIC, Lang.Teach.& Ling.Abstr. **Document type:** academic/scholarly publication.
—BLDSC (6113.184000).

N L P WORLD. (Neuro-Linguistic Programming) see *MEDICAL SCIENCES — Psychiatry And Neurology*

| 410 | | DK | ISSN 0108-8416 |

PD75
N O W E L E. (North-Western European Language Evolution) (Supplement avail.: North-Western European Language Evolution (ISSN 0900-8675)) 1983. s-a. DKK 120. Odense University Press, Campusvej 55, DK-5230 Odense M, Denmark. TEL 66-157999. FAX 66-158126. **Indexed:** Bibl.Ling.
Description: Publishes articles dealing with all aspects of the (pre)-histories of Icelandic, Faroese, Norwegian, Swedish, Danish, Frisian, Dutch, German, English, Gothic and the early Runic language.

| 491.7 947 | | US | |

N W S S NEWS. bi-m. $25 membership; institutions $50. Network of Women in Slavic Studies, Box 75586, Washington, DC 20013. FAX 703-782-0171. E-mail: TOOLS@OASYS.DT.NAVY.MIL. **Document type:** newsletter.
Description: Includes news in the Slavic studies field, job and grant opportunities, Internet news, announcements of meetings, special events and recent publications by members.

| 418 | | BE | ISSN 0167-5257 |

NAAMKUNDE. (Text mainly in Dutch; occasionally in English, German) 1925. 4/yr. 950 BEF (effective 1994). (Katholieke Universiteit te Leuven, Instituut voor Naamkunde) Editions Peeters s.p.r.l., Bondgenotenlaan 153, B-3000 Louvain, Belgium. TEL 32-16-235170. FAX 32-16-228500. (Co-sponsor: Commissie voor Naamkunde en Nederzettingsgeschiedenis te Amsterdam, NE) Ed.Bd. bk.rev.; bibl.; charts; index. **Indexed:** Bibl.Ling., Lang.& Lang.Behav.Abstr. (1978-), M.L.A. **Document type:** academic/scholarly publication.
—SWETS.
Formerly (until 1969): Vereniging voor Naamkunde. Mededelingen (ISSN 0042-3866)
Description: Covers personal and place names as well as topics in theoretical onomastics.

| 410 830 | | GW | ISSN 0936-5761 |

NACHBARSPRACHE NIEDERLAENDISCH. (Text in Dutch, German) 1986. s-a. DM.40. Fachvereinigung Niederlaendisch e.V., Magdalenenstr. 5, 48143 Muenster, Germany. TEL 0251-834447. Eds. Heinz Eickmans, Paul Wolfgang Jaegers. adv.; bk.rev.; bibl.; index. circ. 700. (back issues avail.) **Document type:** academic/scholarly publication.
Description: Studies Dutch language and literature.

LINGUISTICS

410 910   GW   ISSN 0943-0849
NAMENKUNDLICHE INFORMATIONEN. (Supplement avail.) 1964. s-a. DM.12 per no. Universitaet Leipzig, Abteilung Deutsch-Slavische Namenforschung, Augustusplatz 9, 04109 Leipzig, Germany. TEL 0341-7192973. Ed. Anne-Dietlind Krueger. bk.rev. circ. 400. **Indexed:** Bibl.Ling.
Document type: academic/scholarly publication.
Formerly (until vol.15, 1969): Karl-Marx-Universitaet. Leipziger Namenkundlichen Arbeitsgruppe. Informationen.
Description: Devoted to the study of names, such as topographical names and personal names. Covers German as well as English, Slavic and other names.
Refereed Serial

400   US   ISSN 0027-7738
P769
NAMES. 1953. q. $25 to individuals (foreign $30); institutions $35 (foreign $40). American Name Society, c/o Wayne H. Finke, Department of Modern Languages, Baruch College, Box 340, 17 Lexington Ave., New York, NY 10010. TEL 212-387-1570. FAX 212-387-1591. (Editorial addr.: c/o Thomas J. Gasque, Ed., Department of English, northern Illinois University, DeKalb, IL 60115) adv.; bk.rev.; bibl.; index, cum.index: vols.1-51, 16-30. circ. 900.
Indexed: Amer.Bibl.Slavic & E.Eur.Stud., Amer.Hist.& Life, Bibl.Ling., Bull.Signal., Geo.Abstr., Hist.Abstr., Ind.Bk.Rev.Hum., Lang.& Lang.Behav.Abstr. (1987-), Mid.East: Abstr.& Ind. **Document type:** academic/scholarly publication.
—BLDSC (6015.331000); UnCover.
Refereed Serial

400 916.8   SA
NAMES SOCIETY OF SOUTHERN AFRICA. NEWSLETTER/NAAMKUNDEVERENIGING VAN SUIDER-AFRIKA. NUUSBRIEF. (Text in Afrikaans, English) s-a. R.30($30) membership. Names Society of Southern Africa - Naamkundevereniging van Suider-Afrika, c/o Dr. Lucie A. Moeller, Onomastics Research Centre, HSRC, Private Bag X41, Pretoria 0001, South Africa. TEL 27-12-2022164. FAX 27-12-3265362. **Document type:** newsletter.

410   SW   ISSN 0077-2704
DL1
NAMN OCH BYGD; tidskrift foer nordisk ortnamsforskning. (Text in English, German and Scandinavian languages; summaries in English) 1913. a. SEK 135($14) Kungliga Gustav Adolfs Akademien - Royal Gustavus Adolphus Academy, St. Johannesgatan 11, S-75321 Uppsala, Sweden. TEL 018-18 12 89. (Dist. by: Swedish Science Press, P.O. Box 118, S-751 04 Uppsala, Sweden) Ed. Thorsten Andersson. bk.rev. circ. 500. (also avail. in microfiche from IDC; back issues avail.) **Indexed:** Bibl.Ling.
—BLDSC (6015.332400).

400   NO   ISSN 0800-4684
NAMN OG NEMNE/NAMES AND DENOMINATIONS. (Text in Norwegian; occasionally in English or German) 1984. a. NOK 130. (Norsk Namnelag) Alvheim & Eide, Akademisk Forlag, N-5083 Oevre Ervik, Norway. TEL 05-212-403. FAX 05-328-585. Ed. Oddvar Nes. bk.rev. circ. 300. (back issues avail.) **Indexed:** Bibl.Ling. **Document type:** academic/scholarly publication.

491.8   YU   ISSN 0027-8084
PG1201
NAS JEZIK. 1933. 5/yr. 50 din. Institut za Srpskohrvatski Jezik, Knez Mihajlova 35, Belgrade, Serbia, Yugoslavia. TEL 011 63-55-90. Ed. Mitar Pesikan. bk.rev.; index. circ. 1,500. **Indexed:** Bibl.Ling., M.L.A.

491.86   XR   ISSN 0027-8203
PG4004
NASE REC/OUR LANGUAGE. 1917. 5/yr. DM.95. (Czechoslovak Academy of Sciences, Institute for Czech Language) Academia, Publishing House of the Czechoslovak Academy of Sciences, Vodickova 40, 112 29 Prague 1, Czech Republic. TEL 53-93-51. (Dist. in Western countries by: Kubon & Sagner, P.O. Box 34 01 08, D-8000 Munich 34, Germany) Ed. Jan Petr. bk.rev.; index. circ. 2,500. **Indexed:** Bibl.Ling.
Description: Deals with problems of Czech language and language culture in general. Contains articles on the structure of Czech, on its stylistic variants and on the norm of codification of the standard literary language.

NATIONAL ASSOCIATION FOR THE TEACHING OF ENGLISH. NEWSLETTER. see EDUCATION — Teaching Methods And Curriculum

400   JA
NATIONAL LANGUAGE RESEARCH INSTITUTE. ANNUAL REPORT/KOKURITSU KOKUGO KENKYUJO NENPO.* 1951. a. National Language Research Institute - Kokuritsu Kokugo Kenkyujo, 9-14 Nishi-Gaoka 3-chome, Kita-ku, Tokyo 115, Japan.

410   NE   ISSN 0167-806X
P1   CODEN: NLLTDV
NATURAL LANGUAGE AND LINGUISTIC THEORY. (Text in English) 1983. 4/yr. fl.383($200) (effective 1994). Kluwer Academic Publishers, Postbus 17, 3300 AA Dordrecht, Netherlands. TEL 31-78-334911. FAX 31-78-334254. TELEX 29245 KAPG NL. (Dist. by: Kluwer Academic Publishers Group, P.O. Box 322, 3300 AH Dordrecht, Netherlands. TEL 31-78-524400. FAX 31-78-524474; N. America dist. addr.: Box 358, Accord Sta., Hingham, MA 02018-0358. TEL 617-871-6600. FAX 617-871-6528) Ed. Joan Maling. adv.; bk.rev.; index. (also avail. in microform from UMI; reprint service avail. from SWZ) **Indexed:** Arts & Hum.Cit.Ind., ASCA, Bibl.Ling., Curr.Cont., IBR, IBZ, Lang.& Lang.Behav.Abstr. (1983-), Lang.Teach.& Ling.Abstr., M.L.A., Sociol.Abstr., SSCI. **Document type:** academic/scholarly publication.
—BLDSC (6040.728000); Faxon; UnCover; SWETS; UMI. **CCC.**
Description: Provides a forum for discussion of theoretical research that pays close attention to natural language data, providing a channel of communication between researchers of diverse points of view.
Refereed Serial

410   GW
NATURAL LANGUAGE PROCESSING. irreg. Walter de Gruyter und Co., Mouton Publishers, Genthiner Str. 13, 10785 Berlin, Germany. TEL 030-260050. FAX 030-26005251.

401   NE   ISSN 0925-854X
P325   CODEN: NLSEEM
▼**NATURAL LANGUAGE SEMANTICS;** an international journal of semantics and its interfaces in grammar. (Text in English) 1992. 3/yr. fl.303($158.50) (effective 1994). Kluwer Academic Publishers, Postbus 17, 3300 AA Dordrecht, Netherlands. TEL 31-78-334911. FAX 31-78-334254. TELEX 29245 KAPG NL. (Dist. by: Kluwer Academic Publishers Group, P.O. Box 322, 3300 AH Dordrecht, Netherlands. TEL 31-78-524400. FAX 31-78-524474; N. America dist. addr.: Box 358, Accord Sta., Hingham, MA 02018-0358. TEL 617-871-6600. FAX 617-871-6528) Eds. Irene Heim, Angelike Kratzer. bk.rev. (also avail. in microform from UMI; back issues avail.) **Indexed:** Sociol.Abstr. **Document type:** academic/scholarly publication.
—BLDSC (6040.728500); Faxon; UnCover; SWETS; UMI.
Description: Publishes studies on semantics and syntax, with a focus on relations between meaning and structure and on linguistic phenomena rather than methodological and formal foundations.
Refereed Serial

410   YU
NAUCNI SASTANAK SLAVISTA U VUKOVE DANE. REFERATI I SAOPSTENJA. 1971. a. Medjunarodni Slavisticki Centar SR Srbije, Studetski trg 3-1, Belgrade, Yugoslvaia. illus. **Indexed:** Bibl.Ling., M.L.A.

420 375.4   US   ISSN 1061-6993
PS41
NEBRASKA ENGLISH JOURNAL. 1991. q. $20. Creighton University, Department of English, Omaha, NE 68178. TEL 402-280-2822. FAX 402-280-2143. Ed. Kathleen Collins. adv.; bk.rev. circ. 400. **Document type:** academic/scholarly publication.
Formerly: Nebraska English and Language Arts Journal (ISSN 1051-9823)

NEERLANDIA. see LITERARY AND POLITICAL REVIEWS

400   HU   ISSN 0418-4580
PT105
NEMET FILOLOGIAI TANULMANYOK/ARBEITEN ZUR DEUTSCHEN PHILOLOGIE. (Text in German) 1965. irreg., vol.21, 1992. Kossuth Lajos Tudomanyegyetem, Nemet Tanszek, Egyetem Ter 1, 4010 Debrecen, Hungary. bibl. **Indexed:** M.L.A.

NEOPHILOLOGUS; an international journal of modern and mediaeval language and literature. see LITERATURE

NESTOR. see ARCHAEOLOGY — Abstracting, Bibliographies, Statistics

410   US
NETHERLANDS PHONETIC ARCHIVES.* (Text in English) irreg., no.7, 1986. Walter de Gruyter, Inc., 200 Saw Mill River Rd., Hawthorne, NY 10532. TEL 914-747-0110. FAX 914-747-1326. Eds. Marcel P.R. van den Broecke, Vincent J. van Heuven. **Indexed:** Bibl.Ling.
Description: Reports recent advances in the field of linguistics and experimental phonology.

400   GW   ISSN 0342-3816
DIE NEUEREN SPRACHEN; Zeitschrift fuer Forschung, Unterricht und Kontaktstudium auf dem Fachgebiet der modernen Fremdsprachen. (Text in English, French, German, Italian, Spanish) 1952. bi-m. DM.54. Verlag Moritz Diesterweg GmbH, Waechtersbacher Str. 89, 60386 Frankfurt a.M., Germany. TEL 069-42081-0. FAX 069-1301-100. TELEX 413234-MDD. Ed.Bd. adv.; bk.rev.; index, cum.index. circ. 5,100. (reprint service avail. from KTO) **Indexed:** Lang.& Lang.Behav.Abstr., Lang.Teach.& Ling.Abstr., M.L.A. **Document type:** academic/scholarly publication.
—BLDSC (6077.829000); Faxon; SWETS; UMI. **CCC.**
Formerly: Neuphilologische Zeitschrift.

490 350   GW   ISSN 0340-6385
NEUINDISCHE STUDIEN. 1970. irreg., vol.11, 1990. price varies. Harrassowitz Verlag, Taunusstr. 14, 65183 Wiesbaden, Germany. TEL 0611-530-0. FAX 0611-530570. TELEX 4186135. (Subscr. to: Postfach 2929, 65019 Wiesbaden, Germany) Ed.Bd. **Document type:** monographic series.
—BLDSC (6080.850000).

400   FI   ISSN 0028-3754
PB10
NEUPHILOLOGISCHE MITTEILUNGEN. (Text in English, French, German, Italian, Spanish) 1899. q. $46. Uusfilologinen Yhdistys - Modern Language Society, Porthania, PL 4 (Hallituskatu 11), 00014 Helsingin Yliopisto, Finland. Ed. Marjatta Wis. adv.; bk.rev.; abstr.; index. circ. 1,200. (also avail. in microfiche from IDC; reprint service avail. from SWZ) **Indexed:** Arts & Hum.Cit.Ind., Bibl.Ling., Can.Rev.Comp.Lit., Curr.Cont., Ind.Bk.Rev.Hum., Lang.& Lang.Behav.Abstr., Sociol.Abstr. **Document type:** academic/scholarly publication, bulletin.
—BLDSC (6081.270000); Faxon; UnCover; SWETS.

400   GW   ISSN 0028-3983
PB3
NEUSPRACHLICHE MITTEILUNGEN AUS WISSENSCHAFT UND PRAXIS. (Text in English, French, German) 1948. q. DM.55. (Fachverband Moderne Fremdsprachen) Cornelsen Verlagskontor GmbH und Co. KG, Kammerratsheide 66, 33598 Bielefeld, Germany. TEL 0521-9719-0. Ed. Michael Bludau. adv.; bk.rev.; index. circ. 5,000. (tabloid format; also avail. in microform from UMI; reprint service avail. from UMI) **Indexed:** Lang.& Lang.Behav.Abstr., M.L.A. **Document type:** academic/scholarly publication.
—BLDSC (6081.590000); Faxon; UMI.

423.1   US   ISSN 0148-866X
NEW ACRONYMS, INITIALISMS AND ABBREVIATIONS. (Supplement to Acronyms, Initialisms and Abbreviations Dictionary) a. $220 (effective Oct. 1994). Gale Research Inc., 835 Penobscot Bldg., Detroit, MI 48226. TEL 313-961-2242; 800-877-4253. FAX 313-961-6083. TELEX 810-221-7086. Ed. Jennifer Mossman. **Document type:** directory.
Formerly (until 1976): New Acronyms and Initialisms (ISSN 0077-7986)
Description: Directory of acronyms and abbreviations.

NEW CEYLON WRITING; creative and critical writing of Sri Lanka. see LITERATURE

NEW ERA IN EDUCATION. see EDUCATION

NEW GERMAN REVIEW; a journal of Germanic studies. see LITERATURE

400 371.3   US   ISSN 0028-5293
NEW HAMPSHIRE POLYGLOT. (Text in English, French, German, Latin, Russian, Spanish) 1962. q. $15 (effective 1994). New Hampshire Association for Teaching of Foreign Languages, Box 1128, Nashua, NH 03061. TEL 603-888-2250. Ed. Julia T. Bressler. bk.rev. circ. 850. (processed) **Document type:** newsletter.
  Description: Presents study and teaching methods.

NEW SOCIETY OF LETTERS AT LUND. PUBLICATIONS. see *ART*

439   GW   ISSN 0078-0545
PF5601
NIEDERDEUTSCHES WORT; Beitraege zur niederdeutschen Philologie. 1960. irreg. price varies. Aschendorffsche Verlagsbuchhandlung, Soesterstr. 13, 48155 Muenster, Germany. TEL 0251-690-0. FAX 0251-690143. Ed. Jan Goossens. **Indexed:** Bibl.Ling., M.L.A. **Document type:** monographic series.

400   NE   ISSN 0028-9922
PF4
NIEUWE TAALGIDS; tijdschrift voor neerlandici. 1907. 6/yr. fl.86. WoltersgroepGroningen b.v. (Subsidiary of: Wolters Kluwer N.V.), Postbus 58, 9700 MB Groningen, Netherlands. TEL 31-50-226922. FAX 31-50-264866. Ed.Bd. adv.; bk.rev.; abstr.; bibl. **Indexed:** Bibl.Ling., Lang.& Lang.Behav.Abstr., M.L.A. **Document type:** academic/scholarly publication.
  —SWETS.

420.07 371.3   NR   ISSN 0029-0009
NIGERIA ENGLISH STUDIES ASSOCIATION JOURNAL.* 1967. s-a. £N3($6.) Nigeria English Studies Association, c/o University of Ibadan, Ibadan, Nigeria. Ed. Ebo Ubahakwe. adv.; bk.rev. circ. 2,000.
  Description: Presents study and teaching methods.

410   JA
NIHONGO JOURNAL. (Text in English) m. $138. Intercontinental Marketing Corp., I.P.O. Box 5056, Tokyo 100-31, Japan. TEL 81-3-3661-7458. FAX 81-3-3667-9646.

410   JA   ISSN 0914-8051
NIHONGO MAGAZINE. 1971. 4/yr. $69. Intercontinental Marketing Corp., I.P.O. Box 5056, Tokyo 100-31, Japan. TEL 81-3-3667-7458. FAX 81-3-3667-9646.

420   UK   ISSN 0141-6340
DA645
NOMINA; a journal of name studies relating to Great Britain and Ireland. 1977. a. £10 (foreign £12). Society for Name Studies in Britain and Ireland, c/o Anderson, 13 Church St., Chesterton, Cambridge CB4 1DT, England. TEL 0223-357585. Ed.Bd. adv.; bk.rev.; bibl. circ. 250. (back issues avail.) **Indexed:** Bibl.Ling., Br.Archaeol.Abstr., M.L.A. **Document type:** academic/scholarly publication.
  —BLDSC (6116.740000).

400   SA   ISSN 1012-0254
NOMINA AFRICANA. (Text in Afrikaans and English; summaries in Afrikaans, Dutch, English, French, German) 1987. s-a. R.30. Names Society of Southern Africa - Naamkundevereniging van Suider-Afrika, c/o Dr. Lucie A. Moeller, Sec.-Treas., Onomastics Research Centre, HSRC, Private Bag X41, Pretoria 0001, South Africa. TEL 27-12-202-2164. FAX 27-12-326-5362. Ed. J.U. Jacobs. bk.rev.; maps; index. circ. 200. (also avail. in diskette format; back issues avail.) **Indexed:** Bibl.Ling. **Document type:** academic/scholarly publication.
  Description: Contains placenames, personal names, literary and general onomastics.
  Refereed Serial

400   NO   ISSN 0332-5865
P1.A1
NORDIC JOURNAL OF LINGUISTICS. (Text in English) 1972? s-a. NOK 360 in the Nordic countries; elsewhere NOK 400. (Nordic Association of Linguistics) Scandinavian University Press, P.O. Box 2959-Toeyen, N-0608 Oslo, Norway. TEL 472-67-7600. FAX 472-67-7575. (U.S. addr.: Scandinavian University Press, 200 Meacham Ave., Elmont, NY 11003. TEL 516-352-7300) Ed Aake Viberg. bk.rev.; index. circ. 600. (also avail. in microform from UMI; back issues avail.; reprint service avail. from ISI) **Indexed:** Bibl.Ling., Lang.& Lang.Behav.Abstr. (1972-), M.L.A., Psychol.Abstr. —BLDSC (6117.927000); Faxon; UnCover; UMI. CCC.
  Supersedes (1928-1977): Norwegian Journal of Linguistics.
  Description: Concerned with all branches of linguistics. Preference is given to contributions of general theoretical or methodological interests and to studies on Nordic languages (including Finnish and Sami).

439   SW   ISSN 0078-1134
NORDISTICA GOTHOBURGENSIA. (Subseries of Acta Universitatis Gothoburgensis) (Text in Swedish; summaries in English and German) 1965. irreg., no.13, 1990. price varies; also exchange basis. Acta Universitatis Gothoburgensis, PO Box 5096, S-402 22 Goeteborg, Sweden. Ed. Bo Ralph. **Document type:** monographic series.

410   SW   ISSN 0346-6728
NORNA - RAPPORTER. (Text in English, German, and Scandinavian languages) 1973. irreg. price varies. Norna-Foerlaget, P.O. Box135, S-751 04 Uppsala, Sweden. FAX 46-18-18-34-02. (Dist. by: Swedish Science Press, P.O. Box 118, S-751 Uppsala, Sweden) Ed. Thorsten Andersson. bk.rev.; charts. circ. 400. **Indexed:** Bibl.Ling.
  Description: Contains proceedings of conferences within the field of onomastics, annual reports of Scandinavian onomastic research; lists of Scandinavian onomastic scholars.

439.82   NO   ISSN 0800-3076
NORSK LINGVISTISK TIDSSKRIFT. 1983. s-a. NOK 140 to individuals; institutions NOK 250 (effective 1994). Novus Forlag, P.O. Box 748 Sentrum, N-0106 Oslo, Norway. Ed. Ernst Haakon Jahr.

400   US
NORTH CENTRAL NAME SOCIETY. JOURNAL. 1987. a. free to NCNS members. Northern Illinois University, English Department, DeKalb, IL 60115. TEL 815-753-6627. FAX 815-753-1824. Ed. Edward Callary. circ. 100. (back issues avail.) **Document type:** academic/scholarly publication.
  Description: Focuses on all aspects of onomastics.

400   NE   ISSN 0078-1592
NORTH-HOLLAND LINGUISTIC SERIES. 1970. irreg., vol.55, 1992. price varies. Elsevier Science B.V., Books Division, P.O. Box 211, 1000 AE Amsterdam, Netherlands. TEL 31-20-5803911. FAX 31-20-5803705. TELEX 18582 ESPA NL. (Subscr. in U.S. and Canada to: Elsevier Science Inc., Box 882, Madison Sq. Sta., New York, NY 10159. TEL 212-989-5800) **Indexed:** M.L.A. **Document type:** monographic series.
  —BLDSC (6150.003000).
  Refereed Serial

410   US   ISSN 0883-5500
P21
NORTH EAST LINGUISTICS SOCIETY. PROCEEDINGS. Key Title: Proceedings of N E L S. 1976. a. North East Linguistic Society, c/o South College University of Massachusetts, Department of Linguistics, Amherst, MA 01003. **Document type:** proceedings.
  Formerly (until 1982): North Eastern Linguistics Society. Proceedings of the Annual Meeting (ISSN 0742-3209)

410 948   DK   ISSN 0900-8675
P123
NORTH WESTERN EUROPEAN LANGUAGE EVOLUTION. (Supplement to: N O W E L E (ISSN 0108-8416)) irreg. price varies. Odense University Press, Campusvej 55, DK-5230 Odense M, Denmark. TEL 66-157999. FAX 66-158126. Ed.Bd. **Document type:** academic/scholarly publication.
  Description: Publishes articles dealing with all aspects of the (pre-)histories of - and with intra- and extralinguistic factors contributing to change and variation within - Icelandic, Faroese, Norwegian, Swedish, Danish, Frisian, Dutch, German, English, Gothic and the early Runic language.

499.992   ISSN 0029-361X
NORVEGA ESPERANTISTO; Esperantobladet. (Text in Esperanto) 1909. bi-m. NOK 70. Norvega Esperantista Ligo - Norsk Esperanto-Forbund, Olaf Schous vei 18, 0572 Oslo 5, Norway. adv.; bk.rev. circ. 600. **Document type:** bulletin.

410   BO
NOTAS Y NOTICIAS LINGUISTICAS. 1978. m. Bol.$200($12) Instituto Boliviano de Cultura, Instituto Nacional de Estudios Linguisticos, Casilla 8877, La Paz, Bolivia. Ed.Bd. (looseleaf format; back issues avail.)

410   US   ISSN 0736-0673
P1
NOTES ON LINGUISTICS. 1977. q. price varies. Summer Institute of Linguistics, Inc., Academic Publications, 7500 W. Camp Wisdom Rd., Dallas, TX 75236. TEL 214-709-2403. Ed. David Payne. **Indexed:** Bibl.Ling., Lang.& Lang.Behav.Abstr. (1987-). **Document type:** academic/scholarly publication.
  —BLDSC (6167.542500).
  Description: Provides researchers with practical, theoretical and administrative data regarding the field.

410   US   ISSN 0737-6707
NOTES ON LITERACY. no. 3, 1968. q. price varies. Summer Institute of Linguistics, Inc., Academic Publications, 7500 W. Camp Wisdom Rd., Dallas, TX 75236. TEL 214-709-2400. Ed. Steve Walter. circ. 1,000. **Indexed:** Bibl.Ling. **Document type:** academic/scholarly publication.

407 220   US
NOTES ON SCRIPTURE IN USE AND LANGUAGE PROGRAMS. 1981. q. price varies. Summer Institute of Linguistics, Inc., Academic Publications, 7500 W. Camp Rd., Dallas, TX 75236. TEL 214-709-2400. Ed. Doris Porter. circ. 900. (also avail. in microfiche) **Document type:** academic/scholarly publication.
  Formerly (until 1989): Notes on Scripture in Use.

051 371.3   US   ISSN 0163-7088
PE68.U5
NOTES ON TEACHING ENGLISH. 1973. s-a. $5. Georgia-South Carolina College English Association, Valdosta State University, English Dept., Valdosta, GA 31698. TEL 912-333-5946. Eds. Byron Brown, Barbara Stevenson. bk.rev. circ. 400. **Document type:** academic/scholarly publication.

418   US   ISSN 0734-0788
BS449
NOTES ON TRANSLATION. q. price varies. Summer Institute of Linguistics, Inc., Academic Publications, 7500 W. Camp Wisdom Rd., Dallas, TX 75236. TEL 214-709-2400. Ed. K. Barnwell. circ. 1,200. **Document type:** academic/scholarly publication.
  —UnCover.

NOTES PLUS; a quarterly of practical teaching ideas. see *EDUCATION — Teaching Methods And Curriculum*

400   FR   ISSN 0755-7752
NOUVELLE REVUE D'ONOMASTIQUE/JOURNAL OF ONOMASTIC STUDIES. (Text in French; occasionally in German, Italian, Portuguese or Spanish) 1982. a. 300 F. to non-members; members 290 F. Societe Francaise d'Onomastique, 87 rue Vielle-du-Temple, 75003 Paris, France. Ed. Pierre-Henri Billy. adv.; bk.rev. circ. 260. (back issues avail.) **Document type:** bulletin.
  Description: Includes placenames, personal names, divine names, animal names, literary and general onomastics, and methodology.
  Refereed Serial

LINGUISTICS

400   IT
NOVANTIQUA; biblioteca di filologia, curiosita e dialettologia. 1977. irreg., no.13, 1984. price varies. Societa Editrice Napoletana s.r.l., Corso Umberto I 34, Naples, Italy. Ed. Antonio Altamura.

460   MX   ISSN 0185-0121
PC4008
NUEVA REVISTA DE FILOLOGIA HISPANICA. 1947. s-a. $78 to individuals (foreign $90); institutions $90 (foreign $96) for 2 yrs. (effective 1993). Colegio de Mexico, A.C., Departamento de Publicaciones, Camino al Ajusco 20, Codigo Postal 01000, Mexico, D.F., Mexico. TEL 645 5955. FAX 6450464. TELEX 1777585 COLME. Ed. Antonio Alatorre. bk.rev.; bibl.; index. circ. 1,500. (back issues avail.; reprint service avail. from SWZ) **Indexed:** Bibl.Ling., Hisp.Amer.Per.Ind., Ind.Bk.Rev.Hum., M.L.A.
—BLDSC (6184.400000); Faxon; SWETS.

410 400 800   CL   ISSN 0716-6346
NUEVA REVISTA DEL PACIFICO. (Text occasionally in English) 1976. s-a. $15 or exchange basis. Universidad de Playa Ancha de Ciencias de la Educacion, Facultad de Humanidades, Casilla 34-V, Valparaiso, Chile. TEL 281108. FAX 271136. Ed. Daniel Lagos A. bk.rev.; bibl.; charts. circ. 250. **Indexed:** M.L.A.
Incorporates: Alpha.
Description: Studies in language and literature.

450 850   IT
NUOVA RICERCA. 1990. a. L.30000. (Universita degli Studi di Bari, Dipartimento di Linguistica, Filologia e Letteratura Moderna) Schena Editore, Viale Stazione 177, 72015 Fasano di Puglia, Italy. (Edit. addr.: Via De Rossi 233, 70121 Bari, Italy) Ed.Bd. bk.rev. **Document type:** academic/scholarly publication.

410   IO   ISSN 0126-2874
PL5051
NUSA; linguistic studies of Indonesian and other languages in Indonesia. (Text in English) 1975. irreg. (approx. 3/yr.). $32.50. Universitas Katolik Indonesia Atma Jaya, Lembaga Bahasa, P.O. Box 2639, Jakarta 10001, Indonesia. FAX 021-584-352. Ed.Bd. adv.; bk.rev. circ. 450. (back issues avail.) **Indexed:** Bibl.Ling.

410 859   RM
NYELV- ES IRODALOMTUDOMANYI KOZLEMENYEK. vol.24, 1980. 2/yr. 70 lei($42) (Academia Romana) Editura Academiei Romane, Calea Victoriei 125, 71021 Bucharest, Rumania. (Dist. by: Rompresfilatelia, Calea Grivitei 64-66, P.O. Box 12-201, 78104 Bucharest, Rumania) Ed. Szabo Zoltan. bk.rev. **Indexed:** Bibl.Ling., Lang.& Lang.Behav.Abstr., M.L.A.

410   HU   ISSN 0078-2858
NYELVESZETI TANULMANYOK. 1951. irreg., vol.29, 1986. price varies. (Magyar Tudomanyos Akademia) Akademiai Kiado, Publishing House of the Hungarian Academy of Sciences, P.O. Box 245, H-1519 Budapest, Hungary. TEL 181-2134. FAX 166-6466. TELEX 22-6228 AKNYO H.

410   HU   ISSN 0078-2866
NYELVTUDOMANYI ERTEKEZESEK. 1953. irreg., vol.134, 1992. price varies. (Magyar Tudomanyos Akademia, Nyelvtudomanyi Intezet) Akademiai Kiado, Publishing House of the Hungarian Academy of Sciences, P.O. Box 245, H-1519 Budapest, Hungary. TEL 181-2134. FAX 166-6466. TELEX 22-6228 AKNYO H. **Indexed:** Bibl.Ling.

400   HU   ISSN 0029-6791
AS142
NYELVTUDOMANYI KOZLEMENYEK/LINGUISTIC STUDIES. 1862. s-a. $19.50. Magyar Tudomanyos Akademia, Nyelvtudomanyi Intezet, Szinhaz u. 5-9, 1014 Budapest, Hungary. Eds. L. Honti, M. Bakro-Nagy. adv.; bk.rev.; charts; illus.; index. **Indexed:** Bibl.Ling., Lang.& Lang.Behav.Abstr. (1972-), M.L.A.

439.7   SW   ISSN 0345-8768
PD5004
NYSVENSKA STUDIER; tidskrift foer svensk stil- och spraakforskning. 1921. a. SEK 130. Adolf Noreen-Saellskapet Institutionen for Nordiska Spraak, PO Box 513, 75120 Uppsala, Sweden. FAX 46-18-181272. (Dist. by: Almqvist & Wiksell International, P.O. Box 638, 101 28 Stockholm, Sweden) Eds. Lennart Elmevik, Mats Thelander. circ. 600. **Indexed:** Bibl.Ling.
Formerly: Spraak och Stil.
Description: Articles on stylistic and linguistic subjects related to modern Swedish: from the 1520's to the present.

420 375.4   US   ISSN 0192-401X
PE1128.A2   CODEN: ORJOEQ
O R T E S O L JOURNAL. (Oregon Teachers of English to Speakers of Other Languages) 1979. a. $15. Portland State University, Applied Linguistics Department, Portland, OR 97207. TEL 503-725-4142. FAX 503-725-4882. Ed. Marjorie Terdal. adv.; bk.rev. circ. 300. (back issues avail.) **Document type:** academic/scholarly publication.
—BLDSC (6296.105000).

OCCASIONAL PAPERS IN GERMAN STUDIES. see LITERATURE

410   UK   ISSN 0308-2075
OCCASIONAL PAPERS IN LINGUISTICS AND LANGUAGE LEARNING. 1976. irreg. price varies. University of Ulster, Linguistics Panel, Coleraine BT52 1SA, N. Ireland. Ed. R. Thelwall. bibl. circ. 175. **Indexed:** M.L.A.

OCCASIONAL PAPERS IN SLAVIC LANGUAGES AND LITERATURE. see LITERATURE

499   US   ISSN 0029-8115
PL5001
OCEANIC LINGUISTICS. 1962. s-a. $18 to individuals (foreign $19); institutions $24 (foreign $28). University of Hawaii Press, Journals Department, 2840 Kolowalu St., Honolulu, HI 96822. TEL 808-956-8833. FAX 808-988-6052. Ed. Byron W. Bender. adv.; bk.rev.; bibl.; charts; illus.; index. circ. 425. (also avail. in microfilm from UMI; back issues avail.; reprint service avail. from UMI,ISI) **Indexed:** Anthropol.Lit., Bibl.Ling., E.I., Lang.& Lang.Behav.Abstr. (1971-), M.L.A. **Document type:** academic/scholarly publication.
—Faxon; UnCover; UMI.
Description: Focuses on the study of indigenous languages of Oceanic areas.
Refereed Serial

499   US   ISSN 0078-3188
OCEANIC LINGUISTICS. SPECIAL PUBLICATIONS. 1966. irreg., no.22, 1988. price varies. (University of Hawaii Press, Social Science Research Institute) University of Hawaii Press, 2840 Kolowalu St., Honolulu, HI 96822. TEL 808-956-8697. FAX 808-988-6052. TELEX 6712668. Ed. George W. Grace. (reprint service avail. from UMI, ISI) **Indexed:** M.L.A.
—BLDSC (6231.483000).
Description: Presents studies of the languages used in the Pacific region.

410   DK   ISSN 0078-3277
ODENSE UNIVERSITY SLAVIC STUDIES. (Text in English and Russian) 1970. irreg., latest 1986. price varies. Odense University Press, Campusvej 55, DK-5230 Odense M, Denmark. TEL 66-157999. FAX 66-158126. (back issues avail.)

420   DK   ISSN 0078-3293
ODENSE UNIVERSITY STUDIES IN ENGLISH. (Text in English) 1969. irreg. price varies. Odense University Press, Campusvej 55, DK-5230 Odense M, Denmark. TEL 66-157999. FAX 66-158126. (back issues avail.) **Indexed:** M.L.A.
—BLDSC (6235.173600).

400   DK   ISSN 0078-3315
ODENSE UNIVERSITY STUDIES IN LINGUISTICS. 1968. irreg. price varies. Odense University Press, Campusvej 55, DK-5230 Odense M, Denmark. TEL 66-157999. FAX 66-158126. (back issues avail.) **Indexed:** Lang.& Lang.Behav.Abstr. (1968-).

439.5 839.5   DK   ISSN 0078-3331
ODENSE UNIVERSITY STUDIES IN SCANDINAVIAN LANGUAGES AND LITERATURES. (Text in Danish) 1968. irreg. price varies. Odense University Press, Campusvej 55, DK-5230 Odense M, Denmark. TEL 66-157999. FAX 66-158126. (back issues avail.)

410   DK   ISSN 0906-7612
▼**ODENSE WORKING PAPERS IN LANGUAGE AND COMMUNICATION.** 1992. irreg. free. Odense Universitet, Institut for Sprog og Kommunikation, Campusvej 55, DK-5230, Odense M, Denmark. TEL 45-66-15-86-96. FAX 45-65-93-24-83. Ed. Karl-Heinz Pogner. circ. 450. **Document type:** academic/scholarly publication.
Description: Publishes scholarly articles written by members of the Institute of Language and Communication at Odense University and their Danish or foreign colleagues. Each issue is dedicated to a specific topic.

OESTERREICHISCHE AKADEMIE DER WISSENSCHAFTEN. IRANISCHE KOMMISSION. VEROEFFENTLICHUNGEN. see HISTORY — History Of The Near East

410 401   AU
OESTERREICHISCHE AKADEMIE DER WISSENSCHAFTEN. KOMMISSION FUER LINGUISTIK UND KOMMUNIKATIONSFORSCHUNG. VEROEFFENTLICHUNGEN. (Subseries of: Oesterreichische Akademie der Wissenschaften. Philosophisch-Historische Klasse. Sitzungsberichte) 1973. irreg. Verlag der Oesterreichischen Akademie der Wissenschaften, Dr. Ignaz-Seipel-Platz 2, A-1010 Vienna, Austria. FAX 0222-5139541.

420   US   ISSN 0473-9604
OHIO STATE UNIVERSITY. WORKING PAPERS IN LINGUISTICS. 1968. irreg. (2-3/yr.). $15 per no. Ohio State University, Department of Linguistics, 222 Oxley Hall, 1712 Neil Ave., Columbus, OH 43210-1298. TEL 614-292-4052. FAX 614-292-4273. circ. 400. (back issues avail.) **Indexed:** Bibl.Ling., ERIC, Lang.& Lang.Behav.Abstr. (1971-), M.L.A., Sociol.Abstr.
—BLDSC (9350.630000).

410   US
OHIO UNIVERSITY. WORKING PAPERS IN LINGUISTICS AND LANGUAGE TEACHING. 1974. irreg. price varies. Ohio University, Department of Linguistics, 103 Gordy, Athens, OH 45701. TEL 614-593-4564. FAX 614-593-2967. abstr.; bibl.; charts; illus. circ. 250. **Document type:** academic/scholarly publication.
Formerly: Working Papers in Applied Linguistics (ISSN 0163-0016)

OLD ENGLISH NEWSLETTER. see LITERATURE

400   US
OLOGIES AND ISMS; a thematic dictionary. 1979. irreg., 3rd ed., 1986. $97. Gale Research Inc., 835 Penobscot Bldg., Detroit, MI 48226. TEL 313-961-2242. FAX 313-961-6083. TELEX 810-221-7086. Ed.Bd.
Description: Irregularly published guides to systems of belief and action.

410   BE   ISSN 0078-463X
P323
ONOMA; bibliographical and information bulletin. (Text in English) 1950. a. 3000 BEF (effective 1994). (International Council of Onomastic Sciences) International Centre of Onomastics, Blijde-Inkomststraat 21, B-3000 Leuven, Belgium. FAX 32-16-285025. (Subscr. to: Editions Peeters s.p.r.l., Bondgenotenlaan 153, B-3000 Leuven, Belgium. TEL 32-16-235170. FAX 32-16-228500) Eds. K. Roelandts, W. van Langendonck. bk.rev.; bibl.; index. (back issues avail.) **Indexed:** Bibl.Ling., Br.Archaeol.Abstr., M.L.A. **Document type:** bibliography, bulletin.
—BLDSC (6260.940000); SWETS.
Description: Publishes original papers in the field of onomastics, news of recent congresses and meetings, and a comprehensive international bibliography of recent publications in onomastics and related disciplines.
Refereed Serial

491.79 PL ISSN 0078-4648
G104
ONOMASTICA; pismo poswiecone nazewnictwu geograficznemu i osobowemu. (Text in Polish; summaries in French) 1955. a. price varies. (Polska Akademia Nauk, Komitet Jezykoznawstwa) Ossolineum, Publishing House of the Polish Academy of Sciences, Rynek 9, 50-106 Wroclaw, Poland. TEL 48-71-386-25. FAX 48-71-448-103. TELEX 0712771 OSS PL. Ed. Kazimierz Rymut. **Indexed:** Bibl.Ling. **Document type:** academic/scholarly publication.
Description: Devoted to personal and geographical onomastics.

410 CN ISSN 0078-4656
F1004
ONOMASTICA CANADIANA. (Subseries of: Onomastica) (Text and summaries in English, French) 1959. s-a. Can.$20($18) Canadian Society for the Study of Names, c/o Prof. W. Ahrens, Dept. of Languages, Literatures and Linguistics, York University, North York, ON M3J 1P3, Canada. TEL 416-736-5016. FAX 416-736-5735. Ed. Frank R. Hamlin. bk.rev.; index; circ. 180 (paid). (back issues avail.) **Indexed:** Bibl.Ling., Can.Per.Ind., M.L.A. **Document type:** academic/scholarly publication.
—Faxon.
Description: Scholarly study of place and personal names in Canada and abroad.
Refereed Serial

439.31 PL ISSN 0474-1471
ONOMASTICA SLAVOGERMANICA. (Text in German or Polish) 1965. irreg. price varies. (Uniwersytet Wroclawski) Wydawnictwo Uniwersytetu Wroclawskiego, Pl. Uniwersytecki 9-13, 50-137 Wroclaw, Poland. TEL 44-10-06. (Dist. by: Ksiegarnia Uniwersytetu Wroclawskiego, Pl. Uniwersytecki 9-13, 50-137 Wroclaw, Poland) Ed. Bogdan Sicinski. circ. 400. **Indexed:** Bibl.Ling. **Document type:** academic/scholarly publication.

ONTARIO DEAF LIFE. see HANDICAPPED — Hearing Impaired

491.7 891.7 GW
OPERA SLAVICA. NEUE FOLGE. 1961. irreg., vol.25, 1993. price varies. Harrassowitz Verlag, Taunusstr. 14, 65183 Wiesbaden, Germany. TEL 0611-530-0. FAX 0611-530570. TELEX 4186135. (Subscr. to: Postfach 2929, 65019 Wiesbaden, Germany) Ed. Reinhard Lauer. **Indexed:** Bibl.Ling. **Document type:** monographic series.
Formerly (until 1981): Opera Slavica (ISSN 0085-4514)

401 FR ISSN 0220-746X
ORALITE - DOCUMENTS. (Subseries of: Bibliotheque de la S E L A F) 1978. irreg., latest no.6. price varies. Societe d'Etudes Linguistiques et Anthropologiques de France (SELAF), 52 bd St. Michel, 75006 Paris, France. (Dist. by: Editions Peeters s.p.r.l., Bondgenotenlaan 153, B-3000 Louvain, Belgium. TEL 32-16-235170. FAX 32-16-228500) (back issues avail.) **Document type:** monographic series.
Description: Covers topics relating to the linguistics and sociolinguistics of oral traditions.

400 BE ISSN 0030-4379
P2
ORBIS; bulletin international de documentation linquistique. (Text in English, French, German, Italian, Russian, Spanish) 1952. irreg., vol.36, 1993 (for years 1991-1992). 2700 BEF (effective 1994). (Universite Catholique de Louvain, Centre International de Dialectologie Generale) Editions Peeters s.p.r.l., Bondgenotenlaan 153, B-3000 Louvain, Belgium. TEL 32-16-235170. FAX 32-16-228500. Ed. R. Bosteels, P. Swiggers. adv.; bk.rev.; bibl.; charts; illus. (back issues avail.) **Indexed:** Bibl.Ling., Hum.Ind., Mid.East: Abstr.& Ind., Soc.Sci.Ind. **Document type:** academic/scholarly publication.
—SWETS.
Description: Serves as an international forum for scholarly discussion and information exchange on all aspects of the language sciences. Also includes a survey of the contents of current linguistic journals.

439 800 DK ISSN 0108-8025
PD3821
ORD & SAG. 1981. a. free. Aarhus Universitet, Institut for Jysk Sprog- og Kulturforskning, Niels Juels Gade 84, 8200 Aarhus N., Denmark.
TEL 45-8942-1916. Ed. Viggo Soerensen. illus. circ. 1,500. **Indexed:** Bibl.Ling.

ORIENS EXTREMUS; Zeitschrift fuer Sprache, Kunst und Kultur der Laender des fernen Ostens. see ORIENTAL STUDIES

ORIENTALIA RHENO-TRAIECTINA. see ORIENTAL STUDIES

410 IT
ORIENTAMENTI LINGUISTICI. 1977. irreg. price varies. (Universita degli Studi di Pisa, Istituto di Glottologia) Giardini Editori e Stampatori, Via Santa Bibbiana 28, 56100 Pisa, Italy. TEL 050-502531. Ed. Tristano Bolelli.

418.02 SW ISSN 0473-4351
ORTNAMNSSAELLSKAPETS I UPPSALA AARSSKRIFT. (Text in English, German and Swedish; summaries in English) 1936. a. SEK 55($9) Ortnamnssaellskapet i Uppsala - Place-Name Society of Uppsala, P.O. Box 135, 751 04 Uppsala, Sweden. TEL 018-652160. Ed. Karl I. Sandred. bk.rev. circ. 1,000. (back issues avail.) **Indexed:** Bibl.Ling. **Document type:** academic/scholarly publication.

410 II ISSN 0970-0277
P1
OSMANIA PAPERS IN LINGUISTICS. (Text in English) 1975. a. Rs.25($6) Osmania University, Department of Linguistics, Hyderabad 500 007, Andhra Pradesh, India. TEL 868430. adv.; bk.rev. circ. 500. **Indexed:** Lang.& Lang.Behav.Abstr. **Document type:** academic/scholarly publication.
Description: Contains articles in the field of general and applied linguistics.

OUR HERITAGE. see ORIENTAL STUDIES

OXFORD GERMAN STUDIES. see LITERATURE

056.1 US ISSN 1055-1190
OYE!. 1991. 6/yr. (during school term). $25. Scholastic Inc., 555 Broadway, New York, NY 10012-3999. TEL 212-343-6100. Ed. Jacqueline A. Hall.

491.1
P.D. GUNE MEMORIAL LECTURE SERIES. (Text in English, Sanskrit) 1960. irreg. price varies. University of Poona, Centre of Advanced Study in Sanskrit, Ganeshkhind, Poona 411 007, India. TEL 334220. (Subscr. to: Section Officer, Publications Branch, University of Poona, Poona 411 007, India) Ed. V.N. Jha. **Document type:** monographic series.

P M L A. see LITERATURE

410 GW ISSN 0343-4133
P Z L - PAPIERE ZUR LINGUISTIK. (Text in English, German) 1979. 2/yr. DM.48 to individuals; institutions DM.78. Gunter Narr Verlag, Postfach 2567, 72015 Tuebingen, Germany. TEL 07071-78091. FAX 07071-75288. **Document type:** academic/scholarly publication.
—CCC.

PACIFIC COAST PHILOLOGY. see LITERATURE

499 AT ISSN 0078-7531
P11
PACIFIC LINGUISTICS. SERIES A: OCCASIONAL PAPERS. (Includes 5 subseries: Papers in Australian Linguistics (ISSN 0078-9062); Papers in Austronesian Linguistics; Papers in Papuan Linguistics; Papers in Pidgin and Creole Linguistics (ISSN 0811-0026); Papers in South East Asian Linguistics (ISSN 0078-9178)) 1963. irreg. price varies. Australian National University, Research School of Pacific Studies, Pacific Linguistics, Canberra, A.C.T. 0200, Australia, Australia. **Indexed:** Bibl.Ling. **Document type:** academic/scholarly publication.

499 AT ISSN 0078-754X
PACIFIC LINGUISTICS. SERIES B: MONOGRAPHS. 1963. irreg. price varies. Australian National University, Research School of Pacific Studies, Pacific Linguistics, Canberra, A.C.T. 0200, Australia. **Indexed:** Bibl.Ling. **Document type:** academic/scholarly publication, monographic series.

499 AT ISSN 0078-7558
PACIFIC LINGUISTICS. SERIES C: BOOKS. 1965. irreg. price varies. Australian National University, Research School of Pacific Studies, Pacific Linguistics, Canberra, A.C.T. 0200, Australia. **Indexed:** Bibl.Ling. **Document type:** academic/scholarly publication.

499 AT ISSN 0078-7566
PACIFIC LINGUISTICS. SERIES D: SPECIAL PUBLICATIONS. (Includes subseries: Materials in Languages of Indonesia) 1964. irreg. price varies. Australian National University, Research School of Pacific Studies, Pacific Linguistics, Canberra, A.C.T. 0200, Australia. **Indexed:** Bibl.Ling. **Document type:** academic/scholarly publication.
—BLDSC (6330.101000).

410 II
PAKHA SANJAM. (Text in English or Punjabi) 1968. s-a. Punjabi University, Department of Linguistics, Patiala 4, Punjab, India. Ed. Harjeet Singh Gill. adv.; bk.rev. circ. 500.

471 IT ISSN 0390-3141
PAN; studi dell'Istituto di Filologia Latina. 1973. a. exchange basis. Universita degli Studi, Istituto di Filologia Latina, Viale delle Scienze, 90134 Palermo, Italy. **Document type:** academic/scholarly publication.

495.1 MY ISSN 0553-0644
PAN T'AI HSUEH PAO/MAJALLAH PANTAI/UNIVERSITY OF MALAYA. CHINESE LANGUAGE SOCIETY. JOURNAL.* (Text in Chinese, English, Malay) irreg. University of Malaya, Chinese Language Society, Lembah Pantai, 59100 Kuala Lumpur, Malaysia. illus.

410 DK ISSN 0903-2932
PANORAMA IN INTERLINGUA. (Text in Interlingua) 1988. bi-m. DKK 70. Union Mundial pro Interlingua - World Interlingua Union, Hoje Taastrup Blvd. 49 (lejl. 3), DK-2630 Taastrup, Denmark. TEL 45-43-99-03-26. (Subscr. to: Panorama in Interlingua, Juvelvej 25, DK-5210 Odense NV, Denmark) Ed. Thomas Breinstrup. adv.; bk.rev. circ. 1,000.
Incorporates (1981-1987): Heraldo de Interlingua (ISSN 0108-0598); (1964-1987): Currero International de Interlingua (ISSN 0105-8401)
Description: Contains articles in Interlingua about linguistics, international affairs, literature, and Interlingua societies.

410 PL ISSN 0137-2459
P134
PAPERS AND STUDIES IN CONTRASTIVE LINGUISTICS. (Text in English) 1973. irreg., vol.28, 1993. price varies. Adam Mickiewicz University Press, Nowowiejskiego 55, 61-734 Poznan, Poland. TEL 527-380. FAX 61-523130. TELEX 413260 UAM PL. Ed. Jacek Fisiak. adv.; bk.rev. circ. 1,000. (reprint service avail. from EDR) **Indexed:** Bibl.Ling., Lang.& Lang.Behav.Abstr. (1973-), M.L.A. **Document type:** academic/scholarly publication.
—BLDSC (6396.50000).
Description: Addresses contrastive and comparative linguisitics studies; contains contributions from Poland and abroad.

499 AT ISSN 0078-9062
P11
PAPERS IN AUSTRALIAN LINGUISTICS. (Subseries of: Pacific Linguistics. Series A: Occasional Papers (ISSN 0078-7531)) 1967. irreg. price varies. Australian National University, Research School of Pacific Studies, Pacific Linguistics, Canberra, A.C.T. 0200, Australia. TEL 61-6-249-2742. FAX 61-6-249-4896. **Indexed:** Bibl.Ling., M.L.A. **Document type:** academic/scholarly publication.

499 AT
P11
PAPERS IN AUSTRONESIAN LINGUISTICS. (Subseries of Pacific Linguistics. Series A: Occasional Papers) 1991. irreg. price varies. Australian National University, Research School of Pacific Studies, Pacific Linguistics, Canberra, A.C.T. 0200, Australia. cum.index. **Indexed:** M.L.A. **Document type:** academic/scholarly publication.
Formed by the 1991 merger of: Papers in Philippine Linguistics (ISSN 0078-9143) & Papers in Linguistics of Melanesia (ISSN 0078-9127) & Papers in Borneo and Western Austronesian Linguistics (ISSN 0817-6760); Which was formed by the merger of: Papers in Borneo Linguistics (ISSN 0078-9070) & Papers in Western Austronesian Linguistics.

LINGUISTICS

410 UK
▼**PAPERS IN LABORATORY PHONOLOGY.** 1992. irreg. price varies. Cambridge University Press, Edinburgh Bldg., Shaftesbury Rd., Cambridge CB2 2RU, England. TEL 0223-312393. FAX 0223-315052. TELEX 851817256. (N. American addr.: 40 W. 20th St., New York, NY 10011. TEL 212-924-3900. FAX 212-691-3239) **Document type:** proceedings.

499 AT ISSN 1032-5107
P11
PAPERS IN PAPUAN LINGUISTICS. (Subseries of Pacific Linguistics. Series A: Occasional Papers) 1964. irreg. price varies. Australian National University, Research School of Pacific Studies, Pacific Linguistics, Canberra, A.C.T. 0200, Australia. Ed. S.A. Wurm. **Indexed:** Bibl.Ling., M.L.A.
  Supersedes (in 1991): Papers in New Guinea Linguistics (ISSN 0078-9135)

410 AT ISSN 0811-0026
P11
PAPERS IN PIDGIN AND CREOLE LINGUISTICS. (Subseries of Pacific Linguistics. Series A: Occasional Papers (ISSN 0078-7531)) 1978. irreg. price varies. Australian National University, Research School of Pacific Studies, Pacific Linguistics, Canberra, A.C.T. 0200, Australia. TEL 61-6-249-2742. FAX 61-6-249-4896. **Document type:** academic/scholarly publication.

495 AT ISSN 0078-9178
P11
PAPERS IN SOUTH EAST ASIAN LINGUISTICS. (Subseries of Pacific Linguistics. Series A: Occasional Papers (ISSN 0078-7531)) 1967. irreg. price varies. Australian National University, Research School of Pacific Studies, Pacific Linguistics, Canberra, A.C.T. 0200, Australia. TEL 61-6-249-2742. FAX 61-6-249-4896. **Indexed:** M.L.A. **Document type:** academic/scholarly publication.

400 GW ISSN 0341-3195
PAPIERE ZUR TEXTLINGUISTIK/PAPERS IN TEXT LINGUISTICS. irreg., no.68, 1991. price varies. (Universitaet Bielefeld) Helmut Buske Verlag GmbH, Richardstr. 47, 22081 Hamburg, Germany. TEL 040-296842. FAX 040-2993614. Ed.Bd. **Indexed:** Bibl.Ling., M.L.A. **Document type:** monographic series.

400 II
PARKH. (Text in English and Punjabi) 1964. s-a. Rs.4. Panjab University, Publication Bureau, Chandigarh 160014, Union Territory, India. bk.rev.; bibl.; charts. circ. 500-1,000.

PARLANGHE. see LITERATURE

PARNASSOS; an annual literary journal. see HUMANITIES: COMPREHENSIVE WORKS

891.59 AF
PASHTU QUARTERLY. (Text in Pashtu) q. Afghanistan Academy of Sciences, Sher Alikhan St., Kabul, Afghanistan.

PATMA-BANASIRAKAN ANDES/ISTORIKO-FILOLOGICHESKII ZHURNAL. see HISTORY — History Of Europe

418.02 CN
PEDAGOGIE DE LA TRADUCTION. (Text in English, French) 1979. irreg. price varies. University of Ottawa Press, 542 King Edward, Ottawa, ON K1N 6N5, Canada. TEL 613-564-2270. FAX 613-564-9284. Ed. Jean Delisle. **Document type:** monographic series.
  Formerly (until 1993): Cahiers de Traductologie.
  Description: Studies various aspects of translation.

401 BE
LA PENSEE LINGUISTIQUE. 1986. irreg., vol.4, 1993. price varies. Editions Peeters s.p.r.l, Bondgenotenlaan 153, B-3000 Louvain, Belgium. TEL 32-16-235170. FAX 32-16-228500. (back issues avail.) **Document type:** academic/scholarly publication, monographic series.

PERITIA. see HISTORY — History Of Europe

PERSPECTIVES IN NEUROLINGUISTICS, NEUROPSYCHOLOGY, AND PSYCHOLINGUISTICS; a series of monographs and treatises. see MEDICAL SCIENCES — Psychiatry And Neurology

418 DK ISSN 0907-676X
▼**PERSPECTIVES - STUDIES IN TRANSLATOLOGY.** (Text in English) 1993. s-a. (University of Copenhagen, Center for Oversettelsesvidenskab og Leksikografi) Museum Tusculanum Press, University of Copenhagen, Njalsgade 92, DK-2300 Copenhagen S, Denmark. TEL 45-35-32-91-09. FAX 45-35-32-91-13. (Dist. in U.S. and Canada by: Paul & Co, c/o P C S Data Processing, Inc., 360 W. 31st St., New York, NY 10001. TEL 212-564-3730. FAX 212-971-7200) Ed.Bd. **Document type:** academic/scholarly publication.
  Description: Directed to linguists, translators, English philologists.

440 375.4 GW
LE PHARE. 1954. 6/yr. DM.13.20. Beacon-Verlag Koerber oHG, Birkental 13, Postfach 1161, 67098 Bad Duerkheim, Germany. circ. 1,000. (tabloid format)

479 US ISSN 0883-5640
PHI SIGMA IOTA FORUM. (Text and summaries in English and foreign languages) 1922. s-a. $5 to non-members. Phi Sigma Iota Honor Society, Department of Foreign Languages, University of Nevada, Las Vegas, NV 89154. TEL 800-769-7100. FAX 504-769-7105. (Subscr. to: Prof. Santiago Vilas, 5211 Essen La., Ste. 2, Baton Rouge, LA 70809) Ed. Markettta Laurila. adv.: B&W page $450; 10 1/4 x 7 1/2. bk.rev.; play rev.; abstr. circ. 20,000. (tabloid format)
  Former titles: Phi Sigma Iota Newsletter (ISSN 0048-3699); Phi Sigma Iota News Notes (ISSN 0085-4867)

499.211 PH ISSN 0048-3796
P1
PHILIPPINE JOURNAL OF LINGUISTICS. (Text in English, Filipino) 1970. s-a. $40. Linguistic Society of the Philippines, Box 3819, Manila, Philippines. TEL 02-504-611. FAX 02-522-3661. Ed. Andrew B. Gonzalez. bk.rev.; bibl.; charts; illus.; stat. circ. 500. **Indexed:** Bibl.Ling., E.I., Lang.& Lang.Behav.Abstr. (1970-), M.L.A.
  Description: Presents original studies in descriptive, comparative, historical, and area linguistics as well as papers on the application of theory to language teaching.

410 GW ISSN 0079-1598
PHILOLOGEN-JAHRBUCH. a. DM.20. Verlag Jahrbuch der Lehrer der Hoeheren Schulen, Richard Wagner Str. 1, 5000 Cologne 10, Germany. Ed. K. Mueller.

439 NE
PHILOLOGIA FRISICA. (Text in Dutch, English, French, Frisian and German) 1956. triennial. Fryske Akademy, Doelestrjitte 8, 8911 DX Ljouwert-Leeuwarden, Netherlands. TEL 31-58-131414. FAX 31-58-131409.

PHILO (:) LOGICA; rassegna di analisi linguistica ed ironia culturale. see PHILOSOPHY

401 US ISSN 0079-1628
PHILOLOGICAL MONOGRAPHS. 1931. irreg., no.36, 1988. price varies. (American Philological Association) Scholars Press, Box 15399, Atlanta, GA 30333-0399. TEL 404-727-2320. FAX 404-727-2348. Ed. David Blank. circ. 1,000. **Document type:** monographic series.
  Description: Presents papers on classical literature and civilization.

400 US ISSN 0031-7977
P1
PHILOLOGICAL QUARTERLY; devoted to scholarly investigation of the classical and modern languages and literatures. 1922. q. $15 to individuals; institutions $25. University of Iowa, Iowa City, IA 52242. TEL 319-335-0435. Ed. William Kupersmith. bk.rev.; bibl. circ. 2,250. (also avail. in microform from UMI,PMC; microfiche from IDC; reprint service avail. from UMI) **Indexed:** Abstr.Engl.Stud., Arts & Hum.Cit.Ind., Bk.Rev.Ind. (1965-), Child.Bk.Rev.Ind. (1965-), Curr.Cont., Hum.Ind., Lang.& Lang.Behav.Abstr. **Document type:** academic/scholarly publication.
  —BLDSC (6461.430000); Faxon; UnCover; SWETS; UMI.

400 UK ISSN 0079-1636
P11
PHILOLOGICAL SOCIETY TRANSACTIONS. 1842. a. £39.50($81) to individuals; institutions £68($133.50). Basil Blackwell Ltd., 108 Cowley Rd., Oxford OX4 1JF, England. TEL 0865-791100. FAX 0865-791347. TELEX 837022-OXBOOK-G. Ed. J.H.W. Penney. index. (also avail. in microform from SWZ; reprint service avail. from SWZ) **Indexed:** Bibl.Ling., Lang.Teach.& Ling.Abstr.
  —BLDSC (8993.670000); Faxon; UnCover; UMI. **CCC.**

PHILOSOPHY AND RHETORIC. see PHILOSOPHY

PHOENIX; Sri Lanka journal of English in the Commonwealth. see LITERATURE

410 371.9 JA ISSN 0911-0402
PL541
PHONETIC SOCIETY OF JAPAN. BULLETIN. (Text in English, French, Japanese) 1926. 3/yr. 6000 Yen. Phonetic Society of Japan, 5th Fl., Soyosha Bldg., 3-25-6, Higashi-Ueno, Taito-ku, Tokyo 110, Japan. TEL 03-3839-3957. Ed. Teruo Hirayama. adv. circ. 1,100. (reprint service avail.) **Indexed:** Lang.& Lang.Behav.Abstr. (1972-). **Document type:** bulletin.
  —UnCover.

414 SZ ISSN 0031-8388
P215 CODEN: PHNTAW
PHONETICA; international journal of speech science. (Text in English, French, German; summaries in English) 1957. q. 334 SFr.($223) S. Karger AG, Allschwilerstr. 10, P.O. Box, CH-4009 Basel, Switzerland. TEL 061-3061111. FAX 061-3061234. Ed. K. Kohler. adv.; bk.rev.; bibl.; charts; illus.; index. circ. 1,150. (also avail. in microform; reprint service avail. from SWZ) **Indexed:** Bibl.Ling., Biol.Abstr., Curr.Cont., Dent.Ind., Excerp.Med., Ind.Med., Lang.& Lang.Behav.Abstr., Lang.Teach.& Ling.Abstr., M.L.A., SSCI. **Document type:** academic/scholarly publication.
  —Faxon; UnCover; SWETS. **CCC.**

407 US ISSN 0741-6164
PHONETICIAN. (Text in English; occasionally French, German) 1963. 3/yr. $20. International Society of Phonetic Sciences, Institute for Advanced Study of the Communication Process, University of Florida, 50 Dauer Hall, Gainesville, FL 32611. Ed. Harry Hollien. bk.rev. circ. 1,500.

410 US
PHONETICS AND PHONOLOGY. 1989. irreg. Academic Press, Inc., 525 B St., Ste. 1900, San Diego, CA 92101-4495. TEL 619-231-6616. FAX 619-699-6715. (Subscr. to: Order Dept., 6277 Sea Harbor Dr., 4th Fl., Orlando, FL 32887. TEL 800-321-5068) Eds. Stephen R. Anderson, Patricia A. Keating.
  Description: For graduate and research level.

410 UK ISSN 0952-6757
P215
PHONOLOGY. s-a. £30($52) to individuals (overseas £37); institutions £53 (overseas £60 ($92)). Cambridge University Press, Edinburgh Bldg., Shaftesbury Rd., Cambridge CB2 2RU, England. TEL 0223-312393. FAX 0223-315052. TELEX 851817256. (N. American addr.: Cambridge University Press, Journals Dept., 40 W. 20th St., New York, NY 10011. TEL 212-924-3900. FAX 212-691-3239) Eds. Ellen M. Kaisse, Colin J. Ewen. adv. (also avail. in microform from UMI; back issues avail.; reprint service avail. from SWZ) **Indexed:** Bibl.Ling., Lang.& Lang.Behav.Abstr. (1984-). **Document type:** academic/scholarly publication.
  —BLDSC (6465.172000); Faxon; UnCover; SWETS; UMI. **CCC.**
  Formerly (until 1988): Phonology Yearbook (ISSN 0265-8062)
  Description: Combines theoretical and empirical interests to represent the diversity of opinion in the field.

401 302.2 US
▼**PIERCE SEMINAR PAPERS: AN ANNUAL OF SEMIOTIC ANALYSIS.** 1993. a. $35. Berg Pub., 221 Waterman St., Providence, RI 02906-4319. Ed. Michael Shapiro.

450 055.1   DK   ISSN 0108-9935
PIRANESI; Italienische studier. 1983. a. DKK 109. University of Copenhagen, Museum Tusculanum Press, Njalsgade 92, DK-2300 Copenhagen S, Denmark. TEL 45-35-32-91-09.
FAX 45-35-32-91-13. (Dist. in U.S. and Canada by: Paul & Co., c/o P C S Data Processing, Inc., 360 W. 31st St., New York, NY 10001. TEL 212-564-3730. FAX 212-971-7200) Ed.Bd. illus.
Description: Contains articles on various facets of Italian language, history, art and culture.

PLANET; the Welsh internationalist. see *LITERATURE*

410   BE
PLURILINGUA. (Text in English, French, German) 1983. irreg., latest vol.14, 1993. DM.68. Research Centre on Multilingualism, Vrijheidslaan 17, B-1080 Brussels, Belgium. TEL 32-2-4124211.
FAX 32-2-4124200. (Subscr. to: F. Duemmler Verlag, Postfach 1480, 53113 Bonn, Germany) Ed. Peter Hans Nelde. adv. circ. 600. **Document type:** academic/scholarly publication, monographic series, proceedings.

410 371   GW
PO SVETU/PO SWIECIE/PO SVETE. (Text in Czech, Polish and Russian) 1948. 6/yr. DM.23.40. Paedagogischer Zeitschriftenverlag, Postfach 269, 10107 Berlin, Germany. TEL 030-20343431. FAX 030-20343432. illus. circ. 35,000. **Document type:** academic/scholarly publication.
Former titles: Around the World - A Travers le Monde - Po Svetu (ISSN 0323-830X); Durch die Welt.

POETICA; Zeitschrift fuer Sprach- und Literaturwissenschaft. see *LITERATURE*

410 800   JA
POETICA; an international journal of linguistic-literary studies. 1974. 2/yr. $50. Shubun International Co., Ltd., 12-7, 4-chome Komagome, Toshima-ku, Tokyo 170, Japan. TEL 03-915-8290. (Distr. by: Japan Publications Trading Co. Ltd., P.O. Box 5030, Tokyo, Japan) Ed. Shinsuke Ando. **Indexed:** Bibl.Ling., Lang.Teach.& Ling.Abstr.

410   DK   ISSN 0109-2820
POETICA ET ANALYTICA. 1984. irreg. DKK 40. Aarhus University Press, Aarhus University, Bldg. 170, DK-8000 Aarhus, Denmark. FAX 45086-19-84-33.
Formerly: Matieres (ISSN 0107-4946)

499.992   PL   ISSN 0032-2431
POLA ESPERANTISTO/ESPERANTIST'S MAGAZINE;* socio-cultural review. 1906. m. £22. Polski Zwiazek Esperantystow, c/o Ars Polona-Ruch, Krakowskie Przedmiescie 7, Warsaw, Poland. TEL 21-51-33. Ed. Pawel Wimmer. adv.; bk.rev. circ. 1,000.

407   PL
POLITECHNIKA WROCLAWSKA. STUDIUM NAUKI JEZYKOW OBCYCH. PRACE NAUKOWE. MONOGRAFIE. 1980. irreg., no.4, 1988. price varies. Wydawnictwo Politechniki Wroclawskiej, Wybrzeze Wyspianskiego 27, 50-370 Wroclaw, Poland. FAX 22-36-64. TELEX 712559 PWRPL. (Distr. by: Ars Polona-Ruch, Krakowskie Przedmiescie 7, Warsaw, Poland) **Document type:** monographic series.
Formerly: Politechnika Wroclawska. Studium Praktycznej Nauki Jezykow Obcych. Prace Naukowe. Monografie (ISSN 0208-8371)

407   PL   ISSN 0867-356X
POLITECHNIKA WROCLAWSKA. STUDIUM NAUKI JEZYKOW OBCYCH. PRACE NAUKOWE. STUDIA I MATERIALY. (Text in German, Polish, Russian; summaries in English) 1974. irreg., no.25, 1992. price varies. Wydawnictwo Politechniki Wroclawskiej, Wybrzeze Wyspianskiego 27, 50-370 Wroclaw, Poland. FAX 22-36-64. TELEX 712559 PWRPL. (Dist. by: Ars Polona-Ruch, Krakowskie Przedmiescie 7, Warsaw, Poland) circ. 380.
Formerly: Politechnika Wroclawska. Studium Praktycznej Nauki Jezykow Obcych. Prace Naukowe. Studia i Materialy (ISSN 0137-6349)

491.8   PL   ISSN 0137-9712
POLONICA. (Text in Polish; summaries in English) 1975. a. price varies. Polska Akademia Nauk, Instytut Jezyka Polskiego - Polish Academy of Sciences, Institute of Polish Language, Ul. Straszewskiego 27, 31-113 Krakow, Poland. TEL 48-31-222699. FAX 48-31-225929. Ed. Henryk Wrobel. **Indexed:** Bibl.Ling.

POLONISTYKA. see *LITERATURE*

057 943.8   PL   ISSN 0208-4058
POLSKA AKADEMIA NAUK. INSTYTUT SLOWIANOZNAWSTWA. PRACE SLAWISTYCZNE. (Text in Polish; summaries in Russian) irreg., vol.88, 1991. price varies. Polska Akademia Nauk, Instytut Slawistiki - Polish Academy of Sciences, Institute of Slavonic Research, Palac Kultury i Nauki, P.O. Box 24, 00-901 Warsaw. **Document type:** monographic series.
Description: Monographs on Slavonic linguistics, literatures, history, ethnography.

400   PL   ISSN 0079-3485
P9
POLSKA AKADEMIA NAUK. KOMITET JEZYKOZNAWSTWA. PRACE JEZYKOZNAWCZE. (Text in French and Polish) 1954. irreg., vol.124, 1991. price varies. Ossolineum, Publishing House of the Polish Academy of Sciences, Rynek 9, 50-106 Wroclaw, Poland. TEL 48-71-386-25. FAX 48-71-448-103. TELEX 0712771 OSS PL. **Indexed:** Bibl.Ling. **Document type:** monographic series.

491.8   PL   ISSN 0079-4775
POLSKA AKADEMIA NAUK. KOMITET JEZYKOZNAWSTWA. PRACE ONOMASTYCZNE. (Text in Polish; summaries in English, French and German) 1955. irreg., vol.34, 1991. price varies. Ossolineum, Publishing House of the Polish Academy of Sciences, Rynek 9, 50-106 Wroclaw, Poland. TEL 48-71-386-25. FAX 048-448-103. TELEX 0712771 OSS PL. **Document type:** monographic series.

400   PL   ISSN 0079-3272
POLSKA AKADEMIA NAUK. ODDZIAL W KRAKOWIE. KOMISJA FILOLOGII KLASYCZNEJ. PRACE. (Text in English, French, German, Latin and Polish; summaries in English and French) 1960. irreg., no.22, 1991. price varies. Ossolineum, Publishing House of the Polish Academy of Sciences, Rynek 9, 50-106 Wroclaw, Poland. TEL 48-71-386-25. FAX 48-71-448-103. TELEX 0712771 OSS PL. Ed. Marian Plezia. **Document type:** monographic series.
Description: Covers classical philology, ancient history, archeology of the mediterranean world, and the medieval and modern heritage of Poland.

400   PL   ISSN 0079-3310
POLSKA AKADEMIA NAUK. ODDZIAL W KRAKOWIE. KOMISJA JEZYKOZNAWSTWA. PRACE. (Text in Polish, Latin, French; occasionally in English and German) 1964. irreg., no.58, 1990. price varies. Ossolineum, Publishing House of the Polish Academy of Sciences, Rynek 9, 50-106 Wroclaw, Poland. TEL 48-71-386-25. FAX 48-71-448-103. TELEX 0712771 OSS PL. (Dist. by: Ars Polona-Ruch, Krakowskie Przedmiescie 7, Warsaw, Poland) Ed. Franciszek Slawski. **Indexed:** Bibl.Ling. **Document type:** monographic series.
Description: Problems of general Indo-European and Slavic linguistics.

400   PL   ISSN 0079-3329
POLSKA AKADEMIA NAUK. ODDZIAL W KRAKOWIE. KOMISJA JEZYKOZNAWSTWA. WYDAWNICTWA ZRODLOWE. (Text in Polish; summaries in English) irreg. price varies. Ossolineum, Publishing House of the Polish Academy of Sciences, Rynek 9, 50-106 Wroclaw, Poland. TEL 48-71-386-25. FAX 48-71-448-103. TELEX 0712771 OSS PL. **Indexed:** M.L.A. **Document type:** monographic series.

410   PL   ISSN 0032-3802
P19.P6
POLSKIE TOWARZYSTWO JEZYKOZNAWCZE. BIULETYN. (Text in English, German and Polish) irreg., vol.43-45, 1991. price varies. Polskie Towarzystwo Jezykoznawcze - Polish Linguistic Society, Al. Mickiewicza 9-11, 31-120 Krakow, Poland. (Dist. by: Ars Polona-Ruch, Krakowskie Przedmiescie 7, Warsaw, Poland) Ed. K. Polanski. **Indexed:** Bibl.Ling. —BLDSC (2747.900000).

410 800   US   ISSN 1045-6716
P51   CODEN: POLGE2
POLYLINGUA; a college journal of foreign languages. 1990. 3/yr. $20. Michigan Technological University, Department of Humanities, Houghton, MI 49931. TEL 906-487-2447. Ed. Francis Lide.
—UnCover.
Description: Devoted to the language component of foreign language studies.

439.2   NE   ISSN 0032-4205
POMPEBLEDEN; tydskrift foar Fryske Studzje. (Text in Frisian) 1928. 5/yr. fl.25. Stichting Algemiene Fryske Underrjocht Kommisje, P.B. 53, 8900 AB Leeuwarden, Netherlands. TEL 31-58-138045. FAX 31-58-159475. Dir. G.H. Jelsma. adv.; bk.rev.; index. circ. 600.
Description: Covers the study of Frisian language, literature and education.

495   GW   ISSN 0554-7342
PORTA LINGUARUM ORIENTALIUM. 1965. irreg., vol.18, 1989. price varies. Harrassowitz Verlag, Taunusstr. 14, 65183 Wiesbaden, Germany. TEL 0611-530-0. FAX 0611-530570. TELEX 4186135. (Subscr. to: Postfach 2929, 65019 Wiesbaden, Germany) Ed.Bd. **Document type:** monographic series.

410   PL   ISSN 0079-4678
PG6014
POZNANSKIE TOWARZYSTWO PRZYJACIOL NAUK. KOMISJA JEZYKOZNAWCZA. PRACE. (Text in English, German or Polish; summaries in English, French, German) 1962. irreg., vol.13, 1981. price varies. Poznanskie Towarzystwo Przyjaciol Nauk, Ul. Mielzynskiego 27-29, 61-725 Poznan, Poland. (Dist. by: Ars Polona-Ruch, Krakowskie Przedmiescie 7, Warsaw, Poland) Ed. Jerzy Wislocki. **Indexed:** Lang. & Lang.Behav.Abstr.

352   UK   ISSN 0260-4752
PRACTICAL ENGLISH TEACHING; for teachers of English as a foreign language to secondary level. 1980. q. Mary Glasgow Magazines (Subsidiary of: Scholastic Publications Ltd.), 140 Freston Rd., London W10 6TR, England. TEL 071-792-3644.
FAX 071-792-3172. TELEX 311890-MGPUBS. (U.S. subscr. to: Delta Systems, 1400 Miller Pkwy., McHenry IL 60050-7030. TEL 800-823-8270) illus. circ. 14,000. **Indexed:** Cont.Pg.Educ., Lang.Teach.& Ling.Abstr. **Document type:** trade publication.
—SWETS.
Description: Magazine for teachers of English as a foreign language to secondary level

400 220   US   ISSN 0260-0943
PRACTICAL PAPERS FOR THE BIBLE TRANSLATOR. 1950. s-a. $6 ($12 including Technical Papers for the Bible Translator). United Bible Societies, Translation Services Coordinator, 1865 Broadway, New York, NY 10023. FAX 212-582-7245. TELEX 23 62384. Ed. Rev. Euan Fry. adv.; bk.rev.; index, cum.index. circ. 3,000. (also avail. in microform from UMI; microfiche; reprint service avail. from UMI) **Indexed:** Chr.Per.Ind., New Test.Abstr., Old Test.Abstr., Rel.& Theol.Abstr. (1968-), Rel.Ind.One. —BLDSC (1947.830000); UnCover; UMI.
Supersedes in part (since 1972): Bible Translator (ISSN 0006-0844)
Description: Contains practical biblical and linguistic information.

430   US   ISSN 0922-842X
PRAGMATICS AND BEYOND NEW SERIES. Abbreviated title: P A B N S. 1985; N.S. 1988. irreg., vol.25, 1993. price varies. John Benjamins Publishing Co., 821 Bethlehem Pike, Philadelphia, PA 19118. TEL 215-836-1200. FAX 215-836-1204. (And: Amsteldijk 44, P.O. Box 75577, 1070 AN Amsterdam, Netherlands. TEL 020-6762325) Ed.Bd. (back issues avail.) **Indexed:** Bibl.Ling. **Document type:** monographic series. —BLDSC (6598.516200).
Supersedes (in 1988): Pragmatics and Beyond Companion Series (ISSN 0920-3079); Incorporates (1980-1987): Pragmatics and Beyond (ISSN 0166-6258)
Description: Comprehensive, interdisciplinary research in linguistic phenomena.

PRAGMATICS & COGNITION. see *LINGUISTICS — Computer Applications*

410 100   US
PRAGMATICS AND DISCOURSE ANALYSIS.* (Text and summaries in English) 1984. irreg., no.9, 1991. Walter de Gruyter, Inc., 200 Saw Mill River Rd., Hawthorne, NY 10532. TEL 914-747-0110. FAX 914-747-1326. Eds. Fráns H. van Eemeren, Rob Grootendorst.
Description: Contains research on argumentation and speech communication by linguists, philosophers, logicians and cognitive psychologists.

PRAKRIT TEXT SOCIETY. PUBLICATIONS. see *LITERATURE*

LINGUISTICS

491.7 375.4   GW   ISSN 0179-7298
PRAKTIKA; Forum fuer den Russischunterricht. 1986. q. DM.48. Puschkin Buchhandelsgesellschaft mbH, Bonnerstr. 20, 5000 Cologne 1, Germany. TEL 0221-321353. FAX 0221-325952. Ed. Lutz Loescher. circ. 1,000.

491.86   XR   ISSN 0079-4902
PRAMENY CESKE A SLOVENSKE LINGVISTIKY. RADA CESKA. 1970. irreg. price varies. (Ceskoslovenska Akademie Ved) Academia, Publishing House of the Czechoslovak Academy of Sciences, Vodickova 40, 112 29 Prague 1, Czech Republic. TEL 23-63-065. Ed. Josef Vachek.

400 371.3   GW   ISSN 0938-8001
PRAXIS DES NEUSPRACHLICHEN UNTERRICHTS. (Text in English, French, German) 1953. q. DM.39. Cornelsen Verlag GmbH, Mecklenburgische Str. 53, 14197 Berlin, Germany. TEL 030-89785287. FAX 030-89785233. Eds. R. Freudenstein, K. Hinz. adv.; bk.rev.; bibl. circ. 5,000. (tabloid format; also avail. in microform from UMI; reprint service avail. from UMI,KTO) **Indexed:** Lang.& Lang.Behav.Abstr., Lang.Teach.& Ling.Abstr. **Document type:** academic/scholarly publication.
—BLDSC (6603.178500).
   Description: Directed to instructors of French and English in German schools. Covers special problems, new techniques in instruction and methods of teaching.

430 375.4   GW   ISSN 0721-8400
G72
PRAXIS DEUTSCH. bi-m. DM.102.90. Erhard Friedrich Verlag GmbH, Im Brande 17, 30926 Seelze, Germany. TEL 0511-40004-0. (Subscr. to: Postfach 100150, 30917 Seelze, Germany) Ed. Uwe Brinkmann. **Document type:** academic/scholarly publication.
—CCC.

PRE-TEXT; a journal of rhetorical theory. see *HUMANITIES: COMPREHENSIVE WORKS*

440 840   DK   ISSN 0900-9507
PREPUBLICATIONS. (Text in Danish, English, French, Italian, Spanish) 1973. 7/yr. DKK 35. Universite d'Aarhus, Institut d'Etudes Romanes, Niels Juels gade 84, 8200 Aarhus N, Denmark. TEL 45-89-42-19-39. FAX 45-86-16-38-61. Ed. Ole Wehner Rasmussen. index. circ. 300. (back issues avail.) **Indexed:** M.L.A. **Document type:** academic/scholarly publication.

410 407   YU   ISSN 0351-8892
PREVODILAC; casopis Udruzenja Naucnih i Strucnih Prevodilaca Srbije. (Text in Serbo-Croatian) 1982. q. 10000 din.($50) Udruzenje Naucnih i Strucnih Prevodilaca, Kecevska 9, 11000 Belgrade, Serbia, Yugoslavia. TEL 011-444-2997. Ed. Zoran Jovanovic. circ. 2,000.

407   XO   ISSN 1210-1893
PRIATEL'. (Text in Slovak) 1969. 10/yr. 15 Kcs. (Ministerstvo Skolstva, Mladeze a Sportu Slovenskej Republiky) Slovenske Pedagogicke Nakladatelstvo, Sasinkova 5, 815 60 Bratislava, Slovakia. (Subscr. to: Slovart, Gottwaldovo nam. 6, 805-32 Bratislava, Slovakia) Ed. Peter Aich. circ. 16,000.

808 949   YU   ISSN 0350-6673
PG560
PRILOZI ZA KNJIZEVNOST, JEZIK, ISTORIJU I FOLKLOR. (Text in Serbo-Croatian in Cyrillic alphabet) 1921. s-a. 33.60 din. Univerzitet u Beogradu, Filoloski Fakultet, Katedra za Jugoslovenske Knjizevnosti, Studentski trg 3-I, 1100 Belgrade, Serbia, Yugoslavia. FAX 011-630-039. (Subscr. to: Jugoslovenska Knjiga, Trg Republike 5-VIII, 11000 Belgrade, Serbia, Yugoslavia) (Co-sponsors: Fond za Nauku SR Srbije, Vukova Zaduzbina, Geobanka, Investbanka, Institut za Robni Promet) Ed. Miroslav Pantic. circ. 1,000. **Indexed:** Bibl.Ling., M.L.A.
   Description: Articles and notes about Yugoslavian literature, languages, history and folkore.

PRIMARY VOICES K - 6. see *EDUCATION — Teaching Methods And Curriculum*

430 375.4   CN   ISSN 0827-2778
PRISMA CANADA. (Text in English, German) 1975. a. Can.$10. (Saskatchewan Association of Teachers of German) Saskatchewan Teachers' Federation, 507 Frobisher Cres., Saskatoon, SK S7K 4Y8, Canada. TEL 306-931-8980. Ed. Rubi Rubrecht. bk.rev.; charts; illus.; stat. (back issues avail.)
   Formerly: Prisma (ISSN 0380-8815)

PROBLEME DER SEMIOTIK. see *PHILOSOPHY*

410   GW   ISSN 0921-4771
PC1   CODEN: PRUSE2
PROBUS. 1989. 3/yr. DM.80 to individuals; institutions DM.184. Walter de Gruyter and Co., Mouton de Gruyter, Genthiner Str. 13, 10785 Berlin, Germany. TEL 030-26005-0. FAX 030-26005-251. (U.S. addr.: Walter de Gruyter, Inc., 200 Saw Mill River Rd., Hawthorne, NY 10532) Ed. W. Leo Wetzels. **Indexed:** Bibl.Ling., Lang.& Lang.Behav.Abstr. (1989-). **Document type:** academic/scholarly publication.
—Faxon; UnCover; SWETS.
   Description: Discussion of historical and synchronic research in the field of Latin and Romance linguistics, with special emphasis on phonology, morphology, syntax, lexicon and sociolinguistics.

407   US
PROFESSIONAL SPEAKER. 1973. m. membership. National Speakers Association, 1500 S. Priest Dr., Tempe, AZ 85281-6203. TEL 602-968-2552. Ed. Sara Hayden. adv.; bk.rev. circ. 3,600.
   Formerly (until 1992): Speakout.
   Description: Information, trends and ideas on professional speaking.

418.02   UK   ISSN 0955-615X
PROFESSIONAL TRANSLATOR AND INTERPRETER. 1986. 3/yr. £25($50) Institute of Translation and Interpreting, 318a Finchley Rd., London NW3 5HT, England. TEL 071-794-9931. FAX 071-435-2105. (Co-sponsor: Translators Association of the Society of Authors) Ed. M.J. Shields. adv.; bk.rev. circ. 2,000.
   Formerly: I T I News.

499.992   BE   ISSN 0048-5489
PROGRESO. (Text in Ido) no.230, 1972. 3/yr. 500 BEF. Uniono Por la Linguo Internaciona Ido (Reformed Esperanto), Ed. Franz Regnier, 27 Ville du Bois, B-6690 Vielsalm, Belgium. adv.; bk.rev.; bibl.
   Description: Promotes the use of the international language Ido.

PROSPECT; a journal of Australian TESOL. see *EDUCATION — Adult Education*

491.7   PL   ISSN 0137-298X
PRZEGLAD RUSYCYSTYCZNY. (Text in Polish, Russian) 1978. q. price varies. (Polskie Towarzystwo Rusycystyczne) Wydawnictwo Naukowe P W N - Polish Scientific Publishers P W N Ltd., Ul. Miodowa 10, 00-251 Warsaw, Poland. TEL 48-22-260207. FAX 48-22-267163. (Dist. by: Ars Polona, Krakowskie Przedmiescie 7, 00-068 Warsaw, Poland) Ed. W. Zmarzer.
   Description: Publications of Polish studies in Russian philology as well as philosophy, sociology, history, linguistics, methodology, didactics and pedagogy.

410 150   II   ISSN 0377-3132
P1.A1
PSYCHO-LINGUA; a biannual research journal devoted to communicative behavior. (Text in English) 1971. s-a. Rs.100. Psycholinguistic Association of India, c/o Institute of Psychological Services and Behavioural Research, 44-789, Shanti Vihar Colony, Dagnia, Raipur 492 001, India. (Dist. by: National Psychological Corporation, 4-230 Kacheri Ghat, Agra 282 004, India) Ed. V.P. Sharma. adv.; bk.rev.; abstr.; bibl. circ. 250. **Indexed:** Lang.& Lang.Behav.Abstr., Psychol.Abstr. **Document type:** abstracting/indexing.
—BLDSC (6946.277470).

410   US
PUBLICATIONS IN AFRICAN LANGUAGES AND LINGUISTICS.* 1983. irreg., no.10, 1989. Walter de Gruyter, Inc., 200 Saw Mill River Rd., Hawthorne, NY 10532. TEL 914-747-0110. FAX 914-747-1326. Eds. George N. Clements, Didier L. Goyvaerts. **Indexed:** Anthropol.Lit., Bibl.Ling.

PUBLICATIONS ROMANES ET FRANCAISES. see *LITERATURE*

410 800   PK   ISSN 0555-8158
PUSHTO. Cover title: Pashto. (Text in Pushto) N.S. 1969. m. Rs.10. University of Peshawar, Pashto Academy, Peshawar, Pakistan. Ed. Syed Khayat Bokhan. bk.rev. circ. 1,000.

AL-QANTARA; revista de estudios arabes. see *PHILOSOPHY*

QUADERNI DI LINGUE E LETTERATURE. see *LITERATURE*

410   IT   ISSN 0393-1226
P325
QUADERNI DI SEMANTICA; rivista internazionale di semantica teorica e applicata. 1980. s-a. L.65000 (foreign L.110000) (effective 1994). Cooperativa Libraria Universitaria Editrice Bologna, Via Marsala 24, 40126 Bologna, Italy. TEL 051-220736. FAX 051-237758. Ed. Mario Alinei. adv.; index. circ. 500. (back issues avail.) **Indexed:** Bibl.Ling., M.L.A.

410 800   IT   ISSN 0033-4960
F1401
QUADERNI IBERO-AMERICANI; attualita culturale Penisola Iberica America-Latina. (Text in English, Italian, Portuguese and Spanish) 1948. irreg. L.35000($30) (Associazione Studi Iberici (ASI)) Bulzoni Editore, Via dei Liburni 14, 00185 Rome, Italy. TEL 06-4455207. FAX 06-4450355. Dir. Giovanni Maria Bertini. adv.; bk.rev.; cum.index. circ. 800. (back issues avail.)
—SWETS.

469   IT
QUADERNI PORTOGHESI. 1977. s-a. L.40000($40) Giardini Editori e Stampatori, Via Santa Bibbiana 28, 56100 Pisa, Italy. TEL 050-502531. Ed.Bd. **Indexed:** M.L.A.

410   IT
QUADERNO DI LINGUE. 1991. irreg. (Universita degli Studi del Molise) Edizioni Scientifiche Italiane S.p.A., Via Chiatamone 7, 80121 Naples, Italy. TEL 081-7645168. FAX 081-7646477. **Document type:** monographic series.

QUADRANT. see *LITERATURE*

410   CC
QUANGUO ZHONGXUE YOUXIU ZUOWEN XUAN/SELECTED EXCELLENT COMPOSITIONS FROM NATION-WIDE MIDDLE SCHOOLS. (Text in Chinese) m. $50. Jiangsu Jiaoyu Chubanshe - Jiangsu Education Publishing House, 165 Zhongyang Lu, Nanjing, Jiangsu 210009, People's Republic of China. TEL 635549. Ed. Yang Jiuquan. adv. contact: Yuanyuan Qian.

420   US   ISSN 0735-5920
PE1460.A2
QUARTERLY REVIEW OF DOUBLESPEAK. 1973. q. $8. National Council of Teachers of English, Committee on Public Doublespeak, 1111 Kenyon Rd., Urbana, IL 61801. TEL 217-328-3870. FAX 217-328-9645. Ed. William Lutz. bk.rev. circ. 5,000. **Indexed:** Lang.& Lang.Behav.Abstr.
   Formerly: Public Doublespeak Newsletter.

460   UK   ISSN 0033-5940
QUE TAL. (Text in Spanish) 1963. 6/yr. (during school year). Mary Glasgow Magazines (Subsidiary of: Scholastic Publications Ltd.), 140 Freston Rd., London W10 6TR, England. TEL 071-792-3648. FAX 071-792-3172. TELEX 311890-MGPUBS. (U.S. subscr. to: Delta Systems, 1400 Miller Pkwy., McHenry IL 66050-7030. TEL 800-823-8270) illus. (also avail. in microform from UMI; reprint service avail. from BLH, UMI)
   Description: Spanish-language magazine for beginners.

440   CN
QUEBEC (PROVINCE). OFFICE DE LA LANGUE FRANCAISE. RAPPORT D'ACTIVITES. a. Can.$2. (Office de la Langue Francaise) Publications du Quebec, C.P. 1005, Quebec, PQ G1K 7B5, Canada. TEL 800-463-2100. FAX 418-643-6177.

QUELLEN UND UNTERSUCHUNGEN ZUR LATEINISCHEN PHILOLOGIE DES MITTELALTERS. see *CLASSICAL STUDIES*

LINGUISTICS

410 430   GW   ISSN 0170-7558
QUICKBORN; Zeitschrift fuer plattdeutsche Sprache und Dichtung. 1907. q. DM.38 (free to members). Quickborn Vereinigung fuer Niederdeutsche Sprache und Literatur e.V., Alexanderstr. 16, 20099 Hamburg, Germany. TEL 040-240809. Ed. F.W. Michelsen. bk.rev.; film rev.; play rev.; index. circ. 1,000. (back issues avail.)
    Description: Reports on low-German language and literature, theatre, radio.

QUICKBORN BUECHER. see *LITERATURE*

410 800   UK   ISSN 0140-3397
QUINQUEREME; new studies in modern languages. 1978. s-a. £10($24) Claverton Down Bath Quinquereme, School of Modern Languages, The University, Bath BA2 7AY, England. Eds. Peter Wagstaff, David Head. adv.; bk.rev. circ. 400. (also avail. in microfiche; back issues avail.) **Indexed:** Arts & Hum.Cit.Ind., Curr.Cont., Lang.& Lang.Behav.Abstr. —UnCover. **CCC.**

410   US   ISSN 0033-6602
QUINTO LINGO; the multi-lingual magazine. (Text in several languages) 1964-1980; resumed 1982. 6/yr. $27 for 6 nos. American National Heritage Association, Inc., Box 4827, Alexandria, VA 22303-0827. TEL 703-960-6322. Ed. E. Peedo. adv.; bk.rev. circ. 30,000. (also avail. in microform from UMI; audio cassette from UMI; reprint service avail. from UMI) **Document type:** academic/scholarly publication.
—UMI.

420   SI   ISSN 0129-7716
PE1128.A2
R E L C ANNUAL REPORT. (Text in English) 1968. a. $12. Southeast Asian Ministers of Education Organization, Regional Language Centre, 30 Orange Grove Rd., Singapore 1025, Singapore. TEL 737-9044. FAX 734-2753. TELEX RS 55598. charts; stat. circ. 400. (back issues avail.)

407   SI   ISSN 0129-7767
R E L C GUIDELINES; magazine for language teachers. 1979. s-a. $14. Southeast Asian Ministers of Education Organization, Regional Language Centre, 30 Orange Grove Rd., Singapore 1025, Singapore. TEL 737-9044. FAX 734-2753. TELEX RS 55598. (back issues avail.)
—BLDSC (4230.026800).

406 370   SI   ISSN 0033-6882
PE1068.A7
R E L C JOURNAL; a journal of language teaching and research in Southeast Asia. 1970. s-a. $18. Southeast Asian Ministers of Education Organization, Regional Language Centre, 30 Orange Grove Rd., Singapore 1025, Singapore. TEL 737-9044. FAX 734-2753. TELEX RS 55598. adv.; bk.rev. circ. 1,000. (also avail. in microform from UMI; reprint service avail. from UMI) **Indexed:** C.I.J.E., Lang.& Lang.Behav.Abstr., Lang.Teach.& Ling.Abstr., M.L.A., Res.Educ.
—BLDSC (7355.970000); UnCover; SWETS; UMI.

407   SI   ISSN 0217-3077
R E L C NEWSLETTER. s-a. free. Southeast Asian Ministers of Education Organization, Regional Language Centre, 30 Orange Grove Rd., Singapore 1025, Singapore. TEL 737-9044. FAX 7342753. TELEX RS 55598. circ. 3,500. **Document type:** newsletter.

407   SI   ISSN 0129-8844
R E L C OCCASIONAL PAPERS. irreg. $8. Southeast Asian Ministers of Education Organization, Regional Language Centre, 30 Orange Grove Rd., Singapore 1025, Singapore. TEL 737-9044. FAX 7342753. TELEX RS 55598. (back issues avail.)

407   SI
R E L C SEMINAR REPORT. 1970. a. $13. Southeast Asian Ministers of Education Organization, Regional Language Centre, 30 Orange Grove Rd., Singapore 1025, Singapore. TEL 737-9044. FAX 734-2753. TELEX RS 55598. (back issues avail.)

418   CL   ISSN 0033-698X
P9
R L A; revista de linguistica teorica y aplicada. (Text in Spanish; occasionally in English, French; abstracts in English) 1963. a. $7. Universidad de Concepcion, Facultad de Educacion, Humanidades y Arte, Casilla 82-C, Correo 3, Concepcion, Chile. TEL 56-41-234985. FAX 56-41-249108. Ed. Adalberto Salas. adv.; bk.rev. circ. 500. **Indexed:** Bibl.Ling., Bull.Signal., Lang.& Lang.Behav.Abstr. (1970-), Lang.Teach.& Ling.Abstr.
—BLDSC (7863.633000).
    Description: Covers theoretical, descriptive and applied linguistics.

410   CN   ISSN 0229-8651
P99
R S S I. (Recherches Semiotiques - Semiotic Inquiry) (Text and summaries in English and French) 1981. 2/yr. Can.$45 to individuals; students Can.$25. Universite du Quebec a Montreal, Departement d'Etudes Litteraires, C.P. 8888, succ. Centre Ville, Montreal, PQ H3C 3P8, Canada. TEL 514-987-8404. FAX 514-987-8218. Ed. Barbara Havercroft. adv.; bk.rev.; bibl. circ. 500. (also avail. in microform from MML,UMI; reprint service avail. from MML) **Document type:** academic/scholarly publication.
—BLDSC (7309.185000); SWETS.
    Supersedes: Canadian Journal of Research in Semiotics (ISSN 0316-7917)
    Description: Devoted to the empirical and theoretical study of signs, sign systems and processes of signification in all the domains of social and cultural praxis.

430.07   UK   ISSN 0033-7455
DAS RAD. (Text in German) 1964. 6/yr. (during school year). Mary Glasgow Magazines (Subsidiary of: Scholastic Publications Ltd.), 140 Freston Rd., London W10 6TR, Enngland. TEL 071-792-3644. FAX 071-792-3172. TELEX 311890-MGPUBS. (U.S. subscr. to: Delta Systems, 1400 Miller Pkwy., McHenry IL 60050-7030. TEL 800-823-8270) charts; illus. (also avail. in microform from UMI; reprint service avail. from UMI)
    Description: German-language magazine for beginners.

410 809   IT   ISSN 0047-4401
RAGIONI CRITICHE; rivista di studi lingustici e letterari. 1974; N.S 1980. q. L.10000. Aldo Marino Editore, Via Vecchia Ognina 90, 95129 Catania, Italy. Ed. Ermanno Scuderi. adv.; bk.rev.; illus.; cum.index. **Indexed:** M.L.A.

RAJASTHAN UNIVERSITY STUDIES IN ENGLISH. see *LITERATURE*

410 800   US   ISSN 0272-2747
RAM'S HORN. 1980. irreg., approx a., vol.7, 1993. $10. Rassias Foundation, Dartmouth College, 6071 Wentworth Hall, Hanover, NH 03755-3526. TEL 603-646-3719. FAX 603-646-3838. Ed. John A. Rassias. cum.index: vols.1-6. circ. 250. **Document type:** academic/scholarly publication.
    Description: Publishes articles and accounts of successful teaching practices pertaining to the Rassia language method and the Dartmouth intensive language model, incuding classroom experiences, techniques, and pedagogical concerns.

418   IT   ISSN 0033-9725
RASSEGNA ITALIANA DI LINGUISTICA APPLICATA. 1969. 3/yr. L.43000. (Centro Italiano di Linguistica Applicata) Bulzoni Editore, Via Liburni 14, 00185 Rome, Italy. TEL 06-4455207. FAX 06-4450355. Ed. Renzo Titone. adv.; bk.rev.; bibl. circ. 2,000. **Indexed:** Bibl.Ling., C.I.J.E., Lang.& Lang.Behav.Abstr. (1972-), Lang.Teach.& Ling.Abstr., M.L.A.
—BLDSC (7294.310000).

410   NE   ISSN 0922-4777
BF456.R2   CODEN: REWRE8
READING AND WRITING; an interdisciplinary journal. (Text in English) 1989. 4/yr. fl.339($177) (effective 1994). Kluwer Academic Publishers, Postbus 17, 3300 AA Dordrecht, Netherlands. TEL 31-78-334911. FAX 31-78-334254. TELEX 29245 KAPG NL. (Dist. by: Kluwer Academic Publishers Group, P.O. Box 322, 3300 AH Dordrecht, Netherlands. TEL 31-78-524400. FAX 31-78-524474; N. America dist. addr.: Box 358, Accord Sta., Hingham, MA 02018-0358. TEL 617-871-6600. FAX 617-871-6528) Ed. R. Malatesha Joshi. (also avail. in microform from UMI; back issues avail.; reprint service avail. from SWZ) **Indexed:** Bibl.Ling., Curr.Cont., Psychol.Abstr., Psychol.Abstr., Sci.Cit.Ind., SSCI. **Document type:** academic/scholarly publication.
—BLDSC (7300.875000); UnCover; SWETS; UMI. **CCC.**
    Description: Focuses on the interaction among various fields such as linguistics, information processing, neuropsychology, cognitive psychology, speech and hearing sciences, and education. *Refereed Serial*

READING AND WRITING QUARTERLY: OVERCOMING LEARNING DIFFICULTIES. see *EDUCATION — Special Education And Rehabilitation*

READING AROUND SERIES. see *EDUCATION — Teaching Methods And Curriculum*

410   UK   ISSN 0264-2425
    CODEN: RFLAEB
READING IN A FOREIGN LANGUAGE. 1983. s-a. £13 (overseas £15) (effective 1994). International Education Centre, College of St. Mark & St. John, Derriford Rd., Plymouth PL6 8BH, England. FAX 0752-761102. Ed. A.H. Urquhart. adv.; bk.rev. circ. 350. (back issues avail.) **Indexed:** Cont.Pg.Educ., Lang.Teach.& Ling.Abstr. **Document type:** academic/scholarly publication.
—BLDSC (7300.940000); UnCover; SWETS.

413 930.1   US
READING THE PAST. 1987. irreg., vol.9, 1991. price varies. (British Museum) University of California Press, 2120 Berkeley Way, Berkeley, CA 94720. TEL 510-642-4247. FAX 510-643-7127. (Orders to: California-Princeton Fulfillment Services, 1445 Lower Ferry Rd., Ewing, NJ 08618. TEL 800-777-4726. FAX 800-999-1958) (back issues avail.) **Document type:** monographic series.
    Description: Studies all ancient forms of written communication. *Refereed Serial*

410   PR
READINGS IN SPANISH-ENGLISH CONTRASTIVE LINGUISTICS. (Text in English, Spanish) 1973. irreg. Universidad Interamericana de Puerto Rico, San German Campus, Call Box 5100, San German, PR 00753. TEL 809-892-1095. (reprint service avail. from UMI) **Document type:** academic/scholarly publication.

410   SP   ISSN 0210-4822
AS302
REAL ACADEMIA ESPANOLA. BOLETIN. 1914. 3/yr. 5600 ptas.($5.55) per no. Real Academia Espanola, Felipe IV 4, Madrid 14, Spain. **Indexed:** Amer.Hist.& Life, Bibl.Ling., Hist.Abstr., M.L.A. —Faxon; SWETS.

RECHERCHES D'ARCHEOLOGIE, DE PHILOLOGIE ET D'HISTOIRE. see *ARCHAEOLOGY*

418.02   FR
RECHERCHES EN LINGUISTIQUE ETRANGERE. Variant title: Universite de Besancon. Annales Litteraires. 1973. irreg. (Universite de Besancon, Faculte des Lettres et Sciences Humaines) Societe d'Edition les Belles Lettres, 95 Bd. Raspail, Paris 75006, France.

RECHERCHES GERMANIQUES. see *LITERATURE*

410   FR
RECHERCHES LINQUISTIQUES. 1975. irreg. price varies. Universite de Metz, Centre d'Analyse Syntaxique, Metz, France. (Subscr. to: Librairie Klincksieck, 11 rue de Lille, 75007 Paris, France)

REGENSBURGER BEITRAEGE ZUR DEUTSCHEN SPRACH- UND LITERATURWISSENSCHAFT. REIHE A: QUELLEN. see *LITERATURE*

LINGUISTICS

REGENSBURGER BEITRAEGE ZUR DEUTSCHEN SPRACH- UND LITERATURWISSENSCAHFT. REIHE B: UNTERSUCHUNGEN. see *LITERATURE*

400   CN
REGIONAL LANGUAGE STUDIES - NEWFOUNDLAND. 1968. irreg. free to qualified personnel. Memorial University of Newfoundland, Department of English, St. John's, NF A1B 3X9, Canada. TEL 709-737-8983. FAX 709-737-4000. Ed. Graham Shorrocks. bk.rev. circ. 400. **Indexed:** Lang.& Lang.Behav.Abstr., M.L.A.
  Formerly: R L S: Regional Language Studies - Newfoundland (ISSN 0079-9335)

440 375.4   FR   ISSN 1157-1330
REPERES (PARIS, 1970); recherches en didactique du francais langue maternelle. 1970. 2/yr. 155 F. (foreign 180 F.). Institut National de Recherche Pedagogique, 29 rue d'Ulm, 75230 Paris Cedex 05, France. TEL 46-34-90-00.
  Former titles (until 1990): Reperes pour la Renovation de l'Enseignement du Francais (ISSN 0755-7817); (until 1980): Reperes pour la Renovation de l'Enseignement du Francais a l'Ecole Elementaire (ISSN 0755-7906)

496.333   NR   ISSN 1115-4322
RESEARCH IN YORUBA: LANGUAGE & LITERATURE; language and literature. 1991. s-a. $20 to individuals; institutions $30. Yoruba Language and Literature Club, Department of African Language and Literature, Obafemi Awolowo University, Ile-Ife, Nigeria. (Subscr. to: Technicians of the Sacred, 1317 N. San Fernando Blvd., Ste. 310, Burbank, CA 91504) Ed. Lawrence O. Adewole. adv.; bk.rev. **Document type:** academic/scholarly publication.
  Description: Covers all aspects of Yoruba language and literature.

052 301   CN   ISSN 0835-1813
P1
RESEARCH ON LANGUAGE AND SOCIAL INTERACTION. 1987. irreg.? Boreal Publishers and Distributers., Ltd., 11821 39th St., No.102, Edmonton, Alta. T5W 2J4, Canada.
  —BLDSC (7741.752000); Faxon; UnCover; UMI. **CCC.**

400   US   ISSN 0270-4390
REVERSE ACRONYMS, INITIALISMS AND ABBREVIATIONS DICTIONARY. 1972. a. $280 (effective June 1994). Gale Research Inc., 835 Penobscot Bldg., Detroit, MI 48226. TEL 313-961-2242; 800-877-4253. FAX 313-961-6083. TELEX 810-221-7086. Ed. Jennifer Mossman.
  Formerly (until 1976): Reverse Acronyms and Initialisms Dictionary.

REVIEW (CHARLOTTESVILLE). see *LITERATURE*

052   UK   ISSN 0961-6063
REVIEW OF ENGLISH LANGUAGE TEACHING. 1991. irreg. (The British Council) Macmillan Magazines Ltd. (Subsidiary of: Macmillan Publishers Ltd.), 4 Little Essex St., London WC2R 3LF, England. TEL 071-836-6633. Ed. C.J. Brumfit. **Document type:** academic/scholarly publication.
  —BLDSC (7790.365000).

REVIEW OF ENGLISH STUDIES; a quarterly journal of English literature and the English language. see *LITERATURE*

460 375   AG   ISSN 0326-6400
REVISTA ARGENTINA DE LINGUISTICA. (Text in Spanish; summaries in English and Spanish) 1985. 2/yr. Arg.$24 to individuals (foreign $35); institutions Arg.$35 (foreign $45). Casilla de Correo 45, 5511 Gral. Gutierrez, Mendoza, Argentina. TEL 061-978716. Eds. Victor M. Castel, Cesar E. Quiroga Salcedo. adv.; bk.rev.; abstr.; bibl.; charts; stat. circ. 200. (back issues avail.) **Indexed:** Lang.& Lang.Behav.Abstr. (1985-), M.L.A.
  Description: Covers study of linguistics. Includes theory, descriptive sociolinguistics, psycholinguistics, historical linguistics and computational linguistics.

420 375.4   SP   ISSN 0211-5913
PE9
REVISTA CANARIA DE ESTUDIOS INGLESES. 1980. s-a. $25 to individuals; institutions $30. Universidad de La Laguna, Facultad de Filologia, Departamento de Ingles, Secretariado de Publicaciones, San Agustin, 30, 38201 La Laguna-Tenerife, Islas Canarias, Spain. TEL 922-25-81-27. adv.
  ●Also available online.
  —BLDSC (7847.270000).
  Description: Devoted to the English language and literature of the English speaking countries. Includes software reviews.

REVISTA DE COMUNICACAO E LINGUAGENS. see *COMMUNICATIONS*

417 398   SP   ISSN 0034-7981
GR1
REVISTA DE DIALECTOLOGIA Y TRADICIONES POPULARES. 1944. q. 2000 ptas. (foreign 3000 ptas.). Consejo Superior de Investigaciones Cientificas (C.S.I.C.), Instituto de Filologia, Duque de Medinaceli, 6, 28014 Madrid, Spain. TEL 429 20 17. Dir. Julio Caro Baroja. bk.rev.; bibl.; charts; illus.; index. circ. 600. **Indexed:** A.I.C.P., Amer.Hist.& Life, Arts & Hum.Cit.Ind., Bibl.Ling., Hist.Abstr., M.L.A.
  —Faxon.
  Description: Covers the Spanish language in Iberia, and its dialects in America and Europe.

REVISTA DE ESTUDIOS HISPANICOS. see *LITERATURE*

410 056   SP   ISSN 0212-4130
REVISTA DE FILOLOGIA. 1981. a. $20 to individuals; institutions $30. Universidad de La Laguna, Facultad de Filologia, Seretariado de Publicaciones, San Agustin, 30, 38201 La Laguna-Tenerife, Islas Canarias, Spain. adv.
  Description: Devoted to the Spanish and classical languages and literature.

400   SP   ISSN 0210-9174
PQ6001
REVISTA DE FILOLOGIA ESPANOLA. q. 3300 ptas. (foreign 4950 ptas.). Consejo Superior de Investigaciones Cientificas (C.S.I.C.), Instituto de Filologia, Duque de Medinaceli, 6, 28014 Madrid, Spain. Dir. Manuel Alvar. (also avail. in microform from BHP; microfilm from KTO; reprint service avail. from SCH) **Indexed:** Bibl.Ling.
  —SWETS.

400 410   CR   ISSN 0377-628X
REVISTA DE FILOLOGIA Y LINGUISTICA. 1975. s-a. $20. Editorial de la Universidad de Costa Rica, Apdo. 75-2060, Ciudad Universitaria Rodrigo Facio, 2050 San Pedro de Montes de Oca, San Jose, Costa Rica. TEL 506-25-3133. FAX 506-24-9367. TELEX UNICORI 2544. Ed. Enrique Margery P. **Document type:** academic/scholarly publication.

449.9 469.794
499.92   SP   ISSN 1130-8508
REVISTA DE LENGUA Y LITERATURA CATALANA, GALLEGA Y VASCA. 1991. a. Universidad Autonoma de Madrid, Departamento de Filologia Espanola, Carretera de Colmenar, km 15,000, Canto Blanco, 28049 Madrid, Spain. **Document type:** academic/scholarly publication.

420   SP   ISSN 0210-9689
REVISTA "ES". 1971. irreg., no.17, 1993. 1800 ptas. Universidad de Valladolid, Secretariado de Publicaciones, Departamento de Ingles, C. Juan Mambrilla, 14, 47003 Valladolid, Spain. TEL 983-423000. FAX 34-83-290300. **Document type:** monographic series, academic/scholarly publication.

410   SP   ISSN 0210-1874
P9
REVISTA ESPANOLA DE LINGUISTICA. 1971. s-a. 2094 ptas. (effective 1992). (Sociedad Espanola de Linguistica) Editorial Gredos, S.A., Sanchez Pacheco 81, 28002 Madrid, Spain. FAX 341-5192033. Ed.Bd. **Indexed:** Bibl.Ling., Lang.Teach.& Ling.Abstr.
  —SWETS.

410 306.4   PE
REVISTA LATINOAMERICANA DE ESTUDIOS ETNOLINGUISTICOS. (Text in English, Portuguese and Spanish) 1981. irreg., no.7, 1993. $20. E. Iturriaga y Cia., Jiron Ica 441, Ofc. 202-203, Casilla 4640, Lima 100, Peru. Ed. Ignacio Prado Pastor. **Document type:** academic/scholarly publication.
  Description: Covers various topics in Latin American indigenous languages. Includes morphology and syntax, phonology and comparative linguistic studies.

REVISTA LETRAS. see *LITERATURE*

469   PO   ISSN 0870-4139
PC5001
REVISTA PORTUGUESA DE FILOLOGIA. 1978. 2/yr. Esc.800. Universidade de Coimbra, Instituto de Estudos Romanicos, Casa do Castelo, Rua da Sofia 47, Coimbra, Portugal. Ed. Manuel de Paiva Boleo. **Indexed:** Bibl.Ling., M.L.A.

REVISTA SIGNOS DE VALPARAISO; estudios de lengua y literatura. see *LITERATURE*

REVUE BELGE DE PHILOLOGIE ET D'HISTOIRE. see *HISTORY*

410 306.4   BE   ISSN 0778-8118
REVUE D'ETHNOLINGUISTIQUE; cahiers du L A C I T O. (Text in English, French) 1986. a. 1200 BEF (effective 1994). (Laboratoire de Langues et de Civilisations a Tradition Orale, FR) Editions Peeters s.p.r.l., Bondgenotenlaan 153, B-3000 Louvain, Belgium. TEL 32-16-235170. FAX 32-16-228500. Ed.Bd. adv.; bk.rev. (back issues avail.) **Indexed:** Bibl.Ling. **Document type:** academic/scholarly publication.
  Formerly (until 1989): Cahiers du L A C I T O (ISSN 0994-7736).
  Description: Publishes multidisciplinary papers in ethnolinguistics at the intersection of linguistics, ethnology and the natural sciences.

REVUE DE BIBLIOLOGIE. see *LITERATURE*

479   FR   ISSN 0035-1458
PC2
REVUE DE LINGUISTIQUE ROMANE. (Text in French, Italian, Spanish) 1925. s-a. 480 F. to non-members. Societe de Linguistique Romane, 44 av. de la Liberation, Case officielle 3310, 54014 Nancy Cedex, France. TEL 83-96-21-76. FAX 83-97-24-56. adv.; bk.rev.; bibl.; charts; index. circ. 700. (also avail. in microfiche from IDC) **Indexed:** Arts & Hum.Cit.Ind., Bibl.Ling., Ind.Bk.Rev.Hum., Lang.Teach.& Ling.Abstr., M.L.A. **Document type:** bulletin.
  —Faxon; SWETS.

REVUE DE PHILOLOGIE, DE LITTERATURE ET D'HISTOIRE ANCIENNES. see *CLASSICAL STUDIES*

414   FR   ISSN 0035-1660
P1
REVUE DE PHONETIQUE APPLIQUEE. (Text mainly in French; occasionally in English, German) 1965. 4/yr. $42. Didier Erudition, 6 rue de la Sorbonne, 75005 Paris, France. (Subscr. to: Didier Erudition, North American Fullfillment Office, P.O. Box 830350, Birmingham, AL-35283-0350) Ed. R. Renard. bk.rev.; abstr.; bibl.; charts. circ. 100. (also avail. in microform from UMI; reprint service avail. from UMI) **Indexed:** Bibl.Ling., Lang.Behav.Abstr. (1976-), Lang.Teach.& Ling.Abstr., M.L.A.
  —BLDSC (7942.380000); Faxon; SWETS; UMI.

450   FR   ISSN 0035-2047
PQ4001
REVUE DES ETUDES ITALIENNES. 1936. q. 200 F. (foreign 210 F.). Societe des Etudes Italiennes (Paris), Grand Palais-Perron Alexander III, Cours la Reine, 75008 Paris, France. Ed. M. Bec. adv.; bk.rev.; bibl.; index. **Indexed:** Amer.Hist.& Life, Arts & Hum.Cit.Ind., Can.Rev.Comp.Lit., Curr.Cont., Hist.Abstr., M.L.A.

REVUE DES ETUDES LATINES. see *CLASSICAL STUDIES*

REVUE DES ETUDES SLAVES. see *LITERATURE*

LINGUISTICS

440 840   FR   ISSN 0223-3711
REVUE DES LANGUES ROMANES. 1870. s-a. 200 F. Universite de Montpellier III (Universite Paul Valery), Centre d'Etudes Occitanes, B.P. 5043, 34032 Montpellier Cedex 1, France. TEL 67-14-21-54. bk.rev.; bibl.; illus. circ. 1,000. (reprint service avail. from KTO) **Indexed:** Arts & Hum.Cit.Ind., Bibl.Ling., Curr.Cont., M.L.A.
—SWETS.
Description: Main themes are the philology of Romance languages and Occitan literary texts.

499.992   FR   ISSN 0988-6729
REVUE FRANCAISE D'ESPERANTO; Franca Esperantisto. 1908. bi-m. 155 F. Union Francaise pour l'Esperanto, 4 bis, rue de la Cerisaie, 75004 Paris, France. Ed. Herve Gonin. adv.; bk.rev. circ. 2,000.
Incorporates: Esperanto-Actualites.

410   CN   ISSN 0710-0167
P2
REVUE QUEBECOISE DE LINGUISTIQUE; theorique et appliquee. 1971. 4/yr. Can.$35. Association Quebecoise de Linguistique Inc., C.P. 95, Trois-Rivieres, PQ G9A 5E3, Canada. Ed. Henri Wittmann. adv.; bk.rev. circ. 600. (back issues avail.) **Indexed:** Bibl.Ling., Lang.& Lang.Behav.Abstr. (1984-), Lang.Teach.& Ling.Abstr., M.L.A., Pt.de Rep. (1983-), Sociol.Abstr.
—BLDSC (7944.850000); Faxon.
Formerly (until Apr. 1981): Cahier de Linguistique (ISSN 0315-4025)

479   DK   ISSN 0035-3906
REVUE ROMANE. (Text in French, Italian, Spanish) 1966. s-a. DKK 325 (students DKK 162.50). (Koebenhavns Universitet, Institut d'Etudes Romanes - University of Copenhagen) Munksgaard International Publishers Ltd., 35 Noerre Soegade, P.O. Box 2148, DK-1016 Copenhagen K, Denmark. TEL 33-127030. FAX 33-129387. Ed. Hans Peter Lund. bk.rev.; index. circ. 600. **Indexed:** Arts & Hum.Cit.Ind., Bibl.Ling., Curr.Cont., Lang.& Lang.Behav.Abstr., M.L.A.
—BLDSC (7946.030000); Faxon; SWETS. **CCC.**
Refereed Serial

400   RM   ISSN 0035-3957
P1.A1
REVUE ROUMAINE DE LINGUISTIQUE. (Text in English, French, German, Russian, Spanish) 1956. 6/yr. 210 lei($68) (Academia Romana) Editura Academiei Romane, Calea Victoriei 125, 79717 Bucharest, Rumania. (Dist. by: Rompresfilatelia, Calea Grivitei 64-66, P.O. Box 12-201, 78104 Bucharest, Rumania) bk.rev.; index. **Indexed:** Bibl.Ling., Lang.& Lang.Behav.Abstr. (1972-), Lang.Teach.& Ling.Abstr., M.L.A.
—Faxon.
Formerly: Revue de Linguistique.

REVUE RUSSE. see *LITERATURE*

499.992   JA   ISSN 0035-4406
LA REVUO ORIENTA. (Text in Esperanto, Japanese) 1920. m. 3600 Yen. Japana Esperanto Instituto, 12-3, Waseda-machi, Shinjuku-ku, Tokyo 162, Japan. TEL 03-3203-4581. FAX 03-3203-4582. Ed. Satio Ikawa. adv.; bk.rev.; illus. circ. 2,300. **Indexed:** Lang.& Lang.Behav.Abstr.

430   GW
RHEINISCHE MUNDARTEN. 1981. irreg., no.6, 1993. (Landschaftsverband Rheinland, Amt fuer Rheinische Landeskunde) Rheinland Verlag GmbH, Abtei Brauweiler, Postfach 2140, 50250 Pulheim, Germany. TEL 02234-8051. FAX 02234-82503. (Dist. by: Dr. Rudolf Habelt GmbH, Am Buchenhang 1, 53115 Bonn, Germany. TEL 0228-232016. FAX 0228-232017) **Document type:** monographic series.

400 480 470   GW   ISSN 0035-449X
PA3
RHEINISCHES MUSEUM FUER PHILOLOGIE. (Text mainly in German, partly in English, Greek, Latin) 1842. q. DM.184. J.D. Sauerlaender's Verlag, Finkenhofstr. 21, 60322 Frankfurt a.M., Germany. TEL 069-555217. FAX 069-5964344. Ed.Bd. illus.; index. circ. 600. **Indexed:** Bibl.Ling., M.L.A. **Document type:** academic/scholarly publication.
—Faxon; UnCover; SWETS.
Description: Scholarly publication devoted to studies in the literature and history of ancient Greece and Rome.

RHETORIC REVIEW. see *EDUCATION — Higher Education*

410   US   ISSN 0734-8584
PN183
RHETORICA; a journal of the history of rhetoric. 1983. q. $40 to individuals; institutions $59; students $16 (effective 1994). (International Society for the History of Rhetoric) University of California Press, Journals Division, 2120 Berkeley Way, Berkeley, CA 94720. TEL 510-643-7154. FAX 510-642-9117. Ed. Craig Kallendorf. adv.; bk.rev. circ. 850. (also avail. in microform from UMI; back issues avail.) **Indexed:** Arts & Hum.Cit.Ind., Curr.Cont., M.L.A. **Document type:** academic/scholarly publication.
—BLDSC (7960.610300); Faxon; UnCover; SWETS; UMI. **CCC.**
Description: Examines the theory, practice, and cultural context of rhetoric.
Refereed Serial

RIJKSUNIVERSITEIT TE GRONINGEN. NEDERSAKSISCH INSTITUUT. DRIEMAANDELIJKSE BLADEN; taal en volksleven in het oosten van Nederland. see *LITERATURE*

410   SP
RILCE. 1985. 2/yr. 3000 ptas.($37) (Universidad de Navarra, Instituto de Lengua y Cultura Espanolas) Servicio de Publicaciones de la Universidad de Navarra, S.A., Apdo. 177, 31080 Pamplona, Spain. TEL 94 25 2700. Dir. Jesus Canedo.

410   CN   ISSN 0830-9574
LA RIVEREGO. (Text in Esperanto, French) 1986. q. Can.$10. Societe Quebecoise d'Esperanto, 6358-A rue de Bordeaux, Montreal, PQ H2G 2R8, Canada. TEL 514-272-0151. Ed. Sylvain Auclair. adv.; bk.rev. circ. 200. (also avail. in magnetic tape) **Document type:** newsletter.

410   IT
▼**RIVISTA DELLE LINGUE.** 1992. bi-m. Edizioni Linguistic Club, Via Principe Amedeo 15, 00044 Frascati (Rome), Italy.

480   IT   ISSN 0035-6220
RIVISTA DI FILOLOGIA CLASSICA. 1872. q. (foreign L.128000) (effective 1994). Editore Loescher, Via Vittorio Amedeo II, 18, 10121 Turin, Italy. TEL 011-5624622. FAX 011-5625822. Ed.Bd. bk.rev.; bibl.; index. circ. 1,000. (reprint service avail. from KTO) **Indexed:** Bibl.Ling.
—Faxon; SWETS.

450 375.4   IT   ISSN 1120-2726
RIVISTA DI LINGUISTICA. (Text in English) 1989. 2/yr. L.70000 (Europe L.77000; elsewhere L.110000) (effective 1993). Rosenberg & Sellier, Via Andrea Doria, 14, 10123 Turin, Italy. TEL 011-561-39-07. FAX 011-532188. Ed. PierMarco Bertinetto. **Indexed:** Bibl.Ling.

418.02   IT
▼**RIVISTA INTERNAZIONALE DI TECNICA DELLA TRADUZIONE.** 1992. irreg. L.30000($35) for 2 nos. (Universita degli Studi di Trieste, Scuola Superiore di Lingue Moderne per Interpreti e Traduttori) Franca Campanotto Editore, Via Michelini 1, 33100 Udine, Italy. (Edit. addr.: Via B. D'Alviano 15-1, 34144 Trieste, Italy)

450 375.4   IT   ISSN 1122-6331
RIVISTA ITALIANA DI DIALETTOLOGIA; scuola societa territorio. Short title: R I D. 1977. a. L.43000 (foreign L.70000) (effective 1994). (Universita degli Studi di Bologna, Facolta di Lettere e Filosofia, Istituto di Glottologia) Cooperativa Libraria Universitaria Editrice Bologna, Via Marsala 24, 40126 Bologna, Italy. TEL 051-220736. FAX 051-237758. Ed.Bd. **Indexed:** Bibl.Ling., Lang.& Lang.Behav.Abstr.

495.6   US
RIYU XUEXI/LEARNING JAPANESE. (Text in Chinese and Japanese) bi-m. $14.50. China Books & Periodicals, Inc., 2929 24th St., San Francisco, CA 94110. TEL 415-282-2994. FAX 415-282-0994.

495.6   CC
RIYU XUEXI YU YANJIU/STUDIES OF JAPANESE LANGUAGE. (Text in Chinese and Japanese) bi-m. $30.60. Duwai Jingji Maoyi Daxue - Foreign Economics and Trade University, Andingmenwai Xiaoguan, Chaoyang Qu, Beijing 100029, People's Republic of China. TEL 4212161. (Dist. in US by: China Books & Periodicals, Inc., 2929 24th St., San Francisco, CA 94110. TEL 415-282-2994) Ed. Leng Tiezheng.

ROCKY MOUNTAIN REVIEW OF LANGUAGE AND LITERATURE. see *LITERATURE*

491.8   PL   ISSN 0080-3588
PG1
ROCZNIK SLAWISTYCZNY. (Text in French, German and Polish) 1908. a. price varies. (Polska Akademia Nauk, Komitet Slowianoznawstwa) Ossolineum, Publishing House of the Polish Academy of Sciences, Rynek 9, 50-106 Wroclaw, Poland. TEL 48-71-386-25. FAX 48-71-448-103. TELEX 0712771 OSS PL. (Dist. by: Ars Polona-Ruch, Krakowskie Przedmiescie 7, Warsaw, Poland) Ed. F. Slawski. **Indexed:** Bibl.Ling., M.L.A. **Document type:** academic/scholarly publication.
Description: Dissertations on Slavonic studies, bibliographies of published works.

479   US   ISSN 0035-8002
PC1
ROMANCE PHILOLOGY. (Text in several languages) 1947. q. $39 to individuals (foreign $45); institutions $87 (foreign $93); students $24 (foreign $30) (effective 1994). University of California Press, Journals Division, Berkeley, CA 94720. TEL 510-643-7154. FAX 510-642-9117. Ed. Jerry R. Craddock. adv.; bk.rev.; index. circ. 1,200. (also avail. in microform from UMI; back issues avail.; reprint service avail. from UMI) **Indexed:** Arts & Hum.Cit.Ind., Bibl.Ling., Curr.Cont., Hum.Ind., Ind.Bk.Rev.Hum., Lang.& Lang.Behav.Abstr., M.L.A. **Document type:** academic/scholarly publication.
—Faxon; UnCover; SWETS; UMI. **CCC.**
Description: Contains articles on topics of linguistic and literary theory.
Refereed Serial

459 859 940   FR   ISSN 0035-8029
PC2
ROMANIA; revue consacree a l'etude des langues et des litteratures romanes. (Text in English, French, Italian, Spanish) 1872. q. 390 F. (foreign 420 F.). Societe des Amis de la Romania, 19 Rue de la Sorbonne, 75005 Paris, France. Ed. Jacques Monfrin. bk.rev.; index, cum.index. (also avail. in microform from BHP; microfiche from IDC; reprint service avail. from KTO) **Indexed:** Arts & Hum.Cit.Ind., Bibl.Ling., Curr.Cont., Ind.Bk.Rev.Hum. **Document type:** academic/scholarly publication.
—Faxon; UnCover; SWETS.

479.1   BE   ISSN 0080-3855
ROMANICA GANDENSIA. 1953. irreg. price varies. Universiteit Gent, Section de Philologie Romane, Blandijnberg 2, B-9000 Gent, Belgium. TEL 32-9-264-4045. FAX 32-9-264-4195. circ. 600. **Indexed:** M.L.A. **Document type:** monographic series.
Description: Publishes studies in Romance philology.

430 830   SW   ISSN 0080-3863
ROMANICA GOTHOBURGENSIA. (Subseries of Acta Universitatis Gothoburgensis) 1955. irreg., no.41, 1992. price varies; also exchange basis. Acta Universitatis Gothoburgensis, Box 5096, S-402 22 Goeteborg, Sweden. **Document type:** monographic series.

400   SZ   ISSN 0080-3871
ROMANICA HELVETICA. (Text in French, German, or Italian) 1935. irreg., vol.111, 1994. price varies. (Collegium Romanicum Helvetiorum a Curatoribus Vocis Romanicae) Francke Verlag GmbH, Postfach 2560, 72015 Tuebingen, Germany. TEL 07071-78091. FAX 07071-75288. **Document type:** monographic series.

410   IT   ISSN 0391-1950
ROMANICA NEAPOLITANA. 1969. irreg., no.27, 1992. price varies. Liguori Editore s.r.l., Via Mezzocannone 19, 80134 Naples, Italy. TEL 081-5527139. Eds. Francesco Bruni, Alberto Varvaro. **Document type:** monographic series.

410   GW   ISSN 0344-676X
ROMANISTISCHE ARBEITSHEFTE. 1973. irreg., no.37, 1992. price varies. Max Niemeyer Verlag, Postfach 2140, 72011 Tuebingen, Germany. TEL 07071-98940. FAX 07071-989450. (back issues avail.) **Document type:** monographic series.
Description: University course books on Romance languages.

400 GW
ROMANISTISCHE TEXTE UND STUDIEN. 1984. irreg.,
vol.5, 1993. DM.88. Georg Olms Verlag,
Hagentorwall 7, 31134 Hildesheim, Germany.
TEL 05121-1501-0. FAX 05121-150150. (U.S.
subscr. to: 111 W. 57th St., New York, NY 10019.
TEL 212-757-5237) **Document type:** monographic
series.

400 870 GW ISSN 0080-3898
PC3
ROMANISTISCHES JAHRBUCH. 1947. irreg., vol.44,
1993. price varies. (Universitaet Hamburg,
Ibero-Amerikanisches Forschungsinstitut) Walter de
Gruyter und Co., Genthiner Str. 13, 10785 Berlin,
Germany. TEL 030-26005-0. FAX 030-26005251.
TELEX 184027. (U.S. addr.: Walter de Gruyter, Inc.,
200 Saw Mill Rd., Hawthorne, N.Y. 10532) bk.rev.
Indexed: Bibl.Ling., Can.Rev.Comp.Lit., M.L.A.
Document type: monographic series.
—BLDSC (8019.870000).

410 DK ISSN 0106-0821
**ROSKILDE UNIVERSITETSCENTER. LINGVISTGRUPPEN.
ROLIG-PAPIR.** 1974. irreg. free. Roskilde
Universitetscenter, Lingvistgruppen, P.O. Box 260,
4000 Roskilde, Denmark. FAX 46-754410. TELEX
43158-RUBIBL-DK. Eds. Karen Risager, Hartmut
Haberland, Robert Ph8llipson. circ. 350.

491.7 891.7 XR ISSN 0139-9268
ROSSICA OLOMUCENSIA. (Text in Czech or Russian;
summaries in Russian) 1962. a. free. Universita
Palackeho, Filozoficka Fakulta, Katedra Rusistiky,
Krizkovskeho 10, 771 47 Olomouc, Czech Republic.
TEL 42-28-5508371. FAX 42-28-26476. Ed.
Zdenek Pechal. bk.rev. circ. 350. **Indexed:** Bibl.Ling.
Document type: academic/scholarly publication.
Description: Covers studies on Russian literature
and linguistics of the 19th and 20th centuries.

491 II ISSN 0035-9424
RTAM. (Text in English, Hindi, Sanskrit) 1969. s-a.
Rs.20($5.) Akhila Bharatiya Sanskrit Parishad, c/o
Dr. J.P. Sinha, Ed., Mahatma Gandhi Marg,
Hazratganj, Lucknow-226 001, Uttar Pradesh, India.
bk.rev.; index. circ. 200.

947 891.7 UK ISSN 0957-1760
CODEN: RUSIE5
RUSISTIKA. 1959. s-a. £20($40) in the UK; elsewhere
£21. Association for Language Learning, 16 Regent
Pl., Rugby, Warks. CV21 2PN, England.
TEL 44-788-546443. FAX 44-788-544149. Ed.
Margaret Tejerizo. adv.; bk.rev.; film rev.; play rev.;
rec.rev.; abstr.; bibl.; charts; illus.; mkt.; stat.; index.
circ. 1,000. (also avail. in microform from UMI;
reprint service avail. from UMI) **Indexed:** Br.Educ.Ind.,
Br.Hum.Ind., Cont.Pg.Educ., Educ.Ind., Forest.Abstr.,
Lang.& Lang.Behav.Abstr., Lang.Teach.& Ling.Abstr.,
M.L.A. **Document type:** academic/scholarly
publication.
—BLDSC (8052.647590); UnCover; UMI.
Formerly (until 1990): Journal of Russian Studies
(ISSN 0047-276X)
Description: Directed to teachers of Russian in
schools, colleges, and universities, with articles on
language, literature, teaching methodology, and
history.

491.7 370 US ISSN 0036-0252
RUSSIAN LANGUAGE JOURNAL. (Text in English,
Russian) 1947. 3/yr. $25 to individuals; institutions
$30. Russian Language Journal Consortium, c/o
Prof. Munir Sendich, Ed., A-601 Wells Hall,
Department of Linguistics and Language, Michigan
State University, E. Lansing, MI 48824-1027.
TEL 517-355-5079. (Co-sponsors: American
Council of Teachers of Russian; Ohio State
University; American University) adv.; bk.rev.; bibl.;
stat.; cum.index: 1947-1965. circ. 500. (also avail.
in microform from UMI; reprint service avail. from
UMI) **Indexed:** Amer.Bibl.Slavic & E.Eur.Stud.,
Bibl.Ling., C.I.J.E., Can.Rev.Comp.Lit.,
Ind.Bk.Rev.Hum., Lang.& Lang.Behav.Abstr.,
Lang.Teach.& Ling.Abstr., M.L.A. **Document type:**
academic/scholarly publication.
—Faxon; UnCover; UMI.
Formerly: Guide to Teachers of the Russian
Language in America.

491.7 NE ISSN 0304-3487
PG2001 CODEN: RLIND8
RUSSIAN LINGUISTICS; international journal for the
study of the Russian language. (Text in English,
Russian) 1974. 3/yr. fl.393($205.50) (effective
1994). Kluwer Academic Publishers, Postbus 17,
3300 AA Dordrecht, Netherlands.
TEL 31-78-334911. FAX 31-78-334254. TELEX
29245 KAPG NL. (Dist. by: Kluwer Academic
Publishers Group, P.O. Box 322, 3300 AH
Dordrecht, Netherlands. TEL 31-78-524400. FAX
31-78-524474; N. America dist. addr.: Box 358,
Accord Sta., Hingham, MA 02018-0358. TEL
617-871-6600. FAX 617-871-6528) Ed.Bd. adv.;
bk.rev. (also avail. in microform from UMI; reprint
service avail. from SWZ) **Indexed:** Arts &
Hum.Cit.Ind., ASCA, Bibl.Ling., Curr.Cont., IBR, IBZ,
Ind.Bk.Rev.Hum., Lang.& Lang.Behav.Abstr. (1975-),
Lang.Teach.& Ling.Abstr., M.L.A., Sociol.Abstr.
Document type: academic/scholarly publication.
—BLDSC (8052.735000); UnCover; SWETS; UMI.
CCC.
Description: Publishes research on all aspects of
Russian linguistics.
Refereed Serial

RUSSIAN POETICS IN TRANSLATION. see *LITERATURE*

THE RUSSIAN REVIEW; an American quarterly devoted
to Russia past and present. see *HISTORY — History
Of Europe*

375.4 DK ISSN 0108-2442
RUSSISKLAERERFORENINGEN. MEDDELELSER. 1979. q.
membership. Kastanie Alle 3, DK-6000 Kolding,
Denmark. Ed. Anne Bryld. adv.; bk.rev.; illus. circ.
250.

491.7 RU ISSN 0036-0368
RUSSKAYA RECH'. 1967. bi-m. 8.10 Rub. (Rossiiskaya
Akademiya Nauk, Institut Russkogo Yazyka)
Izdatel'stvo Nauka, 90 Profsoyuznaya ul., 117864
Moscow, Russia. (Dist. by: Mezhdunarodnaya Kniga,
ul. Dimitrova D.39, 113095 Moscow, Russia) Ed.
V.V. Ivanov. bk.rev.; bibl.; index. (also avail. in
microform)

491.7 RU
PG2065 CODEN: RINSBP
RUSSKII YAZYK V S.N.G. 1957. q. 0.70 Rub. per issue.
Rossiiskaya Akademiya Obrazovaniya, Smolenskii
bul'var, 4, 119034 Moscow, Russia.
TEL 971-15-63. Ed. M.I. Isaev. circ. 6,000.
Former titles (until 1992): Russkii Yazyk v S.S.S.R.
(ISSN 0868-9539); (until 1991): Russkii Yazyk v
Natsional'noi Shkole (ISSN 0131-6133)

491.7 370 RU ISSN 0131-6141
RUSSKII YAZYK V SHKOLE. 1914. bi-m. $38 (foreign
$41). (Ministerstvo Prosveshcheniya) Izdatel'stvo
Prosveshchenie, 3-i Proezd Mar'inoi Roshchi, 41,
129846 Moscow, Russia. TEL 095-289-1405.
FAX 095-200-4266. TELEX 111999 PARK. (Dist. in
U.S. by: Victor Kamkin Inc. 4956 Boiling Brook
Pkwy, MD 20852. TEL 301-881-5973)
(Co-sponsor: Ministerstvo Narodnogo Obrazovaniya)
Ed. N.M. Shanskii. bk.rev.; bibl.; index. circ.
255,300. **Indexed:** Lang.& Lang.Behav.Abstr.
Description: Aimed at high school and college
teachers of Russian language. Publishes articles on
methodology, as well as practical advice and
recommendations on conducting the lessons.

491.7 370 RU ISSN 0036-0384
RUSSKII YAZYK ZA RUBEZHOM/RUSSIAN ABROAD.
1967. bi-m. 15 Rub. (effective 1991). Institut
Russkogo Yazika im. Pushkina - Pushkin Russian
Language Institute, Ul. Volgina 6, Moscow 117485,
Russia. Ed. A.V. Abramovich. (also avail. in
microform)

491.7 375.4 XO ISSN 0139-8865
RUSTINAR. (Text in Russian) 1966. 10/yr. $24. (Zvaz
Ceskoslovensko-Sovetskeho Priatelstva - Union of
Czechoslovak-Soviet Friendship) Obzor,
Ceskoslovenskej Armady 35, 815 85 Bratislava,
Slovakia. (Co-sponsor: House of Czechoslovak-Soviet
in Bratislava) **Indexed:** Bibl.Ling.

438 430 SW ISSN 0284-7795
**S UND P: SPRACHE UND PRAGMATIK -
ARBEITSBERICHTE.** (Text in German) 1988. irreg.
Lunds Universitet, Helgonabacken 14, S-223-62
Lund, Sweden. **Document type:** academic/scholarly
publication.

410 SI ISSN 0129-8895
**S E A M E O REGIONAL LANGUAGE CENTRE.
ANTHOLOGY SERIES.** (Text in English) irreg. $18.
Southeast Asian Ministers of Education Organization,
Regional Language Centre, 30 Orange Grove Rd.,
Singapore 1025, Singapore. TEL 7379044.
FAX 7342753. TELEX RS 55598. circ. 1,000.
—BLDSC (1542.391000).

407 371.3 AT ISSN 1036-1243
S I L - A A I B OCCASIONAL PAPERS. 1978. irreg. price
varies. Summer Institute of Linguistics, Australian
Aborigines and Islanders Branch, P.O. Berrimah, N.T.
0828, Australia. TEL 089-844488.
FAX 089-844321. Ed. Susanne Hargrave. (back
issues avail.) **Document type:** academic/scholarly
publication.
Formed by the 1990 merger of: Summer Institute
of Linguistics. Australian Aborigines and Islanders
Branch. Work Papers. Series A (ISSN 1030-9853) &
Summer Institute of Linguistics. Australian
Aborigines and Islanders Branch. Work Papers.
Series B (ISSN 1030-9861)
Description: Presents linguistic and cultural data
and analyses, language resource materials, and
practical applications in communication and
translation resulting from research in Australian
Aboriginal and Islander languages.

400 GW ISSN 0942-2919
P204
**S T U F - SPRACHTYPOLOGIE UND
UNIVERSALIENFORSCHUNG.** (Text in English, French,
German) 1948. 4/yr. DM.286 (foreign DM.296).
Akademie Verlag GmbH, Muehlenstr. 33-34, 13187
Berlin, Germany. TEL 030-47889348.
FAX 030-47889357. Ed.Bd. bk.rev.; bibl.; charts;
illus.; index. **Indexed:** Bibl.Ling., Ind.Bk.Rev.Hum.,
Lang.Teach.& Ling.Abstr., M.L.A. **Document type:**
academic/scholarly publication.
—BLDSC (8419.889500); UnCover; SWETS.
Formerly: Zeitschrift fuer Phonetik,
Sprachwissenschaft und Kommunikationsforschung
(ISSN 0044-331X)

400 900 GW ISSN 0080-5297
**SAECHSISCHE AKADEMIE DER WISSENSCHAFTEN,
LEIPZIG. PHILOLOGISCH-HISTORISCHE KLASSE.
ABHANDLUNGEN.** 1896. irreg., vol.73, no.6, 1993.
price varies. Akademie Verlag GmbH, Muehlenstr.
33-34, 13187 Berlin, Germany.
TEL 030-47889348. FAX 030-47889357. **Indexed:**
Bibl.Ling. **Document type:** monographic series.

410 900 GW ISSN 0138-3957
AS182
**SAECHSISCHE AKADEMIE DER WISSENSCHAFTEN,
LEIPZIG. PHILOLOGISCH-HISTORISCHE KLASSE.
SITZUNGSBERICHTE.** irreg., vol.133, no.2, 1993.
price varies. Akademie Verlag GmbH, Muehlenstr.
33-34, 13187 Berlin, Germany.
TEL 030-47889348. FAX 030-47889357. **Indexed:**
Bibl.Ling. **Document type:** monographic series.

SAGA OCH SED. see *FOLKLORE*

491.8 GW
SAGNERS SLAVISTISCHE SAMMLUNG. 1974. irreg.,
vol.10, 1986. price varies. Verlag Otto Sagner,
Postfach 340108, 80328 Munich, Germany.
TEL 089-54218-0. FAX 089-54218218. TELEX
5216711-KUSAD. Ed. Peter Rehder. circ. 250.
Indexed: Bibl.Ling. **Document type:** academic/scholarly
publication.

SAMMLUNG GROOS. see *EDUCATION — Higher
Education*

430 375.4 GW
**SAMMLUNG KURZER GRAMMATIKEN GERMANISCHER
DIALEKTE.** 1880. irreg. price varies. Max Niemeyer
Verlag, Postfach 2140, 72011 Tuebingen,
Germany. TEL 07071-98940.
FAX 07071-989450. Ed.Bd. (back issues avail.)
Document type: monographic series.
Description: Scientific grammars on Germanic
languages including Old and Middle High German,
Gothic, Saxon, Old English and Middle English.

894.541 FI
SANANJALKA. (Text in Finnish; abstracts in English, French or German) 1959. a. FIM 160. Suomen Kielen Seura - Finnish Language Society, Fennicum, Henrikinkatu 3, 20500 Turku, Finland. Ed. Aimo Hakanen. adv.; bk.rev.; abstr. circ. 700. (back issues avail.) **Indexed:** Bibl.Ling. **Document type:** academic/scholarly publication.
Formerly: Suomen Kielen Seuran Vuosikirja (ISSN 0558-4639)
Description: Focuses on Finnish and related languages, Finnish ethnology, literature and folklore, and on comparative religion.

SANKT-PETERBURGSKII UNIVERSITET. VESTNIK. SERIYA 2: ISTORIYA, YAZYKOZNANIE, LITERATUROVEDENIE. see HISTORY

418.02 BU ISSN 0204-8701
PG831
SAPOSTAVITELNO EZIKOZNANIE/CONTRASTIVE LINGUISTICS. (Text in Bulgarian, English, French, German, Russian, Spanish) 1976. 6/yr. $24. Sofiiski Universitet Sv. Kliment Ohridski, 15 Tsar Osvoboditel Blvd., 1040 Sofia, Bulgaria. Ed. Zivko Bojadziev. adv.; bk.rev.; bibl. circ. 1,000. **Indexed:** Lang.& Lang.Behav.Abstr. (1978-), M.L.A. **Document type:** academic/scholarly publication.
—BLDSC (0166.573000).
Description: Publishes articles, review-articles and news-items in the fields of contrastive linguistics, general linguistics, the theory and practice of translation and history of linguistics.

SARGASSO; theater, film, poetry, performance, criticism. see LITERARY AND POLITICAL REVIEWS

410 MY ISSN 0127-2721
PL5101
SARI. (Text in English and Malay-Indo) 1983. s-a. $15 per no. Penerbit Universiti Kebangsaan Malaysia, 43600 UKM Bangi, Selangor, Malaysia.
Description: Publishes research results in Malay studies. Includes language, linguistics, dialects, traditional and modern literary studies.

440 375.4 CN
SASKATCHEWAN ASSOCIATION OF TEACHERS OF FRENCH. BULLETIN DE SERVICE. irreg. (3-4/yr.). Can.$15. Saskatchewan Teachers' Federation, Box 1108, Saskatoon, SK S7K 3N3, Canada. Ed. Raymond C. Anderson.

440 375.4 RU
SBORNIK STATEI PO FRANTSUZSKOI LINGVISTIKE I METODIKE PREPODAVANIYA INOSTRANNOGO YAZIKA V V U ZE. vol.3, 1971. irreg. 0.35 Rub. Moskovskii Gosudarstvennyi Pedagogicheskii Institut Inostrannykh Yazykov, Rostokinskii pr., 13, Moscow B-14, Russia. bibl.
Description: Presents articles on French language study and teaching.

439 839 US ISSN 0036-5637
PD1505
SCANDINAVIAN STUDIES (EUGENE). 1911. q. $40 (foreign $45). Society for the Advancement of Scandinavian Study, c/o Office of Sec. Treas., 3003 JKHB, Brigham Young University, Provo, UT 84602. TEL 801-378-5598. FAX 801-378-4649. Ed. Steven Sondrup. adv.; bk.rev.; bibl. circ. 1,000. (also avail. in microform from UMI; reprint service avail. from UMI) **Indexed:** Amer.Hist.& Life, Arts & Hum.Cit.Ind., Curr.Cont., Hist.Abstr., Hum.Ind., Ind.Bk.Rev.Hum., M.L.A. **Document type:** academic/scholarly publication.
—BLDSC (8087.650000); Faxon; UnCover; UMI.
Description: Examines scholarly articles on philological and linguistic problems of medieval and modern Scandinavian languages; the literatures of Denmark, the Faeroes, Finland (Finno-Swedish and Finnish), Iceland, Norway, and Sweden; the history, society and culture of the North.

439.7 SW ISSN 0280-7750
SCANDINAVIAN WORKING PAPERS ON BILINGUALISM. Spine title: S W P B. 1982-1990; resumed 1992. irreg. SEK 65 per no. University of Stockholm, Institute of Linguistics, Department of Research on Bilingualism, S-106 91 Stockholm, Sweden. **Document type:** academic/scholarly publication.
—BLDSC (8087.689200).

491.8 891.8 DK ISSN 0080-6765
PG1
SCANDO-SLAVICA. (Text in English, French, German, Italian or Russian) 1955. a. DKK 420. (Association of Scandinavian Slavists and Baltologists) Munksgaard International Publishers Ltd., 35 Noerre Soegade, P.O. Box 2148, DK-1016 Copenhagen K, Denmark. TEL 33-127030. FAX 33-129387. Ed. Erik Egeberg. illus.; index. circ. 600. (reprint service avail. from ISI) **Indexed:** Bibl.Ling., Curr.Cont., M.L.A. —Faxon. **CCC.**
Refereed Serial

430.8 375.4 US ISSN 0740-1965
SCHATZKAMMER; der deutschen Sprache, Dichtung und Geschichte. 1975. s-a. $20. c/o Werner Kitzler, Mg. Ed., Department of Modern Languages, Univ. of S. Dakota, 414 E. Clark St., Vermillion, SD 57069. TEL 605-677-6062. FAX 605-677-5073. Ed. Pamela Saur. adv.; bk.rev.; software rev.; cum. index (1975-1993). circ. 1,000. **Indexed:** Lang.& Lang.Behav.Abstr. **Document type:** academic/scholarly publication.
Description: Provides teachers with practical information, especially with regard to classroom application; feature articles, reports, and news items on language, pedagogy, and "Landeskunde" of the German-speaking countries. Includes poems, short works in creative prose, translations by German-American and reference materials.

491.62 IE ISSN 0790-9853
SCHOOL OF CELTIC STUDIES. NEWSLETTER/SCEALA SCOIL AN LEINN CHEILTIGH. (Text in English and Gaelic) 1987. a. free. Dublin Institute for Advanced Studies, School of Celtic Studies, 10 Burlington Rd., Dublin 4, Ireland. TEL 01-6680748.
FAX 01-6680561. **Indexed:** Bibl.Ling. **Document type:** newsletter.

430 UK ISSN 0048-9492
SCHUSS. (Text in German) 1963. 6/yr. (during school year). Mary Glasgow Magazines (Subsidiary of: Scholastic Publications Ltd.), 140 Freston Rd., London W10 6TR, England. TEL 071-792-3644. FAX 071-792-3172. TELEX 311890-MGPUBS. (U.S. subscr. to: Delta Systems, 1400 Miller Pkwy., McHenry IL 60050-7030. TEL 800-823-8270) (also avail. in microform from UMI; reprint service avail. from UMI, BLH)
—UMI.
Description: Directed to intermediate students of German.

437 GW ISSN 0933-7024
SCHWAEDDS. 1980. s-a. DM.25. Schwaedds Verlag, Charlottenstr. 39, 72764 Reutlingen, Germany. TEL 07121-478700. Ed. Wilhelm Koenig. adv.; bk.rev. circ. 2,000. (back issues avail.) **Document type:** bulletin.
Description: Essays, poetry and fiction on and in German dialects.

491.63 UK ISSN 0264-0198
PR8514
SCOTTISH LANGUAGE. (Text in Scots Gaelic, English) 1982. a. £24 to individuals; institutions £150 (effective May 1992). Association for Scottish Literary Studies, c/o University of Aberdeen, Department of English, Aberdeen AB9 2UB, Scotland. Ed. L.D. McClure. adv. circ. 800. (back issues avail.) **Indexed:** Bibl.Ling.
—BLDSC (8210.653000); UnCover.
Description: Covers all aspects of Scottish languages.

439.69 839.69 SW ISSN 0582-3234
DL301
SCRIPTA ISLANDICA. (Text in English and Scandinavian languages) 1950. a. SEK 75 membership. (Islaendska Saellskapet) Scandinavian University Press, P.O. Box 3255, S-103 65 Stockholm, Sweden. FAX 468-20-9982. (Co-sponsor: Swedish Council for Research in the Humanities and Social Sciences) Ed. Claes Aaneman. bk.rev.; index. circ. 250. **Indexed:** Bibl.Ling.

410 US
SECOND LANGUAGE LEARNING. 1991. irreg. price varies. Ablex Publishing Corporation, 355 Chestnut St., Norwood, NJ 07648. TEL 201-767-8450. FAX 201-767-6717. TELEX 135-393. Ed. Robert J. DiPietro.

410 UK ISSN 0267-6583
SECOND LANGUAGE RESEARCH. 1985. 3/yr. £38.50($66) to individuals; institutions £67.50 ($105) (effective 1994). Edward Arnold (Subsidiary of: Hodder Headline plc), Mill Rd., Dunton Green, Sevenoaks, Kent TN13 2YA, England.
TEL 0732-450111. FAX 0732-461321. (Subscr. to: Turpin Distribution Services Ltd., Blackhorse Rd., Letchworth, Herts. SG6 1HN, England) **Indexed:** Bibl.Ling., Lang.& Lang.Behav.Abstr. (1985-), Lang.Teach.& Ling.Abstr. **Document type:** academic/scholarly publication.
—BLDSC (8216.150050); Faxon; UnCover; SWETS; UMI. **CCC.**
Supersedes: Interlanguage Studies Bulletin.
Description: Provides a forum for investigators in non-native language learning; seeks to promote interdisciplinary research that links aquisition studies to neighbouring theoretical and experimental disciplines.

SEFARAD; revista de estudios Hebraicos, Sefardies y de Oriente Proximo. see HISTORY — History Of The Near East

410 US ISSN 0277-0598
PB11
SELECTA (CORVALLIS). (Text in English, French, German, Italian and Spanish) 1950. a. $12. Pacific Northwest Council on Foreign Languages, c/o Foreign Languages & Literatures, Oregon State Univ., Kidd 210, Corvallis, OR 97331-4603. TEL 503-737-3936. Ed. Craig W. Nickisch. adv. circ. 750. (also avail. in microfiche) **Indexed:** Amer.Bibl.Slavic & E.Eur.Stud, M.L.A. **Document type:** academic/scholarly publication.
—BLDSC (8230.840000).
Former titles: Pacific Northwest Council on Foreign Languages. Proceedings (ISSN 0363-8391); Pacific Northwest Conference on Foreign Languages. Proceedings (ISSN 0078-7612); Pacific Northwest Conference of Foreign Language Teachers. Proceedings.
Description: For language professionals at all levels in Alaska, Alberta, British Columbia, Hawaii, Idaho, Montana, Nevada, Oregon, Utah, Washington, and Wyoming.

439 DK ISSN 0108-822X
PD1506
SELSKAB FOR NORDISK FILOLOGI. AARSBERETNING. 1934. biennial. DKK 100. Selskab for Nordisk Filologi, Dansk Sprognaevn, Njalsgade 80, 2300 Copenhagen S, Denmark. TEL 45-31-54-22-11. FAX 45-31-54-03-60. Ed. Henrik Galberg Jacobsen. circ. 300. **Document type:** proceedings.

499.992 DK ISSN 0108-3759
SEMAJNA BULTENO; Europa semajna Esperanto gazeto. (Text in Esperanto) 1976. irreg. (20-25/yr.). DKK 200. Esperanto Domo, Haslevangsvej 30, DK-8210 Aarhus V, Denmark. Ed. Bent Holm. adv.; bk.rev.; illus.
Formerly: Centra Bulteno (ISSN 0108-450X)

SEMEIA; an experimental journal for biblical criticism. see RELIGIONS AND THEOLOGY

SEMINAR; a journal of Germanic studies. see LITERATURE

494.8 II
SEMINAR ON DRAVIDIAN LINGUISTICS. PROCEEDINGS. irreg., 5th, 1975. Rs.25($5) Annamalai University, Publications Division, Annamalainagar P.O., Tamil Nadu, India. Eds. S. Agesthialingom, P.S. Subrahmanyam. bibl. circ. 1,000. **Document type:** proceedings.

499.92 SP ISSN 0582-6152
SEMINARIO DE FILOLOGIA VASCA JULIO DE URQUIJO. ANUARIO; international journal of Basque linguistics and philology. (Supplement avail.) (Text in English, French, Spanish) 1967. 3/yr. 2000 ptas. to individuals (foreign 3000 ptas.); institutions 4000 ptas. (foreign 5000 ptas.). Seminario de Filologia Vasca Julio de Urquijo, Palacio de la Diputacion de Guipuzcoa, Apdo. 1792, 20080 San Sebastian (Guipuzcoa), Spain. bk.rev. **Indexed:** Bibl.Ling.

499.92 SP
SEMINARIO DE FILOLOGIA VASCA JULIO DE URQUIJO. ANUARIO. SUPLEMENTO. 1955. irreg., no. 18, 1990. price varies. Seminario de Filologia Vasca Julio de Urquijo, Palacio de la Diputacion de Guipuzcoa, Apdo. 1792, 20080 San Sebastian, Spain.

LINGUISTICS

410 US ISSN 0922-5072
SEMIOTIC CROSSROADS. Short title: S.C. 1988. irreg., no.5, 1992. price varies. John Benjamins Publishing Co., 821 Bethlehem Pike, Philadelphia, PA 19118. TEL 215-836-1200. FAX 215-836-1204. (And: Amsteldijk 44, P.O. Box 75577, 1070 AN Amsterdam, Netherlands. TEL 020-6762325) Ed.Bd. **Document type:** monographic series.
—BLDSC (8239.497300).
  Description: Covers current semiotic research in France and abroad.

400 GW ISSN 0037-1998
B820
SEMIOTICA. (Text mainly in English and French; occasionally in German and Russian) 1969. 10/yr. DM.850. (International Association for Semiotic Studies) Walter de Gruyter und Co., Mouton de Gruyter, Genthiner Str. 13, 10785 Berlin, Germany. TEL 030-26005-0. FAX 030-26005251. TELEX 184027. (U.S. addr.: Walter de Gruyter, Inc., 200 Saw Mill River Rd., Hawthorne, NY 10532) Ed. Thomas A. Sebeok. adv.; bk.rev.; cum.index: vols. 1-50. circ. 850. **Indexed:** Arts & Hum.Cit.Ind., Bibl.Ling., Commun.Abstr., Curr.Cont., Film Lit.Ind. (1990-), Ind.Bk.Rev.Hum., Psychol.Abstr., RILA. **Document type:** academic/scholarly publication.
—BLDSC (8239.500000); Faxon; UnCover; SWETS. CCC.

410 US ISSN 1054-8386
SEMIOTICS AND THE HUMAN SCIENCES. irreg. price varies. Peter Lang Publishing, Inc., 62 W. 45th St., 4th Fl., New York, NY 10036. TEL 212-302-6740. Ed. Roberta Kevelson. **Document type:** academic/scholarly publication.

SEMIOTIQUE ET BIBLE. see *RELIGIONS AND THEOLOGY*

492 NE ISSN 0169-9911
SEMITIC STUDY SERIES; new series. (Text in English) 1902; N.S. 1952. irreg., vol.6, 1987. E.J. Brill, P.O. Box 9000, 2300 PA Leiden, Netherlands. TEL 31-71-312624. FAX 31-71-317532. TELEX 39296 BRILL NL. (In N. America: E.J. Brill, 24 Hudson St., Kinderhook, NY 12106. TEL 800-962-4406. FAX 518-758-1959) Eds. R.J.M. Gottmeil, M. Jastrow, Jr. **Document type:** monographic series.
  Description: Anthologies and annotated translations (with glossaries) of inscriptions and texts in ancient Semitic languages, including Old Syriac, Aramaic and cuneiform Ugaritic.
  Refereed Serial

492 GW ISSN 0931-2811
SEMITICA VIVA. 1987. irreg., vol.13, 1993. price varies. Harrassowitz Verlag, Taunusstr. 14, 65183 Wiesbaden, Germany. TEL 0611-530-0. FAX 0611-530570. TELEX 4186135. (Subscr. to: Postfach 2929, 65019 Wiesbaden, Germany) Ed. Otto Jastrow. **Document type:** monographic series.

492 GW ISSN 0935-7556
SEMITICA VIVA - SERIES DIDACTICA. 1989. irreg., vol.2, 1992. price varies. Harrassowitz Verlag, Taunusstr. 14, 65183 Wiesbaden, Germany. TEL 0611-530-0. FAX 0611-530570. (Subscr. to: Postfach 2929, 65019 Wiesbaden, Germany) Ed. Otto Jastrow. **Document type:** monographic series.

460 572 914.6 398 US
SERIE DE VOCABULARIOS Y DICCIONARIOS INDIGENAS "MARIANO SILVA Y ACEVES". (Text in Spanish) 1959. irreg., no.30, 1987. price varies. Summer Institute of Linguistics, Inc., Academic Publications, 7500 W. Camp Wisdom Rd., Dallas, TX 75236. (Or: Box 8987 CRB, Tucson, AZ 85738) Eds. Doris Bartholmew, Louise Schoenhals. bibl. circ. 1,000. (also avail. in microfilm; back issues avail.) **Document type:** academic/scholarly publication.

410 PE ISSN 1022-1506
SERIE LINGUISTICA PERUANA. 1963. irreg., no.31, 1993. price varies. Instituto Lingüistico de Verano, Departamento de Estudios Etno-Lingüisticos, Casilla 2492, Lima 100, Peru. FAX 5114-629-629. (Subscr. to: E. Iturriaga y Cia., Jiron Ica 441, Ofc. 202-203, Casilla 4640, Lima 100, Peru) Ed. Mary Ruth Wise. (also avail. in microfiche; back issues avail.) **Indexed:** Lang.& Lang.Behav.Abstr. (1986-), M.L.A. **Document type:** monographic series.
  Description: Covers in depth, various topics in linguistics. Includes morphology, syntax, phonology and comparative linguistics studies.

SERIES IN ENGLISH LANGUAGE AND LITERATURE. see *LITERATURE*

407 II
SERIES IN INDIAN LANGUAGES AND LINGUISTICS. 1972. irreg. price varies. Bahri Publications, 997-A, Street No. 9, Gondpuri, Kalkaji, New Delhi 110 019, India. TEL 644-5710. Ed. Ujjal Singh Bahri. **Document type:** academic/scholarly publication, monographic series.
  Description: Historical and comparative analyses of Indian languages and literature. Includes teaching materials on Indian languages and scripts.

410 II
SERIES IN INDIAN STUDIES IN THEORETICAL AND APPLIED LINGUISTICS. (Text in English) 1991. irreg. Bahri Publications, 997-A, Street No. 9, Gobindpuri, Kalkaji, P.O. Box 4453, New Delhi 110 019, India. TEL 644-8606. FAX 91-11-64601796. Ed. Rajendra Singh. **Document type:** academic/scholarly publication, monographic series.

410 II
SERIES IN SEMIOTICS AND LINGUISTICS. (Text in English) 1989. irreg. price varies. Bahri Publications, 997-A, Street No. 9, P.O. Box 4453, Gobindpuri, Kalkaji, New Delhi 110 019, India. TEL 644-5710. FAX 91-11-64601796. Ed. Ujjal Singh Bahri. **Document type:** monographic series, academic/scholarly publication.

495.1 375.4 CC
SHIJIE HANYU JIAOXUE/CHINESE TEACHING IN THE WORLD. (Text in Chinese) 1987. q. $24. Beijing Yuyan Xueyuan Chubanshe - Beijing Language Institute Press, Beijing Yuyan Xueyuan, Beijing, People's Republic of China. (Dist. in US by: China Books & Periodicals, Inc., 2929 24th St., San Francisco, CA 94110. TEL 415-282-2994) Ed. Zhu Dexi.

410 CC
SHUOXIE YUEKAN/SPEAKING AND WRITING MONTHLY. (Text in Chinese) m. Beijing Shifan Xueyuan - Beijing Normal Institute, 18 Baiguang Lu, Xuanwu-qu, Beijing 100053, People's Republic of China. TEL 3014150. Ed. Gao Yuan.

410 FR ISSN 0223-0100
P2
SIGMA (AIX-EN-PROVENCE). 1976. a. 98 F. Publications de l'Universite de Provence, 29, av. Robert Schumann, 13621 Aix-en-Provence Cedex 1, France. TEL 42-20-09-16. Ed. Rene Rivara. adv.; bk.rev. circ. 300. **Indexed:** Bibl.Ling.
—BLDSC (8275.360000).
  Description: Devoted to research in linguistics, especially in the English language.

420 375.4 FR
SIGMA (MONTPELLIER). a. Universite de Montpellier III (Universite Paul Valery), Centre d'Etudes Linguistiques d'Aix-Montpellier, B.P. 5043, 34032 Montpellier Cedex 1, France. TEL 67-14-20-00.
  Description: Features articles contributed by research workers belonging to the English department of the universities, dealing with linguistics, and related fields.

419 572 US ISSN 0302-1475
HV2350
SIGN LANGUAGE STUDIES. 1972. q. $40 to individuals in U.S. and Canada (elsewhere $50); institutions $60. Linstok Press, Inc., 4020 Blackburn Lane, Burtonsville, MD 20865-1167. Ed. William C. Stokoe. adv.; bk.rev. circ. 485. (also avail. in diskette format) **Indexed:** A.I.C.P., Bibl.Ling., C.I.J.E., DSH Abstr., ERIC, Except.Child.Educ.Abstr., Lang.Teach.& Ling.Abstr., M.L.A., Psychol.Abstr.
—BLDSC (8275.650000); Faxon; UnCover; SWETS. CCC.
  Description: Covers anthropology, linguistics, psychology, sociology as they are related to sign languages and the deaf population.

410 AG
▼**SIGNO Y SENA.** 1992. s-a. Universidad de Buenos Aires, Instituto de Lingüistica, 25 de Mayo 221, 1002 Buenos Aires, Argentina. Ed. Elvira Narvaja de Arnoux. **Document type:** academic/scholarly publication.

419 UK ISSN 1019-9845
SIGNPOST. q. £25 to individuals; institutions £55. International Sign Linguistics Association, Deaf Studies Research Unit, Dept. of Sociology & Social Policy, University of Durham, Elvet Riverside 2, New Elvet, Durham DH1 3TJ, England. TEL 091-374-4752. FAX 091-374-4743. E-mail: G.H.TURNER@DURHAM.AC.UK. Ed. William Edmondson. adv.
—BLDSC (8276.314180).

469 FR
SILLAGES. (Text in French and Portuguese; summaries in English) 1972. a. 15 F.($4.50) Universite de Poitiers, Departement d'Etudes Portugaises et Bresiliennes, 95 Avenue du Recteur Pineau, 86022 Poitiers, France. Ed. R.A. Lawton. circ. 750.
  Description: Presents articles regarding Portuguese language study and teaching.

428 UK ISSN 0950-9585
SIMPLIFIED SPELLING SOCIETY. JOURNAL. Key Title: Journal of the Simplified Spelling Society. 1985. 3/yr. $20. Simplified Spelling Society, 61 Valentine Rd., Birmingham B14 7AJ, England. FAX 021-359-6153. (U.S. subscr. to: Progressive Publishr, 401 E. 32nd St., Rm. 1002, Chicago, IL 60616. TEL 312-225-9181) Ed. Christopher Upward. bk.rev. circ. 300. **Indexed:** Lang.Teach.& Ling.Abstr. **Document type:** academic/scholarly publication.
—BLDSC (4876.350000).
  Former titles (until 1987): Simplified Spelling Society Newsletter (ISSN 0268-5655); Reading and Spelling.
  Description: Contains research on spelling and campaigns for its reform.

SINO-PLATONIC PAPERS. see *HISTORY — History Of Asia*

SISTEMI INTELLIGENTI; rivista quadrimestrale di scienze cognitive e intelligenza artificiale. see *PSYCHOLOGY*

420 375.4 CN
SKYLARK (SASKATOON). 1964. irreg. Can.$20 to non-members. (Saskatchewan English Teachers' Association) Saskatchewan Teachers' Federation, Box 1108, Saskatoon, SK S7K 3N3, Canada. TEL 306-565-6291. Eds. Mable Fleming, Paulette Hubbs. bk.rev.; bibl. circ. 500.
  Description: Covers English language study and teaching.

491 XR ISSN 0037-6736
SLAVIA; casopis pro slovanskou filologii. (Text in English, French, German, Slavic languages) 1922. q. DM.191. (Czechoslovak Academy of Sciences, Institute of Czech and World Literature) Academia, Publishing House of the Czechoslovak Academy of Sciences, Vodickova 40, 112 29 Prague 1, Czech Republic. TEL 53-83-69. (Dist. in Western countries by: Kubon & Sagner, P.O. Box 34 01 08, 8000 Munich 34, Germany) Ed. Slavomir Wollman. (also avail. in microfiche from BHP) **Indexed:** Bibl.Ling., Lang.& Lang.Behav.Abstr.
  Description: Comparative Slavonic philology, i.e. comparative Slavonic linguistics and literature (history and poetics). Modern methods of linguistic theory, general literature, poetics and stylistics; documents and information.

490 PL ISSN 0081-0002
SLAVIA OCCIDENTALIS. (Text in Czech, Polish, Russian; summaries in French) 1922. irreg., vol.37, 1980. price varies. Poznanskie Towarzystwo Przyjaciol Nauk, Ul. Mielzynskiego 27-29, 61-725 Poznan, Poland. (Dist. by: Ars Polona-Ruch, Krakowskie Przedmiescie 7, Warsaw, Poland) Ed. Wladyslaw Kuraszkiewicz. **Indexed:** Bibl.Ling., Lang.& Lang.Behav.Abstr.

LINGUISTICS

410 375   US   ISSN 0037-6752
PG38.U6
SLAVIC AND EAST EUROPEAN JOURNAL. Abbreviated title: S E E J. 1957. q. $20 to members. American Association of Teachers of Slavic and East European Languages, c/o Prof. George Gutsche, Russian - Modern Languages 340, University of Arizona, Tucson, AZ 85721. TEL 602-621-9765. Ed. Michael Naytan. adv.; bk.rev.; index. circ. 2,100. (also avail. in microform from UMI; back issues avail.) **Indexed:** Amer.Bibl.Slavic & E.Eur.Stud, Arts & Hum.Cit.Ind., Bibl.Ling., C.I.J.E., Curr.Cont., Hum.Ind., Ind.Bk.Rev.Hum., Lang.& Lang.Behav.Abstr., Lang.Teach.& Ling.Abstr., M.L.A. **Document type:** newsletter.
—BLDSC (8309.383000); Faxon; UnCover; UMI.

400 800   SW   ISSN 0081-0010
SLAVICA GOTHOBURGENSIA. (Subseries of Acta Universitatis Gothoburgensis) 1958. irreg., no.7, 1980. price varies; also exchange basis. Acta Universitatis Gothoburgensis, Box 5096, S-402 22 Goeteborg, Sweden. Ed. Gunnar Jacobsson. **Document type:** monographic series.
—BLDSC (8309.387500).

057.1   IS   ISSN 0334-3405
PG1
SLAVICA HIEROSOLYMITANA; Slavic studies of the Hebrew University. (Text in English and Russian) 1973. irreg., latest vol.7. Magnes Press, Hebrew University, Jerusalem, P.O. Box 7695, Jerusalem 91076, Israel. TEL 972-2-660341. FAX 972-2-633370. **Indexed:** Bibl.Ling. **Document type:** monographic series.

491.8 891.8   SW   ISSN 0346-8712
SLAVICA LUNDENSIA. (Text in English, German, Slavic and Swedish; summaries in English and Russian) 1973. a. price varies. Lunds Universitet, Slaviska Institutionen, Finngatan 12, S-223 62 Lund, Sweden. TEL 46-10-88-21. FAX 46-10-88-25. Ed. Lars Steensland. circ. 400. (also avail. in microfilm from UMI; back issues avail.) **Indexed:** Bibl.Ling. **Document type:** academic/scholarly publication.

491   DK   ISSN 0106-1313
PG1
SLAVICA OTHINIENSIA. (Text in Danish, English, French, German, Norwegian, Russian, Swedish) 1978. a. free. Odense Universitet, Center for Slaviske Studier, Campusvej 55, DK-5230 Odense M, Denmark. TEL 009-42-66-158600. FAX 66-15-78-92. Eds. Bent Jensen, Jaroslav Vincenc Pavlik. bk.rev. **Indexed:** Bibl.Ling. **Document type:** academic/scholarly publication.

491 891   XO   ISSN 0037-6787
PG1
SLAVICA SLOVACA. (Text in Slavic languages and in English, French or German; summaries in French, German, Russian) 1966. q. 60 Kcs.($18) (Slovenska Akademia Vied, Jazykovedny Ustav) Veda, Publishing House of the Slovak Academy of Sciences, Klemensova 19, 814 30 Bratislava, Slovakia. (Dist. in Western countries by: John Benjamins B.V., Amsteldijk 44, P.O. Box 75577, 1070 AN Amsterdam, Netherlands. TEL 020-6762325) Ed. Jozef Ruricka. **Indexed:** Bibl.Ling., Can.Rev.Comp.Lit.
Description: Covers literary and linguistic problems. For scientists in the field of Slavistics, Slovak language teachers at secondary schools.

491 890   XV   ISSN 0350-6894
SLAVISTICNA REVIJA; journal for linguistics and literary sciences. (Text in Slovenian; summaries in English, German) 1948. q. $8. Slavisticno Drustvo Slovenije, c/o Filozofska Fakulteta, Askerceva 12, YU-61000 Ljubljana, Slovenia. TEL 061-150-337. FAX 061-159-337. Ed. Franc Zadravec. bk.rev.; bibl. circ. 1,200. **Indexed:** Bibl.Ling., M.L.A., Sociol.Abstr.
—SWETS.

491.7 890   GW   ISSN 0583-5429
SLAVISTISCHE BEITRAEGE. (Text in English and German) 1960. irreg. price varies. Verlag Otto Sagner, Postfach 340108, 80328 Munich, Germany. TEL 089-54218-0. FAX 089-54218218. TELEX 5216711-KUSAD. Ed.Bd. circ. 300. (back issues avail.) **Indexed:** Bibl.Ling. **Document type:** academic/scholarly publication.

491.8   GW   ISSN 0583-5445
SLAVISTISCHE STUDIENBUECHER. NEUE FOLGE. 1984. irreg., vol.3, 1989. price varies. Harrassowitz Verlag, Taunusstr. 14, 65183 Wiesbaden, Germany. TEL 0611-530-0. FAX 0611-530570. TELEX 4186135. (Subscr. to: Postfach 2929, 65019 Wiesbaden, Germany) Ed.Bd. **Document type:** monographic series.

490   RU   ISSN 0134-9023
SLAVYANSKAYA FILOLOGIYA. 1964. irreg. 0.72 Rub. Sankt-Peterburgskii Universitet, Universitetskaya Nab. 7-9, St. Petersburg V-164, Russia. bibl.

SLOVACI V ZAHRANICI. see HISTORY — History Of Europe

SLOVENE STUDIES. see HISTORY — History Of Europe

491.87 891.87   XO   ISSN 0037-6981
PG5201
SLOVENSKA REC/SLOVAK LANGUAGE; casopis pre vyskum a kulturu slovenskeho jazyka. 1933. bi-m. 48 Kcs.($16) (Slovenska Akademia Vied, Jazykovedny Ustav L. Stura) Veda, Publishing House of the Slovak Academy of Sciences, Klemensova 19, 814 30 Bratislava, Slovakia. (Dist. in Western countries by: John Benjamins B.V., Amsteldijk 44, P.O. Box 75577, 1070 AN Amsterdam, Netherlands. TEL 020-676-2325) Ed. Frantisek Kocis. bk.rev.; index. circ. 3,000. **Indexed:** Bibl.Ling., Lang.& Lang.Behav.Abstr., M.L.A.
Description: Devoted to the research of Slovak literary language, correct pronunciation, grammatical structure, word stock and stylistic problems.

400   XO   ISSN 0231-6870
SLOVENSKY JAZYK A LITERATURA V SKOLE. 1953. 5/yr. 20 Kcs. (Ministerstvo Skolstva Slovenskej Republiky) Slovenske Pedagogicke Nakladatelstvo, Sasinkova 5, 815 60 Bratislava, Slovakia. Ed. Netalia Ihnatkova. circ. 2,500. **Indexed:** Bibl.Ling.

491.8   XR   ISSN 0037-7031
SLOVO A SLOVESNOST/WORD AND WRITING; casopis pro otazky teorie a kultury jazyka. (Text mainly in Czech; summaries in English, French, German, Russian) 1935. q. DM.124. (Czechoslovak Academy of Sciences, Institute for Czech Language) Academia, Publishing House of the Czechoslovak Academy of Sciences, Vodickova 40, 112 29 Prague 1, Czech Republic. TEL 53-93-51. (Dist. in Western countries by: Kubon & Sagner, P.O. Box 34 01 08, 8000 Munich 34, Germany) Ed. Marie Tesitelova. bk.rev.; bibl.; charts; illus.; stat.; index, cum.index. circ. 1,400. **Indexed:** Bibl.Ling., M.L.A.
Description: Problems at the grammatical, lexical, phonemic and morphemic levels; problems of stylistics, semantics and semiotics, of text theory and communication theory, problems of translation and theory of verse.

491.79   CN   ISSN 0583-6263
SLOVO NA STOROZHI/WORD ON GUARD. 1964. a. Can.$6($6) Ukrainian Language Association, 911 Carling Ave., Ottawa, ON, Canada. TEL 613-225-4447. Ed. J.B. Rudnyckyj. adv.; bk.rev. circ. 500. (back issues avail.) **Indexed:** M.L.A.

SOCIEDAD DE ESTUDIOS VASCOS. CUADERNOS DE SECCION. LENGUA Y LITERATURA. see LITERATURE

469   PO   ISSN 0049-1039
SOCIEDADE DE LINGUA PORTUGUESA. BOLETIM. vol.26, 1975. bi-m. Esc.300. Sociedade de Lingua Portuguesa, Rua S. Jose 41-2, Lisbon, Portugal. Eds. Guilherme Matos, Aldina de Araujo Oliveira. adv.; bk.rev.; abstr.; bibl. circ. 7,000.

490   GW   ISSN 0340-6423
SOCIETAS URALO-ALTAICA. VEROEFFENTLICHUNGEN. 1969. irreg., vol.37, 1993. price varies. Harrassowitz Verlag, Taunusstr. 14, 65183 Wiesbaden, Germany. TEL 0611-530-0. FAX 0611-530570. TELEX 4186135. (Subscr. to: Postfach 2929, 65019 Wiesbaden, Germany) Eds. A.V. Gabain, W. Veenker. **Document type:** monographic series.

475   SP   ISSN 0213-4098
SOCIETAT D'ONOMASTICA. BUTLLETI INTERIOR. (Text in Catalan; occasionally in French or Spanish) 1980. q. membership. Societat d'Onomastica, Palau Dalmases, Montcada, 20, pral., 08003 Barcelona, Spain. TEL 93-212-7546. bk.rev.
Description: Lists the works and research projects of the society's members in the field of onomastics.

410 301.2   FR   ISSN 0249-7069
SOCIETE D'ETUDES LINGUISTIQUES ET ANTHROPOLOGIQUES DE FRANCE. NUMERO SPECIAL. (Supplement to: Bibliotheque de la S E L A F) 1971. irreg., no.24, 1992. price varies. Societe d'Etudes Linguistiques et Anthropologiques de France (SELAF), 52 bd. St. Michel, 75006 Paris, France. TEL 42-08-83-93. (Dist. by: Editions Peeters s.p.r.l., Bondgenotenlaan 153, B-3000 Louvain, Belgium. TEL 32-16-235170. FAX 32-16-228500) **Document type:** monographic series, proceedings.

SOCIETE DE BIBLIOLOGIE ET DE SCHEMATISATION. DOSSIERS. see LITERATURE

406   FR   ISSN 0037-9069
P12
SOCIETE DE LINGUISTIQUE DE PARIS. BULLETIN. (Text in English and French) 1865. s-a. price varies. Editions Klincksieck, 11 rue de Lille, 75005 Paris, France. bk.rev.; abstr.; charts; index. circ. 1,200. (also avail. in microform from BHP) **Indexed:** Bibl.Ling., M.L.A.
—SWETS; UMI.

SOCIETE DES AMERICANISTES. JOURNAL. see ANTHROPOLOGY

SOCIETE FINNO-OUGRIENNE. MEMOIRES/SUOMALAIS-UGRILAISEN SEURAN. TOIMITUKSIA. see ANTHROPOLOGY

400   FI   ISSN 0355-0192
PB10
SOCIETE NEOPHILOLOGIQUE DE HELSINKI. MEMOIRES. (Text in English, French, German) 1893. irreg. price varies. Uusifilologinen Yhdistys - Modern Language Society, Porthania, PL 4 (Hallituskatu 11), 00014 Helsingin Yliopisto, Finland. Ed. Marjatta Wis. cum.index. circ. 500. (back issues avail.) **Document type:** academic/scholarly publication, monographic series.

SOCIETY FOR SLOVENE STUDIES. DOCUMENTATION SERIES. see HISTORY — History Of Europe

410   US
SOCIETY OF FEDERAL LINGUISTS. NEWSLETTER. 1946. irreg., approx. 9/yr. membership. Society of Federal Linguists, Inc., Box 7765, Washington, DC 20044. Ed. E.E. Larson. bk.rev.; circ. 150 (controlled). **Document type:** newsletter.

410 572   FR   ISSN 0295-0251
SOCIOLINGUISTIQUE; systemes de langues et interactions sociales et culturelles. (Subseries of: Bibliotheque de la S E L A F) 1984. irreg., no.6, 1992. price varies. Societe d'Etudes Linguistiques et Anthropologiques de France (SELAF), 52 bd. St. Michel, 75006 Paris, France. TEL 42-08-83-93. (Dist. by: Editions Peeters s.p.r.l., Bondgenotenlaan 153, B-3000 Louvain, Belgium. TEL 32-16-235170. FAX 32-16-228500) Ed. Jean Pierre Caprile. adv.; bk.rev. circ. 500. **Document type:** academic/scholarly publication.

410   PL   ISSN 0208-6808
SOCJOLINGWISTYKA. (Text in Polish; summaries in English, Russian) 1977. a. price varies. Polska Akademia Nauk, Instytut Jezyka Polskiego - Polish Academy of Sciences, Institute of Polish Language, Ul. Straszewskiego 27, 31-113 Krakow, Poland. Ed. Wladyslaw Lubas. **Indexed:** Bibl.Ling.
Description: Studies on social aspects of linguistics and verbal communications.

410   BU
SOFIISKI UNIVERSITET. FAKULTET PO KLASICESKI I NOVI FILOLOGII. GODISNIK/UNIVERSITE DE SOFIA. FACULTE DES LETTRES CLASSIQUES ET MODERNES. ANNUAIRE. (Text in various languages) irreg., vol.71, 1976. price varies. Publishing House of the Bulgarian Academy of Sciences, Acad. G. Bonchev St., Bldg. 6, 1113 Sofia, Bulgaria. bibl. circ. 550. (reprint service avail. from IRC) **Indexed:** Bibl.Ling.
Formerly: Sofiiski Universitet. Fakultet po Zapadni Filologii. Godisnik (ISSN 0584-0252)

491   BU   ISSN 0081-1831
PG1
SOFIISKI UNIVERSITET. FAKULTET PO SLAVIANSKA FILOLOGII. GODISHNIK. (Text in various languages) irreg., vol.63, 1970. price varies. Publishing House of the Bulgarian Academy of Sciences, Acad. G. Bonchev St., Bldg. 6, 1113 Sofia, Bulgaria. Ed. I. Duridanov. bibl. circ. 550. (reprint service avail. from IRC) **Indexed:** Bibl.Ling.

LINGUISTICS

460.07 370   UK   ISSN 0038-0849
EL SOL. (Text in Spanish) 1963. 6/yr. (during school year). £11.75 (effective 1994). Mary Glasgow Magazines (Subsidiary of: Scholastic Publications Ltd.), 140 Freston Rd., London W10 6TR, England. TEL 071-792-3644. FAX 071-792-3172. TELEX 311890-MGPUBS. (U.S. subscr. to: Delta Systems, 1400 Miller Pkwy., McHenry IL 60050-7030. TEL 800-823-8270) charts; illus. circ. 28,000. (also avail. in microfilm from UMI; reprint service avail. from UMI)
—UMI.
    Incorporates (in Jun. 1993): Hoy Dia (ISSN 0018-6856)
    Description: Aims to motivate and educate advanced intermediate-level students of Spanish.

410   CH   ISSN 0259-3777
P9
SOOCHOW JOURNAL OF FOREIGN LANGUAGES AND LITERATURES. Key Title: Dongwu Waiyu Xuebao. (Text in Chinese, English, German, and Japanese) 1985. a. $15. Soochow University, Wai Shuang Hsi, Shih Lin, Taipei, Taiwan, Republic of China. FAX 886-02-8812317. (reprint service avail.) **Document type:** academic/scholarly publication.

440 375.4   US
SOUND AND MEANING; the Roman Jakobson series in linguistics and poetry. 1989. irreg. Duke University, Box 90660, Durham, NC 27708. TEL 919-688-5134. FAX 919-688-4574. Ed. C.H. Van Schooneveld.

496 896   SA   ISSN 0257-2117
    CODEN: SAJLEA
SOUTH AFRICAN JOURNAL OF AFRICAN LANGUAGES. (Text in English) 1981. q. R.80. (African Languages Association of Southern Africa) Foundation for Education, Science & Technology, P.O. Box 1758, Pretoria 0001, South Africa. TEL 27-12-322-6422. Ed. G.J. van Jaarsveld. circ. 620. **Indexed:** Bibl.Ling., Ind.S.A.Per., Sp.Ed.Needs Abstr. **Document type:** academic/scholarly publication.
—CCC.

401   SA   ISSN 1011-8063
SOUTH AFRICAN JOURNAL OF LINGUISTICS/SUID-AFRIKANNSE TYDSKRIF VIR TAALKUNDE. (Text and summaries in Afrikaans, English) 1983. q. R.80. (Linguistics Association of South Africa) Foundation for Education, Science & Technology, P.O. Box 1758, Pretoria 0001, South Africa. TEL 27-12-322-6422. Ed. G.J. van Jaarsveld. adv.; bk.rev. circ. 300. (back issues avail.) **Indexed:** Bibl.Ling. **Document type:** academic/scholarly publication.
    Formerly: Taalfassette.
    Description: Aims to propriate the study of research into Afrikaans, English and Dutch linguistics in South Africa.

SOUTH ASIAN REVIEW. see LITERATURE

406   US   ISSN 0277-335X
PB1
SOUTH ATLANTIC REVIEW. 1935. 4/yr. $30 (effective 1994). South Atlantic Modern Language Association, Drawer 6109, Univ. Sta., Tuscaloosa, AL 35486-6109. FAX 205-348-5298. Ed. Robert F. Bell. adv. contact: Christel Bell. bk.rev.; bibl.; index. circ. 4,300. (also avail. in microfilm from UMI; reprint service avail. from ISI,UMI) **Indexed:** Abstr.Engl.Stud., Amer.Bibl.Slavic & E.Eur.Stud., Amer.Hum.Ind., Arts & Hum.Cit.Ind., Curr.Cont., M.L.A. **Document type:** academic/scholarly publication.
—BLDSC (8348.672000); Faxon; UnCover; UMI.
    Formerly (until 1981): South Atlantic Bulletin.

428.3 380   US   ISSN 1041-794X
PN4071
SOUTHERN COMMUNICATION JOURNAL. 1935. q. $15. Southern States Communication Association, c/o Susan A. Siltanen, Exec. Sec., S.S. Box 5131, University of Southern Mississippi, Speech Communication Department, Hattiesburg, MS 39406-5131. Ed. Keith Erickson. adv.; bk.rev.; illus.; index. circ. 2,500. (also avail. in microform from KTO,UMI; reprint service avail. from KTO) **Indexed:** Abstr.Engl.Stud., Amer.Hist.& Life, C.I.J.E., Commun.Abstr., Hist.Abstr., Ind.Bk.Rev.Hum., Lang.& Lang.Behav.Abstr., Sociol.Abstr.
—BLDSC (8352.980000); Faxon; UnCover; UMI.
    Former titles (until 1988): Southern States Communication Journal; Southern Speech Communication Journal (ISSN 0361-8269); Southern Speech Journal (ISSN 0038-4585)

410   US   ISSN 0737-4143
P1
SOUTHWEST JOURNAL OF LINGUISTICS. (With occasional supplemental issues) (Text mainly in English; occasionally in Spanish) 1975. a. $15 to individuals; institutions $30. University of North Texas and Linguistics Association of the Southwest, University of North Texas, Department of English, Denton, TX 76203-3827. TEL 505-277-7416. FAX 505-277-6355. (Subscr. to: c/o Garland Bills, LASSO, Department of Linguistics, Univ. of New Mexico, Albuquerque, NM 871131) Ed. Alan J. Hudson. adv.; bk.rev. circ. 300. (back issues avail.) **Indexed:** Abstr.Anthropol., Bibl.Ling., Lang.& Lang.Behav.Abstr. (1975-), M.L.A. **Document type:** academic/scholarly publication.
    Formerly: Linguistic Association of the Southwest Journal.
    Description: Contains articles on all areas of linguistics, particularly of the Southwestern U.S.
Refereed Serial

SPANISH STUDIES; modern literature, history and politics. see LITERATURE

460   US   ISSN 0049-1802
SPANISH TODAY. (Text in English and Spanish) 1968. bi-m. $15. Cruzada Spanish Publications, Box 650909, Miami, FL 33265. Ed. Andres Rivero. adv.; bk.rev.; charts; illus.; tr.lit. circ. 10,000. (also avail. in microform from UMI; reprint service avail. from UMI)
—UMI. CCC.

460   DK   ISSN 0109-307X
SPANSKLAERERFORENINGEN. INFORMATIONER. no.6, 1981. q. membership. Spansklaererforeningen, c/o Birgit Christiansen, Overgaden oven Vandet 102, 1.th., 1415 Copenhagen K, Denmark. adv.; illus. circ. 250. **Document type:** bulletin.
    Description: Covers Spanish language study and teaching.

491.7 890   GW   ISSN 0170-1320
SPECIMINA PHILOLOGIAE SLAVICAE. (Text in English, German, Russian and other Slavic languages) 1972. irreg. price varies. Verlag Otto Sagner, Postfach 340108, 80328 Munich, Germany. TEL 089-54218-0. FAX 089-54218218. TELEX 5216711-KUSAD. Eds. Olexa Horbatsch, Gerd Freihof. circ. 100. (back issues avail.) **Indexed:** Bibl.Ling. **Document type:** monographic series.

410   NE   ISSN 0167-6393
    CODEN: SCOMDH
SPEECH COMMUNICATION. 1982. 8/yr. (in 2 vols.; 4 nos./vol.). fl.752($406) (effective 1994). (European Association for Signal Processing) North-Holland (Subsidiary of: Elsevier Science B.V.), P.O. Box 211, 1000 AE Amsterdam, Netherlands. TEL 31-20-5803911. FAX 31-20-5803598. TELEX 18582 ESPA NL. (Subscr. in U.S. and Canada to: Elsevier Science Inc., Box 882, Madison Sq. Sta., New York, NY 10159. TEL 212-989-5800. FAX 212-633-3990) (Co-sponsor: European Speech Communication Association) Ed. Max Wajskop. (back issues avail.) **Indexed:** Lang.& Lang.Behav.Abstr., Lang.Teach.& Ling.Abstr., Psychol.Abstr., Sci.Abstr., SSCI, Tel.Abstr. **Document type:** academic/scholarly publication.
—BLDSC (8411.196000); EI; Faxon; UnCover; SWETS. CCC.
    Description: Covers all theoretical and experimental aspects of speech communication processes. Details speech production, transmission and perception, person to machine communication, phonetics, linguistics, as well as speech and hearing defects and aids.
Refereed Serial

440   FR
SPICAE; cahiers de l'atelier Vincent de Beauvais. 1978. irreg. price varies. (Universite de Nancy II, Centre de Recherches et d'Applications Linguistiques) C N R S Editions, 20-22 rue St. Amand, 75015 Paris, France. TEL 45-33-16-00. FAX 45-33-92-13. TELEX 200 356 F. (Co-sponsor: Institut de Recherche et d'Histoire des Textes) Eds. Helene Nais, Jean Schneider. adv.; bk.rev.; index; circ. 1,500 (controlled).

420.07 370   UK   ISSN 0038-772X
LB1576.A1   CODEN: SPEGE7
SPOKEN ENGLISH; ideas and developments in oral education. 1968. 2/yr. £10. English Speaking Board (International) Ltd., 26a Princes Street, Southport, Merseyside PR8 1EQ, England. TEL 0704-501730. FAX 0704-539637. Ed. Malcolm Dale. adv.; bk.rev.; bibl.; charts; cum.index every 5 yrs. circ. 1,200. **Indexed:** Lang.Teach.& Ling.Abstr. **Document type:** academic/scholarly publication.
—BLDSC (8417.600000).
    Description: Covers English language study and teaching, ideas and developments in oral education, and training in oral communication.

439.5   SW   ISSN 0108-8270
SPRAAK I NORDEN/SPROG I NORDEN. 1970. a. SEK 55. (Nordisk Spraaksekretariat) Almqvist & Wiksell, P.O. Box 1342, S-171 26 Solna, Sweden.

410   NO   ISSN 0333-3825
SPRAAKNYTT. 1973. q. free. Norsk spraakraad - Norwegian Language Council, Postboks 8107 Dep, 0032 Oslo, Norway. TEL 47-22-42-40-20. FAX 47-22-42-76-76. Eds. Dag Gundersen, Kjell Venaas. bk.rev. circ. 20,000. **Document type:** bulletin.
—CCC.
    Description: Presents articles about Norway's two official languages (Nynorsk and Bokmaal); information about new words and approved spellings, and readers' questions.

400   SW   ISSN 0038-8440
PD5004
SPRAAKVAARD. (Text in Danish, Norwegian, Swedish) 1965. q. SEK 110 (typically set in Jan.). Svenska Spraaknaemnden, Lundagatan 42, S-117 27 Stockholm, Sweden. TEL 46-8-668-01-53. FAX 46-8-720-6805. Ed. Margareta Westman. bk.rev.; cum.index. circ. 5,000. (back issues avail.) **Document type:** academic/scholarly publication, bulletin.
    Description: Treats the changes and the evaluation of changes in modern Swedish.

400   GW   ISSN 0038-8459
SPRACHDIENST. 1957. bi-m. DM.60. Gesellschaft fuer deutsche Sprache e.V., Taunusstr. 11, 65183 Wiesbaden, Germany. TEL 0611-520031. FAX 0611-51313. Ed. H. Walther. adv.; bk.rev.; index, cum.index: 1957-1972. circ. 3,200. **Indexed:** M.L.A. **Document type:** academic/scholarly publication.

400   GW   ISSN 0038-8467
DIE SPRACHE; Zeitschrift fuer Sprachwissenschaft. (Text in English, French, German) 1949. 2/yr. DM.128. Harrassowitz Verlag, Taunusstr. 14, 65183 Wiesbaden, Germany. TEL 0611-530-0. FAX 0611-530570. TELEX 4186135. (Subscr. to: Postfach 2929, 65019 Wiesbaden, Germany) Eds. Jochem Schindler, Martin Peters. adv.; bk.rev.; charts; illus.; index. circ. 550. (reprint service avail. from SWZ) **Indexed:** Bibl.Ling., Lang.& Lang.Behav.Abstr. (1972-), Numis.Lit. **Document type:** academic/scholarly publication.
—SWETS.

400   SZ   ISSN 0081-3826
SPRACHE UND DICHTUNG. NEUE FOLGE. 1956. irreg., vol.41, 1990. price varies. Paul Haupt AG, Falkenplatz 14, CH-3001 Bern, Switzerland. TEL 031-3012345. FAX 031-3014669. Ed.Bd. **Indexed:** M.L.A. **Document type:** monographic series.
—CCC.

496   GW   ISSN 0170-5946
PL8000
SPRACHE UND GESCHICHTE IN AFRIKA. Short title: S U G I A. (Text in English, French, German) 1979-1993. irreg., approx. a price varies. (Universitaet Bayreuth, Koeln, Institut fuer Afrikanistik) Helmut Buske Verlag GmbH, Richardstr. 47, 22081 Hamburg, Germany. TEL 040-296842. FAX 040-2993614. **Indexed:** Anthropol.Lit., Bibl.Ling. **Document type:** monographic series.

410   GW   ISSN 0047-472X
P51
SPRACHE UND LITERATUR IN WISSENSCHAFT. 1970. s-a. DM.50. Verlag Ferdinand Schoeningh GmbH, Postfach 2540, 33055 Paderborn, Germany. TEL 05251-127665. FAX 05251-127860. Ed. Annamaria Rucktaeschel. adv.; bk.rev.; bibl. **Indexed:** Lang.& Lang.Behav.Abstr., Lang.Teach.& Ling.Abstr., M.L.A. **Document type:** academic/scholarly publication.
Formerly (until 1978): Linguistik und Didaktik (Paderborn).
Description: Publication devoted to studies in language and linguistics, including language interpretation and use of speech.

430 830   GW
SPRACHE UND LITERATUR IN WISSENSCHAFT UND UNTERRICHT. s-a. DM.48. Verlag Ferdinand Schoeningh GmbH, Juehenplatz 1-3, 33098 Paderborn, Germany. TEL 05251-29010. FAX 05251-290160. (Co-publisher: Wilhelm Fink Verlag) Ed.Bd. index. circ. 2,000. (back issues avail.) **Indexed:** Can.Rev.Comp.Lit., M.L.A. **Document type:** academic/scholarly publication.
—CCC.
Formerly: Linguistik und Didaktik (Munich) (ISSN 0724-9713)

400   GW   ISSN 0038-8505
PB38.G39
DER SPRACHMITTLER; Informationshefte des Sprachendienstes der Bundeswehr. 1963. q. free. Bundesministerium der Verteidigung, S III 4, Postfach 1328, 53003 Bonn, Germany. Ed.Bd. bk.rev.; bibl.; charts. circ. 2,200. **Indexed:** Lang.Teach.& Ling.Abstr.

430   GW   ISSN 0178-644X
SPRACHREPORT; Informationen und Meinungen zur deutschen Sprache. 1986. q. DM.21. Institut fuer Deutsche Sprache, Mannheim, Postfach 101621, 68016 Mannheim, Germany. TEL 0621-15810. FAX 0621-1581200. Ed. Dr. Bernd Biere. bk.rev. circ. 2,000. (back issues avail.) **Document type:** academic/scholarly publication.
Description: Information about German language, communication and linguistics.

430   SZ   ISSN 0038-8513
PF3003
SPRACHSPIEGEL; Schweizerische Zeitschrift fuer die deutsche Muttersprache. 1945. bi-m. 60 SFr. Schweizerischer Verein fuer die Deutsche Sprache, Alpenstr. 7, CH-6004 Lucerne, Switzerland. TEL 041-511910. FAX 041-528678. Ed. Werner Frick. adv. contact: Werner Frick. bk.rev.; index. circ. 1,350. **Indexed:** M.L.A. **Document type:** newsletter.

410   GW   ISSN 0344-8169
SPRACHWISSENSCHAFT. 1977. q. DM.148 (student price DM.120). Universitaetsverlag C. Winter Heidelberg GmbH, Hans-Bunte-Str. 18, 69123 Heidelberg, Germany. Ed.Bd. **Indexed:** Arts & Hum.Cit.Ind., Bibl.Ling., M.L.A. **Document type:** academic/scholarly publication.
—Faxon; SWETS.

410   US   ISSN 0172-620X
SPRINGER SERIES IN LANGUAGE AND COMMUNICATION. 1978. irreg. price varies. Springer-Verlag, 175 Fifth Ave., New York, NY 10010. TEL 212-460-1500. FAX 212-473-6272. (Also: Berlin, Heidelberg, Tokyo and Vienna) Ed. W.J.M. Levelt. (reprint service avail. from ISI) **Document type:** monographic series.
—BLDSC (8424.766500).

407   DK   ISSN 0107-2706
SPROG OG ERHVERV. 1970. 10/yr. membership. Erhvervssprogligt Forbund, P.O. Box 2246, Skindergade 45-47, DK-1019 Copenhagen K, Denmark. TEL 45-33-91-98-00. FAX 45-33-91-68-18. Eds. Jeannette Oersted, Anna Dalsgaard. adv.: B&W page DKK 8000, color page DKK 14570; trim 247 x 181. bk.rev. circ. 11,000. **Document type:** academic/scholarly publication.
Formerly (until 1978): Korrespondenten (ISSN 0107-2714)

410   DK   ISSN 0108-433X
SPROG OG SAMFUND. 1982. q. DKK 50. Modersmaal Selskabet, c/o Gerda Thastum Leffers, Skolebakken 81, DK-2830 Virum, Denmark. Ed. Rasmus Bjoergmose. bk.rev.
Description: Articles, news, reviews relating to the activities of the Mothertongue Society and the Danish language in general.

410   DK
SPROGFORENINGENS ALMANAK. 1984. a. DKK 38. (Sprogforeningen) Dy-Po Bogforlag, Soenderborg, Denmark. (Dist. by: Boghendleres Kommissionsanstalt, Siljangade 6, 2300 Copenhagen S, Denmark)

410
SPUDASMATA; Studien zur Klassischen Philologie und ihren Grenzgebieten. irreg., vol.52, 1993. DM.39.80. Georg Olms Verlag, Hagentorwall 7, 31134 Hildesheim, Germany. TEL 05121-1501-0. FAX 05121-150150. (U.S. subscr. to: 111 W. 57th St., New York, NY 10019. TEL 212-757-5237) Eds. Gottfried Kiefner, Ulrich Koepf. **Document type:** monographic series.

491.1 891.1   II   ISSN 0081-3915
SRI VENKATESWARA UNIVERSITY. DEPARTMENT OF SANSKRIT. SYMPOSIUM. (Text in Sanskrit and English) 1962. irreg., no.4, 1967. Rs.4. Sri Venkateswara University, Department of Sanskrit, Tirupati, Andhra Pradesh, India. Ed. E.R. Sreekrishna Sarma.

SRI VENKATESWARA UNIVERSITY. ORIENTAL JOURNAL. see HISTORY — History Of Asia

400   YU   ISSN 0081-3958
SRPSKA AKADEMIJA NAUKA I UMETNOSTI. ODELJENJE JEZIKA I KNJIZEVNOSTI. GLAS. (Text in Serbo-Croatian; summaries in French, English, German or Russian) N.S. 1951. irreg. price varies. Srpska Akademija Nauka i Umetnosti, Knez Mihailova 35, 11001 Belgrade, Serbia, Yugoslavia. FAX 38-11-182-825. TELEX 72593 SANU YU. (Dist. by: Prosveta, Terazije 16, Belgrade, Serbia, Yugoslavia) circ. 1,000. **Indexed:** Amer.Hist.& Life, Hist.Abstr.

SRPSKA AKADEMIJA NAUKA I UMETNOSTI. ODELJENJE JEZIKA I KNJIZEVNOSTI. POSEBNA IZDANJA. see LITERATURE

407   YU   ISSN 0350-1906
SRPSKI DIJALEKTOLOSKI ZBORNIK. (Text in Serbo-Croatian; summaries in English, French, German, Russian) 1905. a. 1000 din.($34) Srpska Akademija Nauka i Umetnosti, Institut za Srpskohrvatski Jezik - Serbian Academy of Sciences and Arts, Knez Mihailova 35, 11000 Belgrade, Serbia, Yugoslavia. TEL 011-636-590. Ed. Pavle Ivic. bk.rev. circ. 800. **Indexed:** Bibl.Ling.
Description: Papers about Serbo-Croatian languages, other languages spoken in Yugoslavia, Slavic linguistics and general linguistics.

STEM-, SPRAAK- EN TAALPATHOLOGIE. see MEDICAL SCIENCES — Psychiatry And Neurology

STIPENDIEN FUER SPRACHKURSE. see CHILDREN AND YOUTH — For

420   SW
STOCKHOLM STUDIES IN ENGLISH. (Subseries of Acta Universitatis Stockholmiensis) (Text in English) 1937. irreg. price varies. (Stockholms Universitet) A W I International AB, P.O. Box 4627, S-116 91 Stockholm, Sweden. TEL 468-40-8800. FAX 468-641-1180. Eds. Alarik Rynell, Lennart A. Bjork. (back issues avail.) **Indexed:** Bibl.Ling., M.L.A.

400   CI
STRANI JEZICI. 1972. q. 240 din. (Hrvatsko Filolosko Drustvo, Institut za Lingvistiku) Skolska Knjiga, Masarykova 28, Zagreb, Croatia. TEL 41 458-511. Ed. Mirjana Vilke. adv.; bk.rev.; illus.; index. circ. 2,600. **Indexed:** Lang.Teach.& Ling.Abstr.

491.9 891.9   IT   ISSN 0081-6116
STUDI ALBANESI. STUDI E TESTI. 1965. irreg., no.6, 1986. price varies. (Universita degli Studi di Roma, Istituto Studi Albanesi) Casa Editrice Leo S. Olschki, Casella Postale 66, 50100 Florence, Italy. TEL 055-6530684. FAX 055-6530214. Ed. Ernesto Koliqi. circ. 1,000. **Document type:** monographic series.

400   IT
STUDI DI FILOLOGIA ITALIANA. 1927. a., vol.50, 1992. L.80000 (foreign L.110000). (Accademia della Crusca) Licosa S.p.A, Via Duca di Calabria 1-1, 50125 Florence, Italy. **Indexed:** Bibl.Ling.

410   IT
STUDI DI GRAMMATICA ITALIANA. 1971. a., vol.14, 1990. L.70000 (foreign L.100000). (Accademia della Crusca) Licosa S.p.A, Via Duca di Calabria 1-1, 50125 Florence, Italy. **Indexed:** Bibl.Ling., Lang.& Lang.Behav.Abstr. (1977-).

410   IT
STUDI DI LESSICOGRAFIA ITALIANA. 1979. a., vol.11, 1991. L.70000 (foreign L.100000). (Accademia della Crusca) Licosa S.p.A, Via Duca di Calabria 1-1, 50125 Florence, Italy. **Indexed:** Bibl.Ling.

450   IT   ISSN 0049-2361
P47
STUDI E PROBLEMI DI CRITICA TESTUALE. 1970. s-a. L.18000. Via Castiglione 8, 40124 Bologna, Italy. Ed. R. Raffaele Spongano. adv.; bk.rev.; bibl. circ. 600. **Indexed:** Arts & Hum.Cit.Ind., Curr.Cont., M.L.A.

410   IT   ISSN 0085-6827
STUDI E SAGGI LINGUISTICI; supplemento alla rivista l'Italia dialettale. (Text in Italian; summaries in English) 1961. a. L.10000. (Universita degli Studi di Pisa, Istituto di Glottologia) Giardini Editori e Stampatori, Via Santa Bibbiana 28, 56100 Pisa, Italy. TEL 050 502531. Ed. Tristano Bolelli. index. circ. 350. **Indexed:** Bibl.Ling., M.L.A.

440   IT   ISSN 0039-2944
PQ5
STUDI FRANCESI; cultura e civilta letteraria della Francia. (Text in English, French, Italian) 1957. 3/yr. L.125000 (Europe L.140000; elsewhere L.200000) (effective 1993). (Universita degli Studi di Torino, Facolta di Lettere e Filosofia, Istituto di Lingua e Letteratura Francese) Rosenberg & Sellier, Via Andrea Doria 14, 10123 Turin, Italy. TEL 011-561-39-07. FAX 011-532188. Ed. Giorgio Calcagno. bk.rev.; abstr. circ. 1,250. (back issues avail.) **Indexed:** Arts & Hum.Cit.Ind., CERDIC, Curr.Cont., M.L.A.
—Faxon; SWETS.
Description: Covers French civilization and culture. Includes historic studies, French literature and research.

450   IT   ISSN 0039-2987
PA9
STUDI ITALIANI DI FILOLOGIA CLASSICA. 1893; N.S. 1920. s-a. L.100000($95) (effective 1992). Editoriale e Finanziaria Le Monnier, S.p.a., Via A. Meucci 2, Casella Postale 202, 50100 Florence, Italy. Dirs. Umberto Albini, Marcello Gigante. index. (also avail. in microform from SWZ; reprint service avail. from SWZ) **Indexed:** Bibl.Ling.
—UnCover; SWETS.
Description: Covers Classical studies; evaluates how the classical period is related historically to the present.

LINGUISTICS

450   IT   ISSN 0390-6809
P1.A1
STUDI ITALIANI DI LINGUISTICA TEORICA ED APPLICATA. (Text in English, French or Italian) 1972. 3/yr. L.65000. (Universita degli Studi di Bologna, Centro Interfacolta de Linguistica Teorica e Applicata) Liviana Editrice s.r.l., Via Luigi Dottesio 1, 35100 Padua, Italy. TEL 049-8710099. FAX 049-8710261. Ed. Enrico Arcaini. bk.rev.; bibl. circ. 1,500. **Indexed:** Bibl.Ling., Lang.& Lang.Behav.Abstr. (1972-), Lang.Teach.& Ling.Abstr., M.L.A.
—UnCover; SWETS.

400   IT
STUDI LATINI E ITALIANI. 1986. a. $60. (Universita di Roma "La Sapienza", Facolta di Magistero) Herder Editrice e Libreria s.r.l., Piazza Montecitorio, 120, 00186 Rome, Italy. TEL 67-94628. FAX 678-47-51. TELEX 66784751. Ed. V. Ussani. circ. 500. **Document type:** academic/scholarly publication.

450   IT
STUDI LINGUISTICI SALENTINI.* 1965. Associazione Linguistica Salentina, Villa Sebaste, Via per Campi, 73051, Novoli (Lecce), Italy. illus.

410   IT
STUDI MEDIOLATINI E VOLGARI. 1955? a. L.95000 (foreign L.105000) (effective 1994). Pacini Editore s.r.l., Via A. Gherardesca 1, 56014 Ospedaletto (Pisa), Italy. TEL 050-982439. FAX 050-983906. Ed. Valeria Bertolucci. **Indexed:** Bibl.Ling.

420   PL   ISSN 0081-6272
PE1
STUDIA ANGLICA POSNANIENSIA; international review of English Studies. (Text in English) 1969. irreg., vol.25, 1993. price varies. Adam Mickiewicz University Press, Nowowiejskiego 55, 61-734 Poznan, Poland. TEL 527-380. FAX 61-526425. TELEX 413260 UAMPL. Ed. Jacek Fisiak. adv.; bk.rev. circ. 1,300. **Indexed:** Bibl.Ling., Lang.& Lang.Behav.Abstr., Lang.Teach.& Ling.Abstr., M.L.A. **Document type:** academic/scholarly publication.
—BLDSC (8482.361000).
Description: Carries original articles and papers about English linguistics; studies American and English literature.

420   SW   ISSN 0562-2719
STUDIA ANGLISTICA UPSALIENSES. (Subseries of Acta Universitatis Upsaliensis) 1963. irreg. price varies. A W I International AB, P.O. Box 4627, S-116 91 Stockholm, Sweden. TEL 468-640-8800. FAX 468-641-1180. Ed.Bd. (back issues avail.) **Indexed:** Abstr.Engl.Stud., Bibl.Ling.

410 929   SW   ISSN 0280-8633
CS2567
STUDIA ANTHROPONYMICA SCANDINAVICA; tidskrift foer nordisk personnamnsforskning. (Text in English, German, Scandinavian languages; summaries in English) 1983. a. SEK 210 in Sweden; Scandinavia SEK 180; elsewhere SEK 195. Studia Anthroponymica Scandinavica, P.O. Box 135, S-751 04 Uppsala, Sweden. TEL 46-18-18-12-89. FAX 46-18-36-52-77. (Subscr. to: Swedish Science Press, P.O. Box 118, S-751 04 Uppsala, Sweden. TEL 46-18365566) Eds. Thorsten Andersson, Lena Peterson. bk.rev.; charts; illus. circ. 250. (back issues avail.) **Indexed:** Bibl.Ling. **Document type:** academic/scholarly publication.
Description: Publishes articles in the field of Scandinavian personal name research. Presents studies dealing with the etymology, phonology, morphology, semantics, history, sociology and stylistics of names.

499.96   BE   ISSN 0081-6345
DK511.C1
STUDIA CAUCASICA. 1963. irreg., vol.9, 1989. 1000 BEF. Editions Peeters s.p.r.l., Bondgenotenlaan 153, B-3000 Louvain, Belgium. TEL 32-16-235170. FAX 32-16-228500. Ed. A.H. Kuipers. adv.; bk.rev.; illus.; charts. circ. 150. (back issues avail.) **Indexed:** Bibl.Ling., M.L.A. **Document type:** academic/scholarly publication.

491.6   UK   ISSN 0081-6353
PB1001
STUDIA CELTICA. (Text in English and Welsh; occasionally in French and German) 1966. biennial. £20 per double vol. (University of Wales, Board of Celtic Studies) University of Wales Press, 6 Gwennyth St., Cathays, Cardiff CF2 4YD, Wales. TEL 0222-231919. FAX 0222-230908. Ed. J.E. Caerwyn Williams. adv.; bk.rev. circ. 200. (reprint service avail. from UMI) **Indexed:** Bibl.Ling., Br.Archaeol.Abstr., M.L.A. **Document type:** academic/scholarly publication.
Description: Covers Indo-European philology and continental and insular Celtic.

494 410   FI
PH107
STUDIA FENNICA. LINGUISTICA. (Text in English or German) 1933. a. FIM 200. Suomalaisen Kirjallisuuden Seura - Finnish Literature Society, Hallituskatu 1, P.O. Box 259, FIN-00170 Helsinki 17, Finland. TEL 358-0-131231. FAX 358-0-13123220. adv.; bibl. circ. 1,000. **Indexed:** A.I.C.P., Bibl.Ling., M.L.A.
Supersedes in part (in 1991): Studia Fennica (ISSN 0085-6835)
Description: Devoted to linguistics, folkloristics, and ethnology.

439   BE   ISSN 0081-6442
STUDIA GERMANICA GANDENSIA. (Text in Dutch, English, German) 1959. a. 300 BEF. Rijksuniversiteit te Ghent, Faculteit der Letteren en Wijsbegeerte, Blandijnberg 2, B-9000 Ghent, Belgium. Ed. G.A.R. De Smet. index. circ. 150. **Indexed:** Bibl.Ling., M.L.A.
—SWETS.

430   GW   ISSN 0081-6469
P1.A1
STUDIA GRAMMATICA. 1962. irreg., vol.36, 1993. price varies. Akademie Verlag GmbH, Muehlenstr. 33-34, 13187 Berlin, Germany. TEL 030-47889348. FAX 030-47889357. **Indexed:** Lang.& Lang.Behav.Abstr., M.L.A. **Document type:** monographic series.

491.6 941.5   IE   ISSN 0081-6477
PB1201
STUDIA HIBERNICA. 1961. a. I£10. St. Patrick's College, Editorial Committee, Drumcondra, Dublin 9, Ireland. TEL 01-376191. FAX 01-376197. bk.rev. circ. 1,000. **Indexed:** Amer.Hist.& Life, Bibl.Ling., Br.Archaeol.Abstr., Hist.Abstr., M.L.A. **Document type:** academic/scholarly publication.
Description: Devoted to the study of the Irish language and its literature, of Irish history and archaeology, Irish folklore and placenames, and related subjects.

400   IT
STUDIA HISTORICA ET PHILOLOGICA: SECTIO ROMANICA. 1974. irreg. Licosa S.p.A., Via Duca di Calabria 1-1, 50125 Florence, Italy. Ed. R. Picchio. circ. 2,000.

400   IT
STUDIA HISTORICA ET PHILOLOGICA: SECTIO SLAVICA. irreg. price varies. Licosa S.p.A., Via Duca di Calabria 1-1, 50125 Florence, Italy.

400   IT
STUDIA HISTORICA ET PHILOLOGICA: SECTIO SLAVO-ROMANICA. irreg. price varies. Licosa S.p.A., Via Duca di Calabria 1-1, 50125 Florence, Italy. Ed. Riccardo Picchio.

400   NO   ISSN 0039-3193
P9
STUDIA LINGUISTICA; Swedish journal of general linguistics. (Text in English, French) 1947. s-a. $55. Scandinavian University Press, P.O. Box 2959 Toeyen, N-0608 Oslo, Norway. TEL 472-67-7600. FAX 472-67-7575. (U.S. addr.: Scandinavian University Press, 200 Meacham Ave., Elmont, NY 11003. TEL 516-352-7300) Ed. Bengt Sigurd. adv.; bk.rev.; index. **Indexed:** Abstr.Anthropol., Arts & Hum.Cit.Ind., Ind.Bk.Rev.Hum., Lang.& Lang.Behav.Abstr. (1972-), Lang.Teach.& Ling.Abstr., M.L.A.
—Faxon; SWETS; UMI. **CCC.**

407   US
STUDIA LINGUISTICA ET PHILOLOGICA. 1975. irreg. $37.50 per vol. Anma Libri, Box 876, Saratoga, CA 95071. TEL 408-741-1522. **Indexed:** M.L.A. **Document type:** monographic series.
Description: Linguistic and philological studies.

400   NO   ISSN 0039-3274
PB5
STUDIA NEOPHILOLOGICA. (Text in English, German and the Romance languages.) 1928. 2/yr. NOK 485 in the Nordic countries; elsewhere NOK 505. Scandinavian University Press, P.O. Box 2959 Toeyen, N-0608 Oslo, Norway. TEL 472-67-7600. FAX 472-67-7575. (U.S. addr.: Scandinavian University Press, 200 Meacham Ave., Elmont, NY 1103. TEL 516-352-7300) Ed. Lars Hermodsson. bk.rev.; cum.index: vols.1-30. circ. 800. (tabloid format; reprint service avail. from SWZ) **Indexed:** Abstr.Engl.Stud., Arts & Hum.Cit.Ind., Bibl.Ling., Curr.Cont., Ind.Bk.Rev.Hum., Lang.& Lang.Behav.Abstr., M.L.A.
—BLDSC (8483.080000); Faxon; UnCover; SWETS.
Description: Publishes articles on English, German and the Romance languages and literatures.

490   NE   ISSN 0281-4528
STUDIA ORIENTALIA LUNDENSIA. 1983. irreg., vol.4, 1990. price varies. E.J. Brill, P.O. Box 9000, 2300 PA Leiden, Netherlands. TEL 31-71-312624. FAX 31-71-317532. TELEX 39296 BRILL NL. (In N. America: E.J. Brill, 24 Hudson St., Kinderhook, NY 12106. TEL 800-962-4406. FAX 518-758-1959) Ed. Gosta Vitesta. **Document type:** monographic series.
Refereed Serial

410   SW   ISSN 0081-6809
STUDIA PHILOLOGIAE SCANDINAVICAE UPSALIENSIA, (Subseries of Acta Universitatis Upsaliensis) 1961. irreg. price varies; exchange avail. (Uppsala Universitet) A W I International AB, P.O. Box 4627, S-116 91 Stockholm, Sweden. TEL 468-640-8800. FAX 468-641-1180. Ed.Bd.

400   FI   ISSN 0585-5462
STUDIA PHILOLOGICA JYVASKYLAENSIA. (Text in English, Finnish, French, German and Swedish) 1966. irreg. price varies. Jyvaskylan Yliopisto - University of Jyvaskyla, Library, PL 35, 40100 Jyvaskyla 10, Finland. TEL 941-601-211. FAX 603-371. TELEX 28219 JYK SF. Eds. Raija Markkanen, Ellen Sakari. circ. 450. **Document type:** monographic series.

460   SP   ISSN 0210-5438
STUDIA PHILOLOGICA SALMANTICENSIA. 1977. irreg., no.8, 1984. 1200 ptas. Ediciones Universidad de Salamanca, Apdo. 325, 37080 Salamanca, Spain. TEL 923-26-14-54. Dir. Eugenio de Bustos Tovar. **Indexed:** Bibl.Ling. **Document type:** academic/scholarly publication.
Description: Includes studies on Spanish philology.

410   PL   ISSN 0860-2085
STUDIA PHONETICA POSNANIENSIA; an international journal for linguistics and phonetics. (Text in English and Polish; abstracts in English) 1987. irreg., vol.4, 199. price varies. (Adam Mickiewicz University, Institute of Linguistics) Adam Mickiewicz University Press, Nowowiejskiego 55, 61-734 Poznan, Poland. TEL 527-380. Eds. Maria Steffen-Botog, Wieslaw Awedyk. bk.rev.; abstr. circ. 400. (back issues avail.) **Indexed:** Bibl.Ling. **Document type:** academic/scholarly publication.

400   JA   ISSN 0300-1067
P215
STUDIA PHONOLOGICA/ONSEI KAGAKU KENKYU. (Text in English, German or Japanese) 1961. a. free. Kyoto University, Institution for Phonetic Sciences - Kyoto Daigaku Onsei Kagaku Sogo Kenkyu Bukai, Yoshida, Sakyo-ku, Kyoto 606, Japan. FAX 81-75-753-5977. Ed. Shuji Doshita. illus.; circ. 1,000. **Indexed:** Bibl.Ling., Lang.& Lang.Behav.Abstr. (1971-).
—BLDSC (8483.130000).

STUDIA POETICA. see *LITERATURE*

LINGUISTICS 3541

400 PL ISSN 0137-4370
STUDIA POLONISTYCZNE. (Text in Polish; summaries in English, French, German or Russian) 1973. irreg., vol.20, 1994. price varies. Adam Mickiewicz University Press, Nowowiejskiego 55, 61-734 Poznan, Poland. TEL 527-380. FAX 61-526425. TELEX 413260 UAMPL. Eds. Wladyslaw Kuraszkiewicz, Tadeusz Witczak. **Indexed:** Bibl.Ling., Lang.& Lang.Behav.Abstr. **Document type:** academic/scholarly publication.
—BLDSC (8483.158000).
 Description: Contains papers connected with the linguistic, literature and theory of literature problems.

479 420 CI ISSN 0039-3339
STUDIA ROMANICA ET ANGLICA ZAGRABIENSIA. (Editions in English, French, Italian, Spanish) 1956. s-a. 100 din.($20) per no. Sveuciliste u Zagrebu, Filozofski Fakultet, Dure Salaja 3, 41000 Zagreb, Croatia. Ed. Ivo Vidan. **Indexed:** Bibl.Ling., Lang.& Lang.Behav.Abstr., Lang.Teach.& Ling.Abstr.
 Description: Discusses linguistics and the creation of literature from an academic view.

410 HU ISSN 0418-4564
STUDIA ROMANICA UNIVERSITATIS DEBRECENIENSIS DE LUDOVICO KOSSUTH NOMINATAE. SERIES LINGUISTICA. (Text in French) 1964. irreg., vol.5, 1987. Kossuth Lajos Tudomanyegyetem, Roman Nyelvek es Irodalmak Tansek, Egyetem ter 1, 4010 Debrecen, Hungary. bibl.

410 SW ISSN 0562-3022
STUDIA ROMANICA UPSALIENSIA. (Text in French, Italian and Spanish; summaries in English or French) 1961. irreg. (Uppsala University, Acta Universitatis Upsaliensis) A W I International AB, P.O. Box 4627, S-116 91 Stockholm, Sweden. TEL 468-640-8800. FAX 468-641-1180. Ed. Lennart Carlsson. circ. 600. (back issues avail.) **Indexed:** M.L.A.

410 PL ISSN 0137-6608
STUDIA SEMIOTYCZNE. 1968. a. price varies. Polskie Towarzystwo Semiotyczne - Polish Semiotic Society, Palac Kultury i Nauki, pok. 1923, Warsaw, Poland. (Dist. by: Ars Polona-Ruch, Krakowskie Przedmiescie 7, Warsaw, Poland) Ed. Jerzy Pelc. **Indexed:** Bibl.Ling.
 Description: Covers semiotics, linguistics, theory of language.

492 296 NE ISSN 0081-6914
STUDIA SEMITICA NEERLANDICA. 1956. irreg., vol.31, 1993. price varies. Van Gorcum en Co. B.V., P.O. Box 43, 9400 AA Assen, Netherlands. TEL 31-5920-46864. FAX 31-5920-72064. **Document type:** academic/scholarly publication.

491 HU ISSN 0039-3363
PG1
STUDIA SLAVICA ACADEMIAE SCIENTIARUM HUNGARICAE. (Text in English, French, German or Slavic languages) 1955. q. $84 (effective 1992). (Magyar Tudomanyos Akademia) Akademiai Kiado, Publishing House of the Hungarian Academy of Sciences, P.O. Box 245, H-1519 Budapest, Hungary. TEL 181-2134. FAX 166-6466. TELEX 22-6228 AKNYO H. Eds. Ferenc Papp, Attila Hollos. adv.; bk.rev.; bibl.; charts; illus.; index. **Indexed:** Bibl.Ling., Lang.& Lang.Behav.Abstr., M.L.A.
—CCC.
 Description: Publishes essays on linguistics, philological and folkloristic research in Slavonic studies.

400 859 RM ISSN 0039-3444
P19
STUDIA UNIVERSITATIS "BABES-BOLYAI". PHILOLOGIA. (Text in English, French, German, Italian, Rumanian) 1956. q. exchange basis. Universitatea "Babes-Bolyai", Biblioteca Centrala Universitara, Str. Clinicilor Nr. 2, Cluj-Napoca 3400, Rumania. TEL 95-117092. FAX 95-117633. bk.rev.; charts; illus.; index. **Indexed:** Bibl.Ling. **Document type:** academic/scholarly publication.

494 SW ISSN 0081-7015
STUDIA URALICA ET ALTAICA UPSALIENSIA. (Subseries of Acta Universitatis Upsaliensis) (Text in English and Swedish) 1964. irreg. price varies. (Uppsala Universitet) A W I International AB, P.O. Box 4627, S-116 91 Stockholm, Sweden. TEL 468-640-8800. FAX 468-641-1180. Ed. Bo Wickman. bibl.; charts.

494 894 US ISSN 0133-4239
STUDIA URALO-ALTAICA. (Text in English, German, Russian) 1973. irreg., vol.33, 1993. price varies. John Benjamins Publishing Co., 821 Bethlehem Pike, Philadelphia, PA 19118. TEL 215-836-1200. FAX 215-836-1204. (And: Amsteldijk 44, P.O. Box 75577, 1070 AN Amsterdam, Netherlands. TEL 020-6762325) Eds. P. Hajdu, A. Rona-Tas. (back issues avail.) **Indexed:** Bibl.Ling. **Document type:** monographic series.
 Description: Monographs on Uralo-Altaic studies.

491.8 PL ISSN 0081-7090
STUDIA Z FILOLOGII POLSKIEJ I SLOWIANSKIEJ. (Text in Polish; papers and summaries in Slavonic languages) 1955. irreg., vol.30, 1993. price varies. (Polska Akademia Nauk, Komitet Slowianoznawstwa) Wydawnictwo Naukowe PWN, Miodowa 10, 00-251 Warsaw, Poland. TEL 48-22-312738. FAX 48-22-267163. TELEX 813763 PWN PL. Ed. J. Siatkowski. circ. 500. **Indexed:** Bibl.Ling. **Document type:** academic/scholarly publication.

494.3 GW ISSN 0585-5853
P945
STUDIEN ZU DEN BOGAZKOEY-TEXTEN. 1965. irreg., vol.40, 1993. price varies. (Akademie der Wissenschaften und der Literatur, Kommission fuer den Alten Orient) Harrassowitz Verlag, Taunusstr. 14, 65183 Wiesbaden, Germany. TEL 0611-530570. FAX 0611-530570. TELEX 4186135. (Subscr. to: Postfach 2929, 65019 Wiesbaden, Germany) **Indexed:** M.L.A. **Document type:** monographic series.

430 GW
STUDIEN ZUM KLEINEN DEUTSCHEN SPRACHATLAS. 1982. irreg. Max Niemeyer Verlag, Postfach 2140, 72011 Tuebingen, Germany. TEL 07071-98940. FAX 07071-989450. Eds. Werner H. Veith, Wolfgang Putschke. circ. 500. (back issues avail.) **Document type:** monographic series.
 Description: Monographs and collections of essays on dialectological atlases, especially the "Kleiner deutscher Sprachatlas".

053.1 GW
STUDIEN ZUR DEUTSCHEN GRAMMATIK. irreg., no.41, 1994. DM.120. Gunter Narr Verlag, Postfach 2567, 72015 Tuebingen, Germany. TEL 07071-78091. FAX 07071-75288. Ed. Werner Abraham. **Document type:** monographic series.

420 820 GW ISSN 0081-7244
STUDIEN ZUR ENGLISCHEN PHILOLOGIE, NEUE FOLGE. (Text in English or German) 1963. irreg., no.30, 1993. price varies. Max Niemeyer Verlag, Postfach 2140, 72011 Tuebingen, Germany. TEL 07071-98940. FAX 07071-989450. Ed.Bd. (back issues avail.) **Indexed:** M.L.A. **Document type:** monographic series.
 Description: Monographs on English and American literature from the Middle Ages to present.

STUDIEN ZUR INDOLOGIE UND IRANISTIK. see HISTORY — History Of Asia

STUDIER FRA SPROG- OG OLDTIDSFORSKNING. see CLASSICAL STUDIES

400 SW
STUDIER I MODERN SPRAAKVETENSKAP/STOCKHOLM STUDIES IN MODERN PHILOLOGY. (Text in English, French and German) 1898. irreg. (Humanistisk-Samhaellsvetenskapliga Forskning Raadet) A W I International AB, P.O. Box 4627, 116 91 Stockholm, Sweden. TEL 468-640-8800. FAX 468-641-1180. Ed.Bd. **Indexed:** Bibl.Ling.

496 US ISSN 0039-3533
PL8000
STUDIES IN AFRICAN LINGUISTICS. 1970. 3/yr. $16 to individuals (overseas $33); institutions $25 (overseas $42). University of California at Los Angeles, James S. Coleman African Studies Center, 10244 Bunche Hall, UCLA, 405 Hildgard Ave., CA 90024-1310. TEL 310-825-3686. (Co-sponsor: U.C.L.A. Department of Linguistics) Ed.Bd. bibl.; charts. circ. 350. (back issues avail.) **Indexed:** Abstr.Anthropol., Bibl.Ling., Curr.Cont.Africa, Lang.& Lang.Behav.Abstr. (1970-), M.L.A. **Document type:** academic/scholarly publication.
—BLDSC (8488.945000); UnCover; SWETS.
 Description: Descriptive or theoretical articles on linguistics and African languages.

306.4 400 NE
▼**STUDIES IN BILINGUALISM.** 1992. irreg., vol.5, 1992. price varies. John Benjamins Publishing Co., Amsteldijk 44, P.O. Box 75577, 1070 AN Amsterdam, Netherlands. TEL 31-20-6738156. FAX 31-20-6792956. (In N. America: 821 Bethlehem Pike, Philadelphia, PA 19118. TEL 215-836-1200. FAX 215-836-1204) Eds. Kees de Bot, Thom Huebner. (back issues avail.) **Indexed:** Bibl.Ling. **Document type:** monographic series.
 Description: Covers psycholinguistic and sociolinguistic aspects, from childhood bilingualism to political aspects of bilingualism.
 Refereed Serial

410 375.4 GW ISSN 0171-6794
STUDIES IN DESCRIPTIVE LINGUISTICS. (Text in English; summaries in French, German) 1978. irreg. price varies. Julius Groos Verlag, Hertzstr. 6, 69126 Heidelberg, Germany. TEL 06221-303621. FAX 06221-301993. Ed. D. Nehls. circ. 1,000. (back issues avail.) **Indexed:** Bibl.Ling., Lang.& Lang.Behav.Abstr. (1978-). **Document type:** academic/scholarly publication.

415 NE
▼**STUDIES IN DISCOURSE AND GRAMMAR.** 1992. irreg., vol.3, 1993. price varies. John Benjamins Publishing Co., Amsteldijk 44, P.O. Box 75577, 1070 AN Amsterdam, Netherlands. TEL 31-20-6738156. FAX 31-20-6792956. (In N. America: 821 Bethlehem Pike, Philadelphia, PA 19118. TEL 215-836-1200. FAX 215-836-1204) **Indexed:** Bibl.Ling. **Document type:** monographic series.
 Description: Provides a forum for research on grammar as it emerges from and is accounted for by discourse contexts.
 Refereed Serial

STUDIES IN ENGLISH LITERATURE/EIBUNGAKU KENKYU. see LITERATURE

415 US
STUDIES IN GENERATIVE GRAMMAR.* irreg., no.36, 1990. price varies. Walter de Gruyter, Inc., 200 Saw Mill River Rd., Hawthorne, NY 10532. TEL 914-747-0110. FAX 914-747-1326. Eds. Jan Koster, Henk van Riemsdijk. **Indexed:** Bibl.Ling.

411 II
STUDIES IN INDIAN EPIGRAPHY/BHARATIYA PURABHILEKHA PATRIKA. 1975. a. Epigraphical Society of India, University Buildings, Mysore 570005, India. Eds. Z.A. Desai, Ajay Mitra Shastri. illus.

410 II
STUDIES IN INDIAN PLACE NAMES/BHARATIYA STHALANAMA PATRIKA. (Text in English) 1980. a. (Place Names Society of India) Geetha Book House, K.R. Circle, Mysore 570 001, India. Ed. Mandhav N. Katti.

410 100 NE ISSN 0378-4177
P1.A1
STUDIES IN LANGUAGE. (Text in English, French, German) 1977. 2/yr. fl.365($213) (effective 1994). (Foundations of Language Foundation) John Benjamins Publishing Co., Amsteldijk 44, P.O. Box 75577, 1070 AN Amsterdam, Netherlands. TEL 31-20-6738156. FAX 31-20-6792956. (In N. America: 821 Bethlehem Pike, Philadelphia, PA 19118. TEL 215-836-1200. FAX 215-836-1204) Ed.Bd. adv.; bk.rev.; bibl.; index. circ. 800. (back issues avail.; reprint service avail from SWZ) **Indexed:** Abstr.Anthropol., Arts & Hum.Cit.Ind., Bibl.Ling., Ind.Bk.Rev.Hum., Lang.& Lang.Behav.Abstr. (1977-), M.L.A., Math.R. **Document type:** academic/scholarly publication.
—Faxon; UnCover; SWETS. CCC.
 Supersedes: Foundations of Language (ISSN 0015-900X)
 Description: Covers subjects basic to contemporary linguistics and philosophy, focusing on the foundations of language.

LINGUISTICS

410 800 — US — ISSN 0165-7763
STUDIES IN LANGUAGE COMPANION SERIES. Short title: S L C S. (Supplement to: Studies in Language) 1978. irreg., vol.23, 1993. price varies. John Benjamins Publishing Co., 821 Bethlehem Pike, Philadelphia, PA 19118. TEL 215-836-1200. FAX 215-836-1204. (And: Amsteldijk 44, P.O. Box 75577, 1070 AN Amsterdam, Netherlands. TEL 020-6762325) Eds. Werner Abraham, Michael Noonan. **Indexed:** Bibl.Ling., M.L.A., Math.R. **Document type:** monographic series.
—BLDSC (8490.825500).

410 — US
STUDIES IN LANGUAGE LEARNING; an interdisciplinary review of language acquisition, language pedagogy, stylistics, and language planning. 1975. irreg., latest SLL 5:1 (spring 1985). price varies. University of Illinois at Urbana-Champaign, Language Learning Laboratory, G70 Foreign Languages Bldg., 707 S. Mathews Ave., Urbana, IL 61801. TEL 217-333-1719. FAX 217-244-0190. Ed. Bd. bk.rev. circ. 300. (also avail. in microform; back issues avail.) **Indexed:** ERIC, Lang.& Lang.Behav.Abstr. (1976-), Lang.Teach.& Ling.Abstr., Sociol.Abstr. **Document type:** monographic series.

STUDIES IN LINGUISTICS AND PHILOSOPHY. see PSYCHOLOGY

400 — HU
STUDIES IN MODERN PHILOLOGY. (Text in English) 1984. irreg., vol.10, 1992. price varies. Akademiai Kiado, Publishing House of the Hungarian Academy of Sciences, P.O. Box 245, H-1519 Budapest, Hungary. TEL 181-2134. FAX 166-6466. TELEX 22-6228 AKNYO H. Eds. Karoly Manherz, Janos Szavai.

410 — NE — ISSN 0924-4670
STUDIES IN NATURAL LANGUAGE AND LINGUISTIC THEORY. (Text in English) 1985. irreg., vol.29, 1993. price varies. Kluwer Academic Publishers, Postbus 17, P.O. Box 17, 3300 AA Dordrecht, Netherlands. TEL 31-78-334911. FAX 31-78-334254. TELEX 29245 KAPG NL. (Dist. by: Kluwer Academic Publishers Group, P.O. Box 322, 3300 AH Dordrecht, Netherlands. TEL 31-78-524400. FAX 31-78-524474; N. America dist. addr.: Box 358, Accord Sta., Hingham, MA 02018-0358. TEL 617-871-6600. FAX 617-871-6528) Eds. Frank Heny, Joan Maling. **Indexed:** Bibl.Ling. **Document type:** monographic series.
Refereed Serial

430 800 — US — ISSN 0899-9872
STUDIES IN OLD GERMANIC LANGUAGES AND LITERATURES. irreg. Peter Lang Publishing, Inc., 62 W. 45th St., 4th Fl., New York, NY 10036. TEL 212-302-6740. FAX 212-302-7574. Ed. Ernst A. Ebbinghaus. **Document type:** academic/scholarly publication.
Description: Presents monographic studies in Old Germanic dialects (Gothic, Old English, Old Saxon, Old Norse, Old High German), including grammar and text editions; also includes comparative linguistic and literary studies emphasizing the Germanic languages.

499.21 PL5501 — PH — ISSN 0116-0516
STUDIES IN PHILIPPINE LINGUISTICS. (Text in English) 1977. a. $6. Summer Institute of Linguistics, Philippine Branch, P.O. Box 2270 CPO, 1099 Manila, Philippines. TEL 63-2-780061. FAX 63-2-780062. (Co-sponsor: Linguistic Society of the Philippines) Eds. Fe T. Otanes, Hazel Wrigglesworth. bk.rev. circ. 150. (also avail. in microfiche) **Indexed:** Anthropol.Lit., ERIC, Ind.Phil.Per. **Document type:** academic/scholarly publication.

400 P25 — US — ISSN 0039-3738
STUDIES IN PHILOLOGY. 1906. 4/yr. $18 to individuals (foreign $24); institutions $24 (foreign $30). (University of North Carolina at Chapel Hill, Department of English) University of North Carolina Press, Box 2288, Chapel Hill, NC 27515-2288. TEL 919-966-3561. FAX 919-966-3829. Ed. Jerry Mills. adv.; index every 10 yrs. circ. 1,600. (also avail. in microform from MIM,UMI,PMC; microfiche from IDC; reprint service avail. from UMI) **Indexed:** Abstr.Engl.Stud., Arts & Hum.Cit.Ind., Curr.Cont., Hum.Ind., LCR, M.L.A. **Document type:** academic/scholarly publication.
—BLDSC (8491.210000); Faxon; UnCover; SWETS; UMI. CCC.
Refereed Serial

407 P118 — UK — ISSN 0272-2631
STUDIES IN SECOND LANGUAGE ACQUISITION. 1977. q. £28($45) to individuals (overseas £40); institutions £58 (overseas £70 ($89)). Cambridge University Press, Edinburgh Bldg., Shaftesbury Rd., Cambridge CB2 2RU, England. TEL 0223-312393. FAX 0223-315052. TELEX 851817256. (N. American addr.: Cambridge University Press, Journals Dept., 40 W. 20th St., New York, NY 10011. TEL 212-924-3900. FAX 212-691-3239) Ed. Albert Valdman. adv.; bk.rev. (also avail. in microform from UMI; back issues avail.; reprint service avail. from UMI) **Indexed:** Bibl.Ling., C.I.J.E., Lang.& Lang.Behav.Abstr. (1985-), Lang.Teach.& Ling.Abstr. **Document type:** academic/scholarly publication.
—BLDSC (8491.571000); Faxon; UnCover; SWETS; UMI. CCC.
Description: Deals with the acquisition of a second language or languages, whether by formal learning or by assimilation.

410 890 — II
STUDIES IN SEMIOTICS AND LITERATURE. 1979. irreg. price varies. Bahri Publications, 997-A, Street No. 9, Gobindpuri, Kalkaji, New Delhi 110 019, India. TEL 644-5710. Ed. Ujjal Singh Bahri. **Document type:** academic/scholarly publication, monographic series.
Description: Semiotic studies of literature, emphasis on Indian literature.

492 — NE — ISSN 0081-8461
STUDIES IN SEMITIC LANGUAGES AND LINGUISTICS. 1967. irreg., vol.19, 1993. price varies. E. J. Brill, P.O. Box 9000, 2300 PA Leiden, Netherlands. TEL 31-71-312624. FAX 31-71-317532. TELEX 39296 BRILL NL. (In N. America: E.J. Brill, 24 Hudson St., Kinderhook, NY 12106. TEL 800-962-4406. FAX 518-758-1959) (back issues avail.) **Document type:** monographic series.
—BLDSC (8491.575000).
Description: Scholarly monographs on topics in Semitic languages and linguistics, living and dead, including Arabic and Hebrew regional dialects.
Refereed Serial

491 410 PG1 — NE — ISSN 0169-0124 CODEN: SSGLEJ
STUDIES IN SLAVIC AND GENERAL LINGUISTICS. (Text in English, German, Polish or Russian) 1980. irreg. price varies. Editions Rodopi B.V., Keizersgracht 302-304, 1016 EX Amsterdam, Netherlands. TEL 31-20-6227507. FAX 31-20-6380948. (In N. America: 233 Peachtree St. N.E., Ste. 404, Atlanta GA 30303-1504. TEL 800-225-3998. FAX 404-522-7116) Ed.Bd. adv. circ. 500. **Indexed:** Bibl.Ling., M.L.A. **Document type:** monographic series.

STUDIES IN SPEECH PATHOLOGY AND CLINICAL LINGUISTICS. see MEDICAL SCIENCES — Psychiatry And Neurology

410 — US
STUDIES IN THE LINGUISTIC SCIENCES. 1971. s-a. $7.50 per issue. University of Illinois at Urbana-Champaign, Department of Linguistics, 707 S. Mathews, 4088 Foreign Language Bldg., Urbana, IL 61801. TEL 217-333-3563. Ed. Hans Henrich Hock. bk.rev.; bibl. circ. controlled. (back issues avail.) **Indexed:** Lang.& Lang.Behav.Abstr. (1971-), M.L.A., Sociol.Abstr. **Document type:** academic/scholarly publication.
—Faxon.
Formerly: University of Illinois. Department of Linguistics. Working Papers (ISSN 0049-2388)

410 — US
STUDIES IN THE SCIENCES OF LANGUAGE SERIES. 1975. irreg., vol.8, 1991. price varies. John Benjamins Publishing Co., 821 Bethlehem Pike, Philadelphia, PA 19118. TEL 215-836-1200. FAX 215-836-1204. (And: Amsteldijk 44, P.O. Box 75577, 1070 AN Amsterdam, Netherlands. TEL 020-6762325) Ed. D.L. Goyvaerts. (back issues avail.) **Indexed:** Bibl.Ling. **Document type:** monographic series.
Description: Monographs and interdisciplinary studies in linguistics.

410 150 — NE
STUDIES IN THEORETICAL PSYCHOLINGUISTICS. 1983. irreg., vol.19, 1993. price varies. Kluwer Academic Publishers, Postbus 17, 3300 AA Dordrecht, Netherlands. TEL 31-78-334911. FAX 31-78-334254. TELEX 29245 KAPG NL. (Dist. by: Kluwer Academic Publishers Group, P.O. Box 322, 3300 AH Dordrecht, Netherlands. TEL 31-78-524400. FAX 31-78-524474; N. America dist. addr.: Box 358, Accord Sta., Hingham, MA 02018-0358. TEL 617-871-6600. FAX 617-871-6528) Eds. T. Roeper, K. Wexler. **Indexed:** Bibl.Ling. **Document type:** monographic series.
Refereed Serial

STUDIES OF WORLD LITERATURE IN ENGLISH. see LITERATURE

410 — US
STUDIES ON LANGUAGE ACQUISITION. * (Text in English) 1985. irreg., no.9, 1989. Walter de Gruyter, Inc., 200 Saw Mill River Rd., Hawthorne, NY 10532. TEL 914-747-0110. FAX 914-747-1326. Ed.Bd.
Description: Focuses on first language acquisition, second/foreign language acquisition, bilingualism, language loss, and language acquisition in educational settings.

410 — RM — ISSN 0039-405X
STUDII SI CERCETARI LINGVISTICE. 1950. 6/yr. 180 lei($60) (Academia Romana) Editura Academiei Romane, Calea Victoriei 125, 79717 Bucharest, Rumania. (Dist. by: Rompresfilatelia, Calea Grivitei 64-66, P.O. Box 12-201, 78104 Bucharest, Rumania) Ed. I. Coteanu. bk.rev.; charts; index. **Indexed:** Bibl.Ling., Lang.& Lang.Behav.Abstr. (1972-), M.L.A.

THE SUBTLE JOURNAL OF RAW COINAGE. see LITERATURE

SUECANA EXTRANEA; boecker om Sverige och svensk skoenlitteratur paa fraemmande spraak. see BIBLIOGRAPHIES

418 — US — ISSN 1040-4406
SUMMER INSTITUTE OF LINGUISTICS. LANGUAGE DATA. AFRICA SERIES. 1971. irreg., no.21, 1981. price varies. Summer Institute of Linguistics, Inc., Academic Publications, 7500 W. Camp Wisdom Rd., Dallas, TX 75236. TEL 214-709-2403. (also avail. in microfiche) **Document type:** monographic series.

410 — US — ISSN 1040-1113
SUMMER INSTITUTE OF LINGUISTICS. LANGUAGE DATA. AMERINDIAN SERIES. 1973. irreg., no.7, 1979. price varies. Summer Institute of Linguistics, Inc., Academic Publications, 7500 W. Camp Wisdom Rd., Dallas, TX 75236. TEL 214-709-2403. bibl.; charts. (also avail. in microfiche) **Document type:** monographic series.

499 — US — ISSN 1040-4414
SUMMER INSTITUTE OF LINGUISTICS. LANGUAGE DATA. ASIA-PACIFIC SERIES. 1971. irreg., no.13, 1981. price varies. Summer Institute of Linguistics, Inc., Academic Publications, 7500 W. Camp Wisdom Rd., Dallas, TX 75236. TEL 214-709-2403. Ed.Bd. (also avail. in microfiche) **Indexed:** Anthropol.Lit.

498 PM5151 — BL — ISSN 0102-6526
SUMMER INSTITUTE OF LINGUISTICS. SERIE LINGUISTICA. 1973. irreg. price varies. Summer Institute of Linguistics, Departamento de Estudos Tecnicos, SAI-NO Lote D, Bloco 3, 70770-730 Brasilia DF, Brazil. circ. 300. **Indexed:** Lang.& Lang.Behav.Abstr. (1973-). **Document type:** monographic series.
Description: Covers Brazilian indigenous languages.

LINGUISTICS

410 US
SUMMER INSTITUTE OF LINGUISTICS. UNIVERSITY OF NORTH DAKOTA SESSION. WORK PAPERS. vol.25, 1991. a. price varies. Summer Institute of Linguistics, Inc., Academic Publications, 7500 W. Camp Wisdom Rd., Dallas, TX 75236. TEL 214-709-2404. Ed.Bd. (also avail. in microfiche) Indexed: Anthropol.Lit., Bibl.Ling. **Document type:** monographic series.

499 US
SUMMER INSTITUTE OF LINGUISTICS AND THE UNIVERSITY OF TEXAS AT ARLINGTON PUBLICATIONS IN LINGUISTICS. 1958. irreg. price varies. Summer Institute of Linguistics, Inc., Academic Publications, 7500 W. Camp Wisdom Rd., Dallas, TX 75236. TEL 214-709-2403. Eds. W.R Merrifield, D.A. Burquest. Indexed: Anthropol.Lit., Bibl.Ling. **Document type:** monographic series.
    Former titles: S I L Publications in Linguistics (ISSN 1040-0850); S I L Publications on Linguistics and Related Fields (ISSN 0079-7669)
    Description: Provides linguistic descriptions of minority languages throughout the world.

SUOMALAIS-UGRILAISEN SEURAN. AIKAKAUSKIRJA/SOCIETE FINNO-OUGRIENNE. JOURNAL. see ANTHROPOLOGY

491 CI
SUVREMENA METODIKA NASTAVE HRVATSKOG ILI SRPSKOG JEZIKA. 1976. q. 200 din. Skolska Knjiga, Masarykova 28, Zagreb, Croatia. TEL 41 429 111. Ed. Z. Diklic. bk.rev.; film rev.; play rev. circ. 3,000.

SVET LITERATURY/WORLD OF LITERATURE. see LITERATURE

499.992 SZ
SVISA ESPERANTO REVUO;* eldonita de svisa esperanto-societo. (Text in Esperanto) 1903. 9/yr. 30 SFr. Svisa Esperanto-Societo, Zumhofstr. 22, CH-6010 Kriens, Switzerland. TEL 022-44-09-85. Ed. Andres Bickel. adv.; bk.rev.; illus. circ. 600.
    Formerly: Svisa Espero (ISSN 0039-7148)

SVOBODNA SKOLA/FREE THINKING SCHOOL. see LITERATURE

400 SW ISSN 0302-8348
SYDSVENSKA ORTNAMNSSAELLSKAPET. AARSSKRIFT/SOUTH SWEDISH PLACENAME SOCIETY. JOURNAL. (Text in Danish, English, German, Norwegian, Swedish; summaries in English) 1925. a. SEK 40 (effective 1993). Sydsvenska Ortnamnssaellskapets Forlag, Helgonabacken 14, S-223 62 Lund, Sweden. FAX 46-46-152381. Ed. Goeran Hallberg. bk.rev.; index. circ. 500. **Indexed:** Bibl.Ling.

870 410 BE
SYMBOLAE. SERIES C. LINGUISTICA. (Text in Dutch, English, French) 1986. irreg., vol.6, 1989. price varies. Leuven University Press, Krakenstraat 3, B-3000 Leuven, Belgium. TEL 32-16-284175. FAX 32-16-284176. Ed.Bd. **Document type:** academic/scholarly publication.

410 US ISSN 0092-4563
P1
SYNTAX AND SEMANTICS. 1972. irreg., vol.26, 1992. Academic Press, Inc., 525 B St., Ste. 1900, San Diego, CA 92101-4495. TEL 619-231-0926. FAX 619-699-6715. (Subscr. to: Order Dept., 6277 Sea Harbor Dr., 4th Fl., Orlando, FL 32887. TEL 800-321-5068) Ed. Stephen R. Anderson. (reprint service avail. from ISI) Indexed: ASCA, Bibl.Ling., M.L.A.
    —BLDSC (8586.550000); Faxon; UnCover. **CCC.**

SYSTEM; an international journal of educational technology and applied linguistics. see EDUCATION — Teaching Methods And Curriculum

410 371.3 XO
SZOCIALISTA NEVELES. (Text in Hungarian) 1954. 10/yr. 20 Kcs. (Ministry of Education of the Slovak Socialist Republic) Slovenske Pedagogicke Nakladatelstvo, Sasinkova 5, 815 60 Bratislava, Slovakia. (Subscr. to: Slovart, Gottwaldovo nam. 6, 805-32 Bratislava, Slovakia) Ed. Alexander Fibi. circ. 3,000.

410 FR ISSN 0066-9776
T A DOCUMENTS. (Traduction Automatique) 1966. irreg. price varies. Editions Klincksieck, 11 rue de Lille, 75005 Paris, France. (Dist. by: University of Alabama Press, Drawer 2877, University, AL 35486, U.S.A.)

T E J O - TUTMONDE. (Tutmonda Esperantista Junulara Organizo) see CHILDREN AND YOUTH — For

420 375.4 US ISSN 1056-7941
PE1128.A2 CODEN: TEJOEO
T E S O L JOURNAL. 1991. q. membership. Teachers of English to Speakers of Other Languages, 1600 Cameron St., Ste. 300, Alexandria, VA 22314-2751. TEL 703-836-0774. FAX 703-836-7864. Ed. Elliot L. Judd. adv. contact: Maria Minor. bk.rev. circ. 12,000. **Document type:** academic/scholarly publication.
    —UnCover; SWETS.
    Description: Gives practitioners hands-on ideas for everyday applications in diverse ESL and EFL environments. Explores creative strategies for successful teaching.

407 011 371.3 US ISSN 1051-8886
PE1011 CODEN: TESMET
T E S O L MATTERS. 1967. bi-m. membership (effective Nov.). Teachers of English to Speakers of Other Languages, 1600 Cameron St., Ste.300, Alexandria, VA 22314-2751. TEL 703-836-0774. FAX 703-836-7864. Ed. Helen Kornblum. adv. contact: Maria Minor. bk.rev. circ. 20,000. (tabloid format; also avail. in microfilm) **Document type:** newspaper.
    —BLDSC (8796.321300); SWETS.
    Supersedes (in 1991): T E S O L Newsletter (ISSN 0496-9987)
    Description: Offers organizational news and articles about classroom concerns, as well as conference announcements.
    Refereed Serial

420 375.4 US ISSN 0039-8322
PE1128.A2
T E S O L QUARTERLY; a journal for teachers of English to speakers of other languages and of standard English as a second dialect. 1967. q. membership (effective Nov.). Teachers of English to Speakers of Other Languages, 1600 Cameron St., Ste. 300, Alexandria, VA 22314-2751. TEL 703-836-0774. FAX 703-836-7864. Ed. Sandra McKay. adv.; bk.rev.; bibl.; cum.index. circ. 21,000. (also avail. in microform from UMI; reprint service avail. from UMI) **Indexed:** ASCA, C.I.J.E., Cont.Pg.Educ., Curr.Cont., Educ.Ind., Hum.Ind., Ind.Bk.Rev.Hum., Lang.& Lang.Behav.Abstr., Lang.Teach.& Ling.Abstr., M.L.A., Mid.East: Abstr.& Ind., Mult.Ed.Abstr., Res.High.Educ.Abstr., Soc.Sci.Ind., SOMA, Sp.Ed.Needs Abstr., SSCI. **Document type:** academic/scholarly publication.
    —BLDSC (8796.323000); Faxon; UnCover; SWETS; UMI.
    Description: Represents cross-disciplinary interests, both theoretical and practical. Features testing, evaluation, professional preparation, bilingual and adult education and language learning.

406 370 SW ISSN 0039-8438
T N C - AKTUELLT; information fraan Tekniska Nomenklaturcentralen. 1959. 3-4/yr. free. Tekniska Nomenklaturcentralen - Swedish Centre for Technical Terminology, Vaestra vaegen 9 C, 171 46 Solna, Sweden. TEL 46-8-735-85-25. FAX 46-8-273286. Ed.Bd. adv.; bk.rev. (processed)
    —BLDSC (8859.447000).
    Supersedes: T N C Nomenklaturrapport.

439.3 BE ISSN 0039-8691
PF701
TAAL EN TONGVAL; tijdschrift voor dialectologie. 1949. 3/yr. 650 BEF (effective 1992). Seminarie Vlaamse Dialektologie te Gent, Blandijnberg 2, B-9000 Gent, Belgium. FAX 32-9-2644195. (Co-sponsors: Zuidnederlandse Dialektcentrale te Leuven; Dialectencommissie te Amsterdam) Ed. G. DeSchutter. adv.; bk.rev.; bibl. circ. 375. **Indexed:** Bibl.Ling., M.L.A. **Document type:** academic/scholarly publication.
    Description: Presents articles on studies of Dutch dialects.

439.36 SA ISSN 0039-8705
TAALGENOOT. (Text in Afrikaans) 1931. m. R.12. Afrikaanse Taal en Kultuurvereniging, P.O. Box 4585, Johannesburg 2000, South Africa. FAX 27-11-725-1527. Ed. F.J. Kok. adv.; bk.rev. circ. 35,500. **Indexed:** Ind.S.A.Per. **Document type:** academic/scholarly publication.

420 430 440 NE ISSN 0922-1166
DE TALEN; maandblad voor de studie van Frans, Duits en Engels. 1884. 10/yr. fl.99.75. WoltersgroepGroningen b.v. (Subsidiary of: Wolters Kluwer N.V.), Postbus 58, 9700 MB Groningen, Netherlands. TEL 31-50-226922. FAX 31-50-264866. adv.; bk.rev. **Document type:** academic/scholarly publication.
    —SWETS.
    Formerly (until 1988): Drie Talen (ISSN 0012-6187)

TAMIL KALAI; research journal on Tamilology. see HISTORY — History Of Asia

418.02 NE ISSN 0924-1884
TARGET; international periodical of translation studies. (Text in English, French, German) 1989. s-a. fl.142($82) (effective 1994). John Benjamins Publishing Co., Amsteldijk 44, P.O. Box 75577, 1070 AN Amsterdam, Netherlands. TEL 31-20-6738156. FAX 31-20-6792956. (In N. America: 821 Bethlehem Pike, Philadelphia, PA 19118. TEL 215-836-1200. FAX 215-836-1204) Eds. Gideon Toury, Jose Lambert. circ. 650. (back issues avail.) **Indexed:** Bibl.Ling. **Document type:** academic/scholarly publication.
    —BLDSC (8606.100000).
    Description: Studies theoretical, methodological, and descriptive nature of translation. Also reports on current publications and research.

410 NZ ISSN 0494-8440
P11
TE REO. (Text in English, French) 1958. a. NZ.$25 to individuals; institutions NZ$ 35. Linguistic Society of New Zealand, c/o Romance Languages, University, Private Bag 92019, Auckland 1, New Zealand. TEL 64-9-3737999. FAX 64-9-3737449. Ed. R. Harlow. adv.; bk.rev.; bibl.; circ. 350 (paid). **Indexed:** Bibl.Ling., Bull.Signal., E.I., Lang.Teach.& Ling.Abstr., M.L.A. **Document type:** academic/scholarly publication.
    —BLDSC (8612.594000); UnCover.
    Description: Covers descriptive and theoretical linguistics, emphasizes research in indigenous and introduced languages of the South Pacific.
    Refereed Serial

428 375.4 PH ISSN 0116-8037
TEACHING ENGLISH FOR SPECIFIC PURPOSES JOURNAL. (Text in English) 1985. a. P.30($3.20) (De La Salle University, Center for English for Specific Purposes, Language Department) De La Salle University Press, 2401 Taft Ave., Manila, Philippines. TEL 2-59-48-32. FAX 632-521-9094. adv.; bk.rev. circ. 300. **Document type:** academic/scholarly publication.
    Description: Deals with the teaching of writing, principles of testing, criteria for evaluating student performance, and language program evaluation. Includes short articles describing specific and practical principles.

TEACHING ENGLISH TO DEAF AND SECOND LANGUAGE STUDENTS. see EDUCATION — Special Education And Rehabilitation

372 UK ISSN 0969-5141
TEAM (LONDON, 1959). 1959. 6/yr. (during school year). Mary Glasgow Magazines (Subsidiary of: Scholastic Publications Ltd.), 140 Freston Rd., London W10 6TR, England. TEL 071-792-3644. FAX 071-792-3172. TELEX 311890-MGPUBS. (U.S. subscr. to: Delta Systems, 1400 Miller Pkwy., McHenry, IL 60050-7030. TEL 800-823-8270) charts; illus.
    —CCC.
    Supersedes in Jun. 1993): Catch (ISSN 0008-7696); Clockwork (ISSN 0306-1604)
    Description: English-language magazine for intermediate-level E.F.L. students.

LINGUISTICS

220 400 US ISSN 0260-0935
CODEN: BTRAEV
TECHNICAL PAPERS FOR THE BIBLE TRANSLATOR.
1950. s-a. $6 ($12 including Practical Papers for the Bible Translator). United Bible Societies, 1865 Broadway, New York, NY 10023.
TEL 212-408-1468. FAX 212-582-7245. TELEX 23-62384. Ed. Paul Ellingworth. bk.rev.; index, cum.index every 10 yrs. circ. 2,800. (also avail. in microfilm; microfiche; reprint service avail.) Indexed: Chr.Per.Ind., New Test.Abstr., Old Test.Abstr., Rel.& Theol.Abstr. (1968-), Rel.Ind.One.
—BLDSC (1947.830000); UnCover; UMI.
Supersedes in part (in 1972): Bible Translator (ISSN 0006-0844)
Description: Contains technical biblical and linguistic information.

490 II
TELUGU AKADEMI LANGUAGE MONOGRAPH SERIES.
1974. irreg. Rs.16.25($8) Telugu Akademi, Hyderabad 500029, India. **Document type:** monographic series.

491.7 375.4 CN ISSN 0381-9582
TEMA. (Text in English and Ukrainian) 1968. q. Can.$15. (Saskatchewan Teachers of Ukrainian) Saskatchewan Teachers' Federation, Box 1108, Saskatoon, SK S7K 3N3, Canada.
TEL 306-525-0368. Ed. Vera Labach. bk.rev.; film rev.; bibl.; illus.; stat. circ. 200.

418.02 CN ISSN 0225-3194
TERMINOGRAMME; bulletin d'information terminologique et linguistique. 4/yr. Can.$37. (Office de la Langue Francaise) Publications du Quebec, C.P. 1005, Quebec, PQ G1K 7B5, Canada. TEL 800-463-2100. FAX 418-643-6177. (Subscr. to: Service Abonnements, CP 1190, Outremont, PQ H2V 4S7, Canada) Ed.Bd.

410 CN
TERMINOLOGIE. 1968. q. free. Universite Laval, Comite Consultif de la Normalisation et de la Qualite du Francais, Pavillon des Sciences de l'Education, Quebec City, Que. G1K 7P4, Canada.
TEL 418-656-2131. Ed.Bd. circ. 22,000.
Former titles: Comite Consultif de la Normalisation et de la Qualite du Francais a l'Universite Laval. Bulletin; Comite de Terminologie. Bulletin.
Description: Covers university related terminology.

418 EI
TERMINOLOGIE ET TRADUCTION. (Text in Danish, Dutch, English, French, German, Greek, Italian, Portuguese, Spanish) 1964. 3/yr. 35 ECU($28) Commission of the European Communities, Translation Service, Terminology Unit, Batiment Jean Monnet A2-100, L-2920 Luxembourg, Luxembourg.
FAX 4301-4309. TELEX 3423 COMEUR LU.
(Subscr. to: Office for Official Publications of the European Communities, L-2985 Luxembourg, Luxembourg) Ed. Wolfgang Osterheld. bk.rev. circ. 1,100.
—BLDSC (8793.250000).
Formerly: Commission of the European Communities. Terminology and Computer Applications. Translation and Terminology Bulletin (ISSN 0256-7873); **Supersedes (in 1984):** Commission of the European Communities. Terminology Bureau. Terminology Bulletin - Bulletin de Terminologie.
Description: Articles deal with theory, specific translation and training issues.

440 BE ISSN 1015-5716
TERMINOLOGIES NOUVELLES. (Text in French) 1989. 2/yr. free. (Reseau International de Neologie et de Terminologie, CN) Service de la Langue Francaise, 44 Bd Leopold II, B-1080 Brussels, Belgium.
TEL 32-2-4132295. (Co-sponsors: Ministere de la Culture et des Affaires Sociales; Commissariat General aux Relations Internationales; Agence de Cooperation Culturelle et Technique) Eds. Martine Garsou, Marc Van Campenhoudt. bk.rev.; bibl. (back issues avail.) **Document type:** academic/scholarly publication.
Description: Discusses language policy issues throughout the Francophone world, new and emerging usages in the French language, particularly in the fields of science and technology, as well as notes of meetings, new coinages and other linguistic matters.

401 NE
▼**TERMINOLOGY;** international journal of theoretical and applied issues in specialized communication. (Text in English, French) 1994. 2/yr. fl.200($120) (effective 1994). John Benjamins Publishing Co., Amsteldijk 44, P.O. Box 75577, 1070 AN Amsterdam, Netherlands. TEL 31-20-6762325. FAX 31-20-6792956. (In N. America: 821 Bethlehem Pike, Philadelphia, PA 19118. TEL 215-836-1200. FAX 215-836-1204) Eds. Helmi Sonneveld, Kurt Loening. **Document type:** academic/scholarly publication.
Description: Publishes cross-disciplinary studies of systematic solutions of language problems in translation, and related issues such as knowledge representation and transfer, lexicology, computational linguistics, and terminology standardization.

410 FR ISSN 0755-8953
TETRELOGIQUES. 1984. a. (Laboratoire Interdisciplinaire de Recherches sur le Langage) Presses Universitaires de Rennes, 2 rue du Doyen D. Leroy, 35044 Rennes Cedex, France.
TEL 99-54-66-35. FAX 99-33-07-95. **Indexed:** Bibl.Ling.
Description: Studies the sciences as they relate to language.

TEXAS SPEECH COMMUNICATION JOURNAL. see COMMUNICATIONS

TEXAS STUDIES IN LITERATURE AND LANGUAGE; a journal of the humanities. see LITERATURE

TEXT; an interdisciplinary journal for the study of discourse. see HUMANITIES: COMPREHENSIVE WORKS

418.02 GW ISSN 0179-6844
CODEN: TCNTEB
TEXTCONTEXT; Translation, Theorie-Didaktik-Praxis. 1986. q. DM.80. Julius Groos Verlag, Hertzstr. 6, 69126 Heidelberg, Germany. TEL 06221-303621. FAX 06221-301993. Ed.Bd. circ. 400. (reprint service avail. from UMI, back issues avail.) **Indexed:** Bibl.Ling. **Document type:** academic/scholarly publication.
—BLDSC (8800.634700); SWETS.

TEXTE ET L'IDEE. see LITERATURE

TEXTE UND UNTERSUCHUNGEN ZUR GESCHICHTE DER ALTCHRISTLICHEN LITERATUR. see RELIGIONS AND THEOLOGY

492.7 297 UA ISSN 0257-4136
TEXTES ARABES ET ETUDES ISLAMIQUES. (Text in Arabic, French) 1914. irreg., vol.31, 1993. price varies. Institut Francais d'Archeologie Orientale du Caire, P.O. Box 11562 Kasr-el-Aini, 37 Sharia Sheikh Aly Youssef, Mounira, Cairo, Egypt.
TEL 20-2-3548245. FAX 20-2-3544635. (Dist. outside Egypt by: Imprimerie Nationale - D A C F, 27 rue de la Convention, 75732 Paris Cedex 15, France. TEL 33-1-40-58-32-92. FAX 33-1-40-58-30-57) (back issues avail.) **Document type:** monographic series.
Description: Presents critical editions of significant Arabic texts, bibliographies and studies in Islamic history, with an emphasis on Egypt.

492.7 297 UA ISSN 1110-001X
TEXTES ET TRADUCTIONS D'AUTEURS ORIENTAUX. (Text in Arabic, French) 1937. irreg., latest vol.20. price varies. Institut Francais d'Archeologie Orientale du Caire, P.O. Box 11562 Kasr-el-Aini, 37 Sharia Sheikh Aly Youssef, Mounira, Cairo, Egypt.
TEL 20-2-3548245. FAX 20-2-3544635. (Dist. outside Egypt by: Imprimerie Nationale - D A C F, 27 rue de la Convention, 75732 Paris Cedex 15, France. TEL 33-1-40-58-32-92. FAX 33-1-40-58-30-57) bibl. (back issues avail.)
Document type: monographic series.

410 PO ISSN 0120-5455
AS82.A1
TEXTO E CONTEXTO. 1982. q. Esc.1600. Circulo Eros Editora, Rua Infantaria 8, 360, 4700 Braga, Portugal. Ed. Jose Lorite Mena. bk.rev.

TEXTUS; English studies in Italy. see LITERATURE

410 US
THEMATIC STUDIES IN SECOND LANGUAGE LEARNING AND ACQUISITION. 1990. irreg. price varies. Ablex Publishing Corporation, 355 Chestnut St., Norwood, NJ 07648. TEL 201-767-8450.
FAX 201-767-6717. TELEX 135-393. Ed. Robert J. DiPietro.

410 GW ISSN 0301-4428
P1
THEORETICAL LINGUISTICS. 1974. 2/yr. DM.190. Walter de Gruyter und Co., Genthiner Str. 13, 10785 Berlin, Germany. TEL 030-26005-0. FAX 030-26005251. TELEX 184027. (U.S. addr.: Walter de Gruyter, Inc. 200 Saw Mill Rd., Hawthorne, NY 10532) Ed. Helmut Schnelle. adv.; bk.rev. **Indexed:** Arts & Hum.Cit.Ind., Bibl.Ling., Lang.& Lang.Behav.Abstr. (1974-), Lang.Teach.& Ling.Abstr., Math.R. **Document type:** academic/scholarly publication.
—BLDSC (8814.560000); Faxon; UnCover; SWETS. CCC.

410 US ISSN 1051-6670
THEORETICAL STUDIES IN SECOND LANGUAGE ACQUISITION. irreg. Peter Lang Publishing, Inc., 62 W. 45th St., 4th Fl., New York, NY 10036.
TEL 212-302-6740. FAX 212-302-7574. Ed. Simon Belasco. **Document type:** academic/scholarly publication.
Description: Brings together research conducted in "naturalistic" as well as classroom acquisition. Focuses on the acquisition of pragmatic (extralinguistic) knowledge and the acquisition of grammatical (linguistic) knowledge.

400 CK ISSN 0040-604X
THESAURUS. Variant title: Instituto Caro y Cuervo. Boletin. 1945. 3/yr. Col.$7500. Instituto Caro y Cuervo, Seccion de Publicaciones, Apdo. Aereo 51502, Bogota, Colombia. Ed. Jose Manuel Rivas Sacconi. bk.rev.; abstr.; charts; illus.; index, cum.index: vols.1-25 (1945-1970), vols.26-41 (1971-1986). circ. 2,400. **Indexed:** Bibl.Ling., Hisp.Amer.Per.Ind, Lang.Teach.& Ling.Abstr., M.L.A.
—Faxon; SWETS.

439 NE ISSN 0166-4379
TIJDSCHRIFT VOOR TAALBEHEERSING. 1978. 4/yr. fl.99 to individuals; institutions fl.135; students fl.80. WoltersgroepGroningen b.v. (Subsidiary of: Wolters Kluwer N.V.), Postbus 58, 9700 MB Groningen, Netherlands. TEL 31-50-226922. FAX 31-50-264866. Ed.Bd. adv.; bk.rev.
—SWETS.

410 375.9 GW
TIRO. (Text in German and Latin) 1954. 6/yr. DM.7.20. Beacon-Verlag Koerber oHG, Birkental 13, Postfach 1420, 67098 Bad Duerkheim, Germany.

490 375.4 GW
TITO. locosa, lucunda, Seria. 1954. 6/yr. DM.9.60. Beacon Verlag Koerber oHG, Birkental 13, Postfach 1161, 67098 Bad Duerkheim, Germany. circ. 2,500. (tabloid format)

TODAY IN ENGLISH. see CHILDREN AND YOUTH — For

TOHOKU GAKUIN UNIVERSITY REVIEW; essays and studies in English language and literature. see LITERATURE

410 JA ISSN 0389-3081
PB5
TOKAI DAIGAKU KIYO. GAIKOKUGO KYOIKU SENTA/TOKAI UNIVERSITY. FOREIGN LANGUAGE CENTER. BULLETIN. (Text mainly in Japanese; contents page in various languages) 1981. a. free. Tokai Daigaku, Gaikokugo Kyoiku Senta - Tokai University, Foreign Language Center, 1117 Kitakaname, Hiratsuka-shi, Kanagawa-ken 259-12, Japan. circ. 700. **Document type:** bulletin.
Description: Contains articles on languages, literature, and related subjects. Emphasizes articles concerned with psychological insights into literature.

052 GW
TOPICS IN ENGLISH LINGUISTICS. irreg. Walter de Gruyter und Co., Mouton Publishers, Genthiner Str. 13, 10785 Berlin, Germany. TEL 030-260050. FAX 030-26005251. (U.S. addr.: Mouton de Gruyter, Division of Walter de Gruyter, Inc., 200 Saw Mill River Rd., Hawthorne, NY 10532) **Indexed:** Bibl.Ling.

LINGUISTICS

410   **US**
TOPICS IN SOCIOLINGUISTICS.* (Text in English) 1982. irreg., no.9, 1990. Walter de Gruyter, Inc., 200 Saw Mill River Rd., Hawthorne, NY 10532. TEL 914-747-0110. FAX 914-747-1326. Ed. Marinel Gerritsen.

400   **CN**   ISSN 0822-7373
LE TOPONYME. (Text in French) 1983. 2/yr. free. Commission de Toponymie, 1245 Chemin Ste. Foy, PQ G1S 4P2, Canada. TEL 418-643-8660. FAX 418-644-9466. bk.rev. circ. 5,000. **Document type:** bulletin, newsletter, government publication.

TORONTO OLD ENGLISH SERIES. see *LITERATURE*

LA TORRE. see *LITERATURE*

418   **BL**   ISSN 0103-1813
TRABALHOS EM LINGUISTICA APLICADA. 1983. s-a. exchange basis. Universidade Estadual de Campinas, Instituto de Estudos da Linguagem, Caixa Postal 6045, 13081-970 Campinas SP, Brazil. FAX 55-192-391501. **Document type:** academic/scholarly publication.
   Description: Presents studies in applied linguistics.

418.02   **FR**   ISSN 0395-773X
P306.A1
TRADUIRE. (Includes yearbook) 1953. q. 230 F. Societe Francaise des Traducteurs, 22 rue des Martyrs, 75009 Paris, France. TEL 48-78-43-32. FAX 44-53-01-14. Ed. Maurice Voituriez. adv.; bk.rev.; bibl. circ. 2,000. (tabloid format) **Indexed:** Lang.& Lang.Behav.Abstr. (1979-). **Document type:** academic/scholarly publication.
   Description: Features general interest articles on different aspects of translation in the literary, scientific and technical fields, reviews of works, analyses of specialized magazines and technical glossaries.

410   **IT**
TRADUZIONE, SOCIETA E CULTURA. 1991. irreg. (Universita degli Studi di Trieste, Scuola Superiore di Lingue Moderne per Interpreti e Traduttori) Franca Campanotto Editore, Via Michelini 1, 33100 Udine, Italy. TEL 0432-699390. FAX 0432-699390. **Document type:** monographic series.

TRANSLATION (NEW YORK, 1972). see *LITERATURE*

418.02   **US**
TRANSLATION (NEW YORK, 1977); a quarterly samizdat journal of materials for a history of American translation. 1977. q. Translation Index, 175 W. 87th St., No. 24A, New York, NY 10024.

418.02 807   **UK**   ISSN 0968-1361
TRANSLATION AND LITERATURE. a. £21.50. Edinburgh University Press, 22 George Sq., Edinburgh EH8 9LF, Scotland. TEL 031-650-4218. FAX 031-662-0053. Ed. Stuart Gillespie. adv. contact: Kathryn MacLean. **Document type:** academic/scholarly publication.
   Description: Contains articles, notes and reviews on literary translations of all kinds and periods, emphasizing English literature in its foreign relations.
   Refereed Serial

418.02 028.1   **US**   ISSN 0737-4836
PN241.A1
TRANSLATION REVIEW. 1978. 3/yr. $30 to individuals; institutions $125. American Literary Translators Association, University of Texas at Dallas, Box 830688, Richardson, TX 75083-0688. TEL 214-690-2093. FAX 214-705-6303. Ed. Rainer Schulte. adv.; bk.rev. circ. 1,000. (back issues avail.) **Indexed:** Amer.Bibl.Slavic & E.Eur.Stud.; Arts & Hum.Cit.Ind., Curr.Cont., M.L.A.
—BLDSC (9024.908000); Faxon; UnCover; SWETS; UMI.
   Description: Publishes articles on the art and craft of translation, interviews with well known translators, criticisms of recently published translations, profiles of publishers of translations.
   Refereed Serial

410   **US**
TRANSLATION SERVICES DIRECTORY. 1965. biennial. $50 to non-members; members $35. American Translators Association, 1735 Jefferson Davis Hwy., Ste. 903, Arlington, VA 22202-3413. TEL 703-412-1500. FAX 703-412-1501. **Document type:** directory.
   Formerly: A T A Professional Services Directory (ISSN 0567-4263)
   Description: Focuses on ATA active and accredited members who accept translating or interpreting assignments; indexed by subject area, source and target languages.

440 375.4   **FR**   ISSN 0765-1635
TRAVAUX DE DIDACTIQUE DU FRANCAISE LANGUE ETRANGERE. 1979. s-a. 70 F. (foreign 90 F.) Universite de Montpellier (Universite Paul Valery), Centre de Formation Pedagogique pour l'Enseignement du Francais a l'Etranger, B.P. 5043, 34032 Montpellier Cedex 1, France. TEL 67-14-23-26. circ. 300.
   Description: Aims to bring together teacher-trainers, both in France and abroad, and to keep teachers and future teachers informed about the latest research and its applications in the field of teaching French as a foreign-language.

440   **SW**   ISSN 0347-2558
TRAVAUX DE L'INSTITUTE DE LINGUISTIQUE DE LUND. (Text in English, French, German and Swedish) 1959. irreg. price varies. Lund University Press, P.O. Box 141, S-221 00 Lund, Sweden. TEL 46-46-31-20-00. FAX 46-46-30-53-38. Eds. G. Bruce, B. Sigurd. **Document type:** academic/scholarly publication.

410   **BE**   ISSN 0082-6049
TRAVAUX DE LINGUISTIQUE. (Text in French) 1969. s-a. 1950 BEF (Europe 2200 BEF; elsewhere 2250 BEF) (effective 1994). (Rijksuniversiteit te Gent, Dienst voor Franse Linguistiek - State University of Ghent, Department of French Linguistics) Editions Duculot S.A., Av. de Lauzelle 65, B-1348 Louvain-la-Neuve, Belgium. TEL 32-10-471911. FAX 32-10-471925. (Dist. by: De Boeck Universite, Fond Jean-Paques 4, B-1348 Louvain-la-Neuve, Belgium. TEL 32-10-482509. FAX 32-10-482519) Eds. D. Willems, M. Wilmet. adv.; bk.rev. **Indexed:** Bibl.Ling.; Lang.& Lang.Behav.Abstr. (1979-). **Document type:** academic/scholarly publication.
   Description: Covers French and general linguistics and philology.

400   **FR**   ISSN 0082-6057
PC2
TRAVAUX DE LINGUISTIQUE ET DE LITTERATURE. 1963. 2 vols. per yr. price varies. (Universite de Strasbourg II, Centre de Philologie et de Litteratures Romanes) Editions Klincksieck, 11 rue de Lille, 75007 Paris, France. Ed. George Straka. **Indexed:** Lang.& Lang.Behav.Abstr., M.L.A.

375.4   **FR**   ISSN 0995-2411
TRAVAUX LINGUISTIQUES DU C E R L I C O. 1986. irreg., latest no. 5, 1992. (Cercle Linguistique du Centre et de l'Ouest) Presses Universitaires de Rennes, 2 rue du Doyen D. Leroy, 35044 Rennes Cedex, France. TEL 99-54-66-35. FAX 99-33-07-95.
   Description: Promotes linguistic research in the universities of the Grand-Ouest.

420 375.4 384.5   **FR**   ISSN 0989-6686
TRIBUNE VIDEO DES ANGLICISTES. 1987. irreg., latest 1992. (Groupe de Recherche sur les Applications de la Video) Presses Universitaires de Rennes, 2 rue du Doyen D. Leroy, 35044 Rennes Cedex, France. TEL 99-54-66-35. FAX 99-33-07-95.
   Description: Studies the use of video in the teaching of English in high schools and universtties.

410   **GW**
TUDUV-STUDIE. REIHE SPRACH- UND LITERATURWISSENSCHAFTEN. 1975. irreg. price varies. Tuduv Verlagsgesellschaft mbH, Gabelsbergerstr. 15, 8000 Munich 2, Germany.

410   **GW**
TUEBINGER BEITRAEGE ZUR LINGUISTIK. irreg., no.398, 1994. DM.68. Gunter Narr Verlag, Postfach 2567, 72015 Tuebingen, Germany. TEL 07071-78091. FAX 07071-75288. **Document type:** monographic series.

494   **BE**   ISSN 0082-6847
DR401
TURCICA; REVUE D'ETUDES TURQUES. (Supplement avail.: Cahiers Turcica) (Text in English, French, German) 1969. a. 2000 BEF (effective 1994). (Universite des Sciences Humaines de Strasbourg, Association pour le Developpement des Etudes Turques, FR) Editions Peeters s.p.r.l., Bondgenotenlaan 153, B-3000 Louvain, Belgium. TEL 32-16-235170. FAX 32-16-228500. (Co-sponsors: Institut Francais d'Etudes Anatoliennes a Istanbul, TU; Universite de Paris, Institut des Etudes Turques, FR) Ed. I. Melikoff. adv.; bk.rev.; index. **Indexed:** Amer.Hist.& Life, Bibl.Ling., Hist.Abstr. **Document type:** academic/scholarly publication.
—BLDSC (9071.840000).

TURK DILI. see *LITERATURE*

450 370   **UK**   ISSN 0957-1752
TUTTITALIA. 1990. s-a. £20($40) (overseas £21). Association for Language Learning, 16 Regent Pl., Rugby, Warks. CV21 2PN, England. TEL 44-788-546443. FAX 44-788-544149. Ed. Andrew Wilkin. film rev.; play rev.; rec.rev.; abstr.; bibl.; charts; illus.; stat.; index. circ. 1,000. **Document type:** academic/scholarly publication.
—BLDSC (9076.178300).
   Formerly: Association of Teachers of Italian. Journal.
   Description: Contains articles and information for teachers and students of Italian.

410   **SA**   ISSN 0259-9570
TYDSKRIF VIR TAALONDERRIG. (Text in Afrikaans, English) 1966. q. R.40. Rand Afrikaans University, P.O. Box 524, Auckland Park 2006, South Africa. FAX 27-11-489-2790. Ed. Ninon Roets. cum.index. circ. 400. (back issues avail.) **Document type:** academic/scholarly publication.
   Description: Research in language teaching at the secondary and higher education levels.

400   **US**   ISSN 0167-7373
TYPOLOGICAL STUDIES IN LANGUAGE. 1982. irreg., vol.26, 1993. price varies. John Benjamins Publishing Co., 821 Bethlehem Pike, Philadelphia, PA 19118. TEL 215-836-1200. FAX 215-836-1204. (And: Amsteldijk 44, P.O. Box 75577, 1070 AN Amsterdam, Netherlands. TEL 020-6762325) Ed.Bd. (back issues avail.) **Indexed:** Bibl.Ling. **Document type:** monographic series.
—BLDSC (9077.630000).
   Description: Collects data from a wide variety of languages and language typologies.

410   **US**
U C L A OCCASIONAL PAPERS IN LINGUISTICS. 1972. irreg., no.13, 1993. price varies. University of California at Los Angeles, Department of Linguistics, 405 Hilgard Ave., 3125 Campbell Hall, Los Angeles, CA 90024-1543. TEL 310-825-0634. (back issues avail.) **Indexed:** Lang.& Lang.Behav.Abstr. (1984-). **Document type:** academic/scholarly publication.

491.79   **KR**   ISSN 0041-6096
UKRAINS'KA MOVA I LITERATURA V SHKOLI; metodychnyi zhurnal. 1951. m. 13.80 Rub. Ministerstvo Osvity, Yuriya Kotzyubyns'koho 5, Kiev 1, Ukraine. Ed. P.D. Mysnyk. bk.rev.; bibl.; index. circ. 45,950. **Indexed:** Bibl.Ling.

478 499   **GW**
UNITARIO; zurnalo poliglotte de latino moderne. (Text in German and Unitario) 1990. q. DM.16. European Center for the Promotion of Unitario, Postfach 1825, 64608 Bensheim, Germany.

U.S. GEOLOGICAL SURVEY. BOARD ON GEOGRAPHIC NAMES. DECISIONS ON GEOGRAPHIC NAMES IN THE UNITED STATES. see *GEOGRAPHY*

410   **SP**   ISSN 0212-8047
UNIVERSIDAD DE LA LAGUNA. ANUARIOS; ciencias humanas. 1980. a. $15 to individuals; institutions $20. Universidad de la Laguna, Secretariado de Publicaciones, San Agustin, 30, 38201 La Laguna-Tenerife, Islas Canarias, Spain. TEL 922-25-81-27. bk.rev.

LINGUISTICS

410   UY   ISSN 0250-6548
UNIVERSIDAD DE LA REPUBLICA. FACULTAD DE HUMANIDADES Y CIENCIAS. REVISTA. SERIE LINGUISTICA. N.S. 1979. irreg. exchange basis. Universidad de la Republica, Facultad de Humanidades y Ciencias, Seccion Revista, Tristan Narvaja 1674, Montevideo, Uruguay. Dir. Beatriz Martinez Osorio.
   Supersedes in part: Universidad de la Republica. Facultad de Humanidades y Ciencias. Revista.

440 375.4   SP   ISSN 0213-2958
UNIVERSIDAD DE MURCIA. ANALES DE FILOLOGIA FRANCESA. 1985. irreg. 1000 ptas.($10) Universidad de Murcia, Secretariado de Publicaciones e Intercambio Cientifico, Santo Cristo, 1, 30001 Murcia, Spain. TEL 968-363012. FAX 968-363414. Ed. Jesus Ros del Moral. circ. 300. **Document type:** academic/scholarly publication.

410 860   SP   ISSN 0210-4911
UNIVERSIDAD DE MURCIA. ESTUDIOS ROMANICOS. 1978. irreg., vol.3, 1986. 1500 ptas. Universidad de Murcia, Departamento de Filologia Romanica, Secretariado de Publicaciones e Intercambio Cientifico, Santo Cristo 1, 30001 Murcia, Spain.

410   SP
UNIVERSIDAD DE NAVARRA. COLECCION I.L.C.E. 1976. irreg. price varies. (Instituto de Lengua y Cultura Espanola) Ediciones Universidad de Navarra, S.A., Apdo. 396, 31080 Pamplona, Spain. TEL 94 825 6850.

UNIVERSIDAD NACIONAL AUTONOMA DE MEXICO. INSTITUTO DE INVESTIGACIONES FILOSOFICAS. CUADERNOS. see *PHILOSOPHY*

410   BL
UNIVERSIDADE DE SAO PAULO. CENTRO DE ESTUDOS PORTUGUESES. BOLETIM INFORMATIVO. 1975. 2/yr. Universidade de Sao Paulo, Centro de Estudos Portugueses, Cidade Universitaria "Armando de Salles Oliveira", C.P. 8105, 05508 Sao Paulo, Brazil. Ed. Carlos Felipe Moises. bk.rev. circ. 1,500.

410   IT
UNIVERSITA DEGLI STUDI DI FIRENZE. DIPARTIMENTO DI LINGUISTICA. QUADERNI. 1990. irreg. L.30000. Unipress s.a.s., Via Cesare Battisti 231, 35121 Padova, Italy. TEL 049-8752542. FAX 049-8752542. **Indexed:** Bibl.Ling.
   Description: Covers linguistics, historical linguistics and theory of language.

489   IT
UNIVERSITA DEGLI STUDI DI GENOVA. ISTITUTO DI ARCHEOLOGIA E FILOLOGIA CLASSICA "F. DELLA CORTE". PUBBLICAZIONI. 1952. irreg. price varies. Universita degli Studi di Genova, Istituto di Archeologia e Filologia Classica "F. Della Corte", Via Balbi 4, 3p, 16126 Genoa, Italy. TEL 209-97-22. (Dist. by: Tilgher Genova s.a.s., Via Assarotti, 51, 16152 Genoa, Italy) **Document type:** academic/scholarly publication.
   Formerly: Universita degli Studi di Genova. Istituto di Filologia Classica e Medievale. Pubblicazioni (ISSN 0072-0852)

UNIVERSITA DEGLI STUDI DI MACERATA. FACOLTA DI LETTERE E FILOSOFIA. ANNALI. see *ARCHAEOLOGY*

400   IT
UNIVERSITA DI URBINO. ISTITUTO DI LINGUISTICA. QUADERNI. no.4, 1986. irreg., no.6, 1989. price varies. Edizioni Quattroventi, Via Dini 16, Casella Postale 156, 61029 Urbino, Italy. TEL 0722-2588. FAX 0722-320998.

410   RM   ISSN 0379-7880
P1.A1
UNIVERSITATEA "AL. I. CUZA" DIN IASI. ANALELE STIINTIFICE. SECTIUNEA 3E: LINGVISTICA. (Text in English, French, German, Rumanian, Russian, Spanish) 1955. a. 35 lei. Universitatea "Al. I. Cuza" din Iasi, Calea M. Eminescu 11, Jassy, Rumania. (Subscr. to: ILEXIM, Str. 13 Decembrie Nr. 3, Box 136-137, Bucharest, Rumania) Ed. D. Irimia. bk.rev.; abstr.; charts; illus. circ. 300.
   Description: Studies on the general theory of language, linguistics, stylistics and poetics.

410   RM
UNIVERSITATEA BUCURESTI. ANALELE. FILOLOGIE. (Text in English, French, Italian, Rumanian; summaries in Russian) a. $10. Universitatea Bucuresti, Bd. Gh. Gheorghiu-Dej Nr. 64, Bucharest, Rumania.

400   RM   ISSN 0082-4461
UNIVERSITATEA DIN TIMISOARA. ANALELE. STIINTE FILOLOGICE. 1962. a. $30. Universitatea din Timisoara, Faculty of Philology, Bd. Vasile Parvan nr.4, 1900 Timisoara, Rumania. (Subscr. to: ILEXIM, Calea Grivitei 64-66, Box 136-137, Bucharest, Rumania) (Co-sponsor: Ministry of Education) Ed. Simion Mioc. bk.rev. circ. 250. **Indexed:** Bibl.Ling., Lang.& Lang.Behav.Abstr. (1971-).

400   HU   ISSN 0583-5356
UNIVERSITATIS DEBRECENIENSIS DE LUDOVICO KOSSUTH NOMINATAE. INSTITUTI PHILOLOGIAE SLAVICAE. ANNALES. SLAVICA. (Text in several languages) 1961. irreg., vol.26, 1993. $10. Kossuth Lajos Tudomanyegyetem, Szlav Filologiai Tanszek - Kossuth University, Department of Slavic Languages, Egyetem Ter 1, P.O. Box 53, 4010 Debrecen, Hungary. FAX 36-52-10-936. TELEX 72-200 UNIV K H. Ed. Zoltan Hajnady. adv.; bk.rev.; bibl. circ. 700. **Indexed:** Bibl.Ling.

UNIVERSITATIS SCIENTIARUM DEBRECENIENSIS. ACTA CLASSICA. see *CLASSICAL STUDIES*

410   BE   ISSN 0577-1765
UNIVERSITE CATHOLIQUE DE LOUVAIN. CENTRE INTERNATIONAL DE DIALECTOLOGIE GENERALE. TRAVAUX. 1955. a. price varies. (Universite Catholique de Louvain, Centre International de Dialectologie Generale) Editions Peeters s.p.r.l., Bondgenotenlaan 153, B-3000 Louvain, Belgium. TEL 32-16-235170. FAX 32-16-228500. (back issue avail.) **Document type:** monographic series.

UNIVERSITE CATHOLIQUE DE LOUVAIN. FACULTE DE PHILOSOPHIE ET LETTRES. TRAVAUX. see *HUMANITIES: COMPREHENSIVE WORKS*

400   BE   ISSN 0076-1249
UNIVERSITE CATHOLIQUE DE LOUVAIN. INSTITUT DES LANGUES VIVANTES. CAHIERS. (Text in various languages) 1967. irreg., no.30, 1986. Universite Catholique de Louvain, Institut des Langues Vivantes, B-3000 Leuven, Belgium.

400 900   BE   ISSN 0076-1311
UNIVERSITE CATHOLIQUE DE LOUVAIN. RECUEIL DE TRAVAUX D'HISTOIRE ET DE PHILOLOGIE. (Text in Dutch, English, French) 1904. irreg., 6th series, no.31, 1985. price varies. Editions Peeters s.p.r.l., Bondgenotenlaan 153, B-3000 Louvain, Belgium. TEL 32-16-235170. FAX 32-16-228500. TELEX 65981 PULB. **Document type:** academic/scholarly publication.

440 840   DK   ISSN 0107-7392
UNIVERSITE D'ODENSE. ETUDES ROMANES. (Text in Danish, English and French) 1971. irreg. price varies. Odense University Press, Campusvej 55, DK-5230 Odense M, Denmark. TEL 66-157999. FAX 66-158126. (back issues avail.)

410   FR
UNIVERSITE DE GRENOBLE III. INSTITUT DE PHONETIQUE. TRAVAUX. SERIE A: MANUALS. irreg. price varies. Universite de Grenoble III (Universite des Langues et Lettres), Institut de Phonetique, Domaine Universitaire de Saint-Martin-d'Heres, Boite Postale 25-X, 38040 Grenoble Cedex, France. TEL 76-44-82-18.
   Formerly: Universite de Grenoble. Institut de Phonetique. Manuels. Serie A (ISSN 0085-1264)

410   FR   ISSN 0085-1272
UNIVERSITE DE GRENOBLE III. INSTITUT DE PHONETIQUE. TRAVAUX. SERIE B: ETUDES LINGUISTIQUES. 1967. irreg. price varies. Universite de Grenoble III (Universite des Langues et Lettres), Institut de Phonetique, Domaine Universitaire de Saint-Martin-d'Heres, Boite Postal 25-X, 38040 Grenoble Cedex, France. TEL 76-44-82-18.

410   FR   ISSN 0756-7138
                   CODEN: LXIQE2
UNIVERSITE DE LILLE III. LEXIQUE. 1982. a. (University de Lille III) Presses Universitaires de Lille, B.P. 199, 59654 Villeneuve d'Ascq Cedex, France. TEL 20-91-65-35. FAX 20-91-03-95. Ed. Pierre Corbin.

410   ZR
UNIVERSITE DE LUBUMBASHI. CENTRE DE LINGUISTIQUE THEORIQUE ET APPLIQUEE AFRICANISTIQUE. irreg., no.18, 1988. Universite de Lubumbashi, Centre de Linguistique Theorique et Appliquee, B.P. 1607, Lubumbashi, Zaire. **Indexed:** Lang.& Lang..Behav.Abstr. (1975-).
   Formerly: Universite Nationale du Zaire, Lubumbashi. Centre de Linguistique Theorique et Appliquee Africanistique.
   Description: Publishes articles related to Africa especially in the areas of literary and educational linguistics.

410   ZR
UNIVERSITE DE LUBUMBASHI. CENTRE DE LINGUISTIQUE THEORIQUE ET APPLIQUEE. BULLETIN DE LIAISON, ENSEIGNMENT DES LANGUES. 1974. irreg., no.14. $10. Universite de Lubumbashi, Centre de Linguistique Theorique et Appliquee, B.P. 1607, Lubumbashi, Zaire.
   Former titles: Universite National de Zaire, Lubumbashi. Centre de Linguistique Theorique et Applique. Bulletin de Liaison, Enseignment des Langues; Universite Nationale du Zaire, Lubumbashi. Centre de Linguistique Theorique et Appliquee. Bulletin de Liaison.

410   ZR
UNIVERSITE DE LUBUMBASHI. CENTRE DE LINGUISTIQUE THEORIQUE ET APPLIQUEE. LINGUISTIQUE ET SCIENCES HUMAINES. BULLETIN D'INFORMATION. irreg., no.27, 1986. Universite de Lubumbashi, Centre de Linguistique Theorique et Appliquee, B.P. 1607, Lubumbashi, Zaire.
   Former titles: Universite Nationale du Zaire, Lubumbashi. Centre de Linguistique Theorique et Appliquee. Linguistique et Sciences Humaines. Bulletin d'Information; Universite Nationale du Zaire, Lubumbashi. Centre de Linguistique Theorique et Appliquee. Bulletin d'Information.
   Description: Publishes articles on the interaction of languages in Africa as well as African society in general.

UNIVERSITE DE NANCY II. CENTRE DE RECHERCHES ET D'APPLICATIONS PEDAGOGIQUES EN LANGUES. MELANGES. see *EDUCATION — Teaching Methods And Curriculum*

479   FR   ISSN 0081-5918
UNIVERSITE DE STRASBOURG II. CENTRE DE PHILOLOGIE ET LITTERATURES ROMANES. ACTES ET COLLOQUES. 1963. irreg. price varies. (Universite de Strasbourg II, Centre de Philologie et de Litteratures Romanes) Editions Klincksieck, 11 rue de Lille, 75007 Paris, France.

400   FR   ISSN 0081-5934
UNIVERSITE DE STRASBOURG II. INSTITUT DE PHONETIQUE. TRAVAUX. 1970. a. exchange basis. Universite de Strasbourg II, Institut de Phonetique, 22 rue Descartes, 67084 Strasbourg Cedex, France. FAX 88-41-73-54. circ. 600.

UNIVERSITE DE TUNIS. ECOLE NORMALE SUPERIEURE. SECTION A: LETTRES ET SCIENCES HUMAINES. SERIE 1: LANGUE ET LITTERATURE. see *LITERATURE*

UNIVERSITE SAINT-JOSEPH. FACULTE DES LETTRES ET DES SCIENCES HUMAINES. RECHERCHES. SERIE A: LANGUE ARABE ET PENSEE ISLAMIQUE. see *RELIGIONS AND THEOLOGY — Islamic*

410   NE
UNIVERSITEIT VAN AMSTERDAM. INSTITUUT VOOR ALGEMENE TAALWETENSCHAP. PUBLIKATIES. (Text in English and Dutch) 1971. irreg., vol.58, 1991. price varies. Universitat van Amsterdam, Instituut voor Algemene Taalwetenschap, Spuistr. 210, 1012 VT Amsterdam, Netherlands. TEL 020-5253864. FAX 020-5253052. Ed. Hans den Besten. bk.rev. circ. 150. **Indexed:** Bibl.Ling.

491.8 891.8   NO   ISSN 0803-2505
UNIVERSITETET I OSLO. SLAVISK-BALTISK AVDELING. MEDDELELSER. (Text in Norwegian, Russian and English) 1972. irreg. (3-5/yr.). price varies. Universitetet i Oslo, Slavisk-Baltisk Avdeling, P.O. Box 1030, N-0315 Oslo, Norway. FAX 47-22-85-41-40. Ed. Kjetil Ra Hauge. circ. 400. **Document type:** academic/scholarly publication.
   Formerly: Universitetet i Oslo. Slavisk-Baltisk Institutt. Meddelelser.

400   US   ISSN 0068-6484
UNIVERSITY OF CALIFORNIA PUBLICATIONS IN LINGUISTICS. 1945. irreg., vol.121, 1993. price varies. University of California Press, 2120 Berkeley Way, Berkeley, CA 94720. TEL 510-642-4247. FAX 510-643-7127. (Orders to: California-Princeton Fulfillment Services, 1445 Lower Ferry Rd., Ewing, NJ 08618. TEL 800-777-4726. FAX 800-999-1958) Ed.Bd. (reprint service avail. from KTO) **Indexed:** Bibl.Ling. **Document type:** monographic series.
Refereed Serial

400   US   ISSN 0068-6492
PB13
UNIVERSITY OF CALIFORNIA PUBLICATIONS IN MODERN PHILOLOGY. 1909. irreg., vol.127, 1993. price varies. University of California Press, 2120 Berkeley Way, Berkeley, CA 94720. TEL 510-642-4247. FAX 510-643-7127. (Orders to: California-Princeton Fulfillment Services, 1445 Lower Ferry Rd., Ewing, NJ 08618. TEL 800-777-4726. FAX 800-999-1958) Ed.Bd. (back issues avail.) **Document type:** monographic series.
—BLDSC (9105.600000).
Description: Publishes research on the study of languages from the medieval period to the present.
Refereed Serial

410   DK   ISSN 0589-6681
P215
UNIVERSITY OF COPENHAGEN. INSTITUTE OF PHONETICS. ANNUAL REPORT. 1967. a. free. University of Copenhagen, Institute of Phonetics, Njalsgade 96, DK-2300 Copenhagen, Denmark. Ed. Joergen Rishel. circ. 350. (back issues avail.) **Indexed:** Bibl.Ling., M.L.A.

410   GH
UNIVERSITY OF GHANA. INSTITUTE OF AFRICAN STUDIES. COLLECTED LANGUAGE NOTES. no.13, 1972. irreg., latest no.18, 1981. price varies. University of Ghana, Institute of African Studies, Box 73, Legon, Ghana.

496   NR   ISSN 0041-9613
P11
UNIVERSITY OF IBADAN. DEPARTMENT OF LINGUISTICS AND NIGERIAN LANGUAGES. RESEARCH NOTES.* 1967. irreg. University of Ibadan, Department of Linguistics and Nigerian Languages, Ibadan, Nigeria.

410   US
UNIVERSITY OF ILLINOIS AT URBANA-CHAMPAIGN. LANGUAGE LEARNING LABORATORY. TECHNICAL REPORTS. 1981. irreg., no.20, 1992. price varies. University of Illinois at Urbana-Champaign, Language Learning Laboratory, G70 Foreign Languages Bldg., 707 S. Matthews Ave., Urbana, IL 61801. TEL 217-333-1719. FAX 217-244-0190. (back issues avail.) **Document type:** monographic series.

494   II
UNIVERSITY OF KERALA. DEPARTMENT OF TAMIL. RESEARCH PAPERS. (Text in English or Tamil) 1970. a. Rs.30. University of Kerala, Department of Tamil, Kariavattom, Thiruvananthapuram 695 581, Kerala, India. TEL 418919. (Subscr. to: Director of Publications, University of Kerala, Thiruvananthapuram 695 034) Ed. L. Gloria Sundramathy. bk.rev.
Formerly (until 1974): University of Kerala. Department of Tamil. Journal.

410   SZ   ISSN 0256-1565
P1.A1
UNIVERSITY OF LAUSANNE. DEPARTEMENT DES LANGUES ET DES SCIENCES DU LANGAGE. CAHIERS. Short title: Cahiers du DLSL. 1984. s-a. 10 Fr. University of Lausanne, Departement des Langues et des Sciences du Langage, Faculty of Letters, Batiment des Facultes de Sciences Humaines, CH-1015 Lausanne, Switzerland. TEL 021-46 11 11. Ed. G. Peter Winnington. circ. 500.
Description: Prints lectures & papers presented in interdisciplinary seminars organized by the DLSL, psychology and neurology departments of the University of Lausanne.

490   II   ISSN 0076-2237
UNIVERSITY OF MADRAS. KANNADA SERIES.* irreg. University of Madras, Chepauk, Triplicane, Madras 600005, Tamil Nadu, India.

490   II   ISSN 0076-2245
UNIVERSITY OF MADRAS. MALAYALAM SERIES.* irreg. University of Madras, Chepauk, Triplicane, Madras 600005, Tamil Nadu, India.

490   II   ISSN 0076-2261
UNIVERSITY OF MADRAS. SANSKRIT SERIES.* irreg. University of Madras, Chepauk, Triplicane, Madras 600005, Tamil Nadu, India.

490   II   ISSN 0076-227X
UNIVERSITY OF MADRAS. TAMIL SERIES.* irreg. University of Madras, Chepauk, Triplicane, Madras 600005, Tamil Nadu, India.

490   II   ISSN 0076-2288
UNIVERSITY OF MADRAS. TELUGU SERIES.* irreg. University of Madras, Chepauk, Triplicane, Madras 600005, Tamil Nadu, India.

490   II   ISSN 0076-2296
UNIVERSITY OF MADRAS. URDU SERIES.* irreg. University of Madras, Chepauk, Triplicane, Madras 600005, Tamil Nadu, India.

UNIVERSITY OF MANITOBA ANTHROPOLOGY PAPERS. see *ANTHROPOLOGY*

410   US   ISSN 0085-123X
UNIVERSITY OF NORTHERN COLORADO. MUSEUM OF ANTHROPOLOGY. OCCASIONAL PUBLICATIONS IN ANTHROPOLOGY. LINGUISTICS SERIES. 1970. irreg. price varies. University of Northern Colorado, Museum of Anthropology, Attn. George E. Fay, Ed., Greeley, CO 80639. TEL 303-351-1890. circ. 300. (processed)

491.1   II
UNIVERSITY OF POONA. CENTRE OF ADVANCED STUDY IN SANSKRIT. DOCTORAL THESES AND OTHER SANSKRIT & PRAKRIT PUBLICATIONS. (Text in English, Prakrit, Sanskrit) 1961. irreg. price varies. University of Poona, Centre of Advanced Study in Sanskrit, Ganeshkhind, Poona 411 007, India. TEL 334220. (Subscr. to: Section Officer, Publications Branch, University of Poona, Poona 411 007, India) Ed. V.N. Jha. **Document type:** monographic series.

491.1   II   ISSN 0079-3809
UNIVERSITY OF POONA. CENTRE OF ADVANCED STUDY IN SANSKRIT. PUBLICATIONS. (Consists of series: Classes A through G.) (Text in English, Sanskrit) 1965. irreg. price varies. University of Poona, Centre of Advanced Study in Sanskrit, Ganeshkhind, Poona 411 007, India. TEL 334220. (Subscr. to: Section Officer, Publications Branch, University of Poona, Poona 411 007, India) Ed. V.N. Jha. **Document type:** monographic series.

491.1   II
UNIVERSITY OF POONA. CENTRE OF ADVANCED STUDY IN SANSKRIT. SANSKRIT AND PRAKRIT STUDIES. (Text in English, Prakrit, Sanskrit) 1959. irreg. price varies. University of Poona, Centre of Advanced Study in Sanskrit, Ganeshkhind, Poona 411 007, India. TEL 334220. (Subscr. to: Section Officer, Publications Branch, University of Poona, Poona 411 007, India) Ed. V.N. Jha. **Document type:** monographic series.

UNIVERSITY OF RAJASTHAN. STUDIES IN SANSKRIT AND HINDI. see *LITERATURE*

UNIVERSITY OF THE NORTH. COMMUNIQUE. see *EDUCATION*

UNIVERSITY OF TORONTO ROMANCE SERIES. see *LITERATURE*

410   XO   ISSN 0083-4173
PG5201
UNIVERZITA KOMENSKEHO. FILOZOFICKA FAKULTA. ZBORNIK: PHILOLOGICA. (Text of each volume in a different language: i.e. English, French, German, Hungarian, Slovak, Spanish) 1949. a. exchange basis. Univerzita Komenskeho, Filozoficka Fakulta, c/o Ustredna Kniznica Filozofickej Fakulty, Gondova 2, 818 01 Bratislava, Slovakia. illus.; maps. circ. 600. **Document type:** academic/scholarly publication.

375   PL   ISSN 0867-8510
UNIWERSYTET GDANSKI. WYDZIAL HUMANISTYCZNY. STUDIUM JEZYKOW OBCYCH. ZESZYTY NAUKOWE. (Text in English, French, German, Russian and Polish; summaries in German and English) 1976. irreg., latest no.4. price varies. Uniwersytet Gdanski, Wydzial Humanistyczny, c/o Biblioteka Glowna, Ul. Armii Krajowej 110, 81-824 Sopot, Poland. TEL 51-0061. TELEX 051 2247 BMOR PL. (Dist. by: Ars Polona-Ruch, Krakowskie Przedmiescie 7, 00-680 Warsaw, Poland) circ. 250. **Document type:** academic/scholarly publication.
Formerly (until 1990): Uniwersytet Gdanski. Studium Praktycznej Nauki Jezykow Obcych. Zeszyty Naukowe (ISSN 0324-8895).
Description: Contains theoretical and practical essays on developing speaking skills, professionally guided conversation (on different levels of language acquisition), and all types of studies.

400   PL   ISSN 0302-2315
UNIWERSYTET GDANSKI. WYDZIAL HUMANISTYCZNY. ZESZYTY NAUKOWE. FILOLOGIA POLSKA. PRACE JEZYKOZNAWCZE. 1973. irreg. price varies. Uniwersytet Gdanski, Wydzial Humanistyczny, c/o Biblioteka Glowna, Ul. Armii Krajowej 110, 81-824 Sopot, Poland. TEL 51-0061. TELEX 051 2247 BMOR PL. (Dist. by: Ars Polona-Ruch, Krakowskie Przedmiescie 7, 00-680 Warsaw, Poland) Ed. Edward Breza. circ. 250. **Document type:** academic/scholarly publication.
Description: Covers onomastics, stylistics, morphology, dialectics, phraseology, statistical description, and computer translation.

491.7 375.4   PL   ISSN 0208-4678
UNIWERSYTET GDANSKI. WYDZIAL HUMANISTYCZNY. ZESZYTY NAUKOWE. FILOLOGIA ROSYJSKA. (Text in Polish and Russian) 1971. irreg., latest no.18. price varies. Uniwersytet Gdanski, Wydzial Humanistyczny, c/o Biblioteka Glowna, Ul. Armii Krajowej 110, 81-824 Sopot, Poland. TEL 51-0061. TELEX 051 2247 BMOR PL. (Dist. by: Ars Polona-Ruch, Krakowskie Przedmiescie 7, 00-680 Warsaw, Poland) circ. 250. **Document type:** academic/scholarly publication.
Description: Linguistics of the contemporary and historical Russian. Studies in the history of Russian and Soviet literature.

420 375.4   PL   ISSN 1230-6185
P1
UNIWERSYTET GDANSKI. ZESZYTY NAUKOWE. FILOLOGIA ANGIELSKA. (Text in English) 1979. irreg., latest no.10. price varies. Uniwersytet Gdanski, Wydzial Humanistyczny, c/o Biblioteka Glowna, Ul. Armii Krajowej 110, 81-824 Sopot, Poland. TEL 51-0061. TELEX 051-2247 BMOR PL. (Dist. by: Ars Polona-Ruch, Krakowskie Przedmiescie 7, 00-680 Warsaw, Poland) **Document type:** academic/scholarly publication.
Former titles (until 1992): Uniwersytet Gdanski. Wydzial Humanistyczny. Zeszyty Naukowe. Filologia Angielska (ISSN 0239-9121); (until 1982): Uniwersytet Gdanski. Wydzial Humanistyczny. Zeszyty Naukowe. Linguistica et Anglica Gedaniensia (ISSN 0208-5240)
Description: Contains studies on English and American fiction, poetry and drama, on linguistics and on English language teaching.

410   PL   ISSN 1230-6053
UNIWERSYTET GDANSKI. ZESZYTY NAUKOWE. STUDIA SCANDINAVICA. (Text in English, German, Polish and Scandinavia languages) 1978. irreg., latest no.13. price varies. Uniwersytet Gdanski, Wydzial Humanistyczny, c/o Biblioteka Glowna, Ul. Armii Krajowej 110, 81-824 Sopot, Poland. TEL 51-0061. TELEX 051-2247 BMOR PL. (Dist. by: Ars Polona-Ruch, Krakowskie Przedmiescie 7, 00-680 Warsaw, Poland) Ed. Zenon Ciesielski. circ. 250. **Document type:** academic/scholarly publication.
Formerly (until 1991): Uniwersytet Gdanski. Wydzial Humanistyczny. Zeszyty Naukowe. Studia Scandinavica (ISSN 0138-063X)
Description: Includes articles and conference proceedings on literature, culture, linguistics, history, sociopolitical and economic problems of Scandinavian countries.

LINGUISTICS

410   PL   ISSN 0083-4378
PG6014
UNIWERSYTET JAGIELLONSKI. ZESZYTY NAUKOWE. PRACE JEZYKOZNAWCZE. (Text in Polish; summaries in French) 1956. irreg. price varies. Uniwersytet Jagiellonski, Ul. Golegia 24, 31-007 Krakow, Poland. (Dist. by: Ars Polona, Krakowskie Przedmiescie 7, 00-068 Warsaw, Poland) Ed. A. Heinz. circ. 550.
—BLDSC (9512.455000).

491.85   PL   ISSN 0209-3731
UNIWERSYTET SLASKI W KATOWICACH. PRACE NAUKOWE. JEZYK ARTYSTYCZNY. (Text in Polish; summaries in English and Russian) 1978. irreg. price varies. Wydawnictwo Uniwersytetu Slaskiego, Ul. Bankowa 12B, 40-007 Katowice, Poland. TEL 48-32-596-915. FAX 48-32-599-605. TELEX 0315584 USKPL. (Dist. by: CHZ Ars Polona, P.O. Box 1001, 00-950 Warsaw, Poland) Ed. Barbara Woznica. **Document type:** academic/scholarly publication.
Description: Covers: theory of text, linguistic theory of style, structure of narrative text, figurative language, semantics, semiotics and onomastics.

410   PL   ISSN 0208-5550
PB5
UNIWERSYTET SLASKI W KATOWICACH. PRACE NAUKOWE. NEOPHILOLOGICA. (Text in French; summaries in Polish and Russian) 1980. irreg. Wydawnictwo Uniwersytetu Slaskiego, Ul. Bankowa 12B, 40-007 Katowice, Poland. TEL 48-32-596-915. FAX 48-32-599-605. TELEX 0315584 USKPL. (Dist. by: CHS Ars Polona, P.O. Box 1001, 00-950 Warsaw, Poland) Ed. Barbara Woznica. **Document type:** academic/scholarly publication.
Description: Covers French linguistics, particularly syntax and semantics.

491.47   PL   ISSN 0208-5445
UNIWERSYTET SLASKI W KATOWICACH. PRACE NAUKOWE. PRACE JEZYKOZNAWCZE. (Text in Polish and Russian; summaries in English, Polish and Russian) 1969. irreg. price varies. Wydawnictwo Uniwersytetu Slaskiego, Ul. Bankowa 12B, 40-007 Katowice, Poland. TEL 48-32-596-915. FAX 48-32-599-605. TELEX 0315584 USKPL. (Dist. by: CHZ Ars Polona, P.O. Box 1001, 00-950 Warsaw, Poland) Ed. Barbara Woznica. **Indexed:** Bibl.Ling. **Document type:** academic/scholarly publication.
Description: Presents results of synchronus and diachronus studies on the Polish language and Slavonic language studies, principally Russian.

491.85   PL   ISSN 0208-5011
PG6065
UNIWERSYTET SLASKI W KATOWICACH. PRACE NAUKOWE. Z TEORII I PRAKTYKI DYDAKTYCZNEJ JEZYKA POLSKIEGO. (Text in Polish; summaries in English and Russian) 1977. irreg. Wydawnictwo Uniwersytetu Slaskiego, Ul. Bankowa 12B, 40-007 Katowice, Poland. TEL 48-32-596-915. FAX 48-32-599-605. TELEX 0315584 USKPL. (Dist. by: CHZ Ars Polona, P.O. Box 1001, 00-950 Warsaw, Poland) Ed. Barbara Woznica. **Document type:** academic/scholarly publication.
Description: Theoretical problems of teaching Polish language and literature.

430 370   US   ISSN 0042-062X
PF3065
UNTERRICHTSPRAXIS. (Text in English and German) 1967. s-a. $26 (foreign $31). American Association of Teachers of German, Inc., 112 Haddontowne Ct., Ste. 104, Cherry Hill, NJ 08034. TEL 609-795-5553. FAX 609-795-9398. Ed. George Peters. adv.; bk.rev.; bibl.; charts; illus. circ. 5,000. (also avail. in microfiche; reprint service avail. from UMI) **Indexed:** C.I.J.E., Educ.Ind., Lang.& Lang.Behav.Abstr., Lang.Teach.& Ling.Abstr., M.L.A. **Document type:** academic/scholarly publication.
—BLDSC (9121.320000); UnCover; UMI.
Description: Presents articles on language study and teaching methods.

479   GW   ISSN 0083-4580
UNTERSUCHUNGEN ZUR SPRACH- UND LITERATURGESCHICHTE DER ROMANISCHEN VOELKER. 1959. irreg., vol.11, 1986. price varies. (Akademie der Wissenschaften und der Literatur, Mainz, Kommission fuer Romanische Philologie) Franz Steiner Verlag Wiesbaden GmbH, Birkenwaldstr. 44, 70191 Stuttgart, Germany. TEL 0711-2582-0. FAX 0711-2582290. TELEX 723636-DAZ-D. (Subscr. to: Postfach 101061, 70009 Stuttgart, Germany) **Document type:** monographic series.

491.7 375.4   GW   ISSN 0174-0652
URAL-ALTAISCHE JAHRBUECHER. NEUE FOLGE. 1981. a. DM.148. Harrassowitz Verlag, Taunusstr. 14, 65183 Wiesbaden, Germany. TEL 0611-530-0. FAX 0611-530570. TELEX 4186135. (Subscr. to: Postfach 2929, 65019 Wiesbaden, Germany) Ed.Bd. bk.rev. circ. 400. **Indexed:** Bibl.Ling., M.L.A. **Document type:** academic/scholarly publication.

439.2   NE   ISSN 0042-1235
PF1401
US WURK; tydskrift foar Frisistyk. (Text in Dutch, English, French, Frisian, German) 1952. q. fl.25. Rijksuniversitet Groningen, Stifting Freonen Frysk Ynstitut, Oude Kijk in 't Jatstraat 26, 9712 EK Groningen, Netherlands. FAX 31-50-634900. TELEX 53410 RUGRO NL. Ed. O. Vries. charts; index. circ. 300. **Indexed:** Bibl.Ling., Lang.& Lang.Behav.Abstr., M.L.A. **Document type:** academic/scholarly publication.
Description: Scholarly journal on the Frisian language and literature.

UTAH STUDIES IN LITERATURE AND LINGUISTICS. see *LITERATURE*

▼**401**   NE   ISSN 0927-7706
UTRECHT STUDIES IN LANGUAGE AND COMMUNICATION. 1992. irreg. price varies. Editions Rodopi B.V., Keizersgracht 302-304, 1016 EX Amsterdam, Netherlands. TEL 31-20-6227507. FAX 31-20-6380948. (In N. America: 233 Peachtree St., N.E., Ste. 404, Atlanta, GA 30303-1504. TEL 800-225-3998. FAX 404-522-7116) **Document type:** academic/scholarly publication.

407   NE   ISSN 0165-9030
VAN TAAL TOT TAAL. (Text in Dutch, English, French and German) 1956. q. fl.50. Nederlands Genootschap van Vertalers, Prins Hendriklaan 3, 1404 AX Bussum, Netherlands. TEL 31-2159-51798. FAX 31-2159-46903. Ed. Frederick J.A. Mostert. adv.; bk.rev.; index. circ. 1,650. **Indexed:** Lang. & Lang.Behav.Abstr. **Document type:** academic/scholarly publication.
—BLDSC (9143.525000); SWETS.
Description: Features articles and glossaries as well as related subjects for professional translators and interpreters.

410   US   ISSN 0172-7362
VARIETIES OF ENGLISH AROUND THE WORLD. 1979. irreg., vol.T6, 1993. price varies. John Benjamins Publishing Co., 821 Bethlehem Pike, Philadelphia, PA 19118. TEL 215-836-1200. FAX 215-836-1204. (And: Amsteldijk 44, P.O. Box 75577, 1070 AN Amsterdam, Netherlands. TEL 020-6762325) (back issues avail.) **Indexed:** Bibl.Ling. **Document type:** monographic series.
Description: Irregularly published monographs on the English language world-wide.

420 820   PK   ISSN 0042-3483
VENTURE; bi-annual review of English language and literature. (Text in English) 1960. s-a. Rs.10($3.50) University of Karachi, Department of English, University Rd., Karachi 32, Pakistan. Ed. S.A. Ashraf. bk.rev.; bibl.; index. circ. 500.

460 375.4   SP   ISSN 0210-377X
VERBA; anuario galego de filoloxia. 1974. a. 4800 ptas. (effective 1992). Universidade de Santiago, Servicio de Publicacions e Intercambio Cientifico, Campus Universitario, 15706 Santiago de Compostela, Spain. TEL 81-59-35-00. FAX 81-59-39-63. bk.rev.; charts; index, cum.index. circ. 700. (back issues avail.) **Indexed:** Bibl.Ling., Lang.& Lang.Behav.Abstr. (1981-). **Document type:** academic/scholarly publication.

410   US   ISSN 0162-0932
PE1001
VERBATIM; the language quarterly. 1974. q. $16.50. 4 Laurel Heights, Old Lyme, CT 06371. TEL 203-434-2104. (Subscr. to: Verbatim, Box 78008, Indianapolis, IN 46278. TEL 800-999-2266) Ed. Laurence Urdang. adv.; bk.rev.; bibl.; circ. 8,000 (paid). **Indexed:** Arts & Hum.Cit.Ind., Curr.Cont., Lang.& Lang.Behav.Abstr., M.L.A. **Document type:** consumer publication.
—BLDSC (9155.756000).
Description: Contains informative articles and provocative correspondence.

410   FR   ISSN 0182-5887
VERBUM; revue de linguistique. 1978. q. 260 F. (foreign 320 F.). Presses Universitaires de Nancy, 25 rue Baron Louis, 54001 Nancy Cedex, France. TEL 83-37-37-65. Dir. Jean Marie Bonnet. circ. 500. **Indexed:** Bibl.Ling.

430   GW   ISSN 0342-0752
PF5601
VEREIN FUER NIEDERDEUTSCHE SPRACHFORSCHUNG. KORRESPONDENZBLATT. 1875. q. DM.10. Wachholtz Verlag GmbH, Rungestr. 4, 24537 Neumuenster, Germany. TEL 04321-906270. FAX 04321-906275. Ed. Hermann Niebaum. bk.rev.; bibl.; index. circ. 800. (back issues avail.) **Document type:** bulletin.

400 900   IT   ISSN 0042-5079
VICHIANA. 1964. s-a. L.50000 (foreign L.58000) (effective 1994). Loffredo Editore S.p.A., Via Conselvo, 99 H, 80126 Naples, Italy. TEL 081-5937073. FAX 081-5936953. Ed. Armando Salvatore. bk.rev.

460 370   UK   ISSN 0308-4957
CODEN: VIHIEC
VIDA HISPANICA. (Text in English, Portuguese, Spanish) 1990. s-a. £20($40) (overseas £21). Association for Language Learning, 16 Regent Pl., Rugby, Warks. CV21 2PN, England. TEL 44-788-546443. FAX 44-788-544149. Ed. Phil Turk. adv.; bk.rev.; film rev.; play rev.; record rev.; abstr.; bibl.; charts; illus.; mkt.; stat.; index. circ. 1,500. **Document type:** academic/scholarly publication.
—BLDSC (9232.860000).
Description: Contains articles and information for teachers and students of Spanish and Portugese.

VINYAR TENGWAR. see *LITERATURE*

494.541   FI   ISSN 0042-6806
PH101
VIRITTAAJAA. (Text in Finnish; summaries in English or German) 1897. q. FIM 230. Kotikielen Seura - Mother Tongue Society, Fabianinkatu 33, 00170 Helsinki, Finland. Ed. Matti Larjavaara. adv.; bk.rev.; charts; illus.; index, cum.index: 1897-1946; 1947-1956; 1957-1971; 1972-1986. circ. 1,000. (also avail. in microform from UMI) **Indexed:** Bibl.Ling., Lang.& Lang.Behav.Abstr., M.L.A.

491 954   II   ISSN 0083-6621
VISHVESHVARANAND INDOLOGICAL SERIES. (Text in English and Sanskrit) 1950. irreg., vol.73, 1982. price varies. Vishveshvaranand Vedic Research Institute, Sadhu Ashram, Hoshiarpur 146021, Punjab, India. Ed. S. Bhaskaran Nair.

VISIBLE LANGUAGE; the quarterly concerned with all that is involved in our being literate. see *COMMUNICATIONS*

470   FR   ISSN 0042-7306
VITA LATINA. (Text in Latin) 1957. 4/yr. 120 F. Universite de Montpellier (Universite Paul Valery), B.P. 5043, 34032 Montpellier Cedex, France. TEL 67-14-20-00. Ed. Marie-Dominique Joffre. adv.; bk.rev. circ. 800. **Indexed:** Bibl.Ling.
Description: Covers study and teaching of Latin language.

413.028   SP
VOCES (SALAMANCA). (Text in French, Spanish) 1990. a. 1500 ptas. Ediciones Universidad de Salamanca, Apdo. 325, 37080 Salamanca, Spain. TEL 923-26-14-54. (Universite de Caen) Eds. Carmen Codoner, Jean Pierre Etienvre. **Document type:** academic/scholarly publication.
Description: Includes studies in Romance language lexicography.

VOORZETTEN. see *LITERATURE*

LINGUISTICS

491.7 RU
VOPROSY RUSSKOGO YAZYKOZNANIYA. 1976. irreg. 1.21 Rub. per issue. Moskovskii Universitet, Pr. Gertsena 5-7, 103009 Moscow, Russia. Ed. K. Gorshkova. circ. 4,760.

400 RU ISSN 0042-8868
VOPROSY YAZYKOZNANIYA. 1952. bi-m. 32.10 Rub. (Rossiiskaya Akademiya Nauk, Institut Yazykoznaniya) Izdatel'stvo Nauka, 90 Profsoyuznaya ul., 117864 Moscow, Russia. TEL 095-336-0266. FAX 095-420-2220. (Dist. by: Mezhdunarodnaya Kniga, B. Yakimanka 39, 117049 Moscow, Russia) Ed. T.V. Gamkrelidze. bk.rev.; bibl.; charts; index. circ. 2,800. **Indexed:** Bibl.Ling., Lang.& Lang.Behav.Abstr. (1972-).

479 GW ISSN 0042-899X
PC1.A1
VOX ROMANICA; annales helvetici explorandis linguis romanicis destinati. (Text in English, French, German, Italian or Spanish) 1936. a. DM.120. Francke Verlag GmbH, Postfach 2560, 72015 Tuebingen, Germany. TEL 07071-78091. FAX 07071-75288. bk.rev.; bibl.; cum.index. circ. 550. **Indexed:** Bibl.Ling., Lang.& Lang.Behav.Abstr., M.L.A. **Document type:** academic/scholarly publication.
—BLDSC (9258.600000); SWETS. **CCC.**

400 SP ISSN 1130-3271
VOZ Y LETRA; revista de filologia. 1990. s-a. 4600 ptas.($44) Arco Libros, S.A., Juan Bautista de Toledo 28, 28002 Madrid, Spain. TEL 415-36-87. Eds. Manuel Alvar Ezquerra, Jose Lara Garrido.

VRIJE FRIES. see HISTORY — History Of Europe

410 IT ISSN 0393-8255
VS; quaderni di studi semiotici. Variant title: Versus. 1971. 3/yr. L.60000. R C S Libri e Grandi Opere S.p.A., Via Mecenate 91, 20138 Milan, Italy. Ed. Umberto Eco. adv.; bk.rev. **Indexed:** Bibl.Ling.

400 375.4 CC ISSN 1004-5139
WAIGUOYU/JOURNAL OF FOREIGN LANGUAGES. (Text mainly in Chinese, sometimes in English) 1978. bi-m. $31.50. (Shanghai International Studies University) Shanghai Foreign Language Education Press, 550 Dalian Xilu, Shanghai 200083, People's Republic of China. TEL 86-21-5420358. FAX 86-21-5420225. (Dist. in U.S. by: China Books & Periodicals, Inc. 2929 24th St., San Francisco, CA 94110. TEL 415-282-2994) Ed. Dai Weidong. adv.; bk.rev. circ. 5,000. **Document type:** academic/scholarly publication.

400 375.4 CC
WAIYU JIAOXUE YU YANJIU/FOREIGN LANGUAGE TEACHING & RESEARCH. (Text in Chinese; abstracts in English) 1957. q. $18.30. (Foreign Studies University) Foreign Lanaguage Teaching and Research Press, 2 North Xisanhuan Lu, Haidian District, Beijing 100081, People's Republic of China. TEL 842-2277. (Dist. outside China by: China International Book Trading Corp., P.O. Box 399, Beijing, P.R. China; Dist. in U.S. by: China Books and Periodicals, Inc., 2929 24th St., San Francisco, CA 94110. TEL 415-282-2994) Ed. Xu Guozhang. bk.rev. circ. 9,500.

400 CC ISSN 1000-0100
WAIYU XUEKAN/JOURNAL OF FOREIGN LANGUAGES. (Text in Chinese) q. $24.30. Heilongjiang Daxue, Waiyu Xi - Heilongjiang University, Foreign Language Department, Xuefu Lu, Harbin, Heilongjiang 150080, People's Republic of China. TEL 64941. (Dist. in US by: China Books & Periodicals, Inc., 2929 24th St., San Francisco, CA 94110. TEL 415-282-2994)

WELSH JOURNAL OF EDUCATION. see EDUCATION

491.7 GW ISSN 0043-2520
PG1
DIE WELT DER SLAVEN. (Text in English, French, German and Russian) 2/yr. DM.120. Verlag Otto Sagner, Postfach 340108, 80328 Munich, Germany. TEL 089-54218-0. FAX 089-54218218. TELEX 5216711-KUSAD. Ed. Peter Rehder. circ. 450. (back issues avail.) **Indexed:** Arts & Hum.Cit.Ind., Bibl.Ling. **Document type:** academic/scholarly publication.
—SWETS. **CCC.**

410 NR ISSN 0331-0531
WEST AFRICAN JOURNAL OF MODERN LANGUAGES/REVUE OUEST AFRICAINE DES LANGUES VIVANTES. 1976. a. $20. West African Modern Languages Association, c/o University of Maiduguri, Department of Languages and Linguistics, Borno State, Nigeria. Ed. C.M.B. Brann. adv.; bk.rev. circ. 1,000. **Indexed:** M.L.A.

428.3 301 US ISSN 1057-0314
PN4071 CODEN: WJSCDW
WESTERN JOURNAL OF COMMUNICATION. 1937. q. $36 (overseas $40)(includes Communication Reports). Western States Communication Association, c/o Dennis Alexander, Dept. of Communication, University of Utah, Salt Lake City, UT 84112. TEL 801-581-6526. FAX 801-585-6255. Ed. Sandra Petronio. adv.; cum.index. circ. 2,400. (also avail. in microform from UMI; back issues avail.; reprint service avail. from UMI) **Indexed:** Amer.Hist.& Life, C.I.J.E., Commun.Abstr., ERIC, Hist.Abstr., Lang.& Lang.Behav.Abstr., Psychol.Abstr., Sage Pub.Admin.Abstr. **Document type:** monographic series.
—BLDSC (9300.829300); Faxon; UnCover; UMI.
Former titles: Western Journal of Speech Communication (ISSN 0193-6700); Western Speech Communication; Western Speech (ISSN 0043-4205)
Description: Contains information about all areas of communication.

420 820 AU ISSN 0083-9914
PR13
WIENER BEITRAEGE ZUR ENGLISCHEN PHILOLOGIE. (Text in English, German) 1895. irreg., vol.79, 1983. price varies. Wilhelm Braumueller, Universitaets-Verlagsbuchhandlung GmbH, Servitengasse 5, A-1092 Vienna, Austria. TEL 0222-3191159. FAX 0222-3102805. Ed. Siegfried Korninger. index. circ. 600. **Indexed:** M.L.A. **Document type:** academic/scholarly publication.

400 AU ISSN 0083-9922
GN4
WIENER BEITRAEGE ZUR KULTURGESCHICHTE UND LINGUISTIK. 1930. irreg., vol.20, 1981. price varies. (Universitaet Wien, Institut fuer Voelkerkunde) Verlag Ferdinand Berger und Soehne GmbH, Wienerstr. 21-23, A-3580 Horn, Austria. TEL 02982-2317-0. **Document type:** monographic series.

400 800 AU ISSN 0084-0033
WIENER ROMANISTISCHE ARBEITEN. (Text in French, German) 1962. a. price varies. Wilhelm Braumueller, Universitaets Verlagsbuchhandlung GmbH, Servitengasse 5, A-1092 Vienna, Austria. TEL 0222-3191159. FAX 0222-3102805. Ed. Georg Kremnitz. index. circ. 600. **Document type:** academic/scholarly publication.

491.7 AU ISSN 0084-0041
PG1
WIENER SLAVISTISCHES JAHRBUCH/VIENNESE SLAVONIC YEARBOOK. (Text in English, French, German, Polish and Russian) 1950. a. price varies. (Universitaet Wien, Institut fuer Slavische Philologie) Verlag der Oesterreichischen Akademie der Wissenschaften, Dr. Ignaz-Seipel-Platz 2, A-1010 Vienna, Austria. FAX 0222-5139541. Ed.Bd. adv.; bk.rev.; bibl.; illus. **Indexed:** Arts & Hum.Cit.Ind., Bibl.Ling., Can.Rev.Comp.Lit, M.L.A.

400 890 AU ISSN 0258-6819
PG1
WIENER SLAVISTISCHER ALMANACH. (Text in Slavic and other European languages) 1978. 2/yr. DM.116. Gesellschaft zur Foerderung Slavistischer Studien Wien, Teschnergasse 4-17, A-1180 Vienna, Austria. (Subscr. to: Kubon und Sagner, Hesstr. 39, 80798 Munich, Germany) Ed.Bd. bk.rev. circ. 300. (back issues avail.) **Indexed:** Bibl.Ling., M.L.A. **Document type:** bulletin.

400 890 AU ISSN 0258-6835
WIENER SLAVISTISCHER ALMANACH. SONDERBAENDE. (Text in German, Russian) 1980. irreg. price varies. Gesellschaft zur Foerderung Slavistischer Studien Wien, Teschnergasse 4-17, A-1180 Vienna, Austria. (Subscr. to: Kubon und Sagner, Postfach 340108, 80328 Munich, Germany. TEL 089-54218-0. FAX 089-54218218) Eds. Aage Hansen-Loeve, Tilman Reuther. **Document type:** monographic series.

400 AU ISSN 0084-005X
PA3
WIENER STUDIEN. ZEITSCHRIFT FUER KLASSISCHE PHILOLOGIE UND PATRISTIK. (Text in Ancient Greek, English, German and Latin) 1897. a. price varies. (Universitaet Wien, Institut fuer Klassische Philologie) Verlag der Oesterreichischen Akademie der Wissenschaften, Dr. Ignaz-Seipel-Platz 2, A-1010 Vienna, Austria. FAX 0222-5139541. Ed.Bd. adv.; bk.rev.; bibl.; illus. (also avail. in microfiche from IDC; reprint service avail. from KTO) **Indexed:** Bibl.Ling.

370 440 GW ISSN 0043-6089
PF3003
WIRKENDES WORT; deutsche Sprache und Literatur in Forschung und Lehre. 1950. q. DM.90. Bouvier Verlag, Am Hof 28, 53113 Bonn, Germany. TEL 0228-7290141. FAX 0228-7290179. Ed. Heinz Roelleke. adv.; bk.rev.; bibl. index. circ. 3,500. **Indexed:** Bibl.Ling., Can.Rev.Comp.Lit., M.L.A. **Document type:** academic/scholarly publication.
—Faxon. **CCC.**

410 305.4 US ISSN 8755-4550
P120.W66
WOMEN AND LANGUAGE. 1976. s-a. $10 to individuals (Canada $13; elsewhere $18); institutions $15 (Canada $18; elsewhere $20); with membership $15 (effective 1994). George Mason University, Communication Department, 4400 University Dr., Fairfax, VA 22030-4444. TEL 703-993-1099. FAX 703-993-1096. (Co-sponsor: Organization for the Study of Communication Language and Gender) Ed. Anita Taylor. bk.rev.; bibl. circ. 450. (also avail. in microform from UMI; back issues avail.) **Indexed:** Wom.Stud.Abstr. (1976-).
—BLDSC (9343.268000); Faxon; UnCover; UMI.
Description: Features news items and short articles related to women, communication and language.

400 US ISSN 0043-7956
P1
WORD. 1945. 3/yr. $35 to individuals; students $25; institutions $55. International Linguistic Association, c/o Dr. Theodore S. Beardsley, Jr., Treas., Hispanic Society of America, 613 W. 155th St., New York, NY 10032. bk.rev.; bibl.; charts; index. (also avail. in microform from UMI; reprint service avail. from UMI) **Indexed:** A.I.C.P., Bibl.Ling., Ind.Bk.Rev.Hum., Lang.& Lang.Behav.Abstr. (1970-), Lang.Teach.& Ling.Abstr.
—BLDSC (9347.750000); Faxon; UnCover; SWETS; UMI.

410 US ISSN 0043-7980
GV1507.W8
WORD WAYS; journal of recreational linguistics. 1968. q. $20 (effective 1995). A. Ross Eckler, Ed.& Pub., Spring Valley Rd., Morristown, NJ 07960. TEL 201-538-4584. FAX 201-538-4584. adv.; bk.rev. circ. 500. (also avail. in microform from UMI; reprint service avail. from UMI) **Indexed:** Lang.& Lang.Behav.Abstr., M.L.A. **Document type:** academic/scholarly publication.
—BLDSC (9347.950000); Faxon; UnCover; UMI.
Description: Presents short (500-5000 words) expository articles on wordplay (anagrams, palindromes, word squares, pangrams, word ladders). Writing under literary constraint (lipograms, acrostics). Fictional and poetic treatment of wordplay subjects.

370 420 UK ISSN 0883-2919
PE1128.A2
WORLD ENGLISHES; journal of English as an international and intranational language. 1982. 3/yr. £120. Blackwell Publications, Ltd., 108 Cowley Rd., Oxford OX4 1JF, England. TEL 44-865-791155. FAX 44-865-791927. Ed. Braj B. Kachru. (also avail. in microform) **Indexed:** Cont.Pg.Educ., Lang.& Lang.Behav.Abstr. (1986-), Lang.Teach.& Ling.Abstr., Sociol.Abstr. **Document type:** academic/scholarly publication.
—BLDSC (9354.825500); UnCover; SWETS; UMI. **CCC.**
Formerly (until vol.4, no.2, 1985): World Language English (ISSN 0278-4335)
Description: Devoted to the study of global varieties of English in their distinctive cultural and sociolinguistic contexts.
Refereed Serial

WRITING RIGHT. see PUBLISHING AND BOOK TRADE

LINGUISTICS

491.85   PL   ISSN 0084-2990
WROCLAWSKIE TOWARZYSTWO NAUKOWE. KOMISJA JEZYKOWA. ROZPRAWY. (Text in English, German and Polish) 1957. irreg., vol.17, 1991. price varies. Ossolineum, Publishing House of the Polish Academy of Sciences, Rynek 9, Wroclaw, Poland. TEL 48-71-386-25. FAX 48-71-448-103. TELEX 0712771 OSS PL. **Indexed:** Bibl.Ling. **Document type:** academic/scholarly publication.
—BLDSC (8036.060000).
    Description: Papers on Polish and Indo-European linguistics and dialectology.

400 870 880   GW
WUERZBURGER JAHRBUECHER FUER DIE ALTERTUMSWISSENSCHAFT. 1975. a. DM.80. F. Schoeningh Kommissionsverlag, Franziskanerplatz 4, 97070 Wuerzburg, Germany. TEL 031-309810. FAX 031-309818. Eds. Joachim Latacz, Guenter Neumann. circ. 600. **Indexed:** Bibl.Ling. **Document type:** academic/scholarly publication.

490   PL   ISSN 0860-5629
WYZSZA SZKOLA PEDAGOGICZNA IM. KOMISJI EDUKACJI NARODOWEJ W KRAKOWIE. ROCZNIK NAUKOWO-DYDAKTYCZNY. PRACE JEZYKOZNAWCZE. 1970. irreg., no.6, 1991. price varies. Wydawnictwo Naukowe W S P, Ul. Karmelicka 41, 31-128 Krakow, Poland. TEL 33-79-20. (Co-sponsor: Ministerstwo Edukacji Narodowej) Ed. Eugeniusz Pawlowski. illus.

840   PL   ISSN 0239-6556
WYZSZA SZKOLA PEDAGOGICZNA IM. KOMISJI EDUKACJI NARODOWEJ W KRAKOWIE. ROCZNIK NAUKOWO-DYDAKTYCZNY. PRACE ROMANISTYCZNE. 1983. irreg., no.3, 1991. price varies. Wydawnictwo Naukowe W S P, Ul. Karmelicka 41, 31-128 Krakow, Poland. TEL 33-78-20. (Co-sponsor: Ministerstwo Edukacji Narodowej)

WYZSZA SZKOLA PEDAGOGICZNA IM. KOMISJI EDUKACJI NARODOWEJ W KRAKOWIE. ROCZNIK NAUKOWO-DYDAKTYCZNY. PRACE RUSYCYSTYCZNE. see LITERATURE

491.85 891.85   PL
WYZSZA SZKOLA PEDAGOGICZNA IM. KOMISJI EDUKACJI NARODOWEJ W KRAKOWIE. ROCZNIK NAUKOWO-DYDAKTYCZNY. PRACE Z DYDAKTYKI LITERATURY I JEZYKA POLSKIEGO. 1964. irreg., no.4, 1990. price varies. Wydawnictwo Naukowe W S P, Ul. Karmelicka 41, 31-128 Krakow, Poland. TEL 33-78-20. (Co-sponsor: Ministerstwo Edukacji Narodowej)

401
▼**WYZSZA SZKOLA PEDAGOGICZNA, OPOLE. STYLISTYKA.** 1992. irreg. price varies. Wyzsza Szkola Pedagogiczna, Opole, Oleska 48, 45-951 Opole, Poland. TEL 48-22-383-87. (Dist. by: Ars Polona-Ruch, Krakowskie Przedmiescie 7, Warsaw, Poland) Ed. Stanislaw Gajda. **Document type:** academic/scholarly publication.

420 375.4   PL   ISSN 0860-2328
PE1
WYZSZA SZKOLA PEDAGOGICZNA, OPOLE. ZESZYTY NAUKOWE. SERIA A. FILOGOGIA ANGIELSKA. (Text and summaries in English and Polish) 1986. irreg., vol.7, 1993. price varies, avail. on exchange basis. Wyzsza Szkola Pedagogiczna, Opole, Oleska 48, 45-951 Opole, Poland. TEL 48-77-383-87. (Dist. by: Ars Polona-Ruch, Krakowskie Przedmiescie 7, Warsaw, Poland) Eds. Piotr Ruszkiewicz, Piotr Kokietek. **Document type:** academic/scholarly publication.
—BLDSC (9512.478960).

WYZSZA SZKOLA PEDAGOGICZNA, OPOLE. ZESZYTY NAUKOWE. SERIA A. FILOLOGIA GERMANSKA. see LITERATURE

WYZSZA SZKOLA PEDAGOGICZNA, OPOLE. ZESZYTY NAUKOWE. SERIA A. FILOLOGIA POLSKA. see LITERATURE

WYZSZA SZKOLA PEDAGOGICZNA, OPOLE. ZESZYTY NAUKOWE. SERIA A. FILOLOGIA ROSYJSKA. see LITERATURE

410   PL   ISSN 0078-5423
WYZSZA SZKOLA PEDAGOGICZNA, OPOLE. ZESZYTY NAUKOWE. SERIA A. JEZYKOZNAWSTWO. (Text in Polish) 1957. irreg., vol.14, 1993. avail. on exchange; price varies. Wyzsza Szkola Pedagogiczna, Opole, Oleska 48, 45-951 Opole, Poland. TEL 48-77-383-87. (Dist. by: Ars Polona-Ruch, Krakowskie Przedmiescie 7, Warsaw, Poland) Ed. Feliks Pluta. **Document type:** academic/scholarly publication.
—BLDSC (9512.478978).

495.1 375.4   CC
XIAOXUE YUWEN JIAOSHI/ELEMENTARY SCHOOL CHINESE LANGUAGE TEACHER. (Text in Chinese) bi-m. (foreign Y592). Shanghai Jiaoyu Chubanshe - Shanghai Educational Publishing House, 123 Yongfu Road, Shanghai 200031, People's Republic of China. TEL 4377165. (Dist. in US by: China Books & Periodicals, Inc., 2929 24th St., San Francisco, CA 94110. TEL 415-282-2994) Ed. Bao Nanling.

XIAOXUE YUWEN JIAOXUE/ELEMENTARY SCHOOL CHINESE TEACHING. see EDUCATION — Teaching Methods And Curriculum

410   CC
XIAOXUESHENG YUWEN XUEXI/CHINESE STUDIES FOR PUPILS. (Text in Chinese) 1985. m. $50. Jiangsu Jiaoyu Chubanshe - Jiangsu Education Publishing House, 165 Zhongyang Lu, Nanjing, Jiangsu 210009, People's Republic of China. TEL 635549. adv. contact: Yuanyuan Qian. circ. 400,000.

410   US
XINYA. (Text written in romanized Mandarin Chinese) 1982. q. $15 to individuals; institutions $15. Institute for Advanced Communication, Box 254, Swarthmore, PA 19081. TEL 215-543-6286. Ed. Victor H. Mair. adv.; bk.rev. circ. 25,000. (back issues avail.)
    Former titles (until 1991): Xin Tang - New China (ISSN 0731-0897); Xin Talng; (until 1984): Shin Talng.
    Description: Includes stories, poems, essays, illustrated narratives, and articles on language reform.

495.1 375.4   CC
XUE HANYU/LEARNING CHINESE. (Text in Chinese) bi-m. $18.50. Beijing Yuyan Xueyuan - Beijing Language Institute, 15 Xueyuan Lu, Beijing 100083, People's Republic of China. (Dist. in US by: China Books & Periodicals, Inc., 2929 24th St., San Francisco, CA 94110. TEL 415-282-2994) Ed. Sun Junzheng.
    Formerly: Hanyu Xuexi.

400   US
YALE LANGUAGE SERIES. 1963. irreg., latest 1989. Yale University Press, Box 209040, New Haven, CT 06520. TEL 203-432-0940. **Document type:** monographic series.
    Formerly: Yale Linguistic Series (ISSN 0513-4412)

410   BO
YATINATAKI; boletin informativo trilingue. (Text in Aymara, Quechua, Spanish) 1974. m. Bol.$140($8) Instituto Boliviano de Cultura, Instituto Nacional de Estudios Linguisticos, Casilla 8877, La Paz, Bolivia. Ed.Bd. (looseleaf format; back issues avail.)

415   NE   ISSN 0922-3495
                       CODEN: YEMOEQ
YEARBOOK OF MORPHOLOGY. 1988. a. fl.210 (effective 1993). Kluwer Academic Publishers, Postbus 17, 3300 AA Dordrecht, Netherlands. TEL 31-78-334911. FAX 31-78-334254. TELEX 29245 KAPG NL. (Dist. by: Kluwer Academic Publishers Group, P.O. Box 322, 3300 AH Dordrecht, Netherlands. TEL 31-78-524400. FAX 31-78-524474; N. America dist. addr.: Box 358, Accord Sta., Hingham, MA 02018-0358. TEL 617-871-6600. FAX 617-871-6528) Eds. Geert Booij, Jaap van Marle. **Indexed:** Bibl.Ling. **Document type:** academic/scholarly publication.
    Description: Selected studies on specific aspects of morphology in languages throughout the world.
    Refereed Serial

492.49   US   ISSN 0044-0442
PJ5111
YIDISHE SHPRAKH/YIDDISH LANGUAGE. (Text in Yiddish) 1941. irreg. $5. Y I V O Institute for Jewish Research, 1048 Fifth Ave., New York, NY 10028. TEL 212-535-6700. Ed. Mordkhe Schaechter. bk.rev. circ. 1,000. (also avail. in microform) **Indexed:** M.L.A.

420   CC   ISSN 1003-2304
YINGYU SHIJIE/WORLD OF ENGLISH. (Text in Chinese, English) 1981. bi-m. $22.10 (effective 1994). Commercial Press, P.O. Box 1504, Beijing 100005, People's Republic of China. TEL 525-7190. FAX 513-5899. (Dist. in US by: China Books & Periodicals, Inc., 2929 24th St., San Francisco, CA 94110. TEL 415-282-2994) Ed. Chen Yulun. circ. 300,000.

420   CC
YINGYU XUEXI/ENGLISH LANGUAGE LEARNING.* (Text in Chinese and English) m. $26. Beijing Foreign Language Institute, English Department, Suzhou Jie, Haidian Qu, Beijing 100081, People's Republic of China. (Dist. in US by: China Books & Periodicals, Inc., 2929 24th St., San Francisco, CA 94110. TEL 415-282-2994)

420 375.4   CC
YINGYU ZIXUE/ENGLISH SELF-STUDY. (Text in Chinese, English) m. Shanghai Waiguoyu Xueyuan, Yingyu Xi - Shanghai International Studies University, English Department, 119 Xi Tiyuhui Lu, Shanghai 200083, People's Republic of China. TEL 5420900. Ed. Yang Xiaoshi.

410   UK   ISSN 0513-2762
YORKSHIRE DIALECT SOCIETY. SUMMER BULLETIN. 1953. a. £4 (with Transactions). Yorkshire Dialect Society, c/o Librarian, School of English, University of Leeds, Leeds LS2 9JT, England. Ed. M. Shackleton. bk.rev. circ. 650. **Document type:** academic/scholarly publication, bulletin.

410   UK
YORKSHIRE DIALECT SOCIETY TRANSACTIONS. 1897. a. £5 (with Summer Bulletin). Yorkshire Dialect Society, c/o Librarian, School of English, University of Leeds, Leeds LS2 9JT, England. Ed. A. Kellett. circ. 650. (also avail. in microfiche from IDC) **Document type:** academic/scholarly publication.

410 810 960   NR
YORUBA. (Text in English and Yoruba) 1973. s-a. £N2.50($5.50) (Yoruba Studies Association of Nigeria) Onibon-Oje Press and Book Company, Box 3109, Ibadan, Nigeria. Ed. Wande Abimbola. adv.; bk.rev. circ. 2,000.

410   CI
YUGOSLAV SERBO-CROATIAN-ENGLISH CONTRASTIVE PROJECT. SERIES B: STUDIES. (Text in English) 1969. irreg. 50 din. Institute of Linguistics, Zagreb, Djure Salaja 3, 41000 Zagreb, Croatia. Ed. Rudolf Filipovic. circ. 500. **Indexed:** Sociol.Abstr.

495.1   CC   ISSN 1001-8476
YUWEN JIANSHE/CHINESE LANGUAGE PLANNING. (Text in Chinese) 1986. m. $16.20. Guojia Yuyan Wenzi Gongzu Weiyuanhui - State Language Commission, 51 Nanxiajie, Chaoyangmennei, Beijing 100010, People's Republic of China. TEL 554621. (Dist. in US by: China Books & Periodicals, Inc., 2929 24th St., San Francisco, CA 94110. TEL 415-282-0994) Ed. Liu Zhaoxiong. bk.rev. **Document type:** academic/scholarly publication.

495.1 375.4   CC
YUWEN JIAOXUE TONGXUN/BULLETIN OF CHINESE LANGUAGE TEACHING. (Text in Chinese) m. Y15.60($44) Yuwen Bao She, Shanxi Shifan Daxue, Linfen, Shanxi 041004, People's Republic of China. (Dist. outside China by: China International Book Trading Corp., P.O. Box 399, Beijing, P.R.C.; Dist. in US by: China Books & Periodicals, Inc., 2929 24th St., San Francisco, CA 94110) Eds. Sun Quansheng, Jin Baotai.

495.1   CC
YUWEN XUEXI/CHINESE LANGUAGE LEARNING. (Text in Chinese) m. Y18 (foreign Y209). Shanghai Jiaoyu Chubanshe - Shanghai Educational Publishing House, 123 Yongfu Road, Shanghai 200031, People's Republic of China. TEL 4377165. (Dist. outside China by: China International Book Trading Corp., P.O. Box 339, Beijing, P.R.C.; Dist. in US by: China Books & Periodicals, Inc., 2929 24th St., San Francisco, CA 94110) Eds. Chen He, Fan Shougang. **Document type:** academic/scholarly publication.

495.1   CC   ISSN 1000-2979
PL1004
YUWEN YANJIU/CHINESE LANGUAGE RESEARCH. (Text in Chinese) 1980. q. $22.80. (Shanxi Sheng Shehui Kexueyuan) Yuwen Chubanshe, Chaonei Nanxiaojie 51, Beijing, People's Republic of China. (Dist. in US by: China Books & Periodicals, Inc., 2929 24th St., San Francisco, CA 94110. TEL 415-282-2994) **Indexed:** Bibl.Ling.

495.1   CC
YUWEN YUEKAN. (Text in Chinese) 1982. m. Y18. Huanan Shifan Daxue, Zhongwen Xi - South China Normal University, Chinese Department, Shipai, Guangzhou, Guangdong 510631, People's Republic of China. TEL 5516911-2741. (Dist. outside China by: China International Book Trading Corp., P.O. Box 399, Beijing, P.R.C.; Dist. in US by: China Books & Periodicals, Inc., 2929 24th St., San Francisco, CA 94110. TEL 415-282-2994) Ed. Huang Jizhuang. circ. 100,000. **Document type:** academic/scholarly publication.
Description: Covers all aspects of Chinese linguistics.

400 375.4   CC   ISSN 0257-9448
YUYAN JIAOXUE YU YANJIU/LANGUAGE TEACHING & STUDIES. (Text in Chinese) 1979. q. $16.50. Beijing Yuyan Xueyuan - Beijing Language Institute, 15 Xueyuan Lu, Haidian Qu, Beijing 100083, People's Republic of China. TEL 2017531. (Dist. outside China by: China International Book Trading Corp., P.O. Box 399, Beijing, P.R.C.; Dist. in US by: China Books & Periodicals, Inc., 2929 24th St., San Francisco, CA 94110. TEL 415-282-2994) **Indexed:** Bibl.Ling.
—UnCover.

495.1   CC   ISSN 1001-3261
YUYAN WENZI XUE. (Subseries of: Fuyin Baokan Ziliao) (Text in Chinese) m. Y39.90. Zhongguo Renmin Daxue, Shubao Ziliao Zhongxin - China People's University, Book & Newspaper Information Center, P.O. Box 1122, Beijing 100007, People's Republic of China. TEL 441792.
Description: Contains reprints of papers and articles on language and linguistics.

410   GW
Z F F - ZEITSCHRIFT FUER FREMDSPRACHENFORSCHUNG. 1990. s-a. DM.50. (Deutsche Gesellschaft fuer Fremdsprachenforschung) Universitaetsverlag Dr. N. Brockmeyer, Querenburger Hoehe 239, 44801 Bochum, Germany. Ed.Bd. **Document type:** academic/scholarly publication.

410 890   YU   ISSN 0454-4617
ZA CASOPIS: KOVCEZIC. (Text in English, German, Russian and Serbian) 1958. biennial. 4000 din.($4) Vukov i Dositejev Muzej, 9 Jevremova 21, Belgrade, Yugoslavia. TEL 625-161. Ed. J. Saulic. circ. 500.

ZAMBIA MUSEUMS JOURNAL. see *ANTHROPOLOGY*

410   CI
PG1201
ZAVOD ZA HRVATSKI JEZIK. RASPRAVE. (Text in Serbo-Croatian; summaries in English, French, German, Russian) 1968. a. $8. Hrvatski Filoloski Institut, Zavod za Hrvatski Jazik, Strossmayerov Trg 2, 41000 Zagreb, Croatia. TEL 276-007. Ed. Mijo Loncaric. circ. 400. **Indexed:** Lang.& Lang.Behav.Abstr.
Formerly: Zavod za Jezik. Rasprave (ISSN 0351-434X)

891.59   AF
ZAYRAY. (Text in Pashtu) 1938. w. Afghanistan Academy of Sciences, Sher Alikhan St., Kabul, Afghanistan.

491   YU   ISSN 0350-0470
PG13
ZBORNIK ZA SLAVISTIKU/REVIEW OF SLAVIC STUDIES. s-a. Matica Srpska, Matice Srpske 1, Novi Sad, Vojvodina, Yugoslavia. Ed. Milorad Zivancevic.
Indexed: M.L.A.

491   CI
ZBORNIK ZAGREBACKE SLAVISTICKE SKOLE. 1973. irreg. Medjunarodni Slavisticki Centar SR Hrvatske, Djure Salaja 3, Zagreb, Croatia. (Co-sponsor: Sveucilista u Zagrebu, Filozofski Fakultet) Eds. Franjo Grcevic, Mladen Kuzmanovic.

ZEITSCHRIFT FUER AEGYPTISCHE SPRACHE UND ALTERTUMSKUNDE. see *ORIENTAL STUDIES*

410   GW   ISSN 0932-4461
PJ4501
ZEITSCHRIFT FUER ALTHEBRAISTIK. (Text in English, French, German) 1988. s-a. DM.219. W. Kohlhammer GmbH, Hessbruehlstr. 69, 70565 Stuttgart, Germany. TEL 0711-7863-1. (back issues avail.) **Indexed:** Bibl.Ling., Rel.& Theol.Abstr. (1988-). **Document type:** academic/scholarly publication.

ZEITSCHRIFT FUER ANGLISTIK UND AMERIKANISTIK. see *LITERATURE*

410   GW   ISSN 0170-026X
ZEITSCHRIFT FUER ARABISCHE LINGUISTIK/JOURNAL OF ARABIC LINGUISTICS/JOURNAL DE LINGUISTIQUE ARABE. (Text in English, French, German) 1978. irreg., vol.27, 1994. price varies. Harrassowitz Verlag, Taunusstr. 14, 65183 Wiesbaden, Germany. TEL 0611-530-0. FAX 0611-530570. TELEX 4186135. (Subscr. to: Postfach 2929, 65019 Wiesbaden, Germany) Eds. H. Bobzin, O. Jastrow. adv.; bk.rev. circ. 360. (back issues avail.) **Indexed:** Bibl.Ling., Lang.& Lang.Behav.Abstr. (1985-), M.L.A. **Document type:** monographic series.
—BLDSC (4947.165000); SWETS. **CCC**.

491.6   GW   ISSN 0084-5302
ZEITSCHRIFT FUER CELTISCHE PHILOLOGIE. (Text in English, French, German or Irish) 1904; not published 1944-1952. irreg. price varies. Max Niemeyer Verlag, Postfach 2140, 72011 Tuebingen, Germany. TEL 07071-98940. FAX 07071-989450. (also avail. in microfiche from IDC; back issues avail.) **Indexed:** Arts & Hum.Cit.Ind., Bibl.Ling., M.L.A. **Document type:** academic/scholarly publication.
—SWETS.
Description: Essays and reviews on Celtic languages and literature.

430   GW   ISSN 0044-2496
PF3003
ZEITSCHRIFT FUER DEUTSCHE PHILOLOGIE. 1883. q. DM.224 (students DM.204). Erich Schmidt Verlag GmbH & Co. (Berlin), Genthiner Str. 30G, 10785 Berlin, Germany. TEL 030-250085-0. FAX 030-25008521. Ed.Bd. adv.; bk.rev.; bibl.; charts; illus.; index. circ. 1,100. (also avail. in microform from PMC; microfiche from IDC; reprint service avail. from SWZ) **Indexed:** Bibl.Ling., Curr.Cont., Ind.Bk.Rev.Hum., Lang.& Lang.Behav.Abstr., M.L.A. **Document type:** academic/scholarly publication.
—Faxon. **CCC**.

430 830   GW   ISSN 0044-2518
ZEITSCHRIFT FUER DEUTSCHES ALTERTUM UND DEUTSCHE LITERATUR. 1841. 4/yr. DM.198. Franz Steiner Verlag Stuttgart GmbH, Birkenwaldstr. 44, 70191 Stuttgart, Germany. TEL 0711-2582-0. FAX 0711-2582290. TELEX 723636-DAZ-D. (Subscr. to: Postfach 101061, 70009 Stuttgart, Germany) Ed. Franz-Josef Worstbrock. adv.; bk.rev.; bibl.; index. circ. 800. (also avail. in microfiche from IDC; back issues avail.) **Indexed:** Arts & Hum.Cit.Ind., Bibl.Ling., Curr.Cont., Ind.Bk.Rev.Hum., M.L.A. **Document type:** academic/scholarly publication.
—Faxon; UnCover; SWETS. **CCC**.

400   GW   ISSN 0044-1449
PF5001
ZEITSCHRIFT FUER DIALEKTOLOGIE UND LINGUISTIK. (Text in English, German) 1924. 3/yr. DM.140 (supplements priced individually). Franz Steiner Verlag Stuttgart GmbH, Birkenwaldstr. 44, 70191 Stuttgart, Germany. TEL 0711-2582-0. FAX 0711-2582290. TELEX 723636-DAZ-D. (Subscr. to: Postfach 101061, 70009 Stuttgart, Germany) Ed. Joachim Goeschel. adv.; bk.rev.; abstr.; bibl.; charts. circ. 600. (back issues avail.; reprint service avail. from KTO) **Indexed:** Arts & Hum.Cit.Ind., Bibl.Ling., Ind.Bk.Rev.Hum., Lang.& Lang.Behav.Abstr., M.L.A. **Document type:** academic/scholarly publication.
—BLDSC (9457.680000); Faxon; SWETS. **CCC**.
Formerly: Zeitschrift fuer Mundartforschung.

400   GW   ISSN 0341-0838
ZEITSCHRIFT FUER DIALEKTOLOGIE UND LINGUISTIK. BEIHEFTE. irreg., vol.84, 1994. price varies. Franz Steiner Verlag Wiesbaden GmbH, Birkenwaldstr. 44, 70191 Stuttgart, Germany. TEL 0711-2582-0. FAX 0711-2582290. TELEX 723636-DAZ-D. (Subscr. to: Postfach 101061, 70009 Stuttgart, Germany) Ed. Joachim Goeschel. **Document type:** monographic series.

440   GW   ISSN 0044-2747
ZEITSCHRIFT FUER FRANZOESISCHE SPRACHE UND LITERATUR. (Text in English, French, German) 1879. 3/yr. DM.128 (supplements priced individually). Franz Steiner Verlag Stuttgart GmbH, Birkenwaldstr. 44, 70191 Stuttgart, Germany. TEL 0711-2582-0. FAX 0711-2582290. TELEX 723636-DAZ-D. (Subscr. to: Postfach 101061, 70009 Stuttgart, Germany) Eds. Peter Blumenthal, Klaus W. Hempfer. adv.; bk.rev.; bibl.; illus.; index. circ. 500. (also avail. in microfiche from IDC; back issues avail.; reprint service avail. from SWZ) **Indexed:** Bibl.Ling., Curr.Cont., M.L.A. **Document type:** academic/scholarly publication.
—Faxon; SWETS. **CCC**.

440   GW   ISSN 0341-0811
ZEITSCHRIFT FUER FRANZOESISCHE SPRACHE UND LITERATUR. BEIHEFTE. NEUE FOLGE. irreg., vol.21, 1993. price varies. Franz Steiner Verlag Wiesbaden GmbH, Birkenwaldstr. 44, 70191 Stuttgart, Germany. TEL 0711-2582-0. FAX 0711-2582290. TELEX 723636-DAZ-D. (Subscr. to: Postfach 101061, 70009 Stuttgart, Germany) Eds. Klaus W. Hempfer, Peter Blumenthal. **Document type:** monographic series.

430   GW   ISSN 0301-3294
PF3003
ZEITSCHRIFT FUER GERMANISTISCHE LINGUISTIK. 1973. 3/yr. DM.204. Walter de Gruyter und Co., Genthiner Str. 13, 10785 Berlin, Germany. TEL 030-26005-0. FAX 030-26005251. TELEX 184027. (U.S. addr.: Walter de Gruyter, Inc., 200 Saw Mill Rd., Hawthorne, NY 10532) Ed.Bd. adv.; bk.rev.; abstr.; bibl.; index. circ. 2,000. (back issues avail.) **Indexed:** Arts & Hum.Cit.Ind., Bibl.Ling., Curr.Cont., Ind.Bk.Rev.Hum., Lang.& Lang.Behav.Abstr. (1989-). **Document type:** academic/scholarly publication.
—SWETS. **CCC**.

479   GW   ISSN 0049-8661
PC3
ZEITSCHRIFT FUER ROMANISCHE PHILOLOGIE. (Supplement avail.: Romanische Bibliographie) (Text in French, German, Italian, Spanish) 1877. 3/yr. DM.338. Max Niemeyer Verlag, Postfach 2140, 72011 Tuebingen, Germany. TEL 07071-98940. FAX 07071-989450. Ed. Max Pfister. adv.; bk.rev. (also avail. in microfiche from BHP, IDC; back issues avail.; reprint service avail. from SCH) **Indexed:** Arts & Hum.Cit.Ind., Bibl.Ling., Curr.Cont., Lang.& Lang.Behav.Abstr., M.L.A. **Document type:** academic/scholarly publication.
—Faxon; UnCover; SWETS. **CCC**.
Description: Contains essays and reviews concerning Romance languages and literature, especially before the 16th century.

LINGUISTICS — ABSTRACTING, BIBLIOGRAPHIES, STATISTICS

400 830   GW   ISSN 0084-5396
ZEITSCHRIFT FUER ROMANISCHE PHILOLOGIE. BEIHEFTE. (Text in English, French, German, Italian and Spanish) 1906. irreg., no.254, 1993. Max Niemeyer Verlag, Postfach 2140, 72011 Tuebingen, Germany. TEL 07071-98940. FAX 07071-989450. Ed. Max Pfister. (also avail. in microfilm from BHP; back issues avail.) **Document type:** monographic series.
—BLDSC (9485.461000).
   Description: Monographs about Romance literature; critical editions of texts until the 15th century; Romance languages.

ZEITSCHRIFT FUER SEMIOTIK. see *PHILOSOPHY*

491   GW   ISSN 0044-3492
PG1
ZEITSCHRIFT FUER SLAVISCHE PHILOLOGIE. vol.21, 1951. s-a. DM.200 (student DM.150). Universitaetsverlag C. Winter Heidelberg GmbH, Hans-Bunte-Str. 18, 69123 Heidelberg, Germany. Eds. H. Keipert, P. Brang. bk.rev. (reprint service avail. from KTO) **Indexed:** Arts & Hum.Cit.Ind., Bibl.Ling., Curr.Cont., Ind.Bk.Rev.Hum., Lang.& Lang.Behav.Abstr., M.L.A. **Document type:** academic/scholarly publication.
—SWETS.

491 891   GW   ISSN 0044-3506
PG1
ZEITSCHRIFT FUER SLAWISTIK. (Text in English, German) 1956. 4/yr. DM.184 (foreign DM.195). Akademie Verlag GmbH, Muehlenstr. 33-34, 13187 Berlin, Germany. TEL 030-47889348. FAX 030-47889357. Ed.Bd. bk.rev.; abstr.; bibl.; charts; illus.; index, cum.index: 1956-1960. **Indexed:** Arts & Hum.Cit.Ind., Bibl.Ling., Curr.Cont., Lang.& Lang.Behav.Abstr., M.L.A. **Document type:** academic/scholarly publication.
—BLDSC (9486.350000).

430 375.4   GW   ISSN 0721-9067
P3
ZEITSCHRIFT FUER SPRACHWISSENSCHAFT. 1982. s-a. DM.88. Vandenhoeck und Ruprecht, Robert-Bosch-Breite 6, 37079 Goettingen, Germany. TEL 0551-6959-26. FAX 0551-695917. (Subscr. to: 37070 Goettingen, Germany) Ed.Bd. index. circ. 570. **Indexed:** Bibl.Ling. **Document type:** academic/scholarly publication.
—BLDSC (9486.401000); SWETS. **CCC.**

491.7 375.4   CC
ZHONGGUO E YU JIAOXUE/CHINESE JOURNAL OF RUSSIAN TEACHING. (Text in Russian) q. Beijing Waiguoyu Xueyuan - Beijing Foreign Language Institute, Suzhou Jie, Haidian, Beijing 100081, People's Republic of China. TEL 890351. Ed. Wu Fuxiang.

418.02   CC   ISSN 1000-873X
ZHONGGUO FANYI/CHINESE TRANSLATORS JOURNAL. (Text mainly in Chinese; table of contents in English) bi-m. Y6($14.11) (Zhongguo Fanyi Gongzuozhe Xiehui - Translators' Association of China) Waiwen Chuban Faxing Ju - Foreign Languages Publishing and Distribution Administration, 24 Baiwanzhuang Lu, Fuwai, Beijing 100037, People's Republic of China. TEL 861-8327209. (Dist. outside China by: China International Book Trading Corp., P.O. Box 399, Beijing, P.R.C.; Dist. in US by: China Books & Periodicals, Inc., 2929 24th St., San Francisco, CA 94110. TEL 415-282-2994) (Co-sponsor: Zhongguo Duiwai Chuban Gongsi - China Translation and Publishing Corporation) Ed. Ye Junjian.
   Formerly: Translators' Notes.
   Description: Aims to promote the theory and study of translation, exchange of translating experience, and provide commentary on translated works. Includes practice excercises.

495.1   CC   ISSN 0578-1949
ZHONGGUO YUWEN. (Text and summaries in Chinese; table of contents in English) 1952. bi-m. Y10.20($32.90) (Zhongguo Shehui Kexueyuan, Yuwen Yanjiusuo - Chinese Academy of Social Sciences, Language Institute) Shehui Kexue Zazhishe, A-158 Gulou Xidajie, Beijing 100720, People's Republic of China. (Dist. outside China by: China International Book Trading Corp., P.O. Box 399, Beijing, P.R.C.; Dist. in US by: China Books & Periodicals, Inc., 2929 24th St., San Francisco, CA 94110. TEL 415-282-2994) bibl. **Indexed:** Bibl.Ling.
—UnCover.
   Description: Contains linguistic studies on the Chinese language.

410 370   CC   ISSN 1000-7245
ZHONGWEN ZIXIU/CHINESE SELF-STUDY. (Text in Chinese) 1983. m. $25 (effective 1993). Shanghai Jiaoyu Xueyuan - Shanghai Institute of Education, 1045 Huaihai Zhonglu, Shanghai 200031, People's Republic of China. TEL 4375550. Ed. Chen Bixiang. adv. contact: Dakeng Lu. bk.rev. circ. 500.
   Description: Provides self-study materials in Chinese linguistics and literature.

410 370   CC
ZHONGWEN ZIXUE ZHIDAO/GUIDE TO TEACHING YOURSELF CHINESE.* (Text in Chinese) m. East China Normal University, Chinese Department - Huadong Shifan Daxue, Zhongwen Xi, 3663 Zhongshan Beilu, Shanghai 200062, People's Republic of China. TEL 2577577. Ed. Xu Zhongyu.

410   CC   ISSN 1000-419X
ZHONGXUE YUWEN/MIDDLE SCHOOL CHINESE. (Text in Chinese) m. Hubei Daxue, Zhongwen Xi - Hubei University, Department of Chinese, Baoji'an, Wuchang-qu, Wuhan, Hubei 430062, People's Republic of China. TEL 874753. Ed. Deng Xianzheng.

495.1 375.4   US   ISSN 1001-280X
ZHONGXUE YUWEN JIAOXUE/LANGUAGE TEACHING IN MIDDLE SCHOOL. (Text in Chinese) m. $35.90. China Books & Periodicals, Inc., 2929 24th St., San Francisco, CA 94110. TEL 415-282-2994. FAX 415-282-0994.

430 370   GW   ISSN 0341-5864
PF3003
ZIELSPRACHE DEUTSCH; Zeitschrift fuer Unterrichtsmethodik und angewandte Sprachwissenschaft. 1951. 4/yr. DM.34. Max Hueber Verlag, Max-Hueber-Str.4, 85737 Ismaning, Germany. TEL 089-9602-0. FAX 089-9602-358. TELEX 523613-HUEBD. Ed. Elmar Winters-Ohle. adv.; bk.rev. circ. 2,500. (also avail. in microform from SWZ; reprint service avail. from SWZ) **Indexed:** Lang.& Lang.Behav.Abstr., Lang.Teach.& Ling.Abstr., M.L.A. **Document type:** academic/scholarly publication.
—Faxon; SWETS; UMI. **CCC.**
   Formerly: Deutschunterricht fuer Auslaender.
   Description: Focuses on new developments and results in the various fields of applied linguistics and conveys suggestions as to teaching German as a foreign language.

420 374   GW   ISSN 0342-6173
PE1001
ZIELSPRACHE ENGLISCH; Zeitschrift fuer den Englischunterricht in der Erwachsenbildung. (Text in English and German) 1961. 4/yr. DM.34. Max Hueber Verlag, Max-Hueber-Str.4, 85737 Ismaning, Germany. TEL 089-9602-0. FAX 089-9602-358. Ed. A. Schmitz. adv.; bk.rev. circ. 2,800. **Indexed:** Lang.& Lang.Behav.Abstr., Lang.Teach.& Ling.Abstr. **Document type:** academic/scholarly publication.
—BLDSC (9513.132000); UMI. **CCC.**
   Formerly: Englisch an Volkshochschulen (ISSN 0013-8193)
   Description: Covers English study and teaching, including didactics, organization, language, cultural background studies and specialized literature.

440 375.4   GW   ISSN 0342-6203
ZIELSPRACHE FRANZOESISCH; Zeitschrift fuer den Franzoesischunterricht in der Erwachsenbildung. (Text in French and German) 1971. 4/yr. DM.34. (Deutscher Volkshochschulverband, Paedagogische Arbeitsstelle) Max Hueber Verlag, Max-Hueber-Str.4, 85737 Ismaning, Germany. TEL 089-9602-0. FAX 089-9602-358. TELEX 523613-HUEBD. Ed. Albert Raasch. circ. 2,500. **Document type:** academic/scholarly publication.
—**CCC.**
   Description: Covers the organization of study courses, advanced training, methodical, psychological and sociological problems.

LINGUISTICS — Abstracting, Bibliographies, Statistics

016 410   US   ISSN 0165-7267
AMSTERDAM STUDIES IN THE THEORY AND HISTORY OF LINGUISTIC SCIENCE. SERIES 5: LIBRARY AND INFORMATION SOURCES IN LINGUISTICS. Short title: L I S L. (Text in English) 1977. irreg., vol.20, 1990. price varies. John Benjamins Publishing Co., 821 Bethlehem Pike, Philadelphia, PA 19118. TEL 215-836-1200. FAX 215-836-1204. (And: Amsteldijk 44, P.O. Box 75577, 1070 AN Amsterdam, Netherlands. TEL 020-6762325) Ed. E.F.K. Koerner. **Indexed:** M.L.A. **Document type:** monographic series.
   Description: Contains bibliographies, biographies and other reference works concerning linguisitcs.

L'ANNEE PHILOLOGIQUE; bibliographie critique et analytique de l'antiquite greco-latine. see *CLASSICAL STUDIES — Abstracting, Bibliographies, Statistics*

439.3 016   NE   ISSN 0045-186X
BIBLIOGRAFIE VAN DE NEDERLANDSE TAAL- EN LITERATUUR WETENSCHAP. 1970. a. fl.89.50. Stichting Bibliographica Neerlandica, Postbus 90751, 2509 LT The Hague, Netherlands. Ed.Bd. cum.index every 3 years.
● Also available online.

499   NE   ISSN 0920-7104
BIBLIOGRAPHIA DE INTERLINGUA. (Text in Interlingua) 1973. a. free. Servicio de Libros U M I, Zonnegloren 30, 7361 TL Beekbergen, Netherlands. **Document type:** bibliography.
   Description: Lists recent publications in the international language, Interlingua.

BIBLIOGRAPHIE LINGUISTISCHER LITERATUR; bibliography of general linguistics and of English, German and Romance linguistics. see *LITERATURE — Abstracting, Bibliographies, Statistics*

410   BE
BIOBIBLIOGRAPHIES ET EXPOSES. 1956; N.S. 1992. irreg., vol.3, 1993. 300 BEF per no. (effective 1993). Editions Peeters s.p.r.l., Bondgenotenlaan 153, B-3000 Louvain, Belgium. TEL 32-16-235170. FAX 32-16-228500. Ed. P. Swiggers. (back issues avail.) **Document type:** academic/scholarly publication.
   Description: Presents a biographical sketch, and exhaustive bibliography and an essay reviewing the central issues of an author's contributions in linguistics.

C C C C BIBLIOGRAPHY OF COMPOSITION AND RHETORIC. (Conference on College Composition and Communication) see *EDUCATION — Abstracting, Bibliographies, Statistics*

CARIBBEAN ABSTRACTS. see *ANTHROPOLOGY — Abstracting, Bibliographies, Statistics*

410 016   US
CURRENT ESPERANTO BOOK LIST. (Text in English and Esperanto) 1964. s-a. $2. Esperanto League for North America, Box 1129, El Cerrito, CA 94530. TEL 510-653-0998. FAX 510-653-1468. bk.rev.; bibl.; stat. circ. 2,000. **Document type:** bibliography.
   Description: Lists and descriptions of titles in Esperanto and relating to it.

440 840   UK   ISSN 0957-4751
CURRENT RESEARCH IN FRENCH STUDIES AT UNIVERSITIES AND POLYTECHNICS IN THE UNITED KINGDOM AND IRELAND. (Text in English, French) 1969. biennial. £6. Society for French Studies, c/o Dr. John Harris, Ed., University of Bath, Secretary & Registrar's Dept., England. index. circ. 400. (back issues avail.)
   Former titles (until 1988): Current Research in French Studies at Universities and Polytechnics in the United Kindom (ISSN 0263-4538); (until 1982): Current Research in French Studies at Universities and University Colleges in the United Kingdom.

LINGUISTICS — ABSTRACTING, BIBLIOGRAPHIES, STATISTICS

400 016   US
DICTIONARIES, ENCYCLOPEDIAS, AND OTHER WORD-RELATED BOOKS. irreg., 4th ed., 1987. $520. Gale Research Inc., 835 Penobscot Bldg., Detroit, MI 48226. TEL 313-961-2242. FAX 313-961-6083. TELEX 810-221-7086. Ed. Annie M. Brewer.
  Description: Bibliography of word-related reference books.

DIRECTORY OF PERIODICALS PUBLISHING ARTICLES ON ENGLISH AND AMERICAN LITERATURE AND LANGUAGE. see *LITERATURE — Abstracting, Bibliographies, Statistics*

E I. (Excerpta Indonesica) see *ANTHROPOLOGY — Abstracting, Bibliographies, Statistics*

440 016   CN   ISSN 0712-7561
ETUDES STRATEGIQUES ET MILITAIRES (COLLECTION). (Text in English, French) 1981. a. Can.$21. Centre Quebecois de Relations Internationales, Faculte des Sciences Sociales, Universite Laval, Quebec, PQ G1K 7P4, Canada. TEL 418-656-7530. Ed. Claude Basset. circ. 400. **Indexed:** A.B.C.Pol.Sci.
  Formerly (until 1981): Communautes Francophones: Bibliographie, Chroniques.

400 016   FR   ISSN 1157-3740
Z7003
F R A N C I S. 524: SCIENCES DU LANGAGE. 1947. q. 495 F. (outside EEC 525 F.). Centre National de la Recherche Scientifique, Institut de l'Information Scientifique et Technique, 2 allee du Parc de Brabois, 54514 Vandoeuvre-les-Nancy Cedex, France. TEL 83-50-46-00. FAX 83-50-46-50. adv. contact: Veronique Guinvarc'h. cum.index. **Document type:** bibliography.
  ●Also available online. Vendor(s): Telesystemes - Questel.
  Also available on CD-ROM.
  Formerly: Bulletin Signaletique. Part 524: Sciences du Langage (ISSN 0007-5590)

016 840   US   ISSN 0085-0888
Z2173
FRENCH 20 BIBLIOGRAPHY; critical and biographical references for the study of French literature since 1885. 1949. a. $78. (Susquehanna University Press) Associated University Presses, 440 Forsgate Dr., Cranbury, NJ 08512. TEL 609-655-4770. FAX 609-655-8366. Ed. Douglas W. Alden. circ. 700.
  Supersedes: French 7 Bibliography, Critical and Biographical References for the Study of Contemporary French Literature.

GERMANISTIK; internationales Referatenorgan mit bibliographischen Hinweisen. see *LITERATURE — Abstracting, Bibliographies, Statistics*

410 869   SP   ISSN 1130-1163
Z7003
INDICE ESPANOL DE HUMANIDADES. SERIES C: LINGUISTICS AND LITERATURE. 1978. a. 10000 ptas. or exchange basis (effective 1994). Centro de Informacion y Documentacion Cientifica (Cindoc), Pinar 25, 3, 28006 Madrid, Spain. TEL 1-5635482. FAX 1-5642644.
  ●Also available online.
  Also available on CD-ROM.
  Supersedes in part (in 1989): Indice Espanol de Humanidades (ISSN 0210-8488)

410   CK
INSTITUTO LINGUISTICO DE VERANO EN COLOMBIA. BIBLIOGRAFIA. 1975. irreg., vol.13, 1993. $925. Instituto Linguistico de Verano, Departamento de Estudios Tecnicos, Apdo. Aereo 100602, Bogota, Colombia. FAX 2590093. (Dist. in US by: Academic Publications Bookstore, 7500 W. Camp Wisden Rd., Dallas, TX 75236) circ. 1,000. **Document type:** bibliography.

410 572 016   NE   ISSN 0074-0462
KONINKLIJK INSTITUUT VOOR TAAL-, LAND- EN VOLKENKUNDE. BIBLIOGRAPHICAL SERIES. (Text mainly in English; occasionally in Dutch, French) 1965. irreg., no.20, 1992. price varies. K I T L V Press, P.O. Box 9515, 2300 RA Leiden, Netherlands. TEL 31-71-272372. FAX 31-71-272638. (back issues avail.) **Document type:** bibliography, monographic series.

400 370 016   UK   ISSN 0261-4448
PB35
LANGUAGE TEACHING. 1968. q. £26($49) to individuals (overseas £40.50); institutions £54 (overseas 68.50 ($99)). (Center for Information on Language Teaching and Research) Cambridge University Press, Edinburgh Bldg., Shaftesbury Rd., Cambridge CB2 2RU, England. TEL 0223-312393. FAX 0223-315052. TELEX 851817256. (N. American addr.: Cambridge University Press, Journals Dept., 40 W. 20th St., New York, NY 10011. TEL 212-924-3900. FAX 212-691-3239) (Co-sponsor: British Council) Ed. Valerie Kinsella. adv.; bk.rev.; abstr.; bibl.; index, cum.index. (also avail. in microform from UMI; back issues avail.; reprint service avail. from SWZ) **Document type:** abstracting/indexing.
  —BLDSC (5155.711970); Faxon; UnCover; SWETS; UMI. **CCC.**
  Former titles (until 1982): Language Teaching and Linguistics Abstracts (ISSN 0306-6304); (until 1975): Language-Teaching Abstracts (ISSN 0023-8279); English Teaching Abstracts.
  Description: Digests current thinking on both the theoretical and the pracitical aspects of using, learning and teaching language.

016 410   NE   ISSN 0378-4592
LINGUISTIC BIBLIOGRAPHY/BIBLIOGRAPHIE LINGUISTIQUE. (Text in English and French) 1949. a., latest 1993 (for the year 1991). fl.660 (effective 1994). (Unesco International Permanent Committee of Linguists, UN) Kluwer Academic Publishers, Postbus 17, 3300 AA Dordrecht, Netherlands. TEL 31-78-334911. FAX 31-78-334254. TELEX 29245 KAPG NL. (Dist. by: Kluwer Academic Publishers Group, P.O. Box 322, 3300 AH Dordrecht, Netherlands. TEL 31-78-524400. FAX 31-78-524474; N. America dist. addr.: Box 358, Accord Sta., Hingham, MA 02018-0358. TEL 617-871-6600. FAX 617-871-6528) Eds. Mark Janse, Sijmen Tol. **Indexed:** Bibl.Ling. **Document type:** bibliography.
  Description: Contains information on publications in all fields of linguistics, classified by language and subject, with an author index. Each volume contains supplemental information for earlier volumes.
  Refereed Serial

410   UK   ISSN 0267-5498
P1
LINGUISTICS ABSTRACTS. 1985. q. £29.50 to individuals ($67); institutions £87 ($188) (effective 1993). Basil Blackwell Ltd., 108 Cowley Rd., Oxford OX4 1JF, England. TEL 0865-791100. FAX 0865-791347. TELEX 837022-OXBOOK-G. (U.S. subscr. to: 238 Main St., Ste. 501, Cambridge, MA 02142) Ed. David Crystal. adv. circ. 700. (tabloid format; also avail. in microform; back issues avail.) **Indexed:** Bibl.Ling. **Document type:** abstracting/indexing.
  —UMI. **CCC.**

400 016   US   ISSN 0888-8027
Z7001   CODEN: LLBAAZ
LINGUISTICS AND LANGUAGE BEHAVIOR ABSTRACTS. Short title: L L B A. 1967. 5/yr. $235 (including a. cum. index $295). Sociological Abstracts, Inc., Box 22206, San Diego, CA 92192. TEL 619-695-8803. FAX 619-695-0416. adv.; index. cum.index. circ. 900. (back issues avail.) **Document type:** abstracting/indexing.
  ●Also available online. Vendor(s): BRS Online Products (LLBA), DIALOG Information Services, Inc. (File no.36/LLBA).
  —BLDSC (5221.375800); UMI. **CCC.**
  Incorporates (in 1989, vol.12): Reading Abstracts (ISSN 0361-6118); Formerly (until 1985): Language and Language Behavior Abstracts (ISSN 0023-8295)

M L A DIRECTORY OF PERIODICALS; a guide to journals and series in languages and literatures. (Modern Language Association of America) see *LITERATURE — Abstracting, Bibliographies, Statistics*

M L A INTERNATIONAL BIBLIOGRAPHY OF BOOKS AND ARTICLES ON THE MODERN LANGUAGES AND LITERATURES. (Modern Language Association of America) see *LITERATURE — Abstracting, Bibliographies, Statistics*

NOTE US; news from Sociological Abstracts, Linguistics and Language Behavior Abstracts, and Social Planning-Policy & Development Abstracts. see *ABSTRACTING AND INDEXING SERVICES*

410 011   RU
NOVAYA LITERATURA PO SOTSIAL'NYM I GUMANITARNYM NAUKAM. YAZYKOZNANIE; bibliograficheskii ukazatel' 1953. m. $114. Rossiiskaya Akademiya Nauk, Institut Nauchnoi Informatsii po Obshchestvennym Naukam, Ul. Krasikova 28-21, 117418 Moscow V-418, Russia. Ed. V.A. Makarenko.
  Formed by the merger of (1953-1992): Novaya Inostrannaya Literatura po Obshchestvennym Naukam. Yazykoznanie (ISSN 0134-2819); (1954-1992): Novaya Sovetskaya Literatura po Obshchestvennym Naukam. Yazykoznanie (ISSN 0134-2762)

410 800   GW   ISSN 0930-021X
PLATTDEUTSCHE BIBLIOGRAPHIE; laufendes Verzeichnis der Neuerscheinungen und Neuauflagen auf dem Gebiet der Plattdeutschen Sprache und Literatur. 1974. s-a. DM.12. Institut fuer Niederdeutsche Sprache e.V., Schnoor 41, 28195 Bremen, Germany. TEL 0421-324535. Ed. Friedrich W. Michelsen. circ. 500. (back issues avail.) **Document type:** bibliography.
  Description: Covers new literary and linguistic publications in the Low-German dialect (Plattdeutsch).

ROCZNIK SLAWISTYCZNY. see *LINGUISTICS*

479 016   GW   ISSN 0080-388X
ROMANISCHE BIBLIOGRAPHIE/BIBLIOGRAPHIE ROMANE/ROMANCE BIBLIOGRAPHY. (Supplement to: Zeitschrift fuer Romanische Philologie) (Text in German, French and English) 1965. a. price varies. Max Niemeyer Verlag, Postfach 2140, 72011 Tuebingen, Germany. TEL 07071-98940. FAX 07071-989450. Ed. Gustav Ineichen. (back issues avail.) **Document type:** bibliography.
  Description: Bibliography listing reviewed Romance language monographs and essays on literature.

310   AT   ISSN 1031-5020
S I L - A A I B BIBLIOGRAPHY. (In 3 sections: Technical Works, Vernacular-Secular Works, Vernacular-Religious Works) 1972. irreg. Summer Institute of Linguistics, Australian Aborigines and Islanders Branch, P.O. Berrimah, N.T. 0828, Australia. TEL 089-84-4488. FAX 089-844321. **Document type:** bibliography.
  Formerly (until Oct., 1987): S I L - A A B Bibliography.
  Description: Section 1 consists of articles, monographs on linguistics, anthropology, literacy, education; Section 2 consists of several categories of works in Australian languages; Section 3 consists of Bible stories, Scripture portions, complete books of the Bible, Old Testament, summaries and all of New Testament in Australian languages.

418 011   US   ISSN 1055-4750
P51
SECOND LANGUAGE INSTRUCTION - ACQUISITION ABSTRACTS. 1991. biennial. $55 to individuals; institutions $80. Sociological Abstracts, Inc., Box 22206, San Diego, CA 92192-0206. TEL 619-695-8803. FAX 619-695-0416. **Document type:** abstracting/indexing.

410   GW   ISSN 0933-1883
P40.45.E85
SOCIOLINGUISTICA; internationales Jahrbuch fuer Europaeische Soziolinguistik. (Text in English, French and German) 1987. a. price varies. Max Niemeyer Verlag, Postfach 2140, 72011 Tuebingen, Germany. TEL 07071-98940. FAX 07071-989450. Ed.Bd. adv.; bk.rev.; bibl. (back issues avail.) **Indexed:** Bibl.Ling. **Document type:** academic/scholarly publication.
  —BLDSC (8319.579300).
  Description: Covers essays in the field of sociolinguistics of the European languages; includes an updated bibliography.

808.5 371.9   US   ISSN 0081-3656
SPEECH INDEX; an index to 259 collections of orations and speeches for various occasions. 1935. irreg., 4th ed., 1966, supplement 1982. price varies. Scarecrow Press, Inc., 52 Liberty St., Box 4167, Metuchen, NJ 08840. TEL 800-537-7107. Ed. Charity Mitchell. circ. 3,000. **Document type:** abstracting/indexing.

LINGUISTICS — COMPUTER APPLICATIONS

410   **PL**   ISSN 0208-8665
PG6004
STUDIA JEZYKOZNAWCZE. irreg. price varies. (Polish Academy of Sciences, Linguistic Committee) Ossolineum, Publishing House of the Polish Academy of Sciences, Rynek 9, 50-106 Wroclaw, Poland. TEL 48-71-386-25. FAX 48-71-448-103. TELEX 0712771 OSS PL. Ed. J. Siatkowski. **Document type:** abstracting/indexing.
Description: Summaries of linguistic doctoral dissertations.

410   **RU**
YAZYKOZNANIE: OTECHESTVENNAYA LITERATURA; referativnyi zhurnal. 1973. q. $44. Rossiiskaya Akademiya Nauk, Institut Nauchnoi Informatsii po Obshchestvennym Naukam, Ul. Krasikova 28-21, 117418 Moscow V-418, Russia. Ed. F.M. Berezin.
Formerly: Obshchestvennye Nauki v S.S.S.R. Yazykoznanie (ISSN 0202-2087).

410   **RU**
YAZYKOZNANIE: ZARUBEZHNAYA LITERATURA; referativnyi zhurnal. 1973. q.? $32. Rossiiskaya Akademiya Nauk, Institut Nauchnoi Informatsii po Obshchestvennym Naukam, Ul. Krasikova 28-21, 117418 Moscow V-418, Russia. Ed. F.M. Berezin.
Formerly: Obshchestvennye Nauki za Rubezhom. Yazykoznanie (ISSN 0202-2133).

405   **UK**   ISSN 0084-4152
PB1
YEAR'S WORK IN MODERN LANGUAGE STUDIES. 1929-30. a. $204. Modern Humanities Research Association, King's College, London WC2, England. (Vols. 1-29 avail. from: Wm. Dawson & Sons Ltd., Cannon House, Folkstone, Kent, England) Ed. D.A. Wells. index. circ. 850. **Indexed:** Bibl.Ling., Br.Hum.Ind., M.L.A. **Document type:** bibliography.
Description: Critical bibliography of language and literature (modern and Medieval) for all European languages except English.

LINGUISTICS — Computer Applications

ASIAN CLASSICS INPUT PROGRAM. see *RELIGIONS AND THEOLOGY — Buddhist*

490   **SI**
COMMUNICATIONS of C o L I P S. (Text in English) q. S.60 (foreign S$.200). Chinese and Oriental Languages Information Processing Society, c/o Dept. of Information Systems & Computer Science, National University of Singapore, Kent Ridge, Singapore 0511, Singapore. Ed. Kim Teng Lua.
Description: Covers the spectrum of computer processing of Chinese and oriental languages.

410   **UK**
COMPENDIA; computer generated aids to literary and linguistic research. 1968. irreg. price varies. W.S. Maney & Son Ltd., Hudson Rd., Leeds LS9 7DL, England. Ed. R.A. Wisbey. stat. (back issues avail.) **Indexed:** M.L.A. **Document type:** academic/scholarly publication.

410 651.8   **US**   ISSN 0891-2017
P98   CODEN: CLINEE
COMPUTATIONAL LINGUISTICS. 1974. q. $84 to individuals; institutions $98. (Association for Computational Linguistics) M I T Press, 55 Hayward St., Cambridge, MA 02142. TEL 617-253-2889. FAX 617-258-6779. TELEX 921473. E-mail: mit.edu. (Subscr. to: c/o Julia Hirschberg, 2D-450, AT&T Laboratories, 6000 Mountain Ave., Murray Hill, NJ 07974) Ed. James F. Allen. bk.rev.; abstr.; bibl.; stat.; index. circ. 2,500. (also avail. in microfilm; back issues avail.; reprint service avail. from UMI) **Indexed:** A.I.Abstr., Bibl.Ling., Comput.Abstr., Comput.Cont., Comput.Rev., Ind.Med., Lang.& Lang.Behav.Abstr. (1974-), Sci.Abstr.
—BLDSC (3390.601000); EI; Faxon; UnCover; SWETS; UMI; CASDDS. **CCC.**
Formerly: American Journal of Computational Linguistics (ISSN 0362-613X); Supersedes: Finite String (ISSN 0015-2366)
Description: Covers the design and analysis of natural language processing systems. Encompasses research in language, linguistics, and the psychology of language processing and performance.
Refereed Serial

407.8 370   **NE**   ISSN 0958-8221
CODEN: CALLEE
COMPUTER ASSISTED LANGUAGE LEARNING; an international journal. 1990. 3/yr. fl.117.50($65) to individuals; institutions fl.220($121) (effective 1994). Swets & Zeitlinger bv, Heereweg 347, 2161 CA Lisse, Netherlands. TEL 31-2521-35111. FAX 31-2521-15888. TELEX 41325. (Dist. in N. America by: Swets & Zeitlinger, 440 Creamery Way, Ste. A, Exton, PA 19341. TEL 800-447-9387. FAX 610-524-5366) Ed. Keith Cameron. circ. 300. **Document type:** academic/scholarly publication.
—UnCover.
Description: Covers pedagogical principles and applications to computer-assisted language learning, computer assisted translation, applications of AI in language teaching, and other related issues.

410   **US**
DISTRIBUTED LANGUAGE TRANSLATION.* (Text in English) 1986. irreg., no.6, 1989. Walter de Gruyter, Inc., 200 Saw Mill River Rd., Hawthorne, NY 10532. TEL 914-747-0110. FAX 914-747-1326. Ed. Toon Witkam.
Description: Topics in computational linguistics and machine translation.

410   **FR**   ISSN 0085-4786
DOCUMENTS DE LINGUISTIQUE QUANTITATIVE. 1969. irreg. price varies. (Association Jean-Favard pour le Developpement de la Linguistique Quantitative) Editions Jean Favard, 37 rue du Four a Chaux, 91910 St. Sulpice de Favieres, France. Ed. Daniel J. Herault. circ. 850. **Indexed:** Bull.Signal.

492.4   **IS**   ISSN 0792-3252
HEBREW COMPUTATIONAL LINGUISTICS. (Text in Hebrew, summaries in English) 1969. s-a. $28 (effective 1993). (Bar-Ilan University, Department of Hebrew and Semitic Languages) Bar-Ilan University Press, Ramat Gan 52900, Israel. TEL 972-3-5318401. Ed. Maya Fruchtman. (back issues avail.) **Indexed:** Lang.& Lang.Behav.Abstr. (1972-), M.L.A. **Document type:** academic/scholarly publication.

410   **US**   ISSN 1049-2615
I E E E COMPUTER SOCIETY WORKSHOP ON VISUAL LANGUAGES. 1984. a. price varies. (Institute of Electrical and Electronics Engineers, Inc.) I E E E Computer Society Press, 10662 Los Vaqueros Circle, Los Alamitos, CA 90720-1264. TEL 714-821-8380. FAX 714-821-4641. (Subscr. to: 345 E. 47th St., New York, NY 10017-2394) **Document type:** proceedings.
Description: Examines the importance of visual information essential in the communication between personnel, the user and the system.

410   **NE**   ISSN 0929-6174
▼**JOURNAL OF QUANTITATIVE LINGUISTICS.** (Text in English) 1994. 3/yr. fl.150($82) to individuals; institutions fl.260($143) (effective 1994). Swets & Zeitlinger bv, Heereweg 347, 2161 CA Lisse, Netherlands. TEL 31-2521-35111. FAX 31-2521-15888. TELEX 41325. (Dist. in N. America by: Swets & Zeitlinger, 440 Creamery Way, Ste. A, Exton, PA 19341. TEL 800-447-9387. FAX 610-524-5366) Ed. Richard Kohler. **Document type:** academic/scholarly publication.
Description: Discusses research on the quantitative characteristics of language in an exact mathematical form, including issues such as machine learning, statistical parsing, and the application of mathematical methods to linguistic analysis.

410   **UK**   ISSN 1045-926X
CODEN: JVLCE7
JOURNAL OF VISUAL LANGUAGES AND COMPUTING. 1990. q. £86 (effective 1994). Academic Press Ltd. (Subsidiary of: Harcourt Brace & Company Ltd.), 24-28 Oval Rd., London NW1 7DX, England. TEL 44-71-267-4466. FAX 44-71-482-2293. TELEX 25775-ACPRES-G. (Subscr. to: Harcourt Brace & Company Ltd., Foots Cray High St., Sidcup, Kent DA14 5HP, England. TEL 44-81-300-3322. FAX 44-81-309-0807) Eds. S.K. Chang, S. Levialdi. **Document type:** academic/scholarly publication.
—BLDSC (5072.495200); Faxon; UnCover; SWETS.
Description: Directed to researchers, practitioners, and developers to exchange ideas and results for the advancement of visual languages and their implication on the art of computing.

410   **US**
LANGG'UIJ MATTERS. 1970-197?; N.S. 1991. q. free. Translation Company of America, 10 W. 37th St., New York, NY 10018. TEL 212-563-7054. FAX 212-695-2385. Ed. Richard J. Mazziotti. tr.lit. circ. 5,000. **Document type:** newsletter.
Formerly: Translation Talk (ISSN 0041-123X)

410   **NE**   ISSN 0921-5034
LANGUAGE AND COMPUTERS; studies in practical linguistics. (Text in English) 1988. irreg., vol.11, 1994. price varies. Editions Rodopi B.V., Keizersgracht 302-304, 1016 EX Amsterdam, Netherlands. TEL 31-20-6227507. FAX 31-20-6380948. (in N. America: 233 Peachtree St., N.E., Ste. 404, Atlanta GA 30303-1504. TEL 800-225-3998. FAX 404-522-7116) **Document type:** academic/scholarly publication.
Description: Discusses practical applications of linguistic theory.

410 800   **NE**   ISSN 0927-3034
P98   CODEN: LADEEI
▼**LANGUAGES OF DESIGN;** formalisms for word, images and sound. (Text in English) 1992. 4/yr. fl.368($199) (effective 1994). Elsevier Science B.V., P.O. Box 211, 1000 AE Amsterdam, Netherlands. TEL 31-20-5803911. FAX 31-20-5803598. TELEX 18582 ESPA NL. (Subscr. in U.S. and Canada to: Elsevier Science Inc., Box 882, Madison Sq. Sta., New York, NY 10159. TEL 212-989-5800. FAX 212-633-3990) Eds. R.G. Lauzanna, D. Penrose. (also avail. in microform from UMI; back issues avail.) **Document type:** academic/scholarly publication.
—BLDSC (5155.713500).
Description: Interdisciplinary journal devoted to research in formal languages and their use for the generation and analysis of words, images and sound in both literary works and "nonliterary texts," music and visual art, as well as applications of computational methods in visual, audio and textual analyses.
Refereed Serial

001.6 410 800   **UK**   ISSN 0951-1474
P98   CODEN: ALLCB5
LITERARY AND LINGUISTIC COMPUTING. 1986. 4/yr. £70($130) (effective 1994). (Association for Literary and Linguistic Computing) Oxford University Press, Oxford Journals, Walton St., Oxford OX2 6DP, England. TEL 0865-56767. FAX 0865-56646. TELEX 387330-OXPRES-G. (U.S. subscr. to: Oxford University Press Inc., 2001 Evans Rd., Cary, NC 27513. TEL 919-677-0977) Ed. Gordon Dixon. adv. contact: Jane Parker. bk.rev.; bibl.; illus.; index. circ. 900. **Indexed:** Comput.Abstr., Comput.Cont., Comput.Rev., Lang.& Lang.Behav.Abstr. (1986-), Lang.Teach.& Ling.Abstr., M.L.A., Sci.Abstr., Sociol.Abstr. **Document type:** academic/scholarly publication.
—**CCC.**
Incorporated (1973-1986): A L L C Bulletin (ISSN 0305-9855); (1980-1986): A L L C Journal (ISSN 0143-3385)
Description: Covers all aspects of computing applied to literature and language.

410   **NE**   ISSN 0922-6567
P307   CODEN: MACTEZ
MACHINE TRANSLATION. (Text in English) 1986. 4/yr. fl.352($184) (effective 1994). Kluwer Academic Publishers, Postbus 17, 3300 AA Dordrecht, Netherlands. TEL 31-78-334911. FAX 31-78-334254. TELEX 29245 KAPG NL. (Dist. by: Kluwer Academic Publishers Group, P.O. Box 322, 3300 AH Dordrecht, Netherlands. TEL 31-78-524400. FAX 31-78-524474; N. America dist. addr.: Box 358, Accord Sta., Hingham, MA 02018-0358. TEL 617-871-6600. FAX 617-871-6528) Ed. Sergei Nirenburg. adv.; bk.rev.; charts; illus. (also avail. in microform from UMI; back issues avail.; reprint service avail. from SWZ) **Indexed:** Art.Int.Abstr., Bibl.Ling., Comput.Abstr., Comput.Lit.Ind., Eng.Ind., INSPEC, Lang.& Lang.Behav.Abstr., Sci.Abstr., Sociol.Abstr., Zent.Math. **Document type:** academic/scholarly publication.
—BLDSC (5326.515000); EI; SWETS; UMI. **CCC.**
Formerly: Computers and Translation (ISSN 0884-0709)
Description: Publishes articles dealing with theoretical, computational and descriptive aspects of topics that contribute to the advancement of machine translation and machine-aided translation.
Refereed Serial

410   US   ISSN 1049-9865
P98
NOTES ON COMPUTING; a newsletter for academic computing in SIL. 1983. 8/yr. $14. Summer Institute of Linguistics, Inc., JAARS Division, Box 248, Waxhaw, NC 28173. TEL 704-843-6000. FAX 704-843-6200. (Microfiche from: SIL Bookstore, 7500 W. Camp Wisdom Rd., Dallas, TX 75236) Ed. Don Horneman. bk.rev.; cum.index. circ. 1,000. (also avail. in microfiche).
    Former titles (until 1987): Computing (Waxhaw) (ISSN 1049-9911); Notes on Computing (ISSN 0887-9206).

410   NE
▼ PRAGMATICS & COGNITION. (Text in English) 1993. 2/yr. fl.210($120) (effective 1994). John Benjamins Publishing Co., Amsteldijk 44, P.O. Box 75577, 1070 AN Amsterdam, Netherlands. TEL 31-20-6738156. FAX 31-20-6792956. (In N. America: 821 Bethlehem Pike, Philadelphia, PA 19118. TEL 215-836-1200. FAX 215-836-1204) Ed. Marcelo Dascal. Document type: academic/scholarly publication.
    Description: Interdisciplinary journal exploring relations between semiotic systems used by humans, animals and machines, including neurological and biological bases, modeling and simulation, social and cultural variations.
    Refereed Serial

400 510   XR   ISSN 0032-6585
                          CODEN: PBMLAT
PRAGUE BULLETIN OF MATHEMATICAL LINGUISTICS. (Text in English, German or Russian; summaries in English and Russian) 1964. s-a. 10 Kcs.($2) Universita Karlova, Fakulta Matematiky a Fysiky, Ovocny Trh 5, Prague 1, Czech Republic. Ed. Eva Hajicova. bk.rev.; stat.; cum.index: 1964-1973. circ. 800. Indexed: Bibl.Ling., Lang.& Lang.Behav.Abstr. (1972-), M.L.A., Math.R., Sci.Abstr.
—BLDSC (6598.520000).

439   NE
RANDGEBIEDEN; een interdisciplinaire serie. vol.4, 1982. irreg. price varies. Dick Coutinho B.V., Slochterlaan 7, 1405 AL Bussum, Netherlands. TEL 31-2159-49991. FAX 31-2159-47165. bibl. Document type: monographic series.

410 371.394   UK   ISSN 0958-3440
RECALL. 1989. s-a. £30 to Eurocall subscr. (effective 1994). Computers in Teaching Initiative, Centre for Modern Languages, The University of Hull, School of European Languages and Cultures, Hull HU6 7RX, England. TEL 0482-466373. FAX 0482-473816. (Co-sponsor: Eurocall) Ed. June Thompson. adv.; software rev. circ. 2,000. Document type: academic/scholarly publication.
—BLDSC (7303.590500).
    Description: Contains articles of interest to beginners in the fields of computer-assisted language learning (CALL). Includes items concerned with research and developmental work.

410   GW   ISSN 0724-3103
SPRACHWISSENSCHAFT - COMPUTERLINGUISTIK. (Text in English, French and German) 1977. irreg., no.15, 1993. DM.52. A Q Verlag, Weinbergweg 16, 66119 Saarbruecken, Germany. TEL 0681-55118. Document type: monographic series.
—BLDSC (8419.891100).

029.756 400   FR   ISSN 0039-8217
T.A. INFORMATIONS; revue internationale des applications de l'automatisme au langage. 1965. s-a. price varies. (Association pour la Traduction Automatique et la Linguistique Appliquee) Editions Klincksieck, 11 rue de Lille, 75005 Paris, France. bk.rev.; abstr.; charts; illus. circ. 600. (also avail. in microform from SWZ) Indexed: Bibl.Ling.
—Faxon; SWETS.
    Formerly: Traduction Automatique.

USER MODELLING AND USER-ADAPTED INTERACTION; an international journal. see EDUCATION — Computer Applications

LITERARY AND POLITICAL REVIEWS

700   IT   ISSN 0001-1584
A I L A. 1960. w. (Agenzia Internazionale Letteraria Artistica) Francesco Boneschi, Ed. & Pub., Via Giolitti 202, Rome, Italy. bk.rev.; film rev.; music rev.; play rev. circ. 1,200.

323.4   US
A IS A; writings on freedom and individualism. 1971. irreg. $4 for 12 issues. Mega, 9730 Hyne Rd., Brighton, MI 48116. Ed. Dale Haviland. bk.rev.; play rev.; illus. circ. 500. (back issues avail.)
    Formerly: A Is A Newsletter (ISSN 0044-569X)

054   FR   ISSN 1240-9987
A R L I T & CIE. (Annuaire des Revues Litteraires et Compagnie) a. 225 F. B.P. 17, 94404 Vitry Cedex, France.

800   UK   ISSN 0001-320X
LH5
ABERDEEN UNIVERSITY REVIEW. 1913. s-a. £10. Aberdeen University, Alumnus Association, 18 Bon-Accord Sq., Aberdeen, AB9 1YE, Scotland. adv.; bk.rev.; bibl.; illus.; index. circ. 1,300. Indexed: Abstr.Engl.Stud. Document type: academic/scholarly publication.
—BLDSC (0538.020000); UnCover.

ABHANDLUNGEN ZUR KUNST-, MUSIK- UND LITERATURWISSENSCHAFT. see ART

053.1   AU
ACADEMIA; Zeitschrift fuer Politik und Kultur. 1949. bi-m. S.150. Oesterreichischer Cartell-Verband, Lerchenfelderstr. 14, A-1080 Vienna, Austria. FAX 0222-42162233. Ed. C.M. Auer. bk.rev.; film rev.; charts; illus.; stat.; circ. 20,000 (controlled).

ACADEMIE ROYALE DE LANGUE ET DE LITTERATURE FRANCAISES. ANNUAIRES. see LINGUISTICS

056   AG   ISSN 0325-5956
ACCION; en defensa del cooperativismo y del pais. 1966. fortn. Arg.$8000. Instituto Movilizador de Fondos Cooperativos, Rivadavia 1944, 1033 Buenos Aires, Argentina. Ed.Bd. illus.

059.92   MR   ISSN 0001-4869
ACHAAB/PEOPLE; serving the people, the throne, Arabism and Islam. 1952. s-w. DH.120($24.) Achaab Publishing, 12 rue Pormentier, Avenue Temara, Rabat, Morocco. Ed. El Hassan Arbii. adv.; bk.rev.; illus. circ. 2,500. (tabloid format)

056.1   US
ACTIVA. 1976. fortn. Editorial America, S.A., Vanidades Continental Bldg., 6355 N.W. 36th St., Virginia Gardens, FL 33166. TEL 305-871-6400. FAX 305-871-8769. Ed. Elvira Mendoza. adv. circ. 70,000.

ACTIVE VOICE; of the people, by the people, for the people. see POLITICAL SCIENCE

808.8   US
THE ACTS THE SHELFLIFE.* 1980. a. $5. Xexoxial Editions, RR 1 Box 131, La Farge, WI 54639-9601. circ. 500.

054.1   FR
ACTUEL. 1970. m. (11/yr.). 220 F. Societe du Journal Actuel, 33 rue du Faubourg St. Antoine, 75011 Paris, France. TEL 33-1-43-47-50-04. Ed. Frederic Joignot. bk.rev. circ. 171,633. Document type: consumer publication.

891.553   IR
ADABISTAN; farhangi, adabi, hunari, ijtimai. (Text in Persian) 1990. m. IRl.6000 (N. America $125) (effective 1994). Ettela'at Publications, P.O. Box 11365-9365, Khayyam Ave., Tehran 11144, Iran. TEL 98-21-328529. FAX 98-21-3111223. TELEX 212336. Ed. Sayyed Ahmad Sam. circ. 50,000. Document type: consumer publication.
    Description: Covers literary and cultural topics, including art and architecture.

052   IN   ISSN 0044-6181
ADAM AND EVE. (Text in English) vol.5, 1972. m. Rs.10. A & P Publications, 3 Krishnier St., Nungambakkam, Madras 34, India. Ed. Amarlal Nichani. adv.; film rev.; charts; illus.

052   AT   ISSN 0815-5992
ADELAIDE REVIEW. 1984. m. Aus.$20. Adelaide Review, 1 Dequetteville TCF, Kent Town, S.A. 5067, Australia. TEL 08-362-7699. FAX 08-362-7878. Ed. Christopher Pearson. adv.; bk.rev.; illus. circ. 38,500. (back issues avail.)

052   II
ADMINISTRATION. (Text in English) 1973. m. Linge Gowda Detective & Security Chambers, Mysugar Bldg., J.C. Rd., Bangalore 560 002, India. Ed. D. Linge Gowda. adv.; illus. circ. 1,000. Indexed: Mid.East: Abstr.& Ind.

051   US
ADVOCATE (PROVIDENCE). 1973. m. $0.50 per copy. 160 Chace Ave., Providence, RI 02906. Ed. Irwin N. Becker. bibl.; illus. circ. 500.

AERIAL. see LITERATURE — Poetry

059.159   AF
AFGHANISTAN TODAY. (Text in Dari, Pashtu) 1985. bi-m. Block 106, Ansari Wat, Kabul, Afghanistan. Ed. Karim Huquq. circ. 10,500.

AFRICAN INTERPRETER; journal on African and Arab affairs. see BUSINESS AND ECONOMICS

059.927   UA
AHALI. (Text in Arabic) w. (National Progressive Unionist Party) Muassasat al- Ahali, 23 Sharia Abd el-Khaliq Tharwat, Cairo, Egypt. TEL 02-759114. Ed. Mahmoud al-Maragi.

059.927   QA
AL-AHD. (Text in Arabic) 1974. w. Al-Ahd Establishment for Journalism, Printing and Publications Ltd., P.O. Box 2531, Doha, Qatar. TEL 601506. TELEX 4920. Ed. Khalifa al-Hussaini. circ. 13,000.

056   SP   ISSN 1133-2115
AJOBLANCO. 1974. m. 4000 ptas. (Europe 6000 ptas.; elsewhere 10000 ptas.). Ediciones Culturales Odeon, S.A., Aragon 264, 5o - 1a, 08007 Barcelona, Spain. TEL 3-4879748. FAX 3-4877553. Ed. Elisabeth Cabrero. adv. contact: Fernando Gamero. circ. 40,000.
    Description: Covers innovative trends. Provides a forum of opinion and debate.

053   GW
DIE AKTION; Zeitschrift fuer Politik, Literatur, Kunst. 1981. 4/yr. DM.24. Edition Nautilus Verlag Lutz Schulenburg, Am Brink 10, 21029 Hamburg, Germany. TEL 040-7213536. Ed. Lutz Schulenburg. adv.; bk.rev.; film rev. circ. 3,000. (also avail. in microfilm from KTO)

808.8   US   ISSN 0890-1554
PS558.A5
ALABAMA LITERARY REVIEW. 1987. s-a. $9. Troy State University, 253 Smith Hall, Troy State University, Troy, AL 36082. TEL 205-670-3307. FAX 205-670-3519. Ed. Theron Montgomery. bk.rev. circ. 850.
    Description: Presents fiction, poetry, interviews, essays, photographs, graphic art and short drama.

051   US
ALABAMA MAGAZINE. 1936. m. $19.95. Drawer 6161, Montgomery, AL 36106. TEL 205-264-1981. Ed. Wayne Greenhaw. circ. 20,000.

056.1   MX   ISSN 0185-660X
ALARMA. 1963. w. Mex.$4 per no. Publicaciones Llergo, Avda. Ceylan 517, 02300 Mexico D.F., Mexico. TEL 5-587-3855. Ed. Raymundo Medellin R. adv. circ. 1,199,750.

800   US
ALASKA WOMEN. 1990. 4/yr. $30. Attn: G.R. Gardner, Ed., HCR 64, Box 453, Seward, AK 99664. TEL 907-288-3168. adv.; bk.rev.; illus.
    Description: Includes poetry, articles, art, photos, cartoons, interviews, criticism, reviews, non-fiction.

056.1   CK   ISSN 0120-0216
AP63
ALEPH. 1966. 4/yr. $100. Carlos Enrique Ruiz, Ed. & Pub., Apdo. Aereo 1080, Manizales, Colombia. bk.rev. circ. 2,000.

052   AT
ALEXANDRA & EILDON STANDARD. 1886. w. Aus.$45. 49 Grant St., Alexandra, Vic. 3714, Australia. TEL 057 721002. FAX 057-721603. Ed. Geoffrey Heyes. circ. 2,150.

LITERARY AND POLITICAL REVIEWS

052 II
ALIVE. (Text in English) 1940. fortn. Rs.375($15) Delhi Press Patra Prakashan Ltd., Delhi Press Bldg., E-3 Jhandewala Estate, New Delhi 110 055, India. TEL 11-526311. TELEX 31-63053 DEPR IN. Ed. Vishwa Nath. adv.; bk.rev.; illus. circ. 20,000.
Formerly: Caravan (ISSN 0008-6150)
Description: Covers social, political, and business topics.

ALL AREA. see ART

ALLIED ARTS NEWSLETTER. see PUBLIC ADMINISTRATION — Municipal Government

ALLMENDE. see LITERATURE — Poetry

056 AG
ALTERNATIVA CULTURA. m. Arg.$90. Editorial Surcos de Cultura S.R.L., Bustamante 1048, 1832 Lomas de Zamora, Buenos Aires, Argentina. Ed. Claudio Gustavo Basile.

ALTERNATIVE ARCHIVIST. see LIBRARY AND INFORMATION SCIENCES

051 US ISSN 1072-7299
ALTERNATIVE PRESS REVIEW. 1993. 4/yr. $16. C.A.L. Press, Box 1446, Columbia, MO 65205-1446. TEL 314-442-4352. adv.; bk.rev.; circ. 6,000 (paid). Document type: consumer publication.
Description: For people interested in the alternative press.

808.8 301 CN
ALTERNATIVE RESEARCH NEWSLETTER. 1979. q. Can.$1. Alternative Research, Box 1294, Kitchener, Ont. N2G 4G8, Canada. Ed.Bd. adv.; bk.rev.; abstr.; bibl.; index.

055.1 IT
ALTRI TERMINI.* 1972. 3/yr. L.35000. Societa Editrice Napoletana s.r.l., Corso Umberto I, 34, 80138 Naples, Italy. Ed. G. Battista Nazzaro.

800 CQ ISSN 1013-6843
AL-WATWANY/JOURNAL DES COMORES. (Text in French) 1952. s-m. S N E C, Moroni, Comoros.
Supersedes (in 1985): Echo des Comores.

AM ERKER; Zeitschrift fuer Literatur. see LITERATURE

056.1 MX
AMERICA DESDE MEXICO. 1958. m. Mex.$4($.50) per no. Gomez Farias 12, Mexico 21, D.F., Mexico. Dir. Esperanza Gutierrez. adv.

800 001.3 US ISSN 0149-9408
AMERICAN BOOK REVIEW. 1977. bi-m. $24 to individuals; institutions $30. Writers Review, Inc., c/o Publications Center, English Department, Box 494, University of Colorado, Boulder, CO 80309. TEL 303-492-8947. FAX 303-492-5105. Ed. Don Laing. adv.; bk.rev.; illus. circ. 15,000. (tabloid format; back issues avail.) Indexed: Arts & Hum.Cit.Ind., Bk.Rev.Ind. (1978-), Chic.Per.Ind., Child.Bk.Rev.Ind. (1978-), Curr.Cont.
—Faxon.
Description: Guide to current books of literary interest published by the small, large, university, regional, ethnic, women's and other presses.

808.8 US
AMERICAN FORUM;* for the opinionated. 1984. w. $9.95. Vincent F. Palazzolo, Ed. & Pub., 27 Rainbow Ave., Staten Island, NY 10302-2141. TEL 718-720-2153. circ. 3,000. (looseleaf format)

AMERICAN IMAGO; a psychoanalytic journal for culture, science and the arts. see MEDICAL SCIENCES — Psychiatry And Neurology

378 US ISSN 0003-0295
LH1.O8
AMERICAN OXONIAN. 1907. 4/yr. $25. Association of American Rhodes Scholars, Box 1027, Claremont, CA 91711-1027. (Editorial addr.: 11 Lake Rd., Hidden Valley, PA 15502. TEL 814-445-4100) Ed. John Funari. bk.rev.; bibl.; index; circ. 2,400 (paid). —UnCover.

300 378 US ISSN 0003-0937
AP2
AMERICAN SCHOLAR. 1932. q. $23. Phi Beta Kappa Society, 1811 Q St., N.W., Washington, DC 20009. TEL 202-265-3808. FAX 202-986-1601. Ed. Joseph Epstein. adv.; bk.rev.; illus.; index. circ. 26,000. (also avail. in microform from UMI,PMC) Indexed: A.I.P.P., Abstr.Engl.Stud., Acad.Ind., Amer.Bibl.Slavic & E.Eur.Stud., Amer.Hist.& Life, Arts & Hum.Cit.Ind., Biog.Ind., Bk.Rev.Dig., Bk.Rev.Ind. (1965-), C.I.J.E., Chic.Per.Ind., Child.Bk.Rev.Ind. (1965-), Curr.Cont., Film Lit.Ind. (1973-), G.Soc.Sci.& Rel.Per.Lit., Hist.Abstr., Hum.Ind., Ind.Bk.Rev.Hum., Lang.& Lang.Behav.Abstr., M.L.A., Mag.Ind., Mid.East: Abstr.& Ind., P.A.I.S., PMR, PSI, Psychol.Abstr., R.G., Soc.Work Res.& Abstr., SSCI. Document type: academic/scholarly publication.
—BLDSC (0856.400000); Faxon; UnCover; SWETS; UMI.

051 US ISSN 0148-8414
AP2
AMERICAN SPECTATOR. 1967. m. $35. 2020 N. 14th St., Ste. 750, Box 549, Arlington, VA 22201. TEL 703-243-3733. FAX 703-243-6814. Ed. R. Emmett Tyrrell, Jr. adv. contact: John Funk. bk.rev.; film rev.; illus.; index; circ. 200,000 (paid). (also avail. in microfiche from UMI,BHP; back issues avail.; reprint service avail. from ISI) Indexed: Access (1978-1988), Biog.Ind., Bk.Rev.Ind. (1980-), Chic.Per.Ind., Child.Bk.Rev.Ind. (1980-), Mag.Ind., Mid.East: Abstr.& Ind., P.A.I.S., Pop.Per.Ind., R.G. (1988-), Sage Urb.Stud.Abstr. Document type: consumer publication.
●Also available online. Vendor(s): Information Access Co.
Also available on CD-ROM.
—BLDSC (0857.540000); Faxon; UMI.
Former titles (until 1976): Alternative; an American Spectator; Alternative (ISSN 0044-7382)
Description: National magazine of politics and culture.

341.1 JA ISSN 0003-2026
AMPO; Japan-Asia quarterly review. (Text in English) 1969. q. 4000 Yen to individuals (foreign $28); institutions 6000 Yen($40). Pacific Asia Resource Center, Box 5250, Tokyo International, Tokyo, Japan. TEL 03-3291-5901. FAX 03-3295-9453. Eds. Jens Wilkinson, Kiyokazu Koshida. adv.; bk.rev.; bibl.; illus. circ. 2,000. (also avail. in microfilm from UMI) Indexed: HR Rep.
—BLDSC (0859.482400); UnCover; UMI.
Description: Contains cross-cultural articles about politics, ecomonics, and peoples' movements concerning Japan.

808.8 US
ANACHRONISTIC TIME BOMB FUNNIES. q.? $2.50 per no. 1905 Treehouse, Plano, TX 75023. Ed. Nathan Tolzmann.
Description: Contains political and social satires and counterculture themes.

ANALYTICAL PSYCHOLOGY CLUB OF NEW YORK. BULLETIN. see PSYCHOLOGY

800 AT
ANARCHIST AGE MONTHLY REVIEW. 1990. m. Aus.$40. Anarchist Associated Press, Editorial Collective, P.O. Box 20, Parkville, Melbourne, Victoria 3052, Australia. TEL 03-8282856. bk.rev. circ. 500. Document type: newspaper.
Description: Contains articles, letters, and news items from an anarchist perspective.

800 AT
ANARCHIST AGE WEEKLY REVIEW. 1990. w. Aus.$70. Anarchist Associated Press, Editorial Collective, P.O. Box 20, Parkville, Melbourne, Victoria 3052, Australia. bk.rev. circ. 100. Document type: newsletter.
Description: Contains articles, letters, and news items from an anarchist perspective.

ANDERSCHUME - KONTIKI; das Schweizer Magazin fuer den schwulen Mann. see HOMOSEXUALITY

800 US
ANGRY THOREAUAN; stamping out stupidity to eradicate the competition. 1987. q. $8. World Wide Music Union, Box 2246, Anaheim, CA 92814. TEL 714-647-2307. Ed. Rev. Randall Tin-ear. adv.; bk.rev.; film rev. (back issues avail.)
Description: Publishes a wide variety of material, including reviews of both underground and mainstream music, publications, and concerts.

059.91 II ISSN 0003-5203
ANNRINYA. (Text in Bengali) 1969. m. Rs.1.50($1) per copy. S. K. Poddar, Ed. & Pub., 50-8A Gouri Bari Ln., Calcutta 4, India. adv.; bk.rev.; bibl.; charts; film rev.; illus.; stat.; index. circ. 2,500.
Description: Contains literary and cultural items.

057.8 XV ISSN 0003-536X
ANTENA. (Text in Slovenian) 1965. w. $90. Pavliha, Kardeljeva 4, 61000 Ljubljana, Slovenia. Ed. Aleksander Lucu.
Formerly: Horoskop.

800 US
▼**ANTERIOR MONTHLY REVIEW.** 1993. m. $18. Anterior Bitewing Ltd., 7735 Brand Ave., St. Louis, MO 63135-3212. TEL 314-522-6166. Ed. Tom Bergeron.
Description: Includes essays, true first-person experiences, opinions, narratives, humor, and other non-fiction works.

052 TR ISSN 1015-2261
ANTILIA. 1984. 2/yr. University of the West Indies, Faculty of Arts and General Studies, St. Augustine, Trinidad & Tobago, W.I. Ed.Bd.

810 300 US ISSN 0003-5769
AP2
ANTIOCH REVIEW. 1941. q. $30 to individuals; institutions $42. (Antioch College) Antioch Review, Inc., Box 148, Yellow Springs, OH 45387. TEL 513-767-6389. Ed. Robert S. Fogarty. adv.; bk.rev.; index. circ. 4,500. (also avail. in microform from UMI,MIM,PMC; back issues avail.; reprint service avail. from UMI,AMS) Indexed: Abstr.Engl.Stud., Amer.Bibl.Slavic & E.Eur.Stud., Amer.Hist.& Life, Arts & Hum.Cit.Ind., Biog.Ind., Bk.Rev.Ind. (1965-), Child.Bk.Rev.Ind. (1965-), Curr.Cont., Film Lit.Ind. (1973-), Hist.Abstr., Hum.Ind., Ind.Amer.Per.Verse, Ind.Bk.Rev.Hum., Lang.& Lang.Behav.Abstr., M.L.A., Mag.Ind., P.A.I.S., Phil.Ind., Sage Fam.Stud.Abstr., Sociol.Abstr., SSCI. Document type: consumer publication.
—BLDSC (1549.450000); Faxon; UnCover; UMI.

056.1 AG ISSN 0003-6137
AP63
ANTROPOS.* 1969. q. Rodriguez Pena 557, Buenos Aires, Argentina. Ed. Horacio G. Trejo. bk.rev.; illus. Indexed: Psychol.Abstr.

808.8 II
ANUSTUP. (Text in Bengali) 1966. q. Rs.15($1.60) Anustup Prakashani, P-55B, C I T Rd, Calcutta 700010, India. Ed. Anil Acharya. bk.rev.; film rev.; play rev.; abstr. circ. 2,100.

800 IS ISSN 0334-0899
APEREYON. 1983. 4/yr. $20. P.O. Box 3315, Ramat-Hasharon, Israel. TEL 972-3-5496777. Ed. Erez Biton. adv.; bk.rev. circ. 800.
Description: Examines Mediterranean trends in Israeli culture, in relation to Jewish legacy and literature and poetry, and the relationship with Middle Eastern culture.

800 US
APOCALYPSO.* 1984. a. $3.50. Apocalypso Fourth World Ltd., 476 9th Ave., Ste. 1, New York, NY 10018-5603. TEL 212-247-8609. Ed. Oliver Trager. circ. 2,500. (back issues avail.)

AQLAM JOURNAL/PEN. see LITERATURE

054 FR ISSN 0755-883X
AR FALZ; revue d'action culturelle. q. 140 F. (foreign 140 F.). Editions Skol Vreizh, 20 rue de Kerscoff, 29600 Morlaix, France. TEL 98-62-17-20. FAX 98-62-02-38. Document type: bulletin.

ARAB BOOK WORLD. see HISTORY — History Of The Near East

ARBEITSGEMEINSCHAFT DER BIBLIOTHEKEN UND DOKUMENTATIONSSTELLEN DER OST-, OSTMITTEL- UND SUEDOSTEUROPAFORSCHUNG. MITTEILUNGEN. see LIBRARY AND INFORMATION SCIENCES

LITERARY AND POLITICAL REVIEWS

053 800 011   GW   ISSN 0723-2977
CODEN: ARBTEH
ARBITRIUM; Zeitschrift fuer Rezensionen zur germanistischen Literaturwissenschaft. (Text in English, German) 1983. 3/yr. DM.108. Max Niemeyer Verlag, Postfach 2140, 72011 Tuebingen, Germany. TEL 07071-98940. FAX 07071-989450. Eds. W. Fruehwald, Wolfgang Harms. bk.rev.; bibl.; index. circ. 700. (back issues avail.) **Document type:** academic/scholarly publication.
—SWETS. CCC.
   Description: Covers reviews of scholarly books on Germanic literature.

056   SP
ARCHIPIELAGO, CUADERNOS DE CRITICA DE LA CULTURA. q. 3400 ptas. (Europe 5000 ptas.; elsewhere 6600 ptas.). Editorial Pamiela Argitaletxea, Plazuela del Consejo 3-4o, 31001 Pamplona (Irunea), Spain. TEL 948-22-83-02. Ed.Bd. circ. 6,000.

808.8   MP
ARDYN ARMI/PEOPLE'S ARMY. (Text in Mongolian) 1928. bi-m. Ulan Bator, Mongolia. Ed. B. Chantuu.

055.1   IT
AREOPAGO CIRALS. 1975. m. L.20000($27) Piazza Anco Marzio 13, 00122 Rome, Italy. circ. 3,000.

059.919 916.206   UA
AREV. (Text in Armenian) 1915. d. Armenian Liberal Democratic Party, 3 Sharia Soliman Halaby, Cairo, Egypt. TEL 754703. Ed. Avedis Yapoudjian.

051   US
▼**ARGONAUT (SAN FRANCISCO)**. 1993. q. 2250 Geary Blvd., San Francisco, CA 94115. TEL 415-563-6033. FAX 415-563-5934. (Dist. by: Publisher's Group West, 4065 Hollis St., Emeryville, CA 94608. TEL 510-658-3453) Eds. Warren Hinckle, John J. Simon.

ARGUMENTATION; an international journal on reasoning. see PHILOSOPHY

810   US   ISSN 0004-1610
AP2
ARIZONA QUARTERLY; a journal of American literature, culture and theory. 1945. q. $12 to individuals (foreign $16); institutions $16 (foreign $20). University of Arizona, Main Library, Rm. B541, Tucson, AZ 85721. TEL 602-621-6396. Ed. Edgar A. Dryden. adv.; bk.rev.; bibl.; index. circ. 800. (also avail. in microfilm from UMI; back issues avail.; reprint service avail. from KTO) **Indexed:** A.I.P.P., Abstr.Engl.Stud., Amer.Hist.& Life, Amer.Hum.Ind., Chic.Per.Ind., Hist.Abstr., Ind.Bk.Rev.Hum., Ind.Little Mag., M.L.A. **Document type:** academic/scholarly publication.
—BLDSC (1668.490000); Faxon; UnCover; UMI.

808.8   US
ARK (TIBURON). 1973. w. $28. Ark Publishing Co., Box 1054, Tiburon, CA 94920. TEL 415-435-2652. FAX 415-435-0849. Eds. Marilyn Kessler, Barbara Gnoss. adv.; bk.rev.; illus. circ. 3,200. (processed; also avail. in microform from UMI; reprint service avail. from UMI) **Indexed:** Ind.Amer.Per.Verse.
   Former titles: Bleb - The Ark; (until no.13, 1978): Bleb (ISSN 0006-467X)
   Description: Contains articles of local interest.

800   US
▼**ARKANSAS QUARTERLY**; a journal of criticism. 1992. q. $12 (foreign $22). Epiphany Publications, Inc., University of Arkansas, Box 2691, Fayetteville, AR 72701. (Subscr. to: 408 E. Tulsa, Siloam Springs, AR 72761) Ed. Dora Rainey.
   Refereed Serial

059.91   US   ISSN 0004-2366
AP2
ARMENIAN REVIEW. 1948. q. $25 to individuals (foreign $30); institutions $35 (foreign $40). Armenian Review, Inc., 80 Bigelow Ave., Watertown, MA 02172-2012. TEL 617-926-4037. FAX 617-926-1750. Ed. Tatul Sonentz-Papazian. adv.; bk.rev.; illus.; stat. circ. 1,200. (also avail. in microfilm from UMI; reprint service avail. from UMI) **Indexed:** Amer.Bibl.Slavic & E.Eur.Stud., Amer.Hist.& Life, Hist.Abstr., Mid.East: Abstr.& Ind., P.A.I.S. **Document type:** academic/scholarly publication.
—UnCover; UMI.
   Description: Multidisciplinary journal publishing scholarly articles on the history, culture, society, economy of Armenia, its neighbors and Armenian communities abroad.

700   IT
ARS-UOMO; mensile di vita artistica e culturale. 1975. m. L.10000. Bulzoni Editore, Via dei Liburni 14, 00185 Rome, Italy. Ed. Giordana Canti. bk.rev.

808.87   US
ART'S GARBAGE GAZZETTE. 1990. q. $3.50. Art Paul Schlosser's Publishing Company, 214 Dunning, Madison, WI 53704. TEL 608-249-0715. (back issues avail.) **Document type:** newspaper.
   Description: Covers poetry, art, cartoons, jokes, comical gossip and facts.

051   US
▼**AS IF**. 1992. irreg. (2-3/yr.). $7. 1601 Harkrider, Box 3223, Conway, AR 72032. TEL 501-327-9686. Ed. Clint Catalyst. circ. 250.

059.91   US   ISSN 0004-4229
ASBAREZ. (Text in Armenian and English) 1908. 5/wk. $84 (bilingual ed $35). (Armenian Revolutionary Federation) Asbarez Publishing Co., 419 W. Colorado St., Glendale, CA 91204-1537. TEL 818-500-9363. FAX 818-956-1106. Ed.Bd. adv.; bk.rev.; illus. circ. 13,000. (tabloid format; also avail. in microfilm) **Document type:** newspaper.

ASLAN. see *RELIGIONS AND THEOLOGY*

055.91   RM   ISSN 0004-6108
DB721
ASTRA. 1966. m. 5 lei($2.42) Comitetul de Cultura si Educatie Socialista al Judetului Brasov, Str. Mihail Sadoveanu Nr. 3, 2200 Brasov, Rumania. TEL 43179. (Subscr. to: Rompresfilatelia, Calea Grivitei no. 64-66, P.O. Box 12-201, Bucharest, Rumania) Ed. Aurel Ion Brumaru. adv.; bk.rev.; play rev.; illus. circ. 15,000.

ASYLUM ANNUAL. see *LITERATURE — Poetry*

378.1   PR   ISSN 0885-6079
ATENEA. (Text in English, French, Italian, Spanish) 1962. s-a. free to libraries and universities. Universidad de Puerto Rico, Faculty of Arts and Sciences, Mayaguez Campus, Mayaguez, PR 00681. FAX 809-834-3031. Eds. Hilda M. Rodriguez, Lilia Dapaz Strout. bk.rev.; circ. 800 (controlled). **Indexed:** Amer.Hist.& Life, Hist.Abstr., M.L.A. **Document type:** academic/scholarly publication.

056.1   ES
ATENEO DE EL SALVADOR. REVISTA. 1912. 3/yr. Ateneo de El Salvador, 13a Calle Poniente, Centro de Gobierno, San Salvador, El Salvador. TEL 22-9686.

055.1   IT
ATHENA MEDITERRANEA; periodico trimestrale di lettere, storia, arte e cultura varia. 1975. q. L.5000. Piazza Municipio 22, 81031 Aversa, Italy. Ed. Enzo di Grazia.

808.8   UK   ISSN 0262-5113
ATHOLL & BREADALBANE COMMUNITY COMMENT. 1981. 6/yr. £1.20. A B C Comment, Dunkeld St., Aberfeldy, Tayside, Scotland. Ed.Bd. adv.; bk.rev.; illus. circ. 1,000.

051 300 700   US   ISSN 0276-9077
AP2   CODEN: ATLAEO
THE ATLANTIC. 1857. m. $17.94. Atlantic Monthly Co., 745 Boylston, Boston, MA 02116. TEL 617-536-9500. (Subscr. to: Box 2547, Boulder, CO 80322. TEL 800-234-2411) Ed. William Whitworth. adv.; bk.rev.; index. circ. 457,343. (also avail. in microform from UMI,PMC; microfilm from KTO) **Indexed:** Abr.R.G., Acad.Ind., Amer.Bibl.Slavic & E.Eur.Stud., Amer.Hist.& Life, Bk.Rev.Dig., Bk.Rev.Ind. (1965-), Child.Bk.Rev.Ind. (1965-), Film Lit.Ind. (1973-), Fut.Surv., Hist.Abstr., Ind.Bk.Rev.Hum., Mag.Ind., Peace Res.Abstr., PROMT, R.G., TOM.
—BLDSC (1765.897000); Faxon; UnCover; SWETS.
   Former titles (until 1981): Atlantic Monthly (ISSN 0004-6795); (until 1971): Atlantic (ISSN 0160-6506); (until 1932): Atlantic Monthly (ISSN 0160-6514)

808.87   US   ISSN 1061-7000
THE ATROCITY. 1978. m. $10. Absurd Sig, 2419 Greensburg Pike, Pittsburgh, PA 15221. Ed. Hank Roll. adv.; film rev.; illus. circ. 250. (back issues avail.) **Document type:** newsletter.
   Description: Contains humor, cartoons and satire.

808.8   US   ISSN 0889-7433
AURA LITERARY ARTS REVIEW. 1974. s-a. $6. University of Alabama at Birmingham, Box 76, University Center, Birmingham, AL 35294-1150. TEL 205-934-3216. Ed. Mark Valenta. adv.; bk.rev. circ. 600.

051   AT   ISSN 0313-9727
AUSTRALIA - ISRAEL REVIEW. 1975. fortn. Aus.$49($66) Australia-Israel Publications, 578 St. Kilda Rd., 2nd Fl., Melbourne, Vic. 3004, Australia. TEL 03-529-5022. FAX 03-5298-573. TELEX AA100200. Ed. Colin Rubenstein. adv.; bk.rev. circ. 4,600. (back issues avail.) **Document type:** newsletter.
   Description: Reports, comments and analysis of political events in the Middle East and related policies affecting Australia, SE Asia and the Pacific region. Includes comprehensive summary briefing of media reporting of issues concerning the Middle East in Australia and the region.

AUT AUT; rivista di filosofia e di cultura. see *PHILOSOPHY*

320.5   IT   ISSN 0045-1118
AUTONOMI; resistenza, democrazia, Europa unita, periodico di fatti ed opinioni. (Includes supplement) vol.33 No.2. s-a. L.8000 (foreign L.16000). (Associazione Volontari della Liberta e del Circolo-Europa Libera del Piemonte) Autonomi Editore, Torino, Piazza Carignano 8, 10123 Turin, Italy. TEL 541505. Ed. Giuseppe Anacar. adv.; bk.rev.; illus. circ. 3,000.
   Description: Acts as a forum for a variety of political issues.

051   US   ISSN 0005-1918
AP2
AVANT GARDE. 1967. q. $15. Avant-Garde Media, Inc., 80 Central Park W., Ste. 16B, New York, NY 10023. adv.; bk.rev.; illus. circ. 250,000. (also avail. in microform from UMI)

001.3   IT
AVATAR; testimonianza culturale. 1978. m. L.12000. (Associazione Cultura e Umanita, SZ) Associazione Avatar, Via Bellinzona 181, Casella Postale 23, Ponte Chiasso, 22100 Como, Italy. Ed. Giuseppe Antonio Anzelmo.

AXE FACTORY REVIEW. see *LITERATURE*

054   FR
AXE SUD. 4/yr. 25 F. Axe Sud, 11 Place de la Daurade, 31000 Toulouse, France.

AYENEH-E PAZHOOHESH. see *RELIGIONS AND THEOLOGY — Islamic*

059.927   TS
AL-AYYAM. (Text in Arabic) 1969. w. Mu'assasat Dar al- Ayyam for Journalism, Printing, Publishing, P.O. Box 2788, Abu Dhabi, United Arab Emirates. TEL 477184. Ed. Yusuf al-Umran. circ. 10,000.
   Description: Covers cultural and political developments in the U.A.E.

BABY SUE. see *LITERATURE — Poetry*

LITERARY AND POLITICAL REVIEWS

800 US
BACK BAY VIEW; a literary and arts magazine. 1977. s-a. $5 for 4 nos. Back Bay View, Inc., c/o Charlotte A. Boehm, Ed., 33 Karen Dr., Randolph, MA 02368. TEL 617-986-5704. Ed.Bd. circ. 1,000.

820 UK
BACONIANA. 1885. a. £1. Francis Bacon Society Inc., Canonbury Tower, Islington, London N.1, England. Ed.Bd. bk.rev.; bibl.; index. circ. 200.

BAD HAIRCUT. see *POLITICAL SCIENCE*

051 US ISSN 1059-9789
THE BAFFLER. 1988. a. $10 for 2 nos. Box 378293, Chicago, IL 60637. TEL 312-538-3812. Ed. Thomas Frank. bk.rev. circ. 2,500.
 Description: Features critiques of cultural industry excess.

BAGDALA; mesecni list za knjizevnost, umetnost i kulturu. see *LITERATURE*

052 AT
BAIRNSDALE ADVERTISER. 1877. s-w. Aus.$36. James Yeates and Sons Pty. Ltd., Cnr. Macleod and Bailey St., Bairnsdale, Vic. 3875, Australia. TEL 051-521117. Ed. Robert D. Yeates. circ. 7,500.

054.1 FR ISSN 0378-469X
DT470
BALAFON; pour la connaissance de l'Afrique Noire. (Text in French; summaries in English) 1965-1988; resumed. bi-m. 155 F. Air Afrique, 71 rue Desnouettes, 75015 Paris, France. TEL 48-28-40-58. Ed. Guy Leger. adv.; bk.rev.; illus. circ. 100,000.

800.055 914.706 IT ISSN 0392-7660
BALCANICA; storia, cultura, politica. 1982. q. L.50000 (foreign L.100000). Via Conca d'Oro 238, 00141 Rome, Italy. TEL 06-8101700. Ed. Antonio Jerkov. bk.rev.; illus. (back issues avail.) **Indexed**: Amer.Hist.& Life, Hist.Abstr.

059.951 CC
BAN YUE TAN/SEMI-MONTHLY TRIBUNE. (Editions in Chinese and Uighur) 1980. s-m. Y27.50($91.80) (Xinhua News Agency) Ban Yue Tan Zazhishe, No.57, Xuanwumen Xidajie, Beijing 100803, People's Republic of China. TEL 3074433. (Dist. in US by: China Books & Periodicals, Inc., 2929 24th St., San Francisco, CA 94110. TEL 415-282-2994) Ed. Min Fanlu. adv. circ. 5,380,000.

BANASTHALI PATRIKA. see *LITERATURE*

053.1 GW ISSN 0178-9058
PT3895.R8
BANATICA; Beitraege zur deutschen Kultur. q. DM.40. Adam Mueller-Guttenbrunn-Gesellschaft e.V., Ziegelhofstr. 68, 79110 Freiburg, Germany. Ed. Horst Fassel.

808.8 US
BARNEY; modern stone-age magazine. 1981. a. $20 to individuals; institutions $25. Fred & Barney Press, 1140 1-2 Nowita Pl., Venice, CA 90291. TEL 213-392-2886. Ed. Jack Skelley. circ. 500.

053 GW ISSN 0178-000X
BATERIA; Zeitschrift fuer Kunstlerischen Ausdruck. 1982. a. DM.20($15) Wilhelm-Busch-Str. 21, 90427 Nuernberg, Germany. Ed. Manfred Rothenberger. adv. circ. 1,500. (back issues avail.) **Document type**: bulletin.

808.87 US
BAWL STREET JOURNAL; annual lampoon of the financial community. a. $3. Box 445, Wall St. Sta., New York, NY 10005.
 Description: Contains financial wit and humor.

059.915 IR
BAZAR-I RUZ. (Text in Persian) w. Abbasiyan Bldg., 4th Fl., Jumhuri Ave., Tehran, Iran.

055.1 IT ISSN 0005-8351
AP37
BELFAGOR; rassegna di varia umanita. 1946. bi-m. L.63000 (foreign L.98000) (effective 1994). Casa Editrice Leo S. Olschki, Casella Postale 66, 50100 Florence, Italy. TEL 055-6530684. FAX 055-6530214. Ed. Carlo F. Russo. adv.; bk.rev. circ. 3,500. (back issues avail.) **Indexed**: Amer.Hist.& Life, Arts & Hum.Cit.Ind., Can.Rev.Comp.Lit., Curr.Cont., Hist.Abstr., M.L.A. **Document type**: academic/scholarly publication.
 —Faxon.

055 IT ISSN 0394-6584
BENI CULTURALI E AMBIENTE. 1986. m. L.50000. Audiovisivi e Periodici s.r.l., Via Taranto, 21, 00182 Rome, Italy. (Dist. by: Periodici Angelo Patuzzi Spa, Via Zuretti, 25, 20123 Milan, Italy) Ed. Sergio Trasatti.

052 NR ISSN 0331-0213
BENIN REVIEW. 1974. s-a. £N3($6) to individuals; libraries $7.50. Ethiope Publishing Corporation, PMB 1332, Benin City, Nigeria. Eds. Abio la Irele, Pius Oleghe. circ. 50,000. **Indexed**: M.L.A.
 Description: Reviews African art and culture.

057 KR
BEREZIL; literaturno-khudozhnii ta hromads'ko-politychnyi zhurnal. 1956. m. 17.40 Rub. (Spilka Pys'mennykiv Ukrainy) Vydavnytstvo Radyanskii Pismennik, Chkalova, 52, Kiev, Ukraine. Ed. Yu. Stadnychenko. bk.rev.; bibl.; illus. circ. 16,000. **Indexed**: M.L.A.
 Formerly (until 1991): Prapor (ISSN 0130-1608)

808.8 US ISSN 0191-7080
BERKELEY MONTHLY. 1970. m. $10. Klaber Publishing Corp., 1301 59th St., Emeryville, CA 94608-2115. TEL 510-658-9811. FAX 510-658-9902. Eds. Tim Devaney, Mickey Butts. adv.: B&W page $2660, color page $3410. bk.rev.; film rev.; illus.; circ. 75,000 (controlled). **Document type**: newspaper.
 Description: Publishes interviews, investigative journalism with a Bay Area focus, and opinionated arts and cultural essays with a sense of humor.

053.1 GW ISSN 0005-9307
BERLINER LIBERALE ZEITUNG. 1962. 10/yr. (Freie Demokratische Partei, Landesverband Berlin) D.A.V.I.D. GmbH, Im Dol 2-6, 14195 Berlin, Germany. TEL 030-8316445. FAX 030-8316564. Ed. Torsten Mueller. adv.; bk.rev. circ. 5,000. **Document type**: newsletter.

741.5 808.87 US ISSN 0091-2220
E839.5
BEST EDITORIAL CARTOONS OF THE YEAR. 1973. a. $16.95 hardcover; $12.95 paperback. (Association of American Editorial Cartoonists) Pelican Publishing Co., 1101 Monroe St., Gretna, LA 70053. TEL 504-368-1175. FAX 504-368-1195. Ed. Charles Brooks. (back issues avail.)
 —BLDSC (1942.325700).
 Description: Offers a selection of national and international cartoons from members of the association.

808.87 US
THE BEST NEWS OF THE WEEK. 1989. w. $1 per no. Radio Werewolf High Command, Buenaventura Durruti Column Branch, Box 75416, Washington, DC 20013. Ed. Rene Riesel. circ. 2,500. **Document type**: newsletter.
 Description: Contains political humor and satire, largely from a post-modernist and situationist perspective.

800 US
BEST OF AMERICAN LITERATURE. 1987. irreg. price varies. Duke University Press, 6697 College Station, Durham, NC 27708. TEL 919-687-3600. FAX 919-688-4574. Eds. Louis Budd, Edwin Cady.

057 YU ISSN 0351-6016
BIBLIOGRAFIJA RECENZIJA IZ DOMACIH LISTOVA I CASOPISA. (Text in Macedonian, Serbo-Croatian, Slovenian) 1979. q. free. Biblioteka Grada Geograda, Knez Mihajlova 56, 11000 Belgrade, Yugoslavia. TEL 186313. circ. 100.
 Formerly: Bilten Recenzija iz Damacih Listova i Casopisa.

808.87 US
BIGGEST GREATEST CRACKED ANNUAL. a. $1.50. Globe Communications Corp. (New York), 441 Lexington Ave., New York, NY 10017. TEL 800-472-7744. circ. 425,000.
 Description: Contains humorous articles.

808.8 US
BIKINI GIRL; a serial anthology of unconventional literature and graphics. 1976. irreg. $25 per print issue; video cassette issue $47. Box 319, Peter Stuyvesant Sta., New York, NY 10009-0319. TEL 718-633-5015. Ed. Kris Falour; Pub. Lisa Baumgardner. bk.rev.; film rev.; abstr.; illus. circ. 1,500. (also avail. in video cassette; back issues avail.)
 Formerly (until vol.2, no.2, 1981): Blank Tape.

053.1 AU
BILDUNGS-KURIER. 1948. q. S.40. Sozialistische Partei Oberoesterreichs, Landesorganisation, Landstr. 36, A-4020 Linz, Austria. Ed. Max Lotteraner. adv.; bk.rev.; bibl. circ. 4,000.

808.8 US
BIRD EFFORT. 1975. a. $5 to individuals; institutions $6. Bird Effort Press, 25 Mudford Ave., Easthampton, NY 11937. Eds. Robert Long, Josh Dayton. adv.; bk.rev. circ. 500. **Indexed**: Ind.Amer.Per.Verse.

808.81 US ISSN 0897-9057
BIRTH OF TRAGEDY MAGAZINE; the fear issue, the God issue, the power issue, the love issue, the sex issue. (Text in English, Korean, Spanish, Swedish) 1981. a. $2. C.F.Y., Box 6271, Stanford, CA 94309. TEL 415-324-9483. Ed. Eugene S. Robinson. adv. circ. 2,000. (tabloid format; back issues avail.)
 Description: Philosophical inquiry into the darker side of life, love, and death.

059.92 US ISSN 0006-3932
BITZARON: A QUARTERLY OF HEBREW LETTERS. (Text in Hebrew; summaries in English) 1939. q. $18 (foreign $17). (Hebrew Literary Foundation) Bitzaron, Inc., Box 623, Cooper Sta., New York, NY 10003. (Co-sponsor: Institute of Hebrew Culture and Education) Ed. Hayim Leaf. adv.; bk.rev.; play rev.; illus.; stat.; index. circ. 18,800. (also avail. in microfilm from AJP; back issues avail.) **Indexed**: Amer.Hist.& Life, Hist.Abstr., Ind.Heb.Per., M.L.A.
 Supersedes (1939-1978): Bitzaron: The Hebrew Monthly of America.

057.8 CI ISSN 0006-4068
BJELOVARSKI LIST. 1946. w. 100 din. Socijalisticki Savez Radnog Naroda Opcine Bjelovar, Trg Jedinstva 11, Bjelovar, Croatia. Ed. Ivan Matunci.

808 US ISSN 0896-3517
BLACK MOUNTAIN REVIEW. 1987-1988; resumed 1990. a. $6.10 (effective 1992). Lorien House, P.O. Box 1112, Black Mountain, NC 28711-1112. TEL 704-669-6211. Ed. David A. Wilson. bk.rev. circ. 150. (back issues avail.) **Document type**: academic/scholarly publication.
 Description: Articles and essays on specific American authors.

808.87 IE ISSN 0332-253X
BLAZES; Ireland's humour monthly. 1981. m. 20 Essex St., Dublin 2, Ireland. illus.

BOMB; artists, writers, actors, directors. see *ART*

059 II
BOMSEL; fortnightly of Bihar. (Text in English) vol.7, 1975. fortn. Rs.11. Nawal Kishore, Ed. & Pub., Paras Kothi Nayatola, Patna 4, India. adv.; illus.

800 SW
AP48
BONNIERS LITTERAERA MAGASIN. Variant title: B L M. 1932. bi-m. SEK 280. Albert Bonniers Foerlag AB, Box 3159, 103 63 Stockholm 3, Sweden. TEL 08-696-86-42. FAX 08-696-83-59. (Subscr. to: Pressdata, Box 3263, 10365 Stockholm, Sweden) Ed. Stephen Farran-Lee. adv.; bk.rev.; bibl.; illus.; index. circ. 4,000. **Indexed**: Arts & Hum.Cit.Ind., Curr.Cont., M.L.A.
 —SWETS.
 Former titles (until 1991): B L M - Bonniers Litteraera Magasin (ISSN 0005-3198); (until 1941): Bonniers Litteraera Magasin.

LITERARY AND POLITICAL REVIEWS

800 011   US   ISSN 0006-7326
Z1219
BOOK REVIEW DIGEST; an index to reviews of current books. 1905. m. (except Feb. and July) plus q. and a. cumulations. H.W. Wilson Co., 950 University Ave., Bronx, NY 10452. TEL 800-367-6770. FAX 718-590-1617. TELEX 4990003HWILSON. Ed. Martha Mooney. bk.rev.; cum.index 1905-1974; 1975-1984. (also avail. in magnetic tape)
●Also available online. Vendor(s): BRS Online Products, Wilsonline (File BRD).
Also available on CD-ROM. Producer(s): H.W. Wilson (WILSONDISC).
     Description: Includes excerpts to reviews of current adult and juvenile fiction and nonfiction.

BOOKENDS. see *LIBRARY AND INFORMATION SCIENCES*

800   US
BOUILLABAISSE. 1987. s-a. $15. Alpha Beat Press, 31A Waterloo St., New Hope, PA 18938. TEL 215-862-0299. Ed. David Christy. bk.rev.; bibl.; index. circ. 500. (back issues avail.)
     Formed by the merger of: Alpha Beat Soup (ISSN 0838-391X) & Cokefish.
     Description: Reviews and articles on the Beat generation and modern sub-culture, its literature, and poetry.

BRAILLE MIRROR; a current topic magazine. see *HANDICAPPED — Visually Impaired*

808.8   US   ISSN 0103-751X
BRASIL - BRAZIL; a journal of Brazilian literature. (Text in English, Portuguese) 1988. s-a. $15 to individuals; institutions $40. Brown University, Department of Portuguese and Brazilian Studies, Box O, Providence, RI 02912. TEL 401-863-3042. FAX 401-863-7261. Eds. Nelson H. Vieira, Regina Zilberman. adv. **Document type**: academic/scholarly publication.
—UnCover.

051   CN   ISSN 0382-8565
Z1035.A1
BRICK; a literary journal. 1977. 3/yr. $10 to individuals; institutions $14. Brick, P.O. Box 537, Sta. Q, Toronto, ON M4T 2M5, Canada. Ed. Linda Spalding. bk.rev.; illus.; index. circ. 1,200. (back issues avail.) **Indexed**: Br.Ceram.Abstr., Can.Lit.Ind.

052   UK
BRIGHTON VOICE. m. £12. Brighton Voice, Prior House, Tilbury Place, Carlton Hill, Brighton, England. Ed.Bd. adv.; bk.rev. circ. 10,000. (tabloid format)

BROWBEAT. see *MUSIC*

700   GW   ISSN 0937-9509
BRUCKER SZENE; Infos fuer Kunst & Kultur. 1984. m. free. Thomtom Verlag, Schlehdornweg 23, 82256 Fuerstenfeldbruck, Germany. TEL 08141-26246-0. Ed. Thomas Himmler. adv.; bk.rev. circ. 10,000. (back issues avail.)

052   AU
DIE BRUECKE; Kaerntner Kulturzeitschrift. 1975. q. S.230. Amt der Kaerntner Landesregierung, Abteilung 5 - Kultur, Paradeisergasse 7, A-9021 Klagenfurt, Austria. Ed. Ernst Gayer. adv.; bk.rev. circ. 2,300.

800   US
▼**BUBBA MAGAZINE**; celebrating the first bubba president! 1993. q. $2.95 per no. Allison Magazines, 535 Fifth Ave., 28th Fl., New York, NY 10017. TEL 212-867-3516. Ed. Dean King. adv. contact: Logan Ward. illus. circ. 300,000. **Document type**: consumer publication.
     Description: Humorous coverage of the Clinton presidency and related popular culture topics.

053.1   GW
BUECHERKARREN. 4/yr. Verlag Volk und Welt, Otto-Nuschke-Str. 10-11, 1086 Berlin, Germany. TEL 030-203650211. Ed. H.D. Tschoertner. bk.rev.

800   US
BUFFALOON NEWSLETTER. vol.7, no.3, 1993. q. $1.50 per issue. Raisin Blowme & Standard Deviation Productions, 31 W. Northrup Pl., Buffalo, NY 14214. **Document type**: newsletter.

808.8   US
BUG TAR. 1977. 4/yr. $5. Bug Tar Press, Box 1534, San Jose, CA 95109. Ed. Scott Mace. circ. 100.

800   US   ISSN 1053-3605
F869.L8
BUZZ (LOS ANGELES). 1990. 10/yr. $15. Buzz, Inc., 11835 W. Olympic Blvd., Ste. 450, Los Angeles, CA 90064. TEL 310-473-2721. FAX 310-473-2876. Ed. Allan Mayer. adv.; illus. circ. 100,000. **Document type**: consumer publication.
     Incorporates (1985-1993): L.A. Style (ISSN 0895-3465)
     Description: Essays, journalism, photography, and fiction of and for Los Angeles.

052 820   AT   ISSN 0157-3705
C R N L E REVIEWS JOURNAL. 1979. s-a. Aus.$25 to individuals; institutions Aus.$30. Flinders University of South Australia, Centre for Research in the New Literatures in English, Flinders University of South Australia, G.P.O. Box 2100, Adelaide, S.A. 5001. TEL 08-201-2053. FAX 08-201-2556. TELEX AA 89624 FLINDU. Ed.Bd. adv.; bk.rev. circ. 350. (back issues avail.) **Indexed**: Can.Lit.Ind. **Document type**: academic/scholarly publication.

C R O W QUARTERLY REVIEW; a new review of unpublished manuscripts. (Capsule Review of Original Work) see *PUBLISHING AND BOOK TRADE*

808.87   SG
CAFARD LIBERE. 1987. w. 10 rue Tolbiac x autoroute, 3e etage, Dakar, Senegal. TEL 22-84-43. Ed. Laye Bamba Diallo. circ. 10,000.

054.1   FR   ISSN 0222-5956
CAHIERS CONFRONTATION. 1979. s-a. 400 F. for 4 nos. Editions Aubier Montaigne, 13 Quai de Conti, 75006 Paris, France. Ed. Rene Major. adv. circ. 2,500. **Indexed**: M.L.A.

CAHIERS RENAUD BARRAULT. see *THEATER*

054.1   BE
CAHIERS WALLONS. (Text in French, Walloon) 1937. 10/yr. 500 BEF. Relis Namurwes A.S.B.L., 31 rue Godart, B-5002 Namur, Belgium. TEL 32-81-733428. adv.; bk.rev.; bibl. circ. 800. **Document type**: bulletin.
     Description: Promotes literature in the Walloon dialect in the area centered around Namur.

700   CU
CAIMAN BARBUDO. 1966. m. $20 in N. America; S. America $26; Europe $29; others $41. Ediciones Cubanas, Obispo No. 527, Aptdo. 605, Havana, Cuba. Dir. Alex Pausides. circ. 47,000.

800   US
CALENDAR OF LITERARY FACTS. 1990. irreg. $45. Gale Research Inc., 835 Penobscot Bldg., Detroit, MI 48226. TEL 800-877-4253. FAX 313-961-6083. TELEX 810-221-7086. Ed. Samuel J. Rogal.
     Description: Provides views of literary history anywhere, including a wide range of international facts and information on many popular writers.

320.532   CE   ISSN 0045-401X
CALL. (Editions in English and French) 1971. q. Afro Asian Writers Bureau, 73 Castle St., Colombo 8, Sri Lanka. Ed.Bd. bk.rev.; bibl.; charts; illus.

056.1   SP
CAMBIO 16. 1972. w. 13650 ptas. (effective Sep. 1992). Informacion y Revistas S.A., Hermanos Garcia Noblejas 41, 28037 Madrid, Spain. TEL 91-4072700. FAX 91-4070400. Ed. Federico Ysart. adv.; charts.

300   UK   ISSN 0008-2007
CAMBRIDGE REVIEW; a journal of university life and thought. 1879. s-ar. £16($31) to individuals (overseas £24); institutions £36 (overseas £44 ($69)). Cambridge University Press, Edinburgh Bldg., Shaftesbury Rd., Cambridge CB2 2RU, England. TEL 0223-312393. FAX 0223-315052. TELEX 851817256. (N. American addr.: Cambridge University Press, Journals Dept., 40 W. 20th St., New York, NY 10011. TEL 212-924-3900. FAX 212-691-3239) Ed. Nigel Spivey. adv.; bk.rev.; film rev.; music rev.; play rev.; index. (also avail. in microform from UMI; back issues avail.) **Document type**: academic/scholarly publication.
—BLDSC (3015.990000); UnCover; UMI.
     Description: Covers university life and thought through poetry, essays and articles.

055.1   IT   ISSN 0008-2279
CAMMINO ECONOMICO; information bollettin. m. Via G. Verdi 13, 82100 Benevento, Italy. Ed. Esposito Antonio.

CAMPAIGN AUSTRALIA. see *HOMOSEXUALITY*

809   PO
CAMPO GRANDE. 1984. m. Faculdade de Letras de Lisboa, Associacao de Estudantes, Alameda da Universidade, 1699 Lisbon Codex, Portugal. Ed.Bd.

700 301   LB
CAMPUS REVIEW. (Text in English) 1978. m. per no. University of Liberia, University Relation, P.O. Box 9020, Monrovia, Liberia. TEL 221274. adv.; bk.rev. circ. 300.
     Formerly: Revelation.
     Description: Publishes articles of developments that have taken place at the university.

847   FR   ISSN 0008-5405
LE CANARD ENCHAINE; journal satirique paraissant le Mercredi. 1915. w. 287 F. (foreign 410 F.). Editions Marechal, 173 rue St. Honore, 75001 Paris, France. TEL 1-42-60-31-36. FAX 16-14-92-79-787. Dir. A. Ribaud. bk.rev.; film rev.; illus. circ. 520,000. **Document type**: newspaper.
—UMI.

052   UK
CANDOUR. 1953. m. £10 (foreign £12). Candour Publishing Co., Forest House, Liss Forest, Hampshire GU33 7DD, England. Ed. Rosine de Bouneville. adv.; bk.rev. circ. 2,500.
     Description: British "views-letter" covering the role international finance plays in the defense of the sovereignty of Great Britain.

056   SP   ISSN 0213-0467
CANELOBRE. irreg. 1800 ptas. for 4 nos. Instituto de Cultura "Juan Gil-Albert", Departamento de Cultura y Publicaciones, Diputacion Provincial, Alicante, Spain. **Document type**: consumer publication.

808.87   US
CAPITOL COMEDY.* 1988. m. $105. 8801 Jones Mill Rd., Chevy Chase, MD 20815-4726. TEL 202-966-0264. FAX 202-966-0297. Ed. Elaine Bole. circ. 750.
     Description: Contains topical political humor.

052   TR   ISSN 1011-5765
F2155
CARIBBEAN AFFAIRS. 1988. q. T.T.$100($45) (Caribbean $40, Europe $60, Canada $50). Trinidad Express Newspaper Ltd., P.O. Box 1252, Port-of-Spain, Trinidad & Tobago, W.I. TEL 809-623-1711. FAX 809-627-1451. (Co-publisher: Inprint Caribbean Ltd.) Ed. Owen Baptiste. adv.; bk.rev. circ. 1,030.
—BLDSC (3052.595000).
     Description: Features information, issues and events in the Caribbean Basin - from Brazil, Surinam and the Guianas in the South, to Mexico, the Bahamas and Cuba in the North. Written and edited exclusively by Caribbean people.

051 056.1   PR   ISSN 0576-7598
F2183
CARIBBEAN MONTHLY BULLETIN. (Text in English, Spanish) 1963. m. $12 to individuals; institutions $16. Universidad de Puerto Rico, Institute of Caribbean Studies, P.O. Box BM, University Sta., Rio Piedras, PR 00931. Ed. Dale Mathews. bibl. circ. 1,500.

051   JM   ISSN 0008-6495
CARIBBEAN QUARTERLY. 1949. q. Jam.$200($35) University of the West Indies, School of Continuing Studies, Box 42, Kingston 7, Jamaica, W.I. TEL 809-927-1201. FAX 809-927-1920. Ed. Rex Nettleford. adv.; bk.rev.; index. circ. 1,500. (also avail. in microfilm from UMI; back issues avail.; reprint service avail. from KTO) **Indexed**: Abstr.Engl.Stud., Amer.Hist.& Life, Hisp.Amer.Per.Ind., Hist.Abstr., Rural Recreat.Tour.Abstr., World Agri.Econ.& Rural Sociol.Abstr. **Document type**: academic/scholarly publication.
—UnCover; UMI.

LITERARY AND POLITICAL REVIEWS

972.9 800   US   ISSN 0008-6525
AP6
CARIBBEAN REVIEW; a quarterly dedicated to the Caribbean, Latin America and their emigrant groups. 1969. q. $20. Caribbean Review, Inc., 9700 S.W. 67th Ave., Miami, FL 33156. TEL 305-284-8466. FAX 305-284-1019. Ed. Barry B. Levine. adv.; bk.rev.; abstr.; bibl. circ. 5,000. (also avail. in microform from UMI; reprint service avail. from UMI) **Indexed:** Amer.Hist.& Life, Curr.Cont., Hisp.Amer.Per.Ind., Hist.Abstr., HR Rep., I D A, Int.Polit.Sci.Abstr., New Per.Ind., P.A.I.S. —UnCover. **CCC.**
   Supersedes: San Juan Review.

CARILLON (REGINA). see COLLEGE AND ALUMNI

CARTOON WORLD. see ART

800 700   NE   ISSN 0008-7556
AP64
CASTRUM PEREGRINI; deutschsprachige Zeitschrift fuer Literatur-, Kunst- und Geistesgeschichte. (Text in German) 1950. 5/yr. fl.90 (DM.82). Stichting Castrum Peregrini - Castrum Peregrini Presse, P.O. Box 645, 1000 AP Amsterdam, Netherlands. TEL 31-20-6235287. FAX 31-20-6247096. Ed. M.R. Goldschmidt. adv.; bk.rev.; abstr.; illus.; s-a. index. (reprint service avail.) **Indexed:** M.L.A. **Document type:** academic/scholarly publication.

051   CN
CELTIC PAMPLEMOUSSE. 1990. s-a. Can.$2. Lickspittle Ventures, 66 Greyhound Dr., Willowdale, ON M2H 1K3, Canada. TEL 416-495-8360. Ed. Jim Munroe. bk.rev. circ. 200. **Document type:** consumer publication.

056.1   CR   ISSN 0034-9828
CENIT/ZENITH; revista literaria internacional. no.266, 1974. m. free. Academia Hispano Americana Zenith, Apdo. 40, Heredia, Costa Rica. Ed. Amando Cespedes Marin. adv.; illus. circ. 2,000. (processed)

054.1 055.1   SZ   ISSN 0008-896X
CENOBIO; rivista di cultura. (Text mainly in Italian; occasionally in French) 1952. q. 50 SFr. Edizioni Cenobio, Via Streccia 4, P.O. Box 174, CH-6903 Lugano 3, Switzerland. TEL 091-581048. FAX 091-565156. Ed. Riccardo Frigeri. adv.; bk.rev.; bibl.; charts; film rev.; illus.; play rev.; index. circ. 10,000. (back issues avail.) **Indexed:** M.L.A. **Description:** Articles on a wide variety of topics dealing with customs and traditions, history and religion. Contains interviews and poetry.

800   US   ISSN 0273-3323
CENTRAL PARK. 1980. 2/yr. $9.50. (Central Park Trust Fund) Neword Productions, Inc., Box 1446, New York, NY 10023. TEL 212-362-9151. Ed.Bd. adv.; bk.rev.; film rev.; play rev.; illus. circ. 500. (back issues avail.)

CHELSEA HOTEL. see LITERATURE — Poetry

CHERRY. see MEN'S INTERESTS

CHIRICU. see LITERATURE

700 800   FR   ISSN 0009-5001
CHOIX ARTISTIQUE ET LITTERAIRE. 1958. q. free. Editions Flammes Vives, 22 rue du Docteur-Benasson, 95410 Groslay, France. Ed. Jean Aubert. bk.rev.

808.87   US
THE CHOPPING BLOCK. m. $1 per no. Rt. 2, Box 146, Celina, TX 75009. Ed. Kit Lively.
   Description: Contains humor and social satires.

800 200   US   ISSN 0148-3331
PN49
CHRISTIANITY AND LITERATURE. 1951. q. $15 to individuals; institutions $20. Conference on Christianity and Literature, West Georgia College, Carrollton, GA 30118-0001. TEL 206-836-6512. Ed. Robert Snyder. adv.; bk.rev. circ. 1,400. (back issues avail.) **Indexed:** Abstr.Engl.Stud., Amer.Bibl.Slavic & E.Eur.Stud., Arts & Hum.Cit.Ind., CERDIC, Chr.Per.Ind., Curr.Cont., LCR, M.L.A., Rel.& Theol.Abstr. (1989-), Rel.Ind.One. **Document type:** academic/scholarly publication.
   —BLDSC (3181.954000); Faxon; UnCover.
   Formerly: Conference on Christianity and Literature. Newsletter.
   Description: Articles pertaining to the relationship between Christianity and the creation, study, and teaching of literature.

051 301.4157   US   ISSN 0146-7921
HQ75
CHRISTOPHER STREET. 1976. m. $27. That New Magazine Inc., 28 W. 25th St., 4th Fl., New York, NY 10010. TEL 212-627-2120. FAX 212-727-9321. Ed. Thomas Steele. adv.; bk.rev.; film rev.; play rev.; illus.; tr.lit.
   —UMI.

800   US   ISSN 0887-5731
E169.12
CHRONICLES; a magazine of American culture. 1977. m. $28 ($34 outside U.S.). Rockford Institute, 934 N. Main St., Rockford, IL 61103. TEL 815-964-5813. FAX 815-965-1826. (Subscr. to: Box 800, Mt. Morris, IL 61054-8082. TEL 800-877-5459) Ed. Thomas Fleming. adv. contact: Rochelle Frank. bk.rev.; film rev.; play rev.; abstr.; illus.; index. circ. 13,700. (back issues avail.) **Document type:** consumer publication.
   —UnCover.
   Formerly: Chronicles of Culture (ISSN 0163-1187)
   Description: Reviews literature and the arts and examines social and political issues.

056.9   BL
CIENCIAS HUMANAS. 1977. q. $25. Universidade Gama Filho, Rua Manoel Vitorino, CEP 625-Rio de Janeiro, Brazil. Ed. Beneval de Oliveira. adv.; bk.rev. circ. 10,000.

320.9   IT   ISSN 0045-6977
CITTA FUTURA.* (Supplement: Debate) vol.3, 1971. m. L.1500. Via della Vite 13, 00187 Rome, Italy. Ed. Ugu Moretti. adv.; bk.rev.; bibl. circ. 4,500.

CITY LIGHTS REVIEW. see LITERATURE — Poetry

CIVILTA CATTOLICA. see RELIGIONS AND THEOLOGY — Roman Catholic

053.1 055.1 054.1   SZ
CIVITAS; Monatsschrift fuer Politik und Kultur - revue mensuelle politique et culturelle - mensile di politica e culture. (Text in French, German, Italian) 1856. m. 40 SFr. Schweizerischer Studentenverein, Alte Simplonstr. 10, CH-3900 Brig, Switzerland. TEL 028-236200. adv.; bk.rev. circ. 10,000. (back issues avail.) **Indexed:** Amer.Hist.& Life, CERDIC, Hist.Abstr., P.A.I.S.

800   SA
CLASSIC; magazine of creative writing and art. (Text in Afrikaans and English) 1982. biennial. R.1.50($3) (African Writers Association (AWA)) Skotaville Publishers, P.O. Box 32483, Braamfontein, Johannesburg 2017, South Africa. Ed. Jaki Seroke. film rev.; illus.; play rev. circ. 3,000. (back issues avail.) **Indexed:** Ind.S.A.Per.

800   US   ISSN 0090-1237
PQ2605.L2
CLAUDEL STUDIES. 1972. s-a. $15 to individuals; libraries and institutions $20; foreign $20. University of Dallas, Claudel Studies, c/o Moses M. Nagy, Ed., Box 464, Irving, TX 75062-4799. TEL 214-721-5229. Ed. Moses M. Nagy. bk.rev.; bibl. circ. 500. **Indexed:** Arts & Hum.Cit.Ind., Curr.Cont., M.L.A.

051   US
▼**THE CLINTON MONTHLY.** 1994. m. $34.95 ($24.95 by FAX) (Canada $37.95; elsewhere $39.95) (effective 1994). Politically Unique Publications, Box 5656, Buena Park, CA 90622-5656. TEL 800-527-0399. FAX 714-220-9415. Ed. Mark S. Kennedy. adv. **Document type:** newsletter.
   Description: Acts as a forum for public praise and public outrage, providing conservative views and evaluations of how the Clinton administration is handling foreign, domestic, congressional, military and economic policy.

800   US   ISSN 1061-737X
CLUTCH. 1991. 2/yr. $10. Drill Press, 132 Clinton Park, No. 4, San Francisco, CA 94103. TEL 415-695-9773. Eds. Dan Hodge, Lawrence Oberc. circ. 200. (back issues avail.)
   Description: An alternative literary review featuring known, unknown and emerging writers from underground and small presses.

056   AG
CODO A CODO. 1990. q? Junin 146, Buenos Aires C.F., Argentina. Ed. Julio Fernandez.

056   BL
COLECAO ENCANTO RADICAL. Short title: Encanto Radical. no.33, 1983. irreg. Editora Brasiliense S.A., 01416 Rua da Consolacao, 2697, Sao Paulo, Brazil.

056   BL
COLECAO POLEMICAS DO NOSSO TIEMPO. no.5, 1983. irreg. (Livraria Ltda.) Cortez Editora, Rua Bartira, 387, 05009 Sao Paulo, SP, Brazil.

056   BL
COLECAO PRIMEIROS PASSOS. no.98 1983. irreg., latest no.224. Editora Brasiliense S.A., Rua da Consolacao, 2697, 01416 Sao Paulo, Brazil.

COLECCAO N'GOLA. see HISTORY — History Of Africa

056.1   AG
COLECCION ENSAYOS. no.16, 1976. irreg. Editorial Plus Ultra, Viamonte 1755, 1055 Buenos Aires, Argentina. **Document type:** monographic series.

808.8   US
COLONNADES. 1937. a. free. c/o K. Boyle, Faculty Adviser, Box 2252, Elon College, NC 27244. circ. 1,200.

808.8   US   ISSN 1046-3348
COLORADO REVIEW; a journal of contemporary literature. 1955-1969; resumed 1977. s-a. $15 to individuals (foreign $21); institutions $25 (foreign $31). (Colorado State University, English Department) University Press of Colorado, Box 849, Niwot, CO 80544. TEL 303-491-6428. FAX 303-530-5306. Ed. David Milofsky. adv.; bk.rev. circ. 1,500. **Document type:** academic/scholarly publication.
   Formerly (until 1965): Colorado State Review.
   Description: Short fiction, poetry, translations, articles by or interviews with contemporary poets and writers. Includes reviews of recent works of the literary imagination.

810   US   ISSN 1059-8189
PN6010.5
COLUMBIA (NEW YORK, 1975); a magazine of poetry and prose. 1975. s-a. $18. Columbia University, School of the Arts, Writing Division, 404 Dodge Hall, Columbia University, New York, NY 10027. TEL 212-854-4391. (Dist. by: Fine Print, 6448 Hwy. 270 E., Ste. 13104, Austin, TX 78723. TEL 512-452-8709) Ed.Bd. adv. circ. 1,250. (back issues avail.)
   Formerly (until 1991): Columbia, A Magazine of Poetry and Prose (ISSN 0161-486X)
   Description: Presents fiction, poetry and nonfiction by new and established writers.

COLUMBIA REVIEW (NEW YORK). see LITERATURE

051   US
COLUMBUS FREE PRESS.* 1970. m. $15. Columbus Institute for Contemporary Journalism, 203 E. Broad St., Columbus, OH 43215-3701. Ed. Robert Powers. adv.; bk.rev.; illus. circ. 15,000. (also avail. in microfilm from BLH; reprint service avail. from UMI)

808.87   US
COMEDY BUYERS BULLETIN. a. $9. Robert Makinson, Ed. & Pub., Box 023304, Brooklyn, NY 11202-0066. TEL 718-855-5057.

LITERARY AND POLITICAL REVIEWS

808.8 US
▼**COMEDY MAGAZINE.** 1993. bi-m. $19.95. Quality Services Company, 5290 Overpass Rd., Ste. 126, Santa Barbara, CA 93111-9950. TEL 805-964-7841. adv.: B&W page $1600. circ. 50,000. **Document type:** consumer publication.

808.87 US
COMEDY U S A INDUSTRY GUIDE. 1989. a. $59.95 (effective 1993). Laughs Unlimited, Inc., Box 990, New York, NY 10156-0990. TEL 212-628-2850. circ. 5,000. **Document type:** directory, trade publication.
Description: Includes contact information for comedians, comedy writers, their agents, managers and publicists, comedy clubs, and talent coordinators.

051 US
COMEUNITY;* an alternative, independent journal. 1971. irreg. $5. ComeUnity, Margo J. Yazell, Ed., 1000 49th St. N., no.203, Saint Petersburg, FL 33710-6640. adv.; bk.rev. circ. 2,000. (tabloid format; also avail. in microfilm from BLH; back issues avail.)
Description: A non-profit, independent, alternative journal dedicated to the preservation and enhancement of human rights (civil, political, economic, social and cultural).

059.91 IE ISSN 0010-2369
COMHAR. (Text in Irish) 1942. m. I£18. 5 Rae Mhuirfean, Ath Cliath, Ireland. TEL 01-785443. Ed. Tomas Ma Stomoin. adv.; bk.rev.; charts; illus.; index, cum.index: 1942-1981. circ. 2,500.

808.87 US
COMIC HIGHLIGHTS. 1970. m. $125. Tom Adams Productions, Box 10246, Honolulu, HI 96816. TEL 808-373-9800. FAX 808-373-9801. Ed. Tom Adams. adv. circ. 800. (back issues avail.) **Document type:** trade publication.
Formerly: Zoo Keeper.
Description: Covers all areas of today's humor.

808.87 US
COMIC READER.* 1961. m. $19. Street Enterprises, N85W16505 Mary Ct., Menomonee Falls, WI 53051-3032. TEL 414-251-6933. adv. circ. 7,000.
Description: Provides news and descriptions of comic books

051 US ISSN 1055-9639
COMIC RELIEF. 1989. m. $24.75. Page One Publishers and Bookworks, Inc., Box 6606, Eureka, CA 95502. TEL 707-443-2820. FAX 707-445-0270. Ed. Perry Bradford-Wilson; Pub. Perry Bradford-Wilson. adv. circ. 12,000. (back issues avail.) **Document type:** consumer publication.

800 FR ISSN 0180-8214
AP20
COMMENTAIRE. 1978. q. 295 F.($60) (foreign 330 F.). Commentaire, 116 rue du Bac, 75007 Paris, France. TEL 45-49-37-82. FAX 45-44-32-18. Ed. Jean-Claude Casanova. adv. circ. 5,500.
Indexed: ELLIS.
—BLDSC (3331.736000).

296 US ISSN 0010-2601
DS101
COMMENTARY; journal of significant thought and opinion on contemporary issues. 1945. m. $39. American Jewish Committee, 165 E. 56th St., New York, NY 10022. TEL 212-751-4000. FAX 212-751-1174. Ed. Neal Kozodoy. adv.; bk.rev.; index. circ. 25,000. (also avail. in microform from UMI,ISI,KMI; microform from NCR,KTO; reprint service avail. from UMI) **Indexed:** A.B.C.Pol.Sci., Acad.Ind., Amer.Bibl.Slavic & E.Eur.Stud., Amer.Hist.& Life, Bk.Rev.Dig., Bk.Rev.Ind., Chic.Per.Ind., Child.Bk.Rev.Ind. (1965-), Curr.Cont.M.E., Film Lit.Ind. (1973-), Fut.Surv., G.Soc.Sci.& Rel.Per.Lit., Hist.Abstr., Hum.Ind., HR Rep., Hum.Ind., Ind.Bk.Rev.Hum., Ind.Jew.Per., M.L.A., Mag.Ind., Media Rev.Dig., Mid.East: Abstr.& Ind., P.A.I.S., PMR, PROMT, R.G., Rel.Ind.One, RILA, SSCI. **Document type:** academic/scholarly publication.
—BLDSC (3333.600000); Faxon; UnCover; SWETS; UMI.

052 SI ISSN 0084-8956
DS501
COMMENTARY; journal of National University of Singapore Society. 1968-1971; N.S. 1972. irreg. S.$10 per no. (Asian S$12; Elsewhere $10). National University of Singapore Society, 9 Kent Ridge Dr., 0511 Singapore, Singapore. FAX 778-8095. Ed. Zaibun Siraj. bk.rev. circ. 6,000. **Indexed:** Acad.Ind., E.I., G.Soc.Sci.& Rel.Per.Lit., RILA, SSCI.

051 300 US ISSN 0010-3330
AP2
COMMONWEAL. 1924. bi-w. $39. Commonweal Foundation, 15 Dutch St., New York, NY 10038. TEL 212-732-0800. Ed. Margaret O'Brien Steinfels. adv. contact: Ruth Taylor. bk.rev.; film rev.; play rev.; index. circ. 18,000. (also avail. in microform from MIM,PMC,UMI; reprint service avail. from UMI) **Indexed:** A.I.P.P., Acad.Ind., Amer.Bibl.Slavic & E.Eur.Stud., Amer.Hist.& Life, Bk.Rev.Dig., Bk.Rev.Ind. (1965-), Cath.Ind., CERDIC, Child.Bk.Rev.Ind. (1965-), Curr.Lit.Fam.Plan., Film Lit.Ind. (1973-), G.Soc.Sci.& Rel.Per.Lit., Hist.Abstr., M.L.A., Mag.Ind., Media Rev.Dig., Mid.East: Abstr.& Ind., Old Test.Abstr., PMR, R.G. **Document type:** consumer publication.
—BLDSC (3339.340000); Faxon; UnCover; UMI.

329.9 CN ISSN 0010-3357
COMMONWEALTH. 1937. m. Can.$12. Service Printing Co. Ltd., 1122 Saskatchewan Dr., Regina, Sask. S4P 0C4, Canada. TEL 306-525-8321. FAX 306-569-1363. Ed. Leslie Quennell. adv.; bk.rev.; illus. circ. 10,000. (also avail. in microfilm) **Indexed:** So.Pac.Per.Ind.
Description: News on democratic socialist politics in Saskatchewan and across Canada.

800 FR ISSN 0395-6989
PN849.C5
COMMONWEALTH; essays and studies. (Text in English, French) 1975. 2/yr. 130 F. Societe d'Etude des Pays du Commonwealth, Faculte de Langues, 2 Boulevard Gabriel, 21000 Dijon, France. FAX 80-39-56-19. Ed. J.P. Durix. adv.; bk.rev. circ. 600.
—BLDSC (3339.348000).
Description: Devoted to the study of post-colonial anglophone literatures of the world.

COMMONWEALTH NOVEL IN ENGLISH. see *LITERATURE*

055 IT ISSN 1120-7094
COMPARATISTICA. 1989. a. L.45000 (foreign L.55000) (effective 1994). Casa Editrice Leo S. Olschki, Casella Postale 66, 50100 Florence, Italy. TEL 055-6530684. FAX 055-6530214. Ed. E. Caramaschi. **Document type:** academic/scholarly publication.

055.1 IT ISSN 0010-4418
COMPRENDRE; revue de politique de la culture. (Text in French) 1950. irreg. L.65000($53) for 4 nos. Societe Europeenne de Culture, Dorsoduro 909, 30123 Venice, Italy. TEL 041-52-30210. FAX 041-52-31033. Ed. Guiseppe Galasso. bk.rev.; illus.; index. circ. 2,500.

059.92 LE ISSN 0010-5589
CONFERENCES DU CENACLE.* (Text in Arabic) vol.20, 1966. m. Box 1145, Beirut, Lebanon. Ed. Michel Asmar. charts; stat.

056.1 PE ISSN 0010-5600
CONFERENCIAS;* conferencias, discursos, reportajes, articulos, tesis, notas culturales. (Text in English, French, Spanish) 1955. m. S/360.($12) Mario Herrera Gray, Ed. & Pub., Calle Mariano Carranza 306, Lima, Peru. adv.; bk.rev.; charts; illus.; index. circ. 1,000.

051 320 CN ISSN 0227-1311
D839
CONFLICT QUARTERLY. 1980. q. Can.$15($15) University of New Brunswick, Centre for Conflict Studies, Fredericton, N.B. E3B 5A3, Canada. TEL 506-453-4587. Ed. Deborah Stapleford. bk.rev.; cum.index. circ. 500. **Indexed:** Abstr.Mil.Bibl., P.A.I.S.
—BLDSC (3410.654800); Faxon; UnCover. CCC.

800 US ISSN 1055-7334
CONFLUENCE (BELPRE). 1991. a. $5. Bookmasters, Box 336, Belpre, OH 45750. TEL 615-373-2999. FAX 614-373-2999. Ed. Barbara J. McCullough-Cress. bk.rev. circ. 500.
Description: Presents a forum for poetry, fiction, art, photography, interviews, satire, criticism, novel-excerpts, and non-fiction.

800 US
CONFRONTATIONS; a literary journal. 1968. s-a. $10. Long Island University, C.W. Post Center, English Department, Brookville, NY 11548. Ed. Martin Tucker. illus.

051 US
CONNECTION (ALEXANDRIA); libertarian open forum. 1968-1979; resumed after 6 mos. 8/yr. $20. Erwin S. "Filthy Pierre" Strauss, Ed. & Pub., Box 3343, Fairfax, VA 22038-3343. adv.; bk.rev. circ. 100.
Formerly: Libertarian Connection (ISSN 0024-2012)

808.8 US ISSN 0732-7455
CB427
CONTEMPORARY ISSUES CRITICISM. 1982. irreg., vol.2, 1984. $108. Gale Research Inc., 835 Penobscot Bldg., Detroit, MI 48226. TEL 313-961-2242. FAX 313-961-6083. TELEX 810-221-7086. Ed. Robert L. Brubaker.
—BLDSC (3425.184170).

052 UK ISSN 0010-7565
AP4
CONTEMPORARY REVIEW. 1866. m. £36($160) Contemporary Review Co. Ltd., Cheam Business Centre, 14 Upper Mulgrave Rd., Cheam, Surrey SM2 7AZ, England. TEL 081-643-4846. Ed. Richard Mullen. adv.; film rev.; s-a. index. circ. 2,500. (also avail. in microform from PMC,UMI) **Indexed:** Amer.Hist.& Life, Bk.Rev.Ind. (1967-), Br.Hum.Ind., Child.Bk.Rev.Ind. (1967-), Film Lit.Ind. (1973-), Hist.Abstr., Hum.Ind., M.L.A., Mid.East: Abstr.& Ind.
—BLDSC (3425.300000); Faxon; UnCover; SWETS; UMI.
Incorporates: Fortnightly.
Description: Includes home affairs and politics, literature and the arts, history, travel and religion.

CONTEMPORARY VERSE TWO; a magazine of Canadian poetry and criticism. see *LITERATURE — Poetry*

054.1 FR ISSN 0010-7964
CONTREPOINT. (Text in French) 1970. q. 50 F. 4 rue Stockholm, 75008 Paris, France. adv.; bk.rev. circ. 5,000.

COOLIBRI; Kultur Freizeit Programm im Ruhrgebiet. see *MUSEUMS AND ART GALLERIES*

808.87 US ISSN 0733-2904
CORNELL LUNATIC. 1978. q. $10. Cornell Lunatic, Inc., Box 56, Willard Straight Hall, Cornell University, Ithaca, NY 14853. Ed. David Graham. adv.; illus. circ. 2,000. (back issues avail.)
Description: Publishes satire, parody, humor articles, cartoons, poetry, short fiction, and advertising spoofs generally related to campus life at Cornell University. Also features political, social and technical humor items of wider appeal.

055.1 IT ISSN 0589-8366
CORRIERE AFRICANO. 1964. m. Via XX Settembre 49, 00187 Rome, Italy. Ed. Antonio Acone.

055.1 IT
CORRISPONDENZA MERIDIONALE; rassegna di politica, economia, cultura, attualita. m. L.20000. Editrice Pellegrini, Via Roma 74, Casella Postale 158, 87100 Cosenza, Italy.

052 UK
▼**COUNTER CULTURE.** 1992. q. £10 (foreign £14). Third Way Publications Ltd., P.O. Box 1243, London SW7 3PB, England. TEL 071-373-3432. Ed. Patrick Harrington. adv.; bk.rev.; film rev.; play rev.; illus. circ. 1,000. **Document type:** bulletin.

LITERARY AND POLITICAL REVIEWS

808.87 US
CRACKED. 1957. 9/yr. $14.40. Globe Communications Corp. (New York), 441 Lexington Ave., New York, NY 10017. TEL 800-472-7744. FAX 212-286-0072. (And: 5401 N.W. Broken Sound Blvd., Boca Raton, FL 33431) Eds. Lou Silverstone, Andy Simmons. illus. circ. 750,000.
Description: Contains wit and humor.

808.87 US
CRACKED COLLECTORS EDITION. 4/yr. $2.95 per no. Globe Communications Corp. (New York), 441 Lexington Ave., New York, NY 10017. TEL 800-472-7744. FAX 212-286-0072. illus. circ. 450,000.
Description: Contains humorous articles.

808.87 US
CRACKED DIGEST. q. $2 per no. Globe Communications Corp. (New York), 441 Lexington Ave., New York, NY 10017. TEL 800-472-7744.

056 SP ISSN 1130-2186
CREACION. 1990. 3/yr. 3000 ptas. (Europe 4000 ptas.; America 5000 ptas.) (effective 1993). Instituto de Estetica y Teoria de las Artes, P. de la Castellana, 101 2a planta, Madrid, Spain. TEL 91-556-20-44. FAX 91-556-20-53. Dir. Jose Jimenez. adv. circ. 7,000.
Description: Acts as a platform for meeting and debate among creators, critics and philosophers. Also presents contributions in graphic arts.

052 UK ISSN 0260-8278
CREATIVE MIND; magazine of living philosophy. 1978. q. £6 (foreign £10). 70 Main St., Warton, Carnforth, Lancs LA5 9PG. TEL 0524-735924. Ed. Helen Prescott. adv.; bk.rev.; film rev.; play rev.; illus. circ. 1,000. (back issues avail.) **Document type:** newsletter.
Incorporates: Alternatives.

810 700 300 US ISSN 0011-1198
AP2
CRESSET; a review of literature, the arts and public affairs. 1937. m. (Sep.-May). $8.50 to individuals; students $4. (Valparaiso University) Valparaiso University Press, Valparaiso, IN 46383. TEL 219-464-5274. FAX 219-464-5381. Ed. Gail McGrew Eifrig. bk.rev.; film rev.; record rev.; illus. circ. 4,800. **Indexed:** Amer.Hum.Ind., Bk.Rev.Ind. (1965-), Child.Bk.Rev.Ind. (1965-). **Document type:** academic/scholarly publication.
—UnCover.

056.1 AG ISSN 0011-1473
AP63
CRITERIO. 1928. fortn. $80. Kriterion S.A., Junin 627, 1026 Buenos Aires, Argentina. TEL 46-7975. Ed.Bd. adv.; bk.rev.; film rev.; play rev.; index. circ. 3,750.

051 US ISSN 0093-1896
NX1
CRITICAL INQUIRY. 1974. q. $35 to individuals; institutions $84; students $24. University of Chicago Press, Journals Division, 5720 S. Woodlawn Ave., Chicago, IL 60637. TEL 312-753-3347. FAX 312-753-0811. TELEX 25-4603. (Subscr. to: Box 37005, Chicago, IL 60637) Eds. Arnold I. Davidson, W.J.T. Mitchell. adv. circ. 4,200. (also avail. in microform from UMI,PMC; reprint service avail. from UMI,ISI) **Indexed:** Abstr.Engl.Stud., Amer.Hist.& Life, Amer.Hum.Ind., Artbibl.Mod., Arts & Hum.Cit.Ind., Can.Rev.Comp.Lit., Curr.Cont., Film Lit.Ind. (1975-), Hist.Abstr., Hum.Ind., Lang.& Lang.Behav.Abstr., LCR, M.L.A., Mid.East: Abstr.& Ind., Music Artic.Guide, RILA. **Document type:** academic/scholarly publication.
—BLDSC (3487.454000); Faxon; UnCover; SWETS; UMI. **CCC.**
Description: Debates on a variety of topics about literature, art, architecture, film, history, philosophy, and music.
Refereed Serial

CRITICAL QUARTERLY. see *LITERATURE*

800 028 US ISSN 0891-3811
JC599.U5 CODEN: CTRVE3
CRITICAL REVIEW; an interdisciplinary journal. 1987. q. $29 to individuals (foreign $35); institutions $54 (foreign $62). Critical Review Foundation, Inc., 942 Howard St., San Francisco, CA 94103. TEL 415-495-2157. FAX 415-541-0597. Ed. Jeffrey Friedman. adv.; bk.rev.; index. circ. 2,000. (back issues avail.) **Indexed:** Curr.Cont., Ind.Bk.Rev.Hum., Int.Bibl.S.S.Econ., Int.Bibl.S.S.Pol.Sci., Int.Polit.Sci.Abstr., Left Ind. (1990-), Phil.Ind., Polit.Sci.Abstr., Sage Pub.Admin.Abstr., Sociol.Abstr. **Document type:** academic/scholarly publication.
—BLDSC (3487.464000); Faxon; UnCover; UMI.
Description: Contains research and essay-length book reviews on modern authors. Develops and critiques classical liberal theory with an emphasis on political philosophy, economics, sociology, and history.

301 US ISSN 0896-9205
HM1
CRITICAL SOCIOLOGY. 1969. 3/yr. $25 to individuals (foreign $35); institutions $30 (foreign $40). Critical Sociology, University of Oregon, Dept. of Sociology, Eugene, OR 97403. TEL 503-686-5039. FAX 503-346-5026. adv.; bk.rev.; illus.; cum.index. circ. 1,500. (also avail. in microform from UMI) **Indexed:** Abstr.Mil.Bibl., Alt.Press Ind., E.I., Lang.& Lang.Behav.Abstr., Left Ind. (1982-), Mid.East: Abstr.& Ind., Polit.Sci.Abstr., Sociol.Abstr. (1971-), Stud.Wom.Abstr. **Document type:** trade publication.
—BLDSC (3487.485800); Faxon; UnCover; SWETS; UMI.
Formerly: Insurgent Sociologist (ISSN 0047-0384)

800 700 UK ISSN 0011-1570
PR1
CRITICAL SURVEY. 1989. 3/yr. £31($58) (effective 1994). Oxford University Press, Oxford Journals, Walton St., Oxford OX2 6DP, England. TEL 0865-56767. FAX 0865-56646. TELEX 837330-OXPRES-G. (U.S. subscr. to: Oxford University Press Inc., 2001 Evans Rd., Cary, NC 27513. TEL 919-677-0977) Ed. Bryan Loughrey. adv. contact: Jane Parker. bk.rev. circ. 900. **Document type:** academic/scholarly publication.
—BLDSC (3487.488510); UnCover; UMI. **CCC.**
Description: Covers literary and cultural studies. Publishes detailed readings on individual texts, wide ranging debates in the nature of critical practice, discussions of current educational issues, original short stories and poetry.

809 US ISSN 0730-2304
PN2
CRITICAL TEXTS: A REVIEW OF THEORY AND CRITICISM. 1982. 3/yr. $9 to individuals; institutions $15; foreign $20. Department of English and Comparative Literature, 602 Philosophy Hall, Columbia University, New York, NY 10027. TEL 212-749-6956. Ed. Joseph W. Childers. adv.; bk.rev.; bibl. circ. 850. **Indexed:** Amer.Hum.Ind., Artbibl.Mod., M.L.A., Phil.Ind.
—UnCover.
Formerly: Critical Texts: A Newsletter in Critical Theory and the History of Criticism.

053.1 GW ISSN 0011-1597
CRITICON; konservative Zeitschrift. 1970. 4/yr. DM.64. Criticon Verlag GmbH, Knoebelstr. 36, 80538 Munich, Germany. TEL 089-299885. FAX 089-229768. Ed. Caspar Von Schrenck-Notzing. bk.rev.; abstr.; bibl. **Indexed:** M.L.A. **Document type:** consumer publication.

CRITIQUE (WEST VANCOUVER); the juicy embrace between information and transformation. see *NEW AGE PUBLICATIONS*

800 320 FR ISSN 0398-2068
CRITIQUE COMMUNISTE. 1975. m. 240 F. (foreign 300 F.). La Breche, 2 rue Richard Lenoir, 93100 Montreuil, France. TEL 48-59-00-80.
—BLDSC (3487.490330).
Formerly (until 1977): Marx ou Creve (ISSN 0398-205X)

CROSS-BIAS; the newsletter of the friends of Bemerton honoring George Herbert 1593-1633. see *LITERATURE — Poetry*

CROSSCURRENTS. see *SOCIOLOGY*

051 US
CROW; your guide to alternate culture. Variant title: Bill Dale Marcinko's A F T A. 1978. bi-m. $18.95. A F T A Press, Inc., 47 Crater Ave., Wharton, NJ 07885-2023. TEL 201-828-5467. (Alt. addr.: Box A, Wharton, NJ 07885) Ed. Bill Dale Marcinko. adv.; bk.rev.; film rev.; illus. circ. 25,000. (back issues avail.)
Formerly: A F T A (ISSN 0193-7782)

808 US
CRY FOR DAWN. a. $2.50 per no. Cry for Dawn Production Ltd., 360 W. Merrick Rd., Ste. 350, Valley Stream, NY 11580. Ed. Joe Monks.
Description: Covers child molesting, murder, suicide, multilation, racism and other social and political issues.

800 US
▼**CRYSTAL.** 1992. s-a. Box 5713, Takoma Park, MD 20913-5713.
Description: Small literary review.

056.1 SP ISSN 0572-2969
CUADERNO LITERARIO AZOR; literatura, poesia, arte, historia, etc., del ambito de la hispanidad. 1974. q. 4000 ptas.($10) Ediciones Rondas, Peligro 8, 08012 Barcelona, Spain. Ed. Jose Jurado Morales. bk.rev.; bibl.; illus.
Supersedes: Azor (ISSN 0045-1258)

056.1 MX ISSN 0185-156X
AP63
CUADERNOS AMERICANOS. 1942; N.S. 1993. bi-m. Mex.$105($125) (effective 1994). Universidad Nacional Autonoma de Mexico, Apdo. Postal 965, 06000 Mexico, D.F., Mexico. TEL 5489662. FAX 5489662. (Or: Torre I de Humanidades, 2o piso, Ciudad Universitaria, 04510 Mexico D.F., Mexico. TEL 622-19-02. FAX 616-25-15) Dir. Leopoldo Zea. adv.; bk.rev.; bibl.; illus.; index, cum.index: 1942-1971. circ. 2,500. (also avail. in microfilm from BHP) **Indexed:** Amer.Hist.& Life, Anthropol.Lit., Hisp.Amer.Per.Ind., Hist.Abstr., M.L.A.

056 SP
CUADERNOS DE ALZATE; revista vasca de la cultura y las ideas. 1984. 3/yr. 1750 ptas. (Europe 3125 ptas.; America 3875 ptas.) Editorial Pablo Iglesias, Monte Esquinza 30, 2o, 28010 Madrid, Spain. TEL 91-310-43-13. FAX 91-319-45-85. Dir. Jon Juaristi. circ. 1,000.
Description: Aims to reflect the modern and complex Basque society, covering new cultural, artistic, social and scientific experience, and political science.

056.1 AG ISSN 0011-2380
CUADERNOS DE CRITICA.* 1965. q. Charcas 4767, 20 "A" Buenos Aires, Argentina. Ed. Jorge C. Caballero. adv.; bk.rev.

CUADERNOS DE CRITICA. see *PHILOSOPHY*

808.8 320 CU
CUADERNOS DE NUESTRA AMERICA. s-a. $12 in S. America; N. America $14; elsewhere $16. (Centro de Estudio Sobre America) Ediciones Cubanas, Obispo No. 527, Apdo. 605, Havana, Cuba. TEL 32-5556-60.

056.1 AG
CUADERNOS DEL CAMINO. 1978. m. (Instituto Goethe Buenos Aires) Agencia Periodistica CID, Av. de Mayo 666, Buenos Aires, Argentina. Ed. Juan C. Paz.

946 980 SP ISSN 0011-250X
AP63
CUADERNOS HISPANOAMERICANOS; revista mensual de cultura hispanica. 1948. m. 7000 ptas.($75) Instituto de Cooperacion Iberoamericana, Avda. de los Reyes Catolicos 4, Ciudad Universitaria, 28040 Madrid, Spain. TEL 583-83-96. Dir. Felix Grande. bk.rev.; bibl.; illus.; index, circ. 2,000. (reprint service avail. from KTO) **Indexed:** Amer.Hist.& Life, Arts & Hum.Cit.Ind., Curr.Cont., Hisp.Amer.Per.Ind., Hist.Abstr., M.L.A.
—Faxon; SWETS.

056 SP
CUADERNOS NOVENTA. bi-m. 2000 ptas. Publi 92, S.A., Consejo de Ciento 276, 08007 Barcelona, Spain. TEL 93-412-06-40. FAX 93-301-94-74. Dir. Xavier Rubert de Ventos. circ. 5,000.
Description: Publishes analysis and opinion in the Spanish political and cultural context.

LITERARY AND POLITICAL REVIEWS

056.1   CU
CUBA SOCIALISTA. (Summaries in English, French, Spanish) 1966. m. $12 in N. America; S. America $14; Europe $15; elsewhere $21. (Partido Comunista de Cuba, Comite Central) Ediciones Cubanas, Obispo No. 527, Apdo. 605, Havana, Cuba. TEL 22-5895-22-5892. (Subscr. to: Oficina Municipal de Prensa, Dragones No. 456, Havana, Cuba) bk.rev.
    Formerly (until 1981): Pensamiento Critico.

056.1   ES   ISSN 0011-2755
AP63
CULTURA. 1955. q. free. Ministerio de Cultura y Comunicaciones, Direccion de Publicaciones e Impresos, 17 Avda. sur 430, San Salvador, El Salvador. bk.rev.; bibl.; illus.; index, cum.index 1961-1963. circ. 3,000. **Indexed:** Amer.Hist.& Life, Hist.Abstr., M.L.A. **Document type:** government publication.
    Formerly (until 1974): Nueva Cultura (ISSN 0048-1076)

984   BO   ISSN 0011-2763
CULTURA BOLIVIANA.* 1964. m. Bol.$12.($1) Universidad Boliviana Tecnica de Oruro, Departamento de Extension Cultural, Oruro, Bolivia. Dir. Jorge Fajardo. bk.rev.; dance rev.; film rev.; illus.; play rev.; record rev.; index.

810   US
CULTURAL CORRESPONDENCE. 1976. q. $10. 505 West End Ave., New York, NY 10024. TEL 212-787-1784. Ed. Jim Murray. bk.rev.; bibl. circ. 4,000. **Indexed:** Alt.Press Ind.

800.051   US   ISSN 0730-9503
CULTURAL DEMOCRACY. 1980. s-a. $25 to individuals; organizations $50. Alliance for Cultural Democracy, c/o Tripp Mikiah, 1326 Shotwell St., San Francisco, CA 94110. TEL 415-821-9652. FAX 415-546-0578. (Subscr. to: Box 7591, Minneapolis, MN 55407) adv.; bk.rev. circ. 2,000. (back issues avail.)
    Description: Provides a forum for promoting an understanding of the need for integrating cultural, political, and economic democracy in the US.

CULTURAL STUDIES. see *SOCIOLOGY*

300   US
CULTURAL WATCHDOG NEWSLETTER. 1977. m. $15. Ehrenkrantz Enterprises, 33 Baraud Rd., Scarsdale, NY 10583. Ed. Louis Ehrenkrantz. bk.rev. circ. 7,800. **Document type:** newsletter.

059   BD
CULTURE ET SOCIETE. (Text in French) 1978. q. $4. Ministere de la Jeunesse, des Sports et de la Culture, Centre de Civilisation Burundaise, B.P. 1400, Bujumbura, Burundi. Ed.Bd.

055   RM   ISSN 1018-0540
CURIERUL ROMANESC. 1972. m. 2500 lei($30) (effective Feb. 1994). Fundatia Culturala Romana, Aleea Alexandru, no.38, Sector 1, 71273 Bucharest 63, Rumania. TEL 401-212-0510. FAX 401-312-7559. Ed. Ilie Traian. adv.; bk.rev.; play rev. circ. 10,000. (back issues avail.) **Document type:** newspaper.
    Supersedes (in 1989): Tribuna Romaniei.
    Description: Contains political data, economic and social information, a cultural events schedule. Covers history and ethnic interests.

800   US
CYANOSIS. 1990. s-a. $16 per no. Darin DeStefano, Ed. & Pub., 318 Mendocino Ave., Ste.30, Santa Rosa, CA 94115. bk.rev. circ. 1,000,000.
    Description: Presents a forum for unique or experimental fiction, art, photography, letters, novel-excerpts, criticism, satire, plays and non-ficiton.

052 800   FR   ISSN 0992-1893
CYCNOS. (Text in English, French) 1985. 2/yr. 100 F. Centre de Recherche sur les Ecritures de Langue Anglaise, Universite de Nice, Dept. d'Etudes Anglophones, 98 bvd Edouard Herriot, B.P. 209, 06204 Nice Cedex 3, France. FAX 93-37-55-36. Ed. Andre Viola. **Document type:** academic/scholarly publication.

942   UK   ISSN 0024-6204
CYMRO LLUNDAIN/LONDON WELSHMAN. (Text in English, Welsh) 1896. m. 85p. London Welsh Association, 157-163 Gray's Inn Rd., London W.C.1, England. Ed. Raymond Howell. adv.; bk.rev.; charts; illus.; play rev. circ. 3,500.

819 300   CN   ISSN 0011-5827
AP5
DALHOUSIE REVIEW; a Canadian journal of literature and opinion. 1921. q. Can.$19 (foreign Can.$28). Dalhousie University Press Ltd., Sir James Dunn Bldg., Ste. 314, Halifax, NS B3H 3J5, Canada. TEL 902-494-2541. FAX 902-494-2319. TELEX 019-21863-DALUNIV-HFX. Ed. Alan Andrews. adv. contact: Debbie Hills. bk.rev.; index. circ. 800. (also avail. in microfilm from MML,UMI; reprint service avail. from MML,UMI) **Indexed:** Abstr.Engl.Stud., Amer.Hist.& Life, Arts & Hum.Cit.Ind., Bk.Rev.Ind. (1988-), Can.Lit.Ind., Can.Per.Ind., Child.Bk.Rev.Ind. (1988-), CMI, Curr.Cont., Hist.Abstr., Ind.Bk.Rev.Hum., M.L.A., Mid.East: Abstr.& Ind., P.A.I.S.
—BLDSC (3517.750000); Faxon; UnCover.

057.8   CI
DANAS/TODAY; informativno politicki tjednik. 1982. w. 14040 din.($23) Avenija Bratstva i Jedinstva 4, 41000 Zagreb, Croatia. TEL 041-333-333. Ed. Gojko Marinkovic. circ. 56,000. (back issues avail.)

895.1   CC
DANGDAI WENTAN BAO. (Text in Chinese) m. Zhongguo Zuojia Xiehui, Guangdong Fenhui - China Writers' Association, Guangdong Chapter, No. 75, Wende Lu, Guangzhou, Guangdong 510030, People's Republic of China. TEL 331851. Ed. Huang Shusen.

059.91   UK   ISSN 0011-6718
DARPON;* the independent and impartial Bengali quarterly. (Text in Bengali, English) 1968. q. $2. Darpon Publications, 1 Adelaide Villas, Copse Rd., St. Johns, Woking, Surrey, England. Ed. M. Sultan. adv.; bk.rev.; illus. circ. 5,000. (processed)

057.8   CI
DARUVARSKI LIST; glasilo OKSSRN Daruvar. 1975. s-m. 780 din. Narodno Sveuciliste, Informativni Centar Daruvar, Strosmajerova 32A, 43500 Daruvar, Croatia. Ed. Damir Valdgoni.
    Formerly (until 1985): Vjesnik Komune (ISSN 0042-7624)

059.9454   LV   ISSN 0207-4001
PG9145.R1
DAUGAVA. 1977. bi-m. $36 (effective 1994). Izdatel'stvo Daugava, Balasta Dambis 3, LV-1081 Riga, Latvia. TEL 465-996. Ed. R. Dobrovenskij. bk.rev.; circ. 12,000. (paid). **Indexed:** M.L.A.

296   AG   ISSN 0011-703X
AP93
DAVAR; revista literaria. vol.124, 1970. 4/yr. $8. Sociedad Hebraica Argentina, Sarmiento 2233, Buenos Aires, Argentina. Dir. Bernardo Ezequiel Koremblit. bk.rev.; illus. circ. 1,500.

322.4   IE   ISSN 0332-4281
DAWN TRAIN. 1982. 2/yr. £2. Dawn Editorial Collective, 16 Ravensdene Park, Belfast 6, Northern Ireland.

052   UK   ISSN 0011-7080
DAY BY DAY; news commentary and digest of national and international affairs and review of the arts, poems. 1963. m. $17. (Fellowship Party) Loverseed Press, Woolacombe House, 141 Woolacombe Rd., Blackheath, London SE3, England. TEL 01-856-6249. Ed. Ronald Mallone. adv.; bk.rev.; film rev.; music rev.; play rev. circ. 23,000.

056   PE
DEBATE. 1979. bi-m. $40. Apoyo, S.A., Apdo. Postal 671, Lima 100, Peru. FAX 5114-455946. Ed. Augusto Alvarez-Rodrich. adv.; bk.rev. circ. 10,000. **Indexed:** Hisp.Amer.Per.Ind.

052   II
DEBONAIR; Diwana parody. (Text in English) 1972. m. Rs.1.50 per copy. Debonair Publications Private Ltd., 41A Dr E. Moses Rd., Bombay 400 018, India. TEL 22-4941601. Ed. Amrita Shah. circ. 87,500.

059.91   YU   ISSN 0011-7935
AP56
DELO; mesecni knjizevni casopis. (Text in Serbo-Croatian) 1955. m. 5000 din. Nolit, Terazije 27-II, Belgrade, Yugoslavia. Ed. Jovica Acin. adv.; bk.rev.; index. circ. 1,600. (also avail. in microfilm from NRP) **Indexed:** M.L.A.

DEMOCRAZIA E DIRITTO/DEMOCRACY AND LAW. see *LAW*

800   US
▼**THE DESERT GOOD NEIGHBOR.*** 1992. m. $6. Bob Challinor, Ed. & Pub., Box 2279, Mesquite, NV 89024-2279. adv. circ. 5,000.
    Description: Showcases ecologically-oriented poetry, articles, art, photography, interviews, news items, and non-fiction.

056.1   UY
DESTABANDA. 1977. irreg. Mario A. Aiello, Ed. & Pub., Gaboto 1918, Montevideo, Uruguay.

DEUTSCHLAND-MAGAZIN. see *POLITICAL SCIENCE*

053   GW
DIABOLO; Magazin aus Oldenburg. 1984. m. DM.3 per no. Diabolo-Verlag, Bahnhofstr. 10a, 26122 Oldenburg, Germany. TEL 0441-254912. FAX 0441-2489048. Ed. Ruediger Schoen. adv. contact: Ruediger Schoen. circ. 5,011. (back issues avail.) **Document type:** bulletin.

057.8   XV   ISSN 0012-2068
AP58.S55
DIALOGI. (Text in Slovenian) 1965. m. 60 din.($5.90) Zveza Kulturnih Delavcev v Mariboru, Rotovski trg 1, Maribor, Slovenia. Ed. Janez Svajncer. **Indexed:** M.L.A.

DIALOGUE ON LIBERTY. see *POLITICAL SCIENCE*

055.1   IT   ISSN 0012-2335
DIANA (MARCIANISE);* rassegna di politica e di cultura. 1953. bi-m. L.3000($10.) Via Raffaele Musone 175, 81025-Marcianise (Caserta), Italy. illus.

830 700   BE   ISSN 0012-2645
AP15
DIETSCHE WARANDE EN BELFORT; tijdschrift voor letterkunde en geestesleven. (Text in Dutch) 1855. 6/yr. 1600 BEF (effective 1993). Editions Peeters s.p.r.l., Bondgenotenlaan 153, B-3000 Louvain, Belgium. TEL 32-16-235170. FAX 32-16-228500. Ed.Bd. adv.; bk.rev.; index. circ. 3,000. (back issues avail.) **Indexed:** Bibl.Ling., M.L.A. **Document type:** academic/scholarly publication.
—SWETS.

A DIFFERENT LIGHT REVIEW; a catalog of gay and lesbian literature. see *HOMOSEXUALITY*

808.8   US
DIFFICULTIES.* 1979. s-a. $7 per no. c/o Beckett, 131 N. Pearl St., Kent, OH 44240-2219. TEL 216-673-9282. Ed. Tom Beckett. circ. 300.

808.8   US
DIGNITARIES OF THE COUNTER-CLOCKWISE REVOLUTION. 1991. 4/yr. $1 per no. Box 3163, Woonsocket, RI 02895. Ed. Alek Ryan. circ. 300 (paid).

378.1   PH   ISSN 0012-2858
AP8
DILIMAN REVIEW. 1953. q. P.120 (foreign $65). University of the Philippines, 2nd Fl., Palma Hall Annex, University of the Philippines, Diliman, Quezon City 1101, Philippines. TEL 98-24-71. Ed. Eddie E. Escultura. bk.rev.; index. **Indexed:** Ind.Phil.Per., M.L.A. **Document type:** academic/scholarly publication.
—UnCover.

055.1   IT   ISSN 0012-2904
DIMENSIONI; rivista abruzzese di cultura e d'arte. 1957. bi-m. L.2000.($5) Via Bendetto Croce 172, 65100 Pescara, Italy. Ed.Bd. adv.; bk.rev.; bibl.; charts; illus.; index.

055   IT   ISSN 0394-2473
DIORAMA LETTERARIO; mensile di attualita culturali e metapolitiche. 1976. m. L.30000($25) Casella Postale 1364, 50122 Florence, Italy. TEL 055-23-40-714. Ed. Marco Tarchi. bk.rev.; bibl. circ. 2,000. (back issues avail.) **Document type:** bulletin.

LITERARY AND POLITICAL REVIEWS

DIRECTORY OF HUMOR MAGAZINES & HUMOR ORGANIZATIONS IN AMERICA (AND CANADA). see *BIBLIOGRAPHIES*

800　　　　　　　IT　　ISSN 0012-3668
DISCRETIO. 1962. irreg. Via F. M. Penna 20, 97018 Sicily, Italy. Ed. Dr. Giovanni Rossino. circ. 1,000. (tabloid format)
  Description: Translations from modern and classical languages.

057.91　　　　　KR　　ISSN 0012-4354
DNIPRO; literaturno-khudozhnii ta hromads'ko-polltychnyi zhurnal. 1927. m. $85. (Soyuz Molodezhnikh Organizatsii Ukrainy) Vidavnitstvo Molod, Vul. Parkhomenko 38-44, 252119 Kiev, Ukraine. TEL 044-213-1160. Ed. Mykola Lukiv. bk.rev.; bibl.; illus. circ. 71,900. **Indexed:** M.L.A.

DOCUMENTS (NEW YORK). see *ART*

057.1　　　　　　RU　　ISSN 0130-3562
DON; literaturno-khudozhestvennyi i obshchestvenno-politicheskii zhurnal. 1957. m. 24 Rub. Soyuz Pisatelei Rossiiskoi Federatsii, Rostovskoe Oblastnoe Otdelenie, Krasnoarmeiskaya 23, Rostov-na-Donu, GSP-6, Russia. Ed. M.D. Sokolov. bk.rev.; illus. circ. 60,000.

320　　　　　　　GW
DONAU BOTE. bi-m. DM.14. Foerderer Verein "Nemzetor", Ferchenbach Str. 88, 80995 Munich, Germany. TEL 089-1503941. FAX 089-3615610. Ed. Tibor Kecskesi-Tollas. circ. 7,000. **Document type:** newsletter.

DOSTOEVSKY STUDIES. see *LITERATURE*

DOVETAIL. see *RELIGIONS AND THEOLOGY*

800 070.5　　　　UK　　ISSN 1352-7762
▼**DRAGON'S BREATH**; international small press review and monthly newsletter. 1993. m. £2.50. S.A. Publishing, 13 Hazely Combe, Arreton, Isle of Wight PO30 3AJ, England. Ed. Zine Kat. **Document type:** newsletter.

808.8　　　　　　US
▼**DREAM WHIP.** 1992. 4/yr. $4. Box 53832, Lubbock, TX 79453. TEL 806-794-9263. Ed. Bill D. Whip. circ. 44.

808.8　　　　　　US
▼**DREAMWORLDNEWS.** 1990. irreg. $5 per no. Box 614, Northampton, MA 01060. TEL 413-586-4654. Eds. Luke Jaeger, Shoshana Marchand. circ. 200.

890　　　　　　　AA
DRITA. 1960. w. $16. Lidhja e Shkrimtareve dhe e Artisteve te Shqiperise - Union of Writers and Artists of Albania, Baboci 37z, Tirana, Albania. Ed. Zija Cela. bk.rev.; film rev.; illus. (also avail. in microfilm from NRP)

320.5　　　　　　GW　　ISSN 0012-6268
DER DRITTE WEG; freisoziale Alternative zu Kapitalismus und Kommunismus. 1970. m. DM.48. Freisoziale Union, Demokratische Mitte, Feldstr. 46, 20357 Hamburg, Germany. TEL 040-4399717. FAX 02054-84955. Ed. Hans-Bernhard Zill. bk.rev. circ. 3,000.
  Description: Covers capitalism, socialism, and communism and their role in economics, finance, politics, and international politics.

DRUM VOICES; a confluence of literary, cultural and vision arts. see *ETHNIC INTERESTS*

800　　　　　　　US
DRUNKEN BOAT. irreg. Autonomedia, Box 568, Brooklyn, NY 11211-0568. TEL 718-387-6471. Ed. Max Bledman; Pub. Jim Fleming. **Document type:** academic/scholarly publication.

057.1　　　　　　RU　　ISSN 0012-6756
PN6065.R9
DRUZHBA NARODOV. 1938. m. $104. (Soyuz Pisatelei Rossii) Druzhba Narodov, Ul. Vorovskovo 52, 121827 Moscow, Russia. TEL 095-291-6227. (Dist. in U.S. by: Victor Kamkin Inc., 4956 Boiling Brook Pwky., Rockville, MD 20852. TEL 301-881-5973. FAX 301-881-1637) Ed. A. Rudenko-Desnyak. bk.rev.; bibl.; illus.; index. circ. 33,300. **Indexed:** Curr.Dig.Sov.Press, M.L.A.
  —BLDSC (0056.250000).

057.8　　　　　　CI　　ISSN 0012-690X
DUBROVACKI VJESNIK; list Socijalistickog saveza radnog naroda opoine Dubrovnik. 1950. w. 150 din. Socijalisticki Savez Radnog Naroda Opcine Dubrovnik, Frana Bulica 6, 50101 Dubrovnik, Croatia. Ed. Miho Milic.

895　　　　　　　CC　　ISSN 1003-5702
DUFU YANJIU XUEKAN/JOURNAL OF DUFU STUDIES. (Text in Chinese) 1981. q. $30. Chengdu Dufu Yanjiu Xuehui - Chengdu Society of Dufu Studies, Dufu Caotang Bowuguan Nei, Chengdu, Sichuan 610072, People's Republic of China. TEL 769687. (Subscr. to: Sichuan Sheng Xinhua Shudian, Chengdu, Sichuan 610017, P.R.C. TEL 24866) (Co-sponsor: Dufu Caotang Museum) Ed. Zhong Shuliang. adv.: page $500; adv. contact: Pu Younong. **Document type:** academic/scholarly publication.
  Formerly (until 1988): Caotang - Dufu Yanjiu Xuekan.
  Description: Studies the life and poems of Dufu, a famous ancient poet in China.

057.1　　　　　　KR
DZVIN; literaturno-mystets'kyi ta hromads'kopolitychnyi zhurnal. 1940. m. $95. (Soyuz Pisatelei Ukrainy) Vidavnitstvo Kamenyar, Vul. Pidvalna 3, 290006 Lvov, Ukraine. TEL 0322-711949. (Dist. in U.S. by: Victor Kamkin Inc., 4956 Boiling Brook Pkwy., Rockville, MD. TEL 301-881-5973. FAX 301-881-1637) Ed. Roman Fedoriv. bk.rev.; illus. circ. 152,500.
  Formerly (until 1990): Zhovten' (ISSN 0044-4499)

052　　　　　　　NZ
EARWIG. 1969. s-a. NZ.$2 for 5 nos. Earwig Graphics, 10 Norfolk St., Auckland 2, New Zealand. illus. circ. 4,000.

051　　　　　　　FR
EASY SPEAKEASY. 1980. 5/yr. 35 F. Librairie Fernand Nathan, 9 rue Mechain, 75014 Paris, France. Ed. Rosalie Gomes.

ECHO ROOM. see *MUSIC*

056.1　　　　　　PE
ECOS. 1962. m. Jose A. Valencia - Arenas, Apdo. 3758, Lima, Peru. illus. circ. 5,000.

ECRITS DU CANADA FRANCAIS. see *LITERATURE*

056.9　　　　　　BL
EDICOES CADERNOS CULTURAIS;* uma revista de cultura do nordeste para o Brasil. irreg. Cr.$10 per no. Universidade Federal de Pernambuco, Cidade Universitaria, 5000 Recife, PE, Brazil. illus.

941　　　　　　　UK　　ISSN 0267-6672
EDINBURGH REVIEW. 1969. s-a. £10($20) Edinburgh University Press, 22 George Sq., Edinburgh EH8 9LF, Scotland. TEL 031-650-4218. FAX 031-662-0053. Ed. Murdo Macdonald. adv. contact: Kathryn MacLean. bk.rev.; film rev.; bibl.; illus. circ. 1,500. (also avail. in microform from UMI,PMC; microfilm from KTO; reprint service avail. from UMI) **Document type:** academic/scholarly publication.
  —BLDSC (3661.022500).
  Formerly (until 1985): New Edinburgh Review (ISSN 0028-4645)
  Description: Features articles on all aspects of culture (literature, art, philosophy, education).
  Refereed Serial

052　　　　　　　PK　　ISSN 0013-2020
EDUCATOR.* (Text in English) 1965. m. Rs.9($3.) G. Rabbani Mirza, Ed. & Pub., 2 McLeod Rd., Lahore, Pakistan. bk.rev. circ. 1,000.

059.89　　　　　　CY
ELEFTHEROTYPIA TIS DEFTERAS/MONDAY'S FREE PRESS. (Text in Greek) 1980. w. Demoktatiko Komma (DIKO), Hasjisavvas Bldg., Eleftheria Sq., POB 3821, Nicosia, Cyprus.
  Description: Greek-Cypriot right-of-center political review.

ELEMENTS. see *ART*

808.8　　　　　　HU　　ISSN 0424-8848
PN9
ELET ES IRODALOM; irodalmi es politikai hetilap. 1957. w. 360 Ft.($43.50) Lapkiado Vallalat, Lenin krt. 9-11, Budapest 7, Hungary. (Subscr. to: Kultura, P.O. Box 149, H-1389 Budapest, Hungary) Ed. Imre Bata. film rev.; play rev.; illus. circ. 60,000. (looseleaf format)

847　　　　　　　HU　　ISSN 0133-4751
ELETUNK. 1963. m. $14 (effective 1993). (Vas Megye Tanacsa) Kultura, P.O. Box 149, 1389 Budapest 62, Hungary. TEL 361-180-31-94. FAX 361-180-33-06. TELEX 20-2855 KULT H. Ed. Gyorgy Pete. bk.rev. circ. 2,150.

059.89　　　　　　CY
EMBROS/FORWARD. (Text in Greek) 1987. w. Ananeotiko Demokratiko Socialistiko Kinema (AIDSOK), 19 Nikitara St., Ag. Omoloyitae, P.O. Box 3739, Nicosia, Cyprus. Ed. P. Polydorides. circ. 2,500.
  Description: Left-wing political review.

808 808.87　　　　US
EMERALD CITY COMIX & STORIES; fiction, poetry, news, reviews, humor. 1987. bi-m. $12. Wonder Comix, Box 95402, Seattle, WA 98145-2402. TEL 206-527-2598. Ed. Nils Osmar. adv.; bk.rev. circ. 12,000. (tabloid format; back issues avail.)
  Description: Presents short stories and other "word pieces", poetry, cartoons and comics, graphics, news.

EMIGRE; non-stop design - the magazine that ignores boundaries. see *ART*

700　　　　　　　US　　ISSN 0193-5798
ENCLITIC;* the timely taken seriously. 1977. 4/yr. $16 to individuals (foreign $18); institutions $36 (foreign $40). c/o John O'Kane, Ed., 12 Pleasant St., No. 2, Cambridge, MA 02139-3207. Ed. John O'Kane. adv.; bk.rev. circ. 7,500. **Indexed:** Amer.Hum.Ind., Film Lit.Ind. (1982-), Intl.Ind.TV, M.L.A., Sociol.Abstr.
  —BLDSC (3738.516000); UnCover.
  Description: Writing on contemporary politics, ideas and cultural life.

808　　　　　　　US
▼**ENDING THE BEGIN.** 1992. irreg. $2. Box 4816, Seattle, WA 98104-0816. TEL 206-726-0948. Ed. Brad Angell. circ. 100.

500 375.4 820　　SA　　ISSN 0376-8902
ENGLISH IN AFRICA. 1974. s-a. R.20 to individuals; institutions R.28.75; outside Africa £15($20). Rhodes University, Institute for the Study of English in Africa, P.O. Box 94, Grahamstown 6140, South Africa. TEL 27-461-26093. FAX 27-461-25642. Ed. Gareth Cornwell. adv.; bk.rev. circ. 500. **Indexed:** Curr.Cont.Africa, Ind.S.A.Per., M.L.A. **Document type:** academic/scholarly publication.
  —Faxon.

808.8 320　　　　CU　　ISSN 0864-1889
ENIGMA; revista de literatura policiaca. s-a. $12 in N. and S. America; Europe $13; elsewhere $14. (Asociacion Internacional de Escritores Policiacos) Ediciones Cubanas, Obispo No. 527, Apdo. 605, Havana, Cuba. TEL 32-5556-60. (Edit. addr.: UNEAC, 17 y H, Vedado, La Habana, Cuba) Ed. Rodolfo Perez Valero.

056.9　　　　　　BL
ENSAIOS DE OPINIAO; revista mensal de cultura. 1975. m. Cr.$300. Editora Paz e Terra, Rua Sao Jose 90, Centro, Rio de Janeiro, Brazil.

055.1 800　　　　IT　　ISSN 0046-2403
ERA; bimestrale di lettere ed arti. 1971; N.S. 1976. bi-m. L.2500. Via A. Volta 27, 56025 Pontedera (Pisa), Italy. Ed. Salvatore Amodel. bk.rev.; bibl.; illus.

800　　　　　　　US
ERGO!; the bumbershoot literary magazine. 1986. a. $8. Bumbershoot Festival Commission, Box 9750, Seattle, WA 98109-0750. TEL 206-622-5123. FAX 206-622-5154. TELEX 292-992 REEL UR. Ed. Judith Roche. adv.; bk.rev. circ. 1,500. (back issues avail.)

808.8　　　　　　AG
ESCARABAJO DE ORO.* 1972. m. Arg.$3000. c/o Abelardo Castillo, Liliana Heker, Eds., Puyerred 578, Buenos Aires, Argentina. adv.; bk.rev.; bibl.

ESPERANTO. see *LINGUISTICS*

055.1   IT
ESPERIENZE LETTERARIE; rivista trimestrale de critica e di cultura. 1976. q. L.40000. Societa Editrice Napoletana s.r.l., Corso Umberto I 34, 80138 Naples, Italy. Ed. M. Santoro. **Indexed:** M.L.A.

054.1   FR   ISSN 0014-0759
AP20
ESPRIT. 1932. m. 550 F.($92) 212 rue Saint Martin, 75003 Paris, France. TEL 1-48-04-92-90. FAX 48-04-50-53. Ed. Olivier Mongin. adv.; bk.rev.; index. circ. 10,000. **Indexed:** Amer.Hist.& Life (until 1992), Arts & Hum.Cit.Ind., CERDIC, Film Lit.Ind. (1985-), Hist.Abstr. (until 1992), Ind.Bk.Rev.Hum., M.L.A., Pt.de Rep. (1979-).
—Faxon; SWETS.

ETTELA'AT-E SIYASSI EQTESADI; mahnameh siyassi ve eqtesadi. see *POLITICAL SCIENCE*

054.1   FR   ISSN 0014-1941
ETUDES. 1856. m. 450 F. (foreign 550 F.). Assas Editions, 14 rue d'Assas, 75006 Paris, France. TEL 44-39-48-48. FAX 40-49-01-92. Ed. Jean-Yves Calvez. adv.; bk.rev.; abstr.; bibl.; index, cum.index: 1961-1978, 1979-1990. circ. 15,000. **Indexed:** Amer.Hist.& Life, Cath.Ind., CERDIC, Hist.Abstr., Int.Lab.Doc., M.L.A., New Test.Abstr., Phil.Ind., Pt.de Rep. (1979-).
—BLDSC (3816.555000); SWETS.

808.87   GW   ISSN 0423-5975
EULENSPIEGEL. 1946. m. Eulenspiegel GmbH, Franz-Mehring-Platz 1, 10243 Berlin, Germany. TEL 030-58314103. FAX 030-58312203. Eds. Hartmut Berlin, Juergen Nowak. adv. contact: Peter Keller. circ. 138,000. **Document type:** consumer publication.
Formerly (until 1954): Frischer Wind.

050 070.43   FR   ISSN 0180-7897
EUROP. (Supplement avail.) (Text in English, French) 1978. q. 200 F. (foreign 240 F.)(typically set in Jan.). La Fondation Journalistes en Europe, 33 rue du Louvre, 75002 Paris, France. TEL 44-82-20-00. FAX 45-08-42-32. TELEX 240 586. Ed. Jacques Stoufflet. adv.; charts; illus.; stat. circ. 2,300.
Description: Provides an insight into the Europe of tomorrow, undistorted by national preoccupations.

940   FR   ISSN 0014-2751
AP20
EUROPE; revue litteraire mensuel. 1923. m. 450 F. (foreign 550 F.). Scandeditions Europe, 146 rue du Fbg. Poissonniere, 75010 Paris, France. TEL 1-42-81-91-03. FAX 42-82-97-28. Ed. Pierre Gamarra. adv.; bk.rev.; film rev.; music rev.; bibl.; illus.; index. circ. 16,000. (back issues avail.)
Indexed: Curr.Cont., World Text.Abstr.
—BLDSC (3829.455000); Faxon; SWETS.

054.1 320   BE
EUROPE-MAGAZINE. (Text in French) 1944. w. 2400 Fr. Compagnie Internationale d'Editions et de Promotion, Rue Dekens 5, B-1040 Brussels, Belgium. Ed. Maurice Brebart. adv.; bk.rev.; illus. circ. 30,000.
Former titles: Nouvel Europe-Magazine; Europe-Magazine.

800 053   GW   ISSN 0930-8873
DER EVANGELISCHE BUCHBERATER. 1947. q. DM.25. Deutscher Verband Evangelischer Buechereien e.V., Buergerstr. 2, 37073 Goettingen, Germany. TEL 0551-75200. FAX 0551-704415. Ed.Bd. bk.rev.; index. circ. 3,400. (back issues avail.)
Document type: bulletin.

052   CH
EVENSONGS/YEH KO. (Text in Chinese or English) irreg., no.25, 1981. (Evensongs Association) Tamkang University, English Department Evening School, Tamsui, Taipei Hsien, Taiwan 25137, Republic of China. Ed. Chang-Fang Chen. adv.; bk.rev.; illus. circ. 3,000.

052   UK
EVENT SOUTH WEST. 1986. m. £6. Printwest Ltd., 1 Parliament St., Exeter, England. Ed. Rupert Loydell.
Description: Features event listings, art reviews, sports and interviews.

052   UK
EXETER FLYING POST; the campaigning community newspaper. 1976. m. £5. Printwest Ltd., 1 Parliament St., 3rd Fl., Exeter, England. Ed. Patrick Cunningham. adv.; bk.rev.; film rev.; play rev. circ. 1,500. (looseleaf format; back issues avail.)

053   GW   ISSN 0721-6742
EXIL;* Forschung Erkenntnisse Ergebnisse 1933-1945. 1981. 2/yr. DM.39($21) Rheinstr. 20, 60325 Frankfurt a/M., Germany. Ed. Edita Koch. adv.; bk.rev.; index. circ. 600. (back issues avail.)

EXILE. see *LITERATURE*

EXIT 13 MAGAZINE. see *LITERATURE*

057.87   XO   ISSN 0323-2875
EXPRES. 1969. w. Pravda, Gundulicova 12, 882 05 Bratislava, Slovakia. TEL 7-334209. Ed. Karol Hulman. circ. 80,000.

054.1   FR   ISSN 0014-5270
AP20
EXPRESS. 1953. w. $94. Groupe Express S.A., 61 av. Hoche, 75411 Paris Cedex 08, France. TEL 1-40-54-30-00. FAX 44-54-99-72. TELEX 280 805. Ed. Yann de l'Ecotais. adv. circ. 756,600. **Indexed:** CERDIC, Pt.de Rep. (1979-).
—SWETS.

800   US   ISSN 1068-8358
EXPRESSIONS (ST. PAUL). s-a. $10 to individuals in the U.S.; Canada $15; institutions $15. Sefra Kobrin Pitzele, Ed. & Pub., Box 16294, Saint Paul, MN 55116-0294. TEL 612-451-1208. FAX 612-552-1209. adv. contact: Maureen Tracy. bk.rev. circ. 500.
Description: Provides a forum for art, poetry, and fiction by people with either an ongoing medical problem, or a phyical disability. Submission need not be about medical problems.

051   US   ISSN 0740-7815
EXQUISITE CORPSE; a journal of books & ideas. 1981. 6/yr. $20. Illinois State University, Publications Unit, Normal, IL 61790-4241. (Ed. addr.: Box 25051, Baton Rouge, LA 70894. TEL 504-388-2823) Ed. Andrei Codrescu. bk.rev.; film rev.; illus. circ. 3,500. (back issues avail.) **Document type:** academic/scholarly publication.
Description: Iconclastic cultural, political and philosophical commentary on life and the arts, with poetry, fiction and bureau reports from around the world.

FACTSHEET FIVE; the definitive guide to the zine revolution. see *PUBLISHING AND BOOK TRADE*

FAITH AND FORM. see *ARCHITECTURE*

FAITH TODAY; Canada's evangelical news-feature magazine. see *RELIGIONS AND THEOLOGY — Protestant*

053   GW   ISSN 0176-9146
FAMILIENPOLITISCHE INFORMATIONEN. 1962. bi-m. DM.10. Evangelische Aktionsgemeinschaft fuer Familienfragen, Meckenheimer Allee 162, 53115 Bonn, Germany. TEL 0228-634791. FAX 0228-651454. Ed. Gabriele Conen. bk.rev.; index. circ. 3,200. (back issues avail.) **Document type:** newsletter.

808.8 052   UK
FANATIC; a paper of passion. 1977. irreg. price varies. Open Head Press, 2 Blenheim Cresc., London W11 1NN, England. (back issues avail.)

059.91   UK
Y FANER. (Text in Welsh) 1847. w. $40. Gwasg Y Sir, Bala, Gwynedd, Wales. Ed. Hafina Clwyd. adv.; bk.rev.; illus.; play rev.; stat. circ. 6,290.
Formerly: Baner Ac Amserau Cymru (ISSN 0005-4976)

800   US
FASCIST. 1991. irreg? $1 per no. 480 Otis St., St. Paul, MN 55104. bk.rev.
Description: Exposes fascism, propaganda, and existentialism in the form of cartoons, satire, letters, and collages.

FATHERS, BROTHERS, SONS. see *MEN'S STUDIES*

800   NE   ISSN 0167-9392
FAUX TITRE. (Text in English and French) 1980. irreg. vol.77, 1993. price varies. Editions Rodopi B.V., Keizergracht 302-304, 1016 EX Amsterdam, Netherlands. TEL 31-20-6227507. FAX 31-20-6380948. (In N. America: 233 Peachtree St. N.E., Ste. 404, Atlanta GA 30303-1504. TEL 800-225-3998. FAX 404-522-7116) Ed. Keith Busby. circ. 500. **Indexed:** M.L.A. **Document type:** monographic series.
Formerly: Degre Second.
Refereed Serial

051   US
FEED. 1993. q. $16 to individuals; institutions $22. Mark Spot Press, Box 1567, Madison Sq. Sta., New York, NY 10159. Ed. P.J. Mark. illus.

322.4   CH
FEN TOU/STRUGGLE. (Text in Chinese) no.43; 1975. m. Cultural Bldg., 5th Fl., Hsin-yi Rd. Sec. 1, Taipei, Taiwan, Republic of China.

808.87   US
FENGCI YU YOUMO/SATIRE & HUMOR. (Text in Chinese) s-m. $48.50. China Books & Periodicals, Inc., 2929 24th St., San Francisco, CA 94110. TEL 415-282-2994. FAX 415-282-0994. **Document type:** newspaper.

808   IT
FESTA.* 1978. m. L.18000 for 10 nos. Citta Armoniosa, Via Spallanzani 3, 42100 Reggio Emilia, Italy. Ed. Giovanni Riva. illus.

051   US   ISSN 8750-3530
FESTIVAL QUARTERLY.* 1974. 4/yr. $9.90. Main St., Box 419, Intercourse, PA 17534-0419. TEL 717-768-7171. adv. circ. 4,000.

056.1   UY
FICCIONES; revista de cultura. 1977. bi-m. Almiron 5532, Montevideo, Uruguay. Ed. Elena Taboada.

051   US   ISSN 0015-0800
FIFTH ESTATE. 1965. q. $6 to individuals (foreign $8); libraries $10; corporate or government $50. Fifth Estate Newspaper, 4632 Second Ave., Detroit, MI 48201. TEL 313-831-6800. adv.; bk.rev.; film rev.; play rev.; circ. 10,000 (controlled). (tabloid format; also avail. in microform from UMI; reprint service avail. from UMI; back issues avail.) **Indexed:** Alt.Press Ind. **Document type:** newspaper.
—UMI.
Description: Anti-capitalist, pro-anarchist, radical environmental, anti-civilization.

059.92   GW   ISSN 0015-0932
FIKRUN WA FANN. (Text in Arabic) 1963. s-a. free. Inter Nationes e.V., Kennedyallee 91-103, 53175 Bonn, Germany. TEL 0228-880-0. FAX 0228-880457. TELEX 17228308. Ed. Rosemarie Hoell. bk.rev.; illus. circ. 6,000. **Document type:** consumer publication.

808.87   US
FILLMORE BUNGLE. 1975. irreg. $5. Society for the Preservation & Enhancement of the Recognition of Millard Fillmore, Last of the Whigs, 2233 Gabriel Ln., West Palm Beach, FL 33406-5242. TEL 719-684-2102. Ed. Phil Arkow. circ. 300. (back issues avail.) **Document type:** newsletter.
Description: Presents an irreverent look at mediocrity in American life as epitomized by Millard Fillmore, the thirteenth president of the United States.

FINE MADNESS. see *LITERATURE — Poetry*

054.1   FR   ISSN 0015-3486
FLAMMES VIVES. 1948. q. 120 F.($3.60) Editions Flammes Vives, 22 rue du Docteur-Benasson, 95410 Groslay, France. Ed. Jean Aubert. bk.rev.; bibl.; illus. circ. 1,200.

808.8   US   ISSN 0742-2466
FLORIDA REVIEW. 1972. s-a. $7. Department of English, University of Central Florida, Orlando, FL 32816. TEL 407-823-2212. Ed. Russell Kesier. circ. 750.
Description: Contains short stories, poetry and essays.

LITERARY AND POLITICAL REVIEWS

301 808.8   SL
FOCUS. vol.3, 1976. q. Jamawu Publications, P.O. Box 862, Freetown, Sierra Leone. Ed. Fred Awata-Coker. adv.; illus. circ. 5,000.
Description: International socio-economic publication.

FOI ET VIE. see *RELIGIONS AND THEOLOGY*

058.81   DK   ISSN 0015-5845
FOLKEVIRKE; social, kulturel og polistisk oplysning. 1945. q. DKK 90. Folkevirke, Solsortvej 1, 2000 Frederiksberg, Denmark. TEL 45-38-34-83-01. FAX 45-31-19-18-75. Ed. Annemarie Balle. adv. contact: Lise Shjoeth. bk.rev.; illus.; stat.; circ. 2,500 (controlled).
Description: Each issue is devoted to a special theme such as: cultural, social or political.

808.8   US   ISSN 0743-2259
FOOTWORK: THE PATERSON LITERARY REVIEW. 1979. s-a. $10. Passaic County Community College, Poetry Center, College Blvd., Paterson, NJ 07509. TEL 201-684-6555. Ed. Maria Gillan. adv.; bk.rev. circ. 1,000.
Formerly: Footwork Magazine.

051   US   ISSN 0893-5599
FORCED EXPOSURE. 1982. 4/yr. $14. Forced Exposure, Inc., Box 9102, Waltham, MA 02254. TEL 617-562-0507. FAX 617-562-0533. Ed. James Johnson. adv. bk.rev. circ. 15,000. (back issues avail.)

LA FORGE. see *POLITICAL SCIENCE*

052   UK   ISSN 0141-7762
FORTNIGHT. 1970. m. £23 (Europe £26.50; Far East £39; elsewhere £37.50). Fortnight Publications Ltd., 7 Lower Crescent, Belfast BT1 1NR, N. Ireland. TEL 0232-232353. FAX 0232-232650. Ed. Robin Wilson. adv. contact: Julie Tickle. bk.rev.; cum.index vols.1-300. circ. 3,000.
Description: An independent review of politics and the arts.

057.85   PL   ISSN 0015-8402
AS539.5
FORUM. 1965. w. $37. Spoldzielnia Pracy "Tygodnik Forum", Ul. Sniadeckich 10, 00-656 Warsaw, Poland. TEL 48-22-628-9503. FAX 48-22-256140. (Dist. by: Ars Polona-Ruch, Krakowskie Przedmiescie 7, Warsaw, Poland) (Co-publisher: Dom Wydawniczy Herold Press) Ed. Bohdan Herbich. circ. 53,400.
Indexed: Amer.Hist.& Life, Hist.Abstr., Leg.Per.
Description: Contains reprinted articles from foreign periodicals.

FORUM. see *LITERATURE*

301   US
FORUM (LORENTON).* 1976. q. free. Social Concern Committee of Springfield Gardens, Inc., 226-18 Merrick Blvd., Lorenton, NY 11413. TEL 718-978-3700. Ed. E. Cynthia Jenkins. circ. 6,000. **Indexed:** Excerp.Med.

FORUM LIBERAL; liberale Zeitung. see *POLITICAL SCIENCE*

053.1   AU
FORVM; International Zeitschrift fuer kulturelle Freiheit. 1954. 6/yr. DM.30. Gerhard Oberschlick Ed. & Pub., Museumstr. 5, A-1070 Vienna, Austria. FAX 938368. adv.; bk.rev.; film rev.; illus.; play rev.; index; circ. 25,000 (controlled). **Indexed:** Amer.Hist.& Life, CERDIC, Hist.Abstr. **Document type:** consumer publication.
Former titles (until 1980): Neues Forvm (ISSN 0028-3622); (until 1965): Forvm.

378.1   PH   ISSN 0015-8984
FOUNDATION TIME. (Text in English, Filipino) vol.20, 1968. bi-m. P.79.80. Foundation University, Dumaguete City 6200, Philippines. TEL 37-44. Ed. Flixberto F. Abrenica. charts. circ. 2,000.

378.1   US   ISSN 0015-9107
AP2
FOUR QUARTERS. 1951; N.S. 1987. 2/yr. $13 for 2 yrs. La Salle University, 1900 W. Olney Ave., Philadelphia, PA 19141. TEL 215-951-1145. FAX 215-951-1892. Ed. John J. Keenan. bk.rev.; cum.index vols.1-20. circ. 1,000. (also avail. in microform from UMI; reprint service avail. from UMI) **Indexed:** Amer.Hum.Ind., Arts & Hum.Cit.Ind., Curr.Cont., Ind.Amer.Per.Verse, Ind.Little Mag. —BLDSC (4028.054000); Faxon; UnCover; UMI.
Description: Includes fiction, poetry, and essays for the college-educated reader.

FOURTH ESTATE; Canada's national press journal. see *JOURNALISM*

052 700   FR   ISSN 0738-9299
PN771
FRANK; an international journal of contemporary writing and art. (Text in English) 1983. s-a. 220 F.($35) to individuals; institutions 440 F. ($70) for 4 issues. Fonderie Association, 104 rue Edouard Vaillant, 93100 Montreuil, France. TEL 48-59-66-58. FAX 48-59-66-68. Ed. David Applefield. adv.; bk.rev.; illus. circ. 4,000.
Description: Publishes literary and visual art from contemporary writers and artists around the world, both established and emerging, in a broad range of innovative styles, forms, voices, visions, and cultures. Includes interviews and foreign dossiers.

949.3   BE   ISSN 0251-2408
DE FRANSE NEDERLANDEN/PAYS-BAS FRANCAIS. (Text and summaries in Dutch, French) 1976. a. 1200 BEF (Netherlands fl.70; elsewhere 1250 BEF) (effective 1994). Stichting Ons Erfdeel v.z.w., Murissonstraat 260, B-8931 Rekkem, Belgium. TEL 32-56-411201. FAX 32-56-414707. Ed. Jozef Deleu. abstr.; bibl.; charts; illus.; stat. circ. 2,500. **Indexed:** Bibl.Ling.
Description: Covers issues affecting the Francophone community in Belgium and its relations with the Dutch speaking community and with the Netherlands.

FREE RADICAL. see *POLITICAL SCIENCE*

800 410   US   ISSN 0098-9355
PQ1
FRENCH FORUM. (Text in English, French) 1976. 3/yr. $20 to individuals; institutions $45 (effective 1994). French Forum Publishers Inc., Box 130, Nicholasville, KY 40340. TEL 606-885-1446. Eds. Raymond C. La Charite, Virginia A. La Charite. adv.; bk.rev.; bibl. circ. 500. **Indexed:** Arts & Hum.Cit.Ind., Curr.Cont., Ind.Bk.Rev.Hum., M.L.A. **Document type:** academic/scholarly publication. —BLDSC (4034.260000); Faxon; UnCover.
Description: Contains literary criticism.

052   UK   ISSN 0046-5062
FRENDZ.* bi-w. £3.50($14.40) Echidna Epics Co. Ltd., 301 Portobello Rd., London W10 5TR, England. adv.; bk.rev.; film rev.; play rev.; charts; illus. circ. 15,000. (tabloid format)

052   UK
FRIENDSHIP BOOK OF FRANCIS GAY. 1939. a. £2.25. D.C. Thomson and Co. Ltd., 185 Fleet St., London EC4A 2HS, England. (Subscr. to: Subscribers Dept., 9-12 Bank St., Dundee DD1 9HU, Scotland) Ed. Maurice Fleming.

800   UK
THE FROGMORE PAPERS. 1983. bi-a. $20. Frogmore Press, 42 Morehall Ave., Folkstone, Kent CT19 4EF, England. Eds. Jeremy Page. bk.rev. circ. 200. **Document type:** consumer publication.
Description: Reviews poetry and publishes novel extracts, poetry, and short stories

FRONTLINE. see *ETHNIC INTERESTS*

808.8   US
FROZEN WAFFLES.* 1976. irreg. $4.50 per no. Frozen Waffles Press & Tapes, c/o Dave Wade, 329 W. First St., Apt. 5, Bloomington, IN 47401. Eds. Bro Dimitrios, David Wade. circ. 300.

700   IT
FUCK. q. L.10000. Vittorio Baccelli, Ed. & Pub., C.P. 132, 55100 Lucca, Italy. circ. 1,000. (tabloid format)

055.1   IT   ISSN 0016-2876
FUOCO; rassegna di cultura e d'arte. 1953. bi-m. L.20000. (Studium Christi) Edizioni Il Fuoco, Via Giacinto Carini 28, 00152 Rome, Italy. TEL 06-5810969. Ed. Pasquale Magni. bk.rev.; bibl.; illus.; index. circ. 2,000. **Document type:** monographic series.

053.1   AU   ISSN 0016-299X
DIE FURCHE; freie kulturpolitische Wochenschrift. 1945. w. S.760. Die Furche Zeitschriften-Betriebsgesellschaft mbH und Co. KG, Singerstr. 7-VI, A-1010 Vienna, Austria. Ed. Hannes Schopf. adv.; bk.rev.; film rev.; music rev.; play rev.; rec.rev.; charts; illus.; index. circ. 20,000. **Indexed:** Amer.Hist.& Life, Hist.Abstr.

056.1   MX   ISSN 0016-3716
GACETA. 1954. m. Mex.$40000($60) Fondo de Cultura Economica, Av. de la Universidad 975, 03100 Mexico, D.F., Mexico. Ed. Adolfo Castanon Moran. adv.; bk.rev.; abstr.; bibl.; charts; illus.

GAG RECAP. see *ART*

800   UK   ISSN 0016-3929
AP75
GAIRM. (Text in Gaelic) 1952. q. £8 (foreign £10) (typically set in Dec.). Gairm Publications, 29 Waterloo St., Glasgow G2, Scotland. FAX 041-221-1971. Ed. Derick S. Thomson. adv.: Page £150. bk.rev.; illus.; index. circ. 2,000.
Description: Covers Gaelic literary topics, plus fiction, poetry travel, history and current affairs.

051   VE
GALAXIA 71. (Summaries in Portuguese and Spanish) 1971. 3/yr. (with suppl.). $10. Grupo Escritores de Venezuela, Apdo. 4023, Carmelitas 101, Caracas, Venezuela. Ed. Modesto Vargas Lopez. bk.rev.; illus.; circ. 5,000 (controlled). (back issues avail.)

052 800   CN   ISSN 0713-3545
AP5
GAMUT. 1982. q. $10. Artscorp, 238 Davenport Rd., Ste. 171, Toronto, Ont. M5R 1J6, Canada. Eds. Haygo Demir, Alfredo Romano. adv.; bk.rev.; illus. circ. 3,000.

891   IR
GARDOON. (Text in Persian) 1990-1991; resumed 1993. m. IRI.8400 (Europe IRI.14000; N. America IRI.16000) (effective 1993). Damavand Ave No. 4, Kamal Esmail St., P.O. Box 16756-1875, Tehran, Iran. TEL 98-21-753004. Ed. Abbass Maroufi. bk.rev. circ. 20,000.
Description: Publishes critical essays, fiction and poetry by modern Iranian writers, especially younger writers. Also includes translations of world literature.

320 700   UY
GARIBALDI. (Text mainly in Spanish; occasionally in French, Italian, Portuguese) 1986. a. Asociacion Cultural Garibaldina de Montevideo, Florencio Sanchez, 2724, Montevideo, Uruguay. Ed. Carlos Novello. adv.; bibl.; illus.

058   NO
GATEAVISA. (Text in Danish, Norwegian, Swedish) 1970. bi-m. NOK 190($30) (Arbeidskollektivet) Futurum Forlag A-S, Hjelmsgate 3, 0355 Oslo 3, Norway. TEL 02-691284. Ed. A. Engh. adv.; bk.rev.; illus. circ. 8,000. **Document type:** newspaper.
Former titles (until 1988): Glasnost; Gateavisa.
Description: Anarchistic look at social and political subjects.

808.838   US   ISSN 1047-4463
GAUNTLET; exploring the limits of free expression. 1990. s-a. $22 (effective 1994). Gauntlet, Inc., 309 Powell Rd., Springfield, PA 19064. TEL 215-328-5476. FAX 215-328-9949. Ed. Barry Hoffman. adv. contact: Dara Lise. bk.rev.; film rev.; illus. circ. 10,000. **Document type:** academic/scholarly publication.
Description: Covers key issues in censorship in literature, journalism, art and movies, exploring controversial and unreported news, reprinting censored writing and art, with critical essays, author and artist interviews, and a summary of pro- and anti-censorship activities, focusing on the US and Canada.

LITERARY AND POLITICAL REVIEWS

808.838   AT   ISSN 0310-9968
GEGENSCHEIN. 1971. irreg. no.62, 1991. Aus.$1 for 2 nos.; US$1 for 1 no. c/o Eric B. Lindsay, Ed., 6 Hillcrest Ave., Faulconbridge, N.S.W. 2776, Australia. bk.rev. circ. 245.

051   AU
DER GEISTIG SCHAFFENDE. 1949. q. membership. Verband der Geistig Schaffenden Oesterreichs, Wiedener Hauptstr. 23-25, A-1040 Vienna, Austria. Ed. Karl Lengheimer. adv. **Document type:** bulletin.

658 808   US   ISSN 8756-2898
GELOSOPHIST. 1985. irreg. (3-6/yr.). Lone Star Publications of Humor, Box 29000, Ste. 103, San Antonio, TX 78229. Ed. Lauren I. Barnett. bk.rev.; film rev.; play rev.; abstr.; illus.; stat. (looseleaf format; back issues avail.)

053   GW
GEMEINDE-NACHRICHTEN. 1952. w. DM.18. (Gemeinde Sandhausen) Mera-Druck GmbH & Co., Wingertstr. 7, 6902 Sandhausen, Germany. Ed.Bd. adv.; bk.rev.; bibl.; play rev.; stat. circ. 3,500. (looseleaf format) **Document type:** newsletter.

800   US   ISSN 1048-0870
AP2
GENERALIST PAPERS. 1990. 6/yr. $12 (Canada and Mexico $15; elsewhere $20). (Generalist Association, Inc.) Harry Smith, Ed. & Pub., 69 Joralemon St., Brooklyn, NY 11201. bk.rev. circ. 2,200.

052   CN   ISSN 0533-7291
GENERATION (WINDSOR); creative work by the students of the University of Windsor. 1963. s-a. University of Windsor, Windsor, Ont. N9B 3P4, Canada. TEL 519-253-4232. illus.
  Description: Contains poetry, short stories and line drawings.

052 011   US
GEORGE ELIOT - GEORGE HENRY LEWES STUDIES. 1982. s-a. £5($10) Dr. W. Baker, Ed. & Pub., Department of English, Northern Illinois University, Dekalb, IL 60115. TEL 815-753-1857. FAX 815-753-2003. adv.; bk.rev.; index. circ. 400. (back issues avail.) **Document type:** academic/scholarly publication, bibliography.
  Formerly (until 1992): George Eliot - George Henry Lewes Newsletter (ISSN 0953-0754)

053   NE   ISSN 0927-1910
GERMAN MONITOR. 1979. s-a. price varies. Editions Rodopi B.V., Keizersgracht 302-304, 1016 EX Amsterdam, Netherlands. TEL 31-20-6227507. FAX 31-20-6380948. (In N. America: 233 Peachtree St. N.E., Ste. 404, Atlanta GA 30303-1504. TEL 800-225-3998. FAX 404-522-7116) Ed. Ian Wallace. adv.; bk.rev. circ. 500. (back issues avail.) **Document type:** academic/scholarly publication.
—UnCover.
  Formerly (until 1991): G D R Monitor (ISSN 0144-6355)

GESHER. see *RELIGIONS AND THEOLOGY — Judaic*

053.931   NE   ISSN 0016-9730
AP15
GIDS. 1837. m. fl.105 to individuals; students fl.84.50. (Stichting de Gids) Meulenhoff Nederland B.V., Postbus 100, 1000 AC Amsterdam, Netherlands. TEL 31-20-5533500. FAX 31-20-6258511. Ed. Theodor Duquesnoy. adv.; bk.rev.; index. circ. 2,500. **Indexed:** Amer.Hist.& Life, Hist.Abstr., Key to Econ.Sci., M.L.A.
—SWETS.

055.1   IT   ISSN 0017-0526
GIOVANE CRITICA. no.19, 1968. irreg. (5-6/yr.) Via della Trinita dei Pellegrini 19, 00186 Rome, Italy. Ed. Giampiero Mughini. bk.rev.; play rev.

057.8   CI   ISSN 0017-0771
GLAS ISTRE. 1943. w. 20 din. (Socijalisticki Savez Radnog Naroda Istre, Hrvatskog primorja i Gorskog kotara) Glas Istre, Obala Marsala Tita 10, Pula, Croatia. Ed. Santo Kranjac.

057.8   CI   ISSN 0017-0801
GLAS PODRAVINE. 1946. q. 160 din. Socijalisticki Savez Radnog Naroda Opcine Koprivnica, Oruzanska 25, Koprivnica, Croatia. Ed. Vladimir Kuzel.

949.7   BN   ISSN 0017-0828
GLAS TREBINJA; list Socijalistickog saveza radnog naroda opstine Trebinje. 1952. m. 15 din. Socijalisticki Savez Radnog Naroda Opstine Trebinje, Mija Zupcevica 9, Trebinje, Bosnia Hercegovina. Ed. Miso Tica.

800   US   ISSN 1068-0586
▼**GLOBAL CITY REVIEW.** 1993. s-a. $12 (effective 1993). Simon h. Rifkind Center for the Humanities, City College of NY, 138th & Convent, New York, NY 10031. TEL 212-979-5951. Ed. Linsey Abrams. bk.rev. circ. 1,780. **Document type:** consumer publication.
  Description: Contains poetry, fiction, essays and interviews on gender issues, gay and lesbian issues, race, war & peace, environment, language and postmodernism.

055   IT   ISSN 0394-395X
IL GOLFO; periodico di informazione democratica. m? Viale 2 Giugno No. 40, 58023 Follonica, Italy. Ed. Rino Magagnini. illus. circ. 1,000.

808.87   US
GOOFUS OFFICE GAZETTE. 1983. irreg. $15. Goofus Office, 8 Franklin Ave., Apt. 2, Box 259, Pearl River, NY 10965. TEL 914-620-1416. Ed. Samuel T. Godfrey. circ. 250. (back issues avail.)

056   MX
GRAFFITI; literatura, arte, ciencia y politica. 1989. bi-m. Mex.$4000 per no. Revolucion 243-2, Jalapa, Veracruz, Mexico. Ed. Jose Homero.

808.8   CN
GRAMMATEION; the St. Michael's Journal of the Arts. 1975. a. Can.$5. St. Michael's College, Student Union, Box 1, 81 St. Mary St., Toronto, ON M5S 1J4, Canada. TEL 416-926-7268. adv. circ. 1,500.
  Description: Contains prose, poetry, interviews, short drama and art work.

055.1   IT
IL GRANDEVETRO. 1977. bi-m. L.50000. Circolo del Pestival, Via F. Ferrer 1, 56029 Santa Croce sull'Arno (Pisa), Italy. TEL 0571-30988.

054.1   FR   ISSN 0182-0346
GRANDS REPORTAGES. 1978. 11/yr. 230 F. (foreign 310F.). Editions Mondiales, 2 rue des Italiens, 75440 Paris Cedex 09, France. TEL 48-24-46-21. FAX 42-47-14-13. TELEX 643 932. Ed. Jean Weiss. adv. circ. 82,000. **Indexed:** Pt.de Rep. (1989-).

052   UK   ISSN 0017-3231
PN2
GRANTA. 1979. q. £21.95($29.95) Granta Publications Ltd., 2-3 Hanover Yard, Noel Road, Islington, London N1 8BE, England. TEL 071-704-9776. FAX 071-704-0474. (Dist. addr. in U.S.: Granta, Ste. 1316, 250 W. 57th St. New York, NY 10107. TEL 212-246-1313) Ed. Bill Buford. adv.; bk.rev.; charts; illus. circ. 96,000. (also avail. in microform from UMI) **Document type:** academic/scholarly publication.
—BLDSC (4210.900000); Faxon; UnCover; SWETS; UMI.
  Description: Features new fiction, travel and reportage by international writers.

059   UK
GREEK INSTITUTE REVIEW. (Text in English and Greek) 1972. q. £25($50) Greek Institute, 34 Bush Hill Rd., London N21 2DS, England. Ed. Kypros Tofallis. adv.; bk.rev.; bibl.; tr.lit. circ. 1,000.
  Formerly: Greek Review (ISSN 0307-4536)

808.8 614.7   US
GREEN SYNTHESIS (SAN PEDRO); a newsletter and journal for social ecology, deepecology, bioregionalism, eco feminism, and the green movement. 1975. 4/yr. $7.50 to individuals; institutions $13.50 for 10 nos. League for Ecological Democracy, Box 1858, San Pedro, CA 90733. TEL 213-833-2633. Ed.Bd. bk.rev. circ. 8,000. (back issues avail.)
  Formerly: Synthesis (San Pedro).

053   GW
GRENZFRIEDENSHEFTE. 1953. q. DM.24. Grenzfriedensbund e.V., Hafendamm 15, 24937 Flensburg, Germany. TEL 0461-26708. bk.rev. (back issues avail.) **Document type:** bulletin.

053.931   NE   ISSN 0017-4483
DE GROENE AMSTERDAMMER; onafhankelijk weekblad. 1877. w. fl.216.95. N.V. Weekblad de Groene Amsterdammer, Westeinde 16, Box 353, 1000 AJ Amsterdam, Netherlands. adv.; bk.rev. circ. 17,000. **Indexed:** Key to Econ.Sci.

058.7   SW   ISSN 0017-4548
GRONKOPINGS VECKOBLAD.* 1902. m. SEK 145 (effective 1991). Groenkoepings Vedkoblad, P.O. Box 2080, S-103 12 Stockholm, Sweden. Ed. Gunnar Ljusterdal. adv.; illus. circ. 17,000. (tabloid format)

052   GU
GUAM U S O HANDBOOK. a. free. (Guam U S O Council) Glimpses of Guam, Inc., P.O. Box 3191, Agana, Guam 96921. Ed. Dolores Brooks. circ. 15,000.

054   FR   ISSN 1149-0209
GULLIVER. 1990. q. E B A, 106 bd. Diderot, 75012 Paris, France. TEL 43-46-76-34. Dir. Ariane Monod-Sarraut.

GYPSY; literary magazine. see *LITERATURE*

296   US   ISSN 0017-6524
DS101
HADOAR. 1921. bi-w. $36 (effective Sep. 1990). (Histadruth Ivrith of America) Hadoar Association, Inc., 47 W. 34th St., Rm. 609, New York, NY 10001-3012. TEL 212-629-9443. FAX 212-629-9472. Ed. Shlomo Shamir. adv. contact: Harold Galanter. bk.rev.; charts; illus.; index. circ. 3,500. (also avail. in microfilm from AJP) **Document type:** newspaper.

058   SW   ISSN 0345-4789
HAEFTEN FOER KRITISKA STUDIER. Abbreviated title: H f K S. 1968. bi-m. SEK 165 (effective 1990). Foereningen Haeften foer Kritiska Studier, Tomtebogatan 34, 113 38 Stockholm, Sweden. Ed. Goeran Fredriksson. adv.; bk.rev.; bibl. circ. 5,000.

HAIKU ZASSHI ZO. see *LITERATURE — Poetry*

059.91   US   ISSN 0017-677X
HAIRENIK. (Text in Armenian) 1899. w. $60. Hairenik Association, Inc., 80 Bieglow Ave., Watertown, MA 02172. TEL 617-926-3974. Ed. Vatche Proudian. adv.; bk.rev.; illus.

059   MG
HAITENY, HAISORATA, HAIRAHA. 1978. irreg. Academie Malgache, Section 1, B.P. 6217, Tsimbazaza, Antananarivo, Malagasy Republic. circ. 300.

053   GW
HANNOVER VORSCHAU; Veranstaltungen. 1951. m. DM.24. Verkehrsverein Hannover E.V., Friedrichswall 5, 30159 Hannover, Germany. circ. 10,000.
  Formerly: Vorschau Hannover.

HARMONY (SAN FRANCISCO); voices for a just future. see *POLITICAL SCIENCE — Civil Rights*

051   US   ISSN 0017-789X
AP2
HARPER'S MAGAZINE. 1850. m. $18 (effective 1993). Harpers Magazine Foundation, 666 Broadway, New York, NY 10012-2317. TEL 212-614-6500. FAX 212-228-5889. (Subscr. to: Box 7511, Red Oak, IA 51591-0511. TEL 800-444-4653) Ed. Lewis H. Lapham; Pub. John R. MacArthur. adv. contact: Ann Clifford. bk.rev.; index; circ. 205,000 (paid). (also avail. in microfilm from UMI,PMC; back issues avail.; reprint service avail. from UMI) **Indexed:** Acad.Ind., Amer.Bibl.Slavic & E.Eur.Stud., Biog.Ind., Bk.Rev.Ind. (1965-), Child Bk.Rev.Ind. (1965-), Curr.Lit.Fam.Plan., Film Lit.Ind. (1973-), Fut.Surv., Ind.Bk.Rev.Hum., Mag.Ind., Media Rev.Dig., Mid.East Abstr.& Ind., Peace Res.Abstr., R.G., TOM. **Document type:** consumer publication.
—BLDSC (4264.884000); Faxon; UnCover; SWETS; UMI. **CCC.**
  Description: Publishes original fiction, essays, cultural and political commentary, selections of notable statistics, and brief reprints of unusual, controversial or illuminating writings to serve as readings in contemporary society.

LITERARY AND POLITICAL REVIEWS

808.8   US   ISSN 0896-114X
HARRIMAN INSTITUTE FORUM. 1988. m. $35 (foreign $45)(effective Jan. 1994). Columbia University, Harriman Institute, 420 W. 118th St., New York, NY 10027. TEL 212-854-6218. FAX 212-666-3481. Ed. Ronald Meyer. circ. 1,000. (back issues avail.)
—BLDSC (4264.975200); Faxon.

810   US   ISSN 0095-2427
LH1.H3
HARVARD MAGAZINE. 1898. bi-m. $30. Harvard Magazine, Inc., 7 Ware St., Cambridge, MA 02138. TEL 617-495-5746. FAX 617-495-0324. Ed. John T. Bethell; Pub. Laura Freid. adv. contact: Cathryn A. Geppert. bk.rev. circ. 200,000. **Indexed:** Access (1981-), CAD CAM Abstr. (until 1992), Environ.Abstr., Robomat. (until 1992). **Document type:** bulletin.
—BLDSC (4268.200000); CIS; Faxon; UnCover.
Formerly (until 1973): Harvard Bulletin.

053.931   NE   ISSN 0017-8519
HAVENLOODS. 1951. s-w. free. Prins Hendrikkade 14, Rotterdam-3001, Netherlands. adv.; bk.rev.; play rev.; abstr. circ. 266,100.

052   UK
HAWKFRENDZ. 1972. s-a. $3. Zephyr Magazines & Records, P.O. Box 6, Wallasey, Merseyside L45 4SJ, England. Ed. Trevor Hughes. adv.; bk.rev.; rec.rev.; illus. circ. 500.
Former titles: Zephyr; Hawkfriends.

800 700   US   ISSN 0887-5170
HAYDEN'S FERRY REVIEW. 1986. s-a. $10. Arizona State University, Box 871502, Tempe, AZ 85287-1502. TEL 602-965-1243. FAX 602-965-8484. Ed. Salima Keegan. adv. circ. 1,000. (back issues avail.)

327   AI
HAYRENIKY DZAYN. 1965. w. 2.65 Rub. Committee for Cultural Relations with Armenians Abroad, Alaverdian St. 37, Erevan, Armenia. (Subscr. addr.: Soyzpechat', Casian St. 6, Erevan, Armenia) Ed. Levon Zakarian. adv.; bk.rev.; charts; film rev.; illus.; play rev.; stat. circ. 27,000.
Formerly: Areiniki Dzain (ISSN 0017-8705)

051 808.838   US   ISSN 1063-1186
HEARTLAND CRITIQUES. 1980. m. $50. 759 Allen Rd., Independence, MO 64050. TEL 816-254-1868. Ed. Julie Meisinger. bk.rev. circ. 250. (back issues avail.)
Document type: newsletter.
Formerly: Barbra Critiques.
Description: Reviews of 150 romance novels for use by stores, libraries and individuals in the early selection of reading material.

900 700   DR
HELIOS.* 1973. q. Fondo Cultural de la Cuna de America, Jose Reyes 50, Santo Domingo, Dominican Republic. Ed.Bd. adv.; illus. **Indexed:** Arts & Hum.Cit.Ind., Curr.Cont., Fluidex.

HENDERSON COMMUNITY COLLEGE LITERARY MAGAZINE. see *LITERATURE — Poetry*

058   DK   ISSN 0903-9295
HENRY - D R U NYTT; magasin for kultur. 1983. 8/yr. DKK 40. Danmarks Retsforbunds Ungdom, Lyngbyvej 42, 2100 Copenhagen OE, Denmark. TEL 01-204488. Ed. Jette Lehrmann Madsen. illus. circ. 300.
Former titles (until 1987): D R U Nytt; Druiden (ISSN 0109-0119)

808.87   FR
HERISSON. 1936. w. 616 F. Publications Georges Ventillard, 2 a 12 rue de Bellevue, 75019 Paris, France. TEL 42-00-33-05. FAX 42-41-89-40. TELEX PGV 220 409 F. Ed. Philippe Carpentier. illus. circ. 270,000. (tabloid format)

051   US   ISSN 0362-630X
HV5800
HIGH TIMES; the magazine of the counter-culture. 1974. m. $29.95 (foreign $37.95) (effective 1993). Trans-High Corp., 235 Park Ave. S., 5th Fl., New York, NY 10003-1405. TEL 212-387-0500. (Subscr. to: High Times, Box 410, Mt. Morris, IL 61054. TEL 800-827-0228) Ed. Steven Hager. adv. contact: Harry Crossfield Jr. bk.rev.; abstr.; charts; illus.; stat.; tr.lit. circ. 250,000. (back issues avail.) **Document type:** consumer publication.

351 920   US   ISSN 1067-0777
E887.C55
▼**HILLARY CLINTON QUARTERLY.** 1993. q. $15. Maracom, 128C N. State St., Concord, NH 03301. TEL 603-225-8940. Ed. Frank Marafiote. circ. 11,500.
Description: Includes news, commentary, political humor about Hillary Rodham Clinton.

HISPAMERICA; revista de literatura. see *LITERATURE*

HISPANOFILA. see *LITERATURE*

HISPANORAMA. see *LITERATURE*

HISTORIA. see *HISTORY — History Of North And South America*

HISTORICA; rivista trimestrale di cultura. see *HISTORY*

HISTORY TODAY. see *HISTORY*

830   GW
HOFMANNSTHAL JAHRBUCH ZUR EUROPAEISCHEN MODERNE. a. DM.60 for members; non-members DM.98. (Hugo von Hofmannsthal-Gesellschaft) Rombach GmbH Verlagshaus, Loerracherstr. 3, 79115 Freiburg, Germany. TEL 0761-4500-0. FAX 0761-4500212. Ed.Bd. **Document type:** academic/scholarly publication.

808.87   MP
HOH INEED/IRONIC LAUGH. (Text in Mongolian) 1990. m. P.O. 46, Box 971, Ulan Bator, Mongolia. TEL 21425. Ed. J. Chimedtseren.
Description: Features satirical jokes.

837   AU   ISSN 0018-3245
HOHE BRUECKE. 1953. m. S.50. Gluecksstelle Mihalovits, Wipplingerstr. 21, A-1013 Vienna, Austria. Ed. Dr. Heinrich Bohn. adv.; illus.
Description: Contains humorous articles.

949.2   NE   ISSN 0018-3601
HOLLANDS MAANDBLAD. 1959. m. fl.92.50. (Stichting Hollands Maandblad) L.J. Veen Publishers, Herengracht 481, 1017 BT Amsterdam, Netherlands. TEL 31-20-5249800. FAX 31-20-6276851. Ed. J.J. Peereboom. adv.; bk.rev.; play rev.; illus.; index. circ. 2,000.
—SWETS.

378.1   US   ISSN 0018-3644
PS1
HOLLINS CRITIC. 1964. 5/yr. $6 (foreign $7.50). Hollins College, Box 9538, Hollins College, VA 24020. TEL 703-362-6317. FAX 703-362-6642. Ed. John R. Moore. bk.rev.; bibl.; index. circ. 545. (also avail. in microform from UMI; back issues avail.; reprint service avail. from UMI) **Indexed:** A.I.P.P., Abstr.Engl.Stud., Ind.Amer.Per.Verse, LCR, M.L.A. **Document type:** academic/scholarly publication.
—BLDSC (4322.402000); UMI.
Description: Each issue covers a contemporary writer.

808.8 053   GW
HOLZAUGE. 1975. irreg., no.33, 1992. DM.1.50 per no. Schuelerzeitung Holzauge, Remstalgymnasium, 71384 Weinstadt, Germany. TEL 07151-61469. Ed.Bd. adv.; bk.rev. circ. 350.

HONEST ULSTERMAN. see *LITERATURE*

059   FR   ISSN 0769-0088
PB2801
HOR YEZH. (Text in Breton) 1954. irreg. 80 F. for 4 nos. c/o P. Denis, Le Ris, Ploare, 29100 Douarnenez, Brittany, France. **Indexed:** Bibl.Ling., M.L.A.

056.1   PE
HORA DEL HOMBRE. 1943. m. Casilla 2378, Lima 1, Peru. TEL 14-220208. Ed. Jorge Falcon. illus.

808   BE   ISSN 0772-9782
HORIZON; tweemandelijks kultureel tijdschrift. (Text mainly in Flemish, some articles in English) 1985. bi-m. 450 BEF($18) (foreign 600 BEF). Uitgeverij Horizon, Stationstraat 232A, B-1770 Liedekerke, Belgium. TEL 32-53-669465. Ed. Johnny Haelterman. adv.: B&W page 3000 BEF. bk.rev.; film rev.; illus. circ. 200. (back issues avail.)
Description: Publishes fiction, short essays on cultural topics and poetry.

051   XO
HORIZONT. m. $30. (Union of Czechoslovak - Soviet Friendship) Obzor, Ceskoslovenskej Armady 35, 815 85 Bratislava, Slovakia.

051   US
▼**HOT CALALOO.** 1992. 6/yr. $8. Box 429, Riderwood, MD 21139. TEL 410-997-1381. Ed. Michael I. Phillips. adv. circ. 300. **Document type:** newsletter.
Description: Covers current events, culture, sports, poetry, commentary and nostalgia of the Caribbean.

056.1   CL   ISSN 0716-3460
AP63
HOY. 1977. w. $200. Empresa Editora Araucaria Ltda., Monsenor Miller 74, Santiago, Chile. TEL 2236102. FAX 2516191. Dir. Abraham Santibanez. adv.; bk.rev.; illus. circ. 30,000.
Description: Includes articles, opinions and humor on the politics, economy and culture of Chile and the rest of the world.

059.91   SP   ISSN 0018-6902
HRVATSKA REVIJA. (Text mainly in Croatian) 1951. q. $80. Vinko Nikolic, Ed., Apdo. Correos 14030, 08017 Barcelona, Spain. bk.rev.; illus.; music rev.; cum.index: 1951-1988. circ. 1,300.

HUAN QIU/GLOBE. see *POLITICAL SCIENCE — International Relations*

810 700   US   ISSN 0018-702X
AP2
HUDSON REVIEW; a magazine of literature and the arts. 1948. q. $24 (foreign $28). Hudson Review, Inc., 684 Park Ave., New York, NY 10021. TEL 212-650-0020. Eds. Paula Deitz, Frederick Morgan. adv.; bk.rev.; film rev.; music rev.; play rev.; index. circ. 4,500. (also avail. in microform from UMI,MIM; reprint service avail. from UMI) **Indexed:** Abstr.Engl.Stud., Acad.Ind., Amer.Bibl.Slavic & E.Eur.Stud., Amer.Hum.Ind., Arts & Hum.Cit.Ind., Bk.Rev.Ind. (1965-), Can.Rev.Comp.Lit., Child.Bk.Rev.Ind. (1965-), Curr.Cont., Film Lit.Ind. (1973-), Hum.Ind., Ind.Amer.Per.Verse, Ind.Bk.Rev.Hum., Lang.& Lang.Behav.Abstr., M.L.A., Soc.Sci.Ind.
—BLDSC (4335.830000); Faxon; UnCover; SWETS; UMI.

059   DK   ISSN 0106-4959
HUG! 1974. bi-m. DKK 360. Tiderne Skrifter Forlag A-S, Pilestraede 51, 5, DK-1001 Copenhagen K, Denmark. TEL 45-33-32-57-72. FAX 45-33-14-42-05. Ed.Bd. bk.rev.; film rev.; illus. circ. 2,000.

HUMANIST. see *PHILOSOPHY*

055.1   IT   ISSN 0018-7461
HUMANITAS; rivista di cultura. 1946; N.S. 1977. bi-m. L.70000($46) Editrice Morcelliana S.p.A., Via Gabriele Rosa 71, 25100 Brescia, Italy. TEL 030-377522. FAX 030-2400605. Ed. Stefano Minelli. adv.; bk.rev.; film rev.; play rev.; bibl.; illus.; index. circ. 2,500. **Indexed:** CERDIC.

056.9   GW   ISSN 0018-7623
AP1
HUMBOLDT (PORTUGUESE EDITION); revista para o mondo Luso-Brasileiro. 1961. s-a. free. Inter Nationes e.V., Kennedyallee 91-103, 53175 Bonn, Germany. TEL 0228-880-0. FAX 0228-880457. Ed. Margarete Kraft. bk.rev.; illus. circ. 5,300. **Document type:** consumer publication.

053.1 056.1   GW   ISSN 0018-7615
HUMBOLDT (SPANISH EDITION). (Text in Spanish) 1960. 3/yr. free. Inter Nationes e.V., Kennedyallee 91-103, 53175 Bonn, Germany. TEL 0228-880-0. FAX 0228-880457. TELEX 17228308. Ed. Margarete Kraft. bk.rev.; illus. circ. 13,400. **Indexed:** Hisp.Amer.Per.Ind. **Document type:** consumer publication.
Description: Contains Spanish articles about German and Spanish culture. Includes cultural notices of events in Spanish speaking countries.

056   AG
HUMOR. Variant title: Humor Registrado. 1978. w. $180. Ediciones de la Urraca, Venezuela 842, 1095 Buenos Aires, Argentina. TEL 334-5400. FAX 334-1606. Ed. Andres Cascioli. adv. contact: Dante Voccia. bk.rev.; film rev.; play rev. circ. 140,000.
    Description: Contains political satire, comics, and television reviews. Covers ecology, conservation, consumer issues, and sports.

808.87   IO
HUMOR; Majalah Gerrr Nasional. (Text in Indonesian) bi-w. $121. P.T. Orang Lama, Jl. Palmerah Barat No. 38-A Blok B-4, Jakarta 12210, Indonesia. TEL 021-5483569. FAX 021-5305175. TELEX 62797-IA. (Singapore addr.: Media Link, 1 Sophia Rd., No. 04-26, Peace Centre, Singapore 0922. TEL 65-3361725; Japan addr.: Raira Enterprise Co., Ltd., 1-6-8-402, Shimoochiai, Shinjuku-ku, Tokyo 161, Japan. TEL 03-3360-9171) Ed. Sjamsudin Lubis. adv.: B&W page $658, color page $1316; trim 190 X 257. circ. 60,000.
    Description: Features humor and cartoons.

808.87   US
HUMOR DEFENSE. 1981. q. free. (Sarcastics Anonymous) Humor Defense Publishing, Box 10944, 7953 Stonehurst Ct., Pleasanton, CA 94588. TEL 510-462-5710. FAX 510-786-1826. Ed. Virginia Tooper. bk.rev. circ. 600. (looseleaf format) Document type: newsletter.
    Former titles: Sarcastics Anonymous & Laugh Lovers News.
    Description: Explores the positive and negative uses of humor with a light approach.

808.87   US
HUMOR EVENTS & POSSIBILITIES. Abbreviated title: H E P. 1976. q. $25 in DC; elsewhere $20. Workshop Library on World Humor, Box 23334, Washington, DC 20026. TEL 202-484-4949. Ed. Barbara Cummings. bk.rev. circ. 2,000.

808.87   IT
HUMOR GRAPHIC. q. Museo Internazionale dell'Umorismo, Via Arzaga 28, 20146 Milan, Italy. Ed. Luciano Consigli.

943.9 808.8   HU
DB901
HUNGARIAN QUARTERLY. (Text in English) 1960. q. 1200 Ft.($24) to individuals; institutions $35 (effective 1993). Magyar Tavirati Iroda – Hungarian News Agency, Pl. Naphegy ter 8, 1016 Budapest, Hungary. TEL 361-175-6722. FAX 361-118-8297. TELEX 061-22-4371. (Co-sponsor: Ministry of Foreign Affairs) Ed. Miklos Vajda. adv.; bk.rev.; film rev.; play rev.; rec.rev.; illus.; index. circ. 3,000. **Indexed:** Amer.Hist.& Life, Arts & Hum.Cit.Ind., Curr.Cont., Hist.Abstr., IBR, Int.Polit.Sci.Abstr., Key to Econ.Sci., M.L.A., Mid.East: Abstr.& Ind., Music Ind., Rural Recreat.Tour.Abstr., World Agri.Econ.& Rural Sociol.Abstr.
    —BLDSC (4337.058000); Faxon; UnCover.
    Formerly (until 1992): New Hungarian Quarterly (ISSN 0028-5390)
    Description: Includes modern prose and poetry as well as articles on literature, history, sociology, economics, current affairs, the arts, and other aspects of Húngarian life.

HYSTERIA; women, humor and social change. see *WOMEN'S INTERESTS*

053   GW   ISSN 0342-1864
F1408.3
IBEROAMERICANA; Lateinamerika-Spanien-Portugal. (Text in English, German, Portuguese, Spanish) 1977. 4/yr. DM.70($48) students DM.50($32). Vervuert Verlag GmbH, Wielandstr. 40, 60318 Frankfurt a.M., Germany. TEL 069-599615. FAX 069-5978743. Ed.Bd. adv.; bk.rev. circ. 1,000. (back issues avail.) Document type: academic/scholarly publication.
    Description: Contains information about the societies, history, culture, language and literature of Latin-America, Spain and Portugal.

808.8   US   ISSN 1054-1381
ICARUS (NEW YORK); new writing from around the world. 1991. q. $35.80. Rosen Publishing Group, Inc., 29 E. 21st St., New York, NY 10010. TEL 212-777-3017. FAX 212-777-0277. Eds. Roger Rosen, Patra McSharry. circ. 9,000. (back issues avail.)
    Description: Publishes international writing and photo essays to provide a broader perspective on the world for American young adults.

052   UK   ISSN 0264-4940
IDEAS AND PRODUCTIONS; a journal in the history of ideas. 1983. s-a. £6 to individuals; institutions £12. Cambridgeshire College of Arts and Technology (C.C.A.T.), East Rd., Cambridge CB1 1PT, England. TEL 0223 63271. Ed. Edward J. Esche. bk.rev.; illus. (back issues avail.)
    Description: Dedicated to exploring the range of theoretical radicalisms which developed during the 1970s. Each issue considers a particular area of inquiry using new methodologies.

059   RU
DI IDISHE GAS.* (Text in Yiddish; summaries in English, Russian) 1961. m. $109. c/o Soyuz Pisatelei Rossii, Arbat 20, 121918 Moscow, Russia. (Dist. by: Mezhdunarodnaya Kniga, Dimitrov Str. 39, Moscow 113095, Russia; Dist. in U.S. by: Victor Kamkin Inc., 4956 Boiling Brook Pkwy, Rockville, MD 20852. TEL 301-881-5973) Ed. Aron Vergelis. play rev.; bibl.; illus.; stat. (back issues avail.)
    Formerly: Sovietish Heimland (ISSN 0134-4315)

057.8   XV   ISSN 0019-1523
IDRIJSKI RAZGLEDI. (Text in Slovenian) 1956. 2/yr. 90 din.($8.20) Mestni Muzej v Idrii, Idrija, Slovenia. Ed. Joze Car. circ. 1,000.

808   US   ISSN 1067-4128
ILLINOIS REVIEW. 1975. 2/yr. $10 to individuals; institutions $15. Illinois Writers, Inc., 4240 Dept. of English, Illinois State University, Normal, IL 61790-4240. TEL 309-438-7705. Ed. Jim Elledge. adv.; bk.rev. circ. 500. (back issues avail.) Document type: academic/scholarly publication.
    Formerly (until 1993): Illinois Writers Review (ISSN 0733-9526)
    Description: Poetry, prose poems, short stories, novel excerpts, interviews of and by Illinois and national authors. Contains essays and commentary on pressing issues in contemporary writing.

052   UK   ISSN 0046-8703
IMPACT (LONDON); international independent muslim news magazine. 1971. s-m. £42($75) News & Media Ltd., P.O. Box 2493, 233 Seven Sisters Rd., Ste. B, London N4 2BL, England. TEL 071-263-1417. Ed.Bd. adv.; bk.rev. **Indexed:** Per.Islam. (1991-). Document type: newsletter.

055.1   IT   ISSN 0046-8711
IMPEGNO SETTANTA;* rassegna di politica, cultura e attualita. irreg. L.3000. Corso Umberto 22, 91026 Mazara del Vallo (Trapani), Italy. Ed.Bd. adv.; bk.rev.; bibl.; illus.

IMPETUS. see *ART*

051   US
▼**IN YOUR FACE.** 1992. q. $12. Box 6872, Yorkville Sta., New York, NY 10128-0008. Ed. Gina Grega. adv.; bk.rev.; music rev. circ. 400.
    Description: Contains essays, poetry and artwork of a personal, political and sexual nature.

INDEPENDENT (ARLINGTON); a monthly notice of small press periodicals, books and ideas. see *PUBLISHING AND BOOK TRADE*

052   UK   ISSN 0306-4220
K9
INDEX ON CENSORSHIP. 1972. 6/yr. £30 (foreign £36). Writers & Scholars International Ltd., 32 Queen Victoria St., London EC4N 4SS, England. TEL 071-329-6434. FAX 071-329-6461. Ed. Ursula Owen. adv.; bk.rev.; bibl.; index, cum.index: 1972-1988. circ. 10,000. (also avail. in microform; reprint service avail. from ISI) **Indexed:** Alt.Press Ind., Arts & Hum.Cit.Ind., Curr.Cont., HR Rep., M.L.A., Mid.East: Abstr.& Ind., P.A.I.S., Sociol.Abstr. Document type: consumer publication.
    —BLDSC (4377.380000); Faxon; UnCover.
    Description: Reports denials of free speech throughout the world, publishes commentaries on their effects, and prints examples of banned literature.

052   II   ISSN 0019-6304
AP8
INDIAN REVIEW; devoted to the discussion of all topics of interest. (Text in English) 1900. m. Rs.10($5) Manian Natesan, 2-A Cathedral Rd., Madras 600086, India. Ed. M.C. Subhramanyam. bk.rev. **Indexed:** Amer.Hist.& Life, Hist.Abstr.

059   II   ISSN 0300-4007
INDRANIL. (Text in Bengali; summaries in Hindi and English) 1971. m. Rs.8.80($40) P. Ghosh, 5 Dhakuria Kalibari Ln., Calcutta 700031, India. Ed. C.S.D. Chakladar. adv.; bk.rev.; index. circ. 1,000.

051 616.9   US
INFECTED FAGGOT PERSPECTIVES. irreg. $3 per no. Box 26246, Los Angeles, CA 90026. Document type: newsletter.
    Description: Provides real perspectives of living with AIDS.

054   FR   ISSN 0754-023X
INFINI. 1983. 4/yr. 315 F. Gallimard, 5, rue Sebastien Boltin, 75007 Paris, France. TEL 33-1-46-59-89-00. Ed. Philippe Sollers. **Indexed:** Arts & Hum.Cit.Ind., Curr.Cont., M.L.A. —Faxon; SWETS.

052   AT   ISSN 0725-5489
INFOCAB. 1979. m. Aus.$46. Victorian Association of Citizens Advice Bureaux, 9th Fl., 176 Wellington, E. Melbourne, Vic. 3002, Australia, Australia. TEL 03-419-9866. FAX 03-416-3392. Ed. Annette Ryan. bk.rev. circ. 200. (back issues avail.) Document type: newsletter.
    Description: New and updated community information covering the state of Victoria.

320.531   FR
INFORMATION OUVRIERES. 1958. w. 250 F. Mouvement pour un Parti des Travailleurs (MPPT), 87, rue Faubourg-Saint-Denis, 75010 Paris, France. TEL 42-47-13-34. FAX 40-22-01-96. Ed. Jean Pierre Raffi. charts; illus. circ. 20,000.
    Formerly (until 1977): Jeune Revolutionnaire (ISSN 0021-6100)

054   CN   ISSN 0711-2157
INFORMATION PROCHE-ORIENT. 1981. 6/yr. Can.$12($10) Comite Canada - Israel, 1310 Avenue Greene, Ste. 710, Montreal, Que. H3Z 2B2, Canada. TEL 514-934-0771. FAX 514-933-8211. Ed. Gilbert Lemieux. adv. circ. 1,000.
    Formerly: Revue Jonathan (ISSN 0711-026X)

INFORMATIONSBULLETINEN; tidskrift foer sjaelvfoersoerjning, miljoe, energi, odling, kultur, politik, solidaritet och fred. see *POLITICAL SCIENCE*

053.1   GW   ISSN 0863-4564
INITIAL; Zeitschrift fuer Socialwissenschaftlichen Diskurs. 1990. 6/yr. Verlag Volk und Welt, Otto-Nuschke-Str. 10-11, 1086 Berlin, Germany. TEL 030-203650211.

INKSTONE; a magazine of haiku. see *LITERATURE — Poetry*

INROADS. see *MEN'S INTERESTS*

059   NE   ISSN 0167-3696
PR9091
INS AND OUTS; a magazine of awareness. (Text in English) 1978. irreg. $30 for 6 issues. Ins & Outs Press, Box 3759, Amsterdam, Netherlands. Ed. Edward Woods. adv.; bk.rev. circ. 2,500.

808.8   US
INSTEAD OF A MAGAZINE.* 1980. q. $8 to individuals; institutions $17.50. Lysander Spooner Society, Box 0076, Shingleton, CA 96088-0076. TEL 203-456-9005. Ed. Michael Ziesing. adv.; bk.rev. circ. 500.
    Description: Fights all kinds of repression including sexual and racial discrimination.

LITERARY AND POLITICAL REVIEWS

378   US   ISSN 0020-5249
AP2
INTERCOLLEGIATE REVIEW; a journal of scholarship and opinion. 1965. irreg. (2-4/yr.). $18 for 8 nos. Intercollegiate Studies Institute, 14 S. Bryn Mawr, Ste. 100, Bryn Mawr, PA 19010. TEL 215-525-7501. Ed. Dana Peringer. adv.; bk.rev.; illus.; index. circ. 35,000. (also avail. in microform from UMI,MIM; back issues avail.) **Indexed:** Curr.Cont., P.A.I.S. **Document type:** academic/scholarly publication.
—Faxon; UnCover; UMI.
   Incorporates: Academic Reviewer.
   Description: Provides critical commentary on a wide variety of topics related to scholarship and culture.

INTERMEDIAIRE DES CHERCHEURS ET CURIEUX; de questions et responses historiques, litteraires, artistiques et sur toutes autres curiosites. see HISTORY

INTO THE NIGHT; a newsletter for freedom for political prisoners held in the U.S. see POLITICAL SCIENCE — Civil Rights

808.87   UV
INTRUS. 1986. w. c/o Agence Burkinabe de Presse, B.P. 2507, Ouagadougou, Burkina Faso.
   Description: Contains satirical humor.

INVISIBLE CITY. see LITERATURE — Poetry

IRAQ. MINISTRY OF EDUCATION. AL-MU'ALLEM AL-JADID. see EDUCATION

IRIS: A JOURNAL ABOUT WOMEN. see WOMEN'S INTERESTS

052   UK
IRISH POST. 1970. w. £49. Irish Post Ltd., Lex House, 77 South Rd., Southall, Middx. UB1 1SQ, England. TEL 081-574-2058. FAX 081-571-5884. Ed. Donal Mooney. adv.; bk.rev. circ. 78,000.

052 059.916   UK   ISSN 0790-7850
DA925
IRISH REVIEW. 1986. s-a. £12($30) Institute of Irish Studies, Queen's University of Belfast, 8 Fitzwilliam St., Belfast BT9 6AW, Northern Ireland. TEL 0232-439238. Ed.Bd. adv.; bk.rev. circ. 750. **Document type:** academic/scholarly publication.
—BLDSC (4574.721000).
   Description: Provides a general forum for critical and creative writing in English and Irish literature.

ISLAM CAGRISI. see RELIGIONS AND THEOLOGY — Islamic

ISLAMI BAYRLAYK. see RELIGIONS AND THEOLOGY — Islamic

051 960   US   ISSN 0047-1607
DT1
ISSUE; a quarterly journal of opinion. 1972. 2/yr. membership. African Studies Association, Credit Union Bldg., Emory University, Atlanta, GA 30322. TEL 404-329-6410. Ed. Beverly Hawk. adv.; bibl. circ. 3,000. (also avail. in microfilm) **Indexed:** Amer.Hist.& Life, Documentatieblad, Hist.Abstr., HR Rep.
—BLDSC (4583.980000); Faxon; UnCover.

059.91   CI   ISSN 0021-2415
ISTARSKI MOZAIK; casopis za drustvena, knjizevna i umjetnicka pitanja Istre. (Text in Serbocroatian) 1963. q. 12 din.($6.25) Glas Istre, Obala Marsala Tita 10, Pula, Croatia. Ed. Marijan Grakalic.

054.1   FR   ISSN 0021-3187
BX802
ITINERAIRES;* chroniques et documents. 1955. m. 75 F.($16) 4 rue Garanciere, 75006 Paris, France. Dir. Jean Madiran.

808.8   II
JANASUDHA DAILY. (Text in Coloqual) 1978. d. Rs.36. Mahendra Enterprises, Mahendra Nagar, Gollapudi-521225, Vijayawada, India. Ed. Naralasetti Venkateswarl-u. film rev. circ. 5,000.

808.8   II
JANASUDHA MONTHLY. (Text in Coloqual) 1978. m. Rs.36. Mahendra Enterprises, Mahendra Nagar, Gollapudi-521225, Vijayawada, India. Ed. Narasetti Enkateswarl-u. film rev.; illus. circ. 10,000. (also avail. in talking book)

808.8   II
JANASUDHA WEEKLY. (Text in Coloqual) 1978. w. Rs.36. Mahendra Enterprises, Mahendra Nagar, Gollapudi-521225, Vijayawada, India. Ed. Naralasetti Enkateswarl-u. film rev.; illus. circ. 15,000. (also avail. in talking book)

952   JA   ISSN 0021-4590
DS801
JAPAN QUARTERLY. (Text in English) 1954. q. $58. Asahi Shimbunsha - Asahi Shimbun Publishing Co., 3-2, Tsukiji 5-chome, Chuo-ku, Tokyo 104-11, Japan. TEL 03-3545-0131. FAX 03-3544-1428. (Dist. by: Intercontinental Marketing Corp., I.P.O. Box 5056, Tokyo 100-30, Japan. TEL 81-3-3661-7458. FAX 81-3-3667-9646) Ed. Yuji Oishi. adv.; bk.rev.; illus. (also avail. in microform from UMI; back issues avail.; reprint service avail. from UMI) **Indexed:** Acad.Ind., Amer.Hist.& Life, Curr.Cont., Hist.Abstr., M.L.A., Mid.East: Abstr.& Ind., P.A.I.S., Soc.Sci.Ind., SSCI.
—Faxon; UnCover; SWETS; UMI.

JAWAHARLAL NEHRU UNIVERSITY. SCHOOL OF LANGUAGES. JOURNAL. see LINGUISTICS

808.8   HU   ISSN 0447-6425
JELENKOR; irodalmi es muveszeti folyoirat. 1958. m. $20. Jelenkor Irodalmi es Muveszeti Kiado, Szechenyi ter 17, 7621 Pecs, Hungary. (Subscr. to: Hirlapelofizetesi es Lapellatasi Iroda, Lehel u.10A, 1900 Budapest, Hungary) Ed. Istvan Csuhai. bk.rev.; film rev.; music rev.; play rev.; illus.; index. circ. 2,600. (back issues avail.)
   Description: Publishes fine writing and poetry in Hungarian, studies on aesthetics and modern theories of literature, and reviews on modern Hungarian art and Rumanian and Yugoslavian literature.

056.1   MX
JET SET; revista del gran mundo. 1975. m. Mex.$350($41) Corporacion Editorial S.A., Lucio Blanco 435, Col. San Juan Tlihuaca, 02400 Mexico D.F., Mexico. TEL 5-352-0771. Ed. Javier Ortiz Camorlinga. circ. 67,000.

JEWISH AFFAIRS. see ETHNIC INTERESTS

808.8   US
JEWISH BOOK WORLD. 1982. 3/yr. $20. Jewish Book Council, 15 E. 26 St., New York, NY 10010-1579. TEL 212-532-4949. Ed. Carolyn Starman Hessel. adv.; bk.rev. circ. 5,000.

296   UK   ISSN 0021-633X
JEWISH CHRONICLE; the world's leading Jewish newspaper. 1841. w. £163. Jewish Chronicle Publications Ltd., 25 Furnival St., London EC4A 1JT, England. FAX 071-405-9040. TELEX 940-11415. Ed. Ned Temko. adv.; bk.rev.; film rev.; illus.; cum.index. circ. 50,000. (also avail. in microform from RPI) **Document type:** newspaper.

296   US
JEWISH CHRONICLE (YONKERS); serving Southern Westchester. 1968. 13/yr. $15. Jewish Council of Yonkers, 584 N. Broadway, Yonkers, NY 10701. TEL 914-423-5009. FAX 914-423-5077. Ed. Marilyn Shebshaievitz. adv.; bk.rev.; film rev. circ. 6,000. (back issues avail.)

JEWISH QUARTERLY. see ETHNIC INTERESTS

296   UK   ISSN 0021-6801
JEWISH VANGUARD. 1948. q. £1.20. Poale Zion - Labour Zionists, 48 College Rd., Wembley, Middlesex HA9 8RJ, England. TEL 081-904-8483. FAX 081-908-1936. Ed. Reginald Freeson. adv.; bk.rev.; film rev.; play rev.; record rev.; illus. circ. 5,000.

891.8   YU   ISSN 0021-6917
AP115
JEZ.* 1935. w. 520 din. Jez, Nusiceva 6, Belgrade, Yugoslavia. Ed. Radivoje Ivanovic.
   Description: Contains humorous articles.

059.915   IR
JIHAD. (Text in Farsi) 1989. w. Sada-yi Inqilab-i Islami-i Afghanistan, P.O. Box 91460-172, Meshed, Iran. illus.

974 301.16   US   ISSN 0749-4351
JOKESMITH. 1984. q. $40. Edward C. McManus, Ed. & Pub., 44 Queensview Rd., Marlborough, MA 01752. TEL 508-481-0979. FAX 508-481-0979. bk.rev. circ. 800. (looseleaf format; back issues avail.)
   Description: Directed to business and professional speakers with roast lines, presentation remarks, jokes, skits, stories and openers.

700   BL
JOSE;* literatura-critica-arte. 1976. m. Cr.$100. Editora Fontana Ltda, Rua das Marrecas 40 centro, 20031 Rio de Janeiro RJ, Brazil. (Dist. by: Superbancas Ltda. Rua Ubaldino do Amaral 42, Rio de Janeiro, Brazil) Ed. Gastao de Holanda. bk.rev.; bibl.; illus.

JOURNAL OF CROATIAN STUDIES; annual review. see HISTORY — History Of Europe

JOURNAL OF LITERARY STUDIES/TYDSKRIF VIR LITERATUURWETENSKAP. see LITERATURE

JOURNAL OF REGIONAL CRITICISM. see ART

051   US   ISSN 0897-0521
JOURNAL OF THE FANTASTIC IN THE ARTS. 1988. q. $24 (£12.50 in UK). (International Association for the Fantastic in the Arts) Orion Publishing, 3959 Rte. 31, Ste. 210, Liverpool, NY 13090. TEL 315-451-0605. (Subscr. in UK to: Chris Reed, NSFA, P.O. Box 625, Sheffield S1 3GY, England) Ed. Carl Yoke. adv.; bk.rev.; illus. circ. 3,500.
—BLDSC (4983.760000).
   Description: Publishes critical review articles on popular culture and the arts.

JUDAISM; a quarterly journal of Jewish life and thought. see RELIGIONS AND THEOLOGY — Judaic

053   GW   ISSN 0932-660X
JUNGE FREIHEIT; Deutsche Zeitung fuer Politik und Kultur. 1986. m. DM.36 (foreign DM.42). Unitas Germanica e.V., Postfach 1872, 89008 Ulm, Germany. TEL 07661-5653. (Subscr. to: Junge Freiheit Verlag, Postfach 147, 7801 Stegen, Germany) Ed. Dieter Stein. adv.; bk.rev. circ. 35,000.

296   YU   ISSN 0022-748X
KADIMA. (Text in Serbo-Croatian) 1959. m. Savez Jevrejskih Opstina Jugoslavije - Federation of Jewish Communities in Yugoslavia, 7. Jula 71a, Belgrade, Yugoslavia. Ed. David Albahari. circ. 2,500.
   Description: Literary and informative data for Jewish youth.

053.1 952   GW
KAGAMI; Japanischer Zeitschriftenspiegel. 1974. 3/yr. DM.30. Gesellschaft fuer Natur- und Voelkerkunde Ostasiens e.V., Japanisches Seminar, Von Melle-Park 6-VII, 20146 Hamburg, Germany. TEL 040-41234884. Ed. Herbert Worm. bk.rev. circ. 500. **Document type:** newsletter.
   Description: German translations of Japanese essays on political, social and literary current affairs.

700   TR
KAIRI. 1976. a. 22 Fitt St., Woodbrook, Port-of-Spain, Trinidad & Tobago, W.I. Ed. Christopher Laird. bk.rev.; bibl.; illus.

059   II
KALAPATRA. (Text in Hindi) m. Rs.8. F-1422 Krishnanagar, Delhi 110051, India.

070.448   CH   ISSN 1016-4162
KALEIDOSCOPE. Key Title: Zhongwai Zazhi. (Text in Chinese) 1967. m. NT.$1000 in ROC; Hong Kong $50; elsewhere $55. Wang Cheng-Sheng, Ed. & Pub., 108, Lungkiang Rd., Taipei, Taiwan, Republic of China. TEL 02-506-5311. FAX 02-506-6037. (Order in US to: World Journal Bookstore, 141-07 20th Ave., Whitestone, NY 11357. TEL 718-746-8889) adv.; illus.

051   YE
AL-KALIMA; majallat al-muthaqqafiyn al-yamaniyiyn. irreg. 2 rials. Box 1109, Sana'a, Republic of Yemen. Ed. Ibrahim al-Maqhafi. adv.; bk.rev.

059.945   FI   ISSN 0355-4511
KALTIO. 1945. bi-m. FIM 160. Mystintie 21 E, 90230 Oulu, Finland. adv. circ. 1,300.

059.94　　　　FI　　ISSN 0355-0303
AP80
KANAVA. 1932. 9/yr. FIM 260. Yhtyneet Kuvalehdet Oy, Maistraatinportti 1, FIN-00240 Helsinki, Finland. TEL 358-0-156-6524. FAX 358-0-156-6505. TELEX 121364. Ed. Seikko Eskola. adv.: B&W page FIM 3900, color page FIM 5600. bk.rev.; index. circ. 5,680. **Indexed:** M.L.A.
   Formerly: Aika (ISSN 0002-2098)

059.915　　　　　　IR
KAPANK. 1990. bi-m. Kayhan Publications, Ferdowsi Ave., P.O. Box 11365-9631, Tehran 11444, Iran. TEL 021-310251.

057.8　　　　　CI　　ISSN 0022-9059
KARLOVACKI TJEDNIK. 1953. w. 100 din. Socialisticki Savez Radnog Naroda Karlovca, Mihovliceva 2, Karlovac, Croatia. Ed. Jovica Radojcic.

808.87　　　　　PL　　ISSN 0449-9026
KARUZELA. 1957. fortn. Ul. Sienkiewicza 3-5, 90-113 Lodz, Poland. TEL 48-42-331432. TELEX 886265. Ed. Halina Sibisnka. circ. 60,000.

KAYHAN ANDISHE. see *RELIGIONS AND THEOLOGY — Islamic*

059.915　　　　　IR
KAYHAN CARICATURE. (Text in Persian) 1991. m. $259 to N. America (effective 1994). Kayhan Publications, Ferdowsi Ave., P.O. Box 11365-9631, Tehran, Iran. TEL 98-21-3110251. FAX 98-21-3114228. TELEX 212467. **Document type:** consumer publication.

059.915　　　　　IR　　ISSN 1017-4184
KAYHAN FARHANGI. (Text in Persian) 1984. m. $222 to N. America (effective 1994). Kayhan Publications, Ferdowsi Ave., P.O. Box 11365-9631, Teheran, Iran. TEL 98-21-3110251. TELEX 212467. **Document type:** consumer publication.
   Description: Covers political and cultural topics.

053.1　　　　　GW　　ISSN 0930-0503
KETZERBRIEFE. 1985. m. DM.90. (Bund gegen Anpassung) Ahriman Verlag GmbH, Stuebeweg 60, 79108 Freiburg, Germany. TEL 0761-502303. FAX 0761-508001. (Dist. by Thanilo Verlag und Vertriebs GmbH, Postfach 710, 79007 Freiburg, Germany. TEL 0761-508001) (back issues avail.) **Document type:** consumer publication.
   Description: Provides a forum for non-conformist ideas and documentation of persecution for religious and political reasons.

KEVREN. see *POLITICAL SCIENCE*

059.915　　　　　IR
KHAVARAN. (Text in Persian) 1990. m. H. Mir'nizhad, P.O. Box 91735-1497, Meshed, Iran. illus.

052　　　　　II　　ISSN 0023-1282
KICK TO CORRUPTION. (Text in English) 1969. m. Red Rd., Hoshiarpur, India. Ed. S.K. Kapur. adv.; charts; illus.

057.91　　　　　KR　　ISSN 0208-0710
PG3931
KIIV; literaturno-khudozhnii ta hromads'kopolitychnyi zhurnal. 1983. m. 20.40 Rub. (Spika Pys'mennykiv Ukrainy) Vedavnytstvo Radyanskii Pismennik, Chkalova, 52, Kiev, Ukraine. Ed. P.M. Perebyinis. circ. 30,000.

891.553　　　　　IR　　ISSN 1017-415X
KILK - MAHNAMAH-I FARHANGI VA HUNARI/KELK - REVIEW OF ART AND CULTURE. (Text in Farsi) 1990. m. $38 in Asia, Europe; $56 in N. America. P.O. Box 13145-916, Teheran, Iran. Ed. Ali Dehbashi. bk.rev.; film rev.; music rev.; illus.
   Description: Publishes a variety of literary and cultural articles, including art, theatre, music and cultural criticism, poetry, and profiles of poets, musicians and writers.

808.87　　　　　US
KING SIZED CRACKED. a. $14.40. Globe Communications Corp. (New York), 441 Lexington Ave., New York, NY 10017. TEL 800-472-7744. FAX 212-286-0072. Ed. Lou Silverstone. circ. 500,000.
   Description: Consists of humorous articles.

800　　　　　II
KINTU. (Text in Punjabi) 1971. q. Rs.25($5) Agandoot Parkashan, Sahit Sabha, Tapa 148108, India. Ed. Cee Markanda. circ. 5,000. (back issues avail.)

KIRKE OG KULTUR. see *RELIGIONS AND THEOLOGY*

053.1　　　　　GW　　ISSN 0023-2211
AS181
KLUETER BLAETTER; Monatshefte fuer Kultur und Zeitgeschichte. 1949. m. DM.74. Tuermer Verlag Dr. Gert Sudholt, Kreuzanger 8, 82335 Berg, Germany. Ed. Gert Sudholt. adv.; bk.rev. circ. 4,000.

053.9　　　　　BE
KNACK. (Text in Dutch) 1971. w. 4690 BEF. N.V. Roularta Media Group, Meiboomlaan 33, B-8800 Roeselare, Belgium. TEL 02-7366040. FAX 02-7356857. Ed. Frans Verleyen. adv.; bk.rev. circ. 125,000.

057.8　　　　　YU　　ISSN 0023-2416
AP56
KNJIZEVNE NOVINE; list za knjizevnost i kulturu. (Text in Serbo-Croatian) 1949. fortn. 120 din. Knjizevne Novine, Francuska 7, Belgrade, Yugoslavia. Ed. Dragan M. Jeremic. **Indexed:** M.L.A.

KNJIZEVNOST. see *LITERATURE*

051　　　　　US　　ISSN 0738-8640
KNOWLEDGE; dedicated to the dissemination of knowledge for the happiness, health, security, and survival of humankind. 1976. 4/yr. $30. Knowledge, Inc., Knowledge Park, 3863 S.W. Loop 820, Ste. 100, Ft.Worth, TX 76133-2063. TEL 817-292-4270. FAX 817-294-2893. Ed. O.A. Battista. adv.; bk.rev. circ. 1,500. **Indexed:** Curr.Cont., E.I.
   Description: Intellectual, speculative discourses, essays, and articles in pursuit of the enhancement of humankind's physical, emotional, and intellectual lives.

KOMPOST. see *CHILDREN AND YOUTH — For*

320.5　　　　　IO　　ISSN 0023-3188
KOMUNIKASI;* demokrasi, persatuan dan pembangunan berdasarkan pantjasila. 1969. s-m. Rps.600($2.) Yayasan Komunikasi, Matramanx Raya 10 A, Jakarta, Indonesia. Ed. Sabam Sirait.

KOREAN STAMPS. see *PHILATELY*

059.94　　　　　HU　　ISSN 0023-415X
PH3144
KORTARS. 1957. m. $19. (Magyar Irok Szovetsege) Lapkiado Vallalat, Lenin korut 9-11, 1073 Budapest 7, Hungary. TEL 222-408. (Subscr. to: Kultura, Box 149, H-1389 Budapest, Hungary) Ed. Arpad Thiery. adv.; bk.rev. circ. 7,000.

891.7　　　　　RU　　ISSN 0130-2671
KROKODIL. 1922. m. $87 (foreign $116). Bumazhny pr. 14, 101455 Moscow, Russia. TEL 095-250-1086. (Dist. in U.S. by: Victor Kamkin Inc., 4956 Billing Brook Pkwy, Rockville, MD 20852. TEL 301-881-5973) Ed. A.S. Pyanov. illus. circ. 2,200,000. **Indexed:** Curr.Dig.Sov.Press.
   Description: Consists of satire and humor.

057.85　　　　　FR　　ISSN 0023-5148
AP54
KULTURA; szkice, opowiadania, sprawozdania. (Text in Polish) 1947. m. 550 F.($106) Institut Litteraire, 91 Av. de Poissy, Le Mesnil-le-Roi, 78600 Maisons-Laffitte, France. TEL 1-39-62-19-04. FAX 33-1-39-62-57-52. Ed. Jerzy Giedroyc. adv.; bk.rev.; index. circ. 9,500. **Indexed:** Amer.Hist.& Life, Hist.Abstr.

057.85　　　　　PL　　ISSN 0023-5172
AS261
KULTURA I SPOLECZENSTWO. (Text in Polish; tables of contents in English, Russian) q. $32. Polska Akademia Nauk, Komitet Nauk Socjologicznych, Ul. Nowy Swiat 72, 00-330 Warsaw, Poland. Ed. A. Kloskowska. bk.rev.; index. circ. 2,060. **Indexed:** Amer.Hist.& Life, Hist.Abstr., Lang.& Lang.Behav.Abstr.

057.91　　　　　KR　　ISSN 0023-5180
KUL'TURA I ZHYTTYA. (Text in Ukrainian) 1955. s-w. $6. Ministerstvo Kul'tury, Kiev, Ukraine. adv.; bk.rev.; abstr.; bibl.; illus.
   Formerly: Radyans'ka Kul'tura.

057.81　　　　　XN　　ISSN 0047-3731
KULTUREN ZIVOT/CULTURAL LIFE; kultura, umetnost, opstestveni prasanja. (Text in Macedonian) 1956. m. $25 (effective Jan. 1991). Kulturen Zivot, Ruzveltova, 6, P.O. Box 85, 91001 Skopje, Macedonia. Ed. Boris Vishinski. illus. (tabloid format; avail. on records; reprint service avail. from UMI)

053　　　　　GW　　ISSN 0941-4657
KULTURPOLITIK. 1972. q. DM.24 (foreign DM.38). Bundesverband Bildender Kunstler, Meckenheimer Allee 85, 53115 Bonn, Germany. TEL 0228-630406. FAX 0228-696994. Ed.Bd. adv.: B&W page DM.1200; trim 260 x 185. bk.rev. circ. 15,000. **Document type:** trade publication.
   Description: Information on the professional interests of artists.

KUNST UND KULTUR. see *ART*

055.1　　　　　IT
L.G. ARGOMENTI. (Letteratura Giovanile) 1965. q. L.35000 (effective 1992). Comune di Genova, Civiche Biblioteche, Via Archimede, 44, 16142 Genoa, Italy. TEL 10-509181. Ed. Francesco Langella. bk.rev.; index, cum.index every 5 yrs.; circ. 1,500 (controlled). **Document type:** academic/scholarly publication.
   Formerly (until 1977): Minuzzolo (ISSN 0026-5748)

051　　　　　US
L I O N.* (Living in the Ozarks Newsletter) 1973. m. $18 to individuals; institutions $24. First Ozark Press, Box 310, Omaha, AR 72662-0310. adv.; bibl.; illus.

059　　　　　MR
LAMALIF; revue economique, sociale et culturelle. 1966. m. DH.77($15) (foreign 200 F.). Loghlam Presse, 6 bis, Rue Defly-Dieude, Casablanca, Morocco. Ed. Mohamed Loghlam. adv.; bk.rev.; film rev.; bibl.; illus.; stat. circ. 16,000.

LAMBDA BOOK REPORT; a review of contemporary gay and lesbian literature. see *HOMOSEXUALITY*

LANCE. see *COLLEGE AND ALUMNI*

052　　　　　NZ　　ISSN 0023-7930
AP7
LANDFALL; New Zealand arts & letters. 1947. s-a. NZ.$39.95($25) Oxford University Press - New Zealand, P.O. Box 11-149, Auckland 5, New Zealand. TEL 64-9-523-3134. FAX 64-9-524-6723. adv.; bk.rev.; illus.; cum.index every 5 yrs. circ. 1,000. (back issues avail.) **Indexed:** Abstr.Engl.Stud., Amer.Hist.& Life, Arts & Hum.Cit.Ind., Br.Hum.Ind., Curr.Cont., Hist.Abstr., M.L.A., So.Pac.Per.Ind. —BLDSC (5151.550000); Faxon. CCC.
   Description: Publishes stories, poems, literary and cultural commentary, articles on aspects of related arts, work by photographers and artists.

808.8　　　　　CE
LANKA GUARDIAN. (Text in English) 1978. s-m. $45 in Asia; Europe $55; US & Canada $65. (South Asia Media Representatives) Lanka Guardian Publishers, 246 Union Place, Colombo 2, Sri Lanka. Ed. Mervyn de Silva. **Document type:** trade publication.

808.87　　　　　US　　ISSN 0887-6991
LATEST JOKES. 1974. bi-m. $24 (prices typically set in Jan.). Robert Makinson, Ed. & Pub., Box 023304, Brooklyn, NY 11202-0066. TEL 718-855-5057. circ. 250. (back issues avail.)
   Description: Covers short jokes about current events.

808.87　　　　　US
LAUGH FACTORY. 1981. m. $15. Fell Great Publishing Co., 1370 Windsor Rd., Teaneck, NJ 07666. TEL 201-833-0068. Ed. Vince Donato.

800　　　　　FR　　ISSN 0024-0125
LECTURE ET TRADITION; bulletin litteraire, contrerevolutionnaire. 1966. m. 110 F. (foreign 130 F.). Diffusion de la Pensee Francaise, Chire-en-Montreuil, 86190 Vouille, France. TEL 49-51-83-04. FAX 49-51-63-50. Ed. Jean Auguy. adv.; bk.rev.; bibl. circ. 4,000.

052　　　　　UK　　ISSN 0024-0303
LEFT.* m. Brewster Printing Co., Rochester, Kent, England. Ed. Carl Gilleard. adv.; bk.rev. circ. 7,000. (reprint service avail. from KTO)
   Formerly: Focus.

LITERARY AND POLITICAL REVIEWS

800 US ISSN 1056-7429
PS570
LEFT BANK. 1991. s-a. $16. Blue Heron Publishing, 24450 N.W. Hansen Rd., Hillsboro, OR 97124. TEL 503-621-9371. FAX 503-621-9826. Ed. Linny Stovall. adv.; illus. circ. 5,000.
  Description: Showcase for Northwest writers, or those with roots there. Includes fiction, non-fiction, poetry, cartoons, art, interviews.

700 US ISSN 0160-1857
NX180.R45
LEFT CURVE. 1974. irreg. $20 for 3 nos. to individuals; institutions $30. Left Curve Publications, Box 472, Oakland, CA 94604. TEL 510-763-7193. Ed. Csaba Polony. adv.; B&W page $200; trim 8 1/2 x 11. bk.rev.; film rev.; play rev.; illus. circ. 1,200. (also avail. in microform from UMI; back issues avail.; reprint service avail. from UMI.) **Indexed:** Alt.Press Ind., Artbibl.Mod., Left Ind. (1984-).
  —BLDSC (5181.307800).
  Description: Published by artists confronting the crisis of modernity independent of the control of dominant institutions and free from the shackles of instrumental rationality. All cultural forms considered.

LEGAL STUDIES FORUM; an interdisciplinary journal. *see LAW*

053 301.2 GW ISSN 0170-3803
LENDEMAINS; etudes comparees sur la France - vergleichende Frankreichforschung. (Text in German and French) 1975. q. DM.48.60. Dr. Wolfram Hitzeroth Verlag, Franz-Tuczek-Weg 1, 35039 Marburg, Germany. TEL 06421-409261. FAX 06421-409199. Ed.Bd. circ. 950.

056 SP
LETRA INTERNACIONAL. (Avail. in 11 language editions for Spain, France, Italy, Germany, Serbia, Croatia, Czechoslovakia, Hungary, Rumania, Russia and Denmark) q. 2400 ptas. (Europe 3800 ptas.; America 5800 ptas.). Editorial Pablo Iglesias, Monte Esquinza 30, 2o, 28010 Madrid, Spain. TEL 91-310-43-13. FAX 91-319-45-85. Dirs. Luis Goytisolo, Antonin J. Liehm. circ. 10,000.
  Description: Offers a critical, reflective and pluralistic view of the world we live in.

056.9 BL ISSN 0047-441X
LETRAS DA PROVINCIA. 1948. bi-m. Empresa Grafica Editorial Paulista, Rue Dr. Trajano 572, Caixa Postal 109, Limeira, Estado de Sao Paulo, Brazil. Dir. Joao Baptista Petrelli. bk.rev.; bibl. circ. 10,000.

THE LETTER PARADE. *see LITERATURE*

055.1 IT ISSN 0024-130X
LETTERATO; di varia cultura. 1952. m. L.40000. Editrice Pellegrini, Via Roma 74, Casella Postale 158, 87100 Cosenza, Italy. Ed. Luigi Pellegrini. adv.; bk.rev.; bibl.; illus.

809 YU ISSN 0350-4158
LETUNK; tarsadalom, tudomany, kultura. (Text in English, Hungarian, Serbo-Croatian) 1971. bi-m. 250 din. Nisro Forum, Trg. Slobode 1-2, 24000 Subotica, Vojvodina, Yugoslavia. TEL 38-24-26-819. FAX 38-21-56-699. Ed. Tibor Varady. bk.rev.; index. circ. 240,000.

056 SP
LEVIATAN; revista de hechos e ideas. q. 2000 ptas. (Europe 3200 ptas.; America 4800 ptas.). Editorial Pablo Iglesias, Monte Esquinza 30, 2o, 28010 Madrid, Spain. TEL 91-310-43-13. FAX 91-319-45-86. Dir. Salvador Clotas. bk.rev. circ. 8,000.
  Description: Provides a liberal view of the cultural and political scenes.

320 700 US ISSN 0360-1765
AP2
LEVIATHAN (COLORADO SPRINGS); a literary journal. 1974. m. (Oct.-May). $5. Cutler Publications, Inc., The Colorado College, 902 N. Cascade, Colorado Springs, CO 80946. TEL 719-632-4999. Ed. Christina Serkowski. bk.rev. circ. 2,000.
  Description: Journal of poetry, fiction and the visual arts.

800 FR
LIBER. (Supplement to: Frankfurter Allgemeine Zeitung, L'Indice, Le Monde, El Pais, The Times Literary Supplement) bi-m. 52 rue du Cardinal Lemoine, 75005 Paris, France. FAX 47-53-77-69. Ed.Bd.

322.44 NE
LIBERAAL REVEIL. 1959. 4/yr. fl.35 to individuals; students fl.25. Stichting Liberaal Reveil, Prins Hendrikplein 4, 2518 JA The Hague, Netherlands. Ed.Bd. bk.rev. circ. 1,350.

320.9 UK ISSN 0024-1903
LIBERATION NEWS SERVICE.* 1968. w. free. Liberation News Services, 30 Holland Park Gardens, London W.14, England. Ed. Joseph M. Von Haag. bk.rev.; film rev.; play rev.; abstr.; charts; illus.; stat. circ. 1,000. (processed)
  Description: Underground literature.

320.9 II ISSN 0047-4495
DS401
LIBERATION WAR. (Text in English) 1971. m. Rs.12. 23 Lansdowne Pl., Calcutta 29, India. Ed. Asit Sen. bk.rev.

808.8 US ISSN 0272-5959
JC571
LIBERTARIAN DIGEST. 1981. 6/yr. $10 (effective Apr. 1992; typically set in Jan.). 132 Roberts Ln., Ste. 301, Alexandria, VA 22314-4669. TEL 703-683-7769. Ed. Fred Foldvary. adv.; bk.rev. circ. 200. (also avail. in microform)

LIBERTE. *see LITERATURE — Poetry*

330.1 320 100 US ISSN 0894-1408
LIBERTY (PORT TOWNSEND). 1987. bi-m. $19.50 (foreign $24.50). Liberty Publishing, Box 1181, Port Townsend, WA 98368. TEL 206-385-5097. FAX 206-385-3704. Ed. R.W. Bradford. adv.; bk.rev.; film rev. circ. 6,000. (back issues avail.)
  Document type: consumer publication.
  Description: Review of culture, politics and the arts from a libertarian or classical-liberal perspective.

808.8 US ISSN 0894-251X
LIBERTY AND THE PUBLICK GOOD. 1985. q. $50. Institute for Global Action, Inc., Box 677, Bath, OH 44210-0677. TEL 216-666-2815. adv.; bk.rev. circ. 2,000. (tabloid format; back issues avail.)

051 US
LIBERTY REPORT.* m. Liberty Federation, Box 190, Forest, VA 24551. Ed. Martin Mawyer.
  Formerly: Moral Majority Report.

055.1 IT
LIBRIPER. 1978. bi-m. L.4000. Cooperativa Promozione Culturale s.r.l., Via Marruvio 4, 00183 Rome, Italy. Ed. Umberto Amadigi. adv. circ. 10,000.

057.8 CI ISSN 0350-2562
Z2953
LICKI VJESNIK. 1953. fortn. 50 din.($2) (Socijalisticki Savez Radnog Naroda Zajednice Opcina Gospic) Novinsko Informativna Ustanova u Osnivanju, Seste Licke Divizije 3, Gospic, Croatia. Ed. Stjepan Mazar.
  Formerly (until 1977): Licke Novine (ISSN 0024-2888)

059.951 CH
LIEN HO YUEH K'AN. (Text in Chinese) m. NT.$850 in ROC; Hong Kong $32; Asia $54; elsewhere $60. 555 Chung Hsiao E. Rd. Sec. 4, Taipei, Taiwan, Republic of China. TEL 02-768-0091. Ed. Yang Hsi-han. adv.

800 UK ISSN 0266-1500
LINEN HALL REVIEW. 1984. 3/yr. £4 (foreign £5). Linen Hall Library, 17 Donegall Sq., N. Belfast BT1 5GO, N. Ireland. TEL 0232-321707. FAX 0232-438586. Eds. John Gray, Paul Campbell. adv.; bk.rev.; index. circ. 5,000.
  —BLDSC (5221.126000).
  Incorporates: Irish Booklore - New Series.
  Description: A Northern view of the world of Irish books.

808.8 CN
LINK (MONTREAL). 1936. 2/w. Can.$20. Link Publication Society, Concordia Univ., Sir George Williams Campus, 1455 de Maisonneuve St. W., Montreal, PQ H3G 1M8, Canada. TEL 514-848-7405. Eds. Frances Lodico, Andy Riga. adv.; bk.rev.; charts; illus. circ. 16,500. (tabloid format)
  Formed by merger of: Loyola News (ISSN 0024-7073) & Georgian (ISSN 0016-8467)

808.87 IT
LINUS. m. L.30000. Rizzoli Editore-Corriere della Sera, Via A. Rizzoli 2, 20132 Milan, Italy. Ed. F. Serra. adv.

800 US ISSN 0147-2593
PN1009.A1
THE LION AND THE UNICORN; a critical journal of children's literature. 1977. a. $19 to individuals (foreign $22.80); institutions $36 (foreign $39.80). Johns Hopkins University Press, Journals Publishing Division, 2715 N. Charles St., Baltimore, MD 21218. TEL 410-516-6987. FAX 410-516-6968. Eds. Louisa Smith, Jack Zipes. adv.; bk.rev.; bibl. circ. 750. (reprint service avail. from ISI) **Indexed:** Abstr.Engl.Stud., Arts & Hum.Cit.Ind., Curr.Cont., M.L.A.
  —BLDSC (5221.742000); Faxon; UnCover. **CCC.**
  Description: Discusses literature for children.

808.87 XO ISSN 1210-2121
LISIAK. 1967. m. $24. Obzor, Ceskoslovenskej Armady 35, 815 85 Bratislava, Slovakia.
  Description: Includes humorous articles.

053 GW
LITERARISCHER WEIHNACHTSKATALOG. 1877. a. DM.1.95. K.F. Koehler Verlag GmbH, Postfach 800569, 70565 Stuttgart, Germany. FAX 0711-7892-132. adv.; bk.rev. (back issues avail.) **Document type:** catalog.

052 II ISSN 0024-452X
PR1
LITERARY CRITERION. (Text in English) 1952. q. Rs.100($25) c/o English Dept., Bangalore University, Jnana Bharathi, Bangalore 560 056, India. TEL 355299. Eds. C.D. Narasimhaiah, C.N. Srinath. adv.; bk.rev.; cum.index: 1952-1992. circ. 800.
  —BLDSC (5276.634000); Faxon.

800 UK ISSN 0144-4360
NX645
LITERARY REVIEW AND QUARTO. 1979. m. $54. Namara Group, 51 Beak St., London W1R 3LF, England. Ed. Auberon Waugh. adv.; bk.rev. circ. 15,000. **Document type:** academic/scholarly publication.
  —BLDSC (5276.654800).
  Formerly (until 1982): Literary Review.

052 CN ISSN 1188-7494
LITERARY REVIEW OF CANADA; a review of Canadian books on culture, politics and society. 11/yr. Can.$26.70 to individuals; institutions Can.$35. Literary Review of Canada Inc., 3266 Yonge St., Box 1830, Toronto, ON M4N 3P6, Canada. Ed. P.A. Dutil.

LITERARY STUDIES; a quarterly review of literature and criticism from the Panjab. *see LITERATURE*

809 GW ISSN 0024-4643
PN4
LITERATUR IN WISSENSCHAFT UND UNTERRICHT. 1968. q. DM.44. (Universitaet Kiel, Englisches Seminar) Verlag Koenigshausen und Neumann GmbH, Postfach 6007, 97010 Wuerzburg, Germany. TEL 0931-76401. FAX 0931-83620. Ed. Walter T. Rix. adv.; bk.rev.; bibl. circ. 1,700. **Indexed:** Abstr.Engl.Stud., Bibl.Engl.Lang.& Lit., M.L.A. **Document type:** academic/scholarly publication.
  —SWETS.
  Description: Devoted to textual interpretation and close reading of literature in the English and German languages, reviews.

808.8 GW ISSN 0930-2778
LITERATUR-TELEGRAMM; das aktuelle Kulturmagazin. (Text in English, French, German, Italian) 1986. irreg. DM.17.80. Hofmann-Druck Augsburg, Zugspitzstr. 183, 86165 Augsburg, Germany. TEL 0821-791022. (Subscr. to: Anna Gross, Ernst-Moritz-Arndt Str. 19, 8900 Augsburg, Germany) Ed. Benno Griebel. bk.rev. circ. 500.
  Description: Contemporary discussion about cultural development.

800 LI
LITERATURA IR MENAS. 1946. w. $90. Writers' Union, Universiteto 4, 232600 Vilnius, Lithuania. TEL 0122-612-586. FAX 0122-619-696. Ed. Vytautas Rubavicius. adv.; bk.rev. circ. 7,600.

891.79   KR   ISSN 0024-4821
LITERATURNA UKRAYINA. (Text in Ukrainian) 1927. w. $15. (Spilka Pys'mennykiv Ukrainy) Vydavnytstvo Radyanskii Pismennik, Chkalova Str. 52, Kiev, Ukraine. Ed. B. Rogoza. (also avail. in microform)

891.992   AI   ISSN 0024-483X
LITERATURNAYA ARMENIYA. 1958. m. 15 Rub. Soyuz Pisatelei Armeanii, Marchal Bagramyan 3, 385019 Erevan, Armenia. index.

800   RU   ISSN 0233-4305
LITERATURNAYA GAZETA.* 1929. w. $130. Kostyanskii pereulok 13, Moscow 103654, Russia. TEL 095-200-24-17. FAX 095-200-02-38. TELEX 411294. (Subscr. to: Mezhdunarodnaya Kniga, Moscow, G-200, Russia; Dist. in U.S. by: Victor Kamkin Inc., 4956 Boiling Brook Pkwy., Rockville, MD 20852. TEL 301-881-5973) Ed. Arkady Udaltsov. bk.rev.; film rev.; play rev.; abstr. circ. 1,200,000. (also avail. in microform from KTO) Indexed: Curr.Dig.Sov.Press. Document type: newspaper.

059   RU   ISSN 0132-1986
LITERATURNAYA OSETIYA. **LITERATURNO-KHUDOZHESTVENNYI I OBSHCHESTVENNO-POLITICHESKII ZHURNAL.** 1948. q. (Soyuz Pisatelei Severo-Osetinskoi A.S.S.R.) Izdatel'stvo I R, 362040 Ordzhonikidze, Ossetinian A.R., Russia. Ed. Sergey Kabaloev. circ. 1,000.
   Description: Prose and poetry on culture, history and society.

891.7   RU   ISSN 0024-4856
LITERATURNAYA ROSSIYA. 1958. w. $110. (Soyuz Pisatelei Rossii) Izdatel'skoe Ob'edinenie Pisatelei, Tsvetnoi bul. 30, 103662 Moscow, Russia. TEL 095-2004005. FAX 095-2002755. Ed. Ernst Safonov. bk.rev.; illus.; index. circ. 50,000. (also avail. in microform) Indexed: Curr.Dig.Sov.Press. Document type: newspaper.

057.1   RU
LITERATURNOE OBOZRENIE/LITERARY REVIEW. 1973. m. 12 Rub. Izdatel'stvo Sovetskii Pisatel', Ul. Dobroliubova 9-11, 127254 Moscow I-254, Russia. Ed. Leonard Lavlinskii.

800   UK   ISSN 0263-4635
LITMUS. 1974-1985; resumed 1986. 3/yr. $6. Stukeley Press, The City Lt., Stukeley St., Drury Lane, London WC2B 5LJ, England. Ed. Laurie Smith. adv.; bk.rev. circ. 500. (back issues avail.)
   Former titles (until 1982): Limestone Literary Magazine (ISSN 0308-4787); Limestone.

053   GW   ISSN 0944-453X
LIVE MAGAZIN SAAR; das auflagenstaerkste Stadtmagazin im Saarland. 1983. m. DM.24. H und P Verlag, Neumarkt 2, 66117 Saarbruecken, Germany. TEL 0681-5847394. FAX 0681-5846302. Ed. Andreas Hoyer. adv.; bk.rev. circ. 34,700. Document type: consumer publication.

850   IT
LIVORNOCRONACA - IL VERNACOLIERE; periodico politico satirico. 1961. m. L.25000. Mario Cardinali Editore s.r.l., Scali del Corso, 5, 57123 Livorno, Italy. TEL 880226. adv.; illus.; tr.lit. circ. 16,000. (looseleaf format)
   Formerly: Livornocronaca (ISSN 0024-5321)

052 821   UK
LOBBY PRESS NEWSLETTER. (Text mainly in English; occasionally in German and Italian) 1978. bi-m. £1. Lobby Press, 17 Warkworth St., Cambridge CB1 1EG, England. adv.; bk.rev. circ. 300. (looseleaf format)

053   CN   ISSN 0047-4967
LOEGBERG - HEIMSKRINGLA. (Text in English, Icelandic) 1886. w. Can.$37.45($40) Logberg-Heimskringla Inc., 699 Carter Ave., Winnipeg, Man. R3M 2C3, Canada. TEL 204-284-5686. FAX 204-284-5686. Ed. H.K. Danielsdottir. adv.; bk.rev. circ. 1,900. (tabloid format; also avail. in microform from CML)
   Formed by the 1959 merger of: Loegberg (ISSN 0837-3779); Heimskringla (ISSN 0837-3787)

942   UK   ISSN 0024-6085
PR1
LONDON MAGAZINE. 1954. bi-m. £28.50($67) London Magazine Ltd., 30 Thurloe Pl., London SW7, England. TEL 071-589-0618. Ed. Alan Ross. adv.; bk.rev. circ. 4,000. (reprint service avail. from KTO) Indexed: Br.Hum.Ind., Film Lit.Ind. (1973-), Ind.Bk.Rev.Hum. Document type: consumer publication.
   —BLDSC (5293.854000); Faxon; SWETS.
   Description: Features architecture, painting, films, art, fiction, poetry, and memoirs.

808.8   UK   ISSN 0260-9592
LONDON REVIEW OF BOOKS. 1979. fortn. $48. L R B Ltd., Tavistock House South, Tavistock Sq., London WC1H 9JZ, England. TEL 071-388-6751. FAX 071-383-4792. Ed. Mary-Kay Wilmers. adv.; bk.rev.; index. circ. 18,000. (also avail. in microfilm from UMI; reprint service avail. from UMI) Indexed: Bk.Rev.Ind. (1982-), Child.Bk.Rev.Ind. (1982-), RILA. Document type: bibliography.
   —BLDSC (5294.094000); Faxon; SWETS; UMI.

808.87   US
LONE STAR COMEDY SERVICE; a humor service for the professional comedian, public speakers, and broadcasters. 1984. m. Lone Star Publications of Humor, Box 29000, Ste. 103, San Antonio, TX 78229. Ed. Lauren Barnett. (looseleaf format)
   Formerly: Lone Star Comedy Monthly.

808.57   US
LONE STAR HUMOR. 1983. irreg. (4-6/yr.). Lone Star Publications of Humor, Box 29000, Ste. 103, San Antonio, TX 78229. Ed. Lauren I. Barnett. adv.; bk.rev.; film rev.; play rev.; charts; illus.; tr.lit. circ. 1,000. (back issues avail.)
   Formerly: Lone Star (ISSN 0735-1623)

059.91   ER   ISSN 0134-4536
LOOMING. (Text in Estonian) 1923. m. $72 (effective 1993). (Estonian Writers Union) Kirjastus Perioodika, Parnu mnt. 8, 0090 Tallinn, Estonia. TEL 0142-441-262. FAX 0142-442-484. Ed. Andres Langemets. bk.rev.; illus.; index. circ. 25,100. Indexed: M.L.A.

800   US
LOST AND FOUND TIMES. (Text in English or Spanish) 1975. s-a. $20 for 5 nos. Luna Bisonte Prods, 137 Leland Ave., Columbus, OH 43214. TEL 614-846-4126. Ed. John M. Bennett. adv.; bk.rev. circ. 350. (back issues avail.) Indexed: A.I.P.P.
   Description: Avant-garde poetry, verse, and drawings.

051   US
LOUISIANA POLITICAL REVIEW.* bi-m. Box 6, Baton Rouge, LA 70821-0006. TEL 504-388-9520. Ed. John Maginnis.

053   GW
LUEBECKER WOCHENSPIEGEL. 1978. w. free. Luebecker Nachrichten GmbH, P.O. Box 2238, Konigstr. 55, 23552 Lubeck, Germany. Ed. Jorg Loose. circ. 187,000.

LUST & GRATIE; lesbisch cultureel universeel tijdschrift. see HOMOSEXUALITY

056.9   US   ISSN 0024-7413
DP501
LUZO - BRAZILIAN REVIEW; devoted to the culture of the Portuguese speaking world. (Text in English, Portuguese, Spanish) 1963. s-a. $27 to individuals; institutions $77. University of Wisconsin Press, Journal Division, 114 N. Murray St., Madison, WI 53715. TEL 608-262-4952. FAX 608-262-7560. Ed.Bd. adv.; bk.rev.; bibl.; cum.index every 2 yrs. circ. 650. (also avail. in microform from UMI; back issues avail. in microform; reprint service avail. from UMI,KTO) Indexed: Amer.Hist.& Life, Hisp.Amer.Per.Ind., Hist.Abstr., M.L.A. Document type: academic/scholarly publication.
   —BLDSC (5307.550000); Faxon; UnCover; UMI. CCC.

808.81   US   ISSN 0897-6716
LYRA. (Text in English, French, Italian, Spanish) 1988. q. $15. Lyra Society for the Arts, Inc., 317 77th St., N. Bergen, NJ 07047. TEL 201-861-1941. (Subscr. to: Box 3188, Guttenberg, NJ 07093) Eds. Lourdes Gil, Iraida Iturralde. adv.; bk.rev.; film rev. circ. 700. (back issues avail.)
   Description: Multicultural approach to the study of world literature, creative writing and criticism.

M I S INFORMATION. see COMPUTERS

053.9   NE
MAATSTAF. vol.22, 1974. 10/yr. fl.82.50. B.V. de Arbeiderspers, Singel 262, 1016 AC Amsterdam, Netherlands. Ed.Bd. adv.; bibl. circ. 4,500. Indexed: Arts & Hum.Cit.Ind., Curr.Cont., M.L.A.

052   AT
MACARTHUR ADVERTISER. 1935. w. Fairfax Community Newspapers Pty. Ltd., 317 Queen St., Campbelltown, N.S.W. 2560, Australia. FAX 046-284155. Ed. Lisa Harbormann. adv.; bk.rev. circ. 44,300. (tabloid format)

052   CN
MACEDONIA. (Text in English, Macedonian) 1984. m. Can.$20. Macedonian Publishing Co., P.O.B. 291, West Hill Stn., Scarborough, Ont. M1E 4R6, Canada. Ed. Tanas Jovanovski. circ. 2,000. (tabloid format; back issues avail.)

808.87   UK
MAC'S YEAR (YEAR). 1988? a. £2.50. Chapmans Publishers, 141-143 Drury Lane, London WC2B 5TB, England. TEL 01-497-1199.
   Description: Emphasis is on humor.

808.87   US   ISSN 0024-9319
MAD. 1952. m. (8/yr.). $15.50. E.C. Publications, Inc., 485 Madison Ave., New York, NY 10022. TEL 212-752-7685. Eds. Nick Meglin, John Ficarra. illus. circ. 500,000.

051   US
MADWOMAN.* q. $4 per no. SisterSerpents, 1514 Holly Hill Dr., Champaign, IL 61821-2002.
   Description: Contains confessions from radical feminists who fight against patriarchy and misogyny.

053.1   US
MAGAZIN FUER MITARBEITER - WERK UND LEBEN. 1951. fortn. DM.40. Werkschriften-Verlag GmbH, Bachstr. 14, 69121 Heidelberg. TEL 06221-49064. FAX 06221-49066. Ed. Dieter Neumann. adv.; bk.rev. circ. 120,000. (tabloid format) Document type: bulletin.
   Former titles: Magazin fuer Arbeitnehmer - Werk und Leben; Werk und Leben (ISSN 0049-7142)

054.1   LE
MAGAZINE; l'illustre du proche-orient. (Text in French) 1957. w. $300. Editions Orientales S.A.L., P.O. Box 1404, Beirut, Lebanon. TEL 961-1-202070. FAX 961-1-202070. TELEX 41362 EDIORI. (And: 3 rue du Faubourg St Honore, 75008 Paris, France. TEL 33-1-42654940. FAX 33-1-42654944) Ed. Charles Abou Adal; Pub. George Abou Adal. adv.; B&W page $500, color page $800; adv. contact: Mrs. Claude Sabbagha. bk.rev. circ. 17,500. Document type: consumer publication.

052   UK
MAGIC INK.* no.18, 1975. q. Underground Alternative Press Service - Europe, 22 Dane Rd., Margate, Kent, England. Ed. Ian King. bibl.

800   FR   ISSN 1163-7307
MAIN DE SINGE. 1991. q. 250 F. (foreign 300 F.) Editions Comp'Act, 9 place de la Republique, 01420 Seyssel, France. TEL 50-56-13-12. FAX 50-59-02-90. Ed. Dominique Poncel.

808.87   US
MAINEIAC EXPRESS. a. Dog Ear Press, 132 Water St., Gardiner, ME 04345. TEL 207-737-8116.

059.927   SU
MAJALLAH AL-ARABIYYAH. (Text in Arabic) m. P.O. Box 5973, Riyadh 11432, Saudi Arabia. TEL 966-2-4778990. FAX 966-2-4766464. Ed. Hammad Al-Qadi.

508   IR
MAJALLE-YE DANESH-E RUZ. 1973. q. Rs.200. Arak College of Science, Shahpur Ave., Arak, Iran. Ed. Abdolkarim Qarib.

LITERARY AND POLITICAL REVIEWS

052   IE   ISSN 0791-0770
MAKING SENSE. m. 30 Gardiner Place, Dublin 1, Ireland. TEL 01-741045. Ed. Paddy Gillan.

057.99   BW   ISSN 0025-1208
MALADOSTS'. 1953. m. $8.40. Leninsky pr. 79, 220041 Minsk, Belarus. TEL 0172-318543. Ed. A.S. Grochanikov.

800   II
MALAYALAM LITERARY SURVEY. (Text in English) 1977. q. Rs.20. Kerala Sahitya Akademi, Town Hall Rd., Trichur 680020, India. Ed. Erumeli Parameswarsan Pillai. adv.; bk.rev. circ. 1,000.

052   UK   ISSN 0306-5030
MANCHESTER FREE PRESS.* 1971. m. 95p.($4) Moss Side Press, 136 Withington Rd., Manchester 16, England. bk.rev.; film rev. circ. 3,000.

056   PO   ISSN 0872-3303
MANCHETE. 1983. m. Esc.5000($35) Gabinete 1, Imprensa, Promocao e Relacoes Publicas, Ltd., Rua de Sao Bento, 311, 3o Esq., 1200 Lisbon, Portugal. TEL 01-3961771. FAX 01-305688. Ed. Ilidio Francisco Alves. adv. contact: Maria da Luz Braganca. circ. 58,000. (also avail. in microform; back issues avail.)
   Formerly: A Revista; Which superseded in part: Eles e Elas - a Revista (ISSN 0870-8932)
   Description: Contains political, cultural and sports news. Includes articles on politics, arts, fashion, cinema, theater, literature and music.

059.927   SU
AL-MANHAL. (Text in Arabic) 1937. m. P.O. Box 2925, Jeddah 21461, Saudi Arabia. TEL 966-2-6427831. FAX 966-2-6428853. Ed. Nabih Al-Ansari.

MANIPULATOR. see ART

059   II
MANORAMA WEEKLY. (Text in Malayalam) 1937. w. $29. Malayala Manorama Co. Ltd., P.O. Box 26, Kottayam 686 001, Kerala, India. TEL 481-3615. FAX 481-2479. TELEX 0888-201-MNR-IN. Ed. Mammen Varghese. circ. 1,169,023.

059   II
MANORAMA YEAR BOOK. (Text in English) a. Malayala Manorama Co. Ltd., P.O. Box 26, Kottayam 686 001, Kerala, India. TEL 481-3615. FAX 481-2479. TELEX 0888-201-MNR-IN. circ. 126,125.

800 700   UK   ISSN 0950-5091
NX456
MARGIN; at the edge of literature & ideas. 1986. q. £12($20) Common Margins Ltd., Square Inch, Lower Granco St., Dunning PH2 0SQ, Scotland. (U.S. addr.: 1430 Massachusetts Ave., No. 306-17, Cambridge, MA 02138) Eds. Robin Magowan, Walter Perrie. circ. 2,000. (back issues avail.)
   Description: Publishes those who write from the margins of society.

800   GW   ISSN 0025-2948
MARGINALIEN; Zeitschrift fuer Buchkunst und Bibliophilie. 1948. q. DM.90. Aufbau-Verlag Berlin und Weimar, Franzoesische Str. 32, 10117 Berlin, Germany. TEL 030-22350. FAX 030-2298637. (Subscr. to: Inter Abo Betreuungs GmbH, Postfach 53, 12413 Berlin, Germany. TEL 030-68834451. FAX 030-68834490) Ed. Lothar Lang. bibl.; illus. Indexed: M.L.A. Document type: academic/scholarly publication.

800   US   ISSN 0735-1240
MARK. 1977. a. $3. University of Toledo, Graduate Student Association, 2514 Student Union, Toledo, OH 43606. Ed. J.L.G. Bevins, D. Demuth. adv.; bk.rev. circ. 4,000. **Document type:** academic/scholarly publication.
   Description: Examines short stories and poetry worldwide.

MASARYKOVA UNIVERSITA. FILOZOFICKA FAKULTA. SBORNIK PRACI. D: RADA LITERARNEVEDNA. see LITERATURE

059.927   BA
AL-MASIRAH. 1977. w. Al- Masirah Journalism, Printing and Publishing House, P.O. Box 5981, Manama, Bahrain. TEL 258882. FAX 276178. TELEX 7421. Ed. Khalifa Hasan Qassim.

810 300 700   US   ISSN 0025-4878
AS30.M3
MASSACHUSETTS REVIEW; a quarterly of literature, arts and public affairs. 1959. q. $15 to individuals; libraries $20. Massachusetts Review, Inc., Memorial Hall, University of Massachusetts, Amherst, MA 01003. TEL 413-545-2689. Eds. Mary Heath, Paul Jenkins. adv.; bk.rev.; illus.; index. circ. 1,500. (also avail. in microform from UMI; reprint service avail. from UMI) Indexed: A.I.P.P., Abstr.Engl.Stud., Acad.Ind., Amer.Hist.& Life, Arts & Hum.Cit.Ind., Curr.Cont., Film Lit.Ind. (1990-), Hist.Abstr., Hum.Ind., Ind.Bk.Rev.Hum., Ind.Little Mag., Lang.& Lang.Behav.Abstr., M.L.A., Soc.Sci.Ind., Sociol.Abstr.
—BLDSC (5388.690000); Faxon; UnCover; UMI.

800   UK
MASSACRE. 1990. a. £6.50($15) Indelible Inc., BCM 1698, London WC1N 3XX, England. (Dist. by: Central Books, 99 Wallis Rd., London E9 5LN, England. TEL 081-986-4854) Ed. Roberta McKeown. circ. 300. (back issues avail.) **Document type:** academic/scholarly publication.
   Description: Publishes avant-garde surrealistic literary prose, poetry, and artwork. Seeks to promote experimental new writing to a well-educated and liberal readership.

MASSIS. see RELIGIONS AND THEOLOGY — Other Denominations And Sects

MATATU; journal for African culture and society. see LITERATURE

820 300 700   AT   ISSN 0815-953X
AP7
MEANJIN; a magazine of literature, art and discussion. 1940. q. Aus.$30 (foreign Aus.$40). Meanjin Company Ltd., 99 Berry St., Carlton, Vic. 3053, Australia. TEL 03-344-6950. FAX 03-347-2550. Ed. J. Lee. adv.; bk.rev.; index. circ. 3,200. (also avail. in microform) Indexed: Abstr.Engl.Stud., Arts & Hum.Cit.Ind., Aus.P.A.I.S., Bk.Rev.Ind. (1988-), Child.Bk.Rev.Ind. (1988-), Curr.Cont., Gdlns., Ind.Bk.Rev.Hum., Lang.& Lang.Behav.Abstr., M.L.A., So.Pac.Per.Ind.
—BLDSC (5413.540500); Faxon; UnCover.
   Formerly: Meanjin Quarterly (ISSN 0025-6293)

057.8   CI   ISSN 0025-8229
MEDJIMURJE. 1952. w. 150 din. Socijalisticki Savez Radnog Naroda Opstine Cakovec, Uska Ul. 66, Cakovec, Croatia. Ed. Zika Dordevic.

800   SZ
MEMOPRESS AUSGABE D; Dokumentation ueber Informationen aus Politik, Wirtschaft und Religion. (Text in German) 1966. 16/yr. (in 2 vols., 8 nos./vol.). 12.50 SFr. (foreign DM.15). Memopress-Verlag, CH-8215 Hallau, Switzerland. TEL 053-61-31-44. FAX 053-61-40-14. Ed. Emil Rahm. circ. 4,000. **Document type:** abstracting/indexing.
   Supersedes in part: Memo Press: Aktuelle Presse- und Literatur Hinweise mit Kommentar.

800   SZ
MEMOPRESS AUSGABE K; Kurzgefasste Informationen aus Politik, Wirtschaft und Religion mit Kommentar. (Text in German) 1989. 4/yr. 7.50 SFr. Memopress-Verlag, CH-8215 Hallau, Switzerland. TEL 053-61-31-44. FAX 053-61-40-14. Ed. Emil Rahm. bk.rev.; illus. circ. 50,000. **Document type:** abstracting/indexing.
   Supersedes in part: Memo Press: Aktuelle Presse- und Literatur Hinweise mit Kommentar.

053.1   GW   ISSN 0026-0096
AP30
MERKUR; Deutsche Zeitschrift fuer europaeisches Denken. 1947. m. DM.170. Verlag Klett-Cotta, Rotebuehlstr. 77, 70178 Stuttgart, Germany. TEL 0711-6672-0. FAX 0711-616422. Eds. Karl-Heinz Bohrer, Kurt Scheel. adv.: B&W page DM.1200; trim 195 x 112; adv. contact: Horst Flinspach. bk.rev.; film rev.; illus.; index. circ. 5,800. Indexed: Abstr.Engl.Stud., Amer.Hist.& Life, Curr.Cont., Hist.Abstr., Ind.Bk.Rev.Hum., Phil.Ind. **Document type:** academic/scholarly publication.
—BLDSC (5682.245000); Faxon; SWETS. **CCC.**

051   US
MESHUGGAH; a journal of oddball fiction and subversive thought. 1991. 4/yr. $7. Feh! Press, 147 Second Ave., Ste. 603, New York, NY 10003-5701. Ed. Simeon Stylites. adv. circ. 200. **Document type:** consumer publication.
   Description: Contains fiction and essays with the following themes: oddness, satire, irreverence, humor, eccentricity, absurdism, rantings, social criticism.

052 791.43   AT   ISSN 0814-8805
PN3433
METAPHYSICAL REVIEW. 1984. irreg. (approx. 4/yr.). Aus.$35($25) Bruce Gillespie, Ed. & Pub., G.P.O. Box 5195AA, Melbourne, Vic. 3001, Australia. adv.; bk.rev. circ. 200. (back issues avail.)
   Description: Reviews, criticism and discussion of science fiction, fantasy, music, cinema and literature.

MICHIGAN HISTORICAL REVIEW (MT. PLEASANT). see HISTORY — History Of North And South America

810 300   US   ISSN 0026-2420
AS30
MICHIGAN QUARTERLY REVIEW. 1962. q. $13 (foreign $17). University of Michigan, 3032 Rackham Bldg., Ann Arbor, MI 48109-1070. TEL 313-764-9265. Ed. Laurence Goldstein. adv.; bk.rev.; illus.; index. circ. 2,000. (also avail. in microform from UMI; back issues avail.; reprint service avail. from UMI) Indexed: Abstr.Engl.Stud., Amer.Bibl.Slavic & E.Eur.Stud., Amer.Hist.& Life, Amer.Hum.Ind., Arts & Hum.Cit.Ind., Bibl.Engl.Lang.& Lit., Bk.Rev.Ind. (1989-), Child.Bk.Rev.Ind. (1989-), Curr.Cont., Film Lit.Ind. (1986-), Hist.Abstr., Hum.Ind., Ind.Amer.Per.Verse, Ind.Bk.Rev.Hum., LCR, M.L.A., Mich.Mag.Ind., Mid.East: Abstr.& Ind., P.A.I.S. **Document type:** academic/scholarly publication.
—BLDSC (5755.620000); Faxon; UnCover; UMI.
   Description: Presents fiction, poetry, essays, and interviews.

808.8   US   ISSN 0747-8216
MICROCOSM - LYRICAL WAYS. 1981. a. $5. Quixsilver Press, c/o Robert Randolph Medcalf, Jr., Ed., 144 N. Main St., Biglerville, PA 17307. circ. 100.
   Formerly: Apogee - Lyrical Ways.

808.8   US   ISSN 0747-8895
PS501
MID-AMERICAN REVIEW. 1976. s-a. $12. Bowling Green State University, Department of English, c/o George Looney, Ed., Bowling Green State University, Bowling Green, OH 43403. TEL 419-372-2725. (Co-sponsors: Ohio Arts Council; National Endowment for the Arts) adv.; bk.rev.; circ. 1,000 (controlled). Indexed: Amer.Hum.Ind., Lang.& Lang.Behav.Abstr., M.L.A. **Document type:** academic/scholarly publication.
—UnCover.
   Supersedes: Itinerary (Bowling Green).
   Description: Seeks essays and criticism of current literary trends which focus on contemporary authors, poetry, fiction, and poetry and fiction in translation.

053   GW
MID-ZEITSCHRIFT FUER LITERATUR- & ZEITKRITIK. m. DM.50($30) Verlag Herbert D. Debes, Marktstr. 125, 60388 Frankfurt, Germany. TEL 06109-22612. FAX 06109-22113. Ed. Herbert M. Debes. adv.; bk.rev. circ. 30,000. (back issues avail.)

MIDAMERICA (EAST LANSING). see LITERATURE

052   UK   ISSN 0305-0734
HC410.7.A1
THE MIDDLE EAST. 1974. m. £50($90) I.C. Publications Ltd., 7 Coldbath Sq., London EC1R 4LQ, England. TEL 071-713-7711. FAX 071-713-7898. TELEX 8811757-ARABY-G. Ed. Graham Benton. adv.; bk.rev.; illus.; stat. circ. 10,394. (back issues avail.) Indexed: Curr.Cont.M.E., Key to Econ.Sci., Mid.East: Abstr.& Ind., PROMT. **Document type:** consumer publication.
   ●Also available online.
—SWETS; UMI.
   Description: Covers all major political, economic and cultural events.

LITERARY AND POLITICAL REVIEWS

296   US   ISSN 0026-332X
DS149
MIDSTREAM; a monthly Jewish review. 1955. m. $21. Theodor Herzl Foundation, 110 E. 59th St., New York, NY 10022. TEL 212-339-6000. Ed. Joel Carmichael. adv.; bk.rev. circ. 800,000. (also avail. in microform from AJP,UMI; reprint service avail. from UMI) **Indexed**: A.I.P.P., Abstr.Engl.Stud., Amer.Bibl.Slavic & E.Eur.Stud., Amer.Hist.& Life, Amer.Hum.Ind., CERDIC, Curr.Cont.M.E., Film Lit.Ind. (1973-), G.Soc.Sci.& Rel.Per.Lit., Hist.Abstr., HR Rep., Ind.Artic.Jew.Stud., Ind.Bk.Rev.Hum., Mid.East: Abstr.& Ind., P.A.I.S.
—Faxon; UnCover.

808   US   ISSN 0892-5267
MILDRED.* 1987. 2/yr. $12. Mildred Publishing, 961 Birchwood Ln., Schenectady, NY 12309-3118. TEL 518-374-5410. Eds. Ellen Biss, Kathryn Poppino. bk.rev. circ. 350. (back issues avail.)
Description: Features poetry, short stories, reviews, art and photography with a psychological focus.

059.951   HK
MING PAO MONTHLY. (Text in Chinese) m. HK.$130 in Hong Kong; Macao HK.$160; elsewhere HK.$200($26). Ming Pao Tsa Chih Co., 651 King's Rd., 5th Fl., North Point, Hong Kong. TEL 565-3194. FAX 880-9310. Ed. Poon Yiu Ming.

808.87   US
MINNE HA! HA!; the Twin Cities' sorely needed humor magazine. 1978. bi-m. $16. Box 6626 Minnehaha Sta., Minneapolis, MN 55406. TEL 612-491-1818. Ed. Lance Anger. adv.; B&W page $850. bk.rev.; film rev.; play rev.; illus. circ. 22,000. (tabloid format; back issues avail.) **Document type**: newspaper.
Description: Contains fiction, catoons, art, satire, interviews, photos, letters, collages and non-fiction.

954   II   ISSN 0026-5780
MIRA; a monthly journal of Indian culture. (Text in English) 1933. m. (10/yr.) $2.50. 10 Sadhu Vaswani Rd., Poona 1, India. Ed. Gangaram Sajandas. bk.rev.; illus.

800   US
▼**MISNOMER**. 1992. s-a. Box 1395, Prestonsburg, KY 41653. Eds. Jeff Weddle, Eric Cash.
Description: Showcases both established and relatively unknown poetry on a broad range of themes. Includes fiction and non-fiction.

810 300 700   US   ISSN 0026-637X
AS30.M58
MISSISSIPPI QUARTERLY; the journal of Southern culture. 1947. q. $12 (foreign $16). Mississippi State University, College of Arts and Sciences, Box 5272, Mississippi State, MS 39762. TEL 601-325-3069. FAX 601-325-3299. TELEX 785-045. (Subscr. to: Box 5272, Mississippi State, MS 39762) Ed. Robert L. Phillips, Jr. adv.: B&W page $100; trim 4 1/2 x 7 1/2. bk.rev.; bibl.; index. circ. 860. (also avail. in microform from UMI; reprint service avail. from UMI,ISI) **Indexed**: Abstr.Engl.Stud., Amer.Hist.& Life, Amer.Hum.Ind., Arts & Hum.Cit.Ind., Curr.Cont., Hist.Abstr., Hum.Ind., Ind.Bk.Rev.Hum., Lang.& Lang.Behav.Abstr., M.L.A., Sociol.Abstr. **Document type**: academic/scholarly publication.
—BLDSC (5828.928000); Faxon; UnCover; SWETS; UMI.
Description: Publishes contributions in the humanities and the social sciences dealing with the South and Southern authors past and present.

808.8   CN
MITRE; students' literary magazine. (Text in English) 1893. a. Can.$2.50($2.50) Bishop's University, Student's Representative Council, Lennoxville, Que. J1M 1Z7, Canada. TEL 819-569-9551. Ed. Eric Tartiff. adv.; bk.rev.; illus.; circ. controlled. (tabloid format)
Former titles: New Mitre; Mitre.
Description: Short stories, photo essays, poetry and illustrations from the student body of Bishop's University.

947   GW   ISSN 0026-6833
MITTEILUNGEN AUS BALTISCHEM LEBEN. 1955. q. DM.40. Baltische Gesellschaft in Deutschland e.V., Lessingstr. 5, 80336 Munich, Germany. adv.; bk.rev.; charts; illus.; index. circ. 1,000.

057   PL   ISSN 0866-9791
MLODA POLSKA; tygodnik katolicki. 1989. w. $60. Societas Amicorum Catholicae Juventutis Poloniae, c/o Wieslaw Walendziak, Ed., Ul. Targ Drzewny 3-7, 80-886 Gdansk, Poland. TEL 31-17-51. TELEX 0512858 GWP PL. (Subscr. addr. in U.S.: Witold Balaban, P.S.C. 176 Java St., Brooklyn, NY 11222) adv. circ. 30,000.
Description: Presents article on the political and economic situation in Poland from the Catholic and the conservative point of view.

051   US
MOBILE BAY MONTHLY. 1986. m. $15. Box 66200, Mobile, AL 36660. TEL 205-473-6269. FAX 205-479-8822. Ed. Chris McFadyen. adv. circ. 15,000.

051   US   ISSN 0026-7457
AP2
MODERN AGE. 1957. q. $15. Intercollegiate Studies Institute, 14 S. Bryn Mawr Ave., Ste. 100, Bryn Mawr, PA 19010. TEL 215-525-7501. Ed. George A. Panichas. adv.; bk.rev.; index. circ. 3,500. (also avail. in microform from UMI,KTO,MIM; back issues avail.) **Indexed**: Acad.Ind., Amer.Bibl.Slavic & E.Eur.Stud., Amer.Hist.& Life, Bk.Rev.Ind. (1965-), CERDIC, Child.Bk.Rev.Ind. (1965-), Hist.Abstr., Hum.Ind., Ind.Bk.Rev.Hum., Int.Polit.Sci.Abstr., M.L.A., Mid.East: Abstr.& Ind., P.A.I.S., Soc.Sci.Ind.
—BLDSC (5883.560000); Faxon; UnCover; UMI.

MODERN AND CONTEMPORARY FRANCE. see HISTORY — History Of Europe

059.951   CH
MODERN CHINA/CHIN TAI CHUNG-KUO. (Text in Chinese; table of contents in English) bi-m. Modern China, Inc., 11 Chung Shan S. Rd., Taipei, Taiwan, Republic of China. TEL 02-937-3860. (Or: P.O. Box 20, Yangmingshan Post Office, Taipei, Taiwan, ROC) adv.; bk.rev.; illus.
Description: Covers arts, politics, and events in the Republic of China.

808.8   UK   ISSN 0964-2323
THE MODERN REVIEW. 1991. bi-m. $70 for 2 years. 6 Hopgood St., London W12 7JU, England. TEL 081-749-0593. Ed. Toby Young. adv.: B&W page £1000; trim 374 x 257; adv. contact: Wallace Kingston. bk.rev.; film rev. circ. 30,000. (tabloid format; back issues avail.) **Document type**: bulletin.
Description: Low culture for highbrows; imagine People magazine edited by William Shawn.

859.7   RM   ISSN 1018-0419
MOFTUL ROMAN. 1949. m. 336 lei($46) Ministerul Culturii, Piata Presei Libere 1, Sector 1, Bucharest, Rumania. (Subscr. to: Calea Grivitei 66-68, Box 12201, Bucharest, Rumania) Ed. Mihai Ispirescu. illus. circ. 225,000.
Formerly (until 1990): Urzica (ISSN 0042-1200)

057.1   RU   ISSN 0131-2251
                   CODEN: VMEZA4
MOLODAYA GVARDIYA. 1922. m. $88. Izdatel'stvo Molodaya Gvardiya, Novodmitrovskaya ul. 5A, 125015 Moscow, Russia. (Dist. by: Mezhdunarodnaya Kniga, ul. Dimitrova D.39, 113095 Moscow, Russia; Dist. in U.S. by: Victor Kamkin Inc., 4956 Boiling Brook Pkwy, Rockville, MD 20852. TEL 301-881-5973) Ed. A. Ivanov. adv.; bk.rev.; film rev.; play rev.; bibl.; illus. circ. 640,000. **Indexed**: Curr.Dig.Sov.Press.

MONDE LIBERTAIRE. see POLITICAL SCIENCE

051   US
MONTHLY INDEPENDENT TRIBUNE TIMES JOURNAL POST GAZETTE NEWS CHRONICLE BULLETIN; the magazine to which no superlatives apply. 1983. irreg. $.50 per no. 1630 Allston Way, Berkeley, CA 94703. Ed. T.S. Child. circ. 500. (back issues avail.)

MOTHER INDIA; review of culture. see PHILOSOPHY

370   US   ISSN 0362-8841
AP2
MOTHER JONES. 1976. 6/yr. $18 (foreign $28) (effective Jan. 1992). Foundation for National Progress, 1663 Mission St., 2nd Fl., San Francisco, CA 94103. TEL 415-558-8881.
FAX 415-863-5136. (Subscr. to: Box 2606, Boulder, CO 80322) Ed. Jeffrey Klein. adv. circ. 120,000. (also avail. in microform from UMI; magnetic tape; reprint service avail. from UMI, IAC; back issues avail.) **Indexed**: Abstr.Pop.Cult., Acad.Ind., Access (1977-1988), Alt.Press Ind., Bk.Rev.Ind. (1988-), Chic.Per.Ind., Child.Bk.Rev.Ind. (1988-), Curr.Lit.Fam.Plan., Energy Info.Abstr., Environ.Abstr., Fut.Surv., Left Ind. (1982-), Mag.Ind., Media Rev.Dig., New Per.Ind., P.A.I.S., PMR, Pop.Per.Ind., PSI, R.G., Wom.Stud.Abstr. **Document type**: consumer publication.
●Also available online. Vendor(s): CompuServe, Inc., DIALOG Information Services, Inc.
Also available on CD-ROM. Producer(s): University Microfilms International.
—Faxon; UnCover; UMI.
Description: Progressive periodical featuring high quality investigative reporting, political commentary and features.

800   US   ISSN 0145-4773
MOUNTAIN CALL; for the mountains, their people, their culture. 1973. m. $6 to individuals; institutions $10. Mountain Call, Inc., Box 611, Kermit, WV 25674. Ed.Bd. adv.; bk.rev.; charts; illus.; tr.lit.

028.5   II   ISSN 0027-3104
MUKTA. 1961. fortn. Rs.375($15) Delhi Press Patra Prakashan Ltd., Delhi Press Bldg., E-3 Jhandewala Estate, New Delhi 110 055, India. TEL 11-526311. TELEX 31-63053 DEPR IN. Ed. Vishwa Nath. adv.; bk.rev.; film rev.; illus. circ. 45,000.
Description: Contains fiction and self-improvement articles for youth.

055.1   IT   ISSN 0027-3120
AP3
MULINO; rivista trimestrale di cultura e politica. 1951. bi-m. L.120000. Societa Editrice Il Mulino, Strada Maggiore, 37, 40125 Bologna, Italy.
TEL 051-256011. FAX 051-256034. Ed. Giovanni Evangelisti. adv.; bk.rev.; index, cum.index: 1951-1981. circ. 9,000. (tabloid format; back issues avail.) **Indexed**: CERDIC, ELLIS, Lang.& Lang.Behav.Abstr.

327   AG   ISSN 0027-3333
MUNDO NUEVO.* 1966. m. Arg.$6($8.) Instituto Latinoamericano de Relaciones Internacionales, Montevideo 666, Of. 101, Buenos Aires, Argentina. Ed. Horacio Daniel Rodriguez. adv.; bk.rev.; bibl.; cum.index. circ. 10,000.

052   AT
MURRAY PIONEER. 1892. s-w. Aus.$80. Murray Pioneer Pty. Ltd., Box 832, Renmark, S.A. 5341, Australia. FAX 085-865638. Ed. Peter G. Read. adv. circ. 6,915. (back issues avail.)

808.8   US
MUSCADINE; a seniors' literary magazine. 1977. bi-m. $6. Boulder Senior Citizens Center, c/o Lucille Cyphers, 1940 Walnut St., No. 418, Boulder, CO 80302-4459. TEL 303-443-9748. Ed. Milanda Janborn. circ. 400.

MUSIC TEACHERS LIBRARY. see MUSIC

800   US
THE MUSING PLACE. 1986. irreg. (1-2/yr.). $2 per no. 2700 Lakeview, Chicago, IL 60614.
TEL 312-281-3800. FAX 312-281-8790. Eds. Linda Krinsky, Dale Bowman. adv. (back issues avail.) **Document type**: bulletin.
Description: Features poetry, fiction and political and social satire.

MUSLIM WORLD; a journal devoted to the study of Islam and of Christian-Muslim relationships past and present. see RELIGIONS AND THEOLOGY — Islamic

MWENDO. see LITERATURE

057.85   UK   ISSN 0027-5581
MYSL POLSKA/POLISH THOUGHT; dwutygodnik poswiecony zyciu i kulturze narodu. (Text in Polish) 1942. fortn. $30. Trustees of the Polish National Democratic Party, 8 Alma Terrace, Allen St., London W8 6QY, England. TEL 937-1797. Ed. A. Dargas. adv.; bk.rev.; play rev. circ. 2,000.

LITERARY AND POLITICAL REVIEWS

```
800                            US
```
▼ N C L R - NORTH CAROLINA LITERARY REVIEW. 1992. s-a. $15. East Carolina University, Department of English, Greenville, NC 27858-4353. TEL 919-757-6388. FAX 919-757-4889. Ed. Alex Albright. adv.; illus.

```
053                            GW
```
N H Z. (Neue Hanauer Zeitung); Regionalmagazin Main Kinzig Osthessen. 1982. 8/yr. DM.24. Verlag am Freiheitsplatz, Am Freiheitsplatz, 63450 Hanau, Germany. TEL 06181-28180. adv.; bk.rev. circ. 1,200. (back issues avail.)

```
800 700                        PL
```
▼ NA PRZYKLAD; lubelski miesiecznik kulturalny. 1993. m. 10000 Zl. per no. Stowarzyszenie Popierania Tworczosci, Ul. Peowiakow 12, 20-007 Lublin, Poland. TEL 48-81-213-27. Ed. Waldemar Zelazny. adv.; bk.rev.; illus.
  Description: Covers cultural life and history of Lublin region.

NAPJAINK. see *LITERATURE*

```
057.8            CI            ISSN 0027-7975
```
NARODNI LIST. 1862. w. $50. Narodni List, Lenjinovo Setaliste 4, Zadar, Croatia. Ed. Danijel Vucenovic. adv.; bk.rev. circ. 8,500.

```
057.8            BN            ISSN 0027-8106
```
NAS SVIJET. 1965. m. 40 din.($3) Matica Iseljenika Bosne i Hercegovine, Omladinska 5, Sarajevo, Bosnia Hercegovina. Ed. Petar Alfirevic. adv.

```
057.1            RU            ISSN 0027-8238
PG3227
```
NASH SOVREMENNIK; literaturno-khudozhestvennyi i obshchestvenno-politicheskii zhurnal. 1963. m. $104. (Soyuz Pisatelei Rossii) Nash Sovremennik, Tsvetnoi bul.30, Moscow, Russia. TEL 095-200-2424. (Subscr. to: Mezhdunarodnaya Kniga, Moscow, G-200, Russia) Ed. S.Yu. Kunyaev. bk.rev.; illus. circ. 163,757. **Indexed:** Curr.Dig.Sov.Press, M.L.A.
  —BLDSC (0123.975000).

```
320.9 051        US            ISSN 0027-8378
AP2
```
THE NATION. 1865. w. (except the first week in Jan.; bi-w. in July & Aug.) $48 (foreign $66). Nation Company, Inc., 72 Fifth Ave., New York, NY 10011. TEL 212-242-8400. FAX 212-463-9712. (Subscr. to: Box 10763, Des Moines, IA 50340-0763. TEL 800-333-8536) Ed. Victor Navasky. adv.; bk.rev.; film rev.; music rev.; play rev.; s-a. index. circ. 91,077. (also avail. in microfilm from UMI,PMC; back issues avail.; reprint service avail. from UMI) **Indexed:** Acad.Ind., Alt.Press Ind., Amer.Bibl Slavic & E.Eur.Stud., Bk.Rev.Ind., Bk.Rev.Ind. (1965-), Chic.Per.Ind., Child.Bk.Rev.Ind. (1965-), Energy Rev., Film Lit.Ind. (1973-), Fut.Surv., Hlth.Ind., HR Rep., Mag.Ind., Media Rev.Dig., Mid.East: Abstr.& Ind., P.A.I.S., Per.Islam., R.G., SSCI.
  —BLDSC (6015.675000); Faxon; UnCover; SWETS; UMI.

```
338              GW            ISSN 0027-8408
D1050
```
NATION EUROPA; Monatsschrift im Dienst der europaeischen Erneuerung. 1951. m. DM.118. Nation Europa Verlag GmbH, Postfach 2554, 96414 Coburg, Germany. TEL 09561-94596. FAX 09561-99574. adv.; bk.rev.; illus.; maps; index. circ. 7,500.

```
052              AT            ISSN 0156-8221
```
NATION REVIEW. 1958. m. Aus.$15. General Magazine Company (Australia) Pty. Ltd., P.O. Box 1024, Richmond North, Vic. 3121, Australia. TEL 03-429-5599. FAX 03-427-0332. Ed. Geoffrey M. Gold. bk.rev.; film rev.; play rev. circ. 46,000. (tabloid format) **Indexed:** Aus.P.A.I.S.
  Formerly: Nation (ISSN 0027-836X)
  Description: Covers national current affairs and arts criticism.

```
059              II            ISSN 0300-3809
```
NATUN THIKANA. 1972. q. 71-4 Dr. Nilmani Sarkar St., Calcutta 50, India. Eds. Premanshu Bardhan, Anil De. bk.rev.; film rev.; play rev. circ. controlled.

```
800                            CY
```
NEA EPOCHI/NEW EPOCH. (Text in Greek) 1959. bi-m. POB 1581, Nicosia, Cyprus. Ed. Achilleas Pyliotis. circ. 1,500.
  Description: Greek-Cypriot literary review.

NEA HESTIA. see *LITERATURE*

```
808.87           SZ            ISSN 0028-1786
```
NEBELSPALTER; die satirische schweizer Zeitschrift. 1875. w. 118 SFr. (foreign 136 SFr.) E. Loepfe-Benz AG, CH-9400 Rorschach, Switzerland. TEL 071-414341. FAX 071-414313. Ed. Iwan Raschle. adv. contact: Benno Caviezel. bk.rev.; illus.; circ. 38,864 (controlled). **Document type:** newspaper.

```
054              CI
```
NEDELJNA DALMACIJA. 1971. w. 144 din. Slobodna Dalmacija, Splitskog odreda 4, Split, Croatia. Ed. Miro Jajcanin.

```
053              NE            ISSN 0166-0586
```
HET NEDERLANDSE BOEK. 1852. 6/yr. fl.15. Het Nederlandse Boek, Prinsengracht 1065, 1017 JG Amsterdam, Netherlands. TEL 31-20-6233187. Ed. Wim J. Simons. adv.; bk.rev. circ. 20,000.

```
439.31           NE            ISSN 0028-2383
```
NEERLANDIA. 1896. 5/yr. fl.40. Algemeen Nederlands Verbond, J. van Nassaustraat 109, 2596 BS The Hague, Netherlands. TEL 31-70-3245514. FAX 31-70-3246186. Ed.Bd. adv.; bk.rev.; bibl.; index; circ. 3,000 (controlled).
  —SWETS.
  Description: Information and documentation promoting Dutch culture and language, with focus on Dutch-Flemish cooperation in a united Europe.

```
808              US            ISSN 0277-5166
```
NEGATIVE CAPABILITY. 1981. 3/yr. $15 to individuals; institutions $20. Negative Capability Press, 62 Ridgelawn Dr. E., Mobile, AL 36608-2465. TEL 205-343-6163. Ed. Sue Brannan Walker. adv.; bk.rev. circ. 1,000. **Indexed:** Ind.Amer.Per.Verse.

```
800                            US
```
NEIHARDT FOUNDATION NEWSLETTER. 1970. 2/yr. $15 membership. John G. Neihardt Foundation, Inc., Bancroft, NE 68004. TEL 402-648-7971. Eds. Lori Utechtm, Hilda Neihardt. bk.rev. circ. 800. **Document type:** newsletter.

```
057.1            BW            ISSN 0130-7517
```
NEMAN. (Text in Russian) 1952. m. 9.60 Rub. (Sayuz Pismennikaw Belarusi - Union of Writers of Belorus) Neman, Leninsky pr. 39, 220005 Minsk, Belarus. TEL 0172-331461. Ed. A.P. Kudravets. circ. 90,000.

```
320              GW            ISSN 0028-2626
```
NEMZETOR. (Text in Hungarian) 1956. m. $30. Foerderer Verein "Nemzetor", Ferchenbach Str. 88, 80995 Munich, Germany. TEL 089-1503941. FAX 089-3615610. Ed. Tibor Kecskesi-Tollas. adv.; bk.rev.; film rev.; bibl.; charts; illus. circ. 7,000. **Document type:** newsletter.

```
800 700          AA            ISSN 0548-1600
```
NENTORI; revue litteraire et artistique. 1954. m. $20. Lidhja e Shkrimtareve dhe e Artisteve te Shqiperise - Union des Exrivains et Artistes d'Albanie, Baboci 37z, Tirana, Albania. Ed. Kico Blushi. **Indexed:** Bibl.Ling.

```
057              XO
```
NEPMUVELES. (Text in Hungarian) m. $18. (Cultural Institute in Bratislava) Obzor, Ceskoslovenskej Armady 35, 815 85 Bratislava, Slovakia.

```
051              AU
```
NEUE ORDNUNG. 1949. m. S.220. Wappenverlag, Postfach 256, A-1015-Vienna, Austria. Ed. Franz Frank. adv. circ. 4,500. **Indexed:** CERDIC.

```
053.1            GW            ISSN 0028-3347
AP30
```
NEUE RUNDSCHAU. 1890. q. DM.15. S. Fischer Verlag GmbH, Hedderichtstr. 11, 60596 Frankfurt a.M., Germany. FAX 069-6062-319. TELEX 412410. Eds. Guenther Busch, Uwe Wittstock. adv.; bk.rev.; bibl.; index. circ. 7,000. (also avail. in microfilm from BHP) **Indexed:** Arts & Hum.Cit.Ind., Curr.Cont., M.L.A. **Document type:** consumer publication.
  —BLDSC (6077.740000); Faxon; UnCover; SWETS.
  Description: Literary and political essays.

NEUE SAMMLUNG; Vierteljahres-Zeitschrift fuer Erziehung und Gesellschaft. see *EDUCATION*

```
053                            SZ
```
NEUE SOLIDARITAET;* internationale Wochenzeitung fuer Politik Wirtschaft, Wissenschaft und Kunst. 1973. w. DM.100. Azed AG, Dornacherstr. 60-62, CH-4002 Basel, Switzerland. TEL 06121-806955. Ed. Gabriele Liebig. circ. 20,000.

```
057.1            RU            ISSN 0130-741X
```
NEVA. 1955. m. 2300 Rub.($109) per 1/2 year. (Sankt-Peterburgskii Soyuz Pisatelei) Neva Journal Ltd., Nevskii pr. 3, 191065 St. Petersburg, Russia. TEL 812-31265-37. FAX 812-31108-17. (Dist. in U.S. by: Victor Kamkin Inc., 4956 Boiling Brook Pkwy., Rockville, MD 20852. TEL 301-881-5973) Ed. Boris N. Nikol'skii. bk.rev.; film rev.; play rev.; bibl.; charts; illus. circ. 57,000. (also avail. in microform) **Indexed:** Curr.Dig.Sov.Press, M.L.A.

```
051              CN
```
NEW BREED. 1970. m. Can.$24. Native Communications (Wehtamatowin) Co., 173 Second Ave., S., 3rd Fl., Saskatoon, Sask. S7K 1K6, Canada. TEL 306-653-2253. FAX 306-653-3384. Ed. Gary Laplante. adv.; bk.rev. circ. 10,000. (tabloid format; back issues avail.)

```
808.8            US            ISSN 0734-0222
NX503
```
NEW CRITERION. 1982. m. (10/yr.) $36 (effective Sep. 1991). Foundation for Cultural Review, 850 Seventh Ave., New York, NY 10019. TEL 212-247-6980. Ed. Hilton Kramer. adv. contact: Richard Vaughan. bk.rev. circ. 8,000. (also avail. in microfilm from UMI) **Indexed:** Amer.Hum.Ind., Artbibl.Mod., M.L.A., RILA.
  —BLDSC (6082.993000); Faxon; UnCover; UMI.

```
800              US            ISSN 1050-415X
```
NEW DELTA REVIEW. 1984. s-a. $7. English Department, Louisiana State University, Baton Rouge, LA 70803-5001. TEL 504-388-4079. Eds. Nicola Mason, Catherine Williamson. adv.; bk.rev. circ. 500. (back issues avail.)
  —UnCover.
  Description: Features fiction and poetry of rising writers, essays and interviews.

```
808.8 792        US            ISSN 0893-8563
```
NEW DOG. 1986. s-a. $7. A.W. Baker Publishing Company, Inc., 605 W. Poplar Rd., Sterling, VA 22170. (Subscr. to: 3138 N. Southport, 2R, Chicago, IL 60657) Ed. Scott Baker. circ. 1,000. (back issues avail.)

NEW ENGLAND QUARTERLY; a historical review of New England life and letters. see *LITERATURE*

```
051              UK            ISSN 0950-2378
CB428
```
NEW FORMATIONS. 1987. 3/yr. £30 (foreign £32) to individuals; institutions £50 (foreign £52). Lawrence & Wishart, 144a Old South Lambeth Rd., London SW8 1XX, England. TEL 071-820-9281. FAX 071-587-0469. Ed. Judith Squires. adv.; bk.rev. circ. 500. **Indexed:** Amer.Hist.& Life (until 1991), Hist.Abstr. (until 1991). **Document type:** academic/scholarly publication.
  —BLDSC (6084.189000); UnCover. CCC.
  Description: Tackles questions of culture, politics and ideology both through the critical analysis of cultural practices, products and institutions and also by questioning the assumptions of contemporary theory. Engages in a variety of debates: about meaning and power, sexual and cultural difference, modernity and post-modernism, psychoanalysis and post-structuralism, democracy and civil society, aesthetics and style.

NEW HOPE INTERNATIONAL REVIEW. see *LITERATURE — Poetry*

```
051                            US
```
NEW INDICATOR. 1966. bi-w. $8. University of California, San Diego, New Indicator Collective, Student Center B-023, La Jolla, CA 92093. TEL 619-534-2016. Ed.Bd. adv.; bk.rev. circ. 8,500. (tabloid format)

LITERARY AND POLITICAL REVIEWS

320.5   UK   ISSN 0028-6060
HX3
NEW LEFT REVIEW. 1960. 6/yr. $47 to individuals; institutions $93. New Left Review Ltd., 6 Meard St., London W1V 3HR, England. TEL 071-734-8830. FAX 071-734-0059. Ed. Robin Blackburn. adv.; bk.rev. circ. 8,000. (also avail. in microfiche) **Indexed:** Alt.Press Ind., Amer.Hist.& Life, ASSIA, Br.Hum.Ind., Hist.Abstr., Left Ind. (1982-), Mid.East: Abstr.& Ind., P.A.I.S., Soc.Sci.Ind., SSCI, Stud.Wom.Abstr., World Agri.Econ.& Rural Sociol.Abstr. **Document type:** bulletin.
—BLDSC (6084.450000); Faxon; UnCover; SWETS. CCC.

320.5 800   CN   ISSN 0702-7532
NEW LITERATURE AND IDEOLOGY. French edition: Nouvelle Litterature et Ideologie (ISSN 0703-8011) 1969. irreg. Can.$6 for 4 nos. Canadian Cultural Workers Committee, Box 727, Adelaide Station, Toronto, Ont. M5C 2J8, Canada. (Subscr. to: National Publications Centre, Box 727, Adelaide Station, Toronto, Ont., Canada) bk.rev. circ. 5,000. **Indexed:** Abstr.Engl.Stud., Mid.East: Abstr.& Ind. **Incorporates:** Literature and Ideology (ISSN 0024-4740)

052   CN   ISSN 0713-4789
NEW MARITIMES; an independent, regional bi-monthly. (Text in English) 1982. 6/yr. Can.$19.95($25) New Maritimes Editorial Council Society, 6106 Lawrence St., Halifax, NS B3L 1J6, Canada. TEL 902-425-6622. Ed. Scott Milsom. adv.: B&W page $400; trim 8 1/2 x 11. bk.rev. circ. 1,650 (paid). (also avail. in microform from MML; back issues avail.) **Indexed:** Alt.Press Ind., Can.Per.Ind.
●Also available online.

051   US
▼**NEW NOVEL REVIEW.** 1993. s-a. Elmira College, English Department, Elmira, NY 14901. Ed. L. Diamond-Nigh.

808.8   II   ISSN 0258-0381
AP8
NEW QUEST. (Text in English) 1977. 6/yr. Rs.50 to individuals; institutions Rs.75 (foreign $10). Indian Association for Cultural Freedom, Aboli, 850-8A Shivajinagar, Poona 411 004, India. TEL 55744. Eds. M.P. Rege, M.L. Raina. adv.; bk.rev. circ. 1,500. **Indexed:** C.I.J.E., Lang.& Lang.Behav.Abstr., M.L.A. **Supersedes:** Quest.
Description: Aims to promote a free exchange of ideas and contribute to the development of a free culture in India regardless of caste, creed, or sex through creative writing and criticism.

320.9 051   US   ISSN 0028-6583
AP2
NEW REPUBLIC; a journal of opinion. 1914. w. (48/yr., in 2 vols.). $69.97 (effective 1993). 1220 19th St., N.W., Washington, DC 20036. TEL 202-331-7494. FAX 202-331-0275. (Subscr. to: Box 602, Mt. Morris, IL 61054. TEL 800-827-1289) Ed. Martin Peretz. adv.; bk.rev.; film rev.; music rev.; play rev.; s-a. index. circ. 95,000. (also avail. in microform from BLH,UMI,PMC; reprint service avail. from UMI) **Indexed:** Acad.Ind., Amer.Hist.& Life, Biog.Ind., Bk.Rev.Dig., Bk.Rev.Ind. (1965-), Chic.Per.Ind., Child.Bk.Rev.Ind. (1965-), Energy Info.Abstr., Environ.Abstr., Film Lit.Ind. (1973-), Fut.Surv., Hist.Abstr., Hlth.Ind., HR Rep., Lang.& Lang.Behav.Abstr., Mag.Ind., Media Rev.Dig., Mid.East: Abstr.& Ind., Pers.Lit., PMR, R.G., SSCI, Tel.Abstr., Telegen, TOM. **Document type:** consumer publication.
●Also available online. Vendor(s): DIALOG Information Services, Inc.
—BLDSC (6087.740000); Faxon; UnCover; SWETS; UMI.
Description: Commentary on current political, social, economic and cultural issues in the U.S. and around the world, from a liberal viewpoint.

800 910.03   US
NEW SENSE; the literary quarterly of African American students. 1974. s-a. membership. Northwestern University, African American Students, 1914 Sheridan Rd., Evanston, IL 60201. TEL 312-492-3741. Ed. Paula Edwards. bk.rev.; play rev.; film rev.; illus. circ. 1,000. (looseleaf format)

320.9 052   UK   ISSN 0954-2361
AP4   CODEN: NESSEF
NEW STATESMAN & SOCIETY; an independent political and literary review. 1913. w. £70 to individuals; institutions £85. Statesman and Nation Publishing Co., Foundation House, Perseverance Works, 38 Kingsland Rd., London E2 8DQ, England. TEL 071-739-3211. FAX 071-739-9307. TELEX 28449. Ed. Steve Platt. adv.; bk.rev.; film rev.; play rev.; record rev.; index every 6 mos. circ. 22,271. (also avail. in.microform from UMI,PMC; back issues avail.) **Indexed:** Abstr.Engl.Stud., Acad.Ind., ASSIA, Bk.Rev.Dig., Bk.Rev.Ind. (1965-), Br.Hum.Ind., Child.Bk.Rev.Ind. (1965-), Film Lit.Ind. (1973-), GdIns., High.Educ.Curr.Aware.Bull., Hlth.Ind., HRIS, Key to Econ.Sci., Mag.Ind., Media Rev.Dig., Mid.East: Abstr.& Ind., PSI, Soc.Sci.Ind., SOMA, Stud.Wom.Abstr. **Document type:** consumer publication.
—BLDSC (6088.760500); Faxon; UnCover; SWETS; UMI.
Formed by the 1988 merger of: New Statesman (ISSN 0028-6842); (1962-1988): New Society (ISSN 0028-6729)

051   US   ISSN 0886-0629
NEW STUDIES ON THE LEFT. 1973. q. $10 to individuals; institutions $20. Saxifrage Publications Group, 1484 Wicklow St., Boulder, CO 80303. Ed. Ward Churchill. adv.; bk.rev.; bibl. circ. 1,000. (also avail. in microform from UMI; reprint service avail. from UMI) **Indexed:** Alt.Press Ind., Psychol.Abstr. **Document type:** academic/scholarly publication.
Formerly: Issues in Radical Therapy; **Supersedes:** State and Mind (ISSN 0161-1089) & Issues in Cooperation and Power; Former titles (until 1981): Issues in Radical Therapy and Cooperative Power; Issues in Radical Therapy; R T, A Journal of Radical Therapy; Rough Times; Radical Therapist.

051   US   ISSN 0273-9836
NEW TIMES WEEKLY.* 1970. w. $8. New Times, Inc. (Phoenix), Box 2510, Phoenix, AZ 85002. TEL 602-271-0040. Ed. Michael Lacey. adv.; bk.rev.; film rev.; play rev.; illus. circ. 40,000. (tabloid format; also avail. in microform from UMI; reprint service avail. from UMI)
Former titles: New Times (Phoenix) (ISSN 0047-9942) & Arizona Times.

052   UK   ISSN 0954-2116
NEW WELSH REVIEW. 1988. q. £15($28.50) Welsh Academy and University of Wales, Association for the Study of Welsh Writing in English, c/o Robin Reeves, Ed., 49 Park Place, Cardiff CF1 3AH, Wales. TEL 0222-665529. adv.; bk.rev.; film rev. circ. 1,400. (back issues avail.) **Indexed:** M.L.A. **Document type:** academic/scholarly publication.
—BLDSC (6089.194300).
Description: Covers poetry, prose, literary criticism, with special emphasis on the literatures of Wales.

NEW YORK MAGAZINE. see GENERAL INTEREST PERIODICALS — United States

NEW YORK REVIEW OF BOOKS. see PUBLISHING AND BOOK TRADE

810 700   US   ISSN 0028-792X
AP2
THE NEW YORKER. 1925. w. $32 (Canada $65.27; elsewhere $76) (effective 1993). New Yorker Magazine, Inc., 20 W. 43rd St., New York, NY 10036-7440. TEL 212-840-3800. (Subscr. to: Box 56447, Boulder, CO 80322. TEL 800-825-2510) Ed. Tina Brown. adv.; bk.rev.; film rev.; music rev.; play rev.; illus. circ. 808,545. (also avail. in microform from UMI) **Indexed:** A.I.P.P., Abstr.Engl.Stud., Acad.Ind., Bk.Rev.Dig., Bk.Rev.Ind. (1965-), Chic.Per.Ind., Child.Bk.Rev.Ind. (1965-), Deep Sea Res.& Oceanogr.Abstr., Film Lit.Ind. (1973-), GeoRef., Ind.Bk.Rev.Hum., Mag.Ind., Media Rev.Dig., Music Ind., PMR, R.G., RILA, TOM. **Document type:** consumer publication.
—BLDSC (6089.821000); Faxon; UnCover; SWETS.
Description: Contains fiction, poetry, cartoons, longer essays, articles and profiles of artists, writers, politicians, and other notables, for readers interested in cultural issues.

NEWEST REVIEW; a journal of culture and current events in the West. see PUBLISHING AND BOOK TRADE

808.8   GW   ISSN 0720-6542
NIESPULVER. 1967. irreg. DM.2.50. Satire-Verlag, P.O. Box 210 207, 30402 Hannover, Germany. Ed. Hans Firzlaff. adv.; bk.rev.; illus. circ. 20,000.
Former titles: Hannover Extra; Satire (Magazine); Steintor.

800   NR
NIGERIA. WORK IN PROGRESS. (Text in English) 1972. a. £N25. Ahmadu Bello University, Department of English, Zaria, Nigeria. TEL 069-51667. Ed.Bd. adv.; bk.rev. circ. 500.

NIGHTSUN; a journal of poetry, short-short fiction, and interviews. see LITERATURE

059.91   US   ISSN 0029-1161
E184.A7
NOR OR. (Text in Armenian) vol.48, 1970. s-w. $30. (Armenian Democratic Liberal Organization) Nor Or Publishing Co., 1901 N. Allen Ave., Altadena, CA 91001-3421. FAX 818-797-3050. Ed. Sarkis Minassian. adv.; bk.rev.; illus. circ. 2,000.

055.1   IT
NORD;* settimanale indipendente d'informazione. 1964. w. L.5000. Gianni Cerutti, Ed. & Pub., Via Gen. G. Fara 5, 28100 Novara, Italy. adv.; bk.rev.; film rev.; play rev.; illus. circ. 15,000. (looseleaf format)

056.1   AG   ISSN 0029-1242
NORDESTE. 1960. irreg. Universidad Nacional del Nordeste, Facultad de Humanidades, Av. Las Heras 727, Corrientes, Resistencia, Argentina. Ed.Bd. bk.rev.; charts; illus. circ. 2,400.

053   GW   ISSN 0029-1196
DD801.N56
NORDFRIESLAND (BREDSTEDT); Kultur, Politik, Wirtschaft. (Text in German and Frisian) 1965. q. DM.16. Nordfriisk Instituut, Suederstr. 30, 25821 Bredstedt, Germany. TEL 04671-2081. FAX 04671-1333. adv.; bk.rev.; bibl.; charts; illus.; index. circ. 1,900. **Document type:** bulletin.
—CCC.

058   DK   ISSN 0109-3967
NORDICA; tidsskrift for nordisk teksthistorie og aestetik. (Text in Danish, Norwegian and Swedish) 1984. a. DKK 97.60. (Odense Universitet, Nordisk Institut) Odense University Press, Campusvej 55, DK-5230 Odense M, Denmark. TEL 66-157999. FAX 66-158126.

058   SW   ISSN 0029-1501
AP48
NORDISK TIDSKRIFT FOR VETENSKAP, KONST OCH INDUSTRI. (Text in Danish, Norwegian and Swedish) 1878. 6/yr. SEK 200. Letterstedtska Foereningen Nordisk Tidskrift, P.O. Box 34037, S-100 26 Stockholm, Sweden. TEL 08-6567570. FAX 08-6567570. (Distr. by: Foereningen Norden, Hantverkargatan 33, 112 21 Stockholm, Sweden) Ed. Claes Wiklund. bk.rev.; illus.; index. cum.index: 1925-1974, 1975-1984. circ. 2,750. **Document type:** academic/scholarly publication.

058.82   NO   ISSN 0029-1846
DL401
NORSEMAN; a review of current events. (Text in English and Norwegian) 1943. 5/yr. NOK 250($40) (effective 1992). Nordmanns-Forbundet - Norsemen's Federation, Raadhusgt. 23 B, 0158 Oslo, Norway. TEL 47-22-42-75-14. FAX 47-22-42-51-63. Eds. Johan Fr. Heyerdahl, Dina Tolfsby. adv.; bk.rev.; illus.; index. circ. 15,000.
—UnCover. CCC.
Incorporates (1907-1984): Nordmanns-forbundet (ISSN 0800-6954)

051   US   ISSN 0029-2397
AP2
NORTH AMERICAN REVIEW. 1815. bi-m. $18 (effective 1993). c/o Robley Wilson, Ed., University of Northern Iowa, Cedar Falls, IA 50614. TEL 319-273-6455. FAX 319-273-3509. adv.; bk.rev.; illus.; index. circ. 4,700. (also avail. in microform from UMI,PMC; reprint service avail. from UMI) **Indexed:** A.I.P.P., Arts & Hum.Cit.Ind., Bibl.Engl.Lang.& Lit., Bk.Rev.Ind. (1976-), Child.Bk.Rev.Ind. (1976-), Curr.Cont., Hum.Ind., Ind.Little Mag.
—BLDSC (6148.250000); Faxon; UnCover; UMI.

LITERARY AND POLITICAL REVIEWS

052   UK   ISSN 0265-7295
NORTH WIND. 1982. a. £8($18) George MacDonald Society, The Library, King's College, Strand, London WC2R 2LS, England. FAX 071-872-0207. (Subscr. to: c/o R. Johnson, 61 Longdales Rd., Lincoln LN2 2JS, England) Ed. J. Docherty. adv.; bk.rev. circ. 200. **Document type:** academic/scholarly publication.

800   US
▼**NORTHERN CONTOURS.** 1992. irreg.? Plumas County Arts Commission, Box 618, Quincy, CA 95971.
  Description: Bioregional literary review showcasing the literature and art of Northern California. Includes fiction and poetry.

808.8 811   US   ISSN 0899-708X
NORTHLAND QUARTERLY.* 1988. q. $20. Northland Press (Mesa), 222 W. Brown Rd., No. 9, Mesa, AZ 85201-3423. Ed. Jody Wallace. adv.; bk.rev.; film rev. circ. 750. (back issues avail.)

800   US   ISSN 1058-062X
PN75.F7
NORTHROP FRYE NEWSLETTER. 1988. s-a. Roanoke College, Department of English, Salem, VA 24153. TEL 703-375-2365. Ed. Robert Denham. adv.; bk.rev. circ. 500. (back issues avail.) **Document type:** newsletter.

808.87   US   ISSN 1070-5031
THE NOSE. 1989. bi-m. $15 415-621-4946. 60 Federal St., Ste. 502, San Francisco, CA 94107-1430. TEL 415-541-9856. FAX 415-541-9860. E-mail: jacknose@netcom.com. Ed. Jack Boulware; Pub. Michael Johnson. adv.; bk.rev.; music rev.; video rev. circ. 48,000. **Document type:** consumer publication.
  Formerly: San Francisco Nose.
  Description: Satirical investigative magazine with a focus on the Western US.

051   US
NOTES FROM THE DUMP. 1986. s-m. $25. Box 39, Acworth, NH 03601. TEL 508-226-6515. Ed. Terry Ward. circ. 850. (paid) (looseleaf format; back issues avail.) **Document type:** newsletter.

054.1   FR   ISSN 0048-0967
AP20
NOUVELLE ECOLE. 1968. q. 240 F. (students 200 F.). Editions du Labyrinthe, 41 rue Barrault, 75013 Paris, France. Ed. Alain de Benoist. adv.; bk.rev.; bibl.; charts; illus. circ. 10,000.
—BLDSC (6176.770000).

971   CN   ISSN 0029-4756
NOUVELLE FRANCE;* revue du Canada francais. 1957. q. Can.$4. Associes de Neuve-France, 6463 St. Dominique, Montreal, Que., Canada. Ed. Henri Alain. adv. (also avail. in microfiche from BHP)

054.1   FR   ISSN 0029-4802
NOUVELLE REVUE FRANCAISE. 1953. m. 450 F. Editions Gallimard, 5 rue Sebastien-Bottin, 75007 Paris, France. TEL 33-1-46-59-89-00. TELEX 204 121. Ed. Jacques Redad. bk.rev. (reprint service avail. from KTO) **Indexed:** Arts & Hum.Cit.Ind., Curr.Cont., Ind.Bk.Rev.Hum., M.L.A.
—BLDSC (6176.798000); Faxon; UnCover; SWETS.

NOUVELLE TOUR DE FEU; revue de creation poetique. see LITERATURE — Poetry

057   CI   ISSN 0353-8052
DR301
NOVA MATICA. (Text in Croatian and English) 1951. m. 1200 din.($30) Hrvatska Matica Iseljenika, Trnjanska bb, Zagreb, Croatia. TEL 530-002. FAX 38-41-539-111. TELEX MIH YU 22499. Ed. Boris Maruna. adv.; bk.rev. circ. 7,500.
  Formerly: Matica (ISSN 0025-5920)
  Description: Devoted to preserving Croatian culture for emigrants all over the world.

057   XO   ISSN 1210-0943
NOVA SLOBODA. 1946. w. $55. Strana Slobody - Slovak Freedom Party, Obroncov Mieru 8, 816 18 Bratislava, Slovakia.
  Formerly (until 1991): Sloboda (ISSN 0231-6579)

053.1   SZ
AP30
NOVALIS; Zeitschrift fuer europaeisches Denken. 1946. bi-m. 90 SFr. Verlag die Kommenden AG, Steigstr. 59, CH-8201 Schauffhausen, Switzerland. TEL 053-250023. FAX 053-833404. adv.; bk.rev.; illus.; index. circ. 10,000. **Document type:** consumer publication.
  Formerly: Kommenden (ISSN 0023-3005)

NOVAYA GAZETA. see CHILDREN AND YOUTH — For

057.87   XO   ISSN 0323-2891
NOVE SLOVO; bez respektu. 1944. w. Perex, a.s., Pribinova 25, 810 11 Bratislava, Slovakia. TEL 7-50334. Ed. Emil Polak. adv.; color page DM.1610; trim 235 x 135. circ. 15,000.
  Description: Independent publication covers politics, culture, economy.

808.87   XR   ISSN 0862-6561
AP52
NOVY DIKOBRAZ; satiricky tydenik. 1945. w. 76 Kcs.($33) Studio Dobre Nalady, Na Strzi 26, 140 00 Prague 4, Czech Republic. (Subscr. to: Artia, Ve Smeckach 30, 111 27 Prague 1, Czech Republic) Ed. Vaclav Hradecky. illus. circ. 540,000.
  Formerly (until 1990): Dikobraz (ISSN 0012-284X)
  Description: Emphasis is on wit and humor.

057.1   RU   ISSN 0130-7673
NOVYI MIR; literaturno-khudozhestvennyi i obshchestvenno-politicheski zhurnal. 1925. m. $52. (Soyuz Pisatelei Rossii) Novyi Mir, Maly Putinkovsky per. 1-2, 103806 Moscow, Russia. TEL 095-200-0829. (Dist. in U.S. by: Victor Kamkin Inc., 4956 Boiling Brook Pkwy, Rockville, MD 20852. TEL 301-881-5973) Ed. Sergei P. Zalygin. bk.rev.; bibl.; index. circ. 895,000. (also avail. in microform from MIM,UMI; microfilm from KTO; reprint service avail. from UMI) **Indexed:** Arts & Hum.Cit.Ind., Curr.Cont., Curr.Dig.Sov.Press, Lang.& Lang.Behav.Abstr., M.L.A.
—BLDSC (0126.220000).

NOVYI ZHURNAL/NEW REVIEW. see ETHNIC INTERESTS

056.1   SP   ISSN 0029-5795
NUESTRO TIEMPO; revista mensual de cuestiones actuales. 1954. m. 6000 ptas.($70) Servicio de Publicaciones de la Universidad de Navarra, S.A., Apdo. 177, 31080 Pamplona, Spain. TEL 94-25-2700. Ed. Juan Antonio Giner Junquera. adv.; bk.rev.; bibl.; s-a. index. circ. 10,000. **Indexed:** Amer.Hist.& Life, Hist.Abstr.
—CCC.

860   PH
NUEVA HORIZONTE.* (Text in Spanish) w. P.0.30 per no. Sociedad de Escritores Hispano-Filipinos, Herald Building, 61 Muralla, Intramuros, Manila, Philippines. Ed. Francisco C. Palisoc. adv.; illus. (tabloid format)

NUIT BLANCHE; l'actualite du livre. see LITERATURE

808.8 055   IT
NUOVA ANTOLOGIA. 1866. q. L.100000($77) (effective 1994). Fondazione Spadolini Nuova Antologia, via A. Meucci 6, 50015 Grassina, Florence, Italy. adv.; bk.rev. circ. 8,000. **Indexed:** Abstr.Engl.Stud., Amer.Hist.& Life, Hist.Abstr., RILA.

055.1   IT   ISSN 0029-6201
NUOVA RASSEGNA; periodico di attualita-lettere-arti-cinema-teatro. vol.5, 1970. bi-m. L.40000. Editrice Pellegrini, Via Roma 74, Casella Postale 158, 87100 Consenza, Italy. Ed. Luigi Pellegrini-Cosenza. adv.; bk.rev.; film rev.; play rev.; charts; illus.

NUOVA RIVISTA INTERNAZIONALE/NEW INTERNATIONAL REVIEW; problemi della pace e del socialismo. see POLITICAL SCIENCE — International Relations

055.1   IT   ISSN 0029-6295
AP37
NUOVI ARGOMENTI. 1953. q. L.48000 (foreign L.55200). Arnoldo Mondadori Editore S.p.A., Via Sicilia, 137, 00187 Rome, Italy. TEL 06-47497376. Ed.Bd. adv.; bk.rev.; index. circ. 1,900. **Indexed:** M.L.A.

055.1   IT
NUOVI ORIENTAMENTI. 1974. 6/yr. L.12000. Editrice Nuovi Orientamenti, Via B. Tricarico 11, 13014 Gallipoli, Italy. Ed. Luigi Carlo Fontana. illus. circ. 1,500.

055.1   IT   ISSN 0029-6309
NUOVO AGORA OMAGGIO.* vol.3, 1967. q. L.1500. Villa Benia Rapallo, Genoa, Italy. Ed. Vincenzo Mastrangeli. adv.; film rev.; charts; illus.

059.94   FI   ISSN 0027-7126
NYA ARGUS.* 1908. 20/yr. Fmk.17. Postbox 100, 00251 Helsinki 25, Finland. Eds. Nils-Borje Stormbom, Jerker A. Eriksson.

370   CU   ISSN 0029-6961
LA543.7
O C L A E REVISTA. 1967. m. $20 in N. America; S. America $26; Europe $29; elsewhere $41. (Organizacion Continental Latino Americana de Estudiantes - Latin American Continental Students Organization) Ediciones Cubanas, Obispo No. 527, Apdo. 605, Havana, Cuba. Ed. Carlos Font Fernandez. charts; illus. circ. 10,000.

056   UY
O DOS. bi-m. $8. c/o N.N. Arganarz, Ed., Miguelete 1669, Montevideo, Uruguay.

OBEROESTERREICH; Kulturzeitschrift. see ART

057.8   XV   ISSN 0029-7860
OBZORNIK; mesecna ljudska revija Presernove druzbe. (Text in Slovenian) 1953. m. $25. Presernova Druzba, Opekarska 4a, 61000 Ljubljana, Slovenia. TEL 061-218-909. Ed. Emil Cesar. adv.; bk.rev. circ. 3,900. **Indexed:** GeoRef.

OCTOBER. see ART

057.8   BN   ISSN 0029-8387
ODJEK; revija za umjetnost nauku i drustvena pitanja. 1948. fortn. 400 din.($14.60) Kulturno-Prosvjetna Zajednica Bosne i Hercegovine, Otokara Kersovanija 13, Sarajevo, Bosnia Hercegovina. Ed. Cedo Kisic.

057.1   RU   ISSN 0030-0721
OGONEK. 1923. w. $190. Bumazhny per. 14, 101456 Moscow, Russia. TEL 095-283-7964. FAX 095-943-0070. (Dist. in U.S. by: Victor Kamkin Inc., 4956 Boiling Brook Pkwy, Rockville, MD 20852. TEL 301-881-5973) Ed. Lev Gushchin. adv.; charts; stat. circ. 3,200,000. **Indexed:** Curr.Dig.Sov.Press.
—CCC.

700   US
EL OJITO. 1976. a. $3. New Mexico State University, Department of English, Box 3E, Las Cruces, NM 88003. TEL 505-646-3931. adv. circ. 1,000. (back issues avail.)
  Formerly (until 1987): Ojito Review.

057.1   RU   ISSN 0132-0637
OKTYABR'; nezavisimyi literaturno-khudozhestvennyi i publitsisticheskii ezhemesyachnyi zhurnal Rossii. 1924. m. $123. (Soyuz Pisatelei Rossii) Izdatel'stvo Pressa, Ul. Pravdy, 24, Moscow 125047, Russia. TEL 095-214-6205. (Dist. in U.S. by: Victor Kamkin Inc., 4956 Boiling Brook Pkwy, Rockville, MD 20852. TEL 301-881-5973) Ed. A.A. Ananiyev. bk.rev.; index. circ. 115,400. (also avail. in microfilm from KTO) **Indexed:** Curr.Dig.Sov.Press.
—BLDSC (0127.433000).

056.1   PE   ISSN 0472-948X
ONDAS. 1959. m. Jose A. Valencia - Arenas, Apdo. 3758, Lima, Peru. circ. 5,000.

800   US   ISSN 1055-5609
ONE MEADWAY. 1991. s-a. $12. Sarah Lawrence College, 211 W. 92nd St., Box 47, New York, NY 10025. Ed. April Krassner. adv.

OPCION; revista de ciencias humanas y sociales. see SOCIAL SCIENCES: COMPREHENSIVE WORKS

055   IT
GLI ORATORI DEL GIORNO. 1927. bi-m. Via dei Colli dell Farnesina, 144, 00194 Rome, Italy. TEL 36304174. FAX 36301773. Ed. Avvocato Titta Madia.

ORD & SAG. see LINGUISTICS

LITERARY AND POLITICAL REVIEWS

790 YU
OSMEH; humoristicki magazin. 1974. m. 120 din. Dnevnik, Bulevar 23. Oktobra 31, Novi Sad, Yugoslavia. Ed. Ivan Balenovic.

055.1 IT ISSN 0030-6304
AP37
OSSERVATORE POLITICO LETTERARIO.* 1955. m. L.25500. Corso di Porta Nuova 34, 20121 Milan, Italy. Ed. Giuseppe Longo. adv.; bk.rev.; index. circ. 4,000. **Indexed:** M.L.A.

891.8 XN ISSN 0030-6363
OSTEN; satiricno-humoristicen vesnik. (Text in Macedonian) 1945. fortn. 60 din. Nova Makedonija, Bulevar Jugoslavenske Narodne Armije 68, Skopje, Macedonia. Ed. Vlado Jocik.

808.8 070.4836 US
OSTENTATIOUS MIND. 1986. s-a. $5 (foreign $10). (L B and L N Society) Thursday Press, c/o Patricia D. Coscia, Box 7415, JAF Sta., New York, NY 10116-4630. TEL 718-680-3899. adv.; bk.rev.; illus.; index. circ. 200. (looseleaf format; back issues avail.)
Description: Discusses politics, society and the psyche.

051 US
OTTERBEIN MISCELLANY. (Text in English, French and German) 1965-1987; resumed 1991. a. $5. Otterbein College, Westerville, OH 43081. TEL 614-890-3000. Ed. James Bailey. bk.rev.; circ. 300 (controlled).
Description: Forum for Otterbein faculty and staff. Publishes essays, reviews, poetry and short fiction.

059.92 LE ISSN 0002-3965
AL-OUSBOU' AL-ARABI. 1959. w. £L37($200) Editions Orientales S.A.L., P.O. Box 1404, Beirut, Lebanon. TEL 961-1-202070. TELEX 41362 EDIORI. (And: 3 rue du Faubourg St Honore, 75008 Paris, France. TEL 33-1-42654940. FAX 33-1-42654944) Ed. Charles Abou Adal; Pub. George Abou Adal. adv.: B&W page $3500; color page $5000; adv. contact: Chucri Maalouf. illus. circ. 84,086. **Document type:** consumer publication.

059 919 720 IS ISSN 0333-6271
OUT OF JERUSALEM. 1970. q. free. Jerusalem Committee, 36 Keren Hayesod, P.O.B. 1312, Jerusalem, Israel. FAX 972-2-668374. TELEX 26210-SHALMIL. Ed. Daniel Furman. bk.rev. circ. 2,500. **Indexed:** Avery Ind.Archit.Per.
Description: Research reports, press clippings, photo reports on urban planning and cultural and political coexistence in Jerusalem.

052 AT ISSN 0030-7416
AP7
OVERLAND. 1954. q. Aus.$26($40) to individuals; pensioners & students Aus.$20; foreign Aus.$50. Overland Society Ltd., 361 Pigdon St., North Carlton, Vic. 3054, Australia. TEL 03-380-1152. FAX 03-380-2586. adv.; bk.rev.; film rev.; play rev.; illus.; index every 2 yrs. circ. 2,500. (also avail. in microfilm from UMI; reprint service avail. from UMI; back issues avail.) **Indexed:** Arts & Hum.Cit.Ind., Aus.P.A.I.S., Curr.Cont., M.L.A.
—Faxon; UnCover; UMI.
Description: Covers current creative writing in fiction, poetry, literary criticism, history and social comment.

808 792 US
OVERSIGHT. 1989. every 9 m. (Angels Gate Cultural Center) Oversight, Box 29292, Los Angeles, CA 90029-0292. TEL 213-665-5328. Ed. Franklin Odel. adv.; bk.rev.; illus. circ. 2,000. (tabloid format; back issues avail.)
Description: Features artists who work through community arts organizations, including photography, fine arts, fiction, music, film, and news of the Los Angeles art scene.

051 US
OVERTHROW. 1979. m. $10. Youth International Party Information Service, 9 Bleeker St., New York, NY 10012. TEL 212-533-5028. Ed. Alice Torbusch. adv.; bk.rev.; illus.; tr.lit. circ. 15,000. (tabloid format; also avail. in microform from UMI) **Indexed:** Alt.Press Ind.
Supersedes (1973-1978): Yipster Times.

808.8 US
OVERTONE SERIES. 1973. q. $8. Overtone Press, c/o Otis Brown, 8517 Thouron St., Philadelphia, PA 19150. TEL 215-386-4279. Eds. Otis Brown, Beth Brown. circ. 2,500.

052 UK ISSN 0030-7645
LH5
OXFORD. 1932. s-a. membership. Oxford Society, 41 Wellington Sq., Oxford OX1 2JF, England. FAX 0865-270708. Ed. H.A. Hurren. adv.; bk.rev.; illus. circ. 40,000. **Document type:** academic/scholarly publication.

OXFORD MAGAZINE. see LITERATURE

800 US
OXFORD REVIEW. 1985. m. free. Oxford Books, Inc., 360 Pharr Rd., N.E., Atlanta, GA 30305. TEL 404-262-3333. Ed. Doug Merrill. adv.; bk.rev.; video rev.; circ. 227,000 (controlled). (tabloid format) **Document type:** newsletter.
Description: Author interviews, reviews and articles on new developments in the book publishing world.

P N REVIEW. see LITERATURE — Poetry

808.8 800 DK ISSN 0109-4831
P S; tidsskrift for spontan satire, fjollet filosofi, funny fiction and lojerlig ligegyldighed. 1981. irreg. (3-4/yr.). DKK 54. Kreativ Filosofi Forening, Aakjaersvej 3, 6600 Vejen, Denmark. Ed. Bjarne Poulsen. adv.; bk.rev.; illus. circ. 200.
Formerly: Philosophus (ISSN 0108-7460)

808.81 US
PACIFIC REVIEW; a magazine for poetry and prose. 1983. a. $6.50. California State University, San Bernardino, 5500 University Pkwy., San Bernardino, CA 92407. TEL 714-880-5894. Ed. James Brown. adv.; bk.rev.; film rev.; play rev.; illus. circ. 750. (back issues avail.)

051 US
PAGAN PLACE. 1990. irreg., no.5, 1992. $5 for 3 issues. Box 83, New York, NY 10029. TEL 212-249-0630. Ed. Bob Martens.
Description: Covers the latest news, ooze and schmooze from around the world.

056.9 BL
PAGINA ABERTA. 1991. bi-m. Cr.$5000 per no. Editora Brasil Urgente, Rua Melo Palheta, 57, 05002 Sao Paulo, Brazil. TEL 011-872-5671. FAX 011-864-9320. Ed. Andre Singer. circ. 30,000.

056 PE
PAGINAS. no.89, 1988. bi-m. $60 in Latin America; N. America $65; elsewhere $70. Centro de Estudios y Publicaciones, Camilo Carrillo 479, Jesus Maria, Apdo. 11-0107, Lima, Peru. TEL 51-14-33-6453. FAX 51-14-331078. bk.rev.

055 IT
PAGINE DELLA DANTE. c/o Piazza Firenze, 27, Rome, Italy. Ed. E.G. di Giura.

059.951 HK ISSN 1022-6435
PAI SHING SEMI-MONTHLY. (Text in Chinese) 1981. w. HK.$320 (foreign $70). Pai Shing Publishing Ltd., Rm. 1602 Eastern Harbour Centre, 28 Hoi Chak St., North Point, Hong Kong. TEL 852-880-9880. FAX 852-561-9328. Ed. Lau Chi Sun. adv.; illus. circ. 25,000.
Former titles (until Nov. 1993): Pai Shing Newsweek (ISSN 1021-6170); (until Apr. 1993): Pai Shing Semi-Monthly.
Description: Covers news, literary, business and economics, finance, political reviews, real estate, comics, film, music and consumer education.

PAIDEIA; rivista letteraria di informazione bibliografica. see PUBLISHING AND BOOK TRADE

056.1 CU ISSN 0552-9395
PALANTE. 1966. m. $34 in S. America; N. America $36; elsewhere $42. Ediciones Cubanas, Obispo No. 527, Apdo. 605, Havana, Cuba. TEL 7-3-5098. Dir. Rosendo Gutierrez Roman. illus. circ. 235,000.

808.8 700 II
PANDULIPI. (Text in Bengali) 1969. q. Rs.6. Pandulipi Club, 5-1 D.T.N. Chatterji St., Calcutta 50, India. Ed. Debdas Bhattacharya. adv.; bibl. circ. 2,000.

PANEUROPA DEUTSCHLAND. see POLITICAL SCIENCE — International Relations

059.95 HK
PANORAMA MAGAZINE/TA CH'ENG. (Text in Chinese) m. HK.$130 (foreign HK.$170($22)). 1207 Loon Kee Bldg., 267 Des Voeux Rd., Central, Hong Kong. TEL 5532432. adv.

PANURGE. see LITERATURE

808.8 US
PAPER NEWS. 1980. irreg. Vanity Press, 160 Sixth Ave., New York, NY 10013. TEL 212-925-3823. Ed. Tuli Kupferberg. circ. 500.

058 DK ISSN 0901-201X
PARA-NYT;* kritisk forum for off-beat litteratur og pseudovidenskab. 1985. irreg. price varies. Wegner Forlag, Postbox 6, 9320 Hjallerup, Denmark. bk.rev.; illus. circ. 300.
Formed by the merger of (1981-1984): Skeptica (ISSN 0107-2900); (1983-1984): Skeptica Newsletter (ISSN 0109-629X)

059.91 II ISSN 0031-1553
PARABAS. (Text in Bengali) 1970. m. Rs.2.50. 21-B, Quarter-6D, Chittaranjan, West Bengal, India. Ed. Aroon Kumar Chatterjee. bk.rev.; play rev.; circ. controlled.

051 US
PARAMETERS (PORTLAND); an occasional newsletter of critical issues. irreg. Circle Forum, Box 176, Portland, OR 97207. **Indexed:** Air Un.Lib.Ind., Amer.Bibl.Slavic & E.Eur.Stud., PROMT. **Document type:** newsletter.

837 GW ISSN 0031-1855
PARDON;* die Deutsche satirische Monatsschrift. 1962. m. DM.48. Pardon Verlagsgesellschaft mbH, Am Urselback 6, 6000 Frankfurt, Germany. Ed. Hans A. Nikel. adv.; bk.rev.; illus. circ. 220,000.

054.1 FR ISSN 0223-5765
PARLEMENTS ET FRANCOPHONIE. 1969. q. 150 F.($2) Assemblee Internationale des Parlementaires de Langue Francaise, 235 bd. St. Germain, 75007 Paris, France. TEL 47-05-26-87. TELEX AIPLF 202562. adv.; bk.rev.; charts; illus.; stat. circ. 2,000.
Formerly: Revue des Parlementaires de Langue Francaise.

810 US ISSN 0031-2525
HX1
PARTISAN REVIEW. 1934. q. $18. (Boston University) Partisan Review, Inc., 236 Bay State Rd., Boston, MA 02215. TEL 617-353-4260. FAX 617-353-7444. (Subscr. to: Boston University Scholarly Publications, Subscr. Dept., 985 Commonwealth Ave., Rm. 230, Boston, MA 02215. TEL 617-353-4106) Ed. William Phillips. adv.; bk.rev.; film rev.; play rev.; index. circ. 10,000. (also avail. in microform from UMI,PMC; reprint service avail. from UMI) **Indexed:** A.I.P.P., Abstr.Engl.Stud., Acad.Ind., Amer.Bibl.Slavic & E.Eur.Stud., Amer.Hist.& Life, Arts & Hum.Cit.Ind., Bk.Rev.Ind. (1965-), Child.Bk.Rev.Ind. (1965-), Curr.Cont., Film Lit.Ind. (1990-), Hist.Abstr., Hum.Ind., Ind.Bk.Rev.Hum., Lang.& Lang.Behav.Abstr., M.L.A., Mag.Ind., Mid.East: Abstr.& Ind. **Document type:** academic/scholarly publication.
—BLDSC (6407.650000); Faxon; UnCover; SWETS; UMI.

PASSAGES. see ETHNIC INTERESTS

808.8 US ISSN 0731-4663
PASSAIC REVIEW. 1979. s-a. $6. Forstmann Library, 195 Gregory Ave., Passaic, NJ 07055. Ed. Richard P. Quatrone. adv.; bk.rev. circ. 1,000.

800 UK ISSN 0960-3697
PASSPORT. 1990. s-a. £14. 5 Parsonage St., Wistow, Huntingdon, Cambs PE17 2QD, England. TEL 0487-822100. Eds. Mike Gerrard, Thomas McCarthy. circ. 1,000. **Document type:** consumer publication.

322.44 FR
PATRIOTE GUADELOUPEEN.* vol.5, 1974. m. 20 F. Association Generale des Etudiants Guadeloupeens, 85 rue Beaubourg, 75003 Paris, France. Ed. Frantz Succab. bk.rev.; illus.

LITERARY AND POLITICAL REVIEWS

810 US ISSN 0031-3262
PN2
PAUNCH. 1963. 2/yr. $10 to individuals; institutions $14. State University of New York at Buffalo, Department of English, 123 Woodward Ave., Buffalo, NY 14214. TEL 716-836-7332. Ed. Arthur Efron. bk.rev.; cum.index. circ. 200. **Indexed:** A.I.P.P., Abstr.Engl.Stud., Ind.Amer.Per.Verse, M.L.A.
—BLDSC (6412.989000); UnCover.

891.8 XV ISSN 0031-3289
PAVLIHA. (Text in Slovenian) 1944. w. $50. Pavliha, Kardeljeva 4, Ljubljana, Slovenia. Ed. Joze Petelin.

051 US
PEACE PRESS. 1980. 10/yr. $30 membership (low-income $15). Sonoma Country Center for Peace & Justice, 540 Pacific Ave., Santa Rosa, CA 95404. TEL 707-575-8902. Ed.Bd. bk.rev. circ. 2,500.
Formerly (until 1986): Nuke Notes Solidaridad; Formed by the merger of: Peace Network News; Nuke Notes; Solidaridad.
Description: Covers peace, justice and environmental issues in Sonoma County and the rest of the world. Includes a calendar of events.

052 UK
PEACEMAKER. 1973. bi-m. c/o Guy Otten, Ed., 168 Hamilton Rd., Longsight, Manchester M13 OPG, England. bk.rev. circ. 400.

820 SZ ISSN 1013-1191
PEAKE STUDIES; dedicated to the life and work of Mervyn Peake (1911-1968). (Text in English) 1988. s.a. varies. c/o G. Peter Winnington, Ed. & Pub., Les 3 Chasseurs, CH-1413 Orzens, Switzerland. FAX 021-8877976. adv.; bk.rev.; play rev.; illus. (back issues avail.) **Document type:** academic/scholarly publication.

951 HK ISSN 0031-4110
PEKING INFORMERS. 1960. s-m. HK.$800($100) Continental Research Institute, G.P.O. Box 5699, Hong Kong, Hong Kong. Ed. Chow Ching-Wen. (back issues avail.)

810 US ISSN 0097-496X
PS1
PEMBROKE MAGAZINE. 1969. a. $5. (Pembroke State University) The Pilot, Box 60, Pembroke, NC 28372. TEL 919-521-6358. Ed. Shelby Stephenson. adv.; bk.rev.; illus.; cum.index: 1969-73. circ. 600. (also avail. in microfilm from UMI; reprint service avail. from UMI) **Indexed:** A.I.P.P., Amer.Hum.Ind.
—UMI.

800 US
PEMMICAN. a. Box 16374, St. Paul, MN 55116-0374. Ed. Robert Edwards.

PEN IN HAND. see *JOURNALISM*

056 CR
F1421
PENSAMIENTO CENTROAMERICANO. 1960. q. $18 in Central America; S. America $24; N. America $30; Europe $34; Asia $36. Asociacion Libro Libre, Apdo. 1154-1250, Escazu, Costa Rica. FAX 286028. Ed. Xavier Zavala Cuadra. adv.; bk.rev.; bibl.; illus.; stat.; index. circ. 3,000. (also avail. in microform from UMI; reprint service avail. from UMI) **Indexed:** Amer.Hist.& Life, Hisp.Amer.Per.Ind., Hist.Abstr. **Document type:** academic/scholarly publication.
—UMI.
Former titles (until 1992): Revista del Pensamiento Centroamericano (ISSN 0378-3340); (until 1972): Revista Conservadora del Pensamiento Centroamericano (ISSN 0034-7477)

320.531 IT
PENSARE FAENZA/THINKING ABOUT FAENZA. 1904-1924; resumed 1946-1958; resumed 1966. s-m. L.12000. Unione Comunale Partito Socialista Italiano di Faenza, Via 20 Settembre 29, Faenza, Italy. TEL 0546 21055. Ed. Renato Cavina. adv. circ. 4,000. (tabloid format)
Formerly (until 1987): Socialista (ISSN 0037-8275)

055 809 IT
PENSIERO ED ARTE. q. Via Calefati, 379, Bari, Italy. Ed. G. Spinelli de'Santelena.

296 US ISSN 0735-455X
THE PEOPLE TAKE THE LEAD. a. American Jewish Committee, United States Information Service, 065 E. 56th St., New York, NY 10022. TEL 212-751-4000.

051 US ISSN 0048-332X
PEOPLE UNITED TO SAVE HUMANITY. P.U.S.H.-OPERATION PUSH. 1970. m. $3. 930 E. 50th St., Chicago, IL 60615. TEL 312-373-3366. adv.; charts; illus.

051 US ISSN 1071-7250
PEOPLE'S CULTURE. 1990. bi-m. $15. People's Culture, Box 5224, Kansas City, KS 66119. TEL 913-588-1996. Ed. Fred Whitehead. **Document type:** newsletter.
Description: Perspective is based on the great tradition of Midwestern radical and progressive thought and life.

052 RU ISSN 0201-4432
PERESTROIKA. French edition (ISSN 0201-4424) (Edition in English, French, Portuguese) 1990. m. Perestroika Magazine, Editorial Office, 7 Bolshaya Pochtovaya St., Moscow 107082, Russia. Ed. Yekaterina Golubeva.

808.87 KR ISSN 0031-5176
PERETS. (Text in Ukrainian) 1927. fortn. $4.20. Vul. P. Nesterova 4, 252009 Kiev, Ukraine. TEL 044-441-8214. illus. circ. 1,946,900.

056 GT
PERRAJE. irreg.? 14 Avda. 17-12 Interior 13-A, Zona 11, Guatemala City, Guatemala. Ed. Marco Vinicio Mejia.
Description: Independent literary review.

800 FR ISSN 0181-4087
DT348
PEUPLES NOIRS, PEUPLES AFRICAINS. 1978. q. 250 F.($8) Editions des Peuples Noirs, 82, Av. de la Porte-des-Champs, 76000 Rouen, France. TEL 35-89-31-97. bk.rev. circ. 1,500. (back issues avail.) **Indexed:** Curr.Cont.Africa, Documentatieblad.

PHOEBE. see *LITERATURE*

052 DK
PHYSIOGNOMY. (Text in English) 1970. 3/yr. DKK 30($6) Danish Centre for Renewable Energy, c/o David Gould, Ed., Asgard, Sdr. Ydby, DK-7760 Hurup Thy, Denmark. adv. circ. 500.

052 CN ISSN 0710-3034
PIG PAPER. 1975. s-a. $5. Pig Productions, 70 Cotton Drive, Mississauga, Ont. L5G 1Z9, Canada. TEL 416-278-6594. Ed. Gary Pig Gold. adv.; bk.rev.; film rev. circ. 1,000. (back issues avail.)
Description: Humorous overview of the mass media.

PIRANESI; Italienske studier. see *LINGUISTICS*

051 US ISSN 1060-2542
PLAGUE WATCH. (Also avail. on diskette) 1981. q. $23.50 (foreign $30). DeMigalt Media Group, Box 6, Bucyrus, MO 65444-0006. TEL 713-863-0244. FAX 713-864-2607. (And: 519-36 Mie-ken, Owase-shi, Namaida 1113-35, Japan) Ed. John Brisbin. bk.rev.; film rev.; bibl.; stat. circ. 750. (tabloid format; back issues avail.)
●Also available online.
Formerly (until 1991): Journal of Ad-Jective Contagion.
Description: Dedicated to the worldwide tracking of contagious maladies of the body, mind, and spirit.

PLAINSONG. see *LITERATURE — Poetry*

057.8 BU ISSN 0032-0528
AP58.B8
PLAMUK; spisanie za literatura, izkustvo i publitsistika. 1924. m. 6 lv.($8) Suiuz na Bulgarski Pisateli, 5, Ul. Angel Kanchev, Sofia, Bulgaria. (Dist. by: Hemus, 6, Rouski Blvd., 1000 Sofia, Bulgaria) bk.rev.; illus. circ. 11,000. **Indexed:** M.L.A.

PLANET DRUM BUNDLES. see *ENVIRONMENTAL STUDIES*

051 US
PLEIADES MAGAZINE. 1984. s-a. $9. John L. Moravec, Ed. & Pub., 6677 W. Colfax Ave., Ste. D, Box 357, Lakewood, CO 80214. bk.rev. circ. 10,000.

056.1 CK
PLUMA; politica, economia, literatura, arte. 1975. m. Col.$250. Fundacion Pluma, Apdo. Aereo 12190, Bogota D.E., Colombia. Ed. Jorge Valencia Jaramillo. adv.; bk.rev.; film rev.; illus. circ. 70,000.

056.1 AG
PLUMA Y PINCEL; para la difusion del arte y la cultura latinoamericanos. 1976. irreg. Editorial Arte y Letras de America, Nicaragua 5925, Buenos Aires, Argentina. Ed. Romeo Medina.

800 CY
PNEUMATIKI KYPROS/CULTURAL CYPRUS. (Text in Greek) 1960. m. Nicosia, Cyprus. TEL 357-2-659001. Ed. Kypros Chrysanthis.
Description: Explores a variety of original literature.

POET NEWS. see *LITERATURE — Poetry*

800 808 US ISSN 0731-5236
PN1042
POETICS JOURNAL. 1982. irreg. $10 per no. 2639 Russell St., Berkeley, CA 94705. TEL 510-548-1817. Eds. Lyn Hejinian, Barrett Watten. bk.rev. circ. 750.
—UnCover.
Description: Essays on contemporary poetic theory written by poets and other artists.

800 US ISSN 0333-5372
PN1039
POETICS TODAY; an international journal for theory and analysis of literature and communication. (Text in English) 1979. q. $32 to individuals (foreign $40); institutions $72 (foreign $80); students $16 (foreign $24). (Porter Institute for Poetics and Semiotics) Duke University Press, Box 90660, Durham, NC 27708-0660. TEL 919-687-3600. FAX 919-688-4574. Ed. Itamar Even-Zohar. adv.; bk.rev.; index. circ. 1,000. **Indexed:** Arts & Hum.Cit.Ind., Bibl.Ling., Bk.Rev.Ind. (1984-), Can.Rev.Comp.Lit., Child.Bk.Rev.Ind. (1984-), Curr.Cont., Film Lit.Ind. (1990-), Ind.Bk.Rev.Hum., Lang.& Lang.Behav.Abstr., M.L.A.
—BLDSC (6541.745000); Faxon; UnCover; SWETS; UMI. **CCC.**
Refereed Serial

811 FR ISSN 0032-2024
PN3
POETIQUE; revue de theorie et d'analyse litteraires. 1970. q. 330 F. (foreign 360 F.). Editions du Seuil, 27 rue Jacob, 75261 Paris Cedex 06, France. TEL 1-40-46-50-50. FAX 1-40-46-51-43. TELEX 270 024. (Subscr. to: B.S.I., 49 rue de la Vanne, 92120 Montrouge, France) Ed.Bd. adv.; bk.rev.; bibl. **Indexed:** Arts & Hum.Cit.Ind., Bibl.Ling., Can.Rev.Comp.Lit., Curr.Cont., M.L.A.
—Faxon; SWETS. **CCC.**

051 YU ISSN 0353-3832
DR2043
POGLEDI (KRAGUJEVAC)/VIEWS. (Text in Serbian) 1980. fortn. 480 din.($60) N I P "Pogledi", 27 Mart 14, 34000 Kragujevac, Serbia, Yugoslavia. TEL 034 49-031. Ed. Miloslav Samardzic. adv.; bk.rev. circ. 90,000.

057.8 XN ISSN 0032-2245
POGLEDI (SKOPJE); spisanie za opstestveni prasanja. (Text in Macedonian) 1963. bi-m. $9.10. Makedonsko Izdanie na Komunist, Box 313, Skopje, Macedonia. Ed. Dusko Popovski.

808.8 US
POISONED PEN. 1978. q. $20. c/o Jeffrey Meyerson, 8801 Shore Rd., Apt. 6A East, Brooklyn, NY 11209-5409. bk.rev. circ. 350.

059 IS
POLITICA. 1985. 6/yr. $38 (in N. America $55). Politica Association, P.O. Box 23075, Tel Aviv, Israel. TEL 972-3-5101529. FAX 972-3-5100008. Ed. Gideon Samet. adv.; bk.rev.
Description: Focuses on Israeli social, political and cultural concerns.

POLITICA ED ECONOMIA/POLITICS AND ECONOMICS. see *POLITICAL SCIENCE*

055 IT
POLITICA POPOLARE; rassegna di ispirazione sturziana. 1954. m. Via Costantinopoli 84, 80138 Naples, Italy. TEL 091 45-99-49. circ. 2,000.

LITERARY AND POLITICAL REVIEWS

056   EC
POLITICA Y SOCIEDAD. 1984. bi-m. $50. (Archivo de Historia Social Contemporanea) I N F O C, Casilla 235-B, Quito, Ecuador. Eds. Nelson Argones, Alexei Paez.

808.87   SG   ISSN 0850-1807
POLITICIEN. 1977. w. $300. Consortium Africain de Documentation & Presse, Zone B, Villa N: 22B, B.P. 11018, Dakar, Senegal. TEL 24-43-24. Ed. Mam Less Dia.

808   AG
POLITICON; ni a la izquierda, ni a la derecha, ni al centro, arriba. 1986. fortn. Editories Asociados S.A., Maipu 942, 2 piso, Buenos Aires, Argentina. TEL 312-5743.

320.9   YU   ISSN 0032-3381
POLITIKA-EKSPRES; nedeljna revija. 1963. d. 972 din. Politika, Makedonska 29, Belgrade, Yugoslavia. Ed. Bozidar Bogdanovic. (also avail. in microform)

058   DK
POLITIKEN WEEKLY. 1915. w. DKK 8($1) Dagbladet Politiken Ltd., Raadhuspladsen 37, 1585 Copenhagen V, Denmark. TEL 45-33-11-85-11. FAX 45-33-15-41-17. TELEX 16029. Ed. J. Falcon. adv. circ. 8,000.

791   YU   ISSN 0032-339X
POLITIKIN ZABAVNIK. 1939. w. 336 din.($23.50) Politika, Makedonska 29, Belgrade, Yugoslavia. Ed. Radomir Soskic. adv. circ. 260,000.

320.9   SW   ISSN 0032-3489
POLITISK TIDSKRIFT; Centerroerelsens ide- och debatttidskrift. 1941. bi-m. SEK 75 (effective 1991). Foerlaget By och Bygd, P.O. Box 22087, 104 22 Stockholm, Sweden. bk.rev.; illus. circ. 5,200.

057.8   YU   ISSN 0032-3578
POLJA; casopis za kulturu, umetnost i drustvena pitanja. 1955. m. 100 din. (Savez Socijalisticke Omladine Vojvodine, Pokrajinska Konferencija) Tribuna Mladih, Katolicka Porta 5, Box 190, 21000 Novi Sad, Yugoslavia. Ed. Jovan Zivlak. circ. 2,100.

052   AT
PORT STEPHENS EXAMINER. 1893. w. Port Stephens Publishers, 10 William St., Raymond Terrace, N.S.W. 2324, Australia. TEL 049-871411. (Subscr. to: P.O. Box 180, Nelson Bay, N.S.W. 3215, Australia) Ed. Don Comppell. circ. 14,712.

808.8   CN   ISSN 0703-7139
F1051
POSSIBLES. 1976. q. Can.$25 to individuals; institutions Can.$40. Succ. Box 114 Succ. Cote-des-Neiges, Montreal, PQ H3S 2S4, Canada. TEL 514-529-1316. adv.; bk.rev. circ. 2,500. **Indexed**: Lang.& Lang.Behav.Abstr., Pt.de Rep. (1983-).

808.87   US
POSSUM COUNTY NEWS. 1984. q. $11.88 for 12 nos. Poor Ol' George, Box 2572, Owensboro, KY 42302. circ. 12,000.
     Description: Presents humorous and witty anecdotes.

POTATO EYES. see *LITERATURE — Poetry*

808.8   CN   ISSN 0228-3344
POTBOILER MAGAZINE. (Text in English) 1978. s-a. Can.$5($4) Panda Press, Richard's Rd., Roberts Creek, B.C. V0N 2W0, Canada. Ed. L.R. Davidson. adv.; bk.rev.; illus. circ. 275. (back issues avail.)

800   US
POTPOURRI. 1989. m. $9 to individuals; institutions $15. Box 8278, Prairie Valley, KS 66208. Ed. Polly Swafford.

808   US
POULTRY; a magazine of voice. 1980. irreg. (2-3/yr.). $2 per no. Poultry, Inc., Box 4413, Springfield, MA 01101. TEL 413-732-0435. Ed.Bd. bk.rev. circ. 1,000. (tabloid format; back issues avail.)
     Description: Includes parodies, satire and send-ups of contemporary literature, especially poetry.

056.1   SP
PREGON;* revista grafica Navarra. vol.34, 1976. q. 50 ptas. per no. Conde Oliveto, 5, Pamplona, Spain. Ed. Faustino Corella Estella. adv.; illus. **Indexed**: Amer.Hist.& Life, Hist.Abstr.

320 658   NR
PRESIDENT. 1976. m. £N48. New Breed Organisation Ltd., Plot 14, Western Ave., 1, Rafiu Shittu St., Alaka Estate, P.O. Box 385, Surulere, Lagos, Nigeria. TEL 802-6909. FAX 831175. Ed. Chris Okolie.
     Description: Discusses management.

057.8   YU   ISSN 0350-5723
PRIMORSKA SRECANJA; revija za druzboslovje, gospodarstvo in kulturo. 1977. 6/yr. $10. Revija Primorska Srecanja, 65000 Nova Gorica, Slovenia. TEL 065 22 556. bk.rev.; illus.

827   UK   ISSN 0032-888X
AP4   CODEN: PEYEEP
PRIVATE EYE. 1961. fortn. £15. Pressdram Ltd., 6 Carlisle St., London W1V 5RG, England. FAX 44-71-437-0705. Ed. Ian Hilop. adv.; bk.rev.; index. circ. 230,000. (tabloid format)
     Description: Publishes satires and political commentary.

057.8   CI
PRIVLACICA. (Text in Croatian) 1980. bi-m. 1600 din.($4) Cultural Information Center, M. Tita 127, 56251 Privlaka, Croatia. TEL 056 75-449. (also avail. in talking book)

100 055   IT   ISSN 0032-9339
PROBLEMI; periodico quadrimestrale di cultura. 1967. 3/yr. L.90000 (effective 1994). G.B. Palumbo & C. Editore S.p.A., Via Ricasoli 59, 90139 Palermo, Italy. TEL 091-588850. FAX 091-6111848. Ed. Giuseppe Petronio. adv.; bk.rev.; abstr.; bibl.

055   IT
PROCELLARIA. q. Via de Nova, 21c, Reggio, Calabria, Italy. Ed. F. Fiumara.

056.1   EC
PROFESIONAL. 1972. m. Calle Oriente 725, Quito, Ecuador. Ed. Wilson Almeida Munoz. circ. 3,000.

051   US   ISSN 0889-2202
E876
PROGRESSIVE REVIEW. 1966. 9/yr. $16 (foreign $26) (effective 1993). 1739 Connecticut Ave., N.W., Washington, DC 20009. TEL 202-232-5544. FAX 202-234-6222. Ed. Sam Smith. bk.rev.; illus.; cum.index: 1969-1972, 1984-1988. circ. 1,500. (also avail. in microform from UMI; back issues avail.; reprint service avail. from UMI) **Indexed**: Alt.Press Ind. **Document type**: newsletter.
     Former titles (until 1985): D.C. Gazette (ISSN 0011-7153); Capitol East Gazette.
     Description: Newsletter of progressive politics.

059.91   II   ISSN 0033-1201
PRONAB. (Text in Bengali) 1927. m. Rs.25. Swami Nirmalananda, Bharat Sevasram Sangha, 211 Rash Behari Ave., Calcutta 700 019, India. TEL 440-5178. Ed. Swami Atmananda. adv.; bk.rev. circ. 10,000.

808.8   US
PROOF ROCK. 1982. s-a. $5. Proof Rock Press, Box 607, Halifax, VA 24558. Ed. Serena Fusek. adv.; bk.rev. circ. 300.

052   AT
PROSERPINE GUARDIAN. 1904. w. Aus.$36. Whitsunday Printing & Publishing Co., 16 Chapman St., Proserpine, Qld., Australia. TEL 079 451600. FAX 079-452-997. Ed. B.J. Lewis. adv.; bk.rev. circ. 3,030. (back issues avail.)

PROSPETTIVE CULTURALI CALABRESI. see *LITERATURE — Poetry*

057.1   KZ   ISSN 0131-5587
PROSTOR; literaturno-khudozhestvennyi i obshchestvennopoliticheskii zhurnal. (Text and summaries in Russian) 1933. m. 18 Rub. Soyuz Pisatelei Kazakhstana, Alma-Ata, Kazakhstan. TEL 3272-696187. FAX 3272-691058. Ed. R.V. Petrov. adv.; bk.rev.; bibl. circ. 120,000.

055   IT
PROTAGORA. s-a. Via Franco Lucchini, 33, Rome, Italy. Ed. B. Widmar.

800   IT
PUBBLICO; rassegna annuale di fatti letterari. 1977. a. L.10000. Milano Libri Edizioni s.r.l., Via A. Rizzoli 2, 20137 Milan, Italy. Ed. Vittorio Spinazzola. circ. 4,500.

800 001.3   US   ISSN 0899-2363
NX180.S6   CODEN: PUCUE7
PUBLIC CULTURE. 1988. 3/yr. $25 to individuals; institutions $50; students $15. (Society for Transnational Cultural Studies) University of Chicago Press, Journals Division, 5720 S. Woodlawn Ave., Chicago, IL 60637. TEL 312-753-3347. FAX 312-753-0811. (Subscr. to: Box 37005, Chicago, IL 60637) Ed. Carol A. Breckenridge. adv. contact: Cheryl Jones. bk.rev.; illus. circ. 2,500. (back issues avail.) **Indexed**: Film Lit.Ind. (1989-), Left Ind., Sociol.Abstr. **Document type**: academic/scholarly publication.
     —BLDSC (6963.140000); Faxon; UnCover; SWETS.
     Description: Studies political, economic and social aspects of cultural commodity exchange in the postmodern world.
     Refereed Serial

810   US   ISSN 0890-3433
PUCKERBRUSH REVIEW. 1978. 2/yr. $10. Puckerbrush Press, 76 Main St., Orono, ME 04473. TEL 207-581-3832. Ed. Constance Hunting. adv.; bk.rev.; illus.; circ. 250 (paid).
     Description: Interviews Maine writers, features, poetry, fiction and essays with a Maine focus.

055.1   IT   ISSN 0033-4294
PUNGOLO VERDE; arti-science e lettere. 1947. m. L.10000. Box 54, 86100 Campobasso, Italy. Ed. Guido Massarelli. adv.; bk.rev.; illus. circ. 10,000.

320.9   PK   ISSN 0048-6027
PUNJAB PUNCH;* a views weekly. (Text in English) 1971. w. Rs.30. 1 McLeod Rd., Lahore, Pakistan. Ed. Pervez Tahir. adv.; bk.rev.; illus.

059   UK
PUNJABI SAHITYA; magazine of Punjabi life and letters. (Text in Punjabi) 1942. q. £5. c/o H. S. Kalra, Ed., 254 Rowley Gardens, Woodberry Grove, London N4 1HW, England. adv.; bk.rev.; film rev.; play rev.; abstr.; bibl.; charts; illus.; pat.; stat.; tr.lit.; cum.index; circ. 4,000 (controlled).

320   IT
QUADERNI BIANCHI; rivista di cultura politica. 1979. bi-m. L.12000. Piazza S. Ambrogio 21, 20123 Milan, Italy. Ed.Bd.

052   AT   ISSN 0033-5002
AP7
QUADRANT. 1956. 10/yr. Aus.$45 (foreign $54). (Australian Association for Cultural Freedom) Quadrant Magazine Co. Ltd., P.O. Box 1495, Collingwood, Vic. 3066, Australia. TEL 03-4176855. FAX 03-4162980. Ed. Robert Manne. adv.; bk.rev. circ. 6,500. (also avail. in microform; reprint service avail. from KTO) **Indexed**: Aus.P.A.I.S., Child.Lit.Abstr., Gdlns., M.L.A.
     —BLDSC (7168.030000); Faxon; UnCover.
     Description: Conservative review on politics, literature, economics, education, current affairs.

808.87   US
QUAGMIRE; livellafotoorehtsitnemnrevog. 1981. biennial. $25. (National Organization Taunting Safety and Fairness Everywhere) N O T - S A F E, Box 5743 PD, Santa Barbara, CA 93150. TEL 805-969-6217. Ed. Dale Lowdermilk. stat. circ. 1,250. (tabloid format)

810   US   ISSN 0736-4628
PS501
QUARRY WEST; a journal of literature & the arts. 1972. s-a. $12. University of California, Santa Cruz, Porter College, Santa Cruz, CA 95064. TEL 408-429-2155. Ed. Ken Weisner. bk.rev. circ. 750. (back issues avail.)
     Formerly (until 1977): Quarry.

054.1   FR   ISSN 0033-5878
QUATRE VERITES. 1973. m. 600 F. Club des Quatre, 40 rue Jean Jaures, 93170 Bagnolet, France. Ed.Bd. bk.rev.; film rev.; play rev.; charts; illus.; tr.lit. circ. 10,000.

QUEST: MANHATTAN PROPERTIES & COUNTRY ESTATES. see *REAL ESTATE*

LITERARY AND POLITICAL REVIEWS

800 FR
QUESTIONS CLEFS. 1981. q. E.D.I., 29 rue Descartes, Paris 75005, France.

QUINQUEREME; new studies in modern languages. see LINGUISTICS

808.8 US
QUIXOTE, QUIXOTL. q. $20. (Marxist Semi-International) Quixote Press, Inc., 2407 Watts St., Houston, TX 77030-1829. TEL 713-667-6639. Ed. Morris Edelson.
Description: Political satire as an attack on bourgeois decadence.

059.951 CC
QUN YAN/POPULAR TRIBUNE. (Text in Chinese) m. $35.90. (Central Committee of the Chinese Democratic League) Qun Yan Zazhishe, No.1, Dongchang Hutong Beixiang, Dongcheng Qu, Beijing 100006, People's Republic of China. TEL 5127774. (Dist. in US by: China Books & Periodicals, Inc., 2929 24th St., San Francisco, CA 94110. TEL 415-282-0994) Ed. Tao Dayong.
Description: Covers politics, economics, current events, and general interest topics.

QUNZHONG WENHUA/MASS CULTURE; wenhua yishu zonghexing yuekan. see GENERAL INTEREST PERIODICALS — China

R F D; a country journal for gay men everywhere. see HOMOSEXUALITY

059.918 XR ISSN 0862-6375
R O K. (Revue Otevrene Kultury) 1990. 6/yr. 12 Kcs. per issue. Spolecnost Jana Skacela - Jan Skacel Association, Gorkeho 16, 602 00 Brno, Czech Republic. TEL 42-5-4121-3563. Ed. Jiri P. Kriz. adv.: page 10000 Kc. bk.rev. circ. 3,500.

059 UK
RACHNA. 1981. 12/yr. Rachna Publishers, 367 Katherine Rd., London E7 8LT, England. TEL 01-472-2406.
Description: Political and literary articles, poetry and stories concerning immigrants from the Indian subcontinent.

RADICAL BOOKSELLER. see PUBLISHING AND BOOK TRADE

808.8 US ISSN 0742-2768
RAG MAG. 1982. s-a. $10 to individuals; institutions $15. Black Hat Press, 508 Second Ave., Box 12, Goodhue, MN 55027. TEL 612-923-4590; 800-659-2802. Ed. Beverly Voldseth. adv.; bk.rev. circ. 300. **Indexed:** Amer.Hum.Ind.
Formerly (until 1983): Underground Rag Mag.
Description: Eclectic literary magazine of art, poetry and prose.

RAISE THE STAKES; the Planet Drum review. see ENVIRONMENTAL STUDIES

320 US
RAMPART INDIVIDUALIST; a journal of free market libertarian scholarship. 1981. s-a. $18. Rampart Institute, Inc., Box 22231, Carmel, CA 93922-0231. TEL 408-626-8417. Ed. Lawrence Samuels. bk.rev. circ. 500.

RAPPORT; the West Coast review of books. see PUBLISHING AND BOOK TRADE

808.8 US
RASPBERRY PRESS.* 1974. a. $2. Rte. 1, Box 81, Puposky, MN 56667. Ed. Susan Hauser. circ. 300.

055.1 IT ISSN 0033-9482
RASSEGNA DI CULTURA E VITA SCOLASTICA. vol.22, 1968. m. L.2000. Via Giosue Borsi 3, 00197 Rome, Italy. Ed. Paola Di Marcantonio. bk.rev.; abstr.; bibl.; charts; illus.

RATIO; essays in Christian thought. see RELIGIONS AND THEOLOGY

810 US ISSN 1066-1883
RAVEN CHRONICLES; multicultural journal of art, literature and the spoken word. 1991. q. $12 (foreign $15). (Allied Arts Foundation) Raven Chronicles, Box 95918, University Sta., Seattle, WA 98145. TEL 206-543-0249. (Dist. by: Small Changes, 316 Terry Ave. N., Seattle, WA 98109. TEL 206-382-1980) Ed. Phoebe Bosche. circ. 5,000. **Document type:** consumer publication.
Description: Promotes multicultural arts, with a focus on artists and writers from the Pacific Northwest, and provides a forum for critical discussion.

052 UK ISSN 0962-225X
RAVI; Asian newspaper. 1974. w. £22. Ravi Newspapers Ltd., 282 Thornton Rd., Bradford BD8 8JU, England. FAX 0274-721227. Ed. Farida Sheikh. adv.; bk.rev. circ. 8,000. (tabloid format; back issues avail.) **Document type:** newspaper.

800 US
RE-SEARCH. 1981. irreg., no.14, 1992. $40 for 3 issues. Re-Search Publications, 20 Romolo, No. B, San Francisco, CA 94133. TEL 415-362-1465. FAX 415-362-0742. Eds. Andrea Juno, V. Vale. illus. (back issues avail.)
Description: Each issue is devoted to the works of individual writers or specific aspects of American culture, from tattoos, industrial culture, pranks, bizarre music and films to female performance artists.

800 US
REACTIONARY ANNUAL. 1986. a. membership. Elizabeth Linington Society, 1223 Glen Terrace, Glassboro, NJ 08028-1315. Ed. Rinehart S. Potts. adv.; bk.rev. circ. 400. **Document type:** newsletter.

810 US ISSN 0742-9681
READER (HOUGHTON); essay in reader-oriented theory, criticism, and pedagogy. s-a. $10 to individuals (foreign $12); institutions $20 (foreign $22). Michigan Technological University, Department of Humanities, Houghton, MI 49931. TEL 906-487-2447. Ed. Elizabeth A. Flynn.
—UnCover.
Description: Provides reader-oriented approaches to texts including literature, visual images and student writings.

051 US
READER (SAN DIEGO). 1972. w. $165. Box 85803, San Diego, CA 92138. TEL 619-235-3000. FAX 619-231-0489. Ed. James E. Holman. adv.; bk.rev.; film rev.; play rev.; circ. 131,000 (controlled). (tabloid format)

808.8 US ISSN 0034-091X
THE REALIST. 1958-1974; resumed 1985. q. $23 for 12 nos. Box 1230, Venice, CA 90294. Ed. Paul Krassner. circ. 5,000. **Document type:** newsletter.
—UMI.
Description: Satirizes political and social evils.

052 CN
REALITY NOW; for defense of life on Earth. 1983. s-a. Can.$8. R N Publishers, P.O. Box 6326, Station "A", Toronto, Ont. M5W 1P7, Canada. bk.rev. circ. 3,000. (back issues avail.)

808.87 US
REALITY SANDWICH. m. $0.75 per no. Box 2092, Baltimore, MD 21203-2092.
Description: Contains humorous stories about political and social issues.

051 US ISSN 0048-6906
H1
REASON; free minds and free markets. 1968. m. $24 (foreign $34). Reason Foundation, 3415 S. Sepulveda Blvd., Ste. 400, Los Angeles, CA 90034-6060. TEL 310-391-2245. FAX 310-391-4395. (Subscr. to: Box 526, Mt. Morris, IL 61054. TEL 815-734-1102) Ed. Virginia I. Postrel. adv.: B&W page $1100, color page $1540; trim 8 1/4 x 10 7/8. bk.rev.; bibl.; illus.; index. circ. 40,473. (also avail. in microform from UMI; back issues avail.) **Indexed:** Amer.Hist.& Life, Bk.Rev.Ind. (1990-), Child.Bk.Rev.Ind. (1990-), Hist.Abstr., P.A.I.S., Polit.Sci.Abstr., R.G. **Document type:** consumer publication.
—BLDSC (7303.570600); Faxon; UnCover; UMI.
Description: Libertarian journal of opinion providing commentary on current affairs, economics and issues.

800 700 US ISSN 0883-0126
RED BASS. 1981. biennial. $20 for 2 nos. to individuals; institutions and foreign $35. Red Bass Productions, Inc., 105 W. 28th St., New York, NY 10001. TEL 212-239-7470. Ed. Jay Murphy. adv.; bk.rev. circ. 3,000. **Indexed:** Alt.Press Ind., Amer.Hum.Ind., Ind.Amer.Per.Verse.
Description: Explores the interface between art and politics. Presents experimental, innovative and political art and literature, often featuring special themes.

810 US ISSN 0034-1967
PS501
RED CEDAR REVIEW. 1962. s-a. $10. Red Cedar Press, 17C Morrill Hall, Michigan State University, E. Lansing, MI 48824. TEL 517-355-9656. FAX 517-355-7570. Eds. Laura Klynstra, Zachary Chartkoff. circ. 500.
Description: Publishes short stories, plays and poetry.

808.8 320.531 CN ISSN 0711-2270
RED MENACE; a libertarian socialist newsletter. 1975. s-a. Can.$12. Libertarian Socialist Collective, Box 171, Sta. D, Toronto, ON M6P 3J8, Canada. Ed. Ulli Diemer. bk.rev. circ. 1,000. (tabloid format) **Indexed:** Alt.Press Ind. **Document type:** newsletter.

051 US
REIGN OF TOADS. 4/yr. $12. Box 66047, Albany, NY 12206. Ed. Kyle Silfer. **Document type:** newsletter.

053.931 NE ISSN 0034-3749
REKENSCHAP; humanistisch tijdschrift voor wetenschap en cultuur. 1954. q. fl.45. Humanistische Stichting Socrates, Nieuwegracht 69A, Postbus 114, 3500 AC Utrecht, Netherlands. TEL 31-30-318145. FAX 31-30-361704. Ed.Bd. adv.; bk.rev.; illus. circ. 1,500. **Indexed:** Excerp.Med.

055.1 IT ISSN 0034-4745
REPORTAGE; quindicinale d'informazione e attualita. 1962. fortn. L.30000 (foreign L.60000). Via Belvedere 11, 88046 Lamezia Terme (Catanzaro), Italy. TEL 0968-21719. Ed. Rosario Arcuri. adv.; bk.rev.; abstr.; bibl.; charts; illus.; stat. circ. 20,000. (tabloid format)
Description: Political forum featuring news on various topics.

057.86 XR
REPORTER. 1965-1969; resumed 1990. w. 5 Kcs. Novinar, Parizska 9, 110-01 Prague 1, Czech Republic. TEL 232-7633. FAX 232-0775. Ed. Dusan Mrna. circ. 200,000.

054 FR ISSN 1247-8652
▼**REPUBLIQUE INTERNATIONALE DES LETTRES.** 1994. w. 500 F. to individuals (foreign 600 F.); students 400 F. B.P. 66, 75421 Paris Cedex 09, France. TEL 42-80-67-58. FAX 42-80-67-15. Pub. Noel Blandin. bk.rev. **Document type:** newspaper.
Description: Provides a forum for ideas and debate.

057.85 PL
AP54
RES PUBLICA NOWA. 1987. m. $36. Batory Press Sp. z o.o., P.O. Box 856, 00-950 Warsaw 1, Poland. TEL 48-22-263047. Ed. Marcin Krol. adv.; bk.rev. circ. 25,000.
Formerly (until 1992): Res Publica (ISSN 0860-4592)
Description: Intellectual magazine with special interest in politics, culture and economy.

RESPONSABILITA DEL SAPERE. see LITERATURE

RETI - PRATICHE E SAPERI DI DONNE. see POLITICAL SCIENCE

057.8 CI ISSN 0034-6888
REVIJA (OSIJEK); casopis za knjizevnost, kulturu i drustvena pitanja. (Text in Serbo-Croatian) 1961. bi-m. 50 din. Narodno Sveuciliste "Bozidar Maslaric", Centar za Kulturu i Umjetnost, Kuhaceva 29, Osijek 54000, Croatia. Ed. Dejan Rebic.

053.931 NE ISSN 0302-8852
PT5460
REVISOR. 1974. bi-m. fl.86.50 (foreign fl.105). Querido B.V., Singel 262, 1016 AC Amsterdam, Netherlands. TEL 31-20-5511262. FAX 31-20-6203509. Ed.Bd. adv.; bk.rev.; bibl. circ. 6,000. **Indexed:** M.L.A.
—SWETS.

LITERARY AND POLITICAL REVIEWS

056.9   PO   ISSN 0034-6977
REVISTA ALENTEJANA. 1935. m. Esc.80. Casa do Alentejo, Rua das Portas de Santo Antao 58, Lisbon 2, Portugal. Eds. Vitor Santos, Fausto Goncalves. adv.; bk.rev.; film rev.; play rev.; abstr.; bibl.; illus.; tr.lit.; circ. 3,000 (controlled). (tabloid format)

808.2   SP
REVISTA DE MENORCA. 1888. q. 2800 ptas.($5) Ateneo de Mahon, Menorca, Baleares, Spain. Ed.Bd. bk.rev.; bibl.

056.1   SP   ISSN 0034-8635
AP60
REVISTA DE OCCIDENTE. 1923; N.S. 1963, 1975, 1980. m. (11/yr.). 8000 ptas.($102) (elsewhere 9900 ptas.) (effective Oct. 1993). Fundacion Jose Ortega y Gasset, Fortuny, 53, 28010 Madrid, Spain. TEL 310-44-12. FAX 308-40-07. Ed. Magdalena Mora. adv.: B&W page 125000 ptas.; color page 160000 ptas.; adv. contact: Belen Nieto. bk.rev.; illus.; index, cum.index: nos.1-50 in 1985, nos.51-100 in 1989. circ. 20,000. (also avail. in microform; reprint service avail. from KTO) **Indexed:** Abstr.Engl.Stud.; Amer.Hist.& Life; Arts & Hum.Cit.Ind.; Hist.Abstr.
—BLDSC (7869.030000); Faxon; SWETS. **CCC.**
Description: Covers social sciences and humanities. Includes a literary section by Spanish and Spanish American authors.

986.1   CK   ISSN 0034-9852
REVISTA MANIZALES; al servicio de la cultura colombiana y americana. 1940. m. $6. Apdo. Aereo 14-61, Manizales, Caldas, Colombia. Ed. J.B. Jaramillo Meza. adv.; bk.rev.; index.

800   SZ   ISSN 0035-1016
LA REVUE DE BELLES-LETTRES. (Text in French) 1877. q. 60 SFr. (foreign 90 SFr.). (Societe de Belles Lettres de Lausanne et Geneve) Editions Medecine et Hygiene, Case Postale 456, CH-1211 Geneva 4, Switzerland. TEL 022-3469355. FAX 022-3475610. Ed. Olivier Beetschen. adv.; bk.rev.; abstr.; bibl.; illus. circ. 1,400. **Document type:** academic/scholarly publication.
—SWETS. **CCC.**

327   FR   ISSN 0750-9278
AP20
REVUE DES DEUX MONDES; litterature, histoire, arts et sciences. 1829. m. 550 F. (foreign 770 F.). Societe de la Revue des Deux Mondes, 170 rue de Grenelle, 75007 Paris, France. TEL 42-84-22-28. FAX 42-84-22-3974. Ed. Jean Bothorellace. adv.; bk.rev.; film rev.; play rev.; record rev.; index. circ. 15,000. (also avail. in microform from UMI; microfiche from IDC; reprint service avail. from KTO,UMI) **Indexed:** Amer.Hist.& Life; Hist.Abstr.
—BLDSC (7898.300000); Faxon; SWETS; UMI.
Former titles (until 1982): Nouvelle Revue des Deux Mondes (ISSN 0151-914X); (until 1972): Revue des Deux Mondes (ISSN 0035-1962)

054.1   FR   ISSN 0035-3310
REVUE INDEPENDANTE. 1912. bi-m. 90 F. Syndicat des Journalistes et Ecrivains, 206, rue Edouard-Branly, 93100 Montreuil-sous-Bois, France. Ed. Bernard Drupt. bk.rev.; dance rev.; film rev.; play rev.; rec.rev.; illus. circ. 1,500.

957   XO   ISSN 0231-6269
REVUE SVETOVEJ LITERATURY. 1965. 7/yr. $68. (Slovak Literary Fund) Vydavatel'stvo Slovenskly Spisovatel', Laurinska 2, 813 67 Bratislava, Slovakia. bk.rev.
Description: Publishes translations of the works of contemporary authors and classics, not yet published in book form in this country, as well as critical articles, reviews of book translations, and profiles of the foremost Slovak translators.

808.8   US   ISSN 0891-1231
RIDGE REVIEW. 1981. q. $10. Ridge Times Press, Box 90, Mendocino, CA 95460. TEL 707-964-8465. FAX 707-964-7717. Ed.Bd; Pub. Judy Tarbell. adv.; bk.rev.; charts; illus. circ. 3,500. (back issues avail.)
Description: Covers themes concerning the Northern California coastal ridges.

RIFORMA DELLA SCUOLA/SCHOOL REFORM. see EDUCATION

054.1   FR
RIMBAUD VIVANT. 1973. q. 40 F. Amis de Rimbaud, c/o Mme. Suzanne Briet, 24 rue Gutenberg, 92100 Boulogne, France. Ed. Pierre Petitfils. bk.rev.; bibl.
Supersedes: Etudes Rimbaudiennes.

053.1   SZ
RING-POST; Ausblick vom Hauenstein. 1945. m. 15 Fr. Hauenstein-Verlag, Niedergrund 15, CH-4600 Olten 3, Switzerland. bk.rev.
Formerly: Hauenstein Verlag. Mitteilungsblatt (ISSN 0017-839X)

800   US   ISSN 0149-8851
PS501
RIVER STYX. 1975. 3/yr. $20 to individuals; institutions $28. Big River Association, 14 S. Euclid, St. Louis, MO 63108. TEL 314-361-0043. Ed. Vennifer Tabin. adv. circ. 1,200. (back issues avail.) **Indexed:** A.I.P.P.
Description: Multi-cultural publication of literature and art.

808.8   US
RIVERFRONT. 1980. s-a. Metropolitan Technical Community College, Box 3777, Omaha, NE 68103. TEL 402-449-8322. Ed. Jules DeSalvo. circ. 750.

RIVISTA DALMATICA. see HISTORY — History Of Europe

RIVISTA STORICA CALABRESE. see HISTORY — History Of Europe

808.8   US
ROAR. 1979. irreg. $15 per no. Ranger International Productions, Lion Publishing - Roar Recording, Box 71231, Shorewood Sta., Milwaukee, WI 53211-7331. TEL 414-332-7474. FAX 414-332-5251. Ed. Martin F. Rosenblum. bk.rev. circ. 100. (CD format)

ROCKY MOUNTAIN REVIEW OF LANGUAGE AND LITERATURE. see LITERATURE

057   XO
RODINA. bi-m. Pravda, Gundulicova 12, 882-05 Bratislava, Slovakia.

057   XO   ISSN 0231-6560
ROHAC. 1948. w. Slovako-press, Martanovicova 25, 819 10 Bratislava, Slovakia. Ed. Mikulas Sliacky. circ. 30,000.

800   US   ISSN 0886-2249
ROLLING STOCK. 1981. 3/yr. $9 to individuals; institutions $12. University of Colorado, c/o Univ. of Colorado, Campus Box 226, Boulder, CO 80309. TEL 303-442-7631. FAX 303-492-7272. Ed. Jennifer Dunbar Dorn. adv.: B&W page $500. bk.rev. circ. 3,000.
Description: Features essays, columns, stories, interviews, poetry, and art by a diverse group of well-known writers. Serves up serious political comment lightly salted with literary adventure.

808.838   US
ROLLMAG; common sense newsletter. 10/yr. $20. Kenneth Maue, Ed. & Pub., Box 5001, Mill Valley, CA 94942. illus. (looseleaf format) **Document type:** newsletter.
Description: Reflections on contemporary existence, art and culture.

055.91   RM   ISSN 0035-8088
DR201
ROMANIAN REVIEW. French edition: Revue Roumaine (ISSN 0251-3528); German edition: Rumaenische Rundschau (ISSN 1220-3327); Russian edition: Rumunskaya Literatura (ISSN 1220-5060) (Text in English) 1946. m. 360 lei($42) Foreign Languages Press Group "Romania" - Redactia Publicatiilor pentru Strainatate "Romania", Piata Presei Libere Nr. 1, P.O. Box 33-28, 71341 Bucharest, Rumania. TEL 6173836. TELEX 6170487. Ed. Nicolae Sarambei. adv.; bk.rev.; illus. circ. 6,000. **Indexed:** Arts & Hum.Cit.Ind.; Curr.Cont.; M.L.A.
—Faxon.
Description: Deals with Rumanian culture and civilization.

057   XO   ISSN 0231-6714
ROMBOID. 1966. m. $58. (Asociacia Slovenskych Spisovatelov - Association of Slovak Writers) Vydavatel'stvo Slovensky Spisovatel', Laurinska 2, 813 67 Bratislava, Slovakia. **Indexed:** Bibl.Ling.
Description: Features original literary-scientific articles, critiques, reviews, shorter pieces and poems.

059.927   UA
ROSE AL-YUSUF. (Text in Arabic) 1925. w. $180 in N. America (effective 1994). Mu'assasat Ruz al-Yusuf, 89A Sharia Qasr el-Aini, Cairo, Egypt. (Subscr. in N. America to: Al-Ahram International, 405 Lexington Ave., New York, NY 10174. TEL 212-972-6440. FAX 212-286-0285) Ed. Muhammad Tuhami. circ. 35,000.

055.1   IT
IL ROSONE; periodico pugliese di cultura e informazioni. 1978. bi-m. L.50000($45) Edizioni del Rosone, Via Zingarelli 10, Casella Postale 474, 71100 Foggia, Italy. TEL 0881-87659. Ed. Franco Marasca. adv.; bk.rev. circ. 10,000. (back issues avail.)

057.8   YU   ISSN 0035-9793
RUKOVET; casopis za knjizevnost, umetnost i drustvena pitanja. (Text in Serbo-Croatian) 1955. m. $20. (Opstinski Fond Kulture Subotica) N I P "Suboticke Novine", 8 Maksim Gorki St., 24000 Subotica, Yugoslavia. Ed. Milovan Mikovic.
Description: Includes literary, arts and social issues. Contains original works of literature and translations from foreign languages.

056.1   PE
RUNA. 1977. m. S/150 per no. Instituto Nacional de Cultura, Casilla 5247, Lima, Peru. Ed. Mario Razzeto. illus. circ. 10,000.

050   US
RYDER. 1979. m. $12. Out to Lunch Publications, 104 1-2 E. Kirkwood, Apt. 26, Bloomington, IN 47401. TEL 812-339-2001. Ed. Peter Lopilato. adv.; bk.rev.; film rev. circ. 10,000. (also avail. in microfilm)

810   US   ISSN 0038-2876
AP2
S A Q: THE SOUTH ATLANTIC QUARTERLY. 1902. q. $24 to individuals (foreign $32); institutions $54 (foreign $62). Duke University Press, Box 90660, Durham, NC 27708-0660. TEL 919-687-3600. FAX 919-688-4574. Ed. Fredric Jameson. adv.; bk.rev. circ. 1,800. (also avail. in microform from MIM,UMI; reprint service avail. from ISI,UMI) **Indexed:** Abstr.Engl.Stud.; Acad.Ind.; Amer.Bibl.Slavic & E.Eur.Stud., Amer.Hist.& Life, Arts & Hum.Cit.Ind.; Bk.Rev.Ind. (1965-), CERDIC, Child.Bk.Rev.Ind. (1965-), Curr.Cont., Hist.Abstr.; Hum.Ind.; Ind.Bk.Rev.Hum.; LCR, M.L.A.; Mid.East: Abstr.& Ind.; P.A.I.S.
—BLDSC (8348.670000); Faxon; UnCover; SWETS; UMI. **CCC.**
Description: Contains literary and political reviews. Refereed Serial

052   UK   ISSN 0261-1953
S O A P. 1980. 6/yr. £0.60. Selly Oak Alternative Paper, c/o Ms. B. Fay, 64 Oak Tree La., Selly Oak, Birmingham, England. illus.

808.8   US   ISSN 0749-1670
Z716.4
S R R T NEWSLETTER. 1969. 4/yr. $10 to non-members; institutions $20. American Library Association, Social Responsibilities Round Table, 50 E. Huron St., Chicago, IL 60611. TEL 312-944-6780. FAX 312-440-9374. Ed. Thomas L. Wilding. bk.rev.; bibl. circ. 2,000. **Document type:** newsletter.
Formerly: A L A Social Responsibilities Round Table Newsletter (ISSN 0065-9096)
Description: Activities of ALA-SRRT reported.

053.1   GW   ISSN 0036-2115
DD801.S13
SAARBRUECKER HEFTE. 1955. s-a. DM.14.50. Ottweiler Druckerei und Verlag GmbH, Sauermilchstr. 14, 66564 Ottweiler, Germany. Ed.Bd. bk.rev.; illus.; index.

808.87   UK
SABAH AL-KHAIR.* (Text in Arabic) w. c/o Powers Overseas Ltd. (OPMA), Duncan Ho., Dolphin Sq., London SW1, England. Ed. Mofeed Fawzi. circ. 70,000.
Description: Humor and entertainment.

LITERARY AND POLITICAL REVIEWS

808.8   BG
SACHITRA SANDHANI. (Text in Bengali) 1978. w. Tk.2. 68-2 Purana Paltan, Dhaka, Bangladesh. TEL 2-409680. Ed. Gazi Shahabuddin Mahmud. circ. 13,000.

051   US
THE SACRED COW S I G NEWSLETTER. bi-m. $1.50 per no. Special Interest Group of Mensa, 3392 Clemens Dr., St. Charles, MO 63301. Ed. Barbara Koksal. **Document type:** newsletter.
   Description: Presents wide-open debates on racism, sexism, anti-Semitism and other political and social issues.

ST. LOUIS REVIEW. see *RELIGIONS AND THEOLOGY — Roman Catholic*

809   JA
SAITAMA UNIVERSITY. COLLEGE OF LIBERAL ARTS. JOURNAL. (Text in English) vol.26, 1978. irreg. free. Saitama Daigaku, Bungakubu - Saitama University, College of Liberal Arts, 1255 Shimookubo, Urawa-shi, Saitama-ken 338, Japan. circ. 500.

052   II
SAJIT MONTHLY. (Text in English) 1974. m. Rs.1.25 per no. Sajit Print, 2 F Dilkusha St., Calcutta 17, India. Ed. M.M. John.

056.1   MX   ISSN 0300-3388
SALAMANDRA; revista de cultura. 1969. bi-m. $60. Fundacion Cultural Alfonso Reyes Aurrecoechea, A.C., Condominios Constitution, Edif. 41, Depto. 11, 64000 Monterrey, N.L., Mexico. FAX 33-72-64. adv.; bk.rev.; film rev.; bibl.; illus. circ. controlled. (processed) **Indexed:** Biol.Abstr.

052   UK   ISSN 0265-4881
SALISBURY REVIEW; a quarterly magazine of conservative thought. 1982. q. £16($35) (overseas £23). Claridge Press, 33 Canonbury Park S., London N1 2JW, England. TEL 071-226-7791. FAX 071-354-0383. (U.S. addr.: ISI, 14 S. Bryn Mawr Ave., Bryn Mawr, PA 19010-3275) Ed. Roger Scruton. adv.; bk.rev. circ. 800. (back issues avail.) **Indexed:** ASSIA. **Document type:** academic/scholarly publication.
   —BLDSC (8070.921000).

055.1   IT
SALVO IMPREVISTI; quadrimestrale di poesia. 1974. 6/yr. L.30000. Salvo Imprevisti, c/o Mariella Bettarini, Ed., Borgo SS. Apostoli 4, 50123 Florence, Italy. TEL 055-289569. adv.; bk.rev.; bibl.

058.82   NO   ISSN 0036-3928
AP45
SAMTIDEN; tidsskrift for politikk, litteratur og samfunnsspoersmaal. 1890. bi-m. NOK 295 to individuals; libraries NOK 350 (typically set in Jan.). H. Aschehoug & Co. (W. Nygaard) A-S, P.O. Box 363 Sentrum, N-0102-Oslo, Norway. TEL 47-22-40-04-00. FAX 47-22-20-63-95. (Subscr. to: Forlagsentralen, Box 150 Furuset, 1001 Oslo 10, Norway) Ed.Bd. adv.; bk.rev. circ. 4,700. (back issues avail.) **Indexed:** Amer.Hist.& Life (until 1990), Hist.Abstr. (until 1990), M.L.A.
   Description: Focuses on the humanities and social science. Presents in-depth interviews, debates on current issues, and some literary writings both poetry and prose.

800   US
SAN FRANCISCO REVIEW OF BOOKS. 1975. bi-m. $16. 2909 McClure St., Oakland, CA 94609-3504. TEL 510-286-2020. FAX 510-286-0220. Ed. Donald Paul. adv. contact: Paschal Fowlkes. bk.rev.; index; circ. 10,000 (paid). (also avail. in microform from UMI; reprint service avail. from UMI) **Indexed:** Bk.Rev.Ind. (1982-), Chic.Per.Ind., Child.Bk.Rev.Ind. (1982-), New Per.Ind.

800   MX
SAN MIGUEL WRITER. 1988. 2/yr. $10. Aldama 43, San Miguel de Allende, Mexico. TEL 52-465-22225. Ed. Carl Selph. circ. 250. (back issues avail.)
   Description: Features poetry, fiction, art, and political and social satire.

378.1   CU   ISSN 0048-9115
AS71.A1
SANTIAGO. 1971. q. $10 in N. and S. America; Europe $12; others $14. (Universidad de Oriente, Departamento de Extension Universitaria) Ediciones Cubanas, Obispo No. 527, Apdo. 605, Havana, Cuba. Ed. Nils Castro. bk.rev.; illus. **Indexed:** Amer.Hist.& Life, Hist.Abstr.

808.8
SAPIENS.* 1983. s-a. $10. Sapiens Press, 213 Deland Ave., Cherry Hill, NJ 08034-2043. Eds. Bonnie Gordon, Edward Kaplan. circ. 200.

800
SAPPHO'S ISLE. 1988. m. $20. Sappho's Isle, Inc., 960 Willis Ave., Albertson, NY 11507. TEL 516-747-5417. FAX 516-747-5417. Pub. Jean Sidebottom. adv.; bk.rev. circ. 11,000. (tabloid format; back issues avail.) **Document type:** newspaper.

808.8   BG
SAPTAHIKA BICITRA. (Text in Bengali) 1972. w. Tk.6 per. no. Dainik Bangla Group of Publications, 1, DIT Avenue, Dhaka 2, Bangladesh. Ed. Shahadat Chowdhury. adv.; bk.rev. circ. 53,000.

810   US
SARAH LAWRENCE REVIEW. 1957. a. free. Sarah Lawrence College, Writing Department, c/o Thomas Lux, Bronxville, NY 10708. TEL 914-337-0700. circ. 1,500 (controlled).
   Former titles: Sarah Lawrence Literary Review; S.L. Literary Review (ISSN 0036-4746)

808.8 410   PR
SARGASSO; theater, film, poetry, performance, criticism. 1984. s-a. $9 to individuals; institutions $18. Td Imag, Inc., Box 22831, University Sta., Rio Piedras, PR 00931-2831. (Co-sponsor: University of Puerto Rico) Ed. Lowell Fiet. circ. 300. (back issues avail.)

SARMATIAN REVIEW. see *ETHNIC INTERESTS*

055   IT
SATIRA.* 1980. m. Kaos Edizione, Viale Abruzzi 58, 20131 Milan, Italy. Ed. Domenico Nodari.

055.1   IT   ISSN 0036-5742
SCENA ILLUSTRATA; politica, turismo, attualita, arte, cultura. 1865. m. L.35000. Via Cernaia 43, Rome, Italy. Dir. Italo Carlo Sesti. bk.rev.; illus. circ. 24,100.

053.1   SZ   ISSN 0036-7400
AP32
SCHWEIZER MONATSHEFTE; Zeitschrift fuer Politik, Wirtschaft, Kultur. (Text in German; occasionally in French) 1921. m. 80 SFr. Gesellschaft Schweizer Monatshefte, Vogelsangstr. 52, CH-8006 Zurich, Switzerland. Ed.Bd. adv.; bk.rev.; abstr.; index. circ. 2,500. (tabloid format; also avail. in microform from UMI; reprint service avail. from UMI) **Indexed:** Amer.Hist.& Life, Hist.Abstr. **Document type:** consumer publication.
   —BLDSC (8112.350000); Faxon; UMI.

052   UK
THE SCILLONIAN. 1925. biennial. £8 (foreign £10). c/o Clive Tregarthen Mumford, Ed., St. Mary's, Isles of Scilly, Cornwall, England. TEL 0720-22438. bk.rev. circ. 2,500. (back issues avail.)

052   GW   ISSN 0265-5543
SCORPION. 1981. s-m. $30. Scorpion Press, Luetzowstr. 39, 50674 Cologne, Germany. Ed. Michael Walker. adv.; bk.rev.; film rev.; play rev.; bibl.; illus. circ. 2,000. (back issues avail.) **Document type:** academic/scholarly publication.

051   US   ISSN 0360-2672
SCREE. 1973. 5/yr. $8.50 individuals; institutions $10. Duck Down Press, Box 1047, Fallon, NV 89406. Ed. Kirk Robertson. bk.rev.; illus. circ. 1,000. **Indexed:** Access.

051   US   ISSN 0036-9624
SCREW. 1968. w. $75. Milky Way Productions Inc., 116 W. 14th St., Box 432, Old Chelsea Sta., New York, NY 10011. TEL 212-989-8001. FAX 212-924-8154. Ed. Manny Neuhaus. adv.; bk.rev.; film rev.; play rev.; illus.; stat. circ. 175,000. (tabloid format; also avail. in microfilm) **Document type:** newspaper.
   Description: Covers adult literature, political, and social humor.

052   UK   ISSN 0048-9905
SEAR.* no. 46, 1971. m. 75p. Manchester Mensa, c/o Andrew White, 212 Buxton Rd., Davenport, Stockport, Ches, England. Ed.Bd. illus. (processed)

056.1   MX
SEMANA POLITICA. 1955. m. Mex.$35. Antonio Caso 31-1, Mexico 4, D.F., Mexico. Ed. Francisco Arreola, Jr. adv. circ. 21,400.

808.87   CU
SEMINARIA PA'LANTE. w. $50. (Instituto Cubano del Libro) Ediciones Cubanas, Departamento de Exportacion, Obispo No. 461, Apdo. 605, Havana, Cuba. illus. circ. 50,000. (tabloid format)
   Description: Satirical humor magazine with caricatures, photos and text of a humorous nature on the current national and international political, economic, cultural and sport scenes.

808   US   ISSN 0093-9579
P99
SEMIOTEXT(E). Key Title: Semiotexte (New York). 1974. irreg., no.16, 1993. $16 to individuals for 3 nos.; institutions $32. Autonomedia, 55 S. 11th St., P.O. Box 568, Brooklyn, NY 11211-0568. TEL 718-387-6471. Ed. Jim Fleming; Pub. Jim Fleming. adv.; bk.rev. circ. 8,000. **Indexed:** Curr.Cont., M.L.A. **Document type:** academic/scholarly publication.

808.8   US
SENSOR.* 1976. a. $5. c/o George M. Rawlins, Box 22043, San Diego, CA 92192-2043. adv. circ. 700. **Indexed:** Forest Prod.Abstr.
   Formerly: Antenna.

378.1   US   ISSN 0037-2420
PS508.C6
SEQUOIA (STANFORD). 1887. 2/yr. $10. Stanford University, Associated Students, Storke Publications Building, Stanford, CA 94305. TEL 415-497-4331. Eds. Carlos Rodriguez, Mark Clevenger. adv.; bk.rev.; illus. circ. 500. **Indexed:** A.I.P.P.
   Description: Presents poetry, fiction, drama, and art.

052   UK
Y SEREN. 1948. bi-w. (during college term only). free. (University College of North Wales, Bangor Students' Union) Copycat, High St., Bangor, Gwynedd, Wales. Ed. Ingrid Mader. adv.; bk.rev.; film rev.; play rev. circ. 2,000. (tabloid format)
   Former titles: Vox; Graffiti; Forecast (ISSN 0015-7074)

056.1   SP   ISSN 0037-2501
DP302.C57
SERRA D'OR. 1959. m. (July-Aug. combined). 4900 ptas. (Europe 6600 ptas.; elsewhere $75) (effective 1994). Publicacions de l' Abadia de Montserrat, Ausias March 92-98, Apdo. 244, 08013 Barcelona, Spain. TEL 93-2450303. Ed. Maur M. Boix. adv.; bk.rev.; film rev.; play rev.; bibl.; illus.; index. circ. 15,000. **Indexed:** Amer.Hist.& Life, Hist.Abstr.

SEWANEE REVIEW. see *LITERATURE*

057.1   RU
SHANS. 1990. m. 1.90 Rub. Soyuz Predprinimatelei i Arendatorov Urala, Ul. Gor'kogo 10 "A", 45007 Chelyabinsk, Russia. TEL 77-24-04. Ed. A.V. Lobashev. circ. 60,000.

810   US   ISSN 0037-3583
AP2
SHENANDOAH: THE WASHINGTON AND LEE UNIVERSITY REVIEW. 1950. q. $11. Washington and Lee University, Shenandoah, Box 722, Lexington, VA 24450. TEL 703-463-8765. FAX 703-463-8945. Eds. Dabney Stuart, Lynn Williams. adv.: B&W page $200. bk.rev.; index. circ. 1,400. (also avail. in microform from UMI; back issues avail.; reprint service avail. from UMI) **Indexed:** Abstr.Engl.Stud., Amer.Hum.Ind., Arts & Hum.Cit.Ind., Ind.Amer.Per.Verse, Ind.Bk.Rev.Hum., LCR, M.L.A. **Document type:** academic/scholarly publication.
   —BLDSC (8256.375000); Faxon; UnCover; UMI.
   Description: Publishes award-winning fiction, poetry, and essays.

059		JA	

SHOKUN. 1969. m. 10320 Yen. Bungei Shunju Ltd., 3-23, Kioi-cho, Chiyoda-ku, Tokyo 102, Japan. TEL 03-3265-1211. FAX 03-3221-6623. Ed. Kohichi Sasamoto. circ. 100,000.
  Description: Opinion magazine for intellectuals.

800	US	ISSN 1052-648X

SHORT STORY. 1989. s-a. $7. University of Texas, Brownsville, Department of English, 80 Ft. Brown, Brownsville, TX 78520. TEL 210-544-8239. (Co-publisher: University of Northern Iowa) Eds. Mary Rohrberger, Farhat Iftekharuddin. adv.; bk.rev. circ. 800. (back issues avail.) **Document type:** academic/scholarly publication.
  Description: Publishes original short stories, critical essays, and interviews.

808.8	US	ISSN 1059-2210

SIDEWALKS; a magazine for emerging and published writers. 1991. s-a. $8 to individuals; institutions $12. Sidewalks, Box 321, Champlin, MN 55316. TEL 612-421-3512. Ed. Tom Heie. circ. 500. **Indexed:** Ind.Amer.Per.Verse. **Document type:** consumer publication.

056.1		MX	

SIEMPRE!. 1953. w. Vallarta 20, Apdo. 4-033, 06470 Mexico D.F., Mexico. TEL 5-566-9355. FAX 5-546-5130. Ed. Beatriz Pages Rebollas. circ. 185,000.

051	US	ISSN 0891-6926

SIGN OF THE TIMES; a chronicle of decadence in the atomic age. 1981. s-a. $7.50. Studio 403, 221 Boylston Ave., E., Seattle, WA 98102-5608. TEL 206-323-6764. FAX 206-323-6764. Ed. Mark Souder. circ. 750. (back issues avail.) **Document type:** monographic series.

055.1	IT	ISSN 0037-5179

SILARUS; rassegna bimestrale di cultura. (Text in Italian, Latin; summaries in Italian) 1965. bi-m. L.15000. Italo Rocco, Ed. & Pub., Via B. Buozzi 317, Casella Postale 317, 84091 Battipaglia, Salerno, Italy. adv.; bk.rev.; play rev.; abstr.; bibl.; illus. circ. 2,000. **Indexed:** M.L.A.

052	CN	ISSN 0037-5217

SILHOUETTE. 1930. w. Can.$40. McMaster Students Union, Rm. 406, Hamilton Hall, 1280 Main St. W., Hamilton, ON L8S 4K1. TEL 416-525-9140. FAX 416-527-0100. adv.; bk.rev.; film rev.; play rev. circ. 11,000. **Document type:** newspaper.
  Description: Covers university, community, national and international events from a student perspective.

891.553 297		IR	

SIMURGH. 1990. m. Rs.350 per no. M.A. Biramabad, Ed. & Pub., P.O. Box 13145-844, Teheran, Iran.
  Description: Covers literary and Islamic affairs.

700		US	

SKETCH. 1935. s-a. $3. Iowa State University, Government of the Student Body, Memorial Union, 203 Ross Hall, Ames, IA 50010. TEL 515-232-2477. circ. 3,000.
  Description: Features the poetry, prose, photography and artwork of the Iowa State University student population.

800		US	

▼**SKINNER'S IRREGULAR HORSE.** 1993. m. $24 (effective 1994). Dan Sweetland, Ed. & Pub., 2107 E. Jarvis St., Milwaukee, WI 53211. TEL 414-963-9996. (back issues avail.) **Document type:** consumer publication.
  Description: Publishes original fiction and poetry, often from local writers and non-professional writers.

808.87	XR	ISSN 0862-6006

SKRT. 1990. m. 4 Kcs. Novinar, Parizska 9, 110 01 Prague 1, Czech Republic. TEL 2326355. Ed. Eduard Svetlik. circ. 250,000.

800 378.198		US	

SKYLARK. 1972. a. $6. Purdue University Calumet, 2200 169th St., Hammond, IN 46323. TEL 219-989-2262. Ed. Pamela Hunter. adv. circ. 800. (back issues avail.)
  Description: Publishes original writing, art and photography from local and national writers and artists.

808.87		GW	

SLAPSTICK.* 1978. irreg.? DM.2.60 per no. Pardon Verlagsgesellschaft mbH, AM Urselback 6, 6000 Frankfurt, Germany. Ed. Hans A. Nikel.

800			

▼**SLICK TIMES.** 1993. q. $17. Box 1710, Valley Center, CA 92082. TEL 800-937-5425. Ed. Michael Dalton Johnson. **Document type:** newsletter.
  Description: Satirical look at the Clinton presidency.

052		UK	

SLIGHTLY SOILED. 6/yr. £8. c/o Turret Bookshop, 42 Lambs Conduit St., London WC1N 31J, England. Eds. David Crystal, Timothy Cumming. illus.

057	XO	ISSN 0231-7192

SLOVENSKE KUPELE. 1959. q. $20. (Slovakofarma) Obzor, Ceskoslovenskej Armady 35, 815 85 Bratislava, Slovakia. Ed.Bd.

057.8	XV	ISSN 0350-4697

SLOVENSKI CEBELAR. (Text in Slovenian; summaries in English) 1898. m. 250 din.($32) Zveza Cebelarskih Drustev Slovenije, Cankarjeva 3, 61000 Ljubljana, Slovenia. TEL 061-210-992. Ed. Janez Mihelic. adv.; bk.rev.; index. circ. 7,000. (back issues avail.)

943.7	GW	ISSN 0037-7058

SLOWAKEI/SLOVAKIA; kulturpolitische Revue. 1963. a. DM.6. Matus-Cernak-Institut, Kulturelles Zentrum der Slowaken in Deutschland, Postfach 100924, 50449 Cologne, Germany. Ed. Alba Greiner. bk.rev. circ. 1,500.

SMALL PRESS REVIEW - SMALL MAGAZINE REVIEW. see PUBLISHING AND BOOK TRADE

808.8		US	

SNARF.* 1972. s-a. Kitchen Sink Press, Inc., 320 Riverside Dr., Northampton, MA 01060-2717. TEL 414-295-6922. FAX 414-295-6878. Ed. Denis Kitchen. circ. 7,000.
  Description: Contains contributions by top cartoonists: Robert Crumb, Howard Cruse, Drew Friedman and Will Elder.

808.87		US	

SNICKER. 1987. q. $10 for 11 nos. Balducci Publications, 1248 Oak Bark Dr., St. Louis, MO 63146. TEL 314-993-1633. Ed. Rich Balducci. adv. circ. 13,000. (tabloid format)
  Description: Contains sophisticated political and social satires, from professional and novice cartoonists.

SNOECK'S: LITERATUUR KUNST FILM TONEEL MODE REIZEN. see HUMANITIES: COMPREHENSIVE WORKS

051 HX821	US	ISSN 0196-4801

SOCIAL ANARCHISM; a journal of practice & theory. 1980. s-a. $14 for 4 nos. 2743 Maryland Ave., Baltimore, MD 21218. TEL 410-243-6987. Ed. H.J. Ehrlich. adv.; bk.rev. circ. 1,200. **Indexed:** Alt.Press Ind. **Document type:** academic/scholarly publication.
  Description: Essays, reviews, interviews, poetry and graphics concerning anarchism, feminism, political ecology, and community.

320		US	

SOCIALIST REPUBLIC. 1973. 4/yr. $3. Industrial Union Party, Box 533, White Plains, NY 10603. TEL 212-563-8100. (Or: Industrial Union Party, Box 711, Red Bank, NJ 07701. TEL 908-758-0449) Eds. Murray Block, Walter Petrovich. adv.; bk.rev.; bibl. circ. 2,000.
  Formerly: Deleonist.

054.1		FR	

SOCIETE J.K. HUYSMANS. BULLETIN. 1927. irreg., approx. 2/yr. 150 F. membership. Societe J.K. Huysmans, 22 rue Guynemer, 75006 Paris, France. adv.; bk.rev.; circ. 600 (controlled). **Document type:** bibliography, bulletin.

054.1		FR	

SOCIETE LITTERAIRE DES P.T.T. MISSIVES. 1946. q. membership. 6 Impasse Bonne Nouvelle, 75010 Paris, France. Ed. Bernard Rautureau. adv.; bk.rev.; bibl. circ. 6,000.
  Formerly: Societe Litteraire des P.T.T. Bulletin.

057.8 AP58.S55	XV	ISSN 0038-0482

SODOBNOST. (Text in Slovenian) 1953. m. 120 din.($6.85) (Republiska Konferenca Delovnega Ljudstva Slovenije) Drzavna Zalozba Slovenije, Stritarjeva 3-11, Box 50-1, Ljubljana, Slovenia. Ed. Ciril Zlobec. circ. 1,400. **Indexed:** M.L.A.

914.7		LI	

SOGLASIE. (Text in Russian) 1988. w. Zygimantu 26, Vilnius 232600, Lithuania. TEL (0122) 226-206. Ed. Liuba Ciornaya.

051 800		US	

SOMA; left coast culture. 1986. bi-m. $14.95. SOMA Publications, 285 Ninth St., San Francisco, CA 94103. TEL 415-558-8974. FAX 415-558-8253. Eds. Ali Ghanbarian, Rebecca Paoletti. adv.; bk.rev.; film rev.; play rev.; illus. circ. 60,000. (back issues avail.) **Document type:** consumer publication.
  Description: Provides a forum for local and national artists and entertainers, with a special focus on West Coast culture. Includes music and fashion sections.

053.1 AP30	GW	ISSN 0038-1411

SONNTAG; kulturpolitische Wochenzeitung. 1946. w. DM.15.60 (foreign DM.26). Kulturbund der DDR, Otto-Nuscke-Str. 1, 1080 Berlin, Germany. adv.; bk.rev.; dance rev.; film rev.; play rev.; illus.
  Description: Covers theatre, literature, art, architecture, music, film, travel and more. Includes reports and announcements of events in Eastern part of Germany, and international news.

800	FR	ISSN 0993-1406

SORTEZ LA CHIENNE. 1988. a. 60 F. Association Beau Nageur, 48 rue Leon Gambetta, 59000 Lille, France. TEL 20-54-15-48. FAX 20-57-51-34. Ed. J.J. Tachdjian.

055		IT	

IL SOSPIRO DEL TIFOSO; periodico vicentino di sport e cultura. 1964. bi-w. L.15000($12) Pino Dato, Via V. Veneto 13, 36100 Vicenza, Italy. adv. circ. 2,000. (tabloid format; back issues avail.)

850 398	IT	ISSN 0038-1659

SOT LA NAPE; filologje, leterature, folclor. (Text in Friulian, Italian) 1949. q. L.50000($33) membership. (Regione Friuli - Venezia - Giulia) GEAP Pordenone, Via Malignani 41, 33080 Fiume Veneto (PN), Italy. TEL 0432-501598. FAX 0432-511766. (Subscr. to: Societa Filologica Friulana, Via Manin 18, 33100 Udine, Italy) Ed. Andreina Ciceri. adv.; bk.rev.; illus.; index. circ. 3,800. (back issues avail.) **Indexed:** Numis.Lit.

057.91	KR	ISSN 0038-1705

SOTSIALISTYCHNA KUL'TURA. (Text in Ukrainian) m. $6. Ministerstvo Kul'tury, Kiev, Ukraine. Ed. A.P. Varlamov. circ. 47,100.

057.1	RU	ISSN 0868-8230

SOTSIUM. English edition: Socium (Digest). (Text in Russian) 1991. m. 1.30 Rub. Bol'shaya Pochtovaya 7, 107082 Moscow, Russia. TEL 261-33-59. Ed. Aleksandr Zolotarev. adv.; bk.rev.
  Description: Covers the social spheres, questions of politics, philosophy, sociology, business and the history of culture and art.

296.67	IS	ISSN 0082-4585

SOURCES OF CONTEMPORARY JEWISH THOUGHT/MEKEVOT. Title varies: To the Source - El Ha'ayin. (Text in English, French, Spanish, Hebrew) 1968. irreg., no.6, 1975. price varies. World Zionist Organization, Department for Torah Education and Culture in the Diaspora, P.O. Box 92, Jerusalem 91920, Israel. TEL 02-527156. FAX 02-533542. (Subscr. to: Jewish Agency, Publication Service, 515 Park Ave., New York, NY 10022) Ed.Bd.

054.1		FR	

▼**SOUTERRAINES.** (Text in English, French) 1993. irreg. (5-6/yr.). 100 F.($20) for 10 nos. Bruno Pommey, Ed. & Pub., 10 Residence Jean Mace, 28300 Mainvilliers, France. adv.
  Description: Covers publications and music, the alternative culture, mail art.

LITERARY AND POLITICAL REVIEWS

052 659.1   AT
SOUTH EAST MAGAZINE. 1976. w. free. Queanbeyan Publishing Co., 210 Crawford St., Queanbeyan, N.S.W. 2620, Australia. TEL 06-297-3033. FAX 06-297-6201. Ed. R.J. Woods. adv.; bk.rev. circ. 40,000.
Description: Supplement to 18 local newspapers covering the south east region of New South Wales.

051   US   ISSN 0146-809X
F206
SOUTHERN EXPOSURE (DURHAM). 1973. q. $24. Institute for Southern Studies, Box 531, Durham, NC 27702. TEL 919-419-8311. Ed. Eric Bates. adv.; bk.rev.; bibl.; charts; illus.; stat.; s-a. index. circ. 7,500. (also avail. in microfilm from UMI; back issues avail.; reprint service avail. from UMI) **Indexed:** Access (1976-), Alt.Press Ind., Amer.Hist.& Life, Hist.Abstr., Hum.Ind., Lang.& Lang.Behav.Abstr., Sociol.Abstr.
—Faxon; UnCover; UMI.
Description: Covers innovative design, investigative journalism, oral history and profiles.

051 020   US
SOUTHWEST BOOK REVIEW.* 1987. m. $15. 2405 Forest Ave., Austin, TX 78704-5521. TEL 512-443-6618. Ed. Julie Gomoll. adv.; bk.rev. circ. 5,000. (back issues avail.)
Description: Intended for librarians.

810   US   ISSN 0038-4712
AP2
SOUTHWEST REVIEW. 1915. q. $20 to individuals; institutions $25. Southern Methodist University, 307 Fondren Library West, Box 4374, Dallas, TX 75275. TEL 214-768-1037. FAX 214-768-1408. Ed. Willard Spiegelman. adv.; index, cum.index: vols.10-29 (1924-1944), vols.30-60 (1945-1970); circ. 1,500 (paid). (also avail. in microform from UMI; reprint service avail. from UMI) **Indexed:** A.I.P.P., Abstr.Engl.Stud., Abstr.Pop.Cult., Amer.Hist.& Life, Amer.Hum.Ind., Bibl.Engl.Lang.& Lit., Bk.Rev.Ind. (1965-), Child.Bk.Rev.Ind. (1965-), Hist.Abstr., Hum.Ind., Hum.Ind.Amer.Per.Verse, Ind.Bk.Rev.Hum., M.L.A. **Document type:** academic/scholarly publication.
●Also available online.
—BLDSC (8356.900000); Faxon; UnCover; UMI. **CCC.**
Description: Presents the work of writers and scholars from the surrounding states and offers analyses of problems and themes that are distinctly southwestern. Publishes works of good writers, regardless of their locales.

052 820 821   UK   ISSN 0952-4517
SOW'S EAR. (Text in English) 1982. s-a. £1.40($6) per no. 1 Small Lane, Eccleshall, Stafford ST21 6AD, England. Ed. R.J. Ellis. circ. 250. (back issues avail.)
Supersedes: Strange Lime Fruit Stone.
Description: Poetry with features on a single author per issue.

052 700   UK   ISSN 0584-8067
SPANNER (LONDON, 1974). 1974. irreg. £12 for 3 issues to institutions. 14 Hopton Rd., Hereford HR1 1BE, England. TEL 0432-277857. Ed. Allen Fisher. adv.; bk.rev. **Document type:** monographic series.
Description: Promotes innovative and experimental art, poetry and music.

051   FR
SPEAKEASY; English through the news. (Text in English) 1979. 5/yr. 114 F. Librairie Fernand Nathan, 9 rue Mechain, 75680 Paris cedex 14, France. Ed. Michelle Sommers.

054.1   FR
AP20
SPECTACLE DU MONDE - REALITES. 1962. m. 576 F. (foreign 665 F.). Valmonde & Cie, 54 rue Martre, 92586 Clichy Cedex, France. TEL 49-68-18-18. FAX 1-47-35-85-00. Ed. Francois d'Orcival. adv.; bk.rev.; abstr.; bibl.; charts; illus.; stat.; index. circ. 140,000.
Former titles: Spectacle du Monde - Realites - Perspectives; Spectacle du Monde - Spectacle - Perspectives; Spectacle du Monde (ISSN 0038-6944); Incorporates (in 1980): Realites.

827   UK   ISSN 0038-6952
AP4
THE SPECTATOR. 1828. w. £77 (foreign £88). Spectator (1828) Ltd., 56 Doughty St., London WC1N 2LL, England. TEL 071-405-1706. FAX 071-242-0603. TELEX 27124. (Subscr. to: P.O. Box 14, Harold Hill, Romford, Essex RM3 8EQ, England. TEL 0708-381122. FAX 0708-381211) Ed. D. Lawson. adv.; bk.rev.; film rev.; music rev.; play rev.; index. circ. 46,419. (also avail. in microform from UMI,PMC; reprint service avail. from UMI) **Indexed:** Bk.Rev.Ind. (1965-), Br.Hum.Ind., Child.Bk.Rev.Ind. (1965-). **Document type:** consumer publication.
—BLDSC (8408.600000); Faxon; UnCover; SWETS; UMI.

378.1   UK   ISSN 0038-7428
SPHINX; the student magazine for Liverpool. 1892. 3/yr. £4 per no. Liverpool Guild of Undergraduates, Student Union, 2 Bedford St. N., Liverpool 7, England. Ed. Peter Medawar. adv.; bk.rev. circ. 5,000.

055.1   IT   ISSN 1120-6500
SPIRAGLI;* giornale internazionale di cultura. 1978. m. L.20000. Editore S. Vecchio, Contrada S. Giuseppe Tafalia 74-6, 91025 Marsala, Italy. Ed. Gaspare LiCansi. adv. circ. 55,840.

800   US
SPRING (NEW YORK); the journal of the E.E. Cummings Society. 1980. a. $15 to individuals; students $10; libraries $20. Norman Friedman, Ed. & Pub., 33-54 164th St., New York, NY 11358-1442.

057.8   XV   ISSN 0038-8777
SRECANJA. (Text in Slovenian) 1948. bi-m. 200 din. Franciskanska Prokuratura, Presernov trg 4, Ljubljana, Slovenia. Ed. Mihael Vovk. circ. 3,000.

STAND MAGAZINE. see *LITERATURE*

STANFORD CHAPARRAL. see *COLLEGE AND ALUMNI*

STANFORD ITALIAN REVIEW. see *LITERATURE*

057.8   CI   ISSN 0352-2873
START; magazin modernog covjeka. 1969. bi-m. $32. Vjesnik, Avenija Bratstva i Jedinstva 4, 4100 Zagreb, Croatia. Ed. Mladen Plese.

STEAUA. see *LITERATURE*

053.1   IS
DIE STIMME. (Text in German) 1944. m. $50. World Association of Bukowinean Jews, P.O. Box 3653, Tel Aviv 61036, Israel. TEL 972-3-5226619. Ed. Josef N. Rudel. adv.; bk.rev.; play rev. circ. 1,200.

057.1   RU   ISSN 0868-698X
STOLITSA. 1990. w. 7 Rub.($2.98) per issue (effective 1993). Petrovka 22, 101425 Moscow K-51, Russia. TEL 928-23-49. FAX 095-921-2955. TELEX 413739 SU. Ed. Andrei Mal'gin. adv.; bk.rev.; illus. circ. 150,000.

809   US   ISSN 0146-2067
STONY HILLS; news and reviews of the small press. 1977. 3/yr. $15 (includes Small Press News). Diane Kruchkow, Ed. & Pub., RR 1, Box 780, New Sharon, ME 04955. adv.; bk.rev.; cum.index: 1977-1981. circ. 5,000. (tabloid format; back issues avail.) **Indexed:** Access, Bk.Rev.Ind. (1981-1983), Child.Bk.Rev.Ind. (1981-1983).
Formerly: New England Small Press Review.

055   IT
LO STRADONE; il giornale di Corato. 1979. m. L.17000 (foreign L.43000). Lo Stradone, Via Andria 44, 70033 Corato (Bari), Italy. TEL 080-8724205. FAX 8724205. Ed. Emilio D'Angelo. adv.; bk.rev. circ. 3,500. (looseleaf format; back issues avail.)
Description: Focuses on news, sports, politics and local history of Corato, Italy.

800   UK   ISSN 0968-6169
STRANGE ADVENTURES. 1989. irreg. £2($5) per no. S.A. Publishing, 13 Hazely Combe, Arreton, Isle of Wight PO30 3AJ, England. TEL 0983-865668. Ed. Tony Lee. bk.rev.; film rev.; video rev.; illus. (back issues avail.) **Document type:** consumer publication.
Description: Contains interviews, festival and convention reports, film director profiles, movie news and fantasy artwork.

800   IT
STRANIERO/STRANGER/ETRANGER/FREMDE. (Text in English, Italian, occasionally in French, German) 1985. q. L.50000($50) (effective 1994). Via Chiaia 149, 80121 Naples, Italy. TEL 081-426052. Ed. Ignazio Corsaro. circ. 10,000. (back issues avail.)

052   UK
STREETLIFE. 1985. s-a. free. London Borough of Hammersmith and Fulham, Town Hall, King St., London W6 9JU, England. FAX 0741-2685. Ed. Carol Todd. adv.; stat. circ. 86,000. **Document type:** newsletter.
Formerly: London Borough of Hammersmith and Fulham. Review.

059.91   XN   ISSN 0039-2294
STREMEZ; spisanie za literatura, umetnost i kultura. (Text in Macedonian) 1957. 10/yr. 40 din. Interesna Zaednica na Kulturata, Prilep, Joska Jordanoski 2, Prilep, Macedonia. Ed. Branko Ilievski. circ. 1,500.

053.931   BE   ISSN 0039-2324
AP15
STREVEN. (Text in Dutch) 1933. m. 1680 BEF. Streven V.Z.W., Sanderusstraat 5, B-2018 Antwerp, Belgium. Ed. Hugo Rouffaers. adv.; bk.rev.; illus.; index. circ. 2,500. **Indexed:** Hist.Abstr.
—SWETS.

320   UK   ISSN 0260-2563
STUDENT NATIONALIST; the paper for the independent-minded Scot. 1979? irreg. contributions. Federation of Student Nationalists, c/o Student Union, Aberdeen University, Upper Kirkgate, Aberdeen, Scotland. Ed. Eric Herring. illus. circ. 5,000.
Formerly: Nor'-easter.

STUDI STORICI/HISTORICAL STUDIES. see *HISTORY*

808.87   US   ISSN 0095-280X
PS430
STUDIES IN AMERICAN HUMOR. 1974. 4/yr. $10 to individuals; institutions $15. American Humor Publications, Inc., Southwest Texas State University, Department of English, San Marcos, TX 78666. TEL 512-245-2163. Ed. John O. Rosenbalm. adv.; bk.rev. circ. 500. **Indexed:** Abstr.Engl.Stud., M.L.A.
—BLDSC (8489.070000); UnCover.
Incorporates (1974-1984): American Humor (ISSN 0193-7146)

055.1   IT   ISSN 0039-4130
STUDIUM; rivista bimestrale di cultura. 1904. bi-m. L.55000 (foreign L.90000) (effective Jan. 1994). Edizioni Studium, Via Cassiodoro 14, 00193 Rome, Italy. (Subscr. to: C.P. 30100, 00100 Rome 47, Italy) adv.; bk.rev.; bibl.; index. circ. 3,000. (back issues avail.) **Indexed:** Amer.Hist.& Life, Hist.Abstr., M.L.A., RILA. **Document type:** newspaper.
Description: Covers expressions of a working community in a creative and direct way, avoiding criticism. Faces the most significant cultural issues with passages, notes, summaries and reviews.

057.8   YU   ISSN 0039-422X
STVARANJE; casopis za knjizevnost i kulturu. 1946. m. 200 din. Pobjeda, Bulevar Revolucije 11, Box 37, 81000 Titograd, Yugoslavia. Ed.Bd. bk.rev.; index. circ. 2,100. **Indexed:** M.L.A.
—BLDSC (0168.496000).

SUBTERRANEAN SOCIOLOGY NEWSLETTER. see *SOCIOLOGY*

053.1   AU   ISSN 0039-4629
SUEDTIROL IN WORT UND BILD. 1957. q. S.170. Suedtirol Verlag, Defreggerstr. 23, A-6020 Innsbruck, Austria. Ed. Herbert Neuner. adv.; bk.rev.; bibl.; illus. circ. 15,000. **Document type:** consumer publication.

SULFUR; a literary bi-annual of the whole art. see *LITERATURE*

808.8   US   ISSN 0744-9666
AP2
SUN (CHAPEL HILL); a magazine of ideas. 1974. m. $30. Sun Publishing Company, Inc., 107 N. Roberson St., Chapel Hill, NC 27516. TEL 919-942-5282. FAX 919-932-3101. Ed. Sy Safransky. circ. 25,000. (also avail. in microform from UMI; back issues avail.) **Indexed:** Alt.Press Ind.

LITERARY AND POLITICAL REVIEWS

808.0   UK   ISSN 0955-9647
SUNK ISLAND REVIEW. 1989. s-a. $28. Sunk Island Publishing, P.O. Box 74, Lincoln LN1 1QG, England. TEL 0522-575660. Ed. Michael Blackburn. adv.; bk.rev. circ. 1,000. (back issues avail.) **Document type:** bulletin.

808.87   US
SUPER CRACKED. q. $1.50 per no. Globe Communications Corp. (New York), 441 Lexington Ave., New York, NY 10017. TEL 800-472-7744. circ. 400,000.

860   CU
SUPLEMENTO LITERARIO DE REVOLUCION Y CULTURA. 4/yr. Ministerio de Cultura, Direccion de Literatura, Calle 4, No. 205, entre 11 y Linea Vedado, Havana, Cuba.

800   PK
SURAJ MUKHI. (Text in Panjabi) 1978. m. Rs.20. 129-17 Zaildar Rd, Ichhra, Lahore, Pakistan.

800   II
SURGE INTERNATIONAL. (Text in English) 1976. m. Rs.50. B-90, Defence Colony, New Delhi 110024, India. (U.S. dist. addr.: c/o Indrani Rahman, 314 W. 56th St., Apt. 1C, New York, NY 10019) Ed. Uma Vasudev. adv.; bk.rev.

SURPLUS; tijdschrift over literatuur van vrouwen - women's review of books. see *WOMEN'S STUDIES*

058.7   SW   ISSN 0039-677X
AP48
SVENSK TIDSKRIFT. 1911. 9/yr. SEK 220 (effective 1990). Foerlags AB Svensk Tidskrift, Linnegatan 28-30, IV, 114 47 Stockholm, Sweden. FAX 08-6673241. Ed. Rargaretha af Ugglas. adv.; illus.; index. circ. 3,500. **Indexed:** Amer.Hist.& Life, Hist.Abstr.

057.868   XR   ISSN 0039-7032
SVET V OBRAZECH, obrazkovy tydenik. 1945. w. 260 Kcs.($57.20) Novinar, Parizska 9, 110 01 Prague 1, Czech Republic. (Dist. by: Artia, Ve Smeckach 30, 111 27 Prague 1, Czech Republic) Ed. Zdenek Hrabica. adv.; bk.rev.; illus. circ. 150,000.
Description: Covers politics, economics, culture and travel.

057.8   YU   ISSN 0039-7059
SVETLOST. 1935. w. 104 din. Svetlost, 21 Oktobra 66, Kragujevac, Yugoslavia. Ed. Miodrag Stojinovic.

057.8   CI   ISSN 0039-7113
SVIJET (ZAGREB); jugoslavenska zenska revija. 1958. bi-m. $16. Vjesnik, Avenija Bratstva i Jedinstva 4, 41000 Zagreb, Croatia. Ed. Vesna Bluemlmihaljevic.

800   US
SYMPOSIUM SERIES. 1974. irreg., latest no.33. $39.95 per no. Edwin Mellen Press, 415 Ridge St., Box 450, Lewiston, NY 14092. TEL 716-754-2788. FAX 716-754-4056. **Indexed:** Ind.Sci.Rev. **Document type:** monographic series.

058.82   NO   ISSN 0039-7717
AP45
SYN OG SEGN. 1894. 4/yr. NOK 225 to individuals; institutions NOK 300. Det Norske Samlaget, P.O. Box 4672 Sofienberg, N-0506 Oslo, Norway. TEL 47-22-68-76-00. FAX 47-22-68-75-02. Ed. Jan Inge Soerboe. adv.; bk.rev.; illus.; index, cum.index every 25 yrs. circ. 5,000. **Indexed:** M.L.A. **Document type:** academic/scholarly publication.
Description: Essays and interviews about the modern and historical trends of Norwegian and international society; cultural development and conflicts.

290   US
SYNAPSE (BOSTON). 1983. 2/yr. free. Unitarian Universalist Association, 25 Beacon St., Boston, MA 02108-2800. TEL 617-742-2100. FAX 617-367-3237. Ed. Marjorie Agate. adv.; bk.rev.; circ. 10,500 (controlled). (tabloid format; back issues avail.)
Formerly: People Soup (ISSN 0360-8247)

057   XO
T E T. (Termeszet es Tarsadalom) (Text in Hungarian) m. $26. (Socialist Academy of the Slovak Socialist Republic) Obzor, Ceskoslovenskej Armady 35, 815 85 Bratislava, Slovakia.

053   GW
T M. (Trans Media); das medien-kritische Magazin. 1986. m. DM.48. (Buerger Frangen Journalisten) T M Verlags GmbH, Sonnenstr. 4, 91058 Erlangen, Germany. TEL 09131-604030. FAX 09131-604446. Ed. Herbert Eder. adv.; bk.rev.; illus.; stat.; tr.lit. circ. 18,000. (back issues avail.)
Formerly (until 1990): Trans Media.
Description: Media critique, politics and culture.

TABLET. see *RELIGIONS AND THEOLOGY*

TAI SHENG/VOICE OF TAIWAN. see *ETHNIC INTERESTS*

808.8   FR
TAKE IT EASY. 1982. 6/yr. 60 F. Librarie Fernand Nathan, 9 rue Mechain, 75014 Paris, France. Ed. Michelle Somme.

052   UK   ISSN 0049-2884
TALIESIN. 1962. q. £8. Yr. Academi Gymreig - Welsh Language Section, Mount Stuart House, Mount Stuart Sq., Cardiff CF1 6DQ, Wales. TEL 0222-492064. Eds. John Rowlands, Gerwyn Wiliams. bk.rev. circ. 800. (back issues avail.) **Document type:** bulletin.

056.1   CU
TALLER. LITERARIO.* no.22, 1971. q. Universidad de Oriente, Escuela de Letras, Avda. Patricio Lumumba s-n, Santiago de Cuba, Oriente, Cuba. Ed.Bd.

808.8   US
TAMAQUA. 1989. s-a. $10. Parkland College, Humanities Department, 2400 W. Bradley Ave., Champaign, IL 61821-1899. Ed. Bruce Morgan. adv.; bk.rev.; illus. circ. 2,000.
Description: Publishes original fiction, poetry, essays and photography.
Refereed Serial

056.1 800   SP   ISSN 0049-2922
TAMBOR.* vol.13, 1971. m. 125 ptas. Sociedad Cultural Amigos del Arte de Baena, Plaza G. Cascajo 5, Baena, Spain. Ed.Bd. bk.rev.; illus. circ. 700.

059.951   US
T'AN SO/QUEST. Variant title: Tansuo. (Text in Chinese) m. $24. Box 300742, Brooklyn, NY 11230-0011.

059   TR
TAPIA. 1969. w. T.T.$12($30) (Trinidad and Tobago Institute of the West Indies) Tapia House Publishing Co. Ltd., 91 Tunapuna Road, Tunapuna, Trinidad & Tobago, W.I. Ed. Allan Harris. adv.; play rev. circ. 5,000. (tabloid format)

TAPROOT. see *LITERATURE*

057.8   XV   ISSN 0040-1978
TEDNIK. (Text in Slovenian) 1948. w. 1100 SLT. Radio-Tednik, Raiceva 6, Ptuj, Slovenia. TEL 062 771 226. FAX 062-771-223. Ed. Ludvik Kotar. adv. circ. 11,000.

800 780   US   ISSN 0748-836X
TELLUS; the audio magazine series of experimental and innovative sound. 1984. irreg. (1-2/yr.), no.26, 1992. $10 per no. Harvestworks, 596 Broadway, Ste. 602, New York, NY 10012. TEL 212-431-1130. (audio cassette; some issues also avail. in CD format)
Description: Presents original recordings of works by writers, performers and musicians, including stories, performance art, theatrical productions, experimental music, audio portraits of individual artists, and projects completed by artists in residence at the Harvestworks studios in New York. Includes printed notes pertaining to the recorded pieces.

200   FR   ISSN 0244-1462
TEMOIGNAGE CHRETIEN. 1941. w. 600 F. Societe de Presse et d'Edition, 49 rue du Faubourg Poissonniere, 75009 Paris, France. TEL 42-46-37-50. FAX 48-24-33-67. TELEX 290562. (Subscr. to: B.P. 63, F-77932 Perthes Cedex, France. TEL 1-64-38-01-55) Ed. Georges Montaron. adv.; bk.rev.; film rev.; play rev.; tele.rev. circ. 80,000. (tabloid format; also avail. in microform) **Indexed:** CERDIC.
Description: Covers politics, economics, society, culture and religion.

055   IT
TEMPO NUOVO. q. Via Francesco Feo, 34, Naples, Italy. Ed. L. Santucci.

055   IT
TEMPO PRESENTE; rivista mensile di cultura. 1980. m. L.42000. Tempo Presente, Via Virgilio, No. 11, 00193 Rome, Italy. TEL 06 687.3048. Ed.Bd. adv.; bk.rev.

TEMPORARY CULTURE. see *LITERATURE — Science Fiction, Fantasy, Horror*

054.1   FR   ISSN 0040-3075
AP20
TEMPS MODERNES. 1945. m. 200 F. Presses d'Aujourd'hui, 4 rue Ferou, 75006 Paris, France. TEL 1-43-29-08-47. bk.rev.; film rev.; illus. **Indexed:** Arts & Hum.Cit.Ind., Curr.Cont., M.L.A., Pt.de Rep. (1980-).
—BLDSC (8790.300000); SWETS.

800   NE   ISSN 0921-2523
TEORIA LITERARIA: TEXTO Y TEORIA. (Text in Spanish) 1987. irreg. price varies. Editions Rodopi B.V., Keizersgracht 302-304, 1016 EX Amsterdam, Netherlands. TEL 31-20-6227507. FAX 31-20-6380948. (In N. America: 233 Peachtree St. N.E., Ste. 404, Atlanta GA 30303-1504. TEL 800-225-3998. FAX 404-522-7116) Ed. Iris Zavala. circ. 500. **Document type:** monographic series.

055.1   IT
TERZA PAGINA; antigruppo siciliano. (Text in English, Italian and Sicilian) 1950. w. L.25000($50) (Cooperativa Trapani Nuova) Cooperativa Editrice Antigruppo Siciliano, Via Argenteria Km. 4, Trapani, Sicily, Italy. TEL 0923-38681. (Co-sponsor: Cross Cultural Communications) Ed. Nat Scammacca. adv.; bk.rev.; play rev.; illus. circ. 5,000. (tabloid format; back issues avail.)
Formerly: Trapani Nuova (ISSN 0041-1779)
Description: Creative writings and literary essays, including the latest poetic theories and information regarding the poetic movement.

055.1   IT   ISSN 0040-3989
TESTIMONIANZE; quaderni mensili. 1957. 10/yr. L.60000 (effective Jan. 1993). Associazione Culturale Testimonianze, Via dei Roccettini 11, 50016 S. Domenico, Fiesole, Italy. TEL 055-597080. Dir. Lodovico Grassi. adv.; bk.rev.; illus.; index. circ. 7,000. **Indexed:** CERDIC, Old Test.Abstr.
—BLDSC (8796.598000).

051 001.3 300   CN   ISSN 1183-854X
▼**TEXTUAL STUDIES IN CANADA;** Canada's journal of cultural literacy. (Text in English, French) 1992. s-a. Can.$21.40. University College of the Cariboo, English Department, Box 3010, Kamloops, BC V2C 5N3, Canada. TEL 604-828-5000. FAX 604-828-5086. Ed.Bd. adv. contact: Ron Smith. bk.rev.; film rev.illus. circ. 300. **Document type:** academic/scholarly publication.
Description: Dedicated to Canadian cultural texts in all media. Combines discussions of Canadian culture, literature, visual arts and interdisciplinary studies.
Refereed Serial

THEATERZEITSCHRIFT. see *THEATER*

800 700   AT   ISSN 0816-5157
THIRD DEGREE; Australian mythological sights. 1985. a. Third Degree, P.O. Box 123, Broadway, N.S.W. 2007, Australia. TEL 02-3009-674. Ed. Kurt Brereton. circ. 1,500. (back issues avail.)

810   US   ISSN 0741-5958
THIRD RAIL; international arts & literature. 1975. a. $30 for 4 nos. to individuals; libraries $48; foreign $60. Box 46127, Los Angeles, CA 90046. TEL 213-850-7548. Ed. Uri Hertz. adv.; bk.rev. circ. 12,000. (back issues avail.)
Description: Explores new currents in the arts and literary avant-garde traditions.

800   US   ISSN 0734-0117
BL65.P7
THIS WORLD; a journal of religion and public life. 1983. a.? $7.50 (effective 1992). (Elizabethtown College) Science Press, 300 W. Chestnut St., Box 497, Ephrata, PA 17522. TEL 717-367-1151. FAX 717-367-7567. Ed. Paul Gottfried. adv.; bk.rev. circ. 3,000. (also avail. in microform; back issues avail.) **Indexed:** Hum.Ind.
—UnCover; UMI.
Description: Provocative social, political, and religious commentary.
Refereed Serial

L

LITERARY AND POLITICAL REVIEWS

800   US
THUNDER & HONEY; a publication for creative thought. 1983. q. $5. Kummunity Press, Box 11386, Atlanta, GA 30310. TEL 404-688-3376. Ed. Akbar Imhotep.

053.932   BE   ISSN 0040-764X
TIJDSPIEGEL; cultureel blad voor Limburg. 1946. m. 200 Fr. Opperstraat 60-Wijer, 3821 Kozen, Belgium. Ed. Ludo Rolskin. adv.; bk.rev.; illus.; index. circ. 1,500.

TIMARIT MALS OG MENNINGAR. see *LITERATURE*

808.87   GW
TITANIC; das endgueltige Satiremagazin. 1979. m. DM.62 (foreign DM.75). Titanic Verlag Georg Buechner Verlagsbuchhandlung GmbH und Co. KG, Postfach 360440, 109774 Berlin, Germany. TEL 030-2710165. FAX 030-2710149. Ed. Hans Zippert. adv. circ. 65,000.

808   US
TOOK. 1988. irreg. $20. Norton Coker Press, Box 640543, San Francisco, CA 94164-0543. TEL 415-922-0395. Ed. Edward Mycue. bk.rev.; film rev.; play rev.; bibl.; illus. circ. 150. (back issues avail.)
    Description: Includes poetry, plays, stories, criticism, music, art, dance, film, psychology, travel, history, and food.

808   US
TOPSY TURVY-PATAS ARRIBAS.* 1979. m. $6. 4901 E. Sunrise Dr., Apt. 406, Tucson, AZ 85718-4552. TEL 602-747-9352. Ed. Jane Eppinga. circ. 250.

800   CN   ISSN 0714-3508
PK101
TORONTO SOUTH ASIAN REVIEW. 1982. 3/yr. Can.$15($15) Toronto South Asian Review, Box 6996, Sta. A, Toronto, Ont. M5W 1X7, Canada. TEL 416-483-7191. FAX 416-483-7191. Ed. M.G. Vassanji. bk.rev.; index. circ. 500. (also avail. in microform from MML; back issues avail. from Micromedia Ltd.) **Indexed:** Can.Lit.Ind.
    Description: Provides literary and political reviews.

055.1   IT
TORRE. 1953. fortn. L.3000. Via Colombo 24, 92024 Canicatti, Italy. Ed. Giuseppe Alaimo. adv.; bk.rev.

056.9   BL
TOTEM.* q. Faculdade de Filosofia, Ciencias e Letras de Cataguases, Praca Santa Rita 340, Cataguases (MG) 36770, Brazil. Eds. Joaquim Branco, Ronald Werneck. adv.; bk.rev.; film rev.; illus.

TOUCHSTONE (SPRING); literary journal. see *LITERATURE — Poetry*

056.979   SP
A TRABE DE OURO; publicacion galega de pensamento critico. (Text in Gallegan) 1990. q. 3800 ptas. (effective 1990). Grupo Soteblan, S.A., San Marcos s-n, 15890 Santiago de Compostela, Spain. TEL 58-25-71. FAX 58-72-90. Dir. X.L. Mendez Ferrin.

TRADE JOURNAL RECAP. see *ART*

323.4   US   ISSN 0041-1191
AP9
TRANSITION (NEW YORK). 1961-1968; resumed 1971-1977; resumed, no.51, 1991. 4/yr. $27 to individuals; institutions $54 (effective 1994). Oxford University Press, Journals, 200 Madison Ave., New York, NY 10016. TEL 212-679-7300. FAX 212-689-5312. TELEX 6859654. (Subscr. to: Oxford Journals Fulfillment, 2001 Evans Rd., Cary, NC 25713. TEL 919-677-0977. FAX 919-677-1714) Eds. Kwame Anthony Appiah, Henry Louis Gates, Jr. adv.; bk.rev.; illus. circ. 1,600. (also avail. in microform from UMI) **Indexed:** Curr.Cont.Africa. **Document type:** academic/scholarly publication.
    —BLDSC (9020.836000); UnCover; UMI. **CCC.**
    Former titles (until 1977): Ch'indaba (ISSN 0564-108X); (until no.50, 1975): Transition.
    Description: A literary, political and cultural review of modern Africa and the post-colonial world, focusing on Africans and members of the African diaspora.

056   PE
TRAVESIA: REVISTA DE ENSAYO Y POLITICA. 1991. q.? $30. Av. Brasil 4207, Lima 17, Peru. TEL 63-6848. FAX 51-14-816826. Ed. Agustin Haya de la Torre. adv. contact: Eduardo Ballon. **Document type:** academic/scholarly publication.

057.8   XN   ISSN 0041-266X
TRIBINA; vesnik za selo vo SR Makedonija. (Text in Macedonian) 1946. w. 100 din. Nasa Knjiga, Skopje, Partizanski Odredi 17, 91000 Skopje, Macedonia. Ed. Vasko Anastasov.

891.4   II   ISSN 0041-2708
TRIBRITTA; news & literary monthly. (Text in Bengali) 1969. w. Rs.0.50 per copy. Saswati Deb, Ed.& Pub., 3, Tribritta Sarani, Cooch Behar - 736101, West Bengal, India. adv.; bk.rev.; tr.lit. circ. 5,000.

022   IT
TRIMESTRE; storia - politica - societa. q. L.52000 (foreign L.70000). (Istituto di Studi Storici e Politici, Facolta di Scienze Politiche) Trimestre Editrice s.a.s., Via Bolzano, 66020 Sambuceto, Chieti, Italy. TEL 085-206107. FAX 4461000. Ed. Luciano Russi. **Indexed:** M.L.A.

810 300 378   US   ISSN 0041-3097
PS508.C6
TRIQUARTERLY. 1964. 3/yr. $20 to individuals; institutions $30 (effective 1993). Northwestern University, 2020 Ridge Ave., Evanston, IL 60208. TEL 708-491-3490. FAX 708-467-2096. Eds. Reginald Gibbons, Susan Hahn. adv.; bk.rev.; film rev.; play rev.; illus.; cum.index; circ. 5,000 (paid). (also avail. in microform from UMI; back issues avail.; reprint service avail. from KTO) **Indexed:** A.I.P.P., Acad.Ind., Amer.Bibl.Slavic & E.Eur.Stud., Amer.Hist.& Life, Amer.Hum.Ind., Arts & Hum.Cit.Ind., Bk.Rev.Ind. (1986-), Child.Bk.Rev.Ind. (1986-), Curr.Cont., Hist.Abstr., Hum.Ind., LCR, M.L.A.
    —BLDSC (9050.692000); Faxon; UnCover; SWETS; UMI.
    Description: International journal of writing, art, and cultural inquiry.

051 301.412   US   ISSN 0736-928X
HQ1402
TRIVIA; a journal of ideas. 1982. 2/yr. $16 to individuals. Box 9606, N. Amherst, MA 01059-9606. Eds. Erin Rice, Kay Parkhurst. adv.; bk.rev. circ. 2,000. **Indexed:** Alt.Press Ind., Left Ind. (1983-), Stud.Wom.Abstr.
    —BLDSC (9050.777500); UnCover.
    Description: Includes essays, interviews, and experimental forms of literature that combine rigorous thinking without comprimising the feminist tradition.

700   US   ISSN 0742-0692
TUCSON WEEKLY. 1984. w. $25. Tucson Weekly, Inc., Box 2429, Tucson, AZ 85702. TEL 602-795-2143. FAX 602-792-2096. Ed. Dan Huff; Pub. Douglas Biggers. adv.; bk.rev.; circ. 40,000 (controlled). **Document type:** newspaper.

059.94   SW   ISSN 0041-4034
AP95.E4
TULIMULD; eesti kirjanduse ja kultuuri ajakiri. (Text in Estonian) 1950. q. SEK 190 (effective 1990). Bernard Kangro, Ed.& Pub., Skoerdevaegen 1, 222 38 Lund, Sweden. adv.; bk.rev.; illus.; index. circ. 1,000. **Indexed:** M.L.A.

055   IT
TUSCAN SCENE. q. L.30000. Toscana '90, Villa Il Ventaglio, Via Delle Forbici 26, 50100 Florence, Italy. Ed. Giuseppe Mammarella.

051   US
TWILIGHT OF THE IDOLS. 1991. 3/yr. $10. 3739 Balboa St., Ste. 142, San Francisco, CA 94121. TEL 415-665-3666. Ed. John Marmysz. adv.; bk.rev. circ. 600. **Document type:** newsletter.

808.87   US
TWISTED IMAGE NEWSLETTER. 1982. m. $20. 1630 University Ave., No. 26, Berkeley, CA 94703. TEL 510-644-8035. Ed. Ace Backwords. bk.rev.; circ. 4,000. circ. 400 (paid). **Document type:** newsletter.
    Description: Contains comics satirizing hypocrisy, social ills, human adversities, and attempts to relate to the opposite sex.

057.85   PL   ISSN 0041-4727
PG7001
TWORCZOSC. 1945. m. $60. (Ministerstwo Kultury i Sztuki) Agencja Autorska, Ul. Hipoteczna 2, 00-950 Warsaw, Poland. TEL 48-22-628-9507. (Dist. by: Ars Polona-Ruch, Krakowskie Przedmiescie 7, Warsaw, Poland. TEL 48-22-267622) Ed. Jerzy Lisowski. bk.rev.; index. circ. 38,014. **Indexed:** M.L.A.

TYDSKRIF VIR LETTERKUNDE. see *LITERATURE*

808.8   US
U J Q. (Uncle Jam Quarterly) 1973. q. $10 (effective Dec. 1990). Fragments West, Box 670, Lompoc, CA 93438-0670. TEL 805-735-5134. Ed. Edmond Gauthier. adv.; bk.rev. circ. 50,000. (tabloid format) **Document type:** newspaper.
    Formerly: Uncle Jam.
    Description: Covers the arts, books, health and travel humor. Includes exclusive interviews.

056.1   CK
U N A U L A. 1968. s-a. Universidad Autonoma Latinoamericana, Carrera 55 No. 49-51, Apdo. Aereo 3455, Medellin, Colombia.

UGANDA JOURNAL. see *HISTORY — History Of Africa*

053   GW
ULTIMO (MUENSTER); Muensters Stadtmagazin. 1983. fortn. Ultimo Verlag GmbH, Hafenweg 18-20, 48155 Muenster, Germany. TEL 0251-60302. FAX 0251-67698. Ed. Thomas Friedrich. adv. contact: Rainer Liedmeyer. circ. 15,973. **Document type:** consumer publication.
    Description: Information about cultural life in Muenster and its environs.

819   CN
UNDERGROUND. 1969. w. free. Scarborough College Student Press, 1265 Military Trail, West Hill, Ont. M1C 1A4, Canada. TEL 416-978-2011. Ed. Eric Cohen. adv.; bk.rev.; film rev.; illus. circ. 6,000.
    Formerly (until Mar. 1982): Balcony Square (ISSN 0005-4267)

808.8   US   ISSN 1045-3660
UNDERGROUND FOREST - SELVA SUBTERRANEA. (Text in English, Spanish) 1986. a. $12. 1701 Bluebell Ave., Boulder, CO 80302. TEL 303-449-1188. Ed. Joseph Richey; Pubs. Anne Becker, Joseph Richey. adv.; bk.rev.; circ. 5,000 (controlled).
    Formerly: Underground Forest.
    Description: Contains bilingual original works, including investigative articles, politics, literary criticism and nonfiction poems.

808.8   US
UNDERGROUND SURREALIST MAGAZINE; Boston's premiere cartoon. 1987. s-a. $3. Mick Cusimano, Pub. & Ed., Box 2565, Cambridge, MA 02238. TEL 617-787-9513. FAX 617-628-4101. circ. 250. **Document type:** consumer publication.

800   DK   ISSN 0905-1503
UNG OG FRI. 1982. bi-m. DKK 120. Venstres Ungdom, Oesterbrogade 132, 2100 Copenhagen OE, Denmark. Ed. Jesper Beinov. adv.; bk.rev.; illus. circ. 5,000.
    Former titles (until 1989): Liberal Debat (ISSN 0108-8874); Standpunkt (ISSN 0108-8866)

059.951   CH
UNITAS/LIEN HO WEN HSUEH; a literary monthly. (Text in Chinese) m. 7F, 180 Keelung Rd. Sec. 1, Taipei, Taiwan, Republic of China. TEL 02-766-5131. (Dist. in US by: World Journal Bookstore, 377 Broadway, New York, NY 10013. TEL 212-226-5131) Ed. Cheng Chou-yu. adv.

378.1   CL   ISSN 0041-8374
                  CODEN: BOUCAD
UNIVERSIDAD DE CHILE. BOLETIN. 1959. 9/yr. Universidad de Chile, Avda. Bernardo O'Higgins 1058, Casilla 10 D, Santiago, Chile. Ed. Enrique Bello. adv.; bk.rev.; play rev.; bibl.; charts; illus.; maps; stat.; index. circ. 3,000. **Indexed:** Amer.Hist.& Life, Biol.Abstr., Hist.Abstr.

378.1   EC   ISSN 0041-8390
UNIVERSIDAD DE CUENCA. ANALES. 1940. q. free. Universidad de Cuenca, Apdo. 168, Ciudad Universitaria, Cuenca, Ecuador. Dir. Agustin Cuera Tamariz. index. circ. 1,000. **Indexed:** Biol.Abstr.

UNIVERSIDADE DE LISBOA. FACULDADE DE LETRAS. REVISTA. see *LITERATURE*

054 FR ISSN 1159-7593
▼**UNIVERSITE DE PERPIGNAN. COLLECTION ETUDES.** 1992. irreg. price varies. Universite de Perpignan, 52 av. de Villeneuve, 66860 Perpignan Cedex, France. TEL 68-66-22-69. FAX 68-66-20-19. TELEX 505 005 F UNIPERP.

378.1 US ISSN 0041-9524
AS30
UNIVERSITY OF DAYTON REVIEW. 1964. irreg. (approx. 3/yr.). free. (University of Dayton) University of Dayton Press, 300 College Park Ave., Dayton, OH 45469. TEL 513-229-0123. FAX 513-339-3433. Ed. Robert C. Conard. charts; illus.; index. circ. 1,500. **Indexed:** Abstr.Engl.Stud., Amer.Bibl.Slavic & E.Eur.Stud., Amer.Hum.Ind., M.L.A.
—UnCover.

960 GH ISSN 0020-2703
DT1
UNIVERSITY OF GHANA. INSTITUTE OF AFRICAN STUDIES. RESEARCH REVIEW. (Text in English) 1965. 2/yr. $10. University of Ghana, Institute of African Studies, Box 73, Legon, Ghana. Ed. K. Arhin. bk.rev.; charts; illus. circ. 500. **Indexed:** Bibl.Ling., Documentatieblad. **Document type:** academic/scholarly publication.

378.1 CN ISSN 0042-0352
AS42.W5
UNIVERSITY OF WINDSOR REVIEW. (Text in English, French) 1965. s-a. Can.$12. University of Windsor, Windsor, Ont. N9B 3P4, Canada. TEL 519-253-4232. FAX 519-973-7050. Ed. Joseph Quinn. adv.; bk.rev.; bibl.; charts; illus.; index. circ. 500. (also avail. in microform from MIM,UMI; reprint service avail. from UMI) **Indexed:** Abstr.Engl.Stud., Amer.Hist.& Life, Amer.Hum.Ind., Can.Lit.Ind., Can.Per.Ind., CMI, Curr.Cont., Hist.Abstr., Ind.Bk.Rev.Hum., M.L.A. **Document type:** academic/scholarly publication.
—Faxon; UMI.
Description: Contains fiction, poetry and criticism devoted to the arts.

UNMUZZLED OX. see *LITERATURE — Poetry*

296 US ISSN 0042-0506
AP91
UNSER TSAIT. (Text in Yiddish) 1941. 8/yr. $20. Jewish Labor Bund, Coordinating Committee, Atran Center, 25 E. 21st St., 3rd Fl., New York, NY 10010. TEL 212-475-0059. FAX 212-473-5102. Ed. M. Lokiec. **Indexed:** M.L.A.

055.1 IT ISSN 0042-0654
PQ4001
UOMINI E LIBRI. 1965. bi-m. L.40000 (foreign L.100000). Edizioni Effe Emme, Viale. E. Caldara 8, 20122 Milan, Italy. Eds. Mario Miccinesi, Fiora Vincenti. adv.; bk.rev.; bibl.; illus. circ. 7,500. **Indexed:** M.L.A.

UPSTREAM; the Literary Center quarterly. see *LITERATURE — Poetry*

800 US ISSN 8750-0256
PN4784.U53
UTNE READER, the best of the alternative press. 1984. bi-m. $18. Lens Publishing Co., Inc., 1624 Harmon Pl., Suite 330, Minneapolis, MN 55403. TEL 612-338-5040. (Subscr. to: Utne Reader, Box 1974, Marion, OH 43306-1974) Ed. Eric Utne. adv. contact: Michael Tronnes. bk.rev. circ. 305,000. (also avail. in microform from UMI) **Indexed:** Acad.Ind., Alt.Press Ind., Bk.Rev.Ind. (1989-), Child.Bk.Rev.Ind. (1989-), Energy Rev., Mag.Ind. **Document type:** consumer publication.
—UnCover; UMI.
Description: Covers over 1,000 independent, small-circulation magazines, journals and newsletters.

808 US ISSN 0887-8633
V L S. (Voice Literary Supplement) (Supplement to: Village Voice (ISSN 0042-6180)) 1981. m. (10/yr.). $17 (foreign $33). V V Publishing Corporation, 36 Cooper Sq., New York, NY 10003. TEL 212-475-3300. FAX 212-475-2118. (Subscr. to: Department VLS, Box 3000, Denville, NJ 07834-9991. TEL 800-562-1973) Ed. M. Mark. adv. contact: Will Lippincott. bk.rev.; illus. (tabloid format) **Indexed:** Access (1982-), Bk.Rev.Ind. (1982-), Child.Bk.Rev.Ind. (1982-). **Document type:** consumer publication.
Description: Features book reviews, fiction and critical essays.

V O, VIE OUVRIERE. see *GENERAL INTEREST PERIODICALS — Canada*

055.1 IT ISSN 0300-3175
VALORI UMANI; bimestrale di educazione letteraria, scientifica, artistica e di costume. 1967. bi-m. donation. Valori Umani, Via Alessandro Longo 11, 80127 Vomero, Naples, Italy. TEL 5799277. Ed. Pasquale De Orsi. bk.rev.; illus.
Description: Features literary, scientific and artistic articles on customs and traditions of various countries. Articles reflect views of individual authors.

808.8 US
VANISHING CAB. 1976. a. $15 to individuals; institutions $20. 1152 Jackson, No. 8, San Francisco, CA 94133. TEL 415-771-9925. Ed. Jerry Estrin. circ. 815.

808.8 US ISSN 0733-8899
AP2
VANITY FAIR. 1983. m. $15 (foreign $31). Conde Nast Publications Inc., Vanity Fair Magazine, 350 Madison Ave., New York, NY 10017. TEL 212-880-8800. FAX 212-880-8289. (Subscr. to: Box 53516, Boulder, CO 80322. TEL 800-365-0635) Ed. E. Graydon Carter. adv.; illus. circ. 1,013,761. **Indexed:** Access (1984-1991), Music Ind., R.G. (1992-). **Document type:** consumer publication.
—Faxon; UnCover; UMI.
Description: Articles, interviews, and reviews of current trends, ideas, people, and writing.

057.8 CI ISSN 0042-2711
VARAZDINSKE VIJESTI. 1946. w. 150 din.($4.) Socijalisticki Savez Radnog Naroda Varazdin, Opcinske Konferencije SSRN Varazdin, Marsala Tita 66, Varazdin, Croatia. Ed. Stjepan Jalusic. adv.; bk.rev.; abstr.; illus. circ. 10,000.

059 RM ISSN 1220-6334
VATRA; lunar social-cultural. 1894; N.S. 1971. m. 180 lei($20) Uniunea Scriitorilor din Romania, Inspectoratul pentru Cultura al Judetului Mures, Str. Primariei, Nr. 1, 4300 Tirgu-Mures, Rumania. TEL 954-35005. FAX 954-35005. (Subscr. to: Str. Calea Victoriei nr. 133, P.O. Box BCR, Tirgu-Mures 45-10-6-100, Rumania) Ed. Cornel Moraru. adv.; bk.rev.; film rev.; play rev.; illus.; index. circ. 4,000. (back issues avail.)

057.8 CI ISSN 0042-322X
VELIKOGORICKI LIST. 1963. fortn. 72 din. Narodno Sveuciliste Juraj Kokot, Zagrebacka 37, Velika Gorica, Kokot, Croatia. Ed. Ivan Zupetic.

945 IT ISSN 0042-3254
AP37
VELTRO; rivista della civilta italiana. 1957. bi-m. L.80000. Veltro Editrice, Via S. Nicola De' Cesarini 3, 00186 Rome, Italy. Ed. Vincenzo Cappelletti. adv.; bk.rev.; charts; illus.; index, cum.index. circ. 6,000. **Indexed:** Amer.Hist.& Life, Can.Rev.Comp.Lit., Hist.Abstr., M.L.A.

322.4 CU ISSN 0506-6913
AP63
VERDE OLIVO. 1960. m. $21 in N. America; S. America $27; Europe $30; elsewhere $42. (Fuerzas Armadas Revolucionarias) Ediciones Cubanas, Obispo No. 527, Apdo. 605, Havana, Cuba. TEL 7-79-8373. Dir. Eugenio Suarez Perez. charts; illus. circ. 100,000.

808.8 US
VERSION 90.* 1990. bi-m. $18. P M S Cafe Press, Box 383185, Cambridge, MA 02238-3185. Ed.Bd. adv.; bk.rev.

056.9 PO ISSN 0042-4447
AP66
VERTICE; revista de cultura e arte. 1942; N.S. 1988. m. $30. Editorial Caminho, S.A., Alameda de St. Antonio dos Cpuchos, 6-B, 1100 Lisbon, Portugal. TEL 1-542683. FAX 1-534346. TELEX 65792-CAMIN-P. Ed. Francisco Melo. adv.; bk.rev.; charts; illus.; index. **Indexed:** M.L.A.

057.8 XV ISSN 0042-4587
VESTNIK; glasilo obcinskih konferencs ZDL Murska Sobota, Gornja Radgona, Lendava in Ljutomer. (Text in Slovenian) 1949. w. 470 din.($10.) Zavod za Casopisno in Radijsko Dejavnost Murska Sobota, Titova 29-I, Murska Sobota, Slovenia. Ed. Stefan Dravec. adv. circ. 20,000.

820 US ISSN 0886-3865
VICTORIANS INSTITUTE JOURNAL. Abbreviated title: V I J. 1972. a. $10 to individuals; institutions $14 (foreign $17). (Victorians Institute) East Carolina University, Greenville, NC 27834. TEL 919-727-6041. FAX 919-757-4489. Ed. Donald Lawler. illus. circ. 950. (back issues avail.) **Document type:** academic/scholarly publication.
—BLDSC (9232.725000); Faxon.
Description: Presents original critical scholarship in Victorian literature, history, art, culture and ideas.
Refereed Serial

055 IT
IL VIEUSSEUX. 1966. q. L.40000. Gabinetto G. P. Vieusseux, Piazza e Palazzo Strozzi, Florence 50123, Italy. TEL 055-2396743. Ed. Paolo Bagnoli. bk.rev.
Formerly (until 1988): *Antologia Vieusseux.*

810 300 378 US ISSN 0042-675X
AP2
VIRGINIA QUARTERLY REVIEW; a national journal of literature and discussion. 1925. q. $15. University of Virginia, 1 West Range, Charlottesville, VA 22903. TEL 804-924-3124. Ed. Staige Blackford. adv.; bk.rev.; index. (also avail. in microform from UMI,PMC; reprint service avail. from KTO) **Indexed:** Abstr.Engl.Stud., Acad.Ind., Amer.Bibl.Slavic & E.Eur.Stud., Amer.Hist.& Life, Arts & Hum.Cit.Ind., Bk.Rev.Ind. (1965-), Child.Bk.Rev.Ind. (1965-), Curr.Cont., Fut.Surv., Hist.Abstr., Hum.Ind., Ind.Bk.Rev.Hum., P.A.I.S.
—BLDSC (9240.130000); Faxon; UnCover; SWETS; UMI.

056.1 MX ISSN 0185-1969
AP63
VISION; revista interamericana. 1950. 24/yr. $124. Vision, Inc., Arquimedes 199, 60 Piso, 11570 Mexico, D.F., Mexico. TEL 915-203-6734. FAX 915-254-8546. (Subscr. to: Vision, 13 E. 75th St., New York, NY 10021) Ed. Mariano Grondona. adv.; illus. circ. 189,000.
—SWETS.

322.4 US ISSN 0042-7004
VISNYK/HERALD; suspil'no-politychnyi misiachnyk. 1947. m. (except July-Aug.). $8. Organization for Defense of Four Freedoms for Ukraine Inc., Box 304, Cooper Sta., New York, NY 10003. Ed. Viachslav Davydenko. adv.; bk.rev.; illus.; index. circ. 2,000.

059.91 II ISSN 0042-7195
AP8
VISVA - BHARATI QUARTERLY. (Text in English) 1923. q. Rs.80($20) Visva - Bharati, P.O. Santiniketan District, Birbhum, West Bengal, India. Ed. Shyamal Kumar Sarkar. adv.; bk.rev.; bibl.; illus.; index. circ. 1,000. (also avail. in microform from UMI) **Indexed:** G.Indian Per.Lit.

055.1 IT ISSN 0042-725X
AP37
VITA E PENSIERO; rassegna italiana di cultura. 1914. m. (11/yr.). L.38000 (foreign L.65000 ($53)) (effective 1995). (Universita Cattolica del Sacro Cuore) Vita e Pensiero, Largo Gemelli 1, 20123 Milan, Italy. TEL 02-7234-2310. FAX 02-72342260. TELEX 321033 UCATMI 1. Ed. Adriano Bausola. adv.; bk.rev.; bibl.; index. **Indexed:** M.L.A.
Description: Focuses attention on the awareness of religion and the roles it plays in life.

057.91 KR ISSN 0042-7470
VITCHYZNA; literaturno-khudozhnii ta hromads'kopolitychnyi misyachnyk. 1932. m. 24 Rub. (Spilka Pys'mennykiv Ukrainy) Vydavnytstvo Radyanskii Pismennik, Chkalova, 52, Kiev, Ukraine. Ed. O. Glushko. bk.rev.; bibl.; illus. circ. 30,000. **Indexed:** M.L.A.

053.1 SZ
VIVA.* no.16, 1974. bi-m. 12 Fr. Linke Alternative, Postfach 701, 7002 Chur, Switzerland. adv.

800 UK ISSN 0952-7966
VIZ COMIC. 1979. bi-m. £1 per no. John Brown Publishing Ltd., The Boat House, Crabtree Ln., Fulham, London SW6 8NJ, England. TEL 44-71-381-6007. FAX 44-71-381-6903. Ed. Chris Donald. adv. contact: Ronald Hackston. illus. circ. 713,261. (back issues avail.) **Document type:** consumer publication.
Description: Contains humor, satire, and cartoons.

LITERARY AND POLITICAL REVIEWS

053.932   BE   ISSN 0042-7675
DE VLAAMSE GIDS. 1905. bi-m. 800 BEF (foreign 1100 BEF) (effective 1994). Stichting De Vlaamse Gids v.z.w., Willem van Nassaustraat 32, 9000 Gent, Belgium. TEL 32-9-2208224. FAX 32-9-2208736. (Subscr. to: Hoste N.V., Brusselsesteenweg 347, 1730 Kobbegem, Belgium. TEL 32-2-4542201) Ed. Jos Borre. adv.; bk.rev. circ. 9,000. **Indexed:** M.L.A.
—SWETS.

055.1   IT   ISSN 0042-7802
VOCE BRUZIA; indipendente politico letterario. 1961. m. (14/yr.) L.5000. Ed. Ruggiero Magliocchi, Via Nicola Serra 80, Cosenza, Italy. adv.; bk.rev.; film rev.; play rev.; illus. circ. 2,000. **Document type:** newspaper.

THE VOICE OF ZEWAM. see *ETHNIC INTERESTS*

808.87   US   ISSN 1066-2499
VOODOO; the M.I.T. journal of humour. 1919. 4/yr. $10. Massachusetts Institute of Technology, MIT Rm. 50-309, 77 Massachusetts Ave., Cambridge, MA 02139. TEL 617-253-4575. Ed. Kent Lundberg.

320   PO
VOZ DO OPERARIO. 1879. m. Esc.1200. Sociedade de Instrucao e Beneficiencia a Voz do Operario, R. da Voz do Operario, 13, Lisbon-1100, Portugal. TEL 862155. adv.; bk.rev.; illus. circ. 10,000.

057.91   KR   ISSN 0320-8370
VSESVIT; literaturno-khudozhnii ta hromads 'kopolitychnyi zhurnal. 1925. m. 24 Rub. (Silka Pys'mennykiv Ukrainy) Vydavnytstvo Radyanskii Pismennik, Chkalova, 52, Kiev, Ukraine. TEL 293-13-18. Ed. Oleg Mikitenko. bk.rev.; illus. circ. 55,000. **Indexed:** M.L.A.

057.1   RU
VSKHODY. 1990. m.? Novosibirskii Oblastnoi Profsoyuz "Solidarnost'", c/o Vitalii D. Shapran, Ed., Mikroraion "A", dom 56, kv. 53, Berdsk, 633190 Novosibirskaya obl., Russia. TEL 4-00-56. circ. 10,000.

057.91   UK   ISSN 0042-9422
AP58.U5
VYZVOL'NYI SHLYAKH/LIBERATION PATH; Ukrainian political, social, scientific & literary magazine. 1954. m. £30. Ukrainian Publishers Ltd., 200 Liverpool Rd., London N1 1LF, England. TEL 071-607-6266. Ed. I. Dmytriw. bk.rev.; bibl.; charts; stat.; index. circ. 4,800. **Document type:** consumer publication.

059   PK
W U F A. (Text in English) q. Rs.100($30) to individuals; institutions Rs.200($40). Writers Union of Free Afghanistan, P.O. Box 867, Peshawar University, Peshawar, Pakistan. Ed. A. Rasul Amin.

053   GW
WAGE; Magazin fuer Lippe, Kultur und Politik. 1982. m. DM.20. Detmolder Wage e.V., Postfach 1424, 32704 Detmold, Germany. TEL 05231-32396. adv.; bk.rev. circ. 2,000. (back issues avail.)

808.87   US
WAGE SLAVE WORLD NEWS. bi-m. $1 per no. Sensationalist Workers of the World, Box 1217, Madison, WI 53701-1217. (tabloid format) **Document type:** newsletter.
Description: Contains humor and political satires.

942   UK   ISSN 0043-0056
WALES;* the national magazine of literature, the arts and Welsh affairs. 1937. q. 10s. Wales Publications Ltd., 40 Heath St., London N.W.3, England. Ed. Keidrych Rhys. bk.rev.; illus.

053 808.7   GW
WAS LEFFT; Erlanger Stadtzeitung. 1976. bi-m. DM.10($10) Verein zur Foerderung Alternativer Medien e.V., Postfach 3543, 91023 Erlangen, Germany. adv.; bk.rev. circ. 2,500. (microfiche; back issues avail.)

WASCANA REVIEW; of contemporary poetry and short fiction. see *LITERATURE*

WASHINGTON MONTHLY. see *POLITICAL SCIENCE*

052   IE
WATERFORD NEWS & STAR. (Text in English) 1848. w. £43.16. Waterford News & Star, Michael St., Waterford, Ireland. TEL 051-74951. FAX 051-55281. Ed. Peter Doyle. circ. 18,645.
Description: Devoted to the coverage of Waterford City and Waterford County.

059   II
THE WEEK. (Text in English) 1982. w. Rs.800($42) Malayala Manorama Co. Ltd., P.O. Box 26, Kottayam 686 001, Kerala, India. FAX 481-2479. TELEX 0888-201-MNR-IN. Ed. Mammen Mathew. circ. 51,569.

808.87 790.1   US
THE WEEKLY FARCE; Ohio's funniest newspaper. 1988. m. $10 (Canada & Mexico $12; elsewhere $25). Active Communication Inc., Box 394, Berea, OH 44017. TEL 216-362-7979. FAX 216-362-4623. Ed. Ken McEntee. adv.: page $600. (tabloid format) **Document type:** newspaper.
Description: Features humorous coverage of news, politics, sports and the media.

808.8   US
WEIRDO. 1981. a. $7. Last Gasp of San Francisco, 777 Florida St., San Francisco, CA 94110. TEL 415-824-6636. FAX 415-824-1836. Ed. Aline Kominski. bk.rev. circ. 10,000. (back issues avail.)
Description: Contains adult humor and satire.

320.531   AU   ISSN 0508-2757
WELT DER ARBEIT.* 1950. m. S.48. Sozialistische Partei Oesterreichs, Lowellstr. 18ile 97, A-1014 Vienna, Austria. Ed. Kurt Horak. adv. circ. 81,000.

053.1   GW   ISSN 0043-2598
AP30
DIE WELTBUEHNE; Wochenschrift fuer Politik - Kunst - Wirtschaft. 1905. w. DM.100. Verlag der Weltbuehne, Oberwasserstr. 12, Postfach 1437, 10117 Berlin, Germany. TEL 2071435. FAX 2071519. (Subscr. to: Weltbuehne Leserservice, Postfach 103245, 2000 Hamburg 1, Germany) Ed. Helmut Reinhardt. adv.; bk.rev. circ. 25,000.

808.8   US
WELTER. 1967. a. $2 per no. University of Baltimore Publications, English Department, University of Baltimore, 1420 N. Charles St., Baltimore, MD 21201-5779. TEL 410-837-6026. Eds. Daniel Tessitore, Alan Payne. circ. 500.

895.1   CC
WENHUI YUEKAN/ENCOUNTER MONTHLY. (Text in Chinese) m. Y21.60($67.50) Wenhui Bao She, 149, Yuanmingyuan Lu, Shanghai, People's Republic of China. TEL 3211410. (Dist. outside China by: China International Book Trading Corp., P.O. Box 2820, Beijing, P.R.C.; Dist. in US by: China Books & Periodicals, Inc., 2929 24th St., San Francisco, CA 94110. TEL 415-282-2994) illus.

895.1   CC
WENLUN YUEKAN/CRITICISM MONTHLY. (Text in Chinese) m. Hebeisheng Wenlian - Hebei Cultural Workers Association, 2 Shizhuang Lu, Shijiazhuang, Hebei 050000, People's Republic of China. TEL 744870. Ed. Yang Zhenxi.

800   CC
WENXUE ZIYOU TAN/ON LITERARY FREEDOM. (Text in Chinese) q. Tianjin Shi Wenlian, 237 Xinhua Lu, Tianjin 300040, People's Repulic of China. TEL 395034. Ed. Feng Jicai.

895.1   CC
WENYI PINGLUN/LITERARY AND ART REVIEW. (Text in Chinese) bi-m. Heilongjiang Sheng Wenlian, 16, Yaojing Jie, Nangang-qu, Harbin, Heilongjiang 150006, People's Republic of China. TEL 34317. Ed. Li Fucai.

895.1   CC
WENYI PINGLUN JIA. (Text in Chinese) q. Jiangxi Sheng Wenxue Yishu Yanjiusuo, No. 89, Beijing Xilu, Nanchang, Jiangxi 330046, People's Republic of China. TEL 332920. Ed. Yu Yue.

700   CC
WENYI PINGLUN YU PIPING/ART REVIEW AND CRITICISM. (Text in Chinese) bi-m. Zhongguo Yishu Yanjiuyuan - Chinese Academy of Arts, 17 Qianhai Xijie, Beijing 100009, People's Republic of China. TEL 651128. Ed. Chen Yong.

895.1   CC   ISSN 1003-9538
WENYI ZHENGMING. (Text in Chinese) m. Y2 per no. (effective 1994). Jilin Sheng Wenlian, Fu 111, Stalin Street, Changchun, Jilin 130021, People's Republic of China. TEL 86-431-684956. (Dist. overseas by: China International Book Trading Corp., P.O. Box 399, Beijing, P.R. China) Eds. Yang Yinlong, Ren Guomin. adv. contact: Zhu Jing. bk.rev.

808.87   US   ISSN 1045-0491
WE'RE LIVING IN FUNNY TIMES. Short title: Funny Times. 1985. m. $17.50. Susan Wolper & Raymond Lesser, Eds. & Pubs., Box 18530, Cleveland Heights, OH 44118. TEL 216-371-8600. illus.; circ. 49,000 (paid).
Description: Contains a collection of America's best cartoons, comics, and funny stoires.

051 320 100   CN
WEST COAST LIBERTARIAN. 1978. bi-m. Can.$15. Greater Vancouver Libertarian Association, 922 Cloverley St., North Vancouver, BC V7L 1N3, Canada. TEL 604-980-7370. Ed. Kerry Pearson. bk.rev. circ. 400.

WEST COAST LINE; a journal of contemporary writing and criticism. see *LITERATURE*

809   US
WESTERN WRITERS SERIES. 1972. 5/yr. $3.95 per no. Boise State University, Department of English, 1910 University Dr., Boise, ID 83725. TEL 208-385-1246. FAX 208-385-4373. Ed. J. Maguire. bibl. circ. 750. **Indexed:** M.L.A.
Formerly: Discard.

800 700   US
WIDE OPEN MAGAZINE.* 1984. q. $24. Wide Open Press, 3285 Linwood Ave., Santa Rosa, CA 95404-5613. TEL 707-545-3821. Eds. Clif Simms, Lynn L. Simms. adv.: B&W page $150; 8 1/2 x 11. bk.rev. circ. 700. (back issues avail.)
Formerly: Wide Open Magazine of Poetry.
Description: Examines solutions to wide-spread social problems.

053.1   AU
WIENER KULTURKREIS. MITTEILUNGEN. 1975. bi-m. S.30. Wiener Kulturkreis, Prinz-Eugen Str. 3, A-1030 Vienna, Austria. Ed. Aurel Wolfram.

051   US   ISSN 0363-3276
AS36.W79
WILSON QUARTERLY. 1976. 4/yr. $24. Woodrow Wilson International Center for Scholars, 901 D St., S.W., Ste. 704, Washington, DC 20024-2518. TEL 800-876-8828. (Subscr. to: The Wilson Center, Membership Department, Box 420404, Palm Coast, FL 32142-9860) Ed. Jay Tolson. adv.; bk.rev.; bibl.; charts; illus.; stat.; cum.index every 2 yrs. circ. 75,000. (also avail. in microform from UMI) **Indexed:** Amer.Bibl.Slavic & E.Eur.Stud., Amer.Hist.& Life, Amer.Hum.Ind., Bk.Rev.Ind. (1980-), Child.Bk.Rev.Ind. (1980-), Hist.Abstr., Mid.East: Abstr.& Ind., P.A.I.S., Soc.Sci.Ind. **Document type:** academic/scholarly publication.
—BLDSC (9319.082000); Faxon; SWETS; UMI.

800   US   ISSN 0891-1371
AP2
WITNESS (FARMINGTON HILLS). 1987. s-a. $12 to individuals; institutions $18. Oakland Community College, 27055 Orchard Lake Rd., Farmington Hills, MI 48334. TEL 313-471-7740. Ed. Peter Stine. adv.; bk.rev.; circ. 1,500 (paid); 1,500 (controlled). (back issues avail.)
—Faxon.
Description: Literature illuminating political and social issues around globe. Presents writer as witness.

DER WOHLFAHRTSDIENST; Monatsschrift fuer Fragen der Wirtschaft und des Sozialen Lebens. see *SOCIOLOGY*

830 809   GW   ISSN 0340-6318
WOLFENBUETTELER BAROCK - NACHRICHTEN. 1974. 2/yr. DM.80. (Herzog August Bibliothek Wolfenbuettel) Harrassowitz Verlag, Taunusstr. 14, 65183 Wiesbaden, Germany. TEL 0611-530-0. FAX 0611-530570. TELEX 4186135. (Subscr. to: Postfach 2929, 65019 Wiesbaden, Germany) Ed. Martin Bircher. bk.rev.; bibl. circ. 750. (back issues avail.) **Indexed:** M.L.A. **Document type:** academic/scholarly publication.
—SWETS. **CCC.**

LITERARY AND POLITICAL REVIEWS

808.8 305.4 US ISSN 0738-1433
HQ1101
WOMEN'S REVIEW OF BOOKS. 1983. m. (except Aug.). $18 to individuals; institutions $30. (Wellesley College, Center for Research on Women) Women's Review, Inc., Wellesley, MA 02181. TEL 617-283-2087. FAX 617-283-3645. Ed. Linda Gardiner. adv.: B&W page $1550; adv. contact: Anita McClellan. bk.rev.; illus.; circ. 16,000 (paid). (also avail. in microform from UMI) **Indexed:** Alt.Press Ind., Amer.Hum.Ind., Bk.Rev.Ind. (1983-), Child.Bk.Rev.Ind. (1983-), Left Ind. (1986-), Stud.Wom.Abstr., Wom.Stud.Abstr. (1983-).
—BLDSC (9343.420000); UMI. **CCC.**
   Description: Reviews from a feminist perspective; current scholarly and trade books by and about women.

800 UK ISSN 0266-6286
NX1
WORD & IMAGE; a journal of verbal/visual enquiry. 1985. q. £133($224) Taylor & Francis Ltd., Rankine Rd., Basingstoke, Hants RG24 8PR, England. TEL 0256-840366. FAX 0256-479438. TELEX 858540. Ed. John Dixon Hunt. adv.; bk.rev.; film rev.; illus. circ. 750. (back issues avail.) **Indexed:** Amer.Hist.& Life, Artbibl.Mod., Arts & Hum.Cit.Ind., Curr.Cont., Hist.Abstr. **Document type:** academic/scholarly publication.
—BLDSC (9347.837100); Faxon; UnCover; SWETS. **CCC.**
   Description: Intended for literary critics, art historians and critics, linguisticians, cultural and social historians, philosophers and psychologists, as well as the literature departments of literature, art history and media and communications studies.
   Refereed Serial

808.8 US ISSN 0886-8484
WORKING CLASSICS. 1981. q. $10. Red Wheelbarrow Press, 298 Ninth Ave., San Francisco, CA 94118. TEL 415-387-3412. Ed. David Joseph. adv.; bk.rev. circ. 1,000. **Document type:** newsletter.

051 327 US ISSN 0195-8895
AP2
WORLD PRESS REVIEW; news and views from around the world. 1961. m. $24.97 (effective 1993-1994). Stanley Foundation (New York), 200 Madison Ave., Ste. 2104, New York, NY 10016. TEL 212-889-5155. FAX 212-889-5634. TELEX WPRNY62342. (Subscr. to: Box 1997, Marion, OH 43305) Ed. Larry Martz. adv. contact: Cynthia Vought. bk.rev.; illus.; tr.lit.; cum.index: 1961-1972, 1974-1985; circ. 60,000 (paid). (also avail. in microform from UMI; reprint service avail. from UMI) **Indexed:** Acad.Ind., Energy Rev., Hum.Ind., Mag.Ind., P.A.I.S., Peace Res.Abstr., PMR, R.G., Soc.Sci.Ind. **Document type:** consumer publication.
—BLDSC (9358.380000); Faxon; SWETS; UMI.
Former titles (until 1980): Atlas World Press Review (ISSN 0161-6528); (until 1972): Atlas (ISSN 0004-6930)

WORMWOOD REVIEW. see *LITERATURE — Poetry*

052 AT
WORONI. 1948. fortn. Aus.$5($10) Australian National University, Students' Association, Canberra, A.C.T. 2600, Australia. FAX 062-489-062. Ed.Bd. adv.; bk.rev. circ. 2,000.

WRITERS NEWS. see *LITERATURE*

053.1 GW ISSN 0043-9614
WUERZBURG-HEUTE; Mainfraenkische Zeitschrift fuer Kultur und Wirtschaft. 1966. s-a. DM.6. (Universitaetsbund Wuerzburg) Echter Wuerzburg, Fraenkische Gesellschaftsdruckerei und Verlag GmbH, Juliuspromenade 64, 97070 Wuerzburg, Germany. TEL 0931-3091-0. adv. (back issues avail.) **Document type:** bulletin.

WYZSZA SZKOLA PEDAGOGICZNA, OPOLE. ZESZYTY NAUKOWE. SERIA A. FILOGIA ANGIELSKA. see *LINGUISTICS*

056.1 MX ISSN 0043-986X
XALOC. (Text in Catalan) 1964. bi-m. Mex.$200. Ave. Uruguay 40-202, Mexico 1 D.F., Mexico. Ed. Ramon Fabregat. adv.; bk.rev.; illus.

YALE FRENCH STUDIES. see *LITERATURE*

378.1 US ISSN 0044-0124
AP2
YALE REVIEW. 1911. q. $22 to individuals in N. America (elsewhere $33); institutions in N. America $46 (elsewhere $51). Basil Blackwell Inc., 238 Main St., Cambridge, MA 02142. TEL 617-547-7110. FAX 617-547-0789. Ed. J.D. McClatchy. adv.: page $350; trim 4 1/4 x 7 3/4. bk.rev.; rec.rev.; index. circ. 3,750. (also avail. in microform from MIM,UMI,PMC; back issues avail.; reprint service avail. from ISI,SCH,UMI) **Indexed:** A.I.P.P., Abstr.Engl.Stud., Acad.Ind., Amer.Bibl.Slavic & E.Eur.Stud., Arts & Hum.Cit.Ind., Bk.Rev.Dig., Bk.Rev.Ind. (1965-), Child.Bk.Rev.Ind. (1965-), Curr.Cont., Film Lit.Ind. (1973-), Hum.Ind., Ind.Amer.Per.Verse, Ind.Bk.Rev.Hum., LCR, M.L.A., Mag.Ind., Mid.East: Abstr.& Ind., P.A.I.S., R.G. **Document type:** academic/scholarly publication.
—BLDSC (9370.300000); Faxon; UnCover; SWETS; UMI. **CCC.**
   Description: Presents the most intriguing poems and stories from both established and upcoming writers.

800 US
YALE VERNACULAR; an undergraduate publication. 1987. 2/yr. $20. c/o Dean of Student's Office, 1604 A Yale Station, New Haven, CT 06520. TEL 203-432-2900. Ed. Mia Sorgi. adv.; bk.rev.; illus. circ. 3,500. **Document type:** academic/scholarly publication.
   Description: Presents undergraduate literature and art, and interviews with artists and writers.

051 YE
YAMAN AL-JADIYD; a monthly cultural journal. (Text in Arabic) 1971. m. 1.50 din. Ministry of Information and Culture, Sana'a, Republic of Yemen. Ed. 'Abd al-Wudud Sayf.

808.81 US ISSN 0278-9442
YET ANOTHER SMALL MAGAZINE. 1982. a. $2. Andrew Mountain Press, Box 14353, Hartford, CT 06114. TEL 203-549-6723. Ed. Candace C. Hall.

YOUNG SOCIALIST. see *POLITICAL SCIENCE*

059.915 IR
YUL. (Text in Azerbaijani) 1991. m. $222 to N. America (effective 1994). Kayhan Publications, Ferdowsi Ave., P.O. Box 11365-9631, Tehran 11444, Iran. TEL 021-310251. **Document type:** consumer publication.

057.1 RU ISSN 0132-2036
YUNOST'. 1955. m. $98. (Soyuz Pisatelei Rossii) Yunost, Ul. Tverskaya 32-1, Moscow, Russia. (Dist. in U.S. by: Victor Kamkin Inc., 4956 Boiling Brook Pkwy, Rockville, MD 20852. TEL 301-881-5973) Ed. A. Dementev. bk.rev.; film rev.; bibl.; charts; illus.; stat. circ. 999,000. **Indexed:** Curr.Dig.Sov.Press.

051 US ISSN 1060-2070
▼**Z PAPERS.** 1992. q. $20. Institute for Social and Cultural Communications, 116 Saint Botolph St., No.1, Boston, MA 02115-4313. TEL 617-236-5878. FAX 617-247-3179. (back issues avail.) **Document type:** academic/scholarly publication.
   Description: An independent political review of critical thinking on political, cultural, social, ecological and economic goals and program for the United States.

057.1 327 RU ISSN 0044-1554
ZA RUBEZHOM; obozrenie inostrannoi pressy. (Text in Russian) 1932-1938; resumed 1960. w. $114 (foreign $118). Izdatel'stvo Pressa, Ul. Pravdy, 24, Moscow 125865, Russia. TEL 095-257-2387. FAX 095-200-2296. (Dist. in U.S. by: Victor Kamkin Inc., 4956 Boiling Brook Pkwy, Rockville, MD 20852. TEL 301-881-5973) Ed. S. Morozov. illus. circ. 82,727. (tabloid format; also avail. in microform) **Indexed:** Curr.Dig.Sov.Press. **Document type:** newspaper.
   Description: Weekly review of foreign press.

057.8 CI ISSN 0044-1589
AP56
ZADARSKA REVIJA. 1952. bi-m. 300 din.($6.25) Narodni List, Zagrebacka 1, Zadar, Croatia. TEL 057-24070. Ed. of Ante Franic. adv.; bk.rev. circ. 1,000. **Indexed:** M.L.A.

ZANGO/FORUM; Zambian journal of contemporary issues. see *GENERAL INTEREST PERIODICALS — Zambia*

057 CI
ZAVOD ZA KNJIZEVNOST I TEATROLOGIJU. KRONIKA. (Text in Croatian; summaries in German) 1975. biennial. Zavod za Knizevnost i Teatrologiju, Opaticka 18, Zagreb, Croatia. circ. 500.

808.87 CC ISSN 1003-7934
ZAWEN JIE. (Text in Chinese) 1985. bi-m. Y600. Hebei Zawen Xuehui, 12 Hongjun Lu, Shijiazhuang, Hebei 050071, People's Republic of China. TEL 743153. Ed. Du Wenyuan. **Document type:** academic/scholarly publication.

057.8 XV ISSN 0350-8498
ZBORNIK OBCINE GROSUPLJE. (Text in Slovenian; summaries in English, German) 1969. biennial. 500 SLT($10) Obcina Grosuplje, P.O. Box 11, 61290 Grosuplje, Slovenia. FAX 61-783-232. Ed. Mihael Glavan. adv.; bk.rev. circ. 1,000. (back issues avail.)

DIE ZEIT IM BUCH. see *PUBLISHING AND BOOK TRADE*

051 364 US
ZERO HOUR; where culture meets crime. 1988. 2/yr. $12. Zero Hour Publishing, Box 766, Seattle, WA 98111. TEL 206-286-2324. Ed. Jim Jones. adv.; bk.rev. circ. 3,000.
   Description: Examines specific aspects of contemporary society: cults, addiction, pornography.

056.1 VE
ZETA. 1974. w. Pinto a Santa Rosalia, 44, Apdo. 14067, La Candelaria, Caracas, Venezuela. Dir. Rafael Poleo.

057.1 RU ISSN 0130-1616
ZNAMYA; literaturno-khudozhestvennyi i obshchestvenno-politicheskii zhurnal. 1931. m. $125. (Soyuz Pisatelei Rossii) Znamay, Ul. Nikolskaya 8-1, Moscow, Russia. TEL 095-921-2430. (Dist. in U.S. by: Victor Kamkin Inc., 4956 Boiling Brook Pkwy, Rockville, MD 20852. TEL 301-881-5973) Ed. Grigory Ya. Baklanov. adv.; bk.rev.; index. circ. 199,100. **Indexed:** Curr.Dig.Sov.Press.
—BLDSC (0072.165000).

ZUID - AFRIKA; onafhankelijk maandblad, uitgegeven door Z A S M in Amsterdam. see *POLITICAL SCIENCE*

320.531 AU ISSN 0044-5452
H5
ZUKUNFT; Sozialdemokratische Monatsschrift. 1946. m. S.480. (Sozialistische Partei Oesterreichs) Zukunft-Verlagsgesellschaft mbH, Loewelstr. 18, A-1014 Vienna, Austria. TEL 0222-53427206. FAX 0222-5359683. Ed.Bd. adv.: B&W page S.18000; trim 253 x 195. bk.rev.; film rev.; play rev.; illus. circ. 10,000. (tabloid format) **Indexed:** M.L.A. **Document type:** bulletin.

296 US ISSN 0044-5460
ZUKUNFT/FUTURE. (Text in Yiddish) 1892. 5/yr. $25 to individuals; foreign and institutions $30. Congress of Jewish Culture, 25 E. 21st St., New York, NY 10010. TEL 212-505-8040. Ed. Yonia Fain. adv.; bk.rev. circ. 2,000. (also avail. in microfilm from AJP)

057.1 RU ISSN 0321-1878
ZVEZDA; literaturno-khudozhestvennyi i obshchestvenno-politicheskii zhurnal. (Text in Russian; summaries in English) 1924. m. $119. (Soyuz Pisatelei Rossii) Zvezda, Ul. Mokhovaya 20, St. Petersburg D-28, Russia. TEL 095-272-8948. (Dist. in U.S. by: Victor Kamkin Inc., 4956 Boiling Brook Pkwy, Rockville, MD 20852. TEL 301-881-5973) Ed. G.F. Nikolaev. bk.rev.; bibl. circ. 68,080. **Indexed:** Curr.Dig.Sov.Press, M.L.A.
—BLDSC (0071.680000).

968 SA ISSN 0013-2578
1860 SETTLER. 1962. bi-m. $15 per no. S.R. Pather, Ed.& Pub., Box 1233, Durban, Natal, South Africa. **Indexed:** Ind.S.A.Per.

LITERARY AND POLITICAL REVIEWS — ABSTRACTING, BIBLIOGRAPHIES, STATISTICS

053   GW   ISSN 0930-9977
HN1
1999; Zeitschrift fuer Sozialgeschichte des 20 und 21 Jahrhunderts. 1986. q. DM.60. (Hamburger Stiftung fuer Sozialgeschichte des 20. Jahrhunderts) Janus Verlagsgesellschaft, Simon-Meister-Str. 42, 50733 Cologne, Germany. TEL 0221-723432. FAX 0221-737884. Eds. Angelika Ebbinghaus, Klaus Weinhauer. adv.; bk.rev. **Indexed:** Amer.Hist.& Life, Hist.Abstr. **Document type:** academic/scholarly publication.

LITERARY AND POLITICAL REVIEWS — Abstracting, Bibliographies, Statistics

011 020 016   US   ISSN 0002-662X
AI3
ALTERNATIVE PRESS INDEX; an index to alternative and radical publications. 1969. q. $35 to individuals; institutions $175. Alternative Press Center, Inc., Box 33109, Baltimore, MD 21218. TEL 410-243-2471. FAX 410-235-5325. Ed.Bd. bk.rev. circ. 600. (back issues avail.) **Document type:** abstracting/indexing.
    Description: Chronicles progressive articles through its exhaustive efforts at indexing and cross-referencing such journalism.

811   US
BOTTOM LINE PUBLICATIONS.* 1988. m. $25. HC-13, Box 21-AA, Artemas, PA 17211-9405. TEL 814-458-3102. circ. 100.
    Description: Market listing for poets and writers.

GUIDE TO ALTERNATIVE PERIODICALS. see *SOCIAL SCIENCES: COMPREHENSIVE WORKS — Abstracting, Bibliographies, Statistics*

891.1   II
INDIAN LITERARY INDEX; documentation list of creative and critical writings and literary news. (Text in English) 1988. s-a. Rs.80($20) Sahitya Akademi, Rabindra Bhavan, Ferozeshah Rd., New Dehli 110 001, India. Ed. K.C. Dutt. **Document type:** abstracting/indexing.

011 800   UK   ISSN 0950-6217
LIGHT'S LIST OF LITERARY MAGAZINES (YEAR). 1986. a. (with irreg. updates). £0.50($2) per no. Photon Press, 29 Longfield Rd., Tring, Herts HP23 4DG, England. **Document type:** bibliography, directory.
    Description: Lists more than 250 British literary magazines of all types, with addresses and descriptions of content and focus for each publication.

800   US
OLDERR'S FICTION INDEX FOR (YEAR). 1987. a. $58. Gale Research Inc., St. James Press, 835 Penobscot Bldg., Detroit, MI 48226-4232. TEL 800-877-4253. Ed. Stephen Olderr. bk.rev.; abstr.; bibl. **Document type:** abstracting/indexing.
    Description: Lists and categorizes 1,500 adult fiction books per issue. Each entry includes author, title, series, publication information, 1-4 star rating. Contains subject, title, & character indexes.

OLDERR'S YOUNG ADULT FICTION INDEX FOR (YEAR). see *CHILDREN AND YOUTH — Abstracting, Bibliographies, Statistics*

700 800 016   SP   ISSN 0038-6456
DP1
SPANISH CULTURAL INDEX.* (Text in English, French, German and Spanish) 1946. m. Ministerio Espanol de Asuntos Exteriores, Cultural Relations Dept., Palacio de Santa Cruz, Madrid, Spain. bk.rev.; abstr.; bibl.

STATE LIBRARY OF NEW SOUTH WALES. LIBRARY DEPOSIT LIST. see *BIBLIOGRAPHIES*

808.8 016   CN
WINTERGREEN; a directory of progressive periodicals. 1979. a. Can.$5($6) Alternative Research, Box 1294, Kitchener, Ont. N2G 4G8, Canada. Ed.Bd. circ. 1,500. **Document type:** directory.

WORKBOOK. see *ENVIRONMENTAL STUDIES — Abstracting, Bibliographies, Statistics*

LITERATURE

see also Literature–Adventure and Romance; Literature–Mystery and Detective; Literature–Poetry; Literature–Science Fiction, Fantasy, Horror; Publishing and Book Trade

A C D. THE JOURNAL OF THE ARTHUR CONAN DOYLE SOCIETY. see *LITERATURE — Mystery And Detective*

A C I S NEWSLETTER. (American Conference for Irish Studies) see *HISTORY — History Of Europe*

420.07 370   US   ISSN 0001-0898
PE68.U5
A D E BULLETIN. 1964. 3/yr. $21 to individuals; institutions $30. Association of Departments of English, 10 Astor Place, New York, NY 10003-6981. TEL 212-614-6317. FAX 212-477-9863. (Affiliate: Modern Language Association of America) Ed. David Laurence. adv.; bk.rev.; charts; stat. circ. 2,500. (also avail. in microform from MIM,UMI; reprint service avail. from UMI) **Indexed:** C.I.J.E. **Document type:** bulletin.
    —BLDSC (0680.250000); Faxon; UnCover; UMI.
    Description: Presents articles and surveys dealing with professional, pedagogical, curricular, and departmental issues.

891.92   US   ISSN 0003-7583
AP2
A G B U ARARAT; quarterly journal of Armenian literature, history and the arts. 1960. q. $24. Armenian General Benevolent Union, 585 Saddle River Rd., Saddle Brook, NJ 07662. TEL 201-797-7600. Ed. Leo Hamalian. adv.; bk.rev.; film rev.; bibl.; illus.; index. circ. 1,200. (also avail. in microfilm; back issues avail.) **Indexed:** Amer.Bibl.Slavic & E.Eur.Stud.
    —UnCover; UMI.
    Formerly: Ararat.
    Description: Fiction, poetry, and prose related to Armenian history and culture.

A L A N REVIEW. (Assembly on Literature for Adolescents) see *EDUCATION — Teaching Methods And Curriculum*

810   US
▼**A M S HENRY JAMES STUDIES**. 1993. irreg., no.2, 1994. (Abrahams Magazine Service) A M S Press, Inc., 56 E. 13th St., New York, NY 10003. TEL 212-777-4700. FAX 212-995-5413. **Document type:** academic/scholarly publication, monographic series.

830   US   ISSN 1045-6023
A M S STUDIES IN GERMAN LITERATURE AND CULTURE. 1991. irreg. price varies. (Abrahams Magazine Service) A M S Press, Inc., 56 E. 13th St., New York, NY 10003. TEL 212-777-4700. FAX 212-995-5413. **Document type:** monographic series.
    Description: Discusses various aspects of German culture and literature.

800   US   ISSN 0270-2983
A M S STUDIES IN MODERN LITERATURE. 1973. irreg., no.21, 1993. price varies. A M S Press, Inc., 56 E. 13th St., New York, NY 10003. TEL 212-777-4700. FAX 212-995-5413. (back issues avail.)
    —BLDSC (0859.554500).
    Description: Monographs, reference works and bibliographies focusing on various topics and writers of twentieth-century literature, drama and poetry.

800   US
▼**A M S STUDIES IN NINETEENTH-CENTURY LITERATURE AND CULTURE**. 1993. irreg., no.2, 1994. (Abrahams Magazine Service) A M S Press, Inc., 56 E. 13th St., New York, NY 10003. TEL 212-777-4700. FAX 212-995-5413. **Document type:** academic/scholarly publication, monographic series.

800   US   ISSN 0196-6561
A M S STUDIES IN THE EIGHTEENTH CENTURY. 1970. irreg., no.27, 1994. price varies. A M S Press, Inc., 56 E. 13th St., New York, NY 10003. TEL 212-777-4700. FAX 212-995-5413. (back issues avail.) **Indexed:** M.L.A.
    —BLDSC (0859.552000).
    Description: Monographs, reference works and bibliographies on various writers and topics of study in eighteenth-century literature.

A M S STUDIES IN THE MIDDLE AGES. see *HISTORY*

800   US   ISSN 0196-657X
A M S STUDIES IN THE NINETEENTH CENTURY. 1980. irreg., no.14, 1994. A M S Press, Inc., 56 E. 13th St., New York, NY 10003. TEL 212-777-4700. FAX 212-995-5413. (back issues avail.)
    —BLDSC (0859.555000).
    Description: Monographs and reference works on various writers and topics of study in nineteenth-century literature.

800 792.02   US   ISSN 0195-8011
A M S STUDIES IN THE RENAISSANCE. 1976. irreg., no.34, 1994. price varies. A M S Press, Inc., 56 E. 13th St., New York, NY 10003. TEL 212-777-4700. FAX 212-995-5413. (back issues avail.)
    —BLDSC (0859.556000).
    Description: Monographs, reference works and bibliographies on various writers and topics of study in Renaissance literature and drama.

809   US   ISSN 0731-2342
A M S STUDIES IN THE SEVENTEENTH CENTURY. 1986. irreg., no.5, 1993. price varies. (Abrahams Magazine Service) A M S Press, Inc., 56 E. 13th St., New York, NY 10003. TEL 212-777-4700. FAX 212-995-5413.
    —BLDSC (0859.556500).
    Description: Monographs and reference works on various writers and topics of study in seventeenth-century literature, drama and poetry.

810   US   ISSN 0895-769X
PE1
A N Q: A QUARTERLY JOURNAL OF SHORT ARTICLES, NOTES AND REVIEWS. 1988. q. $14 to individuals; institutions $18 (foreign $20). University of Kentucky, Department of English, Lexington, KY 40506-0027. TEL 606-257-6975. FAX 606-323-1072. E-mail: ENGAW@UKCC.UKY.EDU. Ed. Arthur Wrobel. bk.rev.; bibl.; index, cum.index. circ. 600. (also avail. in microform from UMI; reprint service avail. from GMC,KTO,UMI) **Indexed:** Abstr.Engl.Stud., Abstr.Folk.Stud., Amer.Hum.Ind., Arts & Hum.Cit.Ind., Bk.Rev.Ind. (1965-), Child.Bk.Rev.Ind. (1965-), Curr.Cont., Hum.Ind., M.L.A. **Document type:** academic/scholarly publication.
    —BLDSC (1541.824000); Faxon; UnCover; UMI.
    Supersedes (1962-1986): American Notes and Queries (ISSN 0003-0171)
    Description: Contains scholarly articles on all aspects of British and American literature.
    Refereed Serial

A P U PRESS ALASKANA BOOK SERIES. (Alaska Pacific University Press) see *HISTORY — History Of North And South America*

800   RM   ISSN 1220-594X
A R C; litere - arte. 1991. q. $30. Fundatia Culturala Romana, Aleea Alexandru 38, Bucharest, Rumania. TEL 2121403 ext. 104. Ed. George Balaita. circ. 5,000. **Document type:** academic/scholarly publication.
    Description: Contains prose, poetry, essays and art from Rumanians and foreigners.

820   CN   ISSN 0004-1327
PR1
A R I E L. (A Review of International English Literature) 1970. q. Can.$17 to individuals; institutions $25; students Can.$10. University of Calgary, Department of English, CHD 420A, 2500 University Dr. N.W., Calgary, AB T2N 1N4, Canada. TEL 403-220-4657. FAX 403-289-1123. TELEX 03-821545. Ed. Victor J. Ramraj. adv. contact: Mavis Page. bk.rev.; bibl.; index. circ. 1,000. (back issues avail.) **Indexed:** Arts & Hum.Cit.Ind., Br.Hum.Ind., Can.Lit.Ind., Hum.Ind., Ind.Bk.Rev.Hum., M.L.A. **Document type:** academic/scholarly publication.
—BLDSC (1668.349000); Faxon; UnCover.
 Formerly: Review of English Literature.
 Description: Provides critical and scholarly perspectives on literatures in English around the world.

A R P A CAHIERS DE RECHERCHE POETIQUE. (Association de Recherche Poetique en Auvergne) see *LITERATURE — Poetry*

A S C A P BIOGRAPHICAL DICTIONARY. (American Society of Composers, Authors and Publishers) see *MUSIC*

A U L L A; journal of literary criticism, philology & linguistics. (Australian Universities Language and Literature Association) see *LINGUISTICS*

800   GW
AACHENER BEITRAEGE ZUR KOMPARATISTIK. 1977. irreg., no.9, 1992. price varies. Bouvier Verlag Herbert Grundmann, Am Hof 28, 53113 Bonn, Germany. TEL 0228-7290124. FAX 0228-7290179. Ed. Hugo Dyserinck. **Indexed:** M.L.A. **Document type:** monographic series.

AALBORG UNIVERSITETSCENTER. INSTITUT FOR SPROG OG INTERNATIONALE KULTURSTUDIER. ARBEIJDSPAPIRER. see *LINGUISTICS*

895.65   JA
ABIKO QUARTERLY WITH JAMES JOYCE STUDIES; ragwords. (Text in English, Japanese) 1989. q. $40. Laurel Sicks, Ed. & Pub., 8-1-1 Namiki, Abiko-shi, Chiba-ken 270-11, Japan. TEL 0471-84-7904. (Subscr. to: Japan Publications Trading Co., Ltd., P.O. Box 5030, Tokyo International, Tokyo 101, Japan) Ed. Vincent Broderick. adv.: page $200. bk.rev. circ. 600.
 Formerly: Abiko Quarterly Rag.
 Description: Covers fiction, poetry, photography and graphic arts.

869   BL
ACADEMIA AMAZONENSE DE LETRAS. REVISTA. 1918. Cr.$30. Academia Amazonense de Letras, Rua Ramos Ferreira 1009, Manaus, Amazonas, Brazil. Dir. Mario Ypiranga Monteiro.

ACADEMIA ARGENTINA DE LETRAS. BOLETIN. see *LINGUISTICS*

898   BL
ACADEMIA BRASILEIRA DE LITERATURA. REVISTA. 1985. irreg. exchange basis. Academia Brasileira de Literatura, Rua Marques de Abrantes, 127-Apt.904, CEP 22230 Flamengo, Rio de Janeiro, Brazil. Dir. Leodegario A. de Azevedo Filho.

869   BL   ISSN 0065-0447
ACADEMIA CAMPINENSE DE LETRAS. PUBLICACOES. 1958. irreg., no.48, 1991. Cr.$50 or exchange basis. Academia Campinense de Letras, Rua Marechal Deodoro, 525, 13020-000 Campinas SP, Brazil. Ed. Lycurgo de Castro Santos Filho. circ. 200 (controlled). **Document type:** monographic series.

ACADEMIA COLOMBIANA. BOLETIN. see *LINGUISTICS*

800   SP   ISSN 0065-0455
ACADEMIA ESPANOLA, MADRID. ANEJOS DEL BOLETIN. 1959. irreg., latest no.49. price varies. Real Academia Espanola, Calle de Felipe IV No. 4, Madrid 14, Spain.

860   US
ACADEMIA NORTEAMERICANA DE LA LENGUA ESPANOLA. BOLETIN. (Text in Spanish) 1976. irreg. $35 to individuals; institutions $30. Academia Norteamericana de la Lengua Espanola, Box 349, New York, NY 10116. (Subscr. to: Odon Betanzos, 125 Queen St., Staten Island, NY 10314) Ed. Eugenio Chang-Rodriguez. bk.rev.; illus. circ. 3,000. **Indexed:** M.L.A. **Document type:** bulletin.

800   BL   ISSN 0001-3846
AS80
ACADEMIA PAULISTA DE LETRAS. REVISTA. 1937. irreg. free. Academia Paulista de Letras, Largo do Arouche 312, 01219 Sao Paulo, SP, Brazil. Ed. Antonio Soares Amora. bibl. circ. 1,500. **Indexed:** Hisp.Amer.Per.Ind.

860   BL
ACADEMIA PERNAMBUCANA DE LETRAS. REVISTA. 1901. irreg. donation. Academia Pernambucana de Letras, Av. Rui Barbosa, 1596, Gracas, 52050 Recife PE, Brazil. FAX 081-268-2211. bk.rev.; illus. **Document type:** academic/scholarly publication.

800   HU   ISSN 0567-7661
PN1
ACADEMIA SCIENTIARUM HUNGARICA. ACTA LITTERARIA. (Text in English, French, German, Russian) 1957. q. $80 (effective 1992). (Magyar Tudomanyos Akademia) Akademiai Kiado, Publishing House of the Hungarian Academy of Sciences, P.O. Box 245, H-1519 Budapest, Hungary. TEL 181-2134. FAX 166-6466. TELEX 22-6228 AKNYO H. Ed. Katalin Kulin. adv.; bk.rev. **Indexed:** M.L.A. **Document type:** academic/scholarly publication.
—CCC.
 Description: Deals with problems in Hungarian and European literature. Covers the relation between Hungarian and European literatures in the Middle Ages, Renaissance, Reformation, Enlightenment.

840   FR   ISSN 0065-0587
ACADEMIE FRANCAISE. ANNUAIRE; documents et notices sur les membres de l'Academie. 1966. a. 50 F. Academie Francaise, 23 Quai de Conti, 75006 Paris, France. FAX 43-29-47-45.

ACADEMIE ROYALE DE LANGUE ET DE LITTERATURE FRANCAISES. BULLETIN. see *LINGUISTICS*

850 851   IT
L'ACERBA; periodico di tecnica (artistica, letteraria, libraria) culturale. bi-m. L.3000 per no. Corso Mazzini, 137, 63100 Ascoli Piceno, Italy. Dir. Angelo M. Guacci.

800 100   IT   ISSN 0001-494X
ACME. 1948. 3/yr. L.15000. Universita degli Studi di Milano, Facolta di Lettere e Filosofia., Via Festa del Perdono 7, Milan, Italy. Ed. Guido Bezzola. index. circ. 750. **Indexed:** Amer.Hist.& Life, Bibl.Engl.Lang.& Lit., Bibl.Ling., Hist.Abstr.
—Faxon.

860   CL   ISSN 0716-0909
PN1
ACTA LITERARIA. 1975. a. $7. Universidad de Concepcion, Facultad de Educacion, Humanidades y Arte, Departamento de Espanol, Casilla 82-C, Correo 3, Concepcion, Chile. FAX 56-41-249108. TELEX 260004 TEUCO CL. Dir. Luis Munoz G. bk.rev. circ. 600. **Indexed:** M.L.A. **Document type:** academic/scholarly publication.
 Description: Theoretical approach to the study of literature, with emphasis on Hispanic literature.

ACTA NEOPHILOLOGICA. see *LINGUISTICS*

891.85   PL   ISSN 0239-4294
ACTA UNIVERITATIS WRATISLAVIENSIS. PRACE LITERACKIE. MONOGRAFIE. 1956. irreg. price varies. (Uniwersytet Wroclawski) Wydawnictwo Uniwersytetu Wroclawskiego, Pl. Uniwersytecki 9-13, 50-137 Wroclaw, Poland. (Dist. by: Ksiegarnia Uniwersytetu Wroclawskiego, Pl. Uniwersytecki 9-13, 50-137 Wroclaw, Poland) Ed. Leslaw Tatarowski. circ. 500. (also avail. in microfilm) **Document type:** academic/scholarly publication, monographic series.
 Former titles (until 1979): Acta Universitatis Wratislaviensis. Prace Literackie. Studia Monograficzne (ISSN 0239-4286); (until 1978): Acta Universitatis Wratislaviensis. Prace Literackie (ISSN 0079-4767)

800   PL   ISSN 0867-7441
ACTA UNIVERSITATIS WRATISLAVIENSIS. LITERATURA I KULTURA POPULARNA. (Text in Polish; summaries in English or German) 1991. irreg. price varies. (Uniwersytet Wroclawski) Wydawnictwo Uniwersytetu Wroclawskiego, Pl. Uniwersytecki 9-13, 50-137 Wroclaw, Poland. TEL 44-10-06. (Dist. by: Ksiegarnia Uniwersytetu Wroclawskiego, Pl. Uniwersytecki 9-13, 50-137 Wroclaw, Poland) Eds. Jacek Kolbuszewski, Tadeusz Zabski. circ. 250. **Document type:** academic/scholarly publication.

894.511   HU   ISSN 0586-3708
ACTA UNIVERSITATIS DE ATTILA JOZSEF NOMINATAE. ACTA HISTORIAE LITTERARUM HUNGARICARUM. (Text in Hungarian; summaries in English, French, German or Russian) 1961. a. exchange basis. Attila Jozsef University, c/o E. Szabo, Exchange Librarian, Dugonics ter 13, P.O.B. 393, Szeged H-6701, Hungary. (Subscr. to: Kultura, Box 149, H-1389 Budapest, Hungary) Eds. Ferenc Grezsa, Lajos Csetri. circ. 500. **Indexed:** M.L.A. **Document type:** academic/scholarly publication.
 Description: Journal of Hungarian literary criticism from the beginnings to present.

ACTA UNIVERSITATIS DE ATTILA JOZSEF NOMINATAE. ACTA ROMANICA. see *LINGUISTICS*

ACTA UNIVERSITATIS DE ATTILA JOZSEF NOMINATAE. PAPERS IN ENGLISH AND AMERICAN STUDIES. see *LINGUISTICS*

800 370   PL   ISSN 0208-6085
PN9
ACTA UNIVERSITATIS LODZIENSIS: FOLIA LITTERARIA. (Text in Polish; summaries in various languages) 1955-1974; N.S. 1981. irreg. Wydawnictwo Uniwersytetu Lodzkiego, Ul. Jaracz 34, Lodz, Poland. TEL 331671. (Dist. by: Ars Polona-Ruch, Krakowskie Przedmiescie 7, Warsaw, Poland) **Document type:** academic/scholarly publication.
—BLDSC (0585.207400).
 Supersedes in part: Uniwersytet Lodzki. Zeszyty Naukowe. Seria 1: Nauki Humanistyczno-Spoleczne (ISSN 0076-0358)
 Description: Studies in the history of literature, literary epochs and problems. Gives young writers a chance to publish their works.

891.7 100   HU   ISSN 0237-9562
ACTA UNIVERSITATIS SZEGEDIENSIS DE ATTILA JOZSEF NOMINATAE. DISSERTATIONES SLAVICAE. SECTIO HISTORIAE LITTERARUM. Key Title: Dissertationes Slavicae. Sectio Historiae Litterarum. a. Attila Jozsef University, c/o E. Szabo, Exchange Librarian, Dugonics ter 13, P.O. Box 393, Szeged H-6701, Hungary. Ed. Adam Fejer. bk.rev. circ. 350. **Document type:** academic/scholarly publication.
 Supersedes in part (in 1982): Acta Universitatis Szegediensis de Attila Jozsef Nominatae. Dissertationes Slavicae (ISSN 0586-3732)
 Description: Focuses on Russian literature and history of ideas in the nineteenth and twentieth centuries.

ACTA UNIVERSITATIS SZEGEDIENSIS DE ATTILA JOZSEF NOMINATAE. DISSERTATIONES SLAVICAE. SECTIO LINGUISTICA. see *LINGUISTICS*

890   SW   ISSN 0440-9078
ACTA UNIVERSITATIS UPSALIENSIS. HISTORIA LITTERARUM. (Text in English, French, German and Swedish; summaries in French, English and German) 1962. irreg. price varies. (Uppsala University, Historia Litterarum) A W I International AB, P.O. Box 4627, S-116 91 Stockholm, Sweden. TEL 468-640-8800. FAX 468-641-1180. circ. 400. **Indexed:** M.L.A.

830   SW
ACTA UNIVERSITATIS UPSALIENSIS. STUDIA GERMANISTICA UPSALIENSIS. (Text in German) 1964. irreg., latest no.29 1988. A W I International AB, P.O. Box 4627, S-116 91 Stockholm, Sweden. TEL 468-640-8800. FAX 468-641-1180. Ed. John Evert Haerd. **Indexed:** M.L.A. **Document type:** academic/scholarly publication.

ACTA UNIVERSITATIS WRATISLAVIENSIS. ANGLICA WRATISLAVIENSIA. see *LINGUISTICS*

LITERATURE

| 800 | CN | ISSN 0700-8406 |

ACTA VICTORIANA. 1878. s-a. Can.$9($15) 150 Charles St. W., Toronto, ON M5S 1K9, Canada. TEL 416-585-4473. Ed. Simon Archer. illus. circ. 1,800. (back issues avail.)
   Description: Literary journal includes: poetry, short fiction, photography, drama, and interviews.

ACTIVE VOICE; of the people, by the people, for the people. see *POLITICAL SCIENCE*

| 800 | VE | ISSN 0001-7639 |

ACTUAL. 1968-1971; N.S. 1976-1983; N.S. 1983. irreg., no.20, 1991. Universidad de los Andes, Direccion General de Cultura y Extension, Avda. Tulio Febres Cordero, Edificio Administrativo, 4o piso, C.P. 5101, Merida, Venezuela. FAX 074-402655. Ed. Julio Tallaferro. bk.rev.; charts; illus.

| 081 940 | | GW |

▼**AD FONTES.** 1993. irreg., vol.1, 1993. DM.118. Francke Verlag GmbH, Postfach 2560, 72015 Tuebingen, Germany. TEL 07071-78091. FAX 07071-75288. **Document type:** monographic series.

| 830 | AU | ISSN 0001-799X |
| PT2525.Z4 | | |

ADALBERT-STIFTER-INSTITUT DES LANDES OBEROESTERREICH. VIERTELJAHRESSCHRIFT. 1952. s-a. S.140. (Amt der Oberoesterreichischen Landesregierung) Adalbert-Stifter-Institut des Landes Oberoesterreich, Adalbert-Stifter-Platz 1, A-4020 Linz, Austria. TEL 0732-2720-1295. FAX 0732-27201780. Ed. Johann Lachinger. bk.rev.; bibl.; charts; illus.; index every 3 yrs. circ. 750. Indexed: M.L.A. **Document type:** academic/scholarly publication.
   Description: Discusses work and background of Adalbert Stifter, literature of Upper Austria.

ADAM AND EVE. see *LITERARY AND POLITICAL REVIEWS*

| 700 | UK | ISSN 0001-8015 |
| AP1 | | |

ADAM INTERNATIONAL REVIEW. (Text in English and French) 1941. q. £6($10) 28 Emperors Gate, London SW7, England. Ed. Miron Grindea. adv.; bk.rev. circ. 1,250. (back issues avail.) **Indexed:** Br.Hum.Ind., M.L.A.

| 891.4 | II | ISSN 0001-8228 |

ADHUNA SAHITYA.* (Text in Bengali) 1965. q. Rs.2.50($0.50) R.N. Nandy, 2 Bazarpara Main Rd., Halisahar, Parganas 24, West Bengal, India. Ed. S. Mukherjee.
   Formerly: Adhuna.

| 059.915 | IR | ISSN 1017-4095 |

ADINEH. m. $50. G.H. Zakiri, Ed. & Pub., P.O. Box 14185-345, Tehran, Iran. (back issues avail.)

| 800 914.1 | US | ISSN 0736-4970 |

ADRIFT; writings: Irish, Irish-American and ... 1983. s-a. $8. Adrift Editions, 239 E. Fifth St., Apt. 4D, New York, NY 10003. Ed. Thomas McGonigle. adv.; bk.rev. circ. 1,000. (back issues avail.)

| 808 | US | ISSN 8756-1271 |
| P211 | | |

ADVANCES IN WRITING RESEARCH. 1985. irreg., vol.2, 1988. price varies. Ablex Publishing Corporation, 355 Chestnut St., Norwood, NJ 07648. TEL 201-767-8450. FAX 201-767-6717. TELEX 135-393. Ed. Marcia Farr.
   —BLDSC (0712.175000).

| 808 | US | ISSN 1049-1740 |

ADVOCATE (PRATTSVILLE). 1987. bi-m. $12 ($28 to Canada; elsewhere $42.60). P K A Publications, 301A Rolling Hills Park, Prattsville, NY 12468. TEL 518-299-3103. Ed. Remington Wright. adv.; bk.rev. circ. 12,000.
   Formerly (until 1988): Student Advocate.
   Description: Publishes art, fiction, photos and poetry, and promotes careers in writing and the arts.

| 810 | US | |

AEGEAN REVIEW: GREEK ARTS AND LETTERS. 1986. s-a. $10. Wire Press, 220 W. 19th St., Ste. 2A, New York, NY 10011. Ed. Dino Siotis. adv.; bk.rev.; illus. circ. 5,000. **Document type:** academic/scholarly publication.
   Formerly: Aegean Review: Contemporary Greek Arts and Letters (ISSN 0891-7213); Which supersedes (1975-1984, no.13): Coffee House: Contemporary Greek Arts and Letters.

| 790 810 | US | ISSN 1048-3756 |
| PN56.S73 | | |

AETHLON. 1983. s-a. (Sport Literature Association) San Diego State University, San Diego State University Press, San Diego, CA 92182.
   —BLDSC (0730.566000).
   Formerly (until 1988): Arete (ISSN 0894-0827).

| 808 | US | |

AFFINITIES.* 1981. s-a. Latitudes Press, 4722 Little Rd., Arlington, TX 76063-0613. Ed. Robert Bonazzi.

| 806 910.03 | FR | ISSN 0243-7090 |

AFRAM NEWSLETTER. 1975. s-a. free. Universite de Paris III (Sorbonne Nouvelle), Centre d'Etudes Afro-Americaines et des Nouvelles Litteratures en Anglais, 5 rue de l'Ecole de Medecine, 75006 Paris, France. FAX 43-25-74-71. Ed. Michel Fabre. adv.; bk.rev. circ. 350. (processed) **Indexed:** Can.Lit.Ind.

AFRICA; rivista trimestrale di studi e documentazione. see *HISTORY — History Of Africa*

| 051 910.03 | US | |

▼**AFRICAN AMERICAN LITERARY REVIEW.** 1993. q. $12 to individuals; institutions $15 (effective 1994). 5381 La Paseo, No. 105, Ft. Worth, TX 76112. TEL 817-429-6150. FAX 817-336-7527. Ed. Monica Marchi; Pub. John Posey. bk.rev. circ. 800. **Document type:** newsletter.

AFRICAN AMERICAN REVIEW. see *ETHNIC INTERESTS*

AFRICAN ARTS. see *ART*

AFRICAN LANGUAGES AND CULTURES. see *LINGUISTICS*

| 800 | CN | |

AFRICAN LITERATURE ASSOCIATION. BULLETIN. 1974. q. price varies. African Literature Association, Comparative Literature and Film Studies Department, University of Alberta, Edmonton, AB T6G 2E6, Canada. TEL 403-492-5535. FAX 403-492-0692. Ed. Stephen H. Arnold. adv.; bk.rev.; bibl. circ. 850. (back issues avail.) **Document type:** bulletin.
   Formerly: African Literature Association Newsletter (ISSN 0146-4965)

| 896 | FR | ISSN 0245-8160 |

AFRIQUE LITTERAIRE. 1968. q. 150 F. Societe Afrique Litteraire, 2 rue Cretet, 75009 Paris, France. adv.; bk.rev.; bibl.; illus.; index. circ. 2,500. **Indexed:** Curr.Cont., Documentatieblad.
   Formerly (until 1980): Afrique Litteraire et Artistique (ISSN 1149-6835)

| 800 | NR | |

AFRO IMAGE.* 1972. m. £N8. African Cultures Publications Ltd., Mile 2 Ubulunor Rd., Box 20, Ogwashi Uku, Nigeria.

AGADA; an illustrated Jewish literary magazine. see *ETHNIC INTERESTS*

| 990 | US | ISSN 0884-5816 |
| PR3532 | | |

AGE OF JOHNSON; a scholarly annual. 1987. a. $55. A M S Press, Inc., 56 E. 13th St., New York, NY 10003. TEL 212-777-4700. FAX 212-995-5413. Ed. Paul J. Korshin. bk.rev.; index. (back issues avail.) **Document type:** academic/scholarly publication.
   —BLDSC (0736.094500).
   Description: Annual collection of scholarly articles and reviews pertaining to English literature, history and culture during the period of Samuel Johnson's life and circle.

| 810 | US | |

AGNI. 1972. 2/yr. $12 to individuals; institutions $24. (Boston University, Creative Writing Program) Agni Review, Inc., 236 Bay State Rd., Boston, MA 02215-1403. TEL 617-353-5389. Ed. Askold Melnyczuk. adv.: page $200; trim 4 1/2 x 7; adv. contact: Erin Belieu. bk.rev. circ. 1,500. (back issues avail.) **Indexed:** A.I.P.P., Amer.Hum.Ind., Ind.Amer.Per.Verse.
   Formerly: Agni Review (ISSN 0191-3352)
   Description: Includes fiction, poetry, essays and reviews by established and emerging writers, including Derek Walcott, Joyce Carol Oates, Noam Chomsky and Linda Svendsen.

AGORA; an alternative journal of Romanian culture. see *ETHNIC INTERESTS*

AHIJUNA. see *HISTORY — History Of North And South America*

| 800 | FR | ISSN 0065-4787 |

AILLEURS ET DEMAIN; CLASSIQUES.* 1970. irreg. price varies. Editions R. Laffont, 6 Place Saint-Sulpice, Paris 6e, France.

| 889 | GR | |

AIOLIKA GRAMMATA. 1971. bi-m. Dr.40. Hodos Nireos 41, Palaion Phaliron, Athens, Greece. TEL 3600142. circ. 2,000. **Indexed:** M.L.A.

| 820 821 | UK | ISSN 0261-0124 |

AIREINGS. 1980. s-a. £3 (effective 1993). Aireings Publications, 24 Brudenell Rd., Leeds, West Yorkshire LS6 1BD, England. TEL 0532-785893. Ed. Jean Barker. bk.rev. circ. 300.

| 800 300 | II | |

AJKAL. (Editions in Hindi, Urdu) m. Rs.30. Ministry of Information & Broadcasting, Publications Division, Patiala House, Tilak Marg, New Delhi 110001, India. **Document type:** government publication.
   Description: Carries short stories and poems on social, cultural and educational problems of the country.

| 800 | GW | ISSN 0002-2985 |
| PN504 | | |

AKADEMIE DER WISSENSCHAFTEN UND DER LITERATUR, MAINZ. KLASSE DER LITERATUR. ABHANDLUNGEN. 1950. irreg. price varies. Franz Steiner Verlag Wiesbaden GmbH, Birkenwaldstr. 44, 70191 Stuttgart, Germany. TEL 0711-2582-0. FAX 0711-2582290. TELEX 723636-DAZ-D. (Subscr. to: Postfach 101061, 70009 Stuttgart, Germany) index. **Document type:** monographic series.

AKADEMIYA NAUK AZERBAIJANA. IZVESTIYA. SERIYA YAZYKOZNANIE, LITERATURA I ISKUSSTVO. see *LINGUISTICS*

| 890 | II | |

AKS.* (Text in Panjabi) 1950. m. Rs.84. 22-83 W. Patel Nagar, New Delhi 110008, India. TEL 583740. adv.; bk.rev. circ. 27,333.

| 860 | US | ISSN 0044-7064 |

ALALUZ; revista de poesia y narracion. 1969. s-a. $40. University of California, Riverside, Department of Literature & Language, Riverside, CA 92502. TEL 714-787-3406. FAX 714-787-3800. Ed. Ana Maria Fagundo. bk.rev.; bibl. circ. 700. **Document type:** academic/scholarly publication.

| 800 | US | ISSN 0737-268X |
| PN2 | | |

ALASKA QUARTERLY REVIEW. 1982. s-a. $8 to individuals; institutions $10. University of Alaska, Anchorage, College of Arts and Sciences, 3221 Providence Dr., Anchorage, AK 99508. TEL 907-786-4775. Ed. Ronald Spatz. circ. 1,000. (back issues avail.) **Document type:** academic/scholarly publication.
   —UnCover.
   Description: Contains literary short stories, poetry, interviews with contemporary American writers, and essays.

ALBUM, LETRAS Y ARTES. see *ART*

| 800 | IS | ISSN 0334-4827 |

ALEI SIACH; literary conversation. 1974. irreg. IS.24. Brit Takam, Rehov Dobnov 10, Tel Aviv 64 732, Israel. Ed. Yadidiya Yitzhaki. bk.rev. circ. 1,500.
   Description: Contemporary literature and literary research.

LITERATURE

860   AG
ALEJANDRIA. bi-m. Arg.$90($25) Alejandria S.R.L., Larrea 716, Buenos Aires, Argentina. Ed. Jorge Montgomery.

800 300   GT
ALERO. 1973. bi-m. Q.3.50. Universidad de San Carlos de Guatemala, Ciudad Universitaria, Guatemala 12, Guatemala. Ed. Rafael Cuevas del Cid. illus.

800   CN   ISSN 0065-616X
ALEXANDER LECTURES. 1929. irreg. price varies. (University of Toronto, University College) University of Toronto Press, 5201 Dufferin St., Downsview, ON M3H 5T8, Canada. TEL 416-667-7791. FAX 416-667-7832. (U.S. address: 340 Nagel Drive, Cheektowaga, NY 14225) **Document type:** academic/scholarly publication.

ALFA; revista de linguistica. see *LINGUISTICS*

800   HU   ISSN 0401-3174
AP82
ALFOLD. 1950. m. 360 Ft.($5) Csokonai Publishing House, Varga u. 17 er. 10, 4024 Debrecen, Hungary. TEL 52-12626. Ed. Peline Bah Eva. bk.rev. circ. 1,800. **Indexed:** M.L.A. **Document type:** academic/scholarly publication.
   Description: Literary, cultural and critical periodical.

800   US
THE ALGONKIAN. no.11, 1992. m. free. Algonquin Books of Chapel Hill, Box 2225, Chapel Hill, NC 27515-2225. Ed. Bernard Cheltenham Bodoni.

ALIF; journal of comparative poetics. see *LITERATURE — Poetry*

820   II   ISSN 0258-0365
PR1
ALIGARH JOURNAL OF ENGLISH STUDIES. (Text in English) 1976. s-a. Rs.30($6) Aligarh Muslim University, Department of English, Aligarh, Uttar Pradesh, India. Ed. S.M. Jafar Zaki. bk.rev. circ. 350. **Indexed:** M.L.A.
   —BLDSC (0787.821000).

895.65   JA
ALL YOMIMONO; a magazine on popular fiction. (Text in Japanese) 1931. m. 12120 Yen. Bungei-Shunju Ltd., 3-23, Kioicho, Chiyoda-ku, Tokyo 102, Tokyo 102, Japan. TEL 03-3265-1211. FAX 03-3265-4485. Ed. Masaru Nakai. circ. 122,000.

700 500   IT   ISSN 0002-5631
ALLA BOTTEGA; bimestrale di cultura ed arte. 1963. bi-m. L.50000 (foreign L.100000). Via Plinio 38, 20129 Milan, Italy. TEL 224177. Ed. Giuseppe Lucano. adv.; bk.rev.; play rev.; bibl.; illus.; cum.index. circ. 4,000. **Indexed:** M.L.A.

800   US   ISSN 0742-096X
ALLEGHENY REVIEW; a national journal of undergraduate literature. 1983. a. $3.50. Allegheny College, Box 32, Meadville, PA 16335. TEL 814-724-6553. Eds. R. Scott Huth, Katherine Burkett. circ. 1,200. (back issues avail.)

ALLT OM BOECKER. see *LIBRARY AND INFORMATION SCIENCES*

830 770   GW
ALLTAG; die Sensationen des Gewoehnlichen. 1978. q. DM.80. Elefanten Press, Am Treptower Park 28-30, 12435 Berlin, Germany. TEL 030-68834101. Ed.Bd. adv.; bk.rev. circ. 5,000. (back issues avail.) **Document type:** bulletin.

800 700   CN
ALPHA. 1976. irreg. (2-4/yr.). Can.$3. (Acadia University Students Unions) Either Or Publications, Acadia University, Wolfville, N.S. B0P 1X0, Canada. TEL 902-542-2201. Ed. Sian Morris Ross. adv.; bk.rev.; film rev.; play rev.; illus. (back issues avail.) **Indexed:** Can.Lit.Ind.

830   GW   ISSN 0065-6607
ALTDEUTSCHE TEXTBIBLIOTHEK. ERGAENZUNGSREIHE. 1963. irreg., no.108, 1994. price varies. Max Niemeyer Verlag, Postfach 2140, 72011 Tuebingen, Germany. TEL 07071-989494. FAX 07071-989450. (back issues avail.) **Indexed:** M.L.A. **Document type:** monographic series, academic/scholarly publication.
   Description: Critical editions of Old High German and Middle High German manuscripts.

809   GW
ALTE ABENTEUERLICHE REISEBERICHTE. 1966. irreg. price varies. K. Thienemanns Verlag, Blumenstr. 36, 70182 Stuttgart, Germany. TEL 0711-21055-0. FAX 0711-21055-39. circ. 4,000. **Document type:** consumer publication.

800   GW
ALTERTUMSWISSENSCHAFTLICHE TEXTE UND STUDIEN. irreg., vol.27, 1994. DM.64. Georg Olms Verlag, Hagentorwall 7, 31134 Hildesheim, Germany. TEL 05121-1501-0. FAX 05121-150150. (U.S. subscr. to: 111 W. 57th St., New York, NY 10019. TEL 212-757-5237) **Document type:** monographic series.

L'ALTRA EUROPA. see *ART*

850   IT
ALTROQUANDO. 1990. irreg., no.2, 1993. price varies. Liguori Editore s.r.l., Via Mezzocannone 19, 80134 Naples, Italy. TEL 081-5527139. Ed. Sergio Brancato. **Document type:** monographic series.

800   GW   ISSN 0721-0493
AM ERKER; Zeitschrift fuer Literatur. 1977. s-a. DM.30 for 4 nos. Verlag Am Erker, Dahlweg 64, 48153 Muenster, Germany. TEL 0251-793939. Ed. Joachim Feldmann. adv.; bk.rev. circ. 1,000. (back issues avail.) **Document type:** consumer publication.
   Description: Explores experimental literature.

AMACADMY. see *ART*

860   AG
AMARU. m. Casilla de Correo 33, 1824 Sucural Lanus (O), Buenos Aires, Argentina. Ed. Juan C. Gimenez.

810   US
AMATEUR WRITER'S JOURNAL. 1967. q. $8. R.V. Gill Publishing Co., 3653 Harrison St., Bellaire, OH 43906-1142. TEL 614-676-0881. Ed. Rosalind V. Gill. adv.; bibl. circ. 1,500.
   Incorporates: *Four Seasons*.

800   GW   ISSN 0179-4922
AMBACHER SCHRIFTEN. 1986. irreg., vol.7, 1991. Harrassowitz Verlag, Taunusstr. 14, 65183 Wiesbaden, Germany. TEL 0611-530-0. FAX 0611-530-570. TELEX 4186135. (Subscr. to: Postfach 2929, 65019 Wiesbaden, Germany) Ed. Rose-Marie Bonsels. **Document type:** monographic series.

800 700   US   ISSN 1044-2006
AMBERGRIS. 1987. a. $8 for 2 nos. Ambergris Foundation, c/o Mark Kissling, Ed., Box 29919, Cincinnati, OH 45229-0919. adv. circ. 900.
   Description: Publishes essays, art and fiction.

800   UK   ISSN 0002-6972
PR1098
AMBIT; a quarterly of poems, short stories, drawings and criticism. 1959. q. $40. 17 Priory Gardens, London N.6, England. Ed. Martin C.O. Bax. adv.; bk.rev.; illus. circ. 2,000. (also avail. in microfilm from UMI)
   —BLDSC (0808.970000); UMI.

810   US   ISSN 0743-2755
AMELIA. 1984. q. $25. Amelia, 329 "E" St., Bakersfield, CA 93304. TEL 805-323-4064. Eds. Frederick A. Raborg, Jr., Eileen M. Raborg. adv.; B&W page $500, color page $900. bk.rev. circ. 1,352. **Indexed:** Amer.Hum.Ind., Ind.Amer.Per.Verse.
   Description: For the eclectic reader of fiction, poetry, essays, reviews, fine art and sophisticated cartoons.

AMERICAN BENEDICTINE REVIEW. see *RELIGIONS AND THEOLOGY — Roman Catholic*

AMERICAN CLASSICAL REVIEW. see *CLASSICAL STUDIES*

810   US
PN855
AMERICAN COMPARATIVE LITERATURE ASSOCIATION. BULLETIN. 1968. s-a. $6 to non-members. American Comparative Literature Association, Brigham Young University, 3010 JKHB, Provo, UT 84602. TEL 801-378-5529. FAX 801-378-4649. Ed. Larry H. Peer. circ. 800. (back issues avail.) **Document type:** bulletin.
   Former titles (until vol.24, no.1, 1992): A C L A Newsletter (ISSN 0891-3277); (until 1975): American Comparative Literature Association Newsletter (ISSN 0002-8053)
   Description: Includes status of literary studies, proceedings of ACLA, and general information on literary studies, articles and reviews.

AMERICAN DRAMA. see *THEATER*

800   US
AMERICAN FARMER SERIES. (In 2 vols.) 1985. biennial. $7.75 per no. Seven Buffaloes Press, Box 249, Big Timber, MT 59011. TEL 406-932-4168. Ed. Art Cuelho. circ. 750. (back issues avail.)
   Description: Contemporary short stories and poetry on farmer and rancher lifestyles, with emphasis on farms in trouble.

AMERICAN IMAGO; a psychoanalytic journal for culture, science and the arts. see *MEDICAL SCIENCES — Psychiatry And Neurology*

AMERICAN JOURNAL OF GERMANIC LINGUISTICS AND LITERATURES. see *LINGUISTICS*

AMERICAN JOURNAL OF PHILOLOGY. see *LINGUISTICS*

800   US   ISSN 0896-7148
PS1
AMERICAN LITERARY HISTORY. 1989. 4/yr. $29 to individuals; institutions $68 (effective 1994). Oxford University Press, Journals, 200 Madison Ave., New York, NY 10016. TEL 212-679-7300. FAX 212-689-5312. TELEX 6859654. (Subscr. to: Oxford Journals Fulfillment, 2001 Evans Rd., Cary, NC 27513. TEL 919-677-0977. FAX 919-677-1714) Ed. Gordon Hutner. adv.; bk.rev. circ. 1,280. **Document type:** academic/scholarly publication.
   —BLDSC (0840.757500); Faxon; UnCover; SWETS; UMI. **CCC.**
   Description: Covers the study of American literature from the colonial period through the present.

814.008   US   ISSN 0065-9142
PS3
AMERICAN LITERARY SCHOLARSHIP; an annual. 1963. a. price varies. Duke University Press, 6697 College Station, Durham, NC 27708. TEL 919-684-2173. FAX 919-684-8644. Eds. J. Albert Robbins, Warren G. French. (reprint service avail. from ISI,UMI) **Indexed:** M.L.A. **Document type:** academic/scholarly publication.
   —BLDSC (0840.770000).

810   US   ISSN 0002-9831
PS1
AMERICAN LITERATURE; a journal of literary history, criticism, and bibliography. 1929. q. $28 to individuals and secondary schools (foreign $36); institutions $56 (foreign $60); students $14 (foreign $22). Duke University Press, Box 90660, Durham, NC 27708-0660. TEL 919-687-3600. FAX 919-688-4574. Ed. Cathy N. Davidson. adv.; bk.rev.; bibl.; index, cum.index. circ. 5,500. (also avail. in microform from MIM,UMI; reprint service avail. from ISI,UMI,KTO) **Indexed:** Abstr.Engl.Stud., Acad.Ind., Amer.Hist.& Life, Arts & Hum.Cit.Ind., Bk.Rev.Dig., Bk.Rev.Ind. (1965-), Chic.Per.Ind., Child.Bk.Rev.Ind. (1965-), Curr.Bk.Rev.Cit., Curr.Cont., Hist.Abstr., Hum.Ind., Ind.Bk.Rev.Hum., LCR, M.L.A., Ref.Sour., So.Pac.Per.Ind. **Document type:** academic/scholarly publication, bibliography.
   —BLDSC (0840.780000); Faxon; UnCover; SWETS; UMI. **CCC.**
   Refereed Serial

810 US ISSN 1054-7479
PN4877
AMERICAN PERIODICALS; a journal of history, criticism and bibliography. 1991. a. $15. (Research Society for American Periodicals) University of North Texas Press, Journals Division, Box 5096, Denton, TX 76203-5096. TEL 817-565-2134. FAX 817-369-8770. Ed. James T.F. Tanner. adv.; bk.rev.; illus. circ. 500. (back issues avail.) **Indexed:** Amer.Hist.& Life (1991-), Hist.Abstr. (1991-).
—Faxon; UnCover.
Description: General listing of American periodicals.
Refereed Serial

AMERICAN PHILOLOGICAL ASSOCIATION. SPECIAL PUBLICATIONS. see *LINGUISTICS*

810 US ISSN 0569-6941
AMERICAN PHILOLOGICAL ASSOCIATION NEWSLETTER. (Text in English, Greek, Latin) 1960. bi-m. $3 includes membership. American Philological Association, Department of Classics, Holy Cross College, Worcester, MA 01610-2395. TEL 508-793-2253. FAX 508-793-3428. Ed. William J. Ziobro. adv. circ. 3,200. (looseleaf format; back issues avail.) **Document type:** newsletter.
—SWETS.

810 US
AMERICAN RENAISSANCE LITERARY REPORT. 1987. a. Transcendental Books, Box A, Sta. A, Hartford, CT 06126-0160. TEL 203-522-6517. Ed. Kenneth W. Cameron. bk.rev. circ. 150-200. (back issues avail.)
Description: Journal for research scholars and college libraries covering American authors of 19th century.

AMERICAN REVIEW. see *ART*

800 US ISSN 1051-4813
PS648.S5
AMERICAN SHORT FICTION. 1991. q. $24 to individuals; institutions $36. University of Texas Press, Box 7819, Austin, TX 78713-7819. TEL 512-471-4531. FAX 512-320-0668. TELEX 776453 UTEXPRES AUS. Ed. Laura Furman. circ. 1,500.
Description: Offers original fiction from both the famous and the up-and-coming writers of today.

810 US ISSN 0149-9017
PS243
AMERICAN TRANSCENDENTAL QUARTERY; 19th century American literature and culture. Short title: A T Q. 1969. q. $25 (foreign $26). University of Rhode Island, English Department, Kingston, RI 02881. TEL 401-792-2576. Ed. Josie P. Campbell. (also avail. in microfilm from UMI) **Indexed:** Abstr.Engl.Stud., Amer.Hum.Ind., Arts & Hum.Cit.Ind., Curr.Cont., M.L.A. **Document type:** academic/scholarly publication.
—Faxon; UnCover; UMI.
Description: Studies literary works and authors; also publishes nontechnical articles on all other aspects of 19th century and society.

800 US ISSN 0740-9257
AMERICAN UNIVERSITY STUDIES. SERIES 2. ROMANCE LANGUAGES AND LITERATURE. 1982. irreg. Peter Lang Publishing, Inc., 62 W. 45th St., 4th Fl., New York, NY 10036. TEL 212-302-6740. Ed. Kathryn Earle. **Indexed:** Bibl.Ling. **Document type:** academic/scholarly publication.

808.1 US ISSN 0724-1445
AMERICAN UNIVERSITY STUDIES. SERIES 3. COMPARATIVE LITERATURE. 1982. irreg. Peter Lang Publishing, Inc., 62 W. 45th St., 4th Fl., New York, NY 10036. TEL 212-302-6740. Ed. Michael Flamini. **Document type:** academic/scholarly publication.
—BLDSC (0858.077970).

800 US ISSN 0741-0700
AMERICAN UNIVERSITY STUDIES. SERIES 4. ENGLISH LANGUAGE AND LITERATURE. 1983. irreg. Peter Lang Publishing, Inc., 62 W. 45th St., 4th Fl., New York, NY 10036. TEL 212-302-6740. Ed. Michael Flamini. **Indexed:** Bibl.Ling. **Document type:** academic/scholarly publication.
—BLDSC (0858.077980).
Formerly: American University Studies (ISSN 0724-1453)

AMERICAN UNIVERSITY STUDIES. SERIES 17. CLASSICAL LANGUAGE AND LITERATURE. see *CLASSICAL STUDIES*

896 US ISSN 0742-1923
AMERICAN UNIVERSITY STUDIES. SERIES 18. AFRICAN LITERATURE. 1984. irreg. Peter Lang Publishing, Inc., 62 W. 45th St., 4th Fl., New York, NY 10036. TEL 212-302-6740. Ed. Michael Flamini. **Document type:** academic/scholarly publication.

810.9 US ISSN 0743-6645
AMERICAN UNIVERSITY STUDIES. SERIES 19. GENERAL LITERATURE. 1984. irreg. Peter Lang Publishing, Inc., 62 W. 45th St., 4th Fl., New York, NY 10036. TEL 212-302-6740. Ed. Kathryn Earle. **Document type:** academic/scholarly publication.

800 US ISSN 0895-0512
AMERICAN UNIVERSITY STUDIES. SERIES 24. AMERICAN LITERATURE. (Text in English and other West European languages) 1988. irreg. Peter Lang Publishing, Inc., 62 W. 45th St., 4th Fl., New York, NY 10036. TEL 212-302-6740. Ed. Kathryn Earle. **Document type:** academic/scholarly publication.

800 US ISSN 0884-4356
PS501
THE AMERICAN VOICE. 1985. 3/yr. $15. Kentucky Foundation for Women, Inc., 332 W. Broadway, Ste. 1215, Louisville, KY 40202. TEL 502-562-0045. Ed. Frederick Smock. adv.; bk.rev. circ. 2,000. (back issues avail.) **Indexed:** Abstr.Engl.Stud., Amer.Hum.Ind., Ind.Amer.Per.Verse. **Document type:** academic/scholarly publication.
—UnCover.
Description: Covers modern Panamerican literature.

800 US ISSN 1049-815X
PS536.2
AMERICAN WRITING. 1990. s-a. $10 to individuals; institutions $18. Nierika Editions, 4343 Manayunk Ave., Philadelphia, PA 19128. TEL 215-483-7051. Ed. Alexandra Grilikhes. circ. 4,000 (paid). (back issues avail.)
Description: Publishes writing that takes risks.

800 US ISSN 1042-6213
PS508.M4
THE AMERICAS REVIEW (HOUSTON); a review of Hispanic literature and art of the U.S A. (Text in English and Spanish) 1973. 3/yr. $15 to individuals (Canada and Mexico $20; elsewhere $25); institutions $20 (Canada and Mexico $25; elsewhere $30) (effective 1993). Arte Publico Press, University of Houston, Houston, TX 77204-2090. TEL 713-743-2841. FAX 713-743-2847. Eds. Nicolas Kanellos, Evangelina Vigil-Pinon. adv.; bk.rev.; play rev. circ. 1,000. (back issues avail.) **Indexed:** Abstr.Pop.Cult., Bk.Rev.Ind. (1990-), Chic.Per.Ind., Child.Bk.Rev.Ind. (1990-), Hisp.Amer.Per.Ind., M.L.A.
—Faxon; UnCover.
Formerly (until 1986): Revista Chicano-Riquena (ISSN 0360-7860)
Description: Publishes new writing by Hispanics in the United States in their original English or Spanish.

860 MX
AMETRIAS; escritura de creacion. s-a? Universidad de Guadalajara, Apdo. Postal 4-010, 44430 Guadalajara, Jalisco, Mexico.

053.1 GW
AMHERSTER KOLLOQUIEN ZUR DEUTSCHEN LITERATUR. irreg., vol.18, 1993. DM.84. Francke Verlag GmbH, Postfach 2560, 72015 Tuebingen, Germany. TEL 07071-78091. FAX 07071-75288. **Document type:** monographic series.

840 FR ISSN 0044-8133
PQ2613.I2
AMIS D'ANDRE GIDE. BULLETIN. 1968. q. 160 F.($32) Universite de Lyon II, Centre d'Etudes Gidiennes, 18 Quai Claude Bernard, F-69365 Lyon Cedex 07, France. Ed. M. Claude Martin. adv.; bk.rev.; bibl. circ. 1,200. **Indexed:** M.L.A.
—SWETS.

891.857 FR ISSN 0003-181X
AMIS DE MILOSZ. 1967. m. 120 F. Editions Andre Silvaire, 20 rue Domat, 75005 Paris, France. illus.

800 920 FR ISSN 0293-0773
AMIS DE RAMUZ. BULLETIN. 1981. a. 200 F. Les Amis du Ramuz, Universite Francois Rabelais, 3 rue des Tanneurs, F-37000 Tours, France. Ed. J.L. Pierre. adv.; bk.rev. circ. 250. (back issues avail.)

840 FR ISSN 0180-8567
PQ2631.E25
AMITIE CHARLES PEGUY. BULLETIN D'INFORMATIONS ET DE RECHERCHES. 1978. q. 135 F. Amitie Charles Peguy, Chez Francoise Gerbod, 12 rue Notre Dame des Champs, 75006 Paris, France. TEL 45-44-80-38. Ed. Jean Bastaire. bk.rev. circ. 700. **Indexed:** M.L.A. **Document type:** bulletin.
—SWETS.
Formerly: Amitie Charles Peguy. Feuillets.
Description: Articles covering the works of Charles Peguy and his counterparts.

AMON HEN. see *LITERATURE — Science Fiction, Fantasy, Horror*

830 943 NE ISSN 0165-7305
AMSTERDAMER BEITRAEGE ZUR AELTEREN GERMANISTIK. irreg. price varies. Editions Rodopi B.V., Keizersgracht 302-304, 1016 EX Amsterdam, Netherlands. TEL 31-20-6227507. FAX 31-20-6380948. (In N. America: 233 Peachtree St. N.E., Ste. 404, Atlanta, GA 30303-1504. TEL 800-225-3998) **Indexed:** Bibl.Ling. **Document type:** monographic series, academic/scholarly publication.

830 943 NE ISSN 0304-6257
PD3 CODEN: ABAGEV
AMSTERDAMER BEITRAEGE ZUR NEUEREN GERMANISTIK. 1972. irreg., vol.36, 1994. price varies. Editions Rodopi B.V., Keizersgracht 302-304, 1016 EX Amsterdam, Netherlands. TEL 31-20-6227507. FAX 31-20-6380948. (In N. America: 233 Peachtree St. N.E., Ste. 404, Atlanta GA 30303-1504. TEL 800-225-3998) Ed. Gerd Labroisse. circ. 700. **Indexed:** M.L.A. **Document type:** monographic series, academic/scholarly publication.
Description: Covers various aspects of German literature.

AMSTERDAMER PUBLIKATIONEN ZUR SPRACHE UND LITERATUR. see *LINGUISTICS*

821 IE
AN SEANRUD. (Text in English, Irish) 1990. irreg. free. Sunburst Press, 25 Newtown Ave., Blackrock, Co. Dublin, Ireland. Ed. Rudi Holzapfel. bk.rev. circ. 300.

808.8 US ISSN 8755-3910
ANAIS; an international journal. 1983. a. $7.50 (foreign $8.50). Anais Nin Foundation, Box 276, Becket, MA 01223. TEL 413-623-5170. (Subscr. to: 2335 Hidalgo Ave., Los Angeles, CA 90039) Ed. Gunther Stuhlmann. bk.rev. circ. 1,250. **Indexed:** Amer.Hum.Ind. **Document type:** academic/scholarly publication.
—BLDSC (0859.980000); UnCover.
Description: Contains biographical and critical material on Anais Nin and her circle (H. Miller, O. Rank, et al).

ANALECTA CARTUSIANA; review for Carthusian history and spirituality. see *RELIGIONS AND THEOLOGY*

ANALECTA ROMANICA. see *LINGUISTICS*

860 US ISSN 0272-1635
PQ6144
ANALES DE LA LITERATURA ESPANOLA CONTEMPORANEA. (Text and summaries in English and Spanish) 1973. 3/yr. $18 to individuals; institutions $60. (Twentieth Century Spanish Association of America) Society of Spanish and Spanish-American Studies, Department of Spanish and Portuguese, University of Colorado, Campus Box 278, Boulder, CO 80309-0278. TEL 303-492-7308. FAX 303-492-3699. Ed. Luis Gonzalez-del-Valle. adv.; bk.rev.; index. circ. 1,000. (also avail. in microform from UMI; back issues avail.) **Indexed:** Arts & Hum.Cit.Ind., Curr.Cont., M.L.A. **Document type:** academic/scholarly publication.
—BLDSC (0889.850000); UnCover; UMI.
Formed by the 1981 merger of: Anales de la Narrativa Espanola Contemporanea (ISSN 0270-6334); Journal of Spanish Studies: Twentieth Century (ISSN 0092-1807); **Formerly** (1976-1979): Anales de la Novela de Posguerra (ISSN 0145-2363)

LITERATURE

860   SP   ISSN 0212-5889
ANALES DE LITERATURA ESPAÑOLA. Variant title: Universidad de Alicante. Anales. Literatura Espanola. 1982. a. 1500 ptas.($15) (effective 1994). Universidad de Alicante, Departamento de Literatura Espanola, San Vicente del Raspeig, 03090 Alicante, Spain. TEL 96-5903413. FAX 96-5903464. Ed. Guillermo Carnero. adv. **Document type:** academic/scholarly publication.

860   SP   ISSN 0210-4547
ANALES DE LITERATURA HISPANOAMERICANA. 1972. a. 2000 ptas.($22) (Universidad Complutense de Madrid, Seminario de Literatura Hispanoamericana) Editorial Complutense, Donoso Cortes 65, 28015 Madrid, Spain. TEL 394-63-72. FAX 394-63-82. (Co-sponsor: Instituto de Cultura Hispanica) Dir. Juana Martinez Gomez. bk.rev.; bibl.

860   US
ANALES GALDOSIANOS. (Text in English, Spanish) 1966. a. $15. International Association of Galdos Scholars, Cornell University, Department of Romance Studies, Goldwin Smith Hill, Ithaca, NY 14853. Ed. John Kronik. bk.rev. circ. 375. **Indexed:** M.L.A.

800   IT
ANALYSIS: QUADERNI DI ANGLISTICA. (Text in English and Italian) 1983. a. L.16.000($13) Editrice Tecnico Scientifica, Piazza Torricelli 4, I-56100 Pisa, Italy. Ed. Anthony L. Johnson. circ. 500. (back issues avail.) **Indexed:** Lang.Teach.& Ling.Abstr.

ANALYTICAL & ENUMERATIVE BIBLIOGRAPHY. see *BIBLIOGRAPHIES*

ANANDA ACHARYA UNIVERSAL SERIES. see *PHILOSOPHY*

800   II
ANANDA VIKATAN. (Text in Tamil) 1924. w. Rs.156 (foreign RS.990). Vasan Publications Pvt. Ltd., 757, Anna Salai, Madras 600 002, India. TEL 91-44-8264054. FAX 91-44-8267619. TELEX 041-7358 VASN IN. Ed. S. Balasubramanian. circ. 250,000.

800   DK   ISSN 0084-6465
ANDERSENIANA. (Text in Danish; occasionally in English and German; summaries in Danish, English, French, German) 1933. a. DKK 90. Hans Christian Andersen Museum, Hans Jensensstraede 39-43, DK-5000 Odense C, Denmark. TEL 45-66-13-13-72. FAX 45-65-90-86-00. Ed. Niels Oxenvad. adv.; bk.rev.; abstr.; bibl.; illus.; cum.index. circ. 1,000. **Indexed:** Biog.Ind. **Document type:** academic/scholarly publication.

890   II
ANDHRA SACHITRA VARA PATRIKA. (Text in Telugu) 1908. w. Rs.226. Andhra Patrika, 14-14-21 Mallikarjuna Rao St., Gandhinagar, Vijayawada 520 003, India. TEL 61247. Ed. S. Radhakrishna. adv.; bk.rev.; illus. circ. 48,276.

840   FR   ISSN 0180-9350
ANDRE GIDE; la revue des lettres modernes. 1970. irreg., latest no.9, 1991. price varies. Lettres Modernes, 45 rue Saint-Andre, 14123 Fleury sur Orne, France. TEL 31-84-47-06. FAX 31-84-48-09. Ed. Claude Martin. bk.rev. (back issues avail.) **Document type:** academic/scholarly publication.

807   CL
ANDRES BELLO BIBLIOTECA. COLECCION. 1979. m? Editorial Andres Bello, Av. Ricardo Lyon 946, Casilla 4256, Santiago, Chile. FAX 2253600. TELEX 240901 EDJUR CL. Ed. Mercedes Gaju Valles. circ. 10,000.

850   US   ISSN 0899-5273
PQ4001
L'ANELLO CHE NON TIENE; journal of Italian literature. 1988. s-a. $15 to individuals (foreign $20); institutions $25 (foreign $30). Yale University Italian Department, Box 4067, Yale Sta., New Haven, CT 06520-4067. Ed. Ernesto Livorni. bk.rev. **Document type:** academic/scholarly publication.

ANEMONE. see *ART*

800   100   AG
ANFORA; revista cuatrimestral de literatura y filosofia. (Text in Greek, Latin, Spanish) 1987. q. Arg.$750. (Estudio de Abogacia-Dozo Moreno) Agencia Periodistica CID, Avenida de Mayo 666, Capital Federal, Argentina. TEL 30-2471. (Subscr. to: Rodriquez Pena, 545 Capital Federal, Argentina) Ed. Sebastian Dozo Labat. illus. circ. 2,000. (back issues avail.)
Description: Covers literature, philosophy and the distribution of works by certain contemporary writers.

820   UK
ANGELA THIRKELL SOCIETY. JOURNAL. 1981. a. £5. Angela Thirkell Society, c/o Mrs. V. Ramsden, 14 Stanhope Ave., Hosforth, Leeds LS1 5AR, England. (Subscr. addr.: c/o A. Ellis, 32 Carlton Walk, Bath, Avon BA2 4QQ, England) bk.rev. circ. 200. (back issues avail.)

ANGELAKI. see *PHILOSOPHY*

700 800   US
ANGELTREAD;* the lyrian ruse. 1984. q. $8. c/o Tina W. Phillips, Ed., 2100 Madison Ave., Ste. 10H, Charleston, IL 61920-2393. TEL 512-965-4842.

ANGLES. see *LINGUISTICS*

ANGLIA; Zeitschrift fuer englische Philologie. see *LINGUISTICS*

820   DK   ISSN 0066-1805
ANGLISTICA. 1953. irreg. price varies. Rosenkilde og Bagger Ltd., 3 Kronprinsensgade, P.O.Box 2184, DK-1017 Copenhagen, Denmark. Ed. T.J.B. Spencer. circ. 900. **Indexed:** Arts & Hum.Cit.Ind., Curr.Cont. **Document type:** monographic series.

809   GW   ISSN 0179-1389
ANGLISTISCHE FORSCHUNGEN. 1901. irreg. price varies. Universitaetsverlag C. Winter Heidelberg GmbH, Hans-Bunte-Str. 18, 69123 Heidelberg, Germany. (also avail. in microfiche from BHP; microfiche from IDC; reprint service avail. from SWZ) **Indexed:** M.L.A. **Document type:** academic/scholarly publication.

940 820 410   GW
ANGLO-AMERICAN FORUM. (Text in English and German; summaries in English) 1975. irreg. price varies. Peter Lang GmbH Europaeischer Verlag der Wissenschaften, Eschborner Landstr. 42-50, 60489 Frankfurt a.M., Germany. TEL 069-7807050. FAX 069-785893. Ed. Christoph Gutknecht. bk.rev.; abstr.; bibl.; circ. 200 (controlled). (back issues avail.) **Indexed:** M.L.A. **Document type:** monographic series.

ANGOL FILOLOGIAI TANULMANYOK/HUNGARIAN STUDIES IN ENGLISH. see *LINGUISTICS*

800   FR   ISSN 0003-391X
ANNALES DE BRETAGNE ET DES PAYS DE L'OUEST (ANJOU, MAINE, TOURAINE). 1886. q. 220 F. Association pour la Publication des Annales de Bretagne et des Pays de l'Ouest, Universite de Haute Bretagne, 6 av. Gaston Berger, 35043 Rennes, France. index. **Indexed:** Arts & Hum.Cit.Ind., Br.Archaeol.Abstr., Curr.Cont., M.L.A.
—BLDSC (0969.380000).
Formerly (until vol. 81, 1974): Annales de Bretagne.

850   IT
ANNALI ALFIERIANI. irreg. Centro Nazionale di Studi Alfieriani, Via Gaudenzi Ferrari, 9, I-14100 Asti, Italy.

850   US   ISSN 0741-7527
PQ4001
ANNALI D'ITALIANISTICA. 1983. a. $15 to individuals; institutions $29. (University of North Carolina, Chapel Hill, Romance Languages and Literatures) Annali d'Italianistica, Inc., 141 Dey Hall, CB 3170, University of North Carolina, Chapel Hill, NC 27599-3170. Ed. Dino S. Cervigni. adv.; bk.rev. circ. 700. (back issues avail.) **Indexed:** M.L.A.
—BLDSC (1014.600000); UnCover.

843   FR   ISSN 0084-6473
PQ2177.A2
ANNEE BALZACIENNE. 1960. a. 250 F. (foreign 270 F.). (Groupe d'Etudes Balzacienne) Presses Universitaires de France, Departement des Revues, 14 av. du Bois-de-l'Epine, 91003 Evry Cedex, France. TEL 1-60-77-82-05. FAX 1-60-79-20-45. TELEX PUF 600 474 F. (Subscr. to: Maison de Balzac, 47 rue Raynouard, 75016 Paris, France.) **Indexed:** M.L.A.

840   FR   ISSN 0066-3387
ANNUAIRE NATIONAL DES LETTRES. 1948. biennial. Editions Dany Thibaud, 52 rue Labrouste, 75015 Paris, France.

900 800   UK   ISSN 0066-3832
ANNUAL BULLETIN OF HISTORICAL LITERATURE. 1911. a. £35($64) to non-members. (Historical Association) Basil Blackwell Ltd., 108 Cowley Rd., Oxford OX4 1JF, England. TEL 0865-79100. (Subscr. addr.: c/o Marston Book Services, P.O. Box 87, Oxford OX2 ODT, England) Ed. J. Smith. bk.rev.; index. (back issues avail.; reprint service avail. from UMI) **Indexed:** Br.Archaeol.Abstr.

810   US
ANON NINE. irreg. Street Fiction Press, 130 Touro St., Box 625, Newport, RI 01840. TEL 401-847-1067.

810   US   ISSN 0272-4359
PS580
ANOTHER CHICAGO MAGAZINE. Short title: A C M. 1977. s-a. $15. Left Field Press, 3709 N. Kenmore, Chicago, IL 60613. TEL 312-248-7665. Ed. Barry Silesky. adv.; bk.rev. circ. 1,200. (back issues avail.) **Indexed:** Ind.Amer.Per.Verse.
Description: Contains award winning literary fiction, poetry, reviews, essays.

800   US
ANSUDA MAGAZINE. 1979. biennial. $8.95 for 3 nos. Ansuda Publications, Box 158-B, Harris, IA 51345. Ed. Daniel Betz. adv. circ. 300.
Formerly: Pub.
Description: Contains socially-oriented poetry and fiction.

820   US   ISSN 0003-5319
PR1098
ANTAEUS. 1970. s-a. $30 for 4 nos. Ecco Press Ltd., 100 W. Broad St., Hopewell, NJ 08525. TEL 609-466-4748. FAX 609-466-4706. Ed. Daniel Halpern. adv.: page $500; trim 5 x 8. cum.index. nos.1-20, 21, 22-28, 59. circ. 5,000. (back issues avail.) **Indexed:** Amer.Bibl.Slavic & E.Eur.Stud., Amer.Hum.Ind., Arts & Hum.Cit.Ind., Curr.Cont., M.L.A.
—BLDSC (1542.080000); Faxon; UnCover.

800   IT   ISSN 0393-1838
ANTEREM; semestrale di ricerca letteraria. 1976. s-a. $10. Edizioni Anterem, Via Flangini 3, 37121 Verona, Italy. Ed. Flavio Ermini. circ. 2,000.

800   US
▼**ANTERIOR FICTION QUARTERLY.** 1993. 4/yr. $12. Anterior Bitewing Ltd., 7735 Brand Ave., St. Louis, MO 63135-3212. TEL 314-522-6116. Ed. Tom Bergeron.

378.198 800   US
ANTHEON. 1982. s-a. free. City University of New York, Kingsborough Community College, 2001 Oriental Blvd., Brooklyn, NY 11235. TEL 718-934-5603. circ. 500. (back issues avail.)

800   US
ANTIETAM REVIEW. 1982. s-a. $5.25. Washington County Arts Council, 7 W. Franklin St., Hagerstown, MD 21740. TEL 301-791-3132. Ed. Susanne Kass. circ. 1,600. (back issues avail.)
Description: Literary journal carrying short fiction, poetry, photography from the Washington, D.C., area writers and artists, including Pennsylvania.

LITERATURE

800   CN   ISSN 0003-5661
PN2
ANTIGONISH REVIEW. 1970. q. Can.$18. St. Francis Xavier University, Box 135, Antigonish, N.S. B2G 1C0, Canada. TEL 902-867-3962. Ed. George Sanderson. adv.; bk.rev.; illus.; index. circ. 900. (also avail. in microfiche from MML) **Indexed:** Abstr.Engl.Stud.; Arts & Hum.Cit.Ind.; Can.Lit.Ind.; Can.Per.Ind., CMI, Curr.Cont., M.L.A.
—BLDSC (1547.530000); Faxon; UnCover.
Description: Literary quarterly that publishes poetry, fiction, reviews and articles with an emphasis on liveliness.

869   CK
ANTIOQUIA. SECRETARIA DE EDUCACION Y CULTURA. REVISTA CULTURA. 1976. q. Secretaria de Educacion y Cultura, Medellin, Antioquia, Colombia. illus.

820   US   ISSN 0893-5580
PR9600
ANTIPODES; a North American journal of Australian literature. 1987. s-a. $20 to individuals (foreign $27); institutions $35 (foreign $42). American Association of Australian Literary Studies, 190 Sixth Ave., Brooklyn, NY 11217. TEL 718-789-5826. FAX 718-482-5599. Ed. Robert Ross. adv.; bk.rev.; film rev.; play rev.; bibl.; illus. circ. 500. (back issues avail.) **Indexed:** Film Lit.Ind. (1988-). **Document type:** academic/scholarly publication.
Description: Presents both fiction and poetry, and articles about Australian literature for the literary scholar and the general public.

800   AG
ANTOLOGIA; revista literaria. 1974. q. Arg.$800. Ediciones Figaro, Av. Ceballos 274, C.C. 206, 6520 Chivilcoy (BA), Argentina. Ed. Diego B. Rositto. bk.rev. circ. 2,000.

ANUARI DE FILOLOGIA. SECCIO C, LLENGUA I LITERATURA CATALANES. see *LINGUISTICS*

ANUARI DE FILOLOGIA. SECCIO F, ESTUDIOS DE LENGUA Y LITERATURA ESPANOLA. see *LINGUISTICS*

860   MX   ISSN 0543-758X
ANUARIO DE LETRAS. 1961. a. Mex.$7. Universidad Nacional Autonoma de Mexico, Instituto de Investigaciones Filologicas, Ciudad Universitaria, C.P. 04510, Mexico 21 DF, Mexico. **Indexed:** Amer.Hist.& Life, Bibl.Ling., Hisp.Amer.Per.Ind., Hist.Abstr.

800   CU
ANUARIO L L ESTUDIOS LITERARIOS. (Literatura Linguistica) 1967. a. $12 in S. America; N. America $14; elsewhere $16. (Academia de Ciencias de Cuba, Instituto de Literatura y Linguistica) Ediciones Cubanas, Obispo No. 527, Apdo. 605, Havana, Cuba. TEL 32-5556-60.
Supersedes in part: Anuario L - L (ISSN 1015-0978); Which was formerly: L - L (ISSN 0023-6209)

800 700   US   ISSN 0892-0974
L'APACHE;* an international journal of literature and art. 1986. 4/yr. (2 nos. in one). $18 (foreign $25). Box 71, Wheeler, OR 97147. TEL 619-376-3634. Ed. Kathryn Vilips. adv.; bk.rev.; illus. circ. 7,500.
Description: Focuses on short fiction, articles and poetry on the Indians or other ethnic groups.

800   US   ISSN 0890-6408
APALACHEE QUARTERLY. 1973. q. $30 to individuals; institutions $20; foreign $25. Apalachee Press, Box 20106, Tallahassee, FL 32316. Ed.Bd. adv.; bk.rev.; index, cum.index. circ. 500. **Indexed:** Access, Amer.Hum.Ind.

810   US
APOGEE. 1960. a. $1. High Point College, High Point, NC 27262. TEL 919-841-9000. Ed. Susan Warwick. circ. 400 (controlled).

APPALACHIAN JOURNAL; a regional studies review. see *HISTORY — History Of North And South America*

891.7   RU
APPARAT UPRAVLENIYA SOTSIALISTICHESKOGO GOSUDARSTVA. (In 2 parts) 1976. irreg. (Akademiya Nauk S.S.S.R., Institut Gosudarstva i Prava) Izdatel'stvo Yuridicheskaya Literatura, Moscow, Russia. Ed.Bd.

810   US   ISSN 0884-2213
APPEARANCES. 1977. a. $5. 165 W. 26th St., New York, NY 10001. TEL 212-675-3026. Ed.Bd. circ. 900.

800 792   US   ISSN 1071-6785
APPLAUSE THEATRE BOOK REVIEW & CATALOG. 1989. a. $10. Applause Theatre Book Publishers, 211 W. 71st St., New York, NY 10023. TEL 212-595-4735. FAX 212-721-2856. Ed. Glenn Young. adv.; bk.rev. circ. 50,000. **Document type:** catalog.

890   IQ   ISSN 0570-507X
AQLAM JOURNAL/PEN.* (Text in Arabic) 1964. m. ID.1.50($6) Ministry of Culture and Information, Nr au-Husor Sq., Fitruly Qasr as-Salaam Bldg., Baghdad, Iraq. Ed. Sami Mahdi. bk.rev.; bibl.; film rev, play rev.; index. circ. 15,000.

860   UY   ISSN 0066-5606
AQUI. 1983. w. Editorial Arca, Zabala 1322, Esc. 102, Montevideo, Uruguay. Dir. Francisco Jose O'Honelli.

ARAB BOOK GUIDE INTERNATIONAL. see *PUBLISHING AND BOOK TRADE*

890   GW
ARABISTISCHE TEXTE UND STUDIEN. 1986. irreg., vol.5, 1993. DM.49.80. Georg Olms Verlag, Hagentorwall 7, 31134 Hildesheim, Germany. TEL 05121-1501-0. FAX 05121-150150. (U.S. subscr. to: 111 W. 57th St., New York, NY 10019. TEL 212-757-5237) Ed. Ludwig Ammann. **Document type:** monographic series.

AL-ARABIYYA. see *LINGUISTICS*

810 820 410   GW   ISSN 0171-5410
PE3
ARBEITEN AUS ANGLISTIK UND AMERIKANISTIK. (Text in English and German) 1976. 2/yr. DM.64 to individuals; institutions DM.88. Gunter Narr Verlag, Postfach 2567, 72015 Tuebingen, Germany. TEL 07071-78091. FAX 07071-75288. Ed. Bernhard Kettemann. adv.; bk.rev. circ. 200. (back issues avail.) **Indexed:** Bibl.Engl.Lang.& Lit., Bibl.Ling., Curr.Cont., M.L.A. **Document type:** academic/scholarly publication.
—BLDSC (1585.808500); SWETS. **CCC**.

ARBEITEN UND TEXT ZUR SLAVISTIK. see *LINGUISTICS*

ARBITRIUM; Zeitschrift fuer Rezensionen zur germanistischen Literaturwissenschaft. see *LITERARY AND POLITICAL REVIEWS*

810   CN   ISSN 0705-6397
ARC; Canada's national poetry magazine. 1978. s-a. Can.$20 for 2 yrs. Box 7368, Ottawa, ON K1L 8E4, Canada. TEL 613-789-9430. Eds. Nadine McInnis, John Barton. bk.rev. circ. 600. (also avail. in microfiche from MML; back issues avail.) **Indexed:** Can.Per.Ind., CMI, Ind.Amer.Per.Verse. **Document type:** academic/scholarly publication.

830   GW   ISSN 0003-7982
PN851
ARCADIA; Zeitschrift fuer vergleichende Literaturwissenschaft. (Text mainly in German; occasionally in English, French, Italian) 1966. 3/yr. DM.130. Walter de Gruyter und Co., Genthinerstr. 13, 10785 Berlin, Germany. TEL 030-26005-0. FAX 030-26005251. TELEX 184027. (U.S. addr.: Walter de Gruyter, Inc., 200 Saw Mill Rd., Hawthorne, NY 10532) Ed.Bd. adv.; bk.rev.; bibl. **Indexed:** Arts & Hum.Cit.Ind., Can.Rev.Comp.Lit., Curr.Cont., Ind.Bk.Rev.Hum., M.L.A., RILA. **Document type:** academic/scholarly publication.
—Faxon; SWETS. **CCC**.

ARCHIV FUER DAS STUDIUM DER NEUEREN SPRACHEN UND LITERATUREN. see *LINGUISTICS*

ARCHIV FUER REFORMATIONGESCHICHTE. LITERATURBERICHT/ARCHIVE FOR REFORMATION HISTORY. LITERATURE REVIEW. see *RELIGIONS AND THEOLOGY*

840   FR   ISSN 0066-6556
ARCHIVES CLAUDELIENNES; archives des lettres modernes. (Subseries of: Archives des Lettres Modernes) 1958. irreg. price varies. Lettres Modernes, 45 rue Saint-Andre, 14123 Fleury sur Orne, France. TEL 31-84-47-06. FAX 31-84-48-09.

ARCHIVES D'HISTOIRE DOCTRINALE ET LITTERAIRE DU MOYEN AGE. see *PHILOSOPHY*

800   CN   ISSN 0066-6572
ARCHIVES DES LETTRES CANADIENNES. 1961. irreg. price varies. (University of Ottawa, Centre de Recherches de Litterature Canadienne-Francaise) Editions Fides, 165, rue Deslauriers, Ville St.-Laurent, Que. H4N 2S4, Canada. TEL 514-745-4290. FAX 514-745-4299. **Indexed:** RADAR.

809   FR   ISSN 0003-9675
ARCHIVES DES LETTRES MODERNES; etudes de critique et d'histoire litteraire. 1957. irreg. (6-10/yr.), latest no.252, 1991. 570 F. for 60 "cahiers". Lettres Modernes, 45 rue Saint-Andre, 14123 Fleury sur Orne, France. TEL 31-84-47-06. FAX 31-84-48-09. Ed. Michel J. Minard. **Indexed:** M.L.A.

860   CK   ISSN 0066-6734
ARCHIVO EPISTOLAR COLOMBIANO. 1965. irreg. no.24, 1993. price varies. Instituto Caro y Cuervo, Seccion de Publicaciones, Apdo. Aereo 51502, Bogota, Colombia.

056.1   GW   ISSN 0721-0442
ARCHIVUM CALDERONIANUM. (Text in Spanish) 1982. irreg., vol.6, 1991. price varies. Franz Steiner Verlag Wiesbaden GmbH, Birkenwaldstr. 44, 70191 Stuttgart, Germany. TEL 0711-2582-0. FAX 0711-2582290. TELEX 723636-DAZ-D. (Subscr. to: Postfach 101061, 70009 Stuttgart, Germany) Ed. Hans Flasche. **Document type:** monographic series.
—BLDSC (1659.000000).

809   IT   ISSN 0066-6807
ARCHIVUM ROMANICUM. BIBLIOTECA. SERIE 1: STORIA LETTERATURA GRAMMATICA PALEOGRAFIA. (Text in English, French, German, Italian) 1921. irreg., vol.256, 1993. price varies. Casa Editrice Leo S. Olschki, Casella Postale 66, 50100 Florence, Italy. TEL 055-6530684. FAX 055-6530214. circ. 1,000. **Document type:** academic/scholarly publication.

800   PL   ISSN 0066-6904
ARCHIWUM LITERACKIE. (Text in Polish) 1956. irreg., vol.27, 1990. price varies. (Polska Akademia Nauk, Instytut Badan Literackich) Ossolineum, Publishing House of the Polish Academy of Sciences, Rynek 9, 50-106 Wroclaw, Poland. TEL 48-71-386-25. FAX 48-71-448-103. TELEX 0712771 OSS PL. circ. 1,500. **Document type:** monographic series.
—BLDSC (1661.320000).

801   PL   ISSN 0208-7596
ARCHIWUM TLUMACZEN Z TEORII LITERATURY I METODOLOGII BADAN LITERACKICH. 1966. irreg. price varies. Katolicki Uniwersytet Lubelski, Katedra Teorii Literatury, Al. Raclawickie 14, 20-950 Lublin, Poland. Ed. Jozef Japola. index. circ. 225. **Document type:** academic/scholarly publication.

820   PK   ISSN 0254-3028
ARIEL. (Text in English) 1962. a. Rs.25($3) University of Sindh, Department of English, Jamshoro, Sindh, Pakistan. TEL 92-221-71251. Ed. K.M. Larik. bk.rev.; cum.index. circ. 500. **Indexed:** Arts & Hum.Cit.Ind., Curr.Cont., Hum.Ind. **Document type:** academic/scholarly publication.

ARIEL (ENGLISH EDITION); the Israeli review of arts and letters. see *HUMANITIES: COMPREHENSIVE WORKS*

ARISTOS; devoted to the preservation and advancement of traditional values (as opposed to modernism and post-modernism) in the arts. see *ART*

810   US   ISSN 0735-3413
ARIZONA LITERARY MAGAZINE. 1979. a. $6. Arizona Authors' Association, 3509 E. Shea Blvd., Ste. 117, Phoenix, AZ 85028-3339. TEL 602-942-4240. FAX 602-787-8638. Ed. Gerry Benninger.
Formerly (until 1982): Images and Rainbows.

ARIZONA QUARTERLY; a journal of American literature, culture and theory. see *LITERARY AND POLITICAL REVIEWS*

ARIZONA STATE UNIVERSITY. CENTER FOR ASIAN STUDIES. MONOGRAPH SERIES. see *ORIENTAL STUDIES*

839 439 DK ISSN 0107-1475
ARNAMAGNAEAN INSTITUTE AND DICTIONARY. BULLETIN. 1964. biennial. free. Arnamagnaean Institute and Arnamagnaean Dictionary, Njalsgade 76, DK-2300 Copenhagen S, Denmark. TEL 45-31-54-22-11. **Document type:** bulletin.
Formerly (until 1975): Arnamagnaean Institute. Bulletin (ISSN 0066-7765)

800 US
ARNAZELLA. 1976. a. $3.50. 3000 Landerholm Circle, S.E., Bellevue, WA 98007. TEL 206-641-3064. Ed. Jeffrey White. circ. 400. (back issues avail.) **Document type:** bulletin.
Description: Contains poetry, fiction, novels, plays and satire.

800 US ISSN 1043-5778
ARS INTERPRETANDI/ART OF INTERPRETATION. irreg. Peter Lang Publishing, Inc., 62 W. 45th St., 4th Fl., New York, NY 10036. TEL 212-302-6740. FAX 212-302-7574. Ed. Raymond Gay-Crosier. **Document type:** academic/scholarly publication.

800 851 IT ISSN 0393-8263
ARSENALE; trimestrale di letteratura. 1984. q. L.20000($17.50) Edizioni Il Labirinto, Via Leonori 67, 00147 Rome, Italy. Ed. Gianfranco Palmery. adv.; bk.rev. circ. 3,000. (back issues avail.)

ART AND CULTURE. see *ART*

800 700 US
▼**ART & UNDERSTANDING**; the international magazine of literature and art about AIDS. 1991. 6/yr. $22 (Canada $32; elsewhere $42). Art & Understanding, Inc., 25 Monroe St., Ste. 205, New York, NY 12210. TEL 518-426-9010; 800-841-8707. FAX 518-436-5354. Ed. David Waggoner. adv. circ. 40,000.

ART FOR HUMANITY. see *ART*

ART INTERNATIONAL. see *ART*

810 US
ART - LIFE. 1981. 11/yr. $450. Art - Life Limited Editions, Box 23020, Ventura, CA 93002. TEL 805-648-4331. Ed. Gayle Jansen Beede. circ. 800.
Description: Publishes well-crafted poems and short prose.

ARTES. see *ART*

800 US ISSN 0196-691X
ARTFUL DODGE. 1979. a. $10 to individuals; institutions $16. Artful Dodge Publications, Department of English, The College of Wooster, Wooster, OH 44691. TEL 216-262-8353. Ed. Daniel Bourne. adv.; bk.rev.; illus. circ. 1,000. (back issues avail.) **Indexed:** Amer.Hum.Ind.
Description: Publishes new American fiction and poetry, and translations from Eastern Europe and elsewhere. Includes interviews.

840 FR ISSN 0180-9385
ARTHUR RIMBAUD. 1972. a. Lettres Modernes, 45 rue Saint-Andre, 14123 Fleury sur Orne, France. TEL 31-84-47-06. FAX 31-84-48-09. Ed. Louis Forrestier. bk.rev. (back issues avail.)

800 US ISSN 0890-4944
ARTHURIAN INTERPRETATIONS. 1968. 2/yr. $10 (foreign $12.50). Memphis State University, Department of English, Memphis, TN 38152. TEL 901-678-4591. Ed. Henry H. Peyton III. adv.; bk.rev. circ. 500. (back issues avail.) **Indexed:** M.L.A. **Document type:** academic/scholarly publication.
Supersedes (in 1986): Interpretations (ISSN 0196-903X)
Description: Multi-disciplinary journal of Arthurian studies from the beginning to the twentieth century.

800 US ISSN 0261-9946
ARTHURIAN LITERATURE. 1970. a. Boydell & Brewer Inc., Box 41026, Rochester, NY 14604. TEL 716-275-0419. FAX 716-271-8778. **Document type:** academic/scholarly publication.
—BLDSC (1734.073300).

800 US ISSN 0261-9814
ARTHURIAN STUDIES. 1981. irreg., latest no.29. Boydell & Brewer Inc., Box 41026, Rochester, NY 14604. TEL 716-275-0419. FAX 716-271-8778. **Document type:** academic/scholarly publication.
—BLDSC (1734.073400).

ARTPAPER. see *ART*

800 700 US
ARTS INTERNATIONAL. 1981. s-a. $20. Communications International (Washington), Box 53395, Washington, DC 20009. TEL 202-347-4145. FAX 202-328-8724. Ed. H. Hamod. adv. **Document type:** newsletter.
Formerly: Third World News.

890 II
ARUN. (Text in Hindi) 1972. m. Rs.8. Arun Group of Publications, Box 27, Civil Lines, Moradabad, India. adv.; illus.

820.9 GH ISSN 0855-000X
ASEMKA; literary journal. (Text in English or French) 1974. a. $10 to individuals; institutions $20. University of Cape Coast, c/o Dept. of French, Cape Coast, Ghana. TEL 2441-9. Ed. Y.S. Boafo. adv.; bk.rev. circ. 500. **Indexed:** M.L.A. **Document type:** academic/scholarly publication.
Description: Contains studies in literature (mostly African) and languages.
Refereed Serial

850 IT
L'ASINO D'ORO. 1990. s-a. L.42000 (foreign L.56000) (effective 1993). Editore Loescher, Via Vittorio Amedeo II, 18, 10121 Turin, Italy. TEL 011-5624622. FAX 011-5625822. (back issues avail.)
Description: Contains comparative literary studies.

020 US ISSN 1051-3299
ASSISTANT EDITOR; original short articles, fillers, and clip art for library newsletter. 1991. q. $75 (Canada $78; elsewhere $90). Chris Olson & Associates, 857 Twin Harbor Dr., Ste. 1300, Arnold, MD 21012-1027. TEL 410-647-6708. FAX 410-647-0415. (also avail. in diskette format) **Document type:** newsletter.

869 BL
ASSOCIACAO PARAENSE DE ESCRITORES. REVISTA. 1986. s-a. Associacao Paraense de Escritores, Trav. Frutuoso Guimaraes 756, 66020 Campina, Belem, PA, Brazil. Ed. Ronaldo Bandeira.

808 US
ASSOCIATED WRITING PROGRAMS AWARD FOR CREATIVE NONFICTION. 1986. a. price varies. University of Georgia Press, 330 Research Dr., Athens, GA 30602-4901. TEL 706-369-6130. FAX 706-369-6131.

840 FR ISSN 0066-8893
ASSOCIATION DES AMIS D'ALFRED DE VIGNY. BULLETIN. 1968. a. 100 F. membership. Association des Amis d'Alfred de Vigny, 6 av. Constant-Coquelin, 75007 Paris, France. TEL 42-73-12-86. Eds. Andre Jarry, C. Lefranc. adv.; bk.rev. circ. 500. (also avail. in microfiche) **Document type:** bulletin.

800 II ISSN 0066-9083
ASSOCIATION FOR COMMONWEALTH LITERATURE AND LANGUAGE STUDIES. BULLETIN. 1967. s-a. Association for Commonwealth Literature and Language Studies, Indian Branch, Department of English, University of Mysore, Manasagangotri, Mysore 570006, India. **Document type:** bulletin.
Formerly: A C L A L S Newsheet.

ASSOCIATION INTERNATIONALE D'ETUDES DU SUD-EST EUROPEEN. BULLETIN. see *HISTORY — History Of Europe*

840 FR ISSN 0571-5865
PC2012
ASSOCIATION INTERNATIONALE DES ETUDES FRANCAISES. CAHIERS. 1951. a. 150 F. Association Internationale des Etudes Francaises - International Association of French Studies, 11 place Marcelin-Berthelot, 75005 Paris, France. Ed. Sylvain Menant. circ. 1,000. **Document type:** academic/scholarly publication.
—SWETS.

944 FR ISSN 0004-6116
ASTRADO; revue bilingue de Provence. (Text in French, Provencal) 1965. a. 140 F.($30) per no. (effective 1988). Astrado Prouvencalo, 7 rue des Fauvettes, 13130 Berre L'Etang, France. Ed. M. Courty. bk.rev.; illus. circ. 1,000. **Indexed:** M.L.A. **Document type:** academic/scholarly publication.
Description: Centers on one theme every year and includes poems, short-stories, scholarly studies and papers in anthropology, linguistics, literature and history.

AT RANDOM; books and bookpeople from Random House. see *PUBLISHING AND BOOK TRADE*

800 IT
ATALANTA. 1976. irreg., no.2, 1977. price varies. Giardini Editori e Stampatori, Via Santa Bibbiana 28, 56100 Pisa, Italy. TEL 050-502531. Eds. S.G. Mancini, M. Pagnini. **Indexed:** Biol.Abstr.

ATENEO VENETO; rivista di scienze, lettere ed arti. see *SCIENCES: COMPREHENSIVE WORKS*

869 BL
ATENEU ANGRENSE DE LETRAS E ARTES. REVISTA. 1973. q. Cz.$1200. Ateneu Angrense de Letras e Artes, Avda. Raul Pompeia, Casa de Cultura "Brasil dos Reis", 23900 Angra dos Reis, RJ, Brazil. Dir. Alipio Mendes. adv.; bk.rev.; bibl.; index. circ. 5,000. (back issues avail.)

ATHANOR. see *ART*

839.31 NE ISSN 0926-3195
ATLANTIS. 1990. irreg. price varies. Editions Rodopi B.V., Keizersgracht 302-304, 1016 EX Amsterdam, Netherlands. TEL 31-20-6227507. FAX 31-20-6380948. (In N. America: 233 Peachtree St., N.E., Ste. 404, Atlanta, GA 30303-1504. TEL 800-225-3998. FAX 404-522-7116) Eds. Andre Hanou, Karel Bostoen. (back issues avail.) **Document type:** academic/scholarly publication, monographic series.

052 NR ISSN 0004-7007
ATOKA; Yoruba photoplay series. (Text in Yoruba) 1967. s-m. 17.50 n. West African Book Publishers Ltd., Box 3445, Lagos, Nigeria. Ed. Eniola Adeyemi. adv.; illus. circ. 83,000.

860 BL
ATRAVES. 1976. irreg. Livraria Duas Cidades, Rua Bento Freitas 158, 01220 Sao Paulo SP, Brazil. Ed.Bd. illus.

800 US ISSN 1063-0244
▼**AUDIOFILE.** 1992. m. $48. 37 Silver St., Box 109, Portland, ME 04112-0109. TEL 207-774-7563. FAX 207-775-3744. Ed. Robin F. Whitten. adv.; bk.rev.; illus. circ. 1,500. **Document type:** newsletter.
Description: Publishes feature articles and supplementary information for audio collections, libraries, book stores, audio listeners.

806 US
AUGUST DERLETH SOCIETY. NEWSLETTER. 1977. 4/yr. $10 membership. August Derleth Society, Box 481, Sauk City, WI 53583. TEL 608-643-3242. Ed. Kay Price. adv.; bk.rev. circ. 450. **Document type:** newsletter.
Description: Covers the life and writings of August Derleth, and artists and writers associated with him, society activities, and bibliographic items of interest.

AULA. see *SOCIAL SCIENCES: COMPREHENSIVE WORKS*

830 709 GW ISSN 0341-1230
AURORA; Jahrbuch der Eichendorff-Gesellschaft. (Text in German; summaries in English and German) 1953. a. price varies. Jan Thorbecke Verlag GmbH und Co., Postfach 546, 72482 Sigmaringen, Germany. TEL 07571-728-100. FAX 07571-728-280. Ed.Bd. bk.rev.; bibl.; illus.; index. circ. 1,000. (reprint service avail. from KTO) **Indexed:** M.L.A. **Document type:** bulletin.

839.7 SW ISSN 0348-5404
AURORA (SIGTUNA). 1978-1979; resumed 1982. q. Romantiska Foerbundet, c/o K. Salin, Laangsjoehoejden 87, Skallaasen 944, S-125 31 Aelvsjoe, Sweden.

LITERATURE

830 709   GW   ISSN 0171-6530
AURORA-BUCHREIHE. 1974. irreg. price varies. Jan Thorbecke Verlag GmbH und Co., Postfach 546, 72482 Sigmaringen, Germany. TEL 07571-728-100. FAX 07571-728-280. Ed.Bd. circ. 1,000. **Document type:** monographic series.

809 700   GW
AUSGABE; ein Literatur- und Kunstmagazin. 1976. a. DM.20. Armin Hundertmark, Ed.& Pub., Bruesselerstr. 29, 50674 Cologne, Germany. TEL 0221-237944. FAX 0221-249146. adv. **Document type:** bulletin.

800   CN   ISSN 0843-5049
PR9600
AUSTRALIAN AND NEW ZEALAND STUDIES IN CANADA. 1989. s-a. $15. University of Western Ontario, Department of English, London, Ont. N6A 3K7, Canada. TEL 519-679-2111. FAX 519-661-3292. Ed. Thomas E. Tausky. adv. circ. 150.
—Faxon.
Description: Devoted to the study of literature and the related arts in Australia and New Zealand.

830 430   SZ
AUSTRALIAN AND NEW ZEALAND STUDIES IN GERMAN LANGUAGE AND LITERATURE. (Text in English and German) 1971. irreg., vol.17, 1992. 44.60 SFr. Verlag Peter Lang AG, Jupiterstr. 15, CH-3000 Bern 15, Switzerland. TEL 031-9411122. FAX 031-9411131. TELEX 912651-PELA-CH. Eds. Gerhard Schulz, John Asher. circ. 400. (back issues avail.) **Document type:** monographic series.

820   AT   ISSN 1034-0785
AUSTRALIAN BOOK COLLECTOR. 1987. m. Aus.$42. Ross Burnet, Ed. & Pub., P.O. Box 2, Uralla, N.S.W. 2358, Australia. TEL 067-78-4682. FAX 067-78-4516. adv.; bk.rev.; bibl.; illus.; circ. 1,000 (paid). (back issues avail.) **Document type:** consumer publication, trade publication.
Former titles (until 1989): Bookman's Monthly (ISSN 1031-1556) & Book Market.
Description: For the antiquarian trade and collectors.

840 440   AT   ISSN 0004-9468
PQ1
AUSTRALIAN JOURNAL OF FRENCH STUDIES. (Text in English, French) 1964. 3/yr. Aus.$40 (foreign $40). Monash University, Department of Romance Languages, Clayton, Vic. 3168, Australia. TEL 61-3-565-2217. FAX 61-3-565-2137. TELEX AA32691. Ed. Wallace Kirsop. bk.rev.; bibl.; stat.; index. circ. 530. **Indexed:** Amer.Hist.& Life, Arts & Hum.Cit.Ind., Aus.P.A.I.S., Br.Hum.Ind., Can.Rev.Comp.Lit, Curr.Cont., Hist.Abstr., M.L.A. **Document type:** academic/scholarly publication.
—Faxon; UnCover; SWETS.

820   AT   ISSN 0004-9697
PR9400
AUSTRALIAN LITERARY STUDIES. 1963. s-a. Aus.$27.50 to individuals (foreign Aus.$33); institutions Aus.$38.50 (foreign Aus.$40. (University of Queensland, Department of English) University of Queensland Press, P.O. Box 42, St. Lucia, Qld. 4067, Australia. TEL 07-3652740. FAX 07-3651988. (Subscr. to: University of Queensland, P.O. Box 42, St. Lucia, Qld. 4067, Australia) Ed. L.T. Hergenhan. adv.; bk.rev.; bibl.; cum.index every 2 yrs. circ. 1,000. (also avail. in microform from UMI; reprint service avail from UMI) **Indexed:** Abstr.Engl.Stud., Arts & Hum.Cit.Ind., Aus.P.A.I.S., Curr.Cont., Gdlns., Ind.Bk.Rev.Hum., M.L.A., So.Pac.Per.Ind.
—BLDSC (1813.900000); Faxon; UnCover; UMI.

800 920   NE   ISSN 0921-2531
AUSTRALIAN PLAYWRIGHTS; a series of monographs and video programmes. 1987-1991; resumed 199? irreg., vol.5, 1993. Editions Rodopi B.V., Keizersgracht 302-304, 1016 EX Amsterdam, Netherlands. TEL 31-20-6227507. FAX 31-20-6380948. (In N. America: 233 Peachtree St., N.E., Ste. 404, Atlanta, GA 30303-1504. TEL 800-225-3998) (Co-publisher: Humanities Press International Inc.) Ed. Otrum Zuber-Skerritt. play rev.; bibl. **Document type:** monographic series.
Description: Promotes a better understanding of Australian drama through overviews of particular playwrights and their works. Most include videos of interviews with the playwrights.

800   AT   ISSN 0810-4468
AUSTRALIAN SHORT STORIES. 1982. q. Aus.$30($38) Pascoe Publishing Pty. Ltd., P.O. Box 42, Apolo Bay, Vic. 3233, Australia. TEL 052-379-227. FAX 052-376-559. Eds. Bruce Pascoe, Lyn Harwood. adv. circ. 12,000. (back issues avail.)
—CCC.
Description: Contemporary stories from Australia and the world.

800   US   ISSN 1054-058X
AUSTRIAN LITERATURE. (Text in English, German) irreg. Peter Lang Publishing, Inc., 62 W. 45th St., 4th Fl., New York, NY 10036. TEL 212-302-6704. FAX 212-302-7574. Ed. Harry Zohn. **Document type:** academic/scholarly publication.
Description: Provides critical evaluations of Austrian authors, works, currents, or figures from the Middle Ages to the present.

070 800   UK   ISSN 0005-0628
PN101
AUTHOR. 1890. q. £20 non-members. Society of Authors, 84 Drayton Gardens, London SW10 9SB, England. TEL 071-373-6642. FAX 071-373-5768. Ed. Derek Parker. adv.; bk.rev. circ. 6,000. (also avail. in microfilm from UMI; reprint service avail. from UMI) **Indexed:** Br.Hum.Ind. **Document type:** bulletin.
—BLDSC (1825.460000); UMI.

800 340   US
AUTHORS GUILD BULLETIN. 1914. q. membership only. Authors Guild, 330 W. 42nd St., 29th Fl., New York, NY 10036-6902. FAX 212-564-5363. bk.rev. circ. 7,500. **Document type:** trade publication.
Description: Covers business and legal matters of interest to authors.

070 800   US   ISSN 0005-0660
AUTHORSHIP. 1943. bi-m. $18. National Writers Club, 1450 S. Havana, Ste. 424, Aurora, CO 80012. TEL 303-751-7844. FAX 303-751-8593. Ed. Sandy Whelchel. adv.; bk.rev.; charts. circ. 4,000. **Document type:** trade publication.
Description: Discusses creative and compositional techniques.

869   BL
AUTORES AFRICANOS. 1982. irreg. Editora Atica, S.A., Rua Barao de Iguape, 110, Caixa Postal 8656, Sao Paulo, Brazil.

800 900 028.5   US   ISSN 0741-1790
AVALON TO CAMELOT;* issued quarterly on matters Arthurian. 1983. q. $20. Avalon to Camelot, Inc., 4717 N. Lincoln Ave., 3rd Fl., Chicago, IL 60625-2009. Ed. Alan C. Lupack. adv.; bk.rev.; film rev.; bibl.; charts; illus. circ. 2,000. (back issues avail.) **Indexed:** M.L.A.

800 700   NE   ISSN 0921-2515
AVANT GARDE; cahiers interdisciplinaires et internationaux des arts et litteratures au XXe siecle. (Text in English, French, German) 1988. 3/yr. price varies. Editions Rodopi B.V., Keizersgracht 302-304, 1016 EX Amsterdam, Netherlands. TEL 31-20-6227507. FAX 31-20-6380948. (In N. America: 233 Peachtree St., N.E., Ste. 404, Atlanta, GA 30303-1504. TEL 800-225-3998. FAX 404-52-7116) Ed. Fernand Drijkoningen. **Document type:** academic/scholarly publication, monographic series.
—BLDSC (1837.114000); SWETS.
Description: Includes information on research in avant-garde modernism and post-modernism in literature and other arts.

840   FR   ISSN 0067-2610
AVANT-SIECLE. 1967. irreg., no.15, 1978. Lettres Modernes, 45 rue Saint-Andre, 14123 Fleury sur Orne, France. TEL 31-84-47-06. FAX 31-84-48-09. (Dist. outside France by: Librairie Droz S.A., 11, rue Massot, CH-1211 Geneva 12, Switzerland) Ed. Louis Forestier.
Description: Presents modern literature of Western and Eastern Europe. From the "Editions 'Lettres Modernes'."

808   US   ISSN 0899-3750
AVEC; a journal of writing. 1988. s-a. $12. Syntax Projects for the Arts, Box 1059, Penngrove, CA 94951. TEL 707-762-2370. FAX 707-769-0880. Ed. Cydney Chadwick. adv. circ. 1,000. (back issues avail.)
Description: Focuses on experimental poetry and fiction from around the world.

800   UY   ISSN 0067-2637
AVES DEL ARCA.* irreg. Editorial Arca, Colonia 1263, Montevideo, Uruguay.

057.1   RU
AVRORA. 1969. m. Russian Federation Unions of Writers, Ul. Khalturina 4, 191065 St. Petersburg, Russia. TEL (095) 312-13-23. Ed. E. Shevelyov.

059.927   TS
AWRAQ. 1983. w. Al- Waraqun Printing, Publishing and Distribution, P.O. Box 5015, Abu Dhabi, United Arab Emirates. TEL 47700. TELEX 22453 EM. Ed. Hallah Hamid Matouq. circ. 5,000. **Indexed:** Bibl.Ling.
Description: Publishes cultural and literary news, stories, poetry, and analysis of Gulf and Arab world events.

808 700 778.534   US
AXE FACTORY REVIEW. 1985. a. $5. (Axe Factory Center for the Arts) Axe Factory Publications, Box 11186, Philadelphia, PA 19136. TEL 215-331-7389. Eds. Louis McKee, Joesph Farley. adv.; bk.rev. circ. 600.

808 839.7   SW   ISSN 0282-1575
AXPLOCK. 1979-1989; resumed 1991. irreg. (every 2-3 yrs.). Vadsbo Skrivarklubb, c/o I. Svensson, S. Nolgaarden, S-540 15 Vaering, Sweden.

810   US
AZOREAN EXPRESS. 1985. s-a. $6.75 per no. Seven Buffaloes Press, Box 249, Big Timber, MT 59011. Ed. Art Cuelho. circ. 500.

800 070.5   CN   ISSN 0847-7728
B C BOOKWORLD. 1987. q. Can.$10.70 for 5 issues; free to qualified personnel. 3516 W. 13th Ave., Vancouver, BC V6R 2S3, Canada. TEL 604-736-4011. FAX 604-736-4011. Ed. Russell Kelly. adv.; bk.rev.; illus. circ. 45,000. **Document type:** newspaper.

810 811   US   ISSN 0897-5515
PS580
B-CITY. 1983. a. $5. B-City Press, Inc., 517 N. 4th St., DeKalb, IL 60115-3350. TEL 312-871-6175. Ed. Connie Deanovich. circ. 250. (back issues avail.) **Document type:** abstracting/indexing.
Description: Presents modern American poetry and literature.

B L A C. (Black Literature and Arts Congress) see **ETHNIC INTERESTS**

B U M. (Boerne og Ungdoms-Litteratur Magasinet) see **CHILDREN AND YOUTH — For**

BABEL; revue internationale de la traduction - international journal of translation. see **LINGUISTICS**

800 700   US
BABY SPLIT BOWLING NEWS. 1990. q. $16. B S B N Publishing, Box 7205, Minneapolis, MN 55407. Ed. Chilly Most.
Description: Contains liteerature reviews, fictions, non-fictions, and graphis.

BACK BRAIN RECLUSE; new speculative fiction. see **LITERATURE — Science Fiction, Fantasy, Horror**

800 700   YU   ISSN 0005-3880
BAGDALA; mesecni list za knjizevnost, umetnost i kulturu. (Text in Serbo-Croatian) 1959. m. 100 din. Zakiceva 3, Krusevac, Yugoslavia. TEL 037-33-409. Ed. Milos Petrovic. bk.rev. circ. 1,000.

400 800   BX   ISSN 0005-3988
PL5101
BAHANA. 1966. m. B.$1.50($0.75) Ministry of Culture, Youth and Sports, Language and Literature Bureau - Dewan Bahasa dan Pustaka, Jalan Elizabeth II, Bandar Seri Begawan 2604, Brunei Darussalam. FAX 02-241817. TELEX BU-2774. Ed.Bd. adv.; bk.rev.; illus. circ. 3,000.

895.1   CC
BAIHUA YUAN. (Text in Chinese) m. Zhengzhou Shi Wenlian, No. 12, Yihe Lu, Zhengzhou, Henan 450007, People's Republic of China. TEL 449795. Ed. Wang Baomin.

895.1   CC
BAIHUA ZHOU. (Text in Chinese) bi-m. Baihua Zhou Wenyi Chubanshe, No.5, Xinwei Lu, Nanchang, Jiangxi 330002, People's Republic of China. TEL 333180. Ed. Lan Lisheng.

BAIJIA ZUOWEN ZHIDAO. see EDUCATION

BALSA DE LA MEDUSA. see ART

800 US ISSN 0733-0308
BAMBOO RIDGE; the Hawaii writers' quarterly. 1978. q. $16. Bamboo Ridge Press, Box 61781, Honolulu, HI 96839-1781. TEL 808-599-4823. Eds. Eric Chock, Darrell Lum. adv.; bk.rev. circ. 350. (back issues avail.) Indexed: Amer.Hum.Ind.
 Description: Fosters the appreciation, understanding, and creation of literary, visual, and performing arts by or about Hawaii's people.

491.1 891.1 BG
BAMLA EKADEMI GABESHANA PATRIKA. (Former name of issuing body: Bengali Academy) (Text in Bengali) 1957. q. Bangla Academy, Burdwan House, Dhaka 1000, Bangladesh. TEL 2-500131. Indexed: Apic.Abstr.
 Supersedes (1972): Patrika (ISSN 0522-8980)
 Description: Covers Bengali literature and culture.

808.8 US
▼BANAL PROBE. 1992. q. $6. Oyster Publications, Box 4333, Austin, TX 78765. TEL 512-458-8628. Ed. Drucilla B. Blood. circ. 500. (tabloid format; back issues avail.) Document type: newsletter.

820 890 II
BANASTHALI PATRIKA. (Alternate issues in English and Hindi) vol.6, 1971. q. Rs.25($8) Banasthali-Vidyapith, Jaipur, Rajasthan, India. Ed. Rameshwar Gupta. bk.rev.; bibl. circ. 1,000. Indexed: Bibl.Engl.Lang.& Lit., M.L.A.

860 EC
▼BANDA LITERARIA. 1992. s-a.? Red Cultural, Casilla 17-01-312, Quito, Ecuador.

820 UK ISSN 0306-8404
BANDERSNATCH. 1973. irreg. membership. Lewis Carroll Society, 69 Ashby Rd., Woodville, Swadlincote, Derbyshire DE11 7BZ, England. (Subscr. addr.: c/o Roger E. Allen, 146 Headstone Ln., Harrow, Middlesex HA2 6JT, England) Ed. Alfreda Blanchard. bk.rev.; circ. 350 (controlled). Document type: bulletin.

820 BG
BANGLA ACADEMY JOURNAL. (Text in English) vol.4, 1973. s-a. Tk.4($2) Bangla Academy, Burdwan House, Dhaka 1000, Bangladesh. TEL 2-500131. Ed. Mazharul Islam. bk.rev.
 Supersedes: Bengali Academy Journal.
 Description: Discusses literary and cultural topics.

BAOGAO WENXUE/REPORTAGE LITERATURE. see JOURNALISM

850 IT
BARATARIA. 1989. irreg., no.7, 1992. price varies. Liguori Editore s.r.l., Via Mezzocannone, 19, 80134 Naples, Italy. TEL 081-5527139. Eds. Mario DiPinto, Laura Dolfi. Document type: monographic series.

840 700 FR
BARBACANE; revue des pierres et des hommes. vol.11, 1975. a. 40 F. Cercle Culturel et Artisanal de Bonaguil, Chateau de Bonaguil, Saint Front sur Lemance, 47500 Fumel, France. Ed. Max Pons. adv.; bk.rev. circ. 500.

820 UK ISSN 0307-3408
BARD. 1975. s-a. £3($6) Shakespearean Authorship Trust, 11 Old Square, Lincoln's Inn, London WC2A 3TS, England. Ed.Bd. adv.; bk.rev.; bibl. circ. 400.
 Supersedes: Shakespearean Authorship Review.

800 FR ISSN 0067-4222
BAROQUE; revue internationale. 1963. irreg., latest vol.12, 1985. 180 F. (Centre International de Synthese du Baroque) Editions Cocagne, 30 rue de la Banque, 82000 Montauban, France. TEL 63-63-05-67. (back issues avail.) Indexed: M.L.A.
 —SWETS.
 Former titles (until 1966): Journees Internationales d'Etude du Baroque. Actes; (until 1965): Journees Internationales d'Etudes du Baroque.

BASIS; majalah bulanan kebudayaan umum/monthly for culture in general. see ART

830 430 GW ISSN 0067-4508
BASLER STUDIEN ZUR DEUTSCHEN SPRACHE UND LITERATUR. 1954. irreg., vol.66, 1993. Francke Verlag GmbH, Postfach 2560, 72015 Tuebingen, Germany. TEL 07071-78091. FAX 07071-75288. Ed.Bd. Document type: monographic series, academic/scholarly publication.

813 US ISSN 0005-6677
PS3503.A923
BAUM BUGLE. 1957. 3/yr. $15. International Wizard of Oz Club, Inc., 220 N. 11th St., Escanaba, MI 49829. bk.rev.; bibl.; illus. Indexed: M.L.A.
 —UnCover.
 Description: Focuses on the Land of Oz, L. Frank Baum and its other creators, books, films, etc.

491.8 GW
BAUSTEINE ZUR GESCHICHTE DER LITERATUR BEI DEN SLAWEN. irreg., vol.27, 1986. DM.138. Wilhelm Schmitz Verlag, Staufenbergerweg 22, 35457 Lollar, Germany. TEL 06406-2324. Document type: monographic series.

800 296 IS ISSN 0302-8178
PJ5161.A1
BAY ZIKH.* 1972. Komitet far Yidisher Kultur in Yisroel, 228 Bnei Ephraim St., Tel Aviv, Israel.

BAYERISCHE STAATSBIBLIOTHEK. NEW CONTENTS SLAVISTICS. see BIBLIOGRAPHIES

BAZMAVEP. see HISTORY — History Of The Near East

BEAKEN. see LINGUISTICS

800 920 US ISSN 0882-4428
BEAN HOME NEWSLETTER. 1984. q. $12 for two yrs. Friends of Freddy, 5A Laurel Hill Rd., Greenbelt, MD 20770. Ed. Alladine Joroff. circ. 300. (back issues avail.) Document type: newsletter.
 Description: Contains news of the Friends of Freddy and critical evaluations of the writing of Walter R. Brooks.

BEBOP DRAWING CLUB BOOK. see ART

806 US ISSN 0732-2224
PR6003.E282
BECKETT CIRCLE/CERCLE DE BECKETT. 1978. s-a. $12. Samuel Beckett Society, Department of English, Tallahassee, FL 32306. FAX 904-644-0811. Ed. Karen Laughlin. adv.; bk.rev.; play rev.; bibl. circ. 350. (back issues avail.) Document type: newsletter.

891.4 II ISSN 0005-769X
BEDUIN. (Text in Bengali) 1966. a. Rs.12. Rani Suhasini Roy, Tamluk Raj House, Tamluk, Midnapore, West Bengal, India. Ed. Bhabanee Mukhopadhyay.

800 IS ISSN 0334-973X
BE'EMMET; a miscellany of studies, teaching and research in children's literature. 1987. s-a. IS.30. Beit Berl College, Yemima Center for Study and Teaching of Children's Literature, Beit Berl, Doar Beit Berl 44905, Israel. TEL 972-52-906400. FAX 972-52-454104. Ed. Shlomo Har-el. bk.rev.; bibl. circ. 1,000. Document type: academic/scholarly publication.

840 BE
LE BEGUE; la premiere revue facultaire. irreg. (7-8/yr.). 350 Fr. Maison de Droit de Louvain la Neuve, Place Montesquieu, 2 Bte. 45, 1348 Louvain La Neuve, Belgium. TEL 010-47-46-42. Ed. Benoit De Nayer.

895.1 CC ISSN 0476-031X
BEIFANG WENXUE/NORTHERN LITERATURE. (Text in Chinese) 1958. m. Y18($61.20) 16, Yaojing Jie, Nangang, Harbin, Heilongjiang 150006, People's Republic of China. (Dist. outside China by: China International Book Trading Corp., P.O. Box 399, Beijing, P.R.C.; Dist. in US by: China Books & Periodicals, Inc., 2929 24th St., San Francisco, CA 94110. TEL 415-282-2994) Eds. Han Mengjie, Li Fuliang.

895.1 CC
BEIJI GUANG/NORTHERN LIGHTS. (Text in Chinese) bi-m. Beiji Guang Bianjibu - Beiji Guang Magazine, Shengli Lu, Jia Ge Da Qi, Heilongjiang 165000, People's Republic of China. TEL 3968. (Dist. outside China by: China Publications Foreign Trade Corp., P.O. Box 782, Beijing, P.R.C.) Ed. Zhang Lianrong.

LITERATURE 3601

895.1 CC ISSN 0257-0262
BEIJING WENXUE/BEIJING LITERATURE. (Text in Chinese) 1950. m. $61.20. Beijing Wenxue Yuekanshe, Beijing, People's Republic of China. TEL 6031108. (Dist. in US by: China Books & Periodicals, Inc., 2929 24th St., San Francisco, CA 94110. TEL 415-282-2994) Ed. Hao Ran. adv. contact: Weiping Zhong.

BEITRAEGE ZUR DEUTSCHEN PHILOLOGIE. see LINGUISTICS

BEITRAEGE ZUR GESCHICHTE DER DEUTSCHEN SPRACHE UND LITERATUR. see LINGUISTICS

479 GW ISSN 0067-5202
BEITRAEGE ZUR ROMANISCHEN PHILOLOGIE DES MITTELALTERS. 1968. irreg. price varies. Wilhelm Fink Verlag, Ohmstr. 5, 80802 Munich, Germany. Eds. Hans-Wilhelm Klein, Ernstpeter Ruhe. Indexed: Arts & Hum.Cit.Ind., Curr.Cont., M.L.A. Document type: academic/scholarly publication.

895.1 CC
BEIYUE FENG. (Text in Chinese) bi-m. Beiyue Wenyi Chubanshe, 46 Jiefang Lu, Taiyuan, Shanxi 030002, People's Republic of China. TEL 224323. Ed. Yang Wenbin.

800 305.4 070.5 US ISSN 0884-2957
PN471
BELLES LETTRES; a review of books by women. 1985. q. $20 to individuals; students $15; institutions $40. 11151 Captain's Walk Ct., N. Potomac, MD 20878. TEL 301-294-0278. FAX 301-294-0023. (Subscr. to: 615 Anderson Ct., Satellite Beach, FL 32937) Ed. Janet Mulaney. adv.: B&W page $400. bk.rev.; index. circ. 5,000. (also avail. in microform from UMI; back issues avail.) Indexed: Alt.Press Ind., Bk.Rev.Ind. (1988-), Child.Bk.Rev.Ind. (1988-), Wom.Stud.Abstr. (1985-). Document type: consumer publication.
 —BLDSC (1890.357C00); UnCover.
 Description: Founded to preserve, promote, and celebrate women's writing. Reviews scholarly and popular titles and includes interviews, rediscoveries, and retrospectives.

800 US ISSN 1066-2332
THE BELLETRIST REVIEW. 1991. s-a. $12. Marmarc Publications, 17 Farmington Ave., Ste. 290, Plainville, CT 06062. TEL 203-747-2058. Eds. Marlene Dube, Marc F. Saegaert. adv. circ. 500.

810 US ISSN 0734-2934
PS501
BELLINGHAM REVIEW. 1977. 2/yr. $5. Signpost Press, Inc., 1007 Queen St., Bellingham, WA 98226. TEL 206-734-9781. Ed. Knute Skinner. adv.; bk.rev.; illus. circ. 800. Indexed: A.I.P.P.
 Description: Covers the literary arts. Includes poetry, short fiction and drama, drawing, and photographs.

800 US ISSN 0887-4115
BELLOWING ARK; a literary tabloid. 1984. bi-m. $15. Bellowing Ark Society, Box 45637, Seattle, WA 98145. TEL 206-545-8302. Ed. Robert R. Ward. circ. 1,000. (tabloid format; back issues avail.) Indexed: Ind.Amer.Per.Verse.
 Description: Covers material which portrays the human condition as a positive process.

800 US ISSN 0883-9131
BELOIT FICTION JOURNAL. 1985. 2/yr. $9. Box 11, Beloit College, Beloit, WI 53511. TEL 608-363-2308. Ed. Clint McCown. circ. 750. (back issues avail.) Document type: academic/scholarly publication.
 Description: Contains contemporary short stories on any theme or subject, up to fifty pages in length.

891.4 II ISSN 0005-8815
BENGALI LITERATURE.* vol.4, 1970. q. Rs.8($2) 53 Bidhan Palli, Jadavpur, Calcutta 32, India. Ed. Ashis Sanyal. adv.; bk.rev.; bibl; film rev.; play rev.; index. circ. 2,100.

800 CN ISSN 0067-5733
BENT. (Text in English) 1969. irreg., no.7, 1971. Can.$0.25. 1111 Bewdley Avenue, Victoria, B. C., Canada. Ed. Byrd Lukinuk. adv. circ. 300.

LITERATURE

839.7 SW ISSN 0282-4582
BERGLAGSPOETEN; medlemstidning foer Bergslagens poesivaenner. 1982. q. Bergslagspoeten, c/o R. Karlsson, Kompassv. 30, S-711 35 Lindesberg, Sweden.

BERKELEY REVIEW OF BOOKS. see *PUBLISHING AND BOOK TRADE*

800 US
BERN PORTER INTERNATIONAL. 1911. w. $12.50. (Institute of Advanced Thinking) Bern Porter Books, 22 Salmond Rd., Belfast, ME 04915. Ed. Bern Porter. adv.; bk.rev.; film rev.; play rev.; bibl. circ. 265,000. (also avail. in microform from UMI)

890 JA
BESSATSU BUNGEI SHUNJU; a quarterly on popular novels. 1946. q. 4240 Yen. Bungei Shunju Ltd., 3-23, Kioi-cho, Chiyoda-ku, Tokyo 102, Japan. TEL 03-3265-1211. FAX 03-3265-4878. Ed. Kazukiyo Takahashi. circ. 70,000.

810 US ISSN 0888-3742
PS688
BEST AMERICAN ESSAYS. 1986. a. $10.95 (clothbound ed. $21.95). Ticknor & Fields (Subsidiary of: Houghton Mifflin Co.), 215 Park Ave. S., New York, NY 10003. TEL 212-420-5800. (Dist. by: Houghton Mifflin Co., Wayside Rd., Burlington, MA 01803. TEL 800-225-3362) Ed. Robert Atwan.

813.08 US ISSN 0067-6233
PZ1
BEST AMERICAN SHORT STORIES. 1915. a. $10.95 (clothbound ed. £22.95). Ticknor & Fields (Subsidiary of: Houghton Mifflin Co.), 215 Park Ave. S., New York, NY 10003. TEL 212-420-5800. (Dist. by: Houghton Mifflin Co., Wayside Rd., Burlington, MA 01803. TEL 800-225-3362)

813.01 CN ISSN 0703-9476
PZ1
BEST CANADIAN STORIES. 1971. a. $29.95 (clothbound); $15.95 (paperback). Oberon Press, 400-350 Sparks St., Ottawa, ON K1R 7S8, Canada. TEL 613-238-3275. Eds. David Helwig, Maggie Helwig. adv.; bk.rev. circ. 2,500.
 Supersedes: New Canadian Stories (ISSN 0316-7518)
 Description: Collection of the best Canadian stories published during the year.

800 US ISSN 0893-8644
BEST OF LAFAYETTE: THE SOUTHERN WRITER AND ARTIST. bi-m. Amie Lewis, Ed. & Pub., c/o Sew it Seams, 333 11th Pl., Kirkland, WA 98033.

812.5 US ISSN 0067-6284
PN6111
BEST SHORT PLAYS. 1969. a. $10.95. Applause Theatre Book Publishers, 211 W. 71st St., New York, NY 10023. TEL 212-595-4735. FAX 212-721-2856. Eds. Howard Stein, Glenn Young. circ. 10,000.
 Description: Presents 10-12 short plays which represent the range of style and ambition of the current season.

BESTIA. see *FOLKLORE*

891.4 II ISSN 0006-050X
BHARATI TE VIDESHI SAHITA. (Text in Punjabi) 1968. s-a. Punjabi University, Patiala 4, Punjab, India. Ed. Dr. Gurden Singh. bk.rev.

052 II ISSN 0006-0518
BHAVAN'S JOURNAL. 1954. fortn. Rs.156. Bharatiya Vidya Bhavan, Kulapati K.M. Munshi Marg, Bombay 400007, India. Ed. S. Ramakrishnan. adv.; bk.rev. circ. 40,000.

BIBLICAL INTERPRETATION SERIES. see *RELIGIONS AND THEOLOGY*

BIBLIOGRAPHIEN ZUR DEUTSCHEN LITERATUR DES MITTELALTERS. see *LITERATURE — Abstracting, Bibliographies, Statistics*

BIBLIOLOGIA; elementa ad librorum studia pertinentia. see *PUBLISHING AND BOOK TRADE*

860 CK
BIBLIOTECA COLOMBIANA. 1970. irreg., no.40, 1993. price varies. Instituto Caro y Cuervo, Seccion de Publicaciones, Apdo. Aereo 51502, Bogota, Colombia. (back issues avail.)

809 830 SP ISSN 0006-1646
AS302
BIBLIOTECA DE MENENDEZ PELAYO. BOLETIN. 1919. a. 3000 ptas.($34.50) Sociedad "Menendez Pelayo", Santander, Spain. Ed. Manuel Revuelta Sanudo. bk.rev.; index, cum.index: 1919-1960. circ. 600. (also avail. in microform) **Indexed:** Amer.Hist.& Life, Hist.Abstr., M.L.A.
 —BLDSC (2161.440000); Faxon.

860 MX ISSN 0188-476X
PN6
BIBLIOTECA DE MEXICO. 1991. bi-m. Consejo Nacional para la Cultura y las Artes, Plaza de la Ciudadela 4, Centro Historico, Mexico D.F., Mexico. TEL 512-09-27. FAX 510-41-85. illus.

800 IT
BIBLIOTECA DI LETTERATURA E ARTE. 1975. irreg. price varies. Giardini Editori e Stampatori, Via Santa Bibbiana 28, 56100 Pisa, Italy. TEL 050-502531.

850 US
BIBLIOTECA ITALIANA. (Text in English) 1980. irreg., no.6, 1989. price varies. University of California Press, 2120 Berkeley Way, Berkeley, CA 94720. TEL 510-642-4247. FAX 510-643-7127. (Orders to: California-Princeton Fulfillment Services, 1445 Lower Ferry Rd., Ewing, NJ 08618. TEL 800-777-4726. FAX 800-999-1958) (back issues avail.) **Document type:** monographic series.
 Description: Provides translations of Italian Renaissance literature.
 Refereed Serial

860 SP
BIBLIOTECA ROMANICA HISPANICA. 1950. irreg. Editorial Gredos, S.A., Sanchez Pacheco 81, 28002 Madrid, Spain. FAX 341-5192033. **Indexed:** Bibl.Ling.
 Formerly: Biblioteca Romanica Hispanica. Estudios y Ensayos (ISSN 0519-7201)

891.85 PL ISSN 0519-8631
BIBLOTEKA PISARZOW POLSKICH. SERIA A. 1962. irreg. price varies. (Polska Akademia Nauk, Instytut Badan Literackich) Ossolineum, Publishing House of the Polish Academy of Sciences, Rynek 9, 50-106 Wroclaw, Poland. TEL 48-71-386-25. FAX 48-71-448-103. TELEX 0712771 OSS PL. Ed. Jerzy Woronczak. circ. 1,500. **Document type:** monographic series.

891.85 PL ISSN 0519-864X
BIBLIOTEKA PISARZOW POLSKICH. SERIA B. 1953. irreg. price varies. (Polska Akademia Nauk, Instytut Badan Literackich) Ossineum, Publishing House of the Polish Academy of Sciences, Rynek 9, 50-106 Wroclaw, Poland. TEL 48-71-386-24. FAX 48-71-448-103. Ed. Jerzy Woronczak. circ. 1,500.

BIBLIOTHECA ARNAMAGNAEANA; a Jon Helgason condita, auspiciis praesidii Arnamagnaeani. see *LINGUISTICS*

BIBLIOTHECA ARNAMAGNAEANA. SUPPLEMENTUM. see *LINGUISTICS*

BIBLIOTHEQUE D'ETUDES BALKANIQUES. see *LINGUISTICS*

BIBLIOTHEQUE D'HUMANISME ET RENAISSANCE; travaux et documents. see *HISTORY — History Of Europe*

840 FR ISSN 0067-835X
BIBLIOTHEQUE FRANCAISE ET ROMANE. SERIE B: EDITIONS CRITIQUES DE TEXTES. 1962. irreg. price varies. (Universite de Strasbourg II, Centre de Philologie et de Litteratures Romanes) Editions Klincksieck, 11 rue de Lille, 75005 Paris, France. Ed. Georges Straka. **Document type:** academic/scholarly publication.

840 FR ISSN 0067-8368
BIBLIOTHEQUE FRANCAISE ET ROMANE. SERIE C: ETUDES LITTERAIRES. 1960. irreg. price varies. (Universite de Strasbourg II, Centre de Philologie et de Litteratures Romanes) Editions Klincksieck, 11 rue de Lille, 75005 Paris, France. Ed. Paul Vernois. **Document type:** academic/scholarly publication.

840 FR ISSN 0067-8376
BIBLIOTHEQUE FRANCAISE ET ROMANE. SERIE D: INITIATION, TEXTES ET DOCUMENTS. 1964. irreg. price varies. (Universite de Strasbourg II, Centre de Philologie et de Litteratures Romanes) Editions Klincksieck, 11 rue de Lille, 75005 Paris, France. Ed. Georges Straka. **Document type:** academic/scholarly publication.

BIBLIOTHEQUE FRANCAISE ET ROMANE. SERIE E: LANGUE ET LITTERATURE FRANCAISES AU CANADA. see *LINGUISTICS*

840 FR ISSN 0067-8422
BIBLIOTHEQUE INTROUVABLE. (Supplement avail.: Oeuvres Complementaires.) 1966. irreg., latest no. 16, 1990. Lettres Modernes, 45 rue Saint-Andre, 14123 Fleury sur Orne, France. TEL 31-84-47-06. FAX 31-84-48-09. (Dist. outside France by: Librairie Droz S.A., 11, rue Massot, CH-1211 Geneva 12, Switzerland. TEL 022-466666)
 Description: From the series "Editions 'Lettres Modernes'."

800 PO ISSN 0870-4112
BIBLOS. 1925. a. $30. Universidade de Coimbra, Faculdade de Letras, 3049 Coimbra Codex, Portugal. FAX 039-36733. bk.rev. circ. 500.
 —BLDSC (2021.900000).

800 US ISSN 1043-9978
BIG ALLIS. 1989. s-a. 139 Thompson St., Apt. 2, New York, NY 10012. (Dist. by: Segue, 303 E. 8th St., New York, NY 10009; Small Press Distribution, 1814 San Pablo Ave., Berkeley, CA 94702) Eds. Jessica Grim, Melanie Neilson.

811 US
BIG SCREAM. 1974. a. $5. Nada, 2782 Dixie, SW, Grandville, MI 49418. TEL 616-531-1442. Ed. David Cope. circ. 100.
 Description: Exclusivley devoted to poetry, especially objectivist, beat-influenced, with a mind for ecology and Buddhist "right behavior."

BIJDRAGEN TOT DE TAAL-, LAND- EN VOLKENKUNDE. see *ANTHROPOLOGY*

800 PP ISSN 0255-7231
BIKMAUS. 1980. q. K.10. National Research Institute, Cultural Studies Division, P.O. Box 5854, Boroko, NCD, Papua New Guinea. TEL 675-25-3200. FAX 675-25-3042. TELEX NE 22381. Ed. Jack Lahui. adv.; bk.rev.; illus. circ. 3,000. **Indexed:** Abstr.Anthropol., So.Pac.Per.Ind.
 Supersedes: Papua New Guinea Writing.

BIKORET VEPARSHANUT/CRITICISM AND INTERPRETATION; journal for literature, linguistics, history and aesthetics. see *HUMANITIES: COMPREHENSIVE WORKS*

BILINGUAL REVIEW/REVISTA BILINGUE. see *LINGUISTICS*

800 AT ISSN 0156-2142
BILLY BLUE; Sydney, best address on earth. 1968. q. Cogente Pty. Ltd., P.O. Box 728, N. Sydney, N.S.W. 2059, Australia. TEL 2-957-2844. Ed. Ross Renwick. circ. 30,000.

820 BB ISSN 0006-2766
AP6
BIM. 1943. irreg., vol.19, no.73, 1991. B.$8. Ferney, Atlantic Shores, Christ Church, Barbados, W.I. Ed.Bd. adv.; bk.rev.; play rev.; illus. circ. 1,000. (reprint service avail. from KTO)

860 SP ISSN 0213-6511
BITZOC. 1986. q. 6200 ptas. (foreign 7000 ptas.). Basilio Balthasar, Ed. & Pub., Serinya, 9-2o, 07003 Palma de Mallorca, Spain. TEL 971-72-79-39. FAX 971-72-72-34. adv. circ. 2,000.
 Description: Informs on the results and works in progress of modern writers, and what they do and say.

BIULETYN POLONISTYCZNY. see *LINGUISTICS*

BIZA NEIRA (BISE NOIRE); sur l'Auvergne et la civilisation Auvergnate. see HISTORY — History Of Europe

BLACK AUTHORS & PUBLISHED WRITERS DIRECTORY. see BIOGRAPHY

800 US ISSN 0736-9271
BLACK FLY REVIEW. 1979. a. $3. University of Maine at Fort Kent, Fort Kent, MA 04743. Eds. Roland Burns, Wendy Kindred. circ. 700.

810 US ISSN 1047-515X
BLACK ICE. 1984. a. $18 for 3 issues, to individuals. University of Colorado, English Department, Publications Center, Box 494, Boulder, CO 80309. Ed. Mark Amerika. adv. circ. 1,100.
 Description: Publishes hardcore innovative fiction for the End of the World.

BLACK MOUNTAIN REVIEW. see LITERARY AND POLITICAL REVIEWS

896 910.3 NR ISSN 0067-9100
PL8000
BLACK ORPHEUS; journal of African and Afro-American literature. 1957. s-a. £N20($25) (University of Lagos) Lagos University Press, Publishing Division, P.O. Box 132, Akoka, Yaba, Lagos, Nigeria. Ed. T. Vincent. adv.; bk.rev. circ. 2,000. (reprint service avail. from KTO) **Indexed:** Curr.Cont., Documentatieblad, M.L.A. **Document type:** academic/scholarly publication.
 Description: African literature, music, sculpture and other African art forms.

800 US ISSN 0193-6301
PS1
BLACK WARRIOR REVIEW. 1974. s-a. $11 to individuals; institutions $17. (University of Alabama) Black Warrior Review, Box 2936, Tuscaloosa, AL 35486. TEL 205-348-4518. FAX 205-348-4518. Ed. Leigh Ann Sackrider. adv.; bk.rev. circ. 1,800. **Indexed:** Amer.Hum.Ind., Bk.Rev.Ind. (1982), Child.Bk.Rev.Ind. (1982), Hum.Ind., M.L.A. **Document type:** academic/scholarly publication.

BLACK WRITER. see ETHNIC INTERESTS

896 SA
BLACK WRITERS SERIES. 1935. irreg. price varies. Witwatersrand University Press, Wits 2050, South Africa. FAX 27-11-339-3559. TELEX 4-27125 SA. (Dist. by: Hodder and Stoughton Educational Southern Africa, P.O. Box 359, Bergvlei 2012, South Africa.) **Document type:** monographic series.
 Formerly: Bantu Treasury (ISSN 0067-4044)
 Description: Drama, poetry, and essays in African languages.

830 GW ISSN 1010-3597
BLAETTER DER RILKE-GESELLSCHAFT. (Text in English, French and German) 1972. a. (Rilke-Gesellschaft) Jan Thorbecke Verlag Gmbh und Co., Postfach 546, 72482 Sigmaringen, Germany. TEL 07571-728-100. FAX 07571-728-280. Ed.Bd. adv.; bk.rev. circ. 1,000. (back issues avail.) **Document type:** bulletin.

830 AU ISSN 0006-4483
BLAETTER FUER VOLKSLITERATUR. 1962. q. S.100 or membership. Verein der Freunde der Volksliteratur, Lenneisgasse 11-13, A-1140 Vienna, Austria. Ed. Otto Braun. bk.rev. circ. 2,200. (also avail. in microform)

820 US ISSN 0160-628X
PR4147
BLAKE: AN ILLUSTRATED QUARTERLY. 1967. q. $20 individuals (foreign $26); institutions $40 (foreign $46). c/o Morris Eaves, Ed., English Dept., Univ. of Rochester, Rochester, NY 14627. TEL 716-275-3820. FAX 716-442-5769. Eds. Morris Eaves, Morton D. Paley. adv.; bk.rev.; illus.; index. circ. 650. (back issues avail.) **Indexed:** Abstr.Engl.Stud., Amer.Hum.Ind., Arts & Hum.Cit.Ind., Curr.Cont., Ind.Bk.Rev.Hum., M.L.A., RILA.
 —BLDSC (2108.260000); Faxon; UnCover.
 Formerly (until vol.11, 1977): Blake Newsletter (ISSN 0006-453X)

839.7 SW ISSN 0347-3414
BLAND TOMATAR OCH TROLL. 1907. a. SEK 69 (effective 1990). Semic Press AB, P.O. Box 1074, S-172 22 Sundbyberg, Sweden. (Subscr. to: Pressdata AB, P.O. Box 3217, S-103 64 Stockholm, Sweden)

810 US
BLIND ALLEY. 1977. q. $10. Blind Alley Press, Box 1296, Edinburg, TX 78540-1296. Ed. Brian Robertson. circ. 500.

800 US
BLIND IGUANAPRESS. bi-m. $5 per no. 513 Corby Ave., South Bend, IN 46617. Ed. Dan Breen.
 Description: Contains short stories and poems.

808 ISSN 0276-1564
BLOOMSBURY REVIEW. 1980. 6/yr. $16 (Canada $40; elsewhere $52) (effective 1994). Owaissa Communications Company, Inc., Box 8928, Denver, CO 80201. TEL 303-892-0620. FAX 303-892-5620. Ed. Tom Auer; Pub. Tom Auer. adv.: B&W Page $3150; 9 7/8 x 15 1/4; adv. contact: Tom Auer. bk.rev. circ. 50,000. **Indexed:** Bk.Rev.Ind. (1988-), Chic.Per.Ind., Child.Bk.Rev.Ind. (1988-).
 Description: Features interviews, reviews and essays.

800 US
BLUE HORSE. 1966. irreg. Box 6061, Augusta, GA 30906. TEL 706-798-5628. Ed. Jacqueline T. Bradley. bk.rev.

800 US ISSN 1046-0012
PN6071.S33
BLUE LIGHT RED LIGHT; a periodical of speculative fiction and the arts. 1988. a. $15. 496A Hudson St., Ste. F-42, New York, NY 10014. TEL 212-423-3245. Ed. Alma Rodriguez. adv.; bk.rev.; illus. circ. 1,200. (back issues avail.)
 Description: Fuses mainstream writing, magic realism and surrealism together with speculative fiction.

800 398 US
BLUE SMOKE.* 1984. s-a. $3 per no. c/o Bill De Noyelles, Ed., 600 Montview Ave., Apt. D, Rivervale, NJ 07675. TEL 201-391-0336. Eds. Bill De Noyelles, Phil Goon. circ. 300. (back issues avail.)

810 US ISSN 0198-9901
BLUELINE. 1979. a. $6. Potsdam College, English Department, Potsdam, NY 13676. TEL 315-267-2005. FAX 315-267-3256. Ed. Anthony Tyler. bk.rev.; illus.; circ. 400 (controlled). (back issues avail.) **Indexed:** Ind.Amer.Per.Verse.
 Description: Publishes fiction an poetry, with a particular focus on rural life and experiences of nature, and the Adirondacks.

820 CN
BLUENOSE RAMBLER. 1969. q. contributions. Box 32, Western Shore, N.S. BOJ 3MU, Canada. Ed. Blanche Fralic. circ. 450.

808.8 US ISSN 1053-6361
BLUFF CITY. 1990. 2/yr. $9. Box 7697, Elgin, IL 60121. Ed.Bd. circ. 400.
 Description: Publishes short fiction and innovative verse.

800 491.66 940 UK ISSN 0142-3363
PB2101
BOARD OF CELTIC STUDIES. BULLETIN. (Text in English and Welsh) a. £20. (University of Wales, Board of Celtic Studies) University of Wales Press, 6 Gwennyth St., Cathays, Cardiff CF2 4YD, Wales. TEL 0222-231919. FAX 0222-230908. Ed.Bd. circ. 400. (also avail. in microform from UMI; reprint service avail. from UMI) **Indexed:** Abstr.Engl.Stud., Amer.Hist.& Life, Art & Archaeol.Tech.Abstr., Arts & Hum.Cit.Ind., Bibl.Ling., Br.Archaeol.Abstr., Curr.Cont., Geo.Abstr., Hist.Abstr., M.L.A. **Document type:** academic/scholarly publication.
 —BLDSC (2411.720000); UnCover.
 Description: Explores language and literature, archeology and art, history, and law in Celtic studies.

BODENSEE HEFTE; Zeitschrift der Euro-Region Bodensee. see GEOGRAPHY

BOGENS VERDEN; tidsskrift for dansk biblioteksvaesen. see LIBRARY AND INFORMATION SCIENCES

BOGG; a journal of North American and British Commonwealth poetry, prose poems, reviews, and essays on small press publishing. see LITERATURE — Poetry

800 839.7 SW ISSN 0283-8664
BOKBODEN. 1987. q. SEK 50 (effective 1994). Bokboden, Nedre Tjaerna 2, S-780 41 Gagnef, Sweden.

895.1 CC ISSN 1000-4173
BOLAN QUNSHU. (Text in Chinese) 1985. m. Y13.20($35) Guangming Ribao Chubanshe, 106, Yong'an Lu, Beijing 100050, People's Republic of China. (Dist. outside China by: China International Book Trading Corp., P.O. Box 399, Beijing, P.R.C.; Dist. in US by: China Books & Periodicals, Inc., 2929 24th St., San Francisco, CA 94110. TEL 415-282-2994) adv.; bk.rev.
 Description: Contains book reviews, news and articles about books.

860 US ISSN 1064-9824
BOLETIN DE DIVULGACION MARTIANA. (Text in Spanish) 1992. q. D P A International, Box 440817, Houston, TX 77244-0817. TEL 713-558-3052. Ed. Andres D. Puello.

867 SP ISSN 0214-9117
BOLETIN GALEGO DE LITERATURA. 1989. s-a. 2000 ptas. (effective 1993). Universidade de Santiago de Compostela, Servicio de Publicacions e Intercambio Cientifico, Campus Universitario, 15706 Santiago de Compostela, Spain. TEL 81-59-35-00. FAX 81-59-39-63. bk.rev.; illus. circ. 600. (back issues avail.) **Document type:** academic/scholarly publication.

800 080 UY ISSN 0067-9909
BOLSILIBROS.* irreg. Editorial Arca, Colonia 1263, Montevideo, Uruguay.

830 GW ISSN 0068-001X
BONNER ARBEITEN ZUR DEUTSCHEN LITERATUR. 1961. irreg., no.46, 1990. price varies. Bouvier Verlag Herbert Grundmann, Am Hof 28, 53113 Bonn, Germany. TEL 0228-7290124. FAX 0228-7290179. Ed. Benno von Wiese. **Indexed:** M.L.A. **Document type:** monographic series.

BOOK FORUM. see PUBLISHING AND BOOK TRADE

800 UK ISSN 0260-0315
BOOKMARK. 1978. a. £2. College of Education, Language Studies, Moray House, Holyrood Rd., Edinburgh EH8 8AQ, Scotland. TEL 031-556-8455. FAX 031-557-3458. Ed. J. Aldridge. bk.rev.; illus. circ. 400. **Indexed:** Child.Lit.Abstr.

808.8 US
BOOKS ARE EVERYTHING. 1988. q. $25 (foreign $36) (effective 1992). R.C. Holland, Ed. & Pub., 302 Martin Dr., Richmond, KY 40475. TEL 606-624-9176. adv.; bibl.; illus. circ. 3,000.
 Description: Covers vintage paperback collecting, focusing on books from 1938-1965, with features on individual authors, news of interest to collectors, and reproductions of book covers.

808.8 301.4157 US
BOOKS BOHEMIAN; hard-to-find, out-of-print, used. 1977. s-a. free. Books Bohemian, Box 17218, Los Angeles, CA 90017. TEL 213-385-6761. Ed. Robert J. Manners. circ. 1,100. (back issues avail.) **Document type:** catalog.

820 UK ISSN 0954-0334
BOOKS FOR MEN. 1985. q. West & Wilde Bookshop, 25A Dundas St., Edinburgh EH3 6QQ, Scotland. TEL 031-556-0079. FAX 031-558-3717. Ed. Robert Orr. bk.rev. circ. 1,000. (back issues avail.) **Document type:** bibliography.

BORGO BIOVIEWS. see BIOGRAPHY

800 US ISSN 0891-9623
BORGO LITERARY GUIDES. 1991. irreg., no.8, 1993. price varies. Borgo Press, Box 2845, San Bernardino, CA 92406. TEL 909-884-5813. FAX 909-888-4942. Ed. Boden Clarke. index. **Document type:** bibliography.
 Incorporates (1983-1992): Starmont Reference Guides (ISSN 0738-0127)
 Description: Reference guides to literary topics, including awards, bibliographies, directories, cyclopedias, and catalogues.

LITERATURE

BORGO POLITICAL SCENARIOS. see *POLITICAL SCIENCE*

BORGO REFERENCE GUIDES. see *HISTORY*

810 US
BOSTON LITERARY REVIEW. 1985. 2/yr. $9. Box 357, West Somerville, MA 02144. Ed. Gloria Mindock. circ. 500.

BOSTON REVIEW. see *PUBLISHING AND BOOK TRADE*

810 US
BOTTOMFISH. 1976. a. $4. (De Anza College, Language Arts Department) Bottomfish Press, 21250 Stevens Creek Blvd., Cupertino, CA 95014. TEL 408-864-8538. Ed. Robert Scott. circ. 500.
  Description: Publishes fiction and poetry from new and established writers.

800 US ISSN 0885-9337
BOULEVARD; journal of contemporary writing. 1986. 3/yr. $12. Opojaz, Inc., Box 30386, Philadelphia, PA 19103. TEL 215-561-1723. Ed. Richard Burgin. circ. 2,500. **Indexed:** Ind.Amer.Per.Verse.
  Description: Publishes exceptional fiction, poetry and non-fiction by new talents and establishes writers.

800 UK ISSN 0955-3819
BOUND SPIRAL. 1988. s-a. £4 (foreign £6). 72 First Ave., Bush Hill Park, Enfield, Middlesex EN1 1BW, England. Ed. M. Petrucci. adv. circ. 150. (back issues avail.)

800 US ISSN 0190-3659
PN2
BOUNDARY 2; an international journal of literature and culture. 1972. 3/yr. $24 to individuals; institutions $54. Duke University Press, Box 90660, Durham, NC 27708-0660. TEL 919-687-3600. FAX 919-688-4574. Ed. Paul A. Bove. adv.; bk.rev.; illus.; index. circ. 800. **Indexed:** Abstr.Engl.Stud., Abstr.Pop.Cult., Amer.Hum.Ind., Arts & Hum.Cit.Ind., Curr.Cont., Film Lit.Ind. (1990-), Ind.Amer.Per.Verse, Ind.Bk.Rev.Hum., M.L.A.
—BLDSC (2264.273000); Faxon; UnCover; SWETS; UMI.
  Refereed Serial

800 FR
BOUTEILLE A LA MER. irreg. price varies. c/o Ed. Marc Beigbeder, 8 rue Theo-Renaudot, 75015 Paris, France.

800 UK ISSN 0261-0353
BRADFORD OCCASIONAL PAPERS; essays in language, literature and area studies. 1980. a. £6.95. University of Bradford, Modern Languages Department, West Yorks BD7 1DP, England. TEL 0274-733466. FAX 0274-305340. TELEX 51809-UNIBFD-G. Ed.Bd. bk.rev. circ. 200. **Document type:** academic/scholarly publication.
—BLDSC (2265.947000).

830 AU
BRAGI; Vierteljahresschrift fuer Literatur. 1982. q. S.100. Otto R. Braun, Ed. & Pub., Lenneisg. 11 13-5-5, A-1140 Vienna, Austria. circ. 500.

BRAILLE BOOK REVIEW (LARGE PRINT EDITION). see *HANDICAPPED — Visually Impaired*

810 US
BRAINS. 1978. q. $1 per no. David Schnell, Ed. & Pub., 6N 905 Elgin Ave., St. Charles, IL 60174. TEL 708-888-1422.

808 AT ISSN 0725-5543
BRAVE NEW WORD; contemporary Australian short stories and poetry. 1981. s-a. Aus.$12 (foreign Aus.$16). Brave New Word Publishing, 582 Rae St., North Filzroy, Vic. 3068, Australia. TEL 03-482-2530. Ed. Helen Murname. circ. 500.

810 US
BRAVURA. 1960. a. Palomar College, English Department, 1140 W. Mission Rd., San Marcos, CA 92069-1487. TEL 619-744-1150. Ed. Wendy Dougherty. circ. 500.

808 839.7 SW ISSN 0347-3546
BREV; Ljungby Skrivarklubb. 1976. q. SEK 85 (effective 1990). Ljungby Skrivarklubb, P.O. Box 154, S-341 23 Ljungby, Sweden.

700 IT ISSN 0006-968X
BREVE, IL GRUPPO, LA CULTURA, L'IDEE. 1950. m. L.1000. Traversa Merbellina 24, Naples, Italy. Ed. Ettore Capuano. adv.; bk.rev.; abstr.

BRITISH AMATEUR JOURNALIST. see *JOURNALISM*

800 UK
BRITISH AND IRISH AUTHORS: INTRODUCTORY CRITICAL STUDIES. 1967. irreg., latest 1986. price varies. Cambridge University Press, Edinburgh Bldg., Shaftesbury Rd., Cambridge CB2 2RU, England. TEL 0223-312393. FAX 0223-315052. TELEX 851817256. (N. American addr.: Cambridge University Press, Journals Dept., 40 W. 20th St., New York, NY 10011. TEL 212-924-3900. FAX 212-691-3239) Ed. Robin Mayhead. index. **Document type:** monographic series.
  Formerly: British Authors Series (ISSN 0068-1334)

820 UK ISSN 0309-7765
PR4168
BRONTE SOCIETY TRANSACTIONS. 1893. s-a. £10 (foreign £14) (membership only). Bronte Society, c/o Publications Secretary, Bronte Parsonage Museum, Haworth, Keighley, W. Yorskhire BD22 8DR, England. TEL 0535-642323. FAX 0535-647131. adv.; bk.rev.; bibl.; illus.; cum.index; circ. 3,500. (controlled). (also avail. in microform) **Indexed:** Abstr.Engl.Stud., Br.Hum.Ind. **Document type:** academic/scholarly publication.
—UnCover.

810 US
BROWNS MILLS REVIEW. 1980. a. $4. David Vajda, Ed. & Pub., Box 908, Browns Mills, NJ 08015. TEL 609-893-0896. (back issues avail.)

891.6 FR ISSN 0399-7014
PB2801
BRUD NEVEZ. (Text in Breton) 1954. m. 130 F. (foreign 200 F.). 6 rue Beaumarchais, 29200 Brest, Brittany, France. TEL 98-44-89-42. Ed.Bd. adv.; bk.rev.; charts; illus.; index. circ. 500. **Document type:** consumer publication.
  Formerly: Brud ar Yez hag ar Vro (ISSN 0007-2567)

BRULOT. see *POLITICAL SCIENCE — Civil Rights*

830 GW
BRUNNEN JOURNAL. 1988. q. DM.4. Brunnen Verlag GmbH, Postfach 100143, 35331 Giessen, Germany. TEL 0641-6059-0. FAX 0641-6059-40. Ed. Ralf Tibusek. bk.rev. **Document type:** consumer publication.

830 GW ISSN 0178-7241
BUCHJOURNAL. 1985. q. DM.21. (Boersenverein des Deutschen Buchhandels e.V.) Buchhaendler-Vereinigung GmbH, Postfach 100442, 60004 Frankfurt a.M., Germany. TEL 069-1306383. FAX 069-1306201. TELEX 413573-BUCHV-D. adv.; bk.rev. **Document type:** consumer publication.

800 GW ISSN 0176-8220
BUCHREPORT. 1970. w. DM.654. Harenberg Kommunikation Verlags und Medien GmbH & Co. KG, Koenigswall 21, 44137 Dortmund, Germany. TEL 0231-9056-0. FAX 0231-9056111. Ed. Bodo Harenberg. adv.; bk.rev. circ. 4,000. (back issues avail.) **Document type:** bulletin.

800 UK
THE BUDGERIGAR. bi-m. Budgeriagar Society, c/o Alistair Cameron, Ed., 102 Sheriffs Park, Linluthgow, W. Lothian EH49 7SS, Scotland. TEL 44-506-845346. (Subscr. to: The Budgerigar Society, 49-53 Hazelwood Rd., Northampton NN1 1LG, England) adv.; bk.rev. circ. 6,000. (back issues avail.)

841 US ISSN 0007-4128
PQ2191.Z5
BULLETIN BAUDELAIRIEN. (Text in French) 1965. 2/yr. $10 (foreign $14). Vanderbilt University, W. T. Bandy Center for Baudelaire Studies, Box 6325, Sta. B, Nashville, TN 37235. TEL 615-343-0372. Ed. Claude Pichois. bibl.; cum.index: vols.1-20. circ. 200. **Indexed:** M.L.A. **Document type:** academic/scholarly publication.
—Faxon.
  Description: Contains biographical, bibliographical, and documentary articles on Baudelaire and his literary milieu.

840 BE ISSN 0252-1121
LE BULLETIN CELINIEN. 1982. m. 1140 BEF. Marc Laudelout, Ed. & Pub., B.P. 70, 1000 Brussels 22, Belgium. adv.; bk.rev. circ. 500. **Document type:** bulletin.
  Description: Devoted exclusively to the life and literary works of Louis-Ferdinand Celine. Publishes studies, documents, reports of conferences, adaptations of his works for other media, and news of publications on or about Celine.

846 FR ISSN 0338-0548
PQ2631.R63
BULLETIN D'INFORMATIONS PROUSTIENNES. 1975. a. 130 F. Presses de l'Ecole Normale Superieure, 48 bd. Jourdan, 75690 Paris Cedex 14, France. TEL 45-89-08-33. (Co-sponsors: Centre National de la Recherche Scientifique; Institut des Textes et Manuscrits Modernes) Ed. Bernard Brun. adv.; bk.rev. circ. 500. **Document type:** academic/scholarly publication.
—BLDSC (2864.384000); SWETS.

840 801 FR ISSN 0335-508X
BULLETIN DES ETUDES VALERYENNES. 1974. irreg. (2-3/yr.). Universite de Montpellier (Universite Paul Valery), B.P. 5043, 34032 Montpellier Cedex 1, France. TEL 67-14-20-00. **Document type:** academic/scholarly publication.
  Description: Contains all relevant information concerning research on Valery in France and abroad.

BULLETIN HISPANIQUE. see *HISTORY — History Of Europe*

809 BE
BULLETIN JEAN RAY. (Text in Dutch, English and French) 1970. a. 350 Fr. Amis de Jean Ray, 4 rue Vautier, Brussels, Belgium. Ed. Emile Van Balberghe. bk.rev.; bibl. circ. 400.
  Formerly: Cahier Jean Ray.

860 UK ISSN 0007-490X
PC4008
BULLETIN OF HISPANIC STUDIES. (Text mainly in English, Spanish; occasionally in Catalan, French, Portuguese) 1923. q. £25($50) to individuals; institutions £64($135). Liverpool University Press, P.O. Box 147, Liverpool L69 3BX, England. TEL 051-794-2235. FAX 051-708-6502. TELEX 627095-UNIPL-G. Eds. Dorothy Sherman Severin, Ann L. Mackenzie. adv.; bk.rev.; bibl.; illus.; index. circ. 800. (back issues avail.; reprint service avail. from KTO) **Indexed:** Arts & Hum.Cit.Ind., Bibl.Ling., Br.Hum.Ind., Curr.Cont., Ind.Bk.Rev.Hum., M.L.A. **Document type:** academic/scholarly publication.
—BLDSC (2855.910000); Faxon; UnCover; SWETS. CCC.
  Description: Devoted to the language, literature and civilization of Spain, Portugal and Latin America.

860 US ISSN 0007-5108
PQ6098.7
BULLETIN OF THE COMEDIANTES. 1949. s-a. $20 to individuals; institutions $30; students $10. University of California, Riverside, Department of Spanish & Portuguese, Riverside, CA 92521-0222. TEL 909-787-7334. FAX 909-787-2294. (Subscr. to: c/o Prof. Jose Antonio Madrigal, Dept. of Foreign Languages, Auburn University, Auburn, AL 36849) Ed. James Allan Parr. bk.rev. circ. 550. (back issues avail.) **Document type:** academic/scholarly publication.
—Faxon; UnCover; SWETS.
  Description: Specializes in the drama of the Spanish Golden Age.

800 NE ISSN 0167-6520
BUMPER; literatuurmagazine voor het onderwijs. 1978. 3/yr. fl.32.75. WoltersgroepGroningen b.v. (Subsidiary of: Wolters Kluwer N.V.), Postbus 58, 9700 MB Groningen, Netherlands. TEL 31-50-226922. FAX 31-50-364866.
—SWETS.

895 JA ISSN 0389-4029
BUNGAKU/LITERATURE. (Text in Japanese) 1933. q. 4800 Yen. Iwanami Shoten Publishers, 2-5-5 Hitotsubashi, Chiyoda-ku, Tokyo 101-02, Japan. FAX 03-3239-9618. (Dist. overseas by: Japan Publications Trading Co., Ltd., Box 5030, Tokyo International, Tokyo 100-31, Japan; Or: 1255 Howard St., San Francisco, CA 94103) **Indexed:** M.L.A.

890 JA
BUNGAKUKAI; a magazine on serious literature. (Text in Japanese) 1949. m. 10800 Yen. Bungei-Shunju Ltd., 3-23, kioi-cho, Chiyoda-ku, Tokyo 102, Japan. TEL 03-3265-1211. FAX 03-3265-4486. Ed. Tako Shigematsu. circ. 20,000.

800 200 UK ISSN 0954-0970
BUNYAN STUDIES. 1988. irreg., no.4, 1991. £5 (foreign £6) to individuals; institutions £10(foreign £12). Open University, Faculty of Arts, Parsifal College, 527 Finchley Rd., London NW3 7BG, England. TEL 071-794-0575. Ed. W.R. Owens. adv.; bk.rev. circ. 250. (back issues avail.) Indexed: Amer.Hist.& Life (until 1991), Hist.Abstr. (until 1991), Rel.Ind.One. **Document type:** monographic series.
—BLDSC (2930.696100).
  Description: Covers the life and works of John Bunyan and other related topics.

820 UK
PR4329
BURNS CHRONICLE - BURNSIAN. 1892. q. £8 (foreign £9.32). Burns Federation, Dick Institute, Elmbank Avenue, Kilmarnock KAI 3BU, Scotland. Ed. Peter J. Westwood. adv.; bk.rev.; bibl.; illus.; cum.index. circ. 3,000. **Document type:** academic/scholarly publication, newsletter.
—BLDSC (2931.729000).
  Formerly (until 1991): Robert Burns Chronicle (ISSN 0307-8957)

800 UK
BURNS CHRONICLE CLUB DIRECTORY. (Text in English and Scottish) 1892. a. £30. Burns Federation, Dick Institute, Elmbank Ave., Kilmarnock KAI 3BU, Scotland. adv.; bk.rev.; bibl.; charts; illus. circ. 2,700. **Document type:** directory.

820 KE ISSN 0007-6376
PR9344.5
BUSARA.* 1968. s-a. EAs.10($2.50) (University of Nairobi, Department of Literature) Kenya Literature Bureau, Box 30022, Nairobi, Kenya. Ed. K.Gecau. bk.rev. circ. 3,000. (back issues avail.) **Indexed:** Ind.S.A.Per., M.L.A.
  Supersedes: Nexus.

BYDGOSKIE TOWARZYSTWO NAUKOWE. WYDZIAL NAUK HUMANISTYCZNYCH. PRACE. SERIA B (JEZYK I LITERATURA). see LINGUISTICS

BYZANTINA AUSTRALIENSIA. see HISTORY — History Of Europe

810 375.4 US ISSN 0007-8069
PE1101
C E A CRITIC. (Includes: C E A Forum) 1939. 3/yr. $25 to individuals; libraries $30. College English Association, c/o Bege K. Bowers and Patricia Kelvin, Eds., Dept. of English, Youngstown State University, Youngstown, OH 44555. TEL 216-742-3414. FAX 216-742-1998. adv.; index, cum.index. circ. 1,200. (also avail. in microform from UMI; reprint service avail. from UMI) **Indexed:** Abstr.Engl.Stud., Amer.Hum.Ind., Arts & Hum.Cit.Ind., Curr.Cont., M.L.A. **Document type:** academic/scholarly publication.
—BLDSC (3096.790000); Faxon; UnCover; UMI.
  Description: Articles on current research and study on English literature, composition, and language, particularly as they apply to teaching in the college and university classroom.

C E C T A L CONFERENCE PAPERS SERIES. (Centre for English Cultural Tradition and Language) see LINGUISTICS

800 NE ISSN 0925-8612
▼**C E R M E I L.** (Text in French) 1992. irreg. price varies. (Centre d'Etudes et de Recherches sur le Merveilleux, l'Etrange et l'Irreel en Litterature) Editions Rodopi B.V., Keizersgracht 302-304, 1016 EX Amsterdam, Netherlands. TEL 31-20-6227507. FAX 31-20-6380948. (In N. America: 233 Peachtree St., N.E., Ste. 404, Atlanta, GA 30303-1504. TEL 800-225-3998. FAX 404-522-7116) Ed. Gerard Chandes. **Document type:** monographic series.

C L A JOURNAL. (College Language Association) see LINGUISTICS

800 US ISSN 1043-8343
PN851
C N L - WORLD REPORT. 1974. s-a. $35 (foreign $45) includes membership (includes Review of National Literatures). Council on National Literatures, Box 81, Whitestone, NY 11357. TEL 718-767-8380. Ed. Anne Paolucci. adv.; bk.rev. circ. 1,200. (back issues avail.) **Indexed:** M.L.A.
—BLDSC (9359.077000); UnCover.
  Former titles (until 1985): C N L - Quarterly World Report (ISSN 0145-6873); (until Jan. 1978): Council on National Literatures Report.

C R: CENTENNIAL REVIEW. see HUMANITIES: COMPREHENSIVE WORKS

840 NE ISSN 0169-894X
PC2002
C R I N. (Cahiers de Recherche des Instituts Neerlandais de Langue et Litterature Francaise) 1979. 2/yr. price varies. Editions Rodopi B.V., Keizersgracht 302-304, 1016 EX Amsterdam, Netherlands. TEL 31-20-6227507. FAX 31-20-6380948. (In N. America: 233 Peachtree St., N.E., Ste. 404, Atlanta, GA 30303-1504. TEL 800-225-3998. FAX 404-522-7116). Eds. H. Hillenaar, F. Drijkoningen. **Document type:** monographic series.
—BLDSC (2952.128500).

C R N L E REVIEWS JOURNAL. (Centre for Research in the New Literatures in English) see LITERARY AND POLITICAL REVIEWS

800 US ISSN 0883-9980
PR6023.E926
C S L BULLETIN. 1969. m. $10. New York C.S. Lewis Society, York College, Jamaica, NY 11451. Ed. James Como. bk.rev. circ. 550. **Indexed:** M.L.A. **Document type:** bulletin.

810 US
▼**C W M.** 1992. a. $3. 875 Central Pky., Schenectady, NY 12309-6005. TEL 518-356-1621. Ed. Geof Huth. circ. 100.
  Description: Publishes portfolios of divergent works of literature and visual art held together loosely by themes.

800 BL ISSN 0007-9316
CABORE.* 1968. 3/yr. Universidade Federal do Ceara, Faculdade de Letras, Av. da Universidade, Fortaleza, Ceara, Brazil. Ed. Linhares Filho. bk.rev.

839.5 SW ISSN 0348-2057
CAFE EXISTENS; tidskrift foer nordisk litteratur. 1978. q. SEK 275. Cafe Existens, Hantverksbyn i Gerlesborg, S-450 70 Hamburgsund, Sweden.

810 US ISSN 1069-7179
CAFE REVIEW. 1989. q. $12. c/o Yes Books, 20 Danforth St., Portland, ME 04101. TEL 207-775-3233. Eds. Steve Luttrell, Wayne Atherton. circ. 200 (controlled).

840 FR ISSN 0007-9618
CAHIERS BOURBONNAIS; arts, lettres, regionalisme. 1957. q. 250 F. Cour des Dames, 03140 Charroux, France. TEL 70-56-80-61. FAX 70-56-86-06. Dir. M. Jean Pierre Petit. adv.; bk.rev.; illus. circ. 6,000. (also avail. in microfiche)

840 FR ISSN 0575-0415
CAHIERS CHARLES DU BOS. 1955. a. Societe des Amis de Charles Du Bos, 76 bis rue des Saints-Peres, 75007 Paris, France. circ. 400. (back issues avail.)

800 FR ISSN 0007-9650
CAHIERS D'ACTION LITTERAIRE. (Supplement avail.) 1955. 6/yr. 28 F. Jeunesses Litteraires de France, 117 bd. St-Germain, 75006 Paris, France. adv.; bk.rev.; abstr.; illus.; stat.

CAHIERS DE CIVILISATION MEDIEVALE. see HISTORY

CAHIERS DE CIVILISATION MEDIEVALE. SUPPLEMENT. see HISTORY

840 FR
CAHIERS DE JULES ROMAINS. 1976. a. price varies. (Societe des Amis de Jules Romains) Flammarion, 26 rue Racine, 75006 Paris, France.

800 FR ISSN 1248-5691
▼**CAHIERS DE L'EMIGRATION RUSSE.** (Subseries of: Cultures et Societes de l'Est (ISSN 0765-0213)) 1993. irreg., vol.2, 1993. price varies. Institut d'Etudes Slaves, 9 rue Michelet, 75006 Paris, France. TEL 43-26-50-89. FAX 43-26-16-23. (Co-sponsor: Institut de Recherche et d'Etude sur les Nouvelles Institutions a l'Est) **Document type:** academic/scholarly publication.

800 FR
CAHIERS DE L'ENERGUMENE. 1982. 2/yr. $65. Editions Gerard-Julien Salvy, 14 rue du Mail, 75002 Paris, France. Eds. G. Grenier, G.S. Salvy. adv.; bk.rev. circ. 1,800.
  Supersedes (1973-1979): Energumene.

830 430 FR ISSN 0767-7529
CAHIERS DE L'INSTITUT D'ETUDES GERMANIQUES. a. Universite de Montpellier (Universite Paul Valery), Institut d'Etudes Germaniques, B.P. 5043, 34032 Montpellier Cedex 1, France. TEL 67-14-20-00. **Document type:** academic/scholarly publication.
  Description: Specializes in German literature, social studies and linguistics.

CAHIERS DE L'IROISE. see HISTORY — History Of Europe

840 LE ISSN 0007-991X
CAHIERS DE L'ORONTE.* (Text in French) 1965. q. £L22.($15) Immeuble Chidiac, Rue Said Akl, Beirut, Lebanon. Ed. Lody Aoueiss. adv.; bk.rev.; bibl.; charts; illus.; stat.

800 900 FR ISSN 0769-0770
CAHIERS DE L'UNIVERSITE DE PERPIGNAN. 1986. s-a. price varies. Universite de Perpignan, 52 av. de Villeneuve, 66860 Perpignan Cedex, France. TEL 68-66-20-00. FAX 68-66-20-19. TELEX 505 005 F UNIPERP. Ed. Paul Carmignani. adv.; bk.rev.; circ. 300 (controlled). (back issues avail.) **Document type:** academic/scholarly publication.

840 SZ ISSN 0007-9847
CAHIERS DE LA RENAISSANCE VAUDOISE. (Text in French) 1926. irreg. (2-4/yr.). price varies. Place Saint-Francois 5, Case Postale 3414, CH-1002 Lausanne, Switzerland. TEL 021-3121914. FAX 021-3126714. Ed. Yves Gerhard. illus. circ. 5,750. **Document type:** monographic series.
  Description: Essays of political, historical, philosophical and religious essences.

800 FR ISSN 0068-5089
CAHIERS DE SAINT-MICHEL DE CUXA. 1970. a. price varies. Association Culturelle de Cuxa, Centre Permanent de Recherches et d'Etudes Pre-Romanes et Romanes, Abbaye de Saint-Michel de Cuxa, Codalet, 66500 Prades, France. bk.rev. **Indexed:** Avery Ind.Archit.Per., RILA.

808 FR ISSN 0766-4214
CAHIERS DE SEMIOTIQUE TEXTUELLE. 1984. q. (Centre de Semiotique Textuelle) Publidix, Universite de Paris X, 200 Av. de la Republique, 92001 Nanterre, France. TEL 40-97-76-69. FAX 47-21-67-44. Ed. Edmond Marc Lipiansky. **Document type:** academic/scholarly publication.

CAHIERS DU VITREZAIS. see HISTORY — History Of Europe

CAHIERS ELISABETHAINS; late medieval and renaissance English studies. see HISTORY — History Of Europe

CAHIERS HAUT-MARNAIS; revue d'histoire, de lettres et d'art. see HISTORY.

840 FR ISSN 0753-4590
CAHIERS HENRI BOSCO. 1973. a. 120 F. Amitie Henri Bosco, Palais Aurore, 33 bd. Tzarewitch, 06000 Nice, France. Ed. Claude Girault. bk.rev.; cum.index: 1973-1977, 1978-1982. circ. 1,500. (back issues avail.) **Document type:** academic/scholarly publication, bibliography.
  Formerly: Amitie Henri Bosco. Cahiers (ISSN 0399-1121)

840 FR ISSN 1149-8633
CAHIERS LEON BLOY. 1924. a. (Societe des Etudes Bloyennes) A.G. Nizet, 17 rue de la Sorbonne, 75005 Paris, France. Eds. Dominique Millet, Michel Arveiller.

LITERATURE

800   IT
▼**CAHIERS MONTESQUIEU**. 1993. irreg. price varies. (Societe Montesquieu) Ligouri Editore s.r.l., Via Mezzocannone 19, 80134 Naples, Italy. TEL 081-5527139. **Document type:** monographic series.

800   FR   ISSN 0008-0365
CAHIERS NATURALISTES. 1955. a. 175 F. (Societe Litteraire des Amis d'Emile Zola) Editions Grasset et Fasquelle, B.P. 12, 77580 Villers-Morin, France. TEL 47-03-89-41. Dir. Alain Pages. adv.; bk.rev.; bibl.; charts; cum.index. circ. 1,000. (back issues avail.) **Indexed:** M.L.A.

800   FR   ISSN 0084-8239
CAHIERS PAUL-LOUIS COURIER. 1968. s-a. 60 F. Societe des Amis de Paul-Louis Courier, Mairie de Veretz, 37270 Veretz, France. (Subscr. address: c/o M. Quilici, 18 d'Arsonval, 44600 Nazaire, France) Ed. Gabriel Spillebout. adv.; bibl.; illus.

840   FR   ISSN 0008-0454
CAHIERS RACINIENS. 1957. s-a. 60 F. Societe Racinienne, 52 rue Jacques- Dulud, 92200 Neuilly-sur-Seine, France. Ed. M. Jacques Masson-Forestier. bk.rev.; play rev.; bibl.; illus.; tr.lit.; index, cum.index covering 20 issues. circ. 1,000. (Table des Cahiers Raciniens avail.; reprint service avail. from SWZ)

840   FR
CAHIERS SAINT-EXUPERY. a. (Association des Amis d'Antoine de Saint-Exupery) Editions Gallimard, 5 rue Sebastien-Bottin, 75007 Paris, France. illus.

942   FR   ISSN 0220-5610
PR463
CAHIERS VICTORIENS ET EDOUARDIENS. (Text in English, French) 1973. s-a. 150 F. Universite de Montpellier (Universite Paul Valery), Centre d'Etudes et de Recherches Victoriennes et Edouardiennes, B.P. 5043, 34032 Montpellier Cedex 1, France. TEL 67-14-23-93. FAX 67-14-20-52. Ed. J.C. Amalric. adv.; bk.rev. circ. 300. (also avail. in microform from UMI; back issues avail., reprint service avail. from UMI) **Indexed:** Arts & Hum.Cit.Ind., Curr.Cont., M.L.A. **Document type:** academic/scholarly publication.
—BLDSC (2952.413000); Faxon; UnCover; UMI.
Formerly (until 1977): Cahiers d'Etudes et de Recherche Victoriennes (ISSN 0339-2171)
Description: Concerned not only with literature, but with every aspect of the "Victorian and Edwardian" cultural area.

850 851 398   IT
CALABRIA LETTERARIA.* 1954. m. L.24000($14) Rubbettino Editore, Viale dei Pini, 88049 Soveria Mannelli, Italy. Ed. Emilio Frangella. circ. 8,000. (back issues avail.)

CALABRIA NOBILISSIMA. see ART

810   US   ISSN 1040-8339
CALAPOOYA COLLAGE. 1970. a. $5. Calapooya Collage, Box 309, Monmouth, OR 97361. Ed. Thomas L. Ferte. adv.; bk.rev. circ. 1,500. (tabloid format)

CALENDAR OF LITERARY FACTS. see LITERARY AND POLITICAL REVIEWS

820   FR   ISSN 0575-2124
PR1
CALIBAN; litteratures anglaises et nord-americaines. (Text in English or French; summaries in other languages) 1964. a. 90 F. (effective 1994). (Universite de Toulouse II (le Mirail)) Presses Universitaires du Mirail, 56 rue du Taur, 31000 Toulouse, France. TEL 61-22-58-31. FAX 61-21-84-20. Ed. Marcienne Rocard. (back issues avail.) **Indexed:** Abstr.Engl.Stud., M.L.A. **Document type:** academic/scholarly publication.

800   US   ISSN 0890-7269
PN6101
CALIBAN. 1986. s-a. $14 to individuals; institutions $24. Lawrence R. Smith, Ed. & Pub., Box 561, Laguna Beach, CA 92652-0561. TEL 714-497-7437. adv. circ. 1,500. **Indexed:** Ind.Amer.Per.Verse.
Description: International journal of literature, art, and music with a strong emphasis on the avant-garde.

808 910.3   US   ISSN 0161-2492
NX500
CALLALOO; a journal of African-American and African arts and letters. (Text in English, French, Spanish) 1976. 4/yr. $25 to individuals (foreign $42.85); instituions $50 (foreign $67.85). Johns Hopkins University Press, Journals Publishing Division, 2715 N. Charles St., Baltimore, MD 21218. TEL 410-515-6987. FAX 410-516-6998. Ed. Charles H. Rowell. adv.; bk.rev.; film rev.; play rev.; bibl.; illus.; index. circ. 1,359. (back issues avail.) **Indexed:** A.I.P.P., Amer.Hum.Ind., Bk.Rev.Ind. (1987-), Child.Bk.Rev.Ind. (1987-), Ind.Amer.Per.Verse, M.L.A.
—BLDSC (3015.428800); Faxon; UnCover. **CCC.**
Description: Offers a rich mixture of fiction, poetry, plays, critical essays, cultural studies, interviews, and visual art.

CALLIOPE (BRISTOL). see LITERATURE — Poetry

CALLIOPE (PETERBOROUGH); world history for young people. see HISTORY

800   UK
CAMBRENSIS; short story quarterly magazine of Wales. 1987. q. £6. 41 Heol Fach, Cornelly, Bridgend, Mid-Glamorgan CF33 4LN, Wales. TEL 44-656-741994. (Subscr. to: Blackwell's Periodicals Ltd., P.O. Box 40, Hythe Bridge St., Oxford, OX1 2EJ, England) Ed. Arthur Smith. adv.; illus. circ. 500. (back issues avail.)

CAMBRIAN MEDIEVAL CELTIC STUDIES. see HISTORY — History Of Europe

870 880   UK
CAMBRIDGE GREEK AND LATIN CLASSICS. irreg., latest 1985. price varies. Cambridge University Press, Edinburgh Bldg., Shaftesbury Rd., Cambridge CB2 2RU, England. TEL 0223-312393. FAX 0223-315052. TELEX 851817256. (N. American addr.: Cambridge University Press, Journals Dept., 40 W. 20th St., New York, NY 10011. TEL 212-924-3900. FAX 212-924-3239) Eds. E.J. Kenney, P.E. Easterling. **Document type:** academic/scholarly publication.

820   UK
CAMBRIDGE GUIDE TO LITERATURE IN ENGLISH. irreg., 2nd ed., 1994. $49.95. Cambridge University Press, Edinburgh Bldg., Shaftesbury Rd., Cambridge CB2 2RU, England. TEL 0223-312393. FAX 0223-315052. (N. American addr.: Cambridge University Press, Journals Dept., 40 W. 20th St., New York, NY 10011-4211. TEL 800-221-4512) Ed. Ian Ousby.

CAMBRIDGE LATIN TEXTS. see LINGUISTICS

800   UK   ISSN 0008-199X
CAMBRIDGE QUARTERLY. 1964. 4/yr. £51($99) (effective 1994). (Cambridge Quarterly Association) Oxford University Press, Oxford Journals, Walton St., Oxford OX2 6DP, England. TEL 0865-56767. FAX 0865-56646. TELEX 837330-OXPRES-G. (U.S. subscr. to: Oxford University Press Inc., 2001 Evans Rd., Cary, NC 27513. TEL 919-677-0977) Ed.Bd. adv. contact: Jane Parker. bk.rev.; cum.index. circ. 800. **Indexed:** Abstr.Engl.Stud., Arts & Hum.Cit.Ind., Br.Hum.Ind., Curr.Cont., Hum.Ind., Ind.Bk.Rev.Hum., M.L.A., Mid.East: Abstr.& Ind. **Document type:** academic/scholarly publication.
—BLDSC (3015.975000); Faxon; UnCover; SWETS; UMI. **CCC.**
Description: Principally literary criticism, includes articles on painting, sculpture, music and cinema.

056.1   UK
CAMBRIDGE STUDIES IN LATIN AMERICAN AND IBERIAN LITERATURE. 1990. irreg. Cambridge University Press, Edinburgh Bldg., Shaftesbury Rd., Cambridge CB2 2RU, England. TEL 0223-312393. FAX 0223-315052. (N. American addr.: Cambridge University Press, Journals Dept., 40 W. 20th St., New York, NY 10011. TEL 212-924-3900. FAX 212-691-3239) **Document type:** monographic series.

CANADIAN AUTHOR. see PUBLISHING AND BOOK TRADE

800   CN
CANADIAN AUTHORS ASSOCIATION NEWSLINE. q. membership. Canadian Authors Association, 275 Slater St., 5th Fl., Ottawa, ON K1P 5H9, Canada. TEL 613-233-2846. FAX 613-235-8237.

800   UK
CANADIAN C.S. LEWIS JOURNAL. 1979-1993; resumed 1994. q. Robert Stronstad, Ed. & Pub., P.O. Box 1700, Abbotsford, BC, Canada. adv.; bk.rev. circ. 203.

813   CN   ISSN 0045-477X
CANADIAN FICTION. (Text mainly in English; occasionally in French) 1971. q. Can.$32.10 (to institutions and foreign Can.$42.80). Geoffrey Hancock, Ed. & Pub., Box 946, Station F, Toronto, Ont. M4Y 2N9, Canada. TEL 613-548-8249. FAX 613-548-1556. adv.; bk.rev.; illus. circ. 2,000. (also avail. in microform from UMI; reprint service avail. from UMI; back issues avail.) **Indexed:** Abstr.Engl.Stud., Amer.Hum.Ind., Can.Lit.Ind., Can.Per.Ind., CMI, M.L.A.
—UnCover; UMI.

CANADIAN JOURNAL OF IRISH STUDIES. see HUMANITIES: COMPREHENSIVE WORKS

850 945 100   CN   ISSN 0705-3002
PQ4001
CANADIAN JOURNAL OF ITALIAN STUDIES.* (Text in English, French and Italian) 1977. 4/yr. Can.$20($20) to individuals; institutions Can.$30 ($30). c/o Dept. of Modern Languages, Mc Master University, 1280 Main St. W., Hamilton, Ont. L8S 4M2, Canada. TEL 416-525-9140. Ed. Stelio Cro. adv.; bk.rev. circ. 300. **Indexed:** Amer.Hist.& Life, Arts & Hum.Cit.Ind., Can.Rev.Comp.Lit., Curr.Cont., Hist.Abstr., M.L.A.

820 700   CN   ISSN 0225-0500
CANADIAN JOURNAL OF NETHERLANDIC STUDIES/REVUE CANADIENNE D'ETUDES NEERLANDAISES. 1980. s-a. Can.$20 membership. Canadian Association for the Advancement of Netherlandic Studies, Department of French, University of Windsor, Windsor, ON N9B 3P4, Canada. TEL 519-253-4232. FAX 519-973-7050. Ed. Basil D. Kingstone. adv.; bk.rev.; circ. 300 (controlled). **Indexed:** Bibl.Ling., M.L.A. **Document type:** academic/scholarly publication.

819   CN   ISSN 0008-4360
CANADIAN LITERATURE/LITTERATURE CANADIENNE; a quarterly of criticism and review. (Text in English, French) 1959. q. Can.$40 to individuals; institutions Can.$55. University of British Columbia, 223-2029 West Mall, Vancouver, BC V6T 1Z2, Canada. TEL 604-822-2780. FAX 604-822-9452. Ed. W.H. New. adv.; bk.rev.; bibl.; illus. circ. 1,400. (also avail. in microform from UMI; reprint service avail. from CLA,UMI) **Indexed:** Abstr.Engl.Stud., Amer.Hum.Ind., Arts & Hum.Cit.Ind., Bk.Rev.Ind. (1990-), Can.Lit.Ind., Can.Per.Ind., Can.Wom.Per.Ind., Child.Bk.Rev.Ind. (1990-), CMI, Curr.Cont., Hum.Ind., Ind.Bk.Rev.Hum., LCR, M.L.A.
—BLDSC (3037.750000); Faxon; UnCover; SWETS; UMI.
Description: Devoted to the study of all aspects of Canadian writing.

CANADIAN REVIEW OF AMERICAN STUDIES. see HISTORY — History Of North And South America

800 011   CN   ISSN 0319-051X
PN851
CANADIAN REVIEW OF COMPARATIVE LITERATURE/REVUE CANADIENNE DE LITTERATURE COMPAREE. (Text in English and French) 1974. q. Can.$45($40) institutions Can.$70 ($62). (Canadian Comparative Literature Association - Association Canadienne de Litterature Comparee) Academic Printing and Publishing, Box 4218, Edmonton, AB T6E 4T2, Canada. TEL 403-435-5898. FAX 403-435-5852. Ed. Steve Totosy. bk.rev.; abstr.; bibl.; index. circ. 500. **Indexed:** Amer.Bibl.Slavic & E.Eur.Stud., Arts & Hum.Cit.Ind., Can.Rev.Comp.Lit., Curr.Cont., Ind.Bk.Rev.Hum., M.L.A., Mid.East: Abstr.& Ind. **Document type:** academic/scholarly publication.
—BLDSC (3044.640000); Faxon; UnCover; SWETS.

820   CN
CANADIAN SHORT STORY LIBRARY. 1972. irreg. price varies. University of Ottawa Press, 542 King Edward, Ottawa, ON K1N 6N5, Canada. TEL 613-564-2270. FAX 613-564-9284.
Description: Focuses on the short story form.

800 700   US
CANVAS (MADISON). 1987. a. $1. 6189 Helen C. White Hall, Madison, WI 53703. Eds. Mark V. Cushman, William Perry. circ. 500.

LITERATURE

895.1   CC   ISSN 0496-3326
CAOYUAN/PRAIRIE; wenxue yuekan. (Text in Chinese) m. Y12($49.50) Caoyuan Wenxue Yuekan She, 15 Xilin Beilu, Huhhot, Inner Mongolia Autonomous Region 010020, People's Republic of China. (Dist. outside China by: China International Book Trading Corp., P.O. Box 399, Beijing, P.R.C.; Dist. in US by: China Books & Periodicals, Inc., 2929 24th St., San Francisco, CA 94110) Ed. Ding Mao.
    Description: Contains short stories, northern Chinese poetry, prose, and essays.

811 700   CN   ISSN 0315-3754
PR9194.9
CAPILANO REVIEW. 1972. 4/yr. Can.$25 to individuals; Can.$30 to libraries. Capilano College, 2055 Purcell Way, N. Vancouver, BC V7J 3H5, Canada. TEL 604-984-1712. FAX 604-984-4985. Ed. Robert Sherrin. adv.; bk.rev.; illus. circ. 1,000. (also avail. in microform from UMI; reprint service avail. from UMI) **Indexed:** Amer.Hum.Ind., Can.Lit.Ind., Can.Per.Ind.
  —UMI.
    Description: Journal of poetry, art work and short fiction.

CARAVELLE; cahiers du monde hispanique et luso-bresilien. see HISTORY — History Of North And South America

CARIBBEAN REVIEW OF BOOKS. see PUBLISHING AND BOOK TRADE

808   VI   ISSN 0893-1550
THE CARIBBEAN WRITER. 1987. a. $7. University of the Virgin Islands, Caribbean Research Institute, RR 2, Box 10,000, Kingshill, St. Croix, VI 00850. TEL 809-778-0246. FAX 809-778-6750. adv.; bk.rev. circ. 1,000.
    Description: Creative writing: poetry and fiction, with Caribbean as focus.

830.9   CN   ISSN 0317-7254
PT1
CARLETON GERMANIC PAPERS. 1973. a. Can.$4. Carleton University, Department of German, Ottawa, ON K1S 5B6, Canada. TEL 613-788-2116. FAX 613-788-3544. Ed. E.M. Oppenheimer. circ. 140. (back issues avail.) **Indexed:** Curr.Cont., M.L.A. **Document type:** academic/scholarly publication.
  —BLDSC (3053.350000).

CARLYLE ANNUAL; essays on Thomas and Jane Carlyle and their circle. see BIOGRAPHY

CARNEGIE MAGAZINE; dedicated to art, science, literature and music. see ART

808   US   ISSN 0008-6797
CAROLINA QUARTERLY. 1948. 3/yr. $12. University of North Carolina at Chapel Hill, Greenlaw Hall CB 3520, Chapel Hill, NC 27599-3520. TEL 919-962-0244. Ed. Amber Vogel. adv.; bk.rev.; illus. circ. 1,300. (also avail. in microform from UMI; back issues avail.; reprint service avail.from UMI,ISI,KTO) **Indexed:** A.I.P.P., Amer.Hum.Ind., Arts & Hum.Cit.Ind., Bk.Rev.Ind. (1965-), Child.Bk.Rev.Ind. (1965-), Curr.Cont., Ind.Amer.Per.Verse, Ind.Bk.Rev.Hum. **Document type:** academic/scholarly publication.
  —Faxon; UMI.
    Description: Publishes fiction, poetry, essays, reviews and graphic art.

806   US
CAROUSEL; information for writers. 1977. bi-m. $30. Writer's Center, 4508 Walsh St., Bethesda, MD 20815. TEL 301-654-8664. Ed. Allan Lefcowitz. adv.: B&W page $600. bk.rev. circ. 6,000. **Document type:** newsletter.

800   IT
CARTE SCOPERTE. (Text in English and Italian) 1982. q. L.25000. Edizioni del Labirinto, Via Rosario 7, Casella Postale 178, 75100 Matera, Italy. Ed. Gianni Toti.

800 700   IT   ISSN 0008-7025
CARTE SEGRETE;* rivista-libro di letteratura ed arte. 1967. q. L.8000($18) Edizioni Carte Segrete, Piazza Margana 24, 00186 Rome, Italy. Ed. Domenico Javarone. bk.rev.; film rev.; play rev.; abstr.; bibl.; charts; illus.; pat.; tr.lit. circ. 8,000. **Indexed:** M.L.A.

810   US
CASE RESERVE REVIEW. 1982. a. $2. Case Western Reserve University, English Department, 11112 Belflower Rd., Cleveland, OH 44106-7117. TEL 216-368-2355. circ. 1,000.

CASOPIS PRO MODERNI FILOLOGII. see LINGUISTICS

800   UK   ISSN 0069-0961
CASSAL BEQUEST LECTURES. (Text in French) 1961. irreg., no.11, 1991. price varies. University of London, Senate House, Malet St., London WC1E 7HU, England. TEL 071-636-8000. **Document type:** academic/scholarly publication, monographic series.

800 780   FR
CASSETTE GAZETTE; audio magazine. (Text in English) 1971. q. 300 F.($40) Handshake Editions, 83 rue de la Tombe-Issoire, Atelier A2, 75014 Paris, France. Ed. Jim Haynes. circ. 1,000. (back issues avail.)

860   SP
CATALAN REVIEW. 1986. s-a. 4000 ptas.($30) to non-members; members 2000 ptas.($15). (North American Catalan Society, US) Publicacions de l' Abadia de Montserrat, Ausias March 92-98, Barcelona, Spain. Eds. Manuel Duran, Josep Roca-Pons.

849   SP   ISSN 0214-3089
PC3975.E1
CATALAN WRITING. (Text in English) 1988. s-a. Instituco de les Lletres Catalanes, Pg. de Gracia 41, 2n 1a, 08007 Barcelona, Spain. TEL 93-216-80-00. FAX 93-216-01-25. circ. 2,500.
    Description: Provides information on Catalan literature. Promotes the diffusion of works by Catalan writers.

850 700 398   IT
CATALOGO DANTE. 1870. q. Libreria Gozzini, Via Ricasoli 49-103r, 50122 Florence, Italy. TEL 55-212433. FAX 55-211105. circ. 8,200.

810   US   ISSN 0896-7423
CATALYST (ATLANTA); a magazine for heart and mind. 1986. s-a. $10. Catalyst, Inc., 236 Forsyth St., Ste. 400, Atlanta, GA 30303. TEL 404-730-5785. FAX 404-730-7104. Ed. Pearl Cleage. adv.; bk.rev.; illus. circ. 5,000. (back issues avail.)

810   US   ISSN 0145-8310
CATHARTIC. 1974. 2/yr. $5. c/o Patrick M. Ellingham, Ed., Box 1391, Fort Lauderdale, FL 33302. TEL 305-967-9378. adv.; bk.rev.; index. circ. 200. (back issues avail.)
    Description: Poetry magazine devoted to the unknown poet and works from the darker side of life.

800   US   ISSN 1045-9871
PS3505.A87
CATHER STUDIES. 1990. irreg. price varies. University of Nebraska Press, 312 N. 14th St., Box 880484, Lincoln, NE 68588-0484. TEL 402-472-3581. FAX 402-472-6214. Ed. Susan J. Rosowski. **Document type:** academic/scholarly publication.
    Description: Provides a forum for all aspects of Cather scholarship and criticism: biography, various critical approaches to the art of Willa Cather, her literary relationships and reputation, the artistic, historical, intellectual, religious, economic, political, and social background to her work.

800   US   ISSN 1048-8618
PS3505.A87
CATHER YEARBOOK. a. $29.95 to individuals; institutions $29.95. Edwin Mellen Press, 415 Ridge St., Box 450, Lewiston, NY 14092. TEL 800-753-2788. FAX 716-754-4056. Ed.Bd.

800   US   ISSN 1062-6379
▼**CAT'S EAR**; poetry and fiction. 1992. a. $5 to individuals; institutions $10 (effective Aug. 1993). Galliard Group Publishers, Box 946, Kirksville, MO 63501. TEL 816-627-2210. Ed. Tim Rolands. adv.: B&W page $50. circ. 100. (back issues avail.) **Document type:** academic/scholarly publication.
    Description: Profiles today's literature that bridges the gap between academia and the public.

808   US
CAUDA PAVONIS; studies in Hermeticism. 1974. 2/yr. $7.50 to individuals; libraries $10. Washington State University, Department of English, Pullman, WA 99164. TEL 509-335-3023. FAX 509-335-2582. Ed. Stanton J. Linden. bk.rev.; abstr.; bibl. circ. 450. (looseleaf format) **Indexed:** Ind.Bk.Rev.Hum., M.L.A. **Document type:** academic/scholarly publication.
    Description: Publishes scholarly material on all aspects of alchemy and hermeticism and their influence on literature, philosophy, art, religion and the history of science and medicine.

CE MOIS-CI A L'ALLIANCE. see EDUCATION

800 300   PR
CEIBA. 1972. s.a. free. Universidad de Puerto Rico, Administracion de Colegios Regionales, Colegio Universitario Tecnologico de Ponce, Box 7186, Ponce, PR 00732. TEL 809-844-8181. Ed. Luz Ivette Martinez. bk.rev. circ. 1,000. **Indexed:** Hort.Abstr.

800   US   ISSN 0147-3085
PQ6428
CELESTINESCA; boletin informativo internacional. (Text in English, French and Spanish) 1977. s-a. $10 (foreign $15). Michigan State University, Department of Romance Languages, E. Lansing, MI 48824. TEL 517-335-8350. FAX 517-336-3844. Ed. Joseph T. Snow. bk.rev.; play rev.; illus. circ. 360. (processed; back issues avail.) **Indexed:** M.L.A. **Document type:** bulletin.
  —Faxon; UnCover.
    Description: Specializes in the arts, particularly on Fernando de Rojas' Spanish classic, "Celestina," including all other continuations, adaptations, translations, stagings and other tranformations of the work, from 1500 until now.

800   UK   ISSN 0264-0856
CENCRASTUS; Scottish & international literature, arts & affairs. 1979. q. £9 (foreign £12) to individuals; institutions £12(foreign £14). Unit 1, Abbeymount Techbase, 8 Easter Rd., Edinburgh EH8 8EJ, Scotland. TEL 031-661-5687. Eds. Raymond Ross, Thom Nairn. adv.; bk.rev.; charts; illus. circ. 3,000. **Document type:** bulletin.
  —BLDSC (3102.403000).

820   UK   ISSN 0069-164X
CENTRAL LITERARY MAGAZINE. 1873. a. 25p. 45 Sandhills Lane, Barnt Green, Nr. Birmingham, England. Ed. W.H.M. Sparks.

820   FR   ISSN 0240-8864
CENTRE AIXOIS DE RECHERCHES ANGLAISES. ACTES DU COLLOQUE. (Text in French) irreg., no.11, 1990. price varies. Universite de Provence, Service des Publications, 29 av. Robert Schuman, 13621 Aix-en-Provence Cedex 1, France. TEL 42-20-09-16. (back issues avail.)

800   AE   ISSN 0069-1720
CENTRE CULTUREL FRANCAIS, ALGER. RENCONTRES CULTURELLES.* 1970. irreg. price varies. Centre Culturel Francais, 7 rue Medecin-Capitaine Kassani Issad, Algiers, Algeria.

893.3   FR   ISSN 0297-9977
CENTRE D'ETUDES ET DE RECHERCHES AMAZIGH. PUBLICATIONS. 1985. irreg. Editions de la Maison des Sciences de l'Homme, 54 bd. Raspail, 75270 Paris Cedex 06, France. TEL 49-54-20-44. FAX 45-48-83-53.

850   IT   ISSN 1122-0899
CENTRO DI STUDI DI LETTERATURA ITALIANA IN PIEMONTE GUIDO GOZZANO. SAGGI E TESTI. 1965. irreg., no.12, 1993. price varies. Casa Editrice Leo S. Olschki, Casella Postale 66, 50100 Florence, Italy. TEL 055-6530684. FAX 055-6530214. **Document type:** monographic series.

860   US   ISSN 0277-6995
PQ6337
CERVANTES. (Text in English and Spanish) 1981. s-a. $20. Cervantes Society of America, Pomona College, Claremont, CA 91711. TEL 909-621-8937. FAX 909-621-8065. (Subscr. to: William H. Clamurro, Department of Modern Languages, Denison University, Granville, OH 43023) Ed. Michael McGaha. adv.; bk.rev. circ. 350. (back issues avail.) **Indexed:** M.L.A. **Document type:** academic/scholarly publication.
  —Faxon; UnCover; SWETS.

LITERATURE

800 US ISSN 1054-1403
CERVANTES AND HIS TIMES. irreg. Peter Lang Publishing, Inc., 62 W. 45th St., 4th Fl., New York, NY 10036. TEL 212-302-6740. FAX 212-302-7574. Ed. Eduardo Urbina. **Document type:** academic/scholarly publication.
 Description: Publishes manuscripts that contribute to the understanding of Cervantes' work and his times.

891.86 NE ISSN 0009-0468
PG5000
CESKA LITERATURA/CZECH LITERATURE; casopis pro literarni vedu. (Text in Czech; summaries in English, German, Russian) 1953. bi-m. fl.232($140) (effective 1994). (Czech Academy of Sciences, Institute for Czech and World Literature, XR) John Benjamins Publishing Co., Amsteldijk 44, P.O. Box 75577, 1070 AN Amsterdam, Netherlands. TEL 31-20-6738156. FAX 31-20-6739773. (In N. America: 821 Bethlehem Pike, Philadelphia, PA 19118. TEL 215-836-1200. FAX 215-836-1204) Ed. Miroslav Cervenka. bk.rev.; bibl.; illus.; index. circ. 1,850. **Indexed:** Amer.Hist.& Life (until 1990), Arts & Hum.Cit.Ind., Bibl.Ling., Can.Rev.Comp.Lit., Curr.Cont., Hist.Abstr. (until 1990), M.L.A. **Document type:** academic/scholarly publication.
 Description: Studies the history and theory of literatures, especially Czech literature.

CESKY JAZYK A LITERATURA; casopis pro metodiku. see EDUCATION

810 US
CHALLENGING THE LITERARY CANON. 1988. irreg. University of Rochester Press, c/o Robert Easton, Man. Ed., Box 41026, Rochester, NY 14604. TEL 716-275-6208. FAX 716-271-8778. **Document type:** monographic series.

810 US
CHAMINADE LITERARY REVIEW. 1987. 2/yr? $10. 3140 Waialae Ave., Honolulu, HI 96816-1578. TEL 808-735-4723. circ. 350.

891.4 II ISSN 0009-1359
CHANDRABHAGA (WEST BENGAL). (Text in Bengali) 1967. w. Rs.7.50. Ed. Ramanath Sinha, P.O. Suri., Dist. Birbhum, West Bengal, India. circ. 834. **Indexed:** M.L.A.

800 US
CHANEY CHRONICAL. (Companion to: What's New About London, Jack) 1972. irreg. (1-2/yr.). $0.50 per no. London Northwest, 929 South Bay Rd., Olympia, WA 98506. Ed. David H. Schlottman. bk.rev.; bibl. (processed)

895.1 CC
CHANG CHENG/GREAT WALL. (Text in Chinese) bi-m. Hebei Sheng Wenxue Yishu Jie Lianhehui, 2 Shizhuang Lu, Shigang Dajie, Shijiazhuang, Hebei 050000, People's Republic of China. TEL 745373. Ed. Ai Dong.

895.1 US
CHANGJIANG (DUOZHONG WENXUE) CONGKAN/YANGTZE LITERATURE. (Text in Chinese) bi-m. $45.50. China Books & Periodicals, Inc., 2929 24th St., San Francisco, CA 94110. TEL 415-282-2994. FAX 415-282-0994.

895.1 700 CC ISSN 0528-838X
CHANGJIANG WENYI/YANGTZE LITERATURE AND ART. (Text in Chinese) 1949. m. Y25.20($49.50) No. 1, Dong Ting 2 Lu, Wuchang, Wuhan, Hubei 430071, People's Republic of China. TEL 027-611963. (Dist. outside China by: China International Book Trading Corp., P.O. Box 399, Beijing, P.R.C.; Dist. in US by: China Books & Periodicals, Inc., 2929 24th St., San Francisco, CA 94110. TEL 415-282-2994) Ed. Wang Yang. illus. **Document type:** consumer publication.

800 FR ISSN 0395-7845
CHANTS DES PEUPLES. vol.2, 1974. irreg. Editions Caracteres, 7 rue de l'Arbalete, 75005 Paris, France. TEL 43-37-96-98. Ed. Bruno Durocher. illus.

895.1 CC
CHAO SHENG. (Text in Chinese) bi-m. Shantou Shi Wenlian, No. 130, Xinxing Lu, Shantou, Guangdong 515031, People's Republic of China. TEL 254506. Ed. Wu Guoqu.
 Formerly: Shantou Wenyi.

052 800 UK ISSN 0308-2695
CHAPMAN; Scotland's quality literary magazine. (Text in English, Gaelic and Scots) 1970. 4/yr. £12($28) to individuals (overseas £11); institutions £15 ($25) (overseas £19). Chapman Magazine, 4 Broughton Pl., Edinburgh EH1 3RX, Scotland. TEL 031-557-2207. FAX 031-556-9565. Ed. Joy M. Hendry. adv.; bk.rev.; play rev. circ. 2,000. (back issues avail.) **Document type:** consumer publication.
 Description: Publishes poetry, fiction, criticism, reviews, and articles on theater, politics, language, and the arts.

800 US
▼**CHARACTERS IN 19TH-CENTURY LITERATURE.** 1992. triennial. $49.95. Gale Research Inc., 835 Penobscot Bldg., Detroit, MI 48226. TEL 313-961-2242. FAX 313-961-6083. Ed. Kelly King Howes.
 Description: Provides in-depth analyses of more than 2000 memorable characters taken from 300 of the most widely studied works of the previous century.

800 US
CHARACTERS IN 20TH-CENTURY LITERATURE. 1990. irreg. $49.95. Gale Research Inc., 835 Penobscot Bldg., Detroit, MI 48226. TEL 800-877-4253. FAX 313-961-6083. TELEX 810-221-7086. Ed. Laurie Lanzen Harris.
 Description: Covers 20th-century authors and the thousands of characters they create. Provides essays on the most studied characters from over 500 works.

CHARIOTEER; an annual review of modern Greek culture. see GENERAL INTEREST PERIODICALS — Greece

810 US ISSN 0098-9452
PS501
CHARITON REVIEW. 1975. s-a. $7. Northeast Missouri State University, Kirksville, MO 63501. TEL 816-785-4499. Ed. Jim Barnes. adv.; bk.rev. circ. 650. (back issues avail.) **Indexed:** A.I.P.P., Amer.Hum.Ind., Ind.Amer.Per.Verse.
 Description: Contains translations of literary works from the U.S. and around the world, poetry, and fiction.

820 UK ISSN 0308-0951
PR4863
CHARLES LAMB BULLETIN. N.S. 1973. q. $14 to individuals; $21 to institutions. Charles Lamb Society, c/o Willian Ruddick, Ed., 9 Dale View Gardens, Crawcrook, Ryton, Tyne and Wear NE40 4ED, England. bk.rev. circ. 350. (back issues avail.) **Indexed:** Abstr.Engl.Stud., LCR, M.L.A. **Document type:** academic/scholarly publication.
 —BLDSC (3129.934000); Faxon; UnCover.
 Former titles: C.L.S. Bulletin & Charles Lamb Society. Journal.

460 860 US ISSN 0145-8973
PQ7081.A1
CHASQUI. 1972. 2/yr. $9 to individuals; libraries $12. College of William and Mary, Department of Modern Languages, Williamsburg, VA 23187-8795. TEL 804-221-3691. Ed. Howard Fraser. adv.; bk.rev.; bibl. circ. 400. (reprint service avail. from ISI) **Indexed:** Arts & Hum.Cit.Ind., Hisp.Amer.Per.Ind., M.L.A.
 —BLDSC (3132.028200); Faxon; UnCover.

800 US ISSN 0741-9155
CHATTAHOOCHEE REVIEW. 1980. q. $15. DeKalb College, 2101 Womack Rd., Dunwoody, GA 30338. TEL 404-551-3166. FAX 404-551-3201. Ed. Lamar York. adv.; bk.rev.; film rev.; play rev.; cum.index every 5 yrs. (also avail. in microform from UMI; back issues avail.) **Indexed:** Amer.Hum.Ind.
 ●Also available online.
 —UMI.
 Description: Publishes poetry, fictions and essays by established and unacknowledged literary writers.

820 US
CHAUCER LIBRARY. 1978. irreg., no.4, 1989. price varies. University of Georgia Press, 330 Research Dr., Athens, GA 30602-4901. TEL 706-369-4901. FAX 706-369-6131. **Document type:** monographic series.

820 US ISSN 0009-2002
PR1901
CHAUCER REVIEW; a journal of medieval studies and literary criticism. Includes: Chaucer Research Report. 1966. q. $25 to individuals (foreign $32.50); institutions $37.50 (foreign $45). (Modern Language Association, Chaucer Group) Pennsylvania State University Press, Barbara Bldg., Ste. C, 820 N. University Dr., University Park, PA 16802-1003. TEL 814-865-1327. FAX 814-863-1408. Ed. Robert Frank. adv.; bk.rev.; bibl. circ. 1,300. (also avail. in microform from UMI; reprint service avail. from UMI) **Indexed:** Abstr.Engl.Stud., Curr.Cont., Hum.Ind., M.L.A. **Document type:** academic/scholarly publication.
 —Faxon; UnCover; SWETS. CCC.
 Refereed Serial

800 US ISSN 0261-9822
CHAUCER STUDIES. 1970. irreg., latest no.19. Boydell & Brewer Inc., Box 41026, Rochester, NY 14604. TEL 716-275-0419. FAX 716-271-8778. **Document type:** academic/scholarly publication.

810 US ISSN 0009-2185
AP2
CHELSEA; a magazine for poetry, stories, essays, and translations. 1958. s-a. $11 (foreign $14). Chelsea Associates, Inc., Box 5880, Grand Central Sta., New York, NY 10163. TEL 212-988-2276. Ed.Bd. adv.; cum.index. circ. 1,300. (also avail. in microform from UMI; back issues avail.; reprint service avail. from UMI, ISI) **Indexed:** Arts & Hum.Cit.Ind., Curr.Cont., Ind.Amer.Per.Verse.
 —UMI.

820 CN ISSN 0317-0500
PR4453.C4
CHESTERTON REVIEW. 1974. q. Can.$35($35) G.K. Chesterton Society, St. Thomas More College, 1437 College Dr., Saskatoon, Sask. S7N 0W6, Canada. TEL 306-966-8917. FAX 306-966-8904. Ed. J. Ian Boyd. adv.; bk.rev.; bibl.; index. circ. 1,500. **Indexed:** Amer.Hist.& Life, Amer.Hum.Ind., Hist.Abstr., M.L.A. **Document type:** academic/scholarly publication.
 —Faxon; UnCover.

891.4 II ISSN 0009-3432
CHHANDITA. (Text in Bengali) 1965. irreg. (10-12/yr.). Rs.10. B-59 Rabindra Nagar, Calcutta 700018, India. Ed. Gourgopal Das. adv.; bk.rev. circ. 2,500. (also avail. in microform)

800 770
CHICAGO RENAISSANCE.* 1976. a. $5.95. (Chicago Renaissance Workshop) Natural Resources Unlimited, Box 0155, Markham, IL 60426-0155. Ed. Joe H. Mitchell. bk.rev. circ. 3,000.

810 US ISSN 0009-3696
AP2
CHICAGO REVIEW. 1946. q. $15 to individuals (foreign $20); institutions $35 (foreign $40). (University of Chicago, Division of the Humanities) Chicago Review, 5801 S. Kenwood, Chicago, IL 60637. TEL 312-702-0887. FAX 312-702-0887. Ed. David Nicholls. adv.: B&W page $150. bk.rev.; illus.; index. circ. 2,500. (also avail. in microfilm from UMI; back issues avail.; reprint service avail. from UMI) **Indexed:** A.I.P.P., Acad.Ind., Amer.Bibl.Slavic & E.Eur.Stud., Artbibl.Mod., Arts & Hum.Cit.Ind., Curr.Cont., Hum.Ind., Ind.Amer.Per.Verse, Ind.Bk.Rev.Hum., M.L.A. **Document type:** academic/scholarly publication.
 —BLDSC (3172.720000); Faxon; UMI.
 Description: International journal of writing and cultural exchange; includes poetry, fiction, essays, reviews, and interviews.

800 CN ISSN 0315-467X
CHIEN D'OR/GOLDEN DOG. (Text in English and French) 1972. irreg. c/o Editor, English Department, Carleton University, Ottawa, Ont. K1S 5B6, Canada. TEL 613-231-3847. Ed. Michael Gnarowski. illus.
 Supersedes: Yes (ISSN 0044-0353)

CHILDREN'S BOOK REVIEW. see CHILDREN AND YOUTH — For

028.5　　　　　US　　ISSN 0092-8208
PN1009.A1
CHILDREN'S LITERATURE (NEW HAVEN). 1972. a. $16. (Children's Literature Association) Yale University Press, 302 Temple St., Box 209040, New Haven, CT 06520-9040. TEL 203-432-0920. FAX 203-432-0948. Ed. Elizabeth Keyser. bk.rev.; illus.; cum.index every 5 vols. circ. 1,600. **Indexed:** Bk.Rev.Ind. (1990-), Child.Bk.Rev.Ind. (1990-), Child.Lit.Abstr., M.L.A.
—UnCover.
Description: Interdisciplinary journal featuring interpretive essays on various authors, illustrators, genres, periods and issues in children's literature internationally.

CHILDREN'S LITERATURE IN EDUCATION; an international quarterly. see CHILDREN AND YOUTH — About

028.52　　　　　US　　ISSN 0362-4145
PN1009.A1
CHILDREN'S LITERATURE REVIEW. 1976. irreg., vol.25, 1991. $99. Gale Research Inc., 835 Penobscot Bldg., Detroit, MI 48226. TEL 313-961-2242. FAX 313-961-6083. TELEX 810-221-7086. Ed. Gerard J. Senick. bk.rev. **Indexed:** Child.Auth.& Illus.
Description: Provides excerpts from criticism on past and present authors of children's and young adult books.

891.43　　　　　II
CHILDREN'S LITERATURE SERIES. (Text in Hindi) 1951. irreg., vol.29, 1963. price varies. Vishveshvaranand Vedic Research Institute, P.O. Sadhu Ashram, Hoshiarpur 146021, Punjab, India.

810　　　　　US　　ISSN 0894-1696
CHILDREN'S WORLD (ELMONT). m. $25. Vision Publishing House, Inc., 10 Ely Ct., Elmont, NY 11003-4809. TEL 516-285-6763.

820　　　　　HK　　ISSN 0069-3642
CHIMES.* 1961. irreg. free. University of Hong Kong, English Society, Hong Kong. **Indexed:** Ind.Chem.

810　　　　　US　　ISSN 0009-4285
CHIMES (NOTRE DAME). a. free. Saint Mary's College, Notre Dame, IN 46556. TEL 219-284-4000. illus. circ. 1,600.

800　　　　　CC
CHINESE FOLK CULTURE. (Text in Chinese) 1986. q. Y4.20. Zhongguo Minjian Wenyi Xiehui, Shanghai Fenhui - China Folk Literature and Arts Association, Shanghai Chapter, 675 Julu Road, Shanghai 200040, People's Republic of China. TEL 2475446. Ed. Jiang Bin. circ. 3,000.
Formerly (until 1990): Minjian Wenyi Jikan (ISSN 0540-1186)

895.1　　　　　CC　　ISSN 0009-4617
DS777.55
CHINESE LITERATURE; fiction, poetry, art. French edition: Litterature Chinoise (ISSN 1000-9132) (Text in English) 1951. q. $16.50. (Wenhua Bu, Waiwen Ju - Ministry of Culture, Foreign Language Bureau) Zhongguo Wenxue Zazhishe - Chinese Literature Press, 24 Baiwanzhuang Lu, Beijing 100037, People's Republic of China. TEL 832-3291. TELEX 222314-FLPDA-CN. (Dist. by: China International Book Trading Corp., P.O. Box 399, Beijing 100044, P.R.C.; Dist. in US by: China Books & Periodicals Inc., 2929 24th St., San Francisco, CA 94110. TEL 415-282-2994) Ed. He Jingzhi. bk.rev.; illus.; index. circ. 50,000. (also avail. in microform from UMI,MIM) **Indexed:** Arts & Hum.Cit.Ind.
—Faxon; UnCover; SWETS.
Description: Contains new short stories by China's most popular contemporary authors and excerpts from best-selling novels. Includes selections from classical literature, poems, essays, biographical sketches, publishing news and color plates of classical and contemporary art.

895　　　　　US　　ISSN 0887-8099
PL2250
CHINESE LITERATURE: ESSAYS, ARTICLES, REVIEWS. Short title: Clear. 1979. a. $25 to individuals (foreign $35); institutions $50 (foreign $65) (effective 1993). c/o Dept. of Comparative Literature, Ballantine Hall Rm. 402, Indiana University, Bloomington, IN 47405. TEL 812-855-7070. (Subscr. to: Chinese Literature, c/o Ed. Asst., Goodbody Hall 230, Indiana University, Bloomington, IN 47405) Eds. Eugene Eoyang, William Nienhauser. adv.: page $175. **Indexed:** Arts & Hum.Cit.Ind., Curr.Cont., Ind.Bk.Rev.Hum. Document type: academic/scholarly publication.
Formerly (until 1980): Chinese Literature (ISSN 0161-9705)
Description: Publishes original critical essays, articles and reviews on topics in Chinese literature from all periods.
Refereed Serial

800　　　　　CH
THE CHINESE PEN. 1972. q. NT.$400($20) International P.E.N. (Poets, Playwrights, Editors, Essayists, and Novelists), Taipei Chinese Center, 5th Fl., No. 33, Lane 180, Kwang Fu South Rd., Taipei 10553, Taiwan, Republic of China. TEL 02-721-9101. Ed. Pang-yuan Chi. bk.rev.; illus.; cum.index. circ. 2,600. Document type: consumer publication.
Description: Translations of contemporary Chinese short stories, poetry and essays; includes listings of cultural activities in Taiwan. Includes an introduction to new artist with each issue. Contains traditional styles as well.

CHINOPERL PAPERS. see ORIENTAL STUDIES

808　　　　　US　　ISSN 0277-7223
CB226
CHIRICU. (Text in English, Portuguese, Spanish) 1977. a. $5 to individuals; institutions $7. Indiana University, Chicano Riqueno Studies, 849 Ballantine Hall, Bloomington, IN 47405. TEL 812-855-5257. FAX 812-855-8577. Ed. Miguel Angel Vazquez. adv.; bk.rev. circ. 300. **Indexed:** Chic.Per.Ind., M.L.A. Document type: academic/scholarly publication.
Description: Includes scholarly essays, original poetry, fiction, theatre and art by Latinos and non-Latinos interested in Latino issues.

895.74　　　　　KN
CHOSON MUNHAK/KOREAN LITERATURE. (Text in Korean) m. Central Committee of the Korean Writers' Union, Pyongyang, N. Korea.

818　　　　　US
CHRISTMAS: THE ANNUAL OF CHRISTMAS LITERATURE AND ART. 1931. a. $10.95 paper. Augsburg Fortress, 426 S. Fifth St., Box 1209, Minneapolis, MN 55440. TEL 612-330-3300. Ed. Gloria E. Bengtson. circ. 67,000.
Formerly (until 1987): Christmas: An American Annual of Christmas Literature and Art (ISSN 0069-3928)

CHU FENG. see FOLKLORE

895.1　　　　　CC　　ISSN 1003-2738
CHUANQI WENXUE XUANKAN/SELECTED LEGENDARY LITERATURE. (Text in Chinese) 1985. m. Y13.80. Henan Sheng Wenlian, No. 34, Jing 7 Lu, Zhengzhou, Henan 450003, People's Republic of China. TEL 334646. (Dist. overseas by: Jiangsu Publications Import & Export Corp., 56 Gao Yun Ling, Nanjing, Jiangsu, P.R.C.) Ed. Xing Guilun. adv.; bk.rev. circ. 20,000.

895.1　　　　　CC　　ISSN 1001-621X
CHUN FENG/SPRING BREEZE. (Text in Chinese) m. Changchun Shi Wenlian, 11, Jianhe Jie, Changchun, Jilin 130061, People's Republic of China. TEL 822690. Ed. Zhang Shaowu.

895.1　　　　　CH　　ISSN 0303-0849
CHUNG-WAI LITERARY MONTHLY. (Text in Chinese) 1972. m. NT.$1200 to individuals (foreign $64); institutions NT.$1400 (foreign $76). c/o Department of Foreign Languages, National Taiwan University, Roosevelt Rd. Sec. 4, Taipei 106, Taiwan, Republic of China. TEL 886-2-3639652. FAX 886-2-3639395. Ed. Hsien-hao Liao. adv. contact: Chun-yen Chen. bk.rev. Document type: academic/scholarly publication.
Description: Contains articles on literature, literary works, poetry, and translations of foreign literature.

870　　　　　IT　　ISSN 0009-6687
CICERONIANA; rivista di studi Ciceroniani. 1959. irreg. L.20000. Centro di Studi Ciceroniani, Piazza dei Cavalieri di Malta 2, Rome, Italy. Dir. Scevola Mariotti.

810　　　　　US　　ISSN 0009-6849
AS36
CIMARRON REVIEW. 1967. q. $12 (Canada $15). Oklahoma State University, Department of English, 205 Morrill Hall, Stillwater, OK 74078-0135. TEL 405-744-9476. FAX 405-744-6326. Ed. Gordon Weaver. bk.rev.; cum.index every 2 yrs. circ. 700. (also avail. in microfilm from UMI) **Indexed:** Amer.Hum.Ind., Ind.Amer.Per.Verse, M.L.A. Document type: academic/scholarly publication.
—UnCover; UMI.
Description: Publishes fiction, poetry, essays and reviews, with regular features on international literatures.

890 701　　　　　II
CINMAY SMRTI PATHAGARA. (Text in Bengali) 1970. a. Rs.8. 26-8A Mahatma Gandhi Rd., Calcutta 9, India. adv.

700 100　　　　　FR　　ISSN 0069-4177
CIRCE. 1969. irreg. 420 F. for 10 nos. Lettres Modernes, 45 rue Saint-Andre, 14123 Fleury sur Orne, France. TEL 31-84-47-06. FAX 31-84-48-09. Ed. Jean Burgos.

810　　　　　US
CITY RANT. 1989. irreg. $5.95. McOne Press, Box 50174, Austin, TX 78763. TEL 512-477-2269. Ed. John McElhenney. circ. 2,000.

860　　　　　CK　　ISSN 0069-4444
CLASICOS COLOMBIANOS. 1954. irreg., no.8, 1980. price varies. Instituto Caro y Cuervo, Seccion de Publicaciones, Apdo. Aereo 51502, Bogota, Colombia.

CLASSIC; magazine of creative writing and art. see LITERARY AND POLITICAL REVIEWS

800　　　　　US　　ISSN 0896-0011
PN681.5
CLASSICAL AND MEDIEVAL LITERATURE CRITICISM; excerpts from criticism of the works of world authors from classical antiquity through the fourteenth century, from the first appraisals to current evaluations. irreg. (1-2/yr.). $99. Gale Research Inc., 835 Penobscot Bldg., Detroit, MI 48226. TEL 313-961-2242. FAX 313-961-6083. TELEX 810-221-7086. Eds. Dennis Poupard, Jelena O. Krstovic. Document type: academic/scholarly publication.

800　　　　　US　　ISSN 0197-2227
PN883
CLASSICAL AND MODERN LITERATURE: A QUARTERLY. 1980. q. $20 to individuals; institutions $24. C M L, Inc., Box 629, Terre Haute, IN 47808-0629. TEL 812-237-2362. Eds. James O. Loyd, Virginia Leon de Vivero. adv.; bk.rev.; index. circ. 500. **Indexed:** Bk.Rev.Ind. (1982-), Child.Bk.Rev.Ind. (1982-), Curr.Cont., M.L.A. Document type: academic/scholarly publication.
—BLDSC (3274.534000); Faxon; UnCover; SWETS. CCC.
Description: Covers all aspects of classical and modern literatures. Uses the knowledge and depth of the scholar's own discipline to examine problems recurring in both classical and modern literature.

3610 LITERATURE

870 930 UK ISSN 0069-4460
CLASSICAL ASSOCIATION. PROCEEDINGS. 1904. a. £3. Classical Association, St. John's College, Cambridge CB2 1TP, England. Ed. M. Schofield. adv. circ. 4,000. (also avail. in microfilm) **Document type:** proceedings.
  Description: Contains text of presidential address, report of annual formal meeting, news from branches, and a statement of accounts.

CLASSICAL JOURNAL. see *CLASSICAL STUDIES*

850 IT
CLASSICI ITALIANI MINORI. irreg., latest no.18. price varies. Angelo Longo Editore, Via Paolo Costa 33, P.O. Box 431, 48100 Ravenna, Italy. TEL 0544-217026. Ed. Enzo Esposito. circ. 2,000. **Document type:** monographic series.

820 US ISSN 0069-4509
CLASSICS OF BRITISH HISTORICAL LITERATURE. 1970. irreg., no.14, 1984. price varies. University of Chicago Press, 5801 S. Ellis Ave., Chicago, IL 60637. TEL 312-702-7899. Ed. John L. Clive. (reprint service avail. from UMI,ISI)
  Refereed Serial

841 FR ISSN 0755-1959
CLASSIQUES FRANCAIS DU MOYEN AGE. Variant title: C F M A. (Text in ancient French; summaries in French) 1910. q. free. Librairie Honore Champion, 7 quai Malaquais, 75006 Paris, France. TEL 46-34-07-29. FAX 46-34-64-06. Ed. Felix Lecoy. circ. 2,000. (back issues avail) **Indexed:** M.L.A.

808 US
CLEAR BEGINNINGS.* 1981. 3/yr. $3 per no. Clear Beginnings Women's Writers Workshops, c/o Pfender, 5533 38th Ave., N.E., Seattle, WA 98105-2203. Eds. Elizabeth Pfender, Marjorie Mitchell.

808 US
CLIFTON MAGAZINE. 1972. 3/yr. $15. University of Cincinnati, Communications Board, 201 TUC, Mail Location 65, Cincinnati, OH 45221. TEL 513-556-6379. Ed. Eden Casteel. adv.; bk.rev.; play rev.; charts; illus.; cum.index: 1972-1987. circ. 33,500.
  Description: Provides local news stories of concern to university community, as well as fictions and poetry.

800 US
CLINTON ST.. (Text in English; occasionally in Spanish) 1979. 3/yr. $12. Out of the Ashes Press, Box 3588, Portland, OR 97208. TEL 503-222-6039. Ed. David Milholland. adv.; bk.rev.; cum.index: 1979-1988. circ. 50,000. (tabloid format; back issues avail.)
  Formerly: Clinton St. Quarterly.
  Description: Forum of world affairs, literature, the environment and art.

CLIO (FORT WAYNE); a journal of literature, history, and the philosophy of history. see *HISTORY*

CLIPPER STUDIES IN THE THEATER. see *THEATER*

810 US
CLIPS FROM BEAR'S HOME MOVIES. 1985. irreg. $4. Dancing Bear Productions, Box 733, Concord, MA 01742. TEL 617-369-5592. Ed. Craig Ellis. circ. 500.

800 780 700 US ISSN 0740-9311
NX504
CLOCKWATCH REVIEW; a journal of the arts. 1983. 2/yr. $8. Clockwatch Review, Inc., c/o Department of English, Wesleyan University, Bloomington, IL 61702. TEL 309-556-3352. FAX 309-556-3411. Ed. James Plath. adv.; bk.rev.; illus.; index. circ. 1,500. **Indexed:** A.I.P.P., Amer.Hum.Ind., Ind.Amer.Per.Verse.
  Description: Fiction, poetry, and interviews with contemporary artists and musicians.

808 US
CLUES (BOWLING GREEN); a journal of detection. 1980. s-a. $12.50. c/o Mrs. Pat Browne, Ed., Bowling Green State University, Bowling Green, OH 43403. TEL 419-372-7867. FAX 419-372-8095. adv.; bk.rev. circ. 700. **Indexed:** Amer.Bibl.Slavic & E.Eur.Stud., M.L.A.

800 US
COCHRAN'S CORNER. 1986. q. $20 (effective 1992). 1003 Tyler Ct., Waldorf, MD 20602. (And: 5819 Castle Brook, San Antonio, TX 98218) Ed. Debra Tompkins. adv. contact: Eve Williams.
  Description: Contains short stories, poems and articles.

800 US
COE REVIEW. 1972. a. $4. Coe College, Student Senate, 1220 First Ave., Cedar Rapids, IA 52402. TEL 319-399-8539. Ed. Jennifer Beardsley. circ. 500.
  Formerly: Caravan.

800 US ISSN 1050-5873
Z881
COLBY QUARTERLY. 1943. q. $12. Colby College, Waterville, ME 04901. TEL 207-872-3622. Ed. Douglas Archibald. adv.; bibl.; illus.; index. circ. 800. (also avail. in microfilm) **Indexed:** Abstr.Engl.Stud., Amer.Hist.& Life, Arts & Hum.Cit.Ind., Curr.Cont., Hist.Abstr., M.L.A.
  —Faxon; UnCover; UMI.
  Formerly: Colby Library Quarterly (ISSN 0010-0552)

810 US ISSN 0084-8816
COLD-DRILL. 1970. a. $9. Boise State University, Department of English, 1910 University Dr., Boise, ID 83725. TEL 208-385-1999. FAX 208-385-4373. Ed. Tom Trusky. charts; illus.

869 BL
COLECAO DOS AUTORES CELEBRES DA LITERATURA BRASILEIRA. 1988. irreg., latest 1989. Fundacao Casa de Rui Barbosa, Rua Sao Clemente, 134, Botafogo, 22260 Rio de Janeiro, RJ, Brazil. FAX 5371114.

869 BL
COLECAO ESCRITORES BRASILEIROS; antologia e estudos. 1982. irreg. Editora Atica, S.A., Rua Barao de Iguape, 110, Caixa Postal 8656, Sao Paulo, Brazil.

869 PO
COLECCAO ENSAIO. no.3, 1981. irreg. Edicoes Ro, Rua da Tojeirinha, 10, 2735 Cacem, Portugal.

869 PO
COLECCAO LITERATURA. irreg., no.12, 1982. (Instituto Nacional de Investigacao Cientifica, Centro de Linguistica) Universidade de Coimbra, Centro de Estudos Classico y Humanisticos, Faculdade de Letras, Coimbra, Portugal.

800 AG
COLECCION ESTUDIOS LATINOAMERICANOS. 1972. irreg. Fernando Garcia Cambeiro (Dist.), Cochabamba 244, 1150 Buenos Aires, Argentina. Ed. Graciela Maturo. **Indexed:** P.A.I.S.For.Lang.Ind.

808 PY
COLECCION LITERATURA. irreg., no.3, 1983. El Lector, 25 de Mayo y Antequera, Asuncion, Paraguay.

COLECCION MIGUEL SALGUERO. see *ETHNIC INTERESTS*

860 SP
COLECCION POLIEDRO. irreg., no.10, 1981. Ediciones Rayuela, Claudio Coello, 19, Madrid-1, Spain.

860 NQ
COLECCION POPULAR DE LITERATURA NICARAGUENSE. DOCUMENTOS. 1982. irreg. Ministerio de Cultura, Apdo. 3514, Managua, Nicaragua. Ed. Ernesto Cardenal.

808 001.6 US
COLIN'S MAGAZINE. 1991. irreg. (approx. 2/yr.). $7 per no. Poets, Painters, Composers, 10524 35th Ave., S.W., Seattle, WA 98146. TEL 206-937-8155.
  Description: Forum for literary discussion of contemporary culture and technology.

800 US ISSN 1044-1441
COLLAGES & BRICOLAGES; the journal of international writing. (Text mainly in English; occasionally in French, Spanish) 1987. a. $7.50 (effective 1994). Box 86, Clarion, PA 16214. TEL 814-226-5799. (Dist. by: Bernhard DeBoer, Inc., 113 E. Centre St., Nutley, NJ 07110. TEL 201-667-9300) Ed. Marie-Jose Fortis. bk.rev. circ. 700.
  Description: Contains short fiction, short plays, poetry, essays, and interviews.

800 920 NE ISSN 0169-0078
COLLECTION MONOGRAPHIQUE RODOPI EN LITTERATURE FRANCAISE CONTEMPORAINE. (Text in English, French) 1984. irreg., vol.20, 1993. price varies. Editions Rodopi B.V., Keizersgracht 302-304, 1016 EX Amsterdam, Netherlands. TEL 31-20-6227507. FAX 31-20-6380948. (In N. America: 233 Peachtree St., N.E., Ste. 404, Atlanta, GA 30303-1504, USA. TEL 800-225-3998. FAX 404-522-7116; Subscr. in France to: Nordeal, B.P. 139, 30, rue de Verlinghem, F-59832 Lambersart, France) (Co-publisher: Nordeal) **Document type:** monographic series.
  Description: Presents various authors of contemporary French literature and poetry.

840 809 SZ
COLLECTION STENDHALIENNE. (Text in French) 1969. irreg., no.30, 1993. price varies. Librairie Droz S.A., 11, rue Massot, CH-1211 Geneva 12, Switzerland. TEL 022-3466666. FAX 022-3472391. (Subscr. to: Case Postale 389, CH-1211 Geneva 12, Switzerland) Ed. V. Del Litto. **Document type:** monographic series.

895 BE
COLLECTION VIETNAMIENNE. 1973. irreg., no.7, 1985. price varies. Librairie-Editions Thanh-Long, 34 rue Dekens, B-1040 Brussels, Belgium. **Document type:** monographic series.

800 US ISSN 0093-3139
PR1 CODEN: COLTEY
COLLEGE LITERATURE. 1974. 3/yr. $24 to individuals (foreign $29); institutions $48 (foreign $53). West Chester University, 554 New Main, West Chester, PA 19383. TEL 215-436-2901. FAX 215-436-3150. Ed. Kostas Myrsiades. adv.; bk.rev.; index. circ. 900. (also avail. in microfilm from UMI; reprint service avail. from UMI) **Indexed:** Abstr.Engl.Stud., Amer.Bibl.Slavic & E.Eur.Stud., Amer.Hum.Ind., Arts & Hum.Cit.Ind., Bk.Rev.Ind. (1980-), Child.Bk.Rev.Ind. (1980-), Curr.Cont., LCR, M.L.A. **Document type:** academic/scholarly publication.
  —BLDSC (3311.160000); Faxon; UnCover; UMI.
  Description: Presents scholarly criticism dedicated to the needs of college and university teachers by providing them with access to innovative ways of studying and teaching new bodies of literature and experiencing old literatures in new ways.

COLLOQUI CREMONESE. see *ART*

COLLOQUIA GERMANICA; an international journal for Germanic philology and literary criticism. see *LINGUISTICS*

800 PO ISSN 0010-1451
NX7
COLLOQUIO: LETRAS. 1971. q. $65 in Europe; elsewhere $80. Fundacao Calouste Gulbenkian, Av. de Berna 45, 1093 Lisbon, Portugal. TEL 1-7935131. FAX 1-7935139. Dir. David Mourao Ferreira. circ. 4,000.
  —BLDSC (3320.450000); Faxon.

801 SZ ISSN 0179-3780
COLLOQUIUM HELVETICUM; Schweizerhefte fuer allgemeine und vergleichende Literaturwissenschaft. (Text in French, German and Italian) 1985. s.a. 30 SFr.($24) (Schweizerische Gesellschaft fuer Allgemeine und Vergleichende Literaturwissenschaft) Verlag Peter Lang AG, Jupiterstr. 15, CH-3000 Bern 15, Switzerland. TEL 031-9411122. FAX 031-9411131. TELEX 912651-PELA-CH. Ed. Michele Staeuble. **Document type:** academic/scholarly publication.

800 378.1 US ISSN 0010-1982
AP2
COLUMBIA REVIEW (NEW YORK). 1815. a. Columbia University, Columbia Review, 101 Ferris Booth Hall, New York, NY 10027. TEL 212-854-3611. circ. 500. (also avail. in microform) **Indexed:** C.L.I. **Document type:** academic/scholarly publication.
  Description: Literary magazine edited by the students of Columbia University. Includes poetry and prose.

LITERATURE

791.4   US
COMEDY WRITERS ASSOCIATION NEWSLETTER. 1989. q. $20 (prices typically set in Jan.). Robert Makinson, Ed. & Pub., Box 023304, Brooklyn, NY 11202-0066. TEL 718-855-5057. adv.; bk.rev. (looseleaf format; back issues avail.)
  Description: Creation and marketing of jokes, scripts and humorous stories.

791.4   US
COMEDY WRITERS BULLETIN. 1980. a. $9. Robert Makinson, Ed. & Pub., Box 023304, Brooklyn, NY 11202-0066. TEL 718-855-5057.

820   US   ISSN 0069-6412
PR251
COMITATUS; a journal of Medieval and Renaissance studies. 1970. a. $10 to individuals; institutions $15. University of California at Los Angeles, Center for Medieval and Renaissance Studies, 212 Royce Hall, 405 Hilgard Ave., Los Angeles, CA 90024-1485. TEL 310-825-1880. FAX 310-825-0655. Ed. Blair Sullivan. bk.rev. circ. 500. (back issues avail.) **Indexed:** Arts & Hum.Cit.Ind., Curr.Cont., M.L.A. **Document type:** academic/scholarly publication.
  —Faxon.
  Description: Takes an interdisciplinary approach to the study of medieval and Renaissance studies. Articles provided by graduate students and new scholars.
  Refereed Serial

COMMON KNOWLEDGE. see *PHILOSOPHY*

808.8 950 001.3   US   ISSN 0732-6734
PR9080
COMMONWEALTH NOVEL IN ENGLISH. 1982. s-a. $14 to individuals; institutions $16. B S C Center for International Understanding, c/o Sudhakar R. Jamkhandi, Ed., Bluefield St. College, English Dept., Bluefield, WV 24701-2198. FAX 304-325-7747. adv.; bk.rev.; index. circ. 300. (back issues avail.) **Indexed:** Abstr.Engl.Stud., M.L.A.
  —BLDSC (3340.947000).
  Description: Examines the socio-political and economic landscapes in Commonwealth novels.

809   US   ISSN 0275-2069
COMMUNICATION AND THE HUMAN CONDITION. vol.2, 1973. irreg., latest vol.2. price varies. Gordon & Breach Science Publishers, 820 Town Center Dr., Langhorne, PA 19047. TEL 215-750-2642. FAX 215-750-6343. (UK subscr. to: P.O. Box 90, Reading, Berkshire RG1 8JL, England. TEL 0734-560-080) Ed. L. Thayer. **Document type:** monographic series.
  —BLDSC (3359.312000).
  Refereed Serial

700   US   ISSN 0740-8943
PT2603.R397
COMMUNICATIONS FROM THE INTERNATIONAL BRECHT SOCIETY. 1970. s-a. $25. International Brecht Society, c/o W. Lewis, Dept. of Germanic and Slavic Language, University of Georgia, Athens, GA 30602. TEL 404-542-3663. Ed. Michael Gilbert. adv.; bk.rev.; play rev.; bibl. circ. 400. (back issues avail.) **Indexed:** M.L.A.
  —UnCover.

800   SZ   ISSN 0942-8917
▼**COMPAR-A-ISON**; international journal of comparative literature. (Text in English, French, German) 1992. s-a. 80 SFr. Peter Lang AG, Jupiterstr. 15, CH-3000 Bern 15, Switzerland. TEL 031-9411122. FAX 031-9411131. Ed. Michael Jakob. circ. 400. **Document type:** academic/scholarly publication.

800   US   ISSN 0195-7678
PN855
THE COMPARATIST. 1977. a. $15. Southern Comparative Literature Association, Comparatist, c/o Marcel Cornis-Pope, Ed., Department of English, Virginia Commonwealth Univ., Richmond, VA 23284-2005. TEL 804-367-1667. FAX 804-367-2171. bk.rev. circ. 450. **Indexed:** Amer.Bibl.Slavic & E.Eur.Stud, Amer.Hum.Ind., Can.Rev.Comp.Lit, M.L.A. **Document type:** academic/scholarly publication.
  —BLDSC (3363.741400); UnCover.
  Description: A forum for comparative literature.

809   UK   ISSN 0144-7564
PN863   CODEN: CMCRE3
COMPARATIVE CRITICISM; a yearbook. 1979. a. £30($58) to individuals (overseas £37.50); institutions £55 (overseas £62.50 ($94)). (British Comparative Literature Association) Cambridge University Press, Edinburgh Bldg., Shaftesbury Rd., Cambridge CB2 2RU, England. TEL 0223-312393. FAX 0223-315052. TELEX 851817256. (N. American addr.: Cambridge University Press, Journals Dept., 40 W. 20th St., New York, NY 10011. TEL 212-924-3900. FAX 212-691-3239) Ed. Elinor Shaffer. adv. (also avail. in microform from UMI; back issues avail.) **Indexed:** M.L.A. **Document type:** academic/scholarly publication.
  —BLDSC (3363.752750); Faxon; UnCover; SWETS; UMI. **CCC**.
  Description: Examines literary theory and criticism and comparative studies for theme, genre, movement and influence.

809   US   ISSN 0010-4078
PN1601
COMPARATIVE DRAMA. 1967. q. $15 to individuals (foreign $18); institutions $30 (foreign $32.50). Western Michigan University, Department of English, Kalamazoo, MI 49008-3851. TEL 616-387-2576. FAX 616-387-8750. Ed. John H. Stroupe. bk.rev.; bibl.; index. circ. 900. (also avail. in microform from UMI; back issues avail.; reprint service avail. from UMI) **Indexed:** Abstr.Engl.Stud., Amer.Bibl.Slavic & E.Eur.Stud., Arts & Hum.Cit.Ind., Bk.Rev.Ind. (1980-), Can.Rev.Comp.Lit., Child.Bk.Rev.Ind. (1980-), Curr.Cont., Hum.Ind., Ind.Bk.Rev.Hum., LCR, M.L.A., Mid.East: Abstr.& Ind. **Document type:** academic/scholarly publication.
  —BLDSC (3363.755000); Faxon; UnCover; UMI.

800 778.534   US   ISSN 0899-9902
COMPARATIVE LITERARY AND FILM STUDIES: EUROPE, JAPAN, AND THE THIRD WORLD. irreg. Peter Lang Publishing, Inc., 62 W. 45th St., 4th Fl., New York, NY 10036. TEL 212-302-6740. FAX 212-302-7574. Ed. Douglas Radcliff-Umstead. **Document type:** academic/scholarly publication.
  Description: Presents studies on major authors and film makers of the twentieth century who were involved in movements like Surrealism, Futurism, Structuralism, Hermeticism, the New Novel, Neorealism, New German Cinema, and Magic Realism.

809   US   ISSN 0010-4124
PN851
COMPARATIVE LITERATURE. (Text mainly in English; occasionally in French, German, Italian, Spanish) 1949. q. $15 to individuals (foreign $17); institutions $25 (foreign $27). University of Oregon, Comparative Literature, 223 Friendly Hall, Eugene, OR 97403-1233. TEL 503-346-4022. FAX 503-346-4030. Ed. Steven Rendall. bk.rev.; index, cum.index: 1949-1963. circ. 3,000. (also avail. in microfiche from UMI; reprint service avail. from UMI) **Indexed:** Abstr.Engl.Stud., Amer.Bibl.Slavic & E.Eur.Stud., Arts & Hum.Cit.Ind., Bk.Rev.Ind. (1965-), Child.Bk.Rev.Ind. (1965-), Curr.Cont., Hum.Ind., Ind.Bk.Rev.Hum., LCR, M.L.A., Mid.East: Abstr.& Ind. **Document type:** academic/scholarly publication.
  —Faxon; UnCover; SWETS; UMI.

807   CN
COMPARATIVE LITERATURE IN CANADA/LITTERATURE COMPAREE AU CANADA. Variant title: C C L A Bulletin - A C L C Newsletter. s-a. $5. Canadian Comparative Literature Association - Association Canadienne de Litterature Comparee, c/o Universite de Montreal, Montreal, Que H3C 3J7, Canada. Ed. P.A. Robberecht.

809   US   ISSN 0010-4132
PN851
COMPARATIVE LITERATURE STUDIES. 1963. q. $25 to individuals (foreign $32.50); institutions $37.50 (foreign $45). (Pennsylvania State University) Pennsylvania State University Press, Barbara Bldg., Ste. C, 820 N. University Dr., University Park, PA 16802-1003. TEL 814-865-1327. FAX 814-863-1408. Ed. Robert Edwards. adv.; bk.rev.; cum.index: vols.1-10. circ. 1,000. (also avail. in microform from UMI; reprint service avail. from UMI) **Indexed:** Abstr.Engl.Stud., Amer.Bibl.Slavic & E.Eur.Stud., Arts & Hum.Cit.Ind., Bk.Rev.Ind. (1976-), Can.Rev.Comp.Lit., Child.Bk.Rev.Ind. (1976-), Curr.Cont., Hum.Ind., Ind.Bk.Rev.Hum., M.L.A., Mid.East: Abstr.& Ind. **Document type:** academic/scholarly publication.
  —BLDSC (3363.789500); Faxon; UnCover; SWETS. **CCC**.
  Refereed Serial

CONCEPCIONES SOUTHWEST; publicacion de literatura y arte de la Universidad de Nuevo Mexico. see *ART*

800 976   US
CONCHO RIVER REVIEW. 1987. s-a. $12. (Fort Concho Museum) Fort Concho Museum Press, 213 E. Ave. D, San Angelo, TX 76903-7099. TEL 915-657-4441. FAX 915-657-4540. Ed. Terrence Dalrymple. adv. contact: Cora Pugmire.

800   US   ISSN 1068-5359
CONCORD SAUNTERER. 1966-1992; N.S. 1993. a. $20 membership. Thoreau Society, Inc., Thoreau Lyceum, 156 Belknap St., Concord, MA 01742. TEL 508-369-5912. Ed. Ronald Hoag. circ. 1,420. (reprint service avail. from ISI) **Indexed:** Amer.Hum.Ind.

800 940 700   US   ISSN 0891-1908
CONFERENCE ON EDITORIAL PROBLEMS: UNIVERSITY OF TORONTO. 1966. a. $37.50. (University of Toronto) A M S Press, Inc., 56 E. 13th St., New York, NY 10003. TEL 212-777-4700. FAX 212-995-5413. index. (back issues avail.)
  Description: Bibliographical and textual articles taken from the conferences on editorial problems held annually at the University of Toronto.

800 500 600   US   ISSN 1063-1801
▼**CONFIGURATIONS**; a journal of literature, science and technology. 1993. 3/yr. $22 to individuals; institutions $50. (Society for Literature and Science) Johns Hopkins University Press, Journals Publishing Division, 2715 Charles St., Baltimore, MD 21218-4319. TEL 410-516-6987. FAX 410-516-6968. Ed.Bd. **Document type:** academic/scholarly publication.
  —BLDSC (3410.633500); UnCover. **CCC**.

869   BL
CONFLUENCIA. 1991. s-a. exchange basis. Liceu Literario Portugues, Instituto de Lingua Portuguesa, Rua Senador Dantas, 118, 20032 Rio de Janeiro, Brazil. Ed. Evanildo Bechara.

810   US   ISSN 0010-5716
PS501
CONFRONTATION; a literary journal of Long Island University. 1968. s-a. $10. Long Island University, C.W. Post College, Dept. of English, Greenvale, NY 11548. TEL 516-299-2391. Ed. Martin Tucker. bk.rev.; illus. circ. 2,000. (also avail. in microfilm from UMI; back issues avail.; reprint service avail. from UMI, ISI) **Indexed:** A.I.P.P., Arts & Hum.Cit.Ind., Curr.Cont., M.L.A.
  —UMI.

808   US   ISSN 0278-2324
PN6010.5
CONJUNCTIONS; other worlds. 1981. s-a. $18 (foreign $25). Box 118, Bard College, Annandale-on-Hudson, NY 12504. TEL 212-477-1136. FAX 914-758-9654. Ed. Bradford Morrow. adv.: B&W page $350. bk.rev. circ. 7,500. **Indexed:** Ind.Bk.Rev.Hum.
  —Faxon.
  Description: Anthology of contemporary, formally innovative poetry and fiction.

890   FR   ISSN 0589-3496
CONNAISSANCE DE L'ORIENT. COLLECTION UNESCO D'OEUVRES REPRESENTATIVES. 1956. (Unesco, UN) Editions Gallimard, 5 rue Sebastien-Bottin, 75007 Paris, France. TEL 33-1-45-44-39-19.

LITERATURE

CONNECTICUT ENGLISH JOURNAL. see EDUCATION

800   US
CONNECTICUT QUARTERLY. At head of title: C Q. 1979. q. $7.50. Asnuntuck Community College Press, Box 68, Enfield, CT 06082. TEL 203-745-1603. Ed. Carol Haber. bk.rev. circ. 300.

800   US   ISSN 0939-5482
PR1
CONNOTATIONS; a journal of critical debate. 1991. 3/yr. $50. Waxman Publishing Co., Box 1318, New York, NY 10028. Ed. Inge Leimberg. **Document type:** academic/scholarly publication.
    Description: Provides a forum for scholarly communication in the field of English literature form the Middle English period to the present. Focuses on the semantic and stylistic energy of the language of literature in a historical perspective and aims to represent different approaches.

820   NE
▼**THE CONRADIAN.** (Text in English) 1993. a. fl.50 per no. (effective 1993). Editions Rodopi, Keizersgracht 302-304, 1016 EX Amsterdam, Netherlands. TEL 31-20-6227507. FAX 31-20-6380948. (In N. America: 233 Peachtree St., N.E., Ste. 404, Atlanta, GA 30303-1504. TEL 800-225-3998. FAX 404-522-7116) Eds. Robert Hampson, Gene M. Moore. **Document type:** academic/scholarly publication.
    Description: Critical studies of the writings of Joseph Conrad.

820   US   ISSN 0010-6356
PR6005.O4
CONRADIANA; a journal of Joseph Conrad studies. 1968. 3/yr. $19 to individuals; institutions $33. Texas Tech University Press, Box 41037, Lubbock, TX 79409-1037. TEL 806-742-2982; 800-832-4042. FAX 806-742-2979. Ed. David Leon Higdon. adv.; bk.rev.; abstr.; bibl.; illus.; index. circ. 504. (also avail. in microform from UMI) **Indexed:** Abstr.Engl.Stud., Amer.Hum.Ind., Curr.Cont., Ind.Bk.Rev.Hum., M.L.A. **Document type:** academic/scholarly publication.
    —Faxon; UnCover; UMI.

800 700   FR   ISSN 0760-629X
CONSEQUENCES. (Text and summaries in French) 1983. 2/yr. 230 F.($45) outside EEC 310 F. ($61)(effective Jan. 1991). (Centre National des Lettres) Impressions Nouvelles, 93, Quai de Valmy, 75010 Paris, France. Ed. Guy Lelong. adv.; bk.rev.; illus. circ. 1,000. (back issues avail.)

CONSTRUCTIVE CRITICISM; a journal of construct psychology and the arts. see PSYCHOLOGY

CONSTRUCTURA. see LINGUISTICS

CONTEMPORANEA; studi e testi. see HISTORY

839.82 500   NO
PT8890.A1
CONTEMPORARY APPROACHES TO IBSEN. (Text in English) 1951. s-a. price varies. Scandinavian University Press, Box 2959-Toeyen, N-0608 Oslo, Norway. TEL 472-67-7600609. FAX 472-67-7575. (Dist. by: Oxford University Press, Distribution Services, Saxon Way West, Corby, Nothants NN 18 9ES, England; In U.S. dist. by: Oxford University Press, 200 Madison Ave., New York, NY 10016, USA) Eds. Bjoern Hemmer, Vigdis Ystad. bk.rev. (back issues avail.) **Indexed:** M.L.A. **Document type:** academic/scholarly publication.
    —CCC.
    Formerly: Ibsenaarboken (ISSN 0073-4365)

830 943   UK   ISSN 0268-1331
CONTEMPORARY GERMAN STUDIES: OCCASIONAL PAPERS. (Text in English and German) 1985. irreg. (1-2/yr.) £3 per no. University of Strathclyde, Department of Modern Languages, 26 Richmond St., Glasgow G1 1XH, Scotland. TEL 041-552-4400. FAX 041-552-4979. Eds. M. McGowan, M. Pender. circ. 420. (back issues avail.) **Document type:** academic/scholarly publication.
    —BLDSC (3425.181875).
    Description: Presents scholarly and academic research papers on the cultural, political, economic, sociological, literary, and educational issues affecting modern Germany.

809   US   ISSN 0091-3421
PN771
CONTEMPORARY LITERARY CRITICISM SERIES; excerpts from criticism of the works of today's novelists, poets, playwrights, and other creative writers. 1973. irreg., vol.67, 1991. $108 per vol. Gale Research Inc., 835 Penobscot Bldg., Detroit, MI 48226. TEL 313-962-2242. FAX 313-961-6083. TELEX 810-221-7086. Ed. Roger Matuz. cum.index. **Indexed:** Child.Auth.& Illus., Perf.Arts Biog.Master Ind. **Document type:** academic/scholarly publication.
    —BLDSC (3425.190600).
    Description: Compendium of critical works on contemporary creative writers.

800   US   ISSN 0010-7484
PN2
CONTEMPORARY LITERATURE. 1960. 4/yr. $24 to individuals; institutions $61. (University of Wisconsin-Madison, Department of English) University of Wisconsin Press, Journal Division, 114 N. Murray St., Madison, WI 53715. TEL 608-262-4952. FAX 608-262-7560. Ed. Thomas Schaub. adv.; bk.rev.; bibl.; cum.index every 2 yrs. circ. 2,100. (also avail. in microform from UMI; back issues avail., reprint service avail from UMI) **Indexed:** Abstr.Engl.Stud., Amer.Bibl.Slavic & E.Eur.Stud., Amer.Hum.Ind., Arts & Hum.Cit.Ind., Curr.Cont., Hum.Ind., Ind.Bk.Rev.Hum., LCR, M.L.A., Mid.East: Abstr.& Ind. **Document type:** academic/scholarly publication.
    —BLDSC (3425.191000); Faxon; UnCover; SWETS; UMI. CCC.
    Formerly: Wisconsin Studies in Contemporary Literature.

800 700   IT   ISSN 0010-762X
CONTENUTI; bimestrale di lettere e arti. bi-m. L.40000. Editrice Pellegrini, Via Roma 74, Casella Postale 158, 87100 Cosenza, Italy. Ed. Luigi Pellegrini.

850   IT
CONTESTO; rivista di letteratura Italiana. 1977. 3/yr. L.16000($15) Argalia Editore, Via N. Sauro 1, 61029 Urbino, Italy. Dir. Claudio Varese. bibl.

800   SZ
CONTINENT CENDRARS. (Text in French) 1986. a. varies. Universite de Berne, Centre D'Etudes Blaise Cendrars, Laenggassstr. 49, CH-3012 Bern, Switzerland. Ed. Jean-Carlo Flueckiger. bk.rev. **Document type:** bulletin.

808   US   ISSN 0738-9345
CONTRIBUTIONS TO THE STUDY OF WORLD LITERATURE. 1983. irreg. price varies. Greenwood Press, Inc. (Subsidiary of: Greenwood Publishing Group Inc.), 88 Post Rd. W., Box 5007, Westport, CT 06881-5007. TEL 203-226-3571. FAX 203-222-1502. Ed. Leif Sjoberg. index.
    —BLDSC (3461.461000).

869   BL
CONVERGENCIA LUSIADA. (Text in Portuguese, Spanish) 1976. s-a. $50. Centro de Estudos do Real Gabinete Portugues de Leitura, Rua Luis de Camoes 30, 20051-020 Rio de Janeiro RJ, Brazil. TEL 021-221-3138. FAX 021-253-0670. illus. circ. 1,000.
    Formerly: Convergencia.

859   RM   ISSN 0010-8243
CONVORBIRI LITERARE. 1867, N.S. 1972. m. 60 lei($10) Uniunea Scriitorilor din Republica Socialista Romania, Calea Victoriei 115, Bucharest, Rumania. (Subscr. to: ILEXIM, Str. 13 Decembrie Nr. 3, Box 136-137, 70116 Bucharest, Rumania) Ed. Corneliu Sturzu. bk.rev.; bibl. circ. 3,000. **Indexed:** M.L.A.

800 910.09   US   ISSN 1044-3495
COOL TRAVELER; literary publication about "place". 1988. q. $5. Rome Cappuccino Review, 203 S. Market St., Selinsgrove, PA 17870-1813. TEL 215-440-0592. Ed. Bob Moore. adv.; bk.rev. circ. 1,000. (back issues avail.) **Document type:** newsletter.

810 920   US
COOPER SOCIETY NEWSLETTER. 1990. q. $10. James Fenimore Cooper Society, 32 Elm St., Cooperstown, NY 13326-1214. TEL 607-547-2118. Ed. Hugh C. MacDougall. adv.; bk.rev. circ. 125. (back issues avail.; reprint service avail. from UMI) **Document type:** newsletter.
    Description: Covers current scholarship concerning the life and works of James Fenimore Cooper (1789-1851).

800   US
▼**COPPERFIELD'S LITERARY MAGAZINE.** 1992. m. Copperfield's Books, 153 Kentucky St., Petaluma, CA 94952.

808   US
COPULA. q. Copula Press, W. 1114 Indiana St., Spokane, WA 99205. Ed. James Bradford.

CORADDI. see ART

700   US   ISSN 0363-4574
NX1
CORNFIELD REVIEW; an annual of the creative arts. 1976. a. $6. Ohio State University, Marion Campus, 1465 Mt. Vernon Ave., Marion, OH 43302-5695. TEL 614-389-2361. Ed. Stuart Lishan. illus. circ. 750.
    Description: Presents poetry, short fiction and visual art, with an emphasis on Midwestern writers and artists.

801 100   US   ISSN 0270-6687
PS536.2
CORONA. 1980. a. $7 to individuals; institutions $8.50. Montana State University, Department of History and Philosophy, Bozeman, MT 59717. TEL 406-994-5200. Eds. Lynda and Michael Sexson. adv.; bk.rev.; illus. circ. 2,000. (back issues avail.) **Indexed:** Amer.Hum.Ind., M.L.A.

809 839.3   NE
CORPUS SACRAE SCRIPTURAE NEERLANDICAE MEDII AEVII. (Consists of: Catalogus, Miscellanea, Series Maior, Series Minor) 1970. irreg., latest 1984. E.J. Brill, P.O. Box 9000, 2300 PA Leiden, Netherlands. TEL 31-71-312624. FAX 31-71-317532. TELEX 39296 BRILL NL. (In N. America: E.J. Brill, 24 Hudson St., Kinderhook, NY 12106. TEL 800-962-4406. FAX 518-758-1959) Ed. C.C. de Bruin. **Document type:** monographic series, academic/scholarly publication.
    Formerly: Verzameling van Middelnederlandse Bijbelteksten.

800   GW   ISSN 0936-1189
CORVEY JOURNAL; Mitteilungen aus dem Projekt Fuerstliche Bibliothek Corvey. 1989. irreg. Universitaet Paderborn, Projekt Fuerstliche Bibliothek Corvey, Warburgerstr. 100, 33098 Paderborn, Germany. Ed.Bd. **Document type:** monographic series.

810   US
COTTONWOOD. 1965. 3/yr. $15 (foreign $18). Cottonwood Magazine and Press, Box J, 400 Kansas Union, University of Kansas, Lawrence, KS 66045. TEL 913-864-3777. Ed. George F. Wedge. bk.rev.; illus. circ. 500. **Indexed:** Amer.Hum.Ind. **Document type:** academic/scholarly publication.
    Former titles: Cottonwood Review (ISSN 0147-149X); Cottonwood (ISSN 0010-9843)
    Description: Includes a wide variety of poetry and fiction, reviews and interviews.

840   FR   ISSN 0998-6316
COURRIER-EXPRESSION. 1972. s-a. 5 F. Centre Culturel et Sportif de Vulaines, 5 rue Pasteur, Vulaines sur Seine 77870, France. (Affiliate: Federation des Oeuvres Complimentaires de l'Ecole Laique) Ed. Leroux Henry Fonta. circ. 1,000. (tabloid format)

800   US   ISSN 0738-7008
CRAB CREEK REVIEW. (In 3 vols.) 1983. 2/yr. $10 (foreign $13). Crab Creek Review Association, 4462 Whitman Ave., N., Seattle, WA 98103-7347. TEL 206-633-1090. Eds. Linda J. Clifton, Carol Orlock. adv. circ. 500. (back issues avail.) **Indexed:** Ind.Amer.Per.Verse.
    Description: Poetry, short fiction, and translations of poetry and short fiction from Greek, Latin, Chinese, Japanese, and modern work.

LITERATURE

800 US ISSN 0011-0841
PS580 CODEN: CCSCBX
CRAZYHORSE. 1960. s-a. $10. Crazyhorse Association, Department of English, University of Arkansas at Little Rock, 2801 S. University, Little Rock, AR 72204. TEL 501-569-3160. Ed.Bd. adv.; bk.rev. circ. 1,000. (back issues avail.) **Indexed:** M.L.A.
Description: Publishes poetry and short fiction.

808 US ISSN 0887-5308
CRAZYQUILT. 1986. q. $14.95. CrazyQuilt Press, Box 632729, San Diego, CA 92163-2729. TEL 619-688-1023. FAX 619-298-7932. Ed. Jim Kitchen. adv.; bk.rev. circ. 200. (back issues avail.)
Description: Fiction, nonfiction, black and white art and photos, poetry, and drama, as well as interviews with practicing writers.

800 US ISSN 0884-3457
PN6010.5
CREAM CITY REVIEW. 1975. s-a. $10 (effective Jan. 1990). University of Wisconsin-Milwaukee, English Department, Curtin Hall, Box 413, Milwaukee, WI 53201. TEL 414-229-4708. FAX 414-229-6329. Ed. Sandra Nelson. adv.; bk.rev.; film rev.; play rev. circ. 2,500. (back issues avail.) **Indexed:** A.I.P.P., Ind.Amer.Per.Verse. **Document type:** academic/scholarly publication.

820 II
CREATIVE FORUM. 1988. 4/yr. Rs.150($50) Bahri Publications, 997-A St., No. 9, P.O. Box 4453, Gobindpuri, Kalkaji, New Delhi 110 019, India. TEL 6448606. FAX 92-11-64601796. Ed. U.S. Bahri. **Document type:** academic/scholarly publication.

810 US
▼**CREATIVE NONFICTION.** 1993. s-a. $15. Dept. of English, Univ. of Pittsburgh, 526 Cathedral of Learning, Pittsburgh, PA 15260. Ed. Lee Gutkind.
Description: Presents essays of the genre.

CREATIVE WOMAN. see WOMEN'S INTERESTS

810 US
CREATIVE YEARS. bi-m. Coronado Publishers, 5010 N.E. Waldo Rd., Ste. 24, Gainsville, FL 32609-1640. TEL 904-303-7445. Ed. Eloise Henderson.
Formerly: Writers Opportunity.

810 US ISSN 8756-0291
CREEPING BENT. 1984. s-a. $7. 433 West Market St., Bethlehem, PA 18018. TEL 215-866-5613. Ed. Joseph Lucia. bk.rev. circ. 350. (back issues avail.)

800 US ISSN 0749-2871
CRESCENT REVIEW. 1983. s-a. $10. Crescent Review, Inc., 1445 Old Town Rd., Winston-Salem, NC 27106-3143. TEL 202-364-5939. Ed. Guy Nancekeville. adv. circ. 400.
Description: Independent journal devoted only to short stories.

820 UK
CRIMSON CIRCLE MAGAZINE. 1969. q. £8.50 (effective Jan. 1991). Edgar Wallace Society, 7 Devonshire Close, Amersham, Bucks. HP6 5JG, England. TEL 0494-72-5398. Ed. John A. Hogan. bk.rev. circ. 425. **Document type:** newsletter.
Formerly (until 1985): Edgar Wallace Society Newsletter.

800 700 US ISSN 0011-1406
CRISI E LETTERATURA; periodico di lettere filosofia arti. 1961. a. Gaetano Salveti, Ed.& Pub., Via Bu Meliana 12, 00195 Rome, Italy. (Subscr. to: Lago d'Iseo No.21, 00050 Santa Severa, Rome, Italy) bk.rev.; bibl.; illus. circ. 3,000. (tabloid format)

860 US ISSN 0278-7261
PQ6001
CRITICA HISPANICA. (Text in English or Spanish) 1979. s-a. $27 (foreign $38). c/o Gregorio Martin, Ed., Department of Modern Language, Duquesne University, Pittsburgh, PA 15282. TEL 412-434-6415. FAX 412-434-5197. adv.; bk.rev. circ. 500. **Indexed:** Arts & Hum.Cit.Ind., Chic.Per.Ind., Curr.Cont., Ind.Bk.Rev.Hum., M.L.A. **Document type:** academic/scholarly publication.
—Faxon; UnCover.

850 IT ISSN 0390-0142
CRITICA LETTERARIA. 1973. q. L.58000 (foreign L.78000) (effective 1994). Loffredo Editore S.p.A., Via Consalvo, 99-H, 80126 Naples, Italy. TEL 081-5937073. FAX 081-5936953. Ed. Pompeo Giannantonio. bk.rev. circ. 3,000. **Indexed:** Arts & Hum.Cit.Ind., Can.Rev.Comp.Lit., Curr.Cont.
Supersedes: Filologia e Letteratura (ISSN 0015-1777)

820 UK ISSN 0011-1562
AP4 CODEN: CRQUEF
CRITICAL QUARTERLY. 1959. q. £21.50($40) to individuals; institutions £36($65). Basil Blackwell Ltd., 108 Cowley Rd., Oxford OX4 1JF, England. TEL 0865-791100. (Subscr. addr.: c/o Marston Book Services, P.O. Box 87, Oxford OX2 0DT, England) Ed.Bd. adv.; bk.rev.; index. circ. 2,200. (back issues avail.) **Indexed:** Arts & Hum.Cit.Ind., Bk.Rev.Ind. (1988-), Br.Hum.Ind., Child.Bk.Rev.Ind. (1988-), Curr.Cont., Hum.Ind., Ind.Bk.Rev.Hum., M.L.A., Mid.East: Abstr.& Ind. **Document type:** academic/scholarly publication.
—BLDSC (3487.460000); Faxon; UnCover; SWETS; UMI. **CCC.**
Description: Selections of new poetry, literary criticism, contemporary fiction and articles on modern writing.

899 900 100 AT
CRITICAL REVIEW. 1958. a. Aus.$10 (foreign AUS.$12). Australian National University, Research School of Social Sciences, Department of Philosophy, P.O. Box 4, Canberra, A.C.T. 2601, Australia. Ed. S.L. Goldberg. bk.rev. circ. 1,000. (back issues avail.) **Indexed:** Abstr.Engl.Stud., Aus.P.A.I.S., Br.Hum.Ind., Hum.Ind., M.L.A., NRN.
—BLDSC (3487.467000).
Former titles: Critical Review Melbourne (ISSN 0070-1548); Critical Review. Melbourne-Sydney.

CRITICAL REVIEW; an interdisciplinary journal. see LITERARY AND POLITICAL REVIEWS

800 NE ISSN 0923-411X
CRITICAL STUDIES. 1989. irreg., vol.4, 1993. price varies. Editions Rodopi B.V., Keizersgracht 302-304, 1016 EX Amsterdam, Netherlands. TEL 31-20-6227507. FAX 31-20-6380948. (In N. America: 233 Peachtree St., N.E., Ste. 404, Atlanta, GA 30303-1504. TEL 800-225-3998. FAX 404-522-7116) Ed. Myriam Diaz-Diocaretz. **Document type:** monographic series.
—BLDSC (3487.486600).
Refereed Serial

CRITICAL TEXTS: A REVIEW OF THEORY AND CRITICISM. see LITERARY AND POLITICAL REVIEWS

800 700 US ISSN 0011-1589
AS30.W3
CRITICISM; a quarterly for literature and the arts. 1959. q. $28 to individuals; institutions $50 (effective through 1995). Wayne State University Press, 5959 Woodward Ave., Detroit, MI 48202. TEL 313-577-6120. FAX 313-577-6131. Ed. Arthur Marotti. adv.; bk.rev.; illus.; index. circ. 1,175. (also avail. in microform from MIM,UMI; reprint service avail. from UMI,KTO; back issues avail.) **Indexed:** Abstr.Engl.Stud., Bk.Rev.Ind. (1965-), Child.Bk.Rev.Ind. (1965-), Curr.Cont., Film Lit.Ind. (1986-), Hum.Ind., Ind.Bk.Rev.Hum., M.L.A., Mid.East: Abstr.& Ind., RILA. **Document type:** academic/scholarly publication.
—BLDSC (3487.489000); Faxon; UnCover; SWETS; UMI.
Description: Publishes articles on artists, art, and literature from all periods, either individually or in their interrelationships, with an emphasis on post-structuralist critical approaches, feminist and new historicist interpretation.

CRITICON. see LITERATURE — Poetry

801 US ISSN 0011-1619
PN3503
CRITIQUE: STUDIES IN MODERN FICTION. 1956. q. $29 to individuals; institutions $50. (Helen Dwight Reid Educational Foundation) Heldref Publications, 1319 Eighteenth St., N.W., Washington, DC 20036-1802. TEL 202-296-6267. FAX 202-296-5149. Ed. Helen Strang. bk.rev.; index. circ. 1,500. (also avail. in microform; reprint service avail.) **Indexed:** Abstr.Engl.Stud., Arts & Hum.Cit.Ind., Curr.Cont., Hum.Ind., M.L.A. **Document type:** academic/scholarly publication.
—BLDSC (3487.489300); Faxon; UnCover; SWETS; UMI. **CCC.**
Refereed Serial

820 NE ISSN 0924-1426
CROSS - CULTURES; readings in post-colonial literatures in English. (Text in English) 1990. irreg. price varies. Editions Rodopi B.V., Keizersgracht 302-304, 1016 EX Amsterdam, Netherlands. TEL 31-20-6227507. FAX 31-20-6380948. (N. American addr.: 233 Peachtree St., N.E., Ste. 404, Atlanta, GA 30303-1504. TEL 800-225-3998. FAX 404-522-7116) Eds, Hena Maes-Jelinek, Geoffrey Davis. (back issues avail.) **Document type:** academic/scholarly publication, monographic series.

800 700 US ISSN 0739-2354
CROSSCURRENTS; a quarterly. 1980. q. $18. 2200 Glastonbury Rd.; Westlake Village, CA 91361. TEL 818-991-1694. Ed. Linda Brown Michelson. illus. circ. 3,000. (back issues avail.) **Indexed:** Amer.Hum.Ind., Ind.Amer.Per.Verse, M.L.A.
Description: Focused innovative collections of contemporary literature.

820 SA
CRUX. (Text in English) 4/yr. R.15 (effective 1993). Foundation for Education, Science and Technology, P.O. Box 1758, Pretoria 0001, South Africa. TEL 27-12-322-6404. FAX 27-12-320-7803. **Indexed:** Ind.S.A.Per., Lang.Teach.& Ling.Abstr.

CTENAR; mesicnik pro praci s knihou. see LIBRARY AND INFORMATION SCIENCES

CUADERNO LITERARIO AZOR; literatura, poesia, arte, historia, etc., del ambito de la hispanidad. see LITERARY AND POLITICAL REVIEWS

860 SP ISSN 1131-9879
CUADERNOS DE ESTUDIOS DEL SIGLO XVIII. 1991. a. 2500 ptas.($23) Universidad de Oviedo, Instituto Feijoo de Estudios del Siglo XVIII, Fac. de Humidades, 33071 Oviedo, Spain. TEL 98-510-46-71. FAX 98-510-45-13. circ. 500.

CUADERNOS DE INVESTIGACION FILOLOGICA. see LINGUISTICS

CUADERNOS DE LA CATEDRA MIGUEL DE UNAMUNO. see PHILOSOPHY

807 860 AG
CUADERNOS PARA EL ESTUDIO DE LA ESTETICA Y LA LITERATURA. no.8, 1974. irreg. Universidad Nacional del Nordeste, Instituto de Letras, Resistencia, Chaco, Argentina.

700 NQ ISSN 0011-2569
CUADERNOS UNIVERSITARIOS. 1958. 4/yr. C.$12. (Universidad Nacional Autonoma de Nicaragua) Editorial Universitaria de la U N A N, Leon, Nicaragua. Ed. Alejandro Bravo. bk.rev. circ. 1,000. **Indexed:** Amer.Hist.& Life, Hist.Abstr.

CUBA INTERNACIONAL. see POLITICAL SCIENCE

700 IT ISSN 0011-2798
CULTURA NEL MONDO. 1945. q. L.20000. La Cultura nel Mondo, Via Archimede 139, 00197 Rome, Italy. TEL 06-8072575. Ed. Leo Magnino. adv.; bk.rev. circ. 5,000. (also avail. in microform)

809 870 IT ISSN 0391-5654
CULTURA NEOLATINA; revista di filologia romanza. 1941. q. L.100000 (foreign L.120000). Mucchi Editore s.r.l., Via Emilia Est 1527, 41100 Modena, Italy. Ed. Aurelio Roncaglia. (back issues avail.) **Indexed:** Bibl.Ling., M.L.A.
—Faxon; SWETS.

CULTURAL CORRESPONDENCE. see LITERARY AND POLITICAL REVIEWS

LITERATURE

800 659.1 US
CUPID'S DESTINY. 1937. 3/yr. $27. Destiny Syndicate, Box 5637, Reno, NV 89513-5637. Ed. Kelly Williams. adv. circ. 20,000. (back issues avail.)

800 410 US ISSN 0893-5963
CURRENTS IN COMPARATIVE ROMANCE LANGUAGES AND LITERATURES. (Text in English and other West European languages.) 1987. irreg., vol.2, 1988. Peter Lang Publishing, Inc., 62 W. 45th St., 4th Fl., New York, NY 10036. TEL 212-302-6740. FAX 212-302-7574. Eds. Tamara Alvarez-Detrell, Michael G. Paulson. **Document type:** academic/scholarly publication.
—BLDSC (3505.170000).
Description: Concentrates on literary and linguistic works with a comparative basis, usually drawing on two or more Romance language literatures.

800 UK
CURTAINS. 1971. s-a. price varies. Pressed Curtains, 4 Bower St., Maidstone, Kent ME16 8SD, England. Ed. Paul Buck. bk.rev. circ. 400. (processed)

900 800 US ISSN 0737-139X
CUYAHOGA REVIEW. 1983. s-a. $10. Cuyahoga Community College (Western Campus), 11000 Pleasant Valley Rd., Parma, OH 44130. TEL 216-987-5000. Ed. Richard Charnigo. circ. 400. **Indexed:** M.L.A.
—BLDSC (3506.221500).

891.66 UK
CYFRES CLASURON YR ACADEMI. (Text in Welsh) 1980. irreg. price varies. (Welsh Academy) University of Wales Press, 6 Gwennyth St., Cathays, Cardiff CF2 4YD, Wales. TEL 0222-231919. FAX 0222-230908. Ed. P.J. Donovan. **Document type:** academic/scholarly publication.
Description: Covers the classics of Welsh literature previously available only in manuscript form.

820 II
CYGNUS; journal of research in English. (Text in English) 1979. s-a. Rs.30($15) Centre for Commonwealth Literature, Mohana, C-278 Niralanagar, Lucknow-226 007, India. Ed. A.K. Srivastava. circ. 1,000.

820 US ISSN 0011-4936
PR6023.A93
D H LAWRENCE REVIEW. 1968. 3/yr. $14 to individuals (foreign $15); institutions $20. University of Delaware, English Department, 204 Memorial Hall, Newark, DE 19716. TEL 302-454-1480. Ed. Dennis Jackson. adv.; bk.rev.; film rev.; play rev.; bibl.; index; circ. 850 (controlled). (also avail. in microform from UMI; back issues avail.) **Indexed:** Abstr.Engl.Stud., Amer.Hum.Ind., Arts & Hum.Cit.Ind., Curr.Cont., M.L.A. **Document type:** academic/scholarly publication.
—BLDSC (3579.501000); Faxon; UnCover; UMI.

800 US
D H LAWRENCE SOCIETY OF NORTH AMERICA. NEWSLETTER. 1981. s-a. membership. Ohio Northern University, Department of English, Ada, OH 45810. TEL 419-772-2101. (Subscr. to: Nancy Kushigian, Treas., 2919 Whittier Ct., Ann Arbor, MI 48108) Ed. Eleanor H. Green. film rev.; play rev.; bibl.; illus. circ. 250. (looseleaf format; back issues avail.) **Document type:** newsletter.
Description: Contains material of interest to Lawrence scholars and admirers.

800 NE ISSN 0921-2507
D Q R STUDIES IN LITERATURE. (Dutch Quarterly Review) 1986. irreg., latest vol.8, 1990. price varies. Editions Rodopi B.V., Keizersgracht 302-304, 1016 EX Amsterdam, Netherlands. TEL 31-20-6227507. FAX 31-20-6380948. (In N. America: 233 Peachtree St., N.E., Ste. 404, Atlanta, GA 30303-1504. TEL 800-225-3998. FAX 404-522-7116) Ed.Bd. (reprint service avail. from SWZ) **Indexed:** Bibl.Ling. **Document type:** monographic series.
—Faxon; UnCover.
Incorporates (1971-1991): Dutch Quarterly Review of Anglo American Letters (ISSN 0046-0842)

800 410 DK ISSN 0105-208X
D S L'S PRAESENTATIONSHAEFTE. 1975. irreg. DKK 12.20. Danske Sprog- og Litteraturselskab - Society for Danish Language and Literature, Frederiksholms Kanal 18 A, DK-1220 Copenhagen K, Denmark. TEL 45-33-13-06-60. FAX 45-33-14-06-08. circ. 1,200. **Document type:** academic/scholarly publication.
Description: Deals with aspects or editions within the program of this editorial society.

DACOROMANIA; Jahrbuch fuer oestliche Latinitaet. see LINGUISTICS

800 700 US ISSN 0084-9537
NX600.D3
DADA - SURREALISM. 1970. a. $12 to individuals; institutions $15. Association for the Study of Dada and Surrealism, Univ. of Iowa, 425 EPB, Iowa City, IA 52242. TEL 319-335-0330. Ed. Rudolf Kuenzli. adv.; bibl.; illus. (back issues avail.) **Indexed:** Amer.Hum.Ind., Artbibl.Mod., RILA.
Description: Critical essays, previously unpublished documents and extensive bibliographies on Dada and Surrealism.

DALHOUSIE REVIEW; a Canadian journal of literature and opinion. see LITERARY AND POLITICAL REVIEWS

891.7 BW
DALYAGLYADY LITARATURNY ZBORNIK. 1975. a. Vydavetstva Mastatskaya Litaratura, Pr. Masherova 11, 220600 Minsk, Belarus. TEL 0172-234809. Ed.Bd.
Description: Contains translations of foreign literature and poetry into Belorussian.

810 US
DAMASCUS ROAD. 1959. irreg. (approx. a.), latest vol.10. $2.95 per no. c/o C.S. Hanna, Ed., 6271 Hill Dr., Allentown, PA 18104. TEL 215-395-6469. circ. 500. (also avail. in microform from UMI; reprint service avail. from UMI)

800 US
DAN RIVER ANTHOLOGY (YEAR). 1984. a. $12.95. (Conservatory of American Letters) Dan River Press, Box 298, Thomaston, ME 04861-0298. TEL 207-354-0998. Ed. Richard S. Danbury III. circ. 1,000.
Description: Annual collection of fiction and poetry from all over the country.

850 IT
DANAE. 1989. q. Editrice Danae, Via Lucrezio 3, 41012 Carpi (MO), Italy.

DANDELION. see LITERATURE — Poetry

895.1 CC ISSN 0257-0165
DANGDAI/CONTEMPORARY ERA. (Text in Chinese; summaries in Chinese and English) 1979. bi-m. Y22.80($5) Renmin Wenxue Chubanshe - People's Literature Publishing House, 166 Chaonei Dajie, Beijing 100705, People's Republic of China. TEL 55-7553. (Dist. outside China by: China International Book Trading Corp., P.O. Box 399, Beijing, P.R.C.; Dist. in US by: China Books & Periodicals, Inc., 2929 24th St., San Francisco, CA 94110) Ed. Qin Zhaoyang. bk.rev.
Description: Publishes contemporary Chinese literature; novels, novelettes, short stories, poetry, prose, and reportage.

800 US ISSN 1001-1757
DANGDAI WAIGUO WENXUE/CONTEMPORARY FOREIGN LITERATURE. (Text in Chinese) q. $19. China Books & Periodicals, Inc., 2929 24th St., San Francisco, CA 94110. TEL 415-282-2994. FAX 415-282-0994.

895 CC
DANGDAI WENTAN/MODERN LITERARY WORLD. (Text in Chinese) bi-m. (Zhongguo Zuojia Xiehui, Sichuan Fenhui - Chinese Writers Association, Sichuan Chapter) Dangdai Wentan Bianjibu, No.85, Hongxing Zhonglu 2 Duan, Chengdu, Sichuan 610012, People's Republic of China. TEL 660070. Ed. Chen Zhaohong.

800 700 CC
DANGDAI WENYI TANSUO/CONTEMPORARY LITERATURE AND ART STUDY. q.? Zhongguo Zuojia Xiehui, Fujian Fenhui, Wenlian Dalou, Xihong Lu, Fuzhou, Fujian 350002, People's Republic of China. TEL 712657. Ed. Zhang Shilian.

895.1 CC ISSN 1000-7946
DANGDAI XIAOSHUO/CONTEMPORARY NOVELS. (Text in Chinese) 1877. m. $40.40. Jinan Shi Wenlian, No. 104, Jing 10 Lu, Jinan, Shandong 250002, People's Republic of China. TEL 24544. (Dist. by: China International Book Trading Corp., P.O. Box 339, Beijing, P.R. China) Ed. Sun Guozhang. adv. **Document type:** consumer publication.
Former titles (until Jan., 1985): Quan Cheng; (until Apr., 1981): Jinan Wenyi.

895.1 CC
DANGDAI ZUOJIA/MODERN WRITERS. (Text in Chinese) 1986. bi-m. Y3.80 per no. Changjiang Wenyi Chubanshe - Yangtse Literature and Art Publishing House, No. 63, Xiyu Cun, Hankou, Wuhan, Hubei 430022, People's Republic of China. TEL 027-537420. FAX 027-559641. Ed. Tian Zhongquan.
Description: Includes novels and other literary writings.

895.1 CC
DANGDAI ZUOJIA PINGLUN/CONTEMPORARY WRITERS REVIEW. (Text in Chinese; table of contents in English) bi-m. Y13.20. (Zhongguo Zuojia Xiehui, Liaoning Fenhui - China Writers' Association, Liaoning Chapter) Dangdai Zuojia Pinglun Zazhi She, 1 Wenxing Li, Shenyang Lu Erduan, Shenhe Qu, Shenyang, Liaoning 110011, People's Republic of China. (Dist. outside China by: China Publications Foreign Trade Corp., P.O. Box 782, Beijing, P.R.C.) Eds. Chen Yan, Zhang Songkui. adv.
Description: Contains literary criticism, reviews.

839.8 848.9 DK ISSN 0105-8746
DANISH HUMANIST TEXTS AND STUDIES. (Text in various languages) 1977. irreg. price varies. (Kongelige Bibliotek) Museum Tusculanum Press, University of Copenhagen, Njalsgade 92, DK-2300 Copenhagen S, Denmark. TEL 45-35-32-91-09. FAX 45-35-32-91-13. (Dist. in U.S. and Canada by: Paul & Co., c/o P C S Data Processing, Inc., 360 W. 31st St., New York, NY 10001. TEL 212-564-3730. FAX 212-971-7200) Ed. Erland Kolding Nielsen. **Document type:** academic/scholarly publication.
Description: Directed to scholars interested in Danish research within a broad spectrum of the humanities.

839.8 DK ISSN 0906-5369
DANISH LITERARY MAGAZINE. (Text in English) 1991. s-a. DKK 75($25) in Denmark; DKK 120 in Europe; elsewhere DKK 1150. (Ministry of Culture) Danish Literature Information Center, Amaliegade 38, DK-1256 Copenhagen K, Denmark. TEL 45-33-32-07-25. FAX 45-33-91-15-45. (Co-sponsors: Ministry of Foreign Affairs, Ministry of Education) Ed. Lise Bostrup. adv.; bk.rev.; play rev.; bibl.; illus. circ. 10,000. **Document type:** government publication.

850 US ISSN 0070-2862
PQ4331
DANTE STUDIES; with the Annual Report of the Dante Society. 1881. a. price varies. State University of New York Press, State University Plaza, Albany, NY 12246. TEL 800-666-2211. (Avail. from: S U N Y Press, c/o C U P Services, Box 6525, Ithaca, NY 14851) Ed. Anthony L. Pellegrini. adv. circ. 350. (also avail. in microform from UMI; back issues avail.) **Indexed:** M.L.A. **Document type:** academic/scholarly publication.
—UnCover; UMI.
Formerly (until 1980): Dante Society of America. Report with Accompanying Papers.

850 IT ISSN 1122-0856
DANTOLOGIA. 1990. irreg. price varies. (Centro Bibliografico Dantesco) Casa Editrice Leo S. Olschki, Casella Postale 66, 50100 Florence, Italy. TEL 055-6530684. FAX 055-6530214. **Document type:** monographic series.

830   NE   ISSN 0300-693X
PT177
DAPHNIS; Zeitschrift fuer Mittlere Deutsche Literatur. 1972. q. fl.250. Editions Rodopi B.V., Keizersgracht 302-304, 1016 EX Amsterdam, Netherlands. TEL 31-20-6227507. FAX 31-20-6380948. (In N. America: 233 Peachtree St. N.E., Ste. 404, Atlanta, GA 30303-1504. TEL 800-225-3998. FAX 404-522-7116) Ed. Hans-Gert Roloff. adv.; bk.rev. circ. 500. **Indexed**: Arts & Hum.Cit.Ind., Can.Rev.Comp.Lit., Curr.Cont., M.L.A. **Document type**: academic/scholarly publication.
—Faxon; SWETS.

890   IS   ISSN 0334-0686
PJ5001
DAPPIM - RESEARCH IN LITERATURE. (Text in Hebrew; summaries in English) 1984. a. IS.42($30) Haifa University Press, Mount Carmel, Haifa 31999, Israel. TEL 972-4-240601. FAX 972-4-342245. Ed.Bd. circ. 500. **Document type**: academic/scholarly publication.

810   US
DARKNERVE.* q. $10. 1320 Vine St., No. 5, Denver, CO 80206-2051. Ed. Jim Lough.

DAZHONG WENYI. see ART

895.1   CC
DAZHONG XIAOSHUO/POPULAR SHORT STORIES. (Text in Chinese) bi-m. Chunfeng Wenyi Chubanshe, 108 Beiyi Malu, Heping Qu, Shenyang, Liaoning 110001, People's Republic of China. TEL 363198. Ed. Li Qinxue.

810 705   US   ISSN 0070-3141
PS501
DECEMBER; a magazine of the arts and opinion. 1958. irreg. $25 for 4 nos. December Press, Box 302, Highland Park, IL 60035. TEL 708-940-4122. Ed. Curt Johnson. adv.; bk.rev.; film rev.; illus. circ. 1,200. (also avail. in microform from UMI; reprint service avail. from UMI,KTO; back issues avail.)
—UMI.
Description: Fiction and polemics.

800   PO   ISSN 0871-9519
PN851
DEDALUS; revista portuguesa de literatura comparada. 1988. a. Esc.1800 to non-members; members Esc.1600; foreign $20. (Associacao Portuguesa de Literatura Comparada) Edicoes Cosmos, Rua da Emenda, 111-1o, 1200 Lisbon, Portugal. TEL 346-82-01. FAX 347-82-55. circ. 2,000.

800   US   ISSN 0011-7951
PN241.A1
DELOS, a journal of translation for the practitioner, the scholar, and the aficionado. 1988. 2/yr. $15 to individuals (foreign $23); institutions $20 (foreign $28); students $10 (foreign $18). (University of Florida) Harold P. Hanson, Ed. & Pub., 215 Williamson Hall, Gainesville, FL 32611. TEL 904-377-1560. FAX 904-392-0542. adv.; bk.rev. circ. 400. **Document type**: academic/scholarly publication.
—Faxon; UnCover.
Description: Seeks to provide a forum for the discussion of the art of translation and to maintain and invigorate the world's literature by making its best works more widely available in other than the original language.
Refereed Serial

808 960   SG
DEMB AK TEY/YESTERDAY AND TODAY; a journal of myths and legends. (Editions in English and French) q. $18. Centre d'Etude des Civilisations, Ministry of Culture, Dakar, Senegal. Ed.Bd. illus.

810   US   ISSN 0011-9210
DESCANT. 1955. 2/yr. $12 (foreign $18). Texas Christian University, Department of English, Box 32875, Ft. Worth, TX 76129. TEL 817-921-7240. FAX 817-921-7333. Ed. Bd. circ. 400. **Indexed**: Abstr.Engl.Stud., Amer.Hum.Ind., Curr.Cont., M.L.A. **Document type**: academic/scholarly publication.
—UnCover.
Incorporates (in 1979): Quartet (ISSN 0033-586X).
Description: Contains short stories and poetry.

810   CN   ISSN 0382-909X
PR9194
DESCANT. 1970. 4/yr. Can.$22.47 to individuals; institutions Can.$31.03. Descant Arts and Letters Foundation, P.O. Box 314, Sta. P, Toronto, ON M5S 2S8, Canada. TEL 416-603-0223. Ed. Karen Mulhallen. adv.; bk.rev. circ. 1,000. **Indexed**: Amer.Hum.Ind., Arts & Hum.Cit.Ind., Can.Lit.Ind., Can.Per.Ind., CMI, Curr.Cont.
Description: Literary journal publishing poetry, fiction, essays and visuals.

895.9   II
DESH. (Text in Bengali) 1933. w. 6 Prafulla Sarkar St., Calcutta 700 001, India. TEL 33-274880. TELEX 215468. Ed. S. Ghosh. circ. 81,200.

DETSKAYA LITERATURA. see CHILDREN AND YOUTH — About

828.912   CN   ISSN 0707-9141
PR6007.U76
DEUS LOCI; the Lawrence Durrell quarterly. 1977. q. James A. Brigham, Ed. & Pub., c/o Department of English, Okanagan University College, Kelowna, B.C. V1Y 4X8, Canada. TEL 604-762-5445. (back issues avail.) **Document type**: academic/scholarly publication.
Refereed Serial

DEUTSCHE AKADEMIE FUER SPRACHE UND DICHTUNG. JAHRBUCH. see LINGUISTICS

830   GW
DEUTSCHE AKADEMIE FUER SPRACHE UND DICHTUNG. SCHRIFTENREIHE.* 1954. irreg., no.60, 1986. price varies. Luchterhand Literaturverlag, Donnersbergring 18A, 6100 Darmstadt, Germany. **Document type**: academic/scholarly publication.

DEUTSCHE OSTKUNDE; Vierteljahresschrift fuer Wissenschaft, Erziehung und Unterricht. see HISTORY — History Of Europe

830   GW   ISSN 0070-4318
PT105
DEUTSCHE SCHILLER-GESELLSCHAFT. JAHRBUCH. 1957. a. price varies. Alfred Kroener Verlag, Reinsburgstr. 56, 70178 Stuttgart, Germany. FAX 0711-6159946. Ed.Bd. circ. 3,000. **Indexed**: M.L.A.

820   GW
DEUTSCHE SHAKESPEARE-GESELLSCHAFT. JAHRBUCH. 1948. a. price varies, approx. DM.92. Verlag Ferdinand Kamp GmbH & Co. KG, Postfach 101309, 44713 Bochum, Germany. TEL 0234-91420. FAX 0234-9142142. Ed. Werner Habicht. bk.rev. circ. 400. **Indexed**: Abstr.Engl.Stud., Ind.Bk.Rev.Hum., M.L.A. **Document type**: academic/scholarly publication.
Formerly: Deutsche Shakespeare-Gesellschaft West. Jahrbuch (ISSN 0070-4326)
Description: Presents scholarly, critical and theater-oriented articles on Shakespeare and his work.

430 830   GW   ISSN 0070-4334
PT1375
DEUTSCHE TEXTE DES MITTELALTERS. vol.42, 1942. irreg., vol.77, 1992. price varies. Akademie Verlag GmbH, Muehlenstr. 33-34, 13187 Berlin, Germany. TEL 030-47889348. FAX 030-47889357. (also avail. in microfiche from BHP) **Indexed**: M.L.A. **Document type**: monographic series.

850   GW   ISSN 0070-444X
DEUTSCHES DANTE-JAHRBUCH. a. DM.68. (Dante Gesellschaft e.V.) Boehlau Verlag GmbH, Theodor-Heuss-Str. 76, 51149 Cologne, Germany. TEL 02203-307021. FAX 02203-307349. Ed. Marcella Roddewig. **Indexed**: M.L.A. **Document type**: academic/scholarly publication.

810   US
DEVIANCE. 1987. 3/yr. $13. Box 1706, Pawtucket, RI 02862. Ed. Lin Collette. circ. 500.
Description: Publishes poems, satire and translations.

DEVONSHIRE ASSOCIATION FOR THE ADVANCEMENT OF SCIENCE, LITERATURE AND ART. REPORT AND TRANSACTIONS. see ART

410 869   PO   ISSN 0870-8967
AP65
DIACRITICA. 1986. a. Esc.1995($12.50) (effective 1993). Universidade do Minho, Centro de Estudos Portugueses, 4 719 Braga Codex, Portugal. TEL 053-676375. FAX 053-676387. bk.rev. circ. 750. **Document type**: academic/scholarly publication.
Description: Covers university level interests such as theories of literature, philosophy and linguistics.

809   US   ISSN 0300-7162
PN80
DIACRITICS; a review journal of contemporary criticism. 1971. q. $22 to individuals (foreign $30.20); institutions $56 (foreign $64.20). (Cornell University) Johns Hopkins University Press, Journals Publishing Division, 2715 N. Charles St., Baltimore, MD 21218. TEL 410-516-6987. FAX 410-516-6968. Ed. Richard Klein. adv.; bk.rev.; film rev.; bibl.; index, cum.index. circ. 1,290. (also avail. in microform from UMI; back issues avail.; reprint service avail. from SWZ,UMI) **Indexed**: Abstr.Engl.Stud., Amer.Hum.Ind., Arts & Hum.Cit.Ind., Curr.Cont., Film Lit.Ind. (1976-), Ind.Bk.Rev.Hum., Lang.& Lang.Behav.Abstr., LCR, M.L.A.
—BLDSC (3579.616000); Faxon; UnCover; SWETS. CCC.
Description: Features articles in which contributors compare and analyze books on particular theoretical works and develop their own positions on the theses, methods, and theoretical implications of those works.

450   IT   ISSN 0012-2025
DIALETTI D'ITALIA.* (Text in Italian and Italian dialects) 1956; N.S. 1963. m. L.1000. Via Venti Settembre 26, 00187 Rome, Italy. Ed. Maria Teresa Martinozzi.

DIALOGOS HISPANICOS DE AMSTERDAM. see LINGUISTICS

800 300   FR
DIALOGUE. 1978. 2/yr. Universite de Montpellier (Universite Paul Valery), Centre d'Etudes et de Recherches Roumaines et des Traditions Orales Mediterraneennes, B.P. 5043, 34032 Montpellier Cedex 1, France. TEL 67-14-20-00. Ed. J. Lacroix.
Description: Specializes in Rumanian studies. Intended for specialists in the fields of literature, linguistics, cultural anthropology and for those interested in Rumanian and Mediterranean culture.

808   US
DIALOGUE (ANNANDALE).* 1978. s-a. $4. Bard College, Student Association, Box 95, Annandale-on-Huds, NY 12432. TEL 914-758-6822. Ed. Steven R. Bennish. adv.; bk.rev.; illus. circ. 500. (back issues avail.) **Indexed**: CERDIC.

DIANSHI DIANYING WENXUE/T V AND FILM LITERATURE. see MOTION PICTURES

800   RU
DIAPASON; vestnik inostrannoi literatury. 1961. q. $60. Vserosiiskaya Gosudarstvennaya Biblioteka Inostrannoi Literatury, Ul'yanovskaya St., 1, VGBIL "Diapason", Moscow 109189, Russia. TEL 7-095-9157885. FAX 7-095-9162039. TELEX 411234 STACJ SU. Ed. E. Genieva. adv.; bk.rev.; bibl. circ. 3,000. (also avail. in microform)
Formerly (until 1991): Sovremennaya Khudozhestvennaya Literatura za Rubezhom (ISSN 0132-1390)
Description: Informs the academi community, publishers and readers of the books currently published abroad - fiction, criticism, childre's books, new plays and books about theater. Includes critical essays, surveys of the current literary scene all over the world and analytical articles on various aspects of the contemporary literary process.

800   US   ISSN 1056-4861
DIARIST'S JOURNAL. 1988. q. $12. Gazette Publications, Inc., 102 W. Water St., Lansford, PA 18232. TEL 717-645-4692. Ed. Edward Gildea. adv.; bk.rev. circ. 800.
Description: Prints excerpts from diaries people are keeping today. Includes articles on diarists of today and yesterday.

LITERATURE

820 US ISSN 0742-5473
PR4579
DICKENS QUARTERLY. 1970. q. $15. University of Massachusetts, Department of English, Amherst, MA 01003. (Subscr. to: Dickens Society, President's Office, Grawemeyer Hall, Univ. of Louisville, Louisville, KY 40292) Ed. David Paroissien. adv.; bk.rev.; bibl. circ. 500. **Indexed:** Abstr.Engl.Stud.; Amer.Hum.Ind., Arts & Hum.Cit.Ind., Curr.Cont., M.L.A. **Document type:** academic/scholarly publication.
—BLDSC (3580.239000); Faxon; UnCover. **CCC.**
  Supersedes (in 1984): Dickens Studies Newsletter (ISSN 0012-2432)
  Description: Publishes articles, notes, reviews, and a checklist of Dickens studies.

820 US
DICKENS STUDIES ANNUAL: ESSAYS ON VICTORIAN FICTION. 1970. a. $49.50. (City University of New York, Victorian Committee) A M S Press, Inc., 56 E. 13th St., New York, NY 10003. TEL 212-777-4700. FAX 212-995-5413. Ed.Bd. index. (back issues avail.) **Indexed:** Amer.Hum.Ind., M.L.A. **Document type:** academic/scholarly publication.
—BLDSC (3580.240500); UnCover.
  Formerly: Dickens Studies Annual (ISSN 0084-9812)
  Description: Scholarly articles on the life and work of Charles Dickens and other Victorian writers.

800 US ISSN 1054-8777
DICKEN'S UNIVERSE. irreg. Peter Lang Publishing, Inc., 62 W. 45th St., 4th Fl., New York, NY 10036. TEL 212-302-6740. FAX 212-302-7574. Ed. Charlotte Rotkin. **Document type:** academic/scholarly publication.
  Description: Literary series on the life and letters of Charles Dickens.

820 UK ISSN 0012-2440
PR4579
DICKENSIAN. 1905. 3/yr. £9 individuals (overseas £10); institutions £11 (overseas £13). Dickens Fellowship, Eliot College, University of Kent, Canterbury, Kent CT2 7NS, England. TEL 0227-764000. FAX 0227-475471. (Subscr. to: Edward Preston, The Dickens House, 48 Doughty St., London WC1N 2LF, England) Ed. Malcolm Andrews. adv. contact: Edward Preston. bk.rev.; bibl.; illus.; index, cum.index. circ. 1,500. (also avail. in microform from HPL; reprint service avail. from KTO) **Indexed:** Abstr.Engl.Stud., Arts & Hum.Cit.Ind., Br.Hum.Ind., Curr.Cont., Ind.Bk.Rev.Hum., LCR, M.L.A. **Document type:** academic/scholarly publication.
—BLDSC (3580.242000); Faxon; UnCover.

400 US ISSN 0360-215X
PN6081
DICTIONARY OF CONTEMPORARY QUOTATIONS. 1976. triennial. $55. John Gordon Burke Publisher, Inc., Box 1492, Evanston, IL 60204-1492. TEL 708-866-8625.
●Also available online.
  Description: Records contemporary, historically, sociologically and politically significant quotes.

DICTIONARY OF LITERARY BIOGRAPHY. see BIOGRAPHY

DICTIONARY OF LITERARY BIOGRAPHY: DOCUMENTARY SERIES. see BIOGRAPHY

DICTIONARY OF LITERARY BIOGRAPHY YEARBOOK. see BIOGRAPHY

860 US ISSN 0163-0415
PQ6069
DIECIOCHO; Hispanic enlightenment, aesthetics and literary theory. (Text in English, Portuguese, Spanish) 1978. s-a. $12 to individuals; institutions $17 (effective Jan. 1992). c/o Dr. Eva M. Kahiluoto Rudat, Ed., 53 King Charles Ln., Newtown, PA 18940-2312. TEL 215-579-2995. bk.rev. circ. 200. **Indexed:** Arts & Hum.Cit.Ind., Curr.Cont., M.L.A.
—BLDSC (3580.520000); Faxon; UnCover.

800 NE ISSN 0166-5618
DIEPZEE; literaturmagazine voor het onderwijs. 1983. 6/yr. fl.32.75. WoltersgroepGroningen b.v., Postbus 58, 9700 MB Groningen, Netherlands. TEL 31-50-226922. FAX 31-50-264866.
  Formerly: Klapper.

830 US ISSN 0012-2882
AP2
DIMENSION (AUSTIN); contemporary German arts and letters. (Text in English, German) 1968. 3/yr. $16 to individuals; institutions $19. Box 26673, Austin, TX 78755. TEL 512-345-0622. Ed. A. Leslie Willson. index, cum.index: vols.1-10. circ. 800. (also avail. in microform from UMI; reprint service avail. from UMI) **Indexed:** Arts & Hum.Cit.Ind., CERDIC, M.L.A. **Document type:** academic/scholarly publication.
—UMI.

800 US
DIMENSIONS (WATERBURY). 1969. a. free. Naugatuck Community Technical College, Student Legislative Congress, 750 Chase Pkwy., Waterbury, CT 06708. TEL 203-596-8603. Ed. Gloria D. Pond. circ. 1,000. **Document type:** academic/scholarly publication.
  Description: Poetry, verse, drawings, and narrative sketches by students of Mattatuck Community College, Connecticut.

800 US ISSN 1044-4149
DIONYSOS; the literature and addiction triquarterly. 1989. 3/yr. $10 to individuals; institutions $15. University of Wisconsin at Superior, 1800 Grand Ave., Superior, WI 54880. TEL 715-394-8465. FAX 715-394-8454. Ed. Roger Forseth. adv.; bk.rev.; circ. 150 (paid). **Document type:** academic/scholarly publication.
  Former titles: Addiction; Intoxication.
  Description: Contains news notes and articles dealing with the cultural and aesthetic side of intoxication. Covers both the creative and destructive role of drinking and drug use in the lives and works of writers and artists.

800 PY
PQ7081.A1
DISCURSO; revista de estudios iberoamericanos. (Former issuing body: University of Oklahoma, Department of Foreign Languages and Literatures) (Text in English, Portuguese and Spanish) 1983. s-a. $40 to individuals; institutions $60. Ediciones y Arte s.r.l., Rca. Francesa 728, Asuncion, Paraguay. TEL 59521-660-829. FAX 59521-449-677. Dir. Javier Restrepo. adv.; bk.rev.; bibl. circ. 500. (also avail. in microform from UMI; back issues avail.) **Indexed:** M.L.A. **Document type:** academic/scholarly publication.
—Faxon.
  Formerly: Discurso Literario (ISSN 0737-8742)

DISSONANCE. see TECHNOLOGY: COMPREHENSIVE WORKS

800 NE ISSN 0168-9746
DIVER; magazine for reading & literature. (Text in English) 1984. 3/yr. fl.30. WoltersgroepGroningen b.v. (Subsidiary of: Wolters Kluwer N.V.), Postbus 58, 9700 MB Groningen, Netherlands. TEL 31-50-226922. FAX 31-50-264866.

DIVREI HA-AKADEMIA HA-LEUMIT HA-YISRAELIT LEMADAIM. see HUMANITIES: COMPREHENSIVE WORKS

909.6 FR ISSN 0012-4273
DIX-SEPTIEME SIECLE. 1948. q. 300 F. (foreign 350 F.). Societe d'Etude du Dix-Septieme Siecle, Commission de Publication, c/o Universite de Paris Sorbonne, Occident-Moderne, 1 rue Victor Cousin, 75230 Paris Cedex 05, France. TEL 1-40-46-25-13. Dir. Georges Molinie. adv.; bk.rev.; cum.index: 1949-1959, 1960-1969, 1970-1979. circ. 1,500. **Indexed:** Amer.Hist.& Life, Arts & Hum.Cit.Ind., Bull.Signal., Curr.Cont., Hist.Abstr., M.L.A. **Document type:** academic/scholarly publication.
—BLDSC (9725.300000); Faxon; UnCover.
  Description: Publishes news from books or colloques about 17th century studies.

860 US
DOCUMENTACION CERVANTINA. 1978. irreg., no.13, 1993. price varies. Juan de la Cuesta - Hispanic Monographs, 270 Indian Rd., Newark, DE 19711. TEL 302-453-8695. FAX 302-453-8601. Ed. Thomas A. Lathrop. circ. 500. **Indexed:** M.L.A.

830 430 JA ISSN 0387-2831
DOITSU BUNGAKU. s-a. free. Nippon Dokubungakkai, c/o Ikubundo, Hongo 5-30-21, Bunkyo-ku, Tokyo 113, Japan.

800 DK ISSN 0106-4487
DOLPHIN. (Text in English) 1979. a. Aarhus University Press, Aarhus University, Building 170, DK-8000 Aarhus C, Denmark. TEL 86-197033. FAX 86-198433. Ed.Bd. circ. 200.
—BLDSC (3616.620000).
  Description: Studies in English and American literature and language; also media studies.

810 US ISSN 1043-769X
DOMINION REVIEW. 1981. a. $10. Old Dominion University, Department of English, Bal 220, Norfolk, VA 23529. TEL 804-683-4035. Ed.Bd.
  Description: Publishes fiction and poetry.

057.87 891.87 XO
DOMOVA POKLADNICA. a. 30 Kcs. Priroda, Krizkova 9, 815 34 Bratislava, Slovakia.

DONG-A MUNHUA/EAST ASIA CULTURE. see ORIENTAL STUDIES

895.1 CC
DONG HAI/EAST CHINA SEA. (Text in Chinese) m. $36.80. Zhejiang Sheng Wenlian, 9, Jiande Lu, Hangzhou, Zhejiang 310006. TEL 778991. (Dist. in US by: China Books & Periodicals, Inc., 2929 24th St., San Francisco, CA 94110. TEL 415-282-2994)

800 US ISSN 0882-486X
PR6023.E833
DORIS LESSING NEWSLETTER. 1976. s-a. $10 to individuals; libraries $12; foreign $14. Doris Lessing Newsletter, c/o K. Fishburn, English Department, Michigan State University, East Lansing, MI 48824-1036. TEL 517-351-8163. Ed. Ruth Saxton. bk.rev. circ. 200. (back issues avail.) **Document type:** newsletter.
—BLDSC (3619.521000).

820 420 JA ISSN 0046-063X
PE9
DOSHISHA LITERATURE; journal of English literature and philology. (Text in English) 1887-1895; resumed 1927. biennial. 1000 Yen($7) per no. Doshisha University, English Literary Society, Karasuma Imadegawa, Kamikyo-ku, Kyoto 602, Japan. Ed. Isamu Saito. bk.rev. circ. 2,000. **Indexed:** Arts & Hum.Cit.Ind., Curr.Cont., Lang.& Lang.Behav.Abstr. **Document type:** academic/scholarly publication.
  Formerly (until 1956): Doshisha Bungaku.

800 JA ISSN 0286-2832
DOSHISHA STUDIES IN FOREIGN LITERATURE. (Text in English, French, German, Japanese) 1971. irreg. 1000 Yen. Doshisha University, Gaikoku Bungakukai, Tanabe-cho, Kyoto 610-03, Japan. FAX 07746-5-7069. Ed. Osamu Kono. bk.rev. circ. 2,000. **Document type:** academic/scholarly publication.
—BLDSC (3619.743000).

891.7 US
DOSTOEVSKY STUDIES. (Text in English, French, German and Russian) 1980. a. $10. International Dostoevsky Society, c/o Martin P. Rice, University of Tennessee, Department of Germanic and Slavic Languages, Knoxville, TN 37996. TEL 615-974-3421. Ed. Rudolf Neuhaeuser. bk.rev.; bibl. circ. 300. (back issues avail.) **Indexed:** Amer.Bibl.Slavic & E.Eur.Stud, M.L.A.
  Supersedes: International Dostoevsky Society Bulletin (ISSN 0047-0686)

378.1 UK ISSN 0012-589X
DRAGON. (Editions in English and Welsh) 1966. a. University College of Wales, Students' Union, Aberystwyth, Dyfed, Wales. Eds. C. Larner, A. Thomas. adv.; bk.rev.; film rev.; record rev.; illus. circ. 250.
  Description: For students of Aberystwyth, using any literary material freely submitted by the students.

DRAMA CRITICISM. see THEATER

822 UK ISSN 0070-7198
DRAMASCRIPTS SERIES. 1965. irreg., no.4, 1970. price varies. Oleander Press, 17 Stansgate Ave., Cambridge CB2 2QZ, England. (U.S. address: 80 Eighth Ave., Ste. 303, New York, NY 10011) Eds. Philip Ward, Wayne Schlepp. **Document type:** monographic series.

| 800 | | CN | ISSN 0843-445X |

DREAMS & VISIONS; new frontiers in Christian fiction. 1989. 3/yr. Can.$12 to individuals; institutions Can.$15. Skysong Press, R.R. 1, Washago, ON L0K 2B0, Canada. TEL 705-689-6226. Eds. Steve and Wendy Stanton. circ. 200 (paid). (back issues avail.)

| 830 | | SZ | ISSN 0012-6055 |

DREHPUNKT. (Text in German) 1968. 3/yr. 30 SFr. Lenos Verlag, Spalentorweg 12, CH-4051 Basel, Switzerland. (Subscr. to: Postfach 164, CH-4016 Basel, Switzerland) Ed.Bd. adv.; bk.rev.; illus. circ. 1,500.
—CCC.

| 810 | | US | ISSN 0896-6362 |
PS3507.R55

DREISER STUDIES. 1970. s-a. $7 to individuals; institutions $10; outside N. America $15. Indiana State University, Department of English, Terre Haute, IN 47809. TEL 812-237-3163. FAX 812-237-3156. Ed. D. Vancil. bk.rev. circ. 300. (back issues avail.) **Indexed**: Amer.Hum.Ind., Bibl.Engl.Lang.& Lit., Hum.Ind.
—Faxon; UnCover.
Formerly: Dreiser Newsletter (ISSN 0012-6098)
Description: Contains critical and textual essays, notes and reviews, and news on the literature of Theodore Dreiser and his peers.

| 839.7 | | SW | ISSN 0283-6750 |

DROEMSKRINET. 1985. irreg. SEK 20 per no. (effective 1990). Droemskrinet, c/o Ottman, Fraemlingsv. 34, S-126 48 Haegersten, Sweden.

| 810 700 320 | | US | ISSN 0899-5443 |

DRUM (AMHERST); black literary experience. 1969. a. $3. 115 New Africa House, University of Massachusetts, Amherst, MA 01003. TEL 413-545-3185. Ed. Martha Grier-Deen. illus. circ. 4,000. (back issues avail.)

DRYADE; revue artistique et litteraire. see *ART*

| 895.1 | | CC | ISSN 0257-0270 |

DU SHU/READING. (Text in Chinese) 1979. m. Y2.60 per no. (effective Jan. 1994). Shenghuo - Dushu - Xinzhi Sanlian Shudian, Life - Reading - New Knowledge Joint Publishing Co., 166 Chaonei Dajie, Beijing 100706, People's Republic of China. TEL 5120876. FAX 7228848. (Dist. in US by: China Books & Periodicals, Inc., 2929 24th St., San Francisco, CA 94110. TEL 415-282-2994) Ed. Shen Changwen. bk.rev. circ. 50,000.
Description: Offers ideological critiques through reviews and introductions of domestic and foreign books.

| 895.1 | | CC | ISSN 1003-1561 |

DUANPIAN XIAOSHUO/SHORT STORIES. (Text in Chinese) 1956-1963; resumed 1979. m. Y1.80. Jilin Shi Wenlian, 7, Nanjing Jie, Jilin 132001, People's Republic of China. TEL 453031. Ed. Ning Xuancheng. **Document type**: consumer publication.
Formerly (until Jan. 1984): Jiang Cheng.

| 808.8 | | | |

DUCK SOUP. 1978. a. free. North Lake College, 5001 N. MacArthur Blvd., Irving, TX 75038. TEL 214-659-5270. Ed. Nancy Jones. circ. 3,000.
Description: Published contributions from students, faculty and staff of the college.

DUE SOUTH; the biggest guide to what's on in the South. see *ARTS AND HANDICRAFTS*

| 895.1 | | CC | ISSN 1004-1427 |

DUILIAN - MINJIAN DUILIAN GUSHI/ANTITHETICAL COUPLET - FOLK STORIES ABOUT ANTITHETICAL COUPLET. (Text in Chinese) 1985. bi-m. Y1.10. Shanxi Ribao She - Shanxi Daily Publishing Company, 24 Shuangtaji Jie, Taiyuan, Shanxi 030012, People's Republic of China. TEL 446561. FAX 446561-482. Ed. Guo Huarong.

DUITSE KRONIEK; orgaan voor culturele betrekkingen met Duitsland. see *POLITICAL SCIENCE — International Relations*

| 800 780 | | | |

DUMPSTER TIMES. 1989. 4/yr. $10. Dumpster Press, Box 80044, Akron, OH 44308. Ed. Wendy S. Duke. adv.; bk.rev. circ. 300.
Description: Addresses contemporary literature, music and art issues from an anarchist and atheist perspective.

THE DUPLEX PLANET. see *FOLKLORE*

DUQUESNE STUDIES. LANGUAGE AND LITERATURE SERIES. see *LINGUISTICS*

| 820 900 | | UK | ISSN 0012-7280 |

DURHAM UNIVERSITY JOURNAL. (Supplement avail.) 1876. 2/yr. £24 (foreign £27). University of Durham, Department of English Studies, Elvet Riverside, New Elvet, Durham DH1 3JT, England. TEL 091-374-2744. Ed. P.E. Lewis. adv.; bk.rev.; index. circ. 500. (also avail. in microfilm from UMI; back issues avail.; reprint service avail. from UMI) **Indexed**: Abstr.Engl.Stud., Amer.Hist.& Life, Arts & Hum.Cit.Ind., Br.Archaeol.Abstr., Br.Hum.Ind., Curr.Cont., Hist.Abstr., Ind.Bk.Rev.Hum., M.L.A., Mid.East: Abstr.& Ind. **Document type**: academic/scholarly publication.
—BLDSC (3632.450000); Faxon; UnCover.
Description: Articles of academic interest on the arts, humanities, philosophy and Christian theology and church history.

| 891.999 | | NE | ISSN 0927-7501 |

▼**DUTCH STUDIES IN ARMENIAN LANGUAGE AND LITERATURE**. 1992. irreg. Editions Rodopi B.V., Keizersgracht 302-304, 1016 EX Amsterdam, Netherlands. TEL 31-20-6227507. FAX 31-20-6380948. (In N. America: 233 Peachtree St., N.E, Ste. 404, Atlanta, GA 30303-1504. TEL 800-225-3998. FAX 404-522-7116) Eds. Th. van Lint, J.J.S. Weitenberg. **Document type**: monographic series.

DYSKUSJA. see *ETHNIC INTERESTS*

E A C R O T A N A L INFORMATION. (Eastern African Centre for Research on Oral Traditions and African National Languages) see *LINGUISTICS*

E A C R O T A N A L STUDIES & DOCUMENTS. (Eastern African Centre for Research on Oral Traditions and African National Languages) see *LINGUISTICS*

| 810 | | US | ISSN 1054-3376 |

E L F. (Eclectic Literary Forum) 1991. 4/yr. $16 to individuals; institutions $32 (effective 1994). E L F Associates, Inc., Box 392, Tonawanda, NY 14150. TEL 716-693-7006. Ed. Cynthia K. Erbes. adv.; bk.rev. circ. 5,000. (back issues avail.)
Description: Publishes contemporary, well-crafted short fiction, poetry and essays on literary themes, including native American folklore and other special features.

| 820 | | US | ISSN 0013-8304 |
PR1

E L H. (English Literary History) 1931. q. $21 to individuals (foreign $33.20); institutions $69 (foreign $81.20). Johns Hopkins University Press, Journals Publishing Division, 2715 N. Charles St., Baltimore, MD 21218. TEL 410-516-6987. FAX 410-516-6968. Ed. Ronald Paulson. adv. circ. 755. (also avail. in microform from UMI; reprint service avail. from UMI,KTO) **Indexed**: Abstr.Engl.Stud., Acad.Ind., Amer.Hist.& Life, Arts & Hum.Cit.Ind., Curr.Cont., Hist.Abstr., Hum.Ind., LCR, Leg.Cont. M.L.A. **Document type**: academic/scholarly publication.
—BLDSC (3730.650000); Faxon; UnCover; SWETS. CCC.
Description: Presents studies that interpret the historical conditions affecting major works in English and American literature--from the creation of those works to their subsequent life and present status.

| 810 | | US | ISSN 0093-8297 |
PS1629

E S Q; a journal of the American renaissance. 1955. q. $18 to individuals (overseas $25.50); institutions $25 (overseas $32.50) (effective 1994). Washington State University Press, Pullman, WA 99164-5910. TEL 509-335-3518. FAX 509-335-8568. Ed. Robert C. McLean. bk.rev.; bibl.; charts; illus. circ. 625. **Indexed**: Abstr.Engl.Stud., Amer.Hum.Ind., Arts & Hum.Cit.Ind., Curr.Cont., Ind.Bk.Rev.Hum., M.L.A. **Document type**: academic/scholarly publication.
—BLDSC (3811.662000); Faxon; UnCover; SWETS; UMI.
Formerly: Emerson Society Quarterly.

| 830 | | GW | ISSN 0944-5277 |
PT2361.Z49

E.T.A. HOFFMANN JAHRBUCH. MITTEILUNGEN DER E.T.A. HOFFMANN GESELLSCHAFT. 1938. a. DM.50. (E.T.A. Hoffmann Gesellschaft e.V.) Erich Schmidt Verlag GmbH & Co. (Berlin), Genthiner Str. 30G, 10785 Berlin, Germany. TEL 030-250085-0. FAX 030-25008521. bk.rev. circ. 800. (reprint service avail. from SWZ) **Document type**: proceedings.
Formerly (until 1991): E.T.A. Hoffmann-Gesellschaft. Mitteilungen (ISSN 0073-2885)

| 800 | | US | |

EADS BRIDGE; a literary review. 1972. a. $4. St. Louis University, English Department, St. Louis, MO 63108. TEL 314-658-3010. FAX 314-658-3191. Ed. Avis Meyer. circ. 500.
Description: Contains prose, poetry, short stories, essays and graphics.

| 810 | | US | ISSN 0012-8163 |
PS501

EARLY AMERICAN LITERATURE. 1966. 3/yr. $18 to individuals; institutions $24 (foreign $28). (University of North Carolina at Chapel Hill, Department of English) University of North Carolina Press, Box 2288, Chapel Hill, NC 27515-2288. TEL 919-966-3561. FAX 919-966-3829. (Co-sponsor: Modern Language Association of America) Ed. Philip Gura. adv.; bk.rev.; bibl.; cum.index. circ. 800. **Indexed**: Abstr.Engl.Stud., Amer.Hist.& Life, Amer.Hum.Ind., Arts & Hum.Cit.Ind., Curr.Cont., Ind.Bk.Rev.Hum., M.L.A., Rel.Ind.One. **Document type**: academic/scholarly publication.
—BLDSC (3642.930000); Faxon; UnCover; SWETS; UMI.
Refereed Serial

EARLY DRAMA, ART, AND MUSIC REVIEW. see *THEATER*

EARTH'S DAUGHTERS; a feminist arts periodical. see *WOMEN'S INTERESTS*

| 820 780 | | UK | ISSN 1350-2115 |

▼**EASTERN RAINBOW**. 1992. 2/yr. £5 for 4 nos. 17 Farrow Rd., Whaplode Drove, Spalding, Lincs. PE12 OTS, England. TEL 0406-330242. Ed. Paul Rance. adv.: B&W page £35. **Document type**: consumer publication.

| 810 | | US | |

ECHO (GREENVILLE). 1893. s-a. free. Furman University, Board of Student Communications, 3300 Poinsett Hwy., Greenville, SC 29613-0639. TEL 803-294-3209. FAX 803-294-3001. Ed. Ginny Taylor. circ. 3,000. **Document type**: academic/scholarly publication.
Description: Contains student prose, poetry and art.

| 800 | | US | |

ECLECTIC. a. free. West Georgia College, Carrollton, GA 30118. TEL 404-836-6512. circ. 1,000.

| 700 | | CK | ISSN 0012-9410 |
AP63

ECO; revista de la cultura de occidente. 1961. m. $22. Libreria Buchholz, Av. Jimenez de Quesada 8-40, Bogota, Colombia. Ed. J.G. Cobo Borda. bk.rev. circ. 4,500. **Indexed**: Hisp.Amer.Per.Ind., M.L.A.

ECOLE PRATIQUE DES HAUTES ETUDES. CENTRE DE RECHERCHES SUR LE PORTUGAL DE LA RENAISSANCE. SERIES TEXTES. see *HISTORY — History Of Europe*

ECOLES DES LETTRES. SECOND CYCLE. see *EDUCATION — Teaching Methods And Curriculum*

| 840 | | CN | ISSN 0013-0729 |

ECRITS DU CANADA FRANCAIS. 1954. 3/yr. Can.$24 for 4 nos. c/o Paul Beaulieu, 5754 Deom, Montreal, Que. H3S 2N4, Canada. Ed.Bd. adv.; bk.rev.; bibl. circ. 2,500. **Indexed**: Pt.de Rep. (1982-).
—SWETS.

| 860 | | SP | ISSN 0212-0429 |

EDAD DE ORO. 1982. a. (Universidad Autonoma de Madrid, Departamento de Filologia Espanola) Ediciones de la Universidad Autonoma, Vicerrectorado de Extension Univ., 28049 Madrid, Spain.
Description: Dedicated to Spanish literature of the 16th and 17th centuries.

LITERATURE

839.5   NO   ISSN 0013-0818
PN9
EDDA; Scandinavian journal for literary research. (Text in Danish, Norwegian, Swedish; occasionally in English and German) 1914. q. NOK 515 in the Nordic countries; elsewhere NOK 560. Scandinavian University Press, P.O. Box 2959-Toeyen, N-0608 Oslo, Norway. TEL 472-67-7600. FAX 472-67-7575. (U.S. addr.: Scandinavian University Press, 200 Meacham Ave., Elmont, NY 11003. TEL 516-352-7300) Ed. Steinar Grimnes. adv.; bk.rev.; index. circ. 950. **Indexed:** Can.Rev.Comp.Lit, Ind.Bk.Rev.Hum. **Document type:** academic/scholarly publication.
—CCC.
Description: Publishes general literary research by Scandinavian scholars and research on Scandinavian literature by scholars from all countries.

398   PE
EDICIONES DEL PUEBLO. no.38, 1983. irreg. Universidad Nacional "Daniel Aleides Carron", Av. Guzman Blanco 465, Of.204, Lima, Peru.

301.412 800   US
EDITH WHARTON REVIEW. 1984. s-a. $10 to individuals; institutions $20; foreign $15. Edith Wharton Society, Department of English, Long Island University, Brooklyn, NY 11201. TEL 718-403-1050. Ed. Annette Zilversmit. adv.: page $200. bk.rev.; bibl. circ. 450.
Formerly (until 1990): Edith Wharton Newsletter.

EDITING HISTORY. see *HISTORY — History Of North And South America*

809 028.1   GW   ISSN 0931-3079
PN162
EDITIO; internationales Jahrbuch fuer Editionswissenschaft. (Text in English, French and German) 1987. a. DM.96. (Arbeitsgemeinschaft fuer Germanistische Edition) Max Niemeyer Verlag, Postfach 2140, 72011 Tuebingen, Germany. TEL 07071-98940. FAX 07071-989450. Ed. Winfried Woesler. adv.; bk.rev. **Document type:** academic/scholarly publication.
Description: Covers essays and reviews on scholarly editing of works in literature and philosophy.

800   GW
EDITION ORPHEUS. irreg., vol.8, 1993. DM.96. Francke Verlag GmbH, Postfach 2560, 72015 Tuebingen, Germany. TEL 07071-78091. FAX 07071-75288. **Document type:** monographic series.

839 439   DK   ISSN 0070-9069
EDITIONES ARNAMAGNAEANAE. SERIES A. (Text in Danish, English, German, Icelandic, Norwegian , Swedish) 1958. irreg. price varies. Arnamagnaean Commission, Njalsgade 76, DK-2300 Copenhagen S, Denmark. TEL 31-542211. (Dist. by: C.A. Reitzels Boghandel A-S, Noerregade 20, DK-1165 Copenhagen K, Denmark) **Document type:** monographic series, academic/scholarly publication.
Description: Presents critical editions, primarily of Old Norse-Icelandic, mediaeval literature.

839 439   DK   ISSN 0070-9077
EDITIONES ARNAMAGNAEANAE. SERIES B. (Text in Danish, English, German, Icelandic, Norwegian, Swedish) 1960. irreg. price varies. Arnamagnaean Commission, Njalsgade 76, DK-2300 Copenhagen S, Denmark. TEL 31-542211. (Dist. by: C.A. Reitzels Boghandel A-S, Noerregade 20, DK-1165, Copenhagen K, Denmark) **Document type:** monographic series, academic/scholarly publication.
Description: Presents critical editions, primarily of Old Norse-Icelandic, mediaeval literature.

839   DK   ISSN 0070-9085
EDITIONES ARNAMAGNAEANAE. SUPPLEMENTUM. 1963. irreg. Arnamagnaean Commission, Njalsgade 76, DK-2300 Copenhagen S, Denmark. TEL 31-542211. (Dist. by: C.A. Reitzels Boghandel A-S, Noerregade 20, DK-1165 Copenhagen K, Denmark) **Document type:** monographic series, academic/scholarly publication.
Description: Critical editions of primarily Old Norse-Icelandic, mediaeval literature.

EDITOR & PUBLISHER SYNDICATE DIRECTORY; annual directory of syndicate services. see *JOURNALISM*

800   US   ISSN 1060-2658
PS580
EDITOR'S CHOICE; fiction, poetry and art from the U.S. small press. 1980. biennial. $12 paperback; cloth $18. Spirit That Moves Us Press, Inc., Box 820, Jackson Heights, NY 11372-0820. TEL 718-426-8788. Ed. Morty Sklar. bibl.; illus. circ. 3,000. **Indexed:** Amer.Hum.Ind., Ind.Amer.Per.Verse.
Description: Contains selections from small literary presses and magazines, from nominations made by their editors.

800   US   ISSN 1048-8596
THE EDWARDEAN. a. $29.95. Edwin Mellen Press, 415 Ridge St., Box 450, Lewiston, NY 14092. TEL 800-753-2788. FAX 716-754-4056. Ed. Richard Hall. **Document type:** monographic series.
Description: Covers the studies of Jonathan Edwards.

890   SP
EGAN; suplemento de literatura, del boletin de la real sociedad vascongada de los amigo del pais. (Text in Basque) 1948. s-a. 90 ptas. Real Sociedad Vascongada de los Amigos del Pais, Po. Ramon Ma. de Lili, 6-4o, Izqda., Apdo. 992, 20002 San Sebastian, Spain. TEL 285577.

810   UK
EIGHTEEN NINETIES SOCIETY. JOURNAL. 1963. a. membership. Eighteen Nineties Society, 97-D Brixton Rd., London SW9 6EE, England. Ed. G. Krishnamurti. adv.; bk.rev. circ. 750. (processed) **Indexed:** Abstr.Engl.Stud.
Formerly: Francis Thompson Society. Journal (ISSN 0532-5781)

800   CN   ISSN 0840-6286
PN3495
EIGHTEENTH-CENTURY FICTION. 1988. q. Can.$37 to individuals; institutions Can.$57; students Can.$28. University of Toronto Press, Journals Department, 5201 Dufferin St., Downsview, ON M3H 5T8, Canada. TEL 416-667-7781. FAX 416-667-7803. (U.S. addr.: 340 Nagel Dr., Cheektowaga, NY 14225) Ed. David Blewett. adv.; illus.
—BLDSC (3665.227300); Faxon; UnCover. **CCC.**

EIGHTEENTH CENTURY LIFE. see *HISTORY — History Of Europe*

EIGHTEENTH-CENTURY STUDIES. see *HISTORY*

EIGHTEENTH CENTURY: THEORY AND INTERPRETATION. see *HISTORY — History Of Europe*

EIRE - IRELAND; a journal of Irish studies. see *HUMANITIES: COMPREHENSIVE WORKS*

800   FR   ISSN 0397-0051
ELAN; poetique, litteraire et pacifiste. 1955. q. 50 F.($7) Louis Lippens, Ed. & Pub., 31 rue Foch, 59126 Linselles, France. TEL 20-03-48-59. bk.rev.; abstr.; bibl.; illus. (also avail. in microfilm from KTO) **Indexed:** Excerp.Med.

800   US
▼**EL-E-PHANT;** a language arts review. 1993. bi-m. $20. (Contemporary Arts Educational Project) Sun & Moon Press, 6026 Wilshire Blvd., Los Angeles, CA 90026. TEL 213-857-1115. Ed. Douglas Messerli. bk.rev.
Description: Publishes original reviews of current avant garde literary fiction, poetry and theater, with an emphasis on innovation in form or style. Also looks at memorable but ignored works of American poetry, fiction, drama and cinema of the past.

ELEMENTS. see *ART*

810   US
ELEPHANT-EAR. 1983. a. Irvine Valley College, School of Humanities, 5500 Irvine Center Dr., Irvine, CA 92720. TEL 714-559-3341. Ed. Lisa Alvarez. circ. 2,500.

800   IT
ELEUSIS. q. Pen Club di Firenze, Via Cavour, 26, 50129 Florence, Italy. Ed. Vittorio Vettori.

808   CN
ELIXIR. a. Glendon College, Student Union, 2275 Bayview Ave., Toronto, Ont. M4N 3M6, Canada. TEL 416-487-6720. adv. circ. 2,000.

820   AU
ELIZABETHAN AND RENAISSANCE STUDIES. (Text in English) 1972. irreg., no.114, 1992. S.300. Universitaet Salzburg, Institut fuer Englische Sprache, Akademiestr. 24, A-5020 Salzburg, Austria. Ed. James Hogg. circ. 250. **Indexed:** M.L.A. **Document type:** monographic series, academic/scholarly publication.

810   US   ISSN 0160-7545
PS3513.L34
ELLEN GLASGOW NEWSLETTER. 1974. s-a. $5 for 2-yr. membership. Ellen Glasgow Society, c/o Prof. Catherine Rainwater, School of Humanities, St. Edwards University, 3001 S. Congress Ave., Austin, TX 78704-6489. TEL 512-837-6579. bk.rev.; bibl. circ. 200. **Indexed:** M.L.A. **Document type:** newsletter.
Description: Covers Glasgow or people of her time and place. Includes information on related works or references.

800   US   ISSN 1040-1644
ELLIPSIS...; * literature with a certain twist. 1988. s-a. $24 (foreign $32). Ellipsis Press, 59 N. Santa Cruz Ave.ve., Los Gatos, CA 95030. TEL 408-354-1481. FAX 408-354-1463. Ed. Joy Oestreicher. circ. 500. (back issues avail.)
Description: Devoted to literature reflecting the human condition, with a humorous twist.

800   US
EMPIRE!; the N Y State inmate literary arts journal. 1984. a. free. Department of Correctional Services, c/o Paul Gordon, Ed., Arthur Kill Correctional Facility, 2911 Arthur Kill Rd., Staten Island, NY 10309. TEL 718-356-7333. bk.rev. circ. 5,000. (back issues avail.)

800   CN   ISSN 1180-4092
EMPLOI PLUS. (Text in English, French) 1990. s-a. Can.$10. D G R Publication, 125 Principale N. St., Ste. 013, L'Annonciation, Quebec, PQ J0T 1T0, Canada. TEL 819-275-3293. Ed. Daniel G. Reid. bk.rev. circ. 500.

EMPORIA STATE RESEARCH STUDIES. see *HISTORY — History Of North And South America*

800   US   ISSN 0071-0164
ENCORE (BLACKSBURG). 1948. a. $2. National Association of Dramatic and Speech Arts, 208 Cherokee Dr., Blacksburg, VA 24060. TEL 703-552-6862. Ed. H.D. Flowers, II. adv.; bk.rev. circ. 3,000. (also avail. in microform from UMI; reprint service avail. from UMI) **Indexed:** Mag.Ind.
—UMI.
Description: Scholarly and creative writing about black theater and rhetoric.

820   UK   ISSN 0013-8215
PR5
ENGLISH. 1935. 3/yr. £40($90) (effective 1994). The English Association, c/o University of Leicester, 128 Regent Rd., Leicester LE1 7PA, England. TEL 0533-525927. FAX 0533-525928. Eds. Michael Baron, Peter Barry. adv.; bk.rev. (also avail. in microform from UMI; reprint service avail. from UMI) **Indexed:** Abstr.Engl.Stud., Arts & Hum.Cit.Ind., Br.Hum.Ind., Curr.Cont., Ind.Bk.Rev.Hum., Lang.& Lang.Behav.Abstr. **Document type:** academic/scholarly publication.
—BLDSC (3772.600000); Faxon; UnCover; SWETS; UMI.
Description: Publishes literary criticism, publishing essays and reviews aimed at readers in all forms of higher education, but in a style intelligible to all.

800 370   SA
ENGLISH ACADEMY REVIEW. (Text in English) 1984. a. R.27.50 (effective 1992). English Academy of South Africa, P.O. Box 124, 2050 Wits, South Africa. TEL 27-11-716-3683. Ed. Ivan Rabinowitz. adv.; bk.rev.; play rev. circ. 1,100. (back issues avail.) **Indexed:** Documentatieblad. **Document type:** academic/scholarly publication.
Description: Contains South African literature, language and education, and creative writing.

807　　　　　　UK
ENGLISH AND MEDIA MAGAZINE. 1979. s-a. £10.50 to individuals; institutions and foreign £21 (for 3 nos.). English & Media Centre, Ebury Teachers Centre, Sutherland St., London SW1V 4LH, England. TEL 071-828-8560. FAX 071-821-6541. Ed. Michael Simons. adv.; bk.rev. circ. 7,000. (back issues avail.)
　　　Formerly: English Magazine (ISSN 0144-6487)

830
ENGLISH GOETHE SOCIETY. PUBLICATIONS. 1886; N.S. 1972. a. $22. English Goethe Society, University College, Gower St., London W.C.1., England. Ed. Prof. F.M. Fowler. circ. 500.

814　　　　　　UK　　ISSN 0071-0598
ENGLISH INSTITUTE. SELECTED ESSAYS. 1939; N.S. 1978. a. price varies. Routledge, 11 New Fetter Ln., London EC4P 4EE, England. TEL 071-583-9855. FAX 071-583-0701. (reprint service avail. from UMI) **Document type:** monographic series.

810　　　　　　US　　ISSN 0013-8282
PE1
ENGLISH LANGUAGE NOTES. 1963. q. $20 to individuals in N. America (overseas $27); institutions in N. America $40 (overseas $47). University of Colorado, English Language Notes, CB 226, Boulder, CO 80309. TEL 303-492-7176. FAX 303-492-8904. Ed. J. Wallace Donald. adv.; B&W page $250. bk.rev.; bibl.; index. circ. 1,222. (back issues avail; reprint service avail.) **Indexed:** Abstr.Engl.Stud., Arts & Hum.Cit.Ind., Can.Rev.Comp.Lit, Curr.Cont., Hum.Ind., Ind.Bk.Rev.Ind., M.L.A., Ref.Sour. **Document type:** academic/scholarly publication.
　　—BLDSC (3775.040000); Faxon; UnCover; SWETS.
　　　Refereed Serial

820　　　　　　US　　ISSN 0013-8312
PR1
ENGLISH LITERARY RENAISSANCE. 1971. 3/yr. $20 to individuals; libraries $30. University of Massachusetts, Department of English, Amherst, MA 01003. TEL 413-545-2332. Ed. Arthur F. Kinney. adv. circ. 1,100. **Indexed:** Abstr.Engl.Stud., Amer.Hist.& Life, Amer.Hum.Ind., Arts & Hum.Cit.Ind., Curr.Cont., Hist.Abstr., M.L.A. **Document type:** academic/scholarly publication.
　　—BLDSC (3775.065000); Faxon; UnCover; SWETS.
　　　Description: Provides scholarly and critical essays, bibliographies and primary texts of English literary works written in England between 1485-1668. Including studies of the cultural and intellectual background of those texts.

820　　　　　　US　　ISSN 0364-3549
PR1
ENGLISH LITERATURE IN TRANSITION (1880-1920). 1957. q. $18 (effective 1994). Robert Langenfeld, Ed. & Pub., Department of English, University of North Carolina, Greensboro, NC 27412-5001. TEL 919-334-5446. FAX 919-334-3281. Ed. Robert Langenfeld. adv.; bk.rev.; bibl.; cum.index: 1957-1972, 1973-1982. circ. 840. (also avail. in microform from JAI,MIM,UMI; back issues avail.; reprint service avail. from UMI,KTO) **Indexed:** Abstr.Engl.Stud., Arts & Hum.Cit.Ind., Bk.Rev.Ind. (1991-), Child.Bk.Rev.Ind. (1991-), Curr.Cont., Hum.Ind., Ind.Bk.Rev.Ind., M.L.A. **Document type:** academic/scholarly publication.
　　—BLDSC (3775.070000); Faxon; UnCover; UMI.
　　　Formerly: English Fiction in Transition (ISSN 0013-8339)
　　　Description: Contains essays and reviews fiction, poetry and culture in British literature.

080 800　　　　UK　　ISSN 0071-061X
ENGLISH LITTLE MAGAZINES. 1967. irreg., no. 16, 1971. price varies. Frank Cass & Co. Ltd., Gainsborough House, 11 Gainsborough Rd., London E11 1RS, England. TEL 081-530-4226. FAX 081-530-7795. (Dist. in U.S. by: ISBS, 5804 N.E. Hassalo St., Portland, OR 97213-3644) **Document type:** academic/scholarly publication.

ENGLISH QUARTERLY. see EDUCATION — Teaching Methods And Curriculum

ENGLISH STUDIES; a journal of English language and literature. see LINGUISTICS

ENGLISH STUDIES IN AFRICA; a journal of the humanities. see HUMANITIES: COMPREHENSIVE WORKS

820　　　　　　CN　　ISSN 0317-0802
ENGLISH STUDIES IN CANADA. 1975. q. $45 to non-members. Association of Canadian College and University Teachers of English, Department of English, Carleton University, 1125 Colonel By Dr., Ottawa, ON K1S 5B6, Canada. TEL 613-788-2600. FAX 613-788-3544. Ed. D.J. Wurtele. bk.rev. circ. 1,200. **Indexed:** Arts & Hum.Cit.Ind., Can.Lit.Ind., Curr.Cont., Ind.Bk.Rev.Hum., M.L.A. **Document type:** academic/scholarly publication, trade publication.
　　—BLDSC (3775.121000); Faxon; UnCover. **CCC.**

ENLIGHTENMENT BOOK CLUB. see PHILOSOPHY

L'ENNEMI. see ART

860　　　　　　UY　　ISSN 0071-0679
ENSAYO Y TESTIMONIO.* irreg. Editorial Arca, Colonia 1263, Montevideo, Uruguay.

830　　　　　　SZ　　ISSN 1019-2115
▼**ENTWUERFE;** fuer Literatur und Gesellschaft. 1992. bi-m. 70 SFr. (foreign 82 SFr.). Postfach, CH-8023 Zurich, Switzerland. Eds. Margrith Raguth, Markus Buehrer. **Document type:** consumer publication.

809 940　　　　US　　ISSN 0897-4888
PN661
ENVOI; a review journal of medieval literature. 1988. s-a. $15. (Columbia University, Department of English and Comparative Literature) A M S Press, Inc., 56 E. 13th St., New York, NY 10003. TEL 212-777-4700. FAX 212-995-5143. Ed. Paul Spillenger. **Document type:** academic/scholarly publication.
　　—UnCover.
　　　Description: Essays and notices of scholarly books relating to medieval studies with emphasis on medieval literature.

800　　　　　　US
▼**EPIPHANY;** a journal of literature. 1992. q. $12 (foreign $22). Epiphany Publications, Inc., University of Arkansas, Box 2699, Fayetteville, AR 72701. (Subscr. to: 408 E. Tulsa, Siloam Springs, AR 72761) Eds. Gordon Grice, Bob Zordani.

700　　　　　　PY　　ISSN 0013-9726
EPOCA;* revista de cultura. vol.5, 1968. bi-m. 180 g.($5.) Natalicio Talavera No. 336, Asuncion, Paraguay. Ed. Emilio Perez Chaves. bk.rev.; bibl. **Indexed:** Chic. Per.Ind.

810　　　　　　US　　ISSN 0145-1391
AP2
EPOCH (ITHACA); a magazine of contemporary literature. 1947. 3/yr. $11. Cornell University, 251 Goldwin Smith Hall, Ithaca, NY 14853-3201. TEL 607-255-3385. FAX 607-255-1454. Ed. Michael Koch. adv.: B&W page $170; trim 4 1/2 x 7 1/2. bk.rev.; cum.index every 2 yrs. circ. 1,100. (also avail. in microform from UMI; reprint service avail. from UMI) **Indexed:** A.I.P.P., Arts & Hum.Cit.Ind., Ind.Amer.Per.Verse, Ind.Bk.Rev.Hum.
　　—Faxon; UnCover; UMI.

800 900　　　　IT　　ISSN 0394-5618
ERBA D'ARNO. 1980. q. L.33000 (foreign L.60000) (effective 1994). Erba d'Arno, Via Castruccio 1, 50054 Fucecchio (Florence), Italy. TEL 0571-242093. Ed. Piero Malvolti. adv.; bk.rev.; cum.index. circ. 2,000. (back issues avail.)
　　　Description: Covers historical research.

800 900　　　　IT　　ISSN 1120-4923
ERBA D'ARNO. QUADERNI; supplemento a Erba d'Arno. 1986. a. L.10000. Erba d'Arno, Via Castruccio 1, 50054 Fucecchio (Florence), Italy. TEL 0571-242093. Ed. Piero Malvolti. circ. 700.

800　　　　　　FR　　ISSN 1168-9498
▼**L'ERCKMANN - CHATRIAN.** 1992. a. 110 F. Presses Universitaires de Nancy, 25 rue Baron Louis, 54001 Nancy Cedex, France. (Co-publisher: Editions Serpenoise) Ed. Jean-Marie Bonnet. circ. 2,000.

800　　　　　　IE
ERIU; journal devoted to Irish philology and literature. 1904. a. Royal Irish Academy, 19 Dawson St., Dublin 2, Ireland. TEL 01-762570. FAX 01-762346. Ed.Bd. **Indexed:** Bibl.Ling., M.L.A. **Document type:** academic/scholarly publication.

800　　　　　　GW
ERLANGER ROMANISTISCHE DOKUMENTE UND ARBEITEN. irreg., no.13, 1993. DM.87. Stauffenburg Verlag, Postfach 2567, 72015 Tuebingen, Germany. TEL 07071-78091. FAX 07071-75288. Ed.Bd. **Document type:** monographic series.

800 700　　　　AU　　ISSN 0014-0252
EROEFFNUNGEN; Magazin fuer Literatur & bildende Kunst. (Text mainly in German; occasionally in English or Slovene) 1961. q. S.50. Hubert F. Kulterer, Ed. & Pub., Unter-Meidlinger Str. 16-18, A-1120 Vienna, Austria. adv.; bk.rev.; play rev.; illus. circ. 1,500.

808　　　　　　US　　ISSN 0887-5057
EROTIC FICTION QUARTERLY; a journal of erotic & other sexual fiction. 1985. irreg. $9.95 per no. E F Q Publications, Box 424958, San Francisco, CA 94142-4958. Ed. Richard Hiller. circ. 1,000.

ERTONG XIAOSHUO/SHORT STORIES FOR CHILDREN. see CHILDREN AND YOUTH — For

860 100　　　　CK　　ISSN 0120-1263
ESCRITOS. 1974. s-a. $1.50 per no. Universidad Pontificia Bolivariana, Escuela de Educacion y Humanidades, Biblioteca Central - Seccion Canje, Aptdo. 1178, Medellin, Colombia. TEL 2498957. FAX 2396683. TELEX 65047. Ed. Bernardo Lopera. adv.; bk.rev.; bibl. circ. 1,000.

860　　　　　　VE　　ISSN 1011-7989
ESCRITURA: TEORIA Y CRITICA LITERARIAS. 1976. s-a. $15 to individuals; institutions $35. Universidad Central de Venezuela, Consejo de Desarrollo Cientifico y Humanistico, Apdo. 65603, Caracas 1066-A, Venezuela. Ed. Rafael Di Prisco. adv.; bk.rev. circ. 1,000. **Document type:** academic/scholarly publication.
　　　Description: Contains essays and study on theory and literary criticism with special emphasis on Latin American literature.

830　　　　　　AU
ESELSOHR.* 2/yr. G. Pilz, Stifterstrasse 4a, A-4320 Perg, Austria. illus.

840　　　　　　US　　ISSN 0014-0767
ESPRIT CREATEUR; a critical quarterly of French literature. (Text in English and French) 1961. 4/yr. $17 to individuals; institutions $32. Esprit Createur, Inc., Box 25333, Baton Rouge, LA 70894. TEL 504-388-6713. FAX 504-388-6628. Ed. John D. Erickson. adv.; bk.rev.; index. circ. 1,100. (also avail. in microfilm from UMI; reprint service avail. from UMI; back issues avail.) **Indexed:** Amer.Hum.Ind., Arts & Hum.Cit.Ind., Bk.Rev.Ind. (1980-), Child.Bk.Rev.Ind. (1980-), Curr.Cont., M.L.A. **Document type:** academic/scholarly publication.
　　—BLDSC (3811.660200); Faxon; UnCover.

824　　　　　　US　　ISSN 0071-1357
PR13
ESSAYS AND STUDIES.* 1910. a. price varies. Boydell & Brewer, Inc., Box 41026, Rochester, NY 14604. TEL 716-275-0419. FAX 716-271-8778. **Indexed:** Abstr.Engl.Stud., Br.Hum.Ind., M.L.A. **Document type:** monographic series.
　　—Faxon.

809　　　　　　UK　　ISSN 0014-0856
PR1
ESSAYS IN CRITICISM; a quarterly journal of literary criticism. 1951. q. £34($80) Oxford University Press, Oxford Journals, Walton St., Oxford OX2 6DP, England. (U.S. subscr. to: Oxford University Press Inc., 2001 Evans Rd., Cary, NC 27513. TEL 919-677-0977) Eds. Stephen Ward, Christopher Ricks. adv. contact: Jane Parker. bk.rev.; index, cum.index. circ. 2,500. (also avail. in microform from MIM,UMI; back issues avail.; reprint service avail. from SWZ,UMI) **Indexed:** Abstr.Engl.Stud., Acad.Ind., Arts & Hum.Cit.Ind., Br.Hum.Ind., Curr.Cont., Hum.Ind., Ind.Bk.Rev.Hum., M.L.A. **Document type:** academic/scholarly publication.
　　—BLDSC (3811.690000); Faxon; UnCover; SWETS; UMI. **CCC.**
　　　Description: Covers the whole field of English literature from the time of Chaucer to the present day.

LITERATURE

840 844   **AT**   ISSN 0071-139X
PQ12
ESSAYS IN FRENCH LITERATURE. (Text in English and French) 1964. a. Aus.$7. University of Western Australia, Department of French Studies, Nedlands, W.A. 6009, Australia. circ. 400. **Indexed:** Arts & Hum.Cit.Ind., Curr.Cont., M.L.A.
—BLDSC (3811.696000); UnCover.

800   **US**   ISSN 0738-0763
PR6013.R44
ESSAYS IN GRAHAM GREENE; an annual review. 1987. a. $20. Penkevill Publishing Company, Box 212, Greenwood, FL 32443. TEL 904-569-2811. Ed. Peter Wolfe.

809   **US**   ISSN 0094-5404
PN2
ESSAYS IN LITERATURE. 1974. s-a. $8 to individuals; institutions $10 (effective Jan. 1992). Western Illinois University, Department of English, Macomb, IL 61455. TEL 309-298-2212. Ed. Thomas P. Joswick. bibl. circ. 600. **Indexed:** Abstr.Engl.Stud., Amer.Bibl.Slavic & E.Eur.Stud., Arts & Hum.Cit.Ind., Curr.Cont., LCR, M.L.A. **Document type:** academic/scholarly publication.
—BLDSC (3811.699000); Faxon; UnCover; UMI.

800 792   **UK**   ISSN 0308-888X
PN2
ESSAYS IN POETICS. 1976. s-a. £15.50 to individuals (overseas £19.75); institutions £19.75 (overseas £27) (effective 1994). (British Neo-Formalist Circle) Drake Marketing Services Ltd., St. Fagans Rd., Fairwater, Cardiff CF5 3AE, Wales. TEL 0222-560333. FAX 0222-554909. (Co-publisher: Oxon Publishers) Eds. J.M. Andrew, C.R. Pike. adv.; bk.rev. circ. 300. (back issues avail.) **Indexed:** Arts & Hum.Cit.Ind., Curr.Cont., M.L.A. **Document type:** academic/scholarly publication.
—BLDSC (3811.781000); UnCover.

820   **CN**   ISSN 0316-0300
PR9180
ESSAYS ON CANADIAN WRITING. (Text in English) 1974. 3/yr. Can.$20 to individuals; institutions Can.$40 (effective Jan. 1991). Canadian Literary Research Foundation, 1980 Queen St. E., 2nd Fl., Toronto, ON M4L 1J2, Canada. TEL 416-694-3348. FAX 416-698-9906. Ed.Bd. adv.; bk.rev. circ. 1,000. (also avail. in microfilm) **Indexed:** Abstr.Engl.Stud., Amer.Hum.Ind., Bk.Rev.Ind. (1980-), Can.Lit.Ind., Can.Per.Ind., Child.Bk.Rev.Ind. (1980-), CMI, Ind.Bk.Rev.Hum., M.L.A. **Document type:** academic/scholarly publication.
—BLDSC (3811.678000); Faxon; UMI.

ESTRENO; journal on the contemporary Spanish theater. see *THEATER*.

860   **MX**   ISSN 0071-1691
ESTUDIOS DE LITERATURA. 1958. irreg., latest 1983. price varies. Universidad Nacional Autonoma de Mexico, Instituto de Investigaciones Esteticas, Circuito Mtro. Mario de la Cueva, Zona Cultural, Ciudad de la Investigacion en Humanidades, 04000 Mexico, D.F., Mexico.

860   **SP**   ISSN 0071-1705
ESTUDIOS DE LITERATURA CONTEMPORANEA. 1968. irreg. price varies, $3-$5. Real Academia Espanola de la Lengua, Universidad de Santiago de Compostela, Coruna, Spain. circ. 2,000.

ESTUDIOS FILOLOGICOS. see *LINGUISTICS*.

800   **BL**
ESTUDOS BAIANOS. 1970. irreg. Cr.$290. Universidade Federal da Bahia, Centro Editorial e Didatico, Rua A. Viana s-n, Canela, Salvador, Bahia, Brazil. Ed.Bd. circ. 1,000.

830   **BL**   ISSN 0101-837X
PB5
ESTUDOS GERMANICOS. (Two annual issues: one on literature, and one on language) 1980; N.S. 1994. s-a. $5. Universidade Federal de Minas Gerais, Departamento de Letras Germanicas, UFMG-FALE-CESAG, Av. Antonio Carlos, 6627, 31270-901 Belo Horizonte, MG, Brazil. TEL 5531-448-5123. FAX 5531-448-5120. Ed. Julio Yeha. bk.rev. circ. 1,000. **Document type:** academic/scholarly publication.
—BLDSC (3813.064000).

ESTUDOS ITALIANOS EM PORTUGAL. see *ART*.

ESTUDOS LINGUISTICOS E LITERARIOS. see *LINGUISTICS*.

ESTUDOS PORTUGUESES E AFRICANOS. see *SOCIAL SCIENCES: COMPREHENSIVE WORKS*.

800   **US**   ISSN 1074-9535
▼**ETHEREAL DANCES.** 1992. s-a. $5 for 3 issues. Scream Press, 509 Enterprise Dr., Rohnert Park, CA 94928. Ed. Sara Boyd. adv.; illus. circ. 100.

820   **FR**   ISSN 0014-195X
PR1
ETUDES ANGLAISES. (Text in English, French) 1937. q. $70. Didier Erudition, 6 rue de la Sorbonne, 75005 Paris, France. (Subscr. to: Didier Erudition, North American Fulfillment Office, P.O. Box 830350, Birmingham, AL 35283-0350, U.S.A.) Ed. S. Soupel. bk.rev.; bibl.; illus.; index. circ. 1,500. (processed; also avail. in microform from SWZ; reprint service avail. from SWZ) **Indexed:** Abstr.Engl.Stud., Arts & Hum.Cit.Ind., Curr.Cont., Ind.Bk.Rev.Hum., M.L.A.
—BLDSC (3816.760000); Faxon; UnCover; SWETS.

ETUDES BALKANIQUES. see *HISTORY — History Of Europe*.

840   **SZ**   ISSN 0531-9455
ETUDES BAUDELAIRIENNES. 1970. irreg., no.13, 1991. price varies. Editions de la Baconniere S.A., P.O. Box 185, CH-2017 Boudry, Switzerland. TEL 038-421004. Ed. Claude Pichois. (reprint service avail. from UMI) **Document type:** monographic series, academic/scholarly publication.

800   **SZ**   ISSN 0014-2026
ETUDES DE LETTRES. 1926. 4/yr. 60 Fr. Universite de Lausanne, Faculte des Lettres, Batiment Central, CH-1015 Lausanne, Switzerland. Ed. Doris Jakubec. bk.rev.; bibl. circ. 700. **Indexed:** Abstr.Engl.Stud., M.L.A. **Document type:** academic/scholarly publication.

400 900   **SZ**   ISSN 0071-1934
ETUDES DE PHILOLOGIE ET D'HISTOIRE. (Text in English, French) 1967. irreg., no.46, 1992. price varies. Librairie Droz S.A., 11, rue Massot, CH-1211 Geneva 12, Switzerland. TEL 022-3466666. FAX 022-3472391. **Document type:** monographic series, academic/scholarly publication.
—CCC.

ETUDES FINNO-OUGRIENNES. see *LINGUISTICS*.

840 440   **CN**   ISSN 0014-2085
ETUDES FRANCAISES. (Including section bibliographique) (Text in French) 1965. 3/yr. Can.$22.50 to individuals; institutions Can.$38.50. Presses de l'Universite de Montreal, C.P. 6128, Succ. A, Montreal, PQ H3C 3J7, Canada. TEL 514-343-6933. Ed. Ginette Michaud. adv.; bk.rev.; bibl.; index. circ. 1,000. (also avail. in microform from MIM,UMI; reprint service avail. from UMI) **Indexed:** Amer.Hist.& Life, Arts & Hum.Cit.Ind., Can.Lit.Ind., Can.Per.Ind., Hist.Abstr., M.L.A., Pt.de Rep (1979-). **Document type:** academic/scholarly publication.
—BLDSC (3819.530000); Faxon; UMI.

830   **FR**   ISSN 0014-2115
DD1
ETUDES GERMANIQUES. 1946. q. $70. Didier Erudition, 6 rue de la Sorbonne, 75005 Paris, France. (Subscr. to: Didier Erudition, North American Fullfillment Office, P.O. Box 830350, Birmingham, AL 35283-0350, U.S.A.) Ed.Bd. adv.; bk.rev.; charts; index. circ. 2,000. (also avail. in microform from SWZ; reprint service avail. from SWZ) **Indexed:** Arts & Hum.Cit.Ind., Bibl.Ling., Can.Rev.Comp.Lit, Curr.Cont., M.L.A. **Document type:** academic/scholarly publication.
—Faxon; SWETS.

ETUDES IRLANDAISES; revue bilingue d'histoire, civilisation et litterature irlandaises. see *HISTORY — History Of Europe*.

800   **CN**   ISSN 0014-214X
PQ2
ETUDES LITTERAIRES. 1968. 3/yr. Can.$22 to individuals (foreign Can.$26); institutions Can.$36. Presses de l'Universite Laval, Cite Universitaire, Quebec, PQ G1K 7P4, Canada. TEL 418-656-3132. FAX 418-656-3305. Ed. Monique Moser-Verrey. bk.rev. (also avail. in microform from BNQ,UMI; reprint service avail. from UMI) **Indexed:** Arts & Hum.Cit.Ind., Can.Lit.Ind., Can.Rev.Comp.Lit., Curr.Cont., Ind.Bk.Rev.Hum., M.L.A., Pt.de Rep. (1979-). **Document type:** monographic series, academic/scholarly publication.
—Faxon; UMI.
 Description: Each issue devoted to a writer, theme or genre and consists of studies and unedited or little known documents.

840   **GW**
ETUDES LITTERAIRES FRANCAISES. irreg., no.61, 1994. DM.78. Gunter Narr Verlag, Postfach 2567, 72015 Tuebingen, Germany. TEL 07071-78091. FAX 07071-75288. Ed. Alain Niderst. **Document type:** monographic series.

840   **BE**
ETUDES NERVALIENNES ET ROMANTIQUES. (Text in French) 1978. a. 350 BEF. Presses Universitaires de Namur, 8 Rempart de la Vierge, 5000 Namur, Belgium. FAX 32-19-23-03-91. TELEX 59222 FACNAM B. Ed. Pierre Rummens. bk.rev. circ. 750. (back issues avail.) **Document type:** academic/scholarly publication.
 Description: Connected with the publication of the complete works of Gerard de Nerval.

840   **SZ**
ETUDES RABELAISIENNES. (Text in English, French, German, Italian, Spanish) 1956. irreg., vol.29, 1993. price varies. Librairie Droz S.A., 11 rue Massot, CH-1211 Geneva 12, Switzerland. TEL 022-3466666. FAX 022-3472391. circ. 800. **Indexed:** M.L.A. **Document type:** monographic series, academic/scholarly publication.
 Description: Presents studies on the life and work of Francois Rabelais.

ETUDES ROMANES DE LUND. see *LINGUISTICS*.

800   **FR**
ETUDES SUR LES MONDES HISPANOPHONES. no.5, 1965. biennial. price varies. Presses Universitaires de Rennes, 2 rue du Doyen D. Leroy, 35044 Rennes Cedex, France. TEL 99-54-66-35. FAX 99-33-07-95. Ed.Bd. adv.; bk.rev. circ. 500. **Former titles:** Mondes Hispanophone et Lusophone (ISSN 0761-2397); Universite de Haute Bretagne. Centre d'Etudes Hispaniques, Hispano-Americaines et Luso-Bresiliennes. Travaux (ISSN 0080-0929)

800   **US**   ISSN 0146-7220
PS3545.E6
EUDORA WELTY NEWSLETTER. 1977. s-a. $2 (foreign $3). University of Toledo, Department of English, 2801 W. Bancroft, Toledo, OH 43606. TEL 419-537-2318. Ed. W.U. McDonald, Jr. bibl.; cum.index: 1977-1986. circ. 165. (back issues avail.) **Indexed:** Amer.Hum.Ind., LCR, M.L.A. **Document type:** newsletter.
 Description: Provides checklists of Eudora Welty's writing and of secondary materials, information about scholarly works in progress and forthcoming, and bibliographical notes on Welty texts, unrecorded appearances, and location of rare copies or editions.

810   **US**   ISSN 1040-9483
PS3529.N5
EUGENE O'NEILL REVIEW. 1977. 2/yr. $10 to individuals; institutions and foreign $15. Suffolk University, Department of English, c/o Frederick Wilkins, Ed., Boston, MA 02114. TEL 617-573-8272. adv.; bk.rev.; play rev.; abstr.; bibl.; index. circ. 550. (back issues avail.) **Indexed:** Abstr.Engl.Stud., LCR, M.L.A.
—UnCover.
 Formerly (until 1989): Eugene O'Neill Newsletter (ISSN 0733-0456)
 Description: Contains essays on the life and works of Eugene O'Neill, reviews of his plays, news, letters and comments.

830 398 GW ISSN 0531-2159
PT941.E9
EULENSPIEGEL-JAHRBUCH. 1960. a. DM.36. Verlag Peter Lang GmbH, Eschborner Landstr. 42-50, 60489 Frankfurt a.M., Germany. TEL 069-7807050. FAX 069-785893. (Subscr. to: Dieter Scheller, Rathaus, 38170 Schoeppenstedt, Germany) Ed. Werner Wunderlich. adv.; bk.rev. circ. 600. (back issues avail.)

809 GW ISSN 0014-2328
PN4
EUPHORION; Zeitschrift fuer Literaturgeschichte. 1894. 4/yr. DM.148 (students DM.120). Universitaetsverlag C. Winter Heidelberg GmbH, Hans-Bunte-Str. 18, 69123 Heidelberg, Germany. Ed. Wolfgang Adam. adv.; bk.rev.; index, circ. 1,200. (also avail. in microfiche from IDC; reprint service avail. from KTO) **Indexed:** Arts & Hum.Cit.Ind., Can.Rev.Comp.Lit, Curr.Cont. **Document type:** academic/scholarly publication.
— BLDSC (3827.700000); Faxon; UnCover; SWETS.

840 FR ISSN 0046-2667
EUREKA.* 1971. m. c/o Jean LaPlace, Ed., 10 rue Kuss, 75013 Paris, France. bk.rev.

800 RM
EURESIS - CAHIERS ROUMAINS D'ETUDES LITTERAIRES. (Text in English, French; occasionally German, Italian, Spanish) 1973. q. 60 lei($60) (Consiliul Culturii si Educatiei Socialiste) Editura Univers, Piata Presei Libere 1, 79739 Bucharest, Rumania. TEL 40-1-6181762. FAX 40-1-3124970. Ed. Mircea Martin. adv.; bk.rev. circ. 1,000. **Indexed:** Can.Rev.Comp.Lit., M.L.A. **Document type:** academic/scholarly publication.
Formerly: Cahiers Roumains d'Etudes Litteraires (ISSN 0257-7526)
Description: Journal of literary history and theory, criticism, essays. Promotes dialogue between different literatures and intercultural exchange.

820 920 NE ISSN 0923-9855
EUROPEAN JOYCE STUDIES. 1989. a. price varies. Editions Rodopi B.V., Keizersgracht 302-304, 1016 EX Amsterdam, Netherlands. TEL 31-20-6227507. FAX 31-20-6380948. (In N. America: 233 Peachtree St., N.E., Ste. 404, Atlanta, GA 30303-1504. TEL 800-225-3998. FAX 404-522-7116) Eds. Christine van Boheemen, Fritz Senn. **Document type:** academic/scholarly publication.
Description: Offers "European" perspectives on James Joyce's works, their adaptations, annotations, and translations; studies in biography as well as current debates in criticism and Joyce's place in literary history.

800 US
EUROPEAN ROMANTIC REVIEW.* 1990. s-a. $14 to individuals; institutions $22. Box 591402, San Francisco, CA 94159-1402. Ed. Frederick Burwick. bk.rev.

EUROPEAN STUDIES. see HISTORY — History Of Europe

800 US
PR6045.A97
EVELYN WAUGH NEWSLETTER AND STUDIES. 1967. 3/yr. $8. Evelyn Waugh Society, Nassau Community College, State University of New York, Department of English, Garden City, NY 11530. TEL 516-532-7187. Ed. Paul A. Doyle. adv.; bk.rev. circ. 194. **Indexed:** Abstr.Engl.Stud., Amer.Hum.Ind., M.L.A. **Document type:** academic/scholarly publication.
Formerly (until Apr. 1990): Evelyn Waugh Newsletter (ISSN 0014-3693)
Description: Encourages research in the writings of Evelyn Waugh.

800 CN ISSN 0315-3770
EVENT. 1971. 3/yr. Can.$15. Douglas College, P.O. Box 2503, New Westminster, BC V3L 5B2, Canada. TEL 604-527-5293. FAX 604-527-5095. Ed. Dale Zieroth. adv.; bk.rev. circ. 1,000. (also avail. in microfiche from MML; back issues avail.; reprint service avail. from ISI) **Indexed:** Arts & Hum.Cit.Ind., Can.Lit.Ind.
Description: Presents reviews, fiction and poetry.

800 US ISSN 1043-3333
THE EVERGREEN CHRONICLES; a journal of gay and lesbian arts and cultures. 1985. s-a. $15 to individuals (foreign $18); institutions $20 (foreign $30). Box 8939, Minneapolis, MN 55408-0939. TEL 612-371-0382. Eds. Susan Raffo, James Berg. adv.; bk.rev. circ. 1,800. (back issues avail.)
Description: Presents the works exploring gay and lesbian arts and cultures, particularly the works exploring the interweaving of race, culture, class, gender and sexuality.

810 US
▼**EVERMORE.** 1993. q. Poe Foundation, Inc., 1914-16 E. Main St., Richmond, VA 23223. Ed. Agnes Bondurant Marcuson. **Document type:** newsletter.
Description: News and information about the life and work of Edgar Allan Poe, and the activities of the foundation.

850 IT
EX FILTIA. 1987. irreg., vol.4, 1992. L.20000. Biblioteca Civile Angelo Mai, Piazza Vecchia 15, 24100 Bergamo, Italy. FAX 035-240655.

380
THE EXECUTIVE SPEECHWRITER NEWSLETTER; a newsletter of quotes, jokes, stories and ideas for the executive speechwriter. 1986. bi-m. $79. Words, Ink., Emerson Falls, St. Johnsbury, VT 05819. TEL 802-748-4472. FAX 802-748-1939. Joe Taylor Ford, Pres. (back issues avail.) **Document type:** newsletter.
Description: Contains anecdotal information and material for speechwriters.

801 PR
EXEGESIS. 1986. 3/yr. $12. Universidad de Puerto Rico, Colegio Universitario de Humacao, Humacao, PR 00791. TEL 809-850-0000. Ed. Marcos Reyes. bk.rev. circ. 1,500.

809 US ISSN 1041-2573
PN661
EXEMPLARIA; a journal of theory in medieval and Renaissance studies. 1989. s-a. $20 to individuals (foreign $30); institutions $40 (foreign $60). Medieval and Rennaissance Texts and Studies, LNG 99, State University of New York, Binghamton, NY 13902-6000. TEL 607-777-6758. FAX 607-777-2408. Ed. R.A. Shoaf. adv. contact: K.K. Crofoot. circ. 405. **Document type:** academic/scholarly publication.
— BLDSC (3836.227200); Faxon; UnCover.
Description: Concerns with both theoretical and experimental approaches to medieval and Renaissance culture.
Refereed Serial

709 UK
EXETER STUDIES IN AMERICAN & COMMONWEALTH ARTS. 1970. irreg. (1-2/yr.) $10. University of Exeter, Centre for American & Commonwealth Arts, Queens Bldg., Exeter EX 4QH, England. FAX 0392-263108. Ed. R. Maltby. circ. 2,000.
Formerly: American Arts Pamphlet Series.

800 CN
EXILE. 1972. q. $25. Exile Editions Ltd., 69 Sullivan, Toronto, Ont., Canada. TEL 416-977-7937. Ed. Barry Callaghan. circ. 1,200. (also avail. in microfiche) **Indexed:** Arts & Hum.Cit.Ind., Curr.Cont.
Description: Publishes poetry, plays, novels, stories, drawings and paintings.

810 US ISSN 0421-9090
EXILE; contemporary literature. 1953. biennial. free. Denison University, Granville, OH 43023. TEL 614-587-2796. Ed. Ellen Gurly. illus. circ. 1,000. (also avail. in microfiche from BHP) **Indexed:** Arts & Hum.Cit.Ind., Curr.Cont. **Document type:** academic/scholarly publication.
Description: Covers contemporary student literature and art.

800 US ISSN 0195-3516
EXIT; a journal of the arts. 1972. irreg. $10 for 3 nos. Rochester Routes - Creative Arts Projects, 232 Post Ave., Rochester, NY 14619-1313. TEL 716-328-2144. FAX 716-328-7018. Eds. Frank Judge, Mary Whitney. adv.; bk.rev. circ. 2,000.
Formerly: Entrance.

808.81 US ISSN 1054-3937
EXIT 13 MAGAZINE. 1981. a. $67.50 (effective 1994). Tom Plante, Ed. & Pub., 22 Oakwood Ct., Fanwood, NJ 07023. TEL 908-889-5298. adv.; bk.rev. circ. 500. (back issues avail.)
Formerly (until no.4, 1986): Berkeley Works.
Description: Poetic overview of contemporary life, with a strong focus on geography, travel, adventure and nature.

860 US ISSN 0361-9621
PQ6001
EXPLICACION DE TEXTOS LITERARIOS. (Text in Spanish) 1972. s-a. $12 to individuals; libraries $20. California State University, Sacramento, Department of Foreign Languages, 6000 J St., Sacramento, CA 95819. TEL 916-454-6011. Ed. Jorge A. Santana. adv.; bk.rev.; cum.index. circ. 1,000. **Indexed:** Arts & Hum.Cit.Ind., Curr.Cont., Hisp.Amer.Per.Ind., M.L.A.
—Faxon.

810 US ISSN 0014-4940
PR1
THE EXPLICATOR. 1941. q. $29 to individuals; institutions $52. (Helen Dwight Reid Educational Foundation) Heldref Publications, 1319 Eighteenth St., N.W., Washington, DC 20036-1802. TEL 202-296-6267. FAX 202-296-5149. Ed. Nancy Geltman. adv. contact: Raymond Rallo. index, cum.index: vols.1-20, 21-30. circ. 2,200. (also avail. in microform; reprint service avail. from KTO) **Indexed:** Abstr.Engl.Stud., Acad.Ind., Arts & Hum.Cit.Ind., Curr.Cont., Hum.Ind., M.L.A. **Document type:** academic/scholarly publication.
— BLDSC (3842.153000); Faxon; UnCover; UMI. CCC.
Refereed Serial

EXPLORATIONS. see LINGUISTICS

810 US
EXPLORATIONS. 1980. a. $4 (effective 1994). University of Alaska Southeast, English Department, 11120 Glacier Highway, Juneau, AK 99801. TEL 907-789-4618. FAX 907-465-6406. Ed. Art Petersen. circ. 500. (back issues avail.)
Description: Solicits short fiction and poetry from across the nation and awards prizes to winning entries.

EXPLORATIONS IN RENAISSANCE CULTURE. see HUMANITIES: COMPREHENSIVE WORKS

810 US ISSN 0014-5017
EXPLORER (NOTRE DAME). 1960. s-a. $6. Explorer Publications Co., Box 210, Notre Dame, IN 46556. TEL 219-777-3465. Ed. Raymond John Flory. adv.; illus. circ. 200.
Description: Magazine of verse, fiction, and essays.

820 AT ISSN 0085-039X
EXPRESSION. 1964. a. Aus.$2. University of Wollongong, School of Education, P.O. Box 1144, Wollongong, N.S.W. 2500, Australia. Ed. R.W. Colvin. bk.rev. circ. 400.

F A R. see ART

F A R C E. (Fine Arts Research and Communications Enterprises) see ART

820 AT ISSN 0155-476X
F A W N S. 1977. a. Aus.$10. Fellowship of Australian Writers North Shore Regional, P.O. Box 15, Berowra 2081, Australia. TEL 02-4561142. Ed. Bettina Cummins. bk.rev. circ. 150. (back issues avail.)
Description: Contains short stories, articles and poetry written by members.

830 GW ISSN 0175-2200
FACHDIENST GERMANISTIK. 1983. m. DM.84. Iudicium Verlag, Postfach 701067, 81310 Munich, Germany. TEL 089-717868. FAX 089-7142039. Ed. Peter Kapitza. **Document type:** academic/scholarly publication.

FACTSHEET FIVE; the definitive guide to the zine revolution. see PUBLISHING AND BOOK TRADE

808 FR ISSN 0182-1717
PQ1184
FAIRE PART. 1982. a. 180 F. Editions Faire Part, 17, Allee Jean Buclon, 26000 Valence, France. adv.
Description: Presents French prose and poetry works.

3622 LITERATURE

800 US ISSN 1057-7459
FAIRFAX MAGAZINE; the multicultural magazine of short novels, short stories and poetry. 1991. q. $22. C H Fairfax Co., Inc., Box 7047, Baltimore, MD 21216. TEL 410-448-5461. Ed. Paul Fairfax Evans. adv.; bk.rev.; circ. 6,100 (paid). (back issues avail.)
  Description: Contains fiction stories, poetry and one essay. Appeals to a broad, worldwide audience of all ages.

800 US
FAIRLEIGH DICKINSON UNIVERSITY. ARCHIVAL SERIES. irreg., vol.19, 1991. Fairleigh Dickinson University, 223 Montross Ave., Rutherford, NJ 07070-1977.

839.31 NE
FAMA. 1936. 8/yr. free. Stichting het Rijnlands Lyceum, Backershagenlaan 5, 2243 AB Wassenaar, Netherlands. Ed.Bd. adv.; bk.rev.; film rev.; play rev. circ. 1,000.
  Former titles: Krant; Scheepspraat (ISSN 0036-5971)

895.1 CC
FANG CAO. (Text in Chinese) m. Wuhan Shi Wenlian, No. 44, Jiefang Gongyuan Lu, Wuhan, Hubei 430010, People's Republic of China. TEL 24791. Ed. Guan Yonghe.

800 CC
FANG CAO DI. (Text in Chinese) bi-m. Y6. Fang Cao Di Bianjibu, 1-1 Huoyaoku, Huancheng Lu, Fuzhou, Fujian 350001, People's Republic of China. (Dist. overseas by: Jiangsu Publications Import & Export Corp., 56 Gao Yun Ling, Nanjing, Jiangsu, P.R.C.)
  Description: Covers different styles of popular literature, music and critical approaches.

891.439 PK
FANUS. (Text in Urdu) 1978. m. Rs.6. Rukhsanah Siham Mirza, Ludvika Mansion, 689 Central Commercial Area, PECHS, Karachi 29, Pakistan.

810 US
FARCE; Raleigh's review of alternative arts. 1988. 4/yr. $20 (students $12). Paper Plant, Box 543, Raleigh, NC 27602. TEL 919-834-9203. Ed. John Dancy-Jones. circ. 1,000.
  Description: Publishes performative, dramatized works, urban lyrics, and the life of the mind.

FARM. see ART

808 US ISSN 0748-6022
FARMER'S MARKET. 1981. s-a. $10. Midwest Farmer's Market, Inc., Box 1272, Galesburg, IL 61402. Ed.Bd. circ. 500. **Indexed:** Amer.Hum.Ind., Ind.Amer.Per.Verse.
  Description: Creative works of distinguished local, regional, and national writers, poets, and artists, in the Midwestern literary tradition.

FASETTE/FACETS/FACETTEN. see EDUCATION

808 US ISSN 0276-2072
FAT TUESDAY. (Each issue has distinctive title) 1981. a. $5. Fat Tuesday Publications, RD 2, Box 4220, Manada Gap Rd., Grantville, PA 17028. TEL 717-469-7159. Ed. F.M. Cotolo. adv.; illus. circ. 300. (back issues avail.)
  Description: Contains contemporary prose and poetry.

809 US ISSN 0884-2949
PS3511.A86
FAULKNER JOURNAL. 1985. s-a. $12 to individuals; institutions $18. c/o Dawn Trouard, University of Akron, Department of English, Akron, OH 44325-1906. TEL 216-972-5194. FAX 216-972-8817. (Co-sponsors: University of Akron; Boston University) Ed. John T. Matthews. adv.; bibl.; illus. circ. 400. (also avail. in microform from UMI; back issues avail.) **Document type:** academic/scholarly publication.
  —BLDSC (3897.775000); Faxon; UnCover; UMI.
  Description: Publishes scholarly criticism on William Faulkner.

800 920 US ISSN 0733-6357
PS3511.A86
FAULKNER NEWSLETTER & YOKNAPATAWPHA REVIEW. 1981. q. $12.50 (foreign $15) (effective 1992). Yoknapatawpha Press, c/o William Boozer, Ed., 739 Clematis Dr., Nashville, TN 37205. TEL 601-234-0909. FAX 601-234-0800. (Subscr. to: Yoknapatawpha Press, Box 248, Oxford, MS 38655) adv.; bk.rev.; bibl.; illus. circ. 500. (tabloid format; back issues avail.) **Document type:** newsletter, academic/scholarly publication.
  Description: Devoted to the biographical work on the life and works of William Faulkner.

810 US ISSN 0146-5848
FAULT. 1971. s-a. $5. 33513 Sixth St., Union City, CA 94587. TEL 415-489-8561. Ed. Terrance McMahon. circ. 500.

895.1 CC ISSN 1002-803X
FEI TIAN/FLYING APSARAS. (Text in Chinese) 1950. m. Y16.80($58.50) (Gansu Sheng Wenlian) Fei Tian Yuekanshe, 284, Donggang Xilu, Lanzhou, Gansu 730000, People's Republic of China. TEL 25803. (Dist. outside China by: Guoji Shudian - China International Book Trading Corp., P.O. Box 399, Beijing, P.R.C.; Dist. in US by: China Books & Periodicals, Inc., 2929 24th St., San Francisco, CA 94110. TEL 415-282-2994) Ed. Li Yunpeng. adv.; bk.rev. circ. 11,000.
  Formerly (until 1981): Gansu Wenxue.
  Description: Publishes short stories, proses, poems and literary reviews.

800 US ISSN 1040-5607
FELL SWOOP; the all Bohemian review. 1983. s-a. $6. Acre Press, 1521 N. Lopez St., New Orleans, LA 70119. TEL 504-943-5198. Ed. X.J. Dailey. bk.rev. circ. 500. (back issues avail.)
  Description: Geared towards deflating the literature of our day which needs deflating.

FELLOWSHIP IN PRAYER. see RELIGIONS AND THEOLOGY — Other Denominations And Sects

800 301.412 FR ISSN 0150-4185
FEMMES EN LITTERATURE. 1976. irreg. price varies. Editions Klincksieck, 11 rue de Lille, 75005 Paris, France. Dir. Patrice Laurent.

700 AU ISSN 0015-0029
DAS FENSTER; Tiroler Kulturzeitschrift. 1968. s-a. S.160. Tiroler Landesregierung, Kulturabteilung, Sillgasse 8, A-6020 Innsbruck, Austria. (Subscr. to: Haymon Verlag, Kochstr. 10, A-6020 Innsbruck, Austria. TEL 0512-576300) Ed. Wolfgang Pfaundler. adv.; bk.rev.; bibl.; illus. circ. 3,600. **Document type:** consumer publication.

800 FR ISSN 1157-4240
FEUILLETS ROSES/EFFEUILLEE ROSE; revue de litterature erotique. 1991. q. B.P. 17, 26800 Etoile-sur-Rhone, France. TEL 75-60-63-93. FAX 75-60-75-06. Ed. Nigel Gauvin.

810 US ISSN 0046-3736
PN6010.5
FICTION. 1972. 2/yr. (3 nos./vol.). $20 to individuals; institutions $25; foreign $40. c/o City College, Department of English, 138th St. and Convent Ave., New York, NY 10031. TEL 212-650-6319. Ed. Mark J. Mirsky. circ. 3,000. (also avail. in microform from UMI; reprint service avail. from UMI) **Indexed:** Amer.Hum.Ind.
  —UMI.
  Description: Published modern fiction that sets itself serious questions, sometimes in absurd and comic voices, interrogating the nature of the real and fantastic. Representing no particular school of fiction - naturalism, surrealism - except the innovative.

800 US ISSN 1046-1094
FICTION FORUM. 4/yr. $15. Chips Off the Writer's Block, Box 83371, Los Angeles, CA 90083. Ed. Wanda Windham. circ. 500. **Document type:** newsletter.
  Description: Forum for beginners to publish their work and have it critiqued by their peers.

800 US ISSN 0092-1912
PN3311
FICTION INTERNATIONAL. 1973. s-a. $14 to individuals; institutions $28. San Diego State University Press, San Diego, CA 92182. TEL 619-594-6220. Ed. Harold Jaffe. adv. contact: Sheila Dollente. bk.rev.; illus. circ. 1,000. (also avail. in microform from UMI; reprint service avail. from UMI) **Indexed:** Abstr.Engl.Stud., Amer.Hum.Ind., Bk.Rev.Ind. (1980-), Child.Bk.Rev.Ind. (1980-). **Document type:** academic/scholarly publication.
  —BLDSC (3918.715000); UMI.
  Description: Publishes postmodern and innovative short fiction with a theme; recent topics have included women writers from developing nations, pornography and censorship, Japanese fiction, and Mexican fiction.

890 II
FICTION REVIEW; a magazine of creative writing. 1982. m. Vikrant Press, 32 DSIDC Industrial Complex, Wazirpur Delhi 110 052, India. Ed. Jai Vrat. adv.

FILOLOGIA. see LINGUISTICS

FILOLOGIA MODERNA. see LINGUISTICS

FILOLOGIA POLSKA. see LINGUISTICS

FILOZOFSKI FAKULTET - ZADAR. RAZDIO FILOLOSKIH ZNANOSTI. RADOVI. see LINGUISTICS

800 IT
FINISTERE. s-a. Elitropia Edizioni, Casella Postale 421, 42100 Reggio Emilia, Italy.

FINNISCH-UGRISCHE MITTEILUNGEN. see LINGUISTICS

FIREWEED; a feminist quarterly. see WOMEN'S INTERESTS

FIRST LINE/YI XING. see LITERATURE — Poetry

810 US ISSN 1051-1695
FISH DRUM. 1988. irreg. (2-4/yr.) $10 for 4 nos. Fish Drum Magazine, 626 Kathryn Ave., Santa Fe, NM 87501. TEL 505-982-8340. Ed. Robert Winson. bk.rev.; music rev.; circ. 500 (paid). (also avail. in magnetic tape)
  Description: Emphasizes modern, lively poetry and prose, and includes visual art, scores, interviews and literary criticism. Audio issues are all poetry, sometimes with music. Favors local poets.

800 301 US ISSN 0898-0233
FIVE FINGERS REVIEW. 1984. 2/yr. $15. Five Fingers Press, Box 15426, San Francisco, CA 94115-0426. TEL 415-431-8506. FAX 510-655-7904. Ed.Bd. adv. circ. 1,500.
  Description: Publishes poetry, fiction, nonfiction prose, essays and translations from diverse aesthetics and traditions.

821 UK
FIVE LEAVES LEFT. 1983. 3/yr. $10. 12 Colne Rd., Cowling, Keighley, West Yorkshire BD22 OBZ, England. circ. 500.

808 US
FLANNERY O'CONNOR AWARDS FOR SHORT FICTION. 1983. 2/yr. price varies. University of Georgia Press, 330 Research Dr., Athens, GA 30602-4901. TEL 706-369-6130. FAX 706-369-6131.

809 US ISSN 0091-4924
PS3565.C57
FLANNERY O'CONNOR BULLETIN. 1972. a. $7 to individuals; institutions $8. Georgia College, Department of English and Speech, Box 44, Milledgeville, GA 31061. TEL 912-453-4581. Ed. Sarah Gordon. adv.; bk.rev. circ. 1,000. (also avail. in microform from UMI; back issues avail.; reprint service avail. from UMI) **Indexed:** Abstr.Engl.Stud., Amer.Hum.Ind. **Document type:** academic/scholarly publication.
  —UnCover.

FLASH MARKET NEWS. see PUBLISHING AND BOOK TRADE

810 US ISSN 0147-1686
PS580
FLOATING ISLAND. 1976. irreg., no.4, 1989. $15. Floating Island Publications, Box 516, Point Reyes Sta., CA 94956. TEL 415-663-1181. Ed. Michael Sykes. illus. circ. 2,000.
  Description: Occasional anthology of poetry, fiction, photography, and graphic arts.

FLORILEGIUM; annual papers on late antiquity and the Middle Ages. see CLASSICAL STUDIES

810 US
FLOWER; an in-between magazine. 1991. 3/yr. $3 per no. 302 Laurie Court, Stillwater, MN 55082. Ed. Neil Cunningham. adv. circ. 650.
  Description: Publishes poetry that doesn't over-criticize, but offers solutions, poetry that makes you think and imagine.

830 GW ISSN 0724-1194
FLUGASCHE. (Text in English and German) 1980. q. DM.30($22) Flugasche Verlag, Lembergstr. 20, 70188 Stuttgart, Germany. TEL 0711-482446. Ed. Matthias Ulrich. adv.; bk.rev. circ. 2,000. (back issues avail.) **Document type:** consumer publication.

810 US
FOCI. a. Upsala College, 345 Prospect St., East Orange, NJ 07017-3399. TEL 201-266-7000. circ. 800.

FOCUS (KENT). see LITERATURE — Science Fiction, Fantasy, Horror

800 UK
FOCUS ON ROBERT GRAVES AND HIS CONTEMPORARIES. 1972. 2/yr. $10. Nene College, Department of English, Northampton, England. (Co-publisher: University of Maryland, European Division) Ed. Patrick Quinn. bk.rev.; bibl. circ. 800. (processed) **Indexed:** Amer.Hum.Ind., M.L.A.
  Formerly (until no.7, May 1988): Focus on Robert Graves.
  Description: Dedicated to the study of the literature of Robert Graves and of World War I era writers.

FOCUSES. see EDUCATION — Teaching Methods And Curriculum

839.7 SW ISSN 0025-8547
FOERFATTAREN. 1970. 8/yr. SEK 200 (typically set in Jan.). Sveriges Foerfattarfoerbund, Drottninggatan 88 B, 111 36 Stockholm, Sweden. TEL 08-791-89-25. FAX 08-791-22-85. Ed. Maria Rodikova.
  Supersedes: Sveriges Foerfattareforening. Medlemsblad.

FOLIO. see PUBLISHING AND BOOK TRADE

810 US ISSN 0015-5756
FOLIO (BIRMINGHAM). 1965. s-a. $3. A.H. Cather Publishing Co., 2501 Seventh Ave. S., Birmingham, AL 35222. TEL 205-252-6109. circ. 500. (processed; also avail. in microform from UMI) **Indexed:** Tr.& Indus.Ind.

FOLIO (BROCKPORT); essays on foreign languages and literature. see HUMANITIES: COMPREHENSIVE WORKS

808 US
FOLIO (WASHINGTON); a literary journal. 1984. 2/yr. $10. American University, Department of Literature, 4400 Massachusetts Ave., N.W., Washington, DC 20016. TEL 202-885-2971. adv.; bk.rev. circ. 400. (back issues avail.) **Indexed:** Graph.Arts Lit.Abstr.
  Description: Prints quality fiction and poetry by established and new writers.

800 US
FONDAMENTI. q. L.30000. Giardini Editori e Stampatori, Via delle Sorgenti 23, 46010 Agnano Pisano, Italy. Ed. Giuseppe Scarpat.

800 808.81 BE ISSN 0779-0732
FONDATION MAURICE CAREME. (Text in French; special issues in English) 1978. a. free. Fondation Maurice Careme, Av. Nellie Melba, 14, B-1070 Brussels, Belgium. TEL 32-2-5216775. FAX 32-5202086. (Co-sponsor: Les Amis de Maurice Careme) circ. 6,500. **Document type:** bulletin.
  Description: Provides information on films, conferences, poetry readings and competitions in the honor of Maurice Careme, with emphasis on the French language.

830 GW ISSN 0015-6175
PT1863.Z7
FONTANE-BLAETTER. 1965. s-a. DM.8.50 per no. Theodor Fontane Archiv, Postfach 601545, 14415 Potsdam, Germany. TEL 0331-22983. Ed. Manfred Horlitz. adv.; bk.rev. **Indexed:** M.L.A. **Document type:** bibliography, monographic series.
  —SWETS.

052 UK ISSN 0952-3979
FOOLSCAP. 1987. 2/yr. £6($16) (effective 1993). 78 Friars Rd., East Ham, London E6 1LL, England. TEL 081-470-7680. Ed. Judi Benson. circ. 200. (back issues avail.) **Document type:** consumer publication.
  Description: Poetry and prose from well- and little-known writers.

810 US
FOOTBALL: OUR WAY. 1984. 5/yr. $5. Our Way Publications, 5014 Starker Ave., Madison, WI 53716. TEL 608-241-0549. Ed. Dale Jellings. circ. 50.
  Description: Publish literary works related to football.

810 US
FOOTHILL QUARTERLY. 1975. q. $4. Foothill Community College, 12345 El Monte Rd., Los Altos Hills, CA 94022. TEL 415-948-8590. Eds. Richard Maxwell, Neva V. Hacker. circ. 1,000.

800 US ISSN 0749-9132
JF1525.I6
FOREIGN INTELLIGENCE LITERARY SCENE. 1982. 6/yr. $35 (effective 1994). (National Intelligence Study Center) Begell House, Inc., 79 Madison Ave., New York, NY 10016. TEL 212-213-8368. FAX 212-725-1999. Eds. Marjorie W. Cline, Dalton A. West. bk.rev. circ. 1,000. **Document type:** newsletter.
  Description: Reviews scholarly publications on intelligence, and publishes occasional special reports on significant intelligence development.

800 AA
FOREIGN LITERATURE. q. $30. Union des Ecrivains et Artistes d'Albanie, Tirana, Albania.

860 NE ISSN 0925-8620
FORO HISPANICO. 1991. 2/yr. price varies. Editions Rodopi B.V., Keizersgracht 302-304, 1016 EX Amsterdam, Netherlands. TEL 31-20-6227507. FAX 31-20-6380948. (In N. America: 233 Peachtree St., N.E., Ste. 404, Atlanta, GA 30303-1504. TEL 800-225-3998. FAX 404-522-7116) **Document type:** monographic series.
  Description: Covers topics in Spanish language and literature.
  Refereed Serial

860 UY
FORO LITERATIO. 1977. s-a. $7.50. Editorial Geminis, El Uiejo Pancho 2585, Montevideo, Uruguay. (Editorial addr.: Casilla 12013, Montevideo, Uruguay) Ed. Julio Ricci. adv.; bk.rev. circ. 1,000. **Indexed:** Hisp.Amer.Per.Ind.

891.8 CI ISSN 0015-8445
FORUM. (Text in Serbo-Croatian) 1962. 4/yr. 400 din. Jugoslavenska Akademija Znanosti i Umjetnosti, Razred za Suvremenu Knjizevnost, Zrinjski trg. 11, 41000 Zagreb, Croatia. TEL 041 433-849. Ed. Slavko Mihalic. index. **Indexed:** Abstr.Engl.Stud., Leg.Per., M.L.A.

800 NE ISSN 0015-8496
PN9
FORUM DER LETTEREN; tijdschrift voor taal- en letterkunde. 1960. q. fl.53.33 to individuals; institutions fl.62.86; students fl.47.62. (Nederlandse Organisatie voor Zuiver-Wetenschappelijk Onderzoek) Smits B.V., Westeinde 135, 2512 The Hague, Netherlands. Ed.Bd. adv.; index. circ. 1,200. **Indexed:** Amer.Hist.& Life, Bibl.Ling., Hist.Abstr., Ind.Bk.Rev.Hum., M.L.A.
  —SWETS.
  Formerly: Museum.

FORUM FOR MODERN LANGUAGE STUDIES. see LINGUISTICS

FORUM HOMOSEXUALITAET UND LITERATUR. see HOMOSEXUALITY

890 US
FORUM INTERNATIONAL.* (Text in English, Russian) 1976. s-a. $12 for 3 yrs. c/o J. Glad, Ed., 3901 Connecticut Ave., N.W., Ste. 408, Washington, DC 20008. adv.; bibl. circ. 500.
  Formerly: Forum (College Park) (ISSN 0164-288X)

FORUM UNIVERSITAIRE. see SOCIAL SCIENCES: COMPREHENSIVE WORKS

895.1 CC ISSN 1003-9058
FOSHAN WENYI. (Text in Chinese) 1970. m. Y2.80 per no. Foshan Shi Wenhua-ju, No. 36, Xinfeng Lu, Foshan, Guangdong 518000, People's Republic of China. TEL 0757-2288376. Ed. Liu Ning. adv. circ. 500,000. **Document type:** consumer publication.

FOURAH BAY STUDIES IN LANGUAGE AND LITERATURE. see LINGUISTICS

FRANCITE. see LINGUISTICS

800 IT ISSN 1121-7189
▼**FRANCO-ITALICA**; serie storico-letteraria - serie d'histoire litteraire. (Text in French, Italian) 1992. s-a. L.40000 (France 190 F.; elsewhere L.50000). (Universita di Torino, Dipartimento di Scienze Letterarie e Filologiche) Edizioni dell' Orso, Via Piacenza 66, 15100 Alessandria, Italy. Eds. Dario Cecchetti, Daniela Dalla Valle. **Document type:** academic/scholarly publication.

840 440 IT ISSN 1121-953X
FRANCOFONIA; studi e ricerche sulle letterature di lingua francese. 1981. s-a. L.50000 (foreign L.65000) (effective 1994). (Cooperativa Libraria Universitaria Editrice Bologna) Casa Editrice Leo S. Olschki, Casella Postale 66, 50100 Florence, Italy. TEL 055-6530684. FAX 055-6530214. Ed. L. Petroni. **Document type:** academic/scholarly publication.

840 IT
FRANCOFONIA. QUADERNI. 1982. irreg., no.7, 1993. price varies. Casa Editrice Leo S. Olschki, Casella Postale 66, 50100 Florence, Italy. TEL 055-6530684. FAX 055-6530214. **Document type:** monographic series.

FRANKENLAND; Zeitschrift fuer Fraenkische Landeskunde und Kulturpflege. see HISTORY — History Of Europe

830 430 GW ISSN 0071-9226
FRANKFURTER BEITRAEGE ZUR GERMANISTIK. 1967. irreg., vol.15, 1977. price varies. Universitaetsverlag C. Winter Heidelberg GmbH, Hans-Bunte-Str. 18, 69123 Heidelberg, Germany. **Indexed:** M.L.A. **Document type:** monographic series.

081 GW
FRANKFURTER BEITRAEGE ZUR LATEINAMERIKANISTIK. irreg., vol.6, 1994. DM.78. Gunter Narr Verlag, Postfach 2567, 72015 Tuebingen, Germany. TEL 07071-78091. FAX 07071-75288. Ed. Hermann Herlinghaus. **Document type:** monographic series.

FRANKFURTER JUDAISTISCHE BEITRAEGE. see ETHNIC INTERESTS

FRAU OHNE HERZ; eine Zeitschrift fuer Frauen und andere Lesben. see WOMEN'S INTERESTS

800 US
FREE FOCUS. 1985. s-a. $5 (foreign $10). (Women's Literary Guild) Wagner Press, Box 7415, New York, NY 10116-7415. TEL 718-680-3899. Ed. Patricia D. Coscia. adv.; bk.rev.; illus. circ. 200. (looseleaf format; back issues avail.) **Document type:** bibliography.
  Description: Features literature by women.

800 US ISSN 0016-0369
FREE LANCE; a magazine of poetry and prose. 1950. s-a. $2. Free Lance Poets and Prose Workshop, Inc., 6005 Grand Ave., Cleveland, OH 44104. Eds. Casper L. Jordan, Russell Atkins. bk.rev.; charts; play rev.; cum.index: vols.1-13. circ. 500. (also avail. in microfiche from KTO; back issues avail.)

LITERATURE

800   CN
FREE SPEECH MONITOR. 6/yr. Can.$10. Canadian Association for Free Expression Inc., P.O. Box 332, Rexdale, Ont. M9W 5L3, Canada. TEL 416-236-1367. FAX 416-896-4037. Ed. James P. Rae.
Formerly: Free Speech.

820   CN   ISSN 0705-1379
FREELANCE. 1970. m. (10/yr.). Can.$40 membership. Saskatchewan Writers Guild, P.O. Box 3986, Regina, SK S4P 3R9, Canada. Ed. April Davies. circ. 900. **Document type:** newsletter.
Description: Contains news and commentary on issues of interest to writers.

491 891   GW   ISSN 0067-592X
FREIE UNIVERSITAET BERLIN. OSTEUROPA-INSTITUT. SLAVISTISCHE VEROEFFENTLICHUNGEN. (Title varies: Veroeffentlichungen der Abteilung fuer Slavische Sprachen und Literaturen) 1953. irreg., vol.77, 1993. price varies. (Freie Universitaet Berlin, Osteuropa Institut) Harrassowitz Verlag, Taunusstr. 14, 65183 Wiesbaden, Germany. TEL 0611-530-0. FAX 0611-530570. TELEX 4186135. (Subscr. to: Postfach 2929, 65019 Wiesbaden, Germany) Ed.Bd. **Document type:** monographic series.

800   GW   ISSN 0071-9463
AS182
FREIES DEUTSCHES HOCHSTIFT, FRANKFURT AM MAIN. JAHRBUCH. (Text in English and German) 1962. a. varies. Max Niemeyer Verlag, Postfach 2140, 72011 Tuebingen, Germany. TEL 07071-98940. FAX 07071-989450. Ed.Bd. circ. 1,100. (back issues avail.) **Indexed:** M.L.A. **Document type:** academic/scholarly publication.
Description: Studies literature, mostly German, from 1750-1850.

700 800 300   US   ISSN 1052-3952
CR5061.U6
FRENCH AMERICAN REVIEW. 1930. s-a. $16 (foreign $20). American Society of the French Legion of Honor, 22 E. 60th St., New York, NY 10022. TEL 203-542-5539. FAX 203-542-5258. Ed. Sara Vagliano. bk.rev.; index. circ. 950. **Indexed:** M.L.A. **Document type:** academic/scholarly publication.
—UnCover.
Former titles (until winter, 1990): Laurels (ISSN 0270-3793); (until 1979): American Society Legion of Honor Magazine.
Description: Promotes the appreciation in the US of French culture and literature and in France of American culture and literature.

FRENCH - CANADIAN CIVILIZATION RESEARCH CENTER. CAHIERS/CENTRE DE RECHERCHE EN CIVILISATION CANADIENNE - FRANCAISE. CAHIERS. see
HISTORY — History Of North And South America

840 944   UK   ISSN 0016-1128
PQ1
FRENCH STUDIES; a quarterly review. (Supplement avail.: French Studies Bulletin (ISSN 0262-2750)) 1947. q. £35($70) Society for French Studies, c/o Dr. A.W. Raitt, Ed., Taylor Institution, St. Giles', Oxford OX1 3NA, England. bk.rev.; bibl.; tr.lit.; index. circ. 1,900. (back issues avail.; reprint service avail. from SCH) **Indexed:** Amer.Hist.& Life, Arts & Hum.Cit.Ind., Bibl.Ling., Br.Hum.Ind., Curr.Cont., Hist.Abstr., Ind.Bk.Rev.Hum., Mid.East: Abstr.& Ind.
—BLDSC (4034.600000); Faxon; UnCover; SWETS.
Description: Contains articles on French literature and French language with an occasional contribution on other aspects of French culture.

840 944   UK   ISSN 0262-2750
FRENCH STUDIES BULLETIN. (Supplement to French Studies (ISSN 0016-1128)) (Text in English and French) 1981. q. free with subscr. to French Studies. Society for French Studies, c/o G. Chesters, Ed., Dept. of French, University of Hull, Hull HU6 8RX, England. circ. 1,900. (back issues avail.) **Indexed:** Bibl.Ling. **Document type:** bulletin.
—BLDSC (4034.600500); Faxon; UnCover; SWETS.
Description: Contains short notes, opinions and news items on all aspects of French culture and the teaching of French in institutions of higher education.

810   US
FRIENDS OF PEACE PILGRIM. 1987. 3/yr. free. 43480 Cedar Ave., Hemet, CA 92544. TEL 909-927-7678. Ed. John Rush. bk.rev. circ. 10,500. **Document type:** newsletter.
Description: Contains news from Peace Pilgrim friends around the world who have read the Peace Pilgrim literature.

FROGPOND. see LITERATURE — Poetry

809 917.106   CN   ISSN 0829-4976
FROM MY BOOKSHELF; books noted for you. 1972. m. free. George Bonavia International Productions, P.O. Box 826 Sta. B., Ottawa, ON K1P 5P9, Canada. Ed. George Bonavia. bk.rev.
Formerly: International Corner (ISSN 0316-6260)
Description: Reviews books on Canada and Canadian affairs as well as on subjects of interest to ethnocultural groups.

800 410   CH   ISSN 1015-0021
P1
FU JEN STUDIES; literature & linguistics. (Text in English, German, and Spanish) 1968. a. $10 (effective 1993). Fu Jen University, College of Foreign Languages & Literatures - Fu Jen Ta Hsueh, 24205 Hsinchuang, Taipei, Taiwan, Republic of China. FAX 886-2-9021327. Ed. Heliena Krenn. circ. 300. (back issues avail.) **Indexed:** M.L.A. **Document type:** academic/scholarly publication.
—BLDSC (4047.745000).
Description: Presents Chinese and Western literature and linguistics.

800   US
FUEL MAGAZINE. 1991. q. $10. Anaconda Press, Box 146640, Chicago, IL 60614. TEL 312-975-3997. Ed. Andy Lowry. adv. (back issues avail.)
Description: Features poetry, fiction, short stories and art.

895.1   CC   ISSN 0257-0297
FUJIAN WENXUE/FUJIAN LITERATURE. (Text in Chinese) 1951. m. Y18 (foreign 61.20). Fujian Sheng Wenlian, Fenghuang Chi, Xihong Lu, Fuzhou, Fujian 350002, People's Republic of China. TEL 711725. (Dist. in US by: China Books & Periodicals, Inc., 2929 24th St., San Francisco, CA 94110. TEL 415-282-2994) Ed. Cao Haibin.
Description: Published literary works that depict the special economic zones in the province, local towns, as well as relationships between people living on both sides of the Taiwan Straits.

895.65 301.412   JA
FUJINKORON. (Text in Japanese) 1916. m. Chuokoron-Sha Inc., 2-8-7, Kyobashi, Chuo-ku, Tokyo 104, Japan. TEL 03-3563-1261. Ed. Kazuo Matsumura. circ. 257,000.

800   US   ISSN 1065-7983
▼**FURIOUS FICTIONS.** 1992. 3/yr. $13. Furious Fictions, Box 423665, San Francisco, CA 94142. TEL 415-431-0461. Ed. Joseph Lerner. adv.; bk.rev. circ. 1,100. (back issues avail.) **Document type:** academic/scholarly publication.
Description: Devoted exclusively to showcasing experimental short-short fiction by new and emerging poets and writers.

895.1   CC
FURONG. (Text in Chinese) bi-m. Y18($58.80) Hunan Wenyi Chubanshe, 67, Yinpen Nanlu, Changsha, Hunan 410006, People's Republic of China. TEL 82988. (Dist. outside China by: China International Book Trading Corp., P.O. Box 399, Beijing, p.R.C.; Dist. in US by: China Books & Periodicals, Inc., 2929 24th St., San Francisco, CA 94110. TEL 415-282-2994) adv.

809   US
FURTHER STATE(S) OF THE ART; a critical catalogue of new American fiction. 1991. q. $2.50 per no. Marshall Communications, 100 Manhattan Ave., Ste. 1210, Union City, NJ 07087. TEL 201-601-0886. Ed. Phil Leggiere. bk.rev.
Description: Reviews recent American fiction, with an eye for the unconventional and innovative.

G I P. (Germansk Instituts Publikationer) see
LINGUISTICS

800   US
G W REVIEW. 1978. s-a. $6. George Washington University, Marvin Center, 800 21st St., N.W., Ste. 427, Box 20, Washington, DC 20052. Ed. Sara Aitken. bk.rev. circ. 1,000.
Description: Presents poetry, short fiction and interviews.

GALACTIC CENTRAL BIBLIOGRAPHIES. see
BIBLIOGRAPHIES

800   US
▼**GALE'S LITERARY INDEX C D - R O M.** 1993. s-a. $149 for single user; network user $225. Gale Research Inc., 835 Penobscot Bldg., Detroit, MI 48226. (also avail. in diskette format) **Document type:** bibliography.
●Also available on CD-ROM.
Description: Combines and cross-references every Gale literary series index into a single source.

700 800   IT   ISSN 0016-4097
GALLERIA. 1949. bi-m. L.20000. Casa Editrice Salvatore Sciascia, Corso Umberto 111, 93100 Caltanissetta, Italy. Ed. Leonardo Sciascia. adv.; bk.rev.

891.4   II   ISSN 0016-4216
GALPAKABITA. (Text in Bengali) 1967. m. Rs.7($6.) Kamal Kumar Lahiri, 17-1-D Surjya Sen St., Calcutta 12, India. Ed. Krishna Gopal Mullick.

GAMUT. see LITERARY AND POLITICAL REVIEWS

807 860   PE   ISSN 0254-797X
GARABATO; teoria, produccion y critica del texto narrativo. 1983. s-a. Luis Fernando Vidal, Calle Uno 1242 Urbanizacion Corpac, Lima 27, Peru. Ed. Esteban Quiroz Cisneros.

860 700   US   ISSN 8755-3651
EL GATO TUERTO/ONE-EYED CAT; gaceta de arte, literatura, etcetera, etcetera. (Text in English, Spanish) 1984. q. $8 to individuals; institutions $12. Ediciones el Gato Tuerto, Box 210277, San Francisco, CA 94121. TEL 504-866-8598. Ed. Carlota Caulfield. adv.; bk.rev. circ. 1,000. (back issues avail.)
Description: Looks at Hispanic literature.

800   GW   ISSN 0720-2520
GAUKE'S JAHRBUCH. 1980. a. price varies. Gauke Verlag GmbH, Postfach 1320, 24399 Luetenburg, Germany. Eds. Christoph and Gabriele Gauke.

GAUNTLET; exploring the limits of free expression. see
LITERARY AND POLITICAL REVIEWS

869 300   US   ISSN 0276-7910
PQ9470
GAVEA - BROWN; revista bilingue de letras e estudos Luso-Americanos - a bilingual journal of Portuguese-American letters and studies. (Text in English, Portuguese) 1980. a. $10 to individuals; institutions $15. (Center for Portuguese & Brazilian Studies) Ga'vea - Brown Publications, Box O, Brown University, Providence, RI 02912. TEL 401-863-3042. FAX 401-863-3700. TELEX 952095. Eds. One'simo T. Almeida, George Monteiro. bk.rev.; illus. circ. 500. (back issues avail.) **Document type:** academic/scholarly publication.
Description: Covers all things related to the Portuguese presence in North America. Includes studies and creative writing.

GAZZETTA DELLE ARTI. see ART

800   US
GEGENSCHEIN. 1971. irreg., approx. 4/yr. $5 per issue. Gegenschein Press, 421 Hudson St., Ste. 220, New York, NY 10014. TEL 212-989-7845. Ed. Phil Smith. circ. 750 (controlled).
Formerly: Gegenschein Quarterly.

830   GW   ISSN 0016-5883
GEHOERT GELESEN (MUNICH, 1954).
Manuskriptauslese der interessantesten Sendungen des Bayerischen Rundfunks. 1954. m. DM.60. (Bayerischer Rundfunk) Ehrenwirth Verlag, Schwanthaler Str. 91, 80336 Munich, Germany. Ed. Margot Lehner. **Document type:** bulletin.
—CCC.

800		CN

GEIST; the Canadian magazine of ideas and culture. 1990. 5/yr. Can.$16. Geist Foundation, 100 - 1062 Homer St., Vancouver, BC V6B 2W9, Canada. TEL 604-681-9161. FAX 604-669-8250. Ed. Stephan Osborne. adv.; page Can.$300; adv. contact: Amy Francis. bk.rev. circ. 5,000. (back issues avail.) **Document type:** consumer publication.

836.5		NE

GEISTLICHE LITERATUR DER BAROCKZEIT. Short title: G L B. (Supplements avail.) (Text in German, occasionally in Latin) 1979. irreg., latest 1994. A P A, Postbus 122, 3600 AC Maarssen, Netherlands. TEL 31-30-436166. FAX 31-30-420250. Eds. Hans Poernbacher, Guillaume van Gemert. (back issues avail.) **Document type:** monographic series.
 Description: Publishes critical editions and studies of noteworthy texts and authors from southern German Catholic literary and cultural circles of the 17th and 18th centuries.

800		US	ISSN 0016-6928
PN80			

GENRE (NORMAN); forms of discourse and culture. 1968. q. $14 to individuals; institutions $27; foreign $30. University of Oklahoma, Department of English, 760 van Vleet Oval, Norman, OK 73019. TEL 405-325-2908. FAX 405-325-4661. Ed. Ronald Schleifer. adv.; bk.rev. circ. 700. (processed) **Indexed:** Abstr.Engl.Stud., Amer.Hum.Ind., Arts & Hum.Cit.Ind., Can.Rev.Comp.Lit, Curr.Cont., Ind.Bk.Rev.Hum., M.L.A., Mid.East: Abstr.& Ind.
—BLDSC (4116.340000); Faxon; UnCover; SWETS.

800		GW

GEORG FORSTER: SAEMTLICHE SCHRIFTEN, TAGEBUECHER, BRIEFE. (Text in English and German) 1958. irreg., vol.12, 1993. Akademie Verlag GmbH, Muehlenstr. 33-34, 13187 Berlin, Germany. TEL 030-47889348. FAX 030-47889357. **Document type:** monographic series.

800		UK

GEORGE ELIOT REVIEW. 1970. a. £5.50 (effective 1994). George Eliot Fellowship, 71 Stepping Stones Rd., Coventry, W. Midlands CV5 8JT, England. TEL 0203-592231. Eds. Beryl Gray, Graham Handley. adv.; bk.rev. circ. 400. **Indexed:** M.L.A.
 Formerly: George Eliot Fellowship Review.

800 054.1		US

GEORGE SAND STUDIES. Variant title: George Sand Newsletter. (Text in English and French) 1978. s-a. $15 to individuals; institutions $18; students $10. (Friends of George Sand) Hofstra University, Cultural Center, Hempstead, NY 11550. TEL 516-463-5669. FAX 516-564-4306. Ed. Natalie Datlof. adv.; bk.rev.; bibl.; illus. circ. 500. (back issues avail.) **Document type:** newsletter.
 Formerly: Friends of George Sand Newsletter (ISSN 0161-6544)

810		US

GEORGETOWN JOURNAL. 1872. s-a. $10. Georgetown University, Box 6825, 316 Leavey, Washington, DC 20057. TEL 202-687-6951. Ed. George G. Davis. adv.; bk.rev. circ. 2,000.
 Description: Publishes poetry, fiction, essay, photography and art form Georgetown undergraduates, graduates, alumni and professors.

800		US	ISSN 1066-1506

▼**GEORGETOWN REVIEW.** 1992. s-a. $10. 400 East College St., Box 227, Georgetown, KY 40324. TEL 502-863-8308. adv. circ. 1,000.
 Description: Publishes poetry and fiction.

810		US	ISSN 0016-8386
AP2			

THE GEORGIA REVIEW. 1947. q. $18 (foreign $23). University of Georgia, Georgia Review, Athens, GA 30602. TEL 706-542-3481. FAX 706-542-0047. Ed. Stanley W. Lindberg. adv.; bk.rev.; illus.; index. circ. 6,400. (also avail. in microform from UMI; talking book; Braille; back issues avail.; reprint service avail. from UMI) **Indexed:** A.I.P.P., Abstr.Engl.Stud., Amer.Hist.& Life, Bk.Rev.Ind. (1965-), Child.Bk.Rev.Ind. (1965-), Curr.Cont., Film Lit.Ind. (1976-), Hist.Abstr., Hum.Ind., Ind.Bk.Rev.Hum., Lang.& Lang.Behav.Abstr., M.L.A., Sociol.Abstr.
—BLDSC (4158.459000); Faxon; UnCover; UMI.
 Description: Contains fiction, essays, poetry for an interdisciplinary audience.

800		US	ISSN 0884-8696

GEORGIA STATE LITERARY STUDIES. irreg., no.12, 1994. price varies. A M S Press, Inc., 56 E. 13th St., New York, NY 10003. TEL 212-777-4700. FAX 212-995-5413. Ed. Victor A. Kramer. index. (back issues avail.)
—BLDSC (4158.459630).

830		UK	ISSN 0016-8777
AP4			

GERMAN LIFE AND LETTERS. 1936. q. £38($79.50) to individuals; institutions £78.50($165). Basil Blackwell Ltd., 108 Cowley Rd., Oxford OX4 1JF, England. TEL 0865-791100. FAX 0865-791347. TELEX 837022-OXBOOK-G. Ed.Bd. adv.; bk.rev.; index; cum.index. circ. 800. (reprint service avail. from SCH,SWZ) **Indexed:** Arts & Hum.Cit.Ind., Br.Hum.Ind., Can.Rev.Comp.Lit, Curr.Cont., Ind.Bk.Rev.Hum., M.L.A.
—BLDSC (4162.124000); Faxon; UnCover; SWETS; UMI. **CCC.**

GERMAN STUDIES REVIEW. see HISTORY — History Of Europe

GERMANIC REVIEW; devoted to studies dealing with the Germanic languages and literatures. see LINGUISTICS

830		FR

GERMANICA. 2/yr. 100 F. (effective 1992). Universite de Lille III, B.P. 149, F-59653 Villeneuve d'Ascq Cedex, France.

800		GW	ISSN 0016-8904
PB3			

GERMANISCH-ROMANISCHE MONATSSCHRIFT. 1909; N.S. 1950. 4/yr. DM.148 (students DM.120). Universitaetsverlag C. Winter Heidelberg GmbH, Hans-Bunte-Str. 18, 69123 Heidelberg, Germany. Ed. Conrad Wiedemann. adv.; bk.rev.; bibl.; index. circ. 1,100. (also avail. in microfiche from IDC) **Indexed:** Arts & Hum.Cit.Ind., Bibl.Ling., Curr.Cont., Ind.Bk.Rev.Hum., Lang.& Lang.Behav.Abstr., M.L.A., RILA. **Document type:** academic/scholarly publication.
—Faxon; SWETS.

GERMANISTIK (BERLIN). see LINGUISTICS

430		CN	ISSN 0317-4956
PT123.S58			

GERMANO-SLAVICA. (Text in English, French, German) 1973. a. $12. University of Waterloo, Department of Germanic and Slavic Languages and Literature, Waterloo, ON N2L 3G1, Canada. TEL 519-885-1211. FAX 519-885-1211. Ed. Robert Harpiah. adv.; bk.rev. circ. 800. (back issues avail.) **Indexed:** Amer.Bibl.Slavic & E.Eur.Stud., Arts & Hum.Cit.Ind., Bibl.Ling., Curr.Cont., M.L.A.
—UnCover.

GESCHICHTE DES ARABISCHEN SCHRIFTTUMS. see HISTORY — History Of The Near East

800		US	ISSN 0749-7644
PT2603.R397			

GESTUS; a quarterly journal of Brechtian studies. 1985. 6/yr. $35 to individuals; institutions $80. Brecht Society of America, Inc., 59 S. New St., Dover, DE 19901. TEL 302-734-3740. FAX 302-734-9354. TELEX 984038 ESLUND. Ed. Dwight Steward. bk.rev. circ. 250. (also avail. in microform; diskette format)
●Also available online.

GILA QUEEN'S GUIDE TO THE MARKETS. see PUBLISHING AND BOOK TRADE

800		IS

GINAZIM. (Text in Hebrew) 1962. irreg. $7 per no. Association of Hebrew Writers in Israel, Rehov Kaplan 5, Tel Aviv 61070, Israel.

850		IT	ISSN 0017-0496
PQ4001			

GIORNALE STORICO DELLA LETTERATURA ITALIANA. 1883. q. (foreign L.128000) (effective 1994). Editore Loescher, Via Vittorio Amedeo II, 18, 10121 Turin, Italy. TEL 011-5624622. FAX 011-5625822. Ed.Bd. bk.rev.; bibl.; index. **Indexed:** Arts & Hum.Cit.Ind., Bibl.Ling., Can.Rev.Comp.Lit., Curr.Cont., Ind.Bk.Rev.Hum., M.L.A.
—Faxon; SWETS.

808.8 306.84		US

GIRL JOCK. 1990. q. $12. Rox-A-Tronic, Box 882723, San Francisco, CA 94188. TEL 415-282-0833. FAX 415-282-6833. E-mail: roxxiet@aol.com. adv.; bk.rev.
 Description: Covers the lives of women athletes and their admirers. Focuses on a humor-filled depiction of athletic female life, ranging from novice to professional.

820		UK	ISSN 0017-0615
PR4717			

GISSING JOURNAL. 1965. q. £8 to individuals; institutions £12. Gissing Trust, 7 Town Ln., Idle, Bradford BD10 8PR, England. Ed. P. Coustillas. bk.rev.; bibl. circ. 250. (processed) **Indexed:** Abstr.Engl.Stud., M.L.A.
—UnCover.
 Formerly: Gissing Newsletter.
 Description: Concerns George Gissing (1857-1903).

800		US	ISSN 0869-3102

GLAS; new Russian writing. 1991. irreg. (approx. 2/yr.). $40 to individuals; institutions $45 for 4 nos. Zephyr Press, 13 Robinson St., Somerville, MA 02145. TEL 617-628-9726. FAX 617-776-8246. Ed. Natasha Perova. adv. contact: Ed Hogan. circ. 2,000.
 Description: A journal of contemporary Russian literature in English translation.

820 284		UK	ISSN 0269-770X

GLASS (LEICESTER). 1986. irreg. £8. U C C F (Universities and Colleges Christian Fellowship), Literary Studies Group, 38 de Montfort St., Leicester LE1 7GP, England. TEL 01162-551700. FAX 01162-555672. Ed. John Gillespie. bk.rev. circ. 150. (back issues avail.) **Document type:** academic/scholarly publication.
 Description: Aims to develop a Christian understanding of current issues in literary criticism.

800		US	ISSN 1055-7520
PS642			

▼**GLIMMER TRAIN.** 1992. q. $29. Glimmer Train Press, Inc., 812 S.W. Washington St., Ste. 1205, Portland, OR 97205-3216. TEL 503-221-0836. FAX 503-221-0837. Eds. Susan Burmeister, Linda Davies. circ. 16,000.
 Description: Includes short stories, interviews with writers and other artists, and spotlights on short fiction writing from other parts of the world.

810		US

▼**GLOBE LITERARY.** 1993. irreg. 3625 Greenwood North, Seattle, WA 98103. Eds. A. Larcom, D. Sprague. **Document type:** academic/scholarly publication.
 Description: Publishes avant garde prose-poetry, novellas, scientific research and general science non-fiction.

808 701.18		US

GNOME BAKER. 1975. s-a. $15. Tongue Press, Box 23, Kew West, FL 33041. Eds. Madeleine Burnside, Andrew Kelly. adv. circ. 825. (back issues avail.)

GOETEBORGER GERMANISTISCHE FORSCHUNGEN. see LINGUISTICS

830		GW	ISSN 0323-4207
PT2045			

GOETHE-JAHRBUCH. 1880. a. DM.39. (Goethe-Gesellschaft, Weimar) Verlag Hermann Boehlaus Nachfolger, Meyerstr. 50a, 99403 Weimar, Germany. TEL 03643-202071. Ed. Werner Keller. bk.rev. **Indexed:** Arts & Hum.Cit.Ind., Curr.Cont., M.L.A. **Document type:** academic/scholarly publication.
—SWETS.
 Formerly: Goethe-Gesellschaft. Jahrbuch (ISSN 0072-484X)

830		US

GOETHE NEWS AND NOTES. 1980. s-a. membership. Goethe Society of North America, Department of German, University of Calif., Irvine, CA 92717. TEL 714-856-6406. Ed. Meredith Lee. circ. 300. (looseleaf format) **Document type:** newsletter.

830		GW

GOETHE WOERTERBUCH. 1966. a. W. Kohlhammer (Stuttgart), Hessbruehlstr. 69, 70565 Stuttgart, Germany.

LITERATURE

830 US ISSN 0734-3329
PT2046
GOETHE YEARBOOK. 1982. a. $48. (Goethe Society of North America) Camden House, Inc., Box 2025, Columbia, SC 29202. TEL 803-788-8689. FAX 803-736-9455. Ed. Thomas P. Saine. bk.rev.; bibl. circ. 700. (back issues avail.) **Indexed:** M.L.A.
Description: Includes essays on the German poet, novelist and dramatist Goethe and his contemporaries. Includes bibliography of dissertations.

800 AT ISSN 0157-3950
GOING DOWN SWINGING. 1980. a. Aus.$20. Hit and Miss Publications, P.O. Box 64, Coburg, Vic. 3058, Australia. TEL 03-387-4323. FAX 03-484-1552. (Subscr. to: P.O. Box 64, Coburg, Vic. 3058, Australia. TEL 03-387-4323) Eds. Myron Lysenko, Kevin Brophy. bk.rev. circ. 1,100. (back issues avail.)
Description: Covers contemporary prose and fiction.

810 US ISSN 0046-6158
GOOD OLD DAYS. vol.8, 1971. m. $12.97. House of White Birches Publishing, 306 E. Parr Rd., Berne, IN 46711. TEL 219-589-8471. Ed. Ken Tate. adv.; charts; illus.; tr.lit. circ. 72,047. **Document type:** consumer publication.
—UnCover.
Description: Contains photos, cartoons, features and poems from 1900-1949.

810 US ISSN 1058-1871
GOOD OLD DAYS SPECIALS. 1974. bi-m. $9.95. House of White Birches Publishing, 306 E. Parr Rd., Berne, IN 46711. TEL 212-589-8471. Ed. Ken Tate. adv.; charts; illus. circ. 26,933. **Document type:** consumer publication.
Former titles: Fireside Companion (ISSN 1050-480X); Good Old Days Special Issues (ISSN 0160-7510); Good Old Days Specials.
Description: Contains features, photos, cartoons and poems from 1900-1949.

GOTHENBURG STUDIES IN ENGLISH. see LINGUISTICS

800 US ISSN 1073-2659
▼**GOTHIC AND UNREAL.** 1992. q. $4 (effective 1994). Robert S. Robbins, Ed. & Pub., 1997 Misner Rd., Williamsport, PA 17701. TEL 717-326-0139. circ. 100. (looseleaf format; back issues avail.)
Description: Features one short story on the subculture per issue.

800 US
GOTHIC LIGHT. 1991. q. $23.95. 3 South Lancaster, Aurora, IL 60506. TEL 708-897-0382. Ed. Abelardo Arenas. adv. circ. 200. (back issues avail.)
Description: Covers poetry, fiction, novels, art and music.

800 US
GRAB A NICKEL. 1975. irreg. (2-3/yr.). Barbour County Writers' Workshop, Box 2158, Alderson-Broaddus College, Philippi, WV 26416. TEL 304-457-1700. Ed. Barbara Smith. bk.rev. circ. 1,000.

809 US ISSN 0363-8057
PN80
GRADIVA; revista internazionale di lettura italiana - international journal of Italian literature. 1976. a. $25. c/o S. Morandina, Man. Ed., Department of French and Italian, State University of New York at Stony Brook, Stony Brook, NY 11794-3359. (Subscr. to: Box 831, Stony Brook, New York, NY 11790) Ed. Luigi Fontanella. adv.; bk.rev.; abstr.; illus. circ. 300. **Indexed:** Arts & Hum.Cit.Ind., Curr.Cont., M.L.A. **Document type:** academic/scholarly publication.

800 US ISSN 0145-7780
PS580
GRAHAM HOUSE REVIEW. 1976. a. $7.50. (Colgate University) Colgate University Press, Box 5000, Hamilton, NY 13346. TEL 315-824-7271. Eds. Peter Balakian, Bruce Smith. circ. 500. **Indexed:** Ind.Amer.Per.Verse. **Document type:** academic/scholarly publication.
Description: Includes poetry, literary essays and interviews.

810 CN ISSN 0315-7423
PR9194
GRAIN. 1973. 4/yr. Can.$19.95. Saskatchewan Writers Guild, P.O. Box 1154, Regina, SK S4P 3B4, Canada. TEL 306-757-6310. Ed. Elizabeth Philips. circ. 1,500. **Indexed:** Amer.Hum.Ind., Can.Lit.Ind.
Description: International literary and visual arts publication, presenting poetry, short fiction and visual art.

810 US ISSN 0734-5496
PN6010.5
GRAND STREET. 1981. q. $30 to individuals; institutions $40; foreign $40 (effective 1994); newsstand price: $10. (New York Foundation for the Arts) Grand Street Publications, 131 Varick St., Rm. 906, New York, NY 10013. TEL 212-807-6548. FAX 212-807-6544. (Dist. by: W.W. Norton, 500 Fifth Ave., New York, NY 10110; Subscr. to: Dept. GRS, Box 3000, Denville, NJ 07834-9878. TEL 800-807-6548) Ed. Jean Stein; Pub. Jean Stein. adv.: page $450. illus. circ. 5,000. (back issues avail.) **Document type:** consumer publication.
—BLDSC (4210.060750); Faxon.
Description: Essays, stories, poems, art, photography and articles by noted authors, for a cosmopolitan audience.

860 UY ISSN 0072-5439
GRANDES TODOS.* irreg. Editorial Arca, Colonia 1263, Montevideo, Uruguay.

057 GW ISSN 0017-3185
AP50
GRANI; zhurnal literatury, iskusstva, nauki i obshchestvenno-politicheskoi mysli. (Text in Russian) 1946. q. DM.70. Possev-Verlag, Flurscheideweg 15, 65936 Frankfurt a.M., Germany. TEL 069-341265. FAX 069-343841. Ed. E.A. Breitbart-Samsonowa. adv.; bk.rev.; bibl. circ. 2,000. (also avail. in microfilm from KTO; back issues avail.) **Indexed:** M.L.A. **Document type:** academic/scholarly publication.
—CCC.

800 US ISSN 0092-5268
PN171.P75
GRANTS AND AWARDS AVAILABLE TO AMERICAN WRITERS. 1969. biennial. $8 to individuals; institutions $12.50. P E N American Center, 568 Broadway, New York, NY 10012. TEL 212-334-1660. FAX 212-334-2181. Ed. John Morrone. circ. 5,000. **Document type:** directory.
Formerly: List of Grants and Awards Available to American Writers (ISSN 0075-983X)
Description: Directory of prizes, awards, grants, residences and production opportunities for writers of all kinds.

810 US ISSN 1066-4742
GRASSLANDS REVIEW. 1989. 2/yr. $8 to individuals; institutions $20 (effective 1994). N.T. Box 13706, Denton, TX 76203. TEL 817-565-2127. FAX 817-565-6464. Ed. Laura Kennelly. circ. 300.
Description: Publishes original fiction and poetry, especially from new writers.

800 US ISSN 0743-7471
PS648.S5
GRAYWOLF ANNUAL. 1984. a. $8.95. Graywolf Press, 2402 University Ave., Ste. 203, St. Paul, MN 55114. TEL 612-222-8342. FAX 612-641-0036. Ed. Scott Walker. circ. 10,000. (back issues avail.)
Description: Anthology of contemporary fiction or essays, often organized around a social theme or issue (i.e. multi-cultural social change).

810 US ISSN 0196-3147
GREAT CIRCUMPOLAR BEAR CULT. 1976. a. $2. Bear Cult Press, Box 267, Rte. 1, High Bridge, WI 54846. TEL 715-274-2942. Ed. Rick Penn. circ. 500.

GREAT ISSUES OF THE DAY. see POLITICAL SCIENCE

810 US ISSN 0160-2144
PS273
GREAT RIVER REVIEW. 1977. 2/yr. $10. Great River Review, Inc., 211 W. 7th St., Winona, MN 55987. TEL 507-454-6564. Ed. Orval Lund. adv.; bk.rev. circ. 800. (back issues avail.)

809 UK ISSN 0017-386X
GREEK GAZETTE. 1967. m. £50($60) Kyriakos H. Metaxas, Ed. & Pub., 35 Burnham Court, Moscow Rd., London W2 4SW, England. TEL 071-727-1121. FAX 071-727-1444. TELEX 2988839-GRKGZT-G. adv.; bk.rev.; film rev.; play rev.; abstr.; bibl.; charts; illus. circ. 12,000. (tabloid format; also avail. in microfilm)
Description: Historical and literary articles; reviews of all books printed in English on a Greek theme.

GREEK INDEX PROJECT SERIES. see HISTORY — History Of Europe

800 US
▼**GREEN;** literature and art of the natural world. 1994. q. $20 to individuals; institutions $26. Verygraphics, Box 6508, Berkeley, CA 94706. TEL 510-644-4188. Ed. Lily Pond. adv.: B&W page $1570; trim 8 1/2 x 11. circ. 25,000 (paid). **Document type:** consumer publication.
Description: Features essays, poetry, fiction, photography, and other fine arts all dealing with the subject of nature from many cultural perspectives.

800 US ISSN 0895-9307
PS1
GREEN MOUNTAINS REVIEW. 1987. s-a. $12. Johnson State College, Box A58, Johnson, VT 05656. TEL 802-635-2356. Eds. Neil Shepard, Tony Whedon. adv.: B&W page $75; adv. contact: Kate Riley. bk.rev. circ. 1,000. (back issues avail.)
Description: Publishes poetry, fiction, and creative essays by well-known authors and promising newcomers.

810 US ISSN 0017-4009
PS501
GREEN RIVER REVIEW. 1968. 3/yr. $6. Green River Press, Inc., SVSC Box 56, University Center, MI 48710. Ed. Raymond Tyner. bk.rev. circ. 500. **Indexed:** M.L.A.

800 US
GREENHOUSE REVIEW PRESS CHAPBOOK SERIES.* 1975. s-a. $2. Greenhouse Review Press, 3965 Bonny Doon Rd., Santa Cruz, CA 95060. Ed. Gary Young. circ. 500. (back issues avail.)
Supersedes: Greenhouse Review (ISSN 0162-0304)

810 CN ISSN 0824-2992
GREEN'S MAGAZINE; fiction for the family. 1972. q. $12. Green's Educational Publications, Inc., P.O. Box 3236, Regina, SK S4P 3H1, Canada. Ed. David Green. adv.; bk.rev.; illus.; index. circ. 300.

810 US ISSN 0017-4084
GREENSBORO REVIEW. 1966. 2/yr. $8. University of North Carolina at Greensboro, English Department, Greensboro, NC 27412. TEL 919-334-5459. FAX 919-334-3281. Ed. Jim Clark. adv. circ. 600. (also avail. in microfilm from UMI; reprint service avail. from UMI) **Indexed:** A.I.P.P., Amer.Hum.Ind.
—UMI.
Description: Seeks the best prose and poetry, regardless of subject, genre, or style.

GRIDLEY WAVE. see LITERATURE — Science Fiction, Fantasy, Horror

839.6 439.6 IC ISSN 1018-5011
GRIPLA. (Text in English, Icelandic and other Scandinavian languages) 1975. irreg. ISK 3500. Stofnun Arna Magnussonar a Islandi, Arnagardi v. Sudurgoetu, IS-101 Reykjavik, Iceland. TEL 354-1-25540. FAX 354-1-694410. Ed. Jonas Kristjansson. (back issues avail.) **Document type:** academic/scholarly publication, monographic series.
Description: Publishes scholarly articles on Icelandic-Old Norse language, literature and history in the Middle Ages.

850 IT
GROTTA DELLA VIPERA; rivista trimestrale di cultura. 1975. q. L.20000. Via Istria 45, 09100 Cagliari, Italy. Ed. Antonio Cossu. adv.; bk.rev.; illus. circ. 1,000.

820 FR
GROUPE DE RECHERCHE ET D'ETUDES NORD-AMERICAINES. ACTES DU COLLOQUE. (Text in English, French) irreg., no.12, 1990. price varies. Universite de Provence, Service des Publications, 29 av. Robert Schuman, 13621 Aix-en-Provence Cedex 1, France. TEL 42-20-09-16.

LITERATURE

810   CN
GRUB. 1970. q. $12. c/o Dragon Fly, Lake St. Peter, Ont. K0L 2K0, Canada.

800   US
GUADALUPE REVIEW.* 1991. a. $12. Guadalupe Cultural Arts Center, 5619 Sunup Dr., San Antonio, TX 78233-4489. TEL 512-271-3151. Ed. Ray Gonzalez. adv.; illus.

895   CC
GUANGXI WENXUE/GUANGXI LITERATURE. (Text in Chinese) m. Guangxi Wenlian, 28 Jianzhen Lu, Nanning, Guangxi 530023, People's Republic of China. TEL 22120.

895.1   CC   ISSN 0257-022X
GUANGZHOU WENYI/GUANGZHOU LITERATURE. (Text in Chinese) 1976. m. $58.50. Guangzhou Shi Wenlian, CC, Wenhua Dalou, 4th Floor, No. 170, Wende Lu, Guangzhou, Guangdong 510030, People's Republic of China. (Dist. in US by: China Books & Periodicals, Inc., 2929 24th St., San Francisco, CA 94110. TEL 415-282-2994) Ed. Gao Naiyan.

895.1   CC
GUDIAN WENXUE ZHISHI. (Text in Chinese) bi-m. Y7.20. Jiangsu Guji Chubanshe, 165 Zhongyang Lu, Nanjing, Jiangsu 210009, People's Republic of China. Ed.Bd.
    Description: Encourages the reading and study of classical Chinese literature.

895.1   CC
GUDIAN WENXUE ZHISHI/CLASSIC LITERATURE KNOWLEDGE. (Text in Chinese) bi-m. Jiangsu Guji Chubanshe - Jiangsu Classic Literature Publishers, 165 Zhongyang Lu, Nanjing, Jiangsu 210009, People's Republic of China. TEL 631836. Ed. Gao Jiyan.

800   US   ISSN 0160-6565
PN452
GUEST AUTHOR; a directory of speakers. 1978. biennial. $9.95. Hermes Press, 51 Lenox St., Brockton, MA 02401. Eds. Jane Manthorne, Rose Moorachian. circ. 2,000. **Document type:** directory.

810   US   ISSN 0896-2251
GULF COAST (HOUSTON); a journal of literature and fine arts. s-a. $7. University of Houston, Department of English, Creative Writing Program, 4800 Calhoun Rd., Houston, TX 77204-3012. Eds. Mark O'Connor, Randall H. Watson.

GULLIVER; German-English Yearbook. see LINGUISTICS

890   JA
GUNZO. (Text in Japanese) 1946. m. Kodansha Ltd., 12-21 Otowa 2-chome, Bunkyo-ku, Tokyo 112, Japan. TEL 03-5395-3501. FAX 03-5395-5626. TELEX J34509 KODANSHA. Ed. Katsuo Watanabe. circ. 20,000. **Document type:** consumer publication.

895.1   CC   ISSN 1002-6401
GUSHI DAGUAN. (Text in Chinese) 1984. m. Y24. Shandong Wenyi Chubanshe, No. 8, Taibailou Donglu, Jining, Shandong 272117, People's Republic of China. TEL 86-0537-315051. Ed. Sun Yicai. adv. contact: Huo Xiaolin. **Document type:** consumer publication.
    Description: Contains short stories, novels and reportage.

800 028.5   CC
GUSHI DAWANG. (Text in Chinese) m. Shaonian Ertong Chubanshe - Juvenile & Chilren Publishing House, 1538 Yan'an Xilu, Shanghai 200052, People's Republic of China. TEL 2513025. FAX 2512851. Ed. Yu Hexian.

895.1   CC
GUSHI JIA/STORY TELLER. (Text in Chinese) bi-m. Henan Sheng Wenlian, No. 34, Jing 7 Lu, Zhengzhou, Henan 450003, People's Republic of China. TEL 334916. Ed. Du Daoheng.

800   CC   ISSN 1002-2554
GUSHI LIN. (Text in Chinese) 1984. bi-m. Y4.20($2.40) Fujian Sheng Wenlian, Fenghuang Chi, Xihong Lu, Fuzhou, Fujian 350002, People's Republic of China. TEL 32871. (Dist. overseas by: Jiangsu Publications Import & Export Corp., 56 Gao Yun Ling, Nanjing, Jiangsu, P.R.C.) Co-sponsor: Zhongguo Minjian Yishujia Xiehui Fujian Fenhui) Ed. Wang Meitian. adv.
    Description: Publishes ancient and contemporary folk stories, legends and local customs.

895.1   CC
GUSHI SHIJIE. (Text in Chinese) m. Haiyan Chubanshe, No. 73, Nongye Lu, Zhengzhou, Henan 450002, People's Republic of China. TEL 551756. Ed. Gao Mingxing.

895.1   CC   ISSN 0257-0238
GUSHIHUI/STORYTELLER. (Text in Chinese) 1978. m. $58.50. Shanghai Wenyi Chubanshe - Shanghai Literature & Art Press, 74 Shaoxing Lu, Shanghai 200020, People's Republic of China. TEL 4372608. (Dist. in US by: China Books & Periodicals, Inc., 2929 24th St., San Francisco, CA 94110. TEL 415-282-2994)

830   GW
GUSTAV FREYTAG BLAETTER. 1954. a. DM.24 membership. Gustav Freytag Gesellschaft e.V., Bahnhofstr. 71, 40883 Ratingen, Germany. TEL 02102-67341. bk.rev.; bibl.; illus. circ. 500.
    Description: Articles about Gustav Freytag and his times; information for members.

811   US
GUTS.* irregr. Box 15540, Long Beach, CA 90815-0540. Ed. Keith A. Dodson. (back issues avail.)

800   US   ISSN 0176-3148
GYPSY; literary magazine. 1984. s-a. $14. Vergin Press, c/o Belinda Subraman, 10708 Gay Brewer Dr., El Paso, TX 79935. TEL 915-592-3701. Ed. Belinda Subraman. adv.; bk.rev. circ. 1,000. (back issues avail.)
    Description: Features poetry, fiction, interviews and articles, as well as artwork by independent literary and visual artists.

800   US   ISSN 1071-5126
▼**GYPSY BLOOD REVIEW.** (Text in English, Spanish) 1992. q. $15. A P M Press and Publications, Ltd., 6909 Custer Rd., No. 802, Plano, TX 75023-1720. TEL 214-618-1621. (Editorial addr.: 229 N. Locust, No. B, Fayetteville, AR 72701. TEL 501-442-8273) Ed. J. Simpson; Pub. William B. Spier, Jr. adv.; B&W page $50; adv. contact: Stan Q. Faulkner. circ. 250. **Document type:** trade publication.
    Description: Dedicated to compelling sensory communication.

GYPSY LORE SOCIETY. JOURNAL. see ANTHROPOLOGY

820   UK   ISSN 0306-5480
H.G. WELLS SOCIETY NEWSLETTER. 1960. 2/yr. £12 to institutions. H.G. Wells Society, H.G. Wells Centre, Nene College, Eng. Dept., Moulton Park, Northampton NN2 7AL, England. Ed. Sylvia Hardy. bk.rev.; cum.index every five yrs. circ. 300. (looseleaf format; reprint service avail.) **Document type:** newsletter.

800   IS   ISSN 0792-0393
PN1
H S L A. (Hebrew University Studies in Literature and the Arts) (Text in English, French in alternate issues) 1973. s-a. $15. (Hebrew University of Jerusalem, Institute of Languages, Literatures and Arts) Magnes Press, Hebrew University, Jerusalem, P.O. Box 7695, Jerusalem 91076, Israel. TEL 972-2-660341. FAX 972-2-633370. Ed.Bd. circ. 1,000. (back issues avail.) **Indexed:** Abstr.Engl.Stud.; Arts & Hum.Cit.Ind.; Curr.Cont.; M.L.A.; Mid.East: Abstr.& Ind. **Document type:** academic/scholarly publication.
    —UnCover.
    Formerly (until 1983): H S L (ISSN 0333-5690)
    Description: Publishes articles on topics in literature, including stylistic issues, comparative literature and relations between literature and the arts.

810   355.115   US
H V W P IN ACTION. s-a. $15 to individuals; institutions and veterans $8 (includes Veterans' Voice). Hospitalized Veterans Writing Project, Inc., 5920 Nall, Rm. 102, Mission, KS 66202. Ed. Ronnie Millard. circ. 1,585.

830   GW   ISSN 0170-2777
HABELTS DISSERTATIONSDRUCKE. REIHE GERMANISTIK. 1973. irreg. price varies. Dr. Rudolf Habelt GmbH, Am Buchenhang 1, 53115 Bonn, Germany. TEL 0228-232016. FAX 0228-232017. **Document type:** monographic series.

810   US   ISSN 1060-0469
HABERSHAM REVIEW. 1991. 2/yr. $12. Box 10, Demorest, GA 30535. TEL 404-778-3000. FAX 706-776-2811. Eds. David Greene, Lisa Hodgens Lumpkin. adv. contact: Thomas Klump. bk.rev. circ. 600. **Document type:** academic/scholarly publication.
    Description: Publishes poetry, fiction, interviews, satire, reviews with a regional (Southeastern U.S.) focus.

HACIA LA LUZ. see HANDICAPPED — Visually Impaired

895.1   CC
HAI OU/SEA GULL LITERATURE. (Text in Chinese) m. $54. Qingdao Shi Wenlian, No. 25, Xinhaoshan Lu, Qingdao, Shandong 266003, People's Republic of China. TEL 226996. (Dist. in US by: China Books & Periodicals, Inc., 2929 24th St., San Francisco, CA 94110. TEL 415-282-2994) Ed. Xu Banfu.

895.1   CC
HAI YAN. (Text in Chinese) m. Dalian Wenxue Yishujie Lianhehui - Dalian Literary and Art Circle Association, 6 Baiyunshan, Xigang-qu, Dalian, Liaoning 116012, People's Republic of China. TEL 336980. Ed. Bi Fuhua.

810   US
HAIGHT ASHBURY LITERARY JOURNAL. 1980. irreg. (1-2/yr.) $12 for 4 issues. c/o Alice Rogoff, 558 Joost Ave., San Francisco, CA 94127. Ed.Bd. adv.; bk.rev. circ. 3,500. (back issues avail.)
    Description: Publishes poetry, stories, and interviews of writers.

800   CC
HAIXIA/STRAIT. (Text in Chinese) 1981. bi-m. Y3.50($0.70) per no. (effective 1993). Haixia Wenyi Chubanshe - Haixia Literature & Art Publishing House, 27 Degui Xiang, Fuzhou, Fujian 350001, People's Republic of China. TEL 86-591-522384. (Dist. overseas by: Jiangsu Publications Import & Export Corp., 56 Gao Yun Ling, Nanjing, Jiangsu, P.R.C.) Ed. Lin Zhengrang. bk.rev.
    Description: Features writers from both sides of the Taiwan Strait and from overseas Chinese.

808   US   ISSN 0733-6616
HAMBONE. 1974. a. $10 to individuals for two issues; institutions $14. Hambone, 134 Hunelt St., Santa Cruz, CA 95060. TEL 408-426-3072. Ed. Nathaniel Mackey. bk.rev. circ. 700.

820   II   ISSN 0256-2480
PR2807
HAMLET STUDIES; an international journal of research on the tragedy of Hamlet Prince of Denmark. (Text in English) 1979. s-a. $18. R.W. Desai Publishing Company Ltd., Rangoon Villa, 1-10 W. Patel Nagar, New Delhi 110 008, India. TEL 574-7399. Ed. R.W. Desai. adv.; bk.rev. circ. 300. (also avail. in microfilm from GMC; back issues avail.; reprint service avail. from GMC) **Indexed:** Abstr.Engl.Stud.; M.L.A. **Document type:** academic/scholarly publication.
    —BLDSC (4241.472000); UnCover. **CCC.**

HANZI WENHUA/CHINESE CULTURE. see HUMANITIES: COMPREHENSIVE WORKS

808   US
HARBOUR REVIEW. 1982. s-a. $7 for 3 nos. University of Massachusetts, English Department, Boston, MA 02125. Ed. Stephen Strempek. bk.rev.; cum.index: 1982-1984. circ. 500. (back issues avail.)

LITERATURE

810 US
HARD ROW TO HOE. 1982-1987; resumed 1988. 3/yr. $7. Hard Row to Hoe (Subsidiary of: Misty Hill Press), Box 541-I, Healdsburg, CA 95448. TEL 707-433-9786. Ed. Joe E. Armstrong; Pub. Sally Kavste. bk.rev.; circ. 500 (paid). **Document type:** newsletter.
Description: Covers book reviews, short story and poetry of rural America.

810 US
HARP-STRINGS. 1989. 3/yr. $20. 310 S. Adams St., Beverly Hills, FL 32265. Ed. Madelyn Eastlund. circ. 200.

378.1 US ISSN 0017-8004
HARVARD ADVOCATE. 1866. q. $15. Harvard Advocate Trustees, Inc., Advocate House, 21 South St., Cambridge, MA 02138. TEL 617-495-0737. adv.; bk.rev.; film rev.; play rev.; illus. circ. 10,000. (also avail. in microform from UMI; back issues avail.; reprint service avail. from UMI)
—UnCover; UMI.
Description: Contains fiction, poetry, and art work by Harvard College students.

HARVARD CELTIC COLLOQUIUM. PROCEEDINGS. see *LINGUISTICS*

800 420 US ISSN 0073-0513
HARVARD ENGLISH STUDIES. 1970. irreg., vol.17, 1991. Harvard University Press, 79 Garden St., Cambridge, MA 02138. TEL 617-495-2600. FAX 617-495-5898. **Indexed:** M.L.A., Rel.Ind.Two.
—BLDSC (4265.940000).

800 US ISSN 0073-0696
HARVARD STUDIES IN COMPARATIVE LITERATURE. 1910. irreg., no.41, 1991. price varies. Harvard University Press, 79 Garden St., Cambridge, MA 02138. TEL 617-495-2600. FAX 617-495-5898. **Indexed:** M.L.A. **Document type:** monographic series.
Refereed Serial

HARVARD - YENCHING INSTITUTE. MONOGRAPH SERIES. see *HISTORY — History Of Asia*

807 BG
HARVEST: JAHANGIRNAGAR STUDIES IN LITERATURE. (Text in English) vol.2, 1978. a. Tk.15($1) Jahangirnagar University, Department of English, Rm. 223, Savar, Dhaka, Bangladesh. Ed. Nurul Islam. bk.rev. circ. 300.
Formerly (until vol.5, 1983): Jahangirnagar University. Department of English. Bulletin.

800 700 US
HARVESTER. 1972. a. Lincoln Land Community College, Humanities Division, Shephard Rd., Springfield, IL 62794-9256. TEL 217-786-2330. Ed. Mary A. Fortner. circ. 1,000. (back issues avail.)

800 US ISSN 1047-4331
HAWAII PACIFIC REVIEW. 1987. a. $6. Hawaii Pacific University, 1060 Bishop St., Honolulu, HI 96813. TEL 808-544-0214. Ed. Elizabeth Fischel. circ. 500. **Document type:** academic/scholarly publication.
Description: Poetry and fiction with an emphasis on cultural diversity and experimental poetic and narrative techniques. Also includes English translations of poetry in other languages.

810 US ISSN 0093-9625
PS571.H3
HAWAII REVIEW. 1972. 3/yr. $15. University of Hawaii, Board of Publications, 2465 Campus Dr., Honolulu, HI 96822. TEL 808-956-3030. FAX 808-956-9962. (Subscr. to: University of Hawaii, Ka Leo Bldg., 1755 Pope Rd., Bldg. 31-D, Honolulu, HI 96822) Ed. T. Moran. adv.; bk.rev.; illus. circ. 2,000. **Indexed:** A.I.P.P., Amer.Hum.Ind.
Formerly: Hawaii Literary Review (ISSN 0090-8274)

808.8 US ISSN 1066-6176
HEARTLANDS TODAY. 1991. a. $8.50. Bowling Green State University, Firelands College, Firelands Writing Center, 901 Rye Beach Rd., Huron, OH 44839-9791. TEL 419-433-5560. FAX 419-433-9696. Eds. Nancy Dunham, Larry Smith. bk.rev. circ. 500.
Description: Features writing and photography treating the issues and values of the contemporary Midwest. Each volume has a theme.

830 GW ISSN 0073-1560
PT2296.A1
HEBBEL - JAHRBUECHER. a. price varies. (Hebbel-Gesellschaft) Westholsteinische Verlagsanstalt Boyens und Co., Am Wulf-Isebrand-Platz, Postfach 1880, 25746 Heide, Germany. TEL 0481-691-0. Ed.Bd.

830 AU
HEBBEL - MENSCH UND DICHTER IM WERK. irreg., no.4, 1992. price varies. Verband der Wissenschaftlichen Gesellschaften Oesterreichs, Lindengasse 37, A-1070 Vienna, Austria. TEL 932166.

895.1 CC ISSN 1000-9663
HEBEI WENXUE/HEBEI LITERATURE. (Text in Chinese) m. Hebei Sheng Wenxue Yishu Jie Lianhehui, 2 Shizhuang Lu, Shigang Dajie, Shijiazhuang, Hebei 050000, People's Republic of China. TEL 745831.

059.927 001.3 US
HEBREW ANNUAL REVIEW; a journal of biblical and Hebraic studies. 1977. a. $30. Ohio State University, Department of Judaic and Near Eastern Languages and Literatures, 1841 Millikin Rd., Columbus, OH 43210. TEL 614-422-9255. (Subscr. to: Student Book Exchange, 1086 N. High St., Columbus, OH 43201) Ed. Reuben Ahroni. adv. circ. 750. **Indexed:** Bibl.Ling., Lang.& Lang.Behav.Abstr., M.L.A., Rel.& Theol.Abstr. (1982-), Rel.Ind.One, Rel.Ind.One, Sociol.Abstr.

HEBREW STUDIES; a journal devoted to Hebrew language and literature of all periods. see *LINGUISTICS*

800 II
HEENAYANA; literary and cultural quarterly. (Text in Bengali and English) 1974. q. Rs.8($6) Subhas Ghosal, Ed. & Pub., 33-D, Sreemohon Lane, Calcutta 700026, India. adv.; bk.rev. circ. 1,000. (back issues avail.)

830 GW ISSN 0933-8721
HEFTE FUER OSTASIATISCHE LITERATUR. 1985. s-a. DM.28. Iudicium Verlag, Postfach 701067, 81310 Munich, Germany. TEL 089-717868. FAX 089-7142039. **Document type:** academic/scholarly publication.

800 CC
HEHUA DIAN. (Text in Chinese) bi-m. Baoding Shi Wenlian, 14 Yuhua Donglu, Baoding, Hebei 071000, People's Republic of China. TEL 24139. Ed. Hao Jianqi.

053.1 GW
HEIMATJAHRBUCH KREIS AHRWEILER. 1981. a. DM.8.50. Kreisverwaltung Ahrweiler, Wilhelmstr., 53474 Ahrweiler, Germany. TEL 02641-384206. FAX 02641-384456. TELEX 2641915-KVAW. adv.; bk.rev.

830 920 GW ISSN 0073-1692
PT2328
HEINE-JAHRBUCH. 1962. a. DM.25. (Heinrich-Heine-Institut, Duesseldorf) Hoffmann und Campe Verlag, Harvestehuder Weg 42, 20149 Hamburg, Germany. Ed. Joseph A. Kruse. bk.rev. circ. 1,300. **Indexed:** M.L.A. **Document type:** academic/scholarly publication.

800 GW
HEINE SAEKULARAUSGABE: WERKE-BRIEFWECHSEL-LEBENSZEUGNISSE. (Text in French and German) 1970. irreg., vol.18K, 1992. Akademie Verlag GmbH, Muehlenstr. 33-34, 13187 Berlin, Germany. TEL 030-47889348. FAX 030-47889357. **Document type:** monographic series.
Description: Compilation of Heine's work and correspondence, in the original languages.

800 HU ISSN 0017-999X
PN9
HELIKON; vilagirodalmi figyelo. (Text in Hungarian; summaries in French and Russian) 1955. q. $23.50. Magyar Tudomanyos Akademia, Irodalomtudomanyi Intezet, Menesi ut 11-13, 1118 Budapest, Hungary. TEL 36-1-166-5938. FAX 36-1-185-3876. Eds. B. Kopeczi, L. Hopp. adv.; bk.rev.; index. **Indexed:** Amer.Hist.& Life, Hist.Abstr., M.L.A.

840 US ISSN 0160-0923
PA1
HELIOS (LUBBOCK). 1974. s-a. $18 to individuals; institutions $32. (Classical Association of the Southwestern United States) Texas Tech University Press, Box 41037, Lubbock, TX 79409-1037. TEL 806-742-2982; 800-832-4042. FAX 806-742-2979. Ed. Steve M. Oberhelman. adv.; bk.rev. circ. 536. **Indexed:** Arts & Hum.Cit.Ind. **Document type:** academic/scholarly publication.
—BLDSC (4285.330000); Faxon; UnCover.

820 821 AT ISSN 0155-9044
HELIX. 1978. 4/yr. Aus.$12. Victoria College, 119 Maltravers Rd., Ivanhoe 3079, Australia. Ed. David Brooks. adv.; bk.rev.; film rev.; play rev.; illus. circ. 2,000.

880 480 GW ISSN 0018-0084
PA5201
HELLENIKA; Zeitschrift fuer deutsch-griechische kulturelle und wirtschaftliche Zusammenarbeit. 1964. a. DM.20. (Ausgaben Neugriechische Studien) Verlag Ferdinand Kamp, Am Dornbusch 28, 44803 Bochum, Germany. Ed. Isidora Rosenthal-Kamarinea. adv.; bk.rev.; abstr.; bibl. circ. 3,000. **Indexed:** Amer.Hist.& Life, Hist.Abstr., M.L.A.
—BLDSC (4285.465000).

806 US ISSN 0739-7801
HEMINGWAY NEWSLETTER. 1981. s-a. $5. Hemingway Society, c/o Charles M. Oliver, Ed., 1417 Ricky Rd., Charlottesville, VA 22901. bibl.; stat.; circ. 700 (paid). (reprint service avail. from UMI) **Document type:** newsletter.

809 US ISSN 0276-3362
PS3515.E37
HEMINGWAY REVIEW. 1971. s-a. $20 to individuals; institutions $25. Hemingway Society (Chapel Hill, c/o Linda Wagner-Martin, Greenlaw CB 3520, University of North Carolina, Chapel Hill, NC 27599-3520. Ed. Susan F. Beegel. bk.rev.; bibl. circ. 950. (also avail. in microform from UMI; reprint service avail. from UMI) **Indexed:** Abstr.Engl.Stud., Ind.Bk.Rev.Hum., M.L.A. **Document type:** academic/scholarly publication.
—BLDSC (4295.010000); Faxon; UnCover; UMI.
Formerly (until 1981): Hemingway Notes (ISSN 0046-7243)

807 US ISSN 0273-0340
PS2124
HENRY JAMES REVIEW. 1979. 3/yr. $23 to individuals (foreign $28.10); institutions $40 (foreign $45.10). (Henry James Society) Johns Hopkins University Press, Journals Publishing Division, 2715 N. Charles St., Baltimore, MD 21218. TEL 410-516-6987. FAX 410-516-6968. Ed. Daniel Mark Fogel. adv.; bk.rev. circ. 698. **Indexed:** Abstr.Engl.Stud., Ind.Bk.Rev.Hum., LCR, M.L.A.
—Faxon; UnCover. CCC.
Description: Critical essays and reviews by noted critics of James, such as Leon Edel and Adeline Tintner.

800 020 US
HENRY MILLER MEMORIAL LIBRARY. REVIEW. 4/yr. $20. Henry Miller Memorial Library, Big Sur, CA 93920. TEL 408-667-2574. Ed. Jerry Kamstra. adv.

HER OWN WORDS; women's history & literature media. see *WOMEN'S STUDIES*

820 UK ISSN 0073-1927
HERBERT READ SERIES. 1961. irreg. Oleander Press, 17 Stansgate Ave., Cambridge CB2 2QZ, England. (U.S. address: 80 Eighth Ave., Ste. 303, New York, NY 10011) Ed. Philip Ward. **Document type:** monographic series.

830 GW
HERMAEA; germanistische Forschungen N.F. irreg., no.73, 1993. Max Niemeyer Verlag, Postfach 2140, 72011 Tuebingen, Germany. TEL 07071-98940. FAX 07071-989450. Eds. Hans Fromm, Hans-Joachim Maehl. (back issues avail.) **Indexed:** M.L.A. **Document type:** monographic series.
Description: Monographs on German language and literature.

HERODOTE; revue de geographie et de geopolitique. see *GEOGRAPHY*

LITERATURE

809 400 JA ISSN 0387-9348
HERON; essays on language & literature. (Text in English and Japanese) 1966. a. Saitama Daigaku - Saitama University, 255 Shimo-Okubo, Urawa-shi, Saitama-ken 338, Japan. Ed.Bd. circ. 200.
 Description: Articles on American and English literature, English linguistics and Japanology.

800 XO
HET. (Text in Hungarian) w. $65. (Cultural Union of Hungarians in Czechoslovakia - CSEMADOK) Obzor, Ceskoslovenskej Armady 35, 815 85 Bratislava, Slovakia.

810 US ISSN 0888-4153
HIGH PLAINS LITERARY REVIEW. 1986. 3/yr. $20. High Plains Literary Review, Inc., 180 Adams St., Ste. 250, Denver, CO 80206. TEL 303-320-6828. Ed. Robert O. Greer, Jr. adv.; bk.rev. circ. 1,100. (back issues avail.)
 —UnCover.
 Description: Fiction, poetry, interviews, reviews, and essays designed to bridge the gap between academic and commercial literary quarterlies.

059.927 UA ISSN 0378-4010
AL-HILAL. 1893. m. Dar al- Hilal, 16 Sharia Muhammad Ezz el-Arab, Cairo, Egypt. TEL 02-27954. TELEX 92703. Ed. Husain Mones.

810 US
HILL AND HOLLER; southern Appalachian mountains. 1983. a. $6.75 per no. Seven Buffaloes Press, Box 249, Big Timber, MT 59011. Ed. Art Cuelho. circ. 750.
 Description: Lifestyles and culture of Appalachian mountain people.

890 II
HINDI KAHANI. (Text in Hindi) 1977. a. Rs.125($8) Granthayan, 398 Sarvoday Nagar, Sasni Gate, Aligarh 202001, India. Eds. Rakeshgupta, R.K. Chaturvedi. circ. 1,100. (back issues avail.)

800 US ISSN 0363-0471
PQ7081.A1 CODEN: HSPAEC
HISPAMERICA; revista de literatura. (Text in Spanish) 1972. 3/yr. $21 to individuals; institutions $30. c/o Saul Sosnowski, Ed., 5 Pueblo Court, Gaithersburg, MD 20878. TEL 301-948-3494. adv.; bk.rev.; bibl. circ. 1,000. (back issues avail.) **Indexed:** Arts & Hum.Cit.Ind., Curr.Cont., Hisp.Amer.Per.Ind., M.L.A.
 —SWETS.
 Description: Devoted to Spanish-American literature. Publishes essays, bibliographic notes, and reviews, fiction, poetry, and interviews with leading writers.

860 UK ISSN 0952-0570
HISPANIC BILINGUAL TEXTS. 1987. irreg. price varies. Francis Cairns (Publications) Ltd., c/o The University, Leeds LS2 9JT, England.

860 II ISSN 0970-7522
F1408.3
HISPANIC HORIZON. 1985. s-a. Jawaharlal Nehru University, Centre of Spanish Studies, New Delhi 110067, India. TEL 91-11-667676. FAX 91-11-6865886. TELEX 031-73167 JNU IN. Ed. Aparajit Chattopadhyay. bk.rev. circ. 1,000.

800 US ISSN 0893-2395
HISPANIC ISSUES. 1987. s-a. price varies. University of Minnesota Press, 2037 University Ave., S.E., Minneapolis, MN 55455-3092. TEL 800-388-3863. Ed. Nicholas Spadaccini. (back issues avail.) **Document type:** academic/scholarly publication.
 —BLDSC (4315.772400).
 Description: Covers Spanish literary and cultural history.

HISPANIC REVIEW; a quarterly journal devoted to research in the Hispanic languages and literatures. see LINGUISTICS

860 II ISSN 0971-4111
F1401
▼**HISPANISTICA**; Indian journal of Spanish & Latin American Studies. 1993. s-a. Rs.40($10) to individuals; institutions Rs.50 ($15). S.P. Ganguly, Ed. & Pub., B-10-7213 Vasant Kunj, New Delhi 110070, India. TEL 6895515. adv.: page $100; trim 10.5 x 7.5. bk.rev. circ. 1,000. **Document type:** academic/scholarly publication.
 Description: Promotes the interdisciplinary analysis of Hispanic and Indo-Hispanic themes with a focus on literature and culture.

860 US ISSN 0018-2206
PQ6001
HISPANOFILA. (Text in English, Portuguese, Spanish) 1957. 3/yr. $18 to individuals; libraries $21. University of North Carolina at Chapel Hill, Department of Romance Languages, CB 3170, 238 Dey Hall, Chapel Hill, NC 27599-3170. TEL 919-962-1025. Ed. Fred M. Clark. bk.rev.; index, cum.index every 3 yrs. circ. 500. (also avail. in microform from UMI; reprint service avail. from UMI.) **Indexed:** Arts & Hum.Cit.Ind., Can.Rev.Comp.Lit., Curr.Cont., Ind.Bk.Rev.Hum., M.L.A. **Document type:** academic/scholarly publication.
 —BLDSC (4315.785000); Faxon; UnCover; UMI.

860 407 056 370 GW ISSN 0720-1168
HISPANORAMA. (Text in German, Spanish) 1972. 3/yr. DM.40($12) Deutscher Spanischlehrerverband, Braillestr. 17, 90425 Nuernberg, Germany. TEL 0911-351561. FAX 069-513728. Ed. Anton Bemmerlein. adv.; bk.rev.; bibl. circ. 2,000. **Document type:** academic/scholarly publication, bulletin.

100 800 SZ ISSN 0073-2397
HISTOIRE DES IDEES ET CRITIQUE LITTERAIRE. (Text in French; occasionally in English) 1954. irreg. no.325, 1993. price varies. Librairie Droz S.A., 11, rue Massot, CH-1211 Geneva 12, Switzerland. TEL 022-3466666. FAX 022-3472391. circ. 1,500. **Document type:** monographic series.
 —BLDSC (4316.009000). CCC.
 Description: Examines the history of ideas and literary critique from an academic perspective.

810 793 US
HOB-NOB. 1969. s-a. $6 to individuals; libraries $5.50 (effective Jan. 1991). Mildred K. Henderson, Ed. & Pub., 994 Nissley Rd., Lancaster, PA 17601. TEL 717-898-7807. bk.rev. circ. 450.
 Former titles: Hob-Nob Annual; (until 1979): Hob-Nob Quarterly.
 Description: Original prose, poetry, reviews, letters and cartoons.

800 AG
HOJAS LITERARIAS ILUSTRADAS. (Text in Spanish and Yiddish) vol.22, 1976. bi-m. free. Moises Knaphais, Ed. & Pub., Rem. Esc. de San Martin 2670-Dto. C., Buenos Aires, Argentina. adv.; bk.rev.; film rev.; play rev.; charts; illus. circ. 3,000.

895.6 JA
HON. (Text in Japanese) 1977. m. Kodansha Ltd., 12-21 Otowa 2-chome, Bunkyo-ku, Tokyo 112, Japan. TEL 03-5395-3516. FAX 03-3942-7203. TELEX J34509 KODANSHA. Ed. Masaharu Horikoshi. circ. 50,000. **Document type:** consumer publication.
 Description: Publishes short essays.

800 UK ISSN 0018-4543
AP4
HONEST ULSTERMAN. 1968. irreg. (3-4/yr.) £14 to individuals; institutions £17. Ulsterman Publications, 14 Shaw St., Belfast BT4 1PT, N. Ireland. Ed. Tom Clyde. adv.; bk.rev.; cum.index 1968-1985. circ. 1,000. (back issues avail.) **Document type:** bulletin.

895 CC
HONG DOU. (Text in Chinese) m. Nanning Shi Wenlian, Minsheng Lu, Nanning, Guangxi 530012, People's Republic of China. TEL 26093. Ed. Wei Weizu.

895.1 CC
HONG YAN. (Text in Chinese) bi-m. Y21. (Chongqing Wenxue Yishu Jie Lianhehui) Hongyan Wenxue Zazhishe, 30, Chongqing Cun, Zhongshan 3rd Rd., Chongqing 630015, People's Republic of China. TEL 554065. illus.

801.953 CC
HONGLOUMENG XUEKAN/STUDIES ON A DREAM OF RED MANSIONS. (Text in Chinese; table of contents in English) q. Y12.80($34.70) (Zhongguo Yishu Yanjiuyuan - Chinese Art Academy) Wenhua Yishu Chubanshe, 17, Qianhai Xijie, Beijing 100009, People's Republic of China. TEL 651128. (Dist. outside China by: China International Book Trading Corp., P.O. Box 399, Beijing, P.R.C.; Dist. in US by: China Books & Periodicals, Inc., 2929 24th St., San Francisco, CA 94110. TEL 415-282-2994) Ed. Feng Qiyong. bk.rev.
 Description: Presents literary and historical studies on all aspects of the eighteenth-century novel "Hong Lou Meng" (A Dream of Red Mansions).

801.953 CC ISSN 1001-277X
"HONGLOUMENG" YANJIU. (Subseries of: Fuyin Baokan Ziliao) (Text in Chinese) q. Y7. Zhongguo Renmin Daxue, Shubao Ziliao Zhongxin - China People's University, Book & Newspaper Information Center, P.O. Box 1122, Beijing 100007, People's Republic of China. TEL 441792. illus.
 Description: Reprints articles and papers concerning the Qing dynasty novel "Hong Lou Meng" (A Dream of Red Mansions).

810 US
HOOSIER CHALLENGER.* 1956. q. $12. Claire Emerson, Ed. & Pub., 9423 Montgomery Rd., Cincinnati, OH 45242-7602. adv.; bk.rev.; illus.; tr.lit.

800 GW ISSN 0018-4942
DIE HOREN; Zeitschrift fuer Literatur, Grafik und Kritik. 1955. q. DM.48. Verlag fuer Neue Wissenschaft GmbH, Am Alten Hafen 113-115, 27568 Bremerhaven, Germany. TEL 0471-46093. FAX 0471-42765. Ed. Kurt Morawietz. adv.: B&W page DM.900, color page DM.2800; trim 200 x 117. bk.rev. circ. 5,500. (reprint service avail. from KTO) **Document type:** consumer publication.

839.7 FI ISSN 0439-5530
HORISONT. (Text in Swedish) 1954. 6/yr. FIM 150 (SEK 225). Svenska Oesterbottens Litteraturfoerening, Kyrkoesplanaden 19 A 10, 65100 Vasa, Finland. TEL 961-3128426. Ed. Maria Sandin. adv.; bk.rev.; illus.; index. circ. 3,600.

810 US
HORIZONS BEYOND.* 1983. 2/yr. $18. Baker Street Publications, Box 517, Metairie, LA 70004-0517. TEL 504-734-8414. Ed. Sharida Rizzuto. circ. 9,000.

810 US
HORIZONS WEST.* 1983. 2/yr. $18.60. Baker Street Publications, Box 517, Metairie, LA 70004-0517. TEL 504-734-8414. Ed. Sharida Rizzuto. circ. 9,000.

860 861 US
HORIZONTES (PATERSON). 1983. a. $8. Passaic County Community College, Poetry Center, College Blvd., Paterson, NJ 07509. TEL 201-684-6555. Ed. Jose A. Villalongo, Sr. illus. circ. 800.

891.439 PK
HOSHRUBA DA'IJIST. (Text in Urdu) 1978. m. Rs.65. Ali Aufyan Afagi, 20-B Model Town, Lahore, Pakistan.

800 UK ISSN 0305-926X
PR4809.H15
HOUSMAN SOCIETY JOURNAL. 1974. a. £6. Housman Society, Mrs V. Richardson, 1 Warwick Hall Gardens, Bromsgrove B60 2AU, England. adv.; bk.rev.; bibl. circ. 350. (back issues avail.) **Indexed:** M.L.A.

800 US ISSN 0888-3521
HOWLING DOG; a journal of letters, words and lines. 1985. s-a. $10. Parkville Publishing, 8419 Rhode Dr., Utica, MI 48087. TEL 313-254-5334. Ed. Mark Donovan. adv.; bk.rev.; illus. circ. 500. (back issues avail.)
 Description: Contains humor, fiction, poetry and art.

810 US
HOWLING MANSTRA.* 1988. a. $5. 330 6th St., S., Stillwater, MN 55082-4941. TEL 608-785-0810. circ. 150.

LITERATURE

895.15 CC ISSN 1000-789X
HUACHENG. (Text in Chinese) 1979. bi-m. Y36($107.06) Huacheng Chubanshe, No. 11, Shuiyin Lu, Huanshi Donglu, Guangzhou, Guangdong 510075, People's Republic of China. TEL 7768688. (Dist. outside China by: China International Book Trading Corp., P.O. Box 399, Beijing, P.R.C.; Dist. in US by: China Books & Periodicals, Inc., 2929 24th St., San Francisco, CA 94110. TEL 415-282-2994) Ed. Fan Hansheng. adv.

894.2 US
HUADE YUANYE/PRAIRIE OF FLOWERS. (Text in Mongolian) m. $54. China Books & Periodicals, Inc., 2929 24th St., San Francisco, CA 94110. TEL 415-282-2994. FAX 415-282-0994.

895.1 CC ISSN 1000-4823
HUANG HE/YELLOW RIVER. (Text in Chinese) 1985. bi-m. Y18. Shanxi Zuojia Xiehui - Shanxi Writers' Association, Dongsitiao Nanhuamen, Taiyuan, Shanxi 030001, People's Republic of China. TEL 382495. Ed. Shan Quan. adv.: page Y4000. circ. 10,000.
  Description: Contains news, novels, and articles on cultural and social issues.

895.1 CC ISSN 1002-686X
HUAXI; qingnian wenxue yuekan. (Text in Chinese) 1978. m. Y28.80. 27, Shizi Lu, Guiyang, Guizhou 550001, People's Republic of China. Ed.Bd.
  Description: Contains short stories, poetry, prose, and novels.

800 700 PE
HUESO HUMERO. 1979. s-a. $9 per no. Mosca Azul Editores, Conquistadores 1130, Lima 27, Peru. Eds. Mirko Lauer, Abelardo Oquendo. bk.rev. circ. 1,500. **Indexed:** Hisp.Amer.Per.Ind.

895.1 CC ISSN 0439-8106
HUNAN WENXUE/HUNAN LITERATURE. (Text in Chinese) m. $47.70. Hunan Sheng Wenlian, Building No. 17, Dongfeng 2 Cun, Changsha, Hunan 410003, People's Republic of China. TEL 24821. (Dist. in US by: China Books & Periodicals, Inc., 2929 24th St., San Francisco, CA 94110. TEL 415-282-2994) Ed. Wang Yiping.

HUNGARIAN STUDIES NEWSLETTER. see LINGUISTICS

HUNGRY MIND REVIEW; a Midwestern book review. see PUBLISHING AND BOOK TRADE

800 US
THE HUNTED NEWS. 1990. s-a. $6. The Suboubon Press, P.O. Box 9101, Warwick, RI 02889. TEL 401-739-2279. Ed. Michael K. Wood. bk.rev.; film rev, bibl.; circ. 250 (controlled). (back issues avail.)
  Description: Attempts to find writers who move beyond academic or experimental affectation and who try to communicate honestly with their audiences.

810 990 700 US ISSN 0018-7895
Z733.S24
HUNTINGTON LIBRARY QUARTERLY; studies in English and American literature, history, and art. 1937. q. $40 (foreign $48). Huntington Library, Art Collections and Botanical Gardens, 1151 Oxford Rd., San Marino, CA 91108. TEL 818-405-2172. FAX 818-405-0225. Ed. Susan E. Green. bk.rev.; illus.; index. circ. 1,000. (also avail. in microfilm from UMI; reprint service avail. from UMI,KTO) **Indexed:** Abstr.Engl.Stud., Amer.Hist.& Life, Amer.Hum.Ind., Curr.Cont., Hist.Abstr., Hum.Ind., Ind.Bk.Rev.Hum., LCR, M.L.A. **Document type:** academic/scholarly publication.
  —BLDSC (4337.460000); Faxon; UnCover; SWETS; UMI.
  Description: Publishes scholarly articles with special attention to the research fields of the Huntington Library collections, concentrating on the literature, history and art of the 16th to 18th centuries in Britain and America.

800 GW ISSN 0176-8123
HYDRONYMIA EUROPAEA. irreg., vol.9, 1993. price varies. (Akademie der Wissenschaften und der Literatur, Mainz, Klasse Literatur) Franz Steiner Verlag Wiesbaden GmbH, Birkenhahnstr. 44, 70191 Stuttgart, Germany. TEL 0711-2582-0. FAX 0711-2582290. TELEX 723636-DAZ-D. (Subscr. to: Postfach 101061, 70009 Stuttgart, Germany) Ed. Wolfgang P. Schmid. **Document type:** monographic series.

800 US ISSN 1067-9251
▼**HYPOTHESES: NEO-ARISTOTELIAN ANALYSIS.** 1992. q. $10 (Canada $12; elsewhere $15). 70 Sagamore Hill Dr., Port Washington, NY 11050. TEL 516-883-6734. Ed. David R. Eastwood. bk.rev.; abstr.; bibl. circ. 158. **Document type:** academic/scholarly publication, bibliography, newsletter.
  Description: Contains short essays on literature and criticism.

890 KO
HYUNDAE MUNHAK. (Text in Korean) 1955. m. 17000 Won. Mokjung Bldg., 6th Floor, 1361-5 Seocho-dong, Seocho-ku, Seoul, S. Korea. Ed. Kim Kwang-Soo. circ. 200,000.

I B L A. (Institut des Belles Lettres Arabes) see ORIENTAL STUDIES

860 861 VE
I C A M; revista literaria. 1971. q. Bs.210 (foreign Bs.350). Alberto Jose Perez, Ed. & Pub., Apdo. de Correo 127, Barinas 5201A, Venezuela. adv.; bk.rev.; abstr.; bibl.; illus. circ. 2,000. (back issues avail.)

800 US ISSN 0887-3615
I C L A BULLETIN. irreg. (approx. 3/yr.). $15 for 3 years. International Comparative Literature Association, c/o Steven P. Sondrup, Ed., Department of Comparative Literature, Brigham Young University, Provo, UT 84602. TEL 801-378-2579. FAX 801-378-4649. bk.rev. circ. 4,000. **Document type:** bulletin.

800 GW
I J B - REPORT. (Text mainly in German; occasionally in English, French; summaries in English) 1983. q. free. Internationale Jugendbibliothek - International Youth Library, Schloss Blutenburg, 81247 Munich, Germany. TEL 089-8112028. FAX 089-8117553. Ed. Andreas Bode. circ. 3,900.
  Description: News about the children's literature scene and the activities of the library.

809 US ISSN 0271-9061
I.O. EVANS STUDIES IN THE PHILOSOPHY & CRITICISM OF LITERATURE. 1982. irreg., no.18, 1993 (approx. 6/yr.). price varies. Borgo Press, Box 2845, San Bernardino, CA 92406. TEL 909-884-5813. FAX 909-888-4942. Ed. Boden Clarke. **Document type:** monographic series.
  —BLDSC (4563.747400).
  Incorporates (in 1992): Starmont Studies in Literary Criticism (ISSN 0737-1306)
  Description: Includes monographs on general literary topics, histories and discussions of genre fiction, anthologies of essays on specific literary themes, philosophical discussions of literature, and books on related topics.

I U O M A MAGAZINE. (International Union of Mail Artists) see ART

808.82 808 US
I W I NEWSLETTER. 1976? bi-m. $15 to individuals; institutions $20. Illinois Writers, Inc., 4240 Dept. of English, Illinois State University, Normal, IL 61790-4240. TEL 309-438-7705. Ed. Demetrice Worley. bk.rev. circ. 500. **Document type:** newsletter.
  Formerly: I W I Monthly (ISSN 0733-8929); **Supersedes (in 1981):** Illinois Writers' Newsletter.

892.76 UA
IBDA/INNOVATION. (Text in Arabic) 1983. irreg. $12 to individuals; institutions $24. (Al-Hay'ah al-Misriyyah al-Aamah lil-Kuttab) Magallat Ibda', 27 Sharia Abd al-Khaliq Tharwat, P.O. Box 626, Cairo, Egypt. TEL 757691. Ed. Abd al-Qadir al-Qatt. adv.; bk.rev.; illus.
  Description: Publishes short stories, poetry, plays and critical studies on the arts and literature in Egypt.

800 700 IE ISSN 0019-1027
ICARUS. 1950. irreg. (3-7/yr.). £15($20) to individuals; students £8($10). University of Dublin, Regents House, Trinity College, Dublin, Ireland. Ed.Bd. adv.; bk.rev.; film rev. circ. 1,000.

810 US
ICARUS REVIEW. 1989. 2/yr. $6. McOne Press, Box 51074, Austin, TX 78763. TEL 512-477-2269. Ed. Mark Lawrence. circ. 400.

830 GW ISSN 0445-1821
ICH SCHREIBE; Zeitschrift fuer schreibende Arbeiter. vol.13, 1972. 4/yr. DM.11 per no. Zentralhaus-Publikationen, Dittrichring 4, 04109 Leipzig, Germany. Ed. Ursula Dauderstaedt. bk.rev.; bibl.; illus.

800 US ISSN 1064-1777
▼**THE ICONOCLAST (MOHEGAN LAKE).** 1992. 8/yr. $12 (effective 1994). Wagner Labs and Enterprices, 1675 Amazon Rd., Mohegan Lake, NY 10547. TEL 914-528-2553. Ed. Phil Wagner. adv.: Page $35. circ. 250. (back issues avail.)
  Description: Contains poetry, fiction, art and satire, reviews, and essays. Aimed at well-educated readers not satisfied by what is offered by mass media and universities.

296 IS ISSN 0333-838X
PJ5001
IDENTITY. 1980. s-a. $25. Haberman Institute for Literary Research, P.O. Box 166, Lod 71101, Israel. TEL 972-8-244569. FAX 972-8-249466. Ed. Z. Malachi. adv.; bk.rev. circ. 2,000. **Indexed:** Ind.Heb.Per. **Document type:** academic/scholarly publication.
  Description: Studies in Jewish culture and literature.

800 IT
IDRA; semestrale di letteratura. s-a. L.40000. Melangolo, Via di Porta Soprana 3-1, 16123 Genoa, Italy. Ed. Lucio Maninetti.

860 AG ISSN 0019-1663
IGITUR REVISTA LITERARIA. no.4, 1967. q. Republica de Israel 115, Cordoba, Argentina. Ed. Carlos Cullere. adv.; bk.rev.; bibl.

890 IS
IGRA. a. P.O. Box 7145, Jerusalem 91 071, Israel. TEL 02-521201.

813 US
ILLINOIS SHORT FICTION. irreg. University of Illinois Press, 1325 S. Oak St., Champaign, IL 61820. TEL 217-333-0950. FAX 217-244-8082. Refereed Serial

ILOCOS REVIEW. see HISTORY — History Of Australasia And Other Areas

IMAGE. see ORIENTAL STUDIES

IMAGEN DEL CORREO VIEJO; revista del pos-bum. see ART

IMAGERY TODAY. see PSYCHOLOGY

810 US
IMAGINATION MAGAZINE.* 1990. 13/yr. $21. 609 E. Glenwood Lansing Rd., Ste. 20, Glenwood, IL 60425-1961. circ. 100.

850 IT
L'IMMAGINAZIONE. vol.10, 1993. m. L.25000 (foreign L.35000). Edizioni Piero Manni, Via Braccio Martello 36, 73100 Lecce, Italy. TEL 0832-315929. FAX 0832-6314834. bk.rev.

850 IT ISSN 1120-3382
IN OLTRE; letterature e materiali. s-a. L.30000 (foreign L.40000). (Fondazione Ricciotto Canudo) Schena Editore, Viale le Stazione 177, 72015 Fasano (BR), Italy. TEL 080-71-46-81. FAX 80714690. Ed. Lino Angiuli. circ. 1,000 (controlled). **Document type:** academic/scholarly publication.

895.6 JA
IN POCKET. (Text in Japanese) 1983. m. Kodansha Ltd., 12-21 Otowa 2-chome, Bunkyo-ku, Tokyo 112, Japan. TEL 03-5395-3500. FAX 03-5395-5626. TELEX J34509 KODANSHA. Ed. Yoshimi Sugiyama. circ. 80,000. **Document type:** consumer publication.
  Description: Publishes essays and novels.

IN SEARCH OF A SONG. see CHILDREN AND YOUTH — For

808 910.03 US
IN TOUCH (CHICAGO). m. membership. International Black Writers Conference, Box 1030, Chicago, IL 60690. TEL 312-924-3818. bk.rev. **Document type:** newsletter.
  Description: Covers writing competitions, member activities and new books written by Afro-American writers.

INDAGINI E PROSPETTIVE. see POLITICAL SCIENCE

820   US   ISSN 0019-3763
PR5366
INDEPENDENT SHAVIAN. 1962. 3/yr. $18 to libraries and non-members (foreign $20). Bernard Shaw Society, Inc., Box 1159, Madison Sq. Sta., New York, NY 10159-1159. Ed.Bd. adv.; bk.rev.; play rev.; index. circ. 300. (also avail. in microfilm from UMI; reprint service avail. from UMI) **Indexed:** Abstr.Engl.Stud.; M.L.A.
—UMI.

820   II
INDIAN AUTHOR. (Text in English) 1976. q. Rs.20($4) Authors Guild of India, F-12 Jangpura Ext., New Delhi 110 014, India. TEL 11-615063. Ed.Bd. adv.; bk.rev. circ. 2,000. **Document type:** newsletter.

INDIAN HORIZONS. see HISTORY — History Of Asia

INDIAN JOURNAL OF AMERICAN STUDIES. see HISTORY — History Of North And South America

891.1   II   ISSN 0019-5804
AP8
INDIAN LITERATURE. (Text in English) 1957. bi-m. Rs.20($12) National Academy of Letters - Sahitya Akademi, 35 Ferozeshah Rd., Rabindra Bhavan, New Delhi 110 001, India. TEL 38 20 50. Ed. D.S. Rao. adv.; bk.rev.; bibl.; illus.; index, cum.index. circ. 2,500. **Indexed:** Abstr.Engl.Stud., Arts & Hum.Cit.Ind., Curr.Cont., M.L.A.
—Faxon; UnCover.
    Description: Devoted to the dissemination of Indian literature.

820   II   ISSN 0019-6053
PK101
THE INDIAN P.E.N.. (Text in English) 1934. q. Rs.38($7.50) (effective 1993). P.E.N. All-India Centre, Theosophy Hall, 40, New Marine Lines, Bombay 400 020, India. TEL 292175. Ed. Nissim Ezekiel. adv.; bk.rev. circ. 750. **Indexed:** M.L.A.

801 808.1   II
INDIAN WRITER. (Text in English) 1986. q. Rs.20($15) to non-members. Writer's Club, C-23, Annanagar E., Madras 600 102, India. TEL 615370. TELEX 41-24064. Ed P.K. Joy. bk.rev. circ. 900.
    Description: Covers literary news.

810   US
INDIANA ENGLISH. 1966. 3/yr. $10 to non-members. Indiana Council of Teachers of English, Inc., Department of English, Indiana State University, Terre Haute, IN 47809. TEL 812-237-3147. Ed. Robert Perrin. bk.rev. circ. 700 (controlled). **Indexed:** Bibl.Engl.Lang.& Lit.
    Former titles (until 1977): Indiana English Journal (ISSN 0019-6584); Indiana English Leaflet.

800   ISSN 0738-386X
PS536.2
INDIANA REVIEW. 1975. 2/yr. $12 to individuals; institutions $15. 316 N. Jordan Ave., Indiana University, Bloomington, IN 47405. TEL 812-855-3439. Ed. Gretchen Knapp. adv. contact: Jeffrey McKenzie. bk.rev. circ. 2,000. (back issues avail.) **Indexed:** A.I.P.P., Amer.Hum.Ind., Ind.Amer.Per.Verse.
    Formerly: Indiana Writes (ISSN 0149-3361)
    Description: Covers poetry, fiction, non-fiction prose, and personal essays, interviews and translations.

810   US
INDIGENOUS WORLD/MUNDO INDIGENA. (Text in English, Spanish) 1982. 2/yr. $20. 275 Grand View Ave., No. 103, San Francisco, CA 94114. TEL 415-647-1966. circ. 10,000.

800 320   II   ISSN 0378-0856
INDO-IRANICA. (Text in English and Persian) 1946. q. $40. Iran Society, 12 Dr. M. Ishaque Rd., Calcutta 700 016, India. TEL 29-9899. Eds. P.C. Chunder, M.A. Majid. bk.rev.; illus. circ. 750. **Document type:** academic/scholarly publication.
    Description: Features Persian studies (language, literature, relition and culture), and Indian-Iran cultural relations.

491.1 891.1   II
INDOLOGICAL STUDIES. Variant title: University of Delhi. Department of Sanskrit. Journal. (Text in English) 1972. s-a. University of Delhi, Department of Sanskrit, Delhi 110007, India.

860   MX   ISSN 0186-7067
INFAME TURBA. 1986. m. Universidad Autonoma de Puebla, Coordinacion de Difusion Cultural, Reforma 913-altos, C.P. 72000, Puebla, Pue., Mexico. TEL 46 38 91. Ed. Alfonso Velez Pliego. adv.; bk.rev. circ. 2,000.

869   BL
INFAMIA LITERARIA. 1991. s-a. ? R. Joao Adolfo, 118, 14o andar, 01050 Sao Paulo, SP, Brazil. TEL 011-35-2011. FAX 011-37-3940.

810   US
THE INFINITE ONION. 1989. 5/yr. $5. Box 263, Colorado Springs, CO 80901. TEL 719-473-2647. circ. 1,000.

800 700   US   ISSN 1050-7280
INFINITY LIMITED; a journal for the somewhat eccentric. (Text mainly in English; occasionally in French, Spanish) 1988. q. $12.95 to individuals; institutions $15 (effective 1993). Ken and Genie Lester, Eds. & Pubs., Box 2713, Castro Valley, CA 94546-0546. TEL 510-581-8172. adv.; B&W page $100. bk.rev.; illus. circ. 1,000. (back issues avail.) **Document type:** consumer publication.
    Description: Publishes short stories, poems and art.

840   FR   ISSN 0020-0123
PN3
INFORMATION LITTERAIRE; revue illustree paraissant tous les deux mois pendant la periode scolaire. 1949. 5/yr. 235 F. Societe d'Edition les Belles Lettres, 95 bd. Raspail, 75006 Paris, France. Ed. M. Beaujeu. bk.rev.; bibl.; illus.; index. circ. 6,000. (reprint service avail. from KTO)
—BLDSC (4493.685000); Faxon; SWETS.

INFORMER; international poetry magazine. see LITERATURE — Poetry

810   US   ISSN 0885-6664
INKBLOT. 1983. 4/yr. $12. Inkblot Publications, 439 49th St., Ste. 11, Oakland, CA 94609-2158. Ed. Theo Green. circ. 1,000.

INKS: CARTOON AND COMIC ARTS STUDIES. see ART

808.1   US   ISSN 0085-1884
INLET. 1972; suspended. a. free. Virginia Wesleyan College, Department of English, Norfolk, VA 23502. TEL 804-455-3200. Ed. Joseph Harkey. circ. 750.

INNISFREE. see LITERATURE — Poetry

800   GW   ISSN 0443-2460
INSEL-ALMANACH. 1905. a. price varies. Insel-Verlag, Lindenstr. 29, 6000 Frankfurt a.M. 1, Germany. (Dist. by: Suhrkamp Publishers New York Inc., 175 Fifth Ave., New York, NY 10010, USA) bk.rev. circ. 5,000.
    Description: Collection of essays on important writers from the history of world literature.

808   US
INSIDE STORY. 6/yr. $40 membership (Canada $50; elsewhere $75) (includes Storytelling Magazine and National Directory of Storytelling). National Storytelling Association, Box 309, Jonesborough, TN 37659. TEL 615-753-2171. FAX 615-753-9331. **Document type:** newsletter.
    Formerly: Yarnspinner.

800 851 363.35   IT
INSIEME NELLA VALLE E ACCADEMIA INTERNAZIONALE ARTE LETTERE SCIENZE DAFNI; ebdomadario artistico-poetico e di informazione del movimento i.n.v. 1973. m. L.25000. Movimento Independienti per la Pace, Via de Gasperi, 92100 Agrigento, Italy. Ed. Giuseppe Amico. (tabloid format)
    Formerly: Insieme nella Valle.

INSTITUT CATHOLIQUE DE PARIS. REVUE. see GENERAL INTEREST PERIODICALS — France

891.7 947   FR   ISSN 0078-9976
INSTITUT D'ETUDES SLAVES, PARIS. BIBLIOTHEQUE RUSSE. (Text in French or Russian) 1912. irreg., vol.93, 1993. price varies. Institut d'Etudes Slaves, 9 rue Michelet, 75006 Paris, France. **Indexed:** M.L.A. **Document type:** academic/scholarly publication; monographic series.

891.8   FR   ISSN 0079-001X
PG13
INSTITUT D'ETUDES SLAVES, PARIS. TEXTES. 1926. irreg., vol.8, 1968. price varies. Institut d'Etudes Slaves, 9 rue Michelet, 75006 Paris, France.
Document type: academic/scholarly publication.

891 943   FR   ISSN 0079-0028
INSTITUT D'ETUDES SLAVES, PARIS. TRAVAUX. 1923. irreg., vol.37, 1993. price varies. Institut d'Etudes Slaves, 9 rue Michelet, 75006 Paris, France.

800   FR   ISSN 0073-8212
INSTITUT DE RECHERCHE ET D'HISTOIRE DES TEXTES, PARIS. DOCUMENTS, ETUDES ET REPERTOIRES. 1958. irreg., vol.63, 1993. price varies. (Centre National de Recherche Scientifique) C N R S Editions, 20-22 rue St. Amand, 75015 Paris, France. TEL 45-33-16-00. FAX 45-33-92-13. TELEX 200 356 F. (Dist. outside France by: N.V. Brepols, Steenweg op Tielen 68, 2300 Turnhout, Belgium. TEL 32-14-402500. FAX 32-14-428919) adv.; bk.rev.; index. circ. 1,500. (back issues avail.)
Document type: monographic series.

INSTITUT PROVINCIAL D'ETUDES ET RECHERCHES BIBLIOTHECONOMIQUES. MEMOIRES. see BIBLIOGRAPHIES

800   CK   ISSN 0020-370X
INSTITUTO CARO Y CUERVO. NOTICIAS CULTURALES. 1961-1975; N.S. 1982. bi-m. Col.$2500. Instituto Caro y Cuervo, Seccion de Publicaciones, Apdo. Aereo 51502, Bogota, Colombia. Ed.Bd. bk.rev.; bibl.; illus. circ. 4,000.

860   CK
INSTITUTO CARO Y CUERVO. SERIE GRANADA ENTREABIERTA. 1973. irreg., no.65, 1993. price varies. Instituto Caro y Cuervo, Seccion de Publicaciones, Apdo. Aereo 51502, Bogota, Colombia.

860 400   CK   ISSN 0073-9928
INSTITUTO CARO Y CUERVO. SERIE MINOR. 1950. irreg., no.33, 1992. price varies. Instituto Caro y Cuervo, Seccion de Publicaciones, Apdo. Aereo 51502, Bogota, Colombia. (back issues avail.)

800   RM
INSTITUTUL DE SUBINGINERI ORADEA. LUCRARI STIINTIFICE: SERIA LITERATURA. (Text in Rumanian, occasionally in English or French; summaries in English, French, German or Rumanian) irreg. Institutul de Subingineri Oradea, Calea Armatei Rosii Nr. 5, 3700 Oradea, Rumania.
    Formerly: Institutul Pedagogic Oradea. Lucrari Stiintifice: Seria Literatura; which continues in part (in 1973): Institutul Pedagogic Oradea. Lucrari Stiintifice: Seria Filologie; which superseded in part (in 1971): Institutul Pedagogic Oradea. Lucrari Stiintifice: Seria A and Seria B; which was formerly (until 1969): Institutul Pedagogic Oradea. Lucrari Stiintifice.

800   NE   ISSN 0927-3360
INTERACTIONS. irreg. price varies. Editions Rodopi B.V., Keizersgracht 302-304, 1016 EX Amsterdam, Netherlands. TEL 31-20-6227507. FAX 31-20-638-0948. (In N. America: 233 Peachtree St., N.E., Ste. 404, Atlanta, GA 30303-1504. TEL 800-225-3998. FAX 404-522-7116) Ed. Miriam Diaz-Diocaretz.
Document type: academic/scholarly publication.

800   UK
INTERACTIONS. (Text in English, French, German, Spanish) s-a. £8 (France 80 F.; Germany DM.24; Spain 1400 Ptas. Department of German, University College London, Gower St., London WC1E 6BT, England. Ed. Diane M. Moore.
    Description: Publishes literary pieces from France, Germany, Spain, the U.K., and the U.S.

INTERDISCIPLINARITE ETUDES PHILOSOPHIQUES ET LITTERAIRES. see PHILOSOPHY

840   FR   ISSN 0154-5604
PN3
INTERFERENCES. s-a. 20 F. Universite de Rennes II (Universite de Haute Bretagne), Centre d'Histoire et d'Analyse des Textes, 2 rue du Doyen D. Leroy, 35044 Rennes Cedex, France. TEL 99-54-66-35. FAX 99-33-07-95. Ed. Patrick Besnier.
    Description: Studies general and comparative literature.

LITERATURE

840 700　　　　　　FR　　ISSN 0074-1140
INTERFERENCES, ARTS, LETTRES. 1968. irreg. Lettres Modernes, 45 rue Saint-Andre, 14123 Fleury sur Orne, France. TEL 31-84-47-06. FAX 31-84-48-09.

840　　　　　　　　FR　　ISSN 0154-5590
INTERFERENCES: SERIES ETUDES ET TRAVAUX. 1973. irreg. Presses Universitaires de Rennes, 2 rue du Doyen D. Leroy, 35044 Rennes Cedex, France. TEL 99-54-66-35. FAX 99-33-07-95.

800　　　　　　　　US　　ISSN 0888-2452
INTERIM (LAS VEGAS). 1944-1955; resumed 1986. 2/yr. $8 to individuals; institutions $16. c/o A. Wilber Stevens, Ed., Department of English, University of Nevada, Las Vegas, Las Vegas, NV 89154-5034. TEL 702-895-3172. circ. 800.
Indexed: Amer.Hum.Ind., Ind.Amer.Per.Verse.
Description: Publishes poetry and short fiction from international writers.

840 398　　　　　　CN
INTERNATIONAL ARTHURIAN SOCIETY. NEWSLETTER. 1981. s-a. membership. Dalhousie University, Department of French, Halifax, NS B3H 3J5, Canada. TEL 902-494-2430. Ed. Hans R. Runte. circ. controlled. **Document type:** newsletter.

INTERNATIONAL AUTHORS AND WRITERS WHO'S WHO. see BIOGRAPHY

800　　　　　　　　CN　　ISSN 0315-4149
PN3311
INTERNATIONAL FICTION REVIEW. 1974. s-a. Can.$12 to individuals; institutions Can.$15. International Fiction Association, Department of German, Russian, University of New Brunswick, Fredericton, NB, Canada. TEL 506-453-4636. FAX 506-458-8748. Ed. Saad Elkhadem. bk.rev.; index. circ. 600. (also avail. in microform from MML; back issues avail.; reprint service avail.) **Indexed:** Amer.Hum.Ind., Arts & Hum.Cit.Ind., Can.Rev.Comp.Lit., CMI, Curr.Cont., Hum.Ind., Ind.Bk.Rev.Hum., M.L.A., Mid.East: Abstr.& Ind.
—BLDSC (4540.187000); Faxon; UnCover; SWETS.

800 860　　　　　　US　　ISSN 0074-6495
INTERNATIONAL INSTITUTE OF IBERO-AMERICAN LITERATURE. CONGRESS PROCEEDINGS. MEMORIA. (Proceedings published by sponsoring university) 1939. irreg. International Institute of Ibero-American Literature - Institute Internacional de Literatura Iberoamericana, 1312 C.L., University of Pittsburgh, Pittsburgh, PA 15260. TEL 412-624-3359. FAX 412-624-8505. Ed. Keith McDuffie. adv.; bk.rev. (also avail. in microform from UMI; back issues avail.; reprint service avail. from UMI) **Document type:** proceedings.

INTERNATIONAL JOURNAL OF SLAVIC LINGUISTICS AND POETICS. see LINGUISTICS

800 700　　　　　　US
▼**INTERNATIONAL QUARTERLY (TALLAHASSEE);** literature and art in all genres in original English and in translation from any language and for and from all countries for discerning general readers. 1993. q. $19 to individuals; institutions $40. International Quarterly, Inc., Box 10521, Tallahassee, FL 32302-0521. TEL 904-224-5078. FAX 904-224-5127. Ed. Van K. Brock. adv.; bk.rev.; index. circ. 1,500. (back issues avail.)

INTERNATIONAL REVIEW OF AFRICAN AMERICAN ART; an international publication. see ART

830　　　　　　　　GW
INTERNATIONALE ERICH-FRIED-GESELLSCHAFT. JAHRBUCH. 1991. a. (Internationale Erich-Fried-Gesellschaft, AU) Verlag Juergen Haeusser, Frankfurterstr. 64, 64293 Darmstadt, Germany. **Document type:** bulletin.

830　　　　　　　　GW　　ISSN 0340-4528
PT3
INTERNATIONALES ARCHIV FUER SOZIALGESCHICHTE DER DEUTSCHEN LITERATUR. (Text in English, French, German) 1976. s-a. DM.136. Max Niemeyer Verlag, Postfach 2140, 72011 Tuebingen, Germany. TEL 07071-98940.
FAX 07071-989450. Ed.Bd. adv.; bk.rev.; bibl. (back issues avail.) **Indexed:** Arts & Hum.Cit.Ind., Can.Rev.Comp.Lit., Curr.Cont., M.L.A. **Document type:** academic/scholarly publication.
—SWETS.
Description: Essays on social history of German literature, especially 18th through 20th centuries.

840 700　　　　　　US
INTERPLAY; proceedings of symposia in comparative literature and the arts. 1982. irreg., latest no.6. price varies. (University of Southern California, Center for the Humanities, Comparative Literature Program) Undena Publications, Box 97, Malibu, CA 90265. TEL 805-746-5870. FAX 805-746-2728. (Dist. by: Crescent Academic Services, 29528 Madera Ave., Shafter, CA 93263) Ed. Moshe Lazar. (back issues avail.) **Indexed:** Amer.Hist.& Life, Hist.Abstr., M.L.A., PROMT. **Document type:** proceedings.

850　　　　　　　　IT
INTERPRETE. (Text in English or Italian) irreg., latest no.54. price varies. Angelo Longo Editore, Via Paolo Costa 33, P.O. Box 431, 48100 Ravenna, Italy. TEL 0544-217026. Ed. Aldo Scaglione. **Document type:** monographic series.

INTERVENTI CLASSENSI. see ART

INTERZONE. see LITERATURE — Science Fiction, Fantasy, Horror

860　　　　　　　　US　　ISSN 0732-6750
PQ6001
INTI; revista de literatura hispanica. (Text in English, Spanish) 1974. s-a. $25 to individuals; institutions $50 (effective 1993). (Providence College, Department of Modern Languages) Inti Publications, Box 20657, Cranston, RI 02920.
TEL 401-130-7200. FAX 401-865-2057. Ed. Roger B. Carmosino. adv.: B&W page $125. bk.rev.; film rev.; bibl. circ. 1,000. (back issues avail.) **Indexed:** Hisp.Amer.Per.Ind., M.L.A. **Document type:** academic/scholarly publication.
Description: Publishes scholarly discussions of Spanish American and Peninsular literature, creative writing and interviews.
Refereed Serial

800　　　　　　　　IT　　ISSN 0392-6095
INVENTARIO; rivista quadrimestrale di critica e letteratura. q. L.30000. Bi & Gi Editore, Casella Postale 2106, Verona, Italy. Ed. Pino Ruffo.

IO. see ANTHROPOLOGY

820　　　　　　　　UK　　ISSN 0266-2922
IOTA. 1988. 4/yr. £5($8) David Holliday, Ed. & Pub., 67 Hady Cres., Chesterfield, Derbys. S41 0EB, England. TEL 0246-276532. bk.rev. circ. 400.
Description: Contains poetry and literary reviews.

810　　　　　　　　US　　ISSN 0021-065X
PS501
IOWA REVIEW. 1970. 3/yr. $18 to individuals; institutions $20. University of Iowa, Department of English, 308 EPB, Iowa City, IA 52242.
TEL 319-335-0462. Ed. David Hamilton. adv.; bk.rev.; index. circ. 1,500. (also avail. in microform from UMI,KTO) **Indexed:** A.I.P.P., Abstr.Engl.Stud., Access, Amer.Bibl.Slavic & E.Eur.Stud., Amer.Hum.Ind., Bibl.Engl.Lang.& Lit., Ind.Amer.Per.Verse, Ind.Bk.Rev.Hum., Leg.Per., M.L.A. **Document type:** consumer publication.
—BLDSC (4566.600000); Faxon; UnCover; UMI.
Description: Contains fiction, poetry and essays.

808 301.412　　　　US　　ISSN 0271-8227
HQ1438.I7
IOWA WOMAN. 1980. q. $18 (foreign $25). Iowa Woman Endeavors, Inc., Box 680, Iowa City, IA 52244. TEL 319-987-2879. Ed. Marianne Abel. adv.; bk.rev.; circ. 2,000. circ. 2,000 (paid). **Indexed:** Abstr.Pop.Cult., Hum.Ind.
—UnCover.
Description: Fiction, poetry, essays, features, interviews, book reviews and visual arts by women.

860　　　　　　　　FR　　ISSN 0291-2066
IRIS. (Text in English, French, Portugese, Spanish) 1980. a. 75 F. (foreign 100 F.). Universite de Montpellier (Universite Paul Valery), Centre de Recherches sur les Litteratures Iberiques et Iberoamericaines Modernes, B.P. 5043, 34032 Montpellier Cedex 1, France. TEL 67-14-20-00. Ed. P. Jourdan. bk.rev.
—Faxon.
Description: Collection of unpublished poems and texts, studies in Spanish and Latin American poetry, novels, civilization and arts in the 19th and 20th centuries.

IRISH DRAMA SELECTIONS. see THEATER

800　　　　　　　　UK　　ISSN 0140-895X
IRISH LITERARY STUDIES. 1977. irreg. Colin Smythe Ltd., P.O. Box 6, Gerrards Cross, Buckinghamshire SL9 8XA, England. TEL 0753-886000.
FAX 0753-886469. (Pub. in U.S. by: Barnes & Noble Books, 8705 Bollman Place, Savage, MD 20763) circ. 1,200. (reprint service avail. from ISI) **Document type:** monographic series.
—BLDSC (4572.847000).
Description: Monographs and symposia on all aspects of Irish literature.

808 941.606　　　　US　　ISSN 0733-3390
IRISH LITERARY SUPPLEMENT. 1982. s-a. $5 to individuals; libraries and foreign $6. Irish Studies, 114 Paula Blvd., Selden, NY 11784.
TEL 516-698-8243. Ed. Robert G. Lowery. adv.; bk.rev.; illus. circ. 4,000. (also avail. in microfilm) **Indexed:** Amer.Hum.Ind., Bk.Rev.Ind. (1988-), Child.Bk.Rev.Ind. (1988-).
—BLDSC (4572.848000).

800　　　　　　　　US　　ISSN 0075-0816
IRISH PLAY SERIES. 1968. irreg., no.19, 1986. price varies. Proscenium Press, Box 361, Newark, DE 19711. TEL 302-764-8477. Ed. Robert Hogan. (reprint service avail. from UMI) **Document type:** monographic series.

IRISH SLAVONIC STUDIES. see HISTORY — History Of Europe

820　　　　　　　　US
IRISH STUDIES SERIES. irreg. Syracuse University Press, 1600 Jamesville Ave., Syracuse, NY 13244.
TEL 315-443-2597. Ed. Richard Fallis. **Document type:** academic/scholarly publication.

800　　　　　　　　IE　　ISSN 0021-1427
PR8700
IRISH UNIVERSITY REVIEW; a journal of Irish studies. 1970. s-a. $30 to individuals; institutions $40. Rm. K203, Department of English, University College, Belfield, Dublin 4, Ireland. TEL 01-7068260.
FAX 01-7061174. Ed. Christopher Murray. adv.; bk.rev. circ. 1,000. (also avail. in microfiche) **Indexed:** Abstr.Engl.Stud., Arts & Hum.Cit.Ind., Curr.Cont., Ind.Bk.Rev.Hum., M.L.A. **Document type:** academic/scholarly publication.
—BLDSC (4574.880000); Faxon.

894　　　　　　　　HU　　ISSN 0075-0824
IRODALOM - SZOCIALIZMUS. (Text in Hungarian; occasional summaries in German or Russian) 1959. irreg., latest 1990. price varies. (Magyar Tudomanyos Akademia) Akademiai Kiado, Publishing House of the Hungarian Academy of Sciences, P.O. Box 245, 1519 Budapest, Hungary. TEL 181-2134.

800　　　　　　　　US　　ISSN 0075-0832
IRODALOMELMELET KLASSZIKUSAI. 1963. irreg. price varies. (Magyar Tudomanyos Akademia) Akademiai Kiado, Publishing House of the Hungarian Academy of Sciences, P.O. Box 245, H-1519 Budapest, Hungary. TEL 181-2134. FAX 166-6466. TELEX 22-6228 AKNYO H.

809　　　　　　　　HU　　ISSN 0324-4970
IRODALOMTORTENET/LITERARY HISTORY. 1912-1947; N.S. 1949. q. $20. Magyar Irodalomtorteneti Tarsasag, Irodalomtudomanyi Intezet, Menesi ut 11-13, 1118 Budapest, Hungary. Ed. P. Nagy. bk.rev.; bibl. **Indexed:** Amer.Hist.& Life, Hist.Abstr., M.L.A.

809　　　　　　　　HU　　ISSN 0075-0840
IRODALOMTORTENETI FUZETEK. 1950. irreg., vol.132, 1993. price varies. Magyar Tudomanyos Akademia, Irodalomtudomanyi Intezet, Menesi ut 11-13, 1118 Budapest, Hungary. TEL 36-1-166-5938.
FAX 36-1-185-3876. Ed. I. Fenyo. **Indexed:** M.L.A.

809　　　　　　　　HU　　ISSN 0075-0859
IRODALOMTORTENETI KONYVTAR. (Text in Hungarian; occasional summaries in French or German) 1957. irreg., vol.40, 1992. price varies. (Magyar Tudomanyos Akademia) Akademiai Kiado, Publishing House of the Hungarian Academy of Sciences, P.O. Box 245, H-1519 Budapest, Hungary.
TEL 181-2134. FAX 166-6466. TELEX 22-6228 AKNYO H.

LITERATURE

809   HU   ISSN 0021-1486
IRODALOMTORTENETI KOZLEMENYEK/LITERARY HISTORY COMMUNICATIONS. (Text in Hungarian; summaries in English, French, German or Russian) 1891. bi-m. $23. Magyar Tudomanyos Akademia, Irodalomtudomyi Intezet, Menesi ut 11-13, 1118 Budapest, Hungary. TEL 36-1-166-5938. FAX 36-1-185-3876. Ed. P. Koszeghy. adv.; bk.rev.; illus.; index. **Indexed:** M.L.A.

800 800   ISSN 0140-7597
IRON. 1973. 3/yr. $30. Iron Press, 5 Marden Terrace, Cullercoats, North Shields, Tyne & Wear NE30 4PD, England. TEL 091-253-1901. Ed.Bd. adv.; bk.rev. circ. 950. (back issues avail.)
Description: Magazine of contemporary writing and graphics.

810   US
IRON MOUNTAIN REVIEW. 1983. s-a. $5. Emory & Henry College, Box 64, Emory, VA 24327. TEL 703-944-4121. Ed. John Lang. (back issues avail.) **Document type:** academic/scholarly publication.
Description: Contains essays and interviews with contemporary Southern Appalachian writers.

810   US
ISHMAEL. s-a. Rhode Island School of Design, 224 Benefit St., Providence, RI 02903-2723. TEL 401-454-6500. FAX 401-454-6320. (Co-sponsor: Brown University) Eds. Bruce B. Redford, Jane Kallir. illus.

ISLAM AND THE MODERN AGE. see *RELIGIONS AND THEOLOGY — Islamic*

820 770   CN   ISSN 0227-0773
ISLAND (LANTZVILLE). 3/yr. Can.$12 to individuals; institutions Can.$15. Box 256, Lantzville, B.C. V0R 2H0, Canada. Eds. John Marshall, Daphne Marlatt. **Indexed:** Can.Lit.Ind., So.Pac.Per.Ind.

800   AT   ISSN 0156-8124
ISLAND MAGAZINE. 1979. q. Aus.$24 to individuals (foreign Aus.$35); institutions Aus.$34 (foreign Aus.$45). Island Magazine Inc., P.O. Box 207, Sandy Bay, Tas. 7005, Australia. FAX 002-202186. Ed. Cassandra Pybus. adv.; bk.rev. circ. 1,000. (back issues avail.)

700 800   NZ   ISSN 0110-0858
PZ1
ISLANDS; a New Zealand quarterly of arts and letters. 1972. q. NZ.$8. Robin Dudding, Ed. & Pub., 4 Sealy Rd., Torbay, Auckland 10, New Zealand. adv.; bk.rev.; film rev.; play rev.; illus.; index. circ. 2,000. **Indexed:** Abstr.Engl.Stud., So.Pac.Per.Ind.
—CCC.

ISSUE ONE - THE BRIDGE. see *LITERATURE — Poetry*

ISTITUTO NAZIONALE DI STUDI SUL RINASCIMENTO. ATTI DI CONVEGNI. see *HISTORY — History Of Europe*

ISTITUTO NAZIONALE DI STUDI SUL RINASCIMENTO. STUDI E TESTI. see *HISTORY — History Of Europe*

839.5 439   IT   ISSN 0392-6524
ISTITUTO UNIVERSITARIO ORIENTALE. ANNALI. SEZIONE GERMANICA. STUDI NORDICI, STUDI NEDERLANDESI. (Text in Dutch, English, French, German, Italian) 1958; N.S. 1991. a. L.20000. Istituto Universitario Orientale, Piazza San Giovanni, Maggiore 30, 80134 Naples, Italy. TEL 081-5517609. FAX 081-5518550. (Dist. by: Herder Editrice e Libreria, Piazza Montecitorio, 117-120, 00186 Rome Italy) Ed. F. Ferrara. circ. 600. **Document type:** academic/scholarly publication.
Supersedes in part (in 1975): Istituto Universitario Orientale. Annali. Sezione Germanica (ISSN 0077-2763)

830 430   IT   ISSN 0392-6532
ISTITUTO UNIVERSITARIO ORIENTALE. ANNALI. SEZIONE GERMANICA. STUDI TEDESCHI. (Text in German, Italian) 1958; N.S. 1991. a. L.20000. Istituto Universitario Orientale, Piazza San Giovanni, Maggiore 30, 80134 Naples, Italy. TEL 081-5517609. FAX 081-5518550. (Dist. by: Herder Editrice e Libreria, Piazza Montecitorio 117-120, 00186 Rome, Italy) Dir. F. Ferrara. **Document type:** academic/scholarly publication.
Supersedes in part (in 1975): Istituto Universitario Orientale. Annali. Sezione Germanica (ISSN 0077-2763)

800 400   IT
ISTITUTO UNIVERSITARIO ORIENTALE DI NAPOLI. ANNALI. SEZIONE ROMANZA. (Text in French, Italian, Portuguese and Spanish) 1959. 2/yr. L.80000($80) Herder Editrice e Libreria s.r.l., Piazza Montecitorio 117-120, 00186 Rome, Italy. TEL 67-94-628. FAX 678-47-51. TELEX 621427 NATEL. Ed. Raffaele Sirri. **Indexed:** Bibl.Ling. **Document type:** academic/scholarly publication.

810 420 375.4   IT
ISTITUTO UNIVERSITARIO ORIENTALE DI NAPOLI. DIPARTIMENTO DI STUDI LETTERARI E LINGUISTICI DELL'OCCIDENTE. ANNUALI: STUDI DI ANGLISTICA. (Text in English, Italian) 1974. 3/yr. $80. (Istituto Universitario Orientale di Napoli, Dipartimento di Studi Letterari e Linguistici dell'Occidente) Herder Editrice e Libreria s.r.l., Piazza Montecitorio 117-121, 00186 Rome, Italy. TEL 6794628. FAX 6784751.

800 700   CI
ISTRA; kultura, knjizevnost drustvena pitjana. 1963. m. 100 din. Glas Istre, Obala Marsala Tita 10, Pula, Croatia. Ed. Mario Kalcic.

IT GOES ON THE SHELF. see *LITERATURE — Science Fiction, Fantasy, Horror*

800   US   ISSN 0161-4622
NX552.A1
ITALIAN CULTURE. (Former name of issuing body: American Association of University Professors of Italian) (Text in English, French, Italian) 1978. a. $20. American Association for Italian Studies, c/o Dr. Mario Aste, Chair of Languages, University of Lowell, Lowell, MA 01854. TEL 508-934-4000. (Subscr. to: Cinzia Donatelli-Noble, Dept. of French and Italian, Brigham Young University, Provo, UT 84602) adv. contact: Cinzia Donatelli-Noble. bk.rev.; bibl.; illus. circ. 1,000. **Indexed:** M.L.A. **Document type:** academic/scholarly publication.
—BLDSC (4588.332500).

850 450   US   ISSN 0021-2954
DG401
ITALIAN QUARTERLY. 1957. 4/yr. $15 to individuals; institutions $20. Rutgers University, Department of Italian, 84 College Ave., New Brunswick, NJ 08903. TEL 908-932-7031. Ed.Bd. adv.; bk.rev.; index, cum.index. circ. 1,050. (back issues avail) **Indexed:** Amer.Hist.& Life, Arts & Hum.Cit.Ind., Curr.Cont., Hist.Abstr., M.L.A. **Document type:** academic/scholarly publication.
—BLDSC (4588.347000); UnCover.

850   UK   ISSN 0075-1634
PQ4001
ITALIAN STUDIES. 1937. a. £9.50. Society for Italian Studies, c/o Dr. C.S. Cairns, Department of Romance Studies, University College of Wales, Aberystwyth, Dyfed, Wales. Ed. Prof. B. Moloney. adv.; bk.rev.; bibl. circ. 750. (back issues avail.) **Indexed:** Bibl.Ling., Br.Hum.Ind., Ind.Bk.Rev.Hum., M.L.A.

ITALIANIST. see *HISTORY — History Of Europe*

850   IT
ITALIANISTICA. 1972. 3/yr. L.15000. Giardini Editori e Stampatori, Via Santa Bibbiana 28, 56100 Pisa, Italy. adv.; bk.rev. circ. 2,000. **Indexed:** Can.Rev.Comp.Lit., M.L.A.

850 450 370   US   ISSN 0021-3020
PC1068.U6
ITALICA (MADISON). (Text in English, Italian) 1924. q. $30 to individuals; institutions $40. American Association of Teachers of Italian, Department of French and Italian, Ohio State University, 1841 Milliken Rd., Columbus, OH 43210. TEL 614-292-4938. Ed. Albert Mancini. adv.; bk.rev.; bibl.; index. circ. 1,750. (tabloid format; also avail. in microform from UMI; reprint service avail. from UMI) **Indexed:** Arts & Hum.Cit.Ind., Bibl.Ling., C.I.J.E., Curr.Cont., Ind.Bk.Rev.Hum., Lang.Teach.& Ling.Abstr., M.L.A. **Document type:** academic/scholarly publication.
—BLDSC (4588.380000); Faxon; UnCover; UMI.
Description: Represents all levels of the teaching of Italian literature, language and culture.

450 375.4   AU
ITALIENISCHE STUDIEN. (Text in German, Italian) 1978. a. S.300. Istituto Italiano di Cultura, AU, Ungargasse 43, A-1030 Vienna, Austria. TEL 01-7133454. FAX 01-7123716. Ed. Umberto Rinaldi. bk.rev. circ. 500. **Indexed:** Bibl.Ling. **Document type:** academic/scholarly publication.

IWATE UNIVERSITY. FACULTY OF EDUCATION. ANNUAL REPORT/IWATE DAIGAKU KYOIKUGAKUBU KENKYU NENPO. see *SOCIAL SCIENCES: COMPREHENSIVE WORKS*

891.7   BW
IZOBRAZITEL'NOE ISKUSSTVO BELORUSSII. 1977. q. 1.31 Rub. Izdatel'stvo Belarus', Pr. Masherova 11, 220600 Minsk, Belarus. TEL 0172-237734. FAX 0172-209125. circ. 6,000.

891.8   BN   ISSN 0021-3381
PN9
IZRAZ; casopis za knjizevnu i umjetnicku kritiku. 1957. m. $15. (Republican Union of Culture) S O U R Svjetlost, P.O. Box 129, Petra Preradovica 3, 71000 Sarajevo, Bosnia Hercegovina. Ed. Dzevad Karahasan. bk.rev. circ. 1,000. **Indexed:** M.L.A.

807   US   ISSN 0892-8665
J A S N A NEWS. 2/yr. $15 includes membership. Jane Austen Society of North America, 207 Pinecroft Dr., Raleigh, NC 27609. TEL 919-782-3083. (Subscr. to: JASNA, Membership Office, 2650-D Matheson Way, Sacramento, CA 95864) Ed. Paula Stephankowsky. adv. contact: Paula Stepankowsky. illus.; tr.lit. circ. 2,700. (back issues avail.)
Formerly: Jane Austen Society of North America News.
Description: News and activities of the Jane Austen Society of North America.

J E G P: JOURNAL OF ENGLISH AND GERMANIC PHILOLOGY. see *LINGUISTICS*

820   UK   ISSN 0305-8182
PR4612
JABBERWOCKY. 1969. irreg. (2-4/yr.). £8($15) to members; institutions £10($18). Lewis Carroll Society, 69 Ashby Rd., Woodville, Swadlincote, Derbyshire DE11 7BZ, England. Ed. Selwyn H. Goodacre. adv.; bk.rev.; film rev.; play rev.; illus.; bibl.; circ. 400. (back issues avail) **Indexed:** Ind.Bk.Rev.Hum., M.L.A. **Document type:** bulletin.

800   II   ISSN 0448-1143
PN851
JADAVPUR JOURNAL OF COMPARATIVE LITERATURE. (Text mainly in English, occasionally in Bengali; summaries in English) 1961. a. Rs.50($15) Jadavpur University, Department of Comparative Literature, Calcutta 32, India. TEL 9133-473-4044. Ed. Amiya Dev. bk.rev.; index, cum.index vols.1-10. circ. 500. **Indexed:** Abstr.Engl.Stud., M.L.A. **Document type:** academic/scholarly publication.

891.4   II
JADID FAROGH-E-URDU. (Text in Urdu) m. Rs.55. Idara-I-Jadid-Farogh-E-Urdu, 37 Aminabad Park, Lucknow 226018, India. TEL 246135. Ed.Bd. adv.; bk.rev.; illus. circ. 1,200.
Formerly (until 1992): Farogh-I-Urdu (ISSN 0014-8571)

830 407   GW   ISSN 0173-6469
JAHRBUCH DER DEUTSCHDIDAKTIK. 1978. a. price varies. Gunter Narr Verlag, Dischingerweg 5, 72070 Tuebingen, Germany. TEL 07071-78091. FAX 07071-75288. Ed. H. Mueller-Michaels. circ. 750. **Document type:** academic/scholarly publication.

830   SZ
JAHRBUCH FUER INTERNATIONALE GERMANISTIK. 1969. 2/yr. 92 SFr. Verlag Peter Lang AG, Jupiterstr. 15, CH-3000 Bern 15, Switzerland. TEL 031-9411122. FAX 031-9411131. TELEX 912651-PELA-CH. Ed. Hans-Gert Roloff. bibl. **Indexed:** Bibl.Ling., Can.Rev.Comp.Lit., Curr.Cont., M.L.A. **Document type:** academic/scholarly publication.

JAMAICA PICTORIAL. see *MUSIC*

LITERATURE

809 920   US   ISSN 0749-0291
PS3507.I267
JAMES DICKEY NEWSLETTER. 1984. s-a. $5 to individuals; institutions $10. Joyce M. Pair, Ed. & Pub., 2101 Womack Rd., Dunwoody, GA 30338. FAX 404-551-3201. bk.rev. circ. 250. (back issues avail.) **Indexed:** Hum.Ind., M.L.A. **Document type:** academic/scholarly publication, newsletter.
    Description: Publishes critical articles on the writings of James Dickey as well as comparative articles including other writers and works, with an ongoing bibliography of James Dickey's works, and critical writing about him.

820   UK   ISSN 0143-6333
JAMES JOYCE BROADSHEET. 1980. 3/yr. £5($12) University of Leeds, School of English, Leeds LS2 9JT, England. Ed.Bd. adv.; bk.rev.; film rev.; play rev.; illus. circ. 1,000.
    Description: Literary reviews of studies on the author; including essays, review articles, retrospective reviews, verse, translations, news and artwork.

800   US   ISSN 0899-3114
PR6019.09
JAMES JOYCE LITERARY SUPPLEMENT. 1987. s-a. $8. University of Miami, Department of English, Box 248145, Coral Gables, FL 33124. TEL 305-284-2182. FAX 305-284-5635. Ed. Bernard Benstock. adv.; bk.rev. circ. 800. **Document type:** academic/scholarly publication.
    Description: Publishes reviews of books on James Joyce and, occasionally, his contemporaries.

800
JAMES JOYCE NEWESTLATTER. 1969. 3/yr. $15. International James Joyce Foundation, c/o English Dept., Ohio State University, 164 W. 17th Ave., Columbus, OH 43210. TEL 614-292-2061. FAX 614-292-7816. Ed. Morris Beja. bk.rev.; bibl.; charts; illus.; stat. circ. 600. **Document type:** newsletter.
    Formerly: James Joyce Foundation Newsletter.

820   US   ISSN 0021-4183
PR6019.09
JAMES JOYCE QUARTERLY. (Supplement avail.) 1963. q. $17 to individuals (foreign $19); institutions $18 (foreign $20). (University of Tulsa) Academic Publications (Tulsa), 600 S. College Ave., Tulsa, OK 74104. TEL 918-631-2501. FAX 918-631-2033. Ed. Robert Spoo. adv.; bk.rev.; play rev.; bibl.; charts; illus.; cum.index: 1963-1983. circ. 1,400. (also avail. in microform from MIM,UMI; back issues avail.; reprint service avail. from SWZ,UMI) **Indexed:** Abstr.Engl.Stud., Amer.Hum.Ind., Arts & Hum.Cit.Ind., Curr.Cont., Hum.Ind., Ind.Bk.Rev.Hum., LCR, M.L.A.
—BLDSC (4645.700000); Faxon; UnCover; SWETS; UMI.

JAMES WHITE REVIEW; a gay men's literary quarterly. see HOMOSEXUALITY

892.7   UA
JAMI'AT TANTA. KULLIYYAT AL-ADAB. MAJALLAH/TANTA UNIVERSITY. FACULTY OF LITERATURE. JOURNAL. (Text in Arabic) irreg. Tanta University, Faculty of Literature, Tanta, Egypt.

895   JA
JAPANESE LITERATURE TODAY. (Text in English) 1959-1969; N.S. 1976. a. $18.50. Japan P.E.N. Club - Nihon P E N Kurabu, 265 Shuwa Residential Hotel, 9-1-7 Akasaka, Minato-ku, Tokyo, Japan. FAX 03-3402-5951. Ed. Masaaki Kanno. bk.rev. circ. 2,500.
    Supersedes (in 1976): Japan P.E.N. News (ISSN 0075-3300)
    Description: Includes list of translations into foreign languages.

890 430   SZ   ISSN 0721-3719
JAPANESE STUDIES IN GERMAN LANGUAGE AND LITERATURE/JAPANISCHE STUDIEN ZUR DEUTSCHEN SPRACHE UND LITERATUR. (Text in English, German) 1971. irreg. Verlag Peter Lang AG, Jupiterstr. 15, CH-3000 Bern 15, Switzerland. TEL 031-9411122. FAX 031-9411131. TELEX 912651-PELA-CH. circ. 400. **Indexed:** M.L.A. **Document type:** monographic series.

891 301   HU   ISSN 0448-9144
JASZKUNSAG; social and artistic journal. 1954. 6/yr. $30. (Jasz - Nagykun - Szolnok Megyei Onkormanyzat) Verseghy Ferenc Megyei Konyvtar, Kossuth L. ut 2, 5000 Szolnok, Hungary. TEL 36-56-420-610. Ed. Lajos Kormendi. bk.rev.; illus. circ. 1,000. **Document type:** academic/scholarly publication.
    Description: Covers the life, traditions and social conflicts of the people of two historical regions of Eastern Hungary.

JAUNA GAITA. see ART

830   GW   ISSN 0075-3580
PT2456
JEAN-PAUL-GESELLSCHAFT. JAHRBUCH. 1966. a. DM.55. C.H. Beck'sche Verlagsbuchhandlung, Wilhelmstr. 9, 80801 Munich, Germany. TEL 089-38189-338. FAX 089-38189-398. TELEX 5215085-BECK-D. Ed. Kurt Woelfel. bk.rev. circ. 750. **Indexed:** M.L.A. **Document type:** corporate report.

810   US   ISSN 0889-759X
PR6035.H96
JEAN RHYS REVIEW. 1986. s-a. $19 to individuals (foreign $22); institutions $28 (foreign $31). Box 811, Planetarium Sta., New York, NY 10024-0539. TEL 718-884-5854. Ed. Nora Gaines. bk.rev.; bibl. circ. 75. (back issues avail.) **Indexed:** M.L.A. **Document type:** academic/scholarly publication, bibliography.
—BLDSC (4663.465590); UnCover.
    Description: Provides a forum for research-in-progress, bibliography, critical articles and reviews and announcements of forthcoming studies and conferences related to the work of Jean Rhys.

840   FR   ISSN 0981-9185
J'ECRIS; journal d'information technique pour les ecrivains pratiquants. 1987. q. 235 F.($40) 85, rue des Tennerolles, Saint-Cloud 92210, France. Ed. Albert Sigusse. bk.rev. circ. 1,000. (back issues avail.) **Document type:** academic/scholarly publication.

700   US   ISSN 0021-5880
JEOPARDY. 1964. a. $4. College Hall 132, Western Washington University, Department of English, 516 High St., Bellingham, WA 98225. TEL 206-676-3118. bk.rev.; illus. circ. 4,000. (back issues avail.) **Indexed:** A.I.P.P.

840   FR
JEUNESSES LITTERAIRES DE FRANCE. 1955. bi-m. 117 bd. Saint Germain, 75006 Paris, France. Ed. Jean Huguet.

808.5 296   US   ISSN 0896-8152
JEWISH STORYTELLING NEWSLETTER. 1985. 3/yr. $10. 92nd Street Y M - Y W H A Library, Jewish Storytelling Center, 1395 Lexington Ave., New York, NY 10128. TEL 212-415-5544. FAX 212-415-5575. Ed. Peninnah Schram. **Document type:** newsletter.

JEZIK IN SLOVSTVO. see LINGUISTICS

895.1   CC   ISSN 1001-6694
JIANGNAN; daxing wenxue. (Text in Chinese) bi-m. Zhongguo Zuojia Xiehui, Zhejiang Fenhui - China Writers' Association, Zhejiang Chapter, 9, Jiande Lu, Hangzhou, Zhejiang 310006, People's Republic of China.

JIDISCHE SCHTUDIES. see LINGUISTICS

895.1 355   CC
JIEFANGJUN WENYI/LITERATURE AND ART OF PEOPLE'S LIBERATION ARMY. (Text in Chinese) ceased 1992. m. Y1.60($63) (Zhongguo Renmin Jiefangjun - Chinese People's Liberation Army) Jiefangjun Wenyi Chubanshe, A3, Xishiku Maowu Hutong, Beijing 100034, People's Republic of China. (Dist. outside China by: China International Book Trading Corp., P.O. Box 2820, Beijing, P.R.C.; Dist. in US by: China Books & Periodicals, Inc., 2929 24th St., San Francisco, CA 94110. TEL 415-282-2994) Ed. Ling Xingzheng. illus.

895.1   CC
JIN YAOSHI/GOLDEN KEY. (Text in Chinese) q. Nei Menggu Wenxue Yishujie Lianhehui - Inner Mongolian Literary and Art Circle Association, Huhhot, Nei Menggu 010020, People's Republic of China. TEL 663760. Ed. Ya Lin.

JINGU CHUANQI/MODERN AND ANCIENT LEGENDS. see FOLKLORE

895.1   CC
JINSHAN. (Text in Chinese) q. Zhenjiang Wenxue Yishu Jie Lianhehui - Zhenjiang Literary and Art Circle Association, 21 Jiefang Lu, Zhenjiang, Jiangsu 212001, People's Republic of China. TEL 221721. Ed. Chen Tupeng.

895.1   CC   ISSN 0257-2915
JINYANG WENYI. (Text in Chinese) 1957. m. Y36.40. (Shanxi Sheng Qunzhong Yishuguan) Jinyang Wenyi Bianjibu, 1, Houjia Xiang, Taiyuan, Shanxi 030001, People's Republic of China. TEL 3512027376. (Dist. outside China by: China International Book Trading Corp., P.O. Box 399, Beijing, P.R.C.; Dist. in US by: China Books & Periodicals, Inc., 2929 24th St., San Francisco, CA 94110. TEL 415-282-2994) adv.; illus. circ. 15,000. **Document type:** consumer publication.

899.2   II   ISSN 0021-700X
JNANADHARA. (Text in Malayalam) 1969. m. Rs.3.60. P. Haridas, Ed. & Pub., Vakayar P.O., Kouni, Kerala, India. adv.; bk.rev.; film rev.; play rev.; abstr.; illus. circ. 5,000.

200   UK
JOHN CLARE SOCIETY JOURNAL. 1982. a. £7.50($20) John Clare Society, c/o Mrs. J. Mary Moyse, The Stables, 1A West St., Helpston, Peterborough PE6 7DU, England. TEL 0733-252678. Ed. John Goodridge. adv.; bk.rev. circ. 700. (back issues avail.) **Document type:** academic/scholarly publication.
    Description: Examines the life and work of the poet John Clare.

806   US   ISSN 0738-9655
PR2248
JOHN DONNE JOURNAL: STUDIES IN THE AGE OF DONNE. 1982. 2/yr. $20 to individuals; libraries $30. North Carolina State University, Department of English, Box 8105, Raleigh, NC 27695-8105. TEL 919-737-3870. Eds. M. Thomas Hester, R.V. Young. adv.; bk.rev. circ. 450. (back issues avail.) **Indexed:** M.L.A.
—Faxon; UnCover.

820   US   ISSN 0021-728X
PR1
JOHNSONIAN NEWS LETTER. 1940. q. $6 (foreign $6.50). University of Chicago, Department of English, 1050 E. 59th St., Chicago, IL 60637. TEL 312-702-7989. Ed. Stuart Sherman. bk.rev.; cum.index every 5 yrs. circ. 1,800. (back issues avail.) **Document type:** academic/scholarly publication.
    Description: Provides news of interest to students, collectors, and scholars of 18th-century English literature, particularly with reference to Samuel Johnson (1709-1784), English author and lexicographer.

800   GW
JOSEF-ALBERS-SCHOOL. ALMANACH. 1978. s-a. DM.10($6) Zeppelinstr. 20, 46236 Bottrop, Germany. Ed. W. Boschmann. adv. circ. 1,500.

810 770   US   ISSN 1045-084X
THE JOURNAL (COLUMBUS). 1972. 2/yr. $8. Ohio State University, Department of English, 421 Denney Hall, 164 W. 17th Ave., Columbus, OH 43210. TEL 614-292-4076. Eds. Kathy Fagan, Michelle Herman. adv.; bk.rev.; illus. circ. 1,200. (back issues avail.) **Indexed:** A.I.P.P.
    Formerly (until 1987): Ohio Journal.
    Description: Includes contemporary fiction and poetry.

840   FR   ISSN 0249-1524
JOURNAL DES LETTRES ET DE L'AUDIOVISUEL. vol.111, 1976. q. 100 F. Societe des Gens de Lettres de France, Hotel de Massa, 38 rue du Faubourg Saint-Jacques, 75014 Paris, France. bibl. circ. 5,500.
    Formerly: Revue des Lettres (ISSN 0035-2128)

JOURNAL OF AFRO-LATIN AMERICAN STUDIES AND LITERATURES. see *HUMANITIES: COMPREHENSIVE WORKS*

JOURNAL OF AMERICAN DRAMA AND THEATRE. see *THEATER*

800 950   NE   ISSN 0085-2376
PJ7501
JOURNAL OF ARABIC LITERATURE. (Supplement avail.: Studies in Arabic Literature (ISSN 0169-9903)) 1970. 3/yr. fl.98($56) to individuals; institutions fl.145($83) (effective 1994). E.J. Brill, P.O. Box 9000, 2300 PA Leiden, Netherlands. TEL 31-71-312624. FAX 31-71-317532. TELEX 39296 BRILL NL. (In N. America: E.J. Brill, 24 Hudson St., Kinderhook, NY 12106. TEL 800-962-4406. FAX 518-758-1959) Ed. M.M. Badawi. **Indexed:** Arts & Hum.Cit.Ind., Bibl.Ling., Curr.Cont., Ind.Bk.Rev.Hum., M.L.A., Rel.Ind.One. **Document type:** academic/scholarly publication.
—BLDSC (4947.170000); UnCover; SWETS. **CCC.**
  Description: Forum for discussion of Arabic literature (verse and prose), both classical and modern, by Arabs and non-Arabs. Publishes critical essays on individual authors and single works, as well as assessments of trends and movements, and complete short stories.
Refereed Serial

900   II   ISSN 0971-1228
JOURNAL OF AUSTRALIAN LITERATURE. (Text in English) 1990. s.a. Rs.160. c/o Subhas Chandra Saha, Ed., Triburn University, Dept. of English, Agartala 799 004, India.

800 792   US   ISSN 0309-5207
PR6003.E282
JOURNAL OF BECKETT STUDIES. 1976; N.S. 1992. s-a. $15 to individuals; institutions $25. Florida State University, Department of English, Tallahassee, FL 32306. TEL 904-644-6038. FAX 904-644-6038. (Dist. in U.K. by: Calder Publications, 9-15 Neal St., London WC2H 9TU, England. TEL 071-497-1741) Ed. S.E. Gontarski. adv.; bk.rev.; illus. circ. 300. (back issues avail.) **Indexed:** Arts & Hum.Cit.Ind., Curr.Cont., Ind.Bk.Rev.Hum., M.L.A.
—BLDSC (4951.240000); UnCover; SWETS. **CCC.**

819   CN   ISSN 0047-2255
PR9195.7
JOURNAL OF CANADIAN FICTION. (Text in English and French) 1972. q. Can.$18($20) J C F Press Association, 2050 Mackay St., Montreal, Que. H3G 2J1, Canada. Ed. Dr. John R. Sorfleet. adv.; bk.rev.; bibl. circ. 1,500. **Indexed:** Abstr.Engl.Stud., Amer.Hum.Ind., Arts & Hum.Cit.Ind., Bibl.Engl.Lang.& Lit., Can.Lit.Ind., Can.Per.Ind., CMI, Curr.Cont., Hum.Ind., Ind.Bk.Rev.Hum., M.L.A.
—BLDSC (4954.747000).

820   UK   ISSN 0021-9894
PR1
JOURNAL OF COMMONWEALTH LITERATURE. 1965. 3/yr. £58($105) Hans Zell Publishers, P.O. Box 56, Oxford OX1 25J, England. TEL 0342-330-100. FAX 0342-330-191. (Subscr. to: c/o Baileys, 127 Sandgate Rd., Folkestone, Kent CT20 2DN, England. TEL 0303-850501) Ed.Bd. adv.; bibl. circ. 1,200. **Indexed:** Abstr.Engl.Stud., Arts & Hum.Cit.Ind., Br.Hum.Ind., Can.Lit.Ind., Curr.Cont.Africa, Curr.Cont., Hum.Ind., M.L.A., So.Pac.Per.Ind.
—BLDSC (4961.300000); Faxon; UnCover; SWETS; UMI. **CCC.**
  Description: Critical and bibliographical forum in the field of Commonwealth writing.

809   II   ISSN 0252-8169
PN851
JOURNAL OF COMPARATIVE LITERATURE AND AESTHETICS. (Text in English) 1978. s-a. Rs.80($15) (effective 1993). Vishvanatha Kaviraja Institute of Comparative Literature and Aesthetics, B8 Sambalpur University, Jyotivihar 768 019, Orissa, India. TEL 91-663-82-814-75. TELEX 066382-314. Ed. Ananta Charan Sukla. adv.; bk.rev. circ. 1,000. **Indexed:** M.L.A.
—**CCC.**

JOURNAL OF EVOLUTIONARY PSYCHOLOGY. see *PSYCHOLOGY*

400 860   US   ISSN 0147-5460
PC4001
JOURNAL OF HISPANIC PHILOLOGY. 1976. 3/yr. $30 to individuals (foreign $35); institutions $60 (foreign $75). Journal of Hispanic Philology Inc., Department of Modern Languages and Linguistics, Florida State University, Tallahassee, FL 32306. TEL 904-644-8394. FAX 904-644-0524. Ed. Jorge Roman Lagunas. adv.; bk.rev. circ. 500. **Indexed:** Arts & Hum.Cit.Ind., Curr.Cont., Ind.Bk.Rev.Hum., Lang.& Lang Behav.Abstr., M.L.A. **Document type:** academic/scholarly publication.
—Faxon; UnCover; SWETS.

890   II   ISSN 0302-1319
PR9480
JOURNAL OF INDIAN WRITING IN ENGLISH. 1973. s-a. Rs.100($24) G.S. Balarama Gupta, Ed. & Pub., Department of English, Gulbarga University, Gulbarga 585 106, Karnataka, India. adv.: page Rs.2000. bk.rev. circ. 1,500. (back issues avail.) **Indexed:** M.L.A.

JOURNAL OF LATIN AMERICAN LORE. see *FOLKLORE*

JOURNAL OF LITERARY SEMANTICS. see *LINGUISTICS*

800   SA   ISSN 0256-4718
JOURNAL OF LITERARY STUDIES/TYDSKRIF VIR LITERATUURWETENSKAP. (Text in Afrikaans and English) 1985. q. R.28 to individuals; institutions R.36. South African Society for General Literary Studies - Suid-Afrikaanse Vereniging vir Algemene Literatuurwetenskap, c/o UNISA, Dept. of Literary Theory, P.O. Box 392, Pretoria 0001, South Africa. TEL 27-12-4296058. FAX 27-12-4293221. (Co-sponsor: Haum Literary Group) Eds. Ina Graebe, Rory Ryan. bk.rev. circ. 350. (back issues avail.) **Document type:** academic/scholarly publication.
  Description: Forum for discussion of literary theory, methodology, and research. Features articles and reviews aimed at students and lecturers.

JOURNAL OF MEDIEVAL AND RENAISSANCE STUDIES. see *HUMANITIES: COMPREHENSIVE WORKS*

800   II
JOURNAL OF MEDIEVAL INDIAN LITERATURE. 1977. s-a. Panjab University, Department of Medieval Indian Literature, Arts Block No. 3, Panjab University Campus, Chandigarh 160014, India.

JOURNAL OF MENTAL IMAGERY. see *PSYCHOLOGY*

809.4   US   ISSN 0022-281X
PN2
JOURNAL OF MODERN LITERATURE. 1970. 3/yr. $20 to individuals; institutions $25. Temple University, 921 Anderson Hall, Philadelphia, PA 19122. TEL 215-787-8505. FAX 215-204-9620. Ed. Morton P. Levitt. adv.; bk.rev.; bibl.; illus.; index. circ. 1,850. (also avail. in microform from UMI; back issues avail.; reprint service avail. from UMI) **Indexed:** Abstr.Engl.Stud., Amer.Bibl.Slavic & E.Eur.Stud, Amer.Hum.Ind., Arts & Hum.Cit.Ind., Curr.Cont., Film Lit.Ind. (1973-), Hum.Ind., Ind.Bk.Rev.Hum., LCR, M.L.A., Mid.East: Abstr.& Ind.
—BLDSC (5020.685000); Faxon; UnCover; SWETS; UMI.
  Description: Scholarly journal devoted to literary studies of 20th century literature. Coverage includes world literature as well as English and American.

800   US   ISSN 1053-6981
PN212   CODEN: JNLHEY
JOURNAL OF NARRATIVE AND LIFE HISTORY. 1991. q. $35 to individuals (foreign $60); institutions $120 (foreign $145). Lawrence Erlbaum Associates, Inc., 365 Broadway, Hillsdale, NJ 07642. TEL 201-444-4110. FAX 201-666-2394. Ed. Allyssa McCabe. **Document type:** academic/scholarly publication.
—BLDSC (5021.178000); UnCover.
  Description: Provides a forum for encountering diverse approaches to the genres known collectively as narratives and the content of many language games known as life histories.
Refereed Serial

809 806   NZ   ISSN 0112-1227
JOURNAL OF NEW ZEALAND LITERATURE. 1983. s-a. NZ.$24 (overseas NZ.$30). University of Otago, Department of English, P.O. Box 56, Dunedin, New Zealand. TEL 03-479-8636. FAX 64-3-479-2305. TELEX NZ 505601. Ed. L.O. Jones. adv. contact: Janet Wilson. bk.rev. circ. 300. **Document type:** academic/scholarly publication.
  Description: Contains scholarly and critical essays and notes on New Zealand literature.
Refereed Serial

800 300   US   ISSN 0022-3840
AP2
JOURNAL OF POPULAR CULTURE. 1967. q. $35 to individuals; institutions $65. (Modern Language Association of America, Popular Literature Section) Popular Press, Bowling Green State University, Bowling Green, OH 43403. TEL 419-372-7866. (Co-sponsors: Midwest Modern Language Association, Folklore Section; Popular Culture Association) Ed. Ray B. Browne. adv.; bk.rev.; charts; illus.; index. circ. 3,500. (also avail. in microform from MIM,UMI; microfiche from KTO,MIM,UMI; reprint service avail. from UMI) **Indexed:** Abstr.Engl.Stud., Acad.Ind., Amer.Hist.& Life, Artbibl.Mod., Arts & Hum.Cit.Ind., ASSIA, Bk.Rev.Ind. (1976-), CERDIC, Chic.Per.Ind., Child.Bk.Rev.Ind. (1976-), Commun.Abstr., Curr.Cont., Film Lit.Ind. (1973-), Hist.Abstr., Hum.Ind., LCR, M.L.A., Mid.East: Abstr.& Ind., Music Ind., Music Ind., RILA, SSCI.
—BLDSC (5041.130000); Faxon; UnCover; SWETS; UMI.
Refereed Serial

895   US   ISSN 0091-5637
PK1501
JOURNAL OF SOUTH ASIAN LITERATURE. 1963. s-a. $21 to individuals (foreign $22); institutions $27 (foreign $28). Michigan State University, Asian Studies Center, 109 International Center, E. Lansing, MI 48824. TEL 517-353-1680. Eds. Carlo Coppola, Surjit Dulai. bk.rev.; bibl.; index. circ. 350. (also avail. in microform from UMI; reprint service avail. from UMI, ISI) **Indexed:** Arts & Hum.Cit.Ind., Curr.Cont., Ind.Bk.Rev.Hum., M.L.A. **Document type:** academic/scholarly publication.
—UnCover; UMI.
  Formerly: A Quarterly of South Asian Literature (ISSN 0025-0503)

800   FR   ISSN 0294-0442
JOURNAL OF THE SHORT STORY IN ENGLISH. (Text in English) 1983. s-a. 140 Fr. (foreign 165 F.). (Centre d'Etudes et de Recherches sur la Nouvelle en Langue Anglaise) Presses de l'Universite d'Angers, Bibliotheque Universitaire, 5 Blvd. Lavoisier, 49045 Angers, France. TEL 41-35-21-00. (back issues avail.)
  Description: Deals with the 19th and 20th century short stories in English from a historical and textual point-of-view. Includes translations of unpublished short stories and original interviews as well as studies related to the teaching of short stories.

890 300   CN   ISSN 0228-1635
DK508.A2
JOURNAL OF UKRAINIAN STUDIES. (Text in English and Ukrainian) 1976. s-a. $15 to individuals; institutions $20. Canadian Institute of Ukrainian Studies, Department of Slavic Languages & Literatures, University of Toronto, Toronto, ON M5S 1A1, Canada. TEL 403-492-2972. FAX 403-492-4967. Ed. Roman Senkus. adv.; bk.rev.; bibl.; illus.; circ. 250 (paid). (back issues avail.; reprint service avail. from ISI, UMI) **Indexed:** Amer.Bibl.Slavic & E.Eur.Stud., Arts & Hum.Cit.Ind., Bibl.Ling., Curr.Cont., M.L.A. **Document type:** academic/scholarly publication.
—UnCover; UMI.
  Formerly: Journal of Ukrainian Graduate Studies (ISSN 0701-1792)

800   BB   ISSN 0258-8501
JOURNAL OF WEST INDIAN LITERATURE. 1986. s-a. $20. University of the West Indies, Department of English, P.O. Box 64, Bridgetown, Barbados, W.I. TEL 809-425-1310. FAX 809-425-1327. Ed. Mark A. McWatt. adv.; bk.rev.; bibl. circ. 750. (back issues avail.)
  Description: Publishes research in West Indian literature for students and scholars working in that field.

LITERATURE

800 920 US ISSN 1049-0809
PR6019.O9
JOYCE STUDIES ANNUAL. 1990. a. $25 to individuals; institutions $35. University of Texas Press, Box 7819, Austin, TX 78713-7819. TEL 512-471-4531. FAX 512-320-0668. TELEX 776453-UTEXPRES-AUS. Ed. Thomas Staley. adv. circ. 500. (reprint service avail. from UMI) Document type: academic/scholarly publication.
—CCC.
  Description: Publishes articles by leading Joyce scholars on Joyce and closely related topics.

JUGEND UND KULTUR. see *ART*

800 890 DK ISSN 0905-1678
JULEGAVEN. a. DKK 48. Lohses Forlag, Korskarvej 25, DK-7000 Fredericia, Denmark. Ed. Marie Laursen. circ. 300.
  Formerly: Naar Lampen Taendes. Fortaellinger (ISSN 0107-8232)
  Description: Contains fictional and non-fictional religious literature.

895.1 CC
JUN MA/STEED. (Text in Chinese) m. Hulun Bei'er Meng Wenxue Yishu Lianhehui - Hulun Bei'er League Literary and Art Circle Association, Shengli Dajie, Haila'er, Nei Menggu 021008, People's Republic of China. TEL 2145. Ed. Liu Qian.

JUNKANOO. see *THEATER*

JYVASKYLA STUDIES IN THE ARTS. see *ART*

800 GW
K L G: KRITISCHES LEXIKON ZUR DEUTSCHSPRACHIGEN GEGENWARTSLITERATUR. 1979. 3/yr. DM.340. Edition Text und Kritik GmbH, Levelingstr. 6a, 81673 Munich, Germany. TEL 089-432929. FAX 089-433997. Ed. Heinz Ludwig Arnold. Document type: academic/scholarly publication.

800 831 GW
K U L I M U. (Kunst, Literatur & Music) (Text in German, Serbo-Croatian, Slovene) 1974. 3/yr. DM.15($10) Verlag der Zeitschrift fuer Kunst & Literatur & Musik, Marienstr. 6, 93053 Regensburg, Germany. TEL 0941-75805. FAX 0941-760703. Eds. U. Alberts, J. Hachmann. adv.; bk.rev. circ. 1,000. Document type: consumer publication.

KABUL MOJALA. see *PHILOSOPHY*

800 US
KACH NAZAR;* Armenian satirical & critical independent monthly. (Text in Armenian and English) 1970. m. $25 (effective Jan. 1991). Kach Nazar Publishing Co., 319 S. Central Ave., Glendale, CA 91204-1608. Ed. Ovanes Balayan. adv.; bk.rev.; bibl.; illus. circ. 5,000. (tabloid format)

807 US ISSN 0894-6388
KAFKA SOCIETY OF AMERICA. JOURNAL. 1977. 2/yr. $30 to individuals; libraries $25; foreign $35. Temple University, Department of Germanic and Slavic Languages and Literatures, AB 335, Philadelphia, PA 19122. TEL 215-787-8282. Ed. Maria Luise Caputo-Mayr. bk.rev.; bibl. circ. 400. (back issues avail.) Indexed: Amer.Bibl.Slavic & E.Eur.Stud., M.L.A. Document type: academic/scholarly publication.
—UnCover.
  Formerly (until 1983): Kafka Society of America. Newsletter (ISSN 0741-6202)
  Description: Presents papers given at the meetings, other articles, essays, bibliographies, and materials of interest to scholars of Franz Kafka.

800 US
KAIMANA; literary arts Hawaii. 1974. a. $12 membership. Literary Arts Hawaii, Box 11213, Honolulu, HI 96828. Ed. Tony Quagliano. circ. 1,000.
  Former titles: Literary Arts Hawaii; Hawaii Literary Arts Council Newsletter.
  Description: Features fiction, poetry and literary essays.

809 II
KAKATIYA JOURNAL OF ENGLISH STUDIES. Short title: K J E S. (Text in English) 1976. a. Rs.15($2) Kakatiya University, Department of English, Vidyaranyapuri, Warangal 506 009, India. Ed. C. Varadachary. circ. 250. Document type: academic/scholarly publication.

895 II
KALAI MAGAL. (Text in Tamil) 1932. m. P.O. Box 604, Madras 600 004, India. TEL 44-76011. Ed. R. Narayanaswamy. circ. 22,700.

890 700 CE
KALAVA HA SAHITYAYA. (Text in Sinhalese) 1976. irreg. Rs.1. Nava Parapura, 26 Clifford Ave., Colombo 3, Sri Lanka.

KALEIDOSCOPE (AKRON); international magazine of literature, fine arts and disability. see *HANDICAPPED*

305.4 US
▼**KALEIDOSCOPE OF CAROLINA.** 1994. s-a. Betty Glaz, Ed. & Pub., Box 69587, Colombia, SC 29223. TEL 803-736-1559. Document type: academic/scholarly publication.
  Description: Journal of writings by women of South Carolina.

895 II
KALKI. (Text in Tamil) 1941. w. 84-1C Race Course Rd., Guindy, Madras 600 032, India. TEL 48-431543. Ed. K. Rajendran. circ. 88,200.

808 301.412 US ISSN 0735-7885
NX504
KALLIOPE; a journal of women's art. 1979. 3/yr. $12.50 to individuals; institutions $21. Florida Community College, Kalliope Writers' Collective, 3939 Roosevelt Blvd., Jacksonville, FL 32205. TEL 904-381-3511. Ed. Mary Sue Koeppel. bk.rev. circ. 1,250. (also avail. in microform from UMI; back issues avail.)
—UMI.
  Description: Provides a forum for the exchange and sharing of ideas for and by women. Publishes poetry, short fiction and b&w art work. Gives consideration to young and-or emerging artists and writers.

808 301.2 MW
KALULU; bulletin of Malawian oral literature and cultural studies. 1976. irreg. $5. Chancellor College, Writer's Group, Box 280, Zomba, Malawi.

800 340 JA ISSN 0453-1981
KANAZAWA UNIVERSITY. FACULTY OF LAW AND LITERATURE. STUDIES AND ESSAYS. (Text in English and Japanese) 1953. a. Kanazawa Daigaku, Hobungakubu - Kanazawa University, Faculty of Law and Literature, 1-1 Marunouchi, Kanazawa-shi, Ishikawa-ken 920, Japan. bibl.

800 AT ISSN 1036-3262
KANGAROO. (Supplement to: Neucleus (ISSN 1036-4587)) 1980. a. free. University of New England, Armidale Students' Association, Armidale, N.S.W. 2351, Australia. TEL 067-732851. FAX 067-727633.

800 700 CR ISSN 0378-0473
NX1.A1
KANINA; revista de artes y letras. 1976. s-a. $20. Editorial de la Universidad de Costa Rica, Apartado 75-2060, Ciudad Universitaria Rodrigo Facio, 2050 San Pedro, Montes de Oca, San Jose, Costa Rica. TEL 506-25-3133. FAX 506-24-9367. TELEX UNICORI 2544. Dir. Ivonne Robles Mohs. Indexed: Curr.Cont., Hisp.Amer.Per.Ind., M.L.A. Document type: academic/scholarly publication.

800 US ISSN 0022-8990
KARAMU. 1966. a. $5. Karamu Association, English Department, Eastern Illinois University, Charleston, IL 61920. TEL 217-581-5614. Ed. Peggy L. Brayfield. illus. circ. 400. (processed)
  Description: Collection of fiction, poetry, art work, and artistic expression, selected from open submissions and published at Eastern Illinois University.

833 GW ISSN 0300-1989
PT2625.A848
KARL-MAY-GESELLSCHAFT. JAHRBUCH. 1970. a. price varies. (Karl-May-Gesellschaft) Hansa Verlag, Postfach 1480, 25804 Husum, Germany. TEL 04841-6081. FAX 04841-61397. Ed.Bd. adv.; bk.rev. Indexed: M.L.A. Document type: bulletin.

833 GW
KARL-MAY-GESELLSCHAFT. MITTEILUNGEN. 1969. q. membership. Karl-May-Gesellschaft e.V., Maximilienkorso 45, 13465 Berlin, Germany. TEL 030-4061033. Ed. Hansotto Hatzig. adv.; bk.rev. circ. 1,650. (back issues avail.) Document type: bulletin.
  Description: Studies the work and life of German author Karl May (1842-1912).

890 IS ISSN 0334-8547
AL-KARMIL. (Text in Arabic) a. Haifa University, Institute of Middle Eastern Studies, Ha-Carmel, Haifa 31999, Israel. Document type: academic/scholarly publication.

891.4 II ISSN 0022-9318
KATHA-SAHITYA. (Text in Bengali) 1949. m. Rs.60. Mitra & Ghosh Publishers Pvt. Ltd., 10 Shyama Charan Dey St., Calcutta 700 073, India. Ed.Bd. adv.; bk.rev.; tr.lit. circ. 35,750.

820 UK ISSN 0952-4142
KEATS - SHELLEY REVIEW. 1910. a. £7.50. Keats - Shelley Memorial Association, c/o Lord Abinger, Clees Hall, Bures, Suffolk CO8 502, England. TEL 0787-60388. Ed. A.G. Cbmpbell. adv.; bk.rev.; cum.index: vols. 1-20. circ. 1,200. Indexed: Abstr.Engl.Stud., Arts & Hum.Cit.Ind., Curr.Cont., Ind.Bk.Rev.Hum., M.L.A. Document type: bulletin.
—BLDSC (5088.318000).
  Formerly (until 1986): Keats - Shelley Memorial Bulletin (ISSN 0453-4395)

KEEL JA KIRJANDUS. see *LINGUISTICS*

800 US ISSN 0451-6338
KELSEY REVIEW. 1988. a. free. Mercer County Community College, Box B, Trenton, NJ 08690. TEL 609-586-4800. FAX 609-586-2318. Ed. G. Robin Schore. bk.rev. circ. 1,500. (back issues avail.)
  Description: Presents fiction, poetry, essays (all subjects) written by people living and working in Mercer County, NJ.

895.1 CC
KEN CHUN NI. (Text in Chinese) m. Jiangsu Renmin Chubanshe, Qikan Bu - Jiangsu People's Publishing House, 165 Zhongyang Lu, Nanjing, Jiangsu 210009, People's Republic of China. TEL 639518. Ed. Wang Yuanhong.

810 US ISSN 0163-075X
AP2
KENYON REVIEW. 1939; N.S. 1979. 4/yr. $22 to individuals; institutions $24. Kenyon College, Box B, Gambier, OH 43022. TEL 614-427-3339. (Subscr. to: The Kenyon Review, P.O. Box 8062, Syracuse, NY 13217) Ed. Marilyn Hacker. adv.; bk.rev.; index, cum.index (old series): 1939-1963. circ. 3,000. (also avail. in microfilm; reprint service avail. from UMI) Indexed: Abstr.Engl.Stud., Acad.Ind., Amer.Hum.Ind., Bk.Rev.Ind. (1965-), Child.Bk.Rev.Ind. (1965-), Hum.Ind., Ind.Bk.Rev.Hum., M.L.A.
—Faxon; UnCover; SWETS.

800 US
KESTREL CHAPBOOK SERIES. 1982. irreg $4 per no. Holmgangers Press, 95 Carson Ct., Shelter Cove, CA 95589. TEL 707-986-7700. Ed. Gary Elder. circ. 250. (back issues avail.) Document type: monographic series.

810 UK
KEYNOTES. q. membership. Eighteen Nineties Society, 97-D Brixton Rd., London SW9 6EE, England.

KEYSTROKES. see *PUBLISHING AND BOOK TRADE*

KHOJ DARPAN. see *FOLKLORE*

808.8 700 CN
KIDDELIDIVEE BOOKS. 1977. irreg. $3. Kiddelidivee Books, 245 Dunn Ave., Ste. 2111, Toronto, Ont. M6K 1S6, Canada. Ed. Taral Wayne. circ. 900.
  Former titles (until 1987): Hominids, Oh; (until 1986): New Toy; March to the Beat of a Red Shift Drum.
  Description: Includes fiction, essays, reviews, cartoons, illustrations, art portfolios, maps and diagrams covering science fiction, fantasy, comics, autobiography, animation.

KING SAUD UNIVERSITY. JOURNAL. ARTS. see *ART*

813 UK ISSN 0023-1738
PR4856
KIPLING JOURNAL. 1927. q. £20 membership. Kipling Society, P.O. Box 68, Haslemere, Surrey GU27 2YR, England. (U.S. addr.: Secretariat for N. America, Department of English, Rockford College, 5050 E. State St., Rockford IL 61101. TEL 851-226-4183) Ed. G.H. Webb. adv.; bk.rev.; bibl.; illus. circ. 900. **Indexed:** Abstr.Engl.Stud., Br.Hum.Ind., Hum.Ind., M.L.A. **Document type:** academic/scholarly publication.
—BLDSC (5097.330000); UnCover.
Description: Literary and historical review focused on the prose and verse, and life and times, of Rudyard Kipling.

891.92 US ISSN 0017-6613
KIR - OU - KIRK. (Text in Armenian, English) 1956. a. free. Armenian Literary Society - New York, Inc., 77 Everett Rd., Demarest, NJ 07627. TEL 201-767-1494. Ed. Arthur Hamparian. bk.rev.; play rev.; circ. 500 (controlled). **Document type:** academic/scholarly publication.
Formerly: Haghordagroutiun.

890 PK
KIRAN.* (Text in Urdu) 1978. m. Rs.60. 37 Urdu Bazar, Karachi, Pakistan.

KISWAHILI. see LINGUISTICS

820 SA
KLASGIDS. (Text in Afrikaans) 4/yr. R.15 (effective 1993). Foundation for Education, Science and Technology, P.O. Box 1758, Pretoria 0001, South Africa. TEL 27-12-322-6404. FAX 27-12-320-7803. **Indexed:** Ind.S.A.Per., M.L.A.

890 375.4 FR ISSN 1142-3056
KLASK. 1989. a. (Centre de Recherches Bretagne - Pays Celtiques) Presses Universitaires de Rennes, 2 rue du Doyen D. Leroy, 35044 Rennes Cedex, France. TEL 99-54-66-35. FAX 99-33-07-95. **Indexed:** Bibl.Ling.
Description: Studies contemporary literature trends, new approaches to grammar, the evolution of linguistic and cultural practices.

KLAUS GROTH GESELLSCHAFT. JAHRESGABEN. see LINGUISTICS

830 GW ISSN 0075-6318
KLEINE DEUTSCHE PROSADENKMAELER DES MITTELALTERS; Erst und Neuausgaben der Forschungstelle fuer deutsche prosa des Mittelalters. 1965. irreg. price varies. (Seminar fuer Deutsche Philologie) Wilhelm Fink Verlag, Ohmstr. 5, 80802 Munich, Germany. Ed. Georg Steer.

800 GW ISSN 0722-8899
KLEIST-JAHRBUCH. 1980. a. price varies. Erich Schmidt Verlag GmbH & Co. (Bielefeld), Viktoriastr. 44a, 33602 Bielefeld, Germany. TEL 0521-583080. (Subscr. to: Postfach 102451, 33524 Bielefeld, Germany) Ed. Hans Joachim Kreutzer. bk.rev. (back issues avail.) **Document type:** academic/scholarly publication.

859 RM
KNIJEVNI JIVOT. (Text in Serbian) 1957. s-a. 48 lei. Uniunea Scriitorilor din Republica Socialista Romania, Calea Victoriei 115, Bucharest, Rumania. (Subscr. to: ILEXIM, Str. 13 Decembrie Nr. 3, Box 136-137, 70116 Bucharest, Rumania) Ed. Slavomir Gvozdenovici. bk.rev.; abstr.; illus.

900 100 YU
KNJIZEVNA KRITIKA; casopis za umetnicku, istorijsku i filosofsku kritiku. 1970. bi-m. 60000 din.($15) Izdavacko Preduzece Rad, Moshe Pijade 12, Belgrade, Yugoslavia. Ed. Milivoj Srebro. adv.; bk.rev. circ. 1,200. **Indexed:** M.L.A.
Description: Covers criticism and aesthetics in literature.

809 CI ISSN 0455-0463
PN9
KNJIZEVNA SMOTRA; casopis za svjetsku knjizevnost. (Text in Croatian) 1969. q. 120 din.($6.50) Hrvatsko Filolosko Drustvo, Djure Salaja 3, 41000 Zagreb, Croatia. Ed. Zdravko Malic. bk.rev.; illus. circ. 1,500.

057.8 YU ISSN 0023-2408
KNJIZEVNOST. (Text in Serbo-Croatian) 1946. m. $50. Udruzenje za Ekonomiju Samoupravljanja, Zmaj Jovina 12, P.O. Box 611, 11000 Belgrade, Yugoslavia. (Subscr. to: Prosveta, Terazije 16, Belgrade, Yugoslavia) Ed. Vuk Krnjevic. circ. 2,000.

KNJIZEVNOST I JEZIK. see LINGUISTICS

808.068 US ISSN 0271-1990
THE KOBRIN LETTER; concerning children's books about real people, places and things. 1980. 7/yr. $12. 732 Greer Rd., Palo Alto, CA 94303. TEL 415-856-6658. Ed. Dr. Beverly Kobrin. bk.rev. (back issues avail.)
Description: Reviews and recommends the best children's nonfiction literature, kindergarten to young adult.

910.03 323.4 CN ISSN 0835-2445
KOLA. 1987. 2/yr. $12 to individuals; institutions $18. C.P. 1602, Place Bonaventure, Montreal, PQ H5A 1H6, Canada. Ed. Horace I. Goddard. adv.; bk.rev. circ. 300. (back issues avail.) **Document type:** academic/scholarly publication.
Description: Provides a forum for creative artists who have an interest in publicizing works that reflect the black experience around the world.

KONINKLIJKE ACADEMIE VOOR NEDERLANDSE TAAL- EN LETTERKUNDE. JAARBOEK. see LINGUISTICS

400 800 BE ISSN 0770-786X
KONINKLIJKE ACADEMIE VOOR NEDERLANDSE TAAL- EN LETTERKUNDE. VERSLAGEN EN MEDEDELINGEN. 1887; N.S. 1958. irreg. price varies. Koninklijke Academie voor Nederlandse Taal- en Letterkunde, Koningstraat 18, B-9000 Ghent, Belgium. FAX 32-9-3232718. bibl.; illus.; index. **Indexed:** Bibl.Ling., Nutr.Abstr. **Document type:** monographic series.
Supersedes (in 1972): Koninklijke Vlaamse Akademie voor Taal- en Letterkunde. Verslagen en Mededelingen (ISSN 0023-3404)

890 RU ISSN 0259-4412
KONTEKST. a. $3. (Rossiiskaya Akademiya Nauk, Institut Mirovoi Literatury) Izdatel'stvo Nauka, 90 Profsoyuznaya ul., 117864 Moscow, Russia. TEL 095-336-0266. (Dist. by: Mezhdunarodnaya Kniga, B. Yakimanka 39, 117049 Moscow, Russia) Ed.Bd. circ. 7,700.

KONTUREN; Magazin fuer Sprache, Literatur und Landschaft. see LINGUISTICS

830 GW ISSN 0179-0676
KONZEPTE; Magazin fuer eine junge Literatur. fortn. Bundesverband Junger Autoren und Autorinnen e.V., Richard-Wagner-Str. 45, 45128 Essen, Germany. Ed.Bd. adv. contact: Stefan Sprang. **Document type:** bulletin.

KOREANA; a quarterly on Korean culture. see ORIENTAL STUDIES

850 IT
KR 991; quadrimestrale di poesia prosa e immagini. 1990. 3/yr. L.20000. Datanews Editrice, Via Cavour 184-4, 00184 Rome, Italy. TEL 06-463469. FAX 06-4825480. Ed. Miro Renzaglia.

KRATYLOS; kritisches Berichts- und Rezensionsorgan fuer indogermanische und allgemeine Sprachwissenschaft. see LINGUISTICS

KRCKI ZBORNIK. see HISTORY — History Of Europe

800 PL ISSN 0867-1125
KRESY. 1990. q. 120000 Zl.($40) (effective 1994). Stowarzyszenie Literackie "Kresy", Ul. Chopina 5, P.O. Box 383, 20-950 Lublin 1, Poland. Ed. Grzegorz Filip. adv.; bk.rev.

891.4 II ISSN 0023-4737
KRISHANU. (Text and summaries in Bengali) 1968. q. Rs.5($4) Malim Dulta, 18 Surja Sen St., Calcutta, West Bengal, India. Ed. Dinesh Chandra Sinha. adv.; bk.rev.; film rev.; play rev. circ. 1,000.

891.4 II ISSN 0023-4745
KRISHNACHURA. (Text in Bengali) 1970. s-a. Rs.2($0.28) Prodyut Kumar Som, 19 Nagar Bagan, Haltu, Parganas 24, West Bengal, India. Ed. Sumanta Som.

809 HU ISSN 0023-4818
PH3001
KRITIKA. (Summaries in French, German and Russian) 1963. m. $25. (Magyar Tudomanyos Akademia, Irodalomtudomanyi Intezet) Lapkiado Vallalat, Lenin korut 9-11, 1073 Budapest 7, Hungary. TEL 222-408. (Subscr. to: Kultura, Box 149, H-1389 Budapest, Hungary) **Indexed:** Curr.Cont.

839.8 809 NO ISSN 0801-0471
KRITIKKJOURNALEN. 1983. s-a. NOK 395 in the Nordic countries; elsewhere NOK 525. Scandinavian University Press, P.O. Box 2959 Toeyen, N-0608 Oslo, Norway. TEL 47-22-57-54-00. FAX 47-22-57-53-53. Ed.Bd.
Description: Publishes reviews of contemporary Norwegian literature, both fiction and non-fiction.

KRITIKON LITTERARUM; international book review for American, English, Romance and Slavic studies and for linguistics. see LINGUISTICS

809 BE
KTEMATA. (Text in French) 1974. irreg., latest no.10, 1989. 1200 BEF. Editions Peeters s.p.r.l., Bondgenotenlaan 153, B-3000 Louvain, Belgium. TEL 32-16-235170. FAX 32-16-228500. TELEX 65981 PULB. **Document type:** monographic series.

800 KR ISSN 0201-419X
KUL'TURA SLOVA; respublikanskii mezhvidomchyi zbirnyk naukovykh prac. (Text in Ukrainian; summaries in Russian) 1967. s-a. (Akademiya Nauk Ukrainy, Institut Movoznavstva im. O.O. Potebni) Vidavnitstvo Naukova Dumka, Vul. tereshchenkivska 3, 252601 Kiev, Ukraine. TEL 229-02-92. (Dist. by: Mezhdunarodnaya Kniga, B. Yakimanka 39, 117049 Moscow, Russia) Ed. S.Y. Ermolenko.
—BLDSC (0094.740000).

KUMAR. see ART

895.1 355 CC
KUN LUN/ARMY LITERATURE. (Text in Chinese) bi-m. Y22.80($67.80) Jiefangjun Wenyi Chubanshe, A3, Xishiku Maowu Hutong, Beijing 100034, People's Republic of China. (Dist. overseas by: China International Book Trading Corp., P.O. Box 399, Beijing, P.R.C.; Dist. in US by: China Books & Periodicals, Inc., 2929 24th St., San Francisco, CA 94110. TEL 415-282-2994)
Description: Contains short stories, poetry, and prose, emphasizing military themes.

800 II
KUNAPIPI. Association for Commonwealth Literature and Language Studies, Indian Branch, Department of English, University of Mysore, Manasagangotri, Mysore 570006, India. **Indexed:** Curr.Cont.Africa, M.L.A., So.Pac.Per.Ind.
Formerly (until 1979): Commonwealth Newsletter.

800 II
KURINJI QUARTERLY.* (Text in English) 1973. q. Rs.12. 536 Raja Basantha Roy Rd., Calcutta, India. Ed. M. Srinivasan. adv.; bibl
Description: Indian vernacular literature in translation.

KWARTALNIK NEOFILOLOGICZNY. see LINGUISTICS

810 JA ISSN 0454-8132
KYUSHU AMERICAN LITERATURE. (Text in English) 1960. a. (Kyushu American Literature Society - Kyushu Amerika Bungaku-Kai) Kyushu University, College of General Education, 4-2-1 Ropponmatsu, Chuo-ku, Fukuoka 810, Japan. TEL 81-92-731-8745. FAX 81-92-771-4161. adv.; bk.rev.; bibl. circ. 450. **Indexed:** Curr.Cont., M.L.A.
—BLDSC (5135.030000).

800 111.85 400 DK ISSN 0109-5390
L AE S. (Litteratur, Aestetik, Sprog) 1983. s-a. free. Aarhus Universitet, Institut for Nordisk Sprog og Litteratur, Niels Juelsgade 84, DK-8200 Aarhus N, Denmark. TEL 06-136711. Ed.Bd. illus.

L B I NEWS. (Leo Baeck Institute) see HISTORY

810 301.415 US ISSN 1069-5966
L G L C NEWSLETTER. 1983. q. $15. Libertarians for Gay and Lesbian Concerns, Box 447, Chelsea, MI 48118. TEL 313-475-9792. Ed. James L. Hudler. adv.; bk.rev. circ. 300.
Description: Provides a forum for lesbian and gay libertarians.

LITERATURE

L G S N: LESBIAN AND GAY STUDIES NEWSLETTER. see *HOMOSEXUALITY*

L I A S: SOURCES AND DOCUMENTS RELATING TO THE EARLY MODERN HISTORY OF IDEAS.. see *HISTORY*

820   AT   ISSN 0817-458X
L I N Q. (Literature in North Queensland) Variant title: LiNQ. 1971. 3/yr. Aus.$20 to individuals; institutions Aus.$25; overseas Aus.$30. (English Language & Literature Association) James Cook University of North Queensland, Department of English, Townsville, Qld. 4811, Australia. Ed.Bd. bk.rev. circ. 400. **Indexed:** M.L.A.

800   US   ISSN 1043-6928
                             CODEN: LINTEX
L I T: LITERATURE INTERPRETATION THEORY. 1991. 4/yr. 48 ECU (effective 1993). Gordon and Breach Science Publishers, 820 Town Center Dr., Langhorne, PA 19047. TEL 215-750-2642. FAX 215-750-6343. (UK subscr. to: P.O. Box 90, Reading, Berks., RG1 8JL, England. TEL 0734-560-080) Ed. Lee Jacobus. (also avail. in microform) **Document type:** academic/scholarly publication.
—UnCover. **CCC.**
Refereed Serial

LABYRINTHOS. see *ART*

808.8   US
LADIES' FETISH & TABOO SOCIETY. COMPENDIUM OF URBAN ANTHROPOLOGY. 1988. q. $10. Box 542327, Houston, TX 77254-2327. TEL 713-524-5051. FAX 713-524-5064. Ed. Kathy Biehl. circ. 150. **Document type:** consumer publication.
Description: Contains humorous stories of real life happenings.

800   AG   ISSN 0023-7280
LAGRIMAL TRIFURCA. 1968. q. Arg.$2000($20) Ocampo 1812, Rosario, Argentina. Ed. Francisco E. Gandolfo. adv.; bk.rev.; bibl. circ. 1,000. (looseleaf format)

LAMAR LECTURE SERIES. see *HISTORY*

839   NE   ISSN 0165-8204
LAMPAS; tijdschrift voor Nederlandse classici. 5/yr. fl.62.50. Dick Coutinho B.V., Slochterlaan 7, 1405 AL Bussum, Netherlands. TEL 31-2159-49991. FAX 31-2159-47165. Ed.Bd. **Indexed:** Bibl.Ling. **Document type:** academic/scholarly publication.
Description: For Dutch classicists.

809   US   ISSN 0737-0555
PS3515.U274
LANGSTON HUGHES REVIEW. 1982. 2/yr. $10. (Langston Hughes Society) Brown University, Afro-American Studies Program, Box 1904, Providence, RI 02912. TEL 401-863-1813. adv.; bk.rev.; index. circ. 300. (back issues avail.) **Indexed:** M.L.A.
—Faxon; UnCover.
Description: Concerned with the life and writings of Langston Hughes. Articles on information relevant to a critical study of the Hughesian tradition.

LANGUAGE AND CULTURE. see *LINGUISTICS*

LANGUAGE AND LITERATURE. see *LINGUISTICS*

LANGUAGE FORUM. see *LINGUISTICS*

LANGUAGE FORUM MONOGRAPH SERIES. see *LINGUISTICS*

LANGUAGE QUARTERLY. see *LINGUISTICS*

LANGUAGES OF DESIGN; formalisms for word, images and sound. see *LINGUISTICS — Computer Applications*

800 400   FR   ISSN 0457-1320
LANGUES ET STYLES. 1959. irreg., latest no.9, 1983. Lettres Modernes, 45 rue Saint-Andre, 14123 Fleury sur Orne, France. TEL 31-84-47-06. FAX 31-84-48-09. (Dist. outside France by: Librairie Droz S.A., 11, rue Massot, CH-1211 Geneva 12, Switzerland.. TEL 022-466666)
Description: Part of "Editions 'Lettres Modernes'."

LANGUES MODERNES. see *LINGUISTICS*

800
LANNAN SERIES. 1990. irreg., no.3, 1993. price varies. University of California Press, 2120 Berkeley Way, Berkeley, CA 94720. TEL 510-642-4247. FAX 510-643-7127. (Orders to: California-Princeton Fulfillment Services, 1445 Lower Ferry Rd., Ewing, NJ 08618. TEL 800-777-4726. FAX 800-999-1958) (back issues avail.) **Document type:** monographic series.
Description: Covers modern Eastern and Western literature.
Refereed Serial

860   US   ISSN 0888-5613
LATIN AMERICAN INDIAN LITERATURES JOURNAL; a review of American Indian texts and studies. 1977. s-a. $25 to individuals (foreign $31); institutions $36 (foreign $41) (effective 1994). Penn State University, McKeesport, University Dr., McKeesport, PA 15132. TEL 412-675-9466. FAX 412-675-9043. Ed. Mary H. Preuss. adv.; bk.rev.; bibl. circ. 500. (back issues avail.) **Indexed:** Anthropol.Lit., Arts & Hum.Cit.Ind., Bibl.Ling., Curr.Cont., Hisp.Amer.Per.Ind., M.L.A., Rel.Ind.One. **Document type:** academic/scholarly publication.
—BLDSC (5160.064500); Faxon; UnCover.
Supersedes (in 1985): Latin American Indian Literatures (ISSN 0160-8045)

860   US   ISSN 0047-4134
PQ7081.A1
LATIN AMERICAN LITERARY REVIEW. 1972. s-a. $20 to individuals (foreign $28); institutions $36 (foreign $38). (University of Pittsburgh, Department of Hispanic Languages and Literatures) Latin American Literary Review, 121 Edgewood Ave., 1st Fl., Pittsburgh, PA 15218-1513. TEL 412-371-9023. FAX 412-371-9025. Ed. Yvette E. Miller. adv. contact: Susan Wackerbarth. bk.rev.; index. circ. 1,500. (also avail. in microform from UMI) **Indexed:** Arts & Hum.Cit.Ind., Curr.Cont., Hisp.Amer.Per.Ind., M.L.A. **Document type:** academic/scholarly publication.
—BLDSC (5160.075000); Faxon; UnCover; SWETS; UMI.
Description: Essays on and reviews of literature by Latin American writers.

LATIN AMERICAN THEATRE REVIEW; a journal devoted to the theatre and drama of Spanish & Portuguese America. see *THEATER*

859   RM
LATO. (Text in Hungarian) 1953. m. 144 lei. Uniunea Scriitorilor din Republica Socialista Romania, Calea Victoriei 115, Bucharest, Rumania. (Subscr. to: ILEXIM, Str. 13 Decembrie Nr. 3, Box 136-137, 70116 Bucharest, Rumania) Ed. Bela Marko. bk.rev.; film rev.; abstr.; charts; illus. circ. 5,000.
Formerly: Igaz Szo.

808   US   ISSN 0023-9003
PS221
LAUREL REVIEW (MARYVILLE). 1960. s-a. $8 (effective 1992). GreenTower Press, c/o William Trowbridge, Dept. of English, Northwest Missouri State University, Maryville, MO 64468. TEL 816-562-1265. Ed.Bd. adv. circ. 750. (also avail. in microfilm; back issues avail.) **Indexed:** A.I.P.P., Ind.Amer.Per.Verse.
—**CCC.**
Description: Publishes poetry and fiction on any theme.

LAVENDER LIST. see *WOMEN'S INTERESTS*

LEA. see *BIBLIOGRAPHIES*

810 820   US   ISSN 0075-8396
LEBARON RUSSELL BRIGGS PRIZE HONORS ESSAYS IN ENGLISH. 1965. irreg. $5.95. Harvard University, Department of English, Cambridge, MA 02138. (Dist. by: Harvard University Press, 79 Garden St., Cambridge, MA 02138)

LECTOR. see *PUBLISHING AND BOOK TRADE*

808.81   US
THE LEDGE POETRY & FICTION MAGAZINE. 1988. s-a. $15 (for 2 yrs.). 64-65 Cooper Ave., Glendale, NY 11385. Ed. Timothy Monaghan. adv. circ. 500.
Formerly (until 1991): Ledge Poetry and Prose Magazine (ISSN 1046-2724)
Description: Strives to publish quality poetry and fiction that is gritty, arresting and provocative.

900 800   UK   ISSN 0024-0281
AS122
LEEDS PHILOSOPHICAL AND LITERARY SOCIETY. PROCEEDINGS. LITERARY AND HISTORICAL SECTION. 1925. irreg. (1-4/yr.). price varies. Leeds Philosophical and Literary Society, Central Museum, Calverley St., Leeds 2, England. Ed. I.S. Moxon. charts; illus.; index. circ. 650. **Indexed:** Amer.Hist.& Life, Br.Hum.Ind., Hist.Abstr., Sci.Abstr. **Document type:** proceedings.
—BLDSC (6746.900000). **CCC.**
Description: Explores areas of scholarly, literary or historical study.

820   UK   ISSN 0075-8566
PE10
LEEDS STUDIES IN ENGLISH. N.S. 1967. a. price varies. Leeds Studies in English, University of Leeds, School of English, Leeds LS2 9JT, England. Ed. A. Wawn. (reprint service avail. from KTO) **Indexed:** Bibl.Ling., Br.Archaeol.Abstr., M.L.A. **Document type:** academic/scholarly publication.
—BLDSC (5181.305000).
Supersedes: Leeds Studies in English and Kindred Languages.

375.4 420   UK   ISSN 0075-8574
LEEDS TEXTS AND MONOGRAPHS. NEW SERIES. 1966; N.S. 19?? irreg. price varies. Leeds Studies in English, University of Leeds, School of English, Leeds LS2 9JT, England. TEL 0532-334738. FAX 0532-334774. Ed. P. Meredith. **Indexed:** M.L.A. **Document type:** academic/scholarly publication.

800   SP
LEER. m. (11/yr.). 4000 ptas. (foreign 4400 ptas.). Ediciones Intemporales, D. Ramon de la Cruz 88, 1o, 28006 Madrid, Spain. TEL 91-401-71-17. FAX 91-401-75-30. Dir. Heriberto Quesada Porto. bk.rev.
Description: Presents the most interesting works from the large number of books published throughout the year.

800 305.4   US   ISSN 0748-4321
PS149
LEGACY (UNIVERSITY PARK); a journal of American women writers. 1984. s-a. $20 to individuals (foreign $23); institutions $30 (foreign $35). Pennsylvania State University Press, Barbara Bldg., Ste. C, 820 N. University Dr., University Park, PA 16802-1003. TEL 814-865-1327. FAX 814-863-1408. Ed.Bd. adv.; bk.rev. circ. 450. (reprint service avail. from UMI) **Indexed:** Amer.Hist.& Life, Bk.Rev.Ind., Child.Bk.Rev.Ind., Curr.Cont., Hist.Abstr., M.L.A., Wom.Stud.Abstr. (1984-). **Document type:** academic/scholarly publication.
—Faxon; UnCover. **CCC.**
Description: Features articles on American women's literature from the 17th century through the 20th century.
Refereed Serial

052   UK   ISSN 0141-3511
                             CODEN: TLLPAE
LEICESTER LITERARY & PHILOSOPHICAL SOCIETY. TRANSACTIONS. 1879. a. £3($5) Leicester Literary & Philosophical Society, c/o Leicestershire Museums, 96 New Walk, Leicester, England. TEL 0533-715265. Ed. Trevor D. Ford. bk.rev. circ. 300. (back issues avail.) **Document type:** academic/scholarly publication.
—BLDSC (8978.300000).

830   NE   ISSN 0169-8559
LEIDSE GERMANISTISCHE EN ANGLISTISCHE REEKS. 1962. irreg., vol.21, 1983. price varies. E.J. Brill, P.O. Box 9000, 2300 PA Leiden, Netherlands. TEL 31-71-312624. FAX 31-71-317532. TELEX 39296 BRILL NL. (N. America dist. addr.: E.J. Brill, 24 Hudson St., Kinderhook, NY 12106. TEL 800-962-4406. FAX 518-758-1959) (Co-publisher: Leiden University Press) **Document type:** monographic series.
Description: German and English studies of the University of Leiden.

LEIDSE ROMANISTISCHE REEKS. see *LINGUISTICS*

892   IS
LEKET.* (Editions in English and Hebrew) irreg. World Zionist Organization, P.O. Box 92, Jerusalem 91920, Israel. Ed. David Hardan. illus.

850   IT   ISSN 0393-506X
LENGUA; semestrale di poesia e letteratura. 1982. s-a. L.40000. (Associazione Culturale per la Ricerca Poetico-Letteraria delle Lingue) Crocetti Editore, Via E. Falck 53, 20151 Milan, Italy. TEL 02-3538-277. Ed. Gianni D'Elia.

800   IT
▼**LEONE E L'UNICORNO**. 1992. irreg. price varies. Liguori Editore s.r.l., Via Mezzocannone 19, 80134 Naples, Italy. TEL 081-5527139. **Document type:** monographic series.

830   US   ISSN 0075-8833
PT2405.5
LESSING YEARBOOK. (Text in English or German) 1969. a. price varies. (Lessing Society) Wayne State University Press, 5959 Woodward Ave., Detroit, MI 48202. TEL 089-432929. Ed. R. Schade. bk.rev. **Indexed:** M.L.A.
—BLDSC (5184.600000).

891.8   YU   ISSN 0025-5939
AS142
LETOPIS MATICE SRPSKE. 1825. m. 200 din. Matica Srpska, Matice Srpske 1, Novi Sad, Vojvodina, Yugoslavia. Ed. Dimitrije Vucenov. adv.; bk.rev.; bibl.; index.
—BLDSC (0097.375000).

LETRA GRANDE, ARTE Y LITERATURA. see *ART*

860   028.5   SP
LETRAGORDA. 1986. s-a. 1800 ptas. (Europe 2000 ptas.; elsewhere 2500 ptas.). Asociacion para la Promocion de la Lectura, Diego Rodriguez Almela 2, 3o-D, 30007 Murcia, Spain. Dir. Javier Marin Ceballos. circ. 6,000.
Description: Contains information and analysis of children's literature.

800   861   AG   ISSN 0326-2928
PQ7600
LETRAS DE BUENOS AIRES. 1980. 3/yr. $27. Las Heras 3065, 11o A, 1425 Buenos Aires, Argentina. TEL 1-802-1299. Ed. Victoria Pueyrredon. adv.; bk.rev. circ. 6,000. **Document type:** academic/scholarly publication.

800   700   EC
LETRAS DEL ECUADOR. 1944. m. Casa de la Cultura Ecuatoriana, Avda. 6 de Diciembre, Casilla 67, Quito, Ecuador. Dir. Teodoro Vanegas Andrade.

800   700   BL
LETRAS E ARTES. vol.5, 1991. m. Cr.$160 per no. Rua Rumania 14 Laranjeiras, 22240 Rio de Janeiro RJ, Brazil. TEL 285-5496.

860   376   US   ISSN 0277-4356
PQ6055
LETRAS FEMENINAS. (Text in English, Portuguese, Spanish) 1974. 2/yr. $20 to individuals; libraries $25. Asociacion de Literatura Femenina Hispanica, Department of Modern Languages, University of Nebraska, Lincoln, NE 68588-0315. TEL 402-472-3710. FAX 402-472-1123. Ed. Adelaida L. Martinez. adv.; bk.rev. circ. 600. (back issues avail.) **Indexed:** Ind.Amer.Per.Verse, M.L.A. **Document type:** academic/scholarly publication.
—UnCover.

700   MX   ISSN 0024-1245
LETRAS POTOSINAS; vocero de cultura. vol.27, 1969. q. Mex.$40. Luis Chessal Iturbide 505, San Luis Potosi, Mexico. Ed. Jesus C. Perez. adv.; bk.rev.; bibl.

806   383   US   ISSN 0882-3804
LETTER EXCHANGE; a magazine for letter writers. 1982. 3/yr. $20 (effective 1994). Readers' League, Box 6218, Albany, CA 94706. TEL 510-526-7412. Ed. Stephen Sikora. adv.; bk.rev.; circ. 2,000 (paid). **Document type:** consumer publication.
Formerly (until 1983): Readers' League Catalogue of Correspondence.
Description: Publishes items relating to letter writing, including proposed topics of correspondence for persons interested in exchanging letters.

800   US
THE LETTER PARADE. 1985. m. $10. Bonnie Jo Enterprises, Box 52, Comstock, MI 49041. FAX 616-342-9377. Ed. Bonnie Jo. illus. circ. 85. (looseleaf format; back issues avail.) **Document type:** newsletter.
Description: Mostly humorous essays aimed at mainstream.

850   IT
LETTERATURE. 1983. irreg. no.27, 1993. price varies. Liguori Editore s.r.l., Via Mezzocannone, 19, 80134 Naples, Italy. TEL 081-5527139. Ed. GianCarlo Mazzacurati. **Document type:** monographic series.

809   IT
LETTERATURE D'AMERICA. 1980. q. L.40000. (Universita degli Studi di Roma "La Sapienza") Bulzoni Editore, Via dei Liburni 14, 00185 Rome, Italy. Ed. Dario Puccini. **Indexed:** M.L.A.

800   IT
LETTERATURE DI FRONTIERA/LITTERATURES FRONTALIERES. 1991. s-a. L.40000 (foreign L.50000) (effective 1991). Bulzoni Editore, Via dei Liburni 14, 00185 Rome, Italy. TEL 06-4455207. FAX 06-4450355. Ed. Giovanna Trisolini.

850   IT   ISSN 0024-1334
PQ4001
LETTERE ITALIANE. 1949. q. L.75000 (foreign L.95000) (effective 1994). (Universita di Padova e di Torino, Istituti di Letteratura Italiana) Casa Editrice Leo S. Olschki, Casella Postale 66, 50100 Florence, Italy. TEL 055-6530684. FAX 055-6530214. Eds. Vittore Branca, Carlo Ossola. adv.; bk.rev.; cum.index: 1949-1979. circ. 1,200. **Indexed:** Can.Rev.Comp.Lit., Curr.Cont. **Document type:** academic/scholarly publication.
—Faxon; SWETS.

850   IT   ISSN 0075-8892
LETTERE ITALIANE. BIBLIOTECA; studi e testi. 1961. irreg., vol.44, 1993. price varies. Casa Editrice Leo S. Olschki, Casella Postale 66, 50100 Florence, Italy. TEL 055-6530684. FAX 055-6530214. Eds. Vittore Branca, Carlo Ossola. circ. 1,000. **Document type:** monographic series.

850   IT   ISSN 1122-0724
LETTERE ITALIANE. SAGGI. 1959. irreg., no.45, 1993. price varies. Casa Editrice Leo S. Olschki, Casella Postale 66, 50100 Florence, Italy. TEL 055-6530684. FAX 55-6530214. circ. 1,200. **Document type:** monographic series.

850   IT   ISSN 0024-1350
LETTORE DI PROVINCIA; testi - ricerche - critica. 1970. q. L.30000 (foreign L.50000). Angelo Longo Editore, Via Paolo Costa 33, P.O. Box 431, 48100 Ravenna, Italy. TEL 0544-217026. Ed. Tino Dalla Valle. adv.; bk.rev.; bibl. circ. 3,000. **Document type:** academic/scholarly publication.

800   GW
LETTRE INTERNATIONAL. (Text and summaries in German) 1988. q. DM.56. Rosenthalerstr. 13, 10119 Berlin, Germany. TEL 030-30870440. FAX 030-2833128. Eds. Frank Berberich, Antonin Liehm. circ. 30,000. (tabloid format; back issues avail.) **Document type:** bulletin.

800   700   100   FR   ISSN 0024-1369
LETTRES; poesie, philosophie, litterature, arts, critique. 1945. q. 200 F. Editions Andre Silvaire, 20 rue Domat, 75005 Paris, France. illus.

800   AA
LES LETTRES ALBANAISES. (Text in French) q. $12. Lidhja e Shkrimatareve dhe e Artisteve te Shqiperise - Union des Ecrivains et Artistes d'Albanie, Baboci 37z, Tirana, Albania. TEL 42-27989. (Editorial office addr.: Rruga Konferenca e Pezes, Tirana, Albania. TEL 42-22691) Diana Culi.

301.415   GR
LETTRES EOLIENNES/EOLIKA GRAMMATA; revue bimensuelle d'art de Lesbos. 1971. bi-m. Dr.40. 41 Nireos St., P. Faliron, Athens, Greece. TEL 3600142. Ed. K. Valetas. bk.rev.; bibl.

800   900   FR
LETTRES ET CULTURES DE LANGUES FRANCAISES. 1984. 2/yr. 220 F. Association des Ecrivains de Langue Francaise (ADELF), 14 rue Broussais, 75014 Paris, France. TEL 43-21-95-99. Ed. Charles Saint-Prot. adv.; bk.rev. circ. 3,200.

800   FR
LETTRES MEDIEVALES. 1984. irreg. Librairie A.G. Nizet, 3 bis place de la Sorbonne, 75005 Paris, France. TEL 43-54-79-76. Ed. Jacques De Caluwe. circ. 500.

840   CN   ISSN 0382-084X
LETTRES QUEBECOISES; revue de l'actualite litteraire. (Text in French) 1976. q. Can.$20 to individuals; institutions Can.$25. Lettres Quebecoises, 1781 Saint-Hubert, Montreal, PQ H2L 3Z1, Canada. TEL 514-525-9518. FAX 514-525-7537. Ed. Andre Vanasse. adv.; bk.rev.; play rev.; illus. circ. 5,500. (back issues avail.) **Indexed:** C.L.I., Can.Lit.Ind., Can.Per.Ind., M.L.A., Pt.de Rep. (1979-), RADAR.

870   BE   ISSN 0024-1415
LES LETTRES ROMANES. (Supplement avail.) 1947. q. 850 BEF (foreign 950 BEF) (effective 1994). Faculte de Philosophie et Lettres, Place Blaise Pascal 1, B-1348 Louvain-la-Neuve, Belgium. TEL 32-10-474921. FAX 32-10-472579. Ed. G. Jacques. bk.rev.; bibl.; index. circ. 600. (back issues avail.; reprint service avail. from ISI) **Indexed:** Arts & Hum.Cit.Ind., Can.Rev.Comp.Lit., Curr.Cont., Ind.Bk.Rev.Hum. **Document type:** academic/scholarly publication.
—Faxon; UnCover; SWETS.
Description: Publishes original articles on the scientific study of romance language literatures and their history.

850   IT   ISSN 0459-1623
PQ4331
LETTURE CLASSENSI; letture dantesche. (Text in Italian) 1966. a. L.45000. Angelo Longo Editore, Via Paolo Costa 3, P.O. Box 431, 48100 Ravenna, Italy. TEL 0544-217026. adv.; cum.index. circ. 2,000. **Document type:** proceedings.

840   IS   ISSN 0992-0757
DS57
LEVANT. (Text in French) 1984. a. $30. Haifa University, Faculty of Humanities, Ha-Carmel, Haifa 31 999, Israel. FAX 052-584192. circ. 1,000.
Formerly: Approches.

840   FR
LEVANT - CAHIERS DE L'ESPACE MEDITERRANEEN. 1987. a. 95 F. Editions de l'Eclat, Combas, 30250 Sommieres, France. TEL 66-77-87-63. Ed. Michel Elial.

LEVIATA. see *ART*

LEXIS; revista de linguistica y literatura. see *LINGUISTICS*

895   CC
LI JIANG/LI RIVER. (Text in Chinese) q. Li Jiang Chubanshe, 159 Nanhuan Lu, Nanning, Guangxi 541002, People's Republic of China. TEL 223929. Ed. Nie Zhenning.

LIAISON. see *HANDICAPPED — Visually Impaired*

891.6   FR   ISSN 0024-1733
AL LIAMM. (Text in Breton) 1946. bi-m. 150 F. (Association al Liamm) P. Le Bihan, 16 rue des Fours a Chaux, 35400 Saint-Malo, Brittany, France. Ed. R. Huon. adv.; bk.rev.; bibl.; charts; illus. circ. 730. **Indexed:** Bibl.Ling.

LIANHUANHUA YISHU/ART OF PICTORIAL STORIES. see *ART*

810   US   ISSN 0899-8272
HQ450
LIBIDO; the journal of sex and sensibility. 1988. q. $26. Box 146721, Chicago, IL 60614. TEL 312-275-0842. FAX 312-275-0752. Eds. Marianna Beck, Jack Hafferkamp. adv.; bk.rev. circ. 8,000. **Document type:** consumer publication.
Description: Contains articles and erotic stories ranging from the explicit to the titillating.

LIBROS DE MEXICO. see *PUBLISHING AND BOOK TRADE*

028.1   860   PY   ISSN 0257-3555
LIBROS PARAGUAYOS. 1972. a. $25. Distribuidor Internacional Publicaciones Paraguayas, P.O. Box 2507, Ayoreos e-4a y 5a, Asuncion, Paraguay. TEL 595-21-495367. FAX 595-21-447460. Eds. Margarita Kallsen, Sofia Marecky. bk.rev. circ. 1,000. (also avail. in microfiche)

LICHTENBERG-JAHRBUCH. see *BIOGRAPHY*

LIFESTYLES OF THE BODILY DISMEMBERED. see *MOTION PICTURES*

LITERATURE

LIFTOUTS; a review of books and language work. see PUBLISHING AND BOOK TRADE

800 US ISSN 1064-8186
▼LIGHT (CHICAGO). 1992. q. $12. Box 7500, Chicago, IL 60680. TEL 708-853-1028. Ed. John Mella. adv.; bk.rev.; illus. circ. 1,100.
 Description: Contains light verse, satire, word-play, puns, parodies and witty drawings.

LIGHT JOURNEYS. see NEW AGE PUBLICATIONS

808.838 US ISSN 0887-4328
LIGHTHOUSE (AUBURN). 1986. bi-m. $7.95. Lighthouse Publications, Box 1377, Auburn, WA 98071-1377. Eds. Tim Clinton, Lorraine Clinton; Pub. Tim Clinton. circ. 300.
 Formerly: Lighthouse Magazine.
 Description: Presents a variety of fiction for all ages that maintains time-honored values.

850 IT
LIGUORI EDITORE. MONOGRAFIE. 1984. irreg., no.4, 1993. price varies. Liguori Editore s.r.l., Via Mezzocannone, 19, 80134 Naples, Italy. TEL 081-5527139. Eds. G. Mazzacurati, V. Russo. **Document type:** monographic series.

800 PH ISSN 0115-6144
LIKHA; D L S U literary journal. (Text in English and Filipino) 1979. a. P.30($3.20) (De La Salle University, Literature Department) De La Salle University Press, 2401 Taft Ave., Manila, Philippines. TEL 2-59-48-32. FAX 632-521-9094. adv.; bk.rev. circ. 300. **Document type:** academic/scholarly publication.
 Description: Publishes literary works of university faculty and writers.

LILI. (Zeitschrift fuer Literaturwissenschaft und Linguistik) see LINGUISTICS

LILI. BEIHEFTE. (Zeitschrift fuer Literaturwissenschaft und Linguistik) see LINGUISTICS

810 US
LILLIPUT REVIEW. 1989. irreg. (approx. 12/yr.). $1 per no. 207 S. Milvale Ave., Ste. 3, Pittsburgh, PA 15224. Ed. Don Wentworth. circ. 200.
 Description: Publishes poems of ten lines or less.

808 808.81 US ISSN 0899-5966
LIMESTONE; a literary journal. 1979. a. $5. University of Kentucky, Department of English, 1215 Patterson Office Tower, Lexington, KY 40506. TEL 606-257-7008. Ed.Bd. adv.; bk.rev. circ. 1,000. (back issues avail.)
 Formerly: Fabbro (ISSN 0748-2418)
 Description: Attracts quality poetry and short fiction, particularly from Kentucky and Appalachia writers.

800 US ISSN 0267-2634
DA670.L69
LINCOLN RECORD SOCIETY. 1911. irreg., no.82, 1989. Boydell & Brewer Inc., Box 41026, Rochester, NY 14604. TEL 716-275-0419. FAX 716-271-8778. (also avail. in microfiche from IDC)

800 US
LINDEN LANE MAGAZINE. 1982. q. $12. Linden Lane Press, 6724 Crooked Palm Terrace, Hialeah, FL 33024-3718. TEL 609-921-7943. Ed. Heberto Padilla. adv.: page $500. (back issues avail.)
 Description: Covers poetry, fiction, art and photos.

800 IT
LINEA D'OMBRA; mensile di storie, immagini, discussioni e spettacolo. 1983. m. (foreign L.100000). Linea d'Ombra Edizioni s.r.l., Via Gaffurio 4, 20124 Milan, Italy. Ed. Goffredo Fofi; Pub. Lia Sacerdote. adv.; bk.rev.; index.

895 CC
LING SHUI. (Text in Chinese) q. Nannong Diqu Wenlian, You'ai Lu, Nanning, Guangxi 530001, People's Republic of China. TEL 34608. Ed. Huang Quan'an.

800 GW
LINGUA.* (Text in English and German) q. DM.180 to individuals; institutions DM.240. Cobra Verlag, Schlossgang 15, Postfach 1166, 2250 Husum, Germany. Ed. Wendelin Rader. bk.rev.; index.

LINGUA E CULTURA. see LINGUISTICS

800 850 IT
LINGUA E LETTERATURA. 1983. s-a. Istituto Universitario di Lingue Moderne, Piazza Volontari 3, 20145 Milan, Italy. Dir. Carlo Bo. **Indexed:** M.L.A.

LINGUA E LETTERATURA. see LINGUISTICS

LINGUA E STILE. see LINGUISTICS

LINGUISTIC & LITERARY STUDIES IN EASTERN EUROPE. see LINGUISTICS

LINGUISTICA E LETTERATURA. see LINGUISTICS

LINGUISTICA PRAGENSIA. see LINGUISTICS

LINGUISTICA Y LITERATURA. see LINGUISTICS

800 US ISSN 8756-5609
PS3562.I515
LININGTON LINEUP. 1984. bi-m. $12 (foreign $15). (Elizabeth Linington Society) Gloucester Researchers, 1223 Glen Terrace, Glassboro, NJ 08028-1315. TEL 609-589-1571. Ed. Rinehart S. Potts. adv.; bk.rev.; film rev.; abstr.; bibl.; illus. circ. 400. (back issues avail.) **Document type:** newsletter.
 Description: Covers the life and writings of Elizabeth Linington a.k.a. Anne Blaisdell, Lesley Egan, Egan O'Neill, and Dell Shannon.

840 FR
LIRE.* 1975. m. 170 F. Groupe Express, 60732 Chantilly Cedex, France. TEL 44-57-54-48. FAX 47-64-09-41. TELEX 650 009. Ed. Jean-Maurice de Montremy. abstr. circ. 125,070.

830 GW ISSN 0340-7888
LITERARISCHER VEREIN IN STUTTGART. BIBLIOTHEK. Abbreviated title: B L V S. 1842. irreg., vol.316, 1994. price varies. Anton Hiersemann Verlag, Rosenbergstr. 113, 70193 Stuttgart, Germany. TEL 0711-638265. FAX 0711-6369010. (Subscr. to: Postfach 140155, 70071 Stuttgart, Germany) **Document type:** bibliography, monographic series.

830 AU
LITERARISCHES LEBEN IN OESTERREICH. a. Interessengemeinschaft Oesterreichischer Autorrinen und Autoren, Seidengasse 13, A-1070 Vienna, Austria. TEL 01-526204413. **Document type:** bulletin.

891.86 XR ISSN 0862-6618
PG5000
LITERARNI REVUE. 1972. 10/yr. 60 Kcs.($26.40) Obec Ceskych Spisovatel', Narodni tr. 11, 110 00 Prague 1, Czech Republic. TEL 2-2320924. (Subscr. to: Artia, Ve Smeckach 30, 111 27 Prague 1, Czech Republic) (Co-sponsor: Ministerstvo Kultury Ceske Republiky) Ed. Oldrich Rafaj. bk.rev.; illus.; index. circ. 15,000. **Indexed:** M.L.A.
 Formerly (until 1990): Literarni Mesicnik (ISSN 0300-2446)

891.87 780 XO
LITERARNO - MUZEJNY LETOPIS. (Text in Slovak; summaries in German and Russian) 1967. a. price varies. Matica Slovenska, Literarne Muzeum, Ul. Mudronova 26, 036 52 Martin, Slovakia. TEL 42-842-38706. FAX 42-842-32454. Ed. Imrich Sedlak. bk.rev.
 Formerly: Letopis Pamatnika Slovenskej Literatury (ISSN 0075-8841)

891.87 XO ISSN 0075-9872
PG5400
LITERARNY ARCHIV. (Text in Slovak) 1964. biennial. price varies. Matica Slovenska, Archiv Literatury a Umenia, Ul. Mudronova 26, 036 52 Martin, Slovakia. TEL 42-842-38706. FAX 42-842-32454. Ed. Michal Kocak. bk.rev. **Document type:** proceedings.

806 070.5 070 US
PN163
LITERARY AGENTS OF NORTH AMERICA. 1983. biennial. $29.95. Research Associates International, 340 E. 52 St., New York, NY 10022. TEL 212-980-9179. Eds. Arthur Orrmont, Leonie Rosenstiel. adv.
 Formerly: Literary Agents of North America Marketplace (ISSN 8756-2219)

LITERARY CAVALCADE. see CHILDREN AND YOUTH — For

820 II ISSN 0255-2779
LITERARY ENDEAVOUR; a quarterly journal devoted to English studies. (Text in English) 1979. q. Rs.30($70) (New Accents) Dr. L. Adinarayana, Pub., F-3, Block 6, HIG, Opp. Water Tank, Bagh Lingampalli, Hyderanad 500 044, India. Ed. C.R. Nagendran. adv.; bk.rev. circ. 600. **Indexed:** M.L.A. —BLDSC (5276.636050).
 Description: Highlights regional literature. Aims to promote an awareness of modern trends and critical approaches to literature. Includes research and reports of conferences and seminars.

800 II ISSN 0024-4554
AP8
LITERARY HALF-YEARLY. (Text in English) 1960. s-a. Rs.80($20) (Institute of Commonwealth and American Studies and English Language) Literary Press, Anjali 96, 7th Main, Jayalakshmipuram, Mysore 570 012, India. TEL 513030. (Co-sponsor: Centre for Commonwealth Literature and Research) Ed. H.H. Anniah Gowda. adv.; bk.rev.; bibl.; illus.; index. circ. 1,000. (reprint service avail.) **Indexed:** Abstr.Engl.Stud., M.L.A.

800 070 US ISSN 0732-6637
PN4878.3
LITERARY MAGAZINE REVIEW. 1981. q. $12.50 (effective 1992). Kansas State University, English Department, Manhattan, KS 66506. TEL 316-532-6716. Ed. G.W. Clift. bk.rev.; index. circ. 500. (back issues avail.) **Indexed:** Amer.Hum.Ind., Bk.Rev.Ind. (1986-), Child.Bk.Rev.Ind. (1986-). —Faxon; UnCover.
 Description: Devoted to reviews of the specific contents of magazines publishing fiction or poetry.

800 US
LITERARY OLYMPIANS. a. (Literary Olympics, Inc.) Ford - Brown & Co., Box 2764, Boston, MA 02208-2764. Ed. Elizabeth Bartlett.

801 US ISSN 0160-8703
PN56.N16
LITERARY ONOMASTICS STUDIES.* 1974. a. $12. State University of New York at Brockport, State University College, Brockport, NY 14420. TEL 719-395-2269. (Co-sponsor: American Name Society) Ed. Grace Alvarez-Altman. adv.; circ. controlled. **Indexed:** Chic.Per.Ind., M.L.A.

800 028 PK ISSN 0075-9929
LITERARY PRIZES IN PAKISTAN. (Text in English) 1964. a. Rs.4.($1.) National Book Council of Pakistan, Theosophical Hall, M.A. Jinnah Rd., Karachi, Pakistan.
 Formerly: Incentives for Better Books in Pakistan.

800 US ISSN 0024-4589
AP2
LITERARY REVIEW; an international journal of contemporary writing. 1957. q. $18 (foreign $21). Fairleigh Dickinson University, Literary Review, 285 Madison Ave., Madison, NJ 07940. TEL 201-593-8564. Ed. Walter Cummins. adv.; bk.rev.; index. circ. 2,000. (also avail. in microform from MIM,UMI; reprint service avail. from KTO,UMI) **Indexed:** A.I.P.P., Amer.Bibl.Slavic & E.Eur.Stud., Arts & Hum.Cit.Ind., Curr.Cont., Hum.Ind., Ind.Amer.Per.Verse, Ind.Bk.Rev.Hum., M.L.A., Mid.East: Abstr.& Ind. **Document type:** academic/scholarly publication.
 ●Also available online. Vendor(s): Information Access Co..
 —BLDSC (5276.655000); Faxon; UnCover; UMI.

800 070.5 US ISSN 0024-4597
LITERARY SKETCHES; a magazine of interviews, reviews and memorabilia. 1961. m. $7. Olivia Murray Nichols, Ed. & Pub., Box 810571, Dallas, TX 75381-0571. TEL 214-243-8776. adv.; bk.rev.; charts; cum.index: 1962-1986, 1987-1991; circ. 500 (paid). **Indexed:** Abstr.Engl.Stud. **Document type:** newsletter.
 Description: Non-scholarly articles on books and authors of all periods, reviews, trivia, and literary quizzes.

891.4 II ISSN 0024-4600
LITERARY STUDIES; a quarterly review of literature and criticism from the Panjab. (Text in English) 1970. q. Rs.20($10.) Razdan House, Sirhindi Darwaza, Patiala, Panjab, India. Ed. Brij M. Razdan. adv.; bk.rev.

800 700   GW   ISSN 0024-4627
PN4
DER LITERAT; Fachzeitschrift fuer Literatur und Kunst. 1958. m. DM.71. Verlag der Literat, Hohlweg 27, 65812 Bad Soden, Germany. TEL 06174-1764. FAX 06174-24626. Ed. Inka Bohl. adv.; bk.rev.; film rev.; play rev. circ. 3,000. **Document type:** academic/scholarly publication.

LITERATOR; journal of literary criticism and linguistics.
see *LINGUISTICS*

830   GW
LITERATUR. 1983. a. DM.9.80. Lamuv Verlag GmbH, Nikolaikirchhof 7, 37073 Goettingen, Germany. TEL 0551-44024. FAX 0551-41392. Eds. Christoph Heubner, Alwin Meyer. circ. 15,000. (back issues avail.) **Document type:** academic/scholarly publication.

800 831   AU   ISSN 0024-466X
PN4
LITERATUR & KRITIK; oesterreichische Monatsschrift. 1966. 5/yr. S.380. Otto Mueller Verlag, Postfach 167, A-5021 Salzburg, Austria. TEL 0662-881974. FAX 0662-872387. Ed. Karl-Markus Gauss. bk.rev.; index. circ. 2,500. (back issues avail.) **Document type:** academic/scholarly publication.
—Faxon; SWETS.

830   AU
LITERATUR AUS OESTERREICH; Texte zeitgenoessischer Autoren. 1955. bi-m. S.250. (Arbeitsgemeinschaft Literatur) Malek Verlag GmbH, Wienerstr. 127, A-3500 Krems, Austria. FAX 02732-74939. Ed. Johannes Twaroch. adv.; bk.rev.; bibl. circ. 4,000. **Document type:** bibliography.
   Formerly (until 1986): Heimatland (ISSN 0017-9779)

830   GW   ISSN 0930-4010
PT3803.H4
DER LITERATUR BOTE. q. DM.20. (Hessisches Literaturbuero) Dipa-Verlag, Nassauer Str. 1-3, 60439 Frankfurt a.M., Germany. TEL 069-586910. FAX 069-576128.

830   GW   ISSN 0343-1657
PT3
LITERATUR FUER LESER; Zeitschrift fuer Interpretationspraxis und geschichtliche Texterkenntnis. 1968. q. DM.56.80. Peter Lang GmbH Europaeischer Verlag der Wissenschaften, Eschborner Landstr. 42-50, 60489 Frankfurt a.M., Germany. TEL 069-7807050. FAX 069-785893. Ed.Bd. adv.: B&W page DM.800; trim 113 x 184. (back issues avail.) **Document type:** academic/scholarly publication.
—Faxon.
   Description: Collection of critical essays and interpretations of important literary works.

800   GW   ISSN 0178-6857
LITERATUR IN BAYERN. 1985. q. DM.30. Universitaet Muenchen, Institut fuer Bayerische Literaturgeschichte, Karolinenplatz 3, 80333 Munich, Germany. TEL 089-21802402. FAX 089-525598. Ed. Prof. Dietz-Ruediger Moser. adv.; bk.rev. circ. 3,000. **Document type:** academic/scholarly publication.

830
LITERATUR UND GESCHICHTE. EINE SCHRIFTENREIHE. 1970. irreg. price varies. Lothar Stiehm Verlag, Hausackerweg 16, 69118 Heidelberg, Germany. Indexed: M.L.A.

800   GW   ISSN 0075-9937
LITERATUR UND WIRKLICHKEIT. 1967. irreg., latest vol.26. price varies. Bouvier Verlag Herbert Grundmann, Am Hof 28, 53113 Bonn, Germany. TEL 0228-7290124. FAX 0228-7290179. Ed. Karl Otto Conrady. **Document type:** monographic series.

830   GW   ISSN 0938-1767
LITERATUR ZUM ANGEWOEHNEN. 1983. irreg., no.56, 1993. DM.3. M. und N. Boesche, Laurinsteig 14a, 13456 Berlin, Germany. TEL 030-4019009. **Document type:** newspaper.

891.8   PL
LITERATURA. 1972. m. $23. Ul. Koszykowa 6A, 00-562 Warsaw, Poland. (Dist. by: Ars Polona-Ruch, Krakowskie Przedmiescie 7, Warsaw, Poland) Ed. Jacek Syski. bk.rev.; illus. circ. 64,800.
   Supersedes: Wspolczesnosc (ISSN 0510-9744)

800   HU   ISSN 0133-2368
PH3001
LITERATURA. 1974. q. $19.50. Magyar Tudomanyos Akademia, Irodalomtudomanyi Intezet, Menesi ut 11-13, 1118 Budapest, Hungary. TEL 36-1-166-5938. FAX 36-1-185-3876. Ed. B. Pomogats. adv.; bk.rev. Indexed: M.L.A.

800   LI   ISSN 0202-3296
LITERATURA. (Text and summaries in English, German, Lithuanian, Polish, Russian) 1958. 3/yr. price varies. Vilniaus Universitetas - Baltu Filologijos Katedra, c/o Prof. A. Rosinas, Universiteto 3, 2734 Vilnius, Lithuania. (Co-sponsor: Lithuanian Ministry of Culture and Education) Ed. V. Areska. circ. 500. (also avail. in microfilm from KTO) **Document type:** academic/scholarly publication.
—BLDSC (5276.678000).
   Description: Focuses on problems of Lithuanian, Russian, Germanic-Romance and antique literature.

860   US   ISSN 0730-0220
PQ7900
LITERATURA CHILENA; creacion y critica. 1977. irreg. $16 to individuals; institutions $22. Ediciones de la Frontera, Box 3013, Hollywood, CA 90078. Ed. David Valjalo. bk.rev. circ. 3,000.
   Formerly (until 1981): Literatura Chilena en el Exilio (ISSN 0278-7288)

891.7   RU
LITERATURA DREVNEI RUSI. 1975. irreg. 1 Rub. Moskovskii Gosudarstvennyi Pedagogicheskii Institut, Kafedra Russkoi Literatury, Moscow, Russia. circ. 1,000.

891.7   BW   ISSN 0024-4686
LITERATURA I MASTATSTVA. 1932. w. $8.40. (Ministerstvo Kul'tury) Literatura i Mastatstva, Vul. Zakharova 19, 22060 Minsk, Belarus. TEL 0172-332461. Ed. Mikola S. Gil. bk.rev.; illus.; index. (also avail. in microform) **Document type:** newspaper.

499.992   BL   ISSN 0024-4694
LITERATURA KAJERO;* monata kultura kajero en esperanto. (Text in Esperanto) 1968. m. Cr.$10.($3.) Henerik Kocher, Ed. & Pub., Rua Baltasar Lisboa 34, ZC-11 Rio de Janeiro GB, Brazil.

860   MX
LITERATURA MEXICANA. 1990. s-a. Universidad Nacional Autonoma de Mexico, Instituto de Investigaciones Filologicas, Centro de Estudios Literarios, Ciudad Universitaria, Cir. Mario de la Cueva, 04510 Mexico, D.F., Mexico. Ed. Margit Frenk. **Document type:** academic/scholarly publication.
   Refereed Serial

800   PL
LITERATURA NA SWIECIE. m. (Ministerstwo Kultury i Sztuki) Agencja Autorska, Ul. Hipoteczna 2, 00-950 Warsaw, Poland. (Subscr. to: RSW "Prasa-Ksiazka-Ruch" Centrala Kolportazu i Wydawnictw, ul. Towarowa 28, 00-958 Warsaw, Poland; Dist. by: Ars Polona, Krakowskie Przedmiescie 7, Warsaw, Polnad. TEL 48-22-267622) Ed. Waclaw Sadkowski. bk.rev.

891.7   RU
LITERATURA OB ARKHANGEL'SKOI OBLASTI. 1973. a. (Arkhangel'skaya Oblastnaya Biblioteka, Bibliograficheskii Otdel) Severo-Zapadnoe Knizhnoe Izdatel'stvo, Arkhangel'sk, Russia.

869   BL
LITERATURA POPULAR EM VERSO. 1983. irreg. Fundacao Casa de Rui Barbosa, Rua Sao Clemente 134, Botafogo 22260, Rio de Janeiro RJ, Brazil. FAX 5371114.

371.3   RU   ISSN 0130-3414
LITERATURA V SHKOLE. 1914. bi-m. $29. (Ministerstvo Prosveshcheniya) Izdatel'stvo Prosveshchenie, 3-i Proezd Mar'inoi Roshchi, 41, Moscow, Russia. TEL 289-44-34. TELEX 111999 PARK. (Dist. in U.S. by: Victor Kamkin Inc., 4956 Boiling Brook Pkwy, Rockville, MD 20852. TEL 301-881-5973) (Co-sponsor: Ministerstvo Narodnogo Obrazovaniya R.S.F.S.R.) Ed. N.L. Krupina. bk.rev.; bibl.; illus. circ. 286,986.
   Description: Aimed at literature teachers in grades 4-10. Presents materials on classical Russian and modern Soviet literature. Also contains articles on methodology of teaching literature in school.

860   PE
LITERATURAS ANDINAS. 1988. s-a. $12. Instituto de Estudios Cultura y Sociedad en los Andes, San Martin 771, Juaja, Peru.

LITERATURE AND BELIEF. see *RELIGIONS AND THEOLOGY*

052   US   ISSN 0306-1973
AS122.T45
LITERATURE & HISTORY. 1975-1988; N.S. 1990; N.S. 1992. s-a. $40 to individuals; institutions $60. Manchester University Press, Oxford Rd., Manchester MI3 9NR, England. TEL 061-273-5539. FAX 061-274-3346. Ed. Roger Richardson. adv.; bk.rev. circ. 600. Indexed: Abstr.Pop.Cult., Amer.Hist.& Life, Arts & Hum.Cit.Ind., Bk.Rev.Ind. (1984-1990), Child.Bk.Rev.Ind. (1984-1990), Curr.Cont., Hist.Abstr., Ind.Bk.Rev.Hum., LCR, M.L.A. **Document type:** academic/scholarly publication.
—BLDSC (5276.713000); Faxon; UnCover.
   Description: Explores the relations among writing, history, and ideology.

808 610   US   ISSN 0278-9671
PN56.M38
LITERATURE & MEDICINE. 1982. s-a. $20 to individuals (foreign $26.35); institutions $36 (foreign $40.35). (University of Texas Medical Branch at Galveston, Institute for the Medical Humanities) Johns Hopkins University Press, Journals Publishing Division, 2715 N. Charles St., Baltimore, MD 21218. TEL 410-565-6987. FAX 410-565-6998. Ed. Suzanne Poirier. adv. circ. 592. (back issues avail.) Indexed: Arts & Hum.Cit.Ind., Curr.Cont., M.L.A.
—BLDSC (5276.714500); Faxon; UnCover; SWETS; UMI. **CCC.**
   Description: Covers an emerging new specialty in the medical humanities.

809 150   US   ISSN 0024-4759
PN49   CODEN: LIPSA
LITERATURE AND PSYCHOLOGY; a quarterly journal of literary criticism as informed by depth psychology. 1951-1981; resumed 1984. q. $12 to individuals; institutions $20. c/o Morton Kaplan and Richard Feldstein, Eds., Department of English, Rhode Island College, Providence, RI 02908. bk.rev.; bibl. circ. 1,000. (also avail. in microform from UMI; reprint service avail. from SWZ,UMI) Indexed: Abstr.Engl.Stud., Amer.Bibl.Slavic & E.Eur.Stud., Curr.Cont., Film Lit.Ind. (1990-), Hum.Ind., Ind.Bk.Rev.Hum., M.L.A., Mid.East: Abstr.& Ind., Psychol.Abstr.
—BLDSC (5276.715000); Faxon; UnCover; UMI.

839   NE
LITERATURE AND SOCIETY IN THE SEVENTEENTH CENTURY. 1983. irreg. price varies. Dick Coutinho B.V., Slochterlaan 7, 1405 AL Bussum, Netherlands. TEL 31-2159-49991. FAX 31-2159-47165. **Document type:** monographic series.

800 100   US   ISSN 1040-7928
LITERATURE AND THE SCIENCES OF MAN. irreg. Peter Lang Publishing, Inc., 62 W. 45th St., 4th Fl., New York, NY 10036. TEL 212-302-6740. FAX 212-302-7574. Ed. Peter Heller. **Document type:** academic/scholarly publication.

800 700   US   ISSN 0888-3890
LITERATURE AND THE VISUAL ARTS: NEW FOUNDATIONS. irreg. Peter Lang Publishing, Inc., 62 W. 45th St., 4th Fl., New York, NY 10036. TEL 212-302-6740. FAX 212-302-7574. Ed. Ernest B. Gilman. **Document type:** academic/scholarly publication.
—BLDSC (5276.717000).
   Description: Explores the interrelationships of literature and the visual arts, including film.

3642 LITERATURE

800   UK   ISSN 0269-1205
PN49
LITERATURE AND THEOLOGY. 1987. 4/yr. £54($100) (effective 1994). Oxford University Press, Oxford Journals, Walton St., Oxford OX2 6DP, England. TEL 0865-56767. FAX 0865-56646. TELEX 837330-OXPRES-G. (U.S. subscr. to: Oxford University Press Inc., 2001 Evans Rd., Cary, NC 27513. TEL 919-677-0977) Ed. Rev. David Jasper. adv. contact: Jane Parker. bk.rev. circ. 700. **Indexed:** Rel.& Theol.Abstr. (1989-). **Document type:** academic/scholarly publication.
—BLDSC (5276.716000); Faxon; UnCover; SWETS; UMI. **CCC.**
    Description: Interdisciplinary study of serious interest to both theologians and to students of literature.

THE LITERATURE BASE. see *CHILDREN AND YOUTH — For*

800   US   ISSN 0740-2880
LITERATURE CRITICISM 1400 TO 1800. 3/yr. $104 per vol. Gale Research Inc., 835 Penobscot Bldg., Detroit, MI 48226. TEL 313-961-2242. FAX 313-961-6083. Eds. James P. Draper, James E. Pearson, Jr.
    Description: Provides excerpts from criticism of the works of authors who died in these years. Focuses on 8 to 10 authors from all over the world in each volume.

800   US   ISSN 0024-4767
PN2
LITERATURE EAST AND WEST. Short title: L E & W. 1954. q. $10. c/o Department of Oriental and African Languages and Literatures, University of Texas, Austin, 2601 University Ave., Austin, TX 78712. Ed. Michael Hillman. adv.; bk.rev.; index. circ. 500. (also avail. in microform from MIM,UMI; reprint service avail. from UMI,ISI) **Indexed:** Abstr.Engl.Stud., Curr.Cont., M.L.A., Mid.East: Abstr.& Ind.
—UnCover; UMI.

LITERATURE - FILM QUARTERLY. see *MOTION PICTURES*

891.8   XN   ISSN 0024-4791
PG1161
LITERATUREN ZBOR; jezik, literatura, nastavi, prikazi. (Text in Macedonian) 1954. s-a. 15 din.($4.20) Drustvoto za Makedonski Jazik i Literatura, Grigor Prlicev 5, 91000 Skopje, Macedonia. (Co-sponsor: Institut za Makedonski Jazik, Skopje) Ed. Blagoja Karilin. **Indexed:** Bibl.Ling., M.L.A.

891.8   BU   ISSN 0324-0495
LITERATURNA MISAL. (Contents page in English and French) 1957. 10/yr. 1.30 lv. per no. (Bulgarska Akademiia na Naukite, Institut za Literatura) Publishing House of the Bulgarian Academy of Sciences, Acad. G. Bonchev St., Bldg. 6, 1113 Sofia, Bulgaria. (Dist. by: Hemus, 6, Rouski Blvd., 1000 Sofia, Bulgaria) Ed. Pantelei Zarev. bk.rev.; index. circ. 1,660. (reprint service avail. from IRC) **Indexed:** Can.Rev.Comp.Lit., M.L.A.

LITERATURNAYA ROSSIYA. see *LITERARY AND POLITICAL REVIEWS*

891.7   AJ   ISSN 0130-3643
LITERATURNYI AZERBAIDZHAN. (Text in Russian) 1942. bi-m. $42. Soyuz Pisatelei Azerbaidzhana, Ul. Khagani 25, 370000 Baku, Azerbaijan. (Dist. in U.S. by: Victor Kamkin Inc., Boiling Brook Pkwy., Rockville, MD 20852. TEL 301-881-5973. FAX 301-881-1637) Ed. I.P. Tretyakov. bk.rev.; bibl.; charts; illus. circ. 3,460.

891.7   KR
PG3900
LITERATUROZNAVSTVO. 1957. m. (Akademiya Nauk Ukrainy, Institut Literatury im. T.G. Shevchenko) Vidavnitstvo Naukova Dumka, Vul. Tereshchenkivska 3, 25601 Kiev, Ukraine. TEL 044-224-4068. FAX 044-224-7060. (Co-sponsor: Soyuz Pisatelei Ukrainy) Ed. V.G. Belyaev. bk.rev.; bibl.; illus.; index. circ. 2,895.
    Formerly: Radyans'ke Literaturoznavstvo (ISSN 0131-0194)

830   GW   ISSN 0075-997X
PT13
LITERATURWISSENSCHAFTLICHES JAHRBUCH. NEUE FOLGE. 1960. a. price varies. (Goerres-Gesellschaft) Duncker und Humblot GmbH, Postfach 410329, 12113 Berlin, Germany. TEL 030-7900060. FAX 030-79000631. Ed.Bd. bk.rev. **Indexed:** Can.Rev.Comp.Lit., M.L.A. **Document type:** academic/scholarly publication.
—BLDSC (5276.739500).

800   GW
LITFASS; Berliner Zeitschrift fuer Literatur. 1976. q. DM.35.20. U V A, Kronenstr. 3, 10117 Berlin, Germany. Eds. Cornelia Staudacher, Peter Urban-Halle. adv.; bk.rev.; bibl.; illus.; stat.; tr.lit.; index. circ. 4,000. **Document type:** academic/scholarly publication.

800   NE   ISSN 0169-8702
LITTERAE TEXTUALES; a series on manuscripts and their texts. 1972. irreg., latest 1990. price varies. E.J. Brill, P.O. Box 9000, 2300 PA Leiden, Netherlands. TEL 31-71-312624. FAX 31-71-317532. TELEX 39296 BRILL NL. (In N. America: E.J. Brill, 24 Hudson St., Kinderhook, NY 12106. TEL 800-962-4406. FAX 518-758-1959) Eds. A. Gruys, J.P. Gumbert. **Document type:** monographic series.

800   PL   ISSN 0084-3008
LITTERARIA; teoria literatury-metodologia-kultura-humanistyka. 1969. irreg., vol.21, 1989. price varies. (Wroclawskie Towarzystwo Naukowe) Ossolineum, Publishing House of the Polish Academy of Sciences, Rynek 9, 50-106 Wroclaw, Poland. TEL 48-71-386-25. FAX 48-71-448-103. TELEX 0712771 OSS PL. (Co-sponsor: Polska Akademia Nauk) Ed. Jan Trzynadlowski. bk.rev. circ. 700. (also avail. in microfilm) **Document type:** academic/scholarly publication.
    Description: Devoted to Polish literature of the past and present, comparative literature, sociology of literature, and literary criticism.

891.87   XO
LITTERARIA. irreg. price varies. (Slovenska Akademia Vied, Literarnovedny Ustav) Veda, Publishing House of the Slovak Academy of Sciences, Klemensova 19, 814 30 Bratislava, Slovakia. (Dist. by: Slovart, Nam. Slobody 6, 817 64 Bratislava, Slovakia)

800 400   NE   ISSN 0862-8424
PN1
LITTERARIA PRAGENSIA. 1958; N.S. 1991. 2/yr. fl.98($59) (effective 1994). (Czech Academy of Sciences, Institute for Czech and World Literature, XR) John Benjamins Publishing Co., Amsteldijk 44, P.O. Box 75577, 1070 AN Amsterdam, Netherlands. TEL 31-20-6792956. FAX 31-20-6738156. (In N. America: 821 Bethlehem Pike, Philadelphia, PA 19118. TEL 215-836-1200. FAX 215-836-1204) Ed. Zdenek Hrbata. (back issues avail.) **Document type:** academic/scholarly publication.
    Supersedes in part (in 1991): Philologica Pragensia (ISSN 0048-3885)
    Description: Contemporary literary and cultural studies, with an emphasis on literary discourse.

800   FR   ISSN 0047-4800
LITTERATURE. 1971. q. 270 F. Larousse, 17 rue de Montparnasse, 75280 Paris Cedex 06, France. (Dist. by: Gauthier-Villars, Centrale des Revues, 11 rue Gossin, 92543 Montrouge Cedex, France. TEL 1-46-56-52-66) Ed.Bd. bk.rev.; bibl. **Indexed:** Arts & Hum.Cit.Ind., Curr.Cont., M.L.A.
—BLDSC (5277.495000); Faxon; SWETS. **CCC.**

800   CC   ISSN 1000-9132
LITTERATURE CHINOISE. English edition: Chinese Literature (ISSN 0009-4617) (Text in French) q. (Wenhua Bu, Waiwen Ju - China Foreign Languages Publishing and Distribution Administration) Zhongguo Wenxue Zazhishe - Chinese Literature Press, 24 Baiwanzhuang Lu, Beijing 100037, People's Republic of China. TEL 8323291. (Dist. outside China by: China International Book Trading Corp., P.O. Box 399, Beijing, P.R. China) Ed. Yin Shuxun. **Document type:** government publication.

840   FR   ISSN 0563-9751
PN3
LITTERATURES. 1951. s-a. 160 F. to individuals; students 120 F. (effective 1994). (Universite de Toulouse II (le Mirail)) Presses Universitaires du Mirail, 56 rue du Taur, 31000 Toulouse, France. TEL 61-22-58-31. FAX 61-21-84-20. Ed. Claude Sicard. (back issues avail.) **Indexed:** M.L.A. **Document type:** academic/scholarly publication.
—BLDSC (5277.750000).
    Description: Covers French, German, Italian and slavic-language literature; comparative literature; theatrical, musical and cinematographic studies.

LITTLE BALKANS REVIEW; Southeast Kansas literary and graphics quarterly. see *ART*

810   US   ISSN 0024-5054
LITTLE REVIEW. 1969. irreg. $6. Little Review Press, Marshall University, Huntington, WV 25701. TEL 304-696-6499. Ed. John McKernan. bk.rev. circ. 1,000. (also avail. in microfilm from UMI) **Indexed:** Ind.Amer.Per.Verse.
    Description: Focuses on literature; contemporary poetry and poetic theory.

800   US
LIVE LETTERS. 1974. s-a. $20. Center for Live Letters, 156 Hunter St., Kingston, NY 12401. FAX 914-338-5986. bk.rev.; illus. circ. 500. (back issues avail.)
    Formerly: Letters.

860   UK   ISSN 0261-1538
LIVERPOOL MONOGRAPHS IN HISPANIC STUDIES. 1982. irreg. (1-3/yr.). price varies. Francis Cairns (Publications) Ltd., c/o the University, Leeds LS2 9JT, England. Ed. James Higgins. (back issues avail.) **Indexed:** M.L.A. **Document type:** monographic series.

800   UK   ISSN 0076-0188
LLEN CYMRU. (Text in Welsh) 1950. irreg. £5. (Board of Celtic Studies) University of Wales Press, 6 Gwennyth St., Cathays, Cardiff CF2 4YD, Wales. TEL 0222-231919. FAX 0222-230908. Ed. C.W. Lewis. adv.; bk.rev. circ. 250. (also avail. in microfilm from UMI; reprint service avail. from UMI) **Indexed:** M.L.A. **Document type:** academic/scholarly publication.
    Description: Contains research in Welsh language and Welsh literary history.

LO GAI SABER. see *LINGUISTICS*

891.85   PL   ISSN 0079-4791
PG7001
LODZKIE TOWARZYSTWO NAUKOWE. PRACE POLONISTYCZNE. 1951. a. price varies. Lodzkie Towarzystwo Naukowe, Ul. Piotrowska 179, 50-106 Wroclaw, Poland. TEL 48-71-386-25. FAX 48-71-448-103. TELEX 0712771 OSS PL. (Co-sponsor: Polska Akademia Nauk) Ed. Krystyna Poklewska. bk.rev. circ. 800. (also avail. in microfilm) **Document type:** academic/scholarly publication.
—BLDSC (6591.500000).
    Description: Polonistic works on prose and poetry of Polish writers.

800   PL   ISSN 0076-0404
LODZKIE TOWARZYSTWO NAUKOWE. PRACE WYDZIALU JEZYKOZNAWSTWA, NAUKI O LITERATURZE I FILOZOFII. (Text in Polish; summaries in English, French, Russian) 1947. irreg., no.92, 1990. price varies. Ossolineum, Publishing House of the Polish Academy of Sciences, Rynek 9, 50-106 Wroclaw, Poland. TEL 48-71-386-25. FAX 48-71-448-103. TELEX 0712771 OSS PL. (Co-sponsor: Polska Akademia Nauk) **Document type:** monographic series.

800   US
LOEB CLASSICAL LIBRARY. irreg., no.475, 1990. $15.50. Harvard University Press, 79 Garden St., Cambridge, MA 02138. TEL 617-495-2600. FAX 617-495-5898. **Document type:** monographic series.
    Refereed Serial

830 UK
PT1
LONDON GERMAN STUDIES. 1980. irreg., latest 1993. price varies. University of London, Institute of Germanic Studies, 29 Russell Square, London WC1B 5DP, England. TEL 071-580-2711. FAX 071-436-3497. circ. 300. **Document type:** proceedings.
 Description: Selection of essays previously given as lectures at the institute.

820 UK ISSN 0024-614X
LONDON REVIEW.* 1967. s-a. 40p.($0.96) 45 Manor Rd., Ashford, Middx., England. Ed. T.F. Evans. adv. circ. 500.

800 US ISSN 8756-5099
PS536.2
LONG POND REVIEW. 1975. a. $4 per no. to individuals; institutions $5. Long Pond Review Press, Suffolk County Community College, English Dept., 533 College Rd., Selden, NY 11784. TEL 516-451-4110. Ed. Russell Steinke. adv.; bk.rev. circ. 1,000.

800 US ISSN 0895-9773
LONG SHOT. 1982. 2/yr. $20. Long Shot Productions, Box 6238, Hoboken, NJ 07030. Ed.Bd. adv.: B&W page $150. circ. 1,500. (back issues avail.)

800 US ISSN 0741-4242
LONG STORY. 1983. a. $5. 11 Kingston St., North Andover, MA 01845. TEL 508-686-7638. Ed. R.P. Burnham. circ. 800. (back issues avail.) **Indexed:** A.I.P.P., Amer.Hum.Ind.

890 II ISSN 0377-1083
LORE; magazine of new writing. (Text in English) 1974. m. Rs.10. (Delhi Writers' Club) Rami Press, 48 Mandirwali Gali, Yusof Sarai, New Delhi, India. Ed. M. C. Bose. adv.; bk.rev.; bibl.

800 900 US ISSN 0091-2948
NX504
LOST GENERATION JOURNAL. 1973. a. $10. Deloris & Tom Wood, Eds. & Pubs., Rte. 5, Box 134, Salem, MO 65560. TEL 314-729-2545. FAX 314-729-9495. adv.; bk.rev. circ. 500. (back issues avail.) **Indexed:** Abstr.Engl.Stud., Abstr.Pop.Cult., Amer.Hum.Ind., M.L.A. **Document type:** academic/scholarly publication.
 —UnCover. **CCC.**
 Description: Covers American writers, performers and artists in Europe, mainly Paris, France, from 1919 to 1939.

896 892 895 UA
PN2
LOTUS; Afro-Asian writings. 1968. q. Permanent Bureau of Afro-Asian Writers, 104 Sharia Kasr El-Aini, Cairo, Egypt. Ed. Youssef El Sebai. bk.rev.; bibl.; illus.
 Formerly: Afro-Asian Writings (ISSN 0002-0664)

800 US ISSN 0890-0477
LOUISIANA LITERATURE. 1984. s-a. $10 to individuals; institutions $12.50. Southeastern Louisiana University, English Department, Box 792, Hammond, LA 70402. TEL 504-549-2113. Ed. David Hanson. adv.; bk.rev. circ. 650. **Document type:** academic/scholarly publication.
 Formerly: L A Lit - Louisiana Literature.
 Description: Essays relevant to Louisiana's literature, history and art. Includes poetry and fiction.

800 US ISSN 0148-3250
PS501
LOUISVILLE REVIEW. 1976. s-a. $7 (typically set in May). (University of Louisville) Louisville Review Corporation, Louisville, KY 40292. TEL 502-588-6801. Ed. Sena Naslund. circ. 500.
 Description: Contains poetry and fiction, plus children's (K-12) work in the spring.

800 US
LOVE AND ROCKETS. 1982. bi-m. $16.50. Fantagraphics Books, Inc., 7563 Lake City Way, N.E., Seattle, WA 98115. TEL 206-524-1967. FAX 206-524-2104. circ. 22,000. **Document type:** consumer publication.

LOVECRAFT STUDIES. see LITERATURE — Science Fiction, Fantasy, Horror

LOVING BROTHERHOOD NEWSLETTER; a journal for personal and planetary transformation. see HOMOSEXUALITY

810 US
LOWLANDS REVIEW. 1975. s-a. $3 per no. 6048 Perrier, New Orleans, LA 70118. TEL 504-895-5619. Ed. Tom Whalen. bk.rev. circ. 400.

895.1 CC
LU MING. (Text in Chinese) bi-m. Baotou Shi Wenlian - Baotou Municipal Literary and Art Circle Association, Jinrong Dalou (Financial Building), Kundulun-qu, Baotou, Nei Menggu 014010, People's Republic of China. TEL 62935. Ed. Ge Fei.

LU XUN YANJIU YUEKAN/LU XUN STUDIES MONTHLY. see BIOGRAPHY

860 SP ISSN 0214-4581
LUCANOR; revista del cuento literario. 1988. s-a. Apdo. Correos 1138, 31080 Pamplona, Spain. TEL 948-23-37-07.

859 RM
LUCEAFARUL. 1958. w. 208 lei. Uniunea Scriitorilor din Republica Socialista Romania, Calea Victoriei 115, Bucharest, Rumania. (Subscr. to: ILEXIM, Str. 13 Decembrie Nr. 3, Box 136-137, 70116 Bucharest, Rumania) Ed. Nicolae Dan Runtelata. bk.rev.; film rev.; play rev.; charts; illus. circ. 7,000. **Indexed:** M.L.A.

860 CK
LUCIERNAGA. 1981. bi-m. Apartado Aereo 8663, Cali, Colombia.

800 BE
LUCRE-HATIF. 1962. m. 300 Fr. Institut Catholique des Hautes Etudes Commerciales, Cercle des Etudiants, 2 Bd. Brand Whitlock, B-1040 Brussels, Belgium. TEL 02-732-01-50. Ed. Marc Jossart. adv.; bk.rev.; film rev.; illus. circ. 800. (processed)
 Formerly: Confins (ISSN 0010-5694)
 Description: Informs students, teachers, and members of events in the ICHEC. Contains interesting surveys about the students.

LUMEN. see HISTORY

700 800 YU ISSN 0350-4174
LUMINA. (Text in Rumanian) 1946. m. $5.70. Libertatea, Zarka Zrenjanina 7, Pancevo, Serbia, Yugoslavia. Ed. Ion Balan. bibl.

LUMO; Kanada Esperanto-Revuo. see LINGUISTICS

810 US
LUNA NEGRA. 1956. s-a. $2. Kent State University, Department of English, Satterfield Hall, Kent, OH 44242. TEL 216-672-2121. Ed. Maggie Anderson. adv.; illus. circ. 1,500. (processed) **Indexed:** A.I.P.P.
 Former titles: New Kent Quarterly; Human Issue (ISSN 0018-7232)

850 IT
LUNARIONUOVO. bi-m. L.15000. Mario Grasso, Ed. & Pub., Via Duca d'Aosta 90, 95037 San Giovanni La Punta, Italy.

810 US
LUNCH. 1975. q. $6. Fairleigh Dickinson University, 1000 River Rd., Teaneck, NJ 07666-1996. TEL 201-692-2000. Ed. Robert Quatrone. adv. circ. 500.

850 IT
I LUOGHI DELL'ANIMA. 1990. irreg., no.2, 1993. price varies. Liguori Editore s.r.l., Via Mezzocannone 19, 80134 Naples, Italy. TEL 081-5527139. Ed. Elena Vitas. **Document type:** monographic series.

808.81 FR ISSN 0754-927X
LUVAH. 1982. q. 100 F.($15) (effective 1991). Association Luvah, 25220 Amagney, France. Ed. Louis Uccieni. adv. circ. 300. (back issues avail.)

839.71 SW ISSN 0460-0762
LYRIKVAENNEN; tidskrift foer F I B's lyrikklubb. 1954. bi-m. SEK 169 (effective 1990). F I B's Lyrikklubb, P.O. Box 30184, S-104 25 Stockholm, Sweden.

810 US ISSN 0163-755X
PN843
M E L U S. Key Title: Melus. 1974. 4/yr. (in 1 vol.). $40 (foreign $48). Society for the Study of the Multi-Ethnic Literature of the United States, 272 Bartlett Hall, Department of English, University of Massachusetts, Amherst, MA 01003. TEL 413-545-3166. FAX 413-545-3880. Ed. Joseph T. Skerrett, Jr. adv.; bk.rev. circ. 900. (also avail. in microform from UMI) **Indexed:** Abstr.Anthropol., Abstr.Engl.Stud., Amer.Bibl.Slavic & E.Eur.Stud., Amer.Hum.Ind., Arts & Hum.Cit.Ind., Curr.Cont., Hum.Ind. **Document type:** academic/scholarly publication.
 —BLDSC (5546.358000); Faxon; UnCover; UMI.
 Description: Presents research, scholarly essays, and interviews of interest to those concerned with the multiethnic scope of America's literature, including Asian-American, African-American, Hispanic-American, Native-American and immigrant European literature.

800 US ISSN 1073-3027
▼**M F E COLLECTOR'S BOOKLINE;** newsletter for collectors of modern first editions and recent fiction. 1992. m. $135. Box 150119, San Rafael, CA 94915. TEL 415-457-5463. FAX 415-457-5463. Ed. David M. Brown. **Document type:** newsletter.

800 028.5 IS ISSN 0334-2867
MA'AGALAI KERI'A. (Text in Arabic, Hebrew) 1977. s-a. IS.32($25) (Haifa University, Center for Children's Literature) Haifa University Press, Mount Carmel, Haifa 31999, Israel. TEL 972-4-240601. FAX 972-4-342245. Ed. Adir Cohen. circ. 400. **Document type:** academic/scholarly publication.

MAARAV; a journal for the study of the northwest semitic languages and literatures. see LINGUISTICS

890 920 011 IS
MABUA/FOUNTAIN; religious creation in literature, society and thought. (Text and summaries in Hebrew) 1965. a. $20. Association of Religious Writers, 58 King George St., Jerusalem 91074, Israel. Ed. Ya'akov Edelstein. adv.; bk.rev. circ. 2,000. (back issues avail.) **Indexed:** Ind.Heb.Per.

800 700 XN ISSN 0350-3089
MACEDONIAN REVIEW; history, culture, literature, arts. (Text in English) 1971. 3/yr. $20 (effective Jan. 1991). Kulturen Zivot - Cultural Life, Ruzveltova, 6, P.O. Box 85, 91001 Skopje, Macedonia. Ed. Boris Vishinski. bk.rev.; illus. (reprint service avail. from UMI) **Indexed:** Amer.Hist.& Life (1992-), Bibl.Ling., Hist.Abstr. (1992-), M.L.A.

800 US
MACGUFFIN. 1984. 3/yr. $12. Schoolcraft College, English Department, Schoolcraft College, 18600 Haggerty Rd., Livonia, MI 48152. TEL 313-462-4400. Ed. Arthur J. Lindenberg. circ. 500. (back issues avail.)
 Description: Named after a cinematic story technique made famous by Alfred Hitchcock, this literary journal contains an eclectic and wide range of poetry, short fiction, essays, and artwork.

800 976 US ISSN 0885-467X
AS36
MCNEESE REVIEW. 1948. a. $3 (foreign $4.25). McNeese State University, Box 92940, Lake Charles, LA 70609. TEL 318-475-5127. Ed. Benjamin C. Harlow. circ. 200. (back issues avail.) **Indexed:** Abstr.Engl.Stud.
 Description: Presents original, previously unpublished manuscripts and documented research of a scholarly nature.

800 US ISSN 1054-2655
PS681
MAD RIVER; a journal of essays. 1991. 3/yr. $18. Wright State University, 006 U.C., Dayton, OH 45435. TEL 513-873-2031. Ed. Charles S. Taylor. bk.rev. **Document type:** academic/scholarly publication.
 Description: Multidisciplinary journal of essays, original works of art, and reviews of classical and jazz CDs.

895.49 NP
MADHUPARKA. (Text in Nepali) 1986. m. Dharma Path, P.O. Box 23, Kathmandu, Nepal. TEL 222278. Ed. Krishna Bhakta Shrestha. circ. 20,000.

LITERATURE

830 GW
DIE MAERCHEN ZEITSCHRIFT. bi-m. DM.24 (foreign DM.27). Troubadour e.V., Bretthorststr. 140, 32602 Vlotho, Germany. TEL 05733-10801. Ed.Bd. adv. contact: Helga Welsner. Document type: consumer publication.

MAGAZIN POLOVNIKA. see SPORTS AND GAMES — Outdoor Life

800 FR ISSN 0024-9807
PN3
MAGAZINE LITTERAIRE. 1966. m. 335 F. (foreign 450 F.)(effective Mar.1992). Magazine-Expansion, 40, rue des Saints-Peres, 75007 Paris, France. TEL 45-44-14-51. FAX 45-48-86-36. Ed. Jean-Jacques Brochier. adv.; bk.rev. circ. 95,000. Indexed: Pt.de Rep. (1979-).
—BLDSC (5333.470000); Faxon; SWETS.

100 700 US ISSN 0196-8432
MAGIC CHANGES; the biannual for independent artists. 1979. s-a. $5. (Order of the Celestial Otter) Celestial Otter Press, c/o John Sennett, Ed., Box 658, Warrenville, IL 60555-9269. TEL 708-416-3111. adv. contact: Kaela Sennett. bk.rev. circ. 500. (back issues avail.)

808.838 US ISSN 1061-2386
MAGIC REALISM. 1990. 3/yr. $14.95 (effective 1993). Pyx Press, Box 620, Orem, UT 84059-0620. Eds. C. Darren Butler, Julie Thomas. adv. contact: C. Darren Butler. bk.rev. circ. 700. (back issues avail.) Document type: consumer publication.
Formerly (until 1991): Cacophony.
Description: Publishes magic realism and related fiction and poetry, including literary fantasy and folktales, as well as critical articles on the genre.

MAGICAL BLEND; a transformative journey. see NEW AGE PUBLICATIONS

028.1 US ISSN 0163-3058
Z1219
MAGILL'S LITERARY ANNUAL. (Update to: Masterplots and Survey of Contemporary Literature) a. $70. Salem Press, Inc., Magill Books, Box 1097, Englewood Cliffs, NJ 07632. TEL 201-871-3700. FAX 201-871-8668. Ed. F.N. Magill. Indexed: Amer.Bibl.Slavic & E.Eur.Stud. Document type: academic/scholarly publication.
Formerly: Masterplots Annual.
Description: Contains reviews of 200 noteworthy books - fiction, poetry, drama, biography, autobiography, diaries, and memoires - published in the U.S. during the preceding calendar year.

MAGPIES; talking about books for children. see CHILDREN AND YOUTH — About

894.51 HU ISSN 0076-2385
MAGYAR IRODALOMTORTENETIRAS FORRASAI; fontes ad historiam litterariam Hungariae spectantes. 1960. irreg. price varies. (Magyar Tudomanyos Akademia) Akademiai Kiado, Publishing House of the Hungarian Academy of Sciences, P.O. Box 245, H-1519 Budapest, Hungary. TEL 181-2134. FAX 166-6466. TELEX 22-6228 AKNYO H.

891.4 II ISSN 0025-049X
MAHENJODARO. (Text in Bengali) 1959. q. Rs.3. 5514 Natabar Pal Rd., Howrah, West Bengal, India. Ed. Samir Ray. bk.rev.; film rev.; play rev.; abstr.; illus. circ. 2,300.

MAIA; rivista di letterature classiche. see CLASSICAL STUDIES

800 US
MAINE SCHOLAR; a journal of ideas and public affairs. 1988. a. $13 to individuals; institutions $15. University of Maine, Honors Program, 102 Bedford St., Portland, ME 04103. Ed. Wanda P. Whitten.
Description: Provides a public forum for an interdisciplinary approach to public affairs work by faculty, students, and scholars from Maine and across the country.

820 UK ISSN 0025-0848
MAINLY.* 1965. irreg. (2-4/yr.). 2s. 6d. per no.($.75). Carregraff, Graig Las, Talybont, Brecon, Wales. Eds. Lyndon Puw, Chrissie Smith. bk.rev.; illus. circ. 1,000.

830 GW ISSN 0076-2784
MAINZER REIHE. 1960. irreg., no.76. price varies. (Akademie der Wissenschaften und der Literatur, Mainz) Hase und Koehler Verlag KG, Bahnhofstr. 6, 55116 Mainz, Germany. FAX 06131-227952. adv.; bk.rev. Indexed: Math.R. Document type: monographic series.

810 418.02 GW ISSN 0170-9135
MAINZER STUDIEN ZUR AMERIKANISTIK. (Text in English, German) 1972. irreg., no.26, 1992. Peter Lang GmbH Europaeischer Verlag der Wissenschaften, Eschborner Landstr. 42-50, 60489 Frankfurt a.M., Germany. TEL 069-7807050. FAX 069-785893. Eds. Renate von Basdeleben, Winfried Herget. circ. 225. (back issues avail.) Document type: monographic series.

892.7 SY ISSN 0002-4031
PJ6001
MAJMA' AL-LUGHAH AL-ARABIYYAH. MAJALLAH/ACADEMIE ARABE DE DAMAS. REVUE. (Not published 1938-1940) 1921. q. $12 (effective 1994). Academie Arabe de Damas - Arab Language Academy - Majma' al-Lughah al-Arabiyyah bi-Dimashq, P.O. Box 327, Damascus, Syria. TEL 713145. Ed. Dr. Shakir al-Faham. bk.rev.; bibl.; index, cum.index; circ. 2,000 (paid). Document type: academic/scholarly publication.
Description: Covers Arabic culture and traditions in language, history and literature.

800 UK
MAJOR EUROPEAN AUTHOR SERIES. irreg. price varies. Cambridge University Press, Edinburgh Bldg., Shaftesbury Rd., Cambridge CB2 2RU, England. TEL 0223-312393. FAX 0223-315052. TELEX 851817256. (N. American addr.: Cambridge University Press, Journals Dept., 40 W. 20th St., New York, NY 10011. TEL 212-924-3900. FAX 212-691-3239) Document type: monographic series.

800 US
MAJOR 20TH-CENTURY WRITERS. 1991. irreg. Gale Research Inc., 835 Penobscot Bldg., Detroit, MI 48226-4094. TEL 313-961-2242. FAX 313-961-6083. Ed. Bryan Ryan. (also avail. in magnetic tape)
● Also available online. Vendor(s): Mead Data Central, Inc. (GALBIO).
Description: Contains over 1000 bio-bibliographical entries on the most prominent writers of the century.

813 US ISSN 1060-3409
PS3535.A845
MAJORIE KINNAN RAWLINGS JOURNAL OF FLORIDA LITERATURE. 1988. a. $5 to individuals; institutions $10. Illinois State University, Department of English, Normal, IL 61761. TEL 309-438-5776. FAX 309-438-5414. circ. 500. (back issues avail.)
—UnCover.
Formerly (until 1988): Rawlings Journal (ISSN 1052-7583).
Description: Articles, notes, reviews on literature on Florida or by Florida writers.

MAKEDONSKA AKADEMIJA NA NAUKITE I UMETNOSTITE. ODDELENIE ZA LINGVISTIKA I LITERATURNA NAUKA. PRILOZI/MACEDONIAN ACADEMY OF SCIENCES AND ARTS. SECTION OF LINGUISTICS AND LITERARY SCIENCES. CONTRIBUTIONS. see LINGUISTICS

899 MY ISSN 0128-1186
MALAY LITERATURE. (Text in English and Malay) 1967. s-a. M.$20 to individuals (institutions M.$24); foreign individuals $5 (institutions $7). National Language and Literary Agency of Malaysia - Dewan Bahasa dan Pustaka Malaysia, Box 10803, 50926 Kuala Lumpur, Malaysia. FAX 03-2482726. TELEX MA 32683. Ed. S. Jaafar Husin. adv.; bk.rev. circ. 3,000. Indexed: M.L.A.
Formerly (until 1989): Tenggara.
Description: Introduces to the world the literature of the Malay region of Indonesia, Malaysia, Brunei Darussalam and Singapore.

990 FJ ISSN 0379-5268
MANA; South Pacific journal of language and literature. (Text in English) 1973. 2/yr. F.$4. South Pacific Creative Arts Society, c/o IPS, Box 1168, Suva, Fiji. FAX 679-301594. adv.; bk.rev. circ. 1,500. Indexed: M.L.A., So.Pac.Per.Ind.
Formerly: Mana Annual of Creative Writing.

MANG YUAN. see ART

895.1 CC ISSN 1003-9309
MANG ZHONG. (Text in Chinese) m. Y2.10($63) per no. Mang Zhong Zazhishe, 29 Shiwei Lu, Heping-qu, Shengyang, Liaoning 110003, People's Republic of China. TEL 024-2828718. (Dist. in US by: China Books & Periodicals, 2929 24th St., San Francisco, CA 94110. TEL 415-282-2994) Ed. Tang Yaohua.

820 700 PH
MANILA REVIEW; Philippines journal of literature and the arts. (Text in English) 1975. q. P.25($5) Department of Public Information, c/o Bureau of National and Foreign Information, U P L Building, Box 3396, Intramuros, Manila, Philippines. Ed. Gregorio C. Brillantes. bk.rev.; film rev.; charts; illus.

100 700 US
MANIPUR STATE KALA AKADEMI. QUARTERLY JOURNAL. (Text in English) vol.2, 1977. q. Rs.8. Manipur State Kala Akademi, Jawaharlal Nehru Manipur, Dance Academy, Imphal, India. Ed.Bd. bk.rev.

MANNHEIMER BEITRAEGE ZUR SPRACH- UND LITERATURWISSENSCHAFT. see LINGUISTICS

800 808.81 US ISSN 1045-7909
PN771 CODEN: MANOE7
MANOA; a Pacific journal of international writing. 1989. s-a. $18 to individuals (foreign $21); institutions $22 (foreign $26). University of Hawaii Press, Journals Department, 2840 Kolowalu St., Honolulu, HI 96822. TEL 808-948-8833. FAX 808-988-6052. Eds. Robert Shapard, Frank Stewart. adv.; bk.rev.; illus. circ. 530. (back issues avail.; reprint service avail. from UMI) Document type: academic/scholarly publication.
—UMI.
Description: International literary review presents fiction, poetry, artwork and articles of current cultural and literary interest.
Refereed Serial

800 US ISSN 0267-2510
MANUSCRIPT STUDIES. 1985. irreg. Boydell & Brewer Inc., Box 41026, Rochester, NY 14604. TEL 716-275-0419. FAX 716-271-8778.
—BLDSC (5368.242000).

091 900 US ISSN 0025-2603
Z6602
MANUSCRIPTA; a journal devoted to manuscript studies. (Text mainly in English; occasionally in other languages) 1957. 3/yr. $20. St. Louis University, Pius XII Memorial Library, 3650 Lindell Blvd., St. Louis, MO 63108. TEL 314-658-3090. Ed. Charles Ermatinger. adv.; bk.rev.; bibl.; illus.; cum.index. circ. 1,000. (also avail. in microfilm) Indexed: Amer.Bibl.Slavic & E.Eur.Stud., Amer.Hist.& Life, Amer.Hum.Ind., Arts & Hum.Cit.Ind., Cath.Ind., CERDIC, Curr.Cont., Hist.Abstr., Ind.Bk.Rev.Hum., M.L.A., Old Test.Abstr., RILA. Document type: academic/scholarly publication.
—Faxon; UnCover.

800 RM
MANUSCRIPTUM. (Text in Rumanian and original language of manuscript; summaries in English, French, German, Russian) 1970. q. 200 lei per no. ($50/yr.). Muzeul Literaturii Romane, Bd. Dacia, Nr. 12, 71116 Bucharest 1, Rumania. TEL 6-50-20-96. FAX 6-42-41-69. (Subscr. to: Orion s.r.l., Spaliul Independentei nr. 202 A, Sector 6, Bucharest, Rumania. TEL 1-17-34-07) adv.; bk.rev. circ. 2,000. Indexed: M.L.A.
Description: Review of the history of Rumanian literature.

830 700 AU ISSN 0025-2638
PT1141.A2
MANUSKRIPTE; Zeitschrift fuer Literatur, Kunst, Kritik. 1960. 4/yr. S.315. Forum Stadtpark, Stadtpark 1, A-8010 Graz, Austria. TEL 0316-827734. FAX 0316-8253696. Eds. Guenther Waldorf, Alfred Kolleritsch. adv.; bk.rev. circ. 3,000. Document type: academic/scholarly publication.
—Faxon.

895.1 CC
MANZU WENXUE/MANCHU LITERATURE. (Text in Chinese) bi-m. $20.70. Manzu Wenxue Zazhishe, 107 Qijing Jie, Dandong, Liaoning 118000, People's Republic of China. TEL 27950. (Dist. in US by: China Books & Periodicals, Inc., 2929 24th St., San Francisco, CA 94110. TEL 415-282-2994)

830		GW

MARBACHER MAGAZIN. 1976. q. DM.37. Deutsche Schillergesellschaft e.V., Schillerhoehe 8-10, 71672 Marbach a.N., Germany. TEL 07144-848-0. FAX 07144-848-299. **Document type:** academic/scholarly publication.

MARCHE ROMANE. see *LINGUISTICS*

800		BE	ISSN 0025-293X

AP22
MARGINALES; revue des idees et des lettres. 1945. m. $12. Reui Fayt, Bd. General Jacques 159, B-1050 Brussels, Belgium. Ed. Reui Fayt. bk.rev.; play rev.; illus. circ. 1,000.

810		US

MARI SANDOZ HERITAGE. 1971. s-a. $15. Mari Sandoz Heritage Society, c/o Chadron State College, Chadron, NE 69337. TEL 308-432-4451. Ed. Sybil Berndt. adv.; illus. circ. 200. **Document type:** newsletter.

818.409		US	ISSN 1042-5357

MARK TWAIN CIRCULAR. (Supplement to: Mark Twain Journal.) 1987. q. $7 (foreign $8). Mark Twain Circle of America, c/o James S. Leonard, Department of English, The Citadel, Charleston, SC 29409. TEL 803-953-5138. FAX 803-953-7084. Ed. James S. Leonard. adv. circ. 1,050. **Document type:** newsletter.
Description: Contains brief scholarly articles, anecdotes, annotated bibliography of current scholarship, calls for papers, and news of meetings and other Twain-related activities.

817.44		US	ISSN 0025-3499

PS1329
MARK TWAIN JOURNAL. (Supplement avail.: Mark Twain Circular (ISSN 1042-5357)) 1936. s-a. $18 (foreign $20). c/o Department of English, College of Charleston, Charleston, SC 29424. TEL 803-792-5664. Ed. Thomas A. Tenney. adv.; illus.; cum.index. circ. 800. (also avail. in microform from UMI; reprint service avail. from ISI,KTO) Indexed: Abstr.Engl.Stud., Amer.Hum.Ind., Arts & Hum.Cit.Ind., Bibl.Engl.Lang.& Lit., Curr.Cont., LCR, M.L.A., RILA. **Document type:** academic/scholarly publication.
—Faxon; UnCover; UMI.

810		US	ISSN 0272-6378

PS1329
MARK TWAIN SOCIETY BULLETIN. 1978. s-a. $5 (foreign $6). Mark Twain Society, Inc., Box 3225, Elmira, NY 14905. TEL 607-734-6943. Eds. Robert Jerome, Herbert Wisbey. bk.rev.; illus. circ. 500. **Document type:** bulletin.

806		US

MARLOWE SOCIETY OF AMERICA NEWSLETTER. 1980. 2/yr. $15 (foreign $20). Marlowe Society of America, c/o English Department, Box 2275-A, South Dakota State University, Brookings, SD 57007. Ed. Bruce Brandt. circ. 200.

810		US	ISSN 0025-3979

MARQUETTE JOURNAL. 1904. s-a. $12. Marquette University, 1131 W. Wisconsin Ave., Milwaukee, WI 53233. TEL 414-288-7057. FAX 414-288-1979. Ed. Jim Lautenbach. adv. circ. 5,000.
Description: Student publication.

MARYLAND ENGLISH JOURNAL. see *EDUCATION — Teaching Methods And Curriculum*

809 800		XR

MASARYKOVA UNIVERSITA. FILOZOFICKA FAKULTA. SBORNIK PRACI. D: RADA LITERARNEVEDNA. 1955. irreg. (approx. a). price varies. Masarykova Universita, Filozoficka fakulta, A. Novaka 1, 660 88 Brno, Czech Republic. FAX 41-211241. bk.rev. **Document type:** proceedings.
Formerly: Universita J.E. Purkyne. Filozoficka Fakulta. Sbornik Praci. D: Rada Literarnevedna (ISSN 0231-7818)
Description: Covers the theory and history of Czech, Soviet, Russian (pre-revolutionary), and other Slavonic literatures.

MASARYKOVA UNIVERSITA. FILOZOFICKA FAKULTA. SBORNIK PRACI. K: RADA GERMANISTICKO - ANGLISTICKA. see *LINGUISTICS*

MASARYKOVA UNIVERSITA. FILOZOFICKA FAKULTA. SBORNIK PRACI. L: RADA ROMANISTICKA. see *LINGUISTICS*

805		IR

MASHHAD UNIVERSITY. FACULTY OF LETTERS AND HUMANITIES. JOURNAL. (Text in Persian) 1965. q. Rs.250($20) Mashhad University, Faculty of Letters and Humanities, Mashhad 91384, Iran. Ed. M.J. Yahaghi. bk.rev. circ. 1,000. **Document type:** academic/scholarly publication.
Formerly: University of Ferdousi. Faculty of Letters and Humanities. Journal.

890		NE	ISSN 0932-9714
			CODEN: MAATEP

MATATU; journal for African culture and society. (Text in English, French, German) 1987. s-a. fl.45($22.50) to individuals; institutions fl.80($40). Editions Rodopi B.V., Keizersgracht 302-304, 1016 EX Amsterdam, Netherlands. TEL 31-20-6227507. FAX 31-20-6380948. (In N. America: 233 Peachtree St., N.E., Ste. 404, Atlanta, GA 30303-1504. TEL 800-225-3998. FAX 404-522-7116) Ed. Holger G. Ehling. adv.; bk.rev. circ. 500. Indexed: Documentatieblad. **Document type:** academic/scholarly publication.
Description: Concerned with all aspects of Black and African studies.

MATILDA MAGAZINE: LITERARY AND ART MAGAZINE. see *LITERATURE — Poetry*

800		CN	ISSN 0318-3610

MATRIX; writing worth reading. 1975. 3/yr. Can.$15 to individuals; institutions Can.$22. Linda Leith, Ed. & Pub., P.O. Box 100, Ste. Anne de Bellevue, Que. H9X 3L4, Canada. TEL 514-426-8654. FAX 514-426-8658. adv.; bk.rev. circ. 2,000. (also avail. in microfiche from MML) Indexed: Can.Lit.Ind.

800		AT

MATTOID. 1979. 3/yr. Aus.$30. Deakin University, Deakin Literary Society, Vic. 3217, Australia. FAX 052-272018. TELEX DUNIV AA35625. Ed. Brian Edwards. adv.; bk.rev. circ. 650. (back issues avail.)
Description: Literary journal that publishes poetry, fiction, essays, interviews, reviews and graphics.

892		SY

MAWQIF AL-ADABI. (Some numbers issued in combined form) 1971. m. £S1($28) Ittihad al-Kuttab al-Arab - Arab Writers Union, Mezzeh, P.O. Box 3230, Damascus, Syria. Ed. Mohamed Omran. adv.; bk.rev.; illus. circ. 4,000.

810		US

MAXY'S JOURNAL. 1977. 3/yr. $5. Truedog Press, Inc., 216 W. Academy St., Lonoke, AR 72086-3103. TEL 501-676-2467. Ed. Mac Bennett. circ. 500.

MEANJIN; a magazine of literature, art and discussion. see *LITERARY AND POLITICAL REVIEWS*

808		US

MECHANICS, A WRITER'S QUARTERLY.* q. 71 Camelot Rd., Poughkeepsie, NY 12601-5914. Ed. Ginger Bisanz.

890		IE	ISSN 0332-4265

MEDIAEVAL AND MODERN IRISH SERIES. 1931. irreg., vol.25, 1978. Dublin Institute for Advanced Studies, School of Celtic Studies, 10 Burlington Rd., Dublin 4, Ireland. TEL 01-6680748. FAX 01-6680561. **Document type:** monographic series.

890		IE	ISSN 0332-4230

MEDIAEVAL AND MODERN WELSH SERIES. 1957. irreg., vol.9, 1988. Dublin Institute for Advanced Studies, School of Celtic Studies, 10 Burlington Rd., Dublin 4, Ireland. TEL 01-6680748. FAX 01-6680561. **Document type:** monographic series.

800 940		CN	ISSN 0316-0874

MEDIAEVAL SOURCES IN TRANSLATION. 1949. irreg., vol.33, 1990. price varies. Pontifical Institute of Mediaeval Studies, 59 Queen's Park Crescent E., Toronto, ON M5S 2C4, Canada. TEL 416-926-7144. FAX 416-926-7258. (Dist. outside N. America and UK by: N.V. Brepols, Steenweg op Tielen 68, 2300 Turnhout, Belgium. TEL 32-14-415463. FAX 32-14-428919) circ. 1,000. (back issues avail.) **Document type:** monographic series.

MEDIAEVALIA. see *HISTORY — History Of Europe*

MEDIEVAL ACADEMY BOOKS. see *HISTORY — History Of Europe*

MEDIEVAL ACADEMY REPRINTS FOR TEACHING. see *HISTORY — History Of Europe*

800		NE	ISSN 0169-9059

MEDIEVAL AND RENAISSANCE AUTHORS. 1976. irreg., vol.10, 1989. price varies. E.J. Brill, P.O. Box 9000, 2300 PA Leiden, Netherlands. TEL 31-71-312624. FAX 31-71-317532. TELEX 39296 BRILL NL. (In N. America: E.J. Brill, 24 Hudson St., Kinderhook, NY 12106. TEL 800-962-4406. FAX 518-758-1959) Eds. John Norton-Smith, Douglas Gray. (back issues avail.) **Document type:** monographic series.
Refereed Serial

MEDIEVAL AND RENAISSANCE AUTHORS AND TEXTS. see *HISTORY — History Of Europe*

MEDIEVAL AND RENAISSANCE TEXTS. see *HISTORY — History Of Europe*

MEDIEVALIA ET HUMANISTICA; studies in medieval and renaissance culture. see *HISTORY — History Of Europe*

879 410		UK	ISSN 0025-8385

PB1
MEDIUM AEVUM. 1932. s-a. £20 (foreign £25). Society for the Study of Mediaeval Languages and Literature, c/o Dr. D.G. Pattison, Hon. Treas., Magdalen College, Oxford OX1 4AU, England. Ed.Bd. adv.; bk.rev.; index, cum.index: 1932-1957, 1957-1981. circ. 1,100. (also avail. in microfilm; back issues avail.) Indexed: Abstr.Engl.Stud., Arts & Hum.Cit.Ind., Bibl.Ling., Br.Hum.Ind., Can.Rev.Comp.Lit., Hum.Ind., Ind.Bk.Rev.Hum., M.L.A., Mid.East: Abstr.& Ind. **Document type:** academic/scholarly publication.
—BLDSC (5534.790000); Faxon; UnCover; SWETS; UMI.
Description: Articles, notes and reviews on medieval European languages and literature.

056.1		PE

MELIBEA. 1975. irreg. Casimiro Ulloa, 125, Lima, Peru. illus.

810		US	ISSN 0193-8991

PS2386
MELVILLE SOCIETY EXTRACTS. 1969. 4/yr. $7 to individuals (foreign $8); libraries $10. c/o John Wenke, Treas., Department of English, Salisbury State University, Salisbury, MD 21801-6837. Ed. John Bryant. adv.; bk.rev.; illus. circ. 750. (back issues avail.) Indexed: Abstr.Engl.Stud., Amer.Hum.Ind., LCR, M.L.A.
Former titles: Extracts (ISSN 0193-7626); Melville Society Newsletter (ISSN 0076-633X); Incorporates: Melville Society. Special Publication (ISSN 0076-6348)

850 945		IT

▼**MEMORIA DEL TEMPO;** studi e testi medievali e rinascimentali. (Text in English, French, Italian) 1994. irreg. price varies. Angelo Longo Editore, Via Paolo Costa 33, P.O. Box 431, 48100 Ravenna, Italy. TEL 0544-217026. Ed. Michelangelo Picone. circ. 2,000. **Document type:** monographic series.
Description: Contains studies and texts on literature and history from the 15th to 17th centuries.

810		US	ISSN 0025-9233

PS3525.E43
MENCKENIANA. 1962. q. $12 (foreign $15). Enoch Pratt Free Library, 400 Cathedral St., Baltimore, MD 21201-4484. TEL 410-396-5494. FAX 410-837-0582. Ed. Charles Fecher. bk.rev.; bibl. circ. 700. (also avail. in microform from UMI) Indexed: Abstr.Engl.Stud., Amer.Hum.Ind., Curr.Cont., M.L.A. **Document type:** academic/scholarly publication.
—UMI.

MENSUEL 25. see *ART*

820		AT	ISSN 0728-5914

PN2
MERIDIAN; La Trobe University English review. 1982. s-a. Aus.$28 to individuals; institutions Aus.$36.50 (foreign Aus.$39.50). (La Trobe University, Department of English) La Trobe University Press, Bundoora, Vic. 3083, Australia. FAX 03-470-2011. TELEX AA 33143. Ed. John Barnes. adv.; bk.rev. circ. 600.

LITERATURE

800 200   US   ISSN 0894-4857
BX4705.M542
MERTON ANNUAL: STUDIES IN THOMAS MERTON, RELIGION, CULTURE, LITERATURE, AND SOCIAL CONCERNS. 1988. a. $42.50. A M S Press, Inc., 56 E. 13th St., New York, NY 10003. TEL 212-777-4700. FAX 212-995-5413. Ed.Bd. bk.rev.; index.
   Description: Publishes articles about Thomas Merton and matters of major concern in his life and work as a writer, monk, and spiritual leader.

THE MERTON SEASONAL: A QUARTERLY REVIEW. see RELIGIONS AND THEOLOGY

891   LI
METAI. 1991. m. Gedimino pr.37, Vilnius 232600, Lithuania. TEL 0122-617-344. Ed. Juozas Aputis.

METAPHOR AND SYMBOLIC ACTIVITY. see LINGUISTICS

METHODIST HISTORY. see RELIGIONS AND THEOLOGY — Protestant

800   US   ISSN 0543-615X
AP95.L5
METMENYS; kuryba ir analize. (Text in Lithuanian) 1959. s-a. $15. (Metmenys Corp.) A M & M Publications, 7338 S. Sacramento, Chicago, IL 60629. TEL 312-436-5369. Ed. Vytautas Kavolis. bk.rev.; cum.index: 1959-1973, 1973-1985. circ. 1,000. **Indexed:** Amer.Bibl.Slavic & E.Eur.Stud. **Document type:** academic/scholarly publication.

820   UK
▼**METROPOLITAN**; new urban writing. 1993. s-a. £2.50. 19 Victoria Ave., Didsbury, Manchester M20 2GY, England. Eds. Elizabeth Baines, Ailsa Cox. **Document type:** consumer publication.

830   GW
MEZZOTINTO; Zeitschrift fuer Literatur. 1981. a. DM.5. Stiefmuetterchenweg 18, 22607 Hamburg, Germany. TEL 040-806657. Ed. Harry Springer.

MICHIGAN GERMANIC STUDIES. see LINGUISTICS

801   US   ISSN 0076-8103
MICHIGAN SLAVIC CONTRIBUTIONS. (Text in English, Russian and Slavic languages) 1968. irreg., latest 1984. price varies. University of Michigan, Department of Slavic Languages and Literatures, 3040 Modern Language Bldg., Ann Arbor, MI 48109. TEL 313-763-4496. FAX 313-764-3521. Ed. Ladislaw Matejka. **Indexed:** M.L.A. **Document type:** academic/scholarly publication.

890 491.8 375.4   US   ISSN 0543-9930
PG13
MICHIGAN SLAVIC MATERIALS. 1961. a. University of Michigan, Department of Slavic Languages and Literatures, 3040 Modern Language Bldg., Ann Arbor, MI 48109. TEL 313-763-4496. FAX 313-764-3521. Ed. Ladislav Matejka. **Document type:** academic/scholarly publication.

891.7   US
MICHIGAN SLAVIC TRANSLATIONS. 1972. irreg., no.6, 1983. University of Michigan, Department of Slavic Languages and Literatures, 3040 Modern Language Bldg., Ann Arbor, MI 48104. TEL 313-763-4496. FAX 313-764-3521. Ed. Ladislav Matejka. **Document type:** academic/scholarly publication.

890   US
MICHIGAN STUDIES IN THE HUMANITIES. 1980. irreg., vol.7, 1988. University of Michigan, Department of Slavic Languages and Literatures, 3040 Modern Language Bldg., Ann Arbor, MI 48109. TEL 313-763-4496. FAX 313-764-3521. Ed. Ladislav Matejka. **Indexed:** M.L.A. **Document type:** academic/scholarly publication.

800   US   ISSN 0190-2911
MIDAMERICA (EAST LANSING). 1973. a. $7.50 per no. Society for the Study of Midwestern Literature, Ernst Bessey Hall, Michigan State University, East Lansing, MI 48824. TEL 517-355-1855. Ed. David D. Anderson. bk.rev. circ. 1,000. (back issues avail.) **Indexed:** Abstr.Engl.Stud., M.L.A.
   Formerly: Midwestern Annual.

800 808.81 700   US   ISSN 0892-970X
MIDCOASTER. 1986. a. $4.50. Peter Blewett, Ed. & Pub., 2750 N. 45th. St., Milwaukee, WI 53210. TEL 414-442-2807. circ. 500. (back issues avail.)
   Description: Covers short fiction, poetry and art.

420   GW
MIDDLE ENGLISH TEXTS. (Text in English) 1975. irreg., no.24, 1991. Universitaetsverlag C. Winter Heidelberg GmbH, Hans-Bunte-Str. 18, 69123 Heidelberg, Germany. Eds. M. Goerlach, O.S. Pickering. **Document type:** monographic series.

MIDDLEBURY STUDIES IN RUSSIAN LANGUAGE AND LITERATURE. see LINGUISTICS

800 770   US   ISSN 0886-7976
MIDLAND REVIEW. 1985. a. $6.90. Oklahoma State University, English Department, Morrill Hall, Stillwater, OK 74078. TEL 405-744-9474. adv.; bk.rev. circ. 500.
   Description: Covers contemporary literature, literary criticism and art.

809   US
MIDWEST CHESTERTON NEWS. 1988. m. $11. Midwest G.K. Chesterton Society, 740 Spring Rd., Barrington, IL 60010-3142. TEL 708-381-4584. Ed. John Peterson. bibl.; circ. 300 (paid). **Document type:** newsletter.
   Description: Promotes interest in the life and works of English writer Gilbert Keith Chesterton (1874-1936).

800   US   ISSN 0742-5562
P1.A1
MIDWEST MODERN LANGUAGE ASSOCIATION. JOURNAL. 1968. s-a. $15. Midwest Modern Language Association, 302 English-Philosophy Bldg., University of Iowa, Iowa City, IA 52242. TEL 319-335-0331. Ed. Tom Lutz. adv.; bk.rev.; bibl. circ. 2,000. (back issues avail.) **Indexed:** Amer.Hum.Ind., Arts & Hum.Cit.Ind., Curr.Cont.
   —BLDSC (4825.950000); UnCover.
   Formerly (until 1984): Midwest Modern Language Association. Bulletin (ISSN 0026-3419)

810   US
MIDWESTERN MISCELLANY. irreg. membership. Society for the Study of Midwestern Literature, 240 Ernst Bassey Hall, Michigan State University, East Lansing, MI 48824. TEL 517-355-1855. **Indexed:** Mich.Mag.Ind.

800   IS
MIFGASH/LIQA'; majallah fasliyyah adabiyyah 'ibriyyah - 'arabiyyah. (Text in Arabic, Hebrew) 1964. 4/yr. $12 (effective 1994). Histadrut Jewish-Arab Institute - Al-Ma'had al-Yahudi al-Arabi, Beit Berl, Kfar Sabba 44905, Israel. TEL 972-9-450561. FAX 972-9-914473. Ed. Muhammad Hamzah Ghanaaim.
   Supersedes (in 1984): Mifgash.
   Description: Publishes fiction, poetry, novel excerpts, essays and reports of symposia on current cultural issues.

800   US   ISSN 0163-2469
MILFORD SERIES; popular writers of today. 1976. irreg., no.65, 1993 (approx. 6/yr.). price varies. Borgo Press, Box 2845, San Bernardino, CA 92406. TEL 909-884-5813. FAX 909-888-4942. Ed. Dale Salwak. circ. 2,000.
   —BLDSC (6551.700000).
   Incorporates (in 1992): Starmont Reader's Guides (ISSN 0272-7730); (1988-1991): Starmont Contemporary Writers Series (ISSN 0738-0119)
   Description: Series of critical monographs on and interviews with genre and mainstream writers of the twentieth century.

820   US   ISSN 0026-4326
PR3579
MILTON QUARTERLY. 1967. q. $18 to individuals (foreign $28); libraries $28 (foreign $38) (effective 1993). Ohio University English Department, Ellis Hall, Ohio University, Athens, OH 45701-2979. TEL 614-593-2829. (Co-sponsors: Medieval & Renaissance Texts & Studies; S U N Y Binghamton) Ed. Roy C. Flannagan. adv.; bk.rev.; abstr.; illus.; index. circ. 1,100. (also avail. in microform from UMI; back issues avail.; reprint service avail. from UMI, ISI) **Indexed:** Abstr.Engl.Stud., Amer.Hum.Ind., Arts & Hum.Cit.Ind., Curr.Cont., Hum.Ind., Ind.Bk.Rev.Hum., M.L.A. **Document type:** academic/scholarly publication.
   —BLDSC (5774.550000); Faxon; UnCover; UMI. CCC.
   Formerly (until 1969): Milton Newsletter (ISSN 0146-4922)
   Description: Focuses on scholarly articles and texts dealing with John Milton and his milieu.

821.4   US   ISSN 0076-8820
PR3579
MILTON STUDIES. 1969. a. $49.95. University of Pittsburgh Press, 127 N. Bellefield Ave., Pittsburgh, PA 15260. TEL 800-666-2211. FAX 412-624-7380. Ed. Albert Labriola. **Indexed:** Abstr.Engl.Stud., M.L.A. **Document type:** academic/scholarly publication.
   —BLDSC (5774.570000); Faxon; UnCover.

810   US   ISSN 1066-3916
MILWAUKEE UNDERGRADUATE REVIEW. 1989. 2/yr. $6. Box 71079, Milwaukee, WI 53211. Ed. Dean Andrade. circ. 1,000.
   ●Also available online.
   Description: Publishes literary works by undergraduates across the country.

869   BL
MINAS GERAIS SUPLEMENTO LITERARIO. 1966. w. Cr.$150000($200) Imprensa Oficial do Estado, Av. Augusto de Lima, 270, Ramal 197, 30190 Belo Horizonte, MG, Brazil. TEL 031-273-2088. FAX 031-273-3700. TELEX 318227. Ed. Paschoal Motta. bk.rev. circ. 5,000. **Indexed:** M.L.A.

MINAS TIRITH EVENING STAR. see LITERATURE — Science Fiction, Fantasy, Horror

800   CC
MINGZUO XINSHANG/BEST WORKS OF LITERATURE. (Text in Chinese) bi-m. $31.50. Beiyue Wenyi Chubanshe, 46 Jiefang Lu, Taiyuan, Shanxi 030002, People's Republic of China. TEL 227068. (Dist. in US by: China Books & Periodicals, Inc., 2929 24th St., San Francisco, CA 94110. TEL 415-282-2994)

MINJIAN WENXUE. see FOLKLORE

MINJIAN WENXUE LUNTAN/TRIBUNE OF FOLK LITERATURE. see FOLKLORE

800   US   ISSN 0890-0566
MINNESOTA LITERATURE; a newsletter by and for Minnesota writers and supporters of literature. 1973. m. (Sep.-June). $10. 1 Nord Circle, St. Paul, MN 55127. TEL 612-483-3904. Ed. Mary Bround Smith. adv. circ. 750. **Document type:** newsletter.
   Description: Announcements, opportunities, and publication news affecting writers and supporters of literature in the state. Includes opinion essays. Also includes a biannual bibliography of MN presses publications.

810   US   ISSN 0026-5667
AP2
MINNESOTA REVIEW; a journal of committed writing; fiction, poetry, essays, reviews. 1960. s-a. $12 to individuals; institutions $24 (effective 1994). East Carolina University, Department of English, Greenville, NC 27858-4353. TEL 919-757-6388. FAX 919-757-4889. Ed. Jeffrey Williams. adv.; bk.rev.; illus. circ. 1,500. (also avail. in microform from UMI; reprint service avail.) **Indexed:** Abstr.Engl.Stud., Arts & Hum.Cit.Ind., Bk.Rev.Ind. (1989-), Chic.Per.Ind., Child.Bk.Rev.Ind. (1989-), Curr.Cont., Film Lit.Ind. (1976-), M.L.A.
   —BLDSC (5810.463400); Faxon; UnCover; UMI.
   Description: Distinguished fiction, poetry, essays, and reviews on a diverse range of subjects and content.

895.1   CC   ISSN 0257-2850
MINZU WENXUE/JOURNAL OF MINORITY LITERATURE. (Text in Chinese) 1981. m. Y10.80($47.70) Zhongguo Zuojia Xiehui - China Writers' Association, 27, Balizhuang Nanli, Beijing 100025, People's Republic of China. TEL 5005971. (Dist. outside China by: China International Book Trading Corporation, P.O. Box 399, Beijing, P.R.C; Dist. in US by: China Books & Periodicals, Inc., 2929 24th St., San Francisco, CA 94110. TEL 415-282-2994) Ed. Jin Zhe.

895.1   CC
MINZU WENXUE YANJIU/RESEARCH IN NATIONAL MINORITY LITERATURE. (Text in Chinese) 1983. q. $16.50. Zhongguo Shehui Kexueyuan, Minzu Wenxue Yanjiusuo - Chinese Academy of Social Sciences, Institute for National Minority Literature, 5, Jiannei Dajie, Beijing 100732, People's Republic of China. TEL 5137744. (Dist. in US by: China Books & Periodicals, Inc., 2929 24th St., San Francisco, CA 94110. TEL 415-282-2994) Ed. Liu Kuizhi.
    Description: Publishes research articles on folk literature and literature by historical and contemporary writers of China's national minority groups. Also includes important investigative reports on minority literature.

895.1   CC
MINZU ZUOJIA. (Text in Chinese) bi-m. Y9.60. Minzu Zuojia Zazhi She, Urumqi, Xinjiang Weiwuer Zizhiqu, People's Republic of China. (Dist. outside China by: China Publications Foreign Trade Corp., P.O. Box 782, Beijing, P.R.C.) Ed. Zhang Shirong. illus.
    Description: Publishes literature by writers of minority nationalities, especially those in Xinjiang.

MIRAS-I FIRHANGI. see *ARCHAEOLOGY*

MISCELLANEA BYZANTINA MONACENSIA. see *HISTORY — History Of Europe*

820   II   ISSN 0026-5896
MISCELLANY. (Text in English) 1960. bi-m. $18. Writers Workshop, 162-92 Lake Gardens, Calcutta 700045, India. Ed. P. Lal. bk.rev. circ. 1,000.
    Formerly: Writers Workshop Miscellany.

MISSISSIPPI HISTORY NEWSLETTER. see *HISTORY — History Of North And South America*

810   US
MISSISSIPPI MUD. 1973. irreg. $19 for 4 nos. 1336 S.E. Marion St., Portland, OR 97202. TEL 503-236-9962. Ed. Joel Weinstein. adv.; B&W page $800; trim 11 1/2 x 17 1/2. bk.rev. circ. 1,500. (reprint service avail. from UMI,ISI)
    Description: Contains fiction, poetry and artwork.

810   US   ISSN 0047-7559
PS501
MISSISSIPPI REVIEW. 1972. s-a. $15. University of Southern Mississippi, Center for Writers, Box 5144, Southern Station, Hattiesburg, MS 39406. TEL 601-266-4321. FAX 601-266-5757. Ed. Frederick Barthelms. adv.; bk.rev.; index. circ. 1,500. (also avail. in microform from UMI) **Indexed:** A.I.P.P.; Amer.Hum.Ind.
    —Faxon; UnCover; UMI.

810   US   ISSN 0270-3521
MISSISSIPPI VALLEY REVIEW. 1971. 2/yr. $6. Western Illinois University, Department of English, Macomb, IL 61455. TEL 309-298-1514. Ed. Forrest Robinson. circ. 450. **Document type:** academic/scholarly publication.

800   US   ISSN 0191-1961
PS1
MISSOURI REVIEW. 1977. 3/yr. $15. University of Missour at Columbia, 1507 Hillcrest Hall, Columbia, MO 65211. TEL 314-882-4474. Eds. Speer Morgan, Greg Michalson. adv.; bk.rev. circ. 6,000. **Indexed:** Amer.Hum.Ind., M.L.A.
    —Faxon; UnCover.

800   IT   ISSN 0392-6397
MISURE CRITICHE; rivista trimestrale di letteratura e cultura varia. (Text in English, French, Italian) 1970. q. L.48000 (foreign L.80000). Fratelli Conte Editori, Via Andrea d'Isernia, 59, 80122 Naples, Italy. TEL 683667. (Subscr. to: Corso V. Emanuele, 14, 41000 Salerno, Italy) Ed. Gioacchino Paparelli. adv.; bibl. circ. 1,000. (back issues avail.)
    Description: Reviews Italian and comparative literature.

830   US   ISSN 0026-7503
PT3810
MODERN AUSTRIAN LITERATURE. (Text and summaries in English and German) 1961. q. $20 to individuals (foreign $25); libraries $30 (foreign $35). International Arthur Schnitzler Research Association, c/o Donald G. Daviau, Ed., Department of Literatures and Languages, University of California, Riverside, CA 92521. TEL 909-787-5603. FAX 909-684-9202. adv.; bk.rev.; play rev.; abstr.; bibl. circ. 700. (processed; also avail. in microfiche; cards; record; reprint service avail. from UMI) **Indexed:** Amer.Bibl.Slavic & E.Eur.Stud., Arts & Hum.Cit.Ind., Curr.Cont., M.L.A. **Document type:** academic/scholarly publication.
    —BLDSC (5883.695000); Faxon; UnCover; UMI.
    Description: Devoted to 19th and 20th century Austrian literature and culture.

895.1   US   ISSN 0190-2369
PL2303
MODERN CHINESE LITERATURE. 1984. s-a. $15 to individuals; institutions $25; students $10. University of Colorado, Department of Oriental Languages, Campus Box 279, Boulder, CO 80309-0279. TEL 303-492-3486. FAX 303-492-7272. Ed. Howard Goldblatt. adv.; bk.rev. circ. 300. **Indexed:** M.L.A.

822   CN   ISSN 0026-7694
MODERN DRAMA. 1958. q. $27.50 to individuals; institutions $40; students $20. (University of Toronto, Graduate Centre for Study of Drama) University of Toronto Press, Journals Department, 5201 Dufferin St., Downsview, ON M3H 5T8, Canada. TEL 416-667-7781. FAX 416-667-7832. (U.S. addr.: 340 Nagel Dr., Cheektowaga, NY 14225) Ed. J. Astington. adv.; bk.rev.; bibl.; index. circ. 2,260. (back issues avail.) **Indexed:** Acad.Ind., Amer.Bibl.Slavic & E.Eur.Stud., Can.Per.Ind., Curr.Cont., Film Lit.Ind. (1973-), Hum.Ind., Ind.Bk.Rev.Hum., M.L.A., Mid.East: Abstr.& Ind., Ref.Sour.
    —BLDSC (5886.190000); Faxon; UnCover; SWETS; UMI. **CCC.**

813   US   ISSN 0026-7724
PS379
MODERN FICTION STUDIES. Short title: M F S. 1955. 4/yr. $20 to individuals; institutions $35; foreign $35. Purdue University, Department of English, West Lafayette, IN 47907. TEL 317-494-3758. FAX 317-497-3780. Ed. Patrick O'Donnell. bk.rev.; bibl. circ. 3,500. (also avail. in microform from UMI; reprint service avail. from UMI,KTO) **Indexed:** Abstr.Engl.Stud., Acad.Ind., Amer.Bibl.Slavic & E.Eur.Stud., Arts & Hum.Cit.Ind., Bk.Rev.Ind. (1977-), Chic.Per.Ind., Child.Bk.Rev.Ind. (1977-), Curr.Cont., Hum.Ind., Ind.Bk.Rev.Hum., M.L.A., Mid.East: Abstr.& Ind.
    —BLDSC (5886.550000); Faxon; UnCover; SWETS; UMI.
    Description: Devoted to criticism of modern and contemporary narrative and theory.

070.5 899   IS   ISSN 0334-4266
PJ5001
MODERN HEBREW LITERATURE. 1975. s-a. $9. Institute for the Translation of Hebrew Literature, P.O. Box 10051, Ramat Gan 52001, Israel. TEL 972-3-5796830. Ed. Gershon Shaked. bk.rev.; index. circ. 2,000. (also avail. in microform from UMI; reprint service avail. from UMI) **Indexed:** Arts & Hum.Cit.Ind., Curr.Cont., M.L.A., Mid.East: Abstr.& Ind. **Document type:** newspaper.
    —Faxon; UMI.
    Incorporates: Hebrew Book Review.

810.9 296   US   ISSN 0270-9406
PS153.J4
MODERN JEWISH STUDIES ANNUAL. a. c/o Joseph Landis, NSF 35U, Kiely 1309, Queens College, Flushing, NY 11367. TEL 718-520-7067.
    Formerly: Conference on Modern Jewish Studies Annual (ISSN 0270-9392)

400   US   ISSN 0026-7929
PB1
MODERN LANGUAGE QUARTERLY; a journal of literary history. 1940. q. $30 to individuals; institutions $26. University of Washington, Department of English GN-30, Seattle, WA 98195. TEL 206-543-6827. FAX 206-685-2673. Ed. Marshall Brown. bk.rev.; index. circ. 1,600. (also avail. in microform from MIM,UMI,PMC) **Indexed:** Abstr.Engl.Stud., Acad.Ind., Amer.Bibl.Slavic & E.Eur.Stud., Arts & Hum.Cit.Ind., Curr.Cont., Hum.Ind., Ind.Bk.Rev.Hum., M.L.A., Mid.East: Abstr.& Ind. **Document type:** academic/scholarly publication.
    —BLDSC (5887.550000); Faxon; UnCover; SWETS; UMI.
    Description: Focuses on literary scholarship and criticism, medieval to modern, with special emphasis on literary history.

400   UK   ISSN 0026-7937
MODERN LANGUAGE REVIEW. 1905. q. $134. Modern Humanities Research Association, King's College, London WC2 R 2LS, England. (Vols. 1-69 avail. from Wm. Dawson & Sons Ltd., Cannon House, Folkstone, Kent, England) Ed.Bd. bk.rev. circ. 1,800. (also avail. in microfilm from BHP,PMC) **Indexed:** Abstr.Engl.Stud., Arts & Hum.Cit.Ind., Bibl.Ling., Bk.Rev.Ind. (1965-), Br.Hum.Ind., Can.Rev.Comp.Lit., Chic.Per.Ind., Child.Bk.Rev.Ind. (1965-), Curr.Cont., Hum.Ind., Ind.Bk.Rev.Hum., M.L.A., Mid.East: Abstr.& Ind., Ref.Sour., Soc.Sci.Ind.
    —BLDSC (5887.600000); Faxon; UnCover; SWETS.

400   US   ISSN 0047-7729
PB1
MODERN LANGUAGE STUDIES. 1971. 4/yr. $25. Northeast Modern Language Association, English Department, Brown University, Box 1852, Providence, RI 02912. TEL 401-863-3756. Ed. David H. Hirsch. adv.; bk.rev.; bibl. circ. 2,300. (also avail. in microform from UMI) **Indexed:** Abstr.Engl.Stud., Amer.Bibl.Slavic & E.Eur.Stud., Arts & Hum.Cit.Ind., Curr.Cont., Ind.Bk.Rev.Hum., M.L.A., Mid.East: Abstr.& Ind.
    —BLDSC (5887.650000); Faxon; UnCover; UMI.
    Formerly: North East Modern Language Association. Newsletter.

MODERN PHILOLOGY; a journal devoted to research in medieval and modern literature. see *LINGUISTICS*

MODERNA SPRAAK. see *LINGUISTICS*

840   CN   ISSN 0225-1582
MOEBIUS; ecritures et litterature. 1976. q. Can.$30 (foreign Can.$40) to individuals; Can.$45 (foreign Can.$55) to institutions. Editions Triptyque, C.P. 5670, succ. C, Montreal, Que. H2X 3N4, Canada. TEL 514-524-5900. bk.rev. circ. 800. (back issues avail.)

800   II
MOKO. Association for Commonwealth Literature and Language Studies, Indian Branch, Department of English, University of Mysore, Manasagangotri, Mysore 570006, India.

808   UK
MOMENTUM. 1985. 3/yr. £3.40 (foreign £4.40). Wrexham Writers' Workshop, Almere Farm, Rossett, Wrexham, Clwyd LL12 0BY, Wales. Ed. Pamela Goodwin. (back issues avail.)
    Description: Short stories, poems, articles of literary interest.

MONATSHEFTE. see *LINGUISTICS*

895   MP
MONGOL ROMAN/MONGOLIAN NOVEL. (Text in Mongolian) 1989. q. Union of Writers, Ulan Bator, Mongolia. TEL 327863. Ed. Ts. Enkhbat.

800 770 700   US   ISSN 0898-7092
THE MONOCACY VALLEY REVIEW. 1985. s-a. $8. Mount Saint Mary's College, Emmitsburg, MD 21727. TEL 301-447-6122. Ed. William Heath. bk.rev.; illus.; circ. 500 (controlled). **Document type:** bulletin.
    Description: Includes poetry, short fiction, non-fiction prose, reviews, photography and line drawings.

LITERATURE

891.8 940   PL   ISSN 0077-0531
MONOGRAFIE SLAWISTYCZNE. 1959. irreg. vol.52, 1990. price varies. Polska Akademia Nauk, Komitet Slowianoznawstwa, Palac Kultury i Nauki, Pok. 1718, 00-901 Warsaw, Poland. (Dist. by: Ars Polona-Ruch, Krakowskie Przedmiescie 7, Warsaw, Poland) **Document type:** monographic series.

MONOGRAPHS IN MODERN DUTCH STUDIES. see HISTORY — History Of Europe

MONOGRAPHS IN MODERN LANGUAGES. see LINGUISTICS

800   US   ISSN 0196-2604
PS3521.E735
MOODY STREET IRREGULARS; a Jack Kerouac newsletter. (Text in English, French) 1978. s-a. $10 to individuals; institutions $15. Moody Street Irregulars, Inc., Box 157, Clarence Center, NY 14032. Ed. Joy Walsh. adv.; bk.rev.; film rev.; play rev.; bibl.; charts; illus.; stat.; tr.lit. circ. 1,000. (back issues avail.) **Indexed:** M.L.A.
—BLDSC (5966.397000); UnCover.

801   SZ   ISSN 0942-0924
MORGEN-GLANTZ; Zeitschrift der Christian-Knorr-von-Rosenroth-Gesellschaft. 1991. a. 50 SFr. (Christian-Knorr-von-Rosenroth-Gesellschaft) Verlag Peter Lang AG, Jupiterstr. 15, CH-3015 Bern, Switzerland. TEL 031-9411122. FAX 031-9411131. Ed. Michele Battafarano. **Document type:** academic/scholarly publication.

809   CN   ISSN 0027-1276
PN2
MOSAIC (WINNIPEG, 1967); a journal for the interdisciplinary study of literature. (Text in English, French) 1967. q. Can.$22 to individuals; institutions Can.$35. University of Manitoba, 208 Tier Bldg., Winnipeg, MB R3T 2N2, Canada. TEL 204-474-9763. FAX 204-261-9086. (Co-sponsor: Social Sciences and Humanities Research Council of Canada) Ed. Dr. Evelyn J. Hinz. adv.: B&W page $150; adv. contact: Melva Mclean. illus.; index. circ. 1,000. (also avail. in microform from UMI; back issues avail.) **Indexed:** Abstr.Engl.Stud.; Amer.Hum.Ind.; Arts & Hum.Cit.Ind., Can.Lit.Ind., Can.Per.Ind., CMI, Hum.Ind.; Ind.Bk.Rev.Hum.; LCR, M.L.A., RILA, RILM. **Document type:** academic/scholarly publication.
—BLDSC (5967.483500); Faxon; UnCover; SWETS; UMI. **CCC.**
Formerly (until 1978): Journal for the Comparative Study of Literature and Ideas.
Description: Theoretical and practical essays explore literary works or issues from an interdisciplinary perspective.

891.7   RU   ISSN 0131-2332
AP50
MOSKVA; literary magazine. 1957. m. $121. Soyuz Pisatelei Rossii, Moskovskoe Otdelenie, Arbat 20, 121918 Moscow, Russia. TEL 095-291-71-10. (Dist. in U.S. by: Victor Kamkin Inc., 4956 Boiling Brook Pkwy, Rockville, MD 20852. TEL 301-881-5973) Ed. B.N. Krypin. bk.rev.; bibl.; illus.; index. circ. 100,000. **Indexed:** Curr.Dig.Sov.Press.
—BLDSC (0118.550000).

800   CI   ISSN 0006-9833
PG560
MOST/BRIDGE/PONT/PUENTE; jugoslavia revuo pri kroata literaturo. (Text in various languages) N.S. 1981. 4/yr. $12. Drustvo Knjizevnika Hrvatske, Trg Republike 7-l, 41000 Zagreb, Croatia. TEL 041-274-211. Ed. Milivoj Solar. **Indexed:** Amer.Bibl.Slavic & E.Eur.Stud.
Description: Yugoslav review of Croatian literature.

MOSTOVI. see LINGUISTICS

MOVEMENTS IN THE ARTS. see ART

895.1   CC   ISSN 1003-3459
MUDAN/PEONY. (Text in Chinese) 1957. bi-m. Luoyang Shi Wenlian, No. 135, Zhongzhou Zhonglu, Luoyang, Henan 471000, People's Republic of China. TEL 37165. Ed. Han Li.

430 830   GW   ISSN 0077-1872
MUENCHNER GERMANISTISCHE BEITRAEGE. 1968. irreg. price varies. Wilhelm Fink Verlag, Ohmstr. 5, 80802 Munich, Germany. Ed.Bd.

MULIKA. see LINGUISTICS

892   US   ISSN 8755-4925
MUNDUS ARABICUS. 1981. irreg. price varies. Dar Mahjar Inc., Box 56, Cambridge, MA 02238. TEL 617-492-8533. FAX 617-492-8856. Ed.Bd. circ. 350. **Indexed:** Ind.Islam.

892.7   TS
AL-MUNTADA. 1983. m. Dubai Literary Club - Nadi Dubai al-Adabi, P.O. Box 9339, Dubai, United Arab Emirates. TEL 377464. Ed. Ahmed bin Said al-Maktum. circ. 2,000.
Description: Publishes stories, poetry and articles on Arabic literature.

800   NR   ISSN 0331-3468
PR9387.5
MUSE; journal of creative and critical writing from Nsukka. 1963. a. £N2. University of Nigeria, Department of English, Nsukka, Nigeria. Ed. Onyedika L. Okwuonu. adv.; bk.rev. circ. 1,500.

809   IT   ISSN 0392-6931
MUSEUM CRITICUM. vol.10, 1975. irreg. price varies. Giardini Editori e Stampatori, Via Santa Bibbiana 28, 56100 Pisa, Italy. TEL 050 502531. Ed. Benedetto Marzullo.

830   GW   ISSN 1016-1333
MUSIL - FORUM. (Text in English, French, German) 1974. a. DM.45. Internationale Robert-Musil-Gesellschaft, Universitaet, Gebaeude 35, 66041 Saarbruecken, Germany. TEL 0681-3023334. Ed. Juergen Thoeming. bk.rev.; index. circ. 500. **Document type:** consumer publication.

890 069.9   PL   ISSN 0324-8925
PG7001
MUZEUM LITERATURY IM. ADAMA MICKIEWICZA. BLOK-NOTES. 1959. irreg. price varies. Muzeum Literatury im. Adama Mickiewicza, Rynek Starego Miasta 20, 00-272 Warsaw, Poland. TEL 31-40-61. Ed. Malgorzata Kucza-Kuczynska. illus. circ. 600. (back issues avail.)

810 910.03   US
MWENDO. 1973. s-a. $1 per copy. Coe College, Black Student Educational Organization, Box 577, Cedar Rapids, IA 52402. TEL 319-399-8660. Ed. Latonia Williams. bk.rev.; bibl. circ. 350.

895.4   BR
MYAWADDY MAGAZINE. (Text in Burmese, English) 1952. m. Myawaddy Press, 181-3 Sule Pagoda Rd., Yangon, Union of Myanmar. circ. 4,200.

808.838   US
MYSTIC PRESS FICTION. q. $24. Rainbow Way Publications, Rt. 2, Box 173, Canton, MO 63435.
Description: Includes poetry, humor, mysteries, science fiction, fantasy.

850 808   US
N E M L A ITALIAN STUDIES; selected proceedings of the Italian section of N E M L A. (Text in English, Italian) 1977. a. $6. (Northeast Modern Language Association Conference, Italian Section) Prof. Umberto C. Mariani, Ed. & Pub., Rutgers Univ., Dept. of Italian, 84 College Ave., New Brunswick, New Brunswick, NJ 08903. TEL 908-932-7536. FAX 908-932-1686. adv.; bk.rev. circ. 500. (back issues avail.) **Document type:** academic/scholarly publication, proceedings.

830 053.1   AU
N O I INTERNATIONAL; Mensch, Gesellschaft, Kultur, Umwelt. vol.11, 1972. q. S.280. N O I-Verlag, Morrestrasse 13, A-9020 Klagenfurt, Austria. Ed. Dr. Dietfried Schoenemann. bk.rev.; bibl.

891.7   US   ISSN 0894-7120
PG3476.N3
NABOKOVIAN. (Text mainly in English; occasionally in Russian) 1978. s-a. $9 to individuals; institutions $11. Vladimir Nabokov Society, c/o Stephen Jan Parker, Ed., Slavic Languages & Literatures, University of Kansas, Lawrence, KS 66045. TEL 913-864-3313. bk.rev.; bibl. circ. 285. **Indexed:** Amer.Bibl.Slavic & E.Eur.Stud., M.L.A. **Document type:** academic/scholarly publication.
—UnCover.
Formerly (until 1984): Vladimir Nabokov Research Newsletter.

NACHBARSPRACHE NIEDERLAENDISCH. see LINGUISTICS

800   HU   ISSN 0547-1613
NAGYVILAG. 1956. m. $28.50. Szechenyi u. 1, 1054 Budapest, Hungary. TEL 132-1160. Ed. Laszlo Kery. circ. 12,000.
Description: Reviews world literature.

860 028.1   PY   ISSN 1012-5507
NANDE REKO; cuaderno de literatura popular. 1980. s-a. $30. Distribuidor Internacional Publicaciones Paraguayas, P.O. Box 2507, Ayoreos e-4a y 5a, Asuncion, Paraguay. TEL 595-21-495367. FAX 595-21-447460. Ed. Rudi Torga. bk.rev. circ. 1,000.

895   CC
NANFANG WENTAN. (Text in Chinese) bi-m. Guangxi Wenlian, 28 Jianzheng Lu, Nanning, Guangxi 530023, People's Republic of China. TEL 23613. Ed. Li Chaohong.

895   CC
NANFANG WENXUE/SOUTHERN LITERATURE. (Text in Chinese) bi-m. Guilin Shi Wenlian, Rongcheng Lu, Guilin, Guangxi 541001, People's Republic of China. TEL 224578. Ed. Zeng Xianrui.

895.1   CC   ISSN 0257-2885
NANFENG/SOUTH WIND; folk literature of Guizhou. (Text in Chinese) 1983. bi-m. $16.20. Guizhou Sheng Wenlian, 66, Kexue Lu, Guiyang, Guizhou 550002, People's Republic of China. TEL 25616. (Dist. in US by: China Books & Periodicals, Inc., 2929 24th St., San Francisco, CA 94110. TEL 415-282-2994) Ed. Tian Bing.

059.94   HU   ISSN 0547-2075
NAPJAINK. m. $23. Borsod Megyei Lapkiado Vallalat, Bajcsy-Zsilinszky u. 15, 3527 Miskolc, Hungary. (Subscr. to: Kultura, Box 149, H-1389 Budapest, Hungary)

800 700 720   BU   ISSN 0205-1109
NARODNA KULTURA. 1957. w. 6.50 lv. (Komitet za Kultura - Committee for Culture) Foreign Trade Co. "Hemus", 7 Levsky St., 1000 Sofia, Bulgaria. Ed. Koprinka Chervenkova. adv.; bk.rev. circ. 50,000. (also avail. in microfilm from NRP)

860   UY   ISSN 0077-2801
NARRADORES DE ARCA.* irreg. Editorial Arca, Colonia 1263, Montevideo, Uruguay.

NARRATIVA LATINOAMERICANA. see HISTORY — History Of North And South America

800   US   ISSN 1063-3685
PE1425
▼**NARRATIVE.** 1993. 3/yr. $15 to individuals (foreign $19); institutions $36 (foreign $40). (Society for the Study of Narrative Literature) Ohio State University Press, 1070 Carmack Rd., Columbus, OH 43210. TEL 614-292-6930. FAX 614-292-2065. Ed. James Phelan. circ. 1,200. **Document type:** academic/scholarly publication.
—BLDSC (6015.356580); UnCover; UMI.
Description: Publishes works on the English, American and European novel, nonfiction narrative, film, and narrative as used in performance art. Discusses narrative theory, discourse and narrative, and criticism in diverse theoretical modes.

810   US   ISSN 0077-2879
NASSAU REVIEW. 1964. a. free. Nassau Community College, SUNY, Department of English, Garden City, NY 11530. TEL 516-222-7187. Ed. Paul A. Doyle. circ. 1,200. **Indexed:** M.L.A. **Document type:** academic/scholarly publication.
Description: Publishes poems, short stories, essays and research articles for a college and university audience.

810   US   ISSN 0073-1382
NATHANIEL HAWTHORNE JOURNAL. (1979 and 1980 were cancelled) 1971. irreg. $70. Gale Research Inc., 835 Penobscot Bldg., Detroit, MI 48226. TEL 313-961-2242. FAX 313-961-6083. TELEX 810-221-7086. Ed. C.E. Frazer Clark, Jr. **Indexed:** M.L.A.
Description: Articles on the works of Nathaniel Hawthorne.

LITERATURE 3649

806 US ISSN 0890-4197
PS1879
NATHANIEL HAWTHORNE REVIEW. 1975. s-a. $10. Nathaniel Hawthorne Society, Dept. of English, Duquesne University, Pittsburgh, PA 15282. TEL 412-396-5165. FAX 412-396-5197. Ed. Frederick Newberry. adv.: B&W page $75. bk.rev.; bibl. circ. 440. Indexed: Amer.Hum.Ind., M.L.A. **Document type:** academic/scholarly publication, bibliography.
   Formerly: Nathaniel Hawthorne Society. Newsletter (ISSN 0162-9824).
   Description: Contains scholarly essays, notes, queries, reviews and essay reviews, bibliographies and illustrations relating to the life, works, and influence of Nathaniel Hawthorne for academic and professional scholars, as well as for interested readers.

808 US
NATIONAL DIRECTORY OF STORYTELLING. a. $40 membership (Canada $50; elsewhere $75) includes Inside Story and Storytelling Magazine. National Storytelling Association, Box 309, Jonesborough, TN 37659. TEL 615-753-2171. FAX 615-753-9331. **Document type:** directory.
   Description: Guide to professional storytellers, storytelling publications, events and organizations throughout the U.S.

800 US ISSN 0197-8829
NATIONAL ENDOWMENT FOR THE ARTS. APPLICATION GUIDELINES: LITERATURE. Key Title: Literature (Washington). a. free. National Endowment for the Arts, Public Information Office, 1100 Pennsylvania Ave., N.W., Washington, DC 20506. TEL 202-682-5400. **Document type:** government publication.
   Formerly: N E A Grantmaking Programs: Literature.
   Description: Grant application guidelines.

NATIONAL FOUNDATION FOR ADVANCEMENT IN THE ARTS. ANNUAL REPORT. see *ART*

890 JA ISSN 0387-3447
NATIONAL INSTITUTE OF JAPANESE LITERATURE. BULLETIN/KOKUBUNGAKU KENKYU SHIRYOKAN KIYO. (Text in Japanese) 1975. a. free. National Institute of Japanese Literature - Kokubungaku Kenkyu Shiryokan, 1-16-10 Yutokacho, Shinagawa-ku, Tokyo 142, Japan. FAX 03-3785-7051. **Document type:** bulletin.
   —UnCover.

800 US
NATIONAL POETRY MAGAZINE OF THE LOWER EAST SIDE. vol.3, no.1, 1988. q. Box 1351, Cooper Station, New York, NY 10276. Eds. Stephen Paul Miller, Jim Feast.

890 US
NAUKOVE TOVARYSTVO IMENI SHEVCHENKA. UKRAINSKA LITERATURNA BIBLIOTEKA/UKRAINIAN LITERARY LIBRARY. (Text in Ukrainian; summaries in English) 1881. irreg. price varies. Shevchenko Scientific Society, 63 Fourth Ave., New York, NY 10003.

895 CE
NAVA YUGATA. (Text in Sinhala) 1956. fortn. Lake House, D.R. Wijewardene Mawatha 1, Colombo 10, Sri Lanka. TEL 1-21181. Ed. S.N. Senanayake. circ. 57,000.

880 GR ISSN 0028-1735
AP85
NEA HESTIA. 1927. bi-m. $324. G.C. Eleftheroudakis S.A., 4 Nikis St., 10563 Athens, Greece. TEL 01-3222255. FAX 01-3239821. Ed. P. Charis. adv.; bk.rev.; bibl.; illus.; index.

880 GR ISSN 0470-5238
NEA POREIA; magazine on literature. (Text and summaries in Greek) 1955. q. Dr.1600($30) Nea Poreia, 14 Venizelou St., 546 24 Thessaloniki, Greece. TEL 31-273450. Ed. Tilemachos Alaveras. bk.rev.; bibl.; cum.index. circ. 2,000. (back issues avail.)

808 US ISSN 0741-1316
NEBO; a literary journal. 1983. s-a. $6 per no. Arkansas Tech University, Department of English, Russellville, AR 72801. TEL 501-968-0256. Eds. B.C. Hall, Michael Karl Ritchie. bk.rev. circ. 500. (back issues avail.) **Document type:** academic/scholarly publication.

NEBRASKA ENGLISH JOURNAL. see *LINGUISTICS*

800 US ISSN 8755-514X
NEBRASKA REVIEW. 1971. s-a. $10. University of Nebraska at Omaha, College of Fine Arts, Creative Writing Program, Writer's Workshop, Fine Arts Bldg. 212, Omaha, NE 68182-0324. TEL 402-554-2771. Eds. Art Homer, Richard Duggin. adv. circ. 500. Indexed: A.I.P.P., Amer.Hum.Ind.
   Formerly (until 1984): Smackwarm.
   Description: Publishes original literary fiction and poetry.

HET NEDERLANDSE BOEK. see *LITERARY AND POLITICAL REVIEWS*

NEEUROPA. see *ART*

891.553 IR
NEGIN. m. M. Enayat, Ed. & Pub., Vali Asar Ave., Adl St. 52, Teheran, Iran.

NEMET FILOLOGIAI TANULMANYOK/ARBEITEN ZUR DEUTSCHEN PHILOLOGIE. see *LINGUISTICS*

800 NE ISSN 0324-4652
PN851
NEOHELICON; acta comparationis litterarum universarum. (Text in English, French, German, Russian) 1973. s-a. fl.300($174) (effective 1994). (International Comparative Literature Association) John Benjamins Publishing Co., Amsteldijk 44, P.O. Box 75577, 1070 AN Amsterdam, Netherlands. TEL 31-20-6738156. FAX 31-20-6792956. (In N. America: 821 Bethlehem Pike, Philadelphia, PA 19118. TEL 215-836-1200. FAX 215-836-1204) (Co-publisher: Akademiai Kiado, HU) Eds. M. Szabolcsi, G.M. Vajda. bk.rev.; bibl. (back issues avail.) Indexed: Arts & Hum.Cit.Ind., Can.Rev.Comp.Lit., Curr.Cont. **Document type:** academic/scholarly publication.
   —BLDSC (6075.606500); Faxon; SWETS. **CCC**.
   Description: Studies in comparative and world literature.

800 NE ISSN 0028-2677
PB5
NEOPHILOLOGUS; an international journal of modern and mediaeval language and literature. (Text in English, French, German, Italian, Portuguese, Spanish) 1916. 4/yr. fl.324($168.50) (effective 1994). Kluwer Academic Publishers, Postbus 17, 3300 AA Dordrecht, Netherlands. TEL 31-78-334911. FAX 31-78-334254. TELEX 29245 KAPG NL. (Dist. by: Kluwer Academic Publishers Group, P.O. Box 322, 3300 AH Dordrecht, Netherlands. TEL 31-78-524400. FAX 31-78-524474; N. American dist. addr.: Box 358, Accord Sta., Hingham, MA 02018-0358. TEL 617-871-6600. FAX 617-871-6528) Ed.Bd. adv.; abstr.; bibl.; index. circ. 900. (reprint service avail. from SCH,SWZ) Indexed: Abstr.Engl.Stud., Arts & Hum.Cit.Ind., Bibl.Ling., Can.Rev.Comp.Lit, Curr.Cont., Lang.& Lang.Behav.Abstr., M.L.A., Mid.East: Abstr.& Ind. **Document type:** academic/scholarly publication.
   —BLDSC (6075.627000); Faxon; UnCover; SWETS.
   Description: Publishes studies of medieval and modern language and literature, including general linguistics, literary theory and comparative linguistics.
   Refereed Serial

830 GW ISSN 0077-7668
NEUDRUCKE DEUTSCHER LITERATURWERKE. N.S. 1961. irreg., no.46, 1993. price varies. Max Niemeyer Verlag, Postfach 2140, 72011 Tuebingen, Germany. TEL 07071-98940. FAX 07071-989450. (back issues avail.) Indexed: M.L.A. **Document type:** monographic series.
   Continues: Neudrucke Deutscher Literaturwerke des XVI und XVII Jahrhunderts & Neudrucke Deutscher Literaturwerke des XVIII und XIX Jahrhunderts.
   Description: Editions of German literature in the 16th and 17th centuries, in part also the 18th and 19th centuries.

830 GW ISSN 0077-7676
NEUDRUCKE DEUTSCHER LITERATURWERKE. SONDERREIHE. 1964. irreg. price varies. Max Niemeyer Verlag, Postfach 2140, 72011 Tuebingen, Germany. TEL 07071-98940. FAX 07071-989450. (back issues avail.) **Document type:** monographic series.
   Description: Editions of German literature in the 16th and 17th centuries, in part also the 18th and 19th centuries.

830 GW ISSN 0028-3150
PT3
NEUE DEUTSCHE LITERATUR. Short title: N D L. 1953. bi-m. DM.100. Aufbau-Verlag Berlin und Weimar, Franzoesische Str. 32, 10117 Berlin, Germany. TEL 030-22350. FAX 030-2298637. (Subscr. to: Inter Abo Betreuungs GmbH, Postfach 53, 12413 Berlin, Germany. TEL 030-68834451. FAX 030-68834490) Eds. Achim Roscher, Christian Loeser. adv.; bk.rev.; film rev.; play rev.; index. **Document type:** academic/scholarly publication.
   —BLDSC (6077.330000); UnCover; SWETS.

859 RM
NEUE LITERATUR. (Text in German) 1953. m. 144 lei. Uniunea Scriitorilor din Republica Socialista Romania, Calea Victoriei 115, Bucharest, Rumania. (Subscr. to: ILEXIM, Str. 13 Decembrie Nr. 3, Box 136-137, 70116 Bucharest, Rumania) Ed. Arnold Hauser. bk.rev.; play rev.; abstr.; illus.

808.068 371.3
028.5
THE NEW ADVOCATE. 1981-1986 (vol.5); N.S. 1987. 4/yr. $45 (Canada $55; elsewhere $65). (University of Georgia, College of Education) Christopher - Gordon Publishers, Inc., 480 Washington St., Norwood, MA 02062. TEL 617-762-5577. Ed. Joel Taxel. adv.; bk.rev.; charts; illus.; stat.; index. circ. 7,500. (back issues avail.) Indexed: Bk.Rev.Ind. (1990-), Child.Bk.Rev.Ind. (1990-), Child.Lit.Abstr. **Document type:** academic/scholarly publication.
   —BLDSC (6081.725000); Faxon; UnCover.
   Formerly (until 1987): Advocate (Athens) (ISSN 0730-3114)
   Description: Features articles on using children's literature in the K-8 classroom, across the curriculum.

800 100 200 US ISSN 1048-8545
B3090
NEW ATHENAEUM/NEUES ATHENAEUM. (Text in English, German) a. $29.95 to individuals; institutions $29.95. Edwin Mellen Press, 415 Ridge St., Box 450, Lewiston, NY 14092. TEL 716-754-2788. FAX 716-754-4056. Ed. Ruth Richardson. **Document type:** monographic series, academic/scholarly publication.
   Description: Scholarly journal specializing in Schleiermacher and Schlegel Research and other Nineteenth-Century studies.

891 US
NEW BOOKS, SELECTED BOOKS, JOURNALS FROM SLAVICA. m. Slavica Publishers, Inc., Box 14388, Columbus, OH 43214. TEL 614-268-4002. **Document type:** catalog, academic/scholarly publication.
   Description: Lists new and existing scholarly books and journals published or distributed by Slavica. Entries are annotated in detail. Also contains small news items of interest.

807 US
NEW CANTERBURY LITERARY SOCIETY NEWSLETTER. 1973. q. free. (New Canterbury Literary Society) Norman T. Gates, Ed. & Pub., 520 Woodland Ave., Haddonfield, NJ 08033. bk.rev.; circ. 100 (controlled). **Document type:** newsletter.
   Description: Covers the author Richard Aldington (1892-1962).

800 410 AT
NEW CEYLON WRITING; creative and critical writing of Sri Lanka. 1970. irreg. Aus.$20. Post-Colonial Literatures & Language Research Centre, School of English & Linguistics, Nacquarie University, North Ryde, N.S.W. 2109, Australia. TEL 02-805-8776. FAX 02-876-8698. Ed. Yasmine Gooneratne. adv.; bk.rev.; play rev.; abstr.; bibl. circ. 250.

LITERATURE

810 — US — ISSN 0028-4467
NEW COLLAGE MAGAZINE. 1970. 3/yr. $6. (New Collage Foundation) New Collage Press, 5700 N. Tamiami Trail, Sarasota, FL 34243-2197. TEL 813-359-4248. FAX 813-356-5605. Ed. A. McA. Miller. bk.rev. circ. 700. (back issues avail.) **Indexed:** A.I.P.P., Ind.Amer.Per.Verse.

800 — US — ISSN 0891-0073
NEW CONNECTIONS: STUDIES IN INTERDISCIPLINARITY. irreg. Peter Lang Publishing, Inc., 62 W. 45th St., 4th Fl., New York, NY 10036. TEL 212-302-6740. FAX 212-302-7574. Ed. Shirley Paolini. **Document type:** academic/scholarly publication.
—BLDSC (6082.894240).
Description: Focuses on the interrelationships between literature and other arts, science, philosophy, law, psychology, anthropology, and religion.

800 9 — SA — ISSN 1017-5415
AP9
NEW CONTRAST; South African literary journal. (Text in Afrikaans, English) 1960. q. R.60($52) (effective 1994). South African Literary Journal Ltd., P.O. Box 3841, Cape Town 8000, South Africa. Ed.Bd. adv.; bk.rev.; illus.; cum.index every 5 yrs. circ. 500. (back issues avail.) **Indexed:** Ind.S.A.Per., M.L.A.
Formerly: Contrast (ISSN 0589-574X); Incorporates (1983-1990): Upstream (ISSN 0258-7416)
Description: Publishes poetry, short fiction, essays, reviews and journalism by South Africans on issues relating to South Africa.

800 700 — UK
NEW DEPARTURES; international review of literature & the lively arts. 1959. a. $10. c/o Michael Horovitz, Ed., Mullions, Piedmont, Bisley, Stroud, Glos. GL6 7BU, England. adv.; bk.rev. circ. 10,000.

810 974 — US — ISSN 0028-4866
F1
NEW ENGLAND QUARTERLY; a historical review of New England life and letters. 1928. q. $20 to individuals; institutions $25. New England Quarterly, Inc., Meserve Hall, 2nd Fl., Boston, MA 02115. TEL 617-373-2734. FAX 617-373-2661. Ed. William M. Fowler. adv.; bk.rev.; index. circ. 2,500. (also avail. in microform from UMI,PMC; reprint service avail. from UMI) **Indexed:** Abstr.Engl.Stud., Acad.Ind., Amer.Hist.& Life, Arts & Hum.Cit.Ind., Bk.Rev.Ind. (1965-) CERDIC, Child.Bk.Rev.Ind. (1965-) Curr.Cont., Hist.Abstr., Hum.Ind., Ind.Bk.Rev.Hum., M.L.A., Rel.& Theol.Abstr. (1990-).
—Faxon; UnCover; SWETS; UMI.

810 — US — ISSN 1053-1297
PN2
NEW ENGLAND REVIEW. 1978. q. $23 to individuals; institutions $40. (Middlebury College) Middlebury College Publications, Middlebury College, Middlebury, VT 05753. TEL 802-388-3711. FAX 802-388-3711. Eds. David Huddle, William Lychack. adv.; bk.rev. circ. 3,000. (also avail. in microform from UMI; back issues avail.; reprint service avail. from UMI) **Indexed:** A.I.P.P., Amer.Bibl.Slavic & E.Eur.Stud., Arts & Hum.Cit.Ind., Bk.Rev.Ind. (1980-), Child.Bk.Rev.Ind. (1980-), Curr.Cont., Ind.Amer.Per.Verse, Ind.Bk.Rev.Hum., M.L.A.
—Faxon; UnCover; UMI.
Former titles (until 1990): New England Review and Bread Loaf Quarterly (ISSN 0736-2579); (until 1982): New England Review (ISSN 0164-3177)
Description: Contemporary poetry, essays, fiction, reviews, interviews and translations.

830 410 — US — ISSN 0889-0145
NEW GERMAN REVIEW; a journal of Germanic studies. (Text in English, German) 1985. a. $8 to individuals; institutions $10. University of California, Los Angeles, Department of Germanic Languages, 302 Royce Hall, Los Angeles, CA 90034. TEL 213-825-3955. Ed. John-Thomas Siehoff. bk.rev. (back issues avail.) **Document type:** academic/scholarly publication.
Description: Publishes articles on German literature, language, culture and literary theory.

830 — UK — ISSN 0307-2770
PF3001
NEW GERMAN STUDIES. 1973. 3/yr. £5 to individuals; institutions £7. University of Hull, Department of German, Hull HU6 7RX, England. FAX 0482-465991. Eds. A.D. Best, A.R. Deighton. adv.; bk.rev.; index. circ. 250. **Indexed:** M.L.A. **Document type:** academic/scholarly publication.
—BLDSC (6084.217000).

800 — US — ISSN 0145-8388
NEW LAUREL REVIEW. 1971. a. $19 to individuals; libraries $11; foreign $12. (New Orleans Poetry Forum) Smoke Bend Publishing, 828 Lesseps St., New Orleans, LA 70117. TEL 504-947-6001. Ed. Lee Meitzen Grue. adv.; bk.rev. circ. 500. **Indexed:** M.L.A.

378.1 — US — ISSN 0146-4930
PS501
NEW LETTERS; a magazine of writing and art. 1934. q. $17 to individuals; institutions $20. University of Missouri, Kansas City, 5100 Rockhill Rd., Kansas City, MO 64110. TEL 816-235-1168. FAX 816-235-2611. Ed. James McKinley. adv.; bk.rev.; index. circ. 1,500. **Indexed:** A.I.P.P., Abstr.Engl.Stud., Amer.Hum.Ind., Arts & Hum.Cit.Ind., Curr.Cont., Ind.Amer.Per.Verse, Ind.Bk.Rev.Hum., M.L.A.
—Faxon; UnCover.
Former titles (until vol.37, 1971): University Review (ISSN 0042-0379); (until vol.30, 1964): University of Kansas City Review; (until vol.8, 1942): University Review.
Description: Presents contemporary short fiction, poetry, essays, line drawings, and photography.

809 — US — ISSN 0028-6087
PR1
NEW LITERARY HISTORY; a journal of theory and interpretation. 1969. 4/yr. $30 to individuals (foreign $37); institutions $75 (foreign $87). (University of Virginia) Johns Hopkins University Press, Journals Publishing Division, 2715 N. Charles St., Baltimore, MD 21218. TEL 410-516-6987. FAX 410-516-6968. Ed. Ralph Cohen. adv.; index, cum.index: vols.1-10. circ. 2,192. (also avail. in microform from UMI; back issues avail.; reprint service avail. from UMI) **Indexed:** Abstr.Engl.Stud., Amer.Hist.& Life (until 1990), Arts & Hum.Cit.Ind., Bibl.Engl.Lang.& Lit., Can.Rev.Comp.Lit., Curr.Cont., Film Lit.Ind. (1990-), Hist.Abstr. (until 1990), Hum.Ind., Lang.& Lang.Behav.Abstr., LCR, M.L.A., Sociol.Abstr.
—BLDSC (6084.457000); Faxon; UnCover; SWETS. **CCC.**
Description: Focuses on theory and interpretation—the reasons for literary change, the definitions of periods, and the evolution of styles, conventions, and genres.

800 — AT — ISSN 0314-7495
PR9080
NEW LITERATURES REVIEW. 1975. s-a. Aus.$15. University of Wollongong, Department of English, Nothfields Ave., Wollongong, N.S.W. 2522, Australia. TEL 042-214-471. FAX 042-213-477. (Co-sponsor: New Literatures Research Centre) Ed.Bd. adv.; bk.rev. circ. 250. (back issues avail.) **Indexed:** Aus.P.A.I.S., M.L.A., So.Pac.Per.Ind. **Document type:** academic/scholarly publication.

800 — US
THE NEW MOON DIRECTORY. 1988. a. $3.95. Eric L. Watts, Ed. & Pub., 346 Carpenter Dr., No. 51, Atlanta, GA 30328-5030. TEL 404-843-2059. adv.: page $20; adv. contact: Eric Watts. circ. 150. **Document type:** directory.
Description: Lists over 100 publications produced by amateur press associations including subjects such as science fiction, comics, and music.

800 700 — IT — ISSN 0028-6354
NEW MORALITY;* concerned with new literature, art and criticism. (Text in English, French, Italian, Spanish) 1961. q. L.5000.($10) Via della Penna 51, Rome, Italy. Dir. Francine Virduzzo.

810 770 — US — ISSN 0028-6400
AP2
NEW ORLEANS REVIEW. 1968. 4/yr. $30. Loyola University, Box 195, New Orleans, LA 70118. TEL 504-865-2294. Ed. John Mosier. adv.; film rev.; illus. circ. 600. (also avail. in microform from UMI; reprint service avail. from UMI) **Indexed:** A.I.P.P., Abstr.Engl.Stud., Amer.Bibl.Slavic & E.Eur.Stud., Amer.Hum.Ind., Arts & Hum.Cit.Ind., Curr.Cont., Film Lit.Ind. (1980-), Ind.Amer.Per.Verse, Ind.Bk.Rev.Hum., M.L.A.
—BLDSC (6084.843000); Faxon; UnCover; UMI.
Description: Literary journal specializing in poetry, fiction, photography, and film and literary criticism.

808 — US
NEW RAIN. (Text in English, French, Spanish) 1981. a. price varies. Blind Beggar Press, Box 437, Williamsbridge Station, Bronx, NY 10467. TEL 914-683-6792. Ed. Gary Johnston. adv.; illus. circ. 1,000. (back issues avail.)

820 — UK — ISSN 0028-6540
PR3532
NEW RAMBLER. 1941. a. $7. Johnson Society of London, 10 Beaumont Buildings, Oxford OX1 2LL, England. Ed. David Parker. adv.; bk.rev. circ. 300. (back issues avail.) **Indexed:** Abstr.Engl.Stud.

800 700 — US — ISSN 0028-6575
NX1
THE NEW RENAISSANCE; an international magazine of ideas and opinions, emphasizing literature & the arts. 1968. s-a. $19.50 (Canada $21; elsewhere $23) for 3 issues. Friends of the New Renaissance, Inc., 9 Heath Rd., Arlington, MA 02174. Ed. Louise T. Reynolds. bk.rev.; film rev.; play rev.; illus.; index. circ. 1,100. (back issues avail.) **Indexed:** A.I.P.P., Abstr.Engl.Stud., Alt.Press Ind., Amer.Hum.Ind., Ind.Amer.Per.Verse. **Document type:** academic/scholarly publication.
—Faxon; UnCover. **CCC.**

800 770 — US — ISSN 0163-2299
NEW VIRGINIA REVIEW. 1978. 3/yr. $15. New Virginia Review, Inc., 1306 E. Cary St., Ste. 2A, Richmond, VA 23219. TEL 804-782-1043. Ed. Mary Flinn. circ. 2,000.

820 — TR — ISSN 0254-9549
PR9214.5
THE NEW VOICES. (Text in English) 1973. s-a. $10. P.O. Box 3254, Diego Martin, Trinidad & Tobago, W.I. TEL 809-637-4516. Ed. Anson Gonzalez. adv.; bk.rev.; illus. circ. 300.

800 — US — ISSN 0895-6510
NEW WRITER'S MAGAZINE. 1986. bi-m. $14. Sarasota Bay Publishing, Box 5976, Sarasota, FL 34277. TEL 813-953-7903. Ed. George J. Haborak. adv.; bk.rev. circ. 5,000. (back issues avail.) **Document type:** consumer publication.
Description: Features articles for new, aspiring writers with information on how to break into the freelance market.

NEW YORK TIMES BOOK REVIEW. see *PUBLISHING AND BOOK TRADE*

NEW YORK TIMES BOOK REVIEW (MICROFORM EDITIONS). see *PUBLISHING AND BOOK TRADE*

NEW YORK UNIVERSITY STUDIES IN FRENCH CULTURE AND CIVILIZATION. see *HISTORY — History Of Europe*

840 440 — NZ — ISSN 0110-7380
PQ9
NEW ZEALAND JOURNAL OF FRENCH STUDIES. 1980. s-a. NZ.$20. Massey University, Department of European Languages, Palmerston North, New Zealand. TEL 06-356-9099. FAX 06-350-5633. Ed. J. Dunmore. adv.; bk.rev. circ. 200. (back issues avail.) **Document type:** academic/scholarly publication.
—BLDSC (6094.150000); Faxon. **CCC.**
Description: Scholarly articles on all aspects of French language, literature and culture.

NEWORLD; the multicultural magazine of the arts. see *ART*

LITERATURE

810
AP2 US ISSN 0276-5241
NEWPORT REVIEW.* 1979. a. $5. Newport Art Museum, c/o Stuart Blazer, Ed., Box 175, Adamsville, RI 02801-0175. TEL 401-848-2100. adv. circ. 1,000.

800 US ISSN 0737-4011
NEWSBANK REVIEW OF THE ARTS: LITERATURE. 1972. m. (q. and a. cumulations). price varies. NewsBank, Inc., 58 Pine St., New Canaan, CT 06840-5426. TEL 203-966-1100. FAX 203-966-6254. Ed. C. Dyer. bk.rev. (also avail. in microfiche; reprint service avail.)

810 US ISSN 0194-4118
NEWSCRIBES; a literary magazine. 1976. s-a. $5. Newscribes Group, 1223 Newkirk Ave., Brooklyn, NY 11230. Ed. Vincent Campo. adv. circ. 800.

808.87 CN ISSN 0384-1642
NEWSPACKET. 1970. 3/yr. Can.$10. Stephen Leacock Associates, P.O. Box 854, Orillia, ON L3V 6K8, Canada. TEL 705-325-6546. FAX 705-327-6866. Ed. Kathy Hunt. adv.; bk.rev.; illus. circ. 3,500. **Document type:** newsletter.
Description: Newsletter on humor, with emphasis on humor in Canada. Includes news of the Leacock Associates and topical columns.

800 US
NEXUS (DAYTON). 1965. 3/yr. $15. Wright State University, 006 U.C., Dayton, OH 45435. TEL 513-873-5533. FAX 513-873-5536. Ed. Ted Cains. adv.; bk.rev. circ. 2,000. (back issues avail.) **Indexed:** Rel.Ind.One.

NIEUWE TAALGIDS; tijdschrift voor neerlandici. see LINGUISTICS

800 100 US ISSN 0278-6079
NIGHTSUN; a journal of poetry, short-short fiction, and interviews. 1981. a. $6.50. Frostburg State University, Department of English, Frostburg, MD 21532. Ed. Douglas DeMars. adv.; bk.rev. circ. 500. (back issues avail.)

890 JA ISSN 0386-9903
NIHON BUNGAKU/JAPANESE LITERATURE. (Text in Japanese) 1952. m. 930 Yen per no. Nihon Bungaku Kyokai - Japanese Literature Association, 2-17-10 Minami-otsuka, Toshima-ku, Tokyo, Japan. FAX 03-3941-2740. Ed. Senri Sugai. adv.; bk.rev. —UnCover.

808 US ISSN 0029-053X
PS535.5
NIMROD; international journal of prose and poetry. 1956. s-a. $11.50 (foreign $16). Arts and Humanities Council of Tulsa, 2210 S. Main, Tulsa, OK 74114. TEL 918-584-3333. (Dist. by: Council Oak Distributing, 1428 S. St. Louis, Tulsa, OK 74120. TEL 800-247-8850) Ed. Francine Ringold. adv. circ. 4,500. (back issues avail.) **Indexed:** Amer.Hum.Ind., Ind.Amer.Per.Verse. **Document type:** bulletin.

840 US ISSN 0146-7891
PQ1
NINETEENTH CENTURY FRENCH STUDIES. (Text in English and French) 1972. q. $30 to individuals; institutions $34. State University of New York, College at Fredonia, Department of Foreign Languages, Fredonia, NY 14063. TEL 716-673-3387. FAX 716-673-3405. Ed. T. H. Goetz. adv.; bk.rev.; bibl.; index. circ. 800. (also avail. in microfilm from UMI; reprint service avail. from UMI) **Indexed:** Arts & Hum.Cit.Ind., Curr.Cont., Ind.Bk.Rev.Hum., M.L.A. **Document type:** academic/scholarly publication.
—BLDSC (6113.230200); Faxon; UnCover; UMI.

813 US ISSN 0891-9356
PR451
NINETEENTH-CENTURY LITERATURE (BERKELEY). 1945. q. $26 to individuals (foreign $26); institutions $42 (foreign $48); students $17 (foreign $23) (effective 1994). University of California Press, Journals Division, 2120 Berkeley Way, Berkeley, CA 94720. TEL 510-643-7154. FAX 510-642-9917. Eds. G.B. Tennyson, Thomas Wortham. adv.; bk.rev.; index, cum.index. circ. 2,400. (also avail. in microform from UMI; back issues avail.; reprint service avail. from UMI) **Indexed:** Abstr.Engl.Stud., Acad.Ind., Amer.Hist.& Life, Arts & Hum.Cit.Ind., Bk.Rev.Ind. (1986-), Child.Bk.Rev.Ind. (1986-), Curr.Cont., Hist.Abstr., Hum.Ind., Ind.Bk.Rev.Hum., M.L.A., Ref.Sour. **Document type:** academic/scholarly publication.
—BLDSC (6113.230350); Faxon; UnCover; SWETS; UMI. **CCC.**
Formerly: Nineteenth-Century Fiction (ISSN 0029-0564)
Description: Provides new research in scholarship, criticism, comparative studies, and new editions of 19th century English and American literature.
Refereed Serial

800 US
NINETEENTH-CENTURY LITERATURE (ROCHESTER). irreg. University of Rochester Press, c/o Robert Easton, Man. Ed., Box 41026, Rochester, NY 14604. TEL 716-275-6208. FAX 716-271-8778. **Indexed:** Acad.Ind. **Document type:** monographic series.

800 US ISSN 0732-1864
PN761
NINETEENTH-CENTURY LITERATURE CRITICISM. 1981. 3/yr. $108 per vol. (effective Nov. 1991). Gale Research Inc., 835 Penobscot Bldg., Detroit, MI 48226. TEL 313-961-2242. FAX 313-961-6083. TELEX 810-221-7086. Ed. Paula Kepos.

824 US ISSN 1052-0406
PR4023
NINETEENTH-CENTURY PROSE. 1974. 2/yr. $17 to individuals (foreign $23): institutions $35 (foreign $41). University Press of Colorado, Box 849, Niwot, CO 80544. TEL 303-530-5337. FAX 303-530-5306. Ed. Judy Wilson. adv.; bk.rev.; bibl. circ. 400. (back issues avail.) **Indexed:** Abstr.Engl.Stud., Amer.Hum.Ind., Arts & Hum.Cit.Ind., Curr.Cont., LCR, M.L.A. **Document type:** academic/scholarly publication.
—Faxon; UnCover.
Former titles (until 1989): Arnoldian (ISSN 0160-4848); (until 1975): Arnold Newsletter (ISSN 0094-5897)
Description: Devoted exclusively to nonfiction prose writers of the nineteenth century.

800 US ISSN 0893-7931
CB415
NINETEENTH-CENTURY STUDIES. 1987. a. $15 to individuals; institutions $25. (Southeastern Nineteenth-Century Studies Association) The Citadel - The Military College of South Carolina, Department of English, Charleston, SC 29409. TEL 803-953-5140. FAX 803-953-7084. Ed. Suzanne O. Edwards. bk.rev. circ. 250. **Indexed:** M.L.A.
—BLDSC (6113.231630).
Description: Interdisciplinary journal focusing on Nineteenth-Century art, literature, culture, and science.
Refereed Serial

810 US ISSN 0199-3941
NIT & WIT; Chicago's arts magazine. 1977-1985; resumed 1986. bi-m. $12. Nit & Wit Publishing, Box 627, Geneva, IL 60134-0627. TEL 708-232-9496. Eds. Marie Aguirre, Harrison McCormick. adv.; bk.rev.; illus. circ. 6,000. **Indexed:** A.I.P.P.

800 US
NITE-WRITER'S LITERARY ARTS JOURNAL. q. Nite-Owl Press, 3101 Schieck St., Ste. 100, Pittsburgh, PA 10527-4151.

NNIDNID: SURREALITY. see ART

810 US
NOCTURNAL NEWS.* 1983. 3/yr. $11. Baker Street Publications, Box 517, Metairie, LA 70004-0517. TEL 504-734-8414. Ed. Sharida Rizzuto. circ. 9,000.

NONGCUN QINGNIAN/COUNTRY YOUTH. see CHILDREN AND YOUTH — For

NORDEUROPA STUDIEN. see SOCIAL SCIENCES: COMPREHENSIVE WORKS

NORDISTICA GOTHOBURGENSIA. see LINGUISTICS

891.92 AI ISSN 0235-6848
NORK. 1934. m. 18 Rub. Soyuz Pisatelei Armenii, Erevan, Armenia. Ed. R.G. Hovsepyan. bk.rev.; play rev.; bibl.; illus.; stat. circ. 8,000.
Formerly: Sovetakan Grakanutiun (ISSN 0038-5018)

839.82 NO ISSN 0078-1266
PT8301
NORSK LITTERAER AARBOK. (Text mainly in Norwegian, occasionally in Danish and Swedish) 1966. a. NOK 244. Norske Samlaget, P.O. Box 4672 Sofienberg, N-0506 Oslo, Norway. TEL 47-22-68-76-00. FAX 47-22-68-75-02. Eds. H. Skei, E. Vannebo. circ. 1,500. **Indexed:** M.L.A.
Description: Essays on Scandinavian, mainly Norwegian, 20th century literature, and an annotated bibliography of Norwegian research in literature.

800 327 MX
NORTE; revista hispanoamericana. 1929. bi-m. $7 per no. Frente de Afirmacion Hispanista A.C., Lago Ginebra No. 47 C, Mexico 17 D.F., Mexico. Dir. Fredo Arias de la Canal. adv.; illus. circ. 2,000. **Indexed:** Amer.Hist.& Life, Hist.Abstr.

800 US ISSN 0891-4109
NORTH AMERICAN STUDIES IN NINETEENTH-CENTURY GERMAN LITERATURE. (Text in English and other West European languages) 1988. irreg. Peter Lang Publishing, Inc., 62 W. 45th St., 4th Fl., New York, NY 10036. TEL 212-302-6740. Ed. Jeffrey Sammons. **Document type:** academic/scholarly publication.

840 US
NORTH CAROLINA STUDIES IN THE ROMANCE LANGUAGES AND LITERATURES. (Text in English, French, Italian, Latin, Portuguese, Spanish) 1940. irreg., no.231, 1988. price varies. University of North Carolina at Chapel Hill, Department of Romance Languages, CB 3170, 238 Dey Hall, Chapel Hill, NC 27599-3170. TEL 919-962-1025. Ed. Maria A. Salgado. **Indexed:** M.L.A. **Document type:** academic/scholarly publication.
Formerly: Studies in the Romance Languages and Literatures (ISSN 0081-8666)

800 US
NORTH STONE REVIEW. 1971-19??; resumed no.9, 1990. irreg. (1-2/yr.). $15. D Station, Box 14098, Minneapolis, MN 55414. Ed. James Naiden. adv.; bk.rev.; illus. circ. 1,500. (also avail. in microform from UMI; reprint service avail. from UMI)

810 US
NORTHEAST (LA CROSSE). 1962. s-a. $33 to individuals; institutions $38. Juniper Press, 1310 Shorewood Dr., La Crosse, WI 54601. TEL 608-788-0096. Eds. John Judson, Joanne Judson. bk.rev. circ. 400. **Indexed:** A.I.P.P., Ind.Little Mag.
Description: Contains contemporary poetry, short stories, and graphics.

800 US
NORTHEAST JOURNAL. 1978. biennial. $5. Northeast Journal, Box 2321, Providence, RI 02906-0321. Ed. Henry Gould. bk.rev. circ. 500.
Description: Contains original poetry and short prose from around the nation, with an emphasis on Rhode Island and the Northeast.

NORTHERN LIGHTS STUDIES IN CREATIVITY. see ART

800 US ISSN 0190-3012
NORTHERN NEW ENGLAND REVIEW. 1973. a. $5. Franklin Pierce College, Box 825, Rindge, NH 03461. TEL 603-899-5111. Ed. Alexandra Fox. adv.; bk.rev.; circ. 600 (controlled). (back issues avail.) **Indexed:** A.I.P.P., M.L.A.

LITERATURE

800 US
NORTHWARDS JOURNAL. 1986. q. $10. Conservatory of American Letters, Box 298, Thomaston, ME 04861-0298. TEL 207-354-0998. Ed. Robert W. Olmsted. adv. circ. 2,000.
Formerly (until fall 1993): Conservatory of American Letters Newsletter.
Description: Serves as a show case for quality poetry and fiction. Advises members and other writers of things near and dear to the hearts of writers.

810 US ISSN 0029-3423
AP2
NORTHWEST REVIEW. 1957. 3/yr. $14. University of Oregon, Northwest Review, 369 Prince Lucien Campbell Hall, Eugene, OR 97403. TEL 503-346-3957. Ed. John Witte. adv.; bk.rev.; film rev.; play rev. circ. 1,000. (also avail. in microform from UMI; back issues avail.; reprint service avail. from UMI) **Indexed:** A.I.P.P., Amer.Hum.Ind., Ind.Amer.Per.Verse, Ind.Bk.Rev.Hum., M.L.A. **Document type:** academic/scholarly publication.
—BLDSC (6151.950000); Faxon; UnCover; UMI.
Description: Contains original and vital literary and critical works.

811 US
THE NORTHWOODS JOURNAL; a magazine for writers. 1972-1983; resumed 1993. 4/yr. $10 to non-members; Conservatory members free. (Conservatory of American Letters) Northwoods Press, Box 298, Thomaston, ME 04861-0298. TEL 207-354-0998. Ed. Robert W. Olmsted. adv.; bk.rev.; illus. circ. 500.
Supersedes (1972-1983): New Northwoods Journal; Which was formerly: Northwoods Journal (ISSN 0199-6800); Northwoods Newsletter.

070 840 BE ISSN 0029-3717
NOS LETTRES. 1968. m. 750 BEF. Association des Ecrivains Belges de Langue Francaise, Maison des Ecrivains, Chaussee de Wavre 150, B-1050 Brussels, Belgium. TEL 32-2-512-29-68. Ed. Roger Foulon. adv.; bk.rev.; play rev.; illus. circ. 600.
Document type: bulletin.

800 US ISSN 0892-2616
NOSTALGIA (ORANGEBURG); a sentimental state of mind. 1986. s-a. $5. Nostalgia Publications, Box 2224, Orangeburg, SC 29116. TEL 803-534-9844. Ed. Connie Lakey Martin. adv.; bk.rev.; illus. circ. 1,000. (back issues avail.)
Description: Features short stories and poems of a nostalgic content.

NOSTRO TEMPO; settimanale cattolico. see ART

800 180 900 US ISSN 0883-6337
NOTEBOOK/CUADERNO;* a literary journal. (Text in English, some Spanish) 1985. a. $8 to individuals; institutions $10. Esoterica Press, c/o Yoly Zentella, Ed., 1010 Douglas Ave., Ste. 6, Las Vegas, NM 87701-3959. adv.; bk.rev. circ. 200. (back issues avail.) **Indexed:** Amer.Hum.Ind., Chic.Per.Ind.
Description: Humanistic literature emphasizing Latino literature.

800 DK ISSN 0900-2731
NOTER OG OPGAVER TIL ERHVERVS- OG SAMFUNDSBESKRIVELSE H D 1. DEL.* 1975. a. DKK 44.65. (Handelshoejskolen i Koebenhavn) Samfundslitteratur, Copenhagen, Denmark.
Formerly (until 1984): Notat- og Opgavesamling H D 1 til Erhvervs- og Samfundsbeskrivelse (ISSN 0107-6272).

820 AT ISSN 0156-806X
NOTES & FURPHIES. 1978. s-a. Aus.$30 to individuals; institutions Aus.$40. Association for the Study of Australian Literature, c/o University of Tasmania, Humanities, P.O. Box 215, Devonport, Tas. 7310, Australia. TEL 004-247011. FAX 004-241443. Ed. C.A. Cranston. adv.; circ. 500 (paid). (back issues avail.) **Document type:** bulletin, academic/scholarly publication, directory.
Description: Newsletter for undergraduate and post-graduate researchers and academics in Australian literature.

820 UK ISSN 0029-3970
AG305
NOTES AND QUERIES; for readers and writers, collectors and librarians. 1849. 4/yr. £53($100) (effective 1994). Oxford University Press, Oxford Journals, Walton St., Oxford OX2 6DP, England. TEL 0865-56767. FAX 0865-56646. TELEX 837330-OXPRES-G. (U.S. subscr. to: Oxford University Press Inc., 2001 Evans Rd., Cary, NC 27513. TEL 919-677-0977) Ed. E.G. Stanley. adv. contact: Jane Parker. bk.rev.; index, cum.index. circ. 1,500. (also avail. in microform from UMI,PMC) **Indexed:** Abstr.Engl.Stud., Amer.Hist.& Life, Arts & Hum.Cit.Ind., Br.Archaeol.Abstr., Br.Hum.Ind., Curr.Cont., Hist.Abstr., Hum.Ind., Ind.Bk.Rev.Hum., M.L.A., RILA. **Document type:** academic/scholarly publication.
—BLDSC (6165.040000); Faxon; UnCover; SWETS; UMI. **CCC.**
Description: Covers the English language and literature, lexicography, history and scholarly antiquarianism.

800 US ISSN 0029-4047
NOTES ON CONTEMPORARY LITERATURE. 1971. q. $10 to individuals; libraries $20; foreign $20. W.S. Doxey, Ed. & Pub., c/o English Department, West Georgia College, Carollton, GA 30118. TEL 404-836-6512. FAX 404-836-6717. adv.; bk.rev.; index. circ. 250. **Indexed:** Abstr.Engl.Stud., LCR, M.L.A. **Document type:** academic/scholarly publication.
—BLDSC (6166.650000); Faxon; UnCover.

810 US ISSN 0029-4071
PS266.M7
NOTES ON MISSISSIPPI WRITERS. 1968. s-a. $4. University of Southern Mississippi, Department of English, Hattiesburg, MS 39401. TEL 601-266-4319. Ed. Hilton Anderson. bk.rev.; bibl.; index. circ. 250. (back issues avail.) **Indexed:** Abstr.Engl.Stud., M.L.A.
—BLDSC (6167.635000).

840 UK ISSN 0029-4586
PQ1
NOTTINGHAM FRENCH STUDIES. (Text in English and French) 1962. s-a. £12($24) (University of Nottingham, Department of French) Nottingham University Press, Nottingham, England. TEL 0602-515872. FAX 0602-514998. TELEX 37346-UNINOT-G. Ed. Diana Knight. circ. 400. **Indexed:** Arts & Hum.Cit.Ind., Br.Hum.Ind., Curr.Cont., M.L.A. **Document type:** academic/scholarly publication.
—Faxon; UnCover.

800 FR ISSN 0550-1326
PN1
NOUVEAU COMMERCE. (Supplement avail.: Nouveau Commerce de la Lecture (ISSN 0223-3533)) 1963. 2/yr. 310 F. includes supplement. A C N C Nouveau Commerce, Librarie Anima, 3 rue Ravignan, 75018 Paris, France. TEL 1-42-64-05-25. bk.rev.; abstr.; bibl.; cum.index; circ. 1,000 (controlled). (tabloid format)

840 FR ISSN 0223-3533
NOUVEAU COMMERCE DE LA LECTURE. (Supplement to: Nouveau Commerce (ISSN 0550-1326)) 1972. irreg. included in subscr. to Nouveau Commerce. A C N C Nouveau Commerce, 80, rue des Archives, 75003 Paris, France. TEL 42-72-99-03. bk.rev.; abstr.; bibl. circ. 1,000.

840 320 FR ISSN 1161-1006
NOUVEAUX CAHIERS DE L'EST. 1975-1980; resumed 1991. q. 80 F. P O L, 8 villa d'Alesia, 75014 Paris, France. Ed. Dumitru Tsepeneag. bk.rev.
Formerly (until 1980): Cahiers de l'Est (ISSN 0336-5905).

840 920 FR ISSN 0078-2165
NOUVELLE BIBLIOTHEQUE NERVALIENNE. (Consists of two subdivisions: Textes and Etudes et Documents; subdivisions are numbered consecutively within the main series) 1959. irreg. Lettres Modernes, 45 rue Saint-Andre, 14123 Fleury sur Orne, France. TEL 31-84-47-06. FAX 31-84-48-09.

800 PO ISSN 0870-5291
AP65
NOVA SEARA NOVA. 1921-1979; N.S. 1985. bi-m. Esc.750. Empresa de Publicidade Seara Nova, S.A.R.L., Av. Santos Dumont, 57-2, 1000 Lisbon, Portugal. TEL 01-761131. Ed. Ulpiano Nascimento. adv.; bk.rev.; film rev.; play rev.; rec.rev.; charts; illus. circ. 5,000. **Indexed:** M.L.A.
Former titles (until 1985): Seara Nova (ISSN 0870-6719); (until 1979): Seara Nova (ISSN 0870-6662)

NOVA TELLUS. see HUMANITIES: COMPREHENSIVE WORKS

813 US ISSN 0029-5132
PN3311
NOVEL: A FORUM ON FICTION. 1967. 3/yr. $14 to individuals; institutions $20. Brown University, Department of Literature, Box 1984, Providence, RI 02912. TEL 414-863-3756. Ed. Mark Spilka. bk.rev.; index. circ. 1,500. (also avail. in microform from UMI; reprint service avail. from UMI) **Indexed:** Abstr.Engl.Stud., Acad.Ind., Amer.Bibl.Slavic & E.Eur.Stud., Arts & Hum.Cit.Ind., Can.Rev.Comp.Lit., Curr.Cont., Hum.Ind., Ind.Bk.Rev.Hum., M.L.A. **Document type:** academic/scholarly publication.
—BLDSC (6180.235000); Faxon; UnCover; SWETS; UMI.
Description: Contains essays and reviews on novel theory.

808 US ISSN 0897-9812
PN3355
NOVEL & SHORT STORY WRITER'S MARKET. a. $19.95. F & W Publications, Inc., 1507 Dana Ave., Cincinnati, OH 45207. TEL 513-531-2222. Ed. Robin Gee. circ. 35,000.
Formerly (until 1988): Fiction Writer's Market (ISSN 0275-2123)
Description: Provides 1,900 listings of fiction publishers, plus articles on fiction writing and marketing techniques.

800 CN
NOVOID. q.? $2 per no. Box 161, Orillia, Ont. L3V 6H9, Canada. Ed. Colin Hinz.
Description: Contains mimeography, artwork, and articles about publishing, politics and science fiction.

808 333.7 US ISSN 0896-2693
F217.A65
NOW AND THEN. 1984. 3/yr. $10 to individuals; institutions $12 (effective till July, 1994). East Tennessee State University, Center for Appalachian Studies and Services, Box 70556, Johnson City, TN 37614-0556. TEL 615-929-5348. FAX 615-929-5348. Ed. Pat Arnow. bk.rev. circ. 1,600.
●Also available online.
Former Titles: Second Growth; Appalachian Nature and Culture.
Description: Contains poetry, fiction, essays, interviews, photos and graphics focusing on life in the Appalachian mountains.

896 NR
NSUKKA STUDIES IN AFRICAN LITERATURE. 1977. s-a. University of Nigeria, Department of English, Nsukka, Nigeria. (Co-sponsor: Department of Languages) bk.rev. **Indexed:** Arts & Hum.Cit.Ind., Curr.Cont.

056.1 CU
NUEVA GACETA DE CUBA. 1962. m. $20 in N. America; S. America $26; Europe $29; elsewhere $41. (Union de Escritores y Artistas de Cuba) Ediciones Cubanas, Obispo No. 527, Aptdo. 605, Havana, Cuba. illus. circ. 10,000.
Former titles: Nueva Gaceta; Gaceta de Cuba (ISSN 0435-0251)

NUEVA REVISTA DE FILOLOGIA HISPANICA. see LINGUISTICS

NUEVA REVISTA DEL PACIFICO. see LINGUISTICS

860 US ISSN 1048-6380
PQ7081.A1
NUEVO TEXTO CRITICO. (Text in Spanish) 1988. s-a. Stanford University, Department of Spanish and Portuguese, Stanford, CA 94305-2014.

820 CN ISSN 0823-2490
NUIT BLANCHE; l'actualite du livre. 4/yr. Can.$15 (foreign Can.$25). 1026 rue Saint-Jean, No. 403, Quebec, Que. G1R 1R7, Canada. TEL 418-692-1354. FAX 418-692-1355. Ed. A.M. Guerineau. **Indexed:** Pt.de Rep. (1989-).

NUMBER ONE. see LITERATURE — Poetry

800 IT ISSN 0029-6155
NUOVA CORRENTE; rivista di letteratura e filosofia. (Text in Italian; occasionally in English, French, German) 1954. s-a. L.52000 (foreign L.78000) (effective 1994). Tilgher-Genova s.a.s., Via Assarotti 52, 16122 Milan, Italy. TEL 10-8391140. FAX 10-870653. Ed.Bd. adv.; bk.rev.; index. **Indexed:** Abstr.Engl.Stud.
—BLDSC (6184.908500).

NUOVA RICERCA. see LINGUISTICS

850 IT ISSN 0391-8548
NUOVA UNIVERSALE STUDIUM. 1974. irreg., latest no.68. price varies. Edizioni Studium, Via Cassiodoro 14, 00193 Rome, Italy. **Document type:** monographic series.

850 IT
NUVOLE. 1991. bi-m. L.35000 (foreign L.50000). Edizioni Sonda, Via Ciamarella 23-3, 10149 Turin, Italy. TEL 011-218610. FAX 011-293646. Ed. Angelo d'Orsi.

800 CC
NUZI WENXUE/WOMEN'S LITERATURE. (Text in Chinese) m. Shijiazhuang Wenxue Yishu Jie Lianhehui, 19 Tannan Lu, Shijiazhuang, Hebei 050011, People's Republic of China. TEL 45845. Ed. Zhang Guangmin.

NYELV- ES IRODALOMTUDOMANYI KOZLEMENYEK. see LINGUISTICS

840 FR ISSN 0982-4677
NYX. 1987. q. 4 square Saint-Irenee, 75011 Paris, France. Ed. Antoine Chalvin.

891.7 228.5 RU ISSN 0131-2421
O LITERATURE DLYA DETEI. (Text in Russian) 1955. a. Izdatel'stvo Licei, Dom Detskoi Knigi, Nab. Kutuzova 6, 191187 St. Petersburg, Russia. TEL 273-4824. Ed. Alexander L. Kovalenko. adv.; bk.rev. circ. 10,000.
Description: Publishes articles about children's literature and children's reading.

840 FR ISSN 0294-4480
O R A C L. 1982. q. 220 F. Office Regional d'Action Culturelle, Musee Sainte-Croix, 86000 Poitiers, France. TEL 49415900. (Subscr. to: Georges Bonnet, 4 rue de la Trinite, 86000 Poitiers, France) bk.rev. circ. 1,000. (back issues avail.)

820 UK
OASIS (LONDON). 1969. 6/yr. £3 to individuals; institutions £5. Oasis Books, 12 Stevenage Rd., London SW6 6ES, England. TEL 071-726-5059. Ed. Ian Robinson. adv.; bk.rev.; index every 3 yrs. circ. 500. (back issues avail.) **Document type:** bulletin.
Incorporated: Expression (ISSN 0029-7410)

800 910.03 US ISSN 0888-4412
PR1110.B5
OBSIDIAN II: BLACK LITERATURE IN REVIEW. 1975. 3/yr. $12. North Carolina State University, English Department, Box 8105, Raleigh, NC 27695-8105. TEL 919-515-4150. Ed. Gerald Barrax. adv.; bk.rev.; index. circ. 500. (also avail. in microform from UMI; reprint service avail. from UMI) **Indexed:** Amer.Hum.Ind., Arts & Hum.Cit.Ind., Curr.Cont., Ind.Amer.Per.Verse, Ind.Bk.Rev.Hum., M.L.A.
—Faxon; UnCover; UMI.
Formerly: Obsidian: Black Literature in Review (ISSN 0360-6724)
Description: Review for the study and cultivation of creative works in English by black writers worldwide, with scholarly critical studies by all writers on black literature in English.

891.81 BU ISSN 0029-7852
AP4
OBZOR; Bulgarian quarterly review of literature & the arts. (Editions in English, French and Spanish) 1967. q. 4 Iv.($5) (Komitet za Izkustvo i Kultura) Foreign Trade Co. "Hemus", 7 Levsky St., 1000 Sofia, Bulgaria. (Co-sponsor: Suiuz na Bulgarski Pisateli) Ed. Liliana Stefanova. bk.rev.; bibl.; illus.; index. circ. 3,000 (English ed.) (also avail. in microform from UMI; reprint service avail. from UMI) **Indexed:** Arts & Hum.Cit.Ind., Curr.Cont.
—UMI.

430 400 940 UK ISSN 0307-7497
OCCASIONAL PAPERS IN GERMAN STUDIES. (Text in English with German quotations) 1972. irreg. 75p. per no. University of Warwick, Department of German Studies, Coventry CV4 4AL, England. (Co-sponsor: Volkswagen Foundation) Ed. Tony Phelan. circ. 200.

807 407 US ISSN 0739-8972
PG1
OCCASIONAL PAPERS IN SLAVIC LANGUAGES AND LITERATURE. 1982. irreg. University of Washington, Department of Slavic Languages and Literature, DP-32, Seattle, WA 98195. TEL 206-543-6848. Ed. James D. West. **Document type:** academic/scholarly publication.
Description: Presents research papers and covers literature and linguisitcs.

OCTOBER. see ART

809 DK ISSN 0106-2212
ODENSE UNIVERSITET. LABORATORIUM FOR FOLKESPROGLIG MIDDELALDERLITTERATUR. MINDRE SKRIFTER. 1977. irreg. price varies. Odense Universitet, Laboratorium for Folkesproglig Middelalterlitteratur, Odense, Denmark. circ. 100.

800 DK ISSN 0078-3323
ODENSE UNIVERSITY STUDIES IN LITERATURE. (Text in Danish; summaries in English) 1969. irreg., vol.28, 1991. price varies. Odense University Press, Campusvej 55, DK-5230 Odense M, Denmark. TEL 66-157999. FAX 66-158126. (back issues avail.)

ODENSE UNIVERSITY STUDIES IN SCANDINAVIAN LANGUAGES AND LITERATURES. see LINGUISTICS

820 MW
ODI; the muse. (Text in English) 1974. q. $6. Chancellor College, Writers' Group, P.O. Box 280, Zomba, Malawi. Ed. A.J. Nazombe. **Indexed:** M.L.A.

800 700 PL ISSN 0472-5182
AP54
ODRA. 1961. m. $55. (Ministry of Culture) Agencja Autorska, Hipoteczna 2, P.O. Box 133, 00-950 Warsaw, Poland. TEL 48-22-27-6061. FAX 48-22-27-5882. TELEX ZAIKS PL 812472. (Editorial addr.: Redakcja Odry, ul. Podwale 64, Wroslaw, Poland. TEL 255-16) bk.rev. circ. 8,500.
Description: Cultural-social review, includes poetry, prose, essays, art, politics.

ODU; a journal of West African studies. see HISTORY — History Of Africa

830 900 AU ISSN 1013-9966
DB1
OESTERREICH IN GESCHICHTE UND LITERATUR MIT GEOGRAPHIE. 1957. bi-m. S.520. Wilhelm Braumueller, Universitaets-Verlagsbuchhandlung GmbH, Servitengasse 5, A-1092 Vienna, Austria. TEL 0222-3191159. FAX 0222-3102805. adv.; bk.rev.; charts; illus.; index. circ. 1,200. **Indexed:** Amer.Hist.& Life, Hist.Abstr. **Document type:** academic/scholarly publication.
—BLDSC (6303.880000); SWETS.
Formerly (until 1972): Oesterreich in Geschichte und Literatur (ISSN 0029-8743)

838 AU
OESTERREICHISCHE AKADEMIE DER WISSENSCHAFTEN. KOMMISSION FUER LITERATURWISSENSCHAFT. VEROEFFENTLICHUNGEN. (Subseries of: Oesterreichische Akademie der Wissenschaften. Philosophisch-Historische Klasse. Sitzungsberichte) 1973. irreg. Verlag der Oesterreichischen Akademie der Wissenschaften, Dr. Ignaz-Seipel-Platz, A-1010 Vienna, Austria. FAX 0222-5139541.

OESTERREICHISCHE AKADEMIE DER WISSENSCHAFTEN. PHILOSOPHISCH-HISTORISCHE KLASSE. SITZUNGSBERICHTE. see HISTORY — History Of Europe

OESTERREICHISCHE AUTORENZEITUNG. see PATENTS, TRADEMARKS AND COPYRIGHTS

809 840 GW ISSN 0338-1900
PQ2
OEUVRES ET CRITIQUES; revue international d'etude de la reception critique des oeuvres litteraires de langue francaise. (Text in English, French and German) 1976. 2/yr. DM.58 to individuals; institutions DM.88. Gunter Narr Verlag, Postfach 2567, 72015 Tuebingen, Germany. TEL 07071-78091. FAX 07071-75288. Ed. Wolfgang Leiner. adv.; bk.rev.; bibl.; tr.lit. circ. 3,000. (back issues avail.) **Indexed:** Arts & Hum.Cit.Ind., Curr.Cont., M.L.A. **Document type:** academic/scholarly publication.
—UnCover; SWETS. **CCC.**

810 US
OFF MAIN STREET. 1986. a. $3.50. Ferris State College, Languages and Literature Department, Big Rapids, MI 49307. TEL 616-796-8762. Eds. David Vinopal, John Caserta.

811 US
OFFICE NUMBER ONE. 1988. 4/yr. $8.82 for 6 issues. 1708 S. Congress Ave., Austin, TX 78704-3524. TEL 512-445-4489. circ. 2,000.
Description: News from parallel universes and other dimensions.

OHIO REVIEW. see LITERATURE — Poetry

810 US ISSN 0030-1248
OHIOANA QUARTERLY. 1957. q. $20. Ohioana Library Association, 1105 Ohio Departments Bldg., 65 S. Front St., Columbus, OH 43215. TEL 614-466-3831. Ed. Barbara S. Maslekoff. bk.rev.; bibl.; illus. circ. 2,500. **Indexed:** Abstr.Engl.Stud., Amer.Hum.Ind. **Document type:** academic/scholarly publication.
Formerly: Ohioana.

810 960 NR ISSN 0331-0566
PR9898.N5
OKIKE; an African journal of new writing. 1971. 3/yr. $12. Okike Arts Centre, Box 53, Nsukka, Nigeria. Ed. Chinua Achebe. adv.; bk.rev.; illus.; index, cum.index. circ. 5,500. **Indexed:** Arts & Hum.Cit.Ind., Curr.Cont., Curr.Cont.Africa, M.L.A.
—BLDSC (6252.860000).

891.8 YU ISSN 0030-1949
OKTOBAR; list za knjizevnost, umetnost i kulturu. 1966. d. 18 din.($3.) Kulturno Prosvetna Zajednica Opstine Kraljevo, Cara Dusana 32, Kraljevo, Yugoslavia. Ed. Jovan Markovic.

800 429 US ISSN 0030-1973
PE101
OLD ENGLISH NEWSLETTER. 1967. q. $5 to individuals; institutions $10. (Modern Language Association of America, Old English Group) State University of New York at Binghamton, Center for Medieval and Early Renaissance Studies, Binghamton, NY 13901. TEL 607-777-2130. FAX 607-777-2408. Ed. Paul E. Szarmach. bibl. circ. 975. (back issues avail.; reprint service avail. from ISI) **Indexed:** LCR, M.L.A.
—Faxon.

OLD LADY OF THREADNEEDLE STREET. see GENERAL INTEREST PERIODICALS — Great Britain

810 US
OLD RED KIMONO. 1972. a. Floyd College, Humanities Division, Box 1864, Rome, GA 30162. TEL 706-295-6312. FAX 706-295-6610. Eds. Jon Hershey, Ken Anderson. index. circ. 1,500. (processed)
Description: Contains poetry and very short stories that are concise and imagistic, not sentimental or didactic.

850 IT
OLTRANZA; rivista di letteratura ed altro. 3/yr. L.40000. Alfredo Guida Editore, Piazzale E. Fermi 2, 80040 San Sebastiano al Vesuvio, Italy. TEL 081-7713037. (And: Via Port'Alba 19, Naples, Italy. TEL 081-290768) Ed. Ciro Vitiello.

LITERATURE

700   US   ISSN 0316-4055
NX1
ONTARIO REVIEW. 1974. s-a. $12 (foreign $14). O. R. Press, Inc., 9 Honey Brook Dr., Princeton, NJ 08540. TEL 609-737-7497. Ed. Raymond J. Smith. adv.; cum.index: 1974-1987; circ. 1,200 (paid). (also avail. in microfilm; back issues avail.) **Indexed:** A.I.P.P., Amer.Hum.Ind., Ind.Amer.Per.Verse, LCR, M.L.A.
—Faxon.
    Description: Publishes poetry, fiction, essays and graphics by both newer and more established writers and artists, as well as interviews with distinguished authors.

ONTHEBUS. see *LITERATURE — Poetry*

OPEN DEUR. see *ART*

OPERA SLAVICA. NEUE FOLGE. see *LINGUISTICS*

ORAL TRADITION. see *FOLKLORE*

ORBIS; an international journal of poetry and prose. see *LITERATURE — Poetry*

807   DK   ISSN 0105-7510
PN1
ORBIS LITTERARUM; international review of literary studies. (Text in English, French, or German) 1946-1950; resumed 1954. 6/yr. DKK 1050. Munksgaard International Publishers Ltd., 35 Noerre Soegade, P.O. Box 2148, DK-1016 Copenhagen K, Denmark. TEL 33-127030. FAX 33-129387. Ed. Morten Noejgaard. adv.; bk.rev.; index, cum.index: vols.1-8 (1943-1950) in vol.8. circ. 500. (also avail. in microform from SWZ; reprint service avail. from ISI,SWZ) **Indexed:** Arts & Hum.Cit.Ind., Can.Rev.Comp.Lit., Curr.Cont., Ind.Bk.Rev.Hum., M.L.A., Mid.East: Abstr.& Ind.
—Faxon; UnCover. **CCC.**
    Refereed Serial

ORDEN POUR LE MERITE FUER WISSENSCHAFTEN UND KUENSTE. REDEN UND GEDENKWORTE. see *HUMANITIES: COMPREHENSIVE WORKS*

800   UK
ORDINARY LIVES. 1976. irreg. £6.95. Dennis Dobson Books Ltd., 80 Kensington Church St., London W8 4BZ, England.

800 100   US
ORGANICA QUARTERLY; a magazine of arts & activism. 1982. q. $10 (free at health food stores). (Aubrey Organics) Organica Press, 4419 N. Manhattan Ave., Tampa, FL 33614. TEL 813-877-4186. FAX 813-876-8166. Ed. Susan Hussey. bk.rev.; circ. 200,000 (controlled).
    Formerly: Organica (ISSN 0897-2648)

890   PK
ORIENTAL COLLEGE MAGAZINE/MAJALLAT AL-KULLIYAH AL-SHARQIYYAH. (Text in Arabic, English, Urdu) 1925. q. Rs.30. Punjab University, Oriental College, Lahore, Pakistan. TEL 311496. circ. 500 (controlled). **Document type:** academic/scholarly publication.
    Description: Publishes articles on historical, religious and literary topics.

ORIENTALISTISCHE LITERATURZEITUNG; Zeitschrift fuer die Wissenschaft vom ganzen Orient und seinen Beziehungen zu den angrenzenden Kulturkreisen. see *ORIENTAL STUDIES*

800   RM   ISSN 0030-560X
PC601
ORIZONT. 1949. w. 1 lei per no. Uniunea Scriitorilor din Republica Socialista Romania (Timisoara), Str. Rodnei Nr. 1, Timisoara, Rumania. Ed. Ion Ariesanu. bk.rev.; play rev.; bibl.; illus. circ. 5,000.

800 020   US   ISSN 0730-3475
ORO MADRE.* (Text in English, Spanish) 1980. q. $18. Ruddy Duck Press, 1540 Hopkins Rd., Buffalo, NY 14221-1750. Ed. L. Glazier. adv.; bk.rev.; cum.index: 1980-1985. circ. 1,000. (back issues avail.) **Indexed:** Ind.Amer.Per.Verse.

800 930   US   ISSN 0030-5790
ORPHEUS; rivista di umanita classica e cristiana. 1954. s-a. L.40000 (foreign L.70000) (effective 1993). Centro Studi Antico Cristianesimo, Universita di Catania, Facolta di Lettere, 95131 Catania, Sicily, Italy. Ed. Carmelo Curti. adv.; index. circ. 1,200. **Indexed:** Bibl.Ling.

053.5   SZ
ORTE; Schweizer Literaturzeitschrift. 1974. 5/yr. 10 Fr. Orte Verlag, Wirtschaft "Kreuz", CH-9429 Zelg-Wolfhalden, Switzerland. Ed. Werner Bucher. adv.

OSNOVAC. see *ART*

890   XN   ISSN 0352-1362
OSOGOVSKI GLAS. (Text in Macedonian) a. Literaturen Klug "Nadezi", 91320 Kratovo, Macedonia. TEL 0901 81-193.

808   US   ISSN 8756-4696
PS642
OTHER VOICES. 1985. s-a. $20 for 4 nos. to individuals (foreign $30); institutions $24 (foreign $34). Other Voices, Inc., University of Illinois at Chicago, Department of English MC 162, 601 S. Morgan St., Chicago, IL 60607-7120. TEL 312-413-2209. Eds. Sharon Fiffer, Lois Hauselman. adv. circ. 1,500. **Indexed:** Can.Wom.Per.Ind.
    Description: Dedicated to fresh, original and diverse stories and novel-excerpts.

810   US
OTISIAN DIRECTORY. 1988. 4/yr. $8. c/o Jeff Stevens, Box 9183, Cambridge, MA 02139-9183. adv.; bk.rev. circ. 500. **Document type:** directory.
    Description: Publishes fiction, poetry and reviews of alternative publications, with an emphasis on material outside the mainstream.

809   IT   ISSN 0391-2639
OTTO-NOVECENTO; rivista bimestrale di critica letteraria. 1977. bi-m. L.70000 (foreign L.110000) (effective 1994). Edizioni Otto-Novecento, Piazza Giovanni XXIII, no. 2, 21022 Azzate (Va), Italy. FAX 0332-458395. Ed. Umberto Colombo. adv.; bk.rev.

850   IT
OTTO - NOVECENTO RITROVATO. 1985. irreg., no.6, 1990. price varies. Liguori Editore s.r.l., Via Mezzocannone, 19, 80134 Naples, Italy. TEL 081-5527139. Eds. F. Bruni, A. Palermo. **Document type:** monographic series.

800   US
OUROBOROS. 1985. irreg. (2-3/yr.). $4.50 per no. 3912 24th St., Rock Island, IL 61201. Ed. Erskine Carter. circ. 300. (back issues avail.)
    Description: Fiction, poetry and art.

800   US   ISSN 0739-4969
OUTERBRIDGE. 1975. a. $5. City University of New York, College of Staten Island, Department of English 2S-218, 2800 Victory Blvd., Staten Island, NY 10314. TEL 718-982-3651. Ed. Charlotte Alexander. bk.rev.; cum.index in no. 8-9 and no. 18-19. circ. 500. (back issues avail.) **Indexed:** Hum.Ind., Ind.Amer.Per.Verse.
    Description: Seeks professionalism in literature. Regulates theme issues (rural, urban, Southern, war, childhood, interdisciplinary, immigrant-migrant). Slight bias toward new, less published voices.

821   AT   ISSN 0813-5886
PR9614
OUTRIDER. 1984. s-a. Aus.$20 (foreign Aus.$45). (Australia Council Literature Board) Phoenix Publications Brisbane, c/o Prof. M. Jurgensen, P.O. Box 210, Indooroopilly, Qld. 4068, Australia. TEL 07-371-6166. (Co-sponsor: Government of Queensland) Ed. Manfred Jurgensen. adv.; bk.rev. circ. 2,000.
—CCC.
    Description: Publishes literary prose, poetry and articles dealing with literature and culture in Australia.

807   US   ISSN 1069-2215
OWEN WISTER REVIEW. 1978. 2/yr. $10 (foreign $15) (typically set in Sept.). University of Wyoming, Student Publications Board, Box 4238, University Sta., Laramie, WY 82071. TEL 307-766-3819. FAX 307-766-2346. Ed. Georgette Hartley. bk.rev. circ. 500.
    Description: Campus literary publication of an experimental nature including art and literature.

810   US   ISSN 1066-8187
OXALIS. 1988. 3/yr. $18 (effective 1993). Stone Ridge Poetry Society, Box 3993, Kingston, NY 12401. TEL 914-687-7942. Ed. Shirley Powell. adv.; bk.rev. circ. 300. (back issues avail.)

800   US
▼**THE OXFORD AMERICAN;** a magazine from the South. 1992. q. $16. 115 1/2 S. Lamar, Oxford, MS 38655. Ed. Marc Smirnoff. adv.; illus.
    Description: Contains fictions, poetry, and interviews.

820   US
OXFORD ENGLISH MONOGRAPHS. irreg. price varies. Oxford University Press, 200 Madison Ave., New York, NY 10016. TEL 212-679-7300. Ed.Bd. **Indexed:** M.L.A.

830 410   UK   ISSN 0078-7191
PT1
OXFORD GERMAN STUDIES. (Text and summaries in English and German) 1966. a. $35. (Fiedler Foundation) Willem A. Meeuws, Pub., 11 Broad St., Oxford OX1 3AR, England. TEL 0865-242939. FAX 0865-204021. Eds. N. Palmer, T.J. Reed. adv.; bk.rev. circ. 500. (back issues avail.) **Indexed:** Curr.Cont., M.L.A. **Document type:** academic/scholarly publication.
—BLDSC (6321.005000).

800 100   UK   ISSN 0305-1498
OXFORD LITERARY REVIEW; critical analyses of literary, philosophical, political and psycho-analytic theory. 1974. a. £9.50($16.75) to individuals; institutions £20($35). Wadham College, Oxford OX1 3PN, England. FAX 0865-277937. Ed.Bd. adv.; bk.rev. circ. 1,000. **Indexed:** Arts & Hum.Cit.Ind., Curr.Cont., M.L.A. **Document type:** academic/scholarly publication.
—BLDSC (6321.005930); Faxon; UnCover.

811.051   US
OXFORD MAGAZINE. 1985. s-a. $10. Miami University, Department of English, Oxford, OH 45056. TEL 513-529-5256. adv. circ. 250. (back issues avail.)
    Description: National journal publishing new poetry, fiction, and essays.

800   US
OXFORD MODERN LANGUAGE AND LITERATURE MONOGRAPHS. irreg. price varies. Oxford University Press, 200 Madison Ave., New York, NY 10016. TEL 212-679-7300. Ed.Bd. **Indexed:** M.L.A.

OXFORD SLAVONIC PAPERS. see *HISTORY — History Of Europe*

OXFORD THEATRE TEXTS. see *THEATER*

810   US
OYEZ REVIEW. 1966. a. $7.50 for 2 issues. Roosevelt University, 430 S. Michigan Ave., Chicago, IL 60605. TEL 312-341-2017. FAX 312-341-2017. Ed. Angela Lewis. adv.; bk.rev.; illus. circ. 750. (back issues avail.)

800 028.5   US   ISSN 0886-8697
OZ COLLECTOR. 1985. s-a. $2 per no. Book of Wonder, 132 Seventh Ave. at 18th St., New York, NY 10011. TEL 212-989-3270. FAX 212-989-1203. (Subscr. to: Dept. BSB, Box 714, New York, NY 10011) Ed. Peter Glassman. **Document type:** newsletter.

OZ TRADING POST. see *HOBBIES*

OZIANA. see *CLUBS*

800 808.81   IT
L'OZIO; almanacco di letteratura. 1980. s-a. L.35000($37) Edizioni Amadeus, Corso Mazzini 10/39, 31044 Montebelluna, Italy. TEL 0423-85617. FAX 0423-601085. Ed. Antonio Facchin. (back issues avail.; reprint service avail.)

800   UK   ISSN 0074-722X
P E N INTERNATIONAL. bi-a. International P E N, 9-10 Charterhouse Bldgs., London EC1M 7AT, England. TEL 071-253-4308. FAX 071-253-5711. **Document type:** proceedings.

LITERATURE   3655

800   UK   ISSN 1010-4534
P E N INTERNATIONAL. BULLETIN OF SELECTED BOOKS. (Issued with the assistance of UNESCO) (Text and titles in English and French) 1950. s-a. £6($10) International P.E.N., 9-10 Charterhouse Bldgs., London EC1M 7AT, England. TEL 071-253-4308. FAX 071-253-5711. (U.S. address: F.W. Faxon Co., Inc., 15 Southwest Park, Westwood, MA 02090) Ed. Peter Day. bk.rev. circ. 1,600. **Indexed:** Mid.East: Abstr.& Ind. **Document type:** bulletin.
  Formerly (until 1981): International P.E.N. Bulletin of Selected Books (ISSN 0020-823X)

800   US
P E NEWSLETTER. 1971. q. $8. P E N American Center, 568 Broadway, New York, NY 10012. TEL 212-334-1660. FAX 212-334-2181. Ed. Naomi Bliven. circ. 3,500. **Document type:** newsletter.
  Description: Reports on PEN programs in the US and abroad.

820   DK   ISSN 0901-9235
P E O. Key Title: Pre-publications of the English Department of Odense University. 1975. irreg. (Odense University, Department of English) Odense University Press, Campusvej 55, DK-5230 Odense M, Denmark.
  Formerly (until 1983): Pre-publications of the English Institute of Odense University (ISSN 0105-2462)

P - FORM; performance art magazine. see ART

800 406   US   ISSN 0030-8129
PB6
P M L A. 1884. 6/yr. membership; libraries $108 (effective 1995). Modern Language Association of America, 10 Astor Pl., New York, NY 10003. TEL 212-475-9500. FAX 212-477-9863. Ed. Domna Stanton. adv. contact: Cynthia Port. index. circ. 36,000. (also avail. in microfilm from UMI; reprint service avail. from ISI,KTO,UMI) **Indexed:** Abstr.Engl.Stud., Arts & Hum.Cit.Ind., Bibl.Ling., Curr.Cont., Hum.Ind., Lang.& Lang.Behav.Abstr., M.L.A., Mid.East: Abstr.& Ind. **Document type:** academic/scholarly publication.
  —BLDSC (6541.092000); Faxon; UnCover; SWETS; UMI.
  Description: Publishes scholarly and critical articles, professional notes, letters. Lists fellowships, forthcoming meetings.

850   US   ISSN 1042-4822
PQ4835.I7
P S A. 1970. a. $15 to individuals (foreign $20); institutions $30 (foreign $35). Pirandello Society of America, Box 81, Whitestone, NY 11357. TEL 718-767-8380. Ed. A. Paolucci. adv. circ. 600. (back issues avail.) **Document type:** academic/scholarly publication.
  —UnCover.
  Formerly: Pirandello Society Newsletter.
  Description: Articles on Pirandello's work and his influence on contemporary theater. Includes fiction.

800 500   US   ISSN 0886-1102
PN55
P S L S. (Publication of the Society for Literature and Science) 1985. q. $25. Society for Literature and Science, c/o Prof. Kenneth J. Knoespel, Department of Literature, Communication, and Culture, Georgia Institute of Technology, Atlanta, GA 30332-0165. TEL 617-437-2512. adv.; bk.rev. circ. 560. (tabloid format; back issues avail.)
  Description: Surveys the relationship between literature and science and the historical, philosophical, and broader cultural implications of that relationship.

810   US   ISSN 1065-1594
▼**PACIFIC COAST JOURNAL (CAMPBELL).** 1992. irreg., approx. 5/yr. $10 (effective Apr. 1992). French Bread Publications, Box 355, Campbell, CA 95009-0355. Ed. John S. French. bk.rev. circ. 200. (back issues avail.) **Document type:** consumer publication.
  Description: Covers all forms of literature, with a general focus on the West Coast of the U.S. and the Pacific Rim.

800 400   US   ISSN 0078-7469
P1.A1
PACIFIC COAST PHILOLOGY. (Text mainly in English; occasionally in French and German) 1966. a. $6. Philological Association of the Pacific Coast, c/o Cyndia Clegg, Dept. of Humanities, Pepperdine University, Malibu, CA 90263-4225. TEL 310-456-4435. circ. 1,300. **Document type:** academic/scholarly publication.
  —BLDSC (6329.010000).

860   SP
LA PAGINA. (Supplement avail.) q. 2400 ptas. (Europe 4600 ptas.; America 5400 ptas.; elsewhere 7200 ptas.). Pagina Ediciones, S.L., Anchieta 32, 1o-D, 38201 La Laguna, Tenerife, Spain. Dir. Domingo-Luis Hernandez. circ. 8,000.
  Description: Covers literature and its relation to other areas in the humanities.

800   II
PAHAL. (Text in Hindi) 1973. q. Rs.10($5) 763 Agrawal Colony, Jabalpur, India.
  Description: Includes poems, essays and short stories.

810   US   ISSN 0090-5674
PS3531.082
PAIDEUMA; a journal devoted to Ezra Pound scholarship. 1972. 3/yr. $18 to individuals; institutions $35. National Poetry Foundation, 302 Neville Hall, University of Maine, Orono, ME 04469. TEL 207-581-3814. Ed. C.F. Terrell. adv.; bk.rev.; bibl. circ. 1,000. **Indexed:** Abstr.Engl.Stud., Amer.Hum.Ind., Arts & Hum.Cit.Ind., Curr.Cont., Ind.Bk.Rev.Hum., M.L.A. **Document type:** academic/scholarly publication.
  —BLDSC (6333.781000); Faxon; UnCover.

800   US   ISSN 0094-1964
PN6099.6
PAINTBRUSH; a journal of poetry, translations and letters. 1974. s-a. $9 to individuals; institutions $12. Northeast Missouri State University, Language and Literature Division, Kirksville, MO 63501. TEL 816-785-4185. FAX 816-785-4181. Ed. Benjamin Bennani. adv.; bk.rev. circ. 500. (back issues avail.; reprint service avail. from ISI) **Indexed:** Arts & Hum.Cit.Ind., Ind.Amer.Per.Verse, M.L.A.
  —UnCover.

PAINTED BRIDE QUARTERLY. see LITERATURE — Poetry

891.92   LE   ISSN 0030-9613
PAKIN.* (Text in Armenian) 1962. m. Dr. Artin Kazandjian, Pub., Spears St., Box 4176, Beirut, Lebanon. Ed. Gard Sassouny. bk.rev.; illus.; index. circ. 2,000.

860 972   US   ISSN 0277-1535
PQ7070
LA PALABRA. 1979. a. $20. La Palabra, 1616 E. Westchester Dr., Tempe, AZ 85283. Ed. Justo S. Alarcon. **Indexed:** M.L.A.

700   IT   ISSN 0031-0255
PALAESTRA. (Text in Italian and Latin) 1962. bi-m. Via Tiglio S. Biagio, Maddaloni 81024, Italy. Ed. Gaspare Caliendo. bk.rev.; film rev.; play rev.; bibl.; illus.; index, cum.index; circ. 1,000. (controlled). (tabloid format; also avail. in cards)

800   UK
PALATINATE. 1948. 27/yr. £5.25. University of Durham, Students Union, Dunelm House, New Elvet, Durham DH1 3AN, England. TEL 091-3743309. FAX 091-3743328. Ed. Helen Lees. adv.; bk.rev. circ. 4,500. (also avail. in microfilm from UMI; reprint service avail. from UMI) **Document type:** newspaper.
  Formerly: Phalanx.

809   XR   ISSN 0231-5904
PAMATNIK NARODNIHO PISEMNICTVI. SBORNIK. Key Title: Literarni Archiv. (Text in Czech; summaries in English, German) 1966. a. price varies. Pamatnik Narodniho Pisemnictvi - Museum of the Czech Literature, Strahovske Nadv. 132, Prague 1, Czech Republic. TEL 42-2-24511137. FAX 42-2-537063. (Dist. by: Artia, Ve Smeckach 30, 111 27 Prague 1, Czech Republic) bibl.; illus. **Indexed:** Amer.Hist.& Life, Hist.Abstr. **Document type:** academic/scholarly publication.
  Description: Contains research studies on the history of Czech literature and literary criticism.

891.85   PL   ISSN 0031-0514
PG7001
PAMIETNIK LITERACKI. (Text in Polish; contents page in English, Polish, Russian) 1902. q. $88. (Polska Akademia Nauk, Instytut Badan Literackich) Ossolineum, Publishing House of the Polish Academy of Sciences, Rynek 9, 50-106 Wroclaw, Poland. TEL 48-71-386-25. FAX 48-71-448-103. TELEX 0712771 OSS PL. Ed. B. Zakrzewski. bk.rev.; bibl.; index. circ. 1,250. **Indexed:** Arts & Hum.Cit.Ind., Bibl.Ling., Curr.Cont., M.L.A. **Document type:** academic/scholarly publication.
  Description: Devoted to the history and criticism of Polish literature.

891.8   PL   ISSN 0078-866X
D377
PAMIETNIK SLOWIANSKI. 1950. a. price varies. (Polska Akademia Nauk, Komitet Slowianoznawstwa) Ossolineum, Publishing House of the Polish Academy of Sciences, Rynek 9, 50-106 Wroclaw, Poland. TEL 48-71-386-25. FAX 48-71-448-103. TELEX 0712771 OSS PL. Ed. Halina Janaczek-Ivanickova. **Indexed:** Bibl.Ling. **Document type:** academic/scholarly publication.
  Description: Contains Slavonic studies devoted to literature and culture of Slavonic countries and nations.

810   US   ISSN 0031-059X
PAN AMERICAN REVIEW.* (Text mainly in English, occasionally in Spanish) 1970. irreg. $6. Wade Press, Box 3427, Edinburg, TX 78540-3427. Ed. Seth Wade.

810   US   ISSN 0738-8705
PANHANDLER. 1976. s-a. $10 includes Chapbook. University of West Florida, English Department, 11000 Univeristy Pkwy., Pensacola, FL 32514-5751. TEL 904-474-2923. Ed.Bd. adv.; bk.rev. circ. 900. **Indexed:** Amer.Hum.Ind.
  Description: Presents poetry and fiction nationally.

800 808.81   XR   ISSN 0231-6234
PANORAMA OF CZECH LITERATURE. French edition: Panorama de la Litterature Tcheque (ISSN 0231-5068); German edition: Panorama der Tschechischen Literatur (ISSN 0139-9195); Russian edition: Panorama Cheshskoi Litaratury (ISSN 0139-9241); Spanish edition: Panorama de la Literatura Checa (ISSN 0231-6889) (Text in English) 1980. biennial. free. (Union of Czech Writers) Panorama, Halkova 1, 120 72 Prague 2, Czech Republic. (Co-sponsors: Czech Literary Fund, DILIA Theatrical and Literary Agency) Ed. Ivo Kral. circ. 3,000.

808   UK   ISSN 0951-4546
PANURGE. 1984. s-a. £8.50 (foreign £10). Crooked Holme Farm Cottage, Brampton, Cumbria CA8 2AT, England. TEL 06977-41087. Ed. John Murray. adv.; bk.rev.; illus. circ. 1,000. (back issues avail.) **Document type:** consumer publication.
  Description: Short fiction by new and up-and-coming writers.

860   CR   ISSN 0048-2854
PAPEL IMPRESO. 1971. m. free. Ministerio de Cultura, Juventud y Deportes, Departamento de Publicaciones, Apdo. 10227, San Jose, Costa Rica. Ed. Victor Julio Peralta. bibl.; illus.

800
PAPER BAG. 1988. q. $10 (foreign $15). Paper Bag Press, Box 268805, Chicago, IL 60626-8805. TEL 312-285-7972. Ed. Michael H. Brownstein. circ. 500. (back issues avail.)
  Description: Publishes poetry and short short stories.

PAPERBACK INFERNO. see LITERATURE — Science Fiction, Fantasy, Horror

808.838   US
PAPERBACK PREVIEWS. 1966. m. $15 (foreign $30). Box 6781, Albuquerque, NM 87197. TEL 505-345-5925. FAX 505-242-8413. Ed. Annie McDaniels. adv. contact: Gypsy Kemp. bk.rev. circ. 2,500. (tabloid format) **Document type:** catalog.
  Description: Lists all forthcoming titles in paperback in all genres, as well as some hardback and trade titles.

LITERATURE

809 028.5   AT   ISSN 1034-9243
PAPERS: EXPLORATIONS INTO CHILDREN'S LITERATURE. 1990. 3/yr. Aus.$35 (New Zealand Aus.$41.50; elsewhere Aus.$48.50). Magpies Magazine, 10 Armagh St., Victoria Park, W.A. 6100, Australia. TEL 09-361-8288. FAX 09-361-8295. Ed. Alf Mappin.
Description: Contains critical essays - comparative, evaluative and historical - on children's literature.

808   US   ISSN 0736-9123
AS30
PAPERS IN COMPARATIVE STUDIES. 1981. irreg. $10. Ohio State University, Division of Comparative Studies in the Humanities, 308 Dulles Hall, 230 W. 17th Ave., Columbus, OH 43210-1311. TEL 614-292-2559. FAX 614-292-6707. Ed. Marilyn R. Waldman. adv. contact: Brenda Hosey. circ. 200. (back issues avail.) **Document type:** academic/scholarly publication.

400 800   US   ISSN 0031-1294
PR1
PAPERS ON LANGUAGE AND LITERATURE; a quarterly journal for scholars and critics of language and literature. Cover title: P L L: Papers on Language & Literature. 1965. q. $24 to individuals; institutions $48 (foreign $51). Southern Illinois University, Edwardsville, IL 62026-1434. TEL 618-692-2119. FAX 618-692-3509. Eds. Brian Abel Ragen, Jack G. Voller. adv.; bk.rev.; bibl.; index, cum.index. circ. 850. (also avail. in microform from UMI,ISI; reprint service avail. from UMI) **Indexed:** Abstr.Engl.Stud., Amer.Bibl.Slavic & E.Eur.Stud., Arts & Hum.Cit.Ind., Curr.Cont., Hum.Ind., Ind.Bk.Rev.Hum., Lang.& Lang.Behav.Abstr., M.L.A., Mid.East: Abstr.& Ind. **Document type:** academic/scholarly publication.
—BLDSC (6396.950000); Faxon; UnCover; SWETS; UMI.
Description: Papers on literary history, theory, and interpretation, as well as original literary materials such as letters, journals, and notebooks.
Refereed Serial

860   AG
▼**PAPIROS DEL SIGLO VEINTE.*** 1992. m. Arg.$3 per no. Editorial Vinciguerra S.r.l., Av. Juan de Garaz 3746, 1256 Buenos Aires, Argentina. Ed. Lidia Vinciguerra. **Document type:** newspaper.

800   NE   ISSN 0169-9652
PAPYROLOGICA LUGDUNO-BATAVA. 1941. irreg., vol.25, 1991. price varies. E.J. Brill, P.O. Box 9000, 2300 PA Leiden, Netherlands. TEL 31-71-312624. FAX 31-71-317532. TELEX 39296 BRILL NL. (In N. America: E.J. Brill, 24 Hudson St., Kinderhook, NY 12106. TEL 800-962-4406. FAX 518-758-1959) Ed.Bd. **Document type:** monographic series.
Description: Explores international papyrus studies.
Refereed Serial

808   US   ISSN 1055-761X
THE PARADOXIST MOVEMENT. (Text and summaries in English, French, Rumanian) 1991. a. $16.99 (typically set in Sep.). (Paradoxist Association) Xiquan Publishing House, Box 42561, Phoenix, AZ 85080. Ed. Florentin Smarandache. adv.; bk.rev. circ. 500.
Description: Covers avant-garde literature and promotes the Paradoxist Literary Movement originating in Romania in 1980.

800 700   IT   ISSN 0031-1650
PN5
PARAGONE; rivista mensile di arte figurativa e letteratura. 1950. m. L.320000. Casa Ede. Le Lettere, Costa S. Giorgio 28, Florence, Italy. (Dist. by: Licosa, Via Duca di Calabria 1-1, 50125 Florence, Italy) Eds. Cesare Garboli, Mina Gregori. illus.; index. **Indexed:** Artbibl., Arts & Hum.Cit.Ind., Avery Ind.Archit.Per., Can.Rev.Comp.Lit., Curr.Cont., M.L.A., RILA.
—Faxon.

800   CN   ISSN 0838-9624
PARAGRAPH; the Canadian fiction review. 1979. 3/yr. Can.$14 to individuals; institutions Can.$20 (typically set in Jan.). The Mercury Press, 137 Birmingham St., Stratford, ON N5A 2T1, Canada. Ed. Daniel Jones; Pub. Beverley Daurio. adv.; bk.rev.; index. circ. 2,000. (also avail. in microform from MML; back issues avail.) **Indexed:** Can.Lit.Ind., Can.Per.Ind., CMI, Ind.Amer.Per.Verse.
Former titles (until 1990): Cross-Canada Writers' Magazine; Cross-Canada Writers' Quarterly (ISSN 0227-2652); New Writers' News.
Description: Explores contemporary fiction, essays, interviews, opinion, and criticism.

800   UK   ISSN 0264-8334
PN80
PARAGRAPH; a journal of modern critical theory. 1983. 3/yr. £19.75($38.50) Edinburgh University Press, 22 George Sq., Edinburgh EH8 9LF, Scotland. TEL 031-650-4218. FAX 031-662-0053. Ed.Bd. adv. contact: Kathryn MacLean. bk.rev. circ. 1,000. **Document type:** academic/scholarly publication.
—BLDSC (6404.820000); Faxon; UnCover; SWETS; UMI. CCC.
Description: Strives to further the understanding of French critical thought in English-speaking nations. Explores critical theory in general and its application to literature, other arts and society.
Refereed Serial

800   FR   ISSN 0078-9429
PARALOGUE. 1965. irreg., no.5, 1972. Lettres Modernes, 45 rue Saint-Andre, 14123 Fleury sur Orne, France. TEL 31-84-47-06. FAX 31-84-48-09. (Dist. outside France by: Librairie Droz S.A., 11, rue Massot, CH-1211 Geneva 12, Switzerland. TEL 022-466666)
Description: Covers classical literature of France. From the "Editions 'Lettres Modernes'".

808.8   CN
PARANOID TALES OF NEUROSIS. irreg. Can.$2.95($2.50) per no. 19 Tyndall Ave., No. 3, Toronto, ON, Canada. Pub. Joe Deagnon.
Description: Contains a collection of comics with a bent for violence and paranoia.

300   AT   ISSN 0313-6221
CB351
PARERGON. 1971. biennial. Aus.$40. Australian and New Zealand Association for Medieval and Renaissance Studies, University of Sydney, Department of English, Sydney, N.S.W. 2006, Australia. FAX 02-692-2434. TELEX AA26169 UNISYD. Ed. D. Speed. bk.rev. circ. 300. **Indexed:** Arts & Hum.Cit.Ind., Aus.P.A.I.S., Curr.Cont., M.L.A. **Document type:** bulletin.
—BLDSC (6406.298000); UnCover.
Description: Presents scholarly papers on all aspects of Medieval and Renaissance culture.
Refereed Serial

800   US   ISSN 0031-2037
AP4
PARIS REVIEW. 1953. q. $24. Paris Review, Inc., 541 E. 72nd St., New York, NY 10021. TEL 212-861-0016. FAX 212-861-0282. (Subscr. to: 45-39 171st Pl., Flushing, NY 11358) Ed. George A. Plimpton; Pub. Drue Heinz. adv.; B&W page $1000. illus.; cum.index. circ. 12,000. (also avail. in microform from UMI; back issues avail.; reprint service avail. from UMI,ISI) **Indexed:** A.I.P.P., Abstr.Engl.Stud., Acad.Ind., Arts & Hum.Cit.Ind., Curr.Cont., Hum.Ind., Ind.Amer.Per.Verse, Mag.Ind., Soc.Sci.Ind.
—BLDSC (6406.605700); Faxon; UnCover; UMI.

810   FR   ISSN 1146-5948
PN6010.5
PARIS TRANSCONTINENTAL; a magazine of short stories in English. (Text in English) 1990. 2/yr. 120 F.($18) Institut de Monde Anglophone, Sorbonne Nouvelle, 5 rue de l'Ecole de Medecine, 75006 Paris, France. Ed. Claire Larriere. circ. 500.

840   FR   ISSN 0181-5210
PARIS VOICES. 1978. q. 36 F.($9) c/o Shakespeare & Co., 37 rue de la Bucherie, 75005 Paris, France. Ed. Ken Timmerman.

PARISH MAGAZINE - ARTHUR CONAN DOYLE SOCIETY.
see LITERATURE — Mystery And Detective

820   UK   ISSN 0031-210X
PARK.* 1968. q. 25s.($5) Ferry Press, 177 Green Lane, London S.E.9, England. Ed. Andrew Crozier.

PARKH. *see* LINGUISTICS

800 440 375.4   FR   ISSN 1151-941X
PARLANGHE. s-a. 350 F. Geste Editions, Maison des Ruralies, B.P. 1; 79230 Vouille, France. TEL 49-75-67-71. Ed. Michel Gautier.
Description: Studies dialects of the Poitou area.

800   FI   ISSN 0031-2320
PN9
PARNASSO. 1951. 8/yr. FIM 198. (Finnish Cultural Foundation) Yhtyneet Kuvalehdet Oy, Maistraatinportti 1, FIN-00240 Helsinki, Finland. TEL 358-0-156-6524. FAX 358-0-156-6505. TELEX 121364. Ed. Jarkko Laine. adv.: B&W page FIM 4700, color page FIM 6700. bk.rev.; film rev.; play rev.; charts; index. circ. 4,249. **Indexed:** M.L.A.

EL PASEANTE. *see* ART

801   AF
PASHTO ACADEMY. MONTHLY JOURNAL. (Text in Pashto) no.9, 1976. m. Pashto Academy, 26th Saratan Wat, Kabul, Afghanistan.

PASHTU QUARTERLY. *see* LINGUISTICS

809   DK   ISSN 0901-8883
PASSAGE; tidsskrift for litteratur og kritik. 1980. 3/yr. DKK 270. Aarhus Universitet, Institut for Litteraturhistorie, Willemoesgade 15, DK-8000 Aarhus N, Denmark. TEL 45-89-42-18-36. Ed. Peter Nielsen. bk.rev.; illus. **Document type:** academic/scholarly publication.
Formerly: Aarhus Universitet. Institut for Litteraturhistorie. Skrifter (ISSN 0107-8631)

830 701.18   GW   ISSN 0933-7253
NX550.M36
PASSAGEN; Mannheimer Zeitschrift fuer Literatur und Kunst. 1988. bi-m. DM.48. Edition Passagen, Leutweinstr. 23, 68219 Mannheim, Germany. TEL 0621-892928. FAX 0621-8019696. Ed. Helmut Riemenschneider. bk.rev. circ. 4,000. (back issues avail) **Document type:** consumer publication.

PASSAGER; a journal of remembrance and discovery. *see* GERONTOLOGY AND GERIATRICS

808   US   ISSN 0278-0828
PASSAGES NORTH. 1979. s-a. $10. Bay Arts Writers Guild, c/o Kalamazoo College, 1200 Academy St., Kalamazoo, MI 49006-3295. TEL 616-337-7331. Ed. Michael Barrett. adv. circ. 1,500. (back issues avail.) **Indexed:** Amer.Hum.Ind., Ind.Amer.Per.Verse.
Description: Contains poetry, short fiction, essays, photography and graphic art from established and emerging writers and artists.

830   GW   ISSN 0724-0708
PASSAUER PEGASUS; Zeitschrift fuer Literatur. 1983. s-a. DM.20. c/o Karl Krieg, Woerthstr. 8, 94032 Passau, Germany. TEL 0851-56189. adv.; bk.rev. circ. 600. **Document type:** academic/scholarly publication.
Description: New literature in German: poems, short stories, essays.

809   UK   ISSN 0264-8342
PR5136
PATER NEWSLETTER. 1977. s-a. £3($6) Centre for Extra-Mural Studies, Birkbeck College, 26 Russell Sq., London WC1B 5DQ, England. TEL 071-631-6644. FAX 071-631-6688. (U.S. addr.: University of West Virginia, Morgantown, WV 26506. FAX 304-293-5380) Eds. Hayden Ward, Laurel Brake. bk.rev. circ. 100. **Document type:** newsletter.
Description: Contains news, work in progress, articles, reviews, dissertations, and current annotated book and periodical bibliographies on Pater and related topics.

891.4   II   ISSN 0031-3122
PATRANU; world's first mini magazine. (Text in Bengali) 1970. m. Rs.3.40($0.50) K. Chatterjee, Pub., 122-A Ballygunge Gardens, Calcutta 19, India. Ed. A. Chatterji. adv.; bk.rev.; film rev.; play rev.; illus. circ. 5,000. (tabloid format)

810   US
PAX; a journal for peace through culture. 1983. 2/yr. $4 per no. 217 Pershing, San Antonio, TX 78209. Ed. Bryce Milligan. adv. circ. 600.

LITERATURE 3657

820 001.3   UK   ISSN 1351-1653
PEACE & FREEDOM (SPALDING). 1985. 2/yr. £5 for 4 nos. 17 Farrow Rd., Whapload Drove, Spalding, Lincs PE12 OTS, England. TEL 0406-330242. Ed. Paul Rance. adv.: B&W page £35. circ. 300. **Document type:** bulletin.

808   US
PELLENNORATH. 1980. irreg., no.5, 1982. $4 for five issues. Pandemonium Press, 1273 Crest Dr., Encinitas, CA 92024. Ed. R.C. Walker. (back issues avail.)

808   US   ISSN 0031-4242
THE PEN WOMAN. 1922. 6/yr. $7. National League of American Pen Women, Inc., Pen Arts Bldg., 1300 17th St., N.W., Washington, DC 20036. TEL 202-785-1997. adv.; bk.rev.; illus. circ. 5,000. (back issues avail.)
Description: Presents news about members, and articles relating to art, letters, and music. Includes members' poetry, music composition, and artwork, as well as personality profiles.

800   US
PENDRAGON; a literary review. 2/yr. Georgia-South Carolina College English Association, Valdosta State University, English Dept., Valdosta, GA 31698. TEL 912-333-5946. Ed. Heather Tapley. circ. 450. **Document type:** academic/scholarly publication.

PENNSYLVANIA PORTFOLIO; a literary review about Pennsylvania authors, books & libraries. see BIOGRAPHY

800   US   ISSN 8756-5668
PENNSYLVANIA REVIEW. 1985. s-a. $10. University of Pittsburgh, Department of English, 526 C.L., Pittsburgh, PA 15260. TEL 412-624-0026. Ed. Julie Parson-Nesbitt. adv.; bk.rev. circ. 750. (back issues avail.)
Description: Presents contemporary prose and poetry.

PENSIERO ED ARTE. see LITERARY AND POLITICAL REVIEWS

800   UK
PEOPLE LIKE THAT. 1970. irreg. Central London Adult Education Institute, 6 Bolt Court, Fleet St., London E.C.4, England. Ed. Bernard Miller. illus.

800   US   ISSN 0149-0516
PN6010.5
PEQUOD; a journal of contemporary literature and literary criticism. 1974-1984; resumed 1985. 2/yr. $12 to individuals; institutions $18. Pequod Press, Inc., 817 West End Ave., New York, NY 10025. TEL 212-998-8843. FAX 2212-995-4019. Ed. Mark Rudman. adv. circ. 1,200. **Indexed:** A.I.P.P.; Amer.Bibl.Slavic & E.Eur.Stud.; M.L.A.
—Faxon; UnCover.

800   US   ISSN 0740-7890
PERMAFROST; a literary journal. 1977. 2/yr. $7. University of Alaska, Fairbanks, English Department, Fairbanks, AK 99775-0640. TEL 907-474-7193. circ. 500. **Indexed:** A.I.P.P.

PERPJEKJA E JONE/OUR EFFORT. see ART

800   PK
PERSPECTIVE. (Text in English) vol.6, 1972. m. Rs.18($6) Pakistan Publications, Box 183, Shahrah Iraq, Karachi 1, Pakistan. Ed. M. R. Siddiqui. adv.; bk.rev.

809   US   ISSN 0821-0314
PR4036
PERSUASIONS. 1979. a. $15 includes membership. Jane Austen Society of North America, 207 Pinecroft Dr., Raleigh, NC 27609. TEL 919-782-3083. (Subscr. to: JASNA, Membership Office, 2650-D Matheson Way, Sacramento, CA 95864) Ed. Gene Koppel. circ. 2,700. (back issues avail.) **Document type:** academic/scholarly publication.
—UnCover.
Description: Focuses on Jane Austen, her family, her art and her times.

800   US   ISSN 0835-9628
PERSUASIONS, OCCASIONAL PAPERS. 1979. irreg. $15. Jane Austen Society of North America, 207 Pinecroft Dr., Raleigh, NC 27609. TEL 604-988-0479. (Subscr. to: 221 Nevin St., Lancaster, PA 17603) Ed. Gene Koppel. bk.rev.; illus. circ. 150.

890   IS
PESEFAS. 1988. q. IS.60. Eked, P.O. Box 11138, Tel Aviv, Israel. FAX 972-3-5283648. adv.; bk.rev. circ. 2,000.

830   GW
▼**PETER WEISS JAHRBUCH**. 1992. a. (Peter-Weiss-Gesellschaft) Westdeutscher Verlag GmbH, Postfach 5829, 65048 Wiesbaden, Germany. TEL 0611-160230. Ed. Martin Rector. **Document type:** academic/scholarly publication.

800   HU   ISSN 0524-8906
PH3002
PETOFI IRODALMI MUZEUM EVKONYVE/YEARBOOK OF THE LITERARY MUSEUM. 1958. biennial. (Petofi Irodalmi Muzeum - Literature Museum of Petofi) Muzsak, Karolyi Mihaly u. 16, 1054 Budapest, V. ker., Hungary. TEL 36-1-1173-611. FAX 36-1-1171-722. Ed. Ferenc Botka.

800   NQ   ISSN 0031-6652
NX7
EL PEZ Y LA SERPIENTE; revista de cultura. 1961. s-a. C.$41($6) Pablo A. Cuadra, Ed. & Pub., Apdo Postal 192, Managua, Nicaragua. FAX 5052-43569. TELEX 375-2051. bk.rev.; illus. circ. 1,000.
Description: Includes poetry, literary criticism, history, anthropology, and art from the most prominent intellectuals in Central America.

PHI SIGMA IOTA FORUM. see LINGUISTICS

800   GW
PHILOLOGISCHE STUDIEN UND QUELLEN. 1960. irreg., no.128, 1993. Erich Schmidt Verlag GmbH & Co. (Berlin), Genthiner Str. 30G, 10785 Berlin, Germany. TEL 030-2500850. FAX 030-25008521. (Subscr. addr.: Zweigniederlassung Bielefeld, Viktoriastr. 44a, 33602 Bielefeld, Germany) Eds. Hugo Steger, Hartmut Steinecke. **Document type:** monographic series.

PHILOSOPHIA PATRUM; interpretations of patristic texts. see RELIGIONS AND THEOLOGY

PHILOSOPHY AND LITERATURE. see PHILOSOPHY

810   US
PHIZZOGS. 1984. a. Carl Sandburg College, 2232 S. Lake Storey Rd., Galesburg, IL 61401-9576. TEL 309-344-2518. Ed. Paul Merlin. circ. 700.

800   US   ISSN 0270-868X
PHOEBE. 1972. s-a. $8. George Mason University, 4400 University Drive, Fairfax, VA 22030. TEL 703-993-2915. adv.; bk.rev.; illus. circ. 2,500.
Description: Features fiction, poetry, and photographs.

410   CE   ISSN 1017-1622
PR9084.5
PHOENIX; Sri Lanka journal of English in the Commonwealth. 1990. a. Rs.50($4) Sri Lanka Association for Commonwealth Literature and Language Studies, University of Peradeniya, Peradeniya, Sri Lanka. TEL 941-521485. FAX 941-521485. (Subscr. to: Sita Kulatunga, Sri Landa A C L A L S, Open University, Nawal, Nugegoda, Sri Landa) Ed. D.C.R.A. Goonetilleke. bk.rev. circ. 300. **Document type:** academic/scholarly publication.

820   UK
PHOENIX BROADSHEET. 1972. irreg. free. 78 Cambridge St., Leicester LE3 0JP, England. TEL 0533-547419. Ed. Toni Savage. **Document type:** consumer publication.

800   US
PHOENIX LITERATURE. 1929. irreg., latest 1985. price varies. University of Chicago Press, 5801 S. Ellis Ave., Chicago, IL 60637. TEL 312-702-7899. (Subscr. to: 11030 Langley Ave., Chicago, IL 60628)
    Refereed Serial

PICK OF THE YEAR; a selection of 50 recommended books, chosen for families, tried and tested by children, and voted the best of (year). see CHILDREN AND YOUTH — For

PIE/PIADA; rassegna d'illustrazione Romagnola. see FOLKLORE

808   AG
PIE DE PAGINA. 1982. q. Av. Belgrano 2358, 1069 Buenos Aires, Argentina. Eds. Alberto Castro, Gabriela Borgna.

PIEDMONT LITERARY REVIEW. see LITERATURE — Poetry

800   US   ISSN 0195-5799
PIEGAN STORYTELLER. 1976. q. $15 in N. America; elsewhere $20. James Willard Schultz Society, 135 Wildwood Dr., New Bern, NC 28562-9530. Ed. David C. Andrews. adv.; bk.rev.; bibl.; illus. circ. 300.

800   US   ISSN 0261-9849
PIERS PLOWMAN STUDIES. 1987. irreg., latest no.8. Boydell & Brewer Inc., Box 41026, Rochester, NY 14604. TEL 716-275-0419. FAX 716-271-8778. **Document type:** academic/scholarly publication.
—BLDSC (6498.870000).

PIETRA SERENA; ricerca storica e creativita letteraria. see HISTORY — History Of Europe

800   US   ISSN 0362-5214
PS615
PIG IRON; the annual thematic anthology of contemporary literature. 1975. a. $10 to individuals; institutions $12. Pig Iron Press, Box 237, Youngstown, OH 44501. TEL 216-747-6932. Ed. Jim Villani. bibl.; illus. circ. 1,000. (also avail. in microfilm from UMI; back issues avail.) **Indexed:** Ind.Amer.Per.Verse.
Description: Literary anthology series derived from popular culture and modernity.

800   US   ISSN 0192-8716
PIKESTAFF FORUM. 1978. a. $15 for 6 nos. Pikestaff Publications, Inc., Box 127, Normal, IL 61761. TEL 309-452-4831. Eds. Robert D. Sutherland, James R. Scrimgeour. bk.rev.; index. circ. 1,000. (tabloid format; back issues avail.) **Indexed:** Ind.Amer.Per.Verse.
Description: Presents poetry, fiction, commentary and profiles of other editors and magazines. Includes a young writers feature for authors aged 7-17.

810   US
PIMA COLLEGE MAGAZINE. 3/yr. Pima County Community College, 2202 W. Anklam Rd., Tucson, AZ 85709-0001. TEL 602-884-6974. circ. 1,500.

PINTER REVIEW: ANNUAL ESSAYS. see THEATER

852   US   ISSN 1046-557X
PQ4835.I7
PIRANDELLIAN STUDIES. 1985. a. $10 to individuals; institutions, libraries $15; foreign $20. University of Nebraska, Department of Modern Languages & Literatures, 1216 Old Father Hall, Lincoln, NE 68588. TEL 402-472-3883. FAX 402-472-3745. Ed. Walter Centuori. bk.rev. circ. 200. **Document type:** academic/scholarly publication.

891.85   PL   ISSN 0079-211X
PISARZE SLASCY 19 I 20 WIEKU. 1965. irreg. price varies. Slaski Instytut Naukowy, Ul. Graniczna 32, 40-956 Katowice, Poland. (Dist. by: Ars Polona-Ruch, Krakowskie Przedmiescie 7, Warsaw, Poland)

800 700 778.5   CI   ISSN 0351-1936
PITANJA; mjesecnik: drustvo, znanost, kultura. 1969. m. 200 din.($12.50) Savez Socijalisticke Omladine Hrvatske, Zagreb, Centar Drustvenih Djelatnosti, Opaticka 10, 41001 Zagreb, Croatia. Ed. Neven Mates. bk.rev.; film rev.; bibl.; illus.

808.8   US   ISSN 1054-6340
PITTSBURGH QUARTERLY. 1991. q. $12. 36 Haberman Ave., Pittsburgh, PA 15211-2144. Ed. Frank Correnti. adv.

806   AT   ISSN 0311-0753
PLAIN TURKEY. 1973. irreg. Aus.$6. Mt. Isa Writers Workshop, 97 Trainor St., Mt. Isa, Qld. 4825, Australia. Ed. R. Algie.

3658 LITERATURE

890   FR   ISSN 0750-9189
PLANEDENN. 1979. q. 150 F.($24) (foreign 180 F.). Editions Skol Vreizh, 20 rue de Kerscoff, 29600 Morlaix, France. TEL 98-62-17-20. FAX 98-62-02-38.
Description: Contains studies, reviews of theater pieces, news and interviews.

820   UK   ISSN 0048-4288
PLANET; the Welsh internationalist. 1970. bi-m. £12 (foreign £13). P.O. Box 44, Aberystwyth, Dyfed, Wales. TEL 0970-611255. FAX 0970-623311. Ed. John Barnie. bk.rev.; illus.; index. circ. 1,400.
Indexed: Abstr.Engl.Stud. **Document type:** bulletin.

808 200   US
PLANET WALK. 1982. q. $20. Box 701, Inverness, CA 94937. Ed. John Francis. bk.rev. circ. 300.
Formerly: Planet Walker.
Description: Journal of pilgrimage along with news of other pilgrims.

820 920   UK
PLANTAGENET PRODUCTIONS; libraries of spoken word recordings, of stagescripts, and of family papers. 1974. irreg. Westridge (Open Centre), Highclere, Nr. Newbury, Royal Berkshire RG15 9PJ, England. TEL 0635-253322. Ed. Dorothy Rose Gribble.
Document type: newsletter.
Former titles: Milton Traditions; Gribble Annals.
Description: Recordings of poetry, philosophy, narrative (existing titles); stagescripts of short plays, stories suitable for recital; family papers and history.

830   GW   ISSN 0931-3931
PLATTDUETSCH LAND UN WATERKANT. (Text in Low-German (Plattdeutsch)) 1916. s-a. DM.10 (free to members). Quickborn Vereinigung fuer Niederdeutsche Sprache und Literatur e.V., Alexanderstr. 16, 20099 Hamburg, Germany. TEL 040-240809. Ed. Gerd Spiekermann. adv.; bk.rev. circ. 1,000. (back issues avail.)
Description: Short stories, poems, plays and essays in Low-German dialect.

PLAYS & PLAYWRIGHTS. see *THEATER*

890   JA
PLEIADES/SUBARU. (Text in Japanese) 1970. bi-m. 630 Yen. Shueisha Inc., 5-10, 2-chome, Hitotsubashi, Chiyoda-ku, Tokyo 101-50, Japan. TEL 03-3230-6104. Ed. Nobuhiro Kano. circ. 10,000.

800   IT
PLEIADI. irreg.. latest no.45. price varies. Angelo Longo Editore, Via Paolo Costa 33, P.O. Box 431, 48100 Ravenna, Italy. TEL 0544-217026. Ed. Franco Mollia. circ. 2,500. **Document type:** monographic series.

840   FR   ISSN 0248-3696
PLEIN CHANT; cahiers trimestriels de litterature. 1971. q. 180 F. Editions Plein Chant, Bassac, 16120 Chateauneuf-sur-Charente, France. TEL 45-81-93-26. FAX 45-81-92-83. Ed. Edmond Thomas. adv.; bk.rev.; bibl.; illus.; index; circ. 1,000 (controlled). (back issues avail.)
Formerly (until 1979): Plein Chant. Cahiers Poetiques, Litteraires et Champetres (ISSN 0248-3688)

840 700   BE   ISSN 0295-1630
PLEINE MARGE; cahiers de litterature, d'arts plastiques et de critique. (Text in French) 1981. 2/yr. 1200 BEF. Editions Peeters s.p.r.l., Bondgenotenlaan 153, B-3000 Louvain, Belgium. TEL 32-16-235170. FAX 32-16-228500. Ed. J. Chenieux. adv. (back issues avail.) **Document type:** academic/scholarly publication.
Formerly (until 1985): C A S. Champs des Activites Surrealistes (ISSN 0755-0189)

810   US   ISSN 0048-4474
NX1
PLOUGHSHARES; a journal of new writing. 1971. 3/yr. $19 to individuals (foreign $22); institutions $22 (foreign $27). (Emerson College) Ploughshares, Inc., Emerson College, 100 Beacon St., Boston, MA 02116. TEL 617-578-8753. Ed. Don Lee. adv.; bk.rev.; illus.; index, cum.index: vols.1-6. circ. 6,000. (also avail. in microfilm from UMI; back issues avail.; reprint service avail. from UMI) **Indexed:** Amer.Hum.Ind., Arts & Hum.Cit.Ind., Bk.Rev.Ind., Curr.Cont., GeoRef., Ind.Amer.Per.Verse, M.L.A.
●Also available on CD-ROM.
—Faxon; UMI.
Description: Introduces new American writing, guest-edited by major writers.

810   US
PLUCKED CHICKEN. 1978. q. $10. Asphodel Book Shop, 17192 Ravenna Rd., Burton, OH 44021-9733. TEL 216-834-4775. Ed. Will Peterson.

860   MX   ISSN 0185-4925
NX7
PLURAL; critica, arte, literatura, pensamiento. (Text in Spanish) 1971. m. $33 in Mexico and S. America; N. and Central America $30; Europe $43; Africa and Middle East $55; elsewhere $60. Compania Editorial Excelsior S.C.L., Reforma 18, 1er piso, Delegacion Cuauhtemoc, 06600 Mexico, DF, Mexico. TEL 5669360. FAX 5660223. Dir. Jaime Labastida. adv. contact: Arturo Leos Veloz. bk.rev.; illus. circ. 16,000. (tabloid format) **Indexed:** Hisp.Amer.Per.Ind., M.L.A. **Document type:** academic/scholarly publication.
—BLDSC (6541.012000).

800   FR   ISSN 0765-1112
PC2002
PLURIAL; revue de litterature francophone, la femme et la famille traditionnelle. 1988. a. 80 F. Presses Universitaires de Rennes, 2 rue du Doyen D. Leroy, 35044 Rennes Cedex, France. TEL 99-54-66-35. FAX 99-33-07-95.

THE POE MESSENGER. see *LITERATURE — Poetry*

808.83   US
POE STUDIES ASSOCIATION NEWSLETTER. 1973. 2/yr. $8. Poe Studies Association, Worcester Polytechnic Institute, Worcester, MA 01609. TEL 508-831-5383. (Subscr. to: Dennis Eddings, Humanities, Western Oregon State College, Monmouth, OR 97361) Ed. Kent P. Ljungquist. bk.rev.; circ. 250 (paid). **Document type:** academic/scholarly publication, newsletter.
Description: Review of works on Poe and Poe-related activities.

POESIE UND WISSENSCHAFT. SAMMLUNG. see *LITERATURE — Poetry*

POETES ET PROSATEURS DU PORTUGAL. see *LITERATURE — Poetry*

POETIC DRAMA AND POETIC THEORY. see *LITERATURE — Poetry*

800 410   GW   ISSN 0303-4178
P3
POETICA; Zeitschrift fuer Sprach- und Literaturwissenschaft. 1967. q. DM.148. Verlag Ferdinand Schoeningh GmbH, Postfach 2540, 33055 Paderborn, Germany. TEL 05251-127662. FAX 05251-127860. Ed.Bd. adv.; bk.rev.; bibl.; index. circ. 1,000. (back issues avail.) **Indexed:** Bibl.ling., Can.Rev.Comp.Lit., Curr.Cont., Ind.Bk.Rev.Hum., M.L.A. **Document type:** academic/scholarly publication.
—BLDSC (6541.740000). Faxon; SWETS.
Description: Contains essays and discussions on literary theory and history, classical and modern philology. Includes book reviews and bibliography.

800   NE   ISSN 0304-422X
PN45
POETICS; journal for empirical research on literature, the media and the arts. (Text in Dutch, English and French) 1972. 6/yr. fl.467($252) (effective 1994). North-Holland (Subsidiary of: Elsevier Science B.V.), P.O. Box 211, 1000 AE Amsterdam, Netherlands. TEL 31-20-5803911. FAX 31-20-5803598. TELEX 18582 ESPA NL. (Subscr. in U.S. and Canada to: Elsevier Science Inc., Box 882, Madison Sq. Sta., New York, NY 10159. TEL 212-989-5800. FAX 212-633-3990) Ed. C.J. van Rees. bk.rev. (also avail. in microform from UMI; back issues avail.; reprint service avail. from SWZ) **Indexed:** Abstr.Engl.Stud., Arts & Hum.Cit.Ind., Bibl.Ling., Curr.Cont., Ind.Bk.Rev.Hum., Lang.& Lang.Behav.Abstr., Sociol.Abstr. **Document type:** academic/scholarly publication.
—BLDSC (6541.744000); Faxon; SWETS. **CCC.**
Description: Interdisciplinary journal covering theoretical and empirical research in literature, the media and the arts.
Refereed Serial

POETICS JOURNAL. see *LITERARY AND POLITICAL REVIEWS*

POETRY IRELAND REVIEW. see *LITERATURE — Poetry*

POETS & WRITERS MAGAZINE. see *LITERATURE — Poetry*

800 700   US
POETS, PAINTERS, COMPOSERS. 1984. a. $50. Poets, Painters, Composers, 10254 35th Ave., S.W., Seattle, WA 98146. TEL 206-937-8155. Ed. Joseph Keppler. bk.rev.; illus. circ. 300. (back issues avail.)
Description: Multi-media art and literary publication.

810   US
POISON PEN WRITERS NEWS.* 1983. 3/yr. $12. Baker Street Publications, Box 517, Metairie, LA 70004-0517. TEL 504-734-8414. Ed. Sharida Rizzuto. circ. 9,000.
Description: Covers the writers market and writing.

POLICORDO; revista quadrimestale di cultura, letteratura, arte. see *HUMANITIES: COMPREHENSIVE WORKS*

810 320   US
POLIT; a journal of literature and politics. 1977. s-a. $6. Southeastern Massachusetts University, Department of English, North Dartmouth, MA 02747. TEL 617-999-8274. (Co-sponsor: Department of English, University of Alabama, Birmingham) Eds. Robert Waxler, Carl Schinasi.

891   PL   ISSN 0551-3707
POLONISTYKA. 1948. 10/yr. $17.50. (Ministerstwo Edukacji Narodowej) Wydawnictwa Szkolne i Pedagogiczne, Pl. Dabrowskiego 8, 00-950 Warsaw, Poland. TEL 48-22-265451. FAX 48-22-266313. (Dist. by: Ars Polona-Ruch, Krakowskie Przedmiescie 7, Warsaw, Poland) Ed. Bozena Chrzastowska. circ. 10,000. **Indexed:** Bibl.Ling. **Document type:** academic/scholarly publication.
—SWETS.
Description: Presents contemporary literary and linguistic research, with articles on literary studies and on culture, the methodology of teaching Polish, and research on Polish writers' works and different literary epochs.

POLSKA AKADEMIA NAUK. INSTYTUT SLOWIANOZNAWSTWA. PRACE SLAWISTYCZNE. see *LINGUISTICS*

809   PL   ISSN 0554-579X
POLSKA AKADEMIA NAUK. ODDZIAL W KRAKOWIE. KOMISJA HISTORYCZNOLITERACKA. PRACE. (Text in English, French and Polish) 1961. irreg., no.47, 1989. price varies. Ossolineum, Publishing House of the Polish Academy of Sciences, Rynek 9, 50-106 Wroclaw, Poland. TEL 48-71-386-25. FAX 48-71-448-103. TELEX 0712771 OSS PL. Ed. Jan Nowakowski. **Document type:** monographic series.
Description: Presents the history of Polish and other European literature.

POLSKA AKADEMIA NAUK. ODDZIAL W KRAKOWIE. KOMISJA HISTORYCZNOLITERACKA. ROCZNIK. see *HISTORY*

891.8 PL ISSN 0079-3434
POLSKA AKADEMIA NAUK. ODDZIAL W KRAKOWIE. KOMISJA SLOWIANOZNAWSTWA. PRACE. (Text in Polish; summaries in English and Russian) 1962. irreg., no.48, 1990. price varies. Ossolineum, Publishing House of the Polish Academy of Sciences, Rynek 9, 50-106 Wroclaw, Poland. TEL 48-71-386-25. FAX 48-71-448-103. TELEX 0712771 OSS PL. Ed. Ryszard Luzny. **Document type:** monographic series.
  Description: Covers works on Slavonic linguistics and literature.

POLYLINGUA; a college journal of foreign languages. see LINGUISTICS

891.7 BW ISSN 0130-8068
POLYMYA. (Text in Byelorussian) 1922. m. 12 Rub. (Sayuz Pismennikow Belarusi) Polymya, Vul. Zakharova 19, 220600 Minsk, Belarus. TEL 0172-332012. Ed. S.I. Zakonnikov. bk.rev.; play rev.; bibl.; index. circ. 9,500.

POMPEBLEDEN; tydskrift foar Fryske Studzje. see LINGUISTICS

839 NE
POPULAIRE LITERATUUR; een reeks teksten uit de late Middeleeuwen. 1979. irreg. price varies. Dick Coutinho B.V., Slochterlaan 7, 1405 AL Bussum, Netherlands. TEL 31-2159-49991. FAX 31-2159-47165. **Document type:** monographic series.

839 NE
POPULAR ESSAYS FROM THE LATE REPUBLIC. 1983. irreg. price varies. Dick Coutinho B.V., Slochterlaan 7, 1405 AL Bussum, Netherlands. TEL 31-70-2159-49991. FAX 31-2159-47165. **Document type:** monographic series.

808 US ISSN 8756-5978
PORTABLE LOWER EAST SIDE. 1984. 2/yr. $12 to individuals; institutions $20. P L E S, Box 30323, New York, NY 10011-0103. Ed. Arthur Nersesian. adv.; bk.rev. circ. 2,000. (back issues avail.)
—BLDSC (6539.445000).
  Description: Fiction, poetry, photography and non-fiction with a realistic and documentary approach. Each issue focuses on a specific ethnicity or aspect of life in New York City.

800 850 IT
PORTICO. (In 2 parts: Letteratura Italiana; Letteratura Straniera) irreg., latest LI no.100, LS no.134. price varies. Angelo Longo Editore, Via Paolo Costa 33, P.O. Box 431, 48100 Ravenna, Italy. TEL 0544-217026. Ed. Antonio Piromalli. circ. 3,000. **Document type:** monographic series.

800 US
PORTLAND REVIEW MAGAZINE. 1955. 2/yr. $12. Portland State University, Box 751, Portland, OR 97207. TEL 503-725-4533. FAX 503-725-4882. Ed. Dave Tinsley. adv.; bk.rev. circ. 2,000. **Indexed:** Ind.Amer.Per.Verse.
  Former titles: International Portland Review; Portland Review (ISSN 0360-3091)
  Description: Features poetry, fiction, experimental writing, artwork and photography.

869 UK ISSN 0267-5315
DP532
PORTUGUESE STUDIES. (Text mainly in English, occasionally in Portuguese) 1985. a. $62. Modern Humanities Research Association, Kings College, Strand, London WC2R 2LS, England.
—BLDSC (6557.300000); SWETS.
  Description: Devoted to the literature, culture, and history of Portugal, Brazil and the Portuguese-speaking countries in Africa. Includes articles, reviews, literary translation and a survey of research recently completed at universities in the U.K.

POSTCARD ART - POSTCARD FICTION. see ART

800 US ISSN 1053-1920
POSTMODERN CULTURE; an electronic journal of interdisciplinary criticism. (Not avail. in printed format) 1990. 3/yr. $15 to individuals on diskette or fiche; institutions $30 (free electronically). Oxford University Press, Journals, 200 Madison Ave., New York, NY 10010. TEL 212-679-7300. FAX 212-725-2972. (Subscr. to: Oxford Journals Fulfillment, 2001 Evans Rd., Cary, NC 27513. TEL 919-677-0977. FAX 919-677-1714) Eds. Eyal Amiran, John Unsworth. (diskette format; also avail. in microfiche)
● Also available online.
  Description: Review of postmodern literature, cultural and social issues.
  Refereed Serial

800 NE ISSN 0923-0483
POSTMODERN STUDIES. 1989. a. price varies. Editions Rodopi B.V., Keizersgracht 302-304, 1016 EX Amsterdam, Netherlands. TEL 31-20-6227507. FAX 31-20-6380948. (In N. America: 233 Peachtree St., N.E., Ste. 404, Atlanta, GA 30303-1504. TEL 800-225-3998. FAX 404-522-7116) Eds. Theo D'haen, Hans Bertens. (back issues avail.) **Document type:** academic/scholarly publication.
—BLDSC (6563.936500).

806 US
POSTSCRIPT (TARRYTOWN). 1981. q. membership. Washington Irving Society, 150 White Plains Rd., Tarrytown, NY 10591. circ. 150.

808.838 CN ISSN 0226-0840
THE POTTERSFIELD PORTFOLIO; some of the best new fiction, essays, poetry, plays and artwork in English and French from Atlantic Canada and elsewhere. 1979. s-a. Can.$12 (foreign $15). Wild East Publishing Co-operative Ltd., 151 Ryan Ct., Fredericton, NB E3A 2Y9, Canada. TEL 506-472-9251. FAX 506-472-9251. Ed.Bd. adv.: B&W page Can.$300. bk.rev. circ. 1,000. (also avail. in microform from MML) **Indexed:** Amer.Hum.Ind., Can.Lit.Ind., CMI, Ind.Amer.Per.Verse.

800 US ISSN 1058-7691
PR6031.O867
POWYS NOTES. 1985. s-a. $12 membership; institutions $15. Powys Society of North America, Dept. of English, Valparaiso University, Valparaiso, IN 46383. (Subscr. to: Constance Harsh, Dept. of English, Colgate University, Hamilton, NY 13346-1398. TEL 315-824-7294) Ed. Richard Maxwell. bk.rev. circ. 150. **Document type:** academic/scholarly publication.
  Description: Publishes history and criticism relating to literary members of the Powys family.

820 UK ISSN 0309-1619
PR6031.O867
POWYS REVIEW. 1977. a. £6. c/o Belinda Humfrey, Ed., Department of English, Saint David's University College, Lampeter, Dyfed SA48 7ED, Wales. TEL 0570-422351. FAX 0570-423634. adv.; bk.rev.; play rev.; bibl. circ. 1,000. **Indexed:** Arts & Hum.Cit.Ind., Curr.Cont., M.L.A. **Document type:** academic/scholarly publication.
—BLDSC (6579.030000).

891.4 II ISSN 0032-6550
PRAGATI. (Text in Bengali) 1966. m. Rs.10. Nava Niketan, 39B Dent Mission Rd., Calcutta 700 023, India. Ed. Mrinal Chatterjee. adv.; bk.rev.; film rev.; play rev. circ. 1,500.

810 CN ISSN 0821-1124
PRAIRIE FIRE; a Canadian magazine of new writing. 1978. 4/yr. Can.$24 to individuals; institutions Can.$32. Prairie Fire Press, Inc., 423-100 Arthur St., Winnipeg, MB R3B 1H3, Canada. TEL 204-943-9066. FAX 204-942-1555. Ed. Andris Taskans. adv. contact: Tom Dowsett. bk.rev. circ. 1,600 (paid). **Indexed:** Can.Lit.Ind., Ind.Amer.Per.Verse. **Document type:** consumer publication.
  Incorporates: Writers News Manitoba.
  Description: Literary writing and criticism.

820 CN ISSN 0827-2921
PRAIRIE JOURNAL. 1983. s-a. Can.$14 to individuals; institutions Can.$12. Prairie Journal Press, P.O. Box 61203, 217K - 3630 Brentwood Rd. N.W., Calgary, AB T2L 2K6, Canada. Ed. A. Burke. adv.; bk.rev. circ. 500. (also avail. in microform from MML) **Indexed:** Can.Lit.Ind.
  Description: Contains a mix of poetry, fiction, articles, reviews, drama and essays.

810 US ISSN 0032-6682
AP2
PRAIRIE SCHOONER. 1927. q. $20 to individuals; institutions $22. University of Nebraska, Lincoln, 201 Andrews Hall, Lincoln, NE 68588-0334. TEL 402-472-3191. FAX 402-472-4636. TELEX 484-240 U NEBR. (Dist. by: Ingram Periodicals, Box 7000, La Vergne, TN 37086-7000) Ed. Hilda Raz. adv.; bk.rev. circ. 3,200. (also avail. in microfilm from UMI; back issues avail.; reprint service avail. from UMI,KTO) **Indexed:** A.I.P.P., Arts & Hum.Cit.Ind., Bk.Rev.Ind. (1965-), Child.Bk.Rev.Ind. (1965-), Curr.Cont., Hum.Ind., Ind.Bk.Rev.Hum., M.L.A. —BLDSC (6598.554000); Faxon; UnCover; UMI.
  Description: Contains stories, poems, interviews, imaginative essays, translations, plus reviews of current books of poetry and fiction.

800 II
PRAKALPANA SAHITYA/PRAKALPANA LITERATURE. (Text in Bengali and English) 1977. a. Rs.6. c/o Vattacharja Chandan, Ed., P-40 Nandana Park, Calcutta 700 034, India. TEL 91-033-4782347. (Dist. in West by: Flatland, Box 2420, Fort Bragg, CA 95437-2420, USA) bk.rev. circ. 1,000.
  Description: Promotes alternative and experimental Sarbangin poetry, art and literature.

491 891 II
PRAKRIT TEXT SOCIETY. PUBLICATIONS. irreg. price varies. Prakrit Text Society, c/o Lalbhai Dalpatbhai Institute of Indology, Near Gujarat University, P.O. Navarangpura, Ahmedabad 380 009, India. **Document type:** monographic series.

PRAMPRA. see FOLKLORE

801 700 II ISSN 0970-2849
PRATIBHA INDIA; journal of Indian art, culture and literature. (Text in English) 1981. q. Rs.65 (foreign $18). Sneh Bharti - Charitable Trust, B-2, I.P. Staff Flats, Shamnath Marg, Delhi 110 054, India. TEL 292-7815. Eds. Aruna Sitesh, Sitesh Aloke. adv.; bk.rev.; illus. circ. 1,400. **Document type:** academic/scholarly publication.
  Description: Promotes the study and creation of modern Indian literature and poetry. Includes translations of stories and poems from various languages (Bengali, Hindi, Urdu, Tamil, Marathi, as well as others). Features articles on the lives and works of authors and artists, and cultural facets of Indian life.

891.1 II ISSN 0303-2906
PRAYAASA. (Text in English, Hindi) 1975? irreg., latest Mar. 1989. Jawaharlal Nehru University, Literary Club, Cultural Committee, Dean of Students' Office, New Delhi 110 067, India. Eds. Siyaram Sharma (Hindi), Prashant Kumar Misra (English). bibl.; illus.
  Description: Provides a forum for students' essays, analyses, translations and poems. Each issue has separate autonomous English and Hindi sections.

809 US ISSN 0163-4631
PN2
PRECISELY; a critical journal. 1977. 2/yr. $8 for 4 nos. R K Editions, Box 73, Canal St., NY 10013. Eds. Richard Kostelanetz, Stephen Scobie. bk.rev. circ. 300. (back issues avail.) **Indexed:** M.L.A.
  Description: Devoted to extended critical essays on innovative literature of the past three decades.

PREPUBLICATIONS. see LINGUISTICS

800 700 FR ISSN 0336-321X
PRESENCE DES LETTRES ET DES ARTS.* 1964. q. 120 F. Cercle International de la Pensee et des Arts Francais, Arquian, 58310 Saint Amand en Puisage, France. Ed. A. Pourtier. adv.; bk.rev.; illus. circ. 3,000.
  Formerly: Presence des Lettres des Arts (ISSN 0032-7654)

810 US
PRESIDIO. bi-m. $2. Iowa State Penitentiary at Fort Madison, Box 316, Ft. Madison, IA 52627-0316.

LITERATURE

891 RU
PRIAMUR'E MOE; literaturno-khudozhestvennyi sbornik. irreg. 1.05 Rub. Khabarovskoe Knizhnoe Izdatel'stvo, Ul. Lenina, 181, Blagoveshchensk, Russia. illus.

PRILOZI ZA KNJIZEVNOST, JEZIK, ISTORIJU I FOLKLOR. see LINGUISTICS

PRIMAVERA (CHICAGO). see WOMEN'S INTERESTS

800 XV ISSN 0351-1189
PN851
PRIMERJALNA KNJIZEVNOST. (Text in Slovenian; summaries in English, French, German) 1978. s-a. 300 SLT($20) Slovensko Drustvo za Primerjalno Knjizevnost, Askerceva 12, 61000 Ljubljana, Slovenia. TEL 061-156-068. FAX 061-155-253. Ed. Darko Dolinar. bk.rev.; bibl. circ. 500. (back issues avail.) Indexed: M.L.A.
Description: Covers all aspects of comparative literature for literary scholars and students.

800 UK
PRINCESS GRACE IRISH LIBRARY. 1986. irreg. price varies. Colin Smythe Ltd., P.O. Box 6, Gerrards Cross, Buckinghamshire SL9 8XA, England. TEL 0753-886000. FAX 0753-886469. (Dist. in U.S. by: Barnes & Noble Books, 8705 Bollman Place, Savage, MD 20763) circ. 1,200. (reprint service avail. from ISI) Document type: monographic series.
—BLDSC (6612.932300).
Description: Collections of papers given at the Princess Grace Irish Library conferences, or collections of essays commissioned by the Library.

800 UK ISSN 0950-5121
PRINCESS GRACE IRISH LIBRARY LECTURES. 1986. irreg. Colin Smythe Ltd., P.O. Box 6, Gerrards Cross, Buckinghamshire SL9 8XA, England. TEL 0753-886000. FAX 0753-886469. (Dist. in U.S. by: Dufour Editions, Box 449, Chester Springs, PA 19425) circ. 750. (reprint service avail. from ISI) Document type: monographic series.
—BLDSC (6612.932400).
Description: Texts of individual lectures given at the Princess Grace Irish Library.

800 US
PRINCETON ESSAYS IN LITERATURE.. 1964. irreg. price varies. Princeton University Press, 41 William St., Princeton, NJ 08540. TEL 609-258-4900. FAX 609-258-6305. (reprint service avail. from UMI) Document type: monographic series.

PRINCETON LIBRARY OF ASIAN TRANSLATIONS. see ORIENTAL STUDIES

819 CN ISSN 0032-8790
AP5
PRISM INTERNATIONAL; a quarterly journal of contemporary writing. (Text in English) 1959. 4/yr. Can.$16 to individuals; institutions Can.$22. University of British Columbia, Creative Writing Department, E462-1866 Main Mall, Vancouver, BC V6T 1Z1, Canada. TEL 604-822-2514. Ed. Anna Nobile. bk.rev.; cum.index. circ. 1,100. (also avail. in microform from UMI; reprint service avail. from UMI,KTO; back issues avail.) Indexed: Amer.Bibl.Slavic & E.Eur.Stud., Amer.Hum.Ind., Arts & Hum.Cit.Ind., Can.Lit.Ind., Curr.Cont.
—UnCover; UMI.

820 II
PROBITAS; devoted to literature and culture. (Text in English) Rs.3($2) per no. Aruna Printing Works, Berhampur 760002, India.

371 028.5 AU
PROJEKTBUCH. 1956. a. Oesterreichischer Buchklub der Jugend, Mayerhofgasse 6, A-1041 Vienna, Austria. TEL 0222-5051754-0. FAX 0222-505175450. Document type: bulletin.
Formerly (until 1993): Barke (ISSN 0067-4206)

840 FR ISSN 0181-0146
PROMETHEE; magazine bimestriel de creation et de recherches de la pensee. 1972. bi-m. 200 F. Promethee, c/o Octave Prour, Ed., B.P. 166-10, 75463 Paris Cedex 10, France. adv.; bk.rev. circ. 4,000.

PROMISE. see LITERATURE — Poetry

PROOFTEXTS; a journal of Jewish literary history. see RELIGIONS AND THEOLOGY — Judaic

800 100 US ISSN 0734-3027
PROPHETIC VOICES; an international literary journal. 1983. s-a. $14 to individuals; institutions and foreign $16. Heritage Trails Press, 94 Santa Maria Dr., Novato, CA 94947. Ed.Bd. circ. 400. (back issues avail.)
Description: Views the poet as prophet. Concerned with world issues such as the preservation of animals and the environment.

800 UK ISSN 0144-0357
PR750
PROSE STUDIES; history, theory, criticism. 1978. 3/yr. £26($38) to individuals; institutions £70 ($95). Frank Cass & Co. Ltd., Gainsborough House, 11 Gainsborough Rd., London E11 1RS, England. TEL 081-530-4226. FAX 081-530-7795. Eds. Ronald J. Corthell, T.H. Corns. adv.: B&W page £185; adv. contact: Anne Kidson. bk.rev. (back issues avail.) Indexed: Ind.Bk.Rev.Hum., M.L.A. Document type: academic/scholarly publication.
—BLDSC (6927.440000); Faxon; UnCover.
Description: Provides a forum to discuss the history, theory, and criticism of nonfiction prose of all periods.

850 IT
PROSPETTIVE CULTURALI. 1975. bi-m. L.20000. (Associazione Culturale dei Medici Artisti Italiani) Societa Editrice Napoletana s.r.l., Corso Umberto I, 34, 80138 Naples, Italy. Ed. A. Spagnuolo. adv.; bk.rev. circ. 500.
Formerly: Nuove Prospettive Letterarie.

800 700 780 AU ISSN 0555-5027
NX548.A1
PROTOKOLLE; Wiener Halbjahresschrift fuer Literatur, Bildende Kunst und Musik. s-a. S.155. J & V Edition Wien Dachs Verlag GmbH, Rainergasse 38, A-1050 Vienna, Austria. TEL 0222-5458210. FAX 0222-545821027. Ed. Otto Breicha. illus. Indexed: Artbibl.Mod. Document type: consumer publication.
—SWETS.
Description: Journal of literature and the arts.

840 ISSN 0048-5659
PQ2631.R63
PROUST RESEARCH ASSOCIATION NEWSLETTER. (Text in English and French) 1969. s-a. free. Proust Research Association, c/o J. Theodore Johnson, Ed., Department of French and Italian, University of Kansas, Lawrence, KS 66045. TEL 913-864-3388. Ed.Bd. bk.rev.; abstr.; bibl. circ. 250. Indexed: M.L.A.
Description: Forum for the discussion of problems relating to current research on Marcel Proust.

PROVINCETOWN ARTS. see ART

800 700 IS ISSN 0334-4975
PROZA; literary and art magazine. 1976. m. P.O. Box 969, Ramat Gan 52 109, Israel. Ed. Yossi Creme.

PRUDENTIA. see HISTORY

840 440 SZ ISSN 0079-7812
PC7
PUBLICATIONS ROMANES ET FRANCAISES. no.9, 1933. irreg. no.207, 1993. price varies. Librairie Droz S.A., 11, rue Massot, CH-1211 Geneva 12, Switzerland. TEL 022-3466666. FAX 022-3472391. circ. 800. Indexed: M.L.A. Document type: monographic series.
—CCC.
Description: Brings out linguistic, psychological and historical analyses of classical and modern literature.

800 US ISSN 0738-517X
PS580
PUERTO DEL SOL. 1961-1976; resumed 1980. s-a. $7.75. New Mexico State University, Department of English, Box 3E, Las Cruces, NM 88003. TEL 505-646-2345. Ed. Kevin McIlvoy. adv.; bk.rev.; bibl.; illus. circ. 750. Indexed: A.I.P.C.; Amer.Hum.Ind., Chic.Per.Ind., Ind.Amer.Per.Verse.

PULPHOUSE - A FICTION MAGAZINE. see LITERATURE — Science Fiction, Fantasy, Horror

PULPHOUSE FICTION SPOTLIGHT. see LITERATURE — Science Fiction, Fantasy, Horror

800 US
PUN AMERICAN NEWSLETTER; jest for fun. 1989. q. $9.95. Del Mar Publications, 1165 Elmwood Place, Deerfield, IL 60015. TEL 708-945-1790. Ed. Robert S. Aitchison. bk.rev. circ. 600. Document type: newsletter.
Description: Covers puns, pictures, cartoons and photographs mainly contributed by subscribers nation wide.

808.87 CN ISSN 0712-1318
PUNDIT. 1981. m. $20. International Save the Pun Foundation, Box 5040, Sta. A, Toronto, ON M5W 1N4, Canada. TEL 416-922-1100. FAX 416-922-1100. Ed. John S. Crosbie. bk.rev. (looseleaf format) Document type: newsletter.
Description: Seeks to encourage literacy by supplying word-play to members worldwide. Conducts contests involving word games.

378.1 MX ISSN 0033-4367
PUNTO DE PARTIDA. 1967. bi-m. Mex.$15($2.50) Universidad Nacional Autonoma de Mexico, Direccion General de Difusion Cultural, Ciudad Universitaria, Villa Obregon, Mexico 20 D.F., Mexico. Ed. Dir. Eugenia Revueltas. bibl.; illus.

890 BG
PURNASA. (Text in Bengali) 1976. m. Tk.2. Bijan Bihari Goldar, Ed. & Pub., 143 Shahid Samsuzzoha Hall, Rajshahi University, Rajshahi, Bangladesh.

810 US ISSN 0149-7863
PS501
PUSHCART PRIZE: BEST OF THE SMALL PRESSES. 1976. a. $29.50. Pushcart Press, Box 380, Wainscott, NY 11975. TEL 516-324-9300. Ed. Bill Henderson. index. circ. 10,000. (back issues avail.)
Description: Covers selections from small, independent book presses and literary magazines.

PUSHTO. see LINGUISTICS

810 US ISSN 0278-1891
PS3566.Y55
PYNCHON NOTES. 1979. 2/yr. $9 (foreign $12). c/o Bernard Duyfhuizen, Man. Ed., English Dept., Univ. of Wisconsin, Eau Claire, WI 54702-4004. TEL 715-836-3165. FAX 715-836-2380. Eds. John M. Krafft, Khachig Tololyan. adv.; bk.rev.; bibl. circ. 250. Indexed: Abstr.Engl.Stud., LCR, M.L.A. Document type: academic/scholarly publication.
—BLDSC (7161.765000); UnCover.
Description: Notes and essays of any length considering the writings of Thomas Pynchon from any critical angle and in any literary, historical or cultural context.

800 XO ISSN 0231-9047
PYRAMIDA. 1971. m. $94. (Socialist Academy of Slovakia) Obzor, Ceskoslovenskej Armady 35, 815 85 Bratislava, Slovakia.

895.1 CC
QING MING. wenxue shuang yuekan. (Text in Chinese) 1979. bi-m. Y22.80($69.10) 9, Suzhou Rd., Hefei, Anhui 230001, People's Republic of China. (Dist. outside China by: Guoji Shudian - China International Book Trading Corp., P.O. Box 399, Beijing, P.R.C.; Dist. in US by: China Books & Periodicals, Inc., 2929 24th St., San Francisco, CA 94110. TEL 415-282-2994) adv. circ. 160,000. Document type: consumer publication.
Description: Literary magazine that covers stories, prose and reviews.

895.1 CC
QINGCHUN/YOUTH. (Text in Chinese) m. Nanjing Shi Wenlian, 19 Lanyuan, Nanjing, Jiangsu 210018, People's Republic of China. TEL 631931. Ed. Chen Jian.

895.1 CC ISSN 0257-5795
QINGHAI HU/QINGHAI LAKE. (Text in Chinese) 1970. m. $45. Qinghai Sheng Wenlian, No. 12, Huanghe Lu, Xining, Qinghai 810001, People's Republic of China. TEL 45083. (Dist. in US by: China Books & Periodicals, Inc., 2929 24th St., San Francisco, CA 94110. TEL 415-282-2994) Ed. Li Shijing.

895.1   CC
QINGNIAN WENXUE/YOUTH LITERATURE. (Text in Chinese) m. Y1.80($57.60) Zhongguo Qingnian Chubanshe, Qikan Bu - China Youth Press, 21, Dongsi 12 Tiao, Beijing 100708, People's Republic of China. TEL 442125. (Dist. outside China by: China International Book Trading Corp., P.O. Box 399, Beijing, P.R.C.; Dist. in US by: China Books & Periodicals, Inc., 2929 24th St., San Francisco, CA 94110. TEL 415-282-2994) Ed. Chen Haozeng.

895.1   ISSN 1002-2139
QINGNIAN WENXUEJIA/YOUNG WRITERS. (Text in Chinese) 1985. m. Qiqiha'er Shi Wenlian, Tiyuchang Nan 2 Men, Hecheng, Qiqiha'er, Heilongjiang 142, People's Republic of China. TEL 72248. Ed. Guo Dabin.

895.1   CC   ISSN 1003-1669
QINGNIAN ZUOJIA/YOUNG WRITERS; wenxue shuang yuekan. (Text in Chinese) 1981. bi-m. Y15. (Chengdu Shi Xinwen Chubanju - Chengdu News Publishing Bureau) Qingnian Zuojia Zazhishe, 44, Beixin Jie, Chengdu, Sichuan 610016, People's Republic of China. TEL 28719. Ed. Yang Zhengtai. adv.
Description: Publishes prose, poetry, short stories, novelettes, and satirical and humorous stories.

895.1   CC
QIYE WENHUA/ENTERPRISE CULTURE. (Text in Chinese) bi-m. Heilongjiang Zuojia Qiyejia Lianyihui, 16, Yaojing Jie, Nangang-qu, Harbin, Heilongjiang 150006, People's Republic of China. TEL 30993. Ed. Li Chunren.

850   CN   ISSN 0226-8043
PQ4001
QUADERNI D'ITALIANISTICA. 1980. s-a. Can.$20($20) (effective 1991). Canadian Society for Italian Studies, University of Toronto, Dept. of Italian, Toronto, Ont. M5S 1A1, Canada. FAX 416-978-5593. Ed. Massimo Ciavolella. adv.; bk.rev. circ. 450. (reprint service avail. from ISI) Indexed: Arts & Hum.Cit.Ind., Curr.Cont., M.L.A.
—BLDSC (7166.363000).

QUADERNI DEL CARDELLO. see *HISTORY — History Of Europe*

850 410 851   IT   ISSN 1120-9178
QUADERNI DI LINGUE E LETTERATURE. (Text in English, French, German, Modern Greek, Italian, Russian, Spanish) 1976. a. exchange basis. Universita degli Studi di Verona, Facolta di Lingue e Letterature Straniere, 37129 Verona, Italy. TEL 045-8098320. FAX 045-38792. Ed. Anna Maria Babbi. bk.rev. circ. 500. **Document type:** academic/scholarly publication.

QUADERNI DI PIETRA SERENA. see *HISTORY — History Of Europe*

QUADERNI IBERO-AMERICANI; attualita culturale Penisola Iberica America-Latina. see *LINGUISTICS*

850   IT   ISSN 0394-2694
DG975.V38
QUADERNI VENETI. 1985. s-a. L.54000 (foreign L.72000). (Centro Interuniversitario di Studi Veneti) Angelo Longo Editore, Via Paolo Costa 33, P.O. Box 431, 48100 Ravenna, Italy. TEL 0544-217026. Ed. Giorgio Padoan. adv.; index. (back issues avail.) **Document type:** academic/scholarly publication.

800 410   FR
QUADRANT. (Text in French, Portuguese, Spanish) 1984. a. 50 F. Universite de Montpellier (Universite Paul Valery), B.P. 5043, 34032 Montpellier Cedex 1, France. TEL 67-14-20-00. circ. 500. (back issues avail.)
Description: Covers Portuguese and Brazilian literature and linguistics.

895.1   CC
QUANZHOU WENXUE/QUANZHOU LITERATURE. (Text in Chinese) bi-m. Y4.50. Quanzhou Shi Wenlian, 412 Zhongshan Zhonglu, 2nd Floor, Quanzhou, Fujian 362000, People's Republic of China. TEL 222364. (Dist. overseas by: Jiangsu Publications Import & Export Corp., 56 Gao Yun Ling, Nanjing, Jiangsu, P.R.C.) Ed. Chen Zhize.

819   CN   ISSN 0033-5266
PS501
QUARRY. 1952. q. Can.$22.47($21) to individuals; institutions $32 ($35.25). Quarry Press, Inc., Box 1061, Kingston, ON K7L 4Y5, Canada. TEL 613-548-8429. FAX 613-548-1556. Ed. Steve Heighton. adv. contact: Melanie Dugan. bk.rev. circ. 1,000. (also avail. in microfilm from MML; microfiche from UMI) Indexed: Amer.Hum.Ind., C.P.I., Can.Lit.Ind., Can.Per.Ind., CMI, Ind.Amer.Per.Verse.

800   ISSN 1055-1492
QUARRY FARM PAPERS. 1989. irreg. $5 (members $4). Elmira College, Center for Mark Twain Studies, Box EC 7035, Elmira, NY 14901. TEL 607-732-0993. Ed. Darryl Baskin. circ. 1,000. **Document type:** academic/scholarly publication.

810   US   ISSN 0893-3103
PS501
THE QUARTERLY (NEW YORK); the magazine of new writing. 1987-1993; resumed, no.26, 1994. q. $30 (effective 1994). 650 Madison Ave., Ste. 2600, New York, NY 10022. TEL 212-888-4769. (Subscr. to: Gutter Press, 1600 Bathurst St., Ste. 405, Toronto, ON M5P 3H9, Canada. TEL 416-980-5182) Ed. Gordon Lish. adv. circ. 15,000.
Description: Aims to deliver to an international readership the strongest samples of contemporary prose fiction and poetry available in the marketplace.

810   US   ISSN 0194-4231
QUARTERLY WEST. 1976. s-a. $11. University of Utah, Quarterly West, 317 Olpin Union, Salt Lake City, UT 84112. TEL 801-581-3938. Ed. L. Williams. adv.; bk.rev. circ. 1,000. (back issues avail.) Indexed: A.I.P.P., Amer.Hum.Ind., Ind.Amer.Per.Verse. **Document type:** academic/scholarly publication.

800   US   ISSN 0737-3759
F1051
QUEBEC STUDIES. 1983. s-a. $30 to individuals; institutions $40. American Council for Quebec Studies, c/o Karen Gould, Ed., Department of Romance Languages, Bowling Green State University, Bowling Green, OH 43403-0189. TEL 419-372-2667. FAX 419-372-7332. adv.; bk.rev. circ. 800.
—UnCover.
Description: Provides essays on Quebec society and French-Canadian culture.

QUESTION DE. see *PARAPSYCHOLOGY AND OCCULTISM*

800 700   US   ISSN 1041-8385
PN1
QUI PARLE; a journal of literary studies. 1986. s-a. $10 to individuals; institutions $20. University of California, Berkeley, Doreen B. Townsend Center for the Humanities, 460 Stephens Hall, Berkeley, CA 94720. TEL 510-643-9670. FAX 510-643-8245. adv.; bk.rev. circ. 1,000. (back issues avail.) **Document type:** academic/scholarly publication.
—BLDSC (7216.385900); UnCover.
Description: Interdisciplinary journal of contemporary literary theory and criticism.

QUICKBORN; Zeitschrift fuer plattdeutsche Sprache und Dichtung. see *LINGUISTICS*

830   GW
QUICKBORN BUECHER. (Text in German and Low-German (Plattdeutsch)) 1913. a. free to members. Quickborn Vereinigung fuer Niederdeutsche Sprache und Literatur e.V., Alexanderstr. 16, 20099 Hamburg, Germany. TEL 040-240809. adv.; bk.rev. circ. 3,000.

860   SP   ISSN 0211-3325
PN778
QUIMERA. 1980. m. 5000 ptas. (Europe 5500 ptas.; America $60). Montesinos Editor, S.A., Maignon, 26, 3o, 08024 Barcelona, Spain. TEL 93-210-69-06. Ed. Miguel Riera. adv.; bk.rev.; circ. 21,500 (controlled).
—SWETS.
Description: Contains interviews with writers and general articles about literature.

QUINQUEREME; new studies in modern languages. see *LINGUISTICS*

840   FR   ISSN 0048-6493
AP20
QUINZAINE LITTERAIRE. 1966. fortn. 425 F. (foreign 560 F.). S E L I S la Quinzaine Litteraire, 43, rue du Temple, 75004 Paris, France. TEL 48-87-48-58. FAX 48-87-13-01. Ed. Maurice Nadeau. circ. 40,000. (also avail. in microform from UMI; reprint service avail. from UMI) Indexed: Arts & Hum.Cit.Ind., Curr.Cont., M.L.A.
—BLDSC (7218.180000); Faxon; SWETS; UMI.

808 891.82   CI   ISSN 0352-7654
QUORUM; literary journal. (Text in Croatian, English, Serbian) 1986. bi-m. $40. Savez Omladine Hrvatske, Republicki Savjet, Franza Mehringa 14, 41000 Zagreb, Croatia. TEL 041-51-46-79. Ed. Miroslav Micanovic. adv.; bk.rev.; film rev. circ. 2,000.

800   GW   ISSN 0723-0338
PR13
R E A L. YEARBOOK. (Research in English and American Literature) (Text in English) 1982. a. DM.178. Gunter Narr Verlag, Postfach 2567, 72015 Tuebingen, Germany. TEL 07071-78091. FAX 07071-75288. Ed.Bd. adv.; bibl. circ. 800. (back issues avail.) **Document type:** academic/scholarly publication.
—BLDSC (9416.150000); UnCover.

R I F NEWSLETTER. (Reading Is Fundamental, Inc.) see *EDUCATION*

R I S D VOICE. (Rhode Island School of Design) see *ART*

830 920   GW   ISSN 0075-2371
PT2451.Z5
RAABE-GESELLSCHAFT. JAHRBUCH. 1960. a. DM.88. Max Niemeyer Verlag, Postfach 2140, 72011 Tuebingen, Germany. TEL 07071-98940. FAX 07071-989450. Eds. Josef Daum, Hans-Juergen Schrader. bk.rev. circ. 1,000. (reprint service avail. from SWZ) **Document type:** academic/scholarly publication.

800   US   ISSN 0731-4817
PN2
RACKHAM JOURNAL OF THE ARTS AND HUMANITIES. (Text in English, French, German) 1971. a. $4 to individuals; institutions $5. University of Michigan, 411 Mason Hall, Ann Arbor, MI 48109. TEL 313-763-2351. Eds. Thomas Mussio, Mary Lacey. adv. circ. 300. Indexed: Abstr.Engl.Stud., Amer.Hum.Ind., M.L.A.
Formerly: Rackham Literary Studies (ISSN 0360-7887)

RADAR - SEI; rivista mensile di attualita-arte-cultura. see *ART*

810   CN   ISSN 0826-5909
PN771 db .R33
RADDLE MOON. 1978. 2/yr. Can.$12($12) to individuals; institutions Can.$18 (foreign US$18). Raddle Moon Press, 9060 Ardmore Dr., Sidney, BC V8L 3S1, Canada. FAX 604-732-7367. Ed.Bd. adv.; bk.rev.; illus. circ. 700.
Supersedes (in 1984): From an Island (ISSN 0706-8093); Formerly: Introductions from an Island (ISSN 0318-3270)
Description: Publishes post-language-centered and new lyric poetry, open texts and poetics; essays (personal, literary and critical); forums on various topics of current concern, photographs and image-text works.

RADICAL PHILOSOPHY REVIEW OF BOOKS. see *PHILOSOPHY*

891.7   KR   ISSN 0131-8136
RADUGA. 1927. m. 20.40 Rub. (Spilka Pys'mennykiv Ukrainy) Vydavnytstvo Radyanskii Pismennik, Chkalova, 52, Kiev, Ukraine. Ed. A.P. Rogatchenko. bk.rev.; film rev.; play rev.; bibl.; illus. circ. 30,000. (also avail. in microfiche from IDC) Indexed: M.L.A.

RAGIONI CRITICHE; rivista di studi linguistici e letterari. see *LINGUISTICS*

860   BO
RAIZ; revista literaria pedagogica. 1989. m? Bs.3 per no. Casilla 3328, La Paz, Bolivia. TEL 310217. Dir. Jaime Choque Mata.

LITERATURE

820 420 · II · ISSN 0448-1690
PR1
RAJASTHAN UNIVERSITY STUDIES IN ENGLISH. (Text in English) 1963. a. $6. University of Rajasthan, Department of English, Gandhi Nagar, Jaipur 302004, India. Ed. Jasbir Jain. bk.rev. circ. 250. **Indexed:** M.L.A.

800 · US
RAMBUNCTIOUS REVIEW. 1984. a. $10 for 3 nos. Rambunctious Press, Inc., 1221 W. Pratt Blvd., Chicago, IL 60626. Ed.Bd. circ. 300. (back issues avail.)

830 · AU
DIE RAMPE (LINZ). 1975. s-a. S.80. Amt der Oberoesterreich Landesregierung, Kulturabteilung, Spittelwiese 4, A-4010 Linz, Austria. Ed.Bd. adv.; bk.rev. circ. 2,000. **Document type:** government publication.

RAMPIKE MAGAZINE. see ART

RAM'S HORN. see LINGUISTICS

800 · US · ISSN 0275-1607
AS30
RARITAN; a quarterly review. 1981. q. $16 to individuals; institutions $20. Rutgers University, 31 Mine St., New Brunswick, NJ 08903. TEL 908-932-7887. FAX 908-932-7855. Ed. Richard Poirier. adv. contact: Ellen Chafee. bk.rev. circ. 3,500. (also avail. in microform from UMI) **Indexed:** Abstr.Engl.Stud., Amer.Hum.Ind., Arts & Hum.Cit.Ind., Film Lit.Ind. (1989-), Hum.Ind., M.L.A. **Document type:** academic/scholarly publication.
—BLDSC (7291.875000); Faxon; UnCover; UMI.
   Description: Interdisciplinary journal publishing critical writing on literature, film, art, philosophy and anthropology.

850 · IT · ISSN 0033-9423
PQ4001
RASSEGNA DELLA LETTERATURA ITALIANA. 1893. q. L.210000. Casa Ed. Le Lettere, Costa S. Giorgio 28, Florence, Italy. (Dist. by: Licosa, Via Duca di Calabria 1-1, Florence, Italy) Ed. Walter Binni. adv.; bk.rev.; abstr.; bibl.; index. circ. 1,000. **Indexed:** Arts & Hum.Cit.Ind., Can.Rev.Comp.Lit., Curr.Cont., M.L.A.
—Faxon; SWETS.

RASSEGNA MENSILE DI ISRAEL. see RELIGIONS AND THEOLOGY — Judaic

RASSEGNA SOVIETICA; rivista bimestrale di cultura. see ART

800 · RU · ISSN 0235-4241
RASSKAZ. 1978. a. Izdatel'stvo Sovremennik, Horoshevskaya, 62, Moscow 123007, Russia. TEL 941-40-08.
   Description: Presents a collection of the best stories published in the Soviet literary magazines during previous year.

800 · NE
RASTER. 1977. q. fl.95. Uitgeverij De Bezige Bij, Van Miereveldstraat 1, 1071 DW Amsterdam, Netherlands. TEL 020-73-67-31. FAX 020-76-19-48. Ed.Bd. circ. 900.

890 · PK
RAVI. (Issued in 3 parts) (Text in English, Panjabi or Urdu) 1906. a. price varies. Government College, Lahore, Pakistan.

891.4 · XN · ISSN 0034-0227
RAZGLEDI; spisanie za literatura, umetnost i kultura. (Text in Macedonian) 1958. m. 300 din. Ul. Ivo Ribar-Lola 66, Box 345, 91000 Skopje, Macedonia. Ed. Danilo Kocevski. circ. 1,000. **Indexed:** M.L.A.

800 001.3 700 · XN · ISSN 0351-3769
RAZVITOK. (Text in Macedonian) 1963. m. 1600 din.($4) R.O. B.ID. "Mistirkov", Koment Ohridski bb, Bitola, Macedonia. TEL 22-951-097.

800 · US · ISSN 0094-5943
THE READER'S ADVISER; a layman's guide to literature. (In 6 vols.; Vol. 1: The Best in American and British Fiction, Poetry, Essays, Literary Biography, Bibliography, and Reference; Vol. 2: The Best in American and British Drama and World Literature in English Translation; Vol. 3: The Best in General Reference Literature, the Social Sciences, History, and the Arts; Vol. 4: The Best in the Literature of Philosophy and World Religions; Vol. 5: The Best in the Literature of Science, Technology, and Medicine; Vol. 6: Indexes) 1927. irreg., 14th ed., 1993. $500 for 6-vol. set; $110 per vol. R.R. Bowker, A Reed Reference Publishing Company, Part of the Reed Elsevier group, 121 Chanlon Rd., New Providence, NJ 07974. TEL 908-464-6800. FAX 908-555-6688. TELEX 138 755. (Subscr. to: Order Dept., Box 31, New Providence, NJ 07974-9903. TEL 800-521-8110) **Document type:** consumer publication, directory.
   Description: Profiles authors, annotated bibliographies (with prices) of selected in-print works by and about them.

800 · UK · ISSN 0963-472X
READING AIDS. 1988. s-a. West & Wilde Bookshop, 25A Dundas St., Edinburgh EH3 6QQ, Scotland. TEL 031-556-0079. FAX 031-558-3717. Ed. Robert Orr. bk.rev. circ. 5,000. (back issues avail.) **Document type:** bibliography.

809 · AT · ISSN 0155-218X
READING TIME. 1957. q. Aus.$28 (foreign Aus.$38). Children's Book Council of Australia, P.O. Box 62, Ashmont, Wagga Wagga, N.S.W. 2650, Australia. FAX 069-25-4907. Ed. John Cohen. adv.; bk.rev.; index. circ. 2,400. **Indexed:** Aus.P.A.I.S., Child.Lit.Abstr., Gdlns.
—BLDSC (7301.430000).

500 700 800 · SP · ISSN 0034-060X
AS302
REAL ACADEMIA DE CORDOBA DE CIENCIAS, BELLAS LETRAS Y NOBLES ARTES. BOLETIN. 1922. a. 200 ptas. Real Academia de Cordoba de Ciencias, Bellas Letras y Nobles Artes, Ambrosia de Morales 9, Cordoba, Spain. bk.rev.; abstr.; charts; illus.; upd. 3 91130. circ. 500. **Indexed:** Amer.Hist.& Life, Hist.Abstr.

800 · SP
REAL ACADEMIA SEVILLANA DE BUENAS LETRAS. BOLETIN. irreg., latest no.18. price varies. Universidad de Sevilla, Servicio de Publicaciones, Valparaiso 5, 41013 Seville, Spain. TEL 954-2319581. FAX 954-232245.

800 · US
REAL FICTION. 1982. 2/yr. $15 to individuals; institutions $25. 298 9th Ave., San Francisco, CA 94118. Ed. Genevieve Belfiglio. adv. circ. 200.

820 · CN
REAPPRAISALS; Canadian writers. 1974. irreg. University of Ottawa Press, 542 King Edward, Ottawa, ON K1N 6N5, Canada. TEL 613-564-2270. FAX 613-564-9284. Ed. John Moss.
   Description: Articles on Canadian authors or on related topics in English-Canadian literature.

300 · FR · ISSN 0557-6989
E169.1
RECHERCHES ANGLAISES ET AMERICAINES. a. 75 F. Universite de Strasbourg II, Service des Periodiques, 22 rue Descartes, 67084 Strasbourg, France. Ed. A. Bleikasten. **Indexed:** Abstr.Engl.Stud., M.L.A.
—BLDSC (7307.966000).
   Description: Covers English and American culture, literature, and art.

830 430 · FR · ISSN 0399-1989
DD61
RECHERCHES GERMANIQUES. (Text in French, German) 1971. a. price varies. Universite de Strasbourg II, 22 rue Descartes, 67084 Strasbourg, France. Ed. G.L. Fink. bibl. circ. 800. (back issues avail.) **Indexed:** M.L.A.
—SWETS.
   Description: Covers research in German culture and literature.

860 869 791.43 · FR
RECHERCHES IBERIQUES ET CINEMATOGRAPHIQUES. 1960. 2/yr. 119 F. (foreign 139 F.). Universite de Strasbourg II, Institut d'Etudes Iberiques, 25 rue du Marechal Juin, 67084 Strasbourg Cedex, France. TEL 88-36-51-47. Eds. Duarte Mimoso-Ruiz, Jean-Pierre Prevost.
   Former titles: Recherches Iberiques Strasbourg II (ISSN 0755-2807) & Universite de Strasbourg. Institut d'Etudes Latino-Americaines. Travaux.

800 · FR · ISSN 0769-0886
PQ1979
RECHERCHES SUR DIDEROT ET SUR L'ENCYCLOPEDIE. 1986. s-a. 180 F. to members (foreign 220 F.); institutions 250 F. Societe Diderot, 7, Route de la Reine, 92100 Boulogne, France. (Subscr. to: Klincksieck, 8 rue de la Sorbonne, 75005 Paris, France. TEL 43-54-59-53. FAX 43-25-25-53) Ed. Anne-Marie Chouillet. adv.; bk.rev.; illus.

RECORDER (SEARCY). see EDUCATION — Higher Education

RECORDS OF EARLY ENGLISH DRAMA NEWSLETTER. see THEATER

800 · US · ISSN 0300-6425
PN2
RECOVERING LITERATURE; a journal of contextualist criticism. 1972. irreg. (1-3/yr.). $6. Box 805, Alpine, CA 91903. TEL 619-659-0291. Ed. Gerald J. Butler. adv.; bk.rev. circ. 250. (back issues avail.) **Indexed:** Abstr.Engl.Stud. **Document type:** academic/scholarly publication.
—UnCover.

RED BASS. see LITERARY AND POLITICAL REVIEWS

810 · US
RED WEATHER;* poems, translations, essays, reviews. irreg. (approx. 4/yr.). $2.50 per no. c/o Bruce Taylor, 448 W. Grand Ave., Eau Claire, WI 54703-5330. bk.rev. circ. 400.

810 · US · ISSN 0887-5715
REDNECK REVIEW. Variant title: Redneck Review of Literature. 1975. 2/yr. $15 (typically set in Spring). 1326 W. Sheridan Ct., Milwaukee, WI 53209. TEL 414-332-6881. Ed. Penelope Reedy. adv.; bk.rev. circ. 500. **Indexed:** Amer.Hum.Ind.
—UnCover.
   Description: Presents and explores the contemporary literature of the American West. Includes essays, poetry, fiction.

830 · GW · ISSN 0138-340X
PN4
REFERATEDIENST ZUR LITERATURWISSENSCHAFT. 1969. a. DM.48. Foerderungsgesellschaft Wissenschaftliche Neuvorhaben mbH, Forschungsschwerpunkt Literaturwissenschaft, Prenzlauer Promenade 149-152, 13189 Berlin, Germany. TEL 030-4797191. FAX 030-4722023. Ed.Bd. **Document type:** academic/scholarly publication.

860 · AG
REFERENTE; el ojo que mira. 1981. q. Ediciones La Tabla de Esmeralda, Pena 2141, Buenos Aires, Argentina. Ed.Bd.

800 745.1 · US
REFLECT. 1979-1987; resumed 1988. q. $8. 3306 Argonne Ave., Norfolk, VA 23509. TEL 804-857-1097. Ed. William S. Kennedy. adv.; bk.rev. circ. 100.
   Description: Specializes in spiral mode poetry, featuring euphony mysticism and succinct impersonal writing.

811 · US · ISSN 0484-2650
REFLECTION (SPOKANE); Gonzaga's literary magazine. 1960. a. free. Gonzaga University, Spokane, WA 99258. TEL 509-328-4220. FAX 509-484-2818. circ. 800.
   Description: Contains literary pieces (prose and poetry) contributed by both faculty and students.

830 430 375.4 · GW · ISSN 0171-7170
REGENSBURGER BEITRAEGE ZUR DEUTSCHEN SPRACH- UND LITERATURWISSENSCHAFT. REIHE A: QUELLEN. irreg. Peter Lang GmbH Europaeischer Verlag der Wissenschaften, Eschborner Landstr. 42-50, 60489 Frankfurt a.M., Germany. TEL 069-7807050. FAX 069-785893. Ed. Bernhard Gajek. **Document type:** monographic series.

LITERATURE

830 430   **GW**
REGENSBURGER BEITRAEGE ZUR DEUTSCHEN SPRACH- UND LITERATURWISSENSCHAFT. REIHE B: UNTERSUCHUNGEN. irreg., no.56, 1993. Peter Lang GmbH Europaeischer Verlag der Wissenschaften, Eschborner Landstr. 42-50, 60489 Frankfurt a.M., Germany. TEL 069-7807050. FAX 069-785893. Ed. Bernhard Gajek. **Document type:** monographic series.

DER REGGEBOGE/RAINBOW. see *ETHNIC INTERESTS*

894   **HU**   **ISSN 0C80-0570**
REGI MAGYAR PROZAI EMLEKEK. (Text in Hungarian; occasional summaries in German) 1968. irreg. price varies. (Magyar Tudomanyos Akademia) Akademiai Kiado, Publishing House of the Hungarian Academy of Sciences, Box 245, H-1519 Budapest, Hungary. TEL 181-2134. FAX 166-6466. TELEX 22-6228 AKNYO H.

800   **UK**   **ISSN 0757-8237**
REIMPRESSION. 1984. irreg., latest vol.9. Gordon & Breach Science Publishers, P.O. Box 90, Reading, Berkshire RG1 8JL, England. TEL 0734-560080. FAX 0734-568211. TELEX 849870 SCIPUB G. (U.S. addr.: 820 Town Center Dr., Langhorne, PA 19047. TEL 215-750-2642. FAX 215-750-6343) Ed.Bd. **Document type:** monographic series.
Refereed Serial

809.915   **NE**   **ISSN 0925-4757**
PN690.A6
REINARDUS. 1988. a. fl.110($63) (effective 1994). (International Reynard Society) John Benjamins Publishing Co., Amsteldijk 44, P.O. Box 75577, 1070 AN Amsterdam, Netherlands. TEL 31-20-6738156. FAX 31-20-6792956. (In N. America: 821 Bethlehem Pike, Philadelphia, PA 19118. TEL 215-836-1200. FAX 215-836-1204) Eds. Brian Levy, Paul Wackers. (back issues avail.) **Document type:** academic/scholarly publication, monographic series.
Description: Promotes comparative research in the fields of mediaeval comic, satirical, didatic, and allegorical literature, with emphasis on the beast epic, fable and fabliau, including later developments into the modern era.

810   **US**
RELIGION AND LITERATURE. 1957; N.S. vol.8, 1972. 3/yr. $20 to individuals; libraries $25. University of Notre Dame, Department of English, Notre Dame, IN 46556. TEL 219-239-5725. Eds. James Dougherty, Thomas Werge. adv.; bk.rev.; bibl. circ. 500. (processed; also avail. in microform from UMI; back issues avail.) **Indexed:** Abstr.Engl.Stuc., Amer.Hum.Ind., Arts & Hum.Cit.Ind., Cath.Ind., CERDIC, Curr.Cont., M.L.A., Rel.& Theol.Abstr. (1983-), Rel.Ind.One.
—BLDSC (7356.439500); UnCover.
Formerly: Notre Dame English Journal (ISSN 0029-4500)

800 909   **CN**   **ISSN 0034-429X**
CB359
RENAISSANCE AND REFORMATION/RENAISSANCE ET REFORME. (Text in English, French) 1964. q. Can.$28 to individuals; institutions Can.$37. (Canadian Society for Renaissance Studies, Centre for Reformation and Renaissance Studies) University of Guelph, Department of French Studies, Guelph, ON N1G 2W1, Canada. TEL 519-824-4120. FAX 519-763-9572. Ed. Francois Pare. bk.rev.; index. circ. 700. (processed; reprint service avail. from ISI) **Indexed:** Amer.Hist.& Life, Arts & Hum.Cit.Ind., Bk.Rev.Ind. (1980-), Can.Rev.Comp.Lit., Child.Bk.Rev.Ind. (1980-), Curr.Cont., Hist.Abstr., Ind.Bk.Rev.Hum., M.L.A.
—BLDSC (7356.865100); Faxon; UnCover; SWETS.
Description: Multidisciplinary journal on all aspects of the Renaissance, including history, literature, art, music, philosophy, history of science.

RENAISSANCE DRAMA. see *THEATER*

800   **US**
RENAISSANCE PAPERS. 1954. a. $20. Southeastern Renaissance Conference, Box 8105, English Dept., NCSU, Raleigh, NC 27695-8105. TEL 919-737-3866. Eds. Barbara J. Baines, George W. Williams. circ. 500. **Document type:** academic/scholarly publication.

800   **US**   **ISSN 0034-4338**
CB361
RENAISSANCE QUARTERLY. 1954. q. $50 to individuals; institutions $65. Renaissance Society of America, 24 W. 12th St., New York, NY 10011-8604. TEL 212-998-3797. FAX 212-995-4205. Ed.Bd. adv.; bk.rev.; bibl.; illus.; index. circ. 3,000. (also avail. in microform from UMI,KTO; back issues avail; reprint service avail. from KTO) **Indexed:** Abstr.Engl.Stud., Amer.Hist.& Life, Arts & Hum.Cit.Ind., Bk.Rev.Ind. (1980-), Child.Bk.Rev.Ind. (1980-), Curr.Cont., Hist.Abstr., Hum.Ind., Ind.Bk.Rev.Hum., M.L.A., RILA. **Document type:** academic/scholarly publication.
—BLDSC (7356.866000); Faxon; UnCover; SWETS; UMI.
Incorporates: Studies in the Renaissance (ISSN 0081-8658); **Formerly:** Renaissance News.

809   **US**   **ISSN 0034-4346**
PN2
RENASCENCE; essays on values in literature. 1948. q. $20 (foreign $23). Marquette University Press, Coughlin Hall 132, Milwaukee, WI 53233. TEL 414-288-1564. Ed. Andrew Tallon. adv.; bk.rev.; index. circ. 825. (also avail. in microform from UMI; back issues avail.; reprint service avail. from UMI) **Indexed:** Abstr.Engl.Stud., Cath.Ind., Curr.Cont., Hum.Ind., LCR, M.L.A. **Document type:** academic/scholarly publication.
—BLDSC (7356.883000); Faxon; UnCover; UMI.
Description: Concerned with the study of values in literature.

895.1   **CC**   **ISSN 0258-8218**
RENMIN WENXUE/PEOPLE'S LITERATURE. (Text in Chinese) 1950. m. Y23.40($71.10) Zuojia Chubanshe, 10, Nongzhangnan Nanli, Beijing 100026, People's Republic of China. TEL 500-3120. (Dist. outside China by: China International Book Trading Corp., P.O. Box 399, Beijing, P.R.C.; Dist. in US by: China Books & Periodicals, Inc., 2929 24th St., San Francisco, CA 94110. TEL 415-282-2994) Ed. Liu Xinwur.
Description: Contains short stories, essays, poetry. Includes children's literature.

810   **US**   **ISSN 1052-5769**
RENOVATED LIGHTHOUSE; literary magazine. 1986. irreg. $16 for 4 issues (effective 1994). Renovated Lighthouse Publications, Box 340251, Columbus, OH 43234-0251. TEL 614-326-2009. Ed. R. Allen Dodson. circ. 125. (back issues avail.)
Description: Publishes at the cutting edge of modern literary fiction, poetry and art.

860   **CR**   **ISSN 0252-8479**
REPERTORIO AMERICANO. 1974. a. Col.30($8) Universidad Nacional, Instituto de Estudios Latinoamericanos, Apdo. 86, 3000 Heredia, Costa Rica. Ed. Julian Gonzalez. adv.; bk.rev.; bibl.; illus.; cum.index: vols.1-5. circ. 1,000. (tabloid format) **Indexed:** Hisp.Amer.Per.Ind. **Document type:** academic/scholarly publication.

THE REPORT (EUGENE); a fiction writer's magazine. see *LITERATURE — Science Fiction, Fantasy, Horror*

896   **US**   **ISSN 0034-5210**
PL8010
RESEARCH IN AFRICAN LITERATURES. 1970. q. $30 to individuals; institutions $55. Indiana University Press, 601 N. Morton St., Bloomington, IN 47404. TEL 812-855-9449. Ed. Abiola Irele. adv.; bk.rev.; bibl.; charts; illus.; stat.; index. circ. 670. (also avail. in microform from KTO,UMI; reprint service avail. from UMI) **Indexed:** Abstr.Engl.Stud., Anthropol.Lit., Arts & Hum.Cit.Ind., Bibl.Ling., Curr.Cont.Africa, Curr.Cont., Documentatieblad, Hum.Ind., Ind.Bk.Rev.Hum., Lang.& Lang.Behav.Abstr., M.L.A., Sociol.Abstr. **Document type:** academic/scholarly publication.
—BLDSC (7714.380000); Faxon; UnCover; SWETS; UMI.
Description: Features historical, biographical, and theoretical studies of the written and oral literatures of Africa.

RESEARCH IN YORUBA: LANGUAGE & LITERATURE; language and literature. see *LINGUISTICS*

792   **US**   **ISSN 0098-647X**
PR621
RESEARCH OPPORTUNITIES IN RENAISSANCE DRAMA. 1956. a. $6 to individuals; institutions $10. c/o David M. Bergeron, Ed., Department of English, University of Kansas, Lawrence, KS 66045. TEL 913-864-4798. adv.; bk.rev.; play rev.; bibl.; illus. circ. 1,700. **Indexed:** M.L.A. **Document type:** academic/scholarly publication.

RESENA DE LITERATURA, ARTE Y ESPECTACULOS. see *ART*

800   **US**   **ISSN 0048-7384**
RESOURCES FOR AMERICAN LITERARY STUDY. 1972. s-a. $23 to individuals (foreign $27); institutions $30 (foreign $35). Pennsylvania State University Press, Barbara Bldg., Ste. C, 820 N. University Dr., University Park, PA 16802-1003. TEL 814-865-1327. FAX 814-863-1408. Eds. Jackson R. Bryer, Robert Secor. adv.; bk.rev. circ. 600. (also avail. in microform from UMI; back issues avail.; reprint service avail. from UMI) **Document type:** academic/scholarly publication.
—Faxon; UnCover. **CCC**.
Description: Publishes extended reviews of primary documents and research tools for American literary study, including bibliographies, biographies, concordances and other reference works.
Refereed Serial

801 055   **IT**
RESPONSABILITA DEL SAPERE. 1947. s-a. $16. Via G. Carini, 24-28, Rome, Italy. Ed. G. Arcidiacono. bk.rev.

RESPONSE (NEW YORK, 1967); a contemporary Jewish review. see *ETHNIC INTERESTS*

RESPUBLICA LITERARIA NEERLANDICA. see *HISTORY — History Of Europe*

820   **US**   **ISSN 0162-9905**
PR437
RESTORATION: STUDIES IN ENGLISH LITERARY CULTURE, 1660-1700. 1977. s-a. $10 for 6 issues (foreign $20). James Madison University, College of Letters and Sciences, Harrisonburg, VA 22807. TEL 703-568-6261. FAX 703-568-3581. Ed. J.M. Armistead. adv.: B&W page $150; trim 6 x 9. bibl. circ. 500. (back issues avail.) **Indexed:** M.L.A.
—BLDSC (7777.815000); Faxon; UnCover.
Description: Scholarly articles on literature and contexts, annotated bibliography, and announcements.
Refereed Serial

809 420 375.4   **US**   **ISSN 0190-3233**
PR1
REVIEW (CHARLOTTESVILLE). 1979. a. $30. (Virginia Polytechnic Institute and State University) University Press of Virginia, Box 3608 University Sta., Charlottesville, VA 22903. TEL 804-924-3468. FAX 804-982-2655. (Co-sponsor: Pennsylvania State University) Eds. James O. Hoge, James L.W. West III. circ. 1,500. **Document type:** academic/scholarly publication.
Description: Reviews and essays of greater length than in most scholarly journals.

809   **US**   **ISSN 0890-5762**
F1401
REVIEW: LATIN AMERICAN LITERATURE AND ARTS. 1968-1982; resumed 1984. 2/yr. $16 to individuals; institutions $25 (foreign $28). Americas Society, 680 Park Ave., New York, NY 10021. TEL 212-249-8950. FAX 212-517-6247. Ed. Alfred J. MacAdam. adv.: B&W page $700. bk.rev.; film rev.; play rev.; illus. circ. 5,000. (also avail. in microfiche from UMI; back issues avail.) **Indexed:** M.L.A.
—UnCover.
Description: Work in English translation by and about leading Latin American writers as well as articles on Latin American visual and performing arts.

LITERATURE

800 US ISSN 0276-0045
PN3503
REVIEW OF CONTEMPORARY FICTION. 1981. 3/yr. $17 to individuals; institutions $24. Review of Contemporary Fiction, Inc., 4241 Illinois State University, Normal, IL 61790-4241. TEL 309-438-7555. FAX 309-437-7422. Ed. Steven Moore. adv.; bk.rev.; index. circ. 2,780. (also avail. in microform from UMI; back issues avail.) **Indexed:** Amer.Hum.Ind., Bk.Rev.Ind. (1986-), Child.Bk.Rev.Ind. (1986-), LCR, M.L.A. **Document type:** academic/scholarly publication.
—BLDSC (7789.080000); Faxon; UnCover; UMI. **CCC.**
Description: Each issue devoted to one or two significant (but often neglected) contemporary novelists.

820 UK ISSN 0034-6551
PR1
REVIEW OF ENGLISH STUDIES; a quarterly journal of English literature and the English language. 1925; N.S. 1950. q. £62($117) (effective 1994). Oxford University Press, Oxford Journals, Walton St., Oxford OX2 6DP, England. TEL 0865-56767. FAX 0865-56646. TELEX 8373300-OXPRES-G. (U.S. subscr. to: Oxford University Press Inc., 2001 Evans Rd., Cary, NC 27513. TEL 919-677-0977) Ed. R.E. Alton. adv. contact: Jane Parker. bk.rev.; bibl.; index. circ. 2,150. (also avail. in microform from UMI) **Indexed:** Abstr.Engl.Stud., Acad.Ind., Arts & Hum.Cit.Ind., Bibl.Ling., Bk.Rev.Ind. (1965-), Br.Hum.Ind., Child.Bk.Rev.Ind. (1965-), Curr.Cont., Hum.Ind., Ind.Bk.Rev.Hum., Lang.& Lang.Behav.Abstr.
—BLDSC (7790.520000); Faxon; UnCover; SWETS; UMI. **CCC.**
Description: Presents English literature and the English language from the earliest period up to the present day.

800 US ISSN 0034-6640
PN2
REVIEW OF NATIONAL LITERATURES. 1970. a. membership (includes C N L - World Report). Council on National Literatures, Box 81, Whitestone, NY 11357. TEL 718-767-8380. Ed. Anne Paolucci. adv.; bk.rev.; abstr.; bibl. circ. 1,200. (back issues avail.) **Indexed:** Abstr.Engl.Stud., Arts & Hum.Cit.Ind., Curr.Cont., M.L.A., Mid.East: Abstr.& Ind.
—BLDSC (7793.520000); UnCover.

REVISTA AWRAQ. see HISTORY — History Of Europe

869 BL ISSN 0486-6460
PQ9212
REVISTA CAMONIANA. 1964-1971; N.S. 1978. biennial. $10. Universidade de Sao Paulo "Armando de Salles Oliveira", Centro de Estudos Portugueses, Cidade Universitaria, C.P. 8105, 05508 Cidade Universitaria, Sao Paulo, Brazil. Ed. Maria H. Ribeiro da Cunha. bk.rev.; bibl.; illus. circ. 2,000.

700 BL ISSN 0034-7353
REVISTA CAMPINENSE DE CULTURA.* vol.3, 1966. q. Comissao Cultural do Municipio Prefeitura, Municipal de Campina Grande, Paraiba, Brazil. Ed. Elpidio De Almeida. bk.rev.

REVISTA CANARIA DE ESTUDIOS INGLESES. see LINGUISTICS

860 CU ISSN 0008-7157
PN6
REVISTA CASA DE LAS AMERICAS. q. $18 in S. America; N. America $22; elsewhere $30. 3ra y G, Vedado, Habana 10400, Cuba. (Dist. by: Ediciones Cubanas, Obispo No. 526, Apdo. 605, Havana, Cuba; U.S. and Canada subscr. to: Publications Exchange Inc., 8306 Mills Dr., Ste. 241, Miami, FL 33183. TEL 305-256-0162) bk.rev.; play rev.; illus. **Indexed:** Amer.Hist.& Life, Hisp.Amer.Per.Ind., Hist.Abstr., M.L.A.
Description: Contains letters and ideas, articles, essays, fiction, poetry, literary criticism, interviews, art criticism and cultural news from the Latin American and Caribbean countries.

860 SP ISSN 0378-200X
REVISTA CASTILLA. 1980. irreg., vol.16, 1993. 2000 ptas. Universidad de Valladolid, Secretariado de Publicaciones, Departamento de Literatura Espanola, C. Juan Mambrilla, 14, 47003 Valladolid, Spain. TEL 983-423000. FAX 34-83-290300. TELEX 26357. **Document type:** monographic series, academic/scholarly publication.

800 CL ISSN 0048-7651
PQ7900
REVISTA CHILENA DE LITERATURA. 1970. 2/yr. $40. Universidad de Chile, Departamento de Literatura, Casilla 10136, Santiago, Chile. TEL 2725978. FAX 271-68-23. Ed. Hugo Montes. bk.rev.; bibl. circ. 1,000. **Indexed:** Arts & Hum.Cit.Ind., Curr.Cont., Hisp.Amer.Per.Ind., M.L.A. **Document type:** academic/scholarly publication.
Formerly: Facultad de Filosofia y Humanidades. Boletin.

REVISTA CULTULUI MOZAIC/REVIEW OF THE MOSAIC CREED. see RELIGIONS AND THEOLOGY — Judaic

860 US ISSN 0252-8843
PQ7081.A1
REVISTA DE CRITICA LITERARIA LATINOAMERICANA. (Text in Portuguese, Spanish) 1975. s-a. $35. Latinoamericana Editores, 1309 C.L., University of California, Department of Spanish and Portuguese, Berkeley, CA 94720. TEL 510-883-9443. FAX 510-883-9443. Dir. Antonio Cornejo Polar. adv.; bk.rev.; bibl. circ. 1,225. (back issues avail.) **Indexed:** Arts & Hum.Cit.Ind., Chic.Per.Ind., Curr.Cont., Hisp.Amer.Per.Ind., M.L.A. **Document type:** academic/scholarly publication.
—Faxon.

REVISTA DE ESTUDIOS COLOMBIANOS. see HISTORY — History Of North And South America

860 460 US ISSN 0034-818X
REVISTA DE ESTUDIOS HISPANICOS. (Text in English, Spanish) 1967. 3/yr. $21 to individuals; institutions $28.50 (foreign $30); students $17 (typically set in Aug.). Washington University, One Brookings Dr., St. Louis, MO 63130-4899. TEL 314-935-5175. FAX 314-726-3494. Ed. Michael Mudrovic. adv.; bk.rev.; bibl. circ. 600. (also avail. in microform from UMI; back issues avail.; reprint service avail. from UMI) **Indexed:** Arts & Hum.Cit.Ind., Curr.Cont., Ind.Bk.Rev.Hum., M.L.A.
—BLDSC (7854.507000); Faxon; UnCover; UMI. **CCC.**
Description: Articles and reviews of books dealing with the literature of Spain and Latin America.

REVISTA DE FILOLOGIA. see LINGUISTICS

809 RM ISSN 0034-8392
PN9
REVISTA DE ISTORIE SI TEORIE LITERARA. (Text in Rumanian; summaries in English, French, German and Russian) 1952. q. 150 lei to individuals; institutions 300 lei. Academia Romana, Institutul de Istorie si Teorie Literara G. Calinescu, Bd. Schitu Magureanu 1, 70626 Bucharest, Rumania. TEL 14-78-98. (Dist. by: Orion s.r.l., Splaiul Independentei 202A, 6 Bucharest, Rumania) Ed. Zoe Dumitrescu-Busulenga. bk.rev.; abstr.; bibl.; illus.; index. circ. 1,500. **Indexed:** M.L.A.
Formerly: Studii si Cercetari de Istorie Literara si Folclor.

REVISTA DE LENGUA Y LITERATURA CATALANA, GALLEGA Y VASCA. see LINGUISTICS

869 BL ISSN 0101-3505
P1.A1 CODEN: RLETD6
REVISTA DE LETRAS. (Text in Portuguese; summaries in English and Portuguese) 1959-1977; resumed 1980. a. $30 or exchange basis. Universidade Estadual Paulista, Av. Vicente Ferreira 1278, Caixa Posta 603, 17515-901 Marilia SP, Brazil. TEL 0144-33-1844. FAX 0144-22-2504. TELEX 111 9016 UJME BR. bk.rev.; bibl. circ. 1,000. **Indexed:** Hisp.Amer.Per.Ind., Lang.& Lang.Behav.Abstr., M.L.A., Sociol.Abstr.
—BLDSC (7863.605000).
Description: Studies in Brazilian literature.

860 100 SP
REVISTA DE LITERATURA. s-a. 3300 ptas. (foreign 4950 ptas.). Consejo Superior de Investigaciones Cientificas (C.S.I.C.), Instituto de Filologia, Duque de Medinaceli, 6, 28014 Madrid, Spain. Dir. Miguel Angel Garrido.

860 CU ISSN 0138-6948
REVISTA DE LITERATURA CUBANA. 1982. s-a. $14 in S. America; N. America $16; elsewhere $18. (Union de Escritores y Artistas de Cuba (UNEAC)) Ediciones Cubanas, Obispo No. 527, Apdo. 605, Havana, Cuba. Ed.Bd. bk.rev. circ. 10,000.
Description: Presents research and critical studies on authors, works, topics, personages, trends, stages and characteristics of Cuban literature, including bibliographic summaries of literary criticism.

860 VE
REVISTA DE LITERATURA HISPANOAMERICANA. 1971. s-a. $11.20. Universidad de Zulia, Instituto de Investigaciones Literarias, Av. 4 c/c. 74 piso 8, Apdo. Postal 1490, Maracaibo, Venezuela. Dir. Victor Fuenmayor. bk.rev. circ. 1,000.

REVISTA ESTUDIOS; revista trimestral publicada por los fraties de la orden de la merced. see RELIGIONS AND THEOLOGY

860 US ISSN 0034-9593
PQ6001
REVISTA HISPANICA MODERNA; devoted to the study of the literature of Latin America, Portugal and Spain. (Text in English, Portuguese or Spanish) 1934. s-a. $20 to individuals (foreign $25); institutions $30 (foreign $35). Columbia University, Hispanic Institute of the United States, 612 W. 116th St., New York, NY 10027. TEL 212-854-4187. FAX 212-749-0397. Eds. Gonzalo Sobejano, Jaime Alazraki. bk.rev.; charts; illus.; index. circ. 1,200. (also avail. in microform from BHP) **Indexed:** Arts & Hum.Cit.Ind., Curr.Cont., M.L.A. **Document type:** academic/scholarly publication, monographic series.
—Faxon; UnCover; SWETS.

860 US ISSN 0034-9631
PQ7081.A1
REVISTA IBEROAMERICANA. (Text in Portuguese, Spanish) 1938. 4/yr. $40 to individuals (Latin America $25); institutions $60 (Latin America $30). International Institute of Ibero-American Literature - Instituto Internacional de Literature Iberoamericana, 1312 C.L., University of Pittsburgh, Pittsburgh, PA 15260. TEL 412-624-3359. FAX 412-624-8505. Ed. Keith McDuffie. adv.; bk.rev. circ. 1,800. (also avail. in microform from UMI; back issues avail.; reprint service avail. from UMI,KTO) **Indexed:** Arts & Hum.Cit.Ind., Curr.Cont., Hisp.Amer.Per.Ind., M.L.A. **Document type:** academic/scholarly publication.
—Faxon; SWETS; UMI.

869 BL ISSN 0100-0888
PB5
REVISTA LETRAS. 1953. a. exchange only. Universidade Federal do Parana, Setor de Ciencias Humanas, Letras e Artes, Caixa Postal 441, 80001 Curitaba PR, Brazil. TEL 041-264-5545. FAX 041-2642243. TELEX 415100. Ed. Joao Alfredo dal Bello. bk.rev. circ. 700. **Indexed:** M.L.A.

860 AG
▼**REVISTA LITERARIA UNICORNIO;** un caballo con suerte. 1992. bi-m. Arg.$3.50 per no. Unicornio Editor, Vertiz 8852, 7600 Mar del Plata, Argentina. TEL 4-9110. Ed. Carlos Aletto. circ. 7,000. (tabloid format)

400 800 CL ISSN 0035-0451
P9
REVISTA SIGNOS DE VALPARAISO; estudios de lengua y literatura. Variant title: Revista Signos. (Text in Spanish; summaries in English, French and Spanish) 1967. a. $40. (Universidad Catolica de Valparaiso, Instituto de Literatura y Ciencias del Lenguaje) Ediciones Universitarias de Valparaiso, Casilla 1415, Valparaiso, Chile. TEL 032-252900. FAX 032-272746. TELEX 230389 UCVAL CL. Dir. Eduardo Godoy G. bk.rev. circ. 300. **Indexed:** M.L.A. **Document type:** academic/scholarly publication.

800 CU ISSN 0864-1315
REVOLUCION Y CULTURA. 1976. bi-m. $24 in S. America; N. America $26; elsewhere $30. Ministerio de Cultura, Comite Estatal de Colaboracion Economica, Calle 1 No. 201 esq. B Vedado, Havana, Cuba. (Dist. by: Ediciones Cubanas, Obispo No. 527, Apdo. 605, Havana, Cuba) Dir. Romualdo Santos. bk.rev. circ. 20,000. (also avail. in microfilm)

LITERATURE

840 CN ISSN 0839-458X
PQ2625.A716
REVUE ANDRE MALRAUX REVIEW. (Text in English, French) 1969. s-a. Can.$24($24) to individuals; institutions Can.$30($30); foreign Can.$35. c/o Dr. Robert S. Thornberry, Univ. of Alberta, Dept. of Romance Languages, Edmonton, Alta. T6G 2E6, Canada. TEL 403-492-1997. FAX 403-474-8149. (Subscr. to: c/o Prof. Susan McLean McGrath, 615 W. May St., Mount Pleasant, MI 48858) Ed.Bd. bk.rev.; bibl.; cum.index every 3 yrs. circ. 350. **Indexed:** M.L.A.
—UnCover.
Formerly: Melanges Malraux Miscellany (ISSN 0025-892X)
Description: Devoted to all aspects of the life, works and influence of Andre Malraux (1901-1976). Covers aesthetics, psychoanalysis, politics of colonialism, antifascism and anti-Semitism.
Refereed Serial

800 961 US ISSN 0890-6998
PQ3988.N6
REVUE C E L F A N - C E L F A N REVIEW. (Text in English, French) 1981. 3/yr. $7.50 (foreign $10). Center for the Study of the Francophone Literature of North Africa, Department of French and Italian (022-37), Temple University, Philadelphia, PA 19122. TEL 215-787-8529. Ed. Eric Sellin. bk.rev.; bibl.; illus. circ. 200. (back issues avail.)
Description: Scholarly criticism and creative works of French-language literature of North Africa.

860 FR ISSN 0249-6356
REVUE CO-TEXTES. 2/yr. Universite de Montpellier (Universite Paul Valery), B.P. 5043, 34032 Montpellier Cedex 1, France. TEL 67-14-20-00.

800 944 FR ISSN 0373-6075
REVUE D'HISTOIRE DES TEXTES. 1953. a., vol.23, 1993. 350 F. (outside France 2080 BEF) (effective 1994). (Centre National de la Recherche Scientifique, Institut de Recherche et d'Histoire des Textes) C N R S Editions, 20-22 rue St. Amand, 75015 Paris, France. TEL 45-33-16-00. FAX 45-33-92-13. TELEX 200 356 F. (Dist. outside France by: N.V. Brepols, Steenweg op Tielen 68, 2300 Turnhout, Belgium. TEL 32-14-402500. FAX 32-14-428919) adv.; bk.rev.; index; circ. 1,250 (controlled). **Document type:** academic/scholarly publication.
—UnCover.
Formerly (until 1971): Institut de Recherche et d'Histoire des Textes. Bulletin d'Information (ISSN 0073-8204)

809 FR ISSN 0035-2411
PQ2
REVUE D'HISTOIRE LITTERAIRE DE LA FRANCE. 1894. bi-m. 70 ECU($86) (Societe d'Histoire Litteraire de la France) Armand Colin (Subsidiary of: Masson), 103 bd. Saint-Michel, 75005 Paris, France. TEL 1-46-34-19-12. FAX 1-43-26-93-68. TELEX 201 269 F. Ed. Rene Pomeau. adv.; bk.rev.; bibl. circ. 2,700. (also avail. in microfiche from BHP) **Indexed:** Amer.Hist.& Life, Can.Rev.Comp.Lit., Curr.Cont., Hist.Abstr., Ind.Bk.Rev.Hum., M.L.A., RILA.
—Faxon; SWETS.

801 400 FR ISSN 0982-6548
REVUE DE BIBLIOLOGIE. 2/yr. 130 F. Societe de Bibliologie et de Schematisation (S B S), 36 av. d'Italie, Tour Rubis, 75013 Paris, France.
Formed by the merger of: Schema et Schematisation (ISSN 0586-7606); Bulletin d'Informations Internationales de Bibliologie.

809 FR ISSN 0035-1466
PN851
REVUE DE LITTERATURE COMPAREE. (Text in English, French, German, Italian, Spanish) 1921. q. $74. Didier Erudition, 6 rue de la Sorbonne, 75005 Paris, France. (Subscr. to: Didier Erudition, North American Fullfillment Office, P.O. Box 830350, Birmingham, AL-35283-0350) Ed. J. Voisine. adv.; bk.rev.; bibl.; charts; index, cum.index every 10 yrs. circ. 2,000. (also avail. in microfrom from BHP; reprint service avail. from SCH) **Indexed:** Can.Rev.Comp.Lit., Curr.Cont., Ind.Bk.Rev.Hum., M.L.A.
—Faxon; SWETS.
Formerly: Etudes de Litterature Etrangere et Comparee (ISSN 0071-1918)

REVUE DES ETUDES AUGUSTINIENNES. see *RELIGIONS AND THEOLOGY*

891 943 FR ISSN 0080-2557
PG1
REVUE DES ETUDES SLAVES. 1921. q. 450 F. Institut d'Etudes Slaves, 9 rue Michelet, 75006 Paris, France. bk.rev. circ. 700. **Indexed:** Amer.Hist.& Life, Bibl.Ling., Can.Rev.Comp.Lit., Hist.Abstr. **Document type:** academic/scholarly publication.
—Faxon; SWETS.

809 FR ISSN 0035-2136
PN3
REVUE DES LETTRES MODERNES; histoire des idees et des litteratures. 1954. irreg. (6-10/yr.) 940 F. for 50 nos. Lettres Modernes, 45 rue Saint-Andre, 14123 Fleury sur Orne, France. TEL 31-84-47-06. FAX 31-84-48-09. Ed. M.J. Minard. bk.rev.; bibl. **Indexed:** M.L.A.
—SWETS.

840 FR ISSN 0425-4791
REVUE DES LETTRES MODERNES. ETUDES BERNANOSIENNES. 1960. a. 940 F. Lettres Modernes, 45 rue Saint-Andre, 14123 Fleury sur Orne, France. TEL 31-84-47-06. FAX 31-84-48-09. Ed. Michel Esteve. bk.rev. (back issues avail.)

LA REVUE DES REVUES. see *BIBLIOGRAPHIES*

899 MG
REVUE LITTERAIRE ET CULTURELLE DE L'OCEAN INDIEN. (Text in French) 1981. q. $29. Communication et Media Ocean Indien, Rue H. Rabesahala, B.P. 46, Antsakaviro, 101 Antananarivo, Malagasy Republic. TEL 22536. FAX 34534. TELEX 22225. Ed. Henriette Rasendralisoa. adv.; bk.rev. circ. 3,000.

REVUE ROMANE. see *LINGUISTICS*

891 410 FR ISSN 1161-0557
REVUE RUSSE. 1968. s-a. 150 F. Institut d'Etudes Slaves, 9 rue Michelet, 75006 Paris, France. (Co-sponsor: Association Francaise des Russisants) Ed.Bd. bk.rev.; bibl. circ. 600. **Indexed:** Bibl.Ling.
Formerly (until 1991): Enseignement du Russe (ISSN 0300-2608)

808 US ISSN 1047-2207
RHODODENDRON.* (Text in English, French, German, Spanish) 1984. q. $15. Guerilla Poetics, Inc., 196 Harkness Rd., Amherst, MA 01002-9784. TEL 415-324-0206. Ed. Steven Jacobsen. adv.; bk.rev. circ. 250. (back issues avail.)

869 BL
RHYTHMUS. 1981. q. Univerdidade Estadual Paulista Julio De Mesquita Filho, Instituto de Biociencias, Letras e Ciencias Exatas, 15100 Campus de Sao Jose do Rio Preto SP, Brazil.

RICHMOND QUARTERLY. see *HISTORY — History Of North And South America*

439.31 417 NE ISSN 0012-6209
RIJKSUNIVERSITEIT TE GRONINGEN. NEDERSAKSISCH INSTITUUT. DRIEMAANDELIJKSE BLADEN; taal en volksleven in het oosten van Nederland. (Text in Dutch, German) 1902; N.S. 1949. q. fl.25. Stichting Sasland, Postbus 1127, 9701 BC Groningen, Netherlands. Ed. J. van der Kooi. bk.rev.; illus.; maps. circ. 400.
—SWETS.

810 US
RIPPLES;* the poetry and fiction magazine. 1973. 4/yr. $18.50. Shining Waters Press, 2840 Canterbury Rd., Ann Arbor, MI 48104-5021. TEL 313-662-8446. Eds. Jim & Karen Schaefer. adv.; bk.rev. circ. 1,000.

800 US ISSN 1048-129X
PS536.2
RIVER CITY. 1980. s-a. $3 to individuals; institutions $5.56. Memphis State University, Department of English, Memphis, TN 38152. TEL 901-454-4438. Ed. Sharon Bryan. adv.; bk.rev. circ. 2,000.
Formerly (until 1988): Memphis State Review (ISSN 0732-2968)

800 IT
RIVISTA DI LETTERATURE MODERNE E COMPARATE. (Text in English, French and Italian) 1946. q. L.70000 (foreign L.100000) (effective 1994). Pacini Editore s.r.l., Via A. Gherardesca 1, 56014 Ospedaletto (Pisa), Italy. TEL 050-982439. FAX 050-983906. Eds. G. Pellegrini, A. Pizzorusso. adv.; bk.rev. circ. 520. **Indexed:** Arts & Hum.Cit.Ind., Can.Rev.Comp.Lit., Curr.Cont., M.L.A.

800 851 IT
RIVISTA LETTERARIA; quadrimestrale di critica letteraria e cultura varia. 1978. 3/yr. L.12000 (effective Jan. 1993). Giuseppe Amalfitano Editore, Corso Garibaldi, 15, 80074 Casamicciola Terme (Naples), Italy. adv.; bk.rev. (back issues avail.)

RIVISTA ROSMINIANA DI FILOSOFIA E DI CULTURA. see *PHILOSOPHY*

THE ROAD; the journal of history, myth and legend. see *LITERATURE — Science Fiction, Fantasy, Horror*

810 US ISSN 0035-7367
PS50
ROANOKE REVIEW. 1967-1982; resumed 1985. s-a. $5.50. Roanoke College, Department of English, Salem, VA 24505. TEL 703-375-2367. Ed. Robert R. Walter. circ. 300. (processed)

ROBERT E. HOWARD'S FIGHT MAGAZINE. see *LITERATURE — Adventure And Romance*

ROC SCIENCE FICTION ADVANCE. see *LITERATURE — Science Fiction, Fantasy, Horror*

800 700 770 US ISSN 1046-0985
ROCKFORD REVIEW. 1971. q. $15. Rockford Writers' Guild, Box 858, Rockford, IL 61105. Ed. David Ross. circ. 500. (back issues avail.)
Description: Poetry, short fiction, one-act plays, essays, and black and white art work.

ROCKY MOUNTAIN MEDIEVAL AND RENAISSANCE ASSOCIATION. JOURNAL. see *HISTORY — History Of Europe*

800 US ISSN 0361-1299
PB1
ROCKY MOUNTAIN REVIEW OF LANGUAGE AND LITERATURE. 1946. 4/yr. $20 to individuals; institutions $25. Rocky Mountain Modern Language Association, Department of English, Boise State University, Boise, ID 83725. TEL 208-385-3426. FAX 208-385-4373. Ed. Carol A. Martin. adv.; bk.rev.; charts; illus.; circ. 1,200 (paid). **Indexed:** Abstr.Engl.Stud., Amer.Hum.Ind., Arts & Hum.Cit.Ind., Bibl.Engl.Lang.& Lit., Bk.Rev.Ind. (1981-), Chic.Per.Ind., Child.Bk.Rev.Ind. (1981-), Curr.Cont., Lang.& Lang.Behav.Abstr., M.L.A. **Document type:** academic/scholarly publication.
—BLDSC (8002.670000); UnCover.
Formerly: Rocky Mountain Modern Language Association. Bulletin (ISSN 0035-7626)

800 NE ISSN 0923-0416
RODOPI PERSPECTIVES ON MODERN LITERATURE. (Text in English) 1988. irreg., vol.11, 1993. price varies. Editions Rodopi B.V., Keizersgracht 302-304, 1016 EX Amsterdam, Netherlands. TEL 31-20-6227507. FAX 31-20-6380948. (In N. America: 233 Peachtree St., N.E., Ste. 404, Atlanta GA 30303-1504. TEL 800-225-3998. FAX 404-522-7116) Ed. David Bevan. **Document type:** academic/scholarly publication, monographic series.
—BLDSC (8018.757500).

890 II
ROHINI. (Text in Marathi) m. V.S. Kane, Ed. & Pub., White House, Tilak Rd., Pune 411 030, India. circ. 3,000.

813 US ISSN 0145-5753
PS3545.A653
ROHMER REVIEW. 1968. irreg. $3 per no. 4 Forest Ave., Salem, MA 01970-4517. TEL 508-744-0885. Ed. Robert E. Briney. bk.rev.; illus. circ. 400. **Indexed:** Abstr.Pop.Cult.
Description: Covers all aspects of the life and work of British thriller writer Sax Rohmer, creator of Dr. Fu Manchu.

407 US ISSN 0035-7995
PC1
ROMANCE NOTES. (Text in English, French, Italian, Portuguese, Spanish) 1959. 3/yr. $18. University of North Carolina at Chapel Hill, Department of Romance Languages, CB 3170, 238 Dey Hall, Chapel Hill, NC 27599-3170. TEL 919-962-1025. Ed. Ed. Montgomery. cum.index. cum. index. circ. 650. (also avail. in microform; back issues avail.) **Indexed:** Arts & Hum.Cit.Ind., Bibl.Ling., Curr.Cont., M.L.A. **Document type:** academic/scholarly publication.
—BLDSC (8019.460000); Faxon; UnCover; SWETS; UMI.

LITERATURE

ROMANCE OF LIFE. see *ART*

ROMANCE PHILOLOGY. see *LINGUISTICS*

808 US ISSN 0883-1157
P1
ROMANCE QUARTERLY. (Text in English or any Romance language) 1954. q. $35 to individuals; institutions $62. Heldref Publications, 1319 Eighteenth St., N.W., Washington, DC 20036-1802. TEL 202-296-6267. FAX 202-296-5149. Ed. John Neikirk. adv. contact: Raymond Rallo. bk.rev.; index, cum.index. circ. 500. (also avail. in microfilm from UMI; reprint service avail. from UMI) **Indexed:** Arts & Hum.Cit.Ind., Chic.Per.Ind., Curr.Cont., Ind.Bk.Rev.Hum., Lang.& Lang.Behav.Abstr., M.L.A., RILA. **Document type:** academic/scholarly publication.
—BLDSC (8019.474000); Faxon; SWETS; UMI.
Former titles (until 1986): Kentucky Romance Quarterly (ISSN 0364-8664); Kentucky Foreign Language Quarterly (ISSN 0023-0332)
Description: Scholarly articles relating to Romance literature and liguistic topics.

809 UK ISSN 0263-9904
PC1
ROMANCE STUDIES. 1982. s-a. £10 to individuals (foreign £15); institutions £15 (foreign £20). University College of Swansea, School of European Languages, c/o George Evans, Bus. Mgr., School of European Languages, Singleton Park, Swansea, W. Glamorgan SA2 8PP, England. FAX 295710. Ed. Valerie Minogue. adv. circ. 200. **Document type:** academic/scholarly publication.
—BLDSC (8019.480000).
Description: Each issue is devoted to a specific theme or writer.

800 GW ISSN 0557-2614
ROMANFUEHRER; der Inhalt der Romane und Novellen der Weltliteratur. 1952. irreg., vol.28, 1994. DM.178 per no. Anton Hiersemann Verlag, Rosenbergstr. 113, 70193 Stuttgart, Germany. TEL 0711-638265. FAX 0711-6369010. (Subscr. to: Postfach 140155, 70071 Stuttgart, Germany) Ed. Bernd Graef. **Document type:** abstracting/indexing.

859 RM ISSN 0048-8550
AP86
ROMANIA LITERARA. 1954. w. 260 lei($15) Uniunea Scriitorilor din Republica Socialista Romania, Calea Victoriei 115, Bucharest, Rumania. (Subscr. to: ILEXIM, Str. 13 Decembrie Nr. 3, Box 136-137, 70116 Bucharest, Rumania) Dir. Nicolae Manolescu. bk.rev.; film rev.; play rev.; charts; illus. circ. 25,000. (also avail. in microfilm from NRP) **Indexed:** M.L.A.
Supersedes (in 1968): Gazeta Literara.

808.03 US ISSN 0035-8118
PC1
ROMANIC REVIEW. (Text in several languages) 1910. q. $25. Columbia University, c/o Prof. Michael Riffaterre, Ed., 518 Philosophy Hall, Columbia University, New York, NY 10027. TEL 212-854-2500. adv.; bk.rev.; index. circ. 1,500. (also avail. in microfilm from UMI; reprint service avail. from KTO) **Indexed:** Arts & Hum.Cit.Ind., Hum.Ind., Ind.Bk.Rev.Hum., M.L.A.
—BLDSC (8019.770000); Faxon; UnCover; SWETS; UMI.

800 GW
ROMANICA ET COMPARATISTICA. irreg., no.21, 1994. DM.58. Stauffenburg Verlag, Postfach 2567, 72015 Tuebingen, Germany. TEL 07071-78091. FAX 07071-75288. Ed. Maurizio Perugi. **Document type:** monographic series.

ROMANICA GOTHOBURGENSIA. see *LINGUISTICS*

ROMANICA HELVETICA. see *LINGUISTICS*

081 GW
ROMANICA MONACENSIA. irreg., vol.45, 1994. DM.78. Gunter Narr Verlag, Postfach 2567, 72015 Tuebingen, Germany. TEL 07071-78091. FAX 07071-75288. **Document type:** monographic series.

870 GW ISSN 0035-8126
PC3
ROMANISCHE FORSCHUNGEN. (Text in English, French, German, Italian and Spanish) 1883. 4/yr. DM.228. Vittorio Klostermann, Frauenlobstr. 22, 60487 Frankfurt a.M., Germany. TEL 069-774011. FAX 069-708038. (Subscr. to: Postfach 900601, 60446 Frankfurt a.M., Germany) Ed. Wido Hempel. adv.; bk.rev.; bibl.; index. circ. 800. (reprint service avail. from SCH,KTO) **Indexed:** Arts & Hum.Cit.Ind., Bibl.Ling., Curr.Cont., Ind.Bk.Rev.Hum., M.L.A. **Document type:** academic/scholarly publication.
—Faxon; UnCover; SWETS. **CCC.**

890 920 DK ISSN 0106-8253
ROMANSERIER OG SELVBIOGRAFISKE SERIER. a. DKK 124.75. Dansk BiblioteksCenter as, Tempovej 7-11, DK-2750 Ballerup, Denmark. TEL 45-44-97-40-00. FAX 45-44-68-24-42.

800 FR ISSN 0048-8593
ROMANTISME; revue du dix-neuvieme siecle. 1971. 4/yr. 330 F. (Societe des Etudes Romantiques) Editions Centre de Documentation Universitaire et de la Societe d'Edition d'Enseignement Superieur Reunies (CDU & SEDES), 88 bd. Saint Germain, 75005 Paris, France. TEL 43-25-23-23. FAX 46-33-57-15. TELEX EDSEDES 206701F. adv.; bk.rev. **Indexed:** Can.Rev.Comp.Lit., Curr.Cont., M.L.A. —SWETS.

THE ROMANTIST. see *LITERATURE — Science Fiction, Fantasy, Horror*

800 RU
ROMANTIZM V RUSSKOI I SOVETSKOI LITERATURE. 1973. irreg. 68 Rub. Kazanskii Universitet, Ul. Lenina, 4-5, Kazan, Russia.

800 305.412 CN ISSN 0316-1609
ROOM OF ONE'S OWN; a feminist journal of literature and criticism. 1975. q. Can.$20 to individuals (foreign Can.$30); institutions Can.$24 (foreign Can.$35). Growing Room Collective, Box 46160, Sta. D, Vancouver, BC V6J 5G5, Canada. Ed.Bd. adv.; bk.rev.; circ. 1,000 (paid). (also avail. in microform from UMI; back issues avail.; reprint service avail. from UMI) **Indexed:** Amer.Hum.Ind., Can.Lit.Ind., Can.Wom.Per.Ind., M.L.A., Stud.Wom.Abstr.
Description: Publishes fiction, poetry, essays and reviews by, for and about women.

890 II
ROOPVATI. (Text in English, Punjabi) 1970. Rs.7. Pritam Singh, Pleasure Garden Market, Chadni Chowk, Delhi 6, India. Ed. Mrs. Kailash Puri. adv.; bibl.; illus.

ROSSICA OLOMUCENSIA. see *LINGUISTICS*

891.7 RU
ROSSIISKAYA AKADEMIYA NAUK. IZVESTIYA. SERIYA LITERATURY I YAZYKA. 1940. bi-m. $98. Izdatel'stvo Nauka, 90 Profsoyuznaya ul., 117864 Moscow, Russia. TEL 095-336-0266. FAX 095-420-2220. (Dist. by: Mezhdunarodnaju Kniga, B. Yakimanka 39, 117049 Moscow, Russia; Dist. in U.S. by: Victor Kamkin Inc., Boiling Brokk Pkwy., Rockville, MD 20852. TEL 301-881-5973. FAX 301-881-1637) Ed. G.V. Stepanov. **Indexed:** Bibl.Ling.
Formerly: Akademiia Nauk S.S.S.R. Izvestiya. Seriya Literature i Yazyka (ISSN 0321-1711)

800 US
ROUND TABLE: A JOURNAL OF POETRY & FICTION. 1984. a. $7.50. Round Table Publications, Box 18763, Rochester, NY 14618. TEL 716-244-0623. Eds. Alan Lupack, Barbara Tepa Lupack. circ. 125. (back issues avail.).

ROYAL IRISH ACADEMY. PROCEEDINGS. SECTION C: ARCHAEOLOGY, CELTIC STUDIES, HISTORY, LINGUISTICS AND LITERATURE. see *ARCHAEOLOGY*

820 UK
ROYAL SHAKESPEARE COMPANY. PUBLICATION. 1978. a. £3.75. R S C Publications, Barbican Theatre, London EC2Y 8BQ, England. Ed. Simon Trussler.

891.85 PL ISSN 0035-9602
PG7001
RUCH LITERACKI. 1960. bi-m. $28. (Polska Akademia Nauk, Oddzial w Krakowie, Komisja Historycznoliteracka) Ossolineum, Publishing House of the Polish Academy of Sciences, Rynek 9, Wroclaw, Poland. TEL 47-71-386-25. FAX 48-71-448-103. TELEX 0712771 OSS PL. (Co-sponsor: Towarzystwo Literackie Im. A. Mickiewicza) Ed. S. Jaworski. bk.rev.; bibl. circ. 1,700. **Indexed:** M.L.A. **Document type:** academic/scholarly publication.
Description: History of Polish literature in international relations, literary theory, Slavonic literature.

800 GW ISSN 0557-4404
RUECKERT STUDIEN. irreg., vol.5, 1990. (Rueckert Gesellschaft e.V.) Ergon-Verlag, Grombuehlstr. 7, 97080 Wuerzburg, Germany. TEL 0931-280084. FAX 0931-282872. Ed.Bd. **Document type:** monographic series.

800 GW ISSN 0933-9094
RUECKERT ZU EHREN; eine Schriftenreihe der Rueckert Gesellschaft. 1988. irreg., vol.3, 1990. (Rueckert Gesellschaft) Ergon-Verlag, Grombuehlstr. 7, 97080 Wuerzburg, Germany. TEL 0931-280084. FAX 0931-282872. **Document type:** monographic series.

891.4 II ISSN 0035-9963
RUPAMBARA. (Text in English) q. $8. 22B Pratapaditya Rd., Calcutta 26, India. Ed. Swadesh Bharati.

RUSISTIKA. see *LINGUISTICS*

RUSS VON HOELSCHER PUBLISHING REPORT. see *JOURNALISM*

890 NE ISSN 0304-3479
RUSSIAN LITERATURE; Croatian and Serbian, Czech and Slovak, Polish. 1972. 8/yr. (in 2 vols.; 4 nos./vol.). fl.844($456) (effective 1994). North-Holland (Subsidiary of: Elsevier Science B.V.), P.O. Box 211, 1000 AE Amsterdam, Netherlands. TEL 31-20-5803911. FAX 31-20-5803598. TELEX 18582 ESPA NL. (Subscr. in U.S. and Canada to: Elsevier Science Inc., Box 882, Madison Sq. Sta., New York, NY 10159. TEL 212-989-5800. FAX 212-633-3990) Eds. N.A. Nilsson, J. van der Eng. (also avail. in microform from UMI; back issues avail.; reprint service avail. from ISI,SWZ) **Indexed:** Curr.Cont. **Document type:** academic/scholarly publication.
—BLDSC (8052.739000); Faxon; UnCover. **CCC.**
Description: Devoted to special topics of Russian literature with contributions on related subjects in Croatian, Serbian, Czech, Slovak and Polish literatures.
Refereed Serial

891.7 491.7 700 UK
RUSSIAN POETICS IN TRANSLATION. 1973. irreg. price varies. (University of Essex, Department of Literature) R P T Publications, c/o N. Drake, Marketing Services, Deddington, Oxford OX5 4SW, England. FAX 0869-37123. bibl. circ. 800. **Indexed:** M.L.A.

891.7 US ISSN 1061-1975
PN2
RUSSIAN STUDIES IN LITERATURE; a journal of translations. 1964. q. $315 (foreign $347). M.E. Sharpe, Inc., 80 Business Park Dr., Armonk, NY 10504. FAX 914-273-2106. Ed. Deming Brown. adv.; index. **Indexed:** Arts & Hum.Cit.Ind., Curr.Cont., M.L.A.
—BLDSC (8052.931000); Faxon; UnCover; UMI.
Formerly: Soviet Studies in Literature (ISSN 0038-5875)
Refereed Serial

057.1 RU
RUSSKAYA LITERATURA. 1958. q. Institut Russkoi Literatury, Nab. Makarova 4, 199164 St. Petersburg, Russia. Ed. V.V. Skatov.

809 US
RUTGERS AMERICAN WOMEN WRITERS SERIES. 1986. irreg., latest 1991. price varies. Rutgers University Press, 109 Church St., New Brunswick, NJ 08901. TEL 908-932-7762. FAX 908-932-7039. (Dist. by: Rutgers University Press Distribution Center, Box 4869, Hampden Sta., Baltimore, MD 21211. TEL 410-516-6947) **Document type:** monographic series.

800 US
S C L A NEWSLETTER. 1975. biennial. $15 includes membership. Southern Comparative Literature Association, S C L A Newsletter, c/o David Parsell, Dept. of Classical & Modern Languages, Furman University, Greenville, SC 29613. (Subscr. to: c/o Dr. Carolyn Hodges, Department of German, University of Tennessee, Knoxville, TN 37996-0470) bk.rev.; bibl. circ. 500.
  Description: Provides news of the association.

S F W A BULLETIN. (Science-Fiction and Fantasy Writers of America) see LITERATURE — Science Fiction, Fantasy, Horror

800 070.5 US
▼**S H A R P NEWS**. 1992. q. $15 membership (foreign $20; U.K. subscr. £10). Society for the History of Authorship, Reading and Publishing, c/o Jonathan Rose, Drew University, History Department, Madison, NJ 07940. TEL 201-408-3545. FAX 201-408-3768. bibl.; circ. 400 (paid). **Document type:** newsletter.
  Description: Discusses teaching programs, research projects, and course syllabi; lists conferences, lectures, fellowships, employment opportunities, and scholarly publications on the history of book publishing.

S K M. (Schweizer Kontakt) see SOCIOLOGY

800 US ISSN 1064-7767
PQ2664.E84456
S L D. Key Title: Studies on Lucette Desvignes and the Twentieth Century. (Text in English, French) 1991. a. $12 to individuals; institutions $20. (Societe des Amis de Lucette Desvignes) New Paradigm Press, 5413 Neilwoods Dr., Knoxville, TN 37919. TEL 615-588-8878. Ed. Patrick Brady. bk.rev.; circ. 150 (paid). (back issues avail.; reprint service avail.) **Document type:** academic/scholarly publication.
  Description: Covers the work of Lucette Desvignes and other significant twentieth century authors writing in French or English.
  Refereed Serial

830 GW ISSN 0722-7833
PN4
S P I E L. (Siegener Periodikum zur Internationalen Empirischen Literaturwissenschaft) 1982. s-a. DM.69. Peter Lang GmbH Europaeischer Verlag der Wissenschaften, Eschborner Landstr. 42-50, 60489 Frankfurt a.M., Germany. TEL 069-7807050. FAX 069-785893. Ed.Bd. adv.; B&W page DM.400; trim 120 x 190. circ. 200. **Document type:** academic/scholarly publication.
  —BLDSC (8413.799100).

808.838 US
S P W A O SHOWCASE. 1980. a. $5. (Small Press Writers and Artists Organization) Regions Press, c/o Sec./Treas., 13 Southwood Dr., Woodland, CA 95695. TEL 916-661-9231. Ed. Joe Morey. circ. 300.

800 SP ISSN 0213-6449
SABER LEER; revista critica de libros. 1987. m. Fundacion Juan March, Servicio de Informacion y Prensa, Castello, 77, 28006 Madrid, Spain. TEL 435-42-40. FAX 576-34-20. circ. 20,000.

810 640 US
SADIE'S CHATTER. 1972. m. $6. Box 2061, Tulsa, OK 74101. Ed. Doris Gist. adv.; bk.rev.; illus. circ. 1,000.

839.6 949.12 IC ISSN 0558-1257
SAFN TIL SOEGU ISLANDS OG ISLENSKRA BOKMENNTA. 1856. irreg. Hid Islenska Bokmenntafelag, Sidumula 21, P.O. Box 8935, 128 Reykjavik, Iceland. TEL 354-1-67-90-60. FAX 354-1-67-90-95. circ. 700.

800 US ISSN 1056-2591
THE SAGARIN REVIEW; the St. Louis Jewish literary journal. 1991. a. $5 to individuals; institutions $10. c/o The Saul Brodsky Jewish Community Library, 12 Millstone Campus Dr., St. Louis, MO 63146-5776. TEL 314-432-0200. FAX 314-432-6150. Ed. Howard Schwartz. bk.rev.

SAGNERS SLAVISTISCHE SAMMLUNG. see LINGUISTICS

890 II
SAHITYA CHINTA. (Text in Bengali) 1971. s-a. Rs.5 per no. Sahita Chinta Prokashani, 311 Ganguli Bagan Lane, Calcutta 47, India. Ed. Kiranshanker Sengupta. adv.; bk.rev. circ. 1,250.
  Description: Articles on traditions and trends of literary activities in India and abroad, includes short stories, poems and reviews.

916.606 NR ISSN 0795-2864
SAIWA; a journal of communication. (Text in English) 1981. a. £N25($10) Ahmadu Bello University, Department of English, Zaria, Kaduna State, Nigeria. Ed. O.S. Ogede. circ. 500.
  Description: Attempts to break new ground in the praxis and study of African writing.

820 IE
SALMON INTERNATIONAL LITERARY JOURNAL. (Text in English, Gaelic) 1981. 3/yr. £6($22) (Arts Council) Salmon Publishing, The Bridge Mills, Galway, Ireland. TEL 091-62587. Ed. Jessie Lendennie. circ. 1,000.

801 II
SAMBALPUR UNIVERSITY. POST-GRADUATE DEPARTMENT OF ORIYA. JOURNAL. (Text in Oriya) no.2, 1976. a. Sambalpur University, Post Graduate Department of Oriya, Jotibihara, Sambalpur, India.

891.43 II
SAMBODHANA. (Text in Hindi) 1966. q. Rs.1000. Gulfam Khan, Chand Pole, Kankroli 313324, Rajasthan, India. Ed. Omar Mewari. adv.; bk.rev. circ. 1,100.

SAMBRE ET HEURE. see HISTORY

806 NE
▼**SAMUEL BECKETT TODAY - AUJOURD'HUI**. (Text in English, French) 1992. irreg., vol.2, 1994. price varies. Editions Rodopi B.V., Keizersgracht 302-304, 1016 EX Amsterdam, Netherlands. TEL 31-20-6227507. FAX 31-20-6380948. (In N. America: 233 Peachtree St., N.E., Ste. 404, Atlanta, GA 30303-1504. TEL 800-225-3998. FAX 404-522-7116) Eds. Marius Buning, Sjef Houppermans. **Document type:** monographic series, proceedings.

895.1 CC
SAN YUE SAN. Zhuang edition: Sam Nyied Sam. (Editions in Chinese and Zhuang) 1983. bi-m. Y7.50($18.50) Guangxi Minzu Chubanshe, No. 8, Xinghu Lu Bei 2 Li, Nanning, Guangxi 530022, People's Republic of China. TEL 42719. (US subscr. to: China Books & Periodicals, Inc., 2929 24th St., San Francisco, CA 94110) Ed. Wei Wenjun. bk.rev. circ. 20,000.
  Description: Presents folk and contemporary literature by and about minority nationalities in southern China, primarily those in Guangxi. Also publishes research on the history, culture, languages, and customs of various minorities. Columns introduce famous places, persons, drama works, and history pertaining to minority ethnic groups.

378.1 US ISSN 1061-3579
PS1
SANDHILLS REVIEW. 1970. s-a. $14. Sandhills Community College, 2200 Airport Rd., Pinehurst, NC 28374. TEL 919-692-6185. FAX 919-692-2756. Ed. Ronald H. Bayes. adv.; bk.rev.; play rev.; illus. circ. 500. (also avail. in microform from UMI; reprint service avail. from UMI)
Indexed: A.I.P.P.
  —UMI.
  Formerly (until no.42, 1993): St. Andrews Review (ISSN 0036-2751)

810 US
SANDSCRIPT.* 1977. 2/yr. $5. Cape Cod Writers, Inc., 212 Oleander Ave., Ste. 3, Palm Beach, FL 33480-3807. TEL 617-362-6078. Eds. Barbara Oeffner, Jean Lunn. adv.; bk.rev.; illus. circ. 300.

895.1 CC
SANJIAO ZHOU. (Text in Chinese) bi-m. Nantong Wenxue Yishu Jie Lianhehui - Nantong Literary and Art Circle Association, 2 Wenfeng Lu, Nantong, Jiangsu 226001, People's Republic of China. TEL 513929. Ed. Zhang Songlin.

800 US
▼**SANTA BARBARA REVIEW**. 1993. s-a. $10. Box 536, Summerland, CA 93067-0536. Ed. Shelly Lowenkopf. **Document type:** academic/scholarly publication.
  Description: Includes poetry, short fiction and essays.

810 US ISSN 0899-9848
PS659
SANTA MONICA REVIEW. 1988. s-a. $14. Santa Monica College, 1900 Pico Blvd., Santa Monica, CA 90405. TEL 213-450-5150. Ed. James Krusoe. adv. circ. 1,200.
  Description: Presents fiction, poetry and essays by contemporary writers.

895.1 CC ISSN 0257-5809
SANWEN/PROSE MONTHLY. Overseas edition (ISSN 1005-7323) (Text in Chinese) 1980. m. Baihua Wenyi Chubanshe, 189 Zhangzizhong Lu, Heping Qu, Tianjin 300020, People's Republic of China. TEL 7312720. (Dist. in US by: China Books & Periodicals, Inc., 2929 24th St., San Francisco, CA 94110. TEL 415-282-2994)

800 CC
SANWEN BAIJIA. (Text in Chinese) bi-m. Xingtai Diqu Wenlian, 76 Xinxi Jie, Xingtai, Hebei 054001, People's Republic of China. TEL 4084. Ed. Xiao Shanbi.

895.1 CC ISSN 1005-7323
▼**SANWEN HAIWAIBAN/PROSE OVERSEAS EDITION**. (Text in Chinese) 1993. bi-m. Y21($21) Baihua Wenyi Chubanshe, 189 Zhangzishong Lu, Heping Qu, Tianjin 300020, People's Republic of China. TEL 7312720. (Dist. outside China by: Tianjin International Book Trading Corp., Chifeng Dao 130, Heping Qu, Tianjin 300041, P.R. China) Eds. Zheng Faqing, Gan Yiwen.

895.1 CC
SANWEN XUANKAN. (Text in Chinese) m. Y0.98 per no. Henan Sheng Wenlian, No. 34, Jing 7 Lu, Zhengzhou, Henan 450003, People's Republic of China. TEL 334625. Ed. Bian Ka.
  Description: Publishes selected prose.

SARI. see LINGUISTICS

891.4 II ISSN 0036-4797
SARIKA. (Text in Hindi) fortn. $37. Bennett, Coleman & Co., Ltd. (New Delhi), Times House, 7 Bahadur Shah Zafar Marg, New Delhi 110002, India. (U.S. subscr. address: Kalpana, 42-75 Main St., Flushing, NY 11355) Ed. A.N. Mudgil. circ. 40,000.

891.4 II
SARITA. (Text in Hindi) 1945. fortn. Rs.450($17) Delhi Press Patra Prakashan Ltd., Delhi Press Bldg., E-3 Jhandewala Estate, New Delhi 110 055, India. TEL 11-526311. TELEX 31-63053 DEPR IN. Ed. Vishwa Nath. adv.; illus. circ. 275,000.
  Description: Includes fiction, recipes, fashion, film reviews, and regular columns.

890 II ISSN 0303-3074
SARVOTKRUSHTA MARATHI KATHA. (Text in Marathi) vol.9, 1974. a. Rs.16($2) c/o Mrs. Chhaya Kolarkar, Ed., 43-348 Sant Tukaram Nagar, Pimpri, Poona 411018, India. circ. 1,500. (back issues avail.)

890 II ISSN 0581-8532
SATAPITAKA. INDO-ASIAN LITERATURES. 1957. irreg. price varies. (International Academy of Indian Culture) Aditya Prakashan, F-14-65, Model Town II, New Delhi 110 009, India. TEL 91-11-7245584. FAX 91-11-3282047. Ed. Lokesh Chandra. circ. 100. **Document type:** monographic series.

808 US
SATCHELL'S WRITER'S CLUB NEWSLETTER. 1985. q. $2.50 per no. Satchell's Publishing, 3124 Fifth Ave., Richmond, VA 23222. TEL 804-329-2130. Ed. Roswitha Petretschek. illus.

890 II
SATTAR DASHAK. (Text in Bengali) 1971. q. Rs.50. Gita Ganguli, 78-2-71 Biren Roy Rd. W., Calcutta 700061, India. TEL 772026. Ed. Jitesh Gangopadhaya. adv.; page Rs.1000; trim 20 X 15. bk.rev. circ. 15,000. **Document type:** academic/scholarly publication.
  Description: Provides articles on literature, economy and culture.

LITERATURE

SATURDAY EVENING POST. see GENERAL INTEREST PERIODICALS — United States

806 US ISSN 0735-1550
PS3503.E4488
SAUL BELLOW JOURNAL. 1982. 2/yr. $16 to individuals; institutions $15. 6533 Post Oak Dr., West Bloomfield, MI 48322. TEL 313-855-4324. FAX 313-557-6636. Ed. Liela Goldman. bk.rev. circ. 300. **Indexed:** Abstr.Engl.Stud., M.L.A.
—BLDSC (8077.204000); Faxon; UnCover.
Supersedes: Saul Bellow Newsletter.
Description: Critical essays, biographical articles, and annotated bibliography on Saul Bellow and his works.

808 US
SAUL BELLOW SOCIETY NEWSLETTER. vol.4, 1989. q. Brigham Young University, English Department, 3146 Jesse Knight Humanities Bldg., Provo, UT 84602. TEL 801-378-2948.

SAVACOU; a journal of the Caribbean artists movement. see ART

891.8 YU ISSN 0036-519X
SAVREMENIK; mesecni knjizevni casopis. (Text in Serbo-Croatian) 1955. m. $0.05. Knjizevne Novine, Francuska 7, 11000 Belgrade, Yugoslavia. Ed. Pavle Zoric. bk.rev. circ. 1,500. **Indexed:** M.L.A.

800 948 CN ISSN 0823-1796
SCANDINAVIAN - CANADIAN STUDIES/ETUDES SCANDINAVES AU CANADA. (Text in English, French) 1983. a. Can.$15 to individuals; institutions Can.$18. Association for the Advancement of Scandinavian Studies in Canada - Association pour l'Avancement des Etudes Scandinaves au Canada, Department of Languages, Literatures and Linguistics, York University, North York, ON M3J 1P3, Canada. TEL 416-736-5016. FAX 416-736-5735. Ed. Wolfgang P. Ahrens. bk.rev. circ. 250. (back issues avail.) **Document type:** academic/scholarly publication.
Description: Multidisciplinary journal with articles on any Scandinavian related topic; most articles are in the areas of literature, history and political science.

SCANDINAVIAN STUDIES (EUGENE). see LINGUISTICS

800 890 UK ISSN 0036-5653
PT7001
SCANDINAVICA. (Text in English, French, German) 1962. s-a. $45. (School of Modern Languages and European History) Norvik Press, University of East Anglia, Norwich NR4 7TJ, England. TEL 0603-56161. FAX 0603-250599. Ed. Janet Garton. adv.; bk.rev.; bibl.; cum.index every 10 yrs.; circ. 500 (paid). (back issues avail.) **Indexed:** Amer.Hist.& Life (until 1991), Bibl.Ling., Hist.Abstr. (until 1991). **Document type:** academic/scholarly publication.
—Faxon; UnCover; SWETS. **CCC.**

SCANDO-SLAVICA. see LINGUISTICS

800 CN
SCAT!. 1983. a. Can.$10. University of Toronto, Innis College, 2 Sussex Ave., Toronto, Ont. M5S 1A1, Canada. TEL 416-978-4748. Ed. Yukio Koglin. bk.rev. circ. 500. (back issues avail.)

SCAVENGER'S NEWSLETTER. see LITERATURE — Science Fiction, Fantasy, Horror

830 GW ISSN 0937-2644
SCHLESWIG-HOLSTEIN. JAHRBUCH - HEIMATKALENDER. 1938. a. DM.11.90. (Schleswig-Holsteinischer Heimatbund) Heinrich Moeller Soehne GmbH, Bahnhofstr. 12-16, 2370 Rendsburg, Germany. TEL 04331-591101. FAX 04331-591100. adv.; bk.rev.; illus. circ. 10,000.
Formerly: Schleswig-Holsteinischer Heimatkalender.

SCHOOL MAGAZINE. see CHILDREN AND YOUTH — For

830 831 GW ISSN 0174-2132
SCHREIBHEFT; Zeitschrift fuer Literatur. 1977. s-a. DM.60 for 4 issues. Rigodon Verlag, Niederdistr. 18, 45147 Essen, Germany. TEL 0201-778111. FAX 0221-715174. Ed. Norbert Wehr. **Document type:** academic/scholarly publication.

SCHWARZER FADEN; Vierteljahresschrift fuer Lust und Freiheit. see POLITICAL SCIENCE

810 US
SCHWELL. 1978. q. $8. Schwell, 14 Hill Pt., San Francisco, CA 94117. TEL 916-343-5370. circ. 50.

800 PP
SCOPE. irreg. price varies. National Research Institute, Cultural Studies Division, P.O. Box 5854, Boroko, NCD, Papua New Guinea. TEL 675-26-0300. FAX 675-26-0312.

820 UK
SCOTLIT. 1989. s-a. £24 (typically set in May). Association for Scottish Literary Studies (Dundee), c/o Univeristy of Aberdeen, Dept of English, Aberdeen AB9 2UB, Scotland. adv. circ. 3,000.
Supersedes (1974-1987): A S L S Newsletter.
Description: Information about Scottish literature, publications and conferences.

820 UK ISSN 0305-0785
PR8514
SCOTTISH LITERARY JOURNAL. 1974. s-a. £24 to individuals; institutions £40 (typically set in May). Association for Scottish Literary Studies, Dept. of English, University of Aberdeen, Old Aberdeen AB9 2UB, Scotland. TEL 0224-272634. Ed. J.H. Alexander. adv.; bk.rev.; cum.index; circ. 820 (controlled). **Indexed:** Abstr.Engl.Stud., Arts & Hum.Cit.Ind., Curr.Cont., Ind.Bk.Rev.Hum., M.L.A.
—BLDSC (8210.693000); Faxon; UnCover.
Supersedes: Scottish Literary News (ISSN 0048-9794)
Description: Academic journal about Scottish literature of all periods.

800 940 UK ISSN 0265-3273
PG1
SCOTTISH SLAVONIC REVIEW. 1983. 2/yr. £12($25) to individuals; institutions £18($38). University of Glasgow, 53 Southpark Ave., Glasgow G12 8QQ, Scotland. TEL 041-339-5599. FAX 041-330-4808. TELEX 777070-UNIGLA. Ed. Peter Henry. adv.; bk.rev. circ. 400. **Indexed:** Bibl.Ling. **Document type:** academic/scholarly publication.
—BLDSC (8211.240000); Faxon.
Description: Covers the languages, literature, history, cultures and the arts of East Europe. Explores historical and cultural links between Eastern Europe and Scotland.

800 US
SCRIBBLER. 1988. bi-m. Box 671, Madison, AL 35758. TEL 205-837-6434.

890 IE ISSN 0332-4249
SCRIBHINNI GAEILGENA NA BRATHAR MIONUR. (Text in Gaelic) 1952. irreg., vol.11, 1976. Dublin Institute for Advanced Studies, School of Celtic Studies, 10 Burlington Rd., Dublin 4, Ireland. TEL 01-6680748. FAX 01-6680561. **Document type:** monographic series.

820 US ISSN 0190-731X
SCRIBLERIAN AND THE KIT-CATS; a newsjournal devoted to Pope, Swift, and their circle, the Kit-Cats and Dryden. 1968. s-a. $9 to individuals; institutions $12. Temple University, Department of English, Anderson Hall, Rm. 1038, Philadelphia, PA 19122. TEL 215-787-4717. (Co-sponsors: Northeastern University, Goldsmith's College, University of London, Queen's University) Ed. Bill Hatter. adv.; bk.rev.; bibl.; illus. circ. 1,200. (back issues avail.) **Indexed:** Amer.Hum.Ind., Curr.Cont., Ind.Bk.Rev.Hum., M.L.A. —UnCover.
Formerly: Scriblerian (ISSN 0036-9640)

800 AT ISSN 0725-0096
PN2
SCRIPSI. 1981. 3/yr. Aus.$40 to individuals (foreign Aus.$50); institutions Aus.$50 (foreign Aus.$60); students Aus.$30 (foreign Aus.$40). Oxford University Press, Box 2784Y, Melbourne, Vic. 3001, Australia. Eds. Owen Richardson, Andrew Rutherford. adv.; bk.rev. circ. 2,000. (back issues avail.)
—BLDSC (8211.859575); UnCover. **CCC.**
Description: Features Australian and international poetry and fiction.

SCRIPTA ISLANDICA. see LINGUISTICS

800 GW
SCRIPTORALIA. irreg., vol.65, 1994. DM.108. Gunter Narr Verlag, Postfach 2567, 72015 Tuebingen, Germany. TEL 07071-78091. FAX 07071-75288. Ed. Paul Goetsch. **Document type:** monographic series.

870 IE ISSN 0332-4214
SCRIPTORES LATINI HIBERNIAE. (Text in Latin) 1955. irreg., vol.11, 1981. Dublin Institute for Advanced Studies, School of Celtic Studies, 10 Burlington Rd., Dublin 4, Ireland. TEL 01-6680748. FAX 01-6680561. **Document type:** monographic series.
Description: Works in Latin by medieval Irish writers.

860 DR
SCRIPTURA. irreg. Universidad Autonoma de Santo Domingo, Depto. de Letras, Apdo. 1355, Santo Domingo, Dominican Republic. **Indexed:** New Test.Abstr., Rel.Ind.One.

808 384 791.43 US ISSN 0734-8592
PN1993.5.U718
SCRIPTWRITERS MARKET. 1979. a. $28.95. Scriptwriters - Filmmakers Publishing Co., 8033 Sunset Blvd., No. 306, Hollywood, CA 90046. TEL 818-762-3726. Eds. Leslie Gates, David Buffum. adv. circ. 10,000.

800 IT
SCRITTURA SCENICA. 1971. q. L.27000. Bulzoni Editore, Via dei Liburni 14, 00185 Rome, Italy. Dir. Giuseppe Bartolucci. bk.rev.; bibl.

800 CN ISSN 0227-5090
SCRIVENER. 1980. a. Can.$10 for 2 yrs. Scrivener Press, 853 Sherbrooke St. W., Montreal, PQ H3A 2T6, Canada. TEL 514-398-6588. Ed. Susan Brekelmans. adv.; bk.rev. circ. 800.
Description: New Canadian and American poetry, short fiction, essays and art.

810 US
SEASWELLS. 1966. a. $6. Brunswick College, Altama at Fourth, Brunswick, GA 31523-0001. TEL 912-264-7235. circ. 800.
Formerly: Crest.

810 US ISSN 0147-6629
PS536.2
SEATTLE REVIEW. 1978. s-a. $10. University of Washington, Department of English, Padelford Hall, GN-30, Seattle, WA 98195. TEL 206-543-9865. Ed. Donna Gerstenberger. adv. circ. 750. (back issues avail.) **Indexed:** A.I.P.P.
Supersedes: Assay (ISSN 0004-5004)

800 RM ISSN 0037-0517
PN6065.R8
SECOLUL 20; revista de literatura universala. 1961. m. 204 lei($15) Uniunea Scriitorilor Din Republica Socialista Romania, Calea Victoriei 115, Bucharest, Rumania. (Subscr. to: ILEXIM, Str. 13 Decembrie Nr. 3, Box 136-137, 70116 Bucharest, Rumania) Ed. Dan Haulica. bk.rev.; illus.; cum.index. circ. 8,000.

800 US ISSN 1052-5025
SECONDS MAGAZINE. 1986. bi-m. $18. Seconds Magazine Inc., 24 Fifth Ave., Ste. 405, New York, NY 10011. TEL 212-260-0481. (Alt. addr.: Box 2553, Stuyvesant Sta., New York, NY 10009) Ed. Steven Blush. adv. contact: Ken Scrudato. (back issues avail.) **Document type:** consumer publication.
Description: Contains music, art, and literature.

810 811 US ISSN 0095-1730
PS501
SEEMS. 1971. irreg. $16. c/o Karl Elder, Ed., Lakeland College, Box 359, Sheboygan, WI 53081. TEL 414-565-3871. circ. 250. **Indexed:** Access.

895 MY
SEJAHTERA. (Text in English or Malay) a. University of Malaya, Islamic Students' Union - Persatuan Mahasiswa Islam Universiti Malaya, 59100 Kuala Lumpur, Malaysia.

SELECTA (CORVALLIS). see LINGUISTICS

SELECTED WORKS OF JUAN LUIS VIVES. see HISTORY — History Of Europe

SELSKAB FOR NORDISK FILOLOGI. AARSBERETNING. see LINGUISTICS

LITERATURE

430
PF3001   CN   ISSN 0037-1939
SEMINAR; a journal of Germanic studies. (Text in English, French and German) 1965. q. $35. (Canadian Association of University Teachers of German) University of Toronto Press, Journals Department, 5201 Dufferin St., Downsview, ON M3H 5T8, Canada. TEL 416-667-7781. FAX 416-667-7803. (U.S. addr.: 340 Nagel Dr., Cheektowaga, NY 14225) Ed. R. Symington. adv.; bk.rev.; charts; index. circ. 776. **Indexed:** Amer.Bibl.Slavic & E.Eur.Stud., Curr.Cont., Ind.Bk.Rev.Hum., M.L.A.
—BLDSC (8239.352000); UnCover; UMI. **CCC.**

800 051   II   ISSN 1053-9115
SENSATIONS. 1987. s-a. $18 for 2 nos. David Messineo, Ed. & Pub., c/o 2 Radio Ave., A5, Secaucus, NJ 07094. adv.; illus. circ. 200. (back issues avail.) **Document type:** academic/scholarly publication.
Description: First collection of American poetry from 1565 to 1630. Also includes contemporary poetry and fiction.

860   CR
SERIE ESTUDIOS LITERARIOS. 1975. irreg. free (not for international distribution). Ministerio de Cultura, Juventud y Deportes, Dept. de Publicaciones, Apdo. 10227, San Jose, Costa Rica.

800 410   II   ISSN 0254-0193
SERIES IN ENGLISH LANGUAGE AND LITERATURE. (Text in English) 1978. irreg. price varies. Bahri Publications, 997-A, Street No. 9, Gobindpuri, Kalkaji, New Delhi 110 019, India. TEL 644-5710. Ed. Ujjal Singh Bahri. **Document type:** monographic series.
Description: Academic series on English language and literature.

SERIES IN SIKH HISTORY AND CULTURE. see HISTORY — History Of Asia

840   FR   ISSN 0992-2660
SERPENT A PLUMES. q. 225 F. (foreign 275 F.). Association pour le Promotion de la Nouvelle, 78 rue du Bac, 75007 Paris, France. TEL 45-48-58-89. Ed. Pierre Astier.

800   UK   ISSN 0268-117X
THE SEVENTEENTH CENTURY. 1986. s-a. £12 to individuals; institutions £18. University of Durham, Centre for 17th Century Studies, Palace Green, Durham DH1 3RN, England. Ed. R.G. Maber. adv. **Document type:** academic/scholarly publication.
—BLDSC (8253.947900); Faxon.
Description: Interdisciplinary journal concerned with all aspects of the seventeenth century, including literature, theology, philosophy, natural science, music and visual arts.

840 844   UK   ISSN 0265-1068
DC33.4
SEVENTEENTH CENTURY FRENCH STUDIES. (Text in English and French) 1979. a. £7 to individuals; institutions £9. Society for Seventeenth-Century French Studies, French Department, The University, Glasgow G12 8QL, Scotland. TEL 041-339-8855. FAX 041-330-4234. Ed. John Campbell. adv.; bk.rev. circ. 300. **Indexed:** M.L.A. **Document type:** academic/scholarly publication.
Formerly (until 1984): Society for Seventeenth Century French Studies. Newsletter (ISSN 0142-5080)
Description: All aspects of French seventeenth-century culture, literature and history.

800 900   US   ISSN 0037-3028
PR1
SEVENTEENTH - CENTURY NEWS. (Including: Neo-Latin News) 1942. q. $9 (foreign $13) (effective Sep. 1991). (Milton Society of America) Texas A & M University, Department of English, College Station, TX 77843. TEL 409-845-3400. FAX 409-862-2292. Ed. Harrison T. Meserole. adv.; B&W page $250; 8 x 11. bk.rev.; abstr. circ. 1,200. (also avail. in microform from UMI; reprint service avail. from UMI) **Indexed:** Abstr.Engl.Stud., Arts & Hum.Cit.Ind., Bk.Rev.Ind. (1981-), Child.Bk.Rev.Ind. (1981-), Curr.Cont., Ind.Bk.Rev.Hum., M.L.A. **Document type:** academic/scholarly publication.
—Faxon; SWETS; UMI.
Description: Covers all aspects of seventeenth-century culture, English, American and European, with emphasis on literature and history.

800   US   ISSN 0893-6900
SEVENTEENTH - CENTURY TEXTS AND STUDIES. (Text in English and other West European languages) 1987. irreg. Peter Lang Publishing, Inc., 62 W. 45th St., 4th Fl., New York, NY 10036. TEL 212-302-6740. Ed. Anthony Low. **Document type:** academic/scholarly publication.
—BLDSC (8253.953000).
Description: Concerned with English non-dramatic poetry and prose from about the time of Donne and Jonson to the death of Milton.

810   US   ISSN 0037-3052
AP2
SEWANEE REVIEW. 1892. q. $16 to individuals; institution $20. University of the South, Sewanee Review, Sewanee, TN 37383-1000. TEL 615-598-1246. Ed. George Core. adv.; bk.rev. circ. 3,400. (also avail. in microform from KTO; back issues avail.) **Indexed:** A.I.P.P., Abstr.Engl.Stud., Acad.Ind., Arts & Hum.Cit.Ind., Bibl.Engl.Lang.& Lit., Bk.Rev.Ind. (1965-), Child.Bk.Rev.Ind. (1965-), Hum.Ind., Ind.Amer.Per.Verse, Ind.Bk.Rev.Hum., LCR, M.L.A., Mag.Ind.
—Faxon; UnCover; SWETS. **CCC.**

800   US   ISSN 0893-6889
SEXUALITY AND LITERATURE. (Text in English and other West European languages) 1988. irreg. Peter Lang Publishing, Inc., 62 W. 45th St., 4th Fl., New York, NY 10036. TEL 212-302-6740. FAX 212-302-7574. Ed. John Maynard. **Document type:** academic/scholarly publication.

SEZ; a multi-racial journal of poetry & people's culture. see ETHNIC INTERESTS

822.3   SA   ISSN 1011-582X
SHAKESPEARE IN SOUTHERN AFRICA. 1987. a. R.20 in southern Africa; overseas £20($20) (effective 1993). (Shakespeare Society of Southern Africa) Rhodes University, Institute for the Study of English in Africa, P.O. Box 94, Grahamstown 6140, South Africa. TEL 27-461-26093. FAX 27-461-25642. Ed. Laurence Wright. bk.rev.; play rev.; bibl.; illus. circ. 400. (back issues avail.) **Document type:** academic/scholarly publication.
Description: Publishes articles, commentary and reviews on all aspects of Shakespearean studies and performance, with particular emphasis on the response to Shakespeare in southern Africa.
Refereed Serial

800   GW   ISSN 0080-9128
PR2889
SHAKESPEARE - JAHRBUCH. 1864. a. DM.32. (Deutsche Shakespeare Gesellschaft) Verlag Hermann Boehlaus Nachfolger, Meyerstr. 50a, 99403 Weimar, Germany. TEL 03643-202071. Ed. Guenther Klotz. bk.rev. (reprint service avail. from KTO) **Indexed:** M.L.A. **Document type:** academic/scholarly publication.

820   US   ISSN 0037-3214
PR2885
SHAKESPEARE NEWSLETTER. 1951. 4/yr. (Sept.-May). $12 (foreign $14). Iona College, Department of English, New Rochelle, NY 10801. TEL 914-633-2061. Eds. John W. Mahon, Thomas A. Pendleton. adv.; bk.rev.; abstr.; bibl.; film rev.; play rev.; stat.; tr.lit.; index. circ. 2,000. (back issues avail.) **Indexed:** Abstr.Engl.Stud., LCR, M.L.A.
Description: Shakespeare news, digests of scholarly articles, lectures, dissertations, new books, original articles, authorship question, computer scholarship, latest critical and historical discoveries, Shakespeare festivals and programs.

800   US
SHAKESPEARE OXFORD SOCIETY. NEWSLETTER. 1957. q. $25. Shakespeare Oxford Society, c/o Victor Crichton, Membership Chairman, 207 W. 106th St., Apt. 10B, New York, NY 10025. Ed. Morse Johnson. bk.rev. circ. 500.

820   US   ISSN 0037-3222
PR2885
SHAKESPEARE QUARTERLY. 1950. 5/yr. $45 to individuals; institutions $60. Folger Shakespeare Library, 201 E. Capitol St., S.E., Washington, DC 20003-1094. TEL 202-675-0351. FAX 202-544-4623. Ed. Barbara A. Mowat. adv.; bk.rev.; bibl.; illus. circ. 4,000. (also avail. in microform from UMI; microfiche; reprint service avail. from UMI) **Indexed:** Abstr.Engl.Stud., Acad.Ind., Arts & Hum.Cit.Ind., Bk.Rev.Ind. (1986-), Child.Bk.Rev.Ind. (1986-), Curr.Cont., Film Lit.Ind. (1974-), Hum.Ind., Ind.Bk.Rev.Hum., M.L.A.
—BLDSC (8254.586000); Faxon; UnCover; SWETS; UMI.

820   JA   ISSN 0582-9402
SHAKESPEARE STUDIES. (Text in English) 1962. a. 2000 Yen. Shakespeare Society of Japan, 501 Kenkyusha Bldg. 9, 2-chome Kanda-Surugadai, Chiyoda-ku, Tokyo 101, Japan. FAX 03-3233-3398. Ed. Yasunari Takahashi. circ. 1,200. **Indexed:** Hum.Ind., M.L.A. **Document type:** academic/scholarly publication.

809   US   ISSN 0582-9399
PR2885
SHAKESPEARE STUDIES; an annual gathering of research, criticism & review. 1960. a. $48. (Council for Research in the Renaissance) Associated University Presses, 440 Forsgate Dr., Cranbury, NJ 08512. TEL 609-655-4770. FAX 609-655-8366. (Co-publisher: Fairleigh Dickinson University Press) circ. 1,000 (paid). **Indexed:** Hum.Ind., Ind.Bk.Rev.Hum., M.L.A. **Document type:** academic/scholarly publication.
—BLDSC (8254.586500).
Description: Contains research in the Shakespearean era.

822   UK   ISSN 0080-9152
PR2888
SHAKESPEARE SURVEY. 1948. a. price varies. Cambridge University Press, Edinburgh Bldg., Shaftesbury Rd., Cambridge CB2 2RU, England. TEL 0223-312393. FAX 0223-315052. TELEX 851817256. (N. American addr.: Cambridge University Press, Journals Dept., 40 W. 20th St., New York, NY 10011. TEL 212-924-3900. FAX 212-691-3239) Ed. Stanley Wells. index, cum.index: vols. 1-10, 11-10, 21-30. **Indexed:** Abstr.Engl.Stud., Acad.Ind., Arts & Hum.Cit.Ind., Curr.Cont., Hum.Ind., M.L.A. **Document type:** academic/scholarly publication.
—BLDSC (8254.586800); Faxon.

800   US
SHAKESPEARE WORLDWIDE. 1974. a. $45. A M S Press, Inc., 56 E. 13th St., New York, NY 10003. TEL 212-777-4700. FAX 212-995-5413. (back issues avail.)
Formerly: Shakespeare Translation.
Description: Collection of reviews of performances of Shakespeare in non-English speaking countries.

800   US   ISSN 1045-9456
PR2885
SHAKESPEARE YEARBOOK. irreg., latest no.3. $29.95. Edwin Mellen Press, 415 Ridge St., Box 450, Lewiston, NY 14092. TEL 716-754-2788. FAX 716-754-4056. Ed. Holger Klein.
Description: Focuses on cultural continuity.

807   US   ISSN 0883-9123
PR2965
SHAKESPEAREAN CRITICISM. 1984. irreg., vol.16, 1991. $114. Gale Research Inc., 835 Penobscot Bldg., Detroit, MI 48226. TEL 800-877-4253. FAX 313-961-6083. TELEX 810-221-7086. Ed. Sandra Williamson. abstr.; bibl.; illus.
Description: Guide to contemporary forms of Shakespearean criticism.

895.1   CC
SHAN CHA/CAMELLIA; minzu minjian wenxue shuangyuekan. (Text in Chinese) bi-m. $22.50. Yunnan Shehui Kexueyuan, Minzu Wenxue Yanjiusuo - Yunnan Academy of Social Sciences, Institute of Minority Nationalities Literature, 45, Qixiang Lu, Kunming, Yunnan 650032, People's Republic of China. TEL 42039. (Dist. outside China by: China International Book Trading Co., P.O. Box 399, Beijing, P.R.C.; Dist. in US by: China Books & Periodicals, Inc., 2929 24th St., San Francisco, CA 94110. TEL 415-282-2994) Ed. Li Zuanxu.
Description: Contains folk literature and literature of minority nationalities.

LITERATURE

800   NE   ISSN 0956-3083
THE SHANDEAN; an annual volume devoted to Laurence Sterne. 1989. a. £17 to individuals (cloth binding £27); libraries £23 (cloth binding £33) (effective 1994). (Laurence Sterne Trust, UK) The Shandean, P.O. Box 71851, 1008 EB Amsterdam, Netherlands. FAX 31-30-536000. Ed. Peter J. de Voogd. adv.; bk.rev.; illus.; circ. 550 (paid). (back issues avail.) Document type: academic/scholarly publication.
   Description: Publishes previously unpublished material by Laurence Sterne, as well as critical and historical investigations relating to his life and literary works.
   Refereed Serial

895.1   CC   ISSN 0257-5817
SHANDONG WENXUE/SHANDONG LITERATURE. (Text in Chinese) 1980. m. Y15.60($56.70) (Zhongguo Zuojia Xiehui, Shandong Fenhui - China Writers' Association, Shandong Chapter) Shandong Wenxue She, No.10, Honglou Nanlu, Jinan, Shandong 250100, People's Republic of China. TEL 46573. (Dist. overseas by: China International Book Trading Corp., P.O. Box 399, Beijing, P.R.C.; Dist. in US by: China Books & Periodicals, Inc., 2929 24th St., San Francisco, CA 94110) Ed. Qiu Xun. bk.rev.

800   CC   ISSN 1000-4831
SHANGHAI GUSHI/SHANGHAI STORIES. (Text in Chinese) m. Shanghai Qunzhong Yishu-guan - Shanghai Municipal Mass Art Gallery, 226 Huangling Beilu, Shanghai 200003, People's Republic of China. TEL 3278219. Ed. Xu Weixin.

895.1   CC   ISSN 0582-9542
SHANGHAI WENXUE/SHANGHAI LITERATURE; dangdai xintansuo, xinwenxue. (Text in Chinese; table of contents in English) 1959-1963; N.S. 1977. m. Y20.40($72) (Shanghai Wenxue Bianjibu) Shanghai Wenyi Chubanshe - Shanghai Arts Press, 675 Julu Road, Shanghai 200040, People's Republic of China. (Dist. outside China by: China International Book Trading Corp., P.O. Box 399, Beijing, P.R.C.; Dist. in US by: China Books & Periodicals, Inc., 2929 24th St., San Francisco, CA 94110. TEL 415-282-2994) Ed. Ba Jin. adv.
   Formerly: Wenyi Yuebao.

895.1   CC   ISSN 0559-7218
SHANHUA/MOUNTAIN BLOSSOMS (GUIZHOU). (Text in Chinese) m. $49.50. Guizhou Sheng Wenlian, No. 66, Kexue Lu, Guiyang, Guizhou 550002, People's Republic of China. TEL 23844. (Dist. in US by: China Books & Periodicals, Inc., 2929 24th St., San Francisco, CA 94110. TEL 415-282-2994) Ed. Wen Zhiqiang.

810 700   US
SHANKPAINTER. 1970. a. free. Fine Arts Work Center in Provincetown, Inc., Box 565, 24 Pearl St., Provincetown, MA 02657. TEL 508-487-9960. Ed. Joshua Weiner. adv.; bk.rev.; illus.; circ. 700 (controlled). Document type: academic/scholarly publication.
   Description: Publishes the works by the Center's writing and visual fellows.

800   CC
SHANXI MINJIAN WENXUE/SHANXI FOLK LITERATURE. (Text in Chinese) bi-m. Y1.50 per no. Zhongguo Minjian Wenyijia Xiehui, Shanxi Fenhui - China Folk Artists Association, Shanxi Chapter, 62 Yingze Dajie, Taiyuan, Shanxi 030001, People's Republic of China. TEL 4046952. Ed. Liu Qi.

895.1   CC   ISSN 0257-5906
SHANXI WENXUE/SHANXI LITERATURE. (Text in Chinese) 1982. m. $47.70. Shanxi Wenxue Yuekan She, Taiyuan, Shanxi, People's Republic of China. (Dist. by: China Books & Periodicals, Inc., 2929 24th St San Francisco, CA 94110. TEL 415-282-2994)
   Formerly: Fen Shui.

895.1   CC
SHAONAN SHAONU/BOYS AND GIRLS. (Text in Chinese) bi-m. Y10.80. Zhongguo Zuojia Xiehui, Guangdong Fenhui - China Writers' Association, Guangdong Chapter, No. 75, Wende Lu, Guangzhou, Guangdong 510030, People's Republic of China. TEL 330050. Ed. Guan Xizhi.

SHAONIAN WENYI/LITERATURE & ART FOR JUVENILES. see *CHILDREN AND YOUTH — For*

890   IS
AL-SHARQ; literary quarterly. (Text in Arabic) 1970. 4/yr. $50. Al-Mashreq Ltd., P.O. Box 69, Shfaram, Israel. TEL 972-4-966079. FAX 972-4-866129. Ed. Dr. Mahmoud Abassi.

820   UK   ISSN 0037-3346
SHAVIAN. 1946. a. £7($12) Shaw Society, 6 Stanstead Grove, London SE6 4UD, England. (Subscr. to: Mr. D. Sutherland, 155a N. View Rd., London N8 7ND, England) adv.; bk.rev.; cum.index: 1953-1959, 1960-1963. circ. 550. (also avail. in microform from UMI; reprint service avail. from UMI) **Indexed:** Abstr.Engl.Stud., M.L.A. Document type: bulletin.
   —UnCover; UMI.

820   US   ISSN 0741-5842
PR5366
SHAW; the annual of Bernard Shaw Studies. Variant title: Shaw Annual. 1951. a. $35 (foriegn $41) (effective 1993). Pennsylvania State University Press, Barbara Bldg., Ste. C, 820 N. University Dr., University Park, PA 16802-1003. TEL 814-865-1327. FAX 814-863-1408. Ed. Fred D. Crawford. bk.rev.; bibl.; illus.; index, cum.index: 1950-1975. circ. 750. (also avail. in microform from UMI; reprint service avail. from UMI,KTO) **Indexed:** Abstr.Engl.Stud., Amer.Hum.Ind., Curr.Cont., Ind.Bk.Rev.Hum., M.L.A. Document type: academic/scholarly publication.
   —Faxon. CCC.
   Formerly (until 1980): Shaw Review (ISSN 0037-3354)
   Description: Publishes articles on the issues, people, economics, politics, religion, theater, literature and journalism of George Bernard Shaw's period.
   Refereed Serial

800   UK
SHAW SOCIETY NEWSLETTER. 1976. q. £7($12) membership. Shaw Society, 6 Stanstead Grove, London SE6 4UD, England. (Subscr. to: Mr. D.A. Sutherland, 155a North View Rd., London N8 7ND, England) Ed. Barbara Smoker. adv.; bk.rev. circ. 500. (looseleaf format) Document type: newsletter.
   Formerly: Shaw Newsletter (ISSN 0309-0396)

800   CC
SHENZHOU CHUANQI. (Text in Chinese) bi-m. Huashan Wenyi Chubanshe, 45 Beima Lu, Shijiazhuang, Hebei 050071, People's Republic of China. TEL 742501. Ed. Ning Xuancheng.

890   UK
SHETU-BONDHA; the Bengali literary bi-monthly magazine. 1976. bi-m. £2($10) Shetu-Bondha Publications, 113 Harold Rd., London E13 0SG, England. Ed. Khalilur Rahamn. bk.rev. circ. 6,000. (back issues avail.)

895.1   CC   ISSN 0257-5841
PL2653
SHI YUE/OCTOBER; wenxue shuang yuekan. (Text in Chinese) 1978. bi-m. Y22.80($68.20) Beijing Chubanshe, 6, Beisanhuan Zhonglu, Beijing 100011, People's Republic of China. TEL 201-2336. FAX 201-2339. (Dist. overseas by: Guoji Shudian - China International Book Trading Corp., P.O. Box 399, Beijing, P.R.C.; Dist. in US by: China Books & Periodicals, Inc., 2929 24th St., San Francisco, CA 94110. TEL 415-282-2994) Ed. Xie Dajun. circ. 123,000.
   Description: Literary magazine of Beijing.

895.1   CC
SHIDAI WENXUE. (Text in Chinese) bi-m. Zhongguo Zuojia Xiehui, Shandong Fenhui - China Writers' Association, Shandong Chapter, No. 10, Hongjialou Nanlu, Jinan, Shandong 250100, People's Republic of China. TEL 48869. Ed. Feng Deying.

800   CC   ISSN 0583-0206
SHIJIE WENXUE/WORLD LITERATURE. (Text in Chinese; table of contents in English) 1959. bi-m. $47.30. Shehui Kexue Zazhishe, A-158 Gulou Xidajie, Beijing 100720, People's Republic of China. (Dist. in US by: China Books & Periodicals, Inc., 2929 24th St., San Francisco, CA 94110. TEL 415-282-2994)
   Formerly: Yi Wen.
   Description: Introduces modern writers and their works. Also presents important literary trends, critical essays, cultural exchanges, and the latest developments in literature.

810   US   ISSN 0966-5625
SHINY INTERNATIONAL. 1988. q. $12. Shiny International, 39 E. 12th St., Ste. 603, New York, NY 10003.

891.4   II
SHIRAZA. (Editions in Dogri, Gojri, Hindi, Kahmiri, Pahari, Punjabi and Urdu) 1969. bi-m. Rs.10. Jammu and Kashmir Academy of Art, Culture and Languages, Canal Road, Jammu 180001, India. Ed. Amrik Singh. bk.rev.; bibl. circ. 500.

SHOOTING STAR REVIEW; Black literary magazine. see *ETHNIC INTERESTS*

800   US   ISSN 0895-9439
PN3373
SHORT STORY CRITICISM. 1988. irreg., vol.7, 1991. $79. Gale Research Inc., 835 Penobscot Bldg., Detroit, MI 48226-4094. TEL 313-961-2242. FAX 313-961-6083. TELEX 810-221-7086.
   Description: Excerpts significant passages from criticism on the works of the great short story writers of the world throughout history.

810   US   ISSN 0147-7706
PZ1.A1
SHORT STORY INTERNATIONAL. Short title: S S I. 1977. bi-m. $24. International Cultural Exchange, 6 Sheffield Rd., Great Neck, NY 11021. TEL 516-466-4166. (Subscr. to: Box 405, Great Neck, NY 11022) Ed. Sylvia Tankel. circ. 75,000.
   —UnCover.

890   JA
SHOSETSU GENDAI. (Text in Japanese) 1962. m. Kodansha Ltd., 12-21 Otowa 2-chome, Bunkyo-ku, Tokyo 112, Japan. TEL 03-5395-3502. FAX 03-5395-5626. TELEX J34509 KODANSHA. Ed. Shinichi Hirota. circ. 90,000. Document type: consumer publication.
   Description: Publishes serialised novels and short stories for adults.

895.65   JA
SHOSETSU SHINCHO. (Text in Japanese) 1947. m. Shincho-Sha, 71, Yarai-cho, Shinjuku-ku, Tokyo 162, Japan. TEL 03-3266-5235. Ed. Masaji Yokoyama. circ. 360,000.

895.1   CC   ISSN 0583-1288
SHOU HUO/HARVEST: A LITERARY MAGAZINE; a widely circulated national magazine devoted to pure literature. (Text in Chinese) bi-m. Y39 (foreign $70). Shouhuo Wenxue Zazhishe, 675 Julu Lu, Shanghai 200040, People's Republic of China. TEL 2475176. (Dist. outside China by: China International Book Trading Corp., P.O. Box 399, Beijing, P.R.C.; Dist. in US by: China Books & Periodicals, Inc., 2929 24th St., San Francisco, CA 94110. TEL 415-282-2994) Ed. Ba Jin.
   Description: Contains short stories, prose, movie scripts, and other literary works.

SHU LIN/BOOK FOREST. see *PUBLISHING AND BOOK TRADE*

808.87   II
SHUGOOFA; humorous Urdu monthly. (Text in Urdu) 1969. m. Rs.50. 31 Bachelor's Quarters, Moazamjahi Market, Hyderabad 500001, India. TEL 557716. Ed. Dr. S. Mustafa Kamal. adv.; bk.rev.; illus. circ. 2,700.

895.1   US   ISSN 0257-585X
SHUOFANG/SHUOFANG LITERATURE. (Text in Chinese) 1973. m. $44. China Books & Periodicals, Inc., 2929 24th St., San Francisco, CA 94110. TEL 415-282-2994. FAX 415-282-0994.

892.7   TS
SHU'UN ADABIYYAH/LITERARY AFFAIRS. (Text in Arabic) 1987. q. Ittihad Kuttab wa Udaba' al-Imarat - Emirates Writers Union, P.O. Box 4321, Sharjah, United Arab Emirates. TEL 350769. Ed. Muhammad Abdullah al-Muttawi. circ. 2,000.
   Description: Covers contemporary literary issues in the Arab world, with a focus on the U.A.E.

895.1   CC
SICHUAN WENXUE/SICHUAN LITERATURE. (Text in Chinese) 1953. m. Y18. Zhongguo Zuojia Xiehui, Sichuan Fenhui - China Writers' Association, Sichuan Chapter, 85, Sec.2, Hongxing Lu, Chengdu, Sichuan 610012, People's Republic of China. TEL 665271. (Dist. outside China by: China International Book Trading Corp., P.O. Box 399, Beijing, P.R.C.; Dist. in US by: China Books & Periodicals, Inc., 2929 24th St., San Francisco, CA 94110. TEL 415-282-2994) Ed. Deng Yizhong. bk.rev.; illus.
  Formerly (until 1991): Xiandai Zuojia (ISSN 0258-0004)
  Description: Publishes novels, essays, and poetry.

840   FR
SIECLE ECLATE: DADA, SURREALISME ET LES AVANT-GARDES. 1974. irreg. Lettres Modernes, 45 rue Saint-Andre, 14123 Fleury sur Orne, France. TEL 31-84-47-06. FAX 31-84-48-09. circ. 2,500.

860   BO
▼**SIESTA NACIONAL.** 1992. irreg. Producciones AveSol, C. Goitia 155, Cajon Postal 3297, Correo Central, La Paz, Bolivia.

892.4   IS   ISSN 0037-4792
SIFRIYA LAAM. 1958. m. $70. Am Oved Ltd. Publishers, P.O. Box 470, Tel Aviv 61003, Israel. TEL 972-3-291526. FAX 972-2-298911. circ. 20,000. **Document type:** monographic series.

860   US   ISSN 0740-946X
PQ6072
SIGLO XX/20TH CENTURY. (Text and summaries in English and Spanish) 1983. s-a. $25. (Twentieth Century Spanish Association of America) Society of Spanish and Spanish-American Studies, Department of Spanish and Portuguese, University of Colorado, Campus Box 278, Boulder, CO 80309-0278. TEL 303-492-7308. FAX 303-492-3699. Ed. Luis T. Gonzalez. bk.rev.; index. circ. 700. (back issues avail.) **Indexed:** M.L.A. **Document type:** academic/scholarly publication.
  —UnCover.
  Description: Attempts to foster dialogue on twentieth century Spanish and Spanish-American literatures and to facilitate the development of the many critical avenues available to the specialist. *Refereed Serial*

SIGNAL; approaches to children's books. see *CHILDREN AND YOUTH — About*

800   CC   ISSN 1001-0165
SIHAI; dangtai haiwai huaren wenxue. (Text in Chinese) bi-m. Zhongguo Wenlian Chuban Gongsi, 10 Nongzhanguan Nanli, Beijing 100026, People's Republic of China. TEL 5005588. Ed. Qin Mu.
  Description: Presents literary works by Chinese writers living abroad.

830   GW   ISSN 0173-6310
SILHOUETTE; Literatur-International. (Text mainly in German; occasionally in English, Hebrew) 1980. a. DM.10. M. und N. Boesche, Lauristeig 14a, 13456 Berlin, Germany. TEL 030-4019009. Ed. Tilly Boesche-Zacharow. bk.rev. **Document type:** newspaper.

SILLAGES. see *LINGUISTICS*

895.1   US   ISSN 1000-7792
SILU/SILK ROAD. (Text in Chinese) 1978. bi-m. $13.10. (Kashi Wen-lian, CC) China Books & Periodicals, Inc., 2929 24th St., San Francisco, CA 94110. TEL 415-282-2994. FAX 415-282-0994.

810   US   ISSN 0164-1085
PS536.2
SILVERFISH REVIEW. 1979. 2/yr. (Jul., Dec.) $12 to individuals; institutions $15. Box 3541, Eugene, OR 97403. TEL 503-344-5060. Ed. Rodger Moody. adv.; bk.rev. circ. 750. (back issues avail.) **Indexed:** Amer.Hum.Ind., Ind.Amer.Per.Verse.
  Description: Prints poetry, fiction, essays, translations, interviews, reviews and poetry chapbooks.

830   SZ   ISSN 0259-6415
PT1732
SIMPLICIANA; Schriften der Grimmelshausen Gesellschaft. (Text in German) 1979. a. 95 SFr. Verlag Peter Lang AG, Jupiterstr. 15, CH-3000 Bern 15, Switzerland. TEL 031-9411122. FAX 031-9411131. TELEX 912651-PELA-CH. **Document type:** academic/scholarly publication.

800   CL
▼**SIMPSON 7.** 1992. s-a. Sociedad de Escritores de Chile, Almirante Simpson 7, Casilla 4082, Correo Central, Santiago, Chile. Ed. Carlos Olivarez.

890   KO
SIMUNHAK. m. 3000 Won. Simunhak Sa, 34 Hap-dong, Sodaemun-ku, Seoul, S. Korea. Ed. Dok-su Moon. adv.; bk.rev.

810   US   ISSN 0198-9855
PS508.W7
SING HEAVENLY MUSE!; women's poetry and prose. 1978. a. $20 for 3 nos. to individuals; institutions $21. Box 133320, Minneapolis, MN 55414. Ed. Sue Ann Martinson. circ. 500. (back issues avail.)

890   SI   ISSN 0129-3117
SINGAPORE LITERATURE.* (Text in Chinese) 1976. q. S.$19.50 for 10 nos. Singapore Literature Society, 122B Slims Ave., Singapore 1438, Singapore. Ed. Luo-Ming. circ. 8,000.

810   US
SINGLE TODAY.* 1987. 12/yr. $25. 5830 Mt. Moriah Rd., Ste. 27, Memphis, TN 38115-1628. TEL 901-365-3988. Ed. Paula M. Pederson. circ. 15,000.

810   US   ISSN 0891-298X
SINK. 1986. s-a. $5. Sink Press, Box 590095, San Francisco, CA 94159. circ. 250.

800   GW   ISSN 0037-5756
AP30
SINN UND FORM; Beitraege zur Literatur. 1949. bi-m. DM.64.20. Verlag Ruetten und Loening, Franzoesische Str. 32, 10117 Berlin, Germany. TEL 030-22350. FAX 030-2298637. Ed. Sebastian Kleinschmidt. bk.rev.; film rev.; play rev. circ. 3,500. **Indexed:** Arts & Hum.Cit.Ind., Ind.Bk.Rev.Hum., M.L.A. **Document type:** academic/scholarly publication.
  —BLDSC (8285.580000); Faxon; SWETS.

SINO-PLATONIC PAPERS. see *HISTORY — History Of Asia*

800   NE   ISSN 0169-216X
SIRENE. (Text in German) 1985. 3/yr. fl.29. WoltersgroepGroningen b.v. (Subsidiary of: Wolters Kluwer N.V.), Postbus 58, 9700 MB Groningen, Netherlands. TEL 31-50-226922. FAX 31-264866.

SITES. see *ARCHITECTURE*

890   GW
SKANDINAVISTIK; Zeitschrift fuer Sprache, Literatur und Kultur der nordischen Laender. 1970. s-a. DM.46. Verlag J.J. Augustin GmbH, Am Fleth 36-37, 25348 Glueckstadt, Germany. Ed. Otto Oberholzer. **Indexed:** Arts & Hum.Cit.Ind., Bibl.Ling.

839.6 949.12   IC   ISSN 0256-8446
AP41
SKIRNIR; timarit Hins Islenska Bokmenntafelags. 1827. s-a. ISK 2200. Hid Islenska Bokmenntafelag, Sidumula 21, P.O. Box 8935, 128 Reykjavik, Iceland. TEL 354-1-679060. FAX 354-1-679095. Eds. Vilhjalmur Arnason, Astradur Eysteinsson. adv.; bk.rev.; cum.index. circ. 2,000. (back issues avail.) **Indexed:** M.L.A.
  Formerly: Islenzk Sagnabloed.
  Description: Publishes articles on Icelandic literature and culture, as well as on various topics within cultural history, religion, philosophy, and the other humanities.

808   US   ISSN 0737-7002
NX542
SLAVIC AND EAST EUROPEAN ARTS. 1982. 2/yr. $15. (State University of New York, Stony Brook, Department of Germanic and Slavic Languages) Slavic Cultural Center Press, Stony Brook, NY 11794. Ed. E.J. Czerwinski. adv. circ. 1,500.

SLAVIC REVIEW. see *SOCIAL SCIENCES: COMPREHENSIVE WORKS*

SLAVICA LUNDENSIA. see *LINGUISTICS*

SLAVICA SLOVACA. see *LINGUISTICS*

SLAVISTICNA REVIJA; journal for linguistics and literary sciences. see *LINGUISTICS*

SLAVISTISCHE BEITRAEGE. see *LINGUISTICS*

491 940   UK   ISSN 0037-6795
D377.A1
SLAVONIC AND EAST EUROPEAN REVIEW. 1922. q. $150. Modern Humanities Research Association, Kings College, Strand, London WC2R 2LS, England. Ed.Bd. adv.; bk.rev.; illus.; index, cum.index. circ. 1,000. (reprint service avail. from SCH) **Indexed:** Acad.Ind., Amer.Hist.& Life, Arts & Hum.Cit.Ind., Bibl.Ling., Br.Hum.Ind., Hist.Abstr., Hum.Ind., Ind.Bk.Rev.Hum., Lang.& Lang.Behav.Abstr., M.L.A., RILA, SSCI.
  —BLDSC (8309.390000); Faxon; UnCover; SWETS.

800   US
SLIGHTLY WEST. 1985. s-a. $5. Evergreen State College, CAB 380, Olympia, WA 98505. TEL 206-866-6000. Eds. Brian Almquist, Sharon Romeo. circ. 1,000. (back issues avail.)
  Description: Publishes literary works of students at the college.

891.87   XO   ISSN 0037-6973
PG5400
SLOVENSKA LITERATURA/SLOVAK LITERATURE; revue pre literarnu vedu a kritiku. (Text in Slovak; contents page and summaries also in German and Russian) 1954. bi-m. 84 Kcs.($21) (Slovenska Akademia Vied, Literarnovedny Ustav) Veda, Publishing House of the Slovak Academy of Sciences, Klemensova 19, 814 30 Bratislava, Slovakia. (Dist. in Western countries by: John Benjamins B.V., Amsteldijk 44, Amsterdam (Z.), Netherlands) Ed. Dalimir Hajko. adv.; bk.rev.; abstr.; bibl.; cum.index. **Indexed:** Bibl.Ling.
  Description: Evaluates the heritage of Slovak classical literature, and analyzes works and problems of socialist literature.

SLOVENSKA REC/SLOVAK LANGUAGE; casopis pre vyskum a kulturu slovenskeho jazyka. see *LINGUISTICS*

891.87 700   XO   ISSN 0037-7007
SLOVENSKE POHLADY NA LITERATURU A UMENIE. 1846. m. 120 Kcs.($108) (Asociacia Slovenskych Sposovatelov - Association of Slovak Writers) Vydavatel'stvo Slovensky Spisovatel', Laurinska 2, 813 67 Bratislava, Slovakia. (Subscr. to: Slovart, Gottwaldovo nam. 47, 805-32 Bratislava, Slovakia) Ed. Jan Strasser. bk.rev. circ. 6,000.
  Description: For literary scientists, critics, teachers of Slovak in all schools, students, cultural and eductional workers, editors and all those interested in Slovak literature. Contains studies and articles from the history and theory of literature.

810   US   ISSN 0037-721X
SMALL POND MAGAZINE OF LITERATURE; journal of poetry, short fiction and opinion. Variant title: Small Pond. 1964. 3/yr. $9 (effective 1994). Napoleon St. Cyr, Ed. & Pub., Box 664, Stratford, CT 06497. TEL 203-378-4066. adv.; B&W page $40. bk.rev.; cum.index: 1964-69, 1970-74, 1975-78, 1978-81, 1982-84, 1985-88, 1989-91. circ. 300. (also avail. in microform from UMI; reprint service avail. from UMI) **Indexed:** A.I.P.P., Ind.Amer.Per.Verse. **Document type:** academic/scholarly publication.
  —UMI.

810   US   ISSN 0037-7473
SNOWY EGRET. 1922. s-a. $12. Karl Barnebey, Pub., Box 9, Bowling Green, IN 47833. Ed. Philip Repp. bk.rev.; illus. circ. 500. **Indexed:** A.I.P.P.
  Description: Literary, artistic, philosophic and historical responses to nature. Presents artwork, poetry, fiction and non-fiction.

806   AG
SOCIEDAD ARGENTINA DE ESCRITORES. REVISTA. 1975. Sociedad Argentina de Escritores, Cordoba 2054, 1o A, Buenos Aires, Argentina. Ed. Lucila Fevola.
  Formerly: Sociedad Argentina de Escritores. Boletin.

800 410   SP   ISSN 0212-3223
PH5001
SOCIEDAD DE ESTUDIOS VASCOS. CUADERNOS DE SECCION. LENGUA Y LITERATURA. 1982. irreg. Eusko Ikaskuntza, Legazpi, 10-1, 20004 Donostia-San Sebastian, Spain. TEL 425 111.

3672 LITERATURE

840 FR
SOCIETE ACADEMIQUE DES ARTS LIBERAUX DE PARIS. COLLECTION. 1963. 4/yr. free. Societe Academique des Arts Liberaux de Paris, 3 av. de Chanzy, B.P. 49, 94210 la Varenne-St. Hilaire, France. TEL 42-83-36-03. Ed. Claude Cotti. circ. 1,500.
Formerly: Societe Academique des Arts Liberaux de Paris. Anthologie des Societaires (ISSN 0081-072X)

840 FR ISSN 0081-0754
SOCIETE CHATEAUBRIAND. BULLETIN. NOUVELLE SERIE. 1930; N.S. 1957. a. 250 F. Societe Chateaubriand, Secretariat General, 122 bd. de Courcelles, 75017 Paris, France. TEL 42-27-34-41. Ed.Bd. bk.rev. circ. 600. **Document type:** bulletin.

801 400 FR
SOCIETE DE BIBLIOLOGIE ET DE SCHEMATISATION. DOSSIERS. 3/yr. free. Societe de Bibliologie et de Schematisation (S B S), 36 av. d'Italie, Tour Rubis, 75013 Paris, France.
Formerly: Societe de Bibliologie et de Schematisation. Almanach.

800 FR ISSN 0583-8452
PQ2631.R63
SOCIÉTÉ DES AMIS DE MARCEL PROUST ET DES AMIS DE COMBRAY. BULLETIN. 1950. a. 200 F.($45) Societe des Amis de Marcel Proust, 4 rue du docteur Proust, 28120 Illiers-Combray, France. TEL 37-24-30-97. (US addr.: Elyane Dezon-Jones, Dept. of Romance Languages, Washington University, St. Louis, MO 63130. TEL 314-935-5130) Eds. Elyane Dezon-Jones, Jean Milly. adv. contact: Anne Borrel. bk.rev.; bibl. circ. 2,500. (back issues avail.) **Indexed:** M.L.A. **Document type:** academic/scholarly publication, bibliography, bulletin.
—SWETS.
Description: Covers unpublished Proust documents and original studies.

840 FR ISSN 0988-3800
SOCIETE DES ETUDES BLOYENNES. BULLETIN. 1988. bi-m. A.G. Nizet, 17 rue de la Sorbonne, 75005 Paris, France. Ed. Michel Arveiller.

SOCIETE DES SCIENCES ET DES LETTRES DE LODZ. BULLETIN. see SCIENCES: COMPREHENSIVE WORKS

800 700 FR
SOCIETE DES SCIENCES, LETTRES ET ARTS DE BAYONNE. BULLETIN. a. Societe des Sciences, Lettres et Arts de Bayonne, Musee Basque, 1 rue Marengo, 64100 Bayonne, France. (back issues avail.)

820 FR
SOCIETE FRANCAISE SHAKESPEARE. ACTES DU CONGRES. (Text in French) 1981. a. price varies. (Societe Francaise Shakespeare) Librarie Touzot, 38 rue Saint Sulpice, 75278 Paris Cedex 06, France.

800 SW
SOCIETE ROYALE DE LETTRES DE LUND. BULLETIN/KUNGLIGA HUMANISTISKA VETENSKAPSSAMFUNDET I LUND. AARSBERATTELSE. (Text in French) a. A W I International AB, P.O. Box 4267, S-116 91 Stockholm, Sweden. TEL 468-640-8800. FAX 468-641-1180. **Indexed:** Amer.Hist.& Life, Hist.Abstr.

800 FR ISSN 0221-7945
SOCIETE THEOPHILE GAUTIER. BULLETIN. 1977. a. 110 Fr. Universite de Montpellier (University Paul Valery), B.P. 5043, 34032 Montpellier Cedex 1, France. TEL 67-14-20-00. Ed. Claudine Lacoste.

SOCIETY FOR ARMENIAN STUDIES. JOURNAL. see ETHNIC INTERESTS

800 US ISSN 0741-5753
E184.G3
SOCIETY FOR GERMAN - AMERICAN STUDIES. NEWSLETTER. 1979. 4/yr. $20. Society for German - American Studies, c/o William Roba, Treas., 500 Belmont Rd., Bettendorf, IA 52722. TEL 319-359-7531. Ed. La Vern J. Rippley. bk.rev. circ. 1,000. **Document type:** academic/scholarly publication.
Description: Contains articles concerning the society, as well as information about the activities of other organizations with similar purposes. Includes short articles on German-Americana.

850 UK
PQ4835.I7
SOCIETY FOR PIRANDELLO STUDIES. YEARBOOK. 1981. a. £10. Society for Pirandello Studies, Keynes College, University of Kent, Canterbury CT2 7NP, England. FAX 0227-475476. Ed. Elizabeth Schachter. bk.rev.; illus. circ. 300. **Document type:** academic/scholarly publication.
Formerly (until 1991): British Pirandello Society. Yearbook (ISSN 0260-9215)

800 940 700 UK ISSN 0264-8571
SOCIETY FOR RENAISSANCE STUDIES. BULLETIN. 1983. 2/yr. $20 to non-members. Society for Renaissance Studies, c/o Richard Simpson, Hon. Treasurer, 12A Manley St., London NW1 8LT, England. Ed. Constance Blackwell. bk.rev.; tr.lit. circ. 640. (back issues avail.) **Document type:** academic/scholarly publication, bulletin.

SOCIETY FOR THE ADVANCEMENT OF SCANDINAVIAN STUDY. NEWS AND NOTES. see SOCIAL SCIENCES: COMPREHENSIVE WORKS

810 US ISSN 0085-6304
PS501
SOCIETY FOR THE STUDY OF MIDWESTERN LITERATURE. NEWSLETTER. 1971. 3/yr. $5 (includes Midwestern Miscellany). Society for the Study of Midwestern Literature, 240 Ernst Bessey Hall, Michigan State University, East Lansing, MI 48824. TEL 517-355-1855. Ed. David D. Anderson. adv.; bibl. circ. 400. (processed) **Indexed:** Abstr.Engl.Stud., M.L.A., Mich.Mag.Ind.

810 US ISSN 0197-8071
PS261
SOCIETY FOR THE STUDY OF SOUTHERN LITERATURE. NEWSLETTER. Abbreviated title: S S S L. 1968. 2/yr. $4.50 (foreign $5). Society for the Study of Southern Literature, Department of English, Loyola University, New Orleans, LA 70118. TEL 504-865-2476. (Alt. addr.: University of Southern Mississippi, Southern Sta., Box 5078, Hattiesburg, MS 39406-5078) Ed. Stephen Young. bibl. circ. 400. **Document type:** academic/scholarly publication, newsletter.
Description: Reports on scholarly work in progress in Southern literature. Announces special conferences of interest to the membership.

800 CN ISSN 0701-9890
SOCIETY OF THE SEVEN SAGES NEWSLETTER. 1976. a. Dalhousie University, Department of French, Halifax, NS B3H 3J5, Canada. TEL 902-494-2430. Ed. Hans R. Runte. adv.; bk.rev. circ. 120. (back issues avail.) **Document type:** newsletter.
Description: Literary research on the Book of Sinbad and the Seven Sages of Rome.

800 FR ISSN 0985-5939
SOCIOCRITICISM. (Editions in English, French, Spanish) 2/yr. Universite de Montpellier (Universite Paul Valery), B.P. 5043, 34032 Montpellier Cedex 1, France. TEL 67-14-20-00. Ed. Edmond Cros.
—BLDSC (8319.565000); UnCover.
Description: Dedicated to promoting a new conception of the sociohistorical study of literature and culture.

800 301 US ISSN 1043-5727
SOCIOCRITICISM: LITERATURE, SOCIETY, AND HISTORY. irreg. Peter Lang Publishing, Inc., 62 W. 45th St., 4th Fl., New York, NY 10036. TEL 212-302-6740. FAX 212-302-7574. Ed. James F. Gaines. **Document type:** academic/scholarly publication.
Description: Focuses on the early modern period in the Western European literatures (approximately 1550-1850). Examines the relationship between literary art forms and socio-historical structures, tensions, or mentalities.

810 US
SOME FRIENDS. 1972. s-a. $3. Some Friends Press, c/o Terry J. Cooper, Ed., Box 6395, Tyler, TX 75711-6395. TEL 214-597-1258. adv. circ. 500.

810 US
SOME OTHER MAGAZINE. 1978. s-a. $6. Some Other Magazine, 47 Hazen Ct., Wayne, NJ 07470. TEL 201-696-9230. Ed. Robert Richman. adv.; bk.rev. circ. 250. (back issues avail.)

808.068 920 US ISSN 0276-816X
PN451
SOMETHING ABOUT THE AUTHOR. 1971. irreg., vol.67, 1992. $79. Gale Research Inc., 835 Penobscot Bldg., Detroit, MI 48226. TEL 313-961-2242. FAX 313-961-6083. TELEX 810-221-7086. Ed. Donna Olendorf. bibl.; illus.; cum.index. (back issues avail.)
Description: Focuses on contemporary authors and illustrators of children's book, and includes list of works, career and personal data on each author.

895.7 CC
SONGHUA JIANG/SONGHUA RIVER. (Text in Korean) bi-m. Harbin Shi Chaoxianzu Yishuguan - Harbin Korean Art Center, 43, Zhongyang Dajie, Daoli-qu, Harbin, Heilongjiang 150010, People's Republic of China. TEL 415131. Ed. Li Qingzhao.

800 US
SONOMA MANDALA. 1974. a. $6. Sonoma State University, English Department, Rohnert Park, CA 94928. TEL 717-664-2140. FAX 707-664-3902. Ed. Elizabeth Herron. circ. 500. (back issues avail.)
Description: International literary magazine focusing on fiction and poetry.
Refereed Serial

810.8 US ISSN 0275-5203
PS1
SONORA REVIEW. 1980. a. $5 per no. University of Arizona, Department of English, Sonora Review, Tucson, AZ 85721. TEL 602-621-1836. Ed. Tony Brown. bk.rev. circ. 600. (back issues avail.) **Document type:** academic/scholarly publication.
Supersedes: University of Arizona. Department of English. Graduate English Papers (ISSN 0066-7536)
Description: Presents contemporary fiction, nonfiction and poetry.

SOOCHOW JOURNAL OF FOREIGN LANGUAGES AND LITERATURES. see LINGUISTICS

SOUNDINGS (SANTA BARBARA); collections of the University Library. see LIBRARY AND INFORMATION SCIENCES

800 US
SOUNDINGS EAST. 1978. s-a. $6. Salem State College, 352 Lafayette St., Dept. of English, Salem, MA 01970-4589. TEL 508-741-6270. Ed. Betsy Murphy. bk.rev.; illus. circ. 2,500. **Indexed:** A.I.P.P.
Formerly: Soundings (Salem); **Supersedes** (1973-1978): Gone Soft (ISSN 0362-1219)
Description: Contains original poetry, fiction and artwork.

SOUTH AFRICAN JOURNAL OF AFRICAN LANGUAGES. see LINGUISTICS

800 US ISSN 0038-2833
SOUTH & WEST;* an international literary magazine. 1962. q. 2301 Quarry Dr., Van Buren, AR 72956-6440. Ed. Sue Boyd.

492 US ISSN 0275-9527
PK180
SOUTH ASIAN REVIEW.* 1977. s-a. $10. South Asian Literary Association, c/o Univ. of North Florida, Jacksonville, FL 32216. Ed. Satya P. Pachori. circ. 100. **Indexed:** M.L.A.

806 US
SOUTH ATLANTIC MODERN LANGUAGE ASSOCIATION AWARDS. 1977. a. price varies. University of Georgia Press, 330 Research Dr., Athens, GA 30602-4901. TEL 706-369-6130. FAX 706-369-6131.

SOUTH ATLANTIC REVIEW. see LINGUISTICS

810 US ISSN 0038-3163
PS558.S6
SOUTH CAROLINA REVIEW. 1968. 2/yr. $7 to individuals; institutions $8.75; foreign $8.50. Clemson University, Department of English, Clemson, SC 29634-1503. TEL 803-656-3151. Ed. R.J. Calhoun. adv.; bk.rev. circ. 600. (back issues avail.) **Indexed:** A.I.P.P., Abstr.Engl.Stud., Amer.Hum.Ind., Bk.Rev.Ind. (1980-), Child.Bk.Rev.Ind. (1980-), Ind.Amer.Per.Verse, Ind.Bk.Rev.Hum., M.L.A.
—BLDSC (8350.200000); Faxon.

LITERATURE 3673

810   US   ISSN 0038-3368
AP2
SOUTH DAKOTA REVIEW. 1963. 4/yr. $15 (foreign $16). University of South Dakota, Department of English, 414 E. Clark St., Vermillion, SD 57069-2390. TEL 605-677-5229. Ed. John R. Milton. bibl.; illus.; index. circ. 600. (also avail. in microform from UMI; back issues avail.; reprint service avail. from UMI) **Indexed:** A.I.P.P., Abstr.Engl.Stud., Amer.Hum.Ind., Arts & Hum.Cit.Ind., Curr.Cont., Ind.Amer.Per.Verse, M.L.A.
—BLDSC (8351.350000); Faxon; UnCover; UMI.
Description: Includes fiction, poetry, articles and essays, frequently with an eclectic emphasis on the American West.

SOUTHEASTERN FRONT. see ART

SOUTHEASTERN WRITING CENTER ASSOCIATION. SELECTED PAPERS. see EDUCATION — Teaching Methods And Curriculum

820   AT   ISSN 0038-3732
AP7
SOUTHERLY; a review of Australian literature. 1939. q. Aus.$35 (foreign Aus.$45). English Association, Sydney Branch, 2 Belgrave St., Cremorne, N.S.W. 2090, Australia. TEL 02-692-2589. FAX 02-692-4203. (Subscr. to: P.O. Box 187, Rozelle, N.S.W. 2039, Australia) Ed. Elizabeth Webby. adv.; bk.rev.; index. circ. 1,200. (also avail. in microform from UMI; reprint service avail. from UMI) **Indexed:** Abstr.Engl.Stud., Arts & Hum.Cit.Ind., Aus.P.A.I.S., Curr.Cont., Gdlns.
—UMI.
Description: Contains literary criticism, interviews with writers, contemporary stories and poetry.

800   US
SOUTHERN CALIFORNIA ANTHOLOGY. 1983. a. $7.95. University of Southern California, Master of Professional Writing Program, WPH 404, Los Angeles, CA 90089-4034. TEL 213-740-3252. Eds. James Ragan, Richard Paul Aloia, Jr. circ. 1,000. (back issues avail.) **Document type:** academic/scholarly publication.
Description: Presents poetry, short stories, novel excerpts and interviews with writers.

810   US   ISSN 0038-4291
PS261
SOUTHERN LITERARY JOURNAL. 1968. s-a. $17 (foreign $20). (University of North Carolina at Chapel Hill, Department of English) University of North Carolina Press, Box 2288, Chapel Hill, NC 27515-2288. TEL 919-966-3561. FAX 919-966-3829. Eds. Fred Hobson, Kimbal King. adv.; bk.rev.; index. circ. 700. (also avail. in microform from UMI; reprint service avail. from UMI) **Indexed:** Abstr.Engl.Stud., Amer.Hist.& Life, Arts & Hum.Cit.Ind., Curr.Cont., Hist.Abstr., Hum.Ind., Ind.Bk.Rev.Hum., M.L.A. **Document type:** academic/scholarly publication.
—BLDSC (8354.290000); Faxon; UnCover; UMI. Refereed Serial

800   US   ISSN 1042-6604
F209
SOUTHERN READER.* 1989. q. $13. Southern Reader Corporation, Box 3844, Jackson, TN 38303-0844. TEL 601-234-2596. FAX 601-234-2572. Ed. R.J. Bedwell. adv.; bk.rev. circ. 7,000.
Description: Contemporary journalism and fiction on the South.

820   AT   ISSN 0038-4526
PR1
SOUTHERN REVIEW; literary and interdisciplinary essays. 1963. 4/yr. Aus.$25 to individuals; institutions Aus.$40; students and unemployed Aus.$15 (effective 1994). University of Adelaide, Department of English, G.P.O. Box 498, Adelaide, S.A. 5001, Australia. TEL 61-8-303-5627. FAX 61-8-303-4341. Ed.Bd. adv.; bk.rev. page Aus.$100. bk.rev.; index; circ. 500 (paid). (back issues avail.) **Indexed:** Abstr.Engl.Stud., Arts & Hum.Cit.Ind., Aus.P.A.I.S., Curr.Cont., M.L.A. **Document type:** academic/scholarly publication.
—BLDSC (8354.920000); Faxon.
Description: Publishes critical articles, reviews and review articles on literature, literary theory and cultural studies, as well as poems and short stories.

810   US   ISSN 0038-4534
AP2
SOUTHERN REVIEW; a literary and critical quarterly magazine. 1935-1942; resumed 1965. q. $18 to individuals; institutions $35. Southern Review, 43 Allen Hall, Baton Rouge, LA 70803-5005. Eds. James Olney, Dave Smith. adv.; bk.rev.; index. circ. 3,000. (also avail. in microform from UMI; microfiche from KTO; reprint service avail. from UMI,KTO) **Indexed:** A.I.P.P., Abstr.Engl.Stud., Amer.Hist.& Life, Amer.Hum.Ind., Arts & Hum.Cit.Ind., Bk.Rev.Ind. (1976-), Child.Bk.Rev.Ind. (1976-), Curr.Cont., Hist.Abstr., Hum.Ind., Ind.Amer.Per.Verse, Ind.Bk.Rev.Hum.
—BLDSC (8354.932000); Faxon; UnCover; SWETS; UMI.

SOUTHWESTERN (GEORGETOWN). see COLLEGE AND ALUMNI

808   US   ISSN 0276-7155
PS501
SOUTHWESTERN REVIEW. s-a. $2. University of Southwestern Louisiana, Department of English, Box 44691, Lafayette, LA 70504. TEL 318-231-6908. Ed. Laura Ellen Brown. circ. 1,000.
Description: Presents poetry, fiction, black and white photography, and black and white artwork.

810   US   ISSN 0098-499X
SOU'WESTER (EDWARDSVILLE); literary magazine. 1960. 3/yr. $10. Southern Illinois University, Edwardsville, Edwardsville, IL 62026-1438. TEL 618-692-3190. Ed. Fred W. Robbins. circ. 300 (controlled). (back issues avail) **Document type:** academic/scholarly publication.
Description: Contains poetry and short fiction.

891.7   RU   ISSN 0136-8095
SOVETSKAYA LITERATURA, TRADITSII I NOVATORSTVO. 1976. irreg. 0.68 Rub. per issue. Sankt-Peterburgskii Universitet, Universitetskaya Nab. 7-9, St. Petersburg V-164, Russia. Ed. L. Gladkovskaya. circ. 6,550.

891   FR   ISSN 0303-111X
SOVETSKIE LJUDI SEGODNJA/VIE QUOTIDIENNE EN U.R.S.S. PRISE SUR LE VIF. (In two series Textes Litteraires and Dossiers) (Text in Russian; notes and comments in French or Russian) 1969. irreg. price varies. Institut d'Etudes Slaves, 9 rue Michelet, 75006 Paris, France.

SOW'S EAR. see LITERARY AND POLITICAL REVIEWS

820   NZ   ISSN 0313-1459
SPAN. 1975. 2/yr. Aus.$25 to individuals; institutions $40. South Pacific Association for Commonwealth Literature and Language Studies, University of Waikato, Private Bag 1035, Hamilton, New Zealand. Ed. Ralph Grove. bk.rev.; bibl.; cum.index. circ. 250. (back issues avail.) **Document type:** academic/scholarly publication.

860 460   UK
SPANISH STUDIES; modern literature, history and politics. 1979. a. £10 for 4 years. c/o Mrs. Olga Kenyon, E. Pub., 29 Woodsyre, Sydenham Hill, London SE26 6SS, England. TEL 081-670-7073. adv.; bk.rev.; play rev. circ. 300. (back issues avail.) **Document type:** academic/scholarly publication.

SPANISH TODAY. see LINGUISTICS

810   US
SPARROW (SANTA ROSA).* 1972. m. $0.75 per no. Black Sparrow Press, 24 10th St., Santa Rosa, CA 95401-4714. Ed. John Martin. circ. 1,500. **Indexed:** Abstr.Engl.Stud.

890 970.1   US
SPAWNING THE MEDICINE RIVER. 3/yr. $6. Institute of American Indian Arts Press, St. Michael Dr., Santa Fe, NM 87501. Ed. Philip Foss.

SPECIMINA PHILOLOGIAE SLAVICAE. see LINGUISTICS

SPECTRUM (AMHERST). see ART

800 378   US   ISSN 0895-8270
SPECTRUM (PAXTON). 1985. s-a. $7. Anna Maria College, Sunset Lane, Box 72-F, Paxton, MA 01612. TEL 508-849-3450. Ed. Robert Goepfert. bk.rev. circ. 1,000. **Document type:** academic/scholarly publication.
Description: Multidisciplinary presentation of scholarly articles, fiction, poetry, art, and photography.

SPECULUM; a journal of Medieval studies. see HISTORY — History Of Europe

SPECULUM ANNIVERSARY MONOGRAPHS. see HISTORY — History Of Europe

800   IT
SPECULUM ARTIUM. (Text in English, French and Italian) irreg., latest no.19. price varies. Angelo Longo Editore, Via Paolo Costa 33, P.O. Box 431, 48100 Ravenna, Italy. TEL 0544-217026. Ed. Aldo Scaglione. circ. 2,500. **Indexed:** M.L.A. **Document type:** monographic series.

830 301   NE   ISSN 0165-084X
SPEKTATOR; tijdschrift voor neerlandistiek. 1970. 4/yr. fl.87.50 to individuals (foreign fl.115); institutions fl.135 (foreign fl.150) (effective 1994). (Stichting Heliogabalos) Van Gorcum en Co. B.V., P.O. Box 43, 9400 AA Assen, Netherlands. TEL 31-5920-46846. FAX 31-5920-72064. Ed.Bd. adv.; bk.rev.; bibl. circ. 300. **Indexed:** Bibl.Ling., M.L.A., Sociol.Abstr. **Document type:** academic/scholarly publication.
—SWETS.

SPEKTRUM; Vierteljahresschrift fuer Dichtung und Originalgrafik. see ART

830   GW   ISSN 0177-6185
SPEKTRUM DES GEISTES; Literaturkalender. 1951. a. DM.14.80. Husum Druck- und Verlagsgesellschaft mbH, Postfach 1480, 25804 Husum, Germany. TEL 04841-6081. FAX 04841-61397. Eds. Alix and Ingwert Paulsen. adv.; bk.rev. circ. 8,000. **Document type:** academic/scholarly publication.

820   US   ISSN 0038-7347
SPENSER NEWSLETTER. 1970. 3/yr. $6.50 (foreign $11) (effective 1993-94). Kansas State University, Department of English, 122 Denison Hall, Manhattan, KS 66506-0701. TEL 913-532-6716. FAX 913-532-7004. Ed. Jerome S. Dees. adv.; bk.rev.; index. circ. 600. (also avail. in microform from UMI; reprint service avail. from UMI) **Indexed:** Ind.Bk.Rev.Hum. **Document type:** newsletter.
—Faxon; UMI.
Description: Contains book notices, abstract and notices of recent articles, and announcements such as calls for papers and conference listings.

809   CN   ISSN 0319-0188
SPHINX; a magazine of literature and society. 1974. s-a. Can.$3.50 to individuals; institutions Can.$7.50. University of Regina, Department of English, Regina, Sask. S4S 0A2, Canada. Ed.Bd. bk.rev.; illus. circ. 250. (also avail. in microform from MML) **Indexed:** M.L.A.
—BLDSC (8413.615000).

SPHINX WOMEN'S INTERNATIONAL LITERARY ART REVIEW. see ART

839.31   BE   ISSN 0038-7479
SPIEGEL DER LETTEREN; tijdschrift voor Nederlandse literatuurgeschiedenis en voor literatuurwetenschap. (Text in Dutch) 1956. 4/yr. 1280 BEF (effective 1994). Editions Peeters s.p.r.l., Bondgenotenlaan 153, B-3000 Louvain, Belgium. TEL 32-16-235170. FAX 32-16-228500. Ed.Bd. bk.rev.; index. (back issues avail.) **Indexed:** Arts & Hum.Cit.Ind., M.L.A. **Document type:** academic/scholarly publication.

800   US
▼**SPILLED INK.** 1993. q. $3 per no. Box 8362, San Jose, CA 95155. Ed. D.O.C. Curtis.

SPIRAL. see WOMEN'S INTERESTS

LITERATURE

800 US ISSN 0364-4014
PS580
THE SPIRIT THAT MOVES US. 1975 (vol.12). irreg. price varies. Spirit That Moves Us Press, Inc., Box 820, Jackson Heights, NY 11372-0820. TEL 718-426-8788. Ed. Morty Sklar. adv.; index. circ. 2,500. (back issues avail.) **Indexed:** Amer.Hum.Ind., Ind.Amer.Per.Verse.
Description: Presents fiction, poetry and art. Special issues include one of a collection of poetry by Jaroslav Seifert, published before he won the Nobel Prize for literature.

808 796.357 US ISSN 8755-741X
SPITBALL; the literary baseball magazines. 1981. q. $16. c/o Mike Shannon, Ed., 6224 Collegevue, Cincinnati, OH 45224-1922. TEL 513-541-4296. adv.: page $100; adv. contact: Mark Schraf. bk.rev.; film rev.; play rev.; illus. circ. 10,000. (back issues avail.) **Document type:** consumer publication.
Description: Devoted to baseball; includes poetry and fiction, columns on baseball art, memorabilia and classic baseball books.

810 US
SPONTANEOUS COMBUSTION. 1991. irreg. (1-2/yr.) $3.50 for 2 issues. 3320 Vista Rocosa, Escondido, CA 92029. Ed. James C. Kaufman.
Description: Publishes poetry, fiction, art and cartoons.

800 GW ISSN 0038-8475
P3
SPRACHE IM TECHNISCHEN ZEITALTER; Literatur im technischen Zeitalter. 1961. q. DM.50. Aufbau-Verlag Berlin und Weimar, Franzoesische Str. 32, 10117 Berlin, Germany. TEL 030-22350. FAX 030-2298637. (Subscr. to: Inter Abo Betreuungs GmbH, Postfach 53, 12413 Berlin, Germany. TEL 030-68834451. FAX 030-68834490) Eds. Walter Hoellerer, Norbert Miller. adv.; bk.rev.; charts; index. circ. 1,800. **Indexed:** Phil.Ind. **Document type:** academic/scholarly publication.
—SWETS.
Description: Forum for discussing and presenting contemporary and modern literature.

SPRACHE UND LITERATUR IN WISSENSCHAFT UND UNTERRICHT. see LINGUISTICS

800 AU ISSN 0038-8483
P3 CODEN: SPRAEK
SPRACHKUNST; Beitraege zur Literaturwissenschaft. (Text in English, French, German and Russian) 1970. s-a. DM.60. Verlag der Oesterreichischen Akademie der Wissenschaften, Dr. Ignaz-Seipel-Platz 2, A-1010 Vienna, Austria. FAX 0222-5139541. Ed.Bd. bk.rev.; index. **Indexed:** Arts & Hum.Cit.Ind., Can.Rev.Comp.Lit, Ind.Bk.Rev.Hum., M.L.A.

800 US ISSN 0884-1934
SQUARE ONE; a magazine of fiction. 1984. a. $14 for 2 nos. Tarkus Press, Box 11921, Milwaukee, WI 53211. TEL 414-964-1994. Ed. William D. Gagliani. adv. circ. 250. (back issues avail.)
Description: Varied general fiction for well-educated readers interested in the human and inhuman experience.

860 AG
▼**SR. NEON.** 1992. s-a. $9 per no. L.J. Silver s.r.l., Casilla de Correos 149, Suc. 24, 1424 Buenos Aires, Argentina. TEL 01-92-8599. adv.; bk.rev. circ. 500.

SRI AUROBINDO. ARCHIVES AND RESEARCH. see PHILOSOPHY

891.92 491.92 YU ISSN 0081-3990
SRPSKA AKADEMIJA NAUKA I UMETNOSTI. ODELJENJE JEZIKA I KNJIZEVNOSTI. POSEBNA IZDANJA. (Text in Serbo-Croatian; summaries in English, French, German or Russian) 1950. irreg. price varies. Srpska Akademija Nauka i Umetnosti, Knez Mihailova 35, 11001 Belgrade, Serbia, Yugoslavia. FAX 38-11-182-825. TELEX 72593 SANU YU. (Dist. by: Prosveta, Terazije 16, Belgrade, Serbia, Yugoslavia) circ. 1,000.

820 UK ISSN 0038-9366
AP4
STAND MAGAZINE. 1952. q. $25. Stand Magazine, 179 Wingrove Rd., Newcastle-upon-Tyne NE4 9DA, England. TEL 091-273-3280. Ed.Bd. adv.; bk.rev.; cum.index. circ. 4,500. **Indexed:** Abstr.Engl.Stud., Bk.Rev.Ind. (1988-), Child.Bk.Rev.Ind. (1988-), Curr.Cont., Ind.Amer.Per.Verse, Ind.Bk.Rev.Hum. **Document type:** academic/scholarly publication.
—BLDSC (8430.241500); Faxon; UnCover.
Description: Short stories, poetry and reviews.

840 850 US
STANFORD FRENCH & ITALIAN STUDIES. 1975. irreg. (approx. 4 vols./yr.). price varies. (Stanford University, Department of French and Italian) Anma Libri, Box 876, Saratoga, CA 95071. TEL 408-741-1522. Ed. Marc Bertrand. **Indexed:** M.L.A. **Document type:** academic/scholarly publication, monographic series.
Description: Monographs on French and Italian language literature, culture and history.

840 944 US ISSN 0163-657X
PQ1
STANFORD FRENCH REVIEW. (Text in English and French) 1977. s-a. $74.50. (Stanford University, Department of French & Italian) Anma Libri, Box 876, Saratoga, CA 95071. TEL 408-741-1522. Ed. Jean-Pierre Dupu. (back issues avail.; reprint service avail. from ISI) **Indexed:** Arts & Hum.Cit.Ind., Curr.Cont., M.L.A. **Document type:** academic/scholarly publication.
—BLDSC (8431.370000); Faxon; UnCover.
Description: Scholarly articles on French literature, language and culture.

840 US ISSN 0730-6857
PQ4001
STANFORD ITALIAN REVIEW. (Text in English and Italian) 1979. irreg., vol.11, nos.1-2, 1992. $69.50. (Stanford University, Department of French and Italian) Anma Libri, Box 876, Saratoga, CA 95071. TEL 408-741-1522. Ed. John Freccero. **Indexed:** Arts & Hum.Cit.Ind., M.L.A. **Document type:** academic/scholarly publication.
—BLDSC (8432.060000); UnCover.
Description: Scholarly articles on Italian literature, language and culture.

808 US ISSN 0886-666X
STANFORD LITERATURE REVIEW. 1984. s-a. $69.50. (Stanford University, Department of French and Italian) Anma Libri, Box 876, Saratoga, CA 95071. TEL 408-741-1522. Ed. Hans Ulrich Gumbrecht. **Indexed:** M.L.A. **Document type:** academic/scholarly publication.
—BLDSC (8432.280000); UnCover.
Description: Scholarly articles on comparative literature.

808 US
STANFORD LITERATURE STUDIES. 1984. 2/yr. $37.50 per vol. (Stanford University, Department of French and Italian) Anma Libri, Box 876, Saratoga, CA 95071. TEL 408-741-1522. **Document type:** monographic series.
Description: Monographs on French, Italian and comparative literature.

053.1 GW
STAUFFENBURG COLLOQUIUM. irreg., no.33, 1994. DM.68. Stauffenburg Verlag, Postfach 2567, 72015 Tuebingen, Germany. TEL 07071-78091. FAX 07071-75288. Ed. Juergen Schroeder. **Document type:** monographic series.

800 700 RM ISSN 0039-0852
STEAUA. (Text in French and Rumanian) 1953. m. 144 lei($10) Uniunea Scriitorilor din Republica Socialista Romania, Calea Victoriei 115, Bucharest, Rumania. (Subscr. to: Romania, Piata Presei Libere nr. 1, BP 33-28, 71341 Bucharest, Rumania) Ed. Aurel Rau. bk.rev.; illus.; index. circ. 3,500. **Indexed:** M.L.A.

810 US
STEINBECK BIBLIOGRAPHY SERIES. 1986. irreg. price varies. Steinbeck Research Institute, c/o English Dept., Ball State Univ., Muncie, IN 47306. TEL 317-285-5688. Ed. Tetsumaro Hayashi. **Document type:** academic/scholarly publication.

810 016 US
STEINBECK ESSAY SERIES. 1986. irreg. price varies. Steinbeck Research Institute, c/o English Dept., Ball State Univ., Muncie, IN 47306. TEL 317-285-5688. Ed. Tetsumaro Hayashi. **Document type:** academic/scholarly publication.

810 US ISSN 0085-6746
PS3537.T3234
STEINBECK MONOGRAPH SERIES. 1971. irreg., no.13, 1988. price varies. Steinbeck Research Institute, c/o English Dept., Ball State Univ., Muncie, IN 47306. TEL 317-285-5688. Ed. Tetsumaro Hayashi. adv.; bk.rev. circ. 600. (also avail. in microfilm from UMI; reprint service avail. from UMI,KTO) **Indexed:** Abstr.Engl.Stud., Arts & Hum.Cit.Ind., Curr.Cont., M.L.A. **Document type:** monographic series.

810 US ISSN 0039-100X
PS3537.T3234
STEINBECK QUARTERLY. 1968. 2/yr. $25 (foreign $30). Steinbeck Research Institute, c/o English Dept., Ball State Univ., Muncie, IN 47306. TEL 317-285-5688. Ed. Tetsumaro Hayashi. adv.; bk.rev.; abstr.; bibl.; index. circ. 650. (also avail. in microform from UMI; reprint service avail. from UMI,KTO) **Indexed:** Abstr.Engl.Stud., Amer.Hum.Ind., Arts & Hum.Cit.Ind., Curr.Cont., M.L.A. **Document type:** academic/scholarly publication.
—BLDSC (8464.109800); Faxon; UnCover; UMI.
Formerly (until 1969): Steinbeck Newsletter.

830 AU
STERZ; Zeitschrift fuer Literatur, Kunst und Kulturpolitik. 1977. q. S.180($25) Mandellstr. 10, A-8010 Graz, Austria. TEL 0316-824146. Ed.Bd. adv. circ. 8,000.

STILETTO. see LITERATURE — Poetry

809 SW ISSN 0491-0869
STOCKHOLM STUDIES IN HISTORY OF LITERATURE. (Subseries of Acta Universitatis Stockholmiensis) (Text in English and Spanish) 1956. irreg. price varies. (Stockholms Universitet) A W I International AB, P.O. Box 4627, S-116 91 Stockholm, Sweden. TEL 468-640-8800. FAX 468-641-1180. Eds. O. Lindberger, I. Jonsson. (back issues avail.)

890 SW
STOCKHOLM STUDIES IN RUSSIAN LITERATURE. (Subseries of Acta Universitatis Stockholmiensis) (Text in Russian; summaries in English) irreg. price varies. (Stockholms Universitet) A W I International AB, P.O. Box 4627, S-116 91 Stockholm, Sweden. TEL 468-40-8800. FAX 468-41-1180. Ed. Nils Ake Nilsson. **Indexed:** M.L.A.

820 SP
STONY THURSDAY BOOK: CUADERNO DE MADRID. (Text in English, Irish, Spanish or a Celtic language; summaries in English or Spanish for Celtic language texts) 1975. a. I£3 (750 ptas.). Arganzuela, 18, 2o A, 28005 Madrid, Spain. Eds. Liam Liddy, Miguel Ortega. bk.rev.; play rev.; bibl.; illus. circ. 2,000. (back issues avail.) **Document type:** academic/scholarly publication.
Formerly: Stony Thursday Book.

800 945 IT
STORIA E LETTERATURA. 1969. irreg., no.183, 1991. price varies. Edizioni di Storia e Letteratura s.r.l., Via Lancellotti, 18, 00186 Rome, Italy. TEL 6540556. FAX 06-6872567.

808 US ISSN 0742-2113
PN6010.5
STORIES. 1982. 3/yr. $12. Stories and Stories for Children, Inc., Box 1467, Arlington, MA 02174-0022. Ed. Amy R. Kaufman. adv.: B&W page $200; 7 x 10. circ. 5,000.
—UnCover.

820 US ISSN 0081-5861
STORIES FROM THE HILLS. 1970. a. $4. Morris Harvey College Publications, Charleston, WV 25304. TEL 304-346-9471. Ed. William Plumley. circ. 2,000.

800   US   ISSN 1045-0831
PZ1.A1
STORY. 1931. q. $19. F & W Publications, Inc., 1507 Dana Ave., Cincinnati, OH 45207. TEL 513-531-2222. FAX 513-531-4744. Ed. Lois Rosenthal. adv. circ. 25,000. (reprint service avail. from KTO) **Indexed:** Access (1990-).
—UMI.
 Description: Features general interest stories of literary merit.

800   US   ISSN 0039-1999
STORY ART; a magazine for storytellers. 1934. q. $6. National Story League, c/o Gertrude Stirnaman, 3516 Russell, Ste. 6, St. Louis, MO 63104. (Subscr. to: Mrs. Thomas G. Reighart, Ed., 872 High St., No. 5710, Canal Fulton, OH 44614) bk.rev. circ. 3,100. **Document type:** bulletin.

800   US
▼**STORY RHYME GREETING LETTERS.** 1992. a. $5 (Canada $7; elsewhere $8). Story Rhyme Greetings, Box 416, Denver, CO 80201-0416. TEL 303-575-5676. Ed.Bd. **Document type:** newsletter.

800   US
STORYETTE. q. $24. Lott Publishing Co., Box 1107, Santa Monica, CA 90406. TEL 310-397-4217. Ed. Davis Lott. circ. 10,000. (tabloid format)
 Description: Offers short short stories.

800   US   ISSN 1041-0708
STORYQUARTERLY. 1975. 2/yr. $12 for 4 nos. to individuals; institutions $14. StoryQuarterly, Inc., Box 1416, Northbrook, IL 60065. TEL 708-564-8891. (Dist. by: B. DeBoer, 113 Centre St., Nutley, NJ 07110) Eds. Anne Brashler, Diane Williams. adv.; bk.rev.; illus. circ. 1,500. **Indexed:** Amer.Hum.Ind.
—Faxon.

808   US   ISSN 1048-1354
STORYTELLING MAGAZINE. 1984. bi-m. $40 membership (Canada $50; elsewhere $75) includes Inside Story and National Directory of Storytelling. National Storytelling Association, Box 309, Jonesborough, TN 37659. TEL 615-753-2171. FAX 615-753-9331. Ed. Mary C. Weaver. adv.; bk.rev.; illus. circ. 12,000.
—UnCover.
 Formerly (until 1989): National Storytelling Journal (ISSN 0743-1104)
 Description: Showcases contemporary storytelling and the oral tradition and informs readers of developments in the art and its applications, particularly in education and the helping professions.

STORYWORKS. see *CHILDREN AND YOUTH — For*

808   US
STRAITS. 1982. m. $5. Detroit River Press, c/o Glen Mannisto, 39 Moss, Highland Park, MI 48203.

800   US
STREAMS. 1986. a. $5. (Waterways Project) Ten Penny Players, Inc., 393 St. Pauls Ave., Staten Island, NY 10304-2127. TEL 718-442-7429. FAX 718-442-4978. circ. 6,000.
 Description: Anthology of young adult writing from New York City alternative high school and programs students.

839.7 792.9   SW   ISSN 0282-8006
PT9816
STRINDBERGIANA. 1985. a. $30 (typically set in May). Strinbergssaellskapet - Strindberg Society, Drottninggatan 85, S-11160 Stockholm, Sweden. TEL 46-8-11-37-89. FAX 46-8-11-01-41. bk.rev.

809   IT   ISSN 0039-2618
STRUMENTI CRITICI. 1966. 3/yr. L.120000. Societa Editrice Il Mulino, Strada Maggiore, 37, 40125 Bologna, Italy. TEL 051-256011. FAX 051-256034. Ed.Bd. adv.; bk.rev.; bibl.; index. circ. 1,000. (back issues avail.) **Indexed:** Arts & Hum.Cit.Ind., Bibl.Ling., Can.Rev.Comp.Lit., Curr.Cont., M.L.A.
—SWETS.

STUDI ALBANESI. STUDI E TESTI. see *LINGUISTICS*

850   IT
STUDI DANTESCHI (FLORENCE). 1920. a. L.120000($45) (Societa Dantesca Italiana) Casa Ed. Le Lettere, Costa S. Giorgio 28, Florence, Italy. (Dist. by: Licosa, Via Duca di Calabria 1-1, 50125 Florence, Italy) circ. 1,000.

840   IT   ISSN 0585-4768
PQ5
STUDI DI LETTERATURA FRANCESE. (Text in language of authors) 1967. a. price varies. (Universita degli Studi di Milano, Seminario di Lingue e Letterature Neolatine) Casa Editrice Leo S. Olschki, Casella Postale 66, 50100 Florence, Italy. TEL 055-6530684. FAX 055-6530214. Ed. Enea Balmas. circ. 1,000. **Indexed:** M.L.A. **Document type:** academic/scholarly publication.
—SWETS.

STUDI E PROBLEMI DI CRITICA TESTUALE. see *LINGUISTICS*

809   IT
STUDI E TESTI DELL'ANTICHITA. 1975. irreg., no.18, 1984. price varies. Societa Editrice Napoletana s.r.l., Corso Umberto I 34, 80138 Naples, Italy. Ed. Fabio Cupaiuolo.

809 850   IT
STUDI E TESTI DI LETTERATURA ITALIANA. 1974. irreg., no.21, 1984. price varies. Societa Editrice Napoletana s.r.l., Corso Umberto I 34, 80138 Naples, Italy.

STUDI FRANCESI; cultura e civilta letteraria della Francia. see *LINGUISTICS*

830   IT   ISSN 0039-2952
PT5
STUDI GERMANICI. 1935-19??; resumed 1963. 1/yr. L.100000($100) (Istituto Italiano di Studi Germanici) Herder Editrice e Libreria s.r.l., Piazza Montecitorio, 120, 00186 Rome, Italy. TEL 67-94-628. FAX 678-47-51. Ed. Paolo Chiarini. adv.; bk.rev.; bibl. circ. 1,000. **Indexed:** Bibl.Ling. **Document type:** academic/scholarly publication.
 Description: Contains articles and essays on Germanic languages and literatures written by Italian and foreign scholars.

800   IT   ISSN 0585-492X
STUDI ISPANICI. 1962. a. L.185000. Giardini Editori e Stampatori, Via Santa Bibbiana 28, 56100 Pisa, Italy. TEL 050 502531. Ed.Bd. **Indexed:** M.L.A.

850   IT   ISSN 1121-0621
STUDI ITALIANI. 1989. s-a. L.60000 (effective 1993). Edizioni Cadmo, Casella Postale 27, 50014 Fiesole (FI), Italy. TEL 55-599941. FAX 55-598895. Ed.Bd. **Document type:** academic/scholarly publication.

850   IT
STUDI NOVECENTESCHI. 3/yr. L.70000. Giardini Editori e Stampatori, Via Santa Bibbiana 28, 56100 Pisa, Italy. TEL 050 502531. Ed.Bd. **Indexed:** M.L.A.

800 851   IT
STUDI PIEMONTESI. 1972. s-a. L.85000 (foreign L.90000) (effective 1994). Centro Studi Piemontesi, Via O. Revel 15, 10121 Turin, Italy. TEL 537-486. FAX 534777. Ed. Luciano Tamburini. adv.; bk.rev. circ. 1,200. (back issues avail.)
 Description: Literary and historical review of art and the humanities.

850   IT   ISSN 0081-6248
STUDI SECENTESCHI. 1961. a. price varies. Casa Editrice Leo S. Olschki, Casella Postale 66, 50100 Florence, Italy. TEL 055-6530684. FAX 055-6530214. Ed. Martino Capucci. bk.rev.; index. circ. 1,000. **Indexed:** Amer.Hist.& Life, Hist.Abstr., M.L.A., RILA. **Document type:** academic/scholarly publication.

850   IT   ISSN 0081-6256
PQ4646
STUDI TASSIANI. 1951. a. L.40000 (foreign L.80000). Biblioteca Civica Angelo Mai, Centro di Studi Tassiani, Piazza Vecchia 15, 24100 Bergamo, Italy. FAX 035-240655. cum.index: vols.1-10, vols.11-20.

STUDIA ANGLICA POSNANIENSIA; international review of English Studies. see *LINGUISTICS*

880   US   ISSN 0899-9929
STUDIA CLASSICA. irreg. Peter Lang Publishing, Inc., 62 W. 45th St., 4th Fl., New York, NY 10036. TEL 212-302-6740. FAX 212-302-7574. Eds. Anthony J. Podlecki, John C. Overbeck. **Document type:** academic/scholarly publication.
 Description: Examines various aspects of the Graeco-Roman world syntopically.

830   PL   ISSN 0137-2467
PF3003
STUDIA GERMANICA POSNANIENSIA. (Text in German) 1971. irreg., no.21, 1994. price varies. Adam Mickiewicz University Press, Nowowiejskiego 55, 61-734 Poznan, Poland. TEL 527-380. FAX 61-526425. TELEX 413260 UAMPL. Eds. Stefan H. Kaszynski, A. Bzdega. bk.rev.; bibl. **Indexed:** Bibl.Ling., Lang.& Lang.Behav.Abstr. **Document type:** academic/scholarly publication.
—BLDSC (8482.831000).
 Description: An international review of German studies. Contains articles and papers in German linguistics and literature.

800   GW
STUDIA HUMANIORA. irreg., latest vol.24. DM.42. Droste Verlag GmbH, 40196 Duesseldorf, Germany. TEL 0211-5052604. FAX 0211-5052603. **Document type:** monographic series.

800   NE
▼**STUDIA IMAGOLOGICA.** 1992. irreg., vol.3, 1992. price varies. Editions Rodopi B.V., Keizersgracht 302-304, 1016 EX Amsterdam, Netherlands. TEL 31-20-6227507. FAX 31-20-6380948. (In N. America: 233 Peachtree St., N.E., Ste. 404, Atlanta, GA 30303-1504. TEL 800-225-3998. FAX 404-522-7116) Eds. Hugo Dyserinck, Joep Leerssen. (back issues avail.) **Document type:** monographic series.
 Description: Publishes studies in comparative literature.
 Refereed Serial

800   HU   ISSN 0562-2867
PH3001
STUDIA LITTERARIA. (Text in French and Hungarian) 1963. irreg., vol.31, 1993. Kossuth Lajos Tudomanyegyetem, Magyar Irodalomtorteneti Intezet, Egyetem Ter 1, 4010 Debrecen, Hungary. bibl. **Indexed:** M.L.A.

STUDIA MYSTICA. see *PHILOSOPHY*

801 830   HU   ISSN 0209-9403
STUDIA POETICA. (Text in English, German) 1980. irreg. exchange basis. Attila Jozsef University, c/o E. Szabo, Exchange Librarian, Dugonics ter 13, P.O. Box 393, Szeged H-6701, Hungary. (Dist. in Western countries by: Harry Munchberg, Hahnenkleerstr. 14, D-3394 Langelsheim, Germany) Eds. Arpad Bernath, Karoly Csuri. circ. 500.
 Description: Examines literary theory and analysis and attempts to apply the methods of semiotics, linguistics and logical semantics to works of literature.

809   PL   ISSN 0137-4389
STUDIA POLONO-SLAVICA ORIENTALIA. ACTA LITTERARIA. a. price varies. Polska Akademia Nauk, Instytut Slowianoznawstwa, Pracownia Literatur Wschodnioslowianskich, Palac Kultury i Nauki, P.O. Box 24, Warsaw, Poland. (Dist. by: Ars Polona-Ruch, Krakowskie Przedmiescie 7, Warsaw, Poland) Ed. Bazyli Bialokozowicz.

STUDIA ROMANICA ET ANGLICA ZAGRABIENSIA. see *LINGUISTICS*

840   HU   ISSN 0418-4572
STUDIA ROMANICA UNIVERSITATIS DEBRECENIENSIS DE LUDOVICO KOSSUTH NOMINATAE. SERIES LITTERARIA. (Text in French) 1962. irreg., vol.17, 1992. Kossuth Lajos Tudomanyegyetem, Roman Nyelvek es Irodalmak Tanszek, Egyetem Ter 1, 4010 Debrecen, Hungary. bibl.

296   NE   ISSN 0039-3347
DS135.N4
STUDIA ROSENTHALIANA; tijdschrift voor Joodse wetenschap en geschiedenis in Nederland/journal for Jewish literature and history in the Netherlands. (Text in Dutch, English, Hebrew; summaries in English) 1967. s-a. fl.90. (Bibliotheca Rosenthaliana) Van Gorcum en Co. B.V., P.O. Box 43, 9400 AA Assen, Netherlands. TEL 31-5920-46846. FAX 31-5920-72064. Ed.Bd. bk.rev.; circ. 400. **Indexed:** Amer.Hist.& Life, Arts & Hum.Cit.Ind., Bk.Rev.Ind., Hist.Abstr., Hum.Ind. **Document type:** academic/scholarly publication.
—SWETS.

LITERATURE

800   PL   ISSN 0081-6884
PG2025
STUDIA ROSSICA POSNANIENSIA. (Text in Polish and Russian; summaries in English and Russian) 1970. irreg., vol.25, 1993. price varies. Adam Mickiewicz University Press, Nowowiejskiego 55, 61-734 Poznan, Poland. TEL 527-380. FAX 61-526425. TELEX 413260 UAMPL. Eds. Zbigniew Baranski, Leszek Ossowski. bk.rev. circ. 400. **Indexed:** Bibl.Ling., Lang.& Lang.Behav.Abstr. **Document type:** academic/scholarly publication.
—BLDSC (8483.204400).
   Description: Papers in Russian and Polish divided into areas of literature, linguistics and methods of teaching.

800   PL   ISSN 0081-6949
STUDIA STAROPOLSKIE. 1953. irreg., vol.55, 1989. price varies. (Polska Akademia Nauk, Instytut Badan Literackich) Ossolineum, Publishing House of the Polish Academy of Sciences, Rynek 9, 50-106 Wroclaw, Poland. TEL 48-71-386-25. FAX 48-71-448-103. TELEX 0712771 OSS PL. **Document type:** monographic series.

STUDIA UNIVERSITATIS "BABES-BOLYAI". PHILOLOGIA. see *LINGUISTICS*

STUDIA URALO-ALTAICA. see *LINGUISTICS*

800   PL   ISSN 0081-7112
STUDIA Z OKRESU OSWIECENIA. (Text in Polish; summaries in English and French) 1964. irreg., vol.23, 1990. price varies. (Polska Akademia Nauk, Instytut Badan Literackich) Ossolineum, Publishing House of the Polish Academy of Sciences, Rynek 9, 50-106 Wroclaw, Poland. TEL 48-71-386-25. FAX 48-71-448-103. TELEX 0712771 OSS PL. Ed.Bd. bibl. circ. 1,000. **Document type:** monographic series.

830   GW   ISSN 0081-7236
STUDIEN ZUR DEUTSCHEN LITERATUR. 1966. irreg., no.130, 1993. price varies. Max Niemeyer Verlag, Postfach 2140, 72011 Tuebingen, Germany. TEL 07071-98940. FAX 07071-989450. Ed.Bd. (back issues avail.) **Indexed:** M.L.A. **Document type:** monographic series.
   Description: Monographs on German literature, especially since the 17th century.

STUDIEN ZUR ENGLISCHEN PHILOLOGIE, NEUE FOLGE. see *LINGUISTICS*

830   GW   ISSN 0340-594X
STUDIEN ZUR GERMANISTIK, ANGLISTIK UND KOMPARATISTIK. 1970. irreg., vol.121, 1991. price varies. Bouvier Verlag Herbert Grundmann, Am Hof 28, 53113 Bonn, Germany. TEL 0228-7290124. FAX 0228-7290179. Eds. A. Arnold, A. Hass. **Indexed:** M.L.A. **Document type:** monographic series.

800   GW   ISSN 0340-9023
STUDIEN ZUR LITERATUR DER MODERNE. 1976. irreg., vol.22, 1991. price varies. Bouvier Verlag Herbert Grundmann, Am Hof 28, 53113 Bonn, Germany. TEL 0228-7290124. FAX 0228-7290179. Ed. Helmut Koopmann. **Document type:** monographic series.

860 301   GW   ISSN 0340-5990
STUDIEN ZUR LITERATUR- UND SOZIALGESCHICHTE SPANIENS UND LATEINAMERIKAS. 1975. irreg., no.8, 1988. price varies. Bouvier Verlag Herbert Grundmann, Am Hof 28, 53113 Bonn, Germany. TEL 0228-7290124. FAX 0228-7290179. Ed. Martin Franzbach. **Document type:** monographic series.

STUDIES IN AFRICAN AND AFRO-AMERICAN CULTURE. see *HISTORY — History Of Africa*

810   US   ISSN 0091-8083
PS370
STUDIES IN AMERICAN FICTION. 1973. 2/yr. $7 to individuals (foreign $9); institutions $12. Northeastern University, Department of English, Boston, MA 02115. TEL 617-437-3687. Ed. James Nagel. adv.; bk.rev. circ. 1,300. **Indexed:** Abstr.Engl.Stud., Amer.Hum.Ind., Arts & Hum.Cit.Ind., Curr.Cont., Ind.Bk.Rev.Hum., M.L.A. **Document type:** academic/scholarly publication.
—BLDSC (8489.059000); Faxon; UnCover; SWETS.

808 970.1   US   ISSN 0730-3238
STUDIES IN AMERICAN INDIAN LITERATURES. 1977. q. $16 to individuals on limited income; institutions $34 (membership; includes A S A I L Notes). Department of English, California State University at San Bernardino, San Bernardino, CA 92407. TEL 909-880-5824. FAX 909-880-5921. Ed. Rodney Simard. adv.; bk.rev.; bibl. circ. 350. (back issues avail.) **Indexed:** Bibl.Ling.
—UnCover.

STUDIES IN AMERICAN JEWISH LITERATURE. see *ETHNIC INTERESTS*

892.7   NE   ISSN 0169-9903
STUDIES IN ARABIC LITERATURE. (Supplement to: Journal of Arabic Literature (ISSN 0085-2376)) 1971. irreg., no.17, 1994. price varies. E.J. Brill, P.O. Box 9000, 2300 PA Leiden, Netherlands. TEL 31-71-312624. FAX 31-71-317532. TELEX 39296 BRILL NL. (In N. America: E.J. Brill, 24 Hudson St., Kinderhook, NY 12106. TEL 800-962-4406. FAX 518-758-1959) (back issues avail.) **Document type:** monographic series.
   Refereed Serial

808 910.03   US   ISSN 0738-0755
PS153.N5
STUDIES IN BLACK AMERICAN LITERATURE. 1984. a. price varies. Penkevill Publishing Company, Box 212, Greenwood, FL 32443. Eds. Joe Weixlmann, Houston A. Baker, Jr. adv. circ. 500.
—BLDSC (8489.699500).

809   JA
STUDIES IN BRITISH & AMERICAN LITERATURE/EI-BEIBUNGAKU. (Text in English or Japanese) a. Komazawa University, 1-23-1 Komazawa, Setagaya-ku, Tokyo 154, Japan.
   Formerly: Gaikoku Bungaku Kenkyu.

820   US   ISSN 0095-4489
PR4229
STUDIES IN BROWNING AND HIS CIRCLE; a journal of criticism, history and bibliography. 1968. a. $17.50. Baylor University, Armstrong Browning Library, Box 97152, Waco, TX 76798-7152. TEL 817-755-3566. Ed. Roger L. Brooks. bk.rev.; cum.index. circ. 650. **Indexed:** Abstr.Engl.Stud., Amer.Hum.Ind., Arts & Hum.Cit.Ind., Curr.Cont., Ind.Bk.Rev.Hum., M.L.A. **Document type:** newsletter.
—BLDSC (8489.730000).
   Formerly: Browning Newsletter (ISSN 0007-2532)

800   CN   ISSN 0380-6995
PR9180
STUDIES IN CANADIAN LITERATURE. 1976. s-a. Can.$16 to individuals; institutions Can.$22($26). University of New Brunswick, Department of English, Fredericton, NB E3B 5A3, Canada. TEL 506-453-4598. FAX 506-453-4599. Ed. Kathleen Scherf. adv. circ. 700. **Indexed:** Abstr.Engl.Stud., Amer.Hum.Ind., Arts & Hum.Cit.Ind., Can.Lit.Ind., Can.Per.Ind., CMI, Curr.Cont., M.L.A. **Document type:** academic/scholarly publication.
—BLDSC (8489.815000); Faxon; UnCover.

809   US   ISSN 0081-7775
STUDIES IN COMPARATIVE LITERATURE (CHAPEL HILL). (Text in English, French, German, Italian, Latin, and Spanish) 1950. irreg., no.63, 1988. price varies. (University of North Carolina at Chapel Hill, Department of English) University of North Carolina Press, Box 2288, Chapel Hill, NC 27515-2288. TEL 919-966-3561. FAX 919-966-3829. (reprint service avail. from UMI) **Document type:** academic/scholarly publication.
—BLDSC (9116.210000).
   Refereed Serial

820.9 410   JA   ISSN 0039-3649
PR1
STUDIES IN ENGLISH LITERATURE/EIBUNGAKU KENKYU. (Text in English and Japanese) 1919. 3/yr. 7000 Yen. English Literary Society of Japan - Nihon Eibungakkai, 501 Kenkyusha Bldg., 9 Surugadai 2-chome, Kanda, Chiyoda-ku, Tokyo 101, Japan. FAX 03-3233-3398. Ed. Masanori Toyoda. adv.; bk.rev.; cum.index. circ. 3,800. **Indexed:** Curr.Cont.

820   US   ISSN 0039-3657
PR1
STUDIES IN ENGLISH LITERATURE 1500-1900. 1961. q. $25 to individuals; institutions $30 (foreign $35). Rice University, Box 1892, Houston, TX 77251. TEL 713-527-8101. FAX 713-285-5207. Ed. Robert L. Patten. circ. 2,000. (also avail. in microform from UMI; back issues avail.; reprint service avail. from SCH,UMI) **Indexed:** Abstr.Engl.Stud., Acad.Ind., Arts & Hum.Cit.Ind., Biog.Ind., Curr.Cont., Hum.Ind., M.L.A. **Document type:** academic/scholarly publication.
—BLDSC (8490.521000); Faxon; UnCover; SWETS; UMI.
   Description: Each issue covers a different period of literature from the Renaissance through the end of the 19th century, with a review of current scholarship on that period.

890   US
STUDIES IN FRENCH LITERATURE. irreg., latest no.17. $39.95 per no. Edwin Mellen Press, 415 Ridge St., Box 450, Lewiston, NY 14092. TEL 716-754-2788. FAX 716-754-4056. **Document type:** monographic series.

840   US
STUDIES IN GERMAN LANGUAGE AND LITERATURE. irreg., latest vol.14. $39.95 per no. Edwin Mellen Press, 415 Ridge St., Box 450, Lewiston, NY 14092. TEL 716-754-2788. FAX 716-754-4056. **Document type:** monographic series.

800   UK   ISSN 0960-6025
STUDIES IN HOGG AND HIS WORLD. 1982. a. £12.50. James Hogg Society, Department of English Studies, University of Stirling, Stirling FK9 4LA, Scotland. Ed. G.H. Hughes. adv.; bk.rev. circ. 100. **Document type:** academic/scholarly publication.
   Formerly (until 1989): James Hogg Society. Newsletter (ISSN 0263-7022)
   Description: Contains essays and texts concerning the Scottish writer James Hogg (1770-1835) and literature of the Romantic period.

STUDIES IN ISLAM. see *RELIGIONS AND THEOLOGY — Islamic*

800   US   ISSN 1043-5794
STUDIES IN ITALIAN CULTURE: LITERATURE IN HISTORY. irreg. Peter Lang Publishing, Inc., 62 W. 45th St., 4th Fl., New York, NY 10036. TEL 212-302-6740. FAX 212-302-7574. Ed. Aldo Scaglione. **Document type:** academic/scholarly publication.

850   US
STUDIES IN ITALIAN LITERATURE. irreg., latest no.2. $39.95 per no. Edwin Mellen Press, 415 Ridge St., Box 450, Lewiston, NY 14092. TEL 716-754-2788. FAX 716-754-4056. **Document type:** monographic series.

STUDIES IN LANGUAGE COMPANION SERIES. see *LINGUISTICS*

807   US
STUDIES IN MEDIEVAL AND RENAISSANCE TEACHING. 1973. a. $10. c/o J. Hample, Ed., College of Arts and Sciences, Indiana State University, Terre Haute, IN 47809. TEL 812-237-2788. adv.; bk.rev.; film rev.; play rev. circ. 500.
   Formerly (until 1982): Ralph.

STUDIES IN MEDIEVAL CULTURE. see *HISTORY*

890   US
STUDIES IN MIDDLE EASTERN LITERATURES. 1972. irreg., no.11, 1984. price varies. Bibliotheca Islamica, Inc., Box 14474, University Sta., Minneapolis, MN 55414. **Document type:** monographic series.

830   US   ISSN 0888-3904
STUDIES IN MODERN GERMAN LITERATURE. 1987. irreg. Peter Lang Publishing, Inc., 62 W. 45th St., 4th Fl., New York, NY 10036. TEL 212-302-6740. Ed. Peter D.G. Brown. **Document type:** academic/scholarly publication.

STUDIES IN OLD GERMANIC LANGUAGES AND LITERATURES. see *LINGUISTICS*

479 US
STUDIES IN ROMANCE LANGUAGES & LITERATURES.
1970. irreg., latest 1993. price varies. University
Press of Kentucky, 663 S. Limestone St., Lexington,
KY 40508-4008. TEL 606-257-2951.
FAX 606-257-2984. Ed. John E. Keller. (reprint
service avail. from UMI) **Indexed:** M.L.A. **Document
type:** monographic series.
Formerly: Studies in Romance Languages (ISSN
0085-6894)

800 US ISSN 0039-3762
PN751
STUDIES IN ROMANTICISM. 1961. q. $20 to individuals
(foreign $26); institutions $59.50 (foreign $65.50).
Boston University, Graduate School, 236 Bay State
Rd., Boston, MA 02215. TEL 617-353-2505.
(Subscr. to: Boston University Scholarly Publications,
985 Commonwealth Ave., Boston, MA 02215. TEL
617-353-4106) Ed. David Wagenknecht. adv.;
bk.rev.; index, cum.index: vols.1-10. circ. 1,800.
(also avail. in microform from UMI; reprint service
avail. from UMI) **Indexed:** Abstr.Engl.Stud.,
Amer.Hist.& Life, Artbibl.Mod., Can.Rev.Comp.Lit.,
Curr.Cont., Hist.Abstr., Hum.Ind., Ind.Bk.Rev.Hum.,
M.L.A., RILA. **Document type:** academic/scholarly
publication.
—BLDSC (8491.450000); Faxon; UnCover; SWETS;
UMI.
Description: Covers the literature, music and art of
the Romantic period in England, Europe, and
America. Examines Third World parallels.

820 US ISSN 0039-3770
PR8500
STUDIES IN SCOTTISH LITERATURE. 1963. a., latest
vol.26, 1992. $16. G. Ross Roy, Ed.& Pub., c/o
English Dept., University of South Carolina,
Columbia, SC 29208. TEL 803-767-6601.
FAX 803-777-9064. bk.rev.; bibl.; illus.; index. circ.
525. **Indexed:** Abstr.Engl.Stud., Amer.Hum.Ind.,
M.L.A. **Document type:** academic/scholarly
publication.
—BLDSC (8491.570000); Faxon; UnCover.

STUDIES IN SEMIOTICS AND LITERATURE. see
LINGUISTICS

813 US ISSN 0039-3789
PN3311
STUDIES IN SHORT FICTION. 1963. q. $19 to
individuals; libraries $22. Newberry College, 2100
College St., Newberry, SC 29108.
TEL 803-276-5195. FAX 803-321-5232. Ed.
Michael J. O'Shea. bk.rev.; bibl.; index. circ. 1,775.
(also avail. in microform from UMI; reprint service
avail. from UMI) **Indexed:** Abstr.Engl.Stud.,
Abstr.Pop.Cult., Amer.Bibl.Slavic & E.Eur.Stud., Arts
& Hum.Cit.Ind., Bk.Rev.Ind. (1986-),
Child.Bk.Rev.Ind. (1986-), Curr.Cont.,
Hisp.Amer.Per.Ind., Hum.Ind., Ind.Bk.Rev.Hum.,
M.L.A., Mid.East: Abstr.& Ind. **Document type:**
academic/scholarly publication.
—BLDSC (8491.580000); Faxon; UnCover; SWETS;
UMI.
Description: Publishes commentary (scholarship
and criticism) on short fiction.

890 US
STUDIES IN SLAVIC LANGUAGE AND LITERATURE.
1989. irreg. (latest no.7). Edwin Mellen Press, 415
Ridge St., Box 450, Lewiston, NY 14092.
TEL 716-754-8566. FAX 716-754-4335.

899 NE ISSN 0169-0175
STUDIES IN SLAVIC LITERATURE AND POETICS. Short
title: S S P. 1981. irreg., vol.21, 1993. price varies.
Editions Rodopi B.V., Keizersgracht 302-304, 1016
EX Amsterdam, Netherlands. TEL 31-20-6227507.
FAX 31-20-6380948. (In N. America: 233
Peachtree St. N.E., Ste. 404, Atlanta, GA
30303-1504. TEL 800-225-3998. FAX
404-522-7116) Ed.Bd. **Indexed:** M.L.A. **Document
type:** monographic series.

807 US ISSN 0190-2407
PR1901
STUDIES IN THE AGE OF CHAUCER. 1979. a. $30. Ohio
State University, Department of English, 421 Denney
Hall, 164 W. 17th Ave., Columbus, OH 43210.
TEL 614-292-2061. FAX 614-292-1599. (Subscr.
to: Christian Zacher, Center for Medieval &
Renaissance Studies, Ohio State Univ., 322 Dulles
Hall, 230 W. 17th Ave., Columbus, OH
43210-1311) Ed. Lisa J. Kiser. bk.rev.; bibl.; index.
circ. 700. (back issues avail.) **Document type:**
academic/scholarly publication.
—BLDSC (8488.952000); Faxon; UnCover.
Description: Publishes articles dealing with literary
and critical approaches to Chaucer and his
contemporaries and the historical, social and cultural
background to their work, with an annotated
Chaucer bibliography.

800 US ISSN 0149-015X
PS201
STUDIES IN THE AMERICAN RENAISSANCE. 1977. a.
$35. (University of South Carolina) University Press
of Virginia, Box 3608, Charlottesville, VA 22903.
TEL 804-924-3468. FAX 804-982-2655. Ed. Joel
Myerson. bk.rev.; bibl.; illus. circ. 750. **Indexed:**
Amer.Hist.& Life, Amer.Hum.Ind., Hist.Abstr., M.L.A.,
Rel.Ind.One. **Document type:** academic/scholarly
publication.
—BLDSC (8489.090000); Faxon.
Description: Contains articles on the literature of
the American Renaissance.

830 US ISSN 0081-8593
PD25
**STUDIES IN THE GERMANIC LANGUAGES AND
LITERATURES.** 1949. irreg., no.115, 1994. $37.50.
(University of North Carolina at Chapel Hill,
Department of English) University of North Carolina
Press, Box 2288, Chapel Hill, NC 27515-2288.
TEL 919-966-3561. FAX 919-966-3829. (reprint
service avail. from UMI) **Document type:**
academic/scholarly publication.
Refereed Serial

800 US ISSN 0039-3819
PR1
STUDIES IN THE LITERARY IMAGINATION. 1968. s-a.
$5. Georgia State University, Department of English,
Graduate Faculty, University Plaza, Atlanta, GA
30303-3083. TEL 404-658-2900. Ed. Dr. Eugene
Hollahan. circ. 4,000 (controlled). (also avail. in
microform from UMI; back issues avail.; reprint
service avail. from UMI) **Indexed:** Abstr.Engl.Stud.,
Amer.Bibl.Slavic & E.Eur.Stud., Amer.Hum.Ind., Arts
& Hum.Cit.Ind., Film Lit.Ind. (1983-), Hum.Ind.,
M.L.A. **Document type:** academic/scholarly
publication.
—BLDSC (8491.037000); Faxon; UnCover; SWETS;
UMI.

813 US ISSN 0039-3827
PN3311
STUDIES IN THE NOVEL. 1969. q. $15 to individuals;
libraries and other institutions $30 (all foreign $40).
University of North Texas, English Department,
Denton, TX 76203. TEL 817-565-2025. (Subscr.
addr.: Box 13706, North Texas Sta., Denton, TX
76203) Ed. John T. Smith. bk.rev.; bibl.; index. circ.
1,800. (also avail. in microform from UMI; reprint
service avail. from UMI) **Indexed:** Abstr.Engl.Stud.,
Amer.Bibl.Slavic & E.Eur.Stud., Arts & Hum.Cit.Ind.,
Curr.Cont., Hum.Ind., Ind.Bk.Rev.Hum., LCR, M.L.A.,
Mid.East: Abstr.& Ind. **Document type:**
academic/scholarly publication.
—BLDSC (8491.157000); Faxon; UnCover; SWETS;
UMI.

800 US ISSN 0897-9243
STUDIES IN THE ROMANTIC AGE. (Text in English and
other West European languages) 1988. irreg. Peter
Lang Publishing, Inc., 62 W. 45th St., 4th Fl., New
York, NY 10036. TEL 212-302-6740. Ed. Charles I.
Patterson. **Document type:** academic/scholarly
publication.

800 US ISSN 0145-7888
PN771
STUDIES IN TWENTIETH CENTURY LITERATURE. 1976.
s-a. $15 to individuals; institutions $20. Kansas
State University, Department of Modern Languages,
Eisenhower 104, Manhattan, KS 66506-1003.
TEL 913-532-6760. FAX 913-532-7004.
(Co-sponsor: University of Nebraska-Lincoln) Ed.Bd.
adv.; bk.rev.; cum.index. circ. 500. **Indexed:**
Amer.Bibl.Slavic & E.Eur.Stud., Amer.Hum.Ind., Arts
& Hum.Cit.Ind., Curr.Cont., M.L.A., Mid.East: Abstr.&
Ind. **Document type:** academic/scholarly publication.
—BLDSC (8491.832000); Faxon; UnCover.
Description: Devoted to literary theory and
practical criticism of 20th century literature written
in French, German, Russian, and Spanish. Focuses
on poetry, prose, drama, and literary theory.

STUDIES IN WEIRD FICTION. see LITERATURE —
Science Fiction, Fantasy, Horror

800 420 US ISSN 1043-8580
STUDIES OF WORLD LITERATURE IN ENGLISH. irreg.
Peter Lang Publishing, Inc., 62 W. 45th St., 4th Fl.,
New York, NY 10036. TEL 212-302-6740.
FAX 212-302-7574. Ed. Norman R. Cary. **Document
type:** academic/scholarly publication.
Description: Encompasses criticism of modern
English-language literature from outside the United
States, Great Britain, and Ireland; literature by
writers from Canada, Africa, Asia, the Pacific, and
the Caribbean.

800 US ISSN 1056-3970
STUDIES ON THEMES AND MOTIFS IN LITERATURE.
irreg. Peter Lang Publishing, Inc., 62 W. 45th St.,
4th Fl., New York, NY 10036. TEL 212-302-6740.
FAX 212-302-7574. Ed. Horst Daemmrich.
Document type: academic/scholarly publication.
Description: Covers cross-cultural patterns as well
as the entire range of national literatures.

840 940 UK ISSN 0435-2866
PQ2105.A2
STUDIES ON VOLTAIRE AND THE EIGHTEENTH CENTURY.
(Text in English and French) 1955. irreg. (approx.
12/yr.). price varies. Voltaire Foundation, Taylor
Institution, St. Giles, Oxford OX1 3NA, England.
TEL 0865-270250. FAX 0865-270740. Ed. H.T.
Mason. cum.index: 1955-64, 1965-70. (also avail.
in microfiche from VFN; back issues avail.) **Indexed:**
M.L.A. **Document type:** academic/scholarly
publication.

800 300 AT
STUDIO, a journal of Christians writing. 1980. q.
Aus.$40. Studio, 727 Peel St., Albury, N.S.W. 2640,
Australia. TEL 060-21-1135. Ed. Paul Grover.
bk.rev. circ. 300. (back issues avail.)
Formerly: Christians Writing (ISSN 0729-4042)
Description: Presents work of literary merit, offers
a venue for new and aspiring writers, and seeks to
create a sense of community among Christians
writing.

**STUDY GROUP ON EIGHTEENTH-CENTURY RUSSIA.
NEWSLETTER.** see HISTORY — *History Of Europe*

800 GW
STUTTGARTER ARBEITEN ZUR GERMANISTIK. (Text and
summaries in English, German) 1975. irreg. price
varies. Verlag Hans-Dieter Heinz,
Steiermaerkerstrasse 132, 70469 Stuttgart,
Germany. Ed.Bd. circ. 400. (back issues avail.)
Indexed: Bibl.Ling., M.L.A.

801 US ISSN 0039-4238
PE1
STYLE (DEKALB). 1966. q. $24 to individuals;
institutions $36. Northern Illinois University,
Department of English, DeKalb, IL 60115.
TEL 815-753-0611. FAX 815-753-1824. Ed.
Harold E. Mosher, Jr. adv.; bk.rev.; bibl.; circ. 600
(paid). (also avail. in microfilm from UMI; talking
book; Braille; back issues avail.; reprint service avail.
from UMI) **Indexed:** Abstr.Engl.Stud., Arts &
Hum.Cit.Ind., Lang.& Lang.Behav.Abstr., M.L.A.
Document type: academic/scholarly publication.
—BLDSC (8501.803000); Faxon; UnCover; SWETS;
UMI.
Description: Articles analyze stylistic features of
literature, ranging from traditional subjects such as
diction, grammar and metrics, to the theory of
literature, the process of reading, and problems of
narratology.

3678 LITERATURE

869   BL
STYLOS. 1980. irreg., no.43, 1981. Universidade Estadual Paulista Julio de Mesquita Filho, Instituto de Biociencias, Letras e Ciencias Exatas, Rua Cristovao Colombo 2265-J. Nazareth, 15100 Campus de Sao Jose do Rio Preto SP, Brazil.

879.9   US   ISSN 0049-2426
PN2
SUB-STANCE. (Text in English and French) 1971. 3/yr. $23 to individuals; institutions $74. University of Wisconsin Press, Journal Division, 114 N. Murray St., Madison, WI 53715. TEL 608-262-4952. FAX 608-262-7560. Eds. Sydney Levy, Michel Pierssens. adv.; bk.rev.; cum.index: 1971-1978. circ. 750. (processed; also avail. in microform from UMI; reprint service avail. from UMI) **Indexed:** Amer.Hum.Ind., Arts & Hum.Cit.Ind., Curr.Cont., M.L.A., Sociol.Abstr. **Document type:** academic/scholarly publication.
—BLDSC (8503.480000); Faxon; UnCover; UMI. **CCC.**

810   CN   ISSN 0840-7533
SUB-TERRAIN. 1988. 4/yr. $10. Anvil Press Publishers, 175 E. Broadway, Ste. 204-A, Vancouver, BC V5T 1W2, Canada. TEL 604-876-8710. FAX 604-879-2667. (Subscr. to: Box 1575, Sta. A, Vancouver, BC V6C 2P7, Canada) Ed. Brian Kaufman. adv.: page Can.$150. bk.rev. circ. 2,000. **Document type:** trade publication.
Description: Provides a varied mix of fiction, poetry, commentary, art and photography from Canadian, American and international writers and artists.

892   II
SUBH-I-ADAB. (Text in Urdu) 1974. m. Rs.20. Nazir Ahmad Nuri, Mahmood Manzil Gwynne Rd., Lakhnau, India. illus.

808   US
THE SUBTLE JOURNAL OF RAW COINAGE. 1987. m. $10. D B Q P, 875 Central Pkwy., Schenectady, NY 12309-6005. Ed. Geof Huth.
Description: Publishes undefined invented words and short pieces of experimental writing comprised exclusively of invented words, as a means of exploring the creation of language and the invention of meaning.

SUEDOSTDEUTSCHES KULTURWERK. VEROEFFENTLICHUNGEN. REIHE A: KULTUR UND DICHTUNG. see HISTORY — History Of Europe

SUEDOSTDEUTSCHES KULTURWERK. VEROEFFENTLICHUNGEN. REIHE B: WISSENSCHAFTLICHE ARBEITEN. see HISTORY — History Of Europe

SUEDOSTDEUTSCHES KULTURWERK. VEROEFFENTLICHUNGEN. REIHE C: ERINNERUNGEN UND QUELLEN. see HISTORY — History Of Europe

SUEDOSTDEUTSCHES KULTURWERK. VEROEFFENTLICHUNGEN. REIHE D: KLEINE SUEDOSTREIHE. see HISTORY — History Of Europe

830   GW
SUEVICA - BEITRAEGE ZUR SCHWABISCHEN LITERATUR- UND GEISTESGESCHICHTE. 1981. biennial. price varies. (Justinus-Kerner-Verein) Verlag Hans-Dieter Heinz, Steiermaerker Str. 132, 70469 Stuttgart, Germany. Ed. Hartmut Froeschle.
Formerly: Beitraege zur Schwabischen Literatur- und Geistesgeschichte und Mitteilungen des Justinius Kerner-Vereins und Frauenvereins.

895.15   CC   ISSN 1000-7903
SUIBI/RANDOM NOTES. (Text in Chinese) 1979. bi-m. Y18($53.53) Huacheng Chubanshe, No. 11, Shuiyin Lu, Huanshi Donglu, Guangzhou, Guangdong 510075, People's Republic of China. TEL 7768688. (Dist. in US by: China Books & Periodicals, Inc., 2929 24th St., San Francisco, CA 94110. TEL 415-282-2994) Ed. Du Jiankun.

SUID-AFRIKAANSE AKADEMIE VIR WETENSKAP EN KUNS. NUUSBRIEF. see SCIENCES: COMPREHENSIVE WORKS

800   BG
SUJANESHU. (Text in Bengali) m. 15-16 Goalnagar Lane, Dhaka 1, Bangladesh. Eds. Ahmad Rafiq, Kazi Abdul Halim.

800 051   US   ISSN 0730-305X
PS501
SULFUR; a literary bi-annual of the whole art. 1980. 2/yr. $14 to individuals (foreign $18); institutions $20 (foreign $24) (effective 1994). Clayton Eshleman, Ed. & Pub., 210 Washtenaw, Ypsilanti, MI 48197-2526. TEL 313-483-9787. FAX 313-483-9787. (Alt. addr.: c/o English Department, Eastern Michigan University, Ypsilanti, MI 48197) adv.; bibl.; illus. circ. 2,000. (back issues avail.) **Indexed:** Bk.Rev.Ind. (1986-), Child.Bk.Rev.Ind. (1986-), PROMT.
—Faxon; UnCover.
Supersedes (1967-1972): Caterpillar (ISSN 0008-784X)

800   CC
SULIAN WENXUE (LIANKAN)/RUSSIAN LITERATURE. (Text in Chinese) bi-m. $27.50. (Beijing Shifan Daxue - Beijing Normal University) Beijing Shifan Daxue Chubanshe - Beijing Normal University Press, Beijing 100088, People's Republic of China. (Dist. overseas by: China International Book Trading Corp., P.O. Box 399, Beijing, P.R.C.; Dist. in US by: China Books & Periodicals, Inc., 2929 24th St., San Francisco, CA 94110. TEL 415-282-2994) (Co-sponsors: Beijing Waiyu Xueyuan - Beijing Institute of Foreign Languages; Wuhan Daxue - Wuhan University) bk.rev.
Formed by the 1990 merger of: Sulian Wenxue & Dangdai Sulian Wenxue & Esu Wenxue.
Description: Publishes works of Soviet Russian literature, as well as reviews, columns, and literary and publishing news.

808   US   ISSN 0741-0271
SUNRUST. 1983-1991. s-a. $8. Dawn Valley Press, Box 58, New Wilmington, PA 16142. TEL 412-946-2948. Eds. Nancy Esther James, James A. Perkins. bk.rev. circ. 300. (back issues avail.)
Description: Poetry, prose, art and photography emphasizing the moods, places and people of rural America.

SUPLEMENTO LITERARIO DE REVOLUCION Y CULTURA. see LITERARY AND POLITICAL REVIEWS

891.553   IR
SURAH. 1989. m. Rs.250 per no. Hawzah-i Hunari Sazman-i Tablighat-i Islami, 213 Summaiyah St., P.O. Box 1677-15815, Teheran, Iran. illus.

891.439   PK
SURAT. (Text in Urdu) 1979. m. Rs.6. Meyar Publications, Box 3195, Karachi 29, Pakistan. Ed. Sayyid Wajahat Ali.

SURPLUS; tijdschrift over literatuur van vrouwen - women's review of books. see WOMEN'S STUDIES

891.4   II   ISSN 0039-6370
SUSHAMA. (Text in Hindi) 1959. m. Rs.135 (foreign Rs.1150). Shama Magazine, 13-14 Asaf Ali Rd., New Delhi 110002, India. TEL 91-11-732666. FAX 91-11-7521130. TELEX 3161601 SHAMA-IN. Ed. Idrees Dehlvi; Pub. M. Yunus Dehlvi. circ. 80,333. **Document type:** consumer publication.

895 791.43   II
SUSHMITA. (Text in Hindi) 1989. w. 13-14 Asaf Ali Rd., New Delhi 110 002, India. TEL 11-732666. FAX 11-736539. TELEX 3161601. Ed. M. Yunus Dehlvi. circ. 50,000.
Description: Covers literature, films and television.

806 389.7   SW
SVERIGES FOERFATTARFOERBUND. MEDLEMSFOERTECKNING/SWEDISH WRITERS ASSOCIATION. MEMBERSHIP ROLL. a. membership. Sveriges Foerfattarfoerbund, Drottninggatan 88 B, 111 36 Stockholm, Sweden. TEL 08-791-89-25. FAX 08-791-22-85. Ed. Maria Rodikova.

891.7 491.7   NE   ISSN 0862-8440
SVET LITERATURY/WORLD OF LITERATURE. (Text in Czech) 1991. 2/yr. fl.95($57) (effective 1994). (Czech Academy of Sciences, Institute for Czech and World Literature, XR) John Benjamins Publishing Co., Amsteldijk 44, P.O. Box 75577, 1070 AN Amsterdam, Netherlands. TEL 31-20-6738156. FAX 31-20-6792956. (In N. America: 821 Bethlehem Pike, Philadelphia, PA 19118. TEL 215-836-1200. FAX 215-836-1204) bk.rev. (back issues avail.) **Document type:** academic/scholarly publication.
Supersedes in part (1956-1991): Ceskoslovenska Rusistika (ISSN 0009-0638)
Description: Covers European and American literatures with a comparative and interdisciplinary focus, including examinations of interpretative methods.

891.86   XR   ISSN 0039-7075
SVETOVA LITERATURA; revue. 1956. bi-m. 270 Kcs.($61.40) (typically set in Dec.). Spolecnost pro Svetovou Literaturu, Masarykovo nab. 26, 110 00 Prague 1, Czech Republic. Ed. Anna Kareninova. adv.; bk.rev.; illus. circ. 3,000.
Description: Literary review of world literature.

800   US
SVOBODNA SKOLA/FREE THINKING SCHOOL. 1896. m. $5 (foreign $6). (Bohemian Freethinkers Association) Free Thinking Schools, 5701 W. 22nd Pl., Cicero, IL 60650. TEL 708-656-9810. Ed. Savo Roknic. adv.; illus. circ. 600.
Description: Features stories, history and customs of their forefathers.

820   UK
SWANSEA REVIEW. 1975. 3/yr. £1.50. University College of Swansea, Department of English, Mandela House, Singleton Park, Swansea SA2 8PP, Wales. Ed.Bd. adv.; bk.rev.
Formerly (until 1986): Prospect (ISSN 0306-5529)

808   US   ISSN 0277-447X
PN2
SWIFT KICK. 1980. irreg., no.8, 1988. $20 for 4 nos. to individuals; institutions $40. 1711 Amherst St., Buffalo, NY 14214. TEL 716-837-7778. Ed. Robin Kay Willoughby. circ. 150.

810   US   ISSN 1043-1497
PS501
SYCAMORE REVIEW. 1989. s-a. $9. Purdue University, Department of English, W. Lafayette, IN 47907. TEL 317-494-3783. E-mail: sycamore@sage.cc.purdue.edu. Ed. Henry Hughes. adv.; bk.rev. circ. 1,000. (back issues avail.)
Description: Includes fiction, poetry, personal essays, translations and short drama.

820 375.4   AT
SYDNEY STUDIES IN ENGLISH. 1975. a. $8.50. University of Sydney, Department of English, Sydney, N.S.W. 2006, Australia. TEL 02-692-2432. FAX 02-692-2434. Eds. G.A. Wilkes, A.P. Riemer. bk.rev. circ. 1,000. (back issues avail.)
Description: Devoted to criticism and scholarship in English literature and drama.

880.9   US   ISSN 1040-3612
PA1
SYLLECTA CLASSICA. 1989. a. University of Iowa, 112 Schaeffer Hall, Iowa City, IA 52242.
—UnCover.

870   BE
SYMBOLAE. SERIES D. LITERARIA. (Text in Dutch, English) 1987. irreg., vol.6, 1993. price varies. Leuven University Press, Krakenstraat 3, B-3000 Leuven, Belgium. TEL 32-16-284175. FAX 32-16-284176. Ed.Bd. **Document type:** academic/scholarly publication, monographic series.

800   US   ISSN 0039-7709
PB1   CODEN: SYMPEZ
SYMPOSIUM; a quarterly journal in modern foreign literatures. (Text mainly in English; occasionally in French, German, Italian, Portuguese and Spanish) 1946. q. $32 to individuals; institutions $64. (Syracuse University, Department of Romance Languages) Heldref Publications, 1319 Eighteenth St., N.W., Washington, DC 20036-1802. TEL 202-296-6267. FAX 202-296-5149. (Co-sponsor: Helen Dwight Reid Educational Foundation) Ed. Jeanne Bebo. adv. contact: Raymond Rallo. bk.rev. circ. 700. (also avail. in microform; reprint service avail. from KTO) **Indexed:** Hum.Ind., Ind.Bk.Rev.Hum. **Document type:** academic/scholarly publication.
—BLDSC (8582.880000); Faxon; UnCover; SWETS; UMI. **CCC.**
     Refereed Serial

800   US   ISSN 1048-8561
CB351
SYNOPSIS (LEWISTON); a yearly volume of book reviews. a. $29.95 to individuals; institutions $29.95. Edwin Mellen Press, 415 Ridge St., Box 450, Lewiston, NY 14092. TEL 716-754-2788. FAX 716-754-4056. Eds. Guy R. Mermier, Mercedes Vaquero.

850   RM
SYNTHESIS. (Text in English, French, German, Italian, Spanish) 1972. a. 30 lei($42) (Comite National Roumain de Litterature Comparee) Editura Academiei Romane, Calea Victoriei 125, 79717 Bucharest, Rumania. (Dist. by: Rompresfilatelia, Calea Grivitei 64-66, P.O. Box 12-201, 78104 Bucharest, Rumania) Ed. Zoe Dumitrescu Busulenga. bk.rev. **Indexed:** Amer.Hist.& Life, Chem.Infd., Hist.Abstr.

800 200   GW
T H L I. (Textwissenschaft Theologie Hermeneutik Literaturanalyse Informatik) 1991. irreg., vol.9, 1994. DM.68. Francke Verlag GmbH, Postfach 2560, 72015 Tuebingen, Germany. TEL 07071-78091. FAX 07071-75288. Ed. Winfried Bader. **Document type:** monographic series.

860   US   ISSN 1045-8875
E184.M5
T Q S NEWS. (Tonatiuh-Quinto Sol); a contemporary newsletter of eclectic Chicano thought. (Text in English and Spanish) 1976-1982; resumed 1984. q. $16. T Q S Publications (Subsidiary of: Tonatiuh-Quinto Sol International), Box 9275, Berkeley, CA 94709. TEL 510-655-8036. FAX 510-601-6938. Ed. Octavio I. Romano. bk.rev. circ. 1,000. (back issues avail.) **Indexed:** Hisp.Amer.Per.Ind. **Document type:** newsletter.
     Formerly (until Jan. 1989): Grito del Sol Collection; **Supersedes:** Grito del Sol (ISSN 0742-1877)
     Description: News about education, health, literature, research, consumer issues and student scholarships.

800   II
TAGORE INTERNATIONAL. (Text in English) 1985. s-a. Rs.50($10) Tagore Research Institute, Rabindra Charcha Bhavan, 97C S.P. Mukherjee Rd., Calcutta 700 026, India. TEL 42-4386. Ed. Manjula Bose. bk.rev. circ. 500.
     Description: Academic journal and news bulletin on the Bengali poet and writer Rabindranath Tagore.

895.1   CC
TAIGANG WENXUE XUANKAN/SELECTED TAIWAN AND HONG KONG LITERARY WORKS. (Text in Chinese) m. Y26.40. Fujian Sheng Wenlian, Fenghuang Chi, People's Republic of China, Fuzhou, Fujian 350002. TEL 711725. (Dist. overseas by: Jiangsu Publications Import & Export Corp., 56 Gao Yun Ling, Nanjing, Jiangsu, P.R.C.) Ed. Ji Zhong.
     Description: Introduces literary works by overseas Chinese writers in Taiwan, Hong Kong, Macao and other areas.

895.1   CH
TAIWAN LITERATURE/TAI-WAN WEN I. (Text in Chinese) 1964. bi-m. NT.$500 in ROC; Asia $31; elsewhere $35. 6F, No. 1-1, Lane 52, Roosevelt Rd. Sec. 4, Taipei, Taiwan, Republic of China. (Orders to: 3F, No. 65 An-ho Rd., Taipei, Taiwan, R.O.C.) Ed. Wang Ming-Huang. adv.

700 800   NZ   ISSN 0114-4138
TAKAHE. 1989. q. NZ.$24. Takahe Publishing Collective, P.O. Box 13-335, Christchurch 1, New Zealand. TEL 03-3558-337. Ed.Bd. adv. circ. 300.
     Description: Publishes short fiction and poetry (including translations) from emergent and established writers.

808.838   US
TALKING RAVEN; journal of imaginative trouble. 1991. q. $11. ParaTheatrical ReSearch, Box 45758, Seattle, WA 98145. TEL 206-781-5691. adv. circ. 5,000. **Document type:** newspaper.
     Description: Publishes poetry, fiction, essays, brief interviews and artwork, with an emphasis on rebelliousness. Each issue is devoted to a single theme.

800   UK
TALKING STICK MAGAZINE. 1988. q. £10. P.O. Box 3719, London SW17 8XT, England. Eds. Amanda Stick, Caroline Stick. bk.rev. circ. 1,000. **Document type:** academic/scholarly publication.

800   NQ   ISSN 0039-9221
TALLER. 1968; N.S. no.10, 1975. 3/yr. Can.$5. (Universidad Nacional Autonoma de Nicaragua) Editorial Universitaria de la U N A N, Leon, Nicaragua. Ed. Jaime Buitrago. (processed)

860   CL   ISSN 0716-0798
TALLER DE LETRAS. (Some vols. accompanied by supplements) 1971. a. $25. Pontificia Universidad Catolica de Chile, Instituto de Letras, Pte. Batlle y Ordonez, 3300, Campus Oriente U.C., Casilla 6277, Correo 22, Santiago, Chile. FAX 562-2225515. TELEX 240395 PUC VA-CL. Ed. Ileana Cabrera de Hagel. bk.rev.; bibl.; illus.; index. circ. 1,000.

809 895.1   CH   ISSN 0049-2949
PL2250
TAMKANG REVIEW; a journal mainly devoted to comparative studies between Chinese and foreign literatures. (Text in English) 1970. q. NT.$1200($40) Tamkang University, Graduate Institute of Western Languages and Literature, Tamsui, Taipei Hsien, Taiwan 25137, Republic of China. TEL 02-6215656. FAX 02-6211254. Ed. Ming-tu Yang. adv.; bk.rev. circ. 1,000. (back issues avail.) **Indexed:** Arts & Hum.Cit.Ind., Curr.Cont., M.L.A. **Document type:** academic/scholarly publication.
—BLDSC (8601.620000); UnCover.

TANGENT; the science fiction and fantasy short fiction review magazine. see *LITERATURE — Science Fiction, Fantasy, Horror*

895   VN
TAP CHI TAC PHAM VAN HOC. 1987. m. Viet-Nam Writers' Association, 65 Nguyen Du St., Hanoi, Socialist Republic of Vietnam. TEL 52442. Ed. Nguyen Dinh Thi. circ. 15,000.

895   VN
TAP CHI VAN HOC/LITERATURE MAGAZINE. m. Institute of Literature, 20 Ly Thai To St., Hanoi, Socialist Republic of Vietnam. TEL 52895. Ed. Phong Le.

800 792   US   ISSN 0887-9257
TAPROOT. 1984. q. $10. Burning Press, Box 585, Lakewood, OH 44107. Ed. Robert Drake. bk.rev. circ. 250.
     Description: Journal of avant-garde and experimental language, graphic, and audio arts.

810   US
TAPROOT LITERARY REVIEW. 1987. irreg. (1-2/yr.) $7.50. 302 Park Rd., Ambridge, PA 15003. TEL 412-266-8476. Ed. Tikvah Feinstein. circ. 500.

051   US
TASTE OF LATEX; entertainment for the sexually disenfranchised. 3/yr. $5.95 per issue. Box 460122, San Francisco, CA 94146. Ed. Lily Braindrop.
     Description: Includes interviews, artwork, fiction, poetry and editorials.

TEACHERS & WRITERS MAGAZINE. see *EDUCATION — Teaching Methods And Curriculum*

890   PL   ISSN 0867-0633
PN9
TEKSTY DRUGIE. 1972-1981 (no.6-60); resumed 1990 (Apr.). bi-m. $36. Polska Akademia Nauk, Instytut Badan Literackich, Nowy Swiat 72, Palac Staszica, pok. 128, 00-330 Warsaw, Poland. (Co-sponsor: Komitet Nauk o Literaturze Polskiej) Ed. R. Nycz. adv.; bk.rev. circ. 1,500. **Indexed:** M.L.A.
     Formerly (until 1981): Teksty (ISSN 0324-8208)
     Description: Focuses on theory and practice of new approaches to literature, especially to Polish literature.

800   IS   ISSN 0792-1683
TEL AVIV REVIEW. 1988. a. $12 to individuals (foreign $18); institutions $24 (foreign $30). Ah'shav Publishers, 3 Smolenskin St., P.O. Box 3421, Tel Aviv 63415, Israel. TEL 03-5245120. (Dist. worldwide, except in Israel and UK by: Duke University Press, 6697 College Sta., Durham, NC 27708) Ed. Gabriel Moked. adv. circ. 3,700.
     Description: Dedicated to translations from ancient and modern Hebrew literature and to the poetry, fiction, drama and essays of non-Israeli, Jewish and non-Jewish writers.

808 301.4157   US
TELEWOMAN.* 1979. m. $20. Telewoman, Inc., 12091 Glenora Hwy, Sunol, CA 94586-7411. Ed. Anne D'Arcy. adv.; bk.rev.; illus. circ. 500.

TELICOM. see *PHILOSOPHY*

TEMPORARY CULTURE. see *LITERATURE — Science Fiction, Fantasy, Horror*

800 100   US   ISSN 1062-3981
THE TEMPTATION OF SAINT ANTHONY. 1991. w. $10. Martin Bormann's Cranial Splints, Box 8166, Philadelphia, PA 19101-8166. TEL 215-898-0587. Ed. Mark-Jason Doninus. bk.rev.; film rev, play rev. circ. 67,000. (also avail. in magnetic tape; diskette format; back issues avail.) **Document type:** newsletter.
●Also available online.
     Description: Mixed-bag of humor, fiction, bizarre speculation, and observation. Emphasis on life as a work of art, philosophy of consciousness, absurdity and surrealism in everyday things, and Dada.

800   US   ISSN 0497-2384
PS1
TENNESSEE STUDIES IN LITERATURE. 1956. a. price varies. (University of Tennessee at Knoxville, Department of English) University of Tennessee Press, Knoxville, TN 37996-0325. TEL 615-974-3321. bibl.; cum.index. (also avail. in microform from UMI; back issues avail.; reprint service avail. from UMI) **Indexed:** Amer.Hum.Ind., M.L.A. **Document type:** academic/scholarly publication.
—BLDSC (8790.740000).

800   US
TENNESSEE WILLIAMS LITERARY JOURNAL. 1989. s-a. $40. c/o Clare Beth Pierson, Mgr. Ed., 4517 Cleary Ave., Metairie, LA 70000. Ed. W. Kenneth Holditch. adv.; bk.rev.
     Description: Devoted to the study of the life and works of America's premier playwright. Contains critical articles on Tennessee Williams and/or his work, calendar of current production of his plays, news concerning recent publications, and updated bibliographies.

820   UK   ISSN 0082-2841
PR5579
TENNYSON RESEARCH BULLETIN. 1967. a. membership. Tennyson Society, Tennyson Research Centre, Central Library, Free School Ln., Lincoln LN2 1EZ, England. TEL 0522-552866. FAX 0522-552858. Ed.Bd. bk.rev.; index, cum.index every 5 yrs. circ. 500. **Indexed:** M.L.A. **Document type:** bulletin.
—UnCover.

820   UK   ISSN 0082-285X
PR5579
TENNYSON SOCIETY, LINCOLN, ENGLAND. MONOGRAPHS. 1969. irreg., no.11, 1987. membership. Tennyson Society, Tennyson Research Centre, Central Library, Free School Ln., Lincoln LN2 1EZ, England. TEL 0522-552866. FAX 0522-552858. Ed.Bd. circ. 500. **Document type:** monographic series.

LITERATURE

820   UK   ISSN 0307-3572
TENNYSON SOCIETY, LINCOLN, ENGLAND. OCCASIONAL PAPERS. 1974. irreg., no.9, 1993. membership. Tennyson Society, Tennyson Research Centre, Central Library, Free School Ln., Lincoln LN2 1EZ, England. TEL 0522-552866. FAX 0522-552858. **Document type:** monographic series.

820   UK   ISSN 0082-2868
TENNYSON SOCIETY, LINCOLN, ENGLAND. REPORT. 1961. a. free. Tennyson Society, Tennyson Research Centre, Central Library, Free School Ln., Lincoln LN2 1EZ, England. TEL 0522-552866. FAX 0522-552858. circ. 500. **Document type:** bulletin.

800   II
TENOR. (Text in English) 1978. s-a. Rs.50 foreign $10 (effective Sep. 1991). M. Sivaramkrishna, 3-6-226-1, Himayatnagar, Hyderabad 500 029, India. Ed.Bd. adv.; bk.rev. circ. 200.
   Description: Promotes culture, literature and translation.

895   MY
TENQQARA; journal of Southeast Asian literature. (Text in English, Indonesian, Malay) 1967. s-a. $7. Dewan Behasa dan Pustaka, P.O. Box 10803, Kuala Lumpur, Malaysia. adv.; illus.
   Description: Presents literary works and critical essays on and from Malaysia, Philippines, Singapore, and Thailand.

800   US   ISSN 0890-3352
TENSO. vol.8, 1993. 2/yr. $15 to individuals; libraries $20. Societe Guihem IX, c/o Classical & Modern Languages, University of Louisville, Louisville, KY 40292. TEL 502-588-0493. FAX 502-588-8885. (Subscr. to: Elizabeth E. Poe, Department of French and Italian, Tulane University, New Orleans, LA 70118. TEL 504-865-5115) Ed. Wendy Pfeffer. bk.rev.; bibl.; circ. 150 (paid). (back issues avail.) **Indexed:** M.L.A. **Document type:** academic/scholarly publication, bibliography.
   Description: Publishes research on medieval and modern Occitan (Provencal) language and literature; each issue includes notes, announcements, and a linguistic or literary bibliography.

TEORIA LITERARIA: TEXTO Y TEORIA. see *LITERARY AND POLITICAL REVIEWS*

800   IT
TEORIE E OGGETTI SERIE OCRA. 1978. irreg., no.17, 1990. price varies. Liguori Editore s.r.l., Via Mezzocannone 19, 80134 Naples, Italy. TEL 081-5527139. Eds. Giancarlo Mazazcurati. **Document type:** monographic series.
   Supersedes in part: Teorie e Oggetti (ISSN 0392-2154)

895.1   CC   ISSN 1003-6881
TEQU WENXUE/SPECIAL ZONE LITERATURE. (Text in Chinese) 1982. bi-m. Y4.80 per no. Shenzhen Wenlian, 13, Guiyuan Lu, 4th Floor, Shenzhen, Guangdong 518008, People's Republic of China. TEL 5576304. Ed. Dai Musheng. adv.: page $1200; adv. contact: Liu Zhiqiang. illus. circ. 35,000.

808
TERMINO. 1982. q. $6. Box 8905, Cincinnati, OH 45208. TEL 513-232-1548. Eds. Roberto Madrigal Ecay, Manuel F. Ballagas. circ. 5,000.

144   IT
TESTI E STUDI UMANISTICI. irreg., latest no.4. L.30000. Angelo Longo Editore, Via Paolo Costa 33, P.O. Box 431, 48100 Ravenna, Italy. TEL 0544-217026. Eds. Giorgio Padoan, Manlio Pastore Stocchi. circ. 1,500. **Document type:** monographic series.

810   US   ISSN 0885-2685
PS642
TEXAS REVIEW. 1976. s-a. $10. Sam Houston State University, English Department, Huntsville, TX 77340. TEL 409-294-1429. Ed. Paul Ruffin. adv.; bk.rev. circ. 750. **Indexed:** A.I.P.P., M.L.A.
   —BLDSC (8800.100000); UnCover.
   Formerly (until 1979): Sam Houston Literary Review.

810   US   ISSN 0040-4691
AS30
TEXAS STUDIES IN LITERATURE AND LANGUAGE; a journal of the humanities. 1959. q. $24 to individuals; institutions $40. University of Texas Press, Box 7819, Austin, TX 78713. TEL 512-471-4531. Ed. A.C. Hilfer. adv.; index. circ. 1,000. (also avail. in microform from KTO,UMI; reprint service avail. from UMI) **Indexed:** Abstr.Engl.Stud., Amer.Bibl.Slavic & E.Eur.Stud., Arts & Hum.Cit.Ind., Curr.Cont., Hum.Ind., Lang.& Lang.Behav.Abstr., M.L.A., Sociol.Abstr.
   —BLDSC (8800.180000); Faxon; UnCover; SWETS; UMI. **CCC**.
   Description: Publishes essays reflecting a variety of critical approaches and covers all periods of literary history.

TEXT; an interdisciplinary journal for the study of discourse. see *HUMANITIES: COMPREHENSIVE WORKS*

800   US   ISSN 0736-3974
P47
TEXT (NEW YORK); transactions. 1984. a. $49.50. (Society for Textual Scholarship) A M S Press, Inc., 56 E. 13th St., New York, NY 10003. TEL 212-777-4700. FAX 212-995-5413. Eds. D.C. Greetham, W. Speed Hill. (back issues avail.)
   —BLDSC (8800.612500).
   Description: Annual collection of articles on textual scholarship originating from bi-annual conferences held by the Society for Textual Scholarship.

809   US   ISSN 1046-2937
PN2   CODEN: TPQUEI
TEXT AND PERFORMANCE QUARTERLY. 1980. q. Speech Communication Association, 5105 Backlick Rd., Bldg. E., Annandale, VA 22003.
   —BLDSC (8800.620470); Faxon; UnCover; UMI.
   Formerly (until 1989): Literature in Performance (ISSN 0734-0796)

800   GW   ISSN 0933-4769
TEXT UND KONTEXT; Romanische Literaturen und allgemeine Literaturwissenschaft. irreg., vol.12, 1994. price varies. Franz Steiner Verlag Wiesbaden GmbH, Birkenwaldstr. 44, 70191 Stuttgart, Germany. TEL 0711-2582-0. FAX 0711-2582290. TELEX 723636-DAZ-D. (Subscr. to: Postfach 101061, 70009 Stuttgart, Germany) Ed. Klaus W. Hempfer. **Document type:** monographic series.

800   GW   ISSN 0040-5329
PN4
TEXT UND KRITIK; Zeitschrift fuer Literatur. 1962. q. DM.63. Edition Text und Kritik GmbH, Levelingstr. 6a, 81673 Munich, Germany. TEL 089-432929. FAX 089-433997. Ed. Heinz Ludwig Arnold. adv. **Indexed:** Curr.Cont., M.L.A. **Document type:** academic/scholarly publication.
   —SWETS.

800   CN   ISSN 0715-8920
PN3
TEXTE; revue de critique et de theorie litteraire. (Text in English, French) 1981. a. Can.$17 to individuals; institutions Can.$33. Trinity College, Toronto, ON M5S 1H8, Canada. (Subscr. to: 5201 Dufferin St., Downsview, ON M3H 5T8 Canada) Ed. A. Oliver. bk.rev.; circ. 280 (paid). (back issues avail.) **Document type:** academic/scholarly publication.
   —BLDSC (8800.635200).
   Description: Seeks to provide a forum for dialogue between the different approaches to the study of the literary text by bringing together work on a given topic with its critical debates, its analytical bibliographies and indexes.

800   GW
TEXTE DES SPAETEN MITTELALTERS UND DER FRUEHEN NEUZEIT. 1956. irreg., no.36, 1993. Erich Schmidt Verlag GmbH & Co. (Berlin), Genthiner Str. 30G, 10785 Berlin, Germany. TEL 030-2500850. FAX 030-25008521. (Subscr. addr.: Zweigniederlassung Bielefeld, Viktoriastr. 44a, 33602 Bielefeld, Germany) Eds. Karl Stackmann, Stanley N. Werbow. **Document type:** academic/scholarly publication.

830 430   FR   ISSN 0981-1907
TEXTE ET L'IDEE. 1986. a. 70 Fr. (Universite de Nancy II, Centre de Recherches Germaniques) Association le Texte et l'Idee, 23 Blvd. Albert 1er, 54015 Nancy Cedex, France. TEL 80-61-41-22. Ed. Jean-Marie Paul.
   Description: Covers German literature and history of ideas.

808   GW
TEXTEN UND SCHREIBEN. bi-m. DM.57.75 (foreign DM.65.55). Hans Holzmann Verlag GmbH, Gewerbestr. 2, 86825 Bad Woerishofen, Germany. TEL 08247-35401. FAX 08247-354170. Ed. Gabi Neumayer. **Document type:** academic/scholarly publication.

840   SZ
TEXTES LITTERAIRES FRANCAIS. (Text in French) 1895. irreg., no.436, 1993. price varies. Librairie Droz S.A., 11, rue Massot, CH-1211 Geneva 12, Switzerland. TEL 022-3466666. FAX 022-3472391. **Document type:** monographic series.
   Description: Features letters and poetry.

860   MX   ISSN 0185-0830
PQ7081.A1
TEXTO CRITICO. 1975. s-a. Mex.$20($25) Universidad Veracruzana, Centro de Investigaciones Literarias y Semiolinguisticas, Apdo. Postal 369, 91000 Xalapa, Veracruz, Mexico. TEL 28-14-26-56. Ed. Sixto Rodriguez-Hernandez. adv.; bk.rev.; cum.index. circ. 11,000. **Indexed:** Hisp.Amer.Per.Ind. **Document type:** academic/scholarly publication.

820   UK   ISSN 0950-236X
TEXTUAL PRACTICE. 1987. 3/yr. £22 (foreign £24) to individuals; institutions £60 (foreign £65). Routledge, 11 New Fetter Ln., London EC4P 4EE, England. TEL 071-583-9855. FAX 071-583-0701. TELEX 263398-ROUT-G. (Subscr. to: ITPS Ltd., Cheriton House, Andover, Hants SP10 5BE, England. TEL 0264-342919. FAX 0264-342807) Ed. Terence Hawkes. adv.; bk.rev. **Document type:** academic/scholarly publication.
   —BLDSC (8813.780460); Faxon; SWETS. **CCC**.
   Description: Develops the concept of "textuality". Centers on the study of literature, philosophy, law, history of science, sociology, feminism and cultural and media studies.

820 420   IT
TEXTUS; English studies in Italy. 1988. a. L.37000 (foreign L.55000) (effective 1994). (Associazione Italiana di Anglistica) Tilgher-Genova s.a.s., Via Assarotti 52, 16122 Genoa, Italy. TEL 10-8391140. FAX 10-870653. Ed.Bd.

800   NE   ISSN 0927-5754
▼**TEXTXET**; studies in comparative literature. 1993. irreg. price varies. Editions Rodopi B.V., Keizersgracht 302-304, 1016 EX Amsterdam, Netherlands. TEL 31-20-6227507. FAX 31-20-6380948. (in N. America: 233 Peachtree Rd., N.E., Ste. 404, Atlanta, GA 30303-1504. TEL 800-522-7116. FAX 404-522-7116) Eds. C.C. Barfoot, Theo D'haen. **Document type:** academic/scholarly publication.

800   US   ISSN 1064-2463
THACKERAY NEWSLETTER. 1975. s-a. $2.50. Mississippi State University, English Department, Drawer E, Mississippi State, MS 39762. TEL 601-325-3644. Ed. P.L. Shillingsburg. bk.rev. circ. 70. (back issues avail.) **Indexed:** Amer.Hum.Ind., M.L.A.
   Description: News notes, recent studies, and scholarly notes relating to William Makepeace Thackeray.

820   CN   ISSN 0706-5604
PN6147
THALIA; a journal of studies in literary humor. (Text in English; occasionally in French) 1978. s-a. Can.$20 to individuals; libraries Can.$22. Association for the Study of Humor, c/o Jacqueline Tavernier-Courbin, Ed., Dept. of English, University of Ottawa, Ottawa, Ont. K1N 6N5, Canada. TEL 613-564-2311. FAX 613-564-9175. adv.; bk.rev.; illus.; index. circ. 500. (back issues avail.; reprint service avail. from ISI) **Indexed:** Abstr.Engl.Stud., Arts & Hum.Cit.Ind., Curr.Cont., M.L.A.
   —BLDSC (8814.185000); Faxon; UnCover.

LITERATURE

830 920   GW   ISSN 0082-3880
THEODOR-STORM-GESELLSCHAFT. SCHRIFTEN. 1952. a. price varies. Westholsteinische Verlagsanstalt Boyens und Co., Am Wulf-Isebrand-Platz, 25746 Heide, Germany. TEL 0481-691-0. Eds. Karl E. Laage, Friedrich Heitmann.

THIRD DEGREE (NEW YORK). see *LITERATURE — Mystery And Detective*

820   UK
THIRD HALF. 1987. irreg. £2.25 per no. K.T. Publications, 16 Fane Close, Stamford, Lincs PE9 1HG, England. TEL 0780-54193. Ed. Kevin Troop. (back issues avail.) **Document type:** bulletin.

800   UK   ISSN 0268-5418
THOMAS HARDY JOURNAL. 1975. 3/yr £12 (foreign £15). Thomas Hardy Society Ltd., c/o Simon Curtis, Ed., 25 Hawthorn Grove, Heaton Moor, Stockport SK4 4HZ, England. TEL 061-4329075. (Subscr. to: Hon. Treasurer, Thomas Hardy Society, P.O. Box 1438, Dorchester, Dorset DT1 1YH, England) adv.; bk.rev. circ. 1,500. **Document type:** academic/scholarly publication.
—BLDSC (8820.230670); UnCover.
Formerly (until 1985): Thomas Hardy Society. Review (ISSN 0307-1642)
Description: Provides information about the Society's activities. Includes letters, reviews and articles about Hardy's writings, his life and his background.

820   UI   ISSN 0082-416X
PR4752
THOMAS HARDY YEAR BOOK. 1970. a. 4p. Toucan Press, Saravia, Rue des Monts, Delancey Park, St. Sampson, Guernsey, Channel Islands. Eds. J. Stevens Cox, G. Stevens Cox. adv.; bk.rev. circ. 2,000. **Indexed:** Br.Hum.Ind., M.L.A.
Description: Prints scholarly articles on Thomas Hardy and other Victorian authors.

800   SZ   ISSN 0082-4186
PT2625.A44
THOMAS MANN GESELLSCHAFT. BLAETTER. 1958. a. price varies. Thomas Mann Gesellschaft, Raemistr. 5, CH-8001 Zurich, Switzerland. bk.rev. circ. 1,000.

810   US   ISSN 0276-5683
PS3545.O337
THOMAS WOLFE REVIEW. 1977. s-a. $10. Thomas Wolfe Society, c/o John S. Phillipson, Ed., Dept. of English, University of Akron, Akron, OH 44325. TEL 216-972-7470. abstr.; illus. circ. 600. (reprint service avail. from ISI) **Indexed:** Abstr.Engl.Stud., Amer.Hum.Ind., Arts & Hum.Cit.Ind., M.L.A. **Document type:** academic/scholarly publication.
—UnCover.
Formerly: Thomas Wolfe Newsletter (ISSN 0148-1789)

810   US
THOMAS WOLFE SOCIETY. PROCEEDINGS. 1981. a. membership. Thomas Wolfe Society, c/o John S. Phillipson, Dept. of English, University of Akron, Akron, OH 44325. TEL 216-972-7470. circ. 600. **Document type:** proceedings.
Formerly (until 1989): Thomas Wolfe Society. Summer Report and Membership List.

810   US   ISSN 0040-6406
PS3053
THOREAU SOCIETY BULLETIN; devoted to the life and writings of Henry David Thoreau. 1941. q. $20. Thoreau Society, Inc., Dept. of English, East Carolina Univ., Greenville, NC 28758-4353. TEL 919-757-6675. FAX 919-757-4889. Ed. Bradley P. Dean. bk.rev.; bibl.; charts; illus. circ. 2,000. (processed; also avail. in microform from UMI; reprint service avail. from UMI) **Indexed:** Amer.Hum.Ind., LCR, M.L.A.
—UMI.

THORNDYKE FILE. see *LITERATURE — Adventure And Romance*

808.882 100   US   ISSN 0886-6481
THOUGHTS FOR ALL SEASONS; the magazine of epigrams. 1976. irreg., vol.4, 1992. $4.75. Valley Press, 11530 S.W. 99th St., Miami, FL 33176-2516. TEL 305-598-8599. Ed. Michel P. Richard. adv. circ. 1,000. (back issues avail.) **Document type:** consumer publication.
Description: Presents original epigrams and black-and-white illustrations and essays about the epigram as a literary form.

810   US   ISSN 0275-1410
THREEPENNY REVIEW. 1980. q. $16. Box 9131, Berkeley, CA 94709. TEL 510-849-4545. FAX 510-849-4551. Ed. Wendy Lesser. adv.: B&W page $900; trim 12 x 17. bk.rev. circ. 9,000. (tabloid format; also avail. in microfilm from UMI; reprint service avail. from UMI) **Indexed:** Alt.Press Ind., Bk.Rev.Ind. (1981-), Child.Bk.Rev.Ind. (1981-), Ind.Amer.Per.Verse.
—UMI.

820   UK   ISSN 0040-6562
AP4
THRESHOLD. 1957. irreg., no. 31, 1980. price varies. Lyric Players Theatre, 55 Ridgeway St., Belfast 9, N. Ireland. Ed. John Boyd. bk.rev. circ. 1,000.

059.958   BR
THWE - THAUK MAGAZINE. 1946. m. 185 48th St., Yangon, Union of Myanmar.

895.1   CC
TIAN NAN. (Text in Chinese) bi-m. Zhongguo Minjian Wenyijia Xiehui, Guangdong Fenhui - China Folk Artists' Association, Guangdong Chapter, No. 170, Wende Beilu, Guangzhou, Guangdong 510030, People's Republic of China. TEL 346887. Ed. Lin Zesheng.

895.1   CC
TIANCHI/HEAVEN LAKE. (Text in Chinese) 1986. q. Y7.92. Zhongguo Zuojia Xiehui, Yanbian Fenhui, 22, Henan St., Yanji, Jilin 133001, People's Republic of China. TEL 86-433-810587. Ed. Liu Dechang. circ. 6,000.
Description: Covers fictions, poetry, essays and literature theory.

058.396 809   IC   ISSN 0256-8438
PT7351
TIMARIT MALS OG MENNINGAR. 1939. q. ISK 2950. Mal og Menning, Laugavegur 18, 101 Reykjavik, Iceland. TEL 354-1-24240. FAX 354-1-62-35-23. (Subscr. to: P.O. Box 392, 121 Reykjavik, Iceland) Ed. Fridrik Rafnsson. adv.; bk.rev.; illus. circ. 2,000. (back issues avail.)
Description: Publishes original literature, Icelandic and foreign, as well as articles of general cultural interest.

800 700   UK   ISSN 0040-7895
AP4
TIMES LITERARY SUPPLEMENT. 1902. w. $120. Times Supplements Ltd., Admiral House, 66-68 E. Smithfield, London E1 9YY, England. TEL 071-782-3000. FAX 071-782-3200. Ed. Ferdinand Mount. adv.; bk.rev.; illus.; mkt.; index. circ. 25,538. (tabloid format; also avail. in microform from RPI) **Indexed:** Acad.Ind., Bk.Rev.Dig., Bk.Rev.Ind. (1965-), Br.Hum.Ind., Chic.Per.Ind., Child.Bk.Rev.Ind. (1965-), GdIns., Hum.Ind., Mid.East: Abstr.& Ind., Ref.Sour., RILA, RILM. **Document type:** academic/scholarly publication.
—BLDSC (8853.810000).

TIMP LIBER. see *ART*

895.1   SW   ISSN 0803-0391
PL2254
TODAY LITERARY MAGAZINE/JINTIAN. (Text in Chinese) 1978-1980; resumed 1990. q. $32 to individuals; institutions $40. Today Literary Foundation, P.O. Box 50025, S-104 05 Stockholm, Sweden. TEL 46-8-161315. FAX 46-8-155464. Eds. Bei Dao, Chen Maiping.
Description: Contains literature by Chinese writers living in exile, or works by writers still inside the mainland whose works cannot be published in China for political reasons.

820 810 410   JA   ISSN 0385-406X
TOHOKU GAKUIN UNIVERSITY REVIEW; essays and studies in English language and literature. (Text in English and Japanese) 1958. a. 2000 Yen($12) Literary, Economic and Juristic Association, Tohoku Gakuin University, 3-1 Tsuchitoi 1-Chome, Sendai 980, Japan. Ed. Yukio Igarashi. bk.rev. circ. 2,000. **Indexed:** MLA.
—BLDSC (8859.993400).

800   JA   ISSN 0563-6760
TOKAI DAIGAKU KIYO. BUNGAKUBU/TOKAI UNIVERSITY. FACULTY OF LETTERS. BULLETIN. (Text mainly in Japanese; sometimes in English) no.25, 1976. s-a. exchange basis. (Tokai Daigaku, Bungakubu - Tokai University, Faculty of Literature) Tokai Daigaku Shuppankai - Tokai University Press, Shinjuko Tokai Bldg., 27-4 Shinjuku 3-chome, Shinjuku-ku, Tokyo 160, Japan. TEL 03-3356-1541. Ed. Keitaro Syoju. illus.; cum.index: vols.1-25. **Document type:** academic/scholarly publication.
Formerly: Tokai University. Faculty of Literature. Bulletin.

TOME; the dark works of great minds, and the great works of dark minds. see *LITERATURE — Science Fiction, Fantasy, Horror*

TOOK. see *LITERARY AND POLITICAL REVIEWS*

810   US
TOP STORIES. 1979. irreg. (approx. 3/yr.). $14.50 to individuals; institutions $16.50. 228 Seventh Ave., New York, NY 10011. TEL 212-989-3869. Ed. Anne Turyn. circ. 2,000. (back issues avail.)

IL TORCHIO ARTISTICO E LETTERARIO; organo ufficiale di stampa dell'Accademia Culturale d'Europa. see *ART*

940   CN   ISSN 0082-5050
TORONTO MEDAEVAL LATIN TEXTS. 1972. irreg., vol.19, 1990. $6.75 (250 BEF) per no. Pontifical Institute of Mediaeval Studies, 59 Queen's Park Crescent. E., Toronto, ON M5S 2C4, Canada. TEL 416-926-7144. FAX 416-926-7276. (Dist. outside N. America and UK by: N.V. Brepols, Steenweg op Tielen 68, 2300 Turnhout, Belgium. TEL 32-14-415463. FAX 32-14-428919) Ed.Bd. (back issues avail.) **Document type:** monographic series.

809 820   CN
TORONTO OLD ENGLISH SERIES. 1970. irreg. price varies. (University of Toronto, Centre for Medieval Studies) University of Toronto Press, 5201 Dufferin St., Downsview, ON M3H 5T8, Canada. TEL 416-667-7791. FAX 416-667-7832. (U.S. addr.: 340 Nagel Drive, Cheektowaga, NY 14225) Ed. Roberta Frank. **Document type:** academic/scholarly publication.

TORONTO SOUTH ASIAN REVIEW. see *LITERARY AND POLITICAL REVIEWS*

869 469   PR   ISSN 0040-9588
AS74.A1
LA TORRE. 1953. q. $16 to individuals (foreign $18); institutions $28 (foreign $30); students $8. University of Puerto Rico (Rio Piedras Campus), c/o Yudit de Ferdinandy, Mng. Ed., Box 23322, Univ. of Puerto Rico Sta., San Juan, PR 00931-3322. TEL 809 758-0148. FAX 809-753-9116. Ed. Arturo Echavarria. bk.rev.; bibl.; index. circ. 1,000. **Indexed:** Amer.Hist.& Life, Hist.Abstr. **Document type:** academic/scholarly publication.
—Faxon.
Description: Dedicated to literary and linguistic studies with emphasis on Latin American, Caribbean and Spanish literature.

860   AG
TORRE DE PAPEL. bi-m. Av. del Libertador 930, 2 Piso, Buenos Aires, Argentina. bk.rev.

891.85   PL   ISSN 0067-7787
TOWARZYSTWO LITERACKIE IM. A. MICKIEWICZA. BIBLIOTEKA. (Text in Polish) irreg., vol.13, 1992. price varies. Ossolineum, Publishing House of the Polish Academy of Sciences, Rynek 9, 50-106 Wroclaw, Poland. TEL 48-71-386-25. FAX 48-71-448-103. TELEX 0712771 OSS PL. **Document type:** monographic series.

800   JA   ISSN 0285-9602
TOYAMA DAIGAKU KYOIKUGAKUBU KIYO, A. BUNKAKEI/TOYAMA UNIVERSITY. FACULTY OF EDUCATION. MEMOIRS, A. LITERATURE. (Text in English, Japanese; summaries in English) 1953. irreg. (1-2/yr), no.44, 1993. Toyama Daigaku, Kyoikugakubu - Toyama University, Faculty of Education, 3190 Gofuku, Toyama-shi, Toyama-ken 930, Japan. TEL 0764-41-1271. FAX 0764-32-4212. Ed. Tsutomu Anayama. **Document type:** academic/scholarly publication.
—BLDSC (5593.331000).

LITERATURE

800   JA   ISSN 0285-9033
TOYOTA FOUNDATION OCCASIONAL REPORT. (Text in English) 1981. s-a. free. Toyota Foundation, Shinjuku-Mitsui Bldg., 37F, 2-1-1 Nishi-Shinjuku, Shinjuku-ku, Tokyo 163-04, Japan. TEL 03-3344-1701. FAX 03-3342-6911. Eds. Yumiko Himemoto, Becky D. Davis. bk.rev. circ. 4,000.
   Description: Introduces policies, activities, projects, and grantees of the foundation.

820   UK
TRAETHODYDD; cylchgrawn chwarterol at wasanaeth crefydd, diwinyddiaeth, athroniaeth a llenyddiaeth. (Text in Welsh) 1845. q. £1.50. Llyfrfa'r Methodistiaid Calfinaidd, Caernarfon, North Wales. TEL 0970-612959. FAX 0970-627066. Ed. J.E. Caerwyn Williams. bk.rev. circ. 475. **Indexed:** Abstr.Engl.Stud. **Document type:** academic/scholarly publication.

TRANSEUROPEENNES. see *HISTORY — History Of Europe*

800   GW
TRANSFER (TUEBINGEN); Duesseldorfer Materialen zur Literaturuebersetzung. irreg., no.8, 1994. DM.38. Gunter Narr Verlag, Postfach 2567, 72015 Tuebingen, Germany. TEL 07071-78091. Ed.Bd. **Document type:** monographic series.

800   US
TRANSIENT. 1973. irreg., no. 6, 1977. $5. Transient Press, Box 4662, Albuquerque, NM 87106. TEL 505-242-6600. Ed. Ken Saville. circ. 250.
   Formerly: Is.

800   US   ISSN 0093-9307
PN241
TRANSLATION (NEW YORK, 1972). 1972. s-a. $18. Translation Center, 412 Dodge Hall, Columbia University, New York, NY 10027. TEL 212-854-2305. FAX 212-749-0397. Ed. Lori Carlson. adv.: B&W page $300. bk.rev. circ. 2,000. —Faxon.
   Description: Dedicated to finding and publishing the best translations of foreign, contemporary literature.

TRANSLATION AND LITERATURE. see *LINGUISTICS*

TRAVAUX DE LINGUISTIQUE ET DE LITTERATURE. see *LINGUISTICS*

891.1   II
TREND. (Text in English) q. Rs.4. Pathikrit Association, 88-B Bipin Behari Ganguli St., Calcutta 12, India.
   Description: A literary and cultural journal.

TRICYCLE; the Buddhist review. see *RELIGIONS AND THEOLOGY — Buddhist*

800 398   US   ISSN 0360-3385
PN57.T8
TRISTANIA; a journal devoted to Tristan studies. 1975. a. $29.95 to individuals; institutions $19.95. (Tristan Society) Edwin Mellen Press, 415 Ridge St., Box 450, Lewiston, NY 14092. TEL 716-754-2788. FAX 716-754-4056. Ed. Lewis A.M. Sumberg. bk.rev.; bibl. (back issues avail.) **Indexed:** M.L.A.
   —BLDSC (9050.694500).

891.4   II   ISSN 0041-3135
AP8
TRIVENI; a literary and cultural quarterly. (Text in English) 1928. q. Rs.60. Triveni Foundation, 401, Sivasakthi Apts., Barkatpura, Hyderabad 500027, India. Eds.Bhavaraju Narasimha Rao, I.V. Chalapati Rao. adv.; bk.rev. circ. 2,000. **Indexed:** M.L.A.

800 700   UK
TRIVIUM. 1966. a. £8. Saint David's University College, Lampeter, Dyfed SA48 7ED, Wales. FAX 0570-423423. Ed. C.C. Eldridge. adv.; bk.rev. circ. 300. **Indexed:** Abstr.Engl.Stud., Arts & Hum.Cit.Ind., M.L.A. **Document type:** academic/scholarly publication.
   Description: Devoted to the arts and related subjects.

860   SP   ISSN 1132-2373
TROPELIAS; revista de teoria de la literatura y literatura comparada. 1990. a. Universidad de Zaragoza, Departamento de Linguistica General e Hispanica, Ciudad Universitaria s-n, 50009 Zaragoza, Spain. Ed. Tua Blesa.

839.2   NE   ISSN 0041-3348
TROTWAER; literer tydskrift. (Text in Frisian) 1969. bi-m. fl.47.50 to individuals (foreign fl.60); students fl.37.50. Koperative Utjowerij, Postbus 156, 8700 AD Boalsert-Bolsward, Netherlands. TEL 05157-5055. Ed. Koby van der Zwaag-Kampman. adv.; bk.rev.; bibl.; illus. circ. 350. —SWETS.

800   US
TRULY FINE. 1974. irreg. $1.50. Truly Fine Press, Box 891, Bemidji, MN 56601. Ed. Jerry Madson. bk.rev. circ. 500. (back issues avail.)
   Formerly: Truly Fine Press.

895   MP
TSOG/SPARK. 1944. bi-m. Union of Writers, Ulan Bator, Mongolia. TEL 327863. Ed. Ts. Enkhbat.

420.5 809   JA   ISSN 0496-3547
TSUDA REVIEW. (Text in English) 1956. a. exchange basis. Tsuda College - Tsuda Juku Daigaku, 2-1-1 Tsuda-machi, Kodaira-shi, Tokyo 187, Japan. FAX 0423-41-2444. circ. 1,000. **Indexed:** Abstr.Engl.Stud.
   Description: Covers English literature and linguistics.

810   US
TUCUMCARI LITERARY REVIEW. (Text mainly in English; occasionally in Spanish) 1988. bi-m. $12 (foreign $20). 3108 W. Bellevue Ave., Los Angeles, CA 90026. TEL 213-413-0789. Ed. Troxey Kemper. circ. 150.
   Description: Covers poetry, fiction, essays; includes non-fiction articles and nostalgia.

800   US   ISSN 0261-9199
TUDOR INTERLUDES. 1979. irreg., latest no.6. Boydell & Brewer Inc., Box 41026, Rochester, NY 14604. TEL 716-275-0419. FAX 716-271-8778.

808 305.4   US   ISSN 0732-7730
PN471
TULSA STUDIES IN WOMEN'S LITERATURE. 1982. s-a. $12 to individuals (foreign £15); institutions $14 (foreign $16). University of Tulsa, Tulsa Studies in Women's Literature, 600 S. College Ave., Tulsa, OK 74104-3189. TEL 918-631-2503. FAX 918-584-0623. Ed. Holly A. Laird. adv.; bk.rev. circ. 500. (also avail. in microfilm from UMI; back issues avail.) **Indexed:** Arts & Hum.Cit.Ind., Bk.Rev.Ind. (1989-), Child.Bk.Rev.Ind. (1989-), M.L.A., Stud.Wom.Abstr., Wom.Stud.Abstr. (1982-). **Document type:** academic/scholarly publication.
   —BLDSC (9070.480000); Faxon; UnCover.
   Description: Scholarly articles, notes and queries on literature from all time periods and places, including foreign-language literature, and from every genre: poetry, prose, drama, essays, diaries, memoirs, journalism and criticism. Focuses on women and writing, feminist critical and literary theory.

895.1   US
TUO LING/CAMEL BELLS. (Text in Chinese) bi-m. $35.60. China Books & Periodicals, Inc., 2929 24th St., San Francisco, CA 94110. TEL 415-282-2994. FAX 415-282-0994.

494.35   TU   ISSN 0041-4220
TURK DILI. 1933; N.S. 1951. m. $80. Turkish Language Institute - Turk Dil Kurumu, 217 Ataturk Bulvari, Ankara, Turkey. TEL 90-4-4268124. FAX 90-4-4285288. Ed. Ahmet B. Ercilasun. adv.; bk.rev.; bibl.; charts; stat.; index. circ. 11,650. (also avail. in microfiche from IDC) **Document type:** academic/scholarly publication.

830   GW   ISSN 0723-8177
TURMSCHREIBER KALENDER; ein Bayerisches Hausbuch auf das Jahr. 1982. a. DM.19.80. W. Ludwig Verlag, Goethestr. 43, 80336 Munich, Germany. TEL 089-5148-0. FAX 089-5148-229. circ. 11,000. (back issues avail.)

800 811   US   ISSN 0896-5951
TURNSTILE. 1986. a. $6.50. Turnstile Press, Inc., 175 Fifth Ave., Ste. 2348, New York, NY 10010. Ed. Mitchell Nauffets. adv. circ. 1,500. (back issues avail.) **Indexed:** Amer.Hum.Ind.
   Description: A literary forum for new and established writers of poetry and fiction. Includes interviews and original photography.

TUTTESTORIE; racconti letture trame di donne. see *WOMEN'S STUDIES*

810   US   ISSN 0041-4573
PS1329
TWAINIAN. 1939. q. $20 membership. Mark Twain Research Foundation, c/o Hannibal LaGrange College, 2800 Palmyra Rd., Hannibal, MO 63401. TEL 314-221-3675. Ed. Mrs. Chester L. Davis. bk.rev. circ. 400. **Indexed:** Abstr.Engl.Stud., Amer.Hist.& Life, Hist.Abstr.
   Description: Articles and essays on the wisdom of Mark Twain as taught by his life and his writings.

821   AT
TWEED. 1972. q. Aus.$4($5) c/o Janice M. Bostok, Ed., Box 304, Murwillumbah, N.S.W. 2484, Australia. bk.rev.; illus. circ. 200. (back issues avail.)

800   NE   ISSN 0166-1868
DE TWEEDE RONDE; tijdschrift voor literatuur. 1980. q. fl.44. Uitgeverij G.A. van Oorschot, Herengracht 613, 1017 CE Amsterdam, Netherlands. TEL 31-20-6231484. (Editorial addr.: Leidsegracht 35, 1017 NB Amsterdam, Netherlands) Ed.Bd. circ. 2,000.
   Description: Publishes poems, essays and short stories.

800   US   ISSN 0897-7844
TWENTIETH - CENTURY AMERICAN JEWISH WRITERS. irreg. Peter Lang Publishing, Inc., 62 W. 45th St., 4th Fl., New York, NY 10036. TEL 212-302-6740. FAX 212-302-7574. Ed. Daniel Walden. **Document type:** academic/scholarly publication.
   Description: Covers the Jewish writer in 20th Century America.

809   US   ISSN 0276-8178
PN771
TWENTIETH - CENTURY LITERARY CRITICISM; excerpts from criticism of the works of novelists, poets, playwrights, and other creative writers of the era 1900-1960. 1978. irreg., vol.43, 1992. $108. Gale Research Inc., 835 Penobscot Bldg., Detroit, MI 48277-0748. TEL 313-961-2242. FAX 313-961-6083. TELEX 810-221-7086. Ed. Paula Kepos. bibl.; index. (back issues avail.) **Indexed:** Child.Auth.& Illus.
   Description: Covers twentieth century creative writing to 1960.

800   US   ISSN 0041-462X
PN2
TWENTIETH CENTURY LITERATURE; a scholarly and critical journal. 1955. q. $25 to individuals (foreign $30); institutions $30 (foreign $34). Hofstra University, 203 Student Center, Hemstead, NY 11550. TEL 516-463-5460. Ed. William McBrien. adv.; abstr.; bibl.; index. circ. 3,000. (also avail. in microform from MIM,UMI; reprint service avail. from ISI,KTO,UMI) **Indexed:** Abstr.Engl.Stud., Acad.Ind., Arts & Hum.Cit.Ind., Bibl.Engl.Lang.& Lit., Bibl.Ind., Curr.Cont., Hum.Ind., LCR, M.L.A., Mid.East: Abstr.& Ind. **Document type:** academic/scholarly publication.
   —BLDSC (9076.850000); Faxon; UnCover; SWETS; UMI.

051 700
XXIST CENTURY; a new quarterly of art, politics, literature and ideas. 1991. 3/yr. $7.50 per no. Rizzoli International Publishers, Inc., 300 Park Ave. S., New York, NY 10010. TEL 212-387-3400. FAX 212-387-3535. Ed. Gini Alhadeff. illus. **Indexed:** Access (1992-).

TWISTED. see *LITERATURE — Science Fiction, Fantasy, Horror*

820   UK   ISSN 0041-4670
TWO RIVERS.* 1969. q. 32s.($4) 28 Tottenham St., London W.1, England. Eds. Martin Green, Paul Durcan. circ. 1,010.

800   SA   ISSN 0041-476X
TYDSKRIF VIR LETTERKUNDE. (Text in Afrikaans, Dutch) 1951. q. R.20 (effective 1993). (Afrikaanse Skrywerskring) Foundation for Education, Science and Technology - Stigting vir Onderwys, Wetenskap en Tegnologie, Posbus 1758, Pretoria 0001, South Africa. TEL 27-12-322-6404. FAX 27-12-320-7823. (Co-sponsors: Die Afrikaanse Persfonds; Departement Onderwys en Kultuur) Ed. H.J. Pieterse. adv.; bk.rev.; bibl.; illus. circ. 2,000. **Indexed:** Ind.S.A.Per., M.L.A. **Document type:** academic/scholarly publication.
   —SWETS.
   Refereed Serial

810.8 CN ISSN 0226-3440
U.C. REVIEW. Variant title: University College Literary Review. a. University of Toronto, University College, Toronto, Ont. M5S 1A1, Canada. TEL 613-978-2011. illus.

U J D S - STUDIER. see *HISTORY — History Of Europe*

820 SA ISSN 0041-5359
PR1
U N I S A ENGLISH STUDIES. 1963. s-a. R.13.11 (overseas $9) (effective 1994). University of South Africa, Department of English, P.O. Box 392, Pretoria 0001, South Africa. FAX 27-12-429-3221. TELEX 350068. Ed. S.G. Kossick. adv.; bk.rev.; abstr.; bibl.; illus. circ. 2,858. **Indexed:** M.L.A. **Document type:** academic/scholarly publication. —Faxon; UnCover.

808.81 808.81 US ISSN 0362-7012
PS501
U S 1 WORKSHEETS. 1973. a. $10. U S 1 Poets' Cooperative, Box 57, Roosevelt, NJ 08551-0001. (Subscr. to: Postings, Box 1, Ringoes, NJ 08551. TEL 908-782-6492) circ. 500. (back issues avail.) **Indexed:** Ind.Amer.Per.Verse.

800 HU ISSN 0041-5952
AP82
UJ IRAS. 1961. m. $27. (Magyar Irok Szovetsege) Lapkiado Vallalat, Lenin korut 9-11, 1073 Budapest 7, Hungary. TEL 222-408. (Subscr. to: Kultura, Box 149, H-1389 Budapest, Hungary) Ed. Ferenc Juhasz. bk.rev. circ. 20,000. **Indexed:** M.L.A.

890 KR
UKRAINS'KE LITERATUROZNAVSTVO. vol.28, 1977. 1.00 Rub. per no. (L'vovskii Gosudarstvennyi Universitet) Izdatel'stvo Vysshaya Shkola, L'vovskoe Otdelenie, Ul. Universitetskaya, 1, Lvov, Ukraine. Ed. I. Doroshenko. bibl. circ. 1,000.

914.1 941 UK ISSN 0954-3392
ULSTER EDITIONS AND MONOGRAPHS. 1988. irreg. Colin Smythe Ltd., P.O. Box 6, Gerrards Cross, Buckinghamshire SL9 8XA, England. TEL 0753-886000. FAX 0753-886469. circ. 1,200. **Document type:** monographic series. —BLDSC (9082.741800). **Description:** Collections of essays on Northern Irish literary and historical matters.

ULYSSES INTERNATIONAL; magazine du sud en France. see *ETHNIC INTERESTS*

890 JA
UMI/SEA. (Text in Japanese) 1969. m. 9450 Yen. Chuokoron-Sha, Inc., 2-8-7 Kyobashi, Chuo-ku, Tokyo 104, Japan. Ed. Marie Miyata. **Indexed:** Chem.Abstr.

801 CI
UMJETNOST RIJECI/WORD ART; casopis za znanost o knjizevnosti. vol.24, 1980. q. 180 din.($20) Sveuciliste u Zagrebu, Filozofski Fakultet, Dure Salaja 3, 41000 Zagreb, Croatia. (Dist by: IKP "Mladost" Export-Import, Ilica 30, 41000 Zagreb, Croatia) **Indexed:** Bibl.Ling., Can.Rev.Comp.Lit.

800 TZ ISSN 0011-6696
UMMA; a magazine of original writing. (Text in English and Kiswahili) 1966. 2/yr. EAs.15($3) University of Dar es Salaam, Department of Literature, Box 35041, Dar es Salaam, Tanzania. TELEX 41327 UNISCIE TANZANIA. Ed. Clement L. Ndulute. bk.rev. circ. 600. (also avail. in microfilm from UMI; reprint service avail. from KTO,UMI) **Indexed:** Curr.Cont.Africa, M.L.A.
Formerly: Darlite.

800 745.1 US
UNCLE WIGGILY NEWS. m. $17.95. Box 305, Lanc, NY 14086.

890 SW
UNGA DIKTARA. a. Bokfoerlaget Inferi, Box 167, 821 01 Bollnaes 1, Sweden.

808.83 II ISSN 0041-6762
PN2
UNILIT. (Text in English) 1961. m. Rs.35($10) Viswa Sahiti, 6-3-195 New Bhoiguda, Secunderabad 500003, India. Ed. Pothukuchi Sambasivarao. adv.; bk.rev. circ. 2,000. **Indexed:** M.L.A. **Document type:** consumer publication.
Description: Special focus on world problems and scientific material.

800 US
THE UNINTELLIGENCER. q. $1 per no. Box 3194, Bellingham, WA 98227. Ed. J.C. Coleman. circ. 70.
Description: Publishes short fiction, commentary, poetry, comics, and art and contains a trade list.

860 CU ISSN 0041-6770
PQ7081.A1
UNION. 1962. q. $18 in S. America; N. America $25; elsewhere $27. (Union de Escritores y Artistas de Cuba (UNEAC)) Ediciones Cubanas, Obispo No. 527, Aptdo. 605, Havana, Cuba. Ed. Otto Fernandez. bk.rev.; illus. circ. 5,000.

700 SG ISSN 0253-584X
UNIR: ECHO DE SAINT LOUIS. (Includes supplement) 1956. q. 2000 Fr.CFA. (Centre Catholique d'Information) Jean Vast, Ed. & Pub., B.P. 160, 1 rue Neuville, St. Louis, Senegal. TEL 61-10-27. FAX 61-24-08. (Subscr. to: P.J. Vast, 8 rue Duret, B.P. 160, St. Louis, Senegal) adv.; illus. **Document type:** bulletin.
Supersedes (1906-1918): Echo de Saint.

800 US
UNIROD.* 1991. irreg. $10 for 2 issues. An Firsten Tightbell Publishing, c/o Kenward G. Bradley, Ed., 1905 W. Wilson Ave., Apt. 2-A, Chicago, IL 60640-5213.
Description: Includes fiction and art, especially experimental and unusual works.

UNIVERSAL BLACK WRITER. see *ETHNIC INTERESTS*

860 100 SP
UNIVERSIDAD COMPLUTENSE DE MADRID. REVISTA.*
1940. bi-m. Universidad Complutense de Madrid, Facultad de Filosofia y Letras, Ciudad Universitaria, 28040 Madrid, Spain. bk.rev.; bibl. **Indexed:** Amer.Hist.& Life, Hist.Abstr.
Formerly (until 1972): Universidad de Madrid. Revista (ISSN 0541-8607)

860 UY ISSN 0250-6556
PB5
UNIVERSIDAD DE LA REPUBLICA. FACULTAD DE HUMANIDADES Y CIENCIAS. REVISTA. SERIE LETRAS. N.S. 1979. irreg. exchange basis. Universidad de la Republica, Facultad de Humanidades y Ciencias, Seccion Revista, Tristan Narvaja 1674, Montevideo, Uruguay. Dir. Beatriz Martinez Osorio.
Supersedes in part: Universidad de la Republica. Facultad de Humanidades y Ciencias. Revista.

860 VE
UNIVERSIDAD DE LOS ANDES. ESCUELA DE LETRAS. ANUARIO.* 1975. a. exchange basis. Universidad de Los Andes, Escuela de Letras, Via los Chorras de Milla, C.P. 5101, Merida, Venezuela. Ed.Bd.

UNIVERSIDAD DE MURCIA. ESTUDIOS ROMANICOS. see *LINGUISTICS*

860 SP
UNIVERSIDAD DE NAVARRA. DEPARTAMENTO DE LITERATURA ESPANOLA. COLECCION PUBLICACIONES. 1974. irreg., no.9, 1986. price varies. Ediciones Universidad de Navarra, S.A., Apdo. 396, 31080 Pamplona, Spain. TEL 94 825 6850.

UNIVERSIDAD DE SAN CARLOS. REVISTA; artes - literatura - ciencias humanas. see *ART*

800 SP
UNIVERSIDAD DE SEVILLA. COLECCION DE BOLSILLO. irreg., latest no.109. Universidad de Sevilla, Servicio de Publicaciones, Valparaiso 5, 41013 Seville, Spain. TEL 954-231958. FAX 954-232245.

860 UY ISSN 0077-1252
UNIVERSIDAD DE URUGUAY. DEPARTAMENTO DE LITERATURA IBEROAMERICANA PUBLICACIONES.* irreg. Universidad de Uruguay. Departamento de Literatura Iberoamericana, Montevideo, Uruguay.

800 PO
UNIVERSIDADE DE LISBOA. FACULDADE DE LETRAS. REVISTA. 1933. 2/yr. Esc.800($6) Universidade de Lisboa, Faculdade de Letras, Cidade Universitaria, 1699 Lisbon Codex, Portugal. FAX 760063. Ed.Bd. bk.rev.; bibl. circ. 1,500.

869 BL ISSN 0079-9327
PQ9644
UNIVERSIDADE FEDERAL DE MINAS GERAIS. CORPO DISCENTE. REVISTA LITERARIA. Cover title: R L; Revista Literaria. 1966. a. free. Universidade Federal de Minas Gerais, Centro de Extensao da Faculdade de Letras, Av. Antonio Carlos, 6.627-4 Andar-Sala 451, Caixa Postal 905, Belo Horizonte-MG, Brazil. Ed.Bd. bk.rev.; illus. circ. 2,000.
Description: Presents Brazilian poetry, short stories, essays and art.

850 100 IT ISSN 0078-7728
UNIVERSITA DEGLI STUDI DI PADOVA. FACOLTA DI LETTERE E FILOSOFIA. OPUSCOLI ACCADEMICI. 1937. irreg., vol.20, 1993. price varies. Casa Editrice Leo S. Olschki, Casella Postale 66, 50100 Florence, Italy. TEL 055-6530684. FAX 055-6530214. circ. 1,000. **Document type:** monographic series.

850 100 IT ISSN 0078-7736
UNIVERSITA DEGLI STUDI DI PADOVA. FACOLTA DI LETTERE E FILOSOFIA. PUBBLICAZIONI. 1932. irreg., vol.62, 1988. price varies. Casa Editrice Leo S. Olschki, Casella Postale 66, 50100 Florence, Italy. TEL 055-6830684. FAX 055-6530214. circ. 1,000. **Document type:** monographic series.

850 100 IT ISSN 0392-9345
UNIVERSITA DEGLI STUDI DI SIENA. FACOLTA DI LETTERE E FILOSOFIA. ANNALI. 1980. a. price varies. Universita degli Studi di Siena, Facolta di Lettere e Filosofia, Via Fieravecchia 19, 53100 Siena, Italy. Ed. M. Bettini.

UNIVERSITA DI NAPOLI. FACOLTA DI LETTERE E FILOSOFIA. ANNALI. see *HISTORY*

UNIVERSITA PER STRANIERI. ANNALI. see *EDUCATION — International Education Programs*

UNIVERSITAS (ENGLISH EDITION); interdisciplinary journal for the sciences and humanities. see *SCIENCES: COMPREHENSIVE WORKS*

UNIVERSITAS (GERMAN EDITION); Zeitschrift fuer interdisziplinaere Wissenschaft. see *SCIENCES: COMPREHENSIVE WORKS*

850 RM ISSN 0379-7899
PN709.R8
UNIVERSITATEA "AL. I. CUZA" DIN IASI. ANALELE STIINTIFICE. SECTIUNEA 3F: LITERATURA. (Text in English, French, German, Rumanian, Russian) 1955. a. 35 lei. Universitatea "Al. I. Cuza" din Iasi, Calea M. Eminescu 11, Jassy, Rumania. (Subscr. to: ILEXIM, Str. 13 Decembrie Nr. 3, P.O. Box 136-137, Bucharest, Rumania) Ed. Ion Apetroaie. bk.rev.; abstr.; charts; illus. circ. 300.
Description: Covers the history of Rumanian literature, its theories of aesthetics, as well as comparative and universal literature.

UNIVERSITE CATHOLIQUE DE LOUVAIN. FACULTE DE PHILOSOPHIE ET LETTRES. TRAVAUX. see *HUMANITIES: COMPREHENSIVE WORKS*

880 FR ISSN 0065-4981
UNIVERSITE D'AIX-MARSEILLE I. CENTRE D'ETUDES ET DE RECHERCHES HELLENIQUES. PUBLICATIONS. 1958. irreg. Universite d'Aix-Marseille I (Universite de Provence), Centre d'Etudes et de Recherches Helleniques, Service des Publications, 13621 Aix en Provence, France.

UNIVERSITE D'ODENSE. ETUDES ROMANES. see *LINGUISTICS*

800 FR ISSN 0399-0443
F1022
UNIVERSITE DE BORDEAUX III. CENTRE DE RECHERCHES SUR L'AMERIQUE ANGLOPHONE. ANNALES. N.S. 1976. a. 120 F.($20) (typically set in July). Maison des Sciences de l'Homme d'Aquitaine, Esplanade des Antilles, Domaine Universitaire, 33405 Talence Cedex, France. TEL 56-84-68-00. FAX 56-84-68-10. (Dist. by: Presses Universitaires de Bordeaux, Domaine Universitaire, 33405 Talence Cedex, France. TEL 56-84-50-20) Ed. J.F. Beranger. adv. circ. 200. **Document type:** academic/scholarly publication.
●Also available online.
Description: Covers minority literature in the U.S.: Hispanic, Jewish, Indian, Italian and Greek.

LITERATURE

800 700   SZ   ISSN 0041-915X
UNIVERSITE DE LAUSANNE. FACULTE DES LETTRES. PUBLICATIONS. (Text in French; occasionally in English) 1930. irreg., no.34, 1993. price varies. Librairie Droz S.A., 11, rue Massot, CH-1211 Geneva 12, Switzerland. TEL 022-3466666. FAX 022-3472391. **Document type:** monographic series.
—CCC.
   Description: Explores literary, religious and political perspectives of historical studies.

800   SZ   ISSN 0077-7633
UNIVERSITE DE NEUCHATEL. FACULTE DES LETTRES. RECUEIL DE TRAVAUX. 1905. irreg., no.43, 1982. price varies. Librairie Droz S.A., 11, rue Massot, CH-1211 Geneva 12, Switzerland. TEL 022-3466666. FAX 022-3472391. circ. 500. **Document type:** monographic series.
—BLDSC (7329.698000). CCC.
   Description: Covers art, literature, linguistics, banking and architecture of historic and modern Europe.

UNIVERSITE DE POITIERS. CENTRE D'ETUDES SUPERIEURES DE CIVILISATION MEDIEVALE. PUBLICATIONS. see HISTORY

UNIVERSITE DE STRASBOURG II. CENTRE DE PHILOLOGIE ET LITTERATURES ROMANES. ACTES ET COLLOQUES. see LINGUISTICS

UNIVERSITE DE STRASBOURG II. INSTITUT DE PHONETIQUE. TRAVAUX. see LINGUISTICS

890 410   TI
UNIVERSITE DE TUNIS. ECOLE NORMALE SUPERIEURE. SECTION A: LETTRES ET SCIENCES HUMAINES. SERIE 1: LANGUE ET LITTERATURE. 1977. irreg. Universite de Tunis, Ecole Normale Superieure, Tunis, Tunisia.

UNIVERSITETET I OSLO. SLAVISK-BALTISK AVDELING. MEDDELELSER. see LINGUISTICS

820   II
UNIVERSITY OF CALCUTTA. DEPARTMENT OF ENGLISH. JOURNAL. (Text in English) vol.4, 1969. s-a. Rs.15. University of Calcutta, Department of English, Asutosh Bldg., Calcutta 700073, India. Ed. A.K. Dasgupta. bk.rev.; bibl. circ. 1,000.
   Formerly: University of Calcutta. Department of English. Bulletin (ISSN 0008-0691)

UNIVERSITY OF CINCINNATI STUDIES IN HISTORICAL AND CONTEMPORARY EUROPE. see HISTORY — History Of Europe

809   US   ISSN 1048-9576
PN2
UNIVERSITY OF HARTFORD STUDIES IN LITERATURE; a journal of interdisciplinary criticism. 1969. 3/yr. $7.50 to individuals; libraries $9. University of Hartford, English Department, 200 Bloomfield Ave., W. Hartford, CT 06117. TEL 203-243-4574. Ed. Michael Walsh. adv.; bk.rev.; cum.index; circ. 500 (controlled). (also avail. in microform from UMI; reprint service avail. from UMI) **Indexed:** Abstr.Engl.Stud., Amer.Bibl.Slavic & E.Eur.Stud., Amer.Hum.Ind., Arts & Hum.Cit.Ind., Can.Rev.Comp.Lit., Curr.Cont., LCR, M.L.A.
—BLDSC (9110.290000); Faxon; UMI.
   Former titles (until 1989): Studies in Literature (ISSN 0196-2280); (until vol.9, no.2, 1977): Hartford Studies in Literature (ISSN 0017-7989)

UNIVERSITY OF KERALA. DEPARTMENT OF TAMIL. RESEARCH PAPERS. see LINGUISTICS

830   UK   ISSN 0144-9850
UNIVERSITY OF LONDON. INSTITUTE OF GERMANIC STUDIES. BITHELL MEMORIAL LECTURES. 1975. biennial. £2. University of London, Institute of Germanic Studies, 29 Russell Square, London WC1B 5DP, England. TEL 071-580-2711. FAX 071-436-3497. Ed.Bd. circ. 1,000. **Document type:** monographic series.
   Description: Published version of the Institute of Germanic Studies endowed lecture.

830   UK   ISSN 0266-7932
UNIVERSITY OF LONDON. INSTITUTE OF GERMANIC STUDIES. BITHELL SERIES OF DISSERTATIONS. 1979. irreg. University of London, Institute of Germanic Studies, 29 Russell Square, London WC1B 5DP, England. TEL 071-580-2711. FAX 071-436-3497. (Co-sponsor: Modern Humanities Research Association) Ed.Bd. circ. 500. **Document type:** monographic series.
   Description: Theses in German studies previously accepted for a higher degree in a university in the British Isles.

830   UK   ISSN 0076-0811
UNIVERSITY OF LONDON. INSTITUTE OF GERMANIC STUDIES. PUBLICATIONS. 1956. irreg. price varies. University of London, Institute of Germanic Studies, 29 Russell Sq., London WC1B 5DP, England. TEL 071-580-2711. FAX 071-436-3497. circ. 300. **Document type:** proceedings.
—BLDSC (7081.855000).
   Description: Monographs and volumes of essays on topics in German language and literature.

820   US   ISSN 0278-310X
PR5.M5
UNIVERSITY OF MISSISSIPPI STUDIES IN ENGLISH. 1960. a. $20. University of Mississippi, Department of English, University, Lafayette Co., MS 38677. TEL 601-232-7439. Ed. Benjamin F. Fisher IV. adv.; bk.rev. circ. 450. (also avail. in microform from UMI) **Indexed:** Abstr.Engl.Stud., M.L.A.
—UMI.
   Formerly: University of Mississippi. Studies in English. New Series.

491.1 891.1   II   ISSN 0448-1712
UNIVERSITY OF RAJASTHAN. STUDIES IN SANSKRIT AND HINDI. 1965. irreg. University of Rajasthan, Departments of Sanskrit and Hindi, Gandhi Nagar, Jaipur 302004, India.

800   US   ISSN 0888-8787
UNIVERSITY OF TEXAS STUDIES IN CONTEMPORARY SPANISH-AMERICAN FICTION. irreg. Peter Lang Publishing, Inc., 62 W. 45th St., 4th Fl., New York, NY 10036. TEL 212-302-6740. FAX 212-302-7574. Ed. Robert Brody. **Document type:** academic/scholarly publication.

UNIVERSITY OF THE NORTH. COMMUNIQUE. see EDUCATION

820   CN   ISSN 0082-5336
UNIVERSITY OF TORONTO ROMANCE SERIES. (Text in English; occasionally in French) 1949. irreg. price varies. University of Toronto Press, 5201 Dufferin St., Downsview, ON M3H 5T8, Canada. TEL 416-667-7761. FAX 416-667-7832. (U.S. addr.: 340 Nagel Drive, Cheektowaga, NY 14225) **Indexed:** M.L.A. **Document type:** academic/scholarly publication.

UNIVERSITY STUDIES IN MEDIEVAL AND RENAISSANCE LITERATURE. see HISTORY

UNIVERZITA KOMENSKEHO. FILOZOFICKA FAKULTA. ZBORNIK: PHILOLOGICA. see LINGUISTICS

891.85 943   PL   ISSN 0208-4708
UNIWERSYTET GDANSKI. WYDZIAL HUMANISTYCZNY. ZESZYTY NAUKOWE. PRACE HISTORYCZNO-LITERACKIE. (Text in Polish; summaries in English and Russian) 1972. irreg., latest no.16. price varies. Uniwersytet Gdanski, Wydzial Humanistyczny, c/o Biblioteka Glowna, Ul. Armii Krajowej 110, 81-824 Sopot, Poland. TEL 51-0061. TELEX 051-2247 BMOR PL. (Dist. by: Ars Polona-Ruch, Krakowskie Przedmiescie 7, 00-680 Warsaw, Poland) circ. 250. **Document type:** academic/scholarly publication.
   Formerly (until 1972): Wyzsza Szkola Pedagogiczna. Gdanskie Zeszyty Humanistyczne. Prace Historyczno-literackie (ISSN 0072-0488)
   Description: Contains articles and book reviews on the theory and history of literature, particularly Polish literature.

891.85   PL   ISSN 0083-436X
PG7003
UNIWERSYTET JAGIELLONSKI. ZESZYTY NAUKOWE. PRACE HISTORYCZNO-LITERACKIE. (Text mainly in Polish; occasionally in English, French or Russian; summaries in English, French, German, Russian) 1955. irreg. price varies. Uniwersytet Jagiellonski, Ul. Golegia 24, 31-007 Krakow, Poland. (Dist. by: Ars Polona, Krakowskie Przedmiescie 7, 00-068 Warsaw, Poland) Ed. St. Jaworski. circ. 600.

800   PL   ISSN 0208-5038
UNIWERSYTET SLASKI W KATOWICACH. PRACE NAUKOWE. RUSYCYSTYCZNE STUDIA LITERATUROZNAWCZE. (Text in Polish and Russian; summaries in English, Polish or Russian) 1977. irreg. price varies. Wydawnictwo Uniwersytetu Slaskiego, Ul. Bankowa 12B, 40-007 Katowice, Poland. TEL 48-32-596-915. FAX 48-32-599-605. TELEX 0315584 USKPL. (Dist. by: CHZ Ars Polona, P.O. Box 1001, 00-950 Warsaw, Poland) Ed. Barbara Woznica. **Document type:** academic/scholarly publication.
   Description: Covers history and the present image of Russian and Soviet literature: studies of works, groups of works and trends in literary theory.

800   US
UNSHAVED TRUTHS. q. $5 per no. FringeWare, Inc., 2507 Roehampton Dr., Austin, TX 78745-6964. E-mail: fringeware@wixer.cactus.org. Ed. Jon Lebkowsky.

830   GW   ISSN 0083-4564
UNTERSUCHUNGEN ZUR DEUTSCHEN LITERATURGESCHICHTE. 1962. irreg., no.68, 1993. price varies. Max Niemeyer Verlag, Postfach 2140, 72011 Tuebingen, Germany. TEL 07071-98940. FAX 07071-989450. (back issues avail.) **Indexed:** M.L.A. **Document type:** monographic series.
   Description: Monographs on German literature.

800   IT   ISSN 0042-0646
UOMINI E IDEE; rivista di letteratura, sociologia e arte. 1958. bi-m. Via Poggio de Mari 16, 80129 Naples, Italy. Ed. Corrado Piancastelli. adv.; bk.rev.; illus. circ. 5,000.

800 282   US   ISSN 1069-8051
▼**UPSOUTH;** a newsletter for Catholic writers. 1993. m. free. Upsouth, Inc., 3627 Hammett Hill Rd., Bowling Green, KY 42101. TEL 502-843-8018. Ed. Galen Smith, Sr. bk.rev.; film rev.; circ. controlled. (tabloid format; back issues avail.) **Document type:** newsletter.
   Description: Contains articles, essays, and poems on the hobbies, spiritual issues, and religious experiences of Catholic southern writers and seeks to foster a dialogue among the members of this audience. Also shows a strong interest in the culture of the U.S. South.

810 500   US   ISSN 1066-3932
URBANUS - RAIZIRR. 1988. s-a. $8 to individuals; institutions $10. Box 192561, San Francisco, CA 94119-2561. Ed. Peter Drizhal. adv.: B&W page $50. circ. 800.
   Formerly: Urbanus.
   Description: Presents nonmainstream, nonsexist poetry, fiction, and prose.

860   SP   ISSN 0049-5719
UROGALLO; revista literaria y cultural. 1970-1975; resumed 1986. m. 6500 ptas. (foreign 7800 ptas.) (effective Mar. 1994). Ediciones Prensa de la Ciudad, S.A., Carretas 12, 28012 Madrid, Spain. TEL 91-532-62-82. FAX 91-531-01-03. Ed. Encarna Castejon. adv.; bk.rev.; bibl.; illus. circ. 15,000.
   Description: Reports on literary and cultural events in Spain and elsewhere.

899.92   SP
URRUZUNO LITERATUR LEHIAKETA. a.? (Hezkuntza, Unibertsitate eta Ikerketa Saila) Eusko Juarlaritzaren Argitalpen-Zerbitzu Nagusia - Servicio Central de Publicaciones del Gobierno Vasco, Duque de Wellington, 2, 01011 Vitoria-Gasteiz, Spain. circ. 3,000.

US WURK; tydskrift foar Frisistyk. see LINGUISTICS

890 300 TZ ISSN 0856-096X	860 001.3 US ISSN 1075-2021	VIATA CAPITALEI. see *ART*

890 300   TZ   ISSN 0856-096X
UTAFITI; journal of the faculty of arts and social science. 1976. s-a. $25. University of Dar es Salaam, Faculty of Arts and Social Science, TZ , P.O. Box 35051, Dar es Salaam, Tanzania. FAX 48274. Ed. Joseph L. Mbele. bk.rev. circ. 600. Indexed: Curr.Cont.Africa, Documentatieblad. **Document type**: academic/scholarly publication.

800 410   US   ISSN 0171-726X
UTAH STUDIES IN LITERATURE AND LINGUISTICS. irreg. Peter Lang Publishing, Inc., 62 W. 45th St., 4th Fl., New York, NY 10036. TEL 212-302-6740. FAX 212-302-7574. Ed. Wolff A. von Schmidt. **Document type**: academic/scholarly publication.

891.4   II   ISSN 0042-157X
UTHON/PLATFORM.* (Text and summaries in Bengali) 1968. 6/yr. Rs.4($1) (Chandita Prakasani) Raja Rammohan Sarani, Dipok Dey, 107-2 Amherst St., Calcutta 9, India. Ed. Samir Kumar Dey. bk.rev.; illus. circ. 1,500.
  Formerly: Natunkatha.

800   US   ISSN 0167-8175
UTRECHT PUBLICATIONS IN COMPARATIVE LITERATURE. 1983. irreg., vol.30, 1993. price varies. John Benjamins Publishing Co., 821 Bethlehem Pike, Philadelphia, PA 19118. TEL 215-836-1200. FAX 215-836-1204. (And: Amsteldijk 44, P.O. Box 75577, 1070 AN Amsterdam, Netherlands. TEL 020-6762325) (back issues avail.) **Document type**: monographic series.
  —BLDSC (9135.518300).
  Description: Irregularly published monographs in comparative literature.

859   RM   ISSN 1220-6482
UTUNK. (Text in Hungarian) 1946. w. 156 lei. Uniunea Scriitorilor din Republica Socialista Romania, Calea Victoriei 115, Bucharest, Rumania. (Subscr. to: ILEXIM, Str. 13 Decembrie Nr. 3, Box 136-137, 70116 Bucharest, Rumania) Ed. Letay Lajos. bk.rev.; film rev.; play rev.; charts; illus.

890   UZ   ISSN 0134-2258
UZBEK TILI VA ADABIETI. 1958. bi-m. 7.80 Rub. Izdatel'stvo Fan, Pr. M. Gor'kogo 79, Tashkent, Uzbekistan. circ. 19,820.

800 808.81   SZ   ISSN 0259-6512
V W A; revue litteraire. (Text in French) 1983. 2/yr. 75 SFr. V W A, Case Postale 172, 2301 La-Chaux-de-Fonds, Switzerland. TEL 039-282418. FAX 039-282750. Ed.Bd. illus. circ. 1,000. (back issues avail.) **Document type**: bulletin.

860   UY
VAGON. bi-m. Siprocomic Ediciones, Garibaldi 2859, 21-2102, 11600 Montevideo, Uruguay. Ed. Roberto Poy.

891.553   IR   ISSN 0506-3604
VAHID. w. S. Vahidnia, Ed. & Pub., 55 Jomhoori Islami Ave., Jam St., Teheran, Iran.

840   FR   ISSN 0760-5641
VALENCIENNES. 1976. a. 100 F. Presses Universitaires de Valenciennes, Le Mont Houy, 59326 Valenciennes Cedex, France. Ed. J.P. Giusto. adv. circ. 500. (back issues avail.)
  Formerly (until 1981): Cahiers de l'U E R Froissart.

895   VN
VAN NGHE/ARTS AND LETTERS. 1949. w. Vietnamese Writers' Union, 17 Tran Quoc Toan, Hanoi, Socialist Republic of Vietnam. TEL 64430. Ed. Huu Thinh. circ. 40,000.

895   VN   ISSN 0505-0014
VAN NGHE QUAN DOI/ARMY LITERATURE AND ARTS. 1957. m. 4 Ly Nam De St., Hanoi, Socialist Republic of Vietnam. TEL 54378. Ed. Dung Ha. circ. 50,000.

800   TU   ISSN 0042-2762
VARLIK. 1933. m. $40. Varlik Yayinlari A.S., Cagaloglu Yokusu 40, Istanbul, Turkey. FAX 212-5226924. Ed. Filiz Nayir Denizteklin. adv.; bk.rev. circ. 6,000.

VECTOR. see *LITERATURE — Science Fiction, Fantasy, Horror*

860 001.3   US   ISSN 1075-2021
▼**VENEZUELAN LITERATURE AND ARTS JOURNAL/REVISTA DE LITERATURA Y ARTES VENEZOLANAS**. (Text in English, Spanish) 1994. a. $12 to individuals; institutions $20. Hamline University, Mail Stop 50, 1536 Hewitt Ave., St. Paul, MN 55104-1284. FAX 612-641-2956. Ed. Rossi Irausquin-Johnson. circ. 700. (back issues avail.) **Document type**: academic/scholarly publication.
  Description: Seeks to advance the study of Venezuelan literature and arts by serving as a forum for scholarly analysis and evaluation of creative activity from all periods.

860   AG
VENGA QUE LE CUENTO; publicacion periodica aleatoria de narradores Argentinos. no. 1974. irreg. Prudan 1330, Buenos Aires, Argentina. adv.; illus.

VENT - ART. see *ART*

VENTURE; bi-annual review of English language and literature. see *LINGUISTICS*

820   DK   ISSN 0907-1075
EN VERDEN AF ROMANTIK.* 1981. m. DKK 8.75 per no. Winther, Valby, Denmark.
  Formerly (until 1990): Barbara Cartland's Verden af Romantik (ISSN 0108-5174)

800   US   ISSN 0506-7715
IL VERRI. 1956. 4/yr. L.100000. Mucchi Editore s.r.l., Via Emilia Est. 1527, 41100 Modena, Italy. Ed. Luciano Anceschi.

800   SZ   ISSN 0256-9604
VERSANTS; revue suisse des litteratures romanes. (Text in French, Italian and Spanish) 1981. 2/yr. 42 SFr. (Collegium Romanicum, Association des Romanistes Suisses) Editions de la Baconniere S.A., P.O. Box 185, CH-2017 Boudry, Switzerland. TEL 038-421004. **Document type**: academic/scholarly publication.

800 808.81   US   ISSN 0268-3830
VERSE. 1984. 3/yr. $15 to individuals; institutions $21. College of William and Mary, English Department, Box 8795, Williamsburg, VA 23187-8795. TEL 804-221-3922. Ed. Henry Hart. adv.; bk.rev. circ. 800. (back issues avail.)
  Description: International literary publication featuring poems, reviews and essays.

800   US   ISSN 1059-6240
PS536.2
VERSES. 1989. q. $21. (National Authors Registry) Cader Publishing, Ltd., 2899 E. Big Beaver Rd., Ste. 311, Troy, MI 48083. TEL 313-524-0228. FAX 313-524-0124. adv. contact: Albert F. Case, Jr. bk.rev.; circ. 1,000 (paid); 2,000 (controlled).
  Description: Features articles on writing, and showcases new and experienced writers of short fiction, verse and essay-format prose.

891.8   YU   ISSN 0042-4536
VESELI SVET;* humoristicki magazin. (Text in Serbo-Croatian) vol.10, 1970. m. 3 din. Dnevnik, Bulevar 23, Oktobra 31, Novi Sad, Yugoslavia. Ed. Mitar Milosevic.

830   NE   ISSN 0165-4136
VESTDIJKKRONIEK. 1973. q. fl.45. Vestdijkkring, Het Erf 19, 8102 KE Raalte, Netherlands. TEL 05720-54291. Ed.Bd. adv.; bk.rev. circ. 800.
  —SWETS.

IL VESUVIO; fiaccola ercolanese. see *ART*

890   RU
VETER STRANSTVII. 1965. irreg. Izdatel'stvo Fizkul'tura i Sport, Kalyaevskaya ul., 27, 101421 Moscow, Russia. Ed.Bd. illus. circ. 150,000.

810   US   ISSN 0504-0779
PS508.V45
VETERANS' VOICES. 1952. 3/yr. $15. Hospitalized Veterans Writing Project, Inc., 5920 Nall, Rm. 105, Mission, KS 66202. TEL 913-432-1214. Ed. Margaret Cathcart Clark. circ. 6,000.

850   IT
VIA LATTEA; rivista de letteratura. 1988. s-a. L.15000 (foreign L.20000) (effective 1991). Via Piave 2, 95129 Catania, Italy. TEL 095-376890. Ed. Benedetto Macaronio.

VIATA CAPITALEI. see *ART*

859   RM   ISSN 0042-5052
VIATA ROMINEASCA. 1906. m. 144 lei($10) (Uniunea Scriitorilor din Republica Socialista Romania) Foreign Languages Press Group "Romania", Piata Presei Libere 1, 71341 Bucharest, Rumania. TEL 6173836. FAX 6170487. (Subscr. to: ILEXIM, Export-Import Presa, Str. 13 Decembrie Nr. 3, Box 136-137, 70116 Bucharest, Rumania) Ed. Ioanichie Olteanu. bk.rev.; abstr. circ. 2,900. Indexed: M.L.A.

800 700 780   CN   ISSN 0821-6827
VICE VERSA MAGAZINE. 1983. bi-m. Can.$20 to individuals; institutions Can.$30. Editions Vice Versa Inc., C.P. 991, Succ. A, Montreal, Que. H3C 2W9, Canada. TEL 514-393-1853. FAX 514-843-5681. Ed. Lamberto Tassineri. adv.; bk.rev. circ. 10,000. (tabloid format) Indexed: Pt.de Rep. (1989-).
  Formerly: Guernica Review.

821.8   US   ISSN 1060-1503
PR4229
VICTORIAN LITERATURE AND CULTURE. 1973. a. $52.25. (Brawning Institute) A M S Press, Inc., 56 E. 13th St., New York, NY 10003. TEL 212-777-4700. Ed. Adrienne Munich. adv.; illus.; index. circ. 600. Indexed: Arts & Hum.Cit.Ind., Curr.Cont.,
  —BLDSC (2352.500000).
  Formerly (until 1991): Browning Institute Studies (ISSN 0092-4725)
  Description: Material on all aspects of Victorian literary and cultural history.

800   US   ISSN 0042-5192
PR1
VICTORIAN NEWSLETTER. 1952. s-a. $5 (foreign $6). Western Kentucky University, College of Arts and Humanities, CH 106, Bowling Green, KY 42101. TEL 502-745-6338. (Co-sponsor: Modern Language Association) Ed. Ward Hellstrom. bk.rev. circ. 900. (also avail. in microfilm; reprint service avail. from UMI) Indexed: Abstr.Engl.Stud., Avery Ind.Archit.Per. **Document type**: newsletter.
  —BLDSC (9232.655000); Faxon; UnCover; UMI.

VICTORIAN PERIODICALS REVIEW. see *JOURNALISM*

820.9   CN   ISSN 0848-1512
PR461
VICTORIAN REVIEW. 1972. s-a. Can.$20 membership to individuals; institutions Can.$25. Victorian Studies Association of Western Canada, c/o Prof. C. Hosgood, Ed., Dept. of History, University of Lethbridge, Lethbridge, AB T1K 3M4, Canada. TEL 403-329-2543. FAX 403-329-5109. adv.; bk.rev. circ. 250. Indexed: Abstr.Engl.Stud. **Document type**: academic/scholarly publication.
  Formerly: Victorian Studies Association of Western Canada. Newsletter (ISSN 0703-5500)
  Description: Publishes research articles encompassing a wide variety of topics and approaches on all aspects of the nineteenth century.

VICTORIANS INSTITUTE JOURNAL. see *LITERARY AND POLITICAL REVIEWS*

VIET NAM GENERATION; a journal of recent history & contemporary issues. see *MILITARY*

VIGILIA. see *RELIGIONS AND THEOLOGY — Roman Catholic*

800   US
THE VILLAGE IDIOT. (Text mainly in English) 1970. 3/yr. membership only. American Amateur Press Association, c/o Jack W. Bond, 1727 80th St. N., St. Petersburg, FL 33710. (Co-publisher: National Amateur Press Association, c/o Dave Warner, 12311 Winding Ln., Bowie, MD 20715) circ. 300.
  Description: Original poems, pictures, and stories by contemporary authors.

373.4   UK   ISSN 0264-5564
VINAVER STUDIES IN FRENCH. 1984. irreg., latest vol. 4, 1990. £25($44) Francis Cairns (Publications) Ltd., c/o The University, Leeds LS2 9JT, England. (back issues avail.) **Document type**: monographic series.
  —BLDSC (9236.850900).

800 PN9   NO   ISSN 0042-6288
VINDUET; Gyldendal's literary magazine. 1947. q. NOK 275 to individuals; institutions NOK 340; students NOK 200. Gyldendal Norsk Forlag, Sehesteds gt. 4, 0164 Oslo 1, Norway. FAX 22-03-41-05. (Subscr. to: Forlagsentralen, Tidsskriftavd., P.O. Box 150 Furuset, 1001 Oslo 1, Norway) Ed. Merete Morken Andersen. adv.; bk.rev. circ. 3,800. **Indexed:** M.L.A.

810   US
VINTAGE NORTHWEST. 1980. 2/yr. $2.75 per no.(typically set in Jan.). Box 193, Bothell, WA 98011. TEL 206-487-1201. Ed. Lawrence T. Campbell. adv. circ. 500.
    Description: Seasonal literary magazine featuring creative writing only from persons age 50 and older.

800 410   US   ISSN 1054-7606
VINYAR TENGWAR. 1988. bi-m. $12 (Canada $15, elsewhere $18). Elvish Linguistic Fellowship, 2509 Ambling Circle, Crofton, MD 21114. TEL 410-721-5690. Ed. Carl. F. Hostetter. bk.rev.; bibl. circ. 125. (back issues avail.) **Document type:** newsletter.
    Description: Scholarly study of the linguistic works and creations of author and philologist J.R.R. Tolkien.
    Refereed Serial

811   US
VIRGIN MEAT. 1986. 4/yr. $7. 2325 West Ave., K-15, Lancaster, CA 93536. TEL 805-722-1758. Ed. Steve Blum. adv.; bk.rev.; music rev. circ. 300.
    Description: Discusses Gothic fiction and poetry.

809   US
VIRGINIA WOOLF MISCELLANY. 1973. s-a. membership. (Virginia Woolf Society) Sonoma State University, Department of English, Rohnert Park, CA 94928. TEL 707-664-2140. Ed.Bd. bk.rev.; bibl. circ. 1,300. **Indexed:** Abstr.Engl.Stud., Amer.Hum.Ind.
    Description: Forum to exchange information about Virginia Woolf.

VIRITTAAJAA. see LINGUISTICS

891.2   II
VISHVA SAMSKRTAM. (Text in Sanskrit) q. Rs.15. Vishveshvaranand Vedic Research Institute, P.O. Sadhu Ashram, Hoshiarpur 146021, Punjab, India. Ed. Veda Prakasha.
    Description: Presents articles on Sanskrit language, literature and culture.

VISIONARY COMPANY: A MAGAZINE OF THE TWENTIES. see ART

891.4   II   ISSN 0042-7179
VISVA - BHARATI PATRIKA. (Text in Bengali) 1942. q. Rs.23.60. Visva - Bharati University, Publishing Department, 6 Acharya Jagadish Bosh Rd., Calcutta 700017, India. Ed. Surajit Chandra Sinha. adv.; bk.rev.; illus.; index. circ. 2,700.

891.4   II   ISSN 0042-7209
VISWA RACHANA. (Text in Telugu) 1960. fortn. Rs.757. Viswa Sahiti, 6-3-195 New Bhoiguda, Secunderabad 500003, India. Ed. Pothukuchi Sambasivarao. adv.; bk.rev.; film rev.; play rev. circ. 3,000. **Document type:** newspaper.
    Formerly: Viswa Sahiti.
    Description: Special focus on the exchange of world literature.

VLAANDEREN; tijdschrift voor kunst en letteren. see ART

VOCE DI FIUME. see HISTORY

800 700   IT
VOCI DEL NOSTRO TEMPO. 1972. bi-m. Via S. Anna 223, 97100 Ragusa, Italy. Ed. Gerlando Bordore. bibl.; illus.

810   US
VOICES TO AND FROM THE STREETS.* 1982. m. $5. 342 Broadway, Dobbs Ferry, NY 10522-1709. TEL 914-693-0473. Ed. Annie Quintano. circ. 5,000.
    Formerly: Broken Pieces.

840   CN   ISSN 0318-9201
PQ3900
VOIX ET IMAGES. 1976. q. Can.$23 (foreign Can.$25). Universite du Quebec a Montreal, Service des Publications, C.P. 8888, Succ. "A", Montreal, Que. H3C 3P8, Canada. TEL 514-987-7747. Ed. Lucie Robert. **Indexed:** Can.Lit.Ind., M.L.A., Pt.de Rep. (1981-).
    —BLDSC (9251.535000).

808   US
VOLCANO REVIEW.* 1979. s-a. $15. Peninhand Press, 3665 S.E. Tolman, Portland, OR 97202. Ed. Tom Janisse.

830   NE
VOORZETTEN. 1985. irreg. price varies. (Nederlandse Taalunie) Stichting Bibliographia Neerlandica, P.O. Box 90751, 2509 LT The Hague, Netherlands. TEL 31-70-3140285.
    Description: Publication devoted to the integration of the Netherlands and the Dutch speaking community in Belgium, concerning the Dutch language. Each volume covers a single topic.

891.7   RU   ISSN 0042-8795
PN9
VOPROSY LITERATURY. 1957. m. $77. (Soyuz Pisatelei Rossii) Izdatel'stvo Izvestiya, Pl. Pushkina, 5, 103798 Moscow, Russia. TEL 095-209-9100. (Dist. in U.S. by: Victor Kamkin Inc., 4956 Boiling Brook Pkwy., Rockville, MD 20852. TEL 301-881-5973. FAX 301-881-1637) (Co-sponsor: Rossiiskaya Akademiya Nauk, Institut Mirovoi Literatury im. A.M. Gor'kogo) Ed. D.M. Urnov. adv.; bk.rev.; index. circ. 20,000. (also avail. in microfiche from NRP) **Indexed:** Can.Rev.Comp.Lit., Curr.Dig.Sov.Press, M.L.A.
    Description: Literary criticism and scholarship.

800   US   ISSN 1073-5488
VORTEXT; the journal of architecture and romance. 1985-1989; resumed 1993. 3/yr? $10. Vortext, Box 23194, Seattle, WA 98102. Ed. Ezra Mark. bibl.; illus.
    Formerly (until 1993): Phobia.
    Description: Publishes an eclectic assemblage of fragments, notes, bibliographies, and text on architecture, lost love, archaeology, linguistics, and alchemy.

800 374   GW   ISSN 0172-5300
VOX LATINA. 1965. q. DM.28. Societas Latina, Fachbereich 6.3, Universitaet, 66041 Saarbruecken, Germany. Ed. Caelestis Eichenseer. adv.; bk.rev.; index. circ. 1,500. (back issues avail.) **Document type:** academic/scholarly publication.

VOX ROMANICA; annales helvetici explorandis linguis romanicis destinati. see LINGUISTICS

810   US   ISSN 0095-5388
PS301
VOYAGES TO THE INLAND SEA. (Former issuing body: University of Wisconsin-La Crosse) 1971-1979; N.S. 1981. irreg $33 includes Northeast (La Crosse). Juniper Press, 1310 Shorewood Dr., La Crosse, WI 54601. TEL 608-788-0096. Ed. John Judson. circ. 500.

860   MX
VUELTA.* 1976. m. $30. Amigos del Arte A.C., Ave. Contreras 516, piso 3, Col. San Jeronimo Lidice, 10200 Mexico D.F., Mexico. (U.S. subscr. to: Overseas Book Mart, 313 Third St., Bloomington, IN 47401) Ed.Bd. adv.; bk.rev.; illus.; index. circ. 12,000. **Indexed:** Hisp.Amer.Per.Ind., M.L.A.

800   US
WAIGUO WENXUE/FOREIGN LITERATURE. (Text in Chinese) bi-m. $36. China Books & Periodicals, Inc., 2929 24th St., San Francisco, CA 94110. TEL 415-282-2994. FAX 415-282-0994.

800.953   CC   ISSN 1001-2885
WAIGUO WENXUE YANJIU/FOREIGN LITERATURE STUDIES. (Subseries of: Fuyin Baokan Ziliao) (Text in Chinese) 1978. q. Y42($30) Zhongguo Renmin Daxue, Shubao Ziliao Zhongxin - China People's University, Book & Newspaper Information Center, P.O. Box 1122, Beijing 100007, People's Republic of China. TEL 441792. (Dist. in US by: China Books & Periodicals, Inc., 2929 24th St., San Francisco, CA 94110. TEL 415-282-2994)
    Description: Reprints papers and articles on foreign literature.

810   US   ISSN 0737-0679
PS3229
WALT WHITMAN QUARTERLY REVIEW. 1955. q. $12 to individuals; institutions $15. University of Iowa, Department of English, 308 E P B Bldg., Iowa City, IA 52242. (Co-sponsor: Graduate College) Ed. Edwin Folsom. adv.; bk.rev.; bibl.; illus.; cum.index every 5 yrs. circ. 468. (also avail. in microform from MIM,UMI; back issues avail.) **Indexed:** Abstr.Engl.Stud., Amer.Hum.Ind., Arts & Hum.Cit.Ind., Curr.Cont., Ind.Bk.Rev.Hum., M.L.A. **Document type:** academic/scholarly publication.
    —Faxon; UnCover; UMI.
    Former titles (until 1982): Walt Whitman Review (ISSN 0043-017X); Walt Whitman Newsletter.
    Description: Provides scholarly articles and literary criticism about Walt Whitman.

830   GW   ISSN 0930-0279
WALTHARI; Zeitschrift fuer Literatur. 1984. s-a. DM.27. Walthari Verlag, Postfach 440, 66979 Muenchweiler, Germany. Ed. Erich Dauenhauer. bk.rev. (back issues avail.) **Document type:** bulletin.

WANBLI HO/EAGLE'S VOICE. see ETHNIC INTERESTS

800   US   ISSN 1046-6967
PN56.W3
WAR, LITERATURE, AND THE ARTS. Abbreviated title: W L A. 1989. s-a. $10 to individuals; institutions $20. United States Air Force Academy, Department of English, Colorado Springs, CO 80840. TEL 719-472-3930. FAX 719-472-3135. Ed. Donald Anderson. bk.rev. **Indexed:** Amer.Hum.Ind., LCR, M.L.A. **Document type:** academic/scholarly publication.
    —BLDSC (9261.811450); Faxon; UnCover.
    Description: Examines war through artistic depictions from diverse cultural and historical perspectives.

809   ISSN 0083-7210
WARD - PHILLIPS LECTURES IN ENGLISH LANGUAGE AND LITERATURE. 1967. irreg., no.12, 1987. price varies. (University of Notre Dame, Department of English) University of Notre Dame Press, Notre Dame, IN 46556. TEL 219-631-6346. FAX 219-631-8148. (Orders to: Box 635, South Bend, IN 46624) **Indexed:** Cath.Ind. **Document type:** academic/scholarly publication.

819   CN   ISSN 0043-0412
WASCANA REVIEW; of contemporary poetry and short fiction. 1966. s-a. Can.$7 (foreign Can.$8). University of Regina, Regina, SK S4S 0A2, Canada. TEL 306-584-4302. FAX 306-585-4827. Ed. Kathleen Wall. bk.rev. circ. 500. (tabloid format) **Indexed:** Abstr.Engl.Stud., Amer.Hum.Ind., Can.Lit.Ind., M.L.A. **Document type:** academic/scholarly publication.
    Description: Publishes poetry and short fiction, scholarly articles.

808   JA
WASEDA BUNGAKU. m. Kodansha Ltd., P.R. Division, 12-21, Otowa, 2-chome, Bunkyo-ku, Tokyo 112, Japan. Ed. Waseda Bungaku-kai. circ. 3,000.

800   US   ISSN 1041-5874
WATER ROW REVIEW. 1987. q. $10. Water Row Books Inc., Box 438, Sudbury, MA 01776. TEL 508-485-8515. Ed. Cisco Harland. adv.; bk.rev.; bibl. circ. 3,500. (back issues avail.) **Document type:** academic/scholarly publication.
    Description: Dedicated to "Beat" generation authors and their work.

800   US
WAY STATION MAGAZINE.* 1989. 4/yr. $16. 1319 S. Logan St., Lansing, MI 48910. Ed. Randall G. Glumm. adv.; B&W page $160. bk.rev. circ. 500.
    Formerly: Way Station.
    Description: Publishes poetry chaps, poetry collections, fiction, essays, emerging cultures, interviews and letters. Includes photography, B&W art and a wine column.

800   US   ISSN 0363-1230
PN6010.5
WEBSTER REVIEW. 1974. a. $5. (Webster University) Webster Review, Inc., 470 E. Lockwood, Webster Groves, MO 63119. TEL 314-432-2657. Ed. Nancy Schapiro. bk.rev. circ. 600. (back issues avail.) **Indexed:** A.I.P.P., Ind.Amer.Per.Verse, M.L.A.
    Description: Contains works by contemporary American authors and translations of foreign authors.

830   US
WEIMAR AND NOW: GERMAN CULTURAL CRITICISM. (Text in English) 1991. irreg., no.5, 1993. price varies. University of California Press, 2120 Berkeley Way, Berkeley, CA 94720. TEL 510-642-4247. FAX 510-643-7127. (Orders to: California-Princeton Fulfillment Services, 1445 Lower Ferry Rd., Ewing, NJ 08618. TEL 800-777-4726. FAX 800-999-1958) (back issues avail.) **Document type:** monographic series.
   Description: Covers 20th century German literature, art, culture, and history.
   Refereed Serial

800   AU   ISSN 0043-2199
WEIMARER BEITRAEGE; Zeitschrift fuer Literaturwissenschaft, Aesthetik und Kulturwissenschaften. 1955. q. DM.144. Passagen Verlag GmbH, Walfischgasse 15-14, A-1010 Vienna, Austria. TEL 0222-5137761. FAX 0222-5126327. (Subscr. to: Minerva, Postfach 88, A-1201 Vienna, Austria. TEL 01-3302433) Ed. Peter Engelmann. adv.; bk.rev.; index. circ. 1,200. **Indexed:** Arts & Hum.Cit.Ind., Can.Rev.Comp.Lit., Ind.Bk.Rev.Hum., M.L.A. **Document type:** academic/scholarly publication.
   —Faxon; SWETS.

WEISSES MINARETT. see *RELIGIONS AND THEOLOGY — Islamic*

895.1   CC
WEIXING XIAOSHUO XUANKAN. (Text in Chinese) 1984. m. Y9.60. Weixing Xiaoshuo Xuankan Zazhishe, No.5, Xinwei Lu, Nanchang, Jiangxi 330002, People's Republic of China. TEL 0791-332782. FAX 0791-331282. Ed. Li Chun Lin. adv.; page Y3500. bk.rev.
   Description: Provides the best short stories (within 1500 words) recently published worldwide.

820   UK   ISSN 0263-1776
WELLSIAN. 1960. s-a. £10 to institutions. H.G. Wells Society, H.G. Wells Centre, Nene College, Eng. Dept., Moulton Park, Northampton NN2 7AL, England. Ed. Michael Draper. bk.rev.; bibl.; cum.index every 5 yrs. circ. 300. (also avail. in microform from UMI)

DIE WELT DER SLAVEN. see *LINGUISTICS*

895.1   CH
WEN HSUEH TAIWAN/LITERARY TAIWAN. (Text in Chinese) 1982. q. NT.$800 (Europe & USA $60; Asia $55). No. 8, Lane 3, Cheng Yi Rd., Ling Ya District, Kaohsiung, Taiwan, Republic of China. TEL 07-771-2027. FAX 02-716-9964.
   Formerly (until no.28, 1989): Wen Hsueh Chieh.

800   CC   ISSN 1000-6222
WENHUA YICONG. (Text in Chinese) 1980. q. Y4.40. Tianjin Waiyu Xueyuan - Tianjin Foreign Language Institute, 117 Machang Dao, Hexi Qu, Tianjin 300204, People's Republic of China. TEL 390181. Ed. Lu Jiaqi. circ. 2,000.
   Description: Publishes translated articles on world literature, art, history, geography, archaeology, tourism and popular science.

WENHUA YULE/CULTURE & RECREATION. see *LEISURE AND RECREATION*

WENSHI ZHISHI/KNOWLEDGE OF LITERATURE AND HISTORY. see *SOCIAL SCIENCES: COMPREHENSIVE WORKS*

895.1   CC
WENXUE BAO/LITERATURE PRESS. (Text in Chinese) w. $55.50. No. 14, Alley 606, Huaihai Zhonglu, Shanghai 200020, People's Republic of China. (Dist. in US by: China Books & Periodicals, Inc., 2929 24th St., San Francisco, CA 94110) **Document type:** newspaper.

895.1   CC
WENXUE DAGUAN. (Text in Chinese) m. Zhongguo Zuojia Xiehui, Liaoning Fenhui - China Writers' Association, Liaoning Chapter, 7 Shaoshuaifu Houxiang, Chaoyang Jie, Shenhe Qu, Shenyang, Liaoning 110011, People's Republic of China. TEL 443806. Ed. Chi Songnian.

895.1   CC
WENXUE GANG. (Text in Chinese) Ningbo Shi Wenlian, 220, Yaoxing Jie, Ningbo, Zhejiang 315000, People's Republic of China. (Dist. outside China by: China Publications Foreign Trade Corp., P.O. Box 782, Beijing, P.R.C.) Ed. Li Jianshu.

800.953   CC   ISSN 0511-4683
PL2250
WENXUE PINGLUN/LITERARY REVIEW. (Text in Chinese; table of contents in English) 1959. bi-m. Y19.80($50.90) (Zhongguo Shehui Kexueyuan, Wenxue Yanjiusuo - Chinese Academy of Social Sciences, Institute of Literature) Shehui Kexue Zazhishe, 158 A Gulou Xidajie, Beijing 100720, People's Republic of China. (Dist. outside China by: China International Book Trading Corp., P.O. Box 399, Beijing, P.R.C.; Dist. in US by: China Books & Periodicals, Inc., 2929 24th St., San Francisco, CA 94110. TEL 415-282-2994) bk.rev.
   —BLDSC (5276.654540).

895.1   CC
WENXUE PINGLUNJIA/LITERARY CRITICS. (Text in Chinese) bi-m. Y7.80. Zhongguo Zuojia Xiehui, Shandong Fenhui - China Writers' Association, Shandong Chapter, 10, Honglou Nanlu, Jinan, Shandong 250100, People's Republic of China. Eds. Wang Guangdong, Li Jizhao. adv.
   Description: Publishes literary criticism.

895.15   CC
WENXUE QINGNIAN/YOUTH LITERATURE JOURNAL. (Text in Chinese) 1981. m. Wenxue Qingnian Bianjibu, Mu Tse Fang 27, Wenzhou, Zhejiang, People's Republic of China. TEL 3578. Ed. Chen Yushen. circ. 80,000.

895.1   CC
WENXUE SHAONIAN/ADOLESCENT LITERATURE. (Text in Chinese) bi-m. Liaoning Shaonian Ertong Chubanshe, 2, Nanjing Jie 6 Duan 1 Li, Shenyang, Liaoning 110001, People's Republic of China. TEL 365076. Ed. Wu Qingxian.

895.1   CC   ISSN 0257-5914
PL2250
WENXUE YICHAN/LITERARY HERITAGE. (Text in Chinese; table of contents in English) q. Y12($31.50) (Zhongguo Shehui Kexueyuan, Wenxue Yanjiusuo - Chinese Academy of Social Sciences, Institute of Literature) Shehui Kexue Zazhishe, 158 A Gulou Xidajie, Beijing 100720, People's Republic of China. (Dist. outside China by: China International Book Trading Corp., P.O. Box 399, Beijing, P.R.C.; Dist. in U.S. by: China Books & Periodicals, Inc., 2929 24th St., San Francisco, CA 94110) Eds. Xu Gongchi, Lu Huifen.
   —UnCover.

895.1   CC   ISSN 0258-8226
WENYI BAO/LITERATURE & ART GAZETTE. (Text in Chinese) 1949. d. Y182.50. (Zhongguo Zuojia Xiehui - China Writers' Association) Wenyi Bao She, 6th Fl., No. 10, Nongzhanguan Nanli, Beijing 100026, People's Republic of China. TEL 500-5588. (Dist. in US by: China Books & Periodicals, Inc., 2929 24th St., San Francisco, CA 94110. TEL 415-282-2994) Ed. Zheng Bonong. **Document type:** newspaper.

801   CC   ISSN 0257-0254
WENYI LILUN YANJIU/THEORETICAL STUDIES IN LITERATURE AND ART.* (Text in Chinese; table of contents in English) 1980. bi-m. Y11.88($36) East China Normal University, Chinese Department - Huadong Shifan Daxue, Zhongwen Xi, 3663 Zhongshan Beilu, Shanghai 200062, People's Republic of China. (Dist. overseas by: China International Book Trading Corp., P.O. Box 399, Beijing, P.R.C.; Dist. in US by: China Books & Periodicals, Inc., 2929 24th St., San Francisco, CA 94110) (Co-sponsor: Zhongguo Wenyi Lilun Xuehui - Chinese Society of Literature and Art Theory) Eds. Xu Zhongyu, Qian Gurong.

895.1 700   CC   ISSN 0257-5876
WENYI YANJIU/LITERATURE AND ART STUDIES. (Text in Chinese; table of contents in English) 1979. bi-m. Y16.80($36) (Zhongguo Yishu Yanjiuyuan - China Art Institute) Wenhua Yishu Chubanshe, 17, Qianhai Xijie, Xi Cheng Qu, Beijing 100009, People's Republic of China. TEL 651128. (Dist. outside China by: China International Book Trading Corp., P.O. Box 399, Beijing, P.R.C.; Dist. in US by: China Books & Periodicals, Inc., 2929 24th St., San Francisco, CA 94110. TEL 415-282-2994) Ed. Yang Liu.

700   CN   ISSN 1182-4271
AP2
WEST COAST LINE; a journal of contemporary writing and criticism. 1966. 3/yr. Can.$20 to individuals; institutions $30. Simon Fraser University, West Coast Review Publishing Society, 2027 E. Academic Annex, Simon Fraser University, Burnaby, BC V5A 1S6, Canada. TEL 604-291-4287. FAX 604-291-5737. Ed. Roy Miki. adv.; bk.rev.; bibl.; illus.; index. circ. 750. (also avail. in microform from UMI; reprint service avail. from UMI) **Indexed:** Abstr.Engl.Stud., Amer.Hum.Ind., Can.Lit.Ind., Can.Per.Ind., CMI, Ind.Amer.Per.Verse, Ind.Bk.Rev.Hum., M.L.A. **Document type:** academic/scholarly publication.
   —UnCover; UMI. **CCC.**
   Formerly: West Coast Review (ISSN 0043-311X)
   Description: Contains contemporary poetry, fiction, essays, reviews of modern literature. International in scope, but emphasis is on Canadian writing.

800   US
WEST VIRGINIA ASSOCIATION OF COLLEGE ENGLISH TEACHERS. BULLETIN. 1955. a. $2. West Virginia Association of College English Teachers, Department of English, Marshall University, Huntington, WV 25701. TEL 304-696-6600. Ed. Joan F. Gilliland. bk.rev. circ. 200. (back issues avail.) **Indexed:** M.L.A. **Document type:** bulletin.

800 070   CN   ISSN 1184-678X
WEST WORD. 1980. bi-m. Can.$55. Writers Guild of Alberta, 10523 - 100 Ave., Edmonton, AB T5J 0A8, Canada. TEL 403-426-5892. FAX 403-424-7943. adv.; B&W page Can.$165. circ. 1,000.
   Formerly (until 1990): Writers Guild of Alberta. Newsletter (ISSN 0821-4204)

820   AT   ISSN 0043-342X
AP7
WESTERLY. 1956. q. Aus.$24. Centre for Studies in Australian Literature, University of Western Australia, Nedlands, W.A. 6009, Australia. TEL 09-380-2101. FAX 09-380-1030. (Co-sponsors: Australia Council, W.A. Department for the Arts) Ed.Bd. adv.; bk.rev.; illus. circ. 900. **Indexed:** Abstr.Engl.Stud., Arts & Hum.Cit.Ind., Aus.P.A.I.S., Curr.Cont., Gdlns.
   —BLDSC (9300.171500); Faxon. **CCC.**

810   US   ISSN 0043-3462
PS271
WESTERN AMERICAN LITERATURE. 1966. q. $15 to individuals; institutions $30. Western Literature Association, Utah State University, English Dept., Logan, UT 84322-3200. TEL 801-750-1603. FAX 801-750-4099. Ed. Thomas J. Lyon. adv.; bk.rev.; bibl.; index. circ. 1,100. (also avail. in microform from UMI; back issues avail.; reprint service avail. from ISI,UMI) **Indexed:** Abstr.Engl.Stud., Amer.Hist.& Life, Amer.Hum.Ind., Arts & Hum.Cit.Ind., Bk.Rev.Ind. (1981-), Chic.Per.Ind., Child.Bk.Rev.Ind. (1981-), Curr.Cont., Film Lit.Ind. (1990-), Hist.Abstr., Ind.Bk.Rev.Hum., LCR, M.L.A., Ref.Sour. **Document type:** academic/scholarly publication.
   —BLDSC (9300.183000); Faxon; UnCover; UMI.

700 800   US   ISSN 0043-3845
AP2
WESTERN HUMANITIES REVIEW. 1947. q. $20 to individuals; institutions $26. University of Utah, Department of English, Salt Lake City, UT 84112. TEL 801-581-6168. Ed. Barry Weller. index. circ. 1,000. (also avail. in microform from MIM,UMI; back issues avail.; reprint service avail. from SCH,UMI) **Indexed:** A.I.P.P., Abstr.Engl.Stud., Amer.Bibl.Slavic & E.Eur.Stud., Amer.Hist.& Life, Amer.Hum.Ind., Arts & Hum.Cit.Ind., Bk.Rev.Ind. (1965-), Child.Bk.Rev.Ind. (1965-), Curr.Bk.Rev.Cit., Curr.Cont., Film Lit.Ind. (1990-), Hist.Abstr., Ind.Bk.Rev.Hum., LCR, M.L.A., Media Rev.Dig., Mid.East: Abstr.& Ind. **Document type:** academic/scholarly publication.
   —BLDSC (9300.820000); Faxon; UnCover; SWETS; UMI.

WESTWIND (LOS ANGELES); U C L A's journal of the arts. see *ART*

800 700   US
▼**WHAT DID I EAT LAST NIGHT?.** 1993. q. $10 for 6 nos. B S B N Publishing, Box 7205, Minneapolis, MN 55407. Ed. Julian Davis.
   Description: Contains creative writings, poetry and prose.

LITERATURE

800 070.5   US   ISSN 0896-6354
WHAT IS TO BE READ. 1984. bi-m. $25. Cooperative Economics News Service, 1736 Columbia Rd., N.W., Ste. 202, Washington, DC 20009.
TEL 202-387-1753. Ed. Henry Leland. circ. 2,500. (looseleaf format; also avail. in diskette format; back issues avail.) **Document type:** newsletter.
   Description: Read primarily by academic social scientists. Publishes book reviews of current academic, scholarly, and college textbooks in economics, sociology, labor studies, women's studies, urban affairs, and educational software.

810   US   ISSN 0278-4947
WHAT'S COOKING IN CONGRESS?. 1979. biennial. $9.95. (Harian Creative Associates) Harian Creative Press-Books, 47 Hyde Blvd., Ballston Spa, NY 12020. TEL 518-885-7397. Eds. Harry Barba, Marian Barba. circ. 5,000.
   Former titles: Harian Creative Press; Harian Press (ISSN 0017-7776)

800   US
WHAT'S NEW ABOUT LONDON, JACK?. (Companion to Chaney Chronical) 1971. 4/yr. $10. London Northwest, 929 South Bay Rd., Olympia, WA 98506. Ed. David H. Schlottman. adv.; bk.rev.; film rev.; play rev.; bibl. circ. 70. (processed)
   Description: Covers the life and works of the author Jack London.

800 700   US   ISSN 1055-8659
WHETSTONE (BARRINGTON). 1983. a. $6.25. Barrington Area Arts Council, Box 1266, Barrington, IL 60011. TEL 708-382-5626. Ed.Bd. circ. 600. (back issues avail.)
   Description: Presents poetry, short stories, novel excerpts, critical essays, creative non-fictiction and interviews.

808   US
WHICH WAY.* irreg., no. 4, 1982. c/o Don Byrd, 291 State St., Albany, NY 12210-2100. Eds. Jed Rasula, Don Byrd.

808   US
WHISKEY ISLAND MAGAZINE. 1978. 2/yr. $8. Cleveland State University, University Center, Cleveland, OH 44115. TEL 216-687-2056. circ. 2,000.
   Formerly: Dark Tower.

810   US   ISSN 1074-9527
WHISPER; quietly publishing great poems and stories for over 7 years. 1989. s-a. $5. Scream Press, 509 Enterprise Dr., Rohnert Park, CA 94928. E-mail: TONYBOYD@AOL.COM. Ed. Anthony Boyd. adv. circ. 1,000.
   Formerly (until 1993): Helter Skelter.

800   US
WHITE ARMS MAGAZINE.* 1974. q. $5. c/o Dana Wichern, 10215 Hickory Valley Dr., Fort Wayne, IN 46815. illus. circ. 500. (also avail. in microform from UMI)

800   US   ISSN 0882-066X
PS536.2
WIDENER REVIEW; poetry, fiction, essays, reviews. 1984. a. $4. Widener University, Humanities Division, One University Pl., Chester, PA 19013. TEL 215-499-4341. Ed. Michael Clark. bk.rev. circ. 250. (back issues avail.)

800   GW
WIELANDS BRIEFWECHSEL. 1963. irreg., vol.12, 1993. Akademie Verlag GmbH, Muehlenstr. 33-34, 13187 Berlin, Germany. TEL 030-47889348. FAX 030-47889357. **Document type:** monographic series.

830   AU   ISSN 0083-9906
WIENER ARBEITEN ZUR DEUTSCHEN LITERATUR. 1970. a. price varies. Wilhelm Braumueller, Universitaets-Verlagsbuchhandlung GmbH, Servitengasse 5, A-1092 Vienna, Austria. TEL 0222-3191159. FAX 0222-310-2805. Eds. Wendelin Schmidt-Dengler, Werner Welzig. index. circ. 1,000. **Indexed:** M.L.A. **Document type:** academic/scholarly publication.

WIENER BEITRAEGE ZUR ENGLISCHEN PHILOLOGIE. see LINGUISTICS

830 831   AU   ISSN 0250-443X
WIENER - GOETHE - VEREIN. JAHRBUCH. 1878. a. S.250. Verlag Fassbaender, Lichtgasse 10, A-1150 Vienna, Austria. TEL 01-8936497.
FAX 01-8923717. Ed. Herbert Zeman. adv.; bk.rev. circ. 700. (reprint service avail. from KTO) **Document type:** academic/scholarly publication.
   Description: Covers the development of Austrian literature from the 18th to the 20th century.

WIENER ROMANISTISCHE ARBEITEN. see LINGUISTICS

WIENER SLAWISTISCHER ALMANACH. see LINGUISTICS

WIENER SLAWISTISCHER ALMANACH. SONDERBAENDE. see LINGUISTICS

800   US   ISSN 1068-9737
WILD ABOUT WILDE NEWSLETTER. 1986. s-a. $5. Carmel McCaffrey, Ed. & Pub., 2542 Vance Dr., Mt. Airy, MD 21771. TEL 410-875-0699. bk.rev.; play rev. circ. 450. (back issues avail.) **Document type:** newsletter.
   Description: Concerns the work of Oscar Wilde - both his work and any new publications about his work.

810   US
WILD IRIS. 1974. a. $3. Rena Blauner, Ed. & Pub., 706 Albermarle St., El Cerrito, CA 94530.
TEL 415-525-4004. circ. 650.

800   US
WILLA CATHER PIONEER MEMORIAL & EDUCATIONAL FOUNDATION NEWSLETTER. 1957. q. $15. Willa Cather Pioneer Memorial & Educational Foundation, 326 N. Webster, Red Cloud, NE 68970.
TEL 402-746-2653. FAX 402-746-2652. Ed. John J. Murphy. bk.rev.; illus. circ. 2,000. (looseleaf format) **Document type:** newsletter.

378.1   US   ISSN 0043-5600
LH1.W64
WILLIAM AND MARY REVIEW. 1962. s-a. $10. College of William and Mary, Williamsburg, VA 23185.
TEL 804-253-4895. Ed. William Clark. illus. circ. 3,000.
   Description: Publishes fiction, non-fiction, poetry, and visual art in a four-color format.

808   US   ISSN 0196-6286
PS3545.I544
WILLIAM CARLOS WILLIAMS REVIEW. 1975. s-a. $8 to individuals; institutions $10 (effective 1993). William Carlos William Society, University of Texas, Department of English, PAR 108, Austin, TX 78712-1164. TEL 512-471-7842.
FAX 512-471-4909. Ed. Brian Bremen. adv.; bk.rev. circ. 375. (back issues avail.) **Indexed:** Abstr.Engl.Stud.; Amer.Hum.Ind.; Arts & Hum.Cit.Ind., M.L.A. **Document type:** academic/scholarly publication.
—Faxon; UnCover.
   Description: Covers the life and art of the American poet William Carlos Williams (1883-1963). Includes previously unpublished Williams documents, scholarly articles and notes, announcements and current bibliographic listings.

808   US   ISSN 0739-1277
PS571.W2
WILLOW SPRINGS; poetry, translations, fiction, essays, artwork. 1977. s-a. $8. Eastern Washington University, MS-1, Cheney, WA 99004.
TEL 509-458-6429. Ed. Nance Van Winckel. adv.; bk.rev. circ. 1,000. (back issues avail.) **Indexed:** Amer.Hum.Ind. **Document type:** academic/scholarly publication.
   Description: Poetry, fiction, non-fiction.

800   US   ISSN 0361-2481
PS501
WIND. 1971. irreg. $10 for 2 nos. to individuals; institutions $12; foreign $15 (effective 1994). Wind Publications, Box 24548, Lexington, KY 40524.
TEL 606-885-5342. Eds. Steven R. Cope, Charlie G. Hughes. bk.rev. circ. 500. (back issues avail.) **Indexed:** Ind.Amer.Per.Verse.
   Description: Contains poetry, short fiction, essays, reviews of small-press publications, and literary news.

800 700   US   ISSN 0888-0832
WINDHAM PHOENIX. 1985. m. $12. Phoenix Publishing Co., Box 752, Willimantic, CT 06226. Eds. Michael J. Westerfield, Mark Svetz. illus. circ. 1,000. (back issues avail.)

808 700   CN   ISSN 0822-2363
WINDSCRIPT. 1983. a. Can.$8. Saskatchewan Writers Guild, 2049 Lorne St., Regina, SK S4P 2M4, Canada. Ed. Valerie Crowther. adv. circ. 3,500. (back issues avail.)
   Description: Journal of black and white artwork, poetry and prose by Saskatchewan high school students.

810   US   ISSN 0147-3166
PS3501.N4
WINESBURG EAGLE. 1975. s-a. $8. Dept. of English, Virginia Tech, Blacksburg, VA 24061-0112.
TEL 703-231-7721. FAX 703-231-5692. Eds. Charles E. Modlin, Hilbert H. Campbell. adv.; bk.rev. circ. 150. (back issues avail.) **Indexed:** M.L.A.
   Description: Provides critical, biographical and bibliographical articles about Sherwood Anderson.

800 500   US   ISSN 0512-1175
WISCONSIN ACADEMY REVIEW. 1954. q. $15. Wisconsin Academy of Sciences, Arts and Letters, 1922 University Ave., Madison, WI 53705.
TEL 608-263-1692. Ed. Faith B. Miracle. bk.rev. circ. 2,000.
—BLDSC (9325.650000); Faxon.

WISCONSIN ENGLISH JOURNAL. see EDUCATION — Teaching Methods And Curriculum

800 700   US
WITTENBERG REVIEW OF LITERATURE AND ART. 1977. a. Wittenberg University, Box 720, Springfield, OH 45501. TEL 513-327-6231. Ed. Pete Staubitz. illus. circ. 900.

WOLFENBUETTELER BIBLIOTHEKS - INFORMATIONEN. see HISTORY

WOLFENBUETTELER RENAISSANCE MITTEILUNGEN. see HISTORY — History Of Europe

WOLFENBUETTELER STUDIEN ZUR AUFKLAERUNG. SCHRIFTENREIHE. see HISTORY

810   US   ISSN 1042-1491
WOMAN OF MYSTERY. 1986. m. $30. Wom'n, Box 1616, Canal St. Sta., New York, NY 10013.
TEL 212-732-5154. Ed. Amy Lubelski. circ. 600. **Document type:** newsletter.
   Description: Devoted to annotating the mystery novels of Agatha Christie.

WOMAN OF POWER; a magazine of feminism, spirituality, and politics. see WOMEN'S INTERESTS

800 305.4   US   ISSN 0147-1759
PN481
WOMEN & LITERATURE; a journal of women writers and the literary treatment of women. 1974; N.S. 1981. irreg. price varies. Holmes & Meier Publishers, Inc., 160 Broadway E. Wing, New York, NY 10038.
TEL 212-347-0100. FAX 212-347-1313. (U.K. addr.: Book Representation & Distribution, Ltd., 244 A London Rd., Hadleigh, Essex SS7 2DE, England. TEL 702-552912. FAX 702-556095) Ed. Janet M. Todd. adv.; bk.rev.; bibl. (also avail. in microform from MIM,UMI; back issues avail.) **Indexed:** Abstr.Engl.Stud., Amer.Hum.Ind., Arts & Hum.Cit.Ind., Curr.Cont., Hum.Ind., M.L.A., Stud.Wom.Abstr.
   Formerly: Mary Wollstonecraft Journal (ISSN 0193-7103)
   Description: Each volume focuses on a specific theme in literary or artistic criticism.

800 305.4   US   ISSN 1056-4535
WOMEN WRITERS OF ITALY. irregg. price varies. Peter Lang Publishing, Inc., 62 W. 45th St., 4th Fl., New York, NY 10036. TEL 212-302-6740. Ed. Susan Briziarelli. **Document type:** academic/scholarly publication.
   Description: Focuses on Italian women writers, mostly from the nineteenth and twentieth centuries. Includes translations, essays and Italian feminist criticism.

800   US
WOMEN WRITING NEWSLETTER.* 1975. bi-m. $6. c/o Women Writing Press, 151 Oakwook Ln., Ithaca, NY 14850.

WOOLNER INDOLOGICAL SERIES. see PHILOSOPHY

WORD WRAP. see PUBLISHING AND BOOK TRADE

LITERATURE 3689

800 070.5   CN   ISSN 0848-0397
WORD WRAP. 7/yr. free. Manitoba Writers' Guild, 206-100 Arthur St., Winnipeg, MB R3B 1H3, Canada. TEL 204-942-6134. FAX 204-942-5754. Ed. Robyn Deurbrouck. adv.: B&W page Can.$100. circ. 500. pp./issue: 12. **Document type:** newsletter.
   Description: Articles and information of interest to local writers.

800   US   ISSN 0258-0276
WORDS OF WISDOM. 1981. m. $15 to individuals; institutions $20. 612 Front St., Glendora, NJ 08029-1133. Ed. John M. Freiermuth. bk.rev. circ. 200. (back issues avail.)
   Description: Features short stories and poems.

820   US   ISSN 0043-8006
PR1
WORDSWORTH CIRCLE. 1970. q. $20. Temple University, Department of English, Philadelphia, PA 19122. TEL 215-787-4716. adv.; bk.rev.; bibl.; index. circ. 1,000. (also avail. in microform from UMI; back issues avail.) **Indexed:** Abstr.Engl.Stud., Amer.Hum.Ind., Arts & Hum.Cit.Ind., Ind.Bk.Rev.Hum., M.L.A. **Document type:** academic/scholarly publication.
   —BLDSC (9347.990000); Faxon; UnCover; SWETS; UMI.
   Description: Covers the writers and artists who lived during the Romantic Era (1760-1850).

800 001.3   US   ISSN 0886-2060
WORKS AND DAYS; essays in the socio-historical dimensions of literature and the arts. 1979. s-a. $10 to individuals (foreign $15); institutions $20 (foreign $25). Indiana University of Pennsylvania, English Department, 110 Leonard Hall, Indiana, PA 15705. TEL 412-357-6486. FAX 412-357-6213. Ed. David B. Downing. adv.; bk.rev.; index. circ. 300. (back issues avail.) **Indexed:** Hum.Ind. **Document type:** academic/scholarly publication.
   —UnCover.
   Description: Multidisciplinary essays on the relations between literature and arts and their socio-historical and socio-cultural contents.

028   US   ISSN 0196-3570
Z1007
WORLD LITERATURE TODAY; a literary quarterly of the University of Oklahoma. 1927. q. $30 to individuals; institutions $40. 110 Monnet Hall, University of Oklahoma, Norman, OK 73019-0375. TEL 405-325-4531. FAX 405-325-7495. Ed. Djelal Kadir. adv.; bk.rev.; bibl.; index. circ. 2,200. (also avail. in microfilm from UMI; reprint service avail. from KTO,UMI) **Indexed:** Amer.Bibl.Slavic & E.Eur.Stud., Arts & Hum.Cit.Ind., Bk.Rev.Dig., Bk.Rev.Ind. (1977-), Chic.Per.Ind., Child.Bk.Rev.Ind. (1977-), Curr.Cont.Africa, Curr.Cont., Hisp.Amer.Per.Ind., Hum.Ind., Lang.& Lang.Behav.Abstr., M.L.A., Mid.East: Abstr.& Ind.
   —BLDSC (9356.558600); Faxon; UnCover; SWETS; UMI.
   Formerly: Books Abroad (ISSN 0006-7431)
   Description: Presents literary essays and book reviews from all over the world.

820   CN   ISSN 0093-1705
WORLD LITERATURE WRITTEN IN ENGLISH. 2/yr. Can.$20 to individuals; institutions Can.$30. University of Toronto Press, Journals Department, P.O. Box 1280, 1011 Sheppard Ave. W., Downsview, ON M3H 5V4, Canada. TEL 416-667-7781. Ed. Diana Brydon. **Indexed:** Amer.Hum.Ind.
   —BLDSC (9356.558700); UnCover. **CCC.**
   Description: Devoted to the study of literatures in English and in the new englishes written throughout the world and variously termed post-colonial or new literatures in English, Commonwealth literature, contact literature, global English or resistance literature.
   Refereed Serial

WORLD PRESS REVIEW; news and views from around the world. see *LITERARY AND POLITICAL REVIEWS*

800   CN   ISSN 0316-3768
WRIT. 1970. a. Can.$18($18) for 2 yrs. c/o Innis College, 2 Sussex Ave., Toronto, ON M5S 1J5, Canada. TEL 416-978-4871. FAX 416-978-5503. Eds. Roger Greenwald, Richard Lush. adv.; bk.rev.; index. circ. 700. (back issues avail.)
   Description: Presents poetry, fiction, and translations of 20th century authors.

807   US   ISSN 0043-9517
PN101
WRITER (BOSTON). 1887. m. $27 (foreign $35). Writer, Inc., 120 Boylston St., Boston, MA 02116. TEL 617-423-3157. Ed. Sylvia K. Burack. adv. contact: Ann-Margaret Caljouw. bk.rev.; index. circ. 58,174. (microform; also avail. in microform from UMI,PMC) **Indexed:** Child.Lit.Abstr., Mag.Ind., PMR, R.G.
   —Faxon; UnCover; UMI.
   Description: Focuses on writing instruction for all fields.

808   UK   ISSN 0260-2776
WRITER (PENZANCE). 1963. a. £9. United Writers Publications Ltd., Ailsa, Castle Gate, Penzance TR20 8BG, Cornwall, England. Ed. Sydney Sheppard. adv.; bk.rev.; illus.; mkt.; tr.lit. circ. 4,000.
   Incorporates: Writer's Review (ISSN 0043-9568)
   Description: Publication for writers and poets.

808   UK
WRITERS' AND POETS' YEARBOOK. a. United Writers Publications Ltd., Ailsa, Castle Gate, Penzance TR20 8BG, England.

810   US   ISSN 0163-9072
TP1
WRITERS' FORUM (NIWOT). 1974. a. $10 (foreign $13). (University of Colorado at Colorado Springs) University Press of Colorado, Box 849, Niwot, CO 80544. TEL 303-530-5337. FAX 303-530-5306. Ed. Alex Blackburn. adv. circ. 1,000. (also avail. in microfiche; back issues avail.) **Document type:** academic/scholarly publication, trade publication.
   Description: Publishes fiction, poetry, and essays on western American literature.

800   US
WRITERS GAZETTE. 1984. m. $19. Trouvere Company, Rt. 2, Box 290, Eclectic, AL 36024. Ed. Brenda Williamson. adv.; bk.rev. circ. 1,200.
   Formerly: Writer's Gazette Newsletter.

806   US
WRITERS GUILD OF AMERICA, EAST. NEWSLETTER. 1972. m. membership. Writers Guild of America, East, Inc., 555 W. 57th St., New York, NY 10019. TEL 212-767-7800. Ed. Martin G. Waldman. adv.; bk.rev.; circ. 3,500 (controlled). **Document type:** newsletter.

800   US   ISSN 1055-1948
WRITERS GUILD OF AMERICA, WEST. JOURNAL. 1963. 11/yr. $40. Writers Guild of America, West, 8955 Beverly Blvd., West Hollywood, Los Angeles, CA 90048. TEL 310-550-1000. Ed. William A. Meis, Jr. adv.; illus. circ. 10,000.
   Formerly (until Nov. 1988): Writers Guild of America, West. Newsletter (ISSN 0043-9533)
   Description: Looks at TV and screen writing for union members.

897   US   ISSN 0084-2710
PN137
WRITER'S HANDBOOK. 1936. a. $29.95. Writer, Inc., 120 Boylston St., Boston, MA 02116. TEL 617-423-3157. Ed. Sylvia K. Burack. (reprint service avail. from BLH,UMI)
   —BLDSC (9364.710000).
   Description: Provides writing advice and business information from professionals about freelance writing. Lists publishing markets for manuscripts by subject and geographic area.

810   US
THE WRITER'S HAVEN LITMAG. bi-m. Box 413, Joaquin, TX 75954. Ed. Marcella Owens.

WRITERS INK. see *PUBLISHING AND BOOK TRADE*

820   UK   ISSN 0957-3577
WRITERS NEWS. 1959. m. £44.90. Writers News Ltd., P.O. Box 4, Nairn IV12 4HU, Scotland. TEL 0667-54441. (Subscr. to: Stonehart Subscription Services, Writers News, Hainault Road, Little Heath, Romford, RM6 5NP, England) Ed. Richard Bell. adv.; bk.rev. circ. 400.
   Incorporates: Writing Magazine (ISSN 0308-2024); Writing Published (ISSN 0049-8211)
   Description: Publishes articles, short stories, poetry, information for writers and poets.

800   UK   ISSN 0141-5050
WRITERS OF WALES. 1970. irreg. price varies. (Welsh Arts Council) University of Wales Press, 6 Gwennyth St., Cathays, Cardiff CF2 4YD, Wales. TEL 0222-231919. FAX 0222-230908. Eds. Meic Stephens, R. Brinley Jones. **Document type:** academic/scholarly publication.
   Description: Promotes interest in Welsh authors for an English-speaking audience.

800 821   UK   ISSN 0267-1360
WRITERS' OWN MAGAZINE. 1982. q. £6 (foreign £8). 121 Highbury Grove, Clapham, Bedford MK41 6DU, England. TEL 0234-365982. (Subscr. to: Basil Blackwell Ltd., P.O. Box 40, Hythe Bridge Street, Oxford ON 2EU, England) Ed. Eileen M. Pickering. adv.; bk.rev. circ. 150. **Document type:** newsletter.

828   II
WRITERS WORKSHOP LITERARY READER. (Text in English) 1972. irreg. Rs.60 cloth; paperback Rs.15. Writers Workshop, 162-92 Lake Gardens, Calcutta 700045, India. Ed. P. Lal. circ. 1,000.

820   CN   ISSN 0706-1889
WRITING. 1980. 3/yr. Can.$15($18) (outside Canada and US Can.$20). Box 69609, Station "K", Vancouver, B.C. V5K 4W7, Canada. TEL 604-688-6001. Ed. Jeff Derksen. bk.rev.; illus. circ. 750. (back issues avail.) **Indexed:** Can.Lit.Ind.
   Description: A journal of socially committed and experimental poetry and fiction from Canada, the United States and Great Britain.

808 370   US   ISSN 0279-7208
WRITING (MIDDLETOWN); the continuing guide to written communication. 1974. m. (Sep.-May). $7.45 (effective 1993-1994). Weekly Reader Corporation, 245 Long Hill Rd., Middletown, CT 06457. TEL 800-446-3355. FAX 609-786-3360. (Subscr. to: 3000 Cindel Dr., Delran, NJ 08075) Ed. Sandra Maccarone. circ. 152,771 (paid). (also avail. in microfiche from UMI; reprint service avail. from UMI)
   —UMI.
   Formerly (until 1981): Current Media (ISSN 0194-5475)
   Description: Articles, essays, interviews, technical advice, and word challenges pertaining to the craft of writing, for college-bound students. For grades 7-12.

810   US   ISSN 0084-2745
WRITING (SAN FRANCISCO). 1964. irreg., no.43, 1983. price varies. Four Seasons Foundation, Box 31190, San Francisco, CA 94131. (Subscr. to: Subco, Box 160, Monroe, OR 97456) Ed. Donald Allen. circ. 3,000. (also avail. in microfiche from UMI) **Document type:** monographic series.

800 305.4   US   ISSN 1053-7937
WRITING ABOUT WOMEN: FEMINIST LITERARY STUDIES. irreg. Peter Lang Publishing, Inc., 62 W. 45th St., 4th Fl., New York, NY 10036. TEL 212-302-6740. FAX 212-302-7574. Ed. Esther K. Labovitz. **Document type:** academic/scholarly publication.
   Description: Devoted to feminist studies on past and contemporary women authors, exploring social, psychological, political, economic, and historical insights using an interdisciplinary approach.

808   US   ISSN 0277-7789
PE1001
WRITING INSTRUCTOR. 1981. 3/yr. $18 to individuals; institutions $35. T W I (The Writing Instructor), University of Southern California, THH 440 - MC 0354, Los Angeles, CA 90089-3744. Ed. Jennifer Welsh. adv.; bk.rev.; cum.index. circ. 1,000. (back issues avail.) **Document type:** academic/scholarly publication.
   —BLDSC (9364.758500); Faxon; UnCover; UMI.

808   US
WRITING RESEARCH. 1984. irreg. price varies. Ablex Publishing Corporation, 355 Chestnut St., Norwood, NJ 07648. TEL 201-767-8450. FAX 201-767-6717. TELEX 135-393. Ed. Marcia Farr.

WRITTEN COMMUNICATION; a quarterly journal of research, theory, and application. see *COMMUNICATIONS*

LITERATURE

800   GW   ISSN 0341-2172
WUPPERTALER SCHRIFTENREIHE LITERATUR. 1976. irreg., vol.24, 1991. price varies. Bouvier Verlag Herbert Grundmann, Am Hof 28, 53113 Bonn, Germany. TEL 0228-7290124. FAX 0228-7290179. Ed.Bd. **Document type:** monographic series.
    Formerly: Gesamthochschule Wuppertalerschriftenreihe Literaturwissenschaft.

809   PL
WYZSZA SZKOLA PEDAGOGICZNA IM. KOMISJI EDUKACJI NARODOWEJ W KRAKOWIE. ROCZNIK NAUKOWO-DYDAKTYCZNY. PRACE HISTORYCZNOLITERACKIE. 1961. irreg., no.10, 1986. price varies. Wydawnictwo Naukowe W S P, Ul. Karmelicka 41, 31-128 Krakow, Poland. TEL 33-78-20. (Co-sponsor: Ministerstwo Edukacji Narodowej)

WYZSZA SZKOLA PEDAGOGICZNA IM. KOMISJI EDUKACJI NARODOWEJ W KRAKOWIE. ROCZNIK NAUKOWO-DYDAKTYCZNY. PRACE ROMANISTYCZNE. see *LINGUISTICS*

891.7   PL   ISSN 0239-7986
WYZSZA SZKOLA PEDAGOGICZNA IM. KOMISJI EDUKACJI NARODOWEJ W KRAKOWIE. ROCZNIK NAUKOWO-DYDAKTYCZNY. PRACE RUSYCYSTYCZNE. 1964. irreg., no.5, 1987. price varies. Wydawnictwo Naukowe W S P, Ul. Karmelicka 41, 31-128 Krakow, Poland. TEL 33-79-20. (Co-sponsor: Ministerstwo Edukacji Narodowej)

WYZSZA SZKOLA PEDAGOGICZNA IM. KOMISJI EDUKACJI NARODOWEJ W KRAKOWIE. ROCZNIK NAUKOWO-DYDAKTYCZNY. PRACE Z DYDAKTYKI LITERATURY I JEZYKA POLSKIEGO. see *LINGUISTICS*

WYZSZA SZKOLA PEDAGOGICZNA, OPOLE. STYLISTYKA. see *LINGUISTICS*

830 430   PL
▼**WYZSZA SZKOLA PEDAGOGICZNA, OPOLE. ZESZYTY NAUKOWE. SERIA A. FILOLOGIA GERMANSKA.** 1993. irreg. price varies or exchange basis. Wyzsza Szkola Pedagogiczna, Opole, Oleska 48, 45-951 Opole, Poland. TEL 48-22-383-87. (Dist. by: Ars Polona-Ruch, Krakowskie Przedmiescie 7, Warsaw, Poland) Eds. Grazyna Szewczyk, Martin Grinberg. **Document type:** academic/scholarly publication.

890 491.8   PL   ISSN 0324-9050
WYZSZA SZKOLA PEDAGOGICZNA, OPOLE. ZESZYTY NAUKOWE. SERIA A. FILOLOGIA POLSKA. 1975. irreg., vol.30, 1991. price varies or exchange basis. Wyzsza Szkola Pedagogiczna, Opole, Oleska 48, 45-951 Opole, Poland. TEL 48-77-383-87. (Dist. by: Ars Polona-Ruch, Krakowskie Przedmiescie 7, Warsaw, Poland) Ed. Leokadia Pospiech. **Document type:** academic/scholarly publication.
    Incorporates: Wyzsza Szkola Pedagogiczna, Opole. Zeszyty Naukowe. Seria A. Historia Literatury (ISSN 0078-5407)

890   PL   ISSN 0474-2974
HC10
WYZSZA SZKOLA PEDAGOGICZNA, OPOLE. ZESZYTY NAUKOWE. SERIA A. FILOLOGIA ROSYJSKA. (Text in Polish and Russian; summaries in Russian) 1962. irreg., vol.30, 1993. price varies or exchange basis. Wyzsza Szkola Pedagogiczna, Opole, Oleska 48, 45-951 Opole, Poland. TEL 48-77-383-87. (Dist. by: Ars Polona-Ruch, Krakowskie Przedmiescie 7, Warsaw, Poland) Ed. Stanislaw Kochman. **Document type:** academic/scholarly publication.

810   US   ISSN 1058-420X
X I B. 1991. irreg. (1-2/yr.). $10. X I B Publications, Box 262112, San Diego, CA 92126. TEL 619-298-4927. adv. circ. 500.
    Description: Publishes poetry, fiction, art, photos, comics, satire, and collages.

X MAGAZINE; humor and/or music. see *MUSIC*

700 800   US
XALMAN. (Text in English and Spanish) 1974. s-a. $4 to individuals; institutions $10. Casa de la Raza, Inc., 601 E. Montecito St., Santa Barbara, CA 93103. Eds. Armando Vellejo, Manuel Unzueta. film rev.; play rev.; illus. circ. 1,000.

300 001.3   US   ISSN 0887-6681
XAVIER REVIEW. 1980. s-a. $10 to individuals; institutions $15. Xavier University of Louisiana, Box 110C, New Orleans, LA 70125. TEL 504-486-7411. FAX 504-488-3320. Eds. Thomas Bonner Jr., Robert E. Skinner. bk.rev.; circ. 500 (controlled). (back issues avail.) **Indexed:** M.L.A. **Document type:** academic/scholarly publication, monographic series.
    Description: Publishes short fiction, novels in progress, poetry, drama, criticism, literary history and essays.

895.1   CC
XIAMEN WENXUE/XIAMEN LITERATURE. (Text in Chinese) m. Y7.60 (foreign $4.30). Xiamen Shi Wenlian, 2 Gongyuan Nanlu, Xiamen, Fujian 361003, People's Republic of China. TEL 25376. (Dist. overseas by: Jiangsu Publications Import & Export Corp., 56 Gao Yun Ling, Nanjing, Jiangsu, P.R.C.) Ed. Chen Yuanlin.
    Description: Comprehensive treatment of literary activities in the Xiamen Special Economic Zone.

895.1   CC
XIAO XIAOSHUO XUANKAN. (Text in Chinese) m. Zhengzhou Shi Wenlian, No. 12, Yihe Lu, Zhengzhou, Henan 450007, People's Republic of China. TEL 449795. Ed. Wang Baomin.
    Description: Publishes fictional vignettes.

800   CC
XIAOSHUO/SHORT STORIES. (Text in Chinese) q. Zhongguo Qingnian Chubanshe, Qikan Bu - China Youth Press, 21, Dongsi 12 Tiao, Beijing 100708, People's Republic of China. TEL 442125. Ed. Xu Dai.

800   CC
XIAOSHUO JIA/NOVELISTS. (Text in Chinese) bi-m. Baihua Wenyi Chubanshe, 130 Chifeng Dao, Tianjin 300041, People's Republic of China. TEL 704723. Ed. Zheng Faqing.

895.1   CC
XIAOSHUO JIE/WORLD OF NOVELS. (Text in Chinese) 1980. s-m. Y12($67.30) (Nanchang Wenyi Lianhehui - Nanchang Association of Literature and Art) Shanghai Wenyi Chubanshe - Shanghai Literature and Art Press, 74 Shaoxing Lu, Shanghai 200020, People's Republic of China. TEL 4372608. (Dist. in US by: China Books & Periodicals, Inc., 2929 24th St., San Francisco, CA 94110. TEL 415-282-2994) Ed. Feng Zhaopin. adv.; bk.rev. circ. 62,000. (back issues avail.)
    Formerly: Nanyuan Xiaoshuo - Novels of Nanyuan.
    Description: Aims to foster young writers.

895.1   CC
XIAOSHUO LIN. (Text in Chinese) bi-m. (Harbin Shi Wenlian) Xiaoshuo Lin Zazhishe, 91, Tiandi Jie, Daoli-qu, Harbin, Heilongjiang 150010, People's Republic of China. TEL 414197. Ed. Jiang Wei.

895.1   CC   ISSN 1004-2164
XIAOSHUO PINGLUN/SHORT STORY REVIEWS. (Text in Chinese) 1985. bi-m. Y12. (Zhongguo Zuojia Xiehui, Shaanxi Fenhui - China Writers' Association, Shaanxi Chapter) Xiaoshuo Pinglun She, 71, Jianguo Lu, Xi'an, Shaanxi 710001, People's Republic of China. TEL 718615. (Co-sponsor: Zhongguo Xiaoshuo Xuehui) bk.rev. circ. 3,000.
    Description: Publishes literary criticism and comments.

895.1   CC
XIAOSHUO TIANDI. (Text in Chinese) m. Jiangxi Sheng Wenlian, No.104, Bayi Dadao, Nanchang, Jiangxi 330006, People's Republic of China. TEL 65070. Ed. Feng Zhaoping.

895.1   CC   ISSN 0257-5604
XIAOSHUO XUANKAN/SELECTED SHORT STORIES. (Text in Chinese) 1980. m. $71.10. Zuojia Chubanshe, Shatan Beijie 2, Beijing, People's Republic of China. (Dist. in US by: China Books & Periodicals, Inc., 2929 24th St., San Francisco, CA 94110. TEL 415-282-2994)

895.1   CC   ISSN 0257-9413
XIAOSHUO YUEBAO/SHORT STORIES MONTHLY. (Text in Chinese) 1980. m. Y18($61.20) Baihua Wenyi Chubanshe, Chifeng Dao 130, Heping Qu, Tianjin 300041, People's Republic of China. (Dist. outside China by: China International Book Trading Corp., P.O. Box 399, Beijing, P.R.C.; Dist. in US by: China Books & Periodicals, Inc., 2929 24th St., San Francisco, CA 94110. TEL 415-282-2994) Eds. Zheng Faqing, Li Zigan. adv.
    Description: Contains short stories.

XIE ZUO/WRITING. see *JOURNALISM*

895   CC
XIJIANG YUE. (Text in Chinese) bi-m. Wuzhou Shi Wenhua Ju, 102 Dazhongshang Lu, Wuzhou, Guangxi 543000, People's Republic of China. TEL 22347. (Co-sponsor: Wuzhou Shi Wenlian) Ed. Luo Geding.

895.1   CC
XIJU WENXUE/DRAMA LITERATURE. (Text in Chinese) m. Jilin Sheng Xiju Chuangzuo Pinglun Shi, Jianshe Guangchang, Changchun, Jilin 130021, People's Republic of China. TEL 52994. Ed. Li Wenhua.

895.1   CC   ISSN 1002-2260
XIN LIAOZHAI. (Text in Chinese) 1985. bi-m. Y7.80. Shandong Sheng Wenlian, No. 117, Jing 6 Lu, Jinan, Shandong 250001, People's Republic of China. TEL 621475. (Dist. overseas by: China International Book Trading Corp., P.O. Box 399, Beijing, P.R. China) Ed. Li Chuanrui. adv.

895.1   CC   ISSN 0257-5647
XIN WENXUE SHILIAO/HISTORICAL MATERIALS OF NEW LITERATURE. (Text in Chinese) 1978. q. Y14($43.10) Renmin Wenxue Chubanshe - People's Literature Publishing House, 166 Chaonei Dajie, Beijing 100705, People's Republic of China. (Dist. outside China by: China International Book Trading Corp., P.O. Box 399, Beijing, P.R.C.; Dist. in US by: China Books & Periodicals, Inc., 2929 24th St., San Francisco, CA 94110. TEL 415-282-2994) Eds. Niu Han, Chen Zaochun. (back issues avail.)
    Description: Contains articles and investigations in the history of literature.

895.1   CC
XING HUO/SPARK. (Text in Chinese) m. Jiangxi Sheng Wenlian, No. 147, Bayi Dadao, Nanchang, Jiangxi 330046, People's Republic of China. TEL 63230. Ed. Shu Xinbo.

895.1   CC
XINYUAN. (Text in Chinese) bi-m. Shidai Wenyi Chubanshe, Fu 136, Stalin Street, Changchun, Jilin 130022, People's Republic of China. TEL 884440. Ed. Jin Zhongming.

808   CC   ISSN 1000-3584
XIUCI XUEXI/RHETORIC STUDY. (Text in Chinese) 1982. bi-m. Y7.80. (Fudan University, Chinese Language and Literature Institute) Fudan University Press, 220 Handan Rd., Shanghai 200433, People's Republic of China. TEL 5492222. (Dist. in US by: China Books & Periodicals, Inc., 2929 24th St., San Francisco, CA 94110. TEL 415-282-2994) (Co-sponsor: Rhetoric Society of China, East China Branch) Ed. Ni Baoyuan. adv.: page $3000. circ. 9,000 (paid); 300. **Document type:** academic/scholarly publication.
    Description: Promotes rhetoric education and provides hints on how to use Chinese language.

895.4   CC
XIZANG WENXUE/TIBETAN LITERATURE. (Editions in Chinese, Tibetan) bi-m. Y7.20($20.70) (Xizang Wenlian - Tibetan Artists Association) Xizang Wenxue Bianjibu, Lhasa, Xizang (Tibet) 850001, People's Republic of China. TEL 22382. (Dist. in US by: China Books & Periodicals, Inc., 2929 24th St., San Francisco, CA 94110. TEL 415-282-2994)

800   US
XIZQUIL; a place where social consciousness and creative speculation meet. 1990. every 5 mos. $10 for 3 nos. Uncle River, Box 285, Reserve, NM 87830. illus. circ. 225.
    Description: Publishes fiction, poetry, articles and art, realistic and fantastic, that considers how the world works, or might.

LITERATURE 3691

840   US   ISSN 0044-0078
DC1
YALE FRENCH STUDIES. 1948. s-a. price varies. Yale University Press, Box 209040, New Haven, CT 06520. TEL 203-432-0940. Ed. Liliane Greene. adv. circ. 2,500. (also avail. in microform from UMI; reprint service avail. from KTO) **Indexed:** Acad.Ind., Arts & Hum.Cit.Ind., Can.Lit.Ind., Curr.Cont., Hum.Ind., M.L.A.
—BLDSC (9369.970000); UnCover; SWETS; UMI.

800   US   ISSN 0893-5378
PN2
YALE JOURNAL OF CRITICISM; interpretation in the humanities. 1987. s-a. $20.50 to individuals in N. America (elsewhere $30.50); institutions in N. America $57 (elsewhere $89). Basil Blackwell Inc., 238 Main St., Cambridge, MA 02142. TEL 617-547-7110. FAX 617-547-0789. TELEX 837022-OXBOOK-G. Ed.Bd. adv.: page £250; trim 4 x 7 1/2. circ. 1,700. (back issues avail.) **Indexed:** Acad.Ind.
—BLDSC (9370.005000); Faxon; UnCover; SWETS; UMI. **CCC.**
Description: Essays of an interpretive or theoretical nature in all fields of the humanities - literature, history, film studies, anthropology, philosophy, theology, music and the visual arts.

YALE JOURNAL OF LAW & THE HUMANITIES. see *HUMANITIES: COMPREHENSIVE WORKS*

810   US   ISSN 0148-4605
PS501
YALE LITERARY MAGAZINE. 1831. s-a. $35. Box 243A, Yale Sta., New Haven, CT 06520. TEL 203-497-8213. Eds. Carrie Iverson, Andrew Rossi. adv.; bk.rev.; play rev. circ. 5,000. (also avail. in microform from UMI; reprint service avail. from UMI) **Indexed:** A.I.P.P., Amer.Bibl.Slavic & E.Eur.Stud., Hum.Ind., Soc.Sci.Ind.
—BLDSC (9370.240000); Faxon; UMI.
—Former titles (until 1976): Yale Lit (ISSN 0148-4532); Yale Literary Magazine (ISSN 0044-0108)

820 810   US   ISSN 0084-3482
YALE STUDIES IN ENGLISH. 1898. irreg., no.196, 1987. price varies. Yale University Press, Box 209040, New Haven, CT 06520. TEL 203-432-0940. **Indexed:** M.L.A.

895.1   CC   ISSN 1003-4099
YALUJIANG/YALU RIVER. (Text in Chinese) 1946. m. Y20.40($61.20) (Liaoningsheng Zuojia Xiehui - Liaoning Writers' Association) Yalujiang Wenxue Yuekan She - Yalu River Literature Magazine House, No.7, Shaoshuaifu Hou Xiang, Chaoyang Jie, Shenhe Qu, Shenyang, Liaoning 110011, People's Republic of China. TEL 024-443514. (Dist. overseas by: China International Book Trading Corp., P.O. Box 399, Beijing, P.R.C.; Dist. in US by: China Books & Periodicals, Inc., 2929 24th St., San Francisco, CA 94110) Ed. Chi Songnian. bk.rev. circ. 10,000.

895.1   CC   ISSN 1001-6104
YAN HE/YAN RIVER. (Text in Chinese) 1956. m. Y1.50($61.20) (Zhongguo Zuojia Xiehui, Shaanxi Fenhui - China Writers Association, Shaanxi Chapter) Yan He Wenxue Yuekanshe, 71, Jianguo Lu, Xi'an, Shaanxi 710001, People's Republic of China. (Dist. outside China by: China International Book Trading Corp., P.O. Box 399, Beijing, P.R.C.; Dist. in US by: China Books & Periodicals, Inc., 2929 24th St., San Francisco, CA 94110) Ed. Bai Miao. illus.

810.8   US
YARDBIRD READER. Variant title: Y'bird. 1971. s-a. $7.50. Yardbird Publishing Co., Box 2370, Station A, Berkeley, CA 94702. Ed. Glenn Myles. adv.; bk.rev.; illus. circ. 3,000.

059.94   GW   ISSN 0942-2331
YAZIN. (Text in Turkish) 1982. 6/yr. DM.36 (foreign DM.40). Yazin Verlag, Kasselerstr. 1a, 60486 Frankfurt a.M., Germany. TEL 069-70757 14. FAX 069-625645. Ed. Engin Erkiner. adv.; bk.rev.; illus. circ. 2,500. (back issues avail.) **Document type:** consumer publication.

800   US   ISSN 0084-3695
PN851
YEARBOOK OF COMPARATIVE AND GENERAL LITERATURE. (Issued 1952-60 as subseries of University of North Carolina, Studies in Comparative Literature) 1952. a. $17.50 to individuals; libraries $25 per vol. Indiana University, Comparative Literature Program, Ballantine Hall 402, Bloomington, IN 47405. TEL 812-855-2140. FAX 812-855-2688. (Vols.1-11 (1952-62) avail. from Scribner Distribution Center, Inc.: 12 Vreeland Ave., Totowa, NJ 07512) Ed. Gilbert Chaitin. bk.rev. circ. 1,375. (also avail. in microform from UMI; reprint service avail. from UMI) **Indexed:** Abstr.Engl.Stud., Amer.Bibl.Slavic & E.Eur.Stud., Amer.Hum.Ind., Can.Rev.Comp.Lit., Ind.Bk.Rev.Hum., LCR, M.L.A. **Document type:** academic/scholarly publication, bibliography.
—BLDSC (9411.623300); UnCover.
Description: Covers multicultural literary phenomena in all parts of the world, gender studies, interarts studies, film and culture, the theory and practice of translation, the theory, history and teaching of Comparative Literature, and comprehensive reviews of scholarship in these fields.

YEARBOOK OF ENGLISH STUDIES. see *HUMANITIES: COMPREHENSIVE WORKS*

YEARBOOK OF EUROPEAN STUDIES/ANNUAIRE D'ETUDES EUROPEENNES. see *POLITICAL SCIENCE — International Relations*

800   US   ISSN 0741-2827
E184.G3
YEARBOOK OF GERMAN - AMERICAN STUDIES. (Text and summaries in English and German) 1969. a. $20 (foreign $25). Society for German - American Studies, c/o Willaim Roba, Treas., 500 Belmont Rd., Bettendorf, IA 52722. Eds. Helmut Huelsbergen, William Keel. adv.; bk.rev.; bibl. circ. 600. (back issues avail.) **Indexed:** M.L.A. **Document type:** academic/scholarly publication.
—UnCover.
Supersedes (after vol.15): Journal of German - American Studies; **Formerly** (until vol.11, 1976): German - American Studies (ISSN 0046-5836)
Description: Contains articles on German-American history, literature and culture.

YEARBOOK OF INTERDISCIPLINARY STUDIES IN THE FINE ARTS. see *ART*

850   IT   ISSN 1122-1542
YEARBOOK OF ITALIAN STUDIES. 1971. irreg., vol.10, 1993. L.25000 (effective 1994). Edizioni Cadmo, Casella Postale 27, 50014 Fiesole (FI), Italy. TEL 55-59-99-41. FAX 55-59-88-95. Ed. Antonio D'Andrea. circ. 1,500. **Indexed:** M.L.A. **Document type:** academic/scholarly publication.

840 947   US   ISSN 0149-7219
DR201
YEARBOOK OF ROMANIAN STUDIES.* 1976. a. $5. Romanian Studies Association of America, c/o Paul G. Teodorescu, Ed., 307 Pueblo Dr., Salinas, CA 93906-2721. adv.; bk.rev. circ. 250. **Indexed:** Amer.Bibl.Slavic & E.Eur.Stud., M.L.A.

820.6   US   ISSN 0084-4144
PE58
YEAR'S WORK IN ENGLISH STUDIES. 1919. a. price varies. Humanities Press, 165 First Ave., Atlantic Highlands, NJ 07716-1289. TEL 908-872-1441. FAX 908-872-0717. bk.rev.; index. **Indexed:** Br.Hum.Ind., Hum.Ind., M.L.A.
—UMI. **CCC.**
Description: Summarizes and evaluates all books and articles relating to the study of English language and literature.

809   US   ISSN 0742-6224
PR5904
YEATS; an annual of critical and textual studies. 1983. a. University of Michigan Press, Box 1104, Ann Arbor, MI 48106. TEL 313-764-4392. FAX 313-936-0456. TELEX 4320815. Ed. Richard J. Finneran. bk.rev. (reprint service avail. from UMI) **Document type:** academic/scholarly publication.
—UnCover.
Description: Presents current scholarship on W.B. Yeats: articles, annual bibliographies and dissertation abstracts.

YEATS ELIOT REVIEW. see *LITERATURE — Poetry*

808   US   ISSN 0736-9212
PS509.E7
YELLOW SILK; journal of erotic arts. 1981. q. $30 to individuals; institutions $38. Verygraphics, Box 6374, Albany, CA 94706. TEL 510-644-4188. Eds. Lily Pond, Marnie Purple. adv.: B&W page $1006, color page $1645; trim 8 1/2 x 11. bk.rev.; illus. circ. 16,000. (back issues avail.) **Indexed:** Alt.Press Ind., Ind.Amer.Per.Verse. **Document type:** consumer publication.
Description: Publishes erotic literature and art with equal emphasis on craft and erotic content.

296 830   IS   ISSN 0334-9594
YERUSHOLAIMER ALMANAKH. (Text in Yiddish) 1973. a. $15. Yidishe Shrayber Grupe in Yerusholaim - Yiddish Writers Group in Jerusalem, Shederot Eshkol 12-6, Jerusalem, Israel. Ed. Yoysef Kerler. bk.rev.; illus. circ. 700. **Indexed:** M.L.A.

810   US
YESTERDAY'S MAGAZETTE. 1973. 6/yr. $12. Independent Publishing Co., Box 15126, Sarasota, FL 34277. TEL 813-922-7080. Ed. E.P. Burke. circ. 6,500.
Description: Publishes literary works including poetry with a nostalgic theme.

800   US
YIDDISH. 1973. q. $15. c/o Joe Landis, NSF 350, Kiely 1309, Queens College, Flushing, NY 11367. TEL 718-520-7067. Ed. Joseph C. Landis. adv.; bk.rev. circ. 800. (back issues avail.) **Indexed:** Arts & Hum.Cit.Ind., Bibl.Ling., Curr.Cont., M.L.A.

800   CC   ISSN 1001-1897
YILIN/TRANSLATIONS: A QUARTERLY OF FOREIGN LITERATURE; waiguo wenxue jikan. (Text in Chinese) 1979. q. $43.10. Yilin Press, 165 Zhongyang Rd., Nanjing, Jiangsu 210009, People's Republic of China. TEL 86-25-663-1317. FAX 86-25-330-3463. (Dist. in US by: China Books & Periodicals, Inc., 2929 24th St., San Francisco, CA 94110. TEL 415-282-2994) Ed. Li Jingduan. adv. contact: Xie Beng. bk.rev. **Document type:** consumer publication.
Description: Introduces contemporary foreign literary works to Chinese readers.

895.1 791.43   CC
YINGJU XINZUO/NEW FILM AND PLAY SCRIPTS. (Text in Chinese) bi-m. Jiangxi Sheng Wenxue Yishu Yanjiusuo - Jiangxi Institute of Literature and Art, No.89, Beijing Xilu, Nanchang, Jiangxi 330046, People's Republic of China. TEL 332920. Ed. Tao Xuehui.

895.1 791.43   CC   ISSN 1003-0816
YINGSHI WENXUE/FILM AND TELEVISION LITERATURE. (Text in Chinese) 1987. bi-m. Y9. Shandong Sheng Yingshi Zhizuo Zhongxin, No. 55, Wenhua Donglu, Jinan, Shandong 250014, People's Republic of China. TEL 86-0531-657715. Ed. Teng Jingde. adv.: color page Y4000. circ. 8,000 (controlled). **Document type:** trade publication.
●Also available online.
Description: Contains scenarios, reports, and discussions on issues pertaining to film and television industry.

YISHUJIA/ARTIST. see *ART*

YORUBA. see *LINGUISTICS*

895.1   CH
YU SHIH WEN I. (Text in Chinese) m. NT.$700 in ROC; Asia $51; elsewhere $56. 3F, No. 66-1, Chungking S. Rd. Sec. 1, Taipei, Taiwan, Republic of China. TEL 02-311-2832. FAX 02-311-3309. Ed. Tuan Tsai-Hua.

895   CC
YUEDU YU XIEZUO/READING AND WRITING. (Text in Chinese) m. Guangxi Daxue, Zhongwen Xi - Guangxi University, Chinese Department, Nanning, Guangxi 530004, People's Republic of China. TEL 33442. Ed. Liao Chaoran.

YUGNTRUF; Yiddish student quarterly. see *ETHNIC INTERESTS*

895.1   CC   ISSN 0512-9664
YUHUA/RAIN FLOWER. (Text in Chinese) m. (Jiangsu Zuojia Xiehui - Jiangsu Writers Association) Yuhua Bianjibu, 10 Hunan Lu, Nanjing, Jiangsu 210009, People's Republic of China. TEL 638636. Ed. Ye Zhicheng.

YUVA BHARATI; voice of youth. see CHILDREN AND YOUTH — For

891.85   PL   ISSN 0084-4411
PG7001
Z DZIEJOW FORM ARTYSTYCZNYCH W LITERATURZE POLSKIEJ. (Text in Polish) 1963. irreg., vol.74, 1990. price varies. (Polska Akademia Nauk, Instytut Badan Literackich) Ossolineum, Publishing House of the Polish Academy of Sciences, Rynek 9, 50-106 Wroclaw, Poland. TEL 48-71-386-25. FAX 48-71-448-103. TELEX 0712771 OSS PL.
Document type: monographic series.
Description: Series of monographs on artistic forms in Polish literature.

ZA CASOPIS: KOVCEZIC. see LINGUISTICS

809   PL   ISSN 0084-4446
PN1
ZAGADNIENIA RODZAJOW LITERACKICH/PROBLEMES DES GENRES LITTERAIRES. (Text in English, French, German, Italian, Polish, Russian) 1958. irreg. (1-2/yr.). price varies. Lodzkie Towarzystwo Naukowe, Ul. Piotrkska 179, 90-447 Lodz, Poland. TEL 48-42-361026. FAX 48-42-362415. TELEX 884519 PAN PL. (Dist. by: Ars Polona, Krakowskie Przedmiescie 7, 00-068 Warsaw, Poland) (Co-sponsor: Polska Akademia Nauk) Eds. Jan Trzynadlowski, Grzegorz Gazda. bk.rev. circ. 800. **Indexed:** Abstr.Engl.Stud., Can.Rev.Comp.Lit., M.L.A. **Document type:** academic/scholarly publication.
Description: An international periodical devoted to the theory of literature. Authors from various countries.

ZAYRAY. see LINGUISTICS

891.82   YU   ISSN 0084-5183
PG1400
ZBORNIK ISTORIJE KNJIZEVNOSTI/RECUEIL DES TRAVAUX DE L'HISTOIRE DE LA LITTERATURE. (Text in Serbo-Croatian; summaries in English, French, German or Russian) 1960. irreg. price varies. Srpska Akademija Nauka i Umetnosti, Odeljenje Jezika i Knjizevnosti, Knez Mihailova 35, 11001 Belgrade, Serbia, Yugoslavia. FAX 38-11-182-825. TELEX 72593 SANU YU. (Dist. by: Prosveta, Terazije 16, Belgrade, Serbia, Yugoslavia) circ. 1,000. **Indexed:** M.L.A.

891.82   YU   ISSN 0084-5205
ZBORNIK ZA ISTORIJU, JEZIK I KNJIZEVNOST SRPSKOG NARODA. SPOMENICI NA SRPSKOM JEZIKU. (Text in Serbo-Croatian; summaries in English, French, German or Russian) 1960. irreg. price varies. Srpska Akademija Nauka i Umetnosti, Knez Mihailova 35, 11001 Belgrade, Serbia, Yugoslavia. FAX 38-11-182-825. TELEX 72593 SANU YU. (Dist. by Prosveta, Terazije 16, Belgrade, Serbia, Yugoslavia) circ. 1,000.

820 810   GW   ISSN 0044-2305
PR1
ZEITSCHRIFT FUER ANGLISTIK UND AMERIKANISTIK. (Text in English, German) 1953. 4/yr. DM.72. Verlag Langenscheidt KG, Postfach 401120, 80711 Munich, Germany. TEL 089-36096-0. FAX 089-36096258. Ed. Helmut Findeisen. adv.; bk.rev.; bibl.; index. circ. 1,500. **Indexed:** Arts & Hum.Cit.Ind., Bibl.Ling., Can.Rev.Comp.Lit., M.L.A. **Document type:** academic/scholarly publication. —Faxon; UnCover.
Description: Covers literature, literary history, language, linguistics, and semantics. Includes reports of events, and book discussions.

ZEITSCHRIFT FUER ARABISCHE LINGUISTIK/JOURNAL OF ARABIC LINGUISTICS/JOURNAL DE LINGUISTIQUE ARABE. see LINGUISTICS

ZEITSCHRIFT FUER CELTISCHE PHILOLOGIE. see LINGUISTICS

830   SZ   ISSN 0323-7982
PF3003
ZEITSCHRIFT FUER GERMANISTIK. 3/yr. 140 SFr. Verlag Peter Lang AG, Jupiterstr. 15, CH-3000 Bern, Switzerland. TEL 031-9411122. FAX 031-9411131. **Indexed:** Bibl.Ling. **Document type:** academic/scholarly publication. —Faxon; SWETS.
Description: Covers literary history, language, linguistics, semantics, and philosophy. Includes announcements of events, and book discussions.

ZEITSCHRIFT FUER ROMANISCHE PHILOLOGIE. see LINGUISTICS

ZEITSCHRIFT FUER ROMANISCHE PHILOLOGIE. BEIHEFTE. see LINGUISTICS

800   PL   ISSN 0751-0357
ZESZYTY LITERACKIE. 1983. q. 220 F.($40) (Agora-Gazeta Ltd.) Zeszyty Literackie Foundation, Nowy Swiat 27, 00-029 Warsaw, Poland. TEL 48-22-269084. FAX 48-22-261434. Ed. Barbara Torunczyk. adv. contact: Ewa Madej. bk.rev. circ. 10,000.
Description: Includes poetry, prose, essays.

895.1   CC
ZHANGHUI XIAOSHUO. (Text in Chinese) bi-m. Heilongjiang Sheng Wenlian, 16, Yaojing Jie, Nangang-qu, Harbin, Heilongjiang 150006, People's Republic of China. TEL 30826. Ed. Xiao Yingjun.
Description: Publishes a type of traditional Chinese novel with each chapter headed by a couplet giving the gist of its content.

895.1   CC
ZHANJIANG WENXUE/ZHANJIANG LITERATURE. (Text in Chinese) bi-m. Zhanjiang Shi Wenlian, Renmin Dadao Nan, Xiashan, Zhanjiang, Guangdong 224155, People's Republic of China. TEL 224155. Ed. Ou-yang Qi.

800   CC
ZHISHAN. (Text in Chinese) 1979. q. Zhangzhou Shi Wenlian, Shengli Lu, Zhangzhou, Fujian 363000, People's Republic of China. TEL 27182. (Dist. overseas by: Jiangsu Publications Import & Export Corp., 56 Gao Yun Ling, Nanjing, Jiangsu, P.R.C.) Ed. Chen Wenhe.

800   CC
ZHONG WAI SHUZHAI. (Text in Chinese) bi-m. Shanghai Renmen Chubanshe, Qikan Bu - Shanghai People's Publishing House, 54 Shaoxing Lu, Shanghai 200020, People's Republic of China. TEL 4335250. Ed. Wu Shiyu.

895.15   CC   ISSN 1002-7564
ZHONGGUO GUSHI/CHINESE STORIES. (Text in Chinese) 1985. bi-m. Y23. Zhongguo Gushi Zazhishe, 94 Dingziqiao Lu, Wuchang Qu, Wuhan, Hubei 430064, People's Republic of China. TEL 027-712847. (Dist. outside China by: Guoji Shudian - China International Book Trading Corp., P.O. Box 399, Beijing, P.R.C.) adv.; bk.rev. circ. 1,000,000.
Description: Publishes legendary novels, historical stories and biographies.

ZHONGGUO QINGNIAN/CHINESE YOUTH. see CHILDREN AND YOUTH — For

ZHONGGUO QINGNIAN BAO/CHINESE YOUTH DAILY. see CHILDREN AND YOUTH — For

ZHONGGUO TUSHU PINGLUN/CHINA BOOK REVIEW. see PUBLISHING AND BOOK TRADE

895.1   CC   ISSN 1001-2907
ZHONGGUO XIANDAI, DANGDAI WENXUE YANJIU. (Subseries of: Fuyin Baokan Ziliao) (Text in Chinese) m. Y67.20. Zhongguo Renmin Daxue, Shubao Ziliao Zhongxin - China People's University, Book & Newspaper Information Center, P.O. Box 1122, Beijing 100007, People's Republic of China.
Description: Contains reprinted papers and articles on modern and contemporary Chinese literature.

895.1   CC   ISSN 1000-8896
ZHONGGUO XIBU WENXUE. (Text in Chinese) m. Y19.2. Xinjiang Renmin Chubanshe, Qikan Bu - Xinjiang People's Publishing House, 306, Jiefang Lu, Urumqi, Xinjiang 830001, People's Republic of China. TEL 25358. (Dist. outside China by: China Publications Foreign Trade Corp., P.O. Box 782, Beijing, P.R.C.) Ed. Chen Bozhong. adv.; illus.
Description: Publishes short stories, prose, and poetry from the Xinjiang Uighur Autonomous Region and other areas of western China.

895.1   CC
ZHONGGUO ZUOJIA; daxing wenxue shuangyuekan. (Text in Chinese) bi-m. Y22.80($67.80) 2, Shatan Beijie, Beijing 100720, People's Republic of China. (Dist. outside China by: China International Book Trading Corp., P.O. Box 399, Beijing, P.R.C.; Dist. in US by: China Books & Periodicals, Inc., 2929 24th St., San Francisco, CA 94110. TEL 415-282-2994) Ed. Feng Mu. adv.
Description: Contains short stories and essays, as well as interviews with and articles about Chinese writers.

895.1   CC
ZHONGPIAN XIAOSHUO/NOVELETTE. (Text in Chinese) m. Y38.40. Zhongpian Xiaoshuo Bianjibu, 27 Degui Xiang, Fuzhou, Fujian 350001, People's Republic of China. (Dist. overseas by: Jiangsu Publications Import & Export Corp., 56 Gao Yun Ling, Nanjing, Jiangsu, P.R.C.)
Description: Covers critically acclaimed novelettes selected from all the literary magazines and journals in the country as well as novelettes by overseas Chinese writers. Serves as a reference for writers, critics, and libraries.

895.1   CC
ZHONGPIAN XIAOSHUO XUANKAN/SELECTED NOVELLAS. (Text in Chinese) bi-m. Haixia Wenyi Chubanshe, 27 Degui Xiang, Fuzhou, Fujian 350001, People's Republic of China. TEL 533457. Ed. Zhang Jianxing.

895.1   CC
ZHONGSHAN; a literary bi-monthly. (Text in Chinese) 1979. bi-m. Y24($62.40) (Jiangsu Zuojia Xiehui - Jiangsu Writers Association) Zhongshan Bianjibu, 10 Hunan Lu, Nanjing, Jiangsu 210009, People's Republic of China. TEL 86-25-638819. (Dist. in US by: China Books & Periodicals, Inc., 2929 24th St., San Francisco, CA 94110. TEL 415-282-2994) Ed. Fan Xiaotian. adv.; bk.rev.; illus. circ. 20,000. **Document type:** consumer publication.
Description: Contains novels, short stories, fictions, and proses.

895.1   CC
ZHONGWAI GUSHI/CHINESE AND FOREIGN STORIES. (Text in Chinese) bi-m. Zhongguo Minjian Wenyijia Xiehui, Shanxi Fenhui - China Folk Artists' Association, Shanxi Chapter, 62 Yingze Dajie, Taiyuan, Shanxi 030001, People's Republic of China. TEL 446952. (Dist. overseas by: China International Book Trade Corp., P.O. Box 399, Beijing, P.R. China) Ed. Liu Qi.
Description: Contains Chinese and foreign short stories.

ZHONGWAI GUSHI CHUANQI. see LITERATURE — Adventure And Romance

895.1   CC
ZHONGWAI WENXUE/CHINESE AND FOREIGN LITERATURE. (Text in Chinese) bi-m. Chunfeng Wenyi Chubanshe, 108 Beiyi Malu, Shenyang, Liaoning 110001, People's Republic of China. TEL 363198. Ed. Liu Lieheng.

800   CC
ZHUANJI WENXUE/BIOGRAPHICAL LITERATURE. (Text in Chinese) 1984. bi-m. $3. Wenhua Yishu Chubanshe - Culture and Art Publishers, 17 Qianhai Xijie, Beijing 100009, People's Republic of China. TEL 655992. Ed. Liu Jingzi. circ. 50,000.

895.1   CC
ZHUOMUNIAO/WOODPECKER. (Text in Chinese) bi-m. $49.50. Qunzhong Chubanshe, 14, Dongchang'anjie, Beijing 100741, People's Republic of China. TEL 545108. (Dist. in US by: China Books & Periodicals, Inc., 2929 24th St., San Francisco, CA 94110. TEL 415-282-2994) Ed. Sun Zhongyi.

ZLATY MAJ; casopis o detske literature. see CHILDREN AND YOUTH — For

800   VE
ZONA FRANCA. m. Conda esq. Carmelitas, Caracas, Venezuela.

LITERATURE — Abstracting, Bibliographies, Statistics

806 US ISSN 1051-6867
PS3515.U789
ZORA NEALE HURSTON FORUM. 1986. 2/yr. $15 to individuals; institutions $21. Zora Neale Hurston Society, Box 550, Morgan State University, Baltimore, MD 21239. Ed. Ruthe T. Sheffey. bk.rev. circ. 200.
—UnCover.

895.1 CC
ZUOJIA; wenxue yuekan. (Text in Chinese) m. Y18($61.20) 111 Sidalin Dajie, Changchun, Jilin 130021, People's Republic of China. TEL 883677. (Dist. outside China by: China International Book Trading Corp., P.O. Box 399, Beijing, P.R.C.; Dist. in US by: China Books & Periodicals, Inc., 2929 24th St., San Francisco, CA 94110) adv.; bk.rev.

895.1 CC ISSN 0494-1101
PL2250
ZUOPIN. (Text in Chinese) m. $115.50. Zhongguo Zuojia Xiehui, Guangdong Fenhui - China Writers Association, Guangdong Chapter, No. 75, Wende Lu, Guangzhou, Guangdong 510030, People's Republic of China. TEL 334179. (Dist. in US by: China Books & Periodicals, Inc., 2929 24th St., San Francisco, CA 94110. TEL 415-282-2994) Ed. Huang Peiliang.

895.1 CC
ZUOPIN YU ZHENGMING. (Text in Chinese) m. Y1.60 per no. Wenhua Yishu Chubanshe, 17, Qianhai Xijie, Xi Cheng Qu, Beijing 100009, People's Republic of China. (Editorial addr.: P.O. Box 2913, Beijing, P.R.C.) bk.rev.
Description: Contains controversial stories and drama, followed by literary criticism.

ZUOWEN CHENGGONG ZHI LU/WAYS TO A SUCCESSFUL COMPOSITION. see *EDUCATION*

800 US ISSN 1060-9571
▼**ZUZU PETAL QUARTERLY;** of the written arts. 1992. q. $17. Somerset Creamtree Press, Box 4476, Allentown, PA 18105. TEL 215-821-1324. Ed. Tabetha Dunn. bk.rev. circ. 300. **Document type:** academic/scholarly publication.
Description: Literary magazine named after Zuzu Petal, who played George Bailey daughter in the film It's a Wonderful Life. Seeks to expand the literary audience beyond its traditionally academic environs.

800 GW ISSN 0934-6155
ZWISCHEN ORIENT UND OKZIDENT. 1988. irreg., vol.2, 1991. (Rueckert Gesellschaft e.V.) Ergon-Verlag, Grombuehlstr. 7, 97080 Wuerzburg, Germany. TEL 0931-280084. FAX 0931-282872. **Document type:** monographic series.

800 US
▼**ZYX.** 1992. 2/yr. $2. 58-09 205th St., Bayside, NY 11364. Ed. Arnold Skemer. bk.rev. circ. 333. **Document type:** newsletter.
Description: Features avant-garde, innovative fiction criticism.

800 700 ISSN 8756-5633
PS561
ZYZZYVA. 1985. q. $28 to individuals (foreign $48); institutions $36 (effective Dec. 1992). Zyzzyva, Inc., 41 Sutter St., Ste. 1400, San Francisco, CA 94104. TEL 415-255-1282. FAX 415-255-1144. Ed. Howard Junker. adv.; B&W page $500. illus.; index. circ. 4,000. (back issues avail.) **Indexed:** Amer.Hum.Ind., Ind.Amer.Per.Verse.
Description: Highlights West Coast writers and artists.

810 301.412 US ISSN 0094-3320
PS508.W7
13TH MOON; a feminist literary magazine. 1973. irreg. $10 per vol. to individuals; institutions $20. 13th Moon, Inc., Dept. of English, SUNY at Albany, 1400 Washington Ave., Albany, NY 12222. TEL 518-442-4181. FAX 518-442-4599. Ed. Judith E. Johnson. adv.; bk.rev.; illus. circ. 2,000. (back issues avail.) **Indexed:** A.I.P.P., Abstr.Pop.Cult., Amer.Hum.Ind., Ind.Amer.Per.Verse.
Description: Presents poetry, fiction and critical articles with a feminist perspective, includes special focus on translations.

809 FR
27 RUE JACOB. m. Editions du Seuil, 27 rue Jacob, 75261 Paris Cedex 06, France. bk.rev.; abstr.; illus.

LITERATURE — Abstracting, Bibliographies, Statistics

A M S STUDIES IN MODERN LITERATURE. see *LITERATURE*

A M S STUDIES IN THE EIGHTEENTH CENTURY. see *LITERATURE*

A M S STUDIES IN THE NINETEENTH CENTURY. see *LITERATURE*

A M S STUDIES IN THE RENAISSANCE. see *LITERATURE*

A M S STUDIES IN THE SEVENTEENTH CENTURY. see *LITERATURE*

810 016 UK ISSN 0001-3560
PE25
ABSTRACTS OF ENGLISH STUDIES. 1958. 4/yr. £24($35) to individuals; institutions £45($69.50). (University of Calgary, Department of English, CN) Basil Blackwell Ltd., 108 Cowley Road, Oxford OX4 1JF, England. TEL 0865-791100. FAX 0865-791347. TELEX 837022-OXBOOK-G. Eds. Jerve Paquette, W. Monday. index. circ. 1,300. (also avail. in microform from UMI) **Document type:** abstracting/indexing.
—UMI. CCC.
Description: Abstracts from hundreds of journals on American and English literature, world literature and related languages.

AFRICAN STUDIES ABSTRACTS. see *SOCIAL SCIENCES: COMPREHENSIVE WORKS — Abstracting, Bibliographies, Statistics*

AMERICAN HUMANITIES INDEX. see *HUMANITIES: COMPREHENSIVE WORKS — Abstracting, Bibliographies, Statistics*

810 016 US ISSN 0002-9823
PS1
AMERICAN LITERARY REALISM. 1967. 3/yr. $25 (foreign $31). (University of New Mexico, Department of English) McFarland & Company, Inc., Box 611, Jefferson, NC 28640. TEL 910-246-4460. Eds. James Barbour, Robert E. Fleming. adv.; bk.rev.; illus.; index. circ. 600. (reprint service avail. from KTO) **Indexed:** Abstr.Engl.Stud., Amer.Hist.& Life, Amer.Hum.Ind., Arts & Hum.Cit.Ind., Curr.Cont., Hist.Abstr., Ind.Bk.Rev.Hum., M.L.A., Ref.Sour.
—BLDSC (0840.760000); Faxon; UnCover; SWETS.

808.838 US
ANATOMY OF WONDER; a critical guide to science fiction. 1975. irreg., 4th ed., 1994. $52. R.R. Bowker, A Reed Reference Publishing Company, Part of the Reed Elsevier group, 121 Chanlon Rd., New Providence, NJ 07974. TEL 908-464-6800. FAX 908-665-6688. TELEX 138 755. (Subscr. to: Order Dept., Box 31, New Providence, NJ 07974-9903. TEL 800-521-8110) Ed. Neil Barron. **Document type:** directory.

420 016 UK ISSN 0066-3786
Z2011
ANNUAL BIBLIOGRAPHY OF ENGLISH LANGUAGE AND LITERATURE. 1920. a. $216. Modern Humanities Research Association, Kings College, London WC2R 2LS, England. (Vols. 1-39 avail. from: Wm. Dawson & Sons Ltd., Cannon House, Folkstone, Kent, England) Eds. E. Erskine, M.J. De Marr. (also avail. in microform from BHP) **Document type:** bibliography.

016 820 UK ISSN 0307-9864
Z2057
ANNUAL BIBLIOGRAPHY OF SCOTTISH LITERATURE. 1969. a. £9($19) to personal subscriber £11 (24) to institutions. Library Association, Scottish Group, Edinburgh University Library, Edinburgh EH8 9LJ, Scotland. Eds. J. Kidd, R.H. Carnie. adv.; bk.rev. circ. 400. **Indexed:** Abstr.Engl.Stud., LISA. **Document type:** bibliography.

800 016 CN ISSN 0227-1400
Z2019
ANNUAL BIBLIOGRAPHY OF VICTORIAN STUDIES. 1977. a. LITIR Database, c/o Department of English, University of Alberta, Edmonton, Alta. T6G 2E5, Canada. TEL 403-432-3258. Eds. Brahma Chaudhuri, Fred Radford. cum.index every 5 yrs. **Document type:** bibliography.

APPLAUSE THEATRE BOOK REVIEW & CATALOG. see *LITERATURE*

800 FR
Z1000
ARGUS DU LIVRE DE COLLECTION. (Text in English, French) 1981. a. 995 F. Editions du Cercle de la Librairie, 35 rue Gregoire-de-Tours, 75006 Paris, France.
Former titles: Argus du Livre de Collection et de l'Autographe (ISSN 0764-8111); Argus du Livre Ancien et Moderne (ISSN 0242-5823)

AUSTRALIAN BOOK COLLECTOR. see *LITERATURE*

860 016 SP
BIBLIOGRAFIA DE LA LITERATURA HISPANICA. 1960. irreg. Consejo Superior de Investigaciones Cientificas (C.S.I.C.), Instituto de Filologia, Vitruvio, 8, 28006 Madrid, Spain. Ed. Jose Simon Diaz.

860 SP ISSN 1132-0427
BIBLIOGRAFIA DIECIOCHISTA. 1973. a. 2100 ptas.($20) Universidad de Oviedo, Instituto Feijoo de Estudios del Siglo XVIII, Fac. de Humanidades, 33071 Oviedo, Spain. TEL 98-510-46-71. FAX 98-510-45-13. circ. 500. **Document type:** bibliography.
Former titles (until 1987): Centro de Estudios del Siglo XVIII. Boletin. Bibliografia Dieciochista (ISSN 1131-9887); (until 1983): Centro de Estudios del Siglo XVIII. Boletin (ISSN 0210-475X)

809 016 IT
BIBLIOGRAFIA E STORIA DELLA CRITICA. irreg., latest no.9. price varies. Angelo Longo Editore, Via Paolo Costa 33, P.O. Box 431, 48100 Ravenna, Italy. TEL 0544-217026. Ed. Enzo Esposito. circ. 2,000. **Document type:** bibliography.

800 011 YU ISSN 0350-1450
BIBLIOGRAFIJA DOMACIH I STRANIH KNJIGA. (Text in Serbo-Croatian) 1952. 6/yr. Centar za Vojnonaucnu Dokumentaciju i Informaciju, Balkanska 53, Belgrade, Yugoslavia. Ed. Aleksander Nikovic.
Description: Covers contemporary domestic and foreign literature.

059 YU ISSN 0351-1537
BIBLIOGRAFIJA ROTO STAMPE I STRIPOVA. 1974. a. $105. Jugoslovenski Bibliografsko-Informacijski Institut (YUBIN) - Yugoslav Institute for Bibliography and Information, Terazije 26, Belgrade, Serbia, Yugoslavia. FAX 11-687-760. Ed. Radomir Glavicki.

016 830 GW ISSN 0341-9363
BIBLIOGRAPHIE DER DEUTSCHEN SPRACH- UND LITERATURWISSENSCHAFT. 1957. a. DM.208. Vittorio Klostermann, Frauenlobstr. 22, 60487 Frankfurt a.M., Germany. TEL 069-774011. FAX 069-708038. (Subscr. to: Postfach 900601, 60446 Frankfurt a.M., Germany) Ed. Bernhard Kossmann. circ. 2,000. **Document type:** bibliography.
Formerly: Bibliographie der Deutschen Literaturwissenschaft.

016 840 GW ISSN 0523-2465
Z2171
BIBLIOGRAPHIE DER FRANZOESISCHEN LITERATURWISSENSCHAFT. 1960. a. DM.340. Vittorio Klostermann, Frauenlobstr. 22, 60487 Frankfurt a.M., Germany. TEL 069-774011. FAX 069-708038. (Subscr. to: Postfach 900601, 60446 Frankfurt a.M., Germany) Ed. Astrid Klapp-Lehrmann. circ. 1,500. **Document type:** bibliography.

830 430 016 GW ISSN 0172-3960
BIBLIOGRAPHIE LINGUISTISCHER LITERATUR; bibliography of general linguistics and of English, German and Romance linguistics. (Text in English) 1978. a. DM.496. Vittorio Klostermann, Frauenlobstr. 22, 60487 Frankfurt a.M., Germany. TEL 069-774011. FAX 069-708038. (Subscr. to: Postfach 900601, 60446 Frankfurt a.M., Germany) Ed. Berndt Dugall. **Document type:** bibliography.
Formerly (1976-1978): Bibliographie Unselbstaendiger Literatur-Linguistik.

800 SZ
BIBLIOGRAPHIE ZUR DEUTSCHSPRACHIGEN SCHWEIZERLITERATUR. 1976. a. 30 SFr. Bibliotheque Nationale Suisse, Hallwylstr. 15, CH-3003 Bern, Switzerland. Ed. Gaby Rauch. bk.rev. circ. 75. **Document type:** bibliography.

LITERATURE — ABSTRACTING, BIBLIOGRAPHIES, STATISTICS

830   GW   ISSN 0523-2767
BIBLIOGRAPHIEN ZUR DEUTSCHEN LITERATUR DES MITTELALTERS. 1966. irreg., vol.10, 1989. price varies. Erich Schmidt Verlag GmbH & Co. (Bielefeld), Viktoriastr. 44a, 33602 Bielefeld, Germany. TEL 0521-583080. (Subscr. to: Postfach 102451, 33524 Bielefeld, Germany) Eds. Ulrich Pretzel, Wolfgang Bachofer. (back issues avail.) **Indexed:** M.L.A. **Document type:** monographic series.

840   GW   ISSN 0171-0125
BIBLIOGRAPHIEN ZUR ROMANISTIK. (Text in French) 1981. irreg. price varies. Edition Gemini, Juelichstr. 7, 50354 Huerth-Efferen, Germany. TEL 02233-63550. FAX 02233-65866. Ed. Gernot U. Gabel. circ. 200. (back issues avail.) **Document type:** monographic series.

810   US   ISSN 0742-6860
BIBLIOGRAPHIES AND INDEXES IN AMERICAN LITERATURE. 1984. irreg. price varies. Greenwood Press, Inc. (Subsidiary of: Greenwood Publishing Group Inc.), 88 Post Rd. W., Box 5007, Westport, CT 06881-5007. TEL 203-226-3571. FAX 203-222-1502. **Document type:** abstracting/indexing, bibliography.

808.338   US   ISSN 1053-4636
BIBLIOGRAPHIES AND INDEXES IN SCIENCE FICTION, FANTASY, AND HORROR. 1987. irreg. price varies. Greenwood Press, Inc. (Subsidiary of: Greenwood Publishing Group Inc.), 88 Post Rd. W., Box 5007, Westport, CT 06881-5007. TEL 203-226-3571. FAX 203-222-1502. **Document type:** monographic series.

808   US   ISSN 0742-6801
BIBLIOGRAPHIES AND INDEXES IN WORLD LITERATURE. 1984. irreg. price varies. Greenwood Press, Inc. (Subsidiary of: Greenwood Publishing Group Inc.), 88 Post Rd. W., Box 5007, Westport, CT 06881-5007. TEL 203-226-3571. FAX 203-222-1502. **Document type:** abstracting/indexing, bibliography.
—BLDSC (1993.097600).

BIBLIOGRAPHIES OF MODERN AUTHORS. see BIBLIOGRAPHIES

808   II
BIBLIOGRAPHY OF INDIAN WRITING IN ENGLISH SERIES. (Text in English) 1983. irreg. (approx. biennial) Rs.25($5) Concept Publishing Company, A 15-16, Commercial Block, Mohan Garden, New Delhi 110 059, India. TEL 011-5554-042. Ed. Hilda Ponter. bibl. **Document type:** bibliography, monographic series.
Description: Includes biographical factors and critical opinions.

011 899   IS   ISSN 0334-309X
Z7070
BIBLIOGRAPHY OF MODERN HEBREW LITERATURE IN TRANSLATION. 1979. a. $20. Institute for the Translation of Hebrew Literature, P.O. Box 10051, Ramat Gan 52001, Israel. TEL 972-3-5796830. bk.rev.; index. circ. 200. (reprint service avail. from UMI) **Document type:** bibliography.

860   CU
BIBLIOTECA NACIONAL JOSE MARTI. BOLETIN DE ARTE Y CULTURA. 1986. s.a. Biblioteca Nacional Jose Marti, Plaza de la Revolucion, Havana, Cuba. circ. 300.
Formerly: Biblioteca Nacional Jose Marti. Catalogo de Arte y Cultura; Supersedes (in 199?): Biblioteca Nacional Jose Marti. Boletines Bibliograficos.

810   US   ISSN 0742-695X
BIO-BIBLIOGRAPHIES IN AMERICAN LITERATURE. 1984. irreg. price varies. Greenwood Press, Inc., 88 Post Rd. W., Box 5007, Westport, CT 06881-9990. TEL 203-226-3571.

808   US   ISSN 0894-2323
BIO-BIBLIOGRAPHIES IN WORLD LITERATURE. irreg. price varies. Greenwood Press, Inc. (Subsidiary of: Greenwood Publishing Group Inc.), 88 Post Rd. W., Box 5007, Westport, CT 06881-5007. TEL 203-226-3571. FAX 203-222-1502.

BOOK REVIEW INDEX; indexes all reviews in over 500 periodicals. see PUBLISHING AND BOOK TRADE — Abstracting, Bibliographies, Statistics

BOOK REVIEW INDEX: ANNUAL CLOTHBOUND CUMULATIONS. see PUBLISHING AND BOOK TRADE — Abstracting, Bibliographies, Statistics

BOOKS AND ARTICLES ON ORIENTAL SUBJECTS PUBLISHED IN JAPAN. see ORIENTAL STUDIES — Abstracting, Bibliographies, Statistics

BORGO LITERARY GUIDES. see LITERATURE

CARIBBEAN ABSTRACTS. see ANTHROPOLOGY — Abstracting, Bibliographies, Statistics

016 880   US   ISSN 0528-2594
CATALOGUS TRANSLATIONEM ET COMMENTATORIUM; Medieval and Renaissance Latin translations. 1960. irreg., latest vol.7. price varies. Catholic University of America Press, 620 Michigan Ave., N.E., Washington, DC 20064. TEL 202-319-5052. FAX 202-319-5802. (Subscr. to: Box 4852, Hampden Sta., Baltimore, MD 21211. TEL 410-516-6953) (reprint service avail. from UMI)

800   FR
DP501
CENTRE CULTUREL PORTUGAIS. ARCHIVES. 1969. a. 350 F. Centre Culturel Portugais, Fondation Calouste Gulbenkian, 51 Ave. d'Iena, 75116 Paris, France. TEL 47-20-86-84. FAX 40-70-98-79. TELEX GULBENF 620176F. (Subscr. to: Jean Touzot, Editeur Libraire, 38 rue Saint-Sulpice, 75006 Paris, France. TEL 43-26-03-88) Ed. Maria De Lourdes Belchior. bk.rev. circ. 1,000.
—BLDSC (1685.200000).
Formerly: Centro Cultural Portugues. Arquivos (ISSN 0590-966X)

CHILDREN'S AUTHORS AND ILLUSTRATORS; an index to biographical dictionaries. see BIOGRAPHY — Abstracting, Bibliographies, Statistics

CHILDREN'S BOOKS IN PRINT; an author, title, and illustrator index to books for children and young adults. see BIBLIOGRAPHIES

891   US
COMPREHENSIVE BIBLIOGRAPHY OF YUGOSLAV LITERATURE IN ENGLISH. 1984. base vol. (plus updates every 5 yrs.). Slavica Publishers, Inc., Box 14388, Columbus, OH 43214. TEL 614-268-4002. Ed. Vasa D. Mihailovich. (back issues avail.) **Document type:** bibliography.
Description: Provides a thorough listing of all translations and criticisms in English of Yugoslav literature.

840   US
CRITICAL BIBLIOGRAPHY OF FRENCH LITERATURE. 1951. irreg., vol.6, 1980. price varies. Syracuse University Press, 1600 Jamesville Ave., Syracuse, NY 13244. TEL 315-443-2597. Ed. Richard A. Brooks. **Document type:** academic/scholarly publication.

CURRENT RESEARCH IN FRENCH STUDIES AT UNIVERSITIES AND POLYTECHNICS IN THE UNITED KINGDOM AND IRELAND. see LINGUISTICS — Abstracting, Bibliographies, Statistics

015   DK   ISSN 0070-2714
DANIA POLYGLOTTA; literature on Denmark in languages other than Danish and books of Danish interest published abroad. 1947; N.S. 1969. a. price varies. Kongelige Bibliotek, Danish Department, Christians Brygge 8, 1219 Copenhagen K, Denmark. (Avail. on exchange basis from: I.D.E., Denmarks Institut for International Udveksling, Amaliegade 38, DK-1256 Copenhagen K, Denmark) Eds. Sven C. Jacobsen, Jan William Rasmussen.

016   NE   ISSN 0167-2185
DEUTSCHE BUECHER. (Text in German) 1971. q. fl.165. Editions Rodopi B.V., Keizersgracht 302-304, 1016 EX Amsterdam, Netherlands. TEL 31-20-6227507. FAX 31-20-6380948. (In N. America: 233 Peachtree St. N.E., Ste. 404, Atlanta GA 30303-1504. TEL 800-225-3998. FAX 404-522-7116) Ed.Bd. circ. 1,000. **Document type:** academic/scholarly publication.
Formerly (until 1974): Duitse Boek (ISSN 0046-080X)

808.81   US
DIRECTORY OF LITERARY MAGAZINES. 1981. a. $13.50. Council of Literary Magazines and Presses, 154 Christopher St., Ste. 3C, New York, NY 10014-2839. TEL 212-741-9110. FAX 212-741-9112. index. circ. 3,500. **Document type:** directory, bibliography.

050 810 820   US   ISSN 0070-6094
Z2015.P4
DIRECTORY OF PERIODICALS PUBLISHING ARTICLES ON ENGLISH AND AMERICAN LITERATURE AND LANGUAGE.* 1959. irreg., 4th ed. 1975. $10 hardbound; paperback $3.50. Swallow Press, Inc., Box 2080, Chicago, IL 60690-2080. Eds. Donna Gerstenberger, George Hendrick. **Document type:** directory.

E I. (Excerpta Indonesica) see ANTHROPOLOGY — Abstracting, Bibliographies, Statistics

809.02   US   ISSN 0363-4841
PN661
ENCOMIA; bibliographical bulletin of the International Courtly Literature Society. 1975. a. $15. International Courtly Literature Society, c/o Dhira B. Mahoney, Sec.-Treas., Department of English, Arizona State University, Tempe, AZ 85287-0302. TEL 602-965-3168. FAX 602-965-2012. Ed. Maria Dobozy. adv.; bk.rev.; illus. circ. 950. **Indexed:** M.L.A. **Document type:** bibliography.
—BLDSC (3738.523000).

800 011   US   ISSN 0014-083X
AI3
ESSAY AND GENERAL LITERATURE INDEX. 1900. s-a. (a. and 5-yr. cumulations). $120. H.W. Wilson Co., 950 University Ave., Bronx, NY 10452. TEL 800-367-6770. FAX 718-590-1617. TELEX 4990003HWILSON. Ed. John Greenfieldt. cum. index: 1900-1969. (also avail. in magnetic tape) **Document type:** abstracting/indexing.
● Also available online. Vendor(s): BRS Online Products, Wilsonline (File EGL).
Also available on CD-ROM. Producer(s): H.W. Wilson (WILSONDISC).
—BLDSC (3811.671400).
Description: Index to collections of essays and works of a composite nature that have reference value.

800 016   FR   ISSN 1157-3732
Z6513
F R A N C I S. 523: HISTOIRE ET SCIENCES DE LA LITTERATURE. (Text in English, French) 1947. q. 575 F. (outside EEC 605 F.) Centre National de la Recherche Scientifique, Institut de l'Information Scientifique et Technique, 2 allee du Parc de Brabois, 54514 Vandoeuvre-les-Nancy Cedex, France. TEL 83-50-46-00. FAX 83-50-46-50. adv. contact: Veronique Guinvarc'h. cum.index. **Document type:** bibliography.
● Also available online. Vendor(s): Telesystemes - Questel.
Also available on CD-ROM.
Formerly: Bulletin Signaletique. Part 523: Histoire et Sciences de la Litterature (ISSN 0007-5582)

800 011   US   ISSN 0160-4880
Z5916
FICTION CATALOG. quinquennial, plus a. supplement. $98. H.W. Wilson Co., 950 University Ave., Bronx, NY 10452. TEL 800-367-6770. FAX 718-590-2716. TELEX 4990003HWILSON. Ed. Juliette Yaakov. **Document type:** catalog.
Description: An annotated list of the best new and established English-language fiction, with title and subject index.

800   US   ISSN 0271-6607
FRENCH LITERATURE SERIES. 1974. a. $32 (Europe fl.55). University of South Carolina, Department of Foreign Languages, Columbia, SC 29208. TEL 803-777-4881. (Subscr. in N. America: Editions Rodopi, 233 Peachtree St., N.E., Ste. 404, Atlanta, GA 30303-1504. TEL 404-523-1964. FAX 404-522-7116; Elsewhere: Editions Rodopi B.V., Keizersgracht 302-304, 1016 EX Amsterdam, Netherlands. TEL 020-622-75-07. FAX 020-638-09-48) Ed. Freeman G. Henry. bibl. circ. 300. (back issues avail.) **Indexed:** M.L.A. **Document type:** monographic series.

LITERATURE — ABSTRACTING, BIBLIOGRAPHIES, STATISTICS

054.1 944   US   ISSN 0191-9199
Z2172
FRENCH 17; an annual descriptive bibliography of French seventeenth century studies. 1953. a. $10. (Modern Language Association of America, Seventeenth Century French Division) Colorado State University, Department of Foreign Languages, 15 Willard O. Eddy Bldg., Fort Collins, CO 80523. TEL 303-491-6141. FAX 303-491-6797. Ed. J.D. Vedvik. bk.rev. circ. 450. **Document type:** bibliography.
  Former titles: Bibliography of French 17th Century Studies; French 3.
  Description: Provides an annual survey of the work done each year in the general area of 17th century French studies.

800   GW   ISSN 0943-9188
FRITZ-HUESER-INSTITUT FUER DEUTSCHE UND AUSLAENDISCHE ARBEITERLITERATUR. INFORMATIONEN. 1967. irreg. Fritz-Hueser-Institut fuer Deutsche und Auslaendische Arbeiterliteratur, Ostenhellweg 56-58, 44135 Dortmund, Germany. TEL 0231-5023227. Ed. Dr. Rainer Noltenius. circ. 600. **Document type:** bibliography.
  Description: Presents literature of and for the working class from 1848 to the present day.

430 830 016   GW   ISSN 0016-8912
Z2235.A2
GERMANISTIK; internationales Referatenorgan mit bibliographischen Hinweisen. 1960. q. DM.132. Max Niemeyer Verlag, Postfach 2140, 72011 Tuebingen, Germany. TEL 07071-98940. FAX 07071-989450. Ed. Matthias Reifegerste. adv.; bk.rev.; bibl.; index. circ. 1,900. (back issues avail.) **Indexed:** Bibl.Ling., M.L.A. **Document type:** bibliography.
—SWETS. CCC.
  Description: Bibliography listing new works and essays on German language and literature.

GREECE. NATIONAL STATISTICAL SERVICE. CULTURAL STATISTICS. see ART — *Abstracting, Bibliographies, Statistics*

016   US   ISSN 0090-9130
Z1231.P7
INDEX OF AMERICAN PERIODICAL VERSE. 1971. a. Scarecrow Press, Inc., 52 Liberty St., Box 4167, Metuchen, NJ 08840. TEL 800-537-7107. Eds. Rafael Catata, James D. Anderson. circ. 3,000. **Document type:** abstracting/indexing.
  Description: Indexes poems published by periodicals from Canada, the U.S. and Puerto Rico. Includes "little magazines" with limited distribution.

800 016   UK
INDEX OF ENGLISH LITERARY MANUSCRIPTS. 1980. irreg. price varies. Mansell Publishing Ltd., Villiers House, 41-47 Strand, London WC2N 5JE, England. TEL 071-839-4900. FAX 071-839-1804. (Dist. in U.S. by: Cassell, PCS Data Processing Inc., 360 W. 31st St., New York, NY 10001) **Document type:** abstracting/indexing.
  Description: Lists, describes and locates texts by some 270 major British and Irish authors from 1450 to 1900.

800   US   ISSN 0267-2472
INDEX OF MIDDLE ENGLISH PROSE. 1984. irreg., latest no.9. Boydell & Brewer Inc., Box 41026, Rochester, NY 14604. TEL 716-275-0419. FAX 716-271-8788.

INDICE ESPANOL DE HUMANIDADES. SERIES C: LINGUISTICS AND LITERATURE. see LINGUISTICS — *Abstracting, Bibliographies, Statistics*

INTER-AMERICAN REVIEW OF BIBLIOGRAPHY/REVISTA INTERAMERICANA DE BIBLIOGRAFIA. see HUMANITIES: COMPREHENSIVE WORKS — *Abstracting, Bibliographies, Statistics*

820 398   CN   ISSN 0074-1388
Z8045
INTERNATIONAL ARTHURIAN SOCIETY. BIBLIOGRAPHICAL BULLETIN/SOCIETE INTERNATIONALE ARTHURIENNE. BULLETIN BIBLIOGRAPHIQUE. (Text in English and French) 1949. a. $18 to institutions; members $15. International Arthurian Society, c/o Hans R. Runte, Sec.-Treas., Dalhousie University, Department of French, Halifax, NS B3H 3J5, Canada. TEL 902-494-2430. Ed. Keith Busby. bk.rev.; bibl. circ. 1,000. (also avail. in microform from SWZ; back issues avail.; reprint service avail. from SWZ) **Indexed:** MLA. **Document type:** academic/scholarly publication, bibliography, bulletin.
  Supersedes: International Arthurian Society. Report on Congress (ISSN 0074-1396)
  Description: Provides an annotated bibliography of the years work in Arthurian studies.

INTERNATIONAL RARE BOOK PRICES - LITERATURE. see PUBLISHING AND BOOK TRADE — *Abstracting, Bibliographies, Statistics*

INTERNATIONAL RARE BOOK PRICES - MODERN FIRST EDITION. see PUBLISHING AND BOOK TRADE — *Abstracting, Bibliographies, Statistics*

011   SW   ISSN 0349-5426
KOMMUNAL LITTERATUR; foerteckning oever Aktualla Tidskriftsartiklar i Kommunala Fraagor. 1951. bi-m. SEK 295 (effective 1993). Bibliotekstjaenst AB, Box 200, 221 00 Lund, Sweden. TEL 46-180-000. circ. 1,600.
  Formerly (until 1981): Kommunal Litteraturtjaenst (ISSN 0023-3056); (until 1952): Stadsbibliotekets Kommunala Litteraturtjaenst. Tidskriftsoeversikt.

800 011   MX   ISSN 0024-1210
LETRAS;* publicacion literaria y bibliografica. vol.36,1970. bi-m. Libreria y Ediciones Botas S. A., Justo Sierra no. 52, Mexico 1, D.F., Mexico. Ed. Gilberto Basa. bk.rev.; bibl.

850   IT   ISSN 1121-0753
PQ4001
LETTERATURA ITALIANA. AGGIORNAMENTO BIBLIOGRAFICO. 1991. s-a. L.350000 (foreign L.400000). Alcione Edizioni s.r.l., Corso Italia 31, C.P. 554, Trieste, Italy. Ed. Benedetto Aschero. **Document type:** bibliography.

016   US
LEWIS CARROLL SOCIETY OF NORTH AMERICA. CHAPBOOK. Variant title: Carroll Studies. 1975. a. $20. Lewis Carroll Society of North America, 617 Rockford Rd., Silver Spring, MD 20902. Ed. Charles Lovett. circ. 400. **Document type:** academic/scholarly publication, newsletter.

LIBROS PARAGUAYOS. see LITERATURE

LIGHT'S LIST OF LITERARY MAGAZINES (YEAR). see LITERARY AND POLITICAL REVIEWS — *Abstracting, Bibliographies, Statistics*

809 011   US   ISSN 0733-2165
Z2011
LITERARY CRITICISM REGISTER; a monthly listing of studies in English and American literature. 1983. m. $34 to individuals; institutions $59. Literary Criticism Register, Box 2086, DeLand, FL 32721. TEL 904-736-6029. Eds. Sims D. Kline, Nancy W. Kline. adv.; cum.index. circ. 600. **Document type:** abstracting/indexing.
—UnCover.
  Description: Listing of bibliographic information for recent articles, books, and dissertations in the field.

800 016   PL   ISSN 0075-9945
LITERATURA PIEKNA. ADNOTOWANY ROCZNIK BIBLIOGRAFICZNY. 1954. a. 8000 Zl.($28) (Biblioteka Narodowa, Instytut Bibliograficzny) Stowarzyszenie Bibliotekarzy Polskich, Konopczynskiego 5-7, 00-953 Warsaw, Poland. TEL 275296. (Dist. by: Ars Polona-Ruch, Krakowskie Przedmiescie 7, 00-068 Warsaw, Poland) circ. 5,500.

809   RU
PN9
LITERATUROVEDENIE: OTECHESTVENNAYA LITERATURA; referativnyi zhurnal. 1973. q. $44. Rossiiskaya Akademiya Nauk, Institut Nauchnoi Informatsii po Obshchestvennym Naukam, Ul. Krasikova 28-21, 117418 Moscow V-418, Russia. Ed. Ch.G. Guseinov.
  Formerly: Obshchestvennye Nauki v S.S.S.R. Literaturovedenie (ISSN 0202-2095)

809   RU
LITERATUROVEDENIE: ZARUBEZHNAYA LITERATURA; referativnyi zhurnal. 1973. q. $32. Rossiiskaya Akademiya Nauk, Institut Nauchnoi Informatsii po Obshchestvennym Naukam, Ul. Krasikova 28-21, 117418 Moscow V-418, Russia. Ed. L.G. Andreev.
  Formerly: Obshchestvennye Nauki za Rubezhom. Literaturovedenie (ISSN 0202-2117)

890   DK   ISSN 0108-7215
LITTERATUR PAA INDVANDRERSPROG I DANSKE FOLKEBIBLIOTEKER. 1983. a. DKK 1017.75. Dansk BiblioteksCenter as, Tempovej 7-11, 2750 Ballerup, Denmark. TEL 45-44-97-40-00. FAX 45-44-68-24-42.
●Also available online.

800 400 016   US   ISSN 0197-0380
P1.A1
M L A DIRECTORY OF PERIODICALS; a guide to journals and series in languages and literatures. 1979. triennial. $130. Modern Language Association of America, 10 Astor Pl., New York, NY 10003. TEL 212-475-9500. FAX 212-477-9863. Ed. Kathleen Kent. circ. 2,500. **Document type:** directory.
  Description: Provides detailed information of periodicals on language, literature, linguistics and folklore.

400 800 016   US   ISSN 0024-8215
Z7006
M L A INTERNATIONAL BIBLIOGRAPHY OF BOOKS AND ARTICLES ON THE MODERN LANGUAGES AND LITERATURES. (In 5 vols.) 1922. a. $950. Modern Language Association of America, 10 Astor Place, New York, NY 10003. TEL 212-475-9500. FAX 212-477-9863. Ed. Terence Ford. bibl.; index. circ. 3,000. (reprint service avail. from KTO) **Document type:** bibliography.
●Also available online. Vendor(s): Wilsonline. Also available on CD-ROM. Producer(s): SilverPlatter Information, Inc., H.W. Wilson.
  Description: Index of scholarly and critical works; lists journal articles, books, and dissertation abstracts.

808.838   US
Z5917.S36
THE N E S F A INDEX TO SHORT SCIENCE FICTION. 1966. a. $12. New England Science Fiction Association Inc., Box 809, Framingham, MA 01701-0203. FAX 617-253-2311. Ed. Anthony Lewis. circ. 1,000. **Document type:** abstracting/indexing.
  Former titles (until 1986): N.E.S.F.A. Index to the Science Fiction Magazines and Original Anthologies (ISSN 0747-7546); Index to the Science Fiction Magazines (1979) (ISSN 0732-0655); (until 1976): N.E.S.F.A. Index: Science Fiction Magazines and Anthologies (ISSN 0361-3038); (until 1970): Index to the Science Fiction Magazines (ISSN 0579-6059)

809 011   RU
NOVAYA LITERATURA PO SOTSIAL'NYM I GUMANITARNYM NAUKAM. LITERATUROVEDENIE; bibliograficheskii ukazatel' 1992. m. $120. Rossiiskaya Akademiya Nauk, Institut Nauchnoi Informatsii po Obshchestvennym Naukam, Ul. Krasikova 28-21, 117418 Moscow V-418, Russia. Ed. V.A. Makarenko.
  Formed by the merger of (1954-1992): Novaya Inostrannaya Literatura po Obshchestvennym Naukam. Literaturovedenie (ISSN 0134-2797); (1953-1992): Novaya Sovetskaya Literatura po Obshchestvennym Naukam. Literaturovedenie (ISSN 0134-2770)

808   US
PITTSBURGH SERIES IN BIBLIOGRAPHY. 1972. a. price varies. University of Pittsburgh Press, 127 North Bellefield Ave., Pittsburgh, PA 15260. TEL 800-666-2211. FAX 412-624-7380. Ed. Matthew J. Bruccoli. **Document type:** bibliography.

PLATTDEUTSCHE BIBLIOGRAPHIE; laufendes Verzeichnis der Neuerscheinungen und Neuauflagen auf dem Gebiet der Plattdeutschen Sprache und Literatur. see *LINGUISTICS — Abstracting, Bibliographies, Statistics*

800 016   US   ISSN 0554-3037
Z5781
PLAY INDEX. 1949. quinquennial. price varies. H.W. Wilson Co., 950 University Ave., Bronx, NY 10452. TEL 800-367-6770. FAX 718-590-1617. TELEX 4990003HWILSON. Ed. Juliette Yaakov. **Document type**: abstracting/indexing.
    Description: Author, title, and subject index to individual plays and plays in collections, with separate cast analysis.

PLAYWRIGHTS UNION OF CANADA CATALOGUE OF CANADIAN PLAYS. see *THEATER — Abstracting, Bibliographies, Statistics*

808.81   US   ISSN 0736-3966
PN1022
POETRY INDEX ANNUAL. 1982. a. $54.99 (CD-ROM Poemfinder on Disc $300) (effective 1993). Roth Publishing, Inc., 185 Great Neck Rd., Great Neck, NY 11021. TEL 800-899-7684; 516-466-3676. FAX 516-829-7746. (back issues avail.) **Document type**: abstracting/indexing.
    ●Also available on CD-ROM.
    Description: Comprehensive author, title, first line, translator, subject index to poetry in English or English translation published in anthologies in book form during the previous year.

891.85 016   PL   ISSN 0079-3590
POLSKA BIBLIOGRAFIA LITERACKA. 1944. irreg. price varies. Polska Akademia Nauk, Instytut Badan Literackich, Nowy Swiat 72, Palac Staszica, pok.128, 00-330 Warsaw, Poland. (Dist. by: Ars Polona, Krakowskie Przedmiescie 7, 00-068 Warsaw, Poland) Ed. J. Czachowska. circ. 700.

890   SW   ISSN 0348-6133
PT9201
SAMLAREN; tidskrift for svensk litteraturvetenskaplig forskning. (Text and summaries in English, German and Swedish) 1880. a. SEK 160 (effective 1990). (Litteraturvetenskapliga Institutionen) A W I International AB, P.O. Box 4627, S-116 91 Stockholm, Sweden. TEL 468-640-8800. FAX 468-641-1180. Ed. Ulf Wittrock. bk.rev. circ. 1,000. (back issues avail.)

808.838   US
SCIENCE FICTION AND FANTASY RESEARCH INDEX. 1981. irreg., vol.10, 1994. price varies. Box 2845, San Bernardino, CA 92406-2845. TEL 909-884-5813. FAX 909-888-4942. Ed. H.W. Hall. circ. 500. **Document type**: abstracting/indexing.
    Formerly: Science Fiction Research Index.

808 011   US   ISSN 0898-4077
Z5917.S36
SCIENCE FICTION, FANTASY, & HORROR; comprehensive bibliography of books and short fiction published in the English language. 1984. a. price varies. Locus Publications, Box 13305, Oakland, CA 94661. TEL 510-339-9198. FAX 510-399-8144. Eds. Charles N. Brown, William G. Contento. circ. 500. **Document type**: bibliography.
    Former titles: (until 1986): Science Fiction in Print; (until 1985): Science Fiction, Fantasy, and Horror.
    Description: Provides a comprehensive listing of the output in books and magazines for each year by author, title, and subject category.

SENALES; revista bibliografica. see *PUBLISHING AND BOOK TRADE — Abstracting, Bibliographies, Statistics*

800 016   US   ISSN 0360-9774
Z5917.S5
SHORT STORY INDEX; an index to stories in collections and periodicals. 1900. a. (plus 5 yr. cumulation). $90. H.W. Wilson Co., 950 University Ave., Bronx, NY 10452. TEL 800-367-6770. FAX 718-590-1617. TELEX 4990003HWILSON. Ed. Juliette Yaakov. **Document type**: abstracting/indexing.
    ●Also available online. Vendor(s): Wilsonline.

011   UK
TIMES LITERARY SUPPLEMENT INDEX. a. £60. Research Publications International Ltd., P.O. Box 45, Reading RG1 8HF, England. TEL 0734-583247. FAX 0734-591325. (Dist. in the Americas by: Research Publications Inc., 12 Lunar Dr., Drawer AB, Woodbridge, CT 06525. TEL 203-397-2600) **Document type**: abstracting/indexing.
    ●Also available on CD-ROM.

800   DK
UDENLANDSK LITTERATUR I DANSKE FOLKEBIBLIOTEKER. 1972. a. DKK 5044 (incl. supplements). Dansk BiblioteksCenter as, Tempovej 7-11, DK-2750 Ballerup, Denmark. TEL 45-44-97-40-00. FAX 45-44-68-24-42.
    ●Also available online.
    Formerly: Udenlandsk Litteratur i Danske Folkebiblioteker. Skoenlitteratur (ISSN 0106-6641)

830   UK   ISSN 0076-0803
UNIVERSITY OF LONDON. INSTITUTE OF GERMANIC STUDIES. LIBRARY PUBLICATIONS. 1961. irreg. price varies. University of London, Institute of Germanic Studies, 29 Russell Sq., London WC1B 5DP, England. TEL 071-580-2711. FAX 071-436-3497. circ. 300. **Document type**: bibliography.
    Description: Special catalogues and guides relating to the collections of the library of the Institute of Germanic Studies.

016 800   AT   ISSN 0158-3921
VICTORIAN FICTION RESEARCH GUIDES. 1979. irreg. (3-4/yr.). Aus.$40. University of Queensland, Department of English, St. Lucia, Qld. 4072, Australia. TEL 07-365-1442. FAX 07-365-2799. Ed. P.D. Edwards. circ. 100. (back issues avail.) **Indexed**: M.L.A. **Document type**: academic/scholarly publication, monographic series.

810 808.02   US   ISSN 1049-8621
PS129
WHO'S WHO IN WRITERS, EDITORS & POETS IN THE UNITED STATES & CANADA; a biographical directory. biennial, 5th ed., 1994. $97. December Press, Box 302, Highland Park, IL 60035. TEL 708-940-4122. Ed. Curt Johnson. **Document type**: directory.
    Formerly: Who's Who in U S Writers, Editors and Poets (ISSN 0885-4521)
    Description: Gives vital statistics and bibliographies of 10,000 U.S. and Canadian writers, editors and poets.

YEAR'S WORK IN MODERN LANGUAGE STUDIES. see *LINGUISTICS — Abstracting, Bibliographies, Statistics*

ZA CASOPIS: KOVCEZIC. see *LINGUISTICS*

LITERATURE — Adventure And Romance

808.838   IT   ISSN 1120-849X
ACHAB; il corriere dell'avventura. 1990. m. L.50000 (foreign L.120000). Bariletti Editori, Via Paolo Frisi, 9, 00197 Rome, Italy. TEL 06-878931. FAX 06-870628.

808.838   US   ISSN 0739-3881
AFFAIRE DE COEUR; West Coast leading romance publication. 1979. m. $30. Keenan - Snead, Inc., 1555 Washington Ave., San Leandro, CA 94577. TEL 510-357-5665. FAX 510-357-1337. Ed. Louise B. Snead. adv.; bk.rev.; bibl. circ. 115,000. **Document type**: consumer publication.
    Description: Features articles on romance and mystery, including fiction and some non-fiction.

808.838   IT
ALTER-ALTER. 1974. m. L.42000. Rizzoli Editore-Corriere della Sera, Via A. Rizzoli 2, 20132 Milan, Italy. Ed. F. Serra.

808.838   US
ARGOSY (LONG BEACH, 1988); the all-fiction magazine. 1988. q. $15. Richard Kyle Publications, 242 E. Third St., Long Beach, CA 90802-3140. TEL 310-432-5953. Ed. Richard Kyle. adv. contact: D.L. Miles. bk.rev.; illus. circ. 9,500. (back issues avail.)
    Description: Adventure, science fiction and suspense stories in the tradition of the classic pre-WWII all-fiction magazines.

808.838   US   ISSN 1053-3877
PN686.A7
ARTHURIAN YEARBOOK. 1991. a. Garland Publishing, Inc., 1000A Sherman Ave., Hamden, CT 06514.

051   US
AP2
BEST OF SECRETS. 1936. q. Sterling - Macfadden Partnership, 233 Park Ave. S., New York, NY 10003. TEL 212-979-4800. Ed. Claire Clouteir-Le Blanc. adv.
    Formerly: Secrets (ISSN 0037-0649)

056.9   BL   ISSN 0008-5944
CAPRICHO. 1952. m. $90. Editora Abril, S.A., Rua Geraldo Flausino Gomes, 61, 04573-900 Sao Paulo SP, Brazil. TEL 011-534-5344. FAX 011-534-5638. (Subscr. to: Rua do Curtume, 769 CEP 05065-900 Sao Paulo, Brazil. TEL 011-823-9100) Ed. Monica Figueiredo. adv.; bk.rev.; film rev.; music rev.; rec.rev.; video rev.; illus. circ. 250,000. **Document type**: consumer publication.
    Description: For young girls and boys aged 12-18.

056.1   MX
CAPRICHO. 1967. w. Mex.$120($12) Publicaciones Herrerias, S.A., Morelos 16, planta baja, 06040 Mexico D. F., Mexico. TEL 5-512-4903. Ed. Maria Espinosa. adv. circ. 320,000.

808.838   IT
CHARME. m. Edizioni Lancio S.p.A., Via Roccagiovine, 267, 00156 Rome, Italy. TEL 06-411-2651. FAX 06-674-8185. adv.

055.1   IT   ISSN 0009-8426
CLASSICI DEL GIALLO. no.87, 1970. fortn. L.156000 (foreign L.150800). Arnoldo Mondadori Editore S.p.A., Casella Postale 1833, 20101 Milan, Italy. TEL 3199345. Ed. Laura Grimaldi. circ. 1,600.

808   IT
CLASSICO URANIA. 1977. fortn. L.72000 (foreign L.69600). Arnoldo Mondadori Editore S.p.A., Casella Postale 1833, 20101 Milan, Italy. TEL 3199345. Ed. Laura Grimaldi. circ. 10,000.

COMICS INTERVIEW. see *ART*

809.916   US
THE DARK MAN: THE JOURNAL OF ROBERT E. HOWARD STUDIES. 1990. irreg., vol.3, 1993. $5 per no. Necronomicon Press, Box 1304, West Warwick, RI 02893. TEL 401-828-7161. FAX 401-738-6125. Ed. Rusty Burke. bk.rev. (back issues avail.) **Document type**: academic/scholarly publication.
    Description: Covers the life and work of Robert E. Howard, fantasy and horror author, and creator of Conan.

808   IT
DARLING; mensile di fotoromanzi - attualita. vol.8, 1974. m. Edizioni Lancio S.p.A., Via Roccagiovine, 267, 00156 Rome, Italy. TEL 06-411-2651. FAX 06-674-8185. TELEX 622141 LANCIO I. adv.; illus. circ. 235,000.

808.83   GW
EDELWEISS BERG-ROMAN. 1971. w. Zauberkreis Verlag, Karlsruher Str. 22, 76437 Rastatt, Germany. Ed. R. Greiser.

056.1 808.838   MX
ESCANDALO.* 1978. fortn. $47. Corporacion Editorial S.A., Lucio Blanco 435, Col. San Juan Tlihuaca, 02400 Mexico D.F., Mexico. Ed. Javier Ortiz Camorlinga. adv.; film rev, illus. circ. 100,000.

808   GW
FRAGILE; comics handle with care. 1985. q. DM.2. Fragile Comic Group, c/o Michael Hackl, Ed., Stahnsdorferstr. 152a, 14482 Potsdam, Germany. circ. 200. (back issues avail.) **Document type**: consumer publication.

808.838   FR
GALAXIE - BIS. 1962? 24/yr. Societe Nouvelle des Edition Opta, 1 quai de Conti, 75006 Paris, France.

055.1   IT
GRAFFITI.* 1979. m. L.50000($55) Citta Armoniosa, Via Spallanzani 3, 42100 Reggio Emilia, Italy.

LITERATURE — ADVENTURE AND ROMANCE

055.1   IT
GRAND HOTEL. 1946. w. L.91500. Casa Editrice Universo S.p.A., Via M. de Vizzi 35, 20092 Cinisello Balsamo (MI), Italy. Ed. Alberto Tagliati. adv. circ. 450,000.

HEARTLAND CRITIQUES. see *LITERARY AND POLITICAL REVIEWS*

808.838   IT
IDILLIO. m. Edizioni Lancio S.p.A., Via Roccagiovine, 267, 00156 Rome, Italy. TEL 06-411-2651. FAX 06-674-8185. adv.

051   US   ISSN 0020-9813
INTIMATE STORY.* 1948-1982; resumed 1983. m. Charlton Publishers, c/o Miracle Publishing Company, 1275 E. 51 St, Ste. 6H, Brooklyn, NY 11234-2234. TEL 212-868-1210. Ed. Sheila Steinbach. adv. circ. 215,000.

055.1   IT
INVENZIONE.* 1978. m. L.50000($55) Citta Armoniosa, Via Spallanzani 3, 42100 Reggio Emilia, Italy.

ISKATEL. see *CHILDREN AND YOUTH — For*

808.838   IT
KISS. m. Edizioni Lancio S.p.A., Via Roccagiovine, 267, 00156 Rome, Italy. TEL 06-411-2651. FAX 06-674-8185. adv.

808.838   IT
KOLOSSAL. m. Edizioni Lancio S.p.A., Via Roccagiovine, 267, 00156 Rome, Italy. TEL 06-411-2651. FAX 06-674-8185. adv.

808.838   IT
LETIZIA. m. Edizioni Lancio S.p.A., Via Roccagiovine, 267, 00156 Rome, Italy. TEL 06-411-2651. FAX 06-674-8185. adv.

808.838   US   ISSN 1070-8464
▼**LOUIS L'AMOUR WESTERN MAGAZINE.** 1994. bi-m. $14.97 (foreign $19.97). Dell Magazines, 1540 Broadway, New York, NY 10036. TEL 212-354-6500. (Subscr. to: Box 5214, Harlan, IA 51593-4714.. TEL 800-888-0408) Ed. Elana Lore; Pub. Christof Haas-Heye. adv. contact: Fred Sabloff. illus. **Document type:** consumer publication.
  Description: Publishes original Western fiction, reprints classic Spur Award winning stories, interviews and articles on Western-related history and travel.

052   UK
LOVE STORY. m. Argus Specialist Publications Ltd., Argus House, Boundary Way, Hemel Hempstead, Herts. HP2 7ST, England. TEL 0442-66551. FAX 0442-66998. (Subscr. to: Argus Subscription Services, Queensway House, 2 Queensway, Redhill, Surrey, England. TEL 0737-768611) **Document type:** consumer publication.
  Description: Tells stories of love and life.

808.828   UK   ISSN 0262-1118
LOVING. 1970. m. £11.40($36.30) (foreign £17.70). I P C Magazines, Southbank Publishing Group (Subsidiary of: Reed International PLC), King's Reach Tower, Stamford St., London SE1 9LS, England. TEL 071-261-6375. FAX 0444-4406191. TELEX 892084 REEDBP G. (Dist. by: Quadrant Subscription Services, Oakfield House, Perrymount Rd., Haywards Heath, W. Sussex RH16 3DH, England. TEL 0444-440421) Ed. Lorna Read. adv. contact: Nicole Marks. circ. 50,627. **Document type:** consumer publication.
  Incorporates (1987-1990): True Monthly (ISSN 0955-016X)
  Description: Publishes romance fiction and articles on health and beauty topics for a young adult audience.

808.838   IT
LUCKY. m. Edizioni Lancio S.p.A., Via Roccagiovine, 267, 00156 Rome, Italy. TEL 06-411-2651. FAX 06-674-8185. adv.

MANIFEST READER. see *HOMOSEXUALITY*

MANSCAPE. see *HOMOSEXUALITY*

808.838   IT
MARINA. m. Edizioni Lancio S.p.A., Via Roccagiovine, 267, 00156 Rome, Italy. TEL 06-411-2651. FAX 06-674-8185. adv.

MERVEILLES & CONTES/MARVELS & TALES/WUNDER & MAERCHEN/MARAVILLAS & CUENTOS/MERAVIGLIE & RACCONTI. see *FOLKLORE*

808   US   ISSN 0747-1637
MILTON CANIFF'S STEVE CANYON MAGAZINE.* Short title: Steve Canyon Magazine. 1982. q. $40. Kitchen Sink Press, Inc., 320 Riverside Dr., Northampton, MA 01060-2717. TEL 414-295-6922. FAX 414-295-6878. Ed. Peter Poplaski. adv.; bk.rev.; bibl.; charts; illus. circ. 5,000.
  Description: Covers the career of the eighty-year-old active cartoonist. Includes autobiographical material, comic strip reprints & letters.

808.838   DK
MIT LIVS NOVELLE. 1964. 12/yr. DKK 83,75 for 6 mos. Interpresse A-S, Noerregade 7A, DK-1165 Copenhagen K, Denmark. TEL 45-33-33-75-35. FAX 45-33-33-75-05. Ed. Charlotte Weiss. adv. circ. 35,493.

058   SW   ISSN 0345-8083
MITT LIVS NOVELL. med Min Vaerld. 1964. s-w. SEK 548. Semic Press AB, P.O. Box 1074, 172 22 Sundbyberg, Sweden. (Subscr. to: Pressdata AB, P.O. Box 3217, 103 64 Stockholm) Ed. Karin Krausz. circ. 46,200.

051   US   ISSN 0026-8399
MODERN ROMANCES. 1930. m. $14.95. Sterling - Macfadden Partnership, 233 Park Ave. S., New York, NY 10003. TEL 212-979-4800. Ed. Cheryl Clark-King. adv.; illus. (also avail. in microform from MCA)

MUJERES Y MUCHACHA. see *MEN'S INTERESTS*

808.838   US
MYSTERY & ADVENTURE SERIES REVIEW. 1980. s-a. $10 for 4 nos. Fred Woodworth, Ed. & Pub., Box 3488, Tucson, AZ 85722. circ. 700. (back issues avail.)
  Description: Addresses the examination, preservation, and collecting of old juvenile adventure books.

808.838   IT
NOI DUE. m. Edizioni Lancio S.p.A., Via Roccagiovine, 267, 00156 Rome, Italy. TEL 06-411-2651. FAX 06-674-8185. adv.

NOUS DEUX PRESENTE. see *GENERAL INTEREST PERIODICALS — France*

056.1   MX
NOVELA MUSICAL. 1968. w. Mex.$150($15) Publicaciones Herrerias, S.A., Morelos 16, planta baja, 06040 Mexico D.F., Mexico. TEL 5-518-5481. Ed. Maria Espinosa. adv. circ. 300,000.

056.1   MX
NOVELAS DE AMOR. 1960. w. Mex.$3 per no. Publicaciones Herrerias S.A., Morelos 16, planta baja, 06040 Mexico D.F., Mexico. TEL 5-518-5481. Ed. Alicia Ibanez Parkman. adv. circ. 360,000.

808.838   DK   ISSN 0107-5225
NYE VERDENER;* science fiction paa Dansk. 1981. q. DKK 25 per no. Science Fiction Cirklen, Absolonsgade 48, 1658 Copenhagen V, Denmark. illus.

808   UK   ISSN 0955-0135
OH BOY MONTHLY. 1985. m. I P C Magazines, Southbank Publishing Group (Subsidiary of: Reed International PLC), King's Reach Tower, Stamford St., London SE1 9LS, England. TEL 071-261-6375. FAX 0444-440619. TELEX 892084 REEDBP G. (Dist. by: Quadrant Subscription Services, Oakfield House, Perrymount Rd., Haywards Heath, W. Sussex RH16 3DH, England. TEL 0444-440421) Ed. Lorna Read. adv. contact: Nicole Marks. circ. 29,996. **Document type:** consumer publication.
  Incorporates: Photo Love Monthly.

808   US
OMAHA (PRINCETON);* the cat dancer. 1981. bi-m. $15. Kitchen Sink Press, Inc., 320 Riverside Dr., Northampton, MA 01060-2717. TEL 414-295-6922. FAX 414-295-6878. Eds. Reed Waller, Kate Worley. illus. circ. 12,000. (back issues avail; reprint service avail.)

051   US   ISSN 0031-5613
PERSONAL ROMANCES.* 1937-1982; resumed 1983. m. $9. Charlton Publishers, c/o Miracle Publishing Company, 1275 E. 51st St., Ste. 6H, Brooklyn, NY 11234-2234. TEL 212-868-1210. Ed. Sheila Steinbach. adv. circ. 330,000.

808   US
PHOTOROMANCE DARLING.* m. $1.50 per no. Lancio U S A, 55 Maple Ave., Ste. 502, Rockville Center, NY 11570-4267. TEL 212-986-9023. FAX 212-972-9769.

PLOT; il mistero l'avventura la passione. see *LITERATURE — Mystery And Detective*

808   US
PORTENTS.* 1986. 3/yr. $10. 2239 Wilderness, Germantown, TN 38139-5324. Ed. Deb Rasmussen. circ. 350.
  Description: Offers entertaining short stories.

053.1   AU   ISSN 0033-7218
R Z - ILLUSTRIERTE ROMANZEITUNG. 1935. w. S.397. Verlag A. Kirsch, Kaiserstr. 8-10, A-1072 Vienna, Austria. Ed. H. Adfassnig. bk.rev.; film rev.; illus. circ. 59,000.

808.838   IT
RAGAZZA IN. 1979. w. L.700 per no. Lady M, Via Nicotera 24, 00195 Rome, Italy. Ed. Nicola De Feo. adv. circ. 300,000.

808   UK   ISSN 0262-2696
RED LETTER. w. D.C. Thomson & Co. Ltd., Albert Square, Dundee DD1 9QJ, Scotland. **Indexed:** Alt.Press Ind., M.L.A.

052   UK   ISSN 0034-2068
RED STAR WEEKLY. 1929. w. D.C. Thomson & Co. Ltd., Albert Square, Dundee DD1 9QJ, Scotland. adv.

808.838   US
ROBERT E. HOWARD'S FIGHT MAGAZINE. irreg., no.3, 1992. $5.00 per no. Necronomicon Press, Box 1304, West Warwick, RI 02893. TEL 401-828-7161. FAX 401-738-6125.
  Description: Publishes pulp fiction stories.

ROHMER REVIEW. see *LITERATURE*

808.838   US   ISSN 1071-930X
ROMANTIC TIMES MAGAZINE; for readers of romantic and contemporary fiction. 1981. m. $42 (foreign $66) (effective 1993). Romantic Times Publishing Group, 55 Bergen St., Brooklyn, NY 11201. TEL 718-237-1097. FAX 718-624-4231. Ed. Kathryn Falk. adv.; bk.rev. circ. 135,000.
  Incorporates (1986-1991): Rave Reviews.
  Description: Covers romance fiction for readers, writers and booksellers, including publishing industry news and features, profiles of writers, tips for aspiring writers, bookstore news, and reviews of forthcoming books.

056.1   MX   ISSN 0036-0430
RUTAS DE PASION; photo novels. 1965. w. Editorial Mex-Ameris, S.A., Av. Morelos 16, 4o piso, 06040 Mexico, D.F. TEL 5-521-4690. Ed. Dea Maria Revilla. adv.; illus. circ. 115,000.

808   US
SECRETS. 1932. w. D.C. Thomson & Co. Ltd., Albert Square, Dundee DD1 9QJ, Scotland.

808.838   IT
SEGRETISSIMO. 1960. fortn. L.156000 (foreign L.150800). Arnoldo Mondadori Editore S.p.A., Casella Postale 1833, 20101 Milan, Italy. TEL 3199345. Ed. Laura Grimaldi. circ. 12,500.

808.838   US
SHAVERTON. 4/yr. $8. 309 Coghlan St., Vallejo, CA 94590. Ed. Richard Toronto. illus.

808.838   IT
SOGNO. m. Edizioni Lancio S.p.A., Via Roccagiovine, 267, 00156 Rome, Italy. TEL 06-411-2651. FAX 06-674-8185. adv.

STAR WARS COLLECTION TRADING POST. see *HOBBIES*

808.838   US   ISSN 0145-5575
PR6011.R43
THORNDYKE FILE. 1976. s-a. $5. c/o Philip T. Asdell, Ed., R.R. 5, Box 355, Frederick, MD 21701. circ. 100.

LITERATURE — Mystery And Detective

051   US   ISSN 0041-3550
TRUE LOVE. 1931. m. $14.95. Sterling - Macfadden Partnership, 233 Park Ave. S., New York, NY 10003. TEL 212-979-4800. Ed. Cynthia DiMartino. (also avail. in microform from MCA)

808   KE
TRUE LOVE. w. Drum Publications (EA Ltd.), Mutual Bldg., P.O. Box 43372, Kimathi St., Nairobi, Kenya. TEL 23684. Ed. B.B. Garth. circ. 35,000.

808.838   US   ISSN 0199-0020
TRUE ROMANCE. m. $14.95. Sterling - Macfadden Partnership, 233 Park Ave. S., New York, NY 10003. TEL 212-979-4800. Ed. Patricia Byrdsong.

052   UK   ISSN 0262-415X
TRUE ROMANCES. 1934. m. £11.80. Argus Specialist Publications, Ltd., Argus House, Boundary Way, Hemel Hempstead, Herts. HP2 7ST, England. TEL 0442-66551. FAX 0442-66998. (Subscr. to: Argus Subscription Services, Queensway House, 2 Queensway, Redhill, Surrey, England. TEL 0737-768611) Ed. Ann Jaloba. adv.; illus. **Document type:** consumer publication.
   Description: Takes readers to a world of love and romance with which romantics can identify.

052   UK   ISSN 0262-4125
TRUE STORY. 1922. m. £11.80. Argus Specialist Publications Ltd., Argus House, Boundary Way, Hemel Hempstead, Herts. HP2 7ST, England. TEL 0442-66551. FAX 0442-66998. (Subscr. to: Argus Subscription Services, Queensway House, 2 Queensway, Redhill, Surrey, England. TEL 0737-768611) adv.; illus. **Document type:** consumer publication.
   Description: Tells of ordinary people who have faced extraordinary situations and how they coped with these life challenges.

808.838   US   ISSN 0195-3117
TRUE STORY. 1919. m. $14.95 (foreign $19.95). Sterling - Macfadden Partnership, 233 Park Ave. S., New York, NY 10003. TEL 212-979-4800. Ed. Susan Weiner. circ. 750,000.
   Description: Short story romances.

808.838   IT
URANIA. 1952. fortn. L.117000 (foreign L.119600). Arnoldo Mondadori Editore S.p.A., Casella Postale 1833, 20101 Milan, Italy. TEL 3199345. Ed. Laura Grimaldi. circ. 18,000.

808.83   GW   ISSN 0944-6273
WAHRE GESCHICHTEN. 1973. bi-m. DM.3 per no. Verlagsunion Pabel Moewig KG, Karlsruherstr. 31, 76437 Rastatt, Germany. TEL 07222-13-0. FAX 07222-13218. circ. 315,000. **Document type:** consumer publication.

808   JA
WEEKLY NOVELS/SHUKAN SHOSETSU. (Text in Japanese) 1972. fortn. 7200 Yen. Jitsuyo no Nihon Sha, Ltd., 3-9 Ginza, 1-chome, Chuo-ku, Tokyo, Japan. Ed. Nobuyoshi Yoshida.

808.838   US
XENOZOIC TALES. 1987. s-a. $15 for 6 nos. Kitchen Sink Press, Inc., 320 Riverside Dr., Northampton, MA 01060-2717. TEL 414-295-6922. FAX 414-295-6878. Ed. Dave Schreiner. circ. 10,000. (back issues avail.)

808   KO
YADAM & SILHWA. (Text in Korean) 1960. m. 56400 Won. Bupjisa, 30-21 Mukjungdong, Jungku, Seoul, S. Korea. (Subscr. to: Seoul & Records, 3345 N. Clark St., Chicago, IL 60657, U.S.A.) Ed. Kim Jee Wun. illus. circ. 7,000. (also avail. in talking book)

808.03 895.1   CC
ZHONGWAI GUSHI CHUANQI. (Text in Chinese) bi-m. Jiangxi Renmin Chubanshe, Qikan Bu - Jiangxi People's Publishing House, No.5, Xinwei Lu, Nanchang, Jiangxi 330000, People's Republic of China. TEL 333180. Ed. Zhou Rongfang.

LITERATURE — Mystery And Detective

823.912   UK   ISSN 0966-0763
A C D. THE JOURNAL OF THE ARTHUR CONAN DOYLE SOCIETY. 1989. s-a. Arthur Conan Doyle Society, c/o Christopher Roden, Ashcroft, 2 Abbotsford Dr., Penyffordd, Chester CH4 0JG, England. **Document type:** academic/scholarly publication.
   Description: Covers the life and literary works of Sir Arthur Conan Doyle, creator of Sherlock Holmes.

813   US   ISSN 0002-5224
ALFRED HITCHCOCK'S MYSTERY MAGAZINE. 1956. 13/yr. $31.97. Dell Magazines, 1540 Broadway, New York, NY 10036. TEL 212-354-6500. FAX 212-782-8338. (Subscr. to: Box 5124, Harlan, IA 51593-5124. TEL 800-333-3311) Ed. Cathleen Jordan. adv.; B&W page $6090, color page $9890. bk.rev.; film rev.; illus. circ. 245,000. (also avail. in microfilm from UMI) **Indexed:** Amer.Hum.Ind.

813   US   ISSN 0004-217X
PS374.D4
ARMCHAIR DETECTIVE; a quarterly journal of fiction and criticism devoted to the appreciation of mystery, detective and suspense fiction. 1967. q. $26. Otto Pensler, 129 W. 56th St., New York, NY 10019. TEL 212-765-0902. FAX 212-265-5478. Ed. Kate Stine. adv. contact: Jeff Lorber. bk.rev.; film rev.; bibl.; cum.index: vols.1-20. circ. 3,500. (back issues avail.) **Indexed:** Bk.Rev.Ind. (1986-), Child.Bk.Rev.Ind. (1986-), Film Lit.Ind. (1977-), M.L.A. **Document type:** consumer publication.
—CCC.

AUGUST DERLETH SOCIETY. NEWSLETTER. see *LITERATURE*

808.838   US   ISSN 0005-4070
PR4623
BAKER STREET JOURNAL; an irregular quarterly of Sherlockiana. 1946. q. $17.50 (foreign $20). Fordham University Press, University Box L, Bronx, NY 10458-5172. TEL 212-579-2321. FAX 717-633-8900. (Subscr. to: Sheridan Press, 450 Fame Ave., Hanover, PA 17311. TEL 717-632-3535) Ed. Philip A. Shreffler. adv.; bk.rev.; bibl.; illus.; index. circ. 1,600. (also avail. in microform from UMI; back issues avail.; reprint service avail. from UMI) **Indexed:** Abstr.Engl.Stud.; Amer.Hum.Ind., M.L.A.
—BLDSC (1859.980000); Faxon; UnCover. CCC.

808   US
BEST DETECTIVE CASES. bi-m. $1.50 per no. Globe Communications Corp. (New York), 441 Lexington Ave., New York, NY 10017. TEL 800-472-7744.

BOOKS ARE EVERYTHING. see *LITERATURE*

808.838   US
BROWNSTONE MYSTERY GUIDES. 1985. irreg., no.15, 1993. price varies. Brownstone Books (Subsidiary of: Borgo Press), Box 2845, San Bernardino, CA 92406. TEL 909-884-5813. FAX 909-888-4942. Eds. Dale Salwak, Guy M. Townsend. **Document type:** monographic series.
   Formerly: Brownstone Chapbook Series.
   Description: Essays and bibliographies on the mystery writers and themes of our times.

808   US
DETECTIVE CASES. bi-m. Globe Communications Corp. (New York), 441 Lexington Ave., New York, NY 10017. TEL 212-472-4040. Ed. Dominick A. Merle.

808   US
DETECTIVE DRAGNET. bi-m. Globe Communications Corp. (New York), 441 Lexington Ave., New York, NY 10017. TEL 212-472-4040. Ed. Dominick A. Merle.

808   US
DETECTIVE FILES. bi-m. Globe Communications Corp. (New York), 441 Lexington Ave., New York, NY 10017. TEL 800-472-7744. Ed. Dominick A. Merle.

809.916   US   ISSN 0893-0252
PN3448.D4
DROOD REVIEW OF MYSTERY. 1982. bi-m. $20. Jim Huang, Ed. & Pub., Box 50267, Kalamazoo, MI 49005. TEL 616-349-3006. adv.; bk.rev.; index, cum.index; circ. 1,600 (paid). (back issues avail.)
   Description: News and opinion on the latest in mystery, suspense and detective fiction.

808.838   JA
E Q. (Text in Japanese) 1977. bi-m. 3000 Yen. Kobunsha Publishers Co. Ltd., 12-13, 2-chome, Otowa, Bunkyo-ku, Tokyo, Japan. Ed. Hisanori Taniguchi.
   Description: Contains mystery stories.

813   US   ISSN 0013-6328
AP2
ELLERY QUEEN'S MYSTERY MAGAZINE. 1941. 13/yr. $31.97. Dell Magazines, 1540 Broadway, New York, NY 10036. TEL 212-354-6500. FAX 212-782-8338. (Subscr. to: Box 5130, Red Oak, IA 51591-5130. TEL 800-333-3053) Ed. Janet Hutchings. adv.; B&W page $6090, color page $9890. bk.rev.; film rev.; play rev. circ. 230,000. (also avail. in microform from UMI) **Indexed:** Amer.Hum.Ind. **Document type:** consumer publication.

813   US   ISSN 0016-2043
FRONT PAGE DETECTIVE. 7/yr. $12. R G H Publishing Corp., 460 W. 34th St., New York, NY 10001. Ed. Rose Mandelsberg. adv.; illus. **Document type:** consumer publication.

808.838   US   ISSN 0193-533X
PS3537.T733
GAZETTE (NEW YORK). 1979. q. membership. Wolfe Pack, Box 822, Ansonia Sta., New York, NY 10023. Ed. Joel Levy. circ. 500. **Indexed:** Mid.East: Abstr.& Ind.
   Description: Contains material about Nero Wolfe and his creator, Rex Stout.

808.838   IT
GIALLO MONDADORI. 1928. w. L.234000 (foreign L.239200). Arnoldo Mondadori Editore S.p.A., Casella Postale 1833, 20101 Milan, Italy. TEL 3199345. Ed. Laura Grimaldi. circ. 17,500.
   Description: Contains mystery stories.

808.838   US
HARDBOILED. 1988. q. $30 for 6 issues (foreign $36). Gryphon Publications, Box 209, Brooklyn, NY 11228-0209. adv.; bk.rev. circ. 600.
   Formerly: Hardboiled Detective; Which was formed by the merger of: Detective Story Magazine; Hardboiled.
   Description: Publishes original, hard, cutting edge crime fiction and non-fiction by new and professional talent.

808   US
HEADQUARTERS DETECTIVE. bi-m. Globe Communications Corp. (New York), 441 Lexington Ave., New York, NY 10017. TEL 800-472-7744. Ed. Dominick A. Merle.

813   US   ISSN 0020-1847
INSIDE DETECTIVE. 7/yr. $2.50 per issue. R G H Publishing Corp., 460 W. 34th St., New York, NY 10001. Ed. Rose Mandelsberg. adv.; illus. **Document type:** consumer publication.

808.838 057   RU
INTERPOL - MOSKVA. 1991. 12/yr. 10 Rub. P. Severnyi, 1-ya Liniya, d.1, 127204 Moscow, Russia. Ed. Valerii Volodchenko. circ. 250,000.

895.15   CC   ISSN 1001-0459
JINGTAN FENGYUN. (Text in Chinese) 1986. m. Y21.60 (effective 1994). (Fujian Sheng Gong'an Ting - Fujian Provincial Bureau of Public Security) Jingtan Fengyun Publishing House, 12 Hualin Rd., Fuzhou, Fujian 350003, People's Republic of China. TEL 8093034. (Dist. overseas by: Jiangsu Publications Import & Export Corp., 56 Gao Yun Ling, Nanjing, Jiangsu, P.R.C.) Ed. Lin Zhangfu. circ. 250,000. **Document type:** consumer publication.
   Description: Features police stories and foreign detective stories.

058   NO   ISSN 0800-0484
KRIMINAL JOURNALEN.* (Editions in Norwegian and Swedish) 1953. fortn. NOK 400($72) Ernst Poleszynski & Co., P.O. Box 1594 Vika, Oslo 1, Norway. Ed. Dag Loensjoe. adv.; illus. circ. 70,000. (back issues avail.)
—CCC.

LITERATURE — MYSTERY AND DETECTIVE

808.838 US
M W A ANNUAL. 1949. a. membership. Mystery Writers of America, Inc., 17 E. 47th St., 6th fl., New York, NY 10017-1420. TEL 212-888-8171. adv. circ. 3,000.
  Description: Articles and thoughts of various mystery writers in celebration of the Edgar Allan Poe Awards.

808.838 IT
MARTIN MYSTERE. 1982. m. $15. Daim Press, Via Buonarroti 38, 20145 Milan, Italy. TEL 02 46 94 778. Eds. Sergio Bonelli, Alfredo Castelli. circ. 50,000. (back issues avail.)

364.12 US ISSN 0025-5017
AP2
MASTER DETECTIVE. 1929. 7/yr. $2.50 per issue. R G H Publishing Corp., 460 W. 34th St., New York, NY 10001. Ed. Rose Mandelsberg. adv.; bk.rev.; charts; illus.; stat. circ. 175,000. **Document type:** consumer publication.

808.83 AT ISSN 1035-9761
MEAN STREETS. 1990. q. Aus.$25($28) What Goes On Pty. Ltd., 214 Hat Hill Rd., Blackheath, N.S.W. 2785, Australia. TEL 61-47-876049. FAX 61-47-876050. Ed. Stuart Coupe. adv.; bk.rev.; bibl. circ. 6,000. (back issues avail.)
  Description: Covers all areas of crime, mystery and detective fiction, both Australian and international.

808.838 JA
MU. 1979. m. 5880 Yen. Gakken Co. Ltd., 40-5, 4-chome, Kamiikedai, Ohta-ku, Tokyo 145, Japan. Ed. Masao Ota.
  Description: Contains mystery stories.

808.838 371.3 US
▼**MURDER IS ACADEMIC;** the teaching and criticism of crime fiction on campus. 1992. s-a. free. c/o English Department, Hunter College, 695 Park Ave., New York, NY 10021. TEL 212-772-5180. E-mail: BJRHC@CUNYVM.CUNY.EDU. Ed. B.J. Rahn. bk.rev. circ. 800. (tabloid format) **Document type:** academic/scholarly publication, newsletter.
  Description: Offers articles on teaching crime fiction; also contains conference reports for college professors.

808.838 UK ISSN 0963-0473
MURDER MOST FOUL. 1991. q. £6. True Crime Group, P.O. Box 34, Uckfield, E. Sussex, England. TEL 44-0825-761953. FAX 44-0825-768100. Ed. Mike James. adv.: B&W page £1000; trim 190 x 125. circ. 50,000.
  Description: Contains true crime stories from the U.K. and America.

MYSTERY & ADVENTURE SERIES REVIEW. see LITERATURE — Adventure And Romance

808.83 US ISSN 0000-0302
PN3448.D4
MYSTERY & DETECTION ANNUAL.* 1972. a. 152 S. Clark Dr., Beverly Hills, CA 90211. bk.rev. circ. 1,200. **Indexed:** M.L.A.

808.83 US
MYSTERY NOTEBOOK. 1984. irreg. $8.50 per no. Stephen Wright, Ed. & Pub., Box 1341, F.D.R. Sta., New York, NY 10150-1341. bk.rev. circ. 1,000. (back issues avail.)
  Formerly: Stephen Wright's Mystery Notebook (ISSN 0740-8870)
  Description: Essays on specific mysteries and their writers.

808.838 US ISSN 1043-3473
MYSTERY READERS JOURNAL. 1985. q. $22.50 (foreign $35). Mystery Readers International, Box 8116, Berkeley, CA 94707-8116. TEL 510-339-2800. FAX 510-339-8309. Ed. Janet A. Rudolph. bk.rev. circ. 1,500. (back issues avail.) **Document type:** academic/scholarly publication.
  Formerly: Mystery Readers of America Journal.
  Description: Thematic mystery review. Each issue contains articles, interviews, and reviews on a specific theme, as well as special columns, a calendar of events, and other mystery-related material.

808.838 CN ISSN 1192-8700
▼**MYSTERY REVIEW;** a quarterly publication for mystery readers. 1992. q. Can.$21.50($20) C. von Hessert & Associates, P.O. Box 233, Colborne, ON K0K 1S0, Canada. TEL 613-475-4440. FAX 613-475-3400. Ed. Barbara J. Davey. adv. contact: C. von Hessert. bk.rev. circ. 2,000. **Document type:** consumer publication.
  Description: Offers reviews, author interviews, articles of interest to mystery readers.

808.83 US
MYSTERY SCENE. 1985. 6/yr. $35 for 7 nos. (foreign $63.50) (effective 1993). Fedora, Inc., Box 669, Cedar Rapids, IA 52406-0669. TEL 319-363-9868. Ed. Ed Gorman. adv.: B&W page $450; trim 7 1/2 x 9 1/2; adv. contact: Ed Gorman. bk.rev.; bibl.; illus. circ. 8,000. (back issues avail.) **Document type:** trade publication.
  Description: Professional journal for mystery and genre fiction writers, editors and publishers. Includes author interviews, industry news and trends, coverage of recent events and upcoming meetings and conventions.

808.838 US
MYSTERY SCENE PRESS AUTHOR'S CHOICE. 1991. irreg., no.6, 1993. $5.95 per no. Pulphouse Publishing, Inc., Box 1227, Eugene, OR 97440. TEL 503-935-3247. (Co-publisher: Mystery Scene Press) Eds. Martin Greenberg, Ed Gorman; Pub. Dean Wesley Smith.
  Formerly (until 1992): Mystery Scene Author's Choice Monthly.
  Description: Short mystery story collections featuring individual authors.

808.838 JA
MYSTERY STORIES/SHOSETSU SUIRI. (Text in Japanese) 1961. m. 7440 Yen. Futabasha Publishers, 3-28, Higashi-Gokencho, Shinjuku-ku, Tokyo, Japan. Ed. Masaharu Takano.

808.838 US
▼**MYSTERY STREET;** the new wave of crime fiction. 1994. 4/yr. $18. Pulphouse Publishing, Inc., Box 1227, Eugene, OR 97440. TEL 503-935-3247. Ed. Dean Wesley Smith; Pub. Dean Wesley Smith. adv.; illus.
  Description: Crime fiction covering the entire spectrum from police procedural stories, hardboiled, suspense, and thrillers to softboiled and traditional British cozy mysteries.

808.838 US
NEBULOUSFAN.* 1977. irreg., no.10, 1988. (Wing Nuts Wing Club) David Thayer, Ed. & Pub., Box 905, Euless, TX 76039-0905. TEL 817-485-0683. bk.rev.; illus. circ. 200.
  Description: Amateur science fiction humor magazine. Includes fiction, correspondence, humor, criticism, fanzines, cartoons, conventions, art and fun.

808.838 US ISSN 1048-8324
NEW MYSTERY. 1991. q. $37.77. New Mystery Group, 175 Fifth Ave., Ste. 2001, New York, NY 10010-7703. TEL 212-353-1582. FAX 212-353-3495. Ed. Charles Raisch. adv. contact: Linda Wong. bk.rev.; illus. circ. 100,000. (also avail. in microform from UMI) **Document type:** consumer publication.

813 US ISSN 0030-0306
OFFICIAL DETECTIVE STORIES. 1930. 7/yr. $12. R G H Publishing Corp., 460 W. 34th St., New York, NY 10001. Ed. Rose Mandelberg. adv.; bk.rev.; charts; illus.; stat. circ. 265,000. **Document type:** consumer publication.
  Incorporates: Actual Detective.

808 US
P I MAGAZINE; America's private investigation journal. 1988. q. $16. 755 Bronx, Toledo, OH 43609. TEL 419-382-0967. Ed. Bob Mackowiak. illus. circ. 2,000. (back issues avail.)
  Description: Contains stories of real investigators' unsolved cases, investigative techniques, personality profiles and more.

PAPERBACK PARADE. see PUBLISHING AND BOOK TRADE

823.912 UK ISSN 1350-2190
PARISH MAGAZINE - ARTHUR CONAN DOYLE SOCIETY. 1989. s-a. Arthur Conan Doyle Society, c/o Christopher Roden, Ashcroft, 2 Abbotsford Dr., Penyffordd, Chester CH4 0JG, England.

808.838 IT
PLOT; il mistero l'avventura la passione. 1991? bi-m. Via Russo, 42, 40068 San Lazzaro di Savena (BO), Italy. TEL 051-625-52-81. FAX 051-625-79-55. Ed. Massimo Moscati.
  Description: Contains short stories from many genres: horror, love, passion, action, comedy, thriller, detective, adventure, mystery. Includes some criticism.

POE STUDIES ASSOCIATION NEWSLETTER. see LITERATURE

ROHMER REVIEW. see LITERATURE

808.838 US ISSN 1058-8612
SCARLET STREET; the magazine of mystery and horror. 1991. q. $20 (foreign $27). Scarlet Street, Inc., Box 604, Glen Rock, NJ 07452. TEL 201-836-1113. Ed. Richard Valley; Pub. Jesse Lilley. adv.: B&W page $295; trim 8 1/2 x 11; adv. contact: Jill Clarvit. bk.rev. circ. 26,000. **Document type:** consumer publication.
  Description: Covers all mediums: literature, movies, TV, comics and radio.

808.838 US
SERPENTINE MUSE. 1975. q. $10. Adventuresses of Sherlock Holmes, c/o Evelyn Herzog, Man. Ed., 360 W. 21st St., New York, NY 10011. TEL 212-527-7789. Ed. Patricia E. Moran. adv.; bk.rev.; film rev.; play rev.; bibl.; charts; illus.; circ. controlled. (back issues avail.) **Document type:** academic/scholarly publication.
  Formerly: Adventuresses of Sherlock Holmes Newsletter.
  Description: Sherlockiana: scion society of the Baker Street Irregulars.

808.83 UK ISSN 0037-3621
PR4623
SHERLOCK HOLMES JOURNAL. 1952. s-a. £8 (foreign £10). Sherlock Holmes Society of London, c/o Cdr. G.S. Stavert, 3 Outram Rd., Southsea, Hants. PO5 1QP, England. TEL 0705-812104. Ed. N. Utechin. bk.rev.; illus.; cum.index every 2 yrs. circ. 1,600. **Document type:** consumer publication.
  —Faxon; UnCover.

808.838 US ISSN 1040-4937
SHERLOCKIAN TIDBITS. 1987. q. $4. 42 Melrose Pl., Montclair, NJ 07042. Ed. Arnold Korotkin. bk.rev. circ. 221. (back issues avail.) **Document type:** newsletter.
  Description: Covers items of interest pertaining to the adventures, life and times of Sherlock Holmes.

808.838 US
SLEUTH JOURNAL.* 1983. irreg. (2-4/yr.). $28 for 4 issues. Baker Street Publications, Box 517, Metairie, LA 70004-0517. TEL 504-734-8414. Ed. Sharida Rizzuto. circ. 10,000.

808.838 US
SOUTH OF THE MOON. 1968. a. $5 (effective Jan. 1991). American Private Press Association, 562 N. First Ave., Stayton, OR 97383. TEL 503-769-6122. FAX 503-769-4520. Ed. M. Horvat. bk.rev.; film rev. circ. 750.
  Description: Contains a listing of press associations which concentrate on different genres including mystery and detective, science fiction, fantasy, and horror.

813 US ISSN 0038-996X
STARTLING DETECTIVE. 1929. bi-m. $7.20 for 12 nos. Globe Communications Corp. (New York), 441 Lexington Ave., New York, NY 10017. TEL 800-472-7744. Ed. Dominick A. Merle. adv.; illus.

813 US ISSN 0040-6139
THIRD DEGREE (NEW YORK). 1946. m. $65 membership. Mystery Writers of America, Inc., 17 E. 47th St., 6th fl., New York, NY 10017-1420. TEL 212-888-8171. circ. 2,500.

LITERATURE — POETRY

808.838   **US**   **ISSN 0041-3488**
TRUE CONFESSIONS. 1922. m. $14.95. Sterling - Macfadden Partnership, 233 Park Ave. S., New York, NY 10003. TEL 212-979-4800. Ed. Jean Sherbel. adv.; illus. (also avail. in microform from MCA)

808.838   **US**   **ISSN 0041-350X**
TRUE DETECTIVE. 1924. 7/yr. $12. R G H Publishing Corp., 460 W. 34th St., New York, NY 10001. Ed. Rose Mandelsberg. adv.; bk.rev.; charts; illus.; stat. circ. 250,000. **Document type:** consumer publication.

808.838   **US**   **ISSN 0199-0012**
TRUE EXPERIENCE. 1925. m. $14.95. Sterling - Macfadden Partnership, 233 Park Ave. S., New York, NY 10003. TEL 212-979-4800. (Subscr. to: Box 10015, Des Moines, IA 50340) Ed. Jean Wallace.

TRUE POLICE CASES. see CRIMINOLOGY AND LAW ENFORCEMENT

813   **US**   **ISSN 0042-4129**
VERMISSA HERALD;* a journal of Sherlockian affairs. 1967. q. $2. Scowrers & Molly Maguires of San Francisco, 4712 17th St., San Francisco, CA 94117. Ed. William A. Berner. adv.; bk.rev.; bibl. circ. 200.

808.838 820   **UK**
WINTER'S CRIMES. a. MacMillan Press Ltd, Houndmills, Basingstoke, Hants RG2 2XS, England. TEL 0256-29242. FAX 0256-28339. **Document type:** consumer publication.

813.5   **US**   **ISSN 0741-0212**
PZ1
THE YEAR'S BEST MYSTERY AND SUSPENSE STORIES.* 1945. a. $21.95 (effective 1992). Walker & Co., 435 Hudson St., New York, NY 10014-3941. TEL 212-727-8300. FAX 212-727-0984. Ed. Edward D. Hoch.
    Formerly (until 1982): Best Detective Stories of the Year (ISSN 0067-625X)
    Description: Collects outstanding short mystery and suspense stories and novellas from mystery magazines and anthologies.

LITERATURE — Poetry

700   **AG**   **ISSN 0002-4090**
A L A; organo de fomento cultural y de circulacion internacional. vol.11, 1975. q. $10. Conesa 1330, Buenos Aires, Argentina. Dir. Mercedes Fernandez Zalazar. illus. **Indexed:** E.I.

808.81   **US**   **ISSN 0734-7618**
A M S ARS POETICA. 1983. irreg., no.5, 1989. price varies. (Abrahams Magazine Service) A M S Press, Inc., 56 E. 13th St., New York, NY 10003. TEL 212-777-4700. FAX 212-995-5413. (back issues avail.)
    —BLDSC (0859.497000).
    Description: Series of monographs, bibliographies and reference works devoted to particular topics in literature and poetry.

841 800   **FR**
A R P A CAHIERS DE RECHERCHE POETIQUE. 1977. q. 170 Fr.($20) Association de Recherche Poetique en Auvergne, 11 rue Sarrail, 63000 Clermont-Ferrand, France. circ. 500. (back issues avail.)

811   **US**
A VOICE WITHOUT SIDES. 1987. irreg. (approx. 1/yr.). $5 (effective 1993). 875 Central Pkwy., Schenectady, NY 12309-6005. Ed. Geoffrey A. Huth. circ. 30.
    Description: Publishes short avant-garde poetry and visual arts in strange formats.

808.81   **US**   **ISSN 0886-4047**
ABACUS (ELMWOOD). 1984. 8/yr. $26 (effective 1994). Potes & Poets Press, Inc., 181 Edgemont Ave., Elmwood, CT 06110. TEL 203-233-2023. Ed. Peter Ganick. circ. 150. (back issues avail.) **Indexed:** Avery Ind.Archit.Per.
    Description: Experimental and language-centered poetry.

811   **US**
ABBEY; the journal of literary brouhaha. 1970. q. $2. (South Canada Broccoli Federation) White Urp Press, 5360 Fallriver Row Ct., Columbia, MD 21044. Ed. David Greisman. adv.; bk.rev.; play rev.; bibl.; illus.; circ. 200 (controlled).
    Formerly: Hagerstown Cheeseburger Monthly.

811   **US**   **ISSN 0361-1663**
PS325
ABRAXAS. 1968. irreg. $16 (foreign $20). Abraxas Press, Inc., 2518 Gregory St., Madison, WI 53711. TEL 608-238-0175. Ed. Ingrid Swanberg. adv. contact: W.D. Markhardt. bk.rev.; cum.index: 1968-1982. circ. 600. (back issues avail.) **Indexed:** Amer.Hum.Ind.
    Description: Independent, contemporary, small press journal publishing poetry and poetry in translation.

808.81   **UK**   **ISSN 0143-7488**
ACADEMUS POETRY MAGAZINE. 1979. s-a. 38 Courtenay St., Cheltenham, Glos. GL5 4LR, England.

810   **US**
ACADEMY OF AMERICAN POETS. LAMONT POETRY SELECTION AND WALT WHITMAN SELECTION. 1954. a. $45. Academy of American Poets, 584 Broadway, Apt. 1208, New York, NY 10012-3250. **Document type:** bulletin.
    Formerly: Academy of American Poets. Lamont Poetry Selections (ISSN 0515-2003)
    Description: Introduces the winner of the Walt Whitman award, which is an annual first book selection of a previously unpublished poet. The Lamont Poetry Selection is an annual second book award.

L'ACERBA; periodico di tecnica (artistica, letteraria, libraria) culturale. see LITERATURE

861   **MX**   **ISSN 0185-3082**
ACTA POETICA. 1979. a. price varies. Universidad Nacional Autonoma de Mexico, Instituto de Investigaciones Filologicas, Ciudad Universitaria, C.P. 04510, Mexico 21 D.F., Mexico.

841   **FR**   **ISSN 0001-7477**
ACTION POETIQUE. 1950. q. 200 F. (foreign 300 F.). Editions Action Poetique, La Fontaine au Bois Pav. 2, 25 rue J. Mermoz, 77210 Avon, France. Ed. Henri Deluy. adv.; bk.rev.; illus. circ. 2,000.

821   **UK**   **ISSN 0964-0304**
ACUMEN MAGAZINE. 1985. s-a. £5.50($25) (Europe and U.S. £8). 6 The Mount, Higher Furzeham, Brixham, S. Devon TQ5 8QY, England. TEL 0803-851098. Ed. Patricia Oxley. adv.; bk.rev.; circ. 700. (back issues avail.)
    Description: Contains poetry, articles about poetry, and interviews with poets.

ADVOCATE (PRATTSVILLE). see LITERATURE

808.81 700   **US**   **ISSN 0894-2633**
AERIAL. 1985. a. $30 for 3 nos. Edge Books, Box 25642, Washington, DC 20007. TEL 202-333-1544. Ed. Rod Smith. adv.; bk.rev.; bibl. circ. 1,000. (back issues avail.)
    Formerly: Ariel.

811   **US**
AERIE. vol.4, 1974. a. $4.50. University of Southern Indiana, Publication Department, 8600 University Blvd., Evansville, IN 47712. TEL 812-464-1954. FAX 812-464-1960. illus.
    Formerly (until 1979): Moving Finger.

821   **UK**   **ISSN 0002-0796**
AGENDA. 1959. q. £18 to individuals (overseas £20; US $44); libraries and institutions £24 (overseas £26; US $54). Agenda & Editions Charitable Trust, 5 Cranbourne Court, Albert Bridge Rd., London SW11 4PE, England. TEL 44-71-228 0700. Ed. William Cookson. adv.; bk.rev. circ. 2,000. (also avail. in microfilm from UMI) **Indexed:** Abstr.Engl.Stud., Br.Hum.Ind., Geo.Abstr., M.L.A., So.Pac.Per.Ind.
    —BLDSC (0736.242500); UnCover; UMI.

811   **US**
AHSAHTA. 1975. 3/yr. $6.95 per no. Boise State University, Department of English, 1910 University Dr., Boise, ID 83725. TEL 208-385-1246. FAX 208-385-4373. Ed. Tom Trusky. circ. 500.

800 700 770   **US**
AILERON; a literary journal. 1980. a. $15 for 4 nos. Aileron Press, Box 891, Austin, TX 78767-0891. Ed. Ric Williams. circ. 200.
    Description: Poetry with occasional short fiction.

AIREINGS. see LITERATURE

891.43   **II**   **ISSN 0970-096X**
AKAVITA. (Text in Hindi) q. Rs.40($12) Samkaleen Prakashan, 2762 Rajguru Marg, New Delhi 110 055, India. Ed. Krishan Khullar.

831   **GW**   **ISSN 0002-3957**
PT1141.A2
AKZENTE; Zeitschrift fuer Literatur. 1954. bi-m. DM.55.80. Carl Hanser Verlag, Kolbergerstr. 22, 81679 Munich, Germany. TEL 089-998300. FAX 089-984809. (Subscr. to: Postfach 860420, 81631 Munich, Germany) Ed. Michael Krueger. adv.; bk.rev.; index. circ. 4,500. **Indexed:** Arts & Hum.Cit.Ind., Curr.Cont., M.L.A. **Document type:** academic/scholarly publication.
    —Faxon; UnCover; SWETS. CCC.

811   **US**
ALABAMA DOGSHOE MOUSTACHE. 1987. irreg., no.14, 1994. $10. D B Q P, 875 Central Pkwy., Schenectady, NY 12309-6005. Ed. Geof Huth. circ. 100.
    Description: Publishes linquistically daring poetry.

841   **FR**   **ISSN 0294-7749**
ALBATROS. 1978. q. 180 F. (foreign 190 F.) (effective 1991). Academie des Poetes Classiques de France, 40 rue de Bretagne, 75003 Paris, France. Ed. Jean Murail. bk.rev.
    Description: French, and occasionally English modern poetry in the classical form.

811   **US**
ALBATROSS.* 1986. 2/yr. $5. Anabiosis Press, Box 7787, North Port, FL 34287-0787. Eds. Richard Smyth, Richard Brobst. circ. 500.
    Description: Publishes free-style, narrative poetry on environment and nature.

811   **US**
ALDEBARAN. 1971. s-a. $10. c/o Roger Williams University, Old Ferry Rd., Bristol, RI 02809. TEL 401-253-1040. Ed. Quantella Owens. adv.; illus. circ. 200. (back issues avail.)

811   **US**   **ISSN 0002-5089**
PS615
ALDEBARAN REVIEW. 1968. 3/yr. $8. 2209 California, Berkeley, CA 94703. Ed. John Oliver Simon. circ. 1,000. **Indexed:** Access.

821   **UK**   **ISSN 0140-5136**
ALEMBIC. 1973. irreg. $20 for 2 nos. 88 Ashburnham Rd., London NW10 5SE, England. Ed. Robert Hampson. adv.; bk.rev.; bibl. circ. 200. (back issues avail.)

808.81   **UA**
ALIF; journal of comparative poetics. (Text in Arabic, English; occasionally in French) 1981. a. $15 to individuals; institutions $30. American University in Cairo, Department of English and Comparative Literature, P.O. Box 2511, Cairo, Egypt. FAX 355-7565. TELEX 92224 AUCAI UN. Ed. Ferial Ghazoul. adv. circ. 500. (back issues avail.) **Indexed:** Mid.East: Abstr.& Ind. **Document type:** academic/scholarly publication.
    Description: Each issue focuses on a specific theme; responses are articulated by writers in different disciplines and cultures.

851   **IT**
ALIGHIERI. s-a. Piazza Sonnino, 5, Rome, Italy. Ed. A. Vallone. **Indexed:** M.L.A.

ALL AREA. see ART

811   **US**
ALL AVAILABLE LIGHT. 1989. 2/yr. $6. McOne Press, Box 50174, Austin, TX 78763. Ed. Jason Freeman. circ. 200.
    Description: Publishes poems that don't shout their spiritual content, but whisper through language, sound and rhythm.

821   **UK**
ALL IN; wallstickers. (Poster format) 1968. s-a. £1. c/o Nina Steane, Ed., 31 Headlands, Kettering, Northants., England. circ. 50.

LITERATURE — POETRY

831 053   GW   ISSN 0720-3098
PT1141.A2
ALLMENDE. 1981. q. DM.53. Edition Isele, Heidelstr. 9, 79805 Eggingen, Germany. TEL 07746-1418. FAX 07746-2387. Ed.Bd. adv.; index. circ. 1,000. (back issues avail.) **Document type:** consumer publication.

811 780   US
THE ALTERED MIND. 1989. 6/yr. $8. Box 1083, Claremont, CA 91711. TEL 714-949-9531. circ. 800.

811 700   US
ALTERNATIVE PRESS.* 1969. 3/yr. $15. 1207 Henry St., Ann Arbor, MI 48104-4340. Eds. Ann Mikolowski, Ken Mikolowski.

811   US
AMANITA BRANDY. 1980. irreg., no.3, 1992. $6 for 4 nos. ($8 outside U.S.). W. Paul Ganley: Publisher, Box 149, Buffalo, NY 14226-0149. TEL 716-839-2415. circ. 150. (back issues avail.) **Description:** Original fantasy poetry.

811   US
AMERICAN COLLEGIATE POETS. 1975. 2/yr. $12.50. International Publications, Box 44044-L, Los Angeles, CA 90044. TEL 213-755-1814. circ. 500.

808   US   ISSN 1051-5062
PS536.2
AMERICAN LITERARY REVIEW. 1990. s-a. $15. University of North Texas, Box 13615, Denton, TX 76203. TEL 817-565-2271. FAX 817-369-8770. Eds. Scott Cairns, Barb Rodman. adv. circ. 800. **Description:** Publishes previously unpublished poems and short stories in English, representative of all states and both American continents.

AMERICAN OXONIAN. see *LITERARY AND POLITICAL REVIEWS*

800   US   ISSN 0360-3709
PS580
AMERICAN POETRY REVIEW (PHILADELPHIA). 1972. bi-m. $15. World Poetry, Inc., 1721 Walnut St., Philadelphia, PA 19103. TEL 215-496-0439. Ed. David Bonanno. adv.: B&W page $750. bk.rev.; play rev.; illus. circ. 24,000. (tabloid format; also avail. in microfilm from UMI; reprint service avail. from UMI) **Indexed:** A.I.P.P., Amer.Hum.Ind., Arts & Hum.Cit.Ind., Bk.Rev.Ind. (1976-), Child.Bk.Rev.Ind. (1976-), Curr.Cont., Ind.Bk.Rev.Hum., M.L.A., New Per.Ind. —Faxon; SWETS; UMI.

811   US
AMERICAN POETRY SERIES. 1973. irreg. price varies. Ecco Press Ltd., 100 W. Broad St., Hopewell, NJ 08525. TEL 609-466-4748. FAX 609-466-4706.

811   US   ISSN 1057-7998
AMERICAS REVIEW (BERKELEY). 1985. a. $4 to individuals; institutions $6. Box 7681, Berkeley, CA 94707. TEL 510-845-2089. Ed. Gerald Gray. circ. 1,000. **Description:** Publishes poems of a social or political nature. Also sponsors a contest.

821   UK   ISSN 0951-2500
AMMONITE. 1986. irreg. £3.50. Ammonite Publications, 12 Priory Mead, Bruton, Somerset BA10 0DZ, England. TEL 813349. Ed. John Howard Greaves. adv.; bk.rev. circ. 200. (back issues avail.) **Document type:** consumer publication. **Description:** Contains poetry, prose and artwork relating to mythology, science and speculative fiction.

808.81   US
THE AND REVIEW. 1989. 2/yr. $5. 10485 Iams Rd., Plain City, OH 43064. bk.rev.

811   US
ANIMAL TALES. 1989. 6/yr. $19.95. Pet Publications, Box 2220, Payson, AZ 85547-2220. TEL 602-246-7144. Ed. Berta I. Cellers. circ. 400.

808.81   US
▼**ANTERIOR POETRY MONTHLY.** 1993. 12/yr. $15. Anterior Bitewing Ltd., 7735 Brand Ave., St. Louis, MO 63135-2172. TEL 314-522-6166. Ed. Tom Bergeron.

811   US   ISSN 0196-2221
PN6099.6
ANTHOLOGY OF MAGAZINE VERSE AND YEARBOOK OF AMERICAN POETRY. 1980. a. $37.50. Monitor Book Co., Inc., Box 9078, Palm Springs, CA 92263. TEL 619-323-2270. Ed. Alan F. Pater. **Indexed:** Child.Auth.& Illus. **Document type:** monographic series.
    Formerly: Anthology of Magazine Verse (ISSN 0270-3904)
    Description: Preserves the choicest poetry of the year selected from magazines across the United States and Canada.

811   US
ANTI-ISOLATION;* new arts in Wisconsin. 1984. irreg. R.R. 1, Box 131, La Farge, WI 54639-9601. Eds. Miekal and Elizabeth Was. circ. 1,000. **Description:** Seeks innovative poetry, audio and visual arts.

ANTIETAM REVIEW. see *LITERATURE*

861   AG
ANTOLOGIA POETICA DEL PARTIDO DE ESTEBAN ECHEVERRIA. 1979. a. Arg.$10000. (Asociacion de Artes y Letras de Esteban Echeverria) Ediciones Agon, Charcas 3918, 1425 Buenos Aires, Argentina. Dir. Maria E. Dubecq.

849.9   SP   ISSN 1130-202X
ANUARI VERDAGUER; estudis textos ressenyes bibliografia cronica. (Text in Catalan) 1987. a. 2500 ptas. (effective 1994). (Escola Universitaria di Mestres d'Osona) E U M O Editorial, S.A., C. de Miramarges 4, 08500 Vic, Spain. TEL 93-8861044. FAX 3-8891063. Ed.Bd. bk.rev. **Document type:** academic/scholarly publication.

861   MX
ANUARIO DE POESIA. 1989. a. Instituto Nacional de Bellas Artes, Av. Hidalgo 1, 06050 Mexico, D.F., Mexico. Ed. Mario del Valle. circ. 2,000.

861   CK
AQUARIMANTIMA. 1973. irreg. Apdo. Aereo 3845, Medellin, Colombia.

861   AG
AQUARIO; revista internacional de poesia. 1977. irreg. $2.50. Aquario, Paraguay 647, Buenos Aires, Argentina. Eds. Sergio Chaves, Sigfrido Radaelli.

821   UK   ISSN 0003-7303
PR1170
AQUARIUS; poetry magazine. 1968. q. £5($70) c/o Eddie S. Linden, Ed., 116 Sutherland Ave., Flat 10 - Rm. A, London W.9., England. TEL 071-289-4338. adv.; bk.rev. circ. 3,000. **Document type:** academic/scholarly publication. **Description:** Each issue focuses on one of England's great poets.

811   US
AQUATERRA, WATER CONCEPTS FOR THE ECOLOGICAL SOCIETY. 1986. a. $10. Route 7, Box 720, Eureka Springs, AR 72632. TEL 501-253-9431. Pub. Barbara Harmony. circ. 3,000. **Description:** Publishes poems other materials on the theme of water and water related subjects.

811   US
ARACHNE. 1979. q. $18 to individuals; institutions $20. Arachne, Inc., 162 Sturges St., Jamestown, NY 14701. Ed. Susan L. Leach. bk.rev. circ. 500. (back issues avail.) **Document type:** bulletin.

450   GW
ARCHIVIO TEMATICO DELLA LIRICA ITALIANA. 1991. irreg., no.2, 1994. Georg Olms Verlag, Hagentorwall 7, 31134 Hildesheim, Germany. TEL 05121-1501-0. FAX 05121-150150. (U.S. subscr. to: 111 W. 57th St., New York, NY 10019. TEL 212-757-5237) Ed.Bd. **Document type:** monographic series.

808.1   FR   ISSN 0066-734X
ARGUS DE LA POESIE FRANCAISE.* 1971. irreg. 30 F. Association Poesie Vivante France, B.P.8, 01210 Ferney-Voltaire, France.

811   US
THE ARK (CAMBRIDGE). 1970. a. $5. Ark, 35 Highland Ave., Cambridge, MA 02139-1015. TEL 617-547-0852. Ed. Geoffrey Gardner. circ. 1,500. **Description:** Publishes poems including translations.

ARSENAL; surrealist subversion. see *ART*

ARSENALE; trimestrale di letteratura. see *LITERATURE*

ART AND POETRY TODAY. see *ART*

ART ET POESIE. see *ART*

808.81 700
ARTEMIS - ARTISTS AND WRITERS;* artists and writers from the Blue Ridge Mountains. 1977. a. $8. Artemis - Artists and Writers, Inc., Box 21281, Roanoke, VA 24018-0130. TEL 703-774-8440. FAX 703-344-7485. Ed.Bd. circ. 1,200.
    Formerly: Artemis.

811   US
ASH. 1989. 4/yr. $4. 121 Gregory Ave., No. B-7, Passaic, NJ 07055. TEL 201-471-8378. circ. 125.

861 460   US   ISSN 0277-6782
ASOCIACION DE HISPANISTAS DE LAS AMERICAS. PUBLICACIONES. COLECCION MONOGRAFIAS. (Text in English, Spanish) 1981. irreg., no.4, 1992. $5. Asociacion de Hispanistas de las Americas, 3600 S.W. 9th Terrace, Apt. 4, Miami, FL 33135. Ed. Gladys Zaldivar. circ. 500. **Document type:** monographic series.

808.81   US
ASYLUM ANNUAL. 1985. a. $10 to individuals (foreign $12); institutions $15 (foreign $17). Asylum Arts Publishing, Box 6203, Santa Maria, CA 93456. TEL 805-928-8774. Ed. Greg Boyd. adv.; bk.rev. circ. 2,000. **Document type:** consumer publication.
    Formerly: Asylum (ISSN 0896-1344)
    Description: Publishes original short stories and poetry, with an emphasis on dream, dada, surrealism.

811   US
AVALON DISPATCH. irreg. (3-4/yr.). membership. (Avalon Poets) Vernon Payne, Ed. & Pub., 212 W. First St., San Angelo, TX 76901. circ. 500.

861   VE   ISSN 0005-2426
AXIAL.* revista de poesia. 1966. q. Bs.1($1) (Grupo Literario Axial) Editorial Axial, Apartado Postal 62, Merida, Venezuela. Ed. Lubio Cardozo. bk.rev.; bibl.; illus.; circ. 1,000 (controlled).

B-CITY. see *LITERATURE*

811 808.87   US
BABY SUE. 1985. 2/yr. $8. Box 1111, Decatur, GA 30031-1111. TEL 404-875-8951. Ed. Don W. Seven. music rev. circ. 5,000. **Document type:** consumer publication.
    Description: Contains humor and social satires.

808. 780 320   US
BABYFISH LOST ITS MOMMA. q.? $3 per no. Box 11589, Detroit, MI 48211.
    Description: Covers poetry, music and politics.

808.81   US
BACKBOARD. 1976. irreg. free. Backspace Ink, 1131 Galvez Dr., Pacifica, CA 94044. TEL 415-355-4640. Ed. Joanne Shwed. circ. 200. (back issues avail.) **Document type:** newsletter.

BAD HAIRCUT. see *POLITICAL SCIENCE*

811   US
BAD HENRY REVIEW. 1981. s-a. $10. 44 Press, 69 W. Ninth St., Apt. 12-B, New York, NY 10011. FAX 212-473-5144. Ed.Bd. adv.; bk.rev. circ. 750.

811   SP
BAHIA; pliegos poeticos del campo de Gibraltar. 1967. 8/yr. 375 ptas. Ediciones Bahia, Fray Bartolome Bloque 1, 6-A, Algeciras, Cadiz, Spain. Dir. Manuel Fernandez Mota. bibl. circ. 500.

LITERATURE — POETRY

750 700   US   ISSN 1052-3154
BAKUNIN. 1990. s-a. $8 to individuals; institutions and foreign $10. Box 1853, Simi Valley, CA 93062-1853. TEL 805-526-8900. Ed. Jordan Jones. adv.; bk.rev.; illus.
   Description: Focuses on social and sexual criticism, surrealism, and humor. Includes poetry, fiction, art, essays, plays, and reviews.

811   CN   ISSN 0005-4399
BALLSOUT.* 1969. $3. Pendejo Press, 3358 W. First Ave., Vancouver, B.C., Canada. Ed. Bertram Maird. illus.

811   CN
BARBIZON MAGAZINE. 1983. 8/yr. $15. Barbizon House, R.R. 1, Lumby, B.C. V0E 2G0, Canada. TEL 604-547-6621. circ. 2,500.

BARE NIBS. see *THEATER*

808.1   US   ISSN 1063-0929
BARNWOOD. 1980. irreg. (3-4/yr.). $6 for 3 nos. (Barnwood Press Cooperative, Inc.) Barnwood Press, Box 146, Selma, IN 47383-0146. bk.rev. circ. 500.

811   US
BASEBALL: OUR WAY. 1984. 10/yr. $9. Our Way Publications, 5014 Starker Ave., Madison, WI 53716. TEL 608-241-0549. Ed. Dale Jellings. circ. 50.

808.81   US
▼**BE SOMEBODY, BE YOURSELF LETTER;** greetings update. 1992. a. $5 (Canada $7; elsewhere $8). Continnuus, c/o Prosperity & Profits Unlimited, Box 416, Denver, CO 80201-0416. TEL 303-575-5676. Ed.Bd. **Document type:** newsletter.

808.81   US   ISSN 1053-6531
BE SOMEBODY, BE YOURSELF POETRY NEWSLETTER. 1990. a. $2. Continnuus, c/o Prosperity & Profits Unlimited, Box 416, Denver, CO 80201-0416. TEL 303-575-5676. Ed. A Doyle. circ. 1,999. (looseleaf format; also avail. in audio cassette) **Document type:** newsletter.
   Description: Includes self-improvement, motivational, self-direction poetry.

811   US
BEAR CREEK HAIKU. 1991. m. $10. 1177B Bear Mountain Dr., Boulder, CO 80303. TEL 303-494-4868. Ed. Dary Nielsen. circ. 175.

821   UK
BEAT SCENE. 1988. 7/yr. $24 for 4 issues. Beat Scene Press, 27 Court Leet, Binley Woods, Coventry, Warwickshire CV3 2JO, England. TEL 0202-543604. circ. 200.

811   US   ISSN 0005-8661
PS301
BELOIT POETRY JOURNAL. (Supplement avail.: Beloit Poetry Journal. Chapbook) 1950. q. $12 to individuals; institutions $18. Beloit Poetry Journal Foundation, Inc., Box 154, R.F.D. 2, Ellsworth, ME 04605. TEL 207-667-5598. Ed. Marion K. Stocking. bk.rev.; cum.index: 1950-1975. circ. 1,800. (back issues avail.) **Indexed:** Amer.Hum.Ind., Arts & Hum.Cit.Ind., Curr.Cont., Ind.Amer.Per.Verse, Ind.Little Mag.
—Faxon.
   Description: Introduces strong new writers. Includes occasional chapbooks.

811   US   ISSN 0067-5695
BELOIT POETRY JOURNAL. CHAPBOOK. (Included in Beloit Poetry Journal) 1951. irreg., vol.40, 1990 (approx. biennial). $5. Beloit Poetry Journal Foundation, Inc., Box 154, R.F.D. 2, Ellsworth, ME 04605. TEL 207-667-5598. Ed. Marion K. Stocking. circ. 1,800. **Indexed:** Amer.Hum.Ind., Ind.Amer.Per.Verse.

808.81   II
BENGALI INTERNATIONAL.* (Text in English) 1972. bi-m. 107-2 Raja Rammohan Sarani, Calcutta 9, India. Ed. Samir De. adv.

861   BL
BIBLIOTECA ALFA-OMEGA DE POESIA BRASILEIRA: SERIE 1. 1983. irreg. Editora Alfa-Omega, Rua Lisboa, 489, 05413 Sao Paulo, Brazil. TEL (011) 852-6400. TELEX 22888XPSP BR.

BIM. see *LITERATURE*

808.81   US   ISSN 1047-2258
BIRMINGHAM POETRY REVIEW. 1988. 2/yr. $3. English Department, University of Alabama, Birmingham, AL 35294. TEL 205-934-8573. FAX 205-934-4250. Ed. Robert Collins. circ. 600. (back issues avail.)

808.81 700   US   ISSN 8756-0666
BLACK BEAR REVIEW. 1985. s-a. $10. Black Bear Publications, 1916 Lincoln St., Croydon, PA 19021-8026. Eds. Ave Jeanne, Ron Zettlemoyer. adv.; bk.rev.; bibl.; illus. circ. 550.
   Description: Contains poetry, art, and poetry book reviews.

811   US
BLACK BUZZARD REVIEW. 1988. a. $6. Black Buzzard Press, 1110 Seaton La., Falls Church, VA 22046. Ed. Bradley R. Strahan. circ. 300.
   Description: Publishes all types of poetry except typographical poems.

811   US
BLACK JACK & VALLEY GRAPEVINE. 1973. a. $6.75 per no. Seven Buffaloes Press, Box 249, Big Timber, MT 59011. Ed. Art Cuelho. circ. 750.
   Description: Publishes rural poetry, farm and ranch, especially material from the Southern Appalachian region.

811   US
BLACK RIVER REVIEW. 1985. a. $4. 855 Mildred, Lorain, OH 44055-1213. TEL 216-244-9654. Eds. Kaye Coller, Deborah S. Glaefke. adv.; bk.rev. circ. 400.

819   CN   ISSN 0045-2270
BLACKFISH.* 1971. 3/yr. $2. 1851 Moore St., Burnaby 2, B.C., Canada. Eds. B.T. Brett, Allan Safarik. illus.

808.81 700   US   ISSN 0888-529X
BLADES;* a tiny magazine. (Text in English, Portuguese, Spanish) 1977. 3/yr. $2. Poporo Press, 182 Orchard Rd., Newark, DE 19711-5208. Eds. JoAnn Balingit, Francis Poole. circ. 175. (back issues avail.)
   Description: Presents poetry written in the language submitted.

811   US   ISSN 1067-1005
BLANK GUN SILENCER; words and images for the hyperactive Nihilist. 1991. 2/yr. $8. B G S Press, 1240 William St., Racine, WI 53402. TEL 414-639-2406. Ed. Dan Nielsen. bk.rev. circ. 300. (back issues avail.)
   Description: Publishes concise, tight and startling poems from Buk-heads to post-Dada freaks.

808.81   US   ISSN 0737-9269
PS615
BLIND ALLEYS; a journal of contemporary poetry. 1982. s-a. $11 to individuals; institutions $13. 7th Son Press, Rutgers University, Box 29, Camden, NJ 08102. TEL 609-757-6117. Ed. Michael S. Weaver. adv.; bk.rev. circ. 300.

808.81   UK
BLITHE SPIRIT. 1991. 4/yr. £7 (foreign £9). 27 Park St., Westcliff-on-Sea, Essex SSO 7PA, England. TEL 0702-337983. Ed. Richard Goring. circ. 200.
   Description: Contains haiku, senryu, renku, tanka and articles on these forms of poetry.

800
BLUE BUILDINGS.* 1979. irreg. (1-2/yr.). $8 per no. c/o Ruth Doty, 1415 Beaver Ave., Apt. 6, Des Moines, IA 50311-2646. TEL 515-277-4298. Ed.Bd. circ. 500.

811   US
BLUE GUITAR. 1989. 4/yr. $12. 3022 North 5th St., Harrisburg, PA 17110. circ. 300.

811   US
BLUE PIG.* 1968. irreg. $5. 23 Cedar St., Northampton, MA 01060. circ. 250.

811 770   US   ISSN 0886-4187
BLUE PITCHER;* a biannual magazine of poetry and photography. 1986. s-a. $7.50 for 2 yrs. Unicorn Press, Inc., 200 E. Bessemer Ave, Greensboro, NC 27401-1416. TEL 919-852-0281. Ed. Sarah Lindsay. adv.; circ. 1,000 (controlled).

811   US   ISSN 1058-0654
BLUE RYDER. 1989. 6/yr. $12. 511 W. Sullivan St., Olean, NY 14760. TEL 716-372-5667. Ed. Ken Wagner. circ. 600.
   Incorporates: Heathenzine.
   Description: Publishes modernist and experimental poems.

811   US   ISSN 0197-7016
PS580
BLUE UNICORN; a tri-quarterly of poetry. 1977. 3/yr. $14 (foreign $18). Blue Unicorn, Inc., 22 Avon Rd., Kensington, CA 94707. TEL 510-526-8439. Ed.Bd. circ. 500. **Indexed:** A.I.P.P.

810 820   US   ISSN 0882-648X
BOGG; a journal of North American and British Commonwealth poetry, prose poems, reviews, and essays on small press publishing. 1968. irreg. (2-3/yr.). $12 for 3 nos. Bogg Publications, 422 N. Cleveland St., Arlington, VA 22201. TEL 703-243-6019. (UK subscr. to: 31, Belle Vue St., Filey, N. Yorkshire YO14 9HU, England; Canada subscr. to: 380 Wellington St., P.O. Box 23148, London, ON N6A 5N9, Canada; Australia and New Zealand subscr. to: 48 Academy Ave., Mulgrave, Vic. 3170, Australia) Eds. John Elsberg, George Cairncross. bk.rev.; circ. 750 (controlled). (back issues avail.) **Indexed:** Ind.Amer.Per.Verse.

811   US
THE BOHEMIAN. 1977. s-a. $1.50 per no. College of Notre Dame, Department of English, 1500 Ralston Ave., Belmont, CA 94002. Ed. Kate Brady. bk.rev. circ. 300. (back issues avail.)
   Formerly: Cat Feet.
   Description: College literary magazine of poetry and fiction.

808.81   US
BONE & FLESH. 1988. a. $7. Bone & Flesh Publications, Box 349, Concord, NH 03302. Ed. Lester Hirsh. circ. 199. (back issues avail.)

BOOKENDS. see *LIBRARY AND INFORMATION SCIENCES*

808.8   US   ISSN 1065-0342
▼**BORDERLANDS;** Texas poetry review. 1992. 2/yr. $14 to individuals; institutions $16. Borderlands, Box 49818, Austin, TX 78765. Ed.Bd. bk.rev. circ. 500.
   Description: Poetry and essays acknowledging historical, political, social and spiritual connection.

BOTTOM LINE PUBLICATIONS. see *LITERARY AND POLITICAL REVIEWS — Abstracting, Bibliographies, Statistics*

BOUNDARY 2; an international journal of literature and culture. see *LITERATURE*

899   KR
BOYAN. (Text in Ukrainian) 1968. s-a. 0.50 Rub. per no. Vydavnytstvo Radyanskii Pismennik, Chkalova, 52, Kiev, Ukraine. TEL 216-62-72. Ed. L. Golota. circ. 8,000.
   Formerly (until 1992): Poeziya (Kiev) (ISSN 0554-4084)

811   US
BRANCH REDD REVIEW. 1976. irreg., latest no.6. $10 per no. Branch Redd, 4805 B St., Philadelphia, PA 19120. TEL 215-324-1462. Ed. William David Sherman. circ. 400.
   Description: Publishes post-modern poetry.

BRAVE NEW WORD; contemporary Australian short stories and poetry. see *LITERATURE*

808.81   US   ISSN 0275-6080
BRAVO; the poet's magazine. 1980. a. $5. Bravo Editions, c/o John Edwin Cowen, Pub., 1081 Trafalgar St., Teaneck, NJ 07666. TEL 201-836-5922. Ed. Jose Garcia Villa. adv.; page $500. circ. 1,000. (back issues avail.)

808.81   US   ISSN 1052-1569
PS536.2
THE BRIDGE (OAK PARK); a journal of fiction and poetry. 1991. s-a. $8. 14050 Vernon St., Oak Park, MI 48237. Ed. Jack Zucker. adv. circ. 700.

LITERATURE — POETRY

821   **CN**   **ISSN 0382-5272**
BRITISH COLUMBIA MONTHLY. Short title: B.C. Monthly. 1972. irreg. (1-10/yr.). Can.$25 to individuals; institutions Can.$40. B.C. Monthly Press, Box 48884, Sta. Bentall, Vancouver, BC V7X 1A8, Canada. TEL 604-255-9993. Ed. Gerry Gilbert. adv.; bk.rev.; index. circ. 600.
    Description: Provides a key perspective on Canadian poetry.

811   **US**
BROKEN STREETS. 1979. q. $12.50. Broken Streets, 57 Morningside Dr., E., Bristol, CT 06010. Ed. Ron Grossman. adv. circ. 1,000. (back issues avail.)
    Document type: trade publication.
    Description: Christian poetry journal for new and established writers.

807   **UK**
▼**BRONTE SOCIETY GAZETTE.** 1992. m. Bronte Society, Bronte Parsonage Museum, Haworth, England.
    Document type: academic/scholarly publication.
    Description: Aimed at those who study and appreciate the works of Charlotte, Emily, and Anne Bronte.

890   **AT**   **ISSN 0310-2467**
BRONZE SWAGMAN BOOK OF BUSH VERSE. 1972. a. Aus.$9. Winton Tourist Promotion Association, Box 44, Winton, Qld. 4735, Australia. FAX 076-571502. circ. 1,500.

808   **US**
BROOKLYN REVIEW. 1984. a. $5. City University of New York, Brooklyn College, Department of English, Brooklyn, NY 11210. Ed. Tim Gerken.
    Formerly (until 1983): Junction Magazine.
    Description: Publishes poetry and fiction.

811   **US**   **ISSN 1060-2313**
BROWNBAG PRESS. 1989. s-a. $12. Hyacinth House Publications, Box 120, Fayetteville, AR 72702-0120. TEL 501-444-6129. Eds. Shannon Frach, Randal O. Seyler. adv. circ. 400. (back issues avail.) **Document type:** consumer publication.
    Description: Publishes fiction and poetry for a left-of-center audience.

821   **UK**
BROWNING SOCIETY NOTES. 1970. 2/yr. £12.50($35) to individuals; institutions £15($40). Browning Society, c/o Michael Meredith, Ed., The Timbralls, Eton College, Windsor, Berks. SL4 6HB, England. adv.; bk.rev.; index. circ. 225. (processed; back issues avail.) **Indexed:** M.L.A.
    Description: Essays and book reviews on the lives and works of Robert Browning and Elizabeth Barrett Browning.

808.81   **US**   **ISSN 0897-7356**
BRUSSELS SPROUT. 1980. 3/yr. $15 (foreign $20). Box 1551, Mercer Island, WA 98040. TEL 206-232-3239. Ed. Francine Porad. bk.rev. circ. 300. **Document type:** consumer publication.
    Description: International journal of contemporary Haiku and art.

810   **US**
BURNT SIENNA.* 1979. a. $2.50. 2418 Byron St., Berkeley, CA 94702-2029. Ed. Charles Heimler. circ. 1,000.

821   **UK**   **ISSN 0301-7257**
PR4379
BYRON JOURNAL. 1973. a. £15. Byron Society Journal Ltd., 6 Gertrude St., London SW10 0JN, England. TEL 071-352 5112. (US addr.: c/o Marsha Manns, Exec. Dir., Byron Society, American Committee, 259 New Jersey Ave., Collingswood, NJ 08108) Ed.Bd. adv.; bk.rev. circ. 2,000. (back issues avail.) **Indexed:** Arts & Hum.Cit.Ind., Curr.Cont., M.L.A. **Document type:** academic/scholarly publication.
    —BLDSC (2941.550000); UnCover.

808.81   **US**
C A L ANTHOLOGY. (Each vol. has distinctive title) 1987. a. $12.45. (Conservatory of American Letters) Northwoods Press, Box 298, Thomaston, ME 04861-0298. TEL 207-354-0998. Ed. Robert Olmsted. circ. 1,000. **Document type:** monographic series.
    Description: Collections of works by and for members of the non-profit and tax-exempt Conservatory of American Letters of interest to a literary audience.

811   **CN**   **ISSN 0702-7958**
C.S.P. WORLD NEWS. 1962. m. Can.$15. Guy Claude Hamel Foundation, 1307 Bethamy Lane, Gloucester, Ont. K1J 8P3, Canada. TEL 613-741-8675. Ed. Guy F. Claude Hamel. adv.; bk.rev.; film rev. (looseleaf format)

811   **US**
CACANADADADA REVIEW. 1989. 2/yr. $6. Box 1283, Port Angeles, WA 98362. TEL 206-325-5541. Ed. Jack Estes. circ. 300.
    Description: Publishes experimental poetry and satire.

811   **US**   **ISSN 0007-9537**
CAFE SOLO. (Text mainly in English; occasionally in other languages) 1969. q. $30. (India Inc.) Solo Press, c/o Luschei, Box 2814, Atascadero, CA 93422. TEL 805-543-1058. Ed. Glenna Luschei. bk.rev.; illus. circ. 500.

811   **US**
CAFETERIA. 1971. irreg. $3. Cafeteria Press, 1724 Woodland Ave., Modesto, CA 95351. TEL 209-523-8916. Eds. Gordon Preston, Rick Robbins. bk.rev. circ. 300.

CAHIERS DE L'IROISE. see HISTORY — History Of Europe

841   **BE**
CAHIERS NIVELLOIS. 1978. irreg. 250 Fr. Association Culturelle et Dialectale de la Region Nivelloise, Allee des Couterelles 4, 1400 Nivelles, Belgium.

841   **FR**
CAHIERS TRISTAN L'HERMIT. 1979. a. price varies. Rougerie Editeur, Mortemart, 87330 Mezieres-sur-Issoire, France. Ed. M. Carriat. **Indexed:** Can.Rev.Comp.Lit.

CALABRIA LETTERARIA. see LITERATURE

800   **US**
CALLIOPE (BRISTOL). 1977. s-a. $5. Roger Williams University, Creative Writing Program, Bristol, RI 02809. TEL 401-254-3217. FAX 401-254-3480. Ed. Martha Christina. circ. 450. (back issues avail.)
    Description: Publishes poetry and short fiction by established and emerging writers.

CALYX; a journal of art & literature by women. see ART

821   **CN**   **ISSN 0704-5646**
PR9190.2
CANADIAN POETRY; studies, documents, reviews. 1977. s-a. Can.$15 to individuals; institutions Can.$18. c/o Department of English, University of Western Ontario, London, Ont. N6A 3K7, Canada. TEL 519-661-3403. Ed. D.M.R. Bentley. bk.rev. circ. 400. **Indexed:** Amer.Hum.Ind., Hum.Ind., M.L.A. —UnCover.
    Description: Devoted to the study of Canadian poetry from all periods and regions.

821   **US**
CANDELABRUM POETRY MAGAZINE. 1970. s-a. £4. Red Candle Press, 9 Milner Rd., Wisbech PE13 2LR, England. TEL 0945-581067. Ed. M.L. McCarthy. adv.; bk.rev.; cum.index. circ. 1,000. **Document type:** consumer publication.

811 770   **US**   **ISSN 0146-2199**
CAPE ROCK; a journal of poetry. 1964. s-a. $5. Southeast Missouri State University, Department of English, Cape Girardeau, MO 63701. TEL 314-651-2500. Ed. Harvey Hecht. index. circ. 700. (back issues avail.) **Indexed:** A.I.P.P., Ind.Amer.Per.Verse.
    Former titles (until 1975): Cape Rock Journal (ISSN 0008-5812); Cape Rock Quarterly.

861   **AG**
CAPITAL DE LA POESIA. vol.5, 1973. bi-m. Calle Libertad, Casa 16, Barrio los Olivos, Villa Dolores (CBA), Argentina. Ed.Bd.

808.81   **FR**   **ISSN 0008-6134**
CARACTERES; revue internationale de poesie. (Text mainly in French; occasionally in English) 1950. irreg. 150 F. Editions Caracteres, 7 rue de l'Arbalete, 75005 Paris, France. TEL 43-37-96-98. Ed. Bruno Durocher.

CATALYST (SEATTLE). see ART

808.81   **US**   **ISSN 1058-6326**
CATHARSIS. 2/yr. $10. Chips Off the Writer's Block, Box 83371, Los Angeles, CA 90083. Ed. Wanda Windham. circ. 200. **Document type:** newsletter.
    Description: Journal of poetry by beginning poets.

808.81   **US**   **ISSN 1065-9250**
▼**CATHAY.** 1992. 3/yr. $15 to individuals; institutions $25. Paradigm Press, 11 Slater Ave., Providence, RI 02906. Ed.Bd.

811   **US**   **ISSN 0883-9174**
CELEBRATION. 1975. irreg., no.5, 1985. $8 for 4 nos. Prospect Press, 2707 Lawina Rd., Baltimore, MD 21216-1608. TEL 410-542-8785. Ed. William J. Sullivan. circ. 300.

808.81   **US**
CENTER STAGE (MAITLAND).* m. 540 S. Maitland Ave., Maitland, FL 32751.

811   **US**
CENTERING. 1973. irreg. $5 per no. Years Press, ATL EBH, Michigan State University, East Lansing, MI 48824-1033. TEL 517-355-3506. Ed. F. Richard Thomas. circ. 300.
    Description: Each issue focuses on either poetry, or short fiction from one author; past authors included Roger Pfingston, Stephen Dunning, Lee Upton, Dan Seiters, Leonora Smith, Alice Friman.

808.81   **BE**   **ISSN 0771-6443**
CENTRE INTERNATIONAL D'ETUDES POETIQUES. COURRIER. 1954. 4/yr. 800 BEF (effective 1992). Archives et Musee de la Litterature, Bibliotheque Royale, 4 bd. de l'Empereur, B-1000 Brussels, Belgium. TEL 519-55-80. Eds. Fernand Verhesen, Frans de Haes. adv.; bibl. circ. 1,000. **Document type:** academic/scholarly publication.

851   **IT**
CERVO VOLANTE. 10/yr. L.65000. Etrusculudens, Via Bargo 39, 00166 Rome, Italy.

807   **US**   **ISSN 1063-1836**
▼**CHAUCER YEARBOOK;** a journal of late medieval studies. 1992. a. $29.95. Edwin Mellen Press, 415 Ridge St., Box 450, Lewiston, NY 14092. TEL 716-754-2788. FAX 716-754-4056. Eds. Jean E. Jost, Michael N. Salda. **Document type:** academic/scholarly publication.
    Description: Devoted to critical examination of British literature written between 1350 and 1500.

831 053   **GW**
▼**CHELSEA HOTEL.** 1992. s-a. DM.35. Edition Isele, Heidelstr. 9, 79805 Eggingen, Germany. TEL 07746-1418. FAX 07746-2387. circ. 1,500. **Document type:** consumer publication.

811   **US**   **ISSN 1046-8897**
PS501
CHIRON REVIEW; a poetry journal. 1982-1988; resumed 1989. q. $10 to individuals (foreign $20); institutions $24. Chiron Review Press, R.R. 2, Box 111, St. John, KS 67576-2212. TEL 316-792-5025. Ed. Michael Hathaway. adv.; bk.rev. circ. 2,000. (tabloid format; also avail. in microform from UMI; back issues avail.) **Indexed:** Amer.Hum.Ind.
    Formerly (until Mar. 1989): Kindred Spirit (ISSN 0898-5502)

811   **US**
▼**CHRISTIAN POET.** 1992. irreg. $12. 2745 Monterey Hwy., No. 76, San Jose, CA 95111-3129. TEL 408-578-3546. Ed. Richard Soos. bk.rev. circ. 150.
    Description: Publishes single author collections of Christian poetry.

CHUNG-WAI LITERARY MONTHLY. see LITERATURE

CI KAN/VERSES. see MUSIC

808.81   **US**   **ISSN 0891-2386**
CICADA. 1985. q. $14 (foreign $19). Amelia, 329 "E" St., Bakersfield, CA 93304. TEL 805-323-4064. Ed. Frederick A. Raborg. illus. circ. 600.
    Description: Presents oriental poetry forms and related fiction and articles.

LITERATURE — POETRY

811 US
CINCINNATI POETRY REVIEW. 1975. s-a. $3 per no. College of Mount St. Joseph, English Department, Cincinnati, OH 45233. TEL 513-244-4930. FAX 513-224-4222. Ed. Jeffrey Hillard. adv.; bibl. circ. 1,000. (back issues avail.)
Description: Publishes original and unpublished poetry of all kinds.

811 US
CIRCLE (PORTLAND); a periodical of reversible poetry. 1975. biennial. $2 per no. Circle Forum, Box 176, Portland, OR 97207. Ed. J.M. Gates. bk.rev.; circ. controlled. **Indexed:** CERDIC.

811 UK
CIRCLE IN THE SQUARE BROADSHEET. 1966. 2/yr. 30p.($1) Bristol Arts Centre, 415 King Square, Bristol 2, England. Ed. Bill Pickard. circ. 500.
Formerly: Poetry of the Circle in the Square.

811 US
CIRCLETS; an occasional newsletter of reversible poetry. no. 4, 1977. irreg. Circle Forum, Box 176, Portland, OR 97207.

861 US
CIRCULO POETICO; cuadernos de poesia. (Text in English, Spanish) 1970. a. $10 to individuals; institutions $25. Circulo de Cultura Panamericano, 16 Malvern Pl., Verona, NJ 07044. TEL 201-239-3125. Ed. Ana H. Raggi. illus. circ. 800.

808.81 US ISSN 1045-1943
PN6010.5
CITY LIGHTS REVIEW. 1987. a. City Lights Books, 261 Columbus Ave., San Francisco, CA 94133. TEL 415-362-1901. Eds. Lawrence Ferlinghetti, Nancy J. Peters. circ. 5,000.
—BLDSC (3268.374400).

841 FR
CLIVAGES. 1974. irreg., no.8, 1991. price varies. Editions Clivages, 5 rue Sainte-Anastase, 75003 Paris, France. TEL 42-72-40-02. Ed. Jean P. Leger. adv.; illus. circ. 1,250.

808.81 US
CLOUDLINE. biennial. Wind Vein Press, Box 462, Ketchum, ID 83340.

811 US ISSN 1061-5687
COFFEEHOUSE POETS' QUARTERLY. 1990. 4/yr. $8. 3412 Erving Ct., Berthoud, CO 80513. TEL 303-532-3118. Ed. Ray Foreman. circ. 300.
Description: Publishes narrative poems of everyday experience and psychological penetration and insight.

811 US
COKEFISH. 1990. q. $20. Anna Pine, Ed. & Pub., 31A Waterloo St., New Hope, PA 18938. TEL 215-862-0299. bk.rev.

861 PO
COLECCAO FORMA. irreg., no.16, 1983. Editorial Presenca, Lda., Rua Augusto Gil, 35-A, 1000 Lisbon, Portugal.

869 PO
COLECCAO: POESIA (LISBON). 1982. irreg. Edicoes CASO, R. Cons. A. Pedroso, 59-2 E, Lisbon, Portugal.

869 PO
COLECCAO POESIA (PORTO). 1979. irreg., no.23, 1993. price varies. Edicoes Afrontamento, Lda., Rua de Costa Cabral, 859, Apdo. 2009, 4201 Porto Codex, Portugal. TEL 489271. FAX 491777.

861 SP
COLECCION "BAHIA". irreg., no.10, 1979. Ediciones Bahia, Fray Bartolome Bloque 1, Algeciras, Spain. Ed. Manual Fernandez Mota. circ. 700.

861 AG
COLECCION POESIA DEL NUEVO TIEMPO. no.3, 1976. irreg. Ediciones Tres Tiempos, Av. Belgrano 225, Buenos Aires, Argentina. Ed. Sigfrido Radaelli. illus.

861 MX
COLECCION SIGNO Y SOCIEDAD. EL POETA SU TRABAJO. 1980. irreg., no.4, 1985. $5. Universidad Autonoma de Puebla, Apdo. Postal 479, 72000 Puebla, Mexico. TEL 46-38-91. **Document type:** monographic series.

851 IT
COLLANA DI POESIA. 1974; N.S. 1977. irreg., no.26, 1981. price varies. Societa Editrice Napoletana s.r.l., Corso Umberto I 34, 80138 Naples, Italy. Ed. Domenico Rea.

810 US ISSN 1053-1831
COLOR WHEEL. 1990. 2/yr. $8. 700 Elves Press, RR 2 Box 806, Warner, NH 03278-9202. bk.rev. circ. 300.
Description: Publishes ecological, mythological and spiritual poems, fiction, and artwork.

COLUMBIA (NEW YORK, 1975); a magazine of poetry and prose. see LITERARY AND POLITICAL REVIEWS

811 US ISSN 0887-1612
CONDITIONED RESPONSE. 1982. s-a. $6 for 3 nos. Conditioned Response Press, Box 3816, Ventura, CA 93006. Ed. John McKinley. bk.rev. circ. 200. (back issues avail.)

CONFRONTATION; a literary journal of Long Island University. see LITERATURE

808.81 792 US ISSN 0277-7770
CONNECTICUT POETRY REVIEW. 1981. a. $3. Box 818, Stonington, CT 06378. Eds. J. Claire White, Harley More. bk.rev. circ. 500. (back issues avail.) **Indexed:** Amer.Hum.Ind., Ind.Amer.Per.Verse.
Description: Works by noted poets, with each issue focusing on a review of or interview with a noted author.

811 US ISSN 0897-0998
CONNECTICUT RIVER REVIEW; a national journal of poetry. 1978. s-a. $12. Connecticut Poetry Society, Inc., 86 Bellamy Ln., Bethlehem, CT 06751-1203. TEL 203-753-7815. Ed. Robert M. Isaacs. circ. 600. (back issues avail.) **Indexed:** Amer.Hum.Ind.

808.81 CN
CONSPIRACY OF SILENCE. 2/yr. 30 Charles St. W., Ste. 1420, Toronto, Ont. M4Y 1R5, Canada.

811 US
CONTEMPORARY POETRY SERIES. 1969. 4/yr. price varies. University of Georgia Press, 330 Research Dr., Athens, GA 30602-4901. TEL 706-369-6130. FAX 706-369-6131. **Document type:** monographic series.

811 CN ISSN 0831-9502
PR9195.1
CONTEMPORARY VERSE TWO; a magazine of Canadian poetry and criticism. 1975. q. Can.$20 to individuals; institutions Can.$24. P.O. Box 3062, Winnipeg, MB R3C 4E5, Canada. TEL 204-949-1365. Ed.Bd. adv.; bk.rev.; circ. 700 (paid). **Indexed:** Ind.Bk.Rev.Hum.
Formerly (until 1985): C V 2 (ISSN 0319-6879)
Description: Feminist poetry journal that intends to promote, strengthen and unify women.

808.81 US ISSN 1045-2265
CONTEXT SOUTH. 1981. s-a. $10. Context South Foundation, c/o David Breeden, Ed., Box 4504, 2100 Memorial Blvd., Kerrville, TX 78028-5611. TEL 501-972-6095. adv.; bk.rev.; film rev. circ. 500. (back issues avail.)
Former titles (until 1989): Dasein (ISSN 0011-6807); (until 1987): Nycticorax.

851 IT
COOPERATIVA ANTIGRUPPO SICILIANO. 1968. 3/yr. $15. Cooperativa Editrice Antigruppo Siciliano, Villa Schammachanat, Via Argentaria Km 4, Trapani, Sicily, Italy. TEL 0923-38681. (Co-publisher: Cross-Cultural Communications) Ed. Ignazio Navarra. circ. 1,000.

861 AG ISSN 0010-8766
CORMORAN Y DELFIN; revista planetaria de poesia. 1963. q. $4. F.F. Amador, 1805, Olivos, Buenos Aires, Argentina. Ed. Ariel Canzani. cum.index.

808.81 US
CORRIDORS. 1979. Detroit Writer's Guild, c/o Anthony Ambrogio, 820 Notre Dame St., Grosse Pointe, MI 48230-1242. Ed. Jane Dobija. (back issues avail.)
Description: Contains contemporary poetry and fiction by Detroit area writers.

811 US
COYDOG REVIEW. 1984. a. $5. Box 2608, Aptos, CA 95001. TEL 408-761-1824. Ed. Candida Lawrence. circ. 300.
Description: Publishes poems.

811 US
CRAMPED AND WET. 1988. 4/yr. $2 per no. 1012 29th, Sioux City, IA 51104. Ed. Rob Treinen. circ. 150.
Description: Covers poems, art and music.

808.81 US
CRAWLSPACE. 1980. s-a. $3. Crawlspace Press, c/o Dennis Gulling, Ed., 826 N. 1st St., Rockford, IL 61107. circ. 150. (back issues avail.)

890 II
▼**CREATIVE FORUM NEW POETS SERIES.** 1993. 4/yr. Rs.50($10) Bahri Publications, 997-A, Street No. 9, P.O. Box 4453, Gobindpuri, Kalkaji, New Delhi 110 019, India. Eds. R.K. Singh, Ujjal Singh Bahri. **Document type:** monographic series.

811 US
CREATIVE MOMENT WORLD POETRY AND CRITICISM; a semi-annual of creative writing and criticism. 1972. s-a. $4. Poetry Eastwest Publications, 790 Mckay St., Sumter, SC 29150-3217. Ed. Syed Amanuddin. adv.; bk.rev. circ. 300. (also avail. in microfilm from UMI; back issues avail.; reprint service avail. from UMI) **Indexed:** Abstr.Engl.Stud., M.L.A.
Former titles (until 1976): Creative Moment and Poetry Eastwest; (until 1975): Creative Moment (ISSN 0045-897X)

811 US ISSN 0011-0930
CREATIVE WRITING. vol.30, 1979. bi-m. $7. National Poetry Press, Box 218, Agoura, CA 91301. TEL 818-889-7477. Ed. R. Lott. bk.rev. circ. 500.

CRISI E LETTERATURA; periodico di lettere filosofia arti. see LITERATURE

861 860 FR ISSN 0247-381X
CRITICON. (Text in Spanish) 1978. 3/yr. 200 F. (effective 1994). (Universite de Toulouse-Le Mirail) Presses Universitaires du Mirail, 56 rue du Taur, 31000 Toulouse, France. TEL 61-22-58-31. FAX 61-21-84-20. Ed. Robert Jammes. adv.; bk.rev. circ. 500. **Indexed:** M.L.A. **Document type:** academic/scholarly publication.

811 US
CROOKED ROADS. 1989. 3/yr. $5. Wheel of Fire Press, Box 32631, Kansas City, MO 64111. circ. 180.

808.81 US ISSN 0896-4610
CROSS-BIAS; the newsletter of the friends of Bemerton honoring George Herbert 1593-1633. 1975. a. $5. Friends of Bemerton, English Department, c/o Edmund Miller, Ed., English Dept., C.W. Post Campus, Long Island University, Greenvale, NY 11548-0570. TEL 516-299-2391. bibl.; charts. circ. 450. (back issues avail.) **Document type:** academic/scholarly publication.
Description: For scholars interested in George Herbert and seventeeth-century English literature.

811 US ISSN 0318-6075
CROSS COUNTRY; magazine of Canadian-U.S. poetry. 1974. 3/yr. $7.50. Cross Country Press, 32 Haviland Rd., Ridgefield, CT 06877. (And: 27 Tunstall, Senneville, Que. H9X 1T3, Canada) Ed.Bd. adv.; bk.rev.; illus. circ. 500. **Indexed:** Amer.Hum.Ind.

811 US
▼**CROTON BUG.** 1992. irreg. (2-3/yr.). $5 to individuals; institutions $10 per issue. Box 11166, Milwaukee, WI 53211. TEL 414-374-0625. Ed. R.A. Melendez. illus.

808.81 DR ISSN 0257-6457
CUADERNOS DE POETICA. 1983. 3/yr. RD.$45($25) to individuals; institutions RD.$75($30). Editora Alfa y Omega, Apartado Postal 1736, Santo Domingo, Dominican Republic. Ed. Diogenes Cespedes. adv.; bk.rev. circ. 1,000.
Description: Dedicated to poetical theory, literary criticism, linguistics and literary creation.

861 PE ISSN 0011-2550
PQ8450
CUADERNOS TRIMESTRALES DE POESIA. 1951. q. Grupo Poesia, Casilla 151, Trujillo, Peru. circ. 1,000.

811	US
CULTURE CONCRETE.* 1990. 4/yr. $16. Box 410657, San Francisco, CA 94141-0657. TEL 415-285-4286. Ed. Dave Hayman. circ. 14,000.

808.81	US	ISSN 0731-7980
PS580
CUMBERLAND POETRY REVIEW. 1981. s-a. $14 to individuals; institutions $17 (foreign $23). Poetics, Inc., Box 120128, Acklen Sta., Nashville, TN 37212. Ed.Bd. circ. 500. (back issues avail.) **Indexed:** A.I.P.P., Ind.Amer.Per.Verse. —UnCover. **Description:** Devoted to poetry and poetry criticism. Presents poets of diverse origins for a varied audience.

811	US	ISSN 0734-9963
PS501
CUTBANK. 1973. 2/yr. $12. University of Montana, Associated Students, Department of English, Missoula, MT 59812. TEL 406-243-0211. Eds. Francesca Abbate, C.N. Blakemore. adv.; bk.rev. circ. 400. (back issues avail.) **Indexed:** A.I.P.P., ACCESS, Ind.Amer.Per.Verse, Ind.Little Mag. **Document type:** academic/scholarly publication. **Description:** National literary magazine with a Montana focus that inlcudes poetry, fiction, and black-and-white art.

821	UK
CYFRES BARDDONIAETH PWYLLGOR CYFIEITHIADAU YR ACADEMI. (Text in Welsh) 1980. irreg. price varies. (Welsh Academy) University of Wales Press, 6 Gwennyth St., Cathays, Cardiff CF2 4YD, Wales. TEL 0222-231919. FAX 0222-230908. **Document type:** academic/scholarly publication. **Description:** Translations of poetry from many languages (e.g. Polish, Irish, Chinese, and French) into Welsh.

821	CN	ISSN 0383-9575
DANDELION. 1975. s-a. $10. Alexandra Centre, 922 9th Ave. S.E., Calgary, Alta. T2G 0S4, Canada. TEL 403-265-0524. Ed. Barbara Kermode-Scott. adv.; bk.rev. circ. 800.

839	DK	ISSN 0107-4431
DANSK DIGTREGISTER. 1981. a. DKK 2230. Dansk BiblioteksCenter as, Tempovej 7-11, DK-2750 Ballerup, Denmark. TEL 45-44-97-40-00. FAX 45-44-68-24-42.
Formerly: Dansk Digtkatalog.

811	US
DAW RIVER ANTHOLOGY (YEAR). 1984. a. $12.45 (effective 1994). Daw River Anthology, Box 298, Thomaston, ME 04861-0298. Ed. Richard S. Danbury.

811	US
DEAD BEAT POET PRODUCTION.* 1990. 6/yr. 204 Ann Brown Dr., Weatherford, TX 76086-8805. TEL 407-952-0563. circ. 100.

811	US
DEANOTATIONS. 1984. 6/yr. $10. 11919 Moss Point Lane, Reston, VA 22094. TEL 703-471-7907. Ed. Dean Blehert. circ. 400. **Description:** Publishes Dean Blehert's original, humorous poems.

811	US
DEVIL'S MILLHOPPER. 1976. s-a. $5. Devil's Millhopper Press, University of South Carolina at Aiken, 171 University Pkwy., Aiken, SC 29801. TEL 803-641-3239. FAX 803-641-3445. Ed. Stephen Gardner. adv. circ. 500. (back issues avail.)

811	US
DIAL-A-POEM POETS. 1971. 4/yr. $8.98. Giorno Poetry Systems Institute, Inc., 222 Bowery, New York, NY 10012. TEL 212-925-6372. FAX 212-966-7574. Ed. John Giorno. circ. 10,000. (record; also avail. in audio cassette; video cassette; compact disc)

821	II
DIALOGUE INDIA;* Indian poetry review. (Text in English) 6/yr. Rs.50. Dialogue Publications, 5 Pearl Rd., Calcutta 17, India. Ed. Pritish Nandy. bk.rev.; illus. (back issues avail.)
Formerly: Dialogue Calcutta (ISSN 0012-2270)

DICHTER UND ZEICHNER. see *ART*

808.81	II
DIPAVALI. (Text in Marathi) vol.33, 1977. a. Rs.25. Ravindra Kesava Kothavale, 316 Prasad Chambers, Bombay 400 004, India. TEL 8112044. Ed. Ashok Kothavale; Pub. Ravindra K. Kothavale. adv. circ. 10,000.

811	US	ISSN 0734-0605
PS129
DIRECTORY OF AMERICAN POETS AND FICTION WRITERS. 1973. biennial. $25.95 to individuals; institutions $27.95. Poets & Writers, Inc., 72 Spring St., New York, NY 10012. TEL 212-226-3586. FAX 212-226-3963. **Indexed:** Child.Auth.& Illus. **Document type:** directory.
Formed by the merger of: Directory of American Poets; Directory of American Fiction Writers.
Description: Reference for publishers, administrators, agents and others who need access to writers. Lists names and addresses of over 7,000 poets and fiction writers who publish their work in the U.S., with information on each author's publications.

808.81 070.5	US
DIRECTORY OF POETRY PUBLISHERS. a. $17.95 (for 9th ed.). Dustbooks, Box 100, Paradise, CA 95967. TEL 916-877-6110; 800-477-6110. FAX 916-877-0222. circ. 2,000. **Document type:** directory.
Description: Lists poetry publishers worldwide including full data concerning each one.

DISCRETE EPHEMERA. see *ART*

811	US	ISSN 0749-260X
DOG RIVER REVIEW. 1982. s-a. $7. Trout Creek Press, 5976 Billings Rd., Parkdale, OR 97041. TEL 503-352-6494. Ed. Laurence F. Hawkins. bk.rev. circ. 300.

811	US
DOLPHIN-MOON PRESS "SIGNATURES" SERIES. 1985. s-a. $10. Dolphin-Moon Press, Box 22262, Baltimore, MD 21203. circ. 1,000.
Supersedes (1973-1985): Atlantic Triannual; Caim.
Description: Poetry sampling of established and new writers.

811	US
DRAGONFANG.* 1990. 2/yr. $8 for 3 issues. c/o Matthew Steve Schwartz, 7230 Nightingale Ln. No. 3, Holland, OH 43528-9304. TEL 419-878-7246. circ. 150.

811	US	ISSN 0364-359X
PS593.H3
DRAGONFLY; east-west haiku quarterly. 1965. q. $12. Middlewood Press, Box 11236, Salt Lake City, UT 84147-0236. Ed. Richard E. Tice. bk.rev. circ. 400. (processed)
Formerly: Haiku Highlights (ISSN 0017-6664)
Description: Presents English haiku, translations of Japanese haiku, and articles about haiku.

811	US
DREAM JOURNAL.* q. $9. 1508 Taylor St. No. 4, San Francisco, CA 94133.

811	US	ISSN 0897-0238
DREAMS AND NIGHTMARES. 1986. irreg. (approx. q.) $5 for 4 nos. David C. Kopaska-Merkel, Ed. & Pub., 1300 Kicker Rd., Tuscaloosa, AL 35404-3954. TEL 205-553-2284. adv.; illus. circ. 200. (back issues avail.) **Document type:** consumer publication. **Description:** Literary journal of speculative poetry. Introduces new writers.

811	US	ISSN 1062-3612
DRY CRIK REVIEW. 1990. q. $20. Box 51, Lemon Cove, CA 93244. TEL 209-597-2512. Ed. John C. Dofflemyer. adv.; page $250. bk.rev. circ. 45. **Description:** Contains poetry, prose, and art.

DUFU YANJIU XUEKAN/JOURNAL OF DUFU STUDIES. see *LITERARY AND POLITICAL REVIEWS*

811	US	ISSN 1052-4789
DUSTY DOG REVIEWS. 1990. 3/yr. $4.50 (effective 1994). John Pierce, Ed. & Pub., 1904-A Gladden, Gallup, NM 87301. TEL 505-863-2398. bk.rev. circ. 300.
Description: Publishes honest and evaluative reviews of poetry books, magazines and chapbooks.

821	CN
EGORAG. m. Can.$35. 4836 Ross St., Red Deer, Alta. T4N 5E8, Canada.

808	IS
EITIONE 77 LESIFRUT VELETARBUT. (Text in Hebrew) 1977. m. $35. Writers and Artists Association for Literature and Culture in Israel, Box 16452, Tel Aviv, Israel. Ed. Jakob Besser. adv.; bk.rev.

890	II
EK BACHARER SRESTHA KABITA. (Text in Bengali) 1973. a. Rs.4($1) c/o Mrs. Bhaswati Sinha, 36 Ballygunge Place, Calcutta 19, India. Eds. M. Manindra Gupta, Ranjit Sinha. adv.; illus.; stat. circ. 1,000.

808.81	US
ELEVENTH MUSE. 1982. s-a. $8. Poetry West, Box 2413, Colorado Springs, CO 80901. TEL 719-578-5909. Ed.Bd. adv.; bk.rev. circ. 300. (back issues avail.)

810	CN	ISSN 0046-1830
PR9194
ELLIPSE. (Text in English and French) 1969. 2/yr. Can.$12 to individuals; institutions Can.$14. Universite de Sherbrooke, Faculte des Lettres et Sciences Humaines, Box 10, Sherbrooke, PQ J1K 2R1, Canada. TEL 819-821-7277. Eds. Charly Bouchara, Monique Grandmangin. adv.; bibl. circ. 750. (also avail. in microform from MML,UMI; reprint service avail. from UMI) **Indexed:** Amer.Hum.Ind., Can.Lit.Ind., Pt.de Rep. (1982-).

808.81	US	ISSN 0731-0382
EMBERS. 1979. s-a. $11. Embers Horizons, Inc., Box 404, Guilford, CT 06437. TEL 203-453-2328. Ed. Katrina Van Tassel. circ. 500. (back issues avail.)

EMERALD CITY COMIX & STORIES; fiction, poetry, news, reviews, humor. see *LITERARY AND POLITICAL REVIEWS*

808.81 305.4	US	ISSN 1059-6879
PS1541
▼**EMILY DICKINSON JOURNAL.** 1992. s-a. $30 to individuals (foreign $36); institutions $50 (foreign $56). University Press of Colorado, Box 849, Niwot, CO 80544. TEL 303-530-5337. FAX 303-530-5306. Ed. Suzanne Juhasz. **Document type:** academic/scholarly publication. **Description:** Offers a forum for scholarship on Dickinson and her relation to the tradition of American poetry and women's literature.

811	US	ISSN 0271-5023
PS580
EN PASSANT POETRY. 1975. irreg $6. (En Passant Literary Association) En Passant Press, 4612 Sylvanus Dr., Wilmington, DE 19803. Ed. James A. Costello. bk.rev.; illus. circ. 500. **Indexed:** Ind.Amer.Per.Verse.
Formerly: En Passant Poetry Quarterly (ISSN 0363-3780)

841	FR	ISSN 0013-7103
ENCRES VIVES. 1960. q. 200 F. c/o Michel Cosem, Ed., 2 allee des Allobroges, 31770 Colomiers, France. adv.; bk.rev.; film rev. circ. 1,000. **Document type:** newsletter.

ENGLISH. see *LITERATURE*

ENGLISH GOETHE SOCIETY. PUBLICATIONS. see *LITERATURE*

800 808.81	SA	ISSN 0257-2036
ENSOVOORT; a poetry magazine. (Text in Afrikaans and English) 1981. s-a. R.10 to individuals; institutions R.15. Ensovoort, P.O. Box 30314, Les Marais, Pretoria 0038, South Africa. Ed. Johann Lodewik Marais. adv.; bk.rev. circ. 1,000. (back issues avail.) **Indexed:** Ind.S.A.Per.

821	UK	ISSN 0013-9394
PR1225
ENVOI; a poetry magazine. 1957. 3/yr. £9($25) (overseas £10). 44 Rudyard Rd., Biddulph Moor, Stoke-on-Trent, Staffs. ST8 7JN, England. TEL 0782-517892. Ed. Roger Elkin. adv.; bk.rev. circ. 1,000. **Document type:** consumer publication.

EPOCH (ITHACA); a magazine of contemporary literature. see *LITERATURE*

LITERATURE — POETRY

808.81   SP   ISSN 0211-8181
EQUIVALENCIAS/EQUIVALENCES; revista internacional de poesia - international journal of poetry. (Text in English, Spanish and original language of author) 1982. 3/yr. $27. Fundacion Fernando Rielo, Jorge Juan 102, 2nd B, 28009 Madrid, Spain. TEL 575-4091. (Subscr. to: Apdo. de Correos 54, 41450 Constantina (Seville), Spain. TEL 488-00-55; US addr.: 143-48 84th Dr., Briarwood, NY 11435. TEL 718-526-3694) Ed. Justo Jorge Padron. bk.rev. circ. 2,000.
    Description: Offers selections of the latest poetry. Each volume contains a literary essay, biobibliographical notes and a cumulative index of authors.
    Refereed Serial

811   US
EREHWON; journal of lucid poetry. 1966. s-a. $6. Pandemonium Press, 1273 Crest Dr., Encinitas, CA 92024. Ed. R.C. Walker. circ. 200. (back issues avail.)

811   US
▼**ESCHEW OBFUSCATION REVIEW**. 1992. irreg. $5. Pen-Dec Press, 3922 Monte Carlo, Kentwood, MI 49512. Ed. Jim Dewitt.

861   CK   ISSN 0014-0562
ESPARAVEL; gaceta de poesia. 1967. 10/yr. Col.50. Apartado Aereo 2670, Cali, Colombia. Ed. Helcias Martan Gongora. adv.; illus.

ETUDES BAUDELAIRIENNES. see *LITERATURE*

808.81   US
EUTHANASIA ROSES. q.? $1 per no. 759 Cranberry Ridge, Fairbanks, AK 99712. Ed. Yehudi Niemand.

EVENTI E INTERVENTI. see *ART*

811   US   ISSN 0014-4770
EXPERIMENT; a magazine of new poetry. 1944. irreg. $5.20. Experiment Press, 6565 N.E. Windermere Rd., Seattle, WA 98105-2057. TEL 206-527-4172. Ed. Carol Ely Harper. adv.; bk.rev.; illus.; index. circ. 400.

811   US
EXPERIMENTAL BASEMENT. 1991. 3/yr. $8. Experimental Press, 3740 N. Romero Rd., Ste. A-191, Tucson, AZ 85705. TEL 602-293-3287. circ. 150.

821   UK   ISSN 0014-536X
EXPRESSION ONE. 1962. q. £0.75($1.25) c/o Leslie Surridge, Ed., 5 Avon Rd., Waltham Forest, London E17 3RB, England. index. circ. 300.
    Formerly: Expression.

811   US   ISSN 0890-2887
EXPRESSIONS (GREENVILLE); veterans speak issue. 1986. 2/yr. $8. Box 4064, Greenville, DE 19807. FAX 215-255-0476. Ed. Joanne Petrizzi. circ. 350.

F A R C E. (Fine Arts Research and Communications Enterprises) see *ART*

F A W N S. (Fellowship of Australian Writers North Shore Regional) see *LITERATURE*

FANTASY COMMENTATOR. see *LITERATURE — Science Fiction, Fantasy, Horror*

811   US   ISSN 1041-4886
FEDERAL POET. 1943. s-a. $10 (effective 1990). Federal Poets of Washington D.C., Box 65400, Washington, DC 20035. TEL 202-260-5615. Ed. Nancy Allison. adv.; bibl. circ. 200.

808.81   US
FEH!; a journal of odious poetry. 1986. 3/yr. $6. Feh! Press, 147 Second Ave., Ste. 603, New York, NY 10003-5701. Ed. Morgana Malatesta. adv. circ. 150. **Document type**: consumer publication.
    Description: Contains poetry in the following areas: humor, satire, nonsense, eccentricity, madness and social criticism.

811   US
FELICITY.* 1988. m. $15. HC-13, Box 21-AA, Artemas, PA 17211-9405. TEL 814-458-3102. Ed. Kay Weems. circ. 200.

811   CN   ISSN 0015-0630
PR9291.N4
FIDDLEHEAD. 1945. q. $24 to individuals; institutions $28. University of New Brunswick, Campus House, P.O. Box 4400, Fredericton, NB E3B 5A3, Canada. TEL 506-453-3501. FAX 506-453-4599. (Co-sponsors: Canada Council; Provincial Government; Saint Thomas University) Ed. Don McKay. adv.; bk.rev. circ. 1,050. (also avail. in microfilm from MML,UMI; back issues avail.) **Indexed**: Amer.Hum.Ind., Arts & Hum.Cit.Ind., Can.Lit.Ind., Can.Per.Ind., CMI, Curr.Cont., Ind.Bk.Rev.Hum. —Faxon.

811   US   ISSN 0015-0657
PN6099.6
FIELD; contemporary poetry and poetics. 1969. s-a. $12. Oberlin College, Rice Hall, Oberlin, OH 44074. TEL 216-775-8121. FAX 216-775-8124. Eds. David P. Young, Stuart Friebert. bk.rev.; circ. 2,500 (paid). (also avail. in microform from UMI; back issues avail.) **Indexed**: A.I.P.P., Amer.Bibl.Slavic & E.Eur.Stud., Ind.Bk.Rev.Hum. —Faxon.
    Description: Seeks to publish the best in contemporary poetry, poetics and translations of poems.

811   US
FIFTY CELL.* 1975. q. free. Connecticut Correctional Institution, 900 Milldale Rd., Cheshire, CT 06410. TEL 203-272-5391. Ed. D.W. Donzella. illus. circ. 500.

808.81   US   ISSN 0737-4704
PS615
FINE MADNESS. 1982. s-a. $9 (foreign $15). Box 31138, Seattle, WA 98103-1138. Ed.Bd. bk.rev. circ. 800.

808.81   UK
THE FIRESIDE BOOK OF DAVID HOPE. 1968. a. £3.75($6.56) D.C. Thomson & Co. Ltd., 185 Fleet St., London EC4A 2HS, England. (Subscr. to: 80 Kingsway E., Dundee DD4 8SL, Scotland. TEL 0382-23131. FAX 0382-25511) Ed. John Rundle. illus.; index.
    Description: Features new and familiar poems, each illustrated by specifically commissioned color painting designed to appeal to all ages.

895.1   US
FIRST LINE/YI XING. (Text mainly in Chinese; occasionally in English) 1987. q. $10 (foreign $16). c/o Kuan-Fong Institute of East Asian Studies, Pace University, Pace Plaza, NY 10038-1502. (Subscr. to: Box 418, New York, NY 10013-0418) Ed. Yan Li. adv.; illus.
    Description: Contains mainly original poetry by writers from around the world. Accepts contributions from readers. Also includes poetry translations and short prose works.

FLAMMES VIVES. see *LITERARY AND POLITICAL REVIEWS*

FOLIO (WASHINGTON); a literary journal. see *LITERATURE*

FONDATION MAURICE CAREME. see *LITERATURE*

811   US
FOR FOLKS WITH THEIR BOOTS ON. 1990. s-a. $7. Summerhouse Press, Box 1070-B, Challis, ID 83226. TEL 208-879-4475. circ. 3,200.

808.81   US   ISSN 1046-7874
PS615
THE FORMALIST; a journal of metrical poetry. 1990. s-a. $12 to individuals (foreign $15); libraries $14 (foreign $15) (effective 1994). 320 Hunter Dr., Evansville, IN 47711. TEL 812-425-7684. Ed. William Baer. bk.rev. (back issues avail.)
    Description: Devoted entirely to formal, metrical verse and publishing contemporary poetry and translations that participate in the great tradition of metrical poetry from Chaucer to Wilbur.

821   UK   ISSN 0015-7740
FORMAT. 1966. irreg. £5. Stilt Press, c/o Alan & Joan Tucker, The Bookshop, Station Rd., Stroud GL5 3AP, England. FAX 0453-766899. Ed. Alan Tucker. circ. 150 (controlled). (processed) **Document type**: consumer publication.

FRAENKISCHER HAUSKALENDER UND CARITASKALENDER. see *BIOGRAPHY*

807   US   ISSN 1069-1200
PQ2
FRANCOGRAPHIES. (Former name of issuing body: Societe des Professeurs Francais en Amerique) 1930. a. $25 membership. Societe des Professeurs Francais et Francophones d'Amerique, 140 E. 95th St., Ste. 1E, New York, NY 10128. TEL 212-996-2375. FAX 212-996-2367. Ed. J. Macary. adv.; bk.rev. circ. 1,000. **Indexed**: M.L.A. **Document type**: academic/scholarly publication, directory.
    Formerly (until 1991): Societe des Professeurs Francais et Francophones d'Amerique. Bulletin Annuel (ISSN 0887-607X); (until 1981): Societe des Professeurs Francais en Amerique. Bulletin Annuel (ISSN 0081-0916)

FREE LANCE; a magazine of poetry and prose. see *LITERATURE*

808.81   US   ISSN 1041-0945
FREE LUNCH. 1989. 3/yr. $12 (foreign $15) (free to qualified poets). Free Lunch Arts Alliance, Box 7647, Laguna Niguel, CA 92607-7647. Ed. Ron Offen. adv. circ. 1,200. (back issues avail.) **Indexed**: Ind.Amer.Per.Verse. **Document type**: academic/scholarly publication.
    Description: Publishes poetry and news about poetry contests, new markets, and grants.

808.81   US   ISSN 8755-156X
PS593.H3
FROGPOND. 1978. s-a. $20 (foreign $28). Haiku Society of America, 87 Bayard Ave., N. Haven, CT 06473. TEL 203-281-9653. Ed. Sylvia Forges-Ryan. bk.rev. circ. 700. (back issues avail.) **Document type**: academic/scholarly publication.
    Description: Publishes contemporary English-language haiku, with occasional essays, renga and tanka, news briefs, listings of new books of haiku and translations from Japanese and other languages.

811   CN   ISSN 0046-5267
FULL TIDE.* 1936. s-a. membership. Vancouver Poetry Society, c/o 4602 Prospect Rd., North Vancouver, B.C., Canada. Ed. Borghild Valeria.

821   UK   ISSN 0306-1256
GALLERY. 1975. a. £2.50. Gallery Publications, c/o Valerie Sinason, Ed., 3 Honeybourne Rd., London NW6 1HH, England. adv.; bk.rev.; illus. circ. 1,000.

808.81   US   ISSN 0016-4100
GALLEY SAIL REVIEW; a journal of poetry. 1958. 3/yr. $8. 1630 University Ave., Ste. 42, Berkeley, CA 94703. TEL 415-486-0187. Ed. Stanley McNail. bk.rev. circ. 500. **Indexed**: A.I.P.P., Amer.Hum.Ind.
    Description: Seeks to encourage public appreciation of contemporary poetry.

811   US
GANDHABBA. 1984. a. $3.50 to individuals; institutions $4.50; lifetime $50. 622 E. 11th St., New York, NY 10007. TEL 212-533-3893. Ed. Tom Savage. circ. 300.
    Description: Thematical-oriented contemporary poetry.

811   US
GAS. 3/yr. $12. 50 Fell St., San Francisco, CA 94102.

821   UK
GENERA. 1971. irreg. £3 (includes a. review). Colin Simms, Ed. & Pub., Cross Fell Cottage, Gatehead, Gargill, Alston, Cumbria CA9 3EB, England. illus. circ. 1,000. (back issues avail.)
    Formerly: Cuddie Cantos.

808.81 700   US   ISSN 0896-7431
GENERATOR. 1987. a. $7. Generator Press, 8139 Midland Rd., Mentor, OH 44060. TEL 216-951-3209. Ed. John Byrum. bk.rev. circ. 125. (back issues avail.)
    Description: Provides a forum for the intersection and cross-fertilization of language and visual poetries.

GEORG FORSTER: SAEMTLICHE SCHRIFTEN, TAGEBUECHER, BRIEFE. see *LITERATURE*

811 US ISSN 0161-7435
PR3508
GEORGE HERBERT JOURNAL. 1977. s-a. $7 to individuals (foreign $10); institutions $15. c/o Sidney Gottlieb, Ed., English Department, Sacred Heart University, 5151 Park Ave., Fairfield, CT 06432. TEL 203-371-7810. adv.; bk.rev. circ. 450. (back issues avail.) Indexed: Abstr.Engl.Stud.; Amer.Hum.Ind., M.L.A.
—BLDSC (4158.207800); Faxon; UnCover.
  Description: Articles, essays, notes, and reviews on the life and scholarly studies of this English clergyman and poet. Discusses the theologic, social, and literary climate of his period.

808.8 US ISSN 0898-4557
AS30
GETTYSBURG REVIEW. 1988. q. $18 (effective Jan. 1993). Gettysburg College, Gettysburg, PA 17325-1491. FAX 717-337-6775. Ed. Peter Stitt. adv.: B&W page $225; adv. contact: Emily Clarke. bk.rev.; illus.; index. circ. 4,500. Document type: academic/scholarly publication.
—BLDSC (4165.269000); Faxon; UnCover.
  Description: Interdisciplinary magazine of arts and ideas. Features poetry, fiction, essays, essay-reviews and graphics by both beginning and established writers and artists.

811 US ISSN 0016-9633
PS501
GHOST DANCE; the international quarterly of experimental poetry. 1968. irreg. (1-2/yr.). $6. Ghost Dance Press, Dept. of American Thought and Language (EBH), Michigan State University, E. Lansing, MI 48823. Ed. Hugh B. Fox. circ. 300. (also avail. in microfilm from UMI; reprint service avail. from UMI)

808.81 884.55 US
GIORNO POETRY SYSTEMS L P'S, C D'S, CASSETTES & GIORNO VIDEO PAK SERIES. 1967. s-a. Giorno Poetry Systems Institute, Inc., 222 Bowery, New York, NY 10012. TEL 212-925-6372. FAX 212-966-7574. Ed. John Giorno. circ. 17,000.
  Description: Poets working with performance, music and video.

811 US
GLASS WILL. 1986. irreg., latest 1986. $5.95 per no. (Toledo Poets Center) Toledo Poets Center Press, University of Toledo, Toledo, OH 43606. TEL 419-537-2983. Ed. Joel Lipman. circ. 750. (back issues avail.)
  Description: Regional poetry in a book format.

821 UK ISSN 0141-1241
GLOBAL TAPESTRY JOURNAL; mind-opening & post-underground creativity. 1964. irreg £7($22) B.B. Bks, Spring Bank, Longsight Rd., Copster Green, Blackburn, Lancs. BB1 9EU, England. TEL 44-254-249128. Ed. David Cunliffe. adv.; bk.rev.; illus. circ. 1,050. (processed; also avail. in microform)
  Incorporates: P M Newsletter (Blackburn) (ISSN 0030-8145)

811 US
GO MAGAZINE. 1988. 26/yr. free. 1139 N. Laura St., Jacksonville, FL 32206. TEL 904-354-4382. circ. 10,000.

811 US ISSN 1068-2457
GOLDEN ISIS. 1980. q. $10. Golden Isis Press, Box 525, Fort Covington, NY 12937. Ed. Gerina Dunwich. adv.; bk.rev. circ. 3,600.
  Description: Contains pagan art, Wiccan news, reviews, white magick and goddess-inspired poetry.

331.88 IS ISSN 0017-1638
DI GOLDENE KEYT. (Text in Yiddish) 1949. q. $30. Histadrut, Beit Hamlin, 30 Weizmann St., Tel Aviv, Israel. TEL 03-216059. Ed. A. Sutzkever. Indexed: M.L.A.

811 US ISSN 0191-0760
GRAVIDA;* a quarterly journal of poetry. Variant title: Gravida-Bridging. 1972. q. $4. (Women's Poetry Collective) Gravida, Ltd., Box 616, Bethpage, NY 11714-0616. Ed.Bd. bk.rev. circ. 600.

GREAT TAO. see *RELIGIONS AND THEOLOGY — Buddhist*

821 UK ISSN 0017-3967
GREEN ISLAND. 1967. s-a. $75. c/o David A. Kilburn, Ed., Flat 2, 126 Long Acre, London WC2E 9PE, England. illus.; cum.index. circ. 400. Indexed: HR Rep.

GREEN MOUNTAINS REVIEW. see *LITERATURE*

GREEN RIVER REVIEW. see *LITERATURE*

GREENHOUSE REVIEW PRESS CHAPBOOK SERIES. see *LITERATURE*

811 US
GROUND WATER REVIEW.* 1984. irreg. $4.50. Talking Leaves Press, 1915 Altgeld St., South Bend, IN 46614-1605. TEL 219-269-7680. Ed. George Kalamaras. circ. 200.
  Description: Publishes experimental and long poems.

861 PR ISSN 0017-498X
GUAJANA.* 1962. 3/yr. $2.00. Las Palmas 1059, Santurce, PR 00907. Ed. Vicente Rodriguez Nietzsche.

821 UK
GUILDHALL POETS. a. £0.35. 19 Rugwood Rd., Flackwell Heath, High Wycombe HP10 9HA, England.

890 IS ISSN 0333-7588
PJ5041
HADARIM; poetry review. (Text in Hebrew) 1981. s-a. Gordon Gallery Ltd., 95 Ben Yehuda Street, Tel Aviv 63401, Israel. FAX 03-240935. Ed. Helit Yeshurun. adv.; bk.rev. circ. 1,500. (back issues avail.) Indexed: Ind.Heb.Per.

811 US
HAIKU HEADLINES; a monthly newsletter of haiku and senryu. 1988. m. $18 (Canada $20; elsewhere $25). 1347 W. 71st St., Los Angeles, CA 90044. TEL 213-778-5337. David Priebe (Renge). circ. 175.

808.81 US
HAIKU ZASSHI ZO.* (Text in English, French, Hungarian, Japanese, Russian, Sanskrit, Spanish) 1983. s-a. $6. Haiku Zasshi Zo Publishing Co., 325 N. 125th St., Seattle, WA 98133-8123. TEL 206-524-9692. Ed. George Klacsauzky. circ. 800. (back issues avail.)
  Description: Covers haiku poetry and Japanese arts that influence writing haiku.

808.81 US
HALF TONES TO JUBILEE. 1986. a. $4. Pensacola Junior College, 1000 College Blvd., Pensacola, FL 32504. TEL 904-484-1418. FAX 904-484-1826. Eds. Walter F. Spara, Allan Peterson. bk.rev. circ. 500. (back issues avail.)

811 US
HAMMERS; an end of millennium irregular poetry magazine. 1990. 2/yr. $15 for 4 nos. Doublestar Press, 1718 Sherman, Ste. 203, Evanston, IL 60201. TEL 708-328-7555. Ed. Nat David. circ. 500.
  Description: Collection of modern verse.

811 US
HAMPDEN-SYDNEY POETRY REVIEW. 1975. s-a. $5. Hampden-Sydney College, Box 126, Hampden-Sydney, VA 23943. TEL 804-223-8209. Ed. Tom O'Grady. bk.rev. circ. 750. (back issues avail.) Indexed: A.I.P.P.

808.81 NE ISSN 0017-7148
HAND VOL PLUIS.* (Text in Dutch, English and French) 1967. fl.2.50($0.75) Morsestraat 24, The Hague, Netherlands. Ed.Bd.

811 US ISSN 0440-2316
PS580
HANGING LOOSE. 1966. 3/yr. $12.50 to individuals, institutions $15. Hanging Loose Press, 231 Wyckoff St., Brooklyn, NY 11217. TEL 212-206-8465. Ed.Bd. bk.rev.; cum.index every 12 nos. circ. 1,500. (also avail. in microform from UMI; back issues avail.; reprint service avail. from UMI.) Indexed: Ind.Amer.Per.Verse. Document type: consumer publication.
—UMI.
  Formerly: Things (ISSN 0563-4660)
  Description: Includes fiction, poetry, and art, with emphasis on new writers.

811 US
HARBOR REVIEW. 1982. 3/yr. $7 to individuals; institutions $10. University of Massachusetts, English Department, Boston, MA 02125. TEL 617-929-8300. Eds. Charles Grace Anastas, Stephen Strempek. circ. 250.

808.81 US
HARVEST (SALEM). bi-m. 23222 Latona Dr., N.E., Salem, OR 97303.

811 US
HEART & SOUL (HOUSTON).* 1991. 4/yr. $5. 11503 Grapewood Dr., Houston, TX 77089-5433. TEL 713-332-5048. Ed. Rhonda Cook.
  Description: Publishes poems and short stories.

808.81 US ISSN 1042-5381
HEAVEN BONE. 1986. s-a. $16.95. Heaven Bone Press, Box 486, Chester, NY 10918. TEL 914-469-9018. Eds. Kirpal Gordon, Steven Hirsch. adv. contact: Steven Hirsch. bk.rev. circ. 2,000. (back issues avail.)
  Formerly: New Age Literary Arts.
  Description: Includes esoteric and spiritual poetry, stories and reviews. Focus is on spiritual, metaphysical, surrealist and experimental literary concerns.

811 700 US
HEDGEHOG. (Text in English or Spanish) 1983. s-a. $12 to individuals; institutions $13. South Florida Poetry Institute, Box 6124, Fort Lauderdale, FL 33310-6124. TEL 305-421-0980. Ed. M.E. Carlton. adv.; bk.rev. circ. 500. (back issues avail.)
  Former titles (until 1992): South Florida Poetry Institute Presents the Review; South Florida Poetry Review (ISSN 0885-0720)
  Description: Provides a forum for the works of well-known, new and upcoming poets, writers and artists.

HEINE SAEKULARAUSGABE: WERKE-BRIEFWECHSEL-LEBENSZEUGNISSE. see *LITERATURE*

800 II
HELICON.* (Text in English) 1971. m. Rs.10. 10-3C Nepal Bhattacharya St., Calcutta 26, India. Eds. Jyotirmoy Chatterjee, Suddha Sattwa Bovt. adv.

HELIX. see *LITERATURE*

808.81 US ISSN 1044-5331
PS615
HELLAS; a journal of poetry and the humanities. 1990. s-a. $14. 304 S. Tyson Ave., Glenside, PA 19038. TEL 215-884-1086. Ed. Gerald Harnett. adv.; bk.rev. circ. 750. (back issues avail.) Document type: academic/scholarly publication.
  Description: Includes modern poetry with criticism of modern poetry. Provides scholarly articles on Greek, Latin, and Renaissance English, as well as European literature and modern poetry.

811 808.8 US
HENDERSON COMMUNITY COLLEGE LITERARY MAGAZINE. 1988. Henderson Community College, 2660 S. Green St., Henderson, KY 42420. TEL 502-827-1867. Ed. Noelle R. Wallace. illus. (back issues avail.)
  Description: Presents poetry, short stories, and nonfiction prose.

821 II
HESPERUS REVIEW. 1988. q. $10 (effective 1991). Gautam Chandra Chunder, Ed. & Pub., 23 Nirmal Chunder St., Calcutta 700 012, India. TEL 26-8248. adv. circ. 500.

811 US ISSN 0018-1188
HEY LADY. (Supplements avail.) 1969. 10/yr. free. Morgan Press, 1819 N. Oakland Ave., Milwaukee, WI 53202. TEL 414-272-3256. Ed. Edwin H. Burton. illus. circ. 500.

811 US ISSN 0018-179X
HIKA. 1936. 2/yr. $12. Kenyon College, Box B, Gambier, OH 43022. TEL 614-427-2244. Ed.Bd. adv. circ. 2,000. (processed)

LITERATURE — POETRY

811 US ISSN 0018-2036
PS580
HIRAM POETRY REVIEW. 1966. s-a. $8. Hiram College, English Department, Box 162, Hiram, OH 44234. TEL 216-569-5330. Eds. Hale Chatfield, Carol Donley. bk.rev. circ. 500. (also avail. in microform from UMI; back issues avail.; reprint service avail. from UMI) **Indexed:** A.I.P.P., Ind.Amer.Per.Verse, Ind.Bk.Rev.Hum., Ind.Little Mag. **Document type:** academic/scholarly publication.
—UMI.

811 US
HOBO STEW REVIEW.* 1984. 4/yr. $5. Hobo Stew, 71 Marion St., Ste. 2, Somerville, MA 02143-3913. circ. 45.

861 AG ISSN 0327-4640
HOJAS DE POESIA. 1974. irreg. $2.50. Aquario, Paraguay 647, Buenos Aires, Argentina. Eds. Sergio Chaves, Sigfrido Radaelli. (poster format)

811 US ISSN 0147-2631
HOLLOW SPRING REVIEW OF POETRY. 1975. s-a. $6. Hollow Spring Press, R.D. 1, Bancroft Rd., Chester, MA 01011. Ed. Alexander Harvey. adv.; bk.rev. circ. 1,200.

800 US ISSN 0273-303X
HOME PLANET NEWS. 1979. q. $8. Home Planet Publications, Box 415, Stuyvesant Sta., New York, NY 10009. TEL 718-769-2854. Eds. Donald Lev, Enid Dame. adv.; bk.rev.; play rev. circ. 1,000. (tabloid format) **Indexed:** Hum.Ind.
Description: Literary - arts journal emphasizing poetry.

HONEST ULSTERMAN. see LITERATURE

HOOFSTRIKES NEWSLETTER. see ANIMAL WELFARE

821 CN ISSN 0094-9086
PR4803.H44
HOPKINS QUARTERLY. 1974. q. Can.$8($8) Language Studies Dept., Mohawk College, P.O. Box 2034, Hamilton, Ont. L8N 3T2, Canada. TEL 416-575-1212. Ed. Richard F. Giles. adv.; bk.rev.; index. circ. 375. (back issues avail.) **Indexed:** Abstr.Engl.Stud., Amer.Hum.Ind., Arts & Hum.Cit.Ind., Curr.Cont., M.L.A.
—BLDSC (4326.755000); Faxon; UnCover.

861 SP ISSN 0212-9442
HORA DE POESIA. (Text mainly in Spanish; occasionally in other European languages) 1979. s-a. 3450 ptas.($48) (effective 1994). Lentini Editor, Hipolito Lazaro 19-23, Esc. Dcha., Entlo. 3a, 08025 Barcelona, Spain. TEL 93-213-30-40. Ed. Rosa Lentini. adv.; bk.rev.; index. circ. 2,000. (back issues avail.)
Description: Dedicated to Spanish and international poetry. Contains critiques of the latest books, articles and essays.

800 US ISSN 0278-4173
HOT WATER REVIEW. 1976. a. $6. Hot Water Review, Inc., 9 Stuyvesant Oval, No. 5F, New York, NY 10009-1917. FAX 212-674-2737. Ed. Peter Bushyeager. adv. circ. 500.

808.81 301.412 US ISSN 1056-0815
HOUSEWIFE - WRITER'S FORUM. 1988. bi-m. $15. Deneb Publishing, Box 780, Lyman, WY 82937. TEL 307-786-4513. Ed. Diane Wolverton. adv.; bk.rev. circ. 1,500. (back issues avail.)
Description: For the woman writer who juggles husband, kids and housework with the pursuit of being published.

HUACHENG. see LITERATURE

HUAXI; qingnian wenxue yuekan. see LITERATURE

808.81 US ISSN 1047-0158
HUBBUB. 1983. 2/yr. $5. 5344 S.E. 38th, Portland, OR 97202. TEL 503-775-0370. Ed. Lisa Steinman. adv.; bk.rev. circ. 300. (back issues avail.)
Description: Presents contemporary poetry.

808.81 US
HUDSON VALLEY ECHOES; a national journal of prose and poetry. 1985. q. $15 to individuals; institutions $12. Box 7, LaGrangeville, NY 12540. TEL 914-223-5489. Ed. Marcia Grant. illus.

811 US
HWUP!; a forum for poets. 1991. 11/yr. $15 (foreign $18). Box 13743, Tallahassee, FL 32317. TEL 904-893-3878. Ed. Larry Gross. circ. 200.
Description: Discusses pleasures and pitfalls of poetry and promotes a larger market for chapbooks.

I C A M; revista literaria. see LITERATURE

IBDA/INNOVATION. see LITERATURE

813 500 SZ ISSN 0720-8782
AS181
IBYKUS.* Zeitschrift fuer Poesie, Wissenschaft und Staatskunst. 1981. q. DM.35. Azed AG, Dornacherstr. 60-62, CH-4002 Basel, Switzerland. TEL 06121-806955. FAX 06121-884101. adv.; bk.rev. circ. 14,500. (back issues avail.)

811 US ISSN 0019-137X
IDEALS. 1944. 8/yr. $19.95. Ideals Publications Inc., 565 Marriott Dr., Ste. 800, Nashville, TN 37214. TEL 615-885-8270. FAX 615-885-9578. Ed. Patricia Pingry. illus. circ. 274,000. (also avail. in microform from UMI) **Indexed:** Jun.High.Mag.Abstr.
—UMI.

821 AT ISSN 1032-1640
IDIOM 23. 1988. 2/yr. Aus.$8. University of Central Queensland, Rockhampton, Qld. 4702, Australia. TEL 0011-079-360665. Ed. Liz Huf. adv.; illus. circ. 350.
Description: Dedicated to developing the literary arts throughout the Central Queensland region. Includes original short stories, poems and articles.

811 US
IKON. 1982. 2/yr. $9.50. Box 1355, Stuyvesant Sta., New York, NY 10009. Ed. Susan Sherman. circ. 1,750.

821 UK ISSN 0736-4725
ILLUMINATIONS. 1983. a. £10($20) Rathasker Press, Ryde School, Queens Rd., Ryde, Isle of Wight PO33 3BE, England. Ed. Simon Lewis. circ. 500. (back issues avail.)
Description: Features international poetry and short fiction from new and established writers.

821 AT
IMAGO. 1988. 2/yr. Aus.$12.50. Queensland University of Technology, School of Communication, P.O. Box 2434, Brisbane, Qld. 4001, Australia. TEL 07-223-2111. circ. 500. **Document type:** academic/scholarly publication.

851 IT
IMMEDIATI DINTORNI; rassegna di poesia contemporanea. 1990. s-a. L.18000. Mucchi Editore s.r.l., Via Emilia Est, 1527, 41100 Modena, Italy. Ed. Francesco Genitoni.

IMPETUS. see ART

811 PE ISSN 0300-4031
IN TERRIS; revista de poesia. 1967. irreg. Livio Gomez Flores, Ed. & Pub., Francisco Cornejo 847, Tacna, Peru. adv.; bk.rev.; illus. circ. 1,000. (also avail. in microform; back issues avail.)

821 UK
INCEPT.* s-a. £1. c/o Eric Harrison, Ed., 3 Grantley Close, Shalford, Surrey, England.

851 IT
INCOGNITA. 1982. q. L.30000. Societa Editrice Napoletana s.r.l., Corso Umberto 1, 34, 80138 Naples, Italy. Ed. Giancarlo Majorino.

808.81 US
▼**INDEFINITE SPACE.** 1992. s-a. $7. Marcia Arreita & Kevin Joy, Eds. & Pubs., Box 40101, Pasadena, CA 91114.

821 II
INDIAN VERSE; voice of the Indian poets. 1973. q. Rs.10($4) 9-3 Tamer Lane, Calcutta 9, India. Ed.Bd.

INDIAN WRITER. see LITERATURE

808.8 UK ISSN 0020-0840
INFORMER; international poetry magazine. 1966. q. 12s.($1.50) Circle Books, 15 Linkside Ave., Five Mile Drive, Oxford, England. Ed. Keith Armstrong. adv.; bk.rev.; bibl.; illus. circ. 400. (processed)

808.81 UK ISSN 0951-0427
INKSHED - POETRY AND FICTION. 1986. s-a. £5($12) c/o Anthony Smith, Ed. & Pub., 21 Sycamore Ct., Park Grove, Hull HU5 1LS, England. TEL 0482-463534. adv.; bk.rev. circ. 500. (back issues avail.) **Document type:** bulletin.

808.81 950 CN ISSN 0714-2870
INKSTONE; a magazine of haiku. 1983. irreg. Can.$15($15) Keith Southward, Ed. & Pub., P.O. Box 75009, Hudson Bay Post Office, 20 Bloor St. E., Toronto, ON M4C 5H7, Canada. TEL 416-531-5688. bk.rev. circ. 100. (back issues avail.)
Description: Traditional and experimental Haiku poetry.

811 810 US
INNISFREE. 1981. 4/yr. $20. Softspin Press, Box 277, Manhattan Beach, CA 90266. TEL 213-772-5558. FAX 310-546-5862. Ed. Rex Winn. bk.rev. circ. 500. **Document type:** bulletin.

810.8 US ISSN 0094-2715
PS508.C6
INSCAPE (PASADENA). vol.33, 1977. a. $1. Pasadena City College, 1570 E. Colorado Blvd., Pasadena, CA 91106. TEL 818-578-7123. illus.
—BLDSC (4516.776000).
Supersedes (since vol.30): Pipes of Pan.

811 US
INSECTS ARE PEOPLE TOO. 1989. a. $3. Puff 'N' Stuff Productions, Box 146486, Chicago, IL 60614. TEL 312-777-8686. Ed. H.R. Felgenhauer. circ. 1,000.

INSIEME NELLA VALLE E ACCADEMIA INTERNATIONALE ARTE LETTERE SCIENZE DAFNI; ebdomadario artistico-poetico e di informazione del movimento i.n.v. see LITERATURE

861 US
INTERNATIONAL POETRY. (Text in English, French, German, Italian, Portuguese, Spanish) 1973. a. $22. International Writers and Artists Association, Bluffton College, Bluffton, OH 45817. TEL 419-358-3418. Ed. Teresinka Pereira. bk.rev. circ. 500.
Formerly: Poema Convidado.

808.81 US ISSN 0748-9676
INTERNATIONAL UNIVERSITY POETRY QUARTERLY. 1974. q. $300. (International University Foundation) T I U Press, 1301 S. Noland Rd., Independence, MO 64055. TEL 816-461-3633. Ed. John Wayne Johnston. adv.; bk.rev. circ. 425. (looseleaf format; back issues avail.)

051 US ISSN 0147-4936
PN6099.6
INVISIBLE CITY. 1971. irreg. (approx. 1/yr.). $3 to individuals; libraries $5. Red Hill Press, Box 2853, San Francisco, CA 94126. TEL 415-527-1018. Eds. John McBride, Paul Vangelisti. bk.rev. circ. 1,000. (tabloid format; also avail. in microform) **Indexed:** Access.
Formerly: Red Hill Press (ISSN 0034-2009)

821 UK ISSN 0960-5762
ISSUE ONE - THE BRIDGE. 1984. s-a. £1($6) Eon Publications, 2 Tewkesbury Dr., Grimsby, S. Humberside DN34 4TL, England. Ed. Ian Brocklebank. adv. circ. 450.
Formerly (until 1992): Issue One (ISSN 0266-111X)
Description: Publishes works of new and established writers.

811 305.4 US
ITHACA WOMEN'S ANTHOLOGY. 1976. a. $3.80. Box 582, Ithaca, NY 14850. Ed.Bd. circ. 350.

811 US ISSN 1042-7082
PS325
JACARANDA REVIEW. 1985. s-a. $10. University of California, Los Angeles, Department of English, 405 Hilgard Ave., Los Angeles, CA 90024. TEL 310-825-7411. FAX 310-392-0088. Ed. Bruce Kijewski. adv.; bk.rev. circ. 1,500. **Indexed:** Ind.Amer.Per.Verse.
Description: Publishes work by Nobel Prize winners as well as relative unknowns.

LITERATURE — POETRY

811 US ISSN 1074-3251
JACK MACKEREL MAGAZINE. 1990. irreg. (6-8/yr.) $15. Box 80024, Minneapolis, MN 55408-8024. Ed. Greg Bachar. adv.; bk.rev. circ. 750. **Document type:** consumer publication.
Formerly (until 1993): Rowboat.

808.81 FR ISSN 0184-8100
JALONS. 1977. 3/yr. 90 F.($19) for 4 nos. Chris and Jean-Paul Mestas, Eds. & Pubs., 52 av. du Parc de Proce, 44100 Nantes, France. TEL 40-73-20-24. circ. 400.

808.81 II
JAMINRAITU. (Text in Telugu) a. Zamin Ryot Press, 170 Thipparajuvari St, Nellore 524001, India.

JAUNA GAITA. see *ART*

JEOPARDY. see *LITERATURE*

811 US
JOE BOB REPORT. 1985. bi-w. $35 (foreign $70). Joe Bob Briggs Museum of American Culture, 6211 W. Northwest Hwy., Ste. C-123, Dallas, TX 75225. FAX 214-368-2310. (Subscr. to: Box 2002, Dallas, TX 75221) Ed. Tanja Lindstrom. adv.; bk.rev. circ. 2,700. **Document type:** newsletter.
Formerly (until 1993): Joe Bob's We Are the Weird (ISSN 1056-2427)

JOHN CLARE SOCIETY JOURNAL. see *LITERATURE*

841 BE
JOURNAL DES POETES. 1931. 8/yr. 600 BEF($16) Maison Internationale de la Poesie, Chaussee de Wavre 150, B-1050 Brussels, Belgium. FAX 5119122. Eds. A. Haulot, P. Jones. adv.; bk.rev.

808.81 CN ISSN 0705-1328
PR9190.25
JOURNAL OF CANADIAN POETRY. (Text in English, French) 1978-1982; resumed 1986. a. Can.$12.95. Borealis Press Limited, 9 Ashburn Dr., Nepean, ON K2E 6N4, Canada. TEL 613-224-6837. FAX 613-829-7783. Ed. David Staines. adv.; bk.rev. circ. 300. (back issues avail.) **Indexed:** CMI.

811 US ISSN 0363-4205
PS549.N5
JOURNAL OF NEW JERSEY POETS. 1976. s-a. $7. County College of Morris, 214 Center Grove Rd., Randolph, NJ 07869. TEL 201-328-5471. Ed. Sander Zulauf. adv.; bk.rev. circ. 500. **Indexed:** Ind.Amer.Per.Verse. **Document type:** academic/scholarly publication.
—CCC.
Description: Publishes poems written by poets who live or who have lived or worked in New Jersey.

808.81 616.89 US ISSN 0889-3675
CODEN: JPTHEK
JOURNAL OF POETRY THERAPY; the interdisciplinary journal of practice, theory, research, and education. 1987. q. $140 (foreign $165) (effective 1993). (National Association for Poetry Therapy) Human Sciences Press, Inc. (Subsidiary of: Plenum Publishing Corp.), 233 Spring St., New York, NY 10013-1578. TEL 212-620-8000. FAX 212-463-0742. Ed. Nicholas Mazza. adv. (reprint service avail. from UMI) **Indexed:** Soc.Work Res.& Abstr. **Document type:** academic/scholarly publication.
—UMI. CCC.
Description: Addresses the use of poetics in health, mental health, education, and other human service settings, focusing on the use of language in therapy.
Refereed Serial

811 US
JUNCTION. 1973. a. $1.50. City University of New York, Brooklyn College, Graduate Student Organization, La Guardia Hall, Rm. 237C, Brooklyn, NY 11210. TEL 718-780-5485. Ed. Marshall Scott Grossman. bk.rev.; bibl. circ. 250.

861 VE ISSN 0047-3030
K : REVISTA DE POESIA.* 1971. 6/yr. Bs.20($4.) Lubio Cardozo y Juan Pinto, Eds. & Pubs., Apartado 410, Herida, Venezuela. bk.rev.; bibl.; tr.lit.; circ. controlled. (processed)

K U L I M U. (Kunst, Literatur & Music) see *LITERATURE*

808.81 US ISSN 1060-0310
▼**KALAHARI REVIEW.** 1992. 3/yr. $24 to individuals; institutions $30. Kalahari Press, Inc., 4000 Cathedral Ave., N.W., Ste. 138B, Washington, DC 20016. Eds. Ellen Loerke, Patricia D. Norland. illus.
Description: Publishes short stories, poetry, interviews, personal essays, and profiles from the people of southern Africa.

808 II
KALAMI RISHATE. (Text in Punjabi) m. Rs.10. Krishan Lal Parwana, 9 Connaugh Circus, Jullundur 144001, India. bk.rev.

811 700 US
KALDRON. 1976. irreg. (1-2/yr.). $5 price varies. Box 7164, Halcyon, CA 93420-7164. Ed. Karl Kempton. bk.rev. circ. 1,000.
Description: Covers visual poetry from around the world.

851 100 IT
KAMEN'; rivista semestrale di poesia e filosofia. 1991. s-a. L.16000 (foreign L.25000). Editrice Vicolo del Pavone Soc. Coop. a.r.l., Via Romagnosi 80, 29100 Piacenza, Italy. TEL 0523-22777. Ed. Amedeo Anelli.

891.41 II ISSN 0022-9547
KAVITA. (Text in Gujarati) 1967. bi-m. Rs.10 (foreign Rs.160) (effective 1989). Saurashtra Trust, Janmabhoomi Bhavan, Janmabhoomi Marg, Fort, Bombay 400 001, India. TEL 2870831. Ed. Suresh Dalal. adv.; bk.rev. circ. 2,200.
Description: Presents literature, emphasizes poetry.

808.81 II
KAVITA ASIA/ASIAN IDENTITIES; an occasional of Asian poetry, poetics and other reflections. (Text in English) irreg. Rs.75 per no. Asia Poetry Centre, Bharat Bhavan, Shamla Hills, Bhopal, India. TEL 540398. Ed. Ashok Vajpeyi.

811 US
KAVITHA. 1982. s-a. $6. 4408 Wickford Rd., Baltimore, MD 21210. TEL 301-467-4316. Eds. Thomas Dorsett, Kammana Nirmala. circ. 500.

894.811 II
KAVITHAMANDALAM. (Text in Tamil) 1973. m. Rs.5. Vanambadi, 5 East Maada St., Mylapore, Madras 600004, India.
Description: Contains Tamil poetry.

808.81 II
KAVYA BHARATI. (Text in English) 2/yr. Rs.20($2.50) United States Department of English, American College, Madurai 625002, Tamil Dadu, India.

821 US ISSN 0453-4387
PR4836
KEATS - SHELLEY JOURNAL; Keats, Shelley, Byron, Hunt, and their circles. 1952. a. $20 to individuals; institutions $28. Keats - Shelley Association of America, Inc., c/o Stuart Curran, Ed., Dept. of English, University of Pennsylvania, Philadelphia, PA 19104-6273. bk.rev.; bibl. circ. 1,000. (also avail. in microfilm; reprint service avail. from KTO) **Indexed:** Abstr.Engl.Stud., Arts & Hum.Cit.Ind., Curr.Cont., Hum.Ind., Ind.Bk.Rev.Hum., M.L.A., RILA.
—Faxon; UnCover; SWETS. CCC.

821 AT
KHASMIK POETRY QUARTERLY.* 1974. q. Aus.$6. 26 Breillat St., Sydney 2038, Australia. illus.

891 IR
KITAB-I SUBH. (Text in Persian) 1987. a. IRI.300 per no. Daftar-i Nahsr-i Asar-i Hunari, P.O. Box 11365-4655, Tehran, Iran.
Description: Covers modern Iranian poetry and theater.

891 II
KOBISENA. (Text in Bengali and English) 1972. s-a. Rs.4. c/o Vattacharja Chandan, Ed., P-40 Nandana Park, Calcutta 700 034, India. TEL 91-033-4782347. bk.rev. circ. 1,000.
Description: Promotes experimental and avant-garde Sarbangin poetry.

811 US ISSN 1063-5874
KUMQUAT MERINGUE. 1990. irreg. (2-3/yr.). $8. Paragraphics - Penumbra Press, Box 5144, Rockford, IL 61125. TEL 815-968-0713. Ed. Christian Nelson.
Description: Dedicated to the memory of Richard Brautigan.

KUUMBA. see *HOMOSEXUALITY*

800 US ISSN 0896-8705
LACTUCA. 1986. irreg. (2-3/yr.). $10. Lactuca Publications, Box 621, Suffern, NY 10901. TEL 914-356-9236. Ed. Mike Selender. bk.rev. circ. 700. **Indexed:** A.I.P.P., Amer.Hum.Ind., Ind.Amer.Per.Verse.

LAGRIMAL TRIFURCA. see *LITERATURE*

808 UK
THE LAST EVER MELODIC SCRIBBLE. 1984. 3/yr. $6. Pretty Publications, 81 Castlerigg Dr., Burnley, Lancashire BB12 8AT, England. Ed. Andrew Savage. adv.; bk.rev.; illus. circ. 300. (audio cassette; back issues avail.) **Document type:** newsletter.
Formerly: International Melodic Scribble.
Description: Presents rhymed and free verse, both humorous and sad.

821 CN ISSN 0319-6658
LEAGUE OF CANADIAN POETS. NEWSLETTER. no.13, 1974. bi-m. Can.$25 (typically set in Apr.). League of Canadian Poets, 54 Wolseley St., 3rd Fl., Toronto, ON M5T 1A5, Canada. TEL 416-504-1657. FAX 416-947-0159. Ed. Jill Humphries. adv. circ. 400. (back issues avail.)
Description: Information for and about members, poetry market, readings, and contest news.

811 US
LEGACIES IN TIME. 1989. 4/yr. $18. Proving Grounds International, Inc., Box 1074, Jackson, MI 49204. TEL 517-782-1075. circ. 600.

LETRAS DE BUENOS AIRES. see *LITERATURE*

861 NQ
LETRAS DE NICARAGUA. irreg., no.3, 1982. Editorial Nueva Nicaragua, Paseo Salvador Allende, Km. 3 1-2 Carretera Sur, Apdo. Postal RP-073, Managua, Nicaragua. TEL 505-2-664317. FAX 505-2-666520.

811 US
LETTERS FROM LIMERICK. 1980. q. $20. Limerick League, Inc., 1212 Elsworth St., Philadelphia, PA 19147. TEL 215-247-1403. Ed. J. Beauregard Pepys. adv.; bk.rev. circ. 1,500.

808.81 US
LEWISTON POETRY. irreg., latest no.20. $19.95 per no. Edwin Mellen Press, 415 Ridge St., Box 450, Lewiston, NY 14092. TEL 716-754-2788. FAX 716-754-4056. **Document type:** monographic series.

AL LIAMM. see *LITERATURE*

054.1 CN ISSN 0024-2020
AP21
LIBERTE. 1959. bi-m. Can.$30 (foreign $35). Collectif Liberte Inc., C.P. 399, Succ. Outremont, Montreal, PQ H2V 4N3, Canada. FAX 514-524-3145. Ed. Marie-Andree Lamontagne. adv.; bk.rev.; tr.lit. circ. 3,000. (also avail. in microform from UMI; reprint service avail. from UMI, ISI) **Indexed:** Arts & Hum.Cit.Ind., Can.Lit.Ind., Can.Per.Ind., Curr.Cont., Pt.de Rep. (1983-), RADAR. **Document type:** consumer publication.
—BLDSC (5186.763000); UMI.

LIFTOUTS; a review of books and language work. see *PUBLISHING AND BOOK TRADE*

811 US
LIGHTNING SWORD. 1986. irreg. $1 per no. A P K L Publications, Box 371, Woodstock, NY 12498. Ed. Stephen Mark Rafalsky. circ. 1,000.

839.311 NE ISSN 0928-8775
PT5471
LIJN. 1970. q. fl.25. Opwenteling, Cooperatieve Vereniging voor Presentatie van Literatuur U.A., Postbus 6254, 5600 HG Eindhoven, Netherlands. TEL 31-40-455442. Ed.Bd. circ. 500.
Formerly (until 1992): Naar Morgen (ISSN 0027-7355)

LITERATURE — POETRY

811 US ISSN 0743-2909
LIMBERLOST REVIEW. 1976. irreg. (2-3/yr.) $9.95 per no. HC 33, Box 1113, Boise, ID 83706-9702. Ed. Richard Ardinger. circ. 1,000.
Description: Often devoted to the works of poets in the form of chapbooks.

811 US
LIME GREEN BULLDOZERS (AND OTHER RELATED SPECIES).* 1986. 2/yr. $3 per no. 723 N. Highland Ave., Arlington Heights, IL 60004-5515. TEL 806-744-7412. circ. 300.

LIMESTONE; a literary journal. see *LITERATURE*

821 UK ISSN 0459-4541
LINES REVIEW. 1952. q. £10 (foreign £12.50). (Scottish Arts Council) Macdonald Publishers, Edgefield Rd., Loanhead, Midlothian, Scotland. TEL 031-440 0246. FAX 031-440-0315. Ed. Tessa Ransford. adv.; bk.rev.; index. circ. 1,000. **Document type:** bulletin.
Description: Publishes poetry in English, Scots and Gaelic. Includes European languages in translation.

811 US
▼**LINGO;** a journal of the arts. 1993. 2/yr. $10 per no. Hard Press, Box 184, West Stockbridge, MA 02166. illus. (back issues avail.)
Description: Publishes original poetry and translations, essays and interviews with poets and artists.

811 US ISSN 0278-0933
LIPS (MONTCLAIR). 1981. s-a. $6 to individuals; institutions $13. Lips Press, Box 1345, Montclair, NJ 07042. TEL 201-662-1303. Ed. Laura Boss. adv. circ. 1,000. **Indexed:** A.I.P.P., Ind.Amer.Per.Verse.

LITERATUR & KRITIK; oesterreichische Monatsschrift. see *LITERATURE*

831 GW ISSN 0932-4623
LITERATUR UM 11. 1987. s-a. DM.15. (Europae Literae) Diagonal Verlag, Postfach 1248, 45742 Marburg, Germany. TEL 06421-681936. FAX 06421-681733. Eds. Ludwig Legge, Anne Neuschaefer. (back issues avail.) **Document type:** academic/scholarly publication.

800 DK ISSN 0107-0916
LITTERATURTOLKNINGER. 1980. triennial. DKK 617.20. Dansk BiblioteksCenter as, Tempovej 7-11, 2750 Ballerup, Denmark. TEL 45-44-97-40-00. FAX 45-44-68-24-42.

LITTLE REVIEW. see *LITERATURE*

LOBBY PRESS NEWSLETTER. see *LITERARY AND POLITICAL REVIEWS*

808.81 US
LOCKERT LIBRARY OF POETRY IN TRANSLATION. 1967. irreg., latest 1991. price varies. Princeton University Press, 41 William St., Princeton, NJ 08540. TEL 609-258-4900. FAX 609-258-6305. (reprint service avail. from UMI)

841 FR
LOLA-FISH. (Text in English) 1989. 6/yr. $6. Bruno Pommey, Ed. & Pub., 10, Residence Jean Mace, 28300 Mainvilliers, France.

800 US
LONG ISLAND POETRY COLLECTIVE. NEWSLETTER. 1974. 6/yr. membership. Long Island Poetry Collective, Inc., Box 773, Huntington, NY 11743. Ed. Sue Kain. circ. 100.

811 US
LONGHOUSE. 1973. a. $10. Bob Arnold, Ed. & Pub., Jacksonville Stage, Brattleboro, VT 05301. TEL 802-254-4242. bk.rev. circ. 200. **Document type:** newsletter.
Description: Contains works by unknowns and outsiders.

811 US
LOOK QUICK. 1975. irreg. (approx. 2/yr.). $2 per no. Quick Books, Box 222, Pueblo, CO 81002. Eds. Joel Scherzer, Robbie Rubinstein. bk.rev. circ. 200. (also avail. in microfilm; back issues avail.)

811 US ISSN 0734-0699
LOONFEATHER; a magazine of poetry, short prose and graphics. 1979. 2/yr. $7.50. Loonfeather Press, Box 1212, Bemidji, MN 56601. TEL 218-751-4869. Eds. Betty Rossi, Marsh Muirhead; Pub. Betty Rossi. adv. circ. 300. (back issues avail.)

811 US ISSN 0897-6481
LUCIDITY; quarterly journal of verse. 1985. q. $10. Bear House Publishing, RR 02, Box 94, Eureka Springs, AR 72632-9505. TEL 501-253-9351. Ed. Ted. O Badger. bk.rev. circ. 260. (back issues avail.)
Description: Features life-related poetry.

LUCRE-HATIF. see *LITERATURE*

808.81 US ISSN 1051-5968
LULLWATER REVIEW. 1990. 2/yr. $12 to individuals (foreign $15); institutions $15 (foreign $18). Emory University, Box 22036, Atlanta, GA 30322. TEL 404-727-6181. circ. 3,000. (back issues avail.) **Indexed:** Amer.Hum.Ind., Ind.Amer.Per.Verse.

LUVAH. see *LITERATURE*

808.81 US ISSN 1049-4502
LYNX;* a quarterly journal of renga. 1986. q. $15 (foreign $20). Creative Communications, Inc., Box 767, Gualala, CA 95445-0767. TEL 206-274-6661. Ed. Terri Lee Grell. adv.; bk.rev. circ. 1,000. (back issues avail.) **Document type:** trade publication.
Formerly (until 1988): A P A - Renga.
Description: Devoted to renga, the poetry form from which haiku is derived. Contributors include Hiroaki Sato, Jane Reichhold, James Penha, Alexis Rotella, J.I. Lipscomb, Marlene Mountain and Richard Witherspoon.

LYRA. see *LITERARY AND POLITICAL REVIEWS*

811 US ISSN 0024-7820
PS301
LYRIC. 1921. q. $10 (foreign $19). Leslie Mellichamp, Ed. & Pub., 307 Dunton Dr. S.W., Blacksburg, VA 24060. TEL 703-552-3475. index. circ. 900.
Description: Publishes only original, unpublished poetry.

811 US ISSN 0076-1699
LYRICAL IOWA; poetry by Iowa authors. 1946. a. $6. Iowa Poetry Association, 2325 61st St., Des Moines, IA 50322. TEL 515-279-1106. Ed. Lucille Morgan Wilson. circ. 800.

MABUA/FOUNTAIN; religious creation in literature, society and thought. see *LITERATURE*

811 US
MAD POETS REVIEW. 1990. 2/yr. $6. 1074 Hopkins Ave., Glenolden, PA 19036.
Description: Publishes poems of various forms and styles.

811 US
MADISON REVIEW. 1979. s-a. $4 per no. University of Wisconsin, Department of English, Helen C. White Hall, 600 N. Park St., Madison, WI 53706. TEL 608-263-3800. Ed.Bd. adv.; illus. circ. 500.
Supersedes (1968-1979): Bloodroot (Madison); Modine Gunch (ISSN 0026-8763)

818 US ISSN 8755-8785
MAGAZINE OF SPECULATIVE POETRY. 1984. a. $11. Magazine of Speculative Poetry, Box 564, Beloit, WI 53512. Eds. Roger Dutcher, Mark Rich. adv.; bk.rev. circ. 125. (back issues avail.)
Description: Presents poetry, reviews and articles on speculative poetry, the equivalent of speculative fiction.

MAGIRA. see *LITERATURE — Science Fiction, Fantasy, Horror*

808.81 PR
MAIRENA. 1979. s-a. $6 to individuals; institutions $15 (effective Jan. 1992). Manuel de la Puebla, Ed. & Pub., 1656 C. Penasco, Paradise Hills, Rio Piedras, S.J., PR 00926-3127. TEL 809-250-8197. adv.; bk.rev. circ. 1,000. (back issues avail.)
Description: Publishes articles on poetry, analysis, unpublished poems and commentary.

811 CN ISSN 0025-1216
MALAHAT REVIEW. 1967. 4/yr. Can.$18 to individuals; institutions Can.$25. University of Victoria, Box 1700, Victoria, BC V8W 2Y2, Canada. TEL 604-721-8524. FAX 604-721-8653. Ed. Derk Wynand. adv.; bk.rev.; illus.; cum.index: 1967-1977. circ. 1,800. **Indexed:** Abstr.Engl.Stud., Amer.Bibl.Slavic & E.Eur.Stud., Amer.Hum.Ind., Arts & Hum.Cit.Ind., Can.Lit.Ind., Can.Per.Ind., Curr.Cont., Hum.Ind., Ind.Amer.Per.Verse, M.L.A. —Faxon.

MALLIFE. see *ART*

840 SZ ISSN 0076-3748
LA MANDRAGORE QUI CHANTE. 1961. irreg., latest vol.44, 1991. price varies. Editions de la Baconniere S.A., P.O. Box 185, CH-2017 Boudry, Switzerland. TEL 038-421004. (reprint service avail. from UMI) **Document type:** academic/scholarly publication, monographic series.

808 US ISSN 0885-9205
MANHATTAN POETRY REVIEW; a magazine of contemporary American poetry. 1982. a. $7.50 (foreign $12.50). Box 8207, New York, NY 10150. TEL 212-355-6634. Ed. Elaine Reiman-Fenton. circ. 500.

808.81 US ISSN 0275-6889
PN1010
MANHATTAN REVIEW. 1980. a. $10 to individuals; institutions $14. Manhattan Review Press, c/o Philip Fried, Ed., 440 Riverside Dr., Ste. 45, New York, NY 10027. TEL 212-932-1854. adv.; bk.rev. circ. 500. (back issues avail.) **Indexed:** A.I.P.P., Amer.Hum.Ind., Ind.Amer.Per.Verse.
Description: Covers international poetry.

821 UK ISSN 0025-2166
MANIFOLD;* review of poetry and the arts. 1962. q. 12s.($2.) 99 Vera Ave., London N.21, England. bk.rev.

MANIPUR STATE KALA AKADEMI. QUARTERLY JOURNAL. see *LITERATURE*

808.81 US ISSN 0894-2242
MANKATO POETRY REVIEW. 1984. s-a. $5. Mankato State University, English Department, Box 53, Mankato, MN 56001. TEL 507-389-5511. Ed. Roger Sheffer. bk.rev. circ. 200. (back issues avail.)

808.81 US ISSN 0886-5957
MANNA. 1978. s-a. $6 (effective Nov. 1993). FishDown Press, 2966 W. Westcove Dr., W. Valley City, UT 84119-5940. Ed.Bd. circ. 200.
Description: Collection of serious, humorous and inspirational poetry with strong imagery.

MANOA; a Pacific journal of international writing. see *LITERATURE*

MARBACHER MAGAZIN. see *LITERATURE*

808.81 US ISSN 0892-807X
MARYLAND POETRY REVIEW. 1986. s-a. $15. Maryland State Poetry and Literary Society, Drawer H, Catonsville, MD 21228. TEL 410-744-0349. Ed. Rosemary Klein. bk.rev. circ. 1,000. (back issues avail.)
Description: Promotes national and international literary artists.

811 US
MATI. 1975. q. $5.50. Ommation Press, 5548 N. Sawyer Ave., Chicago, IL 60625. Ed. Effie Mihopoulos. adv. circ. 1,000.
Description: Features both academic and experimental poetry.

808.81 800 AT
MATILDA MAGAZINE: LITERARY AND ART MAGAZINE. 1980. q. Aus.$5. (Brunswick Poetry Workshop) Matilda Publications, 7 Mountfield St., Brunswick, Vic. 3056, Australia. Eds. Albert Hayes, Fonda Zenofon. adv.; bk.rev. circ. 1,000.
Former titles: Matilda Literary and Art Magazine (ISSN 0810-2740); Matilda Literary Magazine (ISSN 0159-7841)

LITERATURE — POETRY

808.81 890 US ISSN 8755-7266
MATRIX (URBANA). 1976. a. $8 (effective 1993). (Channing-Murray Foundation) Red Herring Press, c/o Channing-Murray Foundation, 1209 W. Oregon St., Urbana, IL 61801. TEL 217-344-1176. Ed. Ruth S. Walker. circ. 200. (back issues avail.)
   Description: Features poetry on all subjects, diverse styles. Contains selected work by members of Red Herring poetry workshop.

808.81 US
MAYFLY; a magazine of Haiku. 1986. 2/yr. $8. Brooks Books, 4634 Hale Dr., Decatur, IL 62526-1117. TEL 217-877-2966. Ed. Randy Brooks. circ. 200.
   Description: Features Haiku in English.

ME. see ART

808.21 US
ME TOO.* 1974. a. $1.50. Me Too, Inc., 112 W. 34th St., New York, NY 10001. TEL 212-594-9224.

811 US
MEASURE.* 1971. s-a. $6. Tribal Press, c/o Howard McCord, Ed., 15431 San Ridge Rd., Bowling Green, OH 43402. bk.rev. circ. 200-500. (reprint service avail. from KTO)

808.81 BG
MEIRA. (Text in Manipuri) bi-m. Tk.5. Bangladesh Manipuri Sahitya Sangsad, Tapoban, Lamabazar, Sylhet - 3100, Bangladesh. Ed. A.K. Sheram.
   Formerly (until 1989): Dipanvita.

808.81 US ISSN 0025-8954
MELE; international poetry letter. (Text in various languages) 1965. q. $4. University of Hawaii, Department of European Languages and Literature, Honolulu, HI 96822. TEL 808-948-8520. Ed. Stefan Baciu. (processed)

811 US
MELLEN POETRY SERIES. irreg., latest no.20. $9.95 per no. Edwin Mellen Press, 415 Ridge St., Box 450, Lewiston, NY 14092. TEL 716-754-8566. FAX 716-754-4056. **Document type:** monographic series.

821 UK ISSN 0960-4855
MEMES. 1989. irreg. (1-3/yr.). $10. c/o 38 Molesworth Rd., Plympton, Plymouth, Devon PL7 4NT, England. circ. 250. **Document type:** bulletin.
   Description: Compendium of experimental and radical literature (especially poetry).

MENSUEL 25. see ART

811 US
METAPHOR. 1985. 4/yr. $7. 109 Minna St., Ste. 153, San Francisco, CA 94105. TEL 415-641-7231. circ. 250.

811 US
MID COASTER. 1986. a. $4. 2750 North 45th St., Milwaukee, WI 53210-2429. Ed. Peter Blewett. circ. 500.

MIDCOASTER. see LITERATURE

MIDWEST CHESTERTON NEWS. see LITERATURE

811 US ISSN 0745-8738
MIDWEST POETRY REVIEW; a family of poets. 1980. q. $20 (Canada $25; elsewhere $30). River City Publishers, Box 4776, Rock Island, IL 61201. TEL 319-391-1874. Ed. Tom Tilford. adv.: B&W page $120; trim 8 1/2 x 10 1/2. bk.rev. circ. 10,000. **Document type:** academic/scholarly publication.
   Description: Literary magazine by and for poets, devoted only to poetry.

808.5 US ISSN 8756-1549
MIND IN MOTION; a magazine of poetry and short prose. 1985. q. $14 (foreign $18). Mind in Motion Publications, Box 1118, Apple Valley, CA 92307. TEL 619-248-6512. Ed. Celeste Goyer. circ. 350. (back issues avail.)
   Description: General literary quarterly on poetry and short fiction.

808.8 US
MINETTA REVIEW; all-university literary journal. 1974. 2/yr. membership only. New York University, Student Activities, 21 Washington Pl., Box 168, New York, NY 10003. TEL 212-998-4700. Ed. Eddie Pereira. circ. 7,000.

MINJIAN GUSHI/FOLK TALES. see FOLKLORE

800 US
MINOTAUR. 1975. q. $12. Minotaur Press, Box 4039, Felton, CA 95018. Ed. Jim Gove. bk.rev.; circ. 150 (paid); 150 (controlled). (back issues avail.)
   Description: Publishes contemporary poetry.

MIRAGE; the magazine of the arts. see ART

811 US
MIRRORS; international haiku forum. 1988. s-a. $10 (foreign $12). Box 1250, Gualala, CA 95445. TEL 707-882-2226. FAX 707-884-1235. Ed. Jane Reichhold. adv.; bk.rev. circ. 300.
   Description: Subscriber-produced haiku poetry magazine. Contents of each page is totally in the control of the person submitting that page. Includes haiku, senryu, renga, tanka, and haibun.

811 US ISSN 0026-7244
MOCCASIN. 1937. s-a. $12. League of Minnesota Poets, 732 Garfield Ave., North Mankato, MN 56001. Ed. Patricia M. Johnson. circ. 179.

811 US ISSN 0026-7821 PS593.H3
MODERN HAIKU. 1969. 3/yr. $14.25 (effective 1994). Robert Spiess, Ed. & Pub., Box 1752, Madison, WI 53701. TEL 608-233-2738. bk.rev. circ. 675. (back issues avail.) **Indexed:** Ind.Bk.Rev.Hum. **Document type:** academic/scholarly publication.
   Description: Presents haiku and senryu poetry.

811 US ISSN 0026-7848
MODERN IMAGES.* 1968. q. $12.95. Modern Images Poets Committee, c/o Morgan-Mod-Images, 1217 Champaign Ave., Mattoon, IL 61938-3167. Ed. Sue A. Morgan. bk.rev. circ. 100.

811 US
MOONSTONE BLUE, NIGHT ROSES. 1986. irreg. $3 per no. Box 393, Prospect Heights, IL 60070. TEL 708-392-2435. Ed. Allen T. Billy. circ. 250.

808.81 CN ISSN 0228-7404
MOOSEHEAD ANTHOLOGY. 1978. a. Can.$16. Moosehead Press - D C Books, P.O. Box 169, Ayer's Cliff, Que. JOB 1C0, Canada. TEL 819-838-5339. Ed. Robert Allen. bk.rev. circ. 350.
   Formerly: Moosehead Review.

081 US ISSN 0740-1205 PS615
MR. COGITO. 1973. irreg. $9 for 3 nos. Mr. Cogito Press, Humanities, Pacific University, Forest Grove, OR 97116. TEL 503-226-4135. Eds. Robert A. Davies, John M. Gogol. bk.rev. circ. 400.
   Description: Publishes poetry, some emphasis on translations, especially from Eastern and Central European languages. Also graphics; theme contests

808.81 700 US
MUDFISH; art and poetry. 1983. a. $11.50. Box Turtle Press, 184 Franklin St., New York, NY 10013. TEL 212-219-9278. (Dist. by: Bernhard de Boer, Inc., 113 E. Center St., Nutley, NJ 07110) Ed. Jill Hoffman. adv. circ. 1,500. (back issues avail.)
   Description: Contemporary poems interspersed with contemporary art.

808.81 US
MUSE - PIE. 1980. s-a. $5. 73 Pennington Ave., Passaic, NJ 07055. TEL 201-777-3588. Ed. R.W. Grandinetti Rader. circ. 300.

821 CN ISSN 1198-3183
MUSELETTER. s-a. Can.$25 (typically set in Apr.). League of Canadian Poets, 54 Wolseley St., 3rd Fl., Toronto, ON M5T 1A5, Canada. TEL 416-504-1657. FAX 416-947-0159. Ed. Maria Jacobs. adv.; bk.rev. circ. 400. (back issues avail.)
   Description: Essays about poetry, poetry by members.

811 US
MY LEGACY.* 1990. 4/yr. $12. HC-13, Box 21AA, Artemas, PA 17211-9405. TEL 814-458-3102. Ed. Kay Weems. circ. 150.
   Description: Publishes only English poems, no translations.

811 US
N R G. 1976. 2/yr. $4. 6735 S.E. 78th St., Portland, OR 97206. Ed. Dan Raphael. bk.rev.; charts; illus.; stat. circ. 1,000. (tabloid format; back issues avail.)
   Description: Avant-garde poetry.

NATIONAL ENDOWMENT FOR THE ARTS. APPLICATION GUIDELINES: LITERATURE. see LITERATURE

821 IE
NEPTUNE'S KINGDOM; poetry review. (Text in English) 1972. irreg. 10p.($1) per issue. c/o Martin Gleeson, Ed., 5 Victoria Terrace, Kilkee, Co. Clare, Ireland. bk.rev.; illus. circ. 500.

831 GW ISSN 0342-9547
NEUE BEITRAEGE ZUR GEORGE-FORSCHUNG. 1976. a. DM.16.80. Gesellschaft zur Foerderung der Stefan-George-Gedenkstaette Bingen e.V., Nostadtstr. 119, 55411 Bingen a.R., Germany. TEL 06721-44126. (Subscr. to: Verlag Brigitte Guderjahn, Im Anger 5, 6900 Heidelberg, Germany) circ. 400.

808.81 US ISSN 0893-7842
NEW AMERICAN WRITING. 1971. s-a. $12 to individuals; institutions $16; foreign $20. Oink! Press, Inc., 2920 W. Pratt Blvd., Chicago, IL 60645. TEL 312-764-1048. FAX 312-764-1048. Eds. Maxine Chernoff, Paul Hoover. adv.; B&W page $150. bk.rev. circ. 5,000. **Indexed:** Amer.Hum.Ind., Ind.Amer.Per.Verse.
   Formerly (until 1986): Oink! (ISSN 0883-8518)
   Description: Publishes poetry, essays and fiction that emphasize "postmodern" writing, including the New York School, language poetry, and other experiments.

NEW ARCADIAN JOURNAL. see ARCHITECTURE

952 JA ISSN 0911-6567
NEW CICADA; haiku poetry magazine. (Text in English) 1984. s-a. 1000 Yen($6) Tadao Okazaki, Ed. & Pub., 40-11 Kubo, Hobara, Fukushima 960-06, Japan. (back issues avail.) **Document type:** trade publication.
   Description: Devoted to the definition of traditional haiku as a Japanese ballad, and to free-verse haiku.

821 SA
NEW COIN POETRY. 1965. s-a. R.11($14) £7.50. Rhodes University, Institute for the Study of English in Africa, P.O. Box 94, Grahamstown 6140, South Africa. TEL 27-461-26093. FAX 27-461-25642. Ed. Robert Berold. circ. 450. **Indexed:** Ind.S.A.Per.
   Formerly: New Coin (ISSN 0028-4459)

811 US
NEW DAY PUBLICATIONS. 1987. 4/yr. $10. Rte. 4, Box 10, Eupora, MS 39744. TEL 801-258-2935. Ed. Brenda Davis.

NEW DOG. see LITERARY AND POLITICAL REVIEWS

831 LU
NEW EUROPE. 1972. 4/yr. Europeditor, P.O. Box 212, Luxembourg, Luxembourg.

821 UK
NEW HOPE INTERNATIONAL REVIEW. 1980. s-a. £13($35) includes New Hope International Writing and Special Edition Chapbooks. New Hope International, 20 Werneth Ave., Gee Cross, Hyde, Cheshire SK14 5NL, England. TEL 061-351-1878. Ed. Gerald England. adv.; bk.rev.; illus.; cum.index. circ. 1,000. (back issues avail.) **Document type:** bibliography.
   Formerly: New Hope International Review Supplement.
   Description: Review of books, magazines, cassettes, CDs and PC software. Covers literature, music, art, socio-politics, religion and small press.

821 UK
NEW HOPE INTERNATIONAL WRITING. (Text mainly in English; occasionally in other languages) 1980. 6/yr. £13($35) includes New Hope International Review and Special Edition Chapbooks. New Hope International, 20 Werneth Ave., Gee Cross, Hyde, Cheshire SK14 5NL, England. TEL 061-351-1878. Ed. Gerald England. adv.; bk.rev.; cum.index: 1980-1989. circ. 1,000. (back issues avail.) **Document type:** consumer publication.
   Formerly: New Hope International (ISSN 0260-7948); Supersedes: Osgoldcross Review.
   Description: Poetry, prose and original artwork from around the world.

LITERATURE — POETRY

NEW LITERATURE AND IDEOLOGY. see *LITERARY AND POLITICAL REVIEWS*

808.81   US   ISSN 0253-293X
NEW MUSES. 1976. q. price varies. Federation of International Poetry Associations, Drawer 579, Santa Claus, IN 47579. Ed. Carol L. Abell. bk.rev. circ. 2,000.
    Description: Serves the presidents, directors, and members of organizations, societies and groups affiliated with the federation.

NEW ORLEANS REVIEW. see *LITERATURE*

811   US
NEW POETS SERIES - CHESTNUT HILLS PRESS. (Includes subseries: New Poets Series: Stonewall) 1971. 4/yr. price varies. New Poets Series, Inc., 541 Piccadilly Rd., Baltimore, MD 21204. TEL 410-828-0724. Ed. Clarinda Harriss Raymond. circ. 1,000. **Document type:** monographic series.
    Description: Publishes original first collections of poetry from new writers, from around the English speaking world. Also publishes collections by gay and lesbian poets.

811   US   ISSN 0894-6078
NEW PRESS; literary quarterly. 1984. q. $15. 53-35 Hollis Ct. Blvd., Flushing, NY 11365. TEL 718-229-6782. Ed. Robert Dunn. adv. contact: Bob Abramson. circ. 1,600 (paid). (back issues avail.)
    Description: Features short stories, poetry, commentary, and personal journalism with illustrations.

811   US
NEW SINS. 1989. 2/yr. $3. Rane Arroyo, Ed. & Pub., Box 7157, Pittsburgh, PA 15213. TEL 412-621-5611. circ. 200.

821   UK
NEW SPOKES. 1985. 2/yr. £7.50 (foreign £9). c/o The Orchard House, 45 Clophill Rd., Upper Gravenhurst, Bedford MK45 4JH, England. TEL 0462-711195. Eds. Donald Atkinson. bk.rev.; illus. circ. 300.
    Formerly (until 1991): Spokes (ISSN 0268-294X)

808   US
NEW VOICES (METHUEN). 1979. a. $4. 24 Edgewood Terrace, Methuen, MA 01844. TEL 617-685-3087. Ed. Lorraine Moreau-Laverriere. circ. 300. (back issues avail.)

NEW WRITER'S MAGAZINE. see *LITERATURE*

811   US   ISSN 0028-7482
PS580
NEW YORK QUARTERLY. Short title: N Y Q. 1970-1979; resumed 1985. 3/yr. $15 to individuals; institutions $25. National Poetry Foundation, 302 Neville Hall, University of Maine, Orono, ME 04469. Ed. William Packard. adv.; bibl.; cum.index every 10 nos. circ. 3,500. (back issues avail.) **Indexed:** Curr.Cont.

NEW ZEALAND JOURNAL OF FRENCH STUDIES. see *LITERATURE*

808.81   US   ISSN 0743-6882
NEWSLETTER INAGO. 1979. m. $17 (foreign $25) (effective 1993). Del Reitz, Ed & Pub, Box 26244, Tucson, AZ 85726-6244. TEL 602-294-7031. circ. 100. **Document type:** newsletter.

NEXUS (DAYTON). see *LITERATURE*

811   US
NIAGARA MAGAZINE.* 1974. 3/yr. $7 for 4 issues. 17 Burnside St., Upper Montclair, NJ 07043-1324. Ed. Neil Baldwin. circ. 500. (back issues avail.)

811 808.838   US   ISSN 1068-4468
▼**NIGHT SONGS.** 1992. q. $3 (effective Jan. 1992). Gothic Press, 4998 Perkins Rd., Baton Rouge, LA 70808-3043. TEL 504-766-2906. Ed. Gary W. Crawford. circ. 45. (back issues avail.) **Document type:** newsletter.

NIMROD; international journal of prose and poetry. see *LITERATURE*

808 320   US
NO LONGER SILENT. q.? $1 per no. Box 3582, Tucson, AZ 85722. Ed. Eliza Blackweb.
    Description: Contains poems, artworks and essays against violence.

811   US
NOCTURNAL LYRIC.* 1987. 6/yr. $10. Box 77171, San Francisco, CA 94107-0171. circ. 200.

811   US
NOOSPAPERS. 1986. 3/yr. $8. Open Dialogue, Inc., 215 N. Ave. West, Ste. 21, Westfield, NJ 07090. TEL 201-249-0280. circ. 200.

808.81   IT
NORDSEE; poesia in forma di manifesto. (Text in Italian; summaries in English) 1977. q. L.10000. Maurizio Maldini, Ed. & Pub., Via A. Romagnoli, 39, 40137 Bologna, Italy.
    Formerly: Nordsee - Cerchio.

808.81   UK   ISSN 0269-9885
THE NORTH. irreg. (2-3/yr.) £8 for 3 nos. The Poetry Business, 51 Byram Arcade, Westgate, Huddersfield HD1 1ND, W. Yorks., England. TEL 0484-434840. FAX 0484-426566.
    Description: Publishes poetry, criticism, and literary reviews.

811   US
NORTHEASTARTS MAGAZINE. 1990. 2/yr. $10. Boston Arts Organization, Inc., Box 6061, J.F.K. Sta., Boston, MA 02114. Ed. Leigh Donaldson. circ. 1,000.

820   UK   ISSN 0078-1738
NORTHERN HOUSE PAMPHLET POETS. 1964. irreg. price varies. Northern House, 19 Haldane Terrace, Newcastle-upon-Tyne NE2 3AN, England. TEL 091-281-2614. Ed. Jon Silkin. adv.; bk.rev. circ. 1,000. (back issues avail.) **Document type:** consumer publication.
    ● Also available online.

NORTHLAND QUARTERLY. see *LITERARY AND POLITICAL REVIEWS*

811   US
NOSTOC. 1973. s-a. $10. Arts End Books, Box 162, Newton, MA 02168. TEL 508-885-9904. Ed. Marshall Brooks. adv.; bk.rev. circ. 500. (back issues avail.)

807   US
NOTRE DAME TEXTS IN MEDIEVAL CULTURE. irreg. University of Notre Dame Press, Notre Dame, IN 46556. TEL 219-631-6346. FAX 219-631-8148. (Subscr. to: Box 635, South Bend, IN 46624) **Document type:** monographic series, academic/scholarly publication.
    Description: Presents translations of medieval literary texts.

NOUVEAU COMMERCE. see *LITERATURE*

808.81   FR   ISSN 0294-4030
PQ1184
NOUVELLE TOUR DE FEU; revue de creation poetique. 1946. bi-m. 200 F. Editions du Soleil Natal, 8 bis rue Lormier, 91580 Etrechy, France. Ed. Michel Heroult. bk.rev.; illus. circ. 3,000.
    Formerly (until 1982): Tour de Feu (ISSN 0040-9731)

861   BL
NOVA POESIA BRASILEIRA. 1983. 10/yr. $10. Shogun Editora e Arte Ltda., Caixa Postal 43.021, CEP 22052, Rio de Janeiro, Brazil. TEL 021-2559494. circ. 12,000.

861   CL
NUEVA LINEA;* revista de literatura y arte. 1976. q. Esc.45($5) or exchange. Editorial Nueva Linea, Apdo. Postal 14.978, Stgo: 21, Santiago, Chile. Ed. Bd. bk.rev. circ. 1,500.

871   SP
NUEVA POETICA ANDALUZA.* 1981. irreg. Editorial Cajal, Paseo de Almeria 1810, Apdo. 456, 04080 Almeria, Spain.

808.81 700   US   ISSN 0898-1140
PQ7074.5
LA NUEZ; revista internacional de arte y literatura. (Text in Spanish) 1988. 3/yr. $12 to individuals; institutions $15; foreign $18. Box 023617, Brooklyn, NY 11202. Ed. Rafael Bordao. adv.; bk.rev. circ. 1,000.
    Description: Contains poetry, essays, short fiction, criticism, interviews, reviews and original artwork and photography.

808.81 800   US
NUMBER ONE. 1972. a. free. Volunteer State Community College, Humanities Division, Nashville Pike, Gallatin, TN 37066. TEL 615-452-8600. Ed. Jeanne Irelan. circ. 1,000 (controlled).
    Description: Features poetry and short fiction from established writers, faculty and students.

821   UK   ISSN 0950-2858
NUMBERS. 1986. s-a. £4.50($11.50) Numbers Publishing Ltd., 6 Kingston St., Cambridge, Cambs. CB1 2NU, England. TEL 0223-353425. Ed.Bd. adv. circ. 1,000. (back issues avail.)

851   IT
NUOVA RASSEGNA: RIVISTA TRIMESTRALE. q. L.40000. Editrice Pellegrini, Via Roma 74, Casella Postale 158, 87100 Cosenza, Italy. Ed. Luigi Pellegrini-Cosenza. illus.
    Formerly: Poeti della Nuova Italia (ISSN 0032-1982)

811   US
NYCTICORAX (CITRUS HEIGHTS). 1985. 3/yr. $10. 8420 Olivine Ave., Citrus Heights, CA 95610-2721. Ed. John A. Youril. circ. 650.
    Description: Publishes poetry, including translated poems.

808.81   US   ISSN 1060-2232
O. ARS. 1981. s-a. $10. O. Ars, Inc., 21 Rockland Rd., Weare, NH 03281. TEL 603-529-1060. Ed. Don Wellman. adv.; bk.rev. circ. 1,000. (back issues avail.) **Indexed:** M.L.A. **Document type:** bulletin.
    Description: Covers poetry, visual language and theory.

808.81   US   ISSN 0896-3053
O-BLEK; a journal of language arts. 1987. 2/yr. $15 (effective Jan. 1990). Garlic Press Foundation, Inc., Box 1242, Stockbridge, MA 01262. TEL 413-528-0462. Eds. J. Connell McGrath, Peter Gizzi. circ. 300. (back issues avail.)
    Description: Includes prose and poetry with emphasis on experimental and lyric creative writing.

808.81   II
OCARINA; Journal of poetry and aesthetics. (Text in English) 1968. bi-m. price varies. Tagore Institute of Creative Writing, International, Diparun, T-29B, Seventh Ave., Madras 600 090, India. Ed. Amal Ghose. adv.; bk.rev. circ. 5,000.

861   AG
OCTACORDIO. irreg. (every 4-5 mos.). free. P.O. No. 918, 5500 Mendoza, Argentina. TEL 061-252304. Ed. Felicita Clerici. circ. 2,000. (back issues avail.)
    Description: Collection of 8 poems on a subject.

811   US
ODESSA POETRY REVIEW. 1984. 4/yr. $16. RR 1, Box 39, Odessa, MO 64076. Ed. Jim Wyzard. circ. 600.

OEUVRES ET AUTEURS. see *HISTORY — History Of North And South America*

811 810   US   ISSN 0360-1013
AS30
OHIO REVIEW. 1959. 3/yr. $16. Ohio University, Ellis Hall, Athens, OH 45701-2979. TEL 614-593-1900. Ed. Wayne Dodd. adv.; bk.rev.; illus.; index. circ. 3,000. (also avail. in Braille; back issues avail.) **Indexed:** A.I.P.P., Abstr.Pop.Cult., Amer.Hum.Ind., Arts & Hum.Cit.Ind., Curr.Cont., Ind.Amer.Per.Verse, Ind.Bk.Rev.Hum., LCR, M.L.A. —Faxon; UnCover; SWETS.
    Description: Devoted to contemporary American poetry, fiction, and essays.

811   US
OIKOS; a journal of ecology and community. 1980. a. $11.50 for 4 issues. 55 Magnolia Ave., Denville, NJ 07834. circ. 1,200.

808.81   US
OLD HICKORY REVIEW. 1969. s-a. $12. Jackson Writers Group, Box 1178, Jackson, TN 38302. TEL 901-424-3277. (Co-sponsor: Jackson Arts Council) Ed.Bd. circ. 300. (back issues avail.) **Document type:** academic/scholarly publication.
    Description: Focuses on promoting the literary craft and encouraging writers.

LITERATURE — POETRY

840 US ISSN 0381-9132
PN689
OLIFANT. (Text in English, French, German or Spanish) 1973; N.S. 1986. 2/yr. $12 to individuals (foreign $15); institutions $18 (foreign $24). University of Virginia, Dept. of French, Charlottesville, VA 22903. TEL 804-924-4627. Ed. Robert F. Cook. bk.rev.; abstr.; bibl.; index. circ. 450. (back issues avail.) **Indexed:** Amer.Hum.Ind., Can.Rev.Comp.lit, Curr.Cont, M.L.A. **Document type:** academic/scholarly publication.
—Faxon; UnCover; SWETS.
Description: Examines all studies and reviews on the Medieval Romance epic.
Refereed Serial

821 NR
OMABE; poetry from Nsukka. (Text in English) 1972. irreg. (approx. 3/yr.). £N3($4.50) University of Nigeria, Department of English, Nsukka, Nigeria. Ed. Ossie Onuora Enekwe. illus. circ. 1,000. (back issues avail.)
Formerly: Omaba.

808.81 UK ISSN 0308-4752
OMENS; poetry magazine. 1971. q. £1.50($5) 130 Letchworth Rd., Leicester LE3 6HF, England. Eds. John Martin, Sam Brown. adv.; illus. circ. 500. (back issues avail.)

811 US
OMNIFIC.* 1989. 4/yr. $12. HC-13, Box 21AA, Artemas, PA 17211-9045. TEL 814-458-3102. Ed. Kay Weems. circ. 200.

811 070.5 CN ISSN 1192-4411
▼**ON POETS AND POETRY.** 1992. bi-m. Can.$10. J.B. Reid, Ed. & Pub., Box 2041, Winnipeg, Man. R3C 3R3, Canada. TEL 204-774-9743. FAX 204-774-9743. bk.rev. circ. 2,000.
Description: Provides information on poetry markets and poetry by aspiring poets.

811 US ISSN 1043-884X
ONTHEBUS. 1989. 2/yr. $28 to individuals; institutions $33 for 3 nos. Bombshelter Press, 6421 1-2 Orange St., Los Angeles, CA 90048. TEL 213-651-5488. Ed. Jack Grapes. adv.; bk.rev.; illus. circ. 3,000. (back issues avail.)
Description: Contains poetry, stories, interviews, translations, and photographs.

052 UK ISSN 0030-4425
ORBIS; an international journal of poetry and prose. 1968. q. £15($30) 199 The Long Shoot, Nuneaton, Warwickshire CV11 6JQ, England. TEL 203-327440. FAX 203-642402. Ed. Mike Shields. adv.; bk.rev.; illus.; index. circ. 1,000. **Document type:** consumer publication.
Incorporates: Scrip.

821 UK ISSN 0030-459X
ORE. 1954. irreg. (2-3/yr.). £2.15 per no. Eric Ratcliffe, Ed., 7 the Towers, Stevenage, Herts. SG1 1HE, England. adv.; bk.rev. **Document type:** consumer publication.
Description: Poetry reflecting myth, legend and spiritual consciousness.

800 US ISSN 0162-296X
ORPHEUS; the magazine of poems. 1980. 3/yr. $12.50. Illuminati, Box 67E07, Los Angeles, CA 90067-1407. Ed. P. Schneidre. circ. 1,100.

811 US ISSN 0030-5804
ORPHIC LUTE. 1950. q. $12. Dreamcatcher Multiple Arts, 1713 14th Ave., Seattle, WA 98122. TEL 206-323-2115. Ed. David Sparenburg. bk.rev. circ. 1,250. (processed)
Description: Publishes lyric poetry of 40 lines or less, with special focus on ethnic, ecological, mythic and dream related themes. Also publishes short prose pieces.

700 US ISSN 0095-019X
OSIRIS (DEERFIELD); a multilingual poetry journal. (Text in English, French, German, Italian) 1972. s-a. $10. Box 297, Deerfield, MA 01342. TEL 413-774-4027. Ed. Andrea Moorhead. illus. circ. 1,000. **Indexed:** A.I.P.P., Amer.Hum.Ind., Ind.Amer.Per.Verse.
Description: Publishes contemporary poetry in numerous languages, as well as in bilingual format with English translation.

821 UK ISSN 0307-0786
OSTRICH. 1971. q. 60p.($3) Erdesdun Pomes, 10 Greenhaugh Rd., South Wellfield, Whitley Bay, Tyne and Wear NE25 9HF, England. Ed. Keith Armstrong. bk.rev.; illus. circ. 500. (also avail. in microfilm from HPL)

821 UK ISSN 0955-9620
OTTER. 1988. 3/yr. £5. Little Bystock, Richmond Rd., Exeter, England. Ed. R. Skinner. adv. circ. 400.
Description: Publishes the work of writers living in or connected with Devon, England.

OUROBOROS. see *LITERATURE*

821 UK ISSN 0950-7264
OUTPOSTS POETRY QUARTERLY. 1944. q. £12($24) (overseas £15). Hippopotamus Press, 22 Whitewell Rd., Frome, Somerset BA11 4EL, England. TEL 0373-466653. Ed. Roland John. adv.; bk.rev. circ. 2,300. (back issues avail.) **Document type:** academic/scholarly publication.
Formerly: Outposts (ISSN 0030-7297)
Description: Provides a nonbiased forum for new work in poetry and other forms of literature.

811 US
OUTRE. 1986. 2/yr. $1.50 per no. 2251 Helton Dr., Ste. N7, Florence, AL 35630. TEL 205-767-3324. Ed. Jake Berry. circ. 150.

OUTRIDER. see *LITERATURE*

821 UK
OVERSPILL;* for the longer poem. 1972. 5/yr. £1($3.50) c/o Eric Harrison, Ed., Grantley Close, Shalford, Nr. Guildford, Surrey, England. circ. 100. (processed)

811 US
▼**OVERVIEW (WOODRIDGE).** 1992. 2/yr. $10. Overview Ltd., Box 211, Woodridge, NJ 07075. Ed. Joseph Lanciotti. circ. 450.

800 UK
OXFORD POETRY. 1983. 3/yr. £6.50 (foreign £8). (Magdalen College) Oxford Poetry, Oxford OX1 4AU, England. Eds. Sinead Garrigan, Ian Sansom. adv.; bk.rev. circ. 650. (back issues avail.) **Document type:** consumer publication.
Description: Publishes a combination of new poetry, interviews and reviews of new and established poets.

L'OZIO; almanacco di letteratura. see *LITERATURE*

821 UK
P B S ANTHOLOGY. a. £8 membership. Poetry Book Society Ltd., 10 Barley Mow Passage, London W4 4BR, England. TEL 081-994-6477. **Document type:** bulletin.
Former titles: Poetry Bulletin; Poetry Anthology; Poetry Supplement.
Description: Contains new and previously unpublished poems from well-known British poets.

P - FORM; performance art magazine. see *ART*

811 US
P L G C NEWSLETTER. 1975. q. $25 membership. Poets' League of Greater Cleveland, Box 91801, Cleveland, OH 44101. TEL 216-932-8444. Ed. John Byrum. bk.rev.; bibl. circ. 800. **Document type:** newsletter.
Description: Attempts to establish, maintain and improve a regional, cultural, educational, intellectual and social climate in which the practice of art and poetry may prosper.

821 UK ISSN 0144-7076
PN1010
P N REVIEW. 1971. bi-m. £24.50($49) to individuals; institutions £30 ($60). Carcanet Press Ltd., 208 Corn Exchange, Manchester M4 3BQ, England. FAX 44-61-832-0084. Ed. Michael Schmidt. adv.; bk.rev.; cum.index. circ. 2,500. **Indexed:** M.L.A. **Document type:** academic/scholarly publication.
—BLDSC (6541.101000); Faxon; UnCover. **CCC**.
Supersedes (in 1976): Poetry Nation (ISSN 0308-2636); Carcanet (ISSN 0008-624X)
Description: For poets and poetry readers of all ages. Contains poetry, interviews, major essays, and reviews.

811 US
P R C NEWSLETTER AND CALENDAR. 1979. m. membership. Poetry Resource Center of Michigan, 111 E. Kirby, Detroit, MI 48202. Ed. Lee Schreiner. circ. 4,000.
Description: News of poetry in or about Michigan.

PACIFIC REVIEW; a magazine for poetry and prose. see *LITERARY AND POLITICAL REVIEWS*

811 US ISSN 0362-7969
PS580
PAINTED BRIDE QUARTERLY. 1973. q. $16 to individuals; institutions $20. Painted Bride Arts Center, 230 Vine St., Philadelphia, PA 19106. TEL 215-925-9914. Ed.Bd. adv.; bk.rev.; circ. 1,000 (paid). **Indexed:** Amer.Hum.Ind., Ind.Amer.Per.Verse.
Description: Presents poetry, fiction and essays by Pennsylvania writers and their peers nationwide.

811 US ISSN 1053-9247
PAINTED HILLS REVIEW. 1990. 3/yr. $10 to individuals; institutions $12. 2950 Portage Bay W., No. 411, Davis, CA 95616. Eds. Michael Ishii, Kara Kosmatka. bk.rev. circ. 300. **Document type:** consumer publication.
Description: Publishes original poetry and fiction.

861 301.412 CL
PALABRA DE MUJER; revista de poesia latinoamericana. 1990? q. (Poesia Latinoamericana) Editorial Fertil Provincia, Dalmacia 1121, Providencia, Santiago, Chile. TEL 2742240. Ed. Heddy Navarro H.

811 GW ISSN 0179-9711
PALETTE; Zeitschrift fuer Literatur von Randgruppen. 1985. 2/yr. DM.35 for 4 nos. Verein zur Foerderung von Randgruppenkultur e.V., Peuntstr. 10, 96050 Bamberg, Germany. TEL 0951-200599. adv.; bk.rev. circ. 600. (back issues avail.) **Document type:** bulletin.

808.81 US ISSN 0092-5535
PN6099.6
PANJANDRUM POETRY JOURNAL. 1972. irreg. $20 per 3 nos. Panjandrum Press, Inc., 6156 Wilkinson Ave., N. Hollywood, CA 91606-4518. TEL 818-985-7259. Ed. Dennis Koran. circ. 1,250. **Document type:** consumer publication.

PANORAMA OF CZECH LITERATURE. see *LITERATURE*

811 US
PAPER RADIO. 1986. 2/yr. $11 for 3 issues. P.O. Box 4646, Seattle, WA 98104. Ed. Neil S. Kvern. adv.; bk.rev.; illus. circ. 500.
Description: Publishes experimental poetry, art and short stories, humor, weirdness, and surrealism.

811 US
PAPER TOADSTOOL. 1989. irreg. (2-3/yr.). 4946 West Point Way, West Valley, UT 84120. TEL 801-972-8236. circ. 500.
Description: Contains short stories, poems and drawings.

PARLANGHE. see *LITERATURE*

811 US ISSN 0748-8785
PARNASSUS LITERARY JOURNAL. 1975. 3/yr. $12. Kudzu Press, Box 1384, Forest Park, GA 30051. TEL 404-366-3177. Ed. Denver Stull. bk.rev. circ. 200. (back issues avail.)
Description: Collection of poetry and essays pertaining to poetry by unsolicited contributors, emphasizing poetic structure and forms with a neo-romantic content.

811 US ISSN 0048-3028
PN6099.6
PARNASSUS: POETRY IN REVIEW. 1972. s-a. $23 to individuals; institutions $46. Poetry in Review Foundation, 41 Union Sq. W., Rm. 804, New York, NY 10003. TEL 212-463-0889. FAX 212-875-0148. Ed. Herbert Leibowitz. adv.; bk.rev.; index. circ. 2,500. (also avail. in microfilm) **Indexed:** Abstr.Engl.Stud., Amer.Bibl.Slavic & E.Eur.Stud., Amer.Hum.Ind., Arts & Hum.Cit.Ind., Bk.Rev.Ind. (1980-), Child.Bk.Rev.Ind. (1980-), Curr.Cont., Ind.Bk.Rev.Hum., LCR, M.L.A.
—BLDSC (6406.875000); Faxon; UnCover; UMI.
Description: Publishes original poetry and extended critical essays on individual poets and movements.

LITERATURE — POETRY

800 US ISSN 1043-3325
PARTING GIFTS. 1988. s-a. $8. March Street Press, 3413 Wilshire Dr., Greensboro, NC 27408-2923. Ed. Robert Bixby. circ. 100. **Indexed:** Ind.Amer.Per.Verse.
  Description: Experimental poetry and prose.

811 US ISSN 0031-2649
PS571.S8
PASQUE PETALS. 1926. 10/yr. $15. South Dakota State Poetry Society, 909 E. 34the St., Sioux Falls, SD 57105-0326. TEL 605-338-9156. Ed. Barbara Stevens. bk.rev. circ. 200.

811 US ISSN 0749-6761
PATRIOT. 1984. a. $10. Runaway Publications, Box 1172, Ashland, OR 97520-0040. TEL 503-482-2578. Ed. James L. Berkman. circ. 100 (controlled). (back issues avail.) **Document type:** monographic series.
  Description: Looks at the cutting edge of American poetry from a hard line perspective.

821 UK
PAUSE. 1969. 2/yr. $10. National Poetry Foundation, 27 Mill Rd., Fareham, Hampshire, England. Eds. Jonathon Clifford, Helen Robinson. circ. 600.

(808.81) US
(YEAR) PEACE CALENDAR. a. War Resisters League, 339 Lafayette St., New York, NY 10012. TEL 212-228-0450. FAX 212-228-6193.
  Description: Includes one page of poetry or prose with illustrations for each week of the year.

811 US
PEARL. 1987. 3/yr. $15. 3030 E. Second St., Long Beach, CA 90803. TEL 310-434-4523. Ed. Joan Jobe Smith. bk.rev. circ. 500.
  Description: Publishes poerty and short fiction.

811 US ISSN 0031-3696
PS580
PEBBLE; a magazine of poetry. 1968. 2/yr. $1 per no. Best Cellar Press, 118 S. Boswell, Crete, NE 68333-3207. TEL 402-826-4038. Ed. Greg Kuzma. bk.rev. circ. 450.

811 CN
PECKERWOOD. 1987. 3/yr. $2. 1475 King St. W., C 3, Toronto, ON M6K 1J4, Canada. TEL 416-531-4262. Ed. Yuki Hayashi; Pub. Ernie Ourique. circ. 200.

868 US ISSN 0888-322X
PEGASUS. 1986. q. $12.50. Pegasus Publishing, 525 Ave. B, Boulder City, NV 89005. TEL 702-294-1522. Ed. M.E. Hildebrand. circ. 200. (back issues avail.)

808.81 US
THE PEGASUS REVIEW. 1980. bi-m. $8. Pegasus Review, Box 88, Henderson, MD 21640-0088. TEL 410-482-7154. Ed. Art Bounds. circ. 160 (paid). (back issues avail.) **Document type:** newsletter.
  Description: Publishes original short short fiction and poetry in calligraphy.

811 US
PENINHAND.* 1990. 2/yr. $2. Peninhand Press, 3665 S.E. Tolman, Portland, OR 97202. Ed. Tom Janisse. circ. 500.

811 US ISSN 0031-4307
PENINSULA POETS. 1947. s-a. $12. Poetry Society of Michigan, 3781 Lodge Ln., Trenton, MI 48183. Ed. Joye S. Giroux. bk.rev. circ. 300.
  Description: Anthology of poetry by members of the society.

821 UK ISSN 0306-140X
PENNINE PLATFORM; poetry magazine. 1973. 3/yr. £7 (foreign £15). Brian Merrikin Hill, Ed. & Pub., Ingmanthorpe Hall Farm Cottage, Wetherby, W. Yorks. LS22 5EQ, England. TEL 0937-584674. adv.; bk.rev. circ. 350.
  Formerly (until 1975): Platform (Luddendenfoot) (ISSN 0032-1389)

808.81 US
PENTATETTE. 1981. m. $20 includes membership. Limerick Special Interest Group, Box 365, Moffet, CA 94035. bk.rev.

811 US ISSN 0888-9058
PERCEPTIONS (BRUNSWICK); women's poetry for a change. 1982. 3/yr. $15. Temi Rose, Ed. & Pub., 14 Cedar St., No. 2, Brunswick, ME 04011-2309. TEL 207-729-3774. adv.; bk.rev. circ. 300.
  Description: Women's poetry magazine dedicated to the expansion of language and consciousness.

808.81 US ISSN 0890-622X
PEREGRINE; the journal of Amherst Writers & Artists. 1983. a. $5 per no. Amherst Writers & Artists Press, Inc., Box 1076, Amherst, MA 01004. TEL 413-253-3307. FAX 413-253-7764. Ed. Pat Schneider. adv. circ. 500. (back issues avail.) **Document type:** bulletin.

808.81 US
PHASE AND CYCLE. 1988. s-a. $5. Phase and Cycle Press, 3537 E. Prospect, Ft. Collins, CO 80525. TEL 303-482-7573. Ed. Loy Banks. circ. 200. (back issues avail.)
  Description: Publishes poetry for the university community.

811 US
PHOENIX POETS. 1960. irreg., latest 1986. price varies. University of Chicago Press, 5801 S. Ellis Ave., Chicago, IL 60637. TEL 708-702-7899. (Subscr. to: 11030 Langley Ave., Chicago, IL 60628) Ed. Robert von Hallberg.
  Refereed Serial

800 US ISSN 0275-357X
PIEDMONT LITERARY REVIEW. 1976. q. $12. Piedmont Literary Society, 1017 Spanish Moss Ln., Breaux Bridge, LA 70517. Ed. Gail White. bk.rev. circ. 400. (back issues avail.)
  Description: Focuses on poetry, particularly rhymed poetry.

808.81 US
PIG IN A PAMPHLET.* 8/yr. $1 for 3 nos. 119 S. 25th St., Pittsburgh, PA 15203-2277. Ed. Harry Calhoun.

811 US
PIKEVILLE REVIEW. 1987. a. $4. Humanities Dept., Pikeville College, Pikeville, KY 41501. TEL 606-754-4189. Ed. James Alan Riley. circ. 500.

808.81 US
PITT POETRY SERIES. 1968. 7/yr. price varies. University of Pittsburgh Press, 127 North Bellefield Ave., Pittsburgh, PA 15260. TEL 800-666-2211. FAX 412-624-7380. Ed. Ed Ochester.

PITTSBURGH QUARTERLY. see *LITERATURE*

808.81 US ISSN 0554-2324
PIVOT. 1951. a. $5. 250 Riverside Dr., Apt. No. 23, New York, NY 10025. TEL 212-222-1408. (Subscr. to: Pivot Associates, 221 S. Barnard St., State College, PA 16801. TEL 814-238-8887) Ed. Martin Mitchell. adv. circ. 1,500. **Document type:** academic/scholarly publication.

808.8 US ISSN 0730-6172
PLAINS POETRY JOURNAL. 1982. 2/yr. $4.50 per issue; 5 issues $18. Stronghold Press, Box 2337, Bismarck, ND 58502. Ed. Jane Greer. circ. 550. (back issues avail.)
  Description: Presents American poetry.

808.81 US ISSN 0275-0074
PLAINSONG. 1979. irreg. $7 for 2 nos. Plainsong, Inc., Box 8245, Western Kentucky University, Bowling Green, KY 42101. TEL 502-745-5708. Ed.Bd. adv.; bk.rev. circ. 500.

811 US ISSN 1066-6044
PLASTIC TOWER. 1989. 4/yr. $8. Box 702, Bowie, MD 20718. TEL 410-563-2649. Eds. Carol Brown, Roger Kyle-Keith. circ. 200.
  Description: Presents new and established modern poets and a panorama of the 20th Century poetry styles.

821 CN ISSN 0840-707X
PLOWMAN; international poetry art culture. 1988. 4/yr. Can.$10. Box 414, Whitby, ON L1N 5S4, Canada. Ed. T. Scavetta. circ. 10,000. **Document type:** newspaper.
  Description: Publishes holocaust, religion, didactic, ethnic and love works.

811 US ISSN 1072-8821
THE PLUM REVIEW. 1991. 2/yr. $14 to individuals; institutions $18. Box 3557, Washington, DC 20007. Eds. Christina Daub, M. Hammer. bk.rev. circ. 1,000.
  Description: Carries poems, translations, reviews, and interviews with prominent poets.

841 FR ISSN 0152-0032
PN1010
PO & SIE. 1977. q. 215 F. (foreign 235 F.). Editions Belin, 8 rue Ferou, 75278 Paris Cedex 06, France. TEL 46-34-21-42. FAX 43-25-18-29. TELEX 269 355 F. Ed. Michel Deguy. adv.; bk.rev. circ. 500. **Indexed:** M.L.A.

811 US ISSN 0079-2438
POCKET POETS SERIES. 1955. irreg., no.46, 1989. price varies. City Lights Books, 261 Columbus Ave., San Francisco, CA 94133. TEL 415-362-1901.

809 US ISSN 0276-3737
PS2631
THE POE MESSENGER. 1969. a. $5 to libraries. Poe Foundation, Inc., 1914-16 E. Main St., Richmond, VA 23223. Ed. Agnes Bondurant Marcuson. bk.rev.; play rev.; bibl.; illus. circ. 550. (back issues avail.) **Indexed:** Amer.Hum.Ind. **Document type:** academic/scholarly publication.
  Description: Presents poetry, critical and historical information on the life of Edgar Allan Poe, includes list of Foundation activities and events.

811 US ISSN 0032-1885
PS580
POEM. 1967. 2/yr. $10. Huntsville Literary Association, Box 919, Huntsville, AL 35804. TEL 205-536-9038. Ed. N.F. Dillard. index every 6 nos. circ. 600. (back issues avail.) **Indexed:** A.I.P.P.

821 CN
POEMATA. 1986. 6/yr. Can.$20. Canadian Poetry Association, Box 340, Sta. B, London, ON N6A 4W1, Canada. Ed. Wayne Ray.

861 UY ISSN 0079-2462
POESIA.* irreg. Editorial Arca, Colonia 1263, Montevideo, Uruguay.

861 VE ISSN 0032-1893
PQ8544
POESIA DE VENEZUELA. 1963. bi-m. Bs.12($3) or exchange basis. Apdo. Postal 1114, Caracas 1010A, Venezuela. TEL 74-43-61. Ed. Pascual Venegas Filardo. adv.; bk.rev.
  Description: Presents poetry from Venezuela, with emphasis on contemporary poets.

861 AG ISSN 0032-1907
POESIA EN LA CALLE.* 1966. m. Habitante, Chacabuco 1380, Catamarca, Argentina. Ed. Luis Arganaraz.

861 PN
POESIA PANAMENA ACTUAL. 1979. a. price varies. (Direccion Nacional de Extension Cultural, Departamento de Letras) Editorial Mariano Arosemena (INAC), Apdo. 662, Panama 1, Panama. TEL 62-2811.

861 MX ISSN 0188-5154
POESIA Y POETICA. 1990. q. $20 (effective 1993). Universidad Iberoamericana, Departamento de Letras, Prol. Paseo de la Reforma 880, Col. Lomas de Santa Fe, 01210 Mexico DF, Mexico. TEL 5-570-79-49. FAX 5-726-90-48. Ed. Hugo Gola. illus. circ. 700. **Document type:** academic/scholarly publication.
  Description: Presents the best in contemporary poetry.

841 FR
POESIE (YEAR). 1984. 5/yr. 330 F. (foreign 350 F.). (Maison de la Poesie de Paris) Pierre Seghers, 228 bd. Raspail, 75014 Paris, France. TEL 43-20-28-88. FAX 43-21-68-11. adv.; bk.rev.
  Description: Forum for young unknown poets in France as well as the rest of the world.

841 CN ISSN 0846-0655
POESIE AU QUEBEC. a. Ecrits des Forges, c/o Diffusion Collective Radisson, 1497 Laviolette, C.P. 335, Trois-Riviers, PQ G9A 5G4, Canada. TEL 819-379-9813. Ed.Bd.

LITERATURE — POETRY

841 FR ISSN 0048-4563
PQ1160
POESIE PRESENTE. 1971. q. 290 F. Rougerie Editeur, Mortemart, 87330 Mezieres-sur-Issoire, France.
Description: Publishes current French poetry.

811 US ISSN 0364-4022
POESIE - U.S.A..* (Text in French) 1977. q. $10. Pierre E. Chanover, Ed. & Pub., 22605 S.W. 66th St., Ste. 408B, Boca Raton, FL 33428. adv. circ. 500. (back issues avail.)

830 GW
POESIE UND WISSENSCHAFT. SAMMLUNG. 1967. irreg. price varies. Lothar Stiehm Verlag, Hausackerweg 16, 69118 Heidelberg, Germany. **Indexed:** M.L.A.

821 II ISSN 0032-194X
POET. (Six international and six pan-continental issues) (Text in English) 1960. m. $20. World Poetry Society Intercontinental, c/o Dr. Krishna Srinivas, Ed., 118 Raja St., Madras 600042, India. TEL 2350186. bk.rev. circ. 1,000. (also avail. in microfilm from UMI; reprint service avail. from UMI)

811 US
POET (MISHAWAKA); peu a peu. 1973. a. $11.50. Fine Arts Society, 2314 W. Sixth St., Mishawaka, IN 46544. Ed. Doris Nemeth. adv.; illus.; circ. 1,000 (controlled). (reprint service avail. from UMI)

808.81 US
POET (OKLAHOMA CITY). 1989. q. $20. Box 54947, Oklahoma City, OK 73154. Ed. Joy Hall. adv.; illus.

811 US ISSN 0032-1958
PS501
POET AND CRITIC. 1961. 3/yr. $18 (foreign $21). Iowa State University, Department of English, 203 Ross Hall, Ames, IA 50011. TEL 515-294-2180. FAX 515-294-8753. Ed. Neal Bowers. adv.; bk.rev.; illus. circ. 400. (also avail. in microform from UMI; reprint service avail. from UMI) **Indexed:** A.I.P.P., Abstr.Engl.Stud., Arts & Hum.Cit.Ind., Curr.Cont., Ind.Amer.Per.Verse. **Document type:** academic/scholarly publication.
—UMI.

808.81 US ISSN 0032-1966
PN2
POET LORE; a quarterly of world literature. 1889. q. $15 to individuals; institutions $24. Writer's Center, 4508 Walsh St., Bethesda, MD 20815. TEL 301-654-8664. Ed. Philip Jason. adv.; bk.rev.; index. circ. 700. (also avail. in microform from PMC; back issues avail.; reprint service avail.) **Indexed:** A.I.P.P., Amer.Bibl.Slavic & E.Eur.Stud., Arts & Hum.Cit.Ind., Curr.Cont., Ind.Amer.Per.Verse, Ind.Bk.Rev.Hum.
—Faxon; UMI.

810 US
POET MAGAZINE. q. $20. Box 54947, Oklahoma City, OK 73154.
Description: Contains poetry and articles by US and international writers, competition information, awards, poetry book reviews, and tips on writing, publishing and selling work.

811 US
POET NEWS.* 1979. m. $18. Sacramento Poetry Center, 4750 Monterey Way, Sacramento, CA 95822-1258. TEL 916-448-6679. Ed.Bd. adv.; bk.rev. circ. 1,200.
Description: Publishes poetry, essays and articles related to the craft, translations of non-English works and short fiction.

861 PY
POETAS.* 1977. irreg. (Paraguay PEN Centre) Fondo Editor Paraguayo, San Rafael 658, Asuncion, Paraguay.

861 AG
▼**POETAS;** hacedores del patrimonio cultural. 1993. s-a. $2 per no. (avail. on exchange basis). Catamarca 234, 9o M, 1213 Buenos Aires, Argentina. Ed. Cayetano Zemborain.

811 869 BL
POETAS BRASILEIROS DE HOJE (YEAR). a. Shogun Editora e Arte Ltda., Caixa Postal 43.021, CEP 22052 Rio de Janeiro, Brazil. TEL 021-2559494.

808.81 II ISSN 0970-2830
POETCRIT. (Text in English) 1988. s-a. Rs.40($10) Poetcrit, c/o D.C. Chambial, Ed., Maranda 176 102, India. adv. circ. 1,000. (back issues avail.) **Document type:** academic/scholarly publication.
Description: Contains contemporary poetry and poetry criticism.

811 FR ISSN 0079-2470
POETES ET PROSATEURS DU PORTUGAL. 1970-1981. irreg. price varies. Centre Culturel Portugais, Fondation Calouste Gulbenkian, Centre Culturel Portugais, 51, ave. d'Iena, 75116 Paris, France. TEL 1-47-20-86-84. FAX 1-40-70-98-79. (Subscr. to: Jean Touzot, 38 rue Saint-Suplice, 75006 Paris, France. TEL 43-26-03-88) Ed. Maria de Lourdes Belchior. (reprint service avail. from KTO)
—CCC.

820 AU
POETIC DRAMA AND POETIC THEORY. (Text in English) 1972. irreg., no. 104, 1992. S.300. Universitaet Salzburg, Institut fuer Englische Sprache, Akademiestr. 24, A-5020 Salzburg, Austria. Ed. James Hogg. circ. 200. **Document type:** monographic series, academic/scholarly publication.

811 US
POETIC JUSTICE. 1982. irreg. (approx. a.). $10 for 4 issues. 8220 Rayford Dr., Los Angeles, CA 90045. Ed. Alan C. Engebretsen. circ. 200.

811 US ISSN 1054-0776
POETIC PAGE. 1989. 6/yr. $15. Poetic Page, Box 71192, Madison Heights, MI 48071-0192. TEL 313-548-0865. Ed. Denise Martinson. circ. 300.

811 US ISSN 1067-3733
POETIC SPACE. 1983. 2/yr. $10. Box 11157, Eugene, OR 97440. TEL 503-485-2278. FAX 503-485-2478. Eds. Don Hildenbrand, Thomas Strand. adv.: B&W page $100. bk.rev.; film rev, play rev. circ. 800. (back issues avail.)
Description: Features poetry, short fiction, art and black and white sketches.

POETICA; an international journal of linguistic-literary studies. see *LINGUISTICS*

851 IT
POETICA; mensile di poesia e critica diretto da Dante Maffia e Luigi Reina. m. L.25000. EdiSud, Via Leopoldo Cassese, 26, 84100 Salerno (NA), Italy.

811 US
POETIDINGS. 1973. m. $13 membership. New Jersey Poetry Society, c/o Theresa Dean, Box 653, Franklinville, NJ 08322. TEL 609-875-8122. Ed.Bd. adv.; bk.rev. circ. 200. (processed) **Document type:** newsletter.

811 US
POETPOURRI. 1986. s-a. $8. (Comstock Writers' Group, Inc.) Saltfire Press, 907 Comstock Ave., Syracuse, NY 13210. TEL 315-475-0339. Ed.Bd. circ. 500. (back issues avail.)

808.81 II ISSN 0970-7182
POETRY. (Text in English) 1975. s-a. Rs.40 (effective 1993). (Berhampur University, Department of English) Poetry Publications, Jasnal, 2nd Fl., Old Christian St., Berhampur 760 001, India. Ed. N. Mohanty. adv.; bk.rev. circ. 750.

811 US ISSN 0032-2032
PS301
POETRY (CHICAGO). 1912. m. $25. Modern Poetry Association, 60 W. Walton St., Chicago, IL 60610. TEL 312-280-4870. Ed. Joseph Parisi. adv.: B&W page $266; adv. contact: Helen Lothrop Klaviter. bk.rev.; index. circ. 7,500. (also avail. in microform from UMI,PMC; Braille; reprint service avail. from UMI; back issues avail.) **Indexed:** A.I.P.P., Acad.Ind., Access (1980-), Biog.Ind., Bk.Rev.Dig., Bk.Rev.Ind. (1965-), Child.Bk.Rev.Ind. (1965-), Curr.Cont., Ind.Amer.Per.Verse, Ind.Bk.Rev.Hum., Mag.Ind., Pop.Per.Ind.
—Faxon; SWETS; UMI. **CCC.**
Description: Devoted entirely to verse, from Auden to Ashbery, Pound to Pinsky, Stevens to Soto--voices both famous and new. Includes news notes and books received.

811 US ISSN 1072-7426
▼**POETRY (WOODRIDGE).** 1993. s-a. $10 (effective 1994). Overview Ltd., Box 211, Woodridge, NJ 07075. TEL 201-438-9069. FAX 201-778-5111. Ed. Joseph Lanciotti. adv. circ. 1,500. (back issues avail.)

821 UK ISSN 0260-9339
POETRY AND LITTLE PRESS INFORMATION. 1980. bi-a. £4.50. Association of Little Presses, c/o ALP coordinator, 30 Greenhill, Hampstead High St., London NW3 5UA, England. TEL 071-435-1589. Ed. Ian Robinson. circ. 500. **Document type:** consumer publication.
—BLDSC (6541.755000).
Description: Lists poetry and small press publications.

821 UK
POETRY BOOK SOCIETY BULLETIN. 1954. q. £8. Poetry Book Society Ltd., 10 Barley Mow Passage, London W4 4BR, England. TEL 081-994-6477. Ed. Martha Smart. adv.; bk.rev. circ. 2,000. **Document type:** bulletin.
Formerly: New Poems.
Description: Articles and news about contemporary British poetry titles.

821 CN
POETRY CANADA. 1979. q. Can.$17.12($17.85) to individuals; institutions Can.$34.24 ($35.25). Quarry Press, Inc., Box 1061, Kingston, ON K7L 4Y5, Canada. TEL 613-548-8429. FAX 613-548-1556. Eds. Barry Dempster, Bob Hilderley. adv. contact: Melanie Dugan. bk.rev. circ. 1,800. (also avail. in microfilm) **Indexed:** Can.Lit.Ind., CMI, Ind.Amer.Per.Verse.
Formerly: Poetry Canada Review (ISSN 0709-3373)
Description: Features essays on poetry, in-depth interviews, coast-to-coast poetry news articles, and notices of new poetry releases.

808.81 US
POETRY COMICS.* q? $7 for 4 nos. c/o Dave Morice, Ed., Box 3382, Iowa City, IA 52244-3382.

808.81 US
THE POETRY CONNECTION. 1988. bi-m. $5 per no. Sylvia Shichman, Ed. & Pub., 13455 S.W. 16 Ct., Ste. F-405, Pembroke Pines, FL 33027. TEL 305-431-3016. circ. 200. (back issues avail.)
Description: Includes a listing of poetry contests, information on poetry activities and poetry information books.

800 US ISSN 1052-4851
PN1010
POETRY CRITICISM. 1990. biennial. $75. Gale Research Inc., 835 Penobscot Bldg., Detroit, MI 48226-4094. TEL 313-961-2242. FAX 313-961-6083. TELEX 810-221-7086. Ed. Robyn V. Young.
Description: Presents overviews of 12-15 major poets from all time periods and from around the world in each volume.

821 UK
POETRY DURHAM. 1982. 3/yr. £6. University of Durham, School of English, Elvet Riverside, New Elvet, Durham DH1 3JT, England. TEL 091-374-2730. Ed.Bd. adv.; bk.rev. circ. 600. **Document type:** academic/scholarly publication.

811 US ISSN 0197-4009
PN1271
POETRY EAST. 1980. 2/yr. $12. Department of English, De Paul University, 802 W. Belden Ave., Chicago, IL 60614-3214. TEL 312-362-5114. FAX 312-362-5684. Ed. Richard Jones. adv.; bk.rev.; index. circ. 1,500. (back issues avail.) **Indexed:** Ind.Amer.Per.Verse.

811 US ISSN 0737-4747
POETRY FLASH; a poetry review and literary calendar for the West. 1972. m. $15 (foreign $28). Joyce Jenkins, Ed. & Pub., Box 4172, Berkeley, CA 94704. TEL 510-525-5476. Ed. Joyce Jenkins. adv.: page $500; trim 10 x 13 3/4. bk.rev.; illus. circ. 18,000. **Document type:** newspaper.
Description: Covers the entire eclectic spectrum of literary styles and schools. Focuses on poetry, but includes prose, novels and fictions.

POETRY INDEX ANNUAL. see *LITERATURE — Abstracting, Bibliographies, Statistics*

LITERATURE — POETRY

821   IE   ISSN 0332-2998
POETRY IRELAND REVIEW. 1981. q. I£16 (foreign I£24). Bermingham Tower, Upper Yard, Dublin Castle, Dublin 2, Ireland. TEL 01-6714632. FAX 01-6714634. Ed. Pat Boran. adv.; bk.rev. circ. 1,000. (back issues avail.) **Document type:** consumer publication.

808.81   JA
POETRY KANTO. (Text in English, Japanese) 1984. a. free. Kanto Poetry Center, Kanto Gakuin University, 1641 Kamariya, Kanazawa-ku, Yokohama 236, Japan. TEL 045-781-2001. Ed. William I. Elliott. circ. 800. (back issues avail.) **Document type:** trade publication.
    Description: Contains quality contemporary poetry by new and established poets from around the world.

808.81   UK   ISSN 0953-766X
POETRY LONDON NEWSLETTER. 1988. 3/yr. £12 (Europe £12; rest of world £20). Clacton Rd., London E17 8AR, England. (Subscr. to: P.O. Box 4LF, London W1P 4LF, England) Ed. Leon Cych. adv.: full page £100. **Document type:** newsletter.

811   US   ISSN 0048-4601
POETRY MISCELLANY. 1971. 2/yr. $3. University of Tennessee at Chattanooga, Department of English, Chattanooga, TN 37402. TEL 615-755-4269. Ed. Richard Jackson. adv.; bk.rev. circ. 600.

808.81   US
POETRY NEW YORK; a journal of poetry and translation. 1985. a. $4. City University of New York, English Department - Poetry New York, Box 3184, Church St. Sta., New York, NY 10008. (Dist. by: Berhard De Boer, Inc., 113 E. Centre St., Nutley, NJ 07110) Eds. Burt Kimmelman, Tod Thilleman. circ. 500.
    Description: Aims to feature a variety of the most vibrant, provocative and important poetry and translations being written today.

811   US   ISSN 0032-2113
AP2
POETRY NORTHWEST. 1959. q. $10. University of Washington, 4045 Brooklyn Ave. N.E., JA-15, Seattle, WA 98105. TEL 206-685-4750. Ed. David Wagoner. circ. 1,500. **Indexed:** A.I.P.P., Amer.Hum.Ind. **Document type:** academic/scholarly publication.
    Description: Features poetry by young American poets.

821   UK   ISSN 0143-3199
POETRY NOTTINGHAM. 1941. q. £8 (foreign £14). Nottingham Poetry Society, 39 Cavendish Rd., Long Eaton, Nottingham NG10 4HY, England. TEL 0602-461267. Ed. Martin Holroyd. adv.; bk.rev. circ. 300. (back issues avail.) **Document type:** bulletin.

821   UK
POETRY NOW. 1983. q. £8($25) 33 Belgrade Rd., Stoke Newington, London N16, England. Eds. Ravi Mirchandani, Rian Cooney.
    Incorporates (in Oct., 1984): Cambridge Poetry Magazine.

811   US
POETRY OF THE PEOPLE. 1986. m. $8. Box 13077, Gainesville, FL 32604. TEL 904-374-4058. Ed. Paul Cohen. circ. 1,000.
    Description: Publishes satire.

811   US   ISSN 0554-3983
PS301
POETRY PILOT. 1937. q. $25. Academy of American Poets, 584 Broadway, Apt. 1208, New York, NY 10012-3250. **Document type:** bulletin.
    Formerly (until 1943): Doggerel.

821   UK   ISSN 0306-0195
POETRY POST. 1973. 2/yr. £0.75. Ver Poets, 61 & 63 Chiswell Green Lane, St. Albans, Herts AL2 3AL, England. TEL 0727-867005. Ed. May Badman.

808.81   US
POETRY PROJECT NEWSLETTER. 1967. 4/yr. (bi-m. Oct. to May). $20. Poetry Project Ltd., St. Mark's Church in-the-Bowery, 131 E. Tenth St., New York, NY 10003. TEL 212-674-0910. Ed. Jordan Davis. adv. contact: Wanda Phipps. bk.rev. circ. 3,500. **Document type:** newsletter.
    Description: Contains poetry, articles, transcripts of symposia presentations, and annotated calendars of readings and events at the Poetry Project.

821   UK
POETRY QUARTERLY. 1975. irreg. £5.75($15) Curlew Press, Hare Cottage, Kettlesing, Harrogate, Yorks., England. Ed. P.J. Precious.

821   UK   ISSN 0032-2156
PN1010
POETRY REVIEW. 1909. q. £23 to individuals; institutions and libraries £30. Poetry Society Inc., 22 Betterton St., London WC2H 9BU, England. TEL 071-240-4810. FAX 071-240-4818. Ed. Peter Forbes. adv.; bk.rev. circ. 5,000. (reprint service avail. from ISI) **Indexed:** A.I.P.P., Arts & Hum.Cit.Ind., Curr.Cont., Ind.Bk.Rev.Hum., M.L.A. **Document type:** consumer publication.
    —BLDSC (6541.777000); Faxon.
    Description: New poetry, reviews and features on poetry worldwide.

808.81   US
POETRY SOCIETY OF AMERICA NEWSLETTER. a. $40. Poetry Society of America, 15 Gramercy Park, New York, NY 10003. TEL 212-254-9628. Ed. David Rothman. adv.; bk.rev.; tr.lit. circ. 2,700. (back issues avail.) **Document type:** newsletter.
    Description: Interviews, articles and other information of interest to poets.

808.81   II
POETRY TIME; a quarterly of creative literature. (Supplement avail.) (Text in English) q. Rs.40 (foreign $20). Poetry Time Publication, Giri Road, Berhampur 760 005, India. Ed. Laxmi Narayan Mahapatra. adv.; bk.rev. circ. 2,000.
    Description: Includes poems from India and abroad.

811   US   ISSN 1046-0365
PS301
POETRY: U S A QUARTERLY. 1985. q. $10. (National Poetry Association, Inc.) Poetry: U S A Publishers, 2569 Maxwell Ave., Oakland, CA 94601. TEL 510-532-3737. Ed. Jack Foley; Pub. Vernon Edgar. adv.: B&W page $200. index. circ. 10,000. (tabloid format; back issues avail.) **Document type:** newspaper.
    Formerly (until 1989): Poetry: San Francisco Quarterly.
    Description: Includes eclectic articles and poetry, including homeless, prisoner and children's poetry as well an international section.

821   UK   ISSN 0032-2202
PR8954.5
POETRY WALES; Cylchgrawn Cenedlaethol o Farddoniaeth Newydd. (Text mainly in English; occasionally in Welsh) 1965. 4/yr. £10 (outside UK £18). (Welsh Arts Council) Poetry Wales Press, Andmar House, Trewsfield Industrial Estate, Tondu Rd., Bridgend, Mid-Glam. CF31 4LJ, Wales. TEL 0656-767834. Ed. Richard Poole. adv.; bk.rev. circ. 1,000. (reprint service avail. from ISI) **Indexed:** Curr.Cont. **Document type:** academic/scholarly publication.
    —BLDSC (6541.785000); UnCover.
    Description: Covers poetry, critical essays and reviews, often with a Welsh connection.

811 810   US   ISSN 0891-6136
PS129
POETS & WRITERS MAGAZINE. 1972. 6/yr. $18 to individuals; institutions $25. Poets & Writers, Inc., 72 Spring St., New York, NY 10012. TEL 212-226-3586. FAX 212-226-2963. Ed. Darlyn Brewer. adv.: B&W page $1290. circ. 46,000. (also avail. in microform from UMI; reprint service avail. from UMI) **Document type:** trade publication.
    —Faxon; UnCover; UMI.
    Formerly (until 1987): Coda: Poets and Writers Newsletter (ISSN 0091-5645)
    Description: Provides essays, interviews with writers, news and commentary on publishing, political issues and practical topics of interest to writers. Includes coverage of grants and awards, deadlines for applications and calls for manuscript submissions.

808.81   US
POETS AT WORK. 1985. bi-m. $16. Jessee Poet Publications, Box 113, VAMC 325 New Castle Road, Butler, PA 16001. Ed. Jessee Poet. adv. circ. 350. (back issues avail.)
    Description: Publishes contributions of subscribers.

811   US
▼**POET'S FANTASY.** 1992. bi-m. $12. 227 Hatten Ave., Rice Lake, WI 54868. Ed. Gloria A. Stoeckel. circ. 200. (processed) **Document type:** academic/scholarly publication.
    Description: Publishes poetry and articles pertaining to the writing of poetry in different forms.

808.81   US
POET'S FORUM. 1988. m. $50.16 (effective 1992). Dayspring Press, 18600 W. 58 Ave., Golden, CO 80403-1070. TEL 303-279-2462. Ed. John C. Brainerd. adv. circ. 447. (back issues avail.)
    Description: Provides a forum for new and published poetry.

POET'S HANDBOOK; 2,300 poetry publishers. see *BIBLIOGRAPHIES*

808.81   II
POETS INTERNATIONAL. 1983. a. Rs.50($16) 361, 11th Cross, 2nd Block, Jayanagar, Bangalore 560 011, India. TEL 607 818. Eds. Mohamed Fakruddin, D. Litt. adv.; bk.rev. circ. 1,000.

811   US   ISSN 0883-5470
PN1059.M3
POET'S MARKET; where and how to publish your poetry. 1986. a. $19.95. F & W Publications, Inc., 1507 Dana Ave., Cincinnati, OH 45207. TEL 513-531-2222. FAX 513-531-4744. Ed. Christine Martin. index. circ. 25,000.
    Description: Provides 1,700 listings of magazines, chapbook publishers and other markets interested in poetry submissions.

811   US
POET'S NEWSLETTER. 1989. 2/yr. $2.50 per no. 609C Idlewild Cir., Birmingham, AL 35205. TEL 205-323-5690. Ed. Bettye K. Wraye. bk.rev. circ. 200. **Document type:** newsletter.
    Description: Poetry, fiction, essays and interviews.

808.81   US   ISSN 0146-3136
POETS ON:. 1976. s-a. $8. Poets On:, 29 Loring Ave., Mill Valley, CA 94941. TEL 415-381-2824. Ed. Ruth Daigon. bk.rev. circ. 450. **Indexed:** A.I.P.P.
    Description: Explores basic human concerns through poetry, each issue focusing on a specific topic.

821   CN
POETS' PODIUM. q. P.O. Box 60, Verdun, PQ H4G 3E1, Canada. Ed. Harry P. Fox. **Document type:** newsletter.

811   US
POETS' ROUNDTABLE. 1939. 6/yr. $6 (membership). 826 S. Center St., Terre Haute, IN 47807. TEL 812-234-0819. Ed. Esther Alman. circ. 2,000 (controlled).

811   PL   ISSN 0079-2527
POETYKA. ZARYS ENCYKLOPEDYCZNY. 1956. irreg., latest 1987. price varies. (Polska Akademia Nauk, Instytut Badan Literackich) Ossolineum, Publishing House of the Polish Academy of Sciences, Rynek 9, 50-106 Wroclaw, Poland. TEL 48-71-386-25. FAX 48-71-448-103. TELEX 0712771 OSS PL. Ed. Lucylla Pszczolowska. **Document type:** monographic series.
    Description: An Encyclopedic outline on problems of language, prosody, styles and figures in poetry.

899   RU
POEZIYA (MOSCOW). vol.20, 1977. irreg. 0.99 Rub. per issue. Izdatel'stvo Molodaya Gvardiya, Novodmitrovskaya ul. 5A, 125015 Moscow, Russia. Ed. N. Starshinov. illus. circ. 65,000.

841   FR   ISSN 0032-2369
POINTS ET CONTREPOINTS. 1935. q. 80 F. 19 rue Gerando, 75009 Paris, France. Ed. Jean Loisy. adv.; bk.rev.

808.81   FR   ISSN 0766-1924
POLYPHONIES. 1985. 2/yr. 140 F. B.P. 189, 75665 Paris Cedex 14, France. TEL 45-43-68-89. Ed. Pascal Culerrier. bk.rev.
    Description: Opens French literature to major productions of lyric poetry.

808.81 US ISSN 1041-9926
POTATO EYES. 1989. s-a. $11. Nightshade Press, Box 76, Ward Hill, Troy, ME 04987.
TEL 207-948-3427. Eds. Carolyn Page, Roy Zarucchi. bk.rev. circ. 800. (back issues avail.)
Description: Presents poetry, short stories, literary reviews, and art by authors and artists from the United States and Canada.

THE POTTERSFIELD PORTFOLIO; some of the best new fiction, essays, poetry, plays and artwork in English and French from Atlantic Canada and elsewhere. see LITERATURE

851 IT ISSN 0032-5686
POTY CUNTU;* e chiddus cun ti piaci ti lu canci. vol.42, 1967. s-m. L.1200.($3) Accademia Dialettale Siciliana Giovanni Meli, Viale delle Sirene 15, 90149 Palermo, Sicily, Italy. Ed. Dir. Peppino Denaro.
Document type: newspaper.

PRAIRIE JOURNAL. see LITERATURE

811 US
PRINCETON SERIES OF CONTEMPORARY POETS. 1975. irreg. price varies. Princeton University Press, 41 William St., Princeton, NJ 08540.
TEL 609-258-4900. FAX 609-258-6305. (reprint service avail. from UMI) **Document type:** monographic series.

895.65 JA ISSN 0917-1126
PRINTED MATTER. (Text in English) 1977. q. (plus 1 special issue). 3000 Yen. Tels Press, 3-31-14-207 Ikebukuro Honcho, Toshima-ku, Tokyo 170, Japan. TEL 03-3986-7468. Dir. Matthew Zuckerman. circ. 200.

808 US
PROMISE. 1989. q. $6. Bob Murphy, Ed. & Pub., Box 24, Bronston, KY 42518. TEL 606-561-4602. adv. circ. 1,000.
Description: Encourages aspiring writers to submit quality modern poetry and fiction.

851 055 IT
PROSPETTIVE CULTURALI CALABRESI. q. Corso Telesio, 34-36, Cosenza, Italy. Ed. M. Zuccaro.

861 SP
PROVINCIA; coleccion de poesia. 1970. irreg. 2500 ptas.($20) for 6 nos. Institucion "Fray Bernardino de Sahagun", Edificio Fierro, Puerta de la Reina, 1, Leon, Spain. circ. 1,000.

861 AG
PROVINCIA. 1967. s-m. $2. Rafael M. Altamirano, Ed. & Pub., Calle Libertad s-n, Casa 16 B, Barrio los Olivos, 5870 Villa Dolores, Argentina.
TEL 0544-21889. bk.rev.
Description: Covers poetry and other literary works.

821 UK ISSN 0968-5081
PSYCHOPOETICA; a magazine of psychologically-based poetry. 1978. q. £8($16) Psychopoetica Publications, University of Hull, Dept. of Psychology, Hull HU6 7RX, England. TEL 0482-465581. FAX 0482-465599. Ed. Geoff Lowe. bk.rev. circ. 300. (back issues avail.) **Document type:** consumer publication.

811 US
PTOLEMY. 1979. a. $2. David Vajda, Ed. & Pub., Box 908, Browns Mills, NJ 08015. TEL 609-893-0896. circ. 250.

070.5 808.81 US ISSN 1071-7633
PUCK: THE UNOFFICIAL JOURNAL OF THE IRREPRESSIBLE. 1984. 3/yr. $17. Permeable Press, 900 Tennessee, Studio 15, San Francisco, CA 94107-3014. TEL 415-648-2175.
FAX 415-648-2180. E-mail: BCCLARK@IGC.APC.ORG. Ed. Brian C. Clark. bk.rev. circ. 2,000.
Former titles: Xerotic Ephemera; Naked Review; (until 1988): Comet Halley.
Description: Literary journal dedicated to exposing assumptions. Provides a radical reinterpretation of fiction, poetry and reviews.

811 US ISSN 0196-5913
PUDDING MAGAZINE; international journal of applied poetry. 1980. irreg. $15.75 for 3 nos. Pudding House Publications, c/o Pudding House Bed & Breakfast for Writers, 60 N. Main St., Johnstown, OH 43031. Ed. Jennifer Welch Bosveld. adv.; bk.rev. circ. 1,400. **Indexed:** A.I.P.P.
Description: Publishes poetry, essays, articles with particular emphasis on popular culture, and sociology.

861 AG ISSN 0033-4391
PUNTO OMEGA.* 1968. bi-m. Arg.$1000. Envios, Gualeguaychu 882, Buenos Aires, Argentina. Ed. Edmundo J. Knlino. adv.; bk.rev.; bibl.

811 UK
PURPLE HEATHER PUBLICATIONS. 1981. bi-m. £9($24) Yorkshire Arts Association, 12 Granby Terrace, Headingley, Leeds, West Yorkshire LS6 3BB, England. TEL 0532-785878. Ed. Richard Mason. circ. 500. (also avail. in audio cassette; back issues avail.)

821 UK ISSN 0966-5609
PURPLE PATCH. 1976. 6/yr. £6. 8 Beaconview House, Charlemont Farm, West Bromwich, West Midlands, England. TEL 021-588-6642. Ed. Geoff Stevens. bk.rev. **Document type:** consumer publication.

QINGNIAN WENXUE/YOUTH LITERATURE. see LITERATURE

QINGNIAN ZUOJIA/YOUNG WRITERS; wenxue shuang yuekan. see LITERATURE

QUADERNI DI LINGUE E LETTERATURE. see LITERATURE

808 IT ISSN 0079-8274
QUADERNI DI POESIA NEOGRECA. 1967. irreg., no.7, 1987. price varies. Istituto Siciliano di Studi Bizantini e Neoellenici, Via Noto, 34, 90141 Palermo, Italy. TEL 091-625-9541.

800 US ISSN 0748-0873
AP2
QUARTERLY REVIEW OF LITERATURE POETRY SERIES.
Variant title: Q R L Poetry Series. 1943. a. $20 paperback; hardback $40. 26 Haslet Ave., Princeton, NJ 08540. TEL 609-921-6976. Eds. Theodore & Renee Weiss. adv. circ. 3,000. (back issues avail.) **Indexed:** A.I.P.P., Acad.Ind., Arts & Hum.Cit.Ind., Curr.Cont., Ind.Little Mag., R.G. —BLDSC (7207.500000).
Former titles: Quarterly Review of Literature Contemporary Poetry Series; Quarterly Review of Literature (ISSN 0033-5819)
Description: Publishes books of poetry, long poems, poetic plays and books of translations chosen in open competition. Includes photographs, biographies and statements about writing by the authors.

851 IT ISSN 0048-6213
QUASI;* testi poetici e altre approssimazioni. 1971. 2/yr. L.22999. L. Manzuoli, Via Cairoli 86, 50131 Florence, Italy. Eds. Giuseppe Favati, G. Zagarrio. bk.rev.; illus. circ. 1,000. (back issues avail.)

811 US
QUICKENINGS IN TRILLUM LAND. 1974. 2/yr. $4.75. 4344 S.W. Concord, West Seattle, WA 98136. Ed. Jessie T. Haraska. illus.

851 IT ISSN 0390-3656
QUINTA GENERAZIONE; trimestrale di poesia. 1973; N.S. 1992. q. L.25000 (foreign L.30000) (effective 1992). Editrice Forum, Via Pedriali 27, 47100 Forli, Italy. TEL 0543-22763. Ed. Giampaolo Piccari. bk.rev.; bibl.

808.81 II
RABINDRA BHARATI JOURNAL. (Text in English) 1968. irreg., latest issue, 1973. Rs.2. Rabindra Bharati University, 6-4 Dwarkanath Tagore Ln., Calcutta 700007, India. Ed. Ramendranath Mullick. circ. 500.
Description: Contains essays and poems.

811 US ISSN 0148-0162
PS615
RACCOON. 1977. irreg. (2-3/yr.). $15. Ion Books, Inc., Box 111327, Memphis, TN 38111-1327. TEL 901-323-8858. Ed. David Spicer. bk.rev.; index. circ. 500. (back issues avail.) **Indexed:** Amer.Hum.Ind., Ind.Amer.Per.Verse.
—CCC.

RADAR - SEI; rivista mensile di attualita-arte-cultura. see ART

811 US
RAFALE. (Text in English, French) 1977. 4/yr. $10. 126 College Ave., Orono, ME 04469.
TEL 207-581-3764. Ed. Angela Hebert. circ. 4,500.
Description: Encourages the Franco-American artistic expression.

917.306 US ISSN 0891-0545
PK8517
RAFT; a journal of Armenian poetry and criticism. 1987. a. $17.50 to individuals; institutions $30 (for 2 yrs.). c/o John A.C. Greppin, Ed., Cleveland State University, Cleveland, OH 44115.
TEL 216-687-3967. FAX 216-687-9214. adv.; bk.rev.; bibl.; circ. 225 (paid). **Document type:** academic/scholarly publication.
●Also available online.
Description: Intends to serve the needs of those interested in Armenian poetry and criticism who would read it in translation.

808.81 US
RAM - THE LETTER BOX. 1974. q. $25. Fordham University, Box B, Bronx, NY 10458. Ed.Bd. adv.; bk.rev. circ. 6,000.

808.81 US
RANSOM STREET MAGAZINE. q. 323 McMaster St., Chapel Hill, NC 27516.

811 US
RAYSTOWN REVIEW. 1990. a. $3. RD 1, Box 205, Schellsburg, PA 15559. circ. 500.

808.81 US
REALITIES. 1975. m. $5. Realities Library, 2745 Monterey Hwy. No. 76, San Jose, CA 95111. Ed. Richard A. Soos, Jr. bk.rev. circ. 500.
Former titles: Poet; Monthly Poetry Anthology (ISSN 0146-695X); Seven Stars Poetry.

808.81 301.412 US
REBIRTH OF ARTEMIS. 1982. s-a. $9. Astra Publications, 24 Edgewood Terr., Methuen, MA 01844. TEL 617-685-3087. Ed. Lorraine Moreau-Laverriere. circ. 500. (back issues avail.)

811 US ISSN 0147-0396
REBIS CHAPBOOK SERIES. 1977. irreg., unnumbered. Allegany Mountain Press, 111 N. 10th St., Olean, NY 14760. Ed. H. Ruggieri. circ. 300.

811 US
RECORD SUN.* 1969. 4/yr. $8. Poet Papers, Box 8025, Northridge, CA 91327-8025. circ. 8,000.

RED CEDAR REVIEW. see LITERARY AND POLITICAL REVIEWS

811 US
RED DANCEFLOOR.* 1990. 4/yr. $3.50 per no. Box 7392, Van Nuys, CA 91405-7392.
TEL 818-785-7650. Ed. David Goldschlag. circ. 450.

811 US
RED DIRT. 1991. 2/yr. $10 to individuals; institutions and foreign $20. 1630 30th St., Ste. A-307, Boulder, CO 80301. circ. 1,500.

811 US
RED PAGODA; a journal of haiku. 1983. q. $16 (foreign $24). Lewis Sanders, Ed. & Pub., 125 Taylor St., Jackson, TN 38301.
TEL 901-427-7714. bk.rev. circ. 130.

811 028.5
REFLECTIONS (DUNCAN FALLS); the national student poetry magazine for grades K-12. 1980. s-a. $5. Duncan Falls Junior High Journalism Group, Box 368, Duncan Falls, OH 43734. TEL 614-674-5209. Ed. Dean Harper. adv.: B&W page $100. circ. 1,000. (also avail. in Braille; record; video cassette; back issues avail.) **Indexed:** Avery Ind.Archit.Per., ERIC.

808.81 US
RENEGADE (BLOOMFIELD HILLS). 1988. s-a. $5.90. Box 314, Bloomfield Hills, MI 48303. Ed. Michael E. Nowicki. adv.; bk.rev. circ. 100.

RENMIN WENXUE/PEOPLE'S LITERATURE. see LITERATURE

LITERATURE — POETRY

RESONANCE (NEW YORK); new voices for a new age. see NEW AGE PUBLICATIONS

811 US
THE REVIEW (PORTLAND); words and images. 1974. a. $2.50. University of Southern Maine, 96 Falmouth St., Portland, ME 04103. TEL 207-874-6547. Pub. M. Griffin Hane. adv.: B&W page $135; trim 9 3/4 x 6 1/2. bk.rev. circ. 1,000. **Document type:** academic/scholarly publication.
Former titles: Portland Review of the Arts; Presumpscot Review.

811 US
REVIEW LA BOOCHE. 1976. 2/yr. $6. 110 South Ninth, Columbia, MO 65201. circ. 500.

861 AG
REVISTA ACENTO. 1981. bi-m. $10. Fundacion Shaw, Cerrito 1154, Buenos Aires, Argentina. Eds. Juan Forn, Enrique Valiente Noailles. circ. 1,200.

861 SP ISSN 1133-0368
REVISTA ATLANTICA; de poesia. Cover title: Revistatlantica de Poesia. (Text in Spanish; some works are also in original languages: Catalan, English, French, Gallegan, Portuguese) 1991. 3/yr. $70. Diputacion Provincial de Cadiz, Plaza de Espana, s-n, 11006 Cadiz, Spain.
TEL 956-240203. FAX 956-228452. Dir. Jose Ramon Ripoll. circ. 2,500.
Description: Focuses on Spanish and Latinamerican poetry, yet includes translations and original texts from important poets in other languages.

861 CR
REVISTA DE POESIA CENTROAMERICANA. Title varies: Revista Centroamericana de Poesia. 1974. q. Universidad de Costa Rica, Instituto de Estudios Centroamericanos, C.U. Rodrigo Facio, San Pedro de Montes de Oca, San Jose, Costa Rica. Ed. Manlio Argueta. illus.

808.81 US
RHINO. 1976. a. $6. Poetry Forum, 8403 W. Normal Ave., Niles, IL 60714. TEL 708-823-6721. Eds. Kay Meier, Don Hoffman. index. circ. 500. (back issues avail.) **Document type:** academic/scholarly publication.
Description: Publishes free verse poetry and short prose.

821 UK ISSN 0268-5981
THE RIALTO. 1984. 3/yr. £8 (Europe £11; U.S. £15; elsewhere £15.50). 32 Grosvenor Rd., Norwich, NR2 2PZ, England. Eds. Michael Mackmin, John Wakeman. illus. circ. 12,000. (back issues avail.)
Document type: consumer publication.
Description: A magazine of and about new poetry.

831 GW ISSN 0720-0463
RIND UND SCHLEGEL; Zeitschrift fuer Poesie. 1977. q. DM.26. Klaus Friedrich, Ed. & Pub., Ursulastr. 10, 80802 Munich, Germany. TEL 089-342550. adv.; bk.rev. circ. 1,500.
Description: Includes a collection of contemporary poetry.

821 US ISSN 0893-9721
RIVER RAT REVIEW. 1987-1989; resumed no.6, 1992. a. $4. Box 24198, Lexington, KY 40524.
TEL 606-277-8601. Ed. Daryl Rogers. bk.rev. circ. 200. (back issues avail.)

811 US
RIVERRUN. a. $4. Brooklyn College, English Department, Bedford Ave. and Avenue H, Brooklyn, NY 11210. TEL 718-780-5195. Ed. Carlos Serrano.

811 US
RIVERWIND. 1977. a. $2.50. (Hocking College) Riverwind Press, General Studies, Hocking College, Nelsonville, OH 45764. TEL 614-753-3591. Ed.Bd. bk.rev. circ. 400.
Description: Presents literature from many genres.

RIVISTA LETTERARIA; quadrimestrale di critica letteraria e cultura varia. see LITERATURE

ROANOKE REVIEW. see LITERATURE

890 BG
ROBABARA. (Text in Bengali) 1978. w. Tk.4. New Nation Printing Press, 1, Ramkrishna Mission Rd., Dhaka 3, Bangladesh.

811 US ISSN 0300-7936
PS3519.E27
ROBINSON JEFFERS NEWSLETTER. 1962. q. $10. California State University, Department of English, 1250 Bellflower Blvd., Long Beach, CA 90840.
TEL 310-985-4235. FAX 310-985-2369.
(Co-sponsors: California State University, Long Beach; Occidental College) Ed. Robert Brophy. bk.rev.; abstr. circ. 200. (processed; also avail. in microfilm) Indexed: Abstr.Engl.Stud., LCR, M.L.A.
Document type: newsletter.

821 UK ISSN 0144-7262
ROCK DRILL. 1980. irreg. £1.20($4.80) Supranormal Cassettes, 15 Oakapple Rd., Southwick, Sussex BN4 4YL, England. Eds. Robert Sheppard, Penelope Bailey. adv.; bk.rev. circ. 200. (back issues avail.)

ROUND TABLE: A JOURNAL OF POETRY & FICTION. see LITERATURE

813 US ISSN 1072-4524
RUAH. 1991. a. $8 (foreign $9). Power of Poetry, c/o Dominican School of Philosophy & Theology, 2401 Ridge Rd., Berkeley, CA 94709.
TEL 510-763-4057. FAX 510-849-1372. Ed.Bd.
Description: Publishes poetry celebrating faith, spirituality and experience.

RUNDY'S JOURNAL AND CONFEDERATION COURIER. see SPORTS AND GAMES — Ball Games

808.81 US ISSN 0891-2378
S P S M & H. (Shakespeare, Petrarch, Sidney, Milton & Hopkins) 1986. q. $14. Amelia, 329 "E" St., Bakersfield, CA 93304. TEL 805-323-4064. Ed. Frederick A. Raborg, Jr. bk.rev.; illus. circ. 600. (back issues avail.)
Description: Presents sonnets, artricles, fiction about or including sonnets; original illustrations and appropriate sophisticated cartoons.

811 CN
SACRED FIRE. 1990. 4/yr. $20. P.O. Box 91980, West Vancouver, B.C. V7V 4S4, Canada.
TEL 604-922-8745. Ed. Robert Augustus Masters. circ. 20,000.

808.81 US ISSN 0735-4665
PS301
SAGETRIEB. 1982. 3/yr. $18 to individuals; institutions $35. National Poetry Foundation, 302 Neville Hall, University of Maine, Orono, ME 04469.
TEL 207-581-3814. Ed. Carroll F. Terrell. adv.; bk.rev. circ. 300. Indexed: Abstr.Engl.Stud., Amer.Hum.Ind., M.L.A.
—BLDSC (8069.272270); Faxon; UnCover.

808.81 US ISSN 0885-5013
PS508.M4
SAGUARO. (Text in English, Spanish) 1984. a. $10 to individuals; institutions $15. University of Arizona, Mexican American Studies and Research Center, Douglass Bldg., Rm. 315, Tucson, AZ 85721.
TEL 602-621-7551. FAX 602-621-7966. Ed. Charles Tatum. adv. (back issues avail.)

811 US
ST. MAWR. (Text in English, French, Spanish) 1975. s-a. $16.50 (effective Aug. 1991). 496a Hudson St., Ste. K118, New York, NY 10014.
FAX 212-787-9653. Ed. J.H. Kennedy. adv.; charts; illus. circ. 1,000. (also avail. in diskette format; avail. on audio tape)
Formerly (until vol.3, 1977): Veins, Journal of Jazz Poetry.

811 US
SALAD. 1990. 2/yr. $12. Box 64980-306, Dallas, TX 75206. circ. 1,000.

821 IE ISSN 0790-1631
PR8848
SALMON. (Text in English, Gaelic) 1981. 3/yr. £6($22) Salmon Publishing, The Bridge Mills, Galway, Ireland. TEL 091-62587. Ed. Jessie Lendennie. adv. circ. 1,000. (back issues avail.)
Description: Contemporary poetry and short stories primarily by Irish writers, as well as international writers.

831 AU
SALZ; Salzburger Literaturzeitung. 1975. q. S.100. Salzburger Literaturforum Leselampe, Strubergasse 23, A-5020 Salzburg, Austria. TEL 0662-390741. FAX 0662-422411. bk.rev. circ. 6,200. (back issues avail.) **Document type:** consumer publication.

895 II ISSN 0970-0986
SAMKALEEN KALA AUR KAVITA. (Text in Hindi) 1982. q. Rs.80($24) Samkaleen Prakashan, 2762 Rajguru Marg, New Delhi 110 055, India. Ed. Krishan Khullar. adv.; bk.rev.; illus.

811 US ISSN 0196-2884
SAN FERNANDO POETRY JOURNAL. 1978. q. $10. Kent Publications, Inc., 18301 Halsted St., Northridge, CA 91325. TEL 818-349-2080. Ed. Richard Cloke. adv.; bk.rev. circ. 1,000. (back issues avail.) Indexed: Ind.Amer.Per.Verse.
Description: Collection of contemporary, liberal poetry focusing on social, political, and environmental issues.

811 US
SAN MIGUEL QUARTERLY.* 1990. biennial. Box 1375, Mendocino, CA 95460-1375. Ed. John Brander. circ. 400.

SANDHILLS REVIEW. see LITERATURE

SARGASSO; theater, film, poetry, performance, criticism. see LITERARY AND POLITICAL REVIEWS

808.1 CN ISSN 0080-6560
SASKATCHEWAN POETRY BOOK. 1936. biennial. Can.$4. Saskatchewan Poetry Society, 3104 College Avenue, Regina, SK S4T 1V7, Canada.
TEL 306-522-6321. Ed.Bd. circ. 600. (back issues avail.)
Description: Includes brief bibliographical notes on each poet represented.

821 AT
SCARP. 1982. 2/yr. $12. Five Islands Press Cooperative Ltd., P.O. Box 1144, Wollongong, N.S.W. 2500, Australia. TEL 042-270985. circ. 1,000.

808.81 US
SCHLEGEL TRANSLATIONS. irreg., latest no.3. $39.95 per no. Edwin Mellen Press, 415 Ridge St., Box 450, Lewiston, NY 14902. TEL 716-754-2788.
FAX 716-754-4056. **Document type:** monographic series.

SCHREIBHEFT; Zeitschrift fuer Literatur. see LITERATURE

821 UK
SCRATCH. no.5, 1991. 3/yr. £4. Mark Robinson, Ed. & Pub., 24 Nelson St., The Groves, York YO3 7NJ, England.
Description: Small press poetry magazine.

811 US
SCREAM OF THE BUDDHA. 1989. 6/yr. $35. Buddha Rose Publications, Box 548, Hermosa, CA 90254.
TEL 310-543-9673. Ed. Scott Shaw. bk.rev. circ. 1,108.

808.81 US
SCREAM PRESS BROADSHEETS. 1989. a. free. Scream Press, 509 Enterprise Dr., Rohnert Park, CA 94928. Ed. Anthony Boyd. illus. circ. 1,000.

SCREE. see LITERARY AND POLITICAL REVIEWS

808.81 070
SE LA VIE WRITER'S JOURNAL. 1987. q. $16 (foreign $20). Rio Grande Press, Box 71745, Las Vegas, NV 89170-1745. Ed. Rosalie Avara. adv.; bk.rev. circ. 300.
Formerly (until 1989): Se la Vie Poetry Newsletter.
Description: Dedicated to encouraging novice writers, poets and artists by giving them a chance at getting published.

SEEMS. see LITERATURE

811 US ISSN 0037-2145
PN6010.5
SENECA REVIEW. 1970. s-a. $8. Hobart & William Smith Colleges, Geneva, NY 14456.
TEL 315-781-3364. Ed. Deborah Tall. adv.; bk.rev.; illus. circ. 600. (back issues avail.) Indexed: A.I.P.P., Amer.Hum.Ind., Ind.Amer.Per.Verse.
Description: Contemporary poetry, translations and essays on contemporary poetry.

LITERATURE — POETRY

821 UK ISSN 0140-1165
SEPIA. 1977. 3/yr. $3. Kawabata Press, Knill Cross House, Knill Cross, Millbrook, Torpoint, Cornwall, England. Ed. Colin David Webb. bk.rev. circ. 100. **Document type:** consumer publication.
 Description: Poetry and prose.

811 US ISSN 0269-0179
SERIE D'ECRITURE. 1980. a. $9.50. Burning Deck, 71 Elmgrove Ave., Providence, RI 02906. circ. 500.

800 IS ISSN 0334-6137
SEVEN GATES. (Text in English) 1985. irreg., no.7, 1992. IS.25 per no. Eva Avi-Yonah, Ed. & Pub., 15 Bialik St., Jerusalem 96221, Israel. TEL 972-2-435402. illus. circ. 30. (back issues avail.)
 Description: Publishes contemporary poetry by poets from Jerusalem, as well as art and graphic works by Israeli artists.

811 US
SHARING.* 1982. q. $12. (Western Sun Associates, Inc.) Western Sun Publications, 201 S. 1st Ave., Yuma, AZ 85364. Eds. Carson E. Bench, Alex Starch. circ. 200. **Indexed:** Rehabil.Lit.

811 US
SHATTERED WIG REVIEW. 1988. 2/yr. $7. 2407 Maryland Ave., Apt. 1, Baltimore, MD 21218. TEL 410-243-6888. bk.rev. circ. 500.
 Description: Publishes prose poetry and concrete poetry, graphics, stories, and ravings.

895.1 CC
SHI SHEN/POEMS DEITY. (Text in Chinese) m. Hebei Sheng Wenxue Yishu Lianhehui, 2 Shizhuang Lu, Shigang Dajie, Shijiazhuang, Hebei 050000, People's Republic of China. TEL 741808.

895.1 CC ISSN 0583-0230
PL2543
SHIKAN/POETRY. (Text in Chinese) 1957. m. Y15.60($44) (Zhongguo Zuojia Xiehui - China Writers' Association) Shikan She, 10, Nongzhanguan Nanli, Beijing 100026, People's Republic of China. (Dist. overseas by: China International Book Trading Corporation, P.O. Box 2820, Beijing, P.R.C.; Dist. in US by: China Books & Periodicals, Inc., 2929 24th St., San Francisco, CA 94110. TEL 415-282-2994)

895.1 CC
SHILIN. (Text in Chinese) q. Harbin Wenlian, Shilin Bianjibu, 12, Gongchang Jie, Daoli-qu, Harbin, Heilongjiang 150010, People's Republic of China. TEL 410478. Ed. Jiang Wei.

895.1 CC
SHIREN/POET. (Text in Chinese) bi-m. Zhongguo Zuojia Xiehui, Jilin Fenhui - Chinese Writers Association, Jilin Chapter, Fu 111, Stalin Street, Changchun, Jilin 130022, People's Republic of China. TEL 884790. Ed. Lu Ping.

811 US
SHIRIM;* a Jewish poetry journal. 1982. s-a. $7. 1238 E. Wilson Ave., Glendale, CA 91206-5615. Ed. Marc Steven Dworkin. circ. 400.

SICHUAN WENXUE/SICHUAN LITERATURE. see LITERATURE

808.81 284 US ISSN 0889-9118
SILVER WINGS; poems. 1983. q. $7. Poetry on Wings, Inc., Box 1000, Pearblossom, CA 93553-1000. TEL 805-264-3726. Ed. Jackson Wilcox. bk.rev. circ. 450. (back issues avail.)
 Description: Christian ecumenical poetry with a spiritual message.

808.81 US
THE SINGLE HOUND;* the poetry and image of Emily Dickinson. 1989. s-a. $12 to individuals (foreign $15); institutions $20 (foreign $23). Box 276, New Castle, NH 03854-0276. TEL 603-659-2685. Ed. Andrew Leibs. bk.rev. circ. 300. (also avail. in diskette format)
 Description: Explores the poetry and life of Emily Dickinson.

811 US
SISYPHUS.* 1990. 6/yr. $12. 423 Terry Ave., No. 11, Seattle, WA 98104-2417. Ed. Christopher Corbett-Fiacco.

808.81 US ISSN 0893-7095
SLANT: A JOURNAL OF POETRY. 1987. a. $10. University of Central Arkansas, Box 5063, Conway, AR 72035. TEL 501-450-5107. (Subscr. to: UCA, Box 5063, Conway, AR 72035) Ed. James Fowler. circ. 250. (back issues avail.) **Document type:** academic/scholarly publication.
 Description: Presents traditional and modern poetry from all regions.

SLATE & STYLE. see HANDICAPPED — Visually Impaired

811 700 770 US ISSN 0749-0771
SLIPSTREAM (NIAGARA FALLS). 1981. s-a. $15 (includes 2-3 Chapbooks and 1 audio tape). Slipstream Publications, Box 2071, Niagara Falls, NY 14301. TEL 716-282-2616. Ed. Robert Borgatti; Pub. Daniel Sicoli. circ. 300. **Indexed:** Ind.Amer.Per.Verse.
 Description: Publishes strong social commentary and satire in the form of modern poetry, in writing and on audiocassettes.

811 US
SLOW MOTION MAGAZINE.* 1985. s-a. $6. c/o Gilbert Gritz, 30 The Crescent, No.1, Montclair, NJ 07042-2647. Ed.Bd. circ. 250. (back issues avail.)

SMALL POND MAGAZINE OF LITERATURE; journal of poetry, short fiction and opinion. see LITERATURE

821 UK ISSN 0262-852X
SMOKE. 1974. s-a. $5 for 3 nos. Windows Project, 40 Canning St., Liverpool L8 7NP, England. TEL 051-709-3688. Ed. Dave Ward. circ. 1,000. (also avail. in microfiche from BHP; back issues avail.)
 Description: Features poetry, short prose, and art work.

811 US ISSN 1054-1632
SNAIL'S PACE REVIEW. 1991. 2/yr. $7 to individuals; libraries $12. Snail's Pace Press, R.R. 2, Brownell Rd., Box 363, Cambridge, NY 12816. TEL 518-692-9953. Eds. Ken Denberg, Darby Penney. circ. 250.
 Description: Publishes contemporary poetry in all genres and poetry in translation.

811 US ISSN 1046-5006
SNAKE NATION REVIEW. 1989. 4/yr. $20. Snake Nation Press, 110 No. 2 W. Force, Valdosta, GA 31601. TEL 912-249-8334. Ed. Nancy Phillips. circ. 2,000 (paid).

811 US
SNUG. 1988. 2/yr. $2 per no. 1327 High Rd., Ste. Y-6, Tallahassee, FL 32304. TEL 904-224-9196. circ. 100.

841 FR ISSN 0081-0908
SOCIETE DES POETES FRANCAIS. ANNUAIRE. 1902. a. Societe des Poetes Francais, Hotel de Massa, 38 rue du Faubourg Saint-Jacques, 75014 Paris, France.
 Description: Four-year bulletin report of conferences and news of the society, recent awards and prizes given.

841 FR ISSN 0296-6867
SOCIETE DES POETES FRANCAIS. BULLETIN TRIMESTRIEL. no. 173, 1976. 4/yr. membership. Societe des Poetes Francais, 38 rue du Faubourg Saint-Jacques, 75014 Paris, France. **Document type:** bulletin.

808.8 US
SOLO FLYER. 1987. 3/yr. Spare Change Poetry, 2115 Clearview N.E., Massillon, OH 44646. Ed. David B. McCoy. circ. 50.
 Formerly: Quatra.
 Description: Each issue presents poetry by an individual author.

811 US ISSN 0887-2074
SOUTH COAST POETRY JOURNAL. 1986. s-a. $10 to individuals; institutions $12. California State University, Fullerton, Department of English, Fullerton, CA 92634. TEL 714-773-3163. Ed. John J. Brugaletta. adv.; bk.rev.; index. circ. 700. (back issues avail.) **Document type:** academic/scholarly publication.

811 US ISSN 0038-447X
PS580
SOUTHERN POETRY REVIEW. 1958. s-a. $8 (foreign $10). University of North Carolina, Department of English, Charlotte, NC 28223. TEL 704-547-4309. Ed. Ken McLaurin. bk.rev. circ. 1,100. (also avail. in microform from UMI; reprint service avail. from UMI) **Indexed:** Ind.Amer.Per.Verse. **Document type:** academic/scholarly publication.
 —UMI.

SOU'WESTER (EDWARDSVILLE); literary magazine. see LITERATURE

SOW'S EAR. see LITERARY AND POLITICAL REVIEWS

811 US ISSN 1066-3444
SOW'S EAR POETRY REVIEW. 1988. 4/yr. $10. 19435 Pleasant View Dr., Abingdon, VA 24210-6827. TEL 703-628-2651. Eds. Errol Hess, Larry Richman. adv.; bk.rev. circ. 750.
 Formerly: Sow's Ear Poetry Journal.

821 II
SPARK; an anthology of Indian poetry. (Text in English) 1975. s-a. Rs.6($2) per no. Spark Publications, 81 Raja Basanta Roy Rd., Calcutta 700 029, India. Ed. Santosh Kuman Adhikari. adv.; bk.rev. circ. 500.
 Description: Includes poetry, short profiles of poets, views and reviews.

811 US
SPARROW (WEST LAFAYETTE); the politically incorrect verse magazine. 1954. a. $7. Sparrow Press, 103 Waldron St., W. Lafayette, IN 47906. TEL 317-743-0530. Eds. Felix Stefanile, Selma Stefanile. adv.; bk.rev.; illus. circ. 900. (also avail. in microform from UMI; reprint service avail. from UMI) **Indexed:** Ind.Amer.Per.Verse.
 Former titles (until 1991, no.58): Sparrow Poverty Pamphlets (ISSN 0885-9477); (until no.34): Sparrow (ISSN 0038-6588)
 Description: Publishes contemporary sonnets.

SPEKTRUM; Vierteljahresschrift fuer Dichtung und Originalgrafik. see ART

808.81 US ISSN 0195-9468
PR2362
SPENSER STUDIES; a Renaissance poetry annual. 1980. a. $49.50. A M S Press, Inc., 56 E. 13 St., New York, NY 10003. TEL 212-777-4700. FAX 212-995-5413. Eds. Patrick Cullen, Thomas P. Roche, Jr. (back issues avail.) **Indexed:** M.L.A. **Document type:** academic/scholarly publication.
 —UnCover.
 Description: Articles on the works of Edmund Spenser and other Renaissance poets.

SPIRAL. see WOMEN'S INTERESTS

811 US ISSN 0038-7584
PS301
SPIRIT (SOUTH ORANGE); a magazine of poetry. 1934. s-a. $4. Seton Hall University, Department of English, S. Orange, NJ 07079. TEL 201-761-9000. FAX 201-761-9596. Ed. David Rogers. adv.; bk.rev.; index. circ. 650. (also avail. in microform from UMI; reprint service avail. from UMI) **Indexed:** A.I.P.P., Cath.Ind., M.L.A.
 —UMI.

SPONTANEOUS COMBUSTION. see LITERATURE

811 US
SPOON RIVER POETRY REVIEW. 1976. s-a. $12 to individuals; institutions $15. Illinois State University, Publications Unit, Normal, IL 61790-4241. TEL 309-438-7906. Ed. Lucia C. Getsi. adv.; illus. circ. 400. **Indexed:** A.I.P.P. **Document type:** academic/scholarly publication.
 Formerly: Spoon River Quarterly (ISSN 0738-8993)

811 US
SPRING RAIN. 1971. irreg. (2-4/yr.). $10. Spring Rain Press, Box 277, Port Townsend, WA 98368. Ed. Karen Gates. circ. 500.
 Description: Presents previously unpublished poetry.

821 SA ISSN 0258-7211
STAFFRIDER. 1978. q. R.12. Ravan Press (Pty.) Ltd., Box 31134, Braamfontein 2017, Transvaal, South Africa. Ed.Bd. adv.; bk.rev.; play rev. circ. 7,000. **Indexed:** Ind.S.A.Per.

LITERATURE — POETRY

821 UK ISSN 0266-4410
STAPLE. 1983. 4/yr. £12. Tor Cottage, 81 Cavendish Rd., Matlock DE4 3HD, England. TEL 0629-582764. Eds. Donald Measham, Bob Windsor. circ. 600. **Document type:** newsletter.

808.8 US
STAR LINE. 1978. bi-m. $13 membership (Canada and Mexico $15; elsewhere $18). Science Fiction Poetry Association, c/o Mike Arnzen, Sec.-Treas., Box 3712, Moscow, ID 83843-1916. Ed. Margaret B. Simon. adv.; bk.rev.; circ. 250 (paid). **Document type:** newsletter.
Description: Contains poems and critical essays.

STARLIGHT. see RELIGIONS AND THEOLOGY — Protestant

810 US ISSN 1061-6136
▼**STEPHEN CRANE STUDIES.** 1992. s-a. $10 to individuals (foreign $12); institutions $20 (foreign $22). Virginia Polytechnic Institute and State University, Department of English, Blacksburg, VA 24061-0112. TEL 703-231-6501. Ed. Paul Sorrentino.
Description: Journal of notes, queries, and reviews pertaining to the study of Stephen Crane.

821 UK ISSN 0039-1212
STEREO HEADPHONES; an occasional magazine of the new experimental poetries. (Text in English, French, German and Italian) 1969. irreg. (2-3/yr.) £4($7.50) per no. Church Steps, Kersey, Near Ipswich, Suffolk, England. (Also avail from: Nicholas Zurbrugg, Ed., School of Humanities, Griffith University, Nathan, Brisbane, Qld. 4111, Australia) adv.; bk.rev.; bibl.; illus. circ. 1,000. (tabloid format; also avail. in cards)

851 IT ISSN 0393-9480
STEVE; rivista di poesia. (Monographic supplements avail.) 1981. a. L.15000 for 2 yrs. Edizioni del Laboratorio di Poesia, Casella Postale Aperta, 41100 Modena Quattro, Italy. TEL 059-281591. FAX 059-220855. Ed. Carlo Alberto Sitta. adv.; bk.rev. circ. 500.

891 RU
STIKHI. (Subseries of: Repertuar Khudozhestvennoi Samodeyatel'nosti. Seriya-Repertuarnye Sborniki) 1967. irreg. Izdatel'stvo Iskusstvo, Sobinovsky per. 3, 103009 Moscow, Russia.

808.8 US ISSN 1043-9501
PS536.2
STILETTO. 1989. irreg. $21.50. Howling Dog Press, Box 27276, Denver, CO 80224-0276. Ed. Michael Annis. illus.
Description: Offers socially, environmentally and politically conscious poetry, drama, art and essays.

808.81 GU ISSN 1059-7492
STORYBOARD; a journal of Pacific imagery. 1991. a. $5. University of Guam Press, GSR, UOG Sta., Mangilao, Guam 96923. TEL 671-734-9430. FAX 671-734-3676. Ed. Richard Mezo. illus.
Description: Includes poetry, fiction and literary nonfiction.

811 US
STREETFIGHTING AESTHETE. 1991. irreg., approx. triennual. $6 for 3 issues. Pinelands Press, Box 5243, Kreole Station, Moss Point, MS 39562. TEL 601-475-1145. Ed. David Thomas Roberts.
Description: Poetry related to surrealism, folk art, and outsider art.

811 US
STROKER; a poem-prose-art review. 1974. 3/yr. $12. Stroker Press, 124 N. Main St., No.3, Shavertown, PA 18708-1416. Ed. Irving Stettner. adv.; bk.rev. circ. 500.

811 US
STROPHES. 1964. q. $3. National Federation of State Poetry Societies Inc., RR 3, Box 348, Alexandria, IN 46001. TEL 317-754-7082. Ed. Kay Kinnaman. circ. 8,500.
Description: Informs poets of contest news, convention news, poetry news, for members only.

810 320.531 US
STRUGGLE; a magazine of proletarian revolutionary literature. (Text in English; occasionally in Spanish) 1985. q. $6. Marxist-Leninist Party, U S A, Detroit Branch, Box 13261, Harper Sta., Detroit, MI 48213-0261. TEL 313-441-1204. Ed. Tim Hall. bk.rev.; film rev.; play rev. circ. 500. (back issues avail.)
Description: Creative literature attacking the Establishments in the U.S. and abroad. The varied forms range from critique to Marxist call for revolution.

851 IT ISSN 1122-0708
STRUMENTI DI LESSICOGRAFIA LETTERARIA ITALIANA. 1987. irreg., no.10, 1993. price varies. Casa Editrice Leo S. Olschki, Casella Postale 66, 50100 Florence, Italy. TEL 055-6530684. FAX 055-6530214. **Document type:** monographic series.

STUDI PIEMONTESI. see LITERATURE

STUDIA POETICA. see LITERATURE

821 US ISSN 1043-5751
STUDIES IN GERARD MANLEY HOPKINS. 1990. irreg. Peter Lang Publishing, Inc., 62 W. 45th St., 4th Fl., New York, NY 10036. TEL 212-302-6740. FAX 212-302-7574. Ed. Todd K. Bender. **Document type:** academic/scholarly publication.

811 US
STUDIO ONE. 1976. a. free. College of St. Benedict, St. Joseph, MN 56374. circ. 900.

808.81 US
SUBCONSCIOUS SOUP; the magazine of the counterculture. 1991. q. $3 per no. Scott Clark, Ed. & Pub., Box 421272, Kissimmee, FL 34742. TEL 407-932-4597. adv.: B&W color page $75. bk.rev.; circ. 1,000.
Description: As the voice of the counterculture, espouses freedom, sex, drugs, peace, equality, and free expression. Condemns hatred, tyranny, sexism, racism, and homophobia.

841 FR ISSN 0049-2450
SUD; revue litteraire trimestrielle. (Supplement avail.) 1970. 4/yr. 345 F. (foreign 395 F.). 62, rue Sainte, 13001 Marseille, France. TEL 91-33-60-68. Ed. Yves Broussard. adv.; bk.rev. circ. 2,000.

811 861 US
SULPHUR RIVER LITERARY REVIEW. 1977. s-a. $8 per no. Box 402087, Austin, TX 78704-5578. TEL 512-447-6809. Ed. James Michael Robbins. illus. circ. 300. (back issues avail.)
Formerly: Sulphur River Poetry Review.
Description: Publishes poetry, fiction, essays, artwork and photographs.

SULUR. see FOLKLORE

811 US ISSN 0735-7133
PS501
SUN DOG: THE SOUTHEAST REVIEW. 1979. s-a. $8 to individuals; institutions $10. Florida State Student Writing Association, c/o English Dept., Florida State Univ., 406 Williams Bldg., Tallahassee, FL 32306. TEL 904-644-4230. Ed.Bd. adv.; bk.rev. circ. 1,250.
Formerly: Sun Dog.

839.7 920 FI ISSN 0039-6842
CS884
SVENSKA LITTERATURSAELLSKAPET I FINLAND. SKRIFTER. (Text mainly in Swedish; occasionally in other languages) 1886. irreg. (4-8/yr.). price varies. Svenska Litteratursaellskapet i Finland, Marieg. 8, 00170 Helsinki 17, Finland. FAX 358-0-632820. **Document type:** academic/scholarly publication, monographic series.

SWEDISH BOOK REVIEW. see PUBLISHING AND BOOK TRADE

SYCAMORE REVIEW. see LITERATURE

808.81 HU ISSN 0586-3783
SZEP VERSEK. 1964. a. 88 Ft. Magveto Kiado, Vorosmarty ter 1, Budapest V, Hungary. TELEX 223502-MAGVE-H. Ed. Miklos Jovanovics.

808.81 US
T A P J O E. (The Anaprocrustean Poetry Journal of Enumclaw) 1987. s-a. $10 for 4 issues. Red Ink - Black Hole Productions, Box 632, Leavenworth, WA 98826-0632. circ. 200.
Description: Emphasizes poetry with a slant towards environmental or social issues.

861 AG
TABLA REDONDA. 1983. 4/yr. Rincon 110, Buenos Aires, Argentina. Ed. Adela Martinez del Castillo.

TAKAHE. see LITERATURE

808.81 US ISSN 0898-8684
PS325
TALISMAN; a journal of contemporary poetry and poetics. 1988. s-a. $9 to individuals; institutions $13. Box 1117, Hoboken, NJ 07030. TEL 201-798-9093. Ed. Edward Foster. adv.; bk.rev.; circ. 1,000 (paid). **Document type:** trade publication.
Description: Presents poetry, prose and interviews of contemporary artists worldwide.

851 IT
TAM TAM. 1972. q. L.35000($40) Via Val d'Enza 228, 42049 S. Ilario D' Enza (Reggio Emilia), Italy. TEL 0522-674756. Ed. Bianca Maria Bonazzi. adv.; bk.rev. circ. 1,500.

811 US ISSN 0162-1017
PS615
TAMARISK.* 1975. s-a. $10. 1200 Farrell Terr., Rahway, NJ 07065-2729. Eds. Dennis Barone, Deborah Ducoff-Barone. adv.; bk.rev. circ. 300. **Indexed:** A.I.P.P.

811 US ISSN 0896-064X
PS501
TAMPA REVIEW. 1988. s-a. $10. (University of Tampa) University of Tampa Press, 401 W. Kennedy Blvd., Tampa, FL 33606-1490. TEL 813-253-3333. FAX 813-251-0016. Ed. Richard Mathews. adv. circ. 450. **Indexed:** Ind.Amer.Per.Verse.
Supersedes (1972-1987): Abatis; **Formerly:** U T Review.
Description: Features poetry, fiction, articles, essays, interviews, translations and art.

811 US ISSN 0740-9141
PS558.N8
TAR RIVER POETRY. 1978. 2/yr. $10 (effective 1993). East Carolina University, Department of English, Greenville, NC 27858-4353. TEL 919-757-6041. FAX 919-757-4889. Ed. Peter Makuck. adv.; bk.rev.; illus. circ. 650. (tabloid format) **Indexed:** Amer.Hum.Ind., Ind.Amer.Per.Verse.

808.81 IT ISSN 0394-3518
PN1059.E94
TAVERNA DI AUERBACH; rivista internazionale di Poetiche Intermediali. (Text in Italian; summaries in English) 1987. 3/yr. L.35000($30) Hetea Editrice di Enzo Tofani & Co., Via Colleprata, 374, 03011 Alatri (FR), Italy. TEL (0775) 434026. FAX 0775-450096. (Subscr. to: Hetea Editrice di Enzo Tofani & Co., San Quiziano, 03011 Alatri (FR), Italy) Ed. Giovanni Fontana. adv.; bk.rev.; bibl.; illus. circ. 1,000. (back issues avail.) **Document type:** academic/scholarly publication.
Description: Forum dealing with the structure of text, the matter of language and experimentation of all possible textual consistencies.

851 IT
TECHNE; rivista di poesia e non. 1986. a. L.24000($26) Campanino Editore, Via Michelini 1, 33100 Udine, Italy. TEL 055 217882. (Subscr. to: Via del Moro 11, 50123 Florence, Italy) Ed.Bd. (back issues avail.)

811 US
TEMM POETRY MAGAZINE. 1989. m. $12. Split Personality Press, 511 West Sullivan St., Olean, NY 14760. Ed. Ken Wagner. circ. 200.

TEMPORARY CULTURE. see LITERATURE — Science Fiction, Fantasy, Horror

811 US ISSN 0197-890X
PS615
TENDRIL; a poetry magazine. 1977. 3/yr. $12 to individuals; institutions $14. Tendril, Inc., Box 2626, Key West, FL 33045-2626. TEL 617-834-4137. adv.; bibl.; illus.; cum.index: 1977-1980. circ. 1,800. **Indexed:** A.I.P.P., Ind.Amer.Per.Verse.

LITERATURE — POETRY

808 418   US
TERRA POETICA; a multilingual magazine of poetry. 1979. irreg., vol.2, no.2, 1983. $5. State University of New York at Buffalo, Department of Modern Languages, 910 Clemens Hall, Buffalo, NY 14260. TEL 716-636-2191. Ed. Jorge Guitar. circ. 500. (back issues avail.)

811   US
THEATER OF BLOOD. 1990. every 9 months. $7. Pyx Press, Box 620, Orem, UT 84059-0620. Ed. C. Darren Butler. adv.; circ. 500 (paid).
   Description: Examines absurd, intense, horrific, comedic or terrifying poetry, short fiction, and occasionally non-fiction.

808.81   US   ISSN 1041-4851
THEMA. 1990. 3/yr. $16 (foreign $20) (effective 1994). Thema Literary Society, 4312 Napoli Dr., Metairie, LA 70002. TEL 504-887-1263. (Subscr. to: Box 74109, Metairie, LA 70033-4109) Ed. Virginia Howard. circ. 300. (back issues avail.)
   Description: Contains thematically oriented poetry and fiction.

811   US
THEMATIC POETRY QUARTERLY. 1971. q. Audio-Visual Poetry Foundation, 4444 River Forest Rd., Marianna, FL 32446. TEL 904-482-3890. Ed. W.I. Throssell. circ. 100.

811   US
THIRD EYE. 1976. s-a. $2.50. Third Eye Publications, 189 Kelvin Dr., Buffalo, NY 14223. Ed. Patrick Lally. bk.rev. circ. 500. (back issues avail.) **Indexed**: A.I.P.P.

811   US
THIRD LUNG REVIEW. 1985. a. $3. Third Lung Press, Box 361, Conover, NC 28613. TEL 704-465-1254. circ. 150.

811   US   ISSN 0747-9727
THIRTEEN (PORTLANDVILLE). 1982. q. $5. M A F Press, Thirteen Poetry Magazine, Box 392, Portlandville, NY 13834. TEL 607-286-7500. Ed. Ken Stone. bk.rev. circ. 350. **Indexed**: Hum.Ind.

THIS AND THAT. see *CHILDREN AND YOUTH — For*

811   US   ISSN 0362-4846
PS580
THREE RIVERS POETRY JOURNAL. 1973. s-a. $10 for 2 years. Three Rivers Press, P.O. Box 21, Carnegie-Mellon University, Pittsburgh, PA 15213. TEL 412-268-2861. Ed. Gerald Costanzo. adv.; bk.rev. circ. 1,000. (processed; also avail. in microform from UMI) **Indexed**: A.I.P.P.
—UMI.

800   CN   ISSN 0824-7579
TIDEPOOL; anthology of haiku and short poetry. 1984. a. Can.$5($5) Hamilton Haiku Press, 4 E. 23rd St., Hamilton, ON L8V 2W6, Canada. TEL 905-383-2857. Ed. Herb Barrett. circ. 300. (also avail. in microfilm; back issues avail.)

TIME OF SINGING; a magazine of Christian poetry. see *RELIGIONS AND THEOLOGY*

821   AT
TIMESTREAM. 1971. bi-m. Aus.$1. c/o Richard Coady, Ed., Box a360, Sydney South 2000, New South Wales, Australia. circ. controlled.

811   US
TIN WREATH. 1985. q. free. Box 13401, Albany, NY 12212-3401. Ed. David Gonsalves. circ. 250.

861   UY
TORRE DE LOS PANORAMAS. 1972. q. Centro de Investigacion, Informacion y Difusion de la Joven Poesia Uruguaya, Avda. Centenario 3923 Ap. 008 Blok.H., Montevideo, Uruguay. Ed.Bd. adv.; illus. circ. 1,500.

808.8   US
TOUCHSTONE (SPRING); literary journal. 1976. a. $7. Touchstone Press, Box 8308, Spring, TX 77387-8308. Ed. Guida Jackson. adv. bk.rev.; illus.; circ. 1,000 (controlled). (back issues avail.) **Indexed**: Amer.Hum.Ind.

821   CN   ISSN 0495-9701
TOWER. 1951. s-a. Can.$6. Tower Poetry Society, c/o Dundas Public Library, 18 Oglivie St., Dundas, ON L9H 2S2, Canada. Ed. Joanna Lawson. circ. 250. (back issues avail.)

841   FR   ISSN 0041-0276
TRACES; cahiers trimestriels de lettres et d'arts. 1963. q. 88 F. (foreign 96 F.). Editions Traces, 44330 Le Pallet, France. Ed. Michel-Francois Lavaur. bk.rev.; illus. circ. 700. (also avail. in microform from UMI)

808.1   US   ISSN 0085-7378
TREEWELL.* 1968. a. $1. Johnson C. Smith University, 100 Beatties Ford Rd., Charlotte, NC 28216. TEL 704-378-1000. Ed. Carolyn McClair. bk.rev.; illus. circ. 500.

051   US
TRIBE; an American gay journal. 1989. q. $22. Columbia Publishing Co., 234 E. 25th St., Baltimore, MD 21218. Ed.Bd. illus.
   Description: Gay literary journal offering about 100 edited and printed essays, poems and stories.

808.81   UK   ISSN 0269-4824
TUBA. 1976. a. £0.50. Tuba Press, Tunley Cottage, Tunley, Nr. Cirencester, Glos GL7 6LW, England. TEL 0285-760424. Ed. Charlie Hamm. adv.; bk.rev. circ. 500. (back issues avail.) **Document type**: consumer publication.

TURNSTILE. see *LITERATURE*

TWEED. see *LITERATURE*

U.C. REVIEW. see *LITERATURE*

U S 1 WORKSHEETS. see *LITERATURE*

811   HU   ISSN 0082-7312
UJ MAGYAR NEPKOLTESI GYUJTEMENY. 1955. irreg. price varies. (Magyar Tudomanyos Akademia) Akademiai Kiado, Publishing House of the Hungarian Academy of Sciences, P.O. Box 245, H-1519 Budapest, Hungary. TEL 181-2134. FAX 166-6466. TELEX 22-6228 AKNYO H.

811   US
UNBRIDLED LUST!.* 1990. bi-m. $15. Unbridled Lust! Publishing, 114 Sanford St., No. 2, Bangor, ME 04401-6132. TEL 207-866-3535. Eds. Brad Finch, Matt LeClair. circ. 500.

821   CN   ISSN 0838-6749
UNDERPASS. 1987. a. Can.$6.95($6.95) Underpass Press, 574-21, 10405 Jasper Ave., Edmonton, AB T5J 3S2, Canada. Ed. Barry Hammond. adv.; circ. 200 (controlled). (back issues avail.) **Document type**: consumer publication.
   Description: Avant-garde, concrete, urban, discursive prose and poetry.

943.1   US
UNICORN GERMAN SERIES.* (Text in English and German) 1968. irreg. $5 paper; $15 cloth. Unicorn Press, Inc., Box 3307, Greensboro, NC 27402. Ed. Teo Savory. adv.; bk.rev. circ. 2,000. (back issues avail.)

821   CN
UNION SHOP BLUFF. 1990. bi-m. $6. 205A Liverpool St., Cuelph, Ont. N1H 2L6, Canada. TEL 519-767-1998. circ. 120.

861   CK   ISSN 0120-0992
UNIVERSIDAD DE LOS ANDES. CUADERNOS DE FILOSOFIA Y LETRAS. 1973. irreg. Universidad de los Andes, Facultad de Humanidades y Ciencias Sociales, Comite de Publicaciones, Bogota, Colombia. bibl. circ. 1,000.
   Formerly: Universidad de los Andes. Cuadernos de Letras.

811   US   ISSN 0049-5557
PS580
UNMUZZLED OX. 1971. irreg. $20. (Soho Baroque Opera Company, Inc.) Unmuzzled Ox Foundation, Ltd., 105 Hudson St., New York, NY 10013. TEL 212-226-7170. Ed. Michael Andre. adv.; bk.rev.; bibl.; illus.; circ. 20,000 (controlled). **Indexed**: Amer.Hum.Ind., Ind.Amer.Per.Verse. **Document type**: monographic series, trade publication.
   Description: Publishes fiction, original political essays, and poetry.

808.81   US
UPSTREAM; the Literary Center quarterly. 1984. q. $15. Literary Center, Box 85116, Seattle, WA 98105. Ed. Ken Smith. adv.; bk.rev. circ. 1,700.
   Formerly: Literary Center Quarterly.
   Description: Provides a forum for writers and small presses in the Pacific North West.

821   UK   ISSN 0142-128X
URBANE GORILLA. 1970. s-a. £1.50. Raven Publications, 29 Parker's Rd., Sheffield S10 1BN, England. Ed. Ed Tork. adv.; bk.rev. circ. 1,000.

URBANUS - RAIZIRR. see *LITERATURE*

811   US   ISSN 0146-8510
UROBOROS. 1975. 2/yr. $5. Allegany Mountain Press, 111 North Tenth Street, Olean, NY 14760. Eds. Ford & Helen Ruggieri. bk.rev.; bibl.; illus. circ. 500. (also avail. in microfilm) **Indexed**: Access.
   Formerly (until vol. 2, 1976): Allegany Poetry.

890   BG
UTSABA. (Text in Bengali) a. Tk.5. 113 Jagannath Saha Rd., Dhaka 1, Bangladesh. Ed. Syed Zafar Ali.

V W A; revue litteraire. see *LITERATURE*

811   US
VAGABOND CHAPBOOK. vol. 6, 1976. irreg. $1 per no. Vagabond Press, 605 E. 5th Ave., Ellensburg, WA 98926.

841   FR   ISSN 0153-9620
PQ1160
VAGABONDAGES. 1978. 4/yr. 160 F. (foreign 220 F.). Association Paris-Poete, 3 rue Seguier, 75006 Paris, France. adv.; bk.rev.

VARLIK. see *LITERATURE*

821   UK
VER POETS VOICES. 1968. 2/yr. £1.50. Ver Poets, 61 & 63 Chiswell Green Lane, St. Albans, Herts. AL2 3AL, England. TEL 0727-867005. Ed. May Badman.
   Formerly: Ver Poets Broadsheets.

VERSE. see *LITERATURE*

811   US
VERVE. 1989. s-a. $12 (foreign $18). Ron Reichick, Ed. & Pub., Box 3205, Simi Valley, CA 93093. TEL 805-527-8824. bk.rev. circ. 750.

811   US   ISSN 0042-5206
PR500
VICTORIAN POETRY. 1963. q. $18 to individuals; institutions $30. West Virginia University, Victorian Poetry Office, Dept. of English, Morgantown, WV 26506. TEL 304-293-5380. FAX 304-293-7417. Ed. Hayden Ward. adv.; bk.rev.; index, cum.index. circ. 1,200. (also avail. in microfilm from UMI; reprint service avail. from KTO) **Indexed**: Abstr.Engl.Stud., Arts & Hum.Cit.Ind., Curr.Cont., Hum.Ind., Ind.Bk.Rev.Hum., LCR, M.L.A. **Document type**: academic/scholarly publication.
—BLDSC (9232.665000); Faxon; UnCover; SWETS; UMI.
   Description: Examines Victorian poetry from 1830-1914.

821   UK
VISION ON. a. £1.50. Ver Poets, 61 & 63 Chiswell Green Lane, St. Albans, Herts AL2 3AL, England. TEL 0727-867005. Ed. May Badman.

800   US
VISIONS INTERNATIONAL; the world journal of illustrated poetry. 1979. 3/yr. $14. (Visions International Arts Synergy, Inc.) Black Buzzard Press, 1110 Seaton Lane, Falls Church, VA 22046-3920. TEL 703-241-8626. Ed. Bradley R. Strahan. bk.rev.; illus. circ. 800. (back issues avail.) **Indexed**: Amer.Hum.Ind., Ind.Amer.Per.Verse.
   Formerly: Visions (ISSN 0194-1690)
   Description: Contains poetry and translation of poetry from all over the world with original artwork done specifically for the poems.

THE VOICE OF ZEWAM. see *ETHNIC INTERESTS*

LITERATURE — POETRY

809   US
VOICES FROM ASIA. 1990. irreg., no.8, 1989. price varies. University of California Press, 2120 Berkeley Way, Berkeley, CA 94720. TEL 510-643-7127. FAX 510-642-4247. (Orders to: California-Princeton Fulfillment Services, 1445 Lower Ferry Rd., Ewing, NJ 08618. TEL 800-777-4726. FAX 800-999-1958) (back issues avail.) **Document type:** monographic series.
    Description: Examines prose and poetry from throughout southeastern Asia.

811   US   ISSN 0042-8280
VOICES INTERNATIONAL. 1966. q. $10. Voices International, Co., 1115 Gillette Drive, Little Rock, AR 72207. TEL 501-225-0166. Ed. Clovita Rice. adv.; bk.rev. circ. 500.

821   IS   ISSN 0333-676X
VOICES - ISRAEL; magazine of English language poetry from Israel and elsewhere. (Text in English) 1972. a. $13.50. Voices Group of Israeli Poets in English, c/o Mark Levinson, Ed., P.O. Box 5780, Herzliya 46157, Israel. TEL 972-52-552411. adv. circ. 350. (also avail. in diskette format)
    Description: Anthology of English language poetry written by poets in Israel and abroad; includes translations.

808.81   US
VOL. NO. MAGAZINE. (Volume Number); from California - a literary/visual experience. (Text in English; occasionally in Spanish) 1956. a. $5. (Santa Clarita Valley Poets) Los Angeles Poetry Press, 24721 Newhall Ave., Newhall, CA 91321. TEL 805-254-0851. Ed.Bd. adv.; bk.rev. circ. 300. (back issues avail.)

890   US   ISSN 0888-5257
PG3542
VSTRECHI; almanac. (Text in Russian) 1977. a. $10. Encounters, 7738 Woodbine Ave., Philadelphia, PA 19151. TEL 215-477-6172. Ed. Valentina Sinkevich. bk.rev. circ. 500.
    Formerly: Perekrestki (ISSN 0160-5534)

811   US   ISSN 0148-7132
WALLACE STEVENS JOURNAL. 1977. biennial. $25 to individuals; institutions $30 (foreign $35). Wallace Stevens Society, Inc., Box 5750 Clarkson University, Potsdam, NY 13699-5750. TEL 315-268-3987. FAX 315-268-3983. Ed. John N. Serio. adv.; bk.rev.; bibl. circ. 600. **Indexed:** Abstr.Engl.Stud.; Arts & Hum.Cit.Ind., Curr.Cont., M.L.A., Tr.& Indus.Ind. **Document type:** academic/scholarly publication, bibliography.
—BLDSC (9261.497500); Faxon; UnCover.
    Description: Publishes scholarly articles and other works, such as bibliographies, news and comments, poems, telating to the poetry and life of Wallace Stevens.

WALT WHITMAN MUSIC LIBRARY. BULLETIN. see *MUSIC*

811   US
WASHOUT REVIEW.* 1975. irreg. $6. Mildred Publishing, 961 Birchwood Ln., Schenectady, NY 12309-3118. Eds. Ellen Biss, Kathryn Poppino. illus. circ. 500. (back issues avail.)

WATER ROW REVIEW. see *LITERATURE*

811   US   ISSN 0197-4777
WATERWAYS; poetry in the mainstream. 1978. 11/yr. $20. (Waterways Project) Ten Penny Players, Inc., 393 St. Pauls Ave., Staten Island, NY 10304-2127. TEL 718-442-7429. FAX 718-442-4978. Eds. Barbara Fisher, Richard Alan Spiegel. circ. 200. (back issues avail.)
    Formerly: N Y S Waterways Project Magazine.
    Description: Publishes poetry primarily by contemporary Americans (professional and child poets).

808.81   US
WAY DICKIE MAGAZINE. bi-m. Way Dickie Magazine, 184 Center St., E. Aurora, NY 14052. illus.
    Description: Includes poetry, writing, and stuff.

811   US
WE MAGAZINE (SANTA CRUZ). 1986. 4/yr. $15. We Press, Box 1503, Santa Cruz, CA 95061. TEL 408-427-9711. circ. 800.

821   AT   ISSN 1035-0616
WEBBER'S. 1989. 2/yr. $15. 15 McKillop St., Melbourne, Vic. 3000, Australia. TEL 03-670-2418. Ed. Joanna Kenny. circ. 1,000.

WEN HSUEH TAIWAN/LITERARY TAIWAN. see *LITERATURE*

811   US   ISSN 0511-4934
WESLEYAN POETRY PROGRAM. 1959. s-a. Wesleyan University Press, 110 Mt. Vernon St., Middletown, CT 06457. TEL 203-344-7918. FAX 203-344-7977. (Co-publisher: University Press of New England) Ed. Terry Cochran. **Document type:** academic/scholarly publication.

808.7   US   ISSN 0149-6441
PN6010.5
WEST BRANCH. 1977. 2/yr. $7 (effective Sept. 1993). Bucknell University, Bucknell Hall, Lewisburg, PA 17837. TEL 717-524-1853. Eds. Karl Patten, Robert Taylor. bk.rev.; illus. circ. 500. **Indexed:** A.I.P.P., Ind.Amer.Per.Verse.
    Description: Features poetry and fiction.

810   US   ISSN 0049-7223
WEST END;* a magazine of poetry and politics. 1971. s-a. $5. c/o G.D. Kaliss, Ed., 1777 East-West Rd., Ste. 1435, Honolulu, HI 96848-0001. bk.rev.; charts; illus. circ. 1,000.

811   US   ISSN 0890-9024
PS3229
WEST HILLS REVIEW; a Walt Whitman Journal. 1979. a. $6. Walt Whitman Birthplace Association, 246 Old Walt Whitman Rd., Huntington Sta., NY 11746. TEL 516-427-5240. Ed. William A. Fahey. bk.rev. circ. 1,200.

811   US
WESTERFIELD'S REVIEW.* 1976. s-a. $5. Ashford Press, Box 513, Willimantic, CT 06226-0513. Ed. M.J. Westerfield. bk.rev.; illus. circ. 750. (back issues avail.)
    Formerly (until 1981): Sarcophagus.

WESTWORDS. see *ART*

821   UK   ISSN 0307-7276
WEYFARERS. 1972. 3/yr. $15. Guildford Poets Press, 9 White Rose Ln., Woking, Surrey GU22 7JA, England. TEL 0483-762614. Ed. Margaret Pain. bk.rev. circ. 300. **Document type:** newsletter.
    Description: International poetry magazine for all kinds of poetry, especially mainstream of 40 lines or less.

808   CN   ISSN 0827-1828
WHAT; poetry, fiction, drama, criticism. 1985. bi-m. Can.$12($12) to individuals; institutions Can.$24($24). Box 338, Sta. "J", Toronto, Ont. M4J 4Y8, Canada. TEL 416-588-5268. Ed.Bd. adv.: color page $400; trim 11 x 17. bk.rev.; bibl.; play rev. circ. 10,000. (tabloid format; back issues avail.) **Document type:** academic/scholarly publication.

811   US
WHETSTONE (SIERRA VISTA);* a Southwest poetry magazine. 1978. 3/yr. $5. San Pedro Press, c/o Michael Bowden, Ed., 1016 S. Cactus Wren Ln., Sierra Vista, AZ 85635-5404.

811   US
WHISPERING PALM. 1991. m. Box 6523, Lake Worth, FL 33466. circ. 1,500.

811   US
WHITE CLOUDS REVUE. 1987. irreg. (2-3/yr.). $12 for 4 issues. Box 462, Ketchum, ID 83340. circ. 250.

811   US   ISSN 0511-8832
PS3279
WHITTIER NEWSLETTER. 1966. a. free. Whittier Clubs of Haverhill and Amesbury, c/o Howard W. Curtis, Ed., Haverhill Public Library, Haverhill, MA 01830. bk.rev.; bibl. circ. 600. (looseleaf format; back issues avail.)

811   US   ISSN 1068-0780
WHOLE NOTES. (Former name of issuing body: Daedalus Press) 1984. 2/yr. $6 (effective through 1996). Whole Notes Press, Box 1374, Las Cruces, NM 88004. TEL 505-382-7446. Ed. Nancy Peters Hastings. circ. 400. **Document type:** trade publication.
    Description: Features contemporary poetry by new and established writers.

811   US   ISSN 1062-7464
WICKED MYSTIC. 1990. q. $24. Box 3087, Dept. UIPD, Astoria, NY 11103. TEL 718-545-6713. Ed. Andre Scheluchin. adv.: B&W page $95; adv. contact: Clyde Python. **Document type:** consumer publication.
    Description: Is a hard-nosed, uncensored, all-out horror 'zine, strictly for warped, hard-to-offend afficianados of blatant nastiness.

WIELANDS BRIEFWECHSEL. see *LITERATURE*

WIENER - GOETHE - VEREIN. JAHRBUCH. see *LITERATURE*

811   US   ISSN 0893-3375
WINDFALL. 1979. irreg. (approx a.). $5. Windfall Prophets Press, Department of English, University of Wisconsin, Whitewater, WI 53190. TEL 414-472-1036. Ed. Ron Ellis. bk.rev. circ. 300.

808.81   CN   ISSN 0847-1762
WINDHORSE REVIEW. 1982. s-a. Can.$9 to individuals; institutions Can.$12 (effective June 1991). Samurai Press, RR 3, Box 3140, Yarmouth, N.S. B5A 4A7, Canada. TEL 902-742-7945. Ed. John Castlebury. circ. 500.
    Description: Contemplative poetics and art.

811   US   ISSN 0043-5716
PS580
WINDLESS ORCHARD; a quarterly magazine of photography and contemporary poetry. 1970. irreg., no.57, 1993. $20 for 6 nos. Robert Novak, Ed. & Pub., c/o English Dept, Indiana University, Fort Wayne, IN 46805. TEL 219-481-6841. bk.rev.; illus. circ. 300. **Indexed:** Ind.Amer.Per.Verse.

811   US   ISSN 0043-6631
AP2
WISCONSIN REVIEW. 1966. 3/yr. $6. University of Wisconsin at Oshkosh, Box 158, Radford Hall, Oshkosh, WI 54901. TEL 414-424-2267. Ed. Mike Beirne. bk.rev.; play rev.; illus. circ. 400. (back issues avail.)
    Description: Contains new poetry, fiction, reviews, essays, interviews, and artwork.

811   US   ISSN 1052-3162
WITHOUT HALOS. 1983. a. $6. (Ocean County Poets Collective) Without Halos Press, Box 1342, Pt. Pleasant Beach, NJ 08742. Ed. Frank Finale. circ. 1,000. (back issues avail.)

821   UK   ISSN 0043-7107
WIVENHOE PARK REVIEW.* 1966. 4/yr. 25s.($5) Ferry Press, 177 Green Lane, London SE9, England. Ed. A. Crozier. bk.rev. circ. 500.

811   US   ISSN 0195-6183
WOMAN POET. 1980. irreg., latest no.3. $13.95 hardcover; paperback $12.95. Women-in-Literature, Inc., Box 60550, Reno, NV 89506. TEL 702-972-1671. FAX 415-474-6484. Ed. Elaine Dallman. bk.rev. circ. 3,000. (back issues avail.)
—CCC.

811   US   ISSN 8756-5277
WORCESTER REVIEW. 1973. a. $15. Worcester County Poetry Association, 6 Chatham St., Worcester, MA 01609. TEL 508-797-4770. Ed. Rodger Martin. adv.; bk.rev. circ. 1,000. (back issues avail.) **Document type:** academic/scholarly publication.
    Description: Contains poetry, articles about poetry, fiction, critical articles with a New England connection, and graphics.

811   US   ISSN 0043-8154
THE WORLD (NEW YORK). 1966-1984; resumed no.42, 1992. 3/yr. $20. Poetry Project Ltd., St. Marks Church in-the-Bowery, 131 E. Tenth St., New York, NY 10003. TEL 212-674-0910. Ed. Lewis Warsh. **Indexed:** Abstr.Mil.Bibl.

811   US   ISSN 1054-8823
WORLD LETTER; an international literary review. 1991. irreg. $6 per no. Jon Cone, Ed. & Pub., 2726 E. Court St., Iowa City, IA 52245. TEL 319-337-6022. illus. **Indexed:** Amer.Hum.Ind., Ind.Amer.Per.Verse.

811   US
WORLD OF POETRY.* 1975. q. $10. 11419 Cronridge Dr., Ste. 10, Owings Mills, MD 21117-6216. Ed.Bd. circ. 250,000.

WORLD WAR THREE. see *POLITICAL SCIENCE*

LITERATURE — SCIENCE FICTION, FANTASY, HORROR

811 US ISSN 0043-9401
PS580
WORMWOOD REVIEW. 1959. q. $10. Wormwood Books and Magazines, Box 4698, Stockton, CA 95204-0698. TEL 209-466-8231. Ed. M. H. Malone. bk.rev.; bibl.; illus.; cum.index. circ. 700. (also avail. in microform from UMI) **Indexed:** A.I.P.P., Amer.Hum.Ind. **Document type:** academic/scholarly publication.
—UMI.
  Description: Presents prose poems as well as traditional and avant-garde poetry that communicates the current temper of the times.

WRITERS' AND POETS' YEARBOOK. see *LITERATURE*

811 US
WRITERS' BLOC. 1985. 4/yr. $10. Box 212, Marysville, OH 43040. TEL 513-642-8019. circ. 300.

WRITERS' OWN MAGAZINE. see *LITERATURE*

WRITING. see *LITERATURE*

811 US ISSN 0146-0463
XANADU; a literary journal. 1975. a. $5. Long Island Poetry Collective, Inc., Box 773, Huntington, NY 11743. Ed.Bd. circ. 300. (back issues avail.)

XENOPHILIA. see *LITERATURE — Science Fiction, Fantasy, Horror*

811 US
XEROLAGE.* 1985. 4/yr. $10. c/o Elizabeth Was, RR 1 Box 131, La Farge, WI 53639-9601. TEL 608-258-1305. Eds. Miekal & Elizabeth Was. circ. 100.
  Description: Features visual poetry, copy art and collage graphics.

895.1 CC
XINGXING SHIKAN/STAR POETRY JOURNAL. (Text in Chinese) m. Zhongguo Zuojia Xiehui, Sichuan Fenhui - China Writers Association, Sichuan Chapter, 85, Hongxing Lu 2 Duan, Chengdu, Sichuan 610012, People's Republic of China. TEL 660846. Ed. Ye Yanbin.

811 US ISSN 0084-3458
YALE SERIES OF YOUNGER POETS. 1919. a. price varies. Yale University Press, Box 209040, New Haven, CT 06520. TEL 203-432-0940. Ed. James Dickey.

811 US
YARROW; a journal of poetry. 1981. s-a. $1.50 per no. Kutztown State College, English Department, Kutztown, PA 19530. TEL 215-683-4353. Ed. Harry Humes. circ. 350.

820 US ISSN 0704-5700
PS3509.L43
YEATS ELIOT REVIEW. 1974. a. Can.$12 for 2 years to institutions. University of Arkansas at Little Rock, Department of English, Little Rock, AR 72204. Ed. R. Murphy. bk.rev.; bibl. **Indexed:** Abstr.Engl.Stud., Amer.Hum.Ind., Arts & Hum.Cit.Ind., Curr.Cont., Ind.Bk.Rev.Hum., M.L.A. **Document type:** academic/scholarly publication.
—BLDSC (9418.040000); Faxon; UnCover.
  Incorporates: T.S. Eliot Review (ISSN 0318-6342); T.S. Eliot Newsletter (ISSN 0315-1174)

YET ANOTHER SMALL MAGAZINE. see *LITERARY AND POLITICAL REVIEWS*

808.81 US
YOUR ELBOW.* q. $3.50 per no. 1923 St. Clair Ave., No. 8, St. Paul, MN 55105-1667. Ed. Kelly Green.

891.43 II ISSN 0970-0978
YUVA KAVI. (Text in Hindi) q. 40($12) Samkaleen Prakashan, 2762 Rajguru Marg, New Delhi 110 055, India. Ed. Krishan Khullar.

ZHONGGUO XIBU WENXUE. see *LITERATURE*

821 UK ISSN 0260-7654
ZIP; poetry magazine. 1980. irreg. $4. Iris Services Co-operative, 1A Oldham St., Hyde, Cheshire SK14 1LJ, England. Ed. Sandy Gort. adv.; illus. circ. 1,000. **Indexed:** Graph.Arts Lit.Abstr.

811 US ISSN 0888-000X
PS580
ZONE 3. 1986. 2/yr. $8 to individuals; institutions $10 (foreign $11). Austin Peay State University, Center for the Creative Arts, Box 4565, Clarksville, TN 37044. TEL 615-648-7031. Ed. Susan Wallace. adv. circ. 750. **Document type:** academic/scholarly publication.
  Description: Publishes poetry from the US and abroad.

811 US
5 AM. 1987. 2/yr. $6. 1109 Milton Ave., Pittsburgh, PA 15218. circ. 750.
  Description: Publishes mostly poems ignored by other magazines.

811 US
11 X 30 - BROADSIDE. 4/yr. $5. Toledo Poets Center Press, University of Toledo, Toledo, OH 43606-3390. Ed. Joel Lipman. circ. 1,000. **Document type:** newsletter.
  Description: Contains visual language, poetry, literary gossip, and news.

811 US
11TH ST. RUSE. 1988. 3/yr. $1. Urban Groomer, Inc., 322 11th St., Ste. 23, New York, NY 10003. TEL 212-475-5312. circ. 230. circ. 120 (paid). **Document type:** newsletter.
  Description: Provides news about the group and contains comical vocabulary.

LITERATURE — Science Fiction, Fantasy, Horror

808.838 US ISSN 1058-2509
▼**ABERATIONS**; adult horror, science fiction, and dark fantasy. 1992. m. $31 (effective 1992). Experiences Unlimited, 544 Ygnacio Valley Rd., No. 13, Box 8040, Walnut Creek, CA 94596. TEL 510-682-9662. FAX 510-682-9706. Ed. Jon L. Herron. adv. circ. 1,550. (back issues avail.)

808.81 US ISSN 0895-3198
PN3433
ABORIGINAL SCIENCE FICTION. 1986. q. $18 (foreign $21) (effective 1994). (Second Rennaisance Foundation, Inc.) Aboriginal Science Fiction, Box 2449, Woburn, MA 01888-0849. Ed. Charles C. Ryan. adv. contact: Mary Ryan. bk.rev.; film rev.; illus.; circ. 12,400 (paid). (back issues avail.) **Document type:** consumer publication.
  Formerly: Aboriginal S F (ISSN 0888-3475)
  Description: Publishes original science fiction short stories and poetry, developments in science, and news of the science fiction film industry, including forthcoming films.

808.838 US ISSN 1050-0448
AFRAID; the newsletter for the horror professional. m. $25 (foreign $35). Mike Baker, Ed. & Pub., 857 N. Oxford Ave., No. 4, Los Angeles, CA 90029. **Document type:** trade publication, newsletter.

808.838 US ISSN 1043-3686
AFTER HOURS. 1989. 4/yr. $14. Box 538, Sunset Beach, CA 90742. Ed. William G. Raley. adv.; bk.rev. **Document type:** consumer publication.
  Description: Small press fantasy and horror fiction, with author interviews.

808.838 US
AGONIZER. q.? $10. Klingon Society, 2508 Pine St., Philadelphia, PA 19103. Ed. Sue Frank.
  Description: Presents science fiction stories.

808.838 IE
ALBEDO ONE. q. I£7 (foreign I£12). c/o David Murphy, 2 Post Rd., Lusk, Co. Dublin, Ireland. TEL 01-8438017. Ed. Robert Neilson. circ. 180. **Document type:** consumer publication.
  Formerly (until 1991): F T L

808.8 RU
▼**ALIENS.** (Text in English) 1992. q. £1.95($2.95) per no. c/o Yevgeny Maidannikoff, 144 Kashirskoye Hig., Bldg. 2, 115561 Moscow, Russia. (Or: c/o Alexander Vasilkovsky, 36 Pyatidesyatileta Oktyabra av., Apt. 51, 252148, Kiev, Ukraine) Eds. Yevgeny Maidannikoff, Alexander Vasilkovsky.
  Description: Showcases post-Soviet science fiction writing and art for Western audiences, with news of literary and fan activities in the former Soviet Union.

808.838 US ISSN 1058-0751
AMAZING STORIES. 1926. 3/yr. T S R Inc., Box 111, Lake Geneva, WI 53147. TEL 414-248-3625. FAX 414-248-0389. (Subscr. to: T S R Inc., Box 5695, Boston, MA 02206. TEL 800-372-4667) Ed. Kim Mohan. adv./ bk.rev. circ. 7,000. (also avail. in microfilm from KTO) **Document type:** consumer publication.
  Formerly (until 1986): Amazing (ISSN 0279-1706); Which was formed by the 1980 merger of: Fantastic (ISSN 0014-7508); Amazing Stories (ISSN 1060-5401); Former titles: Amazing Science Fiction Stories (ISSN 1060-541X); Amazing Stories (ISSN 0002-6891)
  Description: Publishes science fiction, fantasy, and horror short stories as well as science fact articles and opinion essays.

800 UK ISSN 0306-8781
AMON HEN. bi-m. £15. Tolkien Society, 357 High St., Flat 5, Cheltenham, Glos. GL50 3HT, England. TEL 0242-577232. **Indexed:** Child.Lit.Abstr. **Document type:** bulletin.
  Description: News, reviews, letters, art work and short articles concerning the works of J.R.R. Tolkien.

813 808.838 US ISSN 1059-2113
PZ1.A1
ANALOG SCIENCE FICTION & FACT. 1930. 13/yr. $40.35. Dell Magazines, 1540 Broadway, New York, NY 10036. TEL 212-354-6500. FAX 212-782-8338. (Subscr. to: Box 5133, Harlan, IA 51593-5133. TEL 800-333-4561) Ed. Stanley Schmidt. adv.; bk.rev.; charts; illus.; index. circ. 90,000. (also avail. in microform from UMI; reprint service avail. from UMI) **Indexed:** Acad.Ind., Access (1975-), Bk.Rev.Ind. (1977-), Child.Bk.Rev.Ind. (1977-), Mag.Ind. (1981-). **Document type:** consumer publication.
—Faxon; UnCover.
  Former titles (until 1991): Analog Science Fiction Science Fact (ISSN 0161-2328); Analog Science Fact - Science Fiction (ISSN 0003-2603)

ANATOMY OF WONDER; a critical guide to science fiction. see *LITERATURE — Abstracting, Bibliographies, Statistics*

808.838 UK ISSN 0265-9816
ANSIBLE. 1979-1987; resumed 1991. m. 94 London Rd., Reading, Berks RG1 5AU, England. FAX 0734-669914. Ed. David Langford. bk.rev. **Document type:** newsletter.
  Description: News, commentary and gossip on topics in science fiction.

808.838 RM ISSN 1220-8620
ANTICIPATIA. Variant title: Colectia de Poveresti Stiintifico-Fantastice Anticipatia. 1955-1974; resumed no.466, 1990. m. Societatea Stiinta & Technica S.A., P.O. Box 33-57, Piata Presei Libere nr.1, sector 1, Bucharest, Rumania. Ed. Mihai Dan Pavelescu.

808.838 AG ISSN 0004-1084
ARGENTINE SCIENCE FICTION REVIEW. (Text in English) 1969. 2/yr. $2 per no. Argentine Science Fiction Review Publications, Casilla 3869, Correo Central, Buenos Aires, Argentina. Ed. Hector R. Pessina. adv.; bk.rev.; film rev.; bibl.; illus. circ. 500.

808.838 US ISSN 0883-9824
ARGONAUT (AUSTIN). 1972. s-a. $8 (Canada $10; elsewhere $13). Argo Press, Box 4201, Austin, TX 78765-4201. TEL 512-263-5027. Ed. Michael E. Ambrose. adv.; illus. circ. 750. **Document type:** bulletin.
  Description: Contains original science fiction and weird fantasy.

ARGOSY (LONG BEACH, 1988); the all-fiction magazine. see *LITERATURE — Adventure And Romance*

LITERATURE — SCIENCE FICTION, FANTASY, HORROR

808.838 US
PN6120.95.S33
ASIMOV'S SCIENCE FICTION. 1976. 13/yr. $40.35. Dell Magazines, 1540 Broadway, New York, NY 10036. TEL 212-354-6500. (Subscr. to: Box 5130, Red Oak, IA 51591-5130. TEL 800-333-4108) Ed. Gardner Dozois. adv.; bk.rev. circ. 90,000. (also avail. in microform from UMI; reprint service avail. from UMI) **Indexed:** Amer.Hum.Ind. **Document type:** consumer publication.
Former titles (until Nov. 1992): Isaac Asimov's Science Fiction Magazine (ISSN 1055-2146); (until 1990): Isaac Asimov's Science Fiction (ISSN 1045-6414); (until 1986): Isaac Asimov's Science Fiction Magazine (ISSN 0162-2188)

808.838 US
ATOPOS.* 1990. every 9 mos. $14 for 3 nos. 505 Oakridge Ln., No. 18, New London, WI 54961-9371. TEL 715-845-1421. Ed. Hal H. Hintze. adv.; illus. circ. 500. (back issues avail.)
Description: Publishes speculative fiction, science fiction, horror and fantasy stories and related articles.

808.8 UK ISSN 0954-1918
AUGURIES; science fiction, fantasy & horror magazine. 1982. 2/yr. £7($20) 48 Angelesey Rd., Alverstoke, Gosport, Hants. PO12 2EQ, England. TEL 0705-581220. (U.S. subscr. to: Anne Marsden, 1052 Calle del Cerro, No.708, San Clemente, CA 92672. TEL 714-361-3791) Ed. Nik Morton. adv.; bk.rev.; illus. circ. 200.
Description: Presents traditional science fiction stories.

AUGUST DERLETH SOCIETY. NEWSLETTER. see *LITERATURE*

808.8 AT ISSN 1035-1205
AURELIS; the Australian magazine of fantasy and science fiction. 1990. 2/yr. Aus.$24 (foreign Aus.$39). Chimaera Publications, P.O. Box 538, Mount Waverly, Vic. 3149, Australia. TEL 03-534-1569. FAX 03-534-1569. (Subscr. in U.K. to: Chris Reed, NSFA, P.O. Box 625, Sheffield S1 3GY, England) Ed. Dirk Strasser, Stephen Higgins. adv.; bk.rev. circ. 2,000. **Document type:** trade publication.
Description: Australian science fiction for a wide range of tastes.

808.838 US ISSN 0275-3715
AURORA (MADISON); S F science fiction-speculative feminism. Variant title: Aurora S F. 1975. irreg. (approx. 2/yr.) $10 for 3 nos. Society for the Furtherance and Study of Fantasy and Science Fiction, Inc. (SF3), Box 1624, Madison, WI 53701-1624. Ed. Diane Martin. adv.; bk.rev.; film rev. circ. 500. (back issues avail.) **Indexed:** Stud.Wom.Abstr.
Formerly: Janus.

B C S F A-ZINE. (British Columbia Science Fiction Association) see *CLUBS*

808.81 UK ISSN 0269-9990
BACK BRAIN RECLUSE; new speculative fiction. Short title: B B R. 1984. irreg. approx. 2/yr., no.22, 1994. £11($26) for for issues (effective 1994); newsstand price: £3.50($10). Chris Reed, Ed. & Pub., P.O. Box 625, Sheffield S1 3GY, England. TEL 44-742-824161. FAX 44-742-796395. E-mail: c.s.reed@sheffield.ac.uk. (U.S. subscr. to: Anne Marsden, 1052 Calle del Cerro, No. 708, San Clemente, CA 92672-6068) adv.; bk.rev.; bibl.; illus. **Document type:** consumer publication.
Description: Publishes a variety of innovative and award-winning short fiction, with essays and nonfiction covering the speculative fiction scene around the world.

BANDERSNATCH. see *LITERATURE*

070.5 US
BARRY R. LEVIN SCIENCE FICTION & FANTASY LITERATURE.* vol.6, no., 1993. q. free to qualified personnel. Barry R. Levin Science Fiction & Fantasy Literature, 241 Third Ave., Venice, CA 90291-8615. TEL 310-458-6111. Ed. Barry R. Levin. **Document type:** newsletter, catalog.
Description: Discusses sigificant first and variant editions of science fiction, fantasy and horror books, bibliographic notes, and lists books, manuscripts and associational material available for purchase.

808.838 US
BEST NEW HORROR. 1990. a. $21 (effective 1993). 130 Park View, Wembley, Middx. Ha9 6JU, England. TEL 081-902-1818. Ed. Stephen Jones.
Description: Anthology of recent horror stories by well-known writers, and newcomers to the genre.

813 US ISSN 0095-7119
PZ1.A1
BEST SCIENCE FICTION OF THE YEAR. 1972. a. $2.50. Ballantine Books, 201 E. 50th St., New York, NY 10022. TEL 212-751-2600.

808.838 US
BEYOND SCIENCE FICTION. 1971. a. $5. c/o Rey King, Ed., 414 S. 41st St., Richmond, CA 94804. TEL 415-658-0233. circ. 2,000.
Formerly: Cosmic Circus.

BIBLIOGRAPHIES AND INDEXES IN SCIENCE FICTION, FANTASY, AND HORROR. see *LITERATURE — Abstracting, Bibliographies, Statistics*

808.838 US
▼**BIZARRE BAZAAR.** 1992. a. $8.50. T A L Publications, P.O. Box 1837, Leesburg, VA 22075. TEL 703-777-6324. FAX 703-771-8413. Ed. Stanislaus Tal. circ. 3,000. (back issues avail.) **Document type:** consumer publication.
Description: Anthology series collecting original horror and fantastic fiction.

808.838 US
▼**BIZARRE SEX AND OTHER CRIMES OF PASSION.** 1992. a. $9.50. T A L Publications, P.O. Box 1837, Leesburg, VA 22075. TEL 703-777-6324. FAX 703-771-8413. Stanislaus Tal. circ. 2,000. (back issues avail.) **Document type:** consumer publication.
Description: Features erotic horror literature.

BLACK COUNTRY GHOSTS AND MYSTERIES. see *FOLKLORE*

808.8 GW ISSN 0942-2579
▼**BLIZZ;** das Infozine fuer Science Fiction und Fantasy. 1992. m. DM.40. Utopic Press, Kirchbergstr. 14, 79111 Freiburg, Germany. TEL 0761-807124. Ed. Matthias Hofmann. circ. 250. **Document type:** newsletter.

BLOOMSBURY REVIEW. see *LITERATURE*

BOOKS ARE EVERYTHING. see *LITERATURE*

808.838 US ISSN 0007-6333
BURROUGHS BULLETIN. 1947-1986; N.S. 1990. q. $28 (foreign $35) includes m. newsletter: Gridley Wave. Burroughs Bibliophiles, Edgar Rice Burroughs Collection, Ekstrom Library, University of Louisville, Louisville, KY 40292. TEL 502-588-8729. FAX 502-588-8753. Ed. George T. McWhorter. bk.rev.; film rev.; bibl.; illus. circ. 800. **Document type:** academic/scholarly publication, bulletin.
Description: Publishes scholarly articles on the literary works of Edgar Rice Burroughs, and news of the society's activities.

808.838 UK
BURROUGHSIANA. 1975. q. British E R B Society (Edgar Rice Burroughs), 45 Leith Towers, Brighton Rd., Sutton, Surrey SM2 5BY, England. Ed. Dick Ellingsworth.

808.838 US
CARNAGE HALL. irreg. $4.50 per no. Box 7, Esopus, NY 12429. Ed. David Griffin.

CEMETARY PLOT. see *PARAPSYCHOLOGY AND OCCULTISM*

808.838 US
CEMETERY DANCE. q. $15 (effective 1992). Cemetery Dance Publications, Box 18433, Baltimore, MD 21237. TEL 410-574-3217. Ed. Richard Chizmar. bk.rev.; film rev.; illus. (back issues avail.)
Description: Publishes horror and fantasy short stories, interviews and author profiles.

808.838 CN ISSN 0847-1711
CHAMPAGNE HORROR. 1990. a. $6. Champagne Productions, 2419 Klein Pl., Regina, SK S4V 1M4, Canada. Ed. Cathy Buburuz.
Description: Includes horror fiction, poetry and art.

808.838 UK
CHILLS. no.7, 1993. a. £2.50($6) British Fantasy Society, 2 Harwood Rd., Stockport SK4 1JJ, England. Ed. Peter Coleborn. illus.

CHRONIC RIFT NEWSLETTER. see *COMMUNICATIONS — Television And Cable*

CINEFANTASTIQUE. see *MOTION PICTURES*

810 368 US
CLARION SCIENCE FICTION AND FANTASY WRITER'S WORKSHOP NEWSLETTER. no.9, 1993. s-a. $10 contribution. c/o Mary Sheridan, Lyman Briggs School, 28 E. Holmes, Michigan State University, East Lansing, MI 48825. **Document type:** newsletter.
Description: News of the Clarion science fiction workshop, graduates, and other information relating to science fiction.

808.838 PL
COLLAPS. irreg. membership. Gdanski Klub Fantastyki, P.O. Box 76, 80-325 Gdansk 37, Poland. Dir. Krzysztof Papierkowski. illus.
Description: Science fiction fanzine.

808.838 CN
COMMUNIQUE (EDMONTON). (Text in English, French) bi-m. Can.$25 membership only. S F Canada, c/o Aaron V. Humphrey, Ed., D-10305 114th St., Edmonton, AB T5K 1S2, Canada. **Document type:** newsletter.
Description: News and information for Canadian science fiction writers.

808.838 US
COMPANION IN ZEOR. 1978. irreg. price varies. Karen Litman, Ed. & Pub., 307 Ashland Ave., McKee City, NJ 08232. TEL 609-645-6938. adv.; bk.rev.; film rev.; play rev. circ. 300. (also avail. in audio cassette; also avail. in 4-track audio tape for the visually impaired; back issues avail.)
Description: Dedicated to the writings of Jacqueline Lichtenberg with writings and comments by fans on her various universe-novels, not limited to Sime/Gen.

808.838 UK
CONCATENATION. no.8, 1994. a. free. c/o Jonathan Cowie, Ed., 5 Charlieville Rd., Erith, Kent DA8 1H, England. Ed. Jonathan Cowie. adv. contact: Tony Chester. bk.rev.; film rev.; illus.; circ. 3,000 (controlled). **Document type:** trade publication.
Description: Reviews science and science fiction books, films and videos.

808.8 LI
THE CONTACT. (Text in English) 1990. irreg. Vilnius Science Fiction Club - Dorado, Antakalnio 65-33, 2040 Vilnius, Lithuania. TEL 7-0122-743622. Eds. Gediminas Beresnevicius, Romualdas Buivydas. adv. **Document type:** newsletter.

808.838 US ISSN 0193-6875
CONTRIBUTIONS TO THE STUDY OF SCIENCE FICTION AND FANTASY. 1982. irreg. no.54, 1992. price varies. Greenwood Press, Inc. (Subsidiary of: Greenwood Publishing Group Inc.), 88 Post Rd. W., Box 5007, Westport, CT 06881-5007. TEL 203-226-3571. FAX 203-222-1502. Ed. Marshall Tymn.
—BLDSC (3461.456000).

813 808.838 UK ISSN 0010-9576
COSMOS.* 1969. m. $4.50. c/o Walter Gillings, Ed., 115 Wanstead Park Rd., Ilford, Essex, England. adv.; bk.rev.
Description: Contains science fiction stories.

808.838 US
▼**CRANK! SCIENCE FICTION - FANTASY.** 1993. q. $12. Broken Mirrors Press, Box 380473, Cambridge, MA 02238. Ed. Bryan Cholfin. adv.; circ. 1,200 (paid). **Document type:** consumer publication.
Description: Each issue contains 8 to 10 short stories.

LITERATURE — SCIENCE FICTION, FANTASY, HORROR

808.838 UK
THE EUROPEAN SCIENCE FICTION AND FANTASY REVIEW. 1987. bi-m. £7.99($20) (overseas £11) (effective 1994-1995). Critical Wave Publications, 33 Scott Rd., Olton, Solihull, W. Midlands B92 7LQ, England. TEL 021-706-0108. (Subscr. to: 845 Alum Rock Rd., Ward End, Birmingham B8 2AG, England; U.S. subscr. to: Mary Burns, 23 Kensington Ct., Hempstead, NY 11550; Australian subscr. to: Justin Ackroyd, G.P.O. Box 2708X, Melbourne, Vic. 3001, Australia) Eds. Steve Green, Martin Tudor. adv. contact: Bernie Evans. bk.rev.; film rev.; circ. 1,000 (paid).
Description: Contains science fiction articles and essays, author interviews, and news of conventions.

809.916 US
CRYPT OF CTHULHU; polyp thriller and theological journal. 1981. irreg. (2-3/yr.). no.86, 1994. $6.50 per no. (effective 1994). Necronomicon Press, Box 1304, West Warwick, RI 02893. TEL 401-828-7161. FAX 401-738-6125. Ed. Robert M. Price. adv.; bk.rev.; film rev. circ. 650. (back issues avail.)
Description: Publishes general critical articles examining the literary, biographical and mythological sources of the supernatural fiction of H.P. Lovecraft, creator of the Cthulhu Mythos, and of works by his literary disciples. Occasionally includes fiction by fans and major writers in the field.

808.838 367 US
CUBE. 1983. bi-m. membership. Society for the Furtherance and Study of Fantasy and Science Fiction, Inc. (SF3), Box 1624, Madison, WI 53701-1624. TEL 608-251-6226. Ed. Spike Parsons. bk.rev. circ. 100. (looseleaf format; back issues avail.)

808.838 PL
CZERWONY KARZEL/RED DWARF. (Text in Polish) 1991. irreg. membership. Gdanski Klub Fantastyki, P.O. Box 76, 80-325 Gdansk 37, Poland. Dir. Krzysztof Papierkowski. illus.
Description: Science fiction stories by Polish writers, translations of Western authors, critical articles, and news of science fiction activities in Poland.

808.838 US
THE DARK EIDOLON: THE JOURNAL OF CLARK ASHTON SMITH STUDIES. irreg., no.3, 1993. $5 per no. Necronomicon Press, Box 1304, West Warwick, RI 02893. TEL 401-828-7161. FAX 401-738-6125. Ed. Steve Behrends. bk.rev. **Document type:** academic/scholarly publication.
Description: Publishes essays and reviews examining the life and works of Clark Ashton Smith, poet, author and artist of the macabre.

808.838 UK
DARK HORIZONS. no.31, 1990. irreg. £10($24) membership. British Fantasy Society, c/o Di Wathen, 15 Stanley Rd., Morden, Surrey SM4 5DE, England. Ed. Phil Williams.

THE DARK MAN: THE JOURNAL OF ROBERT E. HOWARD STUDIES. see *LITERATURE — Adventure And Romance*

808.838 US
DARK WINDS;* decadence fantasy magazine. 1982. a. $6. Gibbelin's Gazette Publications, c/o Veron Clark, Ed., 2810 Urbana Dr., Silver Spring, MD 20906-5033. adv.; bk.rev.; illus. circ. 350.
Description: Features nonfiction and poetry.

808.838 US
DARKOVER NEWSLETTER. no.61, 1993. q. $7 (Canada $10; elsewhere $12). Marion Zimmer Bradley, Box 249, Berkeley, CA 94701. TEL 510-644-9222. **Document type:** newsletter.

808.838 US ISSN 1049-0892
DEAD OF NIGHT. 1989. s-a. $9. Dead of Night Publications, 916 Shaker Rd., Ste. 228, Longmeadow, MA 01106-2416. Ed. Lin Stein. adv.; bk.rev.; film rev.; illus. circ. 1,000. (back issues avail.)
Description: Contains horror fiction, fantasy, mystery, science fiction, and vampire-related fiction.

808.838 US
DEATHREALM; the land where horror dwells. 1987. 4/yr. $15.95. T A L Publications, Box 1837, Leesburg, VA 22075. TEL 703-777-6324. FAX 703-771-8413. Ed. Mark Rainey. illus. **Document type:** consumer publication.
Description: Publishes horror fiction and dark fantasy.

808.838 US ISSN 1073-4864
▼**DEEP THOUGHTS;** proceedings of life, the universe, & everything. 1993. a. $15. T L E Press, 3163 J K L B, Provo, UT 84602. TEL 801-378-2456. Eds. Marny K. Parkin, Steve Setzer. circ. 300. **Document type:** academic/scholarly publication, proceedings.
Description: Includes addresses by guests of honor and papers presented at an academic symposium on science fiction and fantasy writing.

808.8 UK
DEMENTIA 13. 1989. 4/yr. £12 (US subscr. £20). 17 Pinewood Ave., Sidcup, Kent DA15 8BB, England. Ed. Pam J. Creais. illus. circ. 100. **Document type:** consumer publication.
Description: Contains horror and fantasy fictions, nonfiction, reviews, interviews and articles.

398 808.81 US
DRACULA NEWS JOURNAL. 1980. q. membership. (Dracula Unlimited) Dracula Press, Penthouse N., 29 Washington Sq. W., New York, NY 10011. TEL 212-533-5018. Ed. James Martin. adv.; bk.rev. circ. 2,500. **Document type:** newsletter.
Description: Concerning vampirism in all its forms and guises.

808.8 UK
DREAM CELL. 1991. irreg. £1 per no. c/o 7 Walmersley Rd., New Moston, Manchester M10 0RS, England. Ed. Shan Schofield.

DREAMS AND NIGHTMARES. see *LITERATURE — Poetry*

808.8 CN ISSN 1183-7020
EDGE DETECTOR. 1991. a. $15 (£9 in UK). Box 36, Sta. H, Montreal, Que. H3G 2K5, Canada. TEL 514-939-4382. FAX 514-939-4382. (Subscr. in UK to: Chris Reed, NSFA, P.O. Box 625, Sheffield S1 3GY, England) Ed. Glenn Grant. circ. 1,000.
Description: Publishes speculative fiction, critical essays and original artwork.

808.838 AT
EIDOLON. vol.4, 1993. q. Aus.$24 (foreign Aus.$44). Eidolon Publications, c/o Richard Scriven, P.O. Box 225, North Perth, WA 6006, Australia. Ed. Jeremy G. Byrne.

808.838 US
ELDRITCH TALES; a magazine of weird fantasy. 1975. q. $24. Eldritch Tales, 1051 Wellington Rd., Lawrence, KS 66049. Ed. Crispin Burnham. adv.; bk.rev.; illus.

808.838 SW ISSN 0349-2397
ENCYCLOPEDIA GALACTICA. 1978-1985; resumed 1989. irreg. Banerg. 11, S-752 37 Uppsala, Sweden. TEL 46-18-54-97-61. Ed. & Pub. John Soeren /Pettersson. bk.rev.

808.838 US ISSN 0891-9593
ESSAYS ON FANTASTIC LITERATURE. 1986. irreg., no.8, 1993. price varies. Borgo Press, Box 2845, San Bernardino, CA 92406. TEL 909-884-5813. FAX 909-888-4942. Ed. Daryl F. Mallett.
Description: Short essays on science fiction and fantasy by critics and professionals in the genre.

808.838 US ISSN 1070-6844
▼**EXPANSE.** 1993. q. $16. Expanse Magazine, Box 43547, Baltimore, MD 21236-0547. TEL 410-483-9332. FAX 410-931-8646. Ed. Steven E. Fick. adv. contact: Eric White. circ. 13,000. **Document type:** consumer publication.
Description: Original science fiction stories, essays and author interviews.

809.9 US ISSN 0014-5483
PN3448.S45
EXTRAPOLATION; journal of the scholarly study of science fiction and fantasy. 1959. q. $18 to individuals; institutions $28. Kent State University Press, Kent, OH 44242-0001. TEL 216-672-7913. Ed. Donald M. Hassler. adv.; bk.rev.; bibl.; cum.index: vols.1-14. circ. 1,000. (also avail. in microform from UMI; reprint service avail. from UMI) **Indexed:** Abstr.Engl.Stud., Acad.Ind., Amer.Bibl.Slavic & E.Eur.Stud., Arts & Hum.Cit.Ind., Bk.Rev.Ind. (1988-), Child.Bk.Rev.Ind. (1988-), Curr.Cont., Hum.Ind., M.L.A. **Document type:** academic/scholarly publication.
—BLDSC (3854.460000); Faxon; UnCover; UMI. CCC.

808.838 UK ISSN 0959-4558
EXUBERANCE. 1990. q. £6.50($15) 34 Croft Close, Chipperfield, Herts. WD4 9PA, England. Ed. Jason R. Smith.
Description: Publishes science fiction.

808.838 US
FANG. m. $28 for 16 nos. Tangram Publishing, Box 752, Belfast, ME 04915. illus.
Description: Horror fiction and art, with author interviews.

133 US ISSN 0164-2111
FANGORIA. 1979. 10/yr. $29.47. Fangoria (Subsidiary of: Starlog Group, Inc.), 475 Park Ave. S., New York, NY 10016. TEL 212-689-2830. FAX 212-889-7933. Ed. Anthony Timpone. adv. circ. 150,000.
Formerly: Fantastica.

808.838 700 GW ISSN 0934-1463
FANTASIA. 1978. q. DM.60($36) Erster Deutscher Fantasy Club e.V., Postfach 1371, 94003 Passau, Germany. Ed. Franz Schroepf. adv.; bk.rev.; film rev.; illus. circ. 800. (back issues avail.) **Document type:** consumer publication.

808.838 US ISSN 0094-2375
FANTASIAE (LOS ANGELES). 1973. m. membership. Fantasy Association, Box 24560, Los Angeles, CA 90024. Ed. Ian M. Slater. bk.rev.; cum.index. circ. 500.

809.916 UK
FANTASTIC WORLDS OF EDGAR RICE BURROUGHS.* 1976. q. £2.50. British E.R.B. Society (Edgar Rice Burroughs), 56 Leith Towers, Brighton Rd., Sutton, Surrey SM2 5BY, England.

808.81 US ISSN 1051-5011
FANTASY COMMENTATOR. 1943. s-a. $10. A. Langley Searles, Ed. & Pub., 48 Highland Cir., Bronxville, NY 10708-5909. TEL 914-961-6799. bk.rev.; bibl.; index; adv. circ. 500 (paid). (back issues avail.) **Document type:** academic/scholarly publication, bibliography.
Description: Devoted to articles, reviews and verse in the area of science-fiction and fantasy.

FANTASYWELT; das Fachmagazin fur Rollenspieler. see *SPORTS AND GAMES*

808.838 UK ISSN 0964-1890
FAR POINT. 1991. 6/yr. £11 (foreign £17). Victoria Publications, P.O. Box 47, Grantham, Lincs. NG31 8RJ, England. bk.rev.; illus. (back issues avail.)
Description: Science fiction and fantasy stories, criticism, and convention news.

808.838 US ISSN 1047-143X
FIGMENT: TALES FROM THE IMAGINATION. 1989. q. $14.50. Figment Press, Box 3128, Moscow, ID 83843-1906. Eds. J.C. Hendee, Barb Hendee. adv.; illus.; index.

808.838 US
FIRST FANDOM MAGAZINE. 1959. 2/yr. membership. Pulp Era Press, 413 Ottokee St., Wauseon, OH 43567-1133. Ed. Lynn A. Hickman. bk.rev.; bibl.; illus.; stat. circ. 350. (processed)
Description: Covers science fiction, with articles on magazines, authors, and artists.

FLICKERS 'N' FRAMES. see *MOTION PICTURES*

LITERATURE — SCIENCE FICTION, FANTASY, HORROR

808.838   UK   ISSN 0144-560X
FOCUS (KENT). 3/yr. £12 includes Matrix, Paperback Inferno and Vector. British Science Fiction Association Ltd., 49 Station Rd., Haxby, York YO3 8LU, England. (Subscr. to: 29 Thornville Rd., Hartlepool, Cleveland TS26 8EW, England) Ed. Cecil Nurse. (back issues avail.) **Document type:** trade publication.
Description: Magazine for those interested in writing science fiction.

808.838   US
FOSFAX. 1973. bi-m. $12 (foreign $18). Falls of the Ohio Science Fiction and Fantasy Association, Box 37281, Louisville, KY 40233-7281. Ed. Tim Lane. adv.: B&W page $25. bk.rev. circ. 300. (also avail. in diskette format)
Description: Covers science fiction topics, scientific discoveries and new books.

808.838   UK   ISSN 0306-4964
PS374.S35
FOUNDATION; the review of science fiction. 1972. 3/yr. £10($20) Science Fiction Foundation, University of York, The King's Manor, York YO1 2EP, England. TEL 0904-433915. Ed. E. James. adv.; bk.rev.; film rev.; bibl.; cum.index. circ. 1,000. (back issues avail.) **Indexed:** M.L.A. **Document type:** academic/scholarly publication.
—BLDSC (4024.855000); UnCover.
Description: Articles on science fiction, by critics and science fiction writers.
Refereed Serial

808.838   US   ISSN 1068-3992
▼**FUTURES PAST**; A visual guidebook to science fiction history. 1992. q. $20 (typically set in June). (Science Fiction Resources Network) The Write Answer, Box 610, Convoy, OH 45832. TEL 419-749-2482. Ed. James Emerson. adv.; bk.rev. circ. 700. **Document type:** academic/scholarly publication.
—UnCover.
Description: Provides a detailed chronicle of the history of modern science fiction from 1926 to the present. Includes comprehensive author bibliographies, profiles and original interviews.

808.838   PL
GALACTICA. irreg. membership. Gdanski Klub Fantastyki, P.O. Box 76, 80-325 Gdansk 37, Poland. Dir. Krzysztof Papierkowski.
Description: Science fiction fanzine.

808.838   US   ISSN 0016-4003
GALAXY. 1950-1980; resumed, N.S. 1994. bi-m. $18 (Canada $28; Europe $30; Pacific Rim $32) (effective 1994). (Institute for the Development of the Harmonious Human Being) Galaxy Magazine, Box 370, Nevada City, CA 95959. TEL 916-432-1839; 800-869-0658. FAX 916-432-1810. Ed. E.J. Gold. adv.; bk.rev.; charts; illus. circ. 10,000. (also avail. in microfiche from UMI; reprint service avail. from UMI) **Indexed:** Amer.Hum.Ind. **Document type:** consumer publication.
Description: Publishes short science fiction stories.

808.838   US   ISSN 1072-4885
▼**GALLEON**. 1993. bi-m. $18. Brave New World Publishing, 4280 Stage Coach Trail, Rockford, IL 61101-6131. TEL 815-969-4885. Ed. Jeff Knoedler. adv.: page $150; trim 7 1/2 x 10.
Description: Contains imaginative fantasy fiction, and short stories.

808.838   UK   ISSN 0955-0933
THE GATE; science fiction and fantasy. 1989. irreg., no.3, 1991. £6 for 4 nos. W Publishing, 28 Saville Rd., Westwood, Peterborough PE3 7PR, England. FAX 0733331511. Ed. Richard Newcombe. bk.rev.; illus. circ. 2,000.

GAUNTLET; exploring the limits of free expression. see LITERARY AND POLITICAL REVIEWS

808.83   UK   ISSN 0968-7777
GHOSTS & SCHOLARS. 1979. 2/yr. £10($20) (effective Oct. 1993). Haunted Library, 36 Hamilton St., Flat 1, Hoole, Chester CH2 3JQ, England. TEL 0244-313685. Ed. Rosemary Pardoe. bk.rev.; illus. circ. 400. (back issues avail.) **Document type:** consumer publication.
Description: Ghost stories in the M.R. James tradition and articles about ghost story writers. Scholarly but not academic.

808.838 813   US   ISSN 0017-419X
GRIDLEY WAVE. 1958; N.S. 1990. m. $28 membership (foreign $35) includes q. Burroughs Bulletin. Burroughs Bibliophiles, Edgar Rice Burroughs Collection, Ekstrom Library, University of Louisville, Louisville, KY 40292. TEL 502-588-8729. FAX 502-588-8753. Ed. George T. McWhorter. bk.rev.; film rev.; bibl.; illus. circ. 800. **Document type:** academic/scholarly publication, bulletin.
Description: Concerns the writings of Edgar Rice Burroughs, and includes news of society activities.

800   US   ISSN 0897-9707
GRUE MAGAZINE. 1985. 3/yr. $13. Hell's Kitchen Productions, Inc., Box 370, Times Sq. Sta., New York, NY 10108-0370. TEL 212-245-2329. Ed. Peggy Nadramia. adv.; illus.; circ. 2,000 (controlled). (back issues avail.)
Description: Contains horror and dark fantasy fiction and poetry.

808.838   CN   ISSN 0700-9917
GUARD THE NORTH. 1970. q. Can.$5. Box 3355, Vancouver, BC V6B 3Y3, Canada. Ed. D. Say. adv.; bk.rev.; film rev. circ. 300.
Description: Contains science fiction stories.

808.838   US   ISSN 1070-6569
▼**HARSH MISTRESS**; science fiction adventures. 1993. q. $14. D.N.A. Publications, Box 13, Greenfield, MA 01302. TEL 413-773-0481. Ed. Warren Lapine; Pub. Warren Lapine. adv.: page $225, color page $725. circ. 6,000.
Description: Specializes in action-adventure oriented science fiction.

808.838   US
HAUNTED JOURNAL.* 1983. irreg. (2-4/yr.). $28 for 4 issues. Baker Street Publications, Box 517, Metairie, LA 70004-0517. TEL 504-734-8414. Ed. Sharida Rizzuto. circ. 9,000.

808.8   US   ISSN 1043-3503
PS648.H6
HAUNTS; tales of unexpected horror and the supernatural. 1984. q. $13. Nightshade Publications, Box 3342, Providence, RI 02906-0742. TEL 401-781-9438. FAX 401-943-0980. Ed. Joseph K. Cherkes. adv.; bk.rev. circ. 1,200. **Document type:** consumer publication.

808.838   JA
HAYAKAWA S F. m. Hayakawa Publishing, Inc., 2-2 Kanda-tacho, Chiyada-ku, Tokyo 101, Japan.

817   US   ISSN 0885-7822
HEAVY METAL; the adult illustrated fantasy magazine. Short title: H M. 1977. bi-m. $12.95. Metal Mammoth, 584 Broadway, Ste. 608, New York, NY 10012. TEL 212-274-8462. FAX 212-274-8969. Ed. Kevin Eastman. adv. contact: Howard Jurofsky. illus. circ. 140,000. (back issues avail.) **Document type:** consumer publication.

808.838   US
HOR-TASY. 1980. irreg. (approx a.). $2.95. Ansuda Publications, Box 158-B, Harris, IA 51345. Ed. Daniel R. Betz.
Description: Publishes psychological horror and pure fantasy, no science fiction.

808.838   US
▼**HORROR**; the news magazine of the horror & dark fantasy field. 1994. m. $36. Wildside Press, 37 Fillmore St., Newark, NJ 07105. TEL 201-246-4532. Ed. John G. Betancourt. bk.rev.; illus. **Document type:** consumer publication.
Description: News, interviews and articles relating to horror publishing in the U.S. and Canada.

808   US   ISSN 0748-2914
HORROR SHOW; an adventure in terror. 1982. q. $14. Phantasm Press, 14848 Misty Springs Ln., Oak Run, CA 96069. TEL 916-472-3540. Ed. David B. Silva. adv.; bk.rev.; film rev. circ. 54,000.
Description: Presents contemporary tales of the macabre, illustrations, and inside tips on the horror field.

808.838   XR
IKARIE. (Text in Czech, Slovak) no.8, 1991. m. Radlickaa 61, 150 02 Prague 5, Czech Republic. Ed. Ondrej Neff. illus.
Description: Science fiction magazine, with original fiction, including foreign writers in translation, interviews, and news of the science fiction world.

808.83   CN   ISSN 0709-8855
IMAGINE; science-fiction et litteratures de l'imaginaire. (Text in French) 1979. q. Can.$20 (effective Jan. 1991). Publications les Imaginoides, 3418 rue de la Paix, Sainte-Foy, PQ G1X 3W6, Canada. TEL 418-658-9966. FAX 418-658-6100. Ed. Marc Lemaire. adv.; bk.rev.; film rev.; play rev.; illus.; index. circ. 600. (back issues avail.)
Description: Covers fiction and studies in the field of science fiction.

808.838   US
INTERFERENCE ON THE BRAIN SCREEN. irreg. $2 per no. c/o Clark, Box 2761, St. Paul, MN 55102.

808.838   UK   ISSN 0264-3596
INTERZONE. 1982. m. £28($52) (effective Jan. 1993). 217 Preston Drove, Brighton BN1 6FL, England. TEL 0273-504710. (N. America dist.: Worldwide Magazine Distributors Ltd., 225 Bysham Park Dr., Unit 14, Woodstock, ON N4T 1P1, Canada. TEL 519-539-0200) Ed. David Pringle. adv.; bk.rev.; film rev.; illus.; cum.index: 1982-1991 in no.50. circ. 10,000. (back issues avail.) **Document type:** consumer publication.
—UnCover.
Incorporates (1991-1993): Million (ISSN 0960-832X)
Description: Specializes in new science fiction and fantasy stories, in addition to reviews, interviews, and more.

808.838   US
IT GOES ON THE SHELF. 1979. a., no.10, 1993. free or exchange basis. Purple Mouth Press, 713 Paul St., Newport News, VA 23605. TEL 804-380-6595. Ed. Ned Brooks. adv.; bk.rev. circ. 350. (also avail. in diskette format) **Document type:** newsletter.
Former titles: Skiffy Thyme; Skiffy Bag.
Description: Reviews books and related materials of interest to science fiction and fantasy readers and collectors.

800   UK
J G B NEWS. irreg. (approx. s-a.). David Pringle, Ed. & Pub., 217 Preston Drove, Brighton BN1 6FL, England. **Document type:** newsletter.
Description: News and articles on the British writer J.G. Ballard, including notes on recent writings and appearances.

808.838   US
J. WAYNE AND ELSIE M. GUNN CENTER FOR THE STUDY OF SCIENCE FICTION NEWSLETTER. 1982. a. J. Wayne and Elsie M. Gunn Center for the Study of Science Fiction, University of Kansas, English Department, Lawrence, KS 66045. TEL 913-864-4520. FAX 913-864-5298. circ. 1,200 (controlled). **Document type:** newsletter.
Description: Describes the programs offered and their status.

808.838   CN
▼**JOURNAL OF CANADIAN CONTENT IN SPECULATIVE LITERATURE**. 1993. q. Can.$20($20) (effective 1994). 112 Monterey Dr., Nepean, ON K2H 7A8, Canada. Ed. James M. Botte.

808.838   SW   ISSN 0345-5599
JULES VERNE - MAGASINET; science fiction nytt. 1940-1948; resumed 1969. bi-m. SEK 175 (effective 1990). Lundwall Fakta och Fantasi, P.O. Box 17030, S-161 17 Bromma, Sweden.
Former titles (until 1948): Vaeckans Aeventyr; (until vol.9, 1942): Jules Verne Magasinet, Veckans Aeventyr; (until vol.36, 1941): Jules Verne - Magasinet.

808.8   LI
KAUKAS. irreg. (2-3/yr.). Radvilenu 56a-35, Kaunas 28, Lithuania. Ed. Gintaras Aleksonis. bk.rev.; film rev.
Description: Publishes science fiction and ... from Lithuanian authors and around the ...

LITERATURE — SCIENCE FICTION, FANTASY, HORROR

808.838   CC
KEHUAN SHIJIE/SCIENCE FICTION WORLD. (Text in Chinese) m. Y21.60. No.11 St. 4, South People's Rd., Chengdu, People's Republic of China. Ed. Yang Xiao. illus. **Document type:** consumer publication.
Description: Publishes original science fiction stories and articles, and Chinese translations of international stories.

808.838   US
LAN'S LANTERN. 1976. irreg. $12. Lan's Lantern, 1305 Cherokee Ave., Royal Oak, MI 48067-3386. Ed. George Laskowski. illus.

813   US   ISSN 1049-5983
THE LEADING EDGE; magazine of science fiction and fantasy. 1981. 3/yr. $8 (effective 1993). T L E Press, 3163 JKHB, Provo, UT 84602. Ed. Michael Carr. adv.: B&W page $70. illus. circ. 500. (back issues avail.)
Description: Publishes science fiction and fantasy short stories, articles and poetry; carries interviews.

808.83   US   ISSN 0047-4959
LOCUS (OAKLAND); the newspaper of the science fiction field. 1968. m. $38 to individuals; institutions $41. Locus Publications, Box 13305, Oakland, CA 94661. TEL 510-339-9198. FAX 510-339-8144. (Subscr. in UK to: Fantast (Medway) Ltd., P.O. Box 23, Upwell Wisbech, Cambs PE14 9BU, England) Ed. Charles N. Brown. adv.; bk.rev.; bibl.; illus.; index. circ. 9,000. (back issues avail.) **Indexed:** Bk.Rev.Ind. (1989-). **Document type:** trade publication.
—UnCover; UMI.
Description: Covers news, people and issues in science fiction of interest to publishers, authors and interested readers. Includes author interviews, comprehensive lists of new and forthcoming books, information on computer technology of interest, science fiction magazines, and timely reports of conventions and awards.

809.916   US   ISSN 0899-8361
LOVECRAFT STUDIES. 1979. 2/yr. $10 (effective 1994). Necronomicon Press, Box 1304, West Warwick, RI 02893. TEL 401-828-7161. FAX 401-738-6125. Ed. S.T. Joshi. bk.rev. (back issues avail.) **Document type:** academic/scholarly publication.
Description: Studies the life and writings of H.P. Lovecraft, horror and supernatural fiction author, and creator of the Cthulhu Mythos.

808.8   UK
THE LYRE. 1991. irreg., no.2, 1993. £2.20($5) per no. Nicholas Mahoney, Ed. & Pub., 275 Lonsdale Ave., Intake, Doncaster DN2 6HJ, England. (Subscr. in U.S. to: Anne Marsden, 1052 Calle del Cerro, No. 708, San Clemente, CA 92672. TEL 714-361-3791)
Description: Original science fiction stories and author interviews.

813   US   ISSN 0024-984X
AP2
THE MAGAZINE OF FANTASY & SCIENCE FICTION. Cover title: Fantasy & Science Fiction. 1949. m. (combined Oct.-Nov.). $26. Mercury Press, Inc., 143 Cream Hill Rd., West Cornwall, CT 06796. TEL 203-672-6376. FAX 203-672-2643. (Submissions and editorial correspondence to: Box 11526, Eugene, OR 97440) Ed. Kristine Rusch; Pub. Ed Ferman. adv. contact: Ed Ferman. bk.rev.; film rev.; charts; illus.; cum.index: vols.1-75, 1949-1988. circ. 61,500. (also avail. in microfilm from UMI) **Indexed:** Amer.Hum.Ind., Bk.Rev.Ind. (1969-), Child.Bk.Rev.Ind. (1969-), Mag.Ind. **Document type:** consumer publication.
Incorporates: Venture Science Fiction.
Description: Contains short stories, novellas, novelettes, and a science column.

830 831 700   GW   ISSN 0934-1455
MAGIRA. 1967. a. $5 per no. Erster Deutscher Fantasy Club e.V., Postfach 1371, 94003 Passau, Germany. Ed. Hubert Strassl. adv.; bk.rev.; bibl.; illus. circ. 1,300. **Document type:** consumer publication.

808.838   UK   ISSN 0308-6674
MALLORN. 1970. a. £15. Tolkien Society, 357 High St., Flat 5, Cheltenham, Glos. GL50 3HT, England. TEL 0242-577232. bk.rev.; bibl. circ. 900. **Indexed:** Child.Lit.Abstr., M.L.A. **Document type:** newsletter.
Description: Essays on elvish language and writings, poetry and art work from members of the Society.

808.838   US   ISSN 0897-9286
PS648.F3
MARION ZIMMER BRADLEY'S FANTASY MAGAZINE. 1988. q. $16 (Canada $24; elsewhere $38). Marion Zimmer Bradley, Box 249, Berkeley, CA 94701. TEL 510-644-9222. Ed. Marion Zimmer Bradley. adv. (back issues avail.) **Document type:** consumer publication.
Description: Contains fantasy artwork, short stories and articles on fiction writing.

810   US
MASIFORM D. (Not published 1991-1992) 1971. a. $7.50 per no. Poison Pen Press, 627 E. Eighth St., Brooklyn, NY 11218. TEL 718-853-8121. Ed. Devra Michele Langsam. illus. circ. 500. (reprint service avail.)
Description: Publishes original fiction based on the Star Trek television shows and movies.

808.838   UK   ISSN 0307-3335
MATRIX; the newsletter of the British Science Fiction Association. 1979. bi-m. £12 includes Focus, Paperback Inferno, and Vector. British Science Fiction Association Ltd., 16 Aviary Pl., Leeds, LS12 2NP, England. (Subscr. to: Membership Secretary, 33 Thornville Rd., Hartlepool, Cleveland TS26 8EW, England) Ed. Jenny Glover. adv.
Formerly: Science Fiction Media News (ISSN 0143-3725)
Description: News and articles on all aspects of science fiction.

800 700   UK   ISSN 0309-1309
PR6031.E183
MERVYN PEAKE REVIEW. 1975. s-a. £14. Mervyn Peake Society, 2 Mount Park Rd., Ealing W5 2RP, England. TEL 081-566-9307. FAX 081-991-0559. adv.; bk.rev.; play rev.; abstr.; illus. circ. 300. (back issues avail.) **Indexed:** Abstr.Engl.Stud., M.L.A. **Document type:** newsletter.
—CCC.
Formerly: Mervyn Peake Society Newsletter.

808.838   US
MIDNIGHT GRAFFITI. 1988. 4/yr. $19.95. 57754 Onaga Trl., Yucca Valley, CA 92284-3939. TEL 619-365-5836. Ed. James van Hise. adv.; bk.rev. circ. 5,000. (back issues avail.)
Description: Small press magazine devoted to the bizarre and the unusual in both fiction and reality. Publishes horror and dark fantasy fiction as well as interviews with writers.

808.838   UK
MIDNIGHT IN HELL; the weirdest tales of fandom. 1990. q. $5 per no. Grave Orc, The Cottage, Smithy Brae, Kilma Colm, Renfrewshire PA13 4EN, Scotland. Ed. George N. Houston. adv.; bibl.; film rev.; circ. 300 (paid). (back issues avail.)
Description: Publishes essays on horror and dark fantasy fan fiction films as well as short fiction. Seeks to attract attention to writers' beginnings in the genres.

808.838   US   ISSN 1058-2517
PS648.H6
MIDNIGHT ZOO; exciting horror, science fiction, fantasy, & science fact. 1990. m. $40 (effective 1993). Experiences Unlimited, 544 Ygnacio Valley Rd., No.13, Box 8040, Walnut Creek, CA 94596. TEL 510-682-9662. FAX 510-682-9706. Ed. Jon L. Herron. circ. 3,000. (back issues avail.)
Formerly (until 1991): Amazing Experiences (ISSN 1051-1725)

808.838   US
MIMOSA. 1981. 2/yr. $2 per no. Box 1270, Germantown, MD 20875. Eds. Dick Lynch, Nicki Lynch.
Description: General interest science fiction fanzine, with emphasis on fan history.

800   US   ISSN 1063-0848
MINAS TIRITH EVENING STAR. 1967. q. $7.50 (Canada $12.50; elsewhere $15). (American Tolkien Society) W.W. Publications, Box 373, Highland, MI 48357-0373. TEL 813-585-0985. Ed. Philip Helms. adv.; bk.rev. circ. 650. (back issues avail.) **Document type:** newsletter.
Description: Examines the works of J.R.R. Tolkien and his son Christopher J.R.R. Tolkieein.

808.838   US
▼**MINDSPARKS.** 1993. m. $18 (overseas $22). Molecudyne Research, Box 1379, Laurel, MD 20725-1379. **Document type:** newsletter.

808.838   US   ISSN 1061-1800
PN3433
MONAD; a journal of science fiction criticism. 1990. irreg., no.3, 1993. $18 for 4 nos. (Writer's Notebook Press) Pulphouse Publishing, Inc., Box 1227, Eugene, OR 97440. TEL 503-935-3247. Ed. Damon Knight; Pub. Dean Wesley Smith. bk.rev.; index. circ. 500.

808.83   US
MYTHIC CIRCLE. 1981. 3/yr. $18 to non-members; members $13. Mythopoeic Society, Box 6707, Altadena, CA 91003-6707. Ed.Bd. circ. 200.
Formerly (until Feb. 1987): Mythellany.
Description: A fantasy writer's workshop in print, includes fiction, poetry and art. Extensive reader feedback is a special feature.

808.83   US   ISSN 0146-9339
PR478.F35
MYTHLORE; a journal of J.R.R. Tolkien, C.S. Lewis, Charles Williams, and the genres of myths and fantasy studies. 1969. q. $13 to individuals; institutions $16. Mythopoeic Society (Los Angeles), 742 S. Garfield Ave., Monterey Park, CA 91754-3951. TEL 213-384-9420. (Subscr. to: P.O. Box 6707, Altadena, CA 91001) Ed. Glen M. Goodknight. adv.; bk.rev.; illus. circ. 1,000. (also avail. in microform from UMI; reprint service avail. from UMI) **Indexed:** Abstr.Engl.Stud., Amer.Hum.Ind., Arts & Hum.Cit.Ind., Curr.Cont., M.L.A.
—BLDSC (6001.050000); UnCover.
Supersedes (1964-1972): Tolkien Journal (ISSN 0040-909X)

808.83   US   ISSN 0146-9347
MYTHPRINT. 1970. m. $12.50. Mythopoeic Society, Box 6707, Altadena, CA 91003-6707. Ed. David Bratman. adv.; bk.rev.; film rev.; illus.; index. circ. 300. **Document type:** newsletter.
Formerly (until 1969): Mythopoeic Society. Bulletin.
Description: Provides information on meetings and conventions.

THE N E S F A INDEX TO SHORT SCIENCE FICTION. (New England Science Fiction Association Inc.) see LITERATURE — Abstracting, Bibliographies, Statistics

808.838   US
NATIONAL FANTASY FAN. m. $12 membership. National Fantasy Fan Federation, c/o Donald Franson, William Center, 1920 Division St., Murphysboro, IL 62966. **Document type:** newsletter.

810   US   ISSN 0741-5567
PS648.S3
NEBULA AWARDS; SFWA's choices for the best science fiction and fantasy of the year. 1965. a. $12.95 paperback; $24.95 hardbound (effective 1994). (Science-fiction and Fantasy Writers of America) Harcourt Brace Co., 15 E. 26th St., New York, NY 10010. TEL 212-614-3000. Ed. James Morrow. **Document type:** trade publication.
Former titles (until 1983): Nebula Award Stories (ISSN 0731-6690); (until 1982): Nebula Winners (ISSN 0162-3818); (until 1977): Nebula Award Stories (ISSN 0077-6408)
Description: Collects award-winning stories, poems, novellas and critical writing of the preceding year.

808.83   US
NECROFILE; the review of horror fiction. 1991. 4/yr. $12 (Canada $15; elsewhere $17.50) (effective 1994). Necronomicon Press, Box 1304, West Warwick, RI 02893. TEL 401-828-7161. FAX 401-738-6125. Eds. Stefan Dziemianowicz, S.T. Joshi. bk.rev.; bibl.; cum.index: nos.1-8 in no.8. (back issues avail.)
Description: Features extended critical reviews of contemporary horror titles, capsule reviews of recent and forthcoming works, and a complete listing of all American and British horror titles published during the preceding three months.

808.838   CN   ISSN 0229-1932
NEW CANADIAN FANDOM. (Text in English, French) 1981. irreg. Can.$2 per no. 53 Mohawk Rd., W., Lethbridge, AB T1K 5J5, Canada. TEL 403-381-4323. Ed. Robert Runte. adv.; bk.rev.; film rev. circ. 500.
Description: Commentary on Canadian speculative fiction, personal essays, and letters.

LITERATURE — SCIENCE FICTION, FANTASY, HORROR

808.8 UK
NEW DAWN FADES. no.9, 1991. irreg. £1.50 per no. 2 Woodfield Ave., Colinston, Edinburgh EH13 0HX, Scotland. Ed. Gavin Boynter.

808.838 US
▼**NEW LOVECRAFT COLLECTOR**. 1993. q. $5 (foreign $6) (effective 1994). Necronomicon Press, Box 1304, West Warwick, RI 02893. TEL 401-828-7161. FAX 401-738-6125. **Document type:** newsletter, bibliography.
  Description: Covers past, present and forthcoming publications and adaptations of works by H.P. Lovecraft, including appearances in anthologies, translations, movies and non-book oddities. Also discusses noteworthy editions, advice to collectors, and a sampling of current prices.

808.838 UK ISSN 0963-0805
NEW MOON; science fiction. 1985. q. £8 (foreign £10). Trevor Jones, Ed. & Pub., 1 Ravenshoe, Godmanchester, Huntingdon, Cambs. PE18 8DE, England. TEL 0480-451600. Ed. George Townsend. bk.rev. circ. 1,000.
  Formerly (until July 1991): Dream Science Fiction.

808 US ISSN 0886-2451
NEW PATHWAYS.* 1986. bi-m. $25 (foreign $36). M G A Services, 725 E. Interstate 30, Ste. 304, Garland, TX 75043-4043. (Subscr. to: Box 863994, Plano, TX 75086-3994) Ed. Michael G. Adkisson. bk.rev.; illus. circ. 1,500.

808.838 UK ISSN 0028-7075
NEW WORLDS. 1946; N.S. 1992. irreg., vol.3, 1994. $13.95 per no. Victor Gollancz Ltd., 14 Henrietta St., Covent Garden, London WC2E 8QJ, England. TEL 44-71-836-2006. FAX 44-71-379-0934. (Dist in U.S. by: Trafalgar Square Publishing, Box 257, North Pomfret, VT 05053. TEL 802-457-1911) Ed. David Garnett. adv.; bk.rev.; charts; film rev.; illus. (also avail. in microform from UMI)
  Description: Publishes original science fiction stories by international writers.

808.838 US ISSN 1052-9438
PN3433
NEW YORK REVIEW OF SCIENCE FICTION. 1988. m. $30 to individuals, institutions $35; Canada $35; elsewhere $42. Dragon Press, Box 78, Pleasantville, NY 10570. TEL 914-769-5545. Eds. Robert Killheffer, Donald G. Keller. adv.; bk.rev.; bibl. circ. 1,000. (back issues avail.)
  Description: Publishes essays and reviews on horror, fantasy and science fiction.

808.838 UK
NEXUS; where science fiction meets reality. 1991. irreg. £25. Paul Brazier, Ed. & Pub., P.O. Box 1123, Brighton BN1 6JS, England. TEL 0273-506698. adv.; bk.rev.
  Description: New science fiction and critical articles.

808.838 PL
NIE Z TEJ ZIEMI/NOT FROM THAT WORLD. 1990. m. Ul. Kopernika 8-18, 00-367 Warsaw, Poland. TEL 48-22-264378. FAX 48-22-279620. Ed. Adam Hollanek. circ. 20,000.
  Description: Covers para-science, ghost stories, and more.

808.838 US
NIEKAS. 1962-1969; resumed 1977. s-a. $15 for 4 nos. Niekas Publications, 380 Morrill St., Gilford, NH 03246. Ed.Bd. bk.rev.; film rev.; illus. circ. 1,000.
  Description: Covers science fiction and fantasy literature genres.

NIGHT SONGS. see *LITERATURE — Poetry*

808.838 UK
NIGHTFALL. no.2, 1990. irreg. £5($10) for 3 nos. 18 Lansdowne Rd., Sydney, Crewe, Cheshire CW1 1JY, England. Ed. Noel K. Hannan. illus.
  Description: Science fiction magazine.

808.838 US
▼**NON-STOP**; alternative science fiction. 1993. q. $18 (Canada $32); newsstand price: $4.95. Box 981, Peck Slip Sta., New York, NY 10272-0981. Ed. K.J. Cypret. adv.; bk.rev.; illus. **Document type:** consumer publication.
  Description: Publishes interviews, critical articles and original science fiction stories.

808.838 US
NOVA EXPRESS. 1987. q. $10 (typically set in Jan.). White Car Publications, Nova Express, P.O. Box 27231, Austin, TX 78755. TEL 512-345-5629. Ed. Michael Sumbera. adv.; bk.rev.; bibl.; index; circ. 750 (paid). (back issues avail.) **Document type:** consumer publication.
  Description: Small press review of science fiction, fantasy and horror, plus interviews.

808.383 PL ISSN 0867-132X
NOWA FANTASTYKA. 1982. m. (plus q. ed. for children and q. comic ed.). Ul. Mokotowska 5-6, 00-640 Warsaw, Poland. TEL 48-22-253475. Ed. Lech Jezmyk. circ. 120,000.
  Formerly (until 1990): Fantastyka (ISSN 0209-1631)

OFFICIAL STAR TREK FAN CLUB OF CANADA. see *COMMUNICATIONS — Television And Cable*

808.838 US
▼**OFFWORLD**; illustrated magazine of science fiction and fantasy. 1993. q. $12. Graphic Image Press, Box 1109, Murray Hill Sta., New York, NY 10156-0604. Ed. Arnaldo Lopez. illus. **Document type:** consumer publication.

850 IT
OLTRE ...; rivista italiana di letteratura di genere fantastico. 1991. q. L.20000 (foreign L.50000). (Associazione Culturale "Il Borghetto") Edizioni Sanesi, Borgo Buio 11, 53045 Montepulciano (SI), Italy. TEL 0578-757535. (Co-sponsor: Universita degli Studi di Siena, Dipartimento di Filologia e Critica della Letteratura) Ed. Giorgio Harold Stuart.

OMNI. see *SCIENCES: COMPREHENSIVE WORKS*

808.838 CN ISSN 0843-476X
ON SPEC; the Canadian magazine of speculative writing. 1989. q. Can.$19.95($18) Copper Pig Collective, Box 4727, Edmonton, AB T6E 5G6, Canada.

808.838 US
ORACLE SCIENCE FICTION AND FANTASY MAGAZINE. 1982. q. $7.20. Science Fiction and Fantasy Productions, Inc., 21111 Mapleridge, Southfield, MI 48075. TEL 313-355-9827. Ed. Dave Lillard. circ. 5,000. (back issues avail.)
  Formerly: Oracle Science Fiction and Fantasy Anthology Magazine (ISSN 0736-2862)

808.838 UK
ORION. 1991. 3/yr. £4.50. Orion, 3 Bower St., Reddish, Stockport, Ches. SK5 6NW, England. Ed. Alan Garside. illus.
  Description: Publishes speculative fiction.

OTHER DIMENSIONS; the journal of multimedia horror. see *MOTION PICTURES*

808.838 US
OTHER WORLDS. 1988. a. $9.95. Gryphon Publications, Box 209, Brooklyn, NY 11228-0209. Ed. Gary Lovisi. adv.; bk.rev. (back issues avail.)

808.838 US
PABLO LENNIS; science fiction, fantasy, science. 1976. m. $12. (Fandom House) Deneb Press, 30 N. 19th St., Lafayette, IN 47904. Ed. John Thiel. adv.; bk.rev.; film rev.; play rev.; charts; illus. circ. 100.
  Description: Aims to promote science fiction and fantasy writing.

808.838 US ISSN 0275-519X
PANDORA. 1978. 2/yr. $15. 2063 Belford Rd., Holly, MI 48442-9456. Ed. Meg MacDonald. bk.rev.; illus. circ. 500. (back issues avail.)
  Description: Focuses on character-intensive science fiction and fantasy stories and poetry.

028.1 UK ISSN 0260-0595
PAPERBACK INFERNO. 1977. 6/yr. £12 includes Focus, Matrix and Vector. British Science Fiction Association Ltd., The Flaxyard, Woodfield Ln., Little Neston, Wirral, Cheshire L62 4BT, England. (Subscr. to: 29 Thornville Rd., Hartlepool, Cleveland TS26 8EW, England) Ed. Andy Sawyer.
  Formerly (until vol.3, 1979): Paperback Parlour.
  Description: Reviews of science fiction paperback books.

PAPERBACK PARADE. see *PUBLISHING AND BOOK TRADE*

PAPERBACK PREVIEWS. see *LITERATURE*

808.8 UK ISSN 0961-4400
PEEPING TOM. 1990. q. £7.50($24) Yew Tree House, 15 Nottingham Rd., Ashby-de-la-Zouch, Leicestershire LE65 1DJ, England. (Subscr. in US to: Anne Marsden, 1052 Calle del Cerro, Ste. 708, San Clemente, CA 92672. TEL 714-361-3791) Ed. Stuart Hughes. adv.: B&W page £10 ($18). circ. 200. **Document type:** consumer publication.
  Description: Menacing and bizarre tales of horror and the macabre.

808.838 UK
PERCHANCE. no.6, 1991. irreg. £1 per no. Jim Johnston, Ed. & Pub., 44 Hillcrest Dr., Doagh Rd., Newtownabbey, Co. Antrim BT36 6EQ, N. Ireland.
  Description: Unusual new stories and scenarios for role-playing game enthusiasts.

808.838 GW
PHANTASTISCHE ZEITEN. 1987. bi-m. DM.30. Trivial Verlag, Marienstr. 3, 30171 Hannover, Germany. TEL 0511-329097. Eds. Kurt Werth, Michael Uffelmann. film rev.; illus. circ. 10,000. (back issues avail.)

POE STUDIES ASSOCIATION NEWSLETTER. see *LITERATURE*

808.83 US ISSN 0090-5224
PS2631
POE STUDIES - DARK ROMANTICISM. 1968. 2/yr. $10 to individuals (overseas $15); institutions $15 (overseas $20) (effective 1994). Washington State University Press, Pullman, WA 99164-5910. TEL 509-335-3518. FAX 509-335-8568. Ed. Alexander Hammond. bk.rev.; bibl. circ. 550. (reprint service avail. from UMI) **Indexed:** Abstr.Engl.Stud., Amer.Hum.Ind., Arts & Hum.Cit.Ind., Curr.Cont., Ind.Bk.Rev.Hum., M.L.A. **Document type:** academic/scholarly publication.
  —Faxon; UnCover; UMI.
  Formerly: Poe Newsletter (ISSN 0032-1877)

808.838 UK ISSN 0968-6185
▼**PREMONITIONS**. 1992. s-a. £2.50 per issue. S.A. Publishing, 13 Hazely Combe, Arreton, Isle of Wight PO30 3AJ, England. TEL 0983-865668. Ed. Tony Lee. adv. **Document type:** consumer publication.

808.838 SA
PROBE. 1970. q. R.36 (foreign R.40). Science Fiction South Africa, P.O. Box 781401, Sandton 2146, South Africa. TEL 011-728-4076. Ed. Cornelius van Niekerk. adv.; bk.rev.; video rev. circ. 200.
  Description: Publishes short science fiction stories, critical articles on science fiction topics, and members' letters and comments.

PSYCHOTRONIC VIDEO. see *COMMUNICATIONS — Video*

808.838 US
PULP VAULT. no.9, 1991. irreg., no.11, 1993. $7.95 per no. (foreign $10). Tattered Pages Press, 6942 N. Oleander, Chicago, IL 60631. TEL 312-763-8763. Ed. Doug Ellis. bibl.
  Description: For pulp-fiction enthusiasts.

808.838 US
PS648.F3
PULPHOUSE - A FICTION MAGAZINE. 1991. m. $39 for 13 nos. (effective 1993). Pulphouse Publishing, Inc., Box 1227, Eugene, OR 97440. TEL 503-935-3247. Ed. Dean Wesley Smith; Pub. Dean Wesley Smith. adv.; bk.rev.; film rev.; video rev.; illus.; tr.lit. circ. 10,000. (back issues avail.) **Document type:** consumer publication.
  Formerly (until no.4, 1991): Pulphouse - A Weekly Fiction Magazine.
  Description: Publishes original science fiction, fantasy, and horror, mystery, westerns and mainstream fiction, with nonfiction and critical articles.

808.838 US
▼**PULPHOUSE FICTION SPOTLIGHT**. 1992. irreg., no.3, 1993. free to Pulphouse subscribers. Pulphouse Publishing, Inc., Box 1227, Eugene, OR 97440. TEL 503-935-3247. Ed. Dean Wesley Smith. adv.; illus. **Document type:** consumer publication, catalog.
  Description: Short horror and fantasy stories, with news of recent Pulphouse releases

LITERATURE — SCIENCE FICTION, FANTASY, HORROR

808.838   AU
QUARBER MERKUR; Franz Rottensteiners unillustrierte Literaturzeitschrift. 1963. s-a. S.140 for 4 issues. Franz Rottensteiner, Ed. & Pub., Marchettigasse 9-17, A-1060 Vienna, Austria. TEL 01-568928. bk.rev. **Document type:** consumer publication.

808.8   UK   ISSN 0959-8642
R E M. 1991. irreg. £7 for 4 nos. R E M Publications, 19 Sandringham Rd., London NW2 5EP, England. TEL 081-451-5787. Ed. Arthur Straker. adv.; bk.rev.; illus. circ. 1,000. **Document type:** consumer publication.
   Description: Alternative science fiction.

808   US
▼**RADIO FREE P K D**. 1993. q. $12 (foreign $16). Noel Productions, 27068 S. La Paz, No. 430, Aliso Viejo, CA 92656. Ed. gregory Lee. **Document type:** newsletter.
   Description: Covers material relating to the life and works of science fiction writer Philip K. Dick.

808.838   US
RADIO FREE THULCANDRA. 1982. q. $3 per no. 11 Lawrence Ave., Malverne, NY 11565-1406. Ed. Marty Helgesen. bk.rev. circ. 150.
   Description: Discusses science fiction issues from a Christian point of view.

800   US
RED LETTER. 6/yr. $6. Box 352, Miamisburg, OH 45343. bk.rev.; film rev.
   Description: News and reviews of interest to horror fans.

808.838   US   ISSN 1058-9406
THE REPORT (EUGENE); a fiction writer's magazine. 1984. 6/yr. $15. Pulphouse Publishing, Inc, Box 1227, Eugene, OR 97440. TEL 503-935-3247. Eds. Christina F. York, J. Steven York; Pub. Dean Wesley Smith. adv. circ. 1,500. (tabloid format; back issues avail.)
   Description: Features articles about anything and everything a science fiction, fantasy or mystery writer could need, covering markets, contracts, writing tips, and sound advice from professional writers.

051   US   ISSN 0035-5518
RIPLEY'S BELIEVE IT OR NOT; true ghost stories. 1964. 7/yr. Western Publishing Co., Inc., Attn.: Whitman Coin Dept., 1220 Mound Ave., Racine, WI 53404. TEL 414-633-2431. Ed. Wallace I. Green.

808.838   US
RISING STAR. 1983. bi-m. $7.50. Star - Sword Publications, 47 Byledge Rd., Manchester, NH 03104. TEL 603-623-9796. Ed. Scott E. Green. adv.; bk.rev. circ. 120. **Document type:** newsletter.
   Description: Publishes market information for writers and artists in the sci-fi, fantasy and horror genres.

808.83   US   ISSN 0889-2326
RIVERSIDE QUARTERLY. 1964. irreg., vol.8, no.4, 1991. $8 for 4 nos. Box 958, Big Sandy, TX 75755-0958. TEL 903-636-5505. Ed. Lee Sapiro. adv.; bk.rev.; film rev.; illus. circ. 1,100. (processed; also avail. in microform from MML,UMI; reprint service avail. from UMI) **Indexed:** Abstr.Engl.Stud., M.L.A. **Document type:** academic/scholarly publication.
   Description: Literary magazine for science-fiction and fantasy. Includes criticism, letters and poetry.

808   UK
THE ROAD; the journal of history, myth and legend. 1980. 3/yr. Widcombe Press, 16 Prior Park Bldgs., Bath, Avon BA2 4NP, England. Ed. Elizabeth Holland. bk.rev. **Document type:** academic/scholarly publication.
   Formerly: New Tolkien Newsletter (ISSN 0260-3268)
   Description: Provides information on research concerned with a group of works allied to Tolkien.

808.838   US
ROC SCIENCE FICTION ADVANCE. 1989. bi-m. free. Penguin Books U S A, Inc., Roc Science Fiction Department, 375 Hudson St., New York, NY 10014. TEL 212-366-2000. Ed. Amy Stout. bk.rev.; illus. (tabloid format) **Document type:** newsletter.
   Formerly: Signet S F Advance.
   Description: Features author interviews and news of upcoming book releases.

808.83   US   ISSN 0161-682X
PS1462
THE ROMANTIST. 1977. irreg. $15. F. Marion Crawford Memorial Society, Saracinesca House, 3610 Meadowbrook Ave., Nashville, TN 37205. TEL 615-292-9695. Ed. John C. Moran. adv.: page $100. bk.rev. circ. 300. (back issues avail.) **Indexed:** M.L.A. **Document type:** academic/scholarly publication.
   Description: Devoted to the study of modern manifestations of the Romantic tradition with emphasis on fantastic and imaginative literature. Contains a special section on Francis Marion Crawford.

808.838   AT
S F COMMENTARY. (Science Fiction) 1969. q. Aus.$35($25) Bruce Gillespie, Ed. & Pub., P.O. Box 5195AA, Melbourne, Vic. 3001, Australia. adv.; bk.rev. circ. 500.
   Description: Contains short reviews of science fiction and fantasy.

813   US   ISSN 1068-395X
PS648.S3
S F R A REVIEW. 1971. 6/yr. $60 (Canada $65; elsewhere $70) (membership). Science Fiction Research Association, c/o Golden Lion Enterprises, 11461 Magnolia Ave., Box 251, Riverside, CA 92406. TEL 909-689-4058. Ed. Daryl F. Mallett. bk.rev.; bibl. circ. 500. **Document type:** newsletter, academic/scholarly publication.
   Formerly (until 1992): Science Fiction Research Association Newsletter (ISSN 0048-9646)

813   US   ISSN 0036-1364
PS374.S35
S F W A BULLETIN. 1965. q. $15. (Science-Fiction and Fantasy Writers of America) Pulphouse Publishing, Inc., Box 1227, Eugene, OR 97440. TEL 503-935-3247. Ed. Dan Hatch; Pub. Dean Wesley Smith. adv.; bk.rev.; illus. circ. 1,500. (also avail. in microform from UMI; reprint service avail. from UMI) **Document type:** bulletin.
   Description: Articles about the business of science-fiction and fantasy writing from professionals in the field.

SCARLET STREET; the magazine of mystery and horror. see *LITERATURE — Mystery And Detective*

070 808   US   ISSN 0894-2617
SCAVENGER'S NEWSLETTER. 1984. m. $14. Janet Fox, Ed. & Pub., 519 Ellinwood, Osage City, KS 66523-1329. TEL 913-528-3538. bk.rev. circ. 1,000. **Document type:** newsletter.
   Description: Provides information about small press markets for science fiction, fantasy, horror, and mystery writers.

808.838   UK   ISSN 0963-2611
SCHEHEREZADE. 1991. irreg. (approx. 4/yr.). £8.50 for 4 nos. Elizabeth Counihan, Ed. & Pub., St. Ives., Maypole Rd., E. Grinstead, W. Sussex RH19 1HL, England. adv.; illus.
   Description: Publishes short fantastic fiction with a non-technological slant, and author interviews.

SCI-FI ENTERTAINMENT. see *COMMUNICATIONS — Television And Cable*

808.838   US
SCIENCE - FANTASY CORRESPONDENT. 1977. 3/yr. $25. c/o Carrollton Clark, 9122 Rosslyn, Arlington, VA 22209. Ed. Willis Conover. illus.

808.83   AT   ISSN 0314-6677
SCIENCE FICTION; a review of speculative literature. 1977. 4/yr. Aus.$24($39) (typically set in Nov.). University of Western Australia, Department of English, c/o Dr. Van Ikin, Ed., Nedlands, W.A. 6009, Australia. TEL 61-9-380-2280. FAX 61-9-380-1030. adv.; bk.rev. circ. 1,000. (back issues avail.) **Document type:** abstracting/indexing.
   Description: Essays, articles and interviews in the field of science fiction.

808.838   US   ISSN 1065-1829
▼**SCIENCE FICTION AGE**. 1992. bi-m. $14.95. Sovereign Media, 457 Carlisle Dr., Herndon, VA 22070. TEL 703-471-1556. FAX 703-471-1559. Ed. Scott Edelman; Pub. Mark Hintz. adv.: B&W page $1275, color page $2075; trim 8 x 10 7/8. bk.rev.; film rev. circ. 75,000. **Document type:** consumer publication.
   Description: Covers science fiction and fantasy.

808.838   US
SCIENCE FICTION AND FANTASY BOOK REVIEW ANNUAL; a magazine of book news, reviews and commentary. 1978. a. $65. Greenwood Press, Inc. (Subsidiary of: Greenwood Publishing Group Inc.), 88 Post Rd. W., Box 5007, Westport, CT 06881-5007. TEL 203-226-3571. FAX 203-222-1502. Ed. Robert A. Collins. adv.; film rev.; abstr.; illus.; tr.lit.; index. circ. 3,000. (back issues avail.) **Indexed:** Bk.Rev.Ind. (1982-1987), Child.Bk.Rev.Ind. (1982-1987).
   Former titles (until 1990): Fantasy Review (ISSN 0747-234X); S F and Fantasy Review; Fantasy Newsletter (ISSN 0199-3151); Incorporates (in 1983): Science Fiction and Fantasy Book Review (ISSN 0163-4348)

SCIENCE FICTION AND FANTASY RESEARCH INDEX. see *LITERATURE — Abstracting, Bibliographies, Statistics*

808.838   US
SCIENCE FICTION AND FANTASY WORKSHOP. 1980. m. $10. 1193 S. 1900 E., Salt Lake City, UT 84108. TEL 801-582-2090. Ed. Kathleen D. Woodbury. circ. 450. (back issues avail.) **Document type:** newsletter.
   Description: Covers writing and marketing of science fiction, fantasy and horror stories of all lengths.

070.5 808   US   ISSN 0195-5365
SCIENCE FICTION CHRONICLE; the monthly science fiction and fantasy newsmagazine. 1979. m. $30. S F Chronicle, Box 022730, Brooklyn, NY 11202-0056. TEL 718-643-9011. FAX 718-643-9011. Ed. Andrew Porter. adv.; bk.rev.; illus.; circ. 6,000 (paid). (also avail. in microform from UMI; diskette format; reprint service avail. from UMI) **Indexed:** Amer.Hum.Ind., Bk.Rev.Ind. (1981-1983, 1985-), Child.Bk.Rev.Ind. (1981-1983, 1985-), M.L.A.
—UnCover; UMI.
   Incorporating (as of 1984): Starship (ISSN 0195-9379); Which was formerly: Algol (ISSN 0002-5364)
   Description: Newsmagazine for professionals and readers with news stories, pre-publication buyer's guide, 550 or more reviews yearly, market news, columns, overseas news, author signings.

SCIENCE FICTION CONVENTION REGISTER. see *MEETINGS AND CONGRESSES*

808.8   US   ISSN 1071-3018
SCIENCE FICTION EYE. Short title: S F Eye. 1987. irreg. (approx. 3/yr.), no.13, 1994. $12.50 for 3 nos. (outside N. America $20); newsstand price: $5. S F Eye, Box 18539, Asheville, NC 28814. TEL 704-684-5575. FAX 704-684-5779. (Subscr. in Japan to: Mari Kotani, 9-11, Tanjo-ga-Oka, Hiratsuka-shi, Kanagawa-ken 254, Japan; Subscr. in the U.K. to: Chris Reed, N.S.F.A., P.O. Box 625, Sheffield S1 3GY, England) Ed. Stephen P. Brown; Pub. Stephen P. Brown. adv.; bk.rev.; music rev.; illus.; circ. 4,500 (paid). **Document type:** consumer publication.
   Description: Contains critical articles, commentary and interviews in the science fiction field and other topics of interest, including fringe science and issues in social and technological change.

SCIENCE FICTION, FANTASY, & HORROR; comprehensive bibliography of books and short fiction published in the English language. see *LITERATURE — Abstracting, Bibliographies, Statistics*

808.838   GW   ISSN 0930-2492
SCIENCE FICTION MEDIA; Informationsdienst fuer science fiction and fantasy. 1984. m. DM.58. Karl-Theodor-Str. 66, 80803 Munich, Germany. TEL 089-3089663. FAX 089-3008806. Ed. Gerd Rottenecker. bk.rev.; film rev.; bibl. circ. 1,000. (back issues avail.) **Document type:** newsletter.

LITERATURE — SCIENCE FICTION, FANTASY, HORROR

808.83 US ISSN 0091-7729
PN3448.S45
SCIENCE-FICTION STUDIES. 1973. 3/yr. $15 to individuals (Canada $17; elsewhere $18); US institutions $22 (Canada $25; elsewhere $26). (DePauw University) S F - T H, Inc., c/o Prof. Arthur B. Evans, Ed., DePauw University, Greencastle, IN 46135-0037. TEL 317-658-4758. FAX 317-658-4177. adv.; bk.rev.; index. circ. 1,200. (also avail. in microform from SWZ; reprint service avail. from SWZ) **Indexed:** Abstr.Engl.Stud., Amer.Hum.Ind., Arts & Hum.Cit.Ind., Bk.Rev.Ind. (1988-), Child.Bk.Rev.Ind. (1988-), Curr.Cont., Hum.Ind., Ind.Bk.Rev.Hum., M.L.A. **Document type:** academic/scholarly publication.
—BLDSC (8145.182000); Faxon; UnCover.
Refereed Serial

808.838 GW ISSN 0048-9654
PN3311
SCIENCE FICTION TIMES. 1959. m. DM.54. Corian Verlag Heinrich Wimmer, Bernhard-Monath-Str. 24a, 86405 Meitingen, Germany. Eds. Uwe Anton, Ronald M. Hahn. adv.; bk.rev.; film rev.; bibl. circ. 1,000.

808.838 US ISSN 0882-1348
SCIFANT. 1986. m. $24. Luna Ventures, Box 398, Suisun, CA 94585. adv.; bk.rev. (also avail. in microfiche; back issues avail.)
Description: Covers science fiction, fantasy, horror, space, and other similar fiction and nonfiction subjects, especially for new writers and artists.

808.838 US ISSN 1059-485X
SCREAM FACTORY. 1988. q. $22 (effective 1993). Deadline Press, Box 2808, Apache Junction, AZ 85220. TEL 408-353-4450. Ed. Peter Enfantino. adv.; film rev. circ. 1,000. **Document type:** academic/scholarly publication.
Description: Contains articles and reviews of horror fiction and films.

808.838 NE ISSN 0168-2776
SHARDS OF BABEL. (Text in English) 1982. bi-m. fl.32($20) for 8 nos. Babel Publications, Caan van Necklaan 63, 2281 BB Rijswijk, Netherlands. TEL 31-70-3950128. Ed. Roelof Goudriaan. adv.: B&W page $90. bk.rev.; bibl. circ. 500.
Description: Comprehensive coverage of European science fiction literary activity, including essays, reviews of new magazines and books from Europe, fan news, and schedules of upcoming events and conventions.

808.838 CN
SOL RISING. no.9, 1993. q? Can.$35 membership. Friends of the Merril Collection, 40 St. George St., Toronto, ON M5S 2E4, Canada. bibl. **Document type:** newsletter.

SOUTH OF THE MOON. see *LITERATURE — Mystery And Detective*

808.838 US ISSN 0271-2512
SPACE AND TIME. 1966. s-a. $10. c/o Gordon Linzner, Ed., 138 W. 70th St., 4-B, New York, NY 10023-4432. TEL 212-595-0894. adv.; illus. circ. 800. **Document type:** consumer publication.
Description: Presents a collection of original fantasy and science fiction.

STAR LINE. see *LITERATURE — Poetry*

808.838 NZ
STAR SONGS - TAU WHETU; New Zealand anthology of science fiction and fantasy. a. Pegapuss Press, c/o Lyn McConchie, Farside Farm, Norsewood, New Zealand. Ed. Jean Weber. illus.

808.838 US
STAR TREK: DEEP SPACE NINE. 4/yr. $25 (foreign $35); with Star Trek: The Next Generation $55 (foreign $75). Starlog Press, 475 Park Ave. S., New York, NY 10016. **Document type:** consumer publication.
Description: Describes episodes of the popular television science fiction series both on the screen and behind the scenes; also features interviews and blueprints of space vehicles.

808.838 US
STAR TREK: THE NEXT GENERATION. 5/yr. $30 (foreign $40); with Star Trek: Deep Space Nine $55 (foreign $75). Starlog Press, 475 Park Ave. S., New York, NY 10016. **Document type:** consumer publication.
Description: Discusses each episode of the popular science fiction television series both on screen and behind the scenes. Features interviews and blueprints of space vehicles.

STAR TREK: THE OFFICIAL FAN CLUB MAGAZINE. see *COMMUNICATIONS — Television And Cable*

808.838 UK ISSN 0955-114X
STARBURST. no.145, 1990. m. £36 (U.S. and Canada $82; rest of world £39). Visual Imagination Ltd., 9 Blades Ct., Deodar Rd., London SW15 2NU, England. TEL 081-875-1520. FAX 081-875-1588. Ed. Stephen Payne. adv.: B&W page £550, color page £825; trim 184 x 268. film rev.; illus. circ. 40,000. **Document type:** consumer publication.
Description: Covers science fiction, horror, and fantasy media events and developments, with interviews and feature articles.

STARLOG; magazine of the future. see *COMMUNICATIONS — Television And Cable*

808.838 UK
▼**STRANGE ATTRACTOR.** 1992. irreg. Rick Cadger, Ed. & Pub., 111 Sundon Rd., Houghton Regis, Dunstable, Beds LU5 5NL, England.
Description: Strange science fiction, fantasy and horror stories.

808.838 US
STRANGE PLASMA. 1989. q. $15 (foreign $23). Edgewood Press, Box 264, Cambridge, MA 02238. Ed. Steve Pasechnick. circ. 500.
Description: Speculative fiction magazine with interviews and critical articles.

808.838 UK
STRING. no.2, 1992. irreg. £1.75 per no. John Weston, Ed. & Pub., 97 St. Peter's Way, Warrington WA2 7BL, England. illus.
Description: Publishes contemporary genre science fiction.

808.838 US ISSN 1050-1045
STUDIES IN WEIRD FICTION. 1987. 2/yr. $10 (effective 1994). Necronomicon Press, Box 1304, West Warwick, RI 02893. TEL 401-828-7161. FAX 401-738-6125. Ed. S.T. Joshi. (back issues avail.) **Document type:** academic/scholarly publication.
Description: Publishes critical articles and reviews in the field of fantasy, horror and supernatural fiction subsequent to Edgar Allan Poe.

808.838 US
▼**SUPERNATURAL MAGAZINE.** 1993. m. $10. Morris Publishing Groups, Box 1563, Cayce, SC 29033. TEL 803-256-1611. Ed. Roy Allen Morris. adv.; bk.rev. (back issues avail.) **Document type:** consumer publication.

T V ZONE. see *COMMUNICATIONS — Television And Cable*

808.838 UK
TALES FROM A HIGH LAND. no.4, 1992. 4/yr. £9 for 6 nos. Calum MacIver, Ed. & Pub., 5 Ferindonald, Sleat, Isle of Skye, Scotland. illus.
Description: Publishes science fiction and fantasy.

808.838 US
▼**TANGENT;** the science fiction and fantasy short fiction review magazine. 1993. bi-m. $18. 1301 S. Scott, No. 14-O, Independence, MO 64052. TEL 816-252-4302. Ed. David A. Truesdale.
Description: Reviews each story appearing in the 10-12 magazines covered. Provides author profiles and photos.

808.838 US
TEKELI-LI! JOURNAL OF TERROR. 1991. q. $20 (foreign $30). Montilla Publications, 106 Hanover Ave., Pawtucket, RI 02861. TEL 401-722-7938. Ed. Jon B. Cooke. bk.rev.; film rev.; bibl.; illus. circ. 1,500. **Document type:** consumer publication.
Description: Devoted to the appreciation of current horror fiction in the tradition of Poe and Lovecraft, with original art, fiction and verse by contemporary writers, author and artist interviews, coverage of the horror small press scene, short critical articles, and reprints of fiction by neglected authors from the past.

800 US ISSN 1055-7644
TEMPORARY CULTURE. 1988. irreg., latest no.8-9, 1994. $6 per no. (effective 1994). Box 43072, Upper Montclair, NJ 07043. Ed. H. Wessells. bk.rev.; illus.; cum.index: nos.1-7; circ. controlled. (back issues avail.)
—CCC.
Formerly (until no.5, 1991): Newsletter of Temporary Culture.
Description: Publishes original artwork, essays, experimental poetry and fiction (especially fantastical or science fiction) extending the boundaries of language and meaning, and mapping the ideological landscapes of the post-industrial environment and culture.
Refereed Serial

808.838 UK
TERRITORIES. 1991. irreg. £1.95 per no. c/o McNair, 65 Niddrie Rd., Strathbungo, Glasgow G42 8PT, Scotland. FAX 3392588. (U.S. subscr. to: NSFA Distribution, 1052 Calle Del Cerro, Ste. 708, San Clemente, CA 92672-6068) Ed. Erich Zaenn. adv.: B&W page £150. bk.rev.
Description: Publishes unconventional fiction and critical articles for science fiction - slipstream enthusiasts.

808.83 AT ISSN 1031-3001
TERROR AUSTRALIS; best Australian horror. 1988; N.S. 1993. a. Aus.$12.95. Hodder & Stoughton Australia Pty Ltd., 10-16 South St., P.O. Box 386, Rydalmere, N.S.W 2116, Australia. TEL 02-638-5299. FAX 02-684-4942. Ed. Leigh D. Blackmore. adv.; bk.rev.; film rev.; play rev.; bibl.; illus. circ. 500. (back issues avail.)
Description: Anthology of dark fantasy by top Australian writers.

808.838 US
THINGS TO COME.* 1953. 14/yr. membership. Science Fiction Book Club, 1540 Broadway, 9th Fl., New York, NY 10036-4021. Ed. Ellen Asher.

808.838 US
THIRTEENTH MOON. 1982. q. $24 (foreign $28) (effective 1994). Tachyon Corporation, 1458 18th St., Box 139, San Francisco, CA 94107. TEL 415-285-5615. Ed. Jacob Weisman. bk.rev.

808.838 US
THUNDER'S SHADOW; collector's magazine. 4/yr. $12. Box 387, Winfield, IL 60190. adv. **Document type:** consumer publication, catalog.
Description: Fantasy and horror fiction and news of collectible books.

808.838 UK
▼**TIME CENTRE TIMES.** 1993. q. £10 in UK; $20 in US; elsewhere £15. Nomads of the Time Streams, International Michael Moorcock Appreciation Society, c/o D.J. Rowe, 18 Laurel Bank, Truss Hill Rd., S. Ascot, Ascot, Berks. SL5 9AL, England. **Document type:** newsletter.

808.838 US
TIME PILOT. 1993. m. $10 (effective 1994). New Legends Group, Box 2567, Bellingham, WA 98227. TEL 206-733-7306. Ed. Gary Bryan. adv. circ. 9,000. (tabloid format; also avail. in diskette format; back issues avail.) **Document type:** newsletter.
●Also available online.
Description: Interactive science fiction newletter in the form of news stories from 500 years into the future.

808.838　　　　　UK
TIME SCREEN; the magazine of British telefantasy. 1984. s-a. £5.90 (foreign £7.30). Engale Marketing, 332 Lytham Rd., South Shore, Blackpool, Lancs. FY4 1DW, England. TEL 0253-48321. FAX 0253-407813. (Subscr. to: Time Screen, 88 Edlington Ln., Doncaster, Lancs. DN4 9LS, England. TEL 0302-854500) Ed. Anthony R. McKay. circ. 2,000. (back issues avail.) **Document type:** academic/scholarly publication.
  Description: Covers science fiction and fantasy television programs made in and for the U.K. Contains interviews, behind-the-scenes information, and lists on all aspects of British television fantasy.

810　　　　　US　　　ISSN 1050-0421
TOME; the dark works of great minds, and the great works of dark minds. 1989. q. $12. Grub St. Publications, 454 Munden Ave., Norfolk, VA 23505. TEL 804-588-0583. Ed. Daivd N. Wilson. adv.; bk.rev. circ. 1,000. (back issues avail.)
  Description: Contains horror, science fiction, fantasy, poetry, artwork, and surrealistic fiction.

808.838　　　　　US
▼**TOMORROW**; speculative fiction. 1992. 6/yr. $18. Unifont Co. Inc., Box 6038, Evanston, IL 60204. TEL 708-864-3668. Ed. Algis Budrys. adv.; illus. **Document type:** consumer publication.
  Description: Contains short stories, novelettes, novellas, and serialized novels from top writers and new talents in science fiction, fantasy, and horror.

808.83　　　　　US
TWISTED. 1985. irreg. $6 per no. Christine Hoard, Ed. & Pub., Box 1249, Palmetto, GA 30268-1249. bk.rev.; film rev.; illus. circ. 300. (back issues avail.) **Document type:** consumer publication.
  Description: Covers horror and fantasy fiction, poetry, art, and reviews.

813　　　　　US　　　ISSN 1068-3267
▼**UNDISCOVERED COUNTRIES JOURNAL**. 1993. bi-m. $23.95. Stars Media, 9792 Edmonds Way, Ste. 252, Edmonds, WA 98020. TEL 206-672-9040. Ed. Michael Breckenridge. adv.; film rev. circ. 1,000.
  Description: Reports science news and contains science fiction, especially Star Trek news, insider NASA reports on space exploration, promotes the Klingon language. Publishes rare photographs.

UNILIT. see LITERATURE

808.838　　　　　US
VAMPIRE JOURNAL.* 1983. irreg. (2-4/yr.). $28. Baker Street Publications, Box 517, Metairie, LA 70004-0517. TEL 504-734-8414. Ed. Sharida Rizzuto. circ. 9,000.
  Description: Devoted to vampirism in literature, legend and film.

808.838　　　　　UK　　　ISSN 0505-0448
VECTOR. 1958. bi-m. £15 membership. British Science Fiction Association Ltd., 60 Bournemouth Rd., Folkestone, Kent CT19 5AZ, England. (Subscr. to: Joanna Raine, Membership Sec., 29 Thornville Rd, Hartlepool, Cleveland TS26 8EV, England; In U.S.: c/o Cy Chauvin, 14248 Wilfred, Detroit, MI 48213) Ed. Catie Cary. adv.; bk.rev.; illus.; index. circ. 1,000. (back issues avail.)
  Description: Devoted to all aspects of science fiction. Includes author interviews and critical articles.

808.838　　　　　PL
WAMPIURS WARS. irreg. membership. Gdanski Klub Fantastyki, P.O. Box 76, 80-325 Gdansk 37, Poland. Dir. Krzysztof Papierkowski.
  Description: Science fiction "fanzine".

808.838　　　　　US
WARP FOUR; the magazine of science fiction, fantasy and horror. 1970. q. $4. c/o John R. Racano, Ed., 113 Cleveland Ave., Colonia, NJ 07067. TEL 201-679-7756. adv.; bk.rev.; illus.

808.838　　　　　US　　　ISSN 8755-7452
WEIRDBOOK. 1968. s-a. $25 for 7 nos. ($30 outside U.S.). W. Paul Ganley: Publisher, Box 149, Buffalo, NY 14226-0149. TEL 716-839-2415. Ed. W. Paul Ganley. illus. circ. 900. (back issues avail.)
  Description: Focuses on fantasy - supernatural fiction, poetry and art.

808.838　　　　　US
WEIRDBOOK ENCORES. 1976. irreg., no.14, 1993. $15 for 6 nos. ($18 outside U.S.). W. Paul Ganley: Publisher, Box 149, Buffalo, NY 14226-0149. TEL 716-839-2415. illus. (back issues avail.) Former titles (until no.11, 1990): Weirdbook Sampler; (until no.10): Eerie Country.
  Description: Supernatural, fantasy and horror short stories and poetry.

WESTWIND (SEATTLE). see CLUBS

808.838　　　　　US
WONDERDISK. (No longer in printed format as of 1993; avail. only on diskette for both Macintosh and Windows.) 1982. q. $32. Wonder Press, Box 58367, Louisville, KY 40268-0367. Ed. Walter Gammons. adv.; bk.rev.; film rev.; illus.; index. circ. 2,000.
  Former titles (until 1993): Wonder; Spectrum Stories.

808.83　　　　　UK　　　ISSN 0954-3902
WORKS; magazine of speculative and imaginative fiction. 1989. 2/yr. £4 (Europe £7; elsewhere £9). Works Publishing, 12 Blakestones Rd., Slaithwaite, Huddersfield, Yorks HD7 5UQ, England. Ed. Dave Hughes. bk.rev. circ. 2,000. **Document type:** consumer publication.

808.838　　　　　US　　　ISSN 0735-3995
WORLD S F NEWSLETTER. 1980. q. $15. World S F, International Science Fiction Association of Professionals, 855 S. Harvard Dr., Palatine, IL 60067-7026. Ed. Jim Goddard. circ. 600. (back issues avail.) **Document type:** newsletter.

808.838　　　　　US
PS509.F3
WORLDS OF FANTASY & HORROR. 1923; N.S. 1994. q. $24 for 6 nos. Terminus Publishing Co., Inc., 123 Crooked Ln., King of Prussia, PA 19406-2570. TEL 610-275-4463. Ed. Darrell Schweitzer; Pub. George Scithers. adv.; bk.rev.; illus.; circ. 8,000 (paid). (back issues avail.) **Document type:** consumer publication.
  Formerly (until 1994): Weird Tales (ISSN 0898-5073)
  Description: Contains fantastic fiction in the tradition of H.P. Lovecraft and Ray Bradbury.

808　　　　　US　　　ISSN 1062-9963
WRITER'S CHAPBOOK SERIES. irreg. Pulphouse Publishing, Inc., Box 1227, Eugene, OR 97440. TEL 503-935-3247. Ed. Dean Wesley Smith; Pub. Dean Wesley Smith. (back issues avail.) **Document type:** monographic series.
  Description: Examines various aspects of the writer's craft, with particular emphasis on science fiction and fantasy writing.

808.8　　　　　US　　　ISSN 1050-5334
XENOPHILIA. 1990. s-a. $7 (foreign $9). 904 Old Town Ct., Cupertino, CA 95014. TEL 408-257-0462. (Subscr. in UK to: Chris Reed, NSFA, P.O. Box 625, Sheffield S1 3GY, England) Ed. Joy Oestreicher. bk.rev.; circ. 200 (controlled).
  Description: Fantastic and unusual poetry focusing on different cultures (real or imagined).

808.838　　　　　UK
XENOS; science fiction - fantasy magazine. 1990. bi-m. £11. S.V. Copestake, 29 Prebend St., Bedford MK40 1QN, England. TEL 0234-49067.
  Description: Publishes new science fiction and fantasy from new writers.

XIZQUIL; a place where social consciousness and creative speculation meet. see LITERATURE

808.838　　　　　US
THE YEAR'S BEST FANTASY AND HORROR; annual collection. 1988. a. $15.95 paperback; $27.95 hardbound (effective 1992). St. Martin's Press, 175 Fifth Ave., New York, NY 10010. TEL 212-674-5151. Eds. Ellen Datlow, Terri Windling.
  Description: Anthology of outstanding new fantasy and horror stories and novellas.

808.838　　　　　US
YEAR'S BEST HORROR STORIES. 1972. a. $5.50 (effective 1993). DAW Books, Inc., 375 Hudson St., New York, NY 10014-3658. TEL 212-366-2096. FAX 212-366-2090. Ed. Karl Edward Wagner.
  Description: Collection of the best horror stories published during the preceding year.

808.838　　　　　US　　　ISSN 0743-1740
PS648.S3
THE YEAR'S BEST SCIENCE FICTION; annual collection. 1984. a. $16.95 paperback (effective 1994). St. Martin's Press, 175 Fifth Ave., New York, NY 10010. TEL 212-674-5151. Ed. Gardner Dozois. bibl. circ. 15,000. (back issues avail.)
  Description: Collects outstanding short science fiction stories from the preceding year, with a list of other noteworthy titles.

808.838　　　　　GW　　　ISSN 0930-0007
ZAUBERZEIT. 1986. bi-m. DM.40 (foreign DM.60). Laurin Verlag, Luruper Chaussee 125, 22761 Hamburg, Germany. TEL 040-896565. Ed. Juergen Pirner. adv.; bk.rev.; index.

808.838　　　　　UK
ZERO HOUR. 1991. irreg. £7 for 4 nos. 20 Thorpe Green Dr., Leymour, Golcar, Huddersfield HD7 4QU, England. (U.S. subscr. to: Anne Marsden, 1052 Calle del Cerro, No. 708, San Clemente, CA 92672. TEL 714-361-3791)
  Description: Strange art and fiction.

808.838　　　　　UK　　　ISSN 1351-5217
▼**THE ZONE**. 1994. 4/yr. £2. S.A. Publishing, 13 Hazely Combe, Arreton, Isle of Wight PO30 3AJ, England. Ed. Tony Lee. **Document type:** consumer publication.

808.838　　　　　US　　　ISSN 0886-8743
2 A M MAGAZINE; horror, fantasy and science fiction. 1986. q. $19 (foreign $23). Two A M Publications, Box 6754, Rockford, IL 61126-1754. TEL 815-397-5901. Ed. Gretta McCombs Anderson. adv.; bk.rev.; film rev.; circ. 2,000 (paid). (back issues avail.) **Document type:** consumer publication.
  Description: Stories, poetry, articles and art for adult readers of fantasy, science fiction and horror literature.

LUMBER AND WOOD

see Forests and Forestry–Lumber and Wood